2021

Harris

Florida

Manufacturers Directory

dun & bradstreet

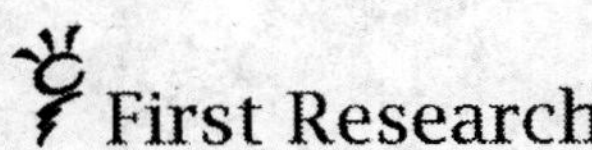

Published December 2021 next update December 2022

Publisher

Mergent Inc.
444 Madison Ave
New York, NY 10022

2021 Mergent Business Press
ISSN 1080-2614
ISBN 978-1-164972-578-3

TABLE OF CONTENTS

SUMMARY OF CONTENTS

Number of Companies.. 19,547
Number of Decision Makers 37,459
Minimum Number of Employees... 4

EXPLANATORY NOTES

How to Cross-Reference in This Directory

Sequential Entry Numbers. Each establishment in the Geographic Section is numbered sequentially (G-0000). The number assigned to each establishment is referred to as its "entry number." To make cross-referencing easier, each listing in the Geographic, SIC, Alphabetic and Product Sections includes the establishment's entry number. To facilitate locating an entry in the Geographic Section, the entry numbers for the first listing on the left page and the last listing on the right page are printed at the top of the page next to the city name.

Source Suggestions Welcome

Although all known sources were used to compile this directory, it is possible that companies were inadvertently omitted. Your assistance in calling attention to such omissions would be greatly appreciated. A special form on the facing page will help you in the reporting process.

Analysis

Every effort has been made to contact all firms to verify their information. The one exception to this rule is the annual sales figure, which is considered by many companies to be confidential information. Therefore, estimated sales have been calculated by multiplying the nationwide average sales per employee for the firm's major SIC/NAICS code by the firm's number of employees. Nationwide averages for sales per employee by SIC/NAICS codes are provided by the U.S. Department of Commerce and are updated annually. All sales—sales (est)—have been estimated by this method. The exceptions are parent companies (PA), division headquarters (DH) and headquarter locations (HQ) which may include an actual corporate sales figure—sales (corporate-wide) if available.

Types of Companies

Descriptive and statistical data are included for companies in the entire state. These comprise manufacturers, machine shops, fabricators, assemblers and printers. Also identified are corporate offices in the state.

Employment Data

The employment figure shown in the Geographic Section includes male and female employees and embraces all levels of the company: administrative, clerical, sales and maintenance. This figure is for the facility listed and does not include other plants or offices. It should be recognized that these figures represent an approximate year-round average. These employment figures are broken into codes A through G and used in the Product and SIC Sections to further help you in qualifying a company. Be sure to check the footnotes on the bottom of pages for the code breakdowns.

Standard Industrial Classification (SIC)

The Standard Industrial Classification (SIC) system used in this directory was developed by the federal government for use in classifying establishments by the type of activity they are engaged in. The SIC classifications used in this directory are from the 1987 edition published by the U.S. Government's Office of Management and Budget. The SIC system separates all activities into broad industrial divisions (e.g., manufacturing, mining, retail trade). It further subdivides each division. The range of manufacturing industry classes extends from two-digit codes (major industry group) to four-digit codes (product).

For example:

Industry Breakdown	Code	Industry, Product, etc.
*Major industry group	20	Food and kindred products
Industry group	203	Canned and frozen foods
*Industry	2033	Fruits and vegetables, etc.

*Classifications used in this directory

Only two-digit and four-digit codes are used in this directory.

Arrangement

1. The **Geographic Section** contains complete in-depth corporate data. This section is sorted by cities listed in alphabetical order and companies listed alphabetically within each city. A County/City Index for referencing cities within counties precedes this section.

IMPORTANT NOTICE: It is a violation of both federal and state law to transmit an unsolicited advertisement to a facsimile machine. Any user of this product that violates such laws may be subject to civil and criminal penalties, which may exceed $500 for each transmission of an unsolicited facsimile. Mergent Inc. provides fax numbers for lawful purposes only and expressly forbids the use of these numbers in any unlawful manner.

2. The **Standard Industrial Classification (SIC) Section** lists companies under approximately 500 four-digit SIC codes. An alphabetical and a numerical index precedes this section. A company can be listed under several codes. The codes are in numerical order with companies listed alphabetically under each code.

3. The **Alphabetic Section** lists all companies with their full physical or mailing addresses and telephone number.

4. The **Product Section** lists companies under unique Harris categories. An index preceding this section lists all product categories in alphabetical order. Companies can be listed under several categories.

USER'S GUIDE TO LISTINGS

GEOGRAPHIC SECTION

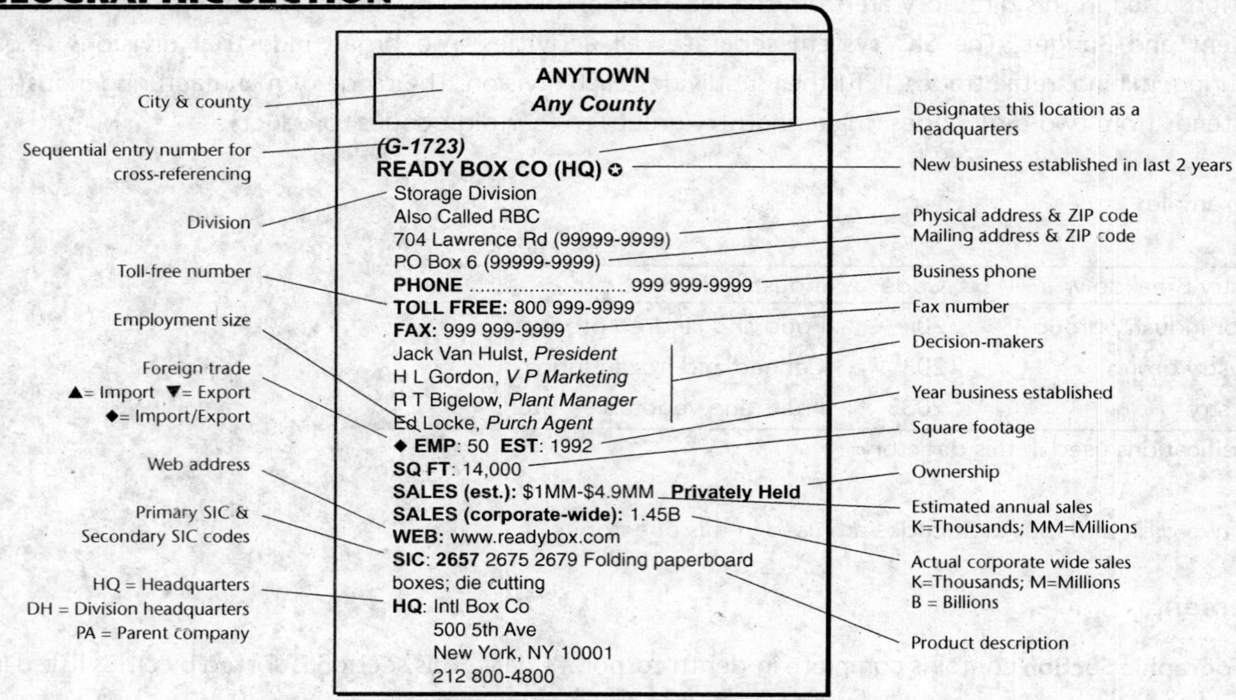

SIC SECTION

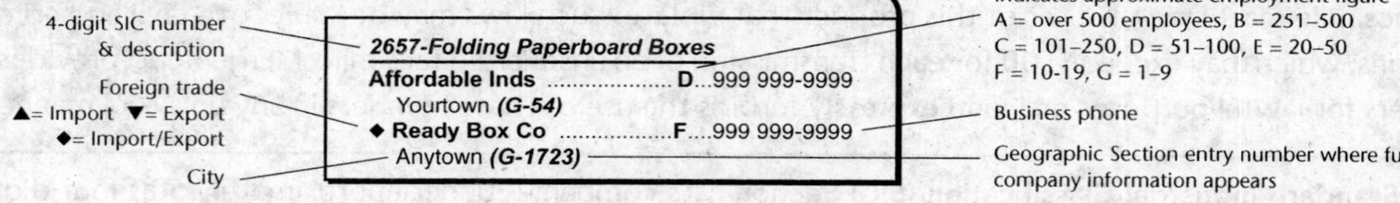

ALPHABETIC SECTION

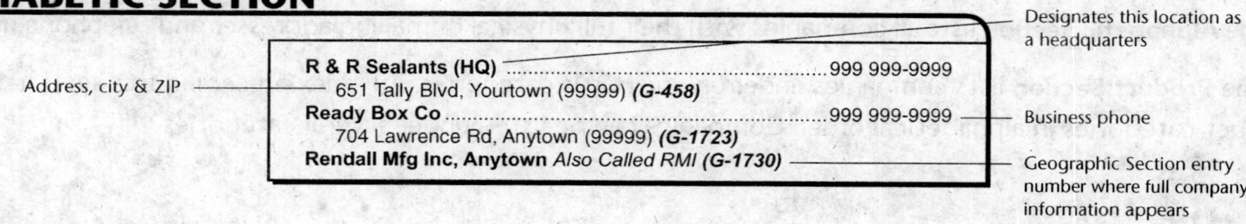

PRODUCT SECTION

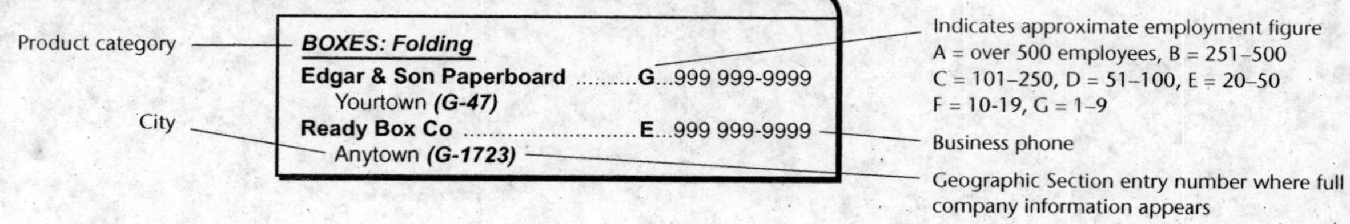

GEOGRAPHIC SECTION

Companies sorted by city in alphabetical order

In-depth company data listed

STANDARD INDUSTRIAL CLASSIFICATIONS

Alphabetical index of classifcation descriptions

Numerical index of classifcation descriptions

Companies sorted by SIC product groupings

ALPHABETIC SECTION

Company listings in alphabetical order

PRODUCT INDEX

Product categories listed in alphabetical order

PRODUCT SECTION

Companies sorted by product and manufacturing service classifications

Florida

County Map

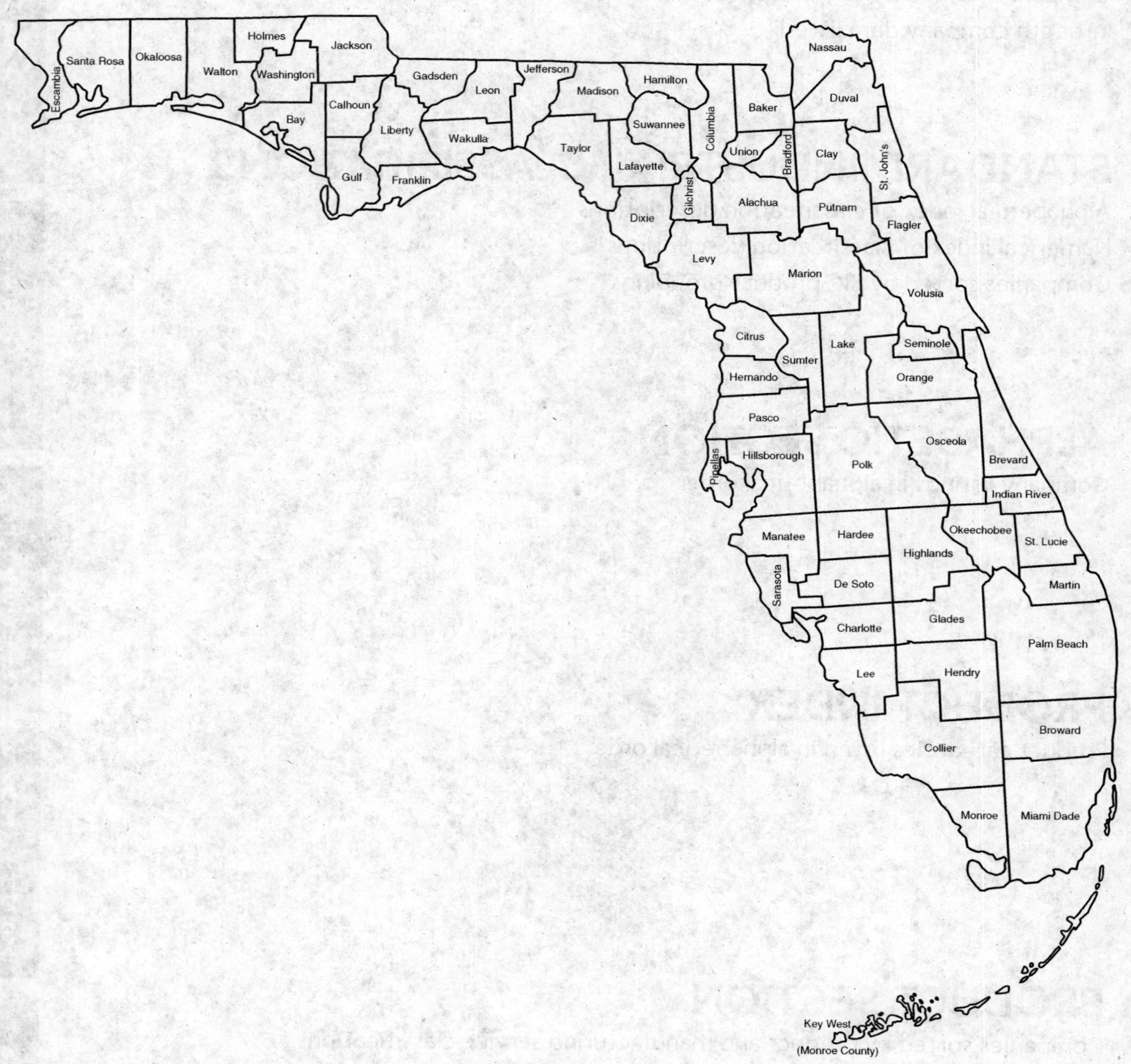

COUNTY/CITY CROSS-REFERENCE INDEX

ENTRY#

Florida City (G-3769)
Hialeah (G-5252)
Hialeah Gardens (G-5697)
Homestead (G-5951)
Key Biscayne (G-7154)
Medley (G-8603)
Miami (G-9020)
Miami Beach (G-10634)
Miami Gardens (G-10731)
Miami Lakes (G-10759)
Miami Shores (G-10884)
Miami Springs (G-10887)
North Bay Village (G-11592)
North Miami (G-11622)
North Miami Beach (G-11666)
Opa Locka (G-12281)
Palmetto Bay (G-13839)
Pinecrest (G-14322)
Princeton (G-15182)
South Miami (G-16811)
Sunny Isles Beach (G-17073)
Surfside (G-17201)
Sweetwater (G-17208)
Virginia Gardens (G-18684)
West Miami (G-18781)

Monroe

Big Pine Key (G-381)
Islamorada (G-6098)
Key Largo (G-7164)
Key West (G-7176)
Marathon (G-8516)
Summerland Key (G-17065)
Tavernier (G-18361)

Nassau

Amelia Island (G-92)
Bryceville (G-1296)
Callahan (G-1322)
Fernandina Beach (G-3730)
Hilliard (G-5706)
Yulee (G-19492)

Okaloosa

Baker (G-299)
Crestview (G-2344)
Destin (G-3183)
Eglin A F B (G-3640)
Eglin Afb (G-3641)
Fort Walton Beach (G-4773)
Holt (G-5948)
Hurlburt Field (G-6044)
Mary Esther (G-8589)
Niceville (G-11562)
Shalimar (G-16774)
Valparaiso (G-18505)

Okeechobee

Okeechobee (G-12172)

Orange

Apopka (G-108)
Belle Isle (G-356)
Christmas (G-1550)
Gotha (G-5040)
Lake Buena Vista (G-7335)
Maitland (G-8455)
Oakland (G-11767)
Ocoee (G-12082)
Orlando (G-12415)
Windermere (G-19225)
Winter Garden (G-19252)
Winter Park (G-19370)
Zellwood (G-19502)

Osceola

Celebration (G-1523)
Kissimmee (G-7214)
Reunion (G-15261)
Saint Cloud (G-15641)

Palm Beach

Belle Glade (G-344)
Boca Raton (G-394)
Boynton Beach (G-870)
Canal Point (G-1331)
Delray Beach (G-3037)
Greenacres (G-5078)
Haverhill (G-5241)
Highland Beach (G-5705)
Hypoluxo (G-6048)
Juno Beach (G-6975)
Jupiter (G-6990)
Lake Harbor (G-7394)
Lake Park (G-7465)
Lake Worth (G-7526)
Lake Worth Beach (G-7601)
Lantana (G-7869)
Loxahatchee (G-8355)
Loxahatchee Groves (G-8367)
Mangonia Park (G-8497)
North Palm Beach (G-11715)
Ocean Ridge (G-12080)
Pahokee (G-13470)
Palm Beach (G-13547)
Palm Beach Gardens
(G-13564)
Palm Springs (G-13771)
Riviera Beach (G-15289)
Royal Palm Beach (G-15461)
South Bay (G-16794)
Tequesta (G-18384)
Wellington (G-18707)
West Palm Beach (G-18782)

Pasco

Dade City (G-2423)
Holiday (G-5732)
Hudson (G-6014)
Land O Lakes (G-7849)
New Port Richey (G-11480)
Port Richey (G-15042)
San Antonio (G-15971)
Spring Hill (G-16870)
Trinity (G-18483)
Wesley Chapel (G-18740)
Zephyrhills (G-19506)

Pinellas

Belleair (G-360)
Belleair Beach (G-362)
Belleair Bluffs (G-363)
Clearwater (G-1558)
Clearwater Beach (G-1948)
Dunedin (G-3569)
Gulfport (G-5132)
Indian Rocks Beach (G-6069)
Indian Shores (G-6070)
Kenneth City (G-7153)
Largo (G-7879)
Madeira Beach (G-8445)
Oldsmar (G-12200)
Ozona (G-13467)
Palm Harbor (G-13715)
Pinellas Park (G-14333)
Redington Beach (G-15259)
Redington Shores (G-15260)
Safety Harbor (G-15488)
Saint Petersburg (G-15687)
Seminole (G-16735)
South Pasadena (G-16833)
St Pete Beach (G-16879)
Tarpon Springs (G-18281)
Tierra Verde (G-18405)
Treasure Island (G-18474)

Polk

Auburndale (G-229)
Bartow (G-305)
Davenport (G-2476)
Dundee (G-3564)
Eloise (G-3656)
Fort Meade (G-4338)
Frostproof (G-4855)
Haines City (G-5137)
Kissimmee (G-7314)
Lake Alfred (G-7331)
Lake Hamilton (G-7390)
Lake Wales (G-7498)
Lakeland (G-7624)
Mulberry (G-11118)
Polk City (G-14568)
Winter Haven (G-19292)

Putnam

Crescent City (G-2338)
East Palatka (G-3603)
Florahome (G-3765)
Grandin (G-5047)
Hollister (G-5754)
Interlachen (G-6079)
Melrose (G-8985)
Palatka (G-13471)

Santa Rosa

Bagdad (G-298)
Gulf Breeze (G-5110)
Jay (G-6961)
Milton (G-10920)
Navarre (G-11465)
Pace (G-13468)

Sarasota

Englewood (G-3670)
Lakewood Ranch (G-7842)
Nokomis (G-11578)
North Port (G-11731)
North Venice (G-11753)
Osprey (G-13410)
Sarasota (G-16327)
Venice (G-18526)

Seminole

Altamonte Springs (G-24)
Casselberry (G-1498)
Chuluota (G-1551)
Fern Park (G-3727)
Geneva (G-5019)
Lake Mary (G-7396)
Longwood (G-8248)
Oviedo (G-13411)
Sanford (G-15984)
Winter Springs (G-19465)

St. Johns

Elkton (G-3648)
Hastings (G-5228)
Jacksonville (G-6935)
Ponte Vedra (G-14922)
Ponte Vedra Beach (G-14929)
Saint Augustine (G-15510)
Saint Johns (G-15673)

St. Lucie

Fort Pierce (G-4667)
Hutchinson Island (G-6047)
Port Saint Lucie (G-15085)
Port St Lucie (G-15166)
Saint Lucie West (G-15686)

Sumter

Bushnell (G-1313)
Center Hill (G-1525)
Lady Lake (G-7330)
Lake Panasoffkee (G-7463)
Oxford (G-13464)
Sumterville (G-17067)
The Villages (G-18389)
Webster (G-18697)
Wildwood (G-19190)

Suwannee

Branford (G-1185)
Live Oak (G-8226)
Mc Alpin (G-8598)
O Brien (G-11766)
Wellborn (G-18706)

Taylor

Perry (G-14291)
Steinhatchee (G-16898)

Union

Lake Butler (G-7337)

Volusia

Daytona Beach (G-2619)
De Land (G-2734)
De Leon Springs (G-2735)
Debary (G-2744)
Deland (G-2951)
Deltona (G-3162)
Edgewater (G-3610)
Holly Hill (G-5755)
Lake Helen (G-7395)
New Smyrna (G-11522)
New Smyrna Beach (G-11524)
Orange City (G-12373)
Ormond Beach (G-13345)
Ponce Inlet (G-14921)
Port Orange (G-15009)
South Daytona (G-16798)

Wakulla

Crawfordville (G-2334)
Panacea (G-13859)
Sopchoppy (G-16785)

Walton

Defuniak Springs (G-2939)
Destin (G-3212)
Freeport (G-4844)
Inlet Beach (G-6077)
Miramar Beach (G-11063)
Mossy Head (G-11094)
Panama City (G-13966)
Ponce De Leon (G-14917)
Santa Rosa Beach (G-16151)

Washington

Chipley (G-1540)
Vernon (G-18587)
Wausau (G-18696)

GEOGRAPHIC SECTION

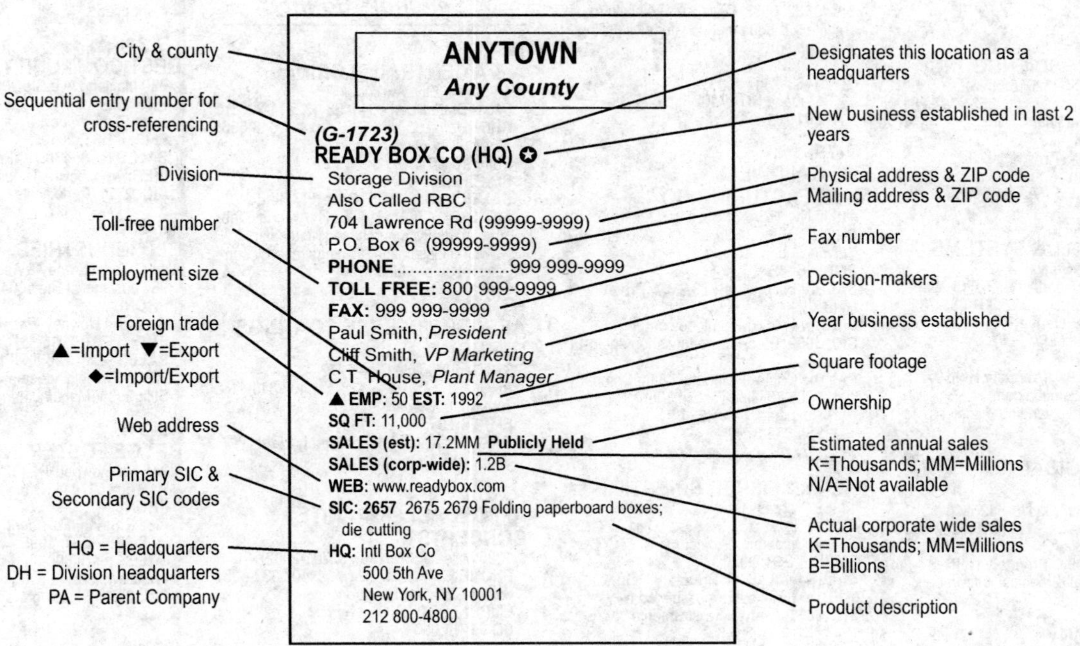

See footnotes for symbols and codes identification.

- This section is in alphabetical order by city.
- Companies are sorted alphabetically under their respective cities.
- To locate cities within a county refer to the County/City Cross Reference Index.

IMPORTANT NOTICE: It is a violation of both federal and state law to transmit an unsolicited advertisement to a facsimile machine. Any user of this product that violates such laws may be subject to civil and criminal penalties which may exceed $500 for each transmission of an unsolicited facsimile. Harris InfoSource provides fax numbers for lawful purposes only and expressly forbids the use of these numbers in any unlawful manner.

Alachua
Alachua County

(G-1)
ALACHUA TODAY INC
14804 Main St (32615-8590)
P.O. Box 2135 (32616-2135)
PHONE..................................386 462-3355
Gail Luparello, *President*
EMP: 6 **EST:** 2000
SQ FT: 1,472
SALES (est): 660.3K **Privately Held**
WEB: www.alachuatoday.com
SIC: 2711 Newspapers, publishing & printing

(G-2)
AMEND SURGICAL INC
14000 Nw 126th Ter (32615-4884)
PHONE..................................844 281-3169
Robby Lane, *CEO*
EMP: 10 **EST:** 2015
SALES (est): 1.1MM **Privately Held**
SIC: 3841 Surgical & medical instruments

(G-3)
AP LIFESCIENCES LLC
12085 Research Dr Ste 155 (32615-6837)
PHONE..................................954 300-7469
Ammon Peck, *COO*
Benjamin Canales, *Senior VP*
Nigel Richards, *Senior VP*
Cuong Nguyen,
EMP: 10 **EST:** 2015
SALES (est): 556.7K **Privately Held**
SIC: 2835 In vitro diagnostics

(G-4)
APPAREL PRINTERS
13201 Rachael Blvd (32615-6688)
P.O. Box 1649 (32616-1649)
PHONE..................................352 463-8850
Harold M Hofstetter, *Owner*
EMP: 7 **EST:** 1988
SQ FT: 6,000
SALES (est): 300K **Privately Held**
WEB: www.apparel-printers.com
SIC: 2262 7389 5199 2759 Screen printing: manmade fiber & silk broadwoven fabrics; sign painting & lettering shop; advertising specialties; screen printing; embroidery products, except schiffli machine

(G-5)
APPLIED GENETIC TECH CORP
14193 Nw 119th Ter Ste 10 (32615-9410)
PHONE..................................386 462-2204
Scott Koenig, *Ch of Bd*
Susan B Washer, *President*
William A Sullivan, *CFO*
Matthew Feinsod, *Chief Mktg Ofcr*
Brian Krex, *General Counsel*
EMP: 78 **EST:** 1999
SQ FT: 21,000
SALES: 500K **Privately Held**
WEB: www.agtc.com
SIC: 2836 8731 Biological products, except diagnostic; biological research

(G-6)
AXOGEN INC (PA)
13631 Progress Blvd # 400 (32615-9409)
PHONE..................................386 462-6800
Karen Zaderej, *Ch of Bd*
Brad Alexander, *Area Mgr*
Phillip Edmondson, *Area Mgr*
Mark Friedman, *Senior VP*
Shawn McCarrey, *Senior VP*
▲ **EMP:** 153 **EST:** 1977
SQ FT: 11,761
SALES: 112.3MM **Publicly Held**
WEB: www.axogeninc.com
SIC: 3845 Electrotherapeutic apparatus

(G-7)
AXOGEN CORPORATION
13631 Progress Blvd # 400 (32615-9409)
P.O. Box 357787, Gainesville (32635-7787)
PHONE..................................386 462-6800
Karen Zaderej, *CEO*
Stacy Arnold, *Vice Pres*
John Engels, *Vice Pres*
Mark Friedman, *Vice Pres*
Brad Hedger, *Vice Pres*
EMP: 32 **EST:** 2002
SALES (est): 13MM
SALES (corp-wide): 112.3MM **Publicly Held**
WEB: www.axogeninc.com
SIC: 3842 Implants, surgical
PA: Axogen, Inc.
13631 Progress Blvd # 400
Alachua FL 32615
386 462-6800

(G-8)
BACK TO GODHEAD INC
Also Called: B T G
13921 Nw 146th Ave (32615-6193)
P.O. Box 430 (32616-0430)
PHONE..................................386 462-0481
Norman Comtois, *President*
▲ **EMP:** 11 **EST:** 1944
SALES (est): 715.7K **Privately Held**
WEB: www.back2godhead.com
SIC: 2721 Magazines: publishing only, not printed on site

(G-9)
BIOENERGETICS PRESS
19802 Old Bellamy Rd (32615-3867)
PHONE..................................386 462-5155
EMP: 10
SALES (est): 557.5K **Privately Held**
SIC: 2741 Misc Publishing

(G-10)
INTERMED GROUP INC (PA)
13301 Nw Us Highway 441 (32615-8512)
PHONE..................................561 586-3667
Rick Staab, *CEO*
Larry Hertzler, *COO*
Scott Nudelman, *COO*
Cristopher Baldwin, *CFO*
Hughie Elliott, *Technology*
EMP: 41 **EST:** 1984
SQ FT: 4,000
SALES (est): 29.8MM **Privately Held**
WEB: www.intermed1.com
SIC: 3841 3842 5047 Surgical & medical instruments; surgical appliances & supplies; medical equipment & supplies

(G-11)
LINDSAY PRECAST INC
13365 Southern Precast Dr (32615-8548)
PHONE..................................800 669-2278
Roland C Lindsay, *President*
Randy Trimm, *Project Mgr*
Mark Severance, *Purchasing*
EMP: 50
SALES (corp-wide): 55.8MM **Privately Held**
WEB: www.lindsayprecast.com
SIC: 3272 Concrete products

PA: Lindsay Precast, Inc.
6845 Erie Ave Nw
Canal Fulton OH 44614
800 837-7788

(G-12)
OPTIMA NEUROSCIENCE INC
11930 Research Cir (32615-6826)
PHONE..................................352 371-8281
Timothy Tucker, *President*
EMP: 6 **EST:** 2009
SALES (est): 700K **Privately Held**
WEB: www.tdt.com
SIC: 3841 Surgical & medical instruments

(G-13)
OPTIMAL VENDING SYSTEMS
Also Called: Optimal Station
22806 Nw County Road 241 (32615-3929)
PHONE..................................301 633-2353
Michele Sparks, *CEO*
Alex Garnier, *Project Mgr*
EMP: 8 **EST:** 2017
SALES (est): 708.9K **Privately Held**
WEB: www.optimalstation.com
SIC: 3581 Automatic vending machines

(G-14)
PIONEER SURGICAL TECHNOLOGY
11621 Research Cir (32615-6825)
PHONE..................................906 225-5629
EMP: 8 **EST:** 2018
SALES (est): 184.9K **Privately Held**
SIC: 3841 Surgical & medical instruments

(G-15)
REGENERATION TECHNOLOGIES INC
11621 Research Cir (32615-6825)
PHONE..................................386 418-8888
Caroline Hartill, *Exec VP*
Keith Koford, *VP Legal*
Eric Baldwin, *Vice Pres*
Johannes Louw, *Vice Pres*
William Cassarly, *Opers Mgr*
EMP: 18 **EST:** 2019
SALES (est): 4.4MM **Privately Held**
SIC: 3841 Surgical & medical instruments

(G-16)
RTI SURGICAL INC
11621 Research Cir (32615-6825)
PHONE..................................386 418-8888
Olivier Visa, *President*
Paul Montague, *VP Human Res*
Jim Borta, *Sales Staff*
Eric Barnum, *Marketing Staff*
Mark Traffas, *Marketing Staff*
EMP: 200 **EST:** 2019
SALES (est): 33.3MM **Privately Held**
WEB: www.rtix.com
SIC: 3841 Surgical & medical instruments

(G-17)
SABINE INC
13301 Nw Us Highway 441 (32615-8512)
PHONE..................................386 418-2000
Doran Oster, *CEO*
Kim Kelley, *CFO*
Michael Mychalczuk, *CTO*
◆ **EMP:** 79 **EST:** 1971
SQ FT: 45,000
SALES (est): 1.1MM
SALES (corp-wide): 29MM **Publicly Held**
WEB: www.clearone.com
SIC: 3699 3931 Electric sound equipment; string instruments & parts
PA: Clearone, Inc.
5225 W Wiley Post Way # 500
Salt Lake City UT 84116
801 975-7200

(G-18)
SANDVIK MINING & CNSTR USA LLC (DH)
13500 Nw County Road 235 (32615-6150)
PHONE..................................386 462-4100
Olof Faxander, *CEO*
David Levy, *Vice Pres*
Kathy Hellriegel, *Purch Dir*
Tim Clayton, *Engineer*
Mats Backman, *CFO*
◆ **EMP:** 150 **EST:** 1998
SQ FT: 70,000
SALES (est): 62.6MM
SALES (corp-wide): 9.9B **Privately Held**
WEB: www.home.sandvik
SIC: 3532 3533 Drills, core; oil field machinery & equipment; water well drilling equipment
HQ: Sandvik, Inc.
1483 Dogwood Way
Mebane NC 27302
201 794-5000

(G-19)
THE CALDWELL MANUFACTURING CO
11600 Nw 173rd St Ste 110 (32615-6059)
PHONE..................................386 418-3525
Wayne Sutton, *Manager*
EMP: 46
SALES (corp-wide): 73.2MM **Privately Held**
WEB: www.caldwellmfgco.com
SIC: 3999 Barber & beauty shop equipment
PA: The Caldwell Manufacturing Company
2605 Manitou Rd Ste 100
Rochester NY 14624
585 352-3790

(G-20)
THERMO FISHER SCIENTIFIC ✪
13859 Progress Blvd (32615-9403)
PHONE..................................781 327-3261
Bonnie Dispagno, *Project Mgr*
EMP: 14 **EST:** 2020
SALES (est): 3MM **Privately Held**
WEB: www.jobs.thermofisher.com
SIC: 3826 Analytical instruments

(G-21)
TUCKER-DAVIS TECHNOLOGIES INC
11930 Research Cir (32615-6826)
PHONE..................................386 462-9622
Timothy J Tucker, *President*
Jennifer Sanders, *Controller*
April Hatfield, *Sales Staff*
Mark Hanus, *Technical Staff*
Christine M Tucker, *Admin Sec*
EMP: 29 **EST:** 1980
SQ FT: 15,000
SALES (est): 5.3MM **Privately Held**
WEB: www.tdt.com
SIC: 3829 3825 Measuring & controlling devices; digital test equipment, electronic & electrical circuits

(G-22)
TUTOGEN MEDICAL INC (DH)
11621 Research Cir (32615-6825)
P.O. Box 2650 (32616-2650)
PHONE..................................386 418-8888
Roy D Crowninshield, *Ch of Bd*
Guy L Mayer, *President*
David C Greenspan, *Vice Pres*
Claude O Pering, *Vice Pres*
Clifton Seliga, *Vice Pres*
EMP: 49 **EST:** 1985
SQ FT: 34,384
SALES (est): 55.8MM
SALES (corp-wide): 101.7MM **Publicly Held**
SIC: 3841 Surgical & medical instruments
HQ: Surgalign Spine Technologies, Inc.
520 Lake Cook Rd Ste 315
Deerfield IL 60015
630 227-3809

Alford
Jackson County

(G-23)
WASHERS-R-US INC
2205 Park Rd (32420-6819)
PHONE..................................850 573-0221
Michael W Baxley, *Partner*
EMP: 7 **EST:** 2008
SALES (est): 62.6K **Privately Held**
WEB: www.washers-r-us.com
SIC: 3452 Washers

Altamonte Springs
Seminole County

(G-24)
A & A CENTRAL FLORIDA
Also Called: Elite Awnings
540 N State Road 434 # 53 (32714-2166)
PHONE..................................407 648-5666
Steve Alvin, *Owner*
EMP: 10 **EST:** 1991
SQ FT: 2,200
SALES (est): 273.2K **Privately Held**
SIC: 2394 1799 5999 5211 Awnings, fabric: made from purchased materials; awning installation; awnings; energy conservation products

(G-25)
AEROSPC/DFENSE COATINGS GA INC
378 Centerpointe Cir # 1272 (32701-3438)
PHONE..................................407 843-1140
Tom Scott, *Owner*
EMP: 8 **EST:** 2008
SALES (est): 161.1K **Privately Held**
SIC: 3479 Metal coating & allied service

(G-26)
AFFORDABLE GRANITE CONCEPTS
1025 Miller Dr Ste 139 (32701-2082)
PHONE..................................407 332-0057
Walter S Pianta, *President*
EMP: 13 **EST:** 2009
SQ FT: 14,000
SALES: 4.5MM **Privately Held**
WEB: www.affordablegraniteconcepts.com
SIC: 3281 Cut stone & stone products

(G-27)
AGM ORLANDO INC
223 Altamonte Commerce Bl (32714-2550)
PHONE..................................407 865-9522
Carmine Parente, *President*
Bill Shoewalter, *Vice Pres*
▲ **EMP:** 5 **EST:** 1998
SQ FT: 4,000
SALES (est): 1MM **Privately Held**
SIC: 3088 Shower stalls, fiberglass & plastic

(G-28)
ALLEGRA MARKETING PRINT DESIGN
620 Douglas Ave Ste 1308 (32714-2546)
PHONE..................................407 848-1721
EMP: 6 **EST:** 2018
SALES (est): 206.3K **Privately Held**
WEB: www.allegramarketingprint.com
SIC: 2752 Commercial printing, offset

(G-29)
ALTAMONTE WOODWORKING CO INC
318 Broadview Ave (32701-6233)
PHONE..................................407 331-0020
Pete Drennan, *Owner*
EMP: 6 **EST:** 1982
SALES (est): 287.6K **Privately Held**
WEB: www.altamontewoodworkingco.com
SIC: 2434 Wood kitchen cabinets

(G-30)
AM CABINETS LLC
628 Alpine St (32701-2634)
PHONE..................................321 663-4319
Yennisey Fenandez, *Manager*
EMP: 6 **EST:** 2017
SALES (est): 993.4K **Privately Held**
WEB: www.amcabinetsllc.com
SIC: 2434 Wood kitchen cabinets

(G-31)
AMRAV INC
Also Called: Frame Tech of Orlando
1026 Miller Dr (32701-2032)
PHONE..................................407 831-1550
Drew Vargo, *President*
Rita Vargo, *Vice Pres*
EMP: 7 **EST:** 1992
SQ FT: 5,000
SALES (est): 579.1K **Privately Held**
SIC: 3555 5084 Printing trades machinery; printing trades machinery, equipment & supplies

(G-32)
BEST COMMUNITY MAGAZINE
260 Maitland Ave Ste 2000 (32701-5510)
PHONE..................................407 571-2980
John Foret, *Principal*
EMP: 6 **EST:** 2010
SALES (est): 179.7K **Privately Held**
WEB: www.bcvdeals.com
SIC: 2721 Periodicals

(G-33)
BLD INDUSTRIES
Also Called: Downey & Associates
987 Josiane Ct Ste 1064 (32701-3665)
PHONE..................................321 207-0050
Benjamin Downey, *Principal*
EMP: 6 **EST:** 2015
SALES (est): 298.3K **Privately Held**
WEB: www.bldindustries.com
SIC: 3999 Manufacturing industries

(G-34)
BRYCE FOSTER INC
215 Rollingwood Trl (32714-3412)
P.O. Box 547841, Orlando (32854-7841)
PHONE..................................800 371-0395
Alec E String, *President*
▲ **EMP:** 9 **EST:** 1995
SALES (est): 690.3K **Privately Held**
WEB: www.brycefoster.com
SIC: 2674 Shipping & shopping bags or sacks

(G-35)
BUBBA ROPE LLC
998 Explorer Cv Ste 130 (32701-7500)
PHONE..................................877 499-8494
Jim Flowers, *General Mgr*
Douglas J Worswick, *Administration*
EMP: 8 **EST:** 2015
SALES (est): 373.3K **Privately Held**
WEB: www.bubbarope.com
SIC: 2298 Ropes & fiber cables; rope, except asbestos & wire

(G-36)
CAPTIVE-AIRE SYSTEMS INC
311 Altamonte Commerce Bl (32714-2553)
P.O. Box 917396, Longwood (32791-7396)
PHONE..................................407 682-9396
Steve Luddy, *Regional Mgr*
Mark Schneider, *Branch Mgr*
Kurt Curtis, *Manager*
Kevin Busta, *Supervisor*
EMP: 22
SALES (corp-wide): 401.1MM **Privately Held**
WEB: www.captiveaire.com
SIC: 3444 Restaurant sheet metalwork
PA: Captive-Aire Systems, Inc.
4641 Paragon Park Rd # 104
Raleigh NC 27616
919 882-2410

(G-37)
CLEAR CHOICE INC
1045 Miller Dr (32701-2067)
PHONE..................................407 830-6968
Brian Smith, *President*
Adam Salinas, *Sales Staff*
Michelle Salinas, *Office Mgr*
EMP: 5 **EST:** 2000
SALES (est): 767.8K **Privately Held**
WEB: www.clearchoicelaminating.com
SIC: 2759 Promotional printing

(G-38)
CONNECTED LIFE SOLUTIONS LLC
Also Called: Consulting
153 Dahlia Dr (32714-2124)
PHONE..................................407 745-1952
Mario Pino, *Mng Member*
Marc Eskenas, *Manager*
Mario J Pino, *Manager*
Ramiro Ruiz, *Manager*
EMP: 10 **EST:** 2014

SALES (est): 440.8K **Privately Held**
WEB: www.connectedls.com
SIC: 7372 8748 7379 8742 Prepackaged software; communications consulting; ; marketing consulting services;

(G-39)
CREATIVE CANVAS CENTL FLA INC
436 Wekiva Rapids Dr (32714-7546)
PHONE..................................407 661-1211
Beverly Costello, *Principal*
Edward Ortiz, *Opers Staff*
Matthew Bello, *Engineer*
Miguel Pozo, *Human Resources*
Michael Betts, *Marketing Staff*
EMP: 12 **EST:** 2014
SALES (est): 319.5K **Privately Held**
SIC: 2211 Canvas

(G-40)
DIGITAL LIVING
4303 Vineland Rd (32714)
PHONE..................................407 332-9998
EMP: 8
SALES (est): 780K **Privately Held**
SIC: 3823 Mfg Process Control Instruments

(G-41)
DJ LIVE PRODUCTIONS LLC
999 Douglas Ave (32714-2064)
PHONE..................................407 383-1740
Austin Beeghly, *Principal*
EMP: 6 **EST:** 2015
SALES (est): 269.8K **Privately Held**
WEB: www.djliveproductions.com
SIC: 3651 5999 3648 Amplifiers: radio, public address or musical instrument; audio-visual equipment & supplies; stage lighting equipment

(G-42)
EDDYS FILTER CHANGE INC
822 Keystone Ave (32701-6410)
PHONE..................................407 448-4498
Edward J Walter, *Principal*
EMP: 6 **EST:** 2009
SALES (est): 79.9K **Privately Held**
SIC: 3569 Filters

(G-43)
EIZO RUGGED SOLUTIONS INC
442 Northlake Blvd # 1008 (32701-5244)
PHONE..................................407 262-7100
Selwyn L Henriques, *President*
Mike Kreischer, *Business Mgr*
Rosemary Penn, *Business Mgr*
Kyana Brooks, *Opers Mgr*
Jeff Grant, *Design Engr*
EMP: 27 **EST:** 1984
SQ FT: 13,000
SALES (est): 9.6MM **Privately Held**
WEB: www.eizorugged.com
SIC: 3577 7371 Graphic displays, except graphic terminals; custom computer programming services
HQ: Eizo Inc.
5710 Warland Dr
Cypress CA 90630
562 431-5011

(G-44)
ETERNAL ELEMENTS LLC
1045 Miller Dr (32701-2067)
PHONE..................................407 830-6968
Michelle Salinas, *Principal*
EMP: 8 **EST:** 2010
SALES (est): 542.5K **Privately Held**
SIC: 2819 Industrial inorganic chemicals

(G-45)
EUROPRINT INC
620 Douglas Ave Ste 1308 (32714-2546)
PHONE..................................407 869-9955
Scott Johnson, *President*
EMP: 13 **EST:** 1994
SQ FT: 5,000
SALES (est): 458.4K **Privately Held**
WEB: www.euromediausa.com
SIC: 2711 Newspapers

(G-46)
FLORIDAS BEST INC
839 Sunshine Ln (32714-3901)
PHONE..................................407 682-9570
James L Toler, *President*
EMP: 6 **EST:** 2011
SALES (est): 601.4K **Privately Held**
WEB: www.floridasbest.com
SIC: 2834 Lip balms

(G-47)
FRESHSURETY CORPORATION
277 Douglas Ave Ste 1002 (32714-3300)
PHONE..................................321 209-8699
John Hodges, *CEO*
EMP: 7 **EST:** 2016
SQ FT: 2,500
SALES (est): 630.1K **Privately Held**
WEB: www.smartfoodstuff.com
SIC: 3679 Electronic circuits; microwave components; antennas, receiving

(G-48)
GF WOODWORKS
1306 Pressview Ave (32701-7742)
P.O. Box 181735, Casselberry (32718-1735)
PHONE..................................407 716-3712
Gary Fliess, *Manager*
EMP: 7 **EST:** 2006
SALES (est): 74.9K **Privately Held**
SIC: 2431 Millwork

(G-49)
GZ DUMPSTERS LLC
1231 Woodridge Ct (32714-1291)
PHONE..................................407 600-0756
Hector Abraham, *Administration*
EMP: 7 **EST:** 2016
SALES (est): 124.3K **Privately Held**
SIC: 3443 Dumpsters, garbage

(G-50)
HUNTED TEES LLC
606 Hattaway Dr (32701-6105)
PHONE..................................407 260-2138
Hurley Constantine, *Principal*
EMP: 6 **EST:** 2016
SALES (est): 114.8K **Privately Held**
SIC: 2759 Screen printing

(G-51)
INNOVATIVE SUPPORT SYSTEMS
1030 Sunshine Ln Ste 1000 (32714-3882)
PHONE..................................407 682-7570
Wood Breazeale, *President*
W Breazeale, *Owner*
Sean Devaney, *Sales Staff*
Peter Gibiser, *Sales Staff*
Patrick Saldana, *Sales Staff*
EMP: 8 **EST:** 2001
SALES (est): 1.4MM **Privately Held**
WEB: www.issifl.com
SIC: 3585 5075 Air conditioning units, complete: domestic or industrial; warm air heating equipment & supplies

(G-52)
LA CIUDAD EN SUS MANOS LLC
555 Forest Lake Dr (32714-2860)
PHONE..................................813 770-4973
Nathaniel Graham, *Principal*
EMP: 6 **EST:** 2013
SALES (est): 120.3K **Privately Held**
WEB: www.laciudadensusmanos.com
SIC: 2741 Miscellaneous publishing

(G-53)
LORENZE & ASSOCIATES INC
1030 Sunshine Ln Ste 1000 (32714-3830)
PHONE..................................407 682-7570
Dewayne Lorenze, *President*
Sharon Lorenze, *Admin Sec*
EMP: 9 **EST:** 1979
SQ FT: 1,800
SALES (est): 704.9K **Privately Held**
SIC: 3585 Heating & air conditioning combination units

(G-54)
M12 LENSES INC
350 Pinestraw Cir (32714-5415)
PHONE..................................407 973-4403
Priyangika Goonetilleke, *Principal*
EMP: 6 **EST:** 2010
SALES (est): 212.4K **Privately Held**
WEB: www.m12lenses.com
SIC: 3851 Ophthalmic goods

(G-55)
MAG CLEANING SOLUTIONS LLC
Also Called: Welding
428 Los Altos Way Apt 204 (32714-3272)
PHONE..................................321 317-3298
Grant Michael Asr, *Branch Mgr*
EMP: 8
SALES (corp-wide): 47.6K **Privately Held**
WEB: www.magweldingllc.com
SIC: 7692 Welding repair
PA: Mag Cleaning Solutions Llc
428 Los Altos Way Apt 204
Altamonte Springs FL

(G-56)
MANNS DIVERSIFIED INDUSTRIES
380 S State Road 434 # 10 (32714-3810)
PHONE..................................407 310-5938
Roy Harold Mann Jr, *Principal*
EMP: 6 **EST:** 2012
SALES (est): 270.2K **Privately Held**
SIC: 3999 Manufacturing industries

(G-57)
NEW SOURCE CORP
107 Hilltop Pl (32701-7604)
PHONE..................................407 830-7771
EMP: 7 **EST:** 2019
SALES (est): 161.8K **Privately Held**
WEB: www.newsourcecorp.com
SIC: 3761 Guided missiles & space vehicles

(G-58)
NORTH AMRCN PRTECTION CTRL LLC
190 N Westmonte Dr (32714-3342)
P.O. Box 161060 (32716-1060)
PHONE..................................407 788-3717
EMP: 7
SALES (est): 659.3K **Privately Held**
SIC: 3462 3568 Iron And Steel Forgings, Nsk

(G-59)
OAKTREE SOFTWARE INC
Also Called: Accordance Bible Software
222 S Westmonte Dr # 251 (32714-4269)
PHONE..................................407 339-5855
Roy B Brown, *President*
Helen Brown, *Vice Pres*
Kristen Linduff, *CFO*
Darin Allen, *Marketing Staff*
Jackie Bolton, *Marketing Staff*
EMP: 10 **EST:** 1989
SALES (est): 2MM **Privately Held**
WEB: www.accordancebible.com
SIC: 7372 Prepackaged software

(G-60)
ORANGE PEEL GAZETTE
760 Mahogany Ln (32714-1326)
PHONE..................................407 312-7335
Jon Richeson, *Principal*
EMP: 6 **EST:** 2001
SALES (est): 139.5K **Privately Held**
WEB: www.orangepeelgazette.com
SIC: 2711 Newspapers, publishing & printing

(G-61)
PARADISE BUILDING MTLS LLC
665 Youngstown Pkwy # 268 (32714-4550)
PHONE..................................407 267-3378
Kevin Fagan,
EMP: 7 **EST:** 2017
SALES (est): 264.2K **Privately Held**
SIC: 3999 Manufacturing industries

(G-62)
PATHFINDER SHIRTS
865 Sunshine Ln (32714-3952)
PHONE..................................407 865-6530
Karen Lillard, *Principal*
EMP: 9 **EST:** 2014
SALES (est): 605.9K **Privately Held**
WEB: www.pathfindershirts.com
SIC: 2759 Screen printing

(G-63)
PAVER WAY LLC
160 N Spring Trl (32714-3461)
PHONE..................................321 303-0968
John Gilmore, *Principal*
EMP: 10 **EST:** 2009
SALES (est): 1.3MM **Privately Held**
SIC: 3531 Pavers

(G-64)
PHARMA RESOURCES INC
380 S State Road 434 (32714-3810)
PHONE..................................973 780-5241
Gregory A Longo, *President*
EMP: 10 **EST:** 2003
SALES (est): 633.1K **Privately Held**
WEB: www.pharmaresourcesint.com
SIC: 2834 Pharmaceutical preparations

(G-65)
PINS FEVER
161 Willow Ave (32714-2117)
PHONE..................................407 619-5314
Edgar Lopez, *Owner*
EMP: 6 **EST:** 2010
SALES (est): 78.9K **Privately Held**
WEB: www.pinsfever.com
SIC: 3452 Pins

(G-66)
PRISTINE LASER CENTER
1180 Spring Cntre S Blvd (32714)
PHONE..................................407 389-1200
Mohammad Eskandari, *Manager*
EMP: 7 **EST:** 2011
SALES (est): 1MM **Privately Held**
WEB: www.pristinelasercenter.com
SIC: 3845 Laser systems & equipment, medical

(G-67)
PRODIGY CUSTOMS
527 Little Wekiva Rd (32714-7403)
PHONE..................................407 832-1752
Frank Serafine, *Principal*
EMP: 7 **EST:** 2005
SALES (est): 81K **Privately Held**
SIC: 2395 Embroidery & art needlework

(G-68)
PROTECTIVE ENCLOSURES CO LLC
Also Called: TV Shield, The
385 Centerpointe Cir # 1319 (32701-3443)
PHONE..................................321 441-9689
Joe Harrell, *General Mgr*
Justin King, *Mng Member*
Jarad King,
▲ **EMP:** 6 **EST:** 2011
SALES (est): 1MM **Privately Held**
WEB: www.protectiveenclosures.com
SIC: 3089 Plastic hardware & building products

(G-69)
RAPID RESPONSE
250 Altmnte Commerce 10 (32714-2535)
PHONE..................................407 774-9877
Donald Dass, *Manager*
EMP: 8 **EST:** 2010
SALES (est): 509.2K **Privately Held**
WEB: www.rapiddeploy.com
SIC: 1389 Construction, repair & dismantling services

(G-70)
RARE CABINETS INC
613 Majorca Ave (32714-2221)
PHONE..................................407 415-3730
Noel F Dowling III, *Principal*
EMP: 6 **EST:** 2015
SALES (est): 162.6K **Privately Held**
WEB: www.rarecabinets.com
SIC: 2434 Wood kitchen cabinets

(G-71)
SAFARI SUN LLC
928 Josiane Ct Ste 1007 (32701-3617)
PHONE..................................407 339-7291
Tara Montano, *Accounts Mgr*
Melissa Battista, *Cust Mgr*
Marlene McQuaig, *Sales Staff*
Heather Eshack, *Marketing Mgr*
John Bohannon, *Asst Office Mgr*
EMP: 30 **EST:** 1980
SQ FT: 6,000
SALES (est): 5.6MM **Privately Held**
WEB: www.safarisun.com
SIC: 2759 Directories, telephone: printing

(G-72)
SEMINOLE METAL FINISHING INC
967 Explorer Cv (32701-7516)
PHONE..................................407 332-8949
Elliott Blackwelder, *President*
Carla Blackwelder, *Vice Pres*
EMP: 15 **EST:** 1987
SALES (est): 1.6MM **Privately Held**
WEB: www.smfi.net
SIC: 3471 7389 Finishing, metals or formed products; electroplating of metals or formed products;

(G-73)
SIGNAGE PLUS LLC
484 Abba St (32714-2447)
PHONE..................................407 668-3567
Gary L Hoenig, *Principal*
EMP: 6 **EST:** 2016
SALES (est): 101.8K **Privately Held**
WEB: www.signage-plus.com
SIC: 3993 Signs & advertising specialties

(G-74)
SIGNATURE PRINTING TECHNOLOGY
682 Youngstown Pkwy # 330 (32714-4565)
PHONE..................................407 963-6291
John Mitchell, *Principal*
EMP: 6 **EST:** 2001
SALES (est): 143.2K **Privately Held**
WEB: www.signatureprinters.com
SIC: 2752 Commercial printing, lithographic

(G-75)
SOPHTECH BA SOLUTIONS LLC
705 Crosby Dr (32714-7218)
PHONE..................................407 389-4011
Lynda D Vidot, *Owner*
EMP: 6 **EST:** 2014
SALES (est): 185.3K **Privately Held**
WEB: www.sophtechba.com
SIC: 7372 Educational computer software

(G-76)
SPECIAL EDITIONSPUBLISHING
Also Called: Special Editions Publishing
999 Douglas Ave Ste 3317 (32714-2063)
P.O. Box 953813, Lake Mary (32795-3813)
PHONE..................................407 862-7737
Albert Sciuto, *President*
Mark Heagy, *Advt Staff*
Rosalyn Porter, *Manager*
Lydia Enriquez, *Bd of Directors*
EMP: 5 **EST:** 1976
SQ FT: 3,000
SALES (est): 456.7K **Privately Held**
SIC: 2721 Magazines: publishing only, not printed on site

(G-77)
SUNSHINE METAL PRODUCTS INC
195 Magnolia St (32701-7512)
PHONE..................................407 331-1300
Benjamin J Coble, *President*
EMP: 5 **EST:** 2003
SQ FT: 4,794
SALES (est): 759.2K **Privately Held**
WEB: www.sunshinemetalproducts.com
SIC: 3444 Sheet metalwork

(G-78)
SUPER LITE ALUMINUM PRODUCTS
Also Called: Racestar Manufacturing
1090 Rainer Dr (32714-3846)
PHONE..................................407 682-2121
Todd A Vallancourt, *President*
Ellen Vallancourt, *Vice Pres*
EMP: 6 **EST:** 2001
SALES (est): 814.2K **Privately Held**
SIC: 3354 Aluminum extruded products

(G-79)
TWO GUYS PLUMBING SUPPLY LLC
1030 Sunshine Ln Ste 1020 (32714-3882)
PHONE..................................321 263-0021
Frank J Altilio, *Vice Pres*
EMP: 10 **EST:** 2010
SALES (est): 834.7K **Privately Held**
SIC: 3088 Plastics plumbing fixtures

(G-80)
ULTIMATE SWIMWEAR INC
247 N Westmonte Dr (32714-3345)
PHONE..................................386 668-8900
Gwyn R Picerne, *President*
EMP: 7 **EST:** 1993
SQ FT: 12,000
SALES (est): 307.2K **Privately Held**
WEB: www.ultimateswimwear.com
SIC: 2339 2329 5699 Bathing suits: women's, misses' & juniors'; bathing suits & swimwear: men's & boys'; bathing suits

(G-81)
UNITED ADVG PUBLICATIONS INC
Also Called: For Rent Media Solutions
225 S Westmonte Dr # 3050 (32714-4215)
PHONE..................................407 297-0832
Sherri Stigmeyer, *Manager*
EMP: 6 **Privately Held**
SIC: 2721 7299 Periodicals; apartment locating service
HQ: United Advertising Publications, Inc.
1331 L St Nw Ste 2
Washington DC 20005
210 377-3116

(G-82)
VEDIC ORIGINS INC
478 E Altamonte Dr # 108 (32701-4628)
PHONE..................................407 712-5614
Chirag Patel, *Principal*
EMP: 7 **EST:** 2010
SALES (est): 154.7K **Privately Held**
SIC: 2833 Vitamins, natural or synthetic: bulk, uncompounded

(G-83)
VINTAGE IRONWORKS LLC
671 Newburyport Ave (32701-2740)
PHONE..................................407 339-2555
William J Walters, *Mng Member*
EMP: 7 **EST:** 2005
SALES (est): 675.8K **Privately Held**
WEB: www.vintageirondoors.com
SIC: 3446 Architectural metalwork

(G-84)
WIZARD LABS
927 Fern St Ste 1000 (32701-2747)
PHONE..................................321 422-0803
EMP: 9 **EST:** 2013
SALES (est): 443.1K **Privately Held**
WEB: www.wizardlabs.us
SIC: 3651 Household audio & video equipment

(G-85)
XOXO BEAUTY STUDIO LLC
937 W State Road 436 # 115 (32714-2927)
Rural Route 937 Fl 436 (32714)
PHONE..................................407 476-7172
Barbara Cherubin, *Owner*
EMP: 6 **EST:** 2018
SALES (est): 42.6K **Privately Held**
WEB: www.xoxobeautystudio.com
SIC: 3999 7231 Eyelashes, artificial; beauty shops; cosmetology & personal hygiene salons; beauty schools

Altha
Calhoun County

(G-86)
WALDEN TIMBER HARVESTING INC
13851 Nw Sand Cut Trl (32421-4940)
PHONE..................................850 674-4884
Troy Walden, *President*
Garnet Walden, *Vice Pres*
EMP: 10 **EST:** 1983
SALES (est): 843.9K **Privately Held**
SIC: 2411 Logging camps & contractors

Altoona
Lake County

(G-87)
NORTHROP GRUMMAN CORPORATION
18510 Nfs 524 (32702)
PHONE..................................352 759-2946
Clyde Colley, *Manager*
EMP: 6 **Publicly Held**
WEB: www.northropgrumman.com
SIC: 3812 Aircraft/aerospace flight instruments & guidance systems
PA: Northrop Grumman Corporation
2980 Fairview Park Dr
Falls Church VA 22042

Alva
Lee County

(G-88)
EZ TRUCK SERVICES INC
19595 N River Rd (33920-3247)
PHONE..................................239 728-3022
Edward P Zengel Sr, *President*
Marie Zengel, *Corp Secy*
Edward A Zengel Jr, *Vice Pres*
EMP: 14 **EST:** 1988
SALES (est): 810.7K **Privately Held**
SIC: 3715 Truck trailers

(G-89)
NPC&UG INC
22021 Luckey Lee Ln (33920-4013)
PHONE..................................239 694-7255
Mitchell Nobles, *Principal*
EMP: 8 **EST:** 2007
SALES (est): 1.2MM **Privately Held**
SIC: 2911 Gases & liquefied petroleum gases

(G-90)
RABER INDUSTRIES INC
2190 Sebastian Ct (33920-3824)
PHONE..................................239 728-5527
Thomas E Raber Jr, *President*
Bill Bolek, *Manager*
Dan Subbert, *Admin Sec*
EMP: 9 **EST:** 2000
SALES (est): 1.8MM **Privately Held**
WEB: www.raberindustries.com
SIC: 3441 Fabricated structural metal

(G-91)
SIMPLY CLOSETS & CABINETS
10105 Amberwood Rd Ste 6 (33920)
PHONE..................................239 994-4264
Barbara Roessner, *Owner*
EMP: 7 **EST:** 2013
SALES (est): 600K **Privately Held**
WEB: www.simplyclosetsandcabinets.com
SIC: 2434 Wood kitchen cabinets

Amelia Island
Nassau County

(G-92)
AMERICAN MAGLEV TECH FLA INC
8030 Frst Cast Hwy Apt 10 (32034)
PHONE..................................404 386-4036
Tony Morris, *CEO*
Jordan Morris, *CFO*
EMP: 10 **EST:** 1994
SALES (est): 940.1K **Privately Held**
WEB: www.american-maglev.com
SIC: 3764 Propulsion units for guided missiles & space vehicles

(G-93)
WELL TRAVELED IMPORTS INC
Also Called: Well Traveled Living
716 S 8th St (32034-3703)
P.O. Box 4, Fernandina Beach (32035-0004)
PHONE..................................904 261-5400
Edwin Hall, *CEO*
Hampton Tanner, *President*
Christine Glumm, *Manager*
▲ **EMP:** 18 **EST:** 1998
SQ FT: 50,000
SALES (est): 4MM **Privately Held**
WEB: www.wtliving.com
SIC: 3645 5021 5023 Garden, patio, walkway & yard lighting fixtures: electric; outdoor & lawn furniture; pottery

Anthony
Marion County

(G-94)
AUSTIN POWDER COMPANY
5299 Ne 97th Street Rd (32617-3952)
P.O. Box 58 (32617-0058)
PHONE..................................352 690-7060
Mike Kaufman, *Manager*
EMP: 8
SALES (corp-wide): 734.5MM **Privately Held**
WEB: www.austinpowder.com
SIC: 2892 Explosives
HQ: Austin Powder Company
25800 Science Park Dr # 300
Cleveland OH 44122
216 464-2400

(G-95)
BEASLEY WELDING LLC
14291 Ne 47th Ave (32617-2513)
PHONE..................................352 595-4086
Daniel Beasley, *Principal*
EMP: 6 **EST:** 2017
SALES (est): 40.8K **Privately Held**
SIC: 7692 Welding repair

(G-96)
KEEPIT NEAT
11630 Ne Jacksonville Rd (32617-2601)
P.O. Box 84 (32617-0084)
PHONE..................................352 867-0541
Brent R Long, *Principal*
EMP: 7 **EST:** 2008
SALES (est): 73.8K **Privately Held**
SIC: 2631 Container, packaging & boxboard

Apalachicola
Franklin County

(G-97)
BUDDY WARD & SONS SEAFOOD
Also Called: Buddy Ward Sons Seafood Trckg
3022 C 30 13 Mile Rd (32320)
P.O. Box 698 (32329-0698)
PHONE..................................850 653-8522
Thomas Ward, *Manager*
EMP: 7 **Privately Held**
WEB: www.13mileseafood.com
SIC: 2092 4212 Seafoods, fresh: prepared; local trucking, without storage
PA: Buddy Ward & Sons Seafood
233 Water St
Apalachicola FL 32320

(G-98)
MIRACLE SEAFOOD MANUFACTURERS
Also Called: S & W Nash Seafood
610 Us Highway 98 (32320-1243)
P.O. Box 494 (32329-0494)
PHONE..................................850 653-2114
Stephen Nash, *Partner*
Wayne Nash, *Partner*
EMP: 6 **EST:** 1972
SQ FT: 2,600
SALES (est): 127.5K **Privately Held**
SIC: 2091 2092 Oysters: packaged in cans, jars, etc.; fresh or frozen packaged fish

Apollo Beach
Hillsborough County

(G-99)
A SIGN SHOP LLC
235 Apollo Beach Blvd # 119 (33572-2251)
PHONE..................................813 334-7765

▲ = Import ▼=Export
◆ =Import/Export

EMP: 6 EST: 2008
SALES (est): 65.9K Privately Held
SIC: 3993 Signs & advertising specialties

(G-100)
ALTERNATIVE MEDICAL ENTPS LLC
Also Called: Altmed Enterprises
6944 N Us Highway 41 (33572-1500)
PHONE.....941 702-9955
Todd Beckwith, *Marketing Staff*
Tyler Hayden, *Manager*
Gary Merlino,
Dave Proffitt, *Administration*
David Clapper,
EMP: 10 EST: 2014
SALES (est): 579.2K Privately Held
WEB: www.muvfl.com
SIC: 2834 Pharmaceutical preparations

(G-101)
DARCY STEPHEN
922 Allegro Ln (33572-2770)
PHONE.....813 645-3375
Darcy Stephen, *Principal*
EMP: 10 EST: 2005
SALES (est): 84.7K Privately Held
SIC: 7372 Prepackaged software

(G-102)
ELSTONS INC
Also Called: Elstons Lmnted Toil Partitions
703 Islebay Dr (33572-3338)
PHONE.....727 527-7929
EMP: 6
SQ FT: 3,200
SALES (est): 1MM Privately Held
SIC: 3088 Mfg Toilet Partitions

(G-103)
EXPRESS CARE OF TAMPA BAY (PA)
6015 Rex Hall Ln (33572-2657)
PHONE.....813 641-0068
Angela Kay Gomes, *Principal*
EMP: 7 EST: 2005
SALES (est): 931.8K Privately Held
WEB: www.expresscareoftampabay.com
SIC: 2741 Miscellaneous publishing

(G-104)
FOUR SEAS DISTILLING CO LLC
Also Called: Copper Bottom Craft Distillery
915 Bunker View Dr (33572-2813)
PHONE.....813 645-0057
Joanne Craig, *Principal*
EMP: 8 EST: 2015
SALES (est): 462.7K Privately Held
SIC: 2085 Distilled & blended liquors

(G-105)
LIFESAVING SYSTEMS CORPORATION
220 Elsberry Rd (33572-2291)
PHONE.....813 645-2748
Samuel G Maness, *CEO*
Jason A Glazer, *President*
Barbara A Maness, *Vice Pres*
Amy O'Hara, *Sales Mgr*
Shelby Lanser, *Sales Staff*
◆ EMP: 36
SQ FT: 20,000
SALES (est): 5.9MM Privately Held
WEB: www.lifesavingsystems.com
SIC: 3842 5099 5999 Personal safety equipment; safety equipment & supplies; safety supplies & equipment

(G-106)
TAMPA CATAMARANS LLC
663 Flamingo Dr (33572-2410)
PHONE.....813 966-4640
Rosemary L Dame, *Manager*
EMP: 6 EST: 2012
SALES (est): 150.3K Privately Held
WEB: www.tampacatamarans.com
SIC: 3949 Sporting & athletic goods

(G-107)
TROPIC GUARD INDUSTRIES LLC
6727 Clair Shore Dr (33572-3359)
PHONE.....813 447-3938
John G Hough, *Principal*
EMP: 7 EST: 2016
SALES (est): 306.4K Privately Held
WEB: www.tropicguardfl.com
SIC: 3999 Manufacturing industries

Apopka
Orange County

(G-108)
ACCURATE REPRODUCTIONS INC
2060 Apopka Blvd (32703-7735)
PHONE.....407 814-1622
Barry West, *President*
EMP: 10 EST: 1988
SQ FT: 10,000
SALES (est): 280.2K Privately Held
SIC: 2221 Fiberglass fabrics

(G-109)
ADVANCED HERMETICS INC
2052 Platinum Rd (32703-7738)
PHONE.....407 464-0539
John Wilson, *President*
Patricia Wilson, *Vice Pres*
▲ EMP: 5 EST: 1988
SQ FT: 5,100
SALES (est): 608.4K Privately Held
WEB: www.advancedhermetics.com
SIC: 3585 Compressors for refrigeration & air conditioning equipment

(G-110)
ALL AMRCAN BLDG STRCTRES CONTR
401 E Cleveland St (32703-7224)
PHONE.....407 466-4959
Lamar Hughley, *Principal*
EMP: 7 EST: 2010
SALES (est): 131.2K Privately Held
SIC: 3448 Prefabricated metal buildings

(G-111)
ALL BECAUSE LLC
Also Called: Printers, The
2098 Sprint Blvd (32703-7761)
PHONE.....407 884-6700
Marcia Van Vliet, *Office Mgr*
John Sciandra, *Mng Member*
John Cravey, *Mng Member*
Terry Cravey, *Admin Sec*
EMP: 7 EST: 2009
SALES (est): 997.8K Privately Held
SIC: 2752 Commercial printing, offset

(G-112)
AMERICAN CCC CERAMIC INC
805 Largo Ct (32703-5960)
PHONE.....321 356-9317
Alberto Cruz, *Principal*
EMP: 6 EST: 2008
SALES (est): 89.4K Privately Held
SIC: 3269 Pottery products

(G-113)
ANDERSONS CAN LINE FBRCTION EQ
2208 Stillwater Ave (32703-9003)
P.O. Box 116, Ocoee (34761-0116)
PHONE.....407 889-4665
Frank L Anderson Jr, *President*
EMP: 13 EST: 1976
SQ FT: 40,000
SALES (est): 4.5MM Privately Held
SIC: 3411 3535 3494 Aluminum cans; conveyors & conveying equipment; valves & pipe fittings

(G-114)
ARTISAN ARMS INC
2516 Jmt Industrial Dr # 105 (32703-2135)
PHONE.....321 299-4053
Philip Picardat, *Principal*
James Krosky, *Principal*
Robert Soong, *Principal*
Lisa Wise-Picardat, *CFO*
EMP: 6 EST: 2009
SALES (est): 506.7K Privately Held
SIC: 3484 Guns (firearms) or gun parts, 30 mm. & below

(G-115)
BAVARIA CORPORATION
Also Called: Bavaria Corp International
515 Cooper Commerce Dr # 10 (32703-5135)
PHONE.....407 880-0322
Peter F Schaeflein, *President*
Bruce Hopkins, *General Mgr*
Faye Reed, *Vice Pres*
Victor Moreno, *Marketing Mgr*
Dennis Koo, *Manager*
◆ EMP: 15 EST: 1986
SQ FT: 15,000
SALES (est): 3.2MM Privately Held
WEB: www.bavariacorp.com
SIC: 2099 5149 Seasonings & spices; seasonings, sauces & extracts

(G-116)
BDJL ENTERPRISES LLC
Also Called: Blue Water Spa Covers
2591 Clark St Ste 208 (32703-2108)
PHONE.....407 678-9960
Brian Keihner, *Mng Member*
Seth Keihner, *Manager*
EMP: 18 EST: 2015
SQ FT: 12,000
SALES (est): 2MM Privately Held
SIC: 3999 Hot tub & spa covers

(G-117)
BEST OF ORLANDO PNTG & STUCCO
3000 Clarcona Rd Lot 763 (32703-8723)
PHONE.....407 947-4174
Gary Baugh, *Principal*
EMP: 9 EST: 2009
SALES (est): 415.9K Privately Held
SIC: 3299 Stucco

(G-118)
BLOEM LLC
3000 Orange Ave (32703-3347)
PHONE.....407 889-5533
EMP: 7
SALES (corp-wide): 11.4MM Privately Held
WEB: www.bloemliving.com
SIC: 3089 Planters, plastic
PA: Bloem, Llc
3301 Hudson Trail Dr
Hudsonville MI 49426
616 622-6344

(G-119)
BOLT SIGNS & MARKETING LLC (PA)
151 Smran Cmmrce Pl Ste A (32703)
PHONE.....407 865-7446
Craig R Lamphere, *Manager*
Lamphere Craig R, *Manager*
EMP: 18 EST: 2010
SALES (est): 137.6K Privately Held
WEB: www.myboltsigns.com
SIC: 3993 Signs & advertising specialties

(G-120)
CELLEC GAMES INC
Also Called: Cg Solutionsgroup
2736 Candlewood Ct (32703-4995)
PHONE.....407 476-3590
Gerard Merritt, *CEO*
Prashanth Yaramosu, *Prgrmr*
EMP: 5 EST: 2011
SALES (est): 782.6K Privately Held
WEB: www.cellecgames.com
SIC: 7372 7389 7371 Educational computer software; ; custom computer programming services

(G-121)
COCA-COLA COMPANY
2659 Orange Ave (32703-3346)
PHONE.....407 886-1568
Katherine Larid, *Manager*
Shannon Wurfel, *Manager*
EMP: 6
SALES (corp-wide): 33B Publicly Held
WEB: www.coca-colacompany.com
SIC: 2086 2087 Bottled & canned soft drinks; fruit juices: concentrated for fountain use; syrups, drink
PA: The Coca-Cola Company
1 Coca Cola Plz Nw
Atlanta GA 30313
404 676-2121

(G-122)
COCA-COLA COMPANY
2651 Orange Ave (32703-3346)
PHONE.....404 676-2121
◆ EMP: 20
SALES (est): 3.2MM Privately Held
SIC: 2086 Carb Sft Drnkbtlcn

(G-123)
COCA-COLA COMPANY
2651 Orange Ave (32703-3346)
PHONE.....407 565-2465
EMP: 7
SALES (corp-wide): 33B Publicly Held
WEB: www.coca-cola.com
SIC: 2087 2086 2033 2037 Concentrates, drink; soft drinks: packaged in cans, bottles, etc.; fruit juices: fresh; fruit juice concentrates, frozen
PA: The Coca-Cola Company
1 Coca Cola Plz Nw
Atlanta GA 30313
404 676-2121

(G-124)
COCA-COLA COMPANY
2501 Orange Ave (32703-3346)
PHONE.....407 358-6758
Oneal Michael, *Opers Staff*
Eric Bennett, *Branch Mgr*
EMP: 6
SALES (corp-wide): 33B Publicly Held
WEB: www.coca-colacompany.com
SIC: 2095 2087 Freeze-dried coffee; fruit juices: concentrated for fountain use
PA: The Coca-Cola Company
1 Coca Cola Plz Nw
Atlanta GA 30313
404 676-2121

(G-125)
COCA-COLA COMPANY DISTRIBUTION
1451 Ocoee Apopka Rd (32703-9209)
PHONE.....407 814-1327
EMP: 11 EST: 2017
SALES (est): 521.1K Privately Held
WEB: www.coca-cola.com
SIC: 2086 Bottled & canned soft drinks

(G-126)
COLLINS MFG INC
672 Johns Rd (32703-6203)
PHONE.....321 322-0280
W John Collins, *President*
Jim Whittaker, *Vice Pres*
Bill Poole, *Opers Mgr*
Ryan Tobyansen, *Production*
Wendy Ritchey, *Human Res Mgr*
EMP: 75 EST: 1995
SQ FT: 37,000
SALES (est): 16.3MM Privately Held
WEB: www.collinsmanufacturing.com
SIC: 3369 Castings, except die-castings, precision

(G-127)
CREATIVE METAL STUDIO INC (PA)
2312 Clark St Ste 3 (32703-2117)
PHONE.....321 206-6112
Bilyana P Vladimirova, *President*
EMP: 22 EST: 2007
SALES (est): 336.7K Privately Held
WEB: www.creativemetalstudioinc.com
SIC: 3446 Architectural metalwork

(G-128)
CREATIVE SIGNS INC
2301 N Hiawassee Rd (32703-2604)
P.O. Box 608070, Orlando (32860-8070)
PHONE.....407 293-9393
Antonio Di Salvatore, *President*
Cheryl Disalvatore, *Treasurer*
EMP: 25 EST: 1982
SALES (est): 4.9MM Privately Held
WEB: www.creativesignsinc.com
SIC: 3993 Signs & advertising specialties

(G-129)
CUSTOM MEDICAL PRODUCTS INC
3909 E Semrn Blvd Ste 599 (32703-6103)
PHONE.................................407 865-7211
Carl Shumate, *President*
EMP: 7 **EST:** 2004
SALES (est): 149.1K **Privately Held**
SIC: 3841 Surgical & medical instruments

(G-130)
DESIGN & PRINT SOLUTIONS INC
Also Called: Romine Reprographics Svcs
553 Sheeler Ave (32703-5555)
PHONE.................................407 703-7861
Chet Carter, *Principal*
EMP: 7 **EST:** 2016
SALES (est): 156.7K **Privately Held**
SIC: 2752 Commercial printing, lithographic

(G-131)
DJ PLASTICS INC
946 Century Ln (32703-3709)
PHONE.................................407 656-6677
Dominick P Dichiria, *President*
Page Bowlen, *President*
EMP: 5 **EST:** 1998
SQ FT: 18,500
SALES (est): 700K **Privately Held**
WEB: www.seelyeinc-orl.com
SIC: 2821 3089 Thermoplastic materials; thermoformed finished plastic products

(G-132)
EARTHMOVER CNSTR EQP LLC
2325 Clark St (32703-2110)
P.O. Box 1649, Windermere (34786-1649)
PHONE.................................407 401-8956
Howard W Abell, *President*
Brian Darville, *Sales Staff*
EMP: 27 **EST:** 2013
SALES (est): 5MM **Privately Held**
SIC: 3537 Industrial trucks & tractors

(G-133)
ELRO MANUFACTURING LLC
516 Cooper Commerce Dr (32703-6223)
PHONE.................................407 410-6006
Robert Asta, *CEO*
Paul Wolmarans, *Ch of Bd*
Philip Klote, *Vice Pres*
EMP: 10 **EST:** 2014
SALES (est): 600K **Privately Held**
WEB: www.elro-mfg.com
SIC: 3441 Fabricated structural metal

(G-134)
EMPIRE DUMPSTERS LLC
927 E Semoran Blvd (32703-5518)
PHONE.................................407 223-8985
Keith A Oelerich, *President*
EMP: 6 **EST:** 2018
SALES (est): 143.2K **Privately Held**
SIC: 3443 Dumpsters, garbage

(G-135)
ENERGY TASK FORCE LLC (HQ)
2501 Clark St Ste 101 (32703-2132)
PHONE.................................407 523-3770
Jay Newell, *Mng Member*
EMP: 15 **EST:** 2000
SQ FT: 38,000
SALES (est): 9.8MM
SALES (corp-wide): 93.4MM **Privately Held**
WEB: www.energytaskforce.com
SIC: 3498 Fabricated pipe & fittings
PA: Venture Management Group, Inc.
110 East Dr Ste 1
Melbourne FL 32904
321 726-8543

(G-136)
ENTERPRISE ELECTRIC LLC
2100 Ocoee Apopka Rd (32703-9210)
PHONE.................................407 884-0668
EMP: 6 **EST:** 2015
SALES (est): 88.3K **Privately Held**
SIC: 3699 1731 Electrical equipment & supplies; electrical work

(G-137)
ENVIROWORKS INC
Also Called: Solartex
3000 Orange Ave (32703-3347)
PHONE.................................407 889-5533
Dave Smith, *President*
EMP: 15 **EST:** 1982
SQ FT: 420,000
SALES (est): 1.2MM
SALES (corp-wide): 1.3B **Privately Held**
WEB: www.enviroworks.co.uk
SIC: 2295 3089 0782 Chemically coated & treated fabrics; flower pots, plastic; plastic hardware & building products; lawn services
HQ: Fiskars Brands, Inc.
7800 Discovery Dr
Middleton WI 53562
866 348-5661

(G-138)
ER PRECISION OPTICAL CORP
1676 E Semoran Blvd (32703-5673)
PHONE.................................407 292-5395
Mark Hess, *President*
Jason Hess, *Vice Pres*
◆ **EMP:** 18 **EST:** 1991
SQ FT: 25,000
SALES (est): 7MM **Privately Held**
WEB: www.eroptics.com
SIC: 3827 Optical instruments & apparatus

(G-139)
ETF WEST LLC
2501 Clark St (32703-2132)
PHONE.................................407 523-3770
EMP: 9 **EST:** 2007
SALES (est): 367.1K **Privately Held**
WEB: www.energytaskforce.com
SIC: 3498 Fabricated pipe & fittings

(G-140)
FINFROCK DESIGN INC
2400 Apopka Blvd (32703-7743)
PHONE.................................407 293-4000
Robert D Finfrock, *President*
Jorge Arboleda, *Vice Pres*
Allen R Finfrock, *Vice Pres*
William A Finfrock, *Vice Pres*
Glenn S Valenta, *Vice Pres*
EMP: 45 **EST:** 2000
SALES (est): 4MM **Privately Held**
WEB: www.finfrock.com
SIC: 3272 Concrete products

(G-141)
FINFROCK INDUSTRIES INC
2400 Apopka Blvd (32703-7743)
P.O. Box 607754, Orlando (32860-7754)
PHONE.................................407 293-4000
Robert D Finfrock, *Ch of Bd*
Jeff Harrison, *Superintendent*
Daniel J Finfrock, *Vice Pres*
William A Finfrock, *Vice Pres*
Chris Farris, *Project Mgr*
EMP: 200
SQ FT: 30,000
SALES (est): 44.7MM **Privately Held**
WEB: www.finfrock.com
SIC: 3272 Prestressed concrete products

(G-142)
FISKARS BRANDS INC
Fiskars Home Leisure Division
3000 Orange Ave (32703-3347)
PHONE.................................407 889-5533
William Denton, *President*
Rob Carroll, *Vice Pres*
Melissa Dunn, *Vice Pres*
Joelle Onorato, *Vice Pres*
Ashley Brantner, *Project Mgr*
EMP: 7
SALES (corp-wide): 1.3B **Privately Held**
WEB: www.gilmour.com
SIC: 2295 3089 Chemically coated & treated fabrics; flower pots, plastic; plastic hardware & building products
HQ: Fiskars Brands, Inc.
7800 Discovery Dr
Middleton WI 53562
866 348-5661

(G-143)
FLORIDA FABRICATION INC
800 Johns Rd (32703-6207)
PHONE.................................407 212-0105
Katherine Starkey, *Principal*
EMP: 13 **EST:** 2013
SALES (est): 3.1MM **Privately Held**
WEB: www.floridafabrication.net
SIC: 3441 Fabricated structural metal

(G-144)
FOLIAGE ENTERPRISES INC
Also Called: Apopka Chief, The
400 N Park Ave (32712-4152)
P.O. Box 880 (32704-0880)
PHONE.................................407 886-2777
John E Ricketson, *President*
Eileen Ricketson, *Vice Pres*
EMP: 32 **EST:** 1923
SQ FT: 8,000
SALES (est): 2MM **Privately Held**
WEB: www.theapopkachief.com
SIC: 2711 Newspapers, publishing & printing

(G-145)
FOSTER & FOSTER WORLDWIDE LLC
635 Lexington Pkwy (32712-4420)
PHONE.................................352 362-9102
Steven Foster,
EMP: 10 **EST:** 2019
SALES (est): 267.5K **Privately Held**
SIC: 1389 Oil consultants

(G-146)
GREATHOUSE SIGNS LLC
156 Holly St (32712-5705)
P.O. Box 1016 (32704-1016)
PHONE.................................407 247-2668
Bob Greathouse, *Principal*
EMP: 7 **EST:** 2010
SALES (est): 167.5K **Privately Held**
WEB: www.greathousesigns.com
SIC: 3993 Signs & advertising specialties

(G-147)
GREEN RHINO ENRGY SLUTIONS LLC (PA)
1451 Ocoee Apopka Rd (32703-9209)
PHONE.................................407 925-5868
Victor Diaz Estrada, *Project Mgr*
Bishoy Rezk, *Electrical Engi*
Nick Bussanich, *VP Bus Dvlpt*
Tom Mangone, *VP Bus Dvlpt*
Mario Wilhelm, *VP Bus Dvlpt*
EMP: 69 **EST:** 2016
SALES (est): 5.9MM **Privately Held**
WEB: www.greenrhino-energy.com
SIC: 3621 Power generators

(G-148)
GUY WINGO SIGNS
Also Called: Capital Signs
2682 Pemberton Dr (32703-9402)
PHONE.................................407 578-1132
Guy Wingo, *Principal*
EMP: 5 **EST:** 2008
SALES (est): 725.3K **Privately Held**
WEB: www.capitalsigndesign.com
SIC: 3993 Electric signs

(G-149)
INVIGICOM INC
205 N Park Ave Ste 110 (32703-4102)
PHONE.................................407 491-6929
David Lamb, *Principal*
Ryan Jorgenson, *Vice Pres*
Lief Sorensen, *Vice Pres*
EMP: 6 **EST:** 2019
SALES (est): 173.6K **Privately Held**
WEB: www.invigicom.com
SIC: 3999 Manufacturing industries

(G-150)
JK2 SCENIC LLC
541 Live Pine Cir (32703-3330)
PHONE.................................407 703-2977
Julie Holmes, *General Mgr*
Tim Bartell,
Paul Holmes,
EMP: 26 **EST:** 2017
SALES (est): 2.3MM **Privately Held**
WEB: www.jk2.com
SIC: 2431 Millwork

(G-151)
JOHN ANDERSEN
923 Ridgeside Ct (32712-4006)
PHONE.................................407 702-4891
John Andersen, *Principal*
EMP: 7 **EST:** 2011
SALES (est): 684.5K **Privately Held**
SIC: 2491 Structural lumber & timber, treated wood

(G-152)
K&T MANUFACTURING INC
557 Cooper Indus Pkwy (32703-6232)
PHONE.................................407 814-7700
Nick Geisel, *CEO*
Rick Liesner, *Vice Pres*
EMP: 5 **EST:** 2001
SALES (est): 759.5K **Privately Held**
WEB: www.kandtmanufacturing.com
SIC: 3441 Fabricated structural metal

(G-153)
K-RACEWAY LLC
1549 Madison Ivy Cir (32712-4430)
PHONE.................................407 889-4314
George Martinez, *Principal*
EMP: 6 **EST:** 2010
SALES (est): 155.1K **Privately Held**
SIC: 3644 Raceways

(G-154)
KHALED W AKKAWI
1349 S Orange Blossom Trl (32703-7605)
PHONE.................................321 396-3108
Khalid Akkawi, *Principal*
EMP: 6 **EST:** 2006
SALES (est): 134.3K **Privately Held**
SIC: 3484 Guns (firearms) or gun parts, 30 mm. & below

(G-155)
LASER CREATIONS INCORPORATED
Also Called: Laser Magic
946 Century Ln (32703-3709)
PHONE.................................800 771-7151
Phillip Kimmell, *President*
Philip Kimmel, *Cust Mgr*
Tish Figueroa, *Director*
▲ **EMP:** 42 **EST:** 1990
SQ FT: 6,000
SALES (est): 1.5MM **Privately Held**
SIC: 3993 3089 5199 Advertising novelties; plastic processing; advertising specialties

(G-156)
LINDLEY FOODS LLC ✪
Also Called: Selma's Cookies
2023 Apex Ct (32703-7720)
PHONE.................................407 884-9433
Stephanie Lindley, *Principal*
EMP: 8 **EST:** 2020
SALES (est): 875.7K **Privately Held**
SIC: 2052 Cookies

(G-157)
MARNIS DOLCE
2928 Rapollo Ln (32712-2431)
PHONE.................................407 915-7607
Annie Resnick, *President*
EMP: 7 **EST:** 2017
SALES (est): 855.3K **Privately Held**
WEB: www.ozlan.us
SIC: 2051 Bread, cake & related products

(G-158)
MATTHEWS INTERNATIONAL CORP
Matthews Envmtl Solutions
2045 Sprint Blvd (32703-7762)
PHONE.................................407 886-5533
Paul Rayhill, *Division Pres*
Michael Tricoche, *Engineer*
Matt Crumbaker, *Sales Staff*
Jessica Walli, *Sales Staff*
Paul Seyler, *Marketing Staff*
EMP: 170
SALES (corp-wide): 1.5B **Publicly Held**
WEB: www.matw.com
SIC: 3569 7699 5085 3567 Cremating ovens; industrial machinery & equipment repair; industrial supplies; industrial furnaces & ovens; nonclay refractories

PA: Matthews International Corporation
2 N Shore Ctr Ste 200
Pittsburgh PA 15212
412 442-8200

(G-159)
MEISHBOY PRODUCTIONS INC
433 Ashley Brooke Ct (32712-3356)
PHONE....................................407 949-1464
Rameish Budhoo, *CEO*
Chan-Denise R Adams, *President*
EMP: 6 **EST:** 2008
SALES (est): 246.5K **Privately Held**
SIC: 2782 Record albums

(G-160)
METAL ROCK INC
174a Semoran Commerce Pl # 103
(32703-4670)
PHONE....................................407 886-6440
▲ **EMP:** 10
SALES (est): 1.1MM **Privately Held**
SIC: 3911 3914 Mfg Custom Jewelry & Pewter Ware

(G-161)
MICRO ENGINEERING INC
1428 E Semrn Blvd Ste 120 (32703-5672)
PHONE....................................407 886-4849
Larry A Laforest, *President*
Joseph Nguyen, *Vice Pres*
William Noble, *Vice Pres*
Samuel Pereira, *Design Engr*
Sharkey Raymond, *Director*
EMP: 36 **EST:** 1981
SALES (est): 4.8MM **Privately Held**
WEB: www.microeng.com
SIC: 3674 3672 Hybrid integrated circuits; printed circuit boards

(G-162)
MJR WOODWORKS LLC
552 Cooper Indus Pkwy (32703-6202)
PHONE....................................407 403-5430
Jason E Ryan, *President*
Matthew Ryan, *Vice Pres*
Matthew Panessidi, *Project Mgr*
EMP: 15 **EST:** 2010
SALES (est): 3.5MM **Privately Held**
WEB: www.mjrwoodworks.com
SIC: 2431 Millwork

(G-163)
MOTOR PROTECTION ELECTRONICS
Also Called: M P E
2464 Vulcan Rd (32703-2015)
PHONE....................................407 299-3825
James E Gallagher, *CEO*
John Evans, *President*
EMP: 10 **EST:** 1983
SQ FT: 6,000
SALES (est): 1.7MM **Privately Held**
WEB: www.mpelectronics.com
SIC: 3625 3613 Motor controls & accessories; switchgear & switchboard apparatus

(G-164)
NEED A DUMPSTER LLC
1733 Benbow Ct Ste 5 (32703-7798)
PHONE....................................888 407-3867
Chiara Carrier, *Mng Member*
EMP: 7 **EST:** 2018
SALES (est): 755.1K **Privately Held**
WEB: www.needadumpsterrent.com
SIC: 3443 Dumpsters, garbage

(G-165)
NEON COWBOYS LLC
2312 Clark St Ste 5 (32703-2117)
PHONE....................................949 514-5557
Asia Hall, *President*
EMP: 5 **EST:** 2015
SALES (est): 436.5K **Privately Held**
WEB: www.neoncowboys.com
SIC: 2813 Neon

(G-166)
NORTHROP GRUMMAN SYSTEMS CORP
2787 S Orange Blossom Trl (32703-4397)
P.O. Box 609555, Orlando (32860-9555)
PHONE....................................407 295-4010
Loshuertos Bill, *Opers Mgr*
Gavin Clark, *Engineer*
Fred Dant, *Engineer*
Virgil Blanton, *Design Engr*
William Zekoll, *Branch Mgr*
EMP: 400 **Publicly Held**
WEB: www.northropgrumman.com
SIC: 3674 3812 Infrared sensors, solid state; search & navigation equipment
HQ: Northrop Grumman Systems Corporation
2980 Fairview Park Dr
Falls Church VA 22042
703 280-2900

(G-167)
OLMSTEAD PUBLISHING LLC
2629 Grassmoor Loop (32712-5005)
PHONE....................................954 559-0192
Phyllis Olmstead, *Owner*
EMP: 6 **EST:** 2011
SALES (est): 179.1K **Privately Held**
WEB: www.olmsteadpublishing.com
SIC: 2741 Miscellaneous publishing

(G-168)
OUM LLC
Also Called: Best Global Source
531 Cooper Indus Pkwy (32703-6232)
PHONE....................................407 886-1511
Kunal Bhakta, *Vice Pres*
Prafulchanbra Bhakta, *Vice Pres*
Janak Bhakta,
EMP: 18 **EST:** 2013
SALES (est): 1.5MM **Privately Held**
SIC: 3672 Printed circuit boards

(G-169)
PALLETS INC
640 Majestic Oak Dr (32712-4082)
PHONE....................................407 492-0857
Carol Scherzer, *Principal*
EMP: 6 **EST:** 2007
SALES (est): 121.5K **Privately Held**
WEB: www.returnofthesun.org
SIC: 2448 Pallets, wood & wood with metal

(G-170)
PIONEER WELDING & FABRICATION
532 Hillend Ct (32712-4732)
PHONE....................................407 880-4997
Paula Marn, *President*
Casey Stroup, *General Mgr*
Kurt Marn, *Vice Pres*
EMP: 5 **EST:** 1991
SALES (est): 1.5MM **Privately Held**
WEB: www.pioneerwelding.com
SIC: 3446 5051 Stairs, fire escapes, balconies, railings & ladders; iron & steel (ferrous) products

(G-171)
PLANE IT SAFE LLC
Also Called: Refreshed Traveler
1135 Ocoee Apopka Rd (32703-9201)
PHONE....................................888 840-0499
Peter Cook, *CEO*
EMP: 5 **EST:** 2018
SALES (est): 393K **Privately Held**
WEB: www.planeitsafe.com
SIC: 3999 Manufacturing industries

(G-172)
PLUMB RITE OF CENTRAL FLORIDA
2850 Overland Rd (32703-9446)
PHONE....................................407 292-0750
Harold H Harris, *Director*
EMP: 5 **EST:** 2001
SALES (est): 465.9K **Privately Held**
SIC: 3432 Plumbing fixture fittings & trim

(G-173)
PRO STREET CHOPPERS INC
917 Suwannee Dr (32703-5935)
PHONE....................................407 389-2047
Robert Alford, *President*
EMP: 6 **EST:** 2004
SALES (est): 122.8K **Privately Held**
SIC: 3751 Motorcycles & related parts

(G-174)
PROTECTIVE COATINGS LLC
344 Longhorn Dr (32712-5357)
PHONE....................................407 535-8535
William F Brunke, *Principal*
EMP: 6 **EST:** 2013
SALES (est): 93.7K **Privately Held**
SIC: 3479 Metal coating & allied service

(G-175)
QCI
2152 Sprint Blvd (32703-7761)
PHONE....................................407 886-6300
Juan Citarella, *President*
EMP: 75 **EST:** 1951
SALES (est): 4.3MM **Privately Held**
SIC: 3822 Water heater controls

(G-176)
QORVO US INC
1818 S Orange Blossom Trl (32703-9419)
PHONE....................................407 886-8860
EMP: 447
SALES (corp-wide): 4B **Publicly Held**
WEB: www.qorvo.com
SIC: 3674 Semiconductors & related devices
HQ: Qorvo Us, Inc.
2300 Ne Brookwood Pkwy
Hillsboro OR 97124
336 664-1233

(G-177)
QUICK ADVERTISING INC
Also Called: Fastsigns
3030 E Semrn Blvd Ste 236 (32703-5953)
PHONE....................................407 774-0003
Roderick A Quick, *President*
EMP: 10 **EST:** 2001
SQ FT: 2,600
SALES (est): 1.6MM **Privately Held**
WEB: www.fastsigns.com
SIC: 3993 Signs & advertising specialties

(G-178)
R & D SLEEVES LLC (PA)
520 W Orange Blossom Trl (32712-3454)
P.O. Box 460, Plymouth (32768-0460)
PHONE....................................407 886-9010
Steven McCoy,
EMP: 24 **EST:** 1981
SALES (est): 2.1MM **Privately Held**
WEB: www.randdsleeves.com
SIC: 2679 2673 Paper products, converted; bags: plastic, laminated & coated

(G-179)
RELIANCE MEDIA INC
515 Cooper Commerce Dr # 140
(32703-6222)
PHONE....................................505 243-1821
Patrick McGuffin, *President*
EMP: 8 **EST:** 1990
SQ FT: 120,000
SALES (est): 282.8K **Privately Held**
WEB: www.new-book-publishing.com
SIC: 2732 2731 7336 Book printing; books: publishing only; commercial art & graphic design

(G-180)
RIGID COATINGS & CASTINGS INC
3290 Overland Rd (32703-9473)
PHONE....................................352 396-8738
Parke Daniel, *Principal*
EMP: 7 **EST:** 2015
SALES (est): 109.2K **Privately Held**
SIC: 3479 Metal coating & allied service

(G-181)
RIGID COATINGS & CASTINGS INC
2585 Clark St (32703-2112)
PHONE....................................352 396-8738
Billy Barham, *Principal*
EMP: 6 **EST:** 2018
SALES (est): 289.3K **Privately Held**
SIC: 3479 Metal coating & allied service

(G-182)
ROCKPACK INC
2549 Clark St (32703-2112)
PHONE....................................407 757-0798
Sheetal Sood, *Principal*
EMP: 32 **EST:** 2015
SALES (est): 4.8MM **Privately Held**
WEB: www.rockpack.net
SIC: 1442 Construction sand & gravel

(G-183)
ROWELL LABORATORIES INC
Also Called: Rowell Labs
174 Semoran Commerce Pl # 110
(32703-1407)
PHONE....................................407 929-9445
Bill Rowell, *President*
EMP: 10 **EST:** 2008
SALES (est): 2MM
SALES (corp-wide): 45.8B **Publicly Held**
WEB: www.rowelllaboratories.com
SIC: 2834 5122 Pharmaceutical preparations; pharmaceuticals
PA: Abbvie Inc.
1 N Waukegan Rd
North Chicago IL 60064
847 932-7900

(G-184)
SEELYE ACQUISITIONS INC
946 Century Ln (32703-3709)
PHONE....................................407 656-6677
Dominick P Dichiria, *CEO*
Paige Bowen, *President*
▲ **EMP:** 7 **EST:** 1978
SQ FT: 18,500
SALES (est): 663K **Privately Held**
WEB: www.seelyeinc-orl.com
SIC: 3548 5084 5162 3087 Welding & cutting apparatus & accessories; welding machinery & equipment; plastics materials; custom compound purchased resins

(G-185)
SELMAS COOKIES INC (PA)
2023 Apex Ct (32703-7720)
P.O. Box 160756, Altamonte Springs
(32716-0756)
PHONE....................................407 884-9433
Selma Sayin, *President*
Dawn Fowler, *CFO*
Karen Brandenburg, *Mktg Dir*
EMP: 30 **EST:** 1990
SQ FT: 20,000
SALES (est): 5MM **Privately Held**
WEB: www.selmas.com
SIC: 2052 5461 Cookies; cookies

(G-186)
SHADES TO YOU LLC
1676 E Semoran Blvd (32703-5673)
PHONE....................................407 889-0049
Nicholas Czesnakowicz, *President*
Robert Czesnakowicz,
▲ **EMP:** 9 **EST:** 1987
SALES (est): 1.4MM **Privately Held**
WEB: www.shadestoyou.windowblindsorlando.com
SIC: 2431 2591 Blinds (shutters), wood; blinds vertical

(G-187)
STA-CON INCORPORATED (PA)
2525 S Orange Blossom Trl (32703-2000)
PHONE....................................407 298-5940
James E Gallagher, *CEO*
Mark S McCartney, *President*
Donna Bender, *General Mgr*
Philip Gallagher, *Vice Pres*
Tommy Wandzilak, *Prdtn Mgr*
EMP: 50 **EST:** 1973
SQ FT: 17,000
SALES (est): 10.3MM **Privately Held**
WEB: www.stacon.com
SIC: 3625 Control equipment, electric

(G-188)
STEVE BAIE ENTERPRISES INC
2456 Clark St (32703-2109)
PHONE....................................407 822-3997
Steve Baie, *President*
EMP: 5 **EST:** 1998
SALES (est): 431.7K **Privately Held**
SIC: 3661 Telephones & telephone apparatus

(G-189)
SUNBELT METALS & MFG INC
920 S Bradshaw Rd (32703-5168)
PHONE....................................407 889-8960
Kevin P Harbin, *President*
Bill Harbin, *General Mgr*
Billy R Harbin, *Corp Secy*
Christopher A Harbin, *Vice Pres*
Johnny Oldaker, *Sales Staff*
EMP: 48 **EST:** 1992

GEOGRAPHIC

SQ FT: 24,000
SALES (est): 12.9MM **Privately Held**
WEB: www.sunbeltmetals.com
SIC: 3441 3443 3444 3446 Building components, structural steel; fabricated plate work (boiler shop); sheet metalwork; architectural metalwork

(G-190)
SUPERIOR TRIM & DOOR INC (PA)
615 Sprior Cmmrce Blvd St (32703-3399)
PHONE..................................407 408-7624
Keith Lemieux, *President*
David Buzzella, *Vice Pres*
▲ **EMP:** 41 **EST:** 1983
SQ FT: 67,500
SALES (est): 2.7MM **Privately Held**
SIC: 2431 3442 Doors, wood; trim, wood; metal doors; moldings & trim, except automobile: metal

(G-191)
TJ CABINETRY INC
2312 Clark St Ste 3 (32703-2117)
PHONE..................................407 801-5124
EMP: 7 **EST:** 2018
SALES (est): 139.2K **Privately Held**
WEB: www.tjcustomcabinets.com
SIC: 2434 Wood kitchen cabinets

(G-192)
TRICOUNTY CHEMICAL CO
2578 Park St Unit 5 (32712)
P.O. Box 917177, Longwood (32791-7177)
PHONE..................................407 682-3550
Terry Schultz, *President*
Pat Schultz, *Admin Sec*
EMP: 7 **EST:** 1986
SALES (est): 546.3K **Privately Held**
SIC: 3949 5999 Swimming pools, except plastic; swimming pool chemicals, equipment & supplies

(G-193)
UNITRON PRCISION MACHINING INC
2482 Clark St (32703-2111)
PHONE..................................407 299-4180
George De Vlugt, *President*
EMP: 10 **EST:** 1977
SQ FT: 1,800
SALES (est): 1.5MM **Privately Held**
WEB: www.unitronmachining.com
SIC: 3599 Machine shop, jobbing & repair

(G-194)
VALVETRAIN AMPLIFICATION
560 Sand Wedge Loop (32712-6054)
PHONE..................................407 886-7656
Richard J Gessner, *Principal*
EMP: 9 **EST:** 2005
SALES (est): 165.1K **Privately Held**
WEB: www.valvetrainamps.com
SIC: 3651 Amplifiers: radio, public address or musical instrument

(G-195)
VERTPAC LLC
520 W Orange Blossom Trl (32712-3454)
PHONE..................................407 886-9010
Stefanos Stamos, *Partner*
Annie Sauceda, *Manager*
EMP: 40 **EST:** 2016
SQ FT: 18,500
SALES (est): 5MM **Privately Held**
WEB: www.vertpac.com
SIC: 2621 5261 Kraft paper; nursery stock, seeds & bulbs

(G-196)
VISION SOURCE INC
9262 Bent Arrow Cv (32703-1965)
PHONE..................................407 435-9958
Letiza Christensen, *Manager*
EMP: 8 **EST:** 2017
SALES (est): 104.7K **Privately Held**
WEB: www.visionsource.com
SIC: 3851 Magnifiers (readers & simple magnifiers)

(G-197)
WINCOR TECHNOLOGY INC ✪
3025 Pinenut Dr (32712-2722)
PHONE..................................407 702-0787
Rameish Budhoo, *Principal*
EMP: 6 **EST:** 2020
SALES (est): 250K **Privately Held**
SIC: 2741

Arcadia
Desoto County

(G-198)
ADAMS BROS CABINETRY INC
9300 Sw Ft Winder St (34269-7003)
PHONE..................................863 993-0501
Ethan M Adams, *Principal*
EMP: 6 **EST:** 2010
SALES (est): 61.1K **Privately Held**
SIC: 2434 Wood kitchen cabinets

(G-199)
ARCADIA THRIFT LLC
129 S Mills Ave (34266-4619)
PHONE..................................863 993-2004
Michael Owens,
EMP: 8 **EST:** 2016
SALES (est): 343.5K **Privately Held**
SIC: 2519 Fiberglass & plastic furniture

(G-200)
BELONGEA INDUSTRIES
6837 Ne Cubitis Ave # 583 (34266-8436)
PHONE..................................574 209-1045
Ronald J Belongea, *Principal*
EMP: 7 **EST:** 2012
SALES (est): 211.8K **Privately Held**
SIC: 3999 Manufacturing industries

(G-201)
CCF HOLDCO LLC
Also Called: Columbia Care Florida
1528 Sw Highway 17 (34266-6436)
PHONE..................................800 714-9215
Nicholas Vita, *Manager*
Michael Abbott, *Manager*
David Hart, *Manager*
EMP: 12 **EST:** 2018
SALES (est): 567.3K **Privately Held**
SIC: 2833 Drugs & herbs: grading, grinding & milling

(G-202)
COOPER TIMBER HARVESTING INC
2056 Ne Newberry Dr (34266-5695)
PHONE..................................863 494-0240
Wayne R Cooper, *President*
Essie E Cooper, *Corp Secy*
EMP: 11 **EST:** 1979
SALES (est): 2MM **Privately Held**
WEB: www.coopertimberfl.com
SIC: 2411 Logging camps & contractors

(G-203)
FINE LINE CUSTOM MILLWORK LLC
1683 Ne Bishop St (34266-5831)
PHONE..................................941 628-9611
Nicole Adams, *Principal*
EMP: 20 **EST:** 2015
SALES (est): 1MM **Privately Held**
SIC: 2499 Laundry products, wood

(G-204)
SANCHEZ MACHINE SHOP LLC
4 S Parker Ave (34266-3349)
P.O. Box 1233 (34265-1233)
PHONE..................................863 494-1212
Enrique Sanchez, *Principal*
EMP: 9 **EST:** 2017
SALES (est): 359.5K **Privately Held**
WEB: www.sanchezmachineshop.com
SIC: 3599 Machine shop, jobbing & repair

(G-205)
SOUTH COUNTRY SHEDS LLC
1460 Sw Price Child St (34266-3851)
PHONE..................................863 491-8700
Orlando Penner,
Mary K Penner,
EMP: 10 **EST:** 2014
SALES (est): 1MM **Privately Held**
WEB: www.southcountrysheds.com
SIC: 2452 Prefabricated wood buildings

(G-206)
TREMRON LLC
Also Called: Tremron Group
3144 Ne Highway 17 (34266-5781)
PHONE..................................863 491-0990
EMP: 14
SALES (corp-wide): 7MM **Privately Held**
WEB: www.tremron.com
SIC: 3271 3272 2951 Blocks, concrete: drystack interlocking; concrete products; asphalt paving mixtures & blocks
PA: Tremron, Llc
2885 Saint Clair St
Jacksonville FL 32254
904 359-5900

Archer
Alachua County

(G-207)
CARSONS CABINETRY AND DESIGN
13411 Sw County Road 346 (32618-4221)
PHONE..................................352 373-8292
Stephen Carson, *President*
EMP: 5 **EST:** 1980
SALES (est): 359.1K **Privately Held**
WEB: www.carsonscabinetry.com
SIC: 2511 5712 Wood household furniture; customized furniture & cabinets

(G-208)
FLORIDA CONCRETE RECYCLING
18515 Sw Archer Rd (32618-4645)
PHONE..................................352 495-2044
Timothy Renfroe, *President*
EMP: 17 **EST:** 1992
SALES (est): 5.1MM **Privately Held**
WEB: www.flcrinc.net
SIC: 3273 Ready-mixed concrete

(G-209)
GOOD LIFE PUBLISHING INC
6906 Sw 134th Ave (32618-4393)
PHONE..................................352 317-6903
James T Byrne, *Principal*
EMP: 7 **EST:** 2010
SALES (est): 172.8K **Privately Held**
WEB: www.ocalasgoodlife.com
SIC: 2741 Miscellaneous publishing

(G-210)
MADDOX FOUNDRY & MCH WORKS LLC
13370 Sw 170th St (32618-3858)
P.O. Box 7 (32618-0007)
PHONE..................................352 495-2121
Chase A Hope, *COO*
Fletcher J Hope, *Officer*
Mary M Hope,
EMP: 30 **EST:** 1905
SQ FT: 100,000
SALES (est): 2MM **Privately Held**
WEB: www.maddoxfoundry.com
SIC: 3321 3325 Gray & ductile iron foundries; steel foundries

Astatula
Lake County

(G-211)
FLORIDA CONCRETE PIPE CORP
25750 C R 561 (34705)
PHONE..................................352 742-2232
Carolyn Sonnentag, *President*
Teresa Whybrew, *Vice Pres*
▲ **EMP:** 14 **EST:** 1987
SQ FT: 800
SALES (est): 812.3K **Privately Held**
WEB: www.floridaconcretepipe.com
SIC: 3272 Pipe, concrete or lined with concrete

(G-212)
L & D DUMPSTERS LLC
25207 Jefferson St (34705-9579)
PHONE..................................352 589-5043
Donna Monroe, *Principal*
EMP: 6 **EST:** 2012
SALES (est): 240.4K **Privately Held**
SIC: 3443 Dumpsters, garbage

(G-213)
MACK CONCRETE INDUSTRIES INC
23902 County Road 561 (34705-9420)
P.O. Box 157 (34705-0157)
PHONE..................................352 742-2333
Betsy Mack Nespeca, *President*
Barbara Mack, *Corp Secy*
EMP: 125 **EST:** 1986
SALES (est): 19.2MM
SALES (corp-wide): 134.5MM **Privately Held**
WEB: www.mackconcrete.com
SIC: 3272 Concrete products, precast
PA: Mack Industries, Inc.
1321 Industrial Pkwy N # 500
Brunswick OH 44212
330 460-7005

(G-214)
MACK INDUSTRIES INC
Also Called: Mack Concrete
23902 County Road 561 (34705-9420)
P.O. Box 157 (34705-0157)
PHONE..................................352 742-2333
Greg Liskey, *Manager*
Ricardo Acevedo, *Technician*
EMP: 6
SALES (corp-wide): 134.5MM **Privately Held**
WEB: www.mackconcrete.com
SIC: 3272 1771 Burial vaults, concrete or precast terrazzo; septic tanks, concrete; manhole covers or frames, concrete; concrete work
PA: Mack Industries, Inc.
1321 Industrial Pkwy N # 500
Brunswick OH 44212
330 460-7005

Astor
Lake County

(G-215)
BOARD SHARK PCB INC
53717 Rivertrace Rd (32102-3514)
PHONE..................................352 759-2100
Cheri Surface, *Principal*
EMP: 6 **EST:** 2016
SALES (est): 159.9K **Privately Held**
WEB: www.boardsharkpcb.com
SIC: 3672 Printed circuit boards

Atlantic Beach
Duval County

(G-216)
AMEE BAY LLC
1701 Mayport Rd (32233-1930)
PHONE..................................904 553-9873
EMP: 28
SALES (corp-wide): 89.1MM **Privately Held**
WEB: www.ameebay.com
SIC: 3731 Shipbuilding & repairing
HQ: Amee Bay, Llc
2702 Denali St Ste 104
Anchorage AK 99503

(G-217)
BEACHES WOODCRAFT INC
14 Dutton Island Rd E (32233-6951)
PHONE..................................904 249-0785
Jerry Hoey, *President*
Jason Hay, *Vice Pres*
Dan Hoey, *Vice Pres*
Jason Hoey, *Vice Pres*
Luke Hoey, *Engineer*
EMP: 15 **EST:** 1978
SQ FT: 7,500
SALES (est): 1.8MM **Privately Held**
WEB: www.beacheswoodcrafts.com
SIC: 2434 2511 Wood kitchen cabinets; wood household furniture

(G-218)
COLONNA SHIPYARD
1701 Mayport Rd (32233-1930)
PHONE..................................904 246-1183
EMP: 6 **EST:** 2015
SALES (est): 108.7K **Privately Held**
WEB: www.colonnaship.com
SIC: 3731 Shipbuilding & repairing

(G-219)
DIRTBAG CHOPPERS INC
27 W 11th St (32233-3460)
PHONE..................................904 725-7600
Jeff Gordon, *CEO*
EMP: 14 **EST:** 2014
SALES (est): 603.8K **Privately Held**
WEB: www.dirtbagchoppersjax.com
SIC: 3751 7389 Motorcycles & related parts;

(G-220)
EARL INDUSTRIES
1543 Main St (32233-1938)
P.O. Box 330089 (32233-0089)
PHONE..................................904 247-1301
EMP: 6 **EST:** 2011
SALES (est): 97.4K **Privately Held**
SIC: 3731 Shipbuilding & repairing

(G-221)
FIRST COAST TRIKKES
510 Mayport Rd (32233-3452)
PHONE..................................904 343-1833
EMP: 6 **EST:** 2015
SALES (est): 80.7K **Privately Held**
WEB: www.firstcoasttrikkes.com
SIC: 3751 Bicycles & related parts

(G-222)
FLORIDA MINING ENTERPRISES LLC
2207 Alicia Ln (32233-5975)
PHONE..................................904 270-2646
David Johnston, *Principal*
EMP: 9 **EST:** 2007
SALES (est): 528.2K **Privately Held**
SIC: 3273 Ready-mixed concrete

(G-223)
GENERAL SIGNS AND SERVICE INC
Also Called: Beach Neon & Sign Co
20 Donner Rd (32233-4209)
PHONE..................................904 372-4238
Randall Ginseg, *President*
Sybil Vinson, *Manager*
EMP: 6 **EST:** 1988
SALES (est): 479.8K **Privately Held**
SIC: 3993 1799 Electric signs; neon signs; sign installation & maintenance

(G-224)
MCG SURFBOARDS
97 Levy Rd (32233-2611)
PHONE..................................904 305-8801
Marcelo Gagliardi, *Principal*
EMP: 6 **EST:** 2012
SALES (est): 126.4K **Privately Held**
SIC: 3949 Surfboards

(G-225)
OCEAN WOODWORKS INC
1701 Mayport Rd Ste 1 (32233-1930)
PHONE..................................904 246-7178
Bill Henry, *President*
Rebecca Henry, *Vice Pres*
EMP: 8 **EST:** 1986
SQ FT: 3,200
SALES (est): 1MM **Privately Held**
WEB: www.oceanwoodworksinc.com
SIC: 2431 Millwork

(G-226)
SANDAR INDUSTRIES INC
1545 Main St (32233-1938)
P.O. Box 330106 (32233-0106)
PHONE..................................904 246-4309
Jason Rodriguez, *Principal*
Peter Rodriguez, *Chairman*
Delia M Rodriguez, *Vice Pres*
Erika Chaves, *Cust Mgr*
Paul Mellion, *Manager*
◆ **EMP:** 22 **EST:** 1975
SQ FT: 10,800
SALES (est): 4.6MM **Privately Held**
WEB: www.sandar.com
SIC: 3545 5084 Precision tools, machinists'; paper manufacturing machinery

(G-227)
TECNICO CORPORATION
490 Levy Rd (32233-2618)
PHONE..................................904 853-6118
Ronald Fett, *Project Mgr*
Jim Pickney, *Manager*
EMP: 17 **Privately Held**
WEB: www.tecnicocorp.com
SIC: 3731 Shipbuilding & repairing
HQ: Tecnico Corporation
831 Industrial Ave
Chesapeake VA 23324

(G-228)
WATTS JUICERY
1013 Atlantic Blvd (32233-3313)
PHONE..................................904 372-0693
Annie Tuttle, *Owner*
Taylor Willneth, *General Mgr*
EMP: 10 **EST:** 2015
SALES (est): 583.1K **Privately Held**
WEB: www.wattsjuicery.com
SIC: 2033 5499 Fruit juices: fresh; juices, fruit or vegetable

Auburndale
Polk County

(G-229)
AGRIFLEET LEASING CORPORATION
100 Thornhill Rd (33823-3938)
PHONE..................................239 293-3976
Robert Swander, *President*
Darren Swander, *Vice Pres*
EMP: 26 **EST:** 1997
SQ FT: 3,000
SALES (est): 4.4MM **Privately Held**
WEB: www.agrifleet.com
SIC: 3523 7519 7359 Fertilizing machinery, farm; utility trailer rental; equipment rental & leasing

(G-230)
BONSAL AMERICAN INC
1511 1st St W (33823-4042)
PHONE..................................863 967-9100
Joseph Jensen, *Manager*
EMP: 6
SALES (corp-wide): 27.5B **Privately Held**
SIC: 3272 Concrete products
HQ: Bonsal American, Inc.
625 Griffith Rd Ste 100
Charlotte NC 28217
704 525-1621

(G-231)
CANTEX INC
101 Gandy Rd (33823-2733)
P.O. Box 365 (33823-0365)
PHONE..................................863 967-4161
John Davies, *Branch Mgr*
EMP: 107
SQ FT: 4,000 **Privately Held**
WEB: www.cantexinc.com
SIC: 3644 3498 3084 Electric conduits & fittings; fabricated pipe & fittings; plastics pipe
HQ: Cantex Inc.
301 Commerce St Ste 2700
Fort Worth TX 76102

(G-232)
CENTER SEAL INC
2714 K Ville Ave (33823-4963)
PHONE..................................863 965-7124
Greg Arnold, *President*
Jamie Arnold, *Corp Secy*
EMP: 8 **EST:** 1995
SQ FT: 7,000
SALES (est): 681.3K **Privately Held**
WEB: www.centerseal.com
SIC: 2451 Mobile homes

(G-233)
CENTRAL FLORIDA SALES & SVC
307 Mckean St (33823-3226)
P.O. Box 402 (33823-0402)
PHONE..................................863 967-6678
Marvin Brown, *President*
Danny Kniskern, *Purch Agent*
Bruce Barber, *Admin Sec*
EMP: 19 **EST:** 1968
SALES (est): 1.7MM **Privately Held**
SIC: 3599 3565 Machine shop, jobbing & repair; packaging machinery

(G-234)
CHEMCLAD LLC
1701 Hobbs Rd (33823-4692)
P.O. Box 1804 (33823-1804)
PHONE..................................863 967-1156
Stephanie S Whiddon, *President*
Conley Whiddon, *Vice Pres*
Shain Brown, *Prdtn Mgr*
Harry W Hazelwood, *Treasurer*
Brittany Craig, *Manager*
▲ **EMP:** 15 **EST:** 1981
SQ FT: 20,000
SALES (est): 3.7MM **Privately Held**
WEB: www.chemclad.com
SIC: 3083 Laminated plastics plate & sheet

(G-235)
COCA-COLA REFRESHMENTS USA INC
705 Main St (33823-4425)
PHONE..................................863 551-3700
Nicole Langone, *Production*
EMP: 6
SALES (corp-wide): 33B **Publicly Held**
WEB: www.coca-cola.com
SIC: 2086 Bottled & canned soft drinks
HQ: Coca-Cola Refreshments Usa, Inc.
2500 Windy Ridge Pkwy Se
Atlanta GA 30339
770 989-3000

(G-236)
COMMERCIAL TRUCK & TRAILER SLS
Also Called: Ctts
507 Us Highway 92 E (33823-4326)
PHONE..................................863 968-9393
George Turner, *Branch Mgr*
EMP: 30
SALES (corp-wide): 375.7MM **Privately Held**
WEB: www.comcar.com
SIC: 3492 Hose & tube fittings & assemblies, hydraulic/pneumatic
HQ: Commercial Truck & Trailer Sales, Inc
502 E Bridgers Ave
Auburndale FL 33823

(G-237)
CUSTOM WLDG & FABRICATION INC
364 Recker Hwy (33823-4075)
P.O. Box 3538, Plant City (33563-0010)
PHONE..................................863 967-1000
Yvonne M Hampton, *President*
Michael E Hampton, *Vice Pres*
EMP: 30 **EST:** 1991
SQ FT: 2,480
SALES (est): 1MM **Privately Held**
WEB: www.customwelding.com
SIC: 3441 1799 Fabricated structural metal; welding on site

(G-238)
CUTRALE FARMS INC
Also Called: Cutrale Citrus Juices
602 Mckean St (33823-4070)
PHONE..................................863 965-5000
Joe A Birge, *President*
Daniel Marques, *Corp Secy*
Andrew Sharrock, *Project Mgr*
Dan Marques, *Opers Mgr*
Antonio Violante, *Purchasing*
▲ **EMP:** 75 **EST:** 1998
SALES (est): 9.7MM **Privately Held**
WEB: www.cutrale.com
SIC: 2033 Fruit juices: fresh

(G-239)
DI JAM HOLDINGS INC
Also Called: Custom Trade Printing.com
123 Main St (33823-3401)
PHONE..................................863 967-6949
James Murray, *President*
EMP: 15 **EST:** 2011
SALES (est): 993.1K **Privately Held**
WEB: www.customtradeprinting.com
SIC: 2752 Commercial printing, lithographic

(G-240)
FI-FOIL COMPANY INC
Also Called: FI Foil Co
612 W Bridgers Ave (33823-3154)
P.O. Box 800 (33823-0800)
PHONE..................................863 965-1846
William A Lippy, *President*
Matt Belman, *Division Mgr*
James Hayes, *Vice Pres*
Douglas F Kinninger, *Vice Pres*
James T Sheridan, *CFO*
◆ **EMP:** 33 **EST:** 2000
SQ FT: 50,000
SALES (est): 8.5MM **Privately Held**
WEB: www.fifoil.com
SIC: 3999 Curling feathers

(G-241)
FLORIDA ALUMINUM AND STEEL INC
100 Thornhill Rd (33823-3938)
PHONE..................................863 967-4191
Darren Swander, *Branch Mgr*
EMP: 10
SALES (corp-wide): 8.9MM **Privately Held**
WEB: www.flasf.com
SIC: 3312 1799 3444 3441 Structural shapes & pilings, steel; ornamental metal work; sheet metalwork; fabricated structural metal
PA: Florida Aluminum And Steel, Inc.
1 Tom Rab Ln
Fort Myers FL
239 936-8153

(G-242)
FLORIDA BREWERY INC
202 Gandy Rd (33823-2726)
P.O. Box 6 (33823-0006)
PHONE..................................863 965-1825
Julie Williams, *President*
Frank Nunez, *Engineer*
Stacey Oakley, *CFO*
◆ **EMP:** 27 **EST:** 1971
SQ FT: 57,863
SALES (est): 6.1MM **Privately Held**
SIC: 2083 2082 Malt; malt beverages; beer (alcoholic beverage)

(G-243)
FLORIDA DISTILLERS CO
Also Called: Florida Caribbean Distillers
425 Recker Hwy (33823-4035)
PHONE..................................863 967-4481
Mike Ryan, *Vice Pres*
Felicie Iris, *Vice Pres*
Lisa Tocci, *Vice Pres*
Liz Nieves, *Production*
Joseph Pickett, *Production*
EMP: 19 **EST:** 2015
SALES (est): 11.8MM
SALES (corp-wide): 30.9MM **Privately Held**
WEB: www.floridadistillers.com
SIC: 2085 Distillers' dried grains & solubles & alcohol
HQ: Imperial Brands, Inc.
100 W Cypress Creek Rd # 1050
Fort Lauderdale FL 33309

(G-244)
GLASRITE INC
627 W Bridgers Ave (33823-3103)
PHONE..................................863 967-8151
Barlow Brannon, *Manager*
◆ **EMP:** 10 **EST:** 2004
SALES (est): 635.3K **Privately Held**
SIC: 2221 Fiberglass fabrics

(G-245)
GTI SYSTEMS INC (PA)
1250 Hobbs Rd (33823-4638)
PHONE..................................863 965-2002

GEOGRAPHIC

Peter Shin, *President*
Danielle Lynch, *Manager*
EMP: 20 **EST:** 2002
SQ FT: 20,000
SALES (est): 7.2MM **Privately Held**
SIC: 3482 3471 3483 3451 Small arms ammunition; anodizing (plating) of metals or formed products; ammunition, except for small arms; screw machine products

(G-246)
J & J WLDG STL FBRCTION FLA IN
364 Recker Hwy (33823-4075)
PHONE..................................813 754-0771
James Davis, *Principal*
EMP: 30 **EST:** 2012
SALES (est): 2.7MM **Privately Held**
WEB: www.jnjwelding.com
SIC: 3441 5051 Fabricated structural metal; structural shapes, iron or steel

(G-247)
JENNINGS MOBILE HM SET UP LLC
1048 Us Highway 92 W (33823-9514)
P.O. Box 1428 (33823-1428)
PHONE..................................863 965-0883
Thomas Jennings,
EMP: 13 **EST:** 2002
SALES (est): 1.7MM **Privately Held**
SIC: 2452 Modular homes, prefabricated, wood

(G-248)
MAGNOLIA MACHINE COMPANY
1088 Us Highway 92 W (33823-9622)
P.O. Box 657 (33823-0657)
PHONE..................................863 965-8201
EMP: 23
SALES (est): 3.1MM **Privately Held**
SIC: 3599 Mfg Industrial Machinery

(G-249)
MASTER-KRAFT CABINETRY
305 Keystone Rd (33823-2343)
PHONE..................................863 661-2083
Jonathan C Ammerman, *President*
▼ **EMP:** 7 **EST:** 2004
SALES (est): 137.2K **Privately Held**
SIC: 2434 Wood kitchen cabinets

(G-250)
PRECISE PAVERS INC
2581 Nelson St (33823-4816)
PHONE..................................863 528-8000
Jose C Gomez, *Principal*
EMP: 11 **EST:** 2012
SALES (est): 701.9K **Privately Held**
SIC: 3531 Pavers

(G-251)
RAT TRAP BAIT COMPANY INC
106 Adams St (33823-3612)
P.O. Box 845 (33823-0845)
PHONE..................................863 967-2148
Ralph Robinson, *President*
Yolanda Dyer, *President*
Charles Davis Jr, *Corp Secy*
Ralph Robbins, *Vice Pres*
Darcy Hurley, *Office Mgr*
EMP: 10 **EST:** 1940
SQ FT: 10,000
SALES (est): 588.2K **Privately Held**
SIC: 3949 3496 2869 2298 Fishing tackle, general; miscellaneous fabricated wire products; industrial organic chemicals; cordage & twine

(G-252)
SEWELL PRODUCTS FLORIDA LLC
Also Called: Kik Custom Products
909 Magnolia Ave (33823-4007)
PHONE..................................863 967-4463
David G Cynamon, *President*
Paul C Anderson, *Senior VP*
Bob Clarke, *Manager*
Richard L Pfab, *Admin Sec*
EMP: 72 **EST:** 1996
SQ FT: 200,000
SALES (est): 24.6MM
SALES (corp-wide): 111.1MM **Privately Held**
WEB: www.kikcorp.com
SIC: 2842 Bleaches, household: dry or liquid
HQ: Kik (Virginia) Llc
27 Mill Ln
Salem VA 24153
540 389-5401

(G-253)
SMITHBILT INDUSTRIES INC (PA)
1061 Us Highway 92 W (33823-4077)
PHONE..................................321 690-0902
Donald E Smith, *President*
Jeanette K Smith, *Corp Secy*
EMP: 75 **EST:** 1982
SQ FT: 40,000
SALES (est): 9.7MM **Privately Held**
WEB: www.smithbilt.com
SIC: 3448 Buildings, portable: prefabricated metal

(G-254)
TAYLOR BUILDING ELEMENTS LLC
116 Van Fleet Ct (33823-2059)
PHONE..................................863 287-2228
Alison A Taylor, *Principal*
EMP: 8 **EST:** 2012
SALES (est): 1.9MM **Privately Held**
SIC: 2819 Industrial inorganic chemicals

(G-255)
WINANS ELECTRIC MOTORS LLC
1150 Us Highway 92 W (33823-4046)
PHONE..................................863 875-5710
Michael Wenners, *Mng Member*
Janet Gangraw,
EMP: 5 **EST:** 1989
SALES (est): 476.1K **Privately Held**
SIC: 3621 Motors & generators

Ave Maria
Collier County

(G-256)
ARTHREX MANUFACTURING INC
6875 Arthrex Commerce Dr (34142-9534)
PHONE..................................239 304-2236
Frank Yacino, *Manager*
Isis Amaro, *Supervisor*
Paul Hobaica MD, *Director*
Tina Ruiz, *Administration*
EMP: 1 **EST:** 2014
SALES (est): 5.2MM
SALES (corp-wide): 7.1MM **Privately Held**
WEB: www.arthrexmedicalcenter.com
SIC: 3999 Manufacturing industries
PA: Arthrex, Inc.
14550 Plantation Rd
Fort Myers FL 33912
239 643-5553

(G-257)
HOUSE DOCTAIR INC ✪
5438 Ferrari Ave (34142-9554)
PHONE..................................239 349-7497
Matthew Foster, *President*
EMP: 10 **EST:** 2020
SALES (est): 216.3K **Privately Held**
WEB: www.housedoctors.com
SIC: 1389 Construction, repair & dismantling services

(G-258)
MASTER CABINETS LLC
5462 Ferrari Ave (34142-9554)
PHONE..................................239 324-9701
Julio C Ordonez, *Vice Pres*
EMP: 6 **EST:** 2017
SALES (est): 279K **Privately Held**
SIC: 2434 Wood kitchen cabinets

Aventura
Miami-Dade County

(G-259)
ACTION CONTROLS INC
Also Called: Aci
3701 N Country Club Dr # 201 (33180-1717)
PHONE..................................253 243-7703
James Waite, *President*
Kristi Waite, *Vice Pres*
EMP: 7
SQ FT: 5,400
SALES (est): 992.6K **Privately Held**
WEB: www.actioncontrols.com
SIC: 3625 Relays & industrial controls

(G-260)
AMERICAN WIRE GROUP INC (PA)
Also Called: Awg
2980 Ne 207th St Ste 901 (33180-1467)
PHONE..................................954 455-3050
Robert Dorfman, *CEO*
Michael Dorfman, *President*
Joshua Dorfman, *COO*
Gerry Goodin, *CFO*
Bill Brewer, *Sales Engr*
◆ **EMP:** 12 **EST:** 2001
SQ FT: 3,000
SALES (est): 15.4MM **Privately Held**
WEB: www.buyawg.com
SIC: 3351 3355 5063 2298 Wire, copper & copper alloy; aluminum wire & cable; wire & cable; power wire & cable; cable, fiber

(G-261)
APPO GROUP INC
7000 Island Blvd Apt 2309 (33160-2474)
PHONE..................................410 992-5500
Stephen Wigler, *President*
Cindy Jones, *Senior VP*
Tom Wuhas, *Senior VP*
Tom Yuhas, *Vice Pres*
Jeanette Leblanc, *Director*
EMP: 7 **EST:** 2013
SALES (est): 595.7K **Privately Held**
WEB: www.appogroup.com
SIC: 7372 Prepackaged software

(G-262)
AYAM BEAUTYCARE LLC
19495 Biscayne Blvd # 608 (33180-2318)
PHONE..................................305 318-2598
Moises Alex Guenoun,
EMP: 6 **EST:** 2019
SALES (est): 258.9K **Privately Held**
WEB: www.ayambeautycare.com
SIC: 2844 Shampoos, rinses, conditioners: hair

(G-263)
BASHERT DIAMONDS INC
3201 Ne 183rd St Apt 408 (33160-2488)
PHONE..................................305 466-1881
Kyla Fajerstein, *President*
EMP: 5 **EST:** 2012
SQ FT: 1,000
SALES (est): 1MM **Privately Held**
WEB: www.bashertdiamonds.com
SIC: 3911 3915 Jewelry, precious metal; diamond cutting & polishing

(G-264)
BERG LLC
3201 Ne 183rd St Apt 704 (33160-2493)
PHONE..................................786 201-2625
Paul L Berg, *Principal*
EMP: 14 **EST:** 2010
SALES (est): 141.8K **Privately Held**
WEB: www.bergpipe.com
SIC: 3312 Blast furnaces & steel mills

(G-265)
BOSSY PRINCESS LLC ✪
18117 Biscayne Blvd # 1194 (33160-2535)
PHONE..................................786 285-4435
Christopher Mesa, *CEO*
Akyng Mesa, *COO*
Nia Mesa, *COO*
Dominique Lewis, *CFO*
EMP: 8 **EST:** 2020
SALES (est): 534.9K **Privately Held**
SIC: 2361 5641 Girls' & children's blouses & shirts; children's & infants' wear stores

(G-266)
CAQUIN GROUP LLC
18851 Ne 29th Ave Ste 700 (33180-2845)
PHONE..................................786 303-2700
Carlos Quintero,
EMP: 10
SALES (est): 450.6K **Privately Held**
WEB: www.caquin.com
SIC: 2631 Container, packaging & boxboard

(G-267)
EGD EURO GOURMET DELI INC
18650 Ne 28th Ct (33180-2931)
PHONE..................................305 937-1515
Monique Seelinger, *President*
Harold Aumenta, *Vice Pres*
Hans Christian Seelinger, *Vice Pres*
EMP: 7 **EST:** 2013
SALES (est): 170.4K **Privately Held**
SIC: 3411 5149 Food & beverage containers; beverage concentrates

(G-268)
EILEEN KRAMER INC
19955 Ne 38th Ct Apt 504 (33180-3428)
PHONE..................................315 395-3831
Eileen Favor Kramer, *Principal*
EMP: 6 **EST:** 2011
SALES (est): 310.8K **Privately Held**
WEB: www.lilbbonnet.com
SIC: 3199 Leather goods

(G-269)
FUTURE SIGNS AND SERVICES INC
3530 Mystic Pointe Dr (33180-4541)
PHONE..................................786 255-0868
Yehoshua Kadosh, *Principal*
EMP: 6 **EST:** 2016
SALES (est): 95.6K **Privately Held**
SIC: 3993 Signs & advertising specialties

(G-270)
GAIN SOLAR LLC
18205 Biscayne Blvd (33160-2106)
P.O. Box 2604, Windermere (34786-2604)
PHONE..................................305 933-1060
Daniel Halberstin,
EMP: 7
SALES (est): 900K **Privately Held**
SIC: 3433 Solar heaters & collectors

(G-271)
GLOBAL PRIME WOOD LLC
2875 Ne 191st St Ste 500 (33180-2832)
PHONE..................................770 292-9200
Cesar Alberto Cemin, *Mng Member*
Leonardo Souza De Zorzi, *Mng Member*
Joao Carlos Nesello, *Mng Member*
▲ **EMP:** 7 **EST:** 2012
SALES (est): 460.4K **Privately Held**
SIC: 2421 1752 Outdoor wood structural products; wood floor installation & refinishing

(G-272)
GOURMET FOOD SOLUTIONS LLC
19950 W Country Club Dr # 101 (33180-4602)
PHONE..................................413 687-3285
Irvin Rhodes, *CEO*
EMP: 30 **EST:** 2014
SALES (est): 2.2MM **Privately Held**
SIC: 2099 Sauces: gravy, dressing & dip mixes

(G-273)
HERBKO INC
3000 Island Blvd Ph 5 (33160-4927)
PHONE..................................305 932-3572
Herbert Sternberg, *President*
Tracey Sternberg, *Vice Pres*
Marlene Sternberg, *CFO*
EMP: 8 **EST:** 1978
SQ FT: 5,000
SALES (est): 415.7K **Privately Held**
SIC: 3944 Games, toys & children's vehicles

▲ = Import ▼=Export
◆ =Import/Export

(G-274)
ITER3D INC
Also Called: Standard 3d Systems
2221 Ne 164th St Ste 296 (33160-3703)
PHONE..................................718 473-0114
EMP: 6
SALES (est): 173.4K **Privately Held**
SIC: 7372 3577 3555 Prepackaged Software Svc Mfg Computer Peripherals Mfg Printing Trades Mach

(G-275)
JMS CORPORATE GROUP LLC
21205 Ne 37th Ave (33180-4051)
PHONE..................................786 219-6114
Juan M Santos, *Mng Member*
EMP: 7
SALES (est): 500K **Privately Held**
SIC: 3714 Motor vehicle parts & accessories

(G-276)
M PET GROUP CORP
2980 Ne 207th St Ste 701 (33180-1465)
PHONE..................................954 455-5003
Isaac Mendal, *President*
EMP: 8 **EST:** 2018
SALES (est): 297.5K **Privately Held**
SIC: 3999 Pet supplies

(G-277)
ONE BIO CORP
19950 W Country Club Dr (33180-4601)
PHONE..................................305 328-8662
Marius Silvasan, *President*
Cris Neely, *CFO*
EMP: 358 **EST:** 2000
SALES (est): 24.1MM **Privately Held**
WEB: www.biooneinc.com
SIC: 2833 Organic medicinal chemicals: bulk, uncompounded; drugs & herbs: grading, grinding & milling; medicinal chemicals

(G-278)
ORBSAT CORP (PA)
18851 Ne 29th Ave Ste 700 (33180-2845)
PHONE..................................305 560-5355
Charles M Fernandez, *Ch of Bd*
David Phipps, *President*
Andrew Cohen, *Senior VP*
Thomas Seifert, *CFO*
Paul R Thomson, *CFO*
EMP: 12 **EST:** 1984
SALES (est): 5.6MM **Publicly Held**
WEB: www.orbsat.com
SIC: 3663 Satellites, communications

(G-279)
ORIGINATES INC
20900 Ne 30th Ave Ste 707 (33180-2164)
PHONE..................................954 233-2500
Meyer Minski, *President*
Jose Minski, *Vice Pres*
Julia Restrepo, *Purch Agent*
◆ **EMP:** 14 **EST:** 1976
SQ FT: 1,500
SALES: 24.4MM **Privately Held**
WEB: www.originates.com
SIC: 2869 Fatty acid esters, aminos, etc.

(G-280)
SERVICES NS 18 LLC
Also Called: Renue Systems South East Fla
19900 E Country Club Dr (33180-3327)
PHONE..................................786 546-3295
Enrique Nessim, *Mng Member*
EMP: 5 **EST:** 2011
SALES (est): 762.9K **Privately Held**
SIC: 2842 Specialty cleaning preparations

(G-281)
SQUEEZE IT CORP ✪
3610 Yacht Club Dr # 213 (33180-3541)
PHONE..................................954 851-2443
Latoya Clark, *President*
EMP: 6 **EST:** 2020
SALES (est): 242.5K **Privately Held**
SIC: 2087 Beverage bases

(G-282)
VMOVILES INC
Also Called: Vmoviles Power Solar Energy
17111 Biscayne Blvd (33160-5097)
PHONE..................................954 609-2510
Francisco Pages, *President*
EMP: 7 **EST:** 2009
SALES (est): 1.9MM **Privately Held**
WEB: www.vmoviles.com
SIC: 3663 Radio & TV communications equipment
PA: Fertiven Operaciones Ca
Urbanizacion El Vinedo
Valencia

Avon Park
Highlands County

(G-283)
AGRA CHEM SALES CO INC
959 S Angelo Lake Rd (33825-6501)
P.O. Box 1356 (33826-1356)
PHONE..................................863 453-6450
Rick Brant, *President*
Bill Engel, *Vice Pres*
◆ **EMP:** 8 **EST:** 1962
SQ FT: 40,000
SALES (est): 636K **Privately Held**
SIC: 2879 Trace elements (agricultural chemicals)

(G-284)
BOWSMITH INC
100 W Monroe St (33825-2254)
P.O. Box 1663 (33826-1663)
PHONE..................................863 453-6666
Ken Berg, *Vice Pres*
Victor Gonzales, *Mfg Staff*
Tonnie Garnett, *Purchasing*
Lee Gipson, *Sales Staff*
Stanley Kirby, *Sales Staff*
EMP: 6
SALES (corp-wide): 11.1MM **Privately Held**
WEB: www.bowsmith.com
SIC: 3069 Tubing, rubber
PA: Bowsmith, Inc.
131 2nd St
Exeter CA 93221
559 592-9485

(G-285)
DESIGNERS TOP SHOP INC
12 N Anoka Ave (33825-3309)
P.O. Box 1952 (33826-1952)
PHONE..................................863 453-3855
Justine Jackson, *President*
Christine Jackson, *Vice Pres*
EMP: 8 **EST:** 1983
SQ FT: 3,500
SALES (est): 303K **Privately Held**
WEB: www.designertopshop.com
SIC: 2759 2395 Screen printing; embroidery & art needlework

(G-286)
DS COATINGS INC
18 S Butler Ave (33825-3804)
PHONE..................................321 848-4719
Daniel Sauls, *Principal*
EMP: 10 **EST:** 2015
SALES (est): 272K **Privately Held**
SIC: 3479 Metal coating & allied service

(G-287)
FLOWERS BKG CO BRADENTON LLC
Also Called: Flowers Baking Company
1202 State Road 64 W (33825-3302)
PHONE..................................941 758-5656
Chris Peer, *Manager*
EMP: 15
SALES (corp-wide): 4.3B **Publicly Held**
WEB: www.flobradconf.com
SIC: 2051 Bread, cake & related products
HQ: Flowers Baking Co. Of Bradenton, Llc
6490 Parkland Dr
Sarasota FL 34243

(G-288)
GPI SIGNS
500 S Lake Ave (33825-3912)
PHONE..................................863 453-4888
EMP: 6 **EST:** 2016
SALES (est): 76.4K **Privately Held**
SIC: 3993 Electric signs

(G-289)
JAHNA CONCRETE INC (PA)
103 County Road 17a W (33825-2239)
PHONE..................................863 453-4353
Frederick W Jahna Jr, *President*
Candis Davis, *Corp Secy*
David Jahna, *Vice Pres*
Dawn Robinson, *Bookkeeper*
Fedeila Jahna, *Shareholder*
EMP: 12
SALES (est): 28MM **Privately Held**
WEB: www.jahnaconcrete.com
SIC: 3271 5032 3273 3272 Blocks, concrete or cinder: standard; concrete mixtures; ready-mixed concrete; concrete products

(G-290)
JAHNA CONCRETE INC
104 S Railroad Ave (33825-3181)
PHONE..................................863 453-4353
EMP: 20
SALES (corp-wide): 28MM **Privately Held**
SIC: 3273 Central-Mixed Concrete
PA: Jahna Concrete Inc
103 County Road 17a W
Avon Park FL 33825
863 453-4353

(G-291)
ON BASE FOODS GROUP LLC
3179 E Pebble Creek Dr (33825)
PHONE..................................248 672-7659
Aaron Schossau, *Manager*
EMP: 10 **EST:** 2019
SALES (est): 553.7K **Privately Held**
SIC: 2013 Canned meats (except baby food) from purchased meat

(G-292)
PEPSI BOTTLING GROUP
Also Called: Pepsico
1006 W Cornell St (33825-3510)
PHONE..................................863 452-9920
EMP: 7 **EST:** 2010
SALES (est): 98.1K **Privately Held**
WEB: www.pepsico.com
SIC: 2086 Carbonated soft drinks, bottled & canned

(G-293)
PLASTIREX LLC
1552 Sun Pure Rd (33825-8713)
PHONE..................................305 471-1111
Janice Roller, *Office Mgr*
Roberto Panzarasa,
Raffaele Chierchia,
Gianpaolo Girardello,
EMP: 17 **EST:** 2018
SALES (est): 4.5MM **Privately Held**
WEB: www.florida-corp.com
SIC: 2821 Carbohydrate plastics

(G-294)
PRO-WELD INC
222 S Forest Ave Unit 1 (33825-3815)
PHONE..................................863 453-9353
Richard Tindell, *President*
EMP: 5 **EST:** 1990
SQ FT: 10,000
SALES (est): 893.1K **Privately Held**
WEB: www.proweldincfl.com
SIC: 7692 Welding repair

(G-295)
SIMCO MACHINE AND TOOL INC
2029 State Road 64 W (33825-8417)
P.O. Box 997 (33826-0997)
PHONE..................................863 452-1151
Drema Zimmerman, *CEO*
EMP: 10 **EST:** 1998
SALES (est): 849K **Privately Held**
WEB: www.simcobox.com
SIC: 3089 Injection molding of plastics

(G-296)
SIMPSON CONSTRUCTION AND ROOFG
418 E Elm St (33825-3206)
PHONE..................................863 443-0710
Thomas Simpson, *President*
EMP: 14 **EST:** 2010
SALES (est): 2.1MM **Privately Held**
WEB: www.simpsonconstructionandroofing.com
SIC: 3842 Clothing, fire resistant & protective

(G-297)
STANDARD INJECTION MOLDING INC
Also Called: Simco
2027 State Road 64 W (33825-8417)
P.O. Box 997 (33826-0997)
PHONE..................................863 452-9090
Drema Zimmerman, *President*
Susan R Crull, *Vice Pres*
EMP: 10 **EST:** 1982
SQ FT: 30,000
SALES (est): 899.4K **Privately Held**
WEB: www.simcobox.com
SIC: 3089 Injection molding of plastics

Bagdad
Santa Rosa County

(G-298)
HOM/ADE FOOD SALES INC
4641 Forsyth St (32530-9401)
PHONE..................................850 623-3845
EMP: 6
SALES (corp-wide): 1B **Publicly Held**
SIC: 2045 Mfg And Distribution Of Frozen Doughs
HQ: Hom/Ade Food Sales Inc
10648 Mac Gregor Dr
Pensacola FL 32514

Baker
Okaloosa County

(G-299)
4F MOBILE WELDING LLC
Also Called: 4f Contracting
6289 Holloway Rd (32531-8131)
PHONE..................................850 537-2290
Aaron Fortner, *Principal*
EMP: 7 **EST:** 2016
SALES (est): 398.4K **Privately Held**
SIC: 7692 Welding repair

(G-300)
BAKER METAL WORKS & SUPPLY LLC (PA)
5846 Highway 189 N (32531-2506)
PHONE..................................850 537-2010
Carrie N Norton,
Jason C Norton,
EMP: 20 **EST:** 2007
SALES (est): 13.6MM **Privately Held**
WEB: www.bakermetalworks.com
SIC: 3444 Metal roofing & roof drainage equipment

(G-301)
BAKER METALWORKS AND SUP INC
5846 Highway 189 N (32531-2506)
PHONE..................................850 537-2010
Carrie N Norton, *President*
EMP: 12 **EST:** 2001
SALES (est): 409.6K **Privately Held**
SIC: 3441 Fabricated structural metal

Bal Harbour
Miami-Dade County

(G-302)
GOYARD MIAMI LLC
Also Called: Maison Goyard
9700 Collins Ave Ste 118 (33154-2200)
PHONE..................................305 894-9235
Deborah Ruiz, *Branch Mgr*
EMP: 30
SALES (corp-wide): 55.2MM **Privately Held**
WEB: www.catalogue.goyard.us
SIC: 3161 Wardrobe bags (luggage)

HQ: Goyard Miami, Llc
20 E 63rd St
New York NY 10065
212 813-0005

(G-303)
MOBA CORP
10155 Collins Ave # 1807 (33154-1655)
PHONE..................................305 868-3700
EMP: 16 **EST:** 1946
SALES (est): 1.2MM **Privately Held**
SIC: 3911 Manufactures Precious Jewelry & Works Of Art With Precious Metals & Stones

(G-304)
WIRE TECH INTERNATIONAL INC
10225 Collins Ave (33154-1443)
PHONE..................................786 258-5746
EMP: 6 **EST:** 2018
SALES (est): 157.5K **Privately Held**
SIC: 3315 Wire & fabricated wire products

Bartow
Polk County

(G-305)
ALL WOOD CABINETRY LLC
Also Called: Ideal Cabinetry
210 Century Blvd (33830-7704)
PHONE..................................866 367-2516
Richard Heley,
Kristi R Dunbar,
◆ **EMP:** 29 **EST:** 2006
SALES (est): 16.2MM **Privately Held**
WEB: www.idealcabinetry.com
SIC: 2434 Wood kitchen cabinets

(G-306)
B & R PROFILES LLC (PA)
216 Homeland Cemetery Rd (33830-8555)
PHONE..................................305 479-8308
Harold Brandan, *Mng Member*
EMP: 26 **EST:** 2015
SALES (est): 3.5MM **Privately Held**
SIC: 3674 Light sensitive devices

(G-307)
BARTOW ETHANOL FLORIDA LC
1705 E Mann Rd (33830-7542)
PHONE..................................863 533-2498
Charles R Ritley, *CEO*
Anthony Senagore, *President*
Jim Munzt, *COO*
James Muntz, *Vice Pres*
Matthew Dunbar, *Controller*
◆ **EMP:** 15 **EST:** 2004
SQ FT: 10,000
SALES (est): 6.3MM **Privately Held**
WEB: www.bartowethanol.com
SIC: 2869 Industrial organic chemicals

(G-308)
BARTOW MACHINE WORKS INC
441 W Vine St (33830-5440)
PHONE..................................863 533-6361
Patrick Frankenburger, *President*
Beverly Heath, *Office Mgr*
Gail Frankenburger, *Admin Sec*
EMP: 7 **EST:** 1941
SQ FT: 10,000
SALES (est): 879.1K **Privately Held**
SIC: 3599 7692 Machine shop, jobbing & repair; welding repair

(G-309)
BEARS METAL WORKS INC
320 S 1st Ave (33830-4900)
PHONE..................................863 537-5644
David Fox, *President*
Phyllis Fox, *Corp Secy*
Kevin Fox, *Vice Pres*
Tim Fox, *Vice Pres*
EMP: 10 **EST:** 1979
SQ FT: 6,000
SALES (est): 1.1MM **Privately Held**
SIC: 3599 Machine shop, jobbing & repair

(G-310)
BEST FABRICATIONS INC
2145 Bravo Ave (33830-6642)
PHONE..................................863 519-6611
Nicholas G Ruys, *CEO*
Anthony Easton, *President*
Pamela Byrd, *Treasurer*
Barry Boucher, *Sales Mgr*
Carolyn Thomas, *Office Mgr*
▼ **EMP:** 15 **EST:** 1992
SQ FT: 18,000
SALES (est): 2.3MM **Privately Held**
WEB: www.bestfab.com
SIC: 3441 Fabricated structural metal

(G-311)
CANDI-LYN CABINETRY
1655 Verona Dr (33830-3123)
PHONE..................................863 860-2505
Jimmy Hicks, *Principal*
EMP: 6 **EST:** 2007
SALES (est): 97.1K **Privately Held**
SIC: 2434 Wood kitchen cabinets

(G-312)
CENTRAL FLORIDA TRUSS INC (PA)
1500 Us Highway 17 N (33830-7602)
P.O. Box 455 (33831-0455)
PHONE..................................863 533-0821
Gary N Newell, *President*
Steven Newell, *Vice Pres*
Larry Braswell, *Manager*
Alec Monies, *Manager*
▼ **EMP:** 20
SQ FT: 2,000
SALES (est): 7.5MM **Privately Held**
WEB: www.cftruss.com
SIC: 2439 Trusses, wooden roof

(G-313)
CORSICANA BEDDING LLC
450 Polk St (33830-3749)
PHONE..................................863 519-5905
Ashley Eakin, *Purch Mgr*
Carroll Moran, *Branch Mgr*
EMP: 41
SALES (corp-wide): 636.6MM **Privately Held**
WEB: www.corsicanamattress.com
SIC: 2515 Mattresses, innerspring or box spring
PA: Corsicana Bedding, Llc
1420 W Mockingbird Ln
Dallas TX 75247
800 323-4349

(G-314)
EPIC METALS CORPORATION
1930 State Road 60 W (33830-9321)
PHONE..................................863 533-7404
Daryl Paw, *Manager*
EMP: 9
SALES (corp-wide): 20.1MM **Privately Held**
WEB: www.epicmetals.com
SIC: 3444 Roof deck, sheet metal
PA: Epic Metals Corporation
11 Talbot Ave
Rankin PA 15104
412 351-3913

(G-315)
ERIE MANUFACTURING INC
1520 Centennial Blvd (33830-7707)
PHONE..................................863 534-3743
Phil Dosso, *President*
EMP: 10 **EST:** 1962
SQ FT: 40,000
SALES (est): 1.9MM **Privately Held**
WEB: www.eriemanufacturinginc.com
SIC: 3535 Conveyors & conveying equipment

(G-316)
HARLEY BOAT CORPORATION
Also Called: Harley Boats
300 S 1st Ave (33830-4935)
PHONE..................................863 533-2800
Howard Harley, *President*
Dorothy E Harley, *Corp Secy*
Richard C Harley, *Vice Pres*
EMP: 5 **EST:** 2007
SQ FT: 26,000
SALES (est): 451.1K **Privately Held**
WEB: www.harleyboats.com
SIC: 3732 Boats, fiberglass: building & repairing

(G-317)
HARLEY SHIPBUILDING CORP
Also Called: Harley Boat
300 S 1st Ave (33830-4935)
PHONE..................................863 533-2800
Howard Harley, *President*
EMP: 9 **EST:** 1997
SALES (est): 756.3K **Privately Held**
WEB: www.harleyshipbuilding.net
SIC: 3732 Boat kits, not models

(G-318)
HCO HOLDING I CORPORATION
2701 State Road 60 W (33830-8750)
PHONE..................................863 533-0522
Jimmy Sellers, *Plant Mgr*
P James Grauer, *Sales & Mktg St*
James Sellers, *Manager*
EMP: 10
SALES (corp-wide): 254.1MM **Privately Held**
SIC: 3531 3241 2952 2851 Asphalt plant, including gravel-mix type; cement, hydraulic; asphalt felts & coatings; paints & allied products; roofing, asphalt & sheet metal
HQ: Hco Holding I Corporation
999 N Pacific Coast Hwy # 80
El Segundo CA 90245
323 583-5000

(G-319)
HINES ENERGY COMPLEX
7700 County Road 555 S (33830-8454)
PHONE..................................863 519-6106
Robert Miller, *President*
EMP: 10 **EST:** 2003
SALES (est): 481.6K **Privately Held**
SIC: 3462 Turbine engine forgings, ferrous

(G-320)
INNOVATED INDUSTRIAL SVCS INC
1416 Chamber Dr (33830-8428)
PHONE..................................863 701-2711
Thomas N Taphorn, *President*
Steven J Hasley, *Vice Pres*
EMP: 12 **EST:** 2000
SQ FT: 2,400
SALES (est): 3.8MM **Privately Held**
WEB: www.innovatedindustrial.com
SIC: 3569 Assembly machines, non-metalworking

(G-321)
KMR CONCRETE INC
2835 State Road 60 E (33830-8917)
P.O. Box 428 (33831-0428)
PHONE..................................863 519-9077
Kennedy M Heidel, *President*
Gary Thomas, *General Mgr*
Ashley Bass, *Manager*
Kerry L Hammock, *Director*
EMP: 25 **EST:** 2005
SQ FT: 400
SALES (est): 2.5MM **Privately Held**
WEB: www.kmrconcrete.com
SIC: 3273 Ready-mixed concrete

(G-322)
L & M PALLET SERVICES INC
1190 Us Highway 17 S (33830-6028)
P.O. Box 1846 (33831-1846)
PHONE..................................863 519-3502
Tim Long, *President*
Eddie Martin, *Vice Pres*
EMP: 15 **EST:** 1999
SALES (est): 1.8MM **Privately Held**
WEB: www.lmpallets.com
SIC: 2448 2441 Pallets, wood; nailed wood boxes & shook

(G-323)
MAINTNNCE RELIABILITY TECH INC
Also Called: M & R Technologies
1421 Chamber Dr (33830-8429)
P.O. Box 2286 (33831-2286)
PHONE..................................863 533-0300
Robert Radford, *President*
James Radford, *Vice Pres*
Marty Thurman, *Vice Pres*
Mike Kautz, *Manager*
Dean Newman, *Manager*
EMP: 35 **EST:** 2004
SQ FT: 9,024
SALES (est): 6MM **Privately Held**
SIC: 3822 Building services monitoring controls, automatic

(G-324)
METAL MART SYSTEMS INC
255 Century Blvd (33830-7705)
PHONE..................................863 533-4040
Henry T Boggs, *President*
Debbie Beckelheimer, *Controller*
▼ **EMP:** 50 **EST:** 1988
SQ FT: 85,000
SALES (est): 8.1MM **Privately Held**
WEB: www.metalmartsystems.com
SIC: 3444 Ducts, sheet metal

(G-325)
MID-FLRIDA LBR ACQISITIONS INC
4281 Echo Ave (33830-6662)
PHONE..................................863 533-0155
Tim Delph, *President*
Vj Creech, *Sales Staff*
EMP: 50 **EST:** 1991
SQ FT: 9,600
SALES (est): 4.8MM **Privately Held**
WEB: www.midflorida.com
SIC: 2439 4226 Trusses, wooden roof; lumber terminal (storage for hire)

(G-326)
PALLET ONE OF MOBILE LLC
6001 Foxtrot Ave (33830-6665)
PHONE..................................251 960-1107
EMP: 18 **EST:** 2019
SALES (est): 260.2K **Privately Held**
SIC: 2448 Pallets, wood

(G-327)
PALLETONE INC (HQ)
6001 Foxtrot Ave (33830-6665)
P.O. Box 819 (33831-0819)
PHONE..................................800 771-1147
Howe Wallace, *President*
Bridget Kennedy Hull, *Vice Pres*
Donnie Isaacson, *Vice Pres*
Gary Creamer, *Safety Mgr*
Casey A Fletcher, *CFO*
◆ **EMP:** 30 **EST:** 2001
SQ FT: 5,000
SALES (est): 35.4MM
SALES (corp-wide): 5.1B **Publicly Held**
WEB: www.palletone.com
SIC: 2448 Pallets, wood
PA: Ufp Industries, Inc.
2801 E Beltline Ave Ne
Grand Rapids MI 49525
616 364-6161

(G-328)
PALLETONE OF TEXAS LP (HQ)
1470 Us Highway 17 S (33830-6627)
P.O. Box 97, New Boston TX (75570-0097)
PHONE..................................903 628-5695
Howe Wallace, *Partner*
▲ **EMP:** 80 **EST:** 1994
SQ FT: 60,000
SALES (est): 31.4MM
SALES (corp-wide): 5.1B **Publicly Held**
WEB: www.ufpi.com
SIC: 2448 Pallets, wood
PA: Ufp Industries, Inc.
2801 E Beltline Ave Ne
Grand Rapids MI 49525
616 364-6161

(G-329)
PALLETONE OF TEXAS LP
1470 Us Highway 17 S (33830-6627)
PHONE..................................863 533-1147
Howe Wallace, *Partner*
EMP: 95 **EST:** 2001
SALES (est): 17MM
SALES (corp-wide): 5.1B **Publicly Held**
WEB: www.palletone.com
SIC: 2448 Pallets, wood
PA: Ufp Industries, Inc.
2801 E Beltline Ave Ne
Grand Rapids MI 49525
616 364-6161

▲ = Import ▼=Export
◆ =Import/Export

(G-330)
PHANTOM SALES GROUP INC
1550 Centennial Blvd (33830-7707)
PHONE..................................888 614-1232
Diane Sehleicher, *CEO*
Diane Arroyo, *President*
Melvin Smith, *Vice Pres*
▲ **EMP:** 7 **EST:** 2009
SALES (est): 685.7K **Privately Held**
WEB: www.phantompumps.com
SIC: 3569 8711 Lubrication equipment, industrial; industrial engineers

(G-331)
ROCKYMOUNTAIN LIFENET
5581 Airport Blvd (33830-6635)
PHONE..................................863 533-5168
Tracy Sanderson, *Manager*
EMP: 6 **EST:** 2002
SALES (est): 83.9K **Privately Held**
SIC: 3721 Helicopters

(G-332)
RSR INDUSTRIAL COATINGS INC
Also Called: Painting & Specialty Coatings
1577 Centennial Blvd (33830-7708)
P.O. Box 1035, Lithia (33547-1035)
PHONE..................................863 537-1110
Sonya Toney, *President*
Rick Toney, *Officer*
EMP: 12 **EST:** 2006
SALES (est): 1.7MM **Privately Held**
WEB: www.rsrcoatings.com
SIC: 3479 1799 2295 Coating of metals & formed products; painting of metal products; sandblasting of building exteriors; sealing or insulating tape for pipe: coated fiberglass

(G-333)
S & S WELDING INC
2850 Us Highway 17 S (33830-7561)
PHONE..................................863 533-2888
Dale J Piechowiak, *President*
Roy Hernandez, *Vice Pres*
Sharon L Piechowiak, *Vice Pres*
Sharon Piechowiak, *Vice Pres*
EMP: 12 **EST:** 1983
SQ FT: 46,000
SALES (est): 5.9MM **Privately Held**
WEB: www.s-swelding.com
SIC: 3444 3449 3446 7692 Sheet metalwork; bars, concrete reinforcing: fabricated steel; architectural metalwork; welding repair

(G-334)
SUPERHEAT FGH SERVICES INC
895 E Lemon St (33830-4926)
PHONE..................................519 396-1324
Jason Aulwurm, *Area Mgr*
Nigel Ford, *Area Mgr*
Gregory Teofilo, *Area Mgr*
Scotty Weatherman, *Business Mgr*
David Ziada, *Business Mgr*
EMP: 7
SALES (corp-wide): 74.8MM **Privately Held**
WEB: www.superheat.com
SIC: 3398 Metal heat treating
PA: Superheat Fgh Services, Inc.
313 Garnet Dr
New Lenox IL 60451
708 478-0205

(G-335)
VALMONT NEWMARK INC
Also Called: Newmark International
4131 Us Highway 17 S (33830-7567)
PHONE..................................863 533-6465
Chris Aycock, *Foreman/Supr*
Tony Gabel, *Engineer*
Ronald Barnett, *Manager*
EMP: 50
SALES (corp-wide): 2.9B **Publicly Held**
SIC: 3272 Pipe, concrete or lined with concrete; panels & sections, prefabricated concrete
HQ: Valmont Newmark, Inc.
2 Perimeter Park S 475w
Birmingham AL 35243
205 968-7200

Bascom
Jackson County

(G-336)
HAY TECH
6468 Wolf Pond Rd (32423-9374)
P.O. Box 65, Donalsonville GA (39845-0065)
PHONE..................................850 592-2424
Steve Crutchfield, *Principal*
EMP: 5 **EST:** 2002
SALES (est): 307.1K **Privately Held**
WEB: www.hay-tech.co.uk
SIC: 2048 7692 Hay, cubed; welding repair

Bay Harbor Islands
Miami-Dade County

(G-337)
ALLIANCE METALS LLC
1111 Kane Concourse # 518 (33154-2029)
PHONE..................................305 343-9536
Larry Gitman, *CEO*
EMP: 6 **EST:** 2017
SALES (est): 1.4MM **Privately Held**
WEB: www.alliancemetalsusa.com
SIC: 3341 Aluminum smelting & refining (secondary)

(G-338)
DEERS HOLDINGS INC
1108 Kane Cncurse Ste 206 (33154)
PHONE..................................805 323-6899
Bentzion Shemtov, *President*
EMP: 3 **EST:** 2016
SALES (est): 5MM **Privately Held**
SIC: 3639 3949 Major kitchen appliances, except refrigerators & stoves; sporting & athletic goods

(G-339)
SAL PRASCHNIK INC
1090 Kane Cncurse Ste 101 (33154)
PHONE..................................305 866-4323
Sal Praschnik, *President*
David Praschnik, *Vice Pres*
EMP: 10 **EST:** 1968
SQ FT: 5,100
SALES (est): 683.4K **Privately Held**
WEB: www.salpraschnik.com
SIC: 3911 6531 Jewelry, precious metal; real estate agents & managers

(G-340)
STITCHNSHIP
1151 97th St (33154-2007)
PHONE..................................216 409-6700
Jeff Pollack, *Principal*
EMP: 6 **EST:** 2017
SALES (est): 115.9K **Privately Held**
SIC: 2395 Embroidery & art needlework

Bell
Gilchrist County

(G-341)
BELL CONCRETE PRODUCTS INC (PA)
2480 N Us Highway 129 (32619-3160)
P.O. Box 7 (32619-0007)
PHONE..................................352 463-6103
Chad A Smith, *President*
Mark Smith, *Vice Pres*
Marilyn Smith, *Treasurer*
▲ **EMP:** 25 **EST:** 1972
SQ FT: 2,000
SALES (est): 5.1MM **Privately Held**
WEB: www.bellconcreteproducts.com
SIC: 3273 3271 Ready-mixed concrete; concrete block & brick

(G-342)
RIDGEWAY TIMBER INC
3949 Nw County Road 341 (32619-3587)
PHONE..................................352 463-6013
Duane J Ridgeway, *President*
Celeste Ridgeway, *Vice Pres*
EMP: 7 **EST:** 2003
SALES (est): 209.9K **Privately Held**
SIC: 2411 Logging

(G-343)
SANTA FE TRUSS COMPANY INC
5079 Sw 80th Ave (32619-1940)
P.O. Box 1298, High Springs (32655-1298)
PHONE..................................386 454-7711
Laurie T Wootton Jr, *President*
EMP: 17 **EST:** 1993
SQ FT: 10,000
SALES (est): 431.5K **Privately Held**
WEB: www.sftruss.com
SIC: 2439 Trusses, wooden roof

Belle Glade
Palm Beach County

(G-344)
ATLANTIC SUGAR ASSOCIATION
26400 County Rd 880 (33430-3127)
P.O. Box 1570 (33430-6570)
PHONE..................................561 996-6541
Val Galan, *Controller*
Eduardo Recio, *Director*
Donald Carson, *Director*
Christopher Hopper, *Director*
Jose F Valdivia Jr, *Director*
EMP: 11 **EST:** 1963
SQ FT: 10,000
SALES (est): 1MM **Privately Held**
SIC: 2061 2062 Raw cane sugar; cane sugar refining

(G-345)
BELLE GLADE ELECTRIC MOTOR SVC
900 Nw 13th St (33430-1710)
PHONE..................................561 996-3333
Bret E Mc Cormick, *President*
Betty Mc Cormick, *Controller*
EMP: 9 **EST:** 1964
SQ FT: 4,800
SALES (est): 610K **Privately Held**
WEB: www.trippmotors.com
SIC: 7694 3825 Electric motor repair; electrical power measuring equipment

(G-346)
CEMEX CNSTR MTLS FLA LLC
Also Called: Belle Glade FL Block
State Rd 80 & Fec Rr (33430)
P.O. Box 1986 (33430-6986)
PHONE..................................561 996-5249
Toll Free:..888 -
Norval Krast, *Branch Mgr*
EMP: 8 **Privately Held**
SIC: 3273 Ready-mixed concrete
HQ: Cemex Construction Materials Florida, Llc
1501 Belvedere Rd
West Palm Beach FL 33406

(G-347)
DIVERSIFIED WELDING INC
714 Nw Avenue L (33430-1808)
P.O. Box 1273 (33430-6273)
PHONE..................................561 996-9398
EMP: 9 **EST:** 2009
SALES (est): 558.3K **Privately Held**
SIC: 7692 Welding repair

(G-348)
GLADES FORMULATING CORPORATION
Also Called: G F C
909 Nw 13th St (33430-1709)
P.O. Box 1690 (33430-6690)
PHONE..................................561 996-4200
Juan Montalvo Jr, *President*
▲ **EMP:** 10
SQ FT: 35,000
SALES (est): 2.5MM **Privately Held**
WEB: www.gladesformulating.com
SIC: 2879 5191 Pesticides, agricultural or household; pesticides

(G-349)
O R WELDING SERVICE LLC
841 Ne 24th St Apt 2 (33430-7902)
PHONE..................................561 707-4325
Oreste Rodriguez, *Principal*
EMP: 6 **EST:** 2015
SALES (est): 183.3K **Privately Held**
SIC: 7692 Welding repair

(G-350)
OKEE-B INC
1125 Ne 18th St (33430-2209)
PHONE..................................561 996-3040
EMP: 58 **EST:** 1995
SALES (est): 6.7MM **Privately Held**
SIC: 3523 7389 Mfg Farm Machinery/Equipment Business Services At Non-Commercial Site

(G-351)
SUGAR CANE GROWERS COOP FLA (PA)
Also Called: Glades Sugar House
1500 George Wedgworth Way (33430-5400)
PHONE..................................561 996-5556
Matthew B Hoffman, *CEO*
Robert J Underbrink, *Ch of Bd*
Antonio L Contreras, *President*
C David Goodlett, *Senior VP*
Jose F Alvarez, *Vice Pres*
▲ **EMP:** 469 **EST:** 1960
SALES (est): 100.6MM **Privately Held**
WEB: www.scgc.org
SIC: 2061 Raw cane sugar

(G-352)
TELLUS PRODUCTS LLC (HQ)
1500 George Wedgworth Way (33430-5400)
P.O. Box 666 (33430-0666)
PHONE..................................561 996-5556
Matthew F Hoffman,
Jose F Alvarez,
Erik J Blomqvist,
Gustavo R Cepero,
Antonio L Contreras,
EMP: 40 **EST:** 2014
SQ FT: 120,000
SALES (est): 25.2MM **Privately Held**
WEB: www.tellusproducts.com
SIC: 2656 Sanitary food containers
PA: Tellus Holdings, Llc
1500 W Sugarhouse Rd
Belle Glade FL 33430
561 829-2600

(G-353)
TRIPP ELECTRIC MOTORS INC
1233 Nw Avenue L (33430-1719)
P.O. Box 1059 (33430-1059)
PHONE..................................561 996-3333
Jimmy Tripp, *President*
Ashley Tripp, *Vice Pres*
▼ **EMP:** 9 **EST:** 1992
SQ FT: 15,000
SALES (est): 2.4MM **Privately Held**
WEB: www.trippmotors.com
SIC: 7694 Electric motor repair

(G-354)
TRU-FLO CORP
924 Nw 13th St (33430-1799)
P.O. Box 248 (33430-0248)
PHONE..................................561 996-5850
Julio Sanchez, *President*
Harold Peacock, *Vice Pres*
EMP: 15 **EST:** 1961
SQ FT: 6,000
SALES (est): 1.9MM **Privately Held**
WEB: www.truflopumps.com
SIC: 3561 3523 Industrial pumps & parts; farm machinery & equipment

(G-355)
WEDGWORTHS INC (PA)
651 Nw 9th St (33430-1747)
P.O. Box 2076 (33430-7076)
PHONE..................................561 996-2076
Dennis Wedgworth, *President*
Brittany Meeks, *Principal*
Barbara Oetzman, *Principal*
Wayne Boynton, *Vice Pres*
James Matthews, *Vice Pres*
▼ **EMP:** 1 **EST:** 1921
SQ FT: 6,000
SALES (est): 5.8MM **Privately Held**
WEB: www.wedgworth.com
SIC: 2875 Fertilizers, mixing only

GEOGRAPHIC

Belle Isle
Orange County

(G-356)
BELLE ISLE FURNITURE LLC (PA)
7210 Seminole Dr Apt 1 (32812-3749)
PHONE..................................407 408-1266
Troy Buswell,
Matt Brannon,
Chris Wyman,
EMP: 2 **EST:** 2018
SALES (est): 5MM **Privately Held**
SIC: 2511 Wood household furniture

(G-357)
EEP
3307 Trentwood Blvd (32812-4848)
PHONE..................................407 380-2828
Stephen Edwards, *Principal*
EMP: 13 **EST:** 2010
SALES (est): 505.2K **Privately Held**
WEB:
www.edwardselectronicprocessing.com
SIC: 3578 Automatic teller machines (ATM)

(G-358)
RESORT POOLSIDE SHOPS INC
2912 Nela Ave (32809-6177)
PHONE..................................407 256-5853
Paul Mullican, *President*
▲ **EMP:** 8 **EST:** 1999
SALES (est): 500K **Privately Held**
SIC: 2369 5611 Beachwear: girls', children's & infants'; clothing, sportswear, men's & boys'

(G-359)
SUNCOAST ASSEMBLERS LLC
2114 Belle Isle Ave (32809-3304)
PHONE..................................407 947-8835
Manuel Antonio Umpierre, *Principal*
EMP: 5 **EST:** 2008
SALES (est): 309.9K **Privately Held**
WEB: www.suncoastassemblers.com
SIC: 3999 Manufacturing industries

Belleair
Pinellas County

(G-360)
MORCENT IMPORT EXPORT INC
Also Called: True Back
1702 Indian Rocks Rd (33756-1656)
PHONE..................................727 442-9735
Rodney D Vincent, *President*
Rodney Vincent, *President*
EMP: 5 **EST:** 1995
SQ FT: 2,500
SALES (est): 453.7K **Privately Held**
WEB: www.trueback.com
SIC: 3841 Ophthalmic instruments & apparatus

(G-361)
TRX INTEGRATION INC
401 Corbett St Ste 470 (33756-7311)
PHONE..................................727 797-4707
EMP: 10
SQ FT: 1,600
SALES (est): 1.6MM **Privately Held**
SIC: 7372 7373 8742 Prepackaged Software

Belleair Beach
Pinellas County

(G-362)
TALON INDUSTRIES INC
111 8th St (33786-3220)
PHONE..................................727 517-0052
Michael Mone, *President*
EMP: 6 **EST:** 2018
SALES (est): 39.6K **Privately Held**
WEB: www.talon-industries.com
SIC: 3999 Manufacturing industries

Belleair Bluffs
Pinellas County

(G-363)
MARLIN DARLIN AIR LLC
2819 West Bay Dr (33770-2619)
P.O. Box 368, Safety Harbor (34695-0368)
PHONE..................................727 726-1136
William Jacobsen, *Administration*
EMP: 8 **EST:** 2005
SALES (est): 174.7K **Privately Held**
SIC: 2451 Mobile homes

(G-364)
SCS SOFTWARE INC
2840 West Bay Dr Ste 125 (33770-2620)
PHONE..................................727 871-8366
Josh Lasov, *VP Opers*
Michael Manter, *Sales Engr*
Henry Abbott, *Technical Staff*
Blaine Moser, *Technical Staff*
EMP: 13 **EST:** 2015
SALES (est): 602.2K **Privately Held**
WEB: www.scscloud.com
SIC: 7372 Prepackaged software

Belleview
Marion County

(G-365)
ACTION PLASTICS INC
11665 Se Us Highway 301 (34420-4427)
PHONE..................................352 342-4122
Harry Severt, *President*
EMP: 5 **EST:** 2006
SALES (est): 320K **Privately Held**
WEB: www.actionplasticsinc.com
SIC: 3089 5162 Plastic containers, except foam; plastics products

(G-366)
AL & SONS MILLWORK INC
6323 Se 113th St (34420-4122)
PHONE..................................352 245-9191
Michael Madore, *President*
Susan Graves, *Office Mgr*
EMP: 36 **EST:** 1978
SQ FT: 27,500
SALES (est): 9MM **Privately Held**
WEB: www.alandsonsmw.com
SIC: 2431 3442 Door frames, wood; doors, wood; metal doors

(G-367)
ASECURE AMERICA INC
10080 Se 67th Ter (34420-9350)
PHONE..................................352 347-7951
Charles Butler, *President*
Tamra Butler, *Manager*
EMP: 7 **EST:** 2003
SALES (est): 82.6K **Privately Held**
SIC: 3699 Security devices

(G-368)
DOLMAR FOODS INC
5920 Se Hames Rd (34420-7312)
P.O. Box 771, Herndon VA (20172-0771)
PHONE..................................262 303-6026
EMP: 15 **EST:** 2012
SALES (est): 585.3K **Privately Held**
SIC: 2099 Food preparations

(G-369)
GATOR FABRICATIONS LLC
3450 Se 132nd Ln (34420-5650)
PHONE..................................352 245-7227
Anthony Hamblen, *Principal*
EMP: 6 **EST:** 2015
SALES (est): 87.2K **Privately Held**
SIC: 3999 Manufacturing industries

(G-370)
HEAT TREATING INCORPORATED
Also Called: H T I
6740 Se 110th St Unit 508 (34420-8433)
PHONE..................................352 245-8811
Steve Knapke, *President*
Rodney E Ingram, *Vice Pres*
Doug Knapke, *Vice Pres*
Chad Tester, *Vice Pres*
Patti Clerc, *Marketing Staff*
EMP: 68
SQ FT: 3,400
SALES (est): 9.4MM **Privately Held**
WEB: www.heattreatinginc.com
SIC: 3398 Metal heat treating

(G-371)
HYDROGEN ONE INC
6880 Se 104th St (34420-9326)
PHONE..................................352 361-6974
Tim Burrall, *Principal*
EMP: 7 **EST:** 2008
SALES (est): 153.6K **Privately Held**
SIC: 2813 Hydrogen

(G-372)
MARION NATURE PARK
12888 Se Us Highway 441 (34420-4566)
PHONE..................................352 817-3077
Kathy Shaw, *Owner*
EMP: 7 **EST:** 2008
SALES (est): 130K **Privately Held**
WEB: www.marionfl.org
SIC: 2752 Commercial printing, lithographic

(G-373)
NOBILITY HOMES INC
Also Called: Nobility Plant 8
6432 Se 115th Ln (34420-4452)
PHONE..................................352 245-5126
Mick Jones, *Manager*
EMP: 50
SQ FT: 31,180
SALES (corp-wide): 41.6MM **Publicly Held**
WEB: www.nobilityhomes.com
SIC: 2451 Mobile homes, except recreational
PA: Nobility Homes, Inc.
3741 Sw 7th St
Ocala FL 34474
352 732-5157

(G-374)
PETROLEUM GROUP LLC
Also Called: Petroimage
6432 Se 115th Ln (34420-4452)
PHONE..................................352 304-5500
Colleen Collins, *Project Mgr*
Dennis Soucey,
Sadiq S Fazal,
EMP: 11 **EST:** 2014
SALES (est): 3.1MM **Privately Held**
WEB: www.petroleum.group
SIC: 2911 Petroleum refining

(G-375)
RAIMONDA INVESTMENT GROUP INC
Also Called: Sign Source The
5911 Se Hames Rd (34420-3321)
P.O. Box 3688 (34421-3688)
PHONE..................................352 347-8899
Ron Raimonda, *President*
EMP: 5 **EST:** 1995
SALES (est): 494K **Privately Held**
SIC: 3993 Signs & advertising specialties

(G-376)
VOICE OF SOUTH MARION
5513 Se 113th St (34420-4039)
P.O. Box 700 (34421-0700)
PHONE..................................352 245-3161
Sandra Walron, *Owner*
EMP: 6 **EST:** 1969
SALES (est): 350K **Privately Held**
WEB: www.thevosm.net
SIC: 2711 Newspapers: publishing only, not printed on site

Beverly Hills
Citrus County

(G-377)
NEW ERA TECHNOLOGY CORP
620 W Sunset Strip Dr (34465-8744)
PHONE..................................352 746-3569
Joan Ward, *President*
Jesse Ward, *Vice Pres*
Joanne Jean, *Admin Sec*
EMP: 10
SQ FT: 10,000
SALES (est): 969.9K **Privately Held**
SIC: 3679 Electronic circuits

(G-378)
PET SERVICES OF FLORIDA LLC
3404 N Lecanto Hwy (34465-3569)
PHONE..................................352 746-6888
Joseph Campbell, *Owner*
EMP: 5 **EST:** 2005
SALES (est): 659.9K **Privately Held**
WEB: www.petctfla.com
SIC: 3829 Medical diagnostic systems, nuclear

(G-379)
SUNCOAST PAVERS INC
3015 W Mustang Blvd (34465-3413)
PHONE..................................352 754-3875
Frank Fleites, *Principal*
EMP: 7 **EST:** 2005
SALES (est): 118.7K **Privately Held**
WEB: www.suncoastpavers.com
SIC: 2951 Asphalt paving mixtures & blocks

(G-380)
VENKATA SAI CORPORATION
3502 N Lecanto Hwy (34465-3512)
PHONE..................................352 746-7076
Kanaka V Yegalapati, *Principal*
EMP: 9 **EST:** 2009
SALES (est): 2.5MM **Privately Held**
SIC: 1311 Crude petroleum production

Big Pine Key
Monroe County

(G-381)
BLUE NATIVE OF FLA KEYS INC
197 Industrial Rd (33043-3408)
PHONE..................................305 345-5305
Louis Perez Jr, *President*
EMP: 6 **EST:** 2017
SALES (est): 566.3K **Privately Held**
WEB: www.bluenativekeys.com
SIC: 3271 Blocks, concrete: landscape or retaining wall

(G-382)
STOCKING FACTORY
30554 5th Ave (33043-3401)
PHONE..................................305 745-2681
Eugenie Livingstone, *Partner*
▲ **EMP:** 5 **EST:** 1989
SALES (est): 585.6K **Privately Held**
WEB: www.stockingfactory.com
SIC: 3999 Christmas tree ornaments, except electrical & glass

Biscayne Park
Miami-Dade County

(G-383)
AUDIO VIDEO IMAGINEERING INC
11853 Griffing Blvd (33161-6242)
PHONE..................................305 947-6991
David Rubinstein, *President*
EMP: 6 **EST:** 1995
SALES (est): 1MM **Privately Held**
WEB: www.wow305.com
SIC: 3651 Audio electronic systems

Blountstown
Calhoun County

(G-384)
BAILEY TIMBER CO INC
19872 State Road 20 W # 2 (32424-4021)
P.O. Box 880 (32424-0880)
PHONE..................................850 674-2080
Aurther Bailey Sr, *President*
Arthur Bailey Jr, *Vice Pres*
EMP: 10 **EST:** 1993
SALES (est): 342.6K **Privately Held**
SIC: 2411 2421 Timber, cut at logging camp; sawmills & planing mills, general

(G-385)
BIG RIVER CYPRESS & HARDWOOD
19431 State Rte 71 N (32424)
P.O. Box 548 (32424-0548)
PHONE..................................850 674-5991
Harry Rogers, *President*
EMP: 18 **EST:** 1992
SALES (est): 619.9K **Privately Held**
SIC: 2421 2426 Sawmills & planing mills, general; hardwood dimension & flooring mills

(G-386)
MIKE BLACKBURN WELDING LLC
19983 Ne Hentz Ave (32424-1080)
PHONE..................................850 643-8464
Sheila A Blackburn, *Principal*
EMP: 7 **EST:** 2009
SALES (est): 300.9K **Privately Held**
SIC: 7692 Welding repair

(G-387)
SOUTHERN CONTRACTING N FL INC
19073 Ne State Road 69 (32424-4742)
P.O. Box 297 (32424-0297)
PHONE..................................850 674-3570
James Clemons Jr, *President*
EMP: 6 **EST:** 2003
SALES (est): 80.3K **Privately Held**
SIC: 1411 Limestone & marble dimension stone

(G-388)
SOUTHERN ROCK & LIME INC (PA)
19073 Ne State Road 69 (32424-4742)
P.O. Box 297 (32424-0297)
PHONE..................................850 674-5089
James E Clemons Jr, *President*
James Clemons Jr, *President*
Peg Frith, *Corp Secy*
Eddie Clemons, *Director*
EMP: 18 **EST:** 2003
SQ FT: 1,679
SALES (est): 8.3MM **Privately Held**
SIC: 1411 Limestone, dimension-quarrying

(G-389)
SOUTHLAND MILLING CO
21474 Se Coastal St (32424-2702)
P.O. Box 351 (32424-0351)
PHONE..................................850 674-8448
John H Schmarje, *President*
EMP: 6 **EST:** 1987
SQ FT: 1,000
SALES (est): 466.4K **Privately Held**
SIC: 2041 5153 Grain mills (except rice); grains

(G-390)
VERTICAL ASSESEMENT ASSOC LLC
17752 Ne Charlie Johns St (32424-1056)
PHONE..................................850 210-0401
Lee Rigby, *President*
Bill Strawn, *Vice Pres*
EMP: 20 **EST:** 2001
SALES (est): 3.3MM **Privately Held**
SIC: 2591 Blinds vertical

Boca Grande
Lee County

(G-391)
AUTOMATED SONIX CORPORATION
5800 Gasparilla Rd (33921-1117)
P.O. Box 1888 (33921-1888)
PHONE..................................941 964-1361
I J Cagan, *President*
EMP: 7 **EST:** 1987
SQ FT: 2,200
SALES (est): 730K **Privately Held**
WEB: www.automatedsonix.com
SIC: 3823 Industrial instrmnts msrmnt display/control process variable

(G-392)
F3 ANALYTICS LLC
16040 Gulf Shores Dr (33921-1399)
P.O. Box 634, Graceville (32440-0634)
PHONE..................................404 551-2600
Nathan Forrester, *CEO*
Matthew Forrester, *Director*
EMP: 6 **EST:** 2008
SALES (est): 89.4K **Privately Held**
WEB: www.f3-analytics.com
SIC: 2621 Paper mills

(G-393)
HOPKINS & DAUGHTER INC
Also Called: Boca Beacon Co
431 Park Ave (33921-1000)
P.O. Box 313 (33921-0313)
PHONE..................................941 964-2995
Philip Hopkins, *President*
Dusty Hopkins, *Publisher*
Marcy Shortuse, *Editor*
Julianne Greenberg, *Advt Staff*
Daniel Godwin, *Art Dir*
EMP: 9 **EST:** 1988
SALES (est): 1.3MM **Privately Held**
WEB: www.bocabeacon.com
SIC: 2711 Newspapers: publishing only, not printed on site

Boca Raton
Palm Beach County

(G-394)
5D BIO GOLD LLC
1725 Avenida Del Sol (33432-1742)
PHONE..................................561 756-8291
Kenneth B Morrow, *Administration*
EMP: 6 **EST:** 2013
SALES (est): 194.3K **Privately Held**
SIC: 2834 Pharmaceutical preparations

(G-395)
A & A PUBLISHING CORP
Also Called: Boca Raton Observer Magazine
950 Peninsula Corporate C (33487-1378)
PHONE..................................561 982-8960
Linda Behmoiras, *President*
Chelsea Greenwood Lassm, *Editor*
Ralph Behmoiras, *Vice Pres*
EMP: 38 **EST:** 2004
SQ FT: 2,000
SALES (est): 2.6MM **Privately Held**
WEB: www.bocaratonobserver.com
SIC: 2721 Magazines: publishing only, not printed on site

(G-396)
ACCENIUS INC ✪
3651 Fau Blvd Ste 400 (33431-6489)
PHONE..................................415 205-6444
Damion Gibbs, *CEO*
EMP: 5 **EST:** 2020
SALES (est): 380.4K **Privately Held**
SIC: 7372 7389 Prepackaged software;

(G-397)
AD VALOREM CORPORATION
2695 Nw 31st St (33434-3629)
PHONE..................................561 488-9966
Neil Segal, *President*
EMP: 7
SQ FT: 1,400
SALES (est): 366.2K **Privately Held**
SIC: 3211 1793 3861 7382 Strengthened or reinforced glass; glass & glazing work; microfilm equipment: cameras, projectors, readers, etc.; security systems services

(G-398)
ADCON TELEMETRY INC (PA)
1001 Nw 51st St Ste 305 (33431-4403)
PHONE..................................561 989-5309
EMP: 8
SALES (est): 1.7MM **Privately Held**
SIC: 3661 Telephone And Telegraph Apparatus

(G-399)
ADMA
5800 Pk Of Commerce Blvd (33487-8222)
PHONE..................................561 989-5800
Maureen Garrity, *Human Resources*
EMP: 25 **EST:** 2018
SALES (est): 1.4MM **Privately Held**
WEB: www.admabiologics.com
SIC: 3999 Manufacturing industries

(G-400)
ADMA BIOLOGICS INC
5800 Pk Of Cmmrce Blvd Nw (33487-8222)
PHONE..................................561 989-5800
Adam Pinkert, *Vice Pres*
EMP: 17 **Publicly Held**
WEB: www.admabiologics.com
SIC: 2836 Plasmas
PA: Adma Biologics, Inc.
465 State Rt 17
Ramsey NJ 07446

(G-401)
ADMA BIOMANUFACTURING LLC
5800 Pk Of Commerce Blvd (33487-8222)
PHONE..................................201 478-5552
Adam Grossman, *Mng Member*
Brian Lenz, *Mng Member*
James Mond, *Mng Member*
EMP: 304 **EST:** 2017
SALES (est): 22.4MM **Publicly Held**
WEB: www.admabiologics.com
SIC: 2836 Biological products, except diagnostic
PA: Adma Biologics, Inc.
465 State Rt 17
Ramsey NJ 07446

(G-402)
ADVANCE CARTS INC
4160 Nw 1st Ave Ste 18 (33431-4263)
PHONE..................................561 320-8674
Marcus Magnusson, *President*
EMP: 14 **EST:** 2014
SALES (est): 981.1K **Privately Held**
WEB: www.advancecarts.com
SIC: 3799 Pushcarts

(G-403)
ADVANCED CMMNICATIONS TECH INC
108 Nw 20th St (33431-7948)
PHONE..................................954 444-4119
Dennis Goodman, *President*
◆ **EMP:** 12 **EST:** 1997
SQ FT: 6,000
SALES (est): 1.5MM **Privately Held**
SIC: 3651 Loudspeakers, electrodynamic or magnetic; microphones

(G-404)
AERO-LINK MARINE & POWER LLC (PA)
2295 Nw Corp Blvd Ste 110 (33431-7329)
PHONE..................................561 404-8181
Paul Kerzner, *Mng Member*
Christos Marinakos,
▲ **EMP:** 6 **EST:** 2010
SALES (est): 585.4K **Privately Held**
WEB: www.aerolinkfl.com
SIC: 3724 Aircraft engines & engine parts

(G-405)
AEROSPACE RETAIL INC ✪
433 Plaza Real Ste 275 (33432-3999)
PHONE..................................888 918-8116
August Knight, *President*
EMP: 15 **EST:** 2020
SALES (est): 893.3K **Privately Held**
SIC: 3429 Aircraft hardware

(G-406)
AEROSPACE TECH GROUP INC
Also Called: Atg
620 Nw 35th St (33431-6404)
PHONE..................................561 244-7400
Simon R Kay, *CEO*
Raymond P Caldiero, *Ch of Bd*
Jeffrey L Booher, *Vice Pres*
Bill Goings, *Vice Pres*
Jacob Newell, *QC Mgr*
▲ **EMP:** 75 **EST:** 1998
SQ FT: 64,000
SALES (est): 22MM **Privately Held**
WEB: www.atgshades.com
SIC: 2591 Window shades

(G-407)
AGRIPURE CBD LLC
12314 Melrose Way (33428-4806)
PHONE..................................561 789-3819
Jeffrey Glasser, *Principal*
EMP: 7 **EST:** 2018
SALES (est): 39.6K **Privately Held**
WEB: www.agripurecbd.com
SIC: 3999

(G-408)
AIR TURBINE TECHNOLOGY INC
1225 Broken Sound Pkwy Nw D (33487-3500)
PHONE..................................561 994-0500
Bill Doyle, *Principal*
Simon Shane, *Chairman*
Terrence Collins, *Senior VP*
Terry Collins, *Manager*
Margot Shane, *Director*
▲ **EMP:** 10 **EST:** 1978
SQ FT: 8,000
SALES (est): 1.9MM **Privately Held**
WEB: www.airturbinetools.com
SIC: 3546 Power-driven handtools

(G-409)
AIRGROUP INC
9858 Glades Rd (33434-3983)
PHONE..................................561 279-0680
Robert Ejr Peach, *President*
EMP: 12 **EST:** 2008
SALES (est): 175.3K **Privately Held**
WEB: www.airgroup.com
SIC: 3569 Lubrication equipment, industrial

(G-410)
AIRSPAN NETWORKS INC (PA)
777 W Yamato Rd Ste 310 (33431-4406)
PHONE..................................561 893-8670
Eric D Stonestrom, *President*
Michelle Krause, *General Mgr*
Uzi Shalev, *COO*
Paul Senior, *Senior VP*
Zigi Avni, *Vice Pres*
▲ **EMP:** 30 **EST:** 1992
SQ FT: 5,400
SALES (est): 63.3MM **Privately Held**
WEB: www.airspan.com
SIC: 3663 Radio & TV communications equipment

(G-411)
ALEVO AUTOMOTIVE INC
301 Ne 51st St Ste 1240 (33431-4931)
PHONE..................................954 593-4215
Stein Christiansen, *Exec VP*
EMP: 7 **EST:** 2009
SALES (est): 457.2K **Privately Held**
SIC: 3711 Automobile assembly, including specialty automobiles

(G-412)
ALL-TAG CORPORATION (PA)
Also Called: All-Tag Security Americas
1155 Broken Sound Pkwy Nw E (33487-3538)
PHONE..................................561 998-9983
Stuart Seidel, *President*
Jeanne Simenc, *Accounts Exec*
▲ **EMP:** 33 **EST:** 2000
SQ FT: 21,000
SALES (est): 5.5MM **Privately Held**
WEB: www.all-tag.com
SIC: 3825 5131 Oscillators, audio & radio frequency (instrument types); labels

(G-413)
ALMACO GROUP INC
7900 Glades Rd Ste 630 (33434-4105)
PHONE..................................561 558-1600
Vilhelm Roberts, *President*
Guillaume Faysse, *Vice Pres*
Mikael Hedberg, *Vice Pres*
Leena Ades, *Admin Asst*
◆ **EMP:** 16 **EST:** 1998
SQ FT: 6,960
SALES (est): 8.3MM **Privately Held**
WEB: www.almaco.cc
SIC: 3731 Shipbuilding & repairing
PA: Almaco Group Oy
Uudenmaantie 100
Piispanristi 20760

(G-414)
ALPHA SUN & SPORT - AS & S LLC
Also Called: Alpha Sun and Sport, Suite 150
2851 S Ocean Blvd Apt 6v (33432-8409)
PHONE..................................954 782-2300
Richard Jobin, *Founder*
Alan McBrearty,
EMP: 6 **EST:** 2010
SQ FT: 5,078
SALES (est): 101.3K **Privately Held**
WEB: www.livingalpha.com
SIC: 3949 Sporting & athletic goods

(G-415)
ALTELIX LLC
1201 Clint Moore Rd (33487-2718)
PHONE..................................561 660-9434
Peter Roth, *President*
EMP: 10 **EST:** 2016
SQ FT: 30,000
SALES (est): 1MM **Privately Held**
WEB: www.altelix.com
SIC: 3663 3678 Antennas, transmitting & communications; electronic connectors

(G-416)
ALUDISC LLC
2127 Nw 53rd St (33496-3451)
PHONE..................................910 299-0911
▲ **EMP:** 40
SALES (est): 9.1MM **Privately Held**
SIC: 3354 3355 Mfg Aluminum Extruded Products Aluminum Rolling/Drawing

(G-417)
ALUMINUM SOLUTIONS GROUP INC
1090 Holland Dr Ste 3 (33487-2719)
PHONE..................................561 999-9932
Mary A Walker, *Principal*
Lee Walker, *Vice Pres*
EMP: 5 **EST:** 2007
SALES (est): 482.9K **Privately Held**
WEB: www.aluminumsolutionsgroup.com
SIC: 3353 Aluminum sheet, plate & foil

(G-418)
AM PAVERS INC
19722 Black Olive Ln (33498-4854)
PHONE..................................954 275-1590
Angela Vicente, *President*
EMP: 7 **EST:** 2005
SALES (est): 124.9K **Privately Held**
SIC: 3531 Pavers

(G-419)
AMARANTH LF SCIENCES PHRM INC
1731 Avenida Del Sol (33432-1742)
PHONE..................................561 756-8291
Walter M Wolf, *CEO*
EMP: 10 **EST:** 2016
SALES (est): 409K **Privately Held**
SIC: 2099 Food preparations

(G-420)
AMERICAN AGGREGATES LLC
9040 Kimberly Blvd Ste 61 (33434-2836)
PHONE..................................813 352-2124
Roberto Servija, *CFO*
EMP: 11 **EST:** 2017
SALES (est): 1.1MM **Privately Held**
SIC: 1081 Metal mining services

(G-421)
AMERICAN BHVIORAL RES INST LLC
Also Called: Relaxium
1515 N Federal Hwy # 300 (33432-1911)
PHONE..................................888 353-1205
Timea Ciliberti, *CEO*
Eric C D, *Mng Member*
EMP: 85 **EST:** 2009
SALES (est): 14.1MM **Privately Held**
WEB: www.tryrelaxium.com
SIC: 2834 Pills, pharmaceutical

(G-422)
AMERICAN HOUSEHOLD INC (DH)
Also Called: Sunbeam Outdoor Products
2381 Nw Executive Ctr Dr (33431-8560)
PHONE..................................561 912-4100
Jerry Levin, *Ch of Bd*
▲ **EMP:** 60 **EST:** 1900
SQ FT: 27,003
SALES (est): 1B
SALES (corp-wide): 9.3B **Publicly Held**
WEB: www.newellbrands.com
SIC: 3631 2514 3421 3634 Barbecues, grills & braziers (outdoor cooking); metal lawn & garden furniture; lawn furniture: metal; scissors, shears, clippers, snips & similar tools; shears, hand; clippers, fingernail & toenail; electric housewares & fans; hair dryers, electric; blenders, electric; food mixers, electric: household; thermometers & temperature sensors; temperature sensors, except industrial process & aircraft; thermometers, liquid-in-glass & bimetal type; geophysical & meteorological testing equipment; blood pressure apparatus

(G-423)
AMERICAN SUGAR REFINING INC
3998 Fau Blvd Ste 100 (33431-6429)
PHONE..................................561 962-8106
EMP: 7
SALES (corp-wide): 2.1B **Privately Held**
WEB: www.asr-group.com
SIC: 2062 Cane sugar refining
HQ: American Sugar Refining, Inc.
1 N Clematis St Ste 200
West Palm Beach FL 33401
561 366-5100

(G-424)
AMI CELEBRITY PUBLICATIONS LLC
1000 American Media Way (33464-1000)
PHONE..................................561 997-7733
David J Pecker, *CEO*
EMP: 160 **EST:** 2011
SALES (est): 4.3MM
SALES (corp-wide): 1.2B **Privately Held**
WEB: www.a360media.com
SIC: 2741 Miscellaneous publishing
PA: Worldwide Media Services Group Inc.
1000 American Media Way
Boca Raton FL 33464
561 989-1342

(G-425)
AMI DIGITAL INC
1000 American Media Way (33464-1000)
PHONE..................................561 997-7733
EMP: 270 **EST:** 2014
SALES (est): 2.4MM
SALES (corp-wide): 1.2B **Privately Held**
WEB: www.a360media.com
SIC: 2741 Miscellaneous publishing
PA: Worldwide Media Services Group Inc.
1000 American Media Way
Boca Raton FL 33464
561 989-1342

(G-426)
AMJ DOT LLC
Also Called: City Fashion, The
22304 Calibre Ct Apt 1304 (33433-5507)
PHONE..................................646 249-0273
Assaf Joseth, *CEO*
Assaf Joseph, *CEO*
Ruth Elmann, *COO*
David Yakobov, *CFO*
▲ **EMP:** 7 **EST:** 2013
SALES (est): 528.6K **Privately Held**
SIC: 2335 5621 Women's, juniors' & misses' dresses; women's clothing stores

(G-427)
APEX FLOOD FIRE MOLD CLNUP INC
1340 Sw 19th Ave (33486-8514)
PHONE..................................305 975-1710
Sagi Dayan, *Principal*
EMP: 8 **EST:** 2008
SALES (est): 103.3K **Privately Held**
SIC: 3544 Industrial molds

(G-428)
AQUATEC SOLUTIONS LLC
140 Nw 11th St (33432-2605)
PHONE..................................561 717-6933
Philip Root, *President*
Sondra Bennett, *Vice Pres*
EMP: 13 **EST:** 2017
SALES (est): 251.2K **Privately Held**
WEB: www.aquatec.com
SIC: 3589 Water treatment equipment, industrial

(G-429)
ARK WOODWORK INC
11184 Mohawk St (33428-3924)
PHONE..................................561 809-7957
EMP: 7 **EST:** 2017
SALES (est): 293.6K **Privately Held**
WEB: www.arkwoodwork.com
SIC: 2431 Millwork

(G-430)
ARTISTIC ELEMENTS INC
400 E Palmetto Park Rd (33432-5018)
PHONE..................................561 750-1554
Leigh A Auger, *President*
EMP: 9 **EST:** 2017
SALES (est): 1MM **Privately Held**
WEB: www.theartisticelements.com
SIC: 2819 Industrial inorganic chemicals

(G-431)
ARTY-SUN LLC
9045 La Fontana Blvd (33434-5636)
PHONE..................................561 705-2222
EMP: 8
SALES (est): 400K **Privately Held**
SIC: 3911 Mfg Precious Metal Jewelry

(G-432)
ATI AGENCY INC
123 Nw 13th St Ste 305b (33432-1645)
PHONE..................................954 895-7909
EMP: 17 **EST:** 2018
SALES (est): 441.6K **Privately Held**
SIC: 3312 Stainless steel

(G-433)
ATKORE INTERNATIONAL INC
1 Town Center Rd (33486-1039)
PHONE..................................800 882-5543
EMP: 8 **Publicly Held**
WEB: www.atkore.com
SIC: 3317 Steel pipe & tubes
HQ: Atkore International, Inc.
16100 Lathrop Ave
Harvey IL 60426

(G-434)
ATM VAULT CORP
2151 Nw Boca Raton Blvd (33431-7456)
PHONE..................................561 441-9294
John Schuttler, *Principal*
EMP: 9 **EST:** 2012
SALES (est): 284.7K **Privately Held**
SIC: 3272 Burial vaults, concrete or precast terrazzo

(G-435)
AVON ASSOC
4101 N Ocean Blvd (33431-5341)
PHONE..................................561 391-7188
Marilyn Schrager, *Principal*
EMP: 5 **EST:** 2005
SALES (est): 630.5K **Privately Held**
SIC: 2821 Plastics materials & resins

(G-436)
B C CABINETRY
10625 Mendocino Ln (33428-1229)
PHONE..................................561 393-8937
Bruce Carlson, *Owner*
EMP: 6 **EST:** 1985
SALES (est): 377.6K **Privately Held**
SIC: 2511 Wood household furniture

(G-437)
B F INDUSTRIES INC
4201 Oak Cir Ste 29 (33431-4237)
PHONE..................................561 368-6662
Sidney Z Bors, *President*
Bob McDonald, *Plant Mgr*
EMP: 10 **EST:** 1972
SQ FT: 10,000
SALES (est): 746K **Privately Held**
WEB: www.bfindustries.com
SIC: 3841 Surgical & medical instruments

(G-438)
B J AND ME INC
Also Called: Insty-Prints
2284 N Dixie Hwy Fl 1 (33431-8025)
PHONE..................................561 368-5470
Howard Rothberg, *President*
Barbara Rothberg, *Vice Pres*
EMP: 5 **EST:** 1984
SQ FT: 1,000
SALES (est): 450K **Privately Held**
WEB: www.instyprints.com
SIC: 2752 7334 2791 2789 Commercial printing, offset; photocopying & duplicating services; typesetting; bookbinding & related work

(G-439)
BA PRECISION PRODUCTS CORP
2920 Nw 2nd Ave Ste 3 (33431-6687)
PHONE..................................561 859-3400
Gary Becher, *President*
EMP: 6 **EST:** 1991
SALES (est): 918.4K **Privately Held**
WEB: www.baprecision.com
SIC: 3599 Machine shop, jobbing & repair

(G-440)
BABBALA LLC
Also Called: Teething Egg, The
2901 Clint Moore Rd (33496-2041)
PHONE..................................844 869-5747
Jessica Luntz, *President*
Dean Luntz, *Vice Pres*
EMP: 5 **EST:** 2015
SALES (est): 589.6K **Privately Held**
WEB: www.theteethingegg.com
SIC: 3069 Teething rings, rubber

(G-441)
BAM INDUSTRIES INC
250 Nw 46th St (33431-4783)
PHONE..................................561 674-2185
Bruce Moorman, *Principal*
EMP: 6 **EST:** 2013
SALES (est): 107.9K **Privately Held**
WEB: www.bam-industries.com
SIC: 3999 Manufacturing industries

(G-442)
BASIC FUN INC (PA)
301 E Yamato Rd Ste 4200 (33431-4933)
PHONE..................................561 997-8901
Jay Foreman, *CEO*
Craig Leaf, *President*
Brad Pedersen, *President*
Jeff Lebron, *General Mgr*
Steven Littman, *COO*
▲ **EMP:** 69 **EST:** 1991
SALES (est): 24MM **Privately Held**
WEB: www.basicfun.com
SIC: 3944 3942 Games, toys & children's vehicles; electronic games & toys; dolls & stuffed toys

(G-443)
BEDDING ACQUISITION LLC (HQ)
Also Called: Hollander Sleep Products
901 W Yamato Rd Ste 250 (33431-4415)
PHONE..................................561 997-6900
Mark Eichhorn, *Mng Member*
Beth Mack,
EMP: 0 **EST:** 2019
SALES (est): 15.4MM **Privately Held**
WEB: www.centrelanepartners.com
SIC: 2392 2221 Cushions & pillows; bedding, manmade or silk fabric

(G-444)
BEDESCHI AMERICA INC (HQ)
2600 N Military Trl # 245 (33431-6330)
PHONE..................................954 602-2175
Rino Bedeschi, *President*
Vladimir Grubacic, *General Mgr*
Thomas C Turano, *Vice Pres*
Marco Bertorelle, *Sales Staff*
Fabio Iurzolla, *Sales Staff*
▲ **EMP:** 94 **EST:** 2004
SALES (est): 53.1MM
SALES (corp-wide): 154.9MM **Privately Held**
WEB: www.bedeschi.com
SIC: 3542 Extruding machines (machine tools), metal

PA: Bedeschi Spa
Via Praimbole 38
Limena PD 35010
049 766-3100

(G-445)
BEI
19657 Waters End Dr # 20 (33434-5716)
PHONE..................................561 488-0759
S Bufferd, *Principal*
EMP: 9 **EST:** 2001
SALES (est): 87.9K **Privately Held**
SIC: 3829 Measuring & controlling devices

(G-446)
BF AMERICAN BUSINESS LLC
22285 Sw 66th Ave Apt 200 (33428-5929)
PHONE..................................561 856-7094
Alberto Bracho, *Manager*
EMP: 6 **EST:** 2015
SALES (est): 204K **Privately Held**
SIC: 3011 Tires & inner tubes

(G-447)
BIG L BRANDS INC (PA)
Also Called: Beer Bread Company
7750 Ne Spanish Trail Ct (33487-1718)
PHONE..................................888 552-9768
Molly Wilson Kohler, *President*
Andrew Yochum, *President*
EMP: 12 **EST:** 2003
SALES (est): 2MM **Privately Held**
WEB: www.biglbrands.com
SIC: 2045 5149 Prepared flour mixes & doughs; groceries & related products

(G-448)
BLACK ICE SOFTWARE LLC (PA)
950 Peninsula Corporate C (33487-1389)
PHONE..................................561 757-4107
Jozsef Nemeth, *CEO*
Amanda Dresser, *Sales Mgr*
Sara Jean, *Accounts Mgr*
Lisa Pither, *Manager*
Ilona Nemeth, *Analyst*
EMP: 6 **EST:** 1987
SQ FT: 1,600
SALES (est): 1.5MM **Privately Held**
WEB: www.blackice.com
SIC: 7372 Prepackaged software

(G-449)
BOCA COATINGS INC
6135 Belleza Ln (33433-1792)
PHONE..................................561 400-8183
Robert Cox, *Principal*
EMP: 6 **EST:** 2013
SALES (est): 71.7K **Privately Held**
SIC: 3479 Metal coating & allied service

(G-450)
BOCA COLOR GRAPHICS INC
139 Nw 3rd St (33432-3824)
PHONE..................................561 391-2229
Joseph W Massarella, *Ch of Bd*
Michael Massarella, *President*
Gerard Massarella, *Vice Pres*
Mike Massarella, *Officer*
Amy Mollica, *Admin Sec*
EMP: 11 **EST:** 1967
SQ FT: 12,000
SALES (est): 1.8MM **Privately Held**
WEB: www.bocacolorgraphics.com
SIC: 2752 2796 2791 2789 Commercial printing, offset; platemaking services; typesetting; bookbinding & related work

(G-451)
BOCA DENTAL SUPPLY LLC
3401 N Federal Hwy # 211 (33431-6007)
PHONE..................................800 768-5691
Alvaro Betancur, *President*
EMP: 9 **EST:** 2015
SALES (est): 319.3K **Privately Held**
WEB: www.bocadentalregenerative.com
SIC: 3843 Dental equipment & supplies

(G-452)
BOCA RATON COMMERCIAL PRINTING
801 N Federal Hwy (33432-2737)
PHONE..................................561 549-0126
Russell Bahrenburg, *Principal*
EMP: 7 **EST:** 2012
SALES (est): 131K **Privately Held**
WEB: www.bocacolorgraphics.com
SIC: 2752 Commercial printing, offset

(G-453)
BOCA RATON OBSERVER
4290 Nw 66th Pl (33496-4028)
PHONE..................................561 702-3086
EMP: 6 **EST:** 2017
SALES (est): 133.4K **Privately Held**
WEB: www.bocaratonobserver.com
SIC: 2711 Newspapers, publishing & printing

(G-454)
BOCA RATON PRINTING CO
1000 Clint Moore Rd # 205 (33487-2807)
PHONE..................................561 395-8404
Dan Garber, *President*
Edward Harper Jr, *Principal*
EMP: 8 **EST:** 1961
SALES (est): 574.6K **Privately Held**
WEB: www.bocaprinting.com
SIC: 2752 2796 2791 Commercial printing, offset; platemaking services; typesetting

(G-455)
BOCA SELF DEFENSE
500 S Ocean Blvd Apt 306 (33432-6288)
PHONE..................................954 903-0913
William Wood, *Owner*
EMP: 6 **EST:** 2014
SALES (est): 155K **Privately Held**
WEB: www.riddledefense.com
SIC: 3812 Defense systems & equipment

(G-456)
BOCA SEMICONDUCTOR CORPORATION
4260 Nw 1st Ave Ste 50 (33431-4264)
PHONE..................................561 226-8500
Richard Rosenstein, *CEO*
L Scott Rosenstein, *President*
EMP: 26 **EST:** 2000
SQ FT: 3,000
SALES (est): 616.3K **Privately Held**
WEB: www.bocasemi.com
SIC: 3674 5065 Transistors; semiconductor devices

(G-457)
BOCA SIGNWORKS
174 Glades Rd (33432-1605)
PHONE..................................561 393-6010
Jason Goulet, *Principal*
EMP: 5 **EST:** 2008
SALES (est): 472.3K **Privately Held**
WEB: www.bocasignworks.com
SIC: 3993 Signs, not made in custom sign painting shops

(G-458)
BOCA STONE DESIGNS
3601 N Dixie Hwy Ste 5 (33431-5901)
PHONE..................................561 362-2085
Rosana Marchelli, *Principal*
EMP: 10 **EST:** 2016
SALES (est): 1.2MM **Privately Held**
WEB: www.bocastonedesign.com
SIC: 3469 Appliance parts, porcelain enameled

(G-459)
BOCA SYSTEMS INC
1065 S Rogers Cir (33487-2816)
PHONE..................................561 998-9600
Larry Gross, *CEO*
Joseph Gross, *Ch of Bd*
Rob Kohn, *Vice Pres*
Robert Kohn, *Vice Pres*
Johnie Ellis, *Accounting Mgr*
▼ **EMP:** 135
SQ FT: 80,000
SALES: 27.8MM **Privately Held**
WEB: www.bocasystems.com
SIC: 3577 Computer peripheral equipment

(G-460)
BONITO & COMPANY LLC
1000 Nw 1st Ave Ste 14 (33432-2601)
PHONE..................................561 451-7494
Deirdre Sours, *Administration*
EMP: 6 **EST:** 2017
SALES (est): 69.5K **Privately Held**
WEB: www.bonitoandcompany.com
SIC: 2323 Men's & boys' neckwear

(G-461)
BPC PLASMA INC
901 W Yamato Rd Ste 101 (33431-4409)
PHONE..................................561 989-5800
EMP: 8
SALES (corp-wide): 657.6MM **Privately Held**
WEB: www.biotestplasma.com
SIC: 2834 8731 Pharmaceutical preparations; biological research; medical research, commercial
HQ: Bpc Plasma, Inc.
901 W Yamato Rd Ste 101
Boca Raton FL 33431

(G-462)
BPC PLASMA INC (DH)
Also Called: Biotest Plasma Center
901 W Yamato Rd Ste 101 (33431-4409)
PHONE..................................561 569-3100
Ilana Carlisle, *CEO*
Stephanie Williams, *Production*
Joan Hoggatt, *Buyer*
Dan Gamache, *Marketing Staff*
Arthur Raymond, *Manager*
EMP: 50 **EST:** 2007
SALES (est): 106.9MM
SALES (corp-wide): 657.6MM **Privately Held**
WEB: www.biotestplasma.com
SIC: 2834 8731 Pharmaceutical preparations; biological research; medical research, commercial
HQ: Grifols Shared Services North America, Inc.
2410 Lillyvale Ave
Los Angeles CA 90032
323 225-2221

(G-463)
BREAST THERMGRPHY OF BRWRD&PLM
10831 Bal Harbor Dr (33498-4544)
PHONE..................................561 852-5789
Renee Katz, *Director*
EMP: 6 **EST:** 2012
SALES (est): 83K **Privately Held**
SIC: 2759 Thermography

(G-464)
BRIAN SLATER & ASSOCIATES LLC
Also Called: Slater Lighting Solutions
5301 N Federal Hwy # 195 (33487-4918)
PHONE..................................561 886-7705
Ginamaria Rivara, *Project Mgr*
Chad Sample, *Sales Staff*
Meta Jamison, *Office Mgr*
Brian Slater,
EMP: 10 **EST:** 2011
SALES (est): 111.9K **Privately Held**
WEB: www.slaterlighting.com
SIC: 3645 Residential lighting fixtures

(G-465)
BRIANAS SALAD LLC
5400 N Dixie Hwy Ste 7 (33487-4902)
PHONE..................................954 608-0953
Maryann Murphy, *Principal*
EMP: 8 **EST:** 2013
SALES (est): 305.4K **Privately Held**
SIC: 2099 Salads, fresh or refrigerated

(G-466)
BRIJOT IMAGING SYSTEMS INC
951 W Yamato Rd Ste 205 (33431-4440)
PHONE..................................407 641-4370
Mitchel J Laskey, *President*
Robert Daly, *Senior VP*
Leon Chlimper, *Vice Pres*
Gregory Chouljian, *Vice Pres*
Troy Techau, *Vice Pres*
▼ **EMP:** 18 **EST:** 2004
SQ FT: 24,000
SALES (est): 2.5MM **Privately Held**
WEB: www.brijot.com
SIC: 3699 Security devices

(G-467)
BROWNBAG POPCORN COMPANY LLC
Also Called: Bbpco
900 Ne 4th St Apt A (33432-4200)
PHONE..................................561 212-5664
Karen Barnes, *Director*
Lynne E Szymanski,
Jill G Fine,
EMP: 7 **EST:** 2014
SALES (est): 480.7K **Privately Held**
WEB: www.brownbagpopcornco.com
SIC: 2064 5145 Popcorn balls or other treated popcorn products; popcorn & supplies

(G-468)
BTB REFINING LLC
925 S Federal Hwy Ste 375 (33432-6144)
PHONE..................................561 999-9916
Kevin G Kirkeide, *Manager*
EMP: 7 **EST:** 2014
SALES (est): 136.3K **Privately Held**
SIC: 2951 Asphalt paving mixtures & blocks

(G-469)
CAPITOL FURNITURE MFG LLC
850 Broken Sound Pkwy Nw (33487-3624)
PHONE..................................954 485-5000
Joan Steele, *Exec VP*
Robert Steinman, *Mng Member*
Kenneth Croll, *Mng Member*
Sheardon Thomas, *IT/INT Sup*
EMP: 8 **EST:** 2014
SQ FT: 2,500
SALES (est): 447.7K **Privately Held**
WEB: www.capitolfurniture.com
SIC: 2512 2511 Upholstered household furniture; wood bedroom furniture

(G-470)
CAPTAIN ZOOM PRODUCTS INC
4976 Bocaire Blvd (33487-1162)
PHONE..................................561 989-9119
Robert Stiller, *President*
Cynthia S Stiller, *Admin Sec*
EMP: 8 **EST:** 2004
SALES (est): 405.1K **Privately Held**
WEB: www.captainzoom.com
SIC: 3652 Compact laser discs, prerecorded

(G-471)
CASEBRIEFS LLC
2234 N Federal Hwy 413 (33431-7710)
PHONE..................................646 240-4401
David E Gray, *Principal*
EMP: 10 **EST:** 2013
SALES (est): 277.2K **Privately Held**
SIC: 2731 Book publishing

(G-472)
CAVASTONE LLC
Also Called: Cavastone By Connie Davalos
506 Nw 77th St (33487-1323)
PHONE..................................561 994-9100
Diego Davalos, *Research*
Norma Davalos, *Mng Member*
Juan C Reyes, *Mng Member*
▲ **EMP:** 7 **EST:** 2006
SALES (est): 3.2MM **Privately Held**
WEB: www.cavastone.com
SIC: 1411 Dimension stone

(G-473)
CBD-ME LLC
4075 Nw 58th Ln (33496-2753)
PHONE..................................847 910-0505
Zachary Greenbaum, *Principal*
EMP: 6 **EST:** 2017
SALES (est): 110.6K **Privately Held**
SIC: 3999

(G-474)
CEAUTAMED WORLDWIDE LLC
Also Called: Greens First
1289 Clint Moore Rd (33487-2718)
PHONE..................................866 409-6262
Ryan Benson, *CEO*
▲ **EMP:** 6 **EST:** 2009
SALES (est): 1.1MM **Privately Held**
WEB: www.greensfirst.com
SIC: 2834 5122 Vitamin preparations; pharmaceuticals

GEOGRAPHIC

(G-475)
CEBEV LLC
2424 N Federal Hwy # 101 (33431-7735)
PHONE..................................918 830-4417
Bill Towler, *General Mgr*
EMP: 5 **EST:** 2016
SQ FT: 1,500
SALES (est): 528.3K **Privately Held**
SIC: 2037 Fruit juices

(G-476)
CELSIUS INC
2424 N Federal Hwy # 208 (33431-7780)
PHONE..................................561 276-2239
John Fieldly, *CEO*
Tony Lau, *Chairman*
William Milmoe, *Chairman*
Bryan Alesiano, *Sales Staff*
Brett Bauer, *Manager*
▼ **EMP:** 18 **EST:** 2004
SQ FT: 3,000
SALES (est): 12.6MM **Publicly Held**
WEB: www.celsius.com
SIC: 2087 Beverage bases
PA: Celsius Holdings, Inc.
2424 N Federal Hwy # 208
Boca Raton FL 33431

(G-477)
CELSIUS HOLDINGS INC (PA)
2424 N Federal Hwy # 208 (33431-7780)
PHONE..................................561 276-2239
John Fieldly, *CEO*
Tony Lau, *Ch of Bd*
William Milmoe, *Ch of Bd*
Edwin F Negron-Carballo, *CFO*
Josh Aronin, *Accountant*
EMP: 81 **EST:** 2005
SQ FT: 2,140
SALES: 130.7MM **Publicly Held**
WEB: www.celsiusholdingsinc.com
SIC: 2086 Iced tea & fruit drinks, bottled & canned

(G-478)
CHANDLER BATS
2401 Nw 2nd Ave Ste 100 (33431-6759)
PHONE..................................484 674-7175
EMP: 6 **EST:** 2019
SALES (est): 287K **Privately Held**
WEB: www.chandlerbats.com
SIC: 3949 Sporting & athletic goods

(G-479)
CIAO GROUP INC (PA)
951 W Yamato Rd Ste 101 (33431-4437)
PHONE..................................347 560-5040
EMP: 20
SALES (est): 1.4MM **Privately Held**
SIC: 3661 4813 6794 Mfg Telecommunications Products & Solutions Franchising Stores

(G-480)
CITY NEWS PUBLISHING LLC
12364 Clearfalls Dr (33428-4845)
PHONE..................................305 332-9101
Gerald S Spielman, *Principal*
EMP: 7 **EST:** 2019
SALES (est): 383.8K **Privately Held**
SIC: 2741 Miscellaneous publishing

(G-481)
CL BOCA RATON LLC
6000 Glades Rd Ste 1234 (33431-7286)
PHONE..................................561 660-9485
Edward W Beiner,
EMP: 6 **EST:** 2007
SALES (est): 257.5K **Privately Held**
WEB: www.bocaratonflocksmiths.com
SIC: 3851 Ophthalmic goods

(G-482)
CLASSIC METAL FABRICATION INC
121 Nw 11th St (33432-2639)
PHONE..................................561 305-9532
Siegfried James Mahar, *President*
EMP: 6 **EST:** 2013
SQ FT: 3,500
SALES (est): 728.6K **Privately Held**
WEB: www.classicmetalfab.com
SIC: 3441 Fabricated structural metal

(G-483)
CLASSIQUE STYLE INC
6590 W Rogers Cir Ste 8 (33487-2739)
PHONE..................................561 995-7557
Dominic Graci, *President*
Stephanie Graci, *Vice Pres*
EMP: 12 **EST:** 1998
SQ FT: 3,000
SALES (est): 433.8K **Privately Held**
WEB: www.classicstylesboca.com
SIC: 3911 Jewelry, precious metal

(G-484)
CLEARLY DERM LLC (PA)
7050 W Palmetto Park Rd # 30
(33433-3426)
PHONE..................................561 353-3376
Brooke Boland, *Med Doctor*
Meredith Hancock, *Med Doctor*
Erika Luceri-Johnson, *Med Doctor*
Andrew Styperek, *Med Doctor*
Andrea Colton MD Faad, *Director*
EMP: 35 **EST:** 2010
SALES (est): 12.7MM **Privately Held**
WEB: www.clearlyderm.com
SIC: 2834 Dermatologicals

(G-485)
CLEVA TECHNOLOGIES LLC
Also Called: Cleva Power
1951 Nw 19th St Ste 101 (33431-7344)
PHONE..................................561 654-5279
Mitchel Robbins, *CEO*
Larry K Canipe, *President*
EMP: 15 **EST:** 2006
SALES (est): 5.2MM **Privately Held**
WEB: www.clevatec.com
SIC: 3691 3694 Alkaline cell storage batteries; battery charging alternators & generators

(G-486)
COASTAL COMMUNICATIONS CORP
Also Called: Corporate & Incentive Travel
2700 N Military Trl # 120 (33431-1809)
PHONE..................................561 989-0600
Harvey Grotsky, *President*
David Middlebrook, *Vice Pres*
Susan Fell, *Manager*
Susan Gregg, *Manager*
Mitch Miller, *Creative Dir*
EMP: 15 **EST:** 1977
SALES (est): 1.4MM **Privately Held**
WEB: www.coastalcomm.net
SIC: 2721 8742 Magazines: publishing only, not printed on site; management consulting services

(G-487)
COMPACT CONTAINER SYSTEMS LLC
2500 N Military Trl # 400 (33431-6344)
PHONE..................................561 392-6910
Charlie Santos Busch, *Mng Member*
EMP: 10 **EST:** 2014
SALES (est): 547.2K **Privately Held**
WEB: www.compactcontainers.com
SIC: 2448 Cargo containers, wood & metal combination

(G-488)
CONSOLIDATED CORDAGE CORP
1707 Avenida Del Sol (33432-1742)
PHONE..................................561 347-7247
Cathleen Materka, *President*
▲ **EMP:** 10 **EST:** 1993
SALES (est): 1.7MM **Privately Held**
WEB: www.consolidatedcordage.com
SIC: 2298 Ropes & fiber cables

(G-489)
COPPERCOM INC
Also Called: Coppercom, A Heico
3600 Fau Blvd Ste 100 (33431-6474)
PHONE..................................561 322-4000
Julian Thomson, *President*
Manuel Vexler, *CTO*
EMP: 70 **EST:** 1997
SQ FT: 15,000
SALES (est): 4.9MM **Privately Held**
WEB: www.heicocompanies.com
SIC: 3661 Telephone & telegraph apparatus
PA: The Heico Companies L L C
70 W Madison St Ste 5600
Chicago IL 60602

(G-490)
COSMETIC SOLUTIONS LLC
6101 Pk Of Commerce Blvd (33487-8208)
PHONE..................................561 226-8600
Mervyn Becker, *President*
Warren Becker, *COO*
Les Herz, *CFO*
Marilyn Esquivia, *Sales Staff*
Lee Rolnick, *Sales Staff*
◆ **EMP:** 50 **EST:** 1992
SQ FT: 40,000
SALES (est): 19.8MM **Privately Held**
WEB: www.naturalskincare.com
SIC: 2844 5122 Cosmetic preparations; cosmetics, perfumes & hair products

(G-491)
CRC PRESS LLC (DH)
Also Called: Critical Review Journals, Crj
6000 Broken Sound Pkwy Nw # 300
(33487-5704)
PHONE..................................561 994-0555
Randy Brehm, *Editor*
Mason Slaine, *Chairman*
Emmett Dages, *COO*
Debbie Rose Amelia, *Vice Pres*
Vivian Espinosa-Kenn, *Controller*
EMP: 30 **EST:** 1913
SQ FT: 40,354
SALES (est): 55.2MM
SALES (corp-wide): 2.2B **Privately Held**
WEB: www.routledge.com
SIC: 2731 Books: publishing only
HQ: Taylor & Francis Limited
Oakfield Road Adams Corner
Aylesbury BUCKS
129 674-7270

(G-492)
CRC PRESS LLC
3848 Fau Blvd Ste 310 (33431-6437)
PHONE..................................561 361-6000
Fenton Markevich, *CEO*
EMP: 37
SALES (corp-wide): 2.2B **Privately Held**
WEB: www.routledge.com
SIC: 2731 Books: publishing only
HQ: Crc Press Llc
6000 Broken Sound Pkwy Nw # 300
Boca Raton FL 33487
561 994-0555

(G-493)
CROWN LEAO INDUSTRIES INC
150 E Palmetto Park Rd # 80
(33432-4827)
PHONE..................................561 866-1218
Achilles A Utsch De Leao, *Principal*
EMP: 8 **EST:** 2015
SALES (est): 310.5K **Privately Held**
WEB: www.cpreo.com
SIC: 3999 Manufacturing industries

(G-494)
CUSTOM INSTALL SOLUTIONS INC
3632 Nw 5th Ter (33431-5746)
PHONE..................................916 601-1190
Peter Gokun, *President*
Mikhail Kosachevich, *Vice Pres*
EMP: 10 **EST:** 2017
SALES (est): 911.7K **Privately Held**
SIC: 2431 7389 Millwork;

(G-495)
DAZMED INC
Also Called: Dazmed Pharmaceuticals
508 Nw 77th St (33487-1323)
PHONE..................................561 571-2020
Amio Das, *President*
EMP: 8 **EST:** 2011
SALES (est): 1.7MM **Privately Held**
WEB: www.dazmed.com
SIC: 2834 Pharmaceutical preparations

(G-496)
DECO LAV INC (PA)
4920 Bocaire Blvd (33487-1162)
PHONE..................................561 274-2110
Robert Mayer, *President*
Courtney Casperson, *Vice Pres*
Linda M Persaud, *Vice Pres*
Tom Santer, *Vice Pres*
Andrea Scott-Knight, *Vice Pres*
▲ **EMP:** 12 **EST:** 2001
SALES (est): 32.6MM **Privately Held**
WEB: www.partners.decolav.com
SIC: 3431 Bathroom fixtures, including sinks

(G-497)
DEFENSTECH INTERNATIONAL INC
Also Called: Defend-X
1080 Holland Dr Ste 1 (33487-2782)
PHONE..................................202 688-1988
Alan R Sporn, *President*
▼ **EMP:** 10 **EST:** 2005
SALES (est): 2.1MM **Privately Held**
WEB: www.defenstech.com
SIC: 3812 Defense systems & equipment

(G-498)
DESIGN & PRINT
199 W Palmetto Park Rd (33432-3809)
PHONE..................................561 361-8299
Carol Inman, *President*
EMP: 5 **EST:** 1991
SALES (est): 339.2K **Privately Held**
SIC: 2752 7336 Commercial printing, lithographic; graphic arts & related design

(G-499)
DEVCON INTERNATIONAL CORP (HQ)
595 S Federal Hwy Ste 500 (33432-5542)
PHONE..................................954 926-5200
Mr Steve Hafen, *CEO*
Mr Donald L Smith, *Principal*
Ms Ann Macdonald, *Senior VP*
Mr Mark M McIntosh, *Senior VP*
Mr Sean Forrest, *CFO*
◆ **EMP:** 229 **EST:** 1951
SALES (est): 4.9MM
SALES (corp-wide): 1.6B **Privately Held**
WEB: www.goldengatecap.com
SIC: 3699 3273 3281 3271 Security devices; ready-mixed concrete; stone, quarrying & processing of own stone products; concrete block & brick; asphalt paving mixtures & blocks; cement
PA: Golden Gate Private Equity Incorporated
1 Embarcadero Ctr Fl 39
San Francisco CA 94111
415 983-2706

(G-500)
DIAGNOSTIC TEST GROUP LLC
Also Called: Clarity Diagnostics
1060 Holland Dr Ste A (33487-2758)
PHONE..................................561 347-5760
Rick Simpson, *CEO*
Dave Wilbert, *President*
Jason Lustig, *CFO*
EMP: 13 **EST:** 2003
SALES (est): 1.5MM **Privately Held**
WEB: www.claritydiagnostics.com
SIC: 3841 Diagnostic apparatus, medical

(G-501)
DILIGENT SERVICES INC ✪
2730 Nw 1st Ave (33431-6606)
PHONE..................................561 368-1478
EMP: 6 **EST:** 2020
SALES (est): 640.6K **Privately Held**
SIC: 7692 Welding repair

(G-502)
DIOXIDE MATERIALS INC
3998 Fau Blvd Ste 300 (33431-6429)
PHONE..................................217 239-1400
Rich Masel, *CEO*
Robert Kutz, *Research*
Amin Salehi-Khojin, *Research*
Jerry Kaczur, *Senior Engr*
Julian Sculley, *CTO*
EMP: 12
SALES: 2.6MM **Privately Held**
WEB: www.dioxidematerials.com
SIC: 2821 8731 3629 Polystyrene resins; commercial research laboratory; electrochemical generators (fuel cells)

▲ = Import ▼=Export
◆ =Import/Export

(G-503)
DIRECT RESPONSE PUBLICATION
Also Called: D R P
315 Se Mizner Blvd # 208 (33432-6086)
PHONE..................................561 620-3010
Richard Giarratana, *President*
Kyle Franch, *General Mgr*
▲ **EMP:** 15 **EST:** 1985
SQ FT: 1,000
SALES (est): 776.2K **Privately Held**
WEB: www.designtrade.net
SIC: 2721 2731 Magazines: publishing only, not printed on site; books: publishing only

(G-504)
DIVINE DOVETAIL
1050 Nw 1st Ave Ste 7 (33432-2603)
PHONE..................................561 245-7601
Chris G Goddard, *Principal*
EMP: 7 **EST:** 2007
SALES (est): 313.4K **Privately Held**
SIC: 3429 Cabinet hardware

(G-505)
DOCTOR PICKLE LLC
1279 W Palmetto Park Rd (33427-0801)
PHONE..................................772 985-5919
Harold Pitts, *Mng Member*
EMP: 17
SALES (est): 1MM **Privately Held**
WEB: www.doctorpickle.com
SIC: 2035 Pickles, sauces & salad dressings

(G-506)
DOLPHINE JEWELRY CONTRACTING
Also Called: Stal Creations
9064 Villa Portofino Cir (33496-1752)
PHONE..................................561 488-0355
Emanuel Friedman, *President*
EMP: 6 **EST:** 1971
SQ FT: 1,600
SALES (est): 89.1K **Privately Held**
SIC: 3911 Jewelry, precious metal

(G-507)
DONNA M WALKER PA
11137 Harbour Springs Cir (33428-1246)
PHONE..................................561 289-0437
Donna Walker, *Principal*
EMP: 6 **EST:** 2008
SALES (est): 288.7K **Privately Held**
SIC: 3842 Walkers

(G-508)
DR PEPPER/SEVEN UP INC
Also Called: Dr. Pepper Snapple
7251 W Plmtt Prk Rd Ste 3 (33433-3487)
PHONE..................................561 995-6260
Kathy Gray, *Branch Mgr*
EMP: 19 **Publicly Held**
WEB: www.drpepper.com
SIC: 2086 Soft drinks: packaged in cans, bottles, etc.
HQ: Dr Pepper/Seven Up, Inc.
6425 Hall Of Fame Ln
Frisco TX 75034
972 673-7000

(G-509)
DRAGONS MIRACLE LLC
160 W Camino Real Ste 154 (33432-5942)
PHONE..................................561 670-5546
Angelo Cairo, *Administration*
EMP: 6 **EST:** 2015
SALES (est): 443.7K **Privately Held**
WEB: www.dragonsmiracle.com
SIC: 2833 Organic medicinal chemicals: bulk, uncompounded

(G-510)
DRY BONEZ INC
22180 Woodset Ln (33428-3805)
PHONE..................................321 926-6399
Helen E Goodall, *Principal*
EMP: 6 **EST:** 2012
SALES (est): 86.8K **Privately Held**
WEB: www.drybonez.com
SIC: 3679 Electronic components

(G-511)
EAGLE ARTISTIC PRINTING INC
10277 Shireoaks Ln (33498-6402)
PHONE..................................973 476-6301
Julia Leung, *Principal*
EMP: 8 **EST:** 2010
SALES (est): 19.4K **Privately Held**
SIC: 2752 Commercial printing, offset

(G-512)
EATON CORPORATION
1225 Broken Sound Pkwy Nw F (33487-3533)
PHONE..................................561 998-4111
Pamela Gorman, *Sales Staff*
Robert Gundlach, *Branch Mgr*
EMP: 6 **Privately Held**
WEB: www.eatonelectrical.com
SIC: 3625 Relays & industrial controls
HQ: Eaton Corporation
1000 Eaton Blvd
Cleveland OH 44122
440 523-5000

(G-513)
ECOSOULIFE USA DIST LLC
3651 Fau Blvd Ste 400 (33431-6489)
PHONE..................................754 212-5456
Romualdo Munoz Jr, *Mng Member*
Brita McGrath,
Yamit Sadok,
EMP: 12 **EST:** 2015
SQ FT: 7,000
SALES (est): 970K **Privately Held**
SIC: 3229 Tableware, glass or glass ceramic

(G-514)
EDGEONE LLC
Also Called: Edgetech
1141 Holland Dr Ste 1 (33487-2737)
PHONE..................................561 995-7767
Robert Trimble, *General Mgr*
David Deveau, *Engineer*
Ricky Pascasio, *VP Sales*
John Spruance, *Manager*
EMP: 10
SALES (corp-wide): 20.3MM **Privately Held**
WEB: www.edgetech.com
SIC: 3826 3812 Analytical instruments; search & navigation equipment
PA: Edgeone Llc
4 Little Brook Rd
West Wareham MA 02576
508 291-0057

(G-515)
EI GLOBAL GROUP LLC
1515 N Federal Hwy # 200 (33432-1911)
PHONE..................................561 999-8989
Steven Megur, *CEO*
Michael Schwartz, *Administration*
Scott Everett,
▲ **EMP:** 8 **EST:** 2006
SALES (est): 1.2MM **Privately Held**
WEB: www.eigpersonalcare.com
SIC: 3089 2844 Novelties, plastic; shampoos, rinses, conditioners: hair

(G-516)
ELEMENT AIRCRAFT SALES LLC
1001 Sw 20th St (33486-6833)
PHONE..................................954 494-2242
Christopher A Blanchard, *Manager*
EMP: 7 **EST:** 2017
SALES (est): 241.6K **Privately Held**
WEB: www.element-aviation.com
SIC: 2819 Industrial inorganic chemicals

(G-517)
ELMRIDGE PROTECTION PDTS LLC
1200 Clint Moore Rd Ste 1 (33487-2731)
PHONE..................................561 244-8337
Jamie Gurvitch, *Business Mgr*
Jonathan Tyfield, *Opers Mgr*
Ira J Gurvitch,
▲ **EMP:** 8 **EST:** 2006
SALES (est): 894.2K **Privately Held**
WEB: www.elmridgeprotection.com
SIC: 3842 Surgical appliances & supplies

(G-518)
ENGLERT ARTS INC
1021 S Rogers Cir Ste 18 (33487-2857)
PHONE..................................561 241-9924
Frank Englert, *President*
Patricia Englert, *Vice Pres*
▼ **EMP:** 9 **EST:** 1979
SQ FT: 3,500
SALES (est): 1MM **Privately Held**
WEB: www.englertarts.com
SIC: 2273 3931 3281 Floor coverings, textile fiber; musical instruments; cut stone & stone products

(G-519)
EPIC PROMOS LLC
6451 E Rogers Cir Ste 3 (33487-2601)
PHONE..................................561 479-8055
Herman Craig, *Principal*
EMP: 11 **EST:** 2016
SALES (est): 1.2MM **Privately Held**
WEB: www.epicpromosfla.com
SIC: 2759 Screen printing

(G-520)
ERAN FINANCIAL SERVICES LLC
3500 Nw Boca Raton Blvd (33431-5851)
PHONE..................................844 411-5483
Shai Levitin, *CEO*
Dan Levitin, *General Mgr*
▲ **EMP:** 26 **EST:** 2007
SQ FT: 6,000
SALES: 46.6MM **Privately Held**
WEB: www.eranindustrial.com
SIC: 3646 6141 Ceiling systems, luminous; consumer finance companies

(G-521)
ERAN GROUP INC
3500 Nw 2nd Ave (33431-5866)
PHONE..................................561 289-5021
Ron Ahayon, *Principal*
EMP: 13 **EST:** 2009
SALES (est): 1MM **Privately Held**
WEB: www.eranindustrial.com
SIC: 3646 Commercial indusl & institutional electric lighting fixtures

(G-522)
ESSENTIAL PUBLISHING GROUP LLC (PA)
1140 Holland Dr Ste 21 (33487-2751)
PHONE..................................410 440-5777
EMP: 7 **EST:** 2017
SALES (est): 456.5K **Privately Held**
WEB: www.cclifeandhome.com
SIC: 2741 Miscellaneous publishing

(G-523)
EUROCRAFT CABINETS INC
1217 Clint Moore Rd (33487-2718)
PHONE..................................561 948-3034
Jeff Canter, *Principal*
▼ **EMP:** 8 **EST:** 2003
SALES (est): 756.8K **Privately Held**
WEB: www.eurocraftcabinets.com
SIC: 2434 Wood kitchen cabinets

(G-524)
EVE CORPORATION (PA)
Also Called: USA Keratin
23085 Addison Lakes Cir (33433-6863)
PHONE..................................305 599-3832
Equel Valdvieso, *President*
EMP: 33 **EST:** 2001
SALES (est): 233.3K **Privately Held**
WEB: www.usakeratin.com
SIC: 2844 Hair preparations, including shampoos

(G-525)
EXELAN PHARMACEUTICALS INC
370 W Cmino Grdns Blvd St (33432)
PHONE..................................561 287-6631
Brian Christensen, *President*
Terri Arndt, *General Mgr*
Deepak Argawal, *CFO*
Sudip Jadhav, *Associate Dir*
EMP: 3
SQ FT: 3,500
SALES: 86.1MM **Privately Held**
WEB: www.exelanpharma.com
SIC: 2834 Pharmaceutical preparations

(G-526)
EXTREME CRAFTS LLC
999 Nw 51st St Ste 100 (33431-4478)
PHONE..................................561 989-7400
Frederick M Middleton, *Mng Member*
EMP: 8 **EST:** 2003
SALES (est): 252.3K **Privately Held**
SIC: 3721 Autogiros

(G-527)
FASTSIGNS2043
2401 N Federal Hwy (33431-7756)
PHONE..................................305 988-5264
Chris Kirby, *CEO*
EMP: 14 **EST:** 2016
SALES (est): 1.1MM **Privately Held**
WEB: www.fastsigns.com
SIC: 3993 Signs & advertising specialties

(G-528)
FIIK SKATEBOARDS LLC (PA)
7050 W Palmetto Park Rd (33433-3426)
PHONE..................................561 316-8234
EMP: 11 **EST:** 2012
SALES (est): 206.3K **Privately Held**
WEB: www.fiik.com
SIC: 3949 Skateboards

(G-529)
FIRST WAVE BIOPHARMA INC
Also Called: Azurrx
777 W Yamato Rd Ste 502 (33431-4475)
PHONE..................................561 589-7020
James Sapirstein, *Ch of Bd*
Daniel Schneiderman, *CFO*
James E Pennington, *Chief Mktg Ofcr*
EMP: 12 **EST:** 2014
SALES (est): 1.5MM **Privately Held**
WEB: www.firstwavebio.com
SIC: 2834 Pharmaceutical preparations

(G-530)
FLEXSHOPPER LLC
2700 N Military Trl # 200 (33431-6394)
PHONE..................................561 922-6609
Brad Bernstein, *President*
John Brann, *Partner*
Justin Metzl, *Vice Pres*
Mario Carballosa, *Engineer*
Alisia Onderlinde, *Bookkeeper*
EMP: 30 **EST:** 2013
SQ FT: 6,400
SALES (est): 17.3MM **Publicly Held**
WEB: www.flexshopper.com
SIC: 3639 2519 3931 Floor waxers & polishers, electric: household; household furniture, except wood or metal: upholstered; musical instruments
PA: Flexshopper, Inc.
901 W Yamato Rd Ste 260
Boca Raton FL 33431

(G-531)
FLORIDA DESIGN INC
621 Nw 53rd St Ste 370 (33487-8241)
PHONE..................................561 997-1660
Jeff Lichtenstein, *President*
Ken Baxley, *Publisher*
Linda Donnelly, *Publisher*
Paul Lichtenstein, *Vice Pres*
Jenny Ortegon, *Human Resources*
EMP: 34 **EST:** 1990
SQ FT: 5,500
SALES (est): 5.7MM **Privately Held**
WEB: www.floridadesign.com
SIC: 2721 Magazines: publishing only, not printed on site

(G-532)
FLORIDA NBTY MANUFACTURING
901 Broken Sound Pkwy Nw (33487-3528)
PHONE..................................561 922-4800
Lynn Boland, *Principal*
EMP: 11 **EST:** 2008
SALES (est): 1.6MM **Privately Held**
SIC: 3999 Manufacturing industries

(G-533)
FLORIDA SOLAR ENERGY LLC
7999 N Federal Hwy # 400 (33487-1673)
PHONE..................................561 206-2324
Sean M O'Day,
EMP: 2 **EST:** 2007
SQ FT: 1,600

SALES (est): 3MM **Privately Held**
WEB: www.floridasolarenergy.com
SIC: 3433 Solar heaters & collectors

(G-534)
FLORIDA STUCCO CORP
21195 Boca Rio Rd (33433-2201)
P.O. Box 880023 (33488-0023)
PHONE..................................561 487-1301
Rick Howell, *President*
Tom Skehan, *Sales Staff*
▼ **EMP:** 21 **EST:** 1980
SQ FT: 13,000
SALES (est): 4MM **Privately Held**
WEB: www.floridastucco.com
SIC: 3299 3949 Stucco; sporting & athletic goods

(G-535)
FLOSPINE LLC
3651 Fau Blvd Ste 400 (33431-6489)
PHONE..................................561 705-3080
Peter Harris, *President*
EMP: 5 **EST:** 2011
SQ FT: 800
SALES (est): 540K **Privately Held**
WEB: www.flospine.com
SIC: 3841 Surgical & medical instruments

(G-536)
FOAM FACTORY INC
10137 Spyglass Way (33498-6448)
PHONE..................................954 485-6700
Stan Regent, *President*
Lori Weiss, *Vice Pres*
◆ **EMP:** 40 **EST:** 1976
SQ FT: 30,000
SALES (est): 2.5MM **Privately Held**
WEB: www.foamfactory.com
SIC: 3086 Packaging & shipping materials, foamed plastic

(G-537)
FOREVER CURRENT MUSIC LLC
20749 Waters Edge Ct (33498-6822)
PHONE..................................213 458-2880
Jarred N Moore, *Principal*
EMP: 6 **EST:** 2016
SALES (est): 91.3K **Privately Held**
WEB: www.forevercurrent.com
SIC: 2741 Miscellaneous publishing

(G-538)
FOREWARN LLC
2650 N Military Trl # 300 (33431-6350)
PHONE..................................561 757-4550
James Reilly, *President*
Aaron Solomon, *Senior VP*
EMP: 5 **EST:** 2017
SALES (est): 1.3MM **Publicly Held**
WEB: www.forewarn.com
SIC: 7372 Prepackaged software
PA: Fluent, Inc.
1 N End Ave Fl 9
New York NY 10282

(G-539)
FRANK BENNARDELLO
8121 Glades Rd (33434)
PHONE..................................561 470-4838
Frank Bennardello, *Principal*
EMP: 6 **EST:** 2007
SALES (est): 151K **Privately Held**
SIC: 3423 Jewelers' hand tools

(G-540)
FRESH START BEVERAGE COMPANY (PA)
Also Called: Fsbc
4001 N Ocean Blvd Apt B30 (33431-5363)
PHONE..................................561 757-6541
Steven Gelerman, *CEO*
Claudette Patron, *President*
Sonia Jackson-Myles, *Principal*
Jack Knott, *Principal*
He Neter Kush Ben Alkebulan, *COO*
EMP: 7 **EST:** 2013
SQ FT: 1,300
SALES (est): 2.4MM **Privately Held**
WEB: www.bananawave.com
SIC: 2087 5149 2086 2023 Beverage bases; groceries & related products; beverage concentrates; beverages, except coffee & tea; iced tea & fruit drinks, bottled & canned; carbonated beverages, nonalcoholic: bottled & canned; dietary supplements, dairy & non-dairy based

(G-541)
FUEL U FAST INC
5660 Wind Drift Ln (33433-5446)
PHONE..................................561 654-0212
Derren Garber, *President*
EMP: 7 **EST:** 2012
SALES (est): 713.6K **Privately Held**
WEB: www.fuelufast.com
SIC: 2869 Fuels

(G-542)
GAS ONE INC (PA)
19688 Oakbrook Cir (33434-3204)
PHONE..................................561 483-0504
Randall E Waltuch, *President*
EMP: 8 **EST:** 2001
SALES (est): 317.3K **Privately Held**
SIC: 1389 Oil & gas field services

(G-543)
GEOCOMMAND INC
3700 Airport Rd Ste 410 (33431-6423)
PHONE..................................561 347-9215
EMP: 6
SQ FT: 700
SALES (est): 672.5K **Privately Held**
SIC: 7372 Prepackaged Software Services

(G-544)
GET SALTED LLC
120 Nw 11th St (33432-2640)
PHONE..................................954 826-3947
Leonard Tonkin, *Principal*
EMP: 6 **EST:** 2016
SALES (est): 251.6K **Privately Held**
WEB: www.get-salted.com
SIC: 2844 Toilet preparations

(G-545)
GLM PUBLISHING LLC
2165 Nw 30th Rd (33431-6367)
PHONE..................................561 409-7696
Guy Mancini, *Principal*
EMP: 7 **EST:** 2013
SALES (est): 251.4K **Privately Held**
WEB: www.seakidstv.com
SIC: 2741 Miscellaneous publishing

(G-546)
GLS ASSOC INC
9170 Long Lake Palm Dr (33496-1786)
PHONE..................................561 451-1999
Gary L Shore, *President*
Elaine H Shore, *Vice Pres*
EMP: 3 **EST:** 1967
SQ FT: 3,000
SALES (est): 15MM **Privately Held**
SIC: 2519 Household furniture, except wood or metal: upholstered

(G-547)
GNS TECHNOLOGIES LLC
5612 Pacific Blvd Apt 704 (33433-6793)
PHONE..................................561 367-3774
Edith Adessa, *Principal*
EMP: 7 **EST:** 2008
SALES (est): 551.8K
SALES (corp-wide): 38.5B **Publicly Held**
WEB: www.dow.com
SIC: 2819 Industrial inorganic chemicals
HQ: The Dow Chemical Company
2211 H H Dow Way
Midland MI 48642
989 636-1000

(G-548)
GOOD JAMS LLC
6450 N Federal Hwy (33487-3155)
PHONE..................................702 379-5551
EMP: 9 **EST:** 2017
SALES (est): 802.1K **Privately Held**
SIC: 2033 Jams, jellies & preserves: packaged in cans, jars, etc.

(G-549)
GORILLADESK LLC
7370 E Country Club Blvd (33487-1538)
PHONE..................................561 245-8614
Christopher Moreschi, *Manager*
EMP: 7 **EST:** 2014
SALES (est): 388.4K **Privately Held**
WEB: www.gorilladesk.com
SIC: 7372 Prepackaged software

(G-550)
GOT IT INC
Also Called: Kitchens, Baths & Closets
107 E Palmetto Park Rd (33432-4818)
PHONE..................................954 899-0001
Paul Remolina, *President*
Holly Sauer, *Vice Pres*
EMP: 8 **EST:** 2015
SALES (est): 411.6K **Privately Held**
SIC: 2514 2394 Metal lawn & garden furniture; canvas awnings & canopies

(G-551)
GRAPHIC PRINTING CORP
751 Park Of Commerce Dr (33487-3626)
PHONE..................................561 994-3586
Matthew Stern, *President*
Yesenia Mayorga, *General Mgr*
Sam Ghanem, *Exec VP*
EMP: 27 **EST:** 1983
SQ FT: 6,000
SALES (est): 5MM **Privately Held**
WEB: www.gpclabels.com
SIC: 2759 Flexographic printing; screen printing

(G-552)
GRINNELL LLC (DH)
Also Called: Grinnell Fire Prtction Systems
1501 Nw 51st St (33431-4438)
PHONE..................................561 988-3658
John F Fort, *CEO*
Jerry Boggess, *Exec VP*
Robert Mead, *Exec VP*
Stephanie Trammell, *Opers Staff*
Steve Konst, *Manager*
▲ **EMP:** 500 **EST:** 1895
SALES (est): 245.4MM **Publicly Held**
WEB: www.tycosimplexgrinnell.com
SIC: 3569 3491 Sprinkler systems, fire: automatic; automatic regulating & control valves; fire hydrant valves; water works valves; gas valves & parts, industrial
HQ: Johnson Controls Fire Protection Lp
6600 Congress Ave
Boca Raton FL 33487
561 988-7200

(G-553)
GROM SOCIAL ENTERPRISES INC (PA)
2060 Nw Boca Raton Blvd (33431-7414)
PHONE..................................561 287-5776
Darren Marks, *Ch of Bd*
Ismael Llera, *Vice Pres*
Melvin Leiner, *CFO*
EMP: 114 **EST:** 2014
SQ FT: 2,100
SALES (est): 6.1MM **Publicly Held**
WEB: www.gromsocial.com
SIC: 7372 Prepackaged software

(G-554)
GULFSTREAM GOODWILL INDS INC
1662 N Federal Hwy (33432-1930)
PHONE..................................561 362-8662
EMP: 31
SALES (corp-wide): 48.6MM **Privately Held**
WEB: www.goggi.org
SIC: 3999 Atomizers, toiletry
PA: Gulfstream Goodwill Industries, Inc.
1715 E Tiffany Dr
Mangonia Park FL 33407
561 848-7200

(G-555)
HAND CARVED CREATIONS
5331 N Dixie Hwy Ste 3 (33487-4920)
PHONE..................................561 893-0292
Errol Palmer, *President*
EMP: 5 **EST:** 2003
SALES (est): 402K **Privately Held**
WEB: www.handcarvedcreation.com
SIC: 2434 Wood kitchen cabinets

(G-556)
HARDWARE PARTS CORPORATION
5030 Champion Blvd 6250 (33496-2473)
PHONE..................................561 994-2121
Bernice Cornfield, *President*
▲ **EMP:** 5 **EST:** 1988
SALES (est): 426.1K **Privately Held**
SIC: 3325 Steel foundries

(G-557)
HOLLANDER HM FSHONS HLDNGS LLC (HQ)
6501 Congress Ave Ste 300 (33487-2840)
PHONE..................................212 302-6571
Marc Pfefferle,
Dennis Maguire, *Maintence Staff*
Chris Baker,
Jeff Hollander,
Dave Sides,
EMP: 15 **EST:** 2009
SALES (est): 509.5MM **Privately Held**
WEB: www.hollander.com
SIC: 2392 Cushions & pillows

(G-558)
HONEYWELL INTERNATIONAL INC
21911 Pine Bark Way (33428-3035)
PHONE..................................561 479-0639
Dan Zbegner, *Manager*
EMP: 6
SALES (corp-wide): 32.6B **Publicly Held**
WEB: www.honeywell.com
SIC: 3724 Aircraft engines & engine parts
PA: Honeywell International Inc.
300 S Tryon St
Charlotte NC 28202
704 627-6200

(G-559)
HOOT/WISDOM MUSIC PUBG LLC
777 Glades Rd (33431-6424)
PHONE..................................561 297-3205
Sid M Breman, *Principal*
EMP: 8 **EST:** 2010
SALES (est): 67.4K **Privately Held**
WEB: www.fau.edu
SIC: 2741 Miscellaneous publishing

(G-560)
HUT GLOBAL INC
Also Called: Volume Cases
131 S Federal Hwy Apt 721 (33432-4961)
P.O. Box 654 (33429-0654)
PHONE..................................561 571-2523
Michael Bordack, *Vice Pres*
EMP: 5 **EST:** 2014
SALES (est): 472.1K **Privately Held**
WEB: www.volumecases.com
SIC: 3161 5045 Cases, carrying; printers, computer

(G-561)
I A I
21362 Placida Ter (33433-2385)
P.O. Box 810591 (33481-0591)
PHONE..................................561 488-6369
Ernestine Gelhardt, *Principal*
EMP: 7 **EST:** 2010
SALES (est): 204.2K **Privately Held**
SIC: 3272 Concrete products

(G-562)
IMAGE 360
6560 E Rogers Cir (33487-2655)
PHONE..................................561 395-0745
Mary Sol Gonzalez, *Principal*
Les Lipman, *Consultant*
EMP: 8 **EST:** 2013
SALES (est): 165.9K **Privately Held**
WEB: www.image360.com
SIC: 3993 Signs & advertising specialties

(G-563)
IMPERX INC (PA)
6421 Congress Ave Ste 204 (33487-2859)
PHONE..................................561 989-0006
Petko Dinev, *President*
Melissa Pangburn, *Opers Staff*

▲ = Import ▼=Export
◆ =Import/Export

Gregory A Pangburn, *CFO*
Joe Neuhausel, *Director*
EMP: 31 **EST:** 2001
SQ FT: 10,833
SALES (est): 10.1MM **Privately Held**
WEB: www.imperx.com
SIC: 3861 Cameras & related equipment

(G-564)
IMPRESSIONS DRY CLEANERS INC
6201 N Federal Hwy Ste 1 (33487-3200)
PHONE..................................561 988-3030
Pete Averill,
EMP: 10 **EST:** 2001
SALES (est): 507K **Privately Held**
WEB: www.mydrycleantogo.com
SIC: 2842 Specialty cleaning preparations

(G-565)
INSTAZORB INTERNATIONAL INC
500 Ne Spanish River Blvd (33431-4515)
P.O. Box 58, Hallandale (33008-0058)
PHONE..................................561 416-7302
Tom Payne, *CEO*
Siren Corn, *Admin Sec*
EMP: 5 **EST:** 1997
SALES (est): 1MM **Privately Held**
WEB: www.instazorb.com
SIC: 3559 Degreasing machines, automotive & industrial

(G-566)
INTEGRAL WD CSTM CABINETRY LLC
Also Called: C.A.c Custom Artisan Cabinetry
176 Glades Rd Ste A (33432-1649)
PHONE..................................561 361-5111
Enzo Barni, *Mng Member*
Elvio Barni,
Jose Barni,
EMP: 11 **EST:** 2015
SQ FT: 11,600
SALES (est): 1MM **Privately Held**
WEB: www.customartisancabinetry.com
SIC: 2434 Wood kitchen cabinets

(G-567)
INTERAVIA SPARES AND SVCS INC
746 Saint Albans Dr (33486-1514)
PHONE..................................954 794-0174
Mariana Oprea, *President*
EMP: 1 **EST:** 2003
SQ FT: 2,000
SALES (est): 3MM **Privately Held**
WEB: www.interaviaspares.com
SIC: 3724 3728 Aircraft engines & engine parts; aircraft parts & equipment

(G-568)
INTERIOR DESIGN
3651 Fau Blvd Ste 200 (33431-6489)
PHONE..................................646 805-0200
Nora Fried, *Business Mgr*
Julie Arkin, *Director*
Mark McMenamin, *Senior Editor*
EMP: 15 **EST:** 2018
SALES (est): 1.5MM **Privately Held**
WEB: www.interiordesign.net
SIC: 2721 Magazines: publishing only, not printed on site

(G-569)
INTERIOR DSIGN MEDIA GROUP LLC
3731 Fau Blvd Ste 1 (33431-6412)
PHONE..................................561 750-0151
Stacey Callahan, *Publisher*
Debby Steiner, *Publisher*
Amy Tambini, *Publisher*
Kate Abney, *Editor*
Mary Bowling, *Editor*
EMP: 70 **EST:** 2010
SALES (est): 6.4MM
SALES (corp-wide): 106.7MM **Privately Held**
WEB: www.luxesource.com
SIC: 2721 Magazines: publishing only, not printed on site
PA: Sandow Media, Llc
3651 Nw 8th Ave Ste 200
Boca Raton FL 33431
561 961-7749

(G-570)
INTERNATIONAL FINISHES INC
7777 Glades Rd (33434-4194)
PHONE..................................561 948-1066
George M Deacon, *Director*
Vicky A Deacon, *Director*
EMP: 13 **EST:** 1995
SALES (est): 536.2K **Privately Held**
SIC: 2843 Finishing agents

(G-571)
INTERTECH WORLDWIDE CORP (PA)
4400 N Federal Hwy # 125 (33431-5187)
PHONE..................................561 395-5441
David A Igdaloff, *President*
Nilma M Igdaloff, *Vice Pres*
▲ **EMP:** 5 **EST:** 1978
SALES (est): 2.7MM **Privately Held**
SIC: 3433 Gas-oil burners, combination

(G-572)
INTRALOCK INTERNATIONAL INC
6560 W Rogers Cir Ste 24 (33487-2746)
PHONE..................................561 447-8282
Thierry Girono, *CEO*
Angie Fratichelli, *Office Mgr*
Mary Jean, *Manager*
Rob Rhees, *Education*
EMP: 9 **EST:** 2019
SALES (est): 539.7K **Privately Held**
WEB: www.intra-lock.com
SIC: 3843 Dental equipment & supplies

(G-573)
INVICTA CORPORATION (PA)
Also Called: A Developmental Stage Company
1160 S Rogers Cir (33487-2786)
PHONE..................................561 995-9980
Alan Yuster, *President*
Leo Gleckel, *Chairman*
Felice Torre, *Vice Pres*
William Reilly, *Treasurer*
Kenneth Brown, *Admin Sec*
EMP: 6 **EST:** 1998
SQ FT: 25,000
SALES (est): 979.4K **Privately Held**
SIC: 3851 Eyeglasses, lenses & frames

(G-574)
ISOCIALMEDIA DIGITAL MARKETING
433 Plaza Real Ste 275 (33432-3999)
PHONE..................................561 510-1124
Celeste Velez, *President*
EMP: 9 **EST:** 2019
SALES (est): 342K **Privately Held**
WEB: www.isocialmedia.business.site
SIC: 2741

(G-575)
JAMERICA INC
11188 Jasmine Hill Cir (33498-1923)
PHONE..................................561 488-6247
John Maslauskas, *Principal*
EMP: 7 **EST:** 2010
SALES (est): 267.4K **Privately Held**
SIC: 2329 Men's & boys' clothing

(G-576)
JARDEN LLC
Also Called: Jarden Consumer Solutions
2381 Nw Executive Ctr Dr (33431-8560)
PHONE..................................561 447-2520
James E Lillie, *CEO*
Eduardo Vega, *Business Mgr*
Jonathan O'Neill, *Engineer*
John Cao, *Sr Project Mgr*
John Costa, *Manager*
EMP: 73
SALES (corp-wide): 9.3B **Publicly Held**
WEB: www.newellbrands.com
SIC: 3089 Plastic containers, except foam
HQ: Jarden Llc
221 River St
Hoboken NJ 07030

(G-577)
JARDEN PLASTIC SOLUTIONS
2381 Nw Executive Ctr Dr (33431-8560)
PHONE..................................864 879-8100
Martin E Franklin, *Principal*
EMP: 9 **EST:** 2010
SALES (est): 476.6K **Privately Held**
SIC: 3089 8748 Injection molding of plastics; systems analysis & engineering consulting services

(G-578)
JAZZIZ MAGAZINE INC
2650 N Military Trl # 140 (33431-6350)
P.O. Box 880189 (33488-0189)
PHONE..................................561 893-6868
Michael Fagien, *President*
Lori Fagien, *Owner*
Brian Zimmerman, *Editor*
Karen Rosenfeld, *CPA*
Geoffrey Fagien, *Adv Dir*
EMP: 23 **EST:** 1983
SQ FT: 2,500
SALES (est): 2.3MM **Privately Held**
WEB: www.jazziz.com
SIC: 2721 3652 Magazines: publishing only, not printed on site; pre-recorded records & tapes

(G-579)
JC VOYAGE LLC
2403 Nw 30th Rd (33431-6214)
PHONE..................................603 686-0065
Jessica Huber, *Mng Member*
Colette Shoemaker, *Mng Member*
EMP: 7 **EST:** 2019
SALES (est): 467.4K **Privately Held**
SIC: 2341 Women's & children's undergarments

(G-580)
JES PUBLISHING CORP
Also Called: Boca Raton Magazine
1000 Clint Moore Rd # 103 (33487-2806)
P.O. Box 820 (33429-0820)
PHONE..................................561 997-8683
Margaret Shuff, *President*
Maureen Hahn, *Research*
John Shuff, *Treasurer*
Gary Kot, *Manager*
Thomas Graziano, *Director*
EMP: 24 **EST:** 1981
SQ FT: 3,208
SALES (est): 3.8MM **Privately Held**
WEB: www.bocamag.com
SIC: 2721 Magazines: publishing only, not printed on site

(G-581)
JKG GROUP
160 Nw 51st St (33431-4226)
PHONE..................................561 866-2850
Josh Aragon, *Director*
EMP: 9 **EST:** 2014
SALES (est): 290.5K **Privately Held**
SIC: 2752 Commercial printing, offset

(G-582)
JO MO ENTERPRISES INC
Also Called: Vince & Sons Pasta Co
20966 Estada Ln (33433-1756)
PHONE..................................708 599-8098
Robert Okon, *President*
Michael Okon, *Vice Pres*
EMP: 8 **EST:** 2013
SQ FT: 10,000
SALES (est): 343.8K **Privately Held**
SIC: 2099 2038 2098 5142 Packaged combination products: pasta, rice & potato; spaghetti & meatballs, frozen; macaroni & spaghetti; dinners, frozen

(G-583)
JODAR INC
354 Ne 5th St (33432-4051)
PHONE..................................561 375-6277
Darin Matera, *Principal*
EMP: 8 **EST:** 2005
SALES (est): 164.3K **Privately Held**
SIC: 3714 Motor vehicle parts & accessories

(G-584)
JUST FUR FUN
8951 Old Pine Rd (33433-3152)
PHONE..................................561 809-6596
Mona B Straub, *Owner*
EMP: 6 **EST:** 2013
SALES (est): 87.9K **Privately Held**
WEB: www.justfurfunonline.com
SIC: 3999 Pet supplies

(G-585)
KAY DIAMOND PRODUCTS LLC
1080 Holland Dr Ste 2 (33487-2782)
PHONE..................................561 994-5400
George Clesi, *QC Mgr*
John Kay, *Mng Member*
Robert Gow,
EMP: 14 **EST:** 2002
SALES (est): 1.2MM **Privately Held**
WEB: www.kaydp.com
SIC: 3291 Abrasive products

(G-586)
KELLSTROM AEROSPACE GROUP INC (HQ)
2500 N Military Trl Ste 4 (33431-6344)
PHONE..................................954 538-2482
Jeff Lund, *President*
Oscar Torres, *COO*
John McKirdy, *Senior VP*
EMP: 21 **EST:** 2015
SALES (est): 50.1MM
SALES (corp-wide): 1B **Privately Held**
WEB: www.aeroequity.com
SIC: 3369 3324 Aerospace castings, nonferrous: except aluminum; aerospace investment castings, ferrous
PA: Ae Industrial Partners, Lp
2500 N Military Trl Ste 4
Boca Raton FL 33431
561 372-7820

(G-587)
KENNETH J MANNING LIGHTING
11170 Malayan St (33428-3914)
PHONE..................................561 702-0169
Ken Manning, *Principal*
EMP: 6 **EST:** 2005
SALES (est): 79K **Privately Held**
SIC: 3648 Lighting equipment

(G-588)
KINETICS USA INC
Also Called: Real Time Labratories
990 S Rogers Cir Ste 5 (33487-2836)
PHONE..................................561 988-8826
Bob Knabe, *President*
▲ **EMP:** 30 **EST:** 1999
SALES (est): 4.2MM
SALES (corp-wide): 4.6B **Privately Held**
WEB: www.elbitsystems.com
SIC: 3823 3492 Fluidic devices, circuits & systems for process control; fluid power valves & hose fittings
HQ: Kinetics Ltd.

Airport City 70199

(G-589)
KNEX INDUSTRIES INC
301 E Yamato Rd Ste 4200 (33431-4933)
PHONE..................................215 997-7722
Michael Araten, *CEO*
Joel Glickman, *President*
Bob Haines, *Senior VP*
Joseph Smith, *Senior VP*
Oscar Doles, *Warehouse Mgr*
◆ **EMP:** 160 **EST:** 1992
SALES (est): 22.9MM **Privately Held**
WEB: www.basicfun.com
SIC: 3944 Games, toys & children's vehicles

(G-590)
KNEX LTD PARTNERSHIP GROUP
301 E Yamato Rd Ste 4200 (33431-4933)
PHONE..................................215 997-7722
Michael Araten, *CEO*
◆ **EMP:** 84 **EST:** 2006
SALES (est): 5MM **Privately Held**
WEB: www.basicfun.com
SIC: 3944 Games, toys & children's vehicles

(G-591)
KOOL LEDZ LLC
21238 Stonewood Dr (33428-1014)
PHONE..................................561 212-5843
Elaine Kuter, *Treasurer*
Angela Herrera,
Camille Filoramo,
EMP: 7 **EST:** 2007
SQ FT: 4,000

GEOGRAPHIC

SALES (est): 1MM **Privately Held**
SIC: 3499 Novelties & giftware, including trophies

(G-592)
KRS GLOBAL BIOTECHNOLOGY INC
Also Called: Krs Global Biotechnology Mfg
791 Park Of Commerce Blvd # 600 (33487-3633)
PHONE..................................888 502-2050
Charles P Richardson, *CEO*
Riccardo Roscetti, *General Mgr*
Mirtha Fonte-Okunski, *CFO*
Viviana Rodriguez, *CFO*
Storm Lefelar, *Officer*
▲ **EMP:** 40 **EST:** 2001
SALES (est): 11.7MM **Privately Held**
WEB: www.krsbio.com
SIC: 2834 5122 Pharmaceutical preparations; drugs, proprietaries & sundries
PA: Cleveland Diabetes Care, Inc.
10752 Deerwood Park Blvd
Jacksonville FL 32256
904 394-2620

(G-593)
KULFI LLC
1100 Holland Dr (33487-2701)
PHONE..................................855 488-4273
Syed Shah, *CEO*
Fred Hassan, *Chairman*
EMP: 30 **EST:** 2013
SALES (est): 4.3MM **Privately Held**
WEB: www.imhealthscience.com
SIC: 2099 8049 Food preparations; dietician; nutritionist

(G-594)
LANCE LASHELLE (PA)
Also Called: Microseal International
6231 Nw 4th Ave (33487-2907)
PHONE..................................425 820-8888
Lance Lashelle, *President*
Ben Wilson, *Data Proc Exec*
EMP: 6 **EST:** 1993
SALES (est): 418K **Privately Held**
SIC: 2269 2262 Finishing plants; finishing plants, manmade fiber & silk fabrics

(G-595)
LANDSLIDE PUBLISHING INC
201 Plaza Real Ste 140 (33432-3959)
PHONE..................................561 392-4717
Richard Schmidt, *Principal*
EMP: 6 **EST:** 2016
SALES (est): 73.1K **Privately Held**
SIC: 2741 Miscellaneous publishing

(G-596)
LASER PHOTO TOOLING SERVICES
Also Called: Lps
5081 N Dixie Hwy (33431-4922)
PHONE..................................561 393-4710
John Leyva, *CEO*
Steven Angona, *Vice Pres*
Jeff Ankenney, *Engineer*
EMP: 15 **EST:** 1987
SQ FT: 5,000
SALES (est): 2.8MM **Privately Held**
WEB: www.l-p-s.com
SIC: 3672 Printed circuit boards

(G-597)
LATITUDE CLEAN TECH GROUP INC
190 Nw Spanish River Blvd # 101 (33431-4217)
PHONE..................................561 417-0687
EMP: 11
SALES (est): 732.3K **Privately Held**
SIC: 3589 Mfg Service Industry Machinery

(G-598)
LAUNDROMART
23182 Sandalfoot Plaza Dr (33428-6627)
PHONE..................................561 487-4343
Lawerence Percipo, *Principal*
EMP: 6 **EST:** 2006
SALES (est): 156K **Privately Held**
SIC: 2499 Hampers, laundry

(G-599)
LEOPARD BRANDS INC
6800 E Rogers Cir (33487-2651)
PHONE..................................954 794-0007
Harris Pollock, *President*
Peter Antonacci, *Treasurer*
▲ **EMP:** 7 **EST:** 2010
SALES (est): 969.7K **Privately Held**
WEB: www.leopardbrands.com
SIC: 2252 Socks

(G-600)
LEXINGTON INTERNATIONAL LLC
Also Called: Hairmax Lasercomb
1040 Holland Dr (33487-2759)
PHONE..................................800 973-4769
Leonard Stillman, *Vice Pres*
Michael Granata, *Accountant*
David Michaels, *Manager*
David M Michaels,
Jessica Rivera, *Graphic Designe*
▲ **EMP:** 30 **EST:** 2000
SALES (est): 5MM **Privately Held**
WEB: www.hairmax.com
SIC: 3845 Laser systems & equipment, medical

(G-601)
LF OF AMERICA CORP
7700 Congress Ave # 1120 (33487-1352)
PHONE..................................561 988-0303
Ferrari Giovanni, *Vice Pres*
Diego Bulgarelli, *Sales Staff*
▲ **EMP:** 5 **EST:** 2002
SQ FT: 40,000
SALES (est): 931.4K **Privately Held**
WEB: www.lfofamerica.com
SIC: 2844 2834 Cosmetic preparations; proprietary drug products

(G-602)
LF SENIOR COMMUNICATIONS GROUP
Also Called: Boomer Times & Senior Life
1515 N Federal Hwy # 300 (33432-1911)
PHONE..................................561 392-4550
Anita Finley, *President*
EMP: 10 **EST:** 1988
SALES (est): 1MM **Privately Held**
SIC: 2711 2721 Newspapers: publishing only, not printed on site; periodicals

(G-603)
LIVE SOURCE
10037 Country Brook Rd (33428-4217)
PHONE..................................561 573-2994
Michelle Trentacoste, *Principal*
Florian Castagneyrol, *Opers Staff*
Brad Morehouse, *Director*
Kurt Wyman, *Officer*
EMP: 6 **EST:** 2010
SALES (est): 118.6K **Privately Held**
SIC: 7372 Prepackaged software

(G-604)
LMI COMPONENTS INC
1181 S Rogers Cir Ste 25 (33487-2726)
PHONE..................................561 994-5896
David Asseraf, *President*
▲ **EMP:** 10 **EST:** 1989
SQ FT: 5,000
SALES (est): 1.4MM **Privately Held**
WEB: www.lmicorp.com
SIC: 3679 3644 3643 Electronic circuits; noncurrent-carrying wiring services; current-carrying wiring devices

(G-605)
MAFEKS INTERNATIONAL LLC
4755 Tech Way Ste 208 (33431)
PHONE..................................561 997-2080
Susan Morgan, *Traffic Mgr*
Natasha Craig, *Sales Staff*
Frieda Foster, *Sales Staff*
Howard McCall Jr,
▼ **EMP:** 16 **EST:** 2003
SQ FT: 3,500
SALES (est): 766.1K **Privately Held**
SIC: 3531 Railway track equipment

(G-606)
MALEMA ENGINEERING CORPORATION (PA)
Also Called: Malema Flow Sensors
1060 S Rogers Cir (33487-2815)
PHONE..................................561 995-0595
Deepak B Malani, *CEO*
Rahul Malani, *Principal*
Sarla Malani, *Principal*
Mannan Bandukwala, *Vice Pres*
Kalash Jhamb, *QC Mgr*
▲ **EMP:** 10 **EST:** 1981
SQ FT: 10,500
SALES (est): 7.3MM **Privately Held**
WEB: www.malema.com
SIC: 3823 3625 Industrial instrmnts msrmnt display/control process variable; flow actuated electrical switches

(G-607)
MARITIME REPLICAS USA LLC
70 Dorset B (33434-3006)
PHONE..................................305 921-9690
Warren R Samut,
EMP: 25 **EST:** 2014
SALES (est): 694.7K **Privately Held**
WEB: www.maritimereplicas.com
SIC: 3944 Boat & ship models, toy & hobby

(G-608)
MARK BENTON ✪
Also Called: Enforty
900 N Federal Hwy (33432-2755)
PHONE..................................754 203-9377
Mark Benton, *Owner*
EMP: 30 **EST:** 2020
SALES (est): 873.4K **Privately Held**
WEB: www.enforty.com
SIC: 2254 Shorts, shirts, slips & panties (underwear): knit

(G-609)
MARKETSHARE LLC
6790 E Rogers Cir (33487-2649)
PHONE..................................631 273-0598
Nancy Mantell, *Principal*
Steven Zaken, *Co-Owner*
David Guarnieri, *Vice Pres*
Monique Greene, *Manager*
Pritika Peddi, *Manager*
EMP: 5 **EST:** 2003
SALES (est): 434.5K **Privately Held**
SIC: 2752 3991 Playing cards, lithographed; toothbrushes, except electric

(G-610)
MARLO ELECTRONICS INC
2412 Nw 35th St (33431-5412)
PHONE..................................561 477-0856
Mark Goddard, *President*
Steven Goddard, *Admin Sec*
EMP: 33 **EST:** 1966
SQ FT: 35,000
SALES (est): 964.8K **Privately Held**
SIC: 3672 Printed circuit boards

(G-611)
MASC ASPEN PARTNERS LLC
17639 Lake Estates Dr (33496-1425)
PHONE..................................212.545-1076
Martin L Markowitz, *Mng Member*
EMP: 6 **EST:** 2005
SALES (est): 83.9K **Privately Held**
SIC: 2752 Commercial printing, lithographic

(G-612)
MCAFEE LLC
19496 Island Court Dr (33434-5153)
PHONE..................................561 477-6626
Harvey Krauser, *Branch Mgr*
EMP: 6
SALES (corp-wide): 2.9B **Publicly Held**
WEB: www.mcafee.com
SIC: 7372 Prepackaged software
HQ: Mcafee, Llc
6220 America Center Dr
San Jose CA 95002

(G-613)
MCCORMICK RESTAURANT SERVICES
7682 Solimar Cir (33433-1035)
PHONE..................................561 706-5554
EMP: 17 **EST:** 2001
SALES (est): 125.1K **Privately Held**
WEB: www.mccormick.com
SIC: 2099 Spices, including grinding

(G-614)
MCILPACK INC
7614 Nw 6th Ave (33487-1319)
PHONE..................................561 988-8545
Susana Arango, *President*
Juan Pinto, *Purchasing*
▲ **EMP:** 13 **EST:** 2002
SALES (est): 2.4MM **Privately Held**
WEB: www.mcilpack.com
SIC: 2844 Cosmetic preparations

(G-615)
MCMILL LLC
4800 N Federal Hwy 302d (33431-3414)
PHONE..................................561 279-3232
Linda McGuffie, *Principal*
EMP: 7 **EST:** 2013
SALES (est): 262.8K **Privately Held**
SIC: 2652 Setup paperboard boxes

(G-616)
MEDATTEND LLC
1200 Clint Moore Rd Ste 5 (33487-2731)
PHONE..................................561 465-2735
Gregory Kis, *Mng Member*
EMP: 10 **EST:** 2016
SALES (est): 474K **Privately Held**
SIC: 3669 Emergency alarms

(G-617)
MEDFARE LLC
6560 W Rogers Cir Ste 13 (33487-2746)
PHONE..................................561 998-9444
Gary Lorenz, *Mng Member*
Amy Lee, *Director*
EMP: 10 **EST:** 1974
SALES (est): 7MM **Privately Held**
WEB: www.medfare.com
SIC: 2752 Commercial printing, offset

(G-618)
MEDIAOPS INC
21455 Halstead Dr (33428-4842)
PHONE..................................516 857-7409
Saleem Padani, *COO*
Parker Yates, *Officer*
EMP: 24 **EST:** 2013
SALES (est): 432.8K **Privately Held**
WEB: www.devops.com
SIC: 7372 Prepackaged software

(G-619)
MERIDIAN CENTRE
6531 Park Of Commerce Blv (33487-8299)
PHONE..................................253 620-4542
Eric Chirinsky, *Manager*
EMP: 7 **EST:** 2011
SALES (est): 114.5K **Privately Held**
SIC: 2421 Building & structural materials, wood

(G-620)
MERIDIAN LIFE SCIENCE INC
1121 Holland Dr Ste 27 (33487-2736)
PHONE..................................561 241-0223
Debbie Colombo, *Branch Mgr*
EMP: 13
SALES (corp-wide): 253.6MM **Publicly Held**
WEB: www.meridianlifescience.com
SIC: 2835 Microbiology & virology diagnostic products
HQ: Meridian Life Science, Inc.
60 Industrial Park Rd
Saco ME 04072
207 283-6500

(G-621)
METRITEK GROUP LLC
370 Camino Gardens Blvd (33432-5816)
PHONE..................................561 995-2414
Robert Jablin, *Mng Member*
Edward Meyer,
EMP: 5 **EST:** 2019
SALES (est): 313.1K **Privately Held**
SIC: 2221 Textile mills, broadwoven: silk & manmade, also glass

(G-622)
MICA PDTS & WD OF BOCA RATON
150 Glades Rd (33432-1605)
PHONE..................................561 395-4686
Gregory Heinmiller, *President*
David L Risley, *Vice Pres*
EMP: 40 **EST:** 1974
SQ FT: 5,000
SALES (est): 3.5MM **Privately Held**
WEB: www.micaproductsandwood.com
SIC: 2434 Wood kitchen cabinets

(G-623)
MICROCOMPUTER SERVICES
1200 S Rogers Cir Ste 8 (33487-5703)
PHONE..................................561 988-7000
Cobden Lyn, *Managing Prtnr*
Brian Davies, *Partner*
EMP: 5 **EST:** 1993
SALES (est): 1.5MM **Privately Held**
WEB: www.mcscompany.com
SIC: 2759 7379 7331 Commercial printing; data processing consultant; direct mail advertising services

(G-624)
MIDWAY LABS USA LLC
6401 Congress Ave Ste 100 (33487-2841)
P.O. Box 480573, Delray Beach (33448-0573)
PHONE..................................561 571-6252
Wilton Colle, *President*
Catherine Colle, *Vice Pres*
Peter Giallorenzo, *CFO*
Christine Hassel, *Executive Asst*
▼ **EMP:** 10 **EST:** 2006
SQ FT: 4,000
SALES (est): 2.1MM **Privately Held**
WEB: www.br.midwaylabsusa.com
SIC: 2833 Medicinals & botanicals

(G-625)
MILANO WORLDWIDE CORP
222 W Yamato Rd Ste 106 (33431-4704)
PHONE..................................561 266-0201
Paula Kruger, *CEO*
Flavia Milano, *President*
▲ **EMP:** 5 **EST:** 2005
SQ FT: 900
SALES (est): 472.7K **Privately Held**
WEB: www.milanoworldwide.com
SIC: 3229 Art, decorative & novelty glassware

(G-626)
MISFIT GAMING
6401 Congress Ave (33487-2843)
PHONE..................................954 347-0906
Ben Spoont, *CEO*
EMP: 99 **EST:** 2016
SALES (est): 3.5MM **Privately Held**
SIC: 3944 Electronic game machines, except coin-operated

(G-627)
MMP-BOCA RATON LLC
Also Called: Nml
1609 Nw 2nd Ave (33432-1654)
PHONE..................................561 392-8626
Michael Orr,
EMP: 11 **EST:** 2008
SALES (est): 1.2MM **Privately Held**
WEB: www.b2bmailer.com
SIC: 2752 Commercial printing, offset

(G-628)
MOBILEHELP LLC (PA)
5050 Conference Way N # 125 (33431-4462)
PHONE..................................561 347-6285
Robert S Flippo, *CEO*
Dennis V Boyle, *President*
Elias Janetis, *Principal*
Scott H Adams, *Chairman*
Ellen Declaire, *Vice Pres*
▲ **EMP:** 70 **EST:** 2006
SQ FT: 45,000
SALES (est): 56.3MM **Privately Held**
WEB: www.mobilehelp.com
SIC: 3841 Biopsy instruments & equipment; diagnostic apparatus, medical; medical instruments & equipment, blood & bone work; instruments, microsurgical: except electromedical

(G-629)
MODERNIZING MEDICINE
Also Called: Gmed
4850 Network Way Ste 200 (33431)
PHONE..................................561 880-2998
Daniel Cane, *CEO*
Joe D Rubinsztain, *President*
Samuel Rubinsztain, *President*
Gabrielle Rubinsztain, *Corp Secy*
Samuel Flicki, *COO*
EMP: 125 **EST:** 1997
SQ FT: 7,500
SALES (est): 24.4MM
SALES (corp-wide): 118.4MM **Privately Held**
WEB: www.modmed.com
SIC: 7372 8099 Application computer software; medical services organization
PA: Modernizing Medicine, Inc.
4850 Network Way Ste 200
Boca Raton FL 33431
561 880-2998

(G-630)
MODERNIZING MEDICINE INC (PA)
4850 Network Way Ste 200 (33431)
PHONE..................................561 880-2998
Daniel Cane, *CEO*
Joe Harpaz, *President*
Patrick Deangelo, *Senior VP*
Nicki Anders, *Vice Pres*
Dan Dalton, *Vice Pres*
EMP: 398 **EST:** 2010
SALES (est): 118.4MM **Privately Held**
WEB: www.modmed.com
SIC: 7372 Application computer software

(G-631)
MONIER LIFETILE INC
135 Nw 20th St (33431-7901)
PHONE..................................561 338-8200
EMP: 7 **EST:** 2019
SALES (est): 178.7K **Privately Held**
SIC: 2952 Asphalt felts & coatings

(G-632)
MONIER LIFETILE LLC
2910 N Federal Hwy (33431-6702)
PHONE..................................561 338-8200
Michael Penny, *CEO*
EMP: 6 **EST:** 2018
SALES (est): 161.8K **Privately Held**
SIC: 2952 Asphalt felts & coatings

(G-633)
MULTITRODE INC
6560 E Rogers Cir (33487-2655)
PHONE..................................561 737-1210
Craig S Parkinson, *Principal*
EMP: 25 **EST:** 2019
SALES (est): 2.9MM **Publicly Held**
WEB: www.xylem.com
SIC: 3561 Pumps & pumping equipment
PA: Xylem Inc.
1 International Dr
Rye Brook NY 10573

(G-634)
N E D LLC
902 Clint Moore Rd # 206 (33487-2800)
PHONE..................................610 442-1017
Nick Riccione, *Principal*
EMP: 7 **EST:** 2010
SALES (est): 291.9K **Privately Held**
SIC: 3841 Surgical & medical instruments

(G-635)
NABI
5800 Pk Of Commerce Blvd (33487-8221)
PHONE..................................561 989-5800
Michael Ramroth, *Principal*
Mike Kulas, *Technician*
EMP: 14 **EST:** 2008
SALES (est): 2.1MM **Privately Held**
WEB: www.nabi-hb.com
SIC: 2834 Pharmaceutical preparations

(G-636)
NATURECITY LLC
990 S Rogers Cir Ste 11 (33487-2835)
PHONE..................................800 593-2563
Beth Giller, *Vice Pres*
Scott Greenberg, *Vice Pres*
Valerie Katzen, *Vice Pres*
Carl M Pradelli, *Mng Member*
Vincent Degiaimo, *Mng Member*
EMP: 9 **EST:** 2002
SALES (est): 1.7MM **Privately Held**
WEB: www.naturecity.com
SIC: 2023 Dietary supplements, dairy & non-dairy based

(G-637)
NAVINTA III INC
1003 Clint Moore Rd (33487-2826)
PHONE..................................561 997-6959
Mahendra Patel, *CEO*
EMP: 7 **EST:** 2016
SALES (est): 8MM **Privately Held**
WEB: www.navinta.com
SIC: 2834 Druggists' preparations (pharmaceuticals)

(G-638)
NEON & SIGN MFG INC
7870 Lago Del Mar Dr (33433-4910)
PHONE..................................443 664-6419
Avinoam Amram, *Principal*
EMP: 6 **EST:** 2005
SALES (est): 118.5K **Privately Held**
SIC: 3993 Signs & advertising specialties

(G-639)
NEURO PHARMALOGICS INC
901 Nw 35th St (33431-6410)
PHONE..................................240 476-4491
David Muth, *President*
Ken Dawson-Scully, *Director*
EMP: 5 **EST:** 2016
SQ FT: 2,000
SALES (est): 367.2K **Privately Held**
SIC: 2834 Pills, pharmaceutical

(G-640)
NEW SENTRY MARKETING INC
Also Called: CPD BOTTLING CLOSURE
878 Nafa Dr (33487-1739)
P.O. Box 189, Newtown PA (18940-0189)
PHONE..................................561 982-9599
Daniel Feldman, *President*
Sally Schultz, *Vice Pres*
EMP: 4 **EST:** 2012
SQ FT: 2,700
SALES: 5.6MM **Privately Held**
SIC: 3085 Plastics bottles

(G-641)
NEW WORLD GOLD CORPORATION (PA)
Also Called: Nwgc
350 Cmino Grdns Blvd Ste (33432)
PHONE..................................561 962-4139
Robert J Honigford, *CEO*
Robert Talbot, *President*
EMP: 61 **EST:** 2008
SALES (est): 8.5MM **Privately Held**
SIC: 1041 Gold ores processing

(G-642)
NEW WORLD HOLDINGS INC
Also Called: New World Medicinals
1080 Holland Dr Ste 1 (33487-2782)
PHONE..................................561 888-4939
Michelle Larkin, *CEO*
Alan Sporn, *CFO*
EMP: 50 **EST:** 2017
SALES (est): 5.8MM **Privately Held**
SIC: 2834 6719 3829 5047 Pharmaceutical preparations; holding companies; medical diagnostic systems, nuclear; medical equipment & supplies; medical instruments & equipment, blood & bone work

(G-643)
NEWBEAUTY MEDIA GROUP LLC
Also Called: Newbeauty Media Group, Lllp
3651 Nw 8th Ave Ste 400 (33431-6489)
PHONE..................................561 961-7600
Adam Sandow, *CEO*
Anna Jimenez, *Editor*
Nicole Wieder, *Business Mgr*
Jennifer Jackolin, *Opers Mgr*
Keith Clements, *Opers Staff*
EMP: 50 **EST:** 2004
SQ FT: 30,000
SALES (est): 16MM
SALES (corp-wide): 106.7MM **Privately Held**
WEB: www.sandow.com
SIC: 2759 5122 Publication printing; cosmetics
PA: Sandow Media, Llc
3651 Nw 8th Ave Ste 200
Boca Raton FL 33431
561 961-7749

(G-644)
NICOLETTE MAYER COLLECTION INC
3750 Ne 6th Dr (33431-6114)
PHONE..................................561 241-6906
Nicolette D Mayer, *President*
Jonathan Ostrow, *CFO*
Richard Barnes, *CIO*
◆ **EMP:** 7 **EST:** 2012
SALES (est): 837.5K **Privately Held**
WEB: www.nicolettemayer.com
SIC: 2679 Wallpaper

(G-645)
NOBLE WOODWORKS INC
22053 Palms Way Apt 106 (33433-8013)
PHONE..................................561 702-2889
Matthew Braun, *Principal*
EMP: 6 **EST:** 2008
SALES (est): 150.7K **Privately Held**
SIC: 2431 Millwork

(G-646)
NOELL DESIGN GROUP INC
1050 Nw 1st Ave Ste 16 (33432-2603)
PHONE..................................561 391-9942
Mark Noell, *President*
EMP: 6 **EST:** 1995
SQ FT: 18,000
SALES (est): 570.6K **Privately Held**
WEB: www.noelldesigngroup.com
SIC: 2511 Wood household furniture

(G-647)
NORDIC GROUP LLC (PA)
2220 Sw 11th Pl (33486-8511)
PHONE..................................561 789-8676
Kai A Makela, *Manager*
EMP: 34 **EST:** 2015
SALES (est): 665.6K **Privately Held**
WEB: www.nordicgrp.com
SIC: 2339 Women's & misses' outerwear

(G-648)
NORDIC LINE INC (PA)
Also Called: Design NS Leather Furniture
1080 Nw 1st Ave (33432-2608)
PHONE..................................561 338-5545
Aki Makela, *President*
Kai Makela, *Vice Pres*
William Cetz, *Sales Mgr*
Vesa Maenanttila, *Manager*
▲ **EMP:** 34 **EST:** 1993
SQ FT: 25,000
SALES (est): 3.2MM **Privately Held**
WEB: www.designns.com
SIC: 2512 5021 Upholstered household furniture; furniture

(G-649)
NOSTALGIC AMERICA INC
102 Ne 2nd St Ste 172 (33432-3908)
P.O. Box 5188, Carefree AZ (85377-5188)
PHONE..................................561 585-1724
Marcia M Berns, *President*
EMP: 10 **EST:** 2001
SALES (est): 610.5K **Privately Held**
WEB: www.nostalgicamerica.com
SIC: 2721 Magazines: publishing only, not printed on site

(G-650)
NOSTALGIC SPECIALTY FOODS INC
399 S Federal Hwy (33432-6025)
PHONE..................................561 391-8600
Leonard Felberbaum, *President*
EMP: 6 **EST:** 1996
SQ FT: 5,000
SALES (est): 427.6K **Privately Held**
SIC: 2051 Bread, cake & related products

(G-651)
NOVAVISION INC (HQ)
951 Broken Sound Pkwy Nw # 320 (33487-3531)
PHONE.................................561 558-2020
David Cantor, *President*
Pam Beidleman, *Controller*
Diana Castillo, *Accountant*
Nicole Inman, *Marketing Staff*
Jose Romano, *Director*
EMP: 10 **EST:** 2010
SQ FT: 3,000
SALES (est): 1.1MM **Publicly Held**
WEB: www.novavision.com
SIC: 3841 Surgical & medical instruments
PA: Vycor Medical, Inc.
951 Broken Sound Pkwy Nw # 320
Boca Raton FL 33487
561 558-2020

(G-652)
OAKBROOK SALES INC
2200 Butts Rd Ste 200 (33431-7451)
PHONE.................................800 773-0979
Al Eder, *Treasurer*
EMP: 12 **EST:** 1996
SALES (est): 179.7K **Privately Held**
SIC: 2099 Food preparations

(G-653)
OLLIE PIPPA INTERNATIONAL INC
Also Called: Plantogen Skin Care
21733 Old Bridge Trl (33428-2847)
P.O. Box 970215 (33497-0215)
PHONE.................................888 851-6533
Elda Argenti, *President*
▲ **EMP:** 5 **EST:** 2003
SALES (est): 323K **Privately Held**
WEB: www.plantogen.com
SIC: 2844 Cosmetic preparations

(G-654)
OMEGA ONE RESEARCH INC
6458 E Rogers Cir (33487-2653)
PHONE.................................561 995-9611
Carole Hersch, *President*
EMP: 5 **EST:** 2000
SALES (est): 1MM **Privately Held**
WEB: www.omegaoneresearch.com
SIC: 3545 Precision tools, machinists'

(G-655)
OPTOELECTRONICS INC
160 W Camino Real (33432-5942)
PHONE.................................954 642-8997
Linda Hufft, *President*
EMP: 14 **EST:** 1974
SQ FT: 13,000
SALES (est): 550.3K **Privately Held**
WEB: www.optoelectronics.com
SIC: 3825 3823 Test equipment for electronic & electrical circuits; industrial instrmnts msrmnt display/control process variable

(G-656)
OSI INTERNATIONAL LLC
164 W Royal Palm Rd (33432-3830)
PHONE.................................561 394-9508
EMP: 6 **EST:** 2019
SALES (est): 209.9K **Privately Held**
WEB: www.osiinternational.com
SIC: 3663 Radio & TV communications equipment

(G-657)
OSMI INC (PA)
7777 Glades Rd Ste 200 (33434-4150)
PHONE.................................561 330-9300
Bernard Mintz, *CEO*
David Mintz, *President*
Neil Mintz, *COO*
Ted Hagberg, *VP Bus Dvlpt*
Perry Slaughter, *Sales Mgr*
◆ **EMP:** 11 **EST:** 1990
SQ FT: 80,000
SALES (est): 13.2MM **Privately Held**
SIC: 3297 Nonclay refractories

(G-658)
OTTICA DANTE AMERICAS LLC
10890 Haydn Dr (33498-6750)
PHONE.................................561 322-0186
Massimo Armiraglio,
Laura Ferrario,
Fabio Massetta,
EMP: 8 **EST:** 2014
SALES (est): 286.4K **Privately Held**
WEB: www.otticadante.com
SIC: 3851 7389 Frames & parts, eyeglass & spectacle; business services

(G-659)
PACIFIC COAST FEATHER LLC (PA)
901 W Yamato Rd Ste 250 (33431-4415)
PHONE.................................206 624-1057
Alex Blanco, *Vice Pres*
Scott Carlson, *Vice Pres*
Pedro Pena, *Plant Mgr*
James Elnathan, *Opers Staff*
Elana Aberge, *VP Finance*
◆ **EMP:** 150
SALES (est): 257MM **Privately Held**
WEB: www.pacificcoast.com
SIC: 2392 Cushions & pillows; comforters & quilts: made from purchased materials

(G-660)
PALLET HOLDINGS LLC (PA)
1200 N Federal Hwy # 207 (33432-2803)
PHONE.................................561 367-0009
Marc Steinberg,
David Davidson,
EMP: 65 **EST:** 2003
SALES (est): 8.6MM **Privately Held**
SIC: 2448 Wood pallets & skids

(G-661)
PARAFLOW ENERGY SOLUTIONS LLC
6501 Congress Ave Ste 100 (33487-2840)
PHONE.................................713 239-0336
Jeff Edwards, *President*
EMP: 25 **EST:** 2015
SALES (est): 2.6MM
SALES (corp-wide): 25.9MM **Privately Held**
SIC: 2843 Surface active agents; emulsifiers, except food & pharmaceutical
PA: Verdant Specialty Solutions Us Llc
24601 Governors Hwy
University Park IL 60484
708 259-1364

(G-662)
PARAMOUNT ELECTRONIC MFG CO
Also Called: Pemco
1551 Sw 6th Ter (33486-7005)
PHONE.................................954 781-3755
Michael De Grandchamp, *President*
EMP: 25 **EST:** 1982
SALES (est): 226.1K
SALES (corp-wide): 4.9MM **Privately Held**
WEB: www.iwdesigners.com
SIC: 3679 Harness assemblies for electronic use: wire or cable
PA: Paramount Industries Inc
1020 Sw 10th Ave Ste 6
Pompano Beach FL 33069
954 781-3755

(G-663)
PARIS INK INC
Also Called: Speedpro Imaging
1020 Holland Dr Ste 119 (33487-5719)
PHONE.................................561 990-1194
Daniel J Paris, *President*
Nathaniel Paris, *Principal*
EMP: 8 **EST:** 2017
SALES (est): 267.1K **Privately Held**
WEB: www.speedpro.com
SIC: 2759 Posters, including billboards: printing

(G-664)
PHOENIX MEDIA NETWORK INC
Also Called: Produce Business Magazine
6531 Pk Of Commerce Blvd (33487-8299)
P.O. Box 810425 (33481-0425)
PHONE.................................561 994-1118
Jim Prevor, *CEO*
Eric Nieman, *Publisher*
Jim Bartelson, *Vice Pres*
Lee Smith, *Vice Pres*
Kate Grace, *Marketing Staff*
EMP: 20 **EST:** 1993
SALES (est): 3.1MM **Privately Held**
WEB: www.phoenixmedianet.com
SIC: 2721 Magazines: publishing only, not printed on site

(G-665)
PIVOTAL THERAPEUTICS US INC
3651 Fau Blvd Ste 400 (33431-6489)
PHONE.................................905 856-9797
Eugene Bortoluzzi, *CEO*
Rachelle Macsweeney, *President*
EMP: 16 **EST:** 2010
SQ FT: 900
SALES (est): 219.6K **Privately Held**
WEB: www.pivotaltherapeutics.us
SIC: 2834 Vitamin, nutrient & hematinic preparations for human use

(G-666)
PIZZA SPICE PACKET LLC
Also Called: Pizza Packet
170 Ne 2nd St Unit 491 (33429-5020)
PHONE.................................718 831-7036
Itchie Gross, *President*
Richard Gross, *Production*
EMP: 7 **EST:** 2009
SALES (est): 496.2K **Privately Held**
WEB: www.pizzapacket.com
SIC: 2038 5142 5411 5812 Pizza, frozen; packaged frozen goods; frozen food & freezer plans, except meat; pizza restaurants

(G-667)
PLUSHBEDS INC
17076 Boca Club Blvd # 4 (33487-1293)
PHONE.................................888 449-5738
Michael Hughes, *Branch Mgr*
EMP: 7 **Privately Held**
SIC: 2515 5712 Mattresses & bedsprings; mattresses
PA: Plushbeds, Inc
5603 Grey Feather Ct
Westlake Village CA

(G-668)
POLY PLASTIC PACKAGING CO INC
Also Called: Polyplastics
18800 Long Lake Dr (33496-1975)
PHONE.................................561 498-9040
EMP: 25 **EST:** 1951
SQ FT: 20,000
SALES (est): 4.1MM **Privately Held**
SIC: 2673 Mfg Bags-Plastic/Coated Paper

(G-669)
POSH CABINETS
9640 Parkview Ave (33428-2916)
PHONE.................................954 444-5441
EMP: 6 **EST:** 2013
SALES (est): 245.3K **Privately Held**
WEB: www.poshcabinets.com
SIC: 2434 Wood kitchen cabinets

(G-670)
POWER POINT GRAPHICS INC
19528 Sedgefield Ter (33498-4643)
PHONE.................................561 351-5599
Leonard Rosenthal, *President*
EMP: 6 **EST:** 1997
SALES (est): 447.9K **Privately Held**
SIC: 2759 7389 Commercial printing; printing broker

(G-671)
PRACTICAL DESIGN PRODUCTS CO
Also Called: P D P
1101 Holland Dr (33487-2762)
PHONE.................................561 995-4023
Jason Bator, *President*
▲ **EMP:** 29 **EST:** 1993
SQ FT: 4,000
SALES (est): 649.4K **Privately Held**
SIC: 3429 Manufactured hardware (general)

(G-672)
PRECISION TURBINES INC (PA)
4710 Nw Boca Raton Blvd (33431-4879)
PHONE.................................561 447-0751
Robert L Spahr, *President*
Susannah Forbes, *Human Resources*
Paul Capes, *Program Mgr*
EMP: 9 **EST:** 2007
SQ FT: 300
SALES (est): 1MM **Privately Held**
WEB: www.precisionturbines.aero
SIC: 3724 Aircraft engines & engine parts

(G-673)
PREMIER PUBLISHING INC
3350 Nw 2nd Ave Ste B38 (33431-6682)
PHONE.................................561 394-9066
EMP: 6 **EST:** 2018
SALES (est): 236.2K **Privately Held**
WEB: www.premierpubinc.com
SIC: 2741 Miscellaneous publishing

(G-674)
PRETTY VULGAR LLC
1141 S Rogers Cir Ste 7 (33487-2789)
PHONE.................................561 465-8831
Katherine Garcia, *Manager*
Lewis Farsedakis,
EMP: 9 **EST:** 2015
SALES (est): 946.6K **Privately Held**
WEB: www.prettyvulgar.com
SIC: 2844 Toilet preparations

(G-675)
PRIVE PORTER LLC
980 N Federal Hwy (33432-2708)
PHONE.................................561 479-9200
Michelle Berk, *Principal*
EMP: 8 **EST:** 2013
SALES (est): 328.8K **Privately Held**
WEB: www.priveporter.com
SIC: 2323 Men's & boys' neckwear

(G-676)
PROJECT MOLD
7666 Cypress Cres (33433-4109)
PHONE.................................561 213-6167
Zev Argov, *Principal*
EMP: 8 **EST:** 2017
SALES (est): 133.8K **Privately Held**
SIC: 3544 Industrial molds

(G-677)
PYROLYZER LLC
750 Ne Spanish River Blvd (33431-6160)
PHONE.................................561 400-1608
Franklin D Canterbury Jr, *Manager*
Franklin Canterbury,
◆ **EMP:** 6 **EST:** 2008
SQ FT: 2,400
SALES (est): 271.8K **Privately Held**
WEB: www.pyrolyzerllc.com
SIC: 1321 Ethane (natural) production

(G-678)
QUARTZ UNLIMITED INC
2255 Glades Rd Ste 324 (33431-8571)
P.O. Box 62019, Sunnyvale CA (94088-2019)
PHONE.................................561 720-7460
Ferenc Ledniczky, *President*
Victoria Gaffney, *Vice Pres*
EMP: 29 **EST:** 1996
SQ FT: 6,000
SALES (est): 370.4K **Privately Held**
SIC: 3679 Quartz crystals, for electronic application

(G-679)
QUARTZ UNLIMITED LLC
5030 Champion Blvd (33496-2473)
PHONE.................................561 306-1243
Ferenc Ledniczky, *Principal*
EMP: 6 **EST:** 2011
SALES (est): 364.3K **Privately Held**
WEB: www.quartzunlimited.com
SIC: 3674 Semiconductors & related devices

(G-680)
RANCHERITOS
8903 Glades Rd Ste A10 (33434-4023)
PHONE.................................561 479-0046
Juan G Maya, *Principal*
EMP: 5 **EST:** 2010
SALES (est): 399.9K **Privately Held**
WEB: www.rancheritosdeboca.com
SIC: 2032 Mexican foods: packaged in cans, jars, etc.

(G-681)
RAYTASH INC (PA)
Also Called: New Choices
1420 Sw 1st St (33486-4470)
PHONE..................................561 347-8863
Ray Tashman, *President*
Myra Tashman, *Vice Pres*
Mona Tashman, *Treasurer*
◆ **EMP:** 5 **EST:** 1982
SALES (est): 431.7K **Privately Held**
SIC: 2511 5021 Wood household furniture; restaurant furniture

(G-682)
RDD INTERNATIONAL INC
301 Ne 51st St Ste 1240 (33431-4931)
PHONE..................................954 422-9909
Andre Serra, *Principal*
EMP: 6 **EST:** 2007
SALES (est): 167.6K **Privately Held**
SIC: 3944 Go-carts, children's

(G-683)
REAL-TIME LABORATORIES LLC (DH)
990 S Rogers Cir Ste 5 (33487-2836)
PHONE..................................561 988-8826
Kevin Sigurdsen, *Engineer*
Cletus Glasener, *Treasurer*
Robert Knabe, *Mng Member*
Thomas Tracy, *Contract Mgr*
Chris Puffer, *Admin Sec*
▲ **EMP:** 53 **EST:** 1979
SQ FT: 20,000
SALES (est): 10.4MM
SALES (corp-wide): 4.6B **Privately Held**
WEB: www.real-timelabs.com
SIC: 3823 Fluidic devices, circuits & systems for process control

(G-684)
REALM LABS LLC
7700 Congress Ave # 3110 (33487-1357)
PHONE..................................561 549-9099
Richard Mann, *Managing Dir*
Annetta Leggett, *Opers Staff*
Andreia Solett, *Accounts Mgr*
Margo Brown,
EMP: 11 **EST:** 2006
SALES (est): 2.6MM **Privately Held**
WEB: www.realmlabs.net
SIC: 2834 Vitamin, nutrient & hematinic preparations for human use

(G-685)
RECREATIONAL SCREEN PRINTING
707 E Palmetto Park Rd (33432-5103)
PHONE..................................561 757-5479
EMP: 6 **EST:** 2015
SALES (est): 140.6K **Privately Held**
SIC: 2759 Screen printing

(G-686)
RED HAWK INDUSTRIES LLC
5100 Town Center Cir # 350 (33486-1037)
PHONE..................................303 779-6272
Nadja Pritchard, *Controller*
Lemay Craig, *Office Admin*
Jeraldine Sulkoski, *Director*
EMP: 8 **EST:** 2017
SALES (est): 240.4K **Privately Held**
WEB: www.adt.com
SIC: 3999 Manufacturing industries

(G-687)
REHYDRADE LLC
Also Called: Dont Fade Rehydrade
131 S Federal Hwy Apt 418 (33432-4949)
PHONE..................................561 419-5656
Zachary Gottfried, *CEO*
Jill Gottfried, *Vice Pres*
EMP: 6 **EST:** 2012
SQ FT: 5,000
SALES (est): 124K **Privately Held**
SIC: 2087 Concentrates, drink

(G-688)
RESERVEAGE
4800 T Rex Ave (33431-4479)
PHONE..................................561 443-5301
Naomi Widdle, *Owner*
Mindy Paris, *VP Sls/Mktg*
Yamit Sadok, *Mktg Dir*
Jamie Oberweger, *Marketing Staff*
James Johnson, *Manager*
▲ **EMP:** 11
SALES (est): 996.9K **Privately Held**
WEB: www.reserveage.tlcchealth.com
SIC: 2834 Pharmaceutical preparations

(G-689)
RJ CAPITAL INC
2200 Glades Rd Ste 305b (33431-7348)
PHONE..................................561 208-7444
Michele Wood, *Branch Mgr*
EMP: 10
SALES (corp-wide): 32.3MM **Privately Held**
WEB: www.idealimage.com
SIC: 3821 Laser beam alignment devices
PA: Rj Capital, Inc
4830 W Kennedy Blvd # 44
Tampa FL 33609
813 289-2500

(G-690)
RM IMAGING INCORPORATED
2499 Glades Rd Ste 206 (33431-7201)
PHONE..................................561 361-8090
Rachael Magro, *President*
Joseph Aucello, *Exec Officer*
Jeffrey Nurge, *Exec Officer*
Elias Robert, *Med Doctor*
EMP: 26 **EST:** 1994
SALES (est): 1MM **Privately Held**
SIC: 3841 8071 Diagnostic apparatus, medical; medical laboratories

(G-691)
RMM CABINETS LLC
1616 Nw 2nd Ave (33432-1655)
PHONE..................................954 588-6353
Shlomo Levi, *Principal*
EMP: 6 **EST:** 2013
SALES (est): 228.6K **Privately Held**
WEB: www.rmmcabinets.com
SIC: 2434 Wood kitchen cabinets

(G-692)
ROCKET VENDING INC
Also Called: Vending Company
19234 S Creekshore Ct (33498-6217)
P.O. Box 970724, Coconut Creek (33097-0724)
PHONE..................................561 672-1373
Michael Fischer, *CEO*
Dori Mirkow, *Vice Pres*
EMP: 10 **EST:** 2007
SALES (est): 703.8K **Privately Held**
WEB: www.domain-for-sale.vereo.com
SIC: 3581 Automatic vending machines

(G-693)
ROKEY CORPORATION
18188 Blue Lake Way (33498-1936)
PHONE..................................561 470-0164
EMP: 5
SALES: 3MM **Privately Held**
SIC: 3429 5199 5961 Mfg /Whol/Ret General Merchandise

(G-694)
ROYAL CROWN DEVELOPERS LLC
9880 Marina Blvd Apt 1513 (33428-6672)
PHONE..................................561 305-4588
Frank Spaziano, *Manager*
EMP: 6 **EST:** 2007
SALES (est): 86.8K **Privately Held**
SIC: 2086 Soft drinks: packaged in cans, bottles, etc.

(G-695)
RUBINELLI WOODWORK INC
8891 Sw 16th St (33433-7966)
PHONE..................................954 445-0537
Paulo Alves, *Principal*
EMP: 8 **EST:** 2007
SALES (est): 82.1K **Privately Held**
SIC: 2431 Millwork

(G-696)
S M D RESEARCH INC
9151 Pine Springs Dr (33428-1458)
PHONE..................................561 451-9895
Stuart P Oakner, *President*
Mark T Brannick, *Treasurer*
▲ **EMP:** 7 **EST:** 1997
SQ FT: 2,000
SALES (est): 275.3K **Privately Held**
SIC: 2899 Chemical preparations

(G-697)
SAFCO SOFTWARE
7654 Solimar Cir (33433-1035)
PHONE..................................561 750-7879
Steven A Fellman, *Principal*
EMP: 6 **EST:** 2010
SALES (est): 105.4K **Privately Held**
WEB: www.gosafco.com
SIC: 7372 Prepackaged software

(G-698)
SAFETEK INTERNATIONAL INC (PA)
6560 W Rogers Cir (33487-2746)
PHONE..................................702 558-8202
Shmuel Shneibalg, *CEO*
Stefan Gudmundsson, *CFO*
EMP: 5 **EST:** 1988
SALES (est): 925.9K **Privately Held**
WEB: www.safetekinternational.com
SIC: 3569 Filters

(G-699)
SANDOW MEDIA LLC
3651 Fau Blvd Ste 200 (33431-6489)
PHONE..................................646 805-0200
Juan Lopez, *Exec VP*
Nicholas Wright, *Exec VP*
Janice Browne, *Vice Pres*
Pamela Jaccarino, *Vice Pres*
Pamela McNally, *Vice Pres*
EMP: 10
SALES (corp-wide): 106.7MM **Privately Held**
WEB: www.sandow.com
SIC: 2721 Magazines: publishing only, not printed on site
PA: Sandow Media, Llc
3651 Nw 8th Ave Ste 200
Boca Raton FL 33431
561 961-7749

(G-700)
SANDOW MEDIA LLC (PA)
Also Called: Sandow Media-Airport Linehaul
3651 Nw 8th Ave Ste 200 (33431-6489)
PHONE..................................561 961-7749
Adam I Sandow, *CEO*
Paul Blum, *CEO*
James Dimonekas, *President*
Erica Holborn, *President*
John Gallo, *Publisher*
▲ **EMP:** 100 **EST:** 2002
SQ FT: 15,000
SALES (est): 106.7MM **Privately Held**
WEB: www.sandow.com
SIC: 2721 Magazines: publishing only, not printed on site

(G-701)
SANOMEDICS INC (PA)
7777 Glades Rd Ste 100 (33434-4150)
PHONE..................................305 433-7814
William Lerner, *Ch of Bd*
David C Langle, *President*
Gary J O'Hara, *CTO*
EMP: 3 **EST:** 1938
SQ FT: 1,200
SALES (est): 5.1MM **Publicly Held**
SIC: 3829 Thermometers, including digital: clinical

(G-702)
SARGEANT MARINE INC
3020 N Military Trl # 100 (33431-1805)
PHONE..................................561 999-9916
Harry J Sargeant, *Ch of Bd*
Daniel Sargeant, *President*
Janet Sargeant, *Corp Secy*
James Sargeant, *Vice Pres*
Suzzane Ghantous, *Bookkeeper*
◆ **EMP:** 15 **EST:** 1984
SALES (est): 2.8MM **Privately Held**
WEB: www.sargeantmarine.com
SIC: 3089 Plastic boats & other marine equipment

(G-703)
SCP COMMERCIAL PRINTING
1100 Holland Dr (33487-2701)
PHONE..................................561 998-0870
Elliot Goldstein, *CEO*
EMP: 9 **EST:** 2000
SALES (est): 162.2K **Privately Held**
WEB: www.scpprinting.com
SIC: 2759 Commercial printing

(G-704)
SENSORMATIC ELECTRONICS LLC
6600 Congress Ave 1b (33487-1213)
PHONE..................................561 912-6000
EMP: 6 **Publicly Held**
WEB: www.sensormatic.com
SIC: 3812 Search & navigation equipment
HQ: Sensormatic Electronics, Llc
6600 Congress Ave
Boca Raton FL 33487
561 912-6000

(G-705)
SENSUS HEALTHCARE INC
851 Broken Sound Pkwy Nw (33487-3616)
PHONE..................................561 922-5808
Joseph C Sardano, *Ch of Bd*
Kalman Fishman, *COO*
Richard Golin, *Exec VP*
Stephen Cohen, *Vice Pres*
Hoi-Bun Suen, *Vice Pres*
EMP: 45 **EST:** 2010
SQ FT: 8,926
SALES: 9.5MM **Privately Held**
WEB: www.sensushealthcare.com
SIC: 3841 Skin grafting equipment

(G-706)
SEP COMMUNICATIONS LLC
Also Called: Make A Statement Gifts
6001 Park Of Commerce Blv (33487-8234)
PHONE..................................561 998-0870
Marty Harris, *Principal*
EMP: 10 **EST:** 2014
SALES (est): 1.4MM **Privately Held**
WEB: www.sepcommunications.com
SIC: 3993 2721 2711 7374 Signs & advertising specialties; periodicals: publishing & printing; commercial printing & newspaper publishing combined; computer graphics service

(G-707)
SFBC LLC
Also Called: Seaboard Folding Box Company
7035 Queenferry Cir (33496-5948)
PHONE..................................978 342-8921
Christopher Morgan, *Vice Pres*
Kevin Trainor, *Vice Pres*
James Alansky, *Purchasing*
William Gentes, *CFO*
Cynthia Lore, *Asst Controller*
EMP: 31 **EST:** 2006
SQ FT: 260,000
SALES (est): 3.4MM **Privately Held**
SIC: 2653 Boxes, corrugated: made from purchased materials

(G-708)
SHILPICO INC
22360 Sands Point Dr (33433-6266)
PHONE..................................561 306-5625
Ravi Shankar, *President*
EMP: 5
SALES (est): 374.5K **Privately Held**
SIC: 3433 Boilers, low-pressure heating: steam or hot water

(G-709)
SHORES AUTOMOTIVE
2544 Nw 2nd Ave (33431-6643)
PHONE..................................561 391-0260
Billy Craven, *Owner*
EMP: 5 **EST:** 2012
SALES (est): 347.4K **Privately Held**
WEB: www.shoresautomotive.com
SIC: 3599 Industrial machinery

(G-710)
SIGNATURE COMPUTER SVCS INC
7040 W Palmetto Park Rd (33433-3411)
PHONE..................................954 421-0950
Scott Gutman, *President*
Vincent C Timphony, *Marketing Staff*
EMP: 9 **EST:** 1999
SQ FT: 1,600
SALES (est): 1.3MM **Privately Held**
WEB: www.signaturecomputer.com
SIC: 3577 Computer peripheral equipment

(G-711)
SIGNIFICANT SOLUTIONS CORP
Also Called: Ai-R.com Got-Leads.com
3003 W Yamato Rd Ste C8 (33434-5337)
PHONE..................................561 703-7703
Christopher Singer, *President*
◆ **EMP:** 8 **EST:** 1993
SQ FT: 2,000
SALES (est): 151.7K **Privately Held**
WEB: www.got-profits.com
SIC: 3999 Novelties, bric-a-brac & hobby kits

(G-712)
SIGNSATIONS INC
5425 N Dixie Hwy Ste 2 (33487-4923)
PHONE..................................561 989-1900
Jack Glover, *President*
Mincy Kien, *Principal*
Roslyn Zimmerman, *Vice Pres*
Jodi Zimmerman, *Treasurer*
EMP: 5 **EST:** 1994
SQ FT: 1,000
SALES (est): 411.7K **Privately Held**
WEB: www.signsations.com
SIC: 3993 7374 Signs & advertising specialties; computer graphics service

(G-713)
SILVERSTAR HOLDINGS LTD (PA)
1900 Glades Rd Ste 265 (33431-8548)
PHONE..................................561 479-0040
Clive Kabatznik, *CEO*
Michael Levy, *Ch of Bd*
Lawrence R Litowitz, *CFO*
Edward L Bernstein, *Director*
Edward Roffman, *Director*
EMP: 2 **EST:** 1995
SQ FT: 1,200
SALES (est): 19.7MM **Privately Held**
WEB: www.silverstarholdings.com
SIC: 7372 Home entertainment computer software

(G-714)
SIMON AND BAKER INC
2901 Clint Moore Rd (33496-2041)
PHONE..................................561 892-0494
Gary Cox, *Principal*
EMP: 6 **EST:** 2008
SALES (est): 82.3K **Privately Held**
WEB: www.poyeen.com
SIC: 2741 Miscellaneous publishing

(G-715)
SIMPLEX TIME RECORDER CO
1501 Nw 51st St (33431-4438)
PHONE..................................561 988-7200
Robert F Chauvin, *Principal*
EMP: 1 **EST:** 2000
SALES (est): 5.5MM **Publicly Held**
WEB: www.simplex-fire.com
SIC: 3669 Emergency alarms
HQ: Johnson Controls Fire Protection Lp
6600 Congress Ave
Boca Raton FL 33487
561 988-7200

(G-716)
SIMPLEXGRINNELL HOLDINGS LLC (DH)
1501 Nw 51st St (33431-4438)
PHONE..................................978 731-2500
James Spicer, *President*
Keith McKinney, *District Mgr*
Terry Reiter, *Opers Mgr*
Steven Kelly, *Project Engr*
Monique Pointer, *VP Human Res*
EMP: 3 **EST:** 1999
SQ FT: 16,000
SALES (est): 2.1B **Publicly Held**
WEB: www.tycosimplexgrinnell.com
SIC: 3579 3669 3699 3822 Time clocks & time recording devices; fire detection systems, electric; security control equipment & systems; thermostats & other environmental sensors
HQ: Tyco International Management Company, Llc
9 Roszel Rd Ste 2
Princeton NJ 08540
609 720-4200

(G-717)
SIMPLICITY ESPORTS LLC
7000 W Plmtt Prk Rd Ste 5 (33433-3424)
PHONE..................................855 345-9467
Jed Kaplan, *CEO*
EMP: 14 **EST:** 2017
SQ FT: 250
SALES (est): 1.1MM
SALES (corp-wide): 1.5MM **Privately Held**
WEB: www.ggsimplicity.com
SIC: 7372 Application computer software
PA: Simplicity Esports And Gaming Company
7000 W Plmtt Prk Rd Ste 5
Boca Raton FL 33433
855 345-9467

(G-718)
SIRS PUBLISHING INC (DH)
Also Called: Sirs Commercial Print
5201 Congress Ave Ste 250 (33487-3601)
PHONE..................................800 521-0600
Fax: 561 995-4065
▲ **EMP:** 98
SQ FT: 50,000
SALES (est): 5.2MM **Publicly Held**
SIC: 2731 2752 2741 Books-Publishing/Printing Lithographic Commercial Printing Misc Publishing
HQ: Voyager Learning Company
17855 Dallas Pkwy Ste 400
Dallas TX 75287
214 932-9500

(G-719)
SJOSTROM INDUSTRIES INC
Also Called: Sjostrom Electronics
1400 Nw 9th Ave Apt 1 (33486-1324)
PHONE..................................561 368-2000
David K Evans, *President*
EMP: 10 **EST:** 1975
SQ FT: 1,000
SALES (est): 679.7K **Privately Held**
SIC: 3825 Digital test equipment, electronic & electrical circuits

(G-720)
SLEEPRITE INDUSTRIES INC
Also Called: Restonic/San Francisco
7087 Mandarin Dr (33433-7411)
P.O. Box 814, Burlingame CA (94011-0710)
PHONE..................................650 344-1980
Jeffrey S Karp, *President*
Elaine Karp, *Corp Secy*
Randall H Karp, *Vice Pres*
▼ **EMP:** 25 **EST:** 1968
SALES (est): 3.8MM **Privately Held**
SIC: 2515 Mattresses, containing felt, foam rubber, urethane, etc.; mattresses, innerspring or box spring

(G-721)
SMARTMATIC CORPORATION (DH)
1001 Broken Sound Pkwy Nw D (33487-3532)
PHONE..................................561 862-0747
Antonio Mugica, *CEO*
Keith Stringfellow, *President*
David Melville, *Principal*
Roger Pinate, *COO*
Paul Babic, *Vice Pres*
▲ **EMP:** 10 **EST:** 2000
SQ FT: 10,000
SALES (est): 38.1MM
SALES (corp-wide): 144MM **Privately Held**
WEB: www.smartmatic.com
SIC: 3571 3579 7372 Electronic computers; voting machines; prepackaged software
HQ: Smartmatic International Holding B.V.
Gustav Mahlerplein 25 C
Amsterdam
207 940-817

(G-722)
SOTA MANUFACTURING INC (PA)
1561 Sw 6th Ave (33486-7001)
PHONE..................................561 368-8007
Noel Gonzales, *CEO*
Brian Burke, *Principal*
EMP: 25 **EST:** 2012
SALES (est): 3MM **Privately Held**
SIC: 3812 3841 3825 Aircraft/aerospace flight instruments & guidance systems; diagnostic apparatus, medical; electrical energy measuring equipment

(G-723)
SOUTHEAST ENERGY INC
23257 State Road 7 # 107 (33428-5448)
PHONE..................................561 883-1051
EMP: 8
SALES: 1MM **Privately Held**
SIC: 2899 5714 1793 Chemical Preparations, Nec, Nsk

(G-724)
SOUTHEAST WOODCRAFTERS INC
1566 Nw 1st Ave (33432-1706)
PHONE..................................561 392-2929
Timothy J Clemmons, *President*
▼ **EMP:** 15 **EST:** 2003
SALES (est): 647.3K **Privately Held**
WEB: www.sewoodcrafters.com
SIC: 2434 Wood kitchen cabinets

(G-725)
SOX LLC
Also Called: Sox Erosion Solutions
950 Pnnsula Corp Cir Ste (33487)
PHONE..................................561 501-0057
Brian Fischer, *Mng Member*
Ryan Leeds,
EMP: 5 **EST:** 2017
SALES (est): 503.8K **Privately Held**
WEB: www.soxerosion.com
SIC: 3999 Permanent wave equipment & machines

(G-726)
SPERANZA THERAPEUTICS CORP
433 Plaza Real Ste 275 (33432-3999)
PHONE..................................844 477-3726
EMP: 7
SALES (est): 277.8K **Privately Held**
SIC: 3841 Surgical & medical instruments

(G-727)
SPETT PRINTING CO INC
Also Called: Egmont Press
4115 Georges Way (33434-5345)
PHONE..................................561 241-9758
Michael Spett, *President*
Lizzie Spett, *Treasurer*
EMP: 5 **EST:** 1941
SQ FT: 1,000
SALES (est): 368.5K **Privately Held**
SIC: 2752 2759 Commercial printing, offset; letterpress printing

(G-728)
SPINNAKER HOLDING COMPANY
Also Called: Minuteman Press
1609 Nw 2nd Ave (33432-1654)
PHONE..................................561 392-8626
Steven Brunk, *President*
Carlene Brunk, *Corp Secy*
Michael Kochersperger, *Graphic Designe*
Israel Salcedo, *Graphic Designe*
EMP: 35 **EST:** 1976
SQ FT: 7,000
SALES (est): 3.2MM **Privately Held**
WEB: www.bocaraton.minutemanpress.com
SIC: 2752 2791 2789 Commercial printing, lithographic; typesetting; bookbinding & related work

(G-729)
STADSON TECHNOLOGY CORPORATION
3651 Fau Blvd Ste 400 (33431-6489)
PHONE..................................561 372-2648
EMP: 24
SALES (corp-wide): 1.2MM **Privately Held**
SIC: 7372 Application Software
PA: Stadson Technology Corporation
751 Park Of Commerce Dr
Boca Raton FL

(G-730)
STAR EDITORIAL INC
1000 American Media Way (33464-1000)
PHONE..................................561 997-7733
David J Pecker, *CEO*
EMP: 6 **EST:** 2010
SALES (est): 285.3K **Privately Held**
WEB: www.a360media.com
SIC: 2711 Newspapers: publishing only, not printed on site

(G-731)
STARMAKERS RISING INC (PA)
17239 Boca Club Blvd # 6 (33487-1073)
PHONE..................................561 989-8999
Eileen Miller, *President*
EMP: 39 **EST:** 1993
SQ FT: 3,000
SALES (est): 6MM **Privately Held**
WEB: www.starmakersrising.com
SIC: 2759 2771 Posters, including billboards: printing; greeting cards

(G-732)
STREAM LINE PUBLISHING INC
Also Called: Fine Art Connoisseur
331 Se Mizner Blvd (33432-6004)
PHONE..................................561 655-8778
B Eric Rhoads, *President*
Adam Jacobson, *Chief*
Tom Elmo, *Vice Pres*
Bob Hogan, *Vice Pres*
Laura Iserman, *Finance*
EMP: 12 **EST:** 1995
SALES (est): 3.1MM **Privately Held**
WEB: www.streamlinepublishing.com
SIC: 2721 Magazines: publishing only, not printed on site

(G-733)
STREAMLINE PUBLISHING INC
331 Se Mizner Blvd (33432-6004)
PHONE..................................561 655-8778
Eric Rhoads, *President*
Tom Elmo, *Vice Pres*
Bob Hogan, *Vice Pres*
Anne Brown, *Marketing Staff*
Gina Ward, *Marketing Staff*
EMP: 9 **EST:** 1987
SQ FT: 5,000
SALES (est): 768.8K **Privately Held**
WEB: www.fineartconnoisseur.com
SIC: 2721 Periodicals

(G-734)
SUN INDALEX LLC
5200 Town Center Cir # 470 (33486-1015)
PHONE..................................561 394-0550
Timothy R J Stubbs, *President*
EMP: 47 **EST:** 2005
SALES (est): 338.8K **Privately Held**
SIC: 3353 Aluminum sheet, plate & foil

(G-735)
SUN MACKIE LLC
5200 Town Center Cir # 470 (33486-1015)
PHONE..................................561 394-0550
Marc J Leder, *CEO*
Rodger R Krouse, *CEO*
Mark Corbidge, *Managing Dir*
Antony Levinson, *Senior VP*
Will Allis, *Vice Pres*
◆ **EMP:** 1437 **EST:** 2002
SALES (est): 26.3MM **Privately Held**
SIC: 3651 Audio electronic systems

(G-736)
SUNBEAM AMERICAS HOLDINGS LLC
2381 Nw Executive Ctr Dr (33431-8560)
PHONE..................................561 912-4100
Jerry W Levin, *Ch of Bd*
EMP: 119 **EST:** 1990
SQ FT: 27,003

▲ = Import ▼=Export
◆ =Import/Export

SALES (est): 612.1K
SALES (corp-wide): 9.3B Publicly Held
SIC: 3631 2514 3421 3634 Barbecues, grills & braziers (outdoor cooking); metal lawn & garden furniture; lawn furniture: metal; scissors, shears, clippers, snips & similar tools; shears, hand; clippers, fingernail & toenail; electric housewares & fans; hair dryers, electric; blenders, electric; food mixers, electric: household; thermometers & temperature sensors; temperature sensors, except industrial process & aircraft; thermometers, liquid-in-glass & bimetal type; geophysical & meteorological testing equipment; blood pressure apparatus
HQ: American Household, Inc.
2381 Nw Executive Ctr Dr
Boca Raton FL 33431
561 912-4100

(G-737)
SUNBEAM LATIN AMERICA LLC (DH)
2381 Executive Ctr Dr (33431-8560)
PHONE..................................786 845-2540
Chris Scherzinger, *President*
Andrew Hutchinson, *General Mgr*
Robert P Totte, *Vice Pres*
Amit Singh, *Treasurer*
Victor J Michaels, *Admin Sec*
◆ EMP: 30 EST: 2000
SALES (est): 18.9MM
SALES (corp-wide): 9.3B Publicly Held
WEB: www.sunbeamhospitality.com
SIC: 3631 Barbecues, grills & braziers (outdoor cooking)
HQ: Sunbeam Products, Inc.
2381 Nw Executive Ctr Dr
Boca Raton FL 33431
561 912-4100

(G-738)
SUNBEAM PRODUCTS INC (HQ)
2381 Nw Executive Ctr Dr (33431-8560)
PHONE..................................561 912-4100
Chris Scherzinger, *CEO*
David Hammer, *President*
Rebecca Pangle, *Business Mgr*
Rocki Rockingham, *Senior VP*
Elcira Garrido, *Assistant VP*
◆ EMP: 290 EST: 1981
SALES (est): 1.8B
SALES (corp-wide): 9.3B Publicly Held
WEB: www.sunbeamhospitality.com
SIC: 3631 3634 3089 Barbecues, grills & braziers (outdoor cooking); electric housewares & fans; hair dryers, electric; blenders, electric; food mixers, electric: household; plastic containers, except foam; plastic kitchenware, tableware & houseware
PA: Newell Brands Inc.
6655 Pachtree Dunwoody Rd
Atlanta GA 30328
770 418-7000

(G-739)
SUPER GRAFIX INC
Also Called: Gulf Stream Gear
2889 Nw 24th Ter (33431-6202)
PHONE..................................561 585-1519
Michael Chernoff, *President*
EMP: 10 EST: 2001
SALES (est): 1.4MM Privately Held
WEB: www.renegadesupergrafix.com
SIC: 2675 Stencils & lettering materials: die-cut

(G-740)
SURGENTEC LLC
911 Clint Moore Rd (33487-2802)
PHONE..................................561 990-7882
Travis Greenhalgh, *Principal*
Lisa Overton, *Opers Staff*
Ricki Goldman, *Sales Staff*
EMP: 11 EST: 2016
SALES (est): 1.1MM Privately Held
WEB: www.surgentec.com
SIC: 3841 Medical instruments & equipment, blood & bone work

(G-741)
T H STONE
4521 N Dixie Hwy (33431-5029)
PHONE..................................561 361-3966
EMP: 6
SALES (est): 1.5MM Privately Held
SIC: 3281 5122 Mfg Cut Stone/Products And Cosmetics/Toiletries

(G-742)
TAYLOR & FRANCIS GROUP LLC (DH)
6000 Broken Sound Pkwy Nw # 300 (33487-5704)
PHONE..................................561 994-0555
Roger Graham Horton, *President*
Kristine Mednansky, *Editor*
Meredith Norwich, *Editor*
Perry Todd, *Editor*
David Varley, *Editor*
▲ EMP: 150 EST: 2004
SQ FT: 36,470
SALES (est): 104.2MM
SALES (corp-wide): 2.2B Privately Held
WEB: www.taylorandfrancis.com
SIC: 2721 2731 Periodicals: publishing only; trade journals: publishing only, not printed on site; books: publishing only; textbooks: publishing only, not printed on site
HQ: Informa Group Limited
Mortimer House 37-41
London W1T 3
207 017-5000

(G-743)
TECHNIFLEX LLC
4400 N Federal Hwy Ste 51 (33431-3426)
PHONE..................................561 235-0844
Serhat Unal,
EMP: 25 EST: 2016
SALES (est): 678.2K Privately Held
SIC: 3999 Atomizers, toiletry

(G-744)
TELIT IOT PLATFORMS LLC (HQ)
5300 Broken Sound Blvd Nw S (33487-3520)
PHONE..................................561 982-9898
Fred Yentz, *President*
Stuart Perry, *Vice Pres*
Jim Wert Jr, *Vice Pres*
David Stalnaker, *Sales Executive*
Lindsay Kelley, *Marketing Staff*
EMP: 114 EST: 2001
SQ FT: 20,000
SALES (est): 51.1MM Privately Held
WEB: www.telit.com
SIC: 3695 7371 5734 Computer software tape & disks: blank, rigid & floppy; computer software development; software, business & non-game

(G-745)
TELSEC CORPORATION
Also Called: E-Tag
1155 Broken Sound Pkwy Nw E (33487-3538)
PHONE..................................561 998-9983
Stuart Seidel, *President*
Andrew Gilbert, *Vice Pres*
▲ EMP: 6 EST: 1994
SQ FT: 6,000
SALES (est): 12MM Privately Held
SIC: 3699 Security control equipment & systems

(G-746)
TENNIER INDUSTRIES INC (PA)
950 Pnnsula Corp Cir Ste (33487)
PHONE..................................561 999-9710
Howard Thier, *CEO*
Steven W Eisen, *CFO*
EMP: 3 EST: 1976
SALES (est): 105MM Privately Held
WEB: www.tennierindustries.com
SIC: 2311 Military uniforms, men's & youths': purchased materials

(G-747)
THEATER EARS INC
20423 State Road 7 Ste F1 (33498-6774)
PHONE..................................561 305-0519
Dan Mangru, *CEO*
EMP: 5 EST: 2013
SALES (est): 486.4K Privately Held
WEB: www.theaterears.com
SIC: 7372 Application computer software

(G-748)
THERAPEUTICSMD INC (PA)
951 W Yamato Rd Ste 220 (33431-4440)
PHONE..................................561 961-1900
Robert G Finizio, *CEO*
John CK Milligan, *CEO*
Tommy G Thompson, *Ch of Bd*
Hugh O'Dowd, *President*
Emilee Cunningham, *Business Mgr*
EMP: 131 EST: 2008
SQ FT: 33,124
SALES: 64.8MM Publicly Held
WEB: www.therapeuticsmd.com
SIC: 2834 Vitamin, nutrient & hematinic preparations for human use

(G-749)
THINGLOBAL LLC
7700 Congress Ave # 1122 (33487-1352)
PHONE..................................561 923-8559
Luiz Serria, *CEO*
Elaine Lignelli, *Mng Member*
Luiz Ferreira, *Manager*
Eliane Lignelli, *Exec Dir*
Kim Huapaya, *Executive*
EMP: 6 EST: 2015
SALES (est): 564.8K Privately Held
WEB: www.thinglobal.com
SIC: 3577 5734 Computer peripheral equipment; computer peripheral equipment

(G-750)
THOR MANUFACTURING INC
7050 W Palmetto Park Rd (33433-3426)
PHONE..................................866 955-8467
EMP: 12 EST: 2008
SALES (est): 91.5K Privately Held
WEB: www.thorpowerproducts.com
SIC: 3999 Atomizers, toiletry

(G-751)
TODAYS RESTAURANT NEWS INC
6165 Old Court Rd Apt 224 (33433-7830)
PHONE..................................561 620-8888
Howard Appell, *Owner*
EMP: 7 EST: 2010
SALES (est): 169.1K Privately Held
WEB: www.trnusa.com
SIC: 2711 Newspapers

(G-752)
TOP SALES CO
17047 Boca Club Blvd 141b (33487-1251)
PHONE..................................561 852-4311
Stuart Nussbaum, *President*
EMP: 6 EST: 1985
SALES (est): 499.1K Privately Held
SIC: 3699 Electrical equipment & supplies

(G-753)
TOTALLY PRODUCTS LLC
1101 S Rogers Cir Ste 10 (33487-2748)
PHONE..................................786 942-9218
Daniel I Rosenfield, *CEO*
EMP: 5 EST: 2009
SALES (est): 592.8K Privately Held
SIC: 2833 Vitamins, natural or synthetic: bulk, uncompounded

(G-754)
TRAINOR METAL PRODUCTS INC
171 Nw 16th St (33432-1606)
P.O. Box 1176 (33429-1176)
PHONE..................................561 395-5520
Jeff Brader, *President*
EMP: 5 EST: 1958
SQ FT: 12,500
SALES (est): 446.8K Privately Held
WEB: www.trainormetal.com
SIC: 2514 Metal lawn & garden furniture

(G-755)
TRI COUNTY PRINTING CO IN
9070 Kimberly Blvd (33434-2855)
PHONE..................................561 477-8487
Joseph Frank, *Principal*
EMP: 6 EST: 2006
SALES (est): 254.7K Privately Held
SIC: 2752 Commercial printing, lithographic

(G-756)
TRIDENT TRADING INC (PA)
Also Called: The Boston Tea Party Kettle Co
6340 Via Tierra (33433-2358)
PHONE..................................561 488-0458
Audrey Ehrenstein, *President*
▲ EMP: 7 EST: 1994
SALES (est): 1.3MM Privately Held
SIC: 3993 5199 3469 3291 Advertising novelties; advertising specialties; metal stampings; abrasive products; specialty cleaning, polishes & sanitation goods

(G-757)
TRIGEANT EP LTD
3020 N Military Trl # 100 (33431-1814)
PHONE..................................561 999-9916
Harry Sargeant III, *Partner*
◆ EMP: 10
SALES (est): 902.4K Privately Held
SIC: 2999 Waxes, petroleum: not produced in petroleum refineries

(G-758)
TRIPLE CROWN PRINTING
5801 Congress Ave (33487-3603)
PHONE..................................561 939-6440
Neal Heller, *Partner*
Richard Siemans, *Partner*
EMP: 35 EST: 2006
SALES (est): 1.6MM Privately Held
SIC: 2759 Commercial printing

(G-759)
TWINLAB CNSLD HOLDINGS INC (PA)
Also Called: TCH
4800 T Rex Ave Ste 305 (33431-4479)
PHONE..................................561 443-4301
David L Van Andel, *Ch of Bd*
Anthony Zolezzi, *President*
Gregory Thomas Grochoski, *Exec VP*
Shari Gottesman, *Senior VP*
Carla Goffstein, *CFO*
EMP: 33 EST: 2013
SQ FT: 13,000
SALES: 66.3MM Publicly Held
WEB: www.tlcchealth.com
SIC: 2833 2023 Vitamins, natural or synthetic: bulk, uncompounded; dietary supplements, dairy & non-dairy based

(G-760)
TWINLAB CONSOLIDATION CORP
4800 T Rex Ave Ste 350 (33431-4447)
PHONE..................................800 645-5626
Naomi Whittel, *CEO*
Yamit Sadok, *Surgery Dir*
EMP: 10 EST: 2017
SALES (est): 2MM
SALES (corp-wide): 66.3MM Publicly Held
WEB: www.twinlab.tlcchealth.com
SIC: 2833 Vitamins, natural or synthetic: bulk, uncompounded
PA: Twinlab Consolidated Holdings Inc.
4800 T Rex Ave Ste 305
Boca Raton FL 33431
561 443-4301

(G-761)
TWINLAB CORPORATION
4800 T Rex Ave Ste 305 (33431-4479)
PHONE..................................800 645-5626
Naomi Whittel, *CEO*
Richard Neuwirth, *Officer*
EMP: 400 EST: 2003
SQ FT: 5,000
SALES (est): 53.1MM
SALES (corp-wide): 87.3MM Privately Held
WEB: www.twinlab.tlcchealth.com
SIC: 2099 2834 2731 2721 Tea blending; vitamin preparations; books: publishing only; statistical reports (periodicals): publishing only; medicinals & botanicals
PA: Twinlab Holdings, Inc.
4800 T Rex Ave Ste 305
Boca Raton FL 33431
800 645-5626

GEOGRAPHIC

(G-762)
TWINLAB HOLDINGS INC (PA)
Also Called: Ideasphere
4800 T Rex Ave Ste 305 (33431-4479)
PHONE..................................800 645-5626
David V Andel, *CEO*
Bill Nicholson, *Vice Ch Bd*
Anthony Robbins, *Vice Ch Bd*
Mark Fox, *President*
Niki Simoneaux, *Senior VP*
EMP: 23 **EST:** 2001
SALES (est): 87.3MM **Privately Held**
WEB: www.twinlab.tlcchealth.com
SIC: 2833 2834 5149 2721 Vitamins, natural or synthetic: bulk, uncompounded; pharmaceutical preparations; groceries & related products; periodicals

(G-763)
TWINLAB HOLDINGS INC
2255 Glades Rd Ste 342w (33431-7379)
PHONE..................................800 645-5626
Joseph Sinicropi, *Branch Mgr*
EMP: 11
SALES (corp-wide): 87.3MM **Privately Held**
WEB: www.twinlab.tlcchealth.com
SIC: 2833 Medicinals & botanicals
PA: Twinlab Holdings, Inc.
4800 T Rex Ave Ste 305
Boca Raton FL 33431
800 645-5626

(G-764)
ULTIMAXX INC
Also Called: Ultimaxx Health
3651 Fau Blvd Ste 400 (33431-6489)
P.O. Box 5308, Frisco TX (75035-0210)
PHONE..................................877 300-3424
Leonard Lomax, *CEO*
Ron Long, *Vice Pres*
EMP: 10 **EST:** 2008
SALES (est): 996.1K **Privately Held**
WEB: www.ultimaxxhealth.com
SIC: 2833 Medicinals & botanicals

(G-765)
UNICO INTERNATIONAL TRDG CORP
Also Called: A World of Wipes
5499 N Federal Hwy Ste P (33487-4993)
PHONE..................................561 338-3338
AVI Tansman, *President*
Avraham AVI Tansman, *President*
Melinda Tansman, *Vice Pres*
Lisa Carey, *Sales Staff*
Joe Doyle, *Marketing Staff*
▲ **EMP:** 6 **EST:** 1991
SALES: 17.5MM **Privately Held**
WEB: www.aworldofwipes.com
SIC: 2844 Towelettes, premoistened

(G-766)
UNION CHEMICAL INDUSTRIES CORP
Also Called: UCI Paints
298 Kingsbridge St (33487-4002)
PHONE..................................716 866-4978
Christopher Cummings, *President*
Richard Devick, *President*
Melissa Patterson Goupe, *VP Opers*
Sam Devick, *Sales Staff*
EMP: 16 **EST:** 1973
SQ FT: 28,000
SALES (est): 3.9MM **Privately Held**
SIC: 2851 Paints & paint additives

(G-767)
UNIQUE INK PRINTING CORP
1934 Sw 8th Ave (33486-6929)
PHONE..................................954 829-2801
Scott Wheeler, *President*
EMP: 7 **EST:** 2014
SALES (est): 211.1K **Privately Held**
SIC: 2752 Commercial printing, lithographic

(G-768)
UNIQUE RECORDING SOFTWARE INC
21218 Saint Andrews Blvd (33433-2435)
PHONE..................................917 854-5403
Nathan Robert, *Principal*
EMP: 5 **EST:** 2004
SALES (est): 322.3K **Privately Held**
WEB: www.ursplugins.com
SIC: 7372 Prepackaged software

(G-769)
UNITED WIRELESS TECH INC
300 Se 5th Ave Apt 8180 (33432-5503)
PHONE..................................561 302-9350
Stephen B Cavayero, *President*
EMP: 15 **EST:** 1993
SQ FT: 20,000
SALES (est): 590.6K **Privately Held**
SIC: 3571 3663 Electronic computers; radio & TV communications equipment

(G-770)
UNIVERSAL TRAINING SFTWR INC
301 Ne 51st St Ste 1240 (33431-4931)
PHONE..................................561 981-6421
Victor Reyes, *Principal*
EMP: 14 **EST:** 1996
SALES: 1.7MM **Privately Held**
WEB: www.utsintel.com
SIC: 7372 Application computer software

(G-771)
US CHUTES CORP
751 Park Of Commerce Dr # 108 (33487-3622)
PHONE..................................860 567-4000
M John Weber Jr, *President*
EMP: 16 **EST:** 1976
SQ FT: 75,000
SALES (est): 475.2K **Privately Held**
SIC: 3443 Chutes, metal plate

(G-772)
US PAVER CO
22809 Horse Shoe Way (33428-5505)
PHONE..................................954 292-4373
EMP: 6 **EST:** 2007
SALES (est): 214.8K **Privately Held**
WEB: www.uspaverco.com
SIC: 3531 Pavers

(G-773)
US SAMPLE CORP
10386 Stonebridge Blvd (33498-6409)
PHONE..................................954 495-4525
Morton Kader, *President*
▲ **EMP:** 22 **EST:** 1991
SQ FT: 60,000
SALES (est): 1.3MM **Privately Held**
SIC: 2782 Sample books
HQ: National Sample Card Company Limited
11500 Boul Armand-Bombardier
Montreal QC

(G-774)
VALIANT TRANSPORT GROUP LLC
Also Called: Triad Electric Vehicles
5030 Chmpn Blvd Ste G11 (33496)
PHONE..................................855 648-7423
James Mason, *Manager*
Cory Grades,
EMP: 30 **EST:** 2012
SQ FT: 3,500
SALES (est): 980K **Privately Held**
SIC: 3711 Cars, electric, assembly of

(G-775)
VARGAS ENTERPRISES INC
2518 Nw 64th Blvd (33496-2008)
PHONE..................................561 989-0908
Peter Stein, *President*
Susan Stein, *Vice Pres*
EMP: 7 **EST:** 1993
SQ FT: 5,000
SALES (est): 164.9K **Privately Held**
SIC: 2331 Women's & misses' blouses & shirts

(G-776)
VEHICLE MAINT PROGRAM INC
Also Called: V M P
3595 N Dixie Hwy Ste 7 (33431-5936)
PHONE..................................561 362-6080
Lindi Brooks Cohen, *President*
Lindy Brooks Cohen, *President*
Penny Brooks, *Corp Secy*
ARI Brooks, *Vice Pres*
EMP: 14 **EST:** 1988
SQ FT: 8,000
SALES (est): 4.8MM **Privately Held**
WEB: www.vmpparts.com
SIC: 2531 5531 5047 Seats, automobile; automobile & truck equipment & parts; automotive parts; medical equipment & supplies

(G-777)
VERSATUS HPC INC
4700 Nw 2nd Ave (33431-4154)
PHONE..................................561 544-8862
Denis Marcelo P Dos Anjos, *Principal*
EMP: 10 **EST:** 2012
SALES (est): 140.4K **Privately Held**
WEB: www.versatushpc.com.br
SIC: 3571 Electronic computers

(G-778)
VERTICAL BRIDGE TOWERS LLC
750 Park Of Commerce (33487)
P.O. Box 743051, Atlanta GA (30374-3051)
PHONE..................................561 948-6367
Alex Gellman, *CEO*
Michael Belski, *Exec VP*
Jim McCulloch, *Vice Pres*
Buddy Norman, *Vice Pres*
Michael Romaniw, *CFO*
EMP: 200 **EST:** 2014
SQ FT: 6,000
SALES (est): 22.3MM **Privately Held**
WEB: www.verticalbridge.com
SIC: 3663 Transmitting apparatus, radio or television

(G-779)
VESERCA GROUP LTD INC
Also Called: Embraer
20694 Nw 27th Ave (33434-4366)
PHONE..................................561 210-7400
Alberto Villasmil, *President*
Antonio Dugarte, *Officer*
◆ **EMP:** 11 **EST:** 2005
SALES (est): 285.2K **Privately Held**
SIC: 3721 5599 Aircraft; aircraft dealers

(G-780)
VIP PRTG NIGHT CLB SUPS LLC
1000 Holland Dr Ste 1 (33487-2723)
PHONE..................................561 603-2846
EMP: 7 **EST:** 2017
SQ FT: 4,800
SALES (est): 206.1K **Privately Held**
WEB: www.vipprintingandnightclubsupplies.com
SIC: 2752 Commercial printing, offset

(G-781)
VOICETHREAD LLC
21747 Westmont Ct (33428-4817)
P.O. Box 970533 (33497-0533)
PHONE..................................919 724-4486
Ben Papell, *CEO*
EMP: 24 **EST:** 2006
SALES (est): 1.7MM **Privately Held**
WEB: www.voicethread.com
SIC: 7372 Educational computer software

(G-782)
VPLENISH NUTRITIONALS INC
101 Plaza Real S Apt 306 (33432-4839)
P.O. Box 1100 (33429-1100)
PHONE..................................954 304-4000
Steven Sponder, *President*
▼ **EMP:** 10 **EST:** 2009
SQ FT: 3,000
SALES (est): 461.2K **Privately Held**
WEB: www.vplenishtheworld.org
SIC: 3999 Manufacturing industries

(G-783)
VYCOR MEDICAL INC (PA)
951 Broken Sound Pkwy Nw # 320 (33487-3531)
PHONE..................................561 558-2020
Peter C Zachariou, *CEO*
Adrian Christopher Liddell, *Ch of Bd*
David Marc Cantor, *President*
Peter Zachariou, *Exec VP*
Pam Beidleman, *Controller*
EMP: 8 **EST:** 2005
SALES: 1.1MM **Publicly Held**
WEB: www.vycormedical.com
SIC: 3841 Surgical & medical instruments

(G-784)
W H L BUSINESS COMMUNICATIONS
Also Called: AlphaGraphics
2880 N Federal Hwy (33431-6802)
PHONE..................................561 361-9202
Wolf H Lehmkuhl, *President*
Alferdo Billings Jr, *General Mgr*
EMP: 8 **EST:** 1998
SALES (est): 806.7K **Privately Held**
WEB: www.alphagraphics.com
SIC: 2752 Commercial printing, lithographic

(G-785)
W R GRACE & CO - CONN
6001 Broken Sound Pkwy # 600 (33487-2766)
PHONE..................................561 982-7776
EMP: 10
SALES (corp-wide): 3B **Publicly Held**
SIC: 3086 2819 Mfg Plastic Foam Products Mfg Industrial Inorganic Chemicals
HQ: W. R. Grace & Co. - Conn.
7500 Grace Dr
Columbia MD 21044
410 531-4000

(G-786)
W2E INTERNATIONAL CORP
2200 Nw Corp Blvd Ste 210 (33431-7307)
PHONE..................................561 362-9595
Steven E Honigman Sq, *Principal*
EMP: 6 **EST:** 2014
SALES (est): 76.5K **Privately Held**
SIC: 1389 Oil & gas field services

(G-787)
WAREHOUSE GOODS LLC
Also Called: Vapeworld
1095 Broken Sound Pkwy Nw # 300 (33487-3503)
PHONE..................................877 865-2260
Eric Hammond, *General Mgr*
Zachary Tapp, *CFO*
Brad Dulin, *Sales Staff*
Adam Stephens, *Marketing Staff*
Karen Fielden, *Manager*
▲ **EMP:** 50 **EST:** 2007
SQ FT: 2,000
SALES (est): 29.9MM
SALES (corp-wide): 138.3MM **Publicly Held**
WEB: www.warehousegoods.com
SIC: 3634 2911 5047 5961 Vaporizers, electric: household; aromatic chemical products; medical equipment & supplies; catalog & mail-order houses
PA: Greenlane Holdings, Inc.
1095 Broken Sound Pkwy Nw # 300
Boca Raton FL 33487
877 292-7660

(G-788)
WEIDER PUBLICATIONS LLC
1000 American Media Way (33464-1000)
PHONE..................................561 998-7424
David Pecker,
EMP: 5 **EST:** 2002
SALES (est): 526.1K **Privately Held**
WEB: www.muscleandfitness.com
SIC: 2741 Miscellaneous publishing

(G-789)
WESTERN DIGITAL CORPORATION
1 Park Pl Ste 240nw (33487-8235)
PHONE..................................561 995-1496
Ron Pack, *Manager*
Cynthia Grace, *Director*
EMP: 6
SALES (corp-wide): 16.9B **Publicly Held**
WEB: www.westerndigital.com
SIC: 3572 Disk drives, computer
PA: Western Digital Corporation
5601 Great Oaks Pkwy
San Jose CA 95119
408 717-6000

(G-790)
WIMBLEDON HEALTH PARTNERS LLC
7000 W Plmtt Prk Rd # 205 (33433-3430)
PHONE..................................800 200-8262
Mitch Rubin, *CEO*

Stewart Whyte, *COO*
Brad Artel,
EMP: 14 **EST:** 2013
SALES (est): 2.5MM **Privately Held**
WEB: www.wimbledonhealthpartners.com
SIC: 3841 8011 Diagnostic apparatus, medical; offices & clinics of medical doctors

(G-791)
WORLD HLTH ENRGY HOLDINGS INC (PA)
1825 Nw Corp Blvd Ste 110 (33431-8554)
PHONE..................................561 870-0440
Giora Rozensweig, *CEO*
EMP: 12 **EST:** 1999
SALES: 98.1K **Publicly Held**
WEB: www.whengroup.com
SIC: 2869 7372 Glycerin; business oriented computer software

(G-792)
WORLDWIDE MEDIA SVCS GROUP INC
1000 American Media Way (33464-1000)
PHONE..................................561 989-1342
David Pecker, *Ch of Bd*
Christopher Polimeni, *Exec VP*
Maydee Ehster, *Manager*
Lyndon Perrine, *Manager*
Adam Butterfield, *Producer*
EMP: 51
SALES (corp-wide): 1.2B **Privately Held**
WEB: www.a360media.com
SIC: 2711 Newspapers, publishing & printing
PA: Worldwide Media Services Group Inc.
1000 American Media Way
Boca Raton FL 33464
561 989-1342

(G-793)
WORLDWIDE MEDIA SVCS GROUP INC (PA)
Also Called: A360 Media
1000 American Media Way (33464-1000)
PHONE..................................561 989-1342
David Pecker, *Ch of Bd*
John Swider, *President*
Dan Solomon, *COO*
Jon P Fine, *Counsel*
Eric Klee, *Vice Pres*
EMP: 50 **EST:** 1952
SALES (est): 1.2B **Privately Held**
WEB: www.a360media.com
SIC: 2741 2711 Miscellaneous publishing; newspapers: publishing only, not printed on site

(G-794)
XELEUM LIGHTING LLC (HQ)
751 Park Of Commerce Dr # 100 (33487-3622)
PHONE..................................954 617-8170
Richard Leaman, *CEO*
Jonathan Cooper, *COO*
Ty Ramsey, *VP Engrg*
Peter Rozendal, *CFO*
▲ **EMP:** 14 **EST:** 2011
SALES (est): 11.6MM **Privately Held**
WEB: www.eiko.com
SIC: 3646 Commercial indusl & institutional electric lighting fixtures

(G-795)
YAREY INC
18840 Mariner Inlet Dr (33498-6366)
PHONE..................................954 520-6015
Alicia Tovar, *President*
EMP: 10 **EST:** 2007
SALES (est): 464.1K **Privately Held**
SIC: 3281 Marble, building: cut & shaped

(G-796)
YESIL INC
23400 Milano Ct (33433-6936)
P.O. Box 220033, Great Neck NY (11022-0033)
PHONE..................................516 858-0244
Musa Suveyke, *President*
EMP: 10 **EST:** 2012
SALES (est): 2MM **Privately Held**
SIC: 2299 7389 Recovering textile fibers from clippings & rags;

(G-797)
YVEL USA INC
6000 Glades Rd Ste 1153 (33431-7254)
PHONE..................................561 391-5119
Eliaz Gabay, *CEO*
Nir Shinuk, *Marketing Staff*
EMP: 9 **EST:** 2015
SALES (est): 349.4K **Privately Held**
WEB: www.yvel.com
SIC: 3172 Cases, jewelry

Bonifay
Holmes County

(G-798)
ARNOLD LUMBER COMPANY INC
3185 Thomas Dr (32425-4239)
PHONE..................................850 547-5733
Joe Jernigan, *CEO*
EMP: 16 **EST:** 1927
SALES (est): 1.8MM **Privately Held**
SIC: 2491 Wood preserving

(G-799)
BD XTREME HOLDINGS LLC
Also Called: Xtreme Boats
2460 Development Cir (32425-6024)
PHONE..................................850 703-1793
Michael Campbell, *Plant Mgr*
Brian Sandberg, *Mng Member*
EMP: 12 **EST:** 2016
SALES (est): 939K **Privately Held**
SIC: 3732 Motorized boat, building & repairing

(G-800)
C2C INNOVATED TECHNOLOGY LLC
3371 Highway 90 (32425-6003)
PHONE..................................251 382-2277
Valarian Couch, *Mng Member*
EMP: 5 **EST:** 2016
SALES (est): 475K **Privately Held**
WEB: www.c2cinnovatedtech.com
SIC: 3825 4911 1731 7622 Network analyzers; ; fiber optic cable installation; computer installation; installation of citizens' band (CB) antennas; computer integrated systems design; computer systems analysis & design; local area network (LAN) systems integrator; value-added resellers, computer systems; software training, computer

(G-801)
CHIPLEY NEWSPAPERS INC
Also Called: Home County Times Advertiser
112 E Virginia Ave (32425-2327)
P.O. Box 67 (32425-0067)
PHONE..................................850 638-0212
Nicole P Barefield, *Principal*
Brenda Taylor, *Office Mgr*
EMP: 7 **EST:** 2016
SALES (est): 387.2K **Privately Held**
WEB: www.washingtoncounty.news
SIC: 2711 Newspapers, publishing & printing

(G-802)
COUNTRY CABINETS
1915 Adolph Whitaker Rd (32425-6515)
PHONE..................................850 547-5477
Neal Reeves, *President*
Barbara Reeves, *Admin Sec*
EMP: 6 **EST:** 1995
SALES (est): 500.7K **Privately Held**
WEB: www.countrycabinets95.com
SIC: 2434 Wood kitchen cabinets

(G-803)
ENVIRONMENTAL MFG & SUPPLY INC
3255 Highway 90 (32425-6011)
P.O. Box 130 (32425-0130)
PHONE..................................850 547-5287
Stacey Coates, *President*
Kyle Coates, *Vice Pres*
▲ **EMP:** 19 **EST:** 1991
SQ FT: 20,000
SALES (est): 5.1MM **Privately Held**
SIC: 3531 Wellpoint systems

(G-804)
HOLMES TOOL & ENGINEERING INC
Also Called: Hte
1019 N Waukesha St (32425-1736)
P.O. Box 95 (32425-0095)
PHONE..................................850 547-4417
Timothy L Steverson, *President*
Brenda G Steverson, *Vice Pres*
Brenda Steverson, *Vice Pres*
Dale Stephens, *Manager*
Ann Sallinger, *Info Tech Mgr*
EMP: 25 **EST:** 1978
SQ FT: 9,500
SALES (est): 6MM **Privately Held**
WEB: www.holmestool.com
SIC: 3599 7692 Machine shop, jobbing & repair; welding repair

(G-805)
PARK CENTRAL INC
Also Called: Aus Manufacturing
704 W Highway 90 (32425-2526)
PHONE..................................850 547-1660
James Rich, *President*
James Sellers, *Vice Pres*
Lea Bryant, *Admin Sec*
EMP: 24 **EST:** 2001
SQ FT: 12,500
SALES (est): 314.7K **Privately Held**
WEB: www.ausmanufacturing.com
SIC: 3599 Machine shop, jobbing & repair

(G-806)
PARTS CENTRAL INC
Also Called: Aus Manufacturing
704 W Highway 90 (32425-2526)
P.O. Box 156 (32425-0156)
PHONE..................................850 547-1660
James Rich, *President*
James Sellers, *Vice Pres*
Lea Bryant, *Administration*
EMP: 13 **EST:** 2001
SALES (est): 2.4MM **Privately Held**
WEB: www.ausmanufacturing.com
SIC: 3433 3599 7692 Burners, furnaces, boilers & stokers; machine shop, jobbing & repair; welding repair

(G-807)
RANDALL BIRGE
2579 Lilly Dr (32425-8403)
PHONE..................................850 373-6131
Randall Birge, *Owner*
EMP: 6 **EST:** 2010
SALES (est): 700K **Privately Held**
SIC: 2411 Logging

(G-808)
STREET TALK AMERICA
1007 N Waukesha St (32425-1736)
PHONE..................................850 547-6186
EMP: 7 **EST:** 2019
SALES (est): 91.8K **Privately Held**
WEB: www.streettalkamerica.com
SIC: 2741 Miscellaneous publishing

Bonita Springs
Lee County

(G-809)
1ST CHICE HRRCANE PRTCTION LLC
Also Called: 1st Choice Windows and Doors
25241 Bernwood Dr Ste 6 (34135-7886)
PHONE..................................239 325-3400
Lance Lustik,
EMP: 18 **EST:** 2017
SALES (est): 3MM **Privately Held**
WEB:
www.1stchoicehurricaneprotection.com
SIC: 2431 Door shutters, wood

(G-810)
ADVANCED INFRSTRCTURE TECH INC
25110 Bernwood Dr # 101 (34135-7813)
P.O. Box 112126, Naples (34108-0136)
PHONE..................................239 992-1700
Brit E Svobova, *President*
Barry Raeburn, *Vice Pres*
EMP: 9 **EST:** 2009
SQ FT: 950
SALES (est): 481.9K **Privately Held**
SIC: 3531 Construction machinery attachments

(G-811)
AEROX AVI OXGN SYSTEMS LLC
25190 Bernwood Dr (34135-7846)
PHONE..................................207 637-2331
EMP: 12
SQ FT: 13,000
SALES (est): 700.3K
SALES (corp-wide): 833.3K **Privately Held**
SIC: 3728 Mfg Aircraft Parts/Equipment
PA: O2 Aero Acquisitions, Llc
8 Morgan Pl
Unionville CT

(G-812)
ALL ABOUT SCREENS
10111 Sunshine Dr (34135-5038)
PHONE..................................239 398-1798
Brian Schatzman, *Principal*
EMP: 7 **EST:** 2005
SALES (est): 234.6K **Privately Held**
WEB: www.allaboutscreensswf.com
SIC: 3448 Screen enclosures

(G-813)
APPLIED MOBILITY DEVICES LLC (PA)
Also Called: Dynamd
8951 Bonita Beach Rd Se (34135-4201)
PHONE..................................833 439-6266
Glorita Cuiffi, *Principal*
Michael L Swank, *Principal*
William Scott, *Mng Member*
EMP: 8 **EST:** 2017
SALES (est): 471.4K **Privately Held**
SIC: 3842 Orthopedic appliances; crutches & walkers

(G-814)
ARTFUL SIGNS
9520 Bonita Beach Rd Se (34135-4517)
PHONE..................................239 431-7356
Donald J Moran, *President*
Robert Viana, *Prdtn Mgr*
EMP: 6 **EST:** 2008
SALES (est): 283.4K **Privately Held**
WEB: www.artfulsigns.com
SIC: 3993 Signs, not made in custom sign painting shops

(G-815)
AVAYA INC
25798 Old Gaslight Dr (34135-8894)
PHONE..................................239 498-2737
Kathy Giamballvo, *Manager*
EMP: 6 **Publicly Held**
WEB: www.avaya.com
SIC: 3661 Telephone & telegraph apparatus
HQ: Avaya Inc.
2605 Meridian Pkwy # 200
Durham NC 27713
908 953-6000

(G-816)
BLIND AND DRAPERY GALLERY INC
24830 S Tamiami Trl # 170 (34134-7032)
PHONE..................................239 948-7611
EMP: 6 **EST:** 2019
SALES (est): 313.4K **Privately Held**
WEB: www.blindanddraperygallery.com
SIC: 2591 Window blinds

(G-817)
BONITA GRANDE MINING LLC
Also Called: Bonita Grande Aggregates
25501 Bonita Grande Dr (34135-6382)
PHONE..................................239 947-6402
Robert Hensley,
EMP: 18 **EST:** 2004
SQ FT: 500
SALES (est): 4.6MM **Privately Held**
SIC: 1442 Sand mining

(G-818)
BONITA PRINTSHOP INC
Also Called: Bonita Print Shop
28210 Old 41 Rd Unit 305 (34135-0839)
PHONE..................................239 992-8522

GEOGRAPHIC

Mark Montgomery, *President*
Jodi Montgomery, *Vice Pres*
EMP: 5 **EST:** 1981
SQ FT: 2,200
SALES (est): 622.6K
SALES (corp-wide): 1.2MM **Privately Held**
WEB: www.bonitaprintshop.com
SIC: 2752 Commercial printing, offset
PA: I-Partner Group, Inc
28200 Old 41 Rd Unit 204
Bonita Springs FL 34135
239 449-4749

(G-819)
BOOSTANE LLC
10981 Harmony Park Dr # 5 (34135-1806)
PHONE..................................239 908-1615
Iam Lehn, *President*
Kelly Herrmann, *Admin Mgr*
Mark Herrmann,
Dave Wesseldyke,
EMP: 10 **EST:** 2013
SQ FT: 5,000
SALES (est): 1.6MM **Privately Held**
WEB: www.boostane.com
SIC: 2911 7389 Fuel additives;

(G-820)
BOSWELL JM & ASSOCIATES INC
Also Called: Homes & Land Magazine
270 3rd St (34134-7323)
PHONE..................................239 949-2311
James M Boswell II, *President*
EMP: 7 **EST:** 1999
SALES (est): 397.3K **Privately Held**
SIC: 2721 Periodicals

(G-821)
BURTON JC COMPANIES INC
Also Called: Ott Welding
24241 Production Cir (34135-7058)
P.O. Box 366056 (34136-6056)
PHONE..................................239 992-2377
Jon C Burton, *President*
Rita Osullivan, *Office Mgr*
Jason Dittman, *Manager*
EMP: 8
SQ FT: 3,400
SALES (est): 2.2MM **Privately Held**
WEB: www.ottwelding.com
SIC: 7692 Welding repair

(G-822)
CABINET COLLECTION INC
24830 S Tamiami Trl (34134-7032)
PHONE..................................239 478-0359
Paulette Southwick, *President*
Andrew Gunn, *Vice Pres*
EMP: 7 **EST:** 2015
SALES (est): 361.8K **Privately Held**
WEB: www.thecabinetcollectioninc.com
SIC: 2434 Wood kitchen cabinets

(G-823)
CAMCO CHEMICAL
3635 Bonita Beach Rd # 3 (34134-4157)
PHONE..................................239 992-4100
Brian J Moffatt, *President*
EMP: 7 **EST:** 2014
SALES (est): 508.5K **Privately Held**
WEB: www.camcochemical.com
SIC: 2899 Chemical preparations

(G-824)
CEMEX PACIFIC HOLDINGS LLC
25061 Old 41 Rd (34135-7041)
PHONE..................................239 992-1400
EMP: 60 **Privately Held**
SIC: 3271 Mfg Concrete
HQ: Cemex Pacific Holdings, Llc
7150 Pollock Dr Ste 100
Las Vegas NV 89119
702 260-9900

(G-825)
COASTLAND SPECIALTIES LLC
28340 Trails Edge Blvd (34134-7586)
PHONE..................................239 910-5401
EMP: 7 **EST:** 2010
SALES (est): 438.7K **Privately Held**
SIC: 3629 Electronic generation equipment

(G-826)
COMMAND PRINT LLC
3250 Bonita Beach Rd # 205 (34134-4190)
PHONE..................................716 583-5175
Fred Sommer,
EMP: 6 **EST:** 2015
SALES (est): 135.1K **Privately Held**
SIC: 2752 7389 Commercial printing, lithographic;

(G-827)
CUSTOMER FIRST INC NAPLES
Also Called: Presstige Printing
10940 Harmony Park Dr (34135-1800)
PHONE..................................239 949-8518
Robert Weidenmiller, *President*
Dave Canty, *President*
Jimmy Deleon, *President*
Dana Winchell, *Cust Mgr*
Joe Colleran, *Manager*
EMP: 31 **EST:** 2001
SALES (est): 8.8MM **Privately Held**
WEB: www.presstigeprinting.com
SIC: 2752 7336 7334 7331 Commercial printing, offset; commercial art & graphic design; photocopying & duplicating services; direct mail advertising services

(G-828)
DA VINCI CABINETRY LLC
25241 Bernwood Dr Ste 7 (34135-7886)
PHONE..................................239 633-7957
Irmantas O Stiega,
EMP: 13 **EST:** 2006
SALES (est): 678.5K **Privately Held**
WEB: www.davincicabinetry.com
SIC: 2434 Wood kitchen cabinets

(G-829)
ERNIES SIGNS
3901 Bonita Beach Rd (34134-4213)
P.O. Box 704 (34133-0704)
PHONE..................................239 992-0800
Joe E Fernandez Jr, *President*
EMP: 7 **EST:** 1972
SQ FT: 1,900
SALES (est): 498.9K **Privately Held**
WEB: www.ernies-signs.com
SIC: 3993 Signs & advertising specialties

(G-830)
FAST SIGNS
Also Called: Fastsigns
28440 Old 41 Rd (34135-7070)
PHONE..................................239 498-7200
Bob Haller Jr, *CEO*
EMP: 7 **EST:** 2015
SALES (est): 182.9K **Privately Held**
WEB: www.fastsigns.com
SIC: 3993 7312 5999 5046 Signs & advertising specialties; outdoor advertising services; banners, flags, decals & posters; commercial equipment

(G-831)
FINAL TOUCH MOLDING CABINETRY
25070 Bernwood Dr (34135-7900)
PHONE..................................239 948-7856
Robert Glownia, *President*
Mike Grenzy, *Business Mgr*
Michael Grenzy, *Manager*
▲ **EMP:** 10 **EST:** 1997
SQ FT: 5,305
SALES (est): 896.3K **Privately Held**
WEB: www.finaltouchmc.com
SIC: 2434 Wood kitchen cabinets

(G-832)
FLOWERS BKG CO BRADENTON LLC
Also Called: Flowers Baking Company
26240 Old 41 Rd (34135-6634)
PHONE..................................941 758-5656
Chris Peer, *Manager*
EMP: 25
SALES (corp-wide): 4.3B **Publicly Held**
WEB: www.flobradconf.com
SIC: 2051 Bread, cake & related products
HQ: Flowers Baking Co. Of Bradenton, Llc
6490 Parkland Dr
Sarasota FL 34243

(G-833)
GEORGE & COMPANY LLC
28771 S Diesel Dr Ste 3 (34135-1808)
P.O. Box 111898, Naples (34108-0132)
PHONE..................................239 949-3650
Shauna Smilanich, *Sales Mgr*
Peter Smilanich, *Mng Member*
▲ **EMP:** 14 **EST:** 2002
SQ FT: 10,000
SALES (est): 1.8MM **Privately Held**
WEB: www.dicegames.com
SIC: 3944 Games, toys & children's vehicles

(G-834)
GLOBAL PHRM COMPLIANCE
4324 Sanctuary Way (34134-8722)
PHONE..................................239 949-4958
Luis Dias Da Silva, *President*
EMP: 6 **EST:** 2015
SALES (est): 177.9K **Privately Held**
SIC: 2834 Pharmaceutical preparations

(G-835)
GUEST SERVICE PUBLICATIONS INC
28026 Pisces Ln (34135-8626)
PHONE..................................516 333-3474
Eric Miller, *President*
EMP: 10 **EST:** 1996
SALES (est): 557.2K **Privately Held**
WEB: www.citimaps.com
SIC: 2752 2741 Publication printing, lithographic; telephone & other directory publishing

(G-836)
GULF COAST INSTALLERS LLC
28720 S Diesel Dr (34135-1820)
P.O. Box 163 (34133-0163)
PHONE..................................239 273-4663
Gabriel A Bava, *Principal*
EMP: 13 **EST:** 2015
SALES (est): 1.8MM **Privately Held**
SIC: 2541 2542 Store & office display cases & fixtures; office & store showcases & display fixtures

(G-837)
GULF COAST MOLD & TOOL CORP
Also Called: Awl Manufactuting
25190 Bernwood Dr (34135-7846)
PHONE..................................239 643-1017
Ralph Shaw, *President*
Bonnie Shaw, *Principal*
Daniel Shaw, *Exec VP*
▼ **EMP:** 16 **EST:** 1993
SQ FT: 18,000
SALES (est): 580.1K **Privately Held**
SIC: 3089 3544 Injection molded finished plastic products; special dies, tools, jigs & fixtures

(G-838)
I-PARTNER GROUP INC (PA)
Also Called: Bonita Print Shop
28200 Old 41 Rd Unit 204 (34135-0836)
PHONE..................................239 449-4749
Mark Pace, *President*
Albert Arguelles, *Vice Pres*
Marian Hack, *Opers Staff*
Jacob Albion, *Web Dvlpr*
EMP: 5 **EST:** 2012
SALES (est): 1.2MM **Privately Held**
WEB: www.ipartnermedia.com
SIC: 2399 Banners, pennants & flags

(G-839)
INSTITUTIONAL EYE CARE LLC
27499 Rvrview Ctr Blvd St (34134-4313)
P.O. Box 366550 (34136-6550)
PHONE..................................866 604-2931
EMP: 12
SALES (est): 1.3MM **Privately Held**
SIC: 3851 8042 Mfg Ophthalmic Goods Optometrist's Office

(G-840)
INTERACTYX AMERICAS INC
3461 Bonita Bay Blvd # 2 (34134-4384)
PHONE..................................888 575-2266
Alfred R Novas, *CEO*
John Hillsman, *Business Mgr*
Jodi Harrison, *Vice Pres*
Jodi L Harrison, *Vice Pres*
Michael Mangan, *Manager*
EMP: 32 **EST:** 2006
SQ FT: 2,339
SALES (est): 878.5K **Privately Held**
WEB: www.topyx.com
SIC: 7372 Application computer software

(G-841)
INTRINSIC INTERVENTIONS INC
223 Dolphin Cove Ct (34134-7456)
PHONE..................................614 205-8465
Kelly Burdge, *Branch Mgr*
EMP: 9
SALES (corp-wide): 81.2K **Privately Held**
WEB: www.myvistaflow.com
SIC: 2899
PA: Intrinsic Interventions Inc.
1604 Pecan St
Nokomis FL

(G-842)
JOHNSON BROS PRCSION PRCAST PD
24263 Production Cir (34135-7058)
PHONE..................................239 947-6734
David L Johnson, *President*
EMP: 25 **EST:** 1988
SQ FT: 15,000
SALES (est): 2MM **Privately Held**
WEB: www.jbprecast.com
SIC: 3272 Concrete products, precast

(G-843)
LIBERTY BALLOONS LLC
10401 Morningside Ln (34135-7730)
PHONE..................................239 947-3338
EMP: 6 **EST:** 2018
SALES (est): 605.9K **Privately Held**
WEB: www.beardeddragongames.com
SIC: 3069 Fabricated rubber products

(G-844)
LOTT QA GROUP INC
27499 Riverview Center Bl (34134-4313)
PHONE..................................201 693-2224
Mark Lott, *CEO*
Michele Licausi, *COO*
EMP: 8 **EST:** 2013
SALES (est): 418K **Privately Held**
SIC: 7372 7371 7379 Business oriented computer software; application computer software; computer software development & applications; computer related consulting services

(G-845)
MIP-TECHNOLOGY CORP
28100 Bonita Grande Dr # 101
(34135-6220)
PHONE..................................239 221-3604
Donald Skelton, *President*
EMP: 6 **EST:** 2012
SALES (est): 397.5K **Privately Held**
SIC: 3826 Photometers

(G-846)
PEREZ INDUSTRIES INC
26364 Old 41 Rd (34135-6658)
PHONE..................................239 992-2444
Baldemar J Perez, *President*
Christina Perez, *Admin Sec*
EMP: 15 **EST:** 1988
SQ FT: 4,900
SALES (est): 2.5MM **Privately Held**
WEB: www.perezindustries.com
SIC: 3353 3444 Aluminum sheet, plate & foil; sheet metalwork

(G-847)
PIZZAROS
24611 Production Cir (34135-7047)
PHONE..................................239 390-0349
Daniel Marshall Snow, *Owner*
EMP: 8 **EST:** 2011
SALES (est): 439.1K **Privately Held**
WEB: www.pizzarosbonita.com
SIC: 3421 Table & food cutlery, including butchers'

(G-848)
PRECISION SCREEN ENCLOSURES
28790 S Diesel Dr (34135-1807)
PHONE..................................239 221-8465

Andrew Fuhrmann, *Principal*
EMP: 6 **EST:** 2018
SALES (est): 88.9K **Privately Held**
WEB: www.premierpoolenclosures.com
SIC: 3448 Screen enclosures

(G-849)
PRESAGE ANALYTICS INC
27500 Rvrview Ctr Blvd St (34134-4325)
PHONE..................................800 309-1704
Paul Griswold, *Principal*
EMP: 7 **EST:** 2019
SALES (est): 323.3K **Privately Held**
WEB: www.presageanalytics.com
SIC: 2034 Dehydrated fruits, vegetables, soups

(G-850)
PRESTIGE BRANDS INTERNATIONAL
26811 S Bay Dr Ste 300 (34134-4358)
PHONE..................................914 524-6800
Matthew M Mannelly, *President*
Jean Boyko, *Senior VP*
John Parkinson, *Senior VP*
Ron Lombardi, *CFO*
Timothy J Connors, *Chief Mktg Ofcr*
EMP: 26 **EST:** 1999
SALES (est): 6.3MM
SALES (corp-wide): 943.3MM **Publicly Held**
WEB: www.prestigebrands.com
SIC: 2834 Pharmaceutical preparations
HQ: Prestige Brands, Inc.
660 White Plains Rd # 250
Tarrytown NY 10591
914 524-6800

(G-851)
R&W DISTRIBUTORS INC
Also Called: R & W Distributors
10919 Enterprise Ave (34135-6864)
PHONE..................................239 948-5735
Steward Miestrich, *President*
EMP: 6
SQ FT: 8,243
SALES (corp-wide): 5.7MM **Privately Held**
WEB: www.rwdist.com
SIC: 3449 Fabricated bar joists & concrete reinforcing bars
PA: R&W Distributors, Inc.
698 Bell Rd
Sarasota FL 34240
941 377-5735

(G-852)
S & S PRECAST INC
25095 Old 41 Rd (34135-7041)
P.O. Box 366098 (34136-6098)
PHONE..................................239 992-8685
Jerry Shannon, *President*
EMP: 11 **EST:** 2007
SALES (est): 2.6MM **Privately Held**
WEB: www.s-sprestress.net
SIC: 3272 Concrete products, precast

(G-853)
SHAW DEVELOPMENT LLC (PA)
25190 Bernwood Dr (34135-7846)
PHONE..................................239 405-6100
Keith Luomala, *President*
Nancy O'Hara, *Corp Secy*
David Dyer, *Vice Pres*
Robert Beckham, *Production*
Paul Cerrito, *Engineer*
◆ **EMP:** 183 **EST:** 1944
SQ FT: 50,000
SALES (est): 65.4MM **Privately Held**
WEB: www.shawdev.com
SIC: 3069 3714 3545 Rubber hardware; exhaust systems & parts, motor vehicle; gas tanks, motor vehicle; machine tool accessories

(G-854)
SMARTADVOCATE LLC (PA)
27299 Riverview Center Bl (34134-4322)
PHONE..................................239 390-1000
Jerrold Parker, *Principal*
Julia Moreland, *VP Sales*
Javier Cobenas, *Administration*
Roy Cronin, *Administration*
EMP: 22 **EST:** 2003
SALES (est): 1.7MM **Privately Held**
WEB: www.smartadvocate.com
SIC: 7372 Business oriented computer software

(G-855)
SOUTHERN PINES INC
26300 Southern Pines Dr (34135-6165)
PHONE..................................239 947-1515
Anthony Tesone, *President*
Joseph Tesone, *Vice Pres*
EMP: 5 **EST:** 1983
SALES (est): 498.1K **Privately Held**
SIC: 2451 Mobile homes

(G-856)
SPIRITWEAR TODAY
28711 N Diesel Dr Unit 9 (34135-1841)
PHONE..................................239 676-7384
Joseph La Rosa, *President*
EMP: 6 **EST:** 2015
SALES (est): 414.3K **Privately Held**
WEB: www.heritagespiritwear.com
SIC: 2752 Commercial printing, offset

(G-857)
SPRINT PRINTING COMPANY LLC
28380 Old 41 Rd Ste 4 (34135-6814)
PHONE..................................239 947-2221
Louisiana Mena,
Martin J Mena,
EMP: 6 **EST:** 2010
SALES (est): 712.4K **Privately Held**
WEB: www.instyprints.com
SIC: 2752 Commercial printing, offset

(G-858)
STRAP SHADE INC
Also Called: Strap Shade
24841 Old 41 Rd (34135-7030)
PHONE..................................239 450-5844
Carlos Kastner, *President*
Paul A Kastner, *COO*
Scott K Presti, *Vice Pres*
EMP: 5
SALES (est): 1MM **Privately Held**
SIC: 3999 Umbrellas, canes & parts

(G-859)
SUNSHINE SPRAY FOAM INSULATION
10923 K Nine Dr (34135-6853)
PHONE..................................239 221-8704
Joceni Sartorio, *President*
EMP: 6 **EST:** 2019
SALES (est): 505K **Privately Held**
WEB: www.sunshinesprayfoamswfl.com
SIC: 1389 Construction, repair & dismantling services

(G-860)
SWF BONITA BEACH INC
3540 Bonita Beach Rd (34134-4158)
PHONE..................................239 466-6600
Tim Anglim, *CEO*
EMP: 55 **Privately Held**
SIC: 2253 Beachwear, knit
PA: Swf Bonita Beach, Inc
17840 San Carlos Blvd
Fort Myers Beach FL 33931

(G-861)
TEDS SHEDS OF TAMPA
10311 Bonita Beach Rd Se (34135-4810)
PHONE..................................239 344-2900
Glenn E Caudill, *President*
EMP: 27 **EST:** 1974
SQ FT: 23,000
SALES (est): 1MM **Privately Held**
SIC: 3448 Farm & utility buildings

(G-862)
TIMILON CORPORATION ✪
24301 Walden Center Dr # 101
(34134-4965)
PHONE..................................239 330-9650
Bill Sanford, *CEO*
EMP: 16 **EST:** 2020
SALES (est): 2.5MM **Privately Held**
WEB: www.timilon.com
SIC: 3564 Air purification equipment

(G-863)
WINDS
Also Called: Mango Bang
4555 Bonita Beach Rd (34134-3985)
PHONE..................................239 948-0777
EMP: 10 **EST:** 2002
SALES (est): 530.8K **Privately Held**
SIC: 2339 Beachwear: women's, misses' & juniors'

Bowling Green
Hardee County

(G-864)
ABBOTT CITRUS LADDERS INC
4060 State Road 62 (33834-4124)
PHONE..................................863 773-6322
Fax: 863 773-6322
EMP: 9
SALES: 800K **Privately Held**
SIC: 2499 Mfg Wood Products

(G-865)
CESARONI AEROSPACE INC
2280 Commerce Ct (33834-2004)
PHONE..................................941 400-1421
Anthony Cesaroni, *President*
Judy V Kiyonaga, *Vice Pres*
Tim Green, *Mfg Staff*
Eric Vianna, *Supervisor*
EMP: 40 **EST:** 1985
SQ FT: 4,000
SALES (est): 4.7MM **Privately Held**
SIC: 3483 Rockets (ammunition)

(G-866)
LENOC CHEMICAL SOLUTIONS INC
2970 Manuel Rd (33834-3058)
PHONE..................................229 499-0665
Bruce J Sperry, *Principal*
EMP: 8 **EST:** 2016
SALES (est): 389.1K **Privately Held**
SIC: 2879 Insecticides & pesticides

(G-867)
PROPLUS PRODUCTS INC
149 County Line Rd E (33834-2850)
P.O. Box 426 (33834-0426)
PHONE..................................863 375-2487
Christina Lyle, *President*
Holly Lyle, *Office Mgr*
EMP: 13 **EST:** 2013
SALES (est): 1.6MM **Privately Held**
WEB: www.proplusproducts.com
SIC: 2873 Fertilizers: natural (organic), except compost

(G-868)
S A FLORIKAN-E LLC
2404 Commerce Ct (33834-2014)
PHONE..................................800 322-8666
Kevin Cundiff, *General Mgr*
Eric Rosenthal, *Mng Member*
John Donegan, *Manager*
Beth Faulkner, *Manager*
Chad Keel, *Manager*
EMP: 60
SALES (corp-wide): 23.3MM **Privately Held**
WEB: www.florikan.com
SIC: 2875 Fertilizers, mixing only
PA: S A Florikan-E Llc
6801 Energy Ct Ste 100
Lakewood Ranch FL 34240
941 379-4048

(G-869)
STREAM2SEA LLC
2498 Commerce Ct (33834-2014)
P.O. Box 907, Wauchula (33873-0907)
PHONE..................................866 960-9513
Autumn P Blum, *CEO*
Mike Malterre, *Exec VP*
Cat Miller, *Accounts Exec*
EMP: 9 **EST:** 2014
SALES (est): 1MM **Privately Held**
WEB: www.stream2sea.com
SIC: 2844 Toilet preparations

Boynton Beach
Palm Beach County

(G-870)
3G ENTERPRISES INC
Also Called: 3g Grpahics Design & Printing
1530 Via De Pepi (33426-8240)
P.O. Box 3672 (33424-3672)
PHONE..................................754 366-7643
Alexandra Grant, *Principal*
EMP: 6 **EST:** 2006
SALES (est): 169.9K **Privately Held**
WEB: www.g3enterprises.com
SIC: 2752 Commercial printing, lithographic

(G-871)
7UP SNAPPLE
Also Called: 7-Up
4895 Park Ridge Blvd (33426-8316)
PHONE..................................561 732-7395
Eric Rogers, *Manager*
EMP: 7 **EST:** 2017
SALES (est): 205.7K **Privately Held**
WEB: www.snapple.com
SIC: 2086 Bottled & canned soft drinks

(G-872)
AD-TAR
26 Bristol Ln (33436-7413)
PHONE..................................561 732-2055
Stuart Adelkoff, *Principal*
EMP: 6 **EST:** 2010
SALES (est): 140.9K **Privately Held**
SIC: 2865 Tar

(G-873)
ADVANCED TRUCK EQUIPMENT INC
1315 Neptune Dr (33426-8403)
PHONE..................................561 424-0442
Kyle J Rathbun, *President*
Deborah A Rathbun, *Corp Secy*
EMP: 22 **EST:** 1957
SQ FT: 26,000
SALES (est): 876.9K **Privately Held**
WEB: www.advtrk.com
SIC: 3713 Truck bodies (motor vehicles)

(G-874)
AMCI TECHNOLOGIES INC
9772 El Clair Ranch Rd (33437-3339)
PHONE..................................561 596-6288
Matthew I Kahn, *Principal*
EMP: 12 **EST:** 2010
SALES (est): 184.2K **Privately Held**
WEB: www.amcitech.com
SIC: 3823 Industrial instrmnts msrmnt display/control process variable

(G-875)
AMERICAN BOTTLING COMPANY
Southeast-Atlantic
4895 Park Ridge Blvd (33426-8316)
PHONE..................................561 732-7395
Rich Kerner, *Manager*
EMP: 17
SQ FT: 3,000 **Publicly Held**
WEB: www.keurigdrpepper.com
SIC: 2086 Soft drinks: packaged in cans, bottles, etc.
HQ: The American Bottling Company
6425 Hall Of Fame Ln
Frisco TX 75034

(G-876)
AMERICAN MOLDING AND PLAS LLC
870 W Industrial Ave # 8 (33426-3643)
PHONE..................................561 676-1987
Angelo J Christopher, *Mng Member*
EMP: 22 **EST:** 2012
SALES (est): 5.1MM **Privately Held**
WEB:
www.americanmoldingandplastics.com
SIC: 3089 Injection molding of plastics

(G-877)
ANTON PAAR QUANTATEC INC
Also Called: Quantachrome Instruments
1900 Corporate Dr (33426-6650)
PHONE..................................561 731-4999

GEOGRAPHIC

Jakob Santner, *Ch of Bd*
Georg Cortolezis-Supp, *President*
Reinhard Eberl, *Vice Pres*
Josh Young, *Project Mgr*
Mark Contessa, *Opers Mgr*
EMP: 5 **EST:** 1922
SQ FT: 45,000
SALES (est): 5.4MM
SALES (corp-wide): 452.3MM **Privately Held**
WEB: www.quantachrome.com
SIC: **3826** 3829 Analytical instruments; measuring & controlling devices
HQ: Anton Paar Gmbh
Anton-Paar-StraBe 20
Graz-Strassgang 8054
316 257-0

(G-878)
APOGEE SERVICES INC
703 Sw 24th Ave (33435-6752)
PHONE..................................561 441-5354
Joy E Wilkie, *President*
Joy Wilkie, *Marketing Staff*
EMP: 15 **EST:** 2004
SALES (est): 350K **Privately Held**
SIC: **3531** Airport construction machinery

(G-879)
APPOINTMENT TEAM INC
1530 W Boynton Beach Blvd (33436-4606)
PHONE..................................561 314-5471
Nicholas Atasoy,
EMP: 10 **EST:** 2018
SALES (est): 641.3K **Privately Held**
SIC: **3699** Security devices

(G-880)
AREWEONLINECOM LLC
1101 N Congress Ave # 202 (33426-3336)
PHONE..................................561 572-0233
Mark Turkel,
James Wright,
EMP: 6 **EST:** 2010
SALES (est): 300.5K **Privately Held**
WEB: www.areweonline.com
SIC: **3695** Computer software tape & disks: blank, rigid & floppy

(G-881)
ATLAS PEAT & SOIL INC (PA)
9621 S State Road 7 (33472-4609)
PHONE..................................561 734-7300
Brian Lulfs, *President*
Michelle Lancianese, *Corp Secy*
Julie Croteau, *Vice Pres*
Margaret Lulfs, *Vice Pres*
Kathryn Vanreeth, *Vice Pres*
◆ **EMP:** 38 **EST:** 1965
SQ FT: 6,400
SALES (est): 7.3MM **Privately Held**
WEB: www.atlaspeatandsoil.com
SIC: **3295** Diatomaceous earth, ground or otherwise treated

(G-882)
BACH WOODWORKING LLC
11170 Sunset Ridge Cir (33473-4870)
PHONE..................................651 329-1220
Andrea Lorbach, *Principal*
EMP: 6 **EST:** 2013
SALES (est): 152.2K **Privately Held**
SIC: **2431** Millwork

(G-883)
BOBS QUICK PRTG & COPY CTR
Also Called: Bob's Printing
812 Chapel Hill Blvd (33435-8111)
PHONE..................................561 278-0203
Fax: 561 272-3828
EMP: 8
SQ FT: 4,000
SALES (est): 850K **Privately Held**
SIC: **2752** Offset Printing & Photo Offset

(G-884)
BRADDCK MTLLGL ARSP SER INC
507 Industrial Way (33426-8770)
PHONE..................................561 622-2200
George Gieger, *Principal*
Steve Hutchinson, *Plant Mgr*
EMP: 12 **EST:** 2008
SALES (est): 1MM **Privately Held**
WEB: www.braddockmt.com
SIC: **3398** Metal heat treating

(G-885)
BURLEYS MMRALS BRIAL VULTS LLC
7111 Ivy Crossing Ln (33436-9415)
PHONE..................................561 284-6983
Kedrick J Burley, *Principal*
EMP: 7 **EST:** 2018
SALES (est): 597.8K **Privately Held**
SIC: **3272** Burial vaults, concrete or precast terrazzo

(G-886)
CANVAS TATTOO LLC
8872 Maple Hill Ct (33473-4855)
PHONE..................................561 870-7929
Giustino M Natale, *President*
EMP: 6 **EST:** 2017
SALES (est): 46.5K **Privately Held**
SIC: **2211** Canvas

(G-887)
CBD DSTRBUTED BY MIAMI CBD INC
416 E Boynton Beach Blvd A (33435-3844)
PHONE..................................561 316-7456
EMP: 6 **EST:** 2017
SALES (est): 112K **Privately Held**
SIC: **3999**

(G-888)
CC LIGHTING INC
11138 Green Lake Dr (33437-1465)
PHONE..................................805 302-5321
Frank C Cotone, *Principal*
EMP: 6 **EST:** 2013
SALES (est): 309.8K **Privately Held**
SIC: **3648** Lighting equipment

(G-889)
CECO INC
Also Called: Caribbean Interior Design Ctr
2951 Sw 14th Pl Ste 39 (33426-9005)
P.O. Box 207 (33425-0207)
PHONE..................................561 265-1111
EMP: 10
SQ FT: 1,600
SALES (est): 590K **Privately Held**
SIC: **2591** Manufactures Window Treatments Including Vertical Blinds Mini Blinds And Window Shades

(G-890)
CLEAR COPY INC
Also Called: 33 Wraps
1304 N Federal Hwy (33435-3233)
PHONE..................................561 369-3900
Steve Feldman, *President*
Bob Feldman, *Vice Pres*
Royce Feldman, *Vice Pres*
Mary Anne Feldman, *Manager*
EMP: 33 **EST:** 1974
SQ FT: 4,000
SALES (est): 1MM **Privately Held**
WEB: www.clearcopyprinting.com
SIC: **2752** Commercial printing, offset

(G-891)
CLOUD INVESTMENT PARTNERS LLLP
1811 Corporate Dr (33426-6646)
PHONE..................................561 266-0845
Declan Treacy, *Partner*
David Weiss, *Partner*
EMP: 4
SALES (est): 3.4MM **Privately Held**
WEB: www.cloudinvestmentpartners.com
SIC: **3324** Aerospace investment castings, ferrous

(G-892)
CONDITION CULTURE LLC
Also Called: Featherlocks
123 Harbors Way (33435-2400)
PHONE..................................786 433-8279
Jennifer Donya,
Alexandra Litowitz,
▲ **EMP:** 11 **EST:** 2011
SALES (est): 1.5MM **Privately Held**
WEB: www.conditionculture.com
SIC: **3999** Hair & hair-based products

(G-893)
CORELLIUM LLC
1301 N Congress Ave # 41 (33426-3320)
PHONE..................................561 502-2420
Amanda Gorton,
EMP: 8 **EST:** 2017
SALES (est): 518.3K **Privately Held**
SIC: **7372** Prepackaged software

(G-894)
CUSTOM INSTRUMENTS LLC
711 N Railroad Ave Unit 3 (33435-3817)
PHONE..................................561 735-9971
Edwyn B Pyron,
Lori Pyron,
EMP: 5 **EST:** 2004
SALES (est): 490K **Privately Held**
SIC: **3549** Metalworking machinery

(G-895)
CUSTOM TRUSS LLC
510 Industrial Ave (33426-3645)
PHONE..................................561 266-3451
Iva Kutlova, *President*
EMP: 10 **EST:** 2008
SALES (est): 2.4MM **Privately Held**
WEB: www.customtrussllc.com
SIC: **2439** Trusses, wooden roof

(G-896)
DELUXE STONE INC
6129 Country Fair Cir (33437-2847)
PHONE..................................561 236-2322
Jimmy Montoya, *Principal*
EMP: 9 **EST:** 2009
SALES (est): 313.1K **Privately Held**
SIC: **2782** Blankbooks & looseleaf binders

(G-897)
DIGICARE BIOMEDICAL TECH INC
107 Commerce Rd (33426-9365)
PHONE..................................561 689-0408
Eduardo Miranda, *President*
Pedro Miranda, *Software Engr*
EMP: 9 **EST:** 1995
SQ FT: 5,000
SALES (est): 2.5MM **Privately Held**
WEB: www.digi-vet.com
SIC: **3841** Surgical & medical instruments

(G-898)
DOUBLE R PUBLISHING
621 Nw 10th Ct (33426-2972)
PHONE..................................305 525-3573
Rebeca Lamas, *Manager*
EMP: 7 **EST:** 2013
SALES (est): 412K **Privately Held**
SIC: **2741** Miscellaneous publishing

(G-899)
DRYER VENT WIZARD OF PB
22 Las Flores (33426-8821)
PHONE..................................561 901-3464
Horatio Chiorean, *Owner*
Wai Chan, *Project Mgr*
Mike Tang, *Project Mgr*
Colleen Martin, *Buyer*
Sean Eberhardt, *Engineer*
EMP: 19 **EST:** 2007
SALES (est): 427.4K **Privately Held**
SIC: **3631** Barbecues, grills & braziers (outdoor cooking)

(G-900)
EAGLE ENGRG & LAND DEV INC
302 Sw 3rd Ave (33435-4823)
P.O. Box 990189, Naples (34116-6067)
PHONE..................................913 948-4320
Lori Schulmeister, *President*
Hugh A House Jr, *President*
EMP: 10
SQ FT: 2,000
SALES (est): 2.5MM **Privately Held**
WEB: www.eaglesitedev.com
SIC: **1422** 1611 1781 1794 Crushed & broken limestone; highway & street construction; water well drilling; excavation & grading, building construction; water distribution or supply systems for irrigation

(G-901)
ECCO DOORS LLC
505 Industrial Way (33426-8770)
PHONE..................................561 392-3533
EMP: 5
SALES (est): 683.6K **Privately Held**
SIC: **2511** Mfg Wood Household Furniture

(G-902)
ENTER YOUR HOURS LLC
2447 Quantum Blvd (33426-8612)
PHONE..................................561 337-7785
Korff S Aaron, *Manager*
EMP: 6 **EST:** 2012
SALES (est): 111.8K **Privately Held**
WEB: www.enteryourhours.com
SIC: **7372** Prepackaged software

(G-903)
EPHS HOLDINGS INC
7694 Colony Palm Dr (33436-1312)
PHONE..................................212 321-0091
Stevan Perry, *President*
Stuart R Ross, *CFO*
EMP: 6 **EST:** 2018
SALES (est): 88.5K **Privately Held**
WEB: www.ephsholdings.com
SIC: **2834** Pharmaceutical preparations

(G-904)
ERICKSON INTERNATIONAL LLC
161 Commerce Rd Ste 2 (33426-9385)
PHONE..................................702 853-4800
Debbie Lindsay, *Branch Mgr*
EMP: 9
SALES (corp-wide): 13.4MM **Privately Held**
WEB: www.aswf.com
SIC: **3211** Window glass, clear & colored
PA: Erickson International, Llc
3135 Marco St
Las Vegas NV 89115
702 853-4800

(G-905)
FIVE STAR FIELD SERVICES
Also Called: Five Star Measurement
3539 S Federal Hwy Apt L (33435-8689)
PHONE..................................347 446-6816
Douglas Asch, *Mng Member*
William Cook,
Keith Stone,
EMP: 7 **EST:** 2008
SQ FT: 1,000
SALES (est): 355K **Privately Held**
SIC: **1389** Measurement of well flow rates, oil & gas

(G-906)
FKP
2950 Commerce Park Dr # 6 (33426-8779)
PHONE..................................561 493-0076
Anne Punter, *President*
EMP: 10 **EST:** 2008
SALES (est): 396.9K **Privately Held**
WEB: www.fkp-us.com
SIC: **3799** Go-carts, except children's

(G-907)
FLORIDA BEST HEARING
4739 N Congress Ave (33426-7940)
PHONE..................................863 402-0094
Guy Steve Reinshuttle, *Principal*
EMP: 22 **EST:** 2018
SALES (est): 358.3K **Privately Held**
SIC: **3842** 8099 Hearing aids; hearing testing service

(G-908)
FRIENDS PROFESSIONAL STY
1521 Neptune Dr (33426-8418)
PHONE..................................561 734-4660
Richard Friend Sr, *President*
Howard Friend, *Corp Secy*
William Friend, *Vice Pres*
EMP: 7 **EST:** 1979
SQ FT: 8,000
SALES (est): 332K **Privately Held**
WEB: www.friendsstationery.com
SIC: **2759** Engraving

(G-909)
GATEWAY WRELESS COMMUNICATIONS
3600 S Congress Ave (33426-8488)
PHONE..................................561 732-6444
EMP: 10

▲ = Import ▼=Export
◆ =Import/Export

SALES (est): 720K Privately Held
SIC: 3663 Wireless Communications

(G-910)
GENERAL CATAGRAPHY INC
4 Estate Dr (33436-6202)
PHONE.................................561 455-4398
Paul Pugliese, *Principal*
EMP: 6 EST: 2016
SALES (est): 309.9K Privately Held
WEB: www.cartographybypaul.com
SIC: 2741 Miscellaneous publishing

(G-911)
GEVAS PCKG CONVERTING TECH LTD
3553 High Ridge Rd (33426-8737)
PHONE.................................561 202-0800
Carlo Gretter, *President*
Thomas Sander, *Partner*
EMP: 5 EST: 1997
SQ FT: 12,000
SALES (est): 911.8K Privately Held
SIC: 3565 Packaging machinery

(G-912)
GFOODZ LLC
10356 Willow Oaks Trl (33473-4860)
PHONE.................................561 703-4505
Sonali Surve, *Mng Member*
EMP: 7 EST: 2016
SALES (est): 100K Privately Held
SIC: 2051 5149 Bakery: wholesale or wholesale/retail combined; bakery products

(G-913)
GOLDEN PRINT INC
2701 Sw 6th St (33435-7511)
PHONE.................................561 833-9661
Christopher Lanni, *President*
EMP: 8 EST: 2018
SALES (est): 165.3K Privately Held
SIC: 2752 Commercial printing, offset

(G-914)
GRAFTON PRODUCTS CORP
Also Called: Grafton Cosmetics
1801 Corporate Dr (33426-6646)
PHONE.................................561 738-2886
Edward Marcus, *President*
Gail Marcus, *Corp Secy*
Jason Marcus, *Vice Pres*
Steven Marcus, *Vice Pres*
David Carroll, *Opers Staff*
▲ EMP: 24 EST: 1962
SQ FT: 17,000
SALES (est): 4.4MM Privately Held
WEB: www.graftoncosmetics.com
SIC: 2844 Perfumes, natural or synthetic; cosmetic preparations

(G-915)
GRANITE IMPORTS INC
1500 Gateway Blvd Ste 250 (33426-7245)
PHONE.................................732 500-2549
▲ EMP: 1
SQ FT: 1,000
SALES (est): 4MM Privately Held
SIC: 1411 Dimension Stone Quarry

(G-916)
HANS RUDOLPH INC
7185 Briella Dr (33437-3763)
PHONE.................................561 877-8775
Hans Rudolph, *President*
EMP: 10 EST: 2015
SALES (est): 90.2K Privately Held
WEB: www.rudolphkc.com
SIC: 3842 Surgical appliances & supplies

(G-917)
ICE CREAM CLUB INC (PA)
1580 High Ridge Rd (33426-8724)
PHONE.................................561 731-3331
Richard Draper, *CEO*
Thomas D Jackson, *Vice Pres*
Michael Scott, *Vice Pres*
Mike Scott, *Vice Pres*
Jim Cummins, *Prdtn Mgr*
▼ EMP: 40 EST: 1982
SQ FT: 16,500
SALES (est): 7.5MM Privately Held
WEB: www.icecreamclub.com
SIC: 2024 Ice cream & frozen desserts; yogurt desserts, frozen

(G-918)
IIS INCORPORATED
3020 High Ridge Rd (33426-8732)
PHONE.................................561 547-4297
Mark A Shymansky, *President*
Catharine Greenman, *Credit Staff*
David Shelfer, *Sales Mgr*
EMP: 7 EST: 2007
SALES (est): 781.4K Privately Held
WEB: www.iisfla.com
SIC: 2394 3089 5039 5199 Canvas awnings & canopies; awnings, fiberglass & plastic combination; awnings; canvas products

(G-919)
IMAGO PRODUCTS
1500 Gateway Blvd Ste 220 (33426-7233)
PHONE.................................888 400-4122
Paul Handerhan, *Owner*
EMP: 7 EST: 2012
SQ FT: 150
SALES (est): 122.2K Privately Held
WEB: www.imagoproducts.com
SIC: 7372 Business oriented computer software

(G-920)
INNOVATIVE INDUS SOLUTIONS INC (PA)
Also Called: I I S
3020 High Ridge Rd (33426-8732)
PHONE.................................561 733-1548
Mark Shymansky, *President*
Rodger Wise, *Vice Pres*
Catharine McIntyre, *Credit Mgr*
▼ EMP: 7 EST: 2001
SQ FT: 12,000
SALES (est): 2.6MM Privately Held
WEB: www.iisfla.com
SIC: 2394 Canvas & related products

(G-921)
INNOVTIVE WIN CNCPTS DOORS INC
4336 Juniper Ter (33436-3023)
PHONE.................................561 493-2303
EMP: 19
SALES: 3MM Privately Held
SIC: 2431 3442 Mfg Millwork Mfg Metal Doors/Sash/Trim

(G-922)
INTERSTATE SIGNCRAFTERS LLC
130 Commerce Rd (33426-9364)
PHONE.................................561 547-3760
Jeff Petersen, *CEO*
Lisa Johnson, *Vice Pres*
Anthony Lipari, *VP Opers*
Valerie Mayer, *VP Finance*
Terri Seldin, *Finance*
▼ EMP: 75
SQ FT: 35,000
SALES (est): 15MM Privately Held
WEB: www.aisigncrafters.com
SIC: 3993 1799 Electric signs; sign installation & maintenance

(G-923)
IRON SIGHT PRECISION LLC
711 N Railroad Ave (33435-3817)
PHONE.................................561 735-9971
Chistopher Rook, *Administration*
EMP: 6 EST: 2016
SALES (est): 96.2K Privately Held
WEB: www.firingpins.com
SIC: 3489 Ordnance & accessories

(G-924)
JET FACTORY LLC
147 Sw 25th Ave (33435-6731)
PHONE.................................305 848-8846
Volker Haseidl, *Branch Mgr*
EMP: 8
SALES (corp-wide): 116.6K Privately Held
SIC: 3999 Barber & beauty shop equipment
PA: Jet Factory Llc
1900 Nw 33rd Ct Ste 5
Pompano Beach FL 33064
786 387-6865

(G-925)
JHN NORTH LLC
3554 Lothair Ave (33436-3122)
PHONE.................................561 294-5613
Juan C Pereyra, *Manager*
EMP: 5 EST: 2018
SALES (est): 330.4K Privately Held
SIC: 3823 Industrial instrmnts msrmnt display/control process variable

(G-926)
KERRY CONSULTING CORP
30 Lawrence Lake Dr (33436-2020)
PHONE.................................561 364-9969
Joel Sarnow, *President*
Doug Pearsall, *Vice Pres*
Linda Sarnow, *Treasurer*
EMP: 10 EST: 2007
SALES (est): 1MM Privately Held
WEB: www.kerryconsultingcorp.com
SIC: 2096 Potato chips & similar snacks

(G-927)
LAP OF AMERICA LC
Also Called: Lap of Amer Laser Applications
161 Commerce Rd Ste 3 (33426-9385)
PHONE.................................561 416-9250
Peter Van Arkel, *CEO*
Caroly Van Arkel, *General Mgr*
Raija Kinnunen, *Finance*
Donald McCreath, *Natl Sales Mgr*
Neil Johnston, *Marketing Staff*
▲ EMP: 7 EST: 1996
SQ FT: 1,500
SALES (est): 1.5MM Privately Held
WEB: www.lap-america.com
SIC: 3699 5085 Laser systems & equipment; industrial supplies

(G-928)
LEGAR INC
303 E Woolbright Rd # 103 (33435-6010)
PHONE.................................561 635-5882
Michael Basnight, *President*
Arlena Richardson, *Chief Mktg Ofcr*
Michael Hursey, *General Counsel*
EMP: 10
SALES (est): 2MM Privately Held
SIC: 2671 Paper coated or laminated for packaging

(G-929)
LJS TOPS & BOTTOMS
Also Called: L J'S Tops & Bottoms
3050 Sw 14th Pl Ste 11 (33426-9020)
PHONE.................................561 736-7868
Lawrence A Walicki, *Partner*
Judy K Walicki, *Partner*
EMP: 24 EST: 1993
SQ FT: 4,000
SALES (est): 2.4MM Privately Held
WEB: www.ljstopsandbottoms.com
SIC: 3799 3949 Golf carts, powered; sporting & athletic goods

(G-930)
M & S COMPUTER PRODUCTS INC
Also Called: Servers 4 Networks
11419 Wingfoot Dr (33437-1629)
PHONE.................................561 244-5400
Marcia Posen, *President*
◆ EMP: 5 EST: 1985
SQ FT: 4,000
SALES (est): 451.3K Privately Held
SIC: 3571 2844 5999 Electronic computers; tonics, hair; business machines & equipment; telephone & communication equipment

(G-931)
MAGELLAN AVIATION GROUP LLLP
1811 Corporate Dr (33426-6646)
PHONE.................................561 266-0845
Larry Grogan, *Partner*
Linda Manfre, *Accountant*
EMP: 6 Privately Held
WEB: www.magellangroup.net
SIC: 3724 Aircraft engines & engine parts
HQ: Magellan Aviation Group Lllp
2345 Township Rd Ste B
Charlotte NC 28273
704 504-9204

(G-932)
MARK WSSER GRAPHIC PRODUCTIONS
Also Called: Mark Weisser Productions
8941 Golden Mountain Cir (33473-3310)
PHONE.................................305 888-7445
Mark Weisser, *President*
EMP: 5 EST: 1992
SQ FT: 1,200
SALES (est): 373.3K Privately Held
SIC: 2759 Advertising literature: printing

(G-933)
MOTOROLA SOLUTIONS INC
2009 Corporate Dr (33426-6653)
PHONE.................................561 369-7164
Tom Pack, *Manager*
EMP: 6
SALES (corp-wide): 7.4B Publicly Held
WEB: www.motorolasolutions.com
SIC: 3663 Radio & TV communications equipment
PA: Motorola Solutions, Inc.
500 W Monroe St Ste 4400
Chicago IL 60661
847 576-5000

(G-934)
MRI SPECIALISTS
1800 W Woolbright Rd # 100 (33426-6398)
PHONE.................................561 369-2144
Richard Bajakian, *President*
Deidra Knevelbaard, *Office Mgr*
Kim Heredia, *Manager*
EMP: 8 EST: 2002
SALES (est): 1MM Privately Held
SIC: 3845 8071 Magnetic resonance imaging device, nuclear; medical laboratories

(G-935)
MULTI CONTACT USA
3814 Lace Vine Ln (33436-3929)
PHONE.................................561 738-5637
Tom Bilinski, *Principal*
Kira Flores, *Production*
EMP: 6 EST: 2005
SALES (est): 222.1K Privately Held
SIC: 3643 Electric connectors

(G-936)
NAMRO INDUSTRIES INC
4336 Juniper Ter (33436-3023)
PHONE.................................561 704-8063
Christine Orman, *Director*
EMP: 8 EST: 2005
SALES (est): 93.5K Privately Held
SIC: 3999 Manufacturing industries

(G-937)
NATURAL BEAUTY WOOD PRODUCTS
Also Called: Creative Metal Products
1120 Se 1st St (33435-6013)
PHONE.................................561 732-0224
Joshua Aron, *Vice Pres*
EMP: 14 EST: 2000
SQ FT: 1,728
SALES (est): 1MM Privately Held
WEB: www.creativemetals.org
SIC: 2431 Staircases, stairs & railings

(G-938)
NUBO BOTTLE COMPANY LLC
526 Bayfront Dr (33435-8644)
PHONE.................................954 283-9057
Abraham K Kohl, *President*
Kirsten Kohl, *Treasurer*
EMP: 7 EST: 2010
SALES (est): 780MM Privately Held
WEB: www.nubobottle.com
SIC: 2086 Water, pasteurized: packaged in cans, bottles, etc.

(G-939)
PEERLESS WIND SYSTEMS
8681 Hawkwood Bay Dr (33473-7822)
PHONE.................................516 249-6900
Jay Moskowitz, *Owner*
Robert Perless, *Vice Pres*
EMP: 8 EST: 2015
SALES (est): 572.2K Privately Held
SIC: 3511 3621 Turbines & turbine generator sets; motors & generators

(G-940)
PLOTKOWSKI INC (PA)
Also Called: Delray's Screens
210 Se 12th Ave Ste 1 (33435-6063)
PHONE..................................561 740-2226
Carol Plotkowski, *President*
Michael Plotkowski, *Vice Pres*
EMP: 9 **EST:** 1960
SQ FT: 10,000
SALES (est): 781.3K **Privately Held**
WEB: www.delrayscreen.net
SIC: 3442 3444 Screens, window, metal; sheet metalwork

(G-941)
POWERBEES INCORPORATED
1375 Gateway Blvd (33426-8304)
PHONE..................................561 797-5927
John Metz, *Principal*
EMP: 7 **EST:** 2010
SALES (est): 153.4K **Privately Held**
WEB: www.powerbees.com
SIC: 3442 Metal doors, sash & trim

(G-942)
PRECISION PRINTING OF COLUMBUS
11831 Fox Hill Cir (33473-7833)
PHONE..................................561 509-7269
Michael Leaventon, *President*
Marc Leaventon, *General Mgr*
Meridith Solomon, *Treasurer*
Barry Leaventon, *Admin Sec*
EMP: 8 **EST:** 1985
SQ FT: 16,000
SALES (est): 164.6K **Privately Held**
SIC: 2752 2791 Commercial printing, lithographic; typesetting

(G-943)
PREMIER PLASTICS LLC (PA)
1500 Gateway Blvd Ste 250 (33426-7245)
PHONE..................................305 805-3333
Albert Esquenazi,
Morris Esquenazi,
▲ **EMP:** 40 **EST:** 2014
SALES (est): 550.6K **Privately Held**
WEB: www.premierplastics.us
SIC: 3999 2392 3861 Barber & beauty shop equipment; bags, garment storage: except paper or plastic film; reels, film

(G-944)
PREMIUM ABSRBENT DSPSABLES LLC
Also Called: Tite-Dri Industries
3030 Sw 13th Pl Ste A (33426-9086)
PHONE..................................561 737-6377
Carlo Gretter, *Mng Member*
EMP: 47 **EST:** 2005
SALES (est): 8.1MM **Privately Held**
WEB: www.titedri.com
SIC: 2673 Bags: plastic, laminated & coated

(G-945)
PRO MILLWORK INSTALLATIONS ✪
1420 Sw 30th Ave (33426-9062)
PHONE..................................561 302-5869
EMP: 6 **EST:** 2020
SALES (est): 716.3K **Privately Held**
WEB: www.pro-millwork.com
SIC: 2431 Millwork

(G-946)
PRODUCTS BY O2 INC
3020 High Ridge Rd # 300 (33426-8732)
PHONE..................................561 392-1892
Olga Galarza, *President*
EMP: 20 **EST:** 2001
SQ FT: 15,000
SALES (est): 2.5MM **Privately Held**
WEB: www.po2labs.com
SIC: 2844 Cosmetic preparations

(G-947)
PURADYN FILTER TECH INC
2017 High Ridge Rd (33426-8713)
PHONE..................................561 547-9499
Edward S Vittoria, *CEO*
Joseph V Vittoria, *Ch of Bd*
Kevin G Kroger, *President*
Elaine Hilton, *Mfg Staff*
Sathish Kannan, *Engineer*
EMP: 20
SQ FT: 25,500
SALES: 1.5MM **Privately Held**
WEB: www.puradyn.com
SIC: 3714 Filters: oil, fuel & air, motor vehicle

(G-948)
PYURE COMPANY INC ✪
2055 High Ridge Rd (33426-8713)
PHONE..................................561 735-3701
Jean Francois Huc, *CEO*
EMP: 23 **EST:** 2020
SALES (est): 3.7MM **Privately Held**
WEB: www.pyure.com
SIC: 3634 Air purifiers, portable

(G-949)
QGISTIX INC
2019 Corporate Dr (33426-6653)
PHONE..................................855 573-3872
Tanja Savic, *Director*
EMP: 9 **EST:** 2019
SALES (est): 198K **Privately Held**
WEB: www.qgistix.com
SIC: 3599 Machine shop, jobbing & repair

(G-950)
QUICKPRINT LINE
2015 Corporate Dr (33426-6653)
P.O. Box 1435, Lake Worth (33460-1435)
PHONE..................................561 740-9930
EMP: 7 **EST:** 2010
SALES (est): 11.6K **Privately Held**
WEB: www.quickprintline.com
SIC: 2752 Commercial printing, offset

(G-951)
RADIAL INC
1903 S Congress Ave # 460 (33426-6559)
P.O. Box 4688 (33424-4688)
PHONE..................................561 737-5151
EMP: 16
SALES (corp-wide): 2.6B **Privately Held**
WEB: www.radial.com
SIC: 7372 Business oriented computer software
HQ: Radial, Inc.
935 1st Ave
King Of Prussia PA 19406
610 491-7000

(G-952)
RAINBOW PRINTING INC
3300 S Congress Ave # 12 (33426-9027)
PHONE..................................561 364-9000
John H Thomas, *President*
Mary Ann Thomas, *Vice Pres*
Shannon Huston,
EMP: 5 **EST:** 1981
SQ FT: 1,500
SALES (est): 699.2K **Privately Held**
WEB: www.printerboyntonbeach.com
SIC: 2752 Commercial printing, offset

(G-953)
RAR INDUSTRIES LLC
9558 Equus Cir (33472-4334)
PHONE..................................561 213-7876
Richard A Recore,
Michelle Recore,
EMP: 6 **EST:** 2007
SALES (est): 240.7K **Privately Held**
SIC: 3999 Atomizers, toiletry

(G-954)
RED BRICK PUBLISHING LLC
6647 Conch Ct (33437-3648)
PHONE..................................718 208-3600
Jason R Margolin, *Manager*
EMP: 8 **EST:** 2001
SALES (est): 180.4K **Privately Held**
SIC: 2741 Miscellaneous publishing

(G-955)
RIBBON PRINTERS UNLIMITED
12104 Oakvista Dr (33437-6352)
PHONE..................................888 546-3310
Everett Kavaler, *President*
EMP: 6 **EST:** 1999
SALES (est): 101.5K **Privately Held**
WEB: www.ribbonprinters.com
SIC: 2752 Commercial printing, offset

(G-956)
ROMEO ROSEAU ECOMMERCE
245 Ne 6th Ave (33435-3875)
PHONE..................................561 633-1352
Vladimir Thelisma, *Owner*
EMP: 10 **EST:** 2016
SALES (est): 57.9K **Privately Held**
SIC: 2741

(G-957)
SEAGATE PRODUCTIONS LLC
1162 Rialto Dr (33436-7198)
PHONE..................................561 506-7750
Oswald Imbert, *Principal*
EMP: 7 **EST:** 2019
SALES (est): 236K **Privately Held**
WEB: www.seagate.com
SIC: 3572 Computer storage devices

(G-958)
SHOWER DOORS UNLIMITED INC
3551 High Ridge Rd (33426-8737)
PHONE..................................561 547-0702
Linda Sorber, *President*
▼ **EMP:** 10 **EST:** 1997
SALES (est): 679.5K **Privately Held**
WEB: www.showerdoorsunlimited.com
SIC: 3431 3231 Shower stalls, metal; products of purchased glass

(G-959)
SHUTTER DOWN ALL WEATHER PROTC
2778 S Evergreen Cir (33426-8656)
PHONE..................................561 856-0655
Stephen Barbieri, *Principal*
EMP: 6 **EST:** 2012
SALES (est): 85K **Privately Held**
SIC: 3442 Shutters, door or window: metal

(G-960)
SODIKART USA
1025 Gateway Blvd (33426-8348)
PHONE..................................561 493-0290
Peter Bekkers, *Principal*
▲ **EMP:** 8 **EST:** 2013
SALES (est): 306K **Privately Held**
WEB: www.sodikartamerica.com
SIC: 3799 Transportation equipment

(G-961)
SOMFY SYSTEMS INC
1200 Sw 35th Ave (33426-8423)
PHONE..................................561 292-3483
Frank Watts, *Manager*
EMP: 17
SALES (corp-wide): 2.6MM **Privately Held**
SIC: 3699 Door opening & closing devices, electrical
HQ: Somfy Systems, Inc.
121 Herrod Blvd
Dayton NJ 08810
609 395-1300

(G-962)
SOUTH FLORIDA STAIRS INC
2901 Commerce Park Dr # 4 (33426-8728)
PHONE..................................561 822-3110
Joshua Cote, *President*
EMP: 15
SALES (est): 5.5MM **Privately Held**
WEB: www.southfloridastairs.com
SIC: 2431 3446 Staircases, stairs & railings; stairs, staircases, stair treads: prefabricated metal

(G-963)
STEPHEN B FINE CABINETRY INC
1154 Sw 28th Ave (33426-7840)
PHONE..................................561 512-2850
Stephen K Biernacki, *Principal*
EMP: 6 **EST:** 2019
SALES (est): 95.8K **Privately Held**
SIC: 2434 Wood kitchen cabinets

(G-964)
SUN-SENTINEL COMPANY INC
4935 Park Ridge Blvd # 1 (33426-8335)
PHONE..................................561 736-2208
Jim Spijfreed, *Manager*
EMP: 8
SALES (corp-wide): 746.2MM **Privately Held**
WEB: www.sun-sentinel.com
SIC: 2711 Newspapers, publishing & printing
HQ: Sun-Sentinel Company, Llc
500 E Broward Blvd # 800
Fort Lauderdale FL 33394
954 356-4000

(G-965)
SUNCOAST HEAT TREAT INC (PA)
507 Industrial Way (33426-8770)
PHONE..................................561 776-7763
Robert H Brisell, *CEO*
Jennifer McPeek, *President*
Steve Hutchinson, *Vice Pres*
Jo Gayne, *Treasurer*
EMP: 11 **EST:** 1983
SQ FT: 43,000
SALES (est): 4.8MM **Privately Held**
SIC: 3398 Metal heat treating

(G-966)
T V TRAC LTD
7 Island Dr (33436-6072)
PHONE..................................516 371-1111
EMP: 6
SALES (est): 510K **Privately Held**
SIC: 3699 Mfg Electrical Equipment/Supplies

(G-967)
TACTICAL PRODUCTS GROUP LLC
1914 Corporate Dr (33426-6650)
PHONE..................................561 265-4066
Robert J Leitner, *COO*
Dan T Lounsbury Jr,
▲ **EMP:** 25 **EST:** 1998
SALES (est): 3.6MM **Privately Held**
WEB: www.tacprogroup.com
SIC: 2329 7381 Men's & boys' sportswear & athletic clothing; protective services, guard

(G-968)
TCR WOODWORKS INC
204 Monterey Sq 31 (33436-2868)
PHONE..................................561 827-6676
Timothy Rosa, *Principal*
EMP: 6 **EST:** 2010
SALES (est): 105.8K **Privately Held**
SIC: 2431 Millwork

(G-969)
TIN-REZ CORP INC
6615 Boynton Beach Blvd (33437-3526)
PHONE..................................561 654-3133
Antony Mitchell, *Principal*
EMP: 11 **EST:** 2012
SALES (est): 1.2MM **Privately Held**
SIC: 3356 Tin

(G-970)
TONER TECHNOLOGIES INC
2900 Commerce Park Dr # 11
(33426-8775)
PHONE..................................561 547-9710
Timothy Burnett, *President*
Timothy J Burnett, *President*
Sherry Burnett, *Vice Pres*
Cheryl Burnett, *CFO*
EMP: 5 **EST:** 1989
SQ FT: 1,800
SALES (est): 881.6K **Privately Held**
WEB: www.toner-tech.com
SIC: 3955 5734 5112 5999 Print cartridges for laser & other computer printers; word processing equipment & supplies; stationery & office supplies; photocopying supplies; photocopy machines; photocopy machine repair

(G-971)
TOWER OPTICAL CORPORATION
3600 S Congress Ave Ste J (33426-8488)
PHONE..................................561 740-2525
Mel Kantor, *President*
Martin Jennings, *General Mgr*
Don Avritt, *Mfg Dir*
Vincent Capozzi, *Sales Staff*
Joel Kramer, *Sales Staff*

EMP: 19 **EST:** 1988
SQ FT: 11,000
SALES (est): 4.2MM **Privately Held**
SIC: 3827 Optical instruments & apparatus

(G-972)
TPG BLACK LLC
2108 Corporate Dr (33426-6644)
PHONE..................................561 777-8989
EMP: 6 **EST:** 2018
SALES (est): 119.6K **Privately Held**
SIC: 3842 Bulletproof vests

(G-973)
VEE INDUSTRIES INC
211 Se 9th Ave (33435-5643)
PHONE..................................561 732-1083
Shawn R Aldous, *President*
John G Rubino, *Vice Pres*
Dee Rubino, *Treasurer*
Verena Edler, *Manager*
David A Aldous, *Admin Sec*
▲ **EMP:** 8 **EST:** 1969
SQ FT: 3,600
SALES (est): 1.4MM **Privately Held**
WEB: www.store.veeindustries.com
SIC: 3643 Current-carrying wiring devices

(G-974)
WINDBRELLA PRODUCTS CORP
2114 Corporate Dr (33426-6655)
PHONE..................................561 734-5222
Glen Kupferman, *President*
Chelsea Heller, *Vice Pres*
▲ **EMP:** 28 **EST:** 1996
SALES (est): 1.4MM **Privately Held**
WEB: www.windbrella.com
SIC: 2211 Umbrella cloth, cotton

(G-975)
WORLDS COLUMBIAN EXONUMIS
802 North Rd (33435-3230)
PHONE..................................561 734-4433
L Tallent-Diddle, *Principal*
EMP: 6 **EST:** 2002
SALES (est): 330.6K **Privately Held**
SIC: 3444 Mail (post office) collection or storage boxes, sheet metal

(G-976)
WORLDWIDE SUPERABRASIVES LLC
Also Called: Wwsa
2921 Commerce Park Dr (33426-8780)
PHONE..................................954 828-9650
Christian Winkel, *Mng Member*
Daniel Herzog, *Manager*
Clara Winkel,
▲ **EMP:** 23 **EST:** 2004
SALES (est): 4.2MM **Privately Held**
WEB: www.wwsa.com
SIC: 3291 Abrasive products

(G-977)
WORLDWIDE TICKETS & LABELS INC
Also Called: Worldwide Ticketcraft
3606 Quantum Blvd (33426-8637)
P.O. Box 168, Fort Smith AR (72902-0168)
PHONE..................................877 426-5754
Erik Covitz, *CEO*
Captiles Vick, *President*
Mark Loomer, *COO*
George Scher, *CFO*
Natasha Gibson, *Accounts Mgr*
◆ **EMP:** 60 **EST:** 1998
SQ FT: 11,000
SALES (est): 11MM **Privately Held**
WEB: www.worldwideticketcraft.com
SIC: 2759 Flexographic printing
PA: Weldon, Williams & Lick, Inc.
711 N A St
Fort Smith AR 72901
479 783-4113

(G-978)
WWSA SOLIDS LLC
2921 Commerce Park Dr (33426-8780)
PHONE..................................561 588-9299
Christian Winkel, *Mng Member*
EMP: 16 **EST:** 2018
SALES (est): 143.5K **Privately Held**
WEB: www.worldwidesolids.com
SIC: 3291 Abrasive products

(G-979)
YKK AP AMERICA INC
8846 Andy Ct Apt C (33436-2489)
PHONE..................................561 736-7808
EMP: 7 **EST:** 2017
SALES (est): 168.3K **Privately Held**
WEB: www.ykkap.com
SIC: 3442 Sash, door or window: metal

Bradenton
Manatee County

(G-980)
AARON TOOL INC
2819 62nd Ave E (34203-5319)
PHONE..................................941 758-9369
John Gardi, *President*
Tony Vincent, *Executive*
EMP: 24 **EST:** 1978
SQ FT: 18,000
SALES (est): 2.3MM **Privately Held**
WEB: www.aaron-tool.com
SIC: 3599 Machine shop, jobbing & repair

(G-981)
ACU GRIND TOOL WORKS INC
2118 58th Ave E (34203-5059)
P.O. Box 68 (34206-0068)
PHONE..................................941 758-6963
Anthony Antony, *President*
Alice Antony, *Vice Pres*
Nick Antony, *Marketing Staff*
EMP: 20 **EST:** 1979
SQ FT: 5,000
SALES (est): 599K **Privately Held**
WEB: www.acugrind.com
SIC: 3599 Machine shop, jobbing & repair

(G-982)
ADEPTUS INDUSTRIES INC
6224 17th St E (34203-5041)
PHONE..................................941 756-7636
Dan L Fraley, *President*
Kenneth Fraley, *Vice Pres*
Patrick Fraley, *Vice Pres*
Richard A Fraley, *Vice Pres*
EMP: 15 **EST:** 1970
SQ FT: 3,500
SALES (est): 556K **Privately Held**
WEB: www.adeptusind.com
SIC: 3599 3444 Machine shop, jobbing & repair; sheet metalwork

(G-983)
ADVANCE CONTROLS INC (PA)
Also Called: A C I
4505 18th St E (34203-3757)
PHONE..................................941 746-3221
Marsha Panuce, *CEO*
David Robertson, *Electrical Engi*
Kenneth J Long, *CFO*
John Garrow, *Admin Sec*
Edward Weiss,
▲ **EMP:** 14 **EST:** 1984
SQ FT: 30,000
SALES (est): 4.8MM **Privately Held**
WEB: www.acicontrols.com
SIC: 3625 5063 Industrial controls: push button, selector switches, pilot; electrical supplies

(G-984)
AER-FLO CANVAS PRODUCTS INC
4455 18th St E (34203-3790)
P.O. Box 1356, Oneco (34264-1356)
PHONE..................................941 747-4151
William W Henning, *President*
Betsy A Henning, *Vice Pres*
Deb Hodge, *Human Resources*
◆ **EMP:** 61 **EST:** 1981
SQ FT: 60,000
SALES (est): 9.8MM **Privately Held**
WEB: www.aerflo.com
SIC: 2394 Tarpaulins, fabric: made from purchased materials

(G-985)
ALPINE INDUSTRIES CORPORATION
2908 29th Ave E Ste A (34208-7460)
PHONE..................................941 749-1900
Fax: 941 748-6616
EMP: 10
SQ FT: 10,000
SALES (est): 590K **Privately Held**
SIC: 3552 Mfg Screen Printing Equipment

(G-986)
ALUMATECH MANUFACTURING INC
6063 17th St E (34203-5002)
P.O. Box 115, Oneco (34264-0115)
PHONE..................................941 748-8880
Jeffrey Gilmore, *President*
EMP: 20 **EST:** 1989
SQ FT: 2,000
SALES (est): 2.5MM **Privately Held**
WEB: www.alumatech1.com
SIC: 2519 5712 Lawn & garden furniture, except wood & metal; furniture stores

(G-987)
AMERICAN BOTTLING COMPANY
2919 62nd Ave E (34203-5320)
PHONE..................................941 758-7010
Edward Clain, *Manager*
EMP: 19 **Publicly Held**
WEB: www.keurigdrpepper.com
SIC: 2086 Soft drinks: packaged in cans, bottles, etc.
HQ: The American Bottling Company
6425 Hall Of Fame Ln
Frisco TX 75034

(G-988)
AMERICAN TORCH TIP COMPANY (PA)
6212 29th St E (34203-5304)
PHONE..................................941 753-7557
John D Walters Jr, *President*
Charles Walters, *Vice Pres*
Jeff Walters, *Vice Pres*
John Spara, *Prdtn Mgr*
Mark Walters, *Treasurer*
◆ **EMP:** 180 **EST:** 1940
SQ FT: 50,000
SALES (est): 50.3MM **Privately Held**
WEB: www.americantorchtip.com
SIC: 3548 Welding apparatus

(G-989)
ANKO PRODUCTS INC
Also Called: Mityflex
6012 33rd St E (34203-5402)
PHONE..................................941 748-2307
Kent Radovich, *President*
Tim Smith, *Vice Pres*
Coya Dryer, *Production*
Patrick Gorman, *Engineer*
Danny Ford, *Controller*
◆ **EMP:** 35 **EST:** 1980
SQ FT: 21,000
SALES (est): 4.4MM **Privately Held**
WEB: www.ankoproducts.com
SIC: 3621 3561 Motors & generators; pumps & pumping equipment

(G-990)
AQUATECTONICA LLC
809 Tallgrass Ln (34212-2651)
PHONE..................................941 592-3071
Christopher Nyers,
EMP: 10 **EST:** 2008
SALES (est): 503.3K **Privately Held**
SIC: 3272 3499 Fountains, concrete; fountains (except drinking), metal

(G-991)
ARMS EAST LLC
Also Called: Avro Arms
2335 63rd Ave E Ste M (34203-5017)
PHONE..................................561 293-2915
Walter Lawlor, *Mng Member*
EMP: 6 **EST:** 2014
SALES (est): 528.4K **Privately Held**
WEB: www.armseastusa.com
SIC: 3482 Small arms ammunition

(G-992)
AUTO TAG OF AMERICA INC (PA)
6015 31st St E (34203-5350)
PHONE..................................941 739-8841
Nick S Gigliotti, *President*
EMP: 54 **EST:** 2001
SALES (est): 974.3K **Privately Held**
WEB: www.autotagamerica.com
SIC: 2679 Tags, paper (unprinted): made from purchased paper

(G-993)
AVON CABINET CORPORATION
5821 24th St E (34203-5028)
PHONE..................................941 755-2866
Edmond Page, *President*
Mark Page, *Vice Pres*
Todd Page, *Vice Pres*
Joy Coblentz, *Sales Staff*
Ileen Sheehan, *Senior Mgr*
◆ **EMP:** 120 **EST:** 1981
SQ FT: 140,000
SALES (est): 10.9MM **Privately Held**
WEB: www.avoncabinet.com
SIC: 2434 Vanities, bathroom: wood

(G-994)
BC SALES
3003 29th Ave E (34208-7418)
PHONE..................................941 708-2727
Bill Cournan, *Owner*
EMP: 7 **EST:** 2010
SALES (est): 149.4K **Privately Held**
WEB: www.bcsalesdeco.com
SIC: 2395 Embroidery products, except schiffli machine

(G-995)
BEACH HOUSE ENGINEERING
1625 50th Avenue Dr E (34203-3772)
P.O. Box 79, Oneco (34264-0079)
PHONE..................................941 727-4488
Terri Norwood, *President*
Brian Bevan, *Partner*
Jan Thompson, *Partner*
EMP: 5
SALES (est): 350K **Privately Held**
SIC: 3714 5091 Motor vehicle parts & accessories; boat accessories & parts

(G-996)
BEAUTY PAVERS LLC
3600 Lk Byshore Dr Unit 1 (34205)
PHONE..................................941 720-3655
Elmar D Martinez, *Manager*
EMP: 7 **EST:** 2014
SALES (est): 90.7K **Privately Held**
SIC: 2951 Asphalt paving mixtures & blocks

(G-997)
BEAVERTAIL SKIFFS INC
4601 15th St E (34203-3617)
PHONE..................................941 705-2090
William D Leslie, *President*
Elizabeth Leslie, *Vice Pres*
EMP: 7 **EST:** 2017
SALES (est): 128.5K **Privately Held**
WEB: www.beavertailskiffs.com
SIC: 3732 Boat building & repairing

(G-998)
BEST CHOICE SOFTWARE INC
1117 30th Ave W (34205-6941)
PHONE..................................941 747-5858
Selden F Decker, *President*
Peter H Hoyt, *Vice Pres*
Bret Bottomley, *Prgrmr*
EMP: 10 **EST:** 2001
SALES (est): 265.3K **Privately Held**
WEB: www.bestchoicesoftware.com
SIC: 7372 Prepackaged software

(G-999)
BIBLE ALLIANCE INC (PA)
12108 10th Ave E (34212-2764)
PHONE..................................941 748-3031
Joseph A Aleppo, *President*
Daniel Madison, *Vice Pres*
Allen Decker, *Commissioner*
EMP: 20 **EST:** 1970
SQ FT: 3,500
SALES (est): 1.6MM **Privately Held**
WEB: www.auroraministries.org
SIC: 3652 Magnetic tape (audio): prerecorded

(G-1000)
BJM ENTERPRISES INC
Also Called: Johnson Printing
1104 9th St W (34205-7333)
PHONE..................................941 746-4171

GEOGRAPHIC

John Johnson, *President*
Sherman Kirkpatrick, *Accounts Exec*
EMP: 13 **EST:** 1977
SQ FT: 2,400
SALES (est): 2.5MM **Privately Held**
WEB: www.johnsonprint.com
SIC: 2752 2796 2791 2789 Commercial printing, offset; platemaking services; typesetting; bookbinding & related work

(G-1001)
BOBS CUSTOM COATINGS LLC
3716 Highland Ave W (34205-2033)
PHONE..................................941 745-9659
Robert W Richardson, *Principal*
EMP: 6 **EST:** 2015
SALES (est): 83.8K **Privately Held**
SIC: 3479 Metal coating & allied service

(G-1002)
BRIDGEPORT CHEMICAL
10516 Firestone Dr (34202-4067)
PHONE..................................941 753-2520
Brad Dillingham, *Principal*
EMP: 7 **EST:** 2010
SALES (est): 278K **Privately Held**
WEB: www.bridgeportchemical.com
SIC: 2869 Laboratory chemicals, organic

(G-1003)
BRUTUS ROLLER LLC
3007 29th Ave E (34208-7418)
PHONE..................................609 393-0007
Cary Wische, *President*
EMP: 5
SALES (est): 388.4K **Privately Held**
WEB: www.brutusroller.com
SIC: 3531 Construction machinery

(G-1004)
BULLETPROOF HITCHES LLC
3145 Lakewood Ranch Blvd # 106 (34211-5004)
PHONE..................................941 251-8110
Gregory Daniel, *Principal*
EMP: 8 **EST:** 2014
SALES (est): 1MM **Privately Held**
WEB: www.bulletproofhitches.com
SIC: 3714 Trailer hitches, motor vehicle

(G-1005)
C & D INDUSTRIAL MAINT LLC
2208 58th Ave E (34203-5062)
PHONE..................................833 776-5833
Tom Hendon, *CEO*
EMP: 14 **EST:** 2018
SALES (est): 2.4MM **Privately Held**
SIC: 3442 5084 3589 5046 Garage doors, overhead: metal; waste compactors; garbage disposers & compactors, commercial; commercial equipment; industrial & commercial equipment inspection service;

(G-1006)
C & H BASEBALL INC (PA)
10615 Tech Ter Ste 100 (34211)
PHONE..................................941 727-1533
Danielle D Huff, *President*
Robert Rex Huff, *Corp Secy*
◆ **EMP:** 8 **EST:** 1946
SQ FT: 6,000
SALES (est): 2.3MM **Privately Held**
WEB: www.chbaseball.com
SIC: 3949 1799 Baseball equipment & supplies, general; welding on site

(G-1007)
C E C CONTROLS COMPANY INC
5306 4th Avenue Cir E (34208-5624)
PHONE..................................941 746-5700
EMP: 13 **EST:** 2014
SALES (est): 263.1K **Privately Held**
SIC: 3823 Industrial instrmnts msrmnt display/control process variable

(G-1008)
C PRODUCTS DEFENSE INC
4555 18th St E (34203-3757)
PHONE..................................941 727-0009
Adel Jamil, *CEO*
Marjorie Hart, *President*
EMP: 20 **EST:** 2011
SALES (est): 2.3MM **Privately Held**
WEB: www.dura-mag.com
SIC: 3484 Guns (firearms) or gun parts, 30 mm. & below

(G-1009)
C2 POWDER COATING LLC
6060 28th St E Ste 1 (34203-5303)
PHONE..................................941 404-2671
Christina Reiss, *Principal*
EMP: 6 **EST:** 2015
SALES (est): 613.4K **Privately Held**
WEB: www.c2powdercoating.com
SIC: 3479 Coating of metals & formed products

(G-1010)
CABINET DESIGNS OF SARASOTA
Also Called: West Wood Manufacturing
6208 B 17th St E (34203)
PHONE..................................941 739-1607
W Russ Edwards, *President*
EMP: 10 **EST:** 1992
SQ FT: 13,000
SALES (est): 822.2K **Privately Held**
WEB: www.westwoodsarasota.com
SIC: 2434 Wood kitchen cabinets

(G-1011)
CABINETS EXTRAORDINAIRE INC
6150 State Road 70 E # 31 (34203-9712)
PHONE..................................618 925-0515
EMP: 19
SALES (corp-wide): 226.3K **Privately Held**
SIC: 2434 Wood kitchen cabinets
PA: Cabinets Extraordinaire Inc
7350 S Tamiami Trl
Sarasota FL 34231
941 961-8453

(G-1012)
CANADA DRY OF FLORIDA
2919 62nd Ave E (34203-5320)
PHONE..................................941 758-7010
Keith Williams, *Manager*
EMP: 6 **EST:** 2007
SALES (est): 158.1K **Privately Held**
WEB: www.canadadry.com
SIC: 2086 Bottled & canned soft drinks

(G-1013)
CARBON MINE SUPPLY LLC
11023 Gatewood Dr Ste 103 (34211-4945)
PHONE..................................606 437-9905
EMP: 8
SQ FT: 10,600
SALES (est): 827.1K **Privately Held**
SIC: 3483 Mfg Ammunition-Except Small Arms

(G-1014)
CARBON RESOURCES INC
9030 58th Dr E Ste 102 (34202-6108)
PHONE..................................941 746-8089
Fred Murrell, *Principal*
EMP: 7 **EST:** 2007
SALES (est): 487.6K **Privately Held**
SIC: 1241 Coal mining services

(G-1015)
CARBON RESOURCES OF FLORIDA (PA)
Also Called: Adaro Envirocoal Americas
9030 58th Dr E Ste 102 (34202-6108)
PHONE..................................941 746-8089
Frederick Murrell, *President*
EMP: 7 **EST:** 1987
SALES (est): 1MM **Privately Held**
WEB: www.carbonresourcesofflorida.com
SIC: 1241 Coal mining services

(G-1016)
CAT 5 HURRICANE PRODUCTS LLC
Also Called: Cat5hp
6112 33rd St E Unit 105 (34203-5401)
PHONE..................................941 752-4692
David E Smith, *Mng Member*
EMP: 11 **EST:** 2007
SALES (est): 1MM **Privately Held**
WEB: www.cat5hp.com
SIC: 3442 Shutters, door or window: metal

(G-1017)
CEH LLC (PA)
Also Called: Ceh Seafood
5510 Tdwter Preserve Blvd (34208-5731)
PHONE..................................941 518-6747
Christopher Hodge, *President*
Maria Hodge,
EMP: 2 **EST:** 2010
SALES (est): 5.3MM **Privately Held**
SIC: 2091 5146 2092 Fish & seafood soups, stews, chowders: canned or packaged; fish & seafoods; seafoods, frozen: prepared

(G-1018)
CENTERLINE TOOL & ENGRG INC
3107 29th Ave E Ste A (34208-7456)
PHONE..................................941 749-5519
George H Nason, *President*
Diane Nason, *Corp Secy*
Matt Nason, *IT/INT Sup*
Constance Crawley,
Gregory Nania,
EMP: 15 **EST:** 1995
SQ FT: 5,000
SALES (est): 1.5MM **Privately Held**
SIC: 3599 Machine shop, jobbing & repair

(G-1019)
CENTRAL FLORIDA PRECAST INC
1910 1st Ave E (34208-1502)
PHONE..................................941 730-2158
Eduardo Solorzano, *Principal*
EMP: 7 **EST:** 2008
SALES (est): 224.6K **Privately Held**
SIC: 3272 Precast terrazo or concrete products

(G-1020)
CITY OF BRADENTON
5600 Natalie Way E (34203-5647)
PHONE..................................941 727-6360
Timothy Parks, *Manager*
EMP: 31
SALES (corp-wide): 62MM **Privately Held**
WEB: www.realizebradenton.com
SIC: 3589 Water treatment equipment, industrial
PA: Bradenton, City Of (Inc)
101 12th St W
Bradenton FL 34205
941 932-9400

(G-1021)
CLINE ALUMINUM DOORS INC
112 32nd Ave W (34205-8909)
PHONE..................................941 746-4104
Cathy Cline, *President*
Robert M Cline, *President*
Rhonda C Zoller, *Corp Secy*
Emma Cline, *Exec VP*
Robert B Ackles, *Vice Pres*
▼ **EMP:** 33 **EST:** 1961
SQ FT: 7,000
SALES (est): 6.2MM **Privately Held**
WEB: www.clinedoors.com
SIC: 3442 3354 Metal doors; aluminum extruded products

(G-1022)
COMPACT BRICK PAVERS INC
1019 Pine Lily Pl (34201)
PHONE..................................727 278-1544
Wagner Santos, *President*
EMP: 6 **EST:** 2009
SALES (est): 71.2K **Privately Held**
SIC: 3531 Pavers

(G-1023)
CONDUIT SPACE RCVERY SYSTEMS L
5204 Lena Rd (34211-9436)
PHONE..................................330 416-0887
Todd Fox, *Chief*
Ron Mason, *Vice Pres*
Kelsey Muller, *Mng Member*
Jorja Allen,
EMP: 15 **EST:** 2013
SALES (est): 1.4MM **Privately Held**
WEB: www.conduitspacerecovery.com
SIC: 3357 Building wire & cable, nonferrous

(G-1024)
COUNTER TOP PUBLISHING INC
3715 35th St W (34205-1803)
PHONE..................................941 321-5811
George J Palino, *Principal*
EMP: 6 **EST:** 2008
SALES (est): 117.3K **Privately Held**
SIC: 2741 Miscellaneous publishing

(G-1025)
CUSTOM CARTS OF SARASOTA LLC
Also Called: Custom Carts of Lakewood Ranch
4515 15th St E (34203-3615)
PHONE..................................941 953-4445
Kurt Didier,
EMP: 45 **EST:** 2016
SALES (est): 5.5MM **Privately Held**
WEB: www.customcarts.com
SIC: 3949 Driving ranges, golf, electronic

(G-1026)
CUSTOM WATERSPORTS EQP INC
1218 50th Avenue Plz W (34207-2538)
PHONE..................................941 753-9949
Julian Shaw, *Principal*
EMP: 7 **EST:** 2015
SALES (est): 131.2K **Privately Held**
SIC: 3599 Industrial machinery

(G-1027)
CUTTING EDGE ARCHTCTRAL MLDNGS
7282 55th Ave E Pmb 176 (34203-8002)
PHONE..................................941 727-1111
Rick D Slawson Mr,
Donald L Greenwood Mr,
Donald J Perella Mr,
EMP: 7 **EST:** 2004
SQ FT: 12,500
SALES (est): 171K **Privately Held**
WEB: www.cuttingedgemoldings.com
SIC: 3299 Moldings, architectural: plaster of paris

(G-1028)
D N MACHINING
2211 60th Dr E (34203-5083)
P.O. Box 316, Tallevast (34270-0316)
PHONE..................................941 727-1684
Robert Didion III, *CEO*
Robby S Didion, *Vice Pres*
Dorothy Didion, *Vice Pres*
EMP: 21 **EST:** 2000
SALES (est): 575.6K **Privately Held**
SIC: 3599 Machine shop, jobbing & repair

(G-1029)
DELUXE EQUIPMENT CO
7817 Alhambra Dr (34209-4834)
P.O. Box 11390 (34282-1390)
PHONE..................................941 753-4184
Sandra E Smith, *President*
EMP: 15 **EST:** 1984
SQ FT: 22,000
SALES (est): 435.1K **Privately Held**
WEB: www.bhcommercialparts.com
SIC: 3556 Bakery machinery; ovens, bakery

(G-1030)
DEPEND-O-DRAIN INC
6012 33rd St E (34203-5402)
PHONE..................................941 756-1710
Kent Radovich, *President*
Patricia Smith, *Master*
◆ **EMP:** 35 **EST:** 1966
SQ FT: 20,000
SALES (est): 9.6MM **Privately Held**
WEB: www.dependodrain.com
SIC: 3494 Valves & pipe fittings

(G-1031)
DIXIE-SOUTHERN ARKANSAS LLC
9135 58th Dr E (34202-9188)
PHONE..................................479 751-9183
EMP: 8
SALES (est): 1.4MM **Privately Held**
SIC: 3441 Structural Metal Fabrication

(G-1032)
DURLACH HOLDINGS INC
6008 28th St E Ste A (34203-5300)
PHONE.................................941 751-1672
Angelo Durlach, *President*
EMP: 18 **EST:** 2005
SQ FT: 20,000
SALES (est): 288.5K **Privately Held**
WEB: www.precaststair.com
SIC: 3272 Concrete products

(G-1033)
DYNOTUNE INC
515 27th St E Ste 4 (34208-1879)
PHONE.................................941 753-8899
Dean Hoffman, *Principal*
EMP: 9 **EST:** 2014
SALES (est): 1.1MM **Privately Held**
WEB: www.dynotunenitrous.com
SIC: 3714 Motor vehicle parts & accessories

(G-1034)
EARTECH INC
3904 9th Ave W (34205-1704)
PHONE.................................941 747-8193
Mark A Krywko, *President*
Marja L Krywko, *Vice Pres*
EMP: 8 **EST:** 1988
SQ FT: 1,500
SALES (est): 550K **Privately Held**
WEB: www.eartechhearingaids.com
SIC: 3842 5999 Hearing aids; autograph supplies

(G-1035)
EDMUNDS METAL WORKS INC
6111 15th St E Ste A (34203-7771)
PHONE.................................941 755-4725
Thomas G Edmunds, *President*
Nina E Edmunds, *COO*
Nina Edmunds, *Opers Mgr*
Judy Edmunds, *CFO*
Judith A Edmunds, *Admin Sec*
EMP: 34 **EST:** 1977
SQ FT: 10,000
SALES (est): 5.4MM **Privately Held**
WEB: www.edmundsmetal.com
SIC: 3599 Machine shop, jobbing & repair

(G-1036)
ELREHA PRINTED CIRCUITS
7522 Plantation Cir (34201-2062)
PHONE.................................727 244-0130
Patrick Scanlan, *Principal*
EMP: 7 **EST:** 2010
SALES (est): 121.1K **Privately Held**
WEB: www.elreha.de
SIC: 3672 Circuit boards, television & radio printed

(G-1037)
EMERSON PRCESS MGT PWR WTR SLT
1401 Manatee Ave W # 400 (34205-6770)
PHONE.................................941 748-8100
Frank Grywalski, *President*
EMP: 24 **EST:** 1993
SQ FT: 6,000
SALES (est): 1.2MM **Privately Held**
SIC: 7372 Word processing computer software

(G-1038)
ENERGY MANAGEMENT PRODUCTS LLC (PA)
Also Called: Led Lighting Solutions
6118 Riverview Blvd (34209-1343)
PHONE.................................410 320-0200
Cara Weisman, *Mng Member*
Kevin Button,
EMP: 5 **EST:** 2011
SALES (est): 851.3K **Privately Held**
WEB: www.ledlightingsolutions.com
SIC: 3646 3647 3641 Commercial indusl & institutional electric lighting fixtures; vehicular lighting equipment; electric lamps

(G-1039)
ETCO INCORPORATED
Also Called: Etco Automotive Products Div
3004 62nd Ave E (34203-5306)
PHONE.................................941 756-8426
Nathan Galla, *Production*
Tom Jacobson, *Sales Mgr*
John Carr, *Sales Mgr*
Paul Richardson, *Sales Mgr*
Deb Freeman, *Sales Staff*
EMP: 110
SQ FT: 19,618
SALES (corp-wide): 25.2MM **Privately Held**
WEB: www.etco.com
SIC: 3644 3714 3061 Terminal boards; motor vehicle parts & accessories; mechanical rubber goods
PA: Etco Incorporated
25 Bellows St
Warwick RI 02888
401 467-2400

(G-1040)
EXTREME CORVETTE CO LLC
6015 28th St E Unit F1 (34203-5341)
PHONE.................................941 524-8942
Axel Jasiek, *Manager*
EMP: 5 **EST:** 2012
SALES (est): 362.2K **Privately Held**
WEB: www.extreme-corvette.com
SIC: 3714 Motor vehicle parts & accessories

(G-1041)
FIRESIDE HOLDINGS INC
Also Called: American Refrigerants
2053 58th Avenue Cir E (34203-5060)
PHONE.................................941 371-0300
Christopher Mussey, *President*
EMP: 7 **EST:** 2019
SALES (est): 681.9K **Privately Held**
SIC: 3585 Refrigeration & heating equipment

(G-1042)
FLORIDA SIGN COMPANY INC
1101 29th Ave W (34205-6993)
PHONE.................................941 747-1000
Charles F Ogle, *President*
Robert A Dring, *Vice Pres*
Bill Runyan, *Prdtn Mgr*
Karen Dring, *Office Mgr*
Charles Ogle, *Executive*
EMP: 14 **EST:** 1955
SQ FT: 13,500
SALES (est): 2.1MM **Privately Held**
WEB: www.floridasign.com
SIC: 3993 Neon signs

(G-1043)
FLOWERS BKG CO BRADENTON LLC
Also Called: Flowers Baking Company
720 9th St E (34208-2025)
PHONE.................................941 758-5656
Chris Peer, *Manager*
EMP: 25
SALES (corp-wide): 4.3B **Publicly Held**
WEB: www.flobradconf.com
SIC: 2051 Bread, cake & related products
HQ: Flowers Baking Co. Of Bradenton, Llc
6490 Parkland Dr
Sarasota FL 34243

(G-1044)
FOUR STAR PRODUCTS INC
6110 33rd St E (34203-5405)
PHONE.................................941 727-6161
Rick Vaal, *President*
Sam Lankford, *Vice Pres*
EMP: 5 **EST:** 1989
SALES (est): 382.8K **Privately Held**
WEB: www.fourstarproducts.com
SIC: 2842 Specialty cleaning, polishes & sanitation goods

(G-1045)
GAMMERLERTECH CORPORATION
Also Called: Gammerler US
3135 Lakewood Ranch Blvd # 107 (34211-5006)
PHONE.................................941 803-0150
Gunter Gammerler, *Principal*
Max Frank, *Sales Staff*
Joe Jastrzebski, *Sales Staff*
Tabitha Trotter-Powell, *Office Mgr*
Mario Banci, *Manager*
EMP: 27 **EST:** 2018
SALES (est): 6.1MM **Privately Held**
WEB: www.gammerlertech.com
SIC: 3555 Printing trades machinery

(G-1046)
GENIUS CENTRAL SYSTEMS INC
2025 Lakewood Ranch Blvd # 202 (34211-4948)
PHONE.................................800 360-2231
Dan Clarke, *CEO*
Leya Avalos, *COO*
Paul Debonis, *COO*
Peter Ceccacci, *Exec VP*
Gordon Lear, *Exec VP*
EMP: 47 **EST:** 2013
SALES (est): 11.9MM **Privately Held**
WEB: www.geniuscentral.com
SIC: 7372 Application computer software

(G-1047)
GLOBAL MARKETING CORP
3752 Summerwind Cir (34209-5809)
PHONE.................................973 426-1088
Christopher D Boyhan, *President*
▲ **EMP:** 20 **EST:** 1981
SALES (est): 445.5K **Privately Held**
WEB: www.globalmarketingcorp.com
SIC: 3469 Household cooking & kitchen utensils, metal

(G-1048)
GLOBAL WRLESS SLTIONS TECH INC
101 Riverfront Blvd # 400 (34205-8812)
PHONE.................................941 744-2511
John Elliott, *President*
Cw Elliott, *Corp Secy*
Joanne Fowkes, *Office Admin*
EMP: 6 **EST:** 2002
SQ FT: 1,500
SALES (est): 390K **Privately Held**
SIC: 3663 Radio & TV communications equipment

(G-1049)
GLOBE TRAILERS FLORIDA INC
3101 59th Avenue Dr E (34203-5311)
PHONE.................................941 753-6425
Leonard H Dobala, *President*
Brian Frater, *Plant Mgr*
Dana Spara, *Purch Mgr*
Jeff Walters, *VP Engrg*
Russ Benuche, *VP Sales*
◆ **EMP:** 40 **EST:** 1985
SQ FT: 60,000
SALES (est): 6.8MM **Privately Held**
WEB: www.globetrailers.com
SIC: 3715 3599 Semitrailers for truck tractors; machine shop, jobbing & repair

(G-1050)
GML COATINGS LLC
10315 Technology Ter (34211-4924)
PHONE.................................941 755-2176
Robin Wilson, *Treasurer*
EMP: 14 **EST:** 2008
SALES (est): 3.9MM **Publicly Held**
WEB: www.gmlcoatings.com
SIC: 3479 Coating of metals & formed products
PA: Primoris Services Corporation
2300 N Field St Ste 1900
Dallas TX 75201

(G-1051)
GOODWILL INDUSTRIES S FLA INC
2563 Lakewood Ranch Blvd (34211-4949)
PHONE.................................941 745-8459
EMP: 113
SALES (corp-wide): 92.8MM **Privately Held**
WEB: www.goodwillsouthflorida.org
SIC: 3999 Barber & beauty shop equipment
PA: Goodwill Industries Of South Florida, Inc.
2121 Nw 21st St
Miami FL 33142
305 325-9114

(G-1052)
GRAND BUFFET
4848 14th St W (34207-2017)
PHONE.................................941 752-3388
Haiyan Lu, *President*
EMP: 9 **EST:** 2015
SALES (est): 74.5K **Privately Held**
WEB: www.grandbuffetfl.com
SIC: 2511 5812 Buffets (furniture); eating places

(G-1053)
GROUND ZERO ELECTROSTATICS INC (PA)
8015 34th Ave E (34211-8408)
P.O. Box 70 (34206-0070)
PHONE.................................941 751-7581
Anthony Murfin, *President*
Alan Garst, *Director*
Lara Jeane Garst, *Assistant*
▲ **EMP:** 5
SQ FT: 1,500
SALES (est): 1.8MM **Privately Held**
WEB: www.gndzero.com
SIC: 3699 5065 Electrostatic particle accelerators; electronic parts & equipment

(G-1054)
GUTHMAN SIGNS LLC
Also Called: Sign Consultants
15777 High Bell Pl (34212-3913)
PHONE.................................941 218-0023
Cordell Guthrie, *General Mgr*
EMP: 5 **EST:** 2017
SALES (est): 333.8K **Privately Held**
WEB: www.guthmansigns.com
SIC: 3993 Signs & advertising specialties

(G-1055)
HAWK RACING
6060 28th St E Ste 5 (34203-5303)
PHONE.................................941 209-1790
Cindy Parlin, *Human Resources*
EMP: 9 **EST:** 2010
SALES (est): 81.5K **Privately Held**
WEB: www.hawk-racing.com
SIC: 3751 Bicycles & related parts

(G-1056)
HERBERT PAVERS INC
3031 46th Ave E (34203-3923)
PHONE.................................941 447-4909
Hebert A Oliveira, *Principal*
EMP: 6 **EST:** 2011
SALES (est): 161.3K **Privately Held**
SIC: 3531 Pavers

(G-1057)
HUDSONS WLDG & FABRICATION INC
10845 Forest Run Dr (34211-9391)
P.O. Box 110096, Lakewood Rch (34211-0002)
PHONE.................................941 355-4858
Kenneth C Hudson, *Vice Pres*
EMP: 6 **EST:** 2011
SALES (est): 152.7K **Privately Held**
WEB: www.hudsonswelding.com
SIC: 7692 Welding repair

(G-1058)
HURRICANE MEDICAL INC
5315 Lena Rd (34211-9442)
PHONE.................................941 753-1517
Dell Bauslaugh, *President*
David Clapp, *Vice Pres*
G Keith Pike, *Treasurer*
J Craig Pike, *Admin Sec*
Dana McKibbin, *Associate*
▲ **EMP:** 25 **EST:** 1999
SQ FT: 1,700
SALES (est): 3.7MM **Privately Held**
WEB: www.hurricanemedical.com
SIC: 3841 Surgical & medical instruments

(G-1059)
IMMUNOTEK BIO CENTERS LLC
825 9th St W (34205-7741)
PHONE.................................337 500-1175
Dmitry Maksimchuck, *Manager*
EMP: 34
SALES (corp-wide): 27MM **Privately Held**
WEB: www.immunotek.com
SIC: 2836 Blood derivatives
PA: Immunotek Bio Centers, L.L.C.
3900 N Causeway Blvd # 1200
Metairie LA 70002
337 500-1175

GEOGRAPHIC

(G-1060)
INNOVATIVE DESIGNS OF SARASOTA
Also Called: IDI
6224 31st St E Ste 8 (34203-5321)
PHONE..................................941 752-7779
Don Beard, *President*
EMP: 6 **EST:** 1988
SQ FT: 5,400
SALES (est): 503.4K **Privately Held**
SIC: 3841 Ophthalmic instruments & apparatus

(G-1061)
INOVART INC
Also Called: Network USA
2304 58th Ave E (34203-5064)
P.O. Box 254, Tallevast (34270-0254)
PHONE..................................941 751-2324
John M Smith, *President*
Mercedez Smith, *Treasurer*
▲ **EMP:** 5 **EST:** 1988
SQ FT: 5,500
SALES (est): 868.8K **Privately Held**
WEB: www.inovart.net
SIC: 2679 Pressed & molded pulp products, purchased material

(G-1062)
ISPG INC
10504 Technology Ter (34211-4927)
PHONE..................................941 896-3999
Maureen F Young, *Corp Secy*
Gerald Luhman, *Vice Pres*
Christopher Young, *Vice Pres*
Chuck Van Epps, *Warehouse Mgr*
Kyle Cancellieri, *Sales Mgr*
▲ **EMP:** 13 **EST:** 2011
SALES (est): 3.5MM **Privately Held**
WEB: www.ispg.com
SIC: 3841 Surgical & medical instruments

(G-1063)
J C INDUSTRIES INC
6105 33rd St E (34203-5414)
P.O. Box 1551, Wauchula (33873-1551)
PHONE..................................863 773-9199
Penny Carlton, *Principal*
EMP: 7 **EST:** 2001
SALES (est): 83.6K **Privately Held**
SIC: 3999 Manufacturing industries

(G-1064)
J L M MACHINE CO INC
2704 29th Ave E (34208-7457)
PHONE..................................941 748-4288
Kelley Graham, *Principal*
Natasha Phifer, *Office Mgr*
EMP: 10 **EST:** 1977
SQ FT: 6,000
SALES (est): 1MM **Privately Held**
WEB: www.jlmmachine.com
SIC: 3599 7692 Machine shop, jobbing & repair; welding repair

(G-1065)
JCB BRICK PAVERS INC
6148 42nd Street Cir E (34203-7011)
PHONE..................................941 739-6089
Susan Oday, *Principal*
EMP: 6 **EST:** 2018
SALES (est): 108.3K **Privately Held**
SIC: 2951 Asphalt paving mixtures & blocks

(G-1066)
JUST LEDS INC
1515 Rye Rd E (34212-9013)
PHONE..................................727 468-4496
Cheryl Collin, *Principal*
EMP: 6 **EST:** 2016
SALES (est): 106.8K **Privately Held**
WEB: www.justledsinc.com
SIC: 3646 Commercial indusl & institutional electric lighting fixtures

(G-1067)
KINETRONICS CORPORATION
5316 Lena Rd (34211-9438)
PHONE..................................941 951-2432
William N Stelcher, *President*
Michael Murdock, *General Mgr*
Carol Stelcher, *Vice Pres*
EMP: 10 **EST:** 1972
SALES (est): 1.5MM **Privately Held**
WEB: www.kinetronics.com
SIC: 3629 Static elimination equipment, industrial

(G-1068)
LAMBS SIGNS INC
Also Called: Signs Now
4230 26th St W (34205-3516)
PHONE..................................941 792-4453
J Brian Lamb, *Owner*
Debra Lamb, *Owner*
Dave Hassall Jr, *Co-Owner*
EMP: 10 **EST:** 2010
SALES (est): 225.8K **Privately Held**
WEB: www.signsnow.com
SIC: 3993 3714 Signs & advertising specialties; motor vehicle parts & accessories

(G-1069)
LED LGHTING SLUTIONS GLOBL LLC
6118 Riverview Blvd (34209-1343)
PHONE..................................855 309-1702
Carrie Weisman, *CEO*
EMP: 8 **EST:** 2015
SALES (est): 556K **Privately Held**
WEB: www.ledlightingsolutions.com
SIC: 3646 Commercial indusl & institutional electric lighting fixtures

(G-1070)
LEXINGTON CUTTER INC
2951 63rd Ave E (34203-5308)
PHONE..................................941 739-2726
Paul J Enander, *President*
Jim Trammell, *Vice Pres*
Laurie Enander, *Admin Sec*
EMP: 22 **EST:** 1947
SQ FT: 15,000
SALES (est): 5MM **Privately Held**
WEB: www.lexingtoncutter.com
SIC: 3541 5084 3545 Machine tools, metal cutting type; industrial machinery & equipment; machine tool accessories

(G-1071)
LIPPERT COMPONENTS INC
Also Called: Sureshade
1900 47th Ter E (34203-3701)
PHONE..................................267 825-0665
EMP: 7
SALES (corp-wide): 2.8B **Publicly Held**
WEB: www.lci1.com
SIC: 3711 Motor vehicles & car bodies
HQ: Lippert Components, Inc.
3501 County Road 6 E
Elkhart IN 46514
574 535-1125

(G-1072)
LIVE WISE NATURALS LLC
13502 4th Plz E (34212-9681)
PHONE..................................866 866-0075
Greg Bulgarelli, *Mng Member*
EMP: 8 **EST:** 2015
SALES (est): 787.7K **Privately Held**
WEB: www.livewisenaturals.com
SIC: 2833 Vitamins, natural or synthetic: bulk, uncompounded

(G-1073)
LYNX PRODUCTS CORP INC
2424 Manatee Ave W # 203 (34205-4954)
P.O. Box 10977 (34282-0977)
PHONE..................................941 727-9676
Greg Winter, *President*
Debra Winter, *Principal*
▲ **EMP:** 6 **EST:** 1999
SQ FT: 1,500
SALES (est): 819.2K **Privately Held**
WEB: www.lynx-products.com
SIC: 3535 5084 Conveyors & conveying equipment; industrial machinery & equipment

(G-1074)
M&L CABINETS INC
7320 Manatee Ave W (34209-3441)
PHONE..................................941 761-8100
Clinton C Hoy, *President*
Ryan Nobles, *Vice Pres*
Clint Hoy, *Manager*
EMP: 7 **EST:** 2018
SALES (est): 652.2K **Privately Held**
WEB: www.mlcabinets.com
SIC: 2434 Wood kitchen cabinets

(G-1075)
MANATEE CABINETS INC
Also Called: Cabinets Unlimited
8700 Cortez Rd W (34210-2209)
PHONE..................................941 792-8656
Jan A Manning, *President*
Marcus Hyde, *Vice Pres*
EMP: 5 **EST:** 1969
SQ FT: 19,000
SALES (est): 667K **Privately Held**
WEB: www.cabinets-unlimited.com
SIC: 2434 Wood kitchen cabinets

(G-1076)
MANATEE PRINTERS INC
1007 30th Ave W (34205-6904)
PHONE..................................941 746-9100
Ronald Pickelsimer, *President*
Patricia Pickelsimer, *Vice Pres*
Mark Pickelsimer, *Opers Staff*
EMP: 20 **EST:** 1964
SQ FT: 6,000
SALES (est): 3.4MM **Privately Held**
WEB: www.manateeprinters.com
SIC: 2752 Letters, circular or form: lithographed; commercial printing, offset

(G-1077)
MED X CHANGE INC (HQ)
525 8th St W (34205-8530)
PHONE..................................941 746-0538
Craig Scherer, *President*
Jcorey Park, *Project Mgr*
Christie Sharp, *Controller*
Chris Danko, *Director*
U Ghaziabad, *Business Dir*
EMP: 25 **EST:** 2001
SALES (est): 7.2MM **Publicly Held**
WEB: www.medxchange.com
SIC: 7372 Prepackaged software

(G-1078)
MILITEK INDUSTRIES LLC
Also Called: Theory Defense Systems
5727 23rd St W (34207-3925)
PHONE..................................941 544-5636
Joshua Wireman,
Dominic Cultrera,
EMP: 6 **EST:** 2017
SALES (est): 174.2K **Privately Held**
SIC: 3495 3443 7699 7389 Gun springs, precision; metal parts; gun parts made to individual order;

(G-1079)
MOBIL BOAT FUEL INC
616 49th St E (34208-5840)
PHONE..................................941 718-3781
William Willis, *Principal*
EMP: 5 **EST:** 2011
SALES (est): 499.8K **Privately Held**
WEB: www.mobil-boat-fuel.com
SIC: 2869 Fuels

(G-1080)
MOJOWAX MEDIA INC
1100 Yale Ave (34207-5250)
PHONE..................................805 550-6013
John J Sullivan, *President*
EMP: 8 **EST:** 2013
SALES (est): 166.8K **Privately Held**
WEB: www.bluesmusicstore.com
SIC: 2759 5961 Publication printing; magazines, mail order; record &/or tape (music or video) club, mail order; books, mail order (except book clubs)

(G-1081)
MORE WOODTURNING MAGAZINE
12728 Fontana Loop (34211-8438)
PHONE..................................508 838-1933
Dennis Daudelin, *Owner*
EMP: 6 **EST:** 2016
SALES (est): 96.5K **Privately Held**
SIC: 2721 Magazines: publishing only, not printed on site

(G-1082)
MOTIONVIBE INNOVATIONS LLC
4031 Caddie Dr E (34203-3429)
PHONE..................................202 285-0235
Nicholas Gerontianos, *CEO*
Jeff Polon, *Research*
EMP: 12
SALES (est): 507.5K **Privately Held**
WEB: www.motionvibe.com
SIC: 7372 Prepackaged software

(G-1083)
MSH BRICK PAVERS INC
5640 Fountain Lake Cir (34207-3765)
PHONE..................................941 822-6472
Desouza Hiago H, *Principal*
EMP: 13 **EST:** 2014
SALES (est): 693K **Privately Held**
SIC: 2951 Asphalt paving mixtures & blocks

(G-1084)
NATIONAL POWDR COATING FLA INC
6004 31st St E (34203-5309)
PHONE..................................941 756-1322
Steve Campbell, *CEO*
Paul Balliette, *President*
EMP: 8 **EST:** 2005
SALES (est): 873.3K **Privately Held**
WEB: www.nationalpowdercoating.com
SIC: 3479 Coating of metals & formed products

(G-1085)
NEW ENGLAND MACHINERY
6204 29th St E (34203-5304)
PHONE..................................941 755-5550
EMP: 25
SALES (est): 4.5MM **Privately Held**
SIC: 3565 Packaging Machinery, Nsk

(G-1086)
NEW ENGLAND MACHINERY INC
Also Called: Nem
2820 62nd Ave E (34203-5305)
P.O. Box 20299 (34204-0299)
PHONE..................................941 755-5550
Judith Nickse, *President*
Geza F Bankuty, *Vice Pres*
Craig Kristoff, *Sales Staff*
John Nieves, *Sales Staff*
Robert Burke, *Manager*
◆ **EMP:** 40 **EST:** 1974
SQ FT: 33,000
SALES (est): 10.7MM **Privately Held**
WEB: www.neminc.com
SIC: 3565 Bottling machinery: filling, capping, labeling

(G-1087)
NORTH AMERICA BIO FUEL CORP
1767 Lakewood Ranch Blvd # 210
(34211-4906)
PHONE..................................877 877-9279
Winston Turner, *President*
EMP: 9
SALES (est): 396.8K **Privately Held**
SIC: 2869 7389 Fluorinated hydrocarbon gases; business services

(G-1088)
NST GLOBAL LLC
Also Called: Sb Tactical
3145 Lakewood Ranch Blvd (34211-5003)
PHONE..................................941 748-2270
Alessandro R Bosco, *CEO*
Jeffry Creamer, *Vice Pres*
Amy Pevear, *Vice Pres*
Lisa Durello, *CFO*
EMP: 26 **EST:** 2008
SALES (est): 3.5MM **Privately Held**
SIC: 3489 5941 Guns or gun parts, over 30 mm.; firearms

(G-1089)
PACEMATE LLC
518 13th St W (34205-7419)
PHONE..................................305 322-5074
David Harrell, *Vice Pres*
Howard Higgins, *Director*
EMP: 6 **EST:** 2016

▲ = Import ▼=Export
◆ =Import/Export

SALES (est): 1.2MM Privately Held
WEB: www.pacemate.com
SIC: 7372 Business oriented computer software
PA: Biocynetic, Llc
518 13th St W
Bradenton FL 34205
305 322-5074

(G-1090)
PACIFIC PAVERS INC
6326 5th Street Cir E (34203-7613)
PHONE....941 238-7854
Julie Nutting, *Principal*
EMP: 6 EST: 2010
SALES (est): 111.2K Privately Held
SIC: 3531 Pavers

(G-1091)
PAD PRINTING TECHNOLOGY CORP
2145 63rd Ave E (34203-5018)
PHONE....941 739-8667
David Berry, *CEO*
EMP: 9 EST: 1995
SQ FT: 8,540
SALES (est): 600K Privately Held
WEB: www.pad-printing.com
SIC: 2752 2759 Commercial printing, offset; laser printing

(G-1092)
PAD PRINTING TECHNOLOGY GROUP
2145 63rd Ave E (34203-5018)
PHONE....941 739-8667
Keith Ekenseair, *CEO*
Tammy Lisko, *Treasurer*
EMP: 10 EST: 2019
SALES (est): 510.8K Privately Held
WEB: www.pad-printing.com
SIC: 2752 Commercial printing, offset

(G-1093)
PADGETT MANUFACTURING INC
2915 62nd Ave E (34203-5320)
PHONE....941 756-8566
Arthur Fowler, *President*
Shirley Fowler, *Corp Secy*
Cleon Fowler, *Vice Pres*
EMP: 68 EST: 1970
SQ FT: 14,000
SALES (est): 3.5MM Privately Held
WEB: www.padgett-inc.com
SIC: 3535 Conveyors & conveying equipment

(G-1094)
PARADISE PUBLISHING GROUP INC
6618 Seven Pines Dr (34203-7870)
PHONE....941 306-2166
Robert Mackin, *Principal*
EMP: 6 EST: 2009
SALES (est): 105.7K Privately Held
SIC: 2741 Miscellaneous publishing

(G-1095)
PHILLIPS PRINTING SERVICES LLC
5103 Lena Rd Unit 107 (34211-9496)
PHONE....941 526-6570
Justin H Phillips, *Principal*
EMP: 8 EST: 2016
SALES (est): 384.5K Privately Held
SIC: 2752 Commercial printing, offset

(G-1096)
PHOSCO ELECTRIC SUPPLY CO INC
1734 5th St W (34205-8302)
P.O. Box 917, Mulberry (33860-0917)
PHONE....941 708-9633
Ken Kelly, *Manager*
EMP: 6
SALES (corp-wide): 4.3MM Privately Held
WEB: www.phosco.net
SIC: 3315 Wire & fabricated wire products
PA: Phosco Electric Supply Co Inc
312 W Canal St
Mulberry FL 33860
863 425-3063

(G-1097)
PIERCE MANUFACTURING INC
1512 38th Ave E (34208-4652)
PHONE....941 748-3900
John Verich, *Vice Pres*
Nancy Krejcarek, *Project Mgr*
Kristina Spang, *Opers Staff*
Rick Kalinski, *Mfg Staff*
Ben Sell, *Mfg Staff*
EMP: 100
SALES (corp-wide): 6.8B Publicly Held
WEB: www.piercemfg.com
SIC: 3711 3792 3715 3714 Fire department vehicles (motor vehicles), assembly of; travel trailers & campers; truck trailers; motor vehicle parts & accessories
HQ: Pierce Manufacturing, Inc.
2600 American Dr
Appleton WI 54914
920 832-3000

(G-1098)
PLASTEC VENTILATION INC
2012 58th Avenue Cir E (34203-5089)
PHONE....941 751-7596
Jean-Jacques Gaudiot, *President*
Jean-Jacqu Gaudiot, *President*
▲ EMP: 5 EST: 2002
SALES (est): 718.1K Privately Held
WEB: www.plastecvent.net
SIC: 3564 Blowers & fans

(G-1099)
PMH HOMES INC
Also Called: Architechtural Foam Systems
14705 21st Ave E (34212-8124)
PHONE....941 234-5121
Philip Michael Heuss, *President*
EMP: 9 EST: 2008
SALES (est): 850K Privately Held
SIC: 3086 Carpet & rug cushions, foamed plastic

(G-1100)
POTTRE GARDENING PRODUCTS LLC
1115 76th St Nw (34209-1032)
PHONE....941 224-8856
Florence C Saldana,
Page Barker,
EMP: 5 EST: 2004
SALES (est): 303.4K Privately Held
SIC: 3524 5191 Lawn & garden equipment; garden supplies

(G-1101)
PRECISION DIRECTIONAL DRLG LLC
5010 60th Dr E (34203-6333)
PHONE....941 320-8308
Carol Gudger, *Branch Mgr*
EMP: 16
SALES (corp-wide): 885.9K Privately Held
SIC: 1381 Directional drilling oil & gas wells
PA: Precision Directional Drilling Llc
3027 59th St
Sarasota FL

(G-1102)
PREFERRED COATINGS LLC
212 Fairway Isles Ln (34212-9325)
PHONE....231 499-3864
Neil W Barnett, *Principal*
EMP: 6 EST: 2016
SALES (est): 141.7K Privately Held
WEB: www.preferredcoatingsllc.net
SIC: 3479 Coating of metals & formed products

(G-1103)
RAPID SWITCH SYSTEMS LLC
4601 15th St E (34203-3617)
PHONE....941 720-7380
William D Leslie, *Manager*
EMP: 7 EST: 2018
SALES (est): 901.7K Privately Held
WEB: www.rapidswitchsystems.com
SIC: 3613 Switchgear & switchboard apparatus

(G-1104)
REFTEC INTERNATIONAL INC
10530 Portal Xing Ste 104 (34211-4914)
PHONE....800 214-4883
Jeff Moore, *CEO*
Chris Lawrence, *CFO*
William Buckles, *Shareholder*
▲ EMP: 31 EST: 1997
SALES (est): 1.1MM Privately Held
WEB: www.reftec.com
SIC: 3585 Refrigeration & heating equipment

(G-1105)
ROAD RUNNER HIGHWAY SIGN INC
4421 12th Street Ct E (34203-3611)
PHONE....941 753-0549
Carol Delagarza, *Principal*
EMP: 8 EST: 2019
SALES (est): 363.9K Privately Held
SIC: 3993 Signs & advertising specialties

(G-1106)
ROCK RIVER TOOL INC
2953 63rd Ave E (34203-5308)
PHONE....941 753-6343
Robert Enander, *President*
Rhonda Stevens, *Mktg Dir*
EMP: 15 EST: 1986
SQ FT: 15,000
SALES (est): 1.4MM Privately Held
WEB: www.rockrivertool.com
SIC: 3545 5085 Cutting tools for machine tools; industrial supplies

(G-1107)
ROSCIOLI INTERNATIONAL INC
Also Called: Donzi Yachts
6111 21st St E (34203-5006)
PHONE....941 755-7411
Dan Hogan, *Purchasing*
Robert Roscioli, *Branch Mgr*
Rita Acosta, *Director*
EMP: 50
SALES (corp-wide): 6.8MM Privately Held
WEB: www.donziyachts.com
SIC: 3732 Boat building & repairing
PA: Roscioli International, Inc.
3201 W State Road 84
Fort Lauderdale FL 33312
941 755-7411

(G-1108)
S & B METAL PRODUCTS S FLA INC
6012 31st St E (34203-5309)
PHONE....941 727-3669
Steve Adlin, *Manager*
Marianne King, *Info Tech Mgr*
EMP: 110 Privately Held
SIC: 3444 Sheet metalwork
PA: S & B Metal Products Of South Florida, Inc.
5301 Gateway Blvd
Lakeland FL 33811

(G-1109)
SAFTRON MANUFACTURING LLC
6012 33rd St E (34203-5402)
PHONE....305 233-5511
Kent W Radovich, *President*
Donna Sandefur, *Sales Mgr*
▼ EMP: 13 EST: 2008
SALES (est): 1.2MM Privately Held
WEB: www.saftron.com
SIC: 3446 Architectural metalwork

(G-1110)
SARASOTA HERALD-TRIBUNE
8713 State Road 70 E (34202-9408)
PHONE....941 745-7808
Patrick Dorsey, *Principal*
EMP: 120
SALES (corp-wide): 272.8MM Privately Held
WEB: www.heraldtribune.com
SIC: 2711 Commercial printing & newspaper publishing combined
HQ: Sarasota Herald-Tribune
801 S Tamiami Trl
Sarasota FL 34236
941 953-7755

(G-1111)
SARASOTA KITCHENS AND CLOSETS
Also Called: Finecraft Cabinetry
5822 24th St E (34203-5027)
PHONE....941 722-7505
EMP: 7 EST: 2018
SALES (est): 463.3K Privately Held
WEB: www.dreamclosetsllc.com
SIC: 2434 Wood kitchen cabinets

(G-1112)
SAY WHAT SCREEN PRTG & EMB INC
Also Called: Make Your Mark Promo .com
10912 8th Ave E (34212-9776)
PHONE....941 745-5822
Marsha Littlefield, *CEO*
Dan Littlefield, *Vice Pres*
▼ EMP: 8 EST: 1997
SQ FT: 7,500
SALES (est): 255.2K Privately Held
WEB: www.makeyourmarkpromo.com
SIC: 3953 2395 Screens, textile printing; embroidery & art needlework

(G-1113)
SEASUCKER LLC
1912 44th Ave E (34203-3798)
PHONE....941 586-2664
Genevieve Casagrande, *President*
Ty Daugherty, *Sales Staff*
Brian Boyd, *Manager*
John Hansen, *Manager*
Charles L Casagrande,
EMP: 22 EST: 2008
SALES (est): 3.7MM Privately Held
WEB: www.seasucker.com
SIC: 3949 Sporting & athletic goods

(G-1114)
SLEUTH INC
Also Called: Slueth Bldg Sys Investigations
3988 E State Road 64 (34208-9059)
PHONE....941 745-9903
Robert L Bergs, *President*
John Horton, *Vice Pres*
Michelle Pressley, *Office Mgr*
EMP: 20 EST: 1982
SQ FT: 790
SALES (est): 3.5MM Privately Held
WEB: www.sleuthleakdetection.com
SIC: 3599 Water leak detectors

(G-1115)
SNAPPLE BEVERAGES
2919 62nd Ave E (34203-5320)
PHONE....941 758-7010
Richard Paul, *Principal*
EMP: 12 EST: 2010
SALES (est): 178.6K Privately Held
WEB: www.snapple.com
SIC: 2086 Soft drinks: packaged in cans, bottles, etc.

(G-1116)
SNOW-NABSTEDT POWER TRANSMISSI
3007 29th Ave E (34208-7418)
PHONE....603 661-5551
Cary Wische, *President*
▲ EMP: 6 EST: 2013
SALES (est): 751.9K Privately Held
WEB: www.snpt.biz
SIC: 3566 Gears, power transmission, except automotive

(G-1117)
SOUTHERN MACHINE TOOL & RBLDRS
2923 62nd Ave E (34203-5367)
PHONE....941 749-0988
Stephen Wendrick, *President*
Kathy Wright, *Treasurer*
EMP: 10 EST: 1979
SQ FT: 10,000
SALES (est): 838.5K Privately Held
SIC: 3599 Machine shop, jobbing & repair

GEOGRAPHIC

(G-1118)
SOUTHERN REINFORCED PLASTICS
Also Called: S R P
2904 29th Ave E Ste F (34208-7424)
PHONE..................................941 746-8793
Robert Biles, *President*
Paula Biles, *Vice Pres*
EMP: 7 **EST:** 1986
SQ FT: 7,500
SALES (est): 300K **Privately Held**
WEB: www.atokaspeedynet.net
SIC: 3089 Injection molding of plastics

(G-1119)
SPRAYING SYSTEMS CO
Also Called: Herman Group
5107 Lena Rd Unit 110 (34211-9494)
PHONE..................................813 259-9400
Ken Schwarz, *Engineer*
Ken Herman, *Manager*
EMP: 7
SALES (corp-wide): 348.1MM **Privately Held**
WEB: www.spray.com
SIC: 3499 Nozzles, spray: aerosol, paint or insecticide
PA: Spraying Systems Co.
200 W North Ave
Glendale Heights IL 60139
630 665-5000

(G-1120)
STERILINE NORTH AMERICA I
872 62nd Street Cir E (34208-6238)
PHONE..................................941 405-2039
EMP: 8 **EST:** 2019
SALES (est): 415.6K **Privately Held**
WEB: www.steriline.it
SIC: 2834 Pharmaceutical preparations

(G-1121)
SUNCOAST ACCRDTED GMLGICAL LAB
4016 Cortez Rd W Ste 1201 (34210-3118)
PHONE..................................941 756-8787
Tom Seguin, *President*
Dave Stieglitz, *Sales Staff*
EMP: 6 **EST:** 1985
SQ FT: 674
SALES (est): 369.3K **Privately Held**
SIC: 3915 7631 3911 6531 Diamond cutting & polishing; watch, clock & jewelry repair; jewelry, precious metal; appraiser, real estate

(G-1122)
SUPER TOOL INC
2951 63rd Ave E (34203-5308)
P.O. Box 20849 (34204-0849)
PHONE..................................941 751-9677
Paul Enander, *President*
Janeen Cabal, *Sales Mgr*
Bryan Enander, *Mktg Dir*
EMP: 20 **EST:** 1989
SQ FT: 10,000
SALES (est): 876.9K **Privately Held**
WEB: www.supertoolinc.com
SIC: 3541 Machine tools, metal cutting type

(G-1123)
SUPERIOR ASPHALT INC
4703 15th St E (34203-3619)
Rural Route 2489, Oneco (34264)
PHONE..................................941 755-2850
Craig W Robson, *President*
Denise Robson, *Corp Secy*
Alan Mulvey, *Vice Pres*
Dan Weaver, *Project Mgr*
Linda Marino, *Administration*
▲ **EMP:** 100
SQ FT: 2,500
SALES (est): 25MM **Privately Held**
WEB: www.superiorasphaltinc.net
SIC: 2951 1771 Asphalt paving mixtures & blocks; blacktop (asphalt) work
PA: Modern Construction Usa, Inc.
4703 15th St E
Bradenton FL 34203
941 727-5215

(G-1124)
SZABO POS DISPLAYS INC
1501 63rd St W (34209-4568)
PHONE..................................941 778-0192
Barbara Szabo, *CEO*
Stephen J Szabo, *President*
EMP: 6 **EST:** 1987
SQ FT: 100,000
SALES (est): 101.4K **Privately Held**
SIC: 3999 2542 3993 3578 Forms: display, dress & show; racks, merchandise display or storage: except wood; signs & advertising specialties; calculating & accounting equipment

(G-1125)
TEAM EDITION APPAREL INC
4208 19th Street Ct E (34208-7336)
PHONE..................................941 744-2041
Giovanna Cipriano, *Vice Pres*
Allen Cotogno, *Director*
◆ **EMP:** 225 **EST:** 1961
SQ FT: 75,000
SALES (est): 64.2MM **Publicly Held**
WEB: www.footlocker-inc.com
SIC: 2329 2396 Athletic (warmup, sweat & jogging) suits: men's & boys'; screen printing on fabric articles
PA: Foot Locker, Inc.
330 W 34th St
New York NY 10001

(G-1126)
TMF PLASTIC SOLUTIONS LLC
4690 19th Street Ct E (34203-3768)
PHONE..................................941 748-2946
Gregory Kuppler, *Mng Member*
Timothy Raymond,
EMP: 21 **EST:** 2016
SALES (est): 5.2MM **Privately Held**
SIC: 3089 Injection molding of plastics

(G-1127)
TORTILLERIA LA RANCHERITA
3010 14th St W (34205-6332)
PHONE..................................941 747-7949
Hilda Vega, *Principal*
EMP: 7 **EST:** 2005
SALES (est): 338.8K **Privately Held**
SIC: 2099 Tortillas, fresh or refrigerated

(G-1128)
TRAKKA USA LLC
4725 Lena Rd Unit 103 (34211-9535)
PHONE..................................505 345-0270
Edwin Daniels, *CEO*
Shawn Mitschelen, *Vice Pres*
Maryellen Mitschelen, *Administration*
Peter Rudaizky,
EMP: 6 **EST:** 2011
SALES (est): 859.3K **Privately Held**
WEB: www.trakkasystems.com
SIC: 3812 Search & navigation equipment

(G-1129)
TRI C PETROLEUM INC
6442 Shoal Creek St Cir (34202-1711)
PHONE..................................941 756-3370
Charles Coleman, *Director*
EMP: 7 **EST:** 2001
SALES (est): 251.2K **Privately Held**
SIC: 1382 Oil & gas exploration services

(G-1130)
TRI-H METAL PRODUCTS INC
5815 21st St E (34203-5004)
PHONE..................................941 753-7311
Rich Hinkle, *President*
Will Hinkle, *Vice Pres*
EMP: 9 **EST:** 2000
SQ FT: 12,000
SALES (est): 1.9MM **Privately Held**
SIC: 3444 Sheet metalwork

(G-1131)
TRINITY MANUFACTURING CORP
6205 31st St E Ste A (34203-5388)
P.O. Box 21105 (34204-1105)
PHONE..................................941 727-9595
James A Fitch Jr, *President*
John Northup, *President*
Paul Goldich, *Vice Pres*
Cheryl Kline, *Purchasing*
Lori Brown, *Manager*
EMP: 29 **EST:** 2003
SQ FT: 9,500
SALES (est): 5.3MM **Privately Held**
WEB: www.trinitymfgcorp.com
SIC: 3679 Harness assemblies for electronic use: wire or cable

(G-1132)
TROPICANA MANUFACTURING CO INC
1001 13th Ave E (34208-2699)
PHONE..................................312 821-1000
Greg Shearson, *President*
▲ **EMP:** 9 **EST:** 2000
SALES (est): 8.1MM
SALES (corp-wide): 70.3B **Publicly Held**
WEB: www.pepsico.com
SIC: 2033 Fruit juices: concentrated, hot pack; fruit juices: fresh
PA: Pepsico, Inc.
700 Anderson Hill Rd
Purchase NY 10577
914 253-2000

(G-1133)
TROPICANA PRODUCTS INC (HQ)
1001 13th Ave E (34208-2699)
P.O. Box 338 (34206-0338)
PHONE..................................941 747-4461
Greg Shearson, *President*
Clay Small, *Senior VP*
Melinda Brown, *Vice Pres*
Paul Carr, *Plant Mgr*
David Schappacher, *Opers Staff*
▲ **EMP:** 1800 **EST:** 1947
SQ FT: 100,000
SALES (est): 1.1B
SALES (corp-wide): 70.3B **Publicly Held**
WEB: www.tropicana.com
SIC: 2033 2037 2086 2048 Fruit juices: fresh; fruit juice concentrates, frozen; fruit drinks (less than 100% juice): packaged in cans, etc.; citrus seed meal, prepared as animal feed
PA: Pepsico, Inc.
700 Anderson Hill Rd
Purchase NY 10577
914 253-2000

(G-1134)
TRUE PLUMBING SVC INC
11729 Meadowgate Pl (34211-3712)
PHONE..................................941 296-5123
Micheal Faulconer, *Owner*
EMP: 9 **EST:** 2018
SALES (est): 1.2MM **Privately Held**
WEB: www.trueplumbing4u.com
SIC: 3432 Plumbing fixture fittings & trim

(G-1135)
ULTIMATE OUTDOOR CABINETRY INC
2864 48th Way E (34203-3814)
PHONE..................................941 713-5295
Walter L Terry, *Principal*
EMP: 6 **EST:** 2012
SALES (est): 123.3K **Privately Held**
WEB: www.ultimateoutdoorcabinetry.com
SIC: 2434 Wood kitchen cabinets

(G-1136)
ULTRABOX INC
5827 17th St E (34203-5043)
P.O. Box 21046 (34204-1046)
PHONE..................................941 371-0000
Boldon Jeffrey, *Principal*
EMP: 10 **EST:** 2013
SALES (est): 270.4K **Privately Held**
WEB: www.ultraboxinc.com
SIC: 2653 Boxes, corrugated: made from purchased materials

(G-1137)
UNITED MANUFACTURING SERVICES
2908 29th Ave E (34208-7460)
PHONE..................................941 224-1692
Rodney Cole, *Principal*
EMP: 7 **EST:** 2016
SALES (est): 255.6K **Privately Held**
SIC: 3999 Manufacturing industries

(G-1138)
US PET IMAGING LLC
Also Called: Imaging For Life
4351 Cortez Rd W (34210-3211)
PHONE..................................941 795-3780
Inita Bedi, *Branch Mgr*
EMP: 6
SALES (corp-wide): 1.1MM **Privately Held**
WEB: www.imagingforlife.net
SIC: 2835 In vitro & in vivo diagnostic substances
PA: Us Pet Imaging Llc
3830 Bee Ridge Rd Ste 100
Sarasota FL 34233
941 921-0383

(G-1139)
VANDALAY INDS MANATEE CNTY LLC
6832 14th St W (34207-5866)
PHONE..................................941 756-6028
Roy Killingsworth, *Principal*
EMP: 6 **EST:** 2010
SALES (est): 176.2K **Privately Held**
SIC: 3999 Manufacturing industries

(G-1140)
VEETHREE ELECTRONICS & MAR LLC
Also Called: Veethree Instruments
2050 47th Ter E (34203-3777)
PHONE..................................941 538-7775
Shekhar Tewatia, *Vice Pres*
Kim Graveline, *Senior Buyer*
Kevin Griffioen, *Technology*
Bill Allen,
Vishal Lalani,
◆ **EMP:** 82 **EST:** 2009
SQ FT: 50,000
SALES (est): 14.8MM **Privately Held**
WEB: www.veethree.com
SIC: 3629 0919 5088 Electronic generation equipment; cultured pearl production; marine supplies

(G-1141)
VISUAL CONCEPTS IN PLASTIC INC
2908 29th Ave E Ste C (34208-7460)
PHONE..................................941 749-1141
Vince Barrentine, *Manager*
EMP: 6 **EST:** 2018
SALES (est): 138K **Privately Held**
SIC: 3089 Plastics products

(G-1142)
VIZCO US INC
1401 Manatee Ave W # 110 (34205-6702)
PHONE..................................941 753-3333
Christopher R Cantolino, *President*
Howard Guard, *Sales Mgr*
◆ **EMP:** 20 **EST:** 2001
SALES (est): 3.5MM **Privately Held**
WEB: www.vizco.com
SIC: 3089 Plastic containers, except foam

(G-1143)
W D H ENTERPRISES INC
Also Called: Copy Right Printing
4230 26th St W (34205-3516)
PHONE..................................941 758-6500
Dave Hassall, *Owner*
Mike Flotow, *Mfg Staff*
Joe Gallantino, *Research*
EMP: 6 **EST:** 1981
SQ FT: 2,500
SALES (est): 713.4K **Privately Held**
SIC: 2752 7331 2791 2789 Commercial printing, offset; direct mail advertising services; typesetting; bookbinding & related work; commercial printing

(G-1144)
W E W ENTERPRISES INC
Also Called: Woodcrafters, The
6103 28th St E Ste A (34203-5386)
PHONE..................................941 751-6610
William E Wilson III, *President*
EMP: 12 **EST:** 1980
SQ FT: 7,000
SALES (est): 345.9K **Privately Held**
SIC: 2434 Wood kitchen cabinets

(G-1145)
WAKE UP BEAUTIFUL
6646 Cortez Rd W (34210-2600)
PHONE..................................941 792-6500
Kathy Yeomans, *Owner*
EMP: 6 **EST:** 2010
SALES (est): 187.4K **Privately Held**
SIC: 2844 Perfumes & colognes

(G-1146)
WEST COAST CASTINGS INC
1211 44th Ave E (34203-3629)
PHONE..................................941 753-2969
Theodore G Boerger, *President*
Susan Boerger, *Vice Pres*
EMP: 13 **EST:** 1948
SQ FT: 12,500
SALES (est): 1.3MM **Privately Held**
WEB: www.westcoastcastings.com
SIC: 3365 Aluminum foundries

(G-1147)
WHEEL SYSTEMS INTL INC
7645 Tralee Way (34202-6010)
PHONE..................................920 235-9888
Shari Medley, *President*
EMP: 11 **EST:** 2003
SALES (est): 389.9K **Privately Held**
WEB: www.medleyglobal.com
SIC: 3448 Garages, portable: prefabricated metal

(G-1148)
WOODTECH GLOBAL INC
Also Called: Graber Cabinets
5822 24th St E (34203-5027)
P.O. Box 110258, Lakewood Rch (34211-0004)
PHONE..................................941 371-0392
Scott Spoerl, *President*
EMP: 10 **EST:** 2016
SALES (est): 1MM **Privately Held**
SIC: 2434 Wood kitchen cabinets

(G-1149)
Z CANS LLC
1111 Brambling Ct (34212-2919)
PHONE..................................941 748-6688
Mary Zimmerman, *Principal*
EMP: 6 **EST:** 2007
SALES (est): 206.4K **Privately Held**
WEB: www.zcans.net
SIC: 3089 Garbage containers, plastic

Brandon
Hillsborough County

(G-1150)
AMERICAN METAL FAB OF CTRL FL
1018 W Brandon Blvd 11b (33511-4101)
PHONE..................................813 653-2788
Roxanna Feldman, *President*
EMP: 5
SQ FT: 2,400
SALES (est): 427.4K **Privately Held**
SIC: 3441 Fabricated structural metal

(G-1151)
AMETRINE LLC
127 Barrington Dr (33511-6449)
PHONE..................................786 300-7946
Darshan Trivedi, *Branch Mgr*
EMP: 10
SALES (corp-wide): 1MM **Privately Held**
WEB: www.ametrinesurfaces.com
SIC: 3281 Table tops, marble
PA: Ametrine Llc
201 Se 2nd Ave
Miami FL 33131
800 864-8127

(G-1152)
BOOKS-A-MILLION INC
839 Brandon Town Ctr Mall (33511-4798)
PHONE..................................813 571-2062
Aji Fabi, *Principal*
EMP: 7
SALES (corp-wide): 847.1MM **Privately Held**
WEB: www.booksamillion.com
SIC: 2741 5942 Miscellaneous publishing; book stores
HQ: Books-A-Million, Inc.
402 Industrial Ln
Birmingham AL 35211
205 942-3737

(G-1153)
COCA COLA BOTTLING CO
599 Lake Kathy Dr (33510-3945)
PHONE..................................813 569-3030
EMP: 25 **EST:** 2017
SALES (est): 691.5K **Privately Held**
WEB: www.coca-cola.com
SIC: 2086 Bottled & canned soft drinks

(G-1154)
COCA-COLA BTLG CENTL FLA LLC
235 W Brandon Blvd (33511-5103)
PHONE..................................832 260-0462
Steven Johnson, *Finance Dir*
EMP: 19 **EST:** 2015
SQ FT: 30,000
SALES (est): 5.5MM **Privately Held**
WEB: www.coca-cola.com
SIC: 2086 Bottled & canned soft drinks

(G-1155)
CONVICTED PRINTING LLC
3005 Rosebud Ln (33511-7542)
PHONE..................................813 304-5568
Ryan J Kole, *Principal*
EMP: 6 **EST:** 2015
SALES (est): 134.5K **Privately Held**
WEB: www.convictedprinting.com
SIC: 2752 Commercial printing, lithographic

(G-1156)
DELTA OIL
823 Bayou Dr (33510)
PHONE..................................813 323-3113
Terry Chaudrey, *President*
EMP: 6 **EST:** 2004
SALES (est): 245.7K **Privately Held**
SIC: 1311 Crude petroleum production

(G-1157)
ERNIES METAL FABRICATING
406 E Windhorst Rd (33510-2530)
PHONE..................................813 679-0816
Ernest Higgins, *Principal*
EMP: 7 **EST:** 2017
SALES (est): 313.3K **Privately Held**
SIC: 3499 Fabricated metal products

(G-1158)
FAST SIGNS OF BRANDON
Also Called: Fastsigns
2020 Brandon Crossing Cir (33511-3674)
PHONE..................................813 655-9036
EMP: 8 **EST:** 2015
SALES (est): 143.4K **Privately Held**
WEB: www.fastsigns.com
SIC: 3993 Signs & advertising specialties

(G-1159)
FLORIDA COCA-COLA BOTTLING CO (DH)
521 Lake Kathy Dr (33510-3945)
PHONE..................................813 569-2600
Jay Ard, *Vice Pres*
Curtis Cattanach, *Marketing Staff*
Denise Jamerson, *Supervisor*
Debra Roach, *Supervisor*
Dan Bottie, *Technical Staff*
◆ **EMP:** 300 **EST:** 1926
SQ FT: 20,000
SALES (est): 888.1MM
SALES (corp-wide): 33B **Publicly Held**
WEB: www.coca-cola.com
SIC: 2086 Bottled & canned soft drinks
HQ: Coca-Cola Refreshments Usa, Inc.
2500 Windy Ridge Pkwy Se
Atlanta GA 30339
770 989-3000

(G-1160)
FRONT LINE PUBLISHING INC
719 Regent Cir S (33511-6931)
PHONE..................................813 480-8033
Joshua J Steinhauer, *Principal*
EMP: 7 **EST:** 2018
SALES (est): 220.5K **Privately Held**
WEB: www.frontlinepublishinginc.com
SIC: 2741 Miscellaneous publishing

(G-1161)
GRIP TOOLING TECHNOLOGIES LLC
1202 Telfair Rd (33510-2978)
PHONE..................................813 654-6832
Thomas Kukucka, *Principal*
EMP: 8 **EST:** 2015
SALES (est): 682.8K **Privately Held**
SIC: 3423 Hand & edge tools

(G-1162)
IDEAL IMAGE BRANDON
1602 Oakfield Dr Ste 105 (33511-0827)
P.O. Box 18191, Tampa (33679-8191)
PHONE..................................813 982-3420
Doh Acebal, *President*
Joe Acebal, *President*
EMP: 6 **EST:** 2005
SALES (est): 453.7K **Privately Held**
WEB: www.idealimage.com
SIC: 3841 Surgical lasers

(G-1163)
IGUANA GRAPHICS INC
1345 Oakfield Dr (33511-4823)
PHONE..................................813 657-7800
Carlos Arias, *President*
EMP: 6 **EST:** 2005
SALES (est): 374K **Privately Held**
WEB: www.goiguana.com
SIC: 2752 Commercial printing, offset

(G-1164)
KING PRINTING & GRAPHICS INC
634 Oakfield Dr (33511-5715)
PHONE..................................813 681-5060
Steve Rabstejnek, *President*
Patty Rabstejnek, *Vice Pres*
EMP: 7 **EST:** 1976
SALES (est): 816.1K **Privately Held**
SIC: 2752 2759 Commercial printing, offset; commercial printing

(G-1165)
LIFELINK CORPORATION
525 E Sadie St (33510-4687)
PHONE..................................813 653-3197
EMP: 6 **EST:** 2010
SALES (est): 239.9K **Privately Held**
WEB: www.lifelinktissuebank.org
SIC: 3821 Clinical laboratory instruments, except medical & dental

(G-1166)
MAGNUM COATINGS INC
802 Lumsden Reserve Dr (33511-5988)
PHONE..................................407 704-0786
Jennifer E Gordon, *Principal*
EMP: 7 **EST:** 2011
SALES (est): 231.9K **Privately Held**
SIC: 3479 Metal coating & allied service

(G-1167)
MICHAEL KORS
909 Brandon Town Ctr Mall (33511-4943)
PHONE..................................813 413-3310
EMP: 6 **EST:** 2018
SALES (est): 433.3K **Privately Held**
WEB: www.locations.michaelkors.com
SIC: 2389 Apparel & accessories

(G-1168)
ORNAMENTAL ALASCO IRON & WLDG
733 Camrose Dr (33510-2158)
PHONE..................................813 254-4883
William Patterson Jr, *Director*
EMP: 6 **EST:** 2001
SALES (est): 130K **Privately Held**
SIC: 7692 Welding repair

(G-1169)
PARAMOUNT DIGITAL PUBG LLC
123 W Bloomingdale Ave # 3 (33511-7400)
PHONE..................................813 489-5029
Grace Macatee, *Mktg Dir*
Donald Fawcett, *Mng Member*
EMP: 10 **EST:** 2011
SALES (est): 591.6K **Privately Held**
SIC: 2741 Miscellaneous publishing

(G-1170)
PATIO PRODUCTS MFG INC
509 S Larry Cir (33511-6040)
PHONE..................................813 681-3806
Al Whitehead, *Principal*
EMP: 8
SALES (est): 463.4K **Privately Held**
WEB: www.patioproductsmfg.com
SIC: 3999 Manufacturing industries

(G-1171)
PATRICK GERMAN INDUSTRIES INC
Also Called: Creative Colors International
1302 Wallwood Dr (33510-2242)
PHONE..................................727 251-3015
German Patrick, *Principal*
EMP: 6 **EST:** 2016
SALES (est): 279.4K **Privately Held**
SIC: 3999 Manufacturing industries

(G-1172)
PATRIOT PERSON DEFENSE
1604 White Dove Ct (33510-2854)
PHONE..................................813 470-8025
John Thies, *President*
EMP: 7 **EST:** 2017
SALES (est): 239.3K **Privately Held**
WEB: www.patriots.com
SIC: 3812 Defense systems & equipment

(G-1173)
PIECEMAKERS LLC
120 N Knights Ave (33510-4324)
PHONE..................................786 517-1829
Andres Tamayo, *Sales Staff*
Vanessa Larsen, *Office Mgr*
Francisco J Villasante, *Mng Member*
Christopher Villasante, *Mng Member*
EMP: 11 **EST:** 2010
SALES (est): 860.4K **Privately Held**
WEB: www.piece-makers.com
SIC: 3441 Fabricated structural metal

(G-1174)
RJH TECHNICAL SERVICES INC
517 Gornto Lake Rd (33510-3919)
P.O. Box 3658 (33509-3658)
PHONE..................................813 655-7947
Dorothy L Hinderliter, *President*
Robert J Hinderliter, *Principal*
Lee Hinderliter, *Purchasing*
Marcus Hinderliter, *Admin Sec*
EMP: 5 **EST:** 1992
SALES (est): 997K **Privately Held**
WEB: www.rjhtechnicalservicesinc.com
SIC: 3825 Internal combustion engine analyzers, to test electronics

(G-1175)
ROCKSTONE BRICK PAVERS
401 S Parsons Ave Ste F (33511-5241)
P.O. Box 7192 (33508-6020)
PHONE..................................813 685-3900
Ronaldo Barcelos, *Principal*
EMP: 6 **EST:** 2011
SALES (est): 103.4K **Privately Held**
WEB: www.rockstonepavers.com
SIC: 3531 Pavers

(G-1176)
ROYAL IDENTITY INCORPORATED
522 Oakfield Dr (33511-5743)
PHONE..................................813 405-4940
Jessi J Johnson, *President*
EMP: 6 **EST:** 2018
SALES (est): 309.1K **Privately Held**
WEB: www.royalidentitypromos.com
SIC: 2759 Commercial printing

(G-1177)
SAND POWER VOLLEYBALL
Also Called: Sandlife Volleyball
1601 Dogwood Ln (33510-2216)
PHONE..................................813 786-8055
Fernando Saavedra, *Principal*
EMP: 6 **EST:** 2016
SALES (est): 298.5K **Privately Held**
SIC: 1442 Construction sand & gravel

GEOGRAPHIC

(G-1178)
SEATTLE ENGRAVING CENTER LLC
1073 E Brandon Blvd (33511-5515)
PHONE..................................206 420-4604
EMP: 6 **EST:** 2016
SALES (est): 435.3K **Privately Held**
WEB: www.seattleengravingcenter.com
SIC: 2759 Currency: engraved

(G-1179)
SIENTRA INC
1302 Guiles Hill Ct (33511-7612)
PHONE..................................813 751-7576
EMP: 9 **EST:** 2017
SALES (est): 132.6K **Privately Held**
WEB: www.sientra.com
SIC: 3842 Surgical appliances & supplies

(G-1180)
SOCRATIC SOLUTIONS INC
220 W Brandon Blvd # 207 (33511-5100)
P.O. Box 414, Lithia (33547-0414)
PHONE..................................813 324-7018
Ryan Lampel, *CEO*
Jennifer Lampel, *Vice Pres*
EMP: 5 **EST:** 2019
SALES (est): 331.1K **Privately Held**
WEB: www.socraticsolutions.us
SIC: 2833 5499 Medicinals & botanicals; tea

(G-1181)
STANFORDS JERKY
3401 Magenta Way (33511-8135)
PHONE..................................813 817-5953
Kyle M Stanford, *Principal*
EMP: 6 **EST:** 2014
SALES (est): 137.5K **Privately Held**
WEB: www.stanfordsjerky.com
SIC: 2013 Sausages & other prepared meats

(G-1182)
TABLE GOLF LLC
667 W Lumsden Rd (33511-5911)
P.O. Box 3290 (33509-3290)
PHONE..................................813 435-6111
EMP: 7
SQ FT: 2,000
SALES: 85K **Privately Held**
SIC: 3944 Mfg Games/Toys

(G-1183)
TWISTED FUSION NUTRITION
Also Called: Reyes Limitless Nutrition
1305 Kingsway Rd (33510-2515)
PHONE..................................646 719-3041
Bryan Reyes, *Owner*
EMP: 10 **EST:** 2019
SALES (est): 420.9K **Privately Held**
SIC: 2429 Shakes (hand split shingles)

(G-1184)
VIMAR STUCCO INC
2546 Edgewater Falls Dr (33511-2295)
PHONE..................................813 966-4831
Franklyn Vicente, *Principal*
EMP: 9 **EST:** 2012
SALES (est): 359.6K **Privately Held**
SIC: 3299 Stucco

Branford
Suwannee County

(G-1185)
BARNES & SONS WOOD PRODUCERS
105 Suwannee Ave Nw (32008-3273)
PHONE..................................386 935-2229
Larry Barnes, *President*
Wesley Barnes, *Vice Pres*
EMP: 5 **EST:** 1970
SQ FT: 3,000
SALES (est): 486K **Privately Held**
SIC: 2411 Pulpwood contractors engaged in cutting

(G-1186)
HATCH ENTERPRISES INC
8199 Us Highway 27 (32008-2680)
P.O. Box 238 (32008-0238)
PHONE..................................386 935-1419
EMP: 5
SQ FT: 2,500
SALES (est): 559.9K **Privately Held**
SIC: 1411 0191 Dolomite Demension-Quarrying And General Farm Primarily Crop

(G-1187)
JOHN LACQUEY ENTERPRISES INC
8125 264th St (32008-2645)
PHONE..................................386 935-1705
John Lacquey, *President*
EMP: 10 **EST:** 2001
SALES (est): 449.4K **Privately Held**
SIC: 2353 Harvest hats, straw

(G-1188)
PINE TOP LOGGING LLC
27687 65th Rd (32008-2510)
PHONE..................................386 365-0857
Donald J Harrison, *Owner*
EMP: 6 **EST:** 2014
SALES (est): 320K **Privately Held**
SIC: 2411 Logging camps & contractors

(G-1189)
TEX ONSITE INC
2169 Ne 120th Loop (32008-7674)
PHONE..................................386 935-4093
Bradley Thomas, *Principal*
EMP: 7 **EST:** 2007
SALES (est): 200K **Privately Held**
WEB: www.texonsite.com.au
SIC: 3825 Engine electrical test equipment

(G-1190)
TW BYRDS SONS INC
11860 E Us 27 (32008-8315)
PHONE..................................386 935-1544
T Jack Byrd, *President*
Paul Byrd, *Vice Pres*
J W Byrd, *Treasurer*
Earl Byrd, *Admin Sec*
Benita Byrd, *Asst Sec*
EMP: 36 **EST:** 1945
SQ FT: 2,500
SALES (est): 2.6MM **Privately Held**
WEB: www.byrdsdepot.com
SIC: 2411 Logging camps & contractors

Bristol
Liberty County

(G-1191)
APALACHEE POLE COMPANY INC
18601 Nw County Road 379a (32321)
P.O. Box 610 (32321-0610)
PHONE..................................850 643-2121
David Powell, *Manager*
Jason Daniels, *Manager*
EMP: 30
SALES (corp-wide): 5MM **Privately Held**
WEB: www.rex-lumber.com
SIC: 2411 2491 Poles, wood: untreated; poles & pole crossarms, treated wood
PA: Apalachee Pole Company, Inc.
1820 Highway 2
Graceville FL 32440
850 263-4457

(G-1192)
C & G TIMBER HARVESTERS INC
10213 Nw Dan Jacobs Ln (32321-3508)
PHONE..................................850 643-1340
Patricia Whitfield, *Principal*
EMP: 6 **EST:** 2003
SALES (est): 97.4K **Privately Held**
SIC: 2411 Logging camps & contractors

(G-1193)
CHARLIE S LOGGING INC
17586 Nw County Road 12 (32321-4068)
PHONE..................................850 643-1145
Lisa Vickers, *Principal*
EMP: 6 **EST:** 2011
SALES (est): 168.6K **Privately Held**
SIC: 2411 Logging

(G-1194)
FLORIDA NORTH LUMBER CO INC
Hwy 12 S (32321)
PHONE..................................850 643-2238
C Finley Mc Rae, *President*
Robert F Mc Rae Jr, *Vice Pres*
EMP: 55 **EST:** 1982
SQ FT: 100,000
SALES (est): 6.1MM **Privately Held**
WEB: www.rex-lumber.com
SIC: 2421 Lumber: rough, sawed or planed

(G-1195)
FLORIDA NORTH LUMBER INC
18601 Nw County Road 12 (32321-4176)
P.O. Box 7, Graceville (32440-0007)
PHONE..................................850 263-4457
C Finley McRae, *President*
EMP: 41 **EST:** 1980
SALES (est): 1.6MM **Privately Held**
WEB: www.rex-lumber.com
SIC: 2421 Sawmills & planing mills, general

(G-1196)
JOHNNY SELLERS LOGGING INC
Turkey Creek Rd (32321)
P.O. Box 582 (32321-0582)
PHONE..................................850 643-5214
Johnny Sellers, *President*
EMP: 9 **EST:** 1995
SALES (est): 892.1K **Privately Held**
SIC: 2411 Logging camps & contractors

(G-1197)
KENNETH P GREEN
Also Called: Kenneth P Green Logging
12977 Nw Pea Ridge Rd (32321-3306)
PHONE..................................850 643-5851
Kenneth P Green, *Owner*
EMP: 6 **EST:** 1972
SALES (est): 311.3K **Privately Held**
SIC: 2411 Logging camps & contractors

(G-1198)
LIBERTY CALHOUN JOURNAL INC
11493 Nw Summers Rd (32321-3364)
P.O. Box 536 (32321-0536)
PHONE..................................850 643-3333
Johnny Eubanks, *President*
Theresa Eubanks, *Vice Pres*
EMP: 9 **EST:** 1981
SALES (est): 784K **Privately Held**
WEB: www.libertycountyflorida.com
SIC: 2711 2791 Newspapers, publishing & printing; typesetting

(G-1199)
MCMILLAN LOGGING INC
15405 Nw Pea Ridge Rd (32321-3660)
P.O. Box 8 (32321-0008)
PHONE..................................850 643-4819
James S McMillan, *President*
EMP: 11 **EST:** 2007
SQ FT: 2,542
SALES (est): 1.2MM **Privately Held**
SIC: 2411 Logging camps & contractors

(G-1200)
MICHAEL P WAHLQUIST
13036 Nw Freeman Rd (32321-3026)
PHONE..................................850 643-5139
Michael P Wahlquist, *Owner*
EMP: 7 **EST:** 2005
SALES (est): 178.5K **Privately Held**
SIC: 3589 Water filters & softeners, household type

(G-1201)
NORTH FLORIDA WOODLANDS INC
Also Called: North Florida Lumber
18601 Nw County Road 12 (32321-4176)
P.O. Box 610 (32321-0610)
PHONE..................................850 643-2238
Ken Betts, *Manager*
EMP: 18
SALES (corp-wide): 2.2MM **Privately Held**
WEB: www.rex-lumber.com
SIC: 2421 Sawmills & planing mills, general
PA: North Florida Woodlands, Inc
1820 Highway 2
Graceville FL 32440
850 263-4457

(G-1202)
REX LUMBER LLC
Highway 12 S (32321)
PHONE..................................850 643-2172
Derik Blesky, *Manager*
EMP: 12
SALES (corp-wide): 68.3MM **Privately Held**
WEB: www.rex-lumber.com
SIC: 2421 Sawmills & planing mills, general
HQ: Rex Lumber, Graceville, Llc
5299 Alabama St
Graceville FL 32440
850 263-2056

(G-1203)
RUBY VANRUM
Also Called: Varnums Rest Home
12167 Nw Freeman Rd (32321-3019)
P.O. Box 6 (32321-0006)
PHONE..................................850 643-5155
Ruby Varnum, *Owner*
EMP: 7 **EST:** 1985
SALES (est): 390.5K **Privately Held**
SIC: 2512 Living room furniture: upholstered on wood frames

Brooksville
Hernando County

(G-1204)
ACCUFORM MANUFACTURING INC
Also Called: Accuform Signs
16228 Flight Path Dr (34604-6875)
PHONE..................................352 799-5434
Wayne D Johnson, *CEO*
Rob Ogilbee, *President*
David B Johnson, *COO*
▲ **EMP:** 270
SQ FT: 100,000
SALES (est): 45.2MM **Privately Held**
WEB: www.accuform.com
SIC: 3993 Signs, not made in custom sign painting shops

(G-1205)
ADAMS ARMS HOLDINGS LLC
21228 Powell Rd (34604-6723)
PHONE..................................727 853-0550
Jason East, *President*
EMP: 35 **EST:** 2019
SALES (est): 4.9MM **Privately Held**
WEB: www.adamsarms.net
SIC: 3484 Guns (firearms) or gun parts, 30 mm. & below

(G-1206)
AIRDYNE AEROSPACE INC
3160 Premier Dr (34604-8299)
PHONE..................................352 593-4163
Ross Neyedly, *President*
Ray Neathery, *CIO*
EMP: 29 **EST:** 2010
SALES (est): 4.7MM **Privately Held**
WEB: www.airdyne-aero.com
SIC: 3728 Aircraft parts & equipment

(G-1207)
AL COVELL ELECTRIC INC
600 S Main St (34601-3764)
P.O. Box 294, Nobleton (34661-0294)
PHONE..................................352 544-0680
James Covell, *President*
Anna Liisa Covell, *Vice Pres*
Bryon Covell, *Director*
EMP: 5 **EST:** 1992
SQ FT: 3,600
SALES (est): 599K **Privately Held**
WEB: www.covellservices.com
SIC: 7694 1731 5999 Electric motor repair; electrical work; motors, electric

▲ = Import ▼=Export
◆ =Import/Export

(G-1208)
AMAX WELDING & FABRICATION
19496 Fort Dade Ave (34601-2414)
P.O. Box 1871 (34605-1871)
PHONE..................................352 544-8484
Brenda J Smith, *President*
Roger D Smith, *Vice Pres*
EMP: 5 **EST:** 2008
SALES (est): 447K **Privately Held**
SIC: 7692 Welding repair

(G-1209)
AME TRITON LLC
Also Called: AME International
2347 Circuit Way (34604-0622)
PHONE..................................352 799-1111
Tim Benoist, *Vice Pres*
Luis Goyeneche, *Vice Pres*
Brett Waggoner, *Vice Pres*
Kyle Sparkman, *Opers Staff*
Jarman Kelly, *Financial Analy*
▲ **EMP:** 23 **EST:** 2007
SQ FT: 19,000
SALES (est): 4.2MM **Privately Held**
WEB: www.ameintl.net
SIC: 3429 Motor vehicle hardware

(G-1210)
AMERICAN INJECTABLES INC ✪
15261 Telcom Dr (34604-0718)
PHONE..................................813 435-6014
Vern Allen, *CEO*
EMP: 12 **EST:** 2020
SALES (est): 1.5MM **Privately Held**
SIC: 2834 Pharmaceutical preparations

(G-1211)
AMERICAN SILICA HOLDINGS LLC
24060 Deer Run Rd (34601-4548)
P.O. Box 68 (34605-0068)
PHONE..................................352 796-8855
EMP: 5
SALES (est): 608.7K **Privately Held**
SIC: 1389 5082 Oil/Gas Field Services Whol Construction/Mining Equipment

(G-1212)
ANTHONY SPAGNA SVC & MAINT INC
3335 Mustang Dr (34604-8113)
P.O. Box 15316 (34604-0116)
PHONE..................................352 796-2109
Anthony Spagna, *President*
EMP: 6 **EST:** 2004
SQ FT: 3,000
SALES (est): 934.1K **Privately Held**
SIC: 3441 Fabricated structural metal

(G-1213)
AVALANCHE CORPORATION
Also Called: Monster Transmission & Prfmce
17109 Old Ayers Rd (34604-6808)
PHONE..................................800 708-0087
Curtis Thomas, *Treasurer*
Eva Thomas, *Office Mgr*
▼ **EMP:** 75 **EST:** 2003
SALES (est): 10.3MM **Privately Held**
SIC: 3714 7539 Rebuilding engines & transmissions, factory basis; torque converter repair, automotive

(G-1214)
BET ER MIX INC
21101 Cortez Blvd (34601-5645)
PHONE..................................352 799-5538
Chuck Jackson, *President*
EMP: 9 **EST:** 2017
SALES (est): 182.1K **Privately Held**
WEB: www.betermix.com
SIC: 3273 Ready-mixed concrete

(G-1215)
BLACK DIAMOND COATINGS INC
6036 Nature Coast Blvd (34602-8286)
PHONE..................................800 270-4050
David Warren, *CEO*
Heather Warren, *Vice Pres*
EMP: 21 **EST:** 2013
SALES (est): 2.8MM **Privately Held**
WEB: www.blackdiamondcoatings.com
SIC: 2851 Paints & allied products

(G-1216)
BREINER MACHINE CO INC
15373 Flight Path Dr (34604-6862)
PHONE..................................352 544-0463
James Breiner, *President*
EMP: 12 **EST:** 1985
SALES (est): 1.9MM **Privately Held**
WEB: www.breinermachineinc.com
SIC: 3444 3599 Sheet metalwork; machine shop, jobbing & repair

(G-1217)
BROOKSVILLE PRINTING INC
712 S Main St (34601-3745)
PHONE..................................352 848-0016
Carl Brady, *President*
C J Brady, *Vice Pres*
EMP: 5 **EST:** 1973
SQ FT: 1,500
SALES (est): 484K **Privately Held**
SIC: 2752 Commercial printing, offset

(G-1218)
CHASCO MACHINE & MANUFACTURING
5071 Cedar Ridge Dr (34601-6535)
PHONE..................................727 815-3510
Jeffrey A Roth, *President*
EMP: 6 **EST:** 1999
SALES (est): 633.1K **Privately Held**
WEB: www.chascomachine.com
SIC: 3599 3469 Catapults; metal stampings

(G-1219)
CHASCO MACHINE & MFG INC
5071 Cedar Ridge Dr (34601-6535)
PHONE..................................352 678-4188
Jeff Roth, *President*
Jeffrey A Roth, *Principal*
▲ **EMP:** 30 **EST:** 2004
SALES (est): 6MM **Privately Held**
WEB: www.chascomachine.com
SIC: 3469 5084 Machine parts, stamped or pressed metal; machine tools & accessories

(G-1220)
CMF TRUSS INC
13521 Ponce De Leon Blvd (34601-8650)
PHONE..................................352 796-5805
Pat Owens, *President*
EMP: 27 **EST:** 1992
SQ FT: 512
SALES (est): 935.9K **Privately Held**
SIC: 2439 Trusses, wooden roof

(G-1221)
COASTAL MFG & FABRICATION INC
16208 Cortez Blvd (34601-8911)
P.O. Box 15815 (34604-0124)
PHONE..................................352 799-8706
Darrell L Witt, *President*
Roxanne M Witt, *Vice Pres*
EMP: 6 **EST:** 2005
SALES (est): 932.3K **Privately Held**
SIC: 3441 2431 Fabricated structural metal; staircases, stairs & railings

(G-1222)
COUNTY OF HERNANDO
Also Called: Lykes Memorial Co Library
238 Howell Ave (34601-2040)
PHONE..................................352 754-4042
Barbara Shiflett, *Manager*
EMP: 10
SQ FT: 15,763
SALES (corp-wide): 240.9MM **Privately Held**
WEB: www.hernandocounty.us
SIC: 2782 Library binders, looseleaf
PA: County Of Hernando
20 N Main St Rm 230
Brooksville FL 34601
352 754-4201

(G-1223)
CREONIX LLC
30167 Power Line Rd (34602-8299)
P.O. Box 21389, Bradenton (34204-1389)
PHONE..................................941 758-3340
Ken Piela, *CEO*
Scott Nickerson, *Director*
EMP: 15 **EST:** 2010
SALES (est): 1.5MM **Privately Held**
WEB: www.creonixllc.com
SIC: 3672 Printed circuit boards

(G-1224)
D A B CONSTRUCTORS INC
3300 Northeast Pkwy (34609)
PHONE..................................352 797-3537
Debrah Bachsmidt, *President*
EMP: 8 **EST:** 2001
SALES (est): 300K **Privately Held**
SIC: 3531 Asphalt plant, including gravel-mix type

(G-1225)
DAY METAL PRODUCTS LLC
119 E Dr M L King Jr Blvd (34601-4043)
P.O. Box 176 (34605-0176)
PHONE..................................352 799-9258
Alan R Day, *Manager*
EMP: 5 **EST:** 2011
SALES (est): 810.6K **Privately Held**
SIC: 3444 Sheet metalwork

(G-1226)
DFA DAIRY BRANDS FLUID LLC
16235 Aviation Loop Dr (34604-6805)
PHONE..................................352 754-1750
Kevin Lampe, *Branch Mgr*
EMP: 8
SALES (corp-wide): 17.8B **Privately Held**
SIC: 2026 5143 Milk processing (pasteurizing, homogenizing, bottling); milk
HQ: Dfa Dairy Brands Fluid, Llc
1405 N 98th St
Kansas City KS 66111
816 801-6455

(G-1227)
DYNO NOBEL INC
14200 Brooksville Rock Rd (34614-1610)
PHONE..................................352 796-9018
Lars Johansen, *CEO*
EMP: 6 **Privately Held**
WEB: www.dynonobel.com
SIC: 2892 Explosives
HQ: Dyno Nobel Inc.
6440 S Millrock Dr # 150
Salt Lake City UT 84121
801 364-4800

(G-1228)
EXCALIBUR MANUFACTURING CORP (PA)
16186 Flight Path Dr (34604-6845)
PHONE..................................352 544-0055
Douglas Schneider, *President*
Wade Thomas, *Corp Secy*
Ellen Schneider, *Vice Pres*
▲ **EMP:** 16 **EST:** 1989
SQ FT: 7,200
SALES (est): 1.5MM **Privately Held**
WEB: www.seawayplastics.com
SIC: 3089 Injection molding of plastics

(G-1229)
FLORIDA LIVING LLC
7410 Dent St (34601-8922)
P.O. Box 10374 (34603-0374)
PHONE..................................352 556-9691
Ronald D McCabe, *Principal*
EMP: 8 **EST:** 2008
SALES (est): 302.5K **Privately Held**
WEB: www.mysinkholerepair.com
SIC: 2741 Miscellaneous publishing

(G-1230)
FSP-GES INC
Also Called: Flagstone Pavers
9070 Old Cobb Rd (34601-8700)
PHONE..................................352 799-7933
Geoff Bond, *President*
Russ Young, *General Mgr*
Kerry Dowling, *Plant Mgr*
Christine Wright, *Sales Mgr*
Shane Cunningham, *Manager*
◆ **EMP:** 25 **EST:** 1999
SQ FT: 20,300
SALES (est): 5.3MM **Privately Held**
WEB: www.flagstonepavers.com
SIC: 3272 Concrete products

(G-1231)
GATOR PRINTING & DESIGN LLC
18628 Cortez Blvd (34601-9012)
PHONE..................................352 593-4168
Ronald R Phillips, *Administration*
EMP: 7 **EST:** 2014
SALES (est): 150.5K **Privately Held**
SIC: 2752 Commercial printing, offset

(G-1232)
GOTG LLC
Also Called: Florida Container Depot
19182 Powell Rd 1 (34604-7059)
PHONE..................................800 381-4684
Annette Cenal, *General Mgr*
Michael McCafrey,
EMP: 5 **EST:** 2009
SALES (est): 484K **Privately Held**
SIC: 3629 4225 5039 Inverters, nonrotating: electrical; power conversion units, a.c. to d.c.: static-electric; warehousing, self-storage;

(G-1233)
HERNANDO LITHOPRINTING INC
Also Called: Hernando Litho Printing
969 Hale Ave (34601-3931)
PHONE..................................352 796-4136
Philip James Myrea, *President*
Barbara Myrea, *Vice Pres*
EMP: 5 **EST:** 1974
SQ FT: 1,200
SALES (est): 316.6K **Privately Held**
SIC: 2752 Commercial printing, offset

(G-1234)
HITECH TRUSS INC ✪
Also Called: Hitek Truss
6179 Nature Coast Blvd (34602-8243)
PHONE..................................352 797-0877
Derrick Rushnell, *President*
EMP: 6 **EST:** 2020
SALES (est): 320K **Privately Held**
SIC: 2439 Trusses, wooden roof

(G-1235)
HITEK PROPERTY LLC
6179 Nature Coast Blvd (34602-8243)
PHONE..................................352 797-0877
Joseph Pastore, *Mng Member*
Robert Eaton,
EMP: 12 **EST:** 2004
SQ FT: 5,000
SALES (est): 2.1MM **Privately Held**
WEB: www.hitektruss.com
SIC: 2439 Trusses, wooden roof

(G-1236)
INDUSTRIAL WELDING & MAINT
10080 Cobb Rd (34601-8710)
P.O. Box 1404 (34605-1404)
PHONE..................................352 799-3432
Curtis B Cannon, *President*
Scott E Dennison, *Vice Pres*
Vera L Cannon, *Treasurer*
EMP: 8 **EST:** 1981
SQ FT: 6,250
SALES (est): 876.3K **Privately Held**
WEB: www.lemasteriwm.com
SIC: 3441 Fabricated structural metal

(G-1237)
INTERCONNECT CABLE TECH CORP
Also Called: Ictc USA
16090 Flight Path Dr (34604-6824)
PHONE..................................352 796-1716
Sareet Majumdar, *President*
Mary Alice Betts, *COO*
Rick Osgood, *Export Mgr*
Paul Sochacki, *Sales Staff*
Kelly Marazita, *Manager*
▲ **EMP:** 75 **EST:** 1988
SQ FT: 45,000
SALES (est): 31.1MM **Privately Held**
WEB: www.ictcusa.com
SIC: 3643 3678 3679 5065 Current-carrying wiring devices; electronic connectors; harness assemblies for electronic use: wire or cable; electronic parts & equipment

(G-1238)
INTREPID MACHINE INC
2305 Circuit Way (34604-0622)
PHONE..................................352 540-9919
Tim M Tabor, *President*
Mike Belle, *Admin Sec*
EMP: 30 **EST:** 1995
SQ FT: 9,000
SALES (est): 3.9MM **Privately Held**
WEB: www.intrepidmachine.com
SIC: 3599 Machine shop, jobbing & repair

(G-1239)
ITCT USA
16090 Flight Path Dr (34604-6824)
PHONE..................................352 799-1466
Gabriel Ocasio, *Supervisor*
Rachel Chou, *Director*
Kerri Coakley, *Director*
EMP: 7 **EST:** 2015
SALES (est): 184.6K **Privately Held**
WEB: www.ictcusa.com
SIC: 3672 Printed circuit boards

(G-1240)
JONI INDUSTRIES INC
16230 Aviation Loop Dr (34604-6804)
PHONE..................................352 799-5456
Gustav Guadagnino, *President*
EMP: 16 **EST:** 1988
SQ FT: 11,000
SALES (est): 2.4MM **Privately Held**
WEB: www.jonipromotionals.com
SIC: 3552 3999 3993 2396 Silk screens for textile industry; novelties, bric-a-brac & hobby kits; signs & advertising specialties; automotive & apparel trimmings; pleating & stitching; screen printing

(G-1241)
KEYLON LIGHTING SERVICES INC
6931 Remington Rd (34602-7443)
PHONE..................................352 279-3249
Kenneth Keylon, *President*
Danny Keylon, *Principal*
EMP: 7 **EST:** 2001
SALES (est): 732K **Privately Held**
SIC: 3646 Commercial indusl & institutional electric lighting fixtures

(G-1242)
KINCAID PLASTICS INC
2400 Corporate Blvd (34604-0621)
PHONE..................................352 754-9979
Jerry L Kincaid, *President*
Maurine Kincaid, *Vice Pres*
David Kincaid, *Manager*
Kayla Kincaid, *Manager*
EMP: 61 **EST:** 1967
SQ FT: 23,500
SALES (est): 15.3MM **Privately Held**
WEB: www.kincaidplastics.com
SIC: 3089 Molding primary plastic; injection molding of plastics

(G-1243)
KINEMATICS AND CONTROLS CORP
15151 Technology Dr (34604-0690)
PHONE..................................352 796-0300
John Rakucewicz, *President*
Anne Rakucewicz, *Comptroller*
EMP: 8 **EST:** 1969
SQ FT: 9,600
SALES (est): 1.4MM **Privately Held**
WEB: www.kcontrols.com
SIC: 3625 3565 Relays & industrial controls; packaging machinery

(G-1244)
LEE MCCULLOUGH INC
Also Called: McCullough Bottled Water
Hud (34606)
P.O. Box 909, Ocala (34478-0909)
PHONE..................................352 796-7100
Fax: 352 351-4468
EMP: 8
SALES: 650K **Privately Held**
SIC: 2086 Mfg Bottled/Canned Soft Drinks

(G-1245)
LEGACY VULCAN LLC
14556 Ponce De Leon Blvd (34601-8422)
P.O. Box 427 (34605-0427)
PHONE..................................352 796-5690
Steve Salantai, *Principal*
Jake Sauer, *Executive*
EMP: 10 **Publicly Held**
WEB: www.vulcanmaterials.com
SIC: 1422 5032 Limestones, ground; limestone
HQ: Legacy Vulcan, Llc
1200 Urban Center Dr
Vestavia AL 35242
205 298-3000

(G-1246)
LHOIST NORTH AMERICA ALA LLC
Also Called: Brooksville Terminal Us11
10245 Cement Plant Rd (34601-8634)
P.O. Box 10448 (34603-0448)
PHONE..................................352 585-3488
Hanspeter Dietiker, *Terminal Mgr*
EMP: 10
SALES (corp-wide): 2.6MM **Privately Held**
SIC: 3274 Lime
HQ: Lhoist North America Of Alabama, Llc
5600 Clearfork Main St # 300
Fort Worth TX 76109
817 732-8164

(G-1247)
LOOPER SPORTS CONNECTION INC
19225 Cortez Blvd (34601-3028)
PHONE..................................352 796-7974
Edward Looper, *CEO*
Jennifer Looper, *Vice Pres*
EMP: 5 **EST:** 2004
SALES (est): 316.6K **Privately Held**
WEB: www.loopersports.com
SIC: 2759 5941 5949 5999 Screen printing; sporting goods & bicycle shops; sewing & needlework; trophies & plaques

(G-1248)
MCR AMRCAN PHARMACEUTICALS INC
16255 Aviation Loop Dr (34604-6805)
PHONE..................................352 754-8587
David Ambrose, *CEO*
Gary Dutton, *President*
Robert Davis, *Director*
EMP: 40 **EST:** 1991
SQ FT: 2,000
SALES (est): 3.3MM **Publicly Held**
WEB: www.mcramerican.com
SIC: 2834 Pharmaceutical preparations
PA: Natural Hitech Petroleum, Inc.
1 Penn Plz Ste 1503
New York NY 10119

(G-1249)
MED-NAP LLC
Also Called: Acme
301 Marianne St (34601-3412)
PHONE..................................352 796-6020
Pierre Sanfacon, *General Mgr*
▲ **EMP:** 12 **EST:** 2013
SQ FT: 10,000
SALES (est): 2.5MM
SALES (corp-wide): 164MM **Publicly Held**
WEB: www.mednap.us
SIC: 2844 Towelettes, premoistened
PA: Acme United Corporation
1 Waterview Dr Ste 200
Shelton CT 06484
800 835-2263

(G-1250)
MICRO MATIC USA INC
15111 Dispense Ln (34604-6879)
PHONE..................................352 799-6331
EMP: 6
SALES (corp-wide): 155.1MM **Privately Held**
WEB: www.micromatic.com
SIC: 3585 Refrigeration & heating equipment
HQ: Micro Matic Usa, Inc.
2386 Simon Ct
Brooksville FL 34604
352 544-1081

(G-1251)
MICRO MATIC USA INC
16121 Flight Path Dr (34604-6846)
PHONE..................................352 544-1081
David Washington, *Branch Mgr*
EMP: 6
SALES (corp-wide): 155.1MM **Privately Held**
WEB: www.micromatic.com
SIC: 3585 Soda fountain & beverage dispensing equipment & parts
HQ: Micro Matic Usa, Inc.
2386 Simon Ct
Brooksville FL 34604
352 544-1081

(G-1252)
MICRO MATIC USA INC (HQ)
2386 Simon Ct (34604-0751)
PHONE..................................352 544-1081
Peter J Muzzonigro, *President*
Chuck Pederson, *Mfg Staff*
Justin Hendrix, *Production*
Kevin Morgan, *Production*
Pat Schumacher, *Regl Sales Mgr*
◆ **EMP:** 44 **EST:** 1984
SQ FT: 18,000
SALES (est): 28.5MM
SALES (corp-wide): 155.1MM **Privately Held**
WEB: www.micromatic.com
SIC: 3491 5087 3585 Industrial valves; liquor dispensing equipment & systems; soda fountain & beverage dispensing equipment & parts
PA: Micro Matic A/S
Holkebjergvej 48
Odense 5250
661 711-22

(G-1253)
MILLWORK AND DESIGN INC
22309 Rodeo Dr (34602-9173)
PHONE..................................352 544-0444
Wayne G Benedict, *President*
John Lovering, *Vice Pres*
Deborah K Benedict, *Admin Sec*
EMP: 8 **EST:** 1987
SQ FT: 10,000
SALES (est): 259K **Privately Held**
SIC: 2431 5211 1796 Millwork; millwork & lumber; installing building equipment

(G-1254)
MONITOR PRODUCTS INC
15400 Flight Path Dr (34604-6823)
PHONE..................................352 544-2620
Carl H Sunden, *President*
John McClure, *Prdtn Mgr*
EMP: 70 **EST:** 1979
SQ FT: 27,000
SALES (est): 9.9MM **Privately Held**
WEB: www.monitorpro.com
SIC: 3443 Heat exchangers, plate type

(G-1255)
MR GS FOODS
Also Called: Eggplant and Dough
15402 Aviation Loop Dr (34604-6856)
PHONE..................................352 799-1806
Mike Guarino, *Owner*
EMP: 13 **EST:** 2009
SALES (est): 562.1K **Privately Held**
WEB: www.mrgsfoods.com
SIC: 2051 Bakery: wholesale or wholesale/retail combined

(G-1256)
NEUBERT AERO CORP
16110 Flight Path Dr (34604-6845)
P.O. Box 320467, Tampa (33679-2467)
PHONE..................................352 345-4828
Timothy W Neubert, *President*
▲ **EMP:** 7 **EST:** 1998
SQ FT: 10,000
SALES (est): 911.9K **Privately Held**
WEB: www.airportnac.com
SIC: 3829 3612 3648 1611 Measuring & controlling devices; lighting transformers, street & airport; airport lighting fixtures: runway approach, taxi or ramp; airport runway construction

(G-1257)
OMNI DISPLAYS LLC
15261 Telcom Dr (34604-0718)
PHONE..................................352 799-9997
EMP: 25
SQ FT: 20,000
SALES (est): 2.3MM **Privately Held**
SIC: 2653 Mfg Corrugated & Solid Fiber Boxes

(G-1258)
PAVERS INC
Also Called: Sun Coast Pavers
14497 Ponce De Leon Blvd (34601-8418)
PHONE..................................352 754-3875
Francisco Fleites, *President*
EMP: 5 **EST:** 2007
SALES (est): 517.8K **Privately Held**
WEB: www.suncoastpavers.com
SIC: 3531 Pavers

(G-1259)
PED-STUART CORPORATION
Also Called: Stuart Promotional Products
15351 Flight Path Dr (34604-6862)
P.O. Box 15550 (34604-0120)
PHONE..................................352 754-6001
Stuart Walasek, *President*
Terry Walasek, *Vice Pres*
EMP: 20 **EST:** 1982
SQ FT: 30,000
SALES (est): 800K **Privately Held**
WEB: www.ped-stuart.com
SIC: 3999 3841 3081 Identification badges & insignia; identification tags, except paper; surgical & medical instruments; unsupported plastics film & sheet

(G-1260)
PEPSI-COLA METRO BTLG CO INC
490 Champion Dr (34601-2726)
PHONE..................................352 797-1160
Gary Logan, *Manager*
EMP: 6
SQ FT: 17,710
SALES (corp-wide): 70.3B **Publicly Held**
WEB: www.pepsico.com
SIC: 2086 5149 Carbonated soft drinks, bottled & canned; groceries & related products
HQ: Pepsi-Cola Metropolitan Bottling Company, Inc.
1111 Westchester Ave
White Plains NY 10604
914 767-6000

(G-1261)
PLAYERS MEDIA GROUP INC
5267 Zenith Garden Loop (34601-6651)
PHONE..................................509 254-4949
Collin Castellaw, *Partner*
EMP: 15 **EST:** 2019
SALES (est): 1.5MM **Privately Held**
SIC: 2836 Culture media

(G-1262)
PRINT SHACK
210 W Jefferson St (34601-2523)
PHONE..................................352 799-2972
Jennie Drummond, *Owner*
EMP: 6 **EST:** 1985
SALES (est): 371.1K **Privately Held**
WEB: www.printshacknc.com
SIC: 2759 2396 Screen printing; automotive & apparel trimmings

(G-1263)
PURE MED MOBILITY INC
1125 W Jefferson St (34601-2423)
P.O. Box 1257 (34605-1257)
PHONE..................................352 366-8008
Joseph Decker, *President*
Barbara Decker, *Vice Pres*
EMP: 6 **EST:** 2019

SALES (est): 114.8K **Privately Held**
WEB: www.puremedmobility.com
SIC: 3751 5012 3842 Motor scooters & parts; motor scooters; canes, orthopedic; crutches & walkers

(G-1264)
RINKER MATERIALS CORP
10311 Cement Plant Rd (34601-8657)
PHONE..................................352 799-7881
EMP: 7 **EST:** 2019
SALES (est): 173.1K **Privately Held**
SIC: 3273 Ready-mixed concrete

(G-1265)
ROGERS SIGN CORP
701 S Lemon Ave (34601-3742)
PHONE..................................352 799-1923
Robert F Rogers, *President*
EMP: 23 **EST:** 1988
SQ FT: 10,062
SALES (est): 600K **Privately Held**
WEB: www.rogerssigncorp.com
SIC: 3993 1799 5085 Electric signs; sign installation & maintenance; signmaker equipment & supplies

(G-1266)
SALERNO PHARMACEUTICALS LP
16255 Aviation Loop Dr (34604-6805)
PHONE..................................352 799-9813
EMP: 6
SQ FT: 18,000
SALES (est): 267.4K **Privately Held**
SIC: 2834 Mfg Pharmaceutical Preparations

(G-1267)
SEATING CONSTRUCTORS USA INC
2347 Circuit Way (34604-0622)
P.O. Box 15258 (34604-0115)
PHONE..................................813 505-7560
Phil Vanderhider, *Owner*
Yvette Vanderhider, *Vice Pres*
EMP: 13 **EST:** 2001
SALES (est): 386.3K **Privately Held**
WEB: www.seatingusa.com
SIC: 2531 Stadium seating

(G-1268)
SHIRLEY L JORDAN COMPANY INC
Also Called: Esco Equipment Supply Co
15270 Flight Path Dr (34604-6849)
PHONE..................................352 754-1117
Jeff Jobe, *CEO*
James Lueras, *Sales Staff*
William Fisher Jr, *Consultant*
◆ **EMP:** 12 **EST:** 1984
SQ FT: 22,000
SALES (est): 2.1MM **Privately Held**
WEB: www.esco.net
SIC: 3559 Automotive related machinery

(G-1269)
SHO ME NUTRICEUTICALS INC
Also Called: Sho ME Natural Products
15431 Flight Path Dr (34604-6851)
PHONE..................................352 797-9600
Chris Reckner, *President*
Theodore C Irving, *Vice Pres*
▲ **EMP:** 42 **EST:** 1998
SQ FT: 11,000
SALES (est): 987.9K **Privately Held**
SIC: 2834 Vitamin, nutrient & hematinic preparations for human use

(G-1270)
SIMS MACHINE & CONTROLS INC
15538 Aviation Loop Dr (34604-6801)
PHONE..................................352 799-2405
Robert Jones, *President*
EMP: 15 **EST:** 1975
SQ FT: 48,000
SALES (est): 478.4K **Privately Held**
WEB: www.simsmachine.com
SIC: 3569 Robots, assembly line: industrial & commercial

(G-1271)
SJG MACHINE INC
316 Marianne St (34601-3411)
PHONE..................................352 345-3656
Scott Gray, *Principal*
EMP: 8 **EST:** 2007
SALES (est): 222.7K **Privately Held**
SIC: 3599 Machine shop, jobbing & repair

(G-1272)
SOUTHERN WOOD SERVICES LLC
6288 California St (34604-8310)
P.O. Box 531, Freeport (32439-0531)
PHONE..................................352 279-3208
Mike Cusic, *Sales Staff*
Ken Gentry, *Manager*
John Paff,
EMP: 5 **EST:** 2008
SALES (est): 431.8K **Privately Held**
SIC: 2411 2421 2611 4212 Timber, cut at logging camp; driving & booming timber; sawdust, shavings & wood chips; pulp mills, mechanical & recycling processing; lumber & timber trucking

(G-1273)
SOUTHWEST EQP FOR HRNANDO CNTY
13484 Chambord St (34613-4865)
PHONE..................................352 596-5142
Paul Arcona, *President*
EMP: 6 **EST:** 2003
SALES (est): 20MM **Privately Held**
SIC: 3555 7699 Printing presses; aircraft & heavy equipment repair services

(G-1274)
SPARTRONICS BROOKSVILLE LLC (DH)
30167 Power Line Rd (34602-8299)
PHONE..................................352 799-6520
Paul Fraipont, *President*
EMP: 100 **EST:** 2013
SALES (est): 31.8MM
SALES (corp-wide): 810.8MM **Privately Held**
WEB: www.sparton.com
SIC: 3674 Microprocessors
HQ: Spartronics, Llc
2333 Reach Rd
Williamsport PA 17701
763 703-4321

(G-1275)
SPARTRONICS BROOKSVILLE LLC
Also Called: Sparton Electronics
30167 Power Line Rd (34602-8299)
PHONE..................................352 799-6520
Billy Sevier, *Senior Buyer*
Pat Webb, *Purchasing*
Fred Coleman, *Engineer*
Jim Fee, *Engineer*
Delana McGuire, *Asst Controller*
EMP: 253
SALES (corp-wide): 810.8MM **Privately Held**
WEB: www.sparton.com
SIC: 3674 3812 Semiconductors & related devices; warfare counter-measure equipment
HQ: Spartronics Brooksville, Llc
30167 Power Line Rd
Brooksville FL 34602
352 799-6520

(G-1276)
SPRING OAKS LLC
7251 Grove Rd (34613-6083)
PHONE..................................352 592-1150
David C Jones,
EMP: 18 **EST:** 2005
SQ FT: 30,195
SALES (est): 2.9MM **Privately Held**
WEB: www.springoaksllc.com
SIC: 2512 Living room furniture: upholstered on wood frames

(G-1277)
SUNSHINE NYLON PRODUCTS INC
16101 Flight Path Dr (34604-6846)
PHONE..................................352 754-9932
Helen Reynolds, *President*
EMP: 6 **EST:** 1979
SQ FT: 7,000
SALES (est): 380.3K **Privately Held**
SIC: 3999 2221 Pet supplies; broadwoven fabric mills, manmade

(G-1278)
TAMPA BAY TIMES
13045 Cortez Blvd (34613-4838)
PHONE..................................352 754-6100
EMP: 7 **EST:** 2019
SALES (est): 288K **Privately Held**
WEB: www.tampabay.com
SIC: 2711 Newspapers, publishing & printing

(G-1279)
TG UNITED INC (PA)
16275 Aviation Loop Dr (34604-6805)
PHONE..................................352 799-9813
David Ambrose, *President*
Robert Davis, *Business Dir*
▼ **EMP:** 5 **EST:** 2004
SQ FT: 12,000
SALES (est): 1MM **Privately Held**
WEB: www.tgunited.com
SIC: 2834 Adrenal pharmaceutical preparations

(G-1280)
THUNDER BAY ENTERPRISES INC
5130 Broad St (34601-5814)
P.O. Box 10186 (34603-0186)
PHONE..................................352 796-9551
Sharon Carty, *Vice Pres*
EMP: 40 **EST:** 2008
SALES (est): 5.4MM **Privately Held**
SIC: 3715 Truck trailers

(G-1281)
TOPLINE HY-LIFT JOHNSON INC (PA)
2251 Topline Way (34604-6892)
PHONE..................................352 799-4668
Chester Staron, *President*
EMP: 28 **EST:** 2004
SQ FT: 300,000
SALES (est): 2.6MM **Privately Held**
SIC: 3764 3519 Engines & engine parts, guided missile; internal combustion engines

(G-1282)
TOPLINE MACHINE & TOOL LLC
2251 Topline Way (34604-6892)
PHONE..................................352 799-4668
Chester A Staron, *Principal*
Chester Staron,
EMP: 6
SALES (est): 277.1K **Privately Held**
WEB: www.toplineauto.com
SIC: 3599 Air intake filters, internal combustion engine, except auto

(G-1283)
TROY THOMPSON INC
20255 Denny Dr (34601-1257)
PHONE..................................813 716-1598
EMP: 5 **EST:** 1994
SQ FT: 2,500
SALES (est): 490.8K **Privately Held**
SIC: 3599 Machine shop, jobbing & repair

(G-1284)
TYCO MACHINE INC
1400 Ponce De Leon Blvd (34601-1670)
P.O. Box 1235 (34605-1235)
PHONE..................................352 544-0210
Michael Ray, *President*
EMP: 6 **EST:** 1999
SQ FT: 5,000
SALES (est): 813K **Privately Held**
SIC: 3531 3599 Construction machinery; machine shop, jobbing & repair

(G-1285)
UNBRIDLED TECHNOLOGIES LLC
Also Called: U Tech
21125 Cortez Blvd (34601-5645)
P.O. Box 344 (34605-0344)
PHONE..................................888 334-8402
Joseph Salway, *CEO*
Christina Walz, *Admin Asst*
EMP: 8 **EST:** 2015
SQ FT: 1,800
SALES (est): 778.1K **Privately Held**
WEB: www.utechcnc.com
SIC: 3541 Machine tools, metal cutting type

(G-1286)
UNIVERSAL MICROWAVE CORP (PA)
6036 Nature Coast Blvd (34602-8286)
PHONE..................................352 754-2200
David Lyle, *President*
Mark Lyle, *Vice Pres*
Lisa Lyle, *Admin Sec*
EMP: 59 **EST:** 1998
SQ FT: 20,000
SALES (est): 7.9MM **Privately Held**
WEB: www.vco1.com
SIC: 3612 3825 Voltage regulators, transmission & distribution; instruments to measure electricity

(G-1287)
VAN-ESS MANUFACTURING INC
15311 Flight Path Dr (34604-6862)
PHONE..................................352 799-1015
Ralph Esposito, *President*
Eugene Van Nostrand, *Corp Secy*
EMP: 5 **EST:** 1982
SQ FT: 3,400
SALES (est): 764.1K **Privately Held**
WEB: www.vanessmanufacturing.com
SIC: 3599 Machine shop, jobbing & repair

(G-1288)
VC DISPLAYS INC
Also Called: Vc Technology
15250 Flight Path Dr (34604-6849)
PHONE..................................352 796-0060
Gregory Potter, *President*
Chen James, *General Mgr*
Gregorypotter, *Principal*
Robert Bauer, *Vice Pres*
Jana Blair, *CFO*
▲ **EMP:** 25 **EST:** 2004
SQ FT: 20,000
SALES (est): 8.1MM **Privately Held**
WEB: www.vcdisplays.com
SIC: 3679 5065 Liquid crystal displays (LCD); electronic parts & equipment

(G-1289)
VENDAPIN LLC (PA)
16381 Cherokee Rd (34601-4202)
PHONE..................................352 796-2693
Darrell Rademacher,
Diane Rademacher,
▲ **EMP:** 10 **EST:** 1999
SQ FT: 1,200
SALES (est): 1.2MM **Privately Held**
WEB: www.vendapin.com
SIC: 3581 Automatic vending machines

(G-1290)
VUFLOW FILTERS CO INC
13370 Chambord St (34613-6812)
PHONE..................................352 597-2607
Thomas R Welte, *President*
Mary Latin, *Admin Sec*
EMP: 5 **EST:** 1978
SALES (est): 398K **Privately Held**
WEB: www.vuflow.com
SIC: 3569 Filters, general line: industrial

(G-1291)
WAYNE DIXON LLC
27340 Popiel Rd (34602-7107)
PHONE..................................352 279-6886
Wayne Dixon, *Manager*
EMP: 8 **EST:** 2005
SALES (est): 412.8K **Privately Held**
SIC: 2451 Mobile homes

(G-1292)
WOOD TELEVISION LLC
Also Called: Tampa Tribune
15299 Cortez Blvd (34613-6005)
PHONE..................................352 544-5200
Dwayne Chichester, *Manager*
EMP: 6
SALES (corp-wide): 4.5B **Publicly Held**
WEB: www.woodtv.com
SIC: 2711 Newspapers, publishing & printing

GEOGRAPHIC

HQ: Wood Television Llc
120 College Ave Se
Grand Rapids MI 49503
616 456-8888

(G-1293)
WOODCRAFTS BY ANGEL INC
Also Called: Tools & More
15400 Shady St (34604-8543)
PHONE..................................352 754-9335
Peggy Niles, *President*
Mark Miles, *Vice Pres*
EMP: 9 **EST:** 1991
SALES (est): 1.4MM **Privately Held**
SIC: 2511 2499 Wood household furniture; wood desks, bookcases & magazine racks; wood lawn & garden furniture; decorative wood & woodwork

(G-1294)
WOODEN IT BE NICE
1442 Culbreath Rd (34602-6119)
PHONE..................................352 797-0427
Mary Firminger, *Principal*
EMP: 7 **EST:** 2005
SALES (est): 119.3K **Privately Held**
SIC: 2499 Wood products

(G-1295)
WOODYS ACRES LLC
4000 Crum Rd (34604-7611)
PHONE..................................352 345-8145
Steven Johnson, *Principal*
EMP: 6 **EST:** 2016
SALES (est): 303.9K **Privately Held**
WEB: www.inductionsolutions.com
SIC: 3714 Motor vehicle parts & accessories

Bryceville
Nassau County

(G-1296)
A&L HALL INVESTMENTS INC
Also Called: (FORMALY NICHOLS TRUCK BODIES, INC.)
1384 Cortez Rd (32009-1304)
PHONE..................................904 781-5080
Arthur H Hall Jr, *President*
Clarence Suggs, *General Mgr*
Linda N Hall, *Corp Secy*
EMP: 36 **EST:** 1954
SQ FT: 19,500
SALES (est): 3.6MM **Privately Held**
SIC: 3713 5012 3441 Truck bodies (motor vehicles); truck bodies; fabricated structural metal

Bunnell
Flagler County

(G-1297)
BEUTLICH PHARMACEUTICALS LLC (PA)
7775 S Us Highway 1 H (32110-3827)
PHONE..................................386 263-8860
Frederic J Beutlich, *General Ptnr*
Heather Wagner, *Sales Mgr*
Jennifer Dilascia, *Sales Staff*
Erlene Thomas, *Mng Member*
Ivone Raposo, *Supervisor*
EMP: 17 **EST:** 1954
SQ FT: 10,000
SALES (est): 7MM **Privately Held**
WEB: www.beutlich.com
SIC: 2834 Druggists' preparations (pharmaceuticals)

(G-1298)
BLAINE E TAYLOR WELDING INC
75 County Road 125 (32110-8703)
PHONE..................................386 931-1242
Blane E Taylor, *Principal*
EMP: 6 **EST:** 2012
SALES (est): 216.9K **Privately Held**
SIC: 7692 Welding repair

(G-1299)
BUILT RGHT KTCHENS OF PALM CAS
7755 S Us Highway 1 (32110-3807)
PHONE..................................386 437-7077
Don Gordon, *Owner*
EMP: 7 **EST:** 1997
SQ FT: 3,000
SALES (est): 735K **Privately Held**
WEB: www.brkitchens.com
SIC: 2434 Wood kitchen cabinets

(G-1300)
ESP PRINTING
4601 E Moody Blvd Ste D5 (32110-7700)
PHONE..................................386 263-2949
Mark Boos, *President*
EMP: 6 **EST:** 2015
SALES (est): 136.1K **Privately Held**
WEB: www.printingesp.com
SIC: 2759 Commercial printing

(G-1301)
KING MOBILE WELDING ANDREW
1645 County Road 302 (32110-7922)
P.O. Box 2425 (32110-2425)
PHONE..................................386 437-1007
Andrew King, *President*
EMP: 5 **EST:** 2008
SALES (est): 418.7K **Privately Held**
SIC: 7692 Welding repair

(G-1302)
M & L TIMBER INC
Sr 11 (32110)
PHONE..................................386 437-0895
M Mitchell Henry, *President*
Doug Henry, *Vice Pres*
EMP: 9 **EST:** 1988
SQ FT: 1,500
SALES (est): 290.2K **Privately Held**
SIC: 2411 Logging camps & contractors

(G-1303)
MCNEILL SIGNS INC
400 Ninth St (32110-6932)
P.O. Box 1093 (32110-1093)
PHONE..................................386 586-7100
Jay McNeil, *President*
EMP: 8
SALES (corp-wide): 3.2MM **Privately Held**
WEB: www.mcneillsigns.com
SIC: 3993 Neon signs; electric signs; advertising artwork
PA: Mcneill Signs Inc
555 S Dixie Hwy E
Pompano Beach FL 33060
561 737-6304

(G-1304)
RAILINGS PLUS INC
1150 State Rd 11 Ste 201 (32110)
PHONE..................................386 437-4501
Mike Adkins, *General Mgr*
Dawn Spoly, *Principal*
EMP: 12 **EST:** 2007
SALES (est): 2.8MM **Privately Held**
WEB: www.railingsplusinc.com
SIC: 3743 Railroad equipment

(G-1305)
RALPH SANTORE & SONS INC
2546 County Road 305 (32110-5350)
P.O. Box 70 (32110-0070)
PHONE..................................386 437-2242
Ralph Santore Jr, *President*
Lloyd Sponenburgh, *General Mgr*
Anthony Santore Jr, *Vice Pres*
Irene Nielsen, *Admin Asst*
◆ **EMP:** 24 **EST:** 1974
SQ FT: 910
SALES (est): 4.5MM **Privately Held**
WEB: www.santorepyro.com
SIC: 2899 7999 Fireworks; fireworks display service

(G-1306)
SIZEMORE WELDING INC
Also Called: Sizemore Ultimate Food Trucks
205 N Bay St (32110-4444)
P.O. Box 1772 (32110-1772)
PHONE..................................386 437-4073
Duane Sizemore, *President*
EMP: 25 **EST:** 1985
SQ FT: 40,000
SALES (est): 4MM **Privately Held**
WEB: www.sizemorewelding.com
SIC: 3714 3599 Motor vehicle parts & accessories; machine shop, jobbing & repair

(G-1307)
T BRAND FERTILIZER INC
801 N Bay St (32110)
P.O. Box 266 (32110-0266)
PHONE..................................386 437-2970
John W Stone, *President*
Thomas Bratcher, *Vice Pres*
Tommie Bennett, *Office Mgr*
EMP: 8 **EST:** 1983
SQ FT: 5,000
SALES (est): 1.4MM **Privately Held**
SIC: 2873 Nitrogenous fertilizers

(G-1308)
TRUSS SYSTEMS LLC
3615 U S 1 S (32110)
PHONE..................................386 255-3009
Lynn McCarthy,
EMP: 6 **EST:** 2013
SALES (est): 411.3K **Privately Held**
SIC: 2439 2452 Trusses, wooden roof; prefabricated wood buildings

(G-1309)
TRUSS SYSTEMS OF VLSIA FLGLER
3615 S Us Highway 1 (32110-3824)
P.O. Box 291250, Port Orange (32129-1250)
PHONE..................................386 255-3009
Lynn Mc Carthy, *President*
James Paytas, *Corp Secy*
Ian Halliday, *Vice Pres*
EMP: 12 **EST:** 1986
SQ FT: 1,600
SALES (est): 629.9K **Privately Held**
WEB: www.webuildtrusses.com
SIC: 2439 2452 Trusses, wooden roof; prefabricated wood buildings

(G-1310)
TUMBLING PINES INC
10987 State Road 11 (32110-5782)
PHONE..................................386 437-2668
Morgan Henry, *President*
Laurel Henry, *Corp Secy*
EMP: 12 **EST:** 1987
SALES (est): 519.6K **Privately Held**
SIC: 2411 4212 Logging camps & contractors; local trucking, without storage

(G-1311)
WORLD CLASS MACHINING INC
Also Called: Holeshot Performance Wheels
6650 S Us Highway 1 (32110-6806)
PHONE..................................386 437-7036
Marlene D Morton, *President*
EMP: 10 **EST:** 1993
SQ FT: 2,500
SALES (est): 1.2MM **Privately Held**
WEB: www.worldclassmachining.com
SIC: 3599 7692 Machine shop, jobbing & repair; welding repair

(G-1312)
WORLD PLATE
2323 N State St Unit 55 (32110-4395)
PHONE..................................386 597-7832
Suzette Negron-Wicklund, *President*
EMP: 6 **EST:** 2017
SALES (est): 303.8K **Privately Held**
WEB: www.world-plate.business.site
SIC: 3471 Plating & polishing

Bushnell
Sumter County

(G-1313)
BUSHNELL SAW MILL INC
5178 W C 48 (33513-8370)
P.O. Box 1240 (33513-0075)
PHONE..................................352 793-2740
Mark Elliott, *President*
Marsha Garcia, *Vice Pres*
EMP: 8 **EST:** 1978
SQ FT: 1,065
SALES (est): 720.6K **Privately Held**
WEB: www.bushnellsawmill.com
SIC: 2421 2426 2411 Lumber: rough, sawed or planed; hardwood dimension & flooring mills; logging

(G-1314)
BUSHNELL TRUSS ENTERPRISES LLC
5240 W C 476 (33513-8558)
P.O. Box 773 (33513-0047)
PHONE..................................352 793-6090
James W Malloy, *President*
Mike Reed, *Plant Mgr*
Claire Malloy, *Treasurer*
EMP: 10 **EST:** 1978
SQ FT: 15,000
SALES (est): 966.7K **Privately Held**
WEB: www.bushnelltruss.com
SIC: 2439 5211 Trusses, wooden roof; lumber products

(G-1315)
CEMEX CNSTR MTLS FLA LLC
Also Called: Rinker Materials
7388 Cr 745 (33513-9042)
PHONE..................................352 793-3048
Mark Robinson, *Branch Mgr*
EMP: 6 **Privately Held**
SIC: 3273 Ready-mixed concrete
HQ: Cemex Construction Materials Florida, Llc
1501 Belvedere Rd
West Palm Beach FL 33406

(G-1316)
COUNTY OF SUMTER
Also Called: Sumter Planning Department
910 N Main St Ste 308 (33513-5006)
PHONE..................................352 689-4460
Brad Cornelius, *Director*
EMP: 9
SALES (corp-wide): 158.7MM **Privately Held**
WEB: www.sumtercountyfl.gov
SIC: 3553 Planing mill machinery
PA: County Of Sumter
7375 Powell Rd Ste 200
Wildwood FL 34785
352 689-4400

(G-1317)
FULL CIRCLE DIRECTIONAL INC
2161 Sw 83rd Pl (33513-5705)
P.O. Box 1465 (33513-0079)
PHONE..................................352 568-0639
George P Mauldin, *CEO*
Kristi Mauldin, *President*
EMP: 5 **EST:** 2009
SALES (est): 889.1K **Privately Held**
SIC: 1381 Directional drilling oil & gas wells

(G-1318)
KNIGHTS FARM FRESH FEEDS INC
5376 Cr 316a (33513-8115)
P.O. Box 670 (33513-0046)
PHONE..................................352 793-2242
Michael R Knight, *President*
Anny Adams, *Administration*
EMP: 6 **EST:** 1984
SQ FT: 4,000
SALES (est): 2.5MM **Privately Held**
WEB: www.knightsfeed.com
SIC: 2048 Cereal-, grain-, & seed-based feeds

(G-1319)
MEMCO INC
Also Called: Memco Enviro Safe
1789 Ec 48 (33513)
P.O. Box 519, Center Hill (33514-0519)
PHONE..................................352 241-2302
Michael S Evans, *President*
John Bolderson, *Project Mgr*
Donnie Wright, *Opers Staff*
◆ **EMP:** 29 **EST:** 1995
SQ FT: 48,000
SALES (est): 3.9MM **Privately Held**
WEB:
www.abovegroundfuelstoragetanks.com
SIC: 3795 Tanks & tank components

▲ = Import ▼=Export
◆ =Import/Export

(G-1320)
RVCC OF FLORIDA
2540 W C 48 (33513-8386)
PHONE..................................352 569-5870
Armando Salinas, *Director*
EMP: 8 **EST:** 2011
SALES (est): 181.3K **Privately Held**
WEB: www.catalog.raritanval.edu
SIC: 3799 Trailer hitches

(G-1321)
SOUTHERN PRE CAST STRUCTURES L
4457 Cr 542h (33513-5536)
P.O. Box 1543 (33513-0080)
PHONE..................................352 569-1128
Danny Hall, *Principal*
EMP: 5 **EST:** 2005
SALES (est): 384.9K **Privately Held**
SIC: 3272 Precast terrazo or concrete products

Callahan
Nassau County

(G-1322)
A & R MATERIAL HANDLING INC
540439 Us Highway 1 (32011-7868)
P.O. Box 1359 (32011-1359)
PHONE..................................904 879-6957
Jack Anders, *President*
EMP: 18 **EST:** 1998
SQ FT: 44,000
SALES (est): 1.2MM **Privately Held**
SIC: 3537 Lift trucks, industrial: fork, platform, straddle, etc.

(G-1323)
AARONS EQUIPMENT REPAIR INC
Also Called: Aaron's Welding & Repair
45417 Zidell Rd (32011-3691)
PHONE..................................904 879-3249
Franklin A Bell, *President*
Dana R Bell, *Admin Sec*
EMP: 9 **EST:** 2014
SALES (est): 285.3K **Privately Held**
SIC: 7692 Welding repair

(G-1324)
G & H RECLAIM LLC
45321 Green Ave (32011-3712)
PHONE..................................904 879-2091
Shari Graham, *Principal*
EMP: 6 **EST:** 2014
SALES (est): 142.7K **Privately Held**
WEB: www.ghreclaims.com
SIC: 2431 Millwork

(G-1325)
J Q BELL & SONS
44247 Bell Ln (32011-7645)
PHONE..................................904 879-1597
Richard Musgrove, *Partner*
Janie B Musgrove, *Partner*
EMP: 7 **EST:** 1950
SALES (est): 728.5K **Privately Held**
SIC: 2411 Pulpwood contractors engaged in cutting

(G-1326)
LOCAL COMMUNITY NEWS INC
54024 Cravey Rd (32011-4600)
P.O. Box 627 (32011-0627)
PHONE..................................904 886-4919
EMP: 8 **EST:** 2015
SALES (est): 89.2K **Privately Held**
WEB: www.floridanewsline.com
SIC: 2711 Newspapers, publishing & printing

(G-1327)
NASSAU PRINTING & OFF SUP INC
542028 Us Highway 1 (32011-8108)
P.O. Box 812 (32011-0812)
PHONE..................................904 879-2305
Jo Ann Thompson, *President*
EMP: 7 **EST:** 1976
SQ FT: 6,072
SALES (est): 879.1K **Privately Held**
WEB: www.nassauprinting.com
SIC: 2752 5943 Commercial printing, offset; office forms & supplies

(G-1328)
RBJ TIMBER INC
44247 Bell Ln (32011-7645)
PHONE..................................904 879-1597
Richard B Musgrove Sr, *President*
Joshua R Musgrove, *Vice Pres*
Janie Musgrove, *Admin Sec*
EMP: 8 **EST:** 2005
SALES (est): 1.1MM **Privately Held**
SIC: 2411 7389 Timber, cut at logging camp;

(G-1329)
SOUTHERN COMPANY ENTP INC
Also Called: Florida Sun Printing
54024 Cravey Rd (32011-4600)
P.O. Box 627 (32011-0627)
PHONE..................................904 879-2101
Mark Thompson, *President*
David Vickers, *President*
Brent Armstrong, *Production*
Christie Anglea,
EMP: 25 **EST:** 1963
SQ FT: 25,000
SALES (est): 3MM **Privately Held**
WEB: www.flasunprinting.com
SIC: 2752 Commercial printing, offset

Campbellton
Jackson County

(G-1330)
BARBER FERTILIZER COMPANY
Also Called: Campbellton Farm Service
5221 Highway 231 (32426-6831)
P.O. Box 234 (32426-0234)
PHONE..................................850 263-6324
Ronald Barber, *Manager*
EMP: 21
SALES (corp-wide): 20.7MM **Privately Held**
SIC: 2873 5191 2875 Fertilizers: natural (organic), except compost; feed; fertilizer & fertilizer materials; fertilizers, mixing only
PA: Barber Fertilizer Company
1011 Airport Rd
Bainbridge GA 39817
229 246-7412

Canal Point
Palm Beach County

(G-1331)
FIVE STONES MINE LLC (PA)
Also Called: Mayaca Materials
18500 Us Highway 441 (33438-9580)
PHONE..................................813 967-2123
Dennis McClelland, *General Mgr*
Peter V De Sanctis, *CPA*
Michael Rendina, *Mng Member*
EMP: 11 **EST:** 2009
SALES (est): 3MM **Privately Held**
WEB: www.mayacamaterials.com
SIC: 1411 Limestone, dimension-quarrying

Candler
Marion County

(G-1332)
TOWNLEY ENGRG & MFG CO INC (PA)
Also Called: Townley Engineering & Mfg Co
10551 Se 110th St Rd (32111)
P.O. Box 221 (32111-0221)
PHONE..................................352 687-3001
J O Townley Jr, *President*
Steven Colquitt, *Vice Pres*
Sarah T Dean, *Vice Pres*
Sara Townley Hall, *Vice Pres*
Parnell Townley, *Vice Pres*
▲ **EMP:** 199
SQ FT: 7,500
SALES (est): 66.8MM **Privately Held**
WEB: www.townley.net
SIC: 3532 3561 3531 3498 Mining machinery; pumps & pumping equipment; construction machinery; fabricated pipe & fittings

(G-1333)
TOWNLEY FOUNDRY & MCH CO INC
10551 Se 110th St Rd (32111)
P.O. Box 221 (32111-0221)
PHONE..................................352 687-3001
J O Townley Jr, *President*
Helen Townley, *Corp Secy*
Sara Townley Dean, *Vice Pres*
Parnell Townley, *Vice Pres*
Martin Harris, *Business Dir*
▲ **EMP:** 56 **EST:** 1982
SQ FT: 7,500
SALES (est): 15.6MM
SALES (corp-wide): 66.8MM **Privately Held**
WEB: www.townley.net
SIC: 3532 Mining machinery
PA: Townley Engineering And Manufacturing Company, Inc.
10551 Se 110th St Rd
Candler FL 32111
352 687-3001

Cantonment
Escambia County

(G-1334)
ALPHA COATINGS INC
3040 Ashfield Estates Rd (32533-8195)
PHONE..................................850 324-9454
Steven Eggart, *Principal*
EMP: 7 **EST:** 2011
SALES (est): 91.9K **Privately Held**
SIC: 3479 Coating of metals & formed products

(G-1335)
ASCEND PRFMCE MTLS OPRTONS LLC
3000 Old Chemstrand Rd (32533-8900)
P.O. Box 68, Gonzalez (32560-0068)
PHONE..................................850 968-7000
Richard Briere, *Plant Mgr*
Andrew Hosmer, *Export Mgr*
Kenneth Krueger, *Engineer*
Connor Manthey, *Engineer*
Cheri Frederick, *Comptroller*
EMP: 600
SQ FT: 6,244
SALES (corp-wide): 1.4B **Privately Held**
WEB: www.ascendmaterials.com
SIC: 2824 5169 2821 5131 Organic fibers, noncellulosic; chemicals & allied products; plastics materials & resins; synthetic fabrics
HQ: Ascend Performance Materials Operations Llc
1010 Travis St Ste 900
Houston TX 77002

(G-1336)
CEREX ADVANCED FABRICS INC
610 Chemstrand Rd (32533-6857)
PHONE..................................850 968-0100
James T Walker, *CEO*
Jim Bostwick, *Vice Pres*
James Crews, *Prdtn Mgr*
Sheldon Ford, *Mfg Staff*
Mike Harris, *Purch Mgr*
▼ **EMP:** 80 **EST:** 1994
SALES (est): 15.4MM **Privately Held**
WEB: www.cerex.com
SIC: 2297 Nonwoven fabrics

(G-1337)
COUCH READY MIX USA INC
3008 S Highway 95a (32533-5800)
PHONE..................................850 236-9042
EMP: 25
SALES (est): 6.1MM **Privately Held**
SIC: 3273 Mfg Ready-Mixed Concrete

(G-1338)
CUSTOM CONTROL SOLUTIONS INC
1520 Power Blvd (32533-5102)
PHONE..................................850 937-8902
Manfred Laner, *President*
Glenn Miller, *Vice Pres*
EMP: 9
SQ FT: 8,000
SALES (est): 2.8MM **Privately Held**
WEB: www.ccsinc-florida.com
SIC: 3613 Control panels, electric

(G-1339)
ES MACHINE SHOP
235 Petty Dr (32533-8686)
PHONE..................................850 968-9300
Ernie Forester, *Principal*
EMP: 6 **EST:** 2009
SALES (est): 89.4K **Privately Held**
SIC: 3599 Machine shop, jobbing & repair

(G-1340)
GIL INDUSTRIES INC
3060 S Highway 95a (32533-5800)
P.O. Box 490, Gonzalez (32560-0490)
PHONE..................................850 479-3400
Fred Shiver, *President*
EMP: 5 **EST:** 1987
SQ FT: 3,000
SALES (est): 535.4K **Privately Held**
WEB: www.gilindustries.com
SIC: 3494 Valves & pipe fittings

(G-1341)
INSULATION DESIGN & DIST LLC
1879 Ziglar Rd (32533-8586)
P.O. Box 67 (32533-0067)
PHONE..................................850 332-7312
William R Ingram, *Mng Member*
EMP: 7 **EST:** 2010
SQ FT: 20,000
SALES (est): 314.5K **Privately Held**
SIC: 3498 Fabricated pipe & fittings

(G-1342)
MATHESON TREIGAS
2898 Old Chemstrand Rd (32533-8965)
PHONE..................................850 679-3024
EMP: 5 **EST:** 2015
SALES (est): 324.1K **Privately Held**
SIC: 2813 Industrial gases

(G-1343)
NINE MILE RACEWAY INC
1281 Lear Ct (32533-5742)
PHONE..................................850 937-1845
Mohammed H Hoque, *President*
EMP: 8 **EST:** 2017
SALES (est): 275K **Privately Held**
SIC: 3644 Raceways

(G-1344)
O NEILL INDUSTRIES INTL INC (PA)
8 E Quintette Rd Ste B (32533-7213)
PHONE..................................850 754-0312
David O'Neill, *President*
Alexander O'Neill, *Treasurer*
EMP: 8 **EST:** 2017
SQ FT: 11,000
SALES (est): 1.1MM **Privately Held**
SIC: 1382 Oil & gas exploration services

(G-1345)
PENSACOLA READY MIX LLC
Pc 3008 Hwy 95 A S (32533)
PHONE..................................850 477-0343
Bobby Linsey, *General Mgr*
EMP: 11 **EST:** 2002
SALES (est): 984.6K **Privately Held**
SIC: 3273 Ready-mixed concrete

(G-1346)
PURIFOY CONSTRUCTION LLC
1425 Muscogee Rd (32533-9150)
PHONE..................................850 206-2900
Tyrone Purifoy,
Coreine Barker,
EMP: 9 **EST:** 2006
SALES (est): 249.9K **Privately Held**
SIC: 3272 1629 1794 Drain tile, concrete; drainage system construction; excavation work

(G-1347)
SERF INC
Also Called: Systems Engrg RES & Facilities
3065 S Highway 29 (32533-8562)
PHONE.................................850 476-8203
Jack W Sparks, *President*
Cheri Sparks, *Corp Secy*
Jeremy Sparks, *Safety Dir*
Jim Jimgilmore, *Sales Engr*
◆ **EMP:** 50 **EST:** 1972
SQ FT: 12,000
SALES (est): 8.8MM **Privately Held**
WEB: www.serfinc.com
SIC: 3569 8711 7692 3561 Assembly machines, non-metalworking; engineering services; welding repair; pumps & pumping equipment; valves & pipe fittings; fabricated plate work (boiler shop)

(G-1348)
SOUTHEASTERN PIPE PRECAST INC
2900 N Highway 95a (32533-7190)
PHONE.................................850 587-7473
EMP: 35
SALES (est): 6.1MM **Privately Held**
SIC: 3272 Mfg Concrete Products

(G-1349)
SOUTHERN ALUMINUM AND STL INC
2501 S Highway 29 (32533-5811)
PHONE.................................850 484-4700
Dj Kusterer, *President*
EMP: 5 **EST:** 1998
SQ FT: 5,140
SALES (est): 737.3K **Privately Held**
WEB: www.southern-aluminum-and-steel-inc.business.site
SIC: 3441 Fabricated structural metal

Cape Canaveral
Brevard County

(G-1350)
AMERICAN BOOM AND BARRIER INC
Also Called: Abbco
720 Mullet Rd Ste M (32920-4520)
PHONE.................................321 784-2110
Randall O'Brien, *President*
Pat Rooney, *Vice Pres*
◆ **EMP:** 21 **EST:** 1977
SQ FT: 42,000
SALES (est): 1.8MM **Privately Held**
WEB: www.acmeboom.com
SIC: 3589 3531 Sewage & water treatment equipment; marine related equipment

(G-1351)
BATECH INC
Also Called: Sunshine Welding
760 Mullet Rd (32920-4504)
PHONE.................................321 784-4838
James L Smith, *President*
David Bragdon, *Vice Pres*
Brandon Smith, *Vice Pres*
Darrell Hunt, *Admin Sec*
▼ **EMP:** 40 **EST:** 1972
SALES (est): 4.4MM **Privately Held**
WEB: www.sunshinewelding.com
SIC: 3429 Marine hardware

(G-1352)
BLINDS SIDE
5801 N Atlantic Ave (32920-3972)
PHONE.................................888 610-8366
EMP: 7 **EST:** 2018
SALES (est): 61.7K **Privately Held**
WEB: www.theblindsside.com
SIC: 2591 Window blinds

(G-1353)
BOEING COMPANY
620 Magellan Rd (32920-4408)
P.O. Box 21105, Kennedy Space Center (32815)
PHONE.................................321 867-6005
Will Tuner, *General Mgr*
EMP: 6
SALES (corp-wide): 58.1B **Publicly Held**
WEB: www.boeing.com
SIC: 3721 Aircraft
PA: The Boeing Company
100 N Riverside Plz
Chicago IL 60606
312 544-2000

(G-1354)
CANAVERAL CUSTOM BOATS INC
774 Mullet Rd (32920-4504)
PHONE.................................321 783-3536
▼ **EMP:** 7
SALES: 1MM **Privately Held**
SIC: 3732 Boatbuilding/Repairing

(G-1355)
CEMEX CNSTR MTLS FLA LLC
Also Called: Port Canaveral FL Canaveral Rm
209 George King Blvd (32920)
PHONE.................................321 636-5121
Larry Jenkins, *Branch Mgr*
Scott Campbell, *Manager*
EMP: 8 **Privately Held**
SIC: 3273 Ready-mixed concrete
HQ: Cemex Construction Materials Florida, Llc
1501 Belvedere Rd
West Palm Beach FL 33406

(G-1356)
DENVER ELEVATOR SYSTEMS INC
7073 N Atlantic Ave (32920-3711)
PHONE.................................800 633-9788
Walter Burns, *President*
EMP: 6 **EST:** 1981
SQ FT: 1,600
SALES (est): 643.3K **Privately Held**
WEB: www.eciamerica.com
SIC: 3672 7629 Printed circuit boards; circuit board repair

(G-1357)
ENVIRO-USA AMERICAN MFR LLC
151 Center St Ste 101 (32920-3727)
PHONE.................................321 222-9551
Jennifer A Vargas, *CFO*
Jennifer Vargas, *CFO*
Luis Vargas, *Sales Staff*
Luis F Vargas,
◆ **EMP:** 21 **EST:** 2009
SALES (est): 6MM **Privately Held**
WEB: www.enviro-usa.com
SIC: 3589 3531 Sewage & water treatment equipment; marine related equipment

(G-1358)
EXCELL COATINGS INC
745 Scallop Dr (32920-4550)
PHONE.................................321 868-7968
Robert Tampa, *President*
Frederick Distasio, *Treasurer*
EMP: 20 **EST:** 1991
SQ FT: 27,000
SALES (est): 3MM **Privately Held**
WEB: www.excellcoatings.com
SIC: 3479 Coating of metals & formed products; painting, coating & hot dipping

(G-1359)
HANSON LEHIGH CEMENT
575 Cargo Rd (32920-4415)
PHONE.................................800 665-6006
EMP: 16 **EST:** 2015
SALES (est): 2.6MM **Privately Held**
WEB: www.lehighhanson.com
SIC: 3273 Ready-mixed concrete

(G-1360)
IMAGE PRINTING & GRAPHICS LLC
Also Called: Jet Press
8649 Villanova Dr (32920-4328)
PHONE.................................321 783-5555
Cheryl Emmons,
Amanda Emmons,
EMP: 6 **EST:** 2004
SALES (est): 860.7K **Privately Held**
SIC: 2752 Commercial printing, offset

(G-1361)
INDIAN RIVER BREWERY CORP
Also Called: Indian Rver Brwing C/Flrida Be
200 Imperial Blvd (32920-4245)
P.O. Box 523 (32920-0523)
PHONE.................................321 728-4114
James Webb, *CEO*
EMP: 21 **EST:** 2013
SALES (est): 5.9MM **Privately Held**
WEB: www.floridabeer.com
SIC: 2082 Beer (alcoholic beverage)

(G-1362)
INTERSTATE ELECTRONICS CORP
Air Force Sta Bldg 54815 (32920)
PHONE.................................321 730-0119
Larry Fitzgerald, *Systems Mgr*
EMP: 71
SQ FT: 3,200
SALES (corp-wide): 3.7B **Publicly Held**
SIC: 3825 3812 3663 Test equipment for electronic & electric measurement; search & navigation equipment; radio & TV communications equipment
HQ: Interstate Electronics Corporation
602 E Vermont Ave
Anaheim CA 92805
714 758-0500

(G-1363)
LEHIGH CEMENT COMPANY LLC
9012 Marlin St (32920-3308)
PHONE.................................321 323-5039
Gary Milla, *Branch Mgr*
EMP: 44
SALES (corp-wide): 20.8B **Privately Held**
WEB: www.lehighwhitecement.com
SIC: 3273 Ready-mixed concrete
HQ: Lehigh Cement Company Llc
300 E John Carpenter Fwy
Irving TX 75062
877 534-4442

(G-1364)
LOCKHEED MARTIN CORPORATION
Pier Rd (32920)
P.O. Box 246 (32920-0246)
PHONE.................................321 853-5194
James Gower, *Engineer*
Ronald Ivey, *Manager*
Brian Ewanyk, *Software Engr*
EMP: 6 **Publicly Held**
WEB: www.lockheedmartin.com
SIC: 3761 3812 8734 Guided missiles & space vehicles; space vehicle guidance systems & equipment; testing laboratories
PA: Lockheed Martin Corporation
6801 Rockledge Dr
Bethesda MD 20817

(G-1365)
MOON EXPRESS INC
Also Called: Moonex
100 Space Port Way (32920-4000)
P.O. Box 489 (32920-0489)
PHONE.................................650 241-8577
Robert D Richards, *CEO*
Jim Cantrell, *General Mgr*
Daven Maharaj, *COO*
Julie Arnold, *Treasurer*
EMP: 30 **EST:** 2010
SALES (est): 4.8MM **Privately Held**
WEB: www.moonexpress.com
SIC: 3761 Guided missiles & space vehicles

(G-1366)
POSM SOFTWARE LLC
8010 N Atl Ave Ste 12 (32920)
P.O. Box 1235 (32920-1235)
PHONE.................................859 274-0041
Robert Katter, *Principal*
Megan Neal, *Manager*
Gene Katter, *Director*
EMP: 9 **EST:** 2016
SALES (est): 173.4K **Privately Held**
WEB: www.posmsoftware.com
SIC: 7372 Prepackaged software

(G-1367)
SIDUS SPACE INC
175 Imperial Blvd (32920-4255)
PHONE.................................321 613-0615
Carol Craig, *CEO*
Mark Mikolajczyk, *Opers Staff*
EMP: 26 **EST:** 2012
SALES (est): 4MM **Privately Held**
WEB: www.sidusspace.com
SIC: 3724 3599 3451 3728 Aircraft engines & engine parts; machine shop, jobbing & repair; screw machine products; aircraft parts & equipment; guided missile & space vehicle parts & auxiliary equipment; satellites, communications

(G-1368)
SPACE EXPLORATION TECH CORP
Cape Cnaveral A Force Sta (32920)
PHONE.................................310 363-6000
Phillip Rench, *Senior Engr*
James Wisnom, *Technology*
EMP: 48
SALES (corp-wide): 2B **Privately Held**
WEB: www.spacex.com
SIC: 3761 Rockets, space & military, complete
PA: Space Exploration Technologies Corp.
1 Rocket Rd
Hawthorne CA 90250
310 363-6000

(G-1369)
SYNERGY COMMUNICATION MGT LLC (PA)
400 Imperial Blvd (32920-4213)
P.O. Box 657 (32920-0657)
PHONE.................................800 749-3160
William R Mays,
Berchet R Mays,
EMP: 14 **EST:** 2013
SALES (est): 19MM **Privately Held**
SIC: 3661 Communication headgear, telephone; headsets, telephone

Cape Coral
Lee County

(G-1370)
A B C CANVAS INC
714 Se 47th Ter (33904-7502)
PHONE.................................239 542-0909
Karen Vogt, *President*
EMP: 5 **EST:** 1972
SQ FT: 5,000
SALES (est): 300K **Privately Held**
WEB: www.abccanvas.com
SIC: 2394 5551 Liners & covers, fabric: made from purchased materials; marine supplies

(G-1371)
ABC SCREEN MASTERS INC
1110 Ne Pine Island Rd # 23 (33909-2188)
PHONE.................................239 772-7336
Robert Bobay, *President*
EMP: 6 **EST:** 1990
SALES (est): 500K **Privately Held**
WEB: www.abcscreenmasters.com
SIC: 3448 1799 5039 5211 Screen enclosures; screening contractor: window, door, etc.; prefabricated structures; screens, door & window

(G-1372)
ACE SHUTTER & SHELVES LLC
422 Sw 2nd Ter (33991-1947)
PHONE.................................239 314-9136
Thomas Archer, *Mng Member*
EMP: 6 **EST:** 2015
SALES (est): 168.4K **Privately Held**
SIC: 2431 2541 Window shutters, wood; cabinets, lockers & shelving

(G-1373)
ACTION MANUFACTURING & SUP INC (PA)
Also Called: Pegasus Water Systems
2602 Ne 9th Ave (33909-2933)
PHONE.................................239 574-3443
Richard Shepard, *President*
Carolyn Eulena Pilgrim, *Vice Pres*
Nick Painter, *Warehouse Mgr*
Lena Pilgrim, *CFO*
Eva Williams, *Technology*
▼ **EMP:** 14 **EST:** 1980

SQ FT: 10,000
SALES (est): 5.9MM Privately Held
WEB: www.actionmfg.com
SIC: 3589 Water purification equipment, household type; water filters & softeners, household type

(G-1374)
ADIRONDACK MEAT COMPANY INC
5335 Mayfair Ct (33904-5971)
PHONE....................518 585-2333
Peter Ward, *President*
Denise Ward, *Vice Pres*
EMP: 11 EST: 2012
SALES (est): 361.4K Privately Held
SIC: 2011 2013 Hides, cured or uncured: from carcasses slaughtered on site; sausages & other prepared meats

(G-1375)
ADVERMARKET CORP
954 Country Club Blvd (33990-3074)
PHONE....................239 541-1144
Benjamin Kiesinger, *President*
EMP: 6 EST: 2017
SALES (est): 482.4K Privately Held
WEB: www.hi-defprinting.com
SIC: 2752 Commercial printing, offset

(G-1376)
ADVERMARKET CORP
4720 Se 15th Ave Ste 205 (33904-9600)
PHONE....................239 542-1020
Benjamin Kiesinger, *President*
EMP: 6 EST: 2005
SALES (est): 525.4K Privately Held
WEB: www.hi-defprinting.com
SIC: 2752 Commercial printing, offset

(G-1377)
AGI-VR/WESSON INC
2673 Ne 9th Ave (33909-2917)
PHONE....................239 573-5132
Thomas A Fliss, *President*
Todd Grabow, *Vice Pres*
Linda S Fliss, *Treasurer*
Jacob Fliss, *Programmer Anys*
▼ EMP: 27
SQ FT: 15,000
SALES (est): 4.6MM Privately Held
WEB: www.vrwesson.com
SIC: 3541 3545 Machine tools, metal cutting type; cutting tools for machine tools

(G-1378)
AMD ORNAMENTAL INC
918 Se 9th Ln Unit A (33990-3120)
PHONE....................239 458-7437
Mark Christian, *President*
EMP: 8 EST: 2008
SALES (est): 670.1K Privately Held
WEB: www.amdornamental.com
SIC: 3446 Ornamental metalwork

(G-1379)
ANCHOR & DOCKING INC
830 Ne 24th Ln Unit G (33909-2939)
PHONE....................239 770-2030
Rune Ilerod, *President*
EMP: 8 EST: 2015
SQ FT: 7,000
SALES (est): 500K Privately Held
SIC: 3462 Anchors, forged

(G-1380)
ANGELA ZIEGLERS WINDOW WASHERS
628 Se 23rd St (33990-2543)
PHONE....................239 849-0310
Angela Ziegler, *Principal*
EMP: 6 EST: 2009
SALES (est): 78.8K Privately Held
SIC: 3452 Washers

(G-1381)
APPLIANCES TO GO USA LLC
741 Del Prado Blvd N # 160 (33909-2297)
PHONE....................239 278-0811
Mickey Rosabo,
EMP: 5 EST: 2008
SQ FT: 10,000
SALES (est): 650.1K Privately Held
WEB: www.appliancestogousa.us
SIC: 3639 Major kitchen appliances, except refrigerators & stoves

(G-1382)
APPLIED COOLING TECHNOLOGY LLC
75 Mid Cape Ter 23 (33991-2012)
PHONE....................239 217-5080
Heather Dutescu, *Engineer*
Nicholas Welford,
Peter Jackson,
◆ EMP: 5 EST: 2007
SQ FT: 12,000
SALES (est): 865.1K Privately Held
WEB: www.appliedcool.com
SIC: 3443 Finned tubes, for heat transfer

(G-1383)
ARCHITCTRAL MTAL FLASHINGS LLC
2659 Ne 9th Ave (33909-2917)
PHONE....................239 221-0123
Darla Bonk, *Vice Pres*
Scott Bonk,
EMP: 16 EST: 2016
SALES (est): 6.6MM Privately Held
WEB: www.architecturalmetalflashings.com
SIC: 3354 Aluminum extruded products

(G-1384)
ART STAIRCASE & WOODWORK LLC
4229 Sw 14th Pl (33914-5682)
PHONE....................239 440-6591
Gregory Ziemba, *Principal*
EMP: 8 EST: 2017
SALES (est): 353.7K Privately Held
SIC: 2431 Millwork

(G-1385)
ATLAS BOAT WORKS INC
2404 Andalusia Blvd (33909-2901)
P.O. Box 150205 (33915-0205)
PHONE....................239 574-2628
Thomas Gamso, *President*
Stan Gamso, *Shareholder*
▼ EMP: 7 EST: 1985
SQ FT: 3,000
SALES (est): 538.5K Privately Held
WEB: www.acadia25.com
SIC: 3732 Boats, fiberglass: building & repairing

(G-1386)
ATM PAVERS INC
2710 Del Prado Blvd S (33904-5788)
PHONE....................239 322-7010
Marcos V De Medeiros, *President*
Jim Adams, *Marketing Staff*
EMP: 7 EST: 2010
SALES (est): 142K Privately Held
SIC: 3531 Pavers

(G-1387)
BACC COATINGS LLC
926 Se 9th St (33990-6204)
PHONE....................239 424-8843
Celia Turner, *Owner*
EMP: 9 EST: 2016
SALES (est): 257.3K Privately Held
SIC: 3479 Metal coating & allied service

(G-1388)
BENCHMARK METALS INC
1003 Se 12th Ave Unit 2 (33990-3018)
PHONE....................239 699-0802
Jason M Guy, *Principal*
EMP: 8 EST: 2019
SALES (est): 513K Privately Held
WEB: www.benchmark-metals.com
SIC: 1081 Metal mining exploration & development services

(G-1389)
BEVERAGE EQUIPMENT REPAIR CO
Also Called: Berco
1020 Ne Pine Island Rd # 201 (33909-2104)
PHONE....................239 573-0683
Michael Depasquale, *President*
Greg Blakely, *Technician*
EMP: 10 EST: 1996
SQ FT: 1,500
SALES (est): 2.1MM Privately Held
WEB: www.beveragerepair.com
SIC: 3585 Refrigeration & heating equipment

(G-1390)
BIG COLOR OUTPUT INC
1327 Lafayette St (33904-9709)
PHONE....................941 540-4441
Harvey L Desnick, *Principal*
EMP: 6 EST: 2018
SALES (est): 55K Privately Held
WEB: www.humansignsllc.com
SIC: 3993 Signs & advertising specialties

(G-1391)
BILLYS WELDING INC
16260 Saddlewood Ln (33991-7514)
PHONE....................239 229-8723
William C Mullen Jr, *Principal*
EMP: 6 EST: 2019
SALES (est): 307.3K Privately Held
SIC: 7692 Welding repair

(G-1392)
BIOBOTANICAL LLC
889 Ne 27th Ln (33909-2957)
PHONE....................239 458-4534
Christopher Mitchell, *Principal*
EMP: 10 EST: 2015
SALES (est): 1.6MM Privately Held
SIC: 2833 Medicinals & botanicals

(G-1393)
BONEFISH BOATS AND TRLRS LLC
1121 Se 12th Pl Ste C (33990-3062)
PHONE....................239 707-4656
Keith Burns, *Principal*
EMP: 6 EST: 2010
SALES (est): 168K Privately Held
SIC: 3799 Boat trailers

(G-1394)
BRAVO INC
Also Called: Bravo Construction Materials
1811 Se 5th Ave (33990-2204)
PHONE....................239 471-8127
Stephen Berge, *President*
Ricco Longo, *Manager*
EMP: 1
SALES (est): 3.5MM Privately Held
WEB: www.bravomaterials.com
SIC: 3523 3524 3531 3537 Cabs, tractors & agricultural machinery; lawn & garden tractors & equipment; backhoes, tractors, cranes, plows & similar equipment; trucks, tractors, loaders, carriers & similar equipment; clamps, surgical

(G-1395)
BREEZE CORPORATION (DH)
Also Called: Fort Meyers Beach Bulletin
2510 Del Prado Blvd S (33904-5750)
P.O. Box 151306 (33915-1306)
PHONE....................239 574-1110
George Ogden Nutting, *President*
Raymond Eckenrode, *Publisher*
Michael Pistella, *Editor*
Robert M Nutting, *Vice Pres*
Edward Rannou, *Production*
EMP: 190 EST: 1890
SQ FT: 13,000
SALES (est): 48.2MM Privately Held
WEB: www.breezenewspapers.com
SIC: 2711 Job printing & newspaper publishing combined
HQ: The Ogden Newspapers Inc
1500 Main St
Wheeling WV 26003
304 233-0100

(G-1396)
BREEZE NEWSPAPERS
2510 Del Prado Blvd S (33904-5750)
PHONE....................239 574-1110
Jim Konig, *Director*
EMP: 7 EST: 2003
SALES (est): 179.2K Privately Held
WEB: www.breezenewspapers.com
SIC: 2711 Newspapers: publishing only, not printed on site

(G-1397)
BULLY WURLD LLC ✪
1103 Country Club Blvd (33990-5009)
PHONE....................201 466-8185
Felix Garcia,
EMP: 6 EST: 2021
SALES (est): 236.5K Privately Held
SIC: 3199 Dog furnishings: collars, leashes, muzzles, etc.: leather

(G-1398)
BWC EQUIPMENT LLC
715 Ne 19th Pl Unit 41 (33909-7410)
PHONE....................239 443-9925
Thorsten R Stein, *Mng Member*
EMP: 8 EST: 2019
SALES (est): 159.4K Privately Held
WEB: www.bwcequipment.com
SIC: 3556 Beverage machinery; ovens, bakery

(G-1399)
CABINET GENIES ✪
1114 Cape Coral Pkwy E (33904-9161)
PHONE....................239 458-8563
EMP: 6 EST: 2020
SALES (est): 465.5K Privately Held
WEB: www.cabinetgenies.com
SIC: 2434 Wood kitchen cabinets

(G-1400)
CABINETS PLUS INC
Also Called: Cabinetsplusfl.com
1056 Ne Pine Island Rd G (33909-2183)
PHONE....................239 574-7020
Phillip Baumstark, *President*
Vicki Baumstark, *Corp Secy*
EMP: 19 EST: 1992
SQ FT: 2,500
SALES (est): 2.5MM Privately Held
WEB: www.cabinetsplusfl.com
SIC: 2541 2434 Cabinets, lockers & shelving; wood kitchen cabinets

(G-1401)
CALNAT INTERNATIONAL INC
2118 Se 1st St (33990-1401)
PHONE....................239 839-2581
Calvin Smith Sr, *President*
Natisha L Smith, *Vice Pres*
EMP: 5 EST: 2005
SALES (est): 2MM Privately Held
WEB: www.calnat.ucanr.edu
SIC: 3312 Tubes, steel & iron; plate, steel; stainless steel; forgings, iron & steel

(G-1402)
CAPE CANDLE LLC
2011 Ne 10th Ter (33909-1762)
PHONE....................239 357-6766
Robert P Sommer, *Principal*
EMP: 6 EST: 2015
SALES (est): 237.7K Privately Held
WEB: www.capecandle.com
SIC: 3999 Candles

(G-1403)
CK PRIME INVESTMENTS INC
Also Called: Action Craft Boats
830 Ne 24th Ln Unit C (33909-2939)
PHONE....................239 574-7800
Chad Kovarik, *Owner*
David Spurlin, *Principal*
EMP: 9 EST: 2015
SALES (est): 952.5K Privately Held
SIC: 3732 Motorized boat, building & repairing

(G-1404)
COLLECTIBLES OF SW FLORIDA
Also Called: Magnetic Bookmarks
1502 Ne 11th Ter (33909-1547)
PHONE....................239 332-2344
Gaby Peden, *President*
Glenn Peden, *Vice Pres*
▲ EMP: 7 EST: 1999
SALES (est): 800K Privately Held
SIC: 3999 Novelties, bric-a-brac & hobby kits

(G-1405)
COLOSSUS PAVERS LLC
2118 Sw 39th St (33914-5429)
PHONE....................239 601-5230

Hector Vara-Monje, *Principal*
EMP: 6 **EST:** 2014
SALES (est): 153.1K **Privately Held**
SIC: 2951 Asphalt paving mixtures & blocks

(G-1406)
CORN-E-LEE WOODCRAFTS
1201 Se 9th Ter (33990-3006)
PHONE..................................239 574-2414
Vaughn Cornelle, *President*
Michael Cornele, *Vice Pres*
EMP: 5 **EST:** 1972
SQ FT: 9,300
SALES (est): 600K **Privately Held**
WEB: www.corneleewoodcraft.com
SIC: 2434 2541 Wood kitchen cabinets; wood partitions & fixtures

(G-1407)
CREATIVE COLORS INTERNATIONAL
Also Called: H & W Creative Colors
1221 Se 9th Ter (33990-3078)
PHONE..................................239 573-8883
Wally Reece, *Partner*
Linda Lakes, *Partner*
EMP: 6 **EST:** 1996
SALES (est): 156.2K **Privately Held**
SIC: 3199 7549 Desk sets, leather; automotive maintenance services

(G-1408)
CUSTOM BUILT SCREEN ENCLOSURES
765 Ne 19th Pl Unit 2 (33909-7803)
PHONE..................................239 242-0224
David Hemed, *CEO*
EMP: 13 **EST:** 1996
SALES (est): 498K **Privately Held**
WEB: www.cbseinc.com
SIC: 3448 Screen enclosures

(G-1409)
D I Y YOGERT
1327 Cape Coral Pkwy E (33904-9816)
PHONE..................................239 471-2177
Kelly Munson, *Owner*
EMP: 7 **EST:** 2012
SALES (est): 239.4K **Privately Held**
WEB: www.diyyogurt.net
SIC: 2024 Yogurt desserts, frozen

(G-1410)
DATA BUOY INSTRUMENTATION LLC
75 Mid Cape Ter Ste 8 (33991-2012)
PHONE..................................239 849-7063
Jeffrey Wingenroth, *Mng Member*
Anthony Harness,
Kahu Trust,
◆ **EMP:** 5 **EST:** 2011
SQ FT: 4,000
SALES (est): 672.1K **Privately Held**
SIC: 3826 7389 Laser scientific & engineering instruments;

(G-1411)
DEKORON UNITHERM LLC (DH)
1531 Commerce Creek Blvd (33909-6502)
PHONE..................................800 633-5015
Paul Brezovsky, *President*
Mike Goddard, *Vice Pres*
Shane Hehir, *Vice Pres*
◆ **EMP:** 34 **EST:** 2004
SQ FT: 30,000
SALES (est): 13.6MM
SALES (corp-wide): 245.5B **Publicly Held**
WEB: www.unithermcc.com
SIC: 3357 Nonferrous wiredrawing & insulating
HQ: Marmon Group Llc
181 W Madison St Ste 2600
Chicago IL 60602
312 372-9500

(G-1412)
DETAILED SERVICES INC
Also Called: Arthur Printing
1518 Se 46th Ln (33904-8635)
PHONE..................................239 542-2452
Robert F Welsh, *President*
Lois M Welsh, *Vice Pres*
Tony Rumreich, *Manager*
EMP: 13 **EST:** 1976
SQ FT: 3,000
SALES (est): 2.2MM **Privately Held**
SIC: 2752 Commercial printing, offset

(G-1413)
DIMENSION MACHINE ENGRG LLC
5201 Sw 28th Pl (33914-6016)
PHONE..................................586 948-3600
Hans Lohr,
Charles Arent,
EMP: 11 **EST:** 1997
SQ FT: 15,000
SALES (est): 196.5K **Privately Held**
SIC: 3544 Special dies, tools, jigs & fixtures

(G-1414)
DIMENSION MACHINE TOOL INC
5201 Sw 28th Pl (33914-6016)
PHONE..................................586 948-3600
Hans Lohr, *President*
EMP: 13 **EST:** 1983
SQ FT: 24,000
SALES (est): 352.4K **Privately Held**
SIC: 3599 3544 Machine shop, jobbing & repair; custom machinery; special dies, tools, jigs & fixtures

(G-1415)
DIRECT IMPRESSIONS INC
1335 Miramar St (33904-9734)
PHONE..................................239 549-4484
Robert Boye, *CEO*
Steve Delaney, *President*
Chris Boye, *Prdtn Mgr*
Rich Boye, *Sales Mgr*
John Panio, *Office Mgr*
EMP: 40 **EST:** 1992
SQ FT: 12,000
SALES (est): 7.8MM **Privately Held**
WEB: www.directimpressions.com
SIC: 2752 7331 Commercial printing, offset; direct mail advertising services

(G-1416)
ECOLOGICAL LABORATORIES INC
2525 Ne 9th Ave (33909-2917)
P.O. Box 24, Matlacha (33993-0024)
PHONE..................................239 573-6650
Nick Simone, *Vice Pres*
Scott Berke, *Sales Mgr*
EMP: 40
SALES (corp-wide): 11.5MM **Privately Held**
WEB: www.microbelift.com
SIC: 2899 5169 2836 Water treating compounds; chemicals & allied products; biological products, except diagnostic
PA: Ecological Laboratories Inc.
4 Waterford Rd
Island Park NY 11558
516 823-3441

(G-1417)
ENERGY HARNESS CORPORATION (PA)
Also Called: Energy Harness Led Lighting
71 Mid Cape Ter Ste 8 (33991-2010)
PHONE..................................239 790-3300
Michael J Fischer, *President*
Peter Lehrer, *Vice Pres*
Dustin Fischer, *Opers Mgr*
Cristiano Rodrigues, *Sales Staff*
Mid Ter, *Sales Staff*
▲ **EMP:** 8 **EST:** 2010
SALES (est): 3.7MM **Privately Held**
WEB: www.energyharness.com
SIC: 3646 Commercial indusl & institutional electric lighting fixtures

(G-1418)
EPOXY2U OF FLORIDA INC
922 Se 14th Pl (33990-3021)
PHONE..................................239 772-0899
Erlan Araujo, *President*
EMP: 9 **EST:** 2018
SALES (est): 785.7K **Privately Held**
WEB: www.epoxy2ufl.com
SIC: 2851 Epoxy coatings

(G-1419)
EURO TRIM INC
17200 Primavera Cir (33909-3024)
PHONE..................................239 574-6646
Peter Geresdi, *Principal*
EMP: 8 **EST:** 2008
SALES (est): 181.6K **Privately Held**
WEB: www.eurotriminc.info
SIC: 3089 Injection molding of plastics

(G-1420)
EVERYTHING PRINTING INC
Also Called: Pioneer Printing and Signs
202 Se 44th St (33904-8426)
PHONE..................................239 541-2679
Robert L Ratcliff, *President*
EMP: 5 **EST:** 2015
SALES (est): 379.6K **Privately Held**
SIC: 2752 Commercial printing, offset

(G-1421)
EXTREME CARE INC
11997 Princess Grace Ct (33991-7536)
PHONE..................................239 898-3709
Maureen Kaufmann, *President*
EMP: 5 **EST:** 2004
SALES (est): 386.1K **Privately Held**
WEB: www.extreme-care-inc.business.site
SIC: 2844 Toilet preparations

(G-1422)
FABWORX LLC
848 Se 9th St (33990-3219)
PHONE..................................239 573-9353
Eric Wirgin,
EMP: 15 **EST:** 1999
SALES (est): 1.7MM **Privately Held**
SIC: 3355 Aluminum rail & structural shapes

(G-1423)
FLATSMASTER MARINE LLC
Also Called: Action Craft
830 Ne 24th Ln Unit C (33909-2939)
PHONE..................................239 574-7800
Paul Guard, *Mng Member*
▼ **EMP:** 10 **EST:** 2009
SQ FT: 34,000
SALES (est): 254.5K **Privately Held**
WEB: www.actioncraft.com
SIC: 3732 Boat building & repairing

(G-1424)
FLORIDA HEALTH PUBLISHING LLC
125 Sw 3rd Pl Ste 205 (33991-2028)
PHONE..................................847 506-2925
Joseph M Mercola, *Principal*
EMP: 6 **EST:** 2016
SALES (est): 89.7K **Privately Held**
SIC: 2741 Miscellaneous publishing

(G-1425)
FLORIDA SW DRONES LLC
1425 Sw 43rd Ter (33914-5665)
PHONE..................................239 785-8337
Gregory Lagrand, *Principal*
EMP: 6 **EST:** 2016
SALES (est): 160.6K **Privately Held**
SIC: 3721 Motorized aircraft

(G-1426)
FORCON PRECISION PRODUCTS LLC
1110 Ne Pine Island Rd (33909-2126)
PHONE..................................239 574-4543
Paul Saalmuller, *Mng Member*
Dale Wheeling,
EMP: 13 **EST:** 1986
SQ FT: 2,800
SALES (est): 800K **Privately Held**
WEB: www.forconprecisionproducts.com
SIC: 3451 Screw machine products

(G-1427)
GATOR POLYMERS LLC
3302 Se 22nd Ave (33904-4421)
PHONE..................................866 292-7306
John R Rasmussen, *Manager*
EMP: 12 **EST:** 2005
SALES (est): 80.9K **Privately Held**
WEB: www.gatorpolymers.com
SIC: 3089 Injection molding of plastics

(G-1428)
GENERATIONS METIER INC (PA)
2818 Nw 43rd Pl (33993-8051)
PHONE..................................239 283-9209
Steven Morrow, *President*
EMP: 26 **EST:** 2006
SALES (est): 148K **Privately Held**
WEB: www.generationsmetier.com
SIC: 2499 Decorative wood & woodwork

(G-1429)
GIRALDO & DONALISIO CORP
3909 Ne 19th Ave (33909-3123)
P.O. Box 4132, Fort Myers (33918-4132)
PHONE..................................239 567-2206
Donalisio Cristiano, *President*
Giraldo Paola, *Director*
▲ **EMP:** 8 **EST:** 2005
SALES (est): 387.8K **Privately Held**
SIC: 3541 3915 Machine tools, metal cutting type; diamond cutting & polishing

(G-1430)
GOLDEN WOOD WORKS LLC
2529 Sw 26th Pl (33914-3827)
PHONE..................................239 677-8540
Timothy Golden, *Manager*
EMP: 7 **EST:** 2012
SALES (est): 257.3K **Privately Held**
SIC: 2431 Millwork

(G-1431)
GREYLOR DYNESCO CO INC
2340 Andalusia Blvd (33909-2901)
PHONE..................................239 574-2011
Michael J Becher, *President*
Amy Chase, *Office Mgr*
Gil Whitmore, *Manager*
▲ **EMP:** 8 **EST:** 1948
SQ FT: 4,500
SALES (est): 1.2MM **Privately Held**
WEB: www.greylor.com
SIC: 3561 5084 Industrial pumps & parts; pumps & pumping equipment

(G-1432)
GULFSHORE CUSTOM WOODWORKS LLC
1012 Nw 36th Ave (33993-9426)
PHONE..................................239 205-0777
Alan Hiebing, *Owner*
EMP: 10 **EST:** 2011
SALES (est): 553.5K **Privately Held**
WEB: www.gulfshorewoodworks.com
SIC: 2431 Millwork

(G-1433)
HANGER PRSTHTICS ORTHOTICS INC
Also Called: Hanger Clinic
323 Del Prado Blvd S (33990-1747)
PHONE..................................239 772-4510
Sam Liang, *President*
EMP: 10 **EST:** 2010
SALES (est): 542.6K **Privately Held**
SIC: 3842 Orthopedic appliances

(G-1434)
HIGH TEMP INDUSTRIES
3808 Sw 6th Ter (33991-1611)
PHONE..................................215 794-0864
Jerold L Bloom, *Principal*
EMP: 9 **EST:** 2012
SALES (est): 216.2K **Privately Held**
WEB: www.high-temp.net
SIC: 3999 Manufacturing industries

(G-1435)
HOME IMPROVER INC
1732 Se 47th Ter (33904-8717)
PHONE..................................239 549-6901
Sean C Campbell, *President*
Ralph Harris, *COO*
EMP: 10 **EST:** 2002
SQ FT: 1,300
SALES (est): 245.5K **Privately Held**
SIC: 2721 Magazines: publishing only, not printed on site

(G-1436)
HOMEMAG INC
1732 Se 47th Ter (33904-8717)
PHONE..................................239 549-6960
Sean Campbell, *President*
Chris Goebel, *President*

EMP: 18 **EST:** 2003
SALES (est): 921.6K **Privately Held**
WEB: www.thehomemag.com
SIC: 2721 Magazines: publishing only, not printed on site

(G-1437)
HOMESHIELD INDUSTRIES CORP
765 Ne 19th Pl (33909-7803)
PHONE..................................239 573-0802
Ricardo A Leon, *Principal*
EMP: 6 **EST:** 2016
SALES (est): 154.8K **Privately Held**
WEB: www.homeshieldwindows.com
SIC: 3999 Manufacturing industries

(G-1438)
HOMEWOOD HOLDINGS LLC
Also Called: Acne Seal Coating and Paving
745 Ne 19th Pl (33909-7807)
PHONE..................................941 740-3655
David C Plummer,
Jennifer D Keese,
EMP: 15 **EST:** 2016
SQ FT: 1,500
SALES (est): 1.5MM **Privately Held**
WEB: www.acmepaving.net
SIC: 3531 Pavers

(G-1439)
HUMAN SIGN
1830 Del Prado Blvd S (33990-4575)
PHONE..................................239 573-4292
Paul Watson, *Principal*
EMP: 14 **EST:** 2007
SALES (est): 524K **Privately Held**
WEB: www.humansignsllc.com
SIC: 3993 Signs & advertising specialties

(G-1440)
JB WOOD WERKS LLC
2550 Sw 27th Ave (33914-3833)
PHONE..................................239 314-4462
Bradley Walker, *Principal*
EMP: 7 **EST:** 2010
SALES (est): 145.2K **Privately Held**
WEB: www.jbwoodwerks.com
SIC: 2431 Millwork

(G-1441)
JDL SURFACE INNOVATIONS INC
922 Se 14th Pl (33990-3021)
PHONE..................................239 772-0077
Roberta Sloat, *Treasurer*
EMP: 22 **EST:** 2010
SALES (est): 1.1MM **Privately Held**
WEB: www.jdlsurfaceinnovations.com
SIC: 3531 1771 7359 Surfacers, concrete grinding; flooring contractor; floor maintenance equipment rental

(G-1442)
JSM CREATIONS INC
16260 Saddlewood Ln (33991-7514)
PHONE..................................239 229-8746
Justin S Mullen, *Principal*
EMP: 8 **EST:** 2013
SALES (est): 533.1K **Privately Held**
SIC: 3648 Decorative area lighting fixtures

(G-1443)
KELTOUR US INC
71 Mid Cape Ter Unit 1/2 (33991-2010)
PHONE..................................239 424-8901
David Jakob, *President*
EMP: 12 **EST:** 2014
SALES (est): 3MM **Privately Held**
WEB: www.keltour.com
SIC: 3569 1731 Liquid automation machinery & equipment; electrical work

(G-1444)
MANUFCTURING SYSTEMS GROUP LLC
1826 Se 5th St (33990-1601)
PHONE..................................727 642-4677
Roy Mapes, *Principal*
EMP: 6 **EST:** 2010
SALES (est): 107.2K **Privately Held**
WEB: www.mfgsysgroup.com
SIC: 7372 Prepackaged software

(G-1445)
MARINE CONCEPTS
2443 Sw Pine Island Rd (33991-1282)
PHONE..................................239 283-0800
John Bower, *Program Mgr*
Del Sturdivant, *Manager*
EMP: 17 **EST:** 2008
SALES (est): 7.5MM **Privately Held**
WEB: www.dcmc-us.com
SIC: 1446 Molding sand mining

(G-1446)
MATTEO GRAPHICS INC
160 Hunter Blvd Ste A1 (33909-2846)
PHONE..................................239 652-1002
Joseph C Trunkett, *President*
Carmen Trunkett, *Vice Pres*
Angela Trunkett, *Officer*
EMP: 13 **EST:** 1989
SALES (est): 1.3MM **Privately Held**
WEB: www.matteographics.com
SIC: 2339 2393 2331 Sportswear, women's; textile bags; women's & misses' blouses & shirts

(G-1447)
MAXXFI LLC
3428 Sw 25th Pl (33914-4875)
PHONE..................................513 289-6521
John Reynolds, *Mng Member*
EMP: 10 **EST:** 2016
SQ FT: 2,500
SALES (est): 420.4K **Privately Held**
WEB: www.nexxgenmobility.com
SIC: 3663 3812 8748 Television antennas (transmitting) & ground equipment; antennas, radar or communications; telecommunications consultant

(G-1448)
MEMBRANE SYSTEMS CORP
3227 Old Burnt Store Rd N (33993-7915)
PHONE..................................239 283-8590
EMP: 6 **Privately Held**
SIC: 3589 Mfg Service Industry Machinery

(G-1449)
MOR SPORTS LLC
1242 Sw Pine Island Rd (33991-2120)
PHONE..................................239 671-5759
EMP: 5 **EST:** 2018
SALES (est): 403.7K **Privately Held**
WEB: www.morsportsgroup.com
SIC: 3949 Sporting & athletic goods

(G-1450)
MOST VALUABLE PAVERS
224 Sw 22nd Pl (33991-1352)
PHONE..................................239 590-5217
Shaun Haag, *President*
EMP: 8 **EST:** 2006
SALES (est): 268.8K **Privately Held**
SIC: 2951 Asphalt paving mixtures & blocks

(G-1451)
NOUMENON CORPORATION
1616 Cape Coral Pkwy W (33914-6979)
PHONE..................................302 296-5460
Linda Higinbotham, *Principal*
EMP: 5 **EST:** 2016
SALES (est): 894.7K **Privately Held**
SIC: 1311 Crude petroleum & natural gas

(G-1452)
NXGEN BRANDS INC (PA)
2322 Se 8th St (33990-2795)
PHONE..................................954 329-2205
Carlos Hurtado, *President*
EMP: 30 **EST:** 2003
SALES (est): 1.7MM **Privately Held**
SIC: 3812 Defense systems & equipment

(G-1453)
ONLINE GERMAN PUBLISHER LLC
1000 Nw 37th Pl (33993-9305)
PHONE..................................239 344-8953
Jens Struck, *President*
EMP: 7 **EST:** 2018
SALES (est): 37.5K **Privately Held**
WEB: www.germanonlinepublisher.com
SIC: 2741 Miscellaneous publishing

(G-1454)
PATRICK INDUSTRIES INC
2443 Sw Pine Island Rd (33991-1282)
PHONE..................................239 283-0800
Andy L Nemeth, *Branch Mgr*
EMP: 90
SALES (corp-wide): 2.4B **Publicly Held**
WEB: www.patrickind.com
SIC: 3429 Marine hardware
PA: Patrick Industries, Inc.
107 W Franklin St
Elkhart IN 46516
574 294-7511

(G-1455)
PRECISION MOLD RESTORATION LLC
204 Ne 23rd Ter (33909-4812)
PHONE..................................239 699-3688
Adam P Welsh, *Manager*
EMP: 6 **EST:** 2016
SALES (est): 375.6K **Privately Held**
WEB: www.precisionmold.net
SIC: 3544 Industrial molds

(G-1456)
PREMIER MANUFACTURING PDTS LLC
730 Ne 19th Pl (33909-5176)
PHONE..................................239 542-0260
Mark Baits, *Principal*
EMP: 12 **EST:** 2018
SALES (est): 737K **Privately Held**
SIC: 2396 Automotive & apparel trimmings

(G-1457)
PRIME HORIZONTAL
5317 Sw 9th Pl (33914-7076)
PHONE..................................239 471-2357
EMP: 6 **EST:** 2014
SALES (est): 68K **Privately Held**
SIC: 3541 Machine tools, metal cutting type

(G-1458)
PROJECT AND CNSTR WLDG INC
Also Called: IMS
2603 Andalusia Blvd (33909-2922)
PHONE..................................239 772-9299
Rolf Nilsen, *President*
Eve Roe, *Bookkeeper*
Leslie Stieffel, *Office Mgr*
◆ **EMP:** 15 **EST:** 1987
SALES (est): 2MM **Privately Held**
WEB: www.imsgroups.com
SIC: 3312 Forgings, iron & steel

(G-1459)
RAY ELECTRIC OUTBOARDS INC
908 Ne 24th Ln Unit 6 (33909-2915)
PHONE..................................239 574-1948
Morton Ray, *President*
▲ **EMP:** 5 **EST:** 1971
SQ FT: 4,000
SALES (est): 738.9K **Privately Held**
WEB: www.rayeo.com
SIC: 3621 5551 Motors, electric; boat dealers

(G-1460)
RIK ENTERPRISES INC
954 Ne Pine Island Rd G (33909-2506)
PHONE..................................239 772-9485
Richard Dahlberg, *President*
EMP: 9 **EST:** 2000
SQ FT: 6,000
SALES (est): 1MM **Privately Held**
WEB: www.rikgraniteshop.com
SIC: 3281 1751 Granite, cut & shaped; cabinet & finish carpentry

(G-1461)
ROCKET INTERNATIONAL INC
2803 Sw 33rd St (33914-4761)
PHONE..................................239 275-0880
John Blanchette, *President*
Cathy Blanchette, *Treasurer*
Armando Almirall, *VP Sales*
Craig Blanchette, *Office Mgr*
Rayleen Rinaldi, *Admin Asst*
EMP: 9
SALES (est): 1.8MM **Privately Held**
WEB: www.rockettrailers.com
SIC: 3799 Boat trailers

(G-1462)
RUDDERS RIVER ROCK
1901 Se 15th Pl Apt A (33990-4591)
PHONE..................................239 574-5656
Robert Rudder, *Partner*
Mark Conway, *Partner*
EMP: 5
SALES (est): 340K **Privately Held**
SIC: 3272 Concrete products

(G-1463)
S4J MANUFACTURING SERVICES INC
2685 Ne 9th Ave (33909-2917)
PHONE..................................239 574-9400
Douglas Gyure, *CEO*
Steven E Gyure, *President*
Douglas S Gyure, *Vice Pres*
EMP: 14 **EST:** 1965
SQ FT: 15,000
SALES (est): 2.2MM **Privately Held**
WEB: www.s4jmfg.com
SIC: 3841 Surgical & medical instruments

(G-1464)
SANDY LENDER INC
2200 Nw 5th St (33993-7591)
PHONE..................................239 272-8613
Sandra Lender, *Principal*
Sandy Lender, *Editor*
EMP: 10 **EST:** 2011
SALES (est): 70.9K **Privately Held**
WEB: www.theasphaltpro.com
SIC: 2721 7389 Magazines: publishing only, not printed on site;

(G-1465)
SATELLITE NOW INC
411 Sw 34th Ter (33914-7824)
PHONE..................................239 945-0520
Suzanne Prytherch, *President*
EMP: 8 **EST:** 2005
SALES (est): 591.9K **Privately Held**
SIC: 3663 Space satellite communications equipment

(G-1466)
SAXTON SIGN FL INC
234 Del Prado Blvd N (33909-2289)
PHONE..................................239 458-0845
EMP: 7 **EST:** 2019
SALES (est): 248.3K **Privately Held**
WEB: www.saxtonsignfl.com
SIC: 3993 Signs & advertising specialties

(G-1467)
SCREENPRINT PLUS INC
1336 Se 47th St (33904-9636)
PHONE..................................239 549-7284
H M Williamson Jr, *President*
Donna Williamson, *Corp Secy*
H M Williamson III, *Vice Pres*
EMP: 46 **EST:** 1986
SQ FT: 15,000
SALES (est): 1.2MM **Privately Held**
WEB: www.screenprintplus.com
SIC: 2261 2397 Screen printing of cotton broadwoven fabrics; schiffli machine embroideries

(G-1468)
SEND IT SWEETLY LLC
1309 Se 47th Ter (33904-9674)
PHONE..................................239 850-5500
Anita R Grant, *Principal*
EMP: 8 **EST:** 2013
SALES (est): 510.5K **Privately Held**
WEB: www.noelachocolate.com
SIC: 2064 Candy & other confectionery products

(G-1469)
SET UP INC
170 Sw 51st St (33914-7126)
PHONE..................................239 542-4142
Jean Bersch, *President*
EMP: 6 **EST:** 1977
SALES (est): 799.1K **Privately Held**
WEB: www.thesetup.com
SIC: 2791 Typesetting

GEOGRAPHIC

(G-1470)
SHORELINE PRINT GROUP
4809 Sw 25th Pl (33914-6618)
PHONE..................................727 481-9358
Robert Groettum, *Principal*
EMP: 6 **EST:** 2014
SALES (est): 111.6K **Privately Held**
WEB: www.shorelineprint.com
SIC: 2752 Commercial printing, offset

(G-1471)
SIGN ON LLC
4519 Del Prado Blvd S B (33904-7525)
PHONE..................................239 800-9454
Gabriel Jacobs, *CEO*
Jacobs Kristian, *Principal*
EMP: 8 **EST:** 2015
SALES (est): 582.5K **Privately Held**
WEB: www.signsandleds.com
SIC: 3993 Signs & advertising specialties

(G-1472)
SILVER ENTERPRISES ASSOC INC
1417 Sw 52nd Ter (33914-7416)
PHONE..................................239 542-0068
Robert McGuire, *Principal*
EMP: 9 **EST:** 2002
SALES (est): 108.5K **Privately Held**
WEB: www.slvx.com
SIC: 3743 Railroad equipment

(G-1473)
SOURCE OF SUP IN POLYURETHANES
2645 Ne 9th Ave Unit 12 (33909-2929)
P.O. Box 7127, Fort Myers (33919-0127)
PHONE..................................239 573-3637
Bart J Derosso, *Principal*
EMP: 3
SALES: 8.4MM **Privately Held**
WEB: www.sosfoams.com
SIC: 3086 Packaging & shipping materials, foamed plastic

(G-1474)
SOUTHERN ALUMINUM INC
674 Stonecrest Ln Ste 4 (33909-2298)
PHONE..................................239 275-3367
Matt Myers, *President*
Stacie Brice, *General Mgr*
Coy Brown, *Purch Mgr*
Shawn Tuggle, *Engineer*
Daniel Watson, *Controller*
EMP: 19 **EST:** 2007
SALES (est): 3.1MM **Privately Held**
WEB: www.southern-aluminum.com
SIC: 3446 Ornamental metalwork

(G-1475)
SOUTHWEST CHOPPERS INC
2123 Ne 3rd Ter (33909-2849)
PHONE..................................239 242-1101
Dave Zink, *General Mgr*
Chris Wallen, *Principal*
EMP: 13 **EST:** 2007
SALES (est): 68.4K **Privately Held**
WEB: www.southwestcycle.net
SIC: 3751 Motorcycles & related parts

(G-1476)
SOUTHWEST FLA NEWSPAPERS INC
308 Se 25th Ter (33904-2763)
PHONE..................................239 574-9733
Moore Karen P, *Principal*
EMP: 8 **EST:** 2013
SALES (est): 88.7K **Privately Held**
WEB: www.breezenewspapers.com
SIC: 2711 Newspapers: publishing only, not printed on site

(G-1477)
SOUTHWEST STEEL GROUP INC
3405 Yucatan Pkwy (33993-9450)
PHONE..................................239 283-8980
EMP: 9
SALES (est): 1.3MM **Privately Held**
SIC: 3441 Structural Metal Fabrication

(G-1478)
SPOSEN SIGNATURE HOMES LLC
2311 Santa Barbara Blvd # 111 (33991-4394)
PHONE..................................239 244-8886
EMP: 11 **EST:** 2019
SALES (est): 1.4MM **Privately Held**
SIC: 3993 Signs & advertising specialties

(G-1479)
STONE HARBOR HOMES LLC
5225 Sw 22nd Pl (33914-6834)
PHONE..................................239 672-7687
Pia Powell, *Principal*
EMP: 6 **EST:** 2015
SALES (est): 363.2K **Privately Held**
WEB: www.stoneharbor4.com
SIC: 2451 Mobile homes, personal or private use

(G-1480)
SUPERIOR FIRE & LF SAFETY INC
1709 Sw 15th Ave (33991-3240)
PHONE..................................850 572-0265
Richard M King, *President*
EMP: 12 **EST:** 2012
SALES (est): 1.1MM **Privately Held**
WEB: www.superiorfiresafetyinc.com
SIC: 3669 Fire alarm apparatus, electric

(G-1481)
SWFL HURRICANE SHUTTERS INC
422 Sw 2nd Ter Ste 214 (33991-1949)
PHONE..................................239 454-4944
Richard Jones, *Principal*
EMP: 7 **EST:** 2007
SALES (est): 93.2K **Privately Held**
SIC: 3442 5023 Shutters, door or window: metal; window furnishings

(G-1482)
SWIFT PRINT SERVICE INC
1431 Se 10th St Unit B (33990-3630)
PHONE..................................239 458-2212
Jerry Kuhen, *President*
Mike Shough, *Mfg Staff*
Victoria Kuhn, *Purchasing*
EMP: 5 **EST:** 1994
SALES (est): 467.2K **Privately Held**
WEB: www.floridaprinter.com
SIC: 2752 Commercial printing, offset

(G-1483)
T & E PAVERS INC
1319 Sw 10th Pl (33991-2912)
PHONE..................................239 243-6229
Tarcilla Vianna, *Principal*
EMP: 6 **EST:** 2009
SALES (est): 86.7K **Privately Held**
SIC: 3531 Pavers

(G-1484)
TDT MANUFACTURING LLC (PA)
2137 Se 19th Pl (33990-3112)
PHONE..................................239 573-7498
Dennis F Walsh, *Manager*
EMP: 7 **EST:** 2018
SALES (est): 93.1K **Privately Held**
SIC: 3999 Manufacturing industries

(G-1485)
THINK OUTLOUD PRINTING
613 Sw Pine Island Rd (33991-1992)
PHONE..................................239 800-3219
EMP: 6 **EST:** 2015
SALES (est): 195.2K **Privately Held**
SIC: 2759 Screen printing

(G-1486)
TOOLINGHOUSE INC
1136 Ne Pine Island Rd (33909-2186)
PHONE..................................239 424-8503
EMP: 6 **EST:** 2011
SALES (est): 122.5K **Privately Held**
WEB: www.toolinghouse.com
SIC: 3545 Machine tool accessories

(G-1487)
TRADEWIND CUSTOM CABINETRY LLC
1213 Cape Coral Pkwy E (33904-9604)
PHONE..................................239 257-3295
Paul Beattie, *Principal*
Mark Zinn, *Broker*
Jill Jones, *Sales Staff*
EMP: 7 **EST:** 2014
SALES (est): 166.7K **Privately Held**
WEB: www.beattiedev.com
SIC: 2434 Wood kitchen cabinets

(G-1488)
TROPIX MARBLE COMPANY
17121 Primavera Cir (33909-3026)
PHONE..................................239 334-2371
Sean W Hassett, *President*
EMP: 18 **EST:** 1958
SALES (est): 2.1MM **Privately Held**
SIC: 3281 5032 Bathroom fixtures, cut stone; brick, stone & related material

(G-1489)
TURBINE GENERATOR MAINT INC (PA)
125 Sw 3rd Pl Ste 300 (33991-2029)
PHONE..................................239 573-1233
David Branton, *CEO*
Robert W Davis, *Finance Dir*
Michael Lake, *Sales Dir*
◆ **EMP:** 25 **EST:** 2007
SQ FT: 8,000
SALES (est): 21.6MM **Privately Held**
WEB: www.turbinegenerator.com
SIC: 3511 Turbines & turbine generator sets

(G-1490)
VEGA
447 Ne 8th Ter (33909-1969)
PHONE..................................239 574-1798
Deborah Vega, *Principal*
EMP: 6 **EST:** 2012
SALES (est): 105.7K **Privately Held**
WEB: www.euphoria4two.com
SIC: 3497 Metal foil & leaf

(G-1491)
VIP DRINKS BOTTLING LLC
2624 Sw 4th Ave (33914-4414)
PHONE..................................239 214-8190
Uwe Rusch, *Principal*
▲ **EMP:** 6 **EST:** 2013
SALES (est): 177K **Privately Held**
SIC: 2086 Soft drinks: packaged in cans, bottles, etc.

(G-1492)
VITERRA AFFORDABLE SHUTTERS
1104 Se 46th Ln Ste 2 (33904-8882)
PHONE..................................239 738-6364
Terry Mc Dermott, *Principal*
EMP: 7 **EST:** 2008
SALES (est): 147.4K **Privately Held**
SIC: 3089 Shutters, plastic

(G-1493)
W E CONNERY BOAT BUILDERS
5787 Sw 9th Ct (33914-8004)
PHONE..................................239 549-8014
Edwin Connery, *Owner*
EMP: 7
SALES (est): 382.8K **Privately Held**
SIC: 3732 3089 Boats, fiberglass: building & repairing; plastic boats & other marine equipment

(G-1494)
WALTZING WATERS INC
1410 Se 10th St (33990-3604)
PHONE..................................239 574-5181
Michael Przystawik, *President*
EMP: 8 **EST:** 1971
SQ FT: 8,000
SALES (est): 1.6MM **Privately Held**
WEB: www.liquidfireworks.com
SIC: 3499 Fountains (except drinking), metal

(G-1495)
WICKED DOLPHIN DISTILLERY
131 Sw 3rd Pl (33991-2011)
PHONE..................................239 565-7947
EMP: 6 **EST:** 2017
SALES (est): 70.4K **Privately Held**
WEB: www.wickeddolphinrum.com
SIC: 2085 Distilled & blended liquors

(G-1496)
XTERIOR SHUTTER SYSTEMS
2523 Sw 24th Ave (33914-2915)
PHONE..................................239 872-2327
EMP: 6 **EST:** 2011
SALES (est): 85.9K **Privately Held**
SIC: 3442 Louvers, shutters, jalousies & similar items

Carrabelle
Franklin County

(G-1497)
DONALD SMITH LOGGING INC
127 Cora Mae Rd (32322-2064)
PHONE..................................850 697-3975
Shirley T Chason, *President*
EMP: 9 **EST:** 1988
SALES (est): 516.1K **Privately Held**
WEB: www.kulinarykingscatering.com
SIC: 2411 4212 Logging; local trucking, without storage

Casselberry
Seminole County

(G-1498)
BIOLIFE PLASMA SERVICES
1385 State Road 436 (32707-6503)
PHONE..................................407 388-1052
EMP: 6 **EST:** 2018
SALES (est): 439.8K **Privately Held**
WEB: www.biolifeplasma.com
SIC: 2836 Plasmas

(G-1499)
CALVERT MANUFACTURING INC
Also Called: Calvert Solutions
228 Colombo Dr (32707-3308)
PHONE..................................407 331-5522
Dana Tucker, *CEO*
Albert A Rollins Jr, *Vice Pres*
EMP: 19 **EST:** 1976
SQ FT: 6,000
SALES (est): 630.1K **Privately Held**
SIC: 3553 8711 Veneer mill machines; consulting engineer

(G-1500)
CHEM GUARD INC
3964 Buglers Rest Pl (32707-4709)
PHONE..................................407 402-2798
David McCullough, *President*
EMP: 11 **EST:** 2008
SALES (est): 84.7K **Privately Held**
WEB: www.chemguard.com
SIC: 2899 Chemical preparations

(G-1501)
CLADDAH CORP
Also Called: Olde Hearth Bread Company
207 Reece Way Ste 1625 (32707-3880)
PHONE..................................407 834-8881
Shannon Talty, *President*
David Talty, *Partner*
Janice Brahm, *Vice Pres*
EMP: 11 **EST:** 1998
SALES (est): 610.5K **Privately Held**
WEB: www.oldehearthbreadcompany.com
SIC: 2051 5461 Bread, all types (white, wheat, rye, etc): fresh or frozen; bakeries

(G-1502)
DARMERICA LLC
198 Wilshire Blvd (32707-5352)
P.O. Box 219, Goldenrod (32733-0219)
PHONE..................................321 219-9111
Wayne Maccinis,
EMP: 10 **EST:** 2016
SALES (est): 810.7K **Privately Held**
WEB: www.attixpharmaceuticals.com
SIC: 2834 Pharmaceutical preparations

(G-1503)
FLORIDA NATURAL FLAVORS INC
170 Lyman Rd (32707-2803)
P.O. Box 181125 (32718-1125)
PHONE..................................407 834-5979
Dave Erdman, *President*
Jeffrey Smail, *General Mgr*
Scott Munson, *Purchasing*
Mark Wilkinson, *Marketing Staff*
Debby Oakes Falls, *Admin Sec*
▼ **EMP:** 35 **EST:** 1983
SQ FT: 32,500
SALES (est): 6.9MM **Privately Held**
WEB: www.floridanaturalflavors.com
SIC: 2087 Flavoring extracts & syrups

(G-1504)
H & H GYPSUM LLC
371 Oleander Way Ste 1325 (32707-3273)
PHONE..................................321 972-5571
Curtis House, *President*
EMP: 7 **EST:** 2017
SALES (est): 225.7K **Privately Held**
SIC: 3275 Gypsum products

(G-1505)
HARRIS AERIAL LLC (PA)
1043 Seminola Blvd (32707-3516)
PHONE..................................407 725-7886
Benjamin Harris, *CEO*
Patrick Burton, *Principal*
Ethan Wash, *Principal*
EMP: 10 **EST:** 2014
SALES: 1.7MM **Privately Held**
WEB: www.harrisaerial.com
SIC: 3861 3721 Aerial cameras; aircraft

(G-1506)
INSTANT LOCATE INC
Also Called: Big League Cards
920 State Road 436 (32707-5633)
PHONE..................................800 431-0812
Alan P Narzissenfeld RES, *President*
EMP: 8 **EST:** 2013
SALES (est): 165.4K **Privately Held**
WEB: www.thenarzgroup.com
SIC: 2752 Commercial printing, lithographic

(G-1507)
J CUBE INC
180 E Trade Winds Rd (32708-3521)
PHONE..................................407 699-6866
Joe Casalese, *Branch Mgr*
EMP: 11
SALES (corp-wide): 94.4K **Privately Held**
WEB: www.j-cube.jp
SIC: 3721 Airplanes, fixed or rotary wing
PA: J Cube Inc
12260 Pescara Ln
Orlando FL

(G-1508)
JET SET PRINTING INC
130 N Cypress Way (32707-3216)
PHONE..................................407 339-1900
Mary Stanley, *President*
EMP: 5 **EST:** 1976
SQ FT: 5,000
SALES (est): 380K **Privately Held**
WEB: www.jetsetprintingorlando.com
SIC: 2759 2791 2789 2752 Screen printing; typesetting; bookbinding & related work; commercial printing, lithographic

(G-1509)
LILES OIL COMPANY
201 Kraft Dr (32707-5746)
PHONE..................................407 739-2083
David L Liles, *President*
David Liles, *Owner*
EMP: 10
SALES (est): 580.1K **Privately Held**
WEB: www.lilesoilco.com
SIC: 2869 Fuels

(G-1510)
MAGNOLIA MILLWORK INTL INC
231 Plaza Oval (32707-2934)
PHONE..................................407 585-3470
David Chauvin, *President*
Charles Palmer, *CFO*
EMP: 7 **EST:** 2014
SALES (est): 130.4K **Privately Held**
SIC: 2431 5211 Millwork; millwork & lumber

(G-1511)
NEV INTERNATIONAL INC
1211 State Road 436 # 141 (32707-6442)
P.O. Box 181428 (32718-1428)
PHONE..................................407 671-0045
▲ **EMP:** 15
SQ FT: 15,000
SALES: 2MM **Privately Held**
SIC: 3711 Mfg Motor Vehicle/Car Bodies

(G-1512)
PERFORMANCE PUMPS INC
321 Oleander Way (32707-3244)
PHONE..................................407 339-6700
Jonathan Kenney, *President*
Michael Hase, *President*
Bradley Share, *Treasurer*
EMP: 25 **EST:** 1994
SALES (est): 1MM **Privately Held**
SIC: 3561 5084 Pumps & pumping equipment; industrial machinery & equipment

(G-1513)
PIPETTE SOLUTIONS LLC
1749 Grand Rue Dr (32707-2427)
PHONE..................................877 974-7388
EMP: 6 **EST:** 2008
SALES (est): 225.4K **Privately Held**
WEB: www.thepipettesolution.com
SIC: 3826 Analytical instruments

(G-1514)
PLATINUM SIGNS AND DESIGN LLC (PA)
352 W Melody Ln (32707-3279)
PHONE..................................407 971-3640
Jayeshbhai Patel, *Mng Member*
EMP: 6 **EST:** 2005
SQ FT: 4,500
SALES (est): 1.1MM **Privately Held**
WEB: www.platinum-signs.com
SIC: 3993 7389 Signs & advertising specialties; advertising, promotional & trade show services; sign painting & lettering shop

(G-1515)
PRECISION QULTY MACHINING INC
207 Reece Way Ste 1601 (32707-3880)
PHONE..................................407 831-7240
Bob Ryan, *President*
Patrick Quinn, *Vice Pres*
EMP: 7 **EST:** 2002
SALES (est): 384K **Privately Held**
SIC: 3599 Custom machinery

(G-1516)
R C SPECIALIZED INTERNATIONAL
1436 State Road 436 (32707-6572)
PHONE..................................407 681-5905
Robert A Michael, *President*
EMP: 8 **EST:** 2007
SALES (est): 131.7K **Privately Held**
SIC: 3714 Motor vehicle parts & accessories

(G-1517)
SAFETY INTL BAGS & STRAPS
160 Lyman Rd (32707-2801)
PHONE..................................407 830-0888
Henry Sanders, *President*
Bonnie Manjura, *Chairman*
◆ **EMP:** 13 **EST:** 1989
SQ FT: 17,000
SALES (est): 762.4K **Privately Held**
SIC: 2393 3842 Canvas bags; restraints, patient

(G-1518)
SIGN-O-SAURUS INC
3008 S Us Highway 17/92 (32707-2911)
PHONE..................................407 677-8965
Alan Migliorato, *Principal*
EMP: 7 **EST:** 2008
SALES (est): 403.5K **Privately Held**
WEB: www.sign-o-saurus.com
SIC: 3993 Signs, not made in custom sign painting shops

(G-1519)
T & C GODBY ENTERPRISES INC
Also Called: Fastsigns
915 State Road 436 (32707-5632)
PHONE..................................407 831-6334
Timm A Godby, *President*
EMP: 27 **EST:** 1992
SQ FT: 2,150
SALES (est): 856.5K **Privately Held**
WEB: www.fastsigns.com
SIC: 3993 Signs & advertising specialties

(G-1520)
THERMOCARBON INC (PA)
391 W Melody Ln (32707-3259)
P.O. Box 181220 (32718-1220)
PHONE..................................407 834-7800
John Boucher, *President*
David Bajune, *Vice Pres*
Frank Cardenas, *Manager*
Irene Miller, *Technical Staff*
EMP: 33 **EST:** 1978
SQ FT: 14,000
SALES (est): 4MM **Privately Held**
WEB: www.dicing.com
SIC: 3545 Diamond cutting tools for turning, boring, burnishing, etc.

(G-1521)
WESOL DISTRIBUTION LLC
1486 Seminola Blvd Unit 1 (32707-3640)
PHONE..................................407 921-9248
Gerald A Wesol, *Mng Member*
EMP: 5 **EST:** 2007
SQ FT: 1,600
SALES (est): 431.5K **Privately Held**
WEB: www.wesoldistribution.com
SIC: 2389 Men's miscellaneous accessories

Cedar Key
Levy County

(G-1522)
1842 DAILY GRIND & MERCANTILE
598 2nd St (32625-5120)
P.O. Box 565 (32625-0565)
PHONE..................................352 543-5004
Terry E Williams, *Principal*
EMP: 7 **EST:** 2016
SALES (est): 132.7K **Privately Held**
SIC: 3599 Grinding castings for the trade

Celebration
Osceola County

(G-1523)
KEMPHARM INC (PA)
1180 Celebration Blvd # 10 (34747-4950)
PHONE..................................321 939-3416
Travis C Mickle, *Ch of Bd*
Sven Guenther, *Exec VP*
Timothy J Sangiovanni, *Vice Pres*
R Laduane Clifton, *CFO*
EMP: 5 **EST:** 2006
SQ FT: 17,000
SALES (est): 13.2MM **Publicly Held**
WEB: www.kempharm.com
SIC: 2834 Pharmaceutical preparations

(G-1524)
ORION TRAVEL TECHNOLOGIES INC (PA)
200 Celebration Pl # 840 (34747-5483)
PHONE..................................407 574-6649
Gary German, *CEO*
EMP: 10
SQ FT: 2,000
SALES (est): 50K **Privately Held**
WEB: www.oriontraveltech.com
SIC: 7372 Business oriented computer software

Center Hill
Sumter County

(G-1525)
CENTRAL BEEF IND LLC
Also Called: Chernin Beef Industries
571 W Kings Hwy (33514-4001)
PHONE..................................352 793-3671
Ida Raye Chernin, *Managing Prtnr*
Randy Bertrand, *Purch Agent*
Adam Chernin,
Alex Chernin,
EMP: 225 **EST:** 1945
SQ FT: 60,000
SALES (est): 21.5MM **Privately Held**
SIC: 2011 Beef products from beef slaughtered on site

(G-1526)
FCS HOLDINGS INC
530 W Kings Hwy (33514-4002)
PHONE..................................352 793-5151
John B Collins, *Manager*
EMP: 38 **Privately Held**
SIC: 1481 Nonmetallic mineral services
PA: Fcs Holdings, Inc.
8500 Us Highway 441
Leesburg FL 34788

Century
Escambia County

(G-1527)
CENTURY MILLWORKS
6082 Industrial Blvd (32535-3312)
P.O. Box 248 (32535-0248)
PHONE..................................850 256-2565
Don Dockens, *President*
Sandra Dockens, *Treasurer*
EMP: 10 **EST:** 1984
SQ FT: 5,000
SALES (est): 452.7K **Privately Held**
WEB: www.centurymillworks.com
SIC: 2431 2434 Doors, wood; wood kitchen cabinets

(G-1528)
SQUEEGEE STITCH GRAPHIX LLC
2940 W Highway 4 (32535-3508)
PHONE..................................850 256-4926
Marsha C Maher, *Principal*
EMP: 6 **EST:** 2009
SALES (est): 144.7K **Privately Held**
WEB: www.squeegeestitchgraphics.com
SIC: 2395 Embroidery & art needlework

Chiefland
Levy County

(G-1529)
AMERICAN TRUSS
6760 Nw 138th Pl (32626-8280)
PHONE..................................352 493-9700
Terry Hassell, *Partner*
EMP: 7 **EST:** 2007
SALES (est): 188.5K **Privately Held**
SIC: 2439 Structural wood members

(G-1530)
AMERICAN TRUSS CHIEFLAND LL
6750 Nw 138th Pl (32626-8280)
PHONE..................................352 493-9700
Michael Martin, *Principal*
EMP: 7 **EST:** 2007
SALES (est): 321.7K **Privately Held**
WEB: www.americantrussofchiefland.com
SIC: 2439 Trusses, wooden roof

(G-1531)
ANDERSON COLUMBIA CO INC
Also Called: Anderson Materials
8191 Nw 160th St (32626)
P.O. Box 2209 (32644-2209)
PHONE..................................352 463-6342
Diana Stevens, *Manager*
EMP: 14

GEOGRAPHIC

SALES (corp-wide): 168.7MM **Privately Held**
WEB: www.andersoncolumbia.com
SIC: 3273 5211 3272 Ready-mixed concrete; cement; concrete products, precast
PA: Anderson Columbia Co., Inc.
871 Nw Guerdon St
Lake City FL 32055
386 752-7585

(G-1532)
B SQUARED OF CHIEFLAND LLC
710 Nw 17th Ave (32626-1736)
P.O. Box 582 (32644-0582)
PHONE..................................352 507-2195
Bradlee Bruner, *Principal*
EMP: 10 **EST:** 2012
SALES (est): 229.4K **Privately Held**
SIC: 2711 Newspapers, publishing & printing

(G-1533)
BAGS UNLIMITED INC
9805 Nw 55th St (32626-6418)
PHONE..................................985 868-3393
Carrie Castell, *Owner*
EMP: 6 **EST:** 1988
SQ FT: 720
SALES (est): 200K **Privately Held**
WEB: www.bagsunlimited.com
SIC: 3069 5699 5162 Bags, rubber or rubberized fabric; work clothing; plastics materials

(G-1534)
CEDAR KEY BEACON
624 W Park Ave (32626-0430)
PHONE..................................352 493-4796
EMP: 6 **EST:** 2017
SALES (est): 98.1K **Privately Held**
SIC: 2711 Newspapers

(G-1535)
CHIEFLAND CRAB COMPANY INC
1606 Sw 4th Pl (32626-0260)
P.O. Box 174, Steinhatchee (32359-0174)
PHONE..................................352 493-4887
EMP: 25
SQ FT: 5,000
SALES (est): 3.3MM **Privately Held**
SIC: 2092 Mfg Fresh/Frozen Packaged Fish

(G-1536)
MARCUS V HALL
14271 Nw 66th Ave (32626-2211)
PHONE..................................352 490-9694
Marcus V Hall, *Owner*
▲ **EMP:** 6
SALES (est): 524.2K **Privately Held**
SIC: 3272 Steps, prefabricated concrete

(G-1537)
PRINT SHOP OF CHIEFLAND INC
Also Called: Print Shop, The
208 N Main St (32626-0802)
P.O. Box 606 (32644-0606)
PHONE..................................352 493-0322
Richard Pelletir, *CEO*
Linda Pelletire, *President*
EMP: 5 **EST:** 1989
SALES (est): 483.8K **Privately Held**
WEB: www.printshopofchiefland.com
SIC: 2752 5999 2759 Commercial printing, offset; rubber stamps; visiting cards (including business): printing

(G-1538)
TRI-COUNTY BULLETIN
624 W Park Ave (32626-0430)
PHONE..................................352 493-4796
Tom Tenbroeck, *Principal*
EMP: 7 **EST:** 2018
SALES (est): 69.2K **Privately Held**
WEB: www.chieflandcitizen.com
SIC: 2711 Newspapers, publishing & printing

(G-1539)
USHER LAND & TIMBER INC
6551 Nw 100th St (32626-4229)
P.O. Box 843 (32644-0843)
PHONE..................................352 493-4221
Ken Griner, *President*
Lynetta Usher Griner, *Corp Secy*
John Fisher, *Vice Pres*
Lynetta Griner, *Admin Sec*
EMP: 24 **EST:** 1950
SQ FT: 2,500
SALES (est): 1.3MM **Privately Held**
WEB: www.usherlandtimber.com
SIC: 2411 4212 Logging; local trucking, without storage

Chipley
Washington County

(G-1540)
ABC FENCE SYSTEMS INC (PA)
963 Industrial Dr (32428-6314)
P.O. Box 119 (32428-0119)
PHONE..................................850 638-8876
Kelly Brock, *President*
Vann Brock, *Corp Secy*
Marlene Brock, *Vice Pres*
EMP: 13
SQ FT: 560
SALES (est): 4MM **Privately Held**
WEB: www.abcfencesystems.com
SIC: 2499 5411 Fencing, wood; grocery stores

(G-1541)
BACK LORY LEE
Also Called: Medical Concepts
403 Cutchins Mill Rd (32428-4397)
PHONE..................................850 638-5430
Lory L Back, *Owner*
Douglas Back, *Owner*
EMP: 8 **EST:** 1993
SQ FT: 1,200
SALES (est): 150K **Privately Held**
WEB: www.medicalconceptschipley.com
SIC: 3841 Surgical & medical instruments

(G-1542)
CORBIN SAND AND CLAY INC
1177 Jackson Ave (32428-2004)
PHONE..................................850 638-8462
Travis Corbin, *CEO*
EMP: 5 **EST:** 2001
SALES (est): 377.6K **Privately Held**
WEB: www.corbinautosales.com
SIC: 1442 Construction sand & gravel

(G-1543)
D & S LOGGING INC
261 Highway 273 (32428-4209)
P.O. Box 935 (32428-0935)
PHONE..................................850 638-5500
Dwayne Taylor, *Principal*
Barry McGaughey, *Vice Pres*
Rex Dwayne Taylor, *Director*
David Morris, *Director*
EMP: 6 **EST:** 1997
SALES (est): 719.1K **Privately Held**
WEB: www.panhandleforestry.net
SIC: 2411 3272 Logging camps & contractors; poles & posts, concrete

(G-1544)
EZY-GLIDE INC
715 7th St (32428-1932)
PHONE..................................850 638-4403
Bobby Padgett, *President*
Bobby R Padgett, *President*
Stephen Padgett, *Officer*
Tyler Padgett, *Officer*
▲ **EMP:** 7 **EST:** 1981
SQ FT: 4,800
SALES (est): 600K **Privately Held**
WEB: www.ezyglide.com
SIC: 3714 Steering mechanisms, motor vehicle; motor vehicle steering systems & parts

(G-1545)
RANDY MORRIS LOGGING INC
4259 Highway 77 (32428-4910)
PHONE..................................850 773-9010
EMP: 12
SQ FT: 3,300
SALES (est): 1.5MM **Privately Held**
SIC: 2411 Logging Contractor

(G-1546)
WASHINGTON COUNTY NEWS (DH)
1364 N Railroad Ave (32428-1456)
PHONE..................................850 638-4242
Nicole Barefield, *Principal*
EMP: 16 **EST:** 1924
SQ FT: 7,000
SALES (est): 8.8MM
SALES (corp-wide): 3.4B **Publicly Held**
WEB: www.washingtoncounty.news
SIC: 2711 Commercial printing & newspaper publishing combined; newspapers, publishing & printing
HQ: Panama City News Herald
501 W 11th St
Panama City FL 32401
850 747-5000

(G-1547)
WEST POINT STEVENS
1414 Main St (32428-6952)
PHONE..................................850 638-9421
John Martin, *General Mgr*
Steve Harr, *Engineer*
EMP: 6 **EST:** 2014
SALES (est): 359.5K **Privately Held**
WEB: www.westpointhome.com
SIC: 2211 Broadwoven fabric mills, cotton

(G-1548)
WESTPOINT HOME INC
1056 Commerce Ave (32428-6395)
PHONE..................................850 415-4100
Terry Ellis, *Engineer*
Vinta Yon, *Human Res Mgr*
Normand Savaria, *Mng Member*
Kristopher Graham, *Manager*
EMP: 397 **Publicly Held**
WEB: www.westpointhome.com
SIC: 2211 Sheets, bedding & table cloths: cotton
HQ: Westpoint Home, Inc.
777 3rd Ave Fl 7
New York NY 10017
212 930-2000

(G-1549)
WESTPOINT HOME INC
Also Called: Home Fashion Source
1414 Main St (32428-6952)
P.O. Box 625 (32428-0625)
PHONE..................................850 415-4100
Steve Harr, *Engineer*
Terry Ellis, *Manager*
Courtney Hoard, *Manager*
EMP: 397 **Publicly Held**
WEB: www.westpointhome.com
SIC: 2211 2392 2391 Broadwoven fabric mills, cotton; household furnishings; curtains & draperies
HQ: Westpoint Home, Inc.
777 3rd Ave Fl 7
New York NY 10017
212 930-2000

Christmas
Orange County

(G-1550)
FLORIDA MANUFACTURED HOME
1722 Duthie Ln (32709-9171)
PHONE..................................407 509-8262
EMP: 6 **EST:** 2019
SALES (est): 190K **Privately Held**
SIC: 3999 Manufacturing industries

Chuluota
Seminole County

(G-1551)
ALICIA DIAGNOSTIC INC
150 W 11th St (32766-9454)
PHONE..................................407 365-8498
Hassan Soltani, *President*
John Tobin, *Vice Pres*
EMP: 10 **EST:** 1989
SQ FT: 5,000
SALES (est): 902.2K **Privately Held**
SIC: 3841 Surgical & medical instruments

(G-1552)
BEFORE WIND BLOWS LLC
282 Osprey Lakes Cir (32766-6664)
PHONE..................................407 977-4833
EMP: 7
SALES (est): 736.5K **Privately Held**
SIC: 3442 Mfg Metal Doors/Sash/Trim

(G-1553)
JSL ENTERPRISES OF ORLANDO
Also Called: Glass Works
1434 Circle Ln (32766-9283)
PHONE..................................386 767-9653
Steven Lovell, *President*
Harry Waltz, *Vice Pres*
▲ **EMP:** 11 **EST:** 1987
SQ FT: 12,500
SALES (est): 350.1K **Privately Held**
SIC: 3231 5231 3211 Products of purchased glass; glass, leaded or stained; flat glass

(G-1554)
SCREEN SAVERS LLC
715 Kyle Ct (32766-9640)
PHONE..................................321 299-8099
Matthew Mendenhall, *Principal*
EMP: 6 **EST:** 2008
SALES (est): 183.2K **Privately Held**
WEB: www.screensaversllc.com
SIC: 3448 Screen enclosures

Citra
Marion County

(G-1555)
A L BAXLEY & SONS INC
1542 E Highway 329 (32113-4238)
P.O. Box 180, Sparr (32192-0180)
PHONE..................................352 629-5137
Daniel Baxley, *Vice Pres*
Tonya Baxley, *Vice Pres*
Glen Davis, *Treasurer*
EMP: 21 **EST:** 1977
SALES (est): 1MM **Privately Held**
WEB: www.albaxleyandsons.com
SIC: 2411 2426 2421 Logging camps & contractors; hardwood dimension & flooring mills; sawmills & planing mills, general

(G-1556)
BLUNTS WELDING LLC
2843 Nw 142nd Pl (32113-3537)
PHONE..................................352 274-6014
Russell C Blunt, *Principal*
EMP: 6 **EST:** 2016
SALES (est): 257.6K **Privately Held**
SIC: 7692 Welding repair

(G-1557)
MEI COMPANIES INC
12150 Ne 7th Ave (32113-4258)
P.O. Box 1672, Anthony (32617-1672)
PHONE..................................352 361-6895
Christopher N Bowden, *CEO*
EMP: 8 **EST:** 2017
SALES (est): 653.2K **Privately Held**
SIC: 1389 Construction, repair & dismantling services

Clearwater
Pinellas County

(G-1558)
180BYTWO
600 Cleveland St (33755-4151)
PHONE..................................202 403-7097
Travis Thomas, *Manager*
Eric Shaffer, *Administration*
EMP: 8 **EST:** 2017
SALES (est): 1.5MM **Privately Held**
WEB: www.180bytwo.com
SIC: 7372 Prepackaged software

(G-1559)
4 HORSEMEN PUBLICATIONS INC
1768 Carlisle St (33755-2305)
PHONE..................................727 698-0476
Erika Lance, *Principal*

EMP: 7 **EST:** 2017
SALES (est): 84K **Privately Held**
SIC: 2741 Miscellaneous publishing

(G-1560)
A J ASSOC MFG & ENGRG CO
Also Called: Aj Associates
5300 115th Ave N (33760-4830)
PHONE..................................727 258-0994
Josephine Zdzierak, *Ch of Bd*
Andrew Zdzierak, *President*
EMP: 13 **EST:** 1991
SQ FT: 2,800
SALES (est): 4.3MM **Privately Held**
WEB: www.ajflorida.com
SIC: 3728 Aircraft parts & equipment

(G-1561)
AAR MANUFACTURING INC
Also Called: AAR Composites
14201 Myerlake Cir (33760-2824)
PHONE..................................727 539-8585
Michael Pentedemos, *President*
Melissa Logan, *Business Mgr*
Dan Fitzpatrick, *VP Opers*
Troy Haas, *Store Mgr*
Devon Mason, *Store Mgr*
EMP: 53
SALES (corp-wide): 1.6B **Publicly Held**
WEB: www.aarcorp.com
SIC: 3728 Aircraft assemblies, subassemblies & parts
HQ: Aar Manufacturing, Inc.
1100 N Wood Dale Rd
Wood Dale IL 60191
630 227-2000

(G-1562)
ACCON MARINE INC
13665 Automobile Blvd (33762-3843)
PHONE..................................727 572-9202
Bernd Czipri, *President*
▲ **EMP:** 13 **EST:** 1980
SQ FT: 19,000
SALES (est): 2.1MM **Privately Held**
WEB: www.acconmarine.com
SIC: 3429 Marine hardware

(G-1563)
ACTRON ENTITIES INC
Also Called: Actron Engineering
13089 60th St N (33760-3915)
PHONE..................................727 531-5871
John Staszewski, *President*
Alana Dergham, *Exec VP*
Heather Eicher, *Buyer*
EMP: 60 **EST:** 2006
SQ FT: 28,500
SALES (est): 10.4MM **Privately Held**
WEB: www.actronengineering.com
SIC: 3444 Sheet metal specialties, not stamped

(G-1564)
ADAMAS INSTRUMENT CORPORATION
13247 38th St N Ste B (33762-4234)
P.O. Box 17558 (33762-0558)
PHONE..................................727 540-0033
Thomas C Smith, *Managing Dir*
EMP: 10 **EST:** 1988
SALES (est): 890.7K **Privately Held**
SIC: 3915 3841 3559 Jewel preparing: instruments, tools, watches & jewelry; diamond cutting & polishing; jewel cutting, drilling, polishing, recutting or setting; ophthalmic instruments & apparatus; semiconductor manufacturing machinery

(G-1565)
ADVANCED ENGINE TECH LLC
Also Called: A E T
3087 Cherry Ln (33759-4306)
PHONE..................................727 744-2935
Rck Pelfrey, *President*
Dale Pelfrey,
EMP: 5 **EST:** 2006
SALES (est): 391.2K **Privately Held**
WEB: www.adv-engine.com
SIC: 2992 3463 3519 Lubricating oils & greases; oils & greases, blending & compounding; engine or turbine forgings, nonferrous; parts & accessories, internal combustion engines

(G-1566)
ADVANCED METAL WORKS INC
1780 Calumet St (33765-1142)
PHONE..................................727 449-9353
Patrick Bogart, *President*
Terri Haire, *Admin Sec*
EMP: 10 **EST:** 1992
SQ FT: 8,000
SALES (est): 2MM **Privately Held**
WEB: www.exometalfab.com
SIC: 3699 Electron beam metal cutting, forming or welding machines

(G-1567)
ADVER-T SCREEN PRINTING INC
408 S Saturn Ave (33755-6550)
PHONE..................................727 443-5525
William Peluso, *President*
Scott Walker, *Vice Pres*
Brian Peluso, *Sales Mgr*
EMP: 15 **EST:** 1978
SQ FT: 4,600
SALES (est): 1.2MM **Privately Held**
WEB: www.advertscreenprinting.com
SIC: 2759 Screen printing

(G-1568)
AEROSONIC LLC
1212 N Hercules Ave (33765-1920)
PHONE..................................727 461-3000
Joe Grote, *President*
Alaine Ferreira, *Production*
Justin Banchy, *Engineer*
Lorenzo Bell, *Engineer*
Jeremiah Callaghan, *Engineer*
EMP: 150 **EST:** 2013
SALES (est): 49MM
SALES (corp-wide): 5.1B **Publicly Held**
WEB: www.aerosonic.com
SIC: 3728 Aircraft parts & equipment
HQ: Transdigm, Inc.
1301 E 9th St Ste 300
Cleveland OH 44114

(G-1569)
AGORA SALES INC
Also Called: Agora Leather Products
4215 E Bay Dr Apt 802 (33764-6970)
PHONE..................................727 490-0499
Tom Ayers, *Sales Mgr*
EMP: 13
SALES (corp-wide): 30.6MM **Privately Held**
WEB: www.agoraedge.com
SIC: 3161 Cases, carrying
PA: Agora Sales, Inc.
2101 28th St N
Saint Petersburg FL 33713
727 321-0707

(G-1570)
AIR AUTHORITIES OF TAMPA INC
4810 110th Ave N Ste 1a (33762-4935)
PHONE..................................727 525-1575
EMP: 5
SALES (est): 674.3K **Privately Held**
SIC: 3822 Mfg Environmental Controls

(G-1571)
AJ ASSOCIATES
11346 53rd St N (33760-4821)
PHONE..................................727 258-0994
Fax: 727 539-0904
EMP: 13
SALES (est): 2.7MM **Privately Held**
SIC: 3728 Mfg Aircraft Parts/Equipment

(G-1572)
AK U TEC MACHINE & TOOL INC
13191 Automobile Blvd (33762-4105)
PHONE..................................727 573-5211
Thomas P McDonald, *President*
Thomas P Mc Donald, *President*
EMP: 5 **EST:** 1989
SQ FT: 3,500
SALES (est): 488.5K **Privately Held**
SIC: 3599 Machine shop, jobbing & repair

(G-1573)
ALEX ROBERT SILVERSMITH INC
625 Pinellas St Unit C (33756-3351)
PHONE..................................727 442-7333
Robert Alex, *President*
EMP: 6 **EST:** 1980
SALES (est): 363.1K **Privately Held**
SIC: 3471 Plating of metals or formed products

(G-1574)
ALL SOUTHERN FABRICATORS INC
5010 126th Ave N (33760-4607)
P.O. Box 658, Pinellas Park (33780-0658)
PHONE..................................727 573-4846
John Stanton, *CEO*
Manuel Santana Jr, *President*
EMP: 43 **EST:** 1967
SQ FT: 40,000
SALES (est): 5.9MM **Privately Held**
WEB: www.allsouthern.com
SIC: 3469 3444 Household cooking & kitchen utensils, metal; sheet metalwork

(G-1575)
ALLBRIGHT ELECTROPOLISHING
5100 Ulmerton Rd Ste 7 (33760-4016)
PHONE..................................727 449-9353
Dustin Colina, *President*
Patrick Bogart, *Principal*
EMP: 5 **EST:** 1997
SQ FT: 4,000
SALES (est): 574.4K **Privately Held**
WEB: www.all-bright.com
SIC: 3471 Electroplating of metals or formed products

(G-1576)
ALLEN INDUSTRIES INC
11351 49th St N (33762-4808)
PHONE..................................727 573-3076
David Allen, *Owner*
Pete Barger, *Exec VP*
Jeff Morrow, *Plant Mgr*
Steve Byrd, *Project Mgr*
Christopher Cummings, *Project Mgr*
EMP: 60
SALES (corp-wide): 45MM **Privately Held**
WEB: www.allenindustries.com
SIC: 3993 Signs, not made in custom sign painting shops
PA: Allen Industries, Inc.
6434 Burnt Poplar Rd
Greensboro NC 27409
336 668-2791

(G-1577)
ALPHA INDUSTRIES INC
701 N Mlk Jr Ave (33755-4210)
PHONE..................................727 443-2673
Loleta Magers, *President*
EMP: 5 **EST:** 1971
SALES (est): 318.5K **Privately Held**
SIC: 3841 Medical instruments & equipment, blood & bone work

(G-1578)
ALTTEC CORPORATION
Also Called: Digital Control Company
4260 114th Ter N (33762-4905)
PHONE..................................727 547-1622
John D Cattel, *President*
EMP: 7 **EST:** 2005
SQ FT: 5,600
SALES (est): 1.2MM **Privately Held**
SIC: 3625 Relays & industrial controls

(G-1579)
AMERICAN DATA SUPPLY INC
Also Called: American Teledata
10870 49th St N (33762-5013)
PHONE..................................866 650-3282
Gil Hunter, *President*
Tim King, *General Mgr*
Monica Welch, *Principal*
Traci Mays, *Sales Staff*
Jim Drake, *Info Tech Mgr*
EMP: 10 **EST:** 1998
SALES (est): 2.2MM **Privately Held**
WEB: www.americanteledata.com
SIC: 3679 1731 1623 3357 Electronic circuits; electrical work; communication line & transmission tower construction; fiber optic cable (insulated); data communication services; fiber optics communications equipment

(G-1580)
AMERICAN INTERNATIONAL MTR SVC
5150 Ulmerton Rd Ste 5 (33760-4013)
PHONE..................................727 573-9501
Dennis D Keihl, *President*
EMP: 6 **EST:** 1979
SQ FT: 4,800
SALES (est): 475.6K **Privately Held**
SIC: 7694 Electric motor repair

(G-1581)
AMERICAN PLASTIC SUP & MFG INC (PA)
Also Called: Design Cncpts By Amrcn Plitics
11601 56th Ct N (33760-4805)
PHONE..................................727 573-0636
Bob Belzer, *President*
Robbin Belzer, *Corp Secy*
Leslie Fields, *Manager*
▲ **EMP:** 20 **EST:** 1985
SQ FT: 12,000
SALES (est): 4.3MM **Privately Held**
WEB: www.americanplasticsupply.com
SIC: 3081 3082 5162 Plastic film & sheet; rods, unsupported plastic; tubes, unsupported plastic; plastics sheets & rods; plastics basic shapes

(G-1582)
AMERICAN TECHNICAL MOLDING INC
Also Called: A T M
1700 Sunshine Dr (33765-1331)
PHONE..................................727 447-7377
Emilia G Opoulos, *CEO*
Emilia Giannakopoulos, *CEO*
Demetre Loulourgas, *President*
Penelope Loulourgas, *Vice Pres*
Dean Riordaner, *Controller*
◆ **EMP:** 91 **EST:** 1978
SQ FT: 140,000
SALES (est): 9.6MM **Privately Held**
WEB: www.atmmolding.com
SIC: 3089 Injection molding of plastics

(G-1583)
AMERICAN TOOL & MOLD INC
Also Called: American Technical Molding
1700 Sunshine Dr (33765-1331)
PHONE..................................727 447-7377
Emilia Loulourgas-Giannakopoul, *CEO*
Demetre Loulourgas, *President*
Penelope Loulourgas, *Vice Pres*
Mark Tardif, *Plant Mgr*
Richard McConnaughey, *Project Mgr*
◆ **EMP:** 180 **EST:** 1978
SQ FT: 150,000
SALES (est): 29.2MM **Privately Held**
WEB: www.a-t-m.com
SIC: 3089 Injection molding of plastics

(G-1584)
AMTECO MACHINE & MANUFACTURING
4652 107th Cir N (33762-5005)
PHONE..................................727 573-0993
Dennis Pavluk, *President*
EMP: 12 **EST:** 1978
SQ FT: 10,000
SALES (est): 156.1K **Privately Held**
WEB: www.rcamachine.com
SIC: 3599 Machine shop, jobbing & repair

(G-1585)
ANZIO IRONWORKS CORP
14605 49th St N Ste 8 (33762-2810)
PHONE..................................727 895-2019
Mike Remo, *President*
David Lydel, *Principal*
EMP: 5
SALES (est): 440K **Privately Held**
WEB: www.anzioironworks.com
SIC: 3949 Sporting & athletic goods

(G-1586)
APYX MEDICAL CORPORATION (PA)
5115 Ulmerton Rd (33760-4004)
PHONE..................................727 384-2323
Charles D Goodwin, *CEO*
Andrew Makrides, *Ch of Bd*
John Andres, *Vice Ch Bd*
Todd Hornsby, *Exec VP*

Moshe Citronowicz, *Senior VP*
EMP: 210 **EST:** 1982
SQ FT: 60,000
SALES: 27.7MM **Publicly Held**
WEB: www.apyxmedical.com
SIC: 3841 Surgical & medical instruments

(G-1587)
ARCHITECTURAL GRAPHICS INC
5500 Rio Vista Dr (33760-3140)
PHONE..................................757 427-1900
Jason Chalaire, *Project Mgr*
EMP: 16
SALES (corp-wide): 199.3MM **Privately Held**
WEB: www.agi.net
SIC: 3993 Signs, not made in custom sign painting shops
PA: Architectural Graphics, Inc.
2655 International Pkwy
Virginia Beach VA 23452
800 877-7868

(G-1588)
ARDEN PHOTONICS LLC
4500 140th Ave N Ste 101 (33762-3848)
PHONE..................................727 478-2651
David Robinson, *President*
Roger Frampton, *Manager*
Alistair Robinson, *Manager*
EMP: 10
SQ FT: 300
SALES (est): 569.2K **Privately Held**
WEB: www.ardenphotonics.com
SIC: 3661 Fiber optics communications equipment

(G-1589)
ARROWHEAD GLOBAL LLC
22033 Us Highway 19 N (33765-2362)
PHONE..................................727 497-7340
Chad Hill, *General Mgr*
Anthony Terranova, *Business Mgr*
Tiffani Hunley, *Manager*
Tara Potter, *Manager*
Tony Frasca, *Officer*
EMP: 7 **EST:** 2013
SQ FT: 1,900
SALES (est): 2.2MM **Privately Held**
WEB: www.arrowheadglobal.com
SIC: 3728 5063 7373 3678 Research & dev by manuf., aircraft parts & auxiliary equip; lugs & connectors, electrical; computer integrated systems design; electronic connectors; fasteners; bolts, nuts, rivets & washers

(G-1590)
ARTISTIC PAVERS
13195 49th St N (33762-4017)
PHONE..................................727 572-1998
Jeffrey Schmitt, *Principal*
EMP: 7 **EST:** 2010
SALES (est): 158.1K **Privately Held**
SIC: 3531 Pavers

(G-1591)
ARTISTIC PAVERS LLC
12700 Automobile Blvd (33762-4719)
PHONE..................................727 573-0918
Robert B Welch,
Sally Welch,
EMP: 15 **EST:** 2017
SALES (est): 3.4MM **Privately Held**
WEB: www.artistic-pavers.com
SIC: 3531 Pavers

(G-1592)
ASAP SIGNS & GRAPHICS OF FLA
509 D St (33756-3337)
PHONE..................................727 443-4878
EMP: 5
SALES: 450K **Privately Held**
SIC: 3993 Signs And Advertising Specialties

(G-1593)
ASCO POWER TECHNOLOGIES LP
14550 58th St N (33760-2805)
PHONE..................................727 450-2730
Andy Malcolm, *Branch Mgr*
Dana Papalardo, *Manager*
EMP: 8
SALES (corp-wide): 177.9K **Privately Held**
WEB: www.ascopower.com
SIC: 3699 Electrical equipment & supplies
HQ: Asco Power Technologies, L.P.
160 Park Ave
Florham Park NJ 07932

(G-1594)
AVT TECHNOLOGY SOLUTIONS LLC
5350 Tech Data Dr (33760-3122)
PHONE..................................727 539-7429
Robert M Dutkowsky, *CEO*
Kimberly Freeman, *Opers Staff*
Cyndi Hash, *Manager*
EMP: 1 **EST:** 2016
SALES (est): 3.9MM
SALES (corp-wide): 37B **Privately Held**
WEB: www.techdata.com
SIC: 7372 Prepackaged software
HQ: Tech Data Corporation
5350 Tech Data Dr
Clearwater FL 33760
727 539-7429

(G-1595)
AXIOM SERVICES INC
Also Called: Axiom International
1805 Drew St (33765-2918)
PHONE..................................727 442-7774
David Greenbaum, *CEO*
Ed Clark, *President*
Catherine Rossi, *Partner*
Hetha Chelin, *Exec VP*
Brendan Haggerty, *Exec VP*
EMP: 35 **EST:** 1984
SQ FT: 10,000
SALES (est): 5.1MM **Privately Held**
WEB: www.axiomint.com
SIC: 7372 7371 Prepackaged software; computer software development

(G-1596)
AYANNA PLASTICS & ENGRG INC
4701 110th Ave N (33762-4912)
PHONE..................................727 561-4329
Daniel R Redmond Jr, *President*
Tammy E Redmond, *Vice Pres*
▲ **EMP:** 32 **EST:** 2001
SQ FT: 12,000
SALES (est): 5.9MM **Privately Held**
WEB: www.ayannaplastics.com
SIC: 3089 Injection molding of plastics

(G-1597)
B & R SALES CORPORATION
11551 43rd St N (33762-4925)
PHONE..................................727 571-2231
William Evans, *President*
EMP: 6 **EST:** 2001
SQ FT: 10,000
SALES (est): 739K **Privately Held**
WEB: www.clearwatermachining.com
SIC: 3089 Injection molding of plastics

(G-1598)
BACKTOCAD TECHNOLOGIES LLC
601 Cleveland St Ste 380 (33755-4178)
PHONE..................................727 303-0383
Andreas Kazmierczak, *Mng Member*
EMP: 6 **EST:** 2009
SALES (est): 1.4MM
SALES (corp-wide): 826.1K **Privately Held**
WEB: www.solutions.backtocad.com
SIC: 7372 Prepackaged software
PA: Kazmierczak Software Gmbh
Raiffeisenstr. 30
Filderstadt 70794
711 518-6692

(G-1599)
BASEWEST INC
4240 116th Ter N (33762-4971)
PHONE..................................727 573-2700
Gary Leegate, *President*
Richard Barnes, *Vice Pres*
David Stanton, *VP Sales*
Nicole Marchini, *Cust Mgr*
Stephanie Coleman, *Manager*
EMP: 44 **EST:** 1991
SQ FT: 12,000
SALES (est): 6.9MM **Privately Held**
WEB: www.basewest.com
SIC: 3647 Vehicular lighting equipment; aircraft lighting fixtures

(G-1600)
BASS AUTO INDUSTRIES LLC
2084 Range Rd (33765-2123)
PHONE..................................727 446-4051
EMP: 7 **EST:** 2018
SALES (est): 572K **Privately Held**
SIC: 3999 Manufacturing industries

(G-1601)
BATTERY POWER SOLUTIONS INC
936 Cleveland St Ste A (33755-4500)
PHONE..................................727 446-8400
Charles Van Breemen, *President*
EMP: 5 **EST:** 2005
SALES (est): 350.8K **Privately Held**
SIC: 3694 Engine electrical equipment

(G-1602)
BAUSCH LOMB SURGICAL INC ✪
21 N Park Place Blvd (33759-3917)
PHONE..................................727 724-6600
Jason Smith, *Vice Pres*
Tracy Gulick, *Engineer*
Alex Lee, *Engineer*
Joshua Allen, *Manager*
Chafik Djellali, *Manager*
EMP: 11 **EST:** 2020
SALES (est): 1.9MM **Privately Held**
WEB: www.bausch.com
SIC: 3851 Ophthalmic goods

(G-1603)
BAYCARE HOME CARE INC
Also Called: Bay Area Prosthetics
1237 S Myrtle Ave (33756-3469)
PHONE..................................727 461-5878
EMP: 10
SALES (corp-wide): 463.9MM **Privately Held**
SIC: 3842 Mfg Surgical Appliances/Supplies
HQ: Baycare Home Care, Inc.
8452 118th Ave
Largo FL 33773

(G-1604)
BCE OF TAMPA BAY INC
14000 63rd Way N (33760-3618)
PHONE..................................727 535-7768
EMP: 6 **EST:** 2019
SALES (est): 161K **Privately Held**
WEB: www.ourprintingdept.com
SIC: 2732 Book printing

(G-1605)
BEACHCHIP TECHNOLOGIES LLC
2655 Ulmerton Rd (33762-3337)
PHONE..................................727 643-8106
Peter Weyant, *Manager*
EMP: 6
SQ FT: 400
SALES (est): 2.1MM **Privately Held**
WEB: www.beachchip.com
SIC: 3559 5045 7379 Electronic component making machinery; computer software;

(G-1606)
BELQUETTE INC
3634 131st Ave N (33762-4262)
PHONE..................................727 329-9483
Brett Weibel, *CEO*
Mark Mombourquette, *Principal*
EMP: 6 **EST:** 2007
SALES (est): 806.6K **Privately Held**
WEB: www.coldesi.com
SIC: 3826 8711 Laser scientific & engineering instruments; acoustical engineering

(G-1607)
BIC CORPORATION
Also Called: Bic Graphic USA
14421 Myerlake Cir (33760-2840)
P.O. Box 23088, Tampa (33623-2088)
PHONE..................................727 536-7895
Joe Cade, *Vice Pres*
Aaron Vollrath, *Vice Pres*
Gerard Krief, *VP Opers*
Albert Saydeh, *Engineer*
Carolynn Miller, *Accountant*
EMP: 800
SALES (corp-wide): 742.7MM **Privately Held**
WEB: www.us.bic.com
SIC: 3951 3952 Pens & mechanical pencils; lead pencils & art goods
HQ: Bic Corporation
1 Bic Way Ste 1 # 1
Shelton CT 06484
203 783-2000

(G-1608)
BIO CEPS INC
15251 Roosevelt Blvd # 204 (33760-3560)
PHONE..................................727 669-7544
EMP: 30
SALES (est): 1.7MM **Privately Held**
SIC: 3841 Mfg Surgical/Medical Instruments

(G-1609)
BL BIO LAB LLC
2021 Sunnydale Blvd # 14 (33765-1202)
PHONE..................................727 900-2707
Marian Kapusta,
EMP: 10 **EST:** 2018
SALES (est): 1.8MM **Privately Held**
WEB: www.blbiolab.com
SIC: 2023 Dietary supplements, dairy & non-dairy based

(G-1610)
BODEN CO INC
Also Called: Adjust-A-Brush
10445 49th St N Ste B (33762-5036)
PHONE..................................727 571-1234
Duane H Newville, *President*
Eric Newville, *Vice Pres*
Marillyn Newville, *CFO*
Kurt Newville, *Executive*
▲ **EMP:** 25 **EST:** 1960
SQ FT: 27,000
SALES (est): 1.3MM **Privately Held**
WEB: www.greenblade.org
SIC: 3991 Brushes, household or industrial

(G-1611)
BOYD INDUSTRIES INC
12900 44th St N (33762-4729)
PHONE..................................727 561-9292
Adrian E Latrace, *President*
Brian Vitoritt, *Project Mgr*
Mark Dietrich, *Opers Mgr*
Aferdit Vinca, *Buyer*
Gloria Herrera, *Engineer*
◆ **EMP:** 60 **EST:** 1957
SQ FT: 63,000
SALES (est): 5.5MM **Privately Held**
WEB: www.boydindustries.com
SIC: 3843 Dental chairs

(G-1612)
BREN TUCK INC
12929 44th St N (33762-4731)
PHONE..................................727 561-7697
Mark Tucker, *President*
▲ **EMP:** 13 **EST:** 2005
SALES (est): 2.4MM **Privately Held**
SIC: 3643 Lightning protection equipment

(G-1613)
BRITO BRICK & PAVERS CORP
6262 142nd Ave N (33760-2757)
PHONE..................................727 214-8760
Robison De Oliveira, *Principal*
EMP: 6 **EST:** 2012
SALES (est): 120.2K **Privately Held**
SIC: 3531 Pavers

(G-1614)
BRUCE R ELY ENTERPRISE INC
Also Called: Designers Plastics
12880 Auto Blvd Ste G (33762)
PHONE..................................727 573-1643
Bruce Ely, *President*
Penny Carrigan, *Corp Secy*
EMP: 18 **EST:** 1975
SQ FT: 32,000

SALES (est): 1.9MM **Privately Held**
SIC: 3089 3993 2542 Plastic hardware & building products; signs & advertising specialties; partitions & fixtures, except wood

(G-1615)
BRYAN NELCO INC
15251 Roosevelt Blvd # 202 (33760-3560)
PHONE..................................727 533-8282
Camille Gianetti, *Principal*
▲ **EMP:** 6 **EST:** 2001
SALES (est): 130.1K **Privately Held**
SIC: 3599 5085 Industrial machinery; industrial supplies

(G-1616)
BUCKLEY PALLETS
2409 Laurelwood Dr (33763-1520)
PHONE..................................727 415-4497
Bonnie Elliott, *Principal*
EMP: 8 **EST:** 2011
SALES (est): 600.1K **Privately Held**
WEB: www.buckleypallets.com
SIC: 2448 Pallets, wood

(G-1617)
BUCKLEY PALLETS LLC
14550 62nd St N 2 (33760-2355)
PHONE..................................727 415-4497
Bonnie Buckley,
EMP: 15 **EST:** 2012
SALES (est): 1.7MM **Privately Held**
WEB: www.buckleypallets.com
SIC: 2448 Wood pallets & skids

(G-1618)
BUSINESS CARD EX TAMPA BAY INC
14000 63rd Way N (33760-3618)
PHONE..................................727 535-7768
Eugene Steslicki, *President*
Kathleen Steslicki, *Vice Pres*
Mark Martinaj, *Manager*
Richard Perez, *Info Tech Mgr*
EMP: 80 **EST:** 1986
SQ FT: 10,000
SALES (est): 14.6MM **Privately Held**
SIC: 2754 2761 2759 Visiting cards: gravure printing; manifold business forms; commercial printing

(G-1619)
C & E INNOVATIVE MGT LLC
Also Called: Fit Like Foots
2454 N Mcmullen Booth Rd (33759-1353)
PHONE..................................727 408-5146
Kyle Bates, *General Mgr*
EMP: 8 **EST:** 2013
SALES (est): 478.3K **Privately Held**
SIC: 2099 8741 Food preparations; management services

(G-1620)
CADCAM SOFTWARE CO
28200 Us Highway 19 N E (33761-2625)
PHONE..................................727 450-6440
Larry Pendelton, *CEO*
EMP: 7 **EST:** 2015
SALES (est): 61.4K **Privately Held**
WEB: www.bobcad.com
SIC: 7372 Prepackaged software

(G-1621)
CAMPBELL MANUFACTURING INC
2151 Logan St (33765-1312)
PHONE..................................727 443-4508
EMP: 6 **EST:** 2017
SALES (est): 125.7K **Privately Held**
WEB: www.bakerwatersystems.com
SIC: 3999 Manufacturing industries

(G-1622)
CELTIC AIRSPARES LLC
28870 Us Highway 19 N # 328 (33761-2596)
PHONE..................................727 431-0482
Ciaran Moloney, *Sales Staff*
Annesley R Martin Mr, *Mng Member*
Ciaran M Moloney,
EMP: 5 **EST:** 2010
SALES (est): 347.4K **Privately Held**
WEB: www.celticairspares.com
SIC: 3721 Aircraft

(G-1623)
CF MOTION INC
4625 E Bay Dr Ste 306 (33764-6868)
PHONE..................................727 458-7092
Israel Menahem, *President*
Sofia Menahem, *Vice Pres*
Mike Menahem, *Admin Sec*
EMP: 8 **EST:** 1998
SALES (est): 1.5MM **Privately Held**
WEB: www.cfmotions.com
SIC: 3663 Antennas, transmitting & communications

(G-1624)
CHARIAN MACHINE & MFG INC
4652 107th Cir N (33762-5005)
PHONE..................................727 561-0150
William W Bronson, *President*
Richard Albritton, *Vice Pres*
Bonnie Bronson, *Treasurer*
EMP: 7 **EST:** 1985
SQ FT: 5,000
SALES (est): 1.2MM **Privately Held**
WEB: www.rcamachine.com
SIC: 3599 Machine shop, jobbing & repair

(G-1625)
CHASSIS KING LLC
1016 Pnc De Leon Blvd (33756-1073)
PHONE..................................727 585-1500
Donald Pratt, *President*
◆ **EMP:** 8 **EST:** 1997
SQ FT: 30,000
SALES (est): 1MM **Privately Held**
WEB: www.chassisking.com
SIC: 3715 Truck trailer chassis

(G-1626)
CJ MULANIX CO INC
2803 Gulf To Bay Blvd (33759-4014)
PHONE..................................716 423-8010
Charles Mulanix, *President*
EMP: 9 **EST:** 2015
SALES (est): 114.7K **Privately Held**
WEB: www.cjmulanixco.com
SIC: 3443 Fabricated plate work (boiler shop)

(G-1627)
CLEARWATER ENGINEERING INC
14605 49th St N Ste 19 (33762-2837)
PHONE..................................727 573-2210
Dave Pratt, *President*
▲ **EMP:** 7 **EST:** 1989
SQ FT: 8,320
SALES (est): 675.6K **Privately Held**
WEB: www.clearwatereng.com
SIC: 3826 3823 1623 Environmental testing equipment; industrial instrmnts msrmnt display/control process variable; water, sewer & utility lines

(G-1628)
CLEARWATER MACHINING INC
Also Called: MACHINE SHOP / DBA B&R SALES
11551 43rd St N (33762-4925)
PHONE..................................727 512-0337
Glenn Erickson, *President*
EMP: 6 **EST:** 2019
SALES (est): 200K **Privately Held**
WEB: www.clearwatermachining.com
SIC: 3599 Machine shop, jobbing & repair

(G-1629)
CMZ INDUSTRIES LLC
27232 Us Highway 19 N (33761-2939)
PHONE..................................727 726-1443
Michael A Bansavage, *Branch Mgr*
EMP: 6
SALES (corp-wide): 92.5K **Privately Held**
SIC: 3999 Barber & beauty shop equipment
PA: Cmz Industries Llc
9273 Rustic Pines Blvd E
Seminole FL

(G-1630)
CNC WORKS SERVICE INC
13584 49th St N Ste 5 (33762-3737)
PHONE..................................813 777-8642
Luis Rivera, *Principal*
Donn B Busby, *Purch Mgr*
EMP: 11 **EST:** 2009
SALES (est): 517.5K **Privately Held**
SIC: 3469 Machine parts, stamped or pressed metal

(G-1631)
COEUR DE LION INC
Also Called: Allied Business Service
1610 N Myrtle Ave (33755-2549)
P.O. Box 1564, Largo (33779-1564)
PHONE..................................727 442-4808
Stanley R Albro, *President*
EMP: 22 **EST:** 1986
SQ FT: 8,000
SALES (est): 1.3MM **Privately Held**
SIC: 2731 Book publishing

(G-1632)
COLE ENTERPRISES INC
Also Called: Florida Research
436 E Shore Dr (33767-2027)
P.O. Box 3129, Clearwater Beach (33767-8129)
PHONE..................................727 441-4101
Robert Cole, *President*
Sandra Cole, *Vice Pres*
EMP: 5 **EST:** 1972
SQ FT: 3,000
SALES (est): 487.3K **Privately Held**
WEB: www.flresearch.com
SIC: 2721 7389 8732 Periodicals: publishing & printing; press clipping service; commercial nonphysical research

(G-1633)
COLORFAST PRINTING & GRAPHICS
Also Called: Colorfast Coml Prtg Grphics Sv
14114 63rd Way N (33760-3616)
PHONE..................................727 531-9506
Milne Sandra J, *President*
Terry Mohamed, *Owner*
Alwin Chan, *Opers Mgr*
EMP: 5 **EST:** 1991
SALES (est): 500K **Privately Held**
WEB: www.colorfastprint.com
SIC: 2752 Commercial printing, offset

(G-1634)
COMMUNITY PHARMACY SVCS LLC
19387 Us Highway 19 N (33764-3102)
PHONE..................................727 431-8261
Linda L Kaczynski, *Director*
EMP: 7 **EST:** 2012
SALES (est): 289K **Privately Held**
WEB: www.chpharmacy.org
SIC: 2834 Pharmaceutical preparations

(G-1635)
CONOPCO INC
5400 118th Ave N (33760-4315)
PHONE..................................727 573-1591
Ken Fregau, *Branch Mgr*
EMP: 20
SALES (corp-wide): 59.9B **Privately Held**
WEB: www.autoclor.com
SIC: 2024 Ice cream, packaged: molded, on sticks, etc.
HQ: Conopco, Inc.
700 Sylvan Ave
Englewood Cliffs NJ 07632
201 894-7760

(G-1636)
CONSOLIDATED POLYMER TECH
4451 110th Ave N (33762-4944)
PHONE..................................727 531-4191
Larry Carpenter, *President*
Rob Klingle, *Corp Secy*
◆ **EMP:** 20 **EST:** 1983
SQ FT: 12,000
SALES (est): 505.2K **Privately Held**
WEB: www.c-flex-cpt.com
SIC: 3082 3842 Tubes, unsupported plastic; surgical appliances & supplies

(G-1637)
CORERX INC
5733 Myerlake Cir (33760-2952)
PHONE..................................727 259-6950
Mohammed S Shekhani, *Vice Pres*
La-Tonya Rouse, *CFO*
EMP: 10 **Privately Held**
WEB: www.corerxpharma.com
SIC: 2834 Pharmaceutical preparations
PA: Corerx, Inc.
14205 Myerlake Cir
Clearwater FL 33760

(G-1638)
CORERX INC (PA)
14205 Myerlake Cir (33760-2824)
PHONE..................................727 259-6950
Todd R Daviau, *CEO*
Mark Licarde, *COO*
Mark J Licarde, *Vice Pres*
Saurabh S Trivedi, *Vice Pres*
James Clark, *Project Mgr*
▲ **EMP:** 198 **EST:** 2006
SQ FT: 9,700
SALES (est): 66.9MM **Privately Held**
WEB: www.corerxpharma.com
SIC: 2834 Pharmaceutical preparations

(G-1639)
CORERX PHARMACEUTICALS INC
14205 Myerlake Cir (33760-2824)
PHONE..................................727 259-6950
Todd Daviau, *CEO*
James Davis, *Vice Pres*
Mark Licarde, *Vice Pres*
Brian McMillan, *Vice Pres*
Bob Berg, *CFO*
EMP: 23 **EST:** 2012
SQ FT: 9,700
SALES (est): 3.9MM **Privately Held**
WEB: www.corerxpharma.com
SIC: 2834 Tablets, pharmaceutical; veterinary pharmaceutical preparations; pills, pharmaceutical

(G-1640)
CORNERSTONE SOFTWARE INC
1356 Hibiscus St (33755-3405)
PHONE..................................727 443-5557
John Welch, *Principal*
Teanna Spence, *Sales Staff*
EMP: 6 **EST:** 2001
SALES (est): 158.2K **Privately Held**
WEB: www.cston.com
SIC: 7372 Prepackaged software

(G-1641)
CREATING TECH SOLUTIONS LLC (PA)
5250 140th Ave N (33760-3728)
P.O. Box 17840 (33762-0840)
PHONE..................................727 914-3001
Milagros Hofius, *CEO*
Mark Hofius, *President*
John McCusker, *COO*
Melanie Giles, *Vice Pres*
EMP: 35 **EST:** 2012
SALES (est): 34.9MM **Privately Held**
WEB: www.crtes.com
SIC: 3692 3629 3825 3691 Primary batteries, dry & wet; battery chargers, rectifying or nonrotating; power conversion units, a.c. to d.c.: static-electric; instrument relays, all types; batteries, rechargeable

(G-1642)
CREATING TECH SOLUTIONS LLC
Also Called: Technology Research
5250 140th Ave N (33760-3728)
P.O. Box 17840 (33762-0840)
PHONE..................................727 914-3001
David Grafe, *Finance*
Mark Steele, *VP Sales*
James Milstead, *Sales Staff*
Ryan Etwaru, *Manager*
Milagros Hofius,
EMP: 36
SALES (corp-wide): 34.9MM **Privately Held**
WEB: www.creatingtechnologysolutions.com
SIC: 3825 3629 Instrument relays, all types; power conversion units, a.c. to d.c.: static-electric
PA: Creating Technology Solutions, Llc
5250 140th Ave N
Clearwater FL 33760
727 914-3001

GEOGRAPHIC

(G-1643)
CREATING TECH SOLUTIONS LLC
Also Called: Patco Electronics
5250 140th Ave N (33760-3728)
P.O. Box 17840 (33762-0840)
PHONE..................................727 914-3001
Milagros Hofius,
EMP: 36
SALES (corp-wide): 34.9MM **Privately Held**
WEB: www.creatingtechnologysolutions.com
SIC: 3692 3691 Primary batteries, dry & wet; storage batteries; batteries, rechargeable
PA: Creating Technology Solutions, Llc
5250 140th Ave N
Clearwater FL 33760
727 914-3001

(G-1644)
CUSTOM SIGN & AWNING
4502 107th Cir N Ste D (33762-5038)
PHONE..................................727 210-0941
Pedro Corodova, *Principal*
EMP: 10 **EST:** 2006
SALES (est): 427.2K **Privately Held**
SIC: 3993 Signs & advertising specialties

(G-1645)
CUTTING EDGE SGNS GRPHICS OF P
12795 49th St N (33762-4604)
PHONE..................................727 546-3700
Jeffery Newburg, *President*
EMP: 5 **EST:** 1996
SALES (est): 637.6K **Privately Held**
WEB: www.thecuttingedgesigns.com
SIC: 3993 2741 7312 Signs, not made in custom sign painting shops; letters for signs, metal; posters: publishing & printing; poster advertising, outdoor

(G-1646)
CYA POWDER COATING LLC
12099 44th St N (33762-5108)
PHONE..................................727 299-9832
Katrina M Lingenfelter, *Mng Member*
EMP: 5 **EST:** 2007
SQ FT: 20,000
SALES (est): 541.9K **Privately Held**
WEB: www.cyapowder.com
SIC: 3479 3471 1799 Coating of metals & formed products; coating, rust preventive; painting of metal products; finishing, metals or formed products; exterior cleaning, including sandblasting

(G-1647)
D & S PALLETS INC
Also Called: D & S Hauling
12195 46th St N (33762-4434)
P.O. Box 18019 (33762-1019)
PHONE..................................727 540-0061
EMP: 52
SALES (est): 2MM **Privately Held**
SIC: 2448 4953 1389 0782 Mfg Wood Pallets/Skids Refuse Systems Oil/Gas Field Services Lawn/Garden Services

(G-1648)
D-REP PLASTICS INC
11345 53rd St N (33760-4822)
PHONE..................................407 240-4154
Daniel Chalich, *President*
EMP: 6 **EST:** 2012
SALES (est): 160.1K **Privately Held**
SIC: 3089 Injection molding of plastics

(G-1649)
DAVIS CONCRETE INC (PA)
1670 Sunshine Dr (33765-1316)
PHONE..................................727 733-3141
EMP: 30 **EST:** 1947
SQ FT: 6,400
SALES (est): 6MM **Privately Held**
WEB: www.davisconcreteinc.com
SIC: 3273 Ready-mixed concrete

(G-1650)
DAVIT MASTER CORP
5560 Ulmerton Rd (33760-4011)
PHONE..................................727 573-4414
Cheryl De Abreau, *Principal*
Chris Deabreau, *Purchasing*
Marilyn Thomas, *Treasurer*
Marty McDonald, *Sales Staff*
▼ **EMP:** 18
SQ FT: 8,000
SALES (est): 4.8MM **Privately Held**
WEB: www.davitmaster.com
SIC: 3536 5551 Davits; marine supplies

(G-1651)
DHS ENTERPRISES INC
5150 Ulmerton Rd Ste 14 (33760-4014)
PHONE..................................727 572-9470
Andrew Kossowski, *President*
EMP: 8 **EST:** 1990
SQ FT: 8,000
SALES (est): 997.4K **Privately Held**
SIC: 3471 Anodizing (plating) of metals or formed products
PA: Veterans Metal Llc
5150 Ulmerton Rd Ste 14
Clearwater FL 33760
727 572-9470

(G-1652)
DILUTION SOLUTIONS INC
2090 Sunnydale Blvd (33765-1201)
PHONE..................................800 451-6628
Pamela M Temko, *President*
Jason Maddox, *Sales Mgr*
EMP: 9 **EST:** 2013
SALES (est): 702.9K **Privately Held**
WEB: www.dilutionsolutions.com
SIC: 3559 Chemical machinery & equipment

(G-1653)
DJ/PJ INC
Also Called: J.W. Appley and Son
13215 38th St N (33762-4229)
PHONE..................................813 907-6359
Doug Jennings, *President*
EMP: 23 **EST:** 2003
SQ FT: 17,000
SALES (est): 4.7MM **Privately Held**
WEB: www.djpjlive.com
SIC: 3499 3599 Machine bases, metal; machine & other job shop work; machine shop, jobbing & repair

(G-1654)
DOT GREEN ENERGY INC
100 Hampton Rd Lot 84 (33759-3955)
PHONE..................................717 505-8686
Herb Andres, *Exec VP*
Kenneth Brody, *Manager*
Ken Brody, *Director*
EMP: 8 **EST:** 2008
SALES (est): 99.7K **Privately Held**
SIC: 2911 8711 Gasoline; energy conservation engineering

(G-1655)
DOUGLAS MACHINES CORP
Also Called: Cyclone Belt Washer
4500 110th Ave N (33762-4907)
PHONE..................................727 461-3477
Paul Claro, *CEO*
David A Ward, *President*
Kevin J Lemen, *Vice Pres*
William J Lever, *Vice Pres*
Susan A Mader, *Vice Pres*
◆ **EMP:** 47 **EST:** 2007
SQ FT: 25,000
SALES (est): 15.8MM
SALES (corp-wide): 99.8MM **Privately Held**
WEB: www.dougmac.com
SIC: 3589 Commercial cleaning equipment
PA: Koda Enterprises Group, Llc
51 Sawyer Rd Ste 420
Waltham MA 02453
781 891-0467

(G-1656)
DOWELS PINS & SHAFTS INC
1975 Calumet St (33765-1108)
P.O. Box 1135, Dunedin (34697-1135)
PHONE..................................727 461-1255
Thomas R Mickelson, *President*
Ellen F Mickelson, *Vice Pres*
Bridget Hammond, *Treasurer*
EMP: 21 **EST:** 1977
SQ FT: 13,500
SALES (est): 1MM **Privately Held**
WEB: www.dowelspinsshafts.com
SIC: 3452 3568 Dowel pins, metal; power transmission equipment

(G-1657)
DOWLING GRAPHICS INC
12920 Automobile Blvd (33762-4723)
PHONE..................................727 573-5997
Denise Dowling, *President*
Dave Kaufman, *Sales Staff*
Drew Adams, *Marketing Staff*
EMP: 26 **EST:** 1990
SQ FT: 21,000
SALES (est): 1.5MM **Privately Held**
WEB: www.dowlinggraphicstoo.com
SIC: 2262 2752 7389 Screen printing: manmade fiber & silk broadwoven fabrics; transfers, decalcomania or dry: lithographed; embroidering of advertising on shirts, etc.

(G-1658)
DPS POWDER COATING
4980 110th Ave N (33760-4813)
PHONE..................................727 573-2797
Art Dorsett, *Owner*
EMP: 8 **EST:** 2005
SALES (est): 600K **Privately Held**
SIC: 3479 Coating of metals & formed products

(G-1659)
DSG CLEARWATER LABORATORY
14333 58th St N (33760-2817)
PHONE..................................727 530-9444
Rick Vanmeter, *General Mgr*
James Haeger, *Controller*
EMP: 11 **EST:** 2014
SALES (est): 289.2K **Privately Held**
WEB: www.dentalservices.net
SIC: 3843 8072 Dental laboratory equipment; artificial teeth production

(G-1660)
DUNRITE METAL FABRICATORS INC
12099 44th St N (33762-5108)
PHONE..................................727 299-9242
David M Lingenfelter, *President*
David Lingenfelter, *President*
EMP: 15 **EST:** 1989
SQ FT: 20,000
SALES (est): 2MM **Privately Held**
WEB: www.dunritemetal.com
SIC: 3599 Machine shop, jobbing & repair

(G-1661)
DUPONT PUBLISHING INC (PA)
Also Called: Dupont Registry
4707 140th Ave N Ste 302 (33762-3840)
PHONE..................................727 573-9339
Steve Chapman, *CEO*
Thomas L Dupont, *Ch of Bd*
Rosemary Nye, *Partner*
David Warner, *Chief*
Audrey Crowder, *Production*
EMP: 80 **EST:** 1984
SALES (est): 15.7MM **Privately Held**
WEB: www.dupontregistry.com
SIC: 2721 Magazines: publishing only, not printed on site

(G-1662)
DURBAL INC
14115 63rd Way N Ste A (33760-3623)
PHONE..................................727 531-3040
Markus Voss, *President*
Monika Voss, *Vice Pres*
Rudolf Swoboda, *Admin Sec*
EMP: 8 **EST:** 1981
SALES (est): 725K **Privately Held**
WEB: www.durbal.com
SIC: 3312 Rods, iron & steel: made in steel mills

(G-1663)
ED PUBLICATIONS INC
2431 Estancia Blvd Bldg B (33761-2608)
PHONE..................................727 726-3592
Don Waitt, *President*
David Fairchild, *Vice Pres*
Teresa Tearno, *Manager*
Caroline Ashe, *Information Mgr*
Kevin Pennington, *Art Dir*
EMP: 10 **EST:** 1990
SQ FT: 2,350
SALES (est): 2MM **Publicly Held**
WEB: www.edpublications.com
SIC: 2741 7389 Directories: publishing only, not printed on site; advertising, promotional & trade show services
PA: Rci Hospitality Holdings, Inc.
10737 Cutten Rd
Houston TX 77066

(G-1664)
EIDSCHUN ENGINEERING INC
2899 Heron Pl (33762-3358)
PHONE..................................727 647-2300
Charles Eidschun, *President*
EMP: 30 **EST:** 1981
SQ FT: 12,500
SALES (est): 2MM **Privately Held**
WEB: www.cycloneproducts.com
SIC: 3559 5084 Electroplating machinery & equipment; industrial machinery & equipment

(G-1665)
ELECTRALED INC
10990 49th St N (33762-5015)
PHONE..................................727 561-7610
Priscilla G Thomas, *President*
Willard Wade Thomas, *Vice Pres*
Vladimir Volochine, *CTO*
▲ **EMP:** 18 **EST:** 2002
SQ FT: 27,000
SALES (est): 4.9MM **Privately Held**
WEB: www.electraled.com
SIC: 3646 Commercial indusl & institutional electric lighting fixtures

(G-1666)
ELECTRO TECHNIK INDUSTRIES INC (PA)
Also Called: RES-Net Microwave
5410 115th Ave N (33760-4841)
P.O. Box 18802 (33762-1802)
PHONE..................................727 530-9555
Darry K Mayo, *President*
Darryl K Mayo, *President*
Geraldine R Mayo, *Corp Secy*
Darryl Mayo, *Vice Pres*
Mark Ewin, *Engineer*
◆ **EMP:** 77 **EST:** 1982
SQ FT: 5,000
SALES (est): 52.6MM **Privately Held**
WEB: www.electrotechnik.com
SIC: 3677 3679 3676 3663 Coil windings, electronic; harness assemblies for electronic use: wire or cable; electronic resistors; radio & TV communications equipment; nonferrous wiredrawing & insulating

(G-1667)
ELECTRO-COMP SERVICES INC
11437 43rd St N (33762-4924)
PHONE..................................727 532-4262
▲ **EMP:** 21
SQ FT: 15,000
SALES (est): 3.2MM **Privately Held**
SIC: 3577 Mfg Computer Peripheral Equipment

(G-1668)
ELITE CNC MACHINING INC
6399 142nd Ave N Ste 122 (33760-2728)
PHONE..................................727 531-8447
S Arthur Hooper, *CEO*
Jack Lavery, *President*
Yolanda Carter, *Controller*
▼ **EMP:** 20 **EST:** 1994
SQ FT: 45,000
SALES (est): 591.8K **Privately Held**
WEB: www.elitecnc.com
SIC: 3599 Machine shop, jobbing & repair

(G-1669)
ELLIOTT DIAMOND TOOL INC
1835 Bough Ave Unit 1 (33760-1541)
P.O. Box 10006, Largo (33773-0006)
PHONE..................................727 585-3839
Mark Elliot, *President*
Mary Lou Elliott, *Vice Pres*
EMP: 18 **EST:** 1972

SALES (est): 1.9MM Privately Held
WEB: www.elliottdiamond.com
SIC: 3545 3425 3541 Drills (machine tool accessories); saw blades for hand or power saws; machine tools, metal cutting type

(G-1670)
EMBROIDME CLEARWATER CO
Also Called: Fully Promoted
26248 Us Highway 19 N (33761-3588)
PHONE.....813 803-0763
Silva Vitelio, *Principal*
EMP: 7 EST: 2015
SALES (est): 76.6K Privately Held
WEB: www.fullypromoted.com
SIC: 2395 Embroidery & art needlework

(G-1671)
ENDEAVOUR CATAMARAN CORP
3703 131st Ave N (33762-4277)
PHONE.....727 573-5377
Robert L Vincent, *President*
EMP: 11 EST: 1991
SQ FT: 52,000
SALES (est): 1.7MM Privately Held
WEB: www.endeavourcats.com
SIC: 3732 Yachts, building & repairing

(G-1672)
ENDO-THERAPEUTICS INC
15251 Roosevelt Blvd # 204 (33760-3560)
PHONE.....727 538-9570
Charles Hardy, *CEO*
Peter Sanchirico, *President*
Robert Querido, *President*
Robert Stuba, *Vice Pres*
Kevin Warren, *Opers Staff*
EMP: 55 EST: 1992
SQ FT: 5,000
SALES (est): 10.4MM Privately Held
WEB: www.endotherapeutics.com
SIC: 3841 Medical instruments & equipment, blood & bone work

(G-1673)
ENGLANDER ENTERPRISES INC
Also Called: Eei Manufacturing Services
703 Grand Central St (33756-3411)
PHONE.....727 461-4755
C Susan Englander, *President*
Kevin McCall, *COO*
Doreen Natale, *Senior Buyer*
Mark Johnson, *Engineer*
Gale Rogers, *Finance*
EMP: 47 EST: 1993
SQ FT: 18,000
SALES (est): 10.2MM Privately Held
WEB: www.eeimfg.com
SIC: 3672 5065 5063 Printed circuit boards; electronic parts & equipment; electrical apparatus & equipment

(G-1674)
ENVIRONMENTAL SERVICES
Also Called: City of Largo
5100 150th Ave N (33760-3502)
PHONE.....727 518-3080
Rich Mushaben, *Supervisor*
Erwin Katy, *Director*
Ernie Muschner, *Officer*
EMP: 27 EST: 1900
SQ FT: 15,344
SALES (est): 3.6MM Privately Held
WEB: www.largo.com
SIC: 3589 Sewage treatment equipment

(G-1675)
EQUIPMENT SALES & SERVICE INC (HQ)
12707 44th St N (33762-4725)
PHONE.....727 572-9197
Robert A Ficocelli, *President*
EMP: 5 EST: 1991
SQ FT: 5,000
SALES (est): 1.6MM Privately Held
WEB: www.magnegas.com
SIC: 2813 Industrial gases

(G-1676)
ERA ORGANICS INC
33 N Garden Ave Ste 120 (33755-6616)
PHONE.....800 579-9817
Tyler Davis, *President*
Linda Clark, *Vice Pres*
Nikki Davis, *Opers Staff*
▼ EMP: 4 EST: 2014
SALES (est): 4.2MM Privately Held
WEB: www.eraorganics.com
SIC: 2834 Dermatologicals

(G-1677)
ES INVESTMENTS LLC (PA)
Also Called: Sun Microstamping Technologies
14055 Us Highway 19 N (33764-7239)
PHONE.....727 536-8822
Bryan Clarke, *President*
Steve McKenzie, *Vice Pres*
Phil Ross, *Vice Pres*
John Bartleman, *Mng Member*
Matt Dlugosz, *Director*
▲ EMP: 150
SQ FT: 110,000
SALES (est): 45.6MM Privately Held
WEB: www.sunmicrostamping.com
SIC: 3469 Stamping metal for the trade

(G-1678)
EZELL PRECISION TOOL CO
Also Called: Legal Components
4733 122nd Ave N (33762-4457)
PHONE.....727 573-3575
Fax: 727 572-6235
▲ EMP: 13
SQ FT: 6,000
SALES (est): 2MM Privately Held
SIC: 3544 Mfg Special Dies & Tools

(G-1679)
F K INSTRUMENT CO INC
Also Called: F K Instrument
2134 Sunnydale Blvd (33765-1274)
PHONE.....727 461-6060
Alfred H Klopfer, *President*
Erich Klopfer, *Vice Pres*
EMP: 59 EST: 1952
SQ FT: 37,200
SALES (est): 9.4MM Privately Held
WEB: www.fk-instrument.com
SIC: 3599 Machine shop, jobbing & repair

(G-1680)
FABMASTER INC
2100 Palmetto St Ste A (33765-2101)
PHONE.....727 216-6750
Danh Tran, *President*
John Gray, *Vice Pres*
EMP: 8 EST: 2009
SALES (est): 854K Privately Held
SIC: 3312 Stainless steel

(G-1681)
FILMFASTENER LLC
12052 49th St N C (33762-4301)
PHONE.....813 926-8721
Frank Fountas,
EMP: 5 EST: 2006
SQ FT: 3,600
SALES (est): 334.2K Privately Held
WEB: www.filmfastener.com
SIC: 3429 Keys, locks & related hardware

(G-1682)
FIRST BLOCK LLC
615 Drew St (33755-4109)
PHONE.....727 462-2526
Jo Beckman, *Accountant*
Fabio Zaniboni, *Manager*
Chiara Basso Zaniboni, *Manager*
EMP: 57 EST: 2014
SALES (est): 8.9MM Privately Held
SIC: 3648 Lighting equipment

(G-1683)
FK INSTRUMENT CO LLC
2134 Sunnydale Blvd (33765-1274)
PHONE.....727 472-2003
Erich Klopfer, *Mng Member*
EMP: 70 EST: 2019
SALES (est): 5.6MM Privately Held
SIC: 3441 Fabricated structural metal

(G-1684)
FLEXIBLE PRTG SOLUTIONS LLC
2070 Weaver Park Dr (33765-2130)
PHONE.....727 446-3014
Curtis B Miller,
EMP: 8 EST: 1999
SQ FT: 6,000
SALES (est): 363.6K Privately Held
WEB: www.flexible-solutions.net
SIC: 2752 Commercial printing, lithographic

(G-1685)
FLORIDA AIR CLEANING INC
13584 49th St N Ste 17 (33762-3737)
P.O. Box 17690 (33762-0690)
PHONE.....727 573-5281
Tom Loudenslagger, *President*
EMP: 6 EST: 1997
SALES (est): 1MM Privately Held
SIC: 3564 Air cleaning systems

(G-1686)
FLORIDA BLOCK & READY MIX LLC (PA)
12795 49th St N (33762-4604)
PHONE.....727 585-2852
Kevin McGinley,
Bruce J Black II,
Mp Diversified Investments,
EMP: 48 EST: 2005
SALES (est): 500.7K Privately Held
SIC: 3273 Ready-mixed concrete

(G-1687)
FLORIDA CANDY FACTORY INC
721 Lakeview Rd (33756-3422)
PHONE.....727 446-0024
Gerald S Rehm, *President*
Joanne McDougall, *Office Mgr*
Richard Barnes, *CIO*
EMP: 18 EST: 1970
SALES (est): 2MM Privately Held
WEB: www.angelmint.com
SIC: 2064 7389 Candy & other confectionery products; packaging & labeling services

(G-1688)
FLORIDA FRAMES INC
12880 Auto Blvd Ste B (33762)
PHONE.....727 572-4064
Greg Brodnick, *President*
Stace Stiverson, *COO*
Debra Brodnick, *Vice Pres*
Holli Miller, *Consultant*
EMP: 17 EST: 1979
SALES (est): 1.7MM Privately Held
WEB: www.floridaframes.com
SIC: 2499 2431 Picture & mirror frames, wood; millwork

(G-1689)
FLORIDA HYTORC
22131 Hwy Us19 (33765)
PHONE.....813 990-9470
Jim Reese, *President*
Andy Craig, *Area Mgr*
EMP: 10
SALES (est): 404.1K Privately Held
WEB: www.floridahytorc.com
SIC: 3541 Machine tools, metal cutting type

(G-1690)
FLORIDA POOL PRODUCTS INC
14550 62nd St N (33760-2355)
P.O. Box 6025 (33758-6025)
PHONE.....727 531-8913
John C Thomas, *CEO*
James P Eisch, *President*
Fred A Thomas, *Chairman*
▲ EMP: 21 EST: 1980
SQ FT: 100,000
SALES (est): 807.7K Privately Held
WEB: www.floridapoolproducts.com
SIC: 3069 3429 3949 3944 Tubing, rubber; manufactured hardware (general); sporting & athletic goods; games, toys & children's vehicles

(G-1691)
FLYTEONE INC
2687 Westchester Dr N (33761-3026)
PHONE.....813 421-1410
Alex Atteberry, *CEO*
Diana L Atteberry, *Admin Sec*
EMP: 5 EST: 2009
SALES (est): 571.4K Privately Held
WEB: www.flyteone.net
SIC: 3592 8742 7363 Valves, aircraft; sales (including sales management) consultant; pilot service, aviation

(G-1692)
FOAM BY DESIGN INC
10606 49th St N (33762-5009)
PHONE.....727 561-7479
Gustavo Trejos, *President*
Amalraj Ramachandran, *Purchasing*
EMP: 50 EST: 2002
SQ FT: 1,000
SALES (est): 5MM Privately Held
WEB: www.foambydesign.com
SIC: 3086 8712 1771 Packaging & shipping materials, foamed plastic; architectural services; concrete work

(G-1693)
FORGE UNLIMITED CO
10880 49th St N (33762-5013)
PHONE.....727 900-7600
Ergun Baltaci, *CEO*
EMP: 7 EST: 2016
SALES (est): 191.7K Privately Held
WEB: www.forgeunlimited.com
SIC: 3993 Signs & advertising specialties; letters for signs, metal

(G-1694)
FRANBIZ INC
2841 Executive Dr Ste 100 (33762-5558)
PHONE.....813 282-1115
Kevin Gordon, *Vice Pres*
EMP: 5 EST: 2019
SALES (est): 611K Privately Held
WEB: www.franbiz.com
SIC: 3535 Conveyors & conveying equipment

(G-1695)
FREEDOM METAL FINISHING INC
5095 113th Ave N (33760-4834)
PHONE.....727 573-2464
Keith Eidschun, *President*
EMP: 25 EST: 1944
SQ FT: 20,000
SALES (est): 3.1MM Privately Held
WEB: www.freedommetalfinishing.com
SIC: 3471 Electroplating & plating; plating of metals or formed products

(G-1696)
FULLERTON 799 INC
5300 115th Ave N (33760-4830)
PHONE.....727 572-7040
Arnold Eichhof, *President*
Beth Flynn, *Corp Secy*
Arne Swanson, *Vice Pres*
▲ EMP: 43 EST: 1982
SQ FT: 60,000
SALES (est): 1.1MM Privately Held
SIC: 3544 3364 Industrial molds; magnesium & magnesium-base alloy die-castings

(G-1697)
G L E M INC
Also Called: Sir Speedy
1878 Drew St (33765-2911)
PHONE.....727 461-5300
Michael G Schratt, *President*
EMP: 5 EST: 1977
SQ FT: 3,000
SALES (est): 411.9K Privately Held
WEB: www.sirspeedy.com
SIC: 2752 7334 2789 Commercial printing, lithographic; mimeographing; bookbinding & related work

(G-1698)
GE AVIATION SYSTEMS LLC
14100 Roosevelt Blvd (33762-3805)
PHONE.....727 532-6370
Diana L Frohn, *Branch Mgr*
EMP: 10
SALES (corp-wide): 79.6B Publicly Held
WEB: www.geaviation.com
SIC: 3812 Aircraft control systems, electronic

GEOGRAPHIC

HQ: Ge Aviation Systems Llc
1 Aviation Way
Cincinnati OH 45215
937 898-9600

(G-1699)
GE AVIATION SYSTEMS LLC
14200 Roosevelt Blvd (33762-2914)
PHONE....................................727 531-7781
David Carrillo, *Engineer*
Kurt Musial, *Engineer*
Wilma Freamon, *Benefits Mgr*
David Miller, *Branch Mgr*
Suzette Pancrazio, *Manager*
EMP: 350
SQ FT: 40,000
SALES (corp-wide): 79.6B **Publicly Held**
WEB: www.geaviation.com
SIC: 3621 3812 Motors & generators; search & navigation equipment
HQ: Ge Aviation Systems Llc
1 Aviation Way
Cincinnati OH 45215
937 898-9600

(G-1700)
GE AVIATION SYSTEMS LLC
14200 Roosevelt Blvd (33762-2914)
P.O. Box 9013 (33758-9013)
PHONE....................................727 539-1631
Normand Barselou, *Engineer*
Kathy Gridley, *Branch Mgr*
EMP: 10
SALES (corp-wide): 79.6B **Publicly Held**
WEB: www.geaviation.com
SIC: 3812 Aircraft control systems, electronic
HQ: Ge Aviation Systems Llc
1 Aviation Way
Cincinnati OH 45215
937 898-9600

(G-1701)
GENCA CORP
13805 58th St N (33760-3716)
PHONE....................................727 524-3622
Fax: 727 531-5700
EMP: 37
SALES (est): 3.2MM **Privately Held**
SIC: 3089 Mfg Plastic Products

(G-1702)
GENERAL HYDRAULIC SOLUTIONS
Also Called: Southcoast Marine Products
10601 47th St N (33762-5003)
PHONE....................................727 561-0719
Kevin Cureton, *President*
Steve Cureton, *Vice Pres*
Rick Passaretti, *Prdtn Mgr*
◆ **EMP:** 6 **EST:** 1999
SALES (est): 843.4K **Privately Held**
WEB: www.ghslift.com
SIC: 3429 Marine hardware

(G-1703)
GENTRY PRINTING COMPANY LLC
2070 Gentry St (33765-2109)
PHONE....................................727 441-1914
Jason Kelly, *President*
Keith Claar,
EMP: 20 **EST:** 1982
SQ FT: 12,000
SALES (est): 4.7MM **Privately Held**
WEB: www.gentryprinting.com
SIC: 2752 Commercial printing, offset

(G-1704)
GOLD EFFECTS INC
13130 56th Ct Ste 609 (33760-4018)
PHONE....................................727 573-1990
Daniel McLaughlin, *President*
Dave Johnston, *Production*
EMP: 6 **EST:** 1992
SALES (est): 612.7K **Privately Held**
WEB: www.goldeffects.com
SIC: 3471 Electroplating of metals or formed products

(G-1705)
GOOEE LLC
1444 S Belcher Rd (33764-2826)
PHONE....................................727 510-0663
Simon Coombes, *Chief Engr*
EMP: 13 **EST:** 2015
SALES (est): 258.1K **Privately Held**
WEB: www.gooee.com
SIC: 7372 Business oriented computer software

(G-1706)
GSSC INC
11692 56th Ct N (33760-4801)
PHONE....................................727 461-6044
John C Hedger, *President*
EMP: 9 **EST:** 2014
SALES (est): 251.9K **Privately Held**
SIC: 3563 Air & gas compressors

(G-1707)
GULF MACHINING INC
5040 110th Ave N (33760-4807)
PHONE....................................727 571-1244
Jerome Peterson, *President*
Jerome A Peterson, *Principal*
Rebecca Lowry, *Vice Pres*
EMP: 14 **EST:** 2013
SALES (est): 1.8MM **Privately Held**
WEB: www.gulfmachining.com
SIC: 3541 Numerically controlled metal cutting machine tools

(G-1708)
GULF PACKAGING CO
1756 Emerald Dr (33756-3665)
PHONE....................................727 441-1117
Jeffrey A Herran, *President*
EMP: 11 **EST:** 1958
SQ FT: 11,000
SALES (est): 516.1K **Privately Held**
WEB: www.floridagulfpackaging.com
SIC: 2652 2657 2671 Boxes, newsboard, metal edged: made from purchased materials; paperboard backs for blister or skin packages; packaging paper & plastics film, coated & laminated

(G-1709)
H & H PUBLISHING CO INC
1231 Kapp Dr (33765-2116)
PHONE....................................727 442-7760
Robert D Hackworth, *President*
Mike Ealy, *IT/INT Sup*
EMP: 6 **EST:** 1978
SQ FT: 2,000
SALES (est): 722.1K **Privately Held**
WEB: www.hhpublishing.com
SIC: 2731 Textbooks: publishing & printing

(G-1710)
HAMMER HAAG STEEL INC
12707 Us Highway 19 N (33764-7213)
PHONE....................................727 216-6903
Constantine Haag, *President*
Denny Fenn, *COO*
Ramon Robles, *Project Mgr*
Pete Shelton, *Project Mgr*
Slava Moukhov, *CFO*
▲ **EMP:** 110
SQ FT: 56,000
SALES (est): 14MM **Privately Held**
WEB: www.hammerhaag.com
SIC: 3599 3441 Machine & other job shop work; building components, structural steel

(G-1711)
HARDER PRCISION COMPONENTS INC
1123 Seminole St (33755-4344)
PHONE....................................727 442-4212
Catherine Katopis, *President*
Cathy Kay, *Executive*
EMP: 26 **EST:** 1960
SQ FT: 6,700
SALES (est): 619.5K **Privately Held**
WEB: www.harderprecision.com
SIC: 3599 Machine shop, jobbing & repair

(G-1712)
HB SEALING PRODUCTS INC (HQ)
Also Called: Hercules Sealing Products
420 Park Place Blvd # 100 (33759-3928)
PHONE....................................727 796-1300
Russell Brown, *CEO*
Ron Garcia, *President*
Russ Petrie, *General Mgr*
Andres Echeverri, *Business Mgr*
Gina Herrera, *COO*
◆ **EMP:** 135 **EST:** 1962
SALES (est): 63.4MM
SALES (corp-wide): 703.5MM **Privately Held**
WEB: www.diplomaplc.com
SIC: 2869 5085 Hydraulic fluids, synthetic base; acetates: amyl, butyl & ethyl; seals, industrial; pistons & valves
PA: Diploma Plc
12 Charterhouse Square
London EC1M
207 549-5700

(G-1713)
HEISLER HARDWOOD INC
1838 N Washington Ave (33755-1861)
PHONE....................................727 410-0401
Keith Heisler, *President*
EMP: 6 **EST:** 2008
SALES (est): 299.8K **Privately Held**
WEB: www.heislerhardwood.com
SIC: 2426 Hardwood dimension & flooring mills

(G-1714)
HENTZEN COATINGS INC
5182 126th Ave N (33760-4615)
PHONE....................................727 572-4474
Nancy Stler, *Admin Mgr*
Ryan Westover, *Technical Staff*
EMP: 10
SALES (corp-wide): 69.5MM **Privately Held**
WEB: www.hentzen.com
SIC: 2851 Lacquer: bases, dopes, thinner; enamels; polyurethane coatings; epoxy coatings
PA: Hentzen Coatings, Inc.
6937 W Mill Rd
Milwaukee WI 53218
414 353-4200

(G-1715)
HOFFSTETTER TOOL & DIE INC
4371 112th Ter N (33762-4930)
PHONE....................................727 573-7775
Ralph Hoffstetter, *President*
Gregory Hoffstetter, *Vice Pres*
Greg Hofstetter, *Vice Pres*
▲ **EMP:** 16 **EST:** 1977
SQ FT: 14,000
SALES (est): 2.1MM **Privately Held**
WEB: www.hoffstettertool.com
SIC: 3469 3544 Metal stampings; special dies, tools, jigs & fixtures

(G-1716)
HONEYWELL AEROSPACE INC
13350 Us Highway 19 N (33764-7290)
PHONE....................................727 539-5197
Kirk Gerber, *CEO*
Alexander Koutsos, *Analyst*
EMP: 6
SALES (corp-wide): 32.6B **Publicly Held**
WEB: www.aerofed.net
SIC: 3812 Search & navigation equipment
HQ: Honeywell Aerospace Inc.
1944 E Sky Harbor Cir N
Phoenix AZ 85034
602 365-3099

(G-1717)
HONEYWELL INTERNATIONAL INC
13350 Us Highway 19 N (33764-7290)
PHONE....................................727 539-5080
Chris Meece, *Engineer*
Will Brito Cardenas, *Supervisor*
Richard Patenaude, *Director*
Vincent Ludovici, *Analyst*
EMP: 453
SALES (corp-wide): 32.6B **Publicly Held**
WEB: www.honeywell.com
SIC: 3812 Aircraft/aerospace flight instruments & guidance systems; navigational systems & instruments; cabin environment indicators
PA: Honeywell International Inc.
300 S Tryon St
Charlotte NC 28202
704 627-6200

(G-1718)
HONEYWELL INTERNATIONAL INC
1221 Us 19 N (33763)
PHONE....................................727 539-3111
EMP: 6
SALES (corp-wide): 32.6B **Publicly Held**
WEB: www.honeywell.com
SIC: 3724 Aircraft engines & engine parts
PA: Honeywell International Inc.
300 S Tryon St
Charlotte NC 28202
704 627-6200

(G-1719)
HONEYWELL INTERNATIONAL INC
13350 Us Highway 19 N (33764-7290)
PHONE....................................727 531-4611
Brian Spiegel, *Principal*
Gwendolyn Grundy, *Senior Buyer*
Kirk Gerber, *Branch Mgr*
EMP: 700
SALES (corp-wide): 32.6B **Publicly Held**
WEB: www.honeywell.com
SIC: 3812 Aircraft control systems, electronic; aircraft/aerospace flight instruments & guidance systems
PA: Honeywell International Inc.
300 S Tryon St
Charlotte NC 28202
704 627-6200

(G-1720)
HONEYWELL INTERNATIONAL INC
13190 56th Ct Ste 403 (33760-4029)
PHONE....................................813 573-1166
Ed Gaunt, *Manager*
EMP: 7
SALES (corp-wide): 32.6B **Publicly Held**
WEB: www.honeywell.com
SIC: 3724 Aircraft engines & engine parts
PA: Honeywell International Inc.
300 S Tryon St
Charlotte NC 28202
704 627-6200

(G-1721)
HOUSE OF METAL LLC
4161 114th Ter N (33762-4904)
PHONE....................................727 540-0637
Douglas Calibey, *Mng Member*
Melody A Calibey, *Mng Member*
EMP: 5 **EST:** 2005
SALES (est): 428.1K **Privately Held**
WEB: www.houseofmetalllc.com
SIC: 7692 Welding repair

(G-1722)
HUTCHINS CO INC
Also Called: S T A Sales
1195 Kapp Dr (33765-2114)
PHONE....................................727 442-6651
Gerry Hutchins, *President*
Rich R Hutchins, *Vice Pres*
Jane Hutchins, *Office Mgr*
▼ **EMP:** 13 **EST:** 1957
SQ FT: 17,000
SALES (est): 2.2MM **Privately Held**
WEB: www.com-pacyachts.com
SIC: 3443 3732 Fabricated plate work (boiler shop); boat building & repairing

(G-1723)
HYDREX LLC
627 Pinellas St Unit C (33756-3326)
PHONE....................................727 443-3900
John Green, *Business Mgr*
Sam Williams, *Business Mgr*
Roscelin Vivas, *Office Admin*
Boud Van Rompay,
▲ **EMP:** 9 **EST:** 2008
SQ FT: 1,500
SALES (est): 428.3K **Privately Held**
WEB: www.hydrex.be
SIC: 3731 Shipbuilding & repairing

(G-1724)
HYMEG CORPORATION
5410 115th Ave N (33760-4841)
P.O. Box 18802 (33762-1802)
PHONE....................................800 322-1953
Darryl Mayo, *CEO*
EMP: 5 **EST:** 2014
SALES (est): 578.7K **Privately Held**
WEB: www.hymeg.com
SIC: 3625 Resistors & resistor units

▲ = Import ▼=Export
◆ =Import/Export

(G-1725)
HYTRONICS CORP
Also Called: Hyco
5410 115th Ave N (33760-4841)
P.O. Box 18802 (33762-1802)
PHONE..................................727 535-0413
Darryl K Mayo, *President*
▲ **EMP:** 69 **EST:** 1967
SALES (est): 3.1MM
SALES (corp-wide): 52.6MM **Privately Held**
WEB: www.hytronicscorp.com
SIC: 3677 3829 3643 3621 Coil windings, electronic; measuring & controlling devices; current-carrying wiring devices; motors & generators; transformers, except electric
PA: Electro Technik Industries, Inc.
5410 115th Ave N
Clearwater FL 33760
727 530-9555

(G-1726)
ICMFG & ASSOCIATES INC
3734 131st Ave N Ste 11 (33762-4222)
PHONE..................................727 258-4995
Tom Coghlan, *CEO*
Michael Doyle, *President*
▲ **EMP:** 9 **EST:** 2010
SALES (est): 95.1K **Privately Held**
WEB: www.icm-associates.com
SIC: 3672 Printed circuit boards

(G-1727)
ICPF DEVELOPMENT GROUP LLC (PA)
Also Called: Led Pro Services
514 N Betty Ln (33755-4708)
PHONE..................................727 474-9927
Banchero Catalina, *Principal*
EMP: 17 **EST:** 2011
SALES (est): 3.6MM **Privately Held**
SIC: 3646 Commercial indusl & institutional electric lighting fixtures

(G-1728)
ICS INEX INSPECTION SYSTEMS
13075 Us Highway 19 N (33764-7224)
PHONE..................................727 535-5502
EMP: 11 **EST:** 2019
SALES (est): 766.4K **Privately Held**
WEB: www.inexvision.com
SIC: 3565 Packaging machinery

(G-1729)
IMAGECARE MAINTENANCE SYSTEMS
14055 46th St N Ste 1108 (33762-3865)
PHONE..................................727 536-8646
Adrienne Slick, *Owner*
Kevin Washington, *Vice Pres*
Nicole Barber, *Manager*
Dolly Hickey, *Manager*
EMP: 14 **EST:** 2007
SALES (est): 379.6K **Privately Held**
WEB: www.stratusunlimited.com
SIC: 3299 Images, small: gypsum, clay or papier mache

(G-1730)
IMPACT MOLDING CLEARWATER LLC
2050 Sunnydale Blvd (33765-1201)
PHONE..................................847 718-9300
Philip Kretekos, *Mng Member*
EMP: 45 **EST:** 2019
SALES (est): 11.4MM
SALES (corp-wide): 137.7MM **Privately Held**
WEB: www.impactmolding.com
SIC: 3069 Floor coverings, rubber
HQ: Thunderbird Parent Plastics Llc
900 Commerce Dr Ste 105
Oak Brook IL

(G-1731)
INDUCTIVE TECHNOLOGIES INC
5410 115th Ave N (33760-4841)
PHONE..................................727 536-7861
John Sellers, *Vice Pres*
EMP: 15 **EST:** 2010
SALES (est): 106.8K **Privately Held**
WEB: www.inductech.com
SIC: 3612 Transformers, except electric

(G-1732)
INSTRUMENT TRANSFORMERS LLC
1907 Calumet St (33765-1190)
P.O. Box 2216, Schenectady NY (12301-2216)
PHONE..................................727 461-9413
James M Koepsell, *President*
I-Pung Hu, *Mng Member*
Bob Criswell, *Info Tech Mgr*
Suzann Lopez, *Info Tech Mgr*
Brenda K Skinner, *Admin Sec*
▲ **EMP:** 500 **EST:** 1975
SQ FT: 170,000
SALES (est): 100.1MM
SALES (corp-wide): 79.6B **Publicly Held**
WEB: www.instrumenttransformers.com
SIC: 3612 Instrument transformers (except portable)
PA: General Electric Company
5 Necco St
Boston MA 02210
617 443-3000

(G-1733)
INTERGLOBAL CAPITAL INC
Also Called: Chassis King
1016 Pnc De Leon Blvd (33756-1073)
PHONE..................................727 585-1500
Donald Pratt, *President*
John Smith, *Principal*
▼ **EMP:** 5 **EST:** 1994
SALES (est): 476.6K **Privately Held**
SIC: 3715 Truck trailers

(G-1734)
INTERPRINT INCORPORATED (HQ)
Also Called: Interprint Web Printing
12350 Us 19 N (33764-7418)
PHONE..................................727 531-8957
James E Morten, *Ch of Bd*
John Rickerman, *President*
James A Morten, *Vice Pres*
Scott Morten, *Vice Pres*
Daniel McCurdy, *Plant Mgr*
▼ **EMP:** 76 **EST:** 1965
SQ FT: 13,000
SALES (est): 13.5MM **Privately Held**
WEB: www.printerusa.com
SIC: 2796 2789 2752 Platemaking services; bookbinding & related work; commercial printing, offset
PA: Morten Enterprises, Inc.
12350 Us Highway 19 N
Clearwater FL 33764
727 531-8957

(G-1735)
INTERSTATE WLDG & FABRICATION
1939 Sherwood St (33765-1932)
PHONE..................................727 446-1449
Charles A Bates Jr, *President*
John C Bates, *Corp Secy*
EMP: 16 **EST:** 1988
SQ FT: 12,000
SALES (est): 2.7MM **Privately Held**
WEB: www.interstatewf.com
SIC: 3441 7692 3444 Building components, structural steel; welding repair; sheet metalwork

(G-1736)
IPC GLOBAL
1062 Cephas Rd (33765-2107)
PHONE..................................727 470-2134
Norbert Heuser, *Owner*
EMP: 7 **EST:** 2012
SALES (est): 341.2K **Privately Held**
WEB: www.hienergy.biz
SIC: 3829 Measuring & controlling devices

(G-1737)
IRONHORSE PRESSWORKS INC
Also Called: Harris Letterpress
406 S Jupiter Ave (33755-6517)
PHONE..................................727 462-9988
Earl Harris, *CEO*
Margaret Harris, *Vice Pres*
Troy Harris, *Vice Pres*
Denise McDonald, *Treasurer*
Denise Milano, *Treasurer*
EMP: 9 **EST:** 1995
SQ FT: 7,000
SALES (est): 727.2K **Privately Held**
SIC: 2752 Commercial printing, offset

(G-1738)
ISLAND PAVER SEALING & PRSSURE
13584 49th St N Ste 2 (33762-3737)
PHONE..................................727 641-3512
Andy Gilley Jr, *Principal*
EMP: 6 **EST:** 2008
SALES (est): 102.6K **Privately Held**
WEB: www.islandpressurewashingservices.com
SIC: 3531 Pavers

(G-1739)
J T WALKER INDUSTRIES INC (PA)
1310 N Hercules Ave Ste A (33765-1940)
PHONE..................................727 461-0501
Peter Desoto, *CEO*
Jay K Poppleton, *President*
Janet L Fasenmyer, *Vice Pres*
Michael Luther, *Vice Pres*
Steve Brush, *Finance Mgr*
◆ **EMP:** 30 **EST:** 1997
SQ FT: 15,000
SALES (est): 250.9MM **Privately Held**
WEB: www.mihvac.com
SIC: 3442 3089 3585 5193 Screens, window, metal; window frames & sash, plastic; parts for heating, cooling & refrigerating equipment; nursery stock

(G-1740)
JAKOBSEN TOOL CO INC
805 Pierce St (33756-5525)
PHONE..................................727 447-1143
Norman Brown, *President*
EMP: 8 **EST:** 1984
SQ FT: 5,300
SALES (est): 568.4K **Privately Held**
SIC: 3599 Machine shop, jobbing & repair

(G-1741)
JAMES REESE ENTERPRISES INC
Also Called: Florida Precision Tool
1714 Misty Plateau Trl (33765-1828)
PHONE..................................727 386-5311
James Reese, *President*
EMP: 10 **EST:** 2012
SALES (est): 1MM **Privately Held**
WEB: www.validity.us
SIC: 3423 8742 Wrenches, hand tools; sales (including sales management) consultant

(G-1742)
JATIGA INC
2660 Enterprise Rd (33763-1105)
PHONE..................................727 793-0079
Jacob Darnell, *Engineer*
Mike Camele, *Accounts Mgr*
Tim Hanser, *Branch Mgr*
EMP: 6
SALES (corp-wide): 19.6MM **Privately Held**
SIC: 3931 5099 Musical instruments; musical instruments
PA: Jatiga, Inc.
9615 Inter Ocean Dr
West Chester OH 45246
859 817-7100

(G-1743)
JIM APPLEYS TRU-ARC INC
5140 110th Ave N (33760-4804)
PHONE..................................727 571-3007
James W Appley II, *President*
Judith H Appley, *Corp Secy*
Larry Macdonald, *Mfg Staff*
EMP: 10 **EST:** 1978
SQ FT: 12,000
SALES (est): 960K **Privately Held**
WEB: www.jimappleystruarc.com
SIC: 3599 3443 7692 3444 Machine shop, jobbing & repair; fabricated plate work (boiler shop); welding repair; sheet metalwork

(G-1744)
JOHN & BETSY HOVLAND
Also Called: Creative Monogramming
2073 Range Rd (33765-2124)
PHONE..................................727 449-2032
John Hovland, *Partner*
Betsy Hovland, *Partner*
EMP: 7 **EST:** 1988
SQ FT: 1,250
SALES (est): 452.2K **Privately Held**
SIC: 2284 Embroidery thread

(G-1745)
JORMAC AEROSPACE INC
13130 56th Ct Ste 604 (33760-4018)
PHONE..................................727 549-9600
Steve Jourdenais, *Owner*
Frank Nelson, *General Mgr*
Brian Barber, *VP Sls/Mktg*
EMP: 15 **EST:** 2011
SALES (est): 434.2K **Privately Held**
WEB: www.jormac.com
SIC: 3812 Aircraft/aerospace flight instruments & guidance systems

(G-1746)
JTL ENTERPRISES (DELAWARE)
Also Called: Hydromassage
15395 Roosevelt Blvd (33760-3500)
PHONE..................................727 536-5566
Paul J Lunter, *President*
Dan Kennedy, *Vice Pres*
Tim Elliott, *Design Engr*
Frank Urino, *Sales Executive*
Hilary Wahlbeck, *Marketing Mgr*
▲ **EMP:** 35 **EST:** 1989
SQ FT: 40,000
SALES (est): 9.1MM **Privately Held**
WEB: www.jtlenterprisesinc.com
SIC: 3841 Surgical & medical instruments

(G-1747)
JW APPLEY AND SON INC
13215 38th St N (33762-4229)
PHONE..................................727 572-4910
Doug Jennings, *President*
Drew Ehehalt, *Sales Executive*
Sue Belmonte, *Admin Sec*
EMP: 25 **EST:** 1931
SQ FT: 17,000
SALES (est): 3MM **Privately Held**
WEB: www.jwappley.com
SIC: 3599 Machine shop, jobbing & repair

(G-1748)
KEMCO SYSTEMS CO LLC (PA)
11500 47th St N (33762-4955)
PHONE..................................727 573-2323
Tom Vanden Heuvel, *President*
Michael Fout, *Vice Pres*
David Lemen, *Vice Pres*
Bill Howard, *Chief Engr*
Ann Elder, *Engineer*
◆ **EMP:** 60 **EST:** 1969
SQ FT: 58,000
SALES (est): 12.2MM **Privately Held**
WEB: www.kemcosystems.com
SIC: 3589 3582 Water treatment equipment, industrial; commercial laundry equipment

(G-1749)
KEN CLEARYS TWO LLC
10900 47th St N (33762-5001)
PHONE..................................727 573-0700
Cleary Kenneth J II,
EMP: 17 **EST:** 2011
SALES (est): 1.8MM **Privately Held**
SIC: 2511 2521 Wood household furniture; wood office furniture

(G-1750)
KINETIC INDUSTRIES LLC
Also Called: Polymatics Plastic Processing
10445 49th St N Ste A (33762-5036)
PHONE..................................727 572-7604
Robert Hoel, *Partner*
Elena Hoel, *Partner*
EMP: 6 **EST:** 1974
SQ FT: 6,200
SALES (est): 763.5K **Privately Held**
WEB: www.polymatics.com
SIC: 3089 3599 3544 Injection molding of plastics; machine shop, jobbing & repair; special dies, tools, jigs & fixtures

GEOGRAPHIC

(G-1751)
KLEIDS ENTERPRISES INC
Also Called: Made To Match Clothing Company
22023 Us Highway 19 N (33765-2362)
P.O. Box 2784, Dunedin (34697-2784)
PHONE..................................727 796-7900
Joanne Kleiderman, *President*
Monroe Kleiderman, *Vice Pres*
EMP: 6 **EST:** 1981
SQ FT: 8,000
SALES (est): 471.5K **Privately Held**
WEB: www.kleids.com
SIC: 2337 2331 Women's & misses' suits & coats; T-shirts & tops, women's: made from purchased materials

(G-1752)
KLOPFER HOLDINGS INC
2134 Sunnydale Blvd (33765-1274)
PHONE..................................727 472-2002
EMP: 70 **EST:** 1978
SALES (est): 3MM **Privately Held**
SIC: 3451 Screw machine products

(G-1753)
KNOTHOLE CREATIONS INC
13205 40th St N (33762-4267)
PHONE..................................727 561-9107
Paul Brown Jr, *President*
David M Brown, *Vice Pres*
David Brown, *Vice Pres*
Anne M Brown, *Treasurer*
Jennifer L Brown, *Admin Sec*
EMP: 5 **EST:** 1992
SQ FT: 7,824
SALES (est): 582K **Privately Held**
WEB: www.knotholecreations.com
SIC: 2434 Wood kitchen cabinets

(G-1754)
KODIAK SOFTWARE INC
832 Narcissus Ave (33767-1336)
PHONE..................................727 599-8839
Susan Broad, *Director*
EMP: 6 **EST:** 2001
SALES (est): 87.6K **Privately Held**
WEB: www.kodiak.com
SIC: 7372 Prepackaged software

(G-1755)
L & N LABEL COMPANY INC
2051 Sunnydale Blvd (33765-1202)
PHONE..................................727 442-5400
Stephen R Sabadosh, *President*
Julee Sabadosh, *Vice Pres*
Dave Gioia, *Manager*
Shelley Johnson, *Executive*
EMP: 25 **EST:** 1977
SQ FT: 9,000
SALES (est): 3.1MM **Privately Held**
WEB: www.lnlabel.com
SIC: 2759 2752 Labels & seals: printing; commercial printing, offset

(G-1756)
LABEL PRINTING SERVICE
1245 N Hercules Ave (33765-1921)
PHONE..................................727 820-1226
Janet Esposito, *Manager*
EMP: 7 **EST:** 2011
SALES (est): 120.6K **Privately Held**
WEB: www.lnlabel.com
SIC: 2752 Commercial printing, lithographic

(G-1757)
LABELPRO INC
Also Called: Grafix
14409 60th St N (33760-2710)
PHONE..................................727 538-2149
Jack Frieder, *President*
EMP: 10 **EST:** 1970
SQ FT: 3,500
SALES (est): 971.8K **Privately Held**
SIC: 3479 3993 2752 2672 Name plates: engraved, etched, etc.; signs & advertising specialties; commercial printing, lithographic; coated & laminated paper; packaging paper & plastics film, coated & laminated

(G-1758)
LETO LLC ✪
Also Called: Sunglo Paint
14483 62nd St N (33760-2722)
PHONE..................................813 486-8049
Christopher S Leto,
EMP: 5 **EST:** 2020
SALES (est): 504K **Privately Held**
SIC: 3479 Painting of metal products

(G-1759)
LFH SOUTHERNSTONE LLC
12520 Automobile Blvd (33762-4415)
PHONE..................................727 538-0123
EMP: 6 **EST:** 2017
SALES (est): 68.5K **Privately Held**
WEB: www.southernstonecabinets.com
SIC: 2434 Wood kitchen cabinets

(G-1760)
LIGHTNING CONNECTING RODS LLC
1630 N Hercules Ave Ste B (33765-1987)
PHONE..................................727 733-2054
Robert S King, *CEO*
EMP: 5 **EST:** 2011
SALES (est): 756.7K **Privately Held**
WEB: www.lightningconnectingrods.com
SIC: 3714 Motor vehicle parts & accessories

(G-1761)
LIGHTNING MASTER CORPORATION
Also Called: Bolt Lightning Protection
2100 Palmetto St Ste A (33765-2101)
PHONE..................................800 749-6800
Bruce Kaiser, *President*
Lindsey Coghlan, *Marketing Staff*
Thao Tran, *Manager*
Lee Howard, *CTO*
▼ **EMP:** 40 **EST:** 1984
SQ FT: 30,000
SALES (est): 7.7MM **Privately Held**
WEB: www.lightningmaster.com
SIC: 3629 Electronic generation equipment

(G-1762)
LITHIONICS BATTERY LLC
1770 Calumet St (33765-1137)
PHONE..................................727 726-4204
Steven Tartaglia, *General Mgr*
Melissa A Tartaglia, *CFO*
Timothy O Sullivan,
▼ **EMP:** 14 **EST:** 2010
SQ FT: 12,000
SALES (est): 2MM **Privately Held**
WEB: www.lithionicsbattery.com
SIC: 3691 Storage batteries

(G-1763)
LITHOTEC COMMERCIAL PRINTING
12350 Us Highway 19 N (33764-7418)
PHONE..................................727 541-4614
Barbara Argyros, *President*
William Argyros, *Vice Pres*
EMP: 10 **EST:** 1969
SQ FT: 13,500
SALES (est): 818.7K **Privately Held**
WEB: www.lithotec.net
SIC: 2752 Commercial printing, offset

(G-1764)
LUCID TECHNOLOGY INC
2380 Drew St Ste 1 (33765-3311)
PHONE..................................727 487-2430
Vadim S Carter, *President*
EMP: 5 **EST:** 2012
SQ FT: 1,800
SALES (est): 338K **Privately Held**
WEB: www.lucidti.com
SIC: 3572 5045 Computer storage devices; computers, peripherals & software

(G-1765)
LUCKE ENTERPRISES INC
Also Called: Fastsigns
2781 Gulf To Bay Blvd (33759-3904)
PHONE..................................727 797-1177
Michael J Lucke, *President*
EMP: 5 **EST:** 1995
SALES (est): 553.4K **Privately Held**
WEB: www.fastsigns.com
SIC: 3993 Signs & advertising specialties

(G-1766)
M AND T PRO COATING INC
2200 Euclid Cir N (33764-6814)
PHONE..................................727 272-4620
Mauricio Torres, *President*
EMP: 7 **EST:** 2016
SALES (est): 96.4K **Privately Held**
SIC: 3479 Metal coating & allied service

(G-1767)
M O PRECISION MOLDERS INC
13750 49th St N (33762-3735)
PHONE..................................727 573-4466
EMP: 14
SQ FT: 15,550
SALES (est): 1.8MM **Privately Held**
SIC: 3089 Injection Molding

(G-1768)
MAC PAPERS INC
Also Called: Florida Graphic Supply
1351 N Arcturas Ave (33765-1903)
PHONE..................................800 582-0049
EMP: 9
SALES (corp-wide): 492.5MM **Privately Held**
WEB: www.macpapers.com
SIC: 3993 5085 Signs & advertising specialties; signmaker equipment & supplies
PA: Mac Papers, Llc
3300 Philips Hwy
Jacksonville FL 32207
904 348-3300

(G-1769)
MAGIC TILT TRAILER MFG CO INC
Also Called: Magic Trailers
2161 Lions Club Rd (33764-6883)
PHONE..................................727 535-5561
Craig Clawson, *President*
Graham Grainger, *Engineer*
Tony Dippolito, *Regl Sales Mgr*
Robert Lyons, *Manager*
▼ **EMP:** 50 **EST:** 1955
SQ FT: 48,000
SALES (est): 8.7MM **Privately Held**
WEB: www.magictilt.com
SIC: 3354 3799 Aluminum extruded products; boat trailers

(G-1770)
MAGNATRONIX CORPORATION INC
Also Called: Fetco
5410 115th Ave N (33760-4841)
PHONE..................................727 536-7861
Roger C Mayo, *President*
Roger Mayo, *President*
John Sellers, *COO*
EMP: 13 **EST:** 1980
SALES (est): 474.8K **Privately Held**
SIC: 3612 Specialty transformers

(G-1771)
MAGNIFICAT HOLDINGS LLC
Also Called: Yo Mama's Foods
1125 Eldridge St (33755-4310)
PHONE..................................727 798-0512
David Habib, *Principal*
▼ **EMP:** 5 **EST:** 2018
SALES (est): 500K **Privately Held**
SIC: 2032 Italian foods: packaged in cans, jars, etc.

(G-1772)
MAGNUM VENUS PLASTECH
5148 113th Ave N (33760-4835)
PHONE..................................727 573-2955
Tom Slay, *Sales Staff*
Dave Miller, *Info Tech Mgr*
EMP: 10 **EST:** 2017
SALES (est): 75.7K **Privately Held**
WEB: www.mvpind.com
SIC: 3296 Mineral wool

(G-1773)
MARINE METAL PRODUCTS CO
2154 Calumet St (33765-1309)
PHONE..................................727 461-5575
Clark M Lea Jr, *President*
Clark M Lea Sr, *Vice Pres*
Mary L Lea, *Treasurer*
Catherine Campbell, *Controller*
Cathy Campbell, *Controller*
▲ **EMP:** 9 **EST:** 1960
SQ FT: 21,000
SALES (est): 1.4MM **Privately Held**
WEB: www.marinemetal.com
SIC: 3949 3561 3523 Buckets, fish & bait; fishing tackle, general; pumps & pumping equipment; farm machinery & equipment

(G-1774)
MARPRO MARINE WAYS LLC
1822 N Belcher Rd (33765-1400)
PHONE..................................727 447-4930
George G Pappas, *Principal*
EMP: 6 **EST:** 2011
SALES (est): 210.1K **Privately Held**
SIC: 3732 Boat building & repairing

(G-1775)
MARYSOL TECHNOLOGIES INC
1444c S Belcher Rd 136 (33764-2877)
PHONE..................................727 712-1523
Dan Bar Joseph, *Principal*
EMP: 9 **EST:** 2003
SALES (est): 810.7K **Privately Held**
WEB: www.marysoltechnologies.com
SIC: 3826 3841 Laser scientific & engineering instruments; surgical lasers

(G-1776)
MATHESON TRI-GAS INC
Also Called: Tri Gas 05
12650 49th St N (33762-4601)
PHONE..................................727 572-8737
Robert Richardson, *Branch Mgr*
EMP: 8 **Privately Held**
WEB: www.mathesongas.com
SIC: 2813 5084 Industrial gases; welding machinery & equipment
HQ: Matheson Tri-Gas, Inc.
3 Mountainview Rd Ste 3 # 3
Warren NJ 07059
908 991-9200

(G-1777)
MATRIX MACHINING & MFG LLC (PA)
1904 Calumet St (33765-1107)
PHONE..................................908 355-1900
Jonathan Barnes, *Partner*
Arun S Samal, *Managing Dir*
Hank Barnes, *Mng Member*
EMP: 10 **EST:** 2014
SQ FT: 6,000
SALES (est): 1.3MM **Privately Held**
SIC: 3599 Machine shop, jobbing & repair

(G-1778)
MCM INDUSTRIES INC
1721 Penny Ln (33756-3685)
P.O. Box 2567, Largo (33779-2567)
PHONE..................................727 259-9894
Eric Dale Frechette, *Principal*
EMP: 8 **EST:** 2008
SALES (est): 250K **Privately Held**
WEB: www.mcmindustries.com
SIC: 3999 Manufacturing industries

(G-1779)
MELITTA NORTH AMERICA INC (DH)
Also Called: Melitta USA
13925 58th St N (33760-3721)
PHONE..................................727 535-2111
Martin T Miller, *President*
Fred Lueck, *Vice Pres*
◆ **EMP:** 100 **EST:** 1996
SQ FT: 104,000
SALES (est): 139.4MM
SALES (corp-wide): 1.8B **Privately Held**
WEB: www.melitta.com
SIC: 2095 3634 5499 Roasted coffee; coffee makers, electric: household; coffee
HQ: Melitta Group Management Gmbh & Co. Kg
Marienstr. 88
Minden 32425
571 404-60

(G-1780)
MELITTA USA INC (DH)
13925 58th St N (33760-3721)
PHONE..................................727 535-2111
Martin Miller, *President*
Fred Lueck, *CFO*
Ed Mitchell, *Admin Sec*

◆ **EMP:** 74 **EST:** 1963
SQ FT: 104,000
SALES (est): 51.5MM
SALES (corp-wide): 1.8B **Privately Held**
WEB: www.melitta.com
SIC: 2095 3634 Coffee roasting (except by wholesale grocers); coffee makers, electric: household

(G-1781)
MERIDIAN SOUTH AVIATION LLC
15875 Fairchild Dr (33762-3510)
P.O. Box 17882 (33762-0882)
PHONE..................................727 536-5387
Michael L Hauser,
EMP: 5 **EST:** 2006
SQ FT: 2,000
SALES (est): 868.9K **Privately Held**
WEB: www.clpilots.com
SIC: 3721 Aircraft

(G-1782)
METAL CULVERTS INC
2148 Pine Forest Dr (33764-5729)
PHONE..................................727 531-1431
Shawn Hapeman, *Manager*
EMP: 23
SQ FT: 27,837
SALES (corp-wide): 19.5MM **Privately Held**
WEB: www.metalculverts.com
SIC: 3444 3312 3317 Culverts, sheet metal; blast furnaces & steel mills; steel pipe & tubes
PA: Metal Culverts, Inc.
711 Heisinger Rd
Jefferson City MO 65109
573 636-7312

(G-1783)
METAL INDUSTRIES INC (HQ)
Also Called: Metal Aire
1985 Carroll St (33765-1909)
PHONE..................................727 441-2651
Jay K Poppleton, *CEO*
Peter Desoto, *CEO*
Grant Tyson, *President*
Mark Paul, *General Mgr*
Janet L Fasenmyer, *Vice Pres*
◆ **EMP:** 200 **EST:** 1949
SQ FT: 700,000
SALES (est): 231.8MM
SALES (corp-wide): 250.9MM **Privately Held**
WEB: www.mihvac.com
SIC: 3585 Parts for heating, cooling & refrigerating equipment
PA: J. T. Walker Industries, Inc.
1310 N Hercules Ave Ste A
Clearwater FL 33765
727 461-0501

(G-1784)
MICA VISIONS INC
2650 Enterprise Rd Ste D (33763-1101)
PHONE..................................727 712-3213
James Hazlett II, *President*
Sean Wall, *Vice Pres*
Mike Francisco, *Prdtn Mgr*
EMP: 5 **EST:** 1989
SQ FT: 5,000
SALES (est): 544K **Privately Held**
WEB: www.micavisions.com
SIC: 2511 Wood household furniture

(G-1785)
MICROSS PRMIER SMCDTR SVCS LLC
Also Called: Micross Components
4400 140th Ave N Ste 140 (33762-3813)
PHONE..................................727 532-1777
Anthony Mastry, *Manager*
EMP: 37 **EST:** 2013
SALES (est): 4.5MM
SALES (corp-wide): 191.4MM **Privately Held**
WEB: www.micross.com
SIC: 3674 Semiconductors & related devices
HQ: Premier Semiconductor Services Llc
1050 Perimeter Rd Ste 201
Manchester NH 03103
267 954-0130

(G-1786)
MID STATE SCREEN GRAPHICS LLC
13183 38th St N (33762-4228)
PHONE..................................727 573-2299
Richard Hawley, *Vice Pres*
Carrie Brightbill, *Vice Pres*
Debbie Sytsma, *Opers Mgr*
EMP: 26 **EST:** 1978
SQ FT: 12,400
SALES (est): 2.7MM
SALES (corp-wide): 48.4MM **Privately Held**
WEB: www.midstatescreengraphics.com
SIC: 2759 Screen printing
PA: Thermopatch Corporation
2204 Erie Blvd E
Syracuse NY 13224
315 446-8110

(G-1787)
MIKE COPE RACE CARS LLC
14152 63rd Way N (33760-3616)
PHONE..................................352 585-2810
Michael S Cope, *Manager*
EMP: 8 **EST:** 2015
SALES (est): 369.7K **Privately Held**
WEB: www.mikecoperacecars.com
SIC: 3711 Automobile assembly, including specialty automobiles

(G-1788)
MJR MANUFACTURING LLC
2519 N Mcmullen Booth Rd (33761-4173)
PHONE..................................727 460-0636
Michel Chabaneix, *Principal*
EMP: 6 **EST:** 2009
SALES (est): 140.2K **Privately Held**
SIC: 3999 Manufacturing industries

(G-1789)
MODERN MAIL PRINT SLUTIONS INC
14201 58th St N (33760-2802)
PHONE..................................727 572-6245
Barbara Cosser, *President*
Corey Cosser, *Vice Pres*
Rick Cosser, *Vice Pres*
Chris Hall, *Vice Pres*
EMP: 30 **EST:** 1976
SQ FT: 19,760
SALES (est): 5.1MM **Privately Held**
WEB: www.modmail.com
SIC: 2752 Commercial printing, offset

(G-1790)
MODERN METAL SYSTEMS INC (PA)
4530 126th Ave N (33762-4703)
PHONE..................................727 573-2255
Gary Wilson, *President*
Vera Wilson, *Treasurer*
▼ **EMP:** 5 **EST:** 1988
SQ FT: 10,960
SALES (est): 872K **Privately Held**
WEB: www.ultraseam.com
SIC: 3444 Sheet metalwork

(G-1791)
MONIN INC
Also Called: Monin Gourmet Flavorings
2100 Range Rd (33765-2125)
PHONE..................................727 461-3033
William Lombardo, *CEO*
Olivier Monin, *President*
Jeremy Coulbeck, *General Mgr*
Jim White, *Managing Dir*
Vittorio Caputi, *Business Mgr*
◆ **EMP:** 151
SQ FT: 200,000
SALES (est): 75.7MM **Privately Held**
WEB: www.monin.com
SIC: 2087 Flavoring extracts & syrups
HQ: Georges Monin Sas
5 Rue Ferdinand De Lesseps
Bourges 18000
248 506-436

(G-1792)
MORTEN ENTERPRISES INC (PA)
12350 Us Highway 19 N (33764-7418)
PHONE..................................727 531-8957
James E Morten, *CEO*
James A Morten, *President*
Scott J Morten, *Vice Pres*
EMP: 14 **EST:** 1965
SQ FT: 13,228
SALES (est): 13.5MM **Privately Held**
SIC: 2752 Commercial printing, offset

(G-1793)
MORTON PLANT MEASE HEALTH CARE
430 Pinellas St (33756-3365)
PHONE..................................727 462-7052
EMP: 831
SALES (corp-wide): 2B **Privately Held**
WEB: www.baycare.org
SIC: 3842 8099 Hearing aids; blood related health services
HQ: Morton Plant Mease Health Care, Inc.
300 Pinellas St
Clearwater FL 33756

(G-1794)
MR BILLS FINE FOODS
1115 Ponce De Leon Blvd (33756-1040)
PHONE..................................727 581-9850
EMP: 6 **EST:** 2011
SALES (est): 382.7K **Privately Held**
WEB: www.mrbillsfinefoods.com
SIC: 2099 Food preparations

(G-1795)
MSP INDUSTRIES LLC
Also Called: Model Screw Products
1500 N Belcher Rd (33765-1301)
PHONE..................................727 443-5764
David Knuepfer Jr,
EMP: 128 **EST:** 2015
SALES (est): 37.4MM **Privately Held**
WEB: www.mspindustriesusa.com
SIC: 3599 3451 Machine shop, jobbing & repair; screw machine products

(G-1796)
MTS PACKAGING SYSTEM INC
12920 Automobile Blvd (33762-4723)
PHONE..................................727 812-2830
EMP: 7 **EST:** 2019
SALES (est): 88.9K **Privately Held**
SIC: 3089 Plastics products

(G-1797)
MTS SALES & MARKETING INC
12920 Automobile Blvd (33762-4723)
PHONE..................................727 812-2830
Todd E Seigel, *President*
EMP: 70 **EST:** 1996
SALES (est): 4.4MM **Publicly Held**
WEB: www.omnicell.com
SIC: 3089 Plastic containers, except foam
HQ: Mts Medication Technologies, Inc.
2003 Gandy Blvd N Ste 800
Saint Petersburg FL 33702
727 576-6311

(G-1798)
MY FAMILYS SEASONINGS LLC
15301 Roosevelt Blvd # 303 (33760-3561)
P.O. Box 5925, Oceanside CA (92052-5925)
PHONE..................................863 698-7968
Christine Quinn, *CEO*
EMP: 10 **EST:** 2005
SALES (est): 900K **Privately Held**
WEB: www.myfamilyseasonings.com
SIC: 2099 5141 Seasonings: dry mixes; groceries, general line

(G-1799)
N C A MANUFACTURING INC
1985 Carroll St (33765-1909)
PHONE..................................727 441-2651
James R Tatum, *Ch of Bd*
Wayne Binder, *Vice Pres*
Andrew M Simurda, *Vice Pres*
▼ **EMP:** 87 **EST:** 1961
SQ FT: 54,000
SALES (est): 8.5MM
SALES (corp-wide): 250.9MM **Privately Held**
WEB: www.ncamfg.com
SIC: 3444 Sheet metalwork
HQ: Metal Industries, Inc.
1985 Carroll St
Clearwater FL 33765
727 441-2651

(G-1800)
NANO ACTIVATED COATINGS INC
507 S Prospect Ave (33756-5625)
PHONE..................................727 437-1099
Robinson Garsha, *Principal*
EMP: 7 **EST:** 2015
SALES (est): 125.6K **Privately Held**
WEB: www.nanoactivatedcoatings.com
SIC: 3479 Metal coating & allied service

(G-1801)
NATIONAL SIGN INC
5651 116th Ave N (33760-4812)
PHONE..................................727 572-1503
Dennis D Devine, *President*
EMP: 10 **EST:** 2003
SALES (est): 675.7K **Privately Held**
SIC: 3993 Signs & advertising specialties

(G-1802)
NATIONAL TRAFFIC SIGNS INC
14521 60th St N (33760-2712)
PHONE..................................727 446-7983
William E Malia, *President*
Barbara Malia, *Treasurer*
Charles Silcox, *Marketing Mgr*
Donna Desanto, *Graphic Designe*
EMP: 9 **EST:** 1962
SQ FT: 5,000
SALES (est): 1.7MM **Privately Held**
WEB: www.ntsigns.com
SIC: 3993 2752 5085 2396 Signs, not made in custom sign painting shops; decals, lithographed; signmaker equipment & supplies; automotive & apparel trimmings

(G-1803)
NATURES BOTANICALS INC
2101 Sunnydale Blvd Ste C (33765-1204)
PHONE..................................727 443-4524
Jimmy Holmlund, *Manager*
EMP: 6 **Privately Held**
WEB: www.naturesbotanicals.com
SIC: 2833 Hormones or derivatives; drugs & herbs: grading, grinding & milling
PA: Natures Botanicals Inc
633 Cleveland St
Clearwater FL

(G-1804)
NAUSET ENTERPRISES INC
Also Called: Affordable Displays
2120 Calumet St Ste 1 (33765-1325)
PHONE..................................727 443-3469
William Brehm, *President*
Rosemary Brehm, *Vice Pres*
EMP: 9 **EST:** 1992
SQ FT: 7,500
SALES (est): 1.2MM **Privately Held**
SIC: 2542 2541 3993 Fixtures: display, office or store: except wood; display fixtures, wood; signs & advertising specialties

(G-1805)
NEAT CLEAN GROUP INC
2523 Marina Key Ln (33763-2162)
PHONE..................................727 459-6079
Zana Lukosiuniene, *Principal*
EMP: 10 **EST:** 2005
SALES (est): 785.2K **Privately Held**
SIC: 3699 Cleaning equipment, ultrasonic, except medical & dental

(G-1806)
NELCO PRODUCTS INC
15251 Roosevelt Blvd # 202 (33760-3560)
PHONE..................................727 533-8282
William Mazzio, *General Mgr*
Matt McGuirk, *General Mgr*
William Dalrymple, *Opers Staff*
Bill Mazzio, *Accounts Exec*
Camille Giannetti, *Manager*
EMP: 8
SALES (corp-wide): 10.7MM **Privately Held**
WEB: www.nelcoproducts.com
SIC: 3398 Metal heat treating
PA: Nelco Products, Inc.
22 Riverside Dr
Pembroke MA 02359
781 826-3010

(G-1807)
NEW NAUTICAL COATINGS INC (HQ)
14805 49th St N (33762-2809)
PHONE..................................727 523-8053
Erik Norrie, *CEO*
David Norrie, *President*
Mike Detmer, *COO*
Tommy Craft, *Vice Pres*
Doug Laue, *CFO*
◆ **EMP:** 30 **EST:** 1978
SQ FT: 39,000
SALES (est): 14.1MM
SALES (corp-wide): 10B **Privately Held**
WEB: www.seahawkpaints.com
SIC: 2851 Marine paints
PA: Akzo Nobel N.V.
Christian Neefestraat 2
Amsterdam
889 697-555

(G-1808)
NEWSPAPER PRINTING COMPANY
12198 44th St N (33762-5109)
PHONE..................................727 572-7488
John Elven, *Owner*
EMP: 9 **EST:** 2013
SALES (est): 102.9K **Privately Held**
WEB: www.npcprinting.com
SIC: 2711 2759 Commercial printing & newspaper publishing combined; commercial printing

(G-1809)
NORDQUIST DIELECTRICS INC
Also Called: EMI Filter Company
12750 59th Way N (33760-3906)
PHONE..................................727 585-7990
Ted Nordquist, *President*
Ann Luce, *Vice Pres*
Eric Nordquist, *Vice Pres*
Kevin T Luce, *Manager*
EMP: 24 **EST:** 1973
SQ FT: 10,000
SALES (est): 2.8MM **Privately Held**
WEB: www.emifiltercompany.com
SIC: 3675 3677 Electronic capacitors; filtration devices, electronic

(G-1810)
NORRIS PRECISION MFG INC
4680 110th Ave N (33762-4951)
P.O. Box 1968, Pinellas Park (33780-1968)
PHONE..................................727 572-6330
Arthur Norris III, *President*
Nancy L Norris, *Corp Secy*
Andrea Just, *Purch Dir*
Richard Nash, *QC Mgr*
Keith Harmon, *Engineer*
EMP: 75
SQ FT: 52,000
SALES (est): 19.6MM **Privately Held**
WEB: www.norrisprecision.com
SIC: 3724 Aircraft engines & engine parts

(G-1811)
NOTE BIN INC
Also Called: Abyde
29399 Us 19 N Ste 360 (33761-2137)
PHONE..................................727 642-8530
Matt Deblasi, *CEO*
EMP: 12 **EST:** 2017
SALES (est): 607.9K **Privately Held**
SIC: 7372 Application computer software

(G-1812)
NUENERGY TECHNOLOGIES CORP
601 Cleveland St Ste 501 (33755-4182)
P.O. Box 329 (33757-0329)
PHONE..................................866 895-6838
Hector M Guevara, *President*
Rolando Alcover, *Vice Pres*
EMP: 7 **EST:** 2009
SALES (est): 263K **Privately Held**
WEB: www.nuenergytech.com
SIC: 3699 Electrical equipment & supplies

(G-1813)
NULAB INC
519 Cleveland St Ste 101 (33755-4009)
PHONE..................................727 446-1126
Hakan Johanson, *Branch Mgr*
EMP: 70 **Privately Held**
WEB: www.nulabinc.com
SIC: 2833 2048 Vitamins, natural or synthetic: bulk, uncompounded; prepared feeds
PA: Nulab, Inc.
2161 Logan St
Clearwater FL 33765

(G-1814)
NUTRITION LABORATORIES INC
2151 Logan St (33765-1312)
PHONE..................................915 496-7531
Hakan Johanson, *CEO*
EMP: 25 **EST:** 2006
SALES (est): 2MM **Privately Held**
WEB: www.nutritionlabs.us
SIC: 2023 Dietary supplements, dairy & non-dairy based

(G-1815)
NUTRITION LABORATORIES INC
2141 Logan St (33765-1312)
PHONE..................................727 442-2747
Hakan Johanson, *President*
Hakkan Johanson, *President*
Brisida Dhembi, *Manager*
▲ **EMP:** 23 **EST:** 2004
SALES (est): 554.4K **Privately Held**
WEB: www.nutritionlabs.us
SIC: 2834 2087 5149 Vitamin preparations; beverage bases; beverage bases, concentrates, syrups, powders & mixes; beverage concentrates

(G-1816)
OCEANIC ELECTRICAL MFG CO INC
1904 Calumet St (33765-1107)
PHONE..................................908 355-1900
C Hank Barnes, *President*
Jon Barnes, *General Mgr*
EMP: 11 **EST:** 1921
SQ FT: 6,000
SALES (est): 309.9K **Privately Held**
WEB: www.oceanicelectric.com
SIC: 3641 Electric lamps & parts for specialized applications

(G-1817)
OMNIVORE TECHNOLOGIES INC
13577 Feather Sound Dr # 390 (33762-5547)
PHONE..................................800 293-4058
Mike Wior, *CEO*
Daniel Singer, *COO*
Feras Ghandour, *Vice Pres*
Matt Haselhoff, *Vice Pres*
Danielle Jaksic, *Vice Pres*
EMP: 55 **EST:** 2013
SQ FT: 3,500
SALES (est): 6MM **Privately Held**
WEB: www.omnivore.io
SIC: 7372 Business oriented computer software

(G-1818)
ONGOING CARE SOLUTIONS INC
11721 Us Highway 19 N (33764-7405)
PHONE..................................727 526-0707
Richard Nace, *President*
Linda Lee, *Vice Pres*
Brian Trokey, *Purch Mgr*
John Kenney, *Treasurer*
Joe Schutte, *Supervisor*
◆ **EMP:** 27 **EST:** 1992
SALES (est): 5MM **Privately Held**
WEB: www.ongoingcare.com
SIC: 3842 Orthopedic appliances; splints, pneumatic & wood

(G-1819)
OPIE CHOICE LLC
Also Called: Futura International
22047 Us Highway 19 N (33765-2363)
PHONE..................................727 726-5157
EMP: 14
SALES (corp-wide): 2MM **Privately Held**
SIC: 7372 Prepackaged Software Services
PA: Opie Choice Llc
3870 Nw 83rd St
Gainesville FL 32606
352 331-3741

(G-1820)
ORD OF AHEPA CH 356 DAILY & T
2555 Enterprise Rd Ste 10 (33763-1150)
PHONE..................................727 791-1040
John Tsagaris, *Principal*
EMP: 7 **EST:** 2011
SALES (est): 23.8K **Privately Held**
SIC: 2711 Newspapers, publishing & printing

(G-1821)
ORIFLOW
2125 Range Rd Ste B (33765-2153)
PHONE..................................727 400-4881
William Bryant, *Principal*
John Gierzak, *Vice Pres*
Tracy Gierzak, *Office Mgr*
EMP: 18 **EST:** 2010
SALES (est): 1.2MM **Privately Held**
WEB: www.oriflow.com
SIC: 3829 Liquid leak detection equipment

(G-1822)
ORIGINCLEAR INC (PA)
13575 58th St N Ste 200 (33760-3739)
PHONE..................................323 939-6645
T Riggs Eckelberry, *Ch of Bd*
Tom Marchesello, *COO*
EMP: 4 **EST:** 2007
SALES: 4.1MM **Publicly Held**
WEB: www.originclear.com
SIC: 3589 2869 Water treatment equipment, industrial; fuels

(G-1823)
OSBORNE METALS
324 S Madison Ave (33756-5727)
PHONE..................................727 441-1703
Wayne Osborne, *Owner*
Manish Jaiswal, *Director*
EMP: 5 **EST:** 1993
SQ FT: 3,000
SALES (est): 449.5K **Privately Held**
WEB: www.osbornemetals.com
SIC: 3444 3452 Sheet metalwork; bolts, nuts, rivets & washers

(G-1824)
PACE TECH INC
2040 Calumet St (33765-1307)
PHONE..................................727 442-8118
Ilhan Bilgutay, *President*
▲ **EMP:** 17 **EST:** 1976
SQ FT: 7,400
SALES (est): 672.3K **Privately Held**
WEB: www.pacetech-med.com
SIC: 3841 Diagnostic apparatus, medical

(G-1825)
PAIR ODICE BREWING CO LLC
4400 118th Ave N Ste 205 (33762-4433)
PHONE..................................727 755-3423
Renee Hurney, *Accounts Mgr*
Julia Rosenthal, *Mng Member*
EMP: 7 **EST:** 2013
SALES (est): 689.2K **Privately Held**
WEB: www.pairodicebrewing.com
SIC: 2082 5921 Malt liquors; liquor stores

(G-1826)
PARKER RESEARCH CORPORATION
2642 Enterprise Rd (33763-1105)
P.O. Box 1406, Dunedin (34697-1406)
PHONE..................................727 796-4066
S John Parker, *President*
Donna Parker, *Executive*
EMP: 12 **EST:** 1963
SALES (est): 1.7MM **Privately Held**
WEB: www.parkerndt.com
SIC: 3829 Measuring & controlling devices

(G-1827)
PCP GROUP LLC
13590 Automobile Blvd (33762-3816)
PHONE..................................727 388-7171
EMP: 6 **EST:** 2019
SALES (est): 124.7K **Privately Held**
WEB: www.pellonprojects.com
SIC: 3944 Games, toys & children's vehicles

(G-1828)
PE MANUFACTURING COMPANY FLA
Also Called: Pemco
11400 47th St N Ste A (33762-4901)
PHONE..................................727 823-8172
Kenneth M Elder, *President*
EMP: 20 **EST:** 2001
SALES (est): 2.2MM **Privately Held**
SIC: 3559 Screening equipment, electric

(G-1829)
PELICAN INTERNATIONAL INC
Also Called: Badaro Group
6140 Ulmerton Rd (33760-3946)
PHONE..................................727 388-9895
John Ellithorpe, *General Mgr*
Anderson Badaro, *Principal*
Meagan Dozier, *Business Mgr*
Cody McCarroll, *Accounts Mgr*
▲ **EMP:** 50 **EST:** 1974
SQ FT: 80,000
SALES (est): 7.3MM **Privately Held**
WEB: www.pelicansinks.com
SIC: 3431 Sinks: enameled iron, cast iron or pressed metal; bathroom fixtures, including sinks

(G-1830)
PHASETRONICS INC (PA)
Also Called: Motortronics
1600 Sunshine Dr (33765-1316)
P.O. Box 5988 (33758-5988)
PHONE..................................727 573-1819
James Mitchell, *President*
Leslie Bennet, *Vice Pres*
Leslie Bennett, *Vice Pres*
Joyce Mitchell, *Vice Pres*
Dave Brun, *Purch Mgr*
◆ **EMP:** 109 **EST:** 1982
SQ FT: 54,000
SALES (est): 30.1MM **Privately Held**
WEB: www.phasetronics.com
SIC: 3625 Control equipment, electric

(G-1831)
PHOENIX TRANSMISSION PARTS INC (PA)
Also Called: Phoenix Trans Parts
12550 44th St N Ste A (33762-5120)
PHONE..................................727 541-0269
Andrew Smith, *President*
Tony Leverso, *Sales Staff*
EMP: 9 **EST:** 2004
SQ FT: 800
SALES (est): 950K **Privately Held**
WEB: www.ptptrans.com
SIC: 3714 7537 Motor vehicle parts & accessories; automotive transmission repair shops

(G-1832)
PIERCE MANUFACTURING INC
Frontline Communications
12770 44th St N (33762-4713)
PHONE..................................727 573-0400
William Mulford, *Project Mgr*
Chris Custer, *Opers Mgr*
Jody Phillips, *Materials Mgr*
Jeff Dickerson, *Opers Spvr*
Richard Motkowicz, *Chief Engr*
EMP: 2222
SALES (corp-wide): 6.8B **Publicly Held**
WEB: www.piercemfg.com
SIC: 3713 3711 Truck & bus bodies; motor vehicles & car bodies
HQ: Pierce Manufacturing, Inc.
2600 American Dr
Appleton WI 54914
920 832-3000

(G-1833)
PINELLAS BLIND AND SHUTTER INC
5100 Ulmerton Rd Ste 22 (33760-4031)
PHONE..................................727 481-4461
James Austin, *Principal*
EMP: 6 **EST:** 2013
SALES (est): 85K **Privately Held**
SIC: 3442 Shutters, door or window: metal

▲ = Import ▼=Export
◆ =Import/Export

(G-1834)
PINELLAS ELECTRIC MOTOR REPAIR
12990 44th St N (33762-4729)
P.O. Box 217, Indian Rocks Beach (33785-0217)
PHONE..................................727 572-0777
Lee C Fletcher, *President*
Christopher Fletcher, *President*
Greg Murin, *Sales Mgr*
▲ **EMP:** 6 **EST:** 1988
SQ FT: 6,500
SALES (est): 687.8K **Privately Held**
WEB: www.pinellaselectricmotor.com
SIC: 7694 5084 Electric motor repair; industrial machinery & equipment

(G-1835)
PIVOTAL SIGN & GRAPHICS INC
2140 Sunnydale Blvd Ste D (33765-1209)
PHONE..................................727 462-2266
William M Waszak, *President*
Mary J Waszak, *Vice Pres*
Meagan Faiola, *Sales Mgr*
EMP: 5 **EST:** 2007
SQ FT: 1,200
SALES (est): 677.4K **Privately Held**
WEB: www.pivotalsign.com
SIC: 3993 Signs & advertising specialties

(G-1836)
PNEUMATIC SCALE ANGELUS
Also Called: Pneumatic Scale Clearwater
5320 140th Ave N (33760-3743)
PHONE..................................727 535-4100
Robert H Chapman, *CEO*
William Morgan, *President*
David M Gianini, *Vice Pres*
Michael McLaughlin, *Vice Pres*
Mike Hayworth, *Engineer*
▲ **EMP:** 70 **EST:** 1990
SQ FT: 48,000
SALES (est): 25.7MM **Privately Held**
WEB: www.psangelus.com
SIC: 3565 Packaging machinery
HQ: Barry-Wehmiller Companies, Inc.
8020 Forsyth Blvd
Saint Louis MO 63105
314 862-8000

(G-1837)
PORTABLE PUMPING SYSTEMS INC
Also Called: Coastal Dewatering
4760 Spring Ave (33762-4435)
P.O. Box 1246, Oldsmar (34677-1246)
PHONE..................................727 518-9191
Don Wendel, *President*
▲ **EMP:** 9 **EST:** 1994
SALES (est): 1.2MM **Privately Held**
WEB: www.portablepumpingsystems.com
SIC: 3561 Pumps & pumping equipment

(G-1838)
POZIN ENTERPRISES INC
Also Called: Sun-Glo Plating Co
14493 62nd St N (33760-2786)
P.O. Box 155, Pinellas Park (33780-0155)
PHONE..................................727 546-8974
Andrew Pozin, *President*
Dave Brackenhamer, *General Mgr*
Bill Farrar, *Purchasing*
EMP: 40 **EST:** 1986
SQ FT: 30,000
SALES (est): 7.8MM **Privately Held**
WEB: www.sun-glo.com
SIC: 3471 3479 Finishing, metals or formed products; electroplating & plating; painting of metal products

(G-1839)
PRECAST AND FOAM WORKS LLC
29757 66th Way N (33761-1607)
PHONE..................................727 657-9195
Gabor Szobolodi, *Principal*
EMP: 6 **EST:** 2014
SALES (est): 559.1K **Privately Held**
WEB: www.precastandfoam.com
SIC: 3272 Precast terrazo or concrete products

(G-1840)
PRECISION LITHO SERVICE INC
Also Called: Pls Print
4250 118th Ave N (33762-5135)
PHONE..................................727 573-1763
John A Blair, *President*
Terry Olson, *Vice Pres*
Jane Cobb, *Treasurer*
Jane Howell, *Treasurer*
Win Hylton, *Admin Sec*
EMP: 53 **EST:** 1984
SQ FT: 32,600
SALES (est): 12.1MM **Privately Held**
WEB: www.plsprint.com
SIC: 2752 Commercial printing, offset

(G-1841)
PRECISION SHAFT TECHNOLOGY
Also Called: PST
1717 Overbrook Ave (33755-1935)
PHONE..................................727 442-1711
Mark Veldhuis, *President*
Arlene Veldhuis, *Office Mgr*
▲ **EMP:** 5 **EST:** 1996
SQ FT: 3,500
SALES (est): 1MM **Privately Held**
WEB: www.pstds.com
SIC: 3714 Motor vehicle parts & accessories

(G-1842)
PRECISION TOOL & MOLD INC
12050 44th St N (33762-5107)
PHONE..................................727 573-4441
Sherry Mowery, *President*
Earl C Mowery, *Vice Pres*
William E Mowery, *Vice Pres*
▲ **EMP:** 16 **EST:** 1981
SQ FT: 11,000
SALES (est): 3.4MM **Privately Held**
WEB: www.precisiontoolmoldinc.com
SIC: 3089 Injection molding of plastics

(G-1843)
PREFERRED MATERIALS
12955 40th St N (33762-4204)
PHONE..................................727 573-3027
EMP: 6 **EST:** 2018
SALES (est): 90.7K **Privately Held**
WEB: www.preferredmaterials.com
SIC: 2951 Asphalt paving mixtures & blocks

(G-1844)
PREMIER SEMICONDUCTOR SVCS LLC
4400 140th Ave N Ste 140 (33762-3813)
PHONE..................................727 532-1777
Kenneth Buckley, *Branch Mgr*
EMP: 6
SALES (corp-wide): 191.4MM **Privately Held**
SIC: 3674 Semiconductors & related devices
HQ: Premier Semiconductor Services Llc
1050 Perimeter Rd Ste 201
Manchester NH 03103
267 954-0130

(G-1845)
PRESSEX INC
12910 Automobile Blvd (33762-4756)
PHONE..................................727 299-8500
Janelle Gabay, *President*
EMP: 14 **EST:** 2007
SQ FT: 18,000
SALES (est): 551.3K **Privately Held**
WEB: www.pressexpromo.com
SIC: 2752 Commercial printing, offset

(G-1846)
PREVAIL SOLUTIONS LLC
19321 Us Highway 19 N # 605 (33764-3144)
PHONE..................................727 210-6600
Benjamin E Wieder, *Managing Prtnr*
Daniel J Wieder, *Mng Member*
Noah A Wieder, *Mng Member*
EMP: 5 **EST:** 2010
SQ FT: 2,000
SALES (est): 413.3K **Privately Held**
WEB: www.chassisformen.com
SIC: 2844 Toilet preparations

(G-1847)
PRINTS 2 GO INC
24129 Us Highway 19 N (33763-5000)
PHONE..................................727 725-1700
Bahaa Tawsik, *President*
EMP: 10 **EST:** 2018
SALES (est): 452.4K **Privately Held**
WEB: www.store.prints2go.us
SIC: 2752 Commercial printing, lithographic

(G-1848)
PRIORITY PRINTING INC
2125 Range Rd Ste B (33765-2153)
PHONE..................................727 446-6605
Fax: 727 446-8514
EMP: 8
SQ FT: 5,000
SALES (est): 1MM **Privately Held**
SIC: 2752 Printing

(G-1849)
PROCYON CORPORATION (PA)
1300 S Highland Ave (33756-6519)
PHONE..................................727 447-2998
Regina W Anderson, *Ch of Bd*
Justice W Anderson, *President*
James B Anderson, *CFO*
EMP: 8 **EST:** 1987
SQ FT: 3,800
SALES: 4.7MM **Publicly Held**
WEB: www.procyoncorp.com
SIC: 2834 Pharmaceutical preparations; dermatologicals

(G-1850)
PROTEX INC
10500 47th St N (33762-5017)
PHONE..................................727 573-4665
Christos J Botsolas, *President*
Dana K Botsolas, *Vice Pres*
EMP: 13 **EST:** 1980
SQ FT: 50,000
SALES (est): 2.1MM **Privately Held**
SIC: 3083 3081 Thermosetting laminates: rods, tubes, plates & sheet; unsupported plastics film & sheet

(G-1851)
PROTO CORP
10500 47th St N (33762-5017)
PHONE..................................727 573-4665
Christos J Botsolas, *President*
Dana K Botsolas, *Vice Pres*
Dana Botsolas, *Vice Pres*
Louis Walton, *Vice Pres*
Ratina Noykathok, *Purchasing*
▼ **EMP:** 100 **EST:** 1980
SQ FT: 110,000
SALES (est): 20.2MM **Privately Held**
WEB: www.protocorporation.com
SIC: 3089 Injection molding of plastics

(G-1852)
PROTOTYPE PLSTIC EXTRUSION INC
3637 131st Ave N (33762-4263)
PHONE..................................727 572-0803
Jeffrey Wells, *President*
Duane Wells, *Treasurer*
◆ **EMP:** 28 **EST:** 1978
SQ FT: 19,000
SALES (est): 1.5MM **Privately Held**
WEB: www.prototypeplastics.com
SIC: 3089 Mfg Plastic Products

(G-1853)
PUBLISHERS PRMOTIONAL SVCS INC
Also Called: Family Reading Club
1383 S Missouri Ave (33756-6500)
PHONE..................................303 431-4080
Lou Carbonaro, *Principal*
EMP: 8 **EST:** 2008
SALES (est): 139.7K **Privately Held**
SIC: 2741 Miscellaneous publishing

(G-1854)
PURE POSTCARDS INC
1938 Byram Dr (33755-1508)
PHONE..................................877 446-2434
Irma Jeanis, *President*
Dru Jeanis, *Senior VP*
EMP: 10 **EST:** 2002
SQ FT: 12,400
SALES (est): 302.6K **Privately Held**
SIC: 2752 Promotional printing, lithographic

(G-1855)
QUALITY CREATIONS INC
10550 47th St N (33762-5017)
PHONE..................................727 571-4332
Tiffiny L Barany, *President*
Tiffiny Barany, *President*
EMP: 6 **EST:** 1993
SALES (est): 582.7K **Privately Held**
WEB: www.quality-creations-inc.com
SIC: 2434 Wood kitchen cabinets

(G-1856)
RANOREX INC
28050 Us Highway 19 N # 303 (33761-2628)
PHONE..................................727 835-5570
Robert Muehlfellner, *President*
Andreas Waschnig, *General Mgr*
Ned Wilbur, *Engineer*
William Silvestri, *Sales Staff*
EMP: 29 **EST:** 2013
SALES (est): 1.7MM
SALES (corp-wide): 201.5MM **Privately Held**
WEB: www.ranorex.com
SIC: 7372 Application computer software
HQ: Ranorex Gmbh
Untere DonaustraBe 13-15/6. Stock
Wien 1020
316 281-328

(G-1857)
RCA MACHINE & MFG INC
4652 107th Cir N (33762-5005)
PHONE..................................727 561-0150
EMP: 7 **EST:** 2019
SALES (est): 64.2K **Privately Held**
WEB: www.rcamachine.com
SIC: 3999 Manufacturing industries

(G-1858)
RES-NET MICROWAVE INC
5410 115th Ave N (33760-4841)
P.O. Box 18802 (33762-1802)
PHONE..................................727 530-9555
Roger Mayo, *President*
▲ **EMP:** 33 **EST:** 1987
SQ FT: 33,000
SALES (est): 2.6MM
SALES (corp-wide): 52.6MM **Privately Held**
WEB: www.electrotechnik.com
SIC: 3679 3663 Microwave components; television broadcasting & communications equipment
PA: Electro Technik Industries, Inc.
5410 115th Ave N
Clearwater FL 33760
727 530-9555

(G-1859)
RETAIL CLOUD TECHNOLOGIES LLC
Also Called: Teamwork Commerce
380 Park Place Blvd # 250 (33759-4930)
PHONE..................................727 210-1700
Michael Mauerer, *CEO*
Carmen Mauerer, *VP Finance*
Michael Maurer, *Mng Member*
Chad Willis, *Mng Member*
EMP: 98 **EST:** 2013
SALES (est): 2.5MM **Privately Held**
WEB: www.retailcloud.com
SIC: 7372 7371 Business oriented computer software; computer software development

(G-1860)
RICH MAID CABINETS INC
Also Called: Innovative Cabinet & Case Work
12706 Daniels Dr (33762-4710)
PHONE..................................727 572-4857
Don Roach, *President*
EMP: 10 **EST:** 1989
SQ FT: 9,000
SALES (est): 1.3MM **Privately Held**
WEB: www.richmaidcabinetsclearwater.com
SIC: 2434 Wood kitchen cabinets

GEOGRAPHIC

(G-1861)
RIVA INDUSTRIES INC
Also Called: Florida Machining Center
4986 113th Ave N (33760-4831)
P.O. Box 86003, Saint Petersburg (33738-6003)
PHONE..................................813 573-1601
William Sponheimer, *President*
Mary Ann Sponheimer, *CFO*
EMP: 7 **EST:** 1984
SQ FT: 5,000
SALES (est): 731.6K **Privately Held**
SIC: 3599 Machine shop, jobbing & repair

(G-1862)
ROBERTS QUALITY PRINTING INC
Also Called: Roberts Printing
2049 Calumet St (33765-1308)
PHONE..................................727 442-4011
Robert T Davis, *President*
J Wayne Nightingale, *Chairman*
Jeanne Davis, *COO*
Kim Blackburn, *Accounts Mgr*
Jack Schero, *Director*
EMP: 45 **EST:** 1968
SQ FT: 28,000
SALES (est): 10.7MM **Privately Held**
WEB: www.robpri.com
SIC: 2752 2796 2791 2789 Commercial printing, offset; platemaking services; typesetting; bookbinding & related work; commercial printing

(G-1863)
ROBOTIC PARKING SYSTEMS INC
12812 60th St N (33760-3959)
PHONE..................................727 539-7275
Royce S Monteverdi, *CEO*
Gerhard Haag, *President*
Juergen Bauer, *Chairman*
Ramanathan Ramasubbu, *COO*
Mary Lou Dewyngaert, *Treasurer*
▲ **EMP:** 12 **EST:** 1994
SQ FT: 165,133
SALES (est): 3.5MM **Privately Held**
WEB: www.roboticparking.com
SIC: 3559 7389 Parking facility equipment & supplies; design, commercial & industrial

(G-1864)
ROLLSHIELD LLC
1151 Kapp Dr (33765-2114)
PHONE..................................727 441-2243
Larry Sgammato, *Sales Associate*
Gregory Moore,
EMP: 16 **EST:** 2006
SALES (est): 3.6MM **Privately Held**
WEB: www.rollshield.com
SIC: 3442 1751 Shutters, door or window: metal; window & door installation & erection

(G-1865)
ROOT INTERNATIONAL INC (PA)
Also Called: Cases2go
4910 Creekside Dr Ste B (33760-4042)
PHONE..................................813 265-1808
David W Root, *President*
Chad Albritton, *Technology*
EMP: 16 **EST:** 1982
SALES (est): 1.2MM **Privately Held**
WEB: www.cases2go.com
SIC: 3086 Packaging & shipping materials, foamed plastic

(G-1866)
RV AIR INC (PA)
628 Cleveland St Apt 1407 (33755-6621)
PHONE..................................309 657-4300
Eddie Rice, *CEO*
Rose Rice, *President*
EMP: 6 **EST:** 2015
SQ FT: 1,000
SALES (est): 738.4K **Privately Held**
WEB: www.rvair.com
SIC: 3564 5075 Filters, air: furnaces, air conditioning equipment, etc.; air filters

(G-1867)
RXENERGY LLC
2449 N Mcmullen Booth Rd (33759-1314)
PHONE..................................727 726-4204
Phil Silberhorn, *Marketing Staff*
Steven Tartaglia,
Brian Newton,
Tim O'Sullivan,
EMP: 10 **EST:** 2010
SALES (est): 535.3K **Privately Held**
WEB: www.rxenergy.com
SIC: 3841 Surgical & medical instruments

(G-1868)
SAMPLETECH
1953 Whitney Way (33760-1618)
PHONE..................................727 239-7055
Matthew Sweadner, *Owner*
EMP: 5
SQ FT: 2,500
SALES (est): 310K **Privately Held**
SIC: 3822 Auto controls regulating residntl & coml environmt & applncs

(G-1869)
SCREAMING BANSHEE LLC
2003 Freedom Dr (33755-1295)
PHONE..................................727 744-6808
EMP: 6 **EST:** 2012
SALES (est): 263.5K **Privately Held**
WEB: www.screaming-banshee.com
SIC: 3714 Motor vehicle parts & accessories

(G-1870)
SCRIBE MANUFACTURING INC (PA)
Also Called: Norwood Promotional Products
14421 Myerlake Cir (33760-2840)
PHONE..................................727 524-7482
Emmanuel Bruno, *CEO*
Fareeha S Amin, *Principal*
Todd Gartman, *Vice Pres*
Bob Keller, *Vice Pres*
Timothy Kelly, *Vice Pres*
EMP: 256 **EST:** 1999
SALES (est): 42.2MM **Privately Held**
SIC: 3951 Pens & mechanical pencils

(G-1871)
SCRIBE OPCO INC (PA)
Also Called: Koozie Group
14421 Myerlake Cir (33760-2840)
P.O. Box 23088, Tampa (33623-2088)
PHONE..................................727 536-7895
Jonathan Fox, *President*
Melissa McCaffrey, *Chairman*
Francine Dupuis, *Vice Pres*
Michael Koichopolos, *Vice Pres*
Jeff Ibberson, *Mfg Mgr*
EMP: 68 **EST:** 2017
SALES (est): 25MM **Privately Held**
WEB: www.kooziegroup.com
SIC: 3951 Pens & mechanical pencils

(G-1872)
SEABOARD MANUFACTURING LLC
13214 38th St N (33762-4268)
PHONE..................................727 497-3572
Shawn McNary, *Managing Prtnr*
Charles Rowland, *Finance Dir*
Tabatha Searles, *Accountant*
Leo J Govoni, *Mng Member*
EMP: 9
SQ FT: 10,000
SALES (est): 202K **Privately Held**
WEB: www.seaboardmfg.com
SIC: 3599 3999 8999 Machine shop, jobbing & repair; atomizers, toiletry; artist

(G-1873)
SENTINEL SQ OFF BLDG MGT & LSG
300 S Duncan Ave Ste 291 (33755-6414)
PHONE..................................727 461-7700
Erika Barrett, *Principal*
EMP: 6 **EST:** 2007
SALES (est): 163.5K **Privately Held**
SIC: 2711 Newspapers, publishing & printing

(G-1874)
SERVICING SOLUTIONS GROUP
28100 Us Highway 19 N # 204 (33761-2635)
PHONE..................................727 216-4477
EMP: 6 **EST:** 2010
SALES (est): 133.7K **Privately Held**
SIC: 1389 Roustabout service

(G-1875)
SERVO TECH INC
Also Called: Servotech
4785 110th Ave N (33762-4912)
PHONE..................................727 573-7998
Radoslav Prissadachky, *President*
EMP: 6 **EST:** 1985
SALES (est): 449.6K **Privately Held**
WEB: www.servotech.com
SIC: 3599 3549 Machine shop, jobbing & repair; metalworking machinery

(G-1876)
SHADOW-CASTER LED LIGHTING LLC
2060 Calumet St (33765-1307)
P.O. Box 82, Dunedin (34697-0082)
PHONE..................................727 474-2877
Steven Uhl, *Opers Staff*
Brian Rogers, *Mng Member*
EMP: 29
SALES (est): 6.8MM **Privately Held**
WEB: www.shadow-caster.com
SIC: 3562 Casters

(G-1877)
SICOMA NORTH AMERICA INC
11300 47th St N (33762-4953)
PHONE..................................800 921-7559
Marianne Johnson, *Principal*
Luca Via Brenta, *Principal*
Michele Via Brenta, *Principal*
Randy Johnson, *Vice Pres*
Gianni Cardoni, *Sales Staff*
▲ **EMP:** 7 **EST:** 2009
SALES (est): 766.6K **Privately Held**
WEB: www.sicomamixers.com
SIC: 3531 Concrete buggies, powered

(G-1878)
SIO CNC MACHINING INC
14241 60th St N (33760-2706)
PHONE..................................727 533-8271
Kouangheu Sio, *President*
Mellissa Malaivanh, *Office Mgr*
EMP: 7 **EST:** 1985
SALES (est): 685.8K **Privately Held**
WEB: www.siomachining.com
SIC: 3599 Machine shop, jobbing & repair

(G-1879)
SKINNY MIXES LLC
Also Called: Gce
2849 Executive Dr Ste 210 (33762-2224)
PHONE..................................727 826-0306
Jordan Engelhardt,
EMP: 9 **EST:** 2009
SALES (est): 1.3MM
SALES (corp-wide): 12.1MM **Privately Held**
WEB: www.skinnymixes.com
SIC: 2087 Flavoring extracts & syrups; beverage bases
PA: Goodwest Industries, Llc
48 Quarry Rd
Douglassville PA 19518
800 948-1922

(G-1880)
SMARTHOME-PRODUCTS INC (PA)
1560 Faulds Rd W (33756-2410)
PHONE..................................727 490-7260
Karl Vantrese, *President*
EMP: 10 **EST:** 2008
SALES (est): 783.8K **Privately Held**
WEB: www.smarthome-products.com
SIC: 3645 Residential lighting fixtures

(G-1881)
SOUTHCOAST MARINE PRODUCTS INC
12550 47th Way N (33762-4441)
PHONE..................................727 573-4821
John R Cureton, *President*
Kevin Cureton, *President*
Richard L Cureton, *Vice Pres*
Steve Cureton, *Vice Pres*
▲ **EMP:** 110 **EST:** 1974
SQ FT: 10,000
SALES (est): 8.8MM **Privately Held**
WEB: www.ghslift.com
SIC: 3429 Marine hardware

(G-1882)
SOUTHERN MFG UPHOLSTERY INC
3670 131st Ave N (33762-4262)
PHONE..................................727 573-1006
Matthew J Argue, *President*
Matthew Argue, *President*
EMP: 13 **EST:** 1988
SALES (est): 1MM **Privately Held**
SIC: 3363 Aluminum die-castings

(G-1883)
SOUTHERNSTONE CABINETS INC
12520 Automobile Blvd (33762-4415)
PHONE..................................727 538-0123
David Baccari, *President*
EMP: 21 **EST:** 1998
SALES (est): 3MM **Privately Held**
WEB: www.southernstonecabinets.com
SIC: 2434 Wood kitchen cabinets

(G-1884)
SPACE MANUFACTURING INC
14271 60th St N (33760-2706)
PHONE..................................727 532-9466
Grace Sokol, *CEO*
Bob Sokol, *President*
EMP: 16 **EST:** 1979
SALES (est): 286.8K **Privately Held**
SIC: 3599 Machine shop, jobbing & repair

(G-1885)
SPACEWERKS INC
13100 56th Ct Ste 711 (33760-4021)
PHONE..................................727 540-9714
Ken Yeager, *President*
EMP: 13 **EST:** 2008
SQ FT: 20,000
SALES (est): 1.5MM **Privately Held**
WEB: www.spacewerksinc.com
SIC: 2431 Moldings, wood: unfinished & prefinished

(G-1886)
SPECTRA CHROME LLC
13130 56th Ct Ste 611 (33760-4018)
PHONE..................................727 573-1990
Todd Hoyt, *Manager*
Daniel A McLaughlin,
▼ **EMP:** 8 **EST:** 2002
SALES (est): 1.4MM **Privately Held**
WEB: www.spectrachrome.com
SIC: 3471 Electroplating of metals or formed products

(G-1887)
SPECTRA METAL SALES INC
Also Called: Alumco
5100 140th Ave N (33760-3753)
P.O. Box 43167, Atlanta GA (30336-0167)
PHONE..................................727 530-5435
Michael Smith, *Manager*
EMP: 10
SALES (corp-wide): 271.2MM **Privately Held**
WEB: www.spectrametals.com
SIC: 3355 5051 5033 Aluminum rolling & drawing; metals service centers & offices; roofing, siding & insulation
PA: Spectra Metal Sales, Inc.
6104 Boat Rock Blvd Sw
Atlanta GA 30336
404 344-4305

(G-1888)
STATEMENT MARINE LLC
12011 49th St N (33762-4302)
PHONE..................................727 525-5235
Craig Barrie, *Principal*
EMP: 13 **EST:** 2008
SALES (est): 693K **Privately Held**
WEB: www.statementmarine.com
SIC: 3732 Boat building & repairing

(G-1889)
STITCH LOGO INC
2165 Sunnydale Blvd Ste H (33765-1211)
PHONE..................................727 446-0228
Christine Lyon, *President*
EMP: 7 **EST:** 1999

SQ FT: 1,500
SALES (est): 1MM Privately Held
WEB: www.stitchlogo.com
SIC: 2395 Embroidery products, except schiffli machine; embroidery & art needlework

(G-1890)
STRATFORD CORPORATION
1555 Sunshine Dr (33765-1315)
PHONE..................................727 443-1573
Alan Conroy, *President*
EMP: 9 EST: 1989
SALES (est): 1.3MM Privately Held
WEB: www.stratfordinc.com
SIC: 2842 Specialty cleaning, polishes & sanitation goods

(G-1891)
SUN BUSINESS SYSTEMS INC (PA)
10900 47th St N (33762-5001)
PHONE..................................727 547-6540
Jim Ellis, *President*
EMP: 5
SQ FT: 9,000
SALES (est): 1.1MM Privately Held
SIC: 2759 Playing cards: printing

(G-1892)
SUN WORKS PLASTICS INC
15373 Roosevelt Blvd # 202 (33760-3507)
PHONE..................................727 573-2343
Brian Myregaard, *President*
Pamela Myregaard, *Vice Pres*
EMP: 8 EST: 1988
SQ FT: 16,000
SALES (est): 892.5K Privately Held
WEB: www.sunworksplastic.com
SIC: 3089 Injection molding of plastics

(G-1893)
SUNCOAST TOOL & GAGE INDS INC
11625 54th St N (33760-4852)
PHONE..................................727 572-8000
Michael Powers, *President*
Lee Dove, *Vice Pres*
Doyle Powers, *Vice Pres*
Lloyd Powers, *Vice Pres*
EMP: 13 EST: 1982
SQ FT: 15,000
SALES (est): 803.1K Privately Held
WEB: www.suncoasttool.com
SIC: 3829 3824 3545 3544 Aircraft & motor vehicle measurement equipment; gauging instruments, thickness ultrasonic; gauges for computing pressure temperature corrections; machine tool accessories; special dies, tools, jigs & fixtures

(G-1894)
SUNDOWN MANUFACTURING INC
4505 131st Ave N Ste 26 (33762-4104)
PHONE..................................727 828-0826
Amy Rose, *Principal*
Dan Casaje, *Plant Mgr*
EMP: 10 EST: 2008
SALES (est): 532.4K Privately Held
WEB: www.sundownmfginc.com
SIC: 3999 Manufacturing industries

(G-1895)
SUNRUI TTNIUM PRCSION PDTS INC
1058 Cephas Rd (33765-2107)
PHONE..................................727 953-7101
Blakenship Angela, *Principal*
EMP: 10 EST: 2015
SALES (est): 589.9K Privately Held
WEB: www.precisiontitaniumproducts.com
SIC: 3356 Titanium

(G-1896)
SUPERIOR ELECTRONICS INC
1140 Kapp Dr (33765-2113)
P.O. Box 2536, Dunedin (34697-2536)
PHONE..................................727 733-0700
Anne Kennedy, *CEO*
Andy Desouza, *President*
Allan Kennedy, *Owner*
Kamill Hilberth, *Principal*
Sherman Desouza, *Vice Pres*
EMP: 34 EST: 1986
SALES (est): 2MM Privately Held
WEB: www.seimfg.com
SIC: 3643 3672 Current-carrying wiring devices; printed circuit boards

(G-1897)
SUPLIAEREOS USA LLC
Also Called: Aero Supply USA
21941 Us Highway 19 N (33765-2359)
PHONE..................................727 754-4915
Robert Ramirez, *COO*
William Tyler, *CFO*
Timothy Garren, *Accounts Mgr*
Michelle Ramirez,
EMP: 7 EST: 2012
SQ FT: 5,000
SALES (est): 1.2MM Privately Held
WEB: www.aerosupplyusa.com
SIC: 3721 3724 3728 3812 Aircraft; aircraft engines & engine parts; aircraft parts & equipment; aircraft/aerospace flight instruments & guidance systems; semiconductors & related devices

(G-1898)
SURFACE FINISHING TECH INC
12200 34th St N Ste A (33762-5608)
PHONE..................................727 577-7777
David Weisberg, *President*
Dale Jackson, *Vice Pres*
Kim Gibson, *Buyer*
EMP: 20 EST: 1996
SQ FT: 38,000
SALES (est): 9.8MM
SALES (corp-wide): 159.5MM Privately Held
WEB: www.technic.com
SIC: 3559 Electroplating machinery & equipment
PA: Technic, Inc.
47 Molter St
Cranston RI 02910
401 781-6100

(G-1899)
SYSTEM ENTERPRISES LLC
Also Called: Funsparks
319 Windward Is (33767-2328)
PHONE..................................888 898-3600
Trisha McCabe, *Sales Staff*
Steven T Mueller,
▲ EMP: 7 EST: 2010
SALES (est): 583.9K Privately Held
WEB: www.system-enterprises.com
SIC: 3944 Games, toys & children's vehicles

(G-1900)
T S E INDUSTRIES INC (PA)
5180 113th Ave N (33760-4835)
PHONE..................................727 573-7676
Robert R Klingel Jr, *CEO*
Mark Cucchiara, *President*
Richard K Klingel, *President*
Richard Catalano, *Counsel*
Brad Klingel, *Vice Pres*
◆ EMP: 188 EST: 1962
SQ FT: 225,000
SALES (est): 59.6MM Privately Held
WEB: www.tse-industries.com
SIC: 3089 3061 2891 2822 Molding primary plastic; mechanical rubber goods; medical & surgical rubber tubing (extruded & lathe-cut); adhesives; synthetic rubber

(G-1901)
T S E INDUSTRIES INC
5260 113th Ave N (33760-4838)
PHONE..................................727 540-1368
Adam Anderson, *Research*
Joe Barker, *Engineer*
Mary Coots, *Controller*
Radhila Petrovich, *Manager*
Tim Carson, *Manager*
EMP: 20
SQ FT: 12,000
SALES (corp-wide): 59.6MM Privately Held
WEB: www.tse-industries.com
SIC: 2821 3089 Thermoplastic materials; molding primary plastic
PA: T S E Industries Inc.
5180 113th Ave N
Clearwater FL 33760
727 573-7676

(G-1902)
TAMPA BAY GRAND PRIX (PA)
12350 Automobile Blvd (33762-4425)
PHONE..................................727 527-8464
Bertrand Ollier, *Owner*
▲ EMP: 5 EST: 2005
SALES (est): 896.4K Privately Held
WEB: www.tampabaygp.com
SIC: 3799 Go-carts, except children's

(G-1903)
TAMPA BAY PUBLICATIONS INC
Also Called: Tampa Bay Magazine
2531 Landmark Dr Ste 101 (33761-3928)
PHONE..................................727 791-4800
Aaron Fodiman, *President*
Fred Horton, *Vice Pres*
Lew Phillips, *Vice Pres*
Mark Maconi, *Treasurer*
M Rosalie Mahoney, *Controller*
EMP: 27 EST: 1986
SQ FT: 1,900
SALES (est): 3.6MM Privately Held
WEB: www.tampabaymagazine.com
SIC: 2721 Magazines: publishing only, not printed on site

(G-1904)
TAMPA MICROWAVE LLC
16255 Bay Vista Dr # 100 (33760-3127)
PHONE..................................813 855-2251
Eric Guerrazzi, *Vice Pres*
Christopher Barry, *Engineer*
Serita Cronin, *Engineer*
Wayne Moore, *Engineer*
Joe Wirth, *Engineer*
EMP: 40 EST: 2011
SALES (est): 12.6MM
SALES (corp-wide): 279.3MM Privately Held
WEB: www.tampamicrowave.com
SIC: 3663 Radio & TV communications equipment
HQ: Thales Defense & Security, Inc.
22605 Gateway Center Dr
Clarksburg MD 20871
240 864-7000

(G-1905)
TAMPA WINES LLC
Also Called: Aspirations Winery
22041 Us Highway 19 N (33765-2363)
PHONE..................................727 799-9463
Bill Linville,
EMP: 7 EST: 2005
SALES (est): 250K Privately Held
SIC: 2084 Wines

(G-1906)
TAMPA YACHT MANUFACTURING LLC
3671 131st Ave N (33762-4263)
P.O. Box 342033, Tampa (33694-2033)
PHONE..................................813 792-2114
Jeff Reinhold, *VP Opers*
Mike Martin, *Supervisor*
Robert L Stevens,
Jeff Aguiar,
CJ Lozano,
EMP: 10 EST: 2006
SALES (est): 1.5MM Privately Held
WEB: www.tampa-yacht.net
SIC: 3732 Yachts, building & repairing

(G-1907)
TECH DATA EDUCATION INC
5350 Tech Data Dr (33760-3122)
PHONE..................................727 539-7429
Charles V Dannewitz, *Director*
EMP: 19 EST: 2018
SALES (est): 1.2MM
SALES (corp-wide): 37B Privately Held
WEB: www.techdata.com
SIC: 7372 Prepackaged software
HQ: Tech Data Corporation
5350 Tech Data Dr
Clearwater FL 33760
727 539-7429

(G-1908)
TECH DATA RESOURCES LLC
5350 Tech Data Dr (33760-3122)
PHONE..................................727 539-7429
EMP: 28 EST: 2001
SALES (est): 1.8MM
SALES (corp-wide): 37B Privately Held
WEB: www.techdata.com
SIC: 7372 Prepackaged software
HQ: Tech Data Corporation
5350 Tech Data Dr
Clearwater FL 33760
727 539-7429

(G-1909)
TECH DATA TENNESSEE INC
5350 Tech Data Dr (33760-3122)
PHONE..................................727 539-7429
Charles V Dannewitz, *Director*
EMP: 22 EST: 1999
SALES (est): 2.6MM
SALES (corp-wide): 37B Privately Held
WEB: www.techdata.com
SIC: 7372 Prepackaged software
HQ: Tech Data Corporation
5350 Tech Data Dr
Clearwater FL 33760
727 539-7429

(G-1910)
TECHNAMOLD INC
5190 110th Ave N (33760-4804)
PHONE..................................727 561-0030
Michael Wilfeard, *President*
Kathleen Wilfeard, *Vice Pres*
EMP: 5 EST: 1992
SQ FT: 4,000
SALES (est): 654.1K Privately Held
SIC: 3544 Industrial molds

(G-1911)
TECHNIFINISH INC
5095 113th Ave N (33760-4834)
PHONE..................................727 576-5955
John S Eidschun, *President*
EMP: 11 EST: 2000
SALES (est): 206.2K Privately Held
SIC: 2269 Finishing plants

(G-1912)
TECHNOLOGY RESEARCH LLC (HQ)
Also Called: T R C
4525 140th Ave N Ste 900 (33762-3864)
PHONE..................................727 535-0572
G Gary Yetman, *CEO*
J Kurt Hennelly, *President*
Richard N Burger, *Corp Secy*
J Bradley Freeman, *Vice Pres*
Douglas B Tilghman, *VP Engrg*
◆ EMP: 92 EST: 1981
SQ FT: 43,000
SALES (est): 61.5MM
SALES (corp-wide): 1.7B Privately Held
WEB: www.southwire.com
SIC: 3613 Control panels, electric; distribution boards, electric
PA: Southwire Company, Llc
1 Southwire Dr
Carrollton GA 30119
770 832-4242

(G-1913)
TEEZE INTERNATIONAL INC
2431 Estancia Blvd (33761-2608)
PHONE..................................727 726-3592
Tyler Waitt, *Principal*
EMP: 8 EST: 2010
SALES (est): 157.9K Privately Held
WEB: www.teezemagazine.com
SIC: 2721 Magazines: publishing only, not printed on site

(G-1914)
TEKNATOOL USA INC
4499 126th Ave N (33762-4768)
PHONE..................................727 954-3433
George Naruns, *President*
Sabrina Latimer, *Analyst*
▲ EMP: 5 EST: 2010
SALES: 5.2MM Privately Held
WEB: www.teknatool.com
SIC: 3553 Woodworking machinery
PA: Teknatool International Limited
7d Dallan Place
Auckland

(G-1915)
TEMPERED GLASS INDUSTRIES INC
11116 47th St N Ste B (33762-4922)
PHONE..................................727 499-0284
Robert C Whitlow, *Principal*
EMP: 20 **EST:** 2006
SALES (est): 841K **Privately Held**
SIC: 3231 Tempered glass: made from purchased glass

(G-1916)
TERLYN INDUSTRIES INC
11256 47th St N (33762-4952)
PHONE..................................727 592-0772
Terence Rushmore, *President*
Lynn Rushmore, *Vice Pres*
Bill Stepp, *Vice Pres*
EMP: 10 **EST:** 1996
SQ FT: 15,000
SALES (est): 1.8MM **Privately Held**
WEB: www.terlyn.com
SIC: 2899 Water treating compounds

(G-1917)
TESS ENTERPRISES INC
13150 38th St N (33762-4221)
PHONE..................................727 573-9701
Richard A Tess, *President*
Sharon Tess, *Vice Pres*
EMP: 7 **EST:** 1997
SQ FT: 11,880
SALES (est): 572.6K **Privately Held**
WEB: www.tessenterprises.com
SIC: 3949 Sporting & athletic goods

(G-1918)
THIERRY BROUZET INC
57 Aster St (33767-1407)
PHONE..................................727 449-0158
Theirry Brouzet, *President*
EMP: 6 **EST:** 2005
SALES (est): 64.5K **Privately Held**
SIC: 1041 Gold ores

(G-1919)
THOMAS SIGN AND AWNING CO INC
4590 118th Ave N (33762-4405)
PHONE..................................727 573-7757
Priscilla Thomas, *President*
W Wade Thomas, *Vice Pres*
Matt Thomas, *VP Opers*
Kiera Harris, *Project Mgr*
Tami Key, *Project Mgr*
▲ **EMP:** 230 **EST:** 1972
SQ FT: 100,000
SALES (est): 45.1MM **Privately Held**
WEB: www.thomassign.com
SIC: 2394 3993 Awnings, fabric: made from purchased materials; electric signs

(G-1920)
THREATTRACK SECURITY INC (HQ)
Also Called: Vipre
311 Park Place Blvd # 300 (33759-3994)
P.O. Box 804, Tarpon Springs (34688-0804)
PHONE..................................855 885-5566
John Lyons, *President*
Dipto Chakravarty, *Exec VP*
Marc Sison, *Engineer*
Stewart D Curly, *CFO*
Alan Rizek, *CFO*
EMP: 130 **EST:** 1994
SALES (est): 150.7MM
SALES (corp-wide): 1.4B **Publicly Held**
WEB: www.vipre.com
SIC: 7372 Business oriented computer software
PA: Davis Ziff Inc
114 5th Ave Fl 15
New York NY 10011
212 503-3500

(G-1921)
TITAN TOOLS LLC ✪
2622 Flournoy Cir S # 23 (33764-1411)
PHONE..................................818 984-1001
Athena Singer, *Mng Member*
Daniel Ashburn, *Mng Member*
EMP: 32 **EST:** 2020
SALES (est): 3.6MM **Privately Held**
SIC: 7372 8299 Application computer software; schools & educational service

(G-1922)
TITANS USA LTD
4371 112th Ter N (33762-4930)
PHONE..................................727 290-9897
Dennis Drew, *President*
Greg Hoffstetter, *Vice Pres*
EMP: 10 **EST:** 2016
SALES (est): 138.9K **Privately Held**
WEB: www.titansusa.com
SIC: 3648 Lighting equipment

(G-1923)
TOM GEORGE YACHT GROUP ✪
17166 Us Highway 19 N (33764-7504)
PHONE..................................727 734-8707
Tom George, *President*
EMP: 6 **EST:** 2021
SALES (est): 54.6K **Privately Held**
WEB: www.tgyg.com
SIC: 3732 7389 Yachts, building & repairing; yacht brokers

(G-1924)
TOPS SOFTWARE
2495 Entp Rd Ste 201 (33763)
PHONE..................................813 960-8300
Teri Perez, *VP Bus Dvlpt*
Sandra Higgins, *Marketing Staff*
Jeffrey Hardy, *Mng Member*
Tricia Berggren, *Manager*
Brianna Sturm, *Manager*
EMP: 12 **EST:** 2017
SALES (est): 902.3K **Privately Held**
WEB: www.topssoft.com
SIC: 7372 Prepackaged software

(G-1925)
TRACKMASTER LLC ✪
22001 Us Highway 19 N (33765-2344)
PHONE..................................727 333-7562
Travis Underwood, *President*
EMP: 6 **EST:** 2020
SALES (est): 86.6K **Privately Held**
WEB: www.trackmastermobility.com
SIC: 3842 Wheelchairs

(G-1926)
TUBOS INC
2775 Diane Ter (33759-1712)
PHONE..................................727 504-0633
EMP: 6 **EST:** 2009
SALES (est): 98.6K **Privately Held**
WEB: www.tubos.biz
SIC: 3296 Acoustical board & tile, mineral wool

(G-1927)
TUTHILL CORPORATION
Also Called: Hansen Plastics Division
2050 Sunnydale Blvd (33765-1201)
PHONE..................................727 446-8593
Chris Duncan, *Senior Buyer*
John Mitchell, *Sales Dir*
Richard D Curtin, *Branch Mgr*
EMP: 60
SQ FT: 18,000
SALES (corp-wide): 144.3MM **Privately Held**
WEB: www.tuthill.com
SIC: 3089 Injection molded finished plastic products
PA: Tuthill Corporation
8500 S Madison St
Burr Ridge IL 60527
630 382-4900

(G-1928)
UNILENS CORP USA
21 N Park Place Blvd (33759-3917)
PHONE..................................727 544-2531
Michael Pecora, *President*
Leonard Barker, *Vice Pres*
Alan Frazer, *QA Dir*
Denis Rehse, *Info Tech Mgr*
EMP: 31 **EST:** 1989
SQ FT: 27,000
SALES (est): 1.6MM **Privately Held**
WEB: www.unilens.com
SIC: 3851 Contact lenses

(G-1929)
UNIVERSAL SOFTWARE SOLUTIONS
Also Called: Networking Dynamics
912 Drew St Ste 104 (33755-4523)
PHONE..................................727 298-8877
Daniel F Kingsbury, *CEO*
Donna Dunbar, *President*
Susanne Zimmerling, *Accounting Mgr*
Pamela Anderson, *Sales Staff*
Annette Welton, *Sales Staff*
EMP: 7 **EST:** 1982
SQ FT: 2,500
SALES (est): 1MM **Privately Held**
SIC: 7372 7371 Prepackaged software; custom computer programming services

(G-1930)
VELA RESEARCH LP
5516 Rio Vista Dr (33760-3107)
PHONE..................................727 507-5300
Mike Reddy, *Partner*
Michele Capps, *Partner*
Kevin Donald, *Partner*
Ken Rubin, *Vice Pres*
James Skupien, *Sales Staff*
EMP: 100 **EST:** 1994
SQ FT: 38,000
SALES (est): 7MM **Privately Held**
WEB: www.vela.com
SIC: 3663 Receiver-transmitter units (transceiver)

(G-1931)
VERIFONE INC
300 Park Place Blvd # 100 (33759-4933)
PHONE..................................727 953-4000
Jennifer Miles, *President*
Rich McGin, *General Mgr*
Simcha Gendelman, *General Mgr*
Greg McFaul, *General Mgr*
Morgan Sellen, *Managing Dir*
EMP: 300
SALES (corp-wide): 695.1MM **Privately Held**
WEB: www.verifone.com
SIC: 3578 Point-of-sale devices
HQ: Verifone, Inc.
2744 N University Dr
Coral Springs FL 33065
800 837-4366

(G-1932)
VERIFONE INC
12501 B 562nd St N (33755)
PHONE..................................727 535-9200
Chris Bolson, *Manager*
Bud Waller, *Technical Staff*
Linda Prahl, *Analyst*
William Rosa, *Analyst*
EMP: 200
SALES (corp-wide): 695.1MM **Privately Held**
WEB: www.verifone.com
SIC: 3578 3577 Point-of-sale devices; computer peripheral equipment
HQ: Verifone, Inc.
2744 N University Dr
Coral Springs FL 33065
800 837-4366

(G-1933)
VISIONTECH COMPONENTS LLC
5120 110th Ave N (33760-4804)
PHONE..................................727 547-5466
Shannon Wren,
EMP: 10
SALES (est): 1MM **Privately Held**
SIC: 3674 Integrated circuits, semiconductor networks, etc.

(G-1934)
VITAMINMED LLC
300 S Duncan Ave Ste 263 (33755-6493)
PHONE..................................727 443-7008
James Miller, *CEO*
David Singer,
EMP: 6 **EST:** 2013
SALES (est): 341.1K **Privately Held**
WEB: www.vitaminmed.com
SIC: 2833 Vitamins, natural or synthetic: bulk, uncompounded

(G-1935)
WALKUP ENTERPRISES INC
Also Called: Gulf Machining
5040 110th Ave N (33760-4807)
PHONE..................................727 571-1244
Fred Walkup, *President*
Mary Walkup, *Treasurer*
EMP: 10 **EST:** 1977
SQ FT: 5,000
SALES (est): 1.1MM **Privately Held**
SIC: 3451 3669 Screw machine products; intercommunication systems, electric

(G-1936)
WALL BED SYSTEMS INC
Also Called: Closet Systems
5040 140th Ave N (33760-3735)
P.O. Box 2042, Wapakoneta OH (45895-0542)
PHONE..................................419 738-5207
Steven Archer, *President*
Eloise Archer, *Corp Secy*
EMP: 8
SALES (est): 1MM **Privately Held**
SIC: 2514 5712 Beds, including folding & cabinet, household: metal; furniture stores

(G-1937)
WEB OFFSET PRINTING CO INC
12198 44th St N (33762-5109)
PHONE..................................727 572-7488
John L Tevlin Jr, *President*
Don Kennedy, *General Mgr*
John L Tevlin, *Vice Pres*
John Tevlin, *Vice Pres*
EMP: 100 **EST:** 1994
SQ FT: 2,500
SALES (est): 9.7MM **Privately Held**
WEB: www.weboffsetprint.com
SIC: 2752 Commercial printing, offset

(G-1938)
WHK BIOSYSTEMS LLC
11345 53rd St N (33760-4822)
PHONE..................................727 209-8402
David J Tottle, *CFO*
Robert R Klingel Jr, *Mng Member*
EMP: 6 **EST:** 2012
SALES (est): 2.8MM
SALES (corp-wide): 59.6MM **Privately Held**
WEB: www.whkbiosystems.com
SIC: 3829 Medical diagnostic systems, nuclear
PA: T S E Industries Inc.
5180 113th Ave N
Clearwater FL 33760
727 573-7676

(G-1939)
WILCOX STEEL COMPANY LLC
1101 Kapp Dr (33765-2114)
PHONE..................................727 443-0461
Jackie A Wilcox Sr, *Owner*
Susan Wilcox Wagner, *Office Mgr*
EMP: 6 **EST:** 1965
SQ FT: 6,400
SALES (est): 300K **Privately Held**
SIC: 3446 3441 Architectural metalwork; fabricated structural metal

(G-1940)
WILLETT PRECISION MACHINING
11339 43rd St N (33762-4915)
PHONE..................................727 573-9299
Debbie Willett, *President*
Kyle P Willett, *Opers Mgr*
Richard Barnes, *CIO*
EMP: 18 **EST:** 1997
SQ FT: 8,432
SALES (est): 1MM **Privately Held**
WEB: www.willettprecision.com
SIC: 3599 Machine shop, jobbing & repair

(G-1941)
WILSON PRINTING USA LLC
1085 Cephas Rd (33765-2108)
PHONE..................................727 536-4173
Thomas R Selenski, *President*
Julie Hale, *COO*
Ella Selenski, *Vice Pres*
Alex Boerma, *Marketing Staff*
Kelsi Hale,
EMP: 7 **EST:** 1969

▲ = Import ▼=Export
◆ =Import/Export

SALES (est): 971.9K **Privately Held**
WEB: www.wilsonprintingusa.com
SIC: 2752 Commercial printing, offset

(G-1942)
WINATIC CORPORATION
5410 115th Ave N (33760-4841)
P.O. Box 18802 (33762-1802)
PHONE..................................727 538-8917
Roger C Mayo, *Chairman*
Geraldine R Mayo, *Treasurer*
EMP: 85 **EST:** 1951
SQ FT: 16,000
SALES (est): 2MM
SALES (corp-wide): 52.6MM **Privately Held**
WEB: www.winatic.com
SIC: 3677 Coil windings, electronic
PA: Electro Technik Industries, Inc.
5410 115th Ave N
Clearwater FL 33760
727 530-9555

(G-1943)
WOODWORKING INC
1458 S Jefferson Ave (33756-2225)
PHONE..................................727 442-6876
Tim Craughan, *Principal*
EMP: 6 **EST:** 2008
SALES (est): 98.7K **Privately Held**
SIC: 2431 Millwork

(G-1944)
WORLD INDUS RESOURCES CORP (HQ)
13100 56th Ct Ste 710 (33760-4021)
PHONE..................................727 572-9991
Leslie Unger, *President*
Robert Thompson, *Controller*
Garvin Callaham, *Credit Mgr*
EMP: 25 **EST:** 1978
SQ FT: 75,000
SALES (est): 123.4MM **Privately Held**
WEB: www.icazalaw.com
SIC: 3999 2542 5113 2671 Music boxes; fixtures: display, office or store: except wood; industrial & personal service paper; waxed paper: made from purchased material

(G-1945)
XSCREAM INC
1780 Calumet St (33765-1142)
PHONE..................................727 449-9353
Patrick Bogart, *President*
EMP: 5 **EST:** 2007
SALES (est): 486.4K **Privately Held**
WEB: www.teamxscream.com
SIC: 3799 All terrain vehicles (ATV)

(G-1946)
XUE WU INC
4445 E Bay Dr Ste 302 (33764-6865)
PHONE..................................727 532-4571
Pin Wu, *Principal*
EMP: 8 **EST:** 2011
SALES (est): 171.2K **Privately Held**
SIC: 3452 Pins

(G-1947)
ZANIBONI LIGHTING LLC
101 N Garden Ave Ste 230 (33755-4197)
PHONE..................................727 213-0410
Chiara Zaniboni, *CEO*
Jo Beckman, *Accountant*
Fabio Zaniboni, *Manager*
▲ **EMP:** 57 **EST:** 2014
SALES (est): 5.1MM **Privately Held**
WEB: www.zanibonilighting.com
SIC: 3648 Lighting equipment

Clearwater Beach
Pinellas County

(G-1948)
ALL AMERICAN WOODWORK
1621 Gulf Blvd Ph D (33767-3900)
PHONE..................................727 210-5214
Miroslaw Wasowski, *President*
EMP: 6 **EST:** 2015
SALES (est): 77.2K **Privately Held**
SIC: 2431 Millwork

Clermont
Lake County

(G-1949)
BLUE EARTH SOLUTIONS INC
13511 Granville Ave (34711-7173)
PHONE..................................352 729-0150
Patricia Cohen, *CEO*
Paul Slufarczyk, *President*
James Cohen Jr, *Vice Pres*
Douglas Vaught, *Vice Pres*
EMP: 25
SALES (est): 2.3MM **Privately Held**
SIC: 2899 Foam charge mixtures

(G-1950)
BLUE HORSESHOE POOLS WEST INC
16334 Arrowhead Trl (34711-8175)
PHONE..................................321 287-8758
Michael P Nieves, *Principal*
EMP: 6 **EST:** 2017
SALES (est): 46.6K **Privately Held**
WEB: www.bhspools.com
SIC: 3462 Horseshoes

(G-1951)
CENTER SAND MINE
16375 Hartwood Marsh Rd (34711-8920)
PHONE..................................800 366-7263
EMP: 6 **EST:** 2007
SALES (est): 95.4K **Privately Held**
SIC: 3281 Stone, quarrying & processing of own stone products

(G-1952)
CIND-AL INC
Also Called: Clasic Fishing Products
13518 Granville Ave (34711-9628)
PHONE..................................863 401-8700
Louie Gibbs, *President*
Damon Albers, *Exec VP*
Dennis C Losey, *CFO*
EMP: 6 **EST:** 1978
SQ FT: 2,500
SALES (est): 599.6K
SALES (corp-wide): 4.9MM **Privately Held**
WEB: www.culprit.com
SIC: 3949 3544 Lures, fishing: artificial; special dies, tools, jigs & fixtures
PA: Classic Fishing Products Inc
13518 Granville Ave
Clermont FL 34711
407 656-6133

(G-1953)
CLASSIC FISHING PRODUCTS INC (PA)
13518 Granville Ave (34711-9628)
PHONE..................................407 656-6133
Louie Gibbs, *President*
Damon Albers, *Exec VP*
Dennis C Losey, *CFO*
▲ **EMP:** 25 **EST:** 1978
SQ FT: 25,000
SALES (est): 4.9MM **Privately Held**
WEB: www.culprit.com
SIC: 3949 5941 Lures, fishing: artificial; sporting goods & bicycle shops

(G-1954)
COCA-COLA CO
16603 Bay Club Dr (34711-8166)
PHONE..................................407 287-4527
Evelyn Bjornson, *Executive*
EMP: 6 **EST:** 2018
SALES (est): 191.7K **Privately Held**
WEB: www.coca-cola.com
SIC: 2086 Bottled & canned soft drinks

(G-1955)
CORINES FRSH FRUITS/VEGETBLES
2530 Citrus Tower Blvd (34711-6893)
PHONE..................................352 708-6247
Tonya D Green, *Principal*
EMP: 6 **EST:** 2019
SALES (est): 62.3K **Privately Held**
SIC: 2037 Fruit juices

(G-1956)
EASY FLEX COUPLINGS LLC
4327 S Highway 27 (34711-5349)
PHONE..................................863 665-9374
Sharon Louwersheimer, *Principal*
EMP: 6 **EST:** 2011
SALES (est): 173.6K **Privately Held**
SIC: 3568 Power transmission equipment

(G-1957)
EXTRA TIME SOLUTIONS
3695 Peaceful Valley Dr (34711-8917)
PHONE..................................407 625-2198
Connie Griggs, *President*
EMP: 11 **EST:** 2012
SALES (est): 1.1MM **Privately Held**
SIC: 3589 7349 Commercial cleaning equipment; building cleaning service

(G-1958)
FLORIDA ENVIROMENTAL CONS
9734 Crenshaw Cir (34711-5320)
P.O. Box 305, Howey In The Hills (34737-0305)
PHONE..................................407 402-2828
Robert Lee Lightsey, *Principal*
▲ **EMP:** 8 **EST:** 2008
SALES (est): 1.8MM **Privately Held**
SIC: 3822 Auto controls regulating residntl & coml environmt & applncs

(G-1959)
FLORIDA MKB HOLDINGS LLC
16212 Sr 50 (34711-6266)
PHONE..................................407 281-7909
Matthew Borisch,
EMP: 25 **EST:** 2012
SALES (est): 23MM
SALES (corp-wide): 2.5MM **Privately Held**
WEB: www.gettommys.com
SIC: 3732 5551 Boat building & repairing; boat dealers
PA: Mkb Holdings, Llc
146 Monroe Center St Nw # 8
Grand Rapids MI 49503
810 423-7035

(G-1960)
FLORIDA ROCK CONCRETE
15150 Pine Valley Blvd (34711-7602)
PHONE..................................407 877-6180
John Baker, *President*
EMP: 7 **EST:** 1957
SQ FT: 720
SALES (est): 176.2K **Privately Held**
SIC: 3273 Ready-mixed concrete

(G-1961)
FRESH MARK CORPORATION
12518 El Viento Rd (34711-9339)
PHONE..................................352 394-7746
Michael D Bowers, *President*
Frank Tislaretz, *Sales Staff*
EMP: 17 **EST:** 1973
SQ FT: 20,000
SALES (est): 250.8K **Privately Held**
WEB: www.freshmark.com
SIC: 2879 3559 Insecticides, agricultural or household; pesticides, agricultural or household; refinery, chemical processing & similar machinery

(G-1962)
GRAPHICS ARTS BINDERY INC
3023 Pinnacle Ct (34711-5942)
P.O. Box 370492, Miami (33137-0492)
PHONE..................................352 394-4077
Jorge Serra, *President*
Josseline Serra, *Corp Secy*
George Serra Jr, *Vice Pres*
EMP: 9 **EST:** 1976
SQ FT: 10,000
SALES (est): 117.8K **Privately Held**
SIC: 2789 Binding only: books, pamphlets, magazines, etc.

(G-1963)
HARTMANS CANINE CENTER LLC
6242 Oil Well Rd (34714-9155)
P.O. Box 136146 (34713-6146)
PHONE..................................352 978-6592
Ai V Hartman, *Principal*
EMP: 7 **EST:** 2017
SALES (est): 154.9K **Privately Held**
SIC: 3231 Cut & engraved glassware: made from purchased glass

(G-1964)
HUESTON STAIR COMPANY
836 W Montrose St Ste 5 (34711-2124)
PHONE..................................314 225-4280
David Hueston, *Principal*
EMP: 6 **EST:** 2017
SALES (est): 225.4K **Privately Held**
WEB: www.huestonstair.com
SIC: 3446 Stairs, staircases, stair treads: prefabricated metal

(G-1965)
KEEPMEFRESH
614 E Highway 50 Ste 122 (34711-3164)
PHONE..................................502 407-7902
Bradley Tinch, *Owner*
EMP: 5 **EST:** 2015
SALES (est): 425K **Privately Held**
SIC: 2389 7389 Footlets;

(G-1966)
L T WELD II LLC
1200 Whitewood Way (34714-7000)
PHONE..................................352 454-2735
James Delucci, *Principal*
EMP: 6 **EST:** 2012
SALES (est): 77.6K **Privately Held**
SIC: 7692 Welding repair

(G-1967)
LEGACY VULCAN LLC
3310 Green Swamp Rd (34714-7227)
PHONE..................................352 394-6196
Frank C Klein, *Manager*
EMP: 10
SQ FT: 260 **Publicly Held**
WEB: www.vulcanmaterials.com
SIC: 1442 5032 Sand mining; gravel; aggregate
HQ: Legacy Vulcan, Llc
1200 Urban Center Dr
Vestavia AL 35242
205 298-3000

(G-1968)
LIGHT AGE PRESS INC
5660 County Road 561 (34714-9795)
PHONE..................................352 242-4530
Sarah Tirri, *Principal*
EMP: 8 **EST:** 2007
SALES (est): 96.3K **Privately Held**
SIC: 2741 Miscellaneous publishing

(G-1969)
MCSKIS
10411 Carlson Cir (34711-7883)
PHONE..................................863 513-0422
EMP: 7 **EST:** 2015
SALES (est): 77.1K **Privately Held**
WEB: www.montecarloskis.com
SIC: 3949 Sporting & athletic goods

(G-1970)
NEWS LEADER INC
Also Called: Sun Publication of Florida
637 8th St (34711-2159)
PHONE..................................352 242-9818
Donna Covert, *President*
EMP: 23 **EST:** 1983
SQ FT: 1,100
SALES (est): 610.8K **Privately Held**
WEB: www.static.newsleader.com
SIC: 2711 Newspapers, publishing & printing

(G-1971)
PRESTIGE/AB READY MIX LLC
Also Called: Prestige A B Ready Mix
17600 State Road 50 (34711-7131)
PHONE..................................407 654-3330
Mike Lane, *Manager*
EMP: 43
SALES (corp-wide): 11.2MM **Privately Held**
SIC: 3273 Ready-mixed concrete
PA: Prestige/Ab Ready Mix, Llc
7228 Westport Pl Ste C
West Palm Beach FL 33413
561 478-9980

GEOGRAPHIC

(G-1972)
REPUBLIC NEWSPAPERS INC
Also Called: South Lake Press
732 W Montrose St (34711-2122)
PHONE..................................352 394-2183
EMP: 10
SALES (corp-wide): 2MM **Privately Held**
SIC: 2711 Newspaper Publisher
PA: Republic Newspapers, Inc
11863 Kingston Pike
Knoxville TN 37934
865 675-6397

(G-1973)
SEAVIN INC (PA)
Also Called: Lakeridge Winery & Vineyards
19239 Us Highway 27 (34715-9025)
PHONE..................................352 394-8627
Charles G Cox, *President*
Jeanne Burgess, *Vice Pres*
Rich Wojcik, *Prdtn Mgr*
Awn M Enix T, *Treasurer*
Denise McLeod, *Consultant*
▲ **EMP:** 35 **EST:** 1990
SQ FT: 22,400
SALES (est): 5.9MM **Privately Held**
WEB: www.seavin.com
SIC: 2084 0172 Wines; grapes

(G-1974)
SECURITY ORACLE INC
3614 Solana Cir (34711-5017)
PHONE..................................352 988-5985
Charles Butler, *CEO*
Vontella Kay Kimball, *President*
EMP: 11 **EST:** 2014
SALES (est): 684.1K **Privately Held**
WEB: www.thesecurityoracle.com
SIC: 7372 7382 1731 Prepackaged software; protective devices, security; safety & security specialization

(G-1975)
TIME IS MONEY CAMPAIGN LLC
16750 Abbey Hill Ct (34711-6353)
PHONE..................................352 255-5273
Denzel Quarterman,
EMP: 12
SALES (est): 487.8K **Privately Held**
SIC: 3651 Music distribution apparatus

Clewiston
Hendry County

(G-1976)
A & J READY MIX INC
Even Rnge 300 398 W El (33440)
PHONE..................................863 228-7154
Alexander Bentancor, *CEO*
Juan Bentancor, *Principal*
EMP: 5 **EST:** 2018
SALES (est): 357.2K **Privately Held**
WEB: www.aj-readymix.com
SIC: 3273 Ready-mixed concrete

(G-1977)
CLEWISTON WATER BTLG CO LLC
615 Commerce Ct (33440-4501)
PHONE..................................863 902-1317
Ernesto Rodriguez Garrido, *Principal*
Ferenc Schafer, *Principal*
Maria Torres, *Admin Asst*
EMP: 7 **EST:** 2014
SQ FT: 8,000
SALES (est): 292.5K **Privately Held**
WEB: www.clewiston-fl.gov
SIC: 2086 Mineral water, carbonated: packaged in cans, bottles, etc.

(G-1978)
D & J MACHINERY INC
728 E Trinidad Ave (33440-3924)
PHONE..................................863 983-3171
James G Swindle, *President*
Alan Case, *Project Engr*
Yavor Kantchev, *Manager*
Joanie L Swindle, *Admin Sec*
EMP: 40 **EST:** 1984
SQ FT: 40,000
SALES (est): 7.7MM **Privately Held**
WEB: www.djmachinery.net
SIC: 3599 Machine shop, jobbing & repair

(G-1979)
EVERGLADES MACHINE INC
1816 Red Rd (33440-9507)
PHONE..................................863 983-0133
William E Rudd, *President*
EMP: 6 **EST:** 1993
SQ FT: 2,400
SALES (est): 980K **Privately Held**
WEB: www.evergladesmachine.com
SIC: 3599 7699 Machine shop, jobbing & repair; agricultural equipment repair services

(G-1980)
FLORIDA SUGAR FARMERS
111 Ponce De Leon Ave (33440-3032)
PHONE..................................863 983-7276
Charles F Shide, *Principal*
EMP: 13 **EST:** 2006
SALES (est): 134.7K **Privately Held**
WEB: www.ussugar.com
SIC: 2062 Cane sugar refining

(G-1981)
GARCIA MINING COMPANY LLC (PA)
6605 Garcia Dr (33440-4309)
PHONE..................................863 902-9777
Joshua Kellam, *Mng Member*
EMP: 13 **EST:** 2018
SALES (est): 1.1MM **Privately Held**
SIC: 1442 Sand mining

(G-1982)
HARE LUMBER & READY MIX INC
425 E Haiti Ave (33440-4699)
PHONE..................................863 983-8725
Leroy Hare, *President*
Sandra Hare, *Corp Secy*
Sarah D Perkins, *Vice Pres*
EMP: 12 **EST:** 1953
SQ FT: 20,000
SALES (est): 2MM **Privately Held**
WEB: www.harereadymixlumber.com
SIC: 3273 5072 5251 Ready-mixed concrete; builders' hardware; builders' hardware

(G-1983)
MAMA BEAR LAWN CARE PRESS
30290 Josie Billie Hwy (33440-9502)
PHONE..................................863 517-5322
EMP: 7 **EST:** 2019
SALES (est): 535K **Privately Held**
SIC: 2741 Miscellaneous publishing

(G-1984)
MIAMI HANG GLIDING CORP
Also Called: Naples Hang Gliding
12655 E State Road 80 (33440-7595)
PHONE..................................863 805-0440
James Gindle, *President*
Doug Wielhouwer, *Vice Pres*
EMP: 6 **EST:** 2010
SALES (est): 460.1K **Privately Held**
SIC: 3721 8331 Hang gliders; job training & vocational rehabilitation services

(G-1985)
NATURAL4NATURALZ LLC ✪
561 Old Farm Pl (33440-4610)
PHONE..................................561 621-1546
Kio Coffie,
Jesmina Elhirech,
EMP: 7 **EST:** 2020
SALES (est): 304.1K **Privately Held**
SIC: 2844 Toilet preparations

(G-1986)
SOUTHERN GRDNS CTRUS HLDG CORP (HQ)
111 Ponce De Leon Ave (33440-3032)
PHONE..................................863 983-8121
Robert Buker, *CEO*
Trist Chapam, *President*
Ricke A Kress, *President*
James Terrill, *President*
Virginia Pena, *Principal*
◆ **EMP:** 4 **EST:** 1990
SQ FT: 40,000
SALES (est): 25.1MM
SALES (corp-wide): 248.3MM **Privately Held**
WEB: www.ussugar.com
SIC: 2037 Fruit juices
PA: United States Sugar Corporation
111 Ponce De Leon Ave
Clewiston FL 33440
863 983-8121

Cocoa
Brevard County

(G-1987)
321 CPR LLC
29 Riverside Dr Ph 601 (32922-8211)
PHONE..................................321 806-3525
Robert Harvey, *Principal*
EMP: 6 **EST:** 2017
SALES (est): 228.1K **Privately Held**
SIC: 3812 Search & navigation equipment

(G-1988)
A & E MACHINE INC
1445 Lake Dr (32922-6284)
P.O. Box 236065 (32923-6065)
PHONE..................................321 636-3110
Art Armellini, *President*
Teresa Vayda, *Manager*
EMP: 17 **EST:** 1982
SQ FT: 3,000
SALES (est): 283.6K **Privately Held**
SIC: 3599 7692 Machine shop, jobbing & repair; welding repair

(G-1989)
A NEW WORLD PRODUCTION
767 Clearlake Rd (32922-5208)
PHONE..................................321 636-6886
John Lingo, *Owner*
▲ **EMP:** 26 **EST:** 1989
SALES (est): 1.7MM **Privately Held**
SIC: 2759 Commercial printing

(G-1990)
ABSOLUTE AUTOMATION & SECURITY
3815 N Highway 1 Ste 101 (32926-5947)
P.O. Box 5687, Titusville (32783-5687)
PHONE..................................321 505-9989
Jason Barati, *President*
EMP: 8 **EST:** 2004
SQ FT: 3,200
SALES (est): 1MM **Privately Held**
WEB: www.absoluteautomation.com
SIC: 3699 Security control equipment & systems

(G-1991)
ADRICK MARINE GROUP INC
581 Cidco Rd (32926-5809)
PHONE..................................321 631-0776
Thomas Vassallo, *CEO*
Susan Vassallo, *Corp Secy*
Richard Vassallo, *Vice Pres*
▼ **EMP:** 12 **EST:** 1978
SQ FT: 10,000
SALES (est): 1.7MM **Privately Held**
WEB: www.adrickmarine.com
SIC: 3585 Refrigeration & heating equipment

(G-1992)
ADVANCED ALUMINUM OF CENTL FLA
155 N Range Rd Ste 13 (32926-5398)
PHONE..................................321 639-1451
William Johns, *President*
Paula Carter, *Vice Pres*
▲ **EMP:** 5 **EST:** 1983
SQ FT: 2,000
SALES (est): 500K **Privately Held**
WEB: www.advancedaluminum.com
SIC: 3355 Structural shapes, rolled, aluminum

(G-1993)
AGTECK INC
150 N Wilson Ave Ste 101 (32922-7260)
PHONE..................................321 305-5930
Win Everett, *President*
Raymond Terranova, *Analyst*
EMP: 20 **EST:** 2013
SALES (est): 900K **Privately Held**
WEB: www.agteck.net
SIC: 3599 8711 Machine shop, jobbing & repair; engineering services

(G-1994)
AMAZON METAL FABRICATORS INC
Also Called: Dotrailings.com
600 Cox Rd Ste C (32926-4248)
PHONE..................................321 631-7574
Donald Benson, *President*
Andrew Benson, *Vice Pres*
Jacominna Benson, *Treasurer*
EMP: 16 **EST:** 1984
SQ FT: 8,000
SALES (est): 350K **Publicly Held**
WEB: www.dotrailing.com
SIC: 3446 Architectural metalwork
PA: Amazon.Com, Inc.
410 Terry Ave N
Seattle WA 98109

(G-1995)
AMERICAN QUALITY MFG INC
310 Shearer Blvd (32922-7248)
PHONE..................................321 636-3434
David McConnell, *President*
Andrew McConnell, *Vice Pres*
▼ **EMP:** 14 **EST:** 1991
SQ FT: 8,500
SALES (est): 1.9MM **Privately Held**
WEB: www.metalsheetfabrication.com
SIC: 3949 Exercise equipment

(G-1996)
ATLANTIC EARTH MATERIALS
2185 W King St (32926-5131)
PHONE..................................321 631-0600
Susan Griffin, *President*
EMP: 10 **EST:** 1996
SALES (est): 902.9K **Privately Held**
SIC: 1442 Gravel & pebble mining

(G-1997)
ATLANTIC WIRE AND RIGGING INC
330 Williams Point Blvd A (32927-4606)
P.O. Box 1249, Sharpes (32959-1249)
PHONE..................................321 633-1552
John L Platt Jr, *President*
Ginger Platt, *Corp Secy*
▼ **EMP:** 7 **EST:** 1992
SQ FT: 10,000
SALES (est): 758.4K **Privately Held**
WEB: www.atlanticwireandrigging.com
SIC: 2298 3312 Slings, rope; wire products, steel or iron

(G-1998)
AYON CYBERSECURITY INC
5155 King St (32926)
PHONE..................................321 953-3033
John H Booher, *President*
EMP: 41 **EST:** 2012
SALES (est): 5.9MM
SALES (corp-wide): 12.5MM **Publicly Held**
WEB: www.videodisplay.com
SIC: 3571 Electronic computers
PA: Video Display Corporation
1868 Tucker Industrial Rd
Tucker GA 30084
770 938-2080

(G-1999)
BRADEN KITCHENS INC
515 Industry Rd S (32926-5874)
PHONE..................................321 636-4700
Peter Profumo, *CEO*
Robert Krick, *President*
Peter Petri, *Vice Pres*
EMP: 31 **EST:** 1964
SQ FT: 50,000
SALES (est): 2.6MM **Privately Held**
WEB: www.bradenkitchens.com
SIC: 2521 3299 2541 2821 Cabinets, office: wood; mica products; wood partitions & fixtures; plastics materials & resins; carpentry work; vanities, bathroom: wood

(G-2000)
BRANDFX LLC
605 Townsend Rd (32926-3321)
PHONE..................................321 632-2063
Tim Tierney, *Branch Mgr*

▲ = Import ▼=Export
◆ =Import/Export

EMP: 44
SALES (corp-wide): 19.3MM **Privately Held**
WEB: www.brandfxbody.com
SIC: 3524 2879 Lawn & garden equipment; pesticides, agricultural or household
PA: Brandfx, Llc
2800 Golden Triangle Blvd
Fort Worth TX 76177
817 431-1131

(G-2001)
BREVARD ROBOTICS
1485 Cox Rd (32926-4743)
P.O. Box 236651 (32923-6651)
PHONE..................................321 637-0367
George Kellgren, *President*
Tobias Obermeit, *Engineer*
EMP: 30 **EST:** 2001
SQ FT: 17,800
SALES (est): 6.8MM **Privately Held**
SIC: 3599 Machine shop, jobbing & repair

(G-2002)
BURR INDUSTRIES LLC
4360 Ponds Dr (32927-8638)
PHONE..................................619 254-2309
Kaleigh A Burr, *Principal*
EMP: 6 **EST:** 2016
SALES (est): 92K **Privately Held**
WEB: www.burrindustriesllc.com
SIC: 3999 Manufacturing industries

(G-2003)
CABINETS -N- MORE INC
6023 Elgin Rd (32927-9038)
PHONE..................................321 355-9548
Vincent Giusto, *Principal*
EMP: 8 **EST:** 2016
SALES (est): 283.6K **Privately Held**
WEB: www.cabinetsnmorefl.com
SIC: 2434 Wood kitchen cabinets

(G-2004)
CEMEX CNSTR MTLS FLA LLC
Also Called: Mat Div-Cocoa Maintenance Shop
3365 E Industry Rd (32926-5841)
PHONE..................................321 632-0500
Tom Helwig, *Branch Mgr*
EMP: 8
SQ FT: 33,631 **Privately Held**
SIC: 3273 5032 5211 Ready-mixed concrete; concrete mixtures; concrete & cinder block
HQ: Cemex Construction Materials Florida, Llc
1501 Belvedere Rd
West Palm Beach FL 33406

(G-2005)
CEMEX MATERIALS LLC
3365 E Industry Rd (32926-5841)
PHONE..................................321 636-5121
EMP: 73 **Privately Held**
SIC: 3273 Ready-mixed concrete
HQ: Cemex Materials Llc
1501 Belvedere Rd
West Palm Beach FL 33406
561 833-5555

(G-2006)
COVINGTON PLASTICS INC
427 Shearer Blvd (32922-4211)
PHONE..................................321 632-6775
Gary Mc Murry, *President*
EMP: 14 **EST:** 1975
SQ FT: 14,700
SALES (est): 1.4MM **Privately Held**
WEB: www.covingtonplastics.com
SIC: 3089 3544 Injection molding of plastics; special dies, tools, jigs & fixtures

(G-2007)
CUTTING EDGE MCH FBRCATION LLC
Also Called: Cocoa Customs RC
534 Saint Johns St Bldg C (32922-7241)
PHONE..................................321 626-0588
Martin Richard Van Buren, *Principal*
EMP: 9 **EST:** 2017
SALES (est): 297.6K **Privately Held**
WEB: www.cuttingedgemnf.com
SIC: 3599 Machine shop, jobbing & repair

(G-2008)
D M T INC
817 N Cocoa Blvd (32922-7510)
PHONE..................................321 267-3931
Scott Glover, *President*
Brandon Glover, *President*
EMP: 14 **EST:** 1981
SALES (est): 1MM **Privately Held**
SIC: 3089 3544 Injection molding of plastics; industrial molds

(G-2009)
DIAMONDBACK BARRELS LLC
4135 Pine Tree Pl (32926-3311)
PHONE..................................321 305-5995
Bobby Fleckinger, *Mng Member*
Stephen Scott Broussard,
EMP: 17 **EST:** 2013
SALES (est): 2.6MM **Privately Held**
WEB: www.diamondbackbarrels.com
SIC: 2429 Barrels & barrel parts

(G-2010)
DIAMONDBACK CNC LLC
3400 Grissom Pkwy (32926-4543)
PHONE..................................321 305-5995
Faith Denman, *Manager*
Bobby Fleckinger,
Fran Fleckinger,
EMP: 33 **EST:** 2006
SALES (est): 4.9MM **Privately Held**
SIC: 3599 Crankshafts & camshafts, machining

(G-2011)
DIAMONDBACK FIREARMS LLC
3400 Grissom Pkwy (32926-4543)
PHONE..................................321 305-5995
Bobby Fleckinger, *President*
Faith Denman, *CFO*
EMP: 18 **EST:** 2009
SALES (est): 8.5MM **Privately Held**
WEB: www.diamondbackfirearms.com
SIC: 3484 Guns (firearms) or gun parts, 30 mm. & below

(G-2012)
DIAMONDBACK MANUFACTURING LLC
1060 Cox Rd Bldg A (32926-4237)
PHONE..................................321 305-5995
Bobby V Fleckinger, *Mng Member*
Faith Denman,
Frances C Fleckinger,
EMP: 18 **EST:** 2012
SALES (est): 132.9K **Privately Held**
WEB: www.diamondbackairboats.com
SIC: 3732 Boat building & repairing

(G-2013)
DIAMONDBACK MANUFACTURING LLC
Also Called: Diamondback Airboats
1060 Cox Rd (32926-4237)
PHONE..................................321 633-5624
Bobby V Fleckinger, *President*
Frances C Fleckinger, *Mng Member*
▼ **EMP:** 40 **EST:** 1989
SQ FT: 15,000
SALES (est): 6MM **Privately Held**
WEB: www.diamondbackairboats.com
SIC: 3732 Boat building & repairing

(G-2014)
DIAMONDBACK TOWERS LLC
1060 Cox Rd Bldg B (32926-4237)
PHONE..................................800 424-5624
Bobby V Fleckinger,
EMP: 18 **EST:** 2012
SALES (est): 1.1MM **Privately Held**
WEB: www.diamondback-marine.com
SIC: 3732 Boat building & repairing

(G-2015)
DR PEPPER/SEVEN UP INC
1313 W King St (32922-8693)
PHONE..................................321 433-3622
EMP: 19 **Publicly Held**
WEB: www.drpepper.com
SIC: 2086 Soft drinks: packaged in cans, bottles, etc.
HQ: Dr Pepper/Seven Up, Inc.
6425 Hall Of Fame Ln
Frisco TX 75034
972 673-7000

(G-2016)
DUTCHY ENTERPRISES LLC
600 Cox Rd Ste A (32926-4248)
PHONE..................................321 877-0700
Robert Reijm, *Mng Member*
Mohan Harrial, *Manager*
EMP: 7 **EST:** 2016
SQ FT: 2,000
SALES (est): 250K **Privately Held**
WEB: www.dutchyenterprises.com
SIC: 3441 8711 Fabricated structural metal; engineering services

(G-2017)
EAST COAST MACHINE INC
3022 Oxbow Cir (32926-4553)
PHONE..................................321 632-4817
Pereric Tapia, *President*
Frederic Meier, *President*
Eric Tapia, *Principal*
Brenda Meier, *Vice Pres*
Tyler Hamlin, *Production*
EMP: 19 **EST:** 1983
SQ FT: 5,000
SALES (est): 2.2MM **Privately Held**
WEB: www.eastcoastmachine.net
SIC: 3499 3599 Fire- or burglary-resistive products; machine shop, jobbing & repair

(G-2018)
EAST COAST METALWORKS LLC
6615 Bethel St (32927-4220)
PHONE..................................321 698-0624
James C Timberlake III, *Mng Member*
EMP: 9 **EST:** 2013
SALES (est): 200K **Privately Held**
SIC: 3499 7692 7389 Fabricated metal products; welding repair;

(G-2019)
ELASTEC INC
401 Shearer Blvd (32922-7249)
PHONE..................................618 382-2525
Jan Hoven, *Business Mgr*
Tammi Crossett, *Engineer*
Greg Gibbs, *Human Res Dir*
Sharon Behnke, *HR Admin*
Jeff Pearce, *Manager*
EMP: 14 **Privately Held**
WEB: www.elastec.com
SIC: 3999 Massage machines, electric: barber & beauty shops
PA: Elastec, Inc.
1309 W Main St
Carmi IL 62821

(G-2020)
EQUIPMENT FABRICATORS INC
655 Cidco Rd (32926-5811)
PHONE..................................321 632-0990
Michael Olsen, *President*
Maryann Spellman, *Human Res Dir*
Ginny Bass, *Administration*
Ellen Cassel, *Administration*
EMP: 32
SQ FT: 16,500
SALES (est): 5MM **Privately Held**
WEB: www.equipmentfab.com
SIC: 3536 3531 Cranes, overhead traveling; construction machinery

(G-2021)
ETCHART LLC
Also Called: Wallpaper For Windows
3732 N Highway 1 Ste 5 (32926-8782)
PHONE..................................321 504-4060
Larry Cashion,
Renee Combs,
EMP: 5 **EST:** 2004
SALES (est): 472.6K **Privately Held**
WEB: www.wallpaperforwindows.com
SIC: 2591 Drapery hardware & blinds & shades

(G-2022)
FLITE TECHNOLOGY INC
2511 Friday Rd (32926-3423)
PHONE..................................321 631-2050
Leo Burch, *President*
Ron Anderson, *Principal*
▲ **EMP:** 13 **EST:** 1981
SQ FT: 3,000
SALES (est): 1.8MM **Privately Held**
WEB: www.flitetech.com
SIC: 3559 3535 3444 Plastics working machinery; conveyors & conveying equipment; sheet metalwork

(G-2023)
FLORIDA GLSD HOLDINGS INC
Also Called: Ocean Potion
851 Greensboro Rd (32926-4516)
PHONE..................................321 633-4644
Steve Taylor, *CEO*
Gerald Woelcke, *CFO*
▼ **EMP:** 180 **EST:** 1989
SQ FT: 75,000
SALES (est): 21.4MM **Privately Held**
WEB: www.sscrllc.com
SIC: 2844 Suntan lotions & oils

(G-2024)
FUN MARINE INC
Also Called: Fiberglass Fabrication
682 Industry Rd S (32926-5825)
PHONE..................................321 576-1100
Larry Wirtzberger, *President*
Seth Kerzner, *Vice Pres*
EMP: 9 **EST:** 1984
SALES (est): 950K **Privately Held**
SIC: 3083 Laminated plastics plate & sheet

(G-2025)
FURNIVAL CABINETRY LLC
7235 Camilo Rd (32927-3040)
PHONE..................................321 638-1223
Ronald E Furnival,
EMP: 9 **EST:** 1999
SALES (est): 914.1K **Privately Held**
WEB: www.furnivalcabinetryllc.com
SIC: 2434 Wood kitchen cabinets

(G-2026)
FURNIVAL CONSTRUCTION LLC
7235 Camilo Rd (32927-3040)
PHONE..................................321 638-1223
Leonard Gallion, *Project Mgr*
Ron Furnival, *Mng Member*
EMP: 10 **EST:** 2014
SALES (est): 809.6K **Privately Held**
WEB: www.furnivalcabinetryllc.com
SIC: 2434 Wood kitchen cabinets

(G-2027)
GEM INDUSTRIES INC
370 Cox Rd (32926-4280)
PHONE..................................321 302-8985
Ann Jeanette Miner, *President*
Garret S Miner, *General Mgr*
EMP: 45 **EST:** 2004
SALES (est): 7.6MM **Privately Held**
WEB: www.gemindustriesincorporated.com
SIC: 3441 Building components, structural steel

(G-2028)
GUARDIAN IGN INTERLOCK MFG INC
Also Called: Guardian Manufacturing
2971 Oxbow Cir Ste A (32926-4500)
PHONE..................................321 205-1730
Charles E Smith, *President*
Steve Smith, *Vice Pres*
Ken Davis, *Opers Dir*
Jeff Stewart, *Chief Engr*
Jeffrey Stewart, *Chief Engr*
▲ **EMP:** 60 **EST:** 1991
SQ FT: 10,000
SALES (est): 24.4MM **Privately Held**
WEB: www.guardianmfg.com
SIC: 3829 Measuring & controlling devices

(G-2029)
HILLSHIRE BRANDS COMPANY
3860 Curtis Blvd Ste 614 (32927-3969)
PHONE..................................321 637-9765
EMP: 7
SALES (corp-wide): 43.1B **Publicly Held**
WEB: www.tysonfoods.com
SIC: 2013 Sausages & other prepared meats
HQ: The Hillshire Brands Company
400 S Jefferson St Ste 1n
Chicago IL 60607
312 614-6000

(G-2030)
IMMUNOTEK BIO CENTERS LLC
1225 W King St (32922-8619)
PHONE..................................404 345-3570
Jerome Parnell III, *Branch Mgr*
EMP: 15
SALES (corp-wide): 27MM **Privately Held**
WEB: www.immunotek.com
SIC: 2836 Blood derivatives
PA: Immunotek Bio Centers, L.L.C.
3900 N Causeway Blvd # 1200
Metairie LA 70002
337 500-1175

(G-2031)
INFOPIA USA LLC
7160 Bright Ave (32927-8005)
PHONE..................................321 225-3620
Bryan Sowards Sowards,
Bryan Sowards,
EMP: 13 **EST:** 2008
SALES (est): 522.4K **Privately Held**
SIC: 3845 Patient monitoring apparatus

(G-2032)
INTERNATIONAL PAINT LLC
3062 Oxbow Cir (32926-4507)
PHONE..................................321 636-9722
EMP: 9
SALES (corp-wide): 10B **Privately Held**
WEB: www.international-pc.com
SIC: 2851 Paints & allied products
HQ: International Paint Llc
6001 Antoine Dr
Houston TX 77091
713 682-1711

(G-2033)
KEL-TEC CNC INDUSTRIES INC
Also Called: Keltec
1505 Cox Rd (32926-4741)
P.O. Box 236009 (32923-6009)
PHONE..................................321 631-0068
George Kellgren, *President*
Derek Kellgren, *General Mgr*
Rubi Kellgren, *Corp Secy*
Chad Enos, *Marketing Staff*
Rick Mueller, *Supervisor*
EMP: 11
SQ FT: 15,000
SALES (est): 2.8MM **Privately Held**
WEB: www.keltecweapons.com
SIC: 3484 Guns (firearms) or gun parts, 30 mm. & below

(G-2034)
MANGO BOTTLING INC
Also Called: Tooter Lingo Liquer
767 Clearlake Rd (32922-5208)
PHONE..................................321 631-1005
John L Lingo, *President*
Pam McCann, *Office Admin*
Jared Shammah, *Business Dir*
▲ **EMP:** 30 **EST:** 1992
SQ FT: 17,000
SALES (est): 5.4MM **Privately Held**
WEB: www.mangobottling.com
SIC: 3085 5182 Plastics bottles; bottling wines & liquors

(G-2035)
MET-CON INC
465 Canaveral Groves Blvd (32926-4663)
P.O. Box 236129 (32923-6129)
PHONE..................................321 632-4880
Billy E Sheffield, *President*
Brian Greer, *Superintendent*
Dennis Dammann, *Vice Pres*
Jeffrey Gibson, *Vice Pres*
Robert Reijm, *Vice Pres*
▼ **EMP:** 100 **EST:** 1979
SQ FT: 100,000
SALES (est): 15.1MM **Privately Held**
WEB: www.metconinc.com
SIC: 3441 1791 1541 Building components, structural steel; structural steel erection; industrial buildings, new construction

(G-2036)
MID FLORIDA STEEL CORP
870 Cidco Rd (32926-5884)
P.O. Box 236006 (32923-6006)
PHONE..................................321 632-8228
Dale Coxwell, *President*
Greg Homes, *Vice Pres*
Rachel Coxwell, *Treasurer*
EMP: 35 **EST:** 1991
SQ FT: 4,000
SALES (est): 1.1MM **Privately Held**
WEB: www.midfloridasteel.com
SIC: 3449 3441 Miscellaneous metalwork; fabricated structural metal

(G-2037)
MTC ENGINEERING LLC
428 Shearer Blvd (32922-7296)
PHONE..................................321 636-9480
Eric Hochstetler,
▲ **EMP:** 26 **EST:** 1966
SQ FT: 13,000
SALES (est): 4.6MM **Privately Held**
WEB: www.mtceng.com
SIC: 3592 Carburetors, pistons, rings, valves

(G-2038)
NEELCO INDUSTRIES INC
420 Shearer Blvd (32922-7250)
PHONE..................................321 632-5303
Robert Martin, *President*
Matt Jerry, *Sales Staff*
EMP: 14 **EST:** 1972
SQ FT: 10,000
SALES (est): 2.1MM **Privately Held**
WEB: www.neelco.biz
SIC: 3523 Fertilizing, spraying, dusting & irrigation machinery

(G-2039)
OB INC (PA)
5020 Scott Rd (32926-2617)
PHONE..................................321 223-0332
Daniel O'Brien, *President*
EMP: 9
SALES (est): 654K **Privately Held**
SIC: 2951 Asphalt paving mixtures & blocks

(G-2040)
PLATING RESOURCES INC
2845 W King St Ste 108 (32926-4803)
PHONE..................................321 632-2435
Judith E Svenson, *CEO*
Eric C Svenson, *President*
EMP: 16 **EST:** 1990
SQ FT: 12,000
SALES (est): 1.3MM **Privately Held**
WEB: www.plating.com
SIC: 2899 Chemical preparations

(G-2041)
PORTABLE-SHADE USA LLC
428 Shearer Blvd (32922-7250)
PHONE..................................321 704-8100
Eric J Hochstetler, *Mng Member*
EMP: 8 **EST:** 2010
SALES (est): 58.9K **Privately Held**
WEB: www.portable-shade.com
SIC: 2394 Canopies, fabric: made from purchased materials

(G-2042)
PRECISION FABG & CLG CO INC
3975 E Railroad Ave (32926-5975)
PHONE..................................321 635-2000
Robert Kelly, *President*
Warren Lambert, *Superintendent*
Todd Gray, *Vice Pres*
David Wilk, *Project Mgr*
Casey Cutright, *Foreman/Supr*
▲ **EMP:** 74 **EST:** 1964
SQ FT: 20,000
SALES (est): 22.1MM **Privately Held**
WEB: www.precgroup.com
SIC: 3823 3769 3494 Industrial instrmnts msrmnt display/control process variable; guided missile & space vehicle parts & auxiliary equipment; valves & pipe fittings
PA: Precision Resources, Inc.
3975 E Railroad Ave
Cocoa FL 32926

(G-2043)
PRECISION RESOURCES INC (PA)
3975 E Railroad Ave (32926-5975)
PHONE..................................321 635-2000
Robert W Kelly, *President*
Robert Kelly, *President*
Todd Gray, *Vice Pres*
Jason Shye, *CFO*
Ed V Hollen, *Treasurer*
EMP: 15 **EST:** 1992
SQ FT: 7,000
SALES: 36.4MM **Privately Held**
WEB: www.precgroup.com
SIC: 3823 1711 8741 Industrial instrmnts msrmnt display/control process variable; warm air heating & air conditioning contractor; mechanical contractor; administrative management

(G-2044)
QUALITY MOLDS USA INC
2402 Cherbourg Rd (32926-5709)
PHONE..................................321 632-6066
William Both, *President*
EMP: 10 **EST:** 2001
SALES (est): 586.2K **Privately Held**
WEB: www.qualitymolds.net
SIC: 3089 Fiberglass doors

(G-2045)
RDS INDUSTRIAL INC
436 Shearer Blvd (32922-7250)
PHONE..................................321 631-0121
Patrick Pacifico, *President*
Fred Garbotz, *President*
Meredith Pacifico, *Executive*
EMP: 18 **EST:** 2009
SQ FT: 10,000
SALES (est): 2.4MM **Privately Held**
WEB: www.rdsindustrial.com
SIC: 3441 3446 Building components, structural steel; architectural metalwork

(G-2046)
REAL FLEET SOLUTIONS LLC
605 Townsend Rd (32926-3321)
PHONE..................................321 631-2414
Cynthia Smith, *Manager*
James Tierney,
EMP: 34 **EST:** 2017
SQ FT: 22,000
SALES (est): 3.2MM **Privately Held**
WEB: www.realfleetsolutions.com
SIC: 3599 Custom machinery

(G-2047)
REYES STUCCO INC
1515 Peachtree St Lot 3 (32922-8668)
PHONE..................................321 557-1319
Cruz M Cifuentes, *Principal*
EMP: 6 **EST:** 2009
SALES (est): 256.2K **Privately Held**
SIC: 3299 Stucco

(G-2048)
RICKS QUALITY PRTG & SIGNS
Also Called: Rick's Quality Printing & Sign
681 Industry Rd S Ste A (32926-5807)
PHONE..................................321 504-7446
Kay Szucs, *President*
Rick Szucs, *Vice Pres*
EMP: 6 **EST:** 1980
SQ FT: 6,400
SALES (est): 355.5K **Privately Held**
SIC: 3993 Signs & advertising specialties

(G-2049)
ROCKET CRAFTERS LAUNCH LLC
Also Called: Vaya Space
305 Brevard Ave (32922-7908)
PHONE..................................321 222-0858
Robert Fabian,
EMP: 7 **EST:** 2018
SALES (est): 402.7K **Privately Held**
SIC: 3761 Ballistic missiles, complete

(G-2050)
SERVICE CORP INTERNATIONAL
Also Called: SCI
Us Hwy 1 Frontenac (32927)
PHONE..................................321 636-6041
Ralph Sutliff, *Manager*
EMP: 7
SALES (corp-wide): 3.5B **Publicly Held**
WEB: www.sci-corp.com
SIC: 3995 Burial caskets
PA: Service Corporation International
1929 Allen Pkwy
Houston TX 77019
713 522-5141

(G-2051)
SMI TOOL & DIE INC
305 Clearlake Rd (32922-6246)
P.O. Box 3113 (32924-3113)
PHONE..................................321 632-6200
Edna Ellery, *President*
Arthur John Ellery, *Vice Pres*
John Ellery, *Vice Pres*
EMP: 6 **EST:** 1979
SQ FT: 9,500
SALES: 130.2K **Privately Held**
WEB: www.smitool.com
SIC: 3599 3443 3728 Machine shop, jobbing & repair; weldments; aircraft parts & equipment

(G-2052)
SOUTHERN TAPE & LABEL INC
1107 Peachtree St (32922-8638)
P.O. Box 3466 (32924-3466)
PHONE..................................321 632-5275
Robert Ramsey, *President*
Joyce Ramsey, *Corp Secy*
EMP: 19
SQ FT: 11,100
SALES (est): 3.1MM **Privately Held**
WEB: www.labelsstl.com
SIC: 2759 Labels & seals: printing

(G-2053)
SPACE COAST INDUSTRIES INC
700 Cox Rd Ste 1 (32926-4249)
P.O. Box 236875 (32923-6875)
PHONE..................................321 633-9336
Wayne W Clark, *President*
EMP: 5 **EST:** 2008
SALES (est): 914K **Privately Held**
SIC: 3799 Trailers & trailer equipment

(G-2054)
SUNTREE TECHNOLOGIES INC
798 Clearlake Rd Ste 2 (32922-5114)
PHONE..................................321 637-7552
EMP: 14 **Privately Held**
WEB: www.suntreetech.com
SIC: 3822 Auto controls regulating residntl & coml environmt & applncs
PA: Suntree Technologies, Inc.
798 Clearlake Rd Ste 2
Cocoa FL 32922

(G-2055)
VAPEX ENVIRONMENTAL TECH INC
2971 Oxbow Cir Ste A (32926-4500)
PHONE..................................407 277-0900
Darrel Resch, *CEO*
Greg Fraser, *President*
Patrick Resch, *Technical Staff*
EMP: 6 **EST:** 2002
SQ FT: 5,000
SALES (est): 1MM **Privately Held**
WEB: www.vapex.com
SIC: 3589 Water treatment equipment, industrial

(G-2056)
VIDEO DISPLAY CORPORATION
Also Called: Vdc Display Systems
5155 King St (32926-2339)
PHONE..................................321 784-4427
Gina Studdard, *General Mgr*
Art Mengel, *Division Pres*
Mary Cairns, *Materials Mgr*
Brian Lawson, *Engineer*
Sherry Balo, *Sales Mgr*
EMP: 60
SALES (corp-wide): 12.5MM **Publicly Held**
WEB: www.videodisplay.com
SIC: 3671 3663 Electron tubes; radio & TV communications equipment
PA: Video Display Corporation
1868 Tucker Industrial Rd
Tucker GA 30084
770 938-2080

Cocoa Beach
Brevard County

(G-2057)
AKMAN INC
2023 N Atl Ave Ste 201 (32931-5096)
PHONE..................................407 948-0562
John Akman, *President*
Beatrice Akman, *Vice Pres*
▼ **EMP:** 5 **EST:** 1983
SQ FT: 4,000
SALES (est): 483.4K **Privately Held**
WEB: www.akman.com
SIC: 3652 Compact laser discs, prerecorded; magnetic tape (audio): prerecorded

(G-2058)
B2B PRINTING CORP
Also Called: Allegra-Rockledge
241 Curacau Dr (32931-3037)
PHONE..................................312 953-7446
Brian Birkholz, *Principal*
EMP: 6 **EST:** 2010
SALES (est): 82.7K **Privately Held**
WEB: www.b2bprintingcorp.com
SIC: 2752 Commercial printing, offset

(G-2059)
CAFM
2023 N Atlantic Ave 223 (32931-5096)
PHONE..................................407 658-6531
Thomas Carney, *Principal*
Dennis Kammerer, *Director*
EMP: 10
SALES (est): 100K **Privately Held**
SIC: 7372 Prepackaged software

(G-2060)
CATHODIC PRTECTION TECH OF FLA
Also Called: C P T
2023 N Atl Ave Ste 251 (32931-5096)
PHONE..................................321 799-0046
James Emory, *President*
EMP: 5 **EST:** 1996
SQ FT: 1,500
SALES (est): 444.6K **Privately Held**
SIC: 2851 3671 Shellac (protective coating); electron tubes

(G-2061)
CITY OF COCOA BEACH
Also Called: Cocoa Bch Wtr Reclamation Dept
1600 Minutemen Cswy (32931-2010)
PHONE..................................321 868-3342
Charles Billias, *Principal*
EMP: 13
SALES (corp-wide): 29.8MM **Privately Held**
WEB: www.cityofcocoabeach.com
SIC: 3589 Sewage & water treatment equipment
PA: City Of Cocoa Beach
2 S Orlando Ave
Cocoa Beach FL 32931
321 868-3200

(G-2062)
EXPRESS BADGING SERVICES INC
1980 N Atl Ave Ste 525 (32931-3273)
PHONE..................................321 784-5925
Joe French, *President*
Joe L French, *Vice Pres*
Laina French, *CFO*
John Coleman, *Manager*
Randy Redding, *Technical Staff*
EMP: 10 **EST:** 1993
SQ FT: 1,500
SALES (est): 500K **Privately Held**
WEB: www.expressbadging.com
SIC: 3999 5734 7382 2399 Identification badges & insignia; computer software & accessories; protective devices, security; emblems, badges & insignia

(G-2063)
GADGETCAT LLC
465 North Shore Dr (32931-2813)
PHONE..................................802 238-3671
Jane Zurn,
EMP: 6 **EST:** 2013
SALES (est): 638.6K **Privately Held**
WEB: www.gadgetcat.com
SIC: 3699 8711 5999 5961 Teaching machines & aids, electronic; electrical or electronic engineering; educational aids & electronic training materials; computer equipment & electronics, mail order

(G-2064)
GARCO MANUFACTURING CO INC
1400 S Orlando Ave (32931-2334)
PHONE..................................321 868-3778
Gary D Cobb, *President*
Alison Capers, *Admin Sec*
EMP: 6 **EST:** 1997
SALES (est): 525.3K **Privately Held**
WEB: www.garcomfg.com
SIC: 2299 Ramie yarn, thread, roving & textiles

(G-2065)
LIT FORKLIFT LLC
151 W Gadsden Ln (32931-3631)
PHONE..................................321 271-4626
Shawn R Marsee, *CEO*
EMP: 6 **EST:** 2013
SALES (est): 172K **Privately Held**
WEB: www.lit-forklift.com
SIC: 3537 7389 Forklift trucks;

(G-2066)
MORGANS ELC MTR & PUMP SVC
Also Called: Morgans Elc Mtr & Pump Svc
157 N Orlando Ave (32931-2973)
PHONE..................................321 960-2209
B Morgan Weglein, *President*
EMP: 9 **EST:** 1994
SALES (est): 278.8K **Privately Held**
SIC: 7694 7699 5261 Electric motor repair; pumps & pumping equipment repair; hydroponic equipment & supplies

(G-2067)
SPACE COAST STORM SHUTTERS LLC
10 West Point Dr (32931-5304)
PHONE..................................410 652-5717
Nicholas Leighty, *Manager*
EMP: 6 **EST:** 2017
SALES (est): 283.5K **Privately Held**
SIC: 3442 Shutters, door or window: metal

Coconut Creek
Broward County

(G-2068)
AIR & POWER SOLUTIONS INC
6810 Lyons Tech Pkwy # 125 (33073-4367)
PHONE..................................954 427-0019
Dale T Keitz, *President*
Marcos Diaz, *Sales Staff*
▼ **EMP:** 6 **EST:** 2003
SALES (est): 545.2K **Privately Held**
WEB: www.airandpowersolutions.com
SIC: 3585 1731 Heating & air conditioning combination units; computer power conditioning

(G-2069)
ALLLIANCE PRECIOUS MTLS GROUP
6820 Lyons Tech Pkwy (33073-4314)
PHONE..................................954 480-8676
Cindy Vandeveer, *Principal*
EMP: 8 **EST:** 2008
SALES (est): 130K **Privately Held**
SIC: 3339 Precious metals

(G-2070)
ATLANTIC JET SUPPORT INC
4801 Johnson Rd Ste 11 (33073-4359)
PHONE..................................954 360-7549
Zlata Archy, *President*
Sarunas Rackauskas, *CFO*
EMP: 8 **EST:** 2004
SQ FT: 5,600
SALES (est): 3.1MM **Privately Held**
WEB: www.ajsupport.com
SIC: 3728 Aircraft parts & equipment

(G-2071)
BOCADELRAY LIFE MAGAZINE
4611 Johnson Rd (33073-4361)
P.O. Box 970335 (33097-0335)
PHONE..................................954 421-9797
Mindi Rudan, *Publisher*
EMP: 7 **EST:** 2006
SALES (est): 167.5K **Privately Held**
SIC: 2721 Magazines: publishing only, not printed on site

(G-2072)
BUCHELLI GLASS INC
5417 Nw 50th Ct (33073-3301)
PHONE..................................954 695-8067
Albert A Berchiolli, *Director*
EMP: 7 **EST:** 2004
SALES (est): 71.3K **Privately Held**
SIC: 3231 Products of purchased glass

(G-2073)
COBEX RECORDERS INC
6601 Lyons Rd Ste F8 (33073-3622)
PHONE..................................954 425-0003
Matthew Levine, *President*
▲ **EMP:** 12 **EST:** 1994
SALES (est): 1.7MM **Privately Held**
WEB: www.cobexrecorders.com
SIC: 3823 Temperature measurement instruments, industrial

(G-2074)
DASS LOGISTICS INC
Also Called: Dass & Associates
6601 Lyons Rd Ste B1 (33073-3605)
PHONE..................................954 837-8339
Joseph Sellers, *President*
EMP: 14 **Privately Held**
WEB: www.jollyplace.com
SIC: 3728 Aircraft parts & equipment
HQ: Dass Logistics, Inc.
6601 Lyons Rd Ste B1
Coconut Creek FL 33073
817 784-6246

(G-2075)
ELITE ALUMINUM CORPORATION
Also Called: Elite Panel Products
4650 Lyons Tech Pkwy (33073-4360)
PHONE..................................954 949-3200
Michael Anoti, *Ch of Bd*
Peter Zadok, *President*
Will Boehmer, *Prdtn Mgr*
Richard Stedding, *Human Resources*
◆ **EMP:** 80 **EST:** 1982
SQ FT: 76,000
SALES (est): 26.5MM **Privately Held**
WEB: www.elitealuminum.com
SIC: 3089 Panels, building: plastic

(G-2076)
EUROPA MANUFACTURING INC
4900 Lyons Tech Pkwy # 7 (33073-4357)
PHONE..................................954 426-2965
Richard Spagna, *President*
Anthony Garofalo, *Engineer*
EMP: 11 **EST:** 2017
SALES (est): 2.7MM **Privately Held**
WEB: www.europamanufacturing.com
SIC: 3444 Sheet metalwork
PA: Sentech Eas Corporation
4900 Lyons Tech Pkwy # 7
Coconut Creek FL 33073

(G-2077)
FORTS SERVICES LLC
4650 Lyons Tech Pkwy (33073-4360)
PHONE..................................786 942-4389
Jesse Lapin-Bertone, *Director*
Daniel Rimon,
Sarita Zadok, *Administration*
EMP: 10 **EST:** 2018
SALES (est): 1.6MM **Privately Held**
WEB: www.fortsservices.com
SIC: 3448 Buildings, portable: prefabricated metal

(G-2078)
GREENWISE BANKCARD
4400 W Sample Rd (33073-3470)
PHONE..................................954 673-0406
Charles Cardona, *Principal*
EMP: 8 **EST:** 2010
SALES (est): 983K **Privately Held**
WEB: www.greenwisebankcard.com
SIC: 3578 Banking machines

(G-2079)
INFINITY MANUFACTURING LLC
4811 Lyons Tech Pkwy (33073-4346)
PHONE..................................954 531-6918
Tyler Howard,
Jim Howard,
EMP: 7 **EST:** 2015
SALES (est): 494K **Privately Held**
SIC: 2842 Sanitation preparations, disinfectants & deodorants

(G-2080)
INGEANT FLORIDA LLC
5163 Woodfield Way (33073-2233)
PHONE..................................954 868-2879
Luis Parra, *General Mgr*
EMP: 8 **EST:** 2011
SALES (est): 167.7K **Privately Held**
SIC: 3661 Communication headgear, telephone

(G-2081)
INNOMED TECHNOLOGIES INC (DH)
6601 Lyons Rd Ste B1 (33073-3605)
PHONE..................................800 200-9842
Ron F Richard, *CEO*
Markus Asch, *Accounting Mgr*
▲ **EMP:** 112 **EST:** 2001
SALES (est): 6.7MM
SALES (corp-wide): 118.5MM **Privately Held**
WEB: www.salterlabs.com
SIC: 3841 Surgical & medical instruments
HQ: Salter Labs, Llc
2710 Northridge Dr Nw A
Grand Rapids MI 49544
847 739-3224

(G-2082)
INNOVATIVE FASTENERS LLC
6601 Lyons Rd Ste I5 (33073-3631)
PHONE..................................561 542-2152
Cid Roberto, *Branch Mgr*
EMP: 10
SALES (corp-wide): 175.6K **Privately Held**
WEB: www.innovativefasteners.com
SIC: 3965 Fasteners
PA: Innovative Fasteners Llc
3495 N Dixie Hwy
Boca Raton FL 33431
561 235-5746

(G-2083)
INTELI DRONE INC
7141 Nw 48th Way (33073-2744)
PHONE..................................954 707-9547
Ruskin Michael, *Principal*
EMP: 8 **EST:** 2014
SALES (est): 97.5K **Privately Held**
WEB: www.intel.com
SIC: 3721 Motorized aircraft

(G-2084)
INTERNATIONAL PRINTING & COPYI
5379 Lyons Rd (33073-2810)
PHONE..................................954 295-5239
Carrie A Sacca, *Principal*
EMP: 7 **EST:** 2007
SALES (est): 252.5K **Privately Held**
SIC: 2752 Commercial printing, lithographic

(G-2085)
JAYNOR FURNISHINGS INC
1603 Abaco Dr (33066-3201)
PHONE..................................954 973-8446
Norma A Golisano, *Principal*
EMP: 6 **EST:** 2015
SALES (est): 62.7K **Privately Held**
SIC: 2221 Broadwoven fabric mills, manmade

(G-2086)
JW MARKETING AND CONSULTING
Also Called: Battery On The Go
6574 N State Road 7 # 27 (33073-3625)
PHONE..................................866 323-0001

Jamie Sasso, *President*
EMP: 10 **EST:** 2009
SALES (est): 318.3K **Privately Held**
WEB: www.batteryonthego.com
SIC: 3692 Primary batteries, dry & wet

(G-2087)
KAPPA METAL USA INC
5497 Wiles Rd Ste 202 (33073-4218)
PHONE..................................954 757-7100
Panagiotis Koutsopodiotis, *President*
EMP: 6 **EST:** 2017
SALES (est): 145.9K **Privately Held**
SIC: 3639 Major kitchen appliances, except refrigerators & stoves

(G-2088)
KO ORTHOTICS INC
5130 Heron Ct (33073-2409)
PHONE..................................954 570-8096
Kristin Orta, *Principal*
EMP: 7 **EST:** 2016
SALES (est): 156.1K **Privately Held**
SIC: 3842 Orthopedic appliances

(G-2089)
MAMA ASIAN NOODLE BAR
4437 Lyons Rd (33073-4387)
PHONE..................................954 973-1670
Robert Kaufman, *Principal*
EMP: 12 **EST:** 2010
SALES (est): 705K **Privately Held**
WEB: www.promenadeatcoconutcreek.com
SIC: 2098 Noodles (e.g. egg, plain & water), dry

(G-2090)
MICHIGAN GROUP INC
5481 Wiles Rd (33073-4259)
PHONE..................................954 328-6341
Ariel Giglio, *President*
EMP: 7 **EST:** 2016
SALES (est): 321.5K **Privately Held**
WEB: www.michigangroup.us
SIC: 3531 Construction machinery

(G-2091)
MOBILE SIGN SERVICE INC
4381 Nw 4th St (33066-1721)
PHONE..................................954 579-8628
Timothy Bucaro, *Director*
EMP: 6 **EST:** 2001
SALES (est): 405.4K **Privately Held**
SIC: 3993 Signs & advertising specialties

(G-2092)
PARODI GENERAL GROUP CORP
5431 Nw 50th Ct (33073-3301)
PHONE..................................954 306-1098
Jose Parodi, *Principal*
EMP: 6 **EST:** 2007
SALES (est): 115.9K **Privately Held**
SIC: 3548 Electric welding equipment

(G-2093)
SENTECH EAS CORPORATION (PA)
4900 Lyons Tech Pkwy # 7 (33073-4357)
PHONE..................................954 426-2965
Richard J Spagna, *President*
Ricky Spagna, *Opers Mgr*
Anthony Garofalo, *Engineer*
Paul Spagna, *Manager*
Lukas A Geiges, *Director*
▲ **EMP:** 18 **EST:** 1990
SALES (est): 6.4MM **Privately Held**
WEB: www.sentecheas.com
SIC: 3812 Detection apparatus: electronic/magnetic field, light/heat

(G-2094)
SERGEANT BRETTS COFFEE LLC
Also Called: Sgt. Bretts Healthy Lifestyles
1991 Nw 38th Ter (33066-3006)
PHONE..................................561 451-0048
EMP: 5 **EST:** 2006
SALES: 900K **Privately Held**
SIC: 2095 4971 2086 3589 Mfg Roasted Coffee Irrigation Systems Mfg Soft Drinks Mfg Svc Industry Mach Water Supply Service

(G-2095)
SIMPSON
7137 Pinecreek Ln (33073-2705)
PHONE..................................954 804-0829
Paul A Simpson, *Principal*
EMP: 12 **EST:** 2012
SALES (est): 237.7K **Privately Held**
WEB: www.simpsondoor.com
SIC: 2431 Millwork

(G-2096)
SMARTBEAR SOFTWARE
4611 Johnson Rd Unit 4 (33073-4361)
PHONE..................................954 312-0188
Douglas McNary, *Principal*
EMP: 8 **EST:** 2013
SALES (est): 159.9K **Privately Held**
WEB: www.smartbear.com
SIC: 7372 Prepackaged software

(G-2097)
STEEL COMPONENTS INC
4701 Johnson Rd Ste 1 (33073-4340)
PHONE..................................954 427-6820
Sammy Shemtov, *President*
Howard Feldsher, *Vice Pres*
Margaret Wong, *Admin Sec*
◆ **EMP:** 15 **EST:** 1997
SALES (est): 2.5MM **Privately Held**
WEB: www.steelcomponentsinc.net
SIC: 3441 Fabricated structural metal

(G-2098)
TRUMETER COMPANY INC (DH)
6601 Lyons Rd Ste H7 (33073-3632)
PHONE..................................954 725-6699
Fred Hickey, *President*
Ron Smith, *Managing Dir*
Stefan Ebert, *Vice Pres*
Sean McNaughton, *VP Opers*
Regina Hickey, *Human Res Mgr*
▲ **EMP:** 3 **EST:** 1994
SALES (est): 7.6MM
SALES (corp-wide): 9.3MM **Privately Held**
WEB: www.trumeter.com
SIC: 3812 3824 3545 Distance measuring equipment; mechanical & electromechanical counters & devices; precision measuring tools
HQ: Trumeter Technologies Limited
4 Floor
Bury LANCS BL9 9
161 674-0960

(G-2099)
UK SALES LLC
5300 W Hillsboro Blvd # 215 (33073-4395)
PHONE..................................561 239-2980
Arnold S Cohen, *Principal*
▲ **EMP:** 6 **EST:** 2009
SALES (est): 67.5K **Privately Held**
SIC: 3312 Stainless steel

(G-2100)
VAL DOR APPAREL LLC (PA)
Also Called: Valdor Apparel
6820 Lyons Tech Cir # 220 (33073-4323)
PHONE..................................954 363-7340
Robert Rothbaum, *Mng Member*
Marcy Rosen, *Director*
Usman Shah, *Director*
Marc Odrobina, *Officer*
Martin Granoff,
◆ **EMP:** 8 **EST:** 2006
SQ FT: 2,200
SALES (est): 35.6MM **Privately Held**
WEB: www.valdorapparel.com
SIC: 2322 2329 2331 2339 Men's & boys' underwear & nightwear; men's & boys' sportswear & athletic clothing; T-shirts & tops, women's: made from purchased materials; women's & misses' outerwear; women's & children's undergarments

(G-2101)
WELL MADE BUS SOLUTIONS LLC
5671 Nw 40th Ter (33073-4057)
PHONE..................................754 227-7268
EMP: 7
SQ FT: 3,800
SALES (est): 675K **Privately Held**
SIC: 3955 5112 Mfg Cartridges & Whol Office Supplies

(G-2102)
WEMERGE INC
3620 W Hillsboro Blvd (33073-2104)
PHONE..................................561 305-2070
Dwayne M Adams, *Principal*
Wemerge Magazine, *Creative Dir*
EMP: 7 **EST:** 2009
SALES (est): 47.2K **Privately Held**
WEB: www.wemerge.com
SIC: 2741 Miscellaneous publishing

(G-2103)
WILLIS AERONAUTICAL SVCS INC
4700 Lyons Tech Pkwy (33073-4309)
PHONE..................................561 272-5402
Don Nunemaker, *President*
Al Landolfi, *Vice Pres*
Susan Leahy, *Vice Pres*
Sue Leahy, *VP Opers*
Stephen Bobal, *CFO*
EMP: 15 **EST:** 2013
SALES (est): 5MM
SALES (corp-wide): 288.6MM **Publicly Held**
WEB: www.willisaero.com
SIC: 3728 3812 7699 Aircraft parts & equipment; aircraft/aerospace flight instruments & guidance systems; aviation propeller & blade repair
PA: Willis Lease Finance Corporation
4700 Lyons Tech Pkwy
Coconut Creek FL 33073
415 408-4700

(G-2104)
XTREME PALLETS INC
5440 Nw 55th Blvd Apt 108 (33073-3789)
PHONE..................................954 302-8915
Silver J Mendez, *Principal*
EMP: 6 **EST:** 2008
SALES (est): 71.5K **Privately Held**
SIC: 2448 Pallets, wood & wood with metal

Coconut Grove
Miami-Dade County

(G-2105)
SPECIAL NUTRIENTS LLC
2766 Sw 37th Ave (33133-2749)
PHONE..................................305 857-9830
Fernando Tamames III, *CEO*
Jesus Martinez, *Manager*
EMP: 18 **EST:** 2018
SQ FT: 3,000
SALES (est): 1.9MM **Privately Held**
WEB: www.specialnutrients.com
SIC: 2048 Feed supplements

Cooper City
Broward County

(G-2106)
ABC COMPONENTS INC
8963 Stirling Rd Ste 5 (33328-5113)
PHONE..................................954 249-6286
Mine Gulec, *President*
Ender Ozelcaglayan, *Sales Mgr*
EMP: 14 **EST:** 2009
SALES (est): 2.3MM **Privately Held**
WEB: www.abccomponents.com
SIC: 3812 3679 Aircraft/aerospace flight instruments & guidance systems; recording & playback apparatus, including phonograph

(G-2107)
ADVANCED GRAPHICS & PRTG INC
5615 Sw 88th Ave (33328-5910)
PHONE..................................954 966-1209
Kevin Comprosky, *Principal*
EMP: 6 **EST:** 2012
SALES (est): 97.8K **Privately Held**
SIC: 2752 Commercial printing, offset

(G-2108)
ALWAYS FUN INC
Also Called: America Mia
5660 Sw 99th Ln (33328-5720)
PHONE..................................954 258-4377
Ernesto Ochoa, *President*
EMP: 7 **EST:** 2009
SALES (est): 264.8K **Privately Held**
SIC: 2721 Periodicals

(G-2109)
ATMOSPHERIC WTR SOLUTIONS INC
12260 Sw 53rd St Ste 603 (33330-3354)
PHONE..................................954 306-6763
Doug Marcille, *CEO*
Howard Ullman, *President*
Reid Goldstein, *Exec VP*
◆ **EMP:** 16 **EST:** 2011
SQ FT: 3,000
SALES (est): 1MM **Privately Held**
WEB: www.atmosphericwatersolutions.com
SIC: 3589 Water purification equipment, household type

(G-2110)
BETROCK INFORMATION SYSTEMS
Also Called: Plantfinder
12330 Sw 53rd St Ste 712 (33330-3355)
PHONE..................................954 981-2821
Irving Betrock, *President*
Bette Betrock, *Vice Pres*
▲ **EMP:** 45 **EST:** 1972
SQ FT: 4,000
SALES (est): 3.4MM **Privately Held**
WEB: www.betrock.com
SIC: 2721 7379 Magazines: publishing only, not printed on site; trade journals: publishing & printing; computer related consulting services

(G-2111)
EMBROIDME - NORTH MIAMI BEACH
10518 Sw 53rd St (33328-5610)
PHONE..................................954 434-2191
James A Foster, *Principal*
EMP: 6 **EST:** 2012
SALES (est): 41.5K **Privately Held**
SIC: 2395 Embroidery & art needlework

(G-2112)
HAPPY MIX LLC
8747 Stirling Rd (33328-5932)
PHONE..................................954 880-0160
Carlos Sabater,
Nannette Sabater,
EMP: 9 **EST:** 2008
SALES (est): 134.5K **Privately Held**
SIC: 2024 Ice cream & ice milk

(G-2113)
JTM INTERNATIONAL INC
5560 Sw 98th Way (33328-5725)
PHONE..................................954 680-3517
Mike Duchrow, *President*
Sherry D Husbands, *President*
EMP: 5
SALES (est): 455.4K **Privately Held**
SIC: 3589 Sewage & water treatment equipment

(G-2114)
MDZ PUBLISHING
5063 Sweetwater Ter (33330-2753)
PHONE..................................954 680-9956
Jonia Fernandez-Marmo, *Principal*
EMP: 6 **EST:** 2009
SALES (est): 123.8K **Privately Held**
SIC: 2741 Miscellaneous publishing

(G-2115)
SKYMO LLC
12260 Sw 53rd St Ste 609 (33330-3320)
PHONE..................................305 676-6739
Raul Santoya, *President*
Reyniel Santoya, *Principal*
EMP: 10 **EST:** 2016
SALES (est): 624.3K **Privately Held**
WEB: www.skymo.net
SIC: 2841 2842 5087 2911 Soap & other detergents; detergents, synthetic organic or inorganic alkaline; degreasing solvent; janitors' supplies; solvents; solvents, organic

▲ = Import ▼=Export
◆ =Import/Export

(G-2116)
SOUTH FLORIDA FABRICATORS LLC
Also Called: All Star Pvc Products
4960 Sw 91st Ter (33328-3524)
PHONE..................................954 802-6782
William Roberson, *Principal*
EMP: 8 **EST:** 2016
SALES (est): 435.7K **Privately Held**
SIC: 3999 Manufacturing industries

(G-2117)
STEVEN PRESS
5820 Sw 115th Ave (33330-4109)
PHONE..................................954 434-3694
Steven Press, *Principal*
EMP: 6 **EST:** 2013
SALES (est): 117.9K **Privately Held**
SIC: 2741 Miscellaneous publishing

Coral Gables
Miami-Dade County

(G-2118)
AERO MECHANICAL INDUSTRIES
121 Alhambra Plz Ste 1700 (33134-4541)
PHONE..................................469 645-1620
EMP: 7 **EST:** 2019
SALES (est): 261K **Privately Held**
SIC: 3728 Aircraft parts & equipment

(G-2119)
AERSALE 23440 LLC
121 Alhambra Plz Ste 1700 (33134-4541)
PHONE..................................305 764-3200
Nicholas Finazzo, *CEO*
Michael Henrickson, *Owner*
Robert Nichols, *COO*
EMP: 1 **EST:** 2011
SALES (est): 5.1MM **Privately Held**
WEB: www.aersale.com
SIC: 3724 Aircraft engines & engine parts
HQ: Aersale, Inc.
121 Alhambra Plz Ste 1700
Coral Gables FL 33134

(G-2120)
AERSALE 26346 LLC
121 Alhambra Plz Ste 1700 (33134-4541)
PHONE..................................305 764-3200
Nicolas Finazzo, *Mng Member*
Michael Henrickson, *Manager*
Doug Meyer,
Robert Nichols,
EMP: 64 **EST:** 1997
SALES (est): 14.7MM **Privately Held**
WEB: www.aersale.com
SIC: 3728 Bodies, aircraft
HQ: Aersale, Inc.
121 Alhambra Plz Ste 1700
Coral Gables FL 33134

(G-2121)
ALVEAN AMERICAS INC
2525 Ponce De Leon Blvd (33134-6037)
PHONE..................................305 606-0770
Julie Decaudin, *Principal*
Megan Conkey, *Associate*
EMP: 13 **EST:** 2015
SALES (est): 603.8K **Privately Held**
WEB: www.alvean.com
SIC: 2061 3556 Raw cane sugar; sugar plant machinery

(G-2122)
AMERICAN ROOFING SERVICES LLC
95 Merrick Way Ste 514 (33134-5310)
PHONE..................................305 250-7115
Mauro Iurman, *Mng Member*
Thyrone Troccolis, *Manager*
Marga Degwitz,
Henry Iurman,
◆ **EMP:** 8 **EST:** 2006
SALES (est): 2.5MM **Privately Held**
WEB: www.amroofs.com
SIC: 2952 Roofing materials

(G-2123)
APAKUS INC
75 Valencia Ave Ste 701 (33134-6132)
PHONE..................................305 403-2603
Vladimir Zhamgotsev, *President*
EMP: 10 **EST:** 2004
SALES (est): 533.2K **Privately Held**
SIC: 2671 2011 Packaging paper & plastics film, coated & laminated; meat packing plants

(G-2124)
AUTOMUNDO PRODUCTIONS INC
Also Called: Automundo Magazine
2520 Coral Way Ste 2 (33145-3431)
PHONE..................................305 541-4198
Jorge Koechlin, *President*
EMP: 6 **EST:** 1983
SALES (est): 546.6K **Privately Held**
SIC: 2721 Magazines: publishing & printing

(G-2125)
BAKERLY LLC (HQ)
2600 S Douglas Rd Ste 410 (33134-6134)
PHONE..................................305 608-4479
Julien Caron, *CEO*
Fabian Milon, *COO*
Tess Fagan, *Project Mgr*
Jonathan Salas, *Regl Sales Mgr*
Andrew Goldemberg, *Sales Staff*
EMP: 25 **EST:** 2015
SQ FT: 100
SALES (est): 7.7MM
SALES (corp-wide): 1MM **Privately Held**
WEB: www.bakerly.com
SIC: 2051 Bakery: wholesale or wholesale/retail combined
PA: Norac
2 A 3
Rennes 35000
299 652-932

(G-2126)
BEES BROTHERS LLC
2990 Ponce De Leon Blvd # 202 (33134-6803)
P.O. Box 141071 (33114-1071)
PHONE..................................305 529-5789
JP Baggini, *General Mgr*
Juan P Baggini, *Mng Member*
Rodrigo Alberton,
Joaquin Mantovani,
▲ **EMP:** 7
SQ FT: 2,000
SALES (est): 23.2MM **Privately Held**
WEB: www.beesbrothersllc.com
SIC: 2099 Honey, strained & bottled

(G-2127)
BLUE STONE USA LLC
1172 S Dixie Hwy 301 (33146-2918)
PHONE..................................305 494-1141
Alex Daian, *Principal*
EMP: 10 **EST:** 2009
SALES (est): 63.6K **Privately Held**
WEB: www.bluestoneusa.com
SIC: 2099 Food preparations

(G-2128)
BUTTERCREAM CPCAKES COF SP INC
1411 Sunset Dr (33143-5824)
PHONE..................................305 669-8181
Kristine E Graulich, *President*
Jose F Cuellar, *Vice Pres*
EMP: 10 **EST:** 2007
SQ FT: 400
SALES (est): 747.7K **Privately Held**
WEB: www.buttercreamcupcakes.com
SIC: 2051 5812 Bakery: wholesale or wholesale/retail combined; coffee shop

(G-2129)
CATALYST PHARMACEUTICALS INC (PA)
355 Alhambra Cir Ste 801 (33134-5075)
PHONE..................................305 420-3200
Patrick J McEnany, *Ch of Bd*
Steven R Miller, *COO*
Jeff D Carmen, *Senior VP*
Jeff Del Carmen, *Senior VP*
Brian Elsbernd, *Senior VP*
EMP: 20 **EST:** 2002
SQ FT: 5,200
SALES: 119MM **Publicly Held**
WEB: www.catalystpharma.com
SIC: 2834 Pharmaceutical preparations

(G-2130)
CE NORTH AMERICA LLC
2600 S Douglas Rd Ph 7 (33134-6143)
PHONE..................................305 392-2200
Mariela Gonzalez, *Opers Mgr*
Manuel Lopez, *CFO*
Julio Caceres, *Controller*
Alberto Gutierrez, *Sales Staff*
Marcelo Teran, *Sales Staff*
◆ **EMP:** 22
SALES: 54.8MM **Privately Held**
WEB: www.cemglobal.com
SIC: 3825 5064 Internal combustion engine analyzers, to test electronics; electric household appliances
PA: Leyva Family Limited Partnership
6950 Nw 77th Ct
Miami FL 33166
305 392-2200

(G-2131)
CLEAN ENERGY ESB INC
600 Biltmore Way Apt 508 (33134-7530)
PHONE..................................202 905-6726
Andrea P Irarrazaval, *CEO*
EMP: 24
SQ FT: 1,100
SALES (est): 500MM **Privately Held**
SIC: 2911 5261 Diesel fuels; fertilizer

(G-2132)
COMMUNCATIONS SURVEILLANCE INC
4000 Ponce De Leon Blvd (33146-1431)
P.O. Box 771373, Miami (33177-0023)
PHONE..................................305 377-1211
Jose M Noy, *President*
Jose Noy, *General Mgr*
Nathaly C Noy, *Senior VP*
Miguel A Noy, *Vice Pres*
EMP: 10 **EST:** 1992
SQ FT: 2,000
SALES (est): 1.1MM **Privately Held**
SIC: 3699 Security control equipment & systems

(G-2133)
CORAL GABLES LIVING
400 University Dr Fl 2 (33134-7114)
P.O. Box 140249, Miami (33114-0249)
PHONE..................................786 552-6464
Joellen Phillips, *Principal*
EMP: 7 **EST:** 2005
SALES (est): 217.1K **Privately Held**
WEB: www.palacecoralgables.com
SIC: 2721 Periodicals: publishing only

(G-2134)
CREATIVE CLTURE MDIA GROUP LLC
5740 Sw 116th St (33156-5033)
PHONE..................................786 237-0206
Nicolas Joseph, *Principal*
EMP: 6 **EST:** 2017
SALES (est): 125.8K **Privately Held**
SIC: 2836 Culture media

(G-2135)
CUSTOM BEACH HUTS LLC
800 S Douglas Rd Ste 300 (33134-3160)
PHONE..................................305 439-3991
Thomas Bache-Wiig, *Principal*
EMP: 8 **EST:** 2014
SALES (est): 332.4K **Privately Held**
WEB: www.custombeach.com
SIC: 2511 Wood household furniture

(G-2136)
DADE ENGINEERING CORP
Also Called: Daeco
6855 Edgewater Dr Apt 1e (33133-7038)
PHONE..................................305 885-2766
Joanne Goodstein, *President*
◆ **EMP:** 10 **EST:** 1953
SALES (est): 600.3K **Privately Held**
WEB: www.dadecoolers.com
SIC: 3448 Panels for prefabricated metal buildings

(G-2137)
DANIEL BUSTAMANTE
1210 Placetas Ave (33146-3243)
PHONE..................................305 779-7777
Daniel Bustamante, *Principal*
EMP: 6 **EST:** 2017
SALES (est): 168.4K **Privately Held**
SIC: 3082 Unsupported plastics profile shapes

(G-2138)
DEL MONTE FRESH PRODUCE NA INC (DH)
241 Sevilla Ave (33134-6622)
P.O. Box 149222, Miami (33114-9222)
PHONE..................................305 520-8400
Mohammad Abu-Ghazaleh, *CEO*
Hani El Naffy, *President*
Kevin Hobbs, *General Mgr*
Anthony Luongo, *General Mgr*
Ana Cristina Fonseca, *Vice Pres*
◆ **EMP:** 50 **EST:** 1952
SQ FT: 48,000
SALES (est): 658.8MM **Privately Held**
WEB: www.freshdelmonte.com
SIC: 2033 5148 Fruits & fruit products in cans, jars, etc.; fruits, fresh
HQ: Del Monte Fresh Produce Company
241 Sevilla Ave Ste 200
Coral Gables FL 33134
305 520-8400

(G-2139)
DIAGEO NORTH AMERICA INC
396 Alhambra Cir (33134-5045)
PHONE..................................305 476-7761
Chris Sherrill, *Sales Staff*
EMP: 51
SALES (corp-wide): 18B **Privately Held**
SIC: 2085 Distilled & blended liquors
HQ: Diageo North America Inc.
3 World Trade Ctr
New York NY 10007
212 202-1800

(G-2140)
ECOSAN LLC
Also Called: American Lab Test & Engrg
2520 Coral Way Ste 2 (33145-3431)
PHONE..................................954 446-5929
Joseph Prieto, *Principal*
▲ **EMP:** 8 **EST:** 2011
SALES (est): 392.7K **Privately Held**
SIC: 2421 Outdoor wood structural products

(G-2141)
EDCA BAKERY CORPORATION
Also Called: Pinocho Bakery
5236 W Flagler St (33134-1168)
PHONE..................................305 448-7843
Carlos Cruz, *President*
Zeus Cruz, *Owner*
EMP: 10 **EST:** 1982
SQ FT: 2,000
SALES (est): 499.5K **Privately Held**
WEB: www.pinochobakery.com
SIC: 2051 5461 Bakery: wholesale or wholesale/retail combined; bakeries

(G-2142)
EDUCATIONAL NETWORKS INC (PA)
901 Ponce De Leon Blvd (33134-3073)
PHONE..................................866 526-0200
Ender Tortop, *CEO*
Kristin Hallowell, *Accounts Mgr*
EMP: 11 **EST:** 2000
SQ FT: 1,071
SALES (est): 2.1MM **Privately Held**
WEB: www.educationalnetworks.net
SIC: 7372 Educational computer software

(G-2143)
ENKI GROUP INC
11555 Sw 82nd Avenue Rd (33156-4308)
PHONE..................................305 773-3502
Antonio Ynastrilla, *President*
EMP: 7 **EST:** 2004
SALES (est): 509K **Privately Held**
SIC: 3812 Defense systems & equipment

(G-2144)
EUROINSOLES INCORPORATED
75 Valencia Ave Ste 201 (33134-6162)
PHONE..................................786 206-6117
Joaquin Santos, *Principal*
EMP: 6 **EST:** 2010
SALES (est): 208.1K **Privately Held**
SIC: 3842 Orthopedic appliances

GEOGRAPHIC

(G-2145)
FASTSIGNS
146 Madeira Ave (33134-4552)
PHONE..................................305 747-7115
EMP: 8 **EST:** 2016
SALES (est): 156.4K **Privately Held**
WEB: www.fastsigns.com
SIC: 3993 Signs & advertising specialties

(G-2146)
FUSSION INTERNATIONAL INC
446 Loretto Ave (33146-2106)
PHONE..................................305 662-4848
Stella Crismanich, *Principal*
EMP: 5 **EST:** 2005
SALES (est): 443K **Privately Held**
SIC: 3161 Luggage

(G-2147)
GABLES ENGINEERING INC
247 Greco Ave (33146-1881)
P.O. Box 140880, Miami (33114-0880)
PHONE..................................305 774-4400
Gary A Galimidi, *President*
Rene Ramos, *General Mgr*
Lauren Colon, *Vice Pres*
Charles Flores, *Mfg Staff*
Tom Eden, *QC Mgr*
EMP: 277 **EST:** 1947
SQ FT: 60,000
SALES (est): 96.6MM **Privately Held**
WEB: www.gableseng.com
SIC: 3812 3365 3369 Aircraft/aerospace flight instruments & guidance systems; aerospace castings, aluminum; aerospace castings, nonferrous: except aluminum

(G-2148)
GALLOWAY FOODS INC
1430 S Dixie Hwy Ste 311 (33146-3173)
PHONE..................................305 670-7600
Pedro Menendez, *Principal*
EMP: 8 **EST:** 2010
SALES (est): 303.5K **Privately Held**
SIC: 2099 Food preparations

(G-2149)
GAMMA INSULATORS CORP (PA)
2121 Ponce De Leon Blvd (33134-5224)
PHONE..................................585 302-0878
Christopher Seguin, *Vice Pres*
◆ **EMP:** 38 **EST:** 2009
SALES (est): 992.3K **Privately Held**
WEB: www.gammainsulators.com
SIC: 3644 Insulators & insulation materials, electrical

(G-2150)
GLOBAL PRINTING SERVICES INC
Also Called: Sir Speedy
3150 Ponce De Leon Blvd (33134-6826)
PHONE..................................305 446-7628
Frank Ley, *President*
Raul Ley, *Vice Pres*
EMP: 5 **EST:** 1988
SQ FT: 2,100
SALES (est): 985.3K **Privately Held**
WEB: www.sirspeedy.com
SIC: 2752 Commercial printing, lithographic

(G-2151)
GLOBAL RECASH LLC
3191 Coral Way (33145-3213)
PHONE..................................818 297-4437
Alfred Urcuyo, *Mng Member*
Derick Brol, *Mng Member*
EMP: 80 **EST:** 2017
SQ FT: 5,000
SALES (est): 7MM **Privately Held**
SIC: 7372 Business oriented computer software

(G-2152)
GRAPHIC CENTER GROUP CORP
Also Called: Office Graphic Design
2150 Coral Way Fl 1 (33145-2629)
PHONE..................................305 961-1649
Oliver Moreno, *CEO*
EMP: 8 **EST:** 2010
SQ FT: 2,000
SALES (est): 500MM **Privately Held**
SIC: 7372 7336 Prepackaged software; graphic arts & related design

(G-2153)
GRUPO EDITORIAL EXPANSION
2800 Ponce De Leon Blvd # 1160 (33134-6913)
PHONE..................................305 374-9003
Dalia Sanchez, *Managing Dir*
German Zimbron, *Director*
EMP: 8 **EST:** 2004
SQ FT: 2,800
SALES (est): 2.4MM
SALES (corp-wide): 300.2MM **Privately Held**
SIC: 2721 Magazines: publishing & printing
HQ: Hearst Expansion, S. De R.L. De C.V.
Av. Constituyentes No. 956
Ciudad De Mexico CDMX 11950

(G-2154)
HERA CASES LLC
6901 Edgewater Dr Apt 315 (33133-7035)
PHONE..................................305 322-8960
Ashley Mouriz, *Manager*
EMP: 5 **EST:** 2018
SALES (est): 324.2K **Privately Held**
WEB: www.heracases.com
SIC: 3523 Farm machinery & equipment

(G-2155)
HERNOL USA INC
201 Alhambra Cir Ste 6 (33134-5107)
PHONE..................................786 263-3341
Juan Zurita, *President*
Jose Gabriel Moran, *Vice Pres*
◆ **EMP:** 30 **EST:** 2015
SQ FT: 200
SALES (est): 2.8MM **Privately Held**
WEB: www.hernolusa.com
SIC: 3069 Hard rubber & molded rubber products

(G-2156)
IBD INDUSTRIAL LLC
Also Called: Axxionflex
1825 Ponce De Leon Blvd (33134-4418)
PHONE..................................786 655-7577
Carlos Martinez, *Mng Member*
EMP: 5 **EST:** 2016
SALES (est): 349.8K **Privately Held**
SIC: 3492 Hose & tube fittings & assemblies, hydraulic/pneumatic

(G-2157)
INGLOTECH USA LLC
2020 Ponce De Leon Blvd # 1108 (33134-4478)
PHONE..................................305 479-2770
Carlos W Astudillo,
Domingo G Bolet,
Concetta G Saladino,
EMP: 6 **EST:** 2011
SALES (est): 326.7K **Privately Held**
SIC: 3694 Engine electrical equipment

(G-2158)
INK PUBLISHING CORPORATION
806 S Douglas Rd Ste 300 (33134-3157)
PHONE..................................786 206-9867
Aracelis Baez, *Human Resources*
Luis Muniz, *Branch Mgr*
EMP: 15
SALES (corp-wide): 116.6MM **Privately Held**
SIC: 2741 Miscellaneous publishing
HQ: Ink Publishing Corporation
800 Suth Dglas Rd Ste 250
Coral Gables FL 33134

(G-2159)
INK PUBLISHING CORPORATION (DH)
800 Suth Dglas Rd Ste 250 (33134)
PHONE..................................786 482-2065
Simon Lesley, *CEO*
Kyra Penn, *Executive*
EMP: 20 **EST:** 2006
SALES (est): 12.9MM
SALES (corp-wide): 116.6MM **Privately Held**
WEB: www.ink-global.com
SIC: 2741 Miscellaneous publishing
HQ: Esubstance Limited
Blackburn House
London NW6 1
207 625-0700

(G-2160)
INTERMAS NETS USA INC
2655 S Le Jeune Rd # 810 (33134-5832)
PHONE..................................305 442-1416
Franois Mouchet, *CEO*
Albert Fort Mauri, *Vice Pres*
EMP: 9 **EST:** 2013
SALES (est): 349K **Privately Held**
WEB: www.intermasgroup.com
SIC: 2258 3089 Net & netting products; netting, plastic

(G-2161)
ISA GROUP CORP
1204 Placetas Ave (33146-3243)
PHONE..................................786 201-8360
Veruska Chalbaud, *Principal*
EMP: 8 **EST:** 2017
SALES (est): 77.8K **Privately Held**
WEB: www.isagroupca.com
SIC: 3552 Textile machinery

(G-2162)
J M ECONO-PRINT INC
303 Camilo Ave (33134-7208)
PHONE..................................305 591-3620
EMP: 8
SQ FT: 4,000
SALES (est): 900K **Privately Held**
SIC: 2752 Offset Printing

(G-2163)
KEY BISCAYNE SMOOTHIE COMPANY
249 Catalonia Ave (33134-6704)
PHONE..................................305 441-7882
Lawrence J Roberts, *Principal*
EMP: 8 **EST:** 2008
SALES (est): 176.8K **Privately Held**
SIC: 2037 Frozen fruits & vegetables

(G-2164)
KIMBERLYN INVESTMENTS CO
2828 Coral Way Ste 309 (33145-3214)
PHONE..................................305 448-6328
Antoniazzi Pablo, *CEO*
EMP: 7 **EST:** 2007
SALES (est): 611K **Privately Held**
SIC: 2911 Petroleum refining

(G-2165)
KITCHENISTA CORP
2332 Galiano St Fl 2 (33134-5402)
PHONE..................................305 400-4992
Naveed Mohammad, *Principal*
▲ **EMP:** 6 **EST:** 2011
SALES (est): 287.3K **Privately Held**
SIC: 3263 Semivitreous table & kitchenware

(G-2166)
KOBALT MUSIC PUBG AMER INC
2100 Ponce De Leon Blvd (33134-5215)
PHONE..................................305 200-5682
Willard Ahdritz, *Manager*
EMP: 52
SALES (corp-wide): 616.1MM **Privately Held**
SIC: 2741 Music book & sheet music publishing
HQ: Kobalt Music Publishing America, Inc.
2 Gansevoort St Fl 6
New York NY 10014
212 247-6204

(G-2167)
KRAFT HEINZ FOODS COMPANY
355 Alhambra Cir Ste 1350 (33134-5037)
PHONE..................................305 428-7152
Jesse Deutsch, *CFO*
EMP: 7
SALES (corp-wide): 26.1B **Publicly Held**
WEB: www.kraftheinzcompany.com
SIC: 2033 Canned fruits & specialties
HQ: Kraft Heinz Foods Company
1 Ppg Pl Ste 3400
Pittsburgh PA 15222
412 456-5700

(G-2168)
KRAFT HEINZ FOODS COMPANY
255 Alhambra Cir Ste 1010 (33134-7405)
PHONE..................................305 476-7000
EMP: 7
SALES (corp-wide): 26.1B **Publicly Held**
WEB: www.kraftheinzcompany.com
SIC: 2033 Canned fruits & specialties
HQ: Kraft Heinz Foods Company
1 Ppg Pl Ste 3400
Pittsburgh PA 15222
412 456-5700

(G-2169)
KRAKEN KOFFEE LLC
Also Called: Kimera Koffee
2555 Ponce De Leon Blvd (33134-6010)
PHONE..................................833 546-3725
Luis F Oviedo, *Mng Member*
Teodoro E Armenteros, *Mng Member*
Alejandro Santoni Fernandez, *Mng Member*
Frank A Pimentel, *Mng Member*
EMP: 6 **EST:** 2014
SALES (est): 434.1K **Privately Held**
WEB: www.kimerakoffee.com
SIC: 2095 Instant coffee

(G-2170)
LA TROPICAL BREWING CO LLC
1825 Ponce De Leon Blvd (33134-4418)
PHONE..................................786 362-5429
Manuel J Portuondo, *Manager*
EMP: 5 **EST:** 1998
SQ FT: 1,000
SALES (est): 352.5K **Privately Held**
SIC: 2085 Distilled & blended liquors

(G-2171)
LAWEX CORPORATION (PA)
Also Called: Trialworks
1550 Madruga Ave Ste 508 (33146-3048)
PHONE..................................305 259-9755
Robb Steinberg, *President*
Vanessa Steinberg, *Vice Pres*
Luana Patriota, *Manager*
Jeanny Collazo, *Software Dev*
EMP: 13 **EST:** 1996
SQ FT: 6,000
SALES (est): 2.2MM **Privately Held**
WEB: www.trialworks.com
SIC: 7372 8111 Business oriented computer software; legal services

(G-2172)
LEFAB COMMERCIAL LLC
Also Called: Morelia Paletas Gourmet
76 Miracle Mile (33134-5404)
PHONE..................................305 456-1306
Gilbert Arismendi, *Mng Member*
Fernando Falasca,
Leonardo Romeri-Arrivillaga,
Leonardo Romero,
EMP: 10 **EST:** 2016
SALES (est): 852.9K **Privately Held**
WEB: www.paletasmorelia.com
SIC: 2024 5143 5451 Ice cream & frozen desserts; ice cream & ices; ice cream (packaged)

(G-2173)
LIT PRINTS INC
4460 Sw 5th St (33134-1947)
PHONE..................................305 951-5122
Jesu Garcia, *Principal*
EMP: 6 **EST:** 2015
SALES (est): 198.8K **Privately Held**
WEB: www.litprints.com
SIC: 2752 Commercial printing, lithographic

(G-2174)
MASSO ESTATE WINERY LLC (PA)
3150 Sw 38th Ave Ste 1303 (33146-1529)
PHONE..................................305 707-7749
Oscar Piloto,
EMP: 19 **EST:** 2011
SQ FT: 1,000
SALES (est): 1MM **Privately Held**
WEB: www,massowinery.com
SIC: 2084 Wines

(G-2175)
MERKARI GROUP INC
Also Called: Direcly
2222 Ponce De Leon Blvd (33134-5039)
PHONE..................................305 748-3260
Francisco A Garcia, *CEO*
EMP: 6 **EST:** 2019
SALES (est): 124.4K **Privately Held**
SIC: 7372 Application computer software

(G-2176)
MIACUCINA LLC
105 Miracle Mile (33134-5405)
PHONE..................................305 444-7383
Maika Dongellini, *Opers Staff*
Jezabel Cruz, *Sales Staff*
Jezabel Flores, *Sales Staff*
Ivonne Pena, *Sales Staff*
Sandhya Murphy, *Office Mgr*
◆ **EMP:** 15 **EST:** 2001
SALES (est): 1.4MM **Privately Held**
WEB: www.miacucina.com
SIC: 2434 Wood kitchen cabinets

(G-2177)
MINEA USA LLC
1550 S Dixie Hwy Ste 216 (33146-3034)
PHONE..................................800 971-3216
Sylvain Mazloum, *President*
Add Loris Mazloum, *Vice Pres*
EMP: 10
SALES: 9MM **Privately Held**
WEB: www.mineagroup.com
SIC: 3639 Major kitchen appliances, except refrigerators & stoves

(G-2178)
MONARQ AMERICAS LLC
Also Called: Monarq Group
55 Merrick Way Ste 202 (33134-5125)
PHONE..................................305 632-7448
Robert De Monchy, *Mng Member*
EMP: 17 **EST:** 2011
SALES (est): 1.3MM **Privately Held**
WEB: www.monarqgroup.com
SIC: 2084 Wines, brandy & brandy spirits

(G-2179)
MONDELEZ GLOBAL LLC
Also Called: Kraft Foods
396 Alhambra Cir Ste 1000 (33134-5095)
PHONE..................................305 774-6273
Tom Boyd, *Vice Pres*
Scott McKallagat, *Foreman/Supr*
Julius Grant, *Production*
Rosie Vansiclen, *Controller*
Steve Zober, *Accounts Mgr*
EMP: 20 **Publicly Held**
WEB: www.mondelezinternational.com
SIC: 2022 Processed cheese
HQ: Mondelez Global Llc
905 W Fulton Market # 20
Chicago IL 60607
847 943-4000

(G-2180)
NANNI USA LLC
306 Alcazar Ave (33134-4318)
PHONE..................................305 450-4853
Marco Ferri,
EMP: 6 **EST:** 2011
SALES (est): 80K **Privately Held**
SIC: 2599 Furniture & fixtures

(G-2181)
NEXOGY INC
2121 Ponce De Leon Blvd # 200
(33134-5256)
PHONE..................................305 358-8952
Carlos Lahrssen, *CEO*
Felipe Lahrssen, *COO*
Juan Carlos Canto, *CFO*
EMP: 27 **EST:** 2005
SALES (est): 3.1MM **Privately Held**
WEB: www.nexogy.com
SIC: 7372 8741 Business oriented computer software; management services

(G-2182)
OUHLALA GOURMET CORP
2655 S Le Jeune Rd # 1011 (33134-5803)
PHONE..................................305 774-7332
Jerome Lesur, *CEO*
Fabian Milon, *Vice Pres*
▲ **EMP:** 18 **EST:** 2008
SQ FT: 20,000
SALES (est): 1.3MM **Privately Held**
SIC: 2033 Fruit juices: packaged in cans, jars, etc.

(G-2183)
OUTDOOR MEDIA INC
Also Called: Lakeland Outdoor Advertising
3195 Ponce De Leon Blvd # 300
(33134-6801)
P.O. Box 141609 (33114-1609)
PHONE..................................305 529-1400
EMP: 5
SALES (est): 750K **Privately Held**
SIC: 2752 Advertising Posters Lithographed

(G-2184)
PENTACLES ENERGY GP LLC
1600 Ponce De Leon Blvd (33134-3988)
P.O. Box 140668 (33114-0668)
PHONE..................................786 552-9931
Miguel Otaola, *Opers Staff*
Gustavo Mancera, *Mng Member*
Alvaro Campins, *Mng Member*
EMP: 8 **EST:** 2010
SALES (est): 737.4K **Privately Held**
WEB: www.pentaclesenergy.com
SIC: 2869 Fuels

(G-2185)
PREMIER DIE CASTING COMPANY
47 S Prospect Dr (33133-7003)
PHONE..................................732 634-3000
Leonard Cordaro, *President*
▲ **EMP:** 60 **EST:** 1945
SALES (est): 6.3MM **Privately Held**
WEB: www.diecasting.com
SIC: 3599 Machine shop, jobbing & repair

(G-2186)
PRETEC DIRECTIONAL DRLG LLC
800 S Douglas Rd Ste 1200 (33134-3165)
PHONE..................................786 220-7667
Robert Apple,
Robert Poteete,
Steven Rooney,
EMP: 10 **EST:** 2016
SALES (est): 15MM
SALES (corp-wide): 6.3B **Publicly Held**
WEB: www.pretecdd.com
SIC: 1381 Directional drilling oil & gas wells
PA: Mastec, Inc.
800 S Douglas Rd Ste 1200
Coral Gables FL 33134
305 599-1800

(G-2187)
PROSTHETIC LABORATORIES
1270 Bird Rd (33146-1110)
PHONE..................................305 250-9900
Pedro Llanes, *President*
EMP: 8 **EST:** 1940
SALES (est): 1MM **Privately Held**
SIC: 3842 5999 Prosthetic appliances; orthopedic appliances; orthopedic & prosthesis applications

(G-2188)
QCI BRITANNIC INC (PA)
1600 Ponce De Leon Blvd # 907
(33134-3991)
P.O. Box 450871, Miami (33245-0871)
PHONE..................................305 860-0102
Ernesto Freund, *President*
Enrique Freund, *Principal*
William Freund, *Principal*
Ricardo Freund, *Vice Pres*
Eduardo Portillo, *CFO*
◆ **EMP:** 9 **EST:** 2000
SALES (est): 2.4MM **Privately Held**
WEB: www.quem.com
SIC: 1481 Nonmetallic mineral services

(G-2189)
RADIATION SHIELD TECH INC
Also Called: R.S.T.
6 Aragon Ave (33134-5300)
P.O. Box 144254 (33114-4254)
PHONE..................................866 733-6766
Ronald Demeo, *President*
Douglas Emery, *Treasurer*
▲ **EMP:** 12 **EST:** 2002
SQ FT: 3,000
SALES (est): 1.8MM **Privately Held**
WEB: www.radshield.com
SIC: 2836 Biological products, except diagnostic

(G-2190)
RAW FOODS INTERNATIONAL LLC
Also Called: Raaw
2600 S Douglas Rd Ste 410 (33134-6134)
PHONE..................................305 856-1991
Simon Decker, *Mng Member*
Paul J Gregg,
EMP: 15 **EST:** 2009
SQ FT: 5,000
SALES (est): 1.3MM **Privately Held**
SIC: 2033 5142 2037 Fruit juices: packaged in cans, jars, etc.; fruits & fruit products in cans, jars, etc.; fruit juices, frozen; fruit juices

(G-2191)
ROSEBANDITS LLC (PA)
740 San Esteban Ave (33146-1216)
PHONE..................................305 778-6370
Freddy Viera, *Principal*
EMP: 9 **EST:** 2010
SALES (est): 64.9K **Privately Held**
WEB: www.lauravangilder.com
SIC: 2741 Miscellaneous publishing

(G-2192)
SAGE IMPORTS CORP
232 Andalusia Ave Ste 201 (33134-5914)
PHONE..................................305 962-0631
Diosana Aleman, *President*
EMP: 9 **EST:** 2011
SALES (est): 269.5K **Privately Held**
SIC: 2099 Food preparations

(G-2193)
SAM-E-NIK CORP
330 Madeira Ave (33134-4240)
PHONE..................................347 992-2123
Carlos Lopez, *Principal*
EMP: 6 **EST:** 2017
SALES (est): 177.6K **Privately Held**
SIC: 3679 Electronic circuits

(G-2194)
SC GASTRONOMIC CREW INC
127 Miracle Mile (33134-5405)
PHONE..................................786 864-1212
Matias Pagano, *Director*
EMP: 30 **EST:** 2016
SALES (est): 1.2MM **Privately Held**
SIC: 2599 Furniture & fixtures

(G-2195)
SESVALIA USA LLC
67 Miracle Mile (33134-5403)
PHONE..................................305 615-1987
Gabriel Serrano,
EMP: 6 **EST:** 2010
SALES (est): 128.6K **Privately Held**
SIC: 2844 Toilet preparations

(G-2196)
SMR MANAGEMENT INC (PA)
Also Called: Sima Group
1728 Coral Way (33145-2794)
PHONE..................................305 529-2488
Roberto Isaias, *President*
Estefano Isaias, *Shareholder*
William Isaias, *Shareholder*
▲ **EMP:** 5 **EST:** 2008
SQ FT: 4,000
SALES (est): 1.5MM **Privately Held**
SIC: 3714 Motor vehicle parts & accessories

(G-2197)
SUKALDE INC (PA)
5271 Sw 8th St Apt 213 (33134-2382)
PHONE..................................786 399-0087
Eduardo J Quintero, *President*
Unai Urtizberea, *Vice Pres*
EMP: 37 **EST:** 2017
SALES (est): 261.3K **Privately Held**
SIC: 2038 Frozen specialties

(G-2198)
TIN MAN CO
2828 Coral Way Ste 207 (33145-3233)
PHONE..................................305 365-1926
Michael Netsky, *CEO*
EMP: 4 **EST:** 2010
SQ FT: 2,000
SALES (est): 72MM **Privately Held**
WEB: www.tinmanco.com
SIC: 3559 8742 Recycling machinery; retail trade consultant

(G-2199)
TITANIC BREWING COMPANY INC
Also Called: Titanic Restaurant & Brewery
5813 Ponce De Leon Blvd (33146-2422)
PHONE..................................305 668-1742
Kevin Rusk, *President*
EMP: 16 **EST:** 1995
SQ FT: 4,000
SALES (est): 1MM **Privately Held**
WEB: www.titanicbrewery.com
SIC: 2082 5812 Beer (alcoholic beverage); Cajun restaurant

(G-2200)
URAL ASSOCIATES INC
Also Called: Journal Housing Science
3608 Anderson Rd (33134-7053)
P.O. Box 140525 (33114-0525)
PHONE..................................305 446-9462
Oktay Ural, *President*
EMP: 6 **EST:** 1972
SALES (est): 353.9K **Privately Held**
WEB: www.housingsciencejournal.com
SIC: 2721 Trade journals: publishing & printing

(G-2201)
UREN NORTH AMERICA LLC
2990 Ponce De Leon Blvd (33134-6803)
P.O. Box 140398 (33114-0398)
PHONE..................................410 924-3478
Julian Wood,
Julie Creese,
Rob Laird,
Ross Stewart,
EMP: 6 **EST:** 2016
SALES (est): 967.3K **Privately Held**
WEB: www.uren.com
SIC: 2038 Breakfasts, frozen & packaged

(G-2202)
US PRECIOUS METALS INC
Also Called: (AN EXPLORATION STAGE COMPANY)
1825 Ponce De Leon Blvd (33134-4418)
PHONE..................................786 814-5804
John Leufray, *CEO*
Michael Green, *CFO*
EMP: 9 **EST:** 1998
SALES (est): 449.3K **Privately Held**
WEB: www.uspr-holdings.com
SIC: 1081 1041 1044 1021 Metal mining exploration & development services; gold ores; silver ores; copper ores

(G-2203)
USA MANUFACTURING GROUP LLC
1130 Alfonso Ave (33146-3210)
PHONE..................................786 253-3152
Gardo Gomez, *Principal*
EMP: 6 **EST:** 2016
SALES (est): 98.2K **Privately Held**
SIC: 3999 Manufacturing industries

(G-2204)
VELTIA USA LLC
2525 Ponce De Leon Blvd # 300
(33134-6037)
PHONE..................................305 298-8262
Ramon AMO, *Mng Member*
EMP: 6 **EST:** 2014
SALES (est): 139.3K **Privately Held**
WEB: www.veltia.com
SIC: 3634 Dryers, electric: hand & face

(G-2205)
VIVALIZE LLC
201 Alhambra Cir Ste 1205 (33134-5150)
PHONE..................................305 614-3952
Isaac G Morhaim, *CEO*
EMP: 6 **EST:** 2019
SALES (est): 604.7K **Privately Held**
SIC: 2834 Pharmaceutical preparations

GEOGRAPHIC

(G-2206)
WEMI SPORTS
Also Called: World Wide Export Management
156 Giralda Ave (33134-5209)
PHONE..................................305 446-5178
Raphael Quevedo, *Director*
▲ **EMP:** 5 **EST:** 2009
SALES (est): 327.4K **Privately Held**
WEB: www.wemisports.com
SIC: 3949 Sporting & athletic goods

(G-2207)
WORLDCITY INC
Also Called: World City
251 Valencia Ave (33134-5905)
PHONE..................................305 441-2244
Ken Roberts, *President*
Alison Klapper Leon, *Vice Pres*
Sari Govantes, *Manager*
Tatiana Panzardi, *Director*
Marilys Rios, *Director*
EMP: 8 **EST:** 1996
SALES (est): 1.8MM **Privately Held**
WEB: www.worldcityweb.com
SIC: 2711 Newspapers

(G-2208)
YELLOW GREEN AEROSPACE INC
Also Called: Ygaero
2525 Ponce De Leon Blvd # 300
(33134-6044)
PHONE..................................954 599-4161
Vanderlei Van Dias, *President*
Vanderlei Dias, *President*
EMP: 7 **EST:** 2016
SALES (est): 1.1MM **Privately Held**
WEB: www.ygaero.com
SIC: 3728 Aircraft parts & equipment

Coral Springs
Broward County

(G-2209)
24/7 SOFTWARE INC
12411 Nw 35th St (33065-2413)
PHONE..................................954 514-8988
Gerald Hwasta, *CEO*
Scott Meyers, *President*
Debbie Popkin, *VP Admin*
Jacob Molz, *Vice Pres*
Bandana Baid, *Finance*
EMP: 15 **EST:** 2007
SQ FT: 4,200
SALES (est): 1.5MM **Privately Held**
WEB: www.247software.com
SIC: 7372 Prepackaged software

(G-2210)
A-1 ROOF TRUSSES LTD COMPANY (PA)
11555 Heron Bay Blvd # 2 (33076-3360)
PHONE..................................270 316-9409
Amanda Wethington, *President*
John Herring, *President*
Robert G Lamb, *Vice Pres*
Michael L Ruede, *Vice Pres*
Bobby Henry, *Opers Staff*
▼ **EMP:** 15 **EST:** 1977
SALES (est): 33.8MM **Privately Held**
WEB: www.a1truss.com
SIC: 2439 3448 Trusses, wooden roof; trusses, except roof: laminated lumber; trusses & framing: prefabricated metal

(G-2211)
ABB ENTERPRISE SOFTWARE INC
Also Called: A B B Automation Technolgy Div
4300 Coral Ridge Dr (33065-7699)
P.O. Box 91089, Raleigh NC (27675-1089)
PHONE..................................954 752-6700
Bharat Chopra, *Business Mgr*
Richard Lindo, *Branch Mgr*
EMP: 170
SALES (corp-wide): 26.1B **Privately Held**
WEB: www.global.abb
SIC: 3823 3566 3625 3613 Controllers for process variables, all types; drives, high speed industrial, except hydrostatic; relays & industrial controls; switchgear & switchboard apparatus
HQ: Abb Inc.
305 Gregson Dr
Cary NC 27511

(G-2212)
ACIC PHARMACEUTICALS INC
11772 W Sample Rd Ste 103 (33065-3166)
PHONE..................................954 341-0795
Luciano Calenti, *President*
Craig Baxter, *Vice Pres*
EMP: 5 **EST:** 2017
SALES (est): 428.6K **Privately Held**
WEB: www.acic.com
SIC: 2834 Pharmaceutical preparations

(G-2213)
ADVANCED CMMNCATIONS HOLDG INC (DH)
Also Called: Advanced Cable Communications
12409 Nw 35th St (33065-2413)
PHONE..................................954 753-0100
Kerry Oslund, *President*
Gary Hoipkemier, *Corp Secy*
Barry Kerr, *Vice Pres*
Michelle Fitzpatrick, *Mktg Dir*
Miguel Bullard, *Technology*
▲ **EMP:** 76 **EST:** 1977
SQ FT: 23,000
SALES (est): 20.3MM
SALES (corp-wide): 2.3B **Publicly Held**
WEB: www.austin.myacc.net
SIC: 2621 2759 2711 2752 Catalog, magazine & newsprint papers; commercial printing; commercial printing & newspaper publishing combined; commercial printing, lithographic
HQ: Schurz Communications, Inc.
1301 E Douglas Rd Ste 200
Mishawaka IN 46545
574 247-7237

(G-2214)
ADVANTAGE MEDICAL ELEC LLC (DH)
Also Called: AMC
11705 Nw 39th St (33065-2511)
PHONE..................................954 345-9800
Cedric Ragsdale, *CFO*
Kim Davis, *Mng Member*
EMP: 13 **EST:** 2015
SALES (est): 5.7MM
SALES (corp-wide): 28.3MM **Privately Held**
WEB: www.lifesync.com
SIC: 3841 Surgical & medical instruments
HQ: Lifesync Corporation
11705 Nw 39th St
Coral Springs FL 33065
954 345-9800

(G-2215)
AEROTEK GEAR & SPLINE INC
11020 Nw 38th St (33065-2773)
PHONE..................................954 543-3473
EMP: 6 **EST:** 2016
SALES (est): 150.4K **Privately Held**
WEB: www.aerotekgear.com
SIC: 3566 Speed changers, drives & gears

(G-2216)
AESINC ADVANCED EQP & SVCS (PA)
Also Called: Advanced Equipment and Svcs
12070 Nw 40th St Ste 2 (33065-7602)
PHONE..................................954 857-1895
Victor De Sousa, *President*
Patricia Osorio, *Vice Pres*
EMP: 9 **EST:** 2016
SALES (est): 1MM **Privately Held**
WEB: www.advancees.com
SIC: 3589 Water treatment equipment, industrial

(G-2217)
AIR SPONGE FILTER COMPANY INC
4224 Nw 120th Ave (33065-7603)
PHONE..................................954 752-1836
Richard Rosen, *Owner*
Elisa Montenero, *Vice Pres*
Moe Adili, *Treasurer*
EMP: 7 **EST:** 1993
SALES (est): 908.8K **Privately Held**
WEB: www.airsponge.com
SIC: 3564 5075 Filters, air: furnaces, air conditioning equipment, etc.; air filters

(G-2218)
AL GAREY & ASSOCIATES INC
Also Called: Decimal Engineering
4300 Coral Ridge Dr (33065-7617)
PHONE..................................954 975-7992
Alan Garey Lee, *President*
Kevin Garey, *Vice Pres*
Wayne Graf, *Production*
Gary Stalzer, *Engineer*
Patrick O 'sullivan, *Manager*
▲ **EMP:** 140 **EST:** 1980
SALES (est): 19.2MM **Privately Held**
WEB: www.decimal.net
SIC: 3444 3599 Forming machine work, sheet metal; machine & other job shop work

(G-2219)
ALDORA ALUMINUM & GL PDTS INC (PA)
Also Called: Smith Mountain
12350 Nw 39th St Ste 102 (33065-2418)
PHONE..................................954 441-5057
Leon Silverstein, *President*
Joel Fletcher, *CFO*
Carin Novellom, *Treasurer*
Andrew Wiegand, *Admin Sec*
◆ **EMP:** 40 **EST:** 2013
SALES (est): 19.8MM **Privately Held**
WEB: www.aldoraglass.com
SIC: 3354 3211 5039 Aluminum extruded products; structural glass; structural assemblies, prefabricated: non-wood; glass construction materials

(G-2220)
AMETEK POWER INSTRUMENT INC
4050 Nw 121st Ave (33065-7612)
PHONE..................................954 344-9822
Frank S Hermance, *CEO*
EMP: 58 **EST:** 1994
SQ FT: 8,400
SALES (est): 5.7MM
SALES (corp-wide): 4.5B **Publicly Held**
WEB: www.ametek.com
SIC: 3829 Measuring & controlling devices
PA: Ametek, Inc.
1100 Cassatt Rd
Berwyn PA 19312
610 647-2121

(G-2221)
AW GATES INC
11285 Sw 1st St (33071-8145)
PHONE..................................954 341-2180
Anthony William Gates, *Owner*
EMP: 9 **EST:** 2008
SALES (est): 418.1K **Privately Held**
SIC: 2421 Building & structural materials, wood

(G-2222)
BABY GUARD INC
Also Called: Baby Guard Pool Fence Co
11947 W Sample Rd (33065-3100)
PHONE..................................954 741-6351
Michael Schatzberg, *President*
Wendy Schatzberg, *Vice Pres*
▲ **EMP:** 19 **EST:** 1989
SQ FT: 2,500
SALES (est): 2.4MM **Privately Held**
WEB: www.babyguardfence.com
SIC: 3315 5211 3949 3496 Fencing made in wiredrawing plants; fencing; sporting & athletic goods; miscellaneous fabricated wire products

(G-2223)
BAGINDD PRINTS
1843 Nw 83rd Dr (33071-6243)
PHONE..................................954 971-9000
Arnold S Reimer, *Partner*
Gloria Reimer, *Partner*
EMP: 10 **EST:** 1978
SQ FT: 25,000
SALES (est): 535.7K **Privately Held**
SIC: 2262 Screen printing: manmade fiber & silk broadwoven fabrics

(G-2224)
BAKER-HILL INDUSTRIES INC
3850 Nw 118th Ave (33065-2543)
PHONE..................................954 752-3090
William Ricci, *President*
Deiter Morlock, *Vice Pres*
Jared Henderson, *Controller*
Matthaw Ricci, *Sales Executive*
Leigh Livesay, *Manager*
EMP: 33 **EST:** 1967
SQ FT: 14,400
SALES (est): 7.4MM **Privately Held**
WEB: www.bakerhillindustries.com
SIC: 3599 Machine shop, jobbing & repair

(G-2225)
BELL BROTHERS ELECTRIC LLC
5222 Nw 110th Ave (33076-2758)
PHONE..................................954 496-0632
Mark A Bell, *Branch Mgr*
EMP: 39
SALES (corp-wide): 631.7K **Privately Held**
WEB: www.bellbrotherselectric.com
SIC: 3699 Bells, electric
PA: Bell Brothers Electric Llc
2436 N Federal Hwy
Lighthouse Point FL

(G-2226)
BLACK COLLEGE TODAY INC
4973 Nw 115th Ter (33076-3201)
P.O. Box 25425, Fort Lauderdale (33320-5425)
PHONE..................................954 344-4469
Steven Mootry, *President*
EMP: 6 **EST:** 1991
SALES (est): 530.6K **Privately Held**
WEB: www.blackcollegetoday.com
SIC: 2721 Magazines: publishing & printing; periodicals: publishing & printing

(G-2227)
BLADES DIRECT LLC
5645 Coral Ridge Dr (33076-3124)
PHONE..................................855 225-2337
Robert Slverstone, *Principal*
Kenny Gills, *Regl Sales Mgr*
Joe Carpone, *Sales Staff*
Micheal D Stewart, *Mng Member*
EMP: 15 **EST:** 2012
SALES (est): 1.1MM **Privately Held**
WEB: www.bladesdirect.net
SIC: 3425 Saw blades & handsaws

(G-2228)
BLIND WIZARD TOO INC
9146 Nw 21st St (33071-6128)
PHONE..................................954 755-3828
Phil Iovino, *President*
EMP: 7 **EST:** 2005
SALES (est): 126.1K **Privately Held**
WEB: www.blindwizard.com
SIC: 2591 Venetian blinds

(G-2229)
BR SIGNS INTERNATIONAL IN
5944 Coral Ridge Dr (33076-3300)
PHONE..................................954 464-7999
William Reicherter, *President*
EMP: 6 **EST:** 2017
SALES (est): 443.5K **Privately Held**
WEB: www.dreamsandvisionsinternational.org
SIC: 3993 Signs & advertising specialties

(G-2230)
CHIPTECH IMAGING LLC
4613 N University Dr # 576 (33067-4602)
PHONE..................................954 827-1401
Steve Ross, *Mng Member*
Barry Kripitzer,
Elizabeth Lawrence,
EMP: 8 **EST:** 2010
SALES (est): 128.8K **Privately Held**
WEB: www.chiptechsolutions.com
SIC: 3572 7389 Magnetic storage devices, computer; document embossing

(G-2231)
CNR PRECISION TOOL INC
8480 Nw 29th Ct (33065-5320)
PHONE..................................954 426-9650
Rosemarie Thomas, *Owner*

Christopher Thomas, *Co-Owner*
EMP: 6 **EST:** 1995
SQ FT: 3,100
SALES (est): 825K **Privately Held**
SIC: 3599 Machine shop, jobbing & repair

(G-2232)
COLD STONE CREAMERY-PARKLAND
6230 Coral Ridge Dr # 110 (33076-3386)
PHONE..................................954 341-8033
Jerry Kestel, *President*
Daniel Toledano, *General Mgr*
EMP: 9 **EST:** 2003
SQ FT: 2,000
SALES (est): 233.9K **Privately Held**
WEB: www.coldstonecreamery.com
SIC: 2024 5812 Ice cream & frozen desserts; ice cream stands or dairy bars

(G-2233)
COLLABORATIVE SFTWR SOLUTIONS
4721 Nw 115th Ave (33076-2154)
PHONE..................................954 753-2025
Rickie Ramcharitar, *Principal*
EMP: 5 **EST:** 2006
SALES (est): 346K **Privately Held**
WEB: www.collaborativesolutions.com
SIC: 7372 Prepackaged software

(G-2234)
CORE ENTERPRISES INCORPORATED
3650 Coral Ridge Dr # 101 (33065-2558)
PHONE..................................954 227-0781
Cornel Opris, *President*
Dennis Cardinale, *Vice Pres*
▲ **EMP:** 6 **EST:** 2001
SQ FT: 4,000
SALES (est): 1MM **Privately Held**
WEB: www.core-enterprises.com
SIC: 3825 3823 3829 Test equipment for electronic & electric measurement; industrial process measurement equipment; gas detectors

(G-2235)
CRYSTAL ART OF FLORIDA INC
11555 Heron Bay Blvd # 2 (33076-3360)
PHONE..................................305 885-5358
George Bock, *President*
Randy Greenberg, *President*
Jim Ehren, *CFO*
Doug Song, *Shareholder*
◆ **EMP:** 2 **EST:** 1993
SQ FT: 1,500
SALES (est): 16MM **Privately Held**
SIC: 3999 5023 Framed artwork; decorative home furnishings & supplies

(G-2236)
DA VINCI SYSTEMS INC
124 Th Ave (33065)
PHONE..................................954 688-5600
John Peeler, *CEO*
Mark Tremallo, *Corp Secy*
Richard Johnson, *Finance*
EMP: 1 **EST:** 1990
SQ FT: 8,000
SALES (est): 4.5MM
SALES (corp-wide): 1.2B **Publicly Held**
WEB: www.blackmagicdesign.com
SIC: 3663 5065 3651 Radio & TV communications equipment; radio & television equipment & parts; closed circuit television; household audio & video equipment
HQ: Jdsu Acterna Holdings Llc
1 Milestone Center Ct
Germantown MD 20876
240 404-1550

(G-2237)
DATA PUBLISHERS INC
Also Called: Parklanders
9602 Nw 36th Mnr (33065-2868)
PHONE..................................954 752-2332
Trulee Abbondanzio, *President*
EMP: 10 **EST:** 1996
SALES (est): 562.7K **Privately Held**
SIC: 2721 Periodicals

(G-2238)
DE LIMA CONSULTANTS GROUP INC
Also Called: Private Label Express
4216 Nw 120th Ave (33065-7603)
PHONE..................................954 933-7030
Robert De Lima, *President*
Peter Cianci, *Business Mgr*
EMP: 12 **EST:** 2010
SALES (est): 2.8MM **Privately Held**
WEB: www.privatelabelexpress.com
SIC: 2833 Vitamins, natural or synthetic: bulk, uncompounded

(G-2239)
DECORAL SYSTEM USA CORPORATION
12477 Nw 44th St (33065-7639)
PHONE..................................954 755-6021
Enrico Piva, *CEO*
Francesca Mella, *COO*
Mirta Duarte, *Vice Pres*
William Grunbaum, *VP Business*
Frank Trecki, *Sales Staff*
EMP: 28 **EST:** 2005
SALES (est): 7MM
SALES (corp-wide): 695.3K **Privately Held**
WEB: www.decoralamerica.com
SIC: 3549 Metalworking machinery
HQ: Decoral System Srl
Viale Del Lavoro 5
Arcole VR 37040
045 763-9101

(G-2240)
DELRAY PIN FACTORY INTL
5304 Nw 84th Ter (33067-2833)
PHONE..................................561 994-1680
Martin Fox, *President*
Barbara Fox, *Vice Pres*
EMP: 5 **EST:** 1990
SALES (est): 409.8K **Privately Held**
WEB: www.delraypin.com
SIC: 3961 3993 Pins (jewelry), except precious metal; advertising novelties

(G-2241)
DFD LOADERS INC
11820 Nw 37th St (33065-2537)
PHONE..................................954 283-8839
David Font, *President*
EMP: 12 **EST:** 2018
SALES (est): 2MM **Privately Held**
WEB: www.dfdloaders.com
SIC: 3537 Trucks, tractors, loaders, carriers & similar equipment

(G-2242)
DYNAMIC DENTAL CORP
3760 Nw 126th Ave (33065-2408)
P.O. Box 9520 (33075-9520)
PHONE..................................954 344-5155
Andres Delvalle, *President*
Andres Del Valle, *President*
Amanda Del Valle, *Vice Pres*
Amanda Delvalle, *Vice Pres*
Andy Delvalle, *Executive*
EMP: 5 **EST:** 1994
SALES (est): 662.7K **Privately Held**
SIC: 3843 7699 Dental equipment; dental instrument repair

(G-2243)
E3 GRAPHICS INC
Also Called: Minuteman Press
9868 W Sample Rd (33065-4006)
PHONE..................................954 510-1302
David B Johnson, *Principal*
EMP: 5 **EST:** 2009
SALES (est): 684.2K **Privately Held**
WEB: www.chanhassen-mn.minutemanpress.com
SIC: 2752 7336 Commercial printing, lithographic; commercial art & graphic design

(G-2244)
FBJ ENGINEERING & DEV LLC
4346 Nw 120th Ave (33065-7610)
PHONE..................................754 423-1309
Fausto Shuguli,
EMP: 6 **EST:** 2017
SALES (est): 208.1K **Privately Held**
SIC: 3999 Manufacturing industries

(G-2245)
FLORIDA MICRO DEVICES INC
4676 Nw 60th Ln (33067-2105)
P.O. Box 970260, Pompano Beach (33097-0260)
PHONE..................................954 973-7200
Francisco Miro, *President*
Miiguel Berthin, *Vice Pres*
EMP: 6 **EST:** 1989
SQ FT: 1,000
SALES (est): 791.3K **Privately Held**
WEB: www.floridamicro.com
SIC: 3674 Microcircuits, integrated (semiconductor)

(G-2246)
FOOT FUNCTION LAB INC
Also Called: Mr Rach
11540 Wiles Rd Ste 1 (33076-2119)
PHONE..................................954 753-2500
Leonard Kerns, *President*
EMP: 5 **EST:** 1979
SQ FT: 2,100
SALES (est): 358.7K **Privately Held**
WEB: www.orthotics.net
SIC: 3842 Surgical appliances & supplies

(G-2247)
FORM SCRIPT - FORM PRINT LLC
9101 W Sample Rd Apt 101 (33065-1629)
PHONE..................................954 345-3727
Jeffrey Malin, *Mng Member*
EMP: 7 **EST:** 2018
SALES (est): 442.5K **Privately Held**
WEB: www.formscript.net
SIC: 2752 Commercial printing, lithographic

(G-2248)
FORTUNE MEDIA GROUP INC
6250 Coral Ridge Dr # 100 (33076-3383)
PHONE..................................954 379-4321
P Douglas Scott, *President*
EMP: 10 **EST:** 2006
SALES (est): 739.5K **Privately Held**
WEB: www.fortunemediagroupinc.com
SIC: 3663 Radio & TV communications equipment

(G-2249)
FROMKIN ENERGY LLC
4630 N University Dr (33067-4626)
PHONE..................................954 683-2509
Lewis Fromkin, *Principal*
EMP: 8 **EST:** 2008
SALES (est): 521.4K **Privately Held**
WEB: www.fromkinenergy.com
SIC: 1311 Crude petroleum & natural gas

(G-2250)
GEAR DRIVEN LLC
4613 N University Dr (33067-4602)
PHONE..................................954 681-8394
Dale A Clement, *Manager*
EMP: 6 **EST:** 2016
SALES (est): 582.2K **Privately Held**
WEB: www.geardriveninc.com
SIC: 3714 Motor vehicle parts & accessories

(G-2251)
HANDAL FOODS LLC
11822 Nw 30th Ct (33065-3324)
PHONE..................................954 753-0649
Abraham Handal, *Principal*
EMP: 6 **EST:** 2012
SALES (est): 392.9K **Privately Held**
SIC: 2099 Food preparations

(G-2252)
HC GRUPO INC
2929 N University Dr # 105 (33065-5047)
PHONE..................................954 227-0150
Francisco Clavel, *President*
Oscar Clavel, *Vice Pres*
EMP: 5 **EST:** 2005
SALES (est): 512.8K **Privately Held**
WEB: www.hardcoconsulting.com
SIC: 3089 3429 Plastic boats & other marine equipment; marine hardware

(G-2253)
HILTON SOFTWARE LLC
2730 N University Dr (33065-5111)
PHONE..................................954 323-2244
Hilton Goldstein,
EMP: 17 **EST:** 2008
SQ FT: 2,730
SALES (est): 2.4MM **Privately Held**
WEB: www.hiltonsoftware.co
SIC: 7372 Prepackaged software

(G-2254)
HILTRONICS CORPORATION
3979 Nw 126th Ave (33065-7609)
PHONE..................................954 341-9100
Stuart Leeman, *President*
Doug Leeman, *Vice Pres*
Stanley Friedman, *Treasurer*
EMP: 7 **EST:** 1993
SQ FT: 3,400
SALES (est): 883.3K **Privately Held**
WEB: www.hiltronicscorp.com
SIC: 3679 Electronic circuits

(G-2255)
HISPACOM INC
Also Called: Icco
9900 W Sample Rd Ste 200 (33065-4044)
PHONE..................................954 255-2622
Carlos Gonzalez, *President*
EMP: 13 **EST:** 1995
SQ FT: 5,000
SALES (est): 527.1K **Privately Held**
SIC: 7372 7371 Prepackaged software; custom computer programming services

(G-2256)
HUGHES CORPORATION
Also Called: Weschler Instruments
4000 Nw 121st Ave (33065-7612)
PHONE..................................954 755-7111
Michael F Dorman, *President*
Matthew Hughes, *Vice Pres*
Luis Gonzalez, *Design Engr*
Ron Wood, *Regl Sales Mgr*
Robert Houston, *Branch Mgr*
EMP: 18
SQ FT: 24,000
SALES (corp-wide): 26.8MM **Privately Held**
WEB: www.weschler.com
SIC: 3825 3823 3613 Measuring instruments & meters, electric; industrial instrmnts msrmnt display/control process variable; switchgear & switchboard apparatus
PA: Hughes Corporation
16900 Foltz Pkwy
Strongsville OH 44149
440 238-2550

(G-2257)
HUNTER GREEN GROUP INC
Also Called: Hunter Green Group, The
4613 N University Dr # 277 (33067-4602)
PHONE..................................954 753-9914
Joel L Barkin, *Director*
EMP: 7 **EST:** 1997
SALES (est): 102.3K **Privately Held**
WEB: www.huntergreengroup.com
SIC: 2759 Commercial printing

(G-2258)
HYDES SCREENING INC
3700 Nw 124th Ave Ste 126 (33065-2432)
PHONE..................................954 345-6743
Christopher Hyde, *Owner*
EMP: 8 **EST:** 1988
SALES (est): 876.9K **Privately Held**
WEB: www.screenpatioenclosures.com
SIC: 3448 1521 1799 Screen enclosures; patio & deck construction & repair; fiberglass work

(G-2259)
ICP ADHESIVES SEALANTS
12505 Nw 44th St (33065-7640)
PHONE..................................954 905-0531
Adrian Robledo, *Sales Staff*
EMP: 6 **EST:** 2016
SALES (est): 123.2K **Privately Held**
SIC: 2891 Sealants

(G-2260)
INMAN ORTHODONTIC LABS INC
3953 Nw 126th Ave (33065-7609)
PHONE..................................954 340-8477
Donald Paul Inman, *President*
Angela Inmanv, *Vice Pres*
EMP: 17 **EST:** 1972
SQ FT: 1,000
SALES (est): 1.8MM **Privately Held**
WEB: www.inmanortho.com
SIC: 3843 8072 Orthodontic appliances; dental laboratories

(G-2261)
INTEGRATED LASER SYSTEMS INC
11383 Lakeview Dr (33071-6332)
PHONE..................................954 489-8282
Patricia Reyes, *Principal*
EMP: 10 **EST:** 2010
SALES (est): 676.5K **Privately Held**
WEB: www.ils-service.com
SIC: 3699 Laser systems & equipment

(G-2262)
ITS A 10 INC
Also Called: It's A "10" Haircare
4613 N University Dr # 478 (33067-4602)
PHONE..................................954 227-7813
Carolyn Plummer, *CEO*
Scott Scharg, *President*
Jules Harris, *Manager*
EMP: 2
SALES: 36.7MM **Privately Held**
WEB: www.itsa10haircare.com
SIC: 3999 Hair & hair-based products

(G-2263)
JENSEN SCIENTIFIC PRODUCTS INC
Also Called: Jensen Inert Products
3773 Nw 126th Ave (33065-2400)
PHONE..................................954 344-2006
Stephen R Little, *President*
◆ **EMP:** 25 **EST:** 1988
SQ FT: 13,000
SALES (est): 3.2MM **Privately Held**
WEB: www.jenseninert.com
SIC: 3221 5049 3821 3498 Vials, glass; scientific & engineering equipment & supplies; laboratory apparatus & furniture; fabricated pipe & fittings; products of purchased glass

(G-2264)
JNC HABITAT INVESTMENTS INC
Also Called: J N C Investments
645 Nw 112th Way (33071-7950)
PHONE..................................954 249-7469
Maria Veliz, *President*
Gil Veliz, *Vice Pres*
EMP: 10 **EST:** 1955
SALES (est): 221.6K **Privately Held**
SIC: 2541 Store & office display cases & fixtures

(G-2265)
JNC WELDING & FABRICATING INC
3769 Nw 126th Ave (33065-2424)
PHONE..................................954 227-9424
James R Noel, *President*
James Noel, *President*
Mick Bonifaz, *Vice Pres*
▲ **EMP:** 21 **EST:** 1999
SQ FT: 12,000
SALES (est): 2.5MM **Privately Held**
WEB: www.jncwelding.com
SIC: 3441 Fabricated structural metal

(G-2266)
JOSEPH MALARA
5944 Coral Ridge Dr (33076-3300)
PHONE..................................352 789-7646
Joseph Malara, *Principal*
EMP: 6 **EST:** 2011
SALES (est): 143.3K **Privately Held**
WEB: www.josephmalara.com
SIC: 3299 Architectural sculptures: gypsum, clay, papier mache, etc.

(G-2267)
JUST SAY PRINT INC
1500 Nw 112th Way (33071-6466)
PHONE..................................954 254-7793
Christopher D Brown, *Principal*
EMP: 7 **EST:** 2012
SALES (est): 181.5K **Privately Held**
SIC: 2752 Commercial printing, lithographic

(G-2268)
KERATRONIX INC
4377 Nw 124th Ave (33065-7634)
PHONE..................................954 753-5741
Michael M Anthony, *President*
Michael Anthony, *Principal*
EMP: 10 **EST:** 2008
SALES (est): 341.7K **Privately Held**
SIC: 2844 Toilet preparations

(G-2269)
KING PHARMACEUTICALS LLC
Also Called: Kings Pharmacy
2814 N University Dr (33065-5010)
PHONE..................................954 575-7085
David Wolman, *Principal*
EMP: 8
SALES (corp-wide): 41.9B **Publicly Held**
SIC: 2834 Pharmaceutical preparations
HQ: King Pharmaceuticals Llc
501 5th St
Bristol TN 37620

(G-2270)
KNOWLES PLASTICS INC
Also Called: Knowles' Mobile Marine
10301 Nw 16th Ct (33071-6518)
PHONE..................................954 232-8756
Jeffrey H Knowles, *President*
Lisa Knowles, *Vice Pres*
EMP: 7 **EST:** 1996
SALES (est): 93.3K **Privately Held**
SIC: 3732 Boats, fiberglass: building & repairing

(G-2271)
L2D OUTDOORS INC
4300 Nw 120th Ave (33065-7610)
PHONE..................................954 757-6116
Lesleyanne Wolff, *Principal*
EMP: 6 **EST:** 2018
SALES (est): 307.6K **Privately Held**
SIC: 3489 Ordnance & accessories

(G-2272)
LEAD 2 DESIGN
4302 Nw 120th Ave (33065-7610)
PHONE..................................954 757-6116
Lesley-Anne Wolff, *Co-Owner*
EMP: 8 **EST:** 2010
SALES (est): 879.9K **Privately Held**
WEB: www.lead2design.com
SIC: 2211 Decorative trim & specialty fabrics, including twist weave

(G-2273)
LEVITA LLC
Also Called: Bedbug Supply
12410 Nw 39th St (33065-2435)
PHONE..................................954 227-7468
Mark Sanders,
Michelle Sanders,
▲ **EMP:** 6 **EST:** 2007
SALES (est): 1MM **Privately Held**
WEB: www.bedbugsupply.com
SIC: 2879 3069 Pesticides, agricultural or household; mattress protectors, rubber

(G-2274)
LEXMARK INTERNATIONAL INC
10866 Nw 14th St (33071-8213)
PHONE..................................954 345-2442
EMP: 159
SALES (corp-wide): 2.5B **Privately Held**
SIC: 3577 Mfg Computer Peripheral Equipment
PA: Lexmark International, Inc.
740 W New Circle Rd
Lexington KY 40511
859 232-2000

(G-2275)
LUPIN RESEARCH INC
4006 Nw 124th Ave (33065-2411)
PHONE..................................800 466-1450
Vinita Gupta, *CEO*
Paul McGarty, *President*
Manjira Sharma, *General Mgr*
Megan Roberts, *Sales Staff*
Jade Ly, *Director*
EMP: 43 **EST:** 2003
SALES (est): 8.7MM **Privately Held**
WEB: www.lupin.com
SIC: 2834 5122 Pharmaceutical preparations; pharmaceuticals
PA: Lupin Limited
3rd Floor, Kalpataru Inspire,
Mumbai MH 40005

(G-2276)
MEATH INDUSTRIES INC
1440 Coral Ridge Dr (33071-5433)
PHONE..................................954 818-0593
Chris Plunkett, *Principal*
EMP: 6 **EST:** 2010
SALES (est): 87.3K **Privately Held**
SIC: 3999 Manufacturing industries

(G-2277)
MEDIA SYSTEMS INC
Also Called: Jiffi Print
3859 Nw 124th Ave (33065-2406)
PHONE..................................954 427-4411
Raed Bakouni, *President*
Terri Bakouni, *Vice Pres*
EMP: 6 **EST:** 2013
SQ FT: 2,200
SALES (est): 446.3K **Privately Held**
WEB: www.mediasystems.com
SIC: 2752 Commercial printing, offset

(G-2278)
MEEK CHIC QUEEN INC
9257 Ramblewood Dr # 1332
(33071-7092)
P.O. Box 1026, Sorrento (32776-1026)
PHONE..................................407 920-8135
Awilda Barrett, *President*
EMP: 6 **EST:** 2012
SALES (est): 57.7K **Privately Held**
SIC: 2335 Women's, juniors' & misses' dresses

(G-2279)
MEGIN US LLC (PA) ✪
11772 W Sample Rd (33065-3166)
PHONE..................................954 341-2965
Rick Goepfert, *Principal*
Gordon Baltzer, *Mng Member*
Craig Shapero,
EMP: 9 **EST:** 2020
SALES (est): 1.1MM **Privately Held**
WEB: www.megin.fi
SIC: 3845 7629 Audiological equipment, electromedical; electrical repair shops

(G-2280)
MEI DEVELOPMENT CORPORATION
11772 W Sample Rd Ste 101 (33065-3166)
PHONE..................................954 341-3302
Sam Moti, *President*
Gordon B Baltzer, *Vice Pres*
Richard McLaughlin, *CFO*
EMP: 10 **EST:** 1997
SALES (est): 1.4MM **Privately Held**
WEB: www.hhshealthcare.com
SIC: 3841 Diagnostic apparatus, medical
PA: The Mei Healthcare Group Llc
11772 W Sample Rd
Coral Springs FL 33065

(G-2281)
METAL SPRAY PAINTING POWDER
3701 Nw 126th Ave Ste 4 (33065-2439)
PHONE..................................954 227-2744
Michael C Landi, *President*
EMP: 7 **EST:** 2013
SALES (est): 875K **Privately Held**
WEB: www.metalspraypainting.com
SIC: 2262 3471 Screen printing: manmade fiber & silk broadwoven fabrics; finishing, metals or formed products

(G-2282)
METHAPHARM INC
11772 W Sample Rd Ste 101 (33065-3166)
PHONE..................................954 341-0795
Luciano Calenti, *President*
Antoniette Walkom, *Vice Pres*
Gordon Baltzer, *Treasurer*
Sharron Brownlee, *Sales Staff*
Brian Frappier, *Sales Staff*
EMP: 5 **EST:** 2000
SQ FT: 2,000
SALES (est): 3.5MM
SALES (corp-wide): 22.1MM **Privately Held**
WEB: www.methapharm.com
SIC: 2834 Pharmaceutical preparations
HQ: Methapharm Inc
81 Sinclair Blvd
Brantford ON N3S 7
519 751-3602

(G-2283)
METRITEK CORPORATION (PA)
849 Nw 126th Ave (33071-4401)
PHONE..................................561 995-2414
Robert Javelin, *President*
Sheli Lopez, *CFO*
Shelley Lopez, *Executive*
Varda Javelin, *Admin Sec*
◆ **EMP:** 106 **EST:** 1986
SALES (est): 12.4MM **Privately Held**
WEB: www.metritek.com
SIC: 2258 Lace, knit

(G-2284)
MICOLE ELECTRIC SIGN COMPANY
10840 Sw 1st Ct (33071-8134)
PHONE..................................954 796-4293
EMP: 5
SALES (est): 423.7K **Privately Held**
SIC: 3993 Mfg Signs/Advertising Specialties

(G-2285)
MICRO CRANE INC
3610 Nw 118th Ave Ste 4 (33065-2552)
PHONE..................................954 755-2225
Charles Helou, *President*
EMP: 6 **EST:** 1979
SALES (est): 221.5K **Privately Held**
SIC: 3577 Computer peripheral equipment

(G-2286)
MOLD EXPERT
2812 Nw 87th Ave (33065-5342)
PHONE..................................954 829-3102
Manuel Galeano, *Principal*
EMP: 8 **EST:** 2010
SALES (est): 141.7K **Privately Held**
SIC: 3544 Industrial molds

(G-2287)
MONAR CORPORATION
9825 W Sample Rd Ste 202 (33065-4040)
PHONE..................................954 650-1930
Naraine Seecharan, *Principal*
Ray Chung, *Executive*
EMP: 7 **EST:** 2004
SALES (est): 1MM **Privately Held**
WEB: www.monarac.net
SIC: 3585 Air conditioning equipment, complete

(G-2288)
MONARCH KNITTING MCHY CORP
9871 Nw 57th Mnr (33076-2825)
PHONE..................................954 345-2091
Harold G Hawkins, *Principal*
EMP: 6
SALES (corp-wide): 8.8MM **Privately Held**
WEB: www.monarchknitting.org
SIC: 3552 Textile machinery
PA: Monarch Knitting Machinery Corp.
115 N Secrest Ave
Monroe NC 28110
704 291-3300

(G-2289)
MONROY AEROSPACE
10908 Nw 17th Mnr (33071-6320)
P.O. Box 8217 (33075-8217)
PHONE..................................954 344-4936
Jose Monroy, *President*
EMP: 5 **EST:** 1986
SALES (est): 407.9K **Privately Held**
WEB: www.monroyaero.com
SIC: 3728 Aircraft assemblies, subassemblies & parts

(G-2290)
MONUMENTAL AIR INC
4333 Nw 64th Ave (33067-3050)
PHONE.................................954 383-9507
Juan Taveras, *Principal*
EMP: 10 **EST:** 2010
SALES (est): 802.3K **Privately Held**
SIC: 3272 Monuments & grave markers, except terrazo

(G-2291)
MRN BIOLOGICS LLC
3732 Nw 126th Ave (33065-2408)
PHONE.................................508 989-6090
Robert O McKie,
EMP: 13 **EST:** 2015
SALES (est): 1.1MM **Privately Held**
SIC: 3821 Clinical laboratory instruments, except medical & dental

(G-2292)
MSC METAL FABRICATION
7600 Wiles Rd Ste B (33067-2003)
PHONE.................................954 344-8343
Samuel Cachola, *Principal*
EMP: 6 **EST:** 2005
SALES (est): 112.5K **Privately Held**
SIC: 3365 3499 Aluminum foundries; fabricated metal products

(G-2293)
MYRLEN INC
3814 Nw 126th Ave (33065-2450)
P.O. Box 8783 (33075-8783)
PHONE.................................800 662-4762
Paul Rose, *Vice Pres*
EMP: 5 **EST:** 2000
SQ FT: 1,800
SALES (est): 499K **Privately Held**
WEB: www.myrlen.com
SIC: 3443 Bins, prefabricated metal plate

(G-2294)
NANOBIOTECH PHARMA INC
5944 Coral Ridge Dr (33076-3300)
PHONE.................................866 568-0178
Gary Mezo, *Principal*
EMP: 6 **EST:** 2015
SALES (est): 160.4K **Privately Held**
SIC: 2834 Pharmaceutical preparations

(G-2295)
NATURAL ETHERCOM
10600 Nw 43rd St (33065-2317)
PHONE.................................954 274-6801
Bryant Anderson, *Principal*
EMP: 6 **EST:** 2012
SALES (est): 246K **Privately Held**
SIC: 2869 Ethers

(G-2296)
NEW WAVE SURGICAL CORP
3700 Nw 124th Ave Ste 135 (33065-2433)
PHONE.................................866 346-8883
Elba Lopez, *Principal*
EMP: 12 **EST:** 2015
SALES (est): 542.9K **Privately Held**
WEB: www.newwavesurgical.com
SIC: 3841 Surgical & medical instruments

(G-2297)
NIDEC MOTOR CORPORATION
Also Called: KB Electronics
12095 Nw 39th St (33065-2516)
PHONE.................................954 346-4900
Thomas Dalton, *President*
Omar Blackwood, *Vice Pres*
Christopher Heumann, *Project Mgr*
Michael Ipolyi, *Production*
Guillermo Cruz, *Engineer*
EMP: 174 **Privately Held**
WEB: www.acim.nidec.com
SIC: 3621 3625 Motors, electric; motor controls & accessories
HQ: Nidec Motor Corporation
8050 West Florissant Ave
Saint Louis MO 63136

(G-2298)
NUTRA PHARMA CORP
4001 Nw 73rd Way (33065-2162)
PHONE.................................954 509-0911
Michael Doherty, *Director*
EMP: 8 **EST:** 2005
SALES (est): 132.6K **Privately Held**
WEB: www.nutrapharma.com
SIC: 2834 Pharmaceutical preparations

(G-2299)
ORKA CABINETS INC
12022 Nw 47th St (33076-3536)
PHONE.................................954 907-2456
Adrian Ortiz Sr, *President*
EMP: 6 **EST:** 2005
SALES (est): 76.1K **Privately Held**
SIC: 2434 Wood kitchen cabinets

(G-2300)
ORVINO IMPORTS & DISTRG INC
11927 W Sample Rd (33065-3164)
PHONE.................................954 785-3100
John Flora, *President*
▲ **EMP:** 14 **EST:** 1995
SALES (est): 866.4K **Privately Held**
WEB: www.orvinowine.com
SIC: 2084 Wines

(G-2301)
ORYZA PHARMACEUTICALS INC
4117 Nw 124th Ave (33065-7633)
PHONE.................................954 881-5481
Jing LI, *Vice Pres*
Kelvin Cui, *CFO*
EMP: 28 **EST:** 2016
SQ FT: 1,000
SALES (est): 3.4MM **Privately Held**
WEB: www.oryzapharma.com
SIC: 2834 Pharmaceutical preparations

(G-2302)
PELICAN BAY PUBLISHING
934 N University Dr (33071-7029)
PHONE.................................954 610-7787
Fred Dias, *Principal*
EMP: 6 **EST:** 2010
SALES (est): 90K **Privately Held**
SIC: 2741 Miscellaneous publishing

(G-2303)
POMPADOUR PRODUCTS INC
1197 Nw 83rd Ave (33071-6720)
PHONE.................................954 345-2700
◆ **EMP:** 30
SQ FT: 22,000
SALES: 1.5MM **Privately Held**
SIC: 3089 3061 Mfg Plastic Products Mfg Mechanical Rubber Goods

(G-2304)
PRINTMOR
Also Called: Printmor Large Format Printing
3941 Nw 126th Ave (33065-7609)
PHONE.................................954 247-9405
Jonathan Buchnik, *Principal*
Jessica Tuszynski, *Graphic Designe*
EMP: 12 **EST:** 2016
SALES (est): 976.2K **Privately Held**
WEB: www.myprintmor.com
SIC: 2752 Commercial printing, lithographic

(G-2305)
RICHARDS MOBILE WELDING
3541 Nw 73rd Way (33065-2136)
PHONE.................................954 913-0487
Richard Sookoo, *Owner*
EMP: 6 **EST:** 2016
SALES (est): 347.3K **Privately Held**
SIC: 7692 Welding repair

(G-2306)
ROCHESTER ELECTRO-MEDICAL INC
11711 Nw 39th St (33065-2511)
PHONE.................................813 994-7519
Kim Davis, *President*
John Baccoli, *Manager*
EMP: 20 **EST:** 1967
SQ FT: 7,500
SALES (est): 5.7MM
SALES (corp-wide): 28.3MM **Privately Held**
WEB: www.rochestersuperstore.com
SIC: 3841 Needles, suture
HQ: Advantage Medical Electronics, Llc
11705 Nw 39th St
Coral Springs FL 33065
954 345-9800

(G-2307)
RPERF TECHNOLOGIES CORP
6584 Nw 56th Dr (33067-3540)
PHONE.................................954 629-2359
Roberto Campos, *Principal*
EMP: 10 **EST:** 2010
SALES (est): 180K **Privately Held**
WEB: www.rperftech.com
SIC: 7372 7379 Educational computer software; computer related consulting services

(G-2308)
RUNAWARE INC
5440 Nw 108th Way (33076-2742)
PHONE.................................954 907-9052
Tim Keys, *CEO*
EMP: 11 **EST:** 2005
SALES (est): 73.7K **Privately Held**
WEB: www.main.runaware.com
SIC: 3652 Pre-recorded records & tapes

(G-2309)
SANTOS GROUP INC (PA)
9736 Nw 1st Mnr (33071-4903)
PHONE.................................954 605-2954
Carmen Santos, *Principal*
EMP: 11 **EST:** 2017
SALES (est): 139.2K **Privately Held**
SIC: 3842 Prosthetic appliances

(G-2310)
SAUGUS VALLEY CORP
Also Called: Sir Speedy
8716 Nw 54th St (33067-2881)
PHONE.................................954 772-4077
Michael Gaby, *President*
EMP: 9 **EST:** 1972
SQ FT: 2,100
SALES (est): 993.3K **Privately Held**
WEB: www.sirspeedy.com
SIC: 2752 2791 2789 Commercial printing, lithographic; typesetting; bookbinding & related work

(G-2311)
SCENTSABILITY CANDLES
11480 W Sample Rd (33065-7054)
PHONE.................................954 234-4405
Bonnie Schmidt, *Director*
EMP: 8 **EST:** 2015
SALES (est): 289.2K **Privately Held**
WEB: www.scentsability.org
SIC: 3999 Candles

(G-2312)
SIGN A RAMA
Also Called: Sign-A-Rama
10200 W Sample Rd (33065-3940)
PHONE.................................954 796-1644
Lisa A Finch, *Vice Pres*
EMP: 9 **EST:** 2010
SALES (est): 291.1K **Privately Held**
WEB: www.signarama.com
SIC: 3993 Signs & advertising specialties

(G-2313)
SIPRADIUS LLC
11834 Wiles Rd (33076-2216)
PHONE.................................954 290-2434
Sergio Ammirata, *Mng Member*
John Iacovelli, *Prgrmr*
EMP: 5 **EST:** 2006
SALES (est): 304.4K **Privately Held**
WEB: www.sipradius.com
SIC: 7372 2741 4813 Operating systems computer software; ; ;

(G-2314)
SONIC LEAK LOCATOR
3871 Jasmine Ln (33065-6062)
PHONE.................................954 340-8924
Scott Makula, *Principal*
EMP: 6 **EST:** 2001
SALES (est): 89.1K **Privately Held**
SIC: 3949 Swimming pools, plastic

(G-2315)
SPIEGEL PAVERS INC
7761 Nw 42nd Pl 1 (33065-1945)
PHONE.................................954 687-5797
Marcio E Vieira, *President*
EMP: 6 **EST:** 2005
SALES (est): 72K **Privately Held**
SIC: 2951 Asphalt paving mixtures & blocks

(G-2316)
STARR WHEEL GROUP INC
3659 Nw 124th Ave (33065-2445)
PHONE.................................954 935-5536
Ray A Starr Jr, *President*
◆ **EMP:** 17 **EST:** 2005
SQ FT: 12,000
SALES (est): 1.5MM **Privately Held**
WEB: www.warriorimport.com
SIC: 3312 Wheels

(G-2317)
SUPERIOR SHADE & BLIND CO INC
11100 Nw 24th St (33065-3645)
PHONE.................................954 975-8122
Alex Fryburg, *Ch of Bd*
David Fryburg, *President*
Robert Fryburg, *Vice Pres*
▼ **EMP:** 20 **EST:** 1981
SALES (est): 1.3MM **Privately Held**
WEB: www.superiorshade.com
SIC: 2591 5131 Blinds vertical; knit fabrics

(G-2318)
SURGIMED CORPORATION
9900 W Sample Rd (33065-4048)
PHONE.................................912 674-7660
Leigh Ann Pettyjohn, *President*
Cira Lavoi, *President*
Luis Arias, *Vice Pres*
Alina Lavoi, *Vice Pres*
◆ **EMP:** 14 **EST:** 1981
SQ FT: 54,000
SALES (est): 1.9MM **Privately Held**
WEB: www.surgimedcorp.com
SIC: 3841 Surgical & medical instruments

(G-2319)
SYNERGY THERMAL FOILS INC
12175 Nw 39th St (33065-2518)
PHONE.................................954 420-9553
Amir Bakhtyari, *President*
▼ **EMP:** 13 **EST:** 2008
SQ FT: 4,000
SALES (est): 2.7MM **Privately Held**
WEB: www.synergythermofoils.com
SIC: 2431 5031 Planing mill, millwork; millwork

(G-2320)
TEAM INKJET
1440 Coral Ridge Dr 339 (33071-5433)
PHONE.................................954 554-3250
Craig S Brockwell, *Principal*
EMP: 8
SQ FT: 5,000
SALES (est): 1.5MM **Privately Held**
SIC: 3955 Print cartridges for laser & other computer printers

(G-2321)
TECHNIPOWER LLC
Also Called: Unipower
210 N University Dr # 700 (33071-7394)
PHONE.................................954 346-2442
Joe Merino, *Vice Pres*
William Kirk, *CFO*
Tom Johnson, *Manager*
▲ **EMP:** 10 **EST:** 1952
SALES (est): 2MM
SALES (corp-wide): 27.1MM **Privately Held**
WEB: www.unipowerco.com
SIC: 3679 3612 3699 3643 Power supplies, all types: static; transformers, except electric; electrical equipment & supplies; current-carrying wiring devices
PA: Unipower, Llc
210 N University Dr # 700
Coral Springs FL 33071
954 346-2442

(G-2322)
TESCO EQUIPMENT LLC
3661 Nw 126th Ave (33065-2426)
PHONE.................................954 752-7994
Joe Ward, *Controller*
Robert Osborn, *Sales Mgr*
Rob Osborn, *Sales Staff*
Bea Osborn,
Doug Robertson,
◆ **EMP:** 42 **EST:** 1936
SQ FT: 30,000

GEOGRAPHIC

SALES (est): 9.2MM **Privately Held**
WEB: www.tescohilift.com
SIC: 3713 3537 3728 Truck & bus bodies; industrial trucks & tractors; aircraft parts & equipment

(G-2323)
TIDWELLS ORTHOTICS AND PROSTHE
4450 Nw 126th Ave Ste 106 (33065-7604)
PHONE..................................954 346-5402
Chris Tidwell, *Principal*
EMP: 8 **EST:** 2006
SALES (est): 797.9K **Privately Held**
WEB: www.tidwellsorthotics.com
SIC: 3842 Orthopedic appliances

(G-2324)
TRIAL SPECTRUM INC
Also Called: Trial Prints
12201 Nw 35th St (33065-2570)
PHONE..................................954 906-5743
Diana Tourtelot, *Chief Mktg Ofcr*
Richard Tourtelot, *Litigation*
EMP: 7 **EST:** 2016
SALES (est): 249.8K **Privately Held**
WEB: www.trialspectrum.com
SIC: 2752 Commercial printing, lithographic

(G-2325)
UNICOMP CORP OF AMERICA
10101 W Sample Rd Stop 1 (33065-3937)
PHONE..................................954 755-1710
Martin Kaplan, *President*
Laura Seiler, *Manager*
EMP: 5 **EST:** 1979
SALES (est): 447.2K **Privately Held**
WEB: www.ucoa.com
SIC: 7372 7371 Application computer software; custom computer programming services

(G-2326)
VERIFONE INC (HQ)
2744 N University Dr (33065-5111)
P.O. Box 641536, San Jose CA (95164-1536)
PHONE..................................800 837-4366
Mike Puli, *CEO*
Paul Galant, *Principal*
Michael Cho, *Counsel*
Jonathan Cross, *Counsel*
Alok Bhanot, *Exec VP*
◆ **EMP:** 190 **EST:** 1981
SALES (est): 574.1MM
SALES (corp-wide): 695.1MM **Privately Held**
WEB: www.verifone.com
SIC: 3578 7372 3577 3575 Point-of-sale devices; operating systems computer software; computer peripheral equipment; computer terminals; engineering services; current-carrying wiring devices
PA: Verifone Systems, Inc.
2744 N University Dr
Coral Springs FL 33065
408 232-7800

(G-2327)
VERIFONE INC
2900 N University Dr (33065-5083)
PHONE..................................754 229-4571
EMP: 8 **EST:** 2019
SALES (est): 254.3K **Privately Held**
WEB: www.verifone.com
SIC: 3578 Calculating & accounting equipment

(G-2328)
VERIFONE SYSTEMS INC (PA)
2744 N University Dr (33065-5111)
PHONE..................................408 232-7800
Mike Pulli, *CEO*
Vin D'Agostino, *Exec VP*
Albert Liu, *Exec VP*
Glen Robson, *Exec VP*
Suzanne Colvin, *Vice Pres*
▲ **EMP:** 193 **EST:** 1981
SALES (est): 695.1MM **Privately Held**
WEB: www.verifone.com
SIC: 3578 7372 Point-of-sale devices; operating systems computer software

(G-2329)
VISTAMATIC LLC
Also Called: Privacy Glass Solutions
11713 Nw 39th St (33065-2511)
PHONE..................................866 466-9525
Carlos Betancur, *Vice Pres*
Jamie Knight, *Vice Pres*
Ewelina Swierczek, *Accounts Mgr*
Kevin Roth, *Mng Member*
EMP: 25 **EST:** 2009
SQ FT: 2,100
SALES (est): 2.5MM **Privately Held**
WEB: www.privacyglasssolutions.com
SIC: 3211 Window glass, clear & colored

(G-2330)
VUTEC CORPORATION
Also Called: Wiremaid Products Division
11711 W Sample Rd (33065-3155)
PHONE..................................954 545-9000
Howard Sinkoff, *President*
Allan Axman, *Vice Pres*
Kevin R Baisely, *Vice Pres*
Kevin Baisley, *Vice Pres*
Raul Passalacqua, *Vice Pres*
◆ **EMP:** 125 **EST:** 1950
SQ FT: 75,000
SALES (est): 22.1MM **Privately Held**
WEB: www.vutec.com
SIC: 3861 3496 Screens, projection; miscellaneous fabricated wire products

Cottondale
Jackson County

(G-2331)
ENVIVA PELLETS COTTONDALE LLC
2500 Green Circle Pkwy (32431-7450)
PHONE..................................850 557-7357
Morten Neraas,
EMP: 24 **EST:** 2015
SALES (est): 6MM **Privately Held**
SIC: 2493 Reconstituted wood products

(G-2332)
INGRAMS BACKHOE DUMPTRUCK SVC
2155 Roark Rd (32431-7629)
PHONE..................................850 718-6042
Rodney L Ingram, *Principal*
EMP: 9 **EST:** 2014
SALES (est): 199.1K **Privately Held**
SIC: 3531 Backhoes

(G-2333)
VAN NEVEL AEROSPACE LLC
1932 Holley Timber Rd (32431-7754)
PHONE..................................337 936-2504
Georges Van Nevel, *President*
EMP: 7 **EST:** 2015
SALES (est): 110K **Privately Held**
WEB: www.vannevelaerospace.com
SIC: 3721 Helicopters

Crawfordville
Wakulla County

(G-2334)
KEVINS MACHINE & ENGRG LLC
2709 Crawfordville Hwy (32327-2158)
PHONE..................................850 519-6516
Kevin W Roberts, *Principal*
EMP: 6 **EST:** 2012
SALES (est): 110.5K **Privately Held**
WEB: www.kevinsmachine.com
SIC: 3599 Machine shop, jobbing & repair

(G-2335)
OXYGENIX MOLD AND ODOR LLC
467 Parkside Cir (32327-7418)
PHONE..................................850 926-5421
EMP: 5
SALES (est): 426.4K **Privately Held**
SIC: 3544 Mfg Dies/Tools/Jigs/Fixtures

(G-2336)
ST MARKS POWDER INC
7121 Coastal Hwy (32327-2918)
P.O. Box 222, Saint Marks (32355-0222)
PHONE..................................850 577-2824
Michael S Wilson, *President*
Guy Cornwell, *Vice Pres*
Jim Dudley, *Engineer*
Chris Beidler, *Project Engr*
Jane Kellett, *Finance*
◆ **EMP:** 340 **EST:** 1998
SALES (est): 97.1MM
SALES (corp-wide): 37.9B **Publicly Held**
WEB: www.gd-ots.com
SIC: 2869 Industrial organic chemicals
HQ: General Dynamics Ordnance And Tactical Systems, Inc.
11399 16th Ct N Ste 200
Saint Petersburg FL 33716
727 578-8100

(G-2337)
WAKULLA NEWS
3119a Crawfordville Hwy (32327-3148)
P.O. Box 307 (32326-0307)
PHONE..................................850 926-7102
Tammie Barfield, *General Mgr*
Keith Blackmar, *Editor*
Eric Stanton, *Production*
Lynda Kinsey, *Advt Staff*
EMP: 10 **EST:** 1895
SALES (est): 620.4K **Privately Held**
WEB: www.thewakullanews.com
SIC: 2711 5943 Newspapers: publishing only, not printed on site; office forms & supplies

Crescent City
Putnam County

(G-2338)
AMERICAN RESPIRATORY SOLUTIONS (PA)
1125 N Summit St Ste C (32112-1721)
P.O. Box 608 (32112-0608)
PHONE..................................386 698-4446
Warren Fletcher, *President*
EMP: 14 **EST:** 1996
SALES (est): 1.3MM **Privately Held**
WEB: www.arscc.com
SIC: 3578 Billing machines

(G-2339)
CHEZ INDUSTRIES LLC
Also Called: Mel Ray Industries
2167 S Us Highway 17 (32112-3903)
P.O. Box 505 (32112-0505)
PHONE..................................386 698-4414
Rita King, *Manager*
Anthony Sanchez,
◆ **EMP:** 11 **EST:** 1987
SQ FT: 56,000
SALES (est): 1.8MM **Privately Held**
WEB: www.melray.com
SIC: 3861 5023 Printing frames, photographic; frames & framing, picture & mirror

(G-2340)
HARTCO INTERNATIONAL
2288 S Us Highway 17 (32112-3900)
PHONE..................................386 698-4668
Kelly Hart, *President*
EMP: 9 **EST:** 2002
SALES (est): 525.5K **Privately Held**
WEB: www.hartcoseats.com
SIC: 3751 Saddles & seat posts, motorcycle & bicycle

(G-2341)
SAMS GAS
2680 S Us Highway 17 (32112-5122)
PHONE..................................386 698-1033
Randy Sams, *Owner*
EMP: 9 **EST:** 2012
SALES (est): 362.3K **Privately Held**
WEB: www.samsgas.com
SIC: 3569 5172 Gas generators; gases, liquefied petroleum (propane)

(G-2342)
SCOTT BREVARD INC
Also Called: King's Office Supply & Prtg Co
306 Central Ave (32112-2608)
PHONE..................................386 698-1121
Scott B King, *Owner*
Rick Scott, *Governor*
EMP: 5 **EST:** 1977
SQ FT: 2,400
SALES (est): 519K **Privately Held**
WEB: www.kingsofficeandprint.com
SIC: 2752 5943 Letters, circular or form: lithographed; office forms & supplies

(G-2343)
STAR SIGHT INNOVATIONS
107 Tangelo Ter (32112-4527)
PHONE..................................307 786-2911
Natalie Corbett, *Vice Pres*
EMP: 6
SALES (est): 421.5K **Privately Held**
SIC: 3432 Lawn hose nozzles & sprinklers

Crestview
Okaloosa County

(G-2344)
BOEING AROSPC OPERATIONS INC
5486 Fairchild Rd Hngr 3 (32539-8411)
PHONE..................................850 682-2746
William Grant, *Site Mgr*
EMP: 15
SALES (corp-wide): 58.1B **Publicly Held**
SIC: 3721 Aircraft
HQ: Boeing Aerospace Operations, Inc.
6001 S A Depo Blvd Ste E
Oklahoma City OK 73150
405 622-6000

(G-2345)
CRESTVIEW READY MIX INC
Also Called: Fort Walton Co
1070 Farmer St (32539-8966)
PHONE..................................850 682-6117
James Campbell, *President*
EMP: 10 **EST:** 1981
SALES (est): 874.5K **Privately Held**
WEB: www.crestviewreadymix.com
SIC: 3273 Ready-mixed concrete

(G-2346)
CYGNUS AEROSPACE INCORPORATED
1001 Industrial Dr (32539-6943)
PHONE..................................850 612-1618
Barry Green, *Opers Staff*
Don Cleveland, *Branch Mgr*
Rick Ballard, *Manager*
EMP: 28
SALES (corp-wide): 3.3MM **Privately Held**
WEB: www.cygnusworld.com
SIC: 3728 Aircraft parts & equipment
PA: Cygnus Aerospace Incorporated
501 Osigian Blvd Ste B
Warner Robins GA 31088
478 333-6110

(G-2347)
EMERALD COAST SIGNS
4563 Rainbird Rise Rd (32539-8231)
P.O. Box 296 (32536-0296)
PHONE..................................850 398-1712
Brad Summers, *CEO*
Bobbie Summers,
EMP: 6 **EST:** 2013
SALES (est): 756.9K **Privately Held**
WEB: www.emeraldcoastsigns.com
SIC: 3993 Signs & advertising specialties

(G-2348)
G2C ENTERPRISES INC
695 Sioux Cir (32536-9516)
PHONE..................................850 398-5368
Rodney Greenway, *CEO*
Beth Suttles, *Admin Sec*
EMP: 11 **EST:** 2007
SALES (est): 396.9K **Privately Held**
SIC: 1442 Construction sand & gravel

▲ = Import ▼=Export
◆ =Import/Export

(G-2349)
G2C ENTERPRISES INC
Also Called: Transand
695 Sioux Cir (32536-9516)
PHONE..................................850 585-4166
Rodney Greenway, *President*
EMP: 10 **EST:** 2003
SALES (est): 530.9K **Privately Held**
SIC: 1442 Construction sand & gravel

(G-2350)
GULF COAST WILBERT INC (PA)
Also Called: Gulf Coast Monuments
100 Martin St (32536-5119)
P.O. Box 455 (32536-0455)
PHONE..................................850 682-8004
David Chapman, *President*
Denise Chapman, *Vice Pres*
EMP: 3 **EST:** 2001
SQ FT: 13,000
SALES (est): 3.6MM **Privately Held**
WEB: www.gulfcoastwilbert.com
SIC: 3272 Burial vaults, concrete or precast terrazzo

(G-2351)
HOT DOG SHOPPE LLC
1308 N Ferdon Blvd (32536-1714)
PHONE..................................850 682-3649
Robert Vogel, *Principal*
EMP: 5 **EST:** 2007
SALES (est): 391.2K **Privately Held**
SIC: 2013 Sausages from purchased meat

(G-2352)
KACHEMAK BAY FLYING SERVICE
Also Called: Kbfs
5545 John Givens Rd (32539-7019)
PHONE..................................850 398-8699
EMP: 13 **EST:** 2007
SALES (est): 500.9K **Privately Held**
WEB: www.s3inc.com
SIC: 3728 Aircraft parts & equipment

(G-2353)
L3 CRESTVIEW AEROSPACE
5486 Fairchild Rd (32539-8410)
PHONE..................................850 682-2746
Claude W Tignor, *Principal*
Stacy L Johnson, *CFO*
Kelley Henderson, *Human Res Mgr*
EMP: 5 **EST:** 2011
SALES (est): 5.2MM
SALES (corp-wide): 3.7B **Publicly Held**
WEB: www.l3harris.com
SIC: 3812 Search & navigation equipment
HQ: L3 Technologies, Inc.
600 3rd Ave Fl 34
New York NY 10016
321 727-9100

(G-2354)
LEEROYS FABRICATION & WLDG LLC
5834 White Oak Dr (32539-9009)
PHONE..................................850 398-1997
Michael Showers, *Principal*
EMP: 6 **EST:** 2018
SALES (est): 231.4K **Privately Held**
SIC: 7692 Welding repair

(G-2355)
PHILLIPS ENERGY INC (HQ)
806 W James Lee Blvd (32536-5135)
PHONE..................................850 682-5127
Rupert E Phillips, *President*
Debora Link, *Vice Pres*
Mark Link, *Vice Pres*
Alan Payne, *Treasurer*
Cathy Hilliard, *Manager*
EMP: 1 **EST:** 2001
SALES (est): 7.6MM
SALES (corp-wide): 19.2MM **Privately Held**
WEB: www.phillipsenergygroup.com
SIC: 2869 Fuels
PA: Phillips Capital Partners, Inc.
42 Busness Cntre Dr Unitt
Miramar Beach FL 32550
850 460-2601

(G-2356)
RED 7 TEES LLC
189 W Oakdale Ave (32536-3513)
PHONE..................................305 793-1440
Christopher Linnel,
EMP: 5 **EST:** 2018
SALES (est): 395.6K **Privately Held**
WEB: www.red7tees.com
SIC: 2759 Screen printing

(G-2357)
SEGERS AEROSPACE CORPORATION
5582 Fairchild Rd (32539-5125)
PHONE..................................850 689-2198
Jeremy Hovater, *General Mgr*
Eric Blakeney, *Engineer*
Scarlett Conner, *Sales Staff*
Joe Labean, *Manager*
Gretchen Harshberger, *Director*
EMP: 33 **Privately Held**
SIC: 3728 Aircraft parts & equipment
PA: Segers Aerospace Corporation
8100 Mcgowin Dr
Fairhope AL 36532

(G-2358)
SIGNS GALORE INC
111 Hammock St (32536-1750)
PHONE..................................850 683-8010
Michael Rutledge, *President*
EMP: 8 **EST:** 1998
SQ FT: 6,440
SALES (est): 938.6K **Privately Held**
WEB: www.signsgaloreinc.com
SIC: 3993 Electric signs

(G-2359)
SOUTHWIRE COMPANY LLC
5680 John Givens Rd (32539-7018)
PHONE..................................850 423-4680
Robert Sires, *Manager*
EMP: 142
SALES (corp-wide): 1.7B **Privately Held**
WEB: www.southwire.com
SIC: 3496 5051 Wire fasteners; wire
PA: Southwire Company, Llc
1 Southwire Dr
Carrollton GA 30119
770 832-4242

(G-2360)
STRIVE DEVELOPMENT CORPORATION
Also Called: Custom Production
3100 Adora Teal Way (32539-7039)
P.O. Box 969 (32536-0969)
PHONE..................................850 689-2124
Elizabeth M Skrovanek, *President*
Michael R Skrovanek, *Vice Pres*
Stanley Zolek, *Vice Pres*
EMP: 18 **EST:** 1999
SQ FT: 7,500
SALES (est): 9.5MM **Privately Held**
WEB: www.customproduction.biz
SIC: 3363 Aluminum die-castings

(G-2361)
WILLIAMS COMMUNICATIONS INC
701 Ashley Dr (32536-9231)
PHONE..................................850 689-6651
Hays Amos, *COO*
Clayton Willis, *Technical Mgr*
Hilarie Geraldi, *Sales Mgr*
Chris Watkins, *Branch Mgr*
Christine Odom, *Manager*
EMP: 7
SALES (corp-wide): 18MM **Privately Held**
WEB: www.wmscom.com
SIC: 3663 Radio & TV communications equipment
PA: Williams Communications Inc
5046 Tenn Capitl Blvd
Tallahassee FL 32303
850 385-1121

(G-2362)
WRONGS WITHOUT WREMEDIES LLC
Also Called: Money Tree Publishing
6256 Bullet Dr (32536-4382)
PHONE..................................850 423-0828
David Gahary, *Principal*
EMP: 8 **EST:** 2015
SALES (est): 153.4K **Privately Held**
SIC: 2741 Miscellaneous publishing

Cross City
Dixie County

(G-2363)
CROSS CITY LUMBER LLC
59 Ne 132nd Ave (32628-3419)
PHONE..................................352 578-8078
Robert McKagen, *CEO*
EMP: 10 **EST:** 2019
SALES (est): 1.3MM **Privately Held**
SIC: 2421 5031 5211 Sawmills & planing mills, general; lumber, plywood & millwork; millwork & lumber

(G-2364)
CROSS CITY VENEER COMPANY INC
106 Ne 180th St (32628-5866)
PHONE..................................352 498-3226
Bolling Jones IV, *President*
David Cannon, *Vice Pres*
EMP: 60 **EST:** 1960
SQ FT: 1,200
SALES: 2.5MM
SALES (corp-wide): 20.7MM **Privately Held**
WEB: www.crosscitydental.com
SIC: 2436 3496 2441 Plywood, softwood; miscellaneous fabricated wire products; nailed wood boxes & shook
PA: Georgia Crate & Basket Co., Inc.
1200 Parnell St
Thomasville GA 31792
229 226-2541

(G-2365)
M & R SEAFOOD INC
Also Called: Suwannee River Shellfish
Hwy 351a (32628)
P.O. Box 1600 (32628-1600)
PHONE..................................352 498-5150
Nabeen Rama, *Owner*
Maggie Bieli, *Manager*
EMP: 10
SALES (corp-wide): 4.8MM **Privately Held**
SIC: 2091 5146 2092 Canned & cured fish & seafoods; fish & seafoods; fresh or frozen packaged fish
PA: M & R Seafood, Inc

Old Town FL
352 543-9395

(G-2366)
REEDS METAL MANUFACTURING INC
16454 Se Highway 19 (32628-3527)
P.O. Box 1690 (32628-1690)
PHONE..................................352 498-0100
Bernard Reed, *President*
Lucas Rollison, *Partner*
EMP: 22 **EST:** 2017
SALES (est): 2MM **Privately Held**
WEB: www.reedsmetals.com
SIC: 3442 3441 Metal doors, sash & trim; fabricated structural metal

(G-2367)
RESOLUTE CROSS CITY LLC
40 Sw 10th St (32628-3558)
PHONE..................................352 498-3363
Kenneth A Shields, *CEO*
Yuri Lewis, *CFO*
Michael Tate, *VP Finance*
Mike Tate, *VP Finance*
Mikka Dey, *Sales Mgr*
◆ **EMP:** 8 **EST:** 2013
SALES (est): 4MM
SALES (corp-wide): 2.9B **Privately Held**
WEB: www.pfresolu.com
SIC: 2426 Dimension, hardwood
PA: Resolute Forest Products Inc
111 Boul Robert-Bourassa Bureau 5000
Montreal QC H3C 2
514 875-2160

(G-2368)
RESOLUTE CROSS CY RE HLDNGS LL
40 Sw 10th St (32628-3558)
PHONE..................................352 498-3363
Charlie Miller, *President*
EMP: 12 **EST:** 2013
SALES (est): 2.2MM
SALES (corp-wide): 2.9B **Privately Held**
WEB: www.resolutefp.com
SIC: 2426 Hardwood dimension & flooring mills
PA: Resolute Forest Products Inc
111 Boul Robert-Bourassa Bureau 5000
Montreal QC H3C 2
514 875-2160

(G-2369)
VAN AERNAM LOGGING & TRUCKING
Also Called: Van Aernam Timber Management
County Rd 351 A (32628)
P.O. Box 2189 (32628-2189)
PHONE..................................352 498-5809
John D Van Aernam, *Partner*
Bobby Van Aernam, *Partner*
Frankin Van Aernam, *Partner*
Karen Van Aernam, *Bookkeeper*
EMP: 18 **EST:** 1989
SALES (est): 2.4MM **Privately Held**
SIC: 2411 0721 Logging camps & contractors; crop planting & protection

Crystal River
Citrus County

(G-2370)
B-SCADA INC (PA)
9030 W Fort Island Trl 9a (34429-8001)
PHONE..................................352 564-9610
Allen Ronald Deserranno, *CEO*
Brian S Thornton, *Vice Pres*
Josephine A Nemmers, *CFO*
Joshua M Weeks, *CTO*
EMP: 14 **EST:** 2001
SALES: 1.9MM **Privately Held**
WEB: www.scada.com
SIC: 7372 Prepackaged software

(G-2371)
CENTRAL MAINTENANCE & WLDG INC
6040 N Suncoast Blvd (34428-6711)
PHONE..................................352 795-2817
Bob Forker, *Branch Mgr*
EMP: 12
SQ FT: 5,280
SALES (corp-wide): 70.8MM **Privately Held**
WEB: www.cmw.cc
SIC: 7692 Welding repair
PA: Central Maintenance And Welding Inc.
2620 E Keysville Rd
Lithia FL 33547
813 229-0012

(G-2372)
CITRUS MOTORSPORTS
7800 W Gulf & Lake Hwy (34429)
PHONE..................................352 564-2453
Charles Allan Pope, *Principal*
Linia Doran, *Manager*
EMP: 11 **EST:** 2006
SALES (est): 160K **Privately Held**
WEB: www.citrusmotorsports.com
SIC: 3711 Motor vehicles & car bodies

(G-2373)
CITRUS PUBLISHING LLC (DH)
Also Called: Citrus County Chronicle, The
1624 N Meadowcrest Blvd (34429-5760)
P.O. Box 1899, Inverness (34451-1899)
PHONE..................................352 563-6363
Mike Abernathy, *President*
Bradford Bautista, *Editor*
Nancy Kennedy, *Editor*
Brian Lapeter, *Editor*
Mike Wright, *Editor*
EMP: 110 **EST:** 1891
SQ FT: 45,000

GEOGRAPHIC

SALES (est): 16.1MM **Privately Held**
WEB: www.chronicleonline.com
SIC: 2711 Newspapers: publishing only, not printed on site
HQ: Landmark Community Newspapers, Llc
601 Taylorsville Rd
Shelbyville KY 40065
502 633-4334

(G-2374)
COLITZ MINING CO INC
Also Called: Crystal River Quarries
7040 N Suncoast Blvd (34428-6726)
PHONE..................................352 795-2409
Frank Colitz, *President*
Edward Colitz, *Vice Pres*
Michelle Colitz, *Vice Pres*
EMP: 10 **EST:** 1940
SQ FT: 1,500
SALES (est): 407.8K **Privately Held**
SIC: 1422 Limestones, ground

(G-2375)
CRYSTAL RIVER QUARRIES INC
Also Called: Red Level Dolomite
7040 N Suncoast Blvd (34428-6726)
P.O. Box 216 (34423-0216)
PHONE..................................352 795-2828
Frank J Colitz Jr, *President*
Edward Colitz, *Corp Secy*
Michelle Colitz, *Vice Pres*
EMP: 24 **EST:** 1959
SQ FT: 1,500
SALES (est): 3.9MM **Privately Held**
SIC: 1422 3274 2951 Dolomite, crushed & broken-quarrying; lime; asphalt paving mixtures & blocks

(G-2376)
CRYSTAL RIVER WATER POLLUTION
302 Nw 11th St (34428-3062)
PHONE..................................352 795-3199
Keith Mullins, *Manager*
EMP: 13 **EST:** 2008
SALES (est): 218.5K **Privately Held**
SIC: 2086 Water, pasteurized: packaged in cans, bottles, etc.

(G-2377)
ELITE CABINET COATINGS
7170 N Ira Martin Ave (34428-6847)
PHONE..................................352 795-2655
Steven Jordan, *Principal*
EMP: 8 **EST:** 2016
SALES (est): 607.4K **Privately Held**
WEB: www.elitecabinetcoatings.com
SIC: 2434 Wood kitchen cabinets

(G-2378)
FRETTO PRINTS INC
Also Called: Shipyard Dog Prints
255 Se Us Highway 19 # 1 (34429-4890)
PHONE..................................904 687-1985
Michael D Fretto, *Principal*
EMP: 7 **EST:** 2010
SALES (est): 181.1K **Privately Held**
SIC: 2752 Commercial printing, lithographic

(G-2379)
HOUSE OF CABINETS LTD INC
4107 N Citrus Ave (34428-6021)
PHONE..................................352 795-5300
Richard Hayden, *President*
Jerry Bass, *Vice Pres*
EMP: 6 **EST:** 1991
SALES (est): 543.9K **Privately Held**
SIC: 2434 Wood kitchen cabinets

(G-2380)
QUANTUM REFLEX INTEGRATION INC
716 Sw Kings Bay Dr (34429-4653)
PHONE..................................352 228-0766
Bruce L Brandes, *Vice Pres*
EMP: 23 **EST:** 2012
SALES (est): 228.5K **Privately Held**
WEB: www.reflexintegration.net
SIC: 3572 Computer storage devices

(G-2381)
SEPARATION TECHNOLOGIES
15760 W Power Line St (34428-6708)
PHONE..................................352 794-4160
Rudy Wiechert, *Manager*
EMP: 6 **EST:** 2015
SALES (est): 402.9K **Privately Held**
SIC: 2899 Chemical preparations

(G-2382)
SIBEX INC (PA)
Also Called: Sibex Systems Division
430 N Suncoast Blvd (34429-5466)
P.O. Box 159, Safety Harbor (34695-0159)
PHONE..................................727 726-4343
Michael J McCarthy, *President*
Glenn Ficco, *Prdtn Mgr*
Mary Drury, *Mfg Spvr*
Wendy Macintyre, *Purch Mgr*
Glenna Mitchell, *Purch Mgr*
EMP: 128 **EST:** 1983
SQ FT: 120,000
SALES (est): 22.8MM **Privately Held**
WEB: www.powerdesignerssibex.com
SIC: 3672 3679 3699 Printed circuit boards; electronic circuits; electrical equipment & supplies

Cutler Bay
Miami-Dade County

(G-2383)
ADVANCED KITCHEN & CABINET
21368 Sw 112th Ave (33189-2934)
PHONE..................................305 251-9344
Yoel L Hernandez Garcia, *Principal*
EMP: 6 **EST:** 2018
SALES (est): 53.7K **Privately Held**
SIC: 2434 Wood kitchen cabinets

(G-2384)
ADVANCED PHARMA RESEARCH INC
10700 Caribbean Blvd # 30 (33189-1232)
PHONE..................................786 234-3709
Jennifer Diaz, *President*
EMP: 15 **EST:** 2016
SALES (est): 1MM **Privately Held**
WEB: www.advancedpharmacr.com
SIC: 2834 Pharmaceutical preparations

(G-2385)
ALL PRO INK
10878 Sw 188th St (33157-6745)
PHONE..................................305 252-7644
Johhny Lester, *Owner*
EMP: 8 **EST:** 2012
SALES (est): 275.6K **Privately Held**
SIC: 2759 Screen printing

(G-2386)
B & R PRODUCTS INC (PA)
18721 Sw 104th Ave (33157-6832)
P.O. Box 970671, Miami (33197-0671)
PHONE..................................305 238-1592
W Robert Millard III, *Exec VP*
Wrobert Millard III, *Vice Pres*
Maria Castellon, *Vice Pres*
Alodel Gray, *Vice Pres*
Gene Henning, *Vice Pres*
▲ **EMP:** 18
SQ FT: 15,000
SALES (est): 8MM **Privately Held**
WEB: www.brpro.com
SIC: 2844 2899 5169 Hair preparations, including shampoos; chemical preparations; chemicals & allied products

(G-2387)
BEAUTIFUL DELUXE INC
9379 Dominican Dr (33189-1622)
PHONE..................................305 498-4995
Lou Casabianca, *Principal*
EMP: 6 **EST:** 2015
SALES (est): 56.5K **Privately Held**
SIC: 2782 Blankbooks & looseleaf binders

(G-2388)
BEAUTY & HEALTH CORPORATION
10871 Sw 188th St Unit 24 (33157-6801)
PHONE..................................305 259-8181
Daniel Leon, *President*
Liz A Ramirez, *Vice Pres*
Vilma P Seife, *Admin Sec*
▲ **EMP:** 5 **EST:** 2008
SQ FT: 1,000
SALES (est): 700K **Privately Held**
WEB: www.linaza.com
SIC: 2023 Dietary supplements, dairy & non-dairy based

(G-2389)
CONTAINER MFG SOLUTIONS
Also Called: Cows USA
10460 Sw 186th St (33157-6701)
PHONE..................................888 805-8785
Ana Frank, *CEO*
Ana M Frank, *CEO*
EMP: 20 **EST:** 2019
SALES (est): 1.1MM **Privately Held**
WEB: www.containermanufacturingsolutions.com
SIC: 2448 Cargo containers, wood & wood with metal

(G-2390)
CUSTOM CARPENTRY PLUS LLC
9801 Bel Aire Dr (33157-7854)
PHONE..................................305 972-3735
Joel Hernandez, *Mng Member*
Maria Carmen Hernandez, *Mng Member*
EMP: 15 **EST:** 2012
SALES (est): 4MM **Privately Held**
SIC: 2434 7389 Wood kitchen cabinets;

(G-2391)
DAISY V CASTILLO VENDOR
10418 Sw 210th Ter (33189-3680)
PHONE..................................305 254-1427
Daisy Castillo, *Owner*
EMP: 6 **EST:** 2010
SALES (est): 158.8K **Privately Held**
WEB: www.knifespa.com
SIC: 2024 Ice cream, bulk

(G-2392)
DANIELS OFFSET PRINTING INC
8541 Franjo Rd (33189-2508)
PHONE..................................305 261-3263
Steve Grimes, *President*
Sue Grimes, *Vice Pres*
EMP: 7 **EST:** 1949
SQ FT: 6,000
SALES (est): 822K **Privately Held**
WEB: www.danielsprinting.net
SIC: 2752 Commercial printing, offset

(G-2393)
DEAKO COATINGS CHEMICAL
10459 Sw 185th Ter (33157-6755)
PHONE..................................305 323-9914
Suzanne Crossland, *Principal*
EMP: 12 **EST:** 1973
SALES (est): 330.5K **Privately Held**
SIC: 2851 Paints & allied products

(G-2394)
GLADIUM LLC
Also Called: Avesani Music
18944 Sw 93rd Ct (33157-7954)
PHONE..................................305 989-2720
Otavio Avesani,
EMP: 6 **EST:** 2015
SALES (est): 240K **Privately Held**
SIC: 3931 Musical instruments

(G-2395)
GLOBAL STONE CORP
10780 Sw 188th St (33157-6779)
PHONE..................................786 601-2459
EMP: 7 **EST:** 2019
SALES (est): 497.2K **Privately Held**
WEB: www.globalstonemiami.com
SIC: 3281 Cut stone & stone products

(G-2396)
GREEN GLOBAL ENERGY SYSTEMS
18868 Sw 80th Ct (33157-7426)
PHONE..................................305 253-3413
Siria Thomas, *President*
Emilio Patrxot, *Exec VP*
Jose Sanchez, *VP Sales*
EMP: 10 **EST:** 2009
SQ FT: 2,000
SALES (est): 520.1K **Privately Held**
WEB: www.greenglobalenergysystems.com
SIC: 3646 5063 Commercial indusl & institutional electric lighting fixtures; lighting fixtures

(G-2397)
HONCHIN INC
Also Called: Signs By Design of Miami
10397 Sw 186th St (33157-6824)
PHONE..................................305 235-3800
Honson Chin, *President*
Ingrid Chin, *Vice Pres*
EMP: 7 **EST:** 1988
SQ FT: 3,000
SALES (est): 748.9K **Privately Held**
WEB: www.signsbydesignofmiami.net
SIC: 3993 Signs & advertising specialties

(G-2398)
INDUSTRIAL CNVEYOR SYSTEMS INC
18693 Sw 103rd Ct (33157-6837)
P.O. Box 972420, Miami (33197-2420)
PHONE..................................305 255-0200
Darrel Padgett, *President*
Diann Padgett, *Admin Sec*
EMP: 10 **EST:** 1978
SQ FT: 16,000
SALES (est): 2.1MM **Privately Held**
WEB: www.icsmachinery.com
SIC: 3523 3531 Barn, silo, poultry, dairy & livestock machinery; soil preparation machinery, except turf & grounds; construction machinery

(G-2399)
LAMB TEC INC
7755 Sw 193rd Ln (33157-7396)
P.O. Box 566073, Miami (33256-6073)
PHONE..................................305 798-6266
Juan F Cordero, *President*
EMP: 7 **EST:** 2000
SALES (est): 200K **Privately Held**
WEB: www.lambtec.com
SIC: 7372 7389 Business oriented computer software;

(G-2400)
LAVISH BLINDS CORP
9822 Sw 222nd Ter (33190-1521)
PHONE..................................786 229-8134
EMP: 6 **EST:** 2019
SALES (est): 124.6K **Privately Held**
WEB: www.lavishblindsmiami.com
SIC: 2591 Window blinds

(G-2401)
LEATHER DOCTOR OF DORAL LLC
18739 Sw 107th Ave (33157-6730)
PHONE..................................786 367-6146
Victor Sevilla, *Principal*
EMP: 6 **EST:** 2010
SALES (est): 220.8K **Privately Held**
WEB: www.leatherdoctormiami.com
SIC: 3111 Leather tanning & finishing

(G-2402)
LIGHT AND SOUND EQUIPMENT INC
Also Called: Lase
10777 Sw 188th St (33157-9001)
PHONE..................................305 233-3737
Robert Wong, *President*
Winston Chin-Quee, *Vice Pres*
Paul Chin-Quee, *Manager*
▼ **EMP:** 5 **EST:** 1984
SALES (est): 499.2K **Privately Held**
SIC: 3651 3648 Speaker systems; lighting equipment

(G-2403)
MAHAN CABINETS
Also Called: D Mahan Cabinets
10471 Sw 184th Ter (33157-6761)
PHONE..................................305 255-3325
Dennis Mahan, *Owner*
EMP: 5 **EST:** 1979
SQ FT: 3,600
SALES (est): 699.8K **Privately Held**
SIC: 2434 2541 Wood kitchen cabinets; wood partitions & fixtures

(G-2404)
MINUTEMAN PRESS
22469 Sw 103rd Ave (33190-1763)
PHONE....................................305 242-6800
Tonya McHugh, *Owner*
EMP: 10 **EST:** 2009
SALES (est): 142.5K **Privately Held**
WEB: www.minutemanpress.com
SIC: 2752 Commercial printing, lithographic

(G-2405)
MWG COMPANY INC
10665 Sw 185th Ter (33157-6798)
P.O. Box 971202, Miami (33197-1202)
PHONE....................................305 232-7344
Ned Scheer, *President*
Jean Gwinn, *Principal*
Judy Scheer, *Admin Sec*
EMP: 8 **EST:** 1984
SQ FT: 1,200
SALES (est): 621K **Privately Held**
WEB: www.mwgco.com
SIC: 3484 Guns (firearms) or gun parts, 30 mm. & below

(G-2406)
ORCHID PRINTING INC
20225 Sw 90th Avenue Rd (33189-1805)
PHONE....................................786 523-3324
Mabel Gonzalez, *Principal*
EMP: 6 **EST:** 2018
SALES (est): 138.2K **Privately Held**
SIC: 2752 Commercial printing, lithographic

(G-2407)
PCS AEROSPACE & MARKETING LLC
7736 Sw 193rd Ln (33157-7394)
PHONE....................................973 352-9159
Michael Sharel, *Branch Mgr*
EMP: 21
SALES (corp-wide): 612K **Privately Held**
WEB: www.pcsaerospace.tech
SIC: 3429 Aircraft hardware
PA: Pcs Aerospace & Marketing Llc
19301 Sw 106th Ave Ste 14
Cutler Bay FL 33157
214 717-5449

(G-2408)
PINTO PALMA SOUND LLC
10665 Sw 190th St # 3103 (33157-7651)
PHONE....................................877 959-1815
Rafael Torres, *Manager*
EMP: 20 **EST:** 2019
SALES (est): 1MM **Privately Held**
SIC: 3596 Truck (motor vehicle) scales

(G-2409)
PRO KITCHEN CABINETS CORP
10675 Sw 190th St Ste 110 (33157-7652)
PHONE....................................786 768-4291
Nelson M Guerra, *Principal*
EMP: 8 **EST:** 2012
SALES (est): 301.6K **Privately Held**
SIC: 2434 Wood kitchen cabinets

(G-2410)
RONNIES WELDING & MACHINE
18640 Sw 104th Ct (33157-6704)
PHONE....................................305 238-0972
Carl Wysong, *President*
Ronald Dennis, *Shareholder*
◆ **EMP:** 7 **EST:** 1959
SALES (est): 901.3K **Privately Held**
WEB: www.ronniesusa.com
SIC: 3532 5084 3546 3531 Drills & drilling equipment, mining (except oil & gas); drilling equipment, excluding bits; power-driven handtools; construction machinery

(G-2411)
SLEEPY DRAGON STUDIOS INC
22814 Sw 88th Path (33190-1358)
PHONE....................................561 714-6156
Juan Borrero, *CEO*
Alex Martinez, *Principal*
Vanessa Velasquez, *Vice Pres*
EMP: 6 **EST:** 2012
SALES (est): 330.3K **Privately Held**
SIC: 7372 7371 7812 7389 Home entertainment computer software; software programming applications; motion picture & video production; ; commercial art & graphic design; creative services to advertisers, except writers

(G-2412)
SOLAIR GROUP LLC
10421 Sw 187th Ter (33157-6726)
PHONE....................................786 269-0160
Todd Dauphinais, *CEO*
Wesley Yale Jr, *President*
Dorothy Tilghman, *COO*
Rafael Aguilar, *CFO*
EMP: 28 **EST:** 2015
SQ FT: 20,000
SALES (est): 2.8MM **Privately Held**
WEB: www.solairgroup.com
SIC: 3728 Aircraft parts & equipment

(G-2413)
SOUTH FLORIDA MARINE
Also Called: Marine Pleasure Craft
19301 Sw 106th Ave Ste 13 (33157-7647)
PHONE....................................305 232-8788
Steven Cefalu, *President*
William Head, *Partner*
EMP: 7 **EST:** 2005
SALES (est): 500K **Privately Held**
WEB: www.southfloridamarineairconditioning.com
SIC: 3531 3585 1711 7623 Marine related equipment; air conditioning equipment, complete; parts for heating, cooling & refrigerating equipment; plumbing, heating, air-conditioning contractors; air conditioning repair; ice making machinery repair service

(G-2414)
SPEED MACHINE SHOP CORP
10755 Sw 190th St Ste 59 (33157-7634)
PHONE....................................305 233-3299
Dario Pava, *President*
EMP: 7 **EST:** 2007
SALES (est): 192.2K **Privately Held**
WEB: www.verde-speed-machine-shop-corp.hub.biz
SIC: 3599 Machine shop, jobbing & repair

(G-2415)
TREADSTONE PERFORMANCE
10340 Sw 187th St (33157-6827)
PHONE....................................305 972-9600
Jason Stone, *Principal*
EMP: 12 **EST:** 2013
SALES (est): 3.7MM **Privately Held**
WEB: www.treadstoneperformance.com
SIC: 3714 Motor vehicle parts & accessories

(G-2416)
TREADSTONE PRFMCE ENGRG INC
9486 Sw 222nd Ln (33190-1467)
PHONE....................................888 789-4586
Jason Stone, *President*
◆ **EMP:** 9 **EST:** 2010
SALES (est): 107.5K **Privately Held**
WEB: www.treadstoneperformance.com
SIC: 3714 Motor vehicle parts & accessories

(G-2417)
TRUBENDZ TECHNOLOGY INC
18495 S Dixie Hwy Ste 213 (33157-6817)
PHONE....................................305 378-9337
Joshua Kunkowski, *President*
EMP: 13
SALES (corp-wide): 620.7K **Privately Held**
WEB: www.trubendz.com
SIC: 3498 Tube fabricating (contract bending & shaping)
PA: Trubendz Technology Inc.
19101 Sw 108th Ave # 19
Cutler Bay FL 33157
305 378-9337

(G-2418)
TRUBENDZ TECHNOLOGY INC (PA)
Also Called: Mandrel Exhaust Systems
19101 Sw 108th Ave # 19 (33157-6797)
PHONE....................................305 378-9337
Joshua Kunkowski, *President*
EMP: 34 **EST:** 2003
SALES (est): 620.7K **Privately Held**
WEB: www.trubendz.com
SIC: 3498 Tube fabricating (contract bending & shaping)

(G-2419)
VERDE SPEED MACHINE SHOP CORP
10780 Sw 190th St (33157-7618)
PHONE....................................305 233-3299
EMP: 5 **EST:** 2018
SALES (est): 414.6K **Privately Held**
SIC: 3599 Machine shop, jobbing & repair

(G-2420)
VIKING KABINETS INC
10445 Sw 186th Ln (33157-6721)
PHONE....................................305 238-9025
Mike Fulford, *President*
Kevin Keenan, *Vice Pres*
▼ **EMP:** 33 **EST:** 1969
SQ FT: 12,000
SALES (est): 1.2MM **Privately Held**
WEB: www.vikingkabinets.com
SIC: 2431 2511 Millwork; wood household furniture

(G-2421)
WILL-RITE INDUSTRIES INC
10853 Sw 188th St (33157-6744)
PHONE....................................305 253-1985
Lyle Glen Willis, *President*
Loreda Willis, *Corp Secy*
Jeffery Willis, *Vice Pres*
EMP: 5 **EST:** 1982
SQ FT: 2,000
SALES (est): 318.2K **Privately Held**
SIC: 2752 Commercial printing, lithographic

(G-2422)
X-TREME WOOD CABINETS CORP
10930 Sw 188th St (33157-6784)
PHONE....................................305 537-8378
Maria Travieso, *Principal*
EMP: 6 **EST:** 2011
SALES (est): 92.2K **Privately Held**
SIC: 2434 Wood kitchen cabinets

Dade City
Pasco County

(G-2423)
BRANNEN WLDG & FABRICATION INC
34117 Ridge Manor Blvd (33523-8937)
P.O. Box 1302, Lady Lake (32158-1302)
PHONE....................................352 583-4849
William Brannen, *Principal*
EMP: 7 **EST:** 2001
SALES (est): 87.9K **Privately Held**
SIC: 7692 Welding repair

(G-2424)
CCA INDUSTRIES INC
13010 Us Highway 301 (33525-5419)
PHONE....................................813 601-6238
Timothy Linville, *President*
EMP: 13 **EST:** 2005
SQ FT: 3,904
SALES (est): 593.9K **Privately Held**
SIC: 3999 Manufacturing industries

(G-2425)
CHAMBERS BODY WORKS INC
16556 Old Johnston Rd (33523-7311)
PHONE....................................352 588-3072
Michael Chambers, *President*
EMP: 5 **EST:** 1991
SALES (est): 439.4K **Privately Held**
WEB: www.airflo.net
SIC: 3799 Trailers & trailer equipment

(G-2426)
CLARKWSTERN DTRICH BLDG SYSTEM
38020 Pulp Dr (33523-6013)
PHONE....................................800 543-7140
Bill Courtney, *Branch Mgr*
EMP: 16 **Privately Held**
WEB: www.clarkdietrich.com
SIC: 3444 Sheet metalwork
HQ: Clarkwestern Dietrich Building Systems Llc
9050 Cntre Pnte Dr Ste 40
West Chester OH 45069

(G-2427)
DELANEY RESOURCES INC
8831 Janmar Rd (33525-0718)
PHONE....................................863 670-5924
John Delaney, *President*
Debra Delaney, *Vice Pres*
EMP: 7 **EST:** 2003
SALES (est): 837.2K **Privately Held**
WEB: www.delaneyresources.com
SIC: 3523 Grading, cleaning, sorting machines, fruit, grain, vegetable

(G-2428)
GENOS CONSTRUCTION INC ✪
12421 Us Highway 301 # 228 (33525-6018)
PHONE....................................234 303-3427
Anthony Geno Martinson, *Principal*
EMP: 62 **EST:** 2021
SALES (est): 3.5MM **Privately Held**
WEB: www.genosconstructioninc.com
SIC: 1389 Construction, repair & dismantling services

(G-2429)
INK & TONER PLUS
10149 Connerly Rd (33525-1661)
PHONE....................................813 783-1650
Barbara Lycans, *Principal*
EMP: 6 **EST:** 2008
SALES (est): 340.4K **Privately Held**
SIC: 3861 Toners, prepared photographic (not made in chemical plants)

(G-2430)
JIM RINALDOS CABINETRY INC
37828 Sky Ridge Cir (33525-0878)
PHONE....................................813 788-2715
Jim Rinaldo, *President*
EMP: 16 **EST:** 1980
SQ FT: 6,500
SALES (est): 619.6K **Privately Held**
WEB: www.jrcab.com
SIC: 2434 Wood kitchen cabinets

(G-2431)
MID FLRIDA LTHERSIR/LEATHERBOY
21710 Us Highway 98 (33523-6600)
PHONE....................................352 615-5851
Raymond Tessier, *Principal*
EMP: 6 **EST:** 2012
SALES (est): 129.7K **Privately Held**
SIC: 3199 Leather goods

(G-2432)
NEW LINE TRANSPORT LLC
Also Called: Trans - Cem Dade City
9931 Old Lakeland Hwy (33525-0702)
PHONE....................................305 223-9200
John Cooper, *Branch Mgr*
EMP: 27 **Privately Held**
SIC: 3271 Concrete block & brick
HQ: New Line Transport, Llc
1501 Belvedere Rd
West Palm Beach FL 33406
561 833-5555

(G-2433)
ROBERTS VAULT CO INC
14621 Roberts Barn Rd (33523-7535)
PHONE....................................352 567-0110
Stephen E Roberts, *President*
C E Roberts, *President*
Craig Roberts, *Vice Pres*
Greg Roberts, *Vice Pres*
Steve Roberts, *Vice Pres*
EMP: 44 **EST:** 1963
SQ FT: 46,000

SALES (est): 6.1MM **Privately Held**
WEB: www.robertsvault.com
SIC: 3272 Burial vaults, concrete or precast terrazzo

(G-2434)
SB MFG LLC
15240 Citrus Country Dr (33523-6003)
PHONE..................................352 458-0137
Michael Bloch, *Principal*
▲ **EMP:** 6 **EST:** 2012
SALES (est): 190.3K **Privately Held**
WEB: www.sbwheelmfg.com
SIC: 3999 Barber & beauty shop equipment

(G-2435)
SOUTH PACIFIC TRADING COMPANY
Also Called: Tampa Bay Copack
15340 Citrus Country Dr (33523-6009)
PHONE..................................352 567-2200
William Foley, *CEO*
Lenne Nicklaus, *Vice Pres*
Valerie Hval, *Treasurer*
Andy Powell, *Director*
Deborah L Nicklaus, *Admin Sec*
▲ **EMP:** 40 **EST:** 2001
SQ FT: 76,000
SALES (est): 5.2MM **Privately Held**
WEB: www.southeast-bottling.com
SIC: 2086 Mineral water, carbonated: packaged in cans, bottles, etc.

(G-2436)
SOUTHEAST BOTTLING & BEV CO
15340 Citrus Country Dr (33523-6009)
PHONE..................................352 567-2200
William Foley, *CEO*
Gregg Nicklaus, *President*
Lenne Nicklaus Ball, *Vice Pres*
Andy Powell, *Vice Pres*
Brandon Farnell, *Production*
▲ **EMP:** 75 **EST:** 2013
SALES (est): 8.8MM **Privately Held**
WEB: www.southeast-bottling.com
SIC: 2086 Soft drinks: packaged in cans, bottles, etc.

(G-2437)
YOS BOTTLING LLC
15240 Citrus Country Dr (33523-6003)
PHONE..................................863 258-6820
Ramon Campos, *Mng Member*
EMP: 10 **EST:** 2019
SALES (est): 726.2K **Privately Held**
SIC: 2087 Beverage bases

Dania
Broward County

(G-2438)
ALL AMERICAN BUILDING PRODUCTS
401 Se 10th St (33004-4536)
PHONE..................................786 718-7300
Javier Martinez, *Principal*
EMP: 6 **EST:** 2010
SALES (est): 150K **Privately Held**
WEB: www.aabpinc.com
SIC: 3448 Prefabricated metal buildings

(G-2439)
BONA ENTERPRISES INC (PA)
255 E Dania Beach Blvd (33004-3083)
PHONE..................................954 927-4889
Frank Bona Jr, *President*
John R Bona, *Director*
EMP: 7 **EST:** 1986
SALES (est): 7.5MM **Privately Held**
SIC: 2426 Flooring, hardwood

(G-2440)
BROWARD MACHINE LLC
2070 Tigertail Blvd Ste D (33004-2111)
PHONE..................................954 920-8004
Joseph T Vennaro, *Principal*
EMP: 6 **EST:** 2015
SALES (est): 262.1K **Privately Held**
WEB: www.browardmachine.com
SIC: 3599 Machine shop, jobbing & repair

(G-2441)
BROWARD YARD & MARINE LLC
Also Called: Broward Marine
750 Ne 7th Ave (33004-2502)
PHONE..................................954 927-4119
Pete Snyder, *Purchasing*
Thomas Lewis, *Mng Member*
Albert Hernandez, *Manager*
◆ **EMP:** 52 **EST:** 1948
SALES (est): 2.1MM **Privately Held**
WEB: www.browardmarine.com
SIC: 3732 4493 Yachts, building & repairing; yacht basins

(G-2442)
BY INVITATION ONLY PUBG INC
850 Ne 3rd St Ste 209 (33004-3418)
PHONE..................................954 922-7100
Michel Karsenti, *President*
EMP: 6 **EST:** 2012
SALES (est): 93.6K **Privately Held**
SIC: 2741 Miscellaneous publishing

(G-2443)
DYNORTHOTICS LTD PARTNERSHIP
1916 Tigertail Blvd (33004-2128)
PHONE..................................954 925-5806
Rich Howell, *Manager*
EMP: 6
SALES (corp-wide): 600K **Privately Held**
WEB: www.palumbobraces.com
SIC: 3842 Braces, elastic
PA: Dynorthotics Limited Partnership
8801 Leesburg Pike
Vienna VA
703 790-0200

(G-2444)
EL CUSTOM WOOD CREATIONS INC
2004 Tigertail Blvd (33004-2145)
PHONE..................................786 337-0014
EMP: 7 **EST:** 2018
SALES (est): 342.5K **Privately Held**
WEB: www.elcustomwoodcreations.com
SIC: 2431 Millwork

(G-2445)
FAMATEL USA LLC
Also Called: Easylife Tech
1221 Stirling Rd Ste 120 (33004-3563)
PHONE..................................754 217-4841
Carlos Latre, *Director*
EMP: 5 **EST:** 2017
SALES (est): 400K
SALES (corp-wide): 22MM **Privately Held**
WEB: www.famatelusa.com
SIC: 3699 3264 3469 Electrical equipment & supplies; insulators, electrical: porcelain; furniture components, porcelain enameled
PA: Fabricacion De Material Electrico Sa
Carretera A-1223 (Km 8)
Peralta De Alcofea 22210
938 634-640

(G-2446)
HKI SOUNDIGITAL USA LLC
345 Bryan Rd (33004-2363)
PHONE..................................786 600-1056
Diogo Ianaconi, *President*
EMP: 8 **EST:** 2016
SALES (est): 482.5K **Privately Held**
SIC: 3651 Amplifiers: radio, public address or musical instrument

(G-2447)
ICEE COMPANY
11 Sw 12th Ave Ste 108 (33004-3527)
PHONE..................................954 966-7502
Jim Shaea, *Manager*
EMP: 10
SALES (corp-wide): 1B **Publicly Held**
WEB: www.icee.com
SIC: 2086 Bottled & canned soft drinks
HQ: The Icee Company
265 Mason Rd
La Vergne TN 37086
800 426-4233

(G-2448)
INTREPID POWERBOATS INC (PA)
805 Ne E 3rd St (33004)
PHONE..................................954 324-4196
Charles K Clinton, *President*
Joe Brenna, *Vice Pres*
Mike Obolsky, *Vice Pres*
Alex Rizo, *Vice Pres*
Doug Denorcy, *Senior Buyer*
▲ **EMP:** 309 **EST:** 1992
SQ FT: 120,000
SALES (est): 54MM **Privately Held**
WEB: www.intrepidpowerboats.com
SIC: 3732 Boats, fiberglass: building & repairing

(G-2449)
IRONCLAD WELDING INC
1205 Sw 4th Ave (33004-3905)
P.O. Box 1868 (33004-1868)
PHONE..................................954 925-7987
William J Stamm, *President*
EMP: 5 **EST:** 1977
SQ FT: 3,000
SALES (est): 523.1K **Privately Held**
WEB: www.ironcladweldinginc.com
SIC: 7692 Welding repair

(G-2450)
MACHINE TOP LLC
720 Sw 4th Ct (33004-3803)
PHONE..................................786 238-8926
Imanuel Hazan, *Principal*
EMP: 14 **EST:** 2014
SALES (est): 674.6K **Privately Held**
WEB: www.machinetopusa.com
SIC: 3599 Machine shop, jobbing & repair

(G-2451)
MARINER INTERNATIONAL TRVL INC
Also Called: Mooring Yacht Brokerage
850 Ne 3rd St Ste 201 (33004-3418)
PHONE..................................954 925-4150
Richard Vass, *Broker*
Dianne Franklin, *Branch Mgr*
Bill Regan, *Consultant*
EMP: 7
SALES (corp-wide): 9.3B **Privately Held**
WEB: www.moorings.com
SIC: 3732 4724 Yachts, building & repairing; travel agencies
HQ: Mariner International Travel, Inc.
93 N Park Place Blvd
Clearwater FL 33759

(G-2452)
MICROMICR CORPORATION
35 Sw 12th Ave Ste 112 (33004-3530)
PHONE..................................954 922-8044
Michael Axelrod, *President*
Chris Schoeller, *COO*
EMP: 19 **EST:** 1990
SQ FT: 16,600
SALES (est): 1.2MM **Privately Held**
WEB: www.micro-micr.com
SIC: 3955 Print cartridges for laser & other computer printers

(G-2453)
MYDOR INDUSTRIES INC
470 Sw 9th St (33004-3836)
PHONE..................................954 927-1140
Marcel Kon, *President*
Stuart Kaufman, *President*
Doris Kaufman, *Corp Secy*
EMP: 6 **EST:** 1983
SQ FT: 6,000
SALES (est): 532.3K **Privately Held**
SIC: 2899 3826 2833 Water treating compounds; water testing apparatus; medicinal chemicals

(G-2454)
NEW T MANAGEMENT INC
255 E Dania Beach Blvd # 2 (33004-3083)
PHONE..................................954 927-4889
Frank J Bona Jr, *Principal*
EMP: 7 **EST:** 2008
SALES (est): 118.2K **Privately Held**
SIC: 2426 Flooring, hardwood

(G-2455)
PAGE ONE LLC
1231 Stirling Rd Ste 107 (33004-3567)
PHONE..................................833 467-2431
Keith Obrien,
EMP: 10 **EST:** 2019
SALES (est): 508.1K **Privately Held**
WEB: www.page.one
SIC: 2741

(G-2456)
PARK PLUS FLORIDA INC
1111 Old Griffin Rd (33004-2224)
PHONE..................................954 929-7511
Colin Lawrence, *President*
Elieser Perez, *Project Engr*
Ron Astrup, *CFO*
Aj Jenkins, *Sales Staff*
EMP: 10 **EST:** 2014
SALES (est): 3MM **Privately Held**
WEB: www.parkplusinc.com
SIC: 3559 Parking facility equipment & supplies

(G-2457)
RABUD INC
110 N Bryan Rd (33004-2244)
PHONE..................................954 925-4199
Ralph Brown, *President*
Patricia Brown, *Corp Secy*
EMP: 7 **EST:** 1976
SQ FT: 45,000
SALES (est): 935.1K **Privately Held**
WEB: www.rabud.com
SIC: 3732 Boat building & repairing

(G-2458)
TECHNICRAFT PLASTICS INC
1253 Stirling Rd (33004-3555)
PHONE..................................954 927-2575
Ken Kholos, *President*
EMP: 15 **EST:** 1996
SQ FT: 17,000
SALES (est): 2.1MM **Privately Held**
WEB: www.technicraftplastics.com
SIC: 3089 Injection molding of plastics

(G-2459)
TOTAL WINDOW INC
1249 Stirling Rd Ste 15 (33004-3554)
PHONE..................................954 921-0109
Stephen Stolow, *President*
Cheryl Stolow, *Corp Secy*
Jesse Stolow, *COO*
Favio Ramirez, *Project Mgr*
Ryan Locke, *Assistant*
▼ **EMP:** 8 **EST:** 1985
SQ FT: 1,200
SALES (est): 1.4MM **Privately Held**
WEB: www.totalwindow.com
SIC: 2591 5023 Window blinds; venetian blinds

(G-2460)
TRAC ECOLOGICAL AMERICA INC
1103 Old Griffin Rd (33004-2224)
PHONE..................................954 583-4922
Kevin Greene, *CEO*
Patrick Leclerc, *President*
▲ **EMP:** 6 **EST:** 2001
SQ FT: 2,000
SALES (est): 1.2MM **Privately Held**
WEB: www.trac-online.com
SIC: 2819 Industrial inorganic chemicals

(G-2461)
WINDWARD ASSOCIATES CORP
265 Bryan Rd (33004-2207)
PHONE..................................954 336-8085
Winfield C Austin, *President*
▼ **EMP:** 12 **EST:** 2004
SALES (est): 376.6K **Privately Held**
SIC: 2434 Wood kitchen cabinets

Dania Beach
Broward County

(G-2462)
AMERICAN EPOXY COATINGS LLC
1340 Stirling Rd Ste 1a (33004-3561)
PHONE..................................954 850-1169

Daniel Bowman, *CEO*
EMP: 10 **EST:** 2017
SALES (est): 781.4K **Privately Held**
WEB: www.americanepoxysystems.com
SIC: 2821 Epoxy resins

(G-2463)
BOGANTEC CORP
1300 Stirling Rd (33004-3545)
PHONE..................................954 217-0023
Francisco J Bogan Sr, *President*
Juan M Bogan Sr, *Vice Pres*
EMP: 8 **EST:** 2010
SALES (est): 1MM **Privately Held**
WEB: www.bogantec.com
SIC: 3531 Marine related equipment

(G-2464)
DANIA CUT HOLDINGS INC
Also Called: Dania Cut Super Yacht Repair
760 Ne 7th Ave (33004-2502)
PHONE..................................954 923-9545
Earl R Macpherson, *President*
Bruce Chee, *Opers Staff*
Jason Harrington, *Director*
▼ **EMP:** 13 **EST:** 2009
SALES (est): 1.6MM **Privately Held**
WEB: www.daniacut.com
SIC: 3732 Yachts, building & repairing

(G-2465)
FLORIDA DERECKTOR INC (PA)
Also Called: Derecktor of Florida
775 Taylor Ln (33004-2536)
PHONE..................................954 920-5756
Cliff Defreitas, *General Mgr*
Eric P Derecktor, *Principal*
Ken Imondi, *COO*
Mark Russell, *Project Mgr*
Galloway Selby, *Project Mgr*
▲ **EMP:** 124 **EST:** 1967
SQ FT: 47,000
SALES (est): 22.7MM **Privately Held**
WEB: www.derecktor.com
SIC: 3732 Yachts, building & repairing

(G-2466)
JOHNSON & JOHNSON
1024 Se 3rd Ave Apt 304 (33004-5210)
PHONE..................................954 534-1141
EMP: 80
SALES (corp-wide): 82.5B **Publicly Held**
SIC: 2676 Mfg Consumer Products & Surgical Appliances
PA: Johnson & Johnson
1 Johnson And Johnson Plz
New Brunswick NJ 08933
732 524-0400

(G-2467)
MADAN CORPORATION (PA)
Also Called: Madan Kosher Foods
130 Sw 3rd Ave (33004-3656)
PHONE..................................954 925-0077
Samuel Weiss, *President*
EMP: 9 **EST:** 1969
SQ FT: 10,000
SALES (est): 848.3K **Privately Held**
SIC: 2038 5812 5084 Frozen specialties; caterers; industrial machinery & equipment

(G-2468)
MARWARE INC
Also Called: Marblue
1206 Stirling Rd Bay 9a-B (33004-3552)
PHONE..................................954 927-6031
Edward W Martin, *CEO*
Maria A Martin, *President*
▲ **EMP:** 38 **EST:** 1993
SQ FT: 6,350
SALES (est): 2.3MM **Privately Held**
SIC: 7372 5065 Prepackaged software; electronic parts & equipment

(G-2469)
MASSIMO & UMBERTO INC
Also Called: Mrs. Pasta
132 Sw 3rd Ave (33004-3656)
PHONE..................................954 993-0842
Umberto Costa, *Principal*
EMP: 5 **EST:** 2010
SALES (est): 800K **Privately Held**
SIC: 2099 Noodles, uncooked: packaged with other ingredients

(G-2470)
MAT INDUSTRIES LLC
1815 Griffin Rd Ste 400 (33004-2252)
PHONE..................................847 821-9630
EMP: 46 **Privately Held**
WEB: www.matholdingsinc.com
SIC: 3563 Air & gas compressors
HQ: Mat Industries, Llc
6700 Wildlife Way
Long Grove IL 60047

(G-2471)
ORTHOSENSOR INC (HQ)
1855 Griffin Rd Ste A310 (33004-2401)
PHONE..................................954 577-7770
Ivan Delevic, *CEO*
Marty Trabish, *General Mgr*
Eric Christopher, *Business Mgr*
Douglas Leach, *Vice Pres*
Jason McIntosh, *Vice Pres*
EMP: 86 **EST:** 2007
SALES (est): 27.5MM
SALES (corp-wide): 14.3B **Publicly Held**
WEB: www.orthosensor.com
SIC: 3845 Electrotherapeutic apparatus
PA: Stryker Corporation
2825 Airview Blvd
Portage MI 49002
269 385-2600

(G-2472)
POSEIDON WINDOW TREATMENTS LLC
1942 Tigertail Blvd (33004-2139)
PHONE..................................954 920-1112
Alina Garcia, *President*
Manny Garcia, *VP Opers*
Alex Garcia, *VP Mktg*
EMP: 7 **EST:** 2012
SQ FT: 9,000
SALES (est): 1.6MM
SALES (corp-wide): 1.7MM **Privately Held**
WEB: www.poseidoninteriors.com
SIC: 2591 Window blinds
PA: Florida International Blind Factory Depot, Inc.
1940 Tigertail Blvd
Dania FL 33004
954 920-1112

(G-2473)
TESLA INC
1949 Tigertail Blvd (33004-2109)
PHONE..................................754 816-3069
Bobby Paris, *Recruiter*
Adrianna Bentley, *Advisor*
EMP: 7
SALES (corp-wide): 31.5B **Publicly Held**
WEB: www.tesla.com
SIC: 3711 Motor vehicles & car bodies
PA: Tesla, Inc.
3500 Deer Creek Rd
Palo Alto CA 94304
650 681-5000

(G-2474)
US METAL FABRICATORS INC
Also Called: US Marine Supply
800 Old Griffin Rd (33004-2745)
PHONE..................................954 921-0800
Jan R Givskov, *President*
Jens E Sorensen, *Director*
EMP: 15 **EST:** 2016
SALES (est): 1.2MM **Privately Held**
SIC: 3441 Fabricated structural metal

(G-2475)
WINE PLUM INC
11 Sw 12th Ave Ste 104 (33004-3527)
PHONE..................................844 856-7586
David Koretz, *CEO*
Justin Dopp, *Vice Pres*
Adam Hoydysh, *Vice Pres*
Weijing LI, *Vice Pres*
EMP: 18 **EST:** 2015
SALES (est): 2.2MM **Privately Held**
WEB: www.plum.wine
SIC: 3632 Household refrigerators & freezers

Davenport
Polk County

(G-2476)
CEMEX CNSTR MTLS FLA LLC
Also Called: Davenport -Block Manufacturing
100 Lem Carnes Rd (33837-2607)
PHONE..................................863 419-2875
Matt Konjezich, *Branch Mgr*
EMP: 9 **Privately Held**
SIC: 3273 Ready-mixed concrete
HQ: Cemex Construction Materials Florida, Llc
1501 Belvedere Rd
West Palm Beach FL 33406

(G-2477)
DAVID GILL ENTERPRISES
110 Hwy 17 92 (33837)
PHONE..................................863 422-5711
David T Gill, *Owner*
EMP: 9 **EST:** 2009
SALES (est): 306.7K **Privately Held**
SIC: 3499 Fabricated metal products

(G-2478)
ER JAHNA INDUSTRIES INC
4949 Sand Mine Rd (33897-3414)
PHONE..................................863 424-0730
Eric Cullop, *Branch Mgr*
EMP: 25
SQ FT: 27,014
SALES (corp-wide): 70.5MM **Privately Held**
WEB: www.jahna.com
SIC: 1499 Gemstone & industrial diamond mining
PA: E.R. Jahna Industries, Inc.
202 E Stuart Ave
Lake Wales FL 33853
863 676-9431

(G-2479)
GILL MANUFACTURING INC
110 S Hwy 17 92 (33837)
P.O. Box 769 (33836-0769)
PHONE..................................863 422-5711
David Gill, *President*
Howard Gill, *Vice Pres*
EMP: 10 **EST:** 1980
SQ FT: 6,000
SALES (est): 1.5MM **Privately Held**
WEB: www.gillmfg.com
SIC: 3441 Fabricated structural metal

(G-2480)
J & N STONE INC (PA)
Also Called: Rich Haven Interiors
135 Bargain Barn Rd (33837-7714)
P.O. Box 1199 (33836-1199)
PHONE..................................863 422-7369
Robert Richards, *President*
Barry Rardain, *Safety Dir*
Derek Deskins, *Accounts Mgr*
Damon Deskins, *Sales Staff*
EMP: 2 **EST:** 1973
SQ FT: 17,600
SALES (est): 5.2MM **Privately Held**
WEB: www.jnstoneveneer.com
SIC: 3281 Cut stone & stone products

(G-2481)
MASCHMEYER CONCRETE CO FLA
4949 Sand Mine Rd (33897-3414)
PHONE..................................863 420-6800
Troy Maschmeyer, *Branch Mgr*
EMP: 15
SALES (corp-wide): 136.2MM **Privately Held**
WEB: www.maschmeyer.com
SIC: 3273 Ready-mixed concrete
PA: Maschmeyer Concrete Company Of Florida
1142 Watertower Rd
Lake Park FL 33403
561 848-9112

(G-2482)
SAMS LED SIGNS & SERVICES
243 Whispering Pines Way (33837-6701)
PHONE..................................407 492-4934
Kian George, *Principal*
EMP: 6 **EST:** 2017
SALES (est): 46K **Privately Held**
SIC: 3993 Signs & advertising specialties

(G-2483)
STANDARD SAND & SILICA COMPANY (PA)
1850 Us Highway 17 92 N (33837-8608)
P.O. Box 1059 (33836-1059)
PHONE..................................863 422-7100
L Baylis I Carnes, *Chairman*
James L Langford, *Vice Pres*
Brent Elliott, *CFO*
Scott Higdon, *Supervisor*
◆ **EMP:** 20 **EST:** 1945
SQ FT: 1,800
SALES (est): 50.3MM **Privately Held**
WEB: www.standardsand.com
SIC: 1446 Industrial sand

(G-2484)
UMBRELLA BUSES INC
Also Called: Umbusa
9800 Us 192 (33897)
PHONE..................................754 457-4004
Zdenek Kozisek, *President*
Melya Tavel, *Principal*
EMP: 7 **EST:** 2019
SALES (est): 535.7K **Privately Held**
SIC: 3829 Fare registers for street cars, buses, etc.

(G-2485)
VERDU-US LLC
741 Caribbean Dr (33897-3940)
PHONE..................................407 776-3017
Hazem Elaeady,
EMP: 10 **EST:** 2017
SALES (est): 589.4K **Privately Held**
WEB: www.verdu-us.com
SIC: 2024 Dairy based frozen desserts

Davie
Broward County

(G-2486)
ABSOLUTE GRAPHICS INC
3721 Sw 47th Ave Ste 302 (33314-2824)
PHONE..................................954 792-3488
Evan R Owen, *President*
▼ **EMP:** 10 **EST:** 1992
SQ FT: 3,000
SALES (est): 1.6MM **Privately Held**
WEB: www.absolutegraphics.us
SIC: 2752 2759 Commercial printing, offset; commercial printing

(G-2487)
ACTAVIS LABORATORIES FL INC (PA)
4955 Orange Dr (33314-3902)
PHONE..................................954 305-4414
Paul M Bisaro, *Director*
EMP: 114 **EST:** 2009
SALES (est): 2.4MM **Privately Held**
SIC: 2834 Pharmaceutical preparations

(G-2488)
ADLER ANB INC
3721 Sw 47th Ave Ste 306 (33314-2826)
PHONE..................................954 581-2572
Michael Auer, *Manager*
EMP: 8 **EST:** 1998
SALES (est): 967.4K **Privately Held**
SIC: 3732 Yachts, building & repairing

(G-2489)
AERO-TRIM CONTROL SYSTEMS INC
4680 Sw 61st Ave (33314-4406)
PHONE..................................954 321-1936
Elyse S Swalley, *Principal*
EMP: 7 **EST:** 2009
SALES (est): 163.6K **Privately Held**
WEB: www.aerotriminc.com
SIC: 3812 Search & navigation equipment

(G-2490)
AIR FLOW SPECIALISTS
5400 S University Dr 206a (33328-5309)
PHONE..................................954 727-9507
Rodney Fritz, *Principal*
EMP: 7 **EST:** 2012

SALES (est): 1.4MM **Privately Held**
WEB: www.airflowspecialists.com
SIC: 3564 Ventilating fans: industrial or commercial

(G-2491)
ALL ABOUT HER
12401 Orange Dr (33330-4341)
PHONE..................................954 559-5175
Errol L Benjamin, *CEO*
EMP: 10 **EST:** 2018
SALES (est): 733.4K **Privately Held**
SIC: 2676 Feminine hygiene paper products

(G-2492)
ALLPRO FBRICATORS ERECTORS INC
3595 Burris Rd (33314-2221)
PHONE..................................954 797-7300
Robert Singh, *President*
EMP: 5 **EST:** 2009
SQ FT: 4,000
SALES (est): 1MM **Privately Held**
WEB: www.allprofab.com
SIC: 3441 Fabricated structural metal

(G-2493)
ALLSTAR SCREEN ENCLOSURES & ST
9460 Poinciana Pl Apt 308 (33324-4881)
PHONE..................................954 266-9757
Thomas B Clay, *Principal*
EMP: 7 **EST:** 2009
SALES (est): 157.3K **Privately Held**
WEB: www.coastalhandyman.net
SIC: 3448 Screen enclosures

(G-2494)
ALPHATRON INDUSTRIES INC
3411 Sw 49th Way Ste 3 (33314-2112)
PHONE..................................954 581-1418
Nick Rezai, *President*
EMP: 5 **EST:** 1985
SQ FT: 5,000
SALES (est): 513.8K **Privately Held**
WEB: www.alphatronindustries.com
SIC: 3548 Resistance welders, electric

(G-2495)
AMERICAN FINE WOODWORK LLC
35 Seville Cir (33324-5447)
PHONE..................................954 261-9793
Christian Almonte, *Principal*
EMP: 6 **EST:** 2016
SALES (est): 246.7K **Privately Held**
SIC: 2431 Millwork

(G-2496)
AMERICAN GENERATOR SVCS LLC
14820 Sw 21st St (33326-2004)
PHONE..................................954 965-1210
James E Oberlander, *Manager*
James Oberlander,
EMP: 12 **EST:** 2007
SALES (est): 1.9MM **Privately Held**
WEB: www.americangeneratorservices.com
SIC: 3621 Motors & generators

(G-2497)
ANDRX CORPORATION (DH)
4955 Orange Dr (33314-3902)
PHONE..................................954 585-1400
Thomas R Giordano, *Senior VP*
Robert I Goldfarb, *Senior VP*
Ian J Watkins, *Senior VP*
Guy Riley, *Maint Spvr*
▲ **EMP:** 230 **EST:** 1992
SQ FT: 69,000
SALES (est): 699.5MM **Privately Held**
WEB: www.andrx.com
SIC: 2834 5122 Pharmaceutical preparations; pharmaceuticals
HQ: Actavis Llc
5 Giralda Farms
Madison NJ 07940
862 261-7000

(G-2498)
ARC ELECTRIC INC
3328 Burris Rd (33314-2215)
PHONE..................................954 583-9800
Omar McFarlane, *President*
Everton Ruddock, *Vice Pres*
Ashley Kay, *Admin Asst*
EMP: 33 **EST:** 2012
SALES (est): 9.6MM **Privately Held**
WEB: www.arcelectricfl.com
SIC: 3699 1731 Electrical equipment & supplies; electrical work

(G-2499)
ARNET PHARMACEUTICAL CORP
Also Called: Natura-Vigor
2525 Davie Rd Ste 330 (33317-7403)
PHONE..................................954 236-9053
Leo Tabacinic, *Ch of Bd*
Jose Tabacinic, *President*
Liliam Lizazo, *Purchasing*
Adam Friedman, *CFO*
Amy Rivero, *Accounts Exec*
◆ **EMP:** 350 **EST:** 1972
SQ FT: 46,000
SALES (est): 89.8MM **Privately Held**
WEB: www.arnetusa.com
SIC: 2834 Pharmaceutical preparations

(G-2500)
AUTHENTIC TRADING INC
11107 Sw 15th Mnr (33324-7190)
PHONE..................................347 866-7241
Ariel Rodriguez, *Principal*
EMP: 7 **EST:** 2010
SALES (est): 117.4K **Privately Held**
SIC: 3691 4911 3556 8731 Storage batteries; ; dairy & milk machinery; energy research

(G-2501)
AVIALL INC
3350 Davie Rd (33314-1647)
PHONE..................................954 625-3930
EMP: 6
SALES (corp-wide): 58.1B **Publicly Held**
WEB: www.shop.boeing.com
SIC: 3721 Airplanes, fixed or rotary wing
HQ: Aviall, Inc.
2750 Rgent Blvd Dfw Arprt Dfw Airport
Dallas TX 75261

(G-2502)
BANASZAK CONCRETE CORP
2401 College Ave (33317-7402)
PHONE..................................954 476-1004
S Howard Banaszak Jr, *President*
S Howard Banaszak Sr, *Vice Pres*
Sarah Lee Banaszak, *Vice Pres*
▼ **EMP:** 20 **EST:** 1964
SALES (est): 749.2K **Privately Held**
WEB: www.banaszakconcrete.com
SIC: 3273 3271 Ready-mixed concrete; blocks, concrete: acoustical

(G-2503)
BNJ NOBLE INC
Also Called: Noble's Jockey Apparel
5408 Stirling Rd (33314-7457)
PHONE..................................954 987-1040
Elizabeth Noble, *President*
EMP: 11 **EST:** 1965
SQ FT: 5,000
SALES (est): 658K **Privately Held**
WEB: www.nobleembroidery.com
SIC: 2253 5699 2397 Jackets, knit; uniforms; schiffli machine embroideries

(G-2504)
C&D CANVAS INC
6110 W Falcons Lea Dr (33331-2981)
PHONE..................................954 924-3433
David Richarson, *Principal*
EMP: 6 **EST:** 2010
SALES (est): 243.4K **Privately Held**
WEB: www.cdcanvasinc.com
SIC: 2394 Canvas & related products

(G-2505)
CABINET GUY 2012 INC
14721 Sw 21st St (33325-4930)
PHONE..................................305 796-5242
Hamid Ahari, *Principal*
EMP: 6 **EST:** 2012
SALES (est): 134.8K **Privately Held**
SIC: 2434 Wood kitchen cabinets

(G-2506)
CBM TRADING INC
10620 Griffin Rd Ste 104 (33328-3213)
P.O. Box 173470, Hialeah (33017-3470)
PHONE..................................954 252-7460
Hanspeter Ehrler, *President*
Peter Edwin, *Owner*
Edward Peters, *Vice Pres*
Doris Brena, *Treasurer*
Persy Sanchez, *Admin Sec*
◆ **EMP:** 5 **EST:** 1998
SQ FT: 1,400
SALES (est): 876.9K **Privately Held**
WEB: www.cbmtrading.net
SIC: 3489 Cannons & howitzers, over 30 mm.

(G-2507)
CELEB LUXURY LLC
6545 Nova Dr Ste 201 (33317-7410)
PHONE..................................954 763-0333
Tammie Hunt, *Vice Pres*
Howard Sperlein, *Vice Pres*
Peggy Sakki, *Opers Staff*
Gretchen Correia, *Sales Staff*
Leanne Weekes, *Pub Rel Staff*
EMP: 13 **EST:** 2014
SQ FT: 11,000
SALES (est): 1.1MM **Privately Held**
WEB: www.celebluxury.com
SIC: 2844 Hair preparations, including shampoos

(G-2508)
CERTIFIED MOLD FREE CORP
2881 W Lake Vista Cir (33328-1106)
PHONE..................................954 614-7100
Gary Rosen, *President*
EMP: 6 **EST:** 2003
SALES (est): 520.8K **Privately Held**
WEB: www.mold-free.org
SIC: 1389 Construction, repair & dismantling services

(G-2509)
COPY-FLOW INC
4727 Orange Dr (33314-3901)
PHONE..................................305 592-0930
Donna Keys, *President*
Jon Keys, *Principal*
Charles Chaddock, *Corp Secy*
EMP: 20 **EST:** 1973
SQ FT: 6,000
SALES (est): 625.9K **Privately Held**
WEB: www.copy-flow.com
SIC: 2752 2789 Commercial printing, offset; promotional printing, lithographic; business form & card printing, lithographic; tag, ticket & schedule printing: lithographic; bookbinding & related work

(G-2510)
CREATIVE COLOR PRINTING INC
3721 Sw 47th Ave Ste 302 (33314-2824)
PHONE..................................954 701-6763
Michael Dubay, *President*
EMP: 8 **EST:** 2013
SALES (est): 173.2K **Privately Held**
WEB: www.creativecolorprinting.net
SIC: 2752 Commercial printing, offset

(G-2511)
CRYNTEL ENTERPRISES LTD INC
10412 W State Road 84 # 1 (33324-4270)
PHONE..................................954 577-7844
Steven Dreyer, *President*
Joel Dreyer, *Vice Pres*
▲ **EMP:** 7 **EST:** 1988
SALES (est): 955.9K **Privately Held**
WEB: www.cryntel.com
SIC: 2426 Parquet flooring, hardwood

(G-2512)
CURRENT
3301 College Ave Asa105 (33314-7721)
PHONE..................................954 262-8455
Michele Manley, *Director*
EMP: 9 **EST:** 1990
SALES (est): 122.9K **Privately Held**
SIC: 2711 8221 Newspapers, publishing & printing; university

(G-2513)
D & D BUILDING CONTRACTORS
Also Called: D & D Millwork Distributors
3380 Sw 50th Ave (33314-2105)
PHONE..................................954 791-2075
David A Green, *President*
Patrick J Brennan, *Vice Pres*
EMP: 8 **EST:** 1986
SQ FT: 1,800
SALES (est): 618.2K **Privately Held**
SIC: 2431 1521 Millwork; single-family housing construction

(G-2514)
DASHCOVERS PLUS DEPOT DISTRS
4431 Sw 64th Ave Ste 104 (33314-3458)
PHONE..................................954 961-7774
Jane Randolph, *President*
Danny Randolph, *Vice Pres*
▲ **EMP:** 5 **EST:** 2003
SALES (est): 582.5K **Privately Held**
WEB: www.dashcover.com
SIC: 3714 Motor vehicle parts & accessories

(G-2515)
DAVIE EMBROIDME
2471 S University Dr (33324-5817)
PHONE..................................954 452-0600
Fernando Corredor, *Principal*
EMP: 10 **EST:** 2006
SALES (est): 664.2K **Privately Held**
WEB: www.fullypromoteddavie.com
SIC: 2759 Screen printing

(G-2516)
DEPENDABLE SHUTTER SERVICE INC
Also Called: Dependable Shutter & Glass
4741 Orange Dr (33314-3901)
PHONE..................................954 583-1411
Wayne C Thompson, *Director*
Mike Waters, *Director*
▼ **EMP:** 35 **EST:** 2001
SALES (est): 6MM **Privately Held**
WEB: www.dependableshutters.com
SIC: 3442 3231 2431 Screen & storm doors & windows; safety glass: made from purchased glass; door shutters, wood

(G-2517)
DOCUVISION INCORPORATED
3650 Hacienda Blvd Ste F (33314-2821)
PHONE..................................954 791-0091
Jim Brodmerkel, *CEO*
John S Leven, *President*
Jackie Leven, *CFO*
Douglas Gonzales, *Supervisor*
EMP: 28 **EST:** 2003
SALES (est): 3.3MM **Privately Held**
WEB: www.docuvis.com
SIC: 2752 Commercial printing, lithographic

(G-2518)
ENERGY CONTROL TECHNOLOGIES
Also Called: Energycontrol.com
10220 W State Road 84 # 9 (33324-4223)
PHONE..................................954 739-8400
Richard E Combs, *President*
Judith L Combs, *Corp Secy*
Nate Mizrahi, *Manager*
Kira Rios,
EMP: 8 **EST:** 1983
SQ FT: 5,000
SALES (est): 1.2MM **Privately Held**
WEB: www.energycontrol.com
SIC: 3825 1711 3823 Electrical energy measuring equipment; plumbing, heating, air-conditioning contractors; industrial instrmnts msrmnt display/control process variable

(G-2519)
ENERGYWARE LLC
17120 Reserve Ct (33331-3526)
PHONE..................................540 809-5902
Tanya Bertamini, *Principal*
EMP: 9 **EST:** 2016

▲ = Import ▼=Export
◆ =Import/Export

SALES (est): 900.6K **Privately Held**
WEB: www.energywarellc.com
SIC: 3648 Lighting equipment

(G-2520)
EVERGREEN RUSH INDUSTRIES INC
473 Sw 126th Ave (33325-3437)
P.O. Box 266862, Fort Lauderdale (33326-6862)
PHONE..................................954 825-9291
Esther Noltion, *Principal*
EMP: 15 **EST:** 2019
SALES (est): 445.4K **Privately Held**
SIC: 3999 Manufacturing industries

(G-2521)
EVOLUTION INTRCNNECT SYSTEMS I
11870 W State Road 84 C (33325-3816)
PHONE..................................954 217-6223
Shawn Chalnick, *Vice Pres*
Marcelo Dutra, *Vice Pres*
Suzette Rebull, *Exec Dir*
EMP: 15 **EST:** 2014
SALES (est): 2.9MM **Privately Held**
WEB: www.evoics.com
SIC: 3699 3643 3612 3613 Extension cords; current-carrying wiring devices; electric connectors; contacts, electrical; power & distribution transformers; auto-transformers, electric (power transformers); switchgear & switchboard apparatus

(G-2522)
EXPRESS TOOLS INC
Also Called: Matco Tools
14521 Sw 21st St (33325-4926)
PHONE..................................954 663-4333
Lazaro Salazar, *Principal*
EMP: 8 **EST:** 2016
SALES (est): 444.9K **Privately Held**
WEB: www.matcotools.com
SIC: 3599 Industrial machinery

(G-2523)
EYES ON GO OPTICAL LLC
4715 Sw 62nd Ave (33314-4460)
PHONE..................................954 242-3243
Carmen Garcia, *Principal*
EMP: 6 **EST:** 2014
SALES (est): 119.3K **Privately Held**
SIC: 3827 Optical instruments & lenses

(G-2524)
FEDS APPAREL
2230 Sw 70th Ave Ste 1 (33317-7131)
PHONE..................................954 932-0685
EMP: 28
SALES (est): 1MM **Privately Held**
SIC: 2353 2321 Mfg Hats/Caps/Millinery Mfg Men's/Boy's Furnishings

(G-2525)
FJH MUSIC COMPANY INC
2525 Davie Rd Ste 360 (33317-7403)
PHONE..................................954 382-6061
Frank J Hackinson, *President*
Gail J Hackinson, *Senior VP*
Giorgi Kerry Hackinson, *Vice Pres*
Kevin Hackinson, *Vice Pres*
Kyle Hackinson, *Vice Pres*
EMP: 30 **EST:** 1988
SQ FT: 33,000
SALES (est): 3MM **Privately Held**
WEB: www.fjhmusic.com
SIC: 2741 Music book & sheet music publishing

(G-2526)
FLORIDA MOLD STOPPERS INC
5520 S University Dr (33328-5333)
PHONE..................................954 445-5560
Earl K Hackworth, *Principal*
EMP: 5 **EST:** 2018
SALES (est): 691.1K **Privately Held**
WEB: www.floridamoldstoppers.com
SIC: 3544 Industrial molds

(G-2527)
FLYER STUDIOS INC
13740 Sw 33rd Ct (33330-4689)
PHONE..................................786 402-9596
Larry M Reyes, *President*
EMP: 12 **EST:** 2017
SALES (est): 313.6K **Privately Held**
WEB: www.flyerstudios.com
SIC: 2752 Commercial printing, offset

(G-2528)
G AND G INDUSTRIES INC
5910 Sw 43rd St (33314-3605)
PHONE..................................754 701-4178
EMP: 5 **EST:** 2017
SALES (est): 321.8K **Privately Held**
SIC: 3499 Fabricated metal products

(G-2529)
G B WELDING & FABRICATION LLC
2397 College Ave (33317-7155)
PHONE..................................954 967-2573
Garrett Bisogno, *President*
Kimberly Bisogno, *Vice Pres*
Joseph Sclater,
EMP: 14 **EST:** 2011
SALES (est): 1.4MM **Privately Held**
WEB: www.gbweldingandfab.com
SIC: 7692 Welding repair

(G-2530)
G F E INC
3030 Burris Rd (33314-2209)
PHONE..................................954 583-7005
Lori Acvedo, *President*
Lori Acevedo, *President*
EMP: 14 **EST:** 1998
SALES (est): 478.5K **Privately Held**
SIC: 3442 3444 3231 Screen & storm doors & windows; sheet metalwork; products of purchased glass

(G-2531)
GATOR DRAIN CLEANING EQUIPMENT
5411 Orange Dr (33314-3816)
PHONE..................................954 584-4441
EMP: 5
SALES (est): 483.4K **Privately Held**
SIC: 3589 Mfg Service Industry Machinery

(G-2532)
GENERAL DEFENSE CORPORATION
4960 Sw 52nd St Ste 413 (33314-5527)
PHONE..................................954 444-0155
Carlos Davidov, *President*
Peter Bratulev, *General Mgr*
EMP: 5 **EST:** 2006
SALES (est): 321K **Privately Held**
WEB: www.generaldefense.com
SIC: 3489 Ordnance & accessories

(G-2533)
GREEN ROADS OF FLORIDA
5150 Sw 48th Way (33314-5513)
PHONE..................................954 626-0574
EMP: 5 **EST:** 2015
SALES (est): 375K **Privately Held**
SIC: 2834 Mfg Pharmaceutical Preparations

(G-2534)
HAC INTERNATIONAL INC
Also Called: Dynofresh
3911 Sw 47th Ave Ste 914 (33314-2818)
PHONE..................................954 584-4530
Howard Cohen, *President*
Maggie Arvelo, *CFO*
▲ **EMP:** 25 **EST:** 1997
SQ FT: 8,000
SALES (est): 6MM **Privately Held**
SIC: 2819 5169 Chemicals, reagent grade: refined from technical grade; chemicals, industrial & heavy

(G-2535)
HICKS INDUSTRIES INC
2257 Sw 66th Ter (33317-7301)
PHONE..................................954 226-5148
Stephen Hatfield, *Manager*
Carmen Alvarez, *Manager*
EMP: 7
SALES (corp-wide): 8.7MM **Privately Held**
WEB: www.hicksindustries.com
SIC: 3272 Burial vaults, concrete or precast terrazzo
PA: Hicks Industries, Inc.
2005 Industrial Park Rd
Mulberry FL 33860
863 425-4155

(G-2536)
HOOPER CORP
6900 Sw 21st Ct (33317-7163)
PHONE..................................954 382-5711
Bob Nichols, *Office Mgr*
EMP: 16 **EST:** 2010
SALES (est): 310K **Privately Held**
WEB: www.hoopercorp.com
SIC: 3699 Electrical equipment & supplies

(G-2537)
INDUSTRIAL SPRING CORP
3129 Peachtree Cir (33328-6706)
PHONE..................................954 524-2558
A W Lidert, *President*
EMP: 11 **EST:** 1969
SALES (est): 985.8K **Privately Held**
WEB: www.industrialspringflorida.com
SIC: 3312 3469 3493 Wire products, steel or iron; metal stampings; steel springs, except wire

(G-2538)
IRONCLAD IMPACT WNDOWS DORS LL
3701 Sw 47th Ave Ste 106 (33314-2830)
PHONE..................................954 743-4321
David Bitton, *Mng Member*
EMP: 7 **EST:** 2019
SALES (est): 311.7K **Privately Held**
WEB: www.ironcladimpactwindows.com
SIC: 2431 Doors & door parts & trim, wood; windows, wood

(G-2539)
J&B CMMNICATION SOLUTIONS CORP
6555 Stirling Rd (33314-7117)
PHONE..................................786 346-7449
Otilio Alvarado, *President*
EMP: 6 **EST:** 2003
SQ FT: 1,000
SALES (est): 600K **Privately Held**
SIC: 3663 Satellites, communications

(G-2540)
KCM MCH SP BROWARD CNTY INC
2394 Sw 66th Ter (33317-7135)
PHONE..................................954 475-8732
Feroz Khan, *President*
◆ **EMP:** 13 **EST:** 2008
SQ FT: 9,500
SALES (est): 1.5MM **Privately Held**
WEB: www.kcmmachine.com
SIC: 3549 Metalworking machinery

(G-2541)
KLEEN WHEELS CORPORATION
Also Called: Perma Cap
5000 Oakes Rd Ste H (33314-2119)
PHONE..................................954 791-9112
David L Weinberg, *President*
John Herzberg, *Vice Pres*
▲ **EMP:** 7 **EST:** 1989
SQ FT: 7,000
SALES (est): 876.9K **Privately Held**
SIC: 3714 3643 Motor vehicle engines & parts; motor vehicle brake systems & parts; current-carrying wiring devices

(G-2542)
KUS USA INC
3350 Davie Rd Ste 203 (33314-1648)
PHONE..................................954 463-1075
Yale Huang, *President*
Nataliya Melcher, *Project Mgr*
Ciarra Ems, *Sales Engr*
Aaron Irvin, *Sales Staff*
Kerry Weston, *Admin Asst*
▲ **EMP:** 25 **EST:** 1996
SQ FT: 32,500
SALES (est): 6.5MM **Privately Held**
WEB: www.kus-usa.com
SIC: 3812 4226 3824 3823 Nautical instruments; liquid storage; liquid meters; liquid level instruments, industrial process type

(G-2543)
LANCASTER INDUSTRIES INC
13974 N Cypress Cove Cir (33325-6749)
PHONE..................................954 916-9293
Dolores Lancaster, *Principal*
EMP: 6 **EST:** 2007
SALES (est): 94.1K **Privately Held**
SIC: 3999 Manufacturing industries

(G-2544)
LAUDERDALE GRAPHICS CORP (PA)
1625 Sw 117th Ave (33325-4648)
PHONE..................................954 450-0800
Boon Tirasitipol, *President*
Yoko Tirasitipol, *Vice Pres*
Tony Lopez, *VP Sales*
John Coyle Jr, *Sales Staff*
▲ **EMP:** 30 **EST:** 1988
SALES (est): 3.1MM **Privately Held**
WEB: www.laudgraphics.com
SIC: 2752 2791 2759 Commercial printing, offset; typesetting; commercial printing

(G-2545)
LEHIGH CEMENT COMPANY LLC
Also Called: Continental Concrete Materials
3575 Sw 49th Way (33314-2123)
PHONE..................................954 581-2812
Rafael Gonzales, *Branch Mgr*
EMP: 44
SALES (corp-wide): 20.8B **Privately Held**
WEB: www.lehighwhitecement.com
SIC: 3273 Ready-mixed concrete
HQ: Lehigh Cement Company Llc
300 E John Carpenter Fwy
Irving TX 75062
877 534-4442

(G-2546)
LEXTM3 SYSTEMS LLC
15751 Sw 41st St Ste 300 (33331-1520)
PHONE..................................954 888-1024
Manuel Consuegra, *Engineer*
Lou Bongiovi, *Director*
Mario Alavrez, *Officer*
Nate Lowery,
EMP: 10 **EST:** 2015
SALES (est): 1.4MM **Privately Held**
WEB: www.lextm3.com
SIC: 3678 3671 3612 3613 Electronic connectors; electron tubes; transformers, except electric; switchgear & switchboard apparatus; relays & industrial controls; current-carrying wiring devices

(G-2547)
LIVE WELL CBDS
12640 Sw 7th Pl (33325-3410)
PHONE..................................954 723-0580
Michelle Lillo, *Principal*
EMP: 6 **EST:** 2017
SALES (est): 141.4K **Privately Held**
SIC: 3999

(G-2548)
MANUFACTURING BY SKEMA INC
3801 Sw 47th Ave Ste 501 (33314-2816)
PHONE..................................954 797-7325
Norberto Grundland, *President*
Patricia Arango, *Vice Pres*
◆ **EMP:** 9 **EST:** 1988
SALES (est): 1MM **Privately Held**
WEB: www.skemainc.com
SIC: 2511 Wood household furniture

(G-2549)
MARINA MEDICAL INSTRUMENTS INC
8190 W State Road 84 (33324-4611)
PHONE..................................954 924-4418
Alexander H Barron, *CEO*
Anthony Zinnanti, *Ch of Bd*
Marina C Zinnanti, *President*
Laura Hucaluk, *CFO*
Brian Holden, *Accounts Mgr*
▲ **EMP:** 25
SQ FT: 11,303
SALES (est): 3.9MM **Privately Held**
WEB: www.marinamedical.com
SIC: 3841 Surgical & medical instruments

(G-2550)
MCDS PRO LLC
2021 Sw 70th Ave Bay 15 (33317-7314)
PHONE.................................954 302-3054
William J Oviedo, *Mng Member*
EMP: 9 **EST:** 2016
SALES (est): 923.2K **Privately Held**
WEB: www.mcdspro.com
SIC: 3441 Fabricated structural metal

(G-2551)
MELMAR CSTM MET FINSHG SVC INC
5990 Sw 42nd Pl (33314-3603)
PHONE.................................954 327-5788
Nils Westberg, *Principal*
EMP: 9 **EST:** 2007
SALES (est): 372.2K **Privately Held**
WEB: www.melimarfinishing.com
SIC: 3471 Electroplating of metals or formed products; plating of metals or formed products

(G-2552)
MERLIN INDUSTRIES INC
2201 College Ave (33317-7343)
PHONE.................................954 472-6891
Larry Maurer, *President*
Dale Schrack, *General Mgr*
Jesse Maurer, *Vice Pres*
EMP: 18 **EST:** 1992
SALES (est): 1.5MM **Privately Held**
WEB: www.merlinindustries.net
SIC: 3441 Fabricated structural metal

(G-2553)
MIL-SAT LLC
12555 Orange Dr (33330-4304)
PHONE.................................954 862-3613
Mary Ann Richardson, *Branch Mgr*
EMP: 9
SALES (corp-wide): 6.9MM **Privately Held**
WEB: www.mil-sat.com
SIC: 3663 Satellites, communications
PA: Mil-Sat Llc
318 Bank St
Surry VA 23883
757 294-9393

(G-2554)
MOHNARK PHARMACEUTICALS INC
5150 Sw 48th Way Ste 604 (33314-5513)
PHONE.................................954 607-4559
Donovan Amritt, *CEO*
EMP: 6 **EST:** 2018
SALES (est): 570.3K **Privately Held**
SIC: 2834 Pharmaceutical preparations

(G-2555)
NAIAD DYNAMICS US INC
3750 Hacienda Blvd Ste A (33314-2825)
P.O. Box 292230, Fort Lauderdale (33329-2230)
PHONE.................................954 797-7566
Vic Kuzmovich, *Branch Mgr*
EMP: 17 **Privately Held**
WEB: www.naiaddynamics.com
SIC: 3731 Shipbuilding & repairing
HQ: Naiad Dynamics Us, Inc.
50 Parrott Dr
Shelton CT 06484

(G-2556)
NATIONAL CHEMICAL SPLY
4151 Sw 47th Ave (33314-4054)
P.O. Box 16785, Fort Lauderdale (33318-6785)
PHONE.................................800 515-9938
Phillip Shaffer, *President*
EMP: 11 **EST:** 2001
SALES (est): 580K **Privately Held**
WEB: www.nationalchemicalsupply.com
SIC: 2819 7389 Industrial inorganic chemicals; swimming pool & hot tub service & maintenance

(G-2557)
NCH MARINE LLC
13325 Sw 28th St (33330-1101)
PHONE.................................754 422-4237
Larry Hill, *Principal*
EMP: 8 **EST:** 2011
SALES (est): 309.8K **Privately Held**
SIC: 2842 Specialty cleaning, polishes & sanitation goods

(G-2558)
NORDIC MADE INC
3801 Sw 47th Ave Ste 503 (33314-2816)
PHONE.................................954 651-6208
Michael Rasmussen, *President*
Bettina D Nowak, *Director*
EMP: 13 **EST:** 2012
SQ FT: 3,000
SALES (est): 3.5MM **Privately Held**
WEB: www.tecosolutions.no
SIC: 3731 Shipbuilding & repairing
HQ: Teco Maritime Group As
Lysaker Torg 45
Lysaker 1366

(G-2559)
OCEAN BIO-CHEM INC (PA)
4041 Sw 47th Ave (33314-4023)
PHONE.................................954 587-6280
Peter G Dornau, *Ch of Bd*
William W Dudman, *COO*
Gregor M Dornau, *Exec VP*
Jeffrey S Barocas, *CFO*
EMP: 22 **EST:** 1973
SQ FT: 12,700
SALES: 55.5MM **Publicly Held**
WEB: www.oceanbiochem.com
SIC: 2842 2992 Polishing preparations & related products; lubricating oils & greases

(G-2560)
OCEAN TEST EQUIPMENT INC
2021 Sw 70th Ave Ste B1 (33317-7334)
PHONE.................................954 474-6603
John Banu, *President*
Gabriela Mirea, *Vice Pres*
▲ **EMP:** 7 **EST:** 1992
SQ FT: 3,000
SALES (est): 895.9K **Privately Held**
WEB: www.oceantestequip.com
SIC: 3812 5049 Nautical instruments; scientific instruments

(G-2561)
OFF THE CHART INC
5400 S University Dr (33328-5312)
PHONE.................................954 654-6541
Mark Beloyan, *Principal*
EMP: 6 **EST:** 2017
SALES (est): 120K **Privately Held**
SIC: 3993 Signs & advertising specialties

(G-2562)
ORANGE SUNSHINE GRAPHICS INC
5051 S State Road 7 # 517 (33314-5659)
PHONE.................................954 797-7425
Pedro Rivas, *President*
Barbara McCraney, *Corp Secy*
Glenda Rivas, *Vice Pres*
▼ **EMP:** 8 **EST:** 1981
SQ FT: 4,000
SALES (est): 947.7K **Privately Held**
WEB: www.customityourway.com
SIC: 2262 Screen printing: manmade fiber & silk broadwoven fabrics

(G-2563)
OZINGA SOUTH FLORIDA INC
2401 College Ave (33317-7402)
PHONE.................................786 422-4694
Justin Ozinga, *President*
EMP: 7 **EST:** 2017
SALES (est): 196.4K **Privately Held**
WEB: www.ozinga.com
SIC: 3273 Ready-mixed concrete

(G-2564)
PALLADIUM SALES LLC
5081 S State Road 7 # 810 (33314-5664)
PHONE.................................754 423-0517
Luis Font,
Edith Font,
EMP: 6 **EST:** 2013
SALES (est): 196.8K **Privately Held**
SIC: 3724 Aircraft engines & engine parts

(G-2565)
PALM BEACH TRIM INC
6900 W State Road 84 (33317-7308)
PHONE.................................561 588-8746
Fax: 561 588-5855
EMP: 50
SALES (est): 6.6MM **Privately Held**
SIC: 2441 2434 Nonclassified Establishment Mfg Wood Boxes/Shook Mfg Wood Kitchen Cabinets

(G-2566)
PARADISE CSTM SCREENING & EMB
2180 Sw 71st Ter (33317-7303)
PHONE.................................954 566-9096
EMP: 21
SALES (est): 1.6MM **Privately Held**
SIC: 2395 2396 Silk Screening & Embroidery

(G-2567)
PAYO LLC
12481 N Stonebrook Cir (33330-1295)
PHONE.................................786 368-8655
Marie Yolete Charles,
▲ **EMP:** 5
SQ FT: 10,000
SALES (est): 356.9K **Privately Held**
SIC: 2051 Bakery: wholesale or wholesale/retail combined

(G-2568)
PEM-AIR LLC
5921 Sw 44th Ct (33314-3640)
PHONE.................................954 321-8726
Virgil D Pizer, *Mng Member*
EMP: 10 **EST:** 2010
SALES (est): 1.1MM **Privately Held**
WEB: www.0338d14.netsolhost.com
SIC: 3728 Aircraft parts & equipment

(G-2569)
PEM-AIR TURBINE ENG SVCS LLC
5921 Sw 44th Ct (33314-3640)
PHONE.................................954 321-8726
Juan Robles, *Sales Staff*
Hope Roetting, *Info Tech Mgr*
Virgil Pizer,
EMP: 10 **EST:** 2013
SALES (est): 1MM **Privately Held**
SIC: 3728 Aircraft parts & equipment

(G-2570)
PETIT CUSTOM WOOD WORKS
3673 W Valley Green Dr (33328-2625)
PHONE.................................954 200-3111
Amberlee Petit, *Principal*
EMP: 6 **EST:** 2016
SALES (est): 58.5K **Privately Held**
SIC: 2499 Laundry products, wood

(G-2571)
PHARMA NATURE LLC
2271 Dorado Ave (33324-6317)
PHONE.................................305 395-4723
Annabella Vizcardo, *Principal*
EMP: 6 **EST:** 2015
SALES (est): 94.4K **Privately Held**
SIC: 2834 Pharmaceutical preparations

(G-2572)
PHARMATECH LLC (PA)
4131 Sw 47th Ave Ste 1403 (33314-4036)
P.O. Box 590671, Fort Lauderdale (33359-0671)
PHONE.................................954 581-7881
Raidel I Figueroa, *CEO*
EMP: 5 **EST:** 2009
SALES (est): 2.4MM **Privately Held**
WEB: www.pharmatech-llc.com
SIC: 2834 8734 Pharmaceutical preparations; testing laboratories

(G-2573)
PHARMATECH LLC
4131 Sw 47th Ave Ste 1405 (33314-4036)
PHONE.................................954 629-2444
Raidel Figueroa, *Officer*
EMP: 15 **Privately Held**
WEB: www.pharmatech-llc.com
SIC: 2834 Pharmaceutical preparations
PA: Pharmatech Llc
4131 Sw 47th Ave Ste 1403
Davie FL 33314

(G-2574)
PL SMOOTHIE LLC
10234 Sw 26th St (33324-7625)
PHONE.................................954 554-0450
Shaukat Umer, *Principal*
EMP: 9 **EST:** 2010
SALES (est): 336K **Privately Held**
SIC: 2037 Frozen fruits & vegetables

(G-2575)
PRINT IT USACOM INC
13660 W State Road 84 (33325-5302)
PHONE.................................954 370-2200
Janice Seidner, *President*
Leigh Seidner, *Vice Pres*
EMP: 5 **EST:** 1992
SALES (est): 470K **Privately Held**
WEB: www.printitusa.com
SIC: 2752 Commercial printing, offset

(G-2576)
PRINTING CONNECTION TOO INC
4960 Sw 52nd St Ste 409 (33314-5527)
PHONE.................................954 584-4197
Larry Peterson, *President*
EMP: 5 **EST:** 1984
SQ FT: 1,650
SALES (est): 456.9K **Privately Held**
WEB: www.pctoo.net
SIC: 2752 Commercial printing, offset

(G-2577)
PURIFY FUELS INC
14113 N Cypress Cove Cir (33325-6736)
PHONE.................................949 842-6159
John Carroll, *CEO*
John Anda, *Ch of Bd*
Pat Gallagher, *Vice Chairman*
Steven Douglas, *COO*
Jay Fountain, *Vice Pres*
EMP: 7 **EST:** 2016
SALES (est): 258.1K **Privately Held**
WEB: www.purifyfuel.com
SIC: 2911 Fuel additives

(G-2578)
QUALITY ANODIZING INCORPORATED
5990 Sw 42nd Pl (33314-3603)
PHONE.................................954 791-8711
Morgan Peterson, *Manager*
EMP: 5 **EST:** 2007
SALES (est): 516.6K **Privately Held**
WEB: www.qualityanodizing.com
SIC: 3471 Electroplating of metals or formed products

(G-2579)
RAINBOW INK PRODUCTS INC
15640 Lancelot Ct (33331-3318)
PHONE.................................954 252-6030
Mr Scott J Lodge, *Principal*
EMP: 6 **EST:** 2010
SALES (est): 160K **Privately Held**
SIC: 2893 Printing ink

(G-2580)
RAND SEARCH LIGHT ADVERTISING
11330 Sw 17th St (33325-4802)
PHONE.................................954 476-7620
Terrie Rand, *Principal*
Peter Nguyen, *CTO*
EMP: 8 **EST:** 1999
SALES (est): 676.9K **Privately Held**
WEB: www.randsearchlight.com
SIC: 3648 Searchlights; floodlights

(G-2581)
RAPIDSPOOLINDUSTRIES INC
3150 Sw 148th Ave (33331-2635)
PHONE.................................954 850-5300
Christofidis Panayiotis T, *Principal*
EMP: 7 **EST:** 2015
SALES (est): 94.7K **Privately Held**
WEB: www.rapidspoolindustries.com
SIC: 3999 Manufacturing industries

(G-2582)
RED BAY BERRY LLC
2983 E Lake Vista Cir (33328-1128)
PHONE.................................954 552-9935
Gil Marcondes, *Principal*
EMP: 6 **EST:** 2013

▲ = Import ▼=Export
◆ =Import/Export

SALES (est): 109.1K **Privately Held**
SIC: 3961 5094 Costume jewelry; jewelry

(G-2583)
RED SMITH FOODS INC
4145 Sw 47th Ave (33314-4006)
PHONE..................................954 581-1996
Stephen F Foster, *President*
Mike Hoffman, *General Mgr*
Jonathan Foster, *Vice Pres*
Tim Foster, *Vice Pres*
David Foster, *Treasurer*
EMP: 22 **EST:** 1973
SQ FT: 12,000
SALES (est): 6.9MM **Privately Held**
WEB: www.redsmithfoods.com
SIC: 2013 Sausages from purchased meat

(G-2584)
REVERSO PUMPS INC
4001 Sw 47th Ave Ste 201 (33314-4030)
PHONE..................................954 523-9396
John Napurano, *President*
Tammy Anstett, *General Mgr*
Dan Bigelow, *Vice Pres*
Heather Kemp, *Buyer*
Francisco Mejia, *Sales Staff*
▲ **EMP:** 17 **EST:** 1993
SQ FT: 6,000
SALES (est): 4.4MM **Privately Held**
WEB: www.reversopumps.com
SIC: 3561 Pumps & pumping equipment

(G-2585)
REX THREE INC
Also Called: Rex 3
15431 Sw 14th St (33326-1937)
PHONE..................................954 452-8301
Julius Miller, *Ch of Bd*
Robert Cannata, *President*
Stephen H Miller, *President*
Jay Kahn, *Vice Pres*
Howard Shusterman, *Vice Pres*
▼ **EMP:** 165 **EST:** 1958
SQ FT: 90,000
SALES (est): 39.4MM **Privately Held**
WEB: www.rex3.com
SIC: 2759 2796 Screen printing; color separations for printing

(G-2586)
ROMCO FUELS INC
10835 Sw 38th Dr (33328-1315)
PHONE..................................954 474-5392
John Romano, *Director*
EMP: 12 **EST:** 2001
SALES (est): 148.9K **Privately Held**
WEB: www.romco.com
SIC: 2869 Fuels

(G-2587)
RTC SOLUTIONS INC
4370 Oakes Rd Ste 700 (33314-2225)
PHONE..................................919 439-8680
Todd Saltzman, *President*
Cheryl Wechter, *Manager*
EMP: 5 **EST:** 2008
SQ FT: 1,500
SALES (est): 891.3K **Privately Held**
WEB: www.rtc-solutions.com
SIC: 3625 Relays & industrial controls

(G-2588)
RUSSELL HOME IMPRVMNT CTR INC
3250 Sw 131st Ter (33330-4607)
PHONE..................................954 436-9186
Ralph Russell, *President*
EMP: 8 **EST:** 1987
SALES (est): 705.7K **Privately Held**
WEB: www.russellhomeimprovement.net
SIC: 3442 Screen & storm doors & windows

(G-2589)
SEAKING INC
Also Called: Seaking USA
2200 Sw 71st Ter (33317-7136)
PHONE..................................954 961-6629
Mark Stevenson, *President*
Paul Fries, *Treasurer*
Marek Stawinski, *Director*
Bruno Wild, *Director*
◆ **EMP:** 25 **EST:** 1990
SQ FT: 20,000
SALES (est): 3.8MM **Privately Held**
WEB: www.seakingusa.com
SIC: 2599 3731 3589 Ship furniture; shipbuilding & repairing; dishwashing machines, commercial

(G-2590)
SEMINOLE STATE SIGNS & LTG
5071 S State Road 7 # 717 (33314-5601)
PHONE..................................954 316-6030
Andrew Wyrosdick, *Vice Pres*
EMP: 8 **EST:** 2015
SALES (est): 329.7K **Privately Held**
SIC: 3993 Signs & advertising specialties

(G-2591)
SHIRTS N THINGS INC
6001 Orange Dr (33314-3609)
PHONE..................................954 434-7480
Steve Chorba, *President*
Renee Chorba, *Corp Secy*
EMP: 5 **EST:** 1980
SQ FT: 2,900
SALES (est): 488.9K **Privately Held**
WEB: www.shirtsnthings.com
SIC: 2759 Screen printing

(G-2592)
SLAINTE WINES INC (PA)
12535 Orange Dr Ste 610 (33330-4307)
PHONE..................................954 474-4547
Chris O'Connor, *President*
Zina O'Connor, *COO*
EMP: 7 **EST:** 2004
SALES (est): 1.3MM **Privately Held**
WEB: www.slaintewines.com
SIC: 2084 Wines

(G-2593)
SLATE SOLUTIONS LLC
7060 W State Road 84 # 12 (33317-7365)
PHONE..................................754 200-6752
Michael J Slate, *President*
EMP: 32 **EST:** 2015
SALES (est): 2.8MM **Privately Held**
WEB: www.slatesolutions.com
SIC: 2389 Men's miscellaneous accessories

(G-2594)
SOUTH FLORIDA CORE DISTRS
2030 Sw 71st Ter Ste C6 (33317-7323)
PHONE..................................954 452-9091
William Lowther, *President*
◆ **EMP:** 5 **EST:** 1991
SALES (est): 422.3K **Privately Held**
SIC: 3694 Distributors, motor vehicle engine

(G-2595)
STAR-BRITE DISTRIBUTING INC
Also Called: Star Brite
4041 Sw 47th Ave (33314-4031)
PHONE..................................954 587-6280
Peter Dornau, *Ch of Bd*
William Dudman, *Vice Pres*
Dornau Gregor M, *Vice Pres*
Jeff Brocas, *CFO*
◆ **EMP:** 35 **EST:** 1973
SQ FT: 300,000
SALES (est): 11.4MM
SALES (corp-wide): 55.5MM **Publicly Held**
WEB: www.starbrite.com
SIC: 2842 Specialty cleaning, polishes & sanitation goods
PA: Ocean Bio-Chem, Inc.
4041 Sw 47th Ave
Davie FL 33314
954 587-6280

(G-2596)
STOLTZ INDUSTRIES INC
9704 E Tree Tops Ct (33328-7105)
PHONE..................................954 792-3270
Carl Stoltz, *President*
▼ **EMP:** 10 **EST:** 1976
SALES (est): 1.8MM **Privately Held**
WEB: www.stoltzind.com
SIC: 3089 Casting of plastic

(G-2597)
SUN BELT GRAPHICS INC
15431 Sw 14th St (33326-1937)
PHONE..................................954 424-3139
Robert Bernstein, *President*
Jerry Garcia, *Production*
EMP: 16 **EST:** 1977
SALES (est): 3.3MM **Privately Held**
SIC: 2752 Color lithography

(G-2598)
SUNBELT DIMENSIONAL INC
15431 Sw 14th St (33326-1937)
PHONE..................................954 424-3139
Robert Bernstein, *President*
Barbara Krane, *General Mgr*
Jose Pagan, *Production*
Peter Gould, *Sales Staff*
EMP: 7 **EST:** 2015
SALES (est): 198.4K **Privately Held**
WEB: www.sunbeltdimensional.net
SIC: 2752 Commercial printing, offset

(G-2599)
SUPER COLOR INC
5905 Sw 58th Ct (33314-7313)
PHONE..................................954 964-4656
Doron Shmueli, *President*
Eddie Shmueli, *Vice Pres*
Ilan Shmueli, *Vice Pres*
▼ **EMP:** 19 **EST:** 1992
SALES (est): 1.6MM **Privately Held**
WEB: www.super-color.com
SIC: 2752 Commercial printing, offset

(G-2600)
SUPERMARKET SERVICES INC
4100 Sw 47th Ave (33314-4007)
PHONE..................................954 525-0439
David Johnson, *President*
Maria Johnson, *Treasurer*
▼ **EMP:** 7 **EST:** 1968
SALES (est): 739.6K **Privately Held**
WEB: www.smsrecyclingequip.com
SIC: 3569 Baling machines, for scrap metal, paper or similar material

(G-2601)
TECHNICAL DRIVE CTRL SVCS INC
Also Called: T D C S
5081 S State Road 7 (33314-5600)
PHONE..................................954 471-6521
Vivian Martens, *President*
Tony Augusto, *Vice Pres*
EMP: 5
SQ FT: 1,500
SALES (est): 659.8K **Privately Held**
SIC: 3625 Control circuit devices, magnet & solid state

(G-2602)
TEND SKIN INTERNATIONAL INC
2090 Sw 71st Ter Ste G9 (33317-7322)
PHONE..................................954 382-0800
Steven E Rosen, *President*
Linda Irons, *Opers Mgr*
David Wood, *QC Mgr*
◆ **EMP:** 13 **EST:** 1994
SQ FT: 6,000
SALES (est): 1.8MM **Privately Held**
WEB: www.tendskin.com
SIC: 2844 5122 5999 7231 Cosmetic preparations; toiletries; toiletries, cosmetics & perfumes; facial salons

(G-2603)
TESCO EQUIPMENT
3400 Burris Rd (33314-2217)
PHONE..................................954 791-9470
Bruce Schoch, *Principal*
EMP: 6 **EST:** 2016
SALES (est): 99.1K **Privately Held**
SIC: 3999 Manufacturing industries

(G-2604)
TG OIL SERVICES
14520 Sw 21st St (33325-4925)
PHONE..................................407 576-9571
Carlos Touzan, *Principal*
EMP: 5 **EST:** 2018
SALES (est): 353.5K **Privately Held**
WEB: www.tgoilservices.com
SIC: 1311 Crude petroleum production

(G-2605)
THERMOVAL SOLENOID VALVES USA
4651 Sw 51st St Ste 808 (33314-5515)
PHONE..................................954 835-5523
EMP: 6 **EST:** 2018
SALES (est): 378.4K **Privately Held**
WEB: www.thermoval.com.br
SIC: 3491 Solenoid valves

(G-2606)
TONER CITY CORP
4137 Stirling Rd Apt 103 (33314-7562)
PHONE..................................954 945-5392
Vince R Charles, *President*
EMP: 9 **EST:** 2017
SQ FT: 1,200
SALES (est): 697.2K **Privately Held**
SIC: 3861 Toners, prepared photographic (not made in chemical plants)

(G-2607)
TOTALLY BANANAS LLC
5081 S State Road 7 # 803 (33314-5664)
PHONE..................................954 674-9421
Joel Kornbluth, *Vice Pres*
Mindy Pheterson, *Vice Pres*
Charles J Pheterson, *Mng Member*
EMP: 12 **EST:** 2009
SALES (est): 1.5MM **Privately Held**
WEB: www.totally-bananas.net
SIC: 2037 Fruits, quick frozen & cold pack (frozen)

(G-2608)
TRUREV LLC
4407 Sw 62nd Ave (33314-3428)
PHONE..................................800 397-3388
Desmond Kameka, *Principal*
Debbie Kameka, *Manager*
EMP: 6 **EST:** 2016
SALES (est): 505K **Privately Held**
WEB: www.trurev.com
SIC: 3599 Industrial machinery

(G-2609)
USA MARINE ENGINES LLC
1540 Sw 106th Ter (33324-7165)
PHONE..................................954 383-1870
Jason Buchanan, *Principal*
EMP: 6 **EST:** 2017
SALES (est): 98.7K **Privately Held**
WEB: www.usamarineengines.com
SIC: 3519 Marine engines

(G-2610)
VEEAM SOFTWARE CORPORATION
15137 Sw 36th St (33331-2734)
PHONE..................................614 339-8200
EMP: 7
SALES (corp-wide): 778.5K **Privately Held**
WEB: www.veeam.com
SIC: 7372 Prepackaged software
HQ: Veeam Software Corporation
8800 Lyra Dr Ste 350
Columbus OH 43240

(G-2611)
WALKING BIRD PUBLICATIONS LLC ✪
3984 Sw 137th Ave (33330-5712)
PHONE..................................954 474-7261
Kristi Tannen, *Manager*
EMP: 6 **EST:** 2020
SALES (est): 41.3K **Privately Held**
SIC: 2741 Miscellaneous publishing

(G-2612)
WAYLOOMOTO LLC
7060 W State Road 84 # 8 (33317-7365)
PHONE..................................954 636-1510
EMP: 5
SALES (est): 310K **Privately Held**
SIC: 3949 Mfg Sporting/Athletic Goods

(G-2613)
WEIGHTECH USA LLC
10384 W State Road 84 # 6 (33324-4251)
PHONE..................................954 666-0877
Joao Paulo Pires,
Carlos Alberto Marin,
EMP: 12 **EST:** 2013
SALES (est): 2.5MM **Privately Held**
WEB: www.weightechusa.com
SIC: 3596 Weighing machines & apparatus

(G-2614)
WILLIS INDUSTRIES INC
5064 S University Dr (33328-4510)
PHONE..................................954 830-6163
Paul Willis, *President*
EMP: 6 **EST:** 2002
SALES (est): 159.4K **Privately Held**
SIC: 3999 Manufacturing industries

(G-2615)
WINDSTONE DEVELOPMENT INTL LC
Also Called: Fastsigns
7080 W State Road 84 (33317-7368)
PHONE..................................954 370-7201
Howard J Willis,
EMP: 15 **EST:** 1999
SALES (est): 285K **Privately Held**
WEB: www.fastsigns.com
SIC: 3993 Signs & advertising specialties

(G-2616)
WIREWORLD BY DAVID SALZ INC
Also Called: Wireworld Cable Technology
6545 Nova Dr Ste 204 (33317-7410)
PHONE..................................954 474-4464
David B Salz, *President*
Bernay Bavone, *COO*
Eric Arocha, *Production*
Leslie Day, *Marketing Mgr*
David Salz, *Manager*
◆ **EMP:** 22 **EST:** 1992
SQ FT: 2,400
SALES (est): 2.9MM **Privately Held**
WEB: www.wireworldcable.com
SIC: 3651 Household audio & video equipment

(G-2617)
YACHT FURNISHING BY ECLIP
7050 W State Road 84 (33317-7364)
PHONE..................................954 792-7339
EMP: 6 **EST:** 2018
SALES (est): 194.1K **Privately Held**
WEB: www.eclipse-yachtfurnishings.com
SIC: 2394 Canvas & related products

(G-2618)
ZINC GUY INC (PA)
3811 Sw 47th Ave Ste 617 (33314-2817)
PHONE..................................954 907-2752
Alberto Spinelli, *President*
EMP: 35 **EST:** 2010
SALES (est): 966.2K **Privately Held**
WEB: www.thezincguy.com
SIC: 3531 5088 Marine related equipment; marine supplies

Daytona Beach
Volusia County

(G-2619)
88 SOUTH ATLANTIC LLC
835 N Beach St (32114-2233)
PHONE..................................386 253-0105
Pinchas Mamane, *Manager*
EMP: 7 **EST:** 2018
SALES (est): 492.2K **Privately Held**
SIC: 3479 Metal coating & allied service

(G-2620)
ACHIEVIA DIRECT INC
Also Called: Achievia Optical Solutions
1440 N Nova Rd Unit 311 (32117-3245)
PHONE..................................386 615-8708
Matthew T Banker, *President*
Donna Neely, *Representative*
▲ **EMP:** 17 **EST:** 2004
SQ FT: 5,000
SALES (est): 415.8K **Privately Held**
WEB: www.achieviaopticalsolutions.com
SIC: 3851 Ophthalmic goods

(G-2621)
ADSIL INC
1901 Mason Ave Ste 101 (32117-5105)
PHONE..................................386 274-1382
Raymond G Smith, *CEO*
Gordon Miller, *Sales Staff*
EMP: 5 **EST:** 1998
SQ FT: 12,000
SALES (est): 1MM **Privately Held**
WEB: www.mymicroguard.com
SIC: 2851 Paints & allied products

(G-2622)
AEROJET ROCKETDYNE INC
Also Called: 3dmt
790 Fentress Blvd (32114-1214)
PHONE..................................386 626-0001
Eileen Drake, *Principal*
Tyler Evens, *Principal*
Greg Jones, *Principal*
Arjun Kampani, *Principal*
Paul Lundstrom, *Principal*
EMP: 9 **EST:** 1945
SALES (est): 740.1K **Privately Held**
WEB: www.rocket.com
SIC: 3728 Aircraft parts & equipment

(G-2623)
AMERICAN LABEL GROUP INC
705 Fentress Blvd (32114-1213)
PHONE..................................386 274-5234
Timothy K Gleason, *President*
Bill Gall, *General Mgr*
Debbie Fristachi,
EMP: 15 **EST:** 2004
SALES (est): 2.3MM **Privately Held**
WEB: www.americancaregroupinc.com
SIC: 2679 Tags & labels, paper

(G-2624)
AMERICRAFT ENTERPRISES INC
2800 S Nova Rd Ste H3 (32119-6141)
PHONE..................................386 756-1100
Gene Blake, *President*
EMP: 6 **EST:** 1989
SALES (est): 442.9K **Privately Held**
WEB: www.americraftboats.com
SIC: 3732 Boat building & repairing

(G-2625)
AMERITECH ENERGY CORPORATION
1500 Beville Rd Ste 606 (32114-5644)
PHONE..................................386 589-7501
David Wise, *CEO*
Warren Ellis, *Corp Secy*
▲ **EMP:** 10 **EST:** 2014
SALES (est): 2.2MM **Privately Held**
WEB: www.ameritechenergy.com
SIC: 3433 Solar heaters & collectors

(G-2626)
AO PRECISION MANUFACTURING LLC
1870 Mason Ave (32117-5101)
PHONE..................................386 274-5882
Steven C Torma, *CEO*
Stephen Koch, *President*
William Dougherty, *Purchasing*
Micky Selimovic, *Engineer*
EMP: 1 **EST:** 1996
SQ FT: 33,000
SALES (est): 14.1MM **Privately Held**
WEB: www.aopmfg.com
SIC: 3484 3489 Small arms; ordnance & accessories
PA: Juno Investments Llc
950 3rd Ave Ste 2300
New York NY 10022

(G-2627)
AQUASOLVE VENTURES LLC
601 Innovation Way # 115 (32114-3865)
PHONE..................................732 570-0707
Yung Wong, *CEO*
Shavin Pinto,
EMP: 6 **EST:** 2013
SALES (est): 218.4K **Privately Held**
WEB: www.aquasolveventures.com
SIC: 3589 5999 Sewage & water treatment equipment; water purification equipment

(G-2628)
ARC TRANSITION LLC (DH)
Also Called: 3dmt
790 Fentress Blvd (32114-1214)
PHONE..................................386 626-0001
Jason T Young, *Mng Member*
EMP: 9 **EST:** 2013
SQ FT: 28,000
SALES (est): 2.8MM
SALES (corp-wide): 2B **Publicly Held**
WEB: www.rocket.com
SIC: 3544 3441 Special dies, tools, jigs & fixtures; fabricated structural metal
HQ: Aerojet Rocketdyne, Inc.
2001 Aerojet Rd
Rancho Cordova CA 95742
916 355-4000

(G-2629)
ART CRETE PRODUCTS INC
1231 S Ridgewood Ave (32114-6127)
PHONE..................................386 252-5118
Ronald Hopkins, *President*
Carol Hopkins, *Corp Secy*
EMP: 10 **EST:** 1989
SQ FT: 3,000
SALES (est): 947.9K **Privately Held**
WEB: www.discoverdaytona.com
SIC: 3272 5211 Cast stone, concrete; masonry materials & supplies

(G-2630)
ATLANTIC CENTRAL ENTPS INC
336 Lpga Blvd (32117-2820)
PHONE..................................386 255-6227
Steven Traulsen, *President*
EMP: 14 **EST:** 1996
SQ FT: 10,800
SALES (est): 3.3MM **Privately Held**
WEB: www.atlanticcentralsteel.com
SIC: 3441 3499 Fabricated structural metal; friction material, made from powdered metal

(G-2631)
BOBS SPACE RACERS INC
427 Whac A Mole Way (32117-2198)
PHONE..................................386 677-0761
Robert Cassata, *CEO*
John Mendes, *President*
Joyce Cassata, *Vice Pres*
Jack D Cook II, *Vice Pres*
Ron Malinowski, *Vice Pres*
◆ **EMP:** 120
SALES (est): 21.7MM **Privately Held**
WEB: www.bobsspaceracers.com
SIC: 3599 Amusement park equipment

(G-2632)
BRADDOCK METALLURGICAL GA INC
400 Fentress Blvd (32114-1208)
PHONE..................................386 267-0955
William K Braddock, *Principal*
James Turgeon, *QC Mgr*
Dan Bieller, *Manager*
EMP: 18 **EST:** 2011
SALES (est): 2.4MM **Privately Held**
WEB: www.braddockmt.com
SIC: 3398 Metal heat treating

(G-2633)
BRADDOCK METALLURGICAL MGT LLC
400 Fentress Blvd (32114-1208)
PHONE..................................386 267-0955
George Gieger, *President*
Eric Dvorscak, *General Mgr*
Rachell Cameron, *QC Mgr*
Koko Sztajer, *QC Mgr*
EMP: 28 **EST:** 2010
SALES (est): 844.9K **Privately Held**
WEB: www.braddockmt.com
SIC: 3398 Metal heat treating

(G-2634)
BRADDOCK MTLLRGCAL - DYTONA IN
400 Fentress Blvd (32114-1208)
PHONE..................................386 267-0955
David Adam, *CFO*
▲ **EMP:** 1 **EST:** 2008
SALES (est): 4.9MM
SALES (corp-wide): 27.4MM **Privately Held**
WEB: www.braddockmt.com
SIC: 3398 Metal heat treating
HQ: Braddock Metallurgical, Inc.
14600 Duval Pl W
Jacksonville FL 32218
386 267-0955

(G-2635)
BRADDOCK MTLLURGICAL HOLDG INC (PA)
400 Fentress Blvd (32114-1208)
PHONE..................................386 323-1500
Steven R Braddock, *CEO*
EMP: 5 **EST:** 2005
SALES (est): 27.4MM **Privately Held**
WEB: www.braddockmt.com
SIC: 3398 Metal heat treating

(G-2636)
BRENDA NAUSED
2043 S Atlantic Ave (32118-5007)
PHONE..................................352 344-4729
Brenda Naused, *Chairman*
EMP: 6 **EST:** 2016
SALES (est): 114.5K **Privately Held**
SIC: 2392 Household furnishings

(G-2637)
CABINET FACTORY OUTLET
1595 N Nova Rd Ste A (32117-3000)
PHONE..................................386 323-0778
Ron Daniels, *Owner*
EMP: 5 **EST:** 2008
SALES (est): 364K **Privately Held**
WEB: www.cabinetfactoryfl.com
SIC: 2434 Wood kitchen cabinets

(G-2638)
CANAM STEEL CORPORATION
1490 Frances Dr (32124-3605)
PHONE..................................386 252-3730
EMP: 7
SALES (corp-wide): 586.3MM **Privately Held**
WEB: www.cscsteelusa.com
SIC: 3441 Building components, structural steel
PA: Canam Steel Corporation
4010 Clay St
Point Of Rocks MD 21777
301 874-5141

(G-2639)
CARLARON INC
421 Ridgewood Ave (32117-4421)
PHONE..................................386 258-1183
Ronald Cornelius, *President*
Carla Cornelius, *Corp Secy*
EMP: 5 **EST:** 1989
SQ FT: 4,400
SALES (est): 453.3K **Privately Held**
SIC: 3993 7389 7311 5999 Signs & advertising specialties; engraving service; advertising consultant; banners

(G-2640)
CENSYS TECHNOLOGIES CORP
1511 Avi Ctr Pkwy Ste 220 (32114)
PHONE..................................850 321-2278
John Lobdell, *Principal*
EMP: 15 **EST:** 2017
SALES (est): 2.2MM **Privately Held**
WEB: www.censystech.com
SIC: 3728 Target drones

(G-2641)
CENTRAL SIGNS LLC
Also Called: Central Signs, LLC
517 Mason Ave (32117-4811)
PHONE..................................386 322-7446
Charles Hutchershon, *CEO*
Charles H Hutchershon,
EMP: 16 **EST:** 2019
SQ FT: 3,930
SALES (est): 1.8MM **Privately Held**
WEB: www.centralsign.net
SIC: 3993 Electric signs

(G-2642)
CLASSIC MAIL CORP
1027 N Nova Rd Ste 109 (32117-4196)
PHONE..................................386 290-0309
Lynn Vanginhoven, *President*
EMP: 8 **EST:** 2018
SALES (est): 412.2K **Privately Held**
WEB: www.classicmailcorp.com
SIC: 2741 Miscellaneous publishing

▲ = Import ▼=Export
◆ =Import/Export

(G-2643)
COASTLINE WHL SGNS LED DISP LL
532 N Segrave St (32114-2618)
PHONE..................................386 238-6200
Nicholas P Florio,
EMP: 10 **EST:** 2013
SALES (est): 560.7K **Privately Held**
WEB: www.coastlinesign.com
SIC: 3993 Electric signs

(G-2644)
COASTLINE WHL SIGNS SVCS LTD
532 N Segrave St (32114-2618)
PHONE..................................386 238-6200
Dan Florio, *Owner*
Nick Florio, *Manager*
EMP: 10 **EST:** 2005
SALES (est): 803.8K **Privately Held**
WEB: www.coastlinesign.com
SIC: 3993 Electric signs

(G-2645)
COLEO LLC ✪
1198 Champions Dr (32124-2024)
PHONE..................................215 436-0902
Cole Vettraino, *Mng Member*
EMP: 11 **EST:** 2021
SALES (est): 465.7K **Privately Held**
SIC: 2051 Bakery: wholesale or whole-sale/retail combined

(G-2646)
COSTA INC (DH)
Also Called: Costa Del Mar
2361 Mason Ave Ste 100 (32117-5163)
PHONE..................................386 274-4000
Chas Macdonald, *CEO*
Eric Thoreux, *President*
Jeffrey J Giguere, *Exec VP*
Michelle Crockett, *Vice Pres*
Charles S Mellen, *Vice Pres*
◆ **EMP:** 634 **EST:** 1916
SALES (est): 282.9MM
SALES (corp-wide): 1.7MM **Privately Held**
WEB: www.costadelmar.com
SIC: 3851 Glasses, sun or glare
HQ: Fgx International Inc.
500 George Washington Hwy
Smithfield RI 02917
401 231-3800

(G-2647)
COUNTER PRODUCTIONS INC
Also Called: New Kitchen Concepts
1052 N Beach St (32117-5044)
PHONE..................................386 673-6500
Kenneth A Chiaravalle, *President*
Clinton Tiffany, *President*
Kimberly Tiffany, *Vice Pres*
Kenneth Chiaravalle, *Treasurer*
EMP: 7 **EST:** 2016
SALES (est): 509.3K **Privately Held**
SIC: 2434 Vanities, bathroom: wood

(G-2648)
CRENSHAW DIE & MANUFACTURING
100 Zaharias Cir (32124-2038)
PHONE..................................949 475-5505
EMP: 12 **EST:** 2012
SALES (est): 79.3K **Privately Held**
WEB: www.crenshawdiemfg.com
SIC: 3544 Special dies & tools

(G-2649)
CRICKET MINI GOLF CARTS INC
1575 Avi Ctr Pkwy Ste 432 (32114)
PHONE..................................386 220-3536
Michael Hampton, *President*
EMP: 18
SALES (est): 210K **Privately Held**
WEB: www.cricketminigolfcarts.com
SIC: 3799 Golf carts, powered

(G-2650)
CUBCO INC
605 Commercial Dr (32117-3440)
PHONE..................................386 254-2706
Stephen Jenkins, *President*
Mary Ann Mahnke, *Bookkeeper*
EMP: 19 **EST:** 1987
SQ FT: 6,500
SALES (est): 2.7MM **Privately Held**
WEB: www.cubcoinc.com
SIC: 2261 2395 2759 Screen printing of cotton broadwoven fabrics; pleating & stitching; screen printing

(G-2651)
D & R SIGNS INC
133 Thomasson Ave (32117-4822)
P.O. Box 290656, Port Orange (32129-0656)
PHONE..................................386 252-2777
Darrell King, *President*
Robin King, *Admin Sec*
EMP: 8 **EST:** 1990
SQ FT: 7,500
SALES (est): 902.1K **Privately Held**
WEB: www.drsignsinc.com
SIC: 3993 Signs & advertising specialties

(G-2652)
DASOPS INC
2425 Dodge Dr (32118-5332)
PHONE..................................386 258-6230
Jerry D Tyser, *President*
EMP: 6 **EST:** 1978
SALES (est): 353.8K **Privately Held**
SIC: 2732 Pamphlets: printing only, not published on site

(G-2653)
DAYTONA DOCK & SEAWALL SERVICE
Rebonner Machine Works
862 Terrace Ave (32114-5742)
PHONE..................................386 255-7909
William Bonner, *Manager*
EMP: 8
SALES (corp-wide): 1.2MM **Privately Held**
WEB: www.daytonadockandseawall.com
SIC: 3544 Special dies, tools, jigs & fixtures
PA: Daytona Dock & Seawall Service Inc
862 Terrace Ave
Daytona Beach FL 32114
386 255-7909

(G-2654)
DAYTONA GLASS WORKS LLC
843 Bill France Blvd (32117-5110)
P.O. Box 10690 (32120-0690)
PHONE..................................386 274-2550
Mike Tomazin, *Vice Pres*
Mel Mathisen, *Mng Member*
EMP: 13 **EST:** 2014
SALES (est): 1.8MM **Privately Held**
WEB: www.daytonaglass.net
SIC: 3679 Quartz crystals, for electronic application

(G-2655)
DAYTONA MAGIC INC
136 S Beach St (32114-4402)
PHONE..................................386 252-6767
Irving Cook, *President*
Harry Allen Gersh, *Vice Pres*
EMP: 5 **EST:** 1966
SQ FT: 2,000
SALES (est): 470K **Privately Held**
WEB: www.daytonamagic.com
SIC: 3999 5945 5092 3944 Magic equipment, supplies & props; hobbies; amusement goods; games, toys & children's vehicles

(G-2656)
DAYTONA TROPHY INC
2413 Bellevue Ave (32114-5615)
PHONE..................................386 253-2806
Stuart Sarjeant, *President*
Rachel L Sarjeant, *Vice Pres*
Catherine Sarjeant, *Treasurer*
James A Sarjeant, *Admin Sec*
EMP: 15 **EST:** 1970
SQ FT: 5,000
SALES (est): 1.1MM **Privately Held**
WEB: www.daytonatrophy.com
SIC: 2261 5999 3993 Screen printing of cotton broadwoven fabrics; trophies & plaques; signs & advertising specialties

(G-2657)
DAYTONA WELDING & FABRICATION
837 Pinewood St (32117-4573)
P.O. Box 7352 (32116-7352)
PHONE..................................386 562-0093
Michael S Lawhorn Sr, *President*
EMP: 10 **EST:** 2013
SALES (est): 535.2K **Privately Held**
WEB: www.daytonawelding.com
SIC: 3441 Fabricated structural metal

(G-2658)
DECORTIVE ELECTRO COATINGS INC
501 Kingston Ave (32114-2025)
PHONE..................................386 255-7878
William A Cottrell Jr, *CEO*
Jason Alexan, *Vice Pres*
EMP: 14 **EST:** 1999
SALES (est): 431.9K **Privately Held**
WEB: www.thecoater.com
SIC: 3479 Coating of metals & formed products

(G-2659)
DRONE DEFENSE SYSTEMS LLC
172 Gray Dove Ct (32119-1390)
PHONE..................................305 607-6708
Sotirios Kaminis, *Principal*
EMP: 5 **EST:** 2016
SALES (est): 367.6K **Privately Held**
WEB: www.dronedefense.systems
SIC: 3721 Motorized aircraft

(G-2660)
EAST COAST ORNAMENTAL WELDING
1794 State Ave (32117-1748)
PHONE..................................386 672-4340
Terry Howard, *President*
Richard Adjemian, *Vice Pres*
EMP: 15 **EST:** 2003
SQ FT: 5,000
SALES (est): 750K **Privately Held**
WEB: www.eastcoastornamentalwelding.com
SIC: 7692 Welding repair

(G-2661)
EDDY STORM PROTECTION
1000 N Nova Rd (32117-4123)
PHONE..................................386 248-1631
James Eddy, *President*
EMP: 9 **EST:** 2000
SALES (est): 1.3MM **Privately Held**
WEB: www.eddystormprotection.com
SIC: 3442 1799 2591 Shutters, door or window: metal; awning installation; window shades

(G-2662)
ELTEC INSTRUMENTS INC (PA)
350 Fentress Blvd (32114-1235)
P.O. Box 9610 (32120-9610)
PHONE..................................386 252-0411
Samuel D Mollenkof, *President*
Samuel S Mollenkof, *Chairman*
Douglas Armstrong, *Vice Pres*
Darla Jones, *Vice Pres*
Virginia Ungewitter, *Treasurer*
EMP: 42 **EST:** 1969
SALES: 6MM **Privately Held**
WEB: www.eltecinstruments.com
SIC: 3812 3823 Infrared object detection equipment; infrared instruments, industrial process type

(G-2663)
ETERNA URN CO INC
126 Carswell Ave (32117-5010)
PHONE..................................386 258-6491
Allan Hannah, *President*
Deborah Hannah, *Corp Secy*
EMP: 5 **EST:** 1974
SQ FT: 7,500
SALES (est): 440K **Privately Held**
WEB: www.eternaurn.com
SIC: 3281 Urns, cut stone

(G-2664)
FABCO METAL PRODUCTS LLC
1490 Frances Dr (32124-3660)
PHONE..................................386 252-3730
Shane King, *President*
Tracy Thomas, *Vice Pres*
Michael Modica, *Project Mgr*
Mark Smith, *Project Mgr*
Nick Jagos, *Info Tech Mgr*
▲ **EMP:** 75 **EST:** 1983
SQ FT: 75,000
SALES (est): 21.5MM
SALES (corp-wide): 586.3MM **Privately Held**
WEB: www.fabcometal.com
SIC: 3441 Fabricated structural metal
HQ: Fabsouth Llc
721 Ne 44th St
Oakland Park FL 33334
954 938-5800

(G-2665)
FEDERAL HEATH SIGN COMPANY LLC
1128 Beville Rd Ste E (32114-5769)
PHONE..................................817 685-9075
Mark Symcox, *Branch Mgr*
Rene Trappmann, *Program Mgr*
Barry Mix, *Administration*
EMP: 17
SALES (corp-wide): 1.8B **Privately Held**
WEB: www.federalheath.com
SIC: 3993 Signs & advertising specialties
HQ: Federal Heath Sign Company, Llc
2300 St Hwy 121
Euless TX 76039

(G-2666)
FLORIDA GRAPHIC PRINTING INC
503 Mason Ave (32117-4811)
PHONE..................................386 253-4532
Patricia Blythe, *President*
Steve Heiden, *Manager*
EMP: 18 **EST:** 1964
SALES (est): 2.4MM **Privately Held**
WEB: www.floridagraphicprinting.com
SIC: 2752 2791 2789 2759 Commercial printing, offset; typesetting; bookbinding & related work; commercial printing; book printing

(G-2667)
GATERMAN PRODUCTS LLC
114 Meadowbrook Cir (32114-1113)
PHONE..................................386 253-1899
Mike Golding, *Marketing Staff*
William C Gaterman, *Manager*
EMP: 5 **EST:** 2005
SALES (est): 389.6K **Privately Held**
WEB: www.gatermanproducts.com
SIC: 3714 Motor vehicle parts & accessories

(G-2668)
GILLA INC (PA)
475 Fentress Blvd Ste L (32114-1236)
PHONE..................................416 843-2881
Graham Simmonds, *Ch of Bd*
Ashish Kapoor, *CFO*
Daniel Yuranyi,
EMP: 8 **EST:** 1995
SALES: 4.6MM **Privately Held**
WEB: www.gilla.com
SIC: 3999 Cigarette & cigar products & accessories

(G-2669)
GRAPHIC SIGN DSIGN CNTL FLA LL
529 Ridgewood Ave (32117-4423)
PHONE..................................386 547-4569
Keith Cook, *Principal*
EMP: 5 **EST:** 2016
SALES (est): 307.8K **Privately Held**
WEB: www.signsofstone.com
SIC: 3993 Signs & advertising specialties

(G-2670)
HALIFAX MEDIA GROUP LLC (HQ)
2339 Beville Rd (32119-8720)
P.O. Box 11826 (32120-1826)
PHONE..................................386 265-6700
Michael Redding, *CEO*
Rick Martin, *COO*
Bernie Szachara, *Senior VP*
Rob Delaney, *Controller*
James Banttari, *Manager*

GEOGRAPHIC

EMP: 300 **EST:** 2011
SALES (est): 405.6MM
SALES (corp-wide): 3.4B **Publicly Held**
WEB: www.gannett.com
SIC: 2711 Newspapers, publishing & printing
PA: Gannett Co., Inc.
7950 Jones Branch Dr
Mc Lean VA 22102
703 854-6000

(G-2671)
HALIFAX MEDIA HOLDINGS LLC (PA)
901 6th St (32117-3352)
P.O. Box 2831 (32120-2831)
PHONE..................................386 681-2404
Michael Redding, *CEO*
Jackson Farrow Jr, *Manager*
Rupert Phillips, *Manager*
Noel Strauss, *Manager*
EMP: 43 **EST:** 2009
SALES (est): 272.8MM **Privately Held**
SIC: 2791 2711 Typesetting; newspapers, publishing & printing

(G-2672)
HALIFAX PLASTIC INC
Also Called: Southeast Plastics
221 Fentress Blvd (32114-1203)
PHONE..................................386 252-2442
Richard Schwarz, *President*
Stephanie Schwarz, *Treasurer*
◆ **EMP:** 15 **EST:** 1981
SQ FT: 35,000
SALES (est): 2.4MM **Privately Held**
SIC: 2759 Screen printing

(G-2673)
HAMSARD USA INC
2330 S Nova Rd Ste A (32119-2574)
PHONE..................................386 761-1830
Iain Whyte, *President*
EMP: 175 **EST:** 2007
SQ FT: 10,000
SALES (est): 45.9MM
SALES (corp-wide): 381.5K **Privately Held**
SIC: 3272 Bathtubs, concrete
HQ: Hamsard 5037 Limited
Estate House
Redditch WORCS

(G-2674)
HIMGC LIMITED
1301 Beville Rd (32119-9009)
PHONE..................................213 443-8729
EMP: 65
SALES (est): 250K **Privately Held**
SIC: 7372 Application computer software

(G-2675)
JAY SQUARED LLC
Also Called: Daytona Helmets International
1810 Mason Ave (32117-5101)
PHONE..................................386 677-7700
Joseph F Linge, *Principal*
▲ **EMP:** 10 **EST:** 1992
SQ FT: 25,500
SALES (est): 1.1MM **Privately Held**
WEB: www.daytonahelmets.com
SIC: 3949 5571 Helmets, athletic; motorcycle parts & accessories

(G-2676)
KENCO 2000 INC
1539 Garden Ave (32117-2109)
PHONE..................................386 672-1590
Raymond Kenneth Webb, *President*
Molly McLaughlin, *Office Mgr*
EMP: 16 **EST:** 1979
SQ FT: 10,000
SALES (est): 820K **Privately Held**
WEB: www.kenco2000inc.com
SIC: 3993 3444 1799 Electric signs; awnings & canopies; sign installation & maintenance

(G-2677)
KT PROPERTIES & DEV INC
500 Walker St (32117-2681)
PHONE..................................386 253-0610
Gregory B Thompson, *President*
EMP: 10 **EST:** 2010
SALES (est): 262K **Privately Held**
SIC: 3272 Septic tanks, concrete

(G-2678)
L D F SERVICES
1111 State Ave (32117-2700)
PHONE..................................386 947-9256
Danny Funicello, *Principal*
EMP: 18 **EST:** 2001
SQ FT: 2,000
SALES (est): 4.6MM **Privately Held**
SIC: 3444 Sheet metalwork

(G-2679)
LAMINAR FLOW SYSTEMS INC
1585 Avi Ctr Pkwy Ste 605 (32114)
PHONE..................................386 253-8833
Robin Thomas, *President*
Sandy Norton, *Accountant*
EMP: 10 **EST:** 1996
SALES (est): 1.2MM **Privately Held**
WEB: www.laminarflowsystems.com
SIC: 3728 Aircraft parts & equipment

(G-2680)
LARSON-BURTON INCORPORATED
1010 N Nova Rd (32117-4123)
PHONE..................................815 637-9500
Jeffrey J Larson, *President*
Dave Burton, *Vice Pres*
EMP: 12 **EST:** 1998
SQ FT: 15,200
SALES (est): 2.1MM **Privately Held**
WEB: www.larsonburton.com
SIC: 3599 Custom machinery

(G-2681)
M & M ENTERPRISES DAYTONA LLC (PA)
1502 State Ave (32117-2229)
PHONE..................................386 672-1554
John Butterfield, *Mng Member*
Christyna Lynch,
▲ **EMP:** 5 **EST:** 1971
SQ FT: 8,000
SALES (est): 733.7K **Privately Held**
WEB: www.mandmenterprisesofdaytona.com
SIC: 2431 Moldings, wood: unfinished & prefinished

(G-2682)
MAITLAND FURNITURE INC
1711 State Ave (32117-1792)
P.O. Box 9787 (32120-9787)
PHONE..................................386 677-7711
EMP: 5
SALES (est): 380K **Privately Held**
SIC: 3949 Mfg Gaming Furniture

(G-2683)
MAT-VAC TECHNOLOGY INC
410 Arroyo Ln (32114-4808)
PHONE..................................386 238-7017
EMP: 10
SQ FT: 40,000
SALES (est): 2MM **Privately Held**
SIC: 3563 5065 7699 3675 Mfg Air/Gas Compressors Whol Electronic Parts Repair Services Mfg Electronic Capacitor

(G-2684)
MICRO AUDIOMETRICS CORPORATION
1901 Mason Ave Ste 104 (32117-5105)
PHONE..................................828 644-0771
Jason Keller, *President*
James Keller, *Vice Pres*
Monica Keller, *Treasurer*
Kathleen Keller, *Admin Sec*
▲ **EMP:** 9 **EST:** 1980
SALES (est): 1.4MM **Privately Held**
WEB: www.earscan.com
SIC: 3845 8711 Audiological equipment, electromedical; engineering services

(G-2685)
MICROGUARD
1901 Mason Ave (32117-5123)
PHONE..................................386 274-1382
EMP: 6 **EST:** 2018
SALES (est): 311.2K **Privately Held**
WEB: www.mymicroguard.com
SIC: 2851 Paints & allied products

(G-2686)
MID-FLORIDA SPORTSWEAR LLC
2415 Bellevue Ave (32114-5615)
PHONE..................................386 258-5632
John Koberg, *President*
Ken Bender, *Vice Pres*
Kenneth Bender, *Vice Pres*
James J Gallagher, *Vice Pres*
Lisa Henson, *Sales Associate*
EMP: 20 **EST:** 1977
SQ FT: 8,000
SALES (est): 3.1MM **Privately Held**
WEB: www.mfswear.com
SIC: 2261 2395 Screen printing of cotton broadwoven fabrics; embroidery & art needlework

(G-2687)
MILLER-LEAMAN INC
800 Orange Ave (32114-4730)
PHONE..................................386 248-0500
Martin Shuster, *President*
Chris Shuster, *Vice Pres*
Judy Letsinger, *Purchasing*
Dave Petrozza, *Electrical Engi*
Robert Leman, *CFO*
▲ **EMP:** 32 **EST:** 1991
SQ FT: 52,000
SALES (est): 7MM **Privately Held**
WEB: www.millerleaman.com
SIC: 3441 Fabricated structural metal

(G-2688)
MINUTEMAN PRESS
201 N Ridgewood Ave (32114-3243)
PHONE..................................386 255-2767
Patrik Franceschi, *Manager*
Trish Carney, *Graphic Designe*
Chrisa Graphics, *Graphic Designe*
EMP: 10 **EST:** 2015
SALES (est): 231.7K **Privately Held**
WEB: www.minutemanpress.com
SIC: 2752 2759 Commercial printing, lithographic; commercial printing

(G-2689)
MOSSBERG GROUP INC
1870 Mason Ave (32117-5101)
PHONE..................................386 274-5882
Johnathan Mossberg, *President*
EMP: 11 **EST:** 2000
SQ FT: 33,000
SALES (est): 416.4K **Privately Held**
WEB: www.iguntechnology.com
SIC: 3484 Small arms

(G-2690)
NEWS-JOURNAL CORPORATION (PA)
Also Called: New Smyrna Daily Journal
901 6th St (32117-8099)
P.O. Box 2831 (32120-2831)
PHONE..................................386 252-1511
Herbert M Davidson Jr, *President*
Georgia M Kaney, *Vice Pres*
David R Kendall, *Vice Pres*
Marc L Davidson, *Treasurer*
Forrest Scot, *Advt Staff*
▲ **EMP:** 800 **EST:** 1927
SQ FT: 300,000
SALES (est): 68.8MM **Privately Held**
WEB: www.news-journalonline.com
SIC: 2711 Newspapers, publishing & printing

(G-2691)
P & L CREECH INC
Also Called: Godawa Septic Tank Service
2960 S Nova Rd (32119-6106)
PHONE..................................386 547-4182
Paul Creech, *President*
Linda Lee Creech, *Vice Pres*
EMP: 6 **EST:** 1947
SQ FT: 2,000
SALES (est): 1.1MM **Privately Held**
SIC: 3089 7359 7699 Septic tanks, plastic; portable toilet rental; septic tank cleaning service

(G-2692)
PAPER PUSHERS OF AMERICA INC
2430 S Atlantic Ave Ste C (32118-5419)
PHONE..................................386 872-7025
Nathaly Encarnacion, *President*
EMP: 6 **EST:** 2019
SALES (est): 83.9K **Privately Held**
SIC: 2752 Commercial printing, lithographic

(G-2693)
PAVEMAX
1120 Enterprise Ct (32117-2692)
PHONE..................................386 206-3113
Doug Cefalo, *Business Mgr*
EMP: 7 **EST:** 2018
SALES (est): 210K **Privately Held**
WEB: www.pavemax.com
SIC: 2951 Asphalt paving mixtures & blocks

(G-2694)
PIP PRINTING
133 W Intl Speedway Blvd (32114)
PHONE..................................386 258-3326
EMP: 8 **EST:** 2012
SALES (est): 131.9K **Privately Held**
WEB: www.pip.com
SIC: 2752 Commercial printing, offset

(G-2695)
POUCHFILL PACKAGING LLC
811 Fentress Ct (32117-5152)
PHONE..................................386 274-1600
Masahiko Tatewaki, *CEO*
Klaus Liedtke, *President*
Packy Bannevans, *Exec VP*
EMP: 15 **EST:** 2017
SALES (est): 2.2MM **Privately Held**
WEB: www.pouchfillpkg.com
SIC: 2087 Flavoring extracts & syrups

(G-2696)
POWER FLOW SYSTEMS INC
795 Fentress Blvd Ste A (32114-1251)
PHONE..................................386 253-8833
Darren Tilman, *President*
Robin Thomas, *President*
EMP: 10 **EST:** 1997
SQ FT: 6,000
SALES (est): 1.6MM **Privately Held**
WEB: www.powerflowsystems.com
SIC: 3728 Aircraft parts & equipment

(G-2697)
PRECISION PRESS LLC
3 Oak Glen Dr (32119-4451)
PHONE..................................386 872-1639
Michelle Stevens, *Owner*
EMP: 6 **EST:** 2012
SALES (est): 122.6K **Privately Held**
SIC: 2741 Miscellaneous publishing

(G-2698)
PRINT ART SCREEN PRINTING INC
340 Marion St (32114-4834)
PHONE..................................386 258-5186
Okan Avcilar, *President*
Cenk Isjener, *Vice Pres*
EMP: 12 **EST:** 2003
SQ FT: 8,000
SALES (est): 2.1MM **Privately Held**
WEB: www.printartdaytona.com
SIC: 2759 2395 Screen printing; embroidery & art needlework

(G-2699)
PRINTING DEPARTMENT LLC
176 Carswell Ave (32117-5010)
PHONE..................................386 253-7990
David Doak, *Principal*
EMP: 7 **EST:** 2019
SALES (est): 350.7K **Privately Held**
WEB: www.tpdflorida.com
SIC: 2752 Commercial printing, lithographic

(G-2700)
PROFESSIONAL SITE & TRNSPT INC
3728 W Intl Spwy Blvd (32124-1030)
PHONE..................................386 239-6800
Christopher R Linsley, *President*
Colette M Linsley, *Vice Pres*
EMP: 10 **EST:** 2000
SQ FT: 500
SALES (est): 1.3MM **Privately Held**
SIC: 1442 Construction sand & gravel

▲ = Import ▼=Export
◆ =Import/Export

(G-2701)
QUALITY PRINTING INC
Also Called: Speedway Press
705 W Intl Speedway Blvd (32114)
PHONE..................................386 255-1565
Craig Solomon, *President*
EMP: 5 **EST:** 1980
SALES (est): 489.3K **Privately Held**
WEB:
www.speedwaypress.ecardbuilder.com
SIC: 2752 Commercial printing, offset

(G-2702)
RANDEL L RDRIGUEZ COATINGS LLC
1227 David Dr (32117-3041)
PHONE..................................386 308-8120
Randel L Rodriguez II,
EMP: 6 **EST:** 2016
SALES (est): 114K **Privately Held**
SIC: 2952 Asphalt felts & coatings

(G-2703)
REPORGRAPHICS UNLIMITED INC
124 Bay St (32114-3234)
PHONE..................................386 253-7990
Ronnie Hames Jr, *President*
EMP: 9 **EST:** 1997
SQ FT: 1,400
SALES (est): 773.6K **Privately Held**
SIC: 2759 Commercial printing

(G-2704)
REX FOX ENTERPRISES INC
Also Called: Fox Furniture
1966 N Nova Rd (32117-1442)
PHONE..................................386 677-3752
Rex A Fox, *President*
Rick Carter, *Treasurer*
EMP: 11 **EST:** 1968
SQ FT: 18,000
SALES (est): 1.5MM **Privately Held**
WEB: www.foxmattress.com
SIC: 2515 5712 Mattresses & foundations; furniture stores; mattresses

(G-2705)
ROSIER MANUFACTURING COMPANY
409 W Intl Speedway Blvd (32114)
P.O. Box 388, Edgewater (32132-0388)
PHONE..................................386 409-7223
Brian Rossiter, *Owner*
Holly Kreitz, *Admin Sec*
EMP: 5 **EST:** 1995
SQ FT: 4,420
SALES (est): 417.4K **Privately Held**
WEB: www.lightninglight.com
SIC: 3089 Plastics products

(G-2706)
ROSSITER MANUFACTURING
409 W Intl Speedway Blvd (32114)
PHONE..................................386 409-7223
Aaron Chasse, *Manager*
EMP: 6 **EST:** 2010
SALES (est): 186K **Privately Held**
SIC: 3999 3296 Manufacturing industries; fiberglass insulation

(G-2707)
S & B METAL PRODUCTS E FLA INC
1811 Holsonback Dr (32117-5113)
PHONE..................................386 274-0092
Steven Campbell, *President*
Lisa Rispoli, *Office Mgr*
Keene Hutchinson, *Manager*
EMP: 36 **EST:** 2007
SALES (est): 5.1MM **Privately Held**
SIC: 3441 Fabricated structural metal

(G-2708)
SCCY INDUSTRIES LLC
Also Called: Sccy Firearms
1800 Concept Ct (32114-1259)
PHONE..................................386 322-6336
Joseph V Roebuck, *CEO*
Beau Hickman, *COO*
Andrew Baez, *Prdtn Mgr*
Nick Tucker, *Opers Staff*
Janine Edwards, *Purchasing*
▲ **EMP:** 147
SQ FT: 5,000
SALES (est): 26.6MM **Privately Held**
WEB: www.sccy.com
SIC: 3484 Guns (firearms) or gun parts, 30 mm. & below

(G-2709)
SCHNEIDDER INDUSTRIES LLC
1690 Dunn Ave Apt 408 (32114-1475)
PHONE..................................850 207-0929
Samuel Quinones, *Principal*
EMP: 6 **EST:** 2014
SALES (est): 105.5K **Privately Held**
WEB: www.schneider.com
SIC: 3999 Manufacturing industries

(G-2710)
SEASIDE ALUMINUM LLC
817 Swift St Ste 130 (32114-2051)
PHONE..................................386 252-4940
Bonnie Bannister, *Mng Member*
EMP: 12 **EST:** 2005
SALES (est): 1.1MM **Privately Held**
SIC: 3441 Fabricated structural metal

(G-2711)
SEE COASTAL MEDIA LLC
404 S Beach St (32114-5036)
P.O. Box 1924 (32115-1924)
PHONE..................................386 562-2213
Debra Smith,
EMP: 6 **EST:** 2009
SALES (est): 123.1K **Privately Held**
WEB: www.daytonabeach.com
SIC: 2721 Magazines: publishing only, not printed on site

(G-2712)
SENSATEK PROPULSION TECH INC
1 Aerospace Blvd (32114-3910)
PHONE..................................850 321-5993
Reamonn Soto, *CEO*
EMP: 10 **EST:** 2016
SALES (est): 1.3MM **Privately Held**
WEB: www.sensatek.com
SIC: 3764 8731 Guided missile & space vehicle propulsion unit parts; commercial physical research

(G-2713)
SHELTAIR DAYTONA BEACH LLC
Also Called: Daytona Beach Jet Center
561 Pearl Harbor Dr (32114-3845)
PHONE..................................386 255-0471
Gerald Holland,
EMP: 31 **EST:** 1988
SQ FT: 75,000
SALES (est): 1.8MM **Privately Held**
WEB: www.daytonabeach.com
SIC: 2911 Jet fuels

(G-2714)
SHOWCASE MARBLE INC
Also Called: Marble Crafters
405 6th St (32117-4305)
PHONE..................................386 253-6646
Richard C Maugeri, *President*
EMP: 17 **EST:** 1988
SQ FT: 60,000
SALES (est): 1MM **Privately Held**
SIC: 3281 3949 2434 Marble, building: cut & shaped; sporting & athletic goods; wood kitchen cabinets

(G-2715)
SIGNS NOW
1440 N Nova Rd Ste 308 (32117-3245)
PHONE..................................386 238-5507
Nancy Thompson, *Principal*
EMP: 5 **EST:** 2011
SALES (est): 303K **Privately Held**
WEB: www.signsnow.com
SIC: 3993 Signs & advertising specialties

(G-2716)
SOUTHEASTERN LTG SOLUTIONS
821 Fentress Ct (32117-5152)
PHONE..................................386 238-1711
Walton M Cox, *Principal*
EMP: 23 **EST:** 2003
SALES (est): 1.2MM **Privately Held**
WEB: www.selightingsolutions.com
SIC: 3993 Signs & advertising specialties

(G-2717)
SOUTHEASTERN TRUCK TOPS INC
402 6th St (32117-4306)
PHONE..................................386 761-0002
Bill Varnadore, *President*
Sharon Varnadore, *Admin Sec*
EMP: 15 **EST:** 1975
SQ FT: 7,496
SALES (est): 2MM **Privately Held**
WEB: www.southeasterntrucktops.com
SIC: 3713 3792 Truck tops; travel trailers & campers

(G-2718)
SPACE COAST DISTRIBUTORS
726 N Segrave St (32114-2020)
PHONE..................................386 239-0305
Ted Bondjuk, *Owner*
EMP: 6 **EST:** 2007
SALES (est): 439.7K **Privately Held**
SIC: 3052 Rubber hose

(G-2719)
STOVER MANUFACTURING LLC
825 Ballough Rd (32114-2256)
PHONE..................................386 238-3775
Burnett R Random, *Principal*
EMP: 7 **EST:** 2012
SALES (est): 59.2K **Privately Held**
SIC: 3999 Manufacturing industries

(G-2720)
STRASSER ENTERPRISES
1504 State Ave (32117-2262)
PHONE..................................386 677-5163
Drew Strasser, *Principal*
EMP: 8 **EST:** 2008
SALES (est): 314.9K **Privately Held**
SIC: 2499 Decorative wood & woodwork

(G-2721)
SUNCOAST HEAT TREAT INC
400 Fentress Blvd (32114-1208)
PHONE..................................386 267-0955
Bruce Sobleski, *Manager*
EMP: 17
SALES (corp-wide): 4.8MM **Privately Held**
SIC: 3398 Metal heat treating
PA: Suncoast Heat Treat, Inc.
507 Industrial Way
Boynton Beach FL 33426
561 776-7763

(G-2722)
TECHNETICS GROUP DAYTONA INC (HQ)
305 Fentress Blvd (32114-1205)
PHONE..................................386 253-0628
Gilles Hudon, *President*
Robert P McKinney, *Vice Pres*
Robert S McLean, *Vice Pres*
Yaakov Abudaram, *Design Engr*
David S Burnett, *Treasurer*
EMP: 138 **EST:** 2006
SQ FT: 59,172
SALES (est): 104.6MM
SALES (corp-wide): 1B **Publicly Held**
WEB: www.enproindustries.com
SIC: 3577 Computer peripheral equipment
PA: Enpro Industries, Inc.
5605 Carnegie Blvd # 500
Charlotte NC 28209
704 731-1500

(G-2723)
TECHNO-SPA MANUFACTURING INC (PA)
Also Called: Cosmo Pro
320 Fentress Blvd (32114-1206)
PHONE..................................386 239-8980
Philippe Hennessy, *President*
◆ **EMP:** 6 **EST:** 1996
SALES (est): 779.8K **Privately Held**
WEB: www.spazonepro.com
SIC: 3999 Hot tubs

(G-2724)
TEL-TRON TECHNOLOGIES CORP (PA)
Also Called: Silversphere Holdings
2570 W Intl Spwy Blvd # 200 (32114-8145)
PHONE..................................386 523-1070
Brian Dawson, *CEO*
Dawson N Rick, *Chairman*
Melinda D Dawson, *Vice Pres*
Rick Taylor, *Vice Pres*
Brian Pabst, *Engineer*
EMP: 50 **EST:** 1945
SALES (est): 11.9MM **Privately Held**
WEB: www.tel-tron.com
SIC: 3625 Control equipment, electric

(G-2725)
TELEDYNE INSTRUMENTS INC
Also Called: Teledyne Odi
1026 N Williamson Blvd (32114-7113)
PHONE..................................386 236-0780
Francis Dunne, *Vice Pres*
Jason Kordek, *Vice Pres*
Debra Holtzman, *Project Mgr*
Patricier Tucker, *Buyer*
Adrian Cheung, *Engineer*
EMP: 250
SALES (corp-wide): 3B **Publicly Held**
WEB: www.teledyne.com
SIC: 3678 Electronic connectors
HQ: Teledyne Instruments, Inc.
16830 Chestnut St
City Of Industry CA 91748
626 934-1500

(G-2726)
THREE BROTHERS BOARDS
212 S Beach St Ste 100 (32114-4403)
PHONE..................................386 310-4927
Roger Murray Jr, *Principal*
▼ **EMP:** 8 **EST:** 2010
SALES (est): 239K **Privately Held**
WEB: www.threebrothersboards.com
SIC: 2499 Oars & paddles, wood

(G-2727)
TIFFANY AND ASSOCIATES INC
Also Called: Independent Printing
500 Mason Ave (32117-4812)
PHONE..................................386 252-7351
Garry L Tiffany, *President*
▼ **EMP:** 27 **EST:** 1943
SQ FT: 10,000
SALES (est): 8.9MM **Privately Held**
WEB: www.printingdaytonabeach.com
SIC: 2752 Lithographing on metal

(G-2728)
TIP TOP PRTG OF VOLUSIA CNTY
1325 Beville Rd (32119-1529)
P.O. Box 1550 (32115-1550)
PHONE..................................386 760-7701
Henry C Winchester Jr, *President*
Bruce Negro, *Business Mgr*
EMP: 6 **EST:** 1961
SALES (est): 624.1K **Privately Held**
WEB: www.tiptopprinting.com
SIC: 2752 7331 5199 Commercial printing, offset; direct mail advertising services; advertising specialties

(G-2729)
UNION ENGINEERING N AMER LLC
Also Called: Pentair Union Engineering N.A.
2361 Mason Ave Ste 100 (32117-5163)
PHONE..................................386 225-4952
Heidi Jorgensen, *Mng Member*
Kimberle Marquardt, *Officer*
◆ **EMP:** 15 **EST:** 1874
SQ FT: 6,000
SALES (est): 4.4MM **Privately Held**
WEB: www.union.dk
SIC: 3569 3556 Gas producers (machinery); brewers' & maltsters' machinery
PA: Pentair Public Limited Company
10 Earlsfort Terrace
Dublin

(G-2730)
V I P PRINTING
133 W Intl Speedway Blvd (32114)
PHONE..................................386 258-3326
William Raymond, *Owner*
Angela Raymond-Jones, *Products*
EMP: 7 **EST:** 1976
SQ FT: 1,000
SALES (est): 750K **Privately Held**
WEB: www.vipprinting.net
SIC: 2752 2791 2789 Commercial printing, offset; typesetting; bookbinding & related work

GEOGRAPHIC

(G-2731)
VALUE PROVIDERS LLC
2441 Bellevue Ave (32114-5615)
P.O. Box 411985, Melbourne (32941-1985)
PHONE..................................321 567-0919
Marc McCoy, *Manager*
EMP: 6 **EST:** 2013
SALES (est): 157.2K **Privately Held**
SIC: 3317 Steel pipe & tubes

(G-2732)
WHITE LABEL LIQUID INC
210 Sentress Blvd (32114)
PHONE..................................386 256-1826
Yaron Elkayan, *CEO*
Carmen Camacho, *Administration*
EMP: 40 **EST:** 2015
SQ FT: 50,000
SALES (est): 4.6MM **Privately Held**
SIC: 3565 Labeling machines, industrial

(G-2733)
WRIGHT PRINTERY INC
735 N Ridgewood Ave (32114-2015)
PHONE..................................386 252-6571
Kim Barker, *President*
Peter Barker, *Vice Pres*
EMP: 5 **EST:** 1927
SQ FT: 1,200
SALES (est): 442.5K **Privately Held**
WEB: www.wrightprintery.com
SIC: 2752 Commercial printing, offset

De Land
Volusia County

(G-2734)
TECHNETICS GROUP LLC
Also Called: Technetics Group Deland
1700 E Intl Speedway Blvd (32724)
PHONE..................................386 736-7373
Chris Surdo, *Vice Pres*
Jeremy Lawrence, *Engineer*
James Boyd, *Branch Mgr*
Tony Eldridge, *Manager*
William Harklerode, *Supervisor*
EMP: 20
SALES (corp-wide): 1B **Publicly Held**
WEB: www.technetics.com
SIC: 3053 3351 Gaskets & sealing devices; copper rolling & drawing
HQ: Technetics Group Llc
5605 Carnegie Blvd # 500
Charlotte NC 28209
704 731-1500

De Leon Springs
Volusia County

(G-2735)
AL-MAR METALS INC
Also Called: Metal Fabricators
1725 Arredondo Grant Rd (32130-3728)
PHONE..................................386 734-3377
Roy Blomquist, *President*
Cynthia Blomquist, *Principal*
Jeremy Blomquist, *Principal*
James Rhodes, *Principal*
EMP: 6 **EST:** 1995
SALES (est): 759.6K **Privately Held**
WEB: www.almarmetals.net
SIC: 3441 Fabricated structural metal

(G-2736)
ALUMINUM CREATIONS
155 Dawson Brown Rd (32130-3526)
PHONE..................................386 451-0113
N Leon Jones, *Principal*
EMP: 12 **EST:** 2001
SALES (est): 506K **Privately Held**
SIC: 3448 Screen enclosures

(G-2737)
ARCO GLOBAS TRADING LLC
Also Called: Arco Globas International
6111 Lake Winona Rd (32130-3544)
PHONE..................................305 707-7702
Abe Citron, *CEO*
Albert Citron, *Vice Pres*
EMP: 28 **EST:** 2012
SQ FT: 12,000
SALES (est): 1.1MM **Privately Held**
SIC: 2085 Cordials & premixed alcoholic cocktails

(G-2738)
EO PAINTER PRINTING COMPANY
4900 Us Highway 17 (32130-3199)
P.O. Box 877 (32130-0877)
PHONE..................................386 985-4877
Sidney Johnston, *President*
Jeff Johnston, *Vice Pres*
Mark Johnston, *Treasurer*
EMP: 10 **EST:** 1878
SALES (est): 885.1K **Privately Held**
WEB: www.eopainterprinting.com
SIC: 2752 Commercial printing, offset

(G-2739)
ERAPSCO
C 0 5612 Johnson Lake Rd (32130)
PHONE..................................386 740-5335
Lynne Moritz, *Principal*
EMP: 9 **EST:** 2014
SALES (est): 121.6K **Privately Held**
SIC: 3812 Sonar systems & equipment

(G-2740)
PARRISH INC
5498 Aragon Ave (32130-3426)
P.O. Box 1127 (32130-1127)
PHONE..................................386 985-4879
Wesley Parrish, *President*
EMP: 7 **EST:** 1994
SALES (est): 400K **Privately Held**
WEB: www.parrishshadetop.com
SIC: 3444 Awnings & canopies

(G-2741)
SDR SPECIALTIES SERVICES LLC
4511n Us Highway 17 (32130-4302)
P.O. Box 533 (32130-0533)
PHONE..................................386 878-6771
Richard D Slanker,
EMP: 7 **EST:** 2012
SALES (est): 388.3K **Privately Held**
WEB: www.sdrspecialtiesservice.com
SIC: 7692 7699 Welding repair; nautical repair services

(G-2742)
SPARTON CORPORATION (DH)
5612 Johnson Lake Rd (32130-3657)
PHONE..................................847 762-5800
Joseph McCormack, *CEO*
Steven Korwin, *Senior VP*
Gordon Madlock, *Senior VP*
Michael A Gaul, *Vice Pres*
James M Lackemacher, *Vice Pres*
▲ **EMP:** 177 **EST:** 1900
SQ FT: 22,000
SALES (est): 570.9MM
SALES (corp-wide): 4.6B **Privately Held**
WEB: www.sparton.com
SIC: 3672 Printed circuit boards

(G-2743)
SPARTON DELEON SPRINGS LLC (DH)
5612 Johnson Lake Rd (32130-3657)
PHONE..................................386 985-4631
Cary B Wood,
Steve M Korwin,
Michael W Osbourne,
Martin Reilly,
Mark Schlei,
▲ **EMP:** 100 **EST:** 1966
SQ FT: 186,000
SALES (est): 26.1MM
SALES (corp-wide): 4.6B **Privately Held**
WEB: www.sparton.com
SIC: 3812 3679 3672 Warfare counter-measure equipment; electronic circuits; printed circuit boards
HQ: Sparton Corporation
5612 Johnson Lake Rd
De Leon Springs FL 32130
847 762-5800

Debary
Volusia County

(G-2744)
ANEW INC
32 Cunningham Rd (32713-3168)
PHONE..................................386 668-7785
David Chapman, *President*
Cindy Connolly, *Marketing Staff*
EMP: 9 **EST:** 1999
SALES (est): 270K **Privately Held**
WEB: www.anewinc.com
SIC: 3841 Medical instruments & equipment, blood & bone work

(G-2745)
ANEW INTERNATIONAL CORPORATION
32 Cunningham Rd (32713-3168)
PHONE..................................386 668-7785
David Chapman, *President*
EMP: 8 **EST:** 1999
SALES (est): 97.8K **Privately Held**
WEB: www.1899267.uscompaniesdata.com
SIC: 3841 Surgical & medical instruments

(G-2746)
COR LABEL LLC ✪
901 S Chrles Rchard Ball (32713-9793)
PHONE..................................407 402-6633
Bryan G Dolbow,
EMP: 5 **EST:** 2020
SALES (est): 442.5K **Privately Held**
WEB: www.corlabel.com
SIC: 2759 Commercial printing

(G-2747)
CORNERSTONE FABRICATION LLC
291 Sprngview Commerce Dr (32713-4838)
PHONE..................................386 310-1110
Jim Hedger Jr, *Mng Member*
Kristine Hedger, *Manager*
EMP: 22 **EST:** 1998
SQ FT: 70,000
SALES (est): 9.2MM **Privately Held**
WEB: www.cornerstonefabrication.com
SIC: 3441 3444 Fabricated structural metal; sheet metal specialties, not stamped

(G-2748)
DYNAMIC ASPECTS INC
108 Fox Chase Ct (32713-4107)
PHONE..................................407 322-1923
James Abbott, *Principal*
Grace Grant, *Manager*
EMP: 8 **EST:** 2004
SALES (est): 418.8K **Privately Held**
WEB: www.dynamicaspects.net
SIC: 3993 1799 Signs & advertising specialties; sign installation & maintenance

(G-2749)
HILOMAST LLC
402 Chairman Ct Ste 100 (32713-4846)
PHONE..................................386 668-6784
Bruce Sousa, *Principal*
Joe Ostermann, *Engineer*
Barry Gardner,
▲ **EMP:** 6 **EST:** 2003
SALES (est): 2.3MM
SALES (corp-wide): 5.1MM **Privately Held**
WEB: www.hilomast.com
SIC: 3663 Radio & TV communications equipment
PA: South Midlands Communications Limited
School Close Chandlers Ford Industrial Estate
Eastleigh HANTS SO53
238 024-6200

(G-2750)
HOFFMAN BROTHERS INC
Also Called: Browning Communications
275 S Chrles Rchard Ball (32713-3718)
PHONE..................................407 563-5004
Dean W O'Brien, *President*
EMP: 21 **EST:** 1985
SQ FT: 13,500
SALES (est): 734.7K **Privately Held**
SIC: 2752 Commercial printing, offset

(G-2751)
MASCHMEYER CONCRETE CO FLA
275 Benson Junction Rd (32713-9789)
PHONE..................................386 668-7801
Richard King, *Branch Mgr*
EMP: 15
SALES (corp-wide): 136.2MM **Privately Held**
WEB: www.maschmeyer.com
SIC: 3273 Ready-mixed concrete
PA: Maschmeyer Concrete Company Of Florida
1142 Watertower Rd
Lake Park FL 33403
561 848-9112

(G-2752)
MICRON FIBER - TECH INC
230 Sprngview Commerce Dr (32713-4853)
PHONE..................................386 668-7895
Lixion Lu, *President*
Ning Jiang, *Vice Pres*
▲ **EMP:** 15 **EST:** 2001
SALES: 2.7MM **Privately Held**
WEB: www.mft-co.com
SIC: 3433 Gas burners, industrial

(G-2753)
PALM LABS ADHESIVES LLC
3063 Enterprise Rd Ste 31 (32713-2715)
PHONE..................................321 710-4850
Roger A Szafranski,
EMP: 10 **EST:** 2014
SALES (est): 896.2K **Privately Held**
WEB: www.palmlabsadhesives.com
SIC: 2891 Adhesives

(G-2754)
RIVER CITY POWERSPORTS LLC
895 Diplomat Dr Unit E (32713-5204)
PHONE..................................386 259-5724
Clint J Furrow, *Principal*
EMP: 7 **EST:** 2011
SALES (est): 289.5K **Privately Held**
WEB: www.rivercitypowersports.com
SIC: 3799 All terrain vehicles (ATV)

(G-2755)
SIGNALVAULT LLC
156 S Charles Richard Bea (32713-3273)
PHONE..................................407 878-6365
Christopher N Gilpin, *Principal*
EMP: 5 **EST:** 2015
SALES (est): 370.6K **Privately Held**
WEB: www.signal-vault.com
SIC: 3699 Security devices

(G-2756)
SPECIALTY STRUCTURES INC
Also Called: Specilty Strctres Instllations
218 Plumosa Rd (32713-3944)
PHONE..................................386 668-0474
Bernd Rennebeck, *President*
Hernan Naya, *Foreman/Supr*
EMP: 10 **EST:** 2011
SALES (est): 1.6MM **Privately Held**
WEB: www.specialty-structures.com
SIC: 3441 Fabricated structural metal

(G-2757)
WHITE SIGN COMPANY LLC
909 S Chrles R Beall Blvd (32713)
PHONE..................................386 516-6156
Joel White, *Principal*
EMP: 6
SALES (est): 177.6K **Privately Held**
WEB: www.whitesigncompany.com
SIC: 3993 Signs & advertising specialties

(G-2758)
WHITE SIGN COMPANY LLC
909 S Charles Richard Bea (32713-9708)
PHONE..................................407 342-7887
Joel White, *Mng Member*
EMP: 5 **EST:** 2007
SQ FT: 8,000

SALES (est): 500K **Privately Held**
WEB: www.whitesigncompany.com
SIC: 3993 Signs & advertising specialties

Deerfield Beach
Broward County

(G-2759)
681 SEAFOOD & SOUTHERN BITES
681 Sw 14th Ct (33441-6437)
PHONE..................................954 573-7320
Juerica Overstreet, *Principal*
EMP: 6 **EST:** 2018
SALES (est): 196.8K **Privately Held**
WEB: www.681-seafood-southern-bites.business.site
SIC: 2092 Fresh or frozen packaged fish

(G-2760)
905 EAST HILLSBORO LLC
Also Called: Aesthetic Mobile Laser Svcs
905 E Hillsboro Blvd (33441-3523)
PHONE..................................954 480-2600
Paul J Miano, *Mng Member*
EMP: 10 **EST:** 2005
SALES (est): 798.9K **Privately Held**
WEB: www.aestheticmobilelaser.com
SIC: 3699 Laser systems & equipment

(G-2761)
AAA STEEL FABRICATORS INC
1669 Sw 45th Way (33442-9003)
PHONE..................................954 570-7211
Thomas Juliano, *President*
Gary Sheriff, *Vice Pres*
EMP: 6 **EST:** 1999
SQ FT: 7,500
SALES (est): 975.4K **Privately Held**
WEB: www.aaasteelfabricators.com
SIC: 3441 Fabricated structural metal

(G-2762)
ACCUPRINT CORPORATION
Also Called: My Print Shop
1061 Sw 30th Ave (33442-8104)
PHONE..................................954 973-9369
Jeff Pottruck, *President*
Carol Mariano, *Manager*
EMP: 11 **EST:** 1988
SQ FT: 2,200
SALES (est): 373.2K **Privately Held**
WEB: www.accuprint.us
SIC: 2752 Commercial printing, offset

(G-2763)
ACCUPRINT MY PRINT SHOP
1061 Sw 30th Ave (33442-8104)
PHONE..................................954 973-9369
Jeffery Pottruck, *Owner*
EMP: 8 **EST:** 1980
SALES (est): 155.7K **Privately Held**
WEB: www.myprintshop.com
SIC: 2759 2752 Screen printing; commercial printing, lithographic

(G-2764)
ADVANCED HAIR PRODUCTS INC
1287 E Nwport Ctr Dr Ste (33442)
PHONE..................................561 347-2799
Carmine Gazero, *CEO*
▲ **EMP:** 8 **EST:** 1990
SQ FT: 2,800
SALES (est): 655.1K **Privately Held**
WEB: www.innovativehair.com
SIC: 3999 Wigs, including doll wigs, toupees or wiglets

(G-2765)
ADVANCED OUTDOOR CONCEPTS INC
Also Called: Cobb America
3840 W Hillsboro Blvd (33442-9478)
PHONE..................................954 429-1428
EMP: 6 **EST:** 2006
SQ FT: 3,000
SALES: 1.2MM **Privately Held**
SIC: 3631 Mfg Household Cooking Equipment

(G-2766)
ADVANCED PUBLIC SAFETY LLC
Also Called: Centralsquare Technologies
400 Fairway Dr Ste 101 (33441-1808)
PHONE..................................954 354-3000
EMP: 1 **EST:** 2001
SALES (est): 6.6MM
SALES (corp-wide): 272.3MM **Privately Held**
WEB: www.centralsquare.com
SIC: 7372 Business oriented computer software
PA: Centralsquare Technologies, Llc
1000 Business Center Dr
Lake Mary FL 32746
800 727-8088

(G-2767)
AERO SOUTH FLORIDA INC
101 Nw 42nd Way (33442-9248)
PHONE..................................954 363-2376
Dimas A Jovel, *President*
EMP: 7 **EST:** 2017
SALES (est): 217K **Privately Held**
SIC: 3728 Aircraft parts & equipment

(G-2768)
AESTHETIC MBL LASER SVCS INC
905 E Hillsboro Blvd (33441-3523)
P.O. Box 8550 (33443-8550)
PHONE..................................954 480-2600
Paul J Miano, *President*
Eduardo Bravo-Leon, *Vice Pres*
EMP: 8 **EST:** 2002
SALES (est): 860.8K **Privately Held**
WEB: www.aestheticmobilelaser.com
SIC: 3841 Surgical lasers

(G-2769)
AIG TECHNOLOGIES INC
5001 Nw 13th Ave Ste B (33064-8649)
PHONE..................................954 433-0618
Stephen Dawes, *President*
Charlene Dawes, *Vice Pres*
Andrea Plante, *Manager*
EMP: 15 **EST:** 1997
SQ FT: 40,000
SALES (est): 4.4MM **Privately Held**
WEB: www.aigtechnologies.net
SIC: 2844 Hair preparations, including shampoos; shampoos, rinses, conditioners: hair; suntan lotions & oils

(G-2770)
AIR DIMENSIONS INC
Also Called: ADI
1371 W Newport Center Dr # 101 (33442-7700)
PHONE..................................954 428-7333
Gregory English, *President*
Tomas Gunther, *Purchasing*
David W English, *Treasurer*
Greg English, *Train & Dev Mgr*
Elizabeth English, *Personnel*
EMP: 22 **EST:** 1971
SQ FT: 12,000
SALES (est): 7.1MM **Privately Held**
WEB: www.airdimensions.com
SIC: 3561 Industrial pumps & parts

(G-2771)
ALL IN ONE CMPLETE HNDYMAN SVC ✪
177 Sw 5th Ct (33441-4620)
PHONE..................................954 708-3463
Craig Baldwin,
EMP: 10 **EST:** 2020
SALES (est): 450.6K **Privately Held**
SIC: 2951 Asphalt paving mixtures & blocks

(G-2772)
ALL PHASE CONSTRUCTION USA LLC
590 Goolsby Blvd (33442-3021)
PHONE..................................754 227-5605
Christopher R Porosky,
EMP: 14 **EST:** 2017
SALES (est): 1.3MM **Privately Held**
WEB: www.allphaseconstructionfl.com
SIC: 3444 Sheet metalwork

(G-2773)
ALL STAR PRINTING INTL
Also Called: Allstar Printing International
2001 W Sample Rd Ste 100 (33064-1346)
PHONE..................................954 974-0333
Morris Spaszwer, *Owner*
EMP: 5 **EST:** 2001
SALES (est): 358.4K **Privately Held**
WEB: www.allstarprintinginc.com
SIC: 2752 Commercial printing, offset

(G-2774)
ALLIANCE CABINETS & MILLWORK
3231 Sw 3rd St (33442-2322)
PHONE..................................407 802-9921
Bruno Romano, *President*
EMP: 6 **EST:** 2010
SALES (est): 400K **Privately Held**
WEB: www.alliancewoodworking.com
SIC: 2431 Millwork

(G-2775)
ALLIED AEROSPACE INTERNATIONAL
1022 E Newport Center Dr (33442-7723)
PHONE..................................954 429-8600
Christopher Abukhalaf, *Principal*
EMP: 6 **EST:** 2016
SALES (est): 203.3K **Privately Held**
WEB: www.alliedaerospaceinc.com
SIC: 3728 Aircraft parts & equipment

(G-2776)
AMERICAN DIESEL AND GAS INC
1911 Nw 40th Ct (33064-8719)
PHONE..................................561 447-8500
Morris Lewitter, *President*
EMP: 18 **EST:** 2001
SALES (est): 767.4K **Privately Held**
SIC: 3519 Engines, diesel & semi-diesel or dual-fuel

(G-2777)
ANCO PRECISION INC
Also Called: Machine Shop
3191 Sw 11th St Ste 200 (33442-8147)
PHONE..................................954 429-3703
David Velardi, *President*
Andrew Velardi, *President*
Terry Velardi, *Corp Secy*
EMP: 6 **EST:** 1976
SQ FT: 3,500
SALES (est): 606.7K **Privately Held**
WEB: www.ancoprecision.com
SIC: 3599 Machine shop, jobbing & repair

(G-2778)
AQUALUMA LLC
3251 Sw 13th Dr Ste A (33442-8166)
PHONE..................................954 234-2512
Alexandra Bader, *Vice Pres*
EMP: 7 **EST:** 2012
SALES (est): 196K **Privately Held**
WEB: www.aqualuma.com
SIC: 3674 Light emitting diodes

(G-2779)
ART WOOD CABINETS CORP
1533 Sw 1st Way (33441-6777)
PHONE..................................754 367-0742
Carlos P Lima, *President*
EMP: 8 **EST:** 2004
SALES (est): 157.5K **Privately Held**
SIC: 2434 Wood kitchen cabinets

(G-2780)
ASHLEY BRYAN INTERNATIONAL INC
1432 E Nwport Ctr Dr Ste (33442)
PHONE..................................954 351-1199
Jerry Isackson, *President*
Bryan Isackson, *Vice Pres*
Sherry Isackson, *Vice Pres*
Travis Belle, *VP Opers*
Sandra Febres, *Project Mgr*
◆ **EMP:** 36 **EST:** 1988
SALES (est): 2.9MM **Privately Held**
WEB: www.bryanashley.ofs.com
SIC: 2531 2519 Public building & related furniture; wicker & rattan furniture

(G-2781)
ASTRO PURE INCORPORATED
Also Called: Astro-Pure Water Purifiers
1441 Sw 1st Way (33441-6753)
PHONE..................................954 422-8966
Roger L Stefl, *President*
Mary Munn, *Vice Pres*
EMP: 10 **EST:** 1970
SQ FT: 2,500
SALES (est): 683.3K **Privately Held**
SIC: 3589 Water purification equipment, household type; water treatment equipment, industrial

(G-2782)
AUDIO INTELLIGENCE DEVICES
637 Jim Moran Blvd (33442-1711)
PHONE..................................954 418-1400
Glen Hower, *President*
William Armour, *CFO*
EMP: 26 **EST:** 1968
SQ FT: 100,000
SALES (est): 957.3K **Privately Held**
WEB: www.aid-nia.com
SIC: 3699 Security control equipment & systems

(G-2783)
BANYAN GAMING LLC
245 Ne 21st Ave Ste 300 (33441-3859)
PHONE..................................954 951-7094
Jason Seelig, *Mng Member*
Roger Cureton, *Technology*
Daniel Lombana, *Technician*
Charles Bernitz,
▲ **EMP:** 14 **EST:** 2015
SQ FT: 6,000
SALES (est): 693.6K **Privately Held**
WEB: www.banyangaming.com
SIC: 3999 Slot machines

(G-2784)
BEEHIVE3D INC ✪
1027 Sw 30th Ave (33442-8104)
PHONE..................................954 560-9513
Doug Hedges, *CEO*
EMP: 6 **EST:** 2020
SALES (est): 1MM **Privately Held**
WEB: www.beehive3d.com
SIC: 3313 Alloys, additive, except copper: not made in blast furnaces

(G-2785)
BLU SLEEP PRODUCTS LLC (PA)
Also Called: Somni Specialty Sleep
1501 Green Rd Ste B (33064-1077)
PHONE..................................866 973-7614
Erasmo Ciccolelle, *Mng Member*
EMP: 2 **EST:** 2014
SQ FT: 23,000
SALES (est): 4MM **Privately Held**
WEB: www.myblusleep.com
SIC: 2515 Mattresses & bedsprings

(G-2786)
BOAIR INC
210 S Military Trl (33442-3017)
P.O. Box 266132, Fort Lauderdale (33326-6132)
PHONE..................................954 426-9226
EMP: 6
SQ FT: 3,500
SALES: 600K **Privately Held**
SIC: 3564 Mfg Of Electro Static Filters

(G-2787)
BOCA TERRY LLC
3000 Sw 15th St Ste G (33442-8198)
PHONE..................................954 312-4400
Ed Cohen, *CFO*
Christi Smith, *Sales Executive*
Jennifer Gulliford, *Manager*
Edward Cohen,
Bruce Cohen,
▲ **EMP:** 10 **EST:** 1997
SALES (est): 1.6MM **Privately Held**
WEB: www.bocaterry.com
SIC: 2384 Robes & dressing gowns

(G-2788)
BOCATECH INC
1020 Nw 6th St Ste A (33442-1720)
PHONE..................................954 397-7070
Abram Ackerman, *President*

Arlene McMachen, *Principal*
Brian Shaw, *Principal*
▲ **EMP:** 5 **EST:** 2005
SALES (est): 500K **Privately Held**
WEB: www.bocatechswitches.com
SIC: 3679 3675 3677 3678 Electronic circuits; condensers, electronic; electronic transformers; electronic connectors

(G-2789)
BRAZILIAN CLSSFIED ADS-CHEI IN
Also Called: Achei USA Newspaper
2001 W Sample Rd Ste 422 (33064-1300)
PHONE..................................954 570-7568
Jose Nunes, *President*
Esterliz Mayer, *Marketing Mgr*
EMP: 7 **EST:** 2001
SQ FT: 1,000
SALES (est): 557.5K **Privately Held**
SIC: 2741 2711 ; newspapers, publishing & printing

(G-2790)
BRITE SHOT INC
600 W Hillsboro Blvd (33441-1609)
PHONE..................................954 418-7125
Peter Ticktin, *President*
Roy McDonald, *Vice Pres*
Irene Conrad, *Treasurer*
Noah Platte, *Manager*
EMP: 10 **EST:** 2009
SALES (est): 931K **Privately Held**
SIC: 3648 Lighting equipment

(G-2791)
BROWARD CUSTOM WOODWORK LLC
401 Jim Moran Blvd (33442-1707)
PHONE..................................352 376-4732
Bill Koelbel, *President*
EMP: 5 **EST:** 1988
SALES (est): 700K
SALES (corp-wide): 190.9MM **Privately Held**
WEB: www.listindustries.com
SIC: 2434 5021 Wood kitchen cabinets; lockers
PA: List Industries Inc.
401 Jim Moran Blvd
Deerfield Beach FL 33442
954 429-9155

(G-2792)
BRRH CORPORATION
3313 W Hillsboro Blvd # 101 (33442-9423)
PHONE..................................954 427-9665
Brian Altschuler, *Vice Pres*
Mindy Shikiar, *Vice Pres*
Lisa Blume, *Human Res Mgr*
Maureen Mann, *Exec Dir*
Brina Watson, *Analyst*
EMP: 47 **Privately Held**
WEB: www.brrh.com
SIC: 3829 Medical diagnostic systems, nuclear
PA: Brrh Corporation
800 Meadows Rd
Boca Raton FL 33486

(G-2793)
BRYAN ASHLEY INC
1432 E Newport Center Dr (33442-7703)
PHONE..................................954 351-1199
Bryan Ashley, *President*
Robert Duban, *Vice Pres*
Bryan Isackson, *Vice Pres*
Brittney Williams, *Vice Pres*
Sandra Febres, *Project Mgr*
EMP: 29 **EST:** 2017
SALES (est): 3.5MM **Privately Held**
WEB: www.bryanashley.ofs.com
SIC: 2599 Hotel furniture

(G-2794)
CAPSTONE COMPANIES INC (PA)
431 Fairway Dr Ste 200 (33441-1823)
PHONE..................................954 252-3440
Stewart Wallach, *President*
Gerry McClinton, *COO*
Johnny Choi, *Opers Mgr*
Aimee Gaudet, *Admin Sec*
Aimee C Brown, *Administration*
EMP: 9 **EST:** 1997
SQ FT: 4,000
SALES: 2.7MM **Publicly Held**
WEB: www.capstonecompaniesinc.com
SIC: 3648 Floodlights

(G-2795)
CAPSTONE INDUSTRIES INC
431 Fairway Dr Ste 200 (33441-1823)
PHONE..................................954 570-8889
Stewart Wallach, *CEO*
Reid Goldstein, *President*
Jerry Mc Clinton, *COO*
Jordan Seals, *Marketing Staff*
Aimee Gaudet, *Director*
▲ **EMP:** 10 **EST:** 1996
SQ FT: 4,000
SALES (est): 1.9MM
SALES (corp-wide): 2.7MM **Publicly Held**
WEB: www.capstoneindustries.com
SIC: 3645 Garden, patio, walkway & yard lighting fixtures: electric
PA: Capstone Companies, Inc.
431 Fairway Dr Ste 200
Deerfield Beach FL 33441
954 252-3440

(G-2796)
CAROLINA WOODWORKS INC
714 Nw 44th Ter Apt 203 (33442-9285)
PHONE..................................954 692-4662
Ecleidivaldo C Araujo, *Principal*
EMP: 7 **EST:** 2007
SALES (est): 82.7K **Privately Held**
SIC: 2431 Millwork

(G-2797)
CAYMAN MANUFACTURING INC
1301 Sw 34th Ave (33442-8153)
PHONE..................................954 421-1170
Donald H Ferguson, *President*
Josh Ferguson, *Mfg Staff*
EMP: 32 **EST:** 1989
SQ FT: 20,000
SALES (est): 2.7MM **Privately Held**
WEB: www.caymanmfg.com
SIC: 2522 2531 Office furniture, except wood; school furniture

(G-2798)
CAYMAN NAT MFG & INSTALLATION
1301 Sw 34th Ave (33442-8153)
PHONE..................................954 421-1170
Donald H Ferguson, *President*
Josh Ferguson, *Sales Staff*
▼ **EMP:** 75 **EST:** 2000
SQ FT: 40,000
SALES (est): 7.2MM **Privately Held**
WEB: www.caymanmfg.com
SIC: 2522 Office cabinets & filing drawers: except wood

(G-2799)
CENTRAL CONCRETE SUPERMIX INC
1817 S Powerline Rd (33442-8164)
PHONE..................................954 480-9333
Frank Perez, *Vice Pres*
Tom Figari, *Branch Mgr*
Noel Bueno, *Info Tech Mgr*
EMP: 10
SALES (corp-wide): 43.8MM **Privately Held**
WEB: www.supermix.com
SIC: 3273 Ready-mixed concrete
PA: Central Concrete Supermix Inc
4300 Sw 74th Ave
Miami FL 33155
305 262-3250

(G-2800)
CHECKPOINT CARD GROUP INC
1801 Green Rd (33064-1052)
PHONE..................................954 426-1331
Anthony Gardner, *President*
Ivan Milo, *Vice Pres*
EMP: 12 **EST:** 2017
SALES (est): 408.3K **Privately Held**
WEB: www.cpcardtech.com
SIC: 3089 Identification cards, plastic

(G-2801)
CHEM-TEC EQUIPMENT CO
Also Called: Chem TEC
3077 Sw 13th Dr (33442-8129)
PHONE..................................954 428-8259
Matthew Donoghue, *President*
Kelly Donoghue, *Admin Sec*
EMP: 11 **EST:** 1967
SQ FT: 10,000
SALES (est): 1.9MM **Privately Held**
WEB: www.chemtec.com
SIC: 3823 3491 Industrial instrmnts msrmnt display/control process variable; industrial valves

(G-2802)
CIRO MANUFACTURING CORPORATION
692 S Military Trl (33442-3000)
PHONE..................................561 988-2139
Leland Cerasani, *President*
▲ **EMP:** 26 **EST:** 2002
SALES (est): 2.7MM **Privately Held**
WEB: www.ciromfg.com
SIC: 3084 Plastics pipe

(G-2803)
COSMO INTERNATIONAL CORP (PA)
Also Called: Cosmo International Fragrances
1341 W Newport Center Dr (33442-7734)
PHONE..................................954 798-4500
Marc Blaison, *President*
J Fernando Belmont, *President*
Janine Belmont, *Vice Pres*
Javier Abadia, *Opers Staff*
Duvan Garcia, *Production*
◆ **EMP:** 50 **EST:** 1976
SQ FT: 90,000
SALES (est): 32.3MM **Privately Held**
WEB: www.cosmo-fragrances.com
SIC: 2869 Perfume materials, synthetic

(G-2804)
COSMO INTERNATIONAL CORP
Also Called: Cosmo International Fragrances
1341 W Newport Center Dr (33442-7734)
PHONE..................................954 798-4500
EMP: 32
SALES (corp-wide): 58MM **Privately Held**
SIC: 2844 Mfg Toilet Preparations
PA: Cosmo International Corp.
2455 E Sunrise Blvd # 720
Fort Lauderdale FL 33442
954 566-1516

(G-2805)
CRAWFORD GLASS DOOR CO
3301 Sw 13th Dr Ste B (33442-8108)
PHONE..................................954 480-6820
Ralph Crawford, *President*
EMP: 10 **EST:** 1991
SQ FT: 6,000
SALES (est): 875.7K **Privately Held**
SIC: 3231 Doors, glass: made from purchased glass

(G-2806)
CREATIVE TEACHING CABINETS
4340 Nw 19th Ave (33064-8710)
PHONE..................................754 205-0886
EMP: 6 **EST:** 2015
SALES (est): 163.3K **Privately Held**
SIC: 2434 Wood kitchen cabinets

(G-2807)
CUSTOM CABINETS DESIGN INC
5000 Nw 3rd Ave (33064-2425)
PHONE..................................561 210-3423
Alvaro Villalobos, *Principal*
EMP: 7 **EST:** 2010
SALES (est): 275.1K **Privately Held**
WEB: www.customcabinetsdesign.com
SIC: 2434 Wood kitchen cabinets

(G-2808)
CUSTOM GRAPHICS INC
1801 Green Rd Ste B (33064-1052)
PHONE..................................954 563-6756
Cathy Cart, *President*
Steven Cart, *Admin Sec*
EMP: 5 **EST:** 1987
SALES (est): 400K **Privately Held**
WEB: www.decalsbycustomgraphics.com
SIC: 2759 Screen printing

(G-2809)
CUSTOM PLASTIC CARD COMPANY
1801 Green Rd Ste A (33064-1052)
P.O. Box 4489 (33442-4489)
PHONE..................................954 426-1331
Tony Gardner, *President*
Deb Devinney, *Advt Staff*
Jordan Manolakis, *Manager*
Bill O'Neill, *Info Tech Mgr*
Anthony B Gardner, *Director*
▲ **EMP:** 80 **EST:** 1983
SQ FT: 45,000
SALES (est): 8.8MM **Privately Held**
WEB: www.customplasticcard.com
SIC: 3089 Injection molding of plastics

(G-2810)
CVE REPORTER INC
3501 West Dr (33442-2000)
PHONE..................................954 421-5566
Steven Fine, *Principal*
Kelly Hampton, *Exec Dir*
EMP: 11 **EST:** 2008
SALES (est): 360.6K **Privately Held**
WEB: www.cvereporter.com
SIC: 2711 Newspapers, publishing & printing

(G-2811)
DAIGLE TOOL & DIE INC
764 Ne 42nd St (33064-4204)
PHONE..................................954 785-9989
Robert V Daigle, *Chairman*
Robert J Daigle, *Vice Pres*
EMP: 7 **EST:** 1982
SQ FT: 12,000
SALES (est): 520.3K **Privately Held**
SIC: 3542 3089 Machine tools, metal forming type; molding primary plastic

(G-2812)
DESIGN-A-RUG INC (PA)
200 N Federal Hwy (33441-3612)
PHONE..................................954 943-7487
Ali R Amjadi, *President*
Fatemeh Amjadi, *Principal*
EMP: 14 **EST:** 1983
SQ FT: 15,000
SALES (est): 1.2MM **Privately Held**
WEB: www.design-a-rug.com
SIC: 2273 5713 Carpets, hand & machine made; carpets

(G-2813)
DIABETEX CARE
1525 Nw 3rd St (33442-1669)
PHONE..................................954 427-9510
Howard Rich, *Principal*
EMP: 7 **EST:** 2010
SALES (est): 142.4K **Privately Held**
SIC: 3841 Surgical & medical instruments

(G-2814)
DIAMOND BLADES 4US
2150 Sw 10th St (33442-7621)
PHONE..................................800 659-5843
Ryan D Fritchen, *Administration*
EMP: 6 **EST:** 2015
SALES (est): 99.7K **Privately Held**
WEB: www.diamondblades4us.us
SIC: 3425 Saw blades & handsaws

(G-2815)
DIZENZO MANUFACTURING INTL
4400 Nw 19th Ave Ste J (33064-8703)
PHONE..................................954 978-4624
Frank Dizenzo, *President*
EMP: 7 **EST:** 1995
SQ FT: 2,400
SALES (est): 800.9K **Privately Held**
SIC: 2591 Window blinds

(G-2816)
DMR CREATIVE MARKETING LLC
321 Goolsby Blvd (33442-3006)
PHONE..................................954 725-3750
Brian Weinman, *President*
Jeffrey Bee, *Exec VP*

▲ = Import ▼=Export
◆ =Import/Export

Eric Moss, *Controller*
◆ **EMP:** 5 **EST:** 2000
SALES (est): 2MM **Privately Held**
WEB: www.dmrcreativem.com
SIC: 2326 Work apparel, except uniforms

(G-2817)
DOORMARK INC
430 Goolsby Blvd (33442-3019)
PHONE..................................954 418-4700
Roy Jacob Van Wyck, *President*
Mark Harmon, *Maint Spvr*
Cindy Vermaas, *Bookkeeper*
Chuck Banner, *Sales Staff*
◆ **EMP:** 44 **EST:** 1994
SALES (est): 7.2MM **Privately Held**
WEB: www.doormark.com
SIC: 2434 Wood kitchen cabinets

(G-2818)
DR JILLS FOOT PADS INC
384 S Military Trl (33442-3007)
PHONE..................................954 573-6557
Jill Scheur, *President*
▼ **EMP:** 10 **EST:** 2002
SALES (est): 2.1MM **Privately Held**
WEB: www.drjillsfootpads.com
SIC: 3842 Foot appliances, orthopedic

(G-2819)
DYNASEL INCORPORATED
114 Grantham A (33442-3401)
PHONE..................................972 733-4447
Naomi Levinson, *President*
Robert Levinson, *Treasurer*
▲ **EMP:** 6 **EST:** 1963
SALES (est): 108.3K **Privately Held**
SIC: 2673 Plastic bags: made from purchased materials

(G-2820)
ECHO PLASTIC SYSTEMS
1801 Green Rd Ste B (33064-1052)
PHONE..................................305 655-1300
Norman Mensh, *President*
Tony Garner, *President*
Doug Upton, *Director*
EMP: 12 **EST:** 1976
SQ FT: 8,500
SALES (est): 879.5K **Privately Held**
SIC: 3083 Laminated plastics plate & sheet

(G-2821)
EDGELINE INDUSTRIES LLC (PA)
1319 E Hillsboro Blvd # 514 (33441-4225)
PHONE..................................954 727-5272
Hector O Huarte,
Nicolas D Huarte,
Dennis J Watts,
◆ **EMP:** 13 **EST:** 2011
SALES (est): 1.8MM **Privately Held**
SIC: 2521 Wood office furniture

(G-2822)
ENDEAVOR MANUFACTURING INC
510 Goolsby Blvd (33442-3021)
PHONE..................................954 752-6828
Stanley S Noreika, *Principal*
EMP: 13 **EST:** 2013
SALES (est): 1.3MM **Privately Held**
WEB: www.emfginc.com
SIC: 3999 Manufacturing industries

(G-2823)
ESQUADRO INC
217 Se 1st Ter (33441-3903)
PHONE..................................754 367-3098
Ebrahim Frederico R, *Principal*
EMP: 8 **EST:** 2014
SALES (est): 293.5K **Privately Held**
SIC: 2434 Wood kitchen cabinets

(G-2824)
FEDERATED PRECISION INC
692 S Military Trl (33442-3000)
P.O. Box 590064, Fort Lauderdale (33359-0064)
PHONE..................................561 288-6500
Keith Smith, *President*
EMP: 20 **EST:** 2011
SQ FT: 22,000
SALES (est): 520.1K **Privately Held**
SIC: 3451 3541 Screw machine products; milling machines; lathes

(G-2825)
FOGMASTER CORPORATION (PA)
1051 Sw 30th Ave (33442-8104)
PHONE..................................954 481-9975
Thomas M Latta, *President*
Steven Hawkins, *Vice Pres*
▲ **EMP:** 8 **EST:** 1982
SQ FT: 21,000
SALES (est): 1.4MM **Privately Held**
WEB: www.fogmaster.com
SIC: 3523 Soil preparation machinery, except turf & grounds

(G-2826)
FORNO DE MINAS USA INC
242 Sw 12th Ave (33442-3104)
PHONE..................................954 840-6533
Rosana Parise, *Officer*
Gustavo Salazar, *Officer*
EMP: 10 **EST:** 2014
SALES (est): 870.9K **Privately Held**
WEB: www.fornodeminas.com
SIC: 2051 Cakes, pies & pastries

(G-2827)
FORUM PUBLISHING GROUP INC (DH)
Also Called: Choice ADS
1701 Green Rd Ste B (33064-1074)
PHONE..................................954 698-6397
Ken Mitchell, *President*
▲ **EMP:** 135 **EST:** 1969
SALES (est): 25.1MM
SALES (corp-wide): 4.5B **Publicly Held**
WEB: www.sun-sentinel.com
SIC: 2711 Newspapers, publishing & printing
HQ: Tribune Media Company
515 N State St Ste 2400
Chicago IL 60654
312 222-3394

(G-2828)
FORUM PUBLISHING GROUP INC
Also Called: Wellington Forum
333 Sw 12th Ave (33442-3107)
PHONE..................................954 596-5650
Keri Lurtz, *Manager*
EMP: 73
SALES (corp-wide): 4.5B **Publicly Held**
WEB: www.sun-sentinel.com
SIC: 2711 2741 Newspapers: publishing only, not printed on site; miscellaneous publishing
HQ: Forum Publishing Group Inc
1701 Green Rd Ste B
Deerfield Beach FL 33064
954 698-6397

(G-2829)
GAM SWISS TURNING INC
355 Sw 33rd Ave (33442-2359)
PHONE..................................954 428-6785
Frank Gamperl, *Principal*
EMP: 8 **EST:** 2008
SALES (est): 162.6K **Privately Held**
WEB: www.gamswissturning.com
SIC: 3599 Machine shop, jobbing & repair

(G-2830)
GBI INTRALOGISTICS SOLUTIONS
1143 W Newport Center Dr (33442-7732)
PHONE..................................954 596-5000
Olga Golubyeva, *Finance*
Nilmani Bhanderi, *Software Engr*
Bogdan Avasiloae, *Administration*
EMP: 25 **EST:** 2016
SALES (est): 5.5MM **Privately Held**
WEB: www.gbisorters.com
SIC: 7372 Application computer software

(G-2831)
GIOVANNI ART IN CUSTOM FURN
1478 Sw 1st Way (33441-6754)
PHONE..................................954 698-1008
Jorge Tenutta, *President*
Patricia Tenutta, *Corp Secy*
EMP: 6 **EST:** 1993
SALES (est): 446.4K **Privately Held**
SIC: 2426 Carvings, furniture: wood

(G-2832)
GLOBAL DIRECTORIES INC
Also Called: Yellow Pages
450 Fairway Dr Ste 204 (33441-1837)
PHONE..................................954 571-8283
EMP: 10
SALES (est): 607K
SALES (corp-wide): 4.9MM **Privately Held**
SIC: 2741 Misc Publishing
PA: Global Directories, Inc.
6440 Sthpint Pkwy Ste 150
Jacksonville FL 32216
904 899-4400

(G-2833)
GULF ASSOCIATES CONTROL INC
Also Called: G A C Inc/Gulf Associates
231 Se 1st Ter (33441-3903)
PHONE..................................954 426-0536
James B Martin Jr, *President*
EMP: 21 **EST:** 1968
SQ FT: 3,750
SALES (est): 385K **Privately Held**
SIC: 3433 Heaters, swimming pool: oil or gas

(G-2834)
H2O INTERNATIONAL INC
3001 Sw 15th St Ste C (33442-8199)
PHONE..................................954 570-3464
Guillermo Guzman, *President*
Ivan Molina, *Technology*
▲ **EMP:** 15 **EST:** 1993
SQ FT: 18,000
SALES (est): 2.2MM **Privately Held**
WEB: www.h2ofilter.com
SIC: 3589 5074 Water purification equipment, household type; water purification equipment

(G-2835)
HANDCRAFT WOODWORKING INC
1498 Nw 3rd St (33442-1647)
PHONE..................................954 418-6356
Jerry A Rowland, *President*
Charles Wieland, *CFO*
Anthony Bilbao, *Manager*
James Woodburn, *Manager*
Joe Barone, *Supervisor*
EMP: 20 **EST:** 1991
SQ FT: 11,600
SALES (est): 3.7MM **Privately Held**
WEB: www.handcraftwoodworking.net
SIC: 2431 Millwork

(G-2836)
HEALTH COMMUNICATIONS INC
Also Called: Hci Books
3201 Sw 15th St (33442-8157)
PHONE..................................954 360-0909
Peter Vegso, *President*
Kate McCormick, *Marketing Staff*
Qiuli Wu, *Database Admin*
◆ **EMP:** 87 **EST:** 1976
SQ FT: 100,000
SALES (est): 13.3MM **Privately Held**
WEB: www.hcibooks.com
SIC: 2741 Miscellaneous publishing; globe covers (maps): publishing & printing

(G-2837)
HENDERSON MACHINE INC
1809 S Powerline Rd # 110 (33442-8196)
PHONE..................................954 419-9789
Daniel Henderson, *President*
Pamela Henderson, *Vice Pres*
EMP: 8 **EST:** 1977
SQ FT: 5,500
SALES (est): 1.5MM **Privately Held**
WEB: www.hendersonmachine.com
SIC: 3599 Machine shop, jobbing & repair

(G-2838)
HERMES 7 COMMUNICATIONS LLC
Also Called: Fastsigns
430 W Hillsboro Blvd (33441-1604)
PHONE..................................954 426-1998
Maria Vilas Fraga,
EMP: 17 **EST:** 2014
SALES (est): 836.2K **Privately Held**
WEB: www.fastsigns.com
SIC: 3993 Signs & advertising specialties

(G-2839)
HOERBGER AUTO CMFORT SYSTEMS L
1191 E Nwport Ctr Dr Ste (33442)
PHONE..................................334 321-2292
Gerhard Schoell,
Helmut Kleiber,
◆ **EMP:** 31 **EST:** 2001
SQ FT: 18,000
SALES (est): 2.4MM **Privately Held**
SIC: 3714 3511 Motor vehicle engines & parts; hydraulic turbine generator set units, complete

(G-2840)
HOERBIGER AMERICA HOLDING INC (PA)
1432 E Nwport Ctr Dr Ste (33442)
PHONE..................................954 422-9850
Franz Gruber, *President*
Heather Henderson, *Corp Secy*
Charles Friess, *Director*
Subodh Gore, *Director*
Juergen Zeschky, *Director*
EMP: 280 **EST:** 2005
SALES (est): 494.1MM **Privately Held**
SIC: 1389 Gas compressing (natural gas) at the fields

(G-2841)
HOERBIGER AMERICA HOLDING INC
Also Called: Corporate It
1191 E Newport Center Dr (33442-7715)
PHONE..................................954 422-9850
Franz Gruber, *President*
EMP: 5004
SALES (corp-wide): 494.1MM **Privately Held**
SIC: 1389 Gas compressing (natural gas) at the fields
PA: Hoerbiger America Holding, Inc.
1432 E Nwport Ctr Dr Ste
Deerfield Beach FL 33442
954 422-9850

(G-2842)
HOFMANN & LEAVY INC
Also Called: Tassel Depot
3251 Sw 13th Dr Ste 3 (33442-8166)
PHONE..................................954 698-0000
Roger S Leavy, *President*
April E Leavy, *Vice Pres*
April Leavy, *VP Mktg*
◆ **EMP:** 100 **EST:** 1864
SQ FT: 22,000
SALES (est): 8.5MM **Privately Held**
WEB: www.tasseldepot.com
SIC: 2298 5085 2396 2782 Wire rope centers; rope, cord & thread; apparel findings & trimmings; furniture trimmings, fabric; sample books

(G-2843)
HOME AIDE DIAGNOSTICS INC
1072 S Powerline Rd (33442-8119)
PHONE..................................954 794-0212
Amgad Girgis, *President*
Akram Girgis, *Vice Pres*
▲ **EMP:** 12 **EST:** 2006
SALES (est): 1.9MM **Privately Held**
WEB: www.homeaide.us
SIC: 3841 Diagnostic apparatus, medical

(G-2844)
HOOD DEPOT INTERNATIONAL INC
710 S Powerline Rd Ste H (33442-8176)
PHONE..................................954 570-9860
Donald Lubowicki, *President*
Max Brand, *Principal*
Sam Lubowicki, *Project Mgr*
Rodney Fritz, *Chief Engr*
▼ **EMP:** 40 **EST:** 1984
SQ FT: 22,000
SALES (est): 8.8MM **Privately Held**
WEB: www.hooddepot.net
SIC: 3564 3444 Blowers & fans; sheet metalwork

(G-2845)
HOSE-MCCANN TELEPHONE CO INC (PA)
Also Called: Hose McCann Communications
1241 W Newport Center Dr (33442-7738)
PHONE..................................954 429-1110
Joan Grande-Butera, *CEO*
Michael Chippolone, *Corp Secy*
Bogen Karlak, *Prdtn Mgr*
Phillip Bester, *Purchasing*
Jim Hebert, *Engineer*
▲ **EMP:** 38 **EST:** 1920
SQ FT: 50,000
SALES (est): 9.4MM **Privately Held**
WEB: www.hose-mccann.com
SIC: 3661 3699 Telephones, sound powered (no battery); electrical equipment & supplies

(G-2846)
HOSPITLITY BEAN CNTERS PLUS IN
1011 Se 4th Ct (33441-5912)
PHONE..................................954 531-1710
Wendy M Janis, *Principal*
EMP: 6 **EST:** 2010
SALES (est): 209K **Privately Held**
SIC: 3131 Counters

(G-2847)
INTERNTNAL SRVILLANCE TECH INC (PA)
Also Called: National Intelligence Academy
160 Sw 12th Ave (33442-3119)
PHONE..................................954 574-1100
Donald A Difrisco, *Principal*
▼ **EMP:** 32 **EST:** 1993
SALES (est): 5MM **Privately Held**
WEB: www.istnia.com
SIC: 3716 7532 5099 5065 Recreational van conversion (self-propelled), factory basis; van conversion; video & audio equipment; video equipment, electronic

(G-2848)
ISOFLEX TECHNOLOGIES INTL LLC
3434 Sw 15th St B (33442-8135)
PHONE..................................561 210-5170
Jonathan Lucco, *Vice Pres*
EMP: 5 **EST:** 2017
SALES (est): 305.1K **Privately Held**
WEB: www.isoflextech.com
SIC: 3714 Motor vehicle parts & accessories

(G-2849)
J & P DEERFIELD INC
1191 W Newport Center Dr (33442-7732)
PHONE..................................954 571-6665
Jason Scherr, *President*
Philip Garroway, *Vice Pres*
▲ **EMP:** 16 **EST:** 1982
SQ FT: 5,100
SALES (est): 2.2MM **Privately Held**
SIC: 3089 2672 Identification cards, plastic; coated & laminated paper

(G-2850)
JET RESEARCH DEVELOPMENT INC
Also Called: Valve Research & Mfg Co
1215 W Newport Center Dr (33442-7738)
PHONE..................................954 427-0404
Paul L Cruz, *President*
Concepcion Y Cruz, *Vice Pres*
Brad Witkowski, *Mfg Mgr*
Tim Johnson, *Sales Staff*
Patricia Kilgallon, *Admin Sec*
EMP: 85 **EST:** 1972
SQ FT: 14,000
SALES (est): 18.2MM **Privately Held**
SIC: 3492 Valves, hydraulic, aircraft; control valves, fluid power: hydraulic & pneumatic

(G-2851)
JIREH WOODWORK INC
3821 Nw 9th Ave (33064-1949)
PHONE..................................954 515-8041
Carlos H Gomes Costa, *Director*
EMP: 7 **EST:** 2005
SALES (est): 91.8K **Privately Held**
SIC: 2431 Millwork

(G-2852)
K20 OIL LLC
1201 S Military Trl (33442-7632)
PHONE..................................954 421-1735
Lui Alvaro, *Principal*
EMP: 6 **EST:** 2015
SALES (est): 1.5MM **Privately Held**
SIC: 1311 Crude petroleum & natural gas

(G-2853)
KEYTAG1 LLC
265 S Federal Hwy (33441-4161)
PHONE..................................203 982-8448
Braunislaw Barski, *Manager*
EMP: 5 **EST:** 2017
SALES (est): 506.1K **Privately Held**
WEB: www.keytag1.com
SIC: 2752 Commercial printing, offset

(G-2854)
KM COATINGS MFG JR
1111 W Newport Center Dr (33442-7732)
PHONE..................................602 253-1168
EMP: 12 **EST:** 2016
SALES (est): 174.7K **Privately Held**
WEB: www.kmcoatings.us
SIC: 3999 Manufacturing industries

(G-2855)
KOSZEGI INDUSTRIES INC
1801 Green Rd Ste E (33064-1052)
PHONE..................................954 419-9544
Brett M Johnson, *President*
James McKenna, *CFO*
▲ **EMP:** 31 **EST:** 1958
SQ FT: 12,000
SALES (est): 3.7MM
SALES (corp-wide): 34.4MM **Publicly Held**
WEB: www.forwardindustries.com
SIC: 3161 3469 3172 2673 Cases, carrying; metal stampings; personal leather goods; bags: plastic, laminated & coated
PA: Forward Industries, Inc.
700 Veterans Memorial Hwy # 10
Hauppauge NY 11788
631 547-3041

(G-2856)
LAMPSHADES OF FLORIDA INC
Also Called: Lampshade Direct
4280 Nw 5th Dr (33442-8032)
PHONE..................................954 491-3377
Morten C Post, *President*
EMP: 17 **EST:** 1979
SALES (est): 1MM **Privately Held**
WEB: www.lampshadesofflorida.com
SIC: 3999 Shades, lamp or candle

(G-2857)
LAPOLLA INDUSTRIES LLC
Also Called: Infiniti Paint & Coatings
720 S Military Trl (33442-3025)
PHONE..................................954 379-0241
Jon Palmisciano, *Vice Pres*
EMP: 12
SALES (corp-wide): 178.9MM **Privately Held**
WEB: www.lapolla.com
SIC: 2952 2851 3069 2891 Roofing felts, cements or coatings; paints & paint additives; foam rubber; adhesives & sealants
HQ: Lapolla Industries, Llc
3315 E Division St
Arlington TX 76011
281 219-4100

(G-2858)
LENCO HOLDINGS LLC
1223 Sw 1st Way (33441-6641)
PHONE..................................305 360-0895
Len Brian, *Mng Member*
▲ **EMP:** 5 **EST:** 2007
SQ FT: 4,000
SALES (est): 653.6K **Privately Held**
WEB: www.lencoholdings.com
SIC: 3542 Mechanical (pneumatic or hydraulic) metal forming machines

(G-2859)
LIST INDUSTRIES INC (PA)
401 Jim Moran Blvd (33442-1781)
PHONE..................................954 429-9155
Herbert List Jr, *President*
Boyd Bryson, *Regional Mgr*
Dave Cole, *Vice Pres*
David Kole, *Vice Pres*
Braden R List, *Vice Pres*
▲ **EMP:** 282 **EST:** 1936
SQ FT: 100,000
SALES (est): 190.9MM **Privately Held**
WEB: www.listindustries.com
SIC: 2542 5021 2541 Lockers (not refrigerated): except wood; lockers; lockers, except refrigerated: wood

(G-2860)
LIST MANUFACTURING INC
401 Jim Moran Blvd (33442-1781)
PHONE..................................954 429-9155
Herbert A List Jr, *President*
EMP: 36 **EST:** 2009
SQ FT: 110,000
SALES (est): 3.9MM
SALES (corp-wide): 190.9MM **Privately Held**
WEB: www.listindustries.com
SIC: 3315 Steel wire & related products
PA: List Industries Inc.
401 Jim Moran Blvd
Deerfield Beach FL 33442
954 429-9155

(G-2861)
LIST PLYMOUTH LLC
401 Jim Moran Blvd (33442-1781)
PHONE..................................954 429-9155
Eric Bello, *CFO*
Alex MAI, *Info Tech Dir*
Herbert A List Jr,
EMP: 25 **EST:** 2007
SQ FT: 150,000
SALES (est): 2.5MM
SALES (corp-wide): 190.9MM **Privately Held**
WEB: www.listindustries.com
SIC: 2542 5021 Lockers (not refrigerated): except wood; lockers
PA: List Industries Inc.
401 Jim Moran Blvd
Deerfield Beach FL 33442
954 429-9155

(G-2862)
LIVING COLOR AQUARIUM CORP
740 S Porwerline Rd Ste E (33442)
PHONE..................................844 522-8265
Daniel Kaufman, *President*
EMP: 20 **EST:** 2016
SQ FT: 100
SALES (est): 719.4K **Privately Held**
SIC: 3231 Products of purchased glass

(G-2863)
LIVING COLOR ENTERPRISES INC
720 S Powerline Rd Ste D (33442-8156)
PHONE..................................954 970-9511
Michael Feder, *CEO*
Mathew Roy, *CEO*
Mat Roy, *President*
Bill Young, *Vice Pres*
Jose Blanco, *Production*
◆ **EMP:** 47 **EST:** 1988
SQ FT: 43,400
SALES (est): 2.1MM **Privately Held**
WEB: www.livingcolor.com
SIC: 3231 Aquariums & reflectors, glass

(G-2864)
LOCAL PAVERS INC
670 Ne 43rd St (33064-4235)
PHONE..................................954 913-6916
Wenceslao Albarran, *Principal*
EMP: 6 **EST:** 2013
SALES (est): 84.5K **Privately Held**
SIC: 2951 Asphalt paving mixtures & blocks

(G-2865)
M VB INDUSTRIES INC
510 Goolsby Blvd 5 (33442-3021)
P.O. Box 4637 (33442-4637)
PHONE..................................954 480-6448
Gared Von Benecke, *President*
Stan Meacham, *Treasurer*
EMP: 26 **EST:** 2000
SQ FT: 11,000
SALES (est): 1.4MM **Privately Held**
WEB: www.mvbindustries.com
SIC: 3541 Drilling machine tools (metal cutting)

(G-2866)
MAHIGAMING LLC
245 Ne 21st Ave Ste 200 (33441-3859)
PHONE..................................561 504-1534
Sean Oxley, *Engineer*
Seher Basak, *Marketing Staff*
Taun E Masterson, *Manager*
Ricardo Paiva, *Consultant*
Gabriel Garcia, *Technical Staff*
EMP: 10 **EST:** 2017
SALES (est): 1.8MM **Privately Held**
WEB: www.mahigaming.com
SIC: 3652 Pre-recorded records & tapes

(G-2867)
MAKAI MARINE INDUSTRIES INC
730 S Deerfield Ave Ste 8 (33441-5362)
PHONE..................................954 425-0203
Marc R Kaiser, *President*
EMP: 6 **EST:** 1982
SALES (est): 29.4K **Privately Held**
SIC: 3563 Air & gas compressors

(G-2868)
MAPEI CORPORATION (DH)
Also Called: North Amrcn Adhesives Coatings
1144 E Newport Center Dr (33442-7725)
PHONE..................................954 246-8888
Luigi Di Geso, *President*
Brenda Gutierrez, *Export Mgr*
Lusanira Morais, *Export Mgr*
Flavio Becerra, *Maint Spvr*
Mike Zalusky, *Maint Spvr*
◆ **EMP:** 120 **EST:** 1985
SALES (est): 619.9MM **Privately Held**
WEB: www.mapei.com
SIC: 2891 5169 Adhesives; chemicals & allied products
HQ: Mapei Spa
Viale Edoardo Jenner 4
Milano MI 20159
023 767-31

(G-2869)
MARTINS PAVERS & POOLS CORP
Also Called: M.T.s Pavers & Pools
220 Nw 40th Ct (33064-2628)
PHONE..................................754 368-4413
Jose C Martins, *Principal*
EMP: 8 **EST:** 2008
SALES (est): 681K **Privately Held**
SIC: 3531 Pavers

(G-2870)
MERGENET MEDICAL INC
1701 W Hillsboro Blvd # 303 (33442-1576)
PHONE..................................561 208-3770
Shara Hernandez, *President*
Charles Lewis, *Director*
Linda Magill, *Director*
EMP: 10 **EST:** 2004
SALES (est): 1MM
SALES (corp-wide): 2.8MM **Privately Held**
WEB: www.mergenetmedical.com
SIC: 3841 Surgical & medical instruments
PA: Mergenet Solutions, Inc.
6601 Lyons Rd Ste B1
Coconut Creek FL 33073
561 558-0129

(G-2871)
MIAMI TECHNICS LLC
457 Goolsby Blvd (33442-3020)
PHONE..................................754 227-5459
EMP: 12 **EST:** 2017
SALES (est): 1.4MM **Privately Held**
WEB: www.miamitechnics.com
SIC: 3728 Aircraft parts & equipment

(G-2872)
MICRO QUALITY CORP
438 S Military Trl (33442-3009)
PHONE..................................954 354-5572
Anne M Yowell, *President*
Gordon Yowell, *Vice Pres*
EMP: 5 **EST:** 2004
SALES (est): 652.8K **Privately Held**
WEB: www.microqualitycorp.com
SIC: 3545 Machine tool accessories

(G-2873)
MINT PRINTS
805 Se 1st Way Ste 8 (33441-5344)
PHONE..................................561 900-5432
Ronny Hantash, *Manager*
EMP: 7 **EST:** 2017
SALES (est): 284K **Privately Held**
WEB: www.mintprints.com
SIC: 2752 Commercial printing, lithographic

(G-2874)
MISC METAL FABRICATION LLC
3001 Sw 15th St Ste A (33442-8199)
PHONE..................................754 264-1026
Juan Vasquez, *Mng Member*
EMP: 10 **EST:** 2012
SQ FT: 12,000
SALES (est): 1MM **Privately Held**
WEB: www.miscmetalfab.com
SIC: 3441 Fabricated structural metal

(G-2875)
MOBILE RVING
2150 Sw 10th St Ste A (33442-7625)
PHONE..................................954 870-7095
EMP: 6 **EST:** 2015
SALES (est): 42.4K **Privately Held**
SIC: 2741 Miscellaneous publishing

(G-2876)
MORI LEE LLC (PA)
3155 Sw 10th St Ste 6a1 (33442-5948)
PHONE..................................954 418-6165
Rick Gross, *Controller*
Chrissy Dodman, *Marketing Mgr*
Gus Cobos, *Info Tech Mgr*
Mitchell Udell,
Madeline Gardner,
▼ **EMP:** 25 **EST:** 1950
SQ FT: 40,000
SALES (est): 8.8MM **Privately Held**
WEB: www.morilee.com
SIC: 2335 Wedding gowns & dresses

(G-2877)
MWI CORPORATION (PA)
Also Called: Mwi Pumps
33 Nw 2nd St (33441-2013)
PHONE..................................954 426-1500
J David Eller, *Ch of Bd*
Dana J Eller, *President*
John Springer, *General Mgr*
Marc Boudet, *Vice Pres*
Daren J Eller, *Vice Pres*
◆ **EMP:** 50 **EST:** 1927
SQ FT: 60,000
SALES (est): 41.8MM **Privately Held**
WEB: www.mwipumps.com
SIC: 3561 7359 Pumps & pumping equipment; equipment rental & leasing

(G-2878)
MY PRINT SHOP INC
1061 Sw 30th Ave (33442-8104)
PHONE..................................954 973-9369
Jeff Pottruck, *President*
EMP: 10 **EST:** 1981
SQ FT: 3,200
SALES (est): 403.8K **Privately Held**
SIC: 2752 2791 2789 Commercial printing, offset; typesetting; bookbinding & related work

(G-2879)
NORES PRECISION INC
44 Se 9th St (33441-5316)
PHONE..................................954 420-0025
James Schlegel, *President*
Rhonda Schlegel, *Vice Pres*
EMP: 48 **EST:** 1945
SQ FT: 8,500
SALES (est): 3.7MM **Privately Held**
WEB: www.noresprecision.com
SIC: 3599 Machine shop, jobbing & repair

(G-2880)
NU-ELEMENT INC
240 Ne 8th Ave (33441-2116)
PHONE..................................561 322-8904
Joseph S Higgins, *President*
EMP: 6 **EST:** 2013
SALES (est): 199.3K **Privately Held**
WEB: www.nuelement.com
SIC: 2819 Industrial inorganic chemicals

(G-2881)
OURO CUSTOM WOODWORK INC
12 Sw 9th St (33441-5346)
P.O. Box 4423 (33442-4423)
PHONE..................................954 428-0735
Mike Ouro, *President*
James J Bugniazet, *Vice Pres*
Carol Morris-Jarrett, *Office Mgr*
EMP: 19 **EST:** 2000
SALES (est): 1.3MM **Privately Held**
WEB: www.ourocustomwoodwork.com
SIC: 2431 Millwork

(G-2882)
PALLET INDUSTRIES INC (DH)
1815 S Powerline Rd (33442-8164)
PHONE..................................954 935-5804
Mitchell Kamps, *President*
Antonio Busto, *Sales Mgr*
EMP: 10 **EST:** 2007
SQ FT: 32,000
SALES (est): 2.8MM
SALES (corp-wide): 1.7B **Privately Held**
WEB: www.palletindustries.com
SIC: 2448 Pallets, wood
HQ: Kamps, Inc.
2900 Peach Ridge Ave Nw
Grand Rapids MI 49534
616 453-9676

(G-2883)
PAVERS SOLUTIONS INC
201 Nw 43rd St (33064-2527)
PHONE..................................754 551-1924
Elvandro F Correa, *Principal*
EMP: 6 **EST:** 2015
SALES (est): 165.4K **Privately Held**
SIC: 2951 Asphalt paving mixtures & blocks

(G-2884)
PAYTON AMERICA INC
Also Called: Payton Group International
1805 S Powerline Rd # 109 (33442-8193)
PHONE..................................954 428-3326
Jim Marinos, *President*
David Yativ, *Vice Pres*
Gil Lucas, *Opers Staff*
Payton Magnetics, *Manager*
Amir Yativ, *Director*
▲ **EMP:** 14 **EST:** 1986
SQ FT: 4,400
SALES (est): 4.5MM **Privately Held**
WEB: www.paytongroup.com
SIC: 3612 Power transformers, electric
PA: Payton Industries Ltd.
3 Haavoda
Ness Ziona 74031

(G-2885)
PEPSICO INC
800 Fairway Dr Ste 400 (33441-1830)
PHONE..................................800 433-2652
Luis Montoya, *Manager*
Andrea Ferrara, *Senior Mgr*
Jonathan Lowry, *Planning*
Amanda Blean, *Associate*
EMP: 6
SALES (corp-wide): 70.3B **Publicly Held**
WEB: www.pepsico.com
SIC: 2086 2096 Bottled & canned soft drinks; iced tea & fruit drinks, bottled & canned; soft drinks: packaged in cans, bottles, etc.; carbonated beverages, nonalcoholic: bottled & canned; corn chips & other corn-based snacks
PA: Pepsico, Inc.
700 Anderson Hill Rd
Purchase NY 10577
914 253-2000

(G-2886)
PERSONAL BRANDS LLC
508 Sw 12th Ave (33442-3110)
PHONE..................................855 426-7765
Joe Davidson, *President*
Piroov Farshar, *COO*
Rebecca Mariolis, *Vice Pres*
EMP: 20 **EST:** 2017
SALES (est): 1.2MM **Privately Held**
WEB: www.thebrandid.com
SIC: 2844 Toilet preparations

(G-2887)
POLENGHI USA INC
720 S Powerline Rd Ste C (33442-8156)
PHONE..................................954 637-4900
Marco Polenghi, *Principal*
EMP: 11 **EST:** 2016
SALES (est): 413.3K **Privately Held**
SIC: 2086 Iced tea & fruit drinks, bottled & canned

(G-2888)
POLYGLASS USA INC (DH)
Also Called: Polyglass Roofg Watering Svcs
1111 W Newport Center Dr (33442-7732)
PHONE..................................954 246-8888
Natalino Zanchetta, *CEO*
Terry Tindal, *Maint Spvr*
Steve Crast, *Research*
Lou Grube, *Research*
Kirk Mulder, *Research*
◆ **EMP:** 65 **EST:** 1991
SALES (est): 112.3MM **Privately Held**
WEB: www.polyglass.us
SIC: 2493 2952 Insulation & roofing material, reconstituted wood; roofing felts, cements or coatings
HQ: Polyglass Spa
Via Dottor Giorgio Squinzi 2
Ponte Di Piave TV 31047
042 275-47

(G-2889)
PREBLE ENTERPRISES INC
Also Called: Precision Aluminum Products
1339 Sw 1st Way (33441-6642)
PHONE..................................954 480-6919
Nick Preble, *President*
Laura Preble, *Corp Secy*
Timothy Preble, *Vice Pres*
EMP: 5 **EST:** 1992
SQ FT: 3,000
SALES (est): 886.3K **Privately Held**
WEB: www.acstands.com
SIC: 3585 Air conditioning condensers & condensing units

(G-2890)
PRIME LIFE NTRTN COMPANYLLC
1239 E Nwport Ctr Dr Ste (33442)
PHONE..................................754 307-7137
Thiago Dias, *CEO*
EMP: 5 **EST:** 2018
SALES (est): 341.6K **Privately Held**
WEB: www.primelifenutrition.org
SIC: 2023 Dietary supplements, dairy & non-dairy based

(G-2891)
PRINT BASICS INC
Also Called: Dpr Print & Promotional
1059 Sw 30th Ave (33442-8104)
PHONE..................................954 354-0700
Ike Abolafia, *CEO*
Lisa M Tanner, *President*
Paul Hendrickson, *General Mgr*
Craig A Tanner, *Vice Pres*
Brian Vecchio, *Prdtn Mgr*
EMP: 27 **EST:** 2002
SQ FT: 3,050
SALES (est): 6.2MM **Privately Held**
WEB: www.printbasics.com
SIC: 2752 Commercial printing, offset

(G-2892)
PRINT E-SOLUTION INC
Also Called: Print Esolutions
409 Goolsby Blvd (33442-3020)
P.O. Box 1004 (33443-1004)
PHONE..................................954 588-5454
Thomas J Wenzel, *President*
EMP: 6
SALES (est): 971.9K **Privately Held**
WEB: www.printesol.com
SIC: 2752 Commercial printing, offset

(G-2893)
PRIORITY 1 SIGNS
1911 Nw 40th Ct (33064-8719)
PHONE..................................954 971-8689
EMP: 10 **EST:** 2014
SALES (est): 450.7K **Privately Held**
SIC: 3993 Signs & advertising specialties

(G-2894)
PRO PAK ENTERPRISES INC
741 Nw 42nd Way (33442-9221)
PHONE..................................888 375-2275
Ralph Droz, *President*
Michael Droz, *Vice Pres*
Debbie Droz, *Director*
EMP: 18 **EST:** 2019
SALES (est): 2.9MM **Privately Held**
SIC: 2673 Plastic bags: made from purchased materials

(G-2895)
PROCRAFT CABINETRY FLORIDA LLC
1850 S Powerline Rd Ste A (33442-8116)
PHONE..................................754 212-2277
Yao Zhao, *President*
Shu Lin,
Xiguang Tang,
EMP: 5 **EST:** 2015
SALES (est): 591.5K **Privately Held**
WEB: www.procraftflorida.com
SIC: 2434 Wood kitchen cabinets

(G-2896)
PRODECO TECHNOLOGIES LLC
1601 Green Rd (33064-1076)
PHONE..................................954 974-6730
▲ **EMP:** 50
SQ FT: 60,000
SALES (est): 10MM **Privately Held**
SIC: 3751 Motorcycles, Bicycles, And Parts, Nsk

(G-2897)
PROSEGUR EAS USA LLC ✪
598 Hillsboro Tech Dr (33441-7732)
PHONE..................................561 900-2744
Matthew P Sack,
EMP: 18 **EST:** 2020
SALES (est): 3.4MM
SALES (corp-wide): 187.9MM **Privately Held**
WEB: www.prosegur-eas.com
SIC: 2679 Tags & labels, paper
PA: Prosegur Services Group, Inc.
512 Herndon Pkwy Ste A
Herndon VA 20170
703 464-4735

(G-2898)
PYLON MANUFACTURING CORP (DH)
600 W Hillsboro Blvd # 4 (33441-1609)
PHONE..................................800 626-4902
Gary Cohen, *CEO*
Michael Fretwell, *President*
Bart Plaumann, *Principal*
Rich Cimino, *Vice Pres*
Richard Cimino, *Vice Pres*
◆ **EMP:** 46 **EST:** 1974
SQ FT: 15,000
SALES (est): 11.9MM **Privately Held**
WEB: www.pylonhq.com
SIC: 3714 Wipers, windshield, motor vehicle
HQ: Qualitor, Inc.
1840 Mcculough St
Lima OH 45801
248 204-8600

(G-2899)
RAMOS WOODWORK LLC
Also Called: IL Mobile
1955 Sw 15th Pl (33442-6101)
PHONE..................................954 861-7679
Eduardo Coutinho Ramos, *Principal*
EMP: 8 **EST:** 2016
SALES (est): 150K **Privately Held**
SIC: 2431 Millwork

(G-2900)
RASKIN INDUSTRIES LLC
710 S Powerline Rd Ste G (33442-8176)
PHONE..................................561 997-6658
Michael Raskin, *CEO*
William Lapis, *COO*
John Hunter, *Vice Pres*
Carlos Franco, *Sales Mgr*
Sofia Tsionis, *Marketing Mgr*
▲ **EMP:** 13 **EST:** 2011
SALES (est): 1.9MM **Privately Held**
WEB: www.raskinind.com
SIC: 3253 Ceramic wall & floor tile

(G-2901)
REDINGTON COUNTERS INC
702 S Military Trl (33442-3025)
PHONE..................................954 725-6699
Bill Fitzsimmons, *Principal*
Michael Demarco, *COO*
Ron Kendzior, *Vice Pres*
Mike Davenport, *Manager*
Richard Woods, *Manager*
EMP: 9 **EST:** 2012
SALES (est): 116K **Privately Held**
SIC: 3829 Measuring & controlling devices

(G-2902)
REGENT LABS INC (PA)
700 W Hillsboro Blvd 2-206 (33441-1695)
PHONE..................................954 426-4889
Eugene RE, *President*
EMP: 6 **EST:** 1979
SQ FT: 8,000
SALES (est): 1.8MM **Privately Held**
WEB: www.regentlabs.com
SIC: 3843 Dental equipment & supplies

(G-2903)
REGENT LABS INC
473 Goolsby Blvd (33442-3020)
PHONE..................................954 426-4889
David Ptak, *Manager*
EMP: 8
SALES (corp-wide): 1.8MM **Privately Held**
WEB: www.regentlabs.com
SIC: 3843 4225 Dental equipment & supplies; general warehousing & storage
PA: Regent Labs, Inc.
700 W Hillsboro Blvd 2-206
Deerfield Beach FL 33441
954 426-4889

(G-2904)
RESOLVERS LLC
711 Se 1st Way Apt 6 (33441-5324)
PHONE..................................954 254-7948
Ron Eisner, *Principal*
EMP: 6 **EST:** 2008
SALES (est): 143.1K **Privately Held**
SIC: 3621 Resolvers

(G-2905)
REYNOSO & ASSOCIATES INC
Also Called: Optimum Power & Envmt Fla
434 Sw 12th Ave (33442-3108)
PHONE..................................954 360-0601
Mia China Ling Reynoso, *President*
Christopher Bachman, *Vice Pres*
EMP: 7 **EST:** 1989
SQ FT: 2,710
SALES (est): 5MM **Privately Held**
SIC: 3694 Engine electrical equipment

(G-2906)
SARGEANT BULK ASPHALT INC
321 E Hillsboro Blvd (33441-3539)
PHONE..................................954 763-4796
Daniel Sargeant, *President*
Harry Sargeant Jr, *Director*
EMP: 8 **EST:** 2014
SALES (est): 474.9K **Privately Held**
WEB: www.sargeantmarine.com
SIC: 2952 Asphalt felts & coatings

(G-2907)
SC ELEARNING LLC
Also Called: Trivantis
400 Fairway Dr Ste 101 (33441-1808)
PHONE..................................561 293-2543
Daniel Bovarnick, *COO*
John Blackmon, *CTO*
Felipe Prieto, *Sr Software Eng*
EMP: 63 **EST:** 2016
SALES (est): 1.5MM **Privately Held**
SIC: 7372 Prepackaged software

(G-2908)
SELECT EUROPE INC
3000 Sw 15th St Ste E (33442-8198)
PHONE..................................407 931-1820
Tony Varol, *President*
Christina Germakopoulos - Varo, *Vice Pres*
◆ **EMP:** 5 **EST:** 2003
SALES (est): 944.8K **Privately Held**
WEB: www.selecteuropeinc.com
SIC: 2091 5146 Seafood products: packaged in cans, jars, etc.; fish & seafoods

(G-2909)
SENELCO IBERIA INC (DH)
500 Nw 12th Ave (33442-1723)
PHONE..................................561 912-6000
Bob Vanourek, *CEO*
▲ **EMP:** 100 **EST:** 1995
SALES (est): 2.9MM **Publicly Held**
WEB: www.sensormatic.com
SIC: 3812 5065 Detection apparatus: electronic/magnetic field, light/heat; security control equipment & systems
HQ: Sensormatic International Inc
6600 Congress Ave
Boca Raton FL 33487
561 912-6000

(G-2910)
SHL PHARMA LLC
588 Jim Moran Blvd (33442-1710)
PHONE..................................954 725-2008
Roger Samuelsson, *CEO*
Lucio Giambattista, *Vice Pres*
Mats Persson, *Vice Pres*
Greg Terranova, *Mfg Mgr*
Kyle Fitzpatrick, *Engineer*
EMP: 20 **EST:** 2010
SALES (est): 9.6MM
SALES (corp-wide): 660.4MM **Privately Held**
WEB: www.shl-medical.com
SIC: 3841 Surgical & medical instruments
PA: Shl Medical Ag
Gubelstrasse 22
Zug ZG 6300
413 680-000

(G-2911)
SIGNGRAPHIX INC
242 S Military Trl (33442-3029)
PHONE..................................954 571-7131
Silvia Lo Monaco, *President*
EMP: 6 **EST:** 2002
SALES (est): 708.7K **Privately Held**
WEB: www.signgraphix.com
SIC: 3993 Signs & advertising specialties

(G-2912)
SINOBEC RESOURCES LLC
1901 Green Rd Ste E (33064-1059)
PHONE..................................561 409-2205
John Lee,
▲ **EMP:** 5 **EST:** 2012
SALES (est): 1MM
SALES (corp-wide): 300K **Privately Held**
WEB: www.sinobecresources.com
SIC: 3365 3354 Masts, cast aluminum; aluminum extruded products
HQ: Commerce Sinobec Inc
4455 Rue Cousens
Saint-Laurent QC H4S 1
514 339-9333

(G-2913)
SKI RIXEN - QUIET WATERS INC
Also Called: Ski Rixen USA
401 S Powerline Rd (33442-8182)
PHONE..................................954 429-0215
Brita Schipner, *President*
EMP: 5 **EST:** 1983
SALES (est): 544.4K **Privately Held**
WEB: www.skirixenusa.com
SIC: 3949 Water skis

(G-2914)
SOUTH FLORIDA PRINT
3413 Sw 14th St (33442-8140)
PHONE..................................561 807-8584
Amir Ben-Haim, *Principal*
EMP: 6 **EST:** 2018
SALES (est): 176.7K **Privately Held**
WEB: www.southfloridaprint.com
SIC: 2752 Commercial printing, offset

(G-2915)
SOUTHEAST PUBLICATIONS USA INC
2150 Sw 10th St Ste A (33442-7625)
PHONE..................................954 368-4686
Wally Warrick, *President*
Wayne Morris, *Vice Pres*
Carol Tims, *Sales Associate*
EMP: 38 **EST:** 1987
SALES (est): 5MM **Privately Held**
SIC: 2741 Miscellaneous publishing

(G-2916)
SOUTHEASTERN MARKETING ASSOCIA
1522 Se 10th St (33441-7165)
PHONE..................................954 421-7388
William Chupp, *Owner*
EMP: 8 **EST:** 2002
SALES (est): 282.9K **Privately Held**
SIC: 7372 Prepackaged software

(G-2917)
STERLING MDR INC
741 Nw 42nd Way (33442-9221)
PHONE..................................954 725-2777
Ralph Droz, *President*
Michael Wood, *Vice Pres*
Yazmin Carbajal, *Sales Staff*
Brian Gutschick, *Sales Staff*
Lisa Costley, *Sales Associate*
EMP: 16 **EST:** 2009
SALES (est): 2.4MM **Privately Held**
SIC: 2673 7389 Bags: plastic, laminated & coated; business services

(G-2918)
SUN-SENTINEL COMPANY LLC
333 Sw 12th Ave (33442-3196)
PHONE..................................954 356-4000
Yvonne Valdez, *Editor*
Charles Ray, *Branch Mgr*
Holly Svekis, *Manager*
EMP: 39
SALES (corp-wide): 746.2MM **Privately Held**
WEB: www.sun-sentinel.com
SIC: 2711 2741 Newspapers, publishing & printing; miscellaneous publishing
HQ: Sun-Sentinel Company, Llc
500 E Broward Blvd # 800
Fort Lauderdale FL 33394
954 356-4000

(G-2919)
SUNSHINE ALANCE CABINETS MLLWK
712 S Military Trl (33442-3025)
PHONE..................................954 621-7444
EMP: 12 **EST:** 2018
SALES (est): 1MM **Privately Held**
SIC: 2434 Wood kitchen cabinets

(G-2920)
SUSTAINABLE CASEWORK INDS LLC
Also Called: SCI
720 S Deerfield Ave Ste 1 (33441-5385)
PHONE..................................954 980-6506
Jonathan R Kaplan, *Mng Member*
EMP: 7 **EST:** 2012
SQ FT: 10,000
SALES (est): 146.7K **Privately Held**
SIC: 3999 Chairs, hydraulic, barber & beauty shop

(G-2921)
T & M INDUSTRIES INC
1106 Se 14th Dr (33441-7227)
PHONE..................................954 778-2238
Tanner Strohmenger, *Principal*
EMP: 11 **EST:** 2018
SALES (est): 54K **Privately Held**
WEB: www.delawarecourt.com
SIC: 3999 Manufacturing industries

(G-2922)
T H L DIAMOND PRODUCTS INC
Also Called: Shark Tools
312 S Powerline Rd (33442-8105)
PHONE..................................954 596-5012
Sean Thompson, *President*
EMP: 7 **EST:** 1999
SALES (est): 600K **Privately Held**
WEB: www.sharkdiamondblade.com
SIC: 3544 Special dies, tools, jigs & fixtures

(G-2923)
TARMAC FLORIDA INC
455 Fairway Dr (33441-1809)
PHONE..................................954 481-2800
Aris Papadopoulos, *President*
EMP: 16 **EST:** 1977
SALES (est): 2MM **Privately Held**
SIC: 3273 Ready-mixed concrete

(G-2924)
TCA POOL INC
350 Sw 32nd Ave (33442-2354)
PHONE..................................954 600-2448
Constantino C Almeida, *Principal*
EMP: 7 **EST:** 2009
SALES (est): 161.3K **Privately Held**
WEB: www.tcapool.com
SIC: 2369 Bathing suits & swimwear: girls', children's & infants'

(G-2925)
TERRY BOCA INC
512 Hillsboro Tech Dr (33441-7732)
PHONE..................................561 893-0333
Jyll Brink, *Accounts Mgr*
Jeffrey Russo, *Sales Executive*
Jennifer Gulliford, *Manager*
Ed Cohen,
Bruce Cohen,
◆ **EMP:** 8 **EST:** 1995
SALES (est): 755.6K **Privately Held**
WEB: www.bocaterry.com
SIC: 2384 2672 Bathrobes, men's & women's: made from purchased materials; cloth lined paper: made from purchased paper

(G-2926)
TIDES MARINE INC
3251 Sw 13th Dr Ste A (33442-8166)
PHONE..................................954 420-0949
Tom Zaniewski, *President*
Jeff Strong, *Principal*
◆ **EMP:** 22 **EST:** 1990
SQ FT: 10,000
SALES (est): 4.9MM **Privately Held**
WEB: www.tidesmarine.com
SIC: 3429 Marine hardware

(G-2927)
TIGHTLINE PUBLICATIONS INC
2795 Sw 11th Pl (33442-5909)
P.O. Box 4397 (33442-4397)
PHONE..................................954 570-7174
Vincent Montella, *President*
Anthony Montella, *Vice Pres*
Gail Monteal, *Treasurer*
EMP: 8 **EST:** 1991
SALES (est): 287.7K **Privately Held**
WEB: www.outdoorcharts.com
SIC: 2741 Miscellaneous publishing

(G-2928)
TITAN AMERICA LLC
Also Called: Tarmac Standard Concrete
455 Fairway Dr Ste 200 (33441-1805)
P.O. Box 8648 (33443-8648)
PHONE..................................954 426-8407
Steven Brown, *Vice Pres*
Thomas Cerullo, *Vice Pres*
Don Ingrassano, *Vice Pres*
George Pantazopoulos, *Vice Pres*
Louis Petrillo, *Vice Pres*
EMP: 50
SALES (corp-wide): 177.9K **Privately Held**
WEB: www.titanamerica.com
SIC: 3273 Ready-mixed concrete
HQ: Titan America Llc
5700 Lake Wright Dr # 300
Norfolk VA 23502
757 858-6500

(G-2929)
TRIVANTIS CORPORATION (HQ)
Also Called: Lectora
400 Fairway Dr Ste 101 (33441-1808)
P.O. Box 1000, Memphis TN (38148-0001)
PHONE..................................513 929-0188
Andrew Scivally, *CEO*
Christie Calahan, *Marketing Staff*
Charles J Beech, *Bd of Directors*
▲ **EMP:** 65 **EST:** 1999
SQ FT: 22,000
SALES (est): 3.3MM **Privately Held**
WEB: www.elearningbrothers.com
SIC: 7372 7371 Publishers' computer software; custom computer programming services

(G-2930)
TURNER ENVIROLOGIC INC
1140 Sw 34th Ave (33442-8183)
PHONE..................................954 422-9566
Thomas K Turner, *President*

Robert Battleson, *Project Mgr*
EMP: 44 **EST:** 1981
SQ FT: 18,000
SALES (est): 6.6MM **Privately Held**
WEB: www.tenviro.com
SIC: 3564 Air purification equipment

(G-2931)
US BUILDING SYSTEMS CORP
401 Fairway Dr Ste 100 (33441-1800)
PHONE..................................954 281-2100
Gary J Rack, *President*
EMP: 15 **EST:** 1991
SQ FT: 12,400
SALES (est): 969.6K **Privately Held**
SIC: 3448 Prefabricated metal buildings

(G-2932)
US PRECISION MANUFACTURING INC
Also Called: Ligi Tool and Engineering
3220 Sw 15th St (33442-8126)
PHONE..................................954 332-2921
Richard Greece, *CEO*
EMP: 20 **EST:** 2018
SALES (est): 5.7MM
SALES (corp-wide): 1.9B **Publicly Held**
WEB: www.ligi.com
SIC: 3599 Machine shop, jobbing & repair
HQ: Rave Llc
430 S Congress Ave Ste 7
Delray Beach FL 33445
561 330-0411

(G-2933)
VINAVIL AMERICAS CORPORATION
1144 E Newport Center Dr (33442-7725)
PHONE..................................954 246-8888
Hemant Shah, *Principal*
▲ **EMP:** 56 **EST:** 1997
SALES (est): 368.3K **Privately Held**
WEB: www.vinavil.com
SIC: 2822 2851 Ethylene-propylene rubbers, EPDM polymers; paints & allied products

(G-2934)
VOLUNTEER CAPITAL LLC
Also Called: Priority One Signs
1911 Nw 40th Ct (33064-8719)
PHONE..................................954 366-6659
William Reicherter, *Mng Member*
EMP: 9 **EST:** 2014
SALES (est): 442.1K **Privately Held**
WEB: www.p1signs.com
SIC: 3993 Signs & advertising specialties

(G-2935)
WECANDO PRINT LLC
424 Sw 12th Ave (33442-3108)
PHONE..................................754 222-9144
Thomas C Letourneau, *Principal*
EMP: 11 **EST:** 2015
SALES (est): 257K **Privately Held**
SIC: 2752 Commercial printing, offset

(G-2936)
WRAP-ART INC
712 S Military Trl (33442-3025)
P.O. Box 6576, Delray Beach (33482-6576)
PHONE..................................954 428-1819
Roberta Tractenberg, *President*
Stanley Tractenberg, *Treasurer*
▲ **EMP:** 9 **EST:** 1998
SQ FT: 5,000
SALES (est): 945K **Privately Held**
WEB: www.wrap-art.com
SIC: 2679 Gift wrap, paper: made from purchased material; novelties, paper: made from purchased material

(G-2937)
WRISTBAND SUPPLY LLC
Also Called: Wristband Specialty
3000 Sw 15th St Ste F (33442-8198)
PHONE..................................954 571-3993
Michael Feingold, *Mng Member*
EMP: 15 **EST:** 2012
SALES (est): 1.6MM **Privately Held**
WEB: www.wristbandsupply.com
SIC: 2389 Arm bands, elastic

(G-2938)
YOU LUCKY DOG INC
947 S Federal Hwy (33441-5753)
PHONE..................................954 428-4648
Tony Mizelle, *Principal*
EMP: 6 **EST:** 2010
SALES (est): 178.2K **Privately Held**
SIC: 3999 Pet supplies

Defuniak Springs
Walton County

(G-2939)
AKASHIC SPIRIT PUBLISHING LLC
610 Rio Ranchero Rd (32433-6997)
PHONE..................................850 974-4944
Douglas Maier, *Principal*
EMP: 6 **EST:** 2012
SALES (est): 115.5K **Privately Held**
WEB: www.akashicspiritpublishing.com
SIC: 2741 Miscellaneous publishing

(G-2940)
CHAUTUQUA VINEYARDS WINERY INC (PA)
Also Called: Emerald Coast Wine Cellars
364 Hugh Adams Rd (32435-3429)
P.O. Box 1308 (32435-1308)
PHONE..................................850 892-5887
Paul Owens, *President*
Sharah Curry, *Manager*
EMP: 10 **EST:** 2005
SALES (est): 1.7MM **Privately Held**
WEB: www.chautauquawinery.com
SIC: 2084 Wines

(G-2941)
DEFUNIAK SPRINGS HERALD BREEZE
740 Baldwin Ave (32435-2598)
P.O. Box 1546 (32435-7546)
PHONE..................................850 892-3232
Gary Woodham, *President*
EMP: 9 **EST:** 1888
SALES (est): 171.6K **Privately Held**
WEB: www.defuniakherald.com
SIC: 2711 Job printing & newspaper publishing combined

(G-2942)
FLORIDA TRANSFORMER INC (DH)
Also Called: Emerald Transformer
4509 St Hwy 83 N (32433-3960)
P.O. Box 507 (32435-0507)
PHONE..................................850 892-2711
Stuart Prior, *CEO*
Mike Burns, *Exec VP*
Mark Newman, *CFO*
Robin Wilson, *CFO*
Thom Rowe, *Natl Sales Mgr*
◆ **EMP:** 120 **EST:** 2006
SQ FT: 100,000
SALES (est): 94.4MM
SALES (corp-wide): 574.1MM **Privately Held**
WEB: www.emeraldtransformer.com
SIC: 3612 Transformers, except electric
HQ: Versatile Processing Group, Inc.
10848 Luna Rd
Dallas TX 75220
317 577-9300

(G-2943)
FORWARD DEFUNIAK INCORPORATED
504 Circle Dr (32435-2565)
PHONE..................................850 830-7663
Bruce Morrison, *Vice Pres*
Daniel Cosson, *Treasurer*
Melinda Henderson, *Exec Dir*
Geneva Lee, *Admin Sec*
EMP: 7 **EST:** 2019
SALES (est): 134.6K **Privately Held**
WEB: www.defuniakherald.com
SIC: 2711 Newspapers, publishing & printing

(G-2944)
LEGACY VULCAN LLC
Also Called: De Funiak Springs Yard
104 Lee S Pl (32435-7720)
PHONE..................................850 951-0562
Buddy Brown, *Manager*
EMP: 7 **Publicly Held**
WEB: www.vulcanmaterials.com
SIC: 3273 Ready-mixed concrete
HQ: Legacy Vulcan, Llc
1200 Urban Center Dr
Vestavia AL 35242
205 298-3000

(G-2945)
ONVOI AVI SUPP AND INSPECT SER
Also Called: Eagle Aviation Maintenance
619 Airpark Rd (32435-4776)
PHONE..................................805 312-3274
Dave Ricker, *Mng Member*
Rich Dobbins, *Mng Member*
EMP: 7 **EST:** 2019
SALES (est): 476K **Privately Held**
WEB: www.monarchaviation.com
SIC: 3721 Aircraft

(G-2946)
PROFESSIONAL PRODUCTS INC
Also Called: Ezy Wrap
54 Hugh Adams Rd (32435-3400)
P.O. Box 589 (32435-0589)
PHONE..................................850 892-5731
Bryan E Kilbey, *CEO*
James Miller, *Principal*
Sarah Kilbey, *Corp Secy*
Dean Stanton, *COO*
Chris Bozeman, *CFO*
◆ **EMP:** 170 **EST:** 1963
SQ FT: 35,000
SALES (est): 21.4MM **Privately Held**
WEB: www.ezywrap.com
SIC: 3842 Orthopedic appliances

(G-2947)
SPECTRAFLEX INC
83 Lancelot Rd (32433-6968)
P.O. Box 1225 (32435-1225)
PHONE..................................850 892-3900
Fax: 850 892-3900
▲ **EMP:** 7
SQ FT: 3,000
SALES (est): 610K **Privately Held**
SIC: 3679 Mfg Electronic Wire And Cable Harness Assemblies

(G-2948)
SUPERIOR ROOF TILE MFG
50 Hugh Adams Rd (32435-3400)
P.O. Box 487 (32435-0487)
PHONE..................................850 892-2299
Jessie Lynn, *President*
Barbara Ferguson, *Manager*
▼ **EMP:** 10 **EST:** 1999
SQ FT: 20,000
SALES (est): 138.1K **Privately Held**
SIC: 3272 Roofing tile & slabs, concrete

(G-2949)
TIKAL PAVERS INC
5991 Coy Burgess Loop (32435-6362)
PHONE..................................850 892-2207
EMP: 5
SALES (est): 624.8K **Privately Held**
SIC: 2951 Mfg Asphalt Mixtures/Blocks

(G-2950)
TROPICANA PRODUCTS INC
400 E Nelson Ave (32433-7443)
PHONE..................................850 610-8849
EMP: 7
SALES (corp-wide): 70.3B **Publicly Held**
WEB: www.tropicana.com
SIC: 2033 Canned fruits & specialties
HQ: Tropicana Products, Inc.
1001 13th Ave E
Bradenton FL 34208
941 747-4461

Deland
Volusia County

(G-2951)
4FRONT SOLUTIONS LLC
3045 Tech Pkwy (32724)
PHONE..................................814 464-2000
Richard P Ward, *President*
EMP: 60 **Privately Held**
WEB: www.4frontsolutions.com
SIC: 3672 Printed circuit boards
HQ: 4front Solutions, Llc
8140 Hawthorne Dr
Erie PA 16509
814 464-2000

(G-2952)
ABRAAHAM ROSA SEASONINGS INC
813a Flight Line Blvd (32724-2059)
PHONE..................................386 453-4827
Ana Rosa-Randolph, *CEO*
Ana Cristina Randolph, *Vice Pres*
EMP: 8 **EST:** 2013
SQ FT: 1,400
SALES (est): 371.5K **Privately Held**
SIC: 2099 Food preparations

(G-2953)
ADVANCED MFG & PWR SYSTEMS INC
Also Called: Amps
1965 Bennett Ave (32724-1928)
PHONE..................................386 822-5565
Chris Ingles, *President*
Debbie Naccarato, *Project Mgr*
Debbi Graham, *Finance Mgr*
Rick Kendrick, *Sales Engr*
◆ **EMP:** 37 **EST:** 1999
SQ FT: 40,000
SALES (est): 8.7MM **Privately Held**
WEB: www.amps.cc
SIC: 3621 Electric motor & generator parts

(G-2954)
AERODYNE RESEARCH LLC
1725 Lexington Ave (32724-2148)
PHONE..................................813 891-6300
Debbie Ingling, *Manager*
William Legard,
EMP: 11 **EST:** 1990
SALES (est): 1.1MM **Privately Held**
WEB: www.flyaerodyne.com
SIC: 2399 Parachutes

(G-2955)
AIR LION INCORP
2609 Old Church Pl (32720-1408)
PHONE..................................386 748-9296
Vasyl Levchenko, *Principal*
EMP: 8 **EST:** 2009
SALES (est): 195.7K **Privately Held**
WEB: www.airlionturbines.com
SIC: 3724 Aircraft engines & engine parts

(G-2956)
ALFA PRODUCTS LLC
425 Nowell Loop (32724-9712)
PHONE..................................901 218-0802
Richard Wilkes, *Principal*
EMP: 6 **EST:** 2013
SALES (est): 114.3K **Privately Held**
WEB: www.wilkeswings.com
SIC: 2035 Pickles, sauces & salad dressings

(G-2957)
ALTI-2 INC
1200 Flight Line Blvd # 5 (32724-2138)
PHONE..................................386 943-9333
Roger F Allen, *President*
Jeremy Gola, *Software Engr*
Carol White, *Admin Asst*
EMP: 19 **EST:** 1999
SQ FT: 5,000
SALES (est): 3.7MM **Privately Held**
WEB: www.alti-2.com
SIC: 3812 Altimeters, standard & sensitive

(G-2958)
APEX GRINDING INC
1857 Patterson Ave Unit 4 (32724-1961)
PHONE..................................386 624-7350

EMP: 5 **EST:** 2018
SALES (est): 372.9K **Privately Held**
WEB: www.apexgrinding.com
SIC: 3999 Custom pulverizing & grinding of plastic materials

(G-2959)
ARC GROUP WORLDWIDE INC (PA)
810 Flight Line Blvd (32724-2055)
PHONE..................................303 467-5236
Drew Kelley, *CEO*
Alan Quasha, *Ch of Bd*
Chris Lak, *Business Mgr*
Sam Vavro, *Business Mgr*
Chris Wilson, *Business Mgr*
EMP: 69 **EST:** 1987
SQ FT: 40,000
SALES: 82.4MM **Privately Held**
WEB: www.arcw.com
SIC: 3499 3462 3812 Friction material, made from powdered metal; flange, valve & pipe fitting forgings, ferrous; antennas, radar or communications

(G-2960)
ARDMORE FARMS LLC
1915 N Woodland Blvd (32720-1799)
PHONE..................................386 734-4634
Kenny Sadai, *Ch of Bd*
James O'Toole, *President*
Thomas A Kolb, *CFO*
▲ **EMP:** 100 **EST:** 1951
SQ FT: 78,000
SALES (est): 24.8MM **Privately Held**
WEB: www.countrypure.com
SIC: 2037 2033 Fruit juices, frozen; fruit juice concentrates, frozen; canned fruits & specialties
PA: Country Pure Foods, Inc.
222 W Main St Ste 401
Akron OH 44308

(G-2961)
ARMOUR COMPANIES LLC
1370 Saratoga St (32724-2136)
PHONE..................................386 740-7459
EMP: 6 **EST:** 2019
SALES (est): 113.8K **Privately Held**
WEB: www.armourhorsestalls.com
SIC: 3999 Manufacturing industries

(G-2962)
BEST PALLETS OF FL LLC
1830 Patterson Ave Unit D (32724-1962)
PHONE..................................386 624-5575
Constantino Delapaz, *Principal*
EMP: 6 **EST:** 2013
SALES (est): 283.4K **Privately Held**
WEB: www.bestpalletsoffl.com
SIC: 2448 Pallets, wood

(G-2963)
CEMEX MATERIALS LLC
2170 State Road 472 (32724-9614)
PHONE..................................386 775-0790
Brad Davis, *Branch Mgr*
EMP: 73
SQ FT: 11,467 **Privately Held**
SIC: 3273 5032 5211 Ready-mixed concrete; concrete mixtures; concrete & cinder block
HQ: Cemex Materials Llc
1501 Belvedere Rd
West Palm Beach FL 33406
561 833-5555

(G-2964)
CONTEMPORARY CARBIDE TECH
1730 Patterson Ave Unit B (32724-1950)
PHONE..................................386 734-0080
Alan Evans, *President*
David Gee, *Vice Pres*
EMP: 16 **EST:** 1997
SQ FT: 5,000
SALES (est): 521.3K **Privately Held**
SIC: 3325 Bushings, cast steel: except investment

(G-2965)
COUNTRY PURE FOODS INC
1915 N Woodland Blvd (32720-1718)
PHONE..................................904 734-4634
EMP: 265
SALES (corp-wide): 4.3B **Privately Held**
SIC: 2037 Mfg Frozen Fruits/Vegetables
HQ: Country Pure Foods, Inc.
681 W Waterloo Rd
Akron OH 44308
330 753-2293

(G-2966)
DAVID SAYNE MASONRY INC
1010 Geryl Way (32724-8063)
PHONE..................................386 873-4696
David Sayne, *President*
Margaret Sayne, *Corp Secy*
EMP: 10
SALES (est): 600K **Privately Held**
SIC: 3241 Masonry cement

(G-2967)
DELAND METAL CRAFT COMPANY
300 W Beresford Ave (32720-7397)
PHONE..................................386 734-0828
Edward J Ray, *President*
Brooke Whitaker, *Vice Pres*
EMP: 9 **EST:** 1967
SQ FT: 7,800
SALES (est): 800K **Privately Held**
WEB: www.delandmetalcraft.com
SIC: 3446 5169 Architectural metalwork; industrial gases

(G-2968)
DELTA MACHINE LLC
1501 Lexington Ave (32724-2117)
PHONE..................................386 738-2204
EMP: 8
SALES (est): 686K **Privately Held**
SIC: 3599 Mfg Industrial Machinery

(G-2969)
DELTA MACHINE & TOOL INC
Also Called: Norco
1212 N Mcdonald Ave (32724-2525)
PHONE..................................386 738-2204
EMP: 20
SQ FT: 5,000
SALES (est): 2.6MM **Privately Held**
SIC: 3542 3089 3544 Mfg Machine Tools-Forming Mfg Plastic Products Mfg Dies/Tools/Jigs/Fixtures

(G-2970)
DIEMECH TURBINE SOLUTION INC
Also Called: Turbine Solution Group
1200 Flight Line Blvd # 1 (32724-2138)
PHONE..................................386 804-0179
Christian H Skoppe, *President*
Marvin Kubaszewski, *General Mgr*
▲ **EMP:** 6 **EST:** 2006
SALES (est): 757.1K **Privately Held**
WEB: www.diemechturbinesolution.com
SIC: 3511 Turbines & turbine generator sets

(G-2971)
DILLCO INC
1842 Patterson Ave (32724-1953)
PHONE..................................386 734-7510
EMP: 16
SQ FT: 2,500
SALES (est): 1.4MM **Privately Held**
SIC: 2759 3089 3499 Contract Screen Printing & Mfg Plastic Hardware Including Wall Light Switch Covers & Picture Frames

(G-2972)
DOBROS INC
803 W New York Ave (32720-5226)
PHONE..................................386 279-0003
Michael Knott, *Owner*
EMP: 8 **EST:** 2011
SALES (est): 724.2K **Privately Held**
WEB: www.dobros.net
SIC: 3421 Table & food cutlery, including butchers'

(G-2973)
EDC CORPORATION
1701 Lexington Ave (32724-2148)
PHONE..................................386 951-4075
Kurt H Prestegard, *Principal*
Donna Bailey, *Info Tech Mgr*
EMP: 5 **EST:** 2008
SALES (est): 450.3K **Privately Held**
WEB: www.edcpma.com
SIC: 3824 Mechanical measuring meters

(G-2974)
EIFF AERODYNAMICS INC
1405 Flight Line Blvd # 18 (32724-2192)
PHONE..................................386 734-3958
Jeff Eiff, *President*
EMP: 11 **EST:** 1996
SALES (est): 272.1K **Privately Held**
WEB: www.eiff.com
SIC: 2399 Parachutes

(G-2975)
ENVIRO WATER SOLUTIONS LLC
Also Called: Pelican Water Systems
3060 Prfmce Cir Ste 2 (32724)
PHONE..................................877 842-1635
Karl Frykman, *President*
Dan Snellback, *Opers Staff*
Margaret Kearney, *Controller*
Robert Prentice, *Marketing Staff*
▼ **EMP:** 79 **EST:** 2013
SALES (est): 8.6MM **Privately Held**
SIC: 3589 5074 Water filters & softeners, household type; water softeners
PA: Pentair Public Limited Company
10 Earlsfort Terrace
Dublin

(G-2976)
F & S CABINETS INC
1307 Yorktown St (32724-2123)
PHONE..................................386 822-9525
Rich Santora, *President*
Murial Santora, *Admin Sec*
EMP: 20 **EST:** 2004
SALES (est): 2.4MM **Privately Held**
SIC: 2521 Cabinets, office: wood

(G-2977)
FABRICO INC
1700 E Intl Speedway Blvd (32724)
PHONE..................................386 736-7373
Patrick Mullane, *President*
Amanda Magee, *CFO*
Bernie Gordon, *Sales Engr*
Mark Lloyd, *Director*
▲ **EMP:** 167 **EST:** 2001
SALES (est): 52.7MM
SALES (corp-wide): 1B **Publicly Held**
WEB: www.technetics.com
SIC: 3053 Gaskets & sealing devices
HQ: Technetics Group Llc
5605 Carnegie Blvd # 500
Charlotte NC 28209
704 731-1500

(G-2978)
FLUID WINGS LLC
1636 Old Daytona St (32724-2023)
PHONE..................................888 245-5843
Scott Roberts, *Mng Member*
EMP: 10 **EST:** 2013
SALES (est): 580.9K **Privately Held**
WEB: www.fluidwings.com
SIC: 2399 Fabricated textile products

(G-2979)
FORTERRA PIPE & PRECAST LLC
Also Called: Hanson Pipe & Products
840 West Ave (32720-3528)
P.O. Box 369 (32721-0369)
PHONE..................................386 734-6228
Rebecca Holiday, *Manager*
EMP: 10
SQ FT: 87,860
SALES (corp-wide): 1.5B **Publicly Held**
WEB: www.forterrabp.com
SIC: 3272 Concrete products
HQ: Forterra Pipe & Precast, Llc
511 E John Carpenter Fwy
Irving TX 75062
469 458-7973

(G-2980)
GRADE A GLASS (PA)
1640 Patterson Ave (32724-1938)
PHONE..................................321 419-6935
Robert Lorden, *President*
Andrea Dunmire, *Mng Member*
EMP: 80 **EST:** 2017
SALES (est): 146.5K **Privately Held**
SIC: 3231 Products of purchased glass

(G-2981)
GRAND PRODUCTS INTERNATIONAL
1601 Essex Ave (32724-2101)
PHONE..................................386 736-3528
Jerry Bullis, *President*
Marcia Macmahon, *Corp Secy*
Carl Fitzwater, *Vice Pres*
Bill W Murphy, *Treasurer*
◆ **EMP:** 6 **EST:** 1990
SQ FT: 1,500
SALES (est): 127.4K **Privately Held**
SIC: 2037 Fruit juices

(G-2982)
GREEN MOUNTAIN SPECIALTIES
2004 Brunswick Ln 5 (32724-2001)
PHONE..................................386 469-0057
Scarlet Marsil, *President*
EMP: 12 **EST:** 2012
SALES (est): 2MM **Privately Held**
WEB: www.support.website-creator.org
SIC: 3315 Steel wire & related products

(G-2983)
HOHOL MARINE PRODUCTS
2741 W New York Ave (32720)
PHONE..................................386 734-0630
Larry Hohol, *Owner*
EMP: 7 **EST:** 2004
SQ FT: 1,000
SALES (est): 164.8K **Privately Held**
WEB: www.theluzernecountyrailroad.com
SIC: 3732 2499 5551 Boat building & repairing; floating docks, wood; boat dealers

(G-2984)
INTELLITEC MOTOR VEHICLES LLC (HQ)
1455 Jacobs Rd (32724-2604)
PHONE..................................386 738-7307
Chris Benham, *Mng Member*
Frank Ellow,
Patrick J O'Neill,
▲ **EMP:** 47 **EST:** 2004
SALES (est): 11.9MM **Privately Held**
WEB: www.intellitec.com
SIC: 3679 Electronic circuits
PA: Nsi Consulting & Development Inc
24079 Research Dr
Farmington Hills MI 48335
248 987-7180

(G-2985)
ISLAND SHUTTER CO INC
Also Called: Hunter Wood Products
1838 Patterson Ave (32724-1924)
PHONE..................................386 738-9455
Chad Hunter, *President*
Joel Hunter, *Manager*
EMP: 27 **EST:** 1993
SALES (est): 724.3K **Privately Held**
WEB: www.islandshutter.com
SIC: 2431 5211 2591 7349 Window shutters, wood; lumber & other building materials; drapery hardware & blinds & shades; window cleaning

(G-2986)
J B NOTTINGHAM & CO INC
Also Called: Duraline
1731 Patterson Ave (32724-1943)
PHONE..................................386 873-2990
John Sclafani, *President*
Lisa Pajonas, *Opers Mgr*
Lisa Sclafani, *Opers Staff*
▲ **EMP:** 49
SQ FT: 25,000
SALES (est): 7.5MM **Privately Held**
WEB: www.jbn-duraline.com
SIC: 3643 3699 3646 3548 Current-carrying wiring devices; electrical equipment & supplies; commercial indusl & institutional electric lighting fixtures; electric welding equipment; switchgear & switchboard apparatus; mechanical rubber goods

▲ = Import ▼=Export
◆ =Import/Export

(G-2987)
JCO METALS INC
Also Called: Parachute Laboratories
1665 Lexington Ave # 106 (32724-2187)
PHONE..................................386 734-5867
Nancy Lariviere, *President*
EMP: 14 **EST:** 1983
SQ FT: 3,000
SALES (est): 248.4K **Privately Held**
WEB: www.jcometals.com
SIC: 3429 Parachute hardware

(G-2988)
JCS BUILDING SALES
4070 N Us Highway 17 (32720-1101)
PHONE..................................386 277-2851
EMP: 6 **EST:** 2017
SALES (est): 118K **Privately Held**
WEB: www.stemetalbuildings.com
SIC: 3448 Prefabricated metal buildings

(G-2989)
JET HELSETH MANUFACTURING INC
1730 Patterson Ave (32724-1950)
PHONE..................................407 324-9001
Andrew Helseth, *CEO*
Jon Thibeault, *COO*
Francine Guillemette, *Project Mgr*
EMP: 32 **EST:** 1995
SQ FT: 12,500
SALES (est): 4MM **Privately Held**
WEB: www.jetmfg.com
SIC: 3599 Machine shop, jobbing & repair

(G-2990)
K & B LANDSCAPE SUPPLIES INC
3900 E State Road 44 (32724-6425)
PHONE..................................800 330-8816
EMP: 5
SALES (est): 991.9K **Privately Held**
SIC: 2499 Mfg Wood Products

(G-2991)
KINGSPAN INSULATED PANELS INC (DH)
Also Called: Kingspan - Asi
726 Summerhill Dr (32724-2021)
PHONE..................................386 626-6789
Russell Shiels, *President*
Peter Wilson, *Managing Dir*
Ilhan Eser, *Vice Pres*
Carlo Vezza, *Vice Pres*
Simon Cousins, *Plant Mgr*
◆ **EMP:** 240 **EST:** 1961
SQ FT: 109,000
SALES (est): 141.1MM **Privately Held**
WEB: www.kingspan.com
SIC: 3448 Prefabricated metal buildings
HQ: Kingspan Insulated Panels Ltd
12557 Coleraine Dr
Bolton ON L7E 3
905 951-5600

(G-2992)
KINGSPAN INSULATED PANELS INC
Also Called: Kingspan Deland Plant
725 Summerhill Dr (32724-2024)
PHONE..................................386 626-6789
EMP: 69 **Privately Held**
WEB: www.kingspan.com
SIC: 3448 Prefabricated metal buildings
HQ: Kingspan Insulated Panels Inc.
726 Summerhill Dr
Deland FL 32724
386 626-6789

(G-2993)
KINGSPAN-MEDUSA INC (HQ)
726 Summerhill Dr (32724-2021)
PHONE..................................386 626-6789
Pat Freeman, *Managing Dir*
Gene M Murtagh, *Principal*
Andrew Williams, *Business Mgr*
Kevin Ogrady, *Opers Dir*
Richard Wenham, *Buyer*
▼ **EMP:** 183 **EST:** 1986
SQ FT: 109,000
SALES (est): 86.7MM **Privately Held**
WEB: www.kingspan.com
SIC: 3448 Prefabricated metal buildings

(G-2994)
KYP GO INC
1551 Lakeside Dr (32720-3014)
PHONE..................................386 736-3770
Robert J Kyp, *President*
Elisabeth Sanda, *Assistant VP*
▲ **EMP:** 10 **EST:** 1964
SQ FT: 10,000
SALES (est): 590K **Privately Held**
WEB: www.kyp-go.com
SIC: 3641 Electric lamps

(G-2995)
MESA INDUSTRIES INC
1560 Lexington Ave (32724-2118)
PHONE..................................386 738-3255
Wanye Estes, *Manager*
Ben Sarmiento, *Director*
EMP: 10
SALES (corp-wide): 13MM **Privately Held**
WEB: www.mesa-intl.com
SIC: 3089 3085 Plastic containers, except foam; plastics bottles
PA: Mesa Industries, Inc.
1208 Eastchester Dr
High Point NC

(G-2996)
MIKE PULVER LLC
703 Deerfoot Rd (32720-7933)
PHONE..................................386 747-8951
Michael D Pulver, *Principal*
EMP: 6 **EST:** 2007
SALES (est): 194K **Privately Held**
SIC: 2434 Wood kitchen cabinets

(G-2997)
MIRAGE SYSTEMS INC
1501a Lexington Ave (32724-2117)
P.O. Box 820 (32721-0820)
PHONE..................................386 740-9222
Dan W Thompson, *President*
Dawn M English, *Vice Pres*
EMP: 15 **EST:** 1996
SQ FT: 5,000
SALES (est): 2.3MM **Privately Held**
WEB: www.miragesys.com
SIC: 3429 3949 5088 Parachute hardware; sporting & athletic goods; aircraft equipment & supplies

(G-2998)
MORGANELLI & ASSOCIATES INC
1401 Saratoga St (32724-2109)
PHONE..................................386 738-3669
Al Morganelli, *President*
Kathy Morganelli, *Corp Secy*
Jenny Malchiodi, *Sales Staff*
EMP: 6 **EST:** 2000
SQ FT: 7,200
SALES (est): 825.6K **Privately Held**
WEB: www.lightandsirenpros.com
SIC: 3669 Emergency alarms

(G-2999)
MORIN CORP
1975 Eidson Dr (32724-2027)
PHONE..................................386 626-6789
Karen Spinney, *Accounting Mgr*
Rick Gordon, *Sales Staff*
EMP: 7 **EST:** 2014
SALES (est): 264.2K **Privately Held**
WEB: www.kingspan.com
SIC: 3448 Prefabricated metal buildings

(G-3000)
MPC CONTAINMENT SYSTEMS LLC (HQ)
880 N Spring Garden Ave (32720-3143)
PHONE..................................773 927-4121
Larry Nunez, *Plant Mgr*
Benjamin Beiler, *Mng Member*
Alan Berman,
Edward E Reicin,
EMP: 65 **EST:** 1979
SALES (est): 13.6MM **Privately Held**
WEB: www.mpccontainment.com
SIC: 3443 Fabricated plate work (boiler shop)

(G-3001)
MPC GROUP LLC (PA)
880 N Spring Garden Ave (32720-3143)
PHONE..................................773 927-4120
Benjamin Beiler, *CEO*
Alan Berman,
Edward Reicin,
EMP: 2 **EST:** 2006
SALES (est): 28.9MM **Privately Held**
WEB: www.mpcgroupllc.com
SIC: 2394 3089 Canvas & related products; plastic processing

(G-3002)
MT-PROPELLER USA INC
1180 Airport Terminal Dr (32724-2112)
PHONE..................................386 736-7762
Gerd Muhlbauer, *President*
Martin Albrecht, *Vice Pres*
Michael Muhlbauer, *Vice Pres*
Eric Greindl, *Sales Dir*
Hoell Josefine, *Sales Mgr*
EMP: 10 **EST:** 1997
SQ FT: 1,500
SALES (est): 750K **Privately Held**
WEB: www.mt-propellerusa.com
SIC: 3728 Accumulators, aircraft propeller

(G-3003)
MY BLANK CANVAS
970 N Spring Garden Ave (32720-0874)
PHONE..................................386 747-5254
Luz M Oyola, *Owner*
EMP: 6 **EST:** 2017
SALES (est): 87.8K **Privately Held**
WEB: www.blankcanvasla.com
SIC: 2211 Canvas

(G-3004)
ON SITE SVCS OF MID FL
265 Damascus Rd (32724-6436)
PHONE..................................407 444-2951
Tim McLaughlin, *Manager*
EMP: 6 **EST:** 2006
SALES (est): 513.3K **Privately Held**
WEB: www.onsiteservicesofmflorida.com
SIC: 7692 Welding repair

(G-3005)
PAIN AWAY LLC
Also Called: Outback Series, The
1515 Detrick Ave (32724-2014)
PHONE..................................800 215-8739
Brandon Godwin, *CEO*
Stacy Godwin, *CFO*
EMP: 7 **EST:** 2016
SALES (est): 362.1K **Privately Held**
SIC: 2833 Medicinals & botanicals

(G-3006)
PALL AEROPOWER CORPORATION
1750 Filter Dr (32724-2000)
PHONE..................................727 849-9999
Nalin Patel, *Engineer*
Terry Flack, *Branch Mgr*
EMP: 458
SALES (corp-wide): 22.2B **Publicly Held**
SIC: 3569 3564 Filters; blowers & fans
HQ: Pall Aeropower Corporation
10540 Ridge Rd Ste 100
New Port Richey FL 34654

(G-3007)
PALL FILTRATION AND SEP
Fluid Dynamics
1750 Filter Dr (32724-2000)
PHONE..................................386 822-8000
Andrew Gorin, *Sales Dir*
Joe Hahn, *Sales Mgr*
Rick Morris, *Branch Mgr*
Eva Chambers, *Manager*
Matt June, *Manager*
EMP: 250
SALES (corp-wide): 22.2B **Publicly Held**
SIC: 3677 3564 Filtration devices, electronic; filters, air: furnaces, air conditioning equipment, etc.
HQ: Pall Filtration And Separations Group Inc.
2120 Greenspring Dr
Lutherville Timonium MD 21093
410 252-0800

(G-3008)
PENNYSAVER
245 S Woodland Blvd (32720-5413)
PHONE..................................718 986-6437
EMP: 6 **EST:** 2019
SALES (est): 67.3K **Privately Held**
SIC: 2711 Newspapers, publishing & printing

(G-3009)
PERFORMANCE DESIGNS INC
1300 E Intl Speedway Blvd (32724)
PHONE..................................386 738-2224
Tony Yrey, *General Mgr*
John Le Blanc, *Vice Pres*
Katie Barbour, *Purchasing*
Katy Barbour, *Purchasing*
Amanda Festi, *Research*
▲ **EMP:** 160 **EST:** 1982
SQ FT: 17,000
SALES (est): 36MM **Privately Held**
WEB: www.performancedesigns.com
SIC: 2399 Parachutes

(G-3010)
REAL GOLD INC
1853 Patterson Ave Unit 4 (32724-1963)
PHONE..................................386 873-4849
Jamie Quick, *President*
Bill Crowley, *Vice Pres*
Tracy Sciulla, *Office Mgr*
EMP: 8 **EST:** 2013
SALES (est): 939.3K **Privately Held**
WEB: www.realgoldinc.com
SIC: 3081 3999 Vinyl film & sheet; atomizers, toiletry

(G-3011)
REFLECTIVITY INC
320 S Spring Garden Ave E (32720-5087)
PHONE..................................386 738-1008
Kathleen S Truba, *President*
EMP: 11 **EST:** 2001
SALES (est): 126.7K **Privately Held**
SIC: 3674 Semiconductors & related devices

(G-3012)
RINKER MATERIALS CORP
2170 State Road 472 (32724-9614)
PHONE..................................386 775-0790
Susan Jensen, *Principal*
EMP: 7 **EST:** 2011
SALES (est): 99.8K **Privately Held**
SIC: 3273 Ready-mixed concrete

(G-3013)
SIMPLY SWEET COMPANY INC (PA)
1431 Orange Camp Rd (32724-7768)
PHONE..................................386 873-6516
Rotondo Donna, *President*
EMP: 5 **EST:** 2015
SALES (est): 360.3K **Privately Held**
WEB: www.simplysweeticecream.com
SIC: 2024 Ice cream & frozen desserts

(G-3014)
SLM BOATS INC
1948 Sunset Ct (32720-2366)
PHONE..................................386 738-4425
Richard Langford, *President*
EMP: 6
SQ FT: 12,000
SALES (est): 350K **Privately Held**
SIC: 3732 Boat building & repairing

(G-3015)
SPORTSANITY
143 N Woodland Blvd (32720-4238)
PHONE..................................386 873-4688
EMP: 6 **EST:** 2017
SALES (est): 170.7K **Privately Held**
SIC: 2759 Screen printing

(G-3016)
SUNNY HILL INTERNATIONAL INC
901 W New York Ave (32720-5144)
PHONE..................................386 736-5757
William R Murphy, *Director*
Leland M Anderson, *Director*
Hector E Viale, *Director*
▼ **EMP:** 7 **EST:** 2004

SALES (est): 2MM **Privately Held**
WEB: www.sunnyhillintl.com
SIC: 2087 Beverage bases

(G-3017)
TCM IMAGINEERING INC
1835 Bennett Ave (32724-1941)
PHONE..................................407 323-6494
Pierre Gauthier, *Executive Asst*
EMP: 12 **EST:** 2014
SALES (est): 1MM **Privately Held**
SIC: 2542 Partitions & fixtures, except wood

(G-3018)
TEAM PLASTICS INC
2025 Eidson Dr (32724-2029)
PHONE..................................386 740-9555
Michael Allen Agee, *President*
Todd Agee, *General Mgr*
Jim Gierhart, *Prdtn Mgr*
Troy Backman, *Engineer*
Troy Agee, *Maintence Staff*
EMP: 45 **EST:** 1991
SALES (est): 5MM **Privately Held**
WEB: www.teamplastics.com
SIC: 3089 Injection molding of plastics

(G-3019)
TECHNETICS GROUP LLC
Technetics Group Burbank
1700 E Intl Speedway Blvd (32724)
PHONE..................................386 736-7373
Kelly Ceiler, *Engineer*
Claudine Andrews, *Manager*
EMP: 126
SALES (corp-wide): 1B **Publicly Held**
WEB: www.technetics.com
SIC: 3053 3351 Gaskets & sealing devices; copper rolling & drawing
HQ: Technetics Group Llc
5605 Carnegie Blvd # 500
Charlotte NC 28209
704 731-1500

(G-3020)
THATCHER CHEMICAL FLORIDA INC (HQ)
Also Called: Thatcher Chemical Company
245 Hazen Rd (32720-3967)
P.O. Box 489 (32721-0489)
PHONE..................................386 734-3966
Lawrence Thatcher, *CEO*
Craig N Thatcher, *President*
Teri Flanders, *Vice Pres*
Michael Walker, *Analyst*
◆ **EMP:** 10 **EST:** 2007
SALES (est): 11.7MM
SALES (corp-wide): 461.7MM **Privately Held**
WEB: www.tchem.com
SIC: 2819 5169 Industrial inorganic chemicals; chemicals & allied products
PA: Thatcher Group, Inc
1905 W Fortune Rd
Salt Lake City UT 84104
801 972-4587

(G-3021)
THREAD GRAPHICS EMBROIDERY
1731 Timber Hills Dr (32724-7980)
PHONE..................................407 688-7026
Kristine Szacik, *President*
EMP: 6 **EST:** 1997
SQ FT: 3,000
SALES (est): 421.1K **Privately Held**
SIC: 2395 Embroidery products, except schiffli machine

(G-3022)
TITAN AMERICA LLC
407 N Spring Garden Ave (32720-3957)
PHONE..................................386 734-5526
Don Podsiadlo, *Principal*
EMP: 6
SQ FT: 4,373
SALES (corp-wide): 177.9K **Privately Held**
WEB: www.titanamerica.com
SIC: 3273 Ready-mixed concrete
HQ: Titan America Llc
5700 Lake Wright Dr # 300
Norfolk VA 23502
757 858-6500

(G-3023)
TITAN SERVICE INDUSTRY LLC
2044 Anchor Ave (32720-2359)
PHONE..................................678 313-4707
Rick Schafrick, *President*
Walter Alvarado,
Richard Schafrick,
EMP: 6 **EST:** 2015
SALES (est): 474.4K **Privately Held**
WEB: www.tsiweld.com
SIC: 7692 1731 7389 1799 Welding repair; safety & security specialization; safety inspection service; welding on site; ; conveyors & conveying equipment

(G-3024)
TOMI AIRCRAFT INC
1310 Flight Line Blvd (32724-2116)
PHONE..................................863 446-3001
Tad Olmsted, *President*
EMP: 6 **EST:** 2014
SALES (est): 1MM **Privately Held**
WEB: www.tomiaircraft.com
SIC: 3728 Aircraft parts & equipment

(G-3025)
TRI-DECK LLC (PA)
3402 Black Willow Trl (32724-1100)
PHONE..................................386 748-3239
David C Solar, *Mng Member*
James Wurst Solar,
EMP: 1 **EST:** 2012
SQ FT: 3,500
SALES (est): 50MM **Privately Held**
WEB: www.trideck.com
SIC: 3949 Skateboards

(G-3026)
TST INDUSTRIES LLC
3625 Royal Fern Cir (32724-1233)
PHONE..................................973 865-1998
Bart P Rogowski, *Principal*
Erica Nocita, *Opers Staff*
EMP: 6 **EST:** 2013
SALES (est): 206.9K **Privately Held**
WEB: www.tstindustries.com
SIC: 3999 Manufacturing industries

(G-3027)
UNINSRED UNTD PRCHUTE TECH LLC
Also Called: Upt Vector
1645 Lexington Ave (32724-2106)
PHONE..................................386 736-7589
Terri Booth, *General Mgr*
Mark Procos, *General Mgr*
Sheryl Bothwell, *Safety Mgr*
Hope Cruz, *Controller*
Thiago Gomes, *Human Res Mgr*
EMP: 85 **EST:** 2006
SQ FT: 12,000
SALES (est): 9.2MM **Privately Held**
WEB: www.uptvector.com
SIC: 3429 Parachute hardware

(G-3028)
UNINSURED RELATIVE WORKSHOP
1645 Lexington Ave (32724-2106)
PHONE..................................386 736-7589
William R Booth,
EMP: 20 **EST:** 1976
SQ FT: 11,000
SALES (est): 502.3K **Privately Held**
WEB: www.uptvector.com
SIC: 3949 Sporting & athletic goods

(G-3029)
USA VIGIL
1400 Flight Line Blvd (32724-2140)
PHONE..................................386 736-8464
Richard Hall, *Principal*
EMP: 6 **EST:** 2010
SALES (est): 117.2K **Privately Held**
WEB: www.vigil.aero
SIC: 2399 Parachutes

(G-3030)
VOLUSIA PRINTING LLC
1919 W Minnesota Ave (32720-2612)
PHONE..................................386 873-7442
Dave Novak, *Manager*
EMP: 6 **EST:** 2018
SALES (est): 83.9K **Privately Held**
WEB: www.volusia.org
SIC: 2752 Commercial printing, lithographic

(G-3031)
WARENSFORD WELL DRILLING INC
329 S Blue Lake Ave (32724-6201)
P.O. Box 326 (32721-0326)
PHONE..................................386 738-3257
Kell Warresnford, *CEO*
William Warrens, *CFO*
EMP: 5 **EST:** 2003
SALES (est): 357.6K **Privately Held**
WEB: www.warensfordwelldrilling.com
SIC: 1389 1381 Oil & gas wells: building, repairing & dismantling; drilling oil & gas wells

(G-3032)
WATERFILTERUSA
3060 Prfmce Cir Ste 2 (32724)
PHONE..................................386 469-0138
Robert Prentice, *Principal*
EMP: 8 **EST:** 2010
SALES (est): 180K **Privately Held**
WEB: www.pelicanwater.com
SIC: 3589 Water filters & softeners, household type

(G-3033)
WEST BOLUSIA BEACON
Also Called: Deland Beacon Newspaper
110 W New York Ave (32720-5416)
PHONE..................................386 734-4622
Barbara Shepard, *President*
Coni Tarby, *Advt Staff*
EMP: 14 **EST:** 1992
SALES (est): 2.8MM **Privately Held**
WEB: www.beacononlinenews.com
SIC: 2711 7313 Newspapers: publishing only, not printed on site; newspaper advertising representative

(G-3034)
WILKINS LAPIDARY ARTS
413 E Kentucky Ave (32724-2431)
PHONE..................................386 734-8470
Mary Wilkins, *Owner*
EMP: 20 **EST:** 2004
SALES (est): 839.3K **Privately Held**
SIC: 3915 Lapidary work, contract or other

(G-3035)
WOOD ASPECTS
1704 Langley Ave Ste D (32724-2188)
PHONE..................................321 800-8875
Eda Abolfathi, *Principal*
EMP: 7 **EST:** 2014
SALES (est): 233K **Privately Held**
WEB: www.woodaspects.com
SIC: 2434 Wood kitchen cabinets

(G-3036)
WOODWORKS FOR YOU
1230 Stevens Ave (32720-5030)
PHONE..................................386 717-4169
Rick Betzel, *Principal*
EMP: 6 **EST:** 2007
SALES (est): 49.9K **Privately Held**
SIC: 2431 Millwork

Delray Beach
Palm Beach County

(G-3037)
A Z PRINTING DELRAY
645 E Atlantic Ave (33483-5325)
PHONE..................................561 330-4154
Steve Sincoff, *Owner*
EMP: 15 **EST:** 2011
SALES (est): 175.3K **Privately Held**
SIC: 2759 Commercial printing

(G-3038)
AA OLDCO INC (PA)
Also Called: Alfred Angelo Bridals
1625 S Congress Ave # 400 (33445-6301)
PHONE..................................215 659-5300
Vincent E Piccione, *President*
Fred Piccione, *Chairman*
Ron Wible, *COO*
Michael Bruzzese, *Vice Pres*
Joe Weltz, *CFO*
▲ **EMP:** 75 **EST:** 1947
SQ FT: 25,000
SALES (est): 18.2MM **Privately Held**
WEB: www.locations.alfredangelo.com
SIC: 2335 Wedding gowns & dresses; gowns, formal

(G-3039)
ABC AWNING & CANVAS CO INC
244 Avenue L (33483-4651)
PHONE..................................321 253-1960
Rue McNay, *President*
EMP: 12 **EST:** 1962
SQ FT: 4,950
SALES (est): 997.8K **Privately Held**
WEB: www.abcawnings.com
SIC: 2394 Awnings, fabric: made from purchased materials

(G-3040)
ADVANCED AUTOMOTIVE DESIGNS
6685 Dana Point Cv (33446-5646)
PHONE..................................561 499-8812
Dov Zucker, *President*
▲ **EMP:** 6 **EST:** 1994
SQ FT: 4,000
SALES (est): 2.1MM **Privately Held**
SIC: 3694 3714 Automotive electrical equipment; motor vehicle electrical equipment

(G-3041)
ADVANCED PRECISION MACHINING
1035 Nw 17th Ave Ste 3 (33445-2518)
PHONE..................................561 243-4567
Mark Burke, *President*
EMP: 8 **EST:** 1997
SQ FT: 5,000
SALES (est): 846K **Privately Held**
WEB: www.advancedprecision.net
SIC: 3599 Machine shop, jobbing & repair

(G-3042)
AFFORDBLE SCREEN ENCLOSURE LLC
5480 Palm Ridge Blvd (33484-1115)
PHONE..................................561 900-8868
Pavel Krutakov, *Principal*
EMP: 7 **EST:** 2016
SALES (est): 1.1MM **Privately Held**
SIC: 3448 Screen enclosures

(G-3043)
ALLEN INDUSTRIES
220 Congress Park Dr (33445-4670)
PHONE..................................561 243-8072
EMP: 7 **EST:** 2018
SALES (est): 46K **Privately Held**
WEB: www.allenindustries.com
SIC: 3993 Electric signs

(G-3044)
ALPER AUTOMOTIVE INC
Also Called: Gwa Alper
335 E Linton Blvd (33483-5023)
PHONE..................................561 342-1501
Gregg Alper, *President*
Bailee Alper, *Mng Member*
EMP: 8 **EST:** 2011
SALES (est): 1MM **Privately Held**
WEB: www.alperautomotive.com
SIC: 3714 Motor vehicle engines & parts

(G-3045)
ALUMINIUM DESIGN PRODUCTS LLC
1055 Sw 15th Ave Ste 1 (33444-1263)
PHONE..................................561 894-8775
Jason Scott Toler, *Vice Pres*
William Toler,
▼ **EMP:** 9 **EST:** 2011
SALES (est): 1.5MM **Privately Held**
WEB: www.aluminumdesignproducts.com
SIC: 3355 Aluminum rolling & drawing

(G-3046)
AMBASSADOR PRINTING COMPANY
Also Called: Ambassador Marketing Group
1025 Nw 17th Ave Ste C (33445-2563)
PHONE..................................561 330-3668

▲ = Import ▼=Export
◆ =Import/Export

Anthony Gentile, *President*
Mario Gentile, *Principal*
Jerold M Ode, *Vice Pres*
EMP: 9 **EST:** 1994
SALES (est): 1.6MM **Privately Held**
WEB: www.ambassadorprinting.com
SIC: 2752 Commercial printing, offset

(G-3047)
ART IN PRINT INC (PA)
Also Called: National Print & Design
8640 Valhalla Dr (33446-9568)
PHONE..................................561 877-0995
David M Ebenstein, *President*
EMP: 10 **EST:** 2015
SQ FT: 12,000
SALES (est): 1.2MM **Privately Held**
WEB: www.nationalprintdesign.com
SIC: 2752 Commercial printing, offset

(G-3048)
AXTONNE INC
Also Called: Precision Plastics
350 Se 1st St (33483-4502)
PHONE..................................510 755-7480
Eric Appelblom, *President*
EMP: 9 **EST:** 2018
SALES (est): 472.4K **Privately Held**
WEB: www.axtonne.com
SIC: 3999 Manufacturing industries

(G-3049)
BANYAN HILL
98 Se 6th Ave Ste 2 (33483-5363)
PHONE..................................561 455-9045
Kristen Barrett, *Manager*
Anthony Planas, *Analyst*
EMP: 6 **EST:** 2017
SALES (est): 116.3K **Privately Held**
WEB: www.banyanhill.com
SIC: 2741 Miscellaneous publishing

(G-3050)
BIRDIE PUBLISHING LLC
701 Se 6th Ave Ste 102 (33483-5186)
PHONE..................................561 332-1826
EMP: 6 **EST:** 2019
SALES (est): 610.5K **Privately Held**
WEB: www.birdiepublishing.com
SIC: 2741 Miscellaneous publishing

(G-3051)
BRANDINE WOODCRAFT INC
601 N Congress Ave # 203 (33445-4703)
PHONE..................................561 266-9360
Fax: 561 266-9361
▲ **EMP:** 5
SQ FT: 5,000
SALES (est): 410K **Privately Held**
SIC: 3944 5945 5999 Mfg Games/Toys Ret Hobbies/Toys/Games Ret Misc Merchandise

(G-3052)
BRILL HYGIENIC PRODUCTS INC
601 N Congress Ave (33445-4646)
PHONE..................................561 278-5600
Alan Brill, *CEO*
David Jablow, *Exec VP*
▲ **EMP:** 12 **EST:** 1991
SQ FT: 4,000
SALES (est): 1.7MM **Privately Held**
WEB: www.brillseat.com
SIC: 3089 Fences, gates & accessories: plastic

(G-3053)
BROOKLYN WATER ENTERPRISES INC
1615 S Congress Ave # 103 (33445-6326)
PHONE..................................877 224-3580
Steven Fassberg, *CEO*
David Ross, *President*
Joseph West, *Vice Pres*
EMP: 32 **EST:** 2007
SALES (est): 4.5MM **Privately Held**
WEB: www.brooklynwaterbagel.com
SIC: 2051 Bakery: wholesale or wholesale/retail combined

(G-3054)
BTB REFINING LLC
25 Seabreeze Ave Ste 300 (33483-7038)
PHONE..................................561 347-5500
EMP: 6 **EST:** 2017
SALES (est): 241.8K **Privately Held**
SIC: 2951 Asphalt paving mixtures & blocks

(G-3055)
CABINETS DIRECT USA
16107 Via Monteverde (33446-2366)
PHONE..................................862 704-6138
EMP: 10 **EST:** 2018
SALES (est): 559.1K **Privately Held**
WEB: www.cabinetsdirectusa.com
SIC: 2434 Wood kitchen cabinets

(G-3056)
CASEY RESEARCH LLC
55 Ne 5th Ave Ste 300 (33483-5461)
PHONE..................................561 455-9043
Mark Arnold, *Mng Member*
EMP: 10 **EST:** 2015
SALES (est): 10MM **Privately Held**
WEB: www.caseyresearch.com
SIC: 2741 Miscellaneous publishing

(G-3057)
CATAPULT LEARNING LL
501 Nw 8th Ave (33444-1701)
PHONE..................................561 573-6025
EMP: 6 **EST:** 2018
SALES (est): 131.9K **Privately Held**
WEB: www.catapultlearning.com
SIC: 3599 Catapults

(G-3058)
CHANNEL LETTER USA CORP
2275 S Federal Hwy # 350 (33483-3337)
PHONE..................................561 243-9699
Shamiroon Little, *Principal*
EMP: 8 **EST:** 2009
SALES (est): 138.6K **Privately Held**
WEB: www.channelletterusa.com
SIC: 3993 Signs & advertising specialties

(G-3059)
CHEM-FREE SYSTEM INC
7168 Cataluna Cir (33446-3176)
PHONE..................................954 258-5415
Edward M Gale, *President*
▼ **EMP:** 9 **EST:** 2011
SALES (est): 564.6K **Privately Held**
WEB: www.chemfreesystemsinc.com
SIC: 2086 Mineral water, carbonated: packaged in cans, bottles, etc.

(G-3060)
CHOCOLATE GUYS LLC
2875 S Congress Ave Ste G (33445-7344)
PHONE..................................561 278-5889
Michelle Ahnell, *Principal*
EMP: 7 **EST:** 2013
SALES (est): 170.1K **Privately Held**
WEB: www.fullman.com
SIC: 2066 5149 Chocolate; chocolate

(G-3061)
COASTAL DOOR & MLLWK SVCS LLC
1300 Sw 10th St (33444-1266)
PHONE..................................561 266-3716
Pat Endres, *Managing Prtnr*
Claudia Arboleda, *Office Mgr*
Pj Hatley, *Mng Member*
EMP: 14 **EST:** 2014
SALES (est): 395.1K **Privately Held**
WEB: www.coastaldms.com
SIC: 2431 Millwork

(G-3062)
COASTAL SCREEN & RAIL LLC
1127 Poinsettia Dr (33444-1221)
PHONE..................................321 917-4605
R Scott Buchanan, *Mng Member*
Michael Spitaletto,
▼ **EMP:** 7 **EST:** 2006
SQ FT: 14,000
SALES (est): 1.8MM **Privately Held**
WEB: www.coastalscreen.com
SIC: 3448 Screen enclosures

(G-3063)
COMMON SENSE PUBLISHING LLC
55 Ne 5th Ave Ste 100 (33483-5461)
PHONE..................................561 510-1713
Amber Mason,
Ryan Markish,
EMP: 130 **EST:** 2010
SALES (est): 50.9MM
SALES (corp-wide): 98.8MM **Privately Held**
WEB: www.palmbeachgroup.com
SIC: 2741 7371 7389 Miscellaneous publishing; computer software development & applications;
PA: Monument & Cathedral Holdings, Inc.
14 W Mount Vernon Pl
Baltimore MD 21201
410 783-8499

(G-3064)
CONVERGENT ACTUARIAL SVCS INC
510 Lavers Cir (33444-7972)
PHONE..................................561 715-4204
Jonathan Evans, *Principal*
EMP: 6 **EST:** 2014
SALES (est): 115.5K **Privately Held**
WEB: www.convergentactuarialservices.com
SIC: 3674 Semiconductors & related devices

(G-3065)
CONVERGENT MARKETING LLC
701 Nw 2nd Ave (33444-3909)
PHONE..................................561 270-7081
Michelle R Bidwell, *Principal*
EMP: 9 **EST:** 2009
SALES (est): 424K **Privately Held**
SIC: 3674 Semiconductors & related devices

(G-3066)
CREATIVE ROUTES PRESS
2815 Hampton Cir E (33445-7158)
PHONE..................................561 213-9800
Jonathan Korman, *Principal*
EMP: 6 **EST:** 2016
SALES (est): 125.8K **Privately Held**
SIC: 2741 Miscellaneous publishing

(G-3067)
CURVCO STEEL STRUCTURES CORP
14545 S Military Trl H (33484-3781)
PHONE..................................800 956-6341
Shawn Davis, *President*
Paul Kraham, *Vice Pres*
EMP: 13 **EST:** 2004
SQ FT: 4,000
SALES (est): 659.9K **Privately Held**
WEB: www.curvcosteelbuildings.com
SIC: 3448 Prefabricated metal buildings

(G-3068)
DAN LIPMAN AND ASSOCIATES
15852 Corintha Ter (33446-9724)
PHONE..................................561 245-8672
Dan Lipman, *President*
Melissa Lipman, *Exec VP*
EMP: 5 **EST:** 1994
SALES (est): 664.9K **Privately Held**
WEB: www.danlipman.com
SIC: 3545 Machine tool attachments & accessories

(G-3069)
DELRAY AWNING INC
80 N Congress Ave (33445-3417)
PHONE..................................561 276-5381
Ricky J Day, *President*
Donald Day, *Vice Pres*
EMP: 15 **EST:** 1959
SQ FT: 4,900
SALES (est): 1.5MM **Privately Held**
WEB: www.delrayawning.com
SIC: 2394 2399 Awnings, fabric: made from purchased materials; banners, made from fabric

(G-3070)
DOUBLE D S TOBACCO
7560 Us Hwy 1 (33446)
PHONE..................................772 871-9910
Don Mills, *Owner*
EMP: 6 **EST:** 2010
SALES (est): 161.4K **Privately Held**
SIC: 3999 Cigarette & cigar products & accessories

(G-3071)
E1W GAMES LLC ✪
14545 S Military Trl J (33484-3781)
PHONE..................................561 255-7370
Mark Friedlander,
EMP: 10 **EST:** 2021
SALES (est): 500K **Privately Held**
SIC: 2741

(G-3072)
EL HARLEY INC
2885 S Congress Ave Ste F (33445-7336)
PHONE..................................561 841-9887
Richard Harley, *President*
Craig Harley, *Vice Pres*
▼ **EMP:** 10 **EST:** 1948
SALES (est): 915.9K **Privately Held**
WEB: www.elharleyinc.com
SIC: 3555 Printing trades machinery

(G-3073)
ENDLESS OCEANS LLC
3125 S Federal Hwy (33483-3221)
PHONE..................................561 274-1990
EMP: 6 **EST:** 2012
SALES (est): 449.3K **Privately Held**
SIC: 3089 3499 5999 7389 Mfg Plastic Products Mfg Misc Fab Metal Prdts Ret Misc Merchandise Business Services Mfg Prdt-Purchased Glass

(G-3074)
EPICCYCLES ✪
14851 Lyons Rd (33446-9010)
PHONE..................................561 450-6470
Alvaro Velez, *Principal*
EMP: 8 **EST:** 2020
SALES (est): 441.2K **Privately Held**
SIC: 3751 Bicycles & related parts

(G-3075)
EPIGENETIX INC
1004 Brooks Ln (33483-6508)
PHONE..................................561 543-7569
Joseph W Collard, *Principal*
EMP: 10 **EST:** 2011
SALES (est): 740.6K **Privately Held**
WEB: www.epigenetix.com
SIC: 2834 Pharmaceutical preparations

(G-3076)
ESSONA ORGANICS INC
14773 Cumberland Dr # 107 (33446-1338)
PHONE..................................716 481-0183
Maria Wydro, *Ch of Bd*
EMP: 7 **EST:** 2006
SALES (est): 213.6K **Privately Held**
WEB: www.essona.com
SIC: 2023 Dietary supplements, dairy & non-dairy based

(G-3077)
EUROMOTION INC
7194 Skyline Dr (33446-2214)
PHONE..................................954 612-0354
Robin Van Der Putten, *President*
▲ **EMP:** 5 **EST:** 2004
SALES (est): 390.2K **Privately Held**
SIC: 3694 Automotive electrical equipment

(G-3078)
FHS ENTERPRISES LLC
Also Called: Florida Salt Scrubs
2875 S Congress Ave Ste D (33445-7344)
PHONE..................................754 214-9379
Geoffrey Schmidt, *Mng Member*
EMP: 5 **EST:** 2012
SALES (est): 621.8K **Privately Held**
SIC: 2844 Toilet preparations

(G-3079)
FOURNIES ASSOCIATES
1226 Nw 19th Ter (33445-2540)
PHONE..................................561 445-5102
Ferdinand F Fournies, *President*
Sandra Fournies, *Partner*
Elizabeth P Fournies, *Vice Pres*
EMP: 7 **EST:** 1971
SALES (est): 700K **Privately Held**
WEB: www.fournies.com
SIC: 2731 8748 Book publishing; business consulting

(G-3080)
FRESH
4801 Linton Blvd (33445-6503)
PHONE..................................561 330-4345
EMP: 8 **EST:** 2011
SALES (est): 500K **Privately Held**
SIC: 3421 Mfg Cutlery

(G-3081)
FRESH BLENDS NORTH AMERICA INC
955 Nw 17th Ave Ste J (33445-2516)
PHONE..................................531 665-8200
James Day, *Managing Prtnr*
Marc Lang, *Vice Pres*
EMP: 10 **EST:** 2016
SALES (est): 3MM **Privately Held**
WEB: www.freshblends.com
SIC: 2037 Frozen fruits & vegetables

(G-3082)
GAIAS FORMULA
827 Sw 17th Ave (33444-1331)
PHONE..................................954 655-8095
Adrianne Cristofaro, *Manager*
EMP: 6 **EST:** 2015
SALES (est): 101.8K **Privately Held**
WEB: www.gaiasformula.com
SIC: 2844 Toilet preparations

(G-3083)
GB ENERGY TECH
2875 S Congress Ave Ste B (33445-7344)
PHONE..................................561 450-6047
Rafael Gonzalez, *Owner*
EMP: 10 **EST:** 2014
SALES (est): 563.5K **Privately Held**
WEB: www.gbenergy.com
SIC: 3674 Solar cells

(G-3084)
GELATO PETRINI LLC
1205 Sw 4th Ave (33444-2276)
PHONE..................................561 600-4088
Dawn Petrini, *Marketing Staff*
Dawn Rachel Petrini,
EMP: 15 **EST:** 2011
SQ FT: 10,000
SALES (est): 1MM **Privately Held**
WEB: www.gelatopetrini.com
SIC: 2024 Ice cream, bulk

(G-3085)
GOODPRESS PUBLISHING LLC
Also Called: Simply The Best Magazine
4731 W Atlantic Ave Ste 5 (33445-3866)
PHONE..................................561 865-8101
Adam Goodkin, *President*
EMP: 5 **EST:** 1999
SQ FT: 3,000
SALES (est): 381.8K **Privately Held**
WEB: www.simplythebestmagazine.com
SIC: 2721 Magazines: publishing & printing

(G-3086)
GRAVITY COLORS USA INC
2428 Bloods Grove Cir (33445-5300)
PHONE..................................561 419-5272
Mate Mayer, *Principal*
EMP: 8 **EST:** 2017
SALES (est): 73.6K **Privately Held**
WEB: www.gravitycolors.com
SIC: 3999 Manufacturing industries

(G-3087)
GREAT ESCAPE PUBLISHING
101 Se 6th Ave Ste A (33483-5261)
PHONE..................................561 860-8266
EMP: 6 **EST:** 2019
SALES (est): 351.5K **Privately Held**
WEB: www.greatescapepublishing.com
SIC: 2741 Miscellaneous publishing

(G-3088)
GRIMES AEROSPACE COMPANY
Aircraft Products Div
12807 Lake Drive Ext (33444-3168)
PHONE..................................407 276-6083
Lee Schwartz, *Branch Mgr*
EMP: 79
SQ FT: 10,000
SALES (corp-wide): 32.6B **Publicly Held**
SIC: 3634 Coffee makers, electric: household
HQ: Grimes Aerospace Company
550 State Route 55
Urbana OH 43078
937 484-2000

(G-3089)
GUARDIAN ESSENTIALS LLC
137 Nw 1st Ave (33444-2611)
PHONE..................................817 401-0200
Kilburn Sherman,
Scott James,
Jeremy Office,
EMP: 6 **EST:** 2016
SQ FT: 2,500
SALES (est): 1MM **Privately Held**
SIC: 2833 Vitamins, natural or synthetic: bulk, uncompounded

(G-3090)
HARDRIVES INDUSTRIES INC
2101 S Congress Ave (33445-7307)
PHONE..................................561 278-0456
George T Elmore, *Principal*
Victor Concepcion, *Project Mgr*
Craig Connors, *Project Mgr*
Chris Sherlock, *Manager*
EMP: 21 **EST:** 2009
SALES (est): 6.7MM **Privately Held**
WEB: www.hardrivespaving.com
SIC: 3999 Manufacturing industries

(G-3091)
INSTASIGN
155 Avenue L (33483-4652)
PHONE..................................561 272-2323
EMP: 6 **EST:** 2018
SALES (est): 297.8K **Privately Held**
WEB: www.instasign.com
SIC: 3993 Signs & advertising specialties

(G-3092)
INTERCOMP
5910 Morningstar Cir (33484-8571)
PHONE..................................407 637-9766
Laura Michaels, *Principal*
EMP: 7 **EST:** 2012
SALES (est): 194.2K **Privately Held**
SIC: 3596 Scales & balances, except laboratory

(G-3093)
IRIS INC
955 Nw 17th Ave Ste D (33445-2516)
PHONE..................................561 921-0847
Jean-Marc Fontaine, *President*
Benjamin Bilges, *Partner*
Sally Daflaar, *General Mgr*
Joe Siegal, *Vice Pres*
Mickey Fried, *Project Mgr*
▲ **EMP:** 8 **EST:** 1997
SALES (est): 4.4MM **Privately Held**
WEB: www.irislink.com
SIC: 7372 Business oriented computer software
HQ: Image Recognition Integrated Systems Group
Rue Du Bosquet 10
Mont-Saint-Guibert 1435
104 513-64

(G-3094)
J T S WOODWORKING INC
75 Nw 18th Ave (33444-1687)
PHONE..................................561 272-7996
Mark Feehan, *President*
EMP: 9 **EST:** 1981
SQ FT: 10,780
SALES (est): 1MM **Privately Held**
WEB: www.jtswoodworking.com
SIC: 2499 2521 2511 Decorative wood & woodwork; wood office furniture; wood household furniture

(G-3095)
JEWELNET CORP
Also Called: K & G Creations
72 Se 6th Ave Apt K (33483-5308)
PHONE..................................561 989-8383
Neil Koppel, *President*
▲ **EMP:** 9 **EST:** 1988
SALES (est): 880.9K **Privately Held**
WEB: www.jewelnet.com
SIC: 3915 Jewelers' materials & lapidary work

(G-3096)
JEWISH BURIAL SOCIETY AMERICA
15310 Strathearn Dr # 11505 (33446-2851)
PHONE..................................954 424-1899
Philip Weinstein, *Principal*
EMP: 6 **EST:** 2002
SALES (est): 98.1K **Privately Held**
SIC: 3272 Burial vaults, concrete or precast terrazzo

(G-3097)
JOE TAYLOR RESTORATION (PA)
855 Nw 17th Ave Ste C (33445-2520)
P.O. Box 970805, Coconut Creek (33097-0805)
PHONE..................................954 972-5390
Robert Taylor, *Principal*
Jessica Baxter, *Sales Staff*
John Dance, *Manager*
Jeremy Kephart, *Manager*
Jesse Diaz, *Admin Asst*
EMP: 35 **EST:** 2012
SALES (est): 13.1MM **Privately Held**
WEB: www.jtrestoration.com
SIC: 3442 Molding, trim & stripping

(G-3098)
JVI MINERALS INC
15108 Ashland Dr Apt F196 (33484-4119)
PHONE..................................561 894-1022
Osmar C Da Costa Souza, *Principal*
EMP: 8 **EST:** 2011
SALES (est): 220.1K **Privately Held**
WEB: www.jviminerals.com
SIC: 2819 Industrial inorganic chemicals

(G-3099)
KC & B CUSTOM INC
Also Called: Kam Tatonetti
2413 N Federal Hwy Unit A (33483-6143)
PHONE..................................561 276-1887
John Kennedy, *President*
John Czulada, *Vice Pres*
EMP: 5 **EST:** 1988
SALES (est): 500K **Privately Held**
WEB: www.everwoodcabinetandtrim.com
SIC: 2434 5211 1751 Wood kitchen cabinets; cabinets, kitchen; cabinet building & installation

(G-3100)
LAB KINGZ LLC ✪
514 Sw 15th Ter (33444-1446)
PHONE..................................561 808-4216
Eric Wakeley Sr, *Mng Member*
EMP: 5 **EST:** 2020
SALES (est): 377.6K **Privately Held**
WEB: www.labkingz.com
SIC: 2833 Vitamins, natural or synthetic: bulk, uncompounded

(G-3101)
LIVING PATTERN LLC
101 Avocado Rd (33444-4226)
PHONE..................................561 596-8205
Jennifer Kiker, *Principal*
EMP: 7 **EST:** 2014
SALES (est): 193K **Privately Held**
WEB: www.livingpattern.studio
SIC: 3543 Industrial patterns

(G-3102)
LUMITEC LLC
1405 Poinsettia Dr Ste 10 (33444-5200)
PHONE..................................561 272-9840
John A Kujawa, *President*
Steve Rotolante, *Electrical Engi*
Karim Kharroubi, *Controller*
Mark Hayward, *Sales Associate*
Sinead Foyle, *Manager*
◆ **EMP:** 34 **EST:** 2007
SALES (est): 9.5MM **Privately Held**
WEB: www.lumiteclighting.com
SIC: 3647 3648 8711 Boat & ship lighting fixtures; underwater lighting fixtures; mechanical engineering; electrical or electronic engineering
HQ: Clarience Technologies, Llc
20600 Civic Center Dr
Southfield MI 48076
716 665-6214

(G-3103)
LUXE VINTAGES LLC
14545 S Military Trl J (33484-3781)
PHONE..................................561 558-7399
Peter Staley,
▲ **EMP:** 7 **EST:** 2007
SALES (est): 632K **Privately Held**
SIC: 2084 Wine cellars, bonded: engaged in blending wines

(G-3104)
MANOTILES LLC ✪
14364 Canalview Dr Apt A (33484-2676)
PHONE..................................954 803-3303
Cynthia Trezona,
EMP: 7 **EST:** 2021
SALES (est): 96.4K **Privately Held**
SIC: 3253 Mosaic tile, glazed & unglazed: ceramic

(G-3105)
MEDLEYCOM INCORPORATED
Also Called: Adultfriendfinder
1615 S Congress Ave # 10 (33445-6300)
PHONE..................................408 745-5418
Anthony Previte, *CEO*
Gavin Towey, *Administration*
EMP: 43 **EST:** 2002
SALES (est): 1.1MM **Privately Held**
WEB: www.medley.com
SIC: 2711 Newspapers, publishing & printing

(G-3106)
MESSER LLC
Linde Eco-Snow System
430 S Congress Ave Ste 7 (33445-4701)
PHONE..................................925 606-2000
EMP: 14
SALES (corp-wide): 1.2B **Privately Held**
SIC: 2813 Commerical Cleaning Equipment
HQ: Messer Llc
200 Somerset Corp Blvd # 7000
Bridgewater NJ 08807
908 464-8100

(G-3107)
METAL SUPPLY AND MACHINING INC
1304 Gwenzell Ave Ste B (33444-1268)
PHONE..................................561 276-4941
C William Packer, *President*
Marc Hirsch, *Vice Pres*
▼ **EMP:** 16 **EST:** 1991
SQ FT: 16,000
SALES (est): 3.6MM **Privately Held**
WEB: www.metalsupplyfl.com
SIC: 3541 5051 3446 3444 Machine tools, metal cutting: exotic (explosive, etc.); metals service centers & offices; architectural metalwork; sheet metalwork; fabricated structural metal

(G-3108)
MM WOOD DESIGNS INC
2859 Cormorant Rd (33444-1068)
PHONE..................................561 602-2775
Manoel L Macedo, *Principal*
EMP: 6 **EST:** 2016
SALES (est): 223.1K **Privately Held**
SIC: 2431 Millwork

(G-3109)
MR MICA WOOD INC
1300 Sw 10th St Ste 3 (33444-1266)
PHONE..................................561 278-5821
John Berube, *President*
Chris Eckert, *Vice Pres*
Dorothy Berube, *Admin Sec*
EMP: 15 **EST:** 1973
SQ FT: 5,000
SALES (est): 433K **Privately Held**
WEB: www.mrmicanwood.com
SIC: 2541 2511 Cabinets, except refrigerated: show, display, etc.: wood; wood household furniture

(G-3110)
MR REAL DEAL BARBQUE LLC ✪
1050 Dotterel Rd Apt 200 (33444-1001)
PHONE..................................561 271-8749
Ronnie Manning,
EMP: 7 **EST:** 2021

▲ = Import ▼=Export
◆ =Import/Export

SALES (est): 255.4K Privately Held
SIC: 2599 Food wagons, restaurant

(G-3111)
MY WILD LIFE PRESS LLC
2155 S Ocean Blvd Apt 1 (33483-6448)
PHONE....515 203-9728
Laura Williams, *Principal*
EMP: 6 EST: 2016
SALES (est): 167K Privately Held
SIC: 2741 Miscellaneous publishing

(G-3112)
P D I S INC
2855 S Congress Ave Ste C (33445-7312)
PHONE....561 243-8442
John W Wilson II, *CEO*
EMP: 10 EST: 1995
SALES (est): 1.8MM Privately Held
SIC: 3599 Custom machinery

(G-3113)
PARKSIDE PUBLISHING LLC
1633 W Classical Blvd (33445-1260)
PHONE....888 386-1115
EMP: 6 EST: 2019
SALES (est): 468.7K Privately Held
WEB: www.parksidepublishingllc.com
SIC: 2741 Miscellaneous publishing

(G-3114)
PEAK PERFORMANCE NUTRIENTS INC
1505 Poinsettia Dr Ste 4 (33444-1272)
PHONE....561 266-1038
Jeff Bielec, *President*
Jennifer Bielec, *Vice Pres*
Louella Bielec, *Sales Mgr*
Edward Bielec, *Director*
▲ EMP: 15 EST: 1997
SQ FT: 15,000
SALES (est): 2.1MM Privately Held
WEB: www.peakperformancenutrients.com
SIC: 2834 Vitamin, nutrient & hematinic preparations for human use

(G-3115)
PETER FOGEL
8108 Summer Shores Dr (33446-3477)
PHONE....561 245-5252
Peter Fogel, *Principal*
EMP: 8 EST: 2010
SALES (est): 407K Privately Held
WEB: www.fogelscorporatecomedy.com
SIC: 3651 Speaker systems

(G-3116)
PHOENIX CUSTOM GEAR LLC
1730 S Federal Hwy # 242 (33483-3309)
PHONE....561 808-7181
William Burbank, *Principal*
EMP: 7 EST: 2018
SALES (est): 485.4K Privately Held
SIC: 2211 Apparel & outerwear fabrics, cotton

(G-3117)
PLASTI-CARD CORPORATION
7901 Clay Mica Ct (33446-2226)
PHONE....305 944-2726
Irwin Feldman, *President*
Steven Feldman, *Vice Pres*
▲ EMP: 13 EST: 1981
SALES (est): 920.4K Privately Held
WEB: www.continentalbizmag.com
SIC: 2752 Commercial printing, offset

(G-3118)
PLASTIMOLD PRODUCTS INC
Also Called: Fort Lauderdale Molding
250 N Congress Ave (33445-3415)
PHONE....561 869-0183
Joseph Parisi, *President*
Cathy Parisi, *Treasurer*
Sue Kibler, *Manager*
▲ EMP: 6 EST: 1991
SQ FT: 8,000
SALES (est): 2.6MM Privately Held
WEB: www.plastimoldproducts.com
SIC: 3089 Injection molding of plastics

(G-3119)
PLATINUM GROUP USA INC
Also Called: Www.tpgus.com
75 N Congress Ave (33445-3416)
P.O. Box 6584 (33482-6584)
PHONE....561 274-7553
Amer Rustom, *CEO*
Robert R Donofrio, *COO*
Azzam Rustom, *Vice Pres*
EMP: 12 EST: 2003
SALES (est): 614.4K Privately Held
SIC: 1382 2834 Oil & gas exploration services; pharmaceutical preparations

(G-3120)
PMR GESTION INC
1100 Sw 10th St (33444-1233)
PHONE....561 501-5190
Guy Gerald, *Principal*
EMP: 9 EST: 2013
SALES (est): 651.9K Privately Held
WEB: www.pmrcc.com
SIC: 3339 Precious metals

(G-3121)
POSITIVEID CORPORATION (PA)
1690 S Congress Ave # 201 (33445-6386)
P.O. Box 880173, Boca Raton (33488-0173)
PHONE....561 805-8000
William J Caragol, *Ch of Bd*
Lyle L Probst, *President*
EMP: 11 EST: 2001
SQ FT: 3,000
SALES: 5.3MM Publicly Held
WEB: www.psidcorp.com
SIC: 2835 In vivo diagnostics

(G-3122)
POWERLINE GROUP INC
8406 Hawks Gully Ave (33446-9678)
PHONE....631 828-1183
Patrick Hinchy, *CEO*
EMP: 105 EST: 2016
SALES (est): 2.8MM Privately Held
WEB: www.thepowerlinegroup.com
SIC: 7372 Application computer software

(G-3123)
PREMIER STONEWORKS LLC
1455 Sw 4th Ave (33444-2274)
PHONE....561 330-3737
Gary Arkin, *Principal*
Glenn Savell, *Director*
◆ EMP: 52 EST: 2010
SALES: 5.7MM Privately Held
WEB: www.premier-stoneworks.com
SIC: 3272 1741 Cast stone, concrete; masonry & other stonework

(G-3124)
PRESTO PRINT II INC
7785 Silver Lake Dr (33446-3337)
PHONE....203 627-2528
Renee Gere, *Principal*
EMP: 7 EST: 2018
SALES (est): 288.8K Privately Held
WEB: www.prestoprint2.com
SIC: 2752 Commercial printing, lithographic

(G-3125)
PRINT IT 4 LESS
601 N Congress Ave # 208 (33445-4646)
PHONE....800 370-5591
EMP: 6 EST: 2018
SALES (est): 92.3K Privately Held
WEB: www.printit4less.com
SIC: 2752 Commercial printing, lithographic

(G-3126)
PRINTING AND PROMOTION SVCS
7320 Amberly Ln Apt 103 (33446-2907)
PHONE....201 612-0800
Phyllis Schinasi, *Principal*
EMP: 7 EST: 2015
SALES (est): 101.5K Privately Held
SIC: 2752 Commercial printing, lithographic

(G-3127)
PROFESSIONAL CTR AT GARDENS
190 Se 5th Ave (33483-5214)
PHONE....561 394-5200
Richard D Gertz, *Principal*
EMP: 10 EST: 2001
SALES (est): 387K Privately Held
SIC: 3069 Fabricated rubber products

(G-3128)
PROGRESSIVE PRINTING SOLUTIONS
Also Called: Progressive Printing Services
601 N Congress Ave # 208 (33445-4646)
PHONE....800 370-5591
Shawn Samai, *President*
Sara I Martinez, *Vice Pres*
EMP: 6 EST: 1992
SQ FT: 3,000
SALES (est): 481.3K Privately Held
WEB: www.progressiveprintingsolutions.com
SIC: 2752 Commercial printing, offset

(G-3129)
PROTEK SYSTEMS INC
1250 Wallace Dr Ste B (33444-4602)
PHONE....561 395-8155
Dennis Chalas, *President*
Alan Austin, *Vice Pres*
Andrew Aukstikalnis, *Opers Staff*
EMP: 7 EST: 1991
SQ FT: 2,500
SALES (est): 1.4MM Privately Held
WEB: www.proteksystem.com
SIC: 3441 Fabricated structural metal

(G-3130)
PSC BUILDING GROUP INC
Also Called: Precision Stone
900 Sw 15th Ave (33444-1322)
PHONE....561 756-6811
Guy Paterra, *Principal*
EMP: 17 EST: 2006
SQ FT: 800
SALES (est): 1.2MM Privately Held
WEB: www.precisionstonecorp.com
SIC: 3281 Cut stone & stone products

(G-3131)
QUALITY SOFTWARE LLC
55 Se 2nd Ave 1 (33444-3615)
PHONE....561 714-2314
Ryan Armstrong, *President*
Ryan F Morrissey, *Principal*
EMP: 24 EST: 2013
SALES (est): 1.3MM Privately Held
SIC: 7372 Prepackaged software

(G-3132)
RAMSTAR CORPORATION
5304 Ventura Dr (33484-8386)
PHONE....561 499-8488
Michael Reale, *Principal*
EMP: 8 EST: 2009
SALES (est): 216.8K Privately Held
SIC: 3599 Machine shop, jobbing & repair

(G-3133)
RANDOLPH CNSTR GROUP INC
1191 N Federal Hwy Ste 1 (33483-5800)
PHONE....954 276-2889
Dwayne Randolph, *President*
Remona Rey, *Vice Pres*
EMP: 6 EST: 2019
SALES (est): 654K Privately Held
WEB: www.randolph-cg.com
SIC: 1389 Construction, repair & dismantling services

(G-3134)
RAVE LLC (HQ)
Also Called: Internano
430 S Congress Ave Ste 7 (33445-4701)
PHONE....561 330-0411
Barry Hopkins, *President*
Rick Greece, *CFO*
Crystal Brazzel, *Admin Sec*
EMP: 32 EST: 1996
SQ FT: 7,500
SALES (est): 13MM
SALES (corp-wide): 1.9B Publicly Held
WEB: www.ravellc.com
SIC: 3826 Analytical instruments
PA: Bruker Corporation
40 Manning Rd
Billerica MA 01821
978 663-3660

(G-3135)
RENAISSANCE CUSTOM WOODWORKING
307 W Mallory Cir (33483-5279)
PHONE....561 212-9885
Scott Lanciano, *Principal*
EMP: 6 EST: 2010
SALES (est): 61.3K Privately Held
SIC: 2431 Millwork

(G-3136)
ROYAL ATLANTIC VENTURES LLC
Also Called: Channel Letter USA
1505 Poinsettia Dr H-9 (33444-1272)
PHONE....561 243-9699
Jason Ditkofsky, *Mng Member*
EMP: 13 EST: 2017
SALES (est): 918.7K Privately Held
SIC: 3993 Signs & advertising specialties

(G-3137)
SAFEGUARD OF SOUTH FLORID
1395 Nw 17th Ave Ste 104 (33445-2552)
PHONE....561 499-7600
Paul Twohig, *Owner*
EMP: 6 EST: 2006
SALES (est): 102.8K Privately Held
SIC: 2599 Furniture & fixtures

(G-3138)
SCHWARZMANN LLC
360 N Congress Ave (33445-3435)
PHONE....561 654-3653
Michael Schluetter, *Mng Member*
Marion Carias,
▲ EMP: 7 EST: 2013
SALES (est): 282.2K Privately Held
WEB: www.schwarzmann.pro
SIC: 2514 Kitchen cabinets: metal

(G-3139)
SEA SIDE SPECIALTIES
Also Called: Tyler Fabricators
1200 S Swinton Ave (33444-2296)
PHONE....561 276-6518
Mico Klingler, *President*
Kelly Klingler, *Vice Pres*
▼ EMP: 7 EST: 1975
SALES (est): 1.5MM Privately Held
WEB: www.tylerfabricators.com
SIC: 3312 Blast furnaces & steel mills

(G-3140)
SHASHI LLC
6926 Royal Orchid Cir (33446-4342)
PHONE....561 447-8800
Natalie L Sudit, *Mng Member*
EMP: 5
SQ FT: 500
SALES (est): 394.6K Privately Held
WEB: www.shashionline.com
SIC: 2252 Socks

(G-3141)
SHIP SHAPE CANVAS AND AWNG LLC
6101 Heliconia Rd (33484-4673)
PHONE....954 480-8889
Richard Daino, *Manager*
EMP: 7 EST: 2017
SALES (est): 132.2K Privately Held
WEB: www.shipshapemarinecanvas.com
SIC: 2394 Canvas & related products

(G-3142)
SIW SOLUTIONS LLC
975 S Congress Ave (33445-4661)
PHONE....561 274-9392
Yida A Lopez, *Principal*
EMP: 70 Privately Held
SIC: 2431 Doors, wood
HQ: Siw Solutions, Llc
401 State Ave N
Warroad MN 56763
888 537-7828

GEOGRAPHIC

(G-3143)
SKILL-METRIC MACHINE & TL INC
1424 Gwenzell Ave 3c (33444-1267)
PHONE..................................561 454-8900
Miguel Leon, *Engineer*
EMP: 25
SQ FT: 11,000
SALES (est): 5.1MM **Privately Held**
WEB: www.skill-metric.com
SIC: 3724 3541 Aircraft engines & engine parts; machine tools, metal cutting type

(G-3144)
SNEIDS INC
Also Called: Sign-A-Rama
2905 S Congress Ave Ste E (33445-7337)
PHONE..................................561 278-7446
Michael Sneiderman, *President*
David Sneiderman, *Vice Pres*
Michelle Laskowski, *Sales Executive*
EMP: 8 **EST:** 1994
SQ FT: 1,600
SALES (est): 651.2K **Privately Held**
WEB: www.sneids.com
SIC: 3993 Signs & advertising specialties

(G-3145)
SPLINTER WOODWORKING INC
738 Dotterel Rd (33444-2087)
PHONE..................................305 731-9334
EMP: 5 **EST:** 2015
SALES (est): 416.1K **Privately Held**
SIC: 2431 5999 Millwork; miscellaneous retail stores

(G-3146)
STEVE PRINTS
15345 Lake Wildflower Rd (33484-4650)
PHONE..................................561 571-2903
Steve Guttman, *Owner*
EMP: 6 **EST:** 2017
SALES (est): 123.8K **Privately Held**
WEB: www.steveprints.com
SIC: 2752 Commercial printing, lithographic

(G-3147)
STRAW GIANT COMPANY
Also Called: Mask Giant
10290 W Atlantic Ave (33448-6901)
P.O. Box 481295 (33448-1295)
PHONE..................................561 430-0729
Gregg Fredman, *CEO*
EMP: 8 **EST:** 2019
SALES (est): 614.1K **Privately Held**
WEB: www.maskgiantcompany.com
SIC: 3842 Clothing, fire resistant & protective

(G-3148)
SUNCOAST STONE INC
151 Nw 18th Ave (33444-1685)
PHONE..................................561 364-2061
Roger Smith, *CEO*
▼ **EMP:** 20 **EST:** 2005
SALES (est): 3.1MM **Privately Held**
WEB: www.suncoast-stone.com
SIC: 3281 Cut stone & stone products

(G-3149)
THRIV INDUSTRIES LLC
402 W Atlantic Ave 65 (33444-2554)
PHONE..................................404 436-3230
Joseph Pritchett,
EMP: 12 **EST:** 2017
SALES (est): 357K **Privately Held**
SIC: 3999 Manufacturing industries

(G-3150)
TIBOR INC
Also Called: Juracsik, Ted Tool & Die
255 N Congress Ave (33445-3418)
PHONE..................................561 272-0770
Ted Juracsik Sr, *President*
Wilma Juracsik, *Corp Secy*
Ted Juracsik Jr, *Vice Pres*
EMP: 40 **EST:** 1960
SQ FT: 20,000
SALES (est): 4.6MM **Privately Held**
WEB: www.tiborreel.com
SIC: 3544 3949 3444 Special dies & tools; reels, fishing; sheet metalwork

(G-3151)
TROPICAL AWNING OF FLORIDA
335 Se 1st Ave Ste A (33444-3581)
PHONE..................................561 276-1144
Monna Simpson, *President*
Robert Scott Simpson, *Corp Secy*
EMP: 12 **EST:** 1952
SQ FT: 8,000
SALES (est): 1MM **Privately Held**
WEB: www.tropicalawning.net
SIC: 2394 Awnings, fabric: made from purchased materials

(G-3152)
TRU CRAFT WOODWORKS LLC
1865 Sw 4th Ave Ste D9 (33444-7998)
PHONE..................................561 441-2742
William A Canty, *Mng Member*
EMP: 6 **EST:** 2009
SALES (est): 54.1K **Privately Held**
SIC: 2431 Millwork

(G-3153)
TRUCRAFT SPECIALTIES INC
1503 Hummingbird Dr (33444-3324)
PHONE..................................561 441-2742
William A Canty, *President*
EMP: 9 **EST:** 2001
SALES (est): 128.2K **Privately Held**
SIC: 2431 Millwork

(G-3154)
VANBERT CORPORATION
1855 Sw 4th Ave Ste B3 (33444-7937)
PHONE..................................561 945-5856
Constantin Chiriac, *CEO*
▲ **EMP:** 6 **EST:** 2013
SALES (est): 750.5K **Privately Held**
WEB: www.vanbertdesign.com
SIC: 2434 Wood kitchen cabinets

(G-3155)
VARIOUS INC (PA)
Also Called: Friendfinder.com
1615 S Congress Ave # 10 (33445-6300)
PHONE..................................561 900-3691
Jonathan Buckheit, *CEO*
Anthony Previte, *CEO*
Tim Pollins, *Editor*
Jason Collins, *Project Mgr*
Marc Glissman, *Project Mgr*
EMP: 149 **EST:** 2010
SALES (est): 30.7MM **Privately Held**
WEB: www.various.com
SIC: 2711 Newspapers

(G-3156)
VENGA LLC
955 Nw 17th Ave (33445-2516)
PHONE..................................561 665-8200
Jamie Day, *Managing Prtnr*
James L Day, *Principal*
Mamadi Niknejad, *Director*
EMP: 9 **EST:** 2007
SALES (est): 428.3K **Privately Held**
SIC: 2086 Bottled & canned soft drinks

(G-3157)
VERITEQ ACQUISITION CORP
220 Congress Park Dr # 200 (33445-4670)
PHONE..................................561 805-8007
Scott R Silverman, *CEO*
EMP: 6 **EST:** 2011
SQ FT: 5,000
SALES (est): 964.2K **Privately Held**
WEB: www.jamm.tech
SIC: 3851 Ophthalmic goods
PA: Veriteq Corporation
11211 S Military Trl # 32
Boynton Beach FL 33436

(G-3158)
VERSAILLES LIGHTING INC
1305 Poinsettia Dr Ste 6 (33444-1251)
PHONE..................................561 945-5744
Maurine Locke, *CEO*
Max Guedj, *President*
EMP: 10 **EST:** 1982
SQ FT: 15,000
SALES (est): 575.2K **Privately Held**
SIC: 3645 3646 5063 Residential lighting fixtures; commercial indusl & institutional electric lighting fixtures; lighting fixtures

(G-3159)
WAY BEYOND BAGELS INC
16850 S Jog Rd Ste 108 (33446-2384)
PHONE..................................561 638-1320
Marcy Speranza, *Manager*
EMP: 10 **EST:** 2001
SALES (est): 498.8K **Privately Held**
WEB: www.waybeyondbagels.com
SIC: 2051 5461 Bakery: wholesale or wholesale/retail combined; bakeries

(G-3160)
WINDSOR IMAGING DELRAY ✪
14590 S Military Trl E1 (33484-3757)
PHONE..................................561 900-0300
EMP: 5 **EST:** 2020
SALES (est): 351.9K **Privately Held**
SIC: 3826 Analytical instruments

(G-3161)
WORRELL WATER TECHNOLOGIES LLC
Also Called: Goodwater Albemarle Co
14 S Swinton Ave (33444-3654)
PHONE..................................434 973-6365
Steven J Keeler,
EMP: 8 **EST:** 2006
SALES (est): 869.9K **Privately Held**
SIC: 1389 Impounding & storing salt water, oil & gas field

Deltona
Volusia County

(G-3162)
A/C CAGES
890 Merrimac St (32725-5776)
PHONE..................................407 446-9259
Brandi N Baker, *Principal*
EMP: 9 **EST:** 2008
SALES (est): 128.8K **Privately Held**
WEB: www.snydercontractingny.com
SIC: 3441 Fabricated structural metal

(G-3163)
BEARDED MOHAWK LLC
2916 Maldive Ct (32738-7935)
PHONE..................................913 680-9829
Merlin Taylor, *Principal*
EMP: 6 **EST:** 2016
SALES (est): 126.8K **Privately Held**
WEB: www.beardedmohawk.us
SIC: 2273 Carpets & rugs

(G-3164)
BKS BAKERY INC
2531 Dumas Dr (32738-5112)
PHONE..................................386 216-0540
Margaret Granito, *Co-Owner*
Theresa Granito, *Co-Owner*
EMP: 8
SQ FT: 1,805
SALES (est): 464.4K **Privately Held**
SIC: 2051 5142 Bakery, for home service delivery; bakery products, frozen

(G-3165)
BYTE SIZE IT LLC
670 Stallings Ave (32738-9268)
PHONE..................................386 785-9311
Timothy McGuire, *Manager*
EMP: 6 **EST:** 2011
SALES (est): 160.5K **Privately Held**
SIC: 2899 Sizes

(G-3166)
CLUPPER LLC
2386 Pavillion Ter (32738-8731)
PHONE..................................386 956-6396
Robert J Clupper III, *Principal*
EMP: 8 **EST:** 2005
SALES (est): 236.2K **Privately Held**
SIC: 3448 Screen enclosures

(G-3167)
CUSTOM MOLDING & CASEWORK INC
1650 Travers Ln (32738-5044)
PHONE..................................407 709-7377
Joseph D Hubbard, *Vice Pres*
EMP: 6 **EST:** 2013
SALES (est): 91.2K **Privately Held**
SIC: 3089 Molding primary plastic

(G-3168)
EDENS GARDEN NATURAL H
3237 Kings Ridge Ter (32725-3079)
PHONE..................................585 353-8547
Devra Lozada,
EMP: 7 **EST:** 2016
SALES (est): 50K **Privately Held**
WEB: www.edensgarden.com
SIC: 2844 Toilet preparations

(G-3169)
FGMG INTERNATIONAL
2820 Lightwood St (32738-9185)
PHONE..................................305 988-7436
Demetris Hardy, *CEO*
EMP: 10
SALES (est): 100K **Privately Held**
SIC: 3651 Music distribution apparatus

(G-3170)
FLORIDA RUST
618 Tradewinds Dr (32738-8761)
PHONE..................................386 259-9940
Sergio G Gallina, *Principal*
EMP: 6 **EST:** 2009
SALES (est): 481.9K **Privately Held**
WEB: www.floridarust.com
SIC: 2842 Rust removers

(G-3171)
FREON & FABRIC
2885 W Huron Dr (32738-1662)
PHONE..................................386 801-5096
Brian Reck Valenzuela, *Owner*
EMP: 6 **EST:** 2017
SALES (est): 233.8K **Privately Held**
SIC: 2869 Freon

(G-3172)
JRS VENTURES LLP
Also Called: Hvac Genius, The
915 Doyle Rd Ste 303-356 (32725-8254)
PHONE..................................715 441-1051
EMP: 6 **EST:** 2018
SALES (est): 217.2K **Privately Held**
WEB: www.jrsventuresinc.squarespace.com
SIC: 3569 3822 Filters; thermostats & other environmental sensors

(G-3173)
LNL LOGISTICS LLC ✪
915 Doyle Rd Ste 303-150 (32725-8254)
PHONE..................................386 977-9276
Lashunda N Lewis, *Principal*
Lashunda Lewis, *Principal*
EMP: 8 **EST:** 2021
SALES (est): 299.2K **Privately Held**
SIC: 3799 Transportation equipment

(G-3174)
M J BOTURLA INDUSTRIES INC
1885 S Lehigh Dr (32738-8645)
PHONE..................................386 574-0811
Phyllis E Boturla, *President*
EMP: 8 **EST:** 2001
SALES (est): 247.8K **Privately Held**
SIC: 3999 Manufacturing industries

(G-3175)
MICHAEL MOORE LLC
1266 Gage Ave (32738-9714)
PHONE..................................407 716-7325
Michael D Moore, *Principal*
EMP: 5 **EST:** 2018
SALES (est): 328.4K **Privately Held**
SIC: 3999 Manufacturing industries

(G-3176)
NATIONWIDE PUBLISHING COMPANY (PA)
Also Called: Claims Pages
537 Deltona Blvd (32725-8017)
PHONE..................................352 253-0017
D Scott Plakon, *President*
Phillip J Imbrenda, *Exec VP*
Alison Post, *Opers Mgr*
EMP: 30 **EST:** 1997
SQ FT: 7,000
SALES (est): 6MM **Privately Held**
SIC: 2741 Telephone & other directory publishing

(G-3177)
PRECISION CABINETRY LLC
2240 E Old Mill Dr (32725-2826)
PHONE...................................386 218-3340
Stephen Theisen, *Manager*
EMP: 6 **EST:** 2014
SALES (est): 78.3K **Privately Held**
WEB: www.precisioncabinetry.com
SIC: 2434 Wood kitchen cabinets

(G-3178)
PREMIUM POWDER COATING
1872 Sweetwater Bnd (32738-3522)
PHONE...................................386 789-0216
Dana Lehman, *Principal*
EMP: 7 **EST:** 2012
SALES (est): 146.3K **Privately Held**
WEB: www.premiumpowdercoating.com
SIC: 3479 Metal coating & allied service

(G-3179)
SERENITY HAIR EXTENSIONS LLC ✪
1235 Providence Blvd R10 (32725-7363)
P.O. Box 11335, Daytona Beach (32120-1335)
PHONE...................................407 917-1788
Marquita Fish, *Mng Member*
EMP: 10 **EST:** 2021
SALES (est): 555.2K **Privately Held**
SIC: 3999 Hair & hair-based products

(G-3180)
SUMMIT HOLSTERS LLC
843 Superior St (32725-5586)
PHONE...................................386 383-4090
Michael Salimbene, *Manager*
EMP: 6 **EST:** 2015
SALES (est): 211.3K **Privately Held**
SIC: 3199 Holsters, leather

(G-3181)
VOLUSIA WASTE INC
1455 Brayton Cir (32725-5684)
PHONE...................................386 878-3322
Gladys E Quiles, *Principal*
EMP: 9 **EST:** 2005
SALES (est): 196.6K **Privately Held**
SIC: 3089 Garbage containers, plastic

(G-3182)
XPRESS FINANCE INC (PA)
807 S Orlando Ave Ste B (32738)
PHONE...................................407 629-0095
David Rasmussen, *Director*
EMP: 13 **EST:** 2005
SALES (est): 321.9K **Privately Held**
WEB: www.xpressfinanceinc.com
SIC: 2741 Miscellaneous publishing

Destin
Okaloosa County

(G-3183)
ARMADA SYSTEMS INC (PA)
Also Called: Asi
508 Mountain Dr (32541-2332)
P.O. Box 307, Mary Esther (32569-0307)
PHONE...................................850 664-5197
Phillip F Robbins, *President*
Tina Smith, *Admin Sec*
▼ **EMP:** 10 **EST:** 1992
SQ FT: 10,000
SALES (est): 1.4MM **Privately Held**
WEB: www.armadahull.com
SIC: 3541 Machine tools, metal cutting type

(G-3184)
BOTE PADDLE BOARDS
383 Harbor Blvd (32541-2323)
PHONE...................................850 460-2250
Corey Cooper, *Principal*
Rob McAbee, *Director*
EMP: 7 **EST:** 2013
SALES (est): 395.1K **Privately Held**
WEB: www.boteboard.com
SIC: 3949 Surfboards

(G-3185)
CARPEDIEM LLC
618 Gulf Shore Dr (32541-3128)
PHONE...................................229 230-1453
David Penney, *Mng Member*
EMP: 18 **EST:** 2019
SALES (est): 2MM **Privately Held**
SIC: 7372 Business oriented computer software

(G-3186)
COASTAL PROMOTIONS INC
128 Indian Bayou Dr (32541-4415)
PHONE...................................850 460-2270
Patricia L Bramlet, *President*
Douglas McWhorter, *Vice Pres*
EMP: 8 **EST:** 1993
SALES (est): 890K **Privately Held**
WEB: www.tasteoffl.com
SIC: 2087 Beverage bases; fruit juices: concentrated for fountain use

(G-3187)
DESTIN MACHINE INC
600 Fourth St (32541-1629)
PHONE...................................850 837-7114
Wayne E Lung, *President*
Norma L Lung, *Corp Secy*
EMP: 5 **EST:** 1980
SQ FT: 3,040
SALES (est): 800K **Privately Held**
WEB: www.destinmachine.embarqspace.com
SIC: 3599 3544 Machine shop, jobbing & repair; special dies, tools, jigs & fixtures

(G-3188)
DESTINATION BVI II INC
36120 Emerald Coast Pkwy (32541-4705)
PHONE...................................850 699-9551
Tim Creehan, *Principal*
Tim Wellborn, *Principal*
EMP: 6 **EST:** 2010
SALES (est): 509.4K **Privately Held**
SIC: 2035 Seasonings, seafood sauces (except tomato & dry)

(G-3189)
ENCORE ANALYTICS LLC
86 Shirah St (32541-3513)
P.O. Box 2247, Santa Rosa Beach (32459-2247)
PHONE...................................866 890-4331
Brooke Boswell, *Manager*
Gary W Toop,
James Price,
EMP: 8 **EST:** 2009
SALES (est): 911.2K **Privately Held**
WEB: www.encore-analytics.com
SIC: 7372 Application computer software

(G-3190)
GIBSON WLDG SHETMETAL VENT INC
335 Mountain Dr (32541-2335)
PHONE...................................850 837-6141
Dean Gibson, *President*
Tina Henschen, *Corp Secy*
EMP: 8 **EST:** 1993
SALES (est): 1MM **Privately Held**
WEB: www.gwsmv.com
SIC: 3444 Booths, spray: prefabricated sheet metal

(G-3191)
GO GREEN MARINE INC
Also Called: Rammo
1234 Arprt Rd Ste 109-110 (32541)
PHONE...................................850 499-5137
Donna Petrucci, *CEO*
Micheal Petrucci, *President*
Mike Petrucci, *President*
Stephen Dugas, *Vice Pres*
EMP: 7 **EST:** 2009
SALES (est): 134.3K **Privately Held**
WEB: www.myrammo.com
SIC: 2841 2873 Soap & other detergents; fertilizers: natural (organic), except compost

(G-3192)
GOTCHA SHUTTERED
4151 Cmmons Dr W Apt 5406 (32541)
PHONE...................................850 450-9137
Michael B Hewitt, *Principal*
EMP: 6 **EST:** 2009
SALES (est): 69.1K **Privately Held**
SIC: 3442 Shutters, door or window: metal

(G-3193)
HART S CERAMIC & STONE INC
981 Highway 98 E Ste 3 (32541-2525)
PHONE...................................850 217-6145
John C Hart, *Principal*
EMP: 6 **EST:** 2010
SALES (est): 80.5K **Privately Held**
SIC: 3269 Pottery products

(G-3194)
HIMES SIGNS INC
4 Commerce Dr Ste 4 # 4 (32541-7350)
P.O. Box 5324 (32540-5324)
PHONE...................................850 837-1159
John Himes, *President*
EMP: 14 **EST:** 1982
SALES (est): 1.5MM **Privately Held**
WEB: www.himessigns.com
SIC: 3993 Electric signs

(G-3195)
INFINITE LASERS LLC
Also Called: Destin Engraving
45 Harbor Blvd (32541-2309)
PHONE...................................850 424-3759
Drew Cooper, *Principal*
EMP: 6 **EST:** 2012
SALES (est): 191.8K **Privately Held**
WEB: www.infinitelaserslic.com
SIC: 3423 Engravers' tools, hand

(G-3196)
LIFES A BCH PUBLICATIONS LLC
124 Benning Dr Ste 7 (32541-2486)
P.O. Box 5731 (32540-5731)
PHONE...................................850 650-2780
Seevers Richard S, *Mng Member*
Richard S Seevers, *Mng Member*
Sarah E Seevers, *Mng Member*
EMP: 9 **EST:** 2003
SALES (est): 857.8K **Privately Held**
WEB: www.lifesabeachllc.com
SIC: 2741 Miscellaneous publishing

(G-3197)
LINX DEFENSE LLC
4507 Furling Ln Ste 205 (32541-5342)
PHONE...................................805 233-2472
Steve Olson, *Owner*
EMP: 6 **EST:** 2017
SALES (est): 394.7K **Privately Held**
WEB: www.linxdefense.com
SIC: 3812 Defense systems & equipment

(G-3198)
LUSH FRESH HANDMADE COSMETICS
4127 Legendary Dr (32541-5393)
PHONE...................................850 650-2434
EMP: 8 **EST:** 2017
SALES (est): 71.5K **Privately Held**
SIC: 2844 Toilet preparations

(G-3199)
NORTH METRO MEDIA
Also Called: Homes & Land of Emerald Coast
4507 Furling Ln Ste 106 (32541-5341)
P.O. Box 1854 (32540-1854)
PHONE...................................850 650-1014
Kate Kelley, *Prdtn Mgr*
Joe Nacchia, *Office Mgr*
EMP: 10 **EST:** 1993
SQ FT: 2,200
SALES (est): 923.6K **Privately Held**
SIC: 2741 Telephone & other directory publishing

(G-3200)
NORTHSIDE PHARMACY LLC
36474c Emerald Coast Pkwy (32541-6700)
PHONE...................................256 398-7500
Jeff South, *Mng Member*
EMP: 7 **EST:** 2013
SALES (est): 211.4K **Privately Held**
SIC: 2834 Pharmaceutical preparations

(G-3201)
PEGASUS AEROSPACE
290 Vinings Way Blvd # 6103 (32541-6803)
PHONE...................................850 376-0991
Eugen Toma, *Principal*
EMP: 8 **EST:** 2017
SALES (est): 199.5K **Privately Held**
WEB: www.pegasp.com
SIC: 3721 Aircraft

(G-3202)
PREMIER SIGN COMPANY LLC
216 Mountain Dr Ste 100 (32541-7300)
PHONE...................................850 621-4524
Anthony Crisafi, *Principal*
EMP: 12 **EST:** 2019
SALES (est): 231.3K **Privately Held**
WEB: www.premiersign.com
SIC: 3993 Signs & advertising specialties

(G-3203)
RB CABINETRY LLC
408 Evergreen Dr Ste A (32541-2202)
P.O. Box 22 (32540-0022)
PHONE...................................850 685-5316
Ronald C Banks, *Branch Mgr*
EMP: 14 **Privately Held**
SIC: 2434 Wood kitchen cabinets
PA: Rb Cabinetry Llc
140 Azalea Dr Ste B
Destin FL

(G-3204)
SAAS TRANSPORTATION INC
3551 Scenic Highway 98 (32541-5748)
PHONE...................................850 650-7709
Ken Pehanick, *President*
EMP: 10 **EST:** 2011
SALES (est): 507.2K **Privately Held**
WEB: www.wisetechglobal.com
SIC: 7372 Application computer software

(G-3205)
SEASIDE PREMIUM CABINETS
4010 Commons Dr W (32541-8420)
PHONE...................................850 533-6801
EMP: 6 **EST:** 2016
SALES (est): 164.7K **Privately Held**
SIC: 2434 Wood kitchen cabinets

(G-3206)
SKATER SOCKS
516 Mountain Dr Ste 104 (32541-7370)
PHONE...................................850 424-6764
EMP: 14 **EST:** 2012
SALES (est): 172.2K **Privately Held**
WEB: www.skatersocks.com
SIC: 2252 Socks

(G-3207)
SMART GROUP TRADERS INC
47 Indian Bayou Dr (32541-4435)
PHONE...................................850 460-5130
Jorge Dijkhuizen, *President*
▲ **EMP:** 8 **EST:** 2012
SALES (est): 688.3K **Privately Held**
WEB: www.smartgrouptradersinc.com
SIC: 1021 1041 1044 5141 Open pit copper ore mining; gold ores mining; silver ores mining; food brokers

(G-3208)
TIMBER CREEK DISTILLING LLC
146 Country Club Dr W (32541-4418)
PHONE...................................408 439-0973
EMP: 9 **EST:** 2015
SALES (est): 307.8K **Privately Held**
WEB: www.timbercreekdistillery.com
SIC: 2085 Distilled & blended liquors

(G-3209)
WANNAGOFAST LLC
403 Juniper St (32541-2611)
PHONE...................................850 585-5168
Blake A Hutchison, *Principal*
EMP: 6 **EST:** 2011
SALES (est): 435.2K **Privately Held**
WEB: www.wannagofast.com
SIC: 2371 Apparel, fur

(G-3210)
WATERHOUSE PRESS LLC
4481 Legendary Dr Ste 200 (32541-5381)
PHONE...................................781 975-6191
Fuchsia Mclnerney, *Principal*
Jesse Kench, *COO*
Yvonne Ellis, *Prdtn Mgr*
Haley Byrd, *Marketing Staff*
Scott Saunders, *Manager*
EMP: 8 **EST:** 2016

GEOGRAPHIC

SALES (est): 1MM **Privately Held**
WEB: www.waterhousepress.com
SIC: 2741 Miscellaneous publishing

(G-3211)
WEIDENHAMER CORPORATION
Also Called: S O S Printing & Office Supply
808 Wild Oak Ave (32541-2646)
P.O. Box 1786 (32540-1786)
PHONE..................................850 837-3190
Thomas Weidenhamer, *President*
Nancy Weidenhamer, *Vice Pres*
EMP: 8 **EST:** 1982
SALES (est): 361.7K **Privately Held**
WEB: www.sos-products.com
SIC: 2752 5943 Commercial printing, offset; office forms & supplies

Destin
Walton County

(G-3212)
BETTER BUILT GROUP INC
66 N Holiday Rd (32550-6936)
PHONE..................................850 803-4044
Rupert E Phillips, *President*
Harold D Daws, *Vice Pres*
James N Perry, *Vice Pres*
Alan Payne, *Treasurer*
Sandra K Phillips, *Admin Sec*
EMP: 8 **EST:** 1995
SALES (est): 154K **Privately Held**
SIC: 2711 Newspapers

(G-3213)
BMW ENTERTAINMENT LLC
Also Called: Village Door, The
136 Fishermans Cv (32550-1822)
PHONE..................................850 502-4590
EMP: 12 **EST:** 2016
SALES (est): 317.2K **Privately Held**
SIC: 2599 Bar, restaurant & cafeteria furniture

Doral
Miami-Dade County

(G-3214)
2N USA LLC
8200 Nw 27th St Ste 107 (33122-1902)
PHONE..................................954 606-6602
Petr Racak, *CEO*
Schaefer Gary, *Opers Staff*
EMP: 7 **EST:** 2015
SALES (est): 466.1K **Privately Held**
WEB: www.2nusa.com
SIC: 3577 Computer peripheral equipment

(G-3215)
3-DIMENSION GRAPHICS INC
8031 Nw 14th St (33126-1611)
PHONE..................................305 599-3277
Jaime Cadena, *Principal*
▼ **EMP:** 30 **EST:** 2000
SQ FT: 15,000
SALES (est): 7.5MM **Privately Held**
WEB: www.threedg.com
SIC: 2752 Commercial printing, offset

(G-3216)
3NSTAR INC
10813 Nw 30th St Ste 100 (33172-2191)
PHONE..................................786 233-7011
Socorro Viayrada, *President*
Veronica Lara, *Admin Asst*
EMP: 10 **EST:** 2013
SALES (est): 835.9K **Privately Held**
WEB: www.3nstar.com
SIC: 3571 2678 Computers, digital, analog or hybrid; mainframe computers; tablets & pads

(G-3217)
7 HOLDINGS GROUP LLC
10450 Nw 29th Ter (33172-2527)
PHONE..................................754 200-1365
Wynn Housel, *CFO*
Lucius French,
EMP: 50
SALES (est): 1.7MM **Privately Held**
SIC: 3829 Thermometers, including digital: clinical

(G-3218)
A & A PRINTING SERVICES LLC
10482 Nw 31st Ter (33172-1215)
PHONE..................................786 597-6022
Lina M Osorio, *Manager*
EMP: 6 **EST:** 2018
SALES (est): 256.8K **Privately Held**
SIC: 2752 Commercial printing, offset

(G-3219)
A & A SHEETMETAL CONTR CORP
3067 Nw 107th Ave (33172-2134)
PHONE..................................305 592-2217
Angel Santos, *President*
Juan Vergara, *Project Mgr*
Lissette Santos, *Admin Sec*
EMP: 60 **EST:** 1985
SQ FT: 10,000
SALES (est): 3.6MM **Privately Held**
WEB: www.aasheetmetal.net
SIC: 3444 Sheet metalwork

(G-3220)
A & S EQUIPMENT CO
1900 Nw 95th Ave (33172-2349)
P.O. Box 228043, Miami (33222-8043)
PHONE..................................305 436-8207
Andrew S Ferrera Jr, *President*
EMP: 15 **EST:** 1996
SALES (est): 702.2K **Privately Held**
SIC: 3537 Forklift trucks

(G-3221)
A&C MICROSCOPES LLC
7925 Nw 12th St Ste 112 (33126-1820)
PHONE..................................786 514-3967
Joe Salgado, *Exec VP*
Michael Lopez,
EMP: 11 **EST:** 2014
SALES (est): 1.1MM **Privately Held**
WEB: www.acmicroscopes.com
SIC: 3827 Microscopes, except electron, proton & corneal

(G-3222)
ABZ MARKETING SOLUTIONS CORP ✪
9716 Nw 29th St (33172-1071)
PHONE..................................305 340-1887
Luis Alzate, *CEO*
EMP: 30 **EST:** 2020
SALES (est): 500K **Privately Held**
SIC: 3699 Security control equipment & systems

(G-3223)
ACER LATIN AMERICA INC
3750 Nw 87th Ave Ste 450 (33178-2430)
PHONE..................................305 392-7000
Mario Teuffer, *General Mgr*
◆ **EMP:** 9 **EST:** 1989
SQ FT: 2,000
SALES (est): 2.1MM **Privately Held**
WEB: www.maintenance.acer-euro.com
SIC: 3571 Minicomputers; personal computers (microcomputers)
HQ: Gateway, Inc.
7565 Irvine Center Dr # 150
Irvine CA 92618
949 471-7000

(G-3224)
ACOLITE CLAUDE UNTD SIGN INC (PA)
Also Called: Acusigns
2555 Nw 102nd Ave Ste 216 (33172-2131)
P.O. Box 522517, Miami (33152-2517)
PHONE..................................305 362-3333
Paul Yesbeck, *President*
Chet Diffenderfer, *Vice Pres*
Andrew Merrill-Facio, *Sales Staff*
Ralph Moreno, *Sales Staff*
EMP: 36 **EST:** 1993
SALES (est): 5.8MM **Privately Held**
WEB: www.acusigns.com
SIC: 3993 Electric signs

(G-3225)
ACOLITE SIGN COMPANY INC
2555 Nw 102nd Ave Ste 216 (33172-2131)
PHONE..................................305 362-3333
Chester Diffenderfer Jr, *President*
Jim Glober, *Vice Pres*
EMP: 7 **EST:** 1938
SALES (est): 436.1K **Privately Held**
WEB: www.acusigns.com
SIC: 3993 Electric signs

(G-3226)
ACOUSTIC COMMUNICATIONS LLC (PA)
5049 Nw 114th Ct (33178-3529)
PHONE..................................305 463-9485
Michael E Reilly,
EMP: 5 **EST:** 2009
SALES (est): 349.5K **Privately Held**
WEB: www.acousticcomm.com
SIC: 3669 8711 Intercommunication systems, electric; acoustical engineering

(G-3227)
ADMIRALTY INDUSTRIES CORP
2654 Nw 97th Ave (33172-1400)
P.O. Box 491532, Key Biscayne (33149-7532)
PHONE..................................305 722-7311
Martin Di Giglio, *CEO*
Elena Perez Roulet, *Vice Pres*
Alicia Diaz, *Admin Sec*
EMP: 3 **EST:** 2008
SALES (est): 3MM **Privately Held**
WEB: www.admiraltyindustries.com
SIC: 3351 3443 Copper & copper alloy pipe & tube; finned tubes, for heat transfer

(G-3228)
AENOVA DORAL MANUFACTURING INC (HQ)
10400 Nw 29th Ter (33172-2527)
PHONE..................................305 463-2270
Ramon Torres, *President*
Otto Prange, *President*
Sue Hammil, *Principal*
Dietmar Rohleder, *Vice Pres*
EMP: 150 **EST:** 2015
SQ FT: 85,000
SALES (corp-wide): 2MM **Privately Held**
WEB: www.healthcareinvest.de
SIC: 2834 Pharmaceutical preparations
PA: Health Care Invest Gmbh
Hermann-Graf-Str. 5
Eisenberg (Pfalz) 67304
635 112-7919

(G-3229)
AENOVA DORAL MANUFACTURING INC
10655 Nw 29th Ter (33172-2197)
PHONE..................................305 463-2263
Prange Otto, *President*
EMP: 18
SALES (corp-wide): 2MM **Privately Held**
SIC: 2834 Pharmaceutical preparations
HQ: Aenova Doral Manufacturing, Inc.
10400 Nw 29th Ter
Doral FL 33172
305 463-2270

(G-3230)
AGRO & CNSTR SOLUTIONS INC
3630 Nw 115th Ave (33178-1863)
PHONE..................................305 593-7011
Lucas Noriega, *CEO*
Pedro Molina, *Vice Pres*
Monica Molina, *Manager*
◆ **EMP:** 11 **EST:** 2009
SQ FT: 6,409
SALES (est): 9.5MM **Privately Held**
WEB: www.agrosolutions.us
SIC: 3523 Farm machinery & equipment

(G-3231)
AGS ENTERPRISES INC
10305 Nw 41st St Ste 210 (33178-2976)
PHONE..................................305 716-7660
Carlos R Perez, *President*
▼ **EMP:** 5 **EST:** 2003
SQ FT: 1,500
SALES (est): 591.2K **Privately Held**
WEB: www.agsenterprisesinc.com
SIC: 3357 Fiber optic cable (insulated)

(G-3232)
ALABAMA MARBLE CO INC
3435 Nw 79th Ave (33122-1017)
PHONE..................................305 718-8000
▲ **EMP:** 15
SQ FT: 45,845
SALES (est): 2.3MM **Privately Held**
SIC: 3261 Mfg Marble Window Items

(G-3233)
ALC GROUP CORP
5900 Nw 99th Ave (33178-2707)
PHONE..................................786 409-7167
EMP: 7 **EST:** 2017
SALES (est): 132.5K **Privately Held**
SIC: 2752 Commercial printing, offset

(G-3234)
ALCO ADVANCED TECHNOLOGIES
10773 Nw 58th St Ste 3707 (33178-2801)
PHONE..................................305 333-0831
Alberto Surijon, *CEO*
EMP: 5 **EST:** 1998
SALES (est): 490K **Privately Held**
WEB: www.alcogroup-la.com
SIC: 3699 Security control equipment & systems

(G-3235)
ALDANA LASER MIAMI INC
10201 Nw 58th St Ste 308 (33178-2737)
PHONE..................................786 681-7752
Aldana J Guillermo, *President*
EMP: 10 **EST:** 2016
SALES (est): 853.7K **Privately Held**
WEB: www.aldanalasermiami.com
SIC: 3827 Optical instruments & lenses

(G-3236)
ALECTRON INC
8810 Nw 24th Ter (33172-2418)
PHONE..................................786 397-6827
Juan Amortegui, *President*
Juan D Montoya, *Vice Pres*
Sandra M Restrepo, *Admin Sec*
EMP: 8 **EST:** 2012
SALES (est): 588K **Privately Held**
WEB: www.alectron.co
SIC: 3699 Electrical equipment & supplies
PA: Almacenes Electron S A S
Calle 12 B Sur 51 54
Medellin

(G-3237)
ALEPH GRAPHICS INC
Also Called: Www.alephgraphics.com
1723 Nw 82nd Ave (33126-1015)
PHONE..................................305 994-9933
Gonzalo D Novas, *President*
Loisa Manitto, *Vice Pres*
Rafael Giraldo, *Sales Mgr*
Elida Barreiro, *Admin Sec*
◆ **EMP:** 6 **EST:** 1996
SALES (est): 776.5K **Privately Held**
WEB: www.alephgraphics.com
SIC: 2752 Commercial printing, lithographic

(G-3238)
ALL AMERICAN KIT & BATH LLC
2900 Nw 77th Ct (33122-1113)
PHONE..................................305 599-9000
Gilbert Ouaknine, *Principal*
EMP: 6 **EST:** 2015
SALES (est): 161.7K **Privately Held**
SIC: 2434 Wood kitchen cabinets

(G-3239)
ALLIED AEROSPACE INC
2223 Nw 79th Ave (33122-1618)
PHONE..................................786 616-8484
Max H Kraushaar, *Principal*
EMP: 13 **EST:** 2017
SALES (est): 2.5MM **Privately Held**
WEB: www.alliedaerospaceinc.com
SIC: 3728 Aircraft parts & equipment

(G-3240)
ALP INDUSTRIES INC
Also Called: American Lifting Products
1828 Nw 82nd Ave (33126-1014)
PHONE..................................786 845-8617
Frank Hill, *General Mgr*
▲ **EMP:** 17 **EST:** 2008
SALES (est): 969.7K **Privately Held**
SIC: 3496 Miscellaneous fabricated wire products

(G-3241)
ALPHATEC COMMUNICATIONS
10570 Nw 27th St Ste 102 (33172-2105)
PHONE..................................518 580-0520
Gary Webster, *President*
EMP: 6 **EST:** 2011
SALES (est): 239.3K **Privately Held**
WEB: www.chenaccountinggroup.com
SIC: 3663 Satellites, communications

(G-3242)
ALTO PRODUCTS CORP AL
6301 Nw 99th Ave (33178-2719)
PHONE..................................305 892-7777
David Landa, *Owner*
Debra D 'angelo, *Vice Pres*
Ray Engel, *Vice Pres*
Justin Martin, *Research*
James Anderson, *Engineer*
EMP: 7 **Privately Held**
WEB: www.altousa.com
SIC: 3714 3568 Transmission housings or parts, motor vehicle; power transmission equipment
PA: Alto Products Corp. Al
1 Alto Way
Atmore AL 36502

(G-3243)
ALVITA PHARMA USA INC
8180 Nw 36th St Ste 100 (33166-6650)
PHONE..................................305 961-1623
Sajan P Unnithan, *Vice Pres*
EMP: 7 **EST:** 2012
SALES (est): 131.3K **Privately Held**
SIC: 2834 Pharmaceutical preparations

(G-3244)
AM WORLDWIDE CORP
7800 Nw 32nd St (33122-1108)
PHONE..................................786 313-3625
Anna Valentina Durante, *Vice Pres*
▼ **EMP:** 11 **EST:** 2013
SALES (est): 116.1K **Privately Held**
WEB: www.radiadores.us
SIC: 3714 Radiators & radiator shells & cores, motor vehicle

(G-3245)
AMC DEVELOPMENT GROUP LLC
Also Called: High Export
10825 Nw 33rd St (33172-2188)
PHONE..................................305 597-8641
Claudia Gomez, *Manager*
◆ **EMP:** 8 **EST:** 2002
SALES (est): 1MM **Privately Held**
SIC: 3577 Encoders, computer peripheral equipment

(G-3246)
AMDS TRADING INC
12301 Nw 116th Ave # 101 (33178-4031)
PHONE..................................305 594-6680
Doumit Shmouni, *Principal*
Diane Aboukhalil, *Principal*
EMP: 7 **EST:** 2004
SALES (est): 118.8K **Privately Held**
WEB: www.royaltymotors.com
SIC: 3537 5084 Trucks, tractors, loaders, carriers & similar equipment; engines & parts, diesel

(G-3247)
AMERICAN WELDING SOCIETY INC (PA)
Also Called: Aws
8669 Nw 36th St Ste 130 (33166-6672)
PHONE..................................305 443-9353
Gary Konarska II, *CEO*
John Bruskotter, *President*
Andrew Davis, *Managing Dir*
Tim Hirthe, *Vice Chairman*
Cassie Burrell, *COO*
▼ **EMP:** 94
SQ FT: 32,000
SALES (est): 33.7MM **Privately Held**
WEB: www.aws.org
SIC: 2721 8611 Magazines: publishing only, not printed on site; trade associations

(G-3248)
AMPER USA LLC
4447 Nw 98th Ave (33178-3361)
PHONE..................................305 717-3101
Ariel Lara, *Principal*
▲ **EMP:** 7 **EST:** 2010
SALES (est): 153.1K **Privately Held**
WEB: www.amper-usa.com
SIC: 3691 3621 Storage batteries; generators for storage battery chargers

(G-3249)
AMTEL SECURITY SYSTEMS INC
1691 Nw 107th Ave (33172-2707)
P.O. Box 490808, Key Biscayne (33149-0808)
PHONE..................................305 591-8200
Suresh Gajwani, *President*
Andy Smith, *Engineer*
◆ **EMP:** 28 **EST:** 1982
SQ FT: 18,000
SALES (est): 2.9MM **Privately Held**
SIC: 3699 1731 7382 Security control equipment & systems; safety & security specialization; security systems services

(G-3250)
ANIMAL AIR SERVICE INC
1952 Nw 93rd Ave (33172-2925)
PHONE..................................305 218-1759
John Ebert, *President*
Rique Valdivieso, *President*
Michael Williams, *Vice Pres*
Brandon Valdivieso, *Treasurer*
EMP: 32 **EST:** 1966
SALES (est): 1.8MM **Privately Held**
WEB: www.animalairmia.com
SIC: 3496 0751 3523 2441 Cages, wire; livestock services, except veterinary; farm machinery & equipment; nailed wood boxes & shook

(G-3251)
APICAL PHARMACEUTICAL CORP
10460 Nw 37th Ter (33178-4200)
PHONE..................................786 331-7200
Bill Bamford, *President*
EMP: 7 **EST:** 2000
SALES (est): 111.2K **Privately Held**
SIC: 2834 Pharmaceutical preparations

(G-3252)
APPAREL INDUSTRIES
5550 Nw 79th Ave (33166-4124)
PHONE..................................786 362-5958
Joan Harris, *President*
EMP: 6 **EST:** 2015
SALES (est): 48.5K **Privately Held**
SIC: 2299 Jute & flax textile products

(G-3253)
APTUM TECHNOLOGIES (USA) INC
2300 Nw 89th Pl (33172-2431)
PHONE..................................877 504-0091
David Alfaro, *Accounts Mgr*
Michael Rivera, *Sales Staff*
Alex SOO, *Sales Staff*
Jonathan Richardson, *Technology*
EMP: 63
SALES (corp-wide): 41.3MM **Privately Held**
WEB: www.aptum.com
SIC: 7372 Business oriented computer software
PA: Aptum Technologies (Usa) Inc.
106 Jefferson St Ste 300
San Antonio TX 78205
604 683-7747

(G-3254)
ARGO CRATES & CONTAINERS
10461 Nw 26th St (33172-2181)
PHONE..................................786 487-4607
Alberto Gomez, *President*
EMP: 5 **EST:** 1999
SALES (est): 422K **Privately Held**
SIC: 2653 Solid fiber boxes, partitions, display items & sheets

(G-3255)
ARTS PRODUCTS LLC (PA)
Also Called: Artscase
8333 Nw 53rd St Ste 450 (33166-4837)
PHONE..................................201 984-7232
JC Martins, *Mng Member*
EMP: 9 **EST:** 2011
SALES (est): 100K **Privately Held**
WEB: www.artscase.com
SIC: 3089 Cases, plastic

(G-3256)
ASTERION BEVERAGES INC
Also Called: Kamsa
3357 Nw 97th Ave (33172-1105)
PHONE..................................866 335-2672
Nicolas Bonilla, *CEO*
EMP: 8 **EST:** 2016
SALES (est): 546.8K **Privately Held**
WEB: www.drinkkamsa.com
SIC: 2086 Carbonated beverages, nonalcoholic: bottled & canned

(G-3257)
ASTROTED INC
3320 Nw 67th Ave Unit 980 (33122-2267)
PHONE..................................786 220-5898
Felipe Tedesco, *Principal*
EMP: 9 **EST:** 2001
SALES (est): 523K **Privately Held**
WEB: www.astroted.site
SIC: 3999 Manufacturing industries

(G-3258)
ATEEI INTERNATIONAL CORP (PA)
8284 Nw 56th St (33166-4018)
PHONE..................................305 597-6408
Luiz D Pereira Ferreira, *President*
EMP: 45 **EST:** 2013
SALES (est): 472.7K **Privately Held**
WEB: www.ateei.com.br
SIC: 3672 Printed circuit boards

(G-3259)
ATG SPECIALTY PRODUCTS CORP
Also Called: Breakthrough Clean Tech
1725 Nw 97th Ave (33172-2301)
PHONE..................................888 455-5499
Erick Navarro, *President*
Tara Yager, *Marketing Mgr*
EMP: 6 **EST:** 2013
SALES (est): 585.6K **Privately Held**
WEB: www.breakthroughclean.com
SIC: 3949 Shooting equipment & supplies, general

(G-3260)
ATRIA INDUSTRY
1866 Nw 82nd Ave (33126-1014)
PHONE..................................786 334-6621
Nicola Atria, *Principal*
EMP: 8 **EST:** 2016
SALES (est): 491K **Privately Held**
WEB: www.atriaindustries.com
SIC: 3999 Manufacturing industries

(G-3261)
AXZES LLC
3401 Nw 82nd Ave Ste 370 (33122-1052)
PHONE..................................786 626-1611
EMP: 7 **EST:** 2019
SALES (est): 315.8K **Privately Held**
WEB: www.axzes.com
SIC: 3652 Pre-recorded records & tapes

(G-3262)
B/E AEROSPACE INC
9835 Nw 14th St (33172-2756)
PHONE..................................305 471-8800
Luis Munoz, *Branch Mgr*
EMP: 6
SALES (corp-wide): 56.5B **Publicly Held**
WEB: www.beaerospace.com
SIC: 3728 Aircraft parts & equipment
HQ: B/E Aerospace, Inc.
1400 Corporate Center Way
Wellington FL 33414
410 266-2048

(G-3263)
BAGS EXPRESS INC
1555 Nw 97th Ave (33172-2815)
PHONE..................................305 500-9849
Alberto Loo, *President*
EMP: 7 **EST:** 1998
SQ FT: 11,000
SALES (est): 666.6K **Privately Held**
WEB: www.polybagsexpress.com
SIC: 2673 Plastic bags: made from purchased materials

(G-3264)
BARU AGENCY INCORPORATED
Also Called: 5 Cents T-Shirt Design
8400 Nw 36th St Ste 450 (33166-6606)
PHONE..................................305 259-8800
Sebastian Jaramillo, *CEO*
EMP: 7 **EST:** 2014
SALES (est): 1.1MM **Privately Held**
SIC: 2396 7336 Screen printing on fabric articles; graphic arts & related design

(G-3265)
BEARING SPECIALIST INC ✪
1908 Nw 94th Ave (33172-2330)
PHONE..................................305 796-3415
EMP: 6 **EST:** 2020
SALES (est): 379.9K **Privately Held**
WEB: www.bspecialist.com
SIC: 3562 Ball & roller bearings

(G-3266)
BELLA VISTA BAKERY INC
Also Called: Tqmuch
2220 Nw 82nd Ave (33122-1509)
PHONE..................................954 759-1920
Christian Pinto, *President*
Alejandra Rocha, *Vice Pres*
Manuel Rivero, *Sales Mgr*
EMP: 50 **EST:** 2010
SALES (est): 3.8MM **Privately Held**
SIC: 2051 Breads, rolls & buns

(G-3267)
BELLAK COLOR CORPORATION
Also Called: Foilmania
9730 Nw 25th St (33172-2201)
P.O. Box 227656, Miami (33222-7656)
PHONE..................................305 854-8525
Manuel S Fernandez, *President*
Manuel J Fernandez, *Vice Pres*
Allen Notkin, *Controller*
Lily Quesad, *Sales Staff*
Sandra Andrade, *Manager*
▼ **EMP:** 45 **EST:** 1961
SQ FT: 3,000
SALES (est): 9MM **Privately Held**
WEB: www.bellak.com
SIC: 2752 2796 Commercial printing, offset; color lithography; platemaking services

(G-3268)
BELZONA INC
2000 Nw 88th Ct (33172-2627)
PHONE..................................305 512-3200
Joel Svendsen, *Branch Mgr*
EMP: 47
SALES (corp-wide): 43.1MM **Privately Held**
WEB: www.belzona.com
SIC: 3732 Boat building & repairing
HQ: Belzona, Inc.
2000 Nw 88th Ct
Doral FL 33172

(G-3269)
BELZONA INC (HQ)
2000 Nw 88th Ct (33172-2627)
PHONE..................................305 594-4994
Joel Svendsen, *President*
Eldana Hunter, *President*
Laura Mendrek, *Business Mgr*
Xi Chen, *Vice Pres*
Hamsely Mirre, *Vice Pres*
◆ **EMP:** 25 **EST:** 1952
SQ FT: 43,000
SALES (est): 26MM
SALES (corp-wide): 43.1MM **Privately Held**
WEB: www.belzonaboats.com
SIC: 2899 5169 Chemical preparations; industrial chemicals
PA: Belzona International Limited
Claro Road
Harrogate HG1 4
142 356-7641

(G-3270)
BEV-CO ENTERPRISES INC
9533 Nw 41st St (33178-2371)
PHONE..................................786 953-7109
Enoc S Martinez, *Branch Mgr*
EMP: 30
SALES (corp-wide): 320.1K **Privately Held**
SIC: 2087 Beverage bases
PA: Bev-Co Enterprises, Inc.
2761 Nw 82nd Ave
Miami FL 33122
786 362-6368

(G-3271)
BG EXPO GROUP LLC
11231 Nw 20th St Unit 140 (33172-1865)
PHONE..................................305 428-3576
Ruben Santamaria, *Mng Member*
EMP: 8 **EST:** 2008
SALES (est): 382.1K **Privately Held**
WEB: www.appledisplays.com
SIC: 2741 7336 ; graphic arts & related design

(G-3272)
BIG RED Q PRINTING SERVICES
2100 Nw 94th Ave (33172-2332)
PHONE..................................305 477-7848
EMP: 6 **EST:** 2016
SALES (est): 128.1K **Privately Held**
WEB: www.regalprintingandgraphics.com
SIC: 2752 Commercial printing, offset

(G-3273)
BIG WOOD MILLWORK SALES INC
10842 Nw 27th St (33172-5907)
PHONE..................................305 471-1155
Rene Picanes, *President*
Lourdes Picanes, *Vice Pres*
EMP: 8 **EST:** 2003
SALES (est): 775.4K **Privately Held**
WEB: www.bigwoodmillwork.com
SIC: 2431 Doors & door parts & trim, wood

(G-3274)
BINCA LLC
10680 Nw 37th Ter (33178-4207)
PHONE..................................305 698-8883
Alexandra Garavito, *Principal*
EMP: 12 **EST:** 2013
SALES (est): 1.8MM **Privately Held**
WEB: www.bincaimaging.com
SIC: 3993 Signs & advertising specialties

(G-3275)
BIOGAIA BIOLOGICS INC
8333 Nw 53rd St Ste 469 (33166-4783)
PHONE..................................786 762-4000
EMP: 7 **EST:** 2018
SALES (est): 161.3K **Privately Held**
WEB: www.biogaia.com
SIC: 2834 Pharmaceutical preparations

(G-3276)
BIOMAR PRODUCTS LLC
9441 Nw 47th Ter (33178-2084)
PHONE..................................800 216-2080
Eduardo Munoz, *Mng Member*
Luz Diana Vasquez, *Mng Member*
EMP: 8 **EST:** 2006
SALES (est): 207.4K **Privately Held**
WEB: www.biomarproducts.com
SIC: 2834 Chlorination tablets & kits (water purification)

(G-3277)
BL BRANDHOUSE LLC
8375 Nw 30th Ter (33122-1916)
PHONE..................................305 600-7181
Jose A Beguiristain, *Administration*
EMP: 7 **EST:** 2016
SALES (est): 275.1K **Privately Held**
WEB: www.brandhousemia.com
SIC: 2759 Screen printing

(G-3278)
BLIX CORPORATE IMAGE LLC
Also Called: Blix Graphics
1352 Nw 78th Ave (33126-1606)
PHONE..................................305 572-9001
Diego Bussano, *President*
German Bussano, *Project Mgr*
Diego L Bussano, *Mng Member*
German N Bussano, *Mng Member*
▼ **EMP:** 10 **EST:** 2005
SALES (est): 1MM **Privately Held**
WEB: www.blixgraphics.com
SIC: 2752 Commercial printing, lithographic

(G-3279)
BLU SENSE
7855 Nw 29th St (33122-1142)
PHONE..................................786 616-8628
Luciano Tartarini, *Owner*
EMP: 5 **EST:** 2014
SALES (est): 308.3K **Privately Held**
SIC: 3645 Fluorescent lighting fixtures, residential

(G-3280)
BLUE CHIP GROUP LLC
Also Called: Vacation Vault
3400 Nw 113th Ct (33178-1836)
PHONE..................................305 863-9094
Robert Perlman, *Mng Member*
EMP: 5 **EST:** 2003
SALES (est): 484.4K **Privately Held**
WEB: www.bluechipgroup.us
SIC: 3499 Safes & vaults, metal

(G-3281)
BONNE SANTE NATURAL MFG INC
Also Called: Millenium Natural Health Pdts
10575 Nw 37th Ter (33178-4209)
PHONE..................................305 594-4990
Darren Minton, *CEO*
Alfonso Cervantes, *President*
Ray Martinez, *Vice Pres*
Edgard Castellanos, *Opers Staff*
Yeni Abreu, *Purchasing*
▼ **EMP:** 33 **EST:** 1998
SQ FT: 16,000
SALES (est): 14.9MM
SALES (corp-wide): 41MM **Privately Held**
WEB: www.milleniumnatural.com
SIC: 2834 Vitamin, nutrient & hematinic preparations for human use
PA: Smart For Life, Inc.
990 Biscayne Blvd # 1203
Miami FL 33132
786 749-1221

(G-3282)
BOSTIC STEEL INC
7740 Nw 34th St (33122-1110)
PHONE..................................305 592-7276
Judith D Bostic, *President*
Michael Belcher, *General Mgr*
Dean D Agati, *Exec VP*
Dean D 'agati, *Exec VP*
Guy Cusano, *Vice Pres*
EMP: 100 **EST:** 1991
SQ FT: 21,000
SALES (est): 28.5MM **Privately Held**
WEB: www.bosticsteel.com
SIC: 3441 Fabricated structural metal

(G-3283)
BPJ INTERNATIONAL LLC
11091 Nw 27th St Ste 204 (33172-5010)
PHONE..................................305 507-8971
EMP: 7
SALES (est): 275K **Privately Held**
SIC: 2844 Mfg Toilet Preparations

(G-3284)
BRAIN FREEZE NITROGEN
3905 Nw 107th Ave Ste 106 (33178-2785)
PHONE..................................786 235-8505
Christi Fraga, *Owner*
EMP: 7 **EST:** 2015
SALES (est): 441.8K **Privately Held**
WEB: www.brainfreezeicecreamlab.com
SIC: 3556 2024 2026 Ice cream manufacturing machinery; ice cream & frozen desserts; yogurt

(G-3285)
BRICKLSER ENGRV MONUMENTS CORP
7964 Nw 14th St (33126-1614)
PHONE..................................786 806-0672
Alexis Butler, *President*
Cody Evans, *President*
James Dixon, *Admin Sec*
EMP: 11 **EST:** 2018
SQ FT: 12,000
SALES (est): 995.8K **Privately Held**
SIC: 3479 6798 5999 Etching & engraving; real estate investment trusts; monuments & tombstones

(G-3286)
BRIDGE TRADING USA LLC
Also Called: Techbtc
2855 Nw 112th Ave Ste 2 (33172-1810)
PHONE..................................877 848-0979
Pablo O Puente, *President*
Betti Vieira, *CFO*
Ivo Cepero, *CTO*
EMP: 10 **EST:** 2008
SQ FT: 3,500
SALES: 2.3MM **Privately Held**
WEB: www.techbtc.com
SIC: 3699 5194 4789 1731 Security devices; tobacco & tobacco products; cargo loading & unloading services; computerized controls installation; fire detection & burglar alarm systems specialization

(G-3287)
BROMIDE MINING LLC
2335 Nw 107th Ave Ste 127 (33172-2165)
PHONE..................................786 477-6229
Kristin Timberlake, *Mng Member*
Oren Goldgraber,
Yehuda Goldgraber,
EMP: 13 **EST:** 2008
SALES (est): 1.3MM **Privately Held**
SIC: 1041 Gold ores mining

(G-3288)
BUENAVIDA IMPORTS LLC
3508 Nw 114th Ave Ste 205 (33178-1841)
PHONE..................................305 988-5992
Maximiliano Martirena, *Mng Member*
EMP: 6 **EST:** 2019
SALES (est): 603.3K **Privately Held**
SIC: 2084 Wines, brandy & brandy spirits

(G-3289)
CAPRA GRAPHICS INC
Also Called: Stedi Press
1625 Nw 79th Ave (33126-1105)
PHONE..................................305 418-4582
George Capra, *President*
Adriana Capra, *Vice Pres*
EMP: 6 **EST:** 1990
SALES (est): 892.9K **Privately Held**
WEB: www.stedipress.com
SIC: 2752 Commercial printing, offset

(G-3290)
CARBEL LLC
2323 Nw 82nd Ave (33122-1512)
PHONE..................................305 599-0832
Francisco J Torrens, *Principal*
Gressia Perez, *Regional Mgr*
EMP: 200 **EST:** 2004
SQ FT: 150,000
SALES (est): 22.2MM **Privately Held**
WEB: www.carbel-wd.com
SIC: 3694 Distributors, motor vehicle engine

(G-3291)
CARIBBEAN EMBLEMS
3555 Nw 79th Ave (33122-1019)
PHONE..................................305 593-8183
Alfredo J Gomez, *President*
Lydia Gomez, *Admin Sec*
EMP: 5 **EST:** 1991
SQ FT: 8,800
SALES (est): 382.9K **Privately Held**
WEB: www.caribbeanemblems.com
SIC: 2395 Embroidery products, except schiffli machine

(G-3292)
CARIBBEAN PAINT COMPANY INC
5295 Nw 79th Ave (33166-4715)
P.O. Box 522550, Miami (33152-2550)
PHONE..................................305 594-4500
George F Sixto, *President*
Ernesto Milian, *Vice Pres*
Silvia R Milian, *Treasurer*
George Sixto, *Office Mgr*
▼ **EMP:** 7 **EST:** 1976
SQ FT: 10,000
SALES (est): 975.4K **Privately Held**
WEB: www.caribbean-paint-company-inc.sbcontract.com
SIC: 2851 Enamels; paints & paint additives; stains: varnish, oil or wax; lacquers, varnishes, enamels & other coatings

(G-3293)
CASA BLINDS INTERIOR CORP
8300 Nw 53rd St (33166-7812)
PHONE..................................786 219-7157
EMP: 6 **EST:** 2019
SALES (est): 57.3K **Privately Held**
SIC: 2591 Window blinds

(G-3294)
CASTONE CREATIONS INC
Also Called: Cast-One
8309 Nw 70th St (33166-2622)
PHONE..................................305 599-3367
Ariel Gonzales, *President*
EMP: 13 **EST:** 2003
SQ FT: 10,000
SALES (est): 1.3MM **Privately Held**
SIC: 3272 Concrete products, precast

(G-3295)
CCM CLLLAR CNNECTION MIAMI INC
1825 Nw 79th Ave (33126-1114)
P.O. Box 228387, Miami (33222-8387)
PHONE..................................305 406-1656
Karim Ben Yahia, *President*
Pascale Vanclee, *Vice Pres*
▲ **EMP:** 22 **EST:** 1995
SALES (est): 1.1MM **Privately Held**
WEB: www.ccmmobile.com
SIC: 3661 Telephones & telephone apparatus

(G-3296)
CENTRAL TURBOS CORP (PA)
1951 Nw 97th Ave (33172-2305)
PHONE..................................305 406-3933
Antonio Tilkian, *President*
Carlos Tilkian, *Vice Pres*
Nina Montiel, *Sales Staff*
Carlos Rudge, *Branch Mgr*
◆ **EMP:** 12 **EST:** 2001
SQ FT: 6,000
SALES (est): 2.9MM **Privately Held**
WEB: www.centralturbos.com
SIC: 3694 3612 Distributors, motor vehicle engine; transformers, except electric

(G-3297)
CHECKSUM SOFTWARE LLC
7979 Nw 21st St (33122-1630)
P.O. Box 25331, Miami (33102-5331)
PHONE..................................786 375-8091
Van Glass,
Leo Salas, *Admin Sec*
EMP: 9 **EST:** 2001
SALES (est): 3MM
SALES (corp-wide): 8.5MM **Privately Held**
WEB: www.advsyscon.com
SIC: 7372 Prepackaged software
PA: Advanced Systems Concepts, Inc.
1180 Hdqters Plz W Towe F
Morristown NJ 07960
973 539-2660

(G-3298)
CIM USA INC
10813 Nw 30th St Ste 108 (33172-2191)
PHONE..................................305 369-1040
Alberto Mucelli, *President*
Mads Petersen, *Exec VP*
Sandro Mucelli, *Vice Pres*
Maria Guzman, *Office Mgr*
▲ **EMP:** 5 **EST:** 1999
SQ FT: 7,000
SALES (est): 3.4MM
SALES (corp-wide): 355.8K **Privately Held**
WEB: www.cim-usa.com
SIC: 3579 Embossing machines for store & office use
HQ: Mf Group Srl
Localita' Braine 54/A
Monzuno BO
051 677-6511

(G-3299)
CIRVEN USA LLC
9681 Nw 45th Ln (33178-4017)
PHONE..................................305 815-2545
Gerardo Serriao, *CEO*
Orlando Diaz, *CFO*
◆ **EMP:** 5 **EST:** 2010
SALES: 1.4MM **Privately Held**
SIC: 3569 Lubricating systems, centralized

(G-3300)
CITY CLORS DGITAL PRTG CTR INC
1470 Nw 79th Ave (33126-1610)
PHONE..................................305 471-0816
Roberto J Infante, *President*
Maria E Infante, *Vice Pres*
EMP: 20 **EST:** 1998
SALES (est): 1.5MM **Privately Held**
WEB: www.citycolors.com
SIC: 2752 Commercial printing, offset

(G-3301)
CLIMAX INC
Also Called: Mechanical Air Concepts
10401 Nw 28th St (33172-2100)
PHONE..................................786 264-6082
Victor Gomez, *President*
EMP: 8 **EST:** 2002
SALES (est): 1MM **Privately Held**
SIC: 3585 Refrigeration & heating equipment

(G-3302)
COFRAN INTERNATIONAL CORP
1540 Nw 94th Ave (33172-2846)
PHONE..................................305 592-2644
Yann Pacreau, *CEO*
Frederick Mas, *President*
▲ **EMP:** 25
SQ FT: 14,000
SALES (est): 4.8MM **Privately Held**
WEB: www.cofrancorp.com
SIC: 2844 7389 Cosmetic preparations; packaging & labeling services

(G-3303)
COJALI USA INC
2200 Nw 102nd Ave Ste 4b (33172-2225)
PHONE..................................305 960-7651
Alberca Venancio, *President*
Emiliano Morales, *Manager*
Carlos Rivas, *Senior Mgr*
EMP: 11 **EST:** 2013
SALES (est): 732.1K **Privately Held**
WEB: www.cojaliusa.com
SIC: 2835 In vitro & in vivo diagnostic substances

(G-3304)
CONCURRENT MFG SOLUTIONS LLC (DH)
10773 Nw 58th St Ste 100 (33178-2801)
PHONE..................................512 637-2540
Gustavo Balleza, *Supervisor*
Tim Ogrady,
▲ **EMP:** 50 **EST:** 2006
SQ FT: 100,000
SALES (est): 20MM **Privately Held**
WEB: www.concurrentmfg.com
SIC: 3679 Electronic circuits
HQ: Cypress Holdings Ltd.
8027 Exchange Dr
Austin TX 78754
512 637-2540

(G-3305)
CONVERLOGIC INTER LLC (PA)
Also Called: Converlogic Americas
2254 Nw 93rd Ave (33172-4801)
PHONE..................................786 623-4747
Jose Luis Horna,
▲ **EMP:** 5 **EST:** 2014
SALES: 927.6K **Privately Held**
WEB: www.converlogic.com
SIC: 3661 Telephone & telegraph apparatus

(G-3306)
COOLTECH HOLDING CORP (HQ)
2100 Nw 84th Ave (33122-1517)
PHONE..................................786 675-5236
Mauricio Diaz, *CEO*
Rein Boigt, *COO*
Alfredo Carrasco, *CFO*
Carlos Padilla, *Controller*
Felipe Rezk, *Chief Mktg Ofcr*
EMP: 4 **EST:** 2016
SALES (est): 5.5MM **Publicly Held**
WEB: www.cooltech.co
SIC: 7372 Prepackaged software

(G-3307)
COQUI RDO PHARMACEUTICALS CORP
Also Called: Coqui Pharma
3125 Nw 84th Ave (33122-1994)
PHONE..................................787 685-5046
Carmen Bigles, *CEO*
EMP: 5 **EST:** 2009
SALES (est): 630.3K **Privately Held**
WEB: www.coquipharma.com
SIC: 2834 7389 Pharmaceutical preparations;

(G-3308)
CORPORATE SIGNS INC
1375 Nw 97th Ave Ste 12 (33172-2855)
PHONE..................................305 500-9313
James Zuniga, *President*
EMP: 6 **EST:** 1998
SALES (est): 445.7K **Privately Held**
WEB: www.corporatesignsinc.com
SIC: 3993 Electric signs

(G-3309)
CORPORATE SIGNS INC
5960 Nw 99th Ave Unit 8 (33178-2712)
PHONE..................................305 500-9313
EMP: 8 **EST:** 2017
SALES (est): 312.5K **Privately Held**
WEB: www.corporatesignsinc.com
SIC: 3993 Signs & advertising specialties

(G-3310)
COSMETICS & CLEANERS INTL LLC
Also Called: C&C Industries
6000 Nw 97th Ave Unit 9 (33178-1639)
PHONE..................................305 592-5504
Andy Boutros, *CEO*
Nakia Thompson, *Asst Controller*
Boutros Andy, *Mng Member*
▼ **EMP:** 30 **EST:** 2010
SQ FT: 50,000
SALES (est): 4.8MM **Privately Held**
WEB: www.cncinds.com
SIC: 2844 Cosmetic preparations

(G-3311)
COTTONIMAGESCOM INC
10481 Nw 28th St (33172-2152)
PHONE..................................305 251-2560
Sandra K Hertzbach, *President*
Scott Hertzbach, *Vice Pres*
▲ **EMP:** 45 **EST:** 2002
SALES (est): 6.8MM **Privately Held**
WEB: www.cottonimages.com
SIC: 2262 2711 Screen printing: manmade fiber & silk broadwoven fabrics; commercial printing & newspaper publishing combined

(G-3312)
CREATIVE HOME AND KITCHEN LLC
Also Called: Kitchenest
2000 Nw 97th Ave Ste 112 (33172-2347)
PHONE..................................786 233-8621
Brokerage Tomahawk, *Mng Member*
EMP: 18 **EST:** 2013
SALES (est): 3.1MM **Privately Held**
WEB: www.creativehomeandkitchen.com
SIC: 3631 Household cooking equipment

(G-3313)
CREATIVE MOLDING CORP
2949 Nw 97th Ct (33172-1099)
PHONE..................................786 251-4241
Gerardo Villegas, *President*
EMP: 12 **EST:** 2005
SALES (est): 314.3K **Privately Held**
SIC: 3089 Molding primary plastic

(G-3314)
CREATIVE SIGNS
2340 Nw 102nd Pl (33172-2517)
PHONE..................................786 636-6969
EMP: 7 **EST:** 2019
SALES (est): 144.6K **Privately Held**
WEB: www.creativesignsinc.com
SIC: 3993 Signs & advertising specialties

(G-3315)
CSC AEROSPACE CORPORATION
9737 Nw 41st St (33178-2924)
PHONE..................................203 300-9760
John B Sawyer, *Principal*
Natalie Caetano, *Principal*
David A Cockrell, *Principal*
EMP: 6 **EST:** 2011
SALES (est): 113.5K **Privately Held**
SIC: 3721 Aircraft

(G-3316)
CURALLUX LLC
1715 Nw 82nd Ave (33126-1015)
PHONE..................................786 888-1875
Carlos Pina, *CEO*
Ray Del Pino, *Purchasing*
Barry Pintar, *Accounts Exec*
Fernando Bermudez, *Sales Staff*
Frances M Brea, *Marketing Staff*
EMP: 50 **EST:** 2012
SQ FT: 21,257
SALES (est): 5.9MM **Privately Held**
WEB: www.capillus.com
SIC: 3845 Electrotherapeutic apparatus

(G-3317)
CUT SERVICES LLC
8264 Nw 58th St (33166-3407)
PHONE..................................305 560-0905
Amedeo Muscelli, *Mng Member*
EMP: 6 **EST:** 2016
SALES (est): 469.2K **Privately Held**
WEB: www.cutservices.com
SIC: 2426 Carvings, furniture: wood

(G-3318)
CYLINDERS ON CEMEX GAS
Also Called: Purchasing Dept
12155 Nw 136th St (33178-3109)
PHONE..................................305 818-4952
Miguel Fernandez, *Branch Mgr*
EMP: 8 **EST:** 2010
SALES (est): 144K **Privately Held**
SIC: 3273 Ready-mixed concrete

(G-3319)
D & L AUTO & MARINE SUPPLIES
5601 Nw 79th Ave (33166-3532)
PHONE..................................305 593-0560
Eleodoro Aguero, *President*
Deborah Aguero, *Shareholder*
▲ **EMP:** 5 **EST:** 1980
SQ FT: 4,000
SALES (est): 1.2MM **Privately Held**
WEB: www.dnlauto.com
SIC: 3694 5013 3625 Automotive electrical equipment; automotive supplies & parts; relays & industrial controls

(G-3320)
D&W FINE PACK LLC
7740 Nw 55th St (33166-4112)
PHONE..................................305 592-4329
Ariel Soler, *President*
EMP: 52
SALES (corp-wide): 900.4MM **Privately Held**
WEB: www.dwfinepack.com
SIC: 3089 Plastic kitchenware, tableware & houseware
HQ: D&W Fine Pack Llc
777 Mark St
Wood Dale IL 60191

(G-3321)
DAISY CRAZY INC
3902 Estepona Ave (33178-2926)
PHONE..................................305 300-5144
Deisy Contreras, *Principal*
▲ **EMP:** 5
SALES (est): 507.2K **Privately Held**
SIC: 2339 2331 2253 Jeans: women's, misses' & juniors'; women's & misses' blouses & shirts; T-shirts & tops, knit

(G-3322)
DAJE INDUSTRIES INC
6020 Nw 99th Ave (33178-2725)
PHONE..................................305 592-7711
Duglay Zavala, *Principal*
EMP: 7 **EST:** 2008
SALES (est): 160.6K **Privately Held**
WEB: www.daje-usa.com
SIC: 3999 Barber & beauty shop equipment

(G-3323)
DANAS SAFTY SUPPLY INC
1622 Nw 82nd Ave (33126-1018)
PHONE..................................305 639-6024
EMP: 15
SALES (est): 2.1MM **Privately Held**
SIC: 3669 Mfg Communications Equipment

(G-3324)
DAYTONA RUBBER COMPANY INC
Also Called: Daytona Cooling Systems
10460 Nw 29th Ter (33172-2527)
PHONE..................................305 513-4105
Rafael Lorenzo, *President*
◆ **EMP:** 11 **EST:** 2010
SALES (est): 217.2K **Privately Held**
SIC: 2822 Synthetic rubber

(G-3325)
DDY MARTINEZ LLC
3105 Nw 107th Ave Ste 400 (33172-2215)
PHONE..................................786 263-2672
Yoanner Martinez,
EMP: 10
SALES (est): 750K **Privately Held**
SIC: 1389 Construction, repair & dismantling services

(G-3326)
DECO ABRUSCI INTERNATIONAL LLC
8485 Nw 29th St (33122-1919)
PHONE..................................305 406-3401
Gregorio Abrusci, *President*
Johnnie Abrusci,
EMP: 12 **EST:** 2014
SALES (est): 1.2MM **Privately Held**
WEB: www.decoabrusci.us
SIC: 2591 8743 Drapery hardware & blinds & shades; sales promotion

(G-3327)
DELTANA ENTERPRISES INC
10820 Nw 29th St (33172-2149)
PHONE..................................305 592-8188
Philip Wong, *President*
Paul Wong, *Principal*
Stewart Donnarae, *CFO*
◆ **EMP:** 20 **EST:** 1977
SQ FT: 60,000
SALES (est): 2.5MM **Privately Held**
WEB: www.deltana.net
SIC: 3441 Fabricated structural metal

(G-3328)
DIAMOND AIRCRAFT LOGICSTICS
11003 Nw 33rd St (33172-5021)
PHONE..................................305 456-8400
Danny Carchi, *CEO*
▲ **EMP:** 5 **EST:** 2012
SALES (est): 500K **Privately Held**
SIC: 3721 Aircraft

(G-3329)
DIGITAL OUTDOOR LLC
Also Called: Lightking Outdoor
8405 Nw 29th St (33122-1924)
PHONE..................................305 944-7945
Timur Colak, *President*
Will Wang, *COO*
EMP: 20 **EST:** 2012
SALES (est): 10MM **Privately Held**
SIC: 3993 Electric signs

(G-3330)
DILOREN INC
8800 Nw 13th Ter (33172-3003)
PHONE..................................786 618-9671
Raul Di Lorenzo, *Manager*
EMP: 7 **EST:** 2015

SALES (est): 288K **Privately Held**
WEB: www.diloren-composites.com
SIC: 3721 Aircraft

(G-3331)
DOLE
10055 Nw 12th St (33172-2761)
PHONE..................................305 925-7900
John Schouten, *Principal*
Alexis Barrios, *Accounts Mgr*
EMP: 9 **EST:** 2014
SALES (est): 251.9K **Privately Held**
SIC: 2099 Food preparations

(G-3332)
DORAL BUILDING SUPPLY CORP
5095 Nw 79th Ave (33166-4711)
PHONE..................................305 471-9797
Cesar F Arellano Jr, *President*
▼ **EMP:** 15 **EST:** 1985
SQ FT: 52,000
SALES (est): 2.7MM **Privately Held**
WEB: www.doral-building-supply-corp.business.site
SIC: 3444 5032 Studs & joists, sheet metal; drywall materials

(G-3333)
DORAL DGTAL REPROGRAPHICS CORP
5701 Nw 79th Ave (33166-3535)
PHONE..................................305 704-3194
Giancarlo Annitto, *President*
Morgan Gregory, *Vice Pres*
Beatrice Berrera, *Sales Mgr*
Beatriz Pereira, *Sales Mgr*
EMP: 6 **EST:** 2006
SALES: 2.7MM **Privately Held**
WEB: www.ddrepro.com
SIC: 2752 7336 2759 Commercial printing, lithographic; art design services; commercial printing; promotional printing; magazines: printing; menus: printing

(G-3334)
DORAL FAMILY JOURNAL LLC
10773 Nw 58th St Ste 96 (33178-2801)
PHONE..................................305 300-4594
Ettore Sabatella, *Manager*
EMP: 6 **EST:** 2016
SALES (est): 103.3K **Privately Held**
WEB: www.doralfamilyjournal.com
SIC: 2711 Newspapers, publishing & printing

(G-3335)
DOTAMED LLC
6332 Nw 99th Ave (33178-2721)
PHONE..................................786 594-0144
Francisco J Franco Velez, *Manager*
Gladys H Largo De Franco, *Manager*
Angelina Da Silva Suarez, *Manager*
John J Franco Velez, *Manager*
▲ **EMP:** 7 **EST:** 2007
SALES (est): 499.4K **Privately Held**
WEB: www.dtmusa.net
SIC: 3843 Dental equipment & supplies

(G-3336)
DS HEALTHCARE GROUP INC (DH)
Also Called: Ds Laboratories
1850 Nw 84th Ave Ste 108 (33126-1027)
PHONE..................................888 404-7770
Fernando Tamez Gutierrez, *CEO*
Carlos Luzuriaga Castro, *COO*
Fernando Tamez, *COO*
Brian Hendricks, *Vice Pres*
Sonya Stoa, *Vice Pres*
EMP: 130 **EST:** 2007
SQ FT: 50,000
SALES: 12.9MM
SALES (corp-wide): 37.3MM **Privately Held**
WEB: www.dslaboratories.com
SIC: 2844 Hair preparations, including shampoos
HQ: Medilogistics Corp
1451 Brickell Ave # 2701
Miami FL 33131
786 856-8311

(G-3337)
DUY DRUGS INC
1730 Nw 79th Ave (33126-1111)
PHONE..................................305 594-3667
Maria Elorzuy, *President*
▲ **EMP:** 10 **EST:** 2004
SALES (est): 773K **Privately Held**
SIC: 2834 Pharmaceutical preparations

(G-3338)
EARTH & SEA WEAR LLC
Also Called: Cover Style
8785 Nw 13th Ter (33172-3013)
PHONE..................................786 332-2236
Augusto Hanimian, *President*
EMP: 40 **EST:** 1993
SQ FT: 12,000
SALES (est): 6.9MM **Privately Held**
SIC: 2339 Bathing suits: women's, misses' & juniors'; sportswear, women's

(G-3339)
EASY FOODS INC (PA)
5900 Nw 97th Ave Unit 14 (33178-1643)
PHONE..................................305 599-0357
William Isaias, *President*
Andres Isaias, *Vice Pres*
Luis N Isaias, *Vice Pres*
Mariadelcarmen Morla, *Vice Pres*
Juan Pablo Viejo, *Vice Pres*
◆ **EMP:** 23 **EST:** 2005
SQ FT: 100,000
SALES (est): 30.7MM **Privately Held**
WEB: www.easyfoodsinc.com
SIC: 2099 Tortillas, fresh or refrigerated

(G-3340)
EEM TECHNOLOGIES CORP (PA)
9590 Nw 40th Street Rd (33178-2971)
PHONE..................................786 606-5993
Ricardo Solorzano, *President*
Eliana Toledo, *Vice Pres*
Juan Soto, *Sales Staff*
EMP: 10 **EST:** 2016
SALES (est): 1.1MM **Privately Held**
WEB: www.eemtechnologies.com
SIC: 3593 3594 7389 3492 Fluid power actuators, hydraulic or pneumatic; fluid power pumps; personal service agents, brokers & bureaus; control valves, fluid power: hydraulic & pneumatic

(G-3341)
EL GLOBAL NEWS
3785 Nw 82nd Ave (33166-6655)
PHONE..................................305 212-1361
EMP: 7 **EST:** 2016
SALES (est): 144.4K **Privately Held**
WEB: www.elglobonews.com
SIC: 2711 Newspapers

(G-3342)
ELIPTER CORP
3900 Nw 79th Ave Ste 482 (33166-6548)
PHONE..................................305 593-8355
Angelo Espinoza, *Principal*
EMP: 7 **EST:** 2010
SALES (est): 112K **Privately Held**
SIC: 3699 Security control equipment & systems

(G-3343)
EMPIRE CORP KIT OF
2846 Nw 79th Ave (33122-1033)
PHONE..................................800 432-3028
Henri Bertuch, *Principal*
EMP: 6 **EST:** 2012
SALES (est): 132.3K **Privately Held**
SIC: 2752 Commercial printing, offset

(G-3344)
ESPERANTO INC
Also Called: Market Logic
8725 Nw 18th Ter Ste 312 (33172-2610)
P.O. Box 228505, Miami (33222-8505)
PHONE..................................305 513-8980
Marcelo Castro, *President*
▲ **EMP:** 15 **EST:** 1994
SQ FT: 2,500
SALES (est): 2MM **Privately Held**
SIC: 2731 Books: publishing only

(G-3345)
EUROKER LLC
3287 Nw 78th Ave (33122-1121)
PHONE..................................305 477-0096
Fernando Jimenez,
EMP: 6 **EST:** 2014
SALES (est): 144.1K **Privately Held**
WEB: www.euroker.com
SIC: 2522 Office furniture, except wood

(G-3346)
EXTREME WOOD WORKS S FLA INC
1520 Nw 79th Ave (33126-1104)
PHONE..................................305 463-8614
Martha Hernandez, *Administration*
EMP: 10 **EST:** 2006
SALES (est): 1MM **Privately Held**
WEB: www.extremewoodworks.com
SIC: 2541 Wood partitions & fixtures; display fixtures, wood

(G-3347)
FASTKIT CORP
11250 Nw 25th St Ste 100 (33172-1820)
PHONE..................................305 599-0839
Jose Fernandez Jr, *President*
Denisse Martinez, *General Mgr*
David Barjun, *COO*
Lidia Fernandez, *Vice Pres*
Yosmar Barrios, *Production*
▲ **EMP:** 38 **EST:** 1986
SALES (est): 8.6MM **Privately Held**
WEB: www.fastkit.com
SIC: 2782 Blankbooks & looseleaf binders

(G-3348)
FASTKIT CORP
11250 Nw 25th St Ste 100 (33172-1820)
PHONE..................................754 227-8234
Jose Fernandez Jr, *Principal*
EMP: 5 **EST:** 1986
SALES (est): 326K **Privately Held**
SIC: 2782 Blankbooks & looseleaf binders

(G-3349)
FCA US LLC
Also Called: Planet Fiat of West Miami
9975 Nw 12th St (33172-2762)
PHONE..................................305 597-2222
EMP: 7
SALES (corp-wide): 102.5B **Privately Held**
WEB: www.stellantis.com
SIC: 3714 Motor vehicle parts & accessories
HQ: Fca Us Llc
1000 Chrysler Dr
Auburn Hills MI 48326

(G-3350)
FELDENKREIS HOLDINGS LLC (PA)
3000 Nw 107th Ave (33172-2133)
PHONE..................................305 592-2830
Oscar Feldenkreis, *President*
George Feldenkreis, *Vice Pres*
Tim Garrett, *VP Sales*
Eric Roberts, *Merchandising*
EMP: 42 **EST:** 2018
SALES (est): 874.8MM **Privately Held**
WEB: www.pery.com
SIC: 2321 Men's & boys' furnishings

(G-3351)
FIPLEX COMMUNICATIONS INC (PA)
2101 Nw 79th Ave (33122-1611)
PHONE..................................305 884-8991
Ron Pitcock, *CEO*
Marta Braun, *Ch of Bd*
Bob Joslin, *Vice Pres*
Matias Goycoechea, *Sales Engr*
Tamara Hernandez, *Sales Staff*
▲ **EMP:** 42 **EST:** 1985
SQ FT: 2,000
SALES (est): 11MM **Privately Held**
WEB: www.fiplex.com
SIC: 3663 Radio & TV communications equipment

(G-3352)
FK IRONS INC
1771 Nw 79th Ave (33126-1112)
PHONE..................................855 354-7667
Gaston A Siciliano Sr, *Principal*
EMP: 35
SQ FT: 20,000
SALES: 4.3MM **Privately Held**
WEB: www.fkirons.com
SIC: 3399 Metal fasteners

(G-3353)
FLOWERS BAKING CO MIAMI LLC
2681 Nw 104th Ct (33172-2172)
PHONE..................................305 599-8457
Willie Prince, *Manager*
EMP: 22
SALES (corp-wide): 4.3B **Publicly Held**
SIC: 2051 Bakery: wholesale or wholesale/retail combined
HQ: Flowers Baking Co. Of Miami, Llc
17800 Nw Miami Ct
Miami FL 33169
305 652-3416

(G-3354)
FLUID HANDLING SUPPORT CORP
6030 Nw 99th Ave Unit 409 (33178-2731)
PHONE..................................786 623-2105
Manuel Escobar, *Branch Mgr*
▼ **EMP:** 12
SALES (corp-wide): 849.4K **Privately Held**
WEB: www.fluid-handling.com
SIC: 2026 Fluid milk
PA: Fluid Handling Support, Corp
11139 Nw 122nd St Unit 6
Medley FL 33178
786 623-2105

(G-3355)
FREEZETONE PRODUCTS LLC
7986 Nw 14th St (33126-1614)
PHONE..................................305 640-0414
Luis M Latour Jr, *Mng Member*
▼ **EMP:** 18 **EST:** 1978
SALES (est): 2.9MM **Privately Held**
WEB: www.freezetoneglobal.com
SIC: 2899 2842 Chemical preparations; specialty cleaning, polishes & sanitation goods

(G-3356)
FRESENIUS KABI USA LLC
1733 Nw 79th Ave (33191-1101)
PHONE..................................847 550-2300
EMP: 35
SALES (corp-wide): 42.9B **Privately Held**
WEB: www.fresenius-kabi.com
SIC: 2834 Pharmaceutical preparations
HQ: Fresenius Kabi Usa, Llc
3 Corporate Dr
Lake Zurich IL 60047
847 550-2300

(G-3357)
GALIX BMEDICAL INSTRUMENTATION
8205 Nw 30th Ter (33122-1913)
PHONE..................................305 534-5905
EMP: 15
SALES (est): 1.8MM **Privately Held**
SIC: 3841 5047 Mfg Surgical/Medical Instruments Whol Medical/Hospital Equipment

(G-3358)
GARFLEX INC (PA)
9594 Nw 41st St Ste 209 (33178-2909)
PHONE..................................305 436-8915
Maria Teresa Santiago, *President*
◆ **EMP:** 72 **EST:** 2017
SQ FT: 1,950
SALES (est): 38.7MM **Privately Held**
SIC: 2241 2389 Rubber thread & yarns, fabric covered; garters

(G-3359)
GEM AEROSPACE
10300 Nw 19th St (33172-2538)
PHONE..................................786 464-5900
Eradin Dejesus, *General Mgr*
Armando Noy, *Opers Mgr*
Olessia Silakova, *Asst Controller*
Osbelto Barroso, *Cust Mgr*
Alejandro Silva, *Cust Mgr*
EMP: 9 **EST:** 2012

SALES (est): 312.6K **Privately Held**
WEB: www.global-engine.com
SIC: 3519 Jet propulsion engines

(G-3360)
GENECELL INTERNATIONAL LLC
2664 Nw 97th Ave (33172-1400)
PHONE..................................305 382-6737
Jose Cirino, *Opers Staff*
Eduardo Cortez, *Mng Member*
Priscilla Pages, *Manager*
EMP: 10 **EST:** 2010
SALES (est): 1.3MM **Privately Held**
WEB: www.genecell.com
SIC: 3821 Autoclaves, laboratory

(G-3361)
GENEL/LANDEC INC
10845 Nw 29th St (33172-5909)
P.O. Box 142161, Miami (33114-2161)
PHONE..................................305 591-9990
James Talamas, *President*
Jim Talamas, *Opers Mgr*
EMP: 6 **EST:** 1980
SQ FT: 2,500
SALES (est): 886K **Privately Held**
WEB: www.genel-landec.com
SIC: 7372 5045 Educational computer software; business oriented computer software; computers

(G-3362)
GENERAL POWER LIMITED INC
9930 Nw 21st St Fl 1 (33172-2212)
PHONE..................................800 763-0359
Luis Lopez, *President*
John Cortiella, *Partner*
Gabriel Lopez, *General Mgr*
Carmen C Moreno De Lopez, *Vice Pres*
◆ **EMP:** 16 **EST:** 1999
SQ FT: 11,000
SALES (est): 4.5MM **Privately Held**
WEB: www.genpowerusa.com
SIC: 3621 Power generators

(G-3363)
GENERAL WELDING SVC ENTPS INC
8115 Nw 56th St (33166-4016)
PHONE..................................305 592-9483
Jose Antonio Cid, *President*
Nancy Cid, *Corp Secy*
Pedro Cid, *Vice Pres*
Juan Cid, *Asst Sec*
EMP: 8 **EST:** 1972
SQ FT: 11,000
SALES (est): 1MM **Privately Held**
SIC: 7692 Welding repair

(G-3364)
GENFLOOR LLC
Also Called: General Floors
6312 Nw 99th Ave (33178-2721)
PHONE..................................305 477-1557
Jose E Calvino,
▲ **EMP:** 7 **EST:** 2010
SQ FT: 8,000
SALES (est): 672.2K **Privately Held**
WEB: www.genfloor.net
SIC: 3589 Floor washing & polishing machines, commercial

(G-3365)
GENSCO LABORATORIES LLC
Also Called: Gensco Pharma
8550 Nw 33rd St Ste 200 (33122-1941)
PHONE..................................754 263-2898
Carlos Alfaras, *President*
Lloyd Ramson, *Accounting Mgr*
Lissa Ajmo, *Manager*
Randi A Press, *Exec Dir*
David Andry, *Director*
EMP: 14 **EST:** 2009
SALES (est): 2.1MM **Privately Held**
WEB: www.genscopharma.com
SIC: 2834 Zinc ointment

(G-3366)
GEORG FISCHER LLC (HQ)
Also Called: GF Piping Systems
10540 Nw 26th St (33172-5932)
PHONE..................................305 418-9150
James Jackson, *Mng Member*
Max Holloway,
EMP: 5 **EST:** 2007
SALES (est): 16.8MM
SALES (corp-wide): 3.5B **Privately Held**
WEB: www.gfps.com
SIC: 3498 Piping systems for pulp paper & chemical industries
PA: Georg Fischer Ag
Amsler-Laffon-Strasse 9
Schaffhausen SH 8200
526 311-111

(G-3367)
GLENNY STONE WORKS INC
3000 Nw 77th Ct (33122-1114)
PHONE..................................786 502-3918
Juan C Glenny, *Principal*
Martin Arzani, *Project Mgr*
EMP: 7 **EST:** 2018
SALES (est): 570.6K **Privately Held**
WEB: www.glennystoneworks.com
SIC: 2434 Wood kitchen cabinets

(G-3368)
GLOBAL ALIMENT INC
7791 Nw 46th St Ste 308 (33166-5484)
PHONE..................................786 536-5261
EMP: 2 **EST:** 2016
SALES: 11.3MM **Privately Held**
WEB: www.globalaliment.com
SIC: 2092 Seafoods, frozen: prepared

(G-3369)
GLOBAL REACH RX PBF LLC
10560 Nw 27th St Ste 101a (33172-5928)
PHONE..................................786 703-1988
Sergio Ruiz, *CEO*
Wayne J Talamas, *President*
EMP: 15 **EST:** 2014
SQ FT: 5,000
SALES (est): 2.1MM **Privately Held**
SIC: 2834 Pharmaceutical preparations

(G-3370)
GLOBALTEK OFFICE SUPPLY INC
Also Called: Globaltek Art & Design
11200 Nw 25th St Ste 123 (33172-1807)
PHONE..................................305 477-2988
Jose Pelucarte, *President*
Oscar Ascanio, *CFO*
Monica Franco, *Controller*
◆ **EMP:** 9 **EST:** 2002
SALES (est): 1.7MM **Privately Held**
WEB: www.globaltek.com
SIC: 3861 Toners, prepared photographic (not made in chemical plants)

(G-3371)
GRAPHINK INCORPORATED
8850 Nw 13th Ter Unit 103 (33172-3012)
PHONE..................................305 468-9463
Vanessa Gramatges, *President*
EMP: 8 **EST:** 2014
SQ FT: 6,000
SALES (est): 910.8K **Privately Held**
WEB: www.graphink.com
SIC: 2752 Business form & card printing, lithographic

(G-3372)
GREAT CIR VNTURES HOLDINGS LLC (PA)
Also Called: Tail Activewear
2105 Nw 86th Ave (33122-1527)
PHONE..................................305 638-2650
Jerry Edwards, *CEO*
Cheryl Maurer, *Vice Pres*
Nikki Miller, *VP Sales*
Sherri Balke, *Sales Staff*
Steve Britt, *Sales Staff*
◆ **EMP:** 58 **EST:** 2006
SQ FT: 38,000
SALES (est): 10MM **Privately Held**
SIC: 2339 Sportswear, women's

(G-3373)
GREENLAM AMERICA INC
Also Called: Greenlam Laminates
8750 Nw 36th St Ste 635 (33178-2778)
PHONE..................................305 640-0388
Jose Somoza, *Regional Mgr*
Rohit Kaul, *Vice Pres*
Vaibhav Sharma, *Vice Pres*
Mohit Agarwal, *CFO*
Agarwal Samarth, *Supervisor*
▲ **EMP:** 12 **EST:** 2008
SALES (est): 2MM **Privately Held**
WEB: www.greenlam.com
SIC: 3589 High pressure cleaning equipment

(G-3374)
GREMED GROUP CORP
8040 Nw 14th St (33126-1612)
PHONE..................................305 392-5331
Felix Perez, *CEO*
Ana Contreras, *Vice Pres*
▲ **EMP:** 20 **EST:** 2004
SQ FT: 16,500
SALES (est): 553K **Privately Held**
SIC: 3841 5047 Surgical & medical instruments; instruments, surgical & medical

(G-3375)
GROVE POWER INC
158 (33122)
PHONE..................................305 599-2045
Jeff Flannery, *President*
James Fahrber, *CFO*
EMP: 7 **EST:** 2009
SALES (est): 173K **Privately Held**
SIC: 3621 Motors & generators

(G-3376)
HALCYON AVIATION CAPITAL LLC ✪
8350 Nw 52nd Ter Ste 301 (33166-7708)
PHONE..................................305 615-1575
Patrice Robinet, *Managing Dir*
EMP: 5 **EST:** 2020
SALES (est): 1.1MM **Privately Held**
WEB: www.halcyonavcap.com
SIC: 3728 Aircraft parts & equipment

(G-3377)
HAMMER HEAD GROUP INC
Also Called: Deco Wraps
8900 Nw 33rd St Ste 100 (33172-1207)
PHONE..................................305 436-5691
Steven Tchira, *CEO*
Maria Gallardo, *Business Mgr*
▲ **EMP:** 30 **EST:** 2016
SALES (est): 4.2MM **Privately Held**
WEB: www.hammerheadcg.com
SIC: 2621 Wrapping & packaging papers

(G-3378)
HANSA OPHTHALMICS LLC
Also Called: United Ophthalmics
4083 Nw 79th Ave (33166-6519)
PHONE..................................305 594-1789
Steven Levesque, *CEO*
EMP: 24 **EST:** 2017
SALES (est): 1MM **Privately Held**
SIC: 3841 Ophthalmic instruments & apparatus

(G-3379)
HERALPIN USA INC
Also Called: Petroheral
10570 Nw 27th St Ste H101 (33172-2105)
PHONE..................................305 218-0174
Rafael Betancourt, *President*
▼ **EMP:** 5 **EST:** 2002
SALES (est): 536.2K **Privately Held**
SIC: 3272 5012 5399 6799 Tanks, concrete; truck tractors; Army-Navy goods; commodity contract trading companies

(G-3380)
HERMES TECHNICAL INTL INC
8227 Nw 54th St (33166-4008)
PHONE..................................305 477-8993
Manuel Ugas, *President*
Nadia Ugas, *Vice Pres*
Vicky Ramirez, *Purchasing*
Sue Arroyo, *Sales Mgr*
Gabriela Cabanillas, *Sales Staff*
▼ **EMP:** 7 **EST:** 1986
SQ FT: 5,000
SALES (est): 1.6MM **Privately Held**
WEB: www.hermestechnical.com
SIC: 3728 Aircraft parts & equipment; brakes, aircraft

(G-3381)
HERNANDEZ ORNAMENTAL INC
1910 Nw 96th Ave (33172-2319)
PHONE..................................305 592-7296
Barbara Hernandez, *President*
Jorge F Hernandez, *President*
Felix Hernandez, *Vice Pres*
EMP: 8 **EST:** 1980
SQ FT: 2,400
SALES (est): 803.3K **Privately Held**
SIC: 3446 Ornamental metalwork

(G-3382)
HIGH END DEFENSE SOLUTIONS LLC
2201 Nw 102nd Pl Ste 4 (33172-2521)
PHONE..................................305 591-7795
Bernd Von Reitzenstein,
▲ **EMP:** 7 **EST:** 2009
SALES (est): 527.6K **Privately Held**
SIC: 3489 Guns, howitzers, mortars & related equipment

(G-3383)
HIGH STANDARD AVIATION INC
5900 Nw 97th Ave Unit 3 (33178-1642)
PHONE..................................305 599-8855
Villasante Francisco, *President*
Alina Villasante, *President*
Francisco Villasante, *Chairman*
Villasante Alina, *Vice Pres*
▲ **EMP:** 49 **EST:** 1991
SQ FT: 25,000
SALES (est): 25.3MM
SALES (corp-wide): 4.5B **Publicly Held**
WEB: www.ametekmro.com
SIC: 3721 4581 3728 Aircraft; aircraft maintenance & repair services; aircraft parts & equipment
PA: Ametek, Inc.
1100 Cassatt Rd
Berwyn PA 19312
610 647-2121

(G-3384)
HIMMEL LOSUNGEN GROUP HLG LLC
4711 Nw 79th Ave Ste 12l (33166-5443)
PHONE..................................786 631-5531
Jefferson Zambrano Angel, *Mng Member*
◆ **EMP:** 5 **EST:** 2015
SQ FT: 625
SALES (est): 1.5MM **Privately Held**
SIC: 3728 Aircraft parts & equipment

(G-3385)
I C T S AMERICA INC
8400 Nw 36th St Ste 450 (33166-6606)
PHONE..................................786 307-2993
Rafael Gonzalez, *President*
Cesar Maraver, *Director*
EMP: 8 **EST:** 2015
SQ FT: 1,200
SALES (est): 223K **Privately Held**
SIC: 1389 Gas field services

(G-3386)
IAMGOLD PURCHASING SVCS INC
Also Called: Rosebel Gold Mines NV
2000 Nw 97th Ave Ste 114 (33172-2347)
PHONE..................................713 671-5973
Gordon Stothart, *President*
Steve Letwin, *President*
L Steve Wagner, *Admin Sec*
◆ **EMP:** 3 **EST:** 1987
SQ FT: 3,000
SALES (est): 5.9MM
SALES (corp-wide): 1B **Privately Held**
WEB: www.iamgold.com
SIC: 1041 Gold ores mining
PA: Iamgold Corporation
401 Bay St Suite 3200
Toronto ON M5H 2
416 360-4710

(G-3387)
IDEA DESIGN STUDIO INC
8562 Nw 56th St (33166-3329)
PHONE..................................305 823-6008
Fabian Forero, *President*
Erika Pallares, *Marketing Staff*
EMP: 10 **EST:** 2006
SQ FT: 500
SALES (est): 800K **Privately Held**
WEB: www.ideadstudio.com
SIC: 2821 7389 Acrylic resins; design, commercial & industrial

GEOGRAPHIC

(G-3388)
IMAGIK INTERNATIONAL CORP
8390 Nw 25th St (33122-1504)
PHONE..................................786 631-5003
Pablo Vadillo, *President*
▲ **EMP**: 15 **EST**: 1994
SALES (est): 4.2MM **Privately Held**
WEB: www.imagikcorp.com
SIC: **3663** Radio & TV communications equipment

(G-3389)
IMC STORAGE
3955 Adra Ave (33178-2907)
PHONE..................................305 418-0069
Agosto Tabana, *President*
Willy Herrera, *Business Mgr*
Engels Jarquin, *Engineer*
Bryan Ramos, *Engineer*
EMP: 5 **EST**: 2012
SALES (est): 12MM **Privately Held**
WEB: www.imcstorage.com
SIC: **3572** Computer auxiliary storage units

(G-3390)
INFINITI DIGITAL EQUIPMENT INC
10500 Nw 29th Ter (33172-2526)
PHONE..................................305 477-6333
Ming Xu, *President*
▲ **EMP**: 8 **EST**: 2005
SALES (est): 686.8K **Privately Held**
WEB: www.infiniti-dt.com
SIC: **3823** Digital displays of process variables

(G-3391)
INTEG CONSTRUCTION INC
2451 Nw 109th Ave Unit 5 (33172-2003)
PHONE..................................305 440-9101
Miguel Saurez, *Principal*
Milagros Suarez, *Co-Owner*
EMP: 7 **EST**: 2016
SQ FT: 2,000
SALES (est): 800K **Privately Held**
WEB: www.integusa.com
SIC: **3824** Mechanical & electromechanical counters & devices

(G-3392)
INTELIATHLETE CORP
5501 Nw 105th Ct (33178-6600)
PHONE..................................305 987-1355
Julissa Nova Romero, *Principal*
EMP: 6 **EST**: 2015
SALES (est): 102.5K **Privately Held**
WEB: www.iot.do
SIC: **7372** Prepackaged software

(G-3393)
INTERNTNAL TECH SLTONS SUP LLC
Also Called: Trugard
2636 Nw 97th Ave (33172-1400)
P.O. Box 226575, Miami (33222-6575)
PHONE..................................305 364-5229
Leonardo J Brito, *Mng Member*
Nataly Bermudez, *Administration*
EMP: 5 **EST**: 2009
SALES (est): 547.4K **Privately Held**
SIC: **1382** 5139 Oil & gas exploration services; boots

(G-3394)
INVERSNES WLLDEL ASOCIADOS INC
8250 Nw 58th St (33166-3407)
PHONE..................................305 591-0931
William Delgado, *Branch Mgr*
EMP: 20
SALES (corp-wide): 1.1MM **Privately Held**
WEB: www.inversioneswilldel.net
SIC: **3441** Railroad car racks, for transporting vehicles: steel
PA: Inversiones Willdel & Asociados, Inc.
4700 Nw 72nd Ave
Miami FL 33166
305 591-0118

(G-3395)
ITALIAN MOONSHINERS INC
8300 Nw 53rd St Ste 350 (33166-7712)
PHONE..................................954 687-4500
Carlo A Lazzari, *Principal*
EMP: 7 **EST**: 2010
SALES (est): 96.6K **Privately Held**
WEB: www.italianmoonshiners.com
SIC: **2085** 2084 Vodka (alcoholic beverage); wines, brandy & brandy spirits

(G-3396)
ITALKRAFT LLC (PA)
2900 Nw 77th Ct (33122-1113)
PHONE..................................305 406-1301
Panos Symvoulidis, *Project Mgr*
Ana Vallejo, *Controller*
Alexandros Xakoustis,
Raul J Gutierrez,
Dirk J Lens,
EMP: 28 **EST**: 2011
SQ FT: 24,645
SALES (est): 6.4MM **Privately Held**
WEB: www.italkraft.com
SIC: **2511** 5712 Vanity dressers: wood; cabinet work, custom

(G-3397)
IVAN & IVAN LLC
Also Called: Inversiones Medicas SIS
1465 Nw 97th Ave (33172-2819)
PHONE..................................305 507-8793
Ivan A Fernandez, *Mng Member*
Krina Fernandez,
EMP: 6 **EST**: 2010
SQ FT: 100
SALES (est): 260.8K **Privately Held**
WEB: www.needlefreesystem.com
SIC: **3841** Surgical & medical instruments

(G-3398)
J D M CORP
Also Called: Modern Display
1551 Nw 93rd Ave (33172-2910)
PHONE..................................305 947-5876
David Milgrom, *President*
Lee Sack, *Vice Pres*
Abraham Bochman, *Treasurer*
▲ **EMP**: 8 **EST**: 1968
SQ FT: 3,000
SALES (est): 936.4K **Privately Held**
SIC: **3993** Electric signs

(G-3399)
J&D OIL FIELD INTL INC
Also Called: J&D Oilfield International
3785 Nw 82nd Ave Ste 206 (33166-6630)
PHONE..................................305 436-0024
Argimiro Malave Leon, *President*
Jose V Rivera, *Vice Pres*
Jose Rivera, *Vice Pres*
Victor A Alezones Rivero, *Vice Pres*
Isabel Verde, *Manager*
EMP: 5 **EST**: 2005
SALES (est): 1.5MM **Privately Held**
WEB: www.jdoilfield.com
SIC: **1389** Oil field services

(G-3400)
JAT POWER LLC
Also Called: Aksa's Generator
8000 Nw 29th St (33122-1077)
PHONE..................................305 592-0103
Joe Niswanger, *CEO*
Rudolph N Niswanger, *Mng Member*
◆ **EMP**: 10 **EST**: 2012
SALES (est): 560.7K **Privately Held**
WEB: www.jatpower.com
SIC: **3621** Generators & sets, electric

(G-3401)
JC TOYS GROUP INC
2841 Nw 107th Ave (33172-2130)
PHONE..................................305 592-3541
Juan L Cerda, *President*
Richard Cerda, *Vice Pres*
Fernando Barroso, *Controller*
Janet Marquez, *Sales Mgr*
Laura Cerda, *Marketing Staff*
◆ **EMP**: 10 **EST**: 1993
SQ FT: 40,000
SALES (est): 2.1MM **Privately Held**
WEB: www.jctoys.com
SIC: **3942** 3944 Dolls & stuffed toys; games, toys & children's vehicles

(G-3402)
JERS GROUP
Also Called: Abam Export
8625 Nw 54th St (33166-3324)
PHONE..................................786 953-6419
Cesar Bolivar, *Owner*
EMP: 5 **EST**: 2014
SALES (est): 662K **Privately Held**
SIC: **3089** Automotive parts, plastic
PA: Serviseguros C.A
Centro Gerencial Mohedano,
Caracas D.F.

(G-3403)
JIMENEZ ENTERPRISES GROUP (PA)
10855 Nw 50th St Apt 204 (33178-3973)
PHONE..................................561 542-7709
Eduardo Jimenez, *President*
EMP: 33 **EST**: 2008
SALES (est): 86.6K **Privately Held**
SIC: **3841** 3743 3011 3613 Surgical & medical instruments; mining locomotives & parts, electric or nonelectric; airplane inner tubes; power circuit breakers

(G-3404)
JLG INDUSTRIES INC
10974 Nw 63rd St (33178-2852)
PHONE..................................786 558-8909
Martin Lacks, *Branch Mgr*
EMP: 114
SALES (corp-wide): 6.8B **Publicly Held**
WEB: www.jlg.com
SIC: **3531** Construction machinery
HQ: Jlg Industries, Inc.
1 Jlg Dr
Mc Connellsburg PA 17233
717 485-5161

(G-3405)
JMP MARINE LLC
Also Called: Jmp USA
2000 Nw 84th Ave Ste 244 (33122-1520)
P.O. Box 162955, Miami (33116-2955)
PHONE..................................305 599-0009
EMP: 27
SALES (est): 2.6MM **Privately Held**
SIC: **3523** Mfg Farm Machinery/Equipment

(G-3406)
KAYVA DISTRIBUTION LLC
Also Called: Blue Sun International
2201 Nw 102nd Pl Ste 4a (33172-2521)
PHONE..................................305 428-2816
Nadia Perez, *Opers Mgr*
Fu Zhou, *Accounts Mgr*
Victor Alvarez, *Mng Member*
▲ **EMP**: 7 **EST**: 2009
SALES (est): 756.5K **Privately Held**
SIC: **2844** 5122 Toilet preparations; cosmetics, perfumes & hair products

(G-3407)
KENDOO TECHNOLOGY INC
1950 Nw 94th Ave Lowr (33172-2324)
PHONE..................................305 592-9688
Harry Chang, *President*
▲ **EMP**: 7 **EST**: 1998
SQ FT: 3,000
SALES (est): 1.5MM **Privately Held**
WEB: www.kendoo.com
SIC: **3691** Batteries, rechargeable

(G-3408)
KITKO CORP
10773 Nw 58th St Ste 87 (33178-2801)
PHONE..................................786 287-8900
EMP: 8
SQ FT: 7,000
SALES (est): 557.4K **Privately Held**
SIC: **3086** Mfg Plastic Foam Products

(G-3409)
KLIMAIRE PRODUCTS INC
2190 Nw 89th Pl (33172-2427)
PHONE..................................305 593-8358
Korkmaz Iltekin, *President*
Idania Sosa, *Sales Staff*
Walter Bolivar, *Department Mgr*
Richard Barnes, *CIO*
◆ **EMP**: 15 **EST**: 1989
SQ FT: 24,000
SALES (est): 3MM **Privately Held**
WEB: www.klimaire.com
SIC: **3585** Air conditioning equipment, complete

(G-3410)
KLYO MEDICAL SYSTEMS INC
1464 Nw 82nd Ave (33126-1508)
PHONE..................................305 330-5025
Luis Torres, *CEO*
Alejandra Cervantes, *Marketing Staff*
EMP: 15 **EST**: 2015
SQ FT: 10,000
SALES (est): 1.9MM **Privately Held**
WEB: www.klyomedical.com
SIC: **3841** Surgical & medical instruments

(G-3411)
KOVER CORP
1375 Nw 97th Ave Ste 12 (33172-2855)
PHONE..................................305 888-0146
Gabriel Conti, *President*
Anais Ramirez, *Sales Mgr*
EMP: 6 **EST**: 2010
SALES (est): 356.6K **Privately Held**
SIC: **2759** Commercial printing

(G-3412)
KR SOLUTIONS GROUP US LLC ✪
1500 Nw 89th Ct Ste 115 (33172-2640)
PHONE..................................305 307-8353
Kristhian Rincon,
EMP: 5 **EST**: 2020
SALES (est): 500K **Privately Held**
WEB: www.krsolutionsgroupllc.com
SIC: **1389** Construction, repair & dismantling services

(G-3413)
KREATIVE DRIVE INC
8953 Nw 23rd St (33172-2404)
PHONE..................................786 845-8605
Rita M Valdes, *Principal*
Jose Otero, *Manager*
EMP: 6 **EST**: 2009
SALES (est): 554.8K **Privately Held**
WEB: www.kreativedrive.com
SIC: **2754** Stationery & invitation printing, gravure

(G-3414)
L C LA FINESTRA
2790 Nw 104th Ct (33172-2175)
PHONE..................................305 599-8093
Bruno Salvoni, *Mng Member*
◆ **EMP**: 20 **EST**: 2001
SQ FT: 13,000
SALES (est): 4MM **Privately Held**
WEB: www.lafinestra.us
SIC: **3442** Metal doors

(G-3415)
LA ESQUINA DEL LE BILLTO
Also Called: La Esquina Del Lechon
8601 Nw 58th St Unit 101 (33166-3312)
PHONE..................................305 477-4225
La Esquina Del Lechon, *Principal*
EMP: 27
SALES (corp-wide): 2.5MM **Privately Held**
WEB: www.secure.esquinalechon.com
SIC: **2013** 5812 Prepared pork products from purchased pork; Mexican restaurant
PA: La Esquina Del Lechon, L.L.C.
7900 Nw 36th St
Doral FL 33166
305 640-3041

(G-3416)
LENNOX GLOBAL LTD (HQ)
Also Called: Lgl Latin America Operations
2335 Nw 107th Ave Ste 132 (33172-2219)
PHONE..................................305 718-2921
Victor Mora, *Managing Dir*
◆ **EMP**: 100 **EST**: 1980
SALES (est): 26MM
SALES (corp-wide): 3.6B **Publicly Held**
WEB: www.lennoxinternational.com
SIC: **3585** Refrigeration & heating equipment
PA: Lennox International Inc.
2140 Lake Park Blvd
Richardson TX 75080
972 497-5000

(G-3417)
LENNOX INDUSTRIES
2335 Nw 107th Ave Ste 132 (33172-2219)
PHONE..................................305 718-2974

Lester Martinez, *Manager*
EMP: 8 **EST:** 2016
SALES (est): 322.1K **Privately Held**
WEB: www.lennox.com
SIC: 3585 Refrigeration & heating equipment

(G-3418)
LOCKHEED MARTIN CORPORATION
8669 Nw 36th St Ste 200 (33166-6640)
PHONE.................................866 562-2363
EMP: 6 **Publicly Held**
WEB: www.lockheedmartin.com
SIC: 3812 Search & navigation equipment
PA: Lockheed Martin Corporation
6801 Rockledge Dr
Bethesda MD 20817

(G-3419)
LORINA INC
8750 Nw 36th St Ste 260 (33178-2499)
PHONE.................................305 779-3085
Jean Pierre Barjon, *President*
Bouchra El Mansour, *Finance*
Caroline Dupoizat, *Marketing Staff*
James Grimes, *Manager*
▲ **EMP:** 13 **EST:** 2000
SALES (est): 7.9MM
SALES (corp-wide): 1MM **Privately Held**
WEB: www.lorina.com
SIC: 2086 Lemonade: packaged in cans, bottles, etc.
HQ: Etablissements Geyer Freres
Route De Sarre Union
Munster 57670
387 016-201

(G-3420)
LTB AEROSPACE LLC
2250 Nw 102nd Pl (33172-2516)
PHONE.................................954 251-1141
Raul M Garcia, *Principal*
EMP: 5 **EST:** 2019
SALES (est): 1MM **Privately Held**
WEB: www.ltbaerospace.com
SIC: 3728 Aircraft parts & equipment

(G-3421)
LUBRICATION GLOBAL LLC
8450 Nw 56th St (33166-3327)
PHONE.................................954 239-9522
Jorge Ramos, *Mng Member*
July Ramos,
Daniel Romero,
EMP: 10 **EST:** 2018
SALES (est): 1.8MM **Privately Held**
SIC: 2992 Lubricating oils & greases

(G-3422)
MAMBO LLC
Also Called: Wgentv
1800 Nw 94th Ave (33172-2329)
PHONE.................................305 860-2544
Olga Echeverri, *General Mgr*
Mauricio Cruz, *Finance Mgr*
EMP: 18 **EST:** 2008
SALES (est): 2.5MM **Privately Held**
SIC: 3663 Radio & TV communications equipment

(G-3423)
MANSUR INDUSTRIES INC
Also Called: Systemone Technolgies
8305 Nw 27th St Ste 107 (33122-1934)
PHONE.................................305 593-8015
Paul Mansur, *President*
Paul I Mansur, *Principal*
EMP: 10 **EST:** 1990
SALES (est): 277.9K **Privately Held**
WEB: www.systemonepartswashers.com
SIC: 3496 Miscellaneous fabricated wire products

(G-3424)
MARAJO DIESEL POWER CORP
1950 Nw 93rd Ave (33172-2925)
PHONE.................................786 212-1485
Elias Novoa, *President*
Ana Beatriz Novoa Silva, *Vice Pres*
EMP: 7 **EST:** 2014
SALES (est): 816.7K **Privately Held**
WEB: www.mdpusa.com
SIC: 3511 Turbines & turbine generator set units, complete

(G-3425)
MARATHON TECHNOLOGY CORP
Also Called: Maracom Marine
8280 Nw 56th St (33166-4018)
PHONE.................................305 592-1340
Robert M Hewitt, *President*
Christine Hewitt, *Treasurer*
EMP: 9 **EST:** 1980
SQ FT: 6,000
SALES (est): 280.1K **Privately Held**
WEB: www.26miles.com
SIC: 3829 5064 Thermometers & temperature sensors; radios

(G-3426)
MASAKA LLC
3105 Nw 107th Ave Ste 601 (33172-2221)
PHONE.................................786 800-8337
Alfonzo Bolivar, *CEO*
Carolina Prince, *Principal*
Carlena Prince, *Manager*
EMP: 10 **EST:** 2013
SALES (est): 1.5MM **Privately Held**
WEB: www.masakatractors.com
SIC: 3462 3531 Construction or mining equipment forgings, ferrous; construction machinery attachments

(G-3427)
MCCLATCHY SHARED SERVICES CTR
3511 Nw 91st Ave (33172-1243)
PHONE.................................305 740-8800
Patrick J Talamantes, *CEO*
Gary B Pruitt, *Ch of Bd*
Christian A Hendricks, *Vice Pres*
Karole M Prager, *Vice Pres*
EMP: 53 **EST:** 1985
SALES (est): 1.7MM **Privately Held**
SIC: 2711 Newspapers, publishing & printing

(G-3428)
MEDIA DIGITTAL LLC
8410 Nw 53rd Ter Ste 107 (33166-4540)
PHONE.................................305 506-0470
EMP: 7
SQ FT: 3,000
SALES (est): 293K **Privately Held**
SIC: 2741 7311 7313 Internet Publishing And Broadcasting Advertising Agency Advertising Representative

(G-3429)
MEDICAL DEFENSE COMPANY INC ✪
1300 Nw 84th Ave (33126-1500)
PHONE.................................954 614-3266
Daniel Niefeld, *Principal*
EMP: 10 **EST:** 2020
SALES (est): 657.5K **Privately Held**
SIC: 3069 Medical sundries, rubber

(G-3430)
MEDTRONIC USA INC
9850 Nw 41st St Ste 450 (33178-2993)
PHONE.................................786 709-4200
Randy Bright, *District Mgr*
Genny Lawrence, *Sales Staff*
Michele Lucisano, *Marketing Staff*
James Hogan, *Branch Mgr*
Caridad Veitia, *Assistant*
EMP: 2026 **Privately Held**
WEB: www.medtronic.com
SIC: 3841 Surgical & medical instruments
HQ: Medtronic Usa, Inc.
710 Medtronic Pkwy
Minneapolis MN 55432
763 514-4000

(G-3431)
MENDELEYES CORP
5401 Nw 110th Ave (33178-3913)
PHONE.................................305 597-7370
Iliana Ruiz, *Vice Pres*
EMP: 6 **EST:** 2016
SALES (est): 71K **Privately Held**
WEB: www.mendeleyes.com
SIC: 7372 Prepackaged software

(G-3432)
MERCAEREO INC
6346 Nw 99th Ave (33178-2721)
PHONE.................................305 307-0672
Mauricio Camacho, *President*
◆ **EMP:** 5 **EST:** 2001
SALES (est): 455.8K **Privately Held**
WEB: www.mercaereo.com.co
SIC: 3812 Aircraft/aerospace flight instruments & guidance systems

(G-3433)
MIAMI HERALD
3500 Nw 89th Ct (33172-1203)
PHONE.................................800 843-4372
Alexandra Villoch, *President*
EMP: 6 **EST:** 2014
SALES (est): 147.8K **Privately Held**
SIC: 2711 Newspapers, publishing & printing

(G-3434)
MIAMI INDUSTRIAL MOTORS INC
8252 Nw 58th St (33166-3407)
PHONE.................................305 593-2370
Mario Garcia Jr, *President*
Ana Carolina Garcia, *Treasurer*
◆ **EMP:** 5 **EST:** 1983
SQ FT: 4,000
SALES (est): 514.2K **Privately Held**
WEB: www.miamiindustrialmotors.co
SIC: 7694 Electric motor repair

(G-3435)
MIAMI NEWS 24 INC
6874 Nw 113th Pl (33178-4547)
PHONE.................................786 331-8141
Tulio Capriles, *Principal*
EMP: 7 **EST:** 2015
SALES (est): 78.2K **Privately Held**
WEB: www.miaminews24.com
SIC: 2711 Newspapers: publishing only, not printed on site

(G-3436)
MIAMI OLIVEOIL & BEYOND LLC
1783 Nw 79th Ave (33126-1112)
PHONE.................................954 632-2762
Samuel Sasson, *Opers Staff*
Miguel Fernandez, *Mng Member*
EMP: 8 **EST:** 2014
SALES (est): 367.7K **Privately Held**
WEB: www.miaoliveoil.com
SIC: 2099 2079 Vinegar; olive oil

(G-3437)
MIAMI TBR LLC
Also Called: Bessie Barnie
1919 Nw 82nd Ave (33126-1011)
PHONE.................................786 275-4773
Theodor Rozenberg, *Mng Member*
EMP: 6 **EST:** 2017
SALES (est): 548.9K **Privately Held**
WEB: www.bessieandbarnie.com
SIC: 3999 5199 5999 Pet supplies; pet supplies; pet supplies

(G-3438)
MILANS MACHINE SHOP & WLDG SVC
8052 Nw 56th St (33166-4015)
PHONE.................................305 592-2447
Milan Baranek, *President*
Eva Baranek, *Admin Sec*
◆ **EMP:** 28 **EST:** 1974
SQ FT: 14,000
SALES (est): 1.8MM **Privately Held**
WEB: www.milansmachineshop.com
SIC: 3599 7692 Machine shop, jobbing & repair; welding repair

(G-3439)
MIRAFLEX CORPORATION
7950 Nw 53rd St Ste 324 (33166-4791)
PHONE.................................786 380-4494
Peter J Montana, *CEO*
EMP: 5 **EST:** 2011
SALES (est): 422.1K **Privately Held**
WEB: www.miraflexglasses.net
SIC: 3851 Eyeglasses, lenses & frames

(G-3440)
MK AVIATION LLC
9471 Nw 12th St (33172-2803)
PHONE.................................305 825-4810
Katrina Ruiz, *Principal*
EMP: 10 **EST:** 2015
SALES (est): 3.1MM **Privately Held**
WEB: www.mkaviationllc.com
SIC: 3728 Aircraft parts & equipment

(G-3441)
MORRIS VALVES INC
5590 Nw 84th Ave Ste C (33166-3335)
PHONE.................................305 477-6525
William Mogollon, *President*
Miriam Escalante, *Vice Pres*
EMP: 7 **EST:** 2010
SALES (est): 411.7K **Privately Held**
WEB: www.morrisvalve.com
SIC: 3491 Industrial valves
PA: Morris Industrial Supplier, C.A.
Carrera Caura, Torre Nekuina
Puerto Ordaz

(G-3442)
MVR COPIADORAS DIGITALES
9649 Nw 33rd St (33172-1100)
PHONE.................................786 366-1842
Luis A Rueda, *Owner*
EMP: 5 **EST:** 2013
SALES (est): 483.8K **Privately Held**
SIC: 3571 Computers, digital, analog or hybrid

(G-3443)
NAVISTAR INC
8600 Nw 36th St Ste 304 (33166-6651)
PHONE.................................305 513-2255
Cesar Longo, *Sales Staff*
Jackie Farinas, *Manager*
Tomas Mascunana, *Retailers*
EMP: 7
SALES (corp-wide): 263.5B **Privately Held**
WEB: www.internationaltrucks.com
SIC: 3711 Truck & tractor truck assembly
HQ: Navistar, Inc.
2701 Navistar Dr
Lisle IL 60532
331 332-5000

(G-3444)
NEW CONCEPTS DISTRS INTL LLC
Also Called: Ncdi
2315 Nw 107th Ave Ste 1b5 (33172-2164)
P.O. Box 227847, Miami (33222-7847)
PHONE.................................305 463-8735
Janice Santiago, *Mng Member*
EMP: 10 **EST:** 2010
SQ FT: 5,000
SALES (est): 1MM **Privately Held**
WEB: www.ncdiusa.com
SIC: 2342 2339 2251 5137 Bras, girdles & allied garments; foundation garments, women's; women's & misses' athletic clothing & sportswear; women's hosiery, except socks; women's & children's lingerie & undergarments

(G-3445)
NOBEL AEROSPACE LLC
1532 Nw 89th Ct (33172-2647)
PHONE.................................786 210-0716
Juan Benitez, *Manager*
EMP: 11 **EST:** 2014
SALES (est): 1.4MM **Privately Held**
WEB: www.nobaero.com
SIC: 3721 Aircraft

(G-3446)
NUPRESS OF MIAMI INC
2050 Nw 94th Ave (33172-2331)
PHONE.................................305 594-2100
Enrique F De La Vega, *President*
Orlando Lopez, *Vice Pres*
Leslie Perez, *Manager*
Henry Reynoso, *Manager*
Greg Rosen, *Manager*
▼ **EMP:** 50 **EST:** 1995
SQ FT: 45,000
SALES (est): 17.7MM **Privately Held**
WEB: www.nupress.com
SIC: 2752 Commercial printing, offset

(G-3447)
O MUSTAD & SON USA INC
2315 Nw 107th Ave Ste 88 (33172-2117)
PHONE.................................206 284-7871
Lars Lemhag, *President*
Edward Galka, *General Mgr*
◆ **EMP:** 38 **EST:** 1969

GEOGRAPHIC

SQ FT: 56,000
SALES (est): 789.5K **Privately Held**
WEB: www.mustad-fishing.com
SIC: 3949 Hooks, fishing
PA: O Mustad & Son As
Raufossvegen 40
Gjovik 2821

(G-3448)
OCTAMETRO LLC
8539 Nw 56th St (33166-3328)
PHONE..................................305 715-9713
Fernando Rodriguez, *Office Mgr*
William Rodriguez, *Office Mgr*
Fernando Rodrguez, *Manager*
Jose Aylagas,
▲ **EMP:** 7 **EST:** 2007
SQ FT: 2,030
SALES (est): 1MM **Privately Held**
WEB: www.octametro.com
SIC: 2599 Furniture & fixtures

(G-3449)
OMZ INDUSTRIES LLC
6010 Nw 99th Ave Unit 102 (33178-2723)
PHONE..................................786 210-6763
Omar Zemmama, *Branch Mgr*
EMP: 15
SALES (corp-wide): 162.4K **Privately Held**
WEB: www.hzindustry.us
SIC: 3999 Barber & beauty shop equipment
PA: Omz Industries Llc
3363 Sheridan St Ste 214
Hollywood FL

(G-3450)
ON-BOARD MEDIA INC
Also Called: Onboard Media
8400 Nw 36th St Ste 500 (33166-6620)
PHONE..................................305 673-0400
Marissa Cosculluela, *President*
Lauren Macleod, *General Mgr*
Lauren McGarrett, *Editor*
Carrie Julier, *Assoc VP*
Rina Alvarado, *Opers Staff*
◆ **EMP:** 90 **EST:** 1990
SQ FT: 13,000
SALES (est): 11.9MM
SALES (corp-wide): 419.1MM **Privately Held**
WEB: www.onboard.com
SIC: 2721 4724 7819 2731 Magazines: publishing only, not printed on site; travel agencies; services allied to motion pictures; book publishing
PA: Lvmh Moet Hennessy Louis Vuitton
22 Avenue Montaigne
Paris 75008
962 177-144

(G-3451)
ORBI SUPPLY INC
8760 Nw 36st Ste 425 (33178)
PHONE..................................305 810-8822
EMP: 6 **EST:** 2011
SALES (est): 61K **Privately Held**
WEB: www.orbisupply.com
SIC: 3151 Welders' gloves

(G-3452)
ORIGINAL PNGUIN DRECT OPRTIONS
3000 Nw 107th Ave (33172-2133)
PHONE..................................305 592-2830
John Griffin, *Principal*
EMP: 12 **EST:** 2010
SALES (est): 1MM **Privately Held**
WEB: www.originalpenguin.com
SIC: 2325 5621 5944 Men's & boys' trousers & slacks; women's clothing stores; watches

(G-3453)
PARAMOUNT DEPOT LLC
7975 Nw 56th St (33166-4012)
PHONE..................................786 275-0107
Rafael Dominguez, *CEO*
Paramount-Yud Gonzalez, *General Mgr*
James C Kennedy, *CFO*
Tomas Cabrerizo,
◆ **EMP:** 19 **EST:** 2005
SALES (est): 2.8MM **Privately Held**
WEB: www.paramountdepot.com
SIC: 1411 5031 Granite dimension stone; flagstone mining; quartzite, dimension-quarrying; lumber, plywood & millwork; kitchen cabinets

(G-3454)
PARINTO GLOBAL ENTERPRISES LLC
Also Called: Tres Leches Factory & Beyond
5213 Nw 79th Ave (33166-4715)
PHONE..................................305 606-3107
Cesar A Liccardo,
Luisa V Liccardo,
Jose C Ortiz,
EMP: 7 **EST:** 2008
SALES (est): 477.8K **Privately Held**
WEB: www.3lechesfactory.com
SIC: 2051 Bakery: wholesale or wholesale/retail combined

(G-3455)
PARKER DAVIS HVAC INTL INC
Also Called: Highseer.com
3250 Nw 107th Ave (33172-2137)
PHONE..................................305 513-4488
Baran Gokce, *CEO*
EMP: 50 **EST:** 2000
SALES (est): 6.7MM **Privately Held**
WEB: www.pdhvac.com
SIC: 3585 5075 Air conditioning equipment, complete; air conditioning units, complete: domestic or industrial; heat pumps, electric; heating & air conditioning combination units; air conditioning & ventilation equipment & supplies

(G-3456)
PD WIRE & CABLE SALES CORP (DH)
9850 Nw 41st St Ste 200 (33178-2987)
PHONE..................................305 648-7790
Manuel Iraola, *President*
Mario Andino, *Senior VP*
Julio Bague, *Senior VP*
A D Leuchtefeld, *Vice Pres*
Edward G Peters, *Vice Pres*
▲ **EMP:** 10 **EST:** 1967
SQ FT: 7,900
SALES (est): 3.4MM **Privately Held**
WEB: www.dodge.com
SIC: 1021 Copper ore mining & preparation
HQ: Phelps Dodge International Corporation
9850 Nw 41st St Ste 200
Doral FL 33178
305 648-7888

(G-3457)
PERKINS POWER CORP
Also Called: Southeast Diesel
5820 Nw 84th Ave (33166-3313)
PHONE..................................904 278-9919
Thomas J Tracy III, *CEO*
Chuck Scott, *General Mgr*
Alexander Colon Sr, *CFO*
Jason Miller, *Sales Mgr*
Jerry Rose, *Manager*
◆ **EMP:** 19 **EST:** 1978
SALES (est): 3.8MM **Privately Held**
WEB: www.perkinspower.com
SIC: 3621 Motors & generators
PA: Southeast Power Group, Inc.
5820 Nw 84th Ave
Doral FL 33166

(G-3458)
PERRY ELLIS INTERNATIONAL INC (HQ)
3000 Nw 107th Ave (33172-2133)
PHONE..................................305 592-2830
Oscar Feldenkreis, *President*
Dawna Ryan, *Area Mgr*
Joseph Roisman, *Exec VP*
Tricia McDermott Thompkins, *Exec VP*
Jack Voith, *Exec VP*
EMP: 350 **EST:** 1967
SQ FT: 240,000
SALES: 874.8MM **Privately Held**
WEB: www.pery.com
SIC: 2325 2339 2337 5611 Men's & boys' trousers & slacks; women's & misses' outerwear; women's & misses' suits & coats; men's & boys' clothing stores; women's clothing stores; men's & boys' dress shirts
PA: Feldenkreis Holdings Llc
3000 Nw 107th Ave
Doral FL 33172
305 592-2830

(G-3459)
PHELPS DODGE INTL CORP (DH)
9850 Nw 41st St Ste 200 (33178-2987)
P.O. Box 942286, Miami (33194-2286)
PHONE..................................305 648-7888
Mathias Sandoval, *President*
Chris Kesl, *Vice Pres*
Keith Macintosh, *Vice Pres*
Walter Barinaga, *Purch Dir*
Juan Arizpe, *Human Res Mgr*
◆ **EMP:** 30 **EST:** 1956
SQ FT: 12,000
SALES (est): 194.6MM **Privately Held**
WEB: www.dodge.com
SIC: 3357 3315 8742 Nonferrous wire-drawing & insulating; steel wire & related products; industrial consultant

(G-3460)
PHOENIX CALIBRATION LTD SRL
1733 Nw 79th Ave (33191-1101)
PHONE..................................786 866-5906
David Weil, *Principal*
EMP: 7 **EST:** 2004
SALES (est): 170.7K **Privately Held**
WEB: www.phoenixcalibrationdr.com
SIC: 3823 Temperature measurement instruments, industrial

(G-3461)
PHOENIX JEWELRY MFG INC
Also Called: Pjm
1499 Nw 79th Ave (33126-1609)
PHONE..................................305 477-2515
Ira Nusbaum, *Corp Secy*
Fred Nusbaum, *Purch Dir*
Fred Nausbaum, *Director*
EMP: 10 **EST:** 1992
SQ FT: 5,000
SALES (est): 1.6MM **Privately Held**
WEB: www.pjminc.com
SIC: 3911 5094 Jewelry, precious metal; jewelry

(G-3462)
PIECEMAKERS LLC
5521 Nw 78th Ave (33166-4119)
PHONE..................................786 517-1829
Francisco Villasante Jr, *Mng Member*
Llobal Alonso,
Alfredo Hernandez,
Jose Mayorga,
EMP: 10 **EST:** 2010
SALES (est): 1MM **Privately Held**
WEB: www.piece-makers.com
SIC: 3441 Fabricated structural metal

(G-3463)
POTTER ROEMER LLC
8306 Nw 14th St (33126-1504)
PHONE..................................786 845-0842
Romer Potter, *Principal*
EMP: 7
SALES (corp-wide): 90MM **Privately Held**
WEB: www.potterroemer.com
SIC: 3669 Emergency alarms
HQ: Potter Roemer, Llc
17451 Hurley St
City Of Industry CA 91744
626 855-4890

(G-3464)
POWER EQUIPMENTS TRADING LLC (PA)
8300 Nw 53rd St Ste 350 (33166-7712)
PHONE..................................305 704-7021
Valmore Gutierrez, *General Mgr*
Francisco Soto, *Purchasing*
Valmore Guitierrez,
▲ **EMP:** 9 **EST:** 2011
SALES (est): 2.1MM **Privately Held**
WEB: www.power-equipments.com
SIC: 3511 3561 5013 Gas turbine generator set units, complete; steam turbines; industrial pumps & parts; pumps, oil & gas

(G-3465)
PPG INDUSTRIES INC
1376 Nw 78th Ave (33126-1606)
PHONE..................................305 477-0541
EMP: 24
SALES (corp-wide): 15.3B **Publicly Held**
SIC: 2851 Mfg Misc Products
PA: Ppg Industries, Inc.
1 Ppg Pl
Pittsburgh PA 15272
412 434-3131

(G-3466)
PRECIOUS METALS XCHANGE GROUP
1890 Nw 95th Ave (33172-2340)
PHONE..................................305 556-1696
Wilmer Tuesta, *President*
EMP: 7 **EST:** 2005
SALES (est): 1MM **Privately Held**
WEB: www.pmxg.com
SIC: 3339 Precious metals

(G-3467)
PRECISION MACHINE TECH LLC
4083 Nw 79th Ave (33166-6519)
PHONE..................................305 594-1789
Wolfgang Reimann,
EMP: 12 **EST:** 2011
SALES (est): 757.9K **Privately Held**
WEB: www.pmt-industries.com
SIC: 3599 3841 3484 Machine shop, jobbing & repair; electrical discharge machining (EDM); surgical & medical instruments; instruments, microsurgical: except electromedical; guns (firearms) or gun parts, 30 mm. & below

(G-3468)
PRECISION MOLD TECH INC
4083 Nw 79th Ave (33166-6519)
P.O. Box 667748, Miami (33166-9405)
PHONE..................................305 594-1789
Enrique Dobrilla, *President*
Govita Dobrilla, *Vice Pres*
EMP: 9 **EST:** 1987
SQ FT: 6,000
SALES (est): 833.7K **Privately Held**
WEB: www.precisionmoldremoval.com
SIC: 3089 Laminating of plastic

(G-3469)
PRESTRESSED SYSTEMS INC
11405 Nw 112th Ct (33178-2163)
PHONE..................................305 556-6699
Vega Emilio R, *Principal*
EMP: 19 **EST:** 2015
SALES (est): 560.7K **Privately Held**
WEB: www.spimiami.com
SIC: 3272 Prestressed concrete products

(G-3470)
PRETZ SNACKS CORP
9755 Nw 46th Ter (33178-1983)
PHONE..................................718 869-2762
David Disla, *Principal*
EMP: 6 **EST:** 2014
SALES (est): 106K **Privately Held**
SIC: 2096 Potato chips & similar snacks

(G-3471)
PROFESSIONAL PET PRODUCTS INC
Also Called: P P P
1873 Nw 97th Ave (33172-2303)
PHONE..................................305 592-1992
John Plant, *President*
Donna Plant, *Corp Secy*
▼ **EMP:** 30 **EST:** 1983
SQ FT: 7,000
SALES (est): 3.4MM **Privately Held**
WEB: www.professionalpetproducts.com
SIC: 3999 3841 Pet supplies; surgical & medical instruments

(G-3472)
PROTEXIN
1833 Nw 79th Ave (33126-1114)
PHONE..................................786 310-7233
Jonathan Sowler, *President*
EMP: 8 **EST:** 2016
SALES (est): 1.3MM **Privately Held**
WEB: www.bio-kult.com
SIC: 2834 Pharmaceutical preparations

(G-3473)
PURE SOURCE LLC
Also Called: Pure Source, The
9750 Nw 17th St (33172-2753)
PHONE..................................305 477-8111
Chad Coston, *Vice Pres*
Manny Garcia, *CFO*
Joel Meyerson,
EMP: 32 **EST:** 2015
SALES (est): 3.8MM **Privately Held**
WEB: www.thepuresource.com
SIC: 2844 Cosmetic preparations

(G-3474)
QUAD INTL INCORPORATED
Also Called: Score Group, The
1629 Nw 84th Ave (33126-1031)
P.O. Box 558150, Miami (33255-8150)
PHONE..................................305 662-5959
John Fox, *President*
Rafael Trinidad, *Software Dev*
EMP: 56 **EST:** 1993
SQ FT: 20,000
SALES (est): 8.2MM **Privately Held**
WEB: www.scorepass.com
SIC: 2741 2721 Miscellaneous publishing; periodicals

(G-3475)
QUICK LIFT INC
8491 Nw 54th St (33166-3320)
PHONE..................................305 471-0147
Salvador Piles, *President*
Maria Piles, *Vice Pres*
▼ **EMP:** 6 **EST:** 1995
SQ FT: 5,000
SALES (est): 897.6K **Privately Held**
WEB: www.quicklift.com
SIC: 3536 Davits

(G-3476)
QUICK PRESS
2600 Nw 87th Ave Ste 16 (33172-1618)
PHONE..................................305 418-8744
Carl Chabouk, *Principal*
EMP: 6 **EST:** 2008
SALES (est): 112.8K **Privately Held**
SIC: 2741 Miscellaneous publishing

(G-3477)
R AND R BROKERAGE CO
Also Called: C & M Products Division
7740 Nw 55th St (33166-4112)
PHONE..................................305 592-4329
Ariel Soler, *Manager*
EMP: 6
SQ FT: 8,000
SALES (corp-wide): 35.5MM **Privately Held**
SIC: 3497 3469 Foil containers for bakery goods & frozen foods; kitchen fixtures & equipment: metal, except cast aluminum
PA: R And R Brokerage Co.
800 Ela Rd
Lake Zurich IL 60047
847 438-4600

(G-3478)
R S APPAREL INC
8454 Nw 58th St (33166-3302)
PHONE..................................305 599-4939
Rudolph Depass, *President*
Audrey Degen, *Director*
◆ **EMP:** 10 **EST:** 1997
SALES (est): 938.2K **Privately Held**
WEB: www.rsapparel.com
SIC: 2221 Apparel & outerwear fabric, manmade fiber or silk

(G-3479)
RADCHEN USA INC
8389 Nw 115th Ct (33178-1959)
PHONE..................................786 270-7628
Luis Fonseca, *Principal*
EMP: 8 **EST:** 2011
SALES (est): 88.6K **Privately Held**
WEB: www.radchenusa.com
SIC: 2099 Food preparations

(G-3480)
RADICA LLC
10471 Nw 36th St (33178-4367)
PHONE..................................954 383-0089
Cristina Barreto, *President*
EMP: 7 **EST:** 2017
SALES (est): 330.8K **Privately Held**
SIC: 2431 Doors & door parts & trim, wood

(G-3481)
RAMI TECHNOLOGY USA LLC (PA)
Also Called: Raltron Electronics
10400 Nw 33rd St Ste 290 (33172-5904)
PHONE..................................305 593-6033
Ross Weiss, *Vice Pres*
Richard Knecht, *CFO*
Alexandre Wolloch,
EMP: 6 **EST:** 2012
SALES (est): 1.6MM **Privately Held**
SIC: 3679 Electronic circuits

(G-3482)
RELU CO
Also Called: PDR OF THE GABLES
7827 Nw 15th St (33126-1109)
PHONE..................................786 717-5665
Edison Recinos, *President*
Ofelia Lucas, *Vice Pres*
EMP: 20 **EST:** 2014
SQ FT: 3,000
SALES (est): 1.6MM **Privately Held**
SIC: 2842 Sanitation preparations, disinfectants & deodorants

(G-3483)
REPWIRE LLC
5500 Nw 106th Ct (33178-6635)
PHONE..................................786 486-1823
Bernardo Pigna, *Mng Member*
Josefina Ruan,
EMP: 2 **EST:** 2014
SALES (est): 9MM **Privately Held**
SIC: 3315 Wire & fabricated wire products

(G-3484)
RESTIFO INVESTMENTS LLC
Also Called: Unlimited Impressions
1424 Nw 82nd Ave (33126-1508)
PHONE..................................305 468-0013
Eligio Restifo,
Reinaldo Restifo,
EMP: 10 **EST:** 2009
SALES (est): 948.7K **Privately Held**
WEB: www.uiprints.com
SIC: 2754 Commercial printing, gravure

(G-3485)
RICOMA INTERNATIONAL CORP
3450 Nw 114th Ave (33178-1840)
PHONE..................................305 418-4421
Frank MA, *President*
Guofeng MA, *President*
WEI Cheng, *Vice Pres*
Valeria Knight, *Marketing Staff*
◆ **EMP:** 7 **EST:** 2008
SALES (est): 1.4MM
SALES (corp-wide): 17.5MM **Privately Held**
WEB: www.ricoma.com
SIC: 3552 Textile machinery
PA: Ricoma (Shenzhen) Co.,Ltd.
201, Bldg. A, Bailian Qimengcheng Industrial Zone, No. 11, Shuit
Shenzhen 51811
755 536-6999

(G-3486)
RINKER MATERIALS CORP CON
12155 Nw 136th St (33178-3109)
PHONE..................................305 818-4952
Johnny Arellano, *Manager*
EMP: 7 **EST:** 2009
SALES (est): 385.3K **Privately Held**
WEB: www.rinkermaterials.com
SIC: 1422 Crushed & broken limestone

(G-3487)
ROBERLO USA INC
8501 Nw 17th St Ste 103 (33126-1099)
PHONE..................................786 334-6191
Jaume Bermudez, *Director*
EMP: 16 **EST:** 2011
SALES (est): 5.2MM
SALES (corp-wide): 1MM **Privately Held**
WEB: www.en.roberlo.us
SIC: 2851 Paints & allied products
HQ: Roberlo Sa
Carretera Nacional Ii (Paratge L Hostal Nou), Km 706,5
Riudellots De La Selva 17457
972 478-060

(G-3488)
ROD-SPEED INC
8901 Nw 109th Ct Unit 903 (33178-1657)
PHONE..................................786 426-3996
Rodrigo Leguizamon, *CEO*
EMP: 6 **EST:** 2010
SALES (est): 280.7K **Privately Held**
WEB: www.westernhemispheres.com
SIC: 3714 Motor vehicle parts & accessories

(G-3489)
RONTAN NORTH AMERICA INC
7859 Nw 46th St Ste 5b (33166-5470)
P.O. Box 226362, Miami (33222-6362)
PHONE..................................305 599-2974
EMP: 20
SALES (est): 2.9MM **Privately Held**
SIC: 3647 Mfg Vehicle Lighting Equipment

(G-3490)
ROSUCA INTERNATIONAL LLC
5639 Nw 113th Ct (33178-3856)
PHONE..................................305 332-5572
Roman Rodriguez, *Mng Member*
EMP: 7 **EST:** 2017
SALES (est): 561.1K **Privately Held**
WEB: www.rosucainternational.com
SIC: 3462 4731 Gear & chain forgings; foreign freight forwarding

(G-3491)
ROVER AEROSPACE INC
Also Called: Altima Technology Devices
2254 Nw 94th Ave (33172-2333)
PHONE..................................305 594-7799
George Delapaz, *President*
Gio Fagueroa, *Admin Sec*
EMP: 7 **EST:** 2000
SALES (est): 787.7K **Privately Held**
SIC: 3812 Acceleration indicators & systems components, aerospace; aircraft/aerospace flight instruments & guidance systems

(G-3492)
ROYAL ANCIENT SUPERFOODS
10530 Nw 37th Ter (33178-4209)
PHONE..................................305 600-1747
Daniel Blanco, *Owner*
EMP: 6 **EST:** 2016
SALES (est): 103.1K **Privately Held**
SIC: 2068 Seeds: dried, dehydrated, salted or roasted

(G-3493)
RUBYQUARTZ TECHNOLOGY LLC
10400 Nw 33rd St Ste 290 (33172-5904)
PHONE..................................305 406-0211
Alexander Wolloch, *Mng Member*
EMP: 12 **EST:** 2010
SALES (est): 1.4MM **Privately Held**
WEB: www.rubyquartz.com
SIC: 3559 Electronic component making machinery

(G-3494)
RVR USA LLC
Also Called: Rvr Elettronica
7782 Nw 46th St 20 (33166-5460)
PHONE..................................305 471-9091
Valentino Biavati, *President*
Angel Ylisastigui, *Director*
▲ **EMP:** 5 **EST:** 2000
SALES (est): 430.2K **Privately Held**
WEB: www.rvrusa.com
SIC: 3663 Radio & TV communications equipment

(G-3495)
SANCHELIMA INTERNATIONAL INC
1783 Nw 93rd Ave (33172-2921)
PHONE..................................305 591-4343
Juan Sanchelima, *President*
Estelle Sanchelima, *Treasurer*
Armando Suarez, *Technology*
◆ **EMP:** 14 **EST:** 1980
SQ FT: 5,400
SALES (est): 6.5MM **Privately Held**
WEB: www.sanchelimaint.com
SIC: 3523 5083 3556 Barn, silo, poultry, dairy & livestock machinery; dairy machinery & equipment; dairy & milk machinery; homogenizing machinery: dairy, fruit, vegetable; pasteurizing equipment, dairy machinery

(G-3496)
SAZON INC
2000 Nw 92nd Ave (33172-2928)
PHONE..................................305 591-9785
Jose A Ortega, *President*
Frank R Unanue Jr, *Vice Pres*
Joseph Unanue, *Vice Pres*
Hiram Carlo, *Plant Mgr*
Javier Madrigal, *Purchasing*
▼ **EMP:** 29 **EST:** 1983
SQ FT: 37,500
SALES (est): 5.8MM **Privately Held**
SIC: 2099 Spices, including grinding

(G-3497)
SDKC CORP
Also Called: Certapro Painters Centl Miami
9624 Nw 47th Ter (33178-2087)
PHONE..................................305 469-7578
Villani-Vertesch Carla, *Principal*
EMP: 9 **EST:** 2014
SALES (est): 667.6K **Privately Held**
SIC: 3732 Boat building & repairing

(G-3498)
SEGUTRONIC INTERNATIONAL INC
11042 Nw 72nd Ter (33178-3663)
PHONE..................................305 463-8551
Fax: 305 463-8552
EMP: 7 **EST:** 1989
SALES: 1MM **Privately Held**
SIC: 3699 Mfg Electrical Equipment/Supplies

(G-3499)
SEPRONET INC
11042 Nw 72nd Ter (33178-3663)
PHONE..................................305 463-8551
EMP: 12
SALES (est): 1.1MM **Privately Held**
SIC: 3699 Mfg Electrical Equipment/Supplies

(G-3500)
SEVEN GROUP USA INC
1681 Nw 79th Ave (33126-1105)
PHONE..................................305 392-9193
Mariela B Aparicio, *President*
EMP: 7 **EST:** 2017
SALES (est): 284.6K **Privately Held**
SIC: 3086 Packaging & shipping materials, foamed plastic

(G-3501)
SHIELD PRODUCTS INC
6010 Nw 99th Ave Unit 110 (33178-2723)
PHONE..................................904 880-6060
Juan P Saenz PHD, *Principal*
EMP: 8 **EST:** 2015
SALES (est): 670K **Privately Held**
WEB: www.shieldproducts.com
SIC: 2899 Chemical preparations

(G-3502)
SHIMA GROUP CORP
10836 Nw 27th St (33172-5907)
PHONE..................................305 463-0288
Fax: 305 262-2155
EMP: 7
SQ FT: 3,000
SALES (est): 790K **Privately Held**
SIC: 2752 Lithographic Commercial Printing

(G-3503)
SIKE USA INC
3004 Nw 82nd Ave (33122-1042)
PHONE..................................786 331-4020
Jorge E Tovar, *President*
Juana I Tovar, *Admin Sec*
EMP: 9 **EST:** 2012
SALES (est): 678.8K **Privately Held**
WEB: www.sikeusa.com
SIC: 3999 5191 Grasses, artificial & preserved; seeds: field, garden & flower

(G-3504)
SILIGOM USA LLC
5930 Nw 99th Ave Unit 9 (33178-2710)
PHONE..................................786 406-6262
Juan J Portela Zardetto, *Mng Member*
Maria L Francetich,
▲ **EMP:** 10 **EST:** 2006
SALES (est): 237.4K **Privately Held**
WEB: www.siligom.com
SIC: 3452 5085 Washers; gaskets

(G-3505)
SOLE INC
8378 Nw 56th St (33166-4020)
PHONE..................................305 513-2603
Gabriel Cardenas, *President*
▲ **EMP:** 5 **EST:** 2000
SQ FT: 1,800
SALES (est): 476.9K **Privately Held**
WEB: www.soleinc.net
SIC: 2519 Garden furniture, except wood, metal, stone or concrete

(G-3506)
SOUTH FLORIDA PALLETS DIST
1951 Nw 89th Pl Ste 100 (33172-2606)
PHONE..................................305 330-7663
Joel Gil, *Principal*
EMP: 13 **EST:** 2017
SALES (est): 347.3K **Privately Held**
WEB: www.sfpallets.com
SIC: 2448 Pallets, wood

(G-3507)
SOUTHEAST POWER GROUP INC (PA)
Also Called: Perkins Power
5820 Nw 84th Ave (33166-3313)
PHONE..................................305 592-9745
Thomas J Tracy III, *President*
Brian Wildasin, *Partner*
Steve Cathels, *Prdtn Mgr*
Rick Mendez, *Warehouse Mgr*
Mike Braswell, *Sales Staff*
◆ **EMP:** 60 **EST:** 1976
SQ FT: 40,000
SALES (est): 31MM **Privately Held**
WEB: www.perkinspower.com
SIC: 3494 3621 5084 5013 Pipe fittings; generators & sets, electric; industrial machinery & equipment; motor vehicle supplies & new parts

(G-3508)
SPANISH PERI & BK SLS INC
Also Called: Publicaciones Internacional
2105 Nw 102nd Ave (33172-2243)
PHONE..................................305 592-3919
Arthur Gelfand, *President*
Joe Bohorques, *Exec VP*
Daniel Gelfand, *Vice Pres*
▼ **EMP:** 75 **EST:** 1974
SQ FT: 30,000
SALES (est): 4.2MM **Privately Held**
SIC: 2721 5192 Magazines: publishing only, not printed on site; magazines

(G-3509)
SPECIALTY FOOD GROUP LLC (HQ)
9835 Nw 14th St (33172-2756)
PHONE..................................305 392-5000
Wissam Amoudi,
▲ **EMP:** 2 **EST:** 2009
SALES (est): 23.5MM
SALES (corp-wide): 119.1MM **Privately Held**
SIC: 2096 Corn chips & other corn-based snacks
PA: Sam's Group Of Companies, Inc.
9835 Nw 14th St
Doral FL 33172
305 392-5000

(G-3510)
SPLIFFPUFF LLC
6961 Nw 111th Ave (33178-3716)
PHONE..................................786 493-4529
Sebastian Arenas,
EMP: 10 **EST:** 2019
SALES (est): 283.1K **Privately Held**
SIC: 3999 Tobacco pipes, pipestems & bits

(G-3511)
STARLOCK INC
Also Called: Elc Security Products
8252 Nw 30th Ter (33122-1914)
PHONE..................................305 477-2303
Alberto L Castro, *President*
▲ **EMP:** 8 **EST:** 2000
SALES (est): 1.3MM **Privately Held**
WEB: www.elc.com.br
SIC: 2673 2677 2754 Bags: plastic, laminated & coated; envelopes; seals: gravure printing

(G-3512)
STONE CRAFT MASTERS LLC
7975 Nw 54th St (33166-4027)
PHONE..................................786 401-7060
Yoel Cruz, *Mng Member*
Christian Carlesi,
EMP: 11 **EST:** 2019
SQ FT: 15,000
SALES (est): 1.8MM **Privately Held**
WEB: www.stonecraftmasters.com
SIC: 3281 Cut stone & stone products

(G-3513)
STONEXCHANGE INC
9605 Nw 13th St (33172-2813)
PHONE..................................305 513-9795
Volkan O Yazici, *President*
◆ **EMP:** 18 **EST:** 2005
SALES (est): 513.3K **Privately Held**
WEB: www.windowsills.com
SIC: 3272 Thresholds, precast terrazzo

(G-3514)
STRUCTRAL PRESTRESSED INDS INC
Also Called: SPI
11405 Nw 112th Ct (33178-2163)
PHONE..................................305 556-6699
Emilio R Vega, *President*
Oswaldo Nordelo, *Prdtn Mgr*
Jorge Hernandez, *Opers Staff*
Alejandro Perez, *Purch Dir*
Edmundo Bendana, *Engineer*
◆ **EMP:** 100 **EST:** 1996
SALES (est): 8.4MM **Privately Held**
WEB: www.spimiami.com
SIC: 3272 Joists, concrete

(G-3515)
STUART-DEAN CO INC
2279 Nw 102nd Pl (33172-2523)
PHONE..................................305 652-9595
Eric Dwyer, *Sales Staff*
Mitchell Figueroa, *Sales Staff*
Mary Ann Degan, *Branch Mgr*
EMP: 13
SALES (corp-wide): 65.4MM **Privately Held**
WEB: www.stuartdean.com
SIC: 3471 Finishing, metals or formed products
PA: Stuart-Dean Co. Inc.
4350 10th St
Long Island City NY 11101
212 273-6900

(G-3516)
SUN PAPER COMPANY
7925 Nw 12th St Ste 321 (33126-1846)
PHONE..................................305 887-0040
Jose R Salgado Sr, *President*
Carlos M Salgado, *Vice Pres*
Graciela Salgado, *Vice Pres*
Jose Salgado Jr, *Vice Pres*
Rita Rodriguez, *Treasurer*
▼ **EMP:** 45 **EST:** 1990
SQ FT: 65,000
SALES (est): 9.5MM **Privately Held**
WEB: www.sunpaper.co
SIC: 2621 Napkin stock, paper; tissue paper; toweling tissue, paper

(G-3517)
SUNSHINE BOTTLING CO
Also Called: Ironbeer Soft Drink
8447 Nw 54th St (33166-3320)
PHONE..................................305 592-4366
Carlos R Blanco, *President*
Teresa Trujillo, *Vice Pres*
Olga Fornet, *Finance*
Richard Barnes, *CIO*
Myra Blanco, *Admin Sec*
◆ **EMP:** 29 **EST:** 1992
SALES (est): 6.7MM **Privately Held**
WEB: www.sunshinebottling.com
SIC: 2086 Soft drinks: packaged in cans, bottles, etc.; fruit drinks (less than 100% juice): packaged in cans, etc.

(G-3518)
SUPERIOR TRUSS SYSTEMS INC
8500 Nw 58th St (33166-3304)
P.O. Box 558247, Miami (33255-8247)
PHONE..................................305 591-9918
Juan Duarte, *President*
Armelio Gomez, *Vice Pres*
Patrick Gomez, *Manager*
EMP: 70 **EST:** 1978
SQ FT: 130,000
SALES (est): 9.8MM **Privately Held**
WEB: www.superiortrusses.com
SIC: 2439 Trusses, wooden roof

(G-3519)
SUPREME INTERNATIONAL LLC (DH)
Also Called: Rafaella
3000 Nw 107th Ave (33172-2133)
P.O. Box 21562, Louisville KY (40221-0562)
PHONE..................................305 592-2830
William V Roberti, *President*
Ronald G Threadgill, *Senior VP*
Terri Gonzalez, *Vice Pres*
Barbara Pereira, *Production*
Moises Kurny, *Natl Sales Mgr*
◆ **EMP:** 712 **EST:** 2002
SQ FT: 190,000
SALES (est): 271.7MM
SALES (corp-wide): 874.8MM **Privately Held**
WEB: www.pery.com
SIC: 2331 2325 Women's & misses' blouses & shirts; men's & boys' trousers & slacks; shorts (outerwear): men's, youths' & boys'; jeans: men's, youths' & boys'
HQ: Perry Ellis International Inc
3000 Nw 107th Ave
Doral FL 33172
305 592-2830

(G-3520)
SURVIVOR INDUSTRIES INC
9399 Nw 13th St (33172-2807)
PHONE..................................805 385-5560
Howard Wallace, *President*
Linda Wallace, *Corp Secy*
▲ **EMP:** 35 **EST:** 1983
SALES (est): 1.8MM **Privately Held**
WEB: www.sosfoodlab.com
SIC: 2099 Food preparations

(G-3521)
SYSTEMONE TECHNOLOGIES INC (PA)
8305 Nw 27th St Ste 107 (33122-1934)
PHONE..................................305 593-8015
Paul I Mansur, *President*
◆ **EMP:** 6 **EST:** 1990
SQ FT: 62,000
SALES (est): 1.6MM **Privately Held**
WEB: www.systemonetechnologies.com
SIC: 3559 Degreasing machines, automotive & industrial

(G-3522)
TAK PAPER CORP
10773 Nw 58th St Ste 651 (33178-2801)
PHONE..................................786 287-8900
EMP: 8
SALES (est): 400K **Privately Held**
SIC: 2674 Mfg Bags-Uncoated Paper

(G-3523)
TAP EXPRESS INC
9625 Nw 33rd St (33172-1100)
PHONE..................................305 468-0038
Michael Walther, *President*
◆ **EMP:** 5 **EST:** 1984
SQ FT: 4,000
SALES (est): 712.5K **Privately Held**
WEB: www.supertap.eu
SIC: 3131 Heel parts for shoes; top lifts, shoe & boot

(G-3524)
TECHNET CORP
10595 Nw 43rd Ter (33178-2265)
PHONE..................................305 582-5369
Andreas Jena, *President*
EMP: 9 **EST:** 2009
SALES (est): 470.5K **Privately Held**
WEB: www.technetllc.com
SIC: 3621 Electric motor & generator parts

(G-3525)
TECHNO CABINETS INC
1681 Nw 97th Ave (33172-2817)
PHONE..................................305 910-9929
Jesus L Govea, *President*
EMP: 7 **EST:** 2015
SALES (est): 375.6K **Privately Held**
WEB: www.technocabinets305.com
SIC: 2434 5211 1751 Wood kitchen cabinets; tile, ceramic; window & door installation & erection

(G-3526)
TECKNO CORP
8640 Nw 101st Pl (33178-2626)
PHONE..................................305 677-3487
Alejandro Paliz, *President*
EMP: 7 **EST:** 2010
SALES (est): 324.5K **Privately Held**
SIC: 3494 Pipe fittings

(G-3527)
TEKTROL INC
11013 Nw 30th St (33172-5070)
PHONE..................................305 305-0937
William F Astbury, *President*
EMP: 9 **EST:** 2000
SALES (est): 154.2K **Privately Held**
SIC: 2759 Embossing on paper

(G-3528)
TERRAFERMA USA CORPORATION
2201 Nw 93rd Ave (33172-4802)
PHONE..................................305 994-7892
Gianni Meneghini, *President*
◆ **EMP:** 13 **EST:** 2009
SALES (est): 259.2K **Privately Held**
WEB: www.artaic.com
SIC: 3231 Decorated glassware: chipped, engraved, etched, etc.

(G-3529)
TM USA INC
1628 Nw 82nd Ave (33126-1018)
PHONE..................................954 801-4649
Jin Park, *President*
EMP: 5 **EST:** 2015
SQ FT: 10,000
SALES (est): 300K **Privately Held**
SIC: 3674 Light emitting diodes

(G-3530)
TRACKING SOLUTIONS CORP
Also Called: TSO Mobile
7791 Nw 46th St Ste 306 (33166-5484)
PHONE..................................877 477-2922
Juan Olano, *President*
Bri Ruiz, *CFO*
Briglig Ruiz, *Manager*
Mauricio Salazar, *Manager*
EMP: 25 **EST:** 2002
SALES (est): 3.3MM
SALES (corp-wide): 10.8MM **Privately Held**
WEB: www.tsomobile.com
SIC: 7372 Prepackaged software
PA: Gpstrackit Holdings, Llc
1080 Holcomb Bridge Rd
Roswell GA 30076
951 296-1316

(G-3531)
TRADEWINDS POWER CORP (HQ)
Also Called: John Deere Authorized Dealer
5820 Nw 84th Ave (33166-3313)
PHONE..................................305 592-9745
Thomas J Tracy III, *CEO*
Jeff Beard, *General Mgr*
Jose Peralta, *COO*
Daniel Santos, *Export Mgr*
Mike Braswell, *Purch Mgr*
◆ **EMP**: 65 **EST**: 1985
SQ FT: 40,000
SALES (est): 27.1MM **Privately Held**
WEB: www.tradewindspower.com
SIC: **3621** 3494 5084 5013 Generators & sets, electric; pipe fittings; industrial machinery & equipment; motor vehicle supplies & new parts

(G-3532)
TRI COUNTY AEROSPACE INC
2080 Nw 96th Ave (33172-2319)
PHONE..................................305 639-3356
Emilio M Brown, *President*
Janet Bishop, *Vice Pres*
Astrid Brown, *Office Mgr*
EMP: 16 **EST**: 2003
SALES (est): 3.8MM **Privately Held**
WEB: www.tcaerospace.com
SIC: **7694** Rewinding services

(G-3533)
TROPICAL PAPER BOX
1401 Nw 78th Ave (33126-1616)
PHONE..................................305 592-5520
Herb Quartin, *Principal*
EMP: 7 **EST**: 2010
SALES (est): 230.2K **Privately Held**
SIC: **2652** Setup paperboard boxes

(G-3534)
TROY INDUSTRIES INC
2100 Nw 102nd Pl (33172-2525)
PHONE..................................305 324-1742
Steve Shapiro, *CEO*
Bernice Shapiro, *President*
Steven Shapiro, *President*
Howard Wilson, *Controller*
◆ **EMP**: 40 **EST**: 1947
SALES (est): 5MM **Privately Held**
WEB: www.troyindustries.com
SIC: **2392** 2842 5099 Polishing cloths, plain; specialty cleaning, polishes & sanitation goods; safety equipment & supplies

(G-3535)
UNICORNIO BAKERY LLC
8255 Lake Dr (33166-7819)
PHONE..................................786 665-1602
Nestor Ferreiro,
EMP: 10 **EST**: 2019
SALES (est): 430.1K **Privately Held**
SIC: **2051** Bakery products, partially cooked (except frozen)

(G-3536)
UNIQUE HITS MUSIC PUBG INC
7302 Nw 107th Pl (33178-3752)
PHONE..................................786 525-9525
Yoel Henriquez, *President*
EMP: 6 **EST**: 2019
SALES (est): 150.4K **Privately Held**
SIC: **2741** Miscellaneous publishing

(G-3537)
UNISCAN LLC ✪
10913 Nw 30th St Ste 101 (33172-5029)
PHONE..................................305 322-7669
Hector Redroban,
Elizabeth Benavides,
EMP: 10 **EST**: 2020
SALES (est): 1.1MM **Privately Held**
SIC: **3577** Magnetic ink & optical scanning devices

(G-3538)
UNISIGNS USA INC
5526 Nw 79th Ave (33166-4124)
PHONE..................................305 509-5232
Karla Barquero, *President*
EMP: 7 **EST**: 2016
SALES (est): 229.8K **Privately Held**
WEB: www.unisignsusa.com
SIC: **3993** Signs & advertising specialties

(G-3539)
USVI PHARMACEUTICALS LLC
1301 Nw 84th Ave Ste 101 (33126-1516)
PHONE..................................305 643-8841
Rick Nielsen, *Principal*
EMP: 9 **EST**: 2006
SQ FT: 5,000
SALES (est): 20.4K **Privately Held**
SIC: **2834** Pharmaceutical preparations

(G-3540)
VALOR LATIN GROUP INC
8320 Nw 14th St (33126-1504)
PHONE..................................305 791-5255
Jose Maleh, *President*
EMP: 5 **EST**: 2016
SALES (est): 444.7K **Privately Held**
WEB: www.valorlg.com
SIC: **3571** Computers, digital, analog or hybrid

(G-3541)
VFM AEROSYSTEMS LLC
10050 Nw 44th Ter Apt 301 (33178-3331)
PHONE..................................786 567-2348
Valery Mesa, *Director*
EMP: 7 **EST**: 2015
SALES (est): 615K **Privately Held**
SIC: **3724** Aircraft engines & engine parts

(G-3542)
VISION CONCEPTS INK INC
8953 Nw 23rd St (33172-2404)
PHONE..................................305 463-8003
Diane G Sardinas, *President*
Manuel Sardinas, *Vice Pres*
EMP: 10 **EST**: 2006
SQ FT: 9,400
SALES (est): 2.2MM **Privately Held**
WEB: www.vcink.com
SIC: **2752** Commercial printing, lithographic; commercial printing, offset

(G-3543)
VISION SOLUTION TECHNOLOGY LL
10367 Nw 41st St (33178-2305)
PHONE..................................305 477-4480
Carlos Romero, *Owner*
EMP: 6 **EST**: 2005
SALES (est): 792.8K **Privately Held**
SIC: **3827** 5048 Optical instruments & lenses; optometric equipment & supplies

(G-3544)
VISTA COLOR CORPORATION
Also Called: Commercial Printer Phrm Prtr
1401 Nw 78th Ave Ste 201 (33126-1616)
PHONE..................................305 635-2000
Jesus E Serrano, *CEO*
Enrique Serrano, *President*
Peter Baljet, *Principal*
Gene Gonzalez, *Vice Pres*
Jesus L Hernandez, *Vice Pres*
▼ **EMP**: 92
SQ FT: 12,500
SALES (est): 12MM **Privately Held**
WEB: www.vistacolor.com
SIC: **2752** Commercial printing, offset

(G-3545)
VOSSEN WHEELS INC
1598 Nw 82nd Ave (33126-1020)
PHONE..................................305 463-7778
EMP: 12 **EST**: 2018
SALES (est): 261.4K **Privately Held**
WEB: www.vossenwheels.com
SIC: **3011** Automobile tires, pneumatic

(G-3546)
VYP SERVICES LLC
Also Called: Caribbean Embroidery Designs
3555 Nw 79th Ave (33122-1019)
PHONE..................................305 593-8183
Pages Garcia, *Principal*
EMP: 7 **EST**: 2012
SALES (est): 227.9K **Privately Held**
SIC: **2395** Embroidery products, except schiffli machine

(G-3547)
WBN LLC
Also Called: AC Dob Led
1630 Nw 82nd Ave (33126-1022)
PHONE..................................786 870-4172
Jin Park, *Mng Member*
EMP: 5 **EST**: 2017
SQ FT: 10,000
SALES (est): 300K **Privately Held**
SIC: **3674** Light emitting diodes

(G-3548)
WEST PALM INSTALLERS INC
5141 Nw 79th Ave Unit 1 (33166-4756)
PHONE..................................305 406-3575
Louis Montalbo, *General Mgr*
EMP: 13 **EST**: 2000
SQ FT: 10,000
SALES (est): 785.8K **Privately Held**
WEB: www.brandernet.com
SIC: **3442** Shutters, door or window: metal

(G-3549)
WIBE NATURAL
10860 Nw 27th St (33172-5906)
PHONE..................................305 594-0158
William P Benard, *Principal*
EMP: 7 **EST**: 2010
SALES (est): 95.9K **Privately Held**
SIC: **2833** Medicinals & botanicals

(G-3550)
WORLD CONTAINER SERVICES LLC
3341 Nw 82nd Ave (33122-1025)
P.O. Box 520275, Miami (33152-0275)
PHONE..................................305 400-4850
Alberto Benitez, *CEO*
Roman Benitez, *Managing Dir*
Angel Abascal, *Opers Mgr*
Patrick Gordon, *CFO*
Jose Aguila, *Mng Member*
EMP: 32 **EST**: 2009
SQ FT: 1,200
SALES (est): 3MM **Privately Held**
WEB: www.worldcontainerservices.com
SIC: **3731** Cargo vessels, building & repairing

(G-3551)
WORLD FUEL CX LLC
9800 Nw 41st St Ste 400 (33178-2980)
PHONE..................................305 428-8000
Michael J Kasbar, *CEO*
Michael Crosby, *Exec VP*
John P Rau, *Exec VP*
Amy Abraham, *Senior VP*
R Alexander Lake, *Senior VP*
EMP: 10 **EST**: 2013
SALES (est): 4.5MM
SALES (corp-wide): 20.3B **Publicly Held**
WEB: www.wfscorp.com
SIC: **2869** Fuels
PA: World Fuel Services Corp
9800 Nw 41st St Ste 400
Doral FL 33178
305 428-8000

(G-3552)
XTS CORP
8870 Nw 18th Ter (33172-2642)
PHONE..................................305 863-7779
Augusto Perez, *President*
▲ **EMP**: 17 **EST**: 2006
SQ FT: 2,500
SALES (est): 479.9K **Privately Held**
WEB: www.xtscorp.com
SIC: **3699** Security devices

(G-3553)
ZIPX PACKAGE SERVICE INC
8401 Nw 17th St (33191-1005)
PHONE..................................305 597-5305
Craig Richard, *Principal*
EMP: 6 **EST**: 2016
SALES (est): 178.5K **Privately Held**
WEB: www.ibcinc.com
SIC: **3086** Packaging & shipping materials, foamed plastic

(G-3554)
ZUMEX USA INC
1573 Nw 82nd Ave (33126-1019)
PHONE..................................305 591-0061
Victor Bertolin, *President*
Sergio Davo, *Vice Pres*
▲ **EMP**: 4 **EST**: 2007
SQ FT: 3,500
SALES (est): 3MM
SALES (corp-wide): 31.8MM **Privately Held**
WEB: www.zumex.com
SIC: **3556** Juice extractors, fruit & vegetable: commercial type
PA: Zumex Group, Sa
Calle Moli (Pol. Industrial Moncada Iii) 2
Moncada 46113
961 301-251

Dover
Hillsborough County

(G-3555)
BINGHAM ON SITE PORTABLES LLC
3640 Sumner Rd (33527-4222)
P.O. Box 749 (33527-0749)
PHONE..................................813 659-0003
Anthony D Bingham, *Mng Member*
Dwayne Bingham Jr,
Linda J Bingham,
EMP: 7 **EST**: 2011
SQ FT: 1,000
SALES (est): 1.1MM **Privately Held**
WEB: www.binghamonsite.com
SIC: **3089** Toilets, portable chemical: plastic

(G-3556)
BINGHAM ON-SITE SEWERS INC
3640 Sumner Rd (33527-4222)
PHONE..................................813 659-0003
Amos Dewayne Bingham Sr, *President*
Linda Jean Bingham, *Corp Secy*
Amos Bingham Jr, *Vice Pres*
Anthony Bingham, *Vice Pres*
Daniel Gildea, *Vice Pres*
EMP: 53 **EST**: 1965
SQ FT: 8,400
SALES (est): 4.8MM **Privately Held**
SIC: **3272** 1711 7699 4959 Septic tanks, concrete; septic system construction; septic tank cleaning service; sanitary services

(G-3557)
C&P INDUSTRIES INC
5021 Durant Rd (33527-6312)
PHONE..................................813 685-3131
Christopher S Frasher, *Principal*
EMP: 6 **EST**: 2009
SALES (est): 119.6K **Privately Held**
SIC: **3999** Manufacturing industries

(G-3558)
DEANS CSTM SHTMTL FABRICATION
5106 Varnadore Ln (33527-5409)
PHONE..................................813 757-6270
Dean Varnadore, *President*
Robin Varnadore, *Vice Pres*
James Register, *Treasurer*
EMP: 9 **EST**: 1985
SQ FT: 7,000
SALES (est): 1.2MM **Privately Held**
SIC: **3444** 1799 Sheet metalwork; welding on site

(G-3559)
FRAZIERS FABRICATION
4730 Durant Rd (33527-6304)
PHONE..................................813 928-1449
Ryan P Frazier, *Manager*
EMP: 8 **EST**: 2015
SALES (est): 253.8K **Privately Held**
WEB: www.ffpcustoms.com
SIC: **3999** Manufacturing industries

(G-3560)
MANNA ON WHEELS INC
2217 Bogaert Rd (33527-5921)
PHONE..................................813 754-2277
EMP: 6 **EST**: 2006
SALES (est): 15.7K **Privately Held**
WEB: www.mannaonwheels.org
SIC: **3312** Wheels

(G-3561)
MARY SYMON
13206 Emerald Acres Ave (33527-3527)
PHONE..................................813 986-4676

GEOGRAPHIC

Mary P Symon, *Principal*
EMP: 7 **EST:** 2010
SALES (est): 116.6K **Privately Held**
SIC: 3644 Raceways

Duette
Manatee County

(G-3562)
MOODY CONSTRUCTION SVCS INC
12450 County Road 39 (34219-6835)
PHONE..................................941 776-1542
Matthew Moody, *President*
EMP: 32 **EST:** 1991
SQ FT: 10,000
SALES (est): 5.8MM **Privately Held**
WEB:
www.moodyconstructionservicesinc.com
SIC: 3441 1541 1542 Fabricated structural metal; renovation, remodeling & repairs: industrial buildings; commercial & office buildings, renovation & repair

(G-3563)
SOUTHSTERN INDUS FBRCATORS LLC
Also Called: Dixie Southern
12650 County Road 39 (34219-6836)
PHONE..................................941 776-1211
David Batts, *Project Mgr*
David Howell,
Jason Howell,
Jonathan Howell,
EMP: 40 **EST:** 2017
SALES (est): 12MM **Privately Held**
WEB: www.dixiesouthern.com
SIC: 3317 3443 3511 Steel pipe & tubes; industrial vessels, tanks & containers; bins, prefabricated metal plate; hoppers, metal plate; missile silos & components, metal plate; hydraulic turbines

Dundee
Polk County

(G-3564)
CHILIPRINT LLC
28597 Hwy 27 (33838-4282)
PHONE..................................863 547-6930
Christopher Chilton, *Principal*
EMP: 8 **EST:** 2010
SALES (est): 288.9K **Privately Held**
SIC: 3993 Signs & advertising specialties

(G-3565)
M&S STRONG WELDING INC
410 Florida Ave (33838-4592)
PHONE..................................623 299-5336
Bernanrdino Meza Cervantes, *President*
EMP: 7 **EST:** 2019
SALES (est): 270.6K **Privately Held**
WEB: www.ms-strong-welding-inc.business.site
SIC: 7692 Welding repair

(G-3566)
MAXIJET INC
8400 Lake Trask Rd (33838-4700)
P.O. Box 1849 (33838-1849)
PHONE..................................863 439-3667
Susan S Thayer, *President*
Tim Geiger, *Plant Mgr*
Thomas A Thayer Jr, *Treasurer*
Virginia Thayer Dunson, *Admin Sec*
EMP: 32 **EST:** 1981
SQ FT: 30,000
SALES (est): 1.2MM **Privately Held**
WEB: www.maxijet.com
SIC: 3523 Irrigation equipment, self-propelled
PA: Thayer Industries Inc
5600 Lake Trask Rd
Dundee FL 33838
813 719-6597

(G-3567)
PHANTOM USA LLC
101 Shepard Ave (33838-4381)
PHONE..................................863 353-5972
Doug Wilson, *Principal*
EMP: 6 **EST:** 2015
SALES (est): 109.9K **Privately Held**
WEB: www.artattackfx.com
SIC: 2752 Commercial printing, lithographic

(G-3568)
PRATT INDUSTRIES INC
Also Called: Corrugating Division
331 Frederick Ave (33838)
P.O. Box 1900 (33838-1900)
PHONE..................................863 439-4184
Steven Roberts, *Design Engr*
Juli Hickey, *Accounts Mgr*
Tomeck Mikler, *Office Mgr*
EMP: 9 **Privately Held**
WEB: www.prattindustries.com
SIC: 2653 Boxes, corrugated: made from purchased materials
PA: Pratt Industries, Inc.
1800 Sarasot Bus Pkwy Ne S
Conyers GA 30013

Dunedin
Pinellas County

(G-3569)
BARTH INDUSTRIES
1701 Hickory Gate Dr S (34698-2413)
PHONE..................................727 787-6392
Harry Barth, *Principal*
EMP: 14 **EST:** 2008
SALES (est): 126.1K **Privately Held**
WEB: www.barthindustries.com
SIC: 3999 Manufacturing industries

(G-3570)
BIOBAG AMERICAS INC
1059 Broadway Ste F (34698-5756)
P.O. Box 369, Palm Harbor (34682-0369)
PHONE..................................727 789-1646
David J Williams, *President*
Alec Brophy, *Chairman*
Tom Goldy, *Business Mgr*
Caroline Stone, *Sales Staff*
Jennifer Pope, *VP Mktg*
▲ **EMP:** 14 **EST:** 2002
SALES (est): 4.4MM **Privately Held**
WEB: www.biobagusa.com
SIC: 2673 Plastic bags: made from purchased materials
HQ: Biobag International As
Trogstadveien 9a
Askim 1807
698 885-90

(G-3571)
CAST ART INTERNATIONAL CORP
762 Marjon Ave (34698-7107)
PHONE..................................727 807-3395
Grazia C Caiazza, *President*
EMP: 9 **EST:** 2010
SALES (est): 108.4K **Privately Held**
SIC: 3272 5211 Silo staves, cast stone or concrete; closets, interiors & accessories

(G-3572)
CERTEK SOFTWARE DESIGNS INC
507 S Paula Dr (34698-2032)
PHONE..................................727 738-8188
David Roberts, *President*
Kurt Golhardt, *Vice Pres*
Mark Barnes, *CFO*
EMP: 9 **EST:** 2003
SALES (est): 1MM **Privately Held**
WEB: www.certek.com
SIC: 7372 Prepackaged software

(G-3573)
CHEVAL COUNTRY CLUB
545 Frederica Ln (34698-5053)
P.O. Box 340465, Tampa (33694-0465)
PHONE..................................813 279-5122
Larry King, *Owner*
Billie Merritt, *Principal*
Itam Antigha, *Personnel*
Ryan Shives, *Director*
EMP: 6 **EST:** 2012
SALES (est): 909K **Privately Held**
WEB: www.playcheval.com
SIC: 3949 7991 Shafts, golf club; athletic club & gymnasiums, membership

(G-3574)
COCA-COLA COMPANY
427 San Christopher Dr (34698-4905)
P.O. Box 979 (34697-0979)
PHONE..................................727 736-7101
Matt Iwanski, *Mfg Staff*
Tim Goodwin, *Opers-Prdtn-Mfg*
Anthony Natal, *Sales Staff*
EMP: 6
SALES (corp-wide): 33B **Publicly Held**
WEB: www.coca-colacompany.com
SIC: 2086 2033 5142 Bottled & canned soft drinks; canned fruits & specialties; packaged frozen goods
PA: The Coca-Cola Company
1 Coca Cola Plz Nw
Atlanta GA 30313
404 676-2121

(G-3575)
CRUISING GIDE PUBLICATIONS INC
2418 Summerwood Ct (34698-2253)
P.O. Box 1017 (34697-1017)
PHONE..................................727 733-5322
Nancy Scott, *President*
Simon Scott, *Vice Pres*
Ashley Scott, *Production*
Maureen Larroux, *Mktg Dir*
◆ **EMP:** 5 **EST:** 1986
SQ FT: 2,000
SALES (est): 529.3K **Privately Held**
WEB: www.cruisingguides.com
SIC: 2741 Atlas, map & guide publishing

(G-3576)
FEWTEK INC
2539 Gary Cir Apt 201 (34698-1748)
PHONE..................................727 736-0533
EMP: 10
SALES: 1.5MM **Privately Held**
SIC: 3824 8721 Mfg Fluid Meter/Counting Devices Accounting/Auditing/Bookkeeping

(G-3577)
FREEDOM ORTHOTICS INC
1714 County Road 1 Ste 23 (34698-3910)
P.O. Box 299 (34697-0299)
PHONE..................................813 833-7871
John I Harrison II, *Principal*
EMP: 7 **EST:** 2016
SALES (est): 126.9K **Privately Held**
WEB: www.freedomorthotics.com
SIC: 3842 Orthopedic appliances

(G-3578)
GATTAS CORP
Also Called: Gattas Marine Services
745 Main St Ste B (34698-5018)
PHONE..................................727 733-5886
Christopher M Gattas, *Director*
EMP: 7 **EST:** 2005
SALES (est): 175.2K **Privately Held**
SIC: 2397 Schiffli machine embroideries

(G-3579)
GEDDIS INC
2221 Paddock Cir (34698-2428)
PHONE..................................800 844-6792
Dave Geddis, *President*
EMP: 10 **EST:** 1978
SALES (est): 527.7K **Privately Held**
WEB: www.surgiclean.com
SIC: 3841 3845 3699 Surgical & medical instruments; electromedical equipment; electrical equipment & supplies

(G-3580)
ILAN CUSTOM WOODWORK LLC (PA)
42 Ventura Dr (34698-8232)
PHONE..................................727 272-5364
Uri Ilan, *Manager*
EMP: 16 **EST:** 2017
SALES (est): 145.7K **Privately Held**
SIC: 2431 Millwork

(G-3581)
IMPACT PROMOTIONAL PUBG LLC
1546 Main St (34698-4642)
PHONE..................................727 736-6228
Peter Klein,
EMP: 11 **EST:** 1996
SALES (est): 404.8K **Privately Held**
WEB: www.impact-i.com
SIC: 2741 Miscellaneous publishing

(G-3582)
KELLER-NGLILLIS DESIGN MFG INC
655 San Christopher Dr (34698-5060)
PHONE..................................727 733-4111
Robert D Keller, *President*
Charles Angelillis, *Corp Secy*
Gerald Keller, *Vice Pres*
Judson Angelillis, *Project Mgr*
Morgan Angelillis, *Admin Mgr*
▼ **EMP:** 12 **EST:** 1955
SQ FT: 30,000
SALES (est): 1.4MM **Privately Held**
WEB: www.kellersales.com
SIC: 3535 3443 Conveyors & conveying equipment; tanks, lined: metal plate

(G-3583)
KITCHEN SINK EXPRESS LLC
1986 Brae Moor Dr (34698-3250)
PHONE..................................800 888-6604
Alicia Taylor, *Principal*
EMP: 6
SALES (est): 491.4K **Privately Held**
SIC: 3365 Household utensils, cast aluminum

(G-3584)
MINUTE MAN PRESS
Also Called: Minuteman Press
1425 Main St Ste C (34698-6247)
PHONE..................................727 791-1115
Courtney Tuttle, *Owner*
EMP: 5 **EST:** 2004
SALES (est): 403.6K **Privately Held**
WEB: www.chanhassen-mn.minuteman-press.com
SIC: 2752 Commercial printing, lithographic

(G-3585)
NU EARTH LABS LLC
150 Douglas Ave (34698-7908)
PHONE..................................727 648-4787
Chris Estey, *CEO*
Tim Bitterman, *Manager*
Angie Chacon, *Manager*
EMP: 50 **EST:** 2016
SALES (est): 4.8MM **Privately Held**
WEB: www.nuearthlabs.com
SIC: 2869 5999 High purity grade chemicals, organic; toiletries, cosmetics & perfumes

(G-3586)
ONE PRICE DRYCLEANERS TAMPA (PA)
1850 Main St (34698-5565)
PHONE..................................727 734-3353
James A Robinson, *President*
Tracy Robinson, *Owner*
EMP: 10 **EST:** 1999
SALES (est): 762.6K **Privately Held**
SIC: 3953 7211 Marking devices; power laundries, family & commercial

(G-3587)
PRINT MART INC
1430 Main St (34698-6201)
PHONE..................................727 796-0064
Neil Stein, *President*
EMP: 5 **EST:** 2014
SALES (est): 316K **Privately Held**
WEB: www.printmart.us
SIC: 2759 Commercial printing

(G-3588)
SINO EAGLE USA INC
1000 Bass Blvd (34698-5801)
PHONE..................................727 259-3570
Jean Raas, *President*
EMP: 17 **EST:** 2011

▲ = Import ▼=Export
◆ =Import/Export

SALES (est): 1.5MM
SALES (corp-wide): 25.6MM **Privately Held**
WEB: www.sinoeaglegroup.com
SIC: **3732** Sailboats, building & repairing
PA: Zhejiang Sino-Eagle Holding Group Co., Ltd.
No.81, Gaoerfu Road, Yinhu Sub-District, Fuya Ng District
Hangzhou 31140
571 634-3261

(G-3589)
STIRLING WINERY
461 Main St (34698-4965)
PHONE..................................727 734-4025
Elinor Fox, *Owner*
EMP: 8 **EST**: 2005
SALES (est): 175.1K **Privately Held**
WEB: www.stirlingwinedunedin.com
SIC: **2084** Wines

(G-3590)
THRILLER CLEARWATER INC
669 Lexington St (34698-8406)
PHONE..................................727 389-2209
EMP: 6 **EST**: 2016
SALES (est): 105.6K **Privately Held**
WEB: www.thrillerclearwater.com
SIC: **3069** Fabricated rubber products

(G-3591)
TWO ROADS CONSULTING LLC
469 Limewood Ave (34698-7220)
PHONE..................................305 395-8821
Perry Warren, *Mng Member*
EMP: 7 **EST**: 2011
SALES (est): 1MM **Privately Held**
WEB: www.tworoadsconsulting.com
SIC: **7372** Business oriented computer software

Dunnellon
Citrus County

(G-3592)
AIR DISTRIBUTORS INC
Also Called: Metal Shop, The
2541 W Dunnellon Rd (34433-2347)
P.O. Box 1829 (34430-1829)
PHONE..................................352 522-0006
James E Jacobs, *President*
Lynn Jacobs, *Admin Sec*
▲ **EMP**: 28 **EST**: 1982
SQ FT: 9,413
SALES (est): 8.9MM **Privately Held**
WEB: www.metalshop.org
SIC: **3444** Sheet metalwork

(G-3593)
DULEY TRUSS INC
2591 W Dunnellon Rd 488 (34433-2347)
P.O. Box 340 (34430-0340)
PHONE..................................352 465-0964
John Duley, *President*
EMP: 27 **EST**: 1983
SQ FT: 7,000
SALES (est): 2.2MM **Privately Held**
WEB: www.duleytruss.com
SIC: **2439** Trusses, wooden roof

Dunnellon
Marion County

(G-3594)
CARLTON MFG INC (PA)
Also Called: Carlton Mfg Associates
20093 E Penn Ave Ste 3 (34432-6061)
P.O. Box 539, Mount Vernon TX (75457-0539)
PHONE..................................352 465-2153
Doug Mercier, *President*
Jean Rowe, *Treasurer*
Robert Behymer, *Admin Sec*
▲ **EMP**: 2 **EST**: 1976
SQ FT: 126,000
SALES: 9.4MM **Privately Held**
SIC: **2512** Living room furniture: upholstered on wood frames

(G-3595)
D & S STEEL
19450 Sw 5th Pl (34431-2101)
PHONE..................................352 489-8791
Vicky Stancil, *Owner*
EMP: 5 **EST**: 1997
SQ FT: 4,000
SALES (est): 535.9K **Privately Held**
SIC: **7692** Welding repair

(G-3596)
DONAU CARBON US LCC
551 N Us Highway 41 (34432-1315)
PHONE..................................352 465-5959
Katharina Wiesauer, *Mng Member*
EMP: 25 **EST**: 2016
SALES (est): 2.8MM **Privately Held**
WEB: www.donau-carbon-us.com
SIC: **2819** Charcoal (carbon), activated

(G-3597)
ELKINS WELDING INC
1620 N Us Highway 41 (34432-1312)
PHONE..................................352 362-4577
EMP: 6 **EST**: 2019
SALES (est): 229.4K **Privately Held**
SIC: **7692** Welding repair

(G-3598)
KASHIBEN SAY LLC
Also Called: Dunnellon Discount Drugs
11150 N Williams St (34432-8363)
PHONE..................................352 489-4960
Tapan J Vora, *Mng Member*
Jittendra Vora,
EMP: 8 **EST**: 2012
SALES (est): 1MM **Privately Held**
WEB: www.dunnellonpharmacy.com
SIC: **2834** 5912 Pharmaceutical preparations; drug stores

(G-3599)
SANDI JOHNSON
10010 Se 125th Ct (34431-7514)
PHONE..................................561 389-1035
Sandi Johnson, *Principal*
Sandra Johnson, *Principal*
EMP: 6 **EST**: 2010
SALES (est): 88.1K **Privately Held**
SIC: **2399** Horse harnesses & riding crops, etc.: non-leather

(G-3600)
STANDARD CARBON LLC
Also Called: Standard Purification
551 N Us Highway 41 (34432-1315)
PHONE..................................352 465-5959
James B Sharpe Jr,
Soohyung Kim,
Nicholas Singer,
▲ **EMP**: 21
SQ FT: 30,000
SALES (est): 8.2MM **Privately Held**
WEB: www.standardpurification.com
SIC: **2819** Industrial inorganic chemicals

(G-3601)
TRIAD EDM INC
14872 Sw 111th St (34432-4731)
PHONE..................................352 489-5336
Joseph J Hytovick, *President*
Vivian Hytovick, *Corp Secy*
EMP: 6 **EST**: 1983
SQ FT: 21,000
SALES (est): 525K **Privately Held**
WEB: www.triadedm.com
SIC: **3544** 3599 Special dies & tools; electrical discharge machining (EDM)

(G-3602)
WATTS WATER TECHNOLOGIES INC
Also Called: Flowmatic
11611 Sw 147th Ct (34432-4759)
PHONE..................................352 465-2000
Renato Trovo, *General Mgr*
Neal Delettre, *Branch Mgr*
Kitae Chang, *Director*
EMP: 6
SALES (corp-wide): 1.5B **Publicly Held**
WEB: www.watts.com
SIC: **3589** Water purification equipment, household type
PA: Watts Water Technologies, Inc.
815 Chestnut St
North Andover MA 01845
978 688-1811

East Palatka
Putnam County

(G-3603)
J M MILLING INC
120 Dog Branch Rd (32131-4161)
PHONE..................................386 546-6826
EMP: 9 **EST**: 2018
SALES (est): 1.1MM **Privately Held**
SIC: **3599** Machine shop, jobbing & repair

(G-3604)
KARNAK CORPORATION
Also Called: Rodents On The Road
147 Pine Tree Rd (32131-4160)
PHONE..................................352 481-4145
Craig Z Sherar, *President*
Jessica R Sherar, *Vice Pres*
EMP: 9 **EST**: 1984
SALES (est): 638K **Privately Held**
SIC: **2048** 7389 Feeds, specialty: mice, guinea pig, etc.;

(G-3605)
PLASTIC MASTERS INTERNATIONAL
327 State Road 207 (32131-4106)
PHONE..................................386 312-9775
Lark James, *President*
Steve James, *Corp Secy*
EMP: 13 **EST**: 1997
SQ FT: 15,000
SALES (est): 2.9MM **Privately Held**
WEB: www.plasticmasters.com
SIC: **2821** Plastics materials & resins

(G-3606)
RYAN MANUFACTURING INC
339b State Road 207 (32131-4106)
PHONE..................................386 325-3644
Mark Ryan, *President*
Marian Ryan, *Manager*
EMP: 10 **EST**: 1987
SQ FT: 8,000
SALES (est): 1.7MM **Privately Held**
WEB: www.ryanmanufacturing.com
SIC: **3443** 3523 Fabricated plate work (boiler shop); farm machinery & equipment

(G-3607)
ST JOHNS TURF CASE
1040 Hstngs Federal Pt Rd (32131-4420)
PHONE..................................352 258-3314
EMP: 17 **EST**: 2019
SALES (est): 3.5MM **Privately Held**
SIC: **3523** Farm machinery & equipment

(G-3608)
TRUE HOUSE INC
150 State Road 207 (32131-4001)
PHONE..................................386 325-9085
Pete Potter, *Principal*
EMP: 110
SALES (corp-wide): 13.6MM **Privately Held**
WEB: www.apextechnology.com
SIC: **2439** Trusses, wooden roof
PA: True House, Inc.
4745 Sutton Park Ct # 501
Jacksonville FL 32224
904 757-7500

(G-3609)
WARWICK LOGGING
Also Called: Warwick, Blane
119 Putnam County Blvd (32131-4020)
P.O. Box 143 (32131-0143)
PHONE..................................386 328-9358
Blane Warwick, *Owner*
EMP: 7 **EST**: 1992
SALES (est): 831.5K **Privately Held**
SIC: **2411** Logging camps & contractors

Edgewater
Volusia County

(G-3610)
ATLANTIC FENCE & PAVERS LLC
3311 Victory Palm Dr (32141-6523)
PHONE..................................386 334-6472
David Isenbarger, *Manager*
EMP: 6 **EST**: 2016
SALES (est): 231K **Privately Held**
WEB: www.atlanticfencepavers.com
SIC: **2951** Asphalt paving mixtures & blocks

(G-3611)
AUTISM PUZZLE ME INC
2945 Lime Tree Dr (32141-5724)
PHONE..................................386 314-4310
Andre Narcisse, *Principal*
EMP: 6 **EST**: 2016
SALES (est): 47K **Privately Held**
WEB: www.autismpuzzleme.com
SIC: **3944** Puzzles

(G-3612)
B&C SIGNS
2525 Guava Dr (32141-5143)
PHONE..................................386 426-2373
Brendon Cahill, *President*
Tanel Cahill, *Vice Pres*
Brendan Cahill, *Info Tech Mgr*
EMP: 5 **EST**: 1996
SQ FT: 3,740
SALES (est): 400K **Privately Held**
WEB: www.bandcsigns.com
SIC: **3993** Electric signs

(G-3613)
BEST IPRODUCTSCOM LLC
111 N Ridgewood Ave (32132-1713)
PHONE..................................386 402-7800
▼ **EMP**: 6 **EST**: 2011
SQ FT: 25,000
SALES: 1MM **Privately Held**
SIC: **3577** Mfg Computer Peripheral Equipment

(G-3614)
BLUE WATER DYNAMICS LLC
Also Called: Dougherty Manufacturing
308 S Old County Rd (32132-1812)
PHONE..................................386 957-5464
Carisa Albrecht, *Vice Pres*
Sarah N Dougherty, *CFO*
Sarah Dougherty,
EMP: 69 **EST**: 2010
SALES (est): 11.6MM **Privately Held**
SIC: **2821** 3089 3448 3469 Plastics materials & resins; prefabricated plastic buildings; buildings, portable: prefabricated metal; ornamental metal stampings; miscellaneous fabricated wire products; tube fabricating (contract bending & shaping)

(G-3615)
BOSTON WHALER INC
100 Whaler Way (32141-7221)
PHONE..................................386 428-0057
John Ward, *President*
Huw S Bower, *President*
Doug Nettles, *Business Mgr*
Anna Collins, *COO*
Jeff Vaughn, *Vice Pres*
◆ **EMP**: 400 **EST**: 1958
SQ FT: 12,000
SALES (est): 83.7MM
SALES (corp-wide): 4.3B **Publicly Held**
WEB: www.bostonwhaler.com
SIC: **3732** Boats, fiberglass: building & repairing
PA: Brunswick Corporation
26125 N Riverwoods Blvd # 500
Mettawa IL 60045
847 735-4700

(G-3616)
BRUNSWICK COMMERCIAL &
100 Whaler Way (32141-7213)
PHONE..................................386 423-2900
Eric Caplan, *President*
◆ **EMP**: 100 **EST**: 2001

SALES (est): 21MM
SALES (corp-wide): 4.3B **Publicly Held**
WEB: www.brunswickcgp.com
SIC: 3732 Motorized boat, building & repairing
PA: Brunswick Corporation
26125 N Riverwoods Blvd # 500
Mettawa IL 60045
847 735-4700

(G-3617)
C & E CABINETS DESIGN LLC
137 W Marion Ave (32132-3552)
PHONE..................................386 410-4281
EMP: 6 **EST:** 2019
SALES (est): 547.6K **Privately Held**
SIC: 3993 Signs & advertising specialties

(G-3618)
CENTROID PRODUCTS INC
2104 Hibiscus Dr (32141-4008)
PHONE..................................386 423-3574
James Tucker, *President*
EMP: 9 **EST:** 1983
SALES (est): 759.5K **Privately Held**
WEB: www.centroidproducts.com
SIC: 3823 Industrial instrmnts msrmnt display/control process variable

(G-3619)
CHOICE PRODUCTS INC
143 W Palm Way (32132-1817)
PHONE..................................386 426-6450
EMP: 15
SALES (est): 1.1MM **Privately Held**
SIC: 3728 3751 Mfg Aircraft Parts/Equipment Mfg Motorcycles/Bicycles

(G-3620)
CUSTOM TUBE PRODUCTS INC
317 Base Leg Dr (32132-1481)
P.O. Box 936 (32132-0936)
PHONE..................................386 426-0670
David S Love, *President*
Sydney S Love, *CFO*
Jake Baker, *Manager*
John Butler, *Technician*
EMP: 15 **EST:** 2003
SQ FT: 20,000
SALES (est): 4.6MM **Privately Held**
WEB: www.customtubeproducts.com
SIC: 3599 3498 Tubing, flexible metallic; fabricated pipe & fittings

(G-3621)
DEW IT RIGHT COATINGS
3122 Umbrella Tree Dr (32141-6104)
PHONE..................................504 272-4981
Duane J Vadnais, *Principal*
EMP: 6 **EST:** 2012
SALES (est): 203.9K **Privately Held**
WEB: www.dewitright.com
SIC: 3479 Metal coating & allied service

(G-3622)
EDGEWATER POWER BOATS LLC
211 Dale St (32132-1417)
P.O. Box 790 (32132-0790)
PHONE..................................386 426-5457
Daniel Robinson, *Regional Mgr*
Chris Phelps, *Opers Staff*
Keith Williams, *Purch Agent*
Kevin Keyes, *Engineer*
Bryan Powderly, *Controller*
◆ **EMP:** 65 **EST:** 2004
SQ FT: 66,000
SALES (est): 18.2MM **Privately Held**
WEB: www.ewboats.com
SIC: 3732 Boat building & repairing

(G-3623)
GLOBAL PUMP DAYTONA
411 Timaquan Trl (32132-2167)
PHONE..................................386 426-2411
Rodney A Mersino Sr, *President*
EMP: 7 **EST:** 2014
SALES (est): 157.4K **Privately Held**
WEB: www.globalpump.com
SIC: 3561 Pumps & pumping equipment

(G-3624)
HYDROPLUS
1712 Fern Palm Dr Ste 7 (32132-5500)
PHONE..................................386 341-2768
John Camp, *Principal*
EMP: 7 **EST:** 2010
SALES (est): 550.5K **Privately Held**
WEB: www.hydroplusengineering.com
SIC: 3829 Pressure & vacuum indicators, aircraft engine

(G-3625)
ILEX ORGANICS LLC ✪
1814 Fern Palm Dr Ste B (32132-3531)
PHONE..................................386 566-3826
Bryon White,
EMP: 15 **EST:** 2021
SALES (est): 528.5K **Privately Held**
SIC: 2043 Coffee substitutes, made from grain

(G-3626)
ISLAMORADA BOATWORKS LLC
4501 S Ridgewood Ave (32141-7350)
PHONE..................................786 393-4752
Thomas Gordon, *Mng Member*
Jean Kayat, *Manager*
EMP: 8 **EST:** 2013
SALES (est): 738.9K **Privately Held**
WEB: www.islamoradaboatworks.com
SIC: 3732 Boat building & repairing

(G-3627)
JAS POWDER COATING LLC
1710 Industrial Ave (32132-3561)
PHONE..................................386 410-6675
EMP: 7 **EST:** 2017
SALES (est): 321.9K **Privately Held**
WEB: www.jaspowdercoating.com
SIC: 3479 Coating of metals & formed products

(G-3628)
JASMINE PURKISS ✪
Also Called: Satchel Group
2526 Hibiscus Dr 108-08 (32141-5004)
PHONE..................................386 244-7726
Jasmine Purkiss, *Principal*
EMP: 11 **EST:** 2020
SALES (est): 306.7K **Privately Held**
SIC: 3161 Satchels

(G-3629)
LEON LEATHER COMPANY INC
Also Called: Desperado Leather
3735 Us Highway 1 (32141-7234)
PHONE..................................386 304-1902
Andrew W Alcantara, *President*
Deborah S Alcantara, *Corp Secy*
▲ **EMP:** 10 **EST:** 1966
SALES (est): 729.1K **Privately Held**
WEB: www.leonleather.com
SIC: 3172 Personal leather goods

(G-3630)
LMN PRINTING CO INC
118 N Ridgewood Ave (32132-1721)
PHONE..................................386 428-9928
Nanette Amalfitano, *President*
Mary Carro, *Corp Secy*
Nora Aly, *Vice Pres*
Noreen Carro, *Vice Pres*
EMP: 18 **EST:** 1990
SQ FT: 2,000
SALES (est): 1.1MM **Privately Held**
WEB: www.lmn-printing.com
SIC: 2752 2731 Commercial printing, offset; book publishing

(G-3631)
MIL-SPEC METAL FINISHING INC
706 W Park Ave Ste A (32132-1412)
PHONE..................................386 426-7188
Isac Possato, *President*
Ronaldo Possato, *Director*
EMP: 6 **EST:** 1990
SALES (est): 1MM **Privately Held**
WEB: www.milspecmetalfinishing.com
SIC: 3471 Decorative plating & finishing of formed products

(G-3632)
PEACE LOVE & CBD
110 Silver Cir (32141-5117)
PHONE..................................386 409-0910
Donna Marie Nichols, *Principal*
EMP: 6 **EST:** 2018
SALES (est): 44.7K **Privately Held**
WEB: www.peaceloveandcbd.net
SIC: 3999

(G-3633)
PORTA PRODUCTS
200 Dale St (32132-1417)
PHONE..................................386 428-7656
Scott S Porta, *Principal*
EMP: 8 **EST:** 2008
SALES (est): 222.8K **Privately Held**
WEB: www.portaproducts.com
SIC: 3732 Motorboats, inboard or outboard: building & repairing

(G-3634)
PUZZLEME NOW INC
2230 Hibiscus Dr (32141-4702)
PHONE..................................386 957-4987
EMP: 6 **EST:** 2014
SALES (est): 223.2K **Privately Held**
SIC: 3944 Puzzles

(G-3635)
R J DOUGHERTY ASSOCIATES LLC
Also Called: Everglades Boats
544 Air Park Rd (32132-3043)
PHONE..................................386 409-2202
Thomas Flocco, *CEO*
Jorge Sotolongo, *Vice Pres*
Rubin Diaz, *QC Mgr*
Ashley Crawford, *Enginr/R&D Asst*
Brian Bohunicky, *CFO*
▼ **EMP:** 250 **EST:** 1997
SQ FT: 115,000
SALES (est): 50.4MM **Privately Held**
WEB: www.evergladesboats.com
SIC: 3732 Boats, fiberglass: building & repairing

(G-3636)
SOUTHERN GRAPHIC MACHINE LLC
3441 Juniper Dr (32141-6811)
PHONE..................................615 812-0778
Jason Black, *President*
EMP: 7
SALES (est): 2MM **Privately Held**
WEB: www.southerngraphic.com
SIC: 3555 Printing trades machinery

(G-3637)
TARMAC AMERICA INC
200 N Flagler Ave (32132-2152)
PHONE..................................386 427-0438
Kevin Shoemaker, *Principal*
EMP: 8 **EST:** 2001
SALES (est): 372.8K **Privately Held**
SIC: 3531 Mixers, concrete

(G-3638)
VIKING AIRCRAFT ENGINES
735 Air Park Rd 3c (32132-3013)
PHONE..................................386 416-8383
Jan L Eggenfellner, *Principal*
EMP: 7 **EST:** 2012
SALES (est): 1.3MM **Privately Held**
WEB: www.vikingaircraftengines.com
SIC: 3728 Aircraft parts & equipment

(G-3639)
WELDING LLC
23 Silver Cir (32141-5114)
PHONE..................................386 478-0323
Randy Bottos, *Principal*
EMP: 8
SALES (est): 88.7K **Privately Held**
SIC: 7692 Welding repair

Eglin A F B
Okaloosa County

(G-3640)
L3 TECHNOLOGIES INC
8th St Bldg 968 (32542)
PHONE..................................850 678-9444
Bill Masek, *Manager*
EMP: 6
SALES (corp-wide): 3.7B **Publicly Held**
WEB: www.l3harris.com
SIC: 3663 Telemetering equipment, electronic
HQ: L3 Technologies, Inc.
600 3rd Ave Fl 34
New York NY 10016
321 727-9100

Eglin Afb
Okaloosa County

(G-3641)
BOEING COMPANY
305 W Choctawhatchee Ave (32542-5701)
P.O. Box 1867 (32542-0867)
PHONE..................................850 882-4912
Robert Moreno, *Branch Mgr*
Jessie Farrington, *Manager*
EMP: 6
SALES (corp-wide): 58.1B **Publicly Held**
WEB: www.boeing.com
SIC: 3721 3663 3761 3764 Airplanes, fixed or rotary wing; helicopters; research & development on aircraft by the manufacturer; airborne radio communications equipment; guided missiles, complete; guided missiles & space vehicles, research & development; propulsion units for guided missiles & space vehicles; guided missile & space vehicle engines, research & devel.; search & navigation equipment; defense systems & equipment; aircraft control systems, electronic; navigational systems & instruments; aircraft body & wing assemblies & parts
PA: The Boeing Company
100 N Riverside Plz
Chicago IL 60606
312 544-2000

(G-3642)
EGLIN AIR FORCE BASE
205 W D Ave Ste 433 (32542-6887)
PHONE..................................850 882-5422
EMP: 66
SALES (corp-wide): 1.1MM **Privately Held**
WEB: www.eglin.af.mil
SIC: 2311 Military uniforms, men's & youths': purchased materials
PA: Eglin Air Force Base
207 W D Ave Ste 125
Eglin Afb FL 32542
850 882-3315

(G-3643)
EGLIN AIR FORCE BASE (PA) ✪
207 W D Ave Ste 125 (32542-6891)
PHONE..................................850 882-3315
Jonas Kemp, *President*
EMP: 116 **EST:** 2020
SALES (est): 1.1MM **Privately Held**
WEB: www.eglin.af.mil
SIC: 2311 Military uniforms, men's & youths': purchased materials

(G-3644)
JAMES TAYLOR ✪
Also Called: Eglin Aero Club
200 W Escambia Rd (32542-5306)
P.O. Box 1588 (32542-0588)
PHONE..................................850 882-5148
Gary Steel, *President*
Cindy Larkins, *Principal*
James Taylor, *Manager*
EMP: 10 **EST:** 2020
SALES (est): 367.6K **Privately Held**
SIC: 3699 Flight simulators (training aids), electronic

(G-3645)
LOCKHEED MARTIN CORPORATION
1404 Nomad Way (32542)
PHONE..................................850 885-3583
EMP: 6 **Publicly Held**
WEB: www.lockheedmartin.com
SIC: 3761 Space vehicles, complete
PA: Lockheed Martin Corporation
6801 Rockledge Dr
Bethesda MD 20817

(G-3646)
LOCKHEED TRAINING FACILITY
1001 Nomad Way Bldg 1404 (32542-6018)
PHONE..................................850 883-2144
EMP: 6 **EST:** 2018

SALES (est): 86K **Privately Held**
SIC: 3721 Aircraft

(G-3647)
RAYTHEON COMPANY
1003 N 2nd St Bldg 130 (32542-5473)
PHONE.................................850 882-8015
William Jefferson, *Principal*
EMP: 6
SALES (corp-wide): 56.5B **Publicly Held**
WEB: www.rtx.com
SIC: 3812 Sonar systems & equipment
HQ: Raytheon Company
870 Winter St
Waltham MA 02451
781 522-3000

Elkton
St. Johns County

(G-3648)
CONAGRA BRANDS INC
Also Called: Conagra Snack Foods
3660 Deerpark Blvd (32033-4019)
PHONE.................................904 417-0964
Christopher Brantley, *Branch Mgr*
EMP: 7
SALES (corp-wide): 11.1B **Publicly Held**
WEB: www.conagrabrands.com
SIC: 2099 Food preparations
PA: Conagra Brands, Inc.
222 Mdse Mart Plz Ste 1
Chicago IL 60654
312 549-5000

(G-3649)
MAS HVAC INC
4010 Deerpark Blvd (32033-2060)
PHONE.................................904 531-3140
Robert Story, *President*
Mitchell Tatar, *Principal*
Ryan Grey, *Engineer*
Matt Kent, *Project Engr*
Daryl Showalter, *VP Bus Dvlpt*
EMP: 14 **EST:** 2010
SQ FT: 2,000
SALES (est): 5.5MM **Privately Held**
WEB: www.mas-hvac.com
SIC: 3585 Air conditioning equipment, complete

(G-3650)
PREFORM LLC
3845 Deerpark Blvd (32033-4063)
PHONE.................................888 826-5161
Helmut Makosch, *Vice Pres*
Judy Welker, *Manager*
Susan Wacha,
EMP: 16 **EST:** 2016
SALES (est): 3.1MM **Privately Held**
WEB: www.preform.us
SIC: 2821 Thermosetting materials

(G-3651)
Q-PAC SYSTEMS INC
4010 Deerpark Blvd (32033-2060)
PHONE.................................229 834-2908
Clark Story, *Principal*
Mathew Kent, *Principal*
Mitchell Tatar, *Principal*
EMP: 30 **EST:** 2014
SQ FT: 2,000
SALES (est): 3.8MM **Privately Held**
WEB: www.q-pac.com
SIC: 3564 Blowers & fans

(G-3652)
VINO DEL GROTTO
4758 Coquina Crossing Dr (32033-4002)
PHONE.................................321 508-1478
Gregory James Good, *Owner*
EMP: 7 **EST:** 2009
SALES (est): 366.6K **Privately Held**
WEB: www.vinodelgrottostaugustine.com
SIC: 2084 Wines

Ellenton
Manatee County

(G-3653)
EASYTURF INC
3203 Us Highway 301 N (34222-2121)
PHONE.................................941 753-3312
EMP: 12
SALES (corp-wide): 354.7K **Privately Held**
WEB: www.easyturf.com
SIC: 3999 0782 1799 Grasses, artificial & preserved; lawn & garden services; artificial turf installation
HQ: Easyturf, Inc.
175 N Industrial Blvd Ne
Calhoun GA 30701
760 745-7026

(G-3654)
PCI COMMUNICATIONS INC
1202 Gary Ave Unit 113 (34222-2012)
P.O. Box 161 (34222-0161)
PHONE.................................941 729-5202
Mark Hildabrandt, *President*
Sam Henson, *Manager*
EMP: 5 **EST:** 1973
SQ FT: 4,000
SALES (est): 565.3K **Privately Held**
WEB: www.pci-directories.com
SIC: 2721 2752 Magazines: publishing only, not printed on site; commercial printing, offset

(G-3655)
SUN CITY BLINDS LLC (PA)
2426 63rd Ter E (34222-2218)
PHONE.................................727 522-6695
EMP: 19 **EST:** 2019
SALES (est): 114.9K **Privately Held**
SIC: 2591 Window blinds

Eloise
Polk County

(G-3656)
UNITED FABRICATION & MAINT
622 Snively Ave (33880-5543)
P.O. Box 399, Eagle Lake (33839-0399)
PHONE.................................863 295-9000
Don Smith, *President*
EMP: 7 **EST:** 1988
SQ FT: 12,000
SALES (est): 1.4MM **Privately Held**
SIC: 3441 1791 Fabricated structural metal; structural steel erection

Englewood
Charlotte County

(G-3657)
ADVANCE CTRL MFG JEAN ANNETTE
9161 Cherry Dr (34224-8942)
PHONE.................................941 697-0846
Lyn Pack, *President*
Gene Pack, *Admin Sec*
EMP: 6 **EST:** 2016
SALES (est): 500K **Privately Held**
SIC: 3625 Relays & industrial controls

(G-3658)
AERO-MARINE TECHNOLOGIES INC
2800 Placida Rd Ste 103 (34224-5576)
PHONE.................................941 205-5420
Joseph N Vaughn, *President*
Theresa L Vaughn, *Corp Secy*
Ethan Fischer, *Vice Pres*
Andrew Etheridge, *Opers Staff*
Terri Vaughn, *CFO*
EMP: 6 **EST:** 1991
SALES (est): 1.1MM **Privately Held**
WEB: www.aero-marinetechnologies.com
SIC: 3599 5088 Machine shop, jobbing & repair; aeronautical equipment & supplies

(G-3659)
CUSTOM STUCCO INC
1921 Michigan Ave (34224-5424)
PHONE.................................941 650-5649
Stephen Heuss, *President*
EMP: 9 **EST:** 2010
SALES (est): 476K **Privately Held**
SIC: 3299 Stucco

(G-3660)
GRAFICO INDUSTRIES INC
7211 Waters Way (34224-8915)
PHONE.................................941 473-2800
Audrey L Lanczki, *President*
EMP: 6 **EST:** 2011
SALES (est): 103.4K **Privately Held**
WEB: www.graficoindustries.com
SIC: 3999 Manufacturing industries

(G-3661)
HARTMANS PRINT CENTER INC
2828 S Mccall Rd Ste 37 (34224-9518)
PHONE.................................941 475-2220
Jim Hartman, *President*
Pat Hartman, *Vice Pres*
EMP: 5 **EST:** 2000
SALES (est): 505.7K **Privately Held**
WEB: www.hartmansprintcenter.com
SIC: 2752 Commercial printing, offset

(G-3662)
KING HAN INC
Also Called: Kings Han Manufacturing
3725 S Access Rd Ste C (34224-7774)
PHONE.................................860 933-8574
Paul Robertson, *President*
Tokcha Robertson, *Owner*
EMP: 5 **EST:** 1997
SQ FT: 2,000
SALES (est): 963K **Privately Held**
WEB: www.kinghaninc.com
SIC: 3825 Frequency meters: electrical, mechanical & electronic

(G-3663)
OMNI MARINE ENTERPRISES LLC
2640 S Mccall Rd (34224-8499)
PHONE.................................941 474-4614
EMP: 6 **EST:** 2019
SALES (est): 369.4K **Privately Held**
WEB: www.omnimarinefl.com
SIC: 7692 Welding repair

(G-3664)
PREMIER TEES
2780 Worth Ave (34224-9159)
PHONE.................................941 681-2688
John Mead, *Owner*
EMP: 7 **EST:** 2010
SALES (est): 185.4K **Privately Held**
WEB: www.premierteesfl.com
SIC: 2759 Screen printing

(G-3665)
QUALITY SOCKET SCREW MFG CORP
2790 Worth Ave (34224-9159)
PHONE.................................941 475-9585
Jean P Feustel, *President*
Tom Feustel, *Vice Pres*
Nancy Cooper, *Bookkeeper*
Rich Saccoccio, *Manager*
EMP: 15 **EST:** 1970
SQ FT: 10,000
SALES (est): 2.4MM **Privately Held**
WEB: www.qualitysocket.com
SIC: 3452 Screws, metal

(G-3666)
RELIABLE CABINET DESIGNS
6900 San Casa Dr Unit 1 (34224-7929)
PHONE.................................941 473-3403
Jerry Weddle, *Owner*
Patti Weddle, *Owner*
Shane Whitmore, *Vice Pres*
EMP: 10 **EST:** 2004
SALES (est): 790K **Privately Held**
WEB: www.reliablecabinetdesigns.com
SIC: 2434 Wood kitchen cabinets

(G-3667)
SOUTHWEST SIGNAL INC
1984 Georgia Ave (34224-5414)
PHONE.................................813 621-4949
Kevin Fitzgerald, *President*
Pam Fitzgerald, *Vice Pres*
EMP: 31 **EST:** 2000
SALES (est): 2.2MM **Privately Held**
SIC: 3648 3669 Street lighting fixtures; traffic signals, electric

(G-3668)
STYLECRAFT CABINETS MFG INC
2780 Ivy St Unit 1 (34224-7773)
PHONE.................................941 474-4824
Larry Carvey, *Corp Secy*
EMP: 9 **EST:** 2018
SQ FT: 11,000
SALES (est): 835.7K **Privately Held**
WEB: www.stylecraftcabinetry.com
SIC: 2434 Wood kitchen cabinets

(G-3669)
TROY INDUSTRIES LLC
6733 Greenview Ln (34224-7658)
PHONE.................................401 241-4231
EMP: 8 **EST:** 2017
SALES (est): 190.7K **Privately Held**
WEB: www.troyindustries.com
SIC: 3999 Manufacturing industries

Englewood
Sarasota County

(G-3670)
CABINET GUY OF ENGLEWOOD INC
150 S Mccall Rd (34223-3233)
PHONE.................................941 475-9454
Barry Saxman, *President*
EMP: 8 **EST:** 2008
SALES (est): 948K **Privately Held**
WEB: www.thecabinetguyenglewood.com
SIC: 2434 Wood kitchen cabinets

(G-3671)
CAR CARE HAVEN LLC
505 Paul Morris Dr (34223-3961)
PHONE.................................855 464-2836
Matthew Bonwill, *CEO*
Nick Obirek, *Mng Member*
Adam Perry, *Mng Member*
EMP: 5 **EST:** 2019
SALES (est): 399.6K **Privately Held**
SIC: 2842 2851 2221 5999 Automobile polish; marine paints; fiberglass fabrics; fiberglass materials, except insulation; polyurethane resins; water, pasteurized: packaged in cans, bottles, etc.

(G-3672)
CATANIAS WINERY LLC
524 Paul Morris Dr Ste B (34223-3972)
PHONE.................................941 321-9650
John Catania Sr, *Principal*
John S Catania, *Manager*
EMP: 5 **EST:** 2010
SALES (est): 300.1K **Privately Held**
WEB: www.cataniaswinery.com
SIC: 2084 Wines

(G-3673)
CINIDYNE SALES INC
1811 Englewood Rd (34223-1822)
PHONE.................................941 473-3914
Edward B Brewer, *Principal*
EMP: 6 **EST:** 2007
SALES (est): 805.6K **Privately Held**
WEB: www.cinidyne.com
SIC: 3861 Photographic equipment & supplies

(G-3674)
CRYSTAL PANEPINTO INC
667 Palomino Trl (34223-3986)
PHONE.................................941 475-9235
Dennis Panepinto, *President*
Donna Panepinto, *Vice Pres*
▲ **EMP:** 8 **EST:** 1989
SALES (est): 164.4K **Privately Held**
SIC: 2431 Windows & window parts & trim, wood

GEOGRAPHIC

(G-3675)
DRAB TO FAB
136 S Mccall Rd (34223-3251)
PHONE....................................941 475-7700
Elizabeth Williams, *Principal*
EMP: 8 **EST:** 2007
SALES (est): 171.4K **Privately Held**
SIC: 2273 Carpets & rugs

(G-3676)
ESSENTIAL OIL UNIVERSITY LLC
Also Called: Perfumery, The
6150 Manasota Key Rd (34223-9253)
PHONE....................................502 498-8804
Robert Pappas PHD, *Mng Member*
▲ **EMP:** 6 **EST:** 2001
SALES (est): 716.8K **Privately Held**
WEB: www.essentialoils.org
SIC: 2869 Perfumes, flavorings & food additives

(G-3677)
FLORIDA HARBOR HOMES INC
850 Bayshore Dr (34223-2202)
PHONE....................................941 284-8363
Russell W Philbrick, *Principal*
EMP: 14 **EST:** 2008
SALES (est): 323.9K **Privately Held**
SIC: 2451 Mobile homes, personal or private use

(G-3678)
HIGHTEC CON PAVERS & CURBING
290 E Langsner St (34223-3447)
PHONE....................................941 412-6077
Darrell Ray Whisler, *Principal*
EMP: 6 **EST:** 2010
SALES (est): 96.1K **Privately Held**
SIC: 3531 Pavers

(G-3679)
IDENTITY STRONGHOLD LLC
563 Paul Morris Dr Unit B (34223-3928)
PHONE....................................941 475-8480
Ted Whitaker, *President*
Mike Lampros, *Sales Staff*
Steven Crimaudo, *Marketing Staff*
Walt Augustinowicz,
▲ **EMP:** 22 **EST:** 2005
SALES (est): 5.6MM **Privately Held**
WEB: www.idstronghold.com
SIC: 3172 5099 Card cases; cases, carrying

(G-3680)
MILLIKEN & MILLIKEN INC
Also Called: Milliken Industries
101 S Mccall Rd (34223-3227)
PHONE....................................941 474-0223
Les Milliken, *CEO*
Shawn Milliken, *President*
Carol M Milliken, *Vice Pres*
▲ **EMP:** 33 **EST:** 1981
SQ FT: 133,000
SALES (est): 5MM **Privately Held**
SIC: 2394 3993 5999 Awnings, fabric: made from purchased materials; signs & advertising specialties; awnings

(G-3681)
RENAISSANCE ENTP GROUP LLC
155 W Dearborn St (34223-3236)
PHONE....................................941 284-7854
Trevor E Charnley, *Principal*
EMP: 5 **EST:** 2008
SALES (est): 549K **Privately Held**
SIC: 3272 Columns, concrete

(G-3682)
REVIEW NEWSPAPERS
370 W Dearborn St Ste B (34223-3167)
PHONE....................................941 474-4351
Tom Newton, *Owner*
Marilyn Johnson, *Sales Staff*
EMP: 6 **EST:** 2004
SALES (est): 229.9K **Privately Held**
SIC: 2711 Newspapers: publishing only, not printed on site

(G-3683)
SHORT STOP PRINT INC
1101 S Mccall Rd Unit A (34223-4233)
PHONE....................................941 474-4313
Gratia Schroeder, *President*
EMP: 6 **EST:** 1982
SQ FT: 2,662
SALES (est): 775.6K **Privately Held**
WEB: www.shortstopprinting.com
SIC: 2752 Commercial printing, offset

(G-3684)
SUN COAST MEDIA GROUP INC
Also Called: Englewood Sun Herald
120 W Dearborn St (34223-3237)
PHONE....................................941 681-3000
Lang Capasso, *Manager*
EMP: 27
SALES (corp-wide): 333.5MM **Privately Held**
WEB: www.yoursun.com
SIC: 2711 Newspapers, publishing & printing
HQ: Sun Coast Media Group, Inc.
23170 Harborview Rd
Port Charlotte FL 33980
941 206-1300

(G-3685)
TOMSONS INC (PA)
6520 Manasota Key Rd (34223-9211)
PHONE....................................248 646-0677
Thomas J Connaughton, *President*
Fay E Stuart, *Admin Sec*
▲ **EMP:** 5 **EST:** 1981
SALES (est): 24.3MM **Privately Held**
SIC: 3069 3089 2741 Hard rubber & molded rubber products; injection molding of plastics; technical manuals: publishing only, not printed on site

Estero
Lee County

(G-3686)
ARTISTIC LABEL COMPANY INC
20050 Sgrove St Unit 1703 (33928)
PHONE....................................401 737-0666
Ellen Kaplan, *President*
EMP: 5 **EST:** 1966
SALES (est): 363K **Privately Held**
WEB: www.artisticlabelcoinc.com
SIC: 2752 Commercial printing, lithographic

(G-3687)
CIMA ACTIVEWEAR LLC
23124 Marsh Landing Blvd (33928-4384)
PHONE....................................239 273-6055
Vanessa Valdes,
EMP: 7 **EST:** 2015
SALES (est): 128.4K **Privately Held**
WEB: www.cimaactivewear.com
SIC: 2339 7389 Women's & misses' athletic clothing & sportswear;

(G-3688)
ESTERO FL
23191 Fashion Dr Unit 309 (33928-2596)
PHONE....................................239 289-9511
EMP: 7 **EST:** 2017
SALES (est): 101.2K **Privately Held**
WEB: www.estero-fl.gov
SIC: 2079 Olive oil

(G-3689)
FLORIDA WEST POGGENPOHL
10800 Corkscrew Rd # 105 (33928-9426)
PHONE....................................239 948-9005
Tony Mannoliti, *President*
EMP: 5 **EST:** 2005
SALES (est): 2MM **Privately Held**
WEB: www.floridacabinets.com
SIC: 2434 Wood kitchen cabinets

(G-3690)
FUEL N GO LLC
10351 Corkscrew Rd (33928-9414)
PHONE....................................239 656-1072
Christian Defilippis, *Owner*
EMP: 7 **EST:** 2009
SALES (est): 328.7K **Privately Held**
SIC: 2869 Fuels

(G-3691)
IMPORTED YARNS LLC
Also Called: Carotex
21561 Pelican Sound Dr # 101 (33928-8935)
PHONE....................................239 405-2974
Mike Cooke,
▲ **EMP:** 7 **EST:** 1999
SALES (est): 6.5MM **Privately Held**
SIC: 2299 7389 Hemp yarn, thread, roving & textiles; brokers, contract services

(G-3692)
NAPLES HMA LLC
Also Called: Physicians Regional - Pine
24231 Walden Center Dr # 201 (34134-5013)
PHONE....................................239 390-2174
C Scott Campbell, *CEO*
Timothy R Parry, *Principal*
EMP: 10 **EST:** 2010
SALES (est): 150.5K **Privately Held**
SIC: 3452 Pins

(G-3693)
PICA SALES AND ENGINEERING
19771 Chapel Trce (33928-1916)
PHONE....................................239 992-9079
EMP: 6
SALES (est): 2.2MM **Privately Held**
SIC: 3672 Mfg Printed Circuit Boards

(G-3694)
RCC CONVEYORS INC (PA)
21569 Oaks Of Estero Cir (33928-3324)
PHONE....................................224 338-8841
Roland Malschafsky, *President*
EMP: 12 **EST:** 2014
SALES (est): 254.8K **Privately Held**
WEB: www.rccc-usa.com
SIC: 3559 Automotive related machinery

(G-3695)
RUGGED INDUSTRIES INC
20041 Legacy Ct (33928-7613)
PHONE....................................239 565-2723
Carl Bierbaum, *Principal*
EMP: 6 **EST:** 2013
SALES (est): 106.3K **Privately Held**
WEB: www.ruggedind.com
SIC: 3999 Manufacturing industries

(G-3696)
SHOWERFLOSS INC
20930 Persimmon Pl (33928-2253)
P.O. Box 3121, Peachtree City GA (30269-7121)
PHONE....................................239 947-2855
Clyde Stewart, *President*
Jill Bauman, *Manager*
EMP: 9 **EST:** 1986
SALES (est): 459.5K **Privately Held**
WEB: www.showerfloss.com
SIC: 3843 Dental equipment & supplies

(G-3697)
STAGEXCHANGE
9156 Estero River Cir (33928-4415)
PHONE....................................239 200-9226
Keith Hopkins, *Principal*
EMP: 6 **EST:** 2016
SALES (est): 132.1K **Privately Held**
WEB: www.teleostbio.com
SIC: 2834 Pharmaceutical preparations

(G-3698)
VISOR VERSA
9510 Coralee Ave (33928-3212)
PHONE....................................239 249-4745
Lori Jo Taylor, *Principal*
Lori Taylor, *Principal*
EMP: 6 **EST:** 2009
SALES (est): 131.3K **Privately Held**
WEB: www.visorversa.com
SIC: 3949 Sporting & athletic goods

Eustis
Lake County

(G-3699)
A LIVING TESTIMONY LLC
Also Called: La Physique'
2119 Bates Ave (32726-3905)
PHONE....................................352 406-0249
Rheba C Turnbull, *Principal*
EMP: 6 **EST:** 2010
SALES (est): 309.2K **Privately Held**
SIC: 2339 Women's & misses' outerwear

(G-3700)
ADVANCED PROSTHETICS AMER INC (DH)
Also Called: Advanced Prosthetics America
601 Mount Homer Rd (32726-6261)
PHONE....................................352 383-0396
Vinit Asar, *CEO*
Samuel M Liang, *President*
EMP: 10 **EST:** 1985
SQ FT: 6,500
SALES (est): 9.3MM
SALES (corp-wide): 1B **Publicly Held**
WEB: www.hangerclinic.com
SIC: 3842 8049 5999 7352 Limbs, artificial; physical therapist; medical apparatus & supplies; medical equipment rental; invalid supplies rental
HQ: Hanger Prosthetics & Orthotics, Inc.
10910 Domain Dr Ste 300
Austin TX 78758
512 777-3800

(G-3701)
AERO DOOR INTERNATIONAL LLC
2770 Dillard Rd (32726-6281)
PHONE....................................407 654-0591
Tara Grey, *General Mgr*
Williams F Mathews,
Paul Blake, *Administration*
John Mathews,
EMP: 13 **EST:** 2011
SALES (est): 1.8MM **Privately Held**
WEB: www.hangardoors.aero
SIC: 3442 Metal doors, sash & trim

(G-3702)
ALL AMERICAN AMPUTEE
601 Mount Homer Rd (32726-6261)
PHONE....................................352 383-0396
Rod Friedland, *CEO*
EMP: 6 **EST:** 1998
SALES (est): 97.1K **Privately Held**
SIC: 3842 Prosthetic appliances

(G-3703)
BILLS PRESTIGE PRINTING INC
640 S Bay St (32726-4860)
PHONE....................................352 589-5833
Bill Honnig, *President*
EMP: 6 **EST:** 1989
SQ FT: 1,000
SALES (est): 560.5K **Privately Held**
WEB: www.billsprestigeprinting.com
SIC: 2759 2752 Commercial printing; commercial printing, lithographic

(G-3704)
C & S FOLIAGE
34910 County Road 439 (32736-9437)
PHONE....................................352 357-4847
Gary Weyers, *Director*
EMP: 6 **EST:** 2005
SALES (est): 91.8K **Privately Held**
SIC: 2499 Wood products

(G-3705)
CBD LIFE FLORIDA INC
3109 Kurt St (32726-6528)
PHONE....................................352 483-8333
Jason C Rein, *Principal*
EMP: 6 **EST:** 2018
SALES (est): 107.8K **Privately Held**
SIC: 3999

(G-3706)
COUNTER IMPRESSIONS LLC
12 S Bay St (32726-4016)
PHONE....................................352 589-4966
Matthew Wilson, *Mng Member*

▲ = Import ▼=Export
◆ =Import/Export

EMP: 10 EST: 2011
SALES (est): 710.4K Privately Held
WEB: www.mycounterimpressions.com
SIC: 3131 Counters

(G-3707)
FLORIDA FOOD PRODUCTS LLC (PA)
2231 W County Road 44 # 1 (32726-2628)
P.O. Box 1300 (32727-1300)
PHONE..................................352 357-4141
Thomas H Brown, *Vice Pres*
Pavan Soma, *Research*
Gerard Bernard, *CFO*
Hannah Mohrenne, *Sales Staff*
Deb Osborne, *Mktg Coord*
◆ EMP: 93 EST: 1954
SQ FT: 160,000
SALES (est): 43.4MM Privately Held
WEB: www.floridafood.com
SIC: 2037 2033 Fruit juices, frozen; vegetable juices: packaged in cans, jars, etc.

(G-3708)
GREEN FUEL SYSTEMS LLC
24745 Lester Way (32736-8473)
PHONE..................................352 483-5005
Douglas E Johnson Jr, *Principal*
EMP: 8 EST: 2008
SALES (est): 391.1K Privately Held
SIC: 2869 Fuels

(G-3709)
INSIGHT CABINETRY LLC
2210 Grant Ave (32726-3208)
PHONE..................................352 818-9708
Crystal Lozenski, *Principal*
EMP: 6 EST: 2015
SALES (est): 171.9K Privately Held
SIC: 2434 Wood kitchen cabinets

(G-3710)
JAMES O CORBETT INC
Also Called: Afab Enterprises
2151 W County Road 44 (32726-2650)
PHONE..................................352 483-1222
James O Corbett, *President*
Sidney Davis, *Treasurer*
EMP: 8 EST: 1992
SQ FT: 6,000
SALES (est): 976.6K Privately Held
WEB: www.afab-ent.com
SIC: 3823 7699 3829 Industrial process control instruments; industrial equipment services; measuring & controlling devices

(G-3711)
KEVCO BUILDERS INC
Also Called: Trim Spot
2104 S Bay St (32726-6357)
P.O. Box 1267, Tavares (32778-1267)
PHONE..................................352 308-8025
Kevin Burkholder, *President*
Gloria Burkholder, *Corp Secy*
EMP: 12 EST: 1980
SQ FT: 6,000
SALES (est): 1MM Privately Held
WEB: www.kevcobuilders.com
SIC: 2431 1521 1751 3442 Doors & door parts & trim, wood; general remodeling, single-family houses; carpentry work; metal doors, sash & trim

(G-3712)
LAKE DOOR AND TRIM INC
1589 Pine Grove Rd (32726-5310)
P.O. Box 449 (32727-0449)
PHONE..................................352 589-5566
Bobby Green, *President*
Karen Green, *Corp Secy*
Don Allison, *Vice Pres*
EMP: 10 EST: 1982
SQ FT: 18,000
SALES (est): 974.5K Privately Held
SIC: 2431 3442 Doors, wood; trim, wood; moldings, wood: unfinished & prefinished; metal doors

(G-3713)
MFT STAMPS
Also Called: My Favorite Things
132 E Magnolia Ave (32726-3418)
PHONE..................................352 360-5797
EMP: 7 EST: 2017
SALES (est): 689.3K Privately Held
WEB: www.mftstamps.com
SIC: 3999 Manufacturing industries

(G-3714)
MJR ENTERPRISES INC
1895 Irma Rd (32726-7136)
PHONE..................................352 483-0735
Michael J Reischmann, *Director*
EMP: 7 EST: 2001
SALES (est): 15.3K Privately Held
WEB: www.mjrcorpusa.com
SIC: 3229 5023 Pressed & blown glass; glassware

(G-3715)
NATIONAL BEVERAGE CORP
Also Called: Shasta Beverages
2221 W Highway 44 (32726-2604)
PHONE..................................352 357-7130
Dennis Darvy, *Opers-Prdtn-Mfg*
EMP: 6
SALES (corp-wide): 1B Publicly Held
WEB: www.nationalbeverage.com
SIC: 2086 Soft drinks: packaged in cans, bottles, etc.
PA: National Beverage Corp.
8100 Sw 10th St Ste 4000
Plantation FL 33324
954 581-0922

(G-3716)
RCD CORPORATION
Also Called: Manufacturer - Distributor
2850 Dillard Rd (32726-6292)
PHONE..................................352 589-0099
Kevin Brogan, *President*
▼ EMP: 9 EST: 1958
SQ FT: 12,000
SALES (est): 3.5MM Privately Held
WEB: www.rcdmastics.com
SIC: 2891 Adhesives & sealants

(G-3717)
STOLLER CHEMICAL CO OF FLORIDA
1451 Pine Grove Rd (32726-5317)
PHONE..................................352 357-3173
Jerry Stoller, *President*
▲ EMP: 10 EST: 1965
SQ FT: 1,200
SALES (est): 481.3K Privately Held
SIC: 2873 Nitrogenous fertilizers

(G-3718)
TIP TOPS OF AMERICA INC
100 S Bay St (32726-4002)
PHONE..................................352 357-9559
James R Budzynski, *CEO*
EMP: 13 EST: 1993
SALES (est): 1.3MM Privately Held
WEB: www.tiptops.com
SIC: 2759 Screen printing

(G-3719)
TIPTOPS INC
100 S Bay St (32726-4002)
PHONE..................................352 357-9559
Marilyn Budzynski, *CEO*
EMP: 8 EST: 1982
SQ FT: 2,000
SALES (est): 650K Privately Held
WEB: www.tiptops.com
SIC: 2396 Screen printing on fabric articles

(G-3720)
US NUTRACEUTICALS INC
Also Called: Valensa International
2751 Nutra Ln (32726-6961)
PHONE..................................352 357-2004
Bill Donovan, *Senior VP*
Anup Chib, *Director*
Muthiah Murugappan, *Director*
Umasudhan Palaniswamy, *Director*
V Ravichandran, *Director*
▲ EMP: 25 EST: 1998
SQ FT: 31,000
SALES (est): 8.9MM Privately Held
WEB: www.valensa.com
SIC: 2833 Alkaloids & other botanical based products
PA: E.I.D Parry (India) Limited
Dare House, New No.2, Old 234,
Chennai TN 60000

Fanning Springs
Gilchrist County

(G-3721)
A MATERIALS GROUP INC
Also Called: Trinity Materials
8191 Nw 160th St (32693-7058)
P.O. Box 2209, Trenton (32693-2181)
PHONE..................................352 463-1254
Doug Anderson, *President*
EMP: 9
SQ FT: 784
SALES (corp-wide): 6.3MM Privately Held
SIC: 3273 Ready-mixed concrete
PA: A Materials Group, Inc.
871 Nw Guerdon St
Lake City FL 32055
386 758-3164

Felda
Hendry County

(G-3722)
PLANTATION BOTANICALS INC
1401 County Rd Ste 830 (33930)
P.O. Box 128 (33930-0128)
PHONE..................................863 675-2984
Michael Huffman, *President*
Eva Huffman, *Vice Pres*
EMP: 23 EST: 1964
SALES (est): 1.1MM Privately Held
WEB: www.plantationmedicinals.com
SIC: 2833 2048 Botanical products, medicinal: ground, graded or milled; prepared feeds

(G-3723)
PLANTATION MEDICINALS INC
1401 County Rd Ste 830 (33930)
P.O. Box 128 (33930-0128)
PHONE..................................863 675-2984
Michael D Huffman, *President*
Eva Huffman, *Corp Secy*
EMP: 12 EST: 1995
SALES (est): 185.8K Privately Held
SIC: 2833 Botanical products, medicinal: ground, graded or milled

(G-3724)
SOUTHWEST PRECISION AG INC
14960 S Sr 29 (33930)
P.O. Box 511 (33930-0511)
PHONE..................................863 674-5799
David Rogers, *President*
Leah Nees, *Office Mgr*
EMP: 9 EST: 2013
SALES (est): 422.6K Privately Held
SIC: 3531 Plows: construction, excavating & grading

Fellsmere
Indian River County

(G-3725)
F T F CONSTRUCTION COMPANY
Also Called: Antiquo Stone By F T F
25 N Myrtle St (32948-7630)
PHONE..................................772 571-1850
Francesco Fornabaio, *President*
Michelle Fornabaio, *Vice Pres*
EMP: 18 EST: 1978
SALES (est): 526.2K Privately Held
SIC: 3272 1521 3281 Concrete products, precast; single-family housing construction; cut stone & stone products

(G-3726)
GAP ANTENNA PRODUCTS INC
99 N Willow St (32948-5334)
PHONE..................................772 571-9922
Richard Henf, *Owner*
Chris Lane, *MIS Dir*
EMP: 8 EST: 1988
SQ FT: 3,000
SALES (est): 864.3K Privately Held
WEB: www.gapantenna.com
SIC: 3663 Radio & TV communications equipment

Fern Park
Seminole County

(G-3727)
ADVANCED TYPESETTING
207 Obrien Rd Ste 101 (32730-2838)
PHONE..................................407 834-1741
Jeffs Kaeser, *Owner*
EMP: 6 EST: 2011
SALES (est): 266K Privately Held
SIC: 2791 Typesetting

(G-3728)
FLEETBOSS GLOBL PSTNING SLTONS
241 Obrien Rd (32730-2802)
PHONE..................................407 265-9559
Larry Carroll, *CEO*
Brian Carroll, *President*
Floyd Honeycutt, *Vice Pres*
Dan Lee, *Mktg Dir*
EMP: 23 EST: 1998
SALES (est): 1.6MM Privately Held
WEB: www.fleetboss.com
SIC: 3663

(G-3729)
HERITAGE CENTL FLA JEWISH NEWS
Also Called: Heritage Newspaper
207 Obrien Rd Ste 101 (32730-2838)
P.O. Box 300742, Casselberry (32730-0742)
PHONE..................................407 834-8277
Jeff Gaeser, *President*
EMP: 10 EST: 1976
SQ FT: 1,100
SALES (est): 753.8K Privately Held
WEB: www.heritagefl.com
SIC: 2752 2711 Newspapers, lithographed only; newspapers, publishing & printing

Fernandina Beach
Nassau County

(G-3730)
ALL POWER PRO INC
995 Egans Creek Ln (32034-5137)
PHONE..................................904 310-3069
Marcin Laura Ann, *Vice Pres*
EMP: 7 EST: 2013
SALES (est): 515.9K Privately Held
WEB: www.all-powerpro.com
SIC: 3621 3585 8741 5084 Motors & generators; refrigeration & heating equipment; management services; engines & parts, diesel; engines, gasoline

(G-3731)
AMELIA ISLAND GRAPHICS
2244 S 8th St (32034-3097)
PHONE..................................904 261-0740
Tony Baia, *Owner*
EMP: 6 EST: 1982
SALES (est): 555.2K Privately Held
WEB: www.ameliaislandgraphics.com
SIC: 2759 7336 Commercial printing; graphic arts & related design

(G-3732)
CARIBBEAN BREEZE INC
1438 E Oak St (32034-4726)
P.O. Box 15849 (32035-3115)
PHONE..................................904 261-7831
David Capps, *President*
Art Adams, *Vice Pres*
Carolyn Capps, *Office Mgr*
▼ EMP: 8 EST: 1992
SALES (est): 2.6MM Privately Held
WEB: www.caribbeanbreeze.com
SIC: 2844 Cosmetic preparations; suntan lotions & oils

GEOGRAPHIC

(G-3733)
COSMETIC CREATIONS INC
1438 E Oak St (32034-4726)
P.O. Box 15849 (32035-3115)
PHONE....................................904 261-7831
Carolyn Capps, *President*
EMP: 7 **EST:** 2014
SALES (est): 905.5K **Privately Held**
WEB: www.cosmeticcreationsspa.com
SIC: 2844 Toilet preparations

(G-3734)
DESIGN IT WRAPS & GRAPHICS LLC
2873 Jamestown Rd (32034-5205)
PHONE....................................904 310-6032
Brent D Knott, *Mng Member*
EMP: 6 **EST:** 2015
SALES (est): 149.1K **Privately Held**
WEB: www.designitgraphics.com
SIC: 3993 Signs & advertising specialties

(G-3735)
DIVERSIFIED PALLETS INC
1894 S 14th St Ste 2 (32034-4717)
PHONE....................................904 491-6800
Ivey Crump Sr, *Principal*
EMP: 10 **EST:** 2007
SALES (est): 170.2K **Privately Held**
SIC: 2448 Pallets, wood & wood with metal

(G-3736)
EARTH VETS INC
96093 Marsh Lakes Dr (32034-0825)
PHONE....................................352 332-9991
Robert Spiegel, *Owner*
EMP: 7 **EST:** 2007
SALES (est): 121.7K **Privately Held**
SIC: 3841 Veterinarians' instruments & apparatus

(G-3737)
ENGINETICS
5142 Sea Chase Dr Unit 5 (32034-5772)
PHONE....................................305 695-8000
EMP: 12 **EST:** 2009
SALES (est): 131.3K **Privately Held**
WEB: www.jp-ice.com
SIC: 3599 Machine shop, jobbing & repair

(G-3738)
FERNANDINA OBSERVER INC
205 Lighthouse Cir (32034-2533)
PHONE....................................904 261-4372
Susan Hardee Steger, *President*
EMP: 8 **EST:** 2016
SALES (est): 93.8K **Privately Held**
WEB: www.fernandinaobserver.com
SIC: 2711 Newspapers

(G-3739)
ISLAND MEDIA PUBLISHING LLC
120 N 15th St (32034-3100)
PHONE....................................904 556-3002
Robert Hicks, *Manager*
▲ **EMP:** 7 **EST:** 2010
SALES (est): 255.5K **Privately Held**
SIC: 2741 Miscellaneous publishing

(G-3740)
JOHN TRENT CONSTRUCTION LLC
1831 Windswept Oak Ln (32034-8996)
PHONE....................................904 753-2942
John Trent, *Mng Member*
Michael Trent,
EMP: 6 **EST:** 2006
SALES (est): 293.2K **Privately Held**
SIC: 3469 Tile, floor or wall: stamped metal

(G-3741)
JOHNSONS MANAGEMENT GROUP INC
1485 S 8th St (32034-3076)
PHONE....................................904 261-4044
Samuel Johnson, *President*
EMP: 7 **EST:** 2003
SQ FT: 1,700
SALES (est): 579.1K **Privately Held**
SIC: 3714 Motor vehicle parts & accessories

(G-3742)
LIGNOTECH FLORIDA LLC
6 Gum St (32034-4280)
P.O. Box 16839 (32035-3131)
PHONE....................................904 577-9077
Peter Morris, *Mng Member*
EMP: 30 **EST:** 2015
SALES (est): 10.3MM
SALES (corp-wide): 1.7B **Publicly Held**
WEB: www.rayonieram.com
SIC: 2861 Gum & wood chemicals
PA: Rayonier Advanced Materials Inc.
1301 Riverplace Blvd # 23
Jacksonville FL 32207
904 357-4600

(G-3743)
MARLIN & BARREL DISTILLERY LLC
115 S 2nd St (32034-4670)
PHONE....................................321 230-4755
Roger Morenc,
EMP: 5 **EST:** 2014
SALES (est): 315.1K **Privately Held**
WEB: www.marlinbarrel.com
SIC: 2085 Distilled & blended liquors

(G-3744)
NELSON RACEWAY LLC
96321 Bay View Dr (32034-6180)
PHONE....................................904 206-1625
Ronald A Nelson, *Owner*
EMP: 6 **EST:** 2016
SALES (est): 327.9K **Privately Held**
SIC: 3644 Raceways

(G-3745)
NETTING PROFESSIONALS LLC
1600 N 14th St (32034-5126)
PHONE....................................904 432-8987
Eli Rogue, *Office Mgr*
EMP: 7
SALES (est): 697K **Privately Held**
WEB: www.nettingpros.com
SIC: 3949 Nets: badminton, volleyball, tennis, etc.

(G-3746)
OLIVE AMELIA LLC
206 Centre St (32034-4239)
PHONE....................................904 310-3603
Kim T Holwell, *Manager*
EMP: 7 **EST:** 2015
SALES (est): 163.6K **Privately Held**
WEB: www.oliveamelia.com
SIC: 2079 Olive oil

(G-3747)
PURPLE DOVE
474311 E State Road 200 (32034-0806)
PHONE....................................904 261-5227
EMP: 9 **EST:** 2010
SALES (est): 151.3K **Privately Held**
WEB: www.micahsplace.org
SIC: 2711 Newspapers

(G-3748)
SWS SERVICES INC
Also Called: Msm Outdoors
1453 S 8th St (32034-3076)
PHONE....................................904 802-2120
Marina Mattioly, *President*
EMP: 12 **EST:** 2017
SALES (est): 1.5MM **Privately Held**
SIC: 3531 Pavers

(G-3749)
WESTROCK CP LLC
600 N 8th St (32034-3319)
PHONE....................................904 261-5551
Bryan Graves, *General Mgr*
Al Thompson, *General Mgr*
Colin Hewett, *Safety Mgr*
Joe Romeo, *Chief Mktg Ofcr*
Chad Erwin, *Technical Staff*
EMP: 110
SALES (corp-wide): 17.5B **Publicly Held**
WEB: www.westrock.com
SIC: 2653 Boxes, corrugated: made from purchased materials
HQ: Westrock Cp, Llc
1000 Abernathy Rd Ste 125
Atlanta GA 30328

(G-3750)
WHITE LADDER INC
1566 Plantation Oaks Ter (32034-5527)
PHONE....................................904 343-9314
Stacy L Miklas, *Vice Pres*
EMP: 6 **EST:** 2005
SALES (est): 103.7K **Privately Held**
SIC: 3446 Ladders, for permanent installation: metal

(G-3751)
XL CARTS INC
474415 E State Road 200 (32034-0802)
PHONE....................................904 277-7111
Kimberly Wilson, *General Mgr*
Anthony Douglas, *Principal*
Garrett Wilson,
EMP: 8 **EST:** 2013
SALES (est): 1.5MM **Privately Held**
WEB: www.xlcarts.com
SIC: 3369 5088 Castings, except die-castings, precision; transportation equipment & supplies

Flagler Beach
Flagler County

(G-3752)
ATHLETIC GUIDE PUBLISHING
509 S Central Ave (32136-3659)
P.O. Box 1050 (32136-1050)
PHONE....................................386 439-2250
Tom Keegan, *Owner*
EMP: 5 **EST:** 1995
SALES (est): 400K **Privately Held**
WEB: www.prepschoolhockeyguide.com
SIC: 2731 Book publishing

(G-3753)
BILL PRAUS STUCCO LLC
625 Cumberland Dr (32136-4033)
P.O. Box 661 (32136-0661)
PHONE....................................386 453-8400
William J Praus Jr, *Principal*
EMP: 6 **EST:** 2007
SALES (est): 71.7K **Privately Held**
SIC: 3299 Stucco

(G-3754)
CONSOLDTED MCH TL HOLDINGS LLC (PA)
712 S Ocean Shore Blvd (32136-3602)
PHONE....................................888 317-9990
Elie Azar,
EMP: 6 **EST:** 2017
SALES (est): 60.9MM **Privately Held**
SIC: 3599 3451 Machine shop, jobbing & repair; screw machine products

(G-3755)
CONTEMPRARY MCHNREY ENGRG SVCS
551 Roberts Rd (32136-3024)
P.O. Box 7 (32136-0007)
PHONE....................................386 439-0937
James A Smith, *President*
Julie M Smith, *Corp Secy*
▲ **EMP:** 20 **EST:** 1958
SQ FT: 60,000
SALES (est): 4.6MM **Privately Held**
SIC: 3743 5084 Railroad equipment; industrial machinery & equipment; controlling instruments & accessories

(G-3756)
REALTY SYSTEMS INC
3165 Old Kings Rd S (32136-4330)
PHONE....................................386 439-0460
EMP: 10 **EST:** 1994
SALES (est): 716.2K **Publicly Held**
SIC: 2451 Mfg Mobile Homes
PA: Equity Lifestyle Properties, Inc.
2 N Riverside Plz Ste 800
Chicago IL 60606

(G-3757)
SEA RAY BOATS INC
Also Called: Manufacturing Facility
1958 Unsinkable St (32136-3001)
PHONE....................................386 439-3401
Dan Goddard, *Branch Mgr*
EMP: 120
SALES (corp-wide): 4.3B **Publicly Held**
WEB: www.searay.com
SIC: 3732 Boats, fiberglass: building & repairing
HQ: Sea Ray Boats, Inc.
800 S Gay St Ste 1200
Knoxville TN 37929
865 522-4181

(G-3758)
WCM GROUP INC
1516 N Daytona Ave (32136-2909)
P.O. Box 1558 (32136-1558)
PHONE....................................516 238-4261
William Minicozzi, *President*
Maureen Minicozzi, *Admin Sec*
EMP: 6 **EST:** 2014
SALES (est): 622K **Privately Held**
WEB: www.wcmgroup.com
SIC: 3999 Barber & beauty shop equipment

Fleming Island
Clay County

(G-3759)
ASPEN PRODUCTS INC
1857 Inlet Cove Ct (32003-7275)
PHONE....................................904 579-4366
George Odonoghue, *Principal*
EMP: 30
SALES (corp-wide): 379.2MM **Privately Held**
WEB: www.aspenpro.com
SIC: 2674 Bags: uncoated paper & multiwall
PA: Aspen Products, Inc.
4231 Clary Blvd
Kansas City MO 64130
816 921-0234

(G-3760)
BARRON BOYZ AUTO ✪
1324 Fairway Village Dr (32003-8398)
PHONE....................................229 403-2656
Antonio Barron, *Owner*
EMP: 10 **EST:** 2021
SALES (est): 150K **Privately Held**
SIC: 3711 Automobile assembly, including specialty automobiles

(G-3761)
EARTHSOIL INC
Also Called: Sellandshipusa
5000-18 Us Hwy 17 S 107 (32003)
PHONE....................................888 282-1920
Gregg Holloway, *President*
EMP: 6 **EST:** 2015
SALES (est): 185K **Privately Held**
WEB: www.earth-soil.com
SIC: 2875 2873 Potting soil, mixed; plant foods, mixed: from plants making nitrog. fertilizers

(G-3762)
ELITE MANUFACTURING US
1860 Indian River Dr (32003-7941)
PHONE....................................919 757-2732
George H Leach, *Owner*
EMP: 6 **EST:** 2017
SALES (est): 93.8K **Privately Held**
SIC: 3599 Machine shop, jobbing & repair

(G-3763)
ELITE MANUFACTURING US LLC
1860 Indian River Dr (32003-7941)
PHONE....................................904 516-4796
EMP: 9 **EST:** 2017
SALES (est): 217.1K **Privately Held**
WEB: www.elitemanufacturingus.com
SIC: 3599 Machine shop, jobbing & repair

(G-3764)
PROPAVERS LLC
1337 Fairway Village Dr (32003-8399)
PHONE....................................904 403-9033
Maria I Castro, *Principal*
EMP: 6 **EST:** 2013
SALES (est): 76.4K **Privately Held**
SIC: 2951 Asphalt paving mixtures & blocks

▲ = Import ▼=Export
◆ =Import/Export

Florahome
Putnam County

(G-3765)
PAVEWAY SYSTEMS INC
114 Indian Lakes Ln (32140-3614)
PHONE....................386 659-1316
Tiffany Albright, *President*
EMP: 10 **EST:** 2011
SALES (est): 1MM **Privately Held**
WEB: www.pavewaysystems.com
SIC: 3999 Manufacturing industries

Floral City
Citrus County

(G-3766)
FERRIS GROVES
7607 S Florida Ave (34436-2739)
P.O. Box 1168 (34436-1168)
PHONE....................352 860-0366
Jim Collette, *Principal*
EMP: 7 **EST:** 2008
SALES (est): 140.8K **Privately Held**
WEB: www.ferrisgroves.com
SIC: 2034 Dehydrated fruits, vegetables, soups

(G-3767)
FLORAL CITY AIRBOAT CO INC
12080 S Hewitt Pt (34436-4246)
PHONE....................352 637-4390
Mike Emrich, *Manager*
EMP: 6
SALES (corp-wide): 1.5MM **Privately Held**
WEB: www.airboatfl.com
SIC: 3732 Boats, fiberglass: building & repairing
PA: Floral City Airboat Company, Inc.
5098 S Florida Ave
Inverness FL 34450
352 637-4390

(G-3768)
INSTANT PRINTING SERVICES INC
Also Called: I P S
8885 E Haines Ct (34436-4261)
PHONE....................727 546-8036
Dan Conroy, *President*
Patty Conroy, *Vice Pres*
EMP: 14 **EST:** 1974
SALES (est): 1.1MM **Privately Held**
WEB: www.instantprintinginc.com
SIC: 2752 7334 2791 2789 Commercial printing, offset; photocopying & duplicating services; typesetting; bookbinding & related work; commercial printing

Florida City
Miami-Dade County

(G-3769)
SOUTHERN PACKAGING MCHY CORP
Also Called: Spmc
550 Nw 3rd Ave (33034-3351)
P.O. Box 349197, Homestead (33034-9197)
PHONE....................305 245-3045
David Raska, *President*
Guillermo Rojas, *Engineer*
EMP: 27 **EST:** 1975
SQ FT: 16,500
SALES (est): 6.7MM **Privately Held**
WEB: www.spmc.biz
SIC: 3565 5084 Packaging machinery; industrial machinery & equipment

Fort Denaud
Hendry County

(G-3770)
AUSTIN POWDER COMPANY
6051 Fort Denaud Rd (33935-0445)
PHONE....................863 674-0504
EMP: 9
SALES (corp-wide): 734.5MM **Privately Held**
WEB: www.austinpowder.com
SIC: 2892 Explosives
HQ: Austin Powder Company
25800 Science Park Dr # 300
Cleveland OH 44122
216 464-2400

Fort Lauderdale
Broward County

(G-3771)
1800FLOWERSCOM
5350 Nw 35th Ter (33309-6334)
PHONE....................954 683-1246
EMP: 8 **EST:** 2019
SALES (est): 291.2K **Privately Held**
WEB: www.1800flowers.com
SIC: 3999 Artificial flower arrangements; flowers, artificial & preserved

(G-3772)
21ST CENTURY CHEMICAL INC
2960 Sw 23rd Ter Ste 108 (33312-4936)
PHONE....................954 689-7111
Bryan Hacht, *President*
EMP: 5 **EST:** 2011
SQ FT: 2,000
SALES (est): 1MM **Privately Held**
WEB: www.21stcenturychemical.com
SIC: 2899 Chemical preparations

(G-3773)
925 NUEVOS CUBANOS INC
925 N Andrews Ave (33311-7440)
PHONE....................954 806-8375
Luis Valdes, *Vice Pres*
EMP: 8 **EST:** 2013
SALES (est): 289.3K **Privately Held**
WEB: www.nuevoscubanos.net
SIC: 2711 Newspapers, publishing & printing

(G-3774)
AAA ABLE APPLIANCE SERVICE
Also Called: A A A Able Air Conditioning
430 N Andrews Ave (33301-3214)
PHONE....................954 791-5222
Robert Murphy, *Owner*
Denise Murphy, *Co-Owner*
EMP: 8 **EST:** 2000
SQ FT: 4,000
SALES (est): 1.6MM **Privately Held**
WEB: www.aaaable.com
SIC: 3585 7623 5722 Refrigeration & heating equipment; refrigeration service & repair; household appliance stores

(G-3775)
ABC IMAGING OF WASHINGTON
714 N Federal Hwy (33304-2733)
PHONE....................954 759-2037
Leon Powell, *Branch Mgr*
EMP: 17
SALES (corp-wide): 124.9MM **Privately Held**
WEB: www.abcimaging.com
SIC: 2759 Publication printing
PA: Abc Imaging Of Washington, Inc
5290 Shawnee Rd Ste 300
Alexandria VA 22312
202 429-8870

(G-3776)
ACCURATE SIGNS LLC
2831 Ne 29th St (33306-1918)
PHONE....................754 779-7519
James E Coppersmith, *Principal*
EMP: 6 **EST:** 2015
SALES (est): 109.2K **Privately Held**
WEB: www.accuratesignsontime.com
SIC: 3993 Signs & advertising specialties

(G-3777)
ACE BLUEPRINTING INC
1770 Nw 64th St Ste 500 (33309-1853)
PHONE....................954 771-0104
Ronald Chin, *President*
Karen Chin, *Vice Pres*
EMP: 10 **EST:** 1983
SALES (est): 712.8K **Privately Held**
WEB: www.aceblueprinting.com
SIC: 2752 Commercial printing, offset

(G-3778)
ACHSAHS DELIGHT BAKERY LLC
3075 Nw 19th St (33311-3284)
PHONE....................954 533-1843
Wayne Jones, *Principal*
Hyacinth C Jones, *Principal*
EMP: 6 **EST:** 2006
SALES (est): 128.6K **Privately Held**
SIC: 2051 Bakery: wholesale or wholesale/retail combined

(G-3779)
ACR ELECTRONICS INC (DH)
5757 Ravenswood Rd (33312-6603)
PHONE....................954 981-3333
Gerald Angeli, *President*
Donna Salmon, *Purchasing*
Irek Gora, *Engineer*
Juan Sanchez, *Engineer*
Bill Cox, *Senior Engr*
▲ **EMP:** 199 **EST:** 1989
SQ FT: 65,000
SALES (est): 58.7MM
SALES (corp-wide): 282.5MM **Privately Held**
WEB: www.acrartex.com
SIC: 3663 3648 Receiver-transmitter units (transceiver); lighting equipment
HQ: Acr Holdings Llc
5757 Ravenswood Rd
Fort Lauderdale FL 33312
954 981-3333

(G-3780)
ACRYLUX PAINT MFG CO INC
6010 Powerline Rd (33309-2014)
PHONE....................954 772-0300
Janet Riedesel, *President*
Andrew Berry, *Opers Mgr*
Trish Davis, *Credit Staff*
Patrick Berry, *Admin Sec*
▼ **EMP:** 11 **EST:** 1959
SQ FT: 14,000
SALES (est): 2.3MM **Privately Held**
WEB: www.acrylux.com
SIC: 2851 5231 Paints, waterproof; paints: oil or alkyd vehicle or water thinned; paint

(G-3781)
ACUDERM INC
5370 Nw 35th Ter Ste 106 (33309-7018)
PHONE....................954 733-6935
Charles R Yeh, *President*
James Foster, *Plant Mgr*
Alan Hartstein, *Controller*
Ralph Theile, *Controller*
Sajivan Ganesh, *Manager*
EMP: 60 **EST:** 1982
SQ FT: 7,000
SALES (est): 11.2MM **Privately Held**
WEB: www.acuderm.com
SIC: 3069 2836 Medical & laboratory rubber sundries & related products; culture media

(G-3782)
ADD HELIUM
3590 Nw 54th St Ste 1 (33309-6366)
PHONE....................239 300-0913
Yvonne Lessmann, *Principal*
Melody Hearndon, *Marketing Mgr*
EMP: 5 **EST:** 2009
SALES (est): 892.8K **Privately Held**
WEB: www.addhelium.com
SIC: 2813 Helium

(G-3783)
ADVANCED MECHANICAL ENTPS INC
217 Sw 28th St (33315-3131)
PHONE....................954 764-2678
Richard Merhige, *President*
Fred Blockland, *Project Mgr*
Teresa Drugatz, *Opers Staff*
Joanna Ramirez, *Mktg Coord*
Christine Battles, *Officer*
◆ **EMP:** 20 **EST:** 1991
SQ FT: 4,200
SALES (est): 3.2MM **Privately Held**
WEB: www.amesolutions.com
SIC: 3731 Shipbuilding & repairing

(G-3784)
ADVANCED SEWING
3619 Nw 19th St (33311-4120)
PHONE....................954 484-2100
Elliot Levontin, *President*
EMP: 5 **EST:** 1986
SQ FT: 3,000
SALES (est): 322.5K **Privately Held**
SIC: 2393 3999 5021 7389 Cushions, except spring & carpet: purchased materials; garden umbrellas; outdoor & lawn furniture; sewing contractor

(G-3785)
AERCAP INC
100 Ne 3rd Ave Ste 800 (33301-1156)
PHONE....................954 760-7777
Aengus Kelly, *CEO*
Wouter Den Dikken, *COO*
Betsy Chatterson, *Assistant VP*
Serge Avakian, *Vice Pres*
Keith Helming, *CFO*
EMP: 29 **EST:** 2014
SALES (est): 556.1K **Privately Held**
WEB: www.aercap.com
SIC: 3721 7359 8711 Aircraft; aircraft rental; aviation &/or aeronautical engineering

GEOGRAPHIC

(G-3786)
AERCAP GROUP SERVICES INC (HQ)
Also Called: Wings Aircraft Finance
100 Ne 3rd Ave Ste 800 (33301-1156)
PHONE....................954 760-7777
Anil Mehta, *President*
David Southard, *Counsel*
David Torres, *Senior VP*
George Arnokouros, *VP Legal*
Scot Kennedy, *VP Legal*
EMP: 275 **EST:** 1999
SALES (est): 11.1MM
SALES (corp-wide): 1B **Privately Held**
WEB: www.aercap.com
SIC: 3721 7359 Aircraft; aircraft rental
PA: Aercap Holdings N.V.
Onbekend Nederlands Adres
Onbekend
353 163-6065

(G-3787)
AERION CORP (PA)
500 Nw 62nd St Ste 400 (33309-6156)
PHONE....................775 337-6682
Tom Vice, *President*
Douglas Coleman, *Exec VP*
Hal Martin, *Vice Pres*
EMP: 20 **EST:** 2002
SALES (est): 6MM **Privately Held**
WEB: www.aerionsupersonic.com
SIC: 3721 Airplanes, fixed or rotary wing

(G-3788)
AGA MACHINE SHOP INC
277 Sw 33rd St (33315-3327)
PHONE....................954 522-1108
Adolfo Gomez, *President*
EMP: 6 **EST:** 2006
SALES (est): 691K **Privately Held**
WEB: www.agamachineshop.com
SIC: 3599 Machine shop, jobbing & repair

(G-3789)
AGM INDUSTRIES INC
1560 Nw 23rd Ave (33311-5149)
PHONE....................954 486-1112
Carmine Parente, *President*
Guido Parente, *Corp Secy*
◆ **EMP:** 16 **EST:** 1986
SQ FT: 16,000
SALES (est): 2.9MM **Privately Held**
WEB: www.acdelete.com
SIC: 3231 Mirrored glass; doors, glass: made from purchased glass

(G-3790)
AIRLINE SUPPORT GROUP INC
2700 W Cypress Creek Rd (33309-1744)
PHONE....................954 971-4567
Joseph Custy, *President*
EMP: 20 **EST:** 1999
SALES (est): 1.1MM **Privately Held**
WEB: www.airlinesupportgroup.net
SIC: 3728 Aircraft parts & equipment

(G-3791)
AIRMARK COMPONENTS INC
2701 Sw 2nd Ave (33315-3129)
PHONE.................................954 522-5370
Louis Moritz, *President*
Kirk Alexander, *Vice Pres*
Yvonne Silva, *Purchasing*
Brian Nee, *Sales Staff*
Wendy Shaver,
EMP: 44 **EST:** 1985
SQ FT: 22,000
SALES (est): 5.7MM **Privately Held**
WEB: www.airmarkcomponents.com
SIC: 3728 Aircraft parts & equipment

(G-3792)
AIRMARK OVERHAUL INC
Also Called: Airmark Engines, Inc.
6001 Nw 29th Ave (33309-1731)
PHONE.................................954 970-3200
David Williams, *President*
William Milburn, *President*
Ernest Moritz, *Treasurer*
◆ **EMP:** 9 **EST:** 1975
SQ FT: 20,000
SALES (est): 736.9K **Privately Held**
WEB: www.airmarkoverhaul.com
SIC: 3724 Aircraft engines & engine parts

(G-3793)
AJ ORIGINALS INC
1710 Ne 63rd Ct (33334-5128)
PHONE.................................954 563-9911
EMP: 8
SALES (est): 1.6MM **Privately Held**
SIC: 2434 2511 2599 2426 Mfg Furniture/Fixtures Mfg Wood Household Furn Mfg Wood Kitchen Cabinet Hdwd Dimension/Flr Mill

(G-3794)
ALBIXON USA LLC
5820 Ne 22nd Way Apt 602 (33308-2647)
PHONE.................................954 297-2000
Jan Haspekl, *President*
EMP: 6 **EST:** 2015
SALES (est): 129.1K **Privately Held**
WEB: www.albixonusa.com
SIC: 3999 Manufacturing industries

(G-3795)
ALCAS USA CORP
5347 Nw 35th Ave (33309-6315)
PHONE.................................305 591-3325
EMP: 7 **EST:** 2015
SALES (est): 484.1K **Privately Held**
SIC: 2024 Ice Cream And Frozen Desserts, Nsk

(G-3796)
ALL AMERICAN BARRICADES
2300 Sw 41st Ave (33317-6927)
PHONE.................................305 685-6124
Ruben G Santos, *President*
Monique Santos, *Vice Pres*
Ali Garces, *Office Mgr*
EMP: 8 **EST:** 1998
SQ FT: 3,000
SALES (est): 1.5MM **Privately Held**
WEB: www.barricades.com
SIC: 3499 Barricades, metal

(G-3797)
ALL LIQUID ENVMTL SVCS LLC
Also Called: Johnson Environmental Services
4600 Powerline Rd (33309-3838)
PHONE.................................800 767-9594
Albert Panzarella, *Principal*
EMP: 39 **EST:** 1933
SALES (est): 12.2MM **Privately Held**
WEB: www.johnsones.com
SIC: 3089 5039 4953 7699 Septic tanks, plastic; septic tanks; liquid waste, collection & disposal; catch basin cleaning

(G-3798)
ALLIED AEROFOAM PRODUCTS LLC
1883 W State Road 84 # 106 (33315-2232)
PHONE.................................731 660-2705
Billy Rust, *Branch Mgr*
EMP: 19
SALES (corp-wide): 45.8MM **Privately Held**
WEB: www.alliedaerofoam.com
SIC: 3086 Plastics foam products
HQ: Allied Aerofoam Products, Llc
1883 W State Road 84 # 106
Fort Lauderdale FL 33315
813 626-0090

(G-3799)
ALLIED AEROFOAM PRODUCTS LLC (HQ)
1883 W State Road 84 # 106 (33315-2232)
PHONE.................................813 626-0090
Kevin M Pocongan, *CEO*
Bill Carrington, *President*
Lambert Willett, *General Mgr*
Angela Murphy, *Purch Dir*
Jeff Aguiar, *CFO*
◆ **EMP:** 70 **EST:** 2002
SALES (est): 45.8MM **Privately Held**
WEB: www.alliedaerofoam.com
SIC: 3086 Plastics foam products

(G-3800)
ALLIED DECALS FLA INC
1001 W Cypress Creek Rd # 320 (33309-1900)
PHONE.................................800 940-2233
EMP: 6 **EST:** 2019
SALES (est): 98.7K **Privately Held**
WEB: www.allieddecals.com
SIC: 2759 Screen printing

(G-3801)
ALLIED DECALS-FLA INC
Also Called: Allied Binders
5225 Nw 35th Ave (33309-3303)
PHONE.................................800 940-2233
Bruce Landis, *President*
Heidi Landis, *Vice Pres*
▼ **EMP:** 16 **EST:** 1978
SQ FT: 11,000
SALES (est): 588K **Privately Held**
SIC: 2759 2782 Screen printing; decals: printing; looseleaf binders & devices

(G-3802)
ALLIED GRAPHICS INC
1220 Nw 23rd Ave (33311-5243)
PHONE.................................954 327-8559
Richard Shea, *President*
Howard Shea, *Corp Secy*
EMP: 5 **EST:** 1967
SALES (est): 732.3K **Privately Held**
SIC: 2893 Letterpress or offset ink

(G-3803)
ALLIED INSULATED PANELS INC
6451 N Federal Hwy # 1204 (33308-1402)
PHONE.................................800 599-3905
Michael D Lassner, *President*
EMP: 8 **EST:** 2018
SALES (est): 550.2K **Privately Held**
WEB: www.alliedbuildings.com
SIC: 3448 Prefabricated metal buildings

(G-3804)
ALLIED STEEL BUILDINGS INC
6451 N Federal Hwy # 1202 (33308-1402)
PHONE.................................800 508-2718
Sergio Plaza, *Vice Pres*
John Barnes, *Prdtn Mgr*
Ursulla Milla, *Human Resources*
Collin Burich, *Accounts Mgr*
Lassner Michael, *Branch Mgr*
EMP: 23 **Privately Held**
WEB: www.alliedbuildings.com
SIC: 3448 Prefabricated metal buildings
PA: Allied Steel Buildings Inc.
6451 N Federal Hwy # 411
Fort Lauderdale FL 33308

(G-3805)
ALLIED STEEL BUILDINGS INC (PA)
6451 N Federal Hwy # 411 (33308-1402)
PHONE.................................954 590-4949
Michael Lassner, *President*
Catherine Soto, *General Mgr*
Alex Andersen, *Business Mgr*
Eric Stephan, *Vice Pres*
Daniel Czaplinski, *Project Mgr*
◆ **EMP:** 17 **EST:** 2003
SQ FT: 5,965
SALES (est): 22.2MM **Privately Held**
WEB: www.alliedbuildings.com
SIC: 3448 Prefabricated metal buildings

(G-3806)
ALLIED STEEL STRUCTURES INC
6400 N Andrews Ave # 200 (33309-2114)
PHONE.................................877 997-8335
Michael Lassner, *President*
Margaret Luebbert, *Accounting Mgr*
Mike Stock, *Sr Project Mgr*
EMP: 16 **EST:** 2003
SALES (est): 327.3K **Privately Held**
WEB: www.alliedbuildings.com
SIC: 3441 Fabricated structural metal

(G-3807)
ALLIED-360 LLC
101 Ne 3rd Ave Ste 300 (33301-1128)
PHONE.................................954 590-4940
Michael Lassner, *President*
Alex Andersen, *Business Mgr*
Guy Susi, *Vice Pres*
Sergio Plaza, *VP Opers*
James McGurk, *Project Mgr*
EMP: 30 **EST:** 2010
SALES (est): 3.1MM **Privately Held**
SIC: 3441 Fabricated structural metal

(G-3808)
ALLSTEEL PROCESSING LC
1250 Nw 23rd Ave (33311-5243)
PHONE.................................954 587-1900
Maria Esquilin, *Human Res Mgr*
Glenn Markus, *Mng Member*
Vanessa Parrilla, *Manager*
Richard Abbott,
EMP: 15 **EST:** 1996
SALES (est): 1.9MM **Privately Held**
WEB: www.allsteelproducts.com
SIC: 3317 Steel pipe & tubes

(G-3809)
ALM MEDIA LLC
Also Called: Miami Daily Business Review
633 S Andrews Ave Ste 100 (33301-2843)
PHONE.................................954 468-2600
Shirley Cohen, *Manager*
Maria Mesa, *Legal Staff*
Nadine Modestil, *Clerk*
EMP: 6
SALES (corp-wide): 202.2MM **Privately Held**
WEB: www.alm.com
SIC: 2711 Newspapers
HQ: Alm Media, Llc
150 E 42nd St
New York NY 10017
212 457-9400

(G-3810)
AM PRIMACLASSE CORP
3015 Ravenswood Rd # 101 (33312-4930)
PHONE.................................305 767-5918
Mattia Casarotto, *President*
EMP: 6 **EST:** 2017
SALES (est): 131.9K **Privately Held**
WEB: www.amdistributions.com
SIC: 3993 Signs & advertising specialties

(G-3811)
AMERICAN CHANGER CORP
Also Called: Hoffman Mint
1400 Nw 65th Pl (33309-1902)
PHONE.................................954 917-3009
Wayne Snihur, *President*
Harry Steinbok, *Principal*
◆ **EMP:** 58 **EST:** 2001
SQ FT: 43,000
SALES (est): 9.7MM **Privately Held**
WEB: www.americanchanger.com
SIC: 3578 Change making machines

(G-3812)
AMERICAN DIAMOND DISTRIBUTORS
Also Called: Beverely's
3600 W Coml Blvd Ste 101 (33309)
PHONE.................................954 485-7808
Jeff Malvin, *President*
Mark Malvin, *Vice Pres*
EMP: 8 **EST:** 1985
SALES (est): 152.4K **Privately Held**
SIC: 3911 Jewelry, precious metal

(G-3813)
AMERICAN IGNITION WIRE LLC
2760 Nw 63rd Ct (33309-1712)
PHONE.................................954 974-6500
Jeff Olefson, *Executive*
Fred Olefson,
EMP: 9 **EST:** 1999
SALES (est): 183.2K **Privately Held**
SIC: 3714 Motor vehicle parts & accessories

(G-3814)
AMERICAN PRTECTIVE COATING INC
Also Called: American Powder Coating
6795 Nw 17th Ave (33309-1521)
PHONE.................................954 561-0999
Robert Symington, *President*
EMP: 22 **EST:** 1990
SQ FT: 10,000
SALES (est): 1.6MM **Privately Held**
WEB: www.apcfl.net
SIC: 3479 Coating of metals & formed products

(G-3815)
AMERICAS BLASTING COATINGS LLC
2020 Sw 36th Ave (33312-4209)
PHONE.................................754 281-6738
Wesley Martin,
EMP: 9 **EST:** 2017
SALES (est): 270K **Privately Held**
WEB: www.americasblasting.com
SIC: 3479 Metal coating & allied service

(G-3816)
AND-DELL CORPORATION
245 Sw 33rd St (33315-3397)
PHONE.................................954 523-6478
Jon A Lobdell, *President*
Beverly Lobdell, *Treasurer*
Mike Stein, *Marketing Staff*
▲ **EMP:** 30 **EST:** 1966
SQ FT: 14,000
SALES (est): 2.9MM **Privately Held**
WEB: www.dellheatrix.com
SIC: 3634 Heating units, electric (radiant heat): baseboard or wall

(G-3817)
ANDREWS WAREHOUSE PARTNERSHIP
1512 E Broward Blvd (33301-2122)
PHONE.................................954 524-3330
Edward D Stone Jr, *Partner*
Joseph J Lalli, *Partner*
EMP: 7 **EST:** 1985
SQ FT: 4,000
SALES (est): 635.6K **Privately Held**
SIC: 2512 Wood upholstered chairs & couches

(G-3818)
APPLE PRINTING & ADVG SPC INC
5055 Nw 10th Ter (33309-3167)
PHONE.................................954 524-0493
Sean Donato, *President*
Kevin Donato, *Vice Pres*
Randolph Bastein, *Production*
EMP: 20 **EST:** 1970
SQ FT: 8,500
SALES (est): 3.3MM **Privately Held**
WEB: www.appleprinting.com
SIC: 2752 2791 2789 Commercial printing, offset; typesetting; bookbinding & related work

(G-3819)
ARCHIMAZE LOGISTICS INC
1776 Nw 38th Ave (33311-4117)
PHONE.................................954 615-7485
Evan Graham, *Principal*
EMP: 9 **EST:** 2012
SALES (est): 394.6K **Privately Held**
WEB: www.forkliftfrenzy.com
SIC: 3061 3559 3462 Automotive rubber goods (mechanical); automotive related machinery; degreasing machines, automotive & industrial; automotive forgings, ferrous: crankshaft, engine, axle, etc.

(G-3820)
ARCHITEXTURE LLC
1008 Guava Isle (33315-1348)
P.O. Box 2095 (33303-2095)
PHONE..................................954 907-8000
Gaia Calcaterra,
EMP: 6 **EST:** 2010
SALES (est): 111K **Privately Held**
WEB: www.coloringbiblepages.com
SIC: 3081 Floor or wall covering, unsupported plastic

(G-3821)
ARGOTEC INC (PA)
2432 Ne 27th Ave (33305-2719)
PHONE..................................954 491-6550
Paul Novakovic, *President*
EMP: 15 **EST:** 1980
SALES (est): 1.3MM **Privately Held**
WEB: www.swmintl.com
SIC: 3699 Underwater sound equipment

(G-3822)
ARKAY DISTRIBUTING INC
401 E Las Olas Blvd # 1400 (33301-2210)
PHONE..................................954 536-8413
Eynald Grattagliano R, *President*
Reynald Grattagliano, *Corp Secy*
Monique Force, *Vice Pres*
Jair Dos Santos Pereira, *Vice Pres*
EMP: 7 **EST:** 2013
SALES (est): 182.3K **Privately Held**
SIC: 2086 Carbonated beverages, nonalcoholic: bottled & canned

(G-3823)
ARMOUR GROUP INC
6700 Powerline Rd (33309-2154)
PHONE..................................954 767-2030
G Robert Tatum, *CEO*
Martine Miller, *President*
EMP: 16 **EST:** 2010
SALES (est): 473.2K **Privately Held**
WEB: www.thearmourgroup.com
SIC: 3711 Cars, armored, assembly of

(G-3824)
ARRIBAS BINDERY SERVICES INC
6701 Nw 15th Way B (33309-1527)
PHONE..................................954 978-8886
Ramon Arriba, *President*
EMP: 5 **EST:** 1999
SALES (est): 477.1K **Privately Held**
SIC: 2789 Binding only: books, pamphlets, magazines, etc.

(G-3825)
ART SIGN CO INC
Also Called: Art Sign & Neon
835 Nw 6th Ave (33311-7222)
PHONE..................................954 763-4410
Joe Dillard, *President*
Stephen Lavene, *Project Mgr*
Tina Mastandrea, *Sales Executive*
Kristina O 'brien, *Mktg Dir*
◆ **EMP:** 80 **EST:** 1947
SQ FT: 2,500
SALES (est): 9.6MM **Privately Held**
WEB: www.artsignfl.com
SIC: 3993 Electric signs; displays & cutouts, window & lobby

(G-3826)
ASBURY MANUFACTURING CO LLC
Also Called: Kold Draft International, LLC
3355 Entp Ave Ste 160 (33331)
PHONE..................................814 453-6761
Christopher Klingensmith, *Engineer*
Oscar Neal Asbury,
◆ **EMP:** 30 **EST:** 1955
SQ FT: 46,285
SALES (est): 7MM
SALES (corp-wide): 208MM **Privately Held**
WEB: www.greenfieldworldtrade.com
SIC: 3585 Ice making machinery
PA: Greenfield World Trade, Inc.
3355 Entp Ave Ste 160
Fort Lauderdale FL 33331
954 202-7419

(G-3827)
ASSA ABLOY HOSPITALITY INC
Also Called: Vingcard
5601 Powerline Rd Ste 305 (33309-2831)
PHONE..................................954 920-0772
Clive Marshall, *Manager*
EMP: 7
SALES (corp-wide): 10.1B **Privately Held**
WEB: www.assaabloyglobalsolutions.com
SIC: 3429 Locks or lock sets
HQ: Assa Abloy Global Solutions, Inc.
631 Interntl Pkwy Ste 100
Richardson TX 75081
972 907-2273

(G-3828)
ASTRONICS DME LLC
6830 Nw 16th Ter (33309-1518)
PHONE..................................954 975-2100
David Burney, *Corp Secy*
Diane Avidor, *Vice Pres*
Frank Cassandra, *Vice Pres*
Sergio Bastiani, *Engineer*
Rigo Armas, *Electrical Engi*
▲ **EMP:** 115 **EST:** 1976
SQ FT: 96,000
SALES (est): 26.2MM
SALES (corp-wide): 502.5MM **Publicly Held**
WEB: www.dmecorp.com
SIC: 3812 Search & navigation equipment
PA: Astronics Corporation
130 Commerce Way
East Aurora NY 14052
716 805-1599

(G-3829)
ATLAS EMBROIDERY LLC
Also Called: Atlas Embroidery & Screen Prtg
2300 Sw 34th St (33312-5061)
PHONE..................................954 625-2411
Mitchell Lombard, *President*
Jacki Murray, *Human Res Mgr*
Jeremy Feinberg, *Director*
Jennifer K Lombard, *Admin Sec*
▼ **EMP:** 95 **EST:** 2002
SQ FT: 16,000
SALES (est): 12.1MM **Privately Held**
WEB: www.atlasembroidery.com
SIC: 2395 Embroidery products, except schiffli machine; embroidery & art needlework

(G-3830)
ATLAS MARINE SYSTEMS INC
1801 S Perimeter Rd # 150 (33309-7139)
PHONE..................................954 735-6767
Mark Loring, *President*
Ray Beutel, *Chairman*
Andrew Ford, *Prdtn Mgr*
John Dale, *Engineer*
Bob Saxon, *Treasurer*
EMP: 18 **EST:** 2002
SALES (est): 536.4K **Privately Held**
WEB: www.atlasmarinesystems.com
SIC: 3679 Electronic loads & power supplies

(G-3831)
ATTACK COMMUNICATIONS INC
Also Called: Vick Houston
1314 E Las Olas Blvd (33301-2334)
PHONE..................................954 300-2716
Steven Vickers, *President*
EMP: 7 **EST:** 1997
SALES (est): 1MM **Privately Held**
WEB: www.attack.ac
SIC: 3651 Household audio & video equipment

(G-3832)
AUDIO STORAGE TECHNOLOGIES
Also Called: Audacity Audio
1540 Ne 60th St (33334-5989)
PHONE..................................954 229-5050
Fred L Clark, *President*
Tom Harrah, *Vice Pres*
EMP: 5 **EST:** 2001
SALES (est): 315.2K **Privately Held**
WEB: www.audiost.com
SIC: 7372 Operating systems computer software

(G-3833)
AUTOMATED PARKING CORPORATION
6555 Nw 9th Ave Ste 106 (33309-2048)
PHONE..................................754 200-8441
Marco Radonic, *CEO*
Paula Voss, *Marketing Staff*
EMP: 7 **EST:** 2016
SALES (est): 908K **Privately Held**
WEB: www.apcpark.com
SIC: 3535 Conveyors & conveying equipment

(G-3834)
AVALON AVIATION INC
1323 Se 17th St Unit 344 (33316-1707)
PHONE..................................954 655-0256
Kevin Maguire, *President*
EMP: 5 **EST:** 2010
SQ FT: 1,600
SALES (est): 466.7K **Privately Held**
SIC: 3728 8711 Aircraft body assemblies & parts; aviation &/or aeronautical engineering

(G-3835)
AWAB LLC
245 Sw 32nd St (33315-3323)
P.O. Box 22248 (33335-2248)
PHONE..................................954 763-3003
J Denny Turner, *President*
Kellie Bucchiere, *General Mgr*
Whitney Turner, *General Mgr*
Valerie Bressler, *Manager*
▼ **EMP:** 5 **EST:** 2000
SALES (est): 1MM **Privately Held**
WEB: www.awabllc.com
SIC: 3492 Hose & tube fittings & assemblies, hydraulic/pneumatic

(G-3836)
B & B BONS LLC
401 E Las Olas Blvd Fl 8 (33301-4205)
PHONE..................................954 940-4900
Sandra A Hoffman, *Principal*
EMP: 6 **EST:** 2010
SALES (est): 876.2K
SALES (corp-wide): 519.4MM **Publicly Held**
WEB: www.bbxcapital.com
SIC: 2064 Candy & other confectionery products
PA: Bluegreen Vacations Holding Corporation
401 E Las Olas Blvd Fl 8
Fort Lauderdale FL 33301
954 940-4900

(G-3837)
BALLISTA TACTICAL SYSTEMS
2881 E Oakland Park Blvd (33306-1813)
PHONE..................................954 260-0765
Shawn Johnson, *CEO*
EMP: 8 **EST:** 2011
SALES (est): 654.8K **Privately Held**
WEB: www.ballistatactical.com
SIC: 3484 3489 Small arms; guns or gun parts, over 30 mm.

(G-3838)
BALPRO POWDER COATING INC
1624 Nw 38th Ave (33311-4137)
PHONE..................................954 797-0520
EMP: 15
SALES (corp-wide): 265.9K **Privately Held**
WEB: www.balpropowdercoating.com
SIC: 3479 Coating of metals & formed products
PA: Balpro Powder Coating Inc
6800 Nw 45th St
Lauderhill FL

(G-3839)
BANDART ENTERPRISES INC
Also Called: PIP Printing
5303 Nw 35th Ter (33309-6328)
PHONE..................................954 564-1224
Jan Geller, *President*
Linda Geller, *Vice Pres*
EMP: 20 **EST:** 2000
SQ FT: 5,400
SALES (est): 4.4MM **Privately Held**
WEB: www.pip.com
SIC: 2752 Commercial printing, offset

(G-3840)
BAS PLASTICS INC
1000 Nw 56th St (33309-2833)
PHONE..................................954 202-9080
Micolas Bara, *President*
▲ **EMP:** 5 **EST:** 1996
SALES (est): 721.4K **Privately Held**
WEB: www.basplastics.com
SIC: 3089 Molding primary plastic

(G-3841)
BAUFORMAT SOUTH-EAST LLC
1511 E Las Olas Blvd (33301-2345)
PHONE..................................201 693-6635
Lothar Birkenfeld, *Principal*
EMP: 9 **EST:** 2017
SALES (est): 588.7K **Privately Held**
SIC: 2434 Wood kitchen cabinets

(G-3842)
BAYSIDE CANVAS YACHT INTERIORS
2830 W State Road 84 # 11 (33312-4826)
PHONE..................................954 792-8535
Sally Moran, *President*
▼ **EMP:** 8 **EST:** 1996
SALES (est): 575.1K **Privately Held**
WEB: www.baysidecanvas.com
SIC: 2394 Canvas & related products

(G-3843)
BBX SWEET HOLDINGS LLC (DH)
401 E Las Olas Blvd (33301-2210)
PHONE..................................954 940-4000
Kevin Coen, *CEO*
Rick Harris, *President*
Alan Levan,
EMP: 11 **EST:** 2013
SALES (est): 156.6MM
SALES (corp-wide): 519.4MM **Publicly Held**
WEB: www.bbxcapital.com
SIC: 2064 5441 Chocolate candy, except solid chocolate; candy

(G-3844)
BCT INTERNATIONAL INC (HQ)
Also Called: B C T
2810 E Oklnd Prk Blvd # 308 (33306-1801)
PHONE..................................305 563-1224
William Wilkerson, *CEO*
Peter Posk, *President*
Ben Fretti, *Senior VP*
Bob Dolan, *Vice Pres*
Gary Hiltbrand, *Vice Pres*
▲ **EMP:** 30 **EST:** 1981
SALES (est): 8MM **Privately Held**
WEB: www.evoprint.com
SIC: 2752 6794 Commercial printing, lithographic; franchises, selling or licensing
PA: Phoenix Group Of Florida, Inc.
3000 Ne 30th Pl Fl 5
Fort Lauderdale FL 33306
954 563-1224

(G-3845)
BELTECH GENERATOR & REWINDING
850 E Coml Blvd Apt 252 (33334)
PHONE..................................954 588-2255
Lindal Gordon, *Branch Mgr*
EMP: 7
SALES (corp-wide): 62.1K **Privately Held**
SIC: 7694 Rewinding services
PA: Beltech Generator And Rewinding Inc
4240 Ne 6th Ave
Oakland Park FL

(G-3846)
BEMA INC
Also Called: Minuteman Press
2301 S Andrews Ave (33316-3947)
PHONE..................................954 761-1919
Dan Kornfield, *President*
EMP: 5 **EST:** 1977
SQ FT: 1,800
SALES (est): 785.3K **Privately Held**
WEB: www.chanhassen-mn.minuteman-press.com
SIC: 2752 Commercial printing, lithographic

GEOGRAPHIC

(G-3847)
BERGERON SAND & ROCK MIN INC (PA)
Also Called: Bergeron Properties & Inv
19612 Sw 69th Pl (33332-1618)
PHONE....................................954 680-6100
Ronald M Bergeron, *President*
Ted Hojara, *Project Mgr*
Phil Desai, *Treasurer*
EMP: 33 **EST:** 1968
SALES (est): 10.7MM **Privately Held**
WEB: www.bergeronland.com
SIC: 1442 Common sand mining; gravel mining

(G-3848)
BETAWAVE LLC ✪
2968 Nw 60th St (33309-1735)
PHONE....................................954 223-8298
Robert Babik, *Mng Member*
EMP: 15 **EST:** 2021
SALES (est): 528.8K **Privately Held**
SIC: 3841 Medical instruments & equipment, blood & bone work

(G-3849)
BI-ADS INC
Also Called: West Side Gazette
545 Nw 7th Ter (33311-8140)
P.O. Box 5304 (33310-5304)
PHONE....................................954 525-1489
Levi Henry Jr, *President*
Sonia Henry, *Corp Secy*
Henry Yvonne, *Vice Pres*
EMP: 15 **EST:** 1971
SQ FT: 3,170
SALES (est): 1MM **Privately Held**
WEB: www.thewestsidegazette.com
SIC: 2711 2752 Newspapers, publishing & printing; commercial printing, lithographic

(G-3850)
BIG EAGLE LLC
3051 W State Road 84 (33312-4821)
PHONE....................................305 586-8766
EMP: 9 **EST:** 2004
SALES (est): 174.2K **Privately Held**
SIC: 3732 Yachts, building & repairing

(G-3851)
BIG SIGN MESSAGE LLC
Also Called: Big Sign Media Group
770 Nw 57th Ct (33309-2028)
PHONE....................................954 235-5717
Tonia L Fralin, *Manager*
EMP: 6 **EST:** 2016
SALES (est): 121.9K **Privately Held**
WEB: www.bigsignmessage.com
SIC: 3993 Signs & advertising specialties

(G-3852)
BIGHAM INSULATION & SUP CO INC
2816 Sw 3rd Ave (33315-3110)
PHONE....................................954 522-2887
Robert E Bryant, *President*
James P Collier Jr, *Vice Pres*
Martin Krutz, *Accountant*
Dominick Palleschi, *Director*
◆ **EMP:** 31 **EST:** 1960
SQ FT: 36,000
SALES (est): 3.5MM **Privately Held**
WEB: www.bighamsparta.com
SIC: 3296 Mineral wool insulation products; fiberglass insulation

(G-3853)
BIMBO BAKERIES USA
6783 Nw 17th Ave (33309-1521)
PHONE....................................954 968-7684
EMP: 12 **EST:** 2019
SALES (est): 389.6K **Privately Held**
WEB: www.bimbobakeriesusa.com
SIC: 2051 Bakery: wholesale or wholesale/retail combined

(G-3854)
BIO-TECH MEDICAL SOFTWARE INC
Also Called: Biotrackthc
6750 N Andrews Ave # 325 (33309-2142)
PHONE....................................800 797-4711
Patrick Vo, *CEO*
Moe Afaneh, *COO*
Gary Greenwood, *Exec VP*
Cody Stiffler, *Vice Pres*
Jenna Smeryage, *Project Mgr*
EMP: 62 **EST:** 2007
SQ FT: 3,000
SALES (est): 14.6MM **Privately Held**
WEB: www.bioscriptrx.com
SIC: 7372 Business oriented computer software

(G-3855)
BIOFLEX MEDICAL MAGNETICS
5970 Sw 32nd Ter (33312-6325)
PHONE....................................954 565-8500
Charles Zablotsky, *CEO*
Theodore Zablotsky, *President*
Willy Moses, *CFO*
▲ **EMP:** 10 **EST:** 1991
SALES (est): 1.2MM
SALES (corp-wide): 2.1MM **Privately Held**
WEB: www.bioflexmedicalmagnetics.com
SIC: 3841 Surgical & medical instruments
PA: Technologies Relevium Inc
1000 Rue Sherbrooke O Bureau 2700
Montreal QC H3A 3
514 824-8559

(G-3856)
BJB MARINE WELDING & SVCS INC
244 Sw 31st St (33315-3322)
PHONE....................................954 909-4967
Warren C Edwards, *Vice Pres*
EMP: 8 **EST:** 2014
SALES (est): 531K **Privately Held**
WEB: www.bjbmarine.com
SIC: 7692 Automotive welding

(G-3857)
BLIND MONKEY
2601 W Broward Blvd (33312-1308)
PHONE....................................954 533-3090
EMP: 7 **EST:** 2019
SALES (est): 197.7K **Privately Held**
WEB: www.blindmonkeykitchen.com
SIC: 2591 Window blinds

(G-3858)
BLUE MARLIN TOWERS INC
3100 W State Road 84 # 20 (33312-4876)
PHONE....................................954 530-9140
Edward R Milo, *Director*
EMP: 6 **EST:** 1993
SQ FT: 2,500
SALES (est): 339.7K **Privately Held**
SIC: 3441 Fabricated structural metal for ships

(G-3859)
BLUE OCEAN PRESS INC
6299 Nw 27th Way (33309-1728)
PHONE....................................954 973-1819
Tom Mounce, *President*
Gregory Von Hausch, *President*
Mary A McKay, *Prdtn Mgr*
Mary McKay, *Prdtn Mgr*
Steve Valdes, *Production*
▲ **EMP:** 46 **EST:** 1984
SQ FT: 30,000
SALES (est): 12.2MM **Privately Held**
WEB: www.blueoceanpress.com
SIC: 2752 7336 7389 2262 Promotional printing, lithographic; graphic arts & related design; apparel pressing service; screen printing: manmade fiber & silk broadwoven fabrics; embroidery products, except schiffli machine; catalog & mail-order houses

(G-3860)
BLUE WATER CHAIRS INC
240 Sw 33rd Ct (33315-3306)
PHONE....................................954 318-0840
Thomas Ackel, *CEO*
Joe Schwab, *President*
▲ **EMP:** 20 **EST:** 1987
SQ FT: 16,000
SALES (est): 1.7MM **Privately Held**
WEB: www.bluewaterchairs.com
SIC: 2511 Chairs, household, except upholstered: wood

(G-3861)
BLUEOCEAN MARINE SERVICES LLC
Also Called: Broward Armature and Generator
340 Sw 21st Ter (33312-1427)
PHONE....................................954 583-9888
Michael L Brochu Sr, *CEO*
Michael W Brochu Jr, *President*
▼ **EMP:** 13 **EST:** 1995
SQ FT: 5,000
SALES (est): 1.3MM **Privately Held**
SIC: 7694 Electric motor repair

(G-3862)
BMC SERVICES INC
2351 Sw 34th St (33312-5046)
PHONE....................................954 587-6337
Ricardo Mejia, *President*
Isabelle Mejia, *Vice Pres*
EMP: 10 **EST:** 2011
SQ FT: 10,000
SALES (est): 833.3K **Privately Held**
WEB: www.bestmarinecarpentry.com
SIC: 2599 1751 Ship furniture; carpentry work

(G-3863)
BOAT ENERGY LLC
714 Nw 57th St (33309-2825)
PHONE....................................954 501-2628
Linda Bernhardt, *VP Sales*
EMP: 6 **EST:** 2013
SALES (est): 518K **Privately Held**
WEB: www.boatenergy.com
SIC: 3519 Marine engines

(G-3864)
BOAT INTERNATIONAL MEDIA INC
Also Called: Duck Walk
1800 Se 10th Ave Ste 340 (33316-2984)
PHONE....................................954 522-2628
Leonardo Careddu, *Publisher*
Stewart Campbell, *Editor*
Lee Franklin, *Editor*
Risa Merl, *Editor*
Marilyn Mower, *Editor*
▲ **EMP:** 3 **EST:** 1997
SALES (est): 3MM
SALES (corp-wide): 11.2MM **Privately Held**
WEB: www.boatinternational.com
SIC: 2721 Magazines: publishing only, not printed on site
HQ: Boat International Media Limited
41-47 Hartfield Road
London SW19

(G-3865)
BOMBARDIIER
Also Called: Bombardier Aircraft Services
4100 Sw 11th Ter (33315-3504)
PHONE....................................954 622-1200
Melissa Bertrand, *Project Mgr*
Joseph Scarfone, *Finance Mgr*
Steve Garrett, *Supervisor*
Cristiane Maia, *Admin Asst*
Zachary Lilly, *Technician*
EMP: 6
SALES (corp-wide): 6.4B **Privately Held**
WEB: www.bombardier.com
SIC: 3721 Aircraft
PA: Bombardier Inc
400 Ch De La Cote-Vertu
Dorval QC H4S 1
514 855-5000

(G-3866)
BONNIER CORPORATION
705 Sw 16th St (33315-1628)
PHONE....................................954 830-4460
Natasha Lloyd, *Principal*
EMP: 8
SALES (corp-wide): 2.4B **Privately Held**
WEB: www.bonniercorp.com
SIC: 2721 Magazines: publishing only, not printed on site
HQ: Bonnier Corporation
480 N Orlando Ave Ste 236
Winter Park FL 32789

(G-3867)
BRADFORD YACHT LIMITED INC
3051 W State Road 84 (33312-4821)
PHONE....................................954 791-3800
Dieter Cosman, *Ch of Bd*
Kathy Nitabach, *Vice Pres*
Colin Lord, *Project Mgr*
◆ **EMP:** 165 **EST:** 1966
SALES (est): 11.6MM **Privately Held**
WEB: www.bradford-marine.com
SIC: 3732 Yachts, building & repairing

(G-3868)
BRIGHT MANUFACTURING LLC (PA)
Also Called: Power Bright Technologies
2933 W Cypress Creek Rd # 202 (33309-1777)
PHONE....................................954 603-4950
Guil Hetzroni,
Daniel Hetzroni,
▲ **EMP:** 5 **EST:** 2008
SALES (est): 936.2K **Privately Held**
WEB: www.powerbright.com
SIC: 3612 Power transformers, electric

(G-3869)
BROWARD CASTING FOUNDRY INC
Also Called: Gatto Furniture
2240 Sw 34th St (33312-5049)
PHONE....................................954 584-6400
Ronald J Gatto, *President*
Ronald J Gatto Jr, *President*
Denise Gatto-Trissel, *Vice Pres*
Lynn Zophres, *Treasurer*
Dawn Brooks, *Admin Sec*
▼ **EMP:** 30 **EST:** 1963
SQ FT: 22,000
SALES (est): 7.3MM **Privately Held**
WEB: www.browardcasting.com
SIC: 3365 Aluminum foundries

(G-3870)
BROWARD POWER TRAIN CO INC
5300 Nw 12th Ave Ste 3 (33309-3164)
PHONE....................................954 772-0881
Lee Minyard, *President*
Charles Minyeard, *Vice Pres*
Sue Minyard, *Treasurer*
Joy Minyard, *Admin Sec*
EMP: 26 **EST:** 1980
SQ FT: 2,000
SALES (est): 3.4MM **Privately Held**
WEB: www.browardpowertrain.com
SIC: 3714 Drive shafts, motor vehicle

(G-3871)
BROWARD SIGNS
1901 S Federal Hwy (33316-3500)
PHONE....................................954 320-9903
Donna A Richards P, *Principal*
EMP: 5 **EST:** 2010
SALES (est): 448.4K **Privately Held**
WEB: www.browardsigns.com
SIC: 3993 Electric signs

(G-3872)
BROWNSUGARBAE LLC
515 E Las Olas Blvd Ste 1 (33301-2296)
PHONE....................................954 554-0318
Ovide Lazarre, *Principal*
Tania Dauphin,
EMP: 9
SALES (est): 62.8K **Privately Held**
SIC: 2051 Bakery: wholesale or wholesale/retail combined

(G-3873)
BRUMATE LLC
201 Nw 22nd Ave (33311-8634)
PHONE....................................317 474-7352
Dylan Jacob,
EMP: 9 **EST:** 2019
SALES (est): 1.7MM **Privately Held**
WEB: www.brumate.com
SIC: 2084 Wine coolers (beverages)

(G-3874)
BUDDY CUSTARD INC
1451 W Cypress Creek Rd (33309-1961)
PHONE....................................561 715-3785
Robert Schlien, *CEO*

Katherine Schlien, *President*
Paul R Smith, *Treasurer*
EMP: 8 **EST:** 2017
SALES (est): 963.1K **Privately Held**
WEB: www.buddycustard.com
SIC: 2048 Prepared feeds

(G-3875)
BUILDERS NOTICE CORPORATION
Also Called: Construction Collections
708 S Andrews Ave (33316-1032)
PHONE..................................954 764-1322
James A Carmel, *CEO*
Kenneth Deangelis, *President*
Regina Durand, *Vice Pres*
EMP: 7 **EST:** 1975
SQ FT: 2,000
SALES (est): 941.3K **Privately Held**
WEB: www.buildersnotice.com
SIC: 2741 7389 Newsletter publishing; process serving service

(G-3876)
BUKKEHAVE INC
6750 N Andrews Ave # 200 (33309-2180)
P.O. Box 13143 (33316-0100)
PHONE..................................954 525-9788
Christian Haar, *CEO*
Morten Frederiksen, *President*
Mark Combs, *Vice Pres*
Rohit Damodar, *Vice Pres*
Bo Dybbro, *CFO*
◆ **EMP:** 7 **EST:** 1996
SALES (est): 11.7MM
SALES (corp-wide): 767.7K **Privately Held**
WEB: www.bukkehave.com
SIC: 1389 5013 Cementing oil & gas well casings; automotive supplies & parts
PA: B1925 Aps
Troensevej 29
Svendborg 5700
632 121-21

(G-3877)
BUSINESS CARDS TOMORROW INC (PA)
Also Called: B C T
2810 E Oklnd Prk Blvd # 308 (33306-1900)
PHONE..................................954 563-1224
Andyara Nahir Mata, *Principal*
Melissa Cooley, *Admin Mgr*
Robert Clarey, *Admin Sec*
Alan Wright, *Admin Asst*
EMP: 52 **EST:** 2011
SALES (est): 1.2MM **Privately Held**
WEB: www.evoprint.com
SIC: 2752 Commercial printing, lithographic

(G-3878)
C MIX CORP
5600 Nw 12th Ave Ste 306 (33309-6600)
PHONE..................................954 670-0208
Fred Rosenfield, *Director*
EMP: 15 **EST:** 2005
SALES (est): 606.5K **Privately Held**
SIC: 3273 Ready-mixed concrete

(G-3879)
C P VEGETABLE OIL INC
Also Called: CP Vegetable Oil
601 Sw 21st Ter Ste 1 (33312-2278)
PHONE..................................954 584-0420
Christian Pellerin, *CEO*
EMP: 11 **EST:** 1998
SALES (est): 6.4MM **Privately Held**
WEB: www.cpvegoil.com
SIC: 2076 Vegetable oil mills
PA: Distributions Christian Pellerin Inc
719 Boul Industriel Bureau 101
Blainville QC J7C 3
450 434-4641

(G-3880)
CAMBRIDGE DIAGNOSTIC PDTS INC
6880 Nw 17th Ave (33309-1524)
PHONE..................................954 971-4040
Roy Gold, *CEO*
Jack H Gold, *CEO*
Gary Gold, *President*
Marc Gold, *Principal*
Jane Walk, *Master*
EMP: 10 **EST:** 1953
SQ FT: 20,000
SALES (est): 2.2MM **Privately Held**
WEB: www.ecamco.com
SIC: 2835 2841 In vitro diagnostics; soap & other detergents

(G-3881)
CAPITAL CONTRACTING & DESIGN (PA)
817 Sw 10th St (33315-1224)
P.O. Box 1333, Plainfield NJ (07061-1333)
PHONE..................................908 561-8411
Donald W Finley, *President*
Mark McQuillan, *Vice Pres*
Silvio Montesdeoca, *CFO*
Scott Angelica, *Sales Executive*
Michele Reese, *Office Mgr*
EMP: 21 **EST:** 1979
SALES (est): 3MM **Privately Held**
WEB: www.captlfix.com
SIC: 2541 2542 Display fixtures, wood; fixtures: display, office or store: except wood

(G-3882)
CAPTAINS FASTENERS CORP
3706 Sw 30th Ave (33312-6707)
PHONE..................................954 533-9259
JC Betancor Santos, *Exec Dir*
EMP: 7 **EST:** 2010
SALES: 2.7MM **Privately Held**
WEB: www.captainsfasteners.com
SIC: 3965 Fasteners

(G-3883)
CARDINAL HEALTH 414 LLC
5601 Powerline Rd Ste 108 (33309-2831)
PHONE..................................954 202-1883
Don Kinney, *Branch Mgr*
EMP: 6
SALES (corp-wide): 152.9B **Publicly Held**
SIC: 2835 2834 Radioactive diagnostic substances; pharmaceutical preparations
HQ: Cardinal Health 414, Llc
7000 Cardinal Pl
Dublin OH 43017
614 757-5000

(G-3884)
CASEWORKS INTERNATIONAL INC
Also Called: Caseworks Factory Store.com
1883 W State Road 84 # 10 (33315-2232)
PHONE..................................954 933-9102
Norman H Alman, *President*
▲ **EMP:** 16 **EST:** 1998
SQ FT: 20,000
SALES (est): 668.6K **Privately Held**
WEB: www.caseworksintl.com
SIC: 3949 2541 Sporting & athletic goods; wood partitions & fixtures

(G-3885)
CAYAGO AMERICAS INC
Also Called: Seabob
1881 W State Road 84 # 104 (33315-2208)
PHONE..................................754 216-4600
Claus Gruner, *CEO*
EMP: 10 **EST:** 2016
SALES: 6.4MM
SALES (corp-wide): 531.1K **Privately Held**
WEB: www.seabob.com
SIC: 3949 Water sports equipment
HQ: Cayago Ag
Flachter Str. 32
Stuttgart 70499
711 993-3970

(G-3886)
CBD LLC
Also Called: Diamond Cbd
3531 Griffin Rd Ste 100 (33312-5444)
PHONE..................................305 615-1194
EMP: 13 **EST:** 2017
SALES (est): 1.2MM **Privately Held**
WEB: www.diamondcbd.com
SIC: 3999

(G-3887)
CD GREETING LLC
3260 Ne 32nd St (33308-7102)
PHONE..................................954 530-1301
EMP: 5
SALES (est): 453.3K **Privately Held**
SIC: 2335 Mfg Women's/Misses' Dresses

(G-3888)
CELIGENEX INC
3233 Ne 34th St Apt 912a (33308-6939)
PHONE..................................954 957-1058
Clyde Goodheart, *Branch Mgr*
EMP: 7
SALES (corp-wide): 67.1K **Privately Held**
SIC: 2834 Powders, pharmaceutical
PA: Celigenex, Inc.
406 S Cypress Rd Apt 303
Pompano Beach FL

(G-3889)
CEMENT-IT INC
2455 E Sunrise Blvd # 11 (33304-3118)
PHONE..................................954 565-7875
Peter Krokstedt, *President*
Jonas Ekberg, *Vice Pres*
◆ **EMP:** 5 **EST:** 1999
SQ FT: 2,000
SALES (est): 1.1MM **Privately Held**
WEB: www.cement-it.com
SIC: 3273 Ready-mixed concrete

(G-3890)
CEMEX MATERIALS LLC
29 Sw 33rd St (33315-3300)
PHONE..................................954 523-9978
David Packard, *Branch Mgr*
EMP: 73 **Privately Held**
SIC: 3273 5032 5211 Ready-mixed concrete; concrete mixtures; concrete & cinder block
HQ: Cemex Materials Llc
1501 Belvedere Rd
West Palm Beach FL 33406
561 833-5555

(G-3891)
CENTRIFUGAL REBABBITTING INC
234 Sw 29th St (33315-3134)
PHONE..................................954 522-3003
Oliver W Street Jr, *President*
EMP: 10 **EST:** 1985
SQ FT: 10,000
SALES (est): 1.1MM **Privately Held**
WEB: www.centrifugalinc.com
SIC: 3562 7699 Ball bearings & parts; roller bearings & parts; nautical repair services

(G-3892)
CF BOATWORKS INC
3340 Sw 2nd Ave (33315-3302)
PHONE..................................954 325-6007
Carol Coffman, *President*
William Coffman, *Vice Pres*
EMP: 5 **EST:** 2007
SALES (est): 350K **Privately Held**
WEB: www.cfboats.com
SIC: 3732 Boat building & repairing

(G-3893)
CG BURGERS (PA)
1732 N Federal Hwy (33305-2543)
PHONE..................................954 618-6450
Shone Sullizan, *Owner*
EMP: 12 **EST:** 2011
SALES (est): 1.2MM **Privately Held**
WEB: www.cgburgers.com
SIC: 2599 Food wagons, restaurant

(G-3894)
CHADWICK S FUEL CO INC
2600 Miami Rd (33316-3960)
PHONE..................................754 224-8773
Stephen L Chadwick, *Principal*
EMP: 6 **EST:** 2010
SALES (est): 150.2K **Privately Held**
SIC: 2869 Fuels

(G-3895)
CHAMPION CONTROLS INC (PA)
811 Nw 57th Pl (33309-2031)
PHONE..................................954 318-3090
Chantal Wedderburn, *CEO*
Marcel V Wedderburn, *Vice Pres*
Patrick Boyd, *Client Mgr*
Gabby Wedderburn, *Manager*
▼ **EMP:** 35 **EST:** 2003
SALES (est): 14MM **Privately Held**
WEB: www.championcontrols.com
SIC: 3613 5063 Control panels, electric; panelboards

(G-3896)
CHARLES & CO LLC
909 Nw 10th Ter (33311-7119)
PHONE..................................404 592-1190
Charles Kline, *Mng Member*
EMP: 12 **EST:** 2012
SALES (est): 1.6MM **Privately Held**
SIC: 3634 Hair curlers, electric

(G-3897)
CHROM INDUSTRIES LLC
3131 Sw 42nd St (33312-6802)
PHONE..................................954 400-5135
Jonas Carreon, *CFO*
Rishi Kukreja,
EMP: 30 **EST:** 2014
SALES (est): 3.2MM **Privately Held**
SIC: 3089 Blow molded finished plastic products

(G-3898)
CHROMALLOY COMPONENT SVCS INC
3600 Nw 54th St (33309-2400)
PHONE..................................954 378-1999
Surizaday Bonachea, *Sales Staff*
Patrick Freeman, *Manager*
Heather Johnston, *Director*
EMP: 71
SALES (corp-wide): 2.9B **Publicly Held**
WEB: www.chromalloy.com
SIC: 3724 Aircraft engines & engine parts
HQ: Chromalloy Component Services, Inc.
303 Industrial Park Rd
San Antonio TX 78226
210 331-2300

(G-3899)
CHROMALLOY MTL SOLUTIONS LLC
3600 Nw 54th St (33309-2400)
PHONE..................................954 378-1999
Jim Guillano, *President*
James Langelotti, *Treasurer*
Catherine Nairn, *Controller*
Amanda Sanders, *Admin Sec*
Michael Blickensderfer,
EMP: 42 **EST:** 2010
SALES (est): 15.8MM
SALES (corp-wide): 2.9B **Publicly Held**
WEB: www.chromalloy.com
SIC: 3511 Turbines & turbine generator sets & parts
HQ: Chromalloy Gas Turbine Llc
4100 Rca Blvd
Palm Beach Gardens FL 33410
561 935-3571

(G-3900)
CIRCUITRONIX LLC (PA)
3131 Sw 42nd St (33312-6802)
PHONE..................................786 364-4458
Rishi C Kukreja, *CEO*
Lina Ochoa, *Opers Mgr*
Paul Silverthorn, *Opers Staff*
Joel Magat, *Engineer*
Rafael Esteves, *Accounts Mgr*
▲ **EMP:** 399 **EST:** 2002
SALES (est): 44.9MM **Privately Held**
WEB: www.circuitronix.com
SIC: 3672 Circuit boards, television & radio printed

(G-3901)
CITRIX SYSTEMS INC (PA)
851 W Cypress Creek Rd (33309-2040)
PHONE..................................954 267-3000
Robert M Calderoni, *Ch of Bd*
Cristiane Rosul, *Managing Dir*
Mark J Schmitz, *COO*
Jeroen M Van Rotterdam, *Exec VP*
Parag Arora, *Vice Pres*
EMP: 600 **EST:** 1989
SQ FT: 317,000
SALES (est): 3.2B **Publicly Held**
WEB: www.citrix.com
SIC: 7372 Prepackaged software; business oriented computer software

(G-3902)
CLARKWSTERN DTRICH BLDG SYSTEM
1001 Nw 58th Ct (33309-1944)
PHONE..................................954 772-6300
EMP: 21 **Privately Held**
SIC: 3441 Structural Metal Fabrication
HQ: Clarkwestern Dietrich Building Systems Llc
9050 Cntre Pnte Dr Ste 40
West Chester OH 45069

(G-3903)
CLASSIC YACHT REFINISHING INC
1881 W State Road 84 # 10 (33315-2208)
PHONE..................................954 760-9626
Ian McDonald, *President*
William Gould, *Project Mgr*
◆ **EMP:** 8 **EST:** 1989
SALES (est): 289.2K **Privately Held**
WEB: www.premieryachtrefinishing.com
SIC: 3732 Yachts, building & repairing

(G-3904)
CLINIGENCE HOLDINGS INC (PA)
2455 E Sunrise Blvd # 1204 (33304-3115)
PHONE..................................678 607-6393
Warren Hosseinion, *Ch of Bd*
Fred Sternberg, *President*
Andrew Barnett, *Exec VP*
Elisa Luqman, *Exec VP*
Michael Bowen, *CFO*
EMP: 6 **EST:** 2000
SALES: 1.5MM **Publicly Held**
WEB: www.igambit.com
SIC: 7372 7389 Business oriented computer software; pay telephone network

(G-3905)
CLOUD BUSINESS FLORIDA LLC
4101 Ravenswood Rd # 325 (33312-5354)
P.O. Box 22548 (33335-2548)
PHONE..................................954 306-3597
Alicia J Gonzalez,
Mark E Owen,
EMP: 6 **EST:** 2013
SALES (est): 62.1K **Privately Held**
WEB: www.cloudbusinessflorida.com
SIC: 7372 Application computer software

(G-3906)
CMA INTERACTIVE CORPORATION
5011 Neptune Ln (33312-5218)
PHONE..................................954 336-6403
Cesar A Cifuentes, *CEO*
EMP: 14 **EST:** 2001
SALES (est): 592K **Privately Held**
WEB: www.cmainteractive.com
SIC: 7372 Prepackaged software

(G-3907)
COGSWELL INNOVATIONS INC
2000 E Oakland Park Blvd # 106 (33306-1120)
PHONE..................................954 245-8877
David L Cogswell, *President*
Corinne Adams, *COO*
Maureen Burke, *Admin Sec*
EMP: 5 **EST:** 2012
SALES (est): 369K **Privately Held**
WEB: www.cogswellinnovations.com
SIC: 2842 Sanitation preparations, disinfectants & deodorants

(G-3908)
COHEN CAPITAL LLC ✪
3020 E Commercial Blvd (33308-4312)
PHONE..................................954 661-8270
Jason Cohen,
EMP: 9 **EST:** 2020
SALES (est): 500K **Privately Held**
SIC: 1389 Construction, repair & dismantling services

(G-3909)
COLAIANNI ITALIAN FLR TILE MFG
Also Called: Italfloor Tile
700 Sw 21st Ter (33312-2234)
PHONE..................................954 321-8244
Cosimo Colaianni, *President*
EMP: 5 **EST:** 1986
SQ FT: 1,500
SALES (est): 447.9K **Privately Held**
SIC: 3253 Wall tile, ceramic

(G-3910)
COLOR-CHROME TECHNOLOGIES INC
Also Called: Wow Innovations
2345 Sw 34th St (33312-5004)
PHONE..................................954 335-0127
Alan Weizman, *President*
EMP: 6 **EST:** 2005
SQ FT: 5,000
SALES (est): 623.1K **Privately Held**
WEB: www.wow-innovations.com
SIC: 2899 8999 Chemical preparations; chemical consultant

(G-3911)
COMMERCIAL PRINTERS INC (PA)
6600 Nw 15th Ave (33309-1503)
PHONE..................................954 781-3737
Jeffery Runde, *President*
Jeffrey W Runde, *President*
William Runde, *President*
Joe Siess, *President*
Elizabeth I Runde, *Corp Secy*
▼ **EMP:** 58 **EST:** 1970
SQ FT: 18,000
SALES (est): 12.3MM **Privately Held**
WEB: www.commercialprintersinc.com
SIC: 2752 2791 2789 2759 Commercial printing, offset; typesetting; bookbinding & related work; commercial printing

(G-3912)
COMMONWEALTH BRANDS INC (HQ)
5900 N Andrews Ave Ste 11 (33309-2367)
PHONE..................................800 481-5814
Kevin Freudenthal, *President*
Russ Mantuso, *President*
Rob Wilkey, *Principal*
Jose Rubiralta, *Regional Mgr*
Ulric Engles, *Vice Pres*
◆ **EMP:** 200 **EST:** 1991
SQ FT: 11,880
SALES (est): 81.7MM
SALES (corp-wide): 42.5B **Privately Held**
WEB: www.imperialbrandsplc.com
SIC: 2111 2131 2621 Cigarettes; smoking tobacco; paper mills
PA: Imperial Brands Plc
123 Winterstoke Road
Bristol BS3 2
117 963-6636

(G-3913)
COMPLETE METAL SOLUTIONS INTL
107 Nw 5th Ave (33311-9141)
P.O. Box 178 (33302-0178)
PHONE..................................954 560-0583
Thomas P McDonough, *President*
EMP: 8 **EST:** 2016
SALES (est): 432.4K **Privately Held**
WEB: www.completemetalsolutions.com
SIC: 3441 Fabricated structural metal

(G-3914)
CONALI EXPRESS CORP
3281 Nw 65th St (33309-1617)
PHONE..................................954 531-9573
Conrado Fernandez, *President*
Alina Fraguela, *Vice Pres*
EMP: 6 **EST:** 2008
SALES (est): 103.8K **Privately Held**
SIC: 2095 Coffee roasting (except by wholesale grocers)

(G-3915)
CONSOLIDATED CIGR HOLDINGS INC
5900 N Andrews Ave # 1100 (33309-2367)
PHONE..................................954 772-9000
Gary R Ellis, *President*
James M Parnofiello, *CFO*
◆ **EMP:** 1410 **EST:** 1993
SQ FT: 19,000
SALES (est): 109MM
SALES (corp-wide): 42.5B **Privately Held**
WEB: www.altadisusa.com
SIC: 2121 Cigars; cigarillos
HQ: Altadis Holdings U.S.A. Inc.
5900 N Andrews Ave # 600
Fort Lauderdale FL 33309
954 772-9000

(G-3916)
CONSTRUCTION SOFTWARE INC
515 E Las Olas Blvd Ste 1 (33301-2296)
P.O. Box 21024, West Palm Beach (33416-1024)
PHONE..................................888 801-0675
Trevor Hadley, *President*
Monai Dupree, *Vice Pres*
Kelvin Brady, *Manager*
Katherine Dunkley, *Manager*
EMP: 5 **EST:** 1991
SALES (est): 500K **Privately Held**
SIC: 7372 7389 Prepackaged software;

(G-3917)
CONTINENTAL SERVICES GROUP
2901 W Broward Blvd (33312-1249)
PHONE..................................954 327-0809
Cherry D Wheeler-Capik, *CEO*
EMP: 8
SALES (corp-wide): 6.4MM **Privately Held**
WEB: www.continentalbloodbank.com
SIC: 2835 In vitro & in vivo diagnostic substances
PA: Continental Services Group Inc
1300 Nw 36th St
Miami FL 33142
305 633-7700

(G-3918)
CONTROL INVESTMENTS INC (PA)
6001 Ne 14th Ave (33334-5007)
PHONE..................................954 491-6660
Matthew W Jones, *President*
David Jones, *Founder*
C David Jones, *Vice Pres*
Courtney Heffield, *Controller*
Carlos Fernandez, *Sales Dir*
EMP: 19 **EST:** 1990
SALES (est): 14.2MM **Privately Held**
WEB: www.advancedcontrolcorp.com
SIC: 3699 Security control equipment & systems

(G-3919)
COUNTY OF BROWARD
Also Called: Public Communications Office P
151 Sw 2nd St Fl 1 (33301-1819)
PHONE..................................954 357-7120
Ramon Canals, *Manager*
EMP: 6 **Privately Held**
WEB: www.broward.org
SIC: 2759 9631 Business forms: printing; public service commission, except transportation: government
PA: County Of Broward
115 S Andrews Ave Ste 409
Fort Lauderdale FL 33301
954 357-7050

(G-3920)
COVIS INC
110 E Broward Blvd # 170 (33301-3503)
PHONE..................................954 315-3835
Andrew Padova, *Principal*
Neal Lohmann, *Principal*
EMP: 7 **EST:** 2016
SALES (est): 338.2K **Privately Held**
WEB: www.covis-inc.com
SIC: 3652 Pre-recorded records & tapes

(G-3921)
CSC TEXTRON
2011 S Perimeter Rd (33309-7135)
PHONE..................................954 776-5862
EMP: 10 **EST:** 2017
SALES (est): 142.8K **Privately Held**
WEB: www.textron.com
SIC: 3728 Aircraft parts & equipment

(G-3922)
CTI GROUP WORLDWIDE SVCS INC
2455 E Sunrise Blvd # 1100 (33304-3113)
PHONE..................................954 568-5900
Robert Upchurch, *President*
Liam Stapleton, *Director*
▲ **EMP:** 2 **EST:** 1992
SQ FT: 1,800
SALES (est): 8MM **Privately Held**
WEB: www.cti-usa.com
SIC: 2326 4729 7361 Work uniforms; airline ticket offices; labor contractors (employment agency)

(G-3923)
CUSTOM CABINET DOORS & MORE IN
1530 Nw 23rd Ave (33311-5149)
PHONE..................................954 318-1881
Scott Ritchey, *Director*
EMP: 8 **EST:** 2005
SALES (est): 904.1K **Privately Held**
WEB: www.customcabinetdoorsandmore.com
SIC: 2434 Wood kitchen cabinets

(G-3924)
CUSTOM CRATE & LOGISTICS CO
280 Sw 33rd St (33315-3328)
PHONE..................................954 527-5742
Scott Janello, *Vice Pres*
Don Janello, *Treasurer*
◆ **EMP:** 9 **EST:** 1968
SQ FT: 10,000
SALES (est): 1.2MM **Privately Held**
WEB: www.customcrateflorida.com
SIC: 2441 4731 Packing cases, wood: nailed or lock corner; shipping cases, wood: nailed or lock corner; freight forwarding; domestic freight forwarding; foreign freight forwarding

(G-3925)
CYALUME TECH HOLDINGS INC (HQ)
910 Se 17th St Ste 300 (33316-2968)
PHONE..................................954 315-4939
Thomas G Rebar, *Ch of Bd*
Yaron Eitan, *Vice Ch Bd*
Zivi Nedivi, *President*
Dale Baker, *COO*
Doug Miller, *Opers Staff*
▲ **EMP:** 100 **EST:** 2008
SQ FT: 8,500
SALES: 41.2MM **Privately Held**
WEB: www.cyalume.com
SIC: 3648 Lighting equipment
PA: Cps Performance Materials Corp.
100 W Main St
Bound Brook NJ 08805
732 469-7760

(G-3926)
CYCLING QUARTERLY LLC
1007 N Federal Hwy 383 (33304-1422)
PHONE..................................786 367-2497
Michael Gale, *Principal*
EMP: 20 **EST:** 2018
SALES (est): 601.3K **Privately Held**
WEB: www.cyclingquarterly.com
SIC: 2741 Miscellaneous publishing

(G-3927)
D & D MBL WLDG FABRICATION INC (PA)
Also Called: D & D Welding
222 Sw 21st Ter (33312-1425)
PHONE..................................954 791-3385
Edmund O Massa, *President*
Diane Jackson, *Exec VP*
Daniel Massa, *Vice Pres*
EMP: 11
SQ FT: 4,000
SALES (est): 15MM **Privately Held**
WEB: www.ddwelding.com
SIC: 7692 3441 Welding repair; fabricated structural metal

▲ = Import ▼=Export
◆ =Import/Export

(G-3928)
D & D WLDG & FABRICATION LLC (PA)
222 Sw 21st Ter (33312-1425)
PHONE..................................954 791-3385
Daniel Massa, *Vice Pres*
EMP: 14 **EST:** 2007
SALES (est): 20MM **Privately Held**
WEB: www.ddwelding.com
SIC: 3441 Fabricated structural metal

(G-3929)
D E B PRINTING & GRAPHICS INC
6500 Nw 15th Ave Ste 100 (33309-1948)
PHONE..................................954 968-0060
Dave Eichner, *Owner*
David Eichner, *Owner*
Richard Barnes, *CIO*
EMP: 5 **EST:** 1999
SALES (est): 752K **Privately Held**
WEB: www.debprinting.com
SIC: 2752 Commercial printing, offset

(G-3930)
DAKOTA PLUMBING PRODUCTS LLC (PA)
800 Nw 65th St Ste B (33309-2006)
PHONE..................................954 987-3430
Jeff Hughes, *Marketing Staff*
David Kaye, *Mng Member*
Nick Borg, *Manager*
▲ **EMP:** 19 **EST:** 2010
SQ FT: 10,000
SALES (est): 2MM **Privately Held**
WEB: www.dakotasinks.com
SIC: 3432 Plumbing fixture fittings & trim

(G-3931)
DALIAN PLATINUM CHEM LTD CORP
200 S Andrews Ave Ste 200 # 200 (33301-2000)
PHONE..................................954 501-0564
Klaus J Grau Sr, *President*
Catalina M Grau Atuesta, *Treasurer*
EMP: 7 **EST:** 2017
SALES (est): 94.4K **Privately Held**
SIC: 2048 Prepared feeds

(G-3932)
DASHCLICKS LLC
2901 Stirling Rd Ste 210 (33312-6531)
PHONE..................................866 600-3369
Chanuka Kodary, *Principal*
EMP: 10 **EST:** 2018
SALES (est): 534.5K **Privately Held**
WEB: www.dashclicks.com
SIC: 7372 Prepackaged software

(G-3933)
DATA PHONE WIRE & CABLE CORP
3420 Sw 14th St (33312-3600)
PHONE..................................954 761-7171
Gary Gunter, *President*
George Burke, *Vice Pres*
EMP: 11 **EST:** 1990
SALES (est): 608.9K **Privately Held**
SIC: 3643 1731 Current-carrying wiring devices; voice, data & video wiring contractor

(G-3934)
DATACORE SOFTWARE CORPORATION (PA)
1901 W Cypress Creek Rd # 200 (33309-1864)
PHONE..................................954 377-6000
Dave Zabrowski, *CEO*
Ziya Aral, *Chairman*
George Teixeira, *Chairman*
Amanda Bedborough, *Vice Pres*
Chris Marczinke, *Vice Pres*
▼ **EMP:** 65 **EST:** 1998
SALES (est): 71.9MM **Privately Held**
WEB: www.datacore.com
SIC: 3695 7372 Computer software tape & disks: blank, rigid & floppy; prepackaged software

(G-3935)
DAYTON-GRANGER INC
Also Called: D G
3299 Sw 9th Ave (33315-3000)
P.O. Box 350550 (33335-0550)
PHONE..................................954 463-3451
Gibbons D Cline, *President*
Kristin K Cline, *Corp Secy*
Sigrun U Cline, *Vice Pres*
Eliana Iglesias, *Buyer*
Phil Abramson, *Manager*
▲ **EMP:** 250 **EST:** 2007
SQ FT: 105,000
SALES (est): 54.3MM **Privately Held**
WEB: www.daytongranger.com
SIC: 3812 3663 3643 Aircraft/aerospace flight instruments & guidance systems; airborne radio communications equipment; current-carrying wiring devices

(G-3936)
DELTA METAL FINISHING INC
101 Ne 3rd Ave Ste 1500 (33301-1181)
P.O. Box 11376, Saint Petersburg (33733-1376)
PHONE..................................954 953-9898
James Humphrey, *President*
Marilyn Humphrey, *Vice Pres*
James Humphry Jr, *Vice Pres*
Steve Humphry, *Vice Pres*
Kimberly Humphry, *Manager*
EMP: 21 **EST:** 1987
SALES (est): 1.7MM **Privately Held**
WEB:
www.deltametalfinishing.business.site
SIC: 3471 Electroplating of metals or formed products

(G-3937)
DESIGNER SIGN SYSTEMS INC
3540 Nw 56th St Ste 201 (33309-2260)
PHONE..................................954 972-0707
Paul Peirson, *President*
Anthony Barbieri, *President*
Lori Porvin, *Opers Staff*
Judith Barbieri, *Treasurer*
EMP: 7 **EST:** 1990
SQ FT: 5,000
SALES (est): 914.8K **Privately Held**
WEB: www.dssfla.com
SIC: 3993 Signs & advertising specialties

(G-3938)
DESIGNERS SPECIALTY CAB CO INC (PA)
Also Called: Designer's Specialty Millwork
1320 Nw 65th Pl (33309-1901)
PHONE..................................954 868-3440
Gladys G Harrison, *President*
EMP: 43 **EST:** 1994
SQ FT: 39,000
SALES (est): 12MM **Privately Held**
WEB: www.designersspecialty.com
SIC: 2431 Interior & ornamental woodwork & trim; woodwork, interior & ornamental; ornamental woodwork: cornices, mantels, etc.; exterior & ornamental woodwork & trim

(G-3939)
DEVATIS INC
2800 W State Road 84 # 11 (33312-4813)
PHONE..................................954 316-4844
EMP: 6 **EST:** 2018
SALES (est): 348.9K **Privately Held**
WEB: www.devatis.com
SIC: 2834 Pharmaceutical preparations

(G-3940)
DICTION WEAR LLC
2851 Nw 11th Pl Apt 3 (33311-5606)
PHONE..................................954 696-5490
Eric Williams,
EMP: 6 **EST:** 2019
SALES (est): 115.9K **Privately Held**
SIC: 2211 Apparel & outerwear fabrics, cotton

(G-3941)
DILLON YARN CORPORATION (PA)
3250 W Coml Blvd Ste 320 (33309)
PHONE..................................973 684-1600
William Cohen, *CEO*
Mitchel Weinberger, *President*
Michelle Oneill, *Controller*
Christopher Jarosz, *VP Finance*
Deirdre Gallenagh, *Human Res Dir*
◆ **EMP:** 158 **EST:** 1920
SQ FT: 20,000
SALES (est): 25MM **Privately Held**
WEB: www.dillonyarn.com
SIC: 2282 2221 Textured yarn; textile warping, on a contract basis

(G-3942)
DIMAR USA INC (PA)
1332 W Mcnab Rd (33309-1120)
PHONE..................................954 590-8573
Anthony Dehart, *CEO*
Ilan Shneor, *Director*
▲ **EMP:** 5 **EST:** 2011
SQ FT: 8,000
SALES (est): 721.7K **Privately Held**
SIC: 3553 Woodworking machinery

(G-3943)
DIRECT SALES AND DESIGN INC
1140 Ne 7th Ave Unit 3 (33304-2018)
PHONE..................................954 522-5477
Omar Fernandez, *Owner*
EMP: 19
SALES (corp-wide): 467.2K **Privately Held**
WEB: www.directsalesanddesign.com
SIC: 3465 Body parts, automobile: stamped metal
PA: Direct Sales And Design Inc
2448 Ne 26th Ter
Fort Lauderdale FL
954 564-0721

(G-3944)
DJ ROOF AND SOLAR SUPPLY LLC
2009 Admirals Way (33316-3643)
PHONE..................................954 557-1992
Daryl Hudson,
EMP: 2 **EST:** 2018
SQ FT: 2,000
SALES (est): 24MM **Privately Held**
SIC: 2952 5033 Roofing materials; roofing & siding materials

(G-3945)
DK INTERNATIONAL ASSOC INC
Also Called: Dkia
1417 Sw 1st Ave (33315-1555)
PHONE..................................954 828-1256
Miller Randy, *Sales Staff*
Daryl Soderman, *Sales Executive*
Daryl E Soderman, *Director*
Katherine H Soderman, *Director*
EMP: 35 **EST:** 2002
SQ FT: 8,000
SALES (est): 8.1MM **Privately Held**
WEB: www.dkia.net
SIC: 3441 Fabricated structural metal

(G-3946)
DOLL MARINE METAL FABRICA ✪
6800 Nw 15th Way (33309-1501)
PHONE..................................954 941-5093
EMP: 6 **EST:** 2020
SALES (est): 453.4K **Privately Held**
SIC: 3499 Fabricated metal products

(G-3947)
DOLLER MARINE SALES & SERVICES
100 Sw 28th St (33315-3130)
PHONE..................................954 463-9988
Ron Doller, *President*
▼ **EMP:** 10 **EST:** 1983
SQ FT: 13,000
SALES (est): 130.6K **Privately Held**
SIC: 3732 5088 5551 Boat building & repairing; marine supplies; boat dealers

(G-3948)
DONS CUSTOM SERVICE INC
Also Called: D C S
900 Ne 3rd Ave (33304-1940)
PHONE..................................954 491-4043
Sandra Potts, *CEO*
Christopher Potts, *Vice Pres*
EMP: 5 **EST:** 1992
SALES (est): 476.5K **Privately Held**
SIC: 3356 Welding rods

(G-3949)
DRAPERY CONTROL SYSTEMS INC (PA)
Also Called: Brambier's Windows & Walls
5545 Nw 35th Ave D (33309-6309)
PHONE..................................305 653-1712
Robert Brambier, *President*
Lyle Brambier, *Vice Pres*
Meaghan Saunders, *Administration*
▼ **EMP:** 16 **EST:** 1973
SALES (est): 4.9MM **Privately Held**
WEB: www.brambiers.com
SIC: 2221 Upholstery, tapestry & wall covering fabrics

(G-3950)
DTF WOODWORKS
4481 Sw 38th Ter (33312-5407)
PHONE..................................954 317-6443
Dale Beswick, *Principal*
EMP: 8 **EST:** 2007
SALES (est): 726.8K **Privately Held**
WEB: www.dtfwoodworks.com
SIC: 2431 Millwork

(G-3951)
DUBHOUSE INC
404 Se 15th St (33316-1942)
PHONE..................................954 524-3658
Michael Pardo, *President*
EMP: 9 **EST:** 1997
SQ FT: 1,000
SALES (est): 3MM **Privately Held**
WEB: www.thedubhouse.net
SIC: 3652 Compact laser discs, prerecorded

(G-3952)
DYNALCO CONTROLS CORPORATION (DH)
5450 Nw 33rd Ave Ste 104 (33309-6353)
PHONE..................................323 589-6181
Nizar Elias, *President*
EMP: 40 **EST:** 1988
SQ FT: 44,400
SALES (est): 17.7MM
SALES (corp-wide): 2.9B **Publicly Held**
SIC: 3829 3694 3823 3825 Measuring & controlling devices; engine electrical equipment; industrial instrmnts msrmnt display/control process variable; instruments to measure electricity; fluid power cylinders & actuators; relays & industrial controls

(G-3953)
DYNAMIC GLUCOSE HLTH CTRS LLC
515 E Las Olas Blvd Ste 1 (33301-2296)
PHONE..................................800 610-6422
Dr John M Magac, *Principal*
Heather Jobe, *Principal*
EMP: 5 **EST:** 2017
SALES (est): 355.9K **Privately Held**
WEB: www.dynamicglucose.com
SIC: 7372 Application computer software

(G-3954)
E & A INDUSTRIES INC
16 Ne 4th St Ste 110e (33301-3262)
PHONE..................................954 278-2428
Terrance Ward, *Principal*
Oz Chowdhry, *Business Anlyst*
EMP: 12 **EST:** 2011
SALES (est): 1MM **Privately Held**
SIC: 3999 Manufacturing industries

(G-3955)
EARL PARKER YACHT REFINISHING
1915 Sw 21st Ave (33312-3113)
PHONE..................................954 791-1811
J Earl Parker, *President*
EMP: 15 **EST:** 1978
SALES (est): 1.4MM **Privately Held**
SIC: 3732 Boat building & repairing

(G-3956)
EASTMAN PERFORMANCE FILMS LLC
Also Called: Suntek Window Films
5553 Ravenswood Rd # 104 (33312-6655)
PHONE..................................954 920-2001
Hilary Thomas, *Manager*

EMP: 7 **Publicly Held**
SIC: 3442 Window & door frames
HQ: Eastman Performance Films, Llc
4210 The Great Rd
Fieldale VA 24089
276 627-3000

(G-3957)
EBWAY LLC
6600 Nw 21st Ave Ste A (33309-1821)
PHONE..................................954 971-4911
Edward Bennett, *President*
▼ **EMP:** 27 **EST:** 1961
SQ FT: 43,000
SALES (est): 8MM **Privately Held**
WEB: www.ebway.com
SIC: 3544 3549 3469 Die sets for metal stamping (presses); metalworking machinery; metal stampings

(G-3958)
EBWAY LLC
6601 Nw 20th Ave (33309-1500)
PHONE..................................954 971-4911
Catherine E Bennett, *Manager*
EMP: 100
SALES (est): 6MM **Privately Held**
WEB: www.ebway.com
SIC: 3544 Die sets for metal stamping (presses)

(G-3959)
ECI PHARMACEUTICALS LLC (PA)
5311 Nw 35th Ter (33309-6328)
PHONE..................................954 486-8181
Bob Franks, *General Mgr*
Ellen Gettenberg, *Vice Pres*
Dusty Snoeberg, *Vice Pres*
Lewis Soars, *Vice Pres*
Michael Wood, *Engineer*
EMP: 23 **EST:** 2010
SQ FT: 20,000
SALES (est): 6.2MM **Privately Held**
WEB: www.ecipharma.com
SIC: 2834 Pharmaceutical preparations

(G-3960)
ECI TELECOM INC (DH)
5100 Nw 33rd Ave Ste 150 (33309-6362)
PHONE..................................954 772-3070
Gerald Degrace, *President*
David Robinson, *General Mgr*
Ron Levin, *Vice Pres*
Patrick Sparks, *VP Opers*
Denise Marr, *Mfg Staff*
EMP: 45 **EST:** 1982
SALES (est): 26.9MM **Privately Held**
WEB: www.info.rbbn.com
SIC: 3661 7373 Telephone & telegraph apparatus; computer integrated systems design

(G-3961)
ECO WATER TECHNOLOGIES CORP
150 N Federal Hwy Ste 200 (33301-1172)
PHONE..................................954 599-3672
Scott Worley, *CEO*
EMP: 6 **EST:** 2017
SALES (est): 2MM **Privately Held**
WEB: www.ecowatertechnologies.com
SIC: 3589 Sewage & water treatment equipment

(G-3962)
EDGEWATER TECHNOLOGIES INC
Also Called: Paradox Marine
1200 Ne 7th Ave Ste 4 (33304-2021)
PHONE..................................954 565-9898
Joseph Patrick Keenan II, *CEO*
Marc Curreri, *COO*
Nicole Lorenzi, *Opers Mgr*
Erin West Keenan, *CFO*
Brian Kane, *CTO*
▲ **EMP:** 10 **EST:** 2005
SQ FT: 1,400
SALES (est): 1.9MM **Privately Held**
WEB: www.edgewatertechnologies.com
SIC: 3699 5065 Security control equipment & systems; security control equipment & systems

(G-3963)
EDIBLE FLAIR INC
220 Florida Ave (33312-1136)
PHONE..................................954 321-3608
Kriss Carlson, *Principal*
EMP: 6 **EST:** 2010
SALES (est): 83K **Privately Held**
SIC: 2899 Flares

(G-3964)
EDISONECOENERGYCOM CORPORATION
528 Sw 5th Ave Apt 3 (33315-1057)
PHONE..................................954 417-5326
Fred Ford, *President*
EMP: 8
SALES (est): 950K **Privately Held**
WEB: www.edisonecosuperstore.com
SIC: 3612 Transformers, except electric

(G-3965)
EES DESIGN LLC
2801 Nw 55th Ct Ste 5e (33309-2501)
PHONE..................................954 541-2660
Eric E Small, *General Mgr*
Maxanne Loew, *General Mgr*
EMP: 14 **EST:** 2011
SALES (est): 1.3MM **Privately Held**
WEB: www.eesdesignllc.com
SIC: 3499 Aerosol valves, metal

(G-3966)
EILEEN RUTH BENDIS
3850 Galt Ocean Dr (33308-7658)
PHONE..................................954 565-5470
Eileen Bendis, *Principal*
EMP: 7 **EST:** 2010
SALES (est): 223.8K **Privately Held**
WEB: www.regencytower.net
SIC: 3443 Towers (bubble, cooling, fractionating, etc.): metal plate

(G-3967)
ELECTROLUX PROFESSIONAL LLC
3225 Sw 42nd St (33312-6810)
PHONE..................................954 327-6778
John Babila, *Branch Mgr*
EMP: 10
SALES (corp-wide): 13.4B **Privately Held**
WEB: www.beyondbyaerus.com
SIC: 3585 3524 Air conditioning units, complete: domestic or industrial; lawn & garden equipment
HQ: Electrolux Professional, Llc
20445 Emerald Pkwy
Cleveland OH 44135
980 236-2000

(G-3968)
ELEMENT SOLUTIONS INC (PA)
500 E Broward Blvd # 1860 (33394-3030)
PHONE..................................561 207-9600
Benjamin Gliklich, *CEO*
Martin E Franklin, *Ch of Bd*
John E Capps, *Exec VP*
Vic Michels, *Vice Pres*
Patricia A Mount, *Vice Pres*
EMP: 257 **EST:** 1922
SALES: 1.8B **Publicly Held**
WEB: www.elementsolutionsinc.com
SIC: 2899 2869 Chemical preparations; hydraulic fluids, synthetic base

(G-3969)
EMBRACE TELECOM INC
Also Called: Blackbox Gps
333 Las Olas Way Cu1 (33301-2363)
PHONE..................................866 933-8986
Martin Moller, *CEO*
EMP: 15 **EST:** 2008
SQ FT: 4,000
SALES (est): 662.9K **Privately Held**
WEB: www.embracetelecom.com
SIC: 3829 Meteorologic tracking systems

(G-3970)
EMBRAER SERVICES INC
276 Sw 34th St (33315-3603)
PHONE..................................954 359-3700
Gary Spulak, *CEO*
Gary J Spulak, *COO*
Gary Kertz, *Controller*
Jack Benabib, *Technology*
Gloobe Tamy, *Admin Sec*
▲ **EMP:** 600 **EST:** 1997
SQ FT: 2,000
SALES (est): 67.2MM **Privately Held**
WEB: www.embraer.com
SIC: 3721 Aircraft
HQ: Embraer Aircraft Holding, Inc.
276 Sw 34th St
Fort Lauderdale FL 33315

(G-3971)
EMOJI BRACELET LLC
3531 Griffin Rd (33312-5444)
PHONE..................................954 987-0515
Kevin Hagen, *Principal*
John Hirsch,
EMP: 8 **EST:** 2016
SALES (est): 384.8K **Privately Held**
WEB: www.emojibracelet.com
SIC: 3961 Bracelets, except precious metal

(G-3972)
ENG GROUP LLC
Also Called: Eng Group LLC Teg , The
5309 Sw 34th Ave (33312-5566)
PHONE..................................954 323-2024
Hedi Enghelberg,
▲ **EMP:** 5 **EST:** 2004
SQ FT: 1,000
SALES (est): 702K **Privately Held**
WEB: www.engautomotivegroup.com
SIC: 3714 4812 2992 Motor vehicle parts & accessories; radio telephone communication; lubricating oils & greases; brake fluid (hydraulic): made from purchased materials; transmission fluid: made from purchased materials; oils & greases, blending & compounding

(G-3973)
EPOC CNG LLC
1300 Nw 65th Pl (33309-1901)
PHONE..................................561 706-4140
Carter Redd, *Mng Member*
EMP: 6 **EST:** 2015
SALES (est): 208K **Privately Held**
SIC: 1389 Gas compressing (natural gas) at the fields

(G-3974)
ERB ROBERTS TILLAGE LLC
401 E Las Olas Blvd (33301-2210)
PHONE..................................352 376-4888
Devansh Mehta,
▲ **EMP:** 6 **EST:** 2011
SALES (est): 1.3MM **Privately Held**
SIC: 3523 Farm machinery & equipment

(G-3975)
EUROSIGN METALWERKE INC
5301 Nw 35th Ave (33309-6315)
PHONE..................................954 717-4426
Alfred M Bulkan, *President*
Andrew R Bulkan, *Corp Secy*
Jerome R Bulkan, *Finance*
◆ **EMP:** 8 **EST:** 1987
SQ FT: 15,680
SALES (est): 1.2MM **Privately Held**
WEB: www.euro-sign.com
SIC: 3469 Automobile license tags, stamped metal

(G-3976)
EVERGLADES ENVELOPE CO INC
6650 Nw 15th Ave (33309-1503)
PHONE..................................954 783-7920
William G Runde, *President*
Paul Royka, *Info Tech Dir*
EMP: 7 **EST:** 1990
SQ FT: 4,000
SALES (est): 2.2MM
SALES (corp-wide): 12.3MM **Privately Held**
WEB: www.evergladesenvelope.com
SIC: 2677 Envelopes
PA: Commercial Printers, Inc.
6600 Nw 15th Ave
Fort Lauderdale FL 33309
954 781-3737

(G-3977)
EVOLIS INC (DH)
3201 W Coml Blvd Ste 110 (33309)
PHONE..................................954 777-9262
Emmanuel Picot P, *CEO*
Gerardo Talavera, *Managing Dir*
Olivier Chevance, *Business Mgr*
Jean-Charles Pichon, *Project Mgr*
Michelle Fourmond, *Buyer*
▲ **EMP:** 11 **EST:** 2004
SQ FT: 1,900
SALES (est): 9.3MM
SALES (corp-wide): 183.7K **Privately Held**
WEB: www.evolis.com
SIC: 3577 Printers, computer; tape print units, computer

(G-3978)
EW PUBLISHING LLC
2820 Ne 30th St Apt 10 (33306-1942)
PHONE..................................305 358-1100
Ellen M White,
EMP: 7 **EST:** 2008
SALES (est): 118.2K **Privately Held**
SIC: 2741 Miscellaneous publishing

(G-3979)
EWHITE LLC
2633 Bayview Dr (33306-1765)
PHONE..................................954 530-3382
Yohann Guarracino, *Principal*
▲ **EMP:** 6 **EST:** 2013
SALES (est): 760.8K **Privately Held**
WEB: www.easy-whitening.com
SIC: 2844 Toilet preparations

(G-3980)
EXALOS INC
824 Se 12th St (33316-2008)
P.O. Box 460007 (33346-0007)
PHONE..................................215 669-4488
Eugene Covell, *President*
Bettina Lambrechts, *Corp Secy*
Philippe Crepelliere, *Manager*
Udo Oehri, *Director*
Christian Velez, *Director*
EMP: 33 **EST:** 2015
SALES (est): 5MM
SALES (corp-wide): 13.1MM **Privately Held**
WEB: www.exalos.com
SIC: 3674 Semiconductors & related devices
PA: Exalos Ag
Wagistrasse 21
Schlieren ZH 8952
434 446-090

(G-3981)
EXCLUSIVE APPAREL LLC
2598 E Sunrise Blvd # 2104 (33304-3230)
PHONE..................................800 859-6260
Naziha Mustafa,
EMP: 13 **EST:** 2016
SQ FT: 800
SALES (est): 414.8K **Privately Held**
SIC: 2389 Men's miscellaneous accessories

(G-3982)
EXIST INC
Also Called: Exist Clothing & Embroidery
1650 Nw 23rd Ave Ste A (33311-4539)
PHONE..................................954 739-7030
Joshua Glickman, *President*
Shaul Ashkenazy, *Vice Pres*
Hava Austin, *CFO*
Stephen Feldschuh, *CFO*
Meyer Coen, *Sales Staff*
◆ **EMP:** 100 **EST:** 1995
SQ FT: 100,000
SALES (est): 14.5MM **Privately Held**
WEB: www.existusa.com
SIC: 2329 5621 Men's & boys' sportswear & athletic clothing; women's clothing stores

(G-3983)
EXODUS MANAGEMENT LLC
Also Called: Exodus Aviation
6750 N Andrews Ave Ste 20 (33309-2173)
PHONE..................................954 995-4407
Juliet Gonzalez, *CEO*
Chris Santana, *Sales Staff*
EMP: 5

SALES (est): 394.1K Privately Held
WEB: www.exodusaviation.com
SIC: 3728 5088 Research & dev by manuf., aircraft parts & auxiliary equip; aircraft & parts; aircraft engines & engine parts; aircraft & space vehicle supplies & parts; aeronautical equipment & supplies

(G-3984)
EXTREME DIGITAL VIDEO INC
3784 Sw 30th Ave (33312-6701)
PHONE....954 792-2818
Mosh Luski, *Principal*
Berry Basile, *Accounts Exec*
EMP: 6 EST: 2009
SALES (est): 167.4K Privately Held
WEB: www.extremedigital.net
SIC: 3699 Security control equipment & systems

(G-3985)
FABRICATION FLORIDA VENTURE
1201 Nw 65th Pl (33309-1942)
PHONE....954 388-5014
Jop Vos, *Principal*
EMP: 6 EST: 2016
SALES (est): 223.7K Privately Held
SIC: 3599 Machine shop, jobbing & repair

(G-3986)
FANWISE LLC
210 S Andrews Ave (33301-1863)
PHONE....954 874-9000
Circe Brett, *VP Finance*
EMP: 6 EST: 2016
SALES (est): 103.1K Privately Held
WEB: www.fanwise.com
SIC: 7372 Prepackaged software

(G-3987)
FASTSIGNS
3328 Griffin Rd (33312-5519)
PHONE....954 404-8341
EMP: 6 EST: 2018
SALES (est): 447.1K Privately Held
WEB: www.fastsigns.com
SIC: 3993 Signs & advertising specialties

(G-3988)
FCT-COMBUSTION INC
5049 Sw 35th Ter Tce (33312-8264)
PHONE....610 725-8840
EMP: 8 EST: 2016
SALES (est): 311.5K Privately Held
WEB: www.fctcombustion.com
SIC: 3823 Industrial instrmnts msrmnt display/control process variable

(G-3989)
FEDERAL EASTERN INTL INC
3516 W Broward Blvd (33312-1012)
PHONE....954 533-4506
EMP: 12 Privately Held
WEB: www.fedeastintl.com
SIC: 3569 Filters
PA: Federal Eastern International, Llc
1523 Chaffee Rd S Unit 12
Jacksonville FL 32221

(G-3990)
FEDERAL MILLWORK CORP
3300 Se 6th Ave (33316-4118)
PHONE....954 522-0653
Richard A Ungerbuehler, *President*
Jon Fox, *Sales Mgr*
◆ EMP: 34 EST: 1939
SQ FT: 55,000
SALES (est): 4.4MM Privately Held
WEB: www.federalmillwork.com
SIC: 2431 Ornamental woodwork: cornices, mantels, etc.

(G-3991)
FEDERAL-MOGUL MOTORPARTS LLC
3499 Sw 42nd St (33312-6829)
PHONE....954 585-2500
Kevin Muilman, *Manager*
EMP: 7
SALES (corp-wide): 15.3B Publicly Held
WEB: www.drivparts.com
SIC: 3714 Motor vehicle parts & accessories
HQ: Federal-Mogul Motorparts Llc
27300 W 11 Mile Rd # 100
Southfield MI 48034
248 354-7700

(G-3992)
FIIK SKATEBOARDS LLC
5300 Powerline Rd Ste 209 (33309-3187)
PHONE....561 405-9541
EMP: 6
SALES (corp-wide): 206.3K Privately Held
WEB: www.fiik.com
SIC: 3949 Skateboards
PA: Fiik Skateboards Llc
7050 W Palmetto Park Rd
Boca Raton FL 33433
561 316-8234

(G-3993)
FINE ARCHTCTRAL MLLWK SHUTTERS
800 Nw 57th Pl (33309-2032)
PHONE....954 491-2055
Richard T Svopa Jr, *President*
EMP: 12 EST: 1996
SALES (est): 220.5K Privately Held
SIC: 2431 2511 2439 2434 Millwork; wood household furniture; structural wood members; wood kitchen cabinets

(G-3994)
FIRST IMPRSEESION SOUTH FLO
1509 Sw 1st Ave (33315-1710)
PHONE....954 525-0342
Margaret Russell, *Principal*
EMP: 6 EST: 2011
SALES (est): 350.8K Privately Held
WEB: www.firstimpressionftl.com
SIC: 2752 Commercial printing, offset

(G-3995)
FIRST LOOK INC
757 Se 17th St 986 (33316-2960)
PHONE....954 240-0530
Herbert Magney, *Director*
EMP: 7 EST: 2005
SALES (est): 86.5K Privately Held
SIC: 3629 Electrical industrial apparatus

(G-3996)
FIVE STAR QUALITY MFG CORP
Also Called: Five Star Shutters
2200 Ne 62nd Ct (33308-2210)
PHONE....954 972-4772
David H Ceccofiglio, *Principal*
◆ EMP: 6 EST: 2010
SALES (est): 160.4K Privately Held
SIC: 3999 Manufacturing industries

(G-3997)
FLIGHT SOURCE LLC
2011 S Perimeter Rd (33309-7135)
PHONE....954 249-8449
Joseph Miller, *Manager*
EMP: 9 EST: 2019
SALES (est): 249K Privately Held
WEB: www.flightsourcepa.com
SIC: 3724 Aircraft engines & engine parts

(G-3998)
FLORIDA AEROSPACE PARTNERSHIP
4019 Sw 30th Ave (33312-6817)
PHONE....954 617-7700
Jerry Ferguson, *Principal*
EMP: 6 EST: 2013
SALES (est): 117.7K Privately Held
SIC: 3721 Aircraft

(G-3999)
FLORIDA ALGAE LLC
540 Sw 11th Ave (33312-2520)
PHONE....954 213-2693
Steven D Schlosser, *Principal*
EMP: 7 EST: 2011
SALES (est): 249.5K Privately Held
SIC: 2099 Food preparations

(G-4000)
FLORIDA FUNERAL SHIPPING CNTRS
Also Called: Flite Rite Industries
1321c Nw 65th Pl Ste C (33309-1991)
PHONE....954 957-9259
Robert Gurin, *President*
Irene Gurin, *Corp Secy*
▼ EMP: 6 EST: 1987
SQ FT: 5,000
SALES (est): 1.2MM Privately Held
SIC: 2448 3281 Cargo containers, wood; burial vaults, stone

(G-4001)
FLORIDA ORDNANCE CORPORATION
4740 Nw 15th Ave (33309-7210)
PHONE....954 493-8691
Israel Schnabel, *President*
▲ EMP: 15 EST: 1976
SQ FT: 15,000
SALES (est): 2.2MM Privately Held
SIC: 3795 Specialized tank components, military

(G-4002)
FLORIDA PACKG & GRAPHICS INC
Also Called: F P G
6680 Nw 16th Ter (33309-1514)
PHONE....954 781-1440
Frances L Long, *President*
John Long, *Vice Pres*
Paul Rivera, *Warehouse Mgr*
EMP: 17 EST: 1972
SQ FT: 28,000
SALES (est): 2.4MM Privately Held
WEB: www.flpginc.com
SIC: 2653 Boxes, corrugated: made from purchased materials

(G-4003)
FLORIDA PWRTRAIN HYDRULICS INC
Also Called: Rowland Specialists
917 Nw 1st St (33311-8901)
PHONE....954 463-7711
Steve Edgell, *Manager*
EMP: 6
SALES (corp-wide): 6.2MM Privately Held
WEB: www.floridapowertrain.com
SIC: 3714 Motor vehicle parts & accessories
PA: Florida Powertrain & Hydraulics, Inc.
2265 W Beaver St
Jacksonville FL 32209
904 354-5691

(G-4004)
FLORIDA SHUTTER FACTORY INC
3069 Nw 26th St (33311-2057)
PHONE....954 687-4793
Mark N Simons, *Principal*
EMP: 9 EST: 2010
SALES (est): 699.3K Privately Held
WEB: www.flshutterfactory.com
SIC: 3442 Louvers, shutters, jalousies & similar items

(G-4005)
FLORIDA SILICA SAND COMPANY (PA)
Also Called: Fss Company
2962 Trivium Cir Ste 106 (33312-4656)
PHONE....954 923-8323
Betty Pegram, *CEO*
Debbie Pegram, *President*
Emily Herwig, *Corp Secy*
Aaron Herwig, *Vice Pres*
Luis Castano, *Facilities Mgr*
◆ EMP: 20
SQ FT: 1,125
SALES (est): 13.2MM Privately Held
WEB: www.fsscompany.com
SIC: 3272 Brick, stone & related material

(G-4006)
FLORIDA SILICA SAND COMPANY
Also Called: Eldorado Stone
2962 Trivium Cir Ste 105 (33312-4656)
PHONE....954 923-8323
Betty Pegram, *CEO*
EMP: 15
SALES (corp-wide): 15MM Privately Held
WEB: www.eldoradostone.com
SIC: 3272 Concrete products, precast
PA: Florida Silica Sand Company
2962 Trivium Cir Ste 106
Fort Lauderdale FL 33312
954 923-8323

(G-4007)
FLORIDA STORM SHUTTERS INC
4898 Sw 24th Ave (33312-5927)
PHONE....954 257-8365
Kenneth Patino, *Principal*
EMP: 7 EST: 2016
SALES (est): 226K Privately Held
WEB: www.floridastormshutters.com
SIC: 3442 Shutters, door or window: metal

(G-4008)
FOAM & PSP INC
3325 Griffin Rd Ste 208 (33312-5500)
PHONE....954 816-5648
Paul Goken, *President*
EMP: 8 EST: 2000
SQ FT: 5,000
SALES (est): 550.5K Privately Held
SIC: 3086 Plastics foam products

(G-4009)
FORECAST TRADING CORPORATION
Also Called: Forecast Products
2760 Nw 63rd Ct (33309-1712)
PHONE....954 979-1120
Jeff Olefson, *President*
Fredric Olefson, *Chairman*
Jessica Olefson, *Corp Secy*
Jefferson Holmes, *Warehouse Mgr*
◆ EMP: 50 EST: 1974
SQ FT: 45,000
SALES (est): 6.7MM
SALES (corp-wide): 1.1B Publicly Held
WEB: www.forecastparts.com
SIC: 3714 Motor vehicle parts & accessories
PA: Standard Motor Products, Inc.
3718 Northern Blvd # 600
Long Island City NY 11101
718 392-0200

(G-4010)
FORTRESS IMPACT WNDOWS DORS LL
6788 Nw 17th Ave (33309-1522)
PHONE....954 621-2395
Mike Betancourt,
Hector Jordan,
EMP: 7 EST: 2016
SALES (est): 2MM Privately Held
SIC: 3442 Screen & storm doors & windows

(G-4011)
FRAMETASTIC INC
Also Called: Foundation Art Services
5470 Nw 10th Ter (33309-2808)
PHONE....954 567-2800
Nicholas A Doherty, *President*
Katherine Doherty, *Treasurer*
▲ EMP: 14 EST: 2002
SQ FT: 24,000
SALES (est): 2MM Privately Held
SIC: 2499 Picture & mirror frames, wood

(G-4012)
FRANK MURRAY & SONS INC
Also Called: Murray Products
1515 Se 16th St (33316-1713)
PHONE....561 845-1366
Vincent Murray, *President*
Lynn Murray-Shea, *Corp Secy*
Michael Murray, *Vice Pres*
▲ EMP: 12 EST: 1982
SQ FT: 9,000

SALES (est): 565.5K **Privately Held**
SIC: 2298 3732 Fishing lines, nets, seines: made in cordage or twine mills; boat building & repairing

(G-4013)
FREEDOM STEEL BUILDING CORP
1883 W State Road 84 # 106 (33315-2232)
PHONE..................................561 330-0447
Sean Hackner, *CEO*
Michael Hackner, *Sales Mgr*
▼ **EMP:** 30 **EST:** 1989
SALES (est): 8.5MM **Privately Held**
WEB: www.freedomsteel.com
SIC: 3449 Curtain walls for buildings, steel

(G-4014)
FT LAUDERDALE WAX
Also Called: Euroteam Wax Center
1912 N Sederal Hwy (33305)
PHONE..................................954 256-9291
Annemarie Healy, *Owner*
EMP: 8 **EST:** 2013
SALES (est): 562.9K **Privately Held**
SIC: 2842 Wax removers

(G-4015)
FUEL REFORMATION INC
1451 W Cypress Creek Rd # 300 (33309-1961)
PHONE..................................954 800-4289
Phillip Brown, *CEO*
Rohan Mowatt, *CTO*
EMP: 3
SALES (est): 15MM **Privately Held**
WEB: www.fuelreformation.com
SIC: 2899 Fuel treating compounds

(G-4016)
G S PRINTERS INC
Also Called: Gold Star Printers
1239 N Flagler Dr (33304-2131)
PHONE..................................305 931-2755
Curt Kreisler, *President*
Sabrina Shores, *Sales Mgr*
Renee Yeoman, *Manager*
EMP: 7 **EST:** 1974
SALES (est): 919.5K **Privately Held**
SIC: 2752 7334 2741 2791 Commercial printing, offset; photocopying & duplicating services; miscellaneous publishing; typesetting; bookbinding & related work; commercial printing

(G-4017)
GA FD SVCS PINELLAS CNTY LLC
Also Called: G A Food Services
1750 W Mcnab Rd (33309-1011)
PHONE..................................954 972-8884
Larry Kotkin, *Manager*
Arnaldo Gonzalez, *Manager*
EMP: 29
SALES (corp-wide): 151.6MM **Privately Held**
WEB: www.sunmeadow.com
SIC: 2038 5812 5142 Frozen specialties; contract food services; packaged frozen goods
PA: G.A. Food Services Of Pinellas County, Llc
12200 32nd Ct N
Saint Petersburg FL 33716
727 388-0075

(G-4018)
GAAB LOCKS LLC
21014 Sheridan St (33332-2310)
PHONE..................................305 788-8515
James Gagel,
Miguel Calancha,
Mariela V De Lellis,
EMP: 5 **EST:** 2019
SALES (est): 384.5K **Privately Held**
SIC: 3429 Keys, locks & related hardware

(G-4019)
GENESIS II SYSTEMS INC
2425 E Coml Blvd Ste 101 (33308)
PHONE..................................954 489-1124
Walter E Apple, *President*
Michelle L Apple, *Admin Sec*
EMP: 8 **EST:** 1994
SQ FT: 1,500
SALES (est): 169.3K **Privately Held**
SIC: 2875 Compost

(G-4020)
GERMKLEEN LLC ✪
716 Nw 6th Ave (33311-7332)
PHONE..................................954 947-5602
David Demerau,
EMP: 5 **EST:** 2020
SALES (est): 313K **Privately Held**
SIC: 2833 Medicinal chemicals

(G-4021)
GIGLIOLA INC
3341 E Oakland Park Blvd (33308-7216)
PHONE..................................954 564-7871
Roberto Pacella, *Principal*
EMP: 6 **EST:** 2010
SALES (est): 99.9K **Privately Held**
SIC: 2051 Cakes, bakery: except frozen

(G-4022)
GK INC (PA)
2724 Ne 35th Dr (33308-6316)
PHONE..................................215 223-7207
William Kowalchuk, *President*
Walter Cavalcanti, *Vice Pres*
Karen Bixler, *Representative*
EMP: 26 **EST:** 1923
SALES (est): 2MM **Privately Held**
SIC: 2514 2522 Medicine cabinets & vanities: metal; office furniture, except wood

(G-4023)
GLOBAL SATELLITE PRPTS LLC
1901 S Andrews Ave (33316-2858)
PHONE..................................954 459-3000
Martin Fierstone, *CEO*
Jeffery Palmer, *Managing Dir*
Khadija Fierstone, *COO*
EMP: 9 **EST:** 2010
SALES (est): 732.4K **Privately Held**
WEB: www.globalsatellite.us
SIC: 3663 Satellites, communications

(G-4024)
GLOBAL TECH LED LLC
1883 W State Road 84 # 106 (33315-2232)
PHONE..................................877 748-5533
Gary Mart Jr, *Partner*
Luis Ivon, *Finance*
Jeffrey Newman,
Ivon Padilla,
▲ **EMP:** 40 **EST:** 2008
SALES (est): 5MM **Privately Held**
WEB: www.fortis-cyber.com
SIC: 3646 Commercial indusl & institutional electric lighting fixtures

(G-4025)
GRAPEVINE USA INC
333 Las Olas Way (33301-2363)
PHONE..................................786 510-9122
EMP: 5 **EST:** 2018
SALES (est): 346.6K **Privately Held**
WEB: www.theinsidersnet.com
SIC: 2741 Miscellaneous publishing

(G-4026)
GRAPHIC DYNAMICS INC
735 Nw 7th Ter (33311-7312)
PHONE..................................954 728-8452
Ken Cooper, *President*
EMP: 5 **EST:** 1992
SQ FT: 7,000
SALES (est): 478.8K **Privately Held**
WEB: www.graphdyn.com
SIC: 2752 Commercial printing, offset

(G-4027)
GRATE IDEAS OF AMERICA LLC
1417 Sw 1st Ave (33315-1555)
PHONE..................................844 292-6044
Charles J Wobby, *Director*
Daryl Soderman,
▼ **EMP:** 8 **EST:** 2010
SALES (est): 340.1K **Privately Held**
WEB: www.grate-ideas.com
SIC: 3429 Fireplace equipment, hardware: andirons, grates, screens

(G-4028)
GREAT VIRTUALWORKS LLC
4100 Sw 28th Way (33312-5200)
PHONE..................................800 606-6518
Alex Domenech, *Vice Pres*
Ken Meares, *Mng Member*
Richard Thompson, *Analyst*
EMP: 17 **EST:** 2013
SALES (est): 1MM **Privately Held**
WEB: www.greatvirtualworks.com
SIC: 2741 Miscellaneous publishing
PA: Great Healthworks, Inc.
4150 Sw 28th Way
Fort Lauderdale FL 33312

(G-4029)
GREEK ISLAND SPICE INC
2905 Sw 2nd Ave (33315-3121)
PHONE..................................954 761-7161
Joanne Theodore, *President*
Jackie Jeffrey, *Office Mgr*
▼ **EMP:** 8 **EST:** 1997
SQ FT: 4,500
SALES (est): 972.5K **Privately Held**
WEB: www.greekisland.com
SIC: 2099 Seasonings & spices

(G-4030)
GREEN APPLICATIONS LLC
Also Called: Star Led
3233 Sw 2nd Ave Ste 200 (33315-3335)
PHONE..................................954 900-2290
Charlie Blanco, *Principal*
Phillip Kloc, *Marketing Staff*
EMP: 40 **EST:** 2016
SALES (est): 1.8MM **Privately Held**
SIC: 3646 5063 Commercial indusl & institutional electric lighting fixtures; lighting fixtures

(G-4031)
GREENTREE MARKETING SVCS INC
1828 Sw 24th Ave (33312-4530)
P.O. Box 460458 (33346-0458)
PHONE..................................800 557-9567
EMP: 10
SALES (corp-wide): 3MM **Privately Held**
WEB: www.greentreemarketingservices.com
SIC: 2711 8742 Commercial printing & newspaper publishing combined; marketing consulting services
PA: Greentree Marketing Services, Inc.
1451 W Cypress Creek Rd
Fort Lauderdale FL 33309
800 557-9567

(G-4032)
GREENWAVE BIODIESEL LLC
420 W Mcnab Rd (33309-2144)
PHONE..................................239 682-7700
Eric N Lesperance,
Jon C Solin,
EMP: 2 **EST:** 2008
SQ FT: 17,000
SALES (est): 3MM **Privately Held**
WEB: www.greenwavebiodiesel.com
SIC: 2869 Fuels

(G-4033)
GUARDIA LLC (PA)
Also Called: Carrier & Tech Solutions LLC
5900 N Andrews Ave Ste 10 (33309-2367)
PHONE..................................954 670-2900
John J Rearer, *CEO*
David G Hampson, *Security Dir*
EMP: 43 **EST:** 2011
SALES (est): 1.3MM **Privately Held**
WEB: www.guardiallc.com
SIC: 7372 Business oriented computer software

(G-4034)
GUARDIAN INDUSTRIES COR
3060 Sw 2nd Ave (33315-3310)
PHONE..................................954 525-3481
EMP: 21 **EST:** 2019
SALES (est): 257.9K **Privately Held**
WEB: www.guardian.com
SIC: 3211 Flat glass

(G-4035)
GULFSTREAM MEDIA GROUP INC
Also Called: Treasure Coastline
1401 E Broward Blvd # 206 (33301-2116)
PHONE..................................954 462-4488
Mark Mc Cormick, *President*
Ileana Llorens, *Editor*
Bernard McCormick, *Vice Pres*
Brian Beach, *Prdtn Mgr*
Mike Romano, *Opers Staff*
EMP: 20 **EST:** 1965
SQ FT: 1,900
SALES (est): 2.3MM **Privately Held**
WEB: www.gulfstreammediagroup.com
SIC: 2721 Magazines: publishing only, not printed on site

(G-4036)
GVI INDUSTRIES INC
350 Nw 55th St (33309-2321)
PHONE..................................954 818-6411
Thomas M Hynes, *Principal*
EMP: 6 **EST:** 2018
SALES (est): 113.3K **Privately Held**
SIC: 3999 Manufacturing industries

(G-4037)
H M J CORPORATION
81 Bay Colony Dr (33308-2001)
PHONE..................................954 229-1873
Howard Bedick, *President*
EMP: 10 **EST:** 1978
SQ FT: 6,500
SALES (est): 150.9K **Privately Held**
SIC: 2331 Women's & misses' blouses & shirts

(G-4038)
HAILEY CIAN LLC
201 Sw 2nd St (33301-1821)
PHONE..................................954 895-7143
Wesley Gleeson, *Principal*
EMP: 7 **EST:** 2012
SALES (est): 354.7K **Privately Held**
SIC: 2893 Printing ink

(G-4039)
HALL FOUNTAINS INC
5500 Nw 22nd Ave (33309-2715)
PHONE..................................954 484-8530
Scott Hall, *President*
Stewart Hall, *Vice Pres*
Brian Hall, *Treasurer*
Todd Hall, *Prgrmr*
Tanya Hall, *Admin Sec*
◆ **EMP:** 17 **EST:** 1965
SQ FT: 20,000
SALES (est): 2.9MM **Privately Held**
WEB: www.hallfountains.com
SIC: 3272 Concrete products

(G-4040)
HAMNER PARKING LOT SERVICE
2151 Ne 55th St (33308-3154)
PHONE..................................954 328-3216
Paul S Wilner, *President*
EMP: 6 **EST:** 1973
SQ FT: 1,000
SALES (est): 653.8K **Privately Held**
SIC: 3272 1629 1611 Cast stone, concrete; tennis court construction; highway & street construction

(G-4041)
HAMWORTHY INC (DH)
2900 Sw 42nd St (33312-6811)
PHONE..................................305 597-7520
▲ **EMP:** 6
SQ FT: 2,000
SALES: 10.3MM **Privately Held**
SIC: 3561 Mfg Pumps/Pumping Equipment

(G-4042)
HARDWARE ONLINE STORE
4343 N Andrews Ave (33309-4743)
PHONE..................................954 565-5678
Corey Golden, *President*
EMP: 10 **EST:** 2015
SALES (est): 302.9K **Privately Held**
SIC: 3429 4813 Manufactured hardware (general);

(G-4043)
HAYES IVY MANUFACTURING
200 Sw 1st Ave Ste 960 (33301-2073)
PHONE..................................954 306-2647
Peter H Knight, *President*
JP Aldana, *Natl Sales Mgr*
EMP: 7 **EST:** 2014
SALES (est): 124.9K **Privately Held**
WEB: www.himi-products.com
SIC: 3999 Barber & beauty shop equipment

▲ = Import ▼=Export
◆ =Import/Export

(G-4044)
HEADHUNTER INC
3380 Sw 11th Ave (33315-2902)
PHONE..................................954 462-5953
Mel Mellinger, *Ch of Bd*
Mark Mellinger, *Vice Pres*
Paul C Mellinger, *Vice Pres*
Jane Mellinger, *Shareholder*
Max Vidaurre, *Internal Med*
◆ **EMP:** 40
SQ FT: 45,000
SALES (est): 10.6MM **Privately Held**
WEB: www.headhunterinc.com
SIC: 3429 5551 Marine hardware; marine supplies

(G-4045)
HEADHUNTER SPEARFISHING CO
1140 Ne 7th Ave Unit 6 (33304-2018)
PHONE..................................954 745-0747
Bradley Thornbrough, *Principal*
EMP: 8 **EST:** 2015
SALES (est): 399.6K **Privately Held**
WEB: www.headhunterspearfishing.com
SIC: 3949 Sporting & athletic goods

(G-4046)
HEADWATERS MANAGEMENT LLC
Also Called: Headwaters Wine and Spirits
1160 N Federal Hwy # 214 (33304-1412)
PHONE..................................608 209-3111
Thomas A Fuchs, *Mng Member*
Twyla Getterte,
EMP: 1 **EST:** 2012
SALES (est): 4MM **Privately Held**
WEB: www.headwaters-wines.com
SIC: 2084 Wines

(G-4047)
HIGH SIERRA TERMINALING LLC
1200 Se 20th St (33316-3596)
PHONE..................................954 764-8818
Lindy R Jones, *Treasurer*
Glenn R Jones, *Mng Member*
John C Wilkinson, *Admin Sec*
John Lynn,
EMP: 19 **EST:** 2006
SQ FT: 20,400
SALES (est): 2.2MM **Privately Held**
SIC: 2952 Asphalt felts & coatings

(G-4048)
HOLLOW METAL DOORS & FRAMES
1947 Sw 28th Ave (33312-4422)
PHONE..................................954 993-0613
Quentin J Gomez R, *Principal*
EMP: 7 **EST:** 2015
SALES (est): 107.6K **Privately Held**
SIC: 3442 Metal doors

(G-4049)
HOLLY SARGENT
1000 Se 4th St Apt 315 (33301-2370)
PHONE..................................954 560-6973
Holly Sargent, *Principal*
EMP: 7 **EST:** 2008
SALES (est): 91.8K **Privately Held**
SIC: 3699 Electrical equipment & supplies

(G-4050)
HOWMEDICA OSTEONICS CORP
505 Nw 65th Ct Ste 102 (33309-6120)
PHONE..................................954 714-7933
Frank Russo, *Manager*
EMP: 49
SALES (corp-wide): 14.3B **Publicly Held**
SIC: 3841 Surgical & medical instruments
HQ: Howmedica Osteonics Corp.
325 Corporate Dr
Mahwah NJ 07430
201 831-5000

(G-4051)
HOWMEDICA OSTEONICS CORP
Also Called: Stryker Spine
2944 Trivium Cir (33312-4659)
PHONE..................................954 791-6078
Nicolas Lluch, *Manager*
EMP: 49
SALES (corp-wide): 14.3B **Publicly Held**
SIC: 3841 Surgical instruments & apparatus
HQ: Howmedica Osteonics Corp.
325 Corporate Dr
Mahwah NJ 07430
201 831-5000

(G-4052)
HUNTER AEROSPACE SUPPLY LLC
3331 Nw 55th St (33309-6306)
P.O. Box 22178 (33335-2178)
PHONE..................................954 321-8848
John Pergolini,
Richard Kosachiner,
Richard Smith,
EMP: 6 **EST:** 2015
SQ FT: 2,500
SALES (est): 476.6K **Privately Held**
WEB: www.hunter.aero
SIC: 3452 3451 Bolts, nuts, rivets & washers; lock washers; rivets, metal; screw machine products

(G-4053)
HUNTSMAN PROPERTIES LLC (PA)
2145 Davie Blvd Ste 101 (33312-3155)
PHONE..................................954 282-1797
David M Huntsman, *President*
EMP: 23 **EST:** 2016
SALES (est): 412.8K **Privately Held**
WEB: www.huntsman.com
SIC: 2821 Plastics materials & resins

(G-4054)
IBI SYSTEMS INC
6842 Nw 20th Ave (33309-1513)
PHONE..................................954 978-9225
Daljeet Singh, *President*
EMP: 6 **EST:** 1987
SQ FT: 4,200
SALES (est): 600K **Privately Held**
WEB: www.ibi-systems.com
SIC: 3571 Electronic computers

(G-4055)
ICARECOM LLC
401 E Las Olas Blvd Ste 1 (33301-2210)
PHONE..................................954 616-5604
James Riley, *CEO*
▼ **EMP:** 19 **EST:** 2012
SQ FT: 8,000
SALES (est): 1.4MM **Privately Held**
SIC: 7372 Application computer software

(G-4056)
IMS PUBLISHING INC
Also Called: Yacht International Magazine
1850 Se 17th St Ste 107 (33316-3051)
PHONE..................................954 761-8777
Michel Karsenti, *President*
EMP: 9 **EST:** 1997
SQ FT: 2,500
SALES (est): 826.9K **Privately Held**
SIC: 2721 Magazines: publishing only, not printed on site

(G-4057)
INDUCTOWELD TUBE CORP
3350 Ne 33rd Ave (33308-7134)
PHONE..................................646 734-7094
Michele Rella, *Principal*
EMP: 7 **EST:** 2016
SALES (est): 531.3K **Privately Held**
SIC: 3312 Blast furnaces & steel mills

(G-4058)
INDUSTRIAL SHADEPORTS INC
6600 Nw 12th Ave Ste 220 (33309-1147)
PHONE..................................954 755-0661
Stanley D Breitweiser, *President*
Agnee E Breitweiser, *Admin Sec*
EMP: 5 **EST:** 2016
SALES (est): 737.4K **Privately Held**
WEB: www.shadeports.com
SIC: 2394 Canvas covers & drop cloths

(G-4059)
INNOVATIVE PRODUCTS LLC
1632 Ne 12th Ter (33305-3131)
PHONE..................................888 764-6478
Seann Pavlik, *President*
Melanie Garcia, *Manager*
EMP: 6 **EST:** 2016
SALES (est): 253.3K **Privately Held**
SIC: 3492 3592 Control valves, fluid power: hydraulic & pneumatic; valves

(G-4060)
INSPECTECH AEROSERVICE INC
902 Sw 34th St (33315-3403)
PHONE..................................954 359-6766
James P Lang, *President*
EMP: 13 **EST:** 1993
SQ FT: 3,500
SALES (est): 565.5K **Privately Held**
WEB: www.inspectech.net
SIC: 3369 Aerospace castings, nonferrous: except aluminum

(G-4061)
INSPIRE ME BRACELETS
3333 Ne 16th Pl (33305-3716)
PHONE..................................404 644-7771
William D Waldbueser, *Owner*
EMP: 10 **EST:** 2017
SALES (est): 400.7K **Privately Held**
SIC: 3961 Bracelets, except precious metal

(G-4062)
INTERMEDIX CORPORATION (DH)
6451 N Federal Hwy # 1000 (33308-1424)
PHONE..................................954 308-8700
Joel Portice, *CEO*
Nicole Cawley, *General Mgr*
Clint Farquhar, *Business Mgr*
Ken Cooke, *COO*
Kenneth Cooke, *COO*
EMP: 70 **EST:** 2005
SALES (est): 328.6MM
SALES (corp-wide): 1.2B **Publicly Held**
WEB: www.r1rcm.com
SIC: 7372 Business oriented computer software
HQ: Intermedix Holdings, Inc.
401 N Michigan Ave # 2700
Chicago IL 60611
312 324-7820

(G-4063)
INTERNATIONAL QUIKSIGNS INC
804 Se 17th St (33316-2930)
PHONE..................................954 462-7446
Paul Rabinowitz, *President*
Brett Selwitz, *Admin Sec*
▼ **EMP:** 13 **EST:** 1990
SALES (est): 539.6K **Privately Held**
WEB: www.quiksignsftl.com
SIC: 3993 5999 Signs, not made in custom sign painting shops; banners

(G-4064)
INTERNATIONAL SHIPYARDS ANCONA
1850 Se 17th St Ste 200 (33316-3050)
PHONE..................................305 371-7722
Edward Sacks, *Principal*
Brian Jupp, *Chief Acct*
Kathleen Deppe, *Human Resources*
Per Bjornsen, *Director*
EMP: 12 **EST:** 2014
SALES (est): 698.3K **Privately Held**
SIC: 3731 Shipbuilding & repairing

(G-4065)
INTERNATIONAL WEATHERIZATION
500 E Broward Blvd # 1710 (33394-3000)
PHONE..................................954 818-3288
Esther Bittelman, *Principal*
EMP: 6 **EST:** 2011
SALES (est): 143.3K **Privately Held**
SIC: 1041 0811 5052 2491 Gold bullion production; gold ores processing; timber tracts, hardwood; gold ore; structural lumber & timber, treated wood

(G-4066)
IRON BRIDGE TOOLS INC
101 Ne 3rd Ave Ste 1800 (33301-1252)
PHONE..................................954 596-1090
Hardy Haenisch, *CEO*
Alissa Robinson, *COO*
EMP: 5 **EST:** 2006
SALES (est): 628.7K **Privately Held**
WEB: www.ironbridgetools.com
SIC: 3423 Hand & edge tools

(G-4067)
ISLAND JOYS
3679 Nw 19th St (33311-4120)
PHONE..................................561 201-6005
EMP: 6 **EST:** 2018
SALES (est): 260K **Privately Held**
WEB: www.islandjoysinc.com
SIC: 2085 Distilled & blended liquors

(G-4068)
ISLAND SALT COMPANY LLC
900 Se 6th St (33301-3010)
PHONE..................................954 610-2590
Claudette A Pagano, *Principal*
EMP: 6 **EST:** 2012
SALES (est): 81.8K **Privately Held**
SIC: 2899 Salt

(G-4069)
ISLANDOOR COMPANY
951 Nw 9th Ave (33311-7211)
PHONE..................................954 524-3667
A J Schwencke, *President*
Rebecca Cabanaugh, *Controller*
EMP: 6 **EST:** 1989
SQ FT: 20,000
SALES (est): 2MM **Privately Held**
SIC: 2431 3442 Doors, wood; metal doors

(G-4070)
ITEG LLC
333 Las Olas Way Cu1 (33301-2363)
PHONE..................................305 399-2510
Sergio Lotero, *Mng Member*
Jose Ayala,
EMP: 10 **EST:** 2013
SALES (est): 2MM **Privately Held**
SIC: 2621 Parchment, securites & bank note papers

(G-4071)
ITG CIGARS INC (HQ)
Also Called: Altadis USA
5900 N Andrews Ave Ste 11 (33309-2367)
PHONE..................................954 772-9000
Gary R Ellis, *CEO*
Rob Wilkey, *President*
Javier Estades, *General Mgr*
Donnie Felts, *Regional Mgr*
Teresa Wadhams, *District Mgr*
◆ **EMP:** 95
SQ FT: 38,000
SALES (est): 216.2MM
SALES (corp-wide): 42.5B **Privately Held**
WEB: www.altadisusa.com
SIC: 2121 Cigars
PA: Imperial Brands Plc
123 Winterstoke Road
Bristol BS3 2
117 963-6636

(G-4072)
J & G EXPLOSIVES LLC
413 Idlewyld Dr (33301-2730)
PHONE..................................407 883-0734
John W Angelini, *Principal*
EMP: 12 **EST:** 2016
SALES (est): 2.8MM **Privately Held**
SIC: 2892 Explosives

(G-4073)
J R WHEELER CORPORATION
Also Called: Structurz Exhibits & Graphics
3748 Sw 30th Ave (33312-6708)
PHONE..................................954 585-8950
Jim Wheeler, *President*
Jarre Mesadieu, *Vice Pres*
EMP: 6 **EST:** 1997
SQ FT: 3,222
SALES (est): 469.3K **Privately Held**
WEB: www.structurz.com
SIC: 3993 Signs & advertising specialties

(G-4074)
JAMES D NALL CO INC (PA)
Also Called: Aqua-Air Manufacturing
1883 W State Road 84 # 106 (33315-2232)
PHONE..................................305 884-8363
James D Nall, *President*
John O'Brien, *Vice Pres*
Marilyn Nall, *Treasurer*
◆ **EMP:** 30 **EST:** 1941

GEOGRAPHIC

SALES (est): 5.6MM **Privately Held**
WEB: www.aquaair.net
SIC: 3585 3429 Air conditioning units, complete: domestic or industrial; manufactured hardware (general)

(G-4075)
JANINE OF LONDON INC
45 Fort Royal Is (33308-6013)
PHONE..................................954 772-3593
Janine Dunn, *President*
Janine Lesley Shamy, *Principal*
Ezra Shamy, *Vice Pres*
▲ **EMP:** 5 **EST:** 1986
SALES (est): 326.9K **Privately Held**
WEB: www.janineoflondonfashions.net
SIC: 2335 Women's, juniors' & misses' dresses

(G-4076)
JAS POWDER COATING LLC
219 Sw 21st Ter (33312-1424)
PHONE..................................954 916-7711
Ellen F Reinig, *Mng Member*
EMP: 7 **EST:** 2011
SQ FT: 12,000
SALES (est): 1.6MM **Privately Held**
WEB: www.jaspowdercoating.com
SIC: 3479 Etching & engraving

(G-4077)
JAVALUTION COFFEE COMPANY
2485 E Sunrise Blvd # 20 (33304-3100)
PHONE..................................954 568-1747
David Briskie, *CEO*
Scott Pumper, *President*
Anthony Sanzari, *COO*
Mike Randolph, *Vice Pres*
Maritza Beck, *Accounts Mgr*
EMP: 14 **EST:** 2003
SQ FT: 8,000
SALES (est): 1.1MM **Privately Held**
WEB: www.gojavafit.biz
SIC: 2095 Roasted coffee

(G-4078)
JEFCO MANUFACTURING INC
718 Nw 1st St (33311-9000)
P.O. Box 14843 (33302-4843)
PHONE..................................954 527-4220
Steve Karden, *President*
Allan Karden, *Vice Pres*
EMP: 20 **EST:** 1976
SQ FT: 12,000
SALES (est): 2.6MM **Privately Held**
WEB: www.jefcomfg.com
SIC: 3429 Manufactured hardware (general)

(G-4079)
JEWELSWEBSCOM
3500 N Sr 7 Ste 103-3 (33319)
PHONE..................................954 993-7744
Jewel Islam, *Principal*
EMP: 6 **EST:** 2015
SALES (est): 132.8K **Privately Held**
WEB: www.jewelswebs.com
SIC: 3915 Jewelers' materials & lapidary work

(G-4080)
JON PAUL INC
Also Called: Jon Paul Jewelers
3353 Galt Ocean Dr 55 (33308-7002)
PHONE..................................954 564-4221
Paul Schroeders, *President*
Mathew Schroeders, *Corp Secy*
EMP: 9 **EST:** 1969
SQ FT: 2,700
SALES (est): 795K **Privately Held**
WEB: www.jonpauljewelers.com
SIC: 3911 5944 Jewelry, precious metal; jewelry, precious stones & precious metals

(G-4081)
JRG SYSTEMS INC
Also Called: Grant Printing
1239 N Flagler Dr (33304-2131)
PHONE..................................954 962-1020
Jim Grant, *President*
Kim Sozio, *General Mgr*
Chad Rodgers, *Principal*
▼ **EMP:** 10 **EST:** 1978
SALES (est): 1.3MM **Privately Held**
WEB: www.grantprintinginc.com
SIC: 2752 2732 2759 Commercial printing, offset; books: printing only; pamphlets: printing only, not published on site; visiting cards (including business): printing

(G-4082)
K C MARINE SERVICES INC
1111 Sw 21st Ave Ste 20 (33312-3139)
PHONE..................................954 766-8100
Kelly Carver, *President*
EMP: 6 **EST:** 1998
SALES (est): 350K **Privately Held**
WEB: www.kcmarineservices.com
SIC: 3732 7699 Yachts, building & repairing; boat repair

(G-4083)
KAI LIMITED
1650 W Mcnab Rd (33309-1009)
PHONE..................................954 957-8586
Scott Zucker, *CEO*
James Pederson, *President*
Robert Crigler, *Vice Pres*
▲ **EMP:** 250 **EST:** 1998
SQ FT: 37,000
SALES (est): 14.9MM **Privately Held**
WEB: www.kailimited.com
SIC: 3679 5065 3357 Electronic circuits; connectors, electronic; nonferrous wiredrawing & insulating

(G-4084)
KARNAK SOUTH INC
1010 Se 20th St (33316-3594)
P.O. Box 13137 (33316-0100)
PHONE..................................954 761-7606
Sima Jelin, *Ch of Bd*
James D Hannah, *President*
Sarah Jelin, *Vice Pres*
Chris Salazar, *Vice Pres*
Robert Andrews, *CFO*
▼ **EMP:** 10 **EST:** 1985
SQ FT: 65,000
SALES (est): 865.8K **Privately Held**
WEB: www.karnakcorp.com
SIC: 2952 3354 2951 Roofing materials; aluminum extruded products; asphalt paving mixtures & blocks

(G-4085)
KB AEROSPACE CO
401 E Las Olas Blvd (33301-2210)
PHONE..................................754 366-9194
Gregory T Dunn, *Principal*
EMP: 7 **EST:** 2010
SALES (est): 204.8K **Privately Held**
WEB: www.kbaerospace.com
SIC: 3721 Aircraft

(G-4086)
KEMET CORPORATION (HQ)
1 E Broward Blvd Ste 200 (33301-1872)
P.O. Box 5928, Greenville SC (29606-5928)
PHONE..................................954 766-2800
William M Lowe Jr, *CEO*
Per Olof Loof, *CEO*
Frank G Brandenberg, *Ch of Bd*
R James Assaf, *Senior VP*
Phillip M Lessner, *Senior VP*
▲ **EMP:** 986 **EST:** 1919
SALES: 1.2B **Privately Held**
WEB: www.kemet.com
SIC: 3675 Electronic capacitors

(G-4087)
KENCO HOSPITALITY INC
1000 Nw 56th St (33309-2833)
PHONE..................................954 921-5434
Gary Kenney, *President*
Mike Wilson, *Plant Mgr*
◆ **EMP:** 62 **EST:** 1994
SQ FT: 17,000
SALES (est): 8.6MM **Privately Held**
WEB: www.kencohospitality.com
SIC: 2392 2391 Bedspreads & bed sets: made from purchased materials; curtains & draperies

(G-4088)
KENCO QUILTING & TEXTILES INC
1000 Nw 56th St (33309-2833)
PHONE..................................954 921-5434
Gary Kenney, *President*
EMP: 14 **EST:** 1971
SQ FT: 17,000
SALES (est): 574.3K **Privately Held**
WEB: www.kencohospitality.com
SIC: 2392 5131 Bedspreads & bed sets: made from purchased materials; drapery material, woven

(G-4089)
KERNO LLC
20958 Sheridan St (33332-2311)
PHONE..................................954 261-5854
Hugo Conde, *Mng Member*
Maite Blanco Fombon,
EMP: 12 **EST:** 2015
SALES (est): 967.1K **Privately Held**
WEB: www.kerno-usa.com
SIC: 3471 Decorative plating & finishing of formed products

(G-4090)
KIZABLE LLC
1125 Ne 16th Ter (33304-2320)
P.O. Box 235, Clearwater (33757-0235)
PHONE..................................727 600-3469
Brian Schroeder, *Exec Dir*
EMP: 8 **EST:** 2011
SALES (est): 715.2K **Privately Held**
SIC: 2064 Fruit & fruit peel confections

(G-4091)
KRON DESIGNS LLC
Also Called: Good Gal Storage G.G.s
6818 Nw 20th Ave (33309-1513)
PHONE..................................954 941-0800
Vanessa Maria Genet,
Veronica Michelle Illsen,
◆ **EMP:** 7 **EST:** 2009
SQ FT: 3,500
SALES (est): 600K **Privately Held**
WEB: www.krondesigns.com
SIC: 3231 2531 2599 Furniture tops, glass: cut, beveled or polished; public building & related furniture; library furniture; school furniture; hotel furniture

(G-4092)
L3 TECHNOLOGIES INC
Also Called: G.A. International
2900 Sw 42nd St (33312-6811)
PHONE..................................305 371-7039
Max Garay, *Branch Mgr*
EMP: 6
SALES (corp-wide): 3.7B **Publicly Held**
WEB: www.l3harris.com
SIC: 3663 3669 3679 3812 Telemetering equipment, electronic; signaling apparatus, electric; microwave components; search & navigation equipment
HQ: L3 Technologies, Inc.
600 3rd Ave Fl 34
New York NY 10016
321 727-9100

(G-4093)
LAGACI INC
Also Called: Lagaci Sport
2201 Stirling Rd Ste 101 (33312-6626)
PHONE..................................954 929-1395
Yuval Lugassy, *CEO*
Shay Y Lugassy, *Vice Pres*
David Lougassy, *Treasurer*
Lagaci Shai, *Manager*
Sela Jonathan, *Info Tech Mgr*
◆ **EMP:** 12 **EST:** 1998
SQ FT: 7,000
SALES (est): 2.1MM **Privately Held**
WEB: www.lagaci.com
SIC: 2339 2325 Women's & misses' outerwear; men's & boys' trousers & slacks

(G-4094)
LAJOIE INVESTMENT CORP
Also Called: Leo Manufacturing
819 Nw 7th Ter (33311-7201)
PHONE..................................954 463-3271
Fax: 954 463-7123
EMP: 10
SQ FT: 15,500
SALES (est): 1.4MM **Privately Held**
SIC: 3444 3585 Mfg Sheet Metalwork Mfg Refrigeration/Heating Equipment

(G-4095)
LASTRADA FURNITURE INC (PA)
Also Called: Lastrada Furniture & Interiors
1785 Nw 38th Ave (33311-4138)
PHONE..................................954 485-6000
Eli Mordehay, *President*
Daniel Leslie, *Sales Mgr*
Eric Denoun, *Executive Asst*
EMP: 18 **EST:** 1995
SQ FT: 50,000
SALES (est): 3.6MM **Privately Held**
SIC: 3553 7389 Furniture makers' machinery, woodworking; interior design services

(G-4096)
LATHAM MARINE INC
280 Sw 32nd Ct (33315-3347)
PHONE..................................954 462-3055
Robert P Latham, *President*
Kathleen Latham, *CFO*
Tom Gongola, *Technician*
EMP: 20 **EST:** 1973
SQ FT: 11,000
SALES (est): 2.5MM **Privately Held**
WEB: www.lathammarine.com
SIC: 3429 3714 3441 3312 Marine hardware; motor vehicle parts & accessories; fabricated structural metal; blast furnaces & steel mills; folding paperboard boxes

(G-4097)
LD TELECOMMUNICATIONS INC
Also Called: Nexogy Sac
2101 W Commercial Blvd (33309-3071)
PHONE..................................954 628-3029
EMP: 56
SALES (corp-wide): 19.6MM **Privately Held**
WEB: www.ldtelecom.com
SIC: 7372 Application computer software
PA: Ld Telecom, Inc
2121 Ponce De Leon Blvd # 200
Coral Gables FL 33134
305 358-8952

(G-4098)
LE PUBLICATIONS INC
Also Called: Life Extension
3600 W Commercial Blvd (33309-3338)
PHONE..................................954 766-8433
Renee Price, *President*
Alexandra Maldonado, *Art Dir*
EMP: 13 **EST:** 2004
SALES (est): 195.7K **Privately Held**
SIC: 2741 Miscellaneous publishing

(G-4099)
LEAN GREEN ENTERPRISES LLC
2125 S Andrews Ave (33316-3431)
PHONE..................................954 525-2971
Scott Frybarger, *Mng Member*
Michael Burgio,
EMP: 5 **EST:** 2009
SALES (est): 426.4K **Privately Held**
WEB: www.hillyork.com
SIC: 3639 Trash compactors, household

(G-4100)
LIFESTYLE MEDIA GROUP LLC
3511 W Commercial Blvd (33309-3331)
PHONE..................................954 377-9470
Jeffrey Dinetz, *Publisher*
Michelle Simon, *Publisher*
Beth Tache, *Publisher*
Michelle Solomon, *Editor*
Dan Fudge, *Vice Pres*
EMP: 12 **EST:** 2013
SALES (est): 2.3MM **Privately Held**
SIC: 2721 Magazines: publishing & printing

(G-4101)
LIQUIGUARD TECHNOLOGIES INC
5807 N Andrews Way (33309-2359)
PHONE..................................954 566-0996
Abbas Sadriwalla, *President*
EMP: 20 **EST:** 2004

▲ = Import ▼=Export
◆ =Import/Export

SALES (est): 2MM Privately Held
WEB: www.liquiguard.com
SIC: 3069 Medical & laboratory rubber sundries & related products

(G-4102)
LONGBOW MARINE INC
1305 Sw 1st Ave (33315-1503)
PHONE....954 616-5737
Simon Addrison, *Principal*
EMP: 8 EST: 2014
SALES (est): 1.4MM Privately Held
WEB: www.longbowmarine.com
SIC: 3429 Aircraft & marine hardware, inc. pulleys & similar items

(G-4103)
LOW CODE IP HOLDING LLC
Also Called: Blazedpath
401 E Las Olas Blvd Ste 1 (33301-2210)
PHONE....833 260-2151
Gustavo Merchan, *Mng Member*
EMP: 8 EST: 2016
SALES (est): 384.2K Privately Held
SIC: 7372 Prepackaged software

(G-4104)
LPS LATH PLST & STUCCO INC
513 Nw 16th Ave (33311-8851)
PHONE....954 444-3727
Eddie Brown, *Principal*
EMP: 8 EST: 2008
SALES (est): 146.3K Privately Held
SIC: 3541 Lathes

(G-4105)
LUXURY BOAT SERVICES INC
Also Called: Marine Electrical Engineer
1990 Sw 9th St 2 (33312-3274)
PHONE....360 451-2888
Joseph D'Alelio, *CEO*
EMP: 5 EST: 2018
SALES (est): 322.9K Privately Held
SIC: 3732 Yachts, building & repairing

(G-4106)
LYTRON PRINT
919 Ne 20th Ave (33304-3037)
PHONE....954 683-1291
Nathalia Hodge, *Principal*
EMP: 6 EST: 2016
SALES (est): 98.2K Privately Held
SIC: 2752 Commercial printing, lithographic

(G-4107)
M AUSTIN FORMAN
888 Se 3rd Ave Ste 501 (33316-1159)
PHONE....954 763-8111
Austin M Forman, *Principal*
EMP: 34 EST: 2008
SALES (est): 635.5K Privately Held
WEB: www.davie-fl.gov
SIC: 3324 Commercial investment castings, ferrous
PA: Town Of Davie
6591 Orange Dr
Davie FL 33314
954 797-1000

(G-4108)
MADDYS PRINT SHOP LLC
5450 Nw 33rd Ave Ste 108 (33309-6353)
PHONE....954 749-0440
Steven Lopata,
Maddy Lopata,
EMP: 8 EST: 1985
SQ FT: 3,500
SALES (est): 890K Privately Held
WEB: www.maddysprintshop.com
SIC: 2752 5699 7374 5999 Commercial printing, offset; T-shirts, custom printed; computer graphics service; banners

(G-4109)
MAGENAV INC
Also Called: Statgear
3530 Nw 53rd St (33309-6340)
PHONE....718 551-1815
Avraham Goldstein, *President*
▲ EMP: 8 EST: 2011
SALES (est): 851.4K Privately Held
WEB: www.statgeartools.com
SIC: 3569 5961 Firefighting apparatus & related equipment; fishing, hunting & camping equipment & supplies: mail order

(G-4110)
MANAGEMENT INTERNATIONAL INC
1828 Se 1st Ave (33316-2802)
PHONE....954 763-8811
Joan McNulty, *President*
Barbara McNulty, *Vice Pres*
Bill McNulty, *Vice Pres*
EMP: 23 EST: 1969
SALES (est): 1.5MM Privately Held
SIC: 2731 2741 Books: publishing only; miscellaneous publishing

(G-4111)
MANNING COMPANY
Also Called: TMC
223 Sw 28th St (33315-3131)
PHONE....954 523-9355
Richard V Manning, *President*
EMP: 7 EST: 1997
SQ FT: 9,000
SALES (est): 651.1K Privately Held
WEB: www.themanningco.com
SIC: 3444 3441 2522 Sheet metalwork; fabricated structural metal; office furniture, except wood

(G-4112)
MANSFIELD INTERNATIONAL INC
3561 N 55th (33301)
PHONE....954 632-3280
Craig Mansfield, *President*
▼ EMP: 7 EST: 2004
SALES (est): 130K Privately Held
SIC: 2241 Cotton narrow fabrics

(G-4113)
MAS ENTRPRSES OF FT LAUDERDALE
Also Called: Consolidated Box
1883 W State Road 84 # 10 (33315-2232)
PHONE....904 356-9606
Mariano Arranz Jr, *President*
Robert Arranz, *Vice Pres*
Mike Trout, *Technology*
Judith Arranz, *Admin Sec*
▼ EMP: 27 EST: 1978
SQ FT: 50,000
SALES (est): 1.6MM Privately Held
SIC: 2653 Boxes, corrugated: made from purchased materials

(G-4114)
MDL MOLDING LLC
1112 Sw 22nd Ter (33312-3048)
PHONE....954 792-3104
Melzar R Deleon, *Manager*
EMP: 6 EST: 2012
SALES (est): 94K Privately Held
SIC: 3089 Molding primary plastic

(G-4115)
MEDIA CREATIONS INC
Also Called: Llumina Press
7101 W Coml Blvd Ste 4e (33319)
PHONE....954 726-0902
Deborah Greenspan, *President*
EMP: 8 EST: 1997
SALES (est): 732K Privately Held
WEB: www.llumina.com
SIC: 2741 Miscellaneous publishing

(G-4116)
MEDIC HEALTHCARE LLC
6750 N Andrews Ave # 200 (33309-2180)
PHONE....954 336-1776
Osullivan James, *Mng Member*
EMP: 7
SQ FT: 1,500
SALES (est): 5MM Privately Held
SIC: 3841 Surgical & medical instruments

(G-4117)
MEGAWATTAGE LLC (PA)
Also Called: Megawattage.com Generators
850 Sw 21st Ter (33312-2236)
PHONE....954 328-0232
Michael Jansen, *President*
Allen Brenner,
EMP: 10 EST: 2006
SQ FT: 10,000
SALES (est): 3.3MM Privately Held
WEB: www.megawattage.com
SIC: 3519 3621 7629 1731 Diesel, semi-diesel or duel-fuel engines, including marine; power generators; electrical equipment repair services; electric power systems contractors; industrial & commercial equipment inspection service; industrial machinery & equipment repair

(G-4118)
METALS USA HOLDINGS CORP (HQ)
4901 Nw 17th Way Ste 405 (33309-3773)
PHONE....954 202-4000
Robert C McPherson, *CEO*
Roger Krohn, *Senior VP*
William A Smith II, *Senior VP*
Daniel L Henneke, *Vice Pres*
Tom Foust, *Manager*
EMP: 651 EST: 2005
SQ FT: 6,700
SALES (est): 266.5MM
SALES (corp-wide): 8.8B Publicly Held
WEB: www.metalsusa.com
SIC: 3272 3354 5051 Building materials, except block or brick: concrete; aluminum extruded products; steel
PA: Reliance Steel & Aluminum Co.
350 S Grand Ave Ste 5100
Los Angeles CA 90071
213 687-7700

(G-4119)
METROPOLIS CORP
2455 E Sunrise Blvd # 909 (33304-3112)
PHONE....954 951-1011
David Brown, *President*
Lex Luthor, *Chief Mktg Ofcr*
Stacey Sterling, *Comms Mgr*
EMP: 50 EST: 2017
SALES (est): 2.6MM Privately Held
WEB: www.metropolis.com
SIC: 3999 Manufacturing industries

(G-4120)
MGM GRANITE & MARBLE COMPANY
5937 Ravenswood Rd Bldg H (33312-6673)
PHONE....954 894-6802
Norman Richie, *CEO*
Irine Carrasquillo, *Vice Pres*
Mike Diaz, *Administration*
EMP: 8 EST: 2003
SALES (est): 482.1K Privately Held
SIC: 3281 Granite, cut & shaped

(G-4121)
MICRO PRINTING INC
2571 Nw 4th Ct (33311-8626)
PHONE....954 676-5757
Alex Buelvas, *President*
Eva Falcone, *Manager*
▼ EMP: 10 EST: 1987
SQ FT: 2,000
SALES (est): 250K Privately Held
WEB: www.micro-printing.com
SIC: 2752 Commercial printing, offset

(G-4122)
MICROSOFT CORPORATION
6750 N Andrews Ave # 400 (33309-2180)
PHONE....425 882-8080
Persio Afonso, *Business Mgr*
Robert Ivanschitz, *Counsel*
Alberto Bustamante, *Sales Mgr*
Jamie McDaniel, *Accounts Exec*
Sarah Didonato, *Corp Comm Staff*
EMP: 200
SALES (corp-wide): 168B Publicly Held
WEB: www.microsoft.com
SIC: 7372 Application computer software
PA: Microsoft Corporation
1 Microsoft Way
Redmond WA 98052
425 882-8080

(G-4123)
MODERN HAPPY HOME LLC
1201 E Sunrise Blvd # 305 (33304-2880)
PHONE....954 436-0055
Carlos Moratinos, *Mng Member*
EMP: 5 EST: 2011
SALES (est): 331.5K Privately Held
WEB: www.modernhappyhome.com
SIC: 2512 Upholstered household furniture

(G-4124)
MONTESINO INTERNATIONAL CORP
1816 N Dixie Hwy (33305-3849)
PHONE....954 767-6185
Mitchell D Ousley, *Principal*
Dan Crilly,
▲ EMP: 9
SALES (est): 845.3K Privately Held
WEB: www.marazullarimar.com
SIC: 3911 Bracelets, precious metal

(G-4125)
MOTUS GI LLC
Also Called: Motus Gi, Inc.
1301 E Broward Blvd # 31 (33301-2152)
PHONE....954 541-8000
Timothy Moran, *Principal*
David Guzman, *Principal*
Jeff Hutchison, *Vice Pres*
EMP: 7 EST: 2015
SALES (est): 1.1MM
SALES (corp-wide): 98K Publicly Held
WEB: www.motusgi.com
SIC: 3841 Surgical & medical instruments
PA: Motus Gi Holdings, Inc.
1301 E Broward Blvd Fl 3
Fort Lauderdale FL 33301
954 541-8000

(G-4126)
MOTUS GI HOLDINGS INC (PA)
1301 E Broward Blvd Fl 3 (33301-2152)
PHONE....954 541-8000
Timothy P Moran, *CEO*
David Hochman, *Ch of Bd*
Mark Pomeranz, *President*
Steven M Bosrock, *Vice Pres*
George G Peters, *Vice Pres*
EMP: 25 EST: 2016
SQ FT: 4,554
SALES (est): 98K Publicly Held
WEB: www.motusgi.com
SIC: 3841 3845 Surgical & medical instruments; electromedical apparatus; colonascopes, electromedical

(G-4127)
MURPHY BED USA INC (PA)
4330 N Federal Hwy (33308-5208)
PHONE....954 493-9001
Jack B Hulse, *President*
▼ EMP: 25 EST: 1991
SALES (est): 2.2MM Privately Held
WEB: www.murphybedusa.com
SIC: 2514 2515 Beds, including folding & cabinet, household: metal; mattresses & bedsprings

(G-4128)
N23D SERVICES LLC ✪
20974 Sheridan St (33332-2311)
PHONE....754 217-3362
Richard Wissinger, *Vice Pres*
Paul Mira,
EMP: 7 EST: 2021
SQ FT: 1,000
SALES (est): 554.6K Privately Held
WEB: www.n23dservices.com
SIC: 3728 Aircraft parts & equipment

(G-4129)
NANAS ORIGINAL STROMBOLI INC
5421 Ne 14th Ave (33334-4928)
PHONE....954 771-6262
Kenneth J Ventura, *President*
Cynthia J Ventura, *Corp Secy*
EMP: 5 EST: 2009
SALES (est): 489.9K Privately Held
WEB: www.nanasoriginalstromboli.com
SIC: 2032 Italian foods: packaged in cans, jars, etc.

(G-4130)
NARDIS ENTERPRISES LLC
2831 Ne 56th Ct (33308-2713)
PHONE....954 529-0691
Angela M Naridis,
EMP: 7 EST: 2006

SALES (est): 396.8K **Privately Held**
WEB: www.bakersstongo.com
SIC: 3411 Food & beverage containers

(G-4131)
NASCO INDUSTRIES INC
Also Called: Industrial Products Div
3541 Nw 53rd St (33309-6391)
PHONE....................954 733-8665
Jason Petrucci, *President*
Ed Brenner, *President*
◆ **EMP:** 24 **EST:** 1959
SQ FT: 17,000
SALES (est): 1.6MM **Privately Held**
WEB: www.nascoindust.com
SIC: 3545 5085 3546 3423 Machine tool attachments & accessories; industrial supplies; power-driven handtools; hand & edge tools

(G-4132)
NATIONAL MULTIPLE LISTING INC (PA)
6511 Bay Club Dr Apt 2 (33308-1806)
PHONE....................954 772-8880
Harris A Small Jr, *President*
▲ **EMP:** 26 **EST:** 1947
SQ FT: 42,000
SALES (est): 1.6MM **Privately Held**
WEB: www.printitondemand.com
SIC: 2752 Commercial printing, offset

(G-4133)
NAUTICAL SPECIALISTS
2841 Ne 36th St (33308-5817)
PHONE....................954 761-7130
Robert Miles, *Principal*
EMP: 5 **EST:** 2007
SALES (est): 910.5K **Privately Held**
WEB: www.nauticalspecialists.com
SIC: 3822 Air conditioning & refrigeration controls

(G-4134)
NAV-X LLC
Also Called: Fortress Marine Anchors
1386 W Mcnab Rd (33309-1132)
PHONE....................954 978-9988
Don M Hallerberg, *Principal*
Alicia Hallerberg, *Corp Secy*
EMP: 20 **EST:** 1986
SQ FT: 12,000
SALES (est): 3.3MM **Privately Held**
WEB: www.fortressanchors.com
SIC: 3463 3462 3369 3354 Aluminum forgings; iron & steel forgings; nonferrous foundries; aluminum extruded products

(G-4135)
NEPTUNE BOAT LIFTS INC
280 Sw 6th St (33301-2822)
PHONE....................954 524-3616
Randy Whitesides, *CEO*
Joshua Billings, *Representative*
▼ **EMP:** 29 **EST:** 2007
SQ FT: 10,000
SALES (est): 950K **Privately Held**
WEB: www.neptuneboatlifts.com
SIC: 3536 Boat lifts

(G-4136)
NEUTRAL GUARD LLC
1401 Sw 34th Ave (33312-3659)
PHONE....................954 249-6600
Larry Konzy, *Principal*
EMP: 7 **EST:** 2010
SALES (est): 185.7K **Privately Held**
WEB: www.thecellphonechipstore.com
SIC: 3842 Surgical appliances & supplies

(G-4137)
NEW RIVER CABINET & FIX INC
750 Nw 57th Ct (33309-2028)
PHONE....................954 938-9200
Joanne R Triviz, *President*
Joannne R Triviz, *President*
Dan Ptak, *COO*
Salvadore Garcia, *Vice Pres*
Christine Rodriguez, *Admin Sec*
▲ **EMP:** 20 **EST:** 1984
SQ FT: 93,000
SALES (est): 933.3K **Privately Held**
SIC: 2541 2542 Cabinets, except refrigerated: show, display, etc.: wood; cabinets: show, display or storage: except wood

(G-4138)
NEW YACHTS COMPANY
2890 W State Road 84 # 103 (33312-4828)
PHONE....................754 223-5907
EMP: 6 **EST:** 2018
SALES (est): 111.3K **Privately Held**
WEB: www.yachtcreators.com
SIC: 3731 Shipbuilding & repairing

(G-4139)
NEW YOU MEDIA LLC
4150 Sw 28th Way (33312-5201)
PHONE....................800 606-6518
Ken Meares, *Mng Member*
EMP: 10 **EST:** 2011
SALES (est): 1MM **Privately Held**
WEB: www.newyou.com
SIC: 2741 Miscellaneous publishing
PA: Great Healthworks, Inc.
4150 Sw 28th Way
Fort Lauderdale FL 33312

(G-4140)
NEWMIL INC
2029 Sw 20th St (33315-1881)
PHONE....................954 444-4471
Sauer Van Den Berg, *President*
Edwin Hibbert, *General Mgr*
EMP: 12 **EST:** 2000
SQ FT: 1,600
SALES (est): 641.2K **Privately Held**
WEB: www.newmilmarine.com
SIC: 2431 Woodwork, interior & ornamental

(G-4141)
NFJB INC
60 Nw 60th St (33309-2332)
PHONE....................954 771-1100
John T Connelly Jr, *President*
Ryan Reynolds, *Purchasing*
Krystal Vega, *Purchasing*
◆ **EMP:** 22 **EST:** 1974
SQ FT: 6,480
SALES (est): 4.2MM **Privately Held**
WEB: www.nauticalfurnishings.com
SIC: 2511 5932 2434 Wood household furniture; used merchandise stores; wood kitchen cabinets

(G-4142)
NORJAC OIL & GAS INC OR J
2525 Barcelona Dr (33301-1558)
PHONE....................954 779-3192
Norm Jackson, *President*
EMP: 6 **EST:** 2001
SALES (est): 149.3K **Privately Held**
SIC: 1389 Oil & gas field services

(G-4143)
NOTICE FOUR LLC
2775 Nw 62nd St (33309-1750)
PHONE....................954 652-1168
Melissa A Notice Ms, *Principal*
EMP: 7 **EST:** 2002
SQ FT: 10,160
SALES (est): 199.1K **Privately Held**
SIC: 3674 Semiconductors & related devices

(G-4144)
NUTOP INTERNATIONAL LLC
2601 E Oklnd Prk Blvd # 601 (33306-1606)
PHONE....................954 909-0010
Wolf M Gerhard, *Mng Member*
Flavio Rego,
EMP: 6 **EST:** 2015
SALES (est): 500K **Privately Held**
SIC: 2833 Vitamins, natural or synthetic: bulk, uncompounded
PA: Nutop Produtos Funcionais Ltda.
Estr. Marica Marques 1055
Santana Do Parnaiba SP

(G-4145)
NYRSTAR US INC
350 E Las Olas Blvd # 800 (33301-4211)
PHONE....................954 400-6464
Michael Morley, *President*
Dan Harrell, *Superintendent*
Julien De Wilde, *Chairman*
Heinz Eigner, *CFO*
Francesco Cappadoro, *Director*
EMP: 111 **EST:** 2007
SALES (est): 17.8MM **Privately Held**
WEB: www.nyrstar.com
SIC: 1081 Metal mining services
HQ: Nyrstar Sales & Marketing Ag
Rue De Jargonnant 1
Genf GE 1207

(G-4146)
OAKLAND PARK SMOOTHIE INC
2765 Ne 19th St (33305-3601)
PHONE....................954 567-0871
Kenneth W Walters, *Principal*
EMP: 6 **EST:** 2010
SALES (est): 111.9K **Privately Held**
SIC: 2037 Frozen fruits & vegetables

(G-4147)
OCTANE SEATING LLC
401 E Las Olas Blvd Ste 1 (33301-2210)
PHONE....................888 627-6743
Peter Goldstein, *President*
Mark Shapiro,
Bruce Tucker,
Martin Vasilev,
▲ **EMP:** 20 **EST:** 2014
SQ FT: 4,000
SALES (est): 2.4MM **Privately Held**
WEB: www.octaneseating.com
SIC: 3111 Upholstery leather

(G-4148)
OHM AMERICAS LLC
Also Called: OHM Power Solutions
3736 Sw 30th Ave (33312-6708)
PHONE....................800 467-7275
Allen Licht,
EMP: 10 **EST:** 2012
SALES (est): 1.7MM **Privately Held**
WEB: www.ohmps.com
SIC: 3679 3677 3612 8711 Electronic loads & power supplies; electronic coils, transformers & other inductors; power & distribution transformers; electrical or electronic engineering; power conversion units, a.c. to d.c.: static-electric

(G-4149)
OMT LLC
3848 Sw 30th Ave (33312-6824)
PHONE....................954 327-1447
Monique Traad, *President*
Daisy Pagang, *Manager*
EMP: 10 **EST:** 2004
SALES (est): 1MM **Privately Held**
WEB: www.omtmedical.com
SIC: 3069 Medical & laboratory rubber sundries & related products

(G-4150)
OP YACHT SERVICES CORP
2015 Sw 20th St Ste 220 (33315-1883)
PHONE....................954 451-3677
Alessandra Lamarca, *Principal*
Osvaldo Palenzuela, *Director*
EMP: 10 **EST:** 2015
SALES (est): 528.8K **Privately Held**
WEB: www.opyachtservices.com
SIC: 3732 Yachts, building & repairing

(G-4151)
ORBUSNEICH MEDICAL INC
5363 Nw 35th Ave (33309-6315)
PHONE....................954 730-0711
Alfred Novak, *Ch of Bd*
Bruce Wayne Johnson, *President*
Joe Velarde, *General Mgr*
David Morrow, *COO*
Robert Cottone, *Vice Pres*
EMP: 30 **EST:** 1996
SQ FT: 11,000
SALES (est): 11.7MM **Privately Held**
WEB: www.orbusneich.com
SIC: 3841 Surgical & medical instruments
PA: Orbusneich Medical Company Limited
Rm 303 & 305 3/F Bldg 20e
Sha Tin NT

(G-4152)
OSLER INCORPORATED (PA)
200 Sw 1st Ave Ste 1250 (33301-2098)
PHONE....................954 767-6339
Leo C Smith, *President*
EMP: 28 **EST:** 2004
SALES (est): 518.2K **Privately Held**
SIC: 1081 Metal mining services

(G-4153)
P S T COMPUTERS INC
Also Called: PST Computers
2808 N Federal Hwy (33306-1426)
PHONE....................954 566-1600
Patrick Guertin, *President*
Alroger Gomes, *Comp Tech*
EMP: 7 **EST:** 1987
SQ FT: 4,500
SALES (est): 1.2MM **Privately Held**
WEB: www.pstcomputers.com
SIC: 3571 5734 1731 Electronic computers; computer peripheral equipment; computer installation

(G-4154)
PALMLAND PAPER CO INC
708 Ne 2nd Ave (33304-2616)
P.O. Box 550848 (33355-0848)
PHONE....................954 764-6910
Bernard Beauregard, *Ch of Bd*
Todd Beauregard, *President*
EMP: 8 **EST:** 1959
SQ FT: 7,500
SALES (est): 840K **Privately Held**
SIC: 2679 Paper products, converted

(G-4155)
PANOFF PUBLISHING INC
Also Called: Ppi Group
6261 Nw 6th Way Ste 100 (33309-6103)
PHONE....................954 377-7777
▲ **EMP:** 60
SQ FT: 2,000
SALES (est): 819.3K **Privately Held**
SIC: 2741 Misc Publishing

(G-4156)
PANTROPIC POWER INC
Also Called: Caterpillar Authorized Dealer
1881 W State Road 84 # 103 (33315-2208)
PHONE....................954 797-7972
Doug Hughes, *Manager*
EMP: 52
SALES (corp-wide): 49.8MM **Privately Held**
WEB: www.pantropic.com
SIC: 3531 5082 Construction machinery; construction & mining machinery
PA: Pantropic Power, Inc.
8205 Nw 58th St
Doral FL 33166
305 477-3329

(G-4157)
PARAMOUNT MOLD LLC
1701 W Cypress Creek Rd (33309-1805)
PHONE....................954 772-2333
Andrew Shelton, *President*
Adrianne D'Antonio, *Human Res Dir*
EMP: 31 **EST:** 2011
SALES (est): 4.2MM **Privately Held**
WEB: www.paramountmold.com
SIC: 3089 Injection molding of plastics

(G-4158)
PARAMOUNT MOLDED PRODUCTS INC
1701 W Cypress Creek Rd (33309-1805)
PHONE....................954 772-2333
Robert H Petrucci, *President*
Richard A Bonopane, *Vice Pres*
Evelyn B Petrucci, *Treasurer*
Joan A Bonopane, *Admin Sec*
▲ **EMP:** 38 **EST:** 1979
SQ FT: 20,000
SALES (est): 4MM **Privately Held**
WEB: www.paramountmold.com
SIC: 3089 Injection molding of plastics

(G-4159)
PARKER BOATWORKS
617 Nw 7th Ave (33311-7306)
PHONE....................954 585-1059
Brian Parker, *President*
EMP: 10 **EST:** 2015
SALES (est): 374.8K **Privately Held**
WEB: www.parkerboatworks.com
SIC: 3732 Boat building & repairing

(G-4160)
PARKSON CORPORATION (DH)
Also Called: Schreiber
1401 W Cypress Creek Rd # 100
(33309-1969)
PHONE..................................954 974-6610
Michael Hill, *President*
Dianne Kaplan, *Principal*
Clare Peeters, *COO*
Bill Maesalu, *Vice Pres*
Michael Miller, *Vice Pres*
◆ **EMP:** 4 **EST:** 1962
SQ FT: 25,000
SALES (est): 48MM
SALES (corp-wide): 1B **Privately Held**
WEB: www.parkson.com
SIC: 3589 Water treatment equipment, industrial
HQ: Axel Johnson Inc.
155 Spring St Fl 6
New York NY 10012
646 291-2445

(G-4161)
PEGASUS CLEAN AIR MTR CARS INC
2400 W Cypress Creek Rd (33309-1824)
PHONE..................................954 682-2000
Jack Trotman, *President*
EMP: 8 **EST:** 2010
SALES (est): 950K **Privately Held**
SIC: 3711 Motor vehicles & car bodies

(G-4162)
PERFECT PAVERS SOUTH FLA LLC
528 Nw 1st Ave (33301-3204)
PHONE..................................954 779-1855
John C Lewis, *Principal*
EMP: 10 **EST:** 2011
SALES (est): 2.3MM **Privately Held**
WEB: www.perfectpavers.com
SIC: 3531 Pavers

(G-4163)
PHARMAMED USA INC
Also Called: Pharmamed Global Distributors
3778 Sw 30th Ave (33312-6701)
PHONE..................................954 533-4462
Julian Lopera, *CEO*
Paula Morato, *CFO*
Andres Otalvaro, *Sales Mgr*
Amy Lee, *Admin Asst*
EMP: 6 **EST:** 2013
SALES (est): 1.7MM **Privately Held**
WEB: www.pharmamed.us
SIC: 2834 Pharmaceutical preparations

(G-4164)
PHARMATECH PHARMATECH LLC
3597 Nw 19th St (33311-4260)
PHONE..................................954 583-8778
EMP: 7 **EST:** 2017
SALES (est): 80.3K **Privately Held**
WEB: www.pharmatech-llc.com
SIC: 2834 Pharmaceutical preparations

(G-4165)
PHLEBOTOMISTS ON WHEELS INC
1451 W Cypress Creek Rd # 300
(33309-1961)
PHONE..................................954 873-7591
Tamika Shontal Williams, *Principal*
EMP: 6 **EST:** 2008
SALES (est): 120.3K **Privately Held**
SIC: 3312 Blast furnaces & steel mills

(G-4166)
PHOENIX GROUP FLORIDA INC (PA)
3000 Ne 30th Pl Fl 5 (33306-1957)
PHONE..................................954 563-1224
William Wilkerson, *Ch of Bd*
Peter Posk, *President*
◆ **EMP:** 2 **EST:** 2003
SALES (est): 8MM **Privately Held**
WEB: www.evoprint.com
SIC: 2752 Commercial printing, lithographic

(G-4167)
PICKLED ART INC
1495 N Federal Hwy (33304-1472)
PHONE..................................954 635-7370
Kaylin M Parrish, *Principal*
EMP: 7 **EST:** 2010
SALES (est): 89.4K **Privately Held**
SIC: 2035 Pickled fruits & vegetables

(G-4168)
PIPE WELDERS INC (PA)
2965 W State Road 84 (33312-4867)
PHONE..................................954 587-8400
George M Irvine Jr, *Ch of Bd*
John Winters, *Vice Pres*
Scot M Coller, *VP Finance*
Shelly Green, *Human Res Mgr*
EMP: 79 **EST:** 1977
SQ FT: 50,000
SALES (est): 23.4MM **Privately Held**
WEB: www.pipewelders.com
SIC: 3441 3732 2394 Fabricated structural metal for ships; boats, fiberglass: building & repairing; canvas & related products

(G-4169)
PIPEWELDERS MARINE INC
2965 W State Road 84 (33312-4867)
PHONE..................................954 587-8400
George Irvine Jr, *Ch of Bd*
George M Irvine III, *President*
Dan Garver, *VP Sls/Mktg*
Scot Coller, *VP Finance*
EMP: 97 **EST:** 1986
SALES (est): 15.6MM
SALES (corp-wide): 23.4MM **Privately Held**
WEB: www.pipewelders.com
SIC: 3429 5551 3444 3441 Marine hardware; boat dealers; sheet metalwork; fabricated structural metal
PA: Pipe Welders, Inc.
2965 W State Road 84
Fort Lauderdale FL 33312
954 587-8400

(G-4170)
PIXELOPTICS INC
6750 N Andrews Ave (33309-2173)
PHONE..................................954 376-1542
Gary Davis, *CEO*
EMP: 6 **EST:** 2007
SALES (est): 307.8K **Privately Held**
SIC: 3851 Frames, lenses & parts, eyeglass & spectacle

(G-4171)
POTNETWORK HOLDINGS INC (PA)
3531 Griffin Rd (33312-5444)
PHONE..................................800 433-0127
Gary Blum, *Ch of Bd*
Lee Lefkowitz, *President*
Kyle L Pritz, *Vice Pres*
EMP: 7 **EST:** 1996
SALES (est): 9.6MM **Privately Held**
WEB: www.potnetworkholding.com
SIC: 2833 5122 5521 Medicinals & botanicals; medicinals & botanicals; automobiles, used cars only

(G-4172)
POWERFICIENT LLC
6250 Nw 27th Way (33309-1729)
PHONE..................................800 320-2535
Gerald P Quindlen, *Principal*
Joseph Pizzella, *Vice Pres*
John Nixdorf, *CFO*
EMP: 32 **EST:** 2015
SALES (est): 2.5MM **Privately Held**
WEB: www.powerficient.com
SIC: 3679 3825 3612 3613 Electronic loads & power supplies; meters, power factor & phase angle; electrical power measuring equipment; voltage regulating transformers, electric power; switches, electric power except snap, push button, etc.

(G-4173)
PRECISION PADDLEBOARDS
429 Seabreeze Blvd 214 (33316-1621)
PHONE..................................954 616-8046
Joshua Vajda, *Principal*
▼ **EMP:** 6 **EST:** 2010
SALES (est): 420.5K **Privately Held**
WEB: www.precisionpaddleboards.com
SIC: 3949 Sporting & athletic goods

(G-4174)
PREGE
1475 W Cypress Creek Rd (33309-1930)
PHONE..................................954 908-1535
Ruben Molina, *Manager*
EMP: 8 **EST:** 2016
SALES (est): 163K **Privately Held**
WEB: www.pregelamerica.com
SIC: 2099 Food preparations

(G-4175)
PREMIER COATINGS LLC
Also Called: Tailored Living
450 Nw 27th Ave (33311-8600)
PHONE..................................954 797-9275
Balsa Baletic,
John Jurlich,
EMP: 20 **EST:** 2006
SALES (est): 1.9MM **Privately Held**
WEB: www.premiercoatingsfl.com
SIC: 2541 1799 Cabinets, lockers & shelving; home/office interiors finishing, furnishing & remodeling

(G-4176)
PREMIER LUXURY GROUP LLC
2860 W State Road 84 Ste (33312-4808)
P.O. Box 846, Dania Beach (33004-0846)
PHONE..................................954 358-9885
C J Butler, *Mng Member*
M Butler,
EMP: 28 **EST:** 2012
SALES (est): 1.9MM **Privately Held**
SIC: 3731 5199 7514 1522 Commercial cargo ships, building & repairing; general merchandise, non-durable; passenger car rental; residential construction; commercial & office building, new construction

(G-4177)
PREMIER PRINTING SOLUTIONS INC
6600 Nw 15th Ave (33309-1503)
PHONE..................................305 490-0244
Stephen F Rothenberg, *President*
Jennifer O'Neill, *Vice Pres*
EMP: 7 **EST:** 1999
SALES (est): 785.6K **Privately Held**
WEB: www.printpremier.com
SIC: 2752 Commercial printing, offset

(G-4178)
PREMIUM PRECIOUS METALS LLC
1883 W State Road 84 # 106 (33315-2232)
PHONE..................................954 367-7513
Marvin Luterman, *Owner*
EMP: 1 **EST:** 2013
SALES (est): 45MM **Privately Held**
WEB: www.premiumpreciousmetals.com
SIC: 3339 Precious metals

(G-4179)
PRESS GOURMET SANDWICHES
6206 N Federal Hwy (33308-1904)
PHONE..................................954 440-0422
Christopher Del Prete, *Owner*
EMP: 9 **EST:** 2015
SALES (est): 512.3K **Privately Held**
WEB: www.pressgourmetsandwiches.com
SIC: 2741 Miscellaneous publishing

(G-4180)
PRINT DYNAMICS
1223 N Flagler Dr (33304-2131)
PHONE..................................954 524-9294
Robert Kesities, *President*
Ashley Keshigian, *Vice Pres*
Eddy Ruiz, *Controller*
Michael Feinstein, *Accounts Exec*
Terry Dent, *Manager*
EMP: 11 **EST:** 2009
SALES (est): 266.7K **Privately Held**
WEB: www.printdynamics.com
SIC: 2752 Commercial printing, offset

(G-4181)
PRINTERS FOR LESS LLC
1217 Ne 12th Ave (33304-2209)
PHONE..................................954 647-0051
Rex Vacca, *Principal*
EMP: 6 **EST:** 2016
SALES (est): 201.9K **Privately Held**
WEB: www.printersforless.net
SIC: 2752 Commercial printing, offset

(G-4182)
PRINTWORLD
4150 Nw 10th Ave (33309-4655)
PHONE..................................754 312-5908
Lorenzo H Jr Pierce, *Principal*
EMP: 6 **EST:** 2016
SALES (est): 179.7K **Privately Held**
SIC: 2752 Commercial printing, lithographic

(G-4183)
PROMARINE BOATS USA
2111 Sw 31st St (33312-4967)
PHONE..................................305 450-2014
Ramon Canela, *Principal*
EMP: 6 **EST:** 2015
SALES (est): 81.4K **Privately Held**
SIC: 3732 Boat building & repairing

(G-4184)
PUMA AERO MARINE INC
622 Ne 14th Ave Apt 10 (33304-2869)
PHONE..................................904 638-5888
Robert EBY, *President*
Charles Rowsell Jr, *CFO*
EMP: 5 **EST:** 2011
SALES (est): 394.3K **Privately Held**
WEB: www.pumamarine.com
SIC: 3731 3721 Shipbuilding & repairing; aircraft

(G-4185)
PURE BRIGHT LIGHTING LLC
711 Bayshore Dr Apt 302 (33304-3964)
PHONE..................................954 780-8700
Bill Balkou, *CEO*
EMP: 7 **EST:** 2013
SALES (est): 578.4K **Privately Held**
WEB: www.purebrightlighting.com
SIC: 3648 Lighting equipment

(G-4186)
PURITAIR LLC
1320 Nw 65th Pl Ste 201 (33309-1901)
PHONE..................................954 281-5105
Alex Techoueyres, *Vice Pres*
EMP: 10
SALES (est): 409.5K **Privately Held**
SIC: 2842 Specialty cleaning, polishes & sanitation goods

(G-4187)
Q INDUSTRIES INC
401 E Las Olas Blvd # 130 (33301-2210)
PHONE..................................954 689-2263
John Moser, *President*
EMP: 9 **EST:** 2003
SALES (est): 308K **Privately Held**
SIC: 3563 Air & gas compressors

(G-4188)
QUALITEST USA LC
401 E Las Olas Blvd Ste 1 (33301-2210)
PHONE..................................877 884-8378
Arash Behzadi, *President*
EMP: 15 **EST:** 2001
SALES (est): 1.9MM **Privately Held**
WEB: www.worldoftest.com
SIC: 3829 3824 Fatigue testing machines, industrial: mechanical; mechanical measuring meters

(G-4189)
QUALITY BAKERY PRODUCTS LLC (DH)
888 E Las Olas Blvd # 700 (33301-2272)
PHONE..................................954 779-3663
David Finch, *Mng Member*
EMP: 6 **EST:** 2010
SALES (est): 11MM **Privately Held**
WEB: www.oldlondonmelba.com
SIC: 2099 Bread crumbs, not made in bakeries

(G-4190)
QUALITY COMPONENTS & ASSEMBLY
440 Nw 27th Ave (33311-8600)
PHONE..................................954 792-5151

John Maschin, *President*
Allison Maschin, *Office Mgr*
EMP: 6 **EST:** 1991
SQ FT: 6,000
SALES (est): 700K **Privately Held**
SIC: 3599 Machine shop, jobbing & repair

(G-4191)
QUALITY MARINE AIR REFRIG
248 Sw 31st St (33315-3322)
PHONE..................................954 560-0084
Gayle Garey, *Owner*
EMP: 7 **EST:** 2017
SALES (est): 533.4K **Privately Held**
WEB: www.qualitymarineair.com
SIC: 3585 Refrigeration & heating equipment

(G-4192)
QUANTUM DEVELOPMENT LLC
3685 Sw 30th Ave (33312-6710)
PHONE..................................954 587-4205
Nick Piper, *Sales Dir*
John T Barth, *Manager*
Terry Allvord, *Technical Staff*
EMP: 8 **EST:** 2015
SALES (est): 129.5K **Privately Held**
WEB: www.quantumstabilizers.com
SIC: 2449 Rectangular boxes & crates, wood

(G-4193)
QUANTUM ENVMTL SLUTIONS ST INC
2699 Stirling Rd Ste C (33312-6517)
PHONE..................................800 975-8721
Stephen N Rosenthal, *President*
Tim Morley, *Vice Pres*
Anne Rosenthal, *Vice Pres*
Neal Rudder, *Treasurer*
Alexandra Zionts, *Admin Sec*
EMP: 6 **EST:** 2010
SQ FT: 2,500
SALES (est): 300K **Privately Held**
SIC: 2842 Degreasing solvent

(G-4194)
QUANTUM LIMIT PARTNERS LLC (PA)
1037 Se 2nd Ct (33301-3627)
PHONE..................................954 849-3720
Glenn C Rice, *CEO*
EMP: 23 **EST:** 2012
SALES (est): 340.7K **Privately Held**
SIC: 3572 Computer storage devices

(G-4195)
QUEUELOGIX LLC
1200 E Las Olas Blvd # 201 (33301-2365)
PHONE..................................404 721-3928
Chris Ragland, *Vice Pres*
EMP: 11 **EST:** 2017
SALES (est): 102.2K **Privately Held**
WEB: www.queuelogix.com
SIC: 7372 Prepackaged software

(G-4196)
QUICK PRINTS LLC
3145 Davie Blvd (33312-2728)
PHONE..................................954 526-9013
William Exemar, *CEO*
EMP: 6 **EST:** 2014
SALES (est): 408.6K **Privately Held**
WEB: www.quickprints.org
SIC: 2752 Commercial printing, offset

(G-4197)
QUICKSERIES PUBLISHING INC
5100 Nw 33rd Ave Ste 247 (33309-6382)
PHONE..................................954 584-1606
Roger G Ledoux, *President*
Steve Arless, *Vice Pres*
Adam Wasserman, *Vice Pres*
Caroline Dussault, *Finance*
Ian Rankine, *Accounts Mgr*
EMP: 52 **EST:** 1993
SQ FT: 26,000
SALES (est): 5MM **Privately Held**
WEB: www.quickseries.com
SIC: 2741 Miscellaneous publishing

(G-4198)
RAPID PRINTER SOLUTIONS
851 Eller Dr (33316-3065)
PHONE..................................954 769-9553
EMP: 7 **EST:** 2016
SALES (est): 101.5K **Privately Held**
WEB: www.rapidprintersolutions.com
SIC: 2752 Commercial printing, offset

(G-4199)
RAY EATON YACHT SERVICE INC
2311 Sw 33rd Ter (33312-4337)
PHONE..................................954 583-8762
Ray Eaton, *President*
Shirley Eaton, *Vice Pres*
EMP: 5 **EST:** 1974
SALES (est): 400.3K **Privately Held**
SIC: 3732 Yachts, building & repairing

(G-4200)
RDT BUSINESS ENTERPRISES INC
3333 Se 14th Ave (33316-4212)
PHONE..................................954 525-1133
Richard D Ticktin, *President*
◆ **EMP:** 13 **EST:** 1992
SQ FT: 50,000
SALES (est): 598.7K **Privately Held**
SIC: 3999 Pet supplies

(G-4201)
REMCO INDUSTRIES INTERNATIONAL
Also Called: Remco Specialty Products Co
917 Nw 8th Ave (33311-7207)
PHONE..................................954 462-0000
Roman Moretth III, *President*
Susan J Moretth, *Admin Sec*
EMP: 18 **EST:** 1992
SQ FT: 18,000
SALES (est): 2.6MM **Privately Held**
WEB: www.remcousa.com
SIC: 3556 Food products machinery

(G-4202)
RENOVATEC ENTERPRISE INC
2590 Nw 4th Ct (33311-8627)
PHONE..................................954 444-8694
Michel Beaulieu, *President*
EMP: 9 **EST:** 1999
SALES (est): 881.6K **Privately Held**
SIC: 2431 Staircases, stairs & railings

(G-4203)
REPUBLIC INDUSTRIES
450 E Las Olas Blvd # 1200 (33301-2292)
PHONE..................................954 627-6000
Michael Jackson, *CEO*
EMP: 6 **EST:** 2017
SALES (est): 119.4K **Privately Held**
SIC: 3441 Fabricated structural metal

(G-4204)
RESCUE METAL FRAMING LLC
2601 Delmar Pl (33301-1577)
PHONE..................................561 660-5945
Drew Rosen, *President*
Bill Ryan, *CFO*
EMP: 12 **EST:** 2018
SQ FT: 130,680
SALES (est): 1.8MM **Privately Held**
SIC: 3442 Metal doors, sash & trim

(G-4205)
RICHARDS AVIATION
1350 River Reach Dr # 506 (33315-1131)
PHONE..................................954 527-2623
Carl Richards, *Principal*
EMP: 9 **EST:** 2007
SALES (est): 196.3K **Privately Held**
SIC: 3812 Aircraft flight instruments

(G-4206)
RIVERHEAD HOUSING INC
3044 Sw 42nd St (33312-6809)
PHONE..................................630 688-6791
Samuel Sosa, *Principal*
Samuel P Sosa, *Principal*
EMP: 7 **EST:** 2012
SALES (est): 131.9K **Privately Held**
SIC: 2452 Prefabricated buildings, wood

(G-4207)
RIVERSTONE SNCTARY - CBD - INC
Also Called: Closets By Design
2101 W Coml Blvd Ste 3500 (33309)
PHONE..................................954 473-1254
Ronald Linares, *CEO*
EMP: 7 **EST:** 2012
SQ FT: 11,000
SALES (est): 114.5K **Privately Held**
WEB: www.closetsbydesign.com
SIC: 2511 Wood household furniture

(G-4208)
RL SCHREIBER INC (PA)
2745 W Cypress Creek Rd (33309-1721)
PHONE..................................954 972-7102
Tom Schreiber, *President*
Chris Carson, *Managing Dir*
Kathleen S Peterson, *Exec VP*
Mary S Massengale, *Vice Pres*
Mary Massengale, *Vice Pres*
◆ **EMP:** 93 **EST:** 1925
SQ FT: 52,000
SALES (est): 25.4MM **Privately Held**
WEB: www.rlschreiber.com
SIC: 2099 2034 2035 2032 Spices, including grinding; soup mixes; pickles, sauces & salad dressings; canned specialties

(G-4209)
RLS LIGHTING INC
205 Ansin Blvd (33311)
PHONE..................................954 458-0345
Gordon Holmes, *President*
▼ **EMP:** 8 **EST:** 1987
SQ FT: 20,000
SALES (est): 664.4K **Privately Held**
SIC: 3648 Outdoor lighting equipment

(G-4210)
ROAD MASTER
203 W State Road 84 (33315-2544)
PHONE..................................561 479-6450
David Benmoha, *Principal*
EMP: 6 **EST:** 2010
SALES (est): 227.7K **Privately Held**
WEB: www.roadmastersf.com
SIC: 3714 Motor vehicle parts & accessories

(G-4211)
ROBERT PETRUCCI INC
1701 W Cypress Creek Rd (33309-1805)
PHONE..................................954 772-2333
Robert Petrucci, *President*
Evelyn Petrucci, *Corp Secy*
EMP: 10 **EST:** 1973
SQ FT: 2,500
SALES (est): 861.3K **Privately Held**
SIC: 3544 Industrial molds

(G-4212)
RONALD A FERGUSON
710 Nw 5th Ave (33311-7328)
PHONE..................................786 488-4019
Ronald A Ferguson, *Principal*
EMP: 7 **EST:** 2010
SALES (est): 95.2K **Privately Held**
WEB: www.bottomlinepress.com
SIC: 2721 Periodicals

(G-4213)
ROPE WORKS INC
262 Sw 33rd St (33315-3328)
PHONE..................................954 525-6575
Bob Nance, *President*
Roger Underwood, *Vice Pres*
Micheal Burrelle, *Director*
▼ **EMP:** 12 **EST:** 2000
SALES (est): 657.3K **Privately Held**
WEB: www.ropeinc.com
SIC: 2298 Ropes & fiber cables

(G-4214)
ROS HOLDING CORPORATION
3201 W State Road 84 (33312-4817)
PHONE..................................954 581-9200
Robert Roscioli, *President*
Sharon Roscioli, *Corp Secy*
EMP: 17 **EST:** 1989
SQ FT: 600
SALES (est): 681K **Privately Held**
SIC: 3732 5551 4493 7389 Fishing boats: lobster, crab, oyster, etc.: small; marine supplies & equipment; boat yards, storage & incidental repair; yacht brokers

(G-4215)
ROSCIOLI INTERNATIONAL INC (PA)
Also Called: Donzi Yachts
3201 W State Road 84 (33312-4869)
PHONE..................................941 755-7411
Robert Roscioli, *President*
Sharon Roscioli, *Corp Secy*
Shawn Schmoll, *Plant Mgr*
EMP: 30 **EST:** 1987
SQ FT: 26,000
SALES (est): 6.8MM **Privately Held**
WEB: www.donziyachts.com
SIC: 3732 Boat building & repairing

(G-4216)
ROSSAM INDUSTRIES INC
811 Nw 57th Pl (33309-2031)
PHONE..................................305 493-5111
William T Frattalone, *President*
Ross John Petrie, *President*
▼ **EMP:** 40 **EST:** 1983
SQ FT: 12,000
SALES (est): 3.6MM **Privately Held**
SIC: 3669 Emergency alarms

(G-4217)
ROTAB INC
20950 Sheridan St (33332-2311)
PHONE..................................954 447-7746
Roy Rolle, *Principal*
▼ **EMP:** 21 **EST:** 2010
SALES (est): 5.6MM **Privately Held**
WEB: www.rotab1.com
SIC: 3465 Body parts, automobile: stamped metal

(G-4218)
ROTH SOUTHEAST LIGHTING LLC
Also Called: Roth Lighting
204 Sw 21st Ter (33312-1425)
PHONE..................................954 423-6640
Marty Capogreco, *Exec VP*
Murray Jesse Maurer, *Mng Member*
David Bowldy,
EMP: 8 **EST:** 2015
SQ FT: 12,000
SALES (est): 2.8MM **Privately Held**
WEB: www.rothsoutheast.com
SIC: 3648 5063 Lighting equipment; light bulbs & related supplies

(G-4219)
ROYAL PRESTIGE
5221 Nw 33rd Ave (33309-6302)
PHONE..................................813 464-9872
Semenia Poblete, *Principal*
EMP: 14 **EST:** 2013
SALES (est): 676.7K **Privately Held**
SIC: 3469 Household cooking & kitchen utensils, metal

(G-4220)
RX FOR FLEAS INC
Also Called: Fleabusters
6555 Powerline Rd Ste 412 (33309-2051)
PHONE..................................954 351-9244
Melvin Yarmouth, *President*
Charles Bayles, *Exec VP*
Robert Yarmuth, *Exec VP*
EMP: 17 **EST:** 1987
SQ FT: 3,000
SALES (est): 1.1MM **Privately Held**
WEB: www.fleabusters.com
SIC: 2834 2879 Powders, pharmaceutical; agricultural chemicals

(G-4221)
SAFE BANKS AND LOCK
2870 Ne 55th Ct (33308-3454)
PHONE..................................954 762-3565
Richard Dragin, *President*
EMP: 7 **EST:** 2007
SALES (est): 453.4K **Privately Held**
WEB: www.bankssafeco.com
SIC: 3499 7382 5044 7699 Locks, safe & vault: metal; security systems services; vaults & safes; lock & key services

(G-4222)
SANCTUARY INTL MINISTRIES
1100 Nw 4th St (33311-8937)
P.O. Box 5272 (33310-5272)
PHONE..................................954 955-7818

Thomas Brown, *Principal*
EMP: 6 **EST:** 2018
SALES (est): 134.8K **Privately Held**
WEB: www.thesanctuaryfl.org
SIC: 3451 Screw machine products

(G-4223)
SANDY FINISHED WOOD INC
3163 Sw 13th Ct (33312-2714)
PHONE..................................954 615-7271
Julio Camacho, *Principal*
EMP: 24
SALES (corp-wide): 77.3K **Privately Held**
SIC: 2499 Laundry products, wood
PA: Sandy Finished Wood Inc
18451 Nw 37th Ave Apt 152
Miami Gardens FL 33056
786 623-8431

(G-4224)
SCI ARCHITECTURAL WDWRK INC
2801 Nw 55th Ct Ste 1w (33309-2501)
PHONE..................................954 247-9601
Alexandre Segura, *President*
Gaston S Galella, *Vice Pres*
Stanton W Reich, *Treasurer*
EMP: 10 **EST:** 2007
SQ FT: 1,500
SALES (est): 374.4K **Privately Held**
WEB: www.sciwoodwork.com
SIC: 2431 Millwork

(G-4225)
SCOTTISH SPIRITS IMPORTS INC
3101 N Federal Hwy # 301 (33306-1018)
PHONE..................................954 332-1116
EMP: 12 **EST:** 2011
SQ FT: 3,200
SALES (est): 810K **Privately Held**
SIC: 2085 Mfg Distilled/Blended Liquor

(G-4226)
SDM ACQUISITION CORPORATION
Also Called: S D Modular Displays
590 Sw 9th St Ste 9 (33315-3848)
PHONE..................................954 462-1919
George Braeunig, *President*
▲ **EMP:** 8 **EST:** 1983
SALES (est): 179.9K **Privately Held**
SIC: 3993 Displays & cutouts, window & lobby

(G-4227)
SEA CANVAS INC
1915 S Federal Hwy (33316-3548)
PHONE..................................954 462-7525
Rafael Tavares, *Principal*
EMP: 8 **EST:** 2016
SALES (est): 249K **Privately Held**
SIC: 2211 Canvas

(G-4228)
SEACOR MARINE LLC
2200 Eller Dr (33316-3069)
P.O. Box 13038 (33316-0101)
PHONE..................................954 523-2200
Oivind Lorentzen, *CEO*
John Gellert, *President*
Charles Fabrikant, *Chairman*
Robert Clemons, *COO*
Jess Llorca, *Exec VP*
EMP: 60 **EST:** 1982
SALES (est): 6.8MM
SALES (corp-wide): 141.8MM **Publicly Held**
WEB: www.seacormarine.com
SIC: 1382 Oil & gas exploration services
PA: Seacor Marine Holdings Inc.
12121 Wickchester Ln # 500
Houston TX 77079
346 980-1700

(G-4229)
SELF MADE DYNASTY LLC ✪
4811 E Pcf View Ter Fl 33 Flr 333 (33309)
PHONE..................................754 303-3134
Marvens Metellus,
EMP: 7 **EST:** 2021
SALES (est): 561.1K **Privately Held**
SIC: 3663 Studio equipment, radio & television broadcasting

(G-4230)
SEN-DURE PRODUCTS INC
6785 Nw 17th Ave (33309-1521)
PHONE..................................954 973-1260
Winston Shutt, *President*
Walter H Shutt III, *President*
Richard Shutt, *Vice Pres*
Winston W Shutt, *Vice Pres*
▼ **EMP:** 61 **EST:** 1928
SQ FT: 20,000
SALES (est): 9.9MM **Privately Held**
WEB: www.sen-dureproducts.com
SIC: 3443 3519 5013 Heat exchangers, condensers & components; marine engines; automotive engines & engine parts

(G-4231)
SHOWER DOORS & MORE INC
1196 Nw 23rd Ave (33311-5738)
PHONE..................................954 358-2014
Lawrence G Giacin, *President*
Page Giacin, *Vice Pres*
◆ **EMP:** 7 **EST:** 1991
SQ FT: 6,000
SALES (est): 1MM **Privately Held**
WEB: www.showerdoors.com
SIC: 3088 5211 2392 Shower stalls, fiberglass & plastic; lumber & other building materials; household furnishings

(G-4232)
SHREDDED TIRE INC
6742 Nw 17th Ave (33309-1522)
PHONE..................................954 970-8565
Richard Spreen, *President*
EMP: 10 **EST:** 2016
SALES (est): 673.6K **Privately Held**
WEB: www.shreddedtire.com
SIC: 3069 Roofing, membrane rubber

(G-4233)
SIGNAL DYNAMICS CORPORATION
Also Called: Backoff Products
6500 Nw 21st Ave Ste 1 (33309-1867)
PHONE..................................904 342-4008
Walter Jakobowski, *President*
Mike Johnson, *Vice Pres*
EMP: 10 **EST:** 1990
SQ FT: 18,000
SALES (est): 269.3K **Privately Held**
WEB: www.signaldynamics.com
SIC: 3714 Motor vehicle parts & accessories

(G-4234)
SIGNARAMA DWNTWN FORT LDERDALE ✪
1422 Se 17th St (33316-1710)
PHONE..................................954 990-4749
Shonagh Baigent, *Principal*
EMP: 8 **EST:** 2020
SALES (est): 330.2K **Privately Held**
WEB: www.downtownsignage.com
SIC: 3993 Signs & advertising specialties

(G-4235)
SIMPLY45 LLC
Also Called: Gosimplyconnect
3490 Sw 30th Ave (33312-6700)
PHONE..................................954 982-2017
EMP: 6 **EST:** 2019
SALES (est): 309.1K **Privately Held**
WEB: www.simply45.com
SIC: 2511 Stools, household: wood

(G-4236)
SINGING MACHINE COMPANY INC (PA)
6301 Nw 5th Way Ste 2900 (33309-6191)
PHONE..................................954 596-1000
Gary Atkinson, *CEO*
Phillip Lau, *Ch of Bd*
Fernando Moreno, *Opers Staff*
Mike Griffin, *Purch Mgr*
Lionel Marquis, *CFO*
▲ **EMP:** 15 **EST:** 1982
SQ FT: 6,500
SALES: 45.8MM **Publicly Held**
WEB: www.singingmachine.com
SIC: 3651 3652 5735 Household audio equipment; tape recorders: cassette, cartridge or reel: household use; prerecorded records & tapes; records, audio discs & tapes

(G-4237)
SINOCARE MEDITECH INC
2400 Nw 55th Ct (33309-2672)
PHONE..................................800 342-7226
Scott Verner, *President*
EMP: 13 **EST:** 2016
SALES (est): 974.6K **Privately Held**
WEB: www.trividiahealth.com
SIC: 3841 8731 Eye examining instruments & apparatus; medical research, commercial
HQ: Trividia Health, Inc.
2400 Nw 55th Ct
Fort Lauderdale FL 33309
954 677-8201

(G-4238)
SINTAVIA LLC (PA)
2500 Sw 39th St (33312-5104)
PHONE..................................954 474-7800
Brian Neff, *CEO*
Doug Hedges, *President*
Sofia Love, *Opers Mgr*
Christopher Arcia, *Mfg Staff*
Alex Bencomo, *QC Mgr*
EMP: 1 **EST:** 2012
SALES (est): 13.5MM **Privately Held**
WEB: www.sintavia.com
SIC: 3471 Finishing, metals or formed products

(G-4239)
SMART MILES LOGISTICS LLC ✪
2420 Nw 31st Ave (33311-2737)
PHONE..................................754 244-2656
Katina Williams,
EMP: 6 **EST:** 2021
SALES (est): 95.5K **Privately Held**
SIC: 3537 Trucks, tractors, loaders, carriers & similar equipment

(G-4240)
SOFT TECH AMERICA INC (PA)
401 E Las Olas Blvd # 1400 (33301-2218)
PHONE..................................954 563-3198
Phillip Thompson, *CEO*
Peter Miller, *Manager*
EMP: 10 **EST:** 1985
SALES (est): 7.4MM **Privately Held**
WEB: www.softtech.com
SIC: 7372 Prepackaged software

(G-4241)
SOGOFISHING LLC
1542 Nw 15th Ave (33311-5467)
PHONE..................................800 308-0259
Thomas Glasco, *CEO*
EMP: 5 **EST:** 2019
SALES (est): 318.8K **Privately Held**
WEB: www.sogofishing.com
SIC: 3949 Sporting & athletic goods; lures, fishing: artificial

(G-4242)
SOLEIL CAPITAL LP (PA)
Also Called: VPR BRANDS
3001 Griffin Rd (33312-5649)
PHONE..................................954 715-7001
Kevin Frija, *Partner*
Daniel Hoff, *Ch Credit Ofcr*
Gary Rep, *Executive*
EMP: 61 **EST:** 2009
SALES: 3.9MM **Privately Held**
WEB: www.vprbrands.com
SIC: 2111 Cigarettes

(G-4243)
SOLIDEXPERTS INC
2005 W Cypress Creek Rd (33309-1878)
PHONE..................................954 772-1903
Michael P Pomper, *President*
Gay Wys, *General Mgr*
Neil Bourgeois, *Admin Sec*
EMP: 12 **EST:** 2005
SALES (est): 2.8MM **Privately Held**
WEB: www.thesolidexperts.com
SIC: 7372 Prepackaged software; application computer software; business oriented computer software; word processing computer software

(G-4244)
SOPHIO SOFTWARE INC (PA)
6300 Ne 1st Ave Ste 201 (33334-1901)
PHONE..................................323 446-2172
Michael B Birnholz, *President*
EMP: 14 **EST:** 1999
SQ FT: 2,000
SALES (est): 1.9MM **Privately Held**
SIC: 7372 Business oriented computer software

(G-4245)
SOUTH FLORIDA GRAPHICS CORP
Also Called: AlphaGraphics
1770 Nw 64th St Ste 500 (33309-1853)
PHONE..................................954 917-0606
Salamon Ojalvo, *President*
Dorita Ojalvo, *Vice Pres*
▼ **EMP:** 9 **EST:** 1996
SALES (est): 955.9K **Privately Held**
WEB: www.aceblueprinting.com
SIC: 2752 Commercial printing, lithographic

(G-4246)
SOUTH FLORIDA PETRO SVCS LLC
2550 Eisenhower Blvd # 11 (33316-3078)
PHONE..................................561 793-2102
Todd Tad, *Director*
Christopher S Vecellio,
Todd Cannon,
▼ **EMP:** 9 **EST:** 2005
SALES (est): 1.3MM **Privately Held**
WEB: www.vecelliogroup.com
SIC: 1311 Crude petroleum & natural gas

(G-4247)
SOUTH FLORIDA SPORT FISHING
2765 Nw 62nd St Ste C (33309-1747)
P.O. Box 5089, Lighthouse Point (33074-5089)
PHONE..................................954 942-7261
Mike Genoun, *President*
Carlos Rodriguez, *Accounts Exec*
Ana Zagazeta, *Advt Staff*
Steve Dougherty, *Assoc Editor*
Micah Simoneaux, *Director*
EMP: 11 **EST:** 2010
SALES (est): 1.5MM **Privately Held**
WEB: www.floridasportfishing.com
SIC: 2721 Magazines: publishing only, not printed on site

(G-4248)
SOUTH FLORIDA SPORT FISHING
Also Called: Sfsf Magazine
2765 Nw 62nd St Ste C (33309-1747)
P.O. Box 5089, Lighthouse Point (33074-5089)
PHONE..................................954 942-7261
Leah Genoun, *President*
EMP: 10 **EST:** 2002
SALES (est): 694.8K **Privately Held**
WEB: www.floridasportfishing.com
SIC: 2721 5961 Magazines: publishing only, not printed on site; catalog sales

(G-4249)
SOUTH FLORIDA WOODWORKERS INC
2873 Sw 16th St (33312-3989)
PHONE..................................954 868-5043
Donald Fenstermaker, *Principal*
EMP: 7 **EST:** 2001
SALES (est): 100.3K **Privately Held**
SIC: 2431 Millwork

(G-4250)
SOUTHERN CROSS BOATWORKS INC
2019 Sw 20th St Ste 111 (33315-1862)
PHONE..................................954 467-5801
Pablo Munoz, *President*
Este Faia Urso, *Vice Pres*
▲ **EMP:** 16 **EST:** 1966
SALES (est): 1.4MM **Privately Held**
WEB: www.southerncrossboatworks.com
SIC: 3732 Boats, fiberglass: building & repairing

(G-4251)
SOUTHLAND POWER & ENRGY CO LLC
Also Called: SP&e
5215 Nw 35th Ave (33309-3303)
PHONE..................................800 217-6040
Kenneth E Sidler, *President*
EMP: 8 **EST:** 2010
SALES (est): 135.8K **Privately Held**
WEB: www.southlandpower.com
SIC: 3433 Heating equipment, except electric

(G-4252)
SPEER LABORATORIES LLC
5821 N Andrews Way (33309-2359)
PHONE..................................954 586-8700
Ian Jones, *Opers Staff*
Amy E Nicolo, *Mng Member*
Matthew Nicolo, *CIO*
Matthew D Nicolo,
EMP: 16 **EST:** 2012
SALES (est): 4.9MM **Privately Held**
WEB: www.speerlaboratories.com
SIC: 2834 Proprietary drug products

(G-4253)
SPICE ISLAND BOAT WORKS INC
505 Se 18th St (33316-2821)
P.O. Box 350504 (33335-0504)
PHONE..................................954 632-9453
Brenda J Moorethomas, *Principal*
EMP: 6 **EST:** 2010
SALES (est): 80K **Privately Held**
SIC: 3732 Boat building & repairing

(G-4254)
SPLASH BEVERAGE GROUP INC
1314 E Las Olas Blvd (33301-2334)
PHONE..................................954 745-5815
Robert Nistico, *President*
Dean Huge, *CFO*
EMP: 3 **EST:** 2012
SALES (est): 4.4MM **Privately Held**
WEB: www.splashbeveragegroup.com
SIC: 2087 5149 Beverage bases, concentrates, syrups, powders & mixes; beverage concentrates
PA: Splash Beverage Group, Inc.
1314 E Las Olas Blvd
Fort Lauderdale FL 33301

(G-4255)
SPRAYMATION DEVELOPMENT CORP
4180 Nw 10th Ave (33309-7014)
PHONE..................................954 484-9700
Grant M Fitzwilliam, *CEO*
Jim McMillen, *Vice Pres*
Michael P Moran, *Vice Pres*
EMP: 31 **EST:** 2019
SALES (est): 4.9MM **Privately Held**
WEB: www.spraymation.com
SIC: 3563 Spraying outfits: metals, paints & chemicals (compressor)

(G-4256)
STANDARD REGISTER INC
4710 Nw 15th Ave (33309-3785)
PHONE..................................954 492-9986
EMP: 19
SALES (corp-wide): 3.8B **Privately Held**
SIC: 2759 Commercial Printing Lithograph Offset
HQ: Standard Register, Inc.
600 Albany St
Dayton OH
937 221-1000

(G-4257)
STANRON CORPORATION
Also Called: Stanron Steel Specialties Div
2770 Nw 63rd Ct (33309-1712)
PHONE..................................954 974-8050
Rick Dunaj, *General Mgr*
Barbara Ciechowski, *Bookkeeper*
EMP: 35
SQ FT: 12,200
SALES (corp-wide): 18MM **Privately Held**
WEB: www.stanron.com
SIC: 3469 3444 Stamping metal for the trade; sheet metalwork
PA: Stanron Corporation
5050 W Foster Ave
Chicago IL 60630
773 777-2600

(G-4258)
STAR PHARMACEUTICALS LLC
2881 E Oakland Park Blvd # 221
(33306-1813)
PHONE..................................800 845-7827
Roseanne Branciforte, *Mng Member*
Gene Branciforte,
EMP: 5 **EST:** 2007
SQ FT: 650
SALES (est): 500K **Privately Held**
WEB: www.starpharm.com
SIC: 2834 Pharmaceutical preparations

(G-4259)
STAR-SEAL OF FLORIDA INC
2740 Nw 55th Ct (33309-2543)
PHONE..................................954 484-8402
Cynthia Thompson, *President*
Alfred Brode, *Principal*
Belinda Broido, *Vice Pres*
Linda Brode, *Treasurer*
◆ **EMP:** 15 **EST:** 1981
SQ FT: 10,000
SALES (est): 1.8MM **Privately Held**
WEB: www.starsealfl.com
SIC: 2951 7699 5169 Coal tar paving materials (not from refineries); industrial equipment services; coal tar products, primary & intermediate

(G-4260)
STARMARK INTERNATIONAL INC
701 S Federal Hwy (33316-1218)
PHONE..................................954 874-9000
Lisa Hoffman, *Vice Pres*
Sue Kane, *Controller*
Sherene Irani, *Marketing Mgr*
Monica Ruiz, *Marketing Staff*
Peggy C Nordeen Estes, *Branch Mgr*
EMP: 7
SALES (corp-wide): 10.8MM **Privately Held**
WEB: www.starmark.com
SIC: 7372 Business oriented computer software
PA: Starmark International, Inc.
210 S Andrews Ave
Fort Lauderdale FL 33301
954 874-9000

(G-4261)
STEELGATE GLOBAL LLC
1800 N Andrews Ave (33311-3933)
P.O. Box 70577 (33307-0577)
PHONE..................................610 909-8509
Steven Bessellieu,
EMP: 6 **EST:** 2009
SALES (est): 250K **Privately Held**
WEB: www.steelgateglobal.com
SIC: 7372 Prepackaged software

(G-4262)
STONEHARDSCAPES INTL INC
5755 Powerline Rd (33309-2001)
PHONE..................................954 989-4050
David Bond, *President*
Arthur H Bond, *Vice Pres*
James S Bond, *Vice Pres*
Michele M Bond, *Treasurer*
Johanna Harrison, *Manager*
EMP: 9 **EST:** 2011
SALES (est): 699.1K **Privately Held**
WEB: www.stonehardscapes.com
SIC: 3272 Building stone, artificial: concrete

(G-4263)
STUART MAGAZINE
1401 E Broward Blvd # 206 (33301-2116)
PHONE..................................954 332-3214
Tracy Auken, *Principal*
Joan Tessmer, *Controller*
Patty Beck, *Manager*
Sowmya Malla, *Manager*
Mark McCormick, *Assoc Editor*
EMP: 17 **EST:** 2010
SALES (est): 372.5K **Privately Held**
WEB: www.magazinemanager.com
SIC: 2721 Magazines: publishing only, not printed on site

(G-4264)
SUN POWER DIESEL INC
413 Sw 3rd Ave (33315-1001)
PHONE..................................954 522-4775
Charlie Podoloff, *Principal*
EMP: 6 **EST:** 2018
SALES (est): 89.6K **Privately Held**
SIC: 3599 Industrial machinery

(G-4265)
SUN-SENTINEL COMPANY LLC (HQ)
Also Called: News & Sun Sentinel Company
500 E Broward Blvd # 800 (33394-3018)
PHONE..................................954 356-4000
Howard Greenberg, *President*
Victoria Ballard, *Editor*
David Selig, *Editor*
Douglas Lyons, *Chairman*
Robyn Motley, *Chairman*
▲ **EMP:** 456 **EST:** 1925
SQ FT: 90,000
SALES (est): 159.7MM
SALES (corp-wide): 746.2MM **Privately Held**
WEB: www.sun-sentinel.com
SIC: 2711 Newspapers, publishing & printing
PA: Tribune Publishing Company
560 W Grand Ave
Chicago IL 60654
312 222-9100

(G-4266)
SUN-SENTINEL COMPANY INC
3585 Nw 54th St (33309-6358)
PHONE..................................954 735-6414
Charles Hare, *Manager*
EMP: 10
SQ FT: 10,480
SALES (corp-wide): 746.2MM **Privately Held**
WEB: www.sun-sentinel.com
SIC: 2711 Newspapers, publishing & printing
HQ: Sun-Sentinel Company, Llc
500 E Broward Blvd # 800
Fort Lauderdale FL 33394
954 356-4000

(G-4267)
SUNSHINE HEALTH PRODUCTS INC
6245 Powerline Rd Ste 106 (33309-2047)
PHONE..................................954 493-5469
Ida Cathie Rhames, *President*
Ralf Morton, *Vice Pres*
▲ **EMP:** 18 **EST:** 2001
SALES (est): 1.3MM **Privately Held**
WEB: www.sunshinehealthproducts.net
SIC: 3843 Dental materials

(G-4268)
SUPERIOR AVIONICS INC
2700 W Cypress Creek Rd (33309-1744)
PHONE..................................954 917-9194
Timothy N Hankins, *President*
EMP: 5 **EST:** 1989
SQ FT: 1,500
SALES (est): 1.1MM **Privately Held**
WEB: www.fdsavionics.com
SIC: 3728 Aircraft parts & equipment

(G-4269)
SURFSKATE INDUSTRIES LLC
614 S Federal Hwy Ste 300 (33301-3192)
PHONE..................................954 349-1116
Michael D Newton, *Principal*
EMP: 6 **EST:** 2010
SALES (est): 119.7K **Privately Held**
WEB: www.surfskate.com
SIC: 3999 Barber & beauty shop equipment

(G-4270)
SUZANO PULP & PAPER
550 W Cypress Creek Rd # 420
(33309-6168)
PHONE..................................954 772-7716
Gerry O'Connor, *Owner*
▲ **EMP:** 6 **EST:** 2006
SALES (est): 498.7K **Privately Held**
WEB: www.suzano.com.br
SIC: 2611 2621 Pulp mills; paper mills

(G-4271)
SYNERGY LABS INC
888 Se 3rd Ave Ste 301 (33316-1159)
PHONE..................................954 525-1133
Lyle J Canida, *President*
Richard Falero, *Mfg Mgr*
Kim Gale, *Purchasing*
Scott Cross, *Chief Mktg Ofcr*
Carlos Zamora, *Mktg Coord*
▼ **EMP:** 32 **EST:** 1992
SALES (est): 11MM **Privately Held**
WEB: www.synergylabs.com
SIC: 2047 Dog food

(G-4272)
SYNERGYLABS LLC
888 Se 3rd Ave Ste 301 (33316-1159)
PHONE..................................954 525-1133
Melodie Chesley, *Opers Staff*
Philip Menard, *Controller*
Phil Menard, *Controller*
Monica Patino, *Sales Mgr*
Karol Berry, *Sales Staff*
◆ **EMP:** 45 **EST:** 2014
SALES (est): 6MM **Privately Held**
WEB: www.synergylabs.com
SIC: 2834 3999 Veterinary pharmaceutical preparations; pet supplies

(G-4273)
T-WIZ PRTG & EMB DESIGNS LLC
464 W Melrose Cir (33312-1805)
PHONE..................................954 280-8949
Davidson Pierre, *CEO*
EMP: 32 **EST:** 2018
SALES (est): 1.1MM **Privately Held**
SIC: 2395 2759 Embroidery & art needlework; commercial printing

(G-4274)
TD FUEL INC
1919 Nw 19th St (33311-3538)
PHONE..................................561 305-2059
Paul Faustin, *President*
Alejandra Perez, *Admin Sec*
▼ **EMP:** 6 **EST:** 2012
SALES (est): 138.8K **Privately Held**
SIC: 2869 Fuels

(G-4275)
TECH COMM INC
511 Se 32nd Ct (33316-4134)
PHONE..................................954 712-7777
Gersald O'Hearn, *President*
EMP: 10 **EST:** 1981
SQ FT: 10,000
SALES (est): 1.7MM **Privately Held**
WEB: www.techcommdf.com
SIC: 3663 Radio broadcasting & communications equipment

(G-4276)
TECNOGRAFIC INC
1010 Nw 51st Pl (33309-3140)
PHONE..................................954 928-1714
Marc Belhoste, *President*
Diane Belhoste, *Vice Pres*
EMP: 20 **EST:** 1983
SQ FT: 12,000
SALES (est): 1MM **Privately Held**
WEB: www.tecnografic.com
SIC: 3531 3732 Marine related equipment; boat building & repairing

(G-4277)
TELLABS INTERNATIONAL INC
1000 Corporate Dr Ste 300 (33334-3688)
PHONE..................................954 492-0120
EMP: 30
SALES (corp-wide): 77.5K **Privately Held**
SIC: 3661 Mfg Telephone/Telegraph Apparatus
HQ: Tellabs International Inc
1415 W Diehl Rd
Naperville IL 60515
630 798-8800

(G-4278)
TESS LLC (DH)
Also Called: T E S S Electrical Sales & Svc
2900 Sw 2nd Ave (33315-3122)
P.O. Box 8564 (33310-8564)
PHONE..................................954 583-6262
Hilda Fleming, *Office Mgr*

Paul Salinex, *Mng Member*
▲ **EMP:** 14 **EST:** 2006
SQ FT: 1,300
SALES (est): 7.4MM
SALES (corp-wide): 2B **Privately Held**
WEB: www.tessllc.us
SIC: 3613 Switchgear & switchboard apparatus
HQ: Rh Marine Netherlands B.V.
Jan Evertsenweg 2
Schiedam 3115
104 871-911

(G-4279)
TEX-COAT LLC
4101 Ravenswood Rd # 218 (33312-5373)
PHONE..................................954 581-0771
Dick Barnes, *Exec VP*
Bill Frazer, *Manager*
EMP: 6
SQ FT: 1,000
SALES (corp-wide): 129.5MM **Privately Held**
WEB: www.texcote.com
SIC: 2851 Paints & allied products
HQ: Tex-Coat Llc
2422 E 15th St
Panama City FL 32405
800 454-0340

(G-4280)
TEXTRON GROUND SUPPORT EQP INC
1800 Sw 34th St (33315-3410)
PHONE..................................954 359-5730
Benjamin Richards, *Branch Mgr*
EMP: 8
SALES (corp-wide): 11.6B **Publicly Held**
WEB: www.textrongse.txtsv.com
SIC: 3537 Trucks, tractors, loaders, carriers & similar equipment; tractors, used in plants, docks, terminals, etc.: industrial
HQ: Textron Ground Support Equipment Inc.
1995 Duncan Dr Nw
Kennesaw GA 30144
770 422-7230

(G-4281)
THOMAS PRINTWORKS
801 N Andrews Ave (33311-7455)
PHONE..................................305 667-4149
EMP: 6 **EST:** 2019
SALES (est): 120.9K **Privately Held**
WEB: www.thomasprintworks.com
SIC: 2752 Commercial printing, lithographic

(G-4282)
THREE D PRODUCTS CORP
6889 Nw 28th Way (33309-1325)
PHONE..................................954 971-6511
Lydia Lopes Woods, *President*
George Woods, *Vice Pres*
Deborah Wood, *Shareholder*
Denise Wood, *Shareholder*
Diana Wood, *Shareholder*
EMP: 5 **EST:** 1995
SALES (est): 303.3K **Privately Held**
SIC: 3251 Ceramic glazed brick, clay

(G-4283)
THROW RAFT LLC
1202 Ne 8th Ave (33304-2002)
PHONE..................................954 366-8004
Troy Faletra, *Mng Member*
EMP: 6 **EST:** 2012
SALES (est): 1.2MM **Privately Held**
WEB: www.throwraft.com
SIC: 3069 5099 5999 Life jackets, inflatable: rubberized fabric; lifesaving & survival equipment (non-medical); alarm & safety equipment stores

(G-4284)
TIGO INC
Also Called: Expose Yourself USA
5967 Nw 31st Ave (33309-2207)
PHONE..................................954 935-5990
Cheryl Tiapago, *President*
Brooke Bradshaw, *General Mgr*
Robert Hernandez, *General Mgr*
Marco Tiapago, *Vice Pres*
▼ **EMP:** 34 **EST:** 2006
SQ FT: 36,000
SALES (est): 3.7MM **Privately Held**
WEB: www.exposeyourselfusa.com
SIC: 3993 Signs & advertising specialties

(G-4285)
TM MARKETING GROUP LLC
3200 S Andrews Ave # 100 (33316-4121)
PHONE..................................954 848-9955
Anthony Munoz, *Mng Member*
EMP: 8 **EST:** 2005
SQ FT: 875
SALES (est): 471.7K **Privately Held**
SIC: 2721 8742 Magazines: publishing only, not printed on site; marketing consulting services

(G-4286)
TOP QUALITY YACHT REFINISHING
1513 Sw 18th Ave (33312-4125)
PHONE..................................954 522-5232
Thanh Van Le, *President*
Binh Le, *Vice Pres*
EMP: 10
SALES (est): 972.2K **Privately Held**
WEB: www.tqyllc.com
SIC: 3732 Yachts, building & repairing

(G-4287)
TORTILLERIA EL TRIUNFO LLC
3981 Sw 12th Ct (33312-3452)
PHONE..................................954 270-7832
EMP: 6 **EST:** 2010
SALES (est): 212.7K **Privately Held**
WEB: www.tortilleriaseltriunfo.com
SIC: 2099 Tortillas, fresh or refrigerated

(G-4288)
TRITON STONE HOLDINGS LLC (PA)
800 Nw 65th St (33309-2006)
PHONE..................................219 669-4890
Josh Kessler, *Mng Member*
Eric Kimmerling,
Randy Mathis,
Sandy McCarter,
Joe Saulkenbery,
▲ **EMP:** 2 **EST:** 2014
SQ FT: 35,000
SALES (est): 48.5MM **Privately Held**
SIC: 3281 5032 1752 3253 Granite, cut & shaped; brick, stone & related material; floor laying & floor work; ceramic wall & floor tile

(G-4289)
TRIVECTA PHARMACEUTICALS INC
1 E Broward Blvd Ste 700 (33301-1876)
PHONE..................................561 856-0842
Lina Garcia, *Principal*
EMP: 12 **EST:** 2017
SALES (est): 943.1K **Privately Held**
WEB: www.trifecta-pharma.com
SIC: 2834 Pharmaceutical preparations

(G-4290)
TRIVIDIA MEDITECH LLC
2400 Nw 55th Ct (33309-2672)
PHONE..................................954 677-9201
Scott Verner, *Manager*
EMP: 11 **EST:** 2019
SALES (est): 1MM **Privately Held**
WEB: www.trividiahealth.com
SIC: 3999 Manufacturing industries

(G-4291)
TWO BROTHERS CULTIVATION LLC
Also Called: Gorilla Boost
817 Se 2nd Ave Apt 518 (33316-1064)
P.O. Box 460193 (33346-0193)
PHONE..................................954 478-2402
Marc Morrow, *Mng Member*
EMP: 26 **EST:** 2014
SALES (est): 1.6MM **Privately Held**
WEB: www.gorillaboost.com
SIC: 2824 Organic fibers, noncellulosic

(G-4292)
UNDERWATER LIGHTS USA LLC
3406 Sw 26th Ter Ste 5 (33312-5010)
PHONE..................................954 760-4447
Ian McDonald, *Mng Member*
Nicole Lippuner, *Manager*
Ian Macdonald, *Technology*
Randal Rash,
EMP: 14 **EST:** 2001
SALES (est): 2.4MM **Privately Held**
WEB: www.underwaterlightsusa.com
SIC: 3646 Commercial indusl & institutional electric lighting fixtures

(G-4293)
UNIQUE ORIGINALS INC
19205 Sw 66th St (33332-1641)
PHONE..................................305 634-2274
Gregory Milu, *President*
▼ **EMP:** 14 **EST:** 1973
SALES (est): 840.5K **Privately Held**
SIC: 2512 2211 2431 Upholstered household furniture; broadwoven fabric mills, cotton; panel work, wood

(G-4294)
UNITED ADVG PUBLICATIONS
3313 W Coml Blvd Ste 130 (33309)
PHONE..................................954 730-9700
Terry Slattey, *Post Master*
EMP: 7 **EST:** 2009
SALES (est): 116.9K **Privately Held**
SIC: 2741 Miscellaneous publishing

(G-4295)
UNITED SHIP SERVICE CORP (PA)
1341 Sw 21st Ter (33312-3116)
PHONE..................................954 583-4588
Erik Engebretsen, *President*
◆ **EMP:** 9 **EST:** 2000
SALES (est): 1.2MM **Privately Held**
WEB: www.uss-us.com
SIC: 3731 Shipbuilding & repairing

(G-4296)
UNITY MARINE INC
2860 W State Road 84 # 118 (33312-4808)
PHONE..................................954 321-1727
Dennis J Cummings, *President*
▲ **EMP:** 9 **EST:** 2007
SALES (est): 129.5K **Privately Held**
SIC: 3086 Packaging & shipping materials, foamed plastic

(G-4297)
UNIVERSAL SIGNS
6045 Nw 31st Ave (33309-2209)
PHONE..................................954 366-1535
EMP: 8 **EST:** 2015
SALES (est): 46K **Privately Held**
WEB: www.universalsignsfl.com
SIC: 3993 Signs & advertising specialties

(G-4298)
UNIWELD PRODUCTS INC (PA)
2850 Ravenswood Rd (33312-4994)
P.O. Box 8427 (33310-8427)
PHONE..................................954 584-2000
David Pearl Sr, *Ch of Bd*
David Foster, *Managing Dir*
David Pearl II, *Exec VP*
Douglas Pearl, *Vice Pres*
Martha Garcia, *Export Mgr*
◆ **EMP:** 250 **EST:** 1949
SQ FT: 100,000
SALES (est): 49.8MM **Privately Held**
WEB: www.uniweld.com
SIC: 3548 3823 Gas welding equipment; welding & cutting apparatus & accessories; pressure gauges, dial & digital

(G-4299)
USA MARINE ENGINES
2600 Sw 3rd Ave (33315-3106)
PHONE..................................954 614-4810
Jason Buchanan, *Principal*
EMP: 11 **EST:** 2019
SALES (est): 2MM **Privately Held**
WEB: www.usamarineengines.com
SIC: 3519 Marine engines

(G-4300)
USA MARITIME ENTERPRISES INC
2600 Esnhwer Blvd Lhigh C Lehigh Cement (33308)
P.O. Box 22723 (33335-2723)
PHONE..................................954 764-8360
Antonio J Orejuela, *President*
Augusto Maldonado, *Vice Pres*
Claudia P Osorio, *Treasurer*
Valerie T Maldonado, *Admin Sec*
EMP: 6 **EST:** 1984
SALES (est): 740K **Privately Held**
WEB: www.usamaritime.us
SIC: 3731 4731 Landing ships, building & repairing; agents, shipping

(G-4301)
V P PRESS INC
Also Called: Discount Printing
3934 Davie Blvd (33312-3406)
PHONE..................................954 581-7531
Vincent Cefalu, *President*
Pamela Cefalu, *Treasurer*
Frank Ramirez, *Admin Sec*
EMP: 10 **EST:** 1980
SQ FT: 2,400
SALES (est): 1.5MM **Privately Held**
WEB: www.vp-press.com
SIC: 2752 2791 2789 Commercial printing, offset; typesetting; bookbinding & related work

(G-4302)
VALLEY SURGICAL INC
1543 Se 13th St (33316-2211)
PHONE..................................954 768-9886
Deran Maloumian, *President*
EMP: 8 **EST:** 2005
SALES (est): 534.3K **Privately Held**
SIC: 3843 Dental equipment & supplies

(G-4303)
VALLEYMEDIA INC
Also Called: Cioreview
200 Se 6th St Ste 505 (33301-3424)
PHONE..................................510 565-7559
Harvi Sachar, *President*
EMP: 22 **EST:** 2015
SALES (est): 2.4MM **Privately Held**
SIC: 2721 Magazines: publishing only, not printed on site

(G-4304)
VAN TIBOLLI BEAUTY CORP
Also Called: GK Hair
4800 Nw 15th Ave Unit E (33309-3781)
PHONE..................................305 390-0044
Vanderlei Tibolla, *President*
Martin Mosley, *COO*
Faisal Kamal, *CFO*
▲ **EMP:** 23 **EST:** 2009
SALES (est): 2.3MM **Privately Held**
WEB: www.gkhair.com
SIC: 2844 3634 Tonics, hair; hair curlers, electric

(G-4305)
VEI TECHNOLOGIES INC
3223 Nw 10th Ter Ste 605 (33309-5940)
PHONE..................................954 653-0210
Jason Bourne, *CEO*
Phyllis Hulse, *Office Mgr*
EMP: 8 **EST:** 2009
SQ FT: 2,500
SALES (est): 167.3K **Privately Held**
WEB: www.vei-systems.net
SIC: 3575 Computer terminals, monitors & components

(G-4306)
VENDORNET
2301 Barbara Dr (33316-3609)
PHONE..................................954 767-8228
EMP: 6 **EST:** 2015
SALES (est): 96.2K **Privately Held**
SIC: 7372 Business oriented computer software

(G-4307)
VERITAS FARMS INC (PA)
1512 E Broward Blvd # 30 (33301-2122)
PHONE..................................561 288-6603
Alexander M Salgado, *CEO*
Dave Smith, *COO*
Erduis Sanabria, *Exec VP*
Spencer Fuller, *Vice Pres*
Rianna Meyer, *Vice Pres*
EMP: 10 **EST:** 2011
SQ FT: 2,145
SALES: 6.2MM **Publicly Held**
WEB: www.theveritasfarms.com
SIC: 2833 Medicinals & botanicals

(G-4308)
VITAL PHARMACEUTICALS INC (PA)
Also Called: Vpx Sports
20311 Sheridan St (33332-2313)
PHONE..................................954 641-0570
John Owoc, *President*
Lorraine Estrada, *Treasurer*
Keoni Kaono, *Sales Staff*
Daisy Grunewald, *Marketing Staff*
Desiree Bolanos, *Manager*
◆ **EMP:** 132 **EST:** 1996
SQ FT: 14,000
SALES (est): 136.2MM **Privately Held**
WEB: www.bangenergy.com
SIC: 2086 Carbonated beverages, nonalcoholic: bottled & canned

(G-4309)
VITAPAK LLC ✪
21070 Sheridan St (33332-2310)
PHONE..................................954 661-0390
Nick Mariano,
EMP: 6 **EST:** 2020
SALES (est): 294.8K **Privately Held**
SIC: 2023 Dietary supplements, dairy & non-dairy based

(G-4310)
VKIDZ INC
Also Called: Time 4 Learning
6300 Ne 1st Ave Ste 203 (33334-1901)
PHONE..................................954 771-0914
John Edelson, *CEO*
Jennifer Eaton, *General Mgr*
Janet Sedano, *Marketing Staff*
Karl Pemsingh, *Prgrmr*
EMP: 10 **EST:** 2004
SALES (est): 2.7MM
SALES (corp-wide): 769.1MM **Privately Held**
WEB: www.time4learning.com
SIC: 7372 Educational computer software
HQ: Cambium Learning Group, Inc.
17855 Dallas Pkwy Ste 400
Dallas TX 75287

(G-4311)
WALRUSS ENTERPRISES INC
Also Called: First Impression Graphic Svcs
1509 Sw 1st Ave (33315-1710)
PHONE..................................954 525-0342
Margaret Russell, *President*
EMP: 9 **EST:** 2011
SALES (est): 309.7K **Privately Held**
SIC: 2759 Commercial printing

(G-4312)
WARDEN ENTERPRISES INC (PA)
Also Called: Clutch House
807 Nw 7th St (33311-7304)
PHONE..................................954 463-4404
Paul Fontanella, *President*
EMP: 6 **EST:** 1975
SQ FT: 10,000
SALES (est): 766.1K **Privately Held**
WEB: www.warden.enterprises
SIC: 3714 Clutches, motor vehicle

(G-4313)
WARFIGHTER FCSED LOGISTICS INC
936 Nw 1st St (33311-8902)
PHONE..................................740 513-4692
Darrell Kem, *CEO*
Ron Wilson, *Vice Pres*
EMP: 15
SQ FT: 1,500
SALES (corp-wide): 2.1MM **Privately Held**
WEB: www.warfighterfocusedlogistics.com
SIC: 3069 3429 Rubber hardware; aircraft & marine hardware, inc. pulleys & similar items; motor vehicle hardware; aircraft hardware; marine hardware
PA: Warfighter Focused Logistics Inc.
936 Nw 1st St
Fort Lauderdale FL 33311
740 513-4692

(G-4314)
WATER PURIFICATION SYSTEMS
2233 S Andrews Ave (33316-3447)
PHONE..................................954 467-8920
EMP: 6 **EST:** 2019
SALES (est): 192.2K **Privately Held**
SIC: 3559 Special industry machinery

(G-4315)
WATERMAKERS INC
2233 S Andrews Ave (33316-3400)
PHONE..................................954 467-8920
Toll Free:..888 -
Joseph Hocher, *President*
David Hocher, *Vice Pres*
Dave Henderson, *Purchasing*
Ann Hocher, *Treasurer*
Kathy Doyley, *Accountant*
◆ **EMP:** 15 **EST:** 1984
SQ FT: 6,000
SALES (est): 3.4MM **Privately Held**
WEB: www.watermakers.com
SIC: 3589 8111 Water purification equipment, household type; water treatment equipment, industrial; legal services

(G-4316)
WATTERA LLC
3131 Sw 42nd St (33312-6802)
PHONE..................................954 400-5135
Rishi Kukreja,
EMP: 20 **EST:** 2012
SQ FT: 3,500
SALES (est): 3.3MM **Privately Held**
SIC: 3089 Injection molding of plastics

(G-4317)
WAYLOO INC
2700 W Cypress Creek Rd (33309-1744)
P.O. Box 668665, Pompano Beach (33066-8665)
PHONE..................................954 914-3192
Nancy Nagamatsu-Silverman, *CEO*
Wayne St James, *Exec VP*
▲ **EMP:** 8 **EST:** 1992
SQ FT: 10,000
SALES (est): 1MM **Privately Held**
WEB: www.wayloo.com
SIC: 2326 2752 7319 2393 Work uniforms; commercial printing, lithographic; distribution of advertising material or sample services; textile bags; men's miscellaneous accessories

(G-4318)
WE BRONZE WHOLESALE LLC
2736 N Federal Hwy (33306-1424)
PHONE..................................954 922-8826
Ed Maslanka,
William Aribu,
▲ **EMP:** 5 **EST:** 2004
SALES (est): 950K **Privately Held**
WEB: www.webronze.com
SIC: 3366 Bronze foundry

(G-4319)
WEBVOIP INC
6400 N Andrews Ave # 490 (33309-2114)
PHONE..................................305 793-2061
David J Rachiele, *President*
EMP: 5 **EST:** 2002
SALES (est): 360.1K **Privately Held**
SIC: 7372 Application computer software

(G-4320)
WESTROCK CP LLC
3251 Sw 1st Ter (33315-3308)
PHONE..................................954 522-3684
John Posch, *Branch Mgr*
EMP: 6
SALES (corp-wide): 17.5B **Publicly Held**
WEB: www.westrock.com
SIC: 2631 Paperboard mills
HQ: Westrock Cp, Llc
1000 Abernathy Rd Ste 125
Atlanta GA 30328

(G-4321)
WHEELS A MILLION
1100 Nw 54th St (33309-2819)
PHONE..................................754 444-2869
Clodoaldo Neto, *Principal*
EMP: 6 **EST:** 2014
SALES (est): 454.4K **Privately Held**
WEB: www.wheelsamillion.com
SIC: 3714 Motor vehicle parts & accessories

(G-4322)
WHOLE ENCHLADA FRESH MXCAN GRI
4115 N Federal Hwy (33308-5530)
PHONE..................................954 561-4040
David Cardaci, *Principal*
EMP: 10 **EST:** 2006
SALES (est): 341.6K **Privately Held**
WEB: www.twefreshmex.com
SIC: 2032 Mexican foods: packaged in cans, jars, etc.

(G-4323)
WHR HOLDINGS LLC
Also Called: Wilkenson Hi-Rise
3402 Sw 26th Ter Ste 10 (33312-5071)
PHONE..................................954 342-4342
Chad George, *CEO*
Michael Bracken, *President*
Michael J Malo,
Stormy Hicks, *Advisor*
▼ **EMP:** 100 **EST:** 2006
SALES (est): 18.5MM **Privately Held**
WEB: www.whrise.com
SIC: 2842 Sanitation preparations, disinfectants & deodorants

(G-4324)
WILKINSON HI-RISE LLC
3402 Sw 26th Ter Ste 10 (33312-5071)
PHONE..................................954 342-4400
Alejandro Tobon, *Opers Mgr*
Michael Bracken, *Mng Member*
Dennis Donohue,
EMP: 120 **EST:** 2001
SALES (est): 10.5MM **Privately Held**
WEB: www.whrise.com
SIC: 3444 5084 3559 Metal housings, enclosures, casings & other containers; processing & packaging equipment; recycling machinery

(G-4325)
WILO USA LLC
Also Called: Scot Pump Company
3001 Sw 3rd Ave Ste 7 (33315-3315)
PHONE..................................954 524-6776
Steve Wilkerson, *Branch Mgr*
EMP: 59
SALES (corp-wide): 37K **Privately Held**
WEB: www.wilo.com
SIC: 3561 Pumps & pumping equipment
HQ: Wilo Usa Llc
9550 W Higgins Rd Ste 300
Rosemont IL 60018

(G-4326)
WIRE PRODUCTS INC OF FLORIDA (PA)
4300 Nw 10th Ave (33309-4603)
PHONE..................................954 772-1477
Thomas J Bourg Jr, *President*
Susan Day, *Corp Secy*
Doug Schleenbaker, *Vice Pres*
Raul Blanco, *Sales Staff*
Derrick D Holmes, *Sales Staff*
◆ **EMP:** 20
SQ FT: 30,000
SALES (est): 8.1MM **Privately Held**
WEB: www.wireproducts.us
SIC: 3496 3315 Concrete reinforcing mesh & wire; wire & fabricated wire products

(G-4327)
WOOL WHOLESALE PLUMBING SUPPLY
Also Called: Pipco
1321 Ne 12th Ave (33304-1898)
PHONE..................................954 763-3632
Carl Wool, *President*
Shirley Wool, *Corp Secy*
▼ **EMP:** 71 **EST:** 1975
SALES (est): 10MM
SALES (corp-wide): 71MM **Privately Held**
WEB: www.woolsupply.com
SIC: 3432 3431 3261 5074 Plumbing fixture fittings & trim; metal sanitary ware; plumbing fixtures, vitreous china; plumbing & hydronic heating supplies
PA: Wool Wholesale Plumbing Supply, Inc.
4340 Sw 74th Ave
Miami FL 33155
305 266-7111

(G-4328)
WORLD WIDE FROZEN FOODS LLC
800 W Cypress Creek Rd (33309-2075)
PHONE..................................954 266-8500
Daniel R Pollak, *Mng Member*
Rigo Ugarte,
▲ **EMP:** 4 **EST:** 2017
SQ FT: 3,300
SALES (est): 6MM **Privately Held**
SIC: 2037 Frozen fruits & vegetables

(G-4329)
WRITE STUFF ENTERPRISES LLC
1001 S Andrews Ave # 120 (33316-1015)
PHONE..................................954 462-6657
Sandy Cruz, *Vice Pres*
Jeffrey L Rodengen,
Amy Major, *Executive Asst*
Marianne Roberts,
EMP: 24 **EST:** 1996
SQ FT: 10,000
SALES (est): 2.1MM **Privately Held**
WEB: www.writestuffbooks.com
SIC: 2731 2752 2721 Books: publishing only; calendar & card printing, lithographic; magazines: publishing only, not printed on site

(G-4330)
YACHT 10 INC
Also Called: Megafend Mooring Products
3001 Sw 3rd Ave Ste 1 (33315-3315)
PHONE..................................954 759-9929
Garry L Gassew, *President*
Nathan Marsack, *Sales Staff*
▲ **EMP:** 6 **EST:** 1986
SQ FT: 2,200
SALES (est): 730.1K **Privately Held**
SIC: 3732 Yachts, building & repairing

(G-4331)
YACHT-MATE PRODUCTS INC
3200 S Andrews Ave Ste 10 (33316-4100)
PHONE..................................954 527-0112
Sandra H Handrahan, *Principal*
EMP: 8 **EST:** 2015
SALES (est): 1.7MM **Privately Held**
WEB: www.yachtmate.com
SIC: 3589 Water treatment equipment, industrial

(G-4332)
YOLO LAS OLAS LLC
200 Sw 2nd St (33301-1822)
PHONE..................................954 522-3002
Timothy Petrillo, *Manager*
EMP: 18 **EST:** 2007
SALES (est): 2.6MM **Privately Held**
WEB: www.lasolasboulevard.com
SIC: 3421 Table & food cutlery, including butchers'

(G-4333)
YOUNGER YOU INC (PA)
Also Called: Nutra-Lift Skin Care
5961 Bayview Dr (33308-2739)
PHONE..................................954 924-4462
Robert Trovato, *President*
EMP: 7 **EST:** 1996
SQ FT: 3,000
SALES (est): 848.3K **Privately Held**
WEB: www.nutra-lift.com
SIC: 2844 Face creams or lotions

(G-4334)
ZENITH ROLLERS LLC
764 Nw 57th Ct (33309-2028)
PHONE..................................954 493-6484
Sashi Ravada,
Shiva Sistla,
▲ **EMP:** 7 **EST:** 2005

▲ = Import ▼=Export
◆ =Import/Export

SALES (est): 922.7K Privately Held
WEB: www.zenithrollersus.com
SIC: 3555 Printing trades machinery

(G-4335)
ZENO FURNITURE & MAT MFG CO
Also Called: Zeno Mattress and Furn Mfg Co
671 Nw 4th Ave (33311-7322)
PHONE 954 764-1212
Joseph Zeno, *President*
EMP: 9 EST: 1960
SQ FT: 15,000
SALES (est): 1.2MM Privately Held
WEB: www.zenomattress.com
SIC: 2515 5712 Mattresses, innerspring or box spring; mattresses

Fort Mc Coy
Marion County

(G-4336)
CIRCLE S MANUFACTURING CO INC
13650 Ne 110th St (32134-7877)
P.O. Box 1440 (32134-1440)
PHONE 352 236-3580
Earla Sogan, *President*
Bruce Sogan, *Vice Pres*
Michael Sogan, *Vice Pres*
Maria Carter, *Treasurer*
Gail Sogan, *Admin Sec*
EMP: 7 EST: 1979
SQ FT: 3,200
SALES (est): 226K Privately Held
WEB: www.circle-s-manufacturing-co-inc.business.site
SIC: 3599 Machine shop, jobbing & repair

(G-4337)
FM MEAT PRODUCTS LTD PARTNR
19798 Ne Highway 315 (32134-7601)
P.O. Box 450 (32134-0450)
PHONE 352 546-3000
Frank Stronach, *Partner*
Corban Russell, *Partner*
EMP: 48 EST: 2013
SALES (est): 9.2MM Privately Held
WEB: www.adenafarms.com
SIC: 2011 Meat packing plants

Fort Meade
Polk County

(G-4338)
NOVAPHOS INC
3200 County Rte 630 W (33841)
PHONE 863 285-8607
Theodore Fowler, *President*
EMP: 40 EST: 2013
SALES (est): 8.2MM Privately Held
WEB: www.novaphos.com
SIC: 2874 Phosphates

(G-4339)
R & H AIR COATINGS INC
524 Water Oak Ct (33841-9631)
PHONE 863 559-6021
Beverly L Reves, *Principal*
EMP: 8 EST: 2017
SALES (est): 313.3K Privately Held
SIC: 3479 Metal coating & allied service

Fort Myers
Lee County

(G-4340)
5571 HALIFAX INC
5571 Halifax Ave (33912-4403)
PHONE 239 454-4999
Daniel R Harper, *President*
Shawn Harper, *Vice Pres*
Ronald E Inge, *Treasurer*
EMP: 42 EST: 1999
SQ FT: 10,651
SALES (est): 1.8MM Privately Held
WEB: www.dssrecycle.com
SIC: 7692 Welding repair

(G-4341)
A QUALLITY PALLET COMPANY
5896 Enterprise Pkwy (33905-5030)
P.O. Box 50975 (33994-0975)
PHONE 239 245-0900
Daniel Crismon, *Principal*
EMP: 7 EST: 2007
SALES (est): 137.2K Privately Held
SIC: 2448 Pallets, wood

(G-4342)
ABSOLUTE PLASTIC SOLUTIONS
2178 Andrea Ln (33912-1986)
PHONE 239 313-7779
Barry J Bowen Jr, *Principal*
EMP: 11 EST: 2012
SALES (est): 2.9MM Privately Held
SIC: 3089 Injection molding of plastics

(G-4343)
ACCOUNTBLE DRCTIONAL DRILLILLC
2511 Palm Ave (33916-5347)
PHONE 239 226-1606
Ralph Andrew, *Manager*
EMP: 6 EST: 2012
SALES (est): 202.1K Privately Held
SIC: 1381 Directional drilling oil & gas wells

(G-4344)
ACE PRESS INC
2133 Broadway (33901-3634)
PHONE 239 334-1118
Tom Jackson, *President*
Stephen Cooper, *CTO*
EMP: 8 EST: 1963
SQ FT: 12,000
SALES (est): 642.3K Privately Held
WEB: www.ace-press.com
SIC: 2752 Commercial printing, offset

(G-4345)
ADVANCED PRECISION MCH US INC
3791 Edison Ave (33916-4705)
PHONE 239 332-2841
Thomas L Pancoast, *Principal*
EMP: 13 EST: 2010
SALES (est): 1MM Privately Held
WEB: www.apmachineshop.com
SIC: 3599 Machine shop, jobbing & repair

(G-4346)
AERO-MACH TCO MANUFACTURING
604 Danley Dr (33907-1529)
PHONE 239 936-7570
Jason White, *President*
EMP: 9 EST: 1974
SQ FT: 4,000
SALES (est): 982.9K
SALES (corp-wide): 11.9MM Privately Held
WEB: www.tcomanufacturing.com
SIC: 3663 Radio & TV communications equipment
PA: Aero-Mach Laboratories, Inc.
7707 E Funston St
Wichita KS 67207
316 682-7707

(G-4347)
AIRO INDUSTRIES INC
2837 Fowler St (33901-6314)
PHONE 239 229-5273
Mark Pruskauer, *President*
Patricia Lamentia, *Vice Pres*
EMP: 7 EST: 2012
SQ FT: 10,500
SALES (est): 880.9K Privately Held
WEB: www.airoind.com
SIC: 3699 Electrical equipment & supplies

(G-4348)
AKJ INDUSTRIES INC (PA)
10175 6 Mile Cypress Pkwy (33966-6993)
PHONE 239 939-1696
Kenneth Burnside, *President*
Daniel Deer, *Vice Pres*
Jerry Nelesen, *Regl Sales Mgr*
Nina Verios, *Admin Asst*
◆ EMP: 9 EST: 1981
SQ FT: 3,000
SALES (est): 9.1MM Privately Held
WEB: www.skifflife.com
SIC: 2899 3559 Carbon removing solvent; degreasing machines, automotive & industrial

(G-4349)
ALICO METAL FABRICATORS LLC
Also Called: Metropolis Iron By Design
16750 Link Ct Ste 205 (33912-5907)
PHONE 239 454-4766
Andrew N Aiken Jr, *Mng Member*
Andrew Aiken Jr, *Mng Member*
EMP: 5 EST: 2009
SALES (est): 647.7K Privately Held
WEB: www.alicometalfabricators.com
SIC: 3441 Fabricated structural metal

(G-4350)
ALL CUT INC NO SELECTION
2910 Hunter St (33916-7608)
PHONE 239 789-1748
EMP: 7 EST: 2018
SALES (est): 254.7K Privately Held
WEB: www.allcut.com
SIC: 3599 Machine shop, jobbing & repair

(G-4351)
ALLENSTEEL INC
16281 Pine Ridge Rd (33908-2689)
PHONE 239 454-1331
Tony Allen, *Owner*
EMP: 8 EST: 2003
SQ FT: 81,100
SALES (est): 145.9K Privately Held
SIC: 3441 Fabricated structural metal

(G-4352)
ALLI CATS INC
Also Called: Fastsigns
12211 S Cleveland Ave (33907-3746)
PHONE 239 274-0744
Paul Hill, *President*
Paul J Hill, *President*
EMP: 5 EST: 2002
SALES (est): 500K Privately Held
WEB: www.fastsigns.com
SIC: 3993 Signs & advertising specialties

(G-4353)
ALLOY CLADDING COMPANY LLC
16170 Old Us 41 (33912-2286)
PHONE 561 625-4550
EMP: 17 EST: 2008
SALES (est): 142.3K Privately Held
WEB: www.alloycladding.com
SIC: 3548 Welding apparatus

(G-4354)
ALTERNATIVE LABORATORIES LLC (PA)
4740 S Cleveland Ave (33907-1311)
PHONE 239 692-9160
Kevin Thomas, *CEO*
Dawn Hollander, *Purchasing*
▲ EMP: 37 EST: 2009
SALES (est): 9.7MM Privately Held
WEB: www.alternativelabs.com
SIC: 2834 Vitamin, nutrient & hematinic preparations for human use

(G-4355)
AMAZON SHEDS AND GAZEBOS INC (PA)
17300 Jean St (33967-6067)
PHONE 239 498-5558
Filiberto Rodriguez, *President*
Zoe Branca, *Sales Mgr*
EMP: 15 EST: 2006
SALES (est): 3.7MM Privately Held
WEB: www.amazonsheds.com
SIC: 2452 3448 Prefabricated wood buildings; prefabricated metal buildings

(G-4356)
AMD AERO INC
14230 Jetport Loop W (33913-7712)
PHONE 239 561-8622
James H Cline, *President*
Barbara Cline, *Corp Secy*
EMP: 13 EST: 1991
SQ FT: 10,000
SALES (est): 395K Privately Held
SIC: 3829 Fuel system instruments, aircraft

(G-4357)
AMERICAN BOTTLING COMPANY
Also Called: Southeast-Atlantic
2236 Hemingway Dr (33912-1917)
PHONE 239 489-0838
Jeff Sutherland, *Manager*
EMP: 17 Publicly Held
WEB: www.keurigdrpepper.com
SIC: 2086 Soft drinks: packaged in cans, bottles, etc.
HQ: The American Bottling Company
6425 Hall Of Fame Ln
Frisco TX 75034

(G-4358)
AMERICAN TRACTION SYSTEMS INC
Also Called: A T S
10030 Amberwood Rd Ste 1 (33913-8521)
PHONE 239 768-0757
Bonne Posma, *President*
Anthony Davis, *Vice Pres*
Juan Pinzon, *Vice Pres*
Car Wilcox, *Vice Pres*
Steve Beeson, *Engineer*
EMP: 20 EST: 2008
SALES (est): 3.6MM Privately Held
WEB: www.americantraction.com
SIC: 3621 Control equipment for electric buses & locomotives

(G-4359)
AMERICAN WINDOWS SHUTTERS INC
Also Called: American Shutter Products Inc
11600 Adelmo Ln (33966-8400)
PHONE 239 278-3066
Cesare Croci, *President*
Spencer Bass, *Sales Staff*
Cindy Rhoton, *Admin Asst*
◆ EMP: 30 EST: 1993
SQ FT: 120,000
SALES (est): 10.8MM
SALES (corp-wide): 441K Privately Held
WEB: www.crocinorthamerica.com
SIC: 3354 Aluminum extruded products
HQ: Croci Italia Srl
Via Emilia 732
Bertinoro FC 47032
054 346-3911

(G-4360)
AMERICUT OF FLORIDA INC
1941 Custom Dr (33907-2101)
PHONE 800 692-2187
Michael Harris, *President*
Kevin Sorrell, *Vice Pres*
EMP: 16 EST: 2013
SALES (est): 728.2K Privately Held
WEB: www.americut.com
SIC: 3541 Sawing & cutoff machines (metalworking machinery)

(G-4361)
AMERITECH POWDER COATING INC
502 South Rd Unit D (33907-2454)
PHONE 239 274-8000
Ovidio Chavez, *President*
Johnathan Kob, *Vice Pres*
EMP: 10 EST: 2002
SALES (est): 984.4K Privately Held
WEB: www.ameritechapc.com
SIC: 3479 Coating of metals & formed products

(G-4362)
AMES TOOLS
5011 Luckett Rd (33905-4417)
PHONE 239 693-1055
EMP: 14 EST: 2016
SALES (est): 91.1K Privately Held
WEB: www.amestools.com
SIC: 3599 Industrial machinery

(G-4363)
ANGEL FERNANDEZ
17601 Laurel Valley Rd (33967-5009)
PHONE 239 580-9714
Angel Fernandez, *Principal*

EMP: 6 EST: 2011
SALES (est): 113.5K Privately Held
SIC: 3589 High pressure cleaning equipment

(G-4364)
ANNA ANDRES
Also Called: USA Today
2442 Dr M L King Blvd Martin (33901)
PHONE....239 335-0233
Anna Andres, *Principal*
EMP: 7 EST: 1997
SALES (est): 242.6K Privately Held
WEB: www.2395404884.com
SIC: 2711 Newspapers, publishing & printing

(G-4365)
ANYTHING DISPLAY
6225 Presidential Ct (33919-3566)
PHONE....239 433-9738
Chris Andrews, *Division Mgr*
EMP: 10 EST: 2011
SALES (est): 505K Privately Held
WEB: www.anythingdisplay.com
SIC: 3993 Signs & advertising specialties

(G-4366)
ARCHITECTURAL METALS S W FL
4700 Laredo Ave (33905-4909)
PHONE....239 334-7433
Chris Mills, *President*
EMP: 25 EST: 1994
SQ FT: 9,600
SALES (est): 3.7MM Privately Held
WEB: www.archmetalsfl.com
SIC: 3444 Sheet metalwork

(G-4367)
AROMA COFFEE SERVICE INC
2168 Andrea Ln (33912-1901)
PHONE....239 481-7262
Karen Long, *President*
Brian Long, *Vice Pres*
Jared Dupre, *Opers Mgr*
Phil Lessor, *Branch Mgr*
EMP: 5 EST: 1986
SQ FT: 1,500
SALES (est): 1.4MM Privately Held
WEB: www.aromacoffee.net
SIC: 2095 5149 5499 Roasted coffee; coffee, green or roasted; coffee

(G-4368)
ATLANTIC BEV GROUP USA INC
2711 1st St Apt 102 (33916-1843)
PHONE....239 334-3016
Albert J Degutis, *President*
Paul F Dumas, *Treasurer*
EMP: 6 EST: 2002
SALES (est): 394.8K Privately Held
SIC: 2087 Concentrates, drink

(G-4369)
ATLANTIC DRINKING WATER SYSTMS
2700 Parker Ave (33905-1958)
PHONE....252 255-1110
Joel Walker, *President*
Karen Walker, *Principal*
EMP: 6 EST: 1985
SALES (est): 258.7K Privately Held
SIC: 3589 Water filters & softeners, household type

(G-4370)
AXI INTERNATIONAL CORPORATION (PA)
5400 Division Dr Ste 1 (33905-5016)
PHONE....239 690-9589
Bruwer Wessel Van Tonder, *CEO*
Islam Nahdi, *President*
Ernest Neafsey, *General Mgr*
Bernard W Keizer, *Corp Secy*
Christian Smith, *COO*
◆ EMP: 29 EST: 1998
SQ FT: 7,000
SALES (est): 6.7MM Privately Held
WEB: www.axi-international.com
SIC: 3823 5169 Combustion control instruments; compressed gas

(G-4371)
BAMM MANUFACTURING INC
Also Called: Handcrafted Pewter
1222 Hemingway Dr (33912-1926)
PHONE....239 277-0776
Angie Winebrenner, *President*
Bonnie Mason, *Vice Pres*
▲ EMP: 5 EST: 2002
SALES (est): 500K Privately Held
SIC: 3499 Novelties & giftware, including trophies

(G-4372)
BARON LLC
4784 Skates Cir (33905-7326)
PHONE....239 691-5783
Cindy Young, *Manager*
EMP: 8 EST: 2005
SALES (est): 331.3K Privately Held
SIC: 3728 Aircraft parts & equipment

(G-4373)
BAYSHORE CONCRETE PRODUCTS INC
Also Called: Bayshore Concrete & Ldscp Mtls
8100 Bayshore Rd (33917-3627)
PHONE....239 543-3001
William De Deugd, *President*
EMP: 1 EST: 1964
SALES (est): 3MM
SALES (corp-wide): 4.1MM Privately Held
WEB: www.bayshoreconcrete.net
SIC: 3272 Concrete products
PA: Tricircle Pavers, Inc.
2709 Jeffcott St
Fort Myers FL 33901
239 332-2325

(G-4374)
BAYSHORE PRECAST CONCRETE INC
Also Called: Bayshore Concrete & Ldscp Mtls
8100 Bayshore Rd (33917-3627)
P.O. Box 51410 (33994-1410)
PHONE....239 543-3001
Willem Dedeugd, *President*
EMP: 7 EST: 1984
SALES (est): 888.5K
SALES (corp-wide): 4.1MM Privately Held
WEB: www.bayshoreconcrete.net
SIC: 3272 Concrete products
PA: Tricircle Pavers, Inc.
2709 Jeffcott St
Fort Myers FL 33901
239 332-2325

(G-4375)
BF ONE LLC
5661 Independence Cir (33912-4419)
PHONE....239 939-5251
Donald D Brooks, *Manager*
EMP: 14 EST: 2006
SALES (est): 244.2K Privately Held
SIC: 3011 Tires & inner tubes

(G-4376)
BOAT LIFT PROS OF SW FLA INC
2559 4th St (33901-2507)
PHONE....239 339-7080
Vincent T Forte, *Principal*
EMP: 11 EST: 2019
SALES (est): 1.3MM Privately Held
WEB: www.theboatliftpros.com
SIC: 3536 Boat lifts

(G-4377)
BOAT LIFTS BY SYNERGY LLC ✪
15864 Brothers Ct Ste B (33912-2248)
PHONE....641 676-4785
Brandon Graham, *Mng Member*
EMP: 6 EST: 2020
SALES (est): 514K Privately Held
SIC: 3536 Boat lifts

(G-4378)
BOAT MASTER ALUMINUM TRAILERS
Also Called: Jdci Enterprises
11950 Amedicus Ln Unit 2 (33907-4062)
PHONE....239 768-2224
Joseph K Isley Jr, *President*
John Kraft, *Purch Mgr*
EMP: 7 EST: 1983
SQ FT: 5,000
SALES (est): 517.9K Privately Held
WEB: www.boat-trailers.com
SIC: 3799 Boat trailers

(G-4379)
BOBS BARRICADES INC
8031 Mainline Pkwy (33912-5931)
PHONE....239 656-1183
David Feise, *Manager*
EMP: 20
SALES (corp-wide): 34.7MM Privately Held
WEB: www.bobsbarricades.com
SIC: 3499 Barricades, metal
PA: Bob's Barricades, Inc.
921 Shotgun Rd
Sunrise FL 33326
954 423-2627

(G-4380)
BRADEN & SON CONSTRUCTION INC
6730 Circle Dr (33905-7624)
PHONE....239 694-8600
Charles Richter, *Owner*
EMP: 6 EST: 2016
SALES (est): 83.6K Privately Held
SIC: 3577 Computer peripheral equipment

(G-4381)
BREEZE CORPORATION
Also Called: Breeze Printing
14051 Jetport Loop (33913-7705)
PHONE....239 425-8860
Linda Mozingo, *Branch Mgr*
EMP: 6 Privately Held
WEB: www.breezenewspapers.com
SIC: 2711 2741 Job printing & newspaper publishing combined; miscellaneous publishing
HQ: The Breeze Corporation
2510 Del Prado Blvd S
Cape Coral FL 33904
239 574-1110

(G-4382)
BREEZE NEWSPAPERS
14051 Jetport Loop (33913-7705)
PHONE....239 574-1116
Scott Blonde, *Principal*
Beth Zedeck, *Advt Staff*
Sonia Santiago, *Executive*
Dede Stuart, *Graphic Designe*
EMP: 11 EST: 2010
SALES (est): 243.5K Privately Held
WEB: www.breezenewspapers.com
SIC: 2711 Newspapers: publishing only, not printed on site

(G-4383)
CABINET KINGS LLC
11595 Kelly Rd Ste 322 (33908-2572)
PHONE....239 288-6740
Christopher Snow, *Mng Member*
EMP: 7 EST: 2011
SALES (est): 492.3K Privately Held
WEB: www.thecabinetkings.com
SIC: 2434 Wood kitchen cabinets

(G-4384)
CABINETSYNC INC
11350 Metro Pkwy Ste 107 (33966-1212)
PHONE....239 690-6122
Dennis Whelpley, *Principal*
EMP: 6 EST: 2007
SALES (est): 77K Privately Held
WEB: www.cabinettrac.com
SIC: 2434 Wood kitchen cabinets

(G-4385)
CALOREX USA LLC
Also Called: Aquatherm Heat Pumps
2213 Andrea Ln Ste 110 (33912-1934)
PHONE....239 482-0606
Ed Hall, *Vice Pres*
Reed Wilson,
EMP: 11 EST: 1977
SQ FT: 10,000
SALES (est): 385.3K Privately Held
WEB: www.aquathermheatpumps.com
SIC: 3585 Heat pumps, electric

(G-4386)
CANNA CONSTRUCTION LLC ✪
1942 Dana Dr (33907-2104)
PHONE....239 450-2141
Clara Sanchez,
EMP: 6 EST: 2021
SALES (est): 150K Privately Held
SIC: 1389 Construction, repair & dismantling services

(G-4387)
CARBON PRESS LLC
1635 Hendry St (33901-2909)
PHONE....239 689-4406
Patrick Wilke, *President*
EMP: 12 EST: 2017
SALES (est): 382.1K Privately Held
WEB: www.carbonpress.com
SIC: 2741 Miscellaneous publishing

(G-4388)
CARFORE LTD
Also Called: Shapley
11650 Chitwood Dr (33908-3258)
PHONE....239 415-2275
Cindy S Carfore, *President*
Carol Yorkson, *Buyer*
▼ EMP: 6 EST: 1938
SQ FT: 4,000
SALES (est): 1MM Privately Held
SIC: 2844 Cosmetic preparations

(G-4389)
CARIBBEAN CBINETS COUNTERS INC
11575 Marshwood Ln (33908-3206)
PHONE....239 292-8073
Fiona Kelly, *Principal*
EMP: 6 EST: 2018
SALES (est): 53.7K Privately Held
SIC: 2434 Wood kitchen cabinets

(G-4390)
CARTER SIGNS INC
Also Called: Carter Signs Scott
6350 Slater Mill Way (33917-6645)
P.O. Box 3648 (33918-3648)
PHONE....239 543-4004
Scott Carter, *President*
EMP: 9 EST: 1956
SALES (est): 779.1K Privately Held
WEB: www.carteroutdoor.com
SIC: 3993 Signs & advertising specialties

(G-4391)
CEMENT INDUSTRIES INC
2925 Hanson St (33916-7507)
PHONE....239 332-1440
Gay R Thompson, *President*
W Brown Thompson III, *Senior VP*
Vickie Dragich, *CFO*
Sharon Thompson, *Treasurer*
Carmi Terrell, *Admin Sec*
EMP: 60
SQ FT: 3,500
SALES (est): 14.5MM Privately Held
WEB: www.cementindustries.com
SIC: 3272 5032 Concrete products, precast; brick, stone & related material

(G-4392)
CEMEX MATERIALS LLC
2040 Ortiz Ave (33905-3721)
PHONE....239 332-0135
Peter Dalenberg, *Branch Mgr*
EMP: 73 Privately Held
SIC: 3273 Ready-mixed concrete
HQ: Cemex Materials Llc
1501 Belvedere Rd
West Palm Beach FL 33406
561 833-5555

(G-4393)
CHARLES THAGGARD INC
1951 Collier Ave Ste A (33901-7931)
PHONE....239 936-8059
Charles E Thaggard, *Director*
EMP: 5 EST: 2002
SQ FT: 2,418
SALES (est): 365.8K Privately Held
SIC: 3993 Signs & advertising specialties

(G-4394)
CHURRICO FACTORY LLC
4125 Cleveland Ave # 1370 (33901-9046)
PHONE..................................239 989-7616
Christian Monroe, *CEO*
EMP: 5 **EST:** 2014
SALES (est): 352.3K **Privately Held**
SIC: 2051 Cakes, bakery: except frozen

(G-4395)
CIANOS TILE & MARBLE INC
Also Called: Cambria
5680 Halifax Ave (33912-4417)
PHONE..................................239 267-8453
Paul Ciano, *President*
Mary Kay Sablotny, *Vice Pres*
EMP: 23 **EST:** 1993
SQ FT: 12,500
SALES (est): 2.2MM **Privately Held**
SIC: 2541 1752 2434 Counter & sink tops; floor laying & floor work; wood kitchen cabinets

(G-4396)
CINTAS CORPORATION
Also Called: Cintas Fire Protection
12771 Westlinks Dr Ste 1 (33913-8074)
PHONE..................................239 693-8722
Jeff Playter, *General Mgr*
Steve Taylor, *Principal*
Barbara Bryan, *Supervisor*
EMP: 7
SQ FT: 1,000
SALES (corp-wide): 7.1B **Publicly Held**
WEB: www.cintas.com
SIC: 2326 7382 2337 7218 Work uniforms; burglar alarm maintenance & monitoring; fire alarm maintenance & monitoring; uniforms, except athletic: women's, misses' & juniors'; industrial uniform supply; wiping towel supply; treated equipment supply: mats, rugs, mops, cloths, etc.; safety equipment
PA: Cintas Corporation
6800 Cintas Blvd
Cincinnati OH 45262
513 459-1200

(G-4397)
CLEARTEL VOICE AND DATA LLC
5433 Harbour Castle Dr (33907-7842)
PHONE..................................239 220-5545
Joshua Beverley, *Mng Member*
EMP: 6 **EST:** 2012
SALES (est): 160.8K **Privately Held**
WEB: www.cleartelvoiceanddata.com
SIC: 3661 Telephone central office equipment, dial or manual

(G-4398)
CLEVER PAVERS INC
2727 Clnl Blvd Apt 204 (33907)
PHONE..................................239 633-7048
Stephanie Raggi, *Vice Pres*
EMP: 6 **EST:** 2005
SALES (est): 77.1K **Privately Held**
SIC: 2951 Asphalt paving mixtures & blocks

(G-4399)
CLINICON CORPORATION
Also Called: Clinical Refractions Perfected
3949 Evans Ave Ste 107 (33901-9341)
PHONE..................................239 939-1345
Fax: 239 939-3675
EMP: 11
SQ FT: 2,000
SALES (est): 790K **Privately Held**
SIC: 3841 8071 Mfg Opthalmology Equipment

(G-4400)
COASTAL CANVAS AND AWNING CO
5761 Independence Cir # 1 (33912-4416)
PHONE..................................239 433-1114
John Desesa, *President*
Danny Martin, *Sales Mgr*
EMP: 15 **EST:** 1975
SALES (est): 1MM **Privately Held**
WEB: www.coastalcanvasandawning.com
SIC: 2394 Awnings, fabric: made from purchased materials

(G-4401)
COASTAL CLOSET CO OF FLA LLC
6361 Mtro Plntn Rd Unit B (33966)
PHONE..................................239 826-3807
EMP: 5 **EST:** 2019
SALES (est): 361.6K **Privately Held**
WEB: www.coastalclosetnaples.com
SIC: 2434 Wood kitchen cabinets

(G-4402)
COASTAL CONCRETE PRODUCTS LLC
Also Called: Coastal Site Development
7742 Alico Rd (33912-6021)
PHONE..................................239 208-4079
David E Torres,
EMP: 30 **EST:** 2010
SALES (est): 6.5MM **Privately Held**
WEB: www.coastalconcreteprod.com
SIC: 3272 1771 1623 1611 Concrete products, precast; concrete work; underground utilities contractor; highway & street construction; highway & street paving contractor

(G-4403)
COASTAL ELECTRIC
5760 Youngquist Rd Ste 9 (33912-2267)
PHONE..................................239 245-7396
EMP: 9 **EST:** 2016
SALES (est): 88.3K **Privately Held**
WEB: www.coastalelectriccooperative.com
SIC: 3699 1731 Electrical equipment & supplies; electrical work

(G-4404)
COASTAL PRECAST OF FLORIDA
7291 Pennsylvania St # 3 (33912-5906)
P.O. Box 370, Estero (33929-0370)
PHONE..................................239 432-0667
Frank Innuzzi, *President*
Kathy Pawlowski, *Office Mgr*
Fred Russell, *Admin Sec*
EMP: 30 **EST:** 2001
SALES (est): 5.4MM **Privately Held**
WEB: www.coastalprecast.com
SIC: 3272 Concrete products, precast

(G-4405)
COASTLINE CBNTRY CSTM MLLWK LL
6440 Metro Plantation Rd (33966-1266)
PHONE..................................239 208-2876
Carl B Maxner, *Mng Member*
Brian J Beaudet,
Danny E Cox,
EMP: 14 **EST:** 2013
SALES (est): 1.6MM **Privately Held**
WEB: www.coastlinecabinetry.com
SIC: 2434 Wood kitchen cabinets

(G-4406)
COLLINS AND DUPONT INTERIORS
5711 Corporation Cir (33905-5009)
PHONE..................................239 694-3400
Sherry Dupont, *Principal*
EMP: 6 **EST:** 2017
SALES (est): 74.4K **Privately Held**
WEB: www.collins-dupont.com
SIC: 2879 Agricultural chemicals

(G-4407)
COMPUTERS AT WORK INC
Also Called: Vtech Io
3033 Winkler Ave Ste 210 (33916-9522)
PHONE..................................239 571-1050
David W Peterson, *President*
Marsha Bewersdorf, *CFO*
Terry Timmins, *Accounts Mgr*
Ruhl Shawn, *Maintence Staff*
EMP: 31 **EST:** 2001
SALES (est): 13MM **Privately Held**
WEB: www.vtechio.com
SIC: 3572 5734 Computer storage devices; computer & software stores

(G-4408)
CONRIC HOLDINGS LLC
Also Called: Conric PR & Marketing
8770 Paseo De Valencia St (33908-9657)
PHONE..................................239 690-9840
Connie Ramos-Williams, *CEO*
Frederick R Williams Jr, *CFO*
Josh Milton, *Mktg Coord*
April Bordeaux, *Director*
EMP: 10 **EST:** 2010
SALES (est): 1.1MM **Privately Held**
WEB: www.conricpr.com
SIC: 2721 8743 7311 Magazines: publishing only, not printed on site; public relations services; advertising agencies

(G-4409)
CONTINENTAL METALS
11921 Wedge Dr (33913-8347)
PHONE..................................734 362-1144
Laurel Dorsey, *Principal*
EMP: 6 **EST:** 2016
SALES (est): 54.1K **Privately Held**
SIC: 3547 Rolling mill machinery

(G-4410)
CORNERSTONE KITCHENS INC
Also Called: Cornerstone Builders S W Fla
3150 Old Metro Pkwy (33916-7517)
PHONE..................................239 332-3020
Anthony Leeber, *President*
▲ **EMP:** 113
SQ FT: 9,000
SALES: 22.3MM **Privately Held**
WEB: www.cornerstonebuildersswfl.com
SIC: 2431 5211 Doors & door parts & trim, wood; lumber & other building materials

(G-4411)
COUNTRYWIDE SCREEN PRINTING
14261 Jetport Loop W (33913-7754)
PHONE..................................239 333-4020
Ted Briones, *Owner*
EMP: 6 **EST:** 2008
SALES (est): 125.6K **Privately Held**
SIC: 2396 Fabric printing & stamping

(G-4412)
COVER PUBLISHING
1385 Sautern Dr (33919-2715)
PHONE..................................239 482-4814
Frank Wanicka, *Principal*
▲ **EMP:** 6 **EST:** 2000
SALES (est): 134.4K **Privately Held**
SIC: 2759 Commercial printing

(G-4413)
CREATIVE CABINET CONCEPTS INC
Also Called: Creative Solid Surfacing
7947 Drew Cir (33967-6005)
PHONE..................................239 939-1313
Stephen Ruffino, *President*
EMP: 16 **EST:** 1982
SQ FT: 20,000
SALES (est): 4.7MM **Privately Held**
SIC: 2541 2434 Cabinets, except refrigerated: show, display, etc.: wood; wood kitchen cabinets

(G-4414)
CREATIVE CARBIDE INC (PA)
7880 Interstate Ct Unit A (33917-2131)
PHONE..................................239 567-0041
Tom Shoecraft Jr, *President*
Rick Brockway, *Data Proc Dir*
EMP: 15 **EST:** 1993
SALES (est): 2.9MM **Privately Held**
WEB: www.creativecarbide.com
SIC: 2819 3568 3545 Carbides; power transmission equipment; machine tool accessories

(G-4415)
CREATIVE CONCEPTS INTL LLC
Also Called: Ready Set Mount
16960 Alico Mission Way (33908-4844)
PHONE..................................888 530-7904
Chris Bugan, *President*
▲ **EMP:** 10 **EST:** 2006
SQ FT: 500
SALES (est): 784.7K **Privately Held**
SIC: 2789 Display mounting

(G-4416)
CREATIVE MARINE
6261 Arc Way (33966-1352)
PHONE..................................239 437-1010
Bobbi Land, *Office Mgr*
Weston Beckwith, *Art Dir*
EMP: 6 **EST:** 2019
SALES (est): 310.9K **Privately Held**
WEB: www.this-creative.com
SIC: 3732 Boat building & repairing

(G-4417)
CRUMBLISS MANUFACTURING CO
Also Called: Crumbliss Test Equipment
5812 Enterprise Pkwy (33905-5001)
PHONE..................................239 693-8588
Ronald Crumbliss, *President*
EMP: 10 **EST:** 1933
SQ FT: 13,000
SALES (est): 692.1K **Privately Held**
WEB: www.crumbliss.com
SIC: 3825 3829 Instruments to measure electricity; measuring & controlling devices

(G-4418)
CRYSTEK CRYSTALS CORPORATION
16850 Oriole Rd Ste 3 (33912-2544)
P.O. Box 60135 (33906-6135)
PHONE..................................239 561-3311
Anthony Mastropole, *CEO*
James J Browne, *Vice Pres*
Luiz Oricchio, *Sales Staff*
Maria Guerra, *Marketing Staff*
James D Hohman, *Admin Sec*
EMP: 30 **EST:** 1996
SQ FT: 25,000
SALES (est): 5.1MM **Privately Held**
WEB: www.crystek.com
SIC: 3679 3825 Crystals & crystal assemblies, radio; instruments to measure electricity

(G-4419)
CURTIS K FOULKS
Also Called: Foulks Forest
2240 Hemingway Dr Ste J (33912-1979)
PHONE..................................239 454-9663
Curtis K Foulks, *Owner*
EMP: 6 **EST:** 1985
SALES (est): 465.8K **Privately Held**
SIC: 2434 Wood kitchen cabinets

(G-4420)
CUSTOM CABINETS SW FLORIDA LLC
5929 Youngquist Rd (33912-2294)
PHONE..................................239 415-3350
Terrence Tripp, *Mng Member*
EMP: 8 **EST:** 2010
SALES (est): 632.8K **Privately Held**
WEB: www.customcabinetsswfl.com
SIC: 2434 1751 5712 Wood kitchen cabinets; cabinet & finish carpentry; cabinet work, custom

(G-4421)
CUSTOM DRAWERS OF SWFL LLC
2861 Work Dr (33916-6556)
PHONE..................................239 226-1699
Robert Nielson, *Principal*
EMP: 6 **EST:** 2016
SALES (est): 178.2K **Privately Held**
WEB: www.customdrawersofswfl.com
SIC: 2434 Wood kitchen cabinets

(G-4422)
CUSTOM MAILBOXES AND SIGNS
13319 5th St (33905-2019)
PHONE..................................239 738-9321
Saby Ibanez, *Principal*
EMP: 7 **EST:** 2014
SALES (est): 187.4K **Privately Held**
WEB: www.mailboxesandsigns.com
SIC: 3993 Signs & advertising specialties

(G-4423)
D & D MACHINE & HYDRAULICS INC
10945 Metro Pkwy (33966-1202)
PHONE..................................239 275-7177
W Jack J Harlan, *President*
Bob Hess, *President*
D Todd McGee, *Corp Secy*
Adam Gray, *Opers Mgr*

GEOGRAPHIC

William F Ballantine, *Director*
▼ **EMP:** 34 **EST:** 1969
SQ FT: 55,000
SALES (est): 6.4MM **Privately Held**
WEB: www.ddpumps.com
SIC: 3561 Pumps & pumping equipment

(G-4424)
D AND S SUPERIOR COATINGS INC
6150 Metro Plantation Rd (33966-1200)
PHONE..................................360 388-6099
Harrison Hubschman, *Administration*
EMP: 6 **EST:** 2016
SALES (est): 456K **Privately Held**
SIC: 3479 Metal coating & allied service

(G-4425)
DARLING INGREDIENTS INC
8181 Katanga Ct (33916-7541)
PHONE..................................239 693-2300
Tom Herrington, *Principal*
Linda Goodspeed, *Director*
EMP: 7
SQ FT: 4,000
SALES (corp-wide): 3.3B **Publicly Held**
WEB: www.darlingii.com
SIC: 2077 Animal & marine fats & oils
PA: Darling Ingredients Inc.
5601 N Macarthur Blvd
Irving TX 75038
972 717-0300

(G-4426)
DAVANTI DOORS LLC
2840 South St (33916-5516)
PHONE..................................239 842-8341
Lisa Esposito, *Principal*
EMP: 9 **EST:** 2015
SALES (est): 144.7K **Privately Held**
WEB: www.prrhosting.com
SIC: 2411 2499 3449 5031 Handle bolts, wood: hewn; handles, wood; bars, concrete reinforcing: fabricated steel; door frames, all materials

(G-4427)
DBI SERVICES LLC
5893 Entp Pkwy Ste A (33905)
PHONE..................................239 218-5204
Paul D Deangelo, *Mng Member*
Joseph G Ferguson, *Admin Sec*
Neal A Deangelo,
EMP: 30 **EST:** 2007
SALES (est): 1.2MM **Privately Held**
WEB: www.dbiservices.com
SIC: 3679 Electronic circuits

(G-4428)
DEAN DAIRY HOLDINGS LLC
3579 Work Dr (33916-7535)
PHONE..................................239 334-1114
Rick Oneill, *Manager*
Kevin Cross, *Supervisor*
EMP: 53
SQ FT: 9,280 **Publicly Held**
WEB: www.deanfoods.com
SIC: 2024 5143 Ice cream & frozen desserts; dairy products, except dried or canned
HQ: Dean Dairy Holdings, Llc
6851 Ne 2nd Ave
Miami FL 33138
305 795-7700

(G-4429)
DEAN STEEL BUILDINGS INC (PA)
2929 Industrial Ave (33901-6437)
PHONE..................................239 334-1051
Nan Dean, *President*
John Amann, *Vice Pres*
Michelle Boyer, *Vice Pres*
William A Clark, *Vice Pres*
Charlotte Edwards, *Vice Pres*
◆ **EMP:** 80
SQ FT: 100,000
SALES (est): 14.2MM **Privately Held**
WEB: www.deansteelbuildings.com
SIC: 3448 1542 Prefabricated metal buildings; commercial & office building, new construction

(G-4430)
DEKSCAPE
17051 Alico Commerce Ct # 3 (33967-8510)
P.O. Box 61421 (33906-1421)
PHONE..................................239 278-3325
Jason Fowler, *President*
EMP: 9 **EST:** 2014
SALES (est): 883.8K **Privately Held**
WEB: www.dekscape.com
SIC: 2851 1771 Lacquers, varnishes, enamels & other coatings; flooring contractor

(G-4431)
DIEMOLD MACHINE COMPANY INC
2350 Bruner Ln (33912-1970)
PHONE..................................239 482-1400
Ulrich K Boehnke, *President*
EMP: 29 **EST:** 1962
SQ FT: 30,000
SALES (est): 5.5MM **Privately Held**
WEB: www.diemoldmachine.com
SIC: 3089 3544 Injection molding of plastics; industrial molds

(G-4432)
DIXIE METALCRAFT INCORPORATED
3050 Warehouse Rd (33916-7615)
PHONE..................................239 337-4299
Gene C Sutton, *President*
Ron Kinchen, *Corp Secy*
Bruce E Bordeaux, *Vice Pres*
EMP: 19 **EST:** 1985
SQ FT: 5,000
SALES (est): 1.1MM **Privately Held**
SIC: 3444 Sheet metalwork

(G-4433)
DIXIE STRUCTURES & MAINTENANCE (PA)
1216 Hopedale Dr (33919-1619)
PHONE..................................205 274-4525
Gwen Blackwell, *President*
Bryan Blackwell, *Senior VP*
EMP: 15 **EST:** 1997
SQ FT: 20,000
SALES (est): 1MM **Privately Held**
WEB: www.dixiestructures.com
SIC: 3312 Structural shapes & pilings, steel

(G-4434)
DNE POT SBOB INC
Also Called: Bob's Top End
11000 Metro Pkwy Ste 10 (33966-1210)
PHONE..................................239 936-8880
Robert Foster, *President*
Georgia Foster, *Vice Pres*
EMP: 10 **EST:** 1978
SQ FT: 2,000
SALES (est): 819.1K **Privately Held**
WEB: www.bobstopend.com
SIC: 2759 Screen printing

(G-4435)
DOLPHIN BOAT LIFTS INC
6440 Topaz Ct (33966-8310)
PHONE..................................239 936-1782
Robert Shenkel, *President*
Joanne Shenkel, *Vice Pres*
EMP: 6 **EST:** 1988
SQ FT: 7,100
SALES (est): 977.6K **Privately Held**
WEB: www.dolphinboatlifts.com
SIC: 3429 1629 Marine hardware; dams, waterways, docks & other marine construction

(G-4436)
DRAKE INC
2920 Rockfill Rd (33916-4886)
PHONE..................................239 590-9199
Terry Drake, *Principal*
EMP: 10 **EST:** 2006
SALES (est): 384.7K **Privately Held**
WEB: www.drakeandcompany.com
SIC: 3273 Ready-mixed concrete

(G-4437)
DRAKE READY MIX INC
2920 Rockfill Rd (33916-4886)
PHONE..................................239 590-9199
Annie Drake, *President*
EMP: 52 **EST:** 2005
SALES (est): 8.1MM **Privately Held**
WEB: www.drakereadymix.com
SIC: 3273 Ready-mixed concrete

(G-4438)
E-Z METALS INC
Also Called: Suncoast Industries of Florida
6133 Idlewild St (33966-1217)
PHONE..................................239 936-7887
Jonathan L Dean, *President*
Rusty Billger, *Vice Pres*
Sharon Hackett, *Treasurer*
Kenneth Berdick, *Shareholder*
Judith Leishure, *Admin Sec*
▲ **EMP:** 27 **EST:** 1987
SQ FT: 32,500
SALES (est): 4.5MM **Privately Held**
SIC: 3441 Fabricated structural metal

(G-4439)
EAGLE READY MIX LLC
16576 Gator Rd (33912-5938)
PHONE..................................239 693-1500
Kevin R Eisenbath, *Mng Member*
Doug Mennemeier,
EMP: 21 **EST:** 2007
SQ FT: 1,879
SALES (est): 3.5MM **Privately Held**
SIC: 3273 Ready-mixed concrete

(G-4440)
EAR-TRONICS INC (PA)
7181 College Pkwy Ste 14 (33907-5642)
P.O. Box 60151 (33906-6151)
PHONE..................................239 275-7655
Robert Hooper, *President*
Terri Hooper, *Corp Secy*
Gale Fagan, *Office Mgr*
Peggy Thomas, *Office Mgr*
EMP: 9 **EST:** 1980
SALES (est): 2.4MM **Privately Held**
WEB: www.eartronics.com
SIC: 3842 5999 8049 Hearing aids; hearing aids; audiologist

(G-4441)
EIDOLON ANALYTICS INC
Also Called: Unisource Graphics and Signs
2487 N Airport Rd (33907-1401)
PHONE..................................239 288-6951
Gina Hyon, *President*
Francisco Colon, *Vice Pres*
Minette La Croix, *CFO*
EMP: 10 **EST:** 2011
SQ FT: 19,000
SALES (est): 1.4MM **Privately Held**
WEB: www.unisourcesigns.com
SIC: 3993 Signs & advertising specialties

(G-4442)
ELECTRNIC SYSTEMS SUTHEAST LLC
5840 Halifax Ave (33912-4418)
PHONE..................................561 955-9006
Michael Monteiro, *Sales Staff*
John Ludwig, *Manager*
Steve Brody,
EMP: 9 **EST:** 2002
SALES (est): 177.4K **Privately Held**
SIC: 3629 Electronic generation equipment

(G-4443)
EMCYTE CORP
4331 Veronica S Shoemaker (33916-2233)
PHONE..................................239 481-7725
Patrick Pennie, *President*
Ewa Profiruk, *President*
Jeanette Acker, *Production*
Glendal S Romanini, *Finance*
Peter Everts, *Officer*
EMP: 20 **EST:** 2008
SALES (est): 2.8MM **Privately Held**
WEB: www.emcyte.com
SIC: 3841 Surgical & medical instruments

(G-4444)
ENTERTAINMENT METALS INC
Also Called: Entertainment Mfg Group
13351 Saddle Rd Ste 205 (33913-9054)
PHONE..................................800 817-2683
Ryan Bringardner, *CEO*
Kevin Kirchner, *President*
John Irvin, *CFO*
Zarko Njezic, *Sales Mgr*
Brinley Mazza, *Marketing Staff*
EMP: 32 **EST:** 2009
SQ FT: 13,393
SALES (est): 2MM **Privately Held**
WEB: www.emfgrp.com
SIC: 3441 Fabricated structural metal

(G-4445)
ETERNITY CABINETS
17000 Alico Commerce Ct (33967-8503)
PHONE..................................239 482-7172
Attira Ila, *Owner*
EMP: 7 **EST:** 2013
SALES (est): 272.9K **Privately Held**
WEB: www.cabinetsforswfl.com
SIC: 2434 Wood kitchen cabinets

(G-4446)
EV PILOTCAR INC
6293 Thomas Rd (33912-2269)
PHONE..................................239 243-8023
Ali Mete Timur, *President*
Sukru Ozkilic, *Vice Pres*
EMP: 7 **EST:** 2019
SALES (est): 629.1K **Privately Held**
WEB: www.pilotcarev.com
SIC: 3711 Cars, electric, assembly of

(G-4447)
EV RIDER LLC
6410 Arc Way Ste A (33966-1413)
PHONE..................................239 278-5054
Juan Rivera, *Mng Member*
Ana Rivera,
◆ **EMP:** 8 **EST:** 2006
SALES (est): 3MM **Privately Held**
WEB: www.evrider.com
SIC: 3944 Scooters, children's

(G-4448)
FBI INDUSTRIES INC
11020 Yellow Poplar Dr (33913-8882)
PHONE..................................239 462-1176
Ryan D Beavers, *Principal*
EMP: 8 **EST:** 2016
SALES (est): 51.3K **Privately Held**
WEB: www.fbirl.com
SIC: 3999 Manufacturing industries

(G-4449)
FF SYSTEMS INC
2840 Hunter St (33916-7617)
PHONE..................................239 288-4255
Benno Forstner, *Principal*
Friedrich Heindl, *Vice Pres*
◆ **EMP:** 7 **EST:** 2010
SQ FT: 13,500
SALES (est): 837.6K **Privately Held**
WEB: www.ffsystems.com
SIC: 3613 Control panels, electric

(G-4450)
FLEXSTAKE INC
2150 Andrea Ln (33912-1901)
PHONE..................................239 481-3539
Robert K Hughes Jr, *President*
Jim Zadrozny, *General Mgr*
John W Hughes, *Vice Pres*
▼ **EMP:** 34 **EST:** 1988
SQ FT: 21,550
SALES (est): 1.8MM **Privately Held**
WEB: www.flexstake.com
SIC: 3231 5091 Reflector glass beads, for highway signs or reflectors; golf equipment

(G-4451)
FLORIDA SALES & MARKETING
11840 Metro Pkwy (33966-8384)
PHONE..................................239 274-3103
Charles Hurt, *Principal*
John Bilvich, *Sales Staff*
Timothy Steger, *Representative*
◆ **EMP:** 20
SALES (est): 3.5MM **Privately Held**
WEB: www.floridamarketingandsales.com
SIC: 3334 Primary aluminum

(G-4452)
FLORIDA STONEWARE TOPS INC
11251 Orange River Blvd (33905-6314)
PHONE..................................239 340-0492
Gerald E Martinez, *President*
EMP: 8 **EST:** 2001

SALES (est): 93.9K **Privately Held**
SIC: 3269 Stoneware pottery products

(G-4453)
FLORIDA STYLE ALUMINUM INC
15481 Old Wedgewood Ct (33908-7208)
PHONE..................................239 689-8662
Andrew McCurdy, *President*
Carol McCurdy, *Vice Pres*
EMP: 7 **EST:** 1994
SQ FT: 6,900
SALES (est): 249.9K **Privately Held**
WEB: www.florida-style.com
SIC: 3231 Scientific & technical glassware: from purchased glass

(G-4454)
FLORIDA WEEKLY
2891 Center Pointe Dr # 300 (33916-9458)
PHONE..................................239 333-2135
Angela Schivinski, *Publisher*
Teresa Kitts, *Executive*
EMP: 7 **EST:** 2019
SALES (est): 444.1K **Privately Held**
SIC: 2711 Newspapers, publishing & printing

(G-4455)
FLORIDAS FINEST INDUSTRIES
5294 Summerlin (33907)
PHONE..................................239 333-1777
Annalisa Xioutas, *President*
Sheri Aws, *Bookkeeper*
EMP: 10 **EST:** 2009
SALES (est): 289.9K **Privately Held**
WEB: www.ffi1.com
SIC: 3999 Manufacturing industries

(G-4456)
FOCUS ON WATER INC
10160 Mcgregor Blvd (33919-1039)
PHONE..................................239 275-1880
Robert L Farnsworth, *President*
Gayle Farnsworth, *Vice Pres*
EMP: 8 **EST:** 2014
SALES (est): 123.3K **Privately Held**
SIC: 3589 Water purification equipment, household type; water treatment equipment, industrial

(G-4457)
FORESTRY RESOURCES INC (PA)
Also Called: Forestry Resources Ecological
4353 Michigan Link (33916-2300)
PHONE..................................239 332-3966
John W Cauthen, *President*
Glen Davis, *CFO*
EMP: 40
SQ FT: 6,500
SALES (est): 15MM **Privately Held**
WEB: www.gomulch.com
SIC: 2499 2875 Mulch, wood & bark; potting soil, mixed

(G-4458)
FORT MYERS DIGITAL LLC
6381 Corp Pk Cir Ste 2 (33966)
PHONE..................................239 482-3086
Dorothy P Kres,
EMP: 8 **EST:** 2012
SALES (est): 556.1K **Privately Held**
WEB: www.fortmyersdigital.com
SIC: 2752 2851 Commercial printing, offset; vinyl coatings, strippable

(G-4459)
FRESCO GROUP INC
Also Called: Styleview Industries
13300 S Clevlnd Ave Ste 5 (33907-3871)
PHONE..................................239 936-8055
Lynn B Myers, *President*
P Fred Biery, *Vice Pres*
EMP: 16 **EST:** 1984
SQ FT: 7,150
SALES (est): 1.2MM **Privately Held**
SIC: 3444 1521 Awnings, sheet metal; patio & deck construction & repair

(G-4460)
FULL THROTTLE CNC INC
3550 Work Dr Unit A2 (33916-7522)
PHONE..................................248 525-1973
David Meyers, *Principal*
EMP: 6 **EST:** 2018
SALES (est): 149.9K **Privately Held**
SIC: 3999 Manufacturing industries

(G-4461)
FUSION INDUSTRIES LLC
16710 Gator Rd (33912-5926)
PHONE..................................239 415-7554
Stevens Jeff, *Mng Member*
Brooke Hendrix, *Admin Asst*
EMP: 14 **EST:** 2011
SALES (est): 1.7MM **Privately Held**
WEB: www.fusionindustriesllc.com
SIC: 3999 Hair & hair-based products

(G-4462)
FUSION INDUSTRIES INTL LLC
16710 Gator Rd (33912-5926)
PHONE..................................239 415-7554
Jeffrey Stevens, *President*
EMP: 6 **EST:** 2014
SALES (est): 893.3K **Privately Held**
WEB: www.fusionindustriesllc.com
SIC: 3281 Curbing, granite or stone

(G-4463)
FUSION WELDING
15865 Brothers Ct (33912-2253)
PHONE..................................239 288-6530
Lisa Beaner, *Principal*
EMP: 13 **EST:** 2011
SALES (est): 1.2MM **Privately Held**
WEB: www.fusion-welding.com
SIC: 7692 Welding repair

(G-4464)
G & F MANUFACTURING INC
Also Called: G&F Mnfctring Mfr Glfstream He
7902 Interstate Ct (33917-2112)
PHONE..................................239 939-7446
Dan Goldberg, *President*
Bill Fields, *Vice Pres*
Jim Fields, *Treasurer*
Eric Watters, *Sales Staff*
Brian Goldberg, *Admin Sec*
EMP: 12 **EST:** 2003
SQ FT: 10,200
SALES (est): 2.1MM **Privately Held**
WEB: www.gulfstreamheatpump.com
SIC: 3561 Industrial pumps & parts

(G-4465)
GA FD SVCS PINELLAS CNTY LLC
5501 Division Dr (33905-5017)
PHONE..................................239 693-5090
Larry Page, *Controller*
Terry White, *Sales Staff*
Abe Pacheco, *Manager*
EMP: 29
SALES (corp-wide): 151.6MM **Privately Held**
WEB: www.sunmeadow.com
SIC: 2038 5812 2099 Frozen specialties; contract food services; food preparations
PA: G.A. Food Services Of Pinellas County, Llc
12200 32nd Ct N
Saint Petersburg FL 33716
727 388-0075

(G-4466)
GARYS CABINETS AND MORE LLC
1945 Custom Dr (33907-2101)
PHONE..................................941 585-8001
Gary Whatley, *Principal*
EMP: 6 **EST:** 2018
SALES (est): 258.7K **Privately Held**
WEB: www.garyscabinets.com
SIC: 2434 Wood kitchen cabinets

(G-4467)
GECKO WOODWORKS
5654 Natoma Dr (33919-2618)
PHONE..................................239 738-8283
Tammie Renz, *Principal*
EMP: 6 **EST:** 2014
SALES (est): 54.1K **Privately Held**
SIC: 2431 Millwork

(G-4468)
GENERTOR SPRCNTER SUTHWEST FLA
16243 S Tamiami Trl (33908-4398)
PHONE..................................608 765-5177
EMP: 6 **EST:** 2019
SALES (est): 201K **Privately Held**
WEB: www.generatorsupercenter.com
SIC: 3621 Motors & generators

(G-4469)
GO MOBILE SIGNS
13468 Palm Beach Blvd C (33905-2168)
PHONE..................................239 245-7803
Joseph H Baker Jr, *President*
EMP: 5 **EST:** 2009
SALES (est): 374.1K **Privately Held**
WEB: www.gomobile-signs.com
SIC: 3993 Signs, not made in custom sign painting shops

(G-4470)
GOLD PLATING SPECIALTIES
17560 Allentown Rd (33967-2961)
PHONE..................................239 851-9323
Jill Stulak, *Principal*
EMP: 5 **EST:** 2001
SALES (est): 331K **Privately Held**
WEB: www.goldplating.com
SIC: 3471 Plating of metals or formed products

(G-4471)
GRATE FIREPLACE & STONE SHOPPE
16611 S Tamiami Trl (33908-4504)
PHONE..................................239 939-7187
William J Stasko Sr, *President*
Susan Stasko, *Vice Pres*
Diane Key, *Treasurer*
Helen Stasko, *Admin Sec*
EMP: 21 **EST:** 1982
SQ FT: 3,000
SALES (est): 572.2K **Privately Held**
WEB: www.gratefireplace.com
SIC: 3272 5719 Fireplaces, concrete; fireplace equipment & accessories

(G-4472)
GREATWOODWORKS
19057 Dogwood Rd (33967-3651)
PHONE..................................239 200-4848
Daniel Nagy, *Principal*
EMP: 7 **EST:** 2016
SALES (est): 231.4K **Privately Held**
SIC: 2431 Millwork

(G-4473)
GREG VALENTINE LLC
Also Called: Valentines Glass & Metal
3590 Old Metro Pkwy (33916-7539)
P.O. Box 60272 (33906-6272)
PHONE..................................239 332-0855
Gregory Valentine, *Principal*
Tim Stewmon, *Principal*
Scott Burden, *Purchasing*
EMP: 30 **EST:** 2014
SALES (est): 2.2MM **Privately Held**
WEB: www.vgmholdings.com
SIC: 3446 1793 Gates, ornamental metal; glass & glazing work

(G-4474)
GULF CAST MTLS STHWEST FLA INC
16121 Lee Rd (33912-2512)
PHONE..................................239 790-0016
Robert W Brown, *President*
Donald J Nelson, *Vice Pres*
Kevin J Berth, *CFO*
EMP: 18 **EST:** 2005
SALES (est): 257K **Privately Held**
WEB: www.texasmaterialsgroup.com
SIC: 3241 Cement, hydraulic

(G-4475)
GULF COAST NON EMERGENCY TRANS
17531 Boat Club Dr (33908-4465)
PHONE..................................239 825-1350
EMP: 8
SALES (est): 679.6K **Privately Held**
SIC: 3842 Surgical Appliances And Supplies, Nsk

(G-4476)
GULF COAST PRECAST INC
2506 Precast Ct (33916-4898)
PHONE..................................239 337-0021
James Gorrell, *President*
Joe D Cavage, *Vice Pres*
EMP: 29 **EST:** 1998
SQ FT: 3,900
SALES (est): 3.1MM **Privately Held**
WEB: www.gulfcoastprecast.com
SIC: 3272 Concrete products

(G-4477)
GULF COAST PRINTING
Also Called: Allez Partnership
11000 Panther Printing Wa (33908-3480)
PHONE..................................239 482-5555
Joe Andersen, *Partner*
EMP: 20 **EST:** 2006
SALES (est): 1.2MM **Privately Held**
SIC: 2759 Commercial printing

(G-4478)
GULF COAST TRUSS CO INC
6115 Idlewild St (33966-1217)
PHONE..................................239 278-1819
Ronald A Newsom, *President*
EMP: 12 **EST:** 2003
SQ FT: 6,000
SALES (est): 503.6K **Privately Held**
WEB: www.gulfcoasttru.mfgpages.com
SIC: 2439 Trusses, wooden roof

(G-4479)
GULFSTREAM BOATWORKS
1811 Rhonda St (33901-8936)
PHONE..................................239 223-2628
Aaron Best, *Owner*
EMP: 6 **EST:** 2010
SALES (est): 63K **Privately Held**
SIC: 3732 Boat building & repairing

(G-4480)
HALL INDUSTRIES INCORPORATED
11850 Regional Ln Unit 6 (33913-8874)
PHONE..................................239 768-0372
Alfred Steinberg, *Branch Mgr*
EMP: 12
SALES (corp-wide): 25.4MM **Privately Held**
WEB: www.hallindustries.com
SIC: 3999 Barber & beauty shop equipment
PA: Hall Industries, Incorporated
514 Mecklem Ln
Ellwood City PA 16117
724 752-2000

(G-4481)
HF SCIENTIFIC INC
16260 Arprt Pk Dr Ste 140 (33913)
PHONE..................................888 203-7248
A Suellen Torregrosa, *CEO*
Srinivas K Bagepalli, *President*
Munish Nanda, *President*
Roberto Vengoechea, *President*
Kenneth R Lepage, *Vice Pres*
▲ **EMP:** 40 **EST:** 1964
SALES (est): 8.9MM
SALES (corp-wide): 1.5B **Publicly Held**
WEB: www.watts.com
SIC: 3821 3625 3826 3823 Laboratory apparatus & furniture; electric controls & control accessories, industrial; analytical instruments; industrial instrmnts msrmnt display/control process variable
PA: Watts Water Technologies, Inc.
815 Chestnut St
North Andover MA 01845
978 688-1811

(G-4482)
HINES BENDING SYSTEMS INC
Also Called: Manufctring Sls Pipe Bnding Eq
6441 Metro Plantation Rd (33966-1257)
PHONE..................................239 433-2132
James Hynes, *President*
Carole Andersen, *Sales Staff*
▲ **EMP:** 16 **EST:** 1975
SQ FT: 1,600
SALES (est): 1.3MM **Privately Held**
WEB: www.hinesbending.com
SIC: 3498 Fabricated pipe & fittings

GEOGRAPHIC

(G-4483)
HINSILBLON LTD INC
Also Called: Hinsilblon Laboratories
12381 S Cleveland Ave (33907-3893)
PHONE..................................239 418-1133
Richard Hindin, *President*
Tim Planker, *Vice Pres*
EMP: 7 **EST:** 1990
SQ FT: 2,500
SALES (est): 672.3K **Privately Held**
WEB: www.hinsilblon.com
SIC: 2842 Deodorants, nonpersonal

(G-4484)
HOMES MAGAZINE INC
Also Called: Homes Real Estate Magazine
2133 Broadway (33901-3634)
PHONE..................................239 334-7168
Robert Kaye, *President*
EMP: 10 **EST:** 1973
SALES (est): 599.3K **Privately Held**
WEB: www.homesmagazine.net
SIC: 2741 Directories: publishing only, not printed on site

(G-4485)
HRE LLC
15860 Pine Ridge Rd (33908-2611)
PHONE..................................317 340-5991
John W Hale, *Principal*
EMP: 6 **EST:** 2012
SALES (est): 152.1K **Privately Held**
WEB: www.hremanifolds.com
SIC: 3714 Motor vehicle parts & accessories

(G-4486)
HUDSON CABINETS & MILLWORK LLC
6261 Metro Plantation Rd (33966-1213)
PHONE..................................239 218-0451
Mark Hudson, *Manager*
EMP: 10 **EST:** 2010
SALES (est): 830.5K **Privately Held**
WEB: www.hudsoncabinets.com
SIC: 2434 Wood kitchen cabinets

(G-4487)
HUGHES FABRICATION
2304 Bruner Ln Ste 1 (33912-2077)
PHONE..................................239 481-1376
EMP: 5
SALES (est): 302.3K **Privately Held**
SIC: 3999 Mfg Misc Products

(G-4488)
IMAGING INITIATIVES INC
Also Called: New York Mri Management
5291 Smmrland Commons Way (33907)
PHONE..................................239 936-3646
Howard Sheridan, *President*
EMP: 7 **EST:** 2001
SALES (est): 280.7K **Privately Held**
SIC: 3845 Magnetic resonance imaging device, nuclear

(G-4489)
IMC-HEARTWAY LLC (PA)
Also Called: Heartway USA
5681 Independence Cir A (33912-4457)
PHONE..................................239 275-6767
Young Ho, *CEO*
Yi-Ting Wang, *President*
▲ **EMP:** 5 **EST:** 2001
SQ FT: 8,500
SALES (est): 3.5MM **Privately Held**
SIC: 3842 5047 Wheelchairs; orthopedic equipment & supplies

(G-4490)
IMM SURVIVOR INC
17030 Alico Center Rd (33967-6063)
PHONE..................................239 454-7020
George Becker, *President*
Mike Nanda, *Sales Staff*
EMP: 10 **EST:** 1982
SQ FT: 12,000
SALES (est): 646.2K **Privately Held**
SIC: 3536 Boat lifts

(G-4491)
IMPACT EDUCATION INC
18180 Old Dominion Ct (33908-4677)
PHONE..................................239 482-0202
Adam Hall, *CEO*
Leonard Hall, *President*
Michael Pangrace, *CIO*
EMP: 7 **EST:** 2000
SALES (est): 197.3K **Privately Held**
SIC: 7372 Educational computer software

(G-4492)
IMPERIAL KITCHENS INC
12541 Metro Pkwy Ste 14 (33966-8349)
PHONE..................................239 208-9359
EMP: 5 **EST:** 2018
SALES (est): 334.8K **Privately Held**
WEB: www.imperialkitchensinc.com
SIC: 2434 Wood kitchen cabinets

(G-4493)
INDUSTRIAL SERVICE SOLUTIONS (PA)
10070 Dnels Intrstate Ct (33913-7876)
PHONE..................................239 288-5230
Wade Stockstill, *CEO*
Steve Belt, *Division Mgr*
Charlie Rainey, *General Mgr*
Niclas Ytterdahl, *Chairman*
Mark Clapp, *Regional Mgr*
EMP: 157 **EST:** 2018
SALES (est): 27.7MM **Privately Held**
WEB: www.iss-na.com
SIC: 7694 3625 5063 6719 Electric motor repair; motor controls, electric; motors, electric; investment holding companies, except banks

(G-4494)
INDUSTRIAL TECHNOLOGY LLC
Also Called: Comtronix US
6310 Techster Blvd Ste 3 (33966-4710)
PHONE..................................877 224-5534
Jimmy Haugen, *Vice Pres*
EMP: 10 **EST:** 2018
SALES (est): 819.8K **Privately Held**
WEB: www.comtronixus.com
SIC: 3571 Electronic computers

(G-4495)
INSECO INC
2897 South St (33916-5515)
PHONE..................................239 939-1072
Michael Daikos, *CEO*
▲ **EMP:** 10 **EST:** 1995
SALES (est): 981K **Privately Held**
WEB: www.woodrx.com
SIC: 2851 Paints & allied products

(G-4496)
ISLAND PARK CUSTOM WOODWORKING
16270 Old Us 41 (33912-2254)
PHONE..................................239 437-9670
John Hayden, *President*
Joe Preel, *Vice Pres*
EMP: 5 **EST:** 1996
SQ FT: 8,000
SALES (est): 500K **Privately Held**
SIC: 2431 Doors & door parts & trim, wood; windows & window parts & trim, wood

(G-4497)
ITT FLYGT CORP
5771 Country Lakes Dr (33905-5502)
PHONE..................................239 633-2553
Chris Stewart, *Manager*
EMP: 6 **EST:** 2017
SALES (est): 113.8K **Privately Held**
SIC: 3561 Pumps & pumping equipment

(G-4498)
J & J CUSTOM MICA INC
9971 Bavaria Rd (33913-8510)
PHONE..................................239 433-2828
Lynn A Dunlavey, *President*
EMP: 17 **EST:** 1989
SQ FT: 6,000
SALES (est): 1.2MM **Privately Held**
SIC: 2434 2541 2517 Wood kitchen cabinets; wood partitions & fixtures; wood television & radio cabinets

(G-4499)
J & J LITHO ENTERPRISES INC (PA)
Also Called: Kwik Kopy Printing
6835 Intl Ctr Blvd Ste 8 (33912-7149)
PHONE..................................239 433-2311
Scott Laden, *President*
Christopher J O'Hern, *Vice Pres*
EMP: 16 **EST:** 1983
SQ FT: 8,000
SALES (est): 2MM **Privately Held**
WEB: www.kkpcanada.ca
SIC: 2752 Commercial printing, offset

(G-4500)
J D ALUMINUM
18161 Sandy Pines Cir (33917-4713)
PHONE..................................239 543-3558
John Deschenes, *Owner*
EMP: 8 **EST:** 1993
SALES (est): 519.8K **Privately Held**
WEB: www.campbellcraneservice.com
SIC: 3448 Screen enclosures

(G-4501)
JBJB HOLDINGS LLC
Also Called: Sign-A-Rama
14110 Clear Water Ln (33907-4711)
PHONE..................................239 267-1975
Jeffery Bayer,
Judith Bayer,
EMP: 5 **EST:** 2001
SQ FT: 2,150
SALES (est): 498K **Privately Held**
WEB: www.signarama.com
SIC: 3993 Signs & advertising specialties

(G-4502)
JDCI ENTERPRISES INC
Also Called: Boatmaster/J D C I Enterprises
11950 Amedicus Ln Unit 2 (33907-4062)
PHONE..................................239 768-2292
Seth Hartt, *Sales Staff*
Marty Adams, *IT Specialist*
Joseph K Isley III, *Director*
▼ **EMP:** 25 **EST:** 1982
SQ FT: 10,000
SALES (est): 4.3MM **Privately Held**
WEB: www.boat-trailers.com
SIC: 3799 3548 Boat trailers; welding & cutting apparatus & accessories

(G-4503)
JFLISZO INDUSTRIES INC
17051 Alico Commerce Ct # 3 (33967-8510)
PHONE..................................239 215-6965
EMP: 7 **EST:** 2018
SALES (est): 389.3K **Privately Held**
WEB: www.dekscape.com
SIC: 3999 Manufacturing industries

(G-4504)
JJ TAYLOR DISTRG FLA INC
Also Called: J J Taylor Distributing Fla
2440 Park 82 Dr 82nd (33905)
PHONE..................................239 267-1006
Jose Rivera, *Vice Pres*
Bria Hoyt, *Safety Mgr*
Frank Caputo, *Opers Staff*
Chris Dehaven, *Buyer*
Mike Buel, *Sales Mgr*
EMP: 6
SALES (corp-wide): 224.4MM **Privately Held**
WEB: www.jjtaylor.com
SIC: 2082 Beer (alcoholic beverage)
HQ: J.J. Taylor Distributing Florida, Inc.
655 N A1a
Jupiter FL 33477

(G-4505)
JML PAVERS LLC
18657 Holly Rd (33967-3626)
PHONE..................................239 240-0082
Juan Maldonado-Loredo, *President*
EMP: 7 **EST:** 2015
SALES (est): 363.9K **Privately Held**
SIC: 2951 Asphalt paving mixtures & blocks

(G-4506)
JOHN MADER ENTERPRISES INC
Also Called: Mader Electric Motors
18161 N Tamiami Trl (33903-1301)
PHONE..................................239 731-5455
Jeremy D Mader, *President*
EMP: 31 **EST:** 1984
SQ FT: 12,000
SALES (est): 6MM **Privately Held**
SIC: 7694 7699 3463 3561 Electric motor repair; pumps & pumping equipment repair; pump, compressor, turbine & engine forgings, except auto; pumps & pumping equipment; pumps, oil well & field; pumps, domestic: water or sump; industrial pumps & parts

(G-4507)
JONATHAN MARIOTTI ENTPS LLC
Also Called: Abaxial Elevator
608 Danley Dr Unit C (33907-1538)
P.O. Box 61361 (33906-1361)
PHONE..................................855 353-8280
EMP: 6
SQ FT: 2,000
SALES (est): 580K **Privately Held**
SIC: 3534 Mfg Elevators/Escalators

(G-4508)
JUPITER INDUSTRIES LLC
9373 Laredo Ave (33905-4633)
PHONE..................................239 225-9041
Buddy Yates, *Manager*
Cliff Yates, *Manager*
James E Phillips,
◆ **EMP:** 8 **EST:** 2008
SALES (est): 774.4K **Privately Held**
WEB: www.jupiter-industries.com
SIC: 3354 Aluminum extruded products

(G-4509)
KDD INC (PA)
Also Called: Mr Shower Door
16431 Domestic Ave (33912-6008)
PHONE..................................239 689-8402
Keith W Daubmann, *President*
Doug Daubmann, *Corp Secy*
William Daubmann, *Senior VP*
▲ **EMP:** 22 **EST:** 2003
SALES (est): 5MM **Privately Held**
SIC: 3088 Shower stalls, fiberglass & plastic

(G-4510)
KEYSTONE BRICK PAVER
11495 Ranchette Rd (33966-1243)
PHONE..................................239 340-6492
Joseph M Barone, *Principal*
EMP: 6 **EST:** 2008
SALES (est): 173.6K **Privately Held**
SIC: 3531 Pavers

(G-4511)
KING BRANDS LLC
9910 Bavaria Rd (33913-8509)
PHONE..................................239 313-2057
Mark Kent, *Prdtn Mgr*
John King, *Mng Member*
Jason King,
Jeff King,
▲ **EMP:** 50 **EST:** 2007
SALES (est): 13.1MM **Privately Held**
WEB: www.kingsbrand.com
SIC: 2037 Fruit juices

(G-4512)
KLOCKE OF AMERICA INC
16260 Arprt Pk Dr Ste 125 (33913)
PHONE..................................239 561-5800
Donald W Hopta, *CEO*
Carsten Klocke, *President*
Eden Sheffield, *Treasurer*
Marie Springsteen, *Admin Sec*
EMP: 60 **EST:** 1996
SALES (est): 2.5MM **Privately Held**
WEB: www.klockeamerica.com
SIC: 3399 Primary metal products

(G-4513)
KRAFT HEINZ FOODS COMPANY
5521 Division Dr (33905-5017)
PHONE..................................239 694-3663
Todd Shuttleworth, *Prdtn Mgr*
Joe Garrard, *Manager*
EMP: 7
SQ FT: 2,700
SALES (corp-wide): 26.1B **Publicly Held**
WEB: www.kraftheinzcompany.com
SIC: 2033 Canned fruits & specialties
HQ: Kraft Heinz Foods Company
1 Ppg Pl Ste 3400
Pittsburgh PA 15222
412 456-5700

(G-4514)
KUHLMAN CORPORATION
2690 Rockfill Rd (33916-4802)
PHONE..................................239 334-3111
Timothy Goligoski, *Branch Mgr*
EMP: 6
SALES (corp-wide): 45.5MM **Privately Held**
WEB: www.kuhlman-corp.com
SIC: 3273 Ready-mixed concrete
PA: Kuhlman Corporation
1845 Indian Wood Cir
Maumee OH 43537
419 897-6000

(G-4515)
LANAI LIGHTS LLC
3411 Hanson St Unit A (33916-6509)
PHONE..................................239 415-2561
David Fiorillo, *Principal*
Wesley Fiorillo, *Sales Staff*
EMP: 8 **EST:** 2010
SALES (est): 543.6K **Privately Held**
WEB: www.lanailights.com
SIC: 3648 Lighting equipment

(G-4516)
LCF PAVERS INC
1825 Linhart Ave Lot 25 (33901-6028)
PHONE..................................239 826-8177
Luiz C Faria, *Principal*
EMP: 6 **EST:** 2013
SALES (est): 226.6K **Privately Held**
SIC: 2951 Asphalt paving mixtures & blocks

(G-4517)
LEE COUNTY FUELS INC
16272 Cutters Ct (33908-3092)
PHONE..................................239 349-5322
John Stephens, *President*
EMP: 5 **EST:** 2007
SALES (est): 1MM **Privately Held**
WEB: www.leecountyfuels.com
SIC: 2869 Fuels

(G-4518)
LEE DESIGNS LLC
3300 Palm Ave (33901-7430)
PHONE..................................239 278-4245
Jeff White, *General Mgr*
Bill Wallace, *Manager*
Kip Thomas,
Michael Johnston,
Rachel Johnston,
EMP: 17 **EST:** 1993
SQ FT: 12,000
SALES (est): 2.1MM **Privately Held**
WEB: www.198051.group1.sites.hubspot.net
SIC: 3993 Electric signs

(G-4519)
LIST DISTILLERY LLC
3680 Evans Ave (33901-8315)
PHONE..................................239 208-7214
Thomas List, *Principal*
Tania Fahnemann,
Thomas Fahnemann,
Renate List,
EMP: 11 **EST:** 2015
SALES (est): 3.1MM **Privately Held**
WEB: www.listdistillery.com
SIC: 2085 Distilled & blended liquors

(G-4520)
MAGIC PRINT COPY CENTER
2133 Broadway (33901-3634)
PHONE..................................239 332-4456
John Totzeke, *Partner*
Jennifer Totzeke, *Partner*
EMP: 8 **EST:** 1982
SQ FT: 1,800
SALES (est): 590.9K **Privately Held**
SIC: 2752 Commercial printing, offset

(G-4521)
MAJIC WHEELS CORP (PA)
Also Called: Dumpster Company
1950 Custom Dr (33907-2102)
PHONE..................................239 313-5672
Denise Houghtaling, *President*
Mark Houghtaling, *Admin Sec*
EMP: 5 **EST:** 2007
SALES (est): 549.3K **Privately Held**
SIC: 3944 Games, toys & children's vehicles

(G-4522)
MARK MCMANUS INC
Also Called: McManus Superboats
15821 Chief Ct (33912-2261)
PHONE..................................239 454-1300
Mark McManus, *President*
Kelli Thurman, *Vice Pres*
▼ **EMP:** 10 **EST:** 1989
SQ FT: 15,000
SALES (est): 1.4MM **Privately Held**
WEB: www.apachepowerboats.com
SIC: 3732 Boats, fiberglass: building & repairing

(G-4523)
MASTER KITCHEN CABINETS
12960 Commerce Lk Dr # 8 (33913-8660)
PHONE..................................239 225-9668
Guillermo Rivera,
EMP: 8 **EST:** 2013
SALES (est): 415.4K **Privately Held**
WEB: www.masterkitchencabinets.com
SIC: 2434 Wood kitchen cabinets

(G-4524)
MAUER SPORTS NUTRITION INC
11309 Wine Palm Rd (33966-5736)
PHONE..................................888 609-2489
Ken Mauer, *CEO*
Tim Braun, *President*
Jamie Best, *CFO*
EMP: 4 **EST:** 2014
SALES (est): 6MM **Privately Held**
SIC: 2064 7389 Granola & muesli, bars & clusters;

(G-4525)
MC DERMOTT ENTERPRISES INC
Also Called: Ideal Helicopter Service
6720 Cadet Ave (33905-7615)
PHONE..................................262 593-8612
Wayne Mc Dermott, *President*
Dodie Mc Dermott, *Corp Secy*
Jeff Mc Dermott, *Vice Pres*
EMP: 6 **EST:** 1962
SALES (est): 586.5K **Privately Held**
SIC: 3721 0851 Helicopters; fire fighting services, forest

(G-4526)
MEDIAWRITE LLC
6835 Intl Ctr Blvd Ste 9 (33912-7149)
PHONE..................................239 344-9988
Lee Lake, *Prdtn Mgr*
Lloyd Wickett,
Dale Odell,
EMP: 6 **EST:** 2014
SALES (est): 357.4K **Privately Held**
WEB: www.mediawrite.com
SIC: 3999 Advertising display products

(G-4527)
MERITS HEALTH PRODUCTS INC
4245 Evans Ave (33901-9311)
PHONE..................................239 772-0579
Chung-Lun Liu, *CEO*
Jonathan Cheng, *Vice Pres*
Rohan Smith, *Prdtn Mgr*
John Gadue, *Production*
Michelle Hendry, *Credit Staff*
◆ **EMP:** 26 **EST:** 1993
SALES (est): 8.7MM **Privately Held**
WEB: www.meritshealth.com
SIC: 3842 5047 Wheelchairs; medical & hospital equipment
PA: Merits Health Products Co., Ltd.
No. 18, Jingke Rd., T.P.M.T Park,
Taichung City 40852

(G-4528)
MERMAID MFG SOUTHWEST FLA INC
Also Called: Mermaid Marine Air
2651 Park Windsor Dr # 203 (33901-8319)
P.O. Box 60205 (33906-6205)
PHONE..................................239 418-0535
William Banfield, *President*
Marilyn Banfield, *Principal*
▲ **EMP:** 15 **EST:** 1983
SQ FT: 8,000
SALES (est): 3.5MM **Privately Held**
WEB: www.mmair.com
SIC: 3585 3429 Air conditioning units, complete: domestic or industrial; manufactured hardware (general)

(G-4529)
MFJR PAVERS LLC
1621 Red Cedar Dr (33907-7645)
PHONE..................................239 440-2580
Martin Franco Jr, *Principal*
EMP: 6 **EST:** 2013
SALES (est): 97.9K **Privately Held**
SIC: 2951 Asphalt paving mixtures & blocks

(G-4530)
MICHAEL L LARVIERE INC
17537 Braddock Rd (33967-2970)
PHONE..................................239 267-2738
Michael L Lariviere, *President*
EMP: 10 **EST:** 2001
SALES (est): 904.1K **Privately Held**
SIC: 1389 Construction, repair & dismantling services

(G-4531)
MICHAEL VALENTINES INC
10660 Clear Lake Loop # 234
(33908-2376)
PHONE..................................239 332-0855
Michael Valentine, *President*
EMP: 13 **EST:** 1992
SALES (est): 621.3K **Privately Held**
SIC: 3441 1793 Fabricated structural metal; glass & glazing work

(G-4532)
MICRO CONTROL SYSTEMS INC
5580 Enterprise Pkwy (33905-5022)
PHONE..................................239 694-0089
Brian W Walterick, *President*
Ronnie Andersen, *Vice Pres*
Robert Toney, *Vice Pres*
John Walterick, *Vice Pres*
Chris Hadsock, *Research*
▲ **EMP:** 37 **EST:** 1994
SQ FT: 9,000
SALES (est): 7.4MM **Privately Held**
WEB: www.mcscontrols.com
SIC: 3674 3822 3625 Microprocessors; auto controls regulating residntl & coml environmt & applncs; relays & industrial controls

(G-4533)
MID-STATE MACHINE COMPANY LLC
4516 Longboat Ln (33919-4641)
PHONE..................................704 636-7029
Larry Schwoeri, *CEO*
Gerald Williams Sr, *Mng Member*
Tim Williams,
EMP: 23 **EST:** 2007
SQ FT: 87,000
SALES (est): 2.1MM **Privately Held**
WEB: www.midstatemachine.com
SIC: 3549 Metalworking machinery

(G-4534)
MIGHTEES LLC
18518 Flamingo Rd (33967-3317)
PHONE..................................201 450-7470
Adam O'Toole, *Principal*
EMP: 6 **EST:** 2016
SALES (est): 136.3K **Privately Held**
SIC: 2759 Screen printing

(G-4535)
MOBIUS BUSINESS GROUP INC
Also Called: Coastal and Mainland Cabinets
1961 Dana Dr (33907-2103)
PHONE..................................239 274-8900
Todd Lesley, *President*
Karen Lesley, *Treasurer*
EMP: 10 **EST:** 1985
SQ FT: 9,500
SALES (est): 1MM **Privately Held**
WEB: www.swflcabinets.com
SIC: 2541 2511 2434 Cabinets, except refrigerated: show, display, etc.: wood; wood household furniture; wood kitchen cabinets

(G-4536)
MOLD BE GONE PLUS
14120 Carlotta St (33905-8621)
PHONE..................................239 672-5321
Luis Alvarez, *Principal*
EMP: 7 **EST:** 2016
SALES (est): 100.6K **Privately Held**
WEB: www.moldbegoneplus.com
SIC: 3544 Industrial molds

(G-4537)
MOREY MACHINING & MFG INC
9350 Workmen Way (33905-5212)
PHONE..................................239 693-8699
Timothy Morey, *President*
Tim Morey, *Engineer*
EMP: 20 **EST:** 2001
SQ FT: 5,400
SALES (est): 2.3MM **Privately Held**
WEB: www.moreymachining.com
SIC: 3599 Machine shop, jobbing & repair

(G-4538)
MOTAZ INC
2441 Hanson St (33901-7343)
PHONE..................................239 334-7699
Jad Awadallah, *Principal*
EMP: 6 **EST:** 2010
SALES (est): 79.7K **Privately Held**
SIC: 3578 Automatic teller machines (ATM)

(G-4539)
MOTOROLA SOLUTIONS
13891 Jetport Loop Ste 9 (33913-7716)
PHONE..................................239 939-7717
EMP: 8 **EST:** 2019
SALES (est): 831.8K **Privately Held**
WEB: www.newsroom.motorolasolutions.com
SIC: 3663 Radio & TV communications equipment

(G-4540)
MR FOAMY SOUTHWEST FL LLC
Also Called: Mr Foamy
3411 Hanson St Unit A (33916-6509)
PHONE..................................239 461-3110
Karen Fiorillo, *President*
Rick Sebastian, *Technology*
Jeffrey Hebert, *Admin Sec*
EMP: 13 **EST:** 2000
SQ FT: 4,000
SALES (est): 1.5MM **Privately Held**
WEB: www.mrfoamy.com
SIC: 2431 Exterior & ornamental woodwork & trim

(G-4541)
MUTUAL INDUSTRIES NORTH INC
2940 Walpear St Unit 1 (33916-7549)
PHONE..................................239 332-2400
John Gregory, *Manager*
EMP: 76
SALES (corp-wide): 32.1MM **Privately Held**
WEB: www.mutualindustries.com
SIC: 2221 3496 2297 Specialty broadwoven fabrics, including twisted weaves; miscellaneous fabricated wire products; nonwoven fabrics
PA: Mutual Industries North, Inc.
707 W Grange Ave Ste 1
Philadelphia PA 19120
215 927-6000

(G-4542)
MWI CORPORATION
Also Called: John Deere Authorized Dealer
4945 Kim Ln (33905-3714)
PHONE..................................239 337-4747
David Berggren, *Manager*
EMP: 10
SQ FT: 3,560

GEOGRAPHIC

SALES (corp-wide): 41.8MM **Privately Held**
WEB: www.mwipumps.com
SIC: 3594 7359 5082 Pumps, hydraulic power transfer; equipment rental & leasing; construction & mining machinery
PA: Mwi Corporation
33 Nw 2nd St
Deerfield Beach FL 33441
954 426-1500

(G-4543)
MZ JAZZY ACCEZZORIEZ
3598 Fowler St (33901-0926)
PHONE..................................239 275-6975
Kimberly A Ladson, *Principal*
EMP: 6 **EST:** 2007
SALES (est): 44K **Privately Held**
SIC: 3961 Costume jewelry

(G-4544)
NATURE MEDRX INC
1342 Clnl Blvd Unit C20 (33907)
PHONE..................................239 215-8557
Vincent Cataldi, *President*
EMP: 12 **EST:** 2015
SQ FT: 2,000
SALES (est): 1.1MM **Privately Held**
SIC: 2834 Vitamin, nutrient & hematinic preparations for human use

(G-4545)
NETEXPRESSUSA INC (PA)
Also Called: Reliabilityweb.com
8991 Daniels Center Dr # 105
(33912-0317)
P.O. Box 425, Blair NE (68008-0425)
PHONE..................................888 575-1245
Terrence J O Hanlon, *President*
Kelly I O Hanlon, *Vice Pres*
Mary Grubisich, *Accountant*
Terry Simpson, *Contract Mgr*
Maura Abad, *Manager*
EMP: 6 **EST:** 2003
SQ FT: 9,000
SALES (est): 1MM **Privately Held**
WEB: www.reliabilityweb.com
SIC: 2721 2731 2741 4813 Magazines: publishing only, not printed on site; books: publishing only; newsletter publishing; ; professional membership organizations

(G-4546)
NFI MASKS LLC ✪
16140 Lee Rd Unit 120 (33912-2520)
PHONE..................................239 990-6546
Todd Raines,
EMP: 30 **EST:** 2020
SALES (est): 1.1MM **Privately Held**
WEB: www.nfimasks.com
SIC: 3821 Incubators, laboratory

(G-4547)
NITE-BRIGHT SIGN COMPANY INC
Also Called: Toucanvas
16061 Pine Ridge Rd (33908-2634)
PHONE..................................239 466-2616
David W Mathey Jr, *President*
David W Mathey III, *Vice Pres*
Linda H Mathey, *Vice Pres*
Lyn Bradford, *Treasurer*
Roland Castonguay, *Sales Staff*
EMP: 23 **EST:** 1945
SQ FT: 30,000
SALES (est): 2.7MM **Privately Held**
WEB: www.nitebright.com
SIC: 3993 Signs, not made in custom sign painting shops

(G-4548)
NO FLOOD INC
17061 Alico Commerce Ct (33967-2512)
PHONE..................................239 776-1671
Richard Downare, *President*
Karen Downare, *Co-Owner*
Ashtin Downare, *Vice Pres*
EMP: 5 **EST:** 2017
SALES (est): 629K **Privately Held**
WEB: www.noflood.com
SIC: 3569 Filters

(G-4549)
NORTHPOINTE BANK
8660 College Pkwy Ste 150 (33919-5816)
PHONE..................................239 308-4532
EMP: 6 **EST:** 2019
SALES (est): 128.9K **Privately Held**
WEB: www.northpointe.com
SIC: 7372 Prepackaged software

(G-4550)
NOVA SOLID SURFACES INC
12350 Crystal Commerce Lo (33966-1097)
PHONE..................................239 888-0975
Monique Pedrosa, *Principal*
EMP: 7 **EST:** 2016
SALES (est): 321K **Privately Held**
WEB: www.novasolidsurfaces.com
SIC: 3999 Manufacturing industries

(G-4551)
NOVUS CLIP SIGNS & VIDEO PROD
12771 Metro Pkwy Ste 1 (33966-1369)
PHONE..................................239 471-5639
Nelson Diaz, *Principal*
EMP: 7 **EST:** 2014
SALES (est): 411.4K **Privately Held**
SIC: 3993 Signs & advertising specialties

(G-4552)
NUTRA-LUXE MD LLC
12801 Commwl Dr Ste 1 (33913)
PHONE..................................239 561-9699
Yvonne Von Berg, *Vice Pres*
Gloria Avendano, *Manager*
Peter Von Berg,
▲ **EMP:** 10 **EST:** 2003
SQ FT: 2,800
SALES (est): 2.5MM **Privately Held**
WEB: www.nutraluxemd.com
SIC: 2844 Cosmetic preparations

(G-4553)
OAI ENTERPRISES LLC
12960 Commerce Lakes Dr (33913-8659)
PHONE..................................239 225-1350
Robert C Irion, *Principal*
EMP: 14 **EST:** 2012
SALES (est): 508K **Privately Held**
WEB: www.enterprise.com
SIC: 3599 Machine shop, jobbing & repair

(G-4554)
OCEANSIDE CUSTOM LLC
4125 Cleveland Ave # 1035 (33901-9046)
PHONE..................................386 341-7507
Cliff Levy, *Branch Mgr*
EMP: 6
SALES (corp-wide): 156.3K **Privately Held**
WEB: www.oceansidecustomllc.com
SIC: 3993 Signs & advertising specialties
PA: Oceanside Custom Llc
120 Botefuhr Ave Apt 4
Daytona Beach FL

(G-4555)
OFFSHORE PERFORMANCE SPC
15881 Chief Ct (33912-2262)
PHONE..................................239 481-2768
Donald D Carter, *President*
Mary Davenport, *General Mgr*
Donald Carter III, *Vice Pres*
Donnie Carter, *Vice Pres*
Mandi Dettmering, *Executive Asst*
▼ **EMP:** 16 **EST:** 1987
SQ FT: 10,000
SALES (est): 6.5MM **Privately Held**
WEB: www.offshoreperformance.com
SIC: 3519 5561 7699 Marine engines; recreational vehicle parts & accessories; marine engine repair

(G-4556)
OGRADY TOOL COMPANY
Also Called: Precision Manufacturing
7721 Hidden Pond Ln (33917-4525)
P.O. Box 3485 (33918-3485)
PHONE..................................239 560-3395
EMP: 17 **EST:** 1946
SALES (est): 3.4MM **Privately Held**
SIC: 3545 7389 Mfg Machine Tool Accessories

(G-4557)
OLDE WORLD CRAFTSMEN INC
15970 Lake Candlewood Dr (33908-1790)
PHONE..................................239 229-3806
George Coffey, *Principal*
EMP: 5 **EST:** 2008
SALES (est): 325.7K **Privately Held**
SIC: 3272 Concrete products

(G-4558)
OMAX HOME INC
1946 Dana Dr (33907-2104)
PHONE..................................239 980-2755
Linas Liaukus, *Principal*
EMP: 13 **EST:** 2017
SALES (est): 570.2K **Privately Held**
WEB: www.omaxcabinets.com
SIC: 2434 Wood kitchen cabinets

(G-4559)
ORNAMENTAL COLUMNS AND STATUES
16179 S Tamiami Trl (33908-4306)
PHONE..................................239 482-3911
Alain Colas, *President*
Bobby Colas, *Vice Pres*
EMP: 18 **EST:** 1978
SQ FT: 1,600
SALES (est): 1.6MM **Privately Held**
WEB: www.ornamentalcolumnsandstatues.com
SIC: 3272 Columns, concrete

(G-4560)
P B C H INCORPORATED
Also Called: High Performance Boats & Cars
7941 Mercantile St (33917-2115)
PHONE..................................239 567-5030
Trond Schou, *President*
◆ **EMP:** 30 **EST:** 1986
SQ FT: 6,000
SALES (est): 4.1MM **Privately Held**
WEB: www.nortechboats.com
SIC: 3732 Motorboats, inboard or outboard: building & repairing

(G-4561)
PACE ENCLOSURES INC
12101 Crystal Condo Rd (33966-8363)
PHONE..................................239 275-3818
Dexter Seriao, *President*
EMP: 18 **EST:** 1999
SALES (est): 3MM **Privately Held**
SIC: 3448 Screen enclosures

(G-4562)
PALM PRNTING/PRINTERS INK CORP
2400 First St Ste 102 (33901-2982)
PHONE..................................239 332-8600
Kimberly L Darrow, *Principal*
Randy S Darrow, *Principal*
Randy Darrow, *Mng Member*
EMP: 23 **EST:** 2001
SALES (est): 2.4MM **Privately Held**
SIC: 2752 3555 2741 7334 Commercial printing, offset; printing presses; art copy: publishing & printing; photocopying & duplicating services

(G-4563)
PALM PRTG STRGC SOLUTIONS LLC
2306 Dr Mrtn Luther King (33901-3624)
PHONE..................................239 332-8600
Kim Darrow, *Managing Prtnr*
Kimberly L Darrow, *Mng Member*
Randy S Darrow,
EMP: 8 **EST:** 2001
SQ FT: 6,000
SALES (est): 750.7K **Privately Held**
WEB: www.theprintshop.tv
SIC: 2752 Commercial printing, offset

(G-4564)
PANTHER PRINTING INC
Also Called: Strategy Marketing Group
11580 Marshwood Ln (33908-3206)
PHONE..................................239 936-5050
Hannah Yolin, *President*
Jennifer Namour, *Principal*
EMP: 21 **EST:** 1996
SALES (est): 2.8MM **Privately Held**
WEB: www.pantherprinting.net
SIC: 2752 Commercial printing, offset

(G-4565)
PAPER FISH PRINTING INC
17251 Alico Center Rd # 5 (33967-6025)
PHONE..................................239 481-3555
Peter Heerwagen, *President*
EMP: 6 **EST:** 1990
SQ FT: 2,500
SALES (est): 901.7K **Privately Held**
WEB: www.paperfish.com
SIC: 2752 2791 Commercial printing, offset; typesetting

(G-4566)
PARKWAY PRINTING INC
6371 Arc Way Ste 1 (33966-1416)
PHONE..................................239 936-6970
Ethel Barbosa, *President*
Steven Barbosa, *General Mgr*
Donna Meridith, *Corp Secy*
EMP: 5 **EST:** 1987
SQ FT: 4,000
SALES (est): 443.4K **Privately Held**
WEB: www.parkwayprinting.biz
SIC: 2752 Commercial printing, offset

(G-4567)
PEPSI-COLA BOTTLING CO TAMPA
3625 Mrtin Lther King Blv (33916-4650)
PHONE..................................239 337-2011
Don Cossairt, *Manager*
Jason Ford, *Manager*
EMP: 224
SQ FT: 1,239
SALES (corp-wide): 70.3B **Publicly Held**
WEB: www.pepsico.com
SIC: 2086 Carbonated soft drinks, bottled & canned
HQ: Pepsi-Cola Bottling Company Of Tampa
11315 N 30th St
Tampa FL 33612
813 971-2550

(G-4568)
POLSON TRANSPORTATION LLC ✪
9032 Pomelo Rd W (33967-3722)
PHONE..................................614 733-9677
Andre G Polson, *CEO*
EMP: 6 **EST:** 2020
SALES (est): 85K **Privately Held**
SIC: 3537 Trucks, tractors, loaders, carriers & similar equipment

(G-4569)
POLYGON SOLUTIONS INC
6461 Metro Plantation Rd (33966-1257)
PHONE..................................239 628-4800
Steven M Derbin, *President*
Peter Bagwell, *Mfg Staff*
EMP: 7 **EST:** 2010
SQ FT: 4,000
SALES (est): 1.3MM **Privately Held**
WEB: www.polygonsolutions.com
SIC: 3545 Machine tool attachments & accessories; broaches (machine tool accessories); tool holders; shaping tools (machine tool accessories)

(G-4570)
POSEIDON BOAT MANUFACTURING
5826 Corporation Cir (33905-5026)
PHONE..................................239 362-3736
Osbel Diaz Pacheco, *Principal*
EMP: 15 **EST:** 2010
SALES (est): 252K **Privately Held**
WEB: www.poseidon2boats.com
SIC: 3999 Manufacturing industries

(G-4571)
POVIA PAINTS INC (PA)
2897 South St (33916-5515)
PHONE..................................239 791-0011
Michael Doikos, *President*
George Doikos, *Vice Pres*
Kostas Doikos, *Vice Pres*
William Doikos, *Shareholder*
EMP: 8 **EST:** 1968
SQ FT: 4,000

SALES (est): 2.6MM **Privately Held**
WEB: www.poviapaints.com
SIC: 2851 5198 5231 Paints & paint additives; paints; paint; paint brushes, rollers, sprayers & other supplies

(G-4572)
PRESS PRINTING ENTERPRISES INC
Also Called: Press Printing Company
3601 Hanson St (33916-6537)
P.O. Box 220 (33902-0220)
PHONE..................................239 598-1500
Larry Luettich, *President*
Carl Luettich, *Corp Secy*
EMP: 27 **EST:** 1964
SQ FT: 23,000
SALES (est): 1.2MM **Privately Held**
WEB: www.pressprinting.com
SIC: 2752 2796 Commercial printing, offset; platemaking services

(G-4573)
PROJECT PROS WOODWORKING INC
17051 Jean St Ste 12 (33967-6066)
PHONE..................................239 454-6800
John Presanzano, *President*
EMP: 8 **EST:** 2005
SALES (est): 252K **Privately Held**
WEB: www.projectproswoodworking.com
SIC: 2434 Wood kitchen cabinets

(G-4574)
PROPRINT OF NAPLES INC (PA)
Also Called: Print Shop, The
5900 Enterprise Pkwy (33905-5003)
PHONE..................................239 775-3553
Ron Eikens, *President*
Frank C Tibbetts, *Vice Pres*
Staci Hamilton, *Manager*
Melissa Steindler, *Manager*
Orvel Bicking, *Admin Sec*
EMP: 15 **EST:** 1985
SALES (est): 3.1MM **Privately Held**
SIC: 2752 7336 Commercial printing, offset; commercial art & graphic design

(G-4575)
PUBLISHERS WHSE SANIBEL ISLAND
20350 Summerlin Rd # 2140 (33908-3741)
PHONE..................................239 267-6151
Linda Somers, *Owner*
EMP: 9 **EST:** 2001
SALES (est): 84K **Privately Held**
SIC: 2741 Miscellaneous publishing

(G-4576)
PULSADERM LLC
12801 Commwl Dr Ste 2 (33913)
PHONE..................................877 474-4038
Yvonne Von Berg, *Mng Member*
EMP: 13 **EST:** 2016
SALES (est): 801.9K **Privately Held**
WEB: www.pulsaderm.com
SIC: 2844 Cosmetic preparations

(G-4577)
QUALITY CABINETS & COUNTERS
7869 Drew Cir Unit 1 (33967-6087)
PHONE..................................239 948-5364
Mary Reynolds, *President*
James Brunco, *Vice Pres*
John Reynolds, *Vice Pres*
Sue Ellen Brunco, *Director*
EMP: 14 **EST:** 2000
SQ FT: 6,049
SALES (est): 2.2MM **Privately Held**
WEB: www.qualitycabinetsandcounters.com
SIC: 2434 Wood kitchen cabinets

(G-4578)
QUALITY RESCREENING
17221 Alico Center Rd # 2 (33967-6019)
P.O. Box 510473, Punta Gorda (33951-0473)
PHONE..................................941 625-9765
Kirk Bruns, *Owner*
EMP: 6 **EST:** 2001
SALES (est): 121.4K **Privately Held**
SIC: 3448 Screen enclosures

(G-4579)
RAPID PRINT SOUTHWEST FLA INC
12244 Treeline Ave Ste 4 (33913-8503)
PHONE..................................239 590-9797
Craig Nelson, *President*
Erin Nelson, *Vice Pres*
EMP: 5 **EST:** 1999
SALES (est): 661K **Privately Held**
WEB: www.rapidprintswfl.com
SIC: 2752 Commercial printing, offset

(G-4580)
REGENCY CUSTOM CABINETS INC
8207 Katanga Ct (33916-7541)
PHONE..................................239 332-7977
Wayne M Jurick, *President*
Ralph Sites, *Vice Pres*
EMP: 12 **EST:** 1981
SQ FT: 9,100
SALES (est): 548.3K **Privately Held**
SIC: 2599 5031 2434 Cabinets, factory; kitchen cabinets; wood kitchen cabinets

(G-4581)
REGENT CABINETRY AND MORE INC
5610 Zip Dr (33905-5028)
PHONE..................................239 693-2207
Kasey Hill, *President*
EMP: 6 **EST:** 2008
SALES (est): 176.9K **Privately Held**
WEB: www.regentcabinets.com
SIC: 2434 Wood kitchen cabinets

(G-4582)
RESOURCE MANAGEMENT ASSOCIATES
Also Called: R M A
1675 Temple Ter Ste 2 (33917-3949)
P.O. Box 4363 (33918-4363)
PHONE..................................239 656-0818
William Rose, *President*
Dave Bartz, *Corp Secy*
Michael Gillern, *Vice Pres*
EMP: 9 **EST:** 2003
SALES (est): 800K **Privately Held**
SIC: 3589 Sewage treatment equipment

(G-4583)
RIANI PAVERS INC
1735 Brantley Rd Apt 2015 (33907-3921)
PHONE..................................239 321-1875
Kesios Z De Araujo, *President*
EMP: 7 **EST:** 2013
SALES (est): 203.9K **Privately Held**
SIC: 2951 Asphalt paving mixtures & blocks

(G-4584)
ROAD BLOCK FABRICATION INC ✪
16140 Lee Rd Unit 100 (33912-2520)
PHONE..................................708 417-6091
Daniel J Martindale, *Principal*
EMP: 6 **EST:** 2020
SALES (est): 274.7K **Privately Held**
WEB: www.roadblockfabrication.com
SIC: 3444 Sheet metalwork

(G-4585)
ROCKET SIGN SUPPLIES LLC
3587 Vrnica S Shmker Blvd (33916-2274)
PHONE..................................239 995-4684
Rayford A Betts, *Principal*
EMP: 6 **EST:** 2012
SALES (est): 343.7K **Privately Held**
WEB: www.rocketsignsuppliesllc.com
SIC: 3993 Signs & advertising specialties

(G-4586)
ROLLERTECH CORP
5845 Corporation Cir (33905-5014)
PHONE..................................239 645-6698
Carlos A Leon, *President*
▲ **EMP:** 10 **EST:** 2008
SALES (est): 294.1K **Privately Held**
SIC: 3442 Shutters, door or window: metal

(G-4587)
ROLSAFE LLC
12801 Commwl Dr Ste 7 (33913)
P.O. Box 51619 (33994-1619)
PHONE..................................239 225-2487
Vernon E Collins, *Mng Member*
Mark Matarazzo,
EMP: 16 **EST:** 2004
SQ FT: 50,000
SALES (est): 1MM **Privately Held**
WEB: www.rolsafe.com
SIC: 3442 Storm doors or windows, metal

(G-4588)
RYAN TIRE & PETROLEUM INC
Also Called: Ryan Petroleum
2650 Edison Ave (33916-5306)
PHONE..................................239 334-1351
Bruce Ryan, *President*
Candy Ryan, *Vice Pres*
EMP: 8 **EST:** 1973
SQ FT: 500
SALES (est): 3.1MM **Privately Held**
SIC: 1389 Construction, repair & dismantling services

(G-4589)
RYDER ORTHOPEDICS INC (PA)
1500 Royal Palm Square Bl (33919-1058)
PHONE..................................239 939-0009
Laura Ryder, *President*
Josh C Ryder, *Vice Pres*
Pat Owen, *Manager*
EMP: 7 **EST:** 1987
SALES (est): 1.1MM **Privately Held**
WEB: www.ryderortho.com
SIC: 3842 Limbs, artificial

(G-4590)
S A FEATHER CO INC
Also Called: S.A. Feather Co., Inc. Florida
5852 Enterprise Pkwy (33905-5001)
PHONE..................................239 693-6363
Darren Samuel, *President*
Kay Isserman, *Corp Secy*
Tamara Stroh-Samuel, *Vice Pres*
▲ **EMP:** 12 **EST:** 1906
SQ FT: 8,000
SALES (est): 1.7MM **Privately Held**
WEB: www.safeathercompany.com
SIC: 3999 Feathers & feather products

(G-4591)
S T WOOTEN CORPORATION
Also Called: Fort Myers Asphalt Plant
16560 Mass Ct (33912-5942)
PHONE..................................239 337-9486
Scott Wooten, *President*
Robert Peterson, *Manager*
EMP: 20
SALES (corp-wide): 319.8MM **Privately Held**
WEB: www.stwcorp.com
SIC: 3531 Asphalt plant, including gravel-mix type
PA: S. T. Wooten Corporation
3801 Black Creek Rd Se
Wilson NC 27893
252 291-5165

(G-4592)
SAFE STRAP LLC
Also Called: Patients First Products
13830 Jtport Cmmerce Pkwy (33913)
PHONE..................................239 461-0033
Paul Giampavolo, *Principal*
EMP: 12 **EST:** 2016
SALES (est): 1.1MM **Privately Held**
WEB: www.ridebelts.com
SIC: 3999 Manufacturing industries

(G-4593)
SAHARA CABINETS INC
13296 Island Rd (33905-1808)
PHONE..................................239 334-1151
Richard Sellars, *President*
Brenda Sellars, *Admin Sec*
Marilyn Lamberg, *Administration*
EMP: 18 **EST:** 1976
SALES (est): 1MM **Privately Held**
WEB: www.saharacabinets.com
SIC: 2434 Wood kitchen cabinets

(G-4594)
SAMINCO INC (PA)
10030 Amberwood Rd Ste 5 (33913-8521)
PHONE..................................239 561-1561
Bonne Posma, *President*
Jon Anderson, *Vice Pres*
Anthony Davis, *Vice Pres*
Cari Wilcox, *Vice Pres*
Shawn Hampton, *Sales Staff*
▲ **EMP:** 35 **EST:** 1992
SQ FT: 18,000
SALES (est): 11.8MM **Privately Held**
WEB: www.samincoinc.com
SIC: 3625 Motor controls & accessories

(G-4595)
SANIBEL PRINT & GRAPHICS
15630 Mcgregor Blvd Ste 1 (33908-2553)
PHONE..................................239 454-1001
Lilburn Horton, *Partner*
David Horton, *Partner*
David Rockifeller, *Partner*
EMP: 5 **EST:** 1976
SALES (est): 317.5K **Privately Held**
WEB: www.eakcleaning.com
SIC: 2752 Commercial printing, offset

(G-4596)
SANTIVA CHRONICLE
12860 Banyan Creek Dr (33908-3082)
PHONE..................................239 437-9324
Shannen Hayes, *Principal*
EMP: 6 **EST:** 2017
SALES (est): 68.9K **Privately Held**
WEB: www.santivachronicle.com
SIC: 2711 Newspapers, publishing & printing

(G-4597)
SASHAY SOURCING LLC
8904 Tropical Ct (33908-9244)
PHONE..................................239 454-4940
Roberto Alcalay, *Mng Member*
EMP: 5 **EST:** 2009
SALES (est): 316.1K **Privately Held**
WEB: www.sashaysourcing.com
SIC: 2321 2389 Men's & boys' furnishings; men's miscellaneous accessories

(G-4598)
SCHWING BIOSET
12290 Treeline Ave (33913-8513)
PHONE..................................239 237-2174
Treavor Eaton, *Sales Staff*
EMP: 9 **EST:** 2017
SALES (est): 221.6K **Privately Held**
WEB: www.schwingbioset.com
SIC: 3561 Pumps & pumping equipment

(G-4599)
SCOTT FISCHER ENTERPRISES LLC (PA)
12730 Commwl Dr Ste 2 (33913)
PHONE..................................844 749-2363
Scott Fischer, *President*
Kimberly Haskins, *CFO*
Sarah Mutka, *Sales Mgr*
Dustin Hughes, *Info Tech Dir*
EMP: 218 **EST:** 2010
SALES (est): 13.3MM **Privately Held**
WEB: www.sfe-us.com
SIC: 3751 Motorcycle accessories

(G-4600)
SCREEN ENCLOSURE SERVICES INC
502 South Rd Unit A (33907-2454)
PHONE..................................239 334-6528
Mark Hansen, *President*
Charles Morgan, *Vice Pres*
EMP: 7 **EST:** 1984
SQ FT: 2,000
SALES (est): 730.7K **Privately Held**
WEB: www.myscreendoctor.com
SIC: 3448 Screen enclosures

(G-4601)
SCREENS FAST
1435 Terra Palma Dr (33901-8845)
PHONE..................................239 565-1211
Kurt Meyer, *President*
EMP: 6 **EST:** 2005
SALES (est): 87.5K **Privately Held**
WEB: www.screens-fast.business.site
SIC: 3448 Prefabricated metal buildings

(G-4602)
SEA KING KANVAS & SHADE INC
Also Called: Sea King Canvas & Shade
15581 Pine Ridge Rd Ste A (33908-2798)
PHONE..................................239 481-3535
Lesley G Beers, *President*
EMP: 5 **EST:** 1988
SQ FT: 5,000
SALES (est): 467.9K **Privately Held**
WEB: www.seakingkanvas.com
SIC: 2394 5999 Shades, canvas: made from purchased materials; canvas products

(G-4603)
SEABREEZE COMMUNICATIONS GROUP
Also Called: Seabreeze Publications
5630 Halifax Ave (33912-4417)
PHONE..................................239 278-4222
Terrence Reid, *President*
Jacquelyn Reid, *Corp Secy*
Margo Williams, *Accounts Exec*
Sherry Whalon, *Director*
EMP: 10 **EST:** 1985
SQ FT: 2,700
SALES (est): 1.3MM **Privately Held**
WEB: www.seabreezecommunications.com
SIC: 2721 6531 2711 Magazines: publishing only, not printed on site; real estate agents & managers; newspapers

(G-4604)
SIGNCRAFT PUBLISHING CO INC
Also Called: Signcraft Magazine
3950 Ellis Rd (33905-6400)
P.O. Box 60031 (33906-6031)
PHONE..................................239 939-4644
William G McIltrot, *President*
John K Mc Iltrot, *Vice Pres*
Thomas D Mc Iltrot, *Treasurer*
Dennis P Mc Iltrot, *Admin Sec*
EMP: 13 **EST:** 1980
SALES (est): 1.6MM **Privately Held**
WEB: www.signcraft.com
SIC: 2721 3993 2731 Trade journals: publishing & printing; signs & advertising specialties; book publishing

(G-4605)
SMART TRACKS INC
6182 Idlewild St (33966-1216)
PHONE..................................239 938-1000
Brian D Rist, *Principal*
EMP: 8 **EST:** 2008
SALES (est): 147.5K **Privately Held**
SIC: 3442 Louvers, shutters, jalousies & similar items

(G-4606)
SOMERO ENTERPRISES INC (PA)
14530 Global Pkwy (33913-8888)
P.O. Box 309, Houghton MI (49931-0309)
PHONE..................................906 482-7252
Jack Cooney, *President*
Lawrence Horsch, *Chairman*
Charles Holmes, *Engineer*
Brad Wymore, *Mktg Dir*
Thomas Anderson, *Director*
◆ **EMP:** 93 **EST:** 1986
SALES (est): 20.5MM **Privately Held**
WEB: www.somero.com
SIC: 3559 Concrete products machinery

(G-4607)
SOUTHERN PAVERS LLC
111 5th St Unit A2 (33907-2448)
PHONE..................................239 940-3671
Jacques Jessica L, *Principal*
EMP: 6 **EST:** 2013
SALES (est): 93.4K **Privately Held**
SIC: 2951 Asphalt paving mixtures & blocks

(G-4608)
SOUTHPOINTE PRECISION
12960 Commerce Lk Dr # 10 (33913-8660)
PHONE..................................239 225-1350
Robert Irion, *Owner*
EMP: 5 **EST:** 2000
SALES (est): 400K **Privately Held**
WEB: www.southpointeprecision.com
SIC: 3544 Special dies & tools

(G-4609)
SOUTHWEST STRL SYSTEMS INC
5774 Corporation Cir (33905-5008)
PHONE..................................239 693-6000
Randy Whalin, *President*
EMP: 35 **EST:** 1987
SQ FT: 35,000
SALES (est): 1.1MM **Privately Held**
SIC: 2439 Trusses, wooden roof

(G-4610)
SPECTRUM ENGINEERING INC
1342 Clnl Blvd Ste D31 (33907)
PHONE..................................239 277-1182
R J Ward, *President*
EMP: 5 **EST:** 1987
SALES (est): 410.3K **Privately Held**
WEB: www.spectrumengineering.net
SIC: 3312 8711 Blast furnaces & steel mills; acoustical engineering

(G-4611)
ST JAPAN USA LLC
8813 E Bay Cir (33908-6684)
PHONE..................................239 433-5566
Richard Shaps, *President*
EMP: 6 **EST:** 2015
SALES (est): 109.9K **Privately Held**
WEB: www.stjapan-usa.com
SIC: 3826 Analytical instruments

(G-4612)
STREAMLINE ALUMINUM INC
12651 Metro Pkwy Ste 1 (33966-1306)
PHONE..................................239 561-7200
Robert H Boehm Jr, *President*
Kenneth R Boehm, *Vice Pres*
Donna Boehm, *Manager*
EMP: 10 **EST:** 1997
SQ FT: 6,000
SALES (est): 1.1MM **Privately Held**
WEB: www.streamlinealuminum.com
SIC: 3334 1761 Primary aluminum; roofing, siding & sheet metal work

(G-4613)
STUART BUILDING PRODUCTS LLC
3601 Work Dr (33916-7552)
PHONE..................................239 461-3100
Stacey Mower, *Manager*
EMP: 9
SALES (corp-wide): 24.8MM **Privately Held**
SIC: 3316 Bars, steel, cold finished, from purchased hot-rolled
PA: Stuart Building Products, Llc
1341 Nw 15th St
Pompano Beach FL 33069
954 971-7264

(G-4614)
STUMP INDUSTRIES LLC
1300 Lee St (33901-2823)
PHONE..................................239 940-5754
Joshua Stump, *Manager*
EMP: 99 **EST:** 2019
SALES (est): 2.7MM **Privately Held**
SIC: 3999 Manufacturing industries

(G-4615)
SUNCOAST ALUMINUM FURN INC
6291 Thomas Rd (33912-2269)
PHONE..................................239 267-8300
Rajiv Varshney, *President*
Rajiv P Varshney, *President*
Raj D Varshney, *Corp Secy*
Prakash C Varshney, *Vice Pres*
Bob Stempka, *Accounting Mgr*
◆ **EMP:** 35 **EST:** 1983
SQ FT: 125,000
SALES (est): 7.4MM **Privately Held**
WEB: www.suncoastfurniture.com
SIC: 2514 Metal household furniture

(G-4616)
SUNCOAST IDENTIFICATION TECH
Also Called: Suncoast Lmntion Idntification
13300 S Cleveland Ave # 56 (33907-3886)
PHONE..................................239 277-9922
Frank Savage, *President*
EMP: 8 **EST:** 1988
SALES (est): 1.1MM **Privately Held**
WEB: www.idsource.com
SIC: 3083 5199 7389 3577 Plastic finished products, laminated; gifts & novelties; laminating service; computer peripheral equipment; coated & laminated paper

(G-4617)
SUNCOAST IDNTFCTION SLTONS LLC
618 Danley Dr (33907-1530)
PHONE..................................239 277-9922
Pat Tinajero,
Cori Savage,
EMP: 10 **EST:** 2004
SALES (est): 1MM **Privately Held**
WEB: www.idsource.com
SIC: 3999 Identification badges & insignia

(G-4618)
SUNSET PAVERS INC
8210 Katanga Ct (33916-7541)
PHONE..................................239 208-7293
EMP: 7 **EST:** 2016
SALES (est): 153.3K **Privately Held**
SIC: 2951 Asphalt paving mixtures & blocks

(G-4619)
SUPER SCREENING INCORPORATED
2971 South St (33916-5517)
PHONE..................................239 931-3224
Andre Fortune, *Owner*
Edward Clevenger, *Vice Pres*
EMP: 9 **EST:** 2004
SALES (est): 118.7K **Privately Held**
SIC: 3429 Fireplace equipment, hardware: andirons, grates, screens

(G-4620)
SURVIVAL ARMOR INC
12621 Corp Lakes Dr Ste 8 (33913)
PHONE..................................239 210-0891
James L McCraney, *President*
Bobbie S Epright, *Principal*
Kenneth Mueller, *Vice Pres*
Kurt Osborne, *Vice Pres*
Chad Childers, *Engineer*
▼ **EMP:** 23 **EST:** 2006
SALES (est): 6MM **Privately Held**
WEB: www.survivalarmor.com
SIC: 3462 Armor plate, forged iron or steel

(G-4621)
SWEETLIGHT SYSTEMS
1506 Alhambra Dr (33901-6607)
PHONE..................................239 245-8159
John Snow, *General Mgr*
EMP: 6 **EST:** 2013
SALES (est): 368.2K **Privately Held**
WEB: www.sweetlightsystems.com
SIC: 3648 Stage lighting equipment

(G-4622)
TAG MEDIA GROUP LLC
Also Called: Gulf Coast Aluminum
16751 Link Ct (33912-5913)
PHONE..................................239 288-0499
Thomas Davis, *Principal*
EMP: 9 **EST:** 2017
SALES (est): 543.6K **Privately Held**
SIC: 2431 3442 5211 Door screens, metal covered wood; window screens, wood frame; screens, window, metal; screens, door & window

(G-4623)
TANTASIA
5100 S Cleveland Ave # 312 (33907-2189)
PHONE..................................239 274-5455
Jim Florig, *President*
EMP: 5
SALES (est): 460K **Privately Held**
SIC: 3648 Sun tanning equipment, incl. tanning beds

(G-4624)
TARZEN INTERNATIONAL LLC
10060 Amberwood Rd Ste 3 (33913-8522)
PHONE..................................239 243-0711
Mikyong K Todd, *Mng Member*
▲ **EMP:** 6 **EST:** 2010
SALES (est): 258.5K **Privately Held**
WEB: www.tarzeninternational.com
SIC: 2434 Wood kitchen cabinets

(G-4625)
TAYLOR L MAX L C
Also Called: Dioxyme
12751 S Cleveland Ave (33907-7732)
PHONE..................................833 346-9963
Marc Schneider, *Director*
Bennett T Schneider,
Madison Schneider,
◆ **EMP:** 5 **EST:** 2014
SALES (est): 614.6K **Privately Held**
WEB: www.dioxyme.com
SIC: 2834 5122 Vitamin preparations; vitamins & minerals

(G-4626)
THOMAS C GIBBS CUSTOM CABINETS
12141 Clover Dr (33905-6802)
PHONE..................................239 872-6279
Thomas Gibbs, *Principal*
EMP: 7 **EST:** 2005
SALES (est): 180.5K **Privately Held**
WEB: www.gibbscabinets.com
SIC: 2434 Wood kitchen cabinets

(G-4627)
THOMAS MIX KITCHENS & BATHS
18070 S Tamiami Trl # 13 (33908-4602)
PHONE..................................239 229-4323
Thomas Mix, *Principal*
EMP: 5 **EST:** 2009
SALES (est): 673.8K **Privately Held**
WEB: www.tmkbinc.com
SIC: 3553 Cabinet makers' machinery

(G-4628)
THOMAS UNITED INC
Also Called: Signs By Tomorrow
12700 Metro Pkwy Ste 3 (33966-1303)
PHONE..................................239 561-7446
Michael Thomas, *President*
Robert Thomas, *President*
Deborah Thomas, *Treasurer*
EMP: 8 **EST:** 1997
SQ FT: 2,400
SALES (est): 872.7K **Privately Held**
WEB: www.signsbytomorrow.com
SIC: 3993 5999 7532 Signs & advertising specialties; banners; lettering, automotive

(G-4629)
THOMPSON MANUFACTURING INC
2700 Evans Ave Unit 1 (33901-5303)
PHONE..................................239 332-0446
EMP: 8
SALES (est): 875.6K **Privately Held**
SIC: 3999 Mfg Misc Products

(G-4630)
THOMPSON SALES GROUP INC
2700 Evans Ave Unit 1 (33901-5303)
PHONE..................................239 332-0446
EMP: 20
SQ FT: 2,000
SALES: 2MM **Privately Held**
SIC: 3272 Mfg Concrete Products

(G-4631)
TITAN MFG INC
6381 Metro Plantation Rd (33966-1289)
PHONE..................................239 939-5152
Thomas J McAtee Jr, *President*
Tom McAtee, *President*
Linda McAtee, *Vice Pres*
EMP: 10 **EST:** 2001
SQ FT: 4,000
SALES (est): 800K **Privately Held**
SIC: 7692 Welding repair

(G-4632)
TOP TRTMENT CSTOMES ACCESORIES
50 Mildred Dr Unit A (33901-9190)
PHONE....................................239 936-4600
Jean Bess, *President*
EMP: 9 **EST:** 1991
SQ FT: 2,500
SALES (est): 828.5K **Privately Held**
SIC: 2591 1799 7641 2392 Window blinds; blinds vertical; venetian blinds; window shades; window treatment installation; upholstery work; household furnishings; curtains & draperies

(G-4633)
TORTILLERIA AMERICA INC
2853 Work Dr Ste 1-2 (33916-6524)
PHONE....................................239 462-2175
EMP: 9
SQ FT: 5,000
SALES: 725K **Privately Held**
SIC: 2099 Mfg Food Preparations

(G-4634)
TOTAL OF FLORIDA
12881 Metro Pkwy (33966-8342)
PHONE....................................239 768-9400
Ken Traaium, *Owner*
EMP: 7 **EST:** 2007
SALES (est): 100.4K **Privately Held**
SIC: 3585 5075 Air conditioning equipment, complete; air conditioning & ventilation equipment & supplies

(G-4635)
TPI ALUMINUM
5612 6th Ave (33907-2915)
P.O. Box 51074 (33994-1074)
PHONE....................................239 332-3900
Timothy W Persinger, *President*
EMP: 8 **EST:** 2010
SALES (est): 528.2K **Privately Held**
WEB: www.tpialum.com
SIC: 3499 Fabricated metal products

(G-4636)
TRAFFIC CONTROL PDTS FLA INC
4020 Edison Ave (33916-4830)
PHONE....................................813 621-8484
Joel Hawkins, *General Mgr*
Richard Barnes, *CIO*
EMP: 16
SALES (corp-wide): 15.5MM **Privately Held**
WEB: www.trafficcontrolproducts.org
SIC: 3499 7359 Barricades, metal; work zone traffic equipment (flags, cones, barrels, etc.)
PA: Traffic Control Products Of Florida, Inc.
5514 Carmack Rd
Tampa FL 33610
813 621-8484

(G-4637)
TRANE US INC
14241 Jtport Loop W Ste 1 (33913)
PHONE....................................239 277-0344
EMP: 8 **Privately Held**
WEB: www.trane.com
SIC: 3585 Refrigeration & heating equipment
HQ: Trane U.S. Inc.
3600 Pammel Creek Rd
La Crosse WI 54601
608 787-2000

(G-4638)
TRASH EXPRESS SW INC
3040 Oasis Grand Blvd # 2104 (33916-1607)
PHONE....................................239 340-5291
George Kavouras, *President*
EMP: 5 **EST:** 2013
SALES (est): 5MM **Privately Held**
SIC: 3443 Dumpsters, garbage

(G-4639)
TROPIC SEAL INDUSTRIES INC
1745 Coral Way (33917-2531)
PHONE....................................239 543-8069
Richard P Dietrich, *President*
EMP: 10 **EST:** 2004
SALES (est): 504.6K **Privately Held**
WEB: www.tropicseal.com
SIC: 3479 Metal coating & allied service

(G-4640)
UNITED RENTALS NORTH AMER INC
5491 Division Dr (33905-5011)
PHONE....................................239 690-0600
Chad Epperly, *Branch Mgr*
James Copeland, *Manager*
Thomas Patterson, *Manager*
EMP: 8
SALES (corp-wide): 8.5B **Publicly Held**
WEB: www.unitedrentals.com
SIC: 3561 7353 Pumps, domestic: water or sump; heavy construction equipment rental
HQ: United Rentals (North America), Inc.
100 Frst Stmford Pl Ste 7
Stamford CT 06902
203 622-3131

(G-4641)
US SIGN AND MILL INC
Also Called: U S Sign and Mill
7981 Mainline Pkwy (33912-5921)
PHONE....................................239 936-9154
Steve Dinkel, *President*
Rene Kilbourne, *Vice Pres*
EMP: 25 **EST:** 1987
SQ FT: 18,213
SALES (est): 3.4MM **Privately Held**
WEB: www.ussignandmill.com
SIC: 3993 Signs & advertising specialties

(G-4642)
USA SHUTTER COMPANY LLC
Also Called: Maestroshield
2141 Flint Dr (33916-4811)
PHONE....................................239 596-8883
Marie Kallstrom, *Mng Member*
Christer Kallstrom, *Mng Member*
EMP: 6 **EST:** 2005
SALES (est): 1MM **Privately Held**
SIC: 3089 5211 Shutters, plastic; door & window products

(G-4643)
UTILITIES STRUCTURES INC
2700 Evans Ave Unit 2 (33901-5303)
P.O. Box 9303 (33902-9303)
PHONE....................................239 334-7757
W Brown Thompson III, *President*
Carmi Thompson, *Principal*
T Nathan Thompson, *Vice Pres*
Gay Rebel Thompson, *Treasurer*
Robin Thompson, *Bookkeeper*
EMP: 18 **EST:** 1988
SQ FT: 4,000
SALES (est): 2.5MM **Privately Held**
WEB: www.utilitiesstructures.com
SIC: 3272 Poles & posts, concrete

(G-4644)
VAULT STRUCTURES INC
Also Called: VSI
3640 Work Dr (33916-7534)
PHONE....................................239 332-3270
Kevin P McNamara, *CEO*
Howard T Ankney, *President*
Jennifer Pendl, *Sales Staff*
◆ **EMP:** 50 **EST:** 1986
SQ FT: 44,000
SALES (est): 13.6MM **Privately Held**
WEB: www.vaultstructures.com
SIC: 3499 Safes & vaults, metal

(G-4645)
VELMAXXX ENTERPRISES INC
Also Called: No No-See-Um
10941 Gladiolus Dr Unit 9 (33908-2685)
P.O. Box 71, Sanibel (33957-0071)
PHONE....................................239 689-4343
Caroline Semerjian, *Principal*
Kip Buntrock, *Sales Staff*
Kimberly Chaffin, *Sales Staff*
EMP: 6 **EST:** 2009
SALES (est): 710.3K **Privately Held**
WEB: www.velmaxxx.net
SIC: 2879 Insecticides & pesticides

(G-4646)
VIANNY CORPORATION
6860 Daniels Pkwy (33912-1571)
PHONE....................................239 888-4536
David Aranda, *CEO*
EMP: 10 **EST:** 2015
SALES (est): 495.5K **Privately Held**
SIC: 2844 5122 Toilet preparations; toilet preparations

(G-4647)
VISIONARE LLC
12251 Towne Lake Dr (33913-8012)
PHONE....................................305 989-7271
Irineu Vitor Leite,
Marina Adami, *Administration*
Geninho Thome,
EMP: 7 **EST:** 2013
SALES (est): 552.8K **Privately Held**
WEB: www.visionare.us
SIC: 3842 Orthopedic appliances

(G-4648)
VISIONS MILLWORK INC
15674 Spring Line Ln (33905-2450)
PHONE....................................239 390-0811
Kim Rose, *President*
John McCallum, *Vice Pres*
Barbara Rose, *Admin Sec*
EMP: 10
SALES (est): 3.9MM **Privately Held**
SIC: 2431 5099 5251 Interior & ornamental woodwork & trim; locks & lock sets; door locks & lock sets

(G-4649)
W C H ENTERPRISES INC
17640 Holly Oak Ave (33967-5141)
PHONE....................................239 267-7549
Cynthia Heisler, *President*
EMP: 5 **EST:** 1997
SALES (est): 328K **Privately Held**
SIC: 2431 Window shutters, wood

(G-4650)
WATER BOY INC
1520 Lee St (33901-2915)
PHONE....................................239 461-0860
Scott McLaughlin, *Principal*
EMP: 11
SALES (corp-wide): 8.7MM **Privately Held**
WEB: www.waterboyinc.com
SIC: 2086 5499 Water, pasteurized: packaged in cans, bottles, etc.; water: distilled mineral or spring
PA: Water Boy, Inc.
4454 19th Street Ct E
Bradenton FL 34203
941 744-9249

(G-4651)
WEAR FUND LLC
93 Mildred Dr Ste B (33901-9044)
PHONE....................................239 313-3907
Samuel S Lewis, *Principal*
EMP: 12 **EST:** 2018
SALES (est): 438.2K **Privately Held**
WEB: www.wearthefund.com
SIC: 2759 Screen printing

(G-4652)
WEST CAST CBNETS CLSETS FLRG I
6385 Presidential Ct # 102 (33919-3547)
PHONE....................................239 481-8109
Benjamin E Payne, *Principal*
EMP: 13 **EST:** 2004
SALES (est): 269.5K **Privately Held**
WEB: www.westcoastdesignbuild.com
SIC: 2434 Wood kitchen cabinets

(G-4653)
WEST COAST CUSTOM CABINETRY
17683 Summerlin Rd 10 (33908-5704)
PHONE....................................239 481-8109
Carrie L Payne, *President*
Benjamin E Payne, *Vice Pres*
Renee Payne, *Admin Sec*
EMP: 11 **EST:** 2004
SALES (est): 325.4K **Privately Held**
WEB: www.westcoastdesignbuild.com
SIC: 2434 Wood kitchen cabinets

(G-4654)
WESTERN FABRICATING LLC
17061 Alico Commerce Ct (33967-2512)
PHONE....................................239 676-5382
EMP: 8 **EST:** 2019
SALES (est): 656.9K **Privately Held**
WEB: www.westernfabricating.com
SIC: 3441 Fabricated structural metal

(G-4655)
WHEELHOUSE DIRECT LLC
17595 S Tamiami Trl # 125 (33908-4570)
PHONE....................................239 246-8788
EMP: 11 **EST:** 2018
SALES (est): 475K **Privately Held**
WEB: www.wheelhousedirect.com
SIC: 2721 Periodicals

(G-4656)
YETMAN INDUSTRIES INC
14701 Bald Eagle Dr (33912-2091)
P.O. Box 62266 (33906-2266)
PHONE....................................239 561-7808
Ronald W Yetman, *Principal*
EMP: 7 **EST:** 2008
SALES (est): 313K **Privately Held**
SIC: 3999 Manufacturing industries

(G-4657)
YOUNGQUIST BROTHERS ROCK INC
15401 Alico Rd (33913-8232)
PHONE....................................239 267-6000
Tim G Youngquist, *President*
Richard Friday, *CFO*
Andy Marquez, *Manager*
EMP: 60
SALES (est): 16.1MM **Privately Held**
WEB: www.youngquistbrothers.com
SIC: 1411 Trap rock, dimension-quarrying

(G-4658)
ZARAGOZA PAVERS INC
19049 Murcott Dr E (33967-3751)
PHONE....................................239 273-6665
Oscar Zaragoza Virgen, *Branch Mgr*
EMP: 8
SALES (corp-wide): 120K **Privately Held**
SIC: 2951 Asphalt paving mixtures & blocks
PA: Zaragoza Pavers Inc.
2802 7th St W
Lehigh Acres FL

(G-4659)
ZBC CABINETRY
3593 Vrnica S Shmker Blvd (33916-2274)
PHONE....................................239 332-2940
Zac Carpenter, *Principal*
EMP: 7 **EST:** 2015
SALES (est): 516.7K **Privately Held**
WEB: www.zbccabinetry.com
SIC: 2434 Wood kitchen cabinets

Fort Myers Beach
Lee County

(G-4660)
BREEZE CORPORATION
Also Called: Fort Myers Beach Shopg Guide
19260 San Carlos Blvd (33931-2245)
PHONE....................................239 765-0400
Robin Calabrese, *Manager*
Chris Strine, *Manager*
Jason Welebny, *Manager*
Richard Barnes, *CIO*
Joe Trupo, *Executive*
EMP: 181
SQ FT: 8,236 **Privately Held**
WEB: www.breezenewspapers.com
SIC: 2711 2741 Newspapers: publishing only, not printed on site; miscellaneous publishing
HQ: The Breeze Corporation
2510 Del Prado Blvd S
Cape Coral FL 33904
239 574-1110

(G-4661)
DIVERSIFIED YACHT SERVICES INC
751 Fishermans Wharf (33931-2203)
PHONE....................................239 765-8700
Richard H Levi, *President*
Ryan Levi, *Exec VP*
Pamela Benad, *Vice Pres*
Greg Collins, *Vice Pres*

GEOGRAPHIC

EMP: 30 EST: 2007
SQ FT: 60,000
SALES (est): 1.5MM
SALES (corp-wide): 99.6MM Privately Held
WEB: www.dysinc.com
SIC: 3732 4493 Yachts, building & repairing; boat yards, storage & incidental repair
PA: Levi Ray & Shoup Inc
2401 W Monroe St
Springfield IL 62704
217 793-3800

(G-4662)
FORT MYERS BCH SOCCER LEAG INC
108 Bay Mar Dr (33931-3808)
PHONE..................................239 353-7567
James Demilia, *Principal*
EMP: 7 EST: 2011
SALES (est): 10.1K Privately Held
WEB: www.fmbsoccer.com
SIC: 2899 Flares

(G-4663)
GRAVITY PRODUCE LLC
4401 Bay Beach Ln Apt 844 (33931-5918)
PHONE..................................269 471-9463
Rockie Rick, *Owner*
EMP: 5 EST: 2005
SALES (est): 511.3K Privately Held
WEB: www.gravitywine.com
SIC: 2084 Wines

(G-4664)
ISLAND SAND PAPER
450 Old San Carlos Blvd (33931-2148)
P.O. Box 7003 (33932-7003)
PHONE..................................239 290-4038
Marjorie Layfield, *Principal*
EMP: 6 EST: 2018
SALES (est): 242.9K Privately Held
SIC: 2711 Newspapers, publishing & printing

(G-4665)
JUVENT MEDICAL INC
3111 Shell Mound Blvd (33931-3629)
PHONE..................................732 748-8866
John Moroney, *President*
EMP: 7 EST: 2003
SQ FT: 12,000
SALES (est): 255.9K Privately Held
SIC: 3842 Cotton & cotton applicators

(G-4666)
SKIP ONE SEAFOOD INC
17650 San Carlos Blvd (33931-3033)
PHONE..................................239 463-8788
EMP: 6
SALES (est): 571.4K Privately Held
SIC: 2092 Mfg Fresh/Frozen Packaged Fish

Fort Pierce
St. Lucie County

(G-4667)
A B SURVEY SUPPLY ENTPS INC
2603 Industrial Avenue 2 (34946-8644)
PHONE..................................772 464-9500
Anwar Bacchus, *President*
Christopher Golding, *Vice Pres*
EMP: 6 EST: 1982
SQ FT: 2,400
SALES (est): 575.9K Privately Held
SIC: 2499 5049 8713 Surveyors' stakes, wood; scientific & engineering equipment & supplies; surveying services

(G-4668)
A-1 ROOF TRUSSES LTD COMPANY
Also Called: A1 Building Components
4451 Saint Lucie Blvd (34946-9035)
PHONE..................................772 409-1010
John Hering, *Branch Mgr*
EMP: 110
SALES (corp-wide): 33.8MM Privately Held
WEB: www.a1truss.com
SIC: 2439 Trusses, wooden roof
PA: A-1 Roof Trusses Ltd., Company
11555 Heron Bay Blvd # 2
Coral Springs FL 33076
270 316-9409

(G-4669)
ADVANCED MACHINE AND TOOL INC
3900 Selvitz Rd (34981-4709)
PHONE..................................772 465-6546
Lloyd D Riley, *President*
Jerry Jacques, *General Mgr*
Mike Bousson, *Mfg Mgr*
John Drumm, *Purchasing*
Clay Becton, *Sales Mgr*
◆ EMP: 65 EST: 1979
SQ FT: 32,000
SALES (est): 9.4MM Privately Held
WEB: www.amtfl.com
SIC: 3599 7692 3544 Machine shop, jobbing & repair; welding repair; special dies, tools, jigs & fixtures

(G-4670)
AERO SHADE TECHNOLOGIES INC
3104 Industrial Avenue 3 # 3106 (34946-8662)
PHONE..................................772 562-2243
John Manchec, *President*
▲ EMP: 5 EST: 1998
SALES (est): 643.5K Privately Held
WEB: www.aero-shade.com
SIC: 2591 Window shades

(G-4671)
AIRFRAME INTERNATIONAL INC
3150 Airmans Dr (34946-9131)
PHONE..................................218 461-9305
Larry Calabrese, *CEO*
Carlos Byrne, *President*
▲ EMP: 14 EST: 1998
SQ FT: 22,000
SALES (est): 700K Privately Held
WEB: www.airframe.net
SIC: 3728 Aircraft parts & equipment

(G-4672)
AMERACAT INC
3340 N Us Highway 1 Ste 1 (34946-8478)
PHONE..................................772 882-9186
Stephen Meitner, *CEO*
Scott Meitner, *President*
EMP: 8 EST: 2009
SALES (est): 501K Privately Held
WEB: www.ameracat.com
SIC: 3732 Boat building & repairing

(G-4673)
AMERICAN BOTTLING COMPANY
Also Called: Canada Dry of Florida
3700 Avenue F (34947-5832)
PHONE..................................772 461-3383
Don Castle, *Sales/Mktg Mgr*
EMP: 17
SQ FT: 30,000 Publicly Held
WEB: www.keurigdrpepper.ca
SIC: 2086 Soft drinks: packaged in cans, bottles, etc.
HQ: The American Bottling Company
6425 Hall Of Fame Ln
Frisco TX 75034

(G-4674)
AMERICAN CONCRETE INDUSTRIES
350 N Rock Rd (34945-3437)
PHONE..................................772 464-1187
Robert L Snowe, *President*
▲ EMP: 30 EST: 1987
SQ FT: 28,750
SALES (est): 6.5MM Privately Held
WEB: www.american-concrete-industries.business.site
SIC: 3272 Concrete products, precast

(G-4675)
AMERICAST PRECAST GENERATOR
3204 Ohio Ave (34947-4673)
PHONE..................................772 971-1958
Charles Pitt, *Manager*
EMP: 13 EST: 2018
SALES (est): 894.2K Privately Held
WEB: www.ameri-casting.com
SIC: 3272 Concrete products

(G-4676)
ANCIENT MOSAIC STUDIOS LLC
4106 Mariah Cir (34947-1771)
PHONE..................................772 460-3145
Stuart A Horowitz, *President*
◆ EMP: 16 EST: 2002
SQ FT: 27,000
SALES (est): 1MM Privately Held
WEB: www.stoneyardinc.com
SIC: 3281 Table tops, marble

(G-4677)
APPLE MACHINE & SUPPLY CO
5900 Orange Ave (34947-1550)
P.O. Box 68 (34954-0068)
PHONE..................................772 466-9353
James R Turner, *President*
EMP: 26 EST: 1984
SQ FT: 12,000
SALES (est): 4.2MM Privately Held
WEB: www.applemachineandsupply.com
SIC: 3599 Machine shop, jobbing & repair

(G-4678)
ARROW POWER BOATS LLC
Also Called: Sonic Boats
309 Angle Rd (34947-2502)
PHONE..................................772 429-8888
Anthony Frisina, *Mng Member*
EMP: 7 EST: 2009
SALES (est): 89K Privately Held
WEB: www.sonicboats.net
SIC: 3731 Commercial cargo ships, building & repairing

(G-4679)
AUTOMATED SERVICES INC
Also Called: A S I
2700 Industrial Avenue 3 (34946-8663)
P.O. Box 650889, Vero Beach (32965-0889)
PHONE..................................772 461-3388
EMP: 17
SQ FT: 22,000 Privately Held
SIC: 3479 2759 2821 2396 Coating/Engraving Svcs Commercial Printing Mfg Plstc Material/Resin Mfg Auto/Apparel Trim

(G-4680)
BEE ELECTRONICS INC
2733 Peters Rd (34945-2613)
PHONE..................................772 468-7477
Robert Lunn, *President*
Mark Lunn, *Sales Mgr*
Andrew Lunn, *Manager*
EMP: 100 EST: 1996
SALES (est): 13.9MM Privately Held
WEB: www.beecase.com
SIC: 3161 5099 Cases, carrying; cases, carrying
PA: U.S. Communications Industries Inc
2733 Peters Rd
Fort Pierce FL 34945
772 468-7477

(G-4681)
BEST INDUSTRIES
15860 W Park Ln (34945-4232)
PHONE..................................772 460-8310
Otto G Wild, *President*
Luis Gil, *Project Mgr*
▼ EMP: 10 EST: 2003
SQ FT: 4,000
SALES (est): 1.3MM Privately Held
WEB: www.bestindustries.net
SIC: 3441 Fabricated structural metal

(G-4682)
BOOTH MANUFACTURING COMPANY
Also Called: Auto Labe
3101 Industrial Ave Ste 2 (34946)
PHONE..................................772 465-4441
Roy Shepherd, *CEO*
Mark Birchall, *Chairman*
Jan Neufeld, *Marketing Staff*
◆ EMP: 30
SQ FT: 25,000
SALES (est): 8.2MM Privately Held
WEB: www.autolabe.com
SIC: 3565 Labeling machines, industrial

(G-4683)
CARIB SEA INC
3434 Industrial 31st St (34946-8613)
P.O. Box 13359 (34979-3359)
PHONE..................................772 461-1113
Richard M Greenfield Jr, *President*
Nancy P Greenfield, *Corp Secy*
Betsey Greenfiled-Moore, *Vice Pres*
Jud McCracken, *Sales Mgr*
Tony Wagner, *Marketing Staff*
◆ EMP: 30 EST: 1971
SQ FT: 50,000
SALES (est): 5.5MM Privately Held
WEB: www.caribsea.com
SIC: 3231 Aquariums & reflectors, glass

(G-4684)
CEI LIQUIDATION INC
Also Called: Red Phoenix Extracts
3495 S Us Highway 1 Ste A (34982-6651)
PHONE..................................281 541-2444
Steven L Sample, *CEO*
Gwendolyn G Sample, *Admin Sec*
◆ EMP: 8 EST: 2008
SALES (est): 365.5K Privately Held
SIC: 3556 Mixers, commercial, food

(G-4685)
CEMEX CNSTR MTLS FLA LLC
Also Called: Agg Trading-W Ft Pierce Term
Glades Cut Off Rd (34981)
PHONE..................................800 992-3639
EMP: 25 Privately Held
SIC: 3273 Ready-mixed concrete
HQ: Cemex Construction Materials Florida, Llc
1501 Belvedere Rd
West Palm Beach FL 33406

(G-4686)
CEMEX CNSTR MTLS FLA LLC
Also Called: East Ft. Pierce FL Readymix
514 S 3rd St (34950-1525)
PHONE..................................772 461-7102
Charles Carew, *Branch Mgr*
EMP: 7 Privately Held
SIC: 3273 Ready-mixed concrete
HQ: Cemex Construction Materials Florida, Llc
1501 Belvedere Rd
West Palm Beach FL 33406

(G-4687)
CHAMBERS TRUSS INC (PA)
3105 Oleander Ave (34982-6496)
PHONE..................................772 465-2012
Robert J Becht, *President*
Phyllis Chambers, *Corp Secy*
Arvin L Rieger, *Vice Pres*
Branden Baird, *Sales Staff*
Heidi Baird, *Info Tech Mgr*
▼ EMP: 90
SALES (est): 9MM Privately Held
WEB: www.chamberstruss.com
SIC: 2439 Trusses, wooden roof

(G-4688)
CITRUS EXTRACTS LLC
3495 S Us Highway 1 Ste A (34982-6651)
P.O. Box 394, Johnston IA (50131-0394)
PHONE..................................772 464-9800
Al Koch, *CEO*
William Howe, *President*
EMP: 15 EST: 2015
SALES (est): 2.6MM Privately Held
WEB: www.allthingscitrus.com
SIC: 2836 Extracts

(G-4689)
CUSTOM METAL CREATIONS LLC
3106 S Brocksmith Rd (34945-4411)
PHONE..................................772 807-0000
Christopher Day,
EMP: 9 EST: 2014
SALES (est): 809.7K Privately Held
WEB: www.custommetalcreations.com
SIC: 3446 Ornamental metalwork

(G-4690)
D & D MBL WLDG FABRICATION INC
Also Called: D & D Welding
5300 Steel Blvd (34946-9129)
PHONE..................................772 489-7900
Martine Vaughn, *Branch Mgr*
EMP: 57
SQ FT: 3,000
SALES (corp-wide): 15MM **Privately Held**
WEB: www.ddwelding.com
SIC: 3446 3441 Architectural metalwork; fabricated structural metal
PA: D & D Mobile Welding And Fabrication, Inc.
222 Sw 21st Ter
Fort Lauderdale FL 33312
954 791-3385

(G-4691)
D O B SIGNS LLC
4475 N Old Dixie Hwy (34946-6405)
PHONE..................................772 466-4913
David H Sheil, *Principal*
EMP: 7 **EST:** 2010
SALES (est): 114.6K **Privately Held**
WEB: www.dobsigns.com
SIC: 3993 Signs & advertising specialties

(G-4692)
DELTA REGIS TOOLS INC
7370 Commercial Cir (34951-4109)
PHONE..................................772 465-4302
Thomas G Deadman, *President*
Bob Deadman, *Vice Pres*
James Deadman, *Sales Staff*
Mark Kotiesen, *Sales Staff*
▲ **EMP:** 20 **EST:** 1996
SALES (est): 4.7MM
SALES (corp-wide): 419.3K **Privately Held**
WEB: www.deltaregis.com
SIC: 3546 5085 7629 Power-driven handtools; industrial tools; electrical repair shops
PA: Deadman Holdings Inc
4120 Ridgeway Dr Unit 23
Mississauga ON L5L 5

(G-4693)
ELEMENT 26 LLC
1810 S Ocean Dr (34949-3361)
PHONE..................................413 519-1146
Philip J Gauthier, *Principal*
EMP: 7 **EST:** 2018
SALES (est): 965.5K **Privately Held**
WEB: www.element26.co
SIC: 2819 Elements

(G-4694)
EM ADAMS INC
7496 Commercial Cir (34951-4111)
P.O. Box 12160 (34979-2160)
PHONE..................................772 468-6550
Richard K Donahue, *President*
Rich Donahue, *Vice Pres*
Richard Donahue, *Vice Pres*
Clifford Snow, *Sales Staff*
◆ **EMP:** 65 **EST:** 1958
SALES (est): 8.4MM **Privately Held**
WEB: www.emadamsco.com
SIC: 3841 5047 Surgical & medical instruments; orthopedic equipment & supplies; therapy equipment

(G-4695)
EP6 GROUP INC
1150 Bell Ave (34982-6581)
PHONE..................................772 332-9100
Leanna Evans, *President*
EMP: 9 **EST:** 2018
SALES (est): 697.6K **Privately Held**
WEB: www.ep6group.com
SIC: 2621 Building & roofing paper, felts & insulation siding

(G-4696)
FASCO EPOXIES INC
2550 N Us Highway 1 (34946-8963)
PHONE..................................772 464-0808
Daniel Delo, *President*
EMP: 13 **EST:** 2015
SALES (est): 2MM **Privately Held**
WEB: www.fascoepoxies.com
SIC: 2891 Epoxy adhesives

(G-4697)
FAUX EFFECTS INTERNATIONAL INC
Also Called: Aqua Finishing Solutions
2700 Industrial Avenue 2 (34946-8646)
PHONE..................................772 778-9044
Raymond P Sandor, *President*
Jane Koehler, *Vice Pres*
Joan Rooney, *Office Mgr*
Bill James, *Technology*
Scot Povlin, *Director*
◆ **EMP:** 42 **EST:** 1986
SQ FT: 31,000
SALES (est): 10.5MM **Privately Held**
WEB: www.fauxfx.com
SIC: 2851 Paints & allied products

(G-4698)
FLORIDA COCA-COLA BOTTLING CO
3939 Saint Lucie Blvd (34946-9025)
PHONE..................................772 461-3636
Bob Johnson, *Manager*
EMP: 403
SALES (corp-wide): 33B **Publicly Held**
WEB: www.coca-cola.com
SIC: 2086 Bottled & canned soft drinks
HQ: Florida Coca-Cola Bottling Company
521 Lake Kathy Dr
Brandon FL 33510
813 569-2600

(G-4699)
GEM FRESHCO LLC
3586 Oleander Ave (34982-6509)
P.O. Box 15009 (34979-5009)
PHONE..................................772 595-0070
EMP: 60
SALES (est): 3.9MM **Privately Held**
SIC: 2033 5142 Canned Fruits And Specialties

(G-4700)
GLOBAL STONE COLLECTION LLC (PA)
1405 N Us Highway 1 (34950-1418)
PHONE..................................772 467-1924
Yesid Medina, *Manager*
EMP: 43 **EST:** 2008
SALES (est): 1.3MM **Privately Held**
WEB: www.globalstonecollection.com
SIC: 2541 Table or counter tops, plastic laminated

(G-4701)
GLOMASTER SIGNS INC
4141 Bandy Blvd (34981-4732)
PHONE..................................772 464-0718
James M Hart, *President*
Rebecca Hart, *Admin Sec*
EMP: 6 **EST:** 1965
SQ FT: 3,000
SALES (est): 818.1K **Privately Held**
WEB: www.glomastersigns.com
SIC: 3993 Signs, not made in custom sign painting shops

(G-4702)
GRAFX BY CAZ (FORT PIERCE)
492 Maple Ave (34982-5949)
PHONE..................................772 284-9258
EMP: 6 **EST:** 2019
SALES (est): 201.7K **Privately Held**
SIC: 2759 Screen printing

(G-4703)
GRAVITYSTORM INC
7402 Fort Walton Ave (34951-1429)
PHONE..................................772 519-3009
Barson Nicholas, *Principal*
EMP: 11 **EST:** 2014
SALES (est): 265.4K **Privately Held**
WEB: www.gravitystorm.us
SIC: 2431 Storm windows, wood

(G-4704)
GREEN MACHINE
5110 La Salle St Apt A (34951-5034)
PHONE..................................772 475-6832
Matthew K Kaiser, *Principal*
EMP: 8 **EST:** 2015
SALES (est): 63.1K **Privately Held**
WEB: www.greenmachinenursery.com
SIC: 3599 Machine shop, jobbing & repair

(G-4705)
HALL METAL CORP
4700 Magnum Dr (34981-4839)
PHONE..................................772 460-0706
Peter D Hall, *President*
EMP: 5 **EST:** 1935
SQ FT: 4,000
SALES (est): 1MM **Privately Held**
WEB: www.hallmetals.net
SIC: 3441 Building components, structural steel

(G-4706)
HOMETOWN NEWS LC (PA)
Also Called: Martin County Hometown News
1102 S Us Highway 1 (34950-5132)
P.O. Box 850 (34954-0850)
PHONE..................................772 465-5656
Lee Mooty, *General Mgr*
Lee Mootym, *CFO*
Carol Deprey, *Sales Staff*
Rodney Bookhardt, *Advt Staff*
Vernon D Smith, *Mng Member*
▲ **EMP:** 45 **EST:** 2002
SQ FT: 5,000
SALES (est): 16MM **Privately Held**
WEB: www.hometowngiftcertificates.com
SIC: 2711 Newspapers, publishing & printing

(G-4707)
IMMUNOTEK BIO CENTERS LLC
2710 S Us Highway 1 (34982-5919)
PHONE..................................772 577-7194
John Bonczak, *Manager*
EMP: 32
SALES (corp-wide): 27MM **Privately Held**
WEB: www.immunotek.com
SIC: 2836 Blood derivatives
PA: Immunotek Bio Centers, L.L.C.
3900 N Causeway Blvd # 1200
Metairie LA 70002
337 500-1175

(G-4708)
INDIAN RIVER ARMATURE INC
120 Lakes End Dr Apt A (34982-6747)
PHONE..................................772 461-2067
Richard M Mc Arthur, *President*
Lela McArthur, *Corp Secy*
EMP: 7 **EST:** 1958
SQ FT: 4,800
SALES (est): 303.7K **Privately Held**
SIC: 7694 5063 Electric motor repair; motors, electric

(G-4709)
ISLAND STYLE HOMES INC
4275 Mariah Cir (34947-1707)
PHONE..................................772 464-6259
Gordon Mock, *President*
Susan Mock, *Vice Pres*
▼ **EMP:** 6 **EST:** 1990
SQ FT: 4,000
SALES (est): 892.3K **Privately Held**
WEB: www.islandstylehomes.com
SIC: 2452 Modular homes, prefabricated, wood

(G-4710)
KYOCERA DCMENT SLTONS STHAST L
480 Okeechobee Rd Ste 101 (34947)
PHONE..................................772 562-0511
Barry Rokaw, *Manager*
EMP: 12
SALES (corp-wide): 17.9MM **Privately Held**
WEB: www.kyoceraegp.com
SIC: 3555 7378 5044 Copy holders, printers'; computer maintenance & repair; office equipment
PA: Kyocera Document Solutions Southeast, Llc
3401 Wd Judge Dr Ste 140
Orlando FL 32808
407 841-2932

(G-4711)
LAS & JB INC
Also Called: Beltran Construction
4840 S Us Highway 1 (34982-7013)
PHONE..................................772 672-5315
Jony Beltran, *President*
Gregg Bozenbury, *Principal*
EMP: 7 **EST:** 2005
SQ FT: 1,500
SALES (est): 700K **Privately Held**
WEB: www.lasjbgranite.com
SIC: 3281 5032 1741 Granite, cut & shaped; granite building stone; masonry & other stonework

(G-4712)
LOST FABRICATION LLC
3811 Crossroads Pkwy (34945-2703)
PHONE..................................772 971-3467
Craig Blazer, *Principal*
EMP: 9 **EST:** 2014
SALES (est): 269.6K **Privately Held**
WEB: www.lostfab.com
SIC: 3999 Manufacturing industries

(G-4713)
LP AUTO & HOME GLASS
2471 Se Sapelo Ave (34952-6770)
PHONE..................................772 335-3697
Harold Gerber, *Principal*
EMP: 10 **EST:** 1998
SALES (est): 547.6K **Privately Held**
SIC: 3231 Enameled glass

(G-4714)
MARTINEZ BUILDERS SUPPLY LLC
Also Called: East Coast Truss
5285 Saint Lucie Blvd (34946-9051)
PHONE..................................772 466-2480
Charlie Martinez, *President*
John Zeitz, *Sales Staff*
EMP: 60 **EST:** 2010
SALES (est): 4MM **Privately Held**
SIC: 2439 Trusses, wooden roof

(G-4715)
MAVERICK BOAT GROUP INC
4551 Saint Lucie Blvd (34946-9002)
PHONE..................................772 465-0631
EMP: 185
SALES (corp-wide): 926.5MM **Publicly Held**
WEB: www.maverickboats.com
SIC: 3732 Boat building & repairing
HQ: Maverick Boat Group, Inc.
3207 Industrial 29th St
Fort Pierce FL 34946
772 465-0631

(G-4716)
MAVERICK BOAT GROUP INC (HQ)
3207 Industrial 29th St (34946-8642)
PHONE..................................772 465-0631
Douglas Deal, *President*
Debbie Spencer, *Purchasing*
Mark Mergott, *Engineer*
Stephen Farinacci, *CFO*
Skip Lyshon, *Sales Mgr*
▼ **EMP:** 155 **EST:** 1984
SQ FT: 103,000
SALES (est): 59.5MM
SALES (corp-wide): 926.5MM **Publicly Held**
WEB: www.maverickboats.com
SIC: 3732 Fishing boats: lobster, crab, oyster, etc.: small; skiffs, building & repairing
PA: Malibu Boats, Inc.
5075 Kimberly Way
Loudon TN 37774
865 458-5478

(G-4717)
MCCAIN SALES OF FLORIDA INC
Also Called: Universal Signs & Accessories
3001 Orange Ave (34947-3634)
PHONE..................................772 461-0665
Dixon Mc Cain, *President*
Pete Wells, *General Mgr*
Steven Mc Cain, *Corp Secy*
Rui Mc Cain, *Vice Pres*
Pam Cowger, *CFO*
▲ **EMP:** 22 **EST:** 1962
SQ FT: 18,000
SALES (est): 3.9MM **Privately Held**
WEB: www.universalsignsfl.com
SIC: 3993 Signs, not made in custom sign painting shops

GEOGRAPHIC

(G-4718)
MIAMI FILTER LLC
Also Called: Miami Tank
7384 Commercial Cir (34951-4109)
PHONE....................................772 466-1440
Jeremy Mulvey, *General Mgr*
Ron Masse, *Parts Mgr*
James D Miller, *Mng Member*
Kevin Mulvey, *Mng Member*
◆ **EMP:** 30 **EST:** 1958
SQ FT: 50,000
SALES (est): 3.4MM **Privately Held**
WEB: www.miamifilter.com
SIC: 3569 Filters, general line: industrial

(G-4719)
MORGAN TECHNICAL SERVICES
5512 Silver Oak Dr (34982-7464)
PHONE....................................772 466-5757
Ron Morgan, *Owner*
EMP: 5 **EST:** 1990
SALES (est): 331.9K **Privately Held**
SIC: 3571 Electronic computers

(G-4720)
MOSAICS LIQUIDATION CO INC
901 S 3rd St (34950-5172)
PHONE....................................772 468-8453
Rickey L Farrell, *Principal*
EMP: 6 **EST:** 1989
SALES (est): 66.7K **Privately Held**
SIC: 3253 Ceramic wall & floor tile

(G-4721)
MSA AIRCRAFT PRODUCTS
3106 Industrial Avenue 3 (34946-8662)
PHONE....................................772 562-2243
John Manchec, *Principal*
EMP: 18 **EST:** 2016
SALES (est): 1.7MM **Privately Held**
WEB: www.msaaircraft.com
SIC: 3728 Aircraft parts & equipment

(G-4722)
NILFISK PRESSURE-PRO LLC
7300 Commercial Cir (34951-4109)
PHONE....................................772 672-3697
Dale Reed, *President*
Jeff Barna, *Vice Pres*
Mike Cecchini, *Design Engr*
Alexis White, *Sales Staff*
EMP: 87 **EST:** 2005
SALES (est): 14.8MM
SALES (corp-wide): 1.7B **Privately Held**
WEB: www.pressure-pro.com
SIC: 3589 High pressure cleaning equipment
PA: Nkt A/S
Vibeholms Alle 20
BrOndby
434 820-00

(G-4723)
OCEANGROWN
7453 Commercial Cir (34951-4112)
PHONE....................................941 921-2401
John S Hartman, *President*
EMP: 16 **EST:** 2005
SALES (est): 4.5MM **Privately Held**
WEB: www.oceangrown.com
SIC: 2873 Fertilizers: natural (organic), except compost

(G-4724)
OFFICE OF MEDICAL EXAMINER
2500 S 35th St (34981-5573)
PHONE....................................772 464-7378
Charles Diggs, *Owner*
EMP: 8 **EST:** 1991
SALES (est): 464.1K **Privately Held**
SIC: 2711 Newspapers, publishing & printing

(G-4725)
ORACLE CORPORATION
2100 Nebraska Ave (34950-4704)
PHONE....................................772 466-0704
Colleen Varana, *Surgery Dir*
EMP: 302
SALES (corp-wide): 40.4B **Publicly Held**
WEB: www.oracle.com
SIC: 7372 Prepackaged software
PA: Oracle Corporation
2300 Oracle Way
Austin TX 78741
737 867-1000

(G-4726)
ORANGE PEEL GAZETTE TREASUR
2721 S 10th St (34982-5808)
PHONE....................................772 489-8005
Frank Winchester, *Owner*
EMP: 6 **EST:** 2005
SALES (est): 234K **Privately Held**
WEB: www.orangepeelgazette.com
SIC: 2711 Newspapers, publishing & printing

(G-4727)
ORCHID ISLAND JUICE CO INC
Also Called: Natalies Orchid Island Juice
330 N Us Highway 1 (34950-4207)
PHONE....................................772 465-1122
Marygrace Sexton, *CEO*
Frank Tranchilla, *General Mgr*
John Martinelli, *Exec VP*
William Martinelli, *Vice Pres*
Jim Zurbey, *Opers Staff*
▼ **EMP:** 85 **EST:** 1990
SQ FT: 65,000
SALES (est): 25.9MM **Privately Held**
WEB: www.orchidislandjuice.com
SIC: 2037 Fruit juices

(G-4728)
ORGANIC LABORATORIES INC (PA)
5520 Glades Cut Off Rd (34981-4615)
PHONE....................................772 286-5581
Patrick Barry, *President*
Rick Barr, *Opers Mgr*
Stan Gibbs, *CFO*
▼ **EMP:** 5 **EST:** 1989
SQ FT: 11,000
SALES (est): 2MM **Privately Held**
WEB: www.organiclabs.com
SIC: 2879 Pesticides, agricultural or household

(G-4729)
PAT COBB PRINTING
1201 Palm Walk Ln (34950-3267)
PHONE....................................772 465-5484
Patricia Cobb, *Principal*
EMP: 6 **EST:** 2008
SALES (est): 82.8K **Privately Held**
SIC: 2752 Commercial printing, lithographic

(G-4730)
PB HOLDCO LLC
Also Called: Pursuit Boats
3901 Saint Lucie Blvd (34946-9025)
PHONE....................................772 465-6006
Neal Hager, *Business Mgr*
Cory Rettenmaier, *Project Mgr*
Stephen Troisi, *Opers Mgr*
Bruce Thompson, *Opers-Prdtn-Mfg*
Audra Sypolt, *Senior Buyer*
EMP: 450
SALES (corp-wide): 926.5MM **Publicly Held**
SIC: 3732 Fishing boats: lobster, crab, oyster, etc.: small
HQ: Pb Holdco, Llc
5075 Kimberly Way
Loudon TN 37774
865 458-5478

(G-4731)
PEPSI-COLA METRO BTLG CO INC
Also Called: Pepsico
3620 Crossroads Pkwy (34945-2709)
PHONE....................................772 464-6150
M Reprints, *Managing Dir*
Ken Willis, *Principal*
Latoya Campbell, *Sales Staff*
Karen Baker, *Clerk*
EMP: 142
SALES (corp-wide): 70.3B **Publicly Held**
WEB: www.pepsico.com
SIC: 2086 Carbonated soft drinks, bottled & canned
HQ: Pepsi-Cola Metropolitan Bottling Company, Inc.
1111 Westchester Ave
White Plains NY 10604
914 767-6000

(G-4732)
PHOENIX METAL PRODUCTS INC
3000 Industrial Avenue 3 (34946-8609)
PHONE....................................772 595-6386
Philip Price III, *President*
William J Wilcox, *Vice Pres*
▼ **EMP:** 24 **EST:** 1995
SQ FT: 14,000
SALES (est): 4.5MM **Privately Held**
WEB: www.phoenixgse.com
SIC: 3441 Fabricated structural metal

(G-4733)
PIERCED CIDERWORKS
411 N 2nd St (34950-3001)
PHONE....................................772 302-3863
EMP: 7 **EST:** 2018
SALES (est): 272.2K **Privately Held**
WEB: www.piercedciderworks.com
SIC: 2084 Wines, brandy & brandy spirits

(G-4734)
PIONEER AG-CHEM INC (PA)
Also Called: Diamond R Fertilizer
4100 Glades Cut Off Rd (34981-4711)
P.O. Box 12489 (34979-2489)
PHONE....................................772 464-9300
Mike Mikles, *President*
John Minton, *Principal*
Wayne Carlton, *Principal*
Roy Childs, *Principal*
Ken Scott, *Chairman*
◆ **EMP:** 40 **EST:** 1973
SQ FT: 21,000
SALES (est): 109.3MM **Privately Held**
SIC: 2873 5191 Nitrogen solutions (fertilizer); fertilizers & agricultural chemicals

(G-4735)
PREMIER FABRICATORS LLC
7413 Commercial Cir (34951-4112)
PHONE....................................772 323-2042
Kenneth A Geremia Jr, *President*
Sherry Curtale, *General Mgr*
Terry W Sloan, *Vice Pres*
EMP: 7 **EST:** 2009
SALES (est): 10K **Privately Held**
WEB: www.premierfabricators.net
SIC: 3441 Fabricated structural metal

(G-4736)
PRESTIGE/AB READY MIX LLC
4190 Selvitz Rd (34981-4728)
PHONE....................................772 468-4666
EMP: 20 **Privately Held**
SIC: 3273 Mfg Ready-Mixed Concrete
HQ: Prestige/Ab Ready Mix, Llc
7228 Westport Pl Ste C
West Palm Beach FL 33413
561 478-9980

(G-4737)
RAYMOND NEWKIRK
Also Called: Rays Pallets
920 Angle Rd (34947-1702)
PHONE....................................772 359-0237
Raymond Newkirk, *Principal*
EMP: 7 **EST:** 2010
SALES (est): 98.3K **Privately Held**
SIC: 2448 Pallets, wood & wood with metal

(G-4738)
RE-BUS LLC
5015 Saint Lucie Blvd (34946-9047)
PHONE....................................772 418-7711
Keith Moody, *Mng Member*
EMP: 6 **EST:** 2015
SALES (est): 900K **Privately Held**
WEB: www.re-bus.net
SIC: 3585 Air conditioning, motor vehicle

(G-4739)
REARDEN STEEL MFG LLC
Also Called: Powerlift Hydraulic Doors Fla
5350 Steel Blvd (34946-9129)
PHONE....................................772 882-8517
Lynn Shepard,
EMP: 8 **EST:** 2015
SALES (est): 1.2MM **Privately Held**
SIC: 3442 Hangar doors, metal

(G-4740)
REDDY ICE CORPORATION
2901 Industrial Avenue 2 (34946-8647)
PHONE....................................772 461-5046
Ronald Forgham, *Treasurer*
EMP: 9 **Privately Held**
WEB: www.reddyice.com
SIC: 2097 Manufactured ice
HQ: Reddy Ice Corporation
5710 Lbj Fwy Ste 300
Dallas TX 75240
214 526-6740

(G-4741)
ROCLA CONCRETE TIE INC
600 S 3rd St (34950-1525)
PHONE....................................772 800-1855
Dana Head, *Branch Mgr*
EMP: 70
SALES (corp-wide): 711.6K **Privately Held**
WEB: www.vossloh-north-america.com
SIC: 3272 Ties, railroad: concrete
HQ: Rocla Concrete Tie, Inc
1819 Denver West Dr # 450
Lakewood CO 80401

(G-4742)
SANDS AT ST LUCIE
2750 S Us Highway 1 (34982-5902)
PHONE....................................772 489-9499
Donna Pepper, *Principal*
EMP: 6 **EST:** 2009
SALES (est): 142.3K **Privately Held**
WEB: www.sandsatstlucie.com
SIC: 2392 Household furnishings

(G-4743)
SCULPTURE HOUSE INC
3804 Crossroads Pkwy (34945-2704)
PHONE....................................609 466-2986
Bruner Barrie, *President*
▲ **EMP:** 10 **EST:** 1918
SQ FT: 10,000
SALES (est): 1.7MM **Privately Held**
WEB: www.sculpturehouse.com
SIC: 3952 Artists' equipment

(G-4744)
SE SMITH LLC
8001 Eden Rd (34951-4914)
PHONE....................................772 461-0482
Susan E Smith, *Principal*
EMP: 7 **EST:** 2012
SALES (est): 274.9K **Privately Held**
WEB: www.sesmithfl.com
SIC: 2741 Miscellaneous publishing

(G-4745)
SEA CAST CURB ADPTORS CRBS LLC
2601 Industrial Avenue 3 (34946-8624)
PHONE....................................772 466-2400
John V Langel, *Administration*
EMP: 12 **EST:** 2017
SALES (est): 1.3MM **Privately Held**
WEB: www.curbsfast.com
SIC: 3441 Building components, structural steel

(G-4746)
SEACOAST AIR CONDITIONING & SH ✪
3108 Industrial 31st St (34946-8610)
PHONE....................................772 466-2400
EMP: 13 **EST:** 2020
SALES (est): 3.8MM **Privately Held**
WEB: www.seacoastair.com
SIC: 3444 Sheet metalwork

(G-4747)
SOUTHEAST ELEVATOR LLC
811 Edwards Rd (34982-6286)
PHONE....................................772 461-0030
Charles McGee, *President*
Stephanie Perdue, *Project Mgr*
Lynn Pellegrino, *Office Mgr*
Travis McGee, *Supervisor*
David Zane, *Admin Sec*
◆ **EMP:** 75 **EST:** 1995

▲ = Import ▼=Export
◆ =Import/Export

SALES (est): 10.3MM **Privately Held**
WEB: www.seelevator.com
SIC: 3534 Elevators & moving stairways

(G-4748)
SOUTHERN TRUSS COMPANIES INC
2590 N Kings Hwy (34951-4019)
PHONE..................................772 464-4160
John C Byers, *President*
Burak Askin, *Engineer*
EMP: 90
SALES (est): 10.2MM **Privately Held**
WEB: www.southerntrusscompanies.com
SIC: 2439 Trusses, wooden roof

(G-4749)
SPECTRA COMPOSITES EAST FLA
7445 Commercial Cir (34951-4112)
PHONE..................................772 461-7747
Ginger Moore, *Branch Mgr*
EMP: 7 **EST:** 2012
SALES (est): 675.1K **Privately Held**
WEB: www.spectracomposites.com
SIC: 3229 Glass fiber products

(G-4750)
ST LUCIE SIGNS LLC
1147 Hernando St (34949-3347)
PHONE..................................772 971-6363
James M Nole, *Manager*
EMP: 7 **EST:** 2017
SALES (est): 372.3K **Privately Held**
SIC: 3993 Signs & advertising specialties

(G-4751)
STANDARD CLAY MINES
3804 Crossroads Pkwy (34945-2704)
PHONE..................................609 466-2986
EMP: 9
SALES: 1MM **Privately Held**
SIC: 3952 Mfg Lead Pencils/Art Goods

(G-4752)
SUNNYLAND USA INC
600 Citrus Ave Ste 200 (34950-4280)
PHONE..................................772 293-0293
Abbasgholi Bayat, *President*
◆ **EMP:** 8 **EST:** 2008
SQ FT: 1,000
SALES (est): 218.8K **Privately Held**
SIC: 2037 Frozen fruits & vegetables

(G-4753)
SUPERMIX CONCRETE
4550 Glades Cut Off Rd (34981-4715)
PHONE..................................305 265-4465
EMP: 92
SALES (corp-wide): 12.3MM **Privately Held**
SIC: 3273 Ready-mixed concrete
PA: Supermix Concrete
4300 Sw 74th Ave
Miami FL 33155
954 858-0780

(G-4754)
TEC AIR INC
2195 N Kings Hwy (34951-4018)
PHONE..................................772 335-8220
Barbara A Macwilliam, *President*
EMP: 6
SALES (est): 353.9K **Privately Held**
WEB: www.tecairllc.com
SIC: 3089 Injection molding of plastics

(G-4755)
TIG TECHNOLOGIES INC
4250 Bandy Blvd (34981-4733)
PHONE..................................561 691-3633
Roy McKee, *President*
Janis McKee, *Vice Pres*
EMP: 6 **EST:** 1994
SQ FT: 5,600
SALES (est): 415.8K **Privately Held**
WEB: www.host2011.hostmonster.com
SIC: 7692 Welding repair

(G-4756)
TOP DRAWER CABINETRY & CARPENT
4101 S Indian River Dr (34982-7766)
PHONE..................................772 370-4624
Thor C Welhaven, *Principal*
EMP: 6 **EST:** 2006
SALES (est): 120.7K **Privately Held**
WEB: www.topdrawer.cc
SIC: 2434 Wood kitchen cabinets

(G-4757)
TRANSITION OF SLC INC
7300 Commercial Cir (34951-4109)
PHONE..................................772 461-4486
Dale Reed, *President*
Shaun Spring, *Production*
Bill Mathews, *Engineer*
John Cooper, *Sales Staff*
Bob Gruetzmacher, *Sales Staff*
EMP: 42 **EST:** 1995
SALES (est): 11.7MM
SALES (corp-wide): 983.9MM **Privately Held**
WEB: www.pressure-pro.com
SIC: 3589 High pressure cleaning equipment
HQ: Nilfisk Ltd.
Unit 18-19
Penrith CA11
176 886-8995

(G-4758)
TRICEN TECHNOLOGIES FLA LLC (PA)
500 Farmers Market Rd # 6 (34982-6663)
PHONE..................................866 620-9407
Christopher Hale, *CEO*
Cynthia Hale, *Vice Pres*
▲ **EMP:** 14 **EST:** 2009
SALES (est): 5.4MM **Privately Held**
WEB: www.tricen.net
SIC: 1389 7389 Pipe testing, oil field service; inspection & testing services; industrial & commercial equipment inspection service; petroleum refinery inspection service; pipeline & power line inspection service

(G-4759)
TROPICANA PRODUCTS INC
6500 Glades Cut Off Rd (34981-4399)
PHONE..................................772 465-2030
Ruth Harrison, *Safety Mgr*
Dick Lineberger, *Engineer*
Tim Kelly, *Director*
EMP: 7
SALES (corp-wide): 70.3B **Publicly Held**
WEB: www.tropicana.com
SIC: 2033 2037 Fruit juices: packaged in cans, jars, etc.; fruit juice concentrates, frozen
HQ: Tropicana Products, Inc.
1001 13th Ave E
Bradenton FL 34208
941 747-4461

(G-4760)
TRUE STONE CORP
7324 Commercial Cir (34951-4109)
PHONE..................................772 334-9797
Leanardo Sanchez, *President*
Sean Yeoman, *Prdtn Mgr*
EMP: 21 **EST:** 2000
SALES (est): 1.3MM **Privately Held**
WEB: www.truestonemasonry.com
SIC: 3272 Stone, cast concrete

(G-4761)
TRUE STONE MASONRY LLC
7324 Commercial Cir (34951-4109)
PHONE..................................772 334-9797
Julie Smith, *CEO*
Troy Smith, *President*
EMP: 11 **EST:** 2015
SALES (est): 1.3MM **Privately Held**
WEB: www.truestonemasonry.com
SIC: 3272 1741 Cast stone, concrete; masonry & other stonework

(G-4762)
TURNER MACHINE & SUPPLY CO
5000 Orange Ave (34947-1303)
PHONE..................................772 464-4550
David Turner, *President*
Charles Turner, *Corp Secy*
EMP: 8 **EST:** 1944
SQ FT: 12,600
SALES (est): 996.7K **Privately Held**
SIC: 3599 3561 3523 Machine shop, jobbing & repair; pumps & pumping equipment; farm machinery & equipment

(G-4763)
TWIN VEE CATAMARANS INC
3101 S Us Highway 1 (34982-6337)
PHONE..................................772 429-2525
Donna Dunshee, *President*
Donna Barnett, *CFO*
▼ **EMP:** 15 **EST:** 2010
SQ FT: 77,300
SALES (est): 2.8MM **Privately Held**
WEB: www.twinvee.com
SIC: 3732 Motorized boat, building & repairing

(G-4764)
TWO WAY RADIO GEAR INC
3245 Okeechobee Rd (34947-4618)
PHONE..................................800 984-1534
David Lloyd, *CEO*
Linda Lloyd, *Principal*
Steven Roberts, *Accounts Exec*
Benny Permuy, *Manager*
Edward Wirsing, *Info Tech Mgr*
▲ **EMP:** 16 **EST:** 2011
SALES (est): 2.2MM **Privately Held**
WEB: www.twowayradiogear.com
SIC: 3669 5045 Intercommunication systems, electric; computer peripheral equipment

(G-4765)
UNCLE CARLOS GELATOS
141 Melody Ln (34950-4402)
PHONE..................................810 523-8506
EMP: 8
SALES (est): 720.1K **Privately Held**
SIC: 2024 Mfg Ice Cream/Frozen Desert

(G-4766)
UNIQUE TOOL & DIE LLC
3343 S Us Highway 1 Ste 4 (34982-6664)
PHONE..................................772 464-5006
William Gates, *President*
Fred St John, *Vice Pres*
EMP: 17 **EST:** 2005
SALES (est): 1.2MM **Privately Held**
WEB: www.utdllc.com
SIC: 3544 Special dies & tools

(G-4767)
US COMMUNICATIONS INDUSTRIES (PA)
2733 Peters Rd (34945-2613)
PHONE..................................772 468-7477
Robert A Lunn, *President*
EMP: 50 **EST:** 1981
SALES (est): 13.9MM **Privately Held**
SIC: 3161 7389 Cases, carrying; telephone answering service

(G-4768)
WARREN HEIM CORP
3107 Industrial 25th St (34946-8620)
PHONE..................................772 466-8265
Nancy Heim, *President*
Chuck Heim, *Vice Pres*
William Heim, *Vice Pres*
EMP: 20 **EST:** 1927
SQ FT: 10,000
SALES (est): 1.6MM **Privately Held**
WEB: www.warrenheimcorp.com
SIC: 2393 2381 Canvas bags; fabric dress & work gloves

(G-4769)
WE SIGN IT INC (PA)
15838 Orange Ave (34945-4213)
PHONE..................................772 577-4400
EMP: 15 **EST:** 2017
SALES (est): 144.2K **Privately Held**
SIC: 3993 Signs & advertising specialties

(G-4770)
WHEELER CONSOLIDATED INC
Also Called: Southern Covert
1031 Digiorgio Rd (34982-6447)
PHONE..................................772 464-4400
Zerion Simpson, *Manager*
EMP: 10
SALES (corp-wide): 75.3MM **Privately Held**
WEB: www.wheeler-con.com
SIC: 3272 3444 3441 2821 Culvert pipe, concrete; sheet metalwork; fabricated structural metal; plastics materials & resins
PA: Wheeler Consolidated, Inc
3620 Sw 61st St Ste 330
Des Moines IA 50321
515 223-1584

(G-4771)
WOODWORKX UNLIMITED INC
103 N 13th St (34950-8829)
PHONE..................................772 882-4197
EMP: 6 **EST:** 2018
SALES (est): 493.4K **Privately Held**
WEB: www.woodworkxunlimited.com
SIC: 2434 Wood kitchen cabinets

(G-4772)
WORLD INDUSTRIAL EQUIPMENT INC
Also Called: Stamm Manufacturing
4850 Orange Ave (34947-3413)
PHONE..................................772 461-6056
John G Stamm, *President*
Raul Cepero, *Sales Staff*
Tom Johns, *Admin Sec*
Chris Dillon, *Government*
◆ **EMP:** 25 **EST:** 1994
SQ FT: 23,859
SALES (est): 5.4MM **Privately Held**
WEB: www.stammequip.com
SIC: 3713 3537 Truck bodies & parts; industrial trucks & tractors

Fort Walton Beach
Okaloosa County

(G-4773)
A AND D PRINTING & MAILING LLC
105 Eglin Pkwy Se (32548-5518)
PHONE..................................850 244-2400
Dale J Andrews,
EMP: 7 **EST:** 2014
SALES (est): 118.3K **Privately Held**
WEB: www.aanddprinting.com
SIC: 2752 Commercial printing, lithographic

(G-4774)
ABLE RAILING & WELDING LLC
170 Park Dr (32548-3517)
PHONE..................................850 243-5444
EMP: 7
SALES (est): 97.6K **Privately Held**
SIC: 7692 Welding Repair

(G-4775)
ANCHOR SCREEN PRINTING LLC
808 South Dr (32547-2253)
PHONE..................................850 243-4200
April Wade, *Principal*
EMP: 6 **EST:** 2012
SALES (est): 764.2K **Privately Held**
WEB: www.anchorscreenprint.com
SIC: 2759 Screen printing

(G-4776)
AND SERVICES ✪
1295 Beverly St (32547-1434)
PHONE..................................850 805-6455
EMP: 6 **EST:** 2020
SALES (est): 88.8K **Privately Held**
WEB: www.andservices.com
SIC: 2842 1711 Specialty cleaning, polishes & sanitation goods; plumbing, heating, air-conditioning contractors

(G-4777)
APPAREL EXPRESSIONS LLC
209b Lang Rd (32547-3120)
P.O. Box 487 (32549-0487)
PHONE..................................850 314-0100
Bret Berglund, *General Mgr*
Sarah J Berglund,
Bret D Berglund,
EMP: 7 **EST:** 2005
SQ FT: 2,000

SALES (est): 907.4K **Privately Held**
WEB: www.promoaxp.com
SIC: 2395 Embroidery products, except schiffli machine; embroidery & art needlework

(G-4778)
ARMSTRONGS PRINTING & GRAPHICS (PA)
30 Walter Martin Rd Ne (32548-4960)
PHONE..................................850 243-6923
Fostine Armstrong, *President*
Bill Kirby, *General Mgr*
Jim Armstrong, *Vice Pres*
EMP: 7 **EST:** 1984
SALES (est): 607.3K **Privately Held**
WEB: www.armstrongsprint.com
SIC: 2752 2791 2789 Commercial printing, offset; typesetting; bookbinding & related work

(G-4779)
BAE SYSTEMS TECH SLTONS SVCS I
715 Hollywood Blvd Nw (32548-3863)
PHONE..................................850 244-6433
Brad West, *Sales Mgr*
Tanya Whitfield, *Sales Mgr*
Ed Pitkus, *Technical Staff*
Kristin Soto, *Analyst*
EMP: 6
SALES (corp-wide): 25.6B **Privately Held**
SIC: 3812 Search & navigation equipment
HQ: Bae Systems Technology Solutions & Services Inc.
520 Gaither Rd
Rockville MD 20850
703 847-5820

(G-4780)
BAE SYSTEMS TECH SLTONS SVCS I
70 Ready Ave Nw (32548-3857)
PHONE..................................850 344-0832
Wayne Patrick, *Prgrmr*
Marilyn Lantzy, *Planning*
EMP: 71
SALES (corp-wide): 25.6B **Privately Held**
SIC: 3812 Search & navigation equipment
HQ: Bae Systems Technology Solutions & Services Inc.
520 Gaither Rd
Rockville MD 20850
703 847-5820

(G-4781)
BAE SYSTEMS TECH SOL SRVC INC
557 Mary Esthr Cut Off Nw (32548-4038)
PHONE..................................850 664-6070
Brian Disco, *Business Mgr*
Mark Henry, *Vice Pres*
Thomas Caras, *Project Mgr*
Ted Traylor, *Project Mgr*
Jim Scott, *Opers Staff*
EMP: 17
SALES (corp-wide): 25.6B **Privately Held**
SIC: 3812 Search & navigation equipment
HQ: Bae Systems Technology Solutions & Services Inc.
520 Gaither Rd
Rockville MD 20850
703 847-5820

(G-4782)
BOEING
20 Hill Ave Nw (32548-3858)
PHONE..................................850 301-6635
Alexandra Amico, *Facilities Mgr*
Jamie Rogers, *Opers Staff*
Randall Calloway, *Production*
Andrew Barrett, *Engineer*
Caesar Directo, *Engineer*
EMP: 20 **EST:** 2016
SALES (est): 3.7MM **Privately Held**
SIC: 3721 Aircraft

(G-4783)
BOEING COMPANY
626 Anchors St Nw (32548-3861)
P.O. Box 835, Shalimar (32579-0835)
PHONE..................................850 301-6613
Doug Engman, *Engineer*
Chris Mazour, *Engineer*
George Ruyan, *Administration*
EMP: 6
SALES (corp-wide): 58.1B **Publicly Held**
WEB: www.boeing.com
SIC: 3721 Airplanes, fixed or rotary wing
PA: The Boeing Company
100 N Riverside Plz
Chicago IL 60606
312 544-2000

(G-4784)
BOTE BOARDS
630 Anchors St Nw (32548-3861)
PHONE..................................850 855-4046
EMP: 6 **EST:** 2018
SALES (est): 259K **Privately Held**
WEB: www.boteboard.com
SIC: 3949 Surfboards

(G-4785)
BRAZILIAN BRICKPAVERS INC
200 Racetrack Rd Ne (32547-1805)
PHONE..................................850 699-7833
Bruno D Suares, *Principal*
EMP: 6 **EST:** 2008
SALES (est): 158.2K **Privately Held**
WEB: www.brazilianbrickpavers.net
SIC: 3531 Pavers

(G-4786)
CATERPLLAR 2 BTTRFLY OTRACH CT
248 Hollywood Blvd Se (32548-5767)
PHONE..................................850 515-1143
Tracy A Orr, *Principal*
EMP: 8 **EST:** 2013
SALES (est): 363.6K **Privately Held**
WEB: www.c2boc.org
SIC: 3531 Construction machinery

(G-4787)
COBHAM MISSION SYSTEM CORP
706 Anchors St Nw (32548-3867)
PHONE..................................850 226-6717
Dennis Shindel, *Principal*
EMP: 8 **EST:** 2011
SALES (est): 748.2K **Privately Held**
WEB: www.cobham.com
SIC: 3812 Search & navigation equipment

(G-4788)
COTERIE CARE INC
701 Ferguson Dr (32547-2025)
PHONE..................................850 325-0422
Chase Newton, *Chairman*
Betty Allen, *Manager*
Cierra Allen, *Manager*
EMP: 14 **EST:** 2018
SALES (est): 629K **Privately Held**
SIC: 2833 Medicinals & botanicals

(G-4789)
CRANE ELECTRONICS INC
84 Hill Ave Nw (32548-3858)
PHONE..................................850 244-0043
Carol Cassidy, *Principal*
Arin Hayrapetian, *Business Mgr*
Charles Jewett, *Business Mgr*
Michael Macone, *Buyer*
Bethany Grace, *Purchasing*
EMP: 99
SALES (corp-wide): 2.9B **Publicly Held**
WEB: www.craneae.com
SIC: 3728 Aircraft parts & equipment
HQ: Crane Electronics, Inc.
16700 13th Ave W
Lynnwood WA 98037
425 882-3100

(G-4790)
DESTIN LOG
2 Eglin Pkwy Ne (32548-4915)
P.O. Box 2949 (32549-2949)
PHONE..................................850 837-2828
Rick Thomason, *Principal*
EMP: 176 **EST:** 1974
SQ FT: 11,000
SALES (est): 3.7MM
SALES (corp-wide): 3.4B **Publicly Held**
WEB: www.thedestinlog.com
SIC: 2711 Newspapers, publishing & printing
HQ: Northwest Florida Daily News
2 Eglin Pkwy Ne
Fort Walton Beach FL 32548
850 863-1111

(G-4791)
DRS ADVANCED ISR LLC
654 Anchors St Nw Ste 1 (32548-3861)
PHONE..................................850 226-4888
Chris Bloomfield, *Principal*
Korey Bales, *Principal*
Dana Mortensen, *Manager*
EMP: 14
SALES (corp-wide): 10.2B **Privately Held**
WEB: www.leonardodrs.com
SIC: 3812 Search & navigation equipment
HQ: Drs Icas, Llc
2601 Mssion Pt Blvd Ste 2
Beavercreek OH 45431

(G-4792)
DRS C3 SYSTEMS INC
645 Anchors St Nw (32548-3803)
PHONE..................................850 302-3909
Alan Dietrich, *President*
EMP: 27 **EST:** 1966
SALES (est): 592.3K **Privately Held**
WEB: www.leonardodrs.com
SIC: 3812 Search & navigation equipment

(G-4793)
DRS CONSOLIDATED CONTROLS
645 Anchors St Nw (32548-3803)
PHONE..................................850 302-3000
William Lynn III, *CEO*
Wade Havlat, *Engineer*
EMP: 14 **EST:** 2010
SALES (est): 1.2MM **Privately Held**
WEB: www.leonardodrs.com
SIC: 3812 Search & navigation equipment

(G-4794)
DRS LEONARDO INC
645 Anchors St Nw (32548-3803)
PHONE..................................850 302-3000
William J Lynn III, *Branch Mgr*
EMP: 6
SALES (corp-wide): 10.2B **Privately Held**
WEB: www.leonardodrs.com
SIC: 3812 Search & navigation equipment
HQ: Leonardo Drs, Inc.
2345 Crystal Dr Ste 1000
Arlington VA 22202
703 416-8000

(G-4795)
DRS LEONARDO INC
640 Lovejoy Rd Nw (32548-3832)
PHONE..................................850 302-3514
EMP: 6
SALES (corp-wide): 10.2B **Privately Held**
WEB: www.leonardodrs.com
SIC: 3812 Search & navigation equipment
HQ: Leonardo Drs, Inc.
2345 Crystal Dr Ste 1000
Arlington VA 22202
703 416-8000

(G-4796)
DRS TRAINING CTRL SYSTEMS LLC (DH)
Also Called: Drs Technologies
645 Anchors St Nw (32548-3803)
PHONE..................................850 302-3000
William J Lynn III, *CEO*
Edwin R Epstein, *President*
Jim Scott, *President*
Robert Viviano, *President*
Larry Azelle, *General Mgr*
EMP: 50 **EST:** 1957
SQ FT: 72,000
SALES (est): 74.7MM
SALES (corp-wide): 10.2B **Privately Held**
WEB: www.leonardodrs.com
SIC: 3812 8713 Radar systems & equipment;
HQ: Leonardo Drs, Inc.
2345 Crystal Dr Ste 1000
Arlington VA 22202
703 416-8000

(G-4797)
E BENTON GRIMSLEY INC
909 Mar Walt Dr (32547-6635)
PHONE..................................850 863-4064
E Benton Grimsley, *Principal*
EMP: 6 **EST:** 2010
SALES (est): 68.7K **Privately Held**
SIC: 3999 Manufacturing industries

(G-4798)
EMERALD COAST COATINGS LLC
705 Anchors St Nw (32548-3868)
PHONE..................................850 424-5244
Kevin Harvey, *President*
EMP: 10 **EST:** 2017
SALES (est): 530.9K **Privately Held**
WEB: www.emeraldcoastcoatings.com
SIC: 3479 Metal coating & allied service

(G-4799)
EMERGENCY STANDBY POWER LLC
Also Called: John Deere Authorized Dealer
17 Duval St (32547-2478)
PHONE..................................850 259-2304
Jennifer Diener, *Office Mgr*
Charles R Jacopetti,
Barbara Jacopetti,
EMP: 16 **EST:** 2007
SALES (est): 2.6MM **Privately Held**
WEB: www.espgenerators.com
SIC: 3621 5082 Generators & sets, electric; construction & mining machinery

(G-4800)
FORT WALTON CONCRETE CO
Also Called: Crestview Ready Mix
26 Industrial St Nw (32548-4814)
P.O. Box 655 (32549-0655)
PHONE..................................850 243-8114
James E Campbell, *President*
Tim Campbell, *Vice Pres*
EMP: 19 **EST:** 1975
SQ FT: 1,500
SALES (est): 1.2MM **Privately Held**
WEB: www.fort-walton-concrete-fwb-fl.business.site
SIC: 3273 Ready-mixed concrete

(G-4801)
FORT WALTON MACHINING INC
635 Anchors St Nw (32548-3803)
PHONE..................................800 223-0881
EMP: 28
SALES (corp-wide): 24MM **Privately Held**
WEB: www.fwmachining.com
SIC: 3599 Machine shop, jobbing & repair
PA: Fort Walton Machining, Inc.
43 Jet Dr Nw
Fort Walton Beach FL 32548
850 244-9095

(G-4802)
FORT WALTON MACHINING INC (PA)
43 Jet Dr Nw (32548-4807)
PHONE..................................850 244-9095
Ken Hill, *CEO*
Jan McDonald, *Chairman*
Tim Jozwiak, *Business Mgr*
Timothy M McDonald, *Corp Secy*
Douglas Huber, *Materials Mgr*
EMP: 103 **EST:** 1987
SQ FT: 105,000
SALES (est): 24MM **Privately Held**
WEB: www.fwmachining.com
SIC: 3599 Machine shop, jobbing & repair

(G-4803)
GRAHAMS WELDING FABRICATION
622 Fairway Ave Ne (32547-1708)
PHONE..................................850 865-0899
Charles F Graham, *President*
Teresa Graham, *Corp Secy*
EMP: 6 **EST:** 1997
SQ FT: 3,000
SALES (est): 333.1K **Privately Held**
SIC: 7692 Welding repair

(G-4804)
GREVAN ARTISTIC VENTURES INC (PA)
Also Called: Artistic Stoneworks
622 Lovejoy Rd Nw (32548-7005)
PHONE..................................850 243-8111
Hanley P Gramillion Jr, *President*
Joel Vanderlick, *Vice Pres*
EMP: 17 **EST:** 2014
SQ FT: 15,000

SALES (est): 1.8MM **Privately Held**
WEB: www.artisticstoneworksinc.com
SIC: 3281 5211 Granite, cut & shaped; cabinets, kitchen

(G-4805)
GS GELATO AND DESSERTS INC
1785 Fim Blvd (32547-1152)
PHONE..................................850 243-5455
Guido Tremolini, *President*
Michelle Popp, *Business Mgr*
Simona Faroni, *Vice Pres*
Maria Pizarro, *QC Mgr*
Tj Rodrigues, *Research*
▲ **EMP:** 50 **EST:** 1998
SALES (est): 17.8MM **Privately Held**
WEB: www.gsgelato.com
SIC: 2024 Ice cream & frozen desserts

(G-4806)
GULF COAST BUSINESS WORLD INC
3 Racetrack Rd Nw (32547-1601)
PHONE..................................850 864-1511
EMP: 10
SQ FT: 8,800
SALES (est): 550K **Privately Held**
SIC: 2752 5943 3993 2791 Lithographic Coml Print Ret Stationery Mfg Signs/Ad Specialties Typesetting Services Bookbinding/Related Work

(G-4807)
GULF SOUTH DISTRIBUTORS INC
Also Called: Kitchen Design Center
707 Anchors St Nw (32548-3868)
PHONE..................................850 244-1522
Richard V Nivens, *President*
EMP: 15 **EST:** 1980
SQ FT: 12,000
SALES (est): 846.5K **Privately Held**
WEB: www.gulfsouthkitchendesign.com
SIC: 2599 2542 2511 Cabinets, factory; partitions & fixtures, except wood; wood household furniture

(G-4808)
HERCO SHEET METAL INC
Also Called: Herco Sheet Metal.
201 Northampton Cir (32547-1462)
PHONE..................................850 244-7424
Warren L Sherman, *CEO*
Christopher Miller, *Principal*
Roberson Mary Pat, *Vice Pres*
Cynthia Miller, *CFO*
EMP: 33 **EST:** 1968
SALES (est): 1.5MM **Privately Held**
WEB: www.hercoinc.net
SIC: 3441 Fabricated structural metal

(G-4809)
HONEYWELL INTERNATIONAL INC
15 Industrial St Nw (32548-4813)
PHONE..................................850 243-8812
EMP: 6
SALES (corp-wide): 32.6B **Publicly Held**
WEB: www.honeywell.com
SIC: 3724 Aircraft engines & engine parts
PA: Honeywell International Inc.
300 S Tryon St
Charlotte NC 28202
704 627-6200

(G-4810)
JEHOVA JIREH WOOD WORK PROF
939 Beal Pkwy Nw (32547-1489)
PHONE..................................850 862-7131
Nicholas R Fanella, *Principal*
EMP: 6 **EST:** 2018
SALES (est): 110.9K **Privately Held**
SIC: 2431 Millwork

(G-4811)
JOHN R CAITO
Also Called: Delta Industries
91 Ready Ave Nw (32548-3848)
PHONE..................................850 612-0179
John R Caito, *Owner*
EMP: 8 **EST:** 2003
SALES (est): 101.9K **Privately Held**
SIC: 3446 5999 Stairs, staircases, stair treads: prefabricated metal; awnings

(G-4812)
KITCHEN & BATH CENTER INC (PA)
Also Called: Marble Works Kit & Bath Ctr
20 Ready Ave Nw (32548-3857)
PHONE..................................850 244-3996
Toll Free:..888 -
Ron Fisher, *President*
Kara Lunsford, *Project Mgr*
Adam Watkins, *Project Mgr*
Melinda Vazquez, *Credit Mgr*
Ruby Bullock, *Office Admin*
EMP: 35 **EST:** 1985
SQ FT: 36,000
SALES (est): 10.7MM **Privately Held**
WEB: www.kitchenandbathcenter.net
SIC: 3272 5211 Art marble, concrete; bathroom fixtures, equipment & supplies; cabinets, kitchen; counter tops

(G-4813)
LOCKHEED MARTIN CORPORATION
91 Hill Ave Nw (32548-7011)
PHONE..................................850 301-4155
EMP: 6 **Publicly Held**
WEB: www.lockheedmartin.com
SIC: 3812 Search & navigation equipment
PA: Lockheed Martin Corporation
6801 Rockledge Dr
Bethesda MD 20817

(G-4814)
MAGNA MANUFACTURING INC
Also Called: Loboy
85 Hill Ave Nw (32548-3846)
P.O. Box 279 (32549-0279)
PHONE..................................850 243-1112
Paul D Owens Jr, *President*
Kenny Watkins, *Vice Pres*
Myleto Stewart, *Sales Staff*
◆ **EMP:** 27 **EST:** 1984
SQ FT: 60,000
SALES (est): 8.7MM **Privately Held**
WEB: www.loboy.com
SIC: 3086 Packaging & shipping materials, foamed plastic; ice chests or coolers (portable), foamed plastic

(G-4815)
MICRO SYSTEMS INC (HQ)
35 Hill Ave Nw (32548-3852)
PHONE..................................850 244-2332
Eric M Demarco, *President*
Michael Fink, *Vice Pres*
Stephen Kesegich, *Prdtn Mgr*
Chip Wells, *Purch Dir*
Darla Pegg, *Purch Mgr*
EMP: 135 **EST:** 1976
SQ FT: 19,758
SALES (est): 32.2MM **Publicly Held**
WEB: www.kratosdefense.com
SIC: 3812 3663 3721 3728 Search & navigation equipment; radio & TV communications equipment; aircraft; aircraft parts & equipment; guided missiles & space vehicles; guided missile & space vehicle parts & auxiliary equipment

(G-4816)
MIX IT UP
909 Santa Rosa Blvd # 551 (32548-5979)
PHONE..................................251 767-1771
Gregory L Baetje, *President*
EMP: 6 **EST:** 2011
SALES (est): 212.6K **Privately Held**
WEB: www.mixitupdrinks.com
SIC: 3273 Ready-mixed concrete

(G-4817)
MONEY TREE ATM MFG LLC
130 Staff Dr Ne (32548-5051)
P.O. Box 4247 (32549-4247)
PHONE..................................850 244-5543
EMP: 5
SQ FT: 15,000
SALES (est): 803.3K
SALES (corp-wide): 1.7MM **Privately Held**
SIC: 3578 7629 Mfg Calculating Equipment Electrical Repair
PA: Integrated Financial Systems Llc
130 Staff Dr Ne
Fort Walton Beach FL 32548
850 244-5543

(G-4818)
MOTOROLA SOLUTIONS INC
73 Eglin Pkwy Ne Unit 302 (32548-4939)
PHONE..................................850 243-4426
Larry Hines, *Manager*
EMP: 6
SALES (corp-wide): 7.4B **Publicly Held**
WEB: www.motorolasolutions.com
SIC: 3663 Radio & TV communications equipment
PA: Motorola Solutions, Inc.
500 W Monroe St Ste 4400
Chicago IL 60661
847 576-5000

(G-4819)
NORTHWEST FLORIDA DAILY NEWS (DH)
2 Eglin Pkwy Ne (32548-4915)
P.O. Box 2949 (32549-2949)
PHONE..................................850 863-1111
James Hutto, *Sales Engr*
Tracy Conner, *Manager*
Roger Underwood, *Director*
EMP: 6 **EST:** 1999
SALES (est): 4.3MM
SALES (corp-wide): 3.4B **Publicly Held**
WEB: www.nwfdailynews.com
SIC: 2711 Newspapers, publishing & printing
HQ: Gatehouse Media, Llc
175 Sullys Trl Fl 3
Pittsford NY 14534
585 598-0030

(G-4820)
PALANJIAN ENTERPRISES INC
Also Called: Bon Appetit French Bakery
420 Mary Esther Cut Off N (32548-4023)
PHONE..................................850 244-2848
Vasken Palanjian, *President*
Janice Palanjian, *Corp Secy*
Arous Palanjian, *Vice Pres*
EMP: 14 **EST:** 1983
SQ FT: 3,751
SALES (est): 640.9K **Privately Held**
SIC: 2051 Bakery: wholesale or wholesale/retail combined

(G-4821)
PANAMA CITY NEWS HERALD
Also Called: Northwest Florida Daily News
2 Eglin Pkwy Ne (32548-4915)
P.O. Box 2949 (32549-2949)
PHONE..................................850 863-1111
Tom Conner, *Principal*
EMP: 239
SQ FT: 36,923
SALES (corp-wide): 3.4B **Publicly Held**
WEB: www.newsherald.com
SIC: 2711 Newspapers, publishing & printing
HQ: Panama City News Herald
501 W 11th St
Panama City FL 32401
850 747-5000

(G-4822)
PITTS FABRICATION LLC
617 James Lee Rd (32547-2319)
PHONE..................................850 259-4548
Joseph M Pitts Sr, *Manager*
EMP: 6 **EST:** 2018
SALES (est): 501.3K **Privately Held**
SIC: 3499 Fabricated metal products

(G-4823)
POSITIVE NOTE NETWORK
116 Maurice Ave Nw (32548-4213)
PHONE..................................712 259-1381
Joanie Beaver, *Principal*
EMP: 7 **EST:** 2017
SALES (est): 84.2K **Privately Held**
SIC: 2741 Miscellaneous publishing

(G-4824)
PROBOTIX
628 Lovejoy Rd Nw Unit 3e (32548-7023)
PHONE..................................844 472-9262
EMP: 5 **EST:** 2017
SALES (est): 333.2K **Privately Held**
SIC: 3699 Electrical equipment & supplies

(G-4825)
R4 INTEGRATION INC
45 Beal Pkwy Ne (32548-4818)
PHONE..................................850 226-6913
Vishnu Nathu, *CEO*
John Parsley, *President*
Robin Labare, *Owner*
Kellie Simpson, *Engineer*
Robert Price, *Manager*
EMP: 25 **EST:** 2008
SALES (est): 1.3MM **Privately Held**
WEB: www.r4-integration.com
SIC: 3721 3728 7373 8711 Aircraft; aircraft parts & equipment; systems engineering, computer related; aviation &/or aeronautical engineering

(G-4826)
RAYTHEON COMPANY
91 Hill Ave Nw Ste 201 (32548-7011)
PHONE..................................850 664-7993
Dennis J Picard, *Ch of Bd*
EMP: 6
SALES (corp-wide): 56.5B **Publicly Held**
WEB: www.rtx.com
SIC: 3812 4581 Search & navigation equipment; airports, flying fields & services
HQ: Raytheon Company
870 Winter St
Waltham MA 02451
781 522-3000

(G-4827)
REICO INC
95 Ready Ave Nw (32548-3848)
PHONE..................................850 243-4400
Donald Wilke, *Vice Pres*
Robert A Pomroy, *Vice Pres*
Howard L Smith, *Admin Sec*
EMP: 10 **EST:** 1969
SQ FT: 10,000
SALES (est): 256.4K **Privately Held**
WEB: www.tslinc.com
SIC: 3663 Radio & TV communications equipment

(G-4828)
RMC EWELL INC
1787 F I M Rd (32547)
PHONE..................................850 863-5040
EMP: 8
SALES (corp-wide): 15.4B **Privately Held**
SIC: 3273 3272 Manufactures Ready Mix Concrete And Concrete Pipe
HQ: Ewell Rmc Inc
801 Mccue Rd
Lakeland FL
863 688-5787

(G-4829)
ROCKY BAYOU ENTERPRISES INC
Also Called: Breeze Boat Lifts
630 Lovejoy Rd Nw (32548-3832)
P.O. Box 226, Niceville (32588-0226)
PHONE..................................850 244-4567
Gregory Teman, *Principal*
Kathleen Teman, *Officer*
EMP: 8 **EST:** 1991
SALES (est): 1MM **Privately Held**
WEB: www.breezeboatlifts.com
SIC: 3536 5551 Boat lifts; marine supplies

(G-4830)
ROGUE INDUSTRIES LLC
217 Miracle Strip Pkwy Se (32548-5819)
PHONE..................................850 797-9228
EMP: 5 **EST:** 2018
SALES (est): 378.8K **Privately Held**
SIC: 3999 Manufacturing industries

(G-4831)
ROLIN INDUSTRIES INC
94 Ready Ave Nw Unit A1 (32548-3523)
P.O. Box 1017 (32549-1017)
PHONE..................................850 654-1704
Linda K Ross, *President*
EMP: 9 **EST:** 1991
SQ FT: 5,000

GEOGRAPHIC

SALES (est): 1MM Privately Held
WEB: www.rolinindustries.com
SIC: 2399 3728 Automotive covers, except seat & tire covers; research & dev by manuf., aircraft parts & auxiliary equip

(G-4832)
SERIGRAPHIA INC
223 Troy St Ne (32548-4483)
PHONE..................................850 243-9743
Greg Keith, *President*
Wendy Aplin, *Office Mgr*
EMP: 20 EST: 1979
SQ FT: 23,000
SALES (est): 523K Privately Held
WEB: www.serigraphia.com
SIC: 2396 Screen printing on fabric articles

(G-4833)
SUN COAST CONVERTERS INC
Also Called: Suncoast Diesel
631 Anchors St Nw (32548-3803)
PHONE..................................850 864-2361
Ronald W Wolverton, *President*
Joan M Webb, *President*
Joe F Penn Jr, *Vice Pres*
Jimmy Chatwell, *Manager*
Luther Taylor, *Manager*
▲ EMP: 8 EST: 1989
SALES (est): 1.5MM Privately Held
WEB: www.suncoastdiesel.com
SIC: 3714 Rebuilding engines & transmissions, factory basis

(G-4834)
TECHNICAL SERVICE LABS INC
Also Called: Tsl-Reico
95 Ready Ave Nw (32548-3800)
PHONE..................................850 243-3722
Andrew J Corbin, *President*
Julia G Gordon, *Corp Secy*
Petropoulos Peter, *Director*
EMP: 34 EST: 1971
SQ FT: 12,000
SALES (est): 1.2MM Privately Held
WEB: www.tslinc.com
SIC: 3679 Electronic circuits

(G-4835)
TECHNOLOGIES DRS UNMANNED INC
645 Anchors St Nw (32548-3803)
PHONE..................................850 302-3909
Mark Newman, *President*
Joe Hart, *Vice Pres*
Nina L Dunn, *Admin Sec*
EMP: 96 EST: 1998
SQ FT: 191,000
SALES (est): 6.7MM
SALES (corp-wide): 10.2B Privately Held
WEB: www.leonardodrs.com
SIC: 3812 Search & navigation equipment
HQ: Leonardo Drs, Inc.
2345 Crystal Dr Ste 1000
Arlington VA 22202
703 416-8000

(G-4836)
UTILIS USA LLC
36 Tupelo Ave Se (32548-5435)
PHONE..................................850 226-7043
Thomas Eggers,
Danny Jura,
EMP: 6 EST: 2006
SQ FT: 13,000
SALES (est): 574.5K Privately Held
WEB: www.uts-systems.com
SIC: 2394 Canvas & related products

(G-4837)
UTS SYSTEMS LLC
36 Tupelo Ave Se Ste A (32548-5435)
PHONE..................................850 226-4301
Aaron Williams, *Production*
Thomas Eggers,
EMP: 7 EST: 2014
SALES (est): 2.1MM Privately Held
WEB: www.uts-systems.com
SIC: 2394 7373 8733 3721 Tents: made from purchased materials; computer integrated systems design; noncommercial research organizations; research & development on aircraft by the manufacturer; commercial physical research

(G-4838)
VER-VAL ENTERPRISES INC
Also Called: Vve
646 Anchors St Nw Ste 8 (32548-7002)
P.O. Box 4550 (32549-4550)
PHONE..................................850 244-7931
Nathaniel Smith Jr, *President*
Rufus Willis, *General Mgr*
Jannie V Smith, *Corp Secy*
Leroy H Harris, *Opers Mgr*
▲ EMP: 10 EST: 1979
SQ FT: 10,000
SALES (est): 1.9MM Privately Held
WEB: www.verval.biz
SIC: 3444 3429 7699 3535 Sheet metal specialties, not stamped; aircraft hardware; aircraft & heavy equipment repair services; conveyors & conveying equipment; aircraft parts & equipment; trailers & trailer equipment

(G-4839)
WALIN TOOLS LLC
642a Anchors St Nw (32548-3861)
PHONE..................................850 226-8632
Michael Neau, *Manager*
Linda Swadling,
EMP: 6 EST: 2008
SALES (est): 500K Privately Held
WEB: www.walintools.com
SIC: 3541 Machine tools, metal cutting type

(G-4840)
WILL WATSON CONSTRUCTION LLC ✪
464 Kanuha Dr (32547-5025)
PHONE..................................850 586-5349
Justin Watson,
EMP: 6 EST: 2020
SALES (est): 300K Privately Held
SIC: 1389 Construction, repair & dismantling services

(G-4841)
WOLVERINE ENGINES
108 Patrick Dr (32547-6766)
PHONE..................................850 462-4160
EMP: 6 EST: 2019
SALES (est): 162.2K Privately Held
WEB: www.turnkeycrateengines.com
SIC: 3569 General industrial machinery

Fort White
Columbia County

(G-4842)
ADVENT GLASS WORKS INC
242 Sw George Gln (32038-8280)
P.O. Box 174 (32038-0174)
PHONE..................................386 497-2050
EMP: 5 EST: 1974
SALES: 350K Privately Held
SIC: 3231 Mfg Products-Purchased Glass

(G-4843)
ENGEDI SPECIALITIES INC
429 Sw Greenwood Ter (32038-8855)
PHONE..................................386 497-1010
EMP: 5
SALES (est): 559.2K Privately Held
SIC: 3353 Mfg Aluminum Sheet/Foil

Freeport
Walton County

(G-4844)
ARSENAL DEMOCRACY LLC
48 Commerce Ln Ste 7 (32439-4557)
PHONE..................................850 296-2122
James P Pechi, *Mng Member*
EMP: 10 EST: 2013
SALES (est): 223.2K Privately Held
WEB: www.arsenaldemocracy.us
SIC: 3484 Machine guns & grenade launchers; guns (firearms) or gun parts, 30 mm. & below

(G-4845)
FLAMINGO PAVERS INC
289 Tropical Way (32439-4789)
PHONE..................................850 974-0094
Alberto M Soares Jr, *President*
EMP: 21 EST: 2005
SALES (est): 1.4MM Privately Held
SIC: 2951 Asphalt paving mixtures & blocks

(G-4846)
FREEPORT TRUSS COMPANY INC
16676 Us Highway 331 S (32439-4101)
PHONE..................................850 835-4541
Keven O Logan, *President*
A O Logan, *Vice Pres*
EMP: 16 EST: 1984
SQ FT: 1,600
SALES (est): 208.3K Privately Held
SIC: 2439 Trusses, wooden roof; trusses, except roof: laminated lumber

(G-4847)
G & S BOATS INC
143 Yacht Dr (32439-3508)
P.O. Box 489 (32439-0489)
PHONE..................................850 835-7700
Curtis Gentry, *President*
Steve Sauer, *Vice Pres*
Marcy Graves, *Manager*
EMP: 10 EST: 1973
SQ FT: 11,999
SALES (est): 679.6K Privately Held
WEB: www.gandsboats.com
SIC: 3732 5551 Yachts, building & repairing; boat dealers

(G-4848)
GREEN AIR GROUP LLC
Also Called: Green Air Controls
902 State Highway 20 E # 104 (32439-3912)
PHONE..................................850 608-3065
Jonathan Michael Green, *Principal*
EMP: 60 EST: 2015
SALES (est): 7.9MM Privately Held
WEB: www.greenairgroup.com
SIC: 3585 Refrigeration & heating equipment

(G-4849)
GULFSTREAM SHIPBUILDING LLC
116 Shipyard Rd (32439-4091)
PHONE..................................850 835-5125
Stuart Reeves, *Mng Member*
EMP: 7 EST: 2013
SALES (est): 317.3K Privately Held
WEB: www.gulfstreamshipyard.net
SIC: 3731 Shipbuilding & repairing

(G-4850)
HI-TEC LABORATORIES INC
9646 State Highway 20 W (32439-2122)
P.O. Box 7068, Destin (32540-7068)
PHONE..................................850 835-6822
John J Magee, *President*
EMP: 48 EST: 1993
SQ FT: 10,000
SALES (est): 1.5MM Privately Held
SIC: 2819 5169 Industrial inorganic chemicals; chemicals & allied products

(G-4851)
PROLINE CHEMICAL & PLASTICS LL
9646 State Highway 20 W (32439-2122)
PHONE..................................850 835-6822
EMP: 9 EST: 2017
SALES (est): 731.9K Privately Held
SIC: 2899 Chemical preparations

(G-4852)
SUPERIOR DOOR WORKS & MORE LLC
37 Caswell Branch Rd (32439-3471)
PHONE..................................850 880-6579
Christy Curnham, *Principal*
EMP: 6 EST: 2010
SALES (est): 137.9K Privately Held
WEB: www.superiordoorworks.com
SIC: 2431 Millwork

(G-4853)
VERONICAS HEALTH CRUNCH LLC
88 Fanny Ann Way (32439-7607)
PHONE..................................352 409-1124
Veronica L Geist, *Principal*
Veronica Geist, *Mng Member*
EMP: 6 EST: 2011
SALES (est): 278.3K Privately Held
WEB: www.veronicashealthcrunch.com
SIC: 2068 Salted & roasted nuts & seeds

(G-4854)
WOODWARDS CABINETS INC
Also Called: Woodwards Custom Cabinets
17921 Us Highway 331 S (32439-9810)
PHONE..................................850 835-0071
Scott Woodward, *Owner*
EMP: 6 EST: 1988
SQ FT: 3,000
SALES (est): 456K Privately Held
WEB: www.woodwardcabinetsinc.com
SIC: 2434 Wood kitchen cabinets

Frostproof
Polk County

(G-4855)
BEN HILL GRIFFIN INC (PA)
Also Called: GRIFFIN FERTILIZER CO
700 S Scenic Hwy Fl 33843 (33843-2443)
P.O. Box 127 (33843-0127)
PHONE..................................863 635-2281
Ben Hill Griffin III, *Ch of Bd*
Ben Hill Griffin IV, *President*
Eugene Mooney, *Exec VP*
Mike Roberts, *Vice Pres*
Aaron Belcher, *Opers Staff*
▲ EMP: 40 EST: 1943
SQ FT: 100,000
SALES: 75.5MM Privately Held
WEB: www.griffinfertilizer.com
SIC: 2875 0174 2033 Fertilizers, mixing only; citrus fruits; fruits: packaged in cans, jars, etc.

(G-4856)
BEN HILL GRIFFIN INC
Griffin Fertilizer Co
72 North Ave (33843-2527)
P.O. Box 188 (33843-0188)
PHONE..................................863 635-2281
Stuart Hurst, *CFO*
Jesse Wooten, *Manager*
EMP: 83
SQ FT: 43,156
SALES (corp-wide): 75.5MM Privately Held
WEB: www.griffinfertilizer.com
SIC: 2875 2879 2873 Fertilizers, mixing only; agricultural chemicals; nitrogenous fertilizers
PA: Ben Hill Griffin, Inc.
700 S Scenic Hwy Fl 33843
Frostproof FL 33843
863 635-2281

(G-4857)
COOK MANUFACTURING GROUP INC
100 E 7th St (33843)
P.O. Box 1175 (33843-1175)
PHONE..................................863 546-6183
Charles Cook, *President*
Vicki Cook, *Vice Pres*
Seth W Turlington, *Vice Pres*
Brian Carruth, *Supervisor*
◆ EMP: 15 EST: 1986
SALES (est): 4.7MM Privately Held
WEB: www.cookmanufacturing.com
SIC: 3585 Evaporative condensers, heat transfer equipment

(G-4858)
CORNELIUS WELDING INC
Also Called: Cwi Industrial Services
221 N Scenic Hwy (33843-2119)
P.O. Box 1104 (33843-1104)
PHONE..................................863 635-3668
Donald L Cornelius, *President*
EMP: 20 EST: 1997
SQ FT: 2,700

▲ = Import ▼=Export
◆ =Import/Export

SALES (est): 2MM Privately Held
WEB: www.cwi-industrial.com
SIC: 7692 Welding repair

(G-4859)
D C INC PRTBLE WLDG FBRICATION
3971 Mammoth Grove Rd (33843)
PHONE....863 533-4483
Don Dumire, *President*
Charlotte Dumire, *Vice Pres*
EMP: 6 EST: 1996
SQ FT: 10,000
SALES (est): 794.8K Privately Held
WEB: www.dcportablewelding.com
SIC: 3444 1799 Sheet metalwork; welding on site

(G-4860)
JUICE TYME INC
Also Called: Bevolution Group
500 S Lake Reedy Blvd (33843-2340)
PHONE....631 424-2850
Dennis Paldin, *Regional Mgr*
EMP: 7
SALES (corp-wide): 2MM Privately Held
WEB: www.bevolutiongroup.com
SIC: 2037 2033 Frozen fruits & vegetables; canned fruits & specialties
HQ: Juice Tyme, Inc.
4401 S Oakley Ave
Chicago IL 60609
773 579-1291

(G-4861)
LEMON-X CORPORATION
Also Called: Bevolution Group
500 S Lake Reedy Blvd (33843-2340)
PHONE....863 635-8400
James Grassi, *Ch of Bd*
Sonia Grassi, *Corp Secy*
Robert Londono, *Plant Mgr*
Daniel Brennan, *Prdtn Mgr*
Luis Gutierrez, *Research*
◆ EMP: 7 EST: 1972
SALES (est): 56K
SALES (corp-wide): 2MM Privately Held
WEB: www.bevolutiongroup.com
SIC: 2087 Cocktail mixes, nonalcoholic
PA: Lx/Jt Intermediate Holdings Inc
4401 S Oakley Ave
Chicago IL 60609
773 369-2652

(G-4862)
NUCOR STEEL FLORIDA INC
22 Nucor Dr (33843)
PHONE....863 546-5800
David A Sumoski, *President*
Tomas A Miller, *Vice Pres*
Brian L Barbery, *Treasurer*
Rae A Eagle, *Admin Sec*
EMP: 5 EST: 2018
SALES (est): 3.7MM
SALES (corp-wide): 20.1B Publicly Held
WEB: www.nucor.com
SIC: 3312 Blast furnaces & steel mills
PA: Nucor Corporation
1915 Rexford Rd Ste 400
Charlotte NC 28211
704 366-7000

(G-4863)
QUALITY PETROLEUM CORP
301 Hwy 630 E (33843-1739)
PHONE....863 635-6708
Shane Weeks, *Owner*
EMP: 6 EST: 2011
SALES (est): 158.9K Privately Held
WEB: www.qualitypetroleum.tripod.com
SIC: 2911 Petroleum refining

Fruitland Park
Lake County

(G-4864)
CUSTOM TIN WORKS LLC
5318 James Rd (34731-6109)
PHONE....352 728-1788
Anthony Cuellar Jr, *Principal*
EMP: 6 EST: 2012
SALES (est): 209.9K Privately Held
SIC: 3356 Tin

(G-4865)
HOME ART CORPORATION
2408 Us Highway 441/27 (34731-2128)
P.O. Box 637 (34731-0637)
PHONE....352 326-3337
Gregory L Kimes, *President*
Jeffrey L Myers, *Corp Secy*
EMP: 16 EST: 1982
SQ FT: 12,790
SALES (est): 1MM Privately Held
WEB: www.homeartcabinets.com
SIC: 2512 2434 Upholstered household furniture; vanities, bathroom: wood

Gainesville
Alachua County

(G-4866)
352INK CORP
Also Called: Allegra Gainesville
327 Nw 23rd Ave Ste 1-4 (32609-8615)
PHONE....352 373-7547
Donald Bailey, *President*
Donald W Bailey, *President*
Karen D Bailey, *Vice Pres*
Karen Bailey, *Vice Pres*
Karen D Bailey, *Vice Pres*
EMP: 5 EST: 1984
SQ FT: 3,000
SALES (est): 500K Privately Held
SIC: 2752 7334 Commercial printing, offset; photocopying & duplicating services

(G-4867)
ACTIONABLE QUALITY ASSURANCE
747 Sw 2nd Ave Ste 170 (32601-7160)
PHONE....352 562-0005
John King, *COO*
Bruce Perkin, *Consultant*
Jacob Rabb, *Info Tech Mgr*
Yuly Virviescas, *Director*
EMP: 11 EST: 2017
SALES (est): 164.5K Privately Held
WEB: www.actionableqa.com
SIC: 7372 Prepackaged software

(G-4868)
AESTHETIC PRINT & DESIGN INC
2618 Ne 18th Ter (32609-3263)
PHONE....352 278-3714
Jonathan M Hamilton, *Director*
EMP: 8 EST: 2005
SALES (est): 210.8K Privately Held
WEB: www.aestheticprint.com
SIC: 2752 Commercial printing, offset

(G-4869)
AGAROSE UNLIMITED INC
707 Nw 13th St (32601-4918)
P.O. Box 817, Alachua (32616-0817)
PHONE....800 850-0659
EMP: 5
SALES (est): 350K Privately Held
SIC: 2899 Suppliers Of Multipurpose Molecular Biology Grade Agarose

(G-4870)
AJB ENTERPRISES OF FLORIDA
9332 Nw 15th Pl (32606-5580)
PHONE....352 331-9569
Fax: 352 495-2969
EMP: 6
SQ FT: 3,000
SALES (est): 125K Privately Held
SIC: 2541 Mfg Wood Partitions/Fixtures

(G-4871)
AKIRA WOOD INC
619 S Main St Ste A (32601-6700)
PHONE....352 375-0691
Hoch Shitama, *President*
Paul Goble, *Project Mgr*
Chip Sawyer, *Design Engr*
Gale Clark, *Treasurer*
Dave Sapp, *Manager*
EMP: 35
SQ FT: 32,000
SALES: 7.3MM Privately Held
WEB: www.akirawood.com
SIC: 2431 Millwork

(G-4872)
ALLFAST FASTENER T
3464 Nw 49th Ave (32605-1070)
PHONE....352 727-8464
EMP: 7 EST: 2019
SALES (est): 70.7K Privately Held
WEB: www.allfastsupply.com
SIC: 3965 Fasteners

(G-4873)
ALTA SYSTEMS INC
6825 Nw 18th Dr (32653-1613)
PHONE....352 372-2534
Jane Er Nesbit, *President*
Richard B Nesbit, *Vice Pres*
Alan Chaset, *Project Dir*
Jasmin Nelson, *Sales Staff*
▼ EMP: 42 EST: 1983
SQ FT: 14,900
SALES (est): 7.5MM Privately Held
WEB: www.altainc.com
SIC: 2752 2791 Commercial printing, offset; typesetting

(G-4874)
AMERICAN OPTIMAL DECISIONS INC
4014 Sw 98th Ter (32608-4662)
PHONE....352 278-2034
Stan Uryasev, *President*
EMP: 7 EST: 2008
SALES (est): 387.5K Privately Held
WEB: www.aorda.com
SIC: 7372 Prepackaged software

(G-4875)
ARGOS
924 S Main St (32601-2025)
PHONE....352 376-6491
Matt Carcaba, *President*
EMP: 12 EST: 2015
SALES (est): 1.5MM Privately Held
WEB: www.argos-us.com
SIC: 3273 Ready-mixed concrete

(G-4876)
ARMALASER INC
5200 Nw 43rd St (32606-4484)
PHONE....800 680-5020
Mary Lou Price, *Principal*
EMP: 9 EST: 2016
SALES (est): 707.5K Privately Held
WEB: www.armalaser.com
SIC: 3949 Sporting & athletic goods

(G-4877)
ASAP SCREEN PRINTING INC
4641 Nw 6th St Ste A (32609-1700)
PHONE....352 505-7574
Larry E Watts, *Principal*
Scott Ronn, *Vice Pres*
EMP: 6 EST: 2006
SALES (est): 400K Privately Held
WEB: www.screenprintingasap.com
SIC: 2759 Screen printing

(G-4878)
ASCENDANTS PUBLISHING LLC
626 Se 2nd Pl Apt 3 (32601-6876)
PHONE....813 391-2745
Vijaya Seixas, *Principal*
EMP: 7 EST: 2016
SALES (est): 41.3K Privately Held
SIC: 2741 Miscellaneous publishing

(G-4879)
ATKINS TECHNICAL INC
6911 Nw 22nd St Ste B (32653-1253)
PHONE....860 349-3473
Carol P Wallace, *President*
Jay McEvoy, *Sales Staff*
Carol Duplessis, *Admin Sec*
EMP: 32 EST: 1957
SALES (est): 528.3K Privately Held
WEB: www.cooper-atkins.com
SIC: 3823 Temperature instruments: industrial process type; humidity instruments, industrial process type

(G-4880)
ATRIS TECHNOLOGY LLC
3417 Nw 97th Blvd Ste 30 (32606-7376)
PHONE....352 331-3100
Lon Davis, *CEO*
Michael Simmons, *Accounts Exec*
Frank Sirmons, *CTO*
Dan Roberts, *Info Tech Dir*
Mauricio Goez, *Technology*
EMP: 12 EST: 1995
SALES (est): 1.2MM Privately Held
WEB: www.atris.com
SIC: 7372 7371 Application computer software; custom computer programming services

(G-4881)
BALLS ROD & KUSTOM LLC
5118 Nw 24th Dr (32605-6227)
PHONE....888 446-2191
Jun A Evangelista, *Principal*
EMP: 9 EST: 2008
SALES (est): 343.8K Privately Held
WEB: www.ballsrodandkustom.com
SIC: 3714 Motor vehicle parts & accessories

(G-4882)
BANYAN BIOMARKERS INC (PA)
132 Nw 76th Dr Ste B (32607-6677)
PHONE....760 710-0460
Henry L Nordhoff, *Ch of Bd*
Steven Richieri, *President*
Maxwell Minch, *Counsel*
Michael Catania, *Vice Pres*
Veronika Shevchenko, *Research*
EMP: 3 EST: 2002
SQ FT: 6,000
SALES (est): 8MM Privately Held
WEB: www.banyanbio.com
SIC: 2835 8731 In vitro diagnostics; biotechnical research, commercial

(G-4883)
BARR SYSTEMS LLC
6241 Nw 23rd St Ste 401 (32653-7110)
PHONE....352 491-3100
Anthony Barr,
EMP: 30
SQ FT: 53,103
SALES (est): 3.8MM Privately Held
WEB: www.barrsystems.com
SIC: 3429 3695 Cabinet hardware; computer software tape & disks: blank, rigid & floppy

(G-4884)
BATH JUNKIE OF GAINESVILLE
7529 Nw 136th St (32653-2474)
PHONE....352 331-3012
Cindy Futral, *CEO*
EMP: 5
SALES (est): 496.8K Privately Held
SIC: 3087 Custom compound purchased resins

(G-4885)
BELLEAIRE PRESS LLC
10000 Sw 52nd Ave Apt 171 (32608-8303)
PHONE....352 377-1870
Tracy D Connors, *Manager*
EMP: 6 EST: 2004
SALES (est): 168.2K Privately Held
WEB: www.belleairepress.com
SIC: 2741 Miscellaneous publishing

(G-4886)
BIGG WILLS WHEELS LLC
125 Nw 23rd Ave Ste D (32609-8611)
PHONE....352 222-6170
William Henderson, *Mng Member*
EMP: 7 EST: 2012
SALES (est): 536.4K Privately Held
WEB: www.bwwcustoms.com
SIC: 3312 Wheels

(G-4887)
BLACK COLLEGE MONTHLY INC
901 Se 18th Ter (32641-9429)
PHONE....352 335-5771
Charles Goston, *Founder*
EMP: 7 EST: 1983
SALES (est): 111.6K Privately Held
SIC: 2721 Magazines: publishing & printing

(G-4888)
BLUAZU LLC
101 Se 2nd Pl Ste 201b (32601-6591)
PHONE....386 697-3743
Richard Allen, *CEO*
James Davis, *Vice Pres*
Jon Stevens, *Senior Engr*

GEOGRAPHIC

EMP: 12 EST: 2013
SALES (est): 1.3MM Privately Held
WEB: www.findmyscout.com
SIC: 3663 Radio & TV communications equipment;

(G-4889)
BOSSHARDT REALTY
5111 Sw 94th St (32608-4175)
PHONE 352 494-1400
Linda Heshmat, *Principal*
EMP: 7 EST: 2006
SALES (est): 54.1K Privately Held
WEB: www.susanbaird.com
SIC: 2431 Millwork

(G-4890)
BUSINESS REPORT OF N CNTRL FL
1314 S Main St (32601-7921)
PHONE 352 275-9469
Scott Schroeder, *Principal*
EMP: 9 EST: 2014
SALES (est): 139.3K Privately Held
WEB: www.gainesvillebizreport.com
SIC: 2711 Newspapers, publishing & printing

(G-4891)
CADUCEUS INTERNATIONAL PUBG
100 Sw 75th St Ste 206 (32607-5777)
PHONE 866 280-2900
Ryan Fagerberg, *President*
Seigfred Fagerberg, *Vice Pres*
Laura Fields, *Controller*
Kristin Polhill, *Accounts Mgr*
Rachel Seaman, *Assistant*
EMP: 10 EST: 2004
SALES (est): 1.6MM Privately Held
WEB: www.cipcourses.com
SIC: 2741 7371 Miscellaneous publishing; computer software development & applications

(G-4892)
CARBONXT INC
3951 Nw 48th Ter Ste 111 (32606-7229)
PHONE 352 378-4950
David Mazyck, *CEO*
Jack Drwiega, *Opers Dir*
Lindsey Costin, *Engineer*
Warren Murphy, *Director*
EMP: 48 EST: 2009
SALES (est): 5.1MM Privately Held
WEB: www.carbonxt.com
SIC: 2819 Charcoal (carbon), activated

(G-4893)
CARDINAL SIGNS INC
6342 Nw 18th Dr Ste 1 (32653-1680)
PHONE 352 376-8494
Paul Randall, *Principal*
EMP: 7 EST: 2006
SALES (est): 155.8K Privately Held
WEB: www.cardinalsigns.net
SIC: 3993 Signs & advertising specialties

(G-4894)
CEMENT PRECAST PRODUCTS INC
2033 Ne 27th Ave (32609-3379)
PHONE 352 372-0953
Michael Harper, *President*
Pat Clark, *Principal*
Jeff Stanford, *Manager*
EMP: 25 EST: 1958
SALES (est): 2.7MM Privately Held
WEB: www.precastfl.com
SIC: 3272 3446 3442 Concrete products, precast; architectural metalwork; metal doors, sash & trim

(G-4895)
CONRAD YELVINGTON DISTRS INC
7605 Nw 13th St (32653-1114)
PHONE 352 336-5049
Jeff Wells, *Principal*
EMP: 7
SALES (corp-wide): 109.9MM Privately Held
WEB: www.cydi.com
SIC: 3295 5261 5032 Perlite, aggregate or expanded; sod; sand, construction
PA: Conrad Yelvington Distributors, Inc.
2328 Bellevue Ave
Daytona Beach FL 32114
386 257-5504

(G-4896)
CONVERGENT ENGINEERING INC
100 Sw 75th St Ste 106 (32607-5775)
PHONE 352 378-4899
Neil R Euliano, *Director*
Thomas Heimann, *Administration*
EMP: 16 EST: 2004
SALES (est): 1.1MM Privately Held
WEB: www.conveng.com
SIC: 3674 Semiconductors & related devices

(G-4897)
CORDAROYS WHOLESALE INC (PA)
3421 W University Ave (32607-2402)
PHONE 352 332-1837
Byron Young, *President*
Jerry Lewicki, *CFO*
John Gassert, *Admin Sec*
▲ EMP: 5 EST: 2000
SQ FT: 6,000
SALES (est): 1MM Privately Held
WEB: www.cordaroys.com
SIC: 2519 5712 ; furniture stores

(G-4898)
CORPORATE ONE HUNDRED INC
Also Called: Tel Test
605 Nw 53rd Ave Ste A17 (32609-1020)
PHONE 352 335-0901
Ezequiel Zetien, *President*
EMP: 21 EST: 1974
SQ FT: 6,000
SALES (est): 5.3MM Privately Held
SIC: 3825 8711 Engine electrical test equipment; engineering services

(G-4899)
COUNTRY SIDE T-SHIRT
2025 Ne County Road 234 (32641-2609)
PHONE 352 372-1015
Theresa Hutchinson, *Owner*
EMP: 6 EST: 1992
SALES (est): 113.9K Privately Held
WEB: www.westside-t-shirts.com
SIC: 2759 Screen printing

(G-4900)
CROM CORPORATION (PA)
250 Sw 36th Ter (32607-2889)
PHONE 352 372-3436
James D Copley Jr, *President*
Stephen Crawford, *President*
Evan Burton, *Superintendent*
Buddy Williams, *Superintendent*
Lars J Balck, *Senior VP*
▲ EMP: 445 EST: 1930
SQ FT: 13,000
SALES (est): 97.1MM Privately Held
WEB: www.cromcorp.com
SIC: 3272 Concrete products

(G-4901)
CYBERTEK COMPUTER SYSTEMS INC
Also Called: Cybertek Computer Solutions
607 Nw 13th St (32601-4975)
P.O. Box 13738 (32604-1738)
PHONE 352 373-9923
Michael Mansingh, *Principal*
EMP: 5 EST: 1995
SALES (est): 472.2K Privately Held
SIC: 7372 7378 5734 Prepackaged software; computer maintenance & repair; computer & software stores

(G-4902)
CYCLO THERAPEUTICS INC (PA)
6714 Nw 16th St Ste B (32653-3975)
P.O. Box 1180, Alachua (32616-1180)
PHONE 386 418-8060
N Scott Fine, *CEO*
Jeffrey L Tate, *COO*
Sharon H Hrynkow, *Senior VP*
Michael Lisjak, *Vice Pres*
Joshua M Fine, *CFO*
EMP: 7 EST: 1992
SQ FT: 2,500
SALES (est): 903.3K Publicly Held
WEB: www.cyclotherapeutics.com
SIC: 2834 Pharmaceutical preparations

(G-4903)
DAILY GREEN
436 Se 2nd St (32601-6772)
PHONE 352 226-8288
EMP: 7 EST: 2013
SALES (est): 129.2K Privately Held
WEB: www.dailygreendowntown.org
SIC: 2711 Newspapers, publishing & printing

(G-4904)
DATAGRID INC
4111 Nw 6th St Ste D (32609-0730)
PHONE 352 371-7608
Bo Gustafson, *President*
EMP: 6 EST: 1999
SQ FT: 3,000
SALES (est): 559.9K Privately Held
WEB: www.datagrid-gnss.com
SIC: 3829 Surveying instruments & accessories

(G-4905)
DIGI-NET TECHNOLOGIES INC (PA)
Also Called: Digichat
4420 Nw 36th Ave Ste A (32606-7222)
PHONE 352 505-7450
Robert Parker, *President*
Todd Chase, *COO*
R Todd Johnson, *Vice Pres*
EMP: 33 EST: 1999
SQ FT: 8,000
SALES (est): 3.9MM Privately Held
WEB: www.digi-net.com
SIC: 7372 4813 Prepackaged software;

(G-4906)
DOCKSIDE AT HORSESHOE BEACH L
6809 Nw 48th Ln (32653-3953)
PHONE 352 377-4616
Frank Darabi, *Principal*
EMP: 7 EST: 2005
SALES (est): 118.9K Privately Held
SIC: 3462 Horseshoes

(G-4907)
DOUBLE ENVELOPE CORPORATION
Also Called: BSC Ventures
2500 Ne 39th Ave (32609-2098)
PHONE 352 375-0738
Brian Sass, *CEO*
Fred G Tucker Jr, *President*
Dalton Miller, *Senior VP*
William Britts, *Vice Pres*
Mike Rubyor, *Accounts Exec*
EMP: 315 EST: 1927
SQ FT: 85,000
SALES (est): 52.1MM
SALES (corp-wide): 126.1MM Privately Held
WEB: www.double-envelope.com
SIC: 2677 Envelopes
HQ: Bsc Ventures Llc
7702 Plantation Rd
Roanoke VA 24019
540 362-3311

(G-4908)
DOUBLE HEADER LLC
3015 Nw 38th St (32606-8119)
PHONE 352 377-4458
Clifford Bickford, *Manager*
EMP: 6 EST: 2011
SALES (est): 14.1K Privately Held
WEB: www.doubleheaderusa.com
SIC: 3542 Headers

(G-4909)
DOWNTOWN PROJECTS I LLC
702 Nw 12th Ave (32601-4118)
PHONE 352 226-8288
Adam Reinhard, *Principal*
EMP: 7 EST: 2013
SALES (est): 225.2K Privately Held
SIC: 2711 Newspapers: publishing only, not printed on site

(G-4910)
DRAGONFLY GRAPHICS INC
319 Sw 3rd Ave (32601-6561)
PHONE 352 375-2144
Joy L Revels, *President*
Joy Revels, *President*
EMP: 6 EST: 1978
SQ FT: 2,700
SALES (est): 921K Privately Held
WEB: www.dragonflygraphics.com
SIC: 2759 Screen printing

(G-4911)
DRSINGH TECHNOLOGIES INC
1912 Nw 67th Pl (32653-1649)
PHONE 352 334-7270
Deepika Singh, *President*
Rajiv K Singh, *President*
Sarah Wilson, *Business Mgr*
Lisa Skeete Tatum,
EMP: 15 EST: 2000
SQ FT: 6,000
SALES (est): 4MM Privately Held
SIC: 7372 Business oriented computer software

(G-4912)
EASYDRIFT LLC
13100 Nw 50th Ave (32606-3561)
PHONE 352 318-3683
Louis Callard, *General Mgr*
▲ EMP: 9 EST: 2009
SALES (est): 364.6K Privately Held
WEB: www.easydriftusa.com
SIC: 3999 Education aids, devices & supplies

(G-4913)
EJCO INC
Also Called: Xerographic Copy Center
927 Nw 13th St (32601-4141)
PHONE 352 375-0797
Eric Hall, *President*
Eric Hill, *President*
Carolyne Salt, *Sales Staff*
Jamie Ault, *Admin Sec*
EMP: 6 EST: 2002
SQ FT: 2,100
SALES (est): 857.1K Privately Held
WEB: www.xerographicgainesville.com
SIC: 2752 Commercial printing, offset

(G-4914)
ELISA TECHNOLOGIES INC
2501 Nw 66th Ct (32653-1693)
PHONE 352 337-3929
Natalie Rosskopf, *Vice Pres*
Bickford Justin, *Treasurer*
Justin Bickford, *Director*
Nick Lafferman, *Director*
EMP: 12 EST: 1990
SQ FT: 4,800
SALES (est): 2.2MM Privately Held
WEB: www.elisa-tek.com
SIC: 2899 8734 Food contamination testing or screening kits; food testing service

(G-4915)
ETECTRX INC
747 Sw 2nd Ave Ste 365ti (32601-6279)
PHONE 321 363-3020
Valerie Sullivan, *President*
Susan L Baumgartner, *Vice Pres*
Judd Sheets, *Engineer*
Emily Dawson, *Controller*
Harry J Travis, *Director*
EMP: 50 EST: 2017
SALES (est): 3.8MM Privately Held
WEB: www.etectrx.com
SIC: 3821 Clinical laboratory instruments, except medical & dental

(G-4916)
EXACTECH INC (HQ)
2320 Nw 66th Ct (32653-1630)
PHONE 352 377-1140
William Petty, *Ch of Bd*
Darin Johnson, *President*
Ray Langenberg, *Managing Dir*
Jeffrey R Binder, *Chairman*
Gary J Miller, *Exec VP*
▲ EMP: 578 EST: 1985
SQ FT: 206,000

▲ = Import ▼=Export
◆ =Import/Export

SALES (est): 257.5MM **Privately Held**
WEB: www.exac.com
SIC: 3842 Surgical appliances & supplies; implants, surgical; orthopedic appliances; trusses, orthopedic & surgical
PA: Osteon Holdings, Inc.
301 Commerce St Ste 3300
Fort Worth TX 76102
817 871-4000

(G-4917)
EXPLORATION SERVICES LLC
4440 Ne 41st Ter (32609-1684)
PHONE..................................352 505-3578
Matt Cannon, *General Mgr*
Craig Bell, *Mng Member*
Randal Ferrell, *Manager*
EMP: 6 **EST:** 2009
SALES (est): 1.3MM **Privately Held**
WEB: www.explorationservicesllc.com
SIC: 1382 8999 Oil & gas exploration services; search & rescue service

(G-4918)
FABCO-AIR INC
Also Called: Bennett Company
3716 Ne 49th Ave (32609-1686)
P.O. Box 5159 (32627-5159)
PHONE..................................352 373-3578
William R Schmidt, *President*
Robbie Severance, *Prdtn Mgr*
Clayton Kight, *Maint Spvr*
Mike Legrow, *QC Mgr*
Chris Schmidt, *Human Res Mgr*
▲ **EMP:** 95 **EST:** 1962
SQ FT: 61,000
SALES (est): 23.8MM
SALES (corp-wide): 3.4B **Privately Held**
WEB: www.fabco-air.com
SIC: 3542 3546 3491 Riveting machines; crimping machinery, metal; power-driven handtools; automatic regulating & control valves
HQ: Festo Corporation
1377 Motor Pkwy Ste 310
Islandia NY 11749
800 993-3786

(G-4919)
FAGERBERG INDUSTRIES LLC
100 Sw 75th St Ste 206 (32607-5777)
PHONE..................................352 318-2254
Ryan Fagerberg, *Principal*
EMP: 11 **EST:** 2009
SALES (est): 241.7K **Privately Held**
WEB: www.cipcourses.com
SIC: 3999 Manufacturing industries

(G-4920)
FLORICAL SYSTEMS INC (PA)
4500 Nw 27th Ave Ste B1 (32606-7042)
PHONE..................................352 372-8326
Jim Moneyhun, *President*
James Moneyhun, *President*
Russ Brannon, *Engineer*
Waltraud Buchanan, *Treasurer*
Jeff Halapin, *Cust Mgr*
EMP: 49 **EST:** 1977
SQ FT: 8,400
SALES (est): 4.3MM **Privately Held**
WEB: www.florical.com
SIC: 3663 Television broadcasting & communications equipment

(G-4921)
FLORIDA NORTH HEARING SOLUTION
Also Called: Mircalear
2228 Nw 44th Pl (32605-1761)
PHONE..................................386 466-0902
Greg Leon, *Vice Pres*
Chad Zandstra, *Project Engr*
David Acrell, *Sr Project Mgr*
Rick Rice, *Sr Project Mgr*
Cathy B McDermott, *Director*
EMP: 11 **EST:** 2011
SALES (est): 108.6K **Privately Held**
SIC: 3842 Hearing aids

(G-4922)
FLORIDA PROBE CORPORATION
3700 Nw 91st St Ste C100 (32606-7307)
PHONE..................................352 372-1142
Charles Gibbs, *President*
John Hirschfeld, *Vice Pres*
Ron Joos, *Vice Pres*
Samuel B Low, *Vice Pres*
Chris Gibbs, *Treasurer*
EMP: 7 **EST:** 1987
SQ FT: 1,500
SALES (est): 1MM **Privately Held**
WEB: www.floridaprobe.com
SIC: 3843 5047 Dental tools; dental equipment & supplies

(G-4923)
FOCAL POINT PUBLISHING LLC
4131 Nw 13th St Ste 200 (32609-1863)
PHONE..................................877 469-9530
Olivia Jannis,
EMP: 8 **EST:** 2018
SALES (est): 200K **Privately Held**
SIC: 2741 Miscellaneous publishing

(G-4924)
FREEMAN PALLETS INC
3530 Se Hawthorne Rd (32641-8858)
PHONE..................................352 328-9326
David Freeman, *President*
EMP: 8 **EST:** 2007
SALES (est): 483K **Privately Held**
WEB: www.freemanpallets.com
SIC: 2448 Pallets, wood

(G-4925)
GAINESVILLE
8039 Sw 67th Rd (32608-7566)
PHONE..................................352 339-0294
Amy Hackett, *Principal*
EMP: 6 **EST:** 2017
SALES (est): 259.2K **Privately Held**
WEB: www.visitgainesville.com
SIC: 2711 Newspapers, publishing & printing

(G-4926)
GAINESVILLE ICE COMPANY
Also Called: GI
508 Se 11th Ave (32601-8078)
PHONE..................................352 378-2604
Richard Bunch, *President*
Nancy Bunch, *Vice Pres*
EMP: 19 **EST:** 1973
SQ FT: 2,500
SALES (est): 5.3MM **Privately Held**
WEB: www.gainesvilleice.com
SIC: 2097 Manufactured ice

(G-4927)
GAINESVILLE IRON WORKS INC
Also Called: Gainesville Ironworks
2341 Nw 66th Ct (32653-1664)
PHONE..................................352 373-4004
Vicki Lowry, *President*
Dean Lowry, *Corp Secy*
EMP: 7 **EST:** 1984
SQ FT: 7,500
SALES (est): 1MM **Privately Held**
WEB: www.gainesvilleironworks.com
SIC: 3446 Stairs, staircases, stair treads: prefabricated metal

(G-4928)
GAINESVILLE SUN
2700 Sw 13th St (32608-2015)
PHONE..................................352 374-5000
Mickie Anderson, *Editor*
Darrell Hartman, *Editor*
Terry Tramell, *Director*
EMP: 11 **EST:** 2010
SALES (est): 568.3K **Privately Held**
WEB: www.gainesville.com
SIC: 2679 Paper products, converted

(G-4929)
GAINESVILLE SUN PUBLISHING CO (HQ)
2700 Sw 13th St (32608-2015)
PHONE..................................352 378-1411
John Fitzwater, *Publisher*
Mickie Anderson, *Editor*
Alan Festo, *Editor*
Kimberly Kanemoto, *Sales Staff*
EMP: 275 **EST:** 1876
SQ FT: 71,000
SALES (est): 36.9MM
SALES (corp-wide): 272.8MM **Privately Held**
WEB: www.gainesville.com
SIC: 2711 Commercial printing & newspaper publishing combined; newspapers, publishing & printing
PA: Halifax Media Holdings, Llc
901 6th St
Daytona Beach FL 32117
386 681-2404

(G-4930)
GAINESVILLE WLDG & FABRICATION
Also Called: Florida Handrail & Fabrication
2327 Ne 19th Dr (32609-3320)
P.O. Box 141985 (32614-1985)
PHONE..................................352 373-0384
Greg Upshaw, *Owner*
EMP: 6 **EST:** 1997
SQ FT: 6,000
SALES (est): 732.4K **Privately Held**
WEB: www.boonewelding.com
SIC: 3441 Building components, structural steel

(G-4931)
GLEIM PUBLICATIONS INC
4201 Nw 95th Blvd (32606-3741)
P.O. Box 12848 (32604-0848)
PHONE..................................352 375-0772
Irvin N Gleim, *President*
Lily Zhao, *Editor*
Larry Gleim, *Vice Pres*
Sean Derek, *Sales Staff*
Sue Hart, *Sales Staff*
◆ **EMP:** 94
SQ FT: 10,000
SALES (est): 11.4MM **Privately Held**
WEB: www.gleim.com
SIC: 2731 8249 7372 8299 Books: publishing only; aviation school; prepackaged software; airline training; catalog & mail-order houses

(G-4932)
GREENTECHNOLOGIES LLC (PA)
3926 Nw 34th Dr (32605-1475)
P.O. Box 357905 (32635-7905)
PHONE..................................352 379-7780
Marla Buchanan, *COO*
Dr Amir Varshovi, *Mng Member*
Marla K Buchanan,
▲ **EMP:** 9 **EST:** 1999
SALES (est): 2.6MM **Privately Held**
WEB: www.green-edge.com
SIC: 2873 8731 Fertilizers: natural (organic), except compost; environmental research

(G-4933)
GRIFFIS LUMBER LLC
9333 Nw 13th St (32653-1094)
PHONE..................................352 372-9965
Elizabeth Conwell, *Manager*
William Gaston,
EMP: 9 **EST:** 2013
SQ FT: 100,000
SALES (est): 877.2K **Privately Held**
WEB: www.gastonmulch.com
SIC: 2421 5199 Sawdust, shavings & wood chips; kiln drying of lumber; baling of wood shavings for mulch

(G-4934)
GUERRILLA PRESS
302 Nw 2nd Ave (32601-5265)
PHONE..................................352 281-7420
Jason Page, *Principal*
EMP: 7 **EST:** 2008
SALES (est): 86.1K **Privately Held**
WEB: www.guerrillapress.net
SIC: 2741 Miscellaneous publishing

(G-4935)
HB FULLER CNSTR PDTS INC
1913 Nw 60th Ln (32653-1648)
PHONE..................................352 372-3931
Dave Sommerness, *Branch Mgr*
EMP: 6
SALES (corp-wide): 2.7B **Publicly Held**
WEB: www.fosterproducts.com
SIC: 2891 Adhesives
HQ: H.B. Fuller Construction Products Inc.
1200 Willow Lake Blvd
Saint Paul MN 55110

(G-4936)
HIGHROLLER FISHING LURE CO LLC
4630 Nw 30th St (32605-1120)
PHONE..................................352 215-2925
Terry J Jertberg, *Owner*
EMP: 7 **EST:** 1999
SQ FT: 1,500
SALES (est): 463.3K **Privately Held**
WEB: www.highroller-lures.myshopify.com
SIC: 3949 Lures, fishing: artificial

(G-4937)
HONDURAS FOOD SERVICES INC
2337 Sw Archer Rd Apt 302 (32608-1005)
PHONE..................................310 940-2071
Carlos Adrian R Roman, *Branch Mgr*
EMP: 27
SALES (corp-wide): 87.1K **Privately Held**
WEB: www.hondurasfoodservice.com
SIC: 2599 Food wagons, restaurant
PA: Honduras Food Services, Inc.
540 Brickell Key Dr # 14
Miami FL

(G-4938)
HONEYWELL INTERNATIONAL INC
1225 Sw 25th Pl (32601-9001)
PHONE..................................352 372-4192
Roslyn Washington, *Manager*
EMP: 6
SALES (corp-wide): 32.6B **Publicly Held**
WEB: www.honeywell.com
SIC: 3724 Aircraft engines & engine parts
PA: Honeywell International Inc.
300 S Tryon St
Charlotte NC 28202
704 627-6200

(G-4939)
HYGREEN INC
3630 Sw 47th Ave Ste 100 (32608-7756)
PHONE..................................352 327-9747
Craig Davehport, *President*
Richard J Melker MD PHD, *CTO*
EMP: 11 **EST:** 2009
SQ FT: 6,000
SALES (est): 348.6K **Privately Held**
WEB: www.hygreen.com
SIC: 3841 5047 Surgical & medical instruments; medical & hospital equipment

(G-4940)
ICM PRINTING CO INC
5510 Sw 41st Blvd Ste 101 (32608-4976)
P.O. Box 141046 (32614-1046)
PHONE..................................352 377-7468
EMP: 12
SQ FT: 20,000
SALES (est): 1.2MM **Privately Held**
SIC: 2752 2791 2789 2759 Lithographic Coml Print Typesetting Services Bookbinding/Related Work Commercial Printing

(G-4941)
IGBO NETWORK LLC
5021 Nw 34th Blvd Ste D (32605-1191)
PHONE..................................352 727-4113
Victor Okorochukw, *Mng Member*
EMP: 10 **EST:** 2012
SALES (est): 268K **Privately Held**
SIC: 2741

(G-4942)
INNOVATIVE MACHINE INC
Also Called: IMI
6115 Nw 123rd Pl (32653-7999)
PHONE..................................386 418-8880
Gary Gillespie, *President*
Keith Monroe, *Vice Pres*
EMP: 10 **EST:** 1999
SQ FT: 5,000
SALES (est): 1.8MM **Privately Held**
WEB: www.imisolutions.com
SIC: 3599 Machine shop, jobbing & repair

(G-4943)
INSTABOOK CORP
12300 Nw 56th Ave (32653-3551)
PHONE....................................352 332-1311
Victor Celorio, *President*
EMP: 5 **EST:** 1997
SQ FT: 2,184
SALES (est): 445.9K **Privately Held**
WEB: www.instabook.net
SIC: 3555 Bookbinding machinery

(G-4944)
INSTY-PRINTS
327 Nw 23rd Ave (32609-8615)
PHONE....................................352 373-7547
EMP: 7 **EST:** 2019
SALES (est): 140.5K **Privately Held**
WEB: www.instyprints.com
SIC: 2752 Commercial printing, lithographic

(G-4945)
INVIVO CORPORATION (DH)
3545 Sw 47th Ave (32608-7691)
PHONE....................................301 525-9683
Stephen Lorenc, *CEO*
Stephan Hohmuth, *Engineer*
Larry Kibler, *Engineer*
Remco Steenbergen, *Treasurer*
Jerret Giammichele, *Accounts Mgr*
▲ **EMP:** 300 **EST:** 1964
SQ FT: 3,000
SALES (est): 113.9MM
SALES (corp-wide): 133.6MM **Privately Held**
WEB: www.usa.philips.com
SIC: 3841 3829 Diagnostic apparatus, medical; measuring & controlling devices
HQ: Philips Medical Systems Mr, Inc
450 Old Niskayuna Rd
Latham NY 12110
518 782-1122

(G-4946)
INVIVO CORPORATION
3600 Sw 47th Ave (32608-7555)
PHONE....................................352 336-0010
Randy Duensing, *Branch Mgr*
EMP: 35
SALES (corp-wide): 133.6MM **Privately Held**
WEB: www.usa.philips.com
SIC: 3826 3845 Magnetic resonance imaging apparatus; electromedical equipment
HQ: Invivo Corporation
3545 Sw 47th Ave
Gainesville FL 32608
301 525-9683

(G-4947)
IRVING PUBLICATIONS LLC
Also Called: Giggle Magazine
5745 Sw 75th St Unit 286 (32608-5504)
PHONE....................................352 219-4688
Nicole B Irving, *Principal*
EMP: 17 **EST:** 2011
SALES (est): 509.5K **Privately Held**
WEB: www.irvingpublications.com
SIC: 2741 Miscellaneous publishing

(G-4948)
JOHN W HOCK COMPANY
Also Called: Hock, John W Co
7409 Nw 23rd Ave (32606-6315)
PHONE....................................352 378-3209
Deborah H Focks, *President*
Dana Focks, *Vice Pres*
John Hock, *Vice Pres*
EMP: 6 **EST:** 1974
SQ FT: 2,000
SALES (est): 882.7K **Privately Held**
WEB: www.johnwhock.com
SIC: 3496 3523 Wire cloth & woven wire products; farm machinery & equipment

(G-4949)
KEVIN JEFFERS INC
Also Called: Jeffcoat Signs
1611 S Main St (32601-8608)
PHONE....................................352 377-2322
Kevin Jeffers, *President*
EMP: 9 **EST:** 1998
SALES (est): 400K **Privately Held**
WEB: www.jeffcoatsigns.com
SIC: 3993 7389 Electric signs; sign painting & lettering shop

(G-4950)
LARRYS MOBILCRETE INC
1104 Nw 50th Ave Ste A (32609-0728)
PHONE....................................352 336-2525
EMP: 7
SALES (est): 520K **Privately Held**
SIC: 3273 Mfg Ready-Mixed Concrete

(G-4951)
LARSON INDUSTRIES
409 Sw 4th Ave (32601-6551)
PHONE....................................352 226-8512
EMP: 6 **EST:** 2018
SALES (est): 266.6K **Privately Held**
SIC: 3999 Manufacturing industries

(G-4952)
LARSON INDUSTRIES INCORPORATED (PA)
409 Sw 4th Ave (32601-6551)
P.O. Box 14715 (32604-4715)
PHONE....................................352 262-0566
Tim Larson, *Principal*
EMP: 17 **EST:** 2012
SALES (est): 388.6K **Privately Held**
SIC: 3999 Manufacturing industries

(G-4953)
LEGACY VULCAN LLC
924 S Main St (32601-2025)
P.O. Box 4667, Ocala (34478-4667)
PHONE....................................352 376-2182
Rick Monghane, *Manager*
EMP: 7
SQ FT: 1,176 **Publicly Held**
WEB: www.vulcanmaterials.com
SIC: 3273 Ready-mixed concrete
HQ: Legacy Vulcan, Llc
1200 Urban Center Dr
Vestavia AL 35242
205 298-3000

(G-4954)
LENNOX INTERNATIONAL INC
605 Nw 53rd Ave Ste A4 (32609-1019)
PHONE....................................352 379-9630
Sanjeev Hingorani, *Manager*
EMP: 9
SALES (corp-wide): 3.6B **Publicly Held**
WEB: www.lennoxinternational.com
SIC: 3585 Refrigeration & heating equipment
PA: Lennox International Inc.
2140 Lake Park Blvd
Richardson TX 75080
972 497-5000

(G-4955)
LITTLE RIVER MARINE
250 Se 10th Ave (32601-7143)
PHONE....................................352 378-5025
William Larson, *Owner*
◆ **EMP:** 8 **EST:** 1977
SALES (est): 1.2MM **Privately Held**
WEB: www.littlerivermarine.com
SIC: 3732 5551 Boats, fiberglass: building & repairing; boat dealers

(G-4956)
MAUPIN HOUSE PUBLISHING INC
2300 Nw 71st Pl (32653-1622)
PHONE....................................800 524-0634
Julia C Graddy, *President*
Robert H Graddy, *Vice Pres*
▲ **EMP:** 5
SQ FT: 13,800
SALES (est): 648.7K **Privately Held**
SIC: 2731 Books: publishing only

(G-4957)
MCCALLUM CABINETS INC
3004 Ne 21st Way (32609-3341)
PHONE....................................352 372-2344
Thomas C McCallum, *President*
Gene McCallum, *Shareholder*
EMP: 14 **EST:** 1982
SQ FT: 5,000
SALES (est): 1.4MM **Privately Held**
WEB: www.mccallumcabinets.com
SIC: 2521 2541 2517 2511 Wood office furniture; wood partitions & fixtures; wood television & radio cabinets; wood household furniture; wood kitchen cabinets

(G-4958)
MCCLUNEYS ORTHPD PRSTHETIS SVC
Also Called: McCluneys Orthpd Prsthtic Srvi
2930 Nw 16th Ave (32605-3733)
PHONE....................................352 373-5754
T Howard Mc Cluney, *President*
Janie Mc Cluney, *Vice Pres*
EMP: 5 **EST:** 1982
SQ FT: 2,000
SALES (est): 449.9K **Privately Held**
SIC: 3842 Orthopedic appliances

(G-4959)
MEDIA EDGE COMMUNICATIONS LLC
Also Called: Media Edge Publishing
3951 Nw 48th Ter Ste 219 (32606-7230)
PHONE....................................352 313-6700
Kevin Brown,
Riquan Liu, *Admin Asst*
EMP: 8 **EST:** 2004
SALES (est): 1MM
SALES (corp-wide): 7MM **Privately Held**
WEB: www.mecgnv.com
SIC: 2741 Miscellaneous publishing
PA: Media Edge Communications Inc
2001 Sheppard Ave E Suite 500
North York ON M2J 4
416 512-8186

(G-4960)
MEGA BOOK INC
Also Called: Megabooks
2937 Ne 19th Dr (32609-3373)
P.O. Box 358659 (32635-8659)
PHONE....................................352 378-4567
Glenda Hogg, *Manager*
EMP: 5 **EST:** 1993
SALES (est): 460.5K **Privately Held**
WEB: www.muscleanatomybook.com
SIC: 2731 Book publishing

(G-4961)
MERCURY SYSTEMS INC
Also Called: Athena Group, The
800 Sw 2nd Ave Ste 300 (32601-6295)
PHONE....................................352 371-2567
Rick Fenoli, *Finance*
EMP: 23
SALES (corp-wide): 924MM **Publicly Held**
WEB: www.mrcy.com
SIC: 3674 7371 7372 7379 Semiconductors & related devices; custom computer programming services; prepackaged software; computer related consulting services; commercial physical research
PA: Mercury Systems, Inc.
50 Minuteman Rd
Andover MA 01810
978 256-1300

(G-4962)
MICAWORKS CABINETRY INC
Also Called: Mica Works Cabinetry
4440 Sw 35th Ter (32608-7596)
PHONE....................................352 336-1707
John R Pedersen, *President*
Luis Deppe, *Prdtn Mgr*
EMP: 9 **EST:** 1996
SALES (est): 1.2MM **Privately Held**
WEB: www.micaworks.com
SIC: 2434 Wood kitchen cabinets

(G-4963)
MILLIKEN & COMPANY
Sivance Plant
5002 Ne 54th Pl (32609-1694)
PHONE....................................352 244-2267
EMP: 7
SALES (corp-wide): 1.6B **Privately Held**
WEB: www.milliken.com
SIC: 2273 Floor coverings, textile fiber
PA: Milliken & Company
920 Milliken Rd
Spartanburg SC 29303
864 503-2020

(G-4964)
MIRAGE MANUFACTURING INC
3001 Ne 20th Way (32609-3396)
PHONE....................................352 377-4146
Kenneth James Fickett, *President*
Dennis Keller, *Vice Pres*
Rebecca Fickett, *Treasurer*
Eric Kraft, *Sales Dir*
EMP: 65 **EST:** 1973
SQ FT: 25,000
SALES (est): 5.2MM **Privately Held**
WEB: www.mirage-mfg.com
SIC: 3732 Boats, fiberglass: building & repairing

(G-4965)
MONTEOCHA COATINGS INC
2607 Ne 56th Ter (32609-5603)
PHONE....................................352 367-3136
Gary Washington, *Principal*
EMP: 7 **EST:** 2013
SALES (est): 165.6K **Privately Held**
SIC: 3479 Metal coating & allied service

(G-4966)
MPH INDUSTRIES INC
Also Called: Boone Welding
2406 Ne 19th Dr (32609-3319)
PHONE....................................352 372-9533
Carl K Bussard Jr, *President*
EMP: 15 **EST:** 1945
SQ FT: 2,500
SALES (est): 1.8MM **Privately Held**
WEB: www.boonewelding.com
SIC: 3498 7692 3441 Fabricated pipe & fittings; welding repair; fabricated structural metal

(G-4967)
MTE INC
8930 Nw 13th St (32653-1033)
PHONE....................................352 371-3898
Paul Bergsma, *Owner*
Marcus Muir, *Admin Sec*
EMP: 5 **EST:** 1996
SQ FT: 1,600
SALES (est): 400K **Privately Held**
WEB: www.mtetooling.com
SIC: 3599 Machine shop, jobbing & repair

(G-4968)
MUNRO INTERNATIONAL INC
Also Called: Molly & Friends
1030 Se 4th St (32601-8004)
PHONE....................................352 337-1535
Thomas M Grant, *President*
EMP: 20
SQ FT: 3,000
SALES (est): 2.6MM **Privately Held**
WEB: www.mollyandfriends.com
SIC: 3999 Pet supplies

(G-4969)
NAYLOR LLC (PA)
Also Called: Naylor Association Solutions
5950 Nw 1st Pl (32607-6060)
PHONE....................................800 369-6220
Alex Debarr, *President*
Jill Andreu, *Publisher*
Troy Woodham, *Publisher*
Shani Calvo, *Editor*
Shelly Neal, *Editor*
EMP: 175 **EST:** 2006
SQ FT: 20,000
SALES (est): 84.3MM **Privately Held**
WEB: www.naylor.com
SIC: 2759 7374 Publication printing; computer graphics service

(G-4970)
NELSON AND AFFILIATES INC
3324 W University Ave (32607-2540)
PHONE....................................352 316-5641
Rick Nelson, *Branch Mgr*
EMP: 18 **Privately Held**
WEB: www.nelsonandaffiliates.com
SIC: 3443 Farm storage tanks, metal plate
PA: Nelson And Affiliates, Inc.
4025 Nw Passage
Tallahassee FL 32303

(G-4971)
NEUROTRONICS INC
4500 Nw 27th Ave Ste C2 (32606-7042)
PHONE....................................352 372-9955
Kazuteru Yanagihara, *President*

Randy Widell, *Vice Pres*
James Schubert, *VP Engrg*
David Pezet, *QC Mgr*
Jay Cushing, *Manager*
EMP: 7 **EST:** 1997
SALES (est): 1.2MM **Privately Held**
WEB: www.neurotronics.com
SIC: 3841 Surgical & medical instruments
PA: Nihon Kohden Corporation
1-31-4, Nishiochiai
Shinjuku-Ku TKY 161-0

(G-4972)
NEXTOWER LLC
11895 Sw 33rd Ln (32608-8815)
PHONE..................................407 907-7984
David H Hudson Boeff, *Owner*
John Collins, *Opers Staff*
EMP: 9 **EST:** 2014
SALES (est): 1MM **Privately Held**
WEB: www.nextower.net
SIC: 3441 Tower sections, radio & television transmission

(G-4973)
NORTH AMRCN SIGNAL SYSTEMS LLC
605 Nw 53rd Ave Ste A17 (32609-1020)
PHONE..................................352 376-8341
Ezequiel Zetien, *Mng Member*
EMP: 9 **EST:** 2009
SALES (est): 800K **Privately Held**
WEB: www.nasignal.com
SIC: 3669 Traffic signals, electric

(G-4974)
OCEAN KITCHEN CABINETS
4445 Sw 35th Ter Ste 200 (32608-8477)
PHONE..................................352 745-7110
Rene Arango, *Principal*
EMP: 8 **EST:** 2015
SALES (est): 310.7K **Privately Held**
WEB: www.ocean-kitchen-cabinets.negocio.site
SIC: 2434 Wood kitchen cabinets

(G-4975)
OLDCASTLE BUILDING PRODUC
Also Called: Old Castle Coastal
3302 Ne 2nd St (32609-2333)
PHONE..................................352 377-1699
Martin Maulden, *President*
EMP: 6 **EST:** 2013
SALES (est): 410.4K **Privately Held**
WEB: www.oldcastlecoastal.com
SIC: 3272 Concrete products

(G-4976)
OPIE CHOICE LLC (PA)
Also Called: Opie Choice Network
3870 Nw 83rd St (32606-5601)
PHONE..................................352 331-3741
Paul Prusakowski, *Mng Member*
EMP: 3 **EST:** 2014
SALES (est): 3.4MM **Privately Held**
WEB: www.opiesoftware.com
SIC: 7372 Application computer software

(G-4977)
ORTHOTIC PRSTHTIC RHBLTTION AS
Also Called: M & M Rehabilitation
6608 Nw 9th Blvd (32605-4207)
PHONE..................................352 331-3399
Frank Vero, *President*
Mark Phelps, *Vice Pres*
EMP: 7 **EST:** 1996
SALES (est): 656.8K **Privately Held**
WEB: www.midflpros.com
SIC: 3842 5999 Limbs, artificial; orthopedic & prosthesis applications

(G-4978)
OXENDINE PUBLISHING INC
412 Nw 16th Ave (32601-4203)
PHONE..................................352 373-6907
W H Oxendine Jr, *President*
EMP: 20 **EST:** 1983
SQ FT: 4,000
SALES (est): 587.4K **Privately Held**
WEB: www.studentleader.com
SIC: 2721 Magazines: publishing only, not printed on site

(G-4979)
PAUL WALES INC
Also Called: Atlas Screen Printing
131 Se 10th Ave (32601-7998)
PHONE..................................352 371-2120
Paul Wales, *President*
Glenda Grosnick, *Sales Mgr*
Annie Orlando, *Admin Sec*
EMP: 19 **EST:** 1976
SQ FT: 14,000
SALES (est): 1.6MM **Privately Held**
WEB: www.wildcotton.com
SIC: 2759 Screen printing

(G-4980)
PEPSI-COLA METRO BTLG CO INC
6335 Nw 18th Dr (32653-1643)
PHONE..................................352 376-8276
Karen Connelly, *Human Resources*
Johanna Reyes, *Manager*
EMP: 6
SQ FT: 28,200
SALES (corp-wide): 70.3B **Publicly Held**
WEB: www.pepsico.com
SIC: 2086 5149 Carbonated soft drinks, bottled & canned; groceries & related products
HQ: Pepsi-Cola Metropolitan Bottling Company, Inc.
1111 Westchester Ave
White Plains NY 10604
914 767-6000

(G-4981)
POWER PRODUCTION MGT INC
408 W University Ave 600b (32601-3239)
PHONE..................................352 263-0766
Aleksey Y Khokhlov, *President*
Jason S Gonos, *Vice Pres*
Peter Poulos, *Project Mgr*
Stefan Schmid, *Design Engr*
Selena Patterson, *Office Mgr*
EMP: 8 **EST:** 2009
SALES (est): 1.4MM **Privately Held**
WEB:
www.powerproductionmanagement.com
SIC: 3674 Semiconductors & related devices

(G-4982)
PRECISION TL ENGRG OF GNSVILLE
2709 Ne 20th Way (32609-3314)
PHONE..................................352 376-2533
Bette J Thibault, *President*
William C Thibault, *Vice Pres*
EMP: 19 **EST:** 1966
SQ FT: 19,000
SALES (est): 461.8K **Privately Held**
WEB: www.pte-fl.com
SIC: 3549 3599 3728 3544 Metalworking machinery; machine shop, jobbing & repair; aircraft parts & equipment; special dies, tools, jigs & fixtures

(G-4983)
PREMIER PARTIES ENTERTAINMENT
805 Nw 13th St (32601-2904)
PHONE..................................352 375-6122
Eric Manin, *President*
Anthony Hernandez, *Vice Pres*
▲ **EMP:** 28 **EST:** 1994
SQ FT: 2,200
SALES (est): 1.4MM **Privately Held**
WEB: www.premiereventco.com
SIC: 2759 7929 7299 7311 Commercial printing; entertainers & entertainment groups; party planning service; advertising agencies

(G-4984)
PS & QS CUSTOM PRINTS LLC
4024 Ne 1st Dr (32609-1702)
PHONE..................................352 231-3961
Patrickk W McDonald, *Branch Mgr*
EMP: 13
SALES (corp-wide): 69K **Privately Held**
SIC: 2752 Commercial printing, lithographic
PA: P's & Q's Custom Prints, Llc
4609 Buchanan Dr
Fort Pierce FL 34982
772 626-7434

(G-4985)
QUANTENA ENERGY PRODUCTGS
1720 Sw 78th St (32607-6601)
PHONE..................................352 332-6630
John Anderson, *President*
EMP: 10 **EST:** 1999
SALES (est): 551K **Privately Held**
SIC: 2951 Asphalt paving mixtures & blocks

(G-4986)
QUICK-MED TECHNOLOGIES INC
902 Nw 4th St (32601-4285)
PHONE..................................352 379-0611
Gregory S Schultz, *Ch of Bd*
Bernd Liesenfeld, *President*
William Toreki, *Vice Pres*
Susan Leander, *Research*
Paul Jenssen, *CFO*
EMP: 7
SQ FT: 3,200
SALES (est): 1MM **Privately Held**
WEB: www.quickmedtech.com
SIC: 3841 8731 Surgical & medical instruments; medical research, commercial

(G-4987)
R & J MFG OF GAINESVILLE
Also Called: Air-Trac
2001 Ne 31st Ave (32609-2506)
PHONE..................................352 375-3130
Loyce Osteen, *President*
James F Osteen, *Vice Pres*
EMP: 6 **EST:** 1974
SQ FT: 20,000
SALES (est): 690.3K **Privately Held**
WEB: www.air-trac.com
SIC: 3822 3585 3564 3433 Air flow controllers, air conditioning & refrigeration; refrigeration & heating equipment; blowers & fans; heating equipment, except electric

(G-4988)
RAD WEAR INC
2135 Nw 40th Ter Ste A (32605-5802)
PHONE..................................352 727-4498
Jennifer Ruland, *President*
Radley Ruland, *Vice Pres*
EMP: 8 **EST:** 2010
SALES (est): 1.1MM **Privately Held**
WEB: www.radweardesigns.com
SIC: 2211 Apparel & outerwear fabrics, cotton

(G-4989)
RAFFERTY HOLDINGS LLC
Also Called: Rafferty Machine and Tool
2722 Nw 74th Pl (32653-1201)
PHONE..................................352 248-0906
Conway Tomlinson,
Celia Gtomlinson,
EMP: 22 **EST:** 1972
SQ FT: 10,000
SALES (est): 2.8MM **Privately Held**
WEB: www.raffertytool.com
SIC: 3544 3599 Special dies & tools; machine shop, jobbing & repair

(G-4990)
RESPITREND INC
3630 Sw 47th Ave (32608-7555)
PHONE..................................407 529-5888
Gerard Bencen, *President*
EMP: 6
SALES (est): 85.2K **Privately Held**
SIC: 3845 Respiratory analysis equipment, electromedical

(G-4991)
RIDGWAY ROOF TRUSS COMPANY
235 Sw 11th Pl (32601-7939)
PHONE..................................352 376-4436
Wells S The Losen, *President*
Jeff Lincoln, *Principal*
Karl The Losen, *Vice Pres*
Wells Losen, *Vice Pres*
Michael Hyde, *VP Opers*
EMP: 100
SQ FT: 10,000
SALES (est): 16.3MM **Privately Held**
WEB: www.ridgwaytruss.com
SIC: 2439 Trusses, wooden roof

(G-4992)
SCAN TECHNOLOGY INC (PA)
10305 Nw 4th Pl (32607-1350)
PHONE..................................931 723-0304
Paul A Flowers, *CEO*
Michael Flowers, *Treasurer*
Stephen Flowers, *Admin Sec*
▼ **EMP:** 6 **EST:** 1979
SQ FT: 1,400
SALES (est): 1.3MM **Privately Held**
WEB: www.scantec.com
SIC: 3577 3643 7389 Magnetic ink recognition devices; readers, sorters or inscribers, magnetic ink; optical scanning devices; current-carrying wiring devices; packaging & labeling services

(G-4993)
SCF PROCESSING LLC
1604 Nw 8th Ave (32603-1004)
PHONE..................................352 377-0858
Siobhan Matthews, *Principal*
EMP: 6 **EST:** 2010
SALES (est): 78.7K **Privately Held**
SIC: 3089 Injection molding of plastics

(G-4994)
SEL WEST COAST INC
817 Ne Waldo Rd (32641-4674)
PHONE..................................352 373-6354
Russ Keaton, *Branch Mgr*
EMP: 21
SALES (corp-wide): 9.5MM **Privately Held**
SIC: 3312 Blast furnaces & steel mills
PA: Sel West Coast, Inc.
7005 E 14th Ave
Tampa FL 33619

(G-4995)
SIGNMASTERS INC
2530 Sw 34th St (32608-1741)
P.O. Box 142530 (32614-2530)
PHONE..................................352 335-7000
Ronald Clark, *President*
EMP: 7 **EST:** 1988
SQ FT: 2,000
SALES (est): 793.3K **Privately Held**
WEB: www.signpower.com
SIC: 3993 Signs, not made in custom sign painting shops

(G-4996)
SILKMASTERS INC
1911 Sw 80th Dr (32607-3499)
PHONE..................................904 372-8958
Shirley Bonamie, *President*
Julie Bonamie, *Corp Secy*
Clifford Bonamie, *Vice Pres*
EMP: 8 **EST:** 1986
SQ FT: 7,800
SALES (est): 658.1K **Privately Held**
WEB: www.silkmasters.com
SIC: 2759 Screen printing

(G-4997)
SIMONSCLUB LLC
8 S Main St (32601-6215)
PHONE..................................352 246-3636
Naji S Semrani, *Manager*
EMP: 24 **EST:** 2014
SALES (est): 1.1MM **Privately Held**
SIC: 2741 Miscellaneous publishing

(G-4998)
SINMAT COMMERCIAL LLC
1912 Nw 67th Pl (32653-1649)
PHONE..................................352 334-7270
Sarah Wilson, *Business Mgr*
Deepika Singh,
Rajiv Singh,
EMP: 15 **EST:** 2012
SQ FT: 22,500
SALES (est): 4.3MM **Privately Held**
WEB: www.entegris.com
SIC: 2819 Industrial inorganic chemicals

(G-4999)
SIRA
912 Nw 13th St (32601-4140)
PHONE..................................352 377-4947
EMP: 6 **EST:** 2019
SALES (est): 122K **Privately Held**
WEB: www.siragainesville.com
SIC: 2499 Decorative wood & woodwork

(G-5000)
SIVANCE LLC (HQ)
5002 Ne 54th Pl (32609-1694)
P.O. Box 1466 (32627-1466)
PHONE..................................352 376-8246
William Carpenter, *Safety Mgr*
Craig Stafford, *Mng Member*
Amy Sweeney, *Manager*
Kathy Hess, *Lab Dir*
James R Richeson,
◆ **EMP:** 116 **EST:** 2009
SALES (est): 56.2MM
SALES (corp-wide): 1.6B **Privately Held**
WEB: www.milliken.com
SIC: 2819 Industrial inorganic chemicals
PA: Milliken & Company
920 Milliken Rd
Spartanburg SC 29303
864 503-2020

(G-5001)
STORTERCHILDS PRINTING CO INC
1540 Ne Waldo Rd (32641-4629)
PHONE..................................352 376-2658
Joe R Davis, *CEO*
Shariq Siraj, *President*
David A Cheadle, *Treasurer*
Sharon Murphy, *Controller*
Dave Hendryx, *Accounts Mgr*
EMP: 24 **EST:** 1949
SQ FT: 21,000
SALES (est): 5.3MM
SALES (corp-wide): 4.7B **Publicly Held**
WEB: www.rrd.com
SIC: 2752 Commercial printing, offset
HQ: Consolidated Graphics, Inc.
5858 Westheimer Rd # 200
Houston TX 77057
713 787-0977

(G-5002)
STOUT DEFENSE PA
5215 Sw 91st Ter (32608-7125)
PHONE..................................352 665-9266
Adam P Stout, *Principal*
EMP: 6 **EST:** 2017
SALES (est): 464.3K **Privately Held**
WEB: www.stoutdefense.com
SIC: 3812 Defense systems & equipment

(G-5003)
STREAMLINE NUMERICS INC
3221 Nw 13th St Ste A (32609-2189)
PHONE..................................352 271-8841
Siddhart Thakur, *President*
EMP: 7
SALES (est): 568K **Privately Held**
WEB: www.snumerics.com
SIC: 3812 Search & navigation equipment

(G-5004)
STRICTLY ECOMMERCE
5210 Ne 49th Ter (32609-1630)
PHONE..................................352 672-6566
Shannon Flesner, *President*
EMP: 5 **EST:** 2007
SALES (est): 346.4K **Privately Held**
WEB: www.strictlytoolboxes.com
SIC: 3999 Atomizers, toiletry

(G-5005)
STRICTLY TOOLBOXES
4820 Ne 49th Rd (32609-1624)
PHONE..................................352 672-6566
Shannon Flesner, *President*
EMP: 9 **EST:** 2013
SALES (est): 1.7MM **Privately Held**
WEB: www.strictlytoolboxes.com
SIC: 3469 Metal stampings

(G-5006)
SWI PUBLISHING INC
116 Sw 40th Ter (32607-2755)
PHONE..................................352 538-1438
Lisa D Wilkinson, *Principal*
EMP: 15 **EST:** 2010
SALES (est): 170.3K **Privately Held**
SIC: 2741 Miscellaneous publishing

(G-5007)
TAPESOUTH INC
1626 Nw 55th Pl (32653-2109)
PHONE..................................904 642-1800
Melissa Norman, *CEO*
Susan S Norman, *President*
James Radtke, *VP Opers*
▲ **EMP:** 8 **EST:** 1993
SQ FT: 15,400
SALES (est): 1.9MM **Privately Held**
WEB: www.tapesouth.com
SIC: 2672 Adhesive papers, labels or tapes: from purchased material

(G-5008)
TARGET COPY GAINESVILLE INC
3422 Sw Archer Rd (32608-2409)
P.O. Box 13955 (32604-1955)
PHONE..................................352 372-1171
Jennifer Ford, *Manager*
EMP: 16
SALES (corp-wide): 9.8MM **Privately Held**
SIC: 2789 7389 7334 2759 Bookbinding & related work; laminating service; blueprinting service; commercial printing
PA: Target Copy Of Gainesville, Inc.
4130 Nw 16th Blvd
Gainesville FL 32605
352 372-2233

(G-5009)
THEISSEN TRAINING SYSTEMS INC
3705 Sw 42nd Ave Ste 2 (32608-2599)
P.O. Box 141917 (32614-1917)
PHONE..................................352 490-8020
Tilman Rumpf, *President*
Omar Silva, *Vice Pres*
Katie Bryan, *Admin Asst*
▲ **EMP:** 56 **EST:** 2001
SALES (est): 11.3MM
SALES (corp-wide): 2MM **Privately Held**
WEB: www.theissentraining.com
SIC: 3499 Fire- or burglary-resistive products
HQ: T.T.S. Theissen Training Systems Gmbh
Schuchardstr. 3
Dusseldorf 40595
211 975-040

(G-5010)
THREAD PIT INC
2708 Ne Waldo Rd (32609-3323)
PHONE..................................352 505-0065
EMP: 6
SALES (est): 716.2K **Privately Held**
SIC: 2759 Commercial Printing

(G-5011)
TOWER PUBLICATIONS INC
Also Called: Senior Times Magazine
4400 Nw 36th Ave (32606-7215)
PHONE..................................352 372-5468
Carlos Delatorre, *President*
Bonita D Delatorre, *Vice Pres*
Larkin Kieffer, *Accounts Exec*
Helen Mincey, *Representative*
Helen Stalnaker, *Representative*
EMP: 15 **EST:** 1999
SQ FT: 3,300
SALES (est): 1.4MM **Privately Held**
WEB: www.towerpublications.com
SIC: 2741 Miscellaneous publishing

(G-5012)
TRENDY ENTERTAINMENT INC
4910 Sw 78th Ln (32608-5196)
PHONE..................................814 384-7123
Marco Dusse, *CEO*
Linda Hoyles, *CFO*
James Reid, *Prgrmr*
EMP: 36 **EST:** 2010
SALES (est): 1.8MM **Privately Held**
WEB: www.chromatic.games
SIC: 7372 Prepackaged software

(G-5013)
TWO TREE INC
24 Nw 33rd Ct Ste A (32607-2556)
PHONE..................................352 284-1763
Thomas L Thompson, *Director*
EMP: 6 **EST:** 2001
SALES (est): 106.9K **Privately Held**
WEB: www.flanaturecoast.com
SIC: 3822 Auto controls regulating residntl & coml environmt & applncs

(G-5014)
US SPARS INC
Also Called: Z Spars
6320 Nw 123rd Pl (32653-1069)
PHONE..................................386 462-3760
Mike Wukotich, *President*
Rick Pantall, *Manager*
◆ **EMP:** 9 **EST:** 1997
SQ FT: 160,000
SALES (est): 1.5MM **Privately Held**
WEB: www.usspars.com
SIC: 2394 3732 Sails: made from purchased materials; boat building & repairing
HQ: Z Diffusion
Z Spars Performance Spars
Perigny 17180
546 442-088

(G-5015)
VERTAEON LLC
747 Sw 2nd Ave Ste 349 (32601-6284)
PHONE..................................404 823-6232
Rekha Menon-Varma,
EMP: 8 **EST:** 2012
SALES (est): 428K **Privately Held**
SIC: 7372 Prepackaged software

(G-5016)
VOS SYSTEMS LLC ✪
304 W University Ave (32601-5208)
PHONE..................................352 317-2954
Omar Ghazzaoui,
EMP: 16 **EST:** 2020
SALES (est): 2.2MM **Privately Held**
SIC: 3699 Electrical equipment & supplies

(G-5017)
XHALE INC (PA)
3630 Sw 47th Ave Ste 100 (32608-7756)
PHONE..................................352 371-8488
Richard R Allen, *CEO*
Thomas Bigger, *President*
Andrew Kersey, *President*
John F Harper, *Chairman*
Lori Herman, *Counsel*
EMP: 8 **EST:** 2005
SALES (est): 802.7K **Privately Held**
WEB: www.xhale.com
SIC: 3841 Surgical & medical instruments

(G-5018)
ZPX LLC
Also Called: Korasana
2106 Nw 4th Pl (32603-1516)
PHONE..................................888 943-8849
Mark G Cruz, *Mng Member*
EMP: 8 **EST:** 2019
SALES (est): 368.7K **Privately Held**
SIC: 3999

Geneva
Seminole County

(G-5019)
CWP SHEET METAL INC
1661 Bandit Way (32732-8520)
PHONE..................................407 349-0926
EMP: 26
SALES (est): 3.1MM **Privately Held**
SIC: 3444 Mfg Sheet Metalwork

(G-5020)
EVOLUTION WOODWORKING
670 Coffee Trl (32732-7279)
PHONE..................................407 221-5031
Stephen Chrismore Hamblin, *Owner*
EMP: 7 **EST:** 2010
SALES (est): 95.5K **Privately Held**
SIC: 2431 Millwork

(G-5021)
F & S MILL WORKS
522 Cemetery Rd (32732-8921)
PHONE..................................407 349-9948
Leon H Flowers, *Principal*
EMP: 6 **EST:** 2003
SALES (est): 155.3K **Privately Held**
SIC: 2434 Wood kitchen cabinets

(G-5022)
FLORIDA STEAM SERVICES INC
349 Whitcomb Dr (32732-9254)
PHONE..................................407 247-8250
David Segrest, *Principal*
Sally Segrest, *Admin Sec*
EMP: 6 **EST:** 1991
SQ FT: 1,400
SALES (est): 446.3K **Privately Held**
SIC: 3317 Welded pipe & tubes

(G-5023)
SUNS EYE INC
2098 Tall Pine Trl (32732-9138)
P.O. Box 39 (32732-0039)
PHONE..................................407 519-4904
Ashley Stollings, *President*
EMP: 6 **EST:** 2013
SALES (est): 525K **Privately Held**
WEB: www.sunseye.com
SIC: 2899 5169 Oils & essential oils; essential oils

Gibsonton
Hillsborough County

(G-5024)
A-FABCO INC
11550 S Us Highway 41 (33534-5209)
P.O. Box 2097 (33534-2097)
PHONE..................................813 677-8790
Robert Harburg, *CEO*
Jerry Harburg, *President*
Dave Barkley, *General Mgr*
Ken Kennedy, *Sales Staff*
▲ **EMP:** 25 **EST:** 1970
SQ FT: 17,250
SALES (est): 4MM **Privately Held**
WEB: www.afabxray.com
SIC: 3443 5072 Nuclear shielding, metal plate; builders' hardware

(G-5025)
ALL STEEL BLDNGS CMPONENTS INC
10159 S Us Highway 41 (33534-4016)
PHONE..................................813 671-8044
Bobby Ramey, *President*
Henry Suggs, *Sales Executive*
▼ **EMP:** 36 **EST:** 2001
SQ FT: 21,600
SALES (est): 8.8MM **Privately Held**
WEB: www.allsteel-buildings.com
SIC: 3448 Prefabricated metal buildings

(G-5026)
BACKYARD CANVAS & SIGNS INC
11225 Restwood Dr (33534-4735)
P.O. Box 1131 (33534-1131)
PHONE..................................813 672-2660
Carter William W, *Principal*
EMP: 7 **EST:** 2017
SALES (est): 100.4K **Privately Held**
WEB: www.backyardcanvas.com
SIC: 3993 Signs & advertising specialties

(G-5027)
BIG BEND FUEL INC
6912 Big Bend Rd (33534-5832)
PHONE..................................727 946-8727
Richard Elkhoury, *Principal*
EMP: 23 **EST:** 2010
SALES (est): 625.2K **Privately Held**
SIC: 2869 Fuels

(G-5028)
GOLD BOND BUILDING PDTS LLC
12949 S Us Highway 41 (33534-5826)
PHONE..................................813 672-8269
EMP: 23
SALES (corp-wide): 41.3MM **Privately Held**
WEB: www.nationalgypsum.com
SIC: 2621 Paper mills
PA: Gold Bond Building Products, Llc
2001 Rexford Rd
Charlotte NC

▲ = Import ▼=Export
◆ =Import/Export

(G-5029)
HJR INDUSTRIES LLC
12726 Kings Lake Dr (33534-3910)
PHONE..................................706 761-1200
Lea Romero, *Principal*
EMP: 8 **EST:** 2017
SALES (est): 308.6K **Privately Held**
SIC: 3999 Manufacturing industries

(G-5030)
INNOVATIVE STEEL TECH INC
12620 S Us Highway 41 (33534-5812)
PHONE..................................813 767-1746
Richard D Biddle, *President*
EMP: 12 **EST:** 2007
SALES (est): 385.3K **Privately Held**
SIC: 3312 Blast furnaces & steel mills

(G-5031)
LIFETIME PRODUCTS GROUP INC
7215 Nundy Ave (33534-4823)
PHONE..................................813 781-9182
EMP: 6 **EST:** 2012
SALES (est): 107K **Privately Held**
SIC: 3999 Manufacturing industries

(G-5032)
SANTIAGO CHOPPER LLC (PA)
10935 Sonora Dr (33534-5456)
PHONE..................................813 671-9097
Christine Bernard, *Principal*
EMP: 22 **EST:** 2011
SALES (est): 148.8K **Privately Held**
WEB: www.santiagochopper.com
SIC: 3714 Motor vehicle parts & accessories

(G-5033)
TAMPA TANK & WELDING INC
12781 S Us Highway 41 (33534-5829)
PHONE..................................813 241-0123
Dale Ison, *Exec VP*
Deborah Hayden, *Controller*
Jody Allans, *Manager*
Randy Kelley, *Manager*
Federico Rivas, *Director*
EMP: 15
SQ FT: 22,332 **Privately Held**
WEB: www.tti-fss.com
SIC: 3446 3443 3441 Architectural metalwork; fabricated plate work (boiler shop); fabricated structural metal
HQ: Tampa Tank & Welding, Inc.
2710 E 5th Ave
Tampa FL 33605
813 623-2675

(G-5034)
TURN KEY INDUSTRIES
9901 Alafia River Ln (33534-4635)
P.O. Box 1306, Riverview (33568-1306)
PHONE..................................813 671-3446
Claudia Haupt, *Owner*
Donny Guedry, *Production*
Dan Belore, *Sales Staff*
EMP: 8 **EST:** 2001
SALES (est): 346.3K **Privately Held**
WEB: www.tkind.com
SIC: 3999 Manufacturing industries

(G-5035)
W R WILLIAMS ENTERPRISES INC
Also Called: Dock Builders Supply
6202 Powell Rd (33534-5800)
P.O. Box 3450, Apollo Beach (33572-1003)
PHONE..................................813 677-2000
William R Williams Jr, *President*
Richard A Tahela, *Vice Pres*
◆ **EMP:** 8 **EST:** 1998
SALES (est): 1.3MM **Privately Held**
WEB: www.dockbuilders.com
SIC: 2499 5072 5251 Floating docks, wood; builders' hardware; builders' hardware

Glen Saint Mary
Baker County

(G-5036)
HOME TOWN JOURNAL
9915 River Oak Dr (32040-5023)
PHONE..................................904 259-9141
Laurie A Wall, *Principal*
EMP: 6 **EST:** 2006
SALES (est): 11.5K **Privately Held**
WEB: www.bestinbaker.com
SIC: 2711 Newspapers, publishing & printing

(G-5037)
NATIONAL PIPE WELDING INC
9473 Smokey Rd (32040-5335)
P.O. Box 1661 (32040-1661)
PHONE..................................904 588-2589
Michelle Fish, *Mng Member*
Lamar Fish,
EMP: 10 **EST:** 2011
SALES (est): 324.6K **Privately Held**
SIC: 7692 Welding repair

(G-5038)
S&J LOGGING INC
10471 Reid Stafford Rd (32040-5227)
PHONE..................................904 237-7774
Shane B Baldwyn, *Principal*
EMP: 6 **EST:** 2008
SALES (est): 93.2K **Privately Held**
SIC: 2411 Logging camps & contractors

(G-5039)
SOUTHERN FUEL INC
7028 E Mount Vernon St (32040-5066)
PHONE..................................904 545-5163
Lynn Driskell, *Principal*
EMP: 6 **EST:** 2010
SALES (est): 442K **Privately Held**
SIC: 2869 Fuels

Gotha
Orange County

(G-5040)
BLUETOAD INC
2225 Lake Nally Woods Dr (34734-4902)
PHONE..................................407 992-8744
Paul Dehart, *CEO*
EMP: 34 **EST:** 2007
SQ FT: 4,700
SALES (est): 5MM **Privately Held**
WEB: www.bluetoad.com
SIC: 2741 Miscellaneous publishing

(G-5041)
PIXIE DUSTED STITCHES
3318 Royal Ascot Run (34734-5116)
PHONE..................................207 776-3277
Diana Solomon, *Principal*
EMP: 6 **EST:** 2015
SALES (est): 54.3K **Privately Held**
WEB: www.pixie-dusted-stitches.com
SIC: 2395 Embroidery & art needlework

Graceville
Jackson County

(G-5042)
APALACHEE POLE COMPANY INC (PA)
1820 Highway 2 (32440-4124)
P.O. Box 7 (32440-0007)
PHONE..................................850 263-4457
C Finley McRae, *President*
Robert McRae Jr, *Vice Pres*
EMP: 2 **EST:** 1986
SQ FT: 6,000
SALES (est): 5MM **Privately Held**
WEB: www.rex-lumber.com
SIC: 2421 Sawmills & planing mills, general

(G-5043)
HARD SURFACE POLISHING LLC
5361 Huckleberry Ln (32440-2058)
PHONE..................................850 360-4140
Cynthia Doman, *Principal*
EMP: 7 **EST:** 2014
SALES (est): 145.7K **Privately Held**
SIC: 3471 Polishing, metals or formed products

(G-5044)
REX LUMBER GRACEVILLE LLC (HQ)
5299 Alabama St (32440-2105)
P.O. Box 7 (32440-0007)
PHONE..................................850 263-2056
Anthony Hanson, *General Mgr*
Matt Pelham, *Project Mgr*
Jason Daniels, *Opers Mgr*
Van Bodin, *Purch Mgr*
David McCroan, *Purchasing*
EMP: 115 **EST:** 1926
SALES (est): 60.5MM
SALES (corp-wide): 68.3MM **Privately Held**
WEB: www.rex-lumber.com
SIC: 2421 Sawmills & planing mills, general
PA: Rex Lumber, Llc
5381 Cliff St
Graceville FL 32440
850 263-4457

(G-5045)
REX LUMBER LLC (PA)
5381 Cliff St (32440-1727)
PHONE..................................850 263-4457
Amber Blackshear, *Sales Staff*
Frank Bondurant, *Mng Member*
Shawn Norris, *Maintence Staff*
EMP: 19 **EST:** 2018
SALES (est): 68.3MM **Privately Held**
WEB: www.rex-lumber.com
SIC: 2421 Sawmills & planing mills, general

Grand Ridge
Jackson County

(G-5046)
PAP-CAP INDUSTRIES LLC
3235 Wisteria Ln (32442-4380)
PHONE..................................850 209-7377
Donna L Wilkie, *Manager*
James Peacock,
EMP: 6 **EST:** 2010
SALES (est): 75.1K **Privately Held**
SIC: 3999 Manufacturing industries

Grandin
Putnam County

(G-5047)
LEGACY VULCAN LLC
1 Mile W On Hwy 100 (32138)
PHONE..................................386 659-2477
Mitchell Johns, *Manager*
EMP: 10 **Publicly Held**
WEB: www.vulcanmaterials.com
SIC: 3273 Ready-mixed concrete
HQ: Legacy Vulcan, Llc
1200 Urban Center Dr
Vestavia AL 35242
205 298-3000

Grant
Brevard County

(G-5048)
CARBONARA LABS INC
4550 S Us Highway 1 (32949-4909)
PHONE..................................321 952-1303
John Carpenter, *President*
Robert Rapp Jr, *Vice Pres*
▲ **EMP:** 10 **EST:** 1974
SALES (est): 798.2K **Privately Held**
WEB: www.carpindustries.com
SIC: 3812 Search & navigation equipment

(G-5049)
JGA LIGHTING LLC
Also Called: JEAN ARCHIBALD DBA JGA ASSOC
3869 Garden Wood Cir (32949)
PHONE..................................772 408-8224
Jean G Archibald,
Douglas W Archibald,
EMP: 7 **EST:** 2013
SALES (est): 462.7K **Privately Held**
WEB: www.bulbwizards.com
SIC: 3229 Bulbs for electric lights

(G-5050)
TRIPLE SEVEN HOME LLC
3385 Grant Rd (32949-8126)
PHONE..................................321 652-5151
Jessica L Lelievre, *Principal*
EMP: 5 **EST:** 2015
SALES (est): 341.5K **Privately Held**
WEB: www.triplesevenhome.com
SIC: 3648 Lighting fixtures, except electric: residential

Green Cove Springs
Clay County

(G-5051)
AMERICAN TRAFFIC SAFETY MTLS
1272 Harbor Rd (32043-8729)
P.O. Box 1449, Orange Park (32067-1449)
PHONE..................................904 284-0284
Sandi Ricketts, *CEO*
Roberta Seay Soldner, *President*
EMP: 23 **EST:** 1997
SQ FT: 5,000
SALES (est): 1.2MM **Privately Held**
WEB: www.atsminc.com
SIC: 2824 Vinyl fibers

(G-5052)
AMMCON CORP
1503 County Road 315 # 204 (32043-8773)
P.O. Box 890, North Plains OR (97133-0890)
PHONE..................................904 863-3196
Josh Grow, *Principal*
Chris Whitlock, *Nursing Mgr*
EMP: 7
SALES (corp-wide): 11.8MM **Privately Held**
WEB: www.ammcon.com
SIC: 3599 Machine shop, jobbing & repair
PA: Ammcon Corp.
21450 Nw West Union Rd
Hillsboro OR 97124
503 645-5206

(G-5053)
ARTEMIS HOLDINGS LLC (HQ)
Also Called: Pyramid Mouldings
4630 County Road 209 S (32043-8182)
PHONE..................................904 284-5611
Ray Hammons, *President*
Gordon Davis, *CFO*
EMP: 141 **EST:** 2014
SALES (est): 51.2MM
SALES (corp-wide): 120.2MM **Privately Held**
WEB: www.rollerdie.com
SIC: 3441 Fabricated structural metal
PA: Roller Die And Forming Company, Inc.
1172 Industrial Blvd
Louisville KY 40219
502 969-1327

(G-5054)
ASHLEY F WARD INC
Also Called: Ashley Ward
3525 Enterprise Way (32043-9334)
PHONE..................................904 284-2848
Brian Storey, *Manager*
EMP: 10
SQ FT: 50,000
SALES (corp-wide): 42.6MM **Privately Held**
WEB: www.ashleyward.com
SIC: 3451 Screw machine products

PA: Ashley F. Ward, Inc.
7490 Easy St
Mason OH 45040
513 398-1414

(G-5055)
B & B TIMBER COMPANY
4880 Highway 17 S (32043-8139)
PHONE..................................904 284-5541
Merrill Batten, *Partner*
Melvin Batten, *Partner*
EMP: 7 **EST:** 1977
SALES (est): 843.3K **Privately Held**
SIC: 2411 Timber, cut at logging camp

(G-5056)
CALLOWAY BARGE LINES INC
967 Bulkhead Rd Pier 5 (32043-8340)
P.O. Box 188 (32043-0188)
PHONE..................................904 284-0503
Latham Smith, *President*
EMP: 9 **EST:** 2001
SALES (est): 286.5K **Privately Held**
SIC: 3441 Boat & barge sections, prefabricated metal

(G-5057)
CAPT LATHAM LLC
967 Bulkhead Rd (32043-8340)
PHONE..................................904 483-6118
Latham Smith, *Principal*
EMP: 7 **EST:** 2016
SALES (est): 94.6K **Privately Held**
WEB: www.smithmaritime.us
SIC: 3731 Shipbuilding & repairing

(G-5058)
CHARDONNAY BOAT WORKS LLC
411 Walnut St (32043-3443)
PHONE..................................703 981-6339
Scott Berg, *Principal*
EMP: 6 **EST:** 2010
SALES (est): 549.8K **Privately Held**
WEB: www.chardonnay.com
SIC: 3732 Boat building & repairing

(G-5059)
COMMERCIAL ENERGY SERVICES
1528 Virgils Way Ste 14 (32043-3781)
PHONE..................................904 589-1059
Shannon Cascarelli, *President*
Tracy Huff, *Vice Pres*
EMP: 10 **EST:** 2008
SALES (est): 976.4K **Privately Held**
SIC: 3646 Commercial indusl & institutional electric lighting fixtures

(G-5060)
ED-GAR LEASING COMPANY INC
1306 Idlewild Ave (32043-3805)
P.O. Box 726 (32043-0726)
PHONE..................................904 284-1900
Garland Deel, *President*
Edna Deel, *Vice Pres*
Edmond Deel, *Treasurer*
EMP: 10 **EST:** 1999
SQ FT: 1,260
SALES (est): 341K **Privately Held**
SIC: 1389 Lease tanks, oil field: erecting, cleaning & repairing

(G-5061)
FOX EQUIPMENT LLC (PA)
965 Bunker Ave (32043-8346)
PHONE..................................904 531-3150
Kevin Simpson, *Engineer*
Barbara Riggs, *Marketing Mgr*
Eric W Fox, *Mng Member*
Jim Garrett, *Manager*
Edward Fox,
EMP: 26 **EST:** 2003
SALES (est): 8.3MM **Privately Held**
WEB: www.foxequipment.com
SIC: 3441 Expansion joints (structural shapes), iron or steel

(G-5062)
FOX MANUFACTURING LLC
965 Bunker Ave (32043-8346)
PHONE..................................904 531-3150
Eric Fox, *Mng Member*
EMP: 6 **EST:** 2011
SALES (est): 39.6K **Privately Held**
SIC: 3999 Manufacturing industries

(G-5063)
GENEVA SYSTEMS INC
712 Simmons Trl (32043-9567)
PHONE..................................352 235-2990
Robert J McMullen, *Principal*
EMP: 7 **EST:** 2008
SALES (est): 354.8K **Privately Held**
WEB: www.genevaservice.com
SIC: 3699 Cleaning equipment, ultrasonic, except medical & dental

(G-5064)
HBP PIPE & PRECAST LLC
4210 Highway 17 S Us (32043-8137)
PHONE..................................904 529-8228
EMP: 36
SALES (corp-wide): 15.6B **Privately Held**
SIC: 3272 Mfg Concrete Products
HQ: Hbp Pipe & Precast Llc
300 E John Carpenter Fwy
Irving TX 75062
972 653-5500

(G-5065)
HERITAGE SIGNS
1282 Energy Cove Ct (32043-4308)
PHONE..................................904 529-7446
Denise Mankinen, *Principal*
Jonathan Knight, *Opers Staff*
Mary Knight, *Sales Staff*
Chuck Knight, *Sales Executive*
EMP: 6 **EST:** 2008
SALES (est): 532.1K **Privately Held**
WEB: www.heritagesignsfl.com
SIC: 3993 Signs & advertising specialties

(G-5066)
HUMIC GROWTH SOLUTIONS INC
938 Hall Park Rd (32043-4934)
PHONE..................................904 329-1012
Kevin Merritt, *President*
EMP: 9
SALES (corp-wide): 10MM **Privately Held**
SIC: 2879 Soil conditioners
PA: Humic Growth Solutions, Inc.
709 Eastport Rd
Jacksonville FL 32218
904 392-7201

(G-5067)
NEW WORLD ENCLOSURES INC
1350 Riviera Dr (32043-8764)
PHONE..................................904 334-4752
Wendy Serrentino, *Principal*
EMP: 12 **EST:** 2007
SALES (est): 660K **Privately Held**
WEB: www.newworldenclosures.com
SIC: 3448 Screen enclosures

(G-5068)
ROLLER DIE + FORMING
4630 County Road 209 S (32043-8182)
PHONE..................................502 804-5571
Cathy Deckard, *Controller*
EMP: 23 **EST:** 2016
SALES (est): 5.8MM **Privately Held**
WEB: www.rollerdie.com
SIC: 3544 Special dies & tools

(G-5069)
RYAN SCIENTIFIC LLC
4035a Reynolds Blvd (32043-8360)
PHONE..................................904 284-6025
Nisa Ryan, *Mng Member*
Dale Ryan, *Mng Member*
EMP: 19 **EST:** 2013
SALES (est): 800K **Privately Held**
SIC: 3296 5063 5999 Fiberglass insulation; electrical supplies; fiberglass materials, except insulation

(G-5070)
RYMAN HOSPITALITY PRPTS INC
625 Oak St (32043-4313)
PHONE..................................904 284-2770
Richard Loftus, *Branch Mgr*
EMP: 544
SALES (corp-wide): 524.4MM **Privately Held**
WEB: www.rymanhp.com
SIC: 3949 Lures, fishing: artificial
PA: Ryman Hospitality Properties, Inc.
1 Gaylord Dr
Nashville TN 37214
615 316-6000

(G-5071)
SHARK TOOTH ENTERPRISES INC
Also Called: R & J Enterprises
981 Martin Ave (32043-8354)
PHONE..................................904 449-8247
Steven W Tyler, *President*
EMP: 20 **EST:** 2008
SQ FT: 28,000
SALES (est): 1.1MM **Privately Held**
WEB: www.rjaquatics.com
SIC: 3231 Aquariums & reflectors, glass

(G-5072)
TAPE TECHNOLOGIES INC
Also Called: Coating Laminating Converting
1272 Harbor Rd (32043-8729)
P.O. Box 56 (32043-0056)
PHONE..................................904 284-0284
Samuel R Phillips, *President*
Michael Tress, *Production*
Tom McTighe, *Natl Sales Mgr*
Sergio Sandoval, *Sales Mgr*
Dana Kominski, *Regl Sales Mgr*
◆ **EMP:** 45 **EST:** 1986
SQ FT: 43,000
SALES (est): 5.3MM **Privately Held**
WEB: www.tapetechnologies.com
SIC: 3081 Unsupported plastics film & sheet

(G-5073)
TRINITY FABRICATORS INC
825 Corporate Sq (32043-3748)
P.O. Box 1826 (32043-1826)
PHONE..................................904 284-9657
Merrill C Westfall, *President*
Damon A Westfall, *Corp Secy*
Daniel M Westfall, *Vice Pres*
EMP: 46 **EST:** 1984
SQ FT: 45,000
SALES (est): 8.1MM **Privately Held**
SIC: 3441 Fabricated structural metal

(G-5074)
U2 CLOUD LLC
1300 Cooks Ln (32043-8988)
PHONE..................................888 370-5433
Diane Wood, *Bookkeeper*
Amanda Juneau, *Accounts Exec*
Joe F Solsona, *Mng Member*
Pete Valentine, *CTO*
Brian Luke, *Software Dev*
EMP: 22 **EST:** 2010
SQ FT: 8,000
SALES (est): 1.3MM **Privately Held**
WEB: www.u2cloud.com
SIC: 7372 Application computer software

(G-5075)
VAC-CON INC (HQ)
969 Hall Park Rd (32043-4940)
PHONE..................................904 284-4200
Darrell Lesage, *President*
Mark Wardlaw, *Regional Mgr*
Greg Hamilton, *Corp Secy*
Todd Masley, *Exec VP*
Alexandra Acevedo-Yates, *Opers Staff*
◆ **EMP:** 271 **EST:** 1987
SALES (est): 69.6MM
SALES (corp-wide): 730.1MM **Privately Held**
WEB: www.vac-con.com
SIC: 3711 3589 Motor vehicles & car bodies; motor trucks, except off-highway, assembly of; sewer cleaning equipment, power
PA: Holden Industries, Inc.
500 Lake Cook Rd Ste 400
Deerfield IL 60015
847 940-1500

(G-5076)
VIRGINIA ELECTRONIC & LTG CORP (PA)
Also Called: Velcorp Gems Vels
1293 Energy Cove Ct (32043-4302)
PHONE..................................904 230-2840
Gregory Stepp, *CEO*
Ray Stephens, *Treasurer*
▲ **EMP:** 5 **EST:** 1994
SQ FT: 1,000
SALES (est): 794.9K **Privately Held**
WEB: www.velcorpgems.com
SIC: 3648 5023 7629 7389 Airport lighting fixtures: runway approach, taxi or ramp; lamps: floor, boudoir, desk; electrical repair shops; design services

(G-5077)
WORTH METALS INC
4135 Highway 17 S (32043-8137)
PHONE..................................904 626-1434
Timothy P Worth, *President*
EMP: 16 **EST:** 2007
SALES (est): 3.3MM **Privately Held**
WEB: www.worthmetalsincfl.com
SIC: 3448 3499 Prefabricated metal buildings; fabricated metal products

Greenacres
Palm Beach County

(G-5078)
CONCRAFT INC (PA)
Also Called: Concraft Patio Products
353 Swain Blvd (33463-3341)
PHONE..................................561 689-0149
Neil Stegall, *President*
Eric Stegall, *Vice Pres*
EMP: 6 **EST:** 1957
SQ FT: 7,500
SALES (est): 950.8K **Privately Held**
SIC: 3272 5999 Concrete products, precast; concrete products, pre-cast

(G-5079)
DECOR CUSTOM WOODWORK LLC ✪
925 Pine Cir (33463-4109)
PHONE..................................561 631-3240
Velma Gayle, *Mng Member*
EMP: 6 **EST:** 2020
SALES (est): 54.1K **Privately Held**
SIC: 2431 Millwork

(G-5080)
ESSENTIAL PUBLISHING GROUP LLC
5319 Lake Worth Rd (33463-3353)
PHONE..................................561 570-7165
EMP: 20
SALES (corp-wide): 456.5K **Privately Held**
WEB: www.cclifeandhome.com
SIC: 2741 Miscellaneous publishing
PA: Essential Publishing Group Llc
1140 Holland Dr Ste 21
Boca Raton FL 33487
410 440-5777

(G-5081)
GOLD BUYERS OF AMERICA LLC
2001 20th Ln (33463-4259)
PHONE..................................877 721-8033
EMP: 184 **Privately Held**
SIC: 3356 Nonferrous Rolling/Drawing
PA: Gold Buyers Of America, Llc
2790 Windham Ct
Delray Beach FL 33445

(G-5082)
HOFFMAN COMMERCIAL GROUP INC (HQ)
Also Called: Hoffman's Chocolates
5190 Lake Worth Rd (33463-3351)
PHONE..................................561 967-2213
Fredrick Meltzer, *CEO*
Jarett Levan, *President*
Chuck Mohr, *President*
Sandra Hoffman, *Exec VP*
Randall Vitale, *Vice Pres*
▲ **EMP:** 30 **EST:** 1975

SQ FT: 15,000
SALES (est): 6MM
SALES (corp-wide): 519.4MM **Publicly Held**
WEB: www.hoffmans.com
SIC: 2064 5145 5441 2066 Candy & other confectionery products; candy; confectionery produced for direct sale on the premises; candy; chocolate candy, solid
PA: Bluegreen Vacations Holding Corporation
401 E Las Olas Blvd Fl 8
Fort Lauderdale FL 33301
954 940-4900

(G-5083)
IMMUNOTEK BIO CENTERS LLC
4560 Lake Worth Rd (33463-3450)
PHONE..................................561 270-6712
Alison Comegys, *Controller*
Rendi Dillard, *Manager*
EMP: 29
SALES (corp-wide): 27MM **Privately Held**
WEB: www.immunotek.com
SIC: 2836 Blood derivatives
PA: Immunotek Bio Centers, L.L.C.
3900 N Causeway Blvd # 1200
Metairie LA 70002
337 500-1175

(G-5084)
KID GROUP INC
4010 S 57th Ave Ste 104 (33463-4301)
PHONE..................................888 805-8851
Keren Aydogan, *President*
EMP: 5 **EST:** 2010
SALES (est): 966.2K **Privately Held**
WEB: www.sepconn.com
SIC: 3679 Electronic circuits

(G-5085)
PURE CANVAS INC
4849 Lake Worth Rd (33463-3461)
PHONE..................................561 818-2655
Derrick Abellard, *President*
EMP: 6 **EST:** 2013
SALES (est): 143.8K **Privately Held**
SIC: 2211 Canvas

(G-5086)
RELCOM INDUSTRIES INC
3900 Woodlake Blvd # 200 (33463-3044)
PHONE..................................561 304-7717
Allan Liebowitz, *Owner*
EMP: 5 **EST:** 2005
SALES (est): 700K **Privately Held**
WEB: www.relcominc.com
SIC: 3679 Electronic circuits

(G-5087)
SAPPHIRE LLC
6432 Melaleuca Ln (33463-3807)
PHONE..................................561 346-7449
Patrick Adams, *Principal*
EMP: 6 **EST:** 2013
SALES (est): 312.8K **Privately Held**
SIC: 3993 Signs & advertising specialties

Greenville
Madison County

(G-5088)
FLORIDA PLYWOODS INC
1228 Nw Us 221 (32331-4268)
P.O. Box 458 (32331-0458)
PHONE..................................850 948-2211
John Maultsby Jr, *President*
Charles Maultsby, *President*
Arthur Maultsby, *Executive*
EMP: 75 **EST:** 1956
SQ FT: 100,000
SALES (est): 7.2MM **Privately Held**
WEB: www.flply.com
SIC: 2434 2493 Wood kitchen cabinets; particleboard products

Greenwood
Jackson County

(G-5089)
L W TIMBER CO INC
3830 Highway 69 (32443-2150)
PHONE..................................850 592-2597
Charles M Leslie, *Director*
EMP: 6
SALES (est): 424.1K **Privately Held**
SIC: 2411 Timber, cut at logging camp

Gretna
Gadsden County

(G-5090)
CDS MANUFACTURING INC
106 Charles Hayes Sr Dr (32332-2406)
PHONE..................................850 875-4651
Melanie D Sembler, *CEO*
Clayton H Sembler, *President*
Michael Mall, *Vice Pres*
Angel Majors, *Controller*
EMP: 52 **EST:** 1999
SALES (est): 8.4MM **Privately Held**
WEB: www.dynalive.net
SIC: 3272 Precast terrazo or concrete products; concrete products, precast; prestressed concrete products

Groveland
Lake County

(G-5091)
ACCU TECH LLC
1506 Max Hooks Rd Ste E (34736-8037)
PHONE..................................407 446-6676
Gary D Akers, *Principal*
EMP: 9 **EST:** 2012
SALES (est): 896.3K **Privately Held**
SIC: 3089 Injection molding of plastics

(G-5092)
ACR FAMILY COMPONENTS LLC
19900 Independence Blvd (34736-8535)
PHONE..................................352 243-0307
Arthur V Raney,
EMP: 29 **EST:** 2006
SALES (est): 11.2MM **Privately Held**
SIC: 3679 Electronic circuits

(G-5093)
AFFORDABLE SIGNS CLERMONT LLC
1502 Max Hooks Rd Ste C (34736-8025)
PHONE..................................352 241-7645
Cindy Graham, *Principal*
EMP: 6 **EST:** 2010
SALES (est): 193.1K **Privately Held**
WEB: www.affordablesignsclermont.com
SIC: 3993 Signs & advertising specialties

(G-5094)
CUSTOM CABINET FACTORY INC
642 W Broad St (34736-2406)
PHONE..................................352 429-7722
Anthony Willis, *President*
Bonny Willis, *Vice Pres*
EMP: 7 **EST:** 1989
SQ FT: 2,184
SALES (est): 850K **Privately Held**
SIC: 2434 Wood kitchen cabinets

(G-5095)
GJCB SIGNS GRAPHICS INC
Also Called: Jds Uniforms
136 S Main Ave (34736-2554)
PHONE..................................352 429-0803
Charles G Thompson, *President*
Jennifer S Thompson, *Vice Pres*
EMP: 11 **EST:** 2014
SALES (est): 304.4K **Privately Held**
WEB: www.linkprintingcf.com
SIC: 3993 Signs & advertising specialties

(G-5096)
GL SHAVINGS LLC
26444 County Road 33 (34736-8651)
PHONE..................................352 360-0063
EMP: 6 **EST:** 2015
SALES (est): 121.5K **Privately Held**
SIC: 2493 Reconstituted wood products

(G-5097)
INTERNL STERILIZATION LAB LLC
Also Called: Isl
217 Sampey Rd (34736-3305)
PHONE..................................352 429-3200
Yasushi Kuki, *President*
Lori Swisher, *Manager*
EMP: 9 **EST:** 1996
SQ FT: 12,080
SALES (est): 1.4MM **Privately Held**
WEB: www.isl-fl.com
SIC: 3842 Sterilizers, hospital & surgical

(G-5098)
JAYSHREE HOLDINGS INC
18830 State Road 19 (34736-8658)
P.O. Box 397 (34736-0397)
PHONE..................................352 429-1000
Sudhir Bhagani, *President*
Jayshree Bhagani, *Vice Pres*
Nitesh Bhagani, *Sales Staff*
EMP: 24 **EST:** 1989
SQ FT: 8,000
SALES (est): 635K **Privately Held**
WEB: www.jayshree.com
SIC: 2099 0139 Seasonings & spices; herb or spice farm

(G-5099)
LAWLESS INDUSTRIES LTD
19994 Independence Blvd (34736-8535)
PHONE..................................352 429-3300
Shawn D Lawless, *President*
EMP: 6 **EST:** 2014
SALES (est): 198.4K **Privately Held**
SIC: 3999 Manufacturing industries

(G-5100)
MAJESTIC WOODWORKS
156 Groveland Farms Rd (34736-2026)
PHONE..................................352 429-2520
Laurie Summers Tueros, *Principal*
EMP: 9 **EST:** 2014
SALES (est): 353.8K **Privately Held**
WEB: www.majesticcustomwood.com
SIC: 2434 Wood kitchen cabinets

(G-5101)
MARITEC INDUSTRIES INC
Also Called: Gambler Bass Boats
20150 Independence Blvd (34736-8528)
PHONE..................................352 429-8888
Thurston R Ackerbloom Jr, *President*
Leonard D Jones, *Vice Pres*
EMP: 55
SQ FT: 45,000
SALES: 10.4MM **Privately Held**
WEB: www.gamblerboats.com
SIC: 3732 Fishing boats: lobster, crab, oyster, etc.: small

(G-5102)
NIAGARA BOTTLING LLC
7633 American Way (34736-8650)
PHONE..................................352 429-3611
Jay Deichler, *Engineer*
David Lockwood, *VP Sales*
Mary Bevins, *Branch Mgr*
Shane Rupe,
EMP: 6
SALES (corp-wide): 151.5MM **Privately Held**
WEB: www.niagarawater.com
SIC: 2086 Water, pasteurized: packaged in cans, bottles, etc.
PA: Niagara Bottling, Llc
1440 Bridgegate Dr
Diamond Bar CA 91765
909 230-5000

(G-5103)
NOVELTY CRYSTAL CORP
21005 Obrien Rd (34736-9590)
PHONE..................................352 429-9036
Rivka Michaeli, *President*
Ed Coslett, *COO*
Asher Michaeli, *Exec VP*
Joseph Michaeli, *Senior VP*
Edward Coslett, *Vice Pres*
▲ **EMP:** 100 **EST:** 1961
SQ FT: 50,000
SALES (est): 8.8MM **Privately Held**
WEB: www.noveltycrystal.com
SIC: 3421 3089 Cutlery; plastic kitchenware, tableware & houseware; kitchenware, plastic

(G-5104)
NOVELTY CRYSTAL CORP
Also Called: Ncc Promotional
21005 Obrien Rd (34736-9590)
PHONE..................................352 429-9036
EMP: 20
SALES (corp-wide): 11.6MM **Privately Held**
SIC: 3089 Mfg Plastic Products
PA: Novelty Crystal Corp.
3015 48th Ave
Long Island City NY 34736
718 458-6700

(G-5105)
POST MORTEM PUBLICATIONS INC
146 E Broad St (34736-4003)
PHONE..................................352 429-1133
James J Baumann, *Principal*
EMP: 8 **EST:** 2010
SALES (est): 113.7K **Privately Held**
SIC: 2741 Miscellaneous publishing

(G-5106)
QUIET FLEX
7730 American Way (34736-8649)
PHONE..................................352 429-3286
EMP: 14 **EST:** 2017
SALES (est): 1.6MM **Privately Held**
WEB: www.quietflex.com
SIC: 3296 Mineral wool

(G-5107)
ROZAR LOGGING INC
847 Crawford Rd (34736-9280)
PHONE..................................352 267-0829
EMP: 7 **EST:** 2019
SALES (est): 98.8K **Privately Held**
SIC: 2411 Logging camps & contractors

(G-5108)
SHIFTED INDUSTRIES
6930 Swamp Dr (34736-8437)
PHONE..................................561 302-8915
Caleb Rennekamp, *Principal*
EMP: 6 **EST:** 2018
SALES (est): 298.4K **Privately Held**
WEB: www.shiftedind.com
SIC: 3999 Manufacturing industries

(G-5109)
VISION WOODWORKING INC
193 Hidden View Dr (34736-8837)
PHONE..................................407 493-9665
Luke Gavin III, *Principal*
Andrea Ranstrom, *Human Resources*
John Stewart, *Manager*
EMP: 7 **EST:** 2009
SALES (est): 91.6K **Privately Held**
WEB: www.visionwoodworking.com
SIC: 2431 Millwork

Gulf Breeze
Santa Rosa County

(G-5110)
A PLUS MARINE SUPPLY INC (PA)
212 Mcclure Dr (32561-7401)
PHONE..................................850 934-3890
Eric W Duntz, *President*
Dana Gonzales, *Corp Secy*
◆ **EMP:** 5 **EST:** 1989
SQ FT: 2,500
SALES (est): 691K **Privately Held**
WEB: www.aplusmarine.com
SIC: 3949 5091 Skin diving equipment, scuba type; diving equipment & supplies

(G-5111)
ALOHA SCREEN PRINTING INC
2635 Gulf Breeze Pkwy (32563-3023)
PHONE.................................850 934-4716
Rodney Lopaka Robello, *President*
Chad Kaipo Robello, *Vice Pres*
EMP: 5 **EST:** 1994
SQ FT: 900
SALES (est): 346.2K **Privately Held**
WEB: www.alohascreenprinting.com
SIC: 2396 2759 Screen printing on fabric articles; screen printing

(G-5112)
ASCEND PRFMCE MTLS OPRTONS LLC
200 Pensacola Beach Rd B3 (32561-4840)
PHONE.................................734 819-0656
Chong Kim, *Branch Mgr*
EMP: 268
SALES (corp-wide): 1.4B **Privately Held**
WEB: www.ascendmaterials.com
SIC: 2821 Plastics materials & resins
HQ: Ascend Performance Materials Operations Llc
1010 Travis St Ste 900
Houston TX 77002

(G-5113)
AVALEX TECHNOLOGIES CORP
2665 Gulf Breeze Pkwy (32563-3023)
PHONE.................................850 470-8464
Tad Ihns, *CEO*
Jurgen R Ihns, *President*
Paul Stephens, *Business Mgr*
Tony Hatten, *Vice Pres*
David Phillips, *Mfg Mgr*
▼ **EMP:** 85 **EST:** 1992
SQ FT: 1,500
SALES (est): 26.2MM **Privately Held**
WEB: www.avalex.com
SIC: 3812 Aircraft control systems, electronic

(G-5114)
COASTAL PADDLE CO LLC
848 Gulf Breeze Pkwy (32561-4723)
PHONE.................................850 916-1600
Randy Cook Jr, *Mng Member*
EMP: 10 **EST:** 2010
SALES (est): 431.2K **Privately Held**
WEB: www.coastalpaddlecompany.com
SIC: 2499 2339 Oars & paddles, wood; women's & misses' accessories

(G-5115)
DARK HORSE SIGNS AND PRTG LLC
6476 Starfish Cv (32563-9079)
PHONE.................................850 684-3833
Caleb Rogers, *Principal*
EMP: 7 **EST:** 2017
SALES (est): 378.2K **Privately Held**
WEB: www.darkhorsesignsandprinting.com
SIC: 2752 Commercial printing, lithographic

(G-5116)
DUPONT FINE HOMES INC
4371 Marilyn Ct (32563-9165)
PHONE.................................850 934-8545
Mrs Ruth D Esser, *Admin Sec*
EMP: 6 **EST:** 2016
SALES (est): 260.7K **Privately Held**
SIC: 2879 Agricultural chemicals

(G-5117)
GULF BREEZE NEWS INC
913 Gulf Breeze Pkwy # 35 (32561-4729)
P.O. Box 1414 (32562-1414)
PHONE.................................850 932-8986
Lisa Newell, *President*
Bob Harriman, *COO*
Laura Lane, *Director*
Gregory Papajohn, *Director*
Victoria Papajohn, *Director*
EMP: 5 **EST:** 2001
SALES (est): 1MM **Privately Held**
WEB: www.gulfbreezenews.com
SIC: 2711 Newspapers, publishing & printing

(G-5118)
GULF COAST SHADES & BLINDS LLC
714 Roanoke Ct (32561-4509)
PHONE.................................850 332-2100
Joseph D Selogy, *Principal*
EMP: 10 **EST:** 2018
SALES (est): 1MM **Privately Held**
WEB: www.gcshadesandblinds.com
SIC: 2591 Window blinds

(G-5119)
HOGENKAMP RESEARCH INC
308 Plantation Hill Rd (32561-4818)
PHONE.................................850 677-1072
James D Doyle, *Owner*
▲ **EMP:** 10 **EST:** 1990
SALES (est): 903.9K **Privately Held**
WEB: www.hogenkampresearch.com
SIC: 2611 Pulp manufactured from waste or recycled paper

(G-5120)
INTEGRATED SURROUNDINGS INC
4333 Gulf Breeze Pkwy (32563-9152)
PHONE.................................850 932-0848
Roy Pedersen, *President*
David Gray, *COO*
Derek Elmore, *Vice Pres*
EMP: 14 **EST:** 2008
SALES (est): 2.4MM **Privately Held**
WEB: www.integratedsurroundings.com
SIC: 3699 1731 Security control equipment & systems; energy management controls

(G-5121)
MORRISSY & CO
204 Fairpoint Dr (32561-4308)
P.O. Box 1434 (32562-1434)
PHONE.................................850 934-4243
EMP: 5
SALES: 300K **Privately Held**
SIC: 7372 Prepackaged Software Services

(G-5122)
NORTH AMERICA WIRELINE LLC
6057 Clay Cir (32563-9715)
PHONE.................................870 365-5401
EMP: 7 **EST:** 2019
SALES (est): 4MM **Privately Held**
WEB: www.awireline.com
SIC: 1389 Oil field services

(G-5123)
NORTH W FLA CNCIL OF BLIND COR
2807 Sandy Ridge Rd (32563-2603)
PHONE.................................850 982-7867
Barbara Reeves, *Principal*
EMP: 6 **EST:** 2018
SALES (est): 84.2K **Privately Held**
SIC: 2591 Window blinds

(G-5124)
POP EM SOCK EMS
675 Gulf Breeze Pkwy (32561-4630)
PHONE.................................850 287-3778
Hannah May, *Principal*
EMP: 6 **EST:** 2018
SALES (est): 119.2K **Privately Held**
SIC: 2252 Socks

(G-5125)
SANDPAPER PUBLISHING INC
7502 Harvest Village Ct (32566-7319)
PHONE.................................850 939-8040
Sandra Kemp, *President*
EMP: 9 **EST:** 1997
SQ FT: 2,400
SALES (est): 991.6K **Privately Held**
WEB: www.navarrepress.com
SIC: 2741 Miscellaneous publishing

(G-5126)
SEPARATION SYSTEMS INC
100 Nightingale Ln A (32561-4300)
PHONE.................................850 932-1433
Joaquin Lubkowitz, *President*
Adela Lubkowitz, *Vice Pres*
Bob Belair, *Sales Staff*
EMP: 10 **EST:** 1990
SQ FT: 1,300
SALES (est): 2.1MM **Privately Held**
WEB: www.separationsystems.com
SIC: 3826 Gas chromatographic instruments

(G-5127)
SQUARED MACHINE & TOOL INC A
1851 Cowen Rd Unit F (32563-4109)
PHONE.................................678 988-2477
Chris Wysoczynski, *Principal*
EMP: 11 **EST:** 2017
SALES (est): 286.7K **Privately Held**
WEB: www.asquaredmachineandtool.com
SIC: 3599 Machine shop, jobbing & repair

(G-5128)
T SALS SHIRT CO
1161 Oriole Beach Rd (32563-3260)
PHONE.................................850 916-9229
Becky Serio, *Owner*
EMP: 10 **EST:** 1972
SALES (est): 984.5K **Privately Held**
WEB: www.salstshirts.com
SIC: 2759 Screen printing

(G-5129)
TASTE OF THAI LLC
3475 Gulf Breeze Pkwy (32563-1402)
PHONE.................................850 581-3340
Viparat B Pippin,
EMP: 5 **EST:** 2012
SALES (est): 397.7K **Privately Held**
WEB: www.tasteofthaillc.com
SIC: 3421 Table & food cutlery, including butchers'

(G-5130)
TOWN STREET PRINT SHOP INC
Also Called: Tmt Printing & Mailing
1142 Bayview Ln (32563-3302)
P.O. Box 18630, Pensacola (32523-8630)
PHONE.................................850 432-8300
Linda Traweek, *Vice Pres*
Dennis Malloy, *Manager*
Angela Tarweek, *Admin Sec*
EMP: 5 **EST:** 1972
SQ FT: 5,000
SALES (est): 500K **Privately Held**
SIC: 2752 7331 2791 2789 Commercial printing, offset; mailing service; typesetting; bookbinding & related work

(G-5131)
VINYL BROS
5668 Gulf Breeze Pkwy # 4 (32563-9524)
PHONE.................................850 396-5977
Cory Malesa, *President*
EMP: 6 **EST:** 2017
SALES (est): 223.4K **Privately Held**
WEB: www.vinylbrosfl.com
SIC: 3993 Signs & advertising specialties

Gulfport
Pinellas County

(G-5132)
BERNAT INDUSTRIES INTL LLC
5133 Gulfport Blvd S (33707-4943)
PHONE.................................727 350-5904
Felana Bernat, *Principal*
EMP: 6 **EST:** 2018
SALES (est): 176K **Privately Held**
SIC: 3999 Manufacturing industries

(G-5133)
FULL BORE DIRECTIONAL INC
4921 15th Ave S (33707-4317)
PHONE.................................727 327-7784
EMP: 5
SQ FT: 900
SALES (est): 500K **Privately Held**
SIC: 1381 Oil/Gas Well Drilling

(G-5134)
GULFCOAST GABBER INC
1419 49th St S (33707-4301)
PHONE.................................727 321-6965
Ken Reichart, *President*
EMP: 6 **EST:** 1986
SALES (est): 613.5K **Privately Held**
WEB: www.thegabber.com
SIC: 2711 Newspapers, publishing & printing

(G-5135)
GULFPORT GRIND INC
5825 20th Ave S (33707-4049)
PHONE.................................727 343-2785
Theodore Kehoe, *Principal*
EMP: 9 **EST:** 2012
SALES (est): 98.6K **Privately Held**
WEB: www.mygulfport.us
SIC: 3599 Grinding castings for the trade

(G-5136)
PFA PUBLISHING
6020 Shore Blvd S (33707-5801)
PHONE.................................727 512-5814
Vernon Fitch, *Principal*
EMP: 11 **EST:** 2007
SALES (est): 97.8K **Privately Held**
WEB: www.pinkfloydarchives.com
SIC: 2741 Miscellaneous publishing

Haines City
Polk County

(G-5137)
AERCON FLORIDA LLC
3701 State Road 544 E (33844-8898)
PHONE.................................863 422-6360
Mike Quaka, *General Mgr*
Mike McCormick, *General Mgr*
Brian Tully, *Technical Mgr*
Nida Pone, *Sales Engr*
◆ **EMP:** 66 **EST:** 2002
SQ FT: 95,000
SALES (est): 12.1MM **Privately Held**
WEB: www.aerconaac.com
SIC: 3272 Concrete products, precast

(G-5138)
CENTRAL ELECTRIC MOTOR SERVICE
313 N 12th St (33844-4403)
P.O. Box 696 (33845-0696)
PHONE.................................863 422-4721
Joey Rulli, *President*
EMP: 10 **EST:** 1969
SQ FT: 6,435
SALES (est): 727.8K **Privately Held**
SIC: 7694 7699 1731 1623 Electric motor repair; pumps & pumping equipment repair; electrical work; pumping station construction

(G-5139)
COST CAST INC
1301 W Commerce Ave (33844-3292)
PHONE.................................863 422-5617
Gary Kallmeyer, *President*
Alex Wilding, *Engineer*
Wendy Huntley, *Office Mgr*
EMP: 17 **EST:** 2017
SALES (est): 1.8MM **Privately Held**
WEB: www.costcast.com
SIC: 3599 Machine shop, jobbing & repair

(G-5140)
COST CAST ALUMINUM CORP
1301 W Commerce Ave (33844-3292)
PHONE.................................863 422-5617
Gary Kallmeyer, *President*
EMP: 32 **EST:** 1966
SQ FT: 9,380
SALES (est): 809.4K **Privately Held**
WEB: www.costcast.com
SIC: 3365 3543 3369 Aluminum foundries; industrial patterns; nonferrous foundries

(G-5141)
CROMER PRINTING INC
Also Called: Cromer International Press
24 N 6th St (33844-4206)
P.O. Box 1268 (33845-1268)
PHONE.................................863 422-8651
Bobbi C Freeman, *President*
Turner Baker, *Manager*
James Robert Freeman, *Manager*
Sharon Lepsic, *Manager*
Margie Wells, *Manager*
EMP: 19 **EST:** 1971

SALES (est): 3.5MM **Privately Held**
WEB: www.cromerprinting.com
SIC: 2752 Commercial printing, offset
PA: The Pamatian Group Inc
997 W Kennedy Blvd Ste A1
Orlando FL 32810
407 291-8387

(G-5142)
ER JAHNA INDUSTRIES INC
Also Called: Haines City Mine
4910 State Road 544 E (33844-8739)
PHONE..................................863 422-7617
Brian Corley, *Sales Staff*
Emil R Jahna, *Marketing Staff*
Dalton Jahna, *Branch Mgr*
Kirk Davis, *Director*
Jake Simmons, *Director*
EMP: 7
SALES (corp-wide): 70.5MM **Privately Held**
WEB: www.jahna.com
SIC: 1442 Construction sand & gravel
PA: E.R. Jahna Industries, Inc.
202 E Stuart Ave
Lake Wales FL 33853
863 676-9431

(G-5143)
FLOYD FABRICATION LLC
2821 Sanderling St (33844-8444)
PHONE..................................330 289-7351
Ben Floyd, *Principal*
EMP: 7 **EST:** 2019
SALES (est): 368.3K **Privately Held**
WEB: www.floydfabrication.com
SIC: 7692 Welding repair

(G-5144)
OLDCASTLE APG SOUTH INC
1980 Marley Dr (33844-9202)
PHONE..................................863 421-7422
▲ **EMP:** 14 **EST:** 2013
SALES (est): 2.8MM **Privately Held**
WEB: www.oldcastlecoastal.com
SIC: 3272 Concrete products

(G-5145)
POWER WTHIN CNSLING CNSLTN LLC
280 Patterson Rd Ste 1 (33844-6261)
PHONE..................................863 242-3023
Cheryl Cyr,
EMP: 5 **EST:** 2018
SALES (est): 335K **Privately Held**
WEB: www.powerwithincc.com
SIC: 3844 Therapeutic X-ray apparatus & tubes

(G-5146)
PRE-TECH INC
3052 Us Highway 17 92 N (33844-9541)
PHONE..................................863 422-5079
Larry E Witherington, *President*
Kathleen Witherington, *Admin Sec*
EMP: 5 **EST:** 1981
SQ FT: 8,000
SALES (est): 451.7K **Privately Held**
WEB: www.pre-tech.net
SIC: 3599 Machine shop, jobbing & repair

(G-5147)
QUALITY METAL WORX
1306 Melbourne Ave (33844-4810)
PHONE..................................863 353-6638
Todd Dunnahoe, *Principal*
EMP: 8 **EST:** 2016
SALES (est): 1.1MM **Privately Held**
WEB: www.quality-metal-worx.business.site
SIC: 3441 7692 Fabricated structural metal; welding repair

(G-5148)
STANDARD SAND & SILICA COMPANY
2 Us Highway 17 92 N (33844-4826)
P.O. Box 1240, Davenport (33836-1240)
PHONE..................................863 419-9673
Brynn Summerlin, *Manager*
Stacee Jackson, *Receptionist*
EMP: 7
SALES (corp-wide): 50.3MM **Privately Held**
WEB: www.standardsand.com
SIC: 3471 1446 Sand blasting of metal parts; abrasive sand mining
PA: Standard Sand & Silica Company
1850 Us Highway 17 92 N
Davenport FL 33837
863 422-7100

(G-5149)
STANDARD TRUSS & ROOF SUP INC
608 N 12th St (33844-4471)
PHONE..................................863 422-8293
James Mc Intee, *President*
David Mc Intee, *Vice Pres*
Steven Mc Intee, *Treasurer*
Sheryl Wolkenhauer, *Admin Sec*
EMP: 25 **EST:** 1978
SQ FT: 23,640
SALES (est): 3.2MM **Privately Held**
SIC: 2439 Trusses, wooden roof

(G-5150)
SUN ORCHARD LLC
1200 S 30th St (33844-9099)
P.O. Box 2008 (33845-2008)
PHONE..................................863 422-5062
Duane Walker, *Engineer*
Scott Mosher, *Controller*
Jean-Marc Rotsaert, *Branch Mgr*
EMP: 100
SALES (corp-wide): 65.2MM **Privately Held**
WEB: www.sunorchard.com
SIC: 2033 Canned fruits & specialties
PA: Sun Orchard, Llc
1198 W Frmont Dr Ste 2350
Miami FL 33131
786 646-9200

(G-5151)
TECHNOLOGY RESEARCH CONS INC
2801 Us Highway 17 92 W (33844-9372)
PHONE..................................863 419-8860
EMP: 7 **EST:** 2019
SALES (est): 289.3K **Privately Held**
SIC: 3728 Aircraft parts & equipment

Hallandale
Broward County

(G-5152)
AQUATIC FABRICATORS OF S FLA
Also Called: Aquatic Wetsuits
2930 Sw 30th Ave Ste A (33009-5142)
PHONE..................................954 458-0400
Gene Sonnabend, *Principal*
Connie Sonnabend, *Admin Sec*
EMP: 6 **EST:** 1991
SQ FT: 2,500
SALES (est): 709K **Privately Held**
WEB: www.wetwear.com
SIC: 3069 Wet suits, rubber

(G-5153)
ATLANTIC SHIP SUPPLY INC
2050 Sw 31st Ave (33009-2027)
PHONE..................................954 961-8885
Adam Notis, *President*
▼ **EMP:** 7 **EST:** 2004
SALES (est): 247K **Privately Held**
SIC: 2674 Shipping & shopping bags or sacks

(G-5154)
CHIPTECH INC (PA)
Also Called: Vertical Cable
2885 Sw 30th Ave (33009-3801)
PHONE..................................954 454-3554
Mike Sattarzadeh, *President*
Jenny Maloney, *Accounting Mgr*
Adam Moore, *Regl Sales Mgr*
◆ **EMP:** 11 **EST:** 1989
SQ FT: 22,000
SALES (est): 7.1MM **Privately Held**
WEB: www.verticalcable.com
SIC: 2298 Cable, fiber

(G-5155)
CORONA PRINTING COMPANY INC
1833 Sw 31st Ave (33009-2020)
PHONE..................................754 263-2914
EMP: 5 **EST:** 2018
SALES (est): 323.8K **Privately Held**
SIC: 2752 Commercial printing, lithographic

(G-5156)
EDDY FLOOR SCRAPER INC
1806 Sw 31st Ave (33009-2024)
PHONE..................................954 981-0715
Stephane Tailly, *CEO*
◆ **EMP:** 5 **EST:** 1999
SQ FT: 9,000
SALES (est): 430.7K **Privately Held**
WEB: www.eddyfloor.com
SIC: 3544 Special dies, tools, jigs & fixtures

(G-5157)
ELEGANT HOUSE INTL LLC
1960 Sw 30th Ave (33009-2005)
PHONE..................................954 457-8836
▲ **EMP:** 5
SQ FT: 20,000
SALES (est): 460.2K **Privately Held**
SIC: 2392 2517 2512 2511 Mfg Household Furnishing Mfg Wd Tv/Radio Cabinets Mfg Uphls Household Furn Mfg Wood Household Furn

(G-5158)
JM OCEAN MAR CANVAS & UPHL INC
1825 Sw 31st Ave (33009-2020)
PHONE..................................786 473-7143
Michael E Pelier P, *Principal*
EMP: 9 **EST:** 2017
SALES (est): 717.8K **Privately Held**
WEB: www.jmmarinecanvas.com
SIC: 2211 Canvas

(G-5159)
MYTON INDUSTRIES INC
1981 S Park Rd (33009-2013)
PHONE..................................954 989-0113
Raymond Leone, *President*
▼ **EMP:** 12 **EST:** 1974
SQ FT: 10,000
SALES (est): 1.6MM **Privately Held**
WEB: www.mytonindustries.com
SIC: 3089 Plastic containers, except foam

(G-5160)
PLASMA CUTTING LLC
3140 W Hllandale Bch Blvd (33009-5100)
PHONE..................................954 558-1371
Andres G A C Gonzalez Sr, *Owner*
EMP: 6 **EST:** 2017
SALES (est): 450.9K **Privately Held**
SIC: 2836 Plasmas

(G-5161)
PRINTEX WORLDWIDE INC
2037 Sw 31st Ave (33009-2031)
PHONE..................................954 518-0722
Gary Walko, *President*
EMP: 6 **EST:** 2002
SALES (est): 441.8K **Privately Held**
WEB: www.printexusa.com
SIC: 2759 Screen printing

(G-5162)
TITANIUM PROF HYRAULICS
1853 Sw 31st Ave (33009-2020)
PHONE..................................917 929-5044
Sheldon Greenbaum, *President*
EMP: 8 **EST:** 2017
SALES (est): 1.1MM **Privately Held**
SIC: 3356 Titanium

(G-5163)
TOPS CABINET
2500 Sw 30th Ave (33009-3020)
PHONE..................................954 544-2006
EMP: 6 **EST:** 2015
SALES (est): 87.1K **Privately Held**
WEB: www.topscabinet.net
SIC: 2434 Wood kitchen cabinets

(G-5164)
TROPICAL ASPHALT LLC
1904 Sw 31st Ave (33009-2022)
PHONE..................................954 983-3434
Richard Zegelbone, *Branch Mgr*
EMP: 15
SALES (corp-wide): 9.7MM **Privately Held**
WEB: www.tropicalroofingproducts.com
SIC: 2952 Asphalt felts & coatings
PA: Tropical Asphalt, Llc
14435 Macaw St
La Mirada CA 90638
714 739-1408

(G-5165)
UNLIMITED CABINET DESIGNS INC
1798 Sw 31st Ave (33009-2023)
PHONE..................................954 923-3269
Gerardo Bernal, *President*
EMP: 10 **EST:** 1988
SQ FT: 100,000
SALES (est): 698.9K **Privately Held**
SIC: 2511 2541 Wood household furniture; cabinets, lockers & shelving

(G-5166)
VENANCIO USA INC
2021 Sw 31st Ave (33009-2031)
PHONE..................................321 418-9489
Adriano Waschow-Medeiros, *Principal*
EMP: 8 **EST:** 2018
SALES (est): 204.1K **Privately Held**
WEB: www.venanciousa.com
SIC: 3999 Manufacturing industries

Hallandale Beach
Broward County

(G-5167)
ABSOLUTE WOOD CREATIONS LLC
200 S Dixie Hwy (33009-5436)
PHONE..................................954 251-2202
AVI Avni,
Rochell Avni,
EMP: 6 **EST:** 2004
SALES (est): 551.6K **Privately Held**
SIC: 2434 Wood kitchen cabinets

(G-5168)
ALAMO USA INC
1117 Ne 10th St (33009-2683)
PHONE..................................954 774-3747
Alexander Aralov, *President*
EMP: 8 **EST:** 2015
SALES (est): 88.6K **Privately Held**
WEB: www.alamo.com
SIC: 3519 Controls, remote, for boats

(G-5169)
AMERICAN IMPACT MEDIA CORP
413 Se 1st Ave (33009-6406)
P.O. Box 1266, Hallandale (33008-1266)
PHONE..................................954 457-9003
Jeffrey Eichner, *President*
Donna Eichner, *Vice Pres*
Kay Garcia, *Prdtn Mgr*
Dina Saman, *Office Mgr*
EMP: 20 **EST:** 1989
SQ FT: 2,500
SALES (est): 3.3MM **Privately Held**
WEB: www.americanimpact.com
SIC: 3661 7922 Message concentrators; radio producers

(G-5170)
ARNO BELO INC
Also Called: Manufacturer
221 W Hllndale Bch Blvd P (33009-5441)
PHONE..................................800 734-2356
Manuel Garrido, *CFO*
Arno Inc, *Administration*
EMP: 6 **EST:** 2016
SALES (est): 401.7K **Privately Held**
WEB: www.arnobelo.com
SIC: 2325 2339 3949 2329 Jeans: men's, youths' & boys'; jeans: women's, misses' & juniors'; sporting & athletic goods; men's & boys' sportswear & athletic clothing

(G-5171)
BIO-PHARM LLC
409 W Hallandale Beach Bl (33009-5301)
PHONE..................................973 223-7163
Amit Shah, *Principal*

EMP: 5 **EST:** 2015
SQ FT: 300
SALES (est): 415K **Privately Held**
SIC: 2834 Pharmaceutical preparations

(G-5172)
BLACKIES WELDNG & BOILER SVC
3101 Sw 25th St (33009-3096)
PHONE..................................954 961-5777
EMP: 6 **EST:** 2013
SALES (est): 334.6K **Privately Held**
SIC: 7692 Welding repair

(G-5173)
BLUUM LAB LLC
470 Ansin Blvd Ste Aa (33009-3106)
PHONE..................................877 341-3339
Yehuda Gabay, *Mng Member*
Elad Barda,
EMP: 16 **EST:** 2015
SALES (est): 1.1MM **Privately Held**
WEB: www.bluumlab.com
SIC: 3999

(G-5174)
BRAZIL AMERICA SRONES INC
723 Sw 6th St Unit 4 (33009-6974)
PHONE..................................305 915-0123
Celso Lima, *Principal*
EMP: 6 **EST:** 2007
SALES (est): 190.2K **Privately Held**
SIC: 2541 Counter & sink tops

(G-5175)
BROWARD SIGN SHOP
1001 N Federal Hwy # 341 (33009-2400)
PHONE..................................305 431-2455
Rosa Becerra, *Principal*
EMP: 6 **EST:** 2010
SALES (est): 101K **Privately Held**
WEB: www.browardsigns.com
SIC: 3993 Signs & advertising specialties

(G-5176)
CALIFORNO CORP
217 Nw 2nd Ave (33009-4008)
PHONE..................................855 553-6766
Shali Zanzuri, *President*
EMP: 8 **EST:** 2016
SALES (est): 400K **Privately Held**
WEB: www.californo.co
SIC: 3556 Ovens, bakery

(G-5177)
CELLPHONE PARTS EXPRESS LLC
2633 Park Ln (33009-3812)
PHONE..................................954 635-5525
Abderrahmane Guennouni,
EMP: 12 **EST:** 2017
SALES (est): 1.3MM **Privately Held**
WEB: www.cpp-express.com
SIC: 3661 Telephone & telegraph apparatus

(G-5178)
COLORTONE INC
226 Nw 4th Ave (33009-4015)
PHONE..................................954 455-0200
Mike Hasson, *President*
Shlomo Hasson, *Vice Pres*
▲ **EMP:** 38 **EST:** 1992
SQ FT: 15,600
SALES (est): 8.3MM **Privately Held**
WEB: www.tiedyeusa.com
SIC: 2269 2261 Chemical coating or treating of narrow fabrics; finishing plants, cotton

(G-5179)
CONRAD PLASTICS LLC
1904 S Ocean Dr Apt 1703 (33009-5962)
PHONE..................................954 391-9515
Javier Solis,
Mariela Zampini,
EMP: 6 **EST:** 2019
SALES (est): 167K **Privately Held**
WEB: www.conradplasticsllc.com
SIC: 3089 Plastic processing

(G-5180)
DAVILA WOODWORKING INC
214 Nw 1st Ave (33009-4002)
PHONE..................................954 458-0460
Carlos Davila Sr, *Partner*
EMP: 6 **EST:** 1985
SALES (est): 511.2K **Privately Held**
WEB: www.davilawoodwork.com
SIC: 2511 Wood household furniture

(G-5181)
DIORA PROFESSIONNEL LLC
Also Called: Keratherapy
1037 Nw 3rd St (33009-3101)
PHONE..................................954 628-5163
Lucas Santino, *Sales Staff*
Lucas Sloan, *Sales Staff*
Alma Socherman, *Mng Member*
Rodrigo Silva, *Technical Staff*
Misha Belfer, *Creative Dir*
◆ **EMP:** 18 **EST:** 2010
SALES (est): 4.8MM **Privately Held**
WEB: www.keratherapy.com
SIC: 2844 Cosmetic preparations

(G-5182)
E&M INNOVATIVE FORAGER LLC (PA)
Also Called: Sunshine Provisions
2649 S Park Rd (33009-3815)
PHONE..................................954 923-0056
Evan S David,
EMP: 24 **EST:** 2014
SALES (est): 3.3MM **Privately Held**
SIC: 2015 2013 Poultry sausage, luncheon meats & other poultry products; sausages & other prepared meats

(G-5183)
FIERO ENTERPRISES INC
203 Nw 5th Ave (33009-4019)
PHONE..................................954 454-5004
Joseph Fiero, *President*
EMP: 10 **EST:** 1971
SQ FT: 19,000
SALES (est): 603.7K **Privately Held**
SIC: 3993 Displays & cutouts, window & lobby

(G-5184)
FINGER MATE INC
Also Called: National Jewellers
2500 E Hallandale Beach B (33009-4883)
P.O. Box 607, Hallandale (33008-0607)
PHONE..................................954 458-2700
Howard Kelrick, *President*
Robert Brooks, *Vice Pres*
Alan Wildstein, *Production*
Kathy Brooks, *Shareholder*
EMP: 21 **EST:** 1964
SQ FT: 2,500
SALES (est): 2.5MM **Privately Held**
WEB: www.fingermate.com
SIC: 3911 5944 3915 Jewelry apparel; jewelry stores; jewelers' materials & lapidary work

(G-5185)
FIRST CASE CASH LLC
225 Holiday Dr (33009-6515)
PHONE..................................954 200-5374
Dmitry Fateev, *Principal*
EMP: 7 **EST:** 2019
SALES (est): 725.2K **Privately Held**
SIC: 3523 Farm machinery & equipment

(G-5186)
FITLETIC SPORTS LLC
1049 Nw 1st Ct (33009-3903)
PHONE..................................305 907-6663
Shifra Pomerantz,
Uri Sharabi,
EMP: 7 **EST:** 2008
SQ FT: 4,000
SALES (est): 1.1MM **Privately Held**
WEB: www.fitletic.com
SIC: 2339 2329 Sportswear, women's; men's & boys' sportswear & athletic clothing

(G-5187)
FIVE STAR SPORTS TICKETS
1755 E Hallandale Bch (33009-4684)
PHONE..................................440 899-2000
Sherry Sabe, *President*
Brian Blume, *Vice Pres*
Bonnie Blume, *Treasurer*
EMP: 10 **EST:** 1990
SQ FT: 1,200
SALES (est): 781.8K **Privately Held**
SIC: 2711 2759 2752 Newspapers; commercial printing; commercial printing, lithographic

(G-5188)
GAR INDUSTRIES CORP
Also Called: Parker Plastics
224 Nw 6th Ave (33009-4022)
PHONE..................................954 456-8088
Alan Roseman, *President*
◆ **EMP:** 14 **EST:** 1970
SQ FT: 10,000
SALES (est): 304.6K **Privately Held**
WEB: www.garindustries.com
SIC: 3171 3172 3161 3949 Handbags, women's; handbags, regardless of material: men's; cases, carrying; sporting & athletic goods; canvas & related products

(G-5189)
GREENTEX AMERICA LLC
520 S Dixie Hwy Ofc 120 (33009-6332)
PHONE..................................305 908-8580
Leon Amitai Liberman, *Mng Member*
Karen Sutton Neirus,
EMP: 10 **EST:** 2018
SALES (est): 371.4K **Privately Held**
SIC: 2759 Publication printing

(G-5190)
HYCOMB USA INC
311 W Ansin Blvd (33009-3114)
PHONE..................................954 251-1691
John Bartos, *President*
Dan Slain, *Director*
▲ **EMP:** 12 **EST:** 2013
SALES (est): 559.5K **Privately Held**
WEB: www.hycombusa.com
SIC: 3469 Porcelain enameled products & utensils

(G-5191)
INTERNATIONAL DOCK PRODUCTS
Also Called: S King Fulton Div
3101 Sw 25th St Ste 106 (33009-3096)
PHONE..................................954 964-5315
Elliot Turk, *President*
Rita Turk, *Corp Secy*
Frank Turk, *Executive*
◆ **EMP:** 15 **EST:** 1991
SQ FT: 6,000
SALES (est): 1.8MM **Privately Held**
WEB: www.dockproducts.com
SIC: 3999 3444 3429 Dock equipment & supplies, industrial; sheet metalwork; manufactured hardware (general)

(G-5192)
ITQLICK INC
2100 E Hlnd Bch Blvd # 203 (33009-3765)
PHONE..................................855 487-5425
Shlomo Lavi, *Principal*
EMP: 7 **EST:** 2017
SALES (est): 70.8K **Privately Held**
WEB: www.itqlick.com
SIC: 7372 Prepackaged software

(G-5193)
JADA FOODS LLC
Also Called: Krunchy Melts
3126 John P Curci Dr # 1 (33009-3827)
PHONE..................................305 319-0263
Moises Mizrahi, *Partner*
Daniel Ginsberg, *Managing Dir*
EMP: 15 **EST:** 2011
SQ FT: 4,950
SALES: 2.3MM **Privately Held**
WEB: www.krunchymelts.com
SIC: 2052 Cookies & crackers

(G-5194)
JPL ASSOCIATES INC
Also Called: Promotional Concepts Team
1250 E Hallandale Beach B (33009-4634)
PHONE..................................954 929-6024
John Lombardo, *President*
Cindy Lombardo, *Vice Pres*
Marc Wright, *Sales Dir*
EMP: 10 **EST:** 2003
SALES (est): 813.4K **Privately Held**
WEB: www.jpl-associates.com
SIC: 3993 7311 Signs & advertising specialties; advertising agencies

(G-5195)
KASULIK II LLC
Also Called: Ragalta
1170 E Hllndale Bch Blvd (33009-4437)
PHONE..................................786 629-8978
Paul Hariton, *CEO*
Ricardo Shneiderman,
▲ **EMP:** 12 **EST:** 2009
SQ FT: 65,000
SALES (est): 3.8MM **Privately Held**
SIC: 3089 5023 Plastic kitchenware, tableware & houseware; home furnishings

(G-5196)
LAKAY VITA LLC
419 N Federal Hwy Apt 209 (33009-3499)
PHONE..................................786 985-7552
Wency Germinal, *CEO*
Sacha Hernandez,
EMP: 5 **EST:** 2019
SALES (est): 505K **Privately Held**
SIC: 2131 5199 Smoking tobacco; general merchandise, non-durable

(G-5197)
LEGACY CNSTR RMDLG CLG SVCS LL
500 N Federal Hwy Ste 631 (33009-2405)
PHONE..................................800 638-9646
Edison Jules,
EMP: 40 **EST:** 2019
SALES (est): 656.4K **Privately Held**
SIC: 1389 Construction, repair & dismantling services

(G-5198)
LILLYS GSTRNMIA ITLANA FLA INC
Also Called: Lillys Gastronomia Italiana FL
370 Ansin Blvd (33009-3107)
PHONE..................................305 655-2111
Fred Botta, *Vice Pres*
EMP: 5 **EST:** 1994
SQ FT: 5,000
SALES (est): 400K **Privately Held**
SIC: 2099 2098 2038 Packaged combination products: pasta, rice & potato; macaroni & spaghetti; frozen specialties

(G-5199)
MIRACLES FOR FUN USA INC
Also Called: Better Sourcing Worldwide
1835 E Hllndale Bch Blvd (33009-4619)
PHONE..................................561 702-8217
Danny Hui, *CEO*
Greg Sanders, *President*
▲ **EMP:** 10 **EST:** 2006
SQ FT: 5,000
SALES (est): 362K **Privately Held**
WEB: www.miracles4funusa.com
SIC: 3229 Glassware, art or decorative

(G-5200)
MN TRADES INC
200 Leslie Dr Ofc (33009-7344)
PHONE..................................954 455-9320
Joao Montoro, *President*
Leandro Montoro, *Vice Pres*
Neuza Montoro, *Treasurer*
EMP: 6 **EST:** 1996
SALES (est): 846.9K **Privately Held**
SIC: 3679 Electronic circuits

(G-5201)
NATURES GIFT CBD
320 Ne 12th Ave Apt 506 (33009-4507)
PHONE..................................954 405-1000
Gratziela Lazarov, *Principal*
EMP: 6 **EST:** 2017
SALES (est): 118.3K **Privately Held**
SIC: 3999

(G-5202)
ON DEMAND SPCLTY ENVELOPE CORP
917 Sw 10th St (33009-6819)
PHONE..................................305 681-5345
Joanne Heller-Mahoney, *President*
Gerry Mahoney, *Vice Pres*
EMP: 16 **EST:** 2011
SQ FT: 10,700
SALES (est): 268.6K **Privately Held**
WEB: www.ondemandenvelope.com
SIC: 2732 Book printing

(G-5203)
PREMIER PLASTICS LLC
500 S Federal Hwy # 2715 (33009-6435)
PHONE..................................305 805-3333
Albert Esquenazi, *Branch Mgr*
EMP: 6
SALES (corp-wide): 550.6K **Privately Held**
WEB: www.premierplastics.us
SIC: 3999 Barber & beauty shop equipment
PA: Premier Plastics, Llc
1500 Gateway Blvd Ste 250
Boynton Beach FL 33426
305 805-3333

(G-5204)
PRINTNOVATIONS INC
125 Sw 4th Ave (33009-5430)
PHONE..................................305 322-4041
Carlos Ochoa, *Principal*
EMP: 6 **EST:** 2011
SALES (est): 127.7K **Privately Held**
SIC: 2759 Commercial printing

(G-5205)
QSRR CORPORATION
Also Called: Bemeals
3126 John P Curci Dr # 4 (33009-3884)
PHONE..................................305 322-9867
Michael Esrubilsky, *CEO*
EMP: 7 **EST:** 2017
SALES (est): 415.7K **Privately Held**
SIC: 2099 7371 Food preparations; computer software development & applications

(G-5206)
QUALITY CBINETS BY STEWART LLC
3120 Sw 19th St Ste 160 (33009-2032)
PHONE..................................954 624-6877
David A Stewart, *Manager*
EMP: 6 **EST:** 2012
SALES (est): 247.2K **Privately Held**
WEB: www.qualitycabinets.net
SIC: 2434 Wood kitchen cabinets

(G-5207)
R-LINES LLC
201 Ansin Blvd (33009-3116)
PHONE..................................954 457-7777
Diana McNally, *Mng Member*
◆ **EMP:** 7 **EST:** 1995
SQ FT: 25,000
SALES (est): 990.9K **Privately Held**
WEB: www.rlines.com
SIC: 2086 Soft drinks: packaged in cans, bottles, etc.

(G-5208)
RENOVASHIP INC
2700 S Park Rd (33009-3833)
PHONE..................................954 342-9062
Dennis P Carbee, *President*
Dennis Rodriguez, *Treasurer*
Oscar Medina, *Admin Sec*
▲ **EMP:** 5 **EST:** 2005
SALES (est): 545.5K **Privately Held**
WEB: www.renovashipinc.com
SIC: 3312 Structural shapes & pilings, steel

(G-5209)
SERVICES ON DEMAND PRINT INC
Also Called: On Demand Envelopes
917 Sw 10th St (33009-6819)
PHONE..................................305 681-5345
Jose Rosario, *Vice Pres*
Antonio Cruz, *Sales Staff*
David Voyasy, *Manager*
▼ **EMP:** 21 **EST:** 1995
SQ FT: 10,000
SALES (est): 465.9K **Privately Held**
WEB: www.ondemandenvelope.com
SIC: 2759 2752 2677 Envelopes: printing; commercial printing, lithographic; envelopes

(G-5210)
SERVISION INC
2100 E Hallandale Beach B (33009-3770)
PHONE..................................305 900-4999
Gidon Tahan, *CEO*
Yaniv Ben, *Vice Pres*
Tamir Alush, *Director*
Brett Schor, *Director*
EMP: 1 **EST:** 2003
SQ FT: 600
SALES (est): 6MM **Privately Held**
WEB: www.servision.net
SIC: 3699 Security devices
HQ: Servision Ltd
1 Eitan
Rishon Lezion 75703

(G-5211)
SMILEFY INC
221 W Hallandale B106 (33009)
PHONE..................................302 465-6606
Ralph Georg, *Principal*
EMP: 10 **EST:** 2017
SALES (est): 283.2K **Privately Held**
WEB: www.smilefy.com
SIC: 2741 8742 ; marketing consulting services

(G-5212)
SOUTH BEACH SKIN CARE INC (PA)
Also Called: Lifecell
701 N Federal Hwy Ste 400 (33009-2452)
PHONE..................................954 606-5057
Chris Suarez, *President*
Amit Suneja, *President*
Esmeralda Woods, *Production*
Https Wwwlink Levitt, *Sales Staff*
Https Wwwlink Monroe, *Consultant*
▲ **EMP:** 14 **EST:** 2009
SALES (est): 3.6MM **Privately Held**
WEB: www.lifecellskin.com
SIC: 2844 Cosmetic preparations

(G-5213)
SOUTH BROWARD BRACE INC
Also Called: Petti, Vince
1920 E Hallndale Bch 702 (33009-4725)
PHONE..................................954 458-0656
Vince Petti, *President*
EMP: 10 **EST:** 1986
SALES (est): 486.1K **Privately Held**
SIC: 3842 Prosthetic appliances

(G-5214)
SOUTH FLORIDA DIGEST INC
Also Called: South Florida Suntimes
305 Nw 10th Ter (33009-3103)
PHONE..................................954 458-0635
Cecile Hiles, *Vice Pres*
EMP: 19 **EST:** 2004
SALES (est): 648.7K **Privately Held**
WEB: www.southfloridasun.net
SIC: 2711 Newspapers, publishing & printing

(G-5215)
STREET LIGHTING EQUIPMENT CORP
2099 S Park Rd (33009-2015)
PHONE..................................954 961-9140
Barry Levine, *President*
Mary Hallenbeck, *Vice Pres*
Martin Levine, *Admin Sec*
◆ **EMP:** 17 **EST:** 1978
SQ FT: 16,000
SALES (est): 2.8MM **Privately Held**
WEB: www.streetlightingfla.com
SIC: 3648 Street lighting fixtures

(G-5216)
SUNGRAF INC
325 W Ansin Blvd (33009-3114)
P.O. Box 260397, Pembroke Pines (33026-7397)
PHONE..................................954 456-8500
Joseph D Cesarotti Jr, *President*
Marianne Cesarotti, *Vice Pres*
EMP: 10 **EST:** 1956
SQ FT: 30,000
SALES (est): 159.7K **Privately Held**
SIC: 3993 3081 3083 2522 Electric signs; plastic film & sheet; laminated plastics plate & sheet; office furniture, except wood; metal household furniture; wood kitchen cabinets

(G-5217)
SYNTEX AMERICA CORPORATION
Also Called: Stntex
409 Nw 10th Ter (33009-3105)
PHONE..................................954 457-1468
Luiz Fernando Valente, *President*
Alessandra Valente, *Vice Pres*
Simone Oliveira, *Treasurer*
EMP: 15 **EST:** 2012
SALES (est): 191.4K **Privately Held**
SIC: 2821 Plastics materials & resins

(G-5218)
TAGS & LABELS PRINTING INC
520 Ne 1st Ave (33009-2417)
PHONE..................................954 455-2867
Peter Applebaum, *President*
Angie Sundar, *Officer*
Brenda Ayotte,
EMP: 21 **EST:** 1976
SQ FT: 10,200
SALES (est): 3.1MM **Privately Held**
WEB: www.tagsandlabels.net
SIC: 2752 Commercial printing, offset

(G-5219)
TAN PRINTING INC
2211 John P Lyons Ln (33009-2173)
PHONE..................................954 986-9869
Henk Tan, *President*
Lilly Lifter, *Vice Pres*
▼ **EMP:** 6 **EST:** 1992
SQ FT: 9,000
SALES (est): 724K **Privately Held**
WEB: www.tanprinting.com
SIC: 2752 Commercial printing, offset

(G-5220)
UNIMD SCRUBS LLC
1850 S Ocean Dr Apt 3407 (33009-7686)
PHONE..................................954 245-1509
Dan Abitan, *CEO*
Imram Lakhani, *COO*
EMP: 6 **EST:** 2015
SALES (est): 74.6K **Privately Held**
SIC: 2211 Scrub cloths

(G-5221)
US PATRIOT INDUSTRIES INC
100 Golden Isles Dr (33009-5885)
PHONE..................................954 802-7402
William Carney, *Mng Member*
Mike Giallombardo, *Director*
Jesse Kearney, *Director*
Tim Masshardt, *Director*
Rob Polumbo, *Director*
EMP: 7 **EST:** 2018
SALES (est): 351.6K **Privately Held**
WEB: www.uspatriotindustries.com
SIC: 3999 Manufacturing industries

(G-5222)
USA ALUMINUM
1880 S Ocean Dr (33009-7610)
PHONE..................................305 303-9121
Claudia Menemdez,
EMP: 6
SQ FT: 5,000
SALES (est): 1MM **Privately Held**
SIC: 3442 Shutters, door or window: metal

(G-5223)
UZZI AMPHIBIOUS GEAR LLC
205 Ansin Blvd (33009-3116)
PHONE..................................954 777-9595
Elan Barshean, *Owner*
EMP: 13 **EST:** 2015
SALES (est): 656.8K **Privately Held**
WEB: www.uzzi.com
SIC: 2339 2326 Service apparel, washable: women's; service apparel (baker, barber, lab, etc.), washable: men's

(G-5224)
WELDING AND FABRICATION INC
3150 W Pembroke Rd (33009-2017)
PHONE..................................973 508-7267
Santiago H Jimenez, *Principal*
EMP: 6 **EST:** 2018
SALES (est): 175.2K **Privately Held**
WEB: www.alswelding.us
SIC: 3441 Fabricated structural metal

(G-5225)
WINSTED THERMOGRAPHERS INC
917 Sw 10th St (33009-6898)
PHONE..................................305 944-7862
Lester Jacobowitz, *President*
Gary Jacobowitz, *Vice Pres*
◆ **EMP:** 19 **EST:** 1971
SQ FT: 20,000
SALES (est): 2.5MM **Privately Held**
WEB: www.winsted-thermo.com
SIC: 2759 2677 Thermography; envelopes

(G-5226)
ZEPPELIN PRODUCTS INC
Also Called: Zep-Pro
3178 W Pembroke Rd (33009-2017)
PHONE..................................954 989-8808
Alon Granovsky, *CEO*
Lebedin German, *President*
German Lebedin, *Data Proc Staff*
◆ **EMP:** 19 **EST:** 1994
SQ FT: 7,500
SALES (est): 1.2MM **Privately Held**
WEB: www.zeppro.com
SIC: 2387 3144 3143 2389 Apparel belts; sandals, women's; sandals, men's; men's miscellaneous accessories

Hampton
Bradford County

(G-5227)
MCCLELLAN LOGGING INC
State Rd 325 (32044)
P.O. Box 108 (32044-0108)
PHONE..................................352 468-1856
Margie McClellan, *President*
Dewey McClellan, *Vice Pres*
EMP: 5 **EST:** 1963
SALES (est): 397.2K **Privately Held**
SIC: 2411 Logging camps & contractors

Hastings
St. Johns County

(G-5228)
HARWIL FIXTURES INC
103 W Saint Johns Ave (32145-4125)
P.O. Box 788 (32145-0788)
PHONE..................................904 692-1051
Louis F Cici, *President*
Bridgitte Cici, *Treasurer*
EMP: 15 **EST:** 1978
SQ FT: 50,000
SALES (est): 3.7MM **Privately Held**
WEB: www.harwilgroup.net
SIC: 2541 Store & office display cases & fixtures; cabinets, except refrigerated: show, display, etc.: wood

(G-5229)
R SMITH PRINTING INC
4820 Joseph St (32145-6316)
PHONE..................................518 827-7700
Robert Smith, *President*
Linda L Quinn, *CFO*
EMP: 6 **EST:** 2005
SQ FT: 8,500
SALES (est): 310K **Privately Held**
SIC: 2752 Commercial printing, offset

Havana
Gadsden County

(G-5230)
APPLIED FIBER HOLDINGS LLC
25 Garrett Dr (32333-3316)
PHONE..................................850 539-7720
Richard Campbell, *Mng Member*
EMP: 30 **EST:** 2003
SALES (est): 2.5MM **Privately Held**
WEB: www.applied-fiber.com
SIC: 2298 Cable, fiber

(G-5231)
APPLIED FIBER MFG LLC
25 Garrett Dr (32333-3316)
PHONE..................................850 539-7720

John Steadman, *COO*
Paul Badeau, *VP Bus Dvlpt*
Casey Davis, *Controller*
Richard Campbell, *Mng Member*
▲ **EMP:** 20 **EST:** 2003
SALES (est): 8.6MM **Privately Held**
WEB: www.applied-fiber.com
SIC: 2298 Cable, fiber

(G-5232)
ARUKI SERVICES LLC
102 Sw 3rd St (32333-1612)
P.O. Box 1228 (32333-1298)
PHONE..................................850 364-5206
Jeffery A Snyder,
EMP: 9 **EST:** 2008
SALES (est): 262.6K **Privately Held**
WEB: www.arukiservices.com
SIC: 3567 5074 Heating units & devices, industrial: electric; heating equipment (hydronic)

(G-5233)
BIG BEND ICE CREAM CO
138 Staghorn Trl (32333-5545)
PHONE..................................850 539-7778
Lauire Shaffer, *President*
EMP: 6 **EST:** 2003
SALES (est): 112.3K **Privately Held**
SIC: 2024 5451 5947 5812 Ice cream & frozen desserts; ice cream (packaged); gifts & novelties; caterers

(G-5234)
BIG BEND TRUSS COMPONENTS INC
52 Salem Rd (32333-6834)
P.O. Box 962 (32333-0962)
PHONE..................................850 539-5351
Keith Jones, *President*
Travis Jones, *Vice Pres*
EMP: 15 **EST:** 1971
SQ FT: 2,120
SALES (est): 1.5MM **Privately Held**
SIC: 2439 8711 Trusses, wooden roof; engineering services

(G-5235)
COASTAL FOREST RESOURCES CO (PA)
Also Called: Coastal Timberlands
8007 Fl Ga Hwy (32333-6382)
PHONE..................................850 539-6432
J Travis Bryant, *President*
James Randolph Light, *Chairman*
Ryan Daniels, *Vice Pres*
Thomas Evans, *Vice Pres*
James Hatch, *Sales Mgr*
◆ **EMP:** 300 **EST:** 1937
SALES (est): 103MM **Privately Held**
WEB: www.coastalplywood.com
SIC: 2436 2491 0811 0851 Plywood, softwood; structural lumber & timber, treated wood; timber tracts; forestry services

(G-5236)
COASTAL PLYWOOD COMPANY
8007 Fl Ga Hwy (32333-6382)
P.O. Box 1128 (32333-1128)
PHONE..................................800 359-6432
Jim Pattillo, *President*
Travis Bryant, *President*
Libby Sumner, *Production*
Kerry Mulford, *QC Dir*
Donnie Vickers, *Sales Mgr*
▼ **EMP:** 354 **EST:** 2003
SALES (est): 43MM
SALES (corp-wide): 103MM **Privately Held**
WEB: www.coastalplywood.com
SIC: 2435 Hardwood veneer & plywood
PA: Coastal Forest Resources Company
8007 Fl Ga Hwy
Havana FL 32333
850 539-6432

(G-5237)
CORRY CABINET COMPANY INC
811 N Main St (32333-1209)
P.O. Box 944 (32333-0944)
PHONE..................................850 539-6455
Henry C Corry Jr, *President*
EMP: 20 **EST:** 1992
SQ FT: 20,295
SALES (est): 2.4MM **Privately Held**
WEB: www.corrycabinets.com
SIC: 2541 Cabinets, except refrigerated: show, display, etc.: wood

(G-5238)
FREEDOM FABRICATION INC
815 N Main St Ste B (32333-1243)
PHONE..................................850 539-4194
Anthony Wickman, *President*
EMP: 10 **EST:** 1992
SQ FT: 6,000
SALES (est): 871.8K **Privately Held**
WEB: www.freedomfabrication.com
SIC: 3842 Orthopedic appliances

(G-5239)
PRIME TECHNOLOGICAL SVCS LLC
Also Called: Teligentems
102 Technology Way (32333-2000)
PHONE..................................850 539-2500
Christopher Eldred, *Branch Mgr*
EMP: 100 **Privately Held**
WEB: www.prime-ems.com
SIC: 3672 8711 Printed circuit boards; electrical or electronic engineering
PA: Prime Technological Services, Llc
2925 Shawnee Industrial W
Suwanee GA 30024

(G-5240)
TMS ENTERPRISES LLC
Also Called: Plant 2
102 Technology Way (32333-2000)
PHONE..................................850 539-2500
Karen Capps, *Vice Pres*
Jeff Hearn, *Production*
Kristopher Miller, *Purch Mgr*
Richard Landry, *Purchasing*
Mike A Wallace, *VP Bus Dvlpt*
EMP: 500 **EST:** 2002
SALES (est): 52.2MM **Privately Held**
WEB: www.teligentems.com
SIC: 3672 Printed circuit boards

Haverhill
Palm Beach County

(G-5241)
WEARABLE NALIA LLC
5081 Palo Verde Pl (33415-1273)
PHONE..................................561 629-5804
Kenya L Glenn, *Principal*
EMP: 7 **EST:** 2008
SALES (est): 253.5K **Privately Held**
WEB: www.wearablenalia.com
SIC: 2395 Embroidery & art needlework

Hawthorne
Alachua County

(G-5242)
ADVANCED METALS LLC
158 Hour Glass Cir (32640-4224)
PHONE..................................352 494-2476
Richard Mahoney, *Owner*
Sherri Sable, *Production*
Nicole Cooper, *Controller*
EMP: 8 **EST:** 2011
SALES (est): 805.9K **Privately Held**
WEB: www.advancedmetals.biz
SIC: 3444 Ducts, sheet metal

(G-5243)
ALL FLORIDA ENGRAVING
17728 S County Road 325 (32640-8301)
PHONE..................................352 213-4572
Louis Wise, *Principal*
EMP: 8 **EST:** 2014
SALES (est): 285.7K **Privately Held**
WEB: www.allfloridaengraving.com
SIC: 2759 Screen printing

(G-5244)
INTERLACHEN CABINETS INC
2010 State Road 20 (32640-5407)
PHONE..................................352 481-6078
Gene Quimby, *President*
EMP: 8 **EST:** 2008
SALES (est): 369.6K **Privately Held**
WEB: www.interlachencabinets.houzz.com
SIC: 2434 Wood kitchen cabinets

(G-5245)
PRESSURE POINT WATER PROOFING
11922 Se 225th Dr (32640-7613)
PHONE..................................352 337-9905
Russell Harris, *President*
EMP: 7 **EST:** 2001
SALES (est): 225K **Privately Held**
WEB: www.pressurepointwaterproofing.com
SIC: 2899 Waterproofing compounds

Hernando
Citrus County

(G-5246)
MERIT SCREW
Also Called: Merit Screw Products
3484 E Hartley Ct (34442-5009)
PHONE..................................352 344-3744
Jack Briscoe, *Partner*
EMP: 5 **EST:** 1973
SQ FT: 4,000
SALES (est): 478.5K **Privately Held**
WEB: www.mspfl.com
SIC: 3451 3599 Screw machine products; machine shop, jobbing & repair

(G-5247)
SKLAR BOV SOLUTIONS INC (PA)
1233 E Norvell Bryant Hwy (34442-4552)
PHONE..................................352 746-6731
Ross Sklar, *CEO*
Darin Brown, *Exec VP*
George D Stroesenreuther, *CFO*
▼ **EMP:** 2 **EST:** 2016
SALES (est): 12MM **Privately Held**
WEB: www.bovsolutions.com
SIC: 3499 Aerosol valves, metal

(G-5248)
TURBINE BROACH COMPANY
521 E Overdrive Cir (34442-9602)
P.O. Box 280, Holder (34445-0280)
PHONE..................................352 795-1163
Timothy Short, *President*
Jeanne Short, *Treasurer*
EMP: 17 **EST:** 1972
SQ FT: 16,688
SALES (est): 2.4MM **Privately Held**
WEB: www.turbinebroach.com
SIC: 3545 Broaches (machine tool accessories)

(G-5249)
VISCOMM PUBLISHING LLC
919 W Pearson St (34442-4986)
PHONE..................................888 511-0900
EMP: 6 **EST:** 2012
SALES (est): 172.8K **Privately Held**
WEB: www.viscommpublishing.com
SIC: 2741 Miscellaneous publishing

Hernando Beach
Hernando County

(G-5250)
AFLG INVSTMNTS-INDUSTRIALS LLC
Hidralmac USA
5000 Calienta St (34607-2900)
PHONE..................................813 443-8203
Doug Joseph, *Managing Dir*
EMP: 10
SALES (corp-wide): 6MM **Privately Held**
SIC: 3542 3569 Mechanical (pneumatic or hydraulic) metal forming machines; liquid automation machinery & equipment
PA: Aflg Investments-Industrials, Llc
701 Suth Hward Ave 106
Tampa FL 33606
813 443-8203

(G-5251)
SON LIFE PRSTHTICS ORTHTICS IN (PA)
4138 Daisy Dr (34607-3339)
PHONE..................................352 596-2257
David Goris, *President*
EMP: 11 **EST:** 1987
SALES (est): 1.5MM **Privately Held**
WEB: www.sonlifeprosthetics.com
SIC: 3842 5999 5661 Prosthetic appliances; orthopedic appliances; artificial limbs; shoes, orthopedic

Hialeah
Miami-Dade County

(G-5252)
3 STARS KITCHEN CABINETS CORP
529 W 28th St (33010-1325)
PHONE..................................786 285-7147
Nelson Monzon, *President*
▲ **EMP:** 6 **EST:** 2013
SALES (est): 276.2K **Privately Held**
WEB: www.3starkitchencabinet.com
SIC: 2434 Wood kitchen cabinets

(G-5253)
3T CORPORATION
7377 Nw 174th Ter Apt 100 (33015-1143)
PHONE..................................786 222-2147
Juan P Sosa Sr, *Principal*
EMP: 6 **EST:** 2015
SALES (est): 198.9K **Privately Held**
SIC: 3564 Blowers & fans

(G-5254)
5301 REALTY LLC
Also Called: Franklin Trade Graphics
950 Se 8th St (33010-5740)
PHONE..................................305 633-9779
Peter Dunne,
Geronimo Alvarez,
Michael Barber,
Robert Dunne,
▼ **EMP:** 149 **EST:** 2002
SQ FT: 70,000
SALES (est): 15.6MM **Privately Held**
SIC: 2752 Commercial printing, lithographic

(G-5255)
A & V REFRIGERATION CORP
997 Se 12th St (33010-5904)
PHONE..................................305 883-0733
Jacob Essenfeld, *President*
Servando Cougil, *Vice Pres*
Alfredo Rodriguez, *Director*
◆ **EMP:** 7 **EST:** 1990
SQ FT: 4,500
SALES (est): 1MM **Privately Held**
WEB: www.av-refrigeration.com
SIC: 3585 7623 Ice making machinery; refrigeration repair service

(G-5256)
A CURV TECH CORP
930 W 23rd St (33010-2014)
PHONE..................................305 888-9631
Ernesto F Sarabia, *President*
Mayra Sarabia, *Corp Secy*
▼ **EMP:** 10 **EST:** 1986
SQ FT: 15,000
SALES (est): 930.3K **Privately Held**
SIC: 3442 Sash, door or window: metal

(G-5257)
A L CUSTOM WOOD CORP
950 W 22nd St (33010-2012)
PHONE..................................305 557-2434
EMP: 7 **EST:** 2019
SALES (est): 389K **Privately Held**
SIC: 2431 Millwork

(G-5258)
A SUPERIOR GARAGE DOOR COMPANY
12195 Nw 98th Ave (33018-2941)
PHONE..................................305 556-6624
Joe Berger, *Partner*
Keith Cotter, *Vice Pres*
Tiffeny Roque, *Manager*
Richard Barnes, *CIO*

EMP: 45 **EST:** 1997
SALES (est): 2.4MM **Privately Held**
SIC: 3442 Garage doors, overhead: metal

(G-5259)
A&C SIGNS SOLUTIONS CORP
1745 W 37th St (33012-4677)
PHONE..................................786 953-5600
Armando J Antelo, *Principal*
EMP: 11 **EST:** 2019
SALES (est): 460.3K **Privately Held**
SIC: 3993 Signs & advertising specialties

(G-5260)
A-1 SPORTSWEAR INC
18820 Nw 84th Ave (33015-5347)
PHONE..................................305 773-7028
Kar Lei Cheung, *President*
Patrick Lei, *Vice Pres*
EMP: 6 **EST:** 1987
SQ FT: 8,000
SALES (est): 110.9K **Privately Held**
SIC: 2339 Athletic clothing: women's, misses' & juniors'

(G-5261)
A1A ELECTRIC SIGNS & NEON INC
Also Called: A1a Signs & Svc.
3655 W 16th Ave Ste 1 (33012-4641)
PHONE..................................305 757-6950
Jorge Bravo, *President*
EMP: 9 **EST:** 1992
SQ FT: 8,000
SALES (est): 1MM **Privately Held**
WEB: www.a1asigns.com
SIC: 3993 Neon signs

(G-5262)
AARG STAIRS & RAILLINGS CORP
2384 W 80th St Ste 7 (33016-5689)
PHONE..................................786 545-6465
Ruben Gonzalez, *Principal*
EMP: 9 **EST:** 2012
SALES (est): 128.6K **Privately Held**
SIC: 3446 Stairs, staircases, stair treads: prefabricated metal

(G-5263)
ABALUX INC
8000 W 26th Ave (33016-2743)
PHONE..................................305 698-9192
Juan D Cabral, *CEO*
EMP: 16 **EST:** 2006
SALES (est): 462.1K **Privately Held**
WEB: www.abaluxgraphics.com
SIC: 3993 Signs & advertising specialties

(G-5264)
AC GRAPHICS INC
1056 E 24th St (33013-4394)
P.O. Box 133220 (33013-0220)
PHONE..................................305 691-3778
Augusto R Casamayor, *President*
Augusto G Casamayor, *COO*
Cliff Conchak, *Vice Pres*
◆ **EMP:** 32 **EST:** 1979
SQ FT: 6,000
SALES (est): 2.2MM **Privately Held**
WEB: www.acgraphics.com
SIC: 2752 Commercial printing, offset

(G-5265)
AC INDUSTRIAL SERVICE INC
Also Called: A C Master Motors & Controls
268 W 23rd St (33010-1524)
PHONE..................................305 887-5541
Oscar Berens, *President*
◆ **EMP:** 10 **EST:** 1979
SQ FT: 5,000
SALES (est): 1.5MM **Privately Held**
WEB: www.ac-industrial.com
SIC: 7694 5084 Electric motor repair; engines & parts, air-cooled

(G-5266)
AC PLASTICS LLC
1627 W 31st Pl (33012-4505)
PHONE..................................305 826-6333
EMP: 7
SALES (est): 530K **Privately Held**
SIC: 3085 Mfg Plastic Bottles

(G-5267)
ACAI INVESTMENTS LLC
Also Called: Dievac Plastics
7803 W 25th Ct (33016-2758)
PHONE..................................305 821-8872
Andres Marino,
EMP: 6 **EST:** 2007
SALES (est): 538.1K **Privately Held**
SIC: 3089 Injection molding of plastics

(G-5268)
ACTIVE LINE CORP
Also Called: Miami Sublimation
915 W 18th St (33010-2322)
PHONE..................................786 766-1944
Boris Litvinov, *President*
◆ **EMP:** 10 **EST:** 1994
SQ FT: 5,000
SALES (est): 728.5K **Privately Held**
SIC: 2395 Embroidery & art needlework

(G-5269)
ADAPTO STORAGE PRODUCTS
625 E 10th Ave (33010-4641)
PHONE..................................305 887-9563
Joe Caridnan, *President*
Jenny Nunez, *Admin Sec*
▼ **EMP:** 20 **EST:** 1999
SQ FT: 106,000
SALES (est): 916.1K **Privately Held**
WEB: www.adapto.com
SIC: 2542 Shelving, office & store: except wood

(G-5270)
ADVANCE PLASTICS UNLIMITED
905 W 19th St (33010-2308)
PHONE..................................305 885-6266
Abraham Kolker, *President*
Elena Kolker, *Corp Secy*
◆ **EMP:** 25 **EST:** 1969
SQ FT: 45,000
SALES (est): 3.3MM **Privately Held**
WEB: www.advanceplasticsindustries.com
SIC: 3085 Plastics bottles

(G-5271)
ADVANCED METAL FAB INC
2247 W 77th St (33016-1867)
PHONE..................................305 557-2008
Olga L Gordillo, *President*
Edward Gordillo Jr, *Vice Pres*
EMP: 10 **EST:** 1986
SQ FT: 5,000
SALES (est): 900K **Privately Held**
SIC: 3599 Machine shop, jobbing & repair

(G-5272)
ADVANCED PRINTING FINSHG INC
Also Called: Boxrus.com
1061 E 32nd St (33013-3523)
PHONE..................................305 836-8581
Omar Martinez, *President*
EMP: 16 **EST:** 2007
SALES (est): 1.6MM **Privately Held**
SIC: 2675 Die-cut paper & board

(G-5273)
AEROWEST MFG CORP
8835 Nw 117th St (33018-1949)
PHONE..................................786 367-6948
Daily Boffill Montano, *CEO*
Daily Boffill-Montano, *General Mgr*
EMP: 5 **EST:** 2006
SALES (est): 897.3K **Privately Held**
WEB: www.aerowestmfg.com
SIC: 3728 3541 Aircraft parts & equipment; drilling machine tools (metal cutting)

(G-5274)
AFFORDABLE METAL INC
3522 E 10th Ct (33013-2916)
PHONE..................................305 691-8082
Silbio Monrable, *President*
Ville Corta, *Vice Pres*
Eduardo Villacorta, *Vice Pres*
▼ **EMP:** 17 **EST:** 2001
SALES (est): 3.8MM **Privately Held**
WEB: www.affordablemetal.com
SIC: 3444 Sheet metal specialties, not stamped

(G-5275)
AGUSTIN REYES INC
2307 W 77th St (33016-1869)
PHONE..................................305 558-8870
Agustin Reyes III, *President*
Ana Maria Reyes, *Vice Pres*
◆ **EMP:** 12 **EST:** 1927
SQ FT: 2,750
SALES (est): 1MM **Privately Held**
WEB: www.agustinreyes.com
SIC: 2844 Cosmetic preparations

(G-5276)
AIRGUIDE MANUFACTURING LLC
795 W 20th St (33010-2429)
PHONE..................................305 888-1631
Douglas Marty Jr, *Vice Pres*
Charles Robinson, *Treasurer*
◆ **EMP:** 150 **EST:** 2003
SQ FT: 52,000
SALES (est): 32.5MM **Privately Held**
WEB: www.airguidemfg.com
SIC: 3446 Architectural metalwork

(G-5277)
ALEXANDER INDUSTRIES INC
905 W 23rd St (33010-2013)
P.O. Box 502, Vernon (32462-0502)
PHONE..................................305 888-9840
George Alexander, *President*
Mary Ann Alexander, *Vice Pres*
Nery Alexander, *Vice Pres*
▲ **EMP:** 6 **EST:** 1972
SQ FT: 10,000
SALES (est): 688.2K **Privately Held**
WEB: www.alexanderindustries.net
SIC: 3556 Food products machinery

(G-5278)
ALL BINDERS & INDEXES INC
Also Called: Delran Business Products
860 W 20th St (33010-2311)
PHONE..................................305 889-9983
Juan Carlos Cruz, *President*
EMP: 22 **EST:** 1993
SQ FT: 7,000
SALES (est): 1MM **Privately Held**
WEB: www.delran.com
SIC: 2789 Binding only: books, pamphlets, magazines, etc.

(G-5279)
ALL MOLDINGS INC
7950 W 26th Ave (33016-2728)
PHONE..................................305 556-6171
EMP: 6
SALES (est): 630K **Privately Held**
SIC: 2491 Wood Preserving

(G-5280)
ALL PRO CHELO CORP
11750 Nw 87th Pl (33018-1974)
PHONE..................................786 317-3914
Magnaset Martinez, *President*
EMP: 6 **EST:** 2011
SALES (est): 181K **Privately Held**
SIC: 2431 5211 Garage doors, overhead: wood; garage doors, sale & installation

(G-5281)
ALLAY PHARMACEUTICAL LLC (PA)
16600 Nw 54th Ave Unit 23 (33014-6109)
PHONE..................................954 336-1136
Rosy Sultana, *CEO*
Maroof H Choudhur, *President*
Abdul M Bhuiyan, *COO*
Abdul Bhuiyan, *COO*
EMP: 7 **EST:** 2006
SQ FT: 13,500
SALES (est): 2.4MM **Privately Held**
WEB: www.allay.us
SIC: 2834 Pharmaceutical preparations

(G-5282)
ALLSTATE SIGNS INC
651 E 17th St (33010-3240)
PHONE..................................305 885-9751
Jose Mastache, *Director*
EMP: 7 **EST:** 2001
SALES (est): 163K **Privately Held**
WEB: www.allstatesign.com
SIC: 3993 Signs & advertising specialties

(G-5283)
ALLURING DESIGN LLC
2657 W 76th St (33016-5616)
PHONE..................................305 582-3481
Fausto Mendez, *CEO*
EMP: 6 **EST:** 2011
SQ FT: 3,000
SALES (est): 200K **Privately Held**
SIC: 2519 Furniture, household: glass, fiberglass & plastic

(G-5284)
ALUMINUM EXPRESS INC
2745 W 78th St (33016-2772)
PHONE..................................954 868-2628
Fax: 305 825-4932
EMP: 5
SALES (est): 410K **Privately Held**
SIC: 2741 Misc Publishing

(G-5285)
ALUMINUM POWDER COATING
16200 Nw 49th Ave (33014-6315)
PHONE..................................305 628-4155
Michael J Buzzella, *Principal*
EMP: 7 **EST:** 2010
SALES (est): 265.3K **Privately Held**
WEB: www.aluminumpowdercoating.com
SIC: 3479 Coating of metals & formed products

(G-5286)
ALUMINUM POWDER COATING LC
16200 Nw 49th Ave (33014-6315)
PHONE..................................305 628-4155
Joseph Buzzella,
Michael Buzzella,
EMP: 10 **EST:** 2002
SQ FT: 24,000
SALES (est): 663.2K **Privately Held**
WEB: www.aluminumpowdercoating.com
SIC: 3479 Coating of metals & formed products

(G-5287)
AMERICAN ALUMINUM DOORS CORP
2214 W 8th Ct (33010-2024)
PHONE..................................305 885-4020
Ramon Ibargollin, *President*
EMP: 13 **EST:** 2001
SALES (est): 29.9K **Privately Held**
SIC: 3353 Aluminum sheet, plate & foil

(G-5288)
AMERICAN ARCHTCTRAL MTLS GL LL
16201 Nw 49th Ave (33014-6314)
PHONE..................................305 688-8778
Donna Rosenberg,
EMP: 7 **EST:** 2009
SALES (est): 1MM **Privately Held**
WEB: www.aamg.us
SIC: 3441 Fabricated structural metal

(G-5289)
AMERICAN ELASTIC & TAPE INC
1675 E 11th Ave (33010-3309)
PHONE..................................305 888-0303
Frank R Zampieri, *President*
Valentin Zampieri, *Vice Pres*
▲ **EMP:** 8 **EST:** 1999
SQ FT: 7,500
SALES (est): 1MM **Privately Held**
WEB: www.americanelastic.com
SIC: 2241 Narrow fabric mills

(G-5290)
AMERICAN FENCE SHOP LLC
4790 E 11th Ave (33013-2130)
PHONE..................................305 681-3511
Isaac Henriquez, *Mng Member*
◆ **EMP:** 18 **EST:** 1995
SQ FT: 5,000
SALES (est): 2MM **Privately Held**
WEB: www.americanfenceshop.com
SIC: 3315 7692 Fence gates posts & fittings: steel; welding repair

(G-5291)
AMERICAN FORCE WHEELS INC
2310 W 76th St (33016-1843)
PHONE..................................786 345-6301
Alireza Shadravan, *President*
Albert Diaz, *Sales Staff*
Nick Chin, *Mktg Dir*
▲ **EMP:** 15 **EST:** 1995
SALES (est): 4MM **Privately Held**
WEB: www.americanforce.com
SIC: 3312 Wheels

(G-5292)
AMERICAN MARINE COVERINGS INC
1065 Se 9th Ct (33010-5815)
PHONE..................................305 889-5355
Philip Lavista, *President*
▼ **EMP:** 11 **EST:** 1972
SQ FT: 2,200
SALES (est): 254.2K **Privately Held**
WEB: www.american-marine.com
SIC: 2394 3429 2512 Canvas & related products; manufactured hardware (general); upholstered household furniture

(G-5293)
AMERICAN MARINE MFG INC
2637 W 76th St (33016-5615)
PHONE..................................305 497-7723
Guillermo Santoya, *President*
Byron Carbonell, *Purch Mgr*
EMP: 5 **EST:** 2016
SALES (est): 434K **Privately Held**
WEB: www.americanmarinewindows.com
SIC: 3731 3442 Lighters, marine: building & repairing; patrol boats, building & repairing; towboats, building & repairing; storm doors or windows, metal

(G-5294)
AMERICAN PROFESSIONAL IR WORK
8320 Nw 103rd St (33016-4657)
PHONE..................................305 556-9522
Mauricio Rivera, *Principal*
EMP: 8 **EST:** 2015
SALES (est): 253.1K **Privately Held**
SIC: 3462 Iron & steel forgings

(G-5295)
AMERICAN S-SHORE PLTING STTCHI
Also Called: Trim Rite Trimmings and Lace
1085 E 31st St (33013-3521)
PHONE..................................305 978-9934
Ike Cortes, *President*
EMP: 8 **EST:** 1972
SQ FT: 12,500
SALES (est): 200K **Privately Held**
WEB: www.americanseashore.com
SIC: 2395 Embroidery & art needlework

(G-5296)
AMERICAN VINYL COMPANY (PA)
Also Called: Avc Plastics
600 W 83rd St (33014-3612)
PHONE..................................305 687-1863
Eric J Wiborg II, *President*
Ryan Wiborg, *General Counsel*
▲ **EMP:** 33 **EST:** 2002
SALES (est): 7.9MM **Privately Held**
WEB: www.avcplastics.com
SIC: 2821 Vinyl resins

(G-5297)
AMERIFAX ACQUISITION CORP
Also Called: Ameri-Fax
7290 W 18th Ln (33014-3704)
PHONE..................................305 828-1701
Lambert Thom, *President*
George Manur, *Vice Pres*
◆ **EMP:** 7 **EST:** 1989
SQ FT: 12,000
SALES (est): 733.1K **Privately Held**
WEB: www.posconcepts.com
SIC: 2679 Paper products, converted

(G-5298)
AMERIGLASS ENGINEERING INC
2246 W 79th St (33016-5520)
PHONE..................................305 558-6227
Samuel F Verdecia, *President*
EMP: 17 **EST:** 2005
SALES (est): 838.2K **Privately Held**
WEB: www.ameriglassinc.com
SIC: 3231 Products of purchased glass

(G-5299)
AMERIKOOLER LLC
575 E 10th Ave (33010-4639)
PHONE..................................305 884-8384
Renato M Alonso, *Chairman*
Juan Madariaga, *COO*
Yoelmir Santana, *Engineer*
Junior Rodriguez, *Design Engr*
Victo Robinson, *Controller*
◆ **EMP:** 220 **EST:** 1986
SQ FT: 210,000
SALES (est): 37.4MM **Privately Held**
WEB: www.amerikooler.com
SIC: 3585 Room coolers, portable

(G-5300)
ANDEAN STONE COMPANY LLC
1050 E 17th St (33010-3318)
PHONE..................................305 460-3320
John B Terry, *General Mgr*
▲ **EMP:** 5 **EST:** 2005
SQ FT: 1,200
SALES (est): 603.9K **Privately Held**
WEB: www.andeanstonecompany.com
SIC: 3281 Cut stone & stone products

(G-5301)
APC ART-PHYL CREATIONS LLC
345 W 75th Pl (33014-4318)
PHONE..................................786 571-4665
Josh Spitz, *Mng Member*
EMP: 6 **EST:** 2013
SALES (est): 159.7K **Privately Held**
SIC: 3965 Hooks, crochet

(G-5302)
APPLIED FIBER CONCEPTS INC
2425 W 8th Ln (33010-2031)
PHONE..................................754 581-2744
Alejandro F Cejas, *President*
Zoila Siu, *QC Mgr*
EMP: 7 **EST:** 2015
SQ FT: 5,000
SALES (est): 1.5MM **Privately Held**
WEB: www.afcarmor.com
SIC: 3423 Tools or equipment for use with sporting arms

(G-5303)
ARCA KNITTING INC (PA)
1060 E 23rd St (33013-4322)
PHONE..................................305 836-0155
Jorge Canals Jr, *President*
Matilde M Canals, *Admin Sec*
EMP: 100 **EST:** 1981
SQ FT: 180,000
SALES (est): 10.1MM **Privately Held**
WEB: www.arcaknitting.com
SIC: 2261 Dyeing cotton broadwoven fabrics

(G-5304)
ARTCRAFT ENGRAVING & PRTG INC
7921 W 26th Ave (33016-2729)
PHONE..................................305 557-9449
Frederick R Narup, *President*
William L Sayers, *Vice Pres*
Patrick Shanahan, *Vice Pres*
William Sayers, *Treasurer*
Erinn Schnur, *Sales Staff*
EMP: 20 **EST:** 1989
SQ FT: 15,000
SALES (est): 2.5MM **Privately Held**
WEB: www.artcraftengraving.com
SIC: 2752 Commercial printing, offset

(G-5305)
ARTEC MANUFACTURING LLC
699 W 17th St (33010-2414)
PHONE..................................305 888-4375
Roy Bustillo, *Mng Member*
EMP: 8 **EST:** 2011
SALES (est): 471.6K **Privately Held**
SIC: 3999 Manufacturing industries

(G-5306)
ARTEC METAL FABRICATION INC
699 W 17th St (33010-2414)
PHONE..................................305 888-4375
Ramon Trujillo, *CEO*
▲ **EMP:** 8 **EST:** 2007
SQ FT: 4,400
SALES (est): 943K **Privately Held**
WEB: www.artecmf.com
SIC: 3441 Fabricated structural metal

(G-5307)
ARTISTIC FENCE CORPORATION
1070 Se 9th Ter Ste B (33010-5832)
P.O. Box 111088 (33011-1088)
PHONE..................................305 805-1976
Ernesto Alvarez, *President*
EMP: 6 **EST:** 1991
SQ FT: 7,485
SALES (est): 600K **Privately Held**
WEB: www.artisticfencenj.com
SIC: 3272 1741 3496 Concrete products, precast; foundation & retaining wall construction; miscellaneous fabricated wire products

(G-5308)
ASEMBLU INC
18520 Nw 67th Ave 208 (33015-3302)
PHONE..................................800 827-4419
EMP: 15
SALES (est): 522.5K **Privately Held**
SIC: 2599 Mfg Furniture/Fixtures

(G-5309)
ASP ALARM & ELEC SUPS INC
7535 W 20th Ave (33014-3728)
PHONE..................................305 556-9047
Mitchell A Delgado, *President*
EMP: 6 **EST:** 2004
SALES (est): 696.8K **Privately Held**
SIC: 3669 Emergency alarms

(G-5310)
ASSOCTION HSPNIC HRITG FSTIVAL
3430 E 1st Ave (33013-2602)
PHONE..................................305 885-5613
Eloy Vazquez, *Principal*
EMP: 6 **EST:** 2006
SALES (est): 190K **Privately Held**
SIC: 2836 Culture media

(G-5311)
ATLAS PAPER MILLS LLC
3725 E 10th Ct (33013-2900)
PHONE..................................305 835-8046
Juan Michelena, *Vice Pres*
EMP: 149
SALES (corp-wide): 2.9B **Privately Held**
WEB: www.resolutetissue.com
SIC: 2621 5113 Toilet tissue stock; industrial & personal service paper
HQ: Atlas Paper Mills, Llc
3301 Nw 107th St
Miami FL 33167
800 562-2860

(G-5312)
ATLAS SOUTH
17301 W Okeechobee Rd (33018-6414)
PHONE..................................305 824-3900
Cynthia Masters, *Principal*
Jorge Rivera, *Site Mgr*
EMP: 6 **EST:** 2010
SALES (est): 96.4K **Privately Held**
SIC: 3823 Industrial instrmnts msrmnt display/control process variable

(G-5313)
AVIATION INTL SOLUTIONS LLC
6043 Nw 167th St Ste A16 (33015-4342)
PHONE..................................305 267-7117
Edgar Caicedo, *Principal*
Carlos Sierra, *Principal*
Claudia Torres,
EMP: 4 **EST:** 2011
SALES (est): 6.2MM **Privately Held**
WEB: www.aviationis.net
SIC: 3721 2531 3429 3728 Helicopters; seats, aircraft; aircraft hardware; rotoblades for helicopters

(G-5314)
B & D PRECISION TOOLS INC
2367 W 8th Ln (33010-2029)
PHONE..................................305 885-1583
Heliodoro Duran, *President*
▼ **EMP:** 31 **EST:** 1978
SQ FT: 24,000
SALES (est): 4.9MM **Privately Held**
SIC: 3544 3949 2591 3089 Dies & die holders for metal cutting, forming, die casting; industrial molds; sporting & athletic goods; drapery hardware & blinds & shades; injection molding of plastics

(G-5315)
B LINE APPAREL INC
4671 E 11th Ave (33013-2115)
P.O. Box 530671, Miami (33153-0671)
PHONE..................................305 953-8300
Fax: 305 953-7909
▼ **EMP:** 12
SQ FT: 20,000
SALES (est): 3.4MM **Privately Held**
SIC: 3552 Mfg Textile Machinery

(G-5316)
BASS INDUSTRIES INC
Also Called: Bass Bulletin and Directory
604 W 18th St (33010-2423)
PHONE..................................305 751-2716
Robert Baron, *President*
Paul Baron, *Vice Pres*
Anne Baron, *Admin Sec*
◆ **EMP:** 37 **EST:** 1961
SQ FT: 19,600
SALES (est): 1.8MM **Privately Held**
WEB: www.bassind.com
SIC: 3993 2542 2519 Displays & cutouts, window & lobby; partitions & fixtures, except wood; furniture, household: glass, fiberglass & plastic

(G-5317)
BAYLEE & COMPANY LLC
Also Called: Baylee Nasco
605 W 17th St (33010-2414)
PHONE..................................305 333-6464
Alina Nasco,
EMP: 5 **EST:** 2016
SQ FT: 13,000
SALES (est): 333.1K **Privately Held**
WEB: www.bayleenasco.com
SIC: 3552 Card clothing, textile machinery

(G-5318)
BEAUTIFUL MAILBOX CO
2360 W 76th St (33016-1843)
PHONE..................................305 403-4820
Andrew Corsetti, *President*
Sherri Corsetti, *Vice Pres*
Seth Valancy, *Controller*
Sheri Corsetti, *VP Sales*
Edward Schissler, *Manager*
EMP: 38 **EST:** 1988
SQ FT: 30,000
SALES (est): 6MM **Privately Held**
WEB: www.beautifulmailbox.com
SIC: 3444 3993 Sheet metalwork; signs & advertising specialties

(G-5319)
BELLA LUNA INC
3650 E 10th Ct (33013-2918)
PHONE..................................305 696-0310
Amelia Costa, *President*
Theresa Costa, *Partner*
Nicolas Trujillo, *Partner*
◆ **EMP:** 21 **EST:** 1995
SQ FT: 15,000
SALES (est): 3.1MM **Privately Held**
WEB: www.lunabella.com
SIC: 3648 3641 Lighting fixtures, except electric: residential; electric lamps

(G-5320)
BELTS INC
2500 W 84th St Unit 8 (33016-5757)
PHONE..................................714 572-3636
Jeff Schwartz, *President*
Esthela Schwartz, *CFO*

EMP: 7 **EST:** 2000
SQ FT: 5,000
SALES (est): 80.9K **Privately Held**
WEB: www.belts.com
SIC: 2387 Apparel belts

(G-5321)
BENITEZ FORKLIFT CORP
18820 Nw 57th Ave Apt 301 (33015-7012)
PHONE..................................786 307-3872
Yeymi Sardubas, *Principal*
▼ **EMP:** 7 **EST:** 2010
SALES (est): 607.9K **Privately Held**
WEB: www.benitezforklift.com
SIC: 3537 Forklift trucks

(G-5322)
BERNARD CAP LLC
620 W 27th St (33010-1214)
PHONE..................................305 822-4800
Lawrence Weinstein, *CEO*
Barry L Showalter, *Treasurer*
Leo Fonseca, *Human Res Mgr*
Phyllis Alfonso, *Cust Mgr*
Lonne Weinstein, *Admin Sec*
◆ **EMP:** 140
SQ FT: 60,000
SALES (est): 19.5MM **Privately Held**
WEB: www.bernardcap.com
SIC: 2353 Hats & caps

(G-5323)
BEST POWDER COATINGS INC
3970 E 10th Ct (33013-2924)
PHONE..................................305 836-9460
Omar Romero Jr, *President*
EMP: 22 **EST:** 1999
SQ FT: 7,500
SALES (est): 1.6MM **Privately Held**
WEB: www.bestpowdercoatings.com
SIC: 3479 Coating of metals & formed products

(G-5324)
BEST PRODUCTS MIX INC
17541 Nw 89th Ct (33018-6693)
PHONE..................................305 512-9920
Luis M Gutierrez, *President*
Maria B Gutierrez, *Vice Pres*
▼ **EMP:** 8
SQ FT: 10,000
SALES (est): 823.8K **Privately Held**
SIC: 3299 Stucco

(G-5325)
BETWELL OIL & GAS COMPANY (PA)
8083 Nw 103rd St (33016-2201)
P.O. Box 22577 (33002-2577)
PHONE..................................305 821-8300
Lowell S Dunn II, *President*
EMP: 5 **EST:** 1981
SQ FT: 10,000
SALES (est): 1.6MM **Privately Held**
SIC: 1381 Directional drilling oil & gas wells

(G-5326)
BIOSCULPTOR CORPORATION
2480 W 82nd St Unit 1 (33016-2735)
PHONE..................................305 823-8300
Alan Finnieston, *President*
Karen Finnieston, *Vice Pres*
EMP: 5 **EST:** 1994
SALES (est): 997.5K **Privately Held**
WEB: www.biosculptor.com
SIC: 3695 3575 7372 3842 Computer software tape & disks: blank, rigid & floppy; computer terminals; prepackaged software; surgical appliances & supplies; manufactured hardware (general)

(G-5327)
BISCAYNE BEDDING INTL LLC
3925 E 10th Ct (33013-2923)
PHONE..................................305 633-4634
Alan Mandell, *President*
Jean Mandell, *Corp Secy*
Stephen Mandell, *Vice Pres*
▼ **EMP:** 25 **EST:** 1949
SQ FT: 15,000
SALES (est): 5.3MM **Privately Held**
WEB: www.biscaynebedding.com
SIC: 2515 Mattresses, innerspring or box spring; box springs, assembled

(G-5328)
BISCHOFF AERO LLC
2583 W 6th Ln (33010-1247)
PHONE..................................305 883-4410
Guillermo Bischoff, *Sales Staff*
Michael Bischoff,
EMP: 15 **EST:** 2006
SQ FT: 10,000
SALES (est): 1.2MM **Privately Held**
WEB: www.bischoffaerospace.com
SIC: 3728 Aircraft parts & equipment

(G-5329)
BLACK OPS LLC
7815 W 4th Ave (33014-4213)
PHONE..................................305 450-0127
Louis J Garcia, *Principal*
◆ **EMP:** 8 **EST:** 2010
SALES (est): 373.3K **Privately Held**
WEB: www.blackopsusa.com
SIC: 2393 Canvas bags

(G-5330)
BOTANICA ODOMIWALE CORP
1301 Palm Ave (33010-3463)
PHONE..................................305 381-5834
Ramon B Ruiz Sr, *Principal*
EMP: 6 **EST:** 2015
SALES (est): 138.4K **Privately Held**
SIC: 2833 Medicinals & botanicals

(G-5331)
BROS WILLIAMS PRINTING
4716 E 10th Ct (33013-2122)
PHONE..................................305 769-9925
Fax: 305 769-9927
EMP: 9
SQ FT: 5,000
SALES: 380K **Privately Held**
SIC: 2759 5199 Commercial Printing Whol Nondurable Goods

(G-5332)
BROS WILLIAMS PRINTING INC
Also Called: Williams Specialities
4716 E 10th Ct (33013-2122)
PHONE..................................305 769-9925
Mario Williams Jr, *President*
Mario J Williams Jr, *President*
EMP: 9 **EST:** 1981
SQ FT: 5,000
SALES (est): 250K **Privately Held**
WEB: www.williamsspecialties.com
SIC: 2752 2791 2789 2759 Commercial printing, offset; typesetting; bookbinding & related work; commercial printing; die-cut paper & board

(G-5333)
BUILDING ENVELOPE SYSTEMS INC
3121 E 11th Ave (33013-3513)
PHONE..................................305 693-0683
▲ **EMP:** 4
SQ FT: 15,000
SALES: 3MM **Privately Held**
SIC: 3442 Mfg Metal Doors/Sash/Trim

(G-5334)
BUILT RIGHT INSTALLERS INTL
7930 W 26th Ave Unit 2 (33016-2718)
PHONE..................................305 362-6010
George Martinez, *CEO*
EMP: 10 **EST:** 1993
SALES (est): 1MM **Privately Held**
WEB: www.barm6ranch.com
SIC: 3535 1796 Unit handling conveying systems; installing building equipment

(G-5335)
BULLET LINE LLC (DH)
Also Called: Bl Acquisition
6301 E 10th Ave Ste 110 (33013-0008)
PHONE..................................305 623-9223
Michael Bernstein, *Vice Pres*
Mark Weiss, *Vice Pres*
Christie Blanco, *Opers Staff*
Deenna Fajardo, *Opers Staff*
Lissette Saldana, *Production*
◆ **EMP:** 404 **EST:** 2006
SQ FT: 250,000
SALES (est): 100.8MM
SALES (corp-wide): 23.1MM **Privately Held**
WEB: www.humphreyline.com
SIC: 3993 Advertising novelties

(G-5336)
BUSINESS CLINIC INC
1475 W Okeechobee Rd # 3 (33010-2860)
PHONE..................................786 473-4573
Antonio Diaz, *Principal*
Tony Diaz, *Consultant*
EMP: 6 **EST:** 2018
SALES (est): 715.2K **Privately Held**
SIC: 2752 Commercial printing, lithographic

(G-5337)
C & G PACKAGING LLC
7305 W 19th Ct (33014-3720)
PHONE..................................305 825-5244
Arnold Coburn, *CEO*
Manuel Gomez, *COO*
EMP: 15 **EST:** 2007
SQ FT: 30,000
SALES: 2.7MM **Privately Held**
WEB: www.cgpacks.com
SIC: 3089 3085 Plastic processing; plastics bottles

(G-5338)
C2 IMAGE & PRINTING INC
7665 Nw 182nd Ter (33015-2942)
PHONE..................................310 892-8316
Claudia Cardenas, *Principal*
EMP: 6 **EST:** 2017
SALES (est): 139.1K **Privately Held**
SIC: 2752 Commercial printing, offset

(G-5339)
CABRERAS SPANISH SAUSAGES LLC
765 W 27th St (33010-1215)
PHONE..................................305 882-1040
Rodolfo Cabrera,
Rafael Cabrera,
Joanna Desten,
▲ **EMP:** 9 **EST:** 2013
SALES (est): 665.4K **Privately Held**
SIC: 2013 Sausages from purchased meat; ham, canned: from purchased meat

(G-5340)
CARGILL MEAT SOLUTIONS CORP
Also Called: Cargill Food Distribution
4220 W 91st Pl Unit 100 (33018-3903)
PHONE..................................305 826-3699
Jerry Mullins, *Branch Mgr*
EMP: 338
SALES (corp-wide): 3B **Privately Held**
WEB: www.cargill.com
SIC: 2011 Meat packing plants
HQ: Cargill Meat Solutions Corp
151 N Main St Ste 900
Wichita KS 67202
316 291-2500

(G-5341)
CG QUALITY WOODWORKS INC
7530 W 19th Ct (33014-3725)
PHONE..................................305 231-3480
Carlos Gomez, *President*
EMP: 7 **EST:** 1998
SALES (est): 973.5K **Privately Held**
WEB: www.cgqualitywoodworks.com
SIC: 2431 Millwork

(G-5342)
CHARLESTON ALUMINUM LLC
1150 Nw 159th Dr (33016)
PHONE..................................305 628-4014
EMP: 11
SALES (corp-wide): 40MM **Privately Held**
SIC: 3334 Primary Aluminum Producer
PA: Charleston Aluminum, Llc
480 Frontage Rd
Gaston SC 29053
803 939-4600

(G-5343)
CHEMSEAL INC
7891 W 25th Ct (33016-2758)
PHONE..................................305 433-8362
Carlos Simanca, *Principal*
EMP: 6 **EST:** 2011
SALES (est): 1.3MM **Privately Held**
WEB: www.chemsealinc.net
SIC: 3491 Industrial valves
PA: Chemseal, C.A.
Avenida Aragua Oeste # 15
Maracay

(G-5344)
CHOLIFT FORKLIFT USA CO
1390 W 42nd St Apt 204 (33012-8710)
PHONE..................................786 483-6930
Guangjun Zhou, *President*
EMP: 6 **EST:** 2017
SALES (est): 97K **Privately Held**
SIC: 3537 Forklift trucks

(G-5345)
CIRON CUSTOM WELDING INC
2954 W 84th St (33018-4914)
PHONE..................................786 259-7589
Ana R Rodriguez, *President*
Ciro Verdecia, *Vice Pres*
EMP: 7 **EST:** 2016
SALES (est): 105.8K **Privately Held**
SIC: 7692 Welding repair

(G-5346)
CJKS DELUXE INC
8920 Nw 187th St (33018-6280)
PHONE..................................786 657-8726
Carlos Martinez, *Principal*
EMP: 6 **EST:** 2017
SALES (est): 115.4K **Privately Held**
SIC: 2782 Blankbooks & looseleaf binders

(G-5347)
CLASSIC PRINTING & FINISH LLC
3140 W 84th St Unit 7 (33018-4913)
PHONE..................................305 817-4242
EMP: 6 **EST:** 2018
SALES (est): 261.7K **Privately Held**
SIC: 2752 Commercial printing, lithographic

(G-5348)
CNC-PRECISION MACHINING CORP
1055 E 26th St (33013-3717)
PHONE..................................786 452-9575
Lucio Castillo, *President*
EMP: 6 **EST:** 1996
SQ FT: 10,000
SALES (est): 864.5K **Privately Held**
WEB: www.cnc-precision.com
SIC: 3599 Machine shop, jobbing & repair

(G-5349)
COBALT AEROSPACE INC
2550 W 78th St Unit 8 (33016-2766)
PHONE..................................305 450-0457
Madai Girard, *Principal*
Tommy Nelms, *Vice Pres*
EMP: 7 **EST:** 2019
SALES (est): 144.8K **Privately Held**
WEB: www.cobaltaerospace.com
SIC: 3647 Aircraft lighting fixtures

(G-5350)
COLOR EXPRESS INC
7990 W 25th Ct (33016-2701)
PHONE..................................305 558-2061
Lee Mc Call, *President*
EMP: 8 **EST:** 1979
SQ FT: 5,000
SALES (est): 775.6K **Privately Held**
WEB: www.colorexpressprinting.com
SIC: 2752 2791 2789 Commercial printing, offset; typesetting; bookbinding & related work

(G-5351)
CONDO ELECTRIC MOTOR REPR CORP
3615 E 10th Ct (33013-2917)
PHONE..................................305 691-5400
Hector Gomez, *President*
Mohamed Hallaj, *Principal*
Jose G Espinola, *Vice Pres*
Hector Gomez Jr, *Treasurer*
Amos Rojas, *Controller*
◆ **EMP:** 30 **EST:** 1976
SQ FT: 20,000

GEOGRAPHIC

SALES (est): 6.3MM **Privately Held**
WEB: www.condoelectric.com
SIC: 7694 Electric motor repair

(G-5352)
CONSTRCTION MTAL FBRCATORS LLC
15913 Nw 49th Ave (33014-6308)
PHONE..................................305 781-9004
Ferenc Schafer, *Manager*
EMP: 6 **EST:** 2017
SALES (est): 396.7K **Privately Held**
SIC: 3499 Fabricated metal products

(G-5353)
CONTROL AND AUTOMTN CONS INC
11300 Nw 87th Ct Ste 125 (33018-4518)
P.O. Box 171825 (33017-1825)
PHONE..................................305 823-8670
Wilky Gonzalez, *President*
Sadiye Gonzalez, *Vice Pres*
Wilky N Gonzales, *Manager*
EMP: 8 **EST:** 1992
SQ FT: 3,600
SALES (est): 927.8K **Privately Held**
WEB: www.controlandautomation.com
SIC: 3699 Security control equipment & systems

(G-5354)
CORAL CLUB TEE SHIRTS INC
3192 W 81st St (33018-5808)
PHONE..................................305 828-6939
Morton Blake, *President*
▼ **EMP:** 9 **EST:** 1990
SQ FT: 8,000
SALES (est): 861.5K **Privately Held**
SIC: 2253 2759 T-shirts & tops, knit; screen printing

(G-5355)
CORDOBA FOODS LLC
4477 E 11th Ave (33013-2534)
PHONE..................................305 733-4768
Karina Mena, *President*
David Mena, *Mng Member*
Karina F Porritiello,
EMP: 20 **EST:** 2004
SQ FT: 1,000
SALES (est): 9.1MM **Privately Held**
WEB: www.gauchoranchfoods.com
SIC: 2033 Barbecue sauce: packaged in cans, jars, etc.

(G-5356)
CORELITE INC (PA)
1060 E 30th St (33013-3520)
PHONE..................................305 921-4292
Pascual Del Cioppo, *President*
Mariella Vazquez, *Vice Pres*
Domenica Del Cioppo, *Treasurer*
Elsa Axelsdottir, *Manager*
Giancarlo Del Cioppo, *Admin Sec*
▲ **EMP:** 11 **EST:** 2011
SQ FT: 25,000
SALES: 9MM **Privately Held**
WEB: www.corelitecomposites.com
SIC: 2436 Softwood veneer & plywood

(G-5357)
CREATIVE MILLWORK INC
7635 W 28th Ave Bay 3 (33016-5107)
PHONE..................................305 885-5474
William Rodriguez, *President*
EMP: 5 **EST:** 1997
SQ FT: 700
SALES (est): 467K **Privately Held**
WEB: www.creative-millwork.com
SIC: 2431 Millwork

(G-5358)
CUSTOM CONTROLS TECHNOLOGY INC
2230 W 77th St (33016-1866)
PHONE..................................305 805-3700
Sheila Gallo, *President*
Gordon Myers, *Vice Pres*
EMP: 26 **EST:** 1987
SQ FT: 15,000
SALES (est): 9MM **Privately Held**
WEB: www.cct-inc.us
SIC: 3625 Relays & industrial controls

(G-5359)
CUSTOM MICA FURNITURE INC
575 W 28th St (33010-1325)
PHONE..................................305 888-8480
Fax: 305 885-2284
EMP: 6
SQ FT: 8,000
SALES (est): 470K **Privately Held**
SIC: 2511 Kitchen Cabinets/Cultured Marble/Granite

(G-5360)
D T WOODCRAFTERS CORP
1677 W 31st Pl (33012-4505)
PHONE..................................305 556-3771
David Thibaudeau, *President*
George Miller, *Plant Mgr*
Maickel Plaza, *Plant Mgr*
Wendy Ackerman, *Controller*
EMP: 29 **EST:** 1989
SQ FT: 16,000
SALES (est): 2.7MM **Privately Held**
WEB: www.dtwoodcrafters.com
SIC: 2541 2434 Store & office display cases & fixtures; wood kitchen cabinets

(G-5361)
D TURIN & COMPANY INC
8045 W 26th Ct (33016-2797)
PHONE..................................305 825-2004
Ronald Plask, *President*
Robert Edelman, *Vice Pres*
David Plask, *Vice Pres*
Kenny Plask, *Vice Pres*
Barbara Spivack, *Vice Pres*
▲ **EMP:** 29 **EST:** 1926
SQ FT: 7,200
SALES (est): 2MM **Privately Held**
WEB: www.dturin.com
SIC: 2353 3911 2752 3961 Hats, caps & millinery; jewelry, precious metal; commercial printing, lithographic; costume jewelry

(G-5362)
DADE DOORS INC
1707 W 32nd Pl (33012-4511)
PHONE..................................305 556-8980
Wilfredo Gonsalez, *President*
▼ **EMP:** 10 **EST:** 1999
SQ FT: 2,000
SALES (est): 800.1K **Privately Held**
WEB: www.dadedoors.com
SIC: 2434 Wood kitchen cabinets

(G-5363)
DADE MADE
478 W 28th St (33010-1324)
PHONE..................................305 846-9482
L Michael Underwood Jr, *President*
EMP: 7 **EST:** 2017
SALES (est): 532.6K **Privately Held**
WEB: www.dademadefab.com
SIC: 7692 Welding repair

(G-5364)
DAILY MULTISERVICES INC
6763 Nw 182nd St Apt 105 (33015-7933)
PHONE..................................786 286-3817
Efrain S Valdes, *Vice Pres*
EMP: 6 **EST:** 2013
SALES (est): 97.9K **Privately Held**
SIC: 2711 Newspapers, publishing & printing

(G-5365)
DAVID VIERA LLC
7828 W 29th Ln Apt 101 (33018-5166)
PHONE..................................305 218-3401
David Viera, *Manager*
EMP: 8 **EST:** 2004
SALES (est): 389K **Privately Held**
WEB: www.dvmiamistairsrailing.com
SIC: 3446 Architectural metalwork

(G-5366)
DEBWAY CORPORATION
2343 W 76th St (33016-1842)
PHONE..................................305 818-6353
Gesualdo Vitale, *President*
Rosanna Vitale, *Vice Pres*
Patrizia Vitlae, *Treasurer*
Mariana Vitale, *Admin Sec*
◆ **EMP:** 6 **EST:** 1991
SQ FT: 9,600
SALES (est): 1.7MM **Privately Held**
WEB: www.debwaycorp.com
SIC: 3562 Ball & roller bearings

(G-5367)
DECO SHADES SOLUTIONS INC
3155 W Okeechobee Rd (33012-4519)
PHONE..................................305 558-9800
Enrique Perez, *Principal*
▼ **EMP:** 6 **EST:** 2012
SALES (est): 371.2K **Privately Held**
SIC: 2591 Drapery hardware & blinds & shades

(G-5368)
DELCONTE PACKAGING INC
757 W 26th St (33010-1211)
PHONE..................................305 885-2800
William Block, *President*
▲ **EMP:** 15 **EST:** 1995
SQ FT: 10,000
SALES (est): 2.3MM **Privately Held**
WEB: www.delcontepackaging.com
SIC: 3089 3993 Plastic containers, except foam; signs & advertising specialties

(G-5369)
DERM-BURO INC
Also Called: G-Forces Div
4675 E 10th Ct (33013-2107)
PHONE..................................305 953-4025
Derrick Visla, *Manager*
EMP: 41
SALES (corp-wide): 3.4MM **Privately Held**
WEB: www.gforces.com
SIC: 3841 Surgical & medical instruments
PA: Derm-Buro, Inc.
229 Newtown Rd
Plainview NY 11803
516 694-8300

(G-5370)
DESIGNER FILMS INC
7485 W 19th Ct (33014-3722)
PHONE..................................305 828-0605
Monica Anderson, *President*
Eduardo Temkin, *Principal*
▲ **EMP:** 16 **EST:** 2010
SQ FT: 15,000
SALES (est): 2.2MM **Privately Held**
WEB: www.designerfilms.com
SIC: 3081 Plastic film & sheet

(G-5371)
DHF MARKETING INC
685 W 25th St (33010-2148)
PHONE..................................305 884-8077
Barry J Richman, *President*
EMP: 14 **EST:** 2003
SQ FT: 28,255
SALES (est): 502.1K **Privately Held**
SIC: 2211 Draperies & drapery fabrics, cotton

(G-5372)
DIAZ BROTHERS CORP
7750 W 24th Ave (33016-5786)
PHONE..................................305 364-4911
Nelson Y Diaz Mendez, *Principal*
EMP: 9 **EST:** 2009
SALES (est): 322.9K **Privately Held**
WEB: www.bandmpaving.com
SIC: 2515 Mattresses & bedsprings

(G-5373)
DILAN ENTERPRISES INC
2339 W 9th Ct (33010-2003)
PHONE..................................305 887-3051
▼ **EMP:** 36
SQ FT: 4,000
SALES (est): 1.5MM **Privately Held**
SIC: 2339 2369 Mfg Women's/Misses' Outerwear Mfg Girl/Youth Outerwear

(G-5374)
DIVITAE INC
570 E 65th St (33013-1161)
PHONE..................................786 585-5556
Gabriel Kohen, *CEO*
EMP: 7 **EST:** 2019
SALES (est): 945.1K **Privately Held**
SIC: 2869 Industrial organic chemicals

(G-5375)
DJ CABINET FACTORY INC
2552 W 3rd Ct (33010-1457)
PHONE..................................786 483-8868
Jose Luis Lopez, *President*
EMP: 7 **EST:** 2006
SALES (est): 285.4K **Privately Held**
SIC: 2434 Vanities, bathroom: wood

(G-5376)
DOBBS & BRODEUR BOOKBINDERS
Also Called: D & B Bookbinders
1030 E 14th St (33010-3312)
PHONE..................................305 885-5215
Edward Lloret, *President*
Anthony Lloret, *Vice Pres*
Jorge Lloret, *Treasurer*
EMP: 8 **EST:** 1975
SQ FT: 8,000
SALES (est): 1.1MM **Privately Held**
WEB: www.db-book-binders-online-store.myshopify.com
SIC: 2789 2796 2782 2759 Binding only: books, pamphlets, magazines, etc.; platemaking services; blankbooks & looseleaf binders; commercial printing

(G-5377)
DON INDUSTRIAL GROUP LLC
7760 W 20th Ave Ste 7 (33016-1829)
PHONE..................................305 290-4237
Reinier Hernandez, *Mng Member*
Melanie Garcia, *Administration*
EMP: 10 **EST:** 2010
SALES (est): 1.3MM **Privately Held**
WEB: www.donindustrialgroup.com
SIC: 3728 Aircraft parts & equipment

(G-5378)
DRT EXPRESS INC
7855 W 2nd Ct Ste 4 (33014-4333)
PHONE..................................305 827-5005
Pok Hao Truong, *Principal*
EMP: 8 **EST:** 2009
SALES (est): 927.4K **Privately Held**
WEB: www.drtexpress.com
SIC: 3312 Wheels

(G-5379)
DTI DESIGN TREND INC
496 W 18th St (33010-2419)
PHONE..................................954 680-8370
Jack Wiener, *President*
EMP: 13 **EST:** 2004
SQ FT: 11,000
SALES (est): 106K **Privately Held**
SIC: 2399 2221 Emblems, badges & insignia; draperies & drapery fabrics, manmade fiber & silk; bedspreads, silk & manmade fiber

(G-5380)
DUCT DESIGN CORPORATION
7850 W 22nd Ave Unit 1 (33016-1873)
PHONE..................................305 827-0110
Rolando Ors, *President*
Maria Ors, *Corp Secy*
Gianni Jimenez, *Project Engr*
EMP: 33 **EST:** 1992
SQ FT: 2,000
SALES (est): 4.9MM **Privately Held**
WEB: www.ductdesign.com
SIC: 3444 Ducts, sheet metal

(G-5381)
DYNABILT TECHNOLOGIES CORP
180 W 22nd St (33010-2208)
P.O. Box 726, Hallandale (33008-0726)
PHONE..................................305 919-9800
Fax: 954 455-9911
EMP: 15
SQ FT: 10,000
SALES: 3MM **Privately Held**
SIC: 3441 Structural Metal Fabrication

(G-5382)
DYNACOLOR GRAPHICS INC
950 Se 8th St (33010-5740)
P.O. Box 699037, Miami (33269-9037)
PHONE..................................305 625-5388
Donald M Duncanson, *President*
Harry Duncanson, *Vice Pres*
▼ **EMP:** 21 **EST:** 1971

SQ FT: 41,000
SALES (est): 696.8K **Privately Held**
WEB: www.dynacolor.com
SIC: 2752 Commercial printing, offset

(G-5383)
E & D KITCHEN CABINET INC
6790 W 6th Ct (33012-6534)
PHONE..................................786 343-8558
Elio Montero, *Principal*
EMP: 7 **EST:** 2010
SALES (est): 251.3K **Privately Held**
SIC: 2434 Wood kitchen cabinets

(G-5384)
E & E WOODCRAFT CORP
1619 W 33rd Pl (33012-4513)
PHONE..................................305 556-1443
Diosmede Cano, *President*
EMP: 10 **EST:** 2005
SALES (est): 489.2K **Privately Held**
WEB: www.eandemillwork.net
SIC: 2431 Millwork

(G-5385)
E C V DISPLAY CORP
2336 W 77th St (33016-1868)
PHONE..................................786 586-1034
Sandra Valdes, *President*
EMP: 6 **EST:** 2009
SALES (est): 94.5K **Privately Held**
SIC: 3993 Signs & advertising specialties

(G-5386)
EASTERN SIGNS LLC
13408 Nw 38th Ct (33014)
PHONE..................................305 542-8274
Jorge L Quintero, *Principal*
EMP: 8 **EST:** 2016
SALES (est): 505.5K **Privately Held**
SIC: 3993 Signs & advertising specialties

(G-5387)
EC CABINETS INC
1511 E 11th Ave (33010-3308)
PHONE..................................305 887-2091
Emilio Cruz, *President*
Yudelka Rosario, *Vice Pres*
EMP: 7 **EST:** 2002
SQ FT: 20,000
SALES (est): 604.2K **Privately Held**
WEB: www.eccabinets.net
SIC: 2434 Wood kitchen cabinets

(G-5388)
ECONOCHANNEL INC
213 Se 10th Ave (33010-5536)
PHONE..................................305 255-2113
Jose Hernandez, *President*
Leida Hernandez, *Vice Pres*
Laura Hernandez, *Controller*
▼ **EMP:** 35 **EST:** 1997
SALES (est): 4.6MM **Privately Held**
WEB: www.econochannel.com
SIC: 3993 Signs & advertising specialties

(G-5389)
ED STEEL FABRICATOR INC
4807 E 10th Ln (33013-2127)
PHONE..................................305 926-4904
EMP: 8 **EST:** 2015
SALES (est): 400K **Privately Held**
WEB: www.edsteelf.com
SIC: 3441 Fabricated structural metal

(G-5390)
EDSUN LIGHTING FIXTURES MFG
569 W 17th St (33010-2412)
P.O. Box 650861, Miami (33265-0861)
PHONE..................................305 888-8849
Guillermina Garcia, *President*
Roy Garcia, *General Mgr*
Isabelle Moraitis, *Vice Pres*
◆ **EMP:** 15 **EST:** 1983
SQ FT: 20,000
SALES (est): 2.1MM **Privately Held**
SIC: 3645 3646 Residential lighting fixtures; commercial indusl & institutional electric lighting fixtures

(G-5391)
EGG ROLL SKINS INC
3251 E 11th Ave (33013-3515)
PHONE..................................305 836-0571
Fernando Chang Muy, *President*
Julio Chiong, *Vice Pres*
Wai Chiu Muy, *Vice Pres*
EMP: 10 **EST:** 1970
SQ FT: 10,000
SALES (est): 152.6K **Privately Held**
SIC: 2051 5812 2099 Rolls, bread type: fresh or frozen; Chinese restaurant; food preparations

(G-5392)
ELITE GRAPHICS
18710 W Oakmont Dr (33015-2904)
P.O. Box 822203, Pembroke Pines (33082-2203)
PHONE..................................305 331-2678
Thomas Crews, *President*
EMP: 6 **EST:** 2015
SALES (est): 86.1K **Privately Held**
SIC: 2396 Fabric printing & stamping

(G-5393)
ELLIS FAMILY HOLDINGS INC
Also Called: Molded Container
6301 E 10th Ave Ste 110 (33013-0008)
PHONE..................................503 785-7400
Melvin W Ellis, *President*
◆ **EMP:** 18 **EST:** 1957
SQ FT: 5,000
SALES (est): 238.6K **Privately Held**
SIC: 3089 3993 Injection molding of plastics; advertising novelties

(G-5394)
EMC REPRESENTATIONS CORP
1198 W 23rd St (33010-1949)
PHONE..................................305 305-1776
Eladio Medina Cabello, *Principal*
EMP: 6 **EST:** 2016
SALES (est): 94.5K **Privately Held**
SIC: 3572 Computer storage devices

(G-5395)
EMJAC INDUSTRIES INC
1075 Hialeah Dr (33010-5551)
PHONE..................................305 883-2194
David Dorta, *President*
Robert Castro, *Business Mgr*
Jeff Cook, *COO*
Kenneth Brown, *Vice Pres*
Terri Dorta, *Vice Pres*
▼ **EMP:** 96
SQ FT: 100,000
SALES (est): 25.9MM **Privately Held**
WEB: www.emjacindustries.com
SIC: 2542 3441 Counters or counter display cases: except wood; fabricated structural metal

(G-5396)
EMPIRE ENTERPRISES
2980 W 84th St Unit 11 (33018-4916)
PHONE..................................786 373-8003
Erick Martinez, *Principal*
EMP: 6 **EST:** 2018
SALES (est): 344K **Privately Held**
SIC: 3999 Manufacturing industries

(G-5397)
EMPIRE STONE AND CABINETS
720 W 27th St (33010-1216)
PHONE..................................305 885-7092
Ralph J Granadillo, *President*
Nicole Granadillo, *Vice Pres*
EMP: 20 **EST:** 2016
SALES (est): 2.3MM **Privately Held**
SIC: 2434 Wood kitchen cabinets

(G-5398)
EMPIRE TRNSPT SOLUTIONS CORP
228 W 18th St (33010-2527)
PHONE..................................305 439-5677
Adolfo A Rumbaut Guzman, *President*
EMP: 6 **EST:** 2017
SALES (est): 300K **Privately Held**
SIC: 3537 Trucks, tractors, loaders, carriers & similar equipment

(G-5399)
ENVIRONMENTAL CONTRACTORS INC
Also Called: E C I
2648 W 78th St (33016-2745)
PHONE..................................305 556-6942
Kelly Moran, *President*
EMP: 16 **EST:** 1985
SQ FT: 6,064
SALES (est): 2.3MM **Privately Held**
WEB: www.hannahindustries.com
SIC: 1481 1541 4212 Overburden removal, nonmetallic minerals; industrial buildings & warehouses; hazardous waste transport

(G-5400)
EXCLUSIVE BATS LLC
10930 Nw 138th St Unit 1 (33018-1139)
PHONE..................................305 450-3858
Roberto Maya, *Principal*
EMP: 5 **EST:** 2016
SALES (est): 424.9K **Privately Held**
WEB: www.exclusivebats.com
SIC: 3949 Sporting & athletic goods

(G-5401)
EXPRESS VISION CARE INC
1550 W 84th St Ste 15 (33014-3368)
PHONE..................................786 587-7404
Raul Lopez, *Manager*
EMP: 10 **EST:** 2012
SALES (est): 1.4MM **Privately Held**
WEB: www.myexpressvisioncare.com
SIC: 3851 Contact lenses

(G-5402)
F & R GENERAL INTERIORS CORP
480 W 20th St (33010-2426)
PHONE..................................305 635-4747
Ruben Rodriguez, *President*
Chris Rodriguez, *Vice Pres*
▼ **EMP:** 13 **EST:** 1984
SALES (est): 2MM **Privately Held**
WEB: www.fandrgeneralinteriors.com
SIC: 2531 2491 Chairs, table & arm; millwork, treated wood

(G-5403)
FAJAS COLOMBIANAS USA LLC
18850 Nw 57th Ave (33015-7018)
PHONE..................................786 326-0002
Juan Pablo Angel,
EMP: 6 **EST:** 2018
SALES (est): 35K **Privately Held**
SIC: 2259 Girdles & other foundation garments, knit

(G-5404)
FALCONPRO INDUSTRIES INC
1690 W 40th St (33012-7043)
PHONE..................................305 556-4456
John Carlos, *President*
Juan Rivero, *Director*
Anna Gonzalez, *Admin Sec*
▼ **EMP:** 6 **EST:** 1983
SQ FT: 4,000
SALES (est): 653.7K **Privately Held**
WEB: www.falconpro.com
SIC: 2842 Deodorants, nonpersonal

(G-5405)
FASHION CONNECTION MIAMI INC
Also Called: Classic Uniforms
900 W 19th St (33010-2309)
PHONE..................................305 882-0782
Sergio Urquiza Jr, *President*
Joseph Urquiza, *Vice Pres*
Maria Urquiza, *Treasurer*
EMP: 9 **EST:** 1977
SQ FT: 15,000
SALES (est): 835.1K **Privately Held**
SIC: 2389 Uniforms & vestments

(G-5406)
FAST FUEL CORP
2274 W 80th St Unit 4 (33016-5550)
PHONE..................................786 251-0373
Ricardo Rivero, *Principal*
EMP: 7 **EST:** 2007
SALES (est): 199.6K **Privately Held**
SIC: 2869 Fuels

(G-5407)
FASTSIGNS
118 Hialeah Dr (33010-5250)
PHONE..................................786 615-2179
EMP: 6 **EST:** 2018
SALES (est): 46K **Privately Held**
WEB: www.fastsigns.com
SIC: 3993 Signs & advertising specialties

(G-5408)
FAULKNER INC OF MIAMI
Also Called: Faulkner Plastics
7275 W 20th Ave (33014-3707)
PHONE..................................305 885-4731
Joseph E McCabe, *President*
Tami L McCabe, *Vice Pres*
Gretchel Zamora, *Sales Staff*
▼ **EMP:** 14 **EST:** 1966
SQ FT: 14,000
SALES (est): 5.4MM **Privately Held**
WEB: www.plasticproductsinc.com
SIC: 3089 Injection molding of plastics

(G-5409)
FDC PRINT LLC
Also Called: Franklin Dodd Communications
950 Se 8th St (33010-5740)
PHONE..................................305 885-8707
Donald Mader, *President*
Maryjo Lynch, *Prdtn Mgr*
Elizabeth Cal, *Engineer*
Robert Cooler, *Engineer*
Ken Justilien, *Accounts Exec*
▼ **EMP:** 71 **EST:** 2011
SALES (est): 15.7MM
SALES (corp-wide): 47.2MM **Privately Held**
WEB: www.franklindodd.com
SIC: 2759 Commercial printing
PA: Southeastern Printing Co Inc
950 Se 8th St
Hialeah FL 33010
772 287-2141

(G-5410)
FEDAN CORP
Also Called: Fedan Tire Co
2280 W 1st Ave (33010-2202)
PHONE..................................305 885-5415
Felix Sanchez Sr, *President*
Mireya Sanchez, *Corp Secy*
Felix J Sanchez Jr, *Vice Pres*
◆ **EMP:** 18 **EST:** 1979
SQ FT: 8,000
SALES (est): 3.7MM **Privately Held**
WEB: www.fedantire.com
SIC: 3011 5531 5014 7534 Retreading materials, tire; automotive tires; tires & tubes; tire retreading & repair shops

(G-5411)
FLORIDA DRAGLINE OPERATION
3163 W 81st St (33018-5807)
PHONE..................................305 824-9755
David White, *Manager*
▲ **EMP:** 7 **EST:** 1995
SALES (est): 330.7K **Privately Held**
SIC: 3531 Excavators: cable, clamshell, crane, derrick, dragline, etc.

(G-5412)
FLORIDA ELECTROMECHANICS INC
7305 W 19th Ct (33014-3720)
P.O. Box 112680 (33011-2680)
PHONE..................................305 825-5244
Manuel Gomez, *President*
EMP: 6 **EST:** 1980
SQ FT: 10,000
SALES (est): 35K **Privately Held**
WEB: www.electrobottles.com
SIC: 3089 3085 Injection molding of plastics; plastics bottles

(G-5413)
FLORIDA FLEXIBLE
2699 W 79th St Unit 1 (33016-2739)
PHONE..................................305 512-2222
Armando Corbett, *President*
EMP: 7 **EST:** 2014
SALES (est): 593.2K **Privately Held**
WEB: www.floridaflex.com
SIC: 2759 Screen printing

(G-5414)
FLORIDA KIT CBNETS AMERCN CORP
9325 W Okeechobee Rd (33016-2183)
PHONE..................................305 828-2830

Carlos Cabrera, *Principal*
EMP: 7 **EST:** 2005
SALES (est): 172.6K **Privately Held**
WEB: www.floridakitchencenters.com
SIC: 2434 Wood kitchen cabinets

(G-5415)
FLORIDA THREAD & TRIMMING
7395 W 18th Ln (33014-3739)
PHONE..................................954 240-2474
Erwin Fein, *President*
Robert Fein, *Corp Secy*
Alan Fein, *Vice Pres*
▼ **EMP:** 7 **EST:** 1968
SQ FT: 10,000
SALES (est): 194.9K **Privately Held**
SIC: 2284 5131 Thread from manmade fibers; notions

(G-5416)
FOREVER SIGNS INC
2400 W 3rd Ct (33010-1439)
PHONE..................................305 885-3411
Arturo Dizcaiano, *President*
Dailyn Gonzalez, *Admin Sec*
▲ **EMP:** 19 **EST:** 2006
SALES (est): 2.2MM **Privately Held**
WEB: www.foreversignsusa.net
SIC: 3993 Electric signs

(G-5417)
FRIENDLY WELDING INC
4600 E 10th Ln (33013-2112)
PHONE..................................786 953-8413
EMP: 11 **Privately Held**
SIC: 7692 Welding Repair
PA: Friendly Welding Inc
17051 Ne 23rd Ave Apt 1k
North Miami Beach FL

(G-5418)
FUTURE KITCHEN CORP
5841 W 3rd Ave (33012-2614)
PHONE..................................786 356-3746
Alien Medina, *Principal*
EMP: 7 **EST:** 2012
SALES (est): 170.5K **Privately Held**
WEB: www.thefuturekitchencorp.com
SIC: 2434 Wood kitchen cabinets

(G-5419)
G PRINT INC
2392 W 80th St Ste 1 (33016-5687)
PHONE..................................305 316-2266
Gilbert A Gutierrez, *President*
EMP: 7 **EST:** 2016
SALES (est): 508.7K **Privately Held**
SIC: 2752 Commercial printing, lithographic

(G-5420)
G S SERVICORE CORP
3630 E 10th Ct (33013-2918)
PHONE..................................305 888-0189
Victor Medina, *President*
Karlos Medina, *Opers Staff*
Sandra Medina, *Admin Sec*
◆ **EMP:** 22 **EST:** 2001
SQ FT: 18,000
SALES (est): 2.6MM **Privately Held**
WEB: www.sgsequipment.com
SIC: 3621 4581 7699 Motors & generators; airport terminal services; industrial equipment services

(G-5421)
G-CAR INC (PA)
235 W 75th Pl (33014-4340)
PHONE..................................305 883-8223
Gerardo Cabrera, *President*
Carlos Cabrera, *Corp Secy*
▲ **EMP:** 60 **EST:** 1985
SQ FT: 35,000
SALES (est): 5.1MM **Privately Held**
SIC: 3714 Steering mechanisms, motor vehicle

(G-5422)
GALAXY AWNING AND SIGNS INC
1620 W 33rd Pl (33012-4514)
PHONE..................................305 262-4224
David Borrell, *Principal*
EMP: 6 **EST:** 2012
SALES (est): 147.7K **Privately Held**
WEB: www.goldenawning.com
SIC: 3993 Signs & advertising specialties

(G-5423)
GAMA TEC CORPORATION
2208 W 79th St (33016-5520)
PHONE..................................305 362-0456
Claudio Gatto, *President*
EMP: 6 **EST:** 1991
SQ FT: 3,000
SALES (est): 580K **Privately Held**
SIC: 3544 Industrial molds

(G-5424)
GARCIA DELUXE SERVICES CORP
1240 W 34th St (33012-4810)
PHONE..................................786 291-4329
Mijail Garcia, *President*
EMP: 6 **EST:** 2018
SALES (est): 144.9K **Privately Held**
SIC: 2782 Blankbooks & looseleaf binders

(G-5425)
GARCIA IRON WORKS
365 W 21st St (33010-2518)
PHONE..................................305 888-0080
Martin Garcia, *Owner*
Alena Garcia, *Opers-Prdtn-Mfg*
EMP: 6 **EST:** 1995
SALES (est): 654.6K **Privately Held**
WEB: www.garciaironwork.com
SIC: 3312 5712 Hot-rolled iron & steel products; furniture stores

(G-5426)
GENERAL IMPACT GL WINDOWS CORP
290 W 78th Rd (33014-4302)
PHONE..................................305 558-8103
Jose Gunida, *President*
Jose Ruiz, *Sales Staff*
▼ **EMP:** 16 **EST:** 2001
SALES (est): 3.2MM **Privately Held**
WEB: www.generalimpact.com
SIC: 3442 Shutters, door or window: metal

(G-5427)
GENERAL PILLOWS & FIBER INC
Also Called: Hygenator Pillow Service
605 W 17th St (33010-2414)
PHONE..................................305 884-8300
Alina G Nasco, *President*
Miguel A Nasco Jr, *Vice Pres*
EMP: 9 **EST:** 2005
SALES (est): 1.1MM **Privately Held**
WEB: www.pillowsandfibers.com
SIC: 2392 Cushions & pillows

(G-5428)
GENERAL STAIR CORPORATION
Also Called: G S C
690 W 83rd St (33014-3612)
PHONE..................................305 769-9900
Saby Behar, *President*
Moises Vaninstein, *Treasurer*
Alejandro Davila, *Finance Mgr*
Rachel Martinez, *Sales Staff*
Raimundo Aleman, *Supervisor*
EMP: 32
SQ FT: 23,000
SALES (est): 2.5MM **Privately Held**
WEB: www.generalstair.com
SIC: 2431 Staircases & stairs, wood

(G-5429)
GESS TECHNOLOGIES LLC
7292 W 20th Ave (33016-1854)
PHONE..................................305 231-6322
Johnny Ferreira, *CEO*
EMP: 13 **EST:** 2003
SALES (est): 561.3K **Privately Held**
WEB: www.gess-inc.com
SIC: 3699 Security devices

(G-5430)
GIFT GIVING CREATIONS CORP
7221 Nw 174th Ter Apt 102 (33015-1106)
PHONE..................................786 239-0229
EMP: 8 **EST:** 2019
SALES (est): 322.3K **Privately Held**
WEB: www.giftgivingcreations.com
SIC: 2759 Screen printing

(G-5431)
GILDA INDUSTRIES INC
2525 W 4th Ave (33010-1339)
PHONE..................................305 887-8286
Juan Blazquez, *President*
Danny Gallardo, *General Mgr*
Jeannice Blazquez, *Vice Pres*
Yamilet Fernandez, *Accounting Mgr*
Carmen E Blazquez, *Director*
◆ **EMP:** 97 **EST:** 1967
SQ FT: 40,000
SALES (est): 13.6MM **Privately Held**
WEB: www.gildaindustries.com
SIC: 2052 Crackers, dry

(G-5432)
GLOBAL INTL INVESTMENTS LLC
6175 Nw 167th St Ste G32 (33015-4362)
PHONE..................................305 825-2288
Dorelis La Capruccia, *Vice Pres*
Pamela Hermoza, *Sales Staff*
EMP: 6 **EST:** 2010
SALES (est): 811.9K **Privately Held**
WEB: www.giillc.net
SIC: 3728 Aircraft parts & equipment

(G-5433)
GOLD NETWORK OF MIAMI INC
17620 Nw 63rd Ct (33015-4484)
PHONE..................................305 343-7355
George Smith, *Principal*
EMP: 8 **EST:** 2011
SALES (est): 181.6K **Privately Held**
SIC: 3571 Personal computers (microcomputers)

(G-5434)
GOURMET 3005 INC
2315 W 77th St (33016-1869)
PHONE..................................786 334-6250
Mario Marquez, *President*
Robinson Avila, *Vice Pres*
EMP: 6 **EST:** 2011
SALES (est): 300K **Privately Held**
WEB: www.eternalwaterheater.com
SIC: 2011 Bacon, slab & sliced from meat slaughtered on site

(G-5435)
GQ INVESTMENTS LLC
Also Called: Fine Art Lamps
3840 W 104th St Unit 20 (33018-1230)
PHONE..................................305 821-3850
Bill Gearhart, *Controller*
Laura Goldblum,
Rene Quintana,
Janina Schardar,
EMP: 140 **EST:** 2018
SQ FT: 125,000
SALES (est): 23.2MM **Privately Held**
SIC: 3645 Wall lamps; table lamps; desk lamps

(G-5436)
GREGG TOOL & DIE CO INC
4725 E 10th Ct (33013-2121)
PHONE..................................305 685-6309
Gregg Jones, *President*
Edith Jones, *Corp Secy*
EMP: 5 **EST:** 1970
SQ FT: 15,000
SALES (est): 610.4K **Privately Held**
WEB: www.greggtool.com
SIC: 3544 3469 Special dies & tools; metal stampings

(G-5437)
GROUP STEEL INC (PA)
3492 W 84th St (33018-4930)
PHONE..................................786 319-1222
Erick Gonzalez, *President*
Angelica Bustamante, *Treasurer*
EMP: 6 **EST:** 2010
SALES (est): 1.5MM **Privately Held**
SIC: 3441 Fabricated structural metal

(G-5438)
GRUPO ERIK USA LLC
3355 W 68th St Apt 120 (33018-1740)
PHONE..................................305 447-2611
Erik Arie De Leeuwerk,
EMP: 6 **EST:** 2019
SALES (est): 117.6K **Privately Held**
WEB: www.grupoerik.com
SIC: 2752 Commercial printing, lithographic

(G-5439)
GUIMAR INC
Also Called: Sir Speedy
1224 E 4th Ave (33010-3502)
PHONE..................................305 888-1547
Maria Noguera, *President*
Maurice Noguera, *Vice Pres*
Mauricio Noguera, *Vice Pres*
Rosa Osorio, *Manager*
David Robidoux, *Executive*
EMP: 14 **EST:** 1980
SQ FT: 3,200
SALES (est): 2.5MM **Privately Held**
WEB: www.sirspeedy.com
SIC: 2752 Commercial printing, lithographic

(G-5440)
GUNDERLIN LTD INC
3625 E 11th Ave (33013-2929)
PHONE..................................305 696-6071
Jay Bass, *President*
Lynn Kislack, *Corp Secy*
Russ Marot, *Vice Pres*
Charlie Sammarco, *Vice Pres*
▼ **EMP:** 95
SQ FT: 100,000
SALES (est): 41.3MM **Privately Held**
WEB: www.gunderlin.com
SIC: 3534 Elevators & equipment

(G-5441)
H GOICOECHEA INC
Also Called: Best Supplier
695 E 10th Ave (33010-4641)
PHONE..................................305 805-3333
Hugo Goicoechea, *President*
▲ **EMP:** 15 **EST:** 2010
SALES (est): 269.7K **Privately Held**
SIC: 2673 Bags: plastic, laminated & coated

(G-5442)
HAMBURG HOUSE INC
6157 Nw 167th St Ste F20 (33015-4360)
PHONE..................................305 557-9913
Peter Auerbach, *President*
▲ **EMP:** 27 **EST:** 1933
SALES (est): 1.3MM **Privately Held**
WEB: www.hamburghouse.com
SIC: 2299 2395 Linen fabrics; embroidery products, except schiffli machine

(G-5443)
HG TRADING CIA INC
1055 Se 9th Ter (33010-5804)
PHONE..................................305 986-5702
Hector Gahaleano, *President*
◆ **EMP:** 7 **EST:** 1997
SALES (est): 116.7K **Privately Held**
SIC: 3251 5032 Brick & structural clay tile; brick, stone & related material

(G-5444)
HIALEAH DISTRIBUTION CORP
Also Called: Beverage Depot
270 W 25th St (33010-1528)
PHONE..................................786 200-2498
Marc Gueron, *CEO*
Viktor Razon, *General Mgr*
EMP: 32 **EST:** 1970
SQ FT: 6,000
SALES (est): 477.8K **Privately Held**
WEB: www.hialeahfl.gov
SIC: 2097 5149 Manufactured ice; soft drinks

(G-5445)
HIALEAH PLATING
4335 E 10th Ave (33013-2513)
PHONE..................................305 953-4143
EMP: 9 **EST:** 2018
SALES (est): 760.2K **Privately Held**
WEB: www.alliedplating.com
SIC: 3471 Electroplating of metals or formed products

(G-5446)
HIALEAH POWDER COATING CORP
1690 W 33rd Pl (33012-4514)
PHONE..................................786 275-4107
Jimmy J Hernandez, *President*
EMP: 12 **EST:** 2014
SALES (est): 859.4K **Privately Held**
SIC: 3479 Etching & engraving

(G-5447)
HIALEAH WELDING & ORNAMENTAL
4295 E 11th Ave (33013-2530)
PHONE..................................305 685-3196
Alberto Ojito, *Owner*
EMP: 6 **EST:** 1968
SQ FT: 5,000
SALES (est): 100K **Privately Held**
SIC: 7692 Welding repair

(G-5448)
HOLPACK CORP
Also Called: Best Bubble Mailers
3840 W 104th St Unit 7 (33018-1230)
PHONE..................................786 565-3969
Benjamin Wainberg, *President*
EMP: 9 **EST:** 2018
SALES (est): 1MM **Privately Held**
WEB: www.holpack.com
SIC: 3089 Blister or bubble formed packaging, plastic

(G-5449)
HOME DESIGN GROUP CORP
220 W 21st St (33010-2517)
PHONE..................................305 888-5836
Javier Barrera, *President*
Dianne Camps, *Admin Sec*
EMP: 6 **EST:** 2003
SALES (est): 339.8K **Privately Held**
SIC: 2434 Wood kitchen cabinets

(G-5450)
HYBRID IMPRESSIONS INC (PA)
8020 W 30th Ct (33018-3853)
PHONE..................................305 392-5029
John Braceras, *President*
▼ **EMP:** 29 **EST:** 2005
SALES (est): 2.1MM **Privately Held**
WEB: www.hybridimpressions.com
SIC: 2752 Commercial printing, lithographic

(G-5451)
IC INDUSTRIES INC
1101 E 33rd St Fl 2 (33013-3528)
P.O. Box 139075 (33013-9075)
PHONE..................................305 696-8330
Harvey Rothstein, *Ch of Bd*
Joel Bachelor, *President*
Wendy Rothstein, *Exec VP*
Matthew Rothstein, *Vice Pres*
◆ **EMP:** 85 **EST:** 1990
SQ FT: 20,000
SALES (est): 21.1MM **Privately Held**
WEB: www.icind.com
SIC: 2653 Boxes, corrugated: made from purchased materials

(G-5452)
ICE BUNKER A&M CORP
717 W 27th St (33010-1215)
PHONE..................................786 368-0924
Yeicsa R Mucarsel, *Principal*
EMP: 10 **EST:** 2018
SALES (est): 510K **Privately Held**
SIC: 3999 Manufacturing industries

(G-5453)
IMPRESSING DESIGN PRINT
17699 Nw 78th Ave (33015-3627)
PHONE..................................786 615-3695
EMP: 6 **EST:** 2016
SALES (est): 92.3K **Privately Held**
WEB: www.goimpressing.com
SIC: 2752 Commercial printing, lithographic

(G-5454)
INTEGRATED COMPONENTS CORP
2592 W 78th St (33016-2773)
PHONE..................................305 824-0484
Juan P Rodriguez, *President*
◆ **EMP:** 17 **EST:** 1993
SQ FT: 11,000
SALES (est): 1.1MM **Privately Held**
SIC: 3089 Injection molded finished plastic products

(G-5455)
INTERNATIONAL IRON WORKS LLC (PA)
3585 E 10th Ct (33013-2915)
PHONE..................................305 835-0190
Juana Ramos,
EMP: 9 **EST:** 2007
SALES (est): 1MM **Privately Held**
SIC: 3312 Structural shapes & pilings, steel

(G-5456)
INTERNATIONAL SOUND CORP
Also Called: Teleview Racing Patrol
1550 W 35th Pl (33012-4626)
PHONE..................................305 556-1000
Ron Sellitto, *Branch Mgr*
Mauricio Morello, *IT/INT Sup*
Don Chambers, *Director*
Darrell Calhoun, *Executive*
EMP: 83
SALES (corp-wide): 14MM **Privately Held**
WEB: www.isctv.com
SIC: 3663 Television broadcasting & communications equipment
PA: International Sound Corporation
7130 Milford Indus Rd
Pikesville MD 21208
410 484-2244

(G-5457)
INTERTEK INTERNATIONAL CORP
Also Called: Intertek Auto-Sun-Shade
401 Se 11th Ave (33010-5737)
PHONE..................................305 883-8700
Ezra David Eskandry, *President*
▲ **EMP:** 52 **EST:** 1985
SQ FT: 20,000
SALES (est): 5.2MM **Privately Held**
SIC: 3714 Motor vehicle parts & accessories

(G-5458)
IVERICA INDUSTRIAL INC
1044 E 29th St (33013-3518)
PHONE..................................305 691-1659
EMP: 10
SQ FT: 6,476
SALES: 500K **Privately Held**
SIC: 2426 2542 Hardwood Dimension/Floor Mill Mfg Partitions/Fixtures-Nonwood

(G-5459)
J C S ENGINEERING & DEV
211 W 22nd St (33010-1593)
PHONE..................................305 888-7911
EMP: 10
SQ FT: 10,000
SALES (est): 1MM **Privately Held**
SIC: 3495 5085 3544 3493 Mfg Wire Springs Whol Industrial Supplies Mfg Dies/Tools/Jigs/Fixt Mfg Steel Spring-Nonwire

(G-5460)
JAFFER WLL DRLLNG A DIV OF AC
1451 Se 9th Ct (33010-5944)
PHONE..................................954 523-6669
Eugene C Friedlander, *Partner*
William J Mc Cluskey, *Partner*
Caroline Urtiaga, *Partner*
EMP: 11 **EST:** 2010
SALES (est): 235.3K **Privately Held**
WEB: www.acschultes.com
SIC: 1381 1711 Directional drilling oil & gas wells; plumbing, heating, air-conditioning contractors

(G-5461)
JAIBA CABINETS INC
8125 W 20th Ave (33014-3231)
PHONE..................................305 364-3646
EMP: 5
SQ FT: 7,000
SALES (est): 542.7K **Privately Held**
SIC: 2434 Mfg Wood Kitchen Cabinets

(G-5462)
JAM CABINETS & INVESTMENTS LLC
Also Called: Cary's Kitchen Cabinets
2795 W 78th St (33016-2772)
PHONE..................................305 823-9020
Jorge Merida, *Mng Member*
Miguel Ferreiro,
Clara D Merida,
EMP: 11 **EST:** 1981
SQ FT: 16,572
SALES (est): 1.3MM **Privately Held**
WEB: www.caryskitchen.com
SIC: 2434 Wood kitchen cabinets

(G-5463)
JANORO FIXTURE MFG CORP
249 W 29th St (33012-5705)
PHONE..................................305 887-2524
James G Sobie, *President*
Rebecca Sobie, *Vice Pres*
Helen Sobie, *Admin Sec*
EMP: 6 **EST:** 1978
SQ FT: 10,000
SALES (est): 561.5K
SALES (corp-wide): 1.4MM **Privately Held**
SIC: 3646 3645 Commercial indusl & institutional electric lighting fixtures; residential lighting fixtures
PA: H L H Sobyco Electrical Supplies Corp
275 W 29th St
Hialeah FL 33012
305 887-2524

(G-5464)
JEB THERMOFOIL OF SOUTH FLA
1065 E 16th St (33010-3315)
PHONE..................................305 887-6214
Antonio Garlovo, *President*
EMP: 8 **EST:** 2017
SALES (est): 372.5K **Privately Held**
WEB: www.florida.intercreditreport.com
SIC: 2431 Doors & door parts & trim, wood

(G-5465)
JESUS CABINETS CORP
1701 W 42nd Pl (33012-8403)
PHONE..................................786 285-1088
Jesus R Piloto, *Principal*
EMP: 6 **EST:** 2010
SALES (est): 116.9K **Privately Held**
SIC: 2434 Wood kitchen cabinets

(G-5466)
JONEL KNITTING MILLS INC
7130 W 12th Ln (33014-4513)
PHONE..................................305 887-7333
Jonel Jankuc, *President*
Donna Jankuc, *Vice Pres*
Jeffrey Jankuc, *Vice Pres*
EMP: 25 **EST:** 1987
SALES (est): 846.9K **Privately Held**
WEB: www.jonelknittingmills.com
SIC: 2253 Knit outerwear mills

(G-5467)
JOSE LEAL ENTERPRISES INC
705 W 20th St (33010-2429)
PHONE..................................305 887-9611
Jose M Leal, *President*
Sandra Leal, *Director*
◆ **EMP:** 65 **EST:** 1968
SQ FT: 40,000
SALES (est): 9.2MM **Privately Held**
WEB: www.wwdrape.com
SIC: 2211 7641 Bedspreads, cotton; draperies & drapery fabrics, cotton; furniture upholstery repair

(G-5468)
JP COSMETICS INC
1687 W 32nd Pl (33012-4509)
PHONE..................................305 231-4963
Eudel Morales, *President*
Juan M Dominguez, *Vice Pres*
Lorenzo C Morales, *Treasurer*
▲ **EMP:** 12 **EST:** 2005
SALES (est): 257.3K **Privately Held**
WEB: www.corlys.com
SIC: 2844 Face creams or lotions

(G-5469)
JRP SCREEN PRINTING INC
8416 Nw 201st Ter (33015-5977)
PHONE..................................305 333-4244
Ido Plasencia, *President*
Ramon Plasencia, *Corp Secy*
Raynier Plasencia, *Treasurer*
EMP: 35 **EST:** 1989
SQ FT: 16,000
SALES (est): 1.9MM **Privately Held**
SIC: 2499 5141 Food handling & processing products, wood; food brokers

(G-5470)
JUAN RODRIGUEZ CABINETRY CORP
221 W 41st St (33012-4345)
PHONE..................................305 467-3878
Juan Rodriguez, *President*
EMP: 8 **EST:** 2015
SALES (est): 371.3K **Privately Held**
SIC: 2434 Wood kitchen cabinets

(G-5471)
KCON INDUSTRIES LLC
6538 Nw 170th Ter (33015-4617)
PHONE..................................917 250-7402
Kendra Concepcion, *President*
Markuss Wallace, *Vice Pres*
EMP: 6 **EST:** 2018
SALES (est): 209K **Privately Held**
SIC: 3999 Barber & beauty shop equipment

(G-5472)
KIBBY FOODS LLC
2315 W 77th St (33016-1869)
PHONE..................................305 456-3635
Samir Mourra, *Mng Member*
Olga M Mourra,
EMP: 10 **EST:** 2007
SALES (est): 453.5K **Privately Held**
WEB: www.kibbyfoods.com
SIC: 2038 Frozen specialties

(G-5473)
KIT RESIDENTIAL DESIGNS INC
5921 Nw 176th St Unit 2 (33015-5133)
PHONE..................................305 796-5940
Louis Gonzales, *President*
EMP: 5 **EST:** 2003
SALES (est): 546.1K **Privately Held**
SIC: 2514 5031 Kitchen cabinets: metal; kitchen cabinets

(G-5474)
KNIGHTSBRIDGE STEEL LLC
507 W 17th St (33010-2412)
PHONE..................................786 532-0290
Shir Keidan,
EMP: 7 **EST:** 2016
SALES (est): 264.5K **Privately Held**
SIC: 3272 Building materials, except block or brick: concrete

(G-5475)
KOKI INTERIORS FURN MFG INC
7680 W 7th Ave (33014-4116)
PHONE..................................305 558-6573
Jose Pelaez, *President*
Magda Pelaez, *Treasurer*
◆ **EMP:** 11 **EST:** 1977
SQ FT: 43,000
SALES (est): 560.5K **Privately Held**
SIC: 2512 Living room furniture: upholstered on wood frames

(G-5476)
KRISTINE WINDOW TREATMENTS LLC
15998 Nw 49th Ave (33014-6309)
PHONE..................................305 623-8302
Howard Rothman,
EMP: 18 **EST:** 2015
SQ FT: 5,000
SALES (est): 1.2MM **Privately Held**
SIC: 2591 Window blinds; venetian blinds; mini blinds; micro blinds

(G-5477)
L AND C SCIENCE AND TECH INC
2205 W 80th St Ste 1 (33016-5759)
PHONE..................................305 200-3531
Agustin F Venero, *President*

GEOGRAPHIC

Yaima Suarez, *Purch Mgr*
Marcelo Mancheno, *Engineer*
Agustin Venero, *Director*
EMP: 7 **EST:** 1990
SALES (est): 800K **Privately Held**
WEB: www.landcscience.com
SIC: 3844 3826 7389 X-ray apparatus & tubes; analytical instruments; spectrometers; design services

(G-5478)
L C CH INTERNATIONAL INC
Also Called: La Caja China
7395 W 18th Ln (33014-3739)
PHONE..................................305 888-1323
Roberto Guerra, *President*
Berta Guerra, *Admin Sec*
▼ **EMP:** 9 **EST:** 2000
SQ FT: 20,200
SALES: 1.9MM **Privately Held**
SIC: 3631 Barbecues, grills & braziers (outdoor cooking)

(G-5479)
L C NPEE
Also Called: National Police Ammunition
451 E 10th Ct (33010-5152)
PHONE..................................888 316-3718
Erik Agazim,
EMP: 30 **EST:** 2009
SALES (est): 3.2MM **Privately Held**
SIC: 3482 Small arms ammunition

(G-5480)
LA AUTENTICA
2294 W 78th St (33016-5525)
PHONE..................................786 409-3779
Manuel Diaz, *President*
Luis N Medina, *General Mgr*
Alejandro Perez, *Vice Pres*
EMP: 9 **EST:** 1991
SQ FT: 4,000
SALES (est): 550K **Privately Held**
SIC: 2053 Pastries (danish): frozen

(G-5481)
LA AUTENTICA FOODS INC
2294 W 78th St (33016-5525)
PHONE..................................305 888-6727
Fabrice Riviere, *President*
▲ **EMP:** 20 **EST:** 1997
SQ FT: 45,000
SALES (est): 1.2MM **Privately Held**
WEB: www.laautenticafood.com
SIC: 2099 5141 Tortillas, fresh or refrigerated; groceries, general line

(G-5482)
LA BODEGUITA DE HIALEAH INC
1044 W 23rd St (33010-1923)
PHONE..................................305 240-7421
Leonardo E De Leon, *Principal*
EMP: 6 **EST:** 2010
SALES (est): 258.8K **Privately Held**
SIC: 3949 Bridges, billiard & pool

(G-5483)
LARRY JOHNSON INC
Also Called: Miami Wall
701 W 25th St (33010-2150)
P.O. Box 28109 (33002-8109)
PHONE..................................305 888-2300
Keith Johnson, *President*
Frank Ortega, *Vice Pres*
EMP: 15 **EST:** 1990
SALES (est): 397K **Privately Held**
SIC: 3442 Window & door frames

(G-5484)
LEO FASHIONS INC
230 W 23rd St (33010-1524)
PHONE..................................305 887-1032
Evelio Villa, *President*
Herminia Villia, *Treasurer*
EMP: 10 **EST:** 1977
SALES (est): 306.5K **Privately Held**
SIC: 2331 2321 Shirts, women's & juniors': made from purchased materials; men's & boys' furnishings

(G-5485)
LEON SIGN S LLC
2330 W 80th St (33016-5589)
PHONE..................................786 333-4694
Ada Valdes, *Principal*
EMP: 6 **EST:** 2010
SALES (est): 114.9K **Privately Held**
SIC: 3993 Signs & advertising specialties

(G-5486)
LIEBHERR CRANES INC
Also Called: Liebherr Nenzing Crane
15101 Nw 112th Ave (33018-3709)
PHONE..................................305 817-7500
Winston Ziegler, *Sales Staff*
Deutsch Helmut, *Manager*
Helmut Deutsch, *Manager*
EMP: 8
SALES (corp-wide): 12.8B **Privately Held**
WEB: www.liebherr.com
SIC: 3531 5082 Cranes, ship; construction & mining machinery
HQ: Liebherr Cranes, Inc.
4100 Chestnut Ave
Newport News VA 23607
757 928-2505

(G-5487)
LISA BAKERY INC
2460 W 1st Ave (33010-1718)
PHONE..................................305 888-8431
Alberto Diaz, *President*
Albert Diaz, *President*
EMP: 8 **EST:** 2000
SALES (est): 536.2K **Privately Held**
SIC: 2051 Bakery: wholesale or wholesale/retail combined

(G-5488)
LOS LATINOS MAGAZINE INC
138 Hialeah Dr (33010-5250)
PHONE..................................305 882-9074
Hercules A Vilchez, *President*
Luis Bilchez, *Vice Pres*
Hercules D Vilchez, *Vice Pres*
Luis E Vilchez, *Treasurer*
Luz Falkowski, *Admin Sec*
EMP: 10 **EST:** 1991
SALES (est): 790K **Privately Held**
SIC: 2721 Magazines: publishing only, not printed on site

(G-5489)
LOVE IS IN THE AIR CORP
Also Called: Wholesalers
2284 W 77th St (33016-1866)
PHONE..................................305 828-8181
Alexander Longa, *President*
Luis Christian Longa, *Vice Pres*
◆ **EMP:** 5 **EST:** 1996
SALES (est): 654.6K **Privately Held**
WEB: www.loveisintheair.net
SIC: 2899 5169 5999 Incense; essential oils; candle shops

(G-5490)
LUFEMOR INC
Also Called: Quick Print Center
5392 W 16th Ave (33012-2165)
PHONE..................................305 557-2162
Luis Morales, *President*
▼ **EMP:** 7 **EST:** 1982
SQ FT: 1,800
SALES (est): 450K **Privately Held**
SIC: 2752 Commercial printing, offset

(G-5491)
LUV & LUV INDUSTRIES INC
3149 W 80th St (33018-7278)
PHONE..................................954 826-6237
Gisele Lemus, *Principal*
EMP: 6 **EST:** 2016
SALES (est): 172.5K **Privately Held**
SIC: 3999 Manufacturing industries

(G-5492)
LUXURY WOODWORKING SOLUTI
3468 W 84th St Unit 108 (33018-4927)
PHONE..................................786 398-1785
EMP: 7 **EST:** 2019
SALES (est): 407.6K **Privately Held**
WEB: www.luxurywoodworkingsolutions.com
SIC: 2431 Millwork

(G-5493)
M & E KITCHEN CABINETS INC
7237 W 29th Ln (33018-5361)
PHONE..................................786 346-9987
Nivaldo Sosa, *Principal*
EMP: 6 **EST:** 2013
SALES (est): 121.4K **Privately Held**
WEB: www.m-ekitchencabinets.business.site
SIC: 2434 Wood kitchen cabinets

(G-5494)
M & H ENTERPRISES INC
589 W 27th St (33010-1321)
PHONE..................................305 885-5945
Fax: 305 885-5989
EMP: 9
SQ FT: 4,000
SALES: 450K **Privately Held**
SIC: 2241 5199 Narrow Fabric Mill Whol Nondurable Goods

(G-5495)
MAC D&D INC
Also Called: Alicia Studio
971 W 53rd St (33012-2418)
PHONE..................................305 821-9452
John David Machleid Jr, *President*
Dianne Machleid, *Corp Secy*
EMP: 7 **EST:** 1960
SQ FT: 3,750
SALES (est): 700.9K **Privately Held**
SIC: 2392 Bedspreads & bed sets: made from purchased materials

(G-5496)
MAG WORKS INC
7725 W 2nd Ct (33014-4307)
P.O. Box 668226, Miami (33166-9413)
PHONE..................................305 823-4440
▼ **EMP:** 22
SQ FT: 35,000
SALES (est): 2.3MM **Privately Held**
SIC: 2514 Mfg Metal Household Furniture

(G-5497)
MAJESTY FOODS LLC
Also Called: Majestic Foods
2740 W 81st St (33016-2732)
PHONE..................................305 817-1888
Carlos Garcia, *Plant Mgr*
Colin Chang,
Carl Barnett,
Gary Tie-Shue,
Henry Tie-Shue,
EMP: 31 **EST:** 2018
SALES (est): 3.4MM **Privately Held**
WEB: www.majestyfoods.com
SIC: 2041 Bread & bread-type roll mixes

(G-5498)
MAJOR LEAGUE SIGNS INC
9103 Nw 171st Ln (33018-6650)
PHONE..................................954 600-5505
Hilda Noriega, *Principal*
EMP: 6 **EST:** 2019
SALES (est): 130.8K **Privately Held**
WEB: www.miamisignandwraps.com
SIC: 3993 Signs & advertising specialties

(G-5499)
MANUFACTURING INC SP ✪
2200 W 77th St (33016-1866)
PHONE..................................305 362-0456
EMP: 8 **EST:** 2020
SALES (est): 1.5MM **Privately Held**
SIC: 3999 Manufacturing industries

(G-5500)
MARAMED PRECISION CORPORATION
Also Called: Maramed Orthopedic Systems
2480 W 82nd St Unit 1 (33016-2735)
PHONE..................................305 823-8300
Alan Finnieston, *President*
Mark Mazloff, *Vice Pres*
EMP: 29 **EST:** 1973
SQ FT: 19,200
SALES (est): 1.1MM **Privately Held**
WEB: www.maramed.com
SIC: 3842 Prosthetic appliances; orthopedic appliances

(G-5501)
MARIA E ACOSTA
4004 W 11th Ln (33012-7743)
PHONE..................................305 231-5543
Maria E Acosta, *Principal*
EMP: 8 **EST:** 2000
SALES (est): 211.6K **Privately Held**
SIC: 2024 Ice cream & frozen desserts

(G-5502)
MARINE FIBERGLASS SPECIALIST
8600 Nw 174th St (33015-3521)
PHONE..................................305 821-6667
Charles Bowden, *Principal*
EMP: 6 **EST:** 2016
SALES (est): 97.4K **Privately Held**
SIC: 3732 Boat building & repairing

(G-5503)
MARINE MANUFACTURING INC
295 W 23rd St (33010-1523)
PHONE..................................305 885-3493
Phil Thun, *President*
Kenneth Murray, *President*
▼ **EMP:** 5 **EST:** 1974
SQ FT: 10,000
SALES (est): 426.8K **Privately Held**
WEB: www.marinemanufacturing.com
SIC: 3429 Marine hardware

(G-5504)
MARITIME REPLICAS AMERICA INC
Also Called: Liners of Legend
1275 W 47th Pl Ste 423 (33012-3453)
PHONE..................................305 386-1958
Warren Sanut, *President*
John Kennedy, *Exec VP*
Rocio Davila, *Vice Pres*
▼ **EMP:** 5 **EST:** 1983
SALES (est): 650K **Privately Held**
WEB: www.maritimereplicas.com
SIC: 3999 Boat models, except toy

(G-5505)
MERENGUITOSCOM LLC
4847 E 10th Ct (33013-2123)
PHONE..................................305 685-2709
Luis Aular, *President*
Ada Tapia, *Principal*
Marisol Osorio, *Administration*
EMP: 7 **EST:** 2011
SALES (est): 154.4K **Privately Held**
SIC: 2051 Bread, cake & related products

(G-5506)
METALCO MFG INC
700 W 20th St (33010-2430)
PHONE..................................305 592-0704
Jesus L Ameijeiras, *Principal*
EMP: 8 **EST:** 2006
SALES (est): 329.1K **Privately Held**
SIC: 3999 Manufacturing industries

(G-5507)
METALWORKS ENGINEERING CORP
1745 W 32nd Pl (33012-4511)
PHONE..................................305 223-0011
Michael A Silva, *President*
Ivan Jerak, *Vice Pres*
Igor Kotlyar, *Opers Staff*
Karel Jerak, *Treasurer*
Senen Jimenez, *Marketing Staff*
EMP: 10 **EST:** 2011
SALES (est): 1.9MM **Privately Held**
WEB: www.metalworkscorp.com
SIC: 3444 Sheet metalwork

(G-5508)
MIAMI CELLOPHANE INC
7485 W 19th Ct (33014-3722)
PHONE..................................786 293-2212
Eduardo Temkin, *President*
◆ **EMP:** 29 **EST:** 1989
SQ FT: 9,000
SALES (est): 831.6K **Privately Held**
SIC: 3081 Unsupported plastics film & sheet

(G-5509)
MIAMI EPIC TEES CORP
10990 Nw 138th St Unit 16 (33018-1233)
PHONE..................................305 224-3465
Fabian Soto, *Owner*
EMP: 5 **EST:** 2018
SALES (est): 330.3K **Privately Held**
WEB: www.miamiepicteesstore.com
SIC: 2759 Screen printing

▲ = Import ▼=Export
◆ =Import/Export

(G-5510)
MIAMI FOODS DISTRS USA INC
Also Called: El Equisteo Sabor
2761 W 77th Pl (33016-5635)
PHONE..............................305 512-3246
Fernando Fernandes, *President*
Maria Gomez, *Principal*
▲ **EMP:** 14 **EST:** 2004
SQ FT: 5,770
SALES (est): 2.3MM **Privately Held**
WEB: www.elexquisitosabor.com
SIC: 2024 5143 Yogurt desserts, frozen; non-dairy based frozen desserts; frozen dairy desserts

(G-5511)
MIAMI GRANDSTAND ENTERTAINMENT
2330 W 79th St (33016-5516)
PHONE..............................305 636-9665
Felipe Perbomo, *President*
▲ **EMP:** 5 **EST:** 1997
SALES (est): 396.3K **Privately Held**
WEB: www.grandstandmiami.com
SIC: 2531 Bleacher seating, portable

(G-5512)
MIAMI METAL ROOFING LLC
Also Called: Miami Metal Deck
16000 Nw 49th Ave A (33014-6311)
PHONE..............................305 749-6356
Gabriel Villabon, *General Mgr*
Dan Dasilva, *Vice Pres*
Tahiry Wilhelm, *Regl Sales Mgr*
Peter Muskovac, *Marketing Staff*
Nelson R Parra Perdomo,
EMP: 16 **EST:** 2014
SALES (est): 350K **Privately Held**
WEB: www.mmdeck.com
SIC: 2952 Roofing materials

(G-5513)
MIAMI TAPE INC
6175 Nw 167th St Ste G38 (33015-4362)
PHONE..............................305 558-9211
Carlos A Garcia Jr, *Vice Pres*
Roberto Page, *Vice Pres*
Antonio Moreno, *Treasurer*
Dario Gonzalez, *Admin Sec*
EMP: 10 **EST:** 1974
SQ FT: 25,300
SALES (est): 960.8K **Privately Held**
WEB: www.miamitape.com
SIC: 3652 Magnetic tape (audio): prerecorded; compact laser discs, prerecorded

(G-5514)
MIAMI TECH INC
1725 W 39th Pl (33012-7016)
P.O. Box 126040 (33012-1600)
PHONE..............................786 354-1115
Jose Behar, *Principal*
EMP: 12 **EST:** 2009
SALES (est): 152.1K **Privately Held**
WEB: www.miamitech.com
SIC: 3444 Sheet metalwork

(G-5515)
MIAMI WALL SYSTEMS INC
701 W 25th St (33010-2150)
PHONE..............................305 888-2300
Larry D Johnson, *CEO*
Keith A Johnson, *President*
Francisco Ortega, *Vice Pres*
Keith Johnson, *Manager*
◆ **EMP:** 110 **EST:** 1974
SQ FT: 30,000
SALES (est): 17.2MM **Privately Held**
WEB: www.miamiwallsystems.com
SIC: 3442 Window & door frames; sash, door or window: metal

(G-5516)
MIGUEL CASA CORP
2005 W 4th Ave (33010-2404)
PHONE..............................305 887-0098
Laude M Pena, *President*
EMP: 9 **EST:** 2009
SALES (est): 336.4K **Privately Held**
SIC: 3421 Table & food cutlery, including butchers'

(G-5517)
MIKES PRECISION INC
1929 W 76th St (33014-3269)
PHONE..............................305 558-6421
EMP: 8
SQ FT: 3,000
SALES: 471.8K **Privately Held**
SIC: 3599 3089 Machine Shop And Injection Molding

(G-5518)
MILLENIUM ENGINE PLATING INC
600 W 84th St (33014-3617)
PHONE..............................305 688-0098
Juan G Yanes, *President*
Leonardo Cowley, *Technical Staff*
EMP: 8 **EST:** 2005
SALES (est): 1.2MM **Privately Held**
WEB: www.meplating.com
SIC: 3471 Electroplating of metals or formed products

(G-5519)
MINI CIRCUITS LAB INC
2160 W 80th St (33016-1846)
PHONE..............................305 558-6381
Harvey Kaylie, *President*
Gloria Kaylie, *Admin Sec*
EMP: 62 **EST:** 1977
SALES (est): 820.8K **Privately Held**
WEB: www.minicircuits.com
SIC: 3679 Electronic switches

(G-5520)
MIO GOURMENT PRODUCTS LLC
616 W 27th St (33010-1214)
PHONE..............................305 219-0253
Iristel Reyes, *Managing Prtnr*
Orlando Cordoves, *Managing Prtnr*
Magaly Vangelder, *Managing Prtnr*
EMP: 10 **EST:** 2015
SALES (est): 677.8K **Privately Held**
SIC: 2096 Potato chips & similar snacks

(G-5521)
MIPE CORP
3960 W 16th Ave Ste 208 (33012-7029)
PHONE..............................305 825-1195
Laude Miguel Pena, *President*
EMP: 6 **EST:** 2011
SALES (est): 245.2K **Privately Held**
SIC: 2086 Carbonated beverages, nonalcoholic: bottled & canned

(G-5522)
MIRAGE WOODWORKING INC
6875 W 7th Ave Apt 608 (33014-4879)
PHONE..............................305 606-7043
Antonio Gomez, *Principal*
EMP: 8 **EST:** 2016
SALES (est): 211.2K **Privately Held**
WEB: www.miragewoodworking.com
SIC: 2431 Millwork

(G-5523)
MISTER CABINET DELUXE INC
Also Called: Mobica Center
2280 W 77th St (33016-1866)
PHONE..............................305 205-3601
Silvio Barreiro, *Principal*
EMP: 9 **EST:** 2016
SALES (est): 506.8K **Privately Held**
WEB: www.mistercabinet.com
SIC: 2434 Wood kitchen cabinets

(G-5524)
MJM CABINET INC
226 W 23rd St (33010-1524)
PHONE..............................786 953-5000
Carlos M Toledo, *President*
Jessie L Rosario, *CFO*
EMP: 6 **EST:** 2009
SQ FT: 50,000
SALES (est): 450K **Privately Held**
WEB: www.mjmcabinet.com
SIC: 2434 Wood kitchen cabinets

(G-5525)
MONTEDANA FUELS
2090 Palm Ave (33010-2620)
PHONE..............................305 887-6754
Henry Izquierdo, *President*
EMP: 9 **EST:** 2014
SALES (est): 586.3K **Privately Held**
SIC: 2869 Fuels

(G-5526)
MONTEVISTA GREETINGS LLC
545 W 17th St (33010-2412)
PHONE..............................305 888-9797
David Edmondson, *Owner*
EMP: 6 **EST:** 2007
SQ FT: 23,642
SALES (est): 201.2K **Privately Held**
SIC: 2771 5112 Greeting cards; greeting cards

(G-5527)
MORALMAR KITCHEN CABINETS
3130 W 15th Ave (33012-4799)
PHONE..............................305 819-8402
Eduardo Moreno, *President*
Noelia Moreno, *Corp Secy*
Andres Baez, *Vice Pres*
EMP: 24 **EST:** 1975
SQ FT: 60,000
SALES (est): 704.3K **Privately Held**
WEB: www.moralmar.com
SIC: 2434 Wood kitchen cabinets

(G-5528)
MORAN TRANSPORT
9829 Nw 129th Ter (33018-7410)
PHONE..............................305 824-3366
Jorge Moran, *Owner*
EMP: 7 **EST:** 2000
SALES (est): 309.9K **Privately Held**
SIC: 3799 Cars, off-highway: electric

(G-5529)
MULTIFIX CBD LLC
3740 E 10th Ct (33013-2920)
PHONE..............................786 487-0792
Felipe E Lopez, *Principal*
EMP: 6 **EST:** 2018
SALES (est): 309.9K **Privately Held**
SIC: 3999

(G-5530)
MWS DRAPERY INC
496 W 18th St (33010-2419)
PHONE..............................305 794-3811
Michael Weiss, *President*
EMP: 28 **EST:** 1961
SALES (est): 533.5K **Privately Held**
SIC: 2391 Curtains & draperies

(G-5531)
MYRIAM INTERIORS INC (PA)
16301 Nw 49th Ave (33014-6316)
PHONE..............................305 626-9898
Myriam Gebara, *President*
Robert Gebara, *Vice Pres*
◆ **EMP:** 8 **EST:** 1976
SALES (est): 1.4MM **Privately Held**
WEB: www.myriaminteriorsmiami.com
SIC: 2591 5714 Blinds vertical; draperies

(G-5532)
NANI SWEETS LLC (PA)
8140 W 30th Ct (33018-3820)
PHONE..............................305 793-1077
Calixto Orta, *Mng Member*
EMP: 6
SALES (est): 250K **Privately Held**
SIC: 2051 Bakery: wholesale or wholesale/retail combined

(G-5533)
NATURAL FRUIT CORP
770 W 20th St (33010-2430)
PHONE..............................305 887-7525
Simon Bravo, *President*
Jorge Bravo, *Vice Pres*
Jonathan Bravo, *Project Mgr*
Delia Llompart, *Manager*
◆ **EMP:** 50 **EST:** 1986
SQ FT: 20,000
SALES (est): 14.3MM **Privately Held**
WEB: www.nfc-fruti.com
SIC: 2037 Frozen fruits & vegetables

(G-5534)
NATURAL WOOD WORKS LLC
2382 W 77th St (33016-1868)
PHONE..............................954 445-1493
Juan Martell, *Principal*
EMP: 7 **EST:** 2010
SALES (est): 85.2K **Privately Held**
SIC: 2431 Millwork

(G-5535)
NEARLY NATURAL LLC
3870 W 108th St Unit 20 (33018-1266)
PHONE..............................800 711-0544
Robbie Singer, *President*
Anita Singer, *Vice Pres*
Dennis Singer, *Vice Pres*
George Blews, *CFO*
Vanessa Vasallo, *Sales Staff*
◆ **EMP:** 12 **EST:** 2002
SALES (est): 5.2MM **Privately Held**
WEB: www.nearlynatural.com
SIC: 3999 5193 Artificial flower arrangements; artificial flowers

(G-5536)
NEIGHBORHOOD PROPERTY MGMT
2150 W 68th St Ste 205 (33016-1802)
PHONE..............................305 819-2361
Augustine Cavrera, *Owner*
EMP: 6 **EST:** 1991
SALES (est): 90.3K **Privately Held**
SIC: 3144 Women's footwear, except athletic

(G-5537)
NEON WORKFORCE TECHNOLOGIES
2300 W 84th St Ste 601 (33016-5773)
PHONE..............................305 458-8244
G Michael McCullars, *President*
EMP: 6 **EST:** 2015
SALES (est): 97.5K **Privately Held**
SIC: 2813 Neon

(G-5538)
NEW MARCO FOODS INC
3251 E 11th Ave (33013-3515)
PHONE..............................305 836-0571
Qing Chen, *Vice Pres*
Jia Zhao, *Director*
EMP: 10 **EST:** 2008
SALES (est): 480.6K **Privately Held**
SIC: 2051 Bread, cake & related products

(G-5539)
NEW STYLE WOOD WORK CORP
2735 W 61st St Apt 104 (33016-5946)
PHONE..............................305 989-9665
Oscar Espinosa, *President*
EMP: 6 **EST:** 2012
SALES (est): 341.7K **Privately Held**
WEB: www.newstylekitchencabinets.com
SIC: 2431 7389 Millwork;

(G-5540)
NEXT DOOR COMPANY
4005 E 10th Ct (33013-2925)
PHONE..............................954 772-6666
Justin Schechter, *President*
James Schechter, *Vice Pres*
Karen Brock, *Sales Staff*
◆ **EMP:** 40 **EST:** 1993
SALES (est): 11.7MM **Privately Held**
WEB: www.nextdoorco.com
SIC: 3442 Metal doors

(G-5541)
NIEFELD GROUP LLC
Also Called: Beautiko
2420 W 80th St Unit 5 (33016-2783)
PHONE..............................786 587-7423
Daniel Niefeld, *Manager*
Bruce Niefeld,
EMP: 7 **EST:** 2016
SQ FT: 2,500
SALES (est): 275.5K **Privately Held**
SIC: 2381 Gloves, work: woven or knit, made from purchased materials

(G-5542)
NISSI ELASTIC CORP
961 E 17th St (33010-3353)
PHONE..............................305 968-3812
Jose H Mejia, *President*
Maria D Mejia, *Senior VP*
EMP: 6 **EST:** 2002
SALES (est): 136.5K **Privately Held**
SIC: 2241 Yarns, elastic: fabric covered

(G-5543)
NOGUERA HOLDINGS LLC
Also Called: NOGHOLD
1635 W 32nd Pl (33012-4509)
PHONE.................................305 846-9144
Michele Reinel, *Administration*
EMP: 9 **EST:** 2013
SALES (est): 329.4K **Privately Held**
SIC: 3711 3842 Cars, armored, assembly of; bulletproof vests

(G-5544)
NOVELTEX MIAMI INC
151 E 10th Ave (33010-5191)
PHONE.................................305 887-8191
Dimis A Maratos, *President*
Anton Maratos, *Vice Pres*
◆ **EMP:** 35 **EST:** 1953
SQ FT: 20,000
SALES (est): 2.9MM **Privately Held**
WEB: www.noveltexmiami.com
SIC: 3089 2499 Plastic processing; decorative wood & woodwork

(G-5545)
NRNB LLC
8520 Nw 174th St (33015-3520)
PHONE.................................203 769-5995
Nancy Gonzalez,
EMP: 7 **EST:** 2017
SALES (est): 39.6K **Privately Held**
SIC: 3999 Manufacturing industries

(G-5546)
NU-VUE INDUSTRIES INC
1055 E 29th St (33013-3517)
PHONE.................................305 694-0397
Maria Guardado, *President*
EMP: 25 **EST:** 1993
SQ FT: 23,000
SALES (est): 3.9MM **Privately Held**
WEB: www.nu-vueindustries.com
SIC: 3479 Galvanizing of iron, steel or end-formed products; aluminum coating of metal products

(G-5547)
NUTRICORP LLC
671 W 18th St (33010-2422)
PHONE.................................305 680-4896
EMP: 8
SALES (corp-wide): 666.8K **Privately Held**
SIC: 2834 Medicines, capsuled or ampuled
PA: Nutricorp Llc
4114 Nw 4th Ter
Miami FL 33126
305 680-4896

(G-5548)
OFFICE FURNITURE BY TEMPO INC
4136 E 10th Ln (33013-2506)
PHONE.................................305 685-3077
Carlos Perez, *President*
Jesus Perez, *Administration*
EMP: 19 **EST:** 1976
SQ FT: 3,000
SALES (est): 1.9MM **Privately Held**
WEB: www.ofbtempo.com
SIC: 2521 Wood office furniture

(G-5549)
ONCA GEAR LLC
2372 W 77th St (33016-1868)
PHONE.................................857 253-8207
Marco Carrizosa, *Mng Member*
EMP: 6 **EST:** 2016
SQ FT: 18,000
SALES (est): 650K
SALES (corp-wide): 165.2K **Privately Held**
WEB: www.oncagear.com
SIC: 2329 Men's & boys' sportswear & athletic clothing
PA: Likentex Sl.
Calle De La Perfumeria (Pol Industria), 21 - Nav 8
Colmenar Viejo
918 467-287

(G-5550)
ONSITE RLBLE FORKLIFT SVCS INC
714 E 28th St (33013-3616)
PHONE.................................305 305-8638
Mayelin Perez, *Vice Pres*
EMP: 10 **EST:** 2013
SALES (est): 1.1MM **Privately Held**
SIC: 3537 Forklift trucks

(G-5551)
OPTICAL HONG KONG
6073 Nw 167th St Ste C20 (33015-4346)
PHONE.................................305 200-5522
Adriel Ovadia,
EMP: 10 **EST:** 2016
SALES (est): 336.9K **Privately Held**
SIC: 3089 Lenses, except optical: plastic

(G-5552)
ORNAMNTAL METAL SPECIALIST INC
7889 Nw 173rd St (33015-3854)
PHONE.................................786 360-5727
Ileana Burns, *President*
Wayne Burns, *Vice Pres*
EMP: 6 **EST:** 2008
SALES (est): 350K **Privately Held**
SIC: 3446 Architectural metalwork

(G-5553)
OSCARS WOODWORKS INC
2431 W 80th St Unit 7 (33016-2785)
PHONE.................................786 543-9200
Oscar Rosas, *Principal*
EMP: 6 **EST:** 2010
SALES (est): 63.7K **Privately Held**
WEB: www.oscarswoodwork.com
SIC: 2431 Millwork

(G-5554)
PANELTRONICS INCORPORATED
11960 Nw 87th Ct Ste 1 (33018-1972)
PHONE.................................305 823-9777
Pedro R Pelaez Sr, *President*
Pedro R Pelaez Jr, *Vice Pres*
Pedro J Pelaez, *Vice Pres*
John Murray, *Engineer*
Jose Verdecia, *Engineer*
EMP: 70 **EST:** 1979
SQ FT: 21,000
SALES (est): 15.4MM **Privately Held**
WEB: www.paneltronics.com
SIC: 3613 Control panels, electric

(G-5555)
PATTY KING INC
Also Called: Patty King Production Plant
2740 W 81st St (33016-2732)
PHONE.................................305 817-1888
Gary Chin, *President*
Colin Chang, *Vice Pres*
Warren Chung, *Vice Pres*
Gary Tieshue, *Vice Pres*
◆ **EMP:** 31 **EST:** 1997
SQ FT: 10,000
SALES (est): 3.7MM **Privately Held**
WEB: www.majestyfoods.com
SIC: 2038 5812 Ethnic foods, frozen; ethnic food restaurants

(G-5556)
PETER PRINTER INC
1355 W 49th St (33012-3223)
PHONE.................................305 558-0147
George Pappas, *President*
Gregory Pappas, *Admin Sec*
EMP: 9 **EST:** 1983
SQ FT: 4,000
SALES (est): 632K **Privately Held**
WEB: www.peterprinter.carlsoncraft.com
SIC: 2752 Commercial printing, offset

(G-5557)
PETROLEUM EQUIPMENT AND MFG CO
Also Called: Pemco
2185 W 76th St (33016-1838)
PHONE.................................305 558-9573
Juan H Tamayo, *President*
Adele Azcuy, *General Mgr*
Iran Tamayo, *Vice Pres*
Ivan Tamayo, *Vice Pres*
Jorge Tamayo, *Treasurer*
◆ **EMP:** 19 **EST:** 1985
SQ FT: 53,000
SALES (est): 5.2MM **Privately Held**
WEB: www.pemcofl.com
SIC: 3491 Gas valves & parts, industrial

(G-5558)
PICASSO EMBROIDERY SYSTEMS
6043 Nw 167th St Ste A25 (33015-4395)
PHONE.................................305 827-9666
Emeric Silberman, *President*
EMP: 10 **EST:** 1996
SQ FT: 4,700
SALES (est): 966.7K **Privately Held**
WEB: www.picassoindustries.com
SIC: 2759 Screen printing

(G-5559)
PLACETAS PALLET CORP
195 W 19th St (33010-2640)
PHONE.................................305 633-4262
Orlando F Mesa, *Principal*
EMP: 7 **EST:** 2010
SALES (est): 169.1K **Privately Held**
SIC: 2448 Pallets, wood

(G-5560)
POLYMERSAN LLC
1181 Se 9th Ter Ste B (33010-5814)
PHONE.................................305 887-3824
Tayfun Oktem, *Principal*
EMP: 8 **EST:** 2018
SALES (est): 451.7K **Privately Held**
WEB: www.polymersan.com
SIC: 2821 Plastics materials & resins

(G-5561)
POLYUMAC INC
1060 E 30th St (33013-3520)
PHONE.................................305 691-9093
Mariella Vazquez, *President*
◆ **EMP:** 30 **EST:** 1996
SQ FT: 36,000
SALES (est): 5.9MM **Privately Held**
WEB: www.polyumac.com
SIC: 3559 Plastics working machinery

(G-5562)
POWER FOAM MANUFACTURING INC
4595 E 10th Ct (33013-2105)
PHONE.................................305 303-2956
Marcio Quintero, *Principal*
EMP: 6 **EST:** 2011
SALES (est): 132.5K **Privately Held**
SIC: 3999 Barber & beauty shop equipment

(G-5563)
PRADERE MANUFACTURING CORP
Also Called: Pradere Office Products
7655 W 20th Ave (33014-3226)
PHONE.................................305 823-0190
Jose Pradere, *President*
Maria Victoria Pradere, *Vice Pres*
Ileana Pradere, *Treasurer*
Michelle Pradere, *IT/INT Sup*
▼ **EMP:** 10 **EST:** 1972
SQ FT: 21,500
SALES (est): 2.6MM **Privately Held**
WEB: www.pradereoffice.com
SIC: 2431 2521 Millwork; chairs, office: padded, upholstered or plain: wood

(G-5564)
PRECISION METAL FABRICATIONS
3600 E 10th Ct 20 (33013-2918)
PHONE.................................305 691-0616
John Sanchez, *President*
EMP: 6 **EST:** 1998
SALES (est): 969.9K **Privately Held**
SIC: 3441 Fabricated structural metal

(G-5565)
PREMIER DISTRIBUTOR OF MIAMI
1635 W 40th St (33012-7065)
PHONE.................................305 821-9671
Cesar Zorrilla, *President*
Nancy Zorrilla, *Admin Sec*
EMP: 5 **EST:** 1991
SQ FT: 4,600
SALES (est): 506.8K **Privately Held**
SIC: 2035 Pickles, sauces & salad dressings

(G-5566)
PRESTO LIFTS
1840 W 49th St Ste 403 (33012-2978)
PHONE.................................786 615-7256
EMP: 8 **EST:** 2018
SALES (est): 75.5K **Privately Held**
WEB: www.prestolifts.com
SIC: 3536 Boat lifts

(G-5567)
PRICE KING 2 LLC
495 W 29th St (33012-5700)
PHONE.................................786 337-8801
Miguel Sanchez, *Principal*
EMP: 6 **EST:** 2010
SALES (est): 72.6K **Privately Held**
SIC: 3421 Table & food cutlery, including butchers'

(G-5568)
PRIME ENTERPRISES LLC
Also Called: Prime Matter Labs
16363 Nw 49th Ave (33014-6316)
PHONE.................................305 625-4929
Mohamed Barakat, *President*
Maged Barakat, *Vice Pres*
Francisco Linares, *Vice Pres*
Courtney Palmer, *Engineer*
Carla Goffstein, *CFO*
◆ **EMP:** 65 **EST:** 1983
SQ FT: 75,000
SALES (est): 22.6MM **Privately Held**
WEB: www.primematterlabs.com
SIC: 2844 Cosmetic preparations

(G-5569)
PRIME PACKAGING INC
16363 Nw 49th Ave (33014-6316)
PHONE.................................305 625-6737
Mohamad Barakat, *President*
Jorge Perdomo, *Purchasing*
Aaron Paas, *Officer*
EMP: 20 **EST:** 2000
SALES (est): 1.5MM **Privately Held**
SIC: 2844 Cosmetic preparations

(G-5570)
PRIME TOPCO LLC ✪
16363 Nw 49th Ave (33014-6316)
PHONE.................................305 625-4929
Mohamed Barakat, *Mng Member*
EMP: 5 **EST:** 2020
SALES (est): 323.6K **Privately Held**
SIC: 2844 Toilet preparations

(G-5571)
PRIME WOODWORK INC
17309 Nw 63rd Ave (33015-4470)
PHONE.................................786 226-5646
Anthony Monico, *Principal*
EMP: 6 **EST:** 2017
SALES (est): 86.7K **Privately Held**
SIC: 2431 Millwork

(G-5572)
PRINT BIG INC
1680 W 33rd Pl (33012-4514)
PHONE.................................305 398-8898
Amarilys Curbelo, *President*
Francisco Ruiz, *Agent*
EMP: 7 **EST:** 2008
SALES (est): 650K **Privately Held**
WEB: www.printbigmiami.com
SIC: 2752 Commercial printing, offset

(G-5573)
PRINT SOLUTION DIGITAL LLC
6540 W 20th Ave Unit 3 (33016-2672)
PHONE.................................305 819-7420
Jairo Palacio, *Principal*
EMP: 6 **EST:** 2003
SALES (est): 382K **Privately Held**
SIC: 2752 Commercial printing, offset

(G-5574)
PRINTHOUSEUSACOM INC
450 W 28th St Ste 2 (33010-1317)
PHONE.................................305 231-0202
Alex Montano, *President*
Raul Montano, *Vice Pres*
EMP: 7 **EST:** 2006

▲ = Import ▼=Export
◆ =Import/Export

SQ FT: 18,000
SALES (est): 1MM Privately Held
WEB: www.printhouseusa.com
SIC: 2759 Commercial printing

(G-5575)
PRINTING EXPRESS
1608 W 68th St (33014-4435)
PHONE.................................305 512-0900
Rafael H Gomez, *Principal*
EMP: 6 EST: 2008
SALES (est): 262.3K Privately Held
WEB: www.printgoodprice.com
SIC: 2752 Commercial printing, offset

(G-5576)
PRO LAB SUPPLY CORPORATION
Also Called: Biochrom
5921 Nw 176th St Unit 5 (33015-5130)
PHONE.................................305 600-0444
Paolo Paparcuri, *President*
Beverley C Paparcuri, *Corp Secy*
Luis Urich, *Vice Pres*
▲ EMP: 6 EST: 1998
SALES (est): 1.1MM Privately Held
WEB: www.biochromcorp.com
SIC: 3821 Laboratory equipment: fume hoods, distillation racks, etc.

(G-5577)
PRODUCTOS LAS DELICIAS INC
Also Called: Nutri D'Light
2954 W 84th St Unit 11 (33018-4914)
P.O. Box 170286 (33017-0286)
PHONE.................................305 760-4223
Martha L Arango, *Principal*
▼ EMP: 7 EST: 2010
SALES (est): 157K Privately Held
WEB: www.productoslasdelicias.com
SIC: 2095 2043 Instant coffee; wheat flakes: prepared as cereal breakfast food

(G-5578)
PROFESSIONAL KITCHEN CABINETS
1035 E 13th St (33010-3752)
PHONE.................................305 888-5660
Jose Valdivia, *President*
EMP: 6 EST: 1977
SQ FT: 4,200
SALES (est): 464.8K Privately Held
WEB: www.professionalkitchencabinet.com
SIC: 2434 Wood kitchen cabinets

(G-5579)
PROLABEL INC
621 W 20th St (33010-2432)
PHONE.................................305 620-2202
Ramon Fernandez, *President*
Tony Sierra, *Vice Pres*
Becky Peffer, *Executive*
▼ EMP: 11 EST: 1995
SQ FT: 15,000
SALES (est): 3MM Privately Held
WEB: www.prolabelinc.com
SIC: 2759 Labels & seals: printing

(G-5580)
PROMAX WELDING INC
8055 W 23rd Ave (33016-5577)
PHONE.................................305 962-5033
Yilian Ramirez, *Principal*
EMP: 7 EST: 2014
SALES (est): 151.1K Privately Held
WEB: www.promaxawning.com
SIC: 7692 Welding repair

(G-5581)
PROMEX LLC
1415 E 11th Ave (33010-3307)
P.O. Box 630716, Miami (33163-0716)
PHONE.................................305 884-2400
Yolanda Eustaquio, *Mng Member*
Diana Salamanca, *Info Tech Mgr*
Alexander Avila,
Priscilla Avila,
EMP: 9 EST: 2005
SALES (est): 2.6MM Privately Held
WEB: www.promexllc.com
SIC: 2844 Toilet preparations

(G-5582)
PTE SYSTEMS INTERNATIONAL LLC (PA)
1950 W 8th Ave (33010-2328)
PHONE.................................305 863-3409
Kenneth Antonelli, *Project Mgr*
Henry Baez, *Purch Mgr*
Larry Casper, *CFO*
Frank Del Valle, *Human Resources*
Brenda Hamilton, *Office Mgr*
EMP: 20 EST: 2013
SALES (est): 11.9MM Privately Held
WEB: www.ptestrand.com
SIC: 3315 Steel wire & related products

(G-5583)
PUPPET WORKSHOP INC (PA)
295 E 10th Ct (33010-5148)
P.O. Box 398077, Miami Beach (33239-8077)
PHONE.................................305 666-2655
Ronnie Burns, *President*
Jerald Burns, *Vice Pres*
Gerald Burns, *Treasurer*
◆ EMP: 222 EST: 1977
SQ FT: 75,000
SALES (est): 21.7MM Privately Held
WEB: www.puppetworkshop.com
SIC: 2369 Girls' & children's outerwear

(G-5584)
PURA VIDA DAIRY INC
Also Called: Yogurico
3130 W 84th St U1 (33018-4977)
PHONE.................................305 817-1762
Lilliana Murillo, *President*
Roman Alvarez, *Vice Pres*
Victor Fermin, *Manager*
▲ EMP: 15 EST: 2008
SQ FT: 3,000
SALES (est): 4.1MM Privately Held
WEB: www.puravidadairy.com
SIC: 2026 Yogurt

(G-5585)
PUROX BRANDS CORP
5801 E 10th Ave Unit 108 (33013-1758)
PHONE.................................305 392-0738
Faisal Khan, *CEO*
Isaac Khan, *Marketing Staff*
EMP: 10 EST: 2016
SALES (est): 698.5K Privately Held
SIC: 2841 Soap & other detergents

(G-5586)
PYRAMIDEYE PRINT CORP
1350 W 34th St (33012-4849)
PHONE.................................786 663-1157
Rosa M Rivero, *Principal*
EMP: 6 EST: 2019
SALES (est): 100.6K Privately Held
WEB: www.pyramideyeprint.business.site
SIC: 2752 Commercial printing, lithographic

(G-5587)
QUALITY 1 APPRAISAL INC
18831 Nw 78th Pl (33015-5272)
PHONE.................................786 859-4085
Jose A Gutierrez Jr, *President*
Janet Mincey, *Treasurer*
Sharon Townsend, *Admin Sec*
EMP: 8 EST: 2006
SALES (est): 245.6K Privately Held
SIC: 2431 Millwork

(G-5588)
QUALITY ARTS LCP LLC
7880 W 25th Ct (33016-2757)
PHONE.................................305 735-2310
Leandro C Perini, *Principal*
EMP: 6 EST: 2017
SALES (est): 178.8K Privately Held
SIC: 2752 Commercial printing, lithographic

(G-5589)
QUALITY PRECISION PDTS CO INC
678 W 27th St (33010-1214)
PHONE.................................305 885-4596
Pedro Capote, *President*
Elida Pascual, *Treasurer*
EMP: 10 EST: 1972
SQ FT: 11,312
SALES (est): 276.6K Privately Held
WEB: www.qualityprecisionproducts.com
SIC: 3451 Screw machine products

(G-5590)
QUALITY RAILINGS MIAMI CORP
460 W 18th St (33010-2419)
PHONE.................................786 400-0462
Alberto Cancio, *CEO*
EMP: 9 EST: 2015
SALES (est): 671.8K Privately Held
WEB: www.qualityrailingsmiami.com
SIC: 2431 3446 Staircases, stairs & railings; railings, prefabricated metal

(G-5591)
QUALITY SIGNS
2736 W 54th St (33016-4082)
PHONE.................................786 261-6242
Leidy Hernandez, *President*
EMP: 6 EST: 2015
SALES (est): 46K Privately Held
SIC: 3993 Signs & advertising specialties

(G-5592)
R & R DOORS CORP
1660 W 33rd Pl (33012-4514)
PHONE.................................305 982-8106
Rogelio Garcia, *President*
EMP: 7 EST: 2010
SQ FT: 5,000
SALES (est): 899.8K Privately Held
WEB: www.rrdoors.com
SIC: 2434 Wood kitchen cabinets

(G-5593)
RALPH & LLERENA PALLETS INC
495 E 47th St (33013-1863)
PHONE.................................305 446-2651
Rafael A Ruiz, *Principal*
EMP: 7 EST: 2010
SALES (est): 152.3K Privately Held
SIC: 2448 Pallets, wood

(G-5594)
RC INVESTMENT CASTING
4570 E 11th Ave (33013-2114)
PHONE.................................305 801-9088
Ronaldo Cruz, *Principal*
EMP: 5 EST: 2009
SALES (est): 398.9K Privately Held
SIC: 3365 Aluminum & aluminum-based alloy castings

(G-5595)
RCS WOOD CRAFTERS LLC
1051 E 24th St (33013-4323)
PHONE.................................305 836-0120
Robert Santos, *Mng Member*
Carlos Santos,
Ivonne Santos,
EMP: 8 EST: 2009
SQ FT: 17,000
SALES (est): 988.9K Privately Held
WEB: www.rcswood.com
SIC: 2434 Wood kitchen cabinets

(G-5596)
REACH INTERNATIONAL INC
Also Called: Reach Cooling Group
625 E 10th Ave (33010-4641)
P.O. Box 667765, Medley (33166-9405)
PHONE.................................305 863-6360
Jun Lou, *President*
Luo Jun, *President*
D I C K Chen, *Exec VP*
Connie Chen, *Vice Pres*
Marcelo Marinelli, *Accounting Mgr*
◆ EMP: 32 EST: 1999
SQ FT: 30,800
SALES (est): 10.6MM Privately Held
WEB: www.reachcooling.com
SIC: 3714 Motor vehicle parts & accessories

(G-5597)
RESOLUTE TISSUE SALES
3725 E 10th Ct (33013-2919)
PHONE.................................800 562-2860
Humberto Falcon, *Purchasing*
Roberto De Leon, *Manager*
EMP: 210 EST: 2019
SALES (est): 11.7MM Privately Held
SIC: 2621 Tissue paper

(G-5598)
RHINO TOOLS INC
18844 Nw 89th Ct (33018-6278)
PHONE.................................305 332-7750
Gilberto Aguilar, *Owner*
EMP: 10
SALES (est): 526.7K Privately Held
WEB: www.rhinotool.com
SIC: 3545 Machine tool accessories

(G-5599)
RHONDA CLANTON
6133 Nw 181st Ter Cir S (33015-5627)
PHONE.................................305 502-7050
Rhonda Clanton, *Principal*
EMP: 8 EST: 1995
SALES (est): 594.7K Privately Held
SIC: 2024 Ice cream & frozen desserts

(G-5600)
RICKS PALLET CO INC
2420 W 3rd Ave (33010-1437)
PHONE.................................305 884-4896
Rick Scarbary, *President*
April Scarbary, *Vice Pres*
▲ EMP: 7 EST: 1993
SALES (est): 650K Privately Held
SIC: 2448 Pallets, wood

(G-5601)
RICOS TOSTADITOS INC
Also Called: Ricos Candy Snack & Bakery
740 W 28th St (33010-1220)
PHONE.................................305 885-7392
Albertina Padron, *President*
Hilda Lopez, *Corp Secy*
Alfred Padron, *Vice Pres*
EMP: 10 EST: 1968
SQ FT: 4,200
SALES (est): 918.7K Privately Held
SIC: 2064 2052 Candy & other confectionery products; cookies & crackers

(G-5602)
RIKA BAKERIES INC
1025 E 24th St (33013-4323)
PHONE.................................305 691-5673
Manuel Sendina, *President*
Roberto Sanchez, *Corp Secy*
EMP: 12 EST: 1964
SQ FT: 7,500
SALES (est): 450K Privately Held
SIC: 2052 Crackers, dry

(G-5603)
ROCCOS CUSTOM CASES CORP
6965 W 2nd Ln (33014-5311)
PHONE.................................305 799-2841
Karthe MA, *Principal*
EMP: 6 EST: 2015
SALES (est): 316.6K Privately Held
SIC: 3523 Farm machinery & equipment

(G-5604)
ROD BISCAYNE MANUFACTURING
425 E 9th St (33010-4547)
PHONE.................................305 884-0808
Eddie M Carman, *President*
Kenneth S Carman, *Vice Pres*
Joseph K Carman, *Shareholder*
Mary Jo Carman, *Admin Sec*
▼ EMP: 5 EST: 1948
SQ FT: 3,500
SALES (est): 380.1K Privately Held
WEB: www.biscaynerod.com
SIC: 3949 Rods & rod parts, fishing

(G-5605)
ROLU WOODCRAFT INC
4733 E 11th Ave (33013-2129)
PHONE.................................305 685-0914
Roberto Palenzuela Sr, *President*
Juana Palenzuela, *Vice Pres*
Luis Palenzuela, *Vice Pres*
EMP: 15 EST: 1969
SQ FT: 14,500
SALES (est): 1MM Privately Held
SIC: 2434 2521 2511 2431 Wood kitchen cabinets; wood office furniture; wood household furniture; millwork

(G-5606)
RQ INC
2443 W 4th Ct (33010-1456)
PHONE..................................305 879-1773
Lisday Bello, *Principal*
EMP: 7 **EST:** 2015
SALES (est): 116.4K **Privately Held**
SIC: 7692 Welding repair

(G-5607)
S P MANUFACTURING LLC
2208 W 79th St (33016-5520)
PHONE..................................305 362-0456
Claudio U Gatto, *Principal*
EMP: 8 **EST:** 2007
SALES (est): 881.9K **Privately Held**
SIC: 3999 Barber & beauty shop equipment

(G-5608)
S&S GLOBAL SUPPLY LLC
730 W 38th Pl (33012)
PHONE..................................786 529-4799
Juma M Salem, *Mng Member*
Hani Salem, *Mng Member*
Sami Salem, *Mng Member*
EMP: 9 **EST:** 2015
SALES (est): 336.8K **Privately Held**
WEB: www.ssglobalsupply.com
SIC: 2515 5021 2512 Mattresses, containing felt, foam rubber, urethane, etc.; furniture; upholstered household furniture

(G-5609)
SAFE PRO INC
1650 W 33rd Pl (33012-4514)
PHONE..................................954 494-5768
Pravin Borkar, *Principal*
EMP: 7 **EST:** 2016
SQ FT: 4,000
SALES (est): 637.9K **Privately Held**
WEB: www.safe-prousa.com
SIC: 3089 Awnings, fiberglass & plastic combination

(G-5610)
SALSA CUBA INC
1275 W 49th St (33012-3220)
PHONE..................................305 993-9757
Angel Pellicier, *Principal*
EMP: 6 **EST:** 2016
SALES (est): 114.8K **Privately Held**
SIC: 2099 Dips, except cheese & sour cream based

(G-5611)
SBC INTERNATIONAL GROUP INC
8000 W 26th Ave (33016-2743)
PHONE..................................305 506-5638
Timothy Acosta, *President*
EMP: 12 **EST:** 2018
SALES (est): 569.8K **Privately Held**
SIC: 3999 Atomizers, toiletry

(G-5612)
SCREEN ART POSTERS INC
4333 E 10th Ln (33013-2526)
PHONE..................................305 681-4641
Beatriz Gallat, *President*
Raymond Gallat, *Vice Pres*
EMP: 23 **EST:** 1957
SQ FT: 14,000
SALES (est): 1.2MM **Privately Held**
SIC: 2759 2396 Screen printing; automotive & apparel trimmings

(G-5613)
SELECT ENGINEERED SYSTEMS INC
Also Called: S E S
7991 W 26th Ave (33016-2799)
PHONE..................................305 823-5410
John Sheppard Sr, *President*
Susan Hancock, *COO*
Rick Muller, *Exec VP*
Charles Brennan, *Engineer*
Sandy Tsairis, *CFO*
▲ **EMP:** 20 **EST:** 1976
SQ FT: 11,000
SALES (est): 3.4MM **Privately Held**
WEB: www.selectses.com
SIC: 3699 3829 3661 3643 Security control equipment & systems; measuring & controlling devices; telephone & telegraph apparatus; current-carrying wiring devices; relays & industrial controls; computer peripheral equipment

(G-5614)
SEMINOLE PRINTING INC
2310 W 78th St (33016-5526)
PHONE..................................305 823-7204
Stephanie Pintado, *President*
EMP: 7 **EST:** 2006
SQ FT: 5,100
SALES (est): 100K **Privately Held**
SIC: 2752 Commercial printing, lithographic

(G-5615)
SEMPRUN & MORALES CORPORATION
Also Called: Minuteman Press
3418 W 84th St Ste 100 (33018-4936)
PHONE..................................305 698-2554
Ana T Morales, *President*
▼ **EMP:** 11 **EST:** 2010
SALES (est): 370.9K **Privately Held**
WEB: www.chanhassen-mn.minuteman-press.com
SIC: 2752 Commercial printing, lithographic

(G-5616)
SEVILLA CABINETS INC
1550 W 34th Pl (33012-4622)
PHONE..................................305 888-2174
Omar Cepero, *President*
EMP: 10 **EST:** 1998
SQ FT: 30,000
SALES (est): 824.3K **Privately Held**
SIC: 2434 Wood kitchen cabinets

(G-5617)
SHARING THREE INC
575 E 10th Ave (33010-4639)
PHONE..................................305 884-8384
Renato Alonso, *President*
Gilbert Gambino, *Purch Mgr*
Danny Acosta, *Accounts Mgr*
Xenia Borges, *Accounts Mgr*
Gilbert Lebron, *Sales Staff*
EMP: 15 **EST:** 2001
SALES (est): 386.8K **Privately Held**
SIC: 3585 Refrigeration & heating equipment

(G-5618)
SHELIA SHINE INC
7725 W 2nd Ct (33014-4307)
PHONE..................................305 557-1729
David J Wallach, *Director*
EMP: 7 **EST:** 2016
SALES (est): 303.5K **Privately Held**
WEB: www.sheilashineinc.com
SIC: 2842 Cleaning or polishing preparations

(G-5619)
SIGNS FACTORY USA INC
7465 W 19th Ct (33014-3722)
PHONE..................................786 717-5474
Alexnader Rodriguez, *Principal*
EMP: 5 **EST:** 2018
SALES (est): 364.3K **Privately Held**
WEB: www.signsfactoryusa.com
SIC: 3993 Signs & advertising specialties

(G-5620)
SILCAR CORP
1475 W 82nd St (33014-3359)
PHONE..................................305 557-8391
Carlos Zayas, *Principal*
EMP: 9 **EST:** 2010
SALES (est): 105.1K **Privately Held**
SIC: 3089 Injection molding of plastics

(G-5621)
SKYLITE SIGNS & SERVICES INC
1640 W 32nd Pl (33012-4510)
PHONE..................................305 362-5015
George Bravo, *President*
EMP: 10 **EST:** 2006
SALES (est): 711.5K **Privately Held**
WEB: www.skylitesignsfl.com
SIC: 3993 Signs & advertising specialties

(G-5622)
SLICK DESIGNS & AP MIAMI INC
3710 E 10th Ct (33013-2920)
PHONE..................................305 836-7950
Sasson Jacoby, *President*
◆ **EMP:** 10 **EST:** 2000
SQ FT: 30,000
SALES (est): 188.6K **Privately Held**
SIC: 2759 Screen printing

(G-5623)
SOBRINO CUSTOM CABINETS INC
2220 W 10th Ct (33010-1911)
PHONE..................................786 564-2699
Darney Suarez, *Principal*
EMP: 7 **EST:** 2013
SALES (est): 252.1K **Privately Held**
WEB: www.sobrinocustomcabinet.wixsite.com
SIC: 2434 Wood kitchen cabinets

(G-5624)
SOS SERVICES ON PRTG CORP
2738 W 68th Pl (33016-5476)
PHONE..................................305 225-6000
Brenda Ardua, *Principal*
EMP: 6 **EST:** 2010
SALES (est): 99.8K **Privately Held**
SIC: 2752 Commercial printing, lithographic

(G-5625)
SOUTH FLORIDA CUTTING
3965 E 10th Ct (33013-2923)
PHONE..................................305 693-6711
EMP: 12
SALES (est): 934.1K **Privately Held**
SIC: 2299 2399 Mfg Textile Goods Mfg Fabricated Textile Products

(G-5626)
SOUTH FLORIDA PAVERS CORP
18506 Nw 67th Ave (33015-3304)
PHONE..................................786 517-9100
Mariana E Lorente MD, *Principal*
EMP: 7 **EST:** 2012
SALES (est): 379.6K **Privately Held**
WEB: www.wbpavers.com
SIC: 3531 Pavers

(G-5627)
SOUTH FLORIDA TECHNOLOGY SVCS
Also Called: Florida Emrgncy Eqp Upfitters
2333 W 3rd Ct (33010-1431)
PHONE..................................786 286-2882
Stephen Crowe, *CEO*
EMP: 10 **EST:** 2006
SALES (est): 606.4K **Privately Held**
SIC: 3999 Badges, metal: policemen, firemen, etc.

(G-5628)
SOUTHEASTERN PRINTING CO INC (PA)
950 Se 8th St (33010-5740)
PHONE..................................772 287-2141
Donald N Mader, *President*
Lawrence Reger, *Chairman*
Suzanne Z Kenik, *Project Mgr*
Diana Gannon, *CFO*
Kenny Justilien, *Sales Staff*
▼ **EMP:** 144 **EST:** 1924
SQ FT: 60,000
SALES (est): 47.2MM **Privately Held**
WEB: www.seprint.com
SIC: 2752 2759 2789 2732 Commercial printing, offset; flexographic printing; bookbinding & related work; book printing

(G-5629)
SOUTHERN WELDING & MECHANICS
592 W 28th St (33010-1326)
PHONE..................................305 772-0961
Luis R Fernandez, *President*
Josbel Fernandez, *Vice Pres*
EMP: 15 **EST:** 2011
SQ FT: 3,000
SALES (est): 5MM **Privately Held**
WEB: www.southernwm.com
SIC: 7692 1711 Welding repair; mechanical contractor

(G-5630)
SOUTHWEST TURBINE INC
4550 E 10th Ct (33013-2106)
PHONE..................................305 769-1765
Lourdes Hermoso, *President*
Maria Bolnoes, *General Mgr*
George Castro, *CFO*
EMP: 6 **EST:** 2002
SALES (est): 97.9K **Privately Held**
SIC: 3511 Turbines & turbine generator sets

(G-5631)
ST JUDAS TADEUS FOUNDRY INC
Also Called: Saint Judas Tadeus Foundry
2160 W 10th Ct (33010-1909)
PHONE..................................305 512-3612
Ildefonso Vega, *President*
Alfonso Vega, *General Mgr*
EMP: 8 **EST:** 1964
SALES (est): 711.5K **Privately Held**
SIC: 3365 3496 Masts, cast aluminum; miscellaneous fabricated wire products

(G-5632)
STAR BEDDING MFG CORP
1053 E 14th St (33010-3311)
PHONE..................................305 887-5209
Richard D Morales, *President*
Maria Morales, *Vice Pres*
Gabriel Morales, *CFO*
▼ **EMP:** 30 **EST:** 1969
SQ FT: 11,200
SALES (est): 502.6K **Privately Held**
WEB: www.starbeddingmfg.com
SIC: 2515 Box springs, assembled

(G-5633)
STAR ENVIROTECH INC
1010 E 31st St (33013-3522)
PHONE..................................714 427-1244
Jim Saffie, *President*
▲ **EMP:** 11 **EST:** 2000
SQ FT: 15,000
SALES (est): 322.6K **Privately Held**
SIC: 3559 Automotive maintenance equipment

(G-5634)
STREAMLINE PERFORMANCE BOATS C ✪
7711 W 22nd Ave (33016-5518)
PHONE..................................305 393-8848
EMP: 12 **EST:** 2020
SALES (est): 1MM **Privately Held**
WEB: www.streamlineboats.com
SIC: 3732 Boat building & repairing

(G-5635)
STRUCTURE GLASS SOLUTIONS LLC
13202 Nw 107th Ave Unit 8 (33018-1289)
PHONE..................................954 499-9450
Flavio Schonholz, *Principal*
Norma Schonholz, *Mng Member*
EMP: 12 **EST:** 2015
SALES (est): 1.9MM **Privately Held**
WEB: www.structuregs.com
SIC: 3211 Structural glass

(G-5636)
STS APPAREL CORP
325 W 74th Pl (33014-5024)
PHONE..................................305 628-4000
Marty Tacher, *CEO*
Marco Tiapago, *President*
Scott Valancy, *Vice Pres*
EMP: 13 **EST:** 1999
SALES (est): 452.1K **Privately Held**
WEB: www.stsmiami.com
SIC: 2395 5699 Emblems, embroidered; T-shirts, custom printed

(G-5637)
SUNNMAN INC
2215 W 9th Ave (33010-2001)
PHONE..................................305 505-6615
Enriqueta M Saldarriaga, *Principal*
EMP: 7 **EST:** 2010

SALES (est): 264.8K **Privately Held**
SIC: 3999 Manufacturing industries

(G-5638)
SUNSHINE AVIONICS LLC
963 W 81st Pl (33014-3515)
PHONE..................................954 517-1294
Leon Gonzalez, *President*
Thomas Irwin, *Treasurer*
Elizabeth Letendre, *Admin Sec*
Judith Vetter, *Asst Sec*
EMP: 6 **EST:** 2008
SALES (est): 2.9MM **Publicly Held**
WEB: www.heico.com
SIC: 3724 Aircraft engines & engine parts
HQ: Heico Aerospace Corporation
3000 Taft St
Hollywood FL 33021
954 987-6101

(G-5639)
SUNSHINE PACKAGING INC
880 W 19th St (33010-2307)
PHONE..................................305 887-8141
Santos Flores, *President*
Eva Monzon, *CFO*
Francisca Flores, *Treasurer*
Eva Flores, *Admin Sec*
▼ **EMP:** 17 **EST:** 1972
SALES (est): 6MM **Privately Held**
WEB: www.sunshinepkg.com
SIC: 2653 2657 Boxes, corrugated: made from purchased materials; folding paperboard boxes

(G-5640)
SUNSHINE WINDOWS MFG INC
1785 W 33rd Pl (33012-4515)
PHONE..................................305 364-9952
Jaime Puerto, *President*
Carolina Sendon, *Vice Pres*
Jose Nunez, *Admin Sec*
◆ **EMP:** 72 **EST:** 1988
SQ FT: 34,500
SALES (est): 14.3MM **Privately Held**
WEB: www.sunshinewindows.com
SIC: 3442 3231 Louvers, shutters, jalousies & similar items; doors, glass: made from purchased glass

(G-5641)
SUNSOF INC (PA)
Also Called: Tomasa Healthy Passion
5821 E 10th Ave (33013-1759)
PHONE..................................305 691-1875
Edgardo Armando, *President*
James Jaroscak, *Vice Pres*
Federico Armando, *CFO*
Sergio Padron, *IT/INT Sup*
▲ **EMP:** 46 **EST:** 2004
SQ FT: 15,000
SALES (est): 6.5MM **Privately Held**
WEB: www.sunsof.com
SIC: 2053 7389 Frozen bakery products, except bread; packaging & labeling services

(G-5642)
SUPERIOR SLEEP TECHNOLOGY INC
705 E 10th Ave (33010-4643)
PHONE..................................305 888-0953
Jesus Lopez Teresa, *President*
EMP: 11 **EST:** 2012
SALES (est): 444.5K **Privately Held**
WEB: www.superiorhd.net
SIC: 2392 Cushions & pillows

(G-5643)
SUPREME PRINTING CORP
3155 W 81st St (33018-5807)
P.O. Box 160308 (33016-0006)
PHONE..................................305 591-2916
Jose Estevez, *President*
Gerardo Estevez, *Corp Secy*
Felipe Estevez, *Vice Pres*
Jerry Estevez, *Admin Sec*
EMP: 7 **EST:** 1984
SALES (est): 670K **Privately Held**
SIC: 2752 2791 Commercial printing, lithographic; typesetting

(G-5644)
SURF LIGHTING INC
210 W 24th St (33010-1526)
P.O. Box 441894, Miami (33144-1894)
PHONE..................................305 888-7851
Geraldine Ossakow, *President*
▲ **EMP:** 18 **EST:** 1960
SQ FT: 35,000
SALES (est): 600K **Privately Held**
WEB: www.surflighting.com
SIC: 3646 3699 3641 Fluorescent lighting fixtures, commercial; electrical equipment & supplies; electric lamps

(G-5645)
SYNERGY CUSTOM FIXTURES CORP
215 Se 10th Ave (33010-5536)
PHONE..................................305 693-0055
Alexander Giron, *President*
Peter Garro, *COO*
Luis Flores, *CFO*
Peter Hernandez, *Manager*
EMP: 150 **EST:** 2010
SQ FT: 60,000
SALES (est): 27.2MM **Privately Held**
WEB: www.synergycustomfixtures.com
SIC: 2541 2542 Store fixtures, wood; office & store showcases & display fixtures; fixtures, store: except wood

(G-5646)
T&Y CABINETS INC
7380 W 20th Ave Ste 102 (33016-5541)
PHONE..................................305 512-0802
Jorge Rivero, *Principal*
EMP: 6 **EST:** 2006
SALES (est): 253.6K **Privately Held**
SIC: 2434 Wood kitchen cabinets

(G-5647)
TEJEDA SHEET METAL & ALUMINUM
651 W 43rd Pl (33012-3852)
PHONE..................................305 609-5477
Aleido Tejeda, *Principal*
EMP: 6 **EST:** 2013
SALES (est): 138.9K **Privately Held**
SIC: 3444 Sheet metalwork

(G-5648)
TERRADES CUSTOM WOODWORKS INC
219 W 27th St (33010-1511)
PHONE..................................305 316-2908
Sergio Terrades, *President*
EMP: 6 **EST:** 2015
SALES (est): 105.1K **Privately Held**
SIC: 2431 Millwork

(G-5649)
TIGER BUSINESS FORMS INC
Also Called: Tiger/Southland
7765 W 20th Ave (33014-3227)
PHONE..................................305 888-3528
Mike Pina, *President*
Millie Pina, *Vice Pres*
▼ **EMP:** 23 **EST:** 1988
SQ FT: 25,000
SALES (est): 3.6MM **Privately Held**
WEB: www.tigerprintingsolutions.com
SIC: 2752 2761 Commercial printing, offset; manifold business forms

(G-5650)
TRIM-LINE OF MIAMI INC
2755 W 81st St (33016-2733)
PHONE..................................305 556-6210
Randell V Hulan, *President*
◆ **EMP:** 10 **EST:** 1978
SQ FT: 8,000
SALES (est): 218.7K **Privately Held**
WEB: www.trimlinegraphicsusa.com
SIC: 2759 7336 Screen printing; commercial art & graphic design

(G-5651)
TROPICAL MFG INC
783 W 18th St (33010-2424)
PHONE..................................305 394-6280
Anna K Janania, *President*
▼ **EMP:** 7 **EST:** 2010
SALES (est): 588.2K **Privately Held**
WEB: www.tropicalmfg.com
SIC: 3999 Manufacturing industries

(G-5652)
TTS FOOD LLC
Also Called: Venfood Disrtibutors
15990 Nw 49th Ave (33014-6309)
PHONE..................................305 622-2726
Tomas Gonzalez, *Mng Member*
Lorelvy M Hurtado,
▲ **EMP:** 6 **EST:** 2011
SQ FT: 5,000
SALES (est): 850K **Privately Held**
WEB: www.venfooddistributors.com
SIC: 2051 Breads, rolls & buns

(G-5653)
TURIN EM INC
8045 W 26th Ct (33016-2731)
PHONE..................................305 825-2004
Martin Mendelson, *President*
Robert Edelman, *Vice Pres*
Ronald Plask, *Treasurer*
EMP: 10 **EST:** 1989
SQ FT: 2,000
SALES (est): 664.3K **Privately Held**
SIC: 2395 Embroidery & art needlework

(G-5654)
TUUCI LLC
1000 Se 8th St Ste A (33010-5781)
PHONE..................................305 634-5116
Dougan H Clarke, *CEO*
David Schutte, *President*
Charles Munroe, *CFO*
John Free, *Controller*
Tom Parker, *General Counsel*
◆ **EMP:** 180 **EST:** 2008
SALES (est): 29.5MM **Privately Held**
WEB: www.tuuci.com
SIC: 2514 Backs & seats for metal household furniture
PA: Tuuci Worldwide, Llc
2900 Nw 35th St
Miami FL 33142

(G-5655)
TUUCI WORLDWIDE
1000 Se 8th St (33010-5780)
PHONE..................................305 634-5116
EMP: 6 **EST:** 2018
SALES (est): 197.4K **Privately Held**
WEB: www.tuuci.com
SIC: 2514 Metal household furniture

(G-5656)
U S HOLDINGS INC (PA)
Also Called: Eagle Manufacturing Group
3200 W 84th St (33018-4908)
PHONE..................................305 885-0301
Alex Debogory Jr, *President*
Lee Fortney, *General Mgr*
Alex L Bogory, *COO*
David H Brunswick, *Vice Pres*
John Debogory, *Vice Pres*
◆ **EMP:** 3 **EST:** 1937
SQ FT: 210,000
SALES (est): 157.6MM **Privately Held**
SIC: 3321 3543 Gray iron castings; foundry patternmaking

(G-5657)
ULTIMATE UMBRELLA COMPANY INC (PA)
Also Called: Tuuci
1000 Se 8th St Ste A (33010-5781)
PHONE..................................305 634-5116
Dougan Clarke, *CEO*
Thomas Parker, *President*
Alexander Kromidas, *Regional Mgr*
Juan Tapia, *Vice Pres*
Patrick N Troy, *Vice Pres*
◆ **EMP:** 398 **EST:** 1998
SALES (est): 28.3MM **Privately Held**
WEB: www.tuuci.com
SIC: 3999 Umbrellas, canes & parts

(G-5658)
UNION PVC INDUSTRIES INC
295 W 27th St (33010-1511)
PHONE..................................305 883-1640
Manuel J Lopez, *Principal*
EMP: 7 **EST:** 2016
SALES (est): 47.3K **Privately Held**
WEB: www.unionpvcindustries.com
SIC: 3999 Manufacturing industries

(G-5659)
UNITED BEDDINGS CORP
421 W 28th St (33010-1323)
PHONE..................................786 333-4795
Edel Sosa, *President*
EMP: 16 **EST:** 2011
SALES (est): 534.7K **Privately Held**
WEB: www.united-beddings-corp.business.site
SIC: 2515 Mattresses, containing felt, foam rubber, urethane, etc.

(G-5660)
UNITED CABINETS CORP
867 W 30th St (33012-5001)
PHONE..................................305 887-5050
Edelso Riveron Jr, *President*
Telma Riveron, *Admin Sec*
EMP: 5 **EST:** 1983
SALES (est): 390.1K **Privately Held**
WEB: www.unitedcabinets.com
SIC: 2434 Wood kitchen cabinets

(G-5661)
UNITED STATES FNDRY & MFG CORP
Also Called: US Foundry
3200 W 84th St (33018-4908)
PHONE..................................305 556-1661
Paula Cavache, *Exec VP*
Diana Vanegas, *Purch Agent*
Juan Mejia, *QC Mgr*
Kingsley Bewley, *Controller*
Rick Terrill, *Manager*
EMP: 10
SALES (corp-wide): 157.6MM **Privately Held**
WEB: www.usfoundry.com
SIC: 3321 3441 Gray iron castings; fabricated structural metal
HQ: United States Foundry & Manufacturing Corporation
8351 Nw 93rd St
Medley FL 33166
305 885-0301

(G-5662)
UNIVERSAL ALUM WINDOWS & DOORS
1675 W 31st Pl (33012-4505)
PHONE..................................305 825-7900
Jose Fernandez, *President*
EMP: 16 **EST:** 1984
SQ FT: 16,500
SALES (est): 701.8K **Privately Held**
SIC: 3442 3231 Sash, door or window: metal; products of purchased glass

(G-5663)
UNIVERSAL CONCRETE & READY MIX
10505 W Okeechobee Rd # 10
(33018-1979)
PHONE..................................305 512-3400
Juan Alvarez, *President*
EMP: 36 **EST:** 1983
SQ FT: 2,800
SALES (est): 5MM **Privately Held**
SIC: 3273 Ready-mixed concrete

(G-5664)
UNIVERSAL KITCHEN CENTER INC
7836 Nw 193rd Ter (33015-6347)
PHONE..................................305 218-5108
Enrique Morales, *President*
EMP: 7 **EST:** 2008
SALES (est): 190.9K **Privately Held**
WEB: www.universalkitchencenter.com
SIC: 2434 Wood kitchen cabinets

(G-5665)
UNLIMITED MARINE MFG INC ✪
2637 W 76th St (33016-5615)
PHONE..................................305 420-6034
Lida Munoz, *CEO*
EMP: 7 **EST:** 2020
SALES (est): 250K **Privately Held**
WEB: www.unlimitedmarinemfg.com
SIC: 3731 Marine rigging

(G-5666)
UP2SPEED PRINTING INC
8081 W 28th Ave (33016-5101)
PHONE..................................850 508-2620

GEOGRAPHIC

Orlando Valdes, *Principal*
EMP: 19 **EST:** 2003
SALES (est): 1MM **Privately Held**
WEB: www.up2speedprinting.com
SIC: 2752 Commercial printing, offset

(G-5667)
US PRECAST CORP
3200 W 84th St (33018-4908)
PHONE..................................305 364-8253
Debra Cloudie, *President*
Ana Sierra, *Human Res Mgr*
Angelo Vega, *Branch Mgr*
Hugo Fernandez, *Executive*
EMP: 29 **EST:** 1916
SALES (est): 1.8MM **Privately Held**
WEB: www.usffab.com
SIC: 3272 Precast terrazo or concrete products

(G-5668)
USA SHEET METAL INC
650 W 18th St (33010-2423)
PHONE..................................786 517-3482
Carlos E Rosa, *President*
Lazaro Reinoso, *Vice Pres*
EMP: 7 **EST:** 2006
SQ FT: 2,000
SALES (est): 1.1MM **Privately Held**
SIC: 3444 Sheet metalwork

(G-5669)
USF FABRICATION INC (PA)
3200 W 84th St (33018-4908)
PHONE..................................305 556-1661
Alexander De Bogory Jr, *President*
Valdez Robert, *Vice Pres*
Jamie Rubin, *Vice Pres*
Marvin Lopez, *Plant Mgr*
Ralph Jimenez, *Production*
▼ **EMP:** 200 **EST:** 1996
SQ FT: 90,000
SALES (est): 54.8MM **Privately Held**
WEB: www.usffab.com
SIC: 3441 Fabricated structural metal

(G-5670)
V & G INDUSTRIES INC
4965 E 10th Ct (33013-1731)
PHONE..................................786 853-1265
Enio Guerrero, *Principal*
EMP: 10 **EST:** 2013
SALES (est): 285.1K **Privately Held**
WEB: www.vandginc.business.site
SIC: 3999 Manufacturing industries

(G-5671)
V A ELECTRICAL MOTORS CENTER
4011 W 18th Ave (33012-7054)
PHONE..................................305 825-3327
Horacio Valdes, *Partner*
Margarita Valdes, *Partner*
▼ **EMP:** 5 **EST:** 1986
SALES (est): 349.9K **Privately Held**
SIC: 7694 Electric motor repair; rebuilding motors, except automotive

(G-5672)
V G CARPENTRY LLC
4855 E 10th Ct (33013-2123)
PHONE..................................786 531-7824
EMP: 8 **EST:** 2018
SALES (est): 538.6K **Privately Held**
SIC: 2434 Wood kitchen cabinets

(G-5673)
V P R A R T LLC
Also Called: Vapor Artillery
2630 W 81st St (33016-2755)
PHONE..................................786 205-4526
Kevin Tellado, *Mng Member*
EMP: 30 **EST:** 2013
SALES (est): 2.5MM **Privately Held**
SIC: 2844 Toilet preparations

(G-5674)
VECELLIO & GROGAN INC
White Rock Quarries Division
18300 Nw 122nd Ave (33018)
P.O. Box 667776, Miami (33166-9405)
PHONE..................................305 822-5322
Eddie Allsopp, *Vice Pres*
Jim Hurley, *Plant Mgr*
Raymond Maddy, *Branch Mgr*
Earon Lee, *Planning*
EMP: 100
SALES (corp-wide): 609.6MM **Privately Held**
WEB: www.vecelliogrogan.com
SIC: 1422 1442 Limestones, ground; construction sand & gravel
HQ: Vecellio & Grogan, Inc.
2251 Robert C Byrd Dr
Beckley WV 25801
304 252-6575

(G-5675)
VEGGIESPETIT POIS INC
2202 W 78th St (33016-5525)
PHONE..................................305 826-7867
Rafael Gabeiras, *President*
Viviana Gabeiras, *Vice Pres*
EMP: 30 **EST:** 1999
SQ FT: 6,000
SALES (est): 4.9MM **Privately Held**
WEB: www.mypetitpois.com
SIC: 2339 Athletic clothing: women's, misses' & juniors'

(G-5676)
VERONICA KNITS INC
490 W 18th St (33010-2419)
PHONE..................................305 887-7333
Jonel Jankuc, *President*
Jeffrey Jankuc, *Vice Pres*
▼ **EMP:** 10 **EST:** 1990
SQ FT: 12,000
SALES (est): 244.2K **Privately Held**
WEB: www.veronica-knits.business.site
SIC: 2253 Skirts, knit

(G-5677)
VET SONIC INC
1099 E 47th St (33013-2139)
PHONE..................................305 681-4486
Eva Engler, *President*
EMP: 7 **EST:** 1963
SALES (est): 107.9K **Privately Held**
SIC: 3843 Dental equipment

(G-5678)
VICTORS CSTM QILTING BEDSPREAD
2765 W 78th St (33016-2741)
PHONE..................................305 362-1990
Victor Chao, *President*
▼ **EMP:** 8 **EST:** 1977
SALES (est): 699.8K **Privately Held**
SIC: 2392 Household furnishings

(G-5679)
VICTORS DIE CUTTING INC
1385 Se 9th Ave (33010-5907)
PHONE..................................305 599-0255
Victor Rodriguez, *President*
Juan Rodriguez, *Vice Pres*
EMP: 5 **EST:** 1989
SALES (est): 462.1K **Privately Held**
WEB: www.victorsdiecut.com
SIC: 3544 Dies, steel rule

(G-5680)
VINTAGE FASHION
2450 W 8th Ln (33010-2032)
PHONE..................................786 631-4048
Ryan Frankel, *President*
◆ **EMP:** 9 **EST:** 2015
SALES (est): 452.8K **Privately Held**
WEB: www.wholesalevintagefashion.com
SIC: 2299 Textile goods

(G-5681)
VITAL GRAPHICS AND SIGNS INC
2131 W 60th St (33016-2602)
PHONE..................................305 557-8181
Luis Gonzalez, *President*
Luis E Gonzalez, *Principal*
Alberto Cabrera, *Vice Pres*
EMP: 5 **EST:** 2010
SQ FT: 3,600
SALES (est): 443.7K **Privately Held**
WEB: www.vital-graphicsprinting.com
SIC: 2752 Commercial printing, lithographic

(G-5682)
VITAL PHARMA RESEARCH INC
2300 W 84th St Ste 303 (33016-5772)
PHONE..................................786 666-0592
Luis Canete, *Principal*
EMP: 5 **EST:** 2014
SALES (est): 412K **Privately Held**
WEB: www.vprfl.org
SIC: 2834 Pharmaceutical preparations

(G-5683)
VOICE PUBLISHING CO INC
Also Called: La Voz De La Calle
4696 E 10th Ct (33013-2108)
P.O. Box 133187 (33013-0187)
PHONE..................................305 687-5555
Vincent Rodriguez, *President*
Juan Suarez, *General Mgr*
Zenaida Moreno, *Editor*
EMP: 7
SQ FT: 1,500
SALES (est): 82K **Privately Held**
WEB: www.lavozdelacalle.net
SIC: 2711 Newspapers

(G-5684)
VP CAST STONE CORP
Also Called: Vp Castone
879 E 25th St 899 (33013-3401)
PHONE..................................305 691-9306
Amanda Munoz Garcia, *President*
Alfredo Estevan, *Vice Pres*
◆ **EMP:** 5 **EST:** 2007
SALES (est): 313.9K **Privately Held**
WEB: www.vpcaststone.com
SIC: 3272 Cast stone, concrete

(G-5685)
WALTER HAAS GRAPHICS INC
123 W 23rd St (33010-2211)
PHONE..................................305 883-2257
Patrick Haas, *President*
Chrisitne Lohmeyer, *Vice Pres*
David Lohmeyer, *Treasurer*
Christopher Haas, *Department Mgr*
Marianne Haas, *Director*
▼ **EMP:** 25 **EST:** 1972
SQ FT: 20,000
SALES (est): 1.9MM **Privately Held**
WEB: www.haasprint.com
SIC: 2759 2396 2752 Screen printing; fabric printing & stamping; commercial printing, lithographic

(G-5686)
WARREN TECHNOLOGY INC
Also Called: Warren Manufacturing
2050 W 73rd St (33016-1816)
P.O. Box 5347 (33014-1347)
PHONE..................................305 556-6933
Winfield L Kelley, *President*
Patricia L Parnell, *Corp Secy*
Dario Vega, *Engineer*
Frank Zavala, *Accounts Mgr*
Scott Hamilton, *Sales Engr*
▲ **EMP:** 200 **EST:** 1986
SQ FT: 40,000
SALES (est): 26.7MM **Privately Held**
WEB: www.warrenhvac.com
SIC: 3585 3564 Air conditioning equipment, complete; heating & air conditioning combination units; ventilating fans: industrial or commercial

(G-5687)
WILLIAMS SPECIALTIES INC
4716 E 10th Ct (33013-2122)
PHONE..................................305 769-9925
Mario Williams Jr, *President*
EMP: 8 **EST:** 2016
SALES (est): 378.1K **Privately Held**
SIC: 2396 Printing & embossing on plastics fabric articles

(G-5688)
WINSTON MANUFACTURING CORP
1745 W 32nd Pl Ste 55 (33012-4511)
PHONE..................................305 822-3344
Bill Newnan, *CEO*
Larry Goldstein, *President*
▲ **EMP:** 8 **EST:** 1993
SQ FT: 18,000
SALES (est): 260K **Privately Held**
SIC: 3172 Personal leather goods

(G-5689)
WORLD OF AWNINGS INC
151 W 21st St (33010-2615)
PHONE..................................305 884-6699
Ignasio Sotolongo, *President*
◆ **EMP:** 10 **EST:** 1992
SALES (est): 818.7K **Privately Held**
WEB: www.aworldofawnings.com
SIC: 2431 2394 Awnings, blinds & shutters, wood; canvas & related products

(G-5690)
WORLDWIDE DRAPERIES WEST LLC
705 W 20th St (33010-2429)
PHONE..................................305 887-9611
Sandra Leal, *Opers Staff*
Jose M Leal, *Manager*
Sandra Lina Leal, *Manager*
EMP: 10 **EST:** 2015
SALES (est): 149.8K **Privately Held**
WEB: www.wwdrape.com
SIC: 2591 Shade, curtain & drapery hardware; curtain & drapery rods, poles & fixtures

(G-5691)
XPRESS PRECISION PRODUCTS INC
4432 E 10th Ct (33013-2523)
PHONE..................................305 685-2127
Leonel Montepeque, *President*
EMP: 6 **EST:** 1996
SALES (est): 897.6K **Privately Held**
SIC: 3599 7692 Machine shop, jobbing & repair; welding repair

(G-5692)
Y&D MACHINE SHOP INC
748 E 51st St (33013-1630)
PHONE..................................786 717-6356
Sandra Delgado, *Vice Pres*
EMP: 10 **EST:** 2018
SALES (est): 261.1K **Privately Held**
SIC: 3599 Machine shop, jobbing & repair

(G-5693)
YOUR DREAMS CABINETS CORP
7635 W 28th Ave (33016-5107)
PHONE..................................305 305-3729
Vanler R Napoles, *President*
Madelaine Napoles, *Vice Pres*
EMP: 6 **EST:** 2008
SALES (est): 781.1K **Privately Held**
WEB: www.kitchencabinetsformiami.com
SIC: 2434 Wood kitchen cabinets

(G-5694)
Z-2 METAL ARTWORK INC
117 W 24th St (33010-2215)
PHONE..................................305 804-4974
Zeron A Raul, *President*
EMP: 6 **EST:** 2018
SALES (est): 78.9K **Privately Held**
SIC: 3471 Plating & polishing

(G-5695)
ZAYAS FASHIONS INC (PA)
665 W 33rd St (33012-5112)
PHONE..................................305 823-1438
Daniel Zayas, *Ch of Bd*
Carlos Zayas, *President*
Lilliam Llanos, *Vice Pres*
Haydee Zayas, *Vice Pres*
EMP: 27 **EST:** 1968
SQ FT: 6,000
SALES (est): 1.9MM **Privately Held**
WEB: www.zayasfashions.com
SIC: 2326 5632 Men's & boys' work clothing; apparel accessories

(G-5696)
ZERONS METAL DESIGNERS INC
115 117 W 24th St (33010)
PHONE..................................305 688-2240
Jose A Zeron, *President*
EMP: 13 **EST:** 2004
SALES (est): 1.2MM **Privately Held**
WEB: www.zeronsmetaldesigners.com
SIC: 3499 3312 Bank chests, metal; stainless steel

▲ = Import ▼=Export
◆ =Import/Export

Hialeah Gardens
Miami-Dade County

(G-5697)
A J W COATINGS CORP
3408 W 84th St Ste 210 (33018-4942)
PHONE.................................786 357-7580
Jhon Sierra, *Principal*
EMP: 6 **EST:** 2015
SALES (est): 68.3K **Privately Held**
SIC: 3479 Metal coating & allied service

(G-5698)
FLORIDA TRUCK PARTS
13115 W Okeechobee Rd # 101 (33018-6056)
PHONE.................................786 251-8614
Nubia Conner, *President*
Nubia Miranda, *Admin Sec*
EMP: 5 **EST:** 2012
SALES (est): 634.1K **Privately Held**
SIC: 3713 Truck bodies & parts

(G-5699)
SOS FOOD LAB LLC (PA)
14802 Nw 107th Ave Unit 5 (33018-1238)
PHONE.................................305 594-9933
Jessica Brack, *CEO*
Stella Koniecpolski, *President*
Ludwig Kahn, *Principal*
Beatrice Ableton, *Vice Pres*
Immanuel Decastro, *Purchasing*
▲ **EMP:** 24 **EST:** 1984
SQ FT: 10,000
SALES (est): 6.1MM **Privately Held**
WEB: www.sosfoodlab.com
SIC: 2099 2086 Food preparations; water, pasteurized: packaged in cans, bottles, etc.

High Springs
Alachua County

(G-5700)
COMMERCIAL GATES AND ELC LLC
Also Called: Greg Pyle Enterprises
27317 Nw 78th Ave (32643-9754)
PHONE.................................386 454-2329
Greg Tyle, *Owner*
EMP: 10 **EST:** 2014
SALES (est): 2MM **Privately Held**
WEB: www.commercialgatesandelectric.com
SIC: 3699 1731 Electrical equipment & supplies; electronic controls installation

(G-5701)
HALCYON MANUFACTURING INC
24587 Nw 178th Pl (32643-2305)
PHONE.................................386 454-0811
Jarrod Jablonski, *President*
Mary Townsend, *Vice Pres*
Corey Jablonski, *Executive*
◆ **EMP:** 30 **EST:** 1999
SALES (est): 4.8MM **Privately Held**
WEB: www.halcyon.net
SIC: 3949 Skin diving equipment, scuba type

(G-5702)
THEMEWORKS INCORPORATED
17594 High Sprng Main St (32643-0529)
PHONE.................................386 454-7500
Robert S Gill, *President*
Joe Gazdun, *Foreman/Supr*
Adam Fritts, *Supervisor*
EMP: 104 **EST:** 1995
SQ FT: 54,000
SALES (est): 13.5MM **Privately Held**
WEB: www.themeworks.com
SIC: 3999 Theatrical scenery

(G-5703)
WOOD SCAPES INTERIORS
26509 W Us Highway 27 (32643-2096)
PHONE.................................386 454-1540
Petra Johnson, *Owner*
EMP: 5 **EST:** 2015
SALES (est): 514.6K **Privately Held**
WEB: www.woodscapesinteriors.com
SIC: 2434 Wood kitchen cabinets

(G-5704)
ZENITHTECH INDUSTRIES INC
27124 Nw 203rd Pl (32643-1600)
PHONE.................................386 454-7630
EMP: 8 **EST:** 2008
SALES (est): 490K **Privately Held**
SIC: 3999 Mfg Misc Products

Highland Beach
Palm Beach County

(G-5705)
ARFONA PRINTING LLC ✪
1121 Bel Air Dr Apt 4 (33487-4229)
PHONE.................................312 339-0215
Justin Marks, *Principal*
Clay Teufel, *Principal*
Mark Teufel, *Manager*
EMP: 8 **EST:** 2020
SALES (est): 431.9K **Privately Held**
SIC: 2752 Commercial printing, lithographic

Hilliard
Nassau County

(G-5706)
G HADDOCK ROWLAND INC
376488 Kings Ferry Rd (32046-6372)
PHONE.................................904 845-2725
Rowland G Haddock, *President*
EMP: 8 **EST:** 1996
SQ FT: 1,305
SALES (est): 733.4K **Privately Held**
SIC: 2411 7389 Logging;

(G-5707)
GEIGER LOGGING INC
28714 Yellow Rose Ln (32046-2339)
P.O. Box 1050 (32046-1050)
PHONE.................................904 845-7534
Zenous R Geiger Jr, *President*
Karyn N Geiger, *Vice Pres*
EMP: 25 **EST:** 1997
SQ FT: 1,000
SALES (est): 3MM **Privately Held**
WEB: www.geiger-logging-inc.business.site
SIC: 2411 Logging camps & contractors

(G-5708)
GREG FRANKLIN ENTERPRISES INC
Also Called: Franklin Equipment
551797 Us Highway 1 (32046-8821)
P.O. Box 809 (32046-0809)
PHONE.................................904 675-9129
Gregory W Franklin, *President*
Carrol E Franklin, *Admin Sec*
EMP: 12 **EST:** 2014
SALES (est): 1.8MM **Privately Held**
SIC: 3524 5231 Blowers & vacuums, lawn; paint brushes, rollers, sprayers & other supplies

(G-5709)
HARRY PICKETT
Also Called: Pickett Logging
37752 Kings Ferry Rd (32046-6526)
PHONE.................................904 845-4643
Harry Pickett, *President*
Julie Pickett, *Vice Pres*
EMP: 8 **EST:** 2002
SQ FT: 2,717
SALES (est): 994.5K **Privately Held**
SIC: 2411 Logging camps & contractors

(G-5710)
HOBBS TRUCKING LLC
15616 County Road 108 (32046-5202)
PHONE.................................904 463-5681
Benjamin F Hobbs, *Principal*
EMP: 6 **EST:** 2017
SALES (est): 309.3K **Privately Held**
SIC: 2411 Logging

(G-5711)
JOHNS & CONNER INC
15924 County Road 108 (32046-6700)
P.O. Box 1319 (32046-1319)
PHONE.................................904 845-4430
Charles E Johns, *Principal*
EMP: 6 **EST:** 2011
SALES (est): 785.5K **Privately Held**
SIC: 2411 Logging camps & contractors

(G-5712)
JOHNS & CONNER LOGGING INC
15924 County Road 108 (32046-6700)
P.O. Box 1319 (32046-1319)
PHONE.................................904 845-4430
Charles E Johns, *President*
EMP: 7 **EST:** 1970
SALES (est): 229.2K **Privately Held**
SIC: 2411 Logging camps & contractors

(G-5713)
JOHNS & CONNOR INC
28244 Pond View Cir (32046-7254)
PHONE.................................904 845-4541
Charles E Johns, *President*
Donald B Connor, *Vice Pres*
EMP: 9 **EST:** 1972
SALES (est): 210.6K **Privately Held**
WEB: www.johnsconner.com
SIC: 2411 Logging camps & contractors

(G-5714)
LARRY C CRIBB
28145 Enterprise Dr (32046-2316)
PHONE.................................904 845-2804
Larry C Cribb, *Principal*
EMP: 6 **EST:** 2010
SALES (est): 160.4K **Privately Held**
SIC: 2491 Structural lumber & timber, treated wood

(G-5715)
P & S LOGGING INC
15864 County Road 108 (32046-6711)
P.O. Box 969 (32046-0969)
PHONE.................................904 845-4256
Timothy R Pickett, *President*
Susan Pickett, *Admin Sec*
EMP: 11 **EST:** 2002
SALES (est): 511K **Privately Held**
SIC: 2411 Logging camps & contractors

(G-5716)
REMAS DRAPERIES ETC INC
27777 Conner Nelson Rd (32046-7607)
PHONE.................................904 845-9300
Latrelle Murphy, *Owner*
Ann Combs, *Manager*
EMP: 7 **EST:** 1958
SQ FT: 5,000
SALES (est): 480.5K **Privately Held**
SIC: 2221 5714 2392 2391 Draperies & drapery fabrics, manmade fiber & silk; draperies; household furnishings; curtains & draperies

(G-5717)
RIVERLAND LOGGING INC
25190 County Road 121 (32046-5368)
PHONE.................................904 845-4326
Mike Van Zant, *President*
EMP: 6 **EST:** 2003
SALES (est): 1MM **Privately Held**
WEB: www.riverlandlogging.com
SIC: 2411 Logging camps & contractors

(G-5718)
SMITH MACHINE SERVICES INC
552121 Us Highway 1 (32046-2326)
P.O. Box 339 (32046-0339)
PHONE.................................904 845-2002
Barry D Smith, *CEO*
EMP: 7 **EST:** 1990
SQ FT: 2,000
SALES (est): 605.5K **Privately Held**
SIC: 3549 Metalworking machinery

(G-5719)
STELLAR ON-SITE LLC
27167 Betina Dr (32046-3500)
PHONE.................................904 945-1908
Charles R Carroll Sr, *Manager*
EMP: 14 **EST:** 2018
SALES (est): 3.6MM **Privately Held**
WEB: www.stellaronsite.com
SIC: 2611 Pulp mills, mechanical & recycling processing

(G-5720)
VAN ZANT TIMBER INCORPORATED
373120 Kings Ferry Rd (32046-6617)
PHONE.................................904 845-4661
John Van Zant, *CEO*
Mary Van Zant, *Corp Secy*
EMP: 6 **EST:** 2002
SQ FT: 2,667
SALES (est): 348.8K **Privately Held**
SIC: 2411 Logging

Hobe Sound
Martin County

(G-5721)
ALUMACART INC
12968 Se Suzanne Dr (33455-9747)
PHONE.................................772 675-2158
Jennifer Knoebel, *President*
▼ **EMP:** 10 **EST:** 2006
SALES (est): 600K **Privately Held**
WEB: www.alumacart.net
SIC: 3449 3498 3334 3446 Miscellaneous metalwork; fabricated pipe & fittings; primary aluminum; architectural metalwork; aluminum extruded products

(G-5722)
ARONS TOWING & RECOVERY INC
12872 Se Suzanne Dr (33455-9713)
P.O. Box 2391, Stuart (34995-2391)
PHONE.................................772 220-1151
Aron Dames, *President*
EMP: 9 **EST:** 1987
SALES (est): 1.1MM **Privately Held**
WEB: www.aronstowingandrecovery.com
SIC: 3711 7549 1629 Wreckers (tow truck), assembly of; towing service, automotive; land clearing contractor

(G-5723)
C MIKE ROACH INC
4847 Se Longleaf Pl (33455-8108)
PHONE.................................864 882-1101
Clyde Roach, *President*
Annie Smith, *Manager*
EMP: 10 **EST:** 2012
SQ FT: 15,000
SALES (est): 2.7MM **Privately Held**
SIC: 3432 Lawn hose nozzles & sprinklers

(G-5724)
EASTGATE PUBLISHING INC
9015 Se Athena St (33455-5501)
PHONE.................................772 286-0101
Robert Ritter, *President*
EMP: 6 **EST:** 1997
SALES (est): 304.4K **Privately Held**
WEB: www.eastgate.com
SIC: 2741 Newsletter publishing

(G-5725)
PRINT DIRECT INC
8183 Se Cumberland Cir (33455-4053)
PHONE.................................772 545-9191
Stephen D Desena, *President*
EMP: 6 **EST:** 2003
SALES (est): 246.7K **Privately Held**
WEB: www.printdirectadvertising.com
SIC: 2752 Commercial printing, offset

(G-5726)
R P M INDUSTRIES INC
Also Called: RPM Displays
8505 Se Gulfstream Pl (33455-4244)
PHONE.................................315 255-1105
Roger P Mueller, *President*
David Hess, *Vice Pres*
Martin Lynch, *Asst Treas*
Roy P Mueller, *VP Sales*
▲ **EMP:** 50 **EST:** 1925
SALES (est): 3MM **Privately Held**
SIC: 3089 5046 2499 Boxes, plastic; plastic hardware & building products; mannequins; shoe trees

GEOGRAPHIC

(G-5727)
SIMPLEPIN LLC ✪
8954 Se Bridge Rd (33455-5311)
PHONE..................................800 727-4136
Metod Popolnik, *Mng Member*
EMP: 10 **EST:** 2020
SALES (est): 1MM **Privately Held**
WEB: www.simplepin.com
SIC: 7372 Application computer software

(G-5728)
TEES PLEASE INC
9278 Se Sharon St (33455-6920)
PHONE..................................857 472-3391
Barbara McLaughlin, *Principal*
EMP: 7 **EST:** 2018
SALES (est): 259K **Privately Held**
WEB: www.tees-please-fla.myshopify.com
SIC: 2759 Screen printing

(G-5729)
TREASURE COAST SEALING CO
8949 Se Bridge Rd (33455-5312)
PHONE..................................772 834-5014
Steve Middleton, *Principal*
EMP: 8 **EST:** 2006
SALES (est): 966.2K **Privately Held**
WEB: www.treasurecoastlandscapelighting.com
SIC: 2911 Asphalt or asphaltic materials, made in refineries

(G-5730)
ULTRA TUFF MANUFACTURING INC
8845 Se Robwyn St (33455-5326)
PHONE..................................970 252-9457
▼ **EMP:** 9 **EST:** 1999
SALES (est): 1.5MM **Privately Held**
WEB: www.tuffcoat.net
SIC: 2851 Paints & allied products

(G-5731)
WIRELESS COVERAGE GROUP INC
11718 Se Federal Hwy # 36 (33455-5303)
PHONE..................................561 429-5032
Robert Rapkin, *President*
Brandon McDougall, *Director*
EMP: 7 **EST:** 2012
SALES (est): 162.5K **Privately Held**
WEB: www.commercial.wirelesscoveragesolutions.com
SIC: 3661 Fiber optics communications equipment

Holiday
Pasco County

(G-5732)
ADMIRAL PRINTING INC
Also Called: Fantasy Escapes
5412 Provost Dr Unit 12 (34690-2904)
PHONE..................................727 938-9589
Leonore Sitton, *President*
Melanie Land, *Production*
Steven Riddle, *Sales Mgr*
Anthony El-Ghoul, *Accounts Exec*
Nate Touchberry, *Accounts Exec*
EMP: 6 **EST:** 1993
SALES (est): 500.7K **Privately Held**
WEB: www.admiral.win.net
SIC: 2759 Screen printing

(G-5733)
AGM PUBLISHING INC
3049 Coldwell Dr (34691-4842)
PHONE..................................727 934-9993
Alfred G Messina, *President*
EMP: 7 **EST:** 2005
SALES (est): 72.5K **Privately Held**
SIC: 2741 Miscellaneous publishing

(G-5734)
ARTEX PUBLISHING INC
3130 Westridge Dr (34691-2538)
PHONE..................................727 944-4117
Les Zielinski, *President*
EMP: 6
SALES (est): 250K **Privately Held**
SIC: 2731 Books: publishing only

(G-5735)
B224 USA CO ✪
2508 Baywood Dr (34690-3801)
PHONE..................................786 598-8805
Stella Valerie Sampsonidi, *President*
EMP: 5 **EST:** 2020
SALES (est): 500K **Privately Held**
SIC: 2844 Perfumes & colognes

(G-5736)
BUZZ POP COCKTAILS CORPORATION (PA)
4407 Buena Vista Ln (34691-5454)
PHONE..................................727 275-9848
Joseph Isaacs, *CEO*
EMP: 12
SQ FT: 1,850
SALES (est): 1.5MM **Privately Held**
WEB: www.buzzpopcocktails.com
SIC: 2085 2024 Cocktails, alcoholic; sorbets, non-dairy based

(G-5737)
BXD ENTERPRISES INC
4148 Louis Ave (34691-5612)
PHONE..................................727 937-4100
Robin Selby, *President*
Gail Selby, *Vice Pres*
▲ **EMP:** 7 **EST:** 1998
SALES (est): 1.3MM
SALES (corp-wide): 15.5MM **Privately Held**
WEB: www.premiere-components.com
SIC: 3053 Oil seals, rubber
HQ: Premiere Seals Holdings, Llc
4148 Louis Ave
Holiday FL 34691
727 937-4100

(G-5738)
CCP FABRICATION
2100 Peggy Dr (34690-4112)
PHONE..................................727 946-6024
Paul Kostopoulos, *Principal*
EMP: 6 **EST:** 2013
SALES (est): 191.3K **Privately Held**
WEB: www.ccpfabrication.com
SIC: 3714 Motor vehicle parts & accessories

(G-5739)
E-SEA RIDER LLC
Also Called: E-Sea Rider Marine Bean Bags
4054 Louis Ave (34691-5600)
PHONE..................................727 863-3333
Patrick M Bennett,
▼ **EMP:** 6 **EST:** 2004
SQ FT: 5,000
SALES (est): 650K **Privately Held**
WEB: www.e-searider.com
SIC: 2519

(G-5740)
EPOXY FLOOR COATINGS LLC
1544 Toledo St (34690-5854)
PHONE..................................920 471-6913
Derek Storch, *Principal*
EMP: 7 **EST:** 2015
SALES (est): 379.2K **Privately Held**
WEB: www.garagefloorcoating.com
SIC: 2851 Epoxy coatings

(G-5741)
GREAT BAY DISTRIBUTORS INC
2310 Starkey Rd (34690)
PHONE..................................727 584-8626
Mark Goodwill, *Finance*
Sandy Ho, *Human Res Dir*
Brian Costanza, *Accounts Mgr*
Jeffrey Patterson, *Accounts Mgr*
Tori Chambers, *Sales Staff*
EMP: 240
SALES (corp-wide): 61.6MM **Privately Held**
WEB: www.greatbaybud.com
SIC: 2082 Beer (alcoholic beverage)
PA: Great Bay Distributors, Inc.
2750 Eagle Ave N
Saint Petersburg FL 33716
727 584-8626

(G-5742)
HARBERSON RV PINELLAS LLC
2112 Us Highway 19 (34691-4347)
PHONE..................................727 937-6176
Mark Hollan, *Manager*
EMP: 23
SALES (corp-wide): 11.9MM **Privately Held**
WEB: www.harbersonrv-pinellas.com
SIC: 3365 7538 5561 Aluminum foundries; general automotive repair shops; recreational vehicle dealers
PA: Harberson Rv Pinellas Llc
17028 Us Highway 19 N
Clearwater FL 33764
727 539-8714

(G-5743)
HARBORTECH PLASTICS LLC
3151 Grand Blvd (34690-2244)
PHONE..................................727 944-2425
Bill D Price, *Engineer*
Billy Price, *Engineer*
Chris Tubergen, *Sales Staff*
EMP: 10 **EST:** 2007
SALES (est): 1.7MM **Privately Held**
WEB: www.harbortechplastics.com
SIC: 3089 Injection molding of plastics

(G-5744)
HIGH NOON UNLIMITED INC
Also Called: High Noon Holsters
4339 Buena Vista Ln (34691-5404)
P.O. Box 1923, Tarpon Springs (34688-1923)
PHONE..................................727 939-2701
Claire V Inabinet, *President*
George B Inabinet III, *COO*
Jim Singleton, *Marketing Staff*
Matthew Punzone, *Manager*
EMP: 8 **EST:** 1997
SQ FT: 4,500
SALES (est): 570K **Privately Held**
WEB: www.highnoonholsters.com
SIC: 3199 Holsters, leather; dog furnishings: collars, leashes, muzzles, etc.: leather

(G-5745)
INFINITE PRINT LLC
1014 Us Highway 19 # 114 (34691-5634)
PHONE..................................727 942-2121
EMP: 6 **EST:** 2017
SALES (est): 456.8K **Privately Held**
WEB: www.infiniteprint.com
SIC: 2752 Commercial printing, offset

(G-5746)
INSTANT PRINTING & COPY CENTER
3307 Us Highway 19 (34691-1847)
PHONE..................................727 849-1199
Robert Wagner, *President*
EMP: 5 **EST:** 2003
SALES (est): 395.1K **Privately Held**
SIC: 2752 Commercial printing, offset

(G-5747)
MARY LAME WROUGHT IRON & ALUM
1022 Us Highway 19 (34691-5635)
PHONE..................................727 934-2879
Richard Price, *President*
Sharon Price, *Treasurer*
Steven Katona, *Admin Sec*
EMP: 9 **EST:** 1952
SQ FT: 10,000
SALES (est): 673.8K **Privately Held**
WEB: www.marylame.com
SIC: 3446 3334 3354 Architectural metalwork; primary aluminum; aluminum extruded products

(G-5748)
PEPSI-COLA BOTTLING CO TAMPA
5406 Whippoorwill Dr (34690-2162)
PHONE..................................727 942-3664
Tomek Targosz, *Engineer*
Berry Joyce, *Manager*
Nicholas Rizzolo, *Maintence Staff*
EMP: 224
SALES (corp-wide): 70.3B **Publicly Held**
WEB: www.pepsico.com
SIC: 2086 Carbonated soft drinks, bottled & canned
HQ: Pepsi-Cola Bottling Company Of Tampa
11315 N 30th St
Tampa FL 33612
813 971-2550

(G-5749)
SUN PRINT MANAGEMENT LLC
5441 Provost Dr (34690-2939)
PHONE..................................727 945-0255
Nikolle Smith, *VP Opers*
Bruce Rushton, *Accounts Exec*
Chelsea Schlimm, *Accounts Exec*
Peter Wagner, *Mng Member*
Kristen Loring, *Manager*
EMP: 49 **EST:** 2006
SALES (est): 12.6MM **Privately Held**
WEB: www.sunprint.com
SIC: 2752 3955 7699 5112 Commercial printing, lithographic; print cartridges for laser & other computer printers; photocopy machine repair; laserjet supplies; business machine & electronic equipment rental services

(G-5750)
SUNCOAST TONER CARTRIDGE INC
5441 Provost Dr (34690-2939)
PHONE..................................727 945-0255
Peter Wagner, *President*
Jack Thompson, *Corp Secy*
Stephen Miklos, *Vice Pres*
Steve Miklos, *Vice Pres*
EMP: 12 **EST:** 1995
SQ FT: 3,000
SALES (est): 618.2K **Privately Held**
WEB: www.sunprint.com
SIC: 3955 Print cartridges for laser & other computer printers

(G-5751)
VICTORY CUSTOM CABINETRY
2623 Grand Blvd (34690-3002)
PHONE..................................727 937-2284
Victor Samulian, *Principal*
EMP: 6 **EST:** 2004
SALES (est): 53K **Privately Held**
SIC: 2434 Wood kitchen cabinets

(G-5752)
VOODOO FAB LLC
4717 Bartelt Rd (34690-5534)
PHONE..................................727 916-0014
Charles R Lee, *Manager*
EMP: 6 **EST:** 2017
SALES (est): 169.5K **Privately Held**
SIC: 3714 Motor vehicle body components & frame

(G-5753)
WROBEL INDUSTRIES INC
1004 Us Highway 19 # 202 (34691-5632)
PHONE..................................727 560-6850
Hayden Wrobel, *President*
EMP: 7 **EST:** 2007
SALES (est): 104.1K **Privately Held**
SIC: 3999 Manufacturing industries

Hollister
Putnam County

(G-5754)
KEY LOGGING
229 Lynn Dr (32147)
P.O. Box 486 (32147-0486)
PHONE..................................386 328-6984
Randall Key Jr, *President*
EMP: 6 **EST:** 2001
SALES (est): 742.3K **Privately Held**
SIC: 2411 Logging camps & contractors

Holly Hill
Volusia County

(G-5755)
AMERICAN TECHNICAL FURN LLC
831 Carswell Ave (32117-3513)
PHONE..................................866 239-4204
John Ashman, *COO*

Greg Schmidt, *Sales Mgr*
Dayna Slater, *Clerk*
EMP: 5 **EST:** 2012
SALES (est): 6MM **Privately Held**
WEB: www.americantechnicalfurniture.com
SIC: 2599 Factory furniture & fixtures

(G-5756)
AQUARIAN BATH INC
46 High Ridge Rd (32117-1875)
PHONE..................................310 919-0220
Cory Trusty, *Principal*
EMP: 6 **EST:** 2012
SALES (est): 251.5K **Privately Held**
WEB: www.aquarianbath.com
SIC: 2844 Toilet preparations

(G-5757)
CC MACHINE INC (PA)
Also Called: Custom Wheel
618 Ridgewood Ave Ste B (32117-3604)
PHONE..................................888 577-0144
John Purner, *President*
▲ **EMP:** 17 **EST:** 1992
SQ FT: 8,000
SALES (est): 2.7MM **Privately Held**
SIC: 3714 Motor vehicle parts & accessories

(G-5758)
INSPEC SOLUTIONS LLC (PA)
330 Carswell Ave (32117-4416)
P.O. Box 730732, Ormond Beach (32173-0732)
PHONE..................................866 467-7320
Timothy Alderson, *Business Mgr*
Mohamed Yousef, *Manager*
Kimberly Brown, *Manager*
EMP: 30 **EST:** 2017
SALES (est): 3.7MM **Privately Held**
WEB: www.inspecsolutions.net
SIC: 2844 5999 Toilet preparations; cosmetics

(G-5759)
KENCO SIGNS AWNING LLC
1538 Garden Ave (32117-2110)
PHONE..................................386 672-1590
Raymond Webb, *Owner*
EMP: 15 **EST:** 2003
SQ FT: 1,900
SALES (est): 1.5MM **Privately Held**
WEB: www.kenco2000inc.com
SIC: 3993 Electric signs

(G-5760)
MOTORSPORT MARKETING INC
Also Called: Classic Motor Sport
915 Ridgewood Ave (32117-3519)
PHONE..................................386 239-0523
Timothy P Suddard, *President*
Marjorie J Suddard, *Vice Pres*
Kevin Maffett, *Sales Dir*
Nicole Suddard, *Mktg Coord*
Rick Goolsby, *Manager*
▼ **EMP:** 30 **EST:** 1984
SQ FT: 4,800
SALES (est): 4.6MM **Privately Held**
WEB: www.grassrootsmotorsports.com
SIC: 2721 Magazines: publishing only, not printed on site

(G-5761)
TOWNSEND SIGNS INC
515 Lpga Blvd (32117-2626)
PHONE..................................386 255-1955
Alan Townsend, *President*
John Townsend, *Vice Pres*
Tom Townsend, *Vice Pres*
Dena Townsend, *Admin Sec*
EMP: 8 **EST:** 1980
SQ FT: 4,500
SALES (est): 999.3K **Privately Held**
WEB: www.signsbytownsend.com
SIC: 3993 3444 Electric signs; displays & cutouts, window & lobby; sheet metalwork

Hollywood
Broward County

(G-5762)
4 FUEL LLC
2004 Grant St (33020-3546)
PHONE..................................954 929-5803
Isaac Arguetty, *Principal*
EMP: 7 **EST:** 2016
SALES (est): 74.4K **Privately Held**
SIC: 2869 Industrial organic chemicals

(G-5763)
A1 CUSTOM MICA INC
5805 Plunkett St (33023-2347)
PHONE..................................954 893-0063
Michael Bencivenga, *President*
Harry Malles, *Vice Pres*
EMP: 5 **EST:** 1987
SQ FT: 2,000
SALES (est): 800K **Privately Held**
WEB: www.a1custommica.com
SIC: 2434 Wood kitchen cabinets

(G-5764)
AB ELECTRIC MOTORS & PUMPS
6013 Johnson St (33024-6027)
PHONE..................................954 322-6900
Domingo Garcia, *President*
Jesus Garcia, *Sales Staff*
EMP: 25 **EST:** 2001
SALES (est): 1.8MM **Privately Held**
WEB: www.abemap.com
SIC: 3621 Electric motor & generator parts

(G-5765)
AGISUPREME LLC
2252 Hayes St (33020-3438)
PHONE..................................818 232-6699
Irit Bruchim,
EMP: 24 **EST:** 2017
SALES (est): 745K **Privately Held**
SIC: 3441 Fabricated structural metal

(G-5766)
AIR MARSHALL INC
2870 Stirling Rd Ste 110 (33020-1113)
PHONE..................................954 843-0991
Donald Marshall Jr, *President*
Karen Cruz, *Controller*
Camille Urquhart, *Sales Staff*
EMP: 14
SQ FT: 25,000
SALES (est): 2.2MM **Privately Held**
WEB: www.air-marshall.com
SIC: 3724 Aircraft engines & engine parts

(G-5767)
AIRCRAFT TECHNOLOGY INC
Also Called: ATI
3000 Taft St (33021-4441)
PHONE..................................954 744-7602
Ryan Sadonis, *Engineer*
Thomas Irwin, *CFO*
Carlos Ibanez, *Director*
Elizabeth Letendre, *Admin Sec*
EMP: 40 **EST:** 1985
SQ FT: 25,000
SALES (est): 10.4MM **Publicly Held**
WEB: www.heico.com
SIC: 3724 Aircraft engines & engine parts
HQ: Heico Aerospace Holdings Corp.
3000 Taft St
Hollywood FL 33021
954 987-4000

(G-5768)
ALICO LIGHTING GROUP INC
140 S Dixie Hwy Unit 101 (33020-7332)
PHONE..................................305 542-2648
EMP: 6 **EST:** 2006
SQ FT: 2,400
SALES: 2MM **Privately Held**
SIC: 3643 Mfg Conductive Wiring Devices

(G-5769)
ALL GREEN RECYCLING INC
811 Se 16th St Ste 105 (33024)
PHONE..................................754 204-3707
Carlos Moreno, *President*
EMP: 10 **EST:** 2010
SALES (est): 78.5K **Privately Held**
WEB: www.allgreenrecycling.com
SIC: 2611 Pulp manufactured from waste or recycled paper

(G-5770)
ALLEGRA PRINT SIGNS MAIL
5846 Stirling Rd (33021-1527)
PHONE..................................954 963-3886
EMP: 6 **EST:** 2014
SALES (est): 141.9K **Privately Held**
WEB: www.allegramarketingprint.com
SIC: 3993 2752 Signs & advertising specialties; commercial printing, offset

(G-5771)
ALMI INTL PLASTIC INDS INC
2227 N Federal Hwy (33020-2229)
PHONE..................................954 920-6836
Abraham Lalo, *CEO*
▼ **EMP:** 6 **EST:** 1982
SQ FT: 6,000
SALES (est): 762.1K **Privately Held**
WEB: www.almi.co.il
SIC: 2671 Plastic film, coated or laminated for packaging

(G-5772)
ANNETTE M WELLINGTON HALL INC
5830 Sheridan St (33021-3253)
PHONE..................................954 437-9880
Annette M Wellington, *Principal*
EMP: 9 **EST:** 2008
SALES (est): 319.9K **Privately Held**
SIC: 2511 Wood household furniture

(G-5773)
AQUA PURE WATER CO INC
1246 Funston St (33019-2218)
PHONE..................................954 744-4210
Valerie Galsky, *Principal*
EMP: 7 **EST:** 2012
SALES (est): 151.7K **Privately Held**
WEB: www.aquapure-water.com
SIC: 2086 Pasteurized & mineral waters, bottled & canned

(G-5774)
ARCO COMPUTER PRODUCTS LLC
Also Called: Data Protection Solutions
3100 N 29th Ct Ste 100 (33020-1321)
PHONE..................................954 925-2688
Itzik Levy, *Mng Member*
EMP: 5 **EST:** 1989
SQ FT: 3,000
SALES (est): 712.2K **Privately Held**
WEB: www.ezd2d.com
SIC: 3577 Computer peripheral equipment

(G-5775)
ARTWORKS PRINTING ENTERPRISES
5922 Liberty St (33021-3843)
PHONE..................................954 893-7984
Sergio Pellecer, *President*
Gloria Pellecer, *Vice Pres*
EMP: 5 **EST:** 1991
SALES (est): 431.3K **Privately Held**
WEB: www.artworksprinting.com
SIC: 2752 2759 5199 Commercial printing, offset; screen printing; advertising specialties

(G-5776)
ATI BY SEA CO
11251 Rockinghorse Rd (33026-1355)
PHONE..................................954 483-0526
Mohammed A Hussain, *Principal*
EMP: 8 **EST:** 2008
SALES (est): 196.1K **Privately Held**
SIC: 3312 Stainless steel

(G-5777)
ATK SALES CORP
121 S 61st Ter Ste B (33023-1376)
PHONE..................................954 701-0465
Kravatz Alane, *Principal*
EMP: 6 **EST:** 2014
SALES (est): 78.8K **Privately Held**
SIC: 3764 Propulsion units for guided missiles & space vehicles

(G-5778)
AUDIOSHARK INC
2635 Sherman St (33020-1948)
PHONE..................................954 591-9252
Robert Harvey, *Principal*
EMP: 7 **EST:** 2007
SALES (est): 98K **Privately Held**
WEB: www.audioshark.org
SIC: 3651 Household audio & video equipment

(G-5779)
AUTOMATED PAPER CONVERTERS
400 S Dixie Hwy (33020-4914)
PHONE..................................954 925-0721
Placido Barbeite, *President*
William Chouinard, *Sales Staff*
Larry Lipsitz, *Sales Staff*
Robert L Blumfield, *Admin Sec*
EMP: 7 **EST:** 1988
SALES (est): 857.7K **Privately Held**
WEB: www.apcinc.net
SIC: 2679 Paper products, converted

(G-5780)
AWNINGS OF HOLLYWOOD INC
Also Called: American Made Awnings
5828 Washington St (33023-1947)
PHONE..................................954 963-7717
Gerald Thompson, *President*
Chris Thompson, *Vice Pres*
Lori Roman, *Human Res Mgr*
Brent Lalor, *Department Mgr*
Daniel Robinson, *Manager*
▼ **EMP:** 30 **EST:** 1972
SALES (est): 6.4MM **Privately Held**
WEB: www.thompsonarchitecturalproducts.com
SIC: 3446 2394 Stairs, fire escapes, balconies, railings & ladders; shades, canvas: made from purchased materials

(G-5781)
BABY FOOD CHEF LLC
Also Called: Soapy Chef, The
2905 W Aviary Dr (33026-3635)
PHONE..................................305 335-5990
Leanna Blacher, *Principal*
EMP: 6 **EST:** 2012
SALES (est): 375.2K **Privately Held**
WEB: www.babyfoodchef.com
SIC: 2099 Food preparations

(G-5782)
BACH DIAMONDS
2910 Oakwood Blvd (33020-7122)
PHONE..................................954 921-4069
Ted Olson, *Manager*
EMP: 7 **EST:** 1996
SALES (est): 125.4K **Privately Held**
SIC: 3915 Diamond cutting & polishing

(G-5783)
BAER FAMILY WOODWORKING
5815 Buchanan St (33021-5617)
PHONE..................................954 297-2991
Anthony Baer, *Owner*
EMP: 6 **EST:** 2016
SALES (est): 54.1K **Privately Held**
SIC: 2431 Millwork

(G-5784)
BAPTIST COMMUNICATIONS MISSION (HQ)
3400 Raleigh St (33021-3122)
PHONE..................................954 981-2271
Phil Brown, *Director*
Arthur Edgar, *Director*
Mickey Searcy, *Director*
EMP: 18 **EST:** 1975
SALES (est): 3.6MM
SALES (corp-wide): 103.5MM **Privately Held**
SIC: 2731 7812 Pamphlets: publishing & printing; audio-visual program production
PA: The International Mission Board Of The Southern Baptist Convention
3806 Monument Ave
Richmond VA 23230
804 353-0151

(G-5785)
BELT CORP
4032 N 29th Ave (33020-1012)
PHONE..................................954 505-7400
Patricia Villa, *Assistant*
EMP: 7 **EST:** 2019
SALES (est): 527.4K **Privately Held**
WEB: www.belt.com.co
SIC: 3312 Blast furnaces & steel mills

GEOGRAPHIC

(G-5786)
BEST MANUFACTURING COMPANY
3282 N 29th Ct (33020-1320)
PHONE....................................954 922-1443
Eugene J Monsignore, *President*
Nancy Monsignore, *Corp Secy*
Eugene Monsignore Sr, *Shareholder*
◆ **EMP:** 10 **EST:** 1954
SQ FT: 20,000
SALES (est): 818.4K **Privately Held**
WEB: www.bestmanufacturing.8m.com
SIC: 3496 5031 Lath, woven wire; woven wire products; building materials, exterior; building materials, interior

(G-5787)
BETTER AIR NORTH AMERICA LLC
4651 Sheridan St Ste 335 (33021-3400)
PHONE....................................844 447-7624
Taly Dery, *CEO*
Dery Taly, *Supervisor*
EMP: 8 **EST:** 2015
SALES (est): 1.2MM **Privately Held**
SIC: 3564 Air purification equipment

(G-5788)
BLUE RIBBON TAG & LABEL CORP (PA)
4035 N 29th Ave (33020-1011)
PHONE....................................954 922-9292
Daniel Ferreiro, *President*
Dan Ferreiro, *Vice Pres*
Secundino Ferreiro, *Treasurer*
▼ **EMP:** 30
SQ FT: 30,000
SALES (est): 6MM **Privately Held**
WEB: www.blueribbonlabel.com
SIC: 2672 2752 Labels (unprinted), gummed: made from purchased materials; tags, lithographed

(G-5789)
BLUE RIBBON TAG & LABEL OF PR
4035 N 29th Ave (33020-1011)
PHONE....................................787 858-5300
Robert Schwartztol, *President*
Secundino Ferreiro, *Vice Pres*
Victor Torres, *Vice Pres*
EMP: 10
SQ FT: 12,000
SALES (est): 966.4K
SALES (corp-wide): 6MM **Privately Held**
WEB: www.blueribbonlabel.com
SIC: 2759 Tags: printing
PA: Blue Ribbon Tag & Label Corp.
4035 N 29th Ave
Hollywood FL 33020
954 922-9292

(G-5790)
BRISTOLS ELITE
3326 Garfield St (33021-5416)
PHONE....................................954 651-3574
Chris Bristol, *Principal*
EMP: 6 **EST:** 2017
SALES (est): 125.4K **Privately Held**
SIC: 2621 Paper mills

(G-5791)
BROWNIE LADY LLC
3925 Hyde Park Cir (33021-3046)
PHONE....................................954 989-0630
Marla I Robbins, *Manager*
EMP: 6 **EST:** 2010
SALES (est): 180.2K **Privately Held**
WEB: www.thebrownielady.com
SIC: 2052 Cookies & crackers

(G-5792)
BUSINESS FORWARD INC
Also Called: Signs Now
3286 N 29th Ct (33020-1320)
PHONE....................................954 967-6730
Alan Bleiweiss, *President*
Elizabeth Fairchild, *Opers Dir*
EMP: 5 **EST:** 2004
SALES (est): 366.1K **Privately Held**
WEB: www.signsnow.com
SIC: 3993 Signs & advertising specialties

(G-5793)
CAAMACOSTA INC
5400 N 35th St (33021-2324)
PHONE....................................954 987-5895
Daniel Caamano, *Principal*
EMP: 7 **EST:** 2012
SALES (est): 100.9K **Privately Held**
SIC: 2051 Bread, all types (white, wheat, rye, etc): fresh or frozen

(G-5794)
CALUMET ELECTRONICS
2500 Hollywood Blvd # 309 (33020-6615)
PHONE....................................954 668-7689
Sandra A Landers, *Principal*
EMP: 6 **EST:** 2018
SALES (est): 129.7K **Privately Held**
WEB: www.calumetelectronics.com
SIC: 3672 Printed circuit boards

(G-5795)
CARD USA INC
201 N Ocean Dr Ste 200 (33019-1784)
PHONE....................................954 862-1300
Marc Rochman, *CEO*
Samuel Fridman, *President*
Samuel Guy Fridman, *COO*
Samuel G Fridman, *COO*
Janissa Khal, *Marketing Staff*
▼ **EMP:** 15 **EST:** 1996
SQ FT: 6,300
SALES (est): 2MM **Privately Held**
WEB: www.cardusa.com
SIC: 3089 5199 Identification cards, plastic; cards, plastic: unprinted

(G-5796)
CARLO MORELLI
Also Called: All Spring Manufacturing Inds
1926 Hollywood Blvd (33020-4532)
PHONE....................................954 241-1426
Carlo Moreilli, *Owner*
Carlo Morelli, *Owner*
EMP: 6 **EST:** 2013
SALES (est): 481K **Privately Held**
SIC: 3495 Wire springs

(G-5797)
CGC INDUSTRIES INC
200 N Dixie Hwy (33020-6705)
PHONE....................................954 923-2428
Stefan Pandos, *President*
EMP: 7 **EST:** 2005
SALES (est): 93.6K **Privately Held**
SIC: 3999 Manufacturing industries

(G-5798)
CHARITEES LLC
3475 Sheridan St Ste 310 (33021-3660)
PHONE....................................561 542-4616
Jeffrey R Firestone, *Principal*
EMP: 6 **EST:** 2018
SALES (est): 80.6K **Privately Held**
SIC: 2759 Screen printing

(G-5799)
CITY OF HOLLYWOOD
Also Called: Hollywood Water Trtmnt Plant
3441 Hollywood Blvd Fl 2 (33021-6910)
PHONE....................................954 967-4230
Taylor Calhoun, *Manager*
EMP: 11
SALES (corp-wide): 220.3MM **Privately Held**
WEB: www.hollywoodfl.org
SIC: 3589 4941 Water treatment equipment, industrial; water supply
PA: Hollywood, City Of (Inc)
2600 Hollywood Blvd Ste B
Hollywood FL 33020
954 921-3231

(G-5800)
CKS PACKAGING INC
4020 N 29th Ter (33020-1020)
PHONE....................................954 925-9049
John Beasley, *Plant Mgr*
Mike Nance, *Opers Mgr*
Joseph Bernard, *Prdtn Mgr*
James Eberle, *Maint Mgr*
Bryn Davies, *Facilities Mgr*
EMP: 100
SALES (corp-wide): 411.1MM **Privately Held**
WEB: www.ckspackaging.com
SIC: 3089 3085 Plastic containers, except foam; plastics bottles
PA: C.K.S. Packaging, Inc.
350 Great Sw Pkwy
Atlanta GA 30336
404 691-8900

(G-5801)
CLASSIC CANVAS & UPHOLSTERY
1934 Cleveland St (33020-3134)
PHONE....................................954 850-4994
Elvin Torres, *Principal*
EMP: 6 **EST:** 2018
SALES (est): 180.5K **Privately Held**
SIC: 2211 Canvas

(G-5802)
COCA-COLA COMPANY
3350 Pembroke Rd (33021-8200)
PHONE....................................954 985-5000
Rebecca Marquis, *General Mgr*
Melissa Cerda-Richards, *Regional Mgr*
Toris McGhee, *Area Mgr*
Carmen Neri, *Business Mgr*
Tanika Cabral, *Vice Pres*
EMP: 6
SALES (corp-wide): 33B **Publicly Held**
WEB: www.coca-colacompany.com
SIC: 2086 Bottled & canned soft drinks
PA: The Coca-Cola Company
1 Coca Cola Plz Nw
Atlanta GA 30313
404 676-2121

(G-5803)
COCA-COLA COMPANY
2700 Sw 32nd Ave (33023-7702)
PHONE....................................954 961-8564
Kelly Mulligan, *Branch Mgr*
EMP: 6
SALES (corp-wide): 33B **Publicly Held**
WEB: www.coca-colacompany.com
SIC: 2086 2087 Bottled & canned soft drinks; concentrates, drink
PA: The Coca-Cola Company
1 Coca Cola Plz Nw
Atlanta GA 30313
404 676-2121

(G-5804)
CONCEPT ONE CUSTOM CABINE
5807 Dawson St (33023-1977)
PHONE....................................954 829-3505
Alphanso Brown, *Principal*
EMP: 6 **EST:** 2009
SALES (est): 62.9K **Privately Held**
SIC: 2434 Wood kitchen cabinets

(G-5805)
COSMESIS SKINCARE INC
Also Called: Goldfaden Skincare
3816 Hollywood Blvd (33021-6750)
PHONE....................................954 963-5090
Robert Goldfaden, *CEO*
EMP: 5 **EST:** 2004
SALES (est): 781.5K **Privately Held**
WEB: www.cosmesisskincare.com
SIC: 2844 Face creams or lotions

(G-5806)
CRYOTHRAPY PAIN RLIEF PDTS INC
3460 Laurel Oaks Ln (33021-8441)
PHONE....................................954 364-8192
Hugo Torres, *President*
Gustavo Romero, *Sales Mgr*
◆ **EMP:** 6 **EST:** 2004
SALES (est): 379.8K **Privately Held**
SIC: 2834 Pharmaceutical preparations

(G-5807)
CSI AEROSPACE INC
3000 Taft St (33021-4441)
PHONE....................................954 961-9800
Jon Walkup, *Principal*
EMP: 21 **EST:** 2017
SALES (est): 2.6MM **Publicly Held**
WEB: www.heico.com
SIC: 3724 Aircraft engines & engine parts
PA: Heico Corporation
3000 Taft St
Hollywood FL 33021

(G-5808)
DALE PHOTO AND DIGITAL INC
2960 Simms St (33020-1511)
PHONE....................................954 925-0103
Elaine Farkas, *CFO*
Juliana Farkas, *Director*
David Farkas, *Director*
EMP: 9 **EST:** 2010
SALES (est): 529.4K **Privately Held**
WEB: www.leicastoremiami.com
SIC: 3861 Photographic equipment & supplies

(G-5809)
DARNEL INC
Also Called: Crescent Garden
2331 Thomas St (33020-2038)
P.O. Box 10192, Uniondale NY (11555-0192)
PHONE....................................954 929-0085
Eli Papir, *President*
Paula Douer, *Vice Pres*
Joanne Papir, *Vice Pres*
Paul Siegel, *Accounts Mgr*
◆ **EMP:** 11 **EST:** 1974
SALES (est): 3.7MM **Privately Held**
WEB: www.darnelfabrics.com
SIC: 3089 Molding primary plastic

(G-5810)
DESIGNERS PLUMBING STUDIO INC
3040 N 29th Ave Ste F (33020-1312)
PHONE....................................954 920-5997
Maria De Fatima Rodriguez, *Director*
EMP: 6 **EST:** 2004
SALES (est): 376.9K **Privately Held**
WEB: www.designersplumbingstudio.com
SIC: 3432 Plumbing fixture fittings & trim

(G-5811)
DHSS LLC
Also Called: Sleep Group Solutions
2035 Harding St Ste 200 (33020-2797)
PHONE....................................305 830-0327
Frances Reschtszaid, *Principal*
EMP: 25 **EST:** 2017
SALES (est): 1.5MM **Privately Held**
WEB: www.health.mo.gov
SIC: 3841 Diagnostic apparatus, medical

(G-5812)
DISTINCTIVE CREAT INTR WKSHP I
2126 Pierce St (33020-4412)
PHONE....................................954 921-1861
Linda Crawford, *President*
Patricia Vanik, *Vice Pres*
EMP: 13 **EST:** 1983
SQ FT: 2,500
SALES (est): 1MM **Privately Held**
WEB: www.distinctiveworkroom.com
SIC: 2211 2392 Draperies & drapery fabrics, cotton; shade cloth, window: cotton; upholstery, tapestry & wall coverings: cotton; bedspreads & bed sets: made from purchased materials

(G-5813)
DREAMBOAT CANVAS LLC
3710 Harrison St Apt 3 (33021-7472)
PHONE....................................954 536-2415
Alexandrina Dec, *Principal*
EMP: 6 **EST:** 2013
SALES (est): 136.5K **Privately Held**
SIC: 2211 Canvas

(G-5814)
ECO CONCEPTS INC
3607 N 29th Ave (33020-1003)
P.O. Box 260850, Pembroke Pines (33026-7850)
PHONE....................................954 920-9700
EMP: 13
SALES (est): 3.4MM **Privately Held**
SIC: 2842 2841 Mfg Polishes & Sanitation Goods Soaps & Other Detergents

(G-5815)
ELECTRA AUTOMOTIVE CORP
1001 N 21st Ave (33020-3536)
PHONE....941 623-5563
George Burgos, *President*
EMP: 6 **EST:** 2016
SALES (est): 392.7K **Privately Held**
SIC: 3711 Cars, electric, assembly of

(G-5816)
ENSIDA ENERGY AFS LLC
2315 Sw 32nd Ave (33023-7709)
PHONE....954 364-2296
EMP: 6 **EST:** 2017
SALES (est): 162K **Privately Held**
WEB: www.ensidaenergy.com
SIC: 3714 Motor vehicle parts & accessories

(G-5817)
ESTUMKEDA LTD
Also Called: Micco Aircraft Company
6300 Stirling Rd (33024-2153)
PHONE....954 966-6300
Sandy Miller, *Manager*
Facundo Giacobbe, *Manager*
Rebecca Petrie, *Manager*
Allen Pettigrew, *Exec Dir*
Douglas Zepeda, *Tech/Comp Coord*
EMP: 13 **EST:** 1994
SQ FT: 40,000
SALES (est): 654.4K **Privately Held**
WEB: www.semtribe.com
SIC: 3721 Aircraft

(G-5818)
EVERGREEN SWEETENERS INC (PA)
1936 Hollywood Blvd # 20 (33020-4524)
PHONE....954 381-7776
Arthur Green, *CEO*
Tom Robinson, *General Mgr*
Craig Green, *Co-President*
William Green, *Co-President*
Carole Green, *Corp Secy*
◆ **EMP:** 10 **EST:** 1985
SQ FT: 4,107
SALES (est): 10.3MM **Privately Held**
WEB: www.esweeteners.com
SIC: 2099 5149 Sugar; sugar, refined

(G-5819)
FACTORY DIRECT CAB REFACING
1060 Scarlet Oak St (33019-4810)
PHONE....954 445-6635
Perry Blank, *Owner*
EMP: 9 **EST:** 2012
SALES (est): 236.5K **Privately Held**
WEB: www.factorydirectrenovations.com
SIC: 2434 Wood kitchen cabinets

(G-5820)
FASTSIGNS
2841 Hollywood Blvd (33020-4226)
PHONE....954 416-3434
Evren Brandao, *Owner*
Edson Brandao, *Sales Staff*
EMP: 10 **EST:** 2015
SALES (est): 287K **Privately Held**
WEB: www.fastsigns.com
SIC: 3993 5999 Signs & advertising specialties; banners, flags, decals & posters

(G-5821)
FINISHING GROUP OF FLORID
3997 Pembroke Rd (33021-8126)
PHONE....954 981-2171
John M Hofmann, *President*
EMP: 8 **EST:** 2017
SALES (est): 302.6K **Privately Held**
SIC: 3471 Plating & polishing

(G-5822)
FLORIDA FACTORY AGENTS INC
5701 Sheridan St (33021-3241)
PHONE....754 264-9432
Stanley Hernandez, *Principal*
EMP: 7 **EST:** 2018
SALES (est): 39.6K **Privately Held**
WEB: www.floridafactoryagents.com
SIC: 3999 Manufacturing industries

(G-5823)
FLORIDA RUM COMPANY LLC
Also Called: Ziami Distillery
2901 Simms St Unit D (33020-1510)
PHONE....305 791-1221
Victor Olshansky, *CEO*
EMP: 40 **EST:** 2017
SALES (est): 3.9MM **Privately Held**
WEB: www.ziamirum.com
SIC: 2085 2841 5087 2869 Distilled & blended liquors; neutral spirits, except fruit; soap & other detergents; cleaning & maintenance equipment & supplies; alcohols, non-beverage; alcohols, industrial: denatured (non-beverage); wines, brandy & brandy spirits; wines; wine coolers (beverages); bottling wines & liquors

(G-5824)
FMC MARKETING INC
2001 N 32nd Ave (33021-4423)
PHONE....201 417-1767
EMP: 6 **EST:** 2019
SALES (est): 91.5K **Privately Held**
SIC: 3544 Special dies, tools, jigs & fixtures

(G-5825)
FULL LF NATURAL HLTH PDTS LLC
1932 Hollywood Blvd (33020-4524)
PHONE....954 889-4019
Guido Guevara, *Principal*
EMP: 6 **EST:** 2007
SALES (est): 549.3K **Privately Held**
WEB: www.fulllifedirect.com
SIC: 2023 Dietary supplements, dairy & non-dairy based

(G-5826)
FULL LIFE DIRECT LLC
1932 Hollywood Blvd (33020-4524)
PHONE....800 305-3043
Joseph Kalachy,
EMP: 10 **EST:** 2017
SALES (est): 800K **Privately Held**
WEB: www.fulllifedirect.com
SIC: 2834 Vitamin preparations

(G-5827)
FUNCTION PLEASE LLC (PA)
Also Called: Sleep Please
2001 Tyler St Ste 5 (33020-4566)
PHONE....305 792-7900
Sandro Starna,
EMP: 4 **EST:** 2013
SQ FT: 3,000
SALES (est): 10.8MM **Privately Held**
SIC: 2023 5499 Dietary supplements, dairy & non-dairy based; vitamin food stores

(G-5828)
GOURMET PARISIEN INC
Also Called: Chef Philippe
1943 Sherman St (33020-2124)
P.O. Box 331007, Brooklyn NY (11233-7007)
PHONE....305 778-0756
Fermin Ribes, *President*
Pierre Bahri, *Vice Pres*
▲ **EMP:** 5 **EST:** 2008
SALES (est): 1.3MM **Privately Held**
WEB: www.compagniedesdesserts.com
SIC: 2024 Ice cream & frozen desserts
HQ: La Compagnie Des Desserts
Zone Industrielle Des Corbieres
Lezignan Corbieres 11200
468 276-288

(G-5829)
GRAPH-PLEX INC
2830 N 28th Ter (33020-1523)
PHONE....954 920-0905
Carl Schwartz, *President*
Denise Webster, *Corp Secy*
EMP: 16 **EST:** 1975
SQ FT: 3,000
SALES (est): 2.2MM **Privately Held**
WEB: www.graphplex.com
SIC: 3993 Displays & cutouts, window & lobby; signs, not made in custom sign painting shops

(G-5830)
GREEN BULLION FINCL SVCS LLC
3613 N 29th Ave (33020-1003)
PHONE....954 960-7000
Howard Mofsin,
EMP: 8 **EST:** 2007
SALES (est): 319.2K **Privately Held**
SIC: 3911 Jewelry, precious metal

(G-5831)
GREENGOOD ENERGY CORP
Also Called: Cngas Group
3389 Sheridan St Ste 410 (33021-3606)
PHONE....954 417-6117
Charles Wainer, *CEO*
Humberto Puppo, *COO*
Alejandro Dejtiar, *CTO*
EMP: 9 **EST:** 2008
SQ FT: 1,000
SALES (est): 6MM **Privately Held**
SIC: 3563 Air & gas compressors

(G-5832)
GREZZO USA LLC
1109 Pelican Ln (33019-5040)
PHONE....954 885-0331
Guillermo Rondon, *Principal*
Maria Diaz, *Principal*
EMP: 9 **EST:** 2019
SALES (est): 537.4K **Privately Held**
SIC: 3144 Women's footwear, except athletic

(G-5833)
GRIFFON GRAPHICS INC
Also Called: Le Soleil De La Floride
2117 Hollywood Blvd (33020-6706)
PHONE....954 922-1800
Yves Beauchamp, *CEO*
EMP: 7 **EST:** 1983
SALES (est): 696.5K **Privately Held**
WEB: www.lesoleildelafloride.com
SIC: 2711 Newspapers: publishing only, not printed on site

(G-5834)
GTECHUSA INC
3390 N 40th St (33021-1938)
PHONE....786 281-1803
Guy Ben AMI, *Principal*
EMP: 6 **EST:** 2011
SALES (est): 181.9K **Privately Held**
WEB: www.gtech-usa.com
SIC: 3572 Computer storage devices

(G-5835)
HARVEY BRANKER AND ASSOC PA
Also Called: Harvey Covington Thomas S Fla
3816 Hollywood Blvd # 203 (33021-6750)
PHONE....954 966-4445
Roderick Harvey, *General Ptnr*
EMP: 10 **EST:** 2000
SQ FT: 2,000
SALES (est): 634.5K **Privately Held**
SIC: 2759 8721 Commercial printing; accounting, auditing & bookkeeping

(G-5836)
HEALTHIER CHOICES MGT CORP (PA)
3800 N 28th Way (33020-1114)
PHONE....305 600-5004
Jeffrey Holman, *Ch of Bd*
Christopher Santi, *President*
John A Ollet, *CFO*
◆ **EMP:** 111 **EST:** 1987
SQ FT: 10,000
SALES: 13.9MM **Publicly Held**
WEB: www.healthiercmc.com
SIC: 2111 5411 Cigarettes; grocery stores

(G-5837)
HEICO AEROSPACE CORPORATION (DH)
3000 Taft St (33021-4441)
PHONE....954 987-6101
Eric A Mendelson, *CEO*
Luis J Morell, *President*
Steven Wall, *Business Mgr*
Jeff Biederwolf, *Vice Pres*
Vivian Miller, *Purch Agent*
▲ **EMP:** 31 **EST:** 1957
SQ FT: 140,000
SALES (est): 203.6MM **Publicly Held**
WEB: www.heico.com
SIC: 3724 3812 Aircraft engines & engine parts; search & navigation equipment
HQ: Heico Aerospace Holdings Corp.
3000 Taft St
Hollywood FL 33021
954 987-4000

(G-5838)
HEICO AEROSPACE HOLDINGS CORP (HQ)
3000 Taft St (33021-4441)
PHONE....954 987-4000
Eric Mendelson, *CEO*
Laurans Mendelson, *Principal*
James R Reum, *Exec VP*
Thomas S Irwin, *Treasurer*
Steven Walker, *Controller*
▲ **EMP:** 4 **EST:** 1997
SALES (est): 669.4MM **Publicly Held**
WEB: www.heico.com
SIC: 3724 Aircraft engines & engine parts

(G-5839)
HEICO AEROSPACE PARTS CORP
Also Called: Flight Specialties Components
300 Taft St (33019-3536)
PHONE....440 995-3661
David Peters, *Branch Mgr*
EMP: 6 **Publicly Held**
WEB: www.heico.com
SIC: 3724 Aircraft engines & engine parts
HQ: Heico Aerospace Parts Corporation
375 Alpha Park
Highland Heights OH 44143
954 987-6101

(G-5840)
HEICO CORPORATION (PA)
3000 Taft St (33021-4441)
PHONE....954 987-4000
Laurans A Mendelson, *Ch of Bd*
Eric A Mendelson, *President*
Victor H Mendelson, *President*
Niall Porter, *General Mgr*
Gregg Tuttle, *General Mgr*
▲ **EMP:** 372 **EST:** 1957
SQ FT: 7,000
SALES: 1.7B **Publicly Held**
WEB: www.heico.com
SIC: 3724 3728 7699 Aircraft engines & engine parts; aircraft training equipment; aircraft & heavy equipment repair services; aircraft flight instrument repair

(G-5841)
HEICO ELECTRONIC TECH CORP (HQ)
Also Called: Heico Electronic Tech Group
3000 Taft St (33021-4441)
PHONE....954 987-6101
Laurans A Mendelson, *CEO*
EMP: 40 **EST:** 1996
SQ FT: 5,000
SALES (est): 323.9MM **Publicly Held**
WEB: www.heico.com
SIC: 3724 Aircraft engines & engine parts

(G-5842)
HEICO FLIGHT SUPPORT CORP (HQ)
3000 Taft St (33021-4441)
PHONE....954 987-4000
Eric Mendelson, *President*
John Pfohl, *Opers Mgr*
Carlos L Macau, *CFO*
Carlos Macau, *Treasurer*
Nick Dague, *Director*
EMP: 25 **EST:** 2012
SALES (est): 63.3MM **Publicly Held**
WEB: www.heico.com
SIC: 3724 Aircraft engines & engine parts

(G-5843)
HOLLYWOOD LODGING INC
2601 N 29th Ave (33020-1508)
PHONE....305 803-7455
Nayan C Patel, *Principal*
EMP: 9 **EST:** 2015
SALES (est): 383.2K **Privately Held**
SIC: 2499 Wood products

(G-5844)
HOLLYWOOD MACHINE SHOP INC
5835 Rodman St (33023-1939)
PHONE..................................954 893-6103
Carlos A Delascagigas, *President*
EMP: 7 **EST:** 2009
SALES (est): 420K **Privately Held**
SIC: 3599 Machine shop, jobbing & repair

(G-5845)
HOLLYWOOD WOODWORK INC
2951 Pembroke Rd (33020-5634)
PHONE..................................954 920-5009
Yves Desmarais, *CEO*
Drake Barber, *Vice Pres*
Connie Fuller, *Vice Pres*
Paul Des Marais, *Vice Pres*
Ed Williams, *Project Mgr*
◆ **EMP:** 100 **EST:** 1968
SQ FT: 52,500
SALES (est): 25.9MM **Privately Held**
WEB: www.hollywoodwoodwork.com
SIC: 2431 Millwork

(G-5846)
HOLLYWOOD WOODWORK LLC
2951 Pembroke Rd (33020-5634)
PHONE..................................954 920-5009
Yves Demsmarais, *Mng Member*
Tony Parkinson,
Robert M Perrotti,
EMP: 14 **EST:** 2006
SQ FT: 5,000
SALES (est): 600.2K **Privately Held**
WEB: www.hollywoodwoodwork.com
SIC: 2431 Interior & ornamental woodwork & trim

(G-5847)
HURST AWNING COMPANY INC (PA)
3613 N 29th Ave (33020-1003)
P.O. Box 566330, Miami (33256-6330)
PHONE..................................305 693-0600
Garmendia Magali B, *President*
Frank S Cornelius, *President*
Garcia Jose Luis, *Vice Pres*
Maggie Garmendia, *Treasurer*
▼ **EMP:** 31 **EST:** 1957
SQ FT: 60,000
SALES (est): 3.6MM **Privately Held**
WEB: www.amdaluminum.com
SIC: 3444 Awnings, sheet metal

(G-5848)
INFUPHARMA LLC
6720 Tyler St (33024-7526)
PHONE..................................305 301-3389
Michel Rizo, *Principal*
EMP: 5 **EST:** 2008
SALES (est): 476.3K **Privately Held**
SIC: 2834 Pharmaceutical preparations

(G-5849)
J LEA LLC
Also Called: Grand Band
916 N 20th Ave (33020-3532)
PHONE..................................954 921-1422
Joy Ziefer,
EMP: 9 **EST:** 2010
SALES (est): 447.3K **Privately Held**
WEB: www.thegrandband.com
SIC: 3172 Wallets

(G-5850)
JA ENGINEERING II CORP (HQ)
3000 Taft St (33021-4441)
PHONE..................................954 744-7560
Thomas S Irwin, *Principal*
EMP: 1 **EST:** 2010
SALES (est): 5.2MM **Publicly Held**
WEB: www.heico.com
SIC: 3724 Aircraft engines & engine parts

(G-5851)
JAMES TESTA
Also Called: Testa & Sons Signs
5621 Johnson St (33021-5631)
PHONE..................................954 962-5840
James Testa, *Owner*
▼ **EMP:** 10 **EST:** 1969
SQ FT: 4,000
SALES (est): 1.1MM **Privately Held**
WEB: www.testasigns.com
SIC: 3993 Signs, not made in custom sign painting shops

(G-5852)
JC MARINE SERVICE FABRICA ✪
3000 N 22nd Ave (33020-1404)
PHONE..................................954 913-8185
EMP: 5 **EST:** 2020
SALES (est): 324.3K **Privately Held**
WEB: www.jcmarineservice.com
SIC: 3599 Industrial machinery

(G-5853)
JERAE INC
6031 Hollywood Blvd (33024-7935)
PHONE..................................954 989-6665
James Dauria, *Principal*
EMP: 10 **EST:** 2007
SALES (est): 291.6K **Privately Held**
SIC: 3089 Tires, plastic

(G-5854)
JET AVION CORPORATION
Also Called: Heico Parts Group
3000 Taft St (33021-4441)
PHONE..................................954 987-6101
Rick Stine, *President*
Mike Sego, *Senior VP*
Jack Lewis, *Vice Pres*
Vivian Miller, *Purch Agent*
Joe Randolph, *Project Engr*
▲ **EMP:** 70 **EST:** 1970
SQ FT: 140,000
SALES (est): 40.4MM **Publicly Held**
WEB: www.heico.com
SIC: 3724 Aircraft engines & engine parts
HQ: Heico Aerospace Holdings Corp.
3000 Taft St
Hollywood FL 33021
954 987-4000

(G-5855)
JRMETAL ORNAMENTAL
3725 Pembroke Rd Ste A11 (33021-8296)
PHONE..................................954 989-2607
Jose Obando, *Principal*
EMP: 8 **EST:** 2006
SALES (est): 277.7K **Privately Held**
WEB: www.jrmetalornamental.com
SIC: 3549 Metalworking machinery

(G-5856)
KEYSTONE 75 INC
Also Called: Best Made Flags
5620 Dewey St (33023-1916)
PHONE..................................954 430-1880
Greg Grant, *President*
EMP: 5 **EST:** 1974
SALES (est): 343K **Privately Held**
WEB: www.southfloridaflags.com
SIC: 2399 5999 Banners, pennants & flags; flags; banners

(G-5857)
L7 APPAREL & DENIM COMPANY LLC
1900 Taylor St (33020-4513)
PHONE..................................954 867-8124
Jeffery Gibbs, *Principal*
EMP: 6 **EST:** 2019
SALES (est): 46.5K **Privately Held**
SIC: 2211 Denims

(G-5858)
LEDRADIANT LLC
615 N 21st Ave (33020-4049)
PHONE..................................305 901-1313
Alfredo Kiersz, *Mng Member*
▲ **EMP:** 6 **EST:** 2014
SALES (est): 605K **Privately Held**
WEB: www.ledradiant.com
SIC: 3646 3229 Commercial indusl & institutional electric lighting fixtures; bulbs for electric lights

(G-5859)
LG-TEC CORPORATION
2021 Coolidge St (33020-2427)
PHONE..................................305 770-4005
Gustavo O Fazio, *President*
Hector O Huarte, *President*
◆ **EMP:** 8 **EST:** 2007
SQ FT: 7,000
SALES (est): 1.1MM **Privately Held**
WEB: www.lg-tec.com
SIC: 2241 Zipper tape

(G-5860)
LIGHTHOUSE EXPRESS WORLD INC
3880 N 28th Ter (33020-1118)
PHONE..................................754 210-6196
Caleb Outten, *President*
EMP: 7 **EST:** 2016
SALES (est): 234.8K **Privately Held**
WEB: www.lighthouseexpressworld.com
SIC: 2741 Miscellaneous publishing

(G-5861)
LIP TRADING CO
3460 N 34th Ave (33021-2507)
PHONE..................................954 987-0306
William Lipsitz, *President*
Malu Lipsitz, *Treasurer*
▼ **EMP:** 6 **EST:** 1975
SQ FT: 4,000
SALES (est): 454.2K **Privately Held**
SIC: 3861 5048 5043 Photographic equipment & supplies; ophthalmic goods; photographic equipment & supplies

(G-5862)
LOREN/WTP
3040 N 29th Ave (33020-1311)
PHONE..................................954 846-9800
EMP: 8 **EST:** 2016
SALES (est): 63.4K **Privately Held**
SIC: 3366 Machinery castings: brass

(G-5863)
LP WATCH GROUP INC
Also Called: Lucien Piccard
101 S State Road 7 # 201 (33023-6736)
PHONE..................................954 985-3827
David Koss, *President*
Sol Friedman, *Chairman*
Elena Koss, *Vice Pres*
Dev Dhar, *CFO*
▲ **EMP:** 20 **EST:** 2001
SQ FT: 38,000
SALES (est): 1.1MM **Privately Held**
SIC: 3873 5094 Clocks, assembly of; watches & parts

(G-5864)
LSJ CORP
2301 N 21st Ave (33020-2114)
PHONE..................................954 920-0905
Carl I Schwartz, *President*
EMP: 7 **EST:** 2005
SALES (est): 92.8K **Privately Held**
SIC: 3993 Signs & advertising specialties

(G-5865)
LUCIEN PICCARD/ARNEX WATCH CO
101 S State Road 7 # 201 (33023-6736)
PHONE..................................954 241-2745
Alexander Blau, *President*
Sol Mermelstein, *Vice Pres*
▲ **EMP:** 100 **EST:** 1983
SALES (est): 5.8MM **Privately Held**
SIC: 3873 Watches & parts, except crystals & jewels

(G-5866)
LUNION LOGISTICS LLC ✪
4000 Hollywood Blvd 555s (33021-6751)
PHONE..................................866 586-4660
Kathy Stfleur, *CEO*
EMP: 10 **EST:** 2021
SALES (est): 570.9K **Privately Held**
SIC: 3537 Trucks: freight, baggage, etc.: industrial, except mining

(G-5867)
MACGYVER MACHINE SERVICES INC
1722 Sheridan St (33020-2275)
PHONE..................................352 455-0413
Joseph Pacsuta, *Principal*
EMP: 6 **EST:** 2015
SALES (est): 109.6K **Privately Held**
SIC: 3599 Machine shop, jobbing & repair

(G-5868)
MADISON MILLWORK & CABINET CO
5746 Dawson St Ste A (33023-1908)
PHONE..................................954 966-7551
Glenn Hauser, *President*
EMP: 26 **EST:** 1997
SQ FT: 6,000
SALES (est): 2.4MM **Privately Held**
WEB: www.madisonmillwork.net
SIC: 2511 1751 Wood household furniture; cabinet & finish carpentry; cabinet building & installation; finish & trim carpentry

(G-5869)
MARINIZE PRODUCTS CORP
3986 Pembroke Rd (33021-8127)
PHONE..................................954 989-7990
Martin Panich, *CEO*
Gary Edwards, *Treasurer*
EMP: 7 **EST:** 1986
SALES (est): 248.8K **Privately Held**
SIC: 2842 Cleaning or polishing preparations

(G-5870)
MAS EDITORIAL CORP
Also Called: 305 Media Solutions
1596 Trailhead Ter (33021-1410)
PHONE..................................305 748-0124
Martin Rodriguez Gambaro, *President*
EMP: 6 **EST:** 2015
SALES (est): 336.5K **Privately Held**
SIC: 7372 2721 Publishers' computer software; magazines: publishing & printing

(G-5871)
MAXOGEN GROUP LLC
2719 Hollywood Blvd (33020-4821)
PHONE..................................305 814-0734
Eugene Zavolotsky, *CEO*
EMP: 45 **EST:** 2015
SALES (est): 1MM **Privately Held**
WEB: www.maxogengroup.com
SIC: 3824 Mechanical & electromechanical counters & devices

(G-5872)
MAYERS JWLY CO HOLLYWOOD INC (PA)
Also Called: W C Edge Jewelry Co Division
2002 Grant St (33020-3546)
PHONE..................................954 921-1422
Sam Ziefer, *President*
Martin Gayer, *Corp Secy*
▼ **EMP:** 55
SQ FT: 15,000
SALES (est): 4.5MM **Privately Held**
SIC: 3911 Jewelry, precious metal

(G-5873)
MAYMAAN RESEARCH LLC
3904 N 29th Ave (33020-1010)
PHONE..................................954 374-9376
Eitan Shmueli, *Principal*
EMP: 7 **EST:** 2019
SALES (est): 244.7K **Privately Held**
WEB: www.maymaan.com
SIC: 3621 Motors & generators

(G-5874)
MERIT DIAMOND CORPORATION
1900 Tyler St Fl 3 (33020-4517)
PHONE..................................954 883-3660
Gagi Kaplan, *Ch of Bd*
Neil Bobrow, *COO*
Josef Fraiman, *Exec VP*
Gerson Delgado, *Asst Director*
▲ **EMP:** 30 **EST:** 1981
SQ FT: 15,000
SALES (est): 4.5MM **Privately Held**
WEB: www.meritdiamond.com
SIC: 3911 Jewelry, precious metal

(G-5875)
METRO SIGNS INC
Also Called: Wrapfink
1220 S State Road 7 (33023-6711)
PHONE..................................954 410-4343
Bruno V Dede, *President*
David Metrosigns, *Sales Executive*
Abbey Freese, *Marketing Staff*
Sofia Christina, *Manager*
Jose Alfonso, *Creative Dir*

EMP: 25 **EST:** 1993
SALES (est): 3.8MM **Privately Held**
WEB: www.metrogroupmiami.com
SIC: 3993 Electric signs

(G-5876)
MIA LED LIGHTING INC
2925 Adams St (33020-4717)
PHONE..................................786 440-2856
Jorge L Diaz, *President*
EMP: 6 **EST:** 2016
SALES (est): 222.7K **Privately Held**
SIC: 3648 Lighting equipment

(G-5877)
MILLER SIGNS LLC
2501 N 69th Ave (33024-3750)
PHONE..................................786 395-9420
Rodolfo Baldini, *Principal*
EMP: 7 **EST:** 2016
SALES (est): 55.7K **Privately Held**
WEB: www.millersignsllc.com
SIC: 3993 Signs & advertising specialties

(G-5878)
MOHAWK INDUSTRIES INC
2500 Sw 32nd Ave (33023-7703)
PHONE..................................918 272-0184
EMP: 8 **EST:** 2019
SALES (est): 277.4K **Privately Held**
WEB: www.mohawkind.com
SIC: 2273 Finishers of tufted carpets & rugs

(G-5879)
MOLD R US INC
6596 Taft St (33024-4009)
PHONE..................................954 850-6653
Doron Ibgui, *Principal*
EMP: 5 **EST:** 2010
SALES (est): 467.7K **Privately Held**
WEB: www.moldrus.net
SIC: 3544 Industrial molds

(G-5880)
NATURAL HATS AND MORE LLC
5801 Wiley St (33023-2355)
PHONE..................................954 549-0819
EMP: 23
SALES (corp-wide): 64.5K **Privately Held**
SIC: 2353 Hats, caps & millinery
PA: Natural Hats And More Llc
307 Sw 2nd Ave
Dania FL

(G-5881)
NEOCABINET INC
1623 Plunkett St (33020-6443)
PHONE..................................310 927-1008
Georgy Proskuryakov, *Principal*
EMP: 7 **EST:** 2017
SALES (est): 76.2K **Privately Held**
WEB: www.neocabinet.com
SIC: 2434 Wood kitchen cabinets

(G-5882)
NEX-XOS WORLDWIDE LLC (PA)
Also Called: Xmre
3922 Pembroke Rd (33021-8127)
PHONE..................................305 433-8376
Saul Mishkin, *President*
Juan Shehin, *COO*
Harold Rabinowitz, *Controller*
Nani Chlimper, *Natl Sales Mgr*
Nani Chlinper, *Sales Mgr*
EMP: 14 **EST:** 2010
SQ FT: 21,250
SALES (est): 4MM **Privately Held**
WEB: www.nex-xos.com
SIC: 2099 Packaged combination products: pasta, rice & potato

(G-5883)
NIBA DESIGNS INC (PA)
Also Called: Niba Collections
3609 N 29th Ave (33020-1003)
PHONE..................................305 456-6230
Beth Arrowood, *CEO*
John Berryman, *President*
Manny Hodak, *CFO*
Laura Tonello, *Regl Sales Mgr*
Whitney Roberts, *Sales Staff*
EMP: 10 **EST:** 2006
SALES (est): 3.7MM **Privately Held**
WEB: www.nibadesigns.com
SIC: 2273 2299 Carpets & rugs; linen fabrics

(G-5884)
NOTE IT
Also Called: Bee Inspired Handmade
915 Weeping Willow Way (33019-4811)
PHONE..................................954 593-8616
Patti Ruiter, *Owner*
EMP: 7 **EST:** 2008
SALES (est): 205.6K **Privately Held**
SIC: 2759 5199 Invitations: printing; gifts & novelties

(G-5885)
OCON ENTERPRISE INC
821 N 21st Ave (33020-3505)
P.O. Box 221721 (33022-1721)
PHONE..................................954 920-6700
Don J O'Connell, *President*
A Dawn O'Connell, *CFO*
EMP: 81 **EST:** 1985
SQ FT: 10,000
SALES (est): 7MM **Privately Held**
SIC: 3911 5094 Jewelry, precious metal; jewelry

(G-5886)
PALLADIO BEAUTY GROUP LLC
3912 Pembroke Rd (33021-8127)
PHONE..................................954 922-4311
Philip Solomon,
EMP: 15 **EST:** 2012
SALES (est): 1.6MM **Privately Held**
WEB: www.palladiobeauty.com
SIC: 2844 Toilet preparations

(G-5887)
PB GROUP LLC
Also Called: Palladio Beauty Group
3912 Pembroke Rd (33021-8127)
PHONE..................................954 922-4311
Philip Solomon, *CEO*
Cristina Martinho, *Vice Pres*
Lee Khandeece, *Marketing Staff*
Maria Torres, *Manager*
Kayla Ciruolo, *Creative Dir*
▲ **EMP:** 20
SQ FT: 15,000
SALES (est): 4.1MM **Privately Held**
WEB: www.palladiobeauty.com
SIC: 2844 5199 Toilet preparations; general merchandise, non-durable

(G-5888)
PEERLESS INSTRUMENT CO INC
2030 Coolidge St (33020-2428)
PHONE..................................954 921-6006
Thomas Brady, *President*
Martin Ignac, *Vice Pres*
Daniel A Lippiello, *Vice Pres*
Paul Sadhai, *Plant Supt*
Dustin Johnson, *Production*
EMP: 38 **EST:** 1968
SQ FT: 16,000
SALES (est): 4.1MM **Privately Held**
WEB: www.peerlessinstrument.com
SIC: 3599 Machine shop, jobbing & repair

(G-5889)
PEMBROKE OFFICE INDUSTRIES LLC
1500 S 66th Ave (33023-2103)
PHONE..................................954 589-1329
Luiz C Gastaldo, *Director*
EMP: 6 **EST:** 2014
SALES (est): 250.1K **Privately Held**
SIC: 3999 Manufacturing industries

(G-5890)
PERFECTUS PET FOOD LLC
3300 Oakwood Blvd (33020-7104)
PHONE..................................800 774-3296
Donald Radcliffe, *CEO*
Gregory Eastwood, *Vice Pres*
EMP: 5 **EST:** 2019
SQ FT: 3,000
SALES (est): 438.8K **Privately Held**
WEB: www.perfectuspetfood.com
SIC: 2048 Dry pet food (except dog & cat)

(G-5891)
PHG KENDALL LLC
Also Called: Prime Hotel Group US
4651 Sheridan St Ste 480 (33021-3430)
PHONE..................................954 392-8788
Larry M Abbo, *CEO*
Patrick King, *Purchasing*
Bob Wilkins, *Purchasing*
Leonardo Benatar, *Project Engr*
Mariano Macchi, *Accounting Mgr*
EMP: 19 **EST:** 2009
SALES (est): 9.5MM **Privately Held**
SIC: 3241 3429 Cement, hydraulic; builders' hardware

(G-5892)
PLASTIX USA LLC
900 N Federal Hwy Ste 104 (33020-3589)
PHONE..................................305 891-0091
ARI A Birol,
Eda Birol,
▲ **EMP:** 82 **EST:** 2011
SALES (est): 5MM **Privately Held**
WEB: www.plastixdunnage.com
SIC: 2673 3086 Plastic bags: made from purchased materials; packaging & shipping materials, foamed plastic

(G-5893)
PODGO PRINTING LLC
3810 N 29th Ave (33020-1008)
PHONE..................................954 874-9100
Robert Podgorowiez, *President*
Mitchell I Podgorowiez,
EMP: 6 **EST:** 2019
SALES (est): 395.5K **Privately Held**
WEB: www.podgoprinting.com
SIC: 2752 Commercial printing, offset

(G-5894)
PREFERRED SIGNS INC
1906 N Dixie Hwy (33020-2340)
PHONE..................................954 922-0126
Howard Weber, *President*
Mark Weber, *Vice Pres*
EMP: 9 **EST:** 1973
SQ FT: 8,000
SALES (est): 833.4K **Privately Held**
WEB: www.preferredsigns.com
SIC: 3993 Electric signs

(G-5895)
PRINTSHAQCOM INC
1654 Jackson St (33020-5110)
PHONE..................................954 678-7286
Annette Filecci, *Principal*
EMP: 7 **EST:** 2011
SALES (est): 119.6K **Privately Held**
WEB: www.printshaq.com
SIC: 2752 Commercial printing, lithographic

(G-5896)
PUBLI SIGNS
250 N Dixie Hwy Unit 5 (33020-6736)
PHONE..................................954 927-4411
Gerard Bensadon, *Principal*
EMP: 5 **EST:** 2007
SALES (est): 412.6K **Privately Held**
WEB: www.publisigns.com
SIC: 3993 Electric signs

(G-5897)
QUALITEL INC
2414 N Federal Hwy (33020-2234)
PHONE..................................954 464-3991
Jeronimo Monteiro, *Principal*
EMP: 22 **EST:** 2009
SALES (est): 458.9K **Privately Held**
WEB: www.qualitel.com
SIC: 3672 Printed circuit boards

(G-5898)
QUALITY SCREEN ENCLOSURE LLC
3800 Hillcrest Dr Apt 210 (33021-7937)
PHONE..................................954 226-1980
Pavel A Lebedev, *Manager*
EMP: 6 **EST:** 2017
SALES (est): 403.1K **Privately Held**
WEB: www.qualityscreenenclosure.com
SIC: 3448 Screen enclosures

(G-5899)
QUIET TECHNOLOGY AEROSPACE INC
4100 N 29th Ter (33020-1022)
PHONE..................................305 687-9808
Fernando Birbragher, *CEO*
Barry Fine, *President*
Ben Brown, *Vice Pres*
Richard Brown, *Vice Pres*
Martha Durand, *Controller*
▲ **EMP:** 47 **EST:** 2000
SQ FT: 50,029
SALES (est): 9.5MM **Privately Held**
WEB: www.qtaerospace.com
SIC: 3728 Aircraft parts & equipment

(G-5900)
R R H INC
Also Called: Advanced Color Graphics Group
5900 Johnson St (33021-5638)
P.O. Box 531518, Miami (33153-1518)
PHONE..................................954 966-1209
Rudy Ambra, *CEO*
Harry Jordan, *President*
EMP: 15 **EST:** 1981
SQ FT: 4,500
SALES (est): 351.2K **Privately Held**
SIC: 2752 Commercial printing, offset

(G-5901)
RICKEYS WORLD FAMOUS SAUCE INC
4799 Hollywood Blvd (33021-6503)
PHONE..................................954 829-9464
Evelyn Mitchell, *CEO*
William Mitchell, *President*
Lisa Solito, *Vice Pres*
◆ **EMP:** 15 **EST:** 1955
SQ FT: 4,000
SALES (est): 318.8K **Privately Held**
SIC: 2035 Pickles, sauces & salad dressings

(G-5902)
RODEN INTERNATIONAL INC (PA)
2806 N 29th Ave (33020-1506)
PHONE..................................954 929-1900
Gabriela Berenstein, *President*
Victor Berenstein, *Treasurer*
▲ **EMP:** 18 **EST:** 1989
SQ FT: 12,000
SALES (est): 1.2MM **Privately Held**
WEB: www.zackusa.com
SIC: 3914 3469 Stainless steel ware; table tops, porcelain enameled

(G-5903)
RSD INDUSTRIES INC
1612 Funston St (33020-6412)
PHONE..................................954 240-3660
Robert S Driscoll, *Principal*
EMP: 6 **EST:** 2009
SALES (est): 73.7K **Privately Held**
SIC: 3999 Manufacturing industries

(G-5904)
SCHEDUALL SCHEDUALL SCHEDUALL
2719 Hollywood Blvd (33020-4821)
PHONE..................................954 334-5400
Isis Thomson, *Human Res Mgr*
EMP: 10 **EST:** 2019
SALES (est): 718.3K **Privately Held**
WEB: www.xytechsystems.com
SIC: 2741 Miscellaneous publishing

(G-5905)
SEA AND SHORE CUSTOM CANVAS UP
3629 Washington St (33021-8215)
PHONE..................................954 983-3060
EMP: 5
SALES (est): 344.5K **Privately Held**
SIC: 2211 Cotton Broadwoven Fabric Mill

(G-5906)
SEIMENS INDUSTRIES INC
3402 Bridge Rd (33026-1244)
PHONE..................................954 364-6600
Sheermohame Zulfiquar, *Manager*
EMP: 7 **EST:** 2014
SALES (est): 144.2K **Privately Held**
SIC: 3999 Manufacturing industries

GEOGRAPHIC

(G-5907)
SERV-PAK CORP
5844 Dawson St (33023-1910)
PHONE..................................954 962-4262
Joel Mahler, *President*
◆ **EMP:** 10 **EST:** 1984
SQ FT: 4,000
SALES (est): 1MM **Privately Held**
WEB: www.serv-pak.com
SIC: 3081 2759 Packing materials, plastic sheet; commercial printing

(G-5908)
SIMULATED ENVMT CONCEPTS INC
Also Called: SEC
3937 Pembroke Rd (33021-8126)
PHONE..................................754 263-3184
Ella Frenkel, *President*
Allen Licht, *COO*
Ilya Spivak, *Vice Pres*
◆ **EMP:** 16 **EST:** 1993
SQ FT: 5,000
SALES (est): 2.2MM **Privately Held**
SIC: 3634 Massage machines, electric, except for beauty/barber shops

(G-5909)
SMART SNACKS LLC
2007 Johnson St (33020-3508)
PHONE..................................954 860-8833
Tammy Cohen, *Managing Dir*
EMP: 6 **EST:** 2012
SALES (est): 483.5K **Privately Held**
SIC: 2052 Cookies

(G-5910)
SNAPPY STRUCTURES INC
Also Called: Agg International
2324 Hayes St (33020-3440)
PHONE..................................954 926-6611
Joe Sparacino, *President*
▲ **EMP:** 15 **EST:** 1974
SQ FT: 12,000
SALES (est): 411K **Privately Held**
WEB: www.snappyusa.com
SIC: 3354 3441 Aluminum extruded products; fabricated structural metal

(G-5911)
SOLUTION ASSET MANAGEMENT LLC
1918 Harrison St (33020-5081)
PHONE..................................786 288-9408
EMP: 8
SALES (est): 602.1K **Privately Held**
SIC: 1389 Oil/Gas Field Services

(G-5912)
SOUTH BROWARD PRINTING INC
Also Called: Sir Speedy
5845 Hollywood Blvd Ste C (33021-6312)
PHONE..................................954 962-1309
Dan Lotford, *President*
Brian Doerner, *Sales Executive*
▼ **EMP:** 5 **EST:** 1972
SALES (est): 357.2K **Privately Held**
WEB: www.sirspeedy.com
SIC: 2752 2791 2789 Commercial printing, lithographic; typesetting; bookbinding & related work

(G-5913)
SPA COVER INC
Also Called: Douglas Marine
2310 Hayes St (33020-3440)
PHONE..................................954 923-8801
Judith L Brosseau, *President*
▼ **EMP:** 12 **EST:** 1981
SQ FT: 12,000
SALES (est): 2.7MM **Privately Held**
WEB: www.spacoverinc.net
SIC: 3999 Hot tub & spa covers

(G-5914)
SPARKS CABINETRY
1685 S State Road 7 (33023-6700)
PHONE..................................954 367-2750
Dennis Getsee, *Principal*
EMP: 7 **EST:** 2013
SALES (est): 187.8K **Privately Held**
WEB: www.sparkscabinetry.com
SIC: 2434 Wood kitchen cabinets

(G-5915)
STANLEY INDUSTRIES OF S FLA (PA)
Also Called: Gallery Industries
3001 S Ocean Dr Apt 1423 (33019-2874)
PHONE..................................954 929-8770
Robert Alexander, *President*
Steven Alexander, *Corp Secy*
Jerome Alexander, *Vice Pres*
◆ **EMP:** 9 **EST:** 1976
SQ FT: 6,000
SALES (est): 654K **Privately Held**
SIC: 2325 2321 2335 2331 Men's & boys' trousers & slacks; men's & boys' furnishings; women's, juniors' & misses' dresses; women's & misses' blouses & shirts; textiles, woven; cloth cutting, bolting or winding

(G-5916)
SUN-ART DESIGNS INC
2808 N 29th Ave (33020-1506)
PHONE..................................954 929-6622
Yoave Bitton, *President*
Shahar Bitton, *Business Anlyst*
▼ **EMP:** 20 **EST:** 1989
SQ FT: 22,000
SALES (est): 908.1K **Privately Held**
WEB: www.sunartdesign.com
SIC: 3999 7336 Barber & beauty shop equipment; silk screen design

(G-5917)
SUNRAY REFLECTIONS INC
956 Harrison St (33019-1623)
PHONE..................................305 305-6350
Jeffrey Langer, *Director*
EMP: 8 **EST:** 2001
SALES (est): 152.3K **Privately Held**
WEB: www.colorreflections.com
SIC: 3993 Signs & advertising specialties

(G-5918)
SUNSHINE DRIVEWAYS INC
7750 Nw 35th St (33024-2213)
P.O. Box 841123 (33084-3123)
PHONE..................................954 394-7373
Danilo A De Jesus, *President*
EMP: 6 **EST:** 2006
SALES (est): 63.2K **Privately Held**
SIC: 3271 Paving blocks, concrete

(G-5919)
SURF STYLE INC
4100 N 28th Ter (33020-1116)
PHONE..................................954 926-6666
Doron Malinasky, *President*
Eliyahu Levy, *Vice Pres*
EMP: 30 **EST:** 1989
SQ FT: 20,000
SALES (est): 721.4K **Privately Held**
WEB: www.surfstyle.com
SIC: 2329 Men's & boys' sportswear & athletic clothing

(G-5920)
TAIE INC (PA)
Also Called: Minuteman Press
4171 N State Road 7 (33021-1510)
PHONE..................................954 966-0233
Saied Taie Tehrani, *President*
Kevin Taie, *Vice Pres*
Keven Taie Tehrani, *Vice Pres*
Rhea E Taie Tehrani, *Treasurer*
Diane Bryan, *Office Mgr*
EMP: 11 **EST:** 1983
SQ FT: 3,600
SALES (est): 1.9MM **Privately Held**
WEB: www.chanhassen-mn.minutemanpress.com
SIC: 2752 2789 2759 Commercial printing, lithographic; bookbinding & related work; commercial printing

(G-5921)
TAKE A BED LLC
1915 Hollywood Blvd (33020-4546)
PHONE..................................407 734-8857
Fernando Fortini,
EMP: 7 **EST:** 2017
SALES (est): 193K **Privately Held**
WEB: www.takeabed.com
SIC: 7372 Application computer software

(G-5922)
TER PRINTS USA INC
Also Called: Miami Offset
3613 N 29th Ave (33020-1003)
PHONE..................................305 953-7789
Kurlandski Guy, *President*
Serhat Ilicak, *President*
◆ **EMP:** 30 **EST:** 1999
SQ FT: 65,000
SALES (est): 1.4MM **Privately Held**
SIC: 2711 Newspapers

(G-5923)
TERMINE RAVIOLI MANUFACTURING (PA)
Also Called: Mimi's Ravioli
5714 Johnson St (33021-5634)
PHONE..................................954 983-3711
Frank Billisi, *President*
Linda Billisi, *Co-Owner*
EMP: 10 **EST:** 1972
SQ FT: 10,000
SALES (est): 1.6MM **Privately Held**
WEB: www.mimisravioli.com
SIC: 2098 5499 5149 Macaroni products (e.g. alphabets, rings & shells), dry; gourmet food stores; macaroni

(G-5924)
TIAS MILKSHAKES AND MORE
6768 Stirling Rd (33024-1844)
PHONE..................................954 391-8753
Aracelis Caraballo, *Principal*
EMP: 9 **EST:** 2011
SALES (est): 280.8K **Privately Held**
SIC: 2026 Yogurt

(G-5925)
TREBOR USA CORP
Also Called: Door Shop, The
3901 N 29th Ave (33020-1009)
PHONE..................................954 922-1620
Gratien Proulx, *President*
Micheline Proulx, *President*
Jocelyn Vinet, *Vice Pres*
Marcia Doyle Krutek, *CFO*
Yves Surprenant, *Admin Sec*
◆ **EMP:** 11 **EST:** 1999
SALES (est): 2.4MM **Privately Held**
WEB: www.treborusa.com
SIC: 3442 Metal doors

(G-5926)
TRIARCH INTERNATIONAL INC
Also Called: Triach Industries
4811 Sarazen Dr (33021-2367)
PHONE..................................305 622-3400
Bernard Rogover, *President*
David Labell, *Exec VP*
Howard Rogover, *Vice Pres*
◆ **EMP:** 14 **EST:** 1973
SQ FT: 94,838
SALES (est): 1.4MM **Privately Held**
WEB: www.triarchindustries.com
SIC: 3648 Lighting equipment

(G-5927)
TRICAB (USA) INC
3876 Pembroke Rd (33021-8108)
PHONE..................................754 210-5490
Arthur Raymond, *President*
EMP: 7 **EST:** 2015
SALES (est): 301.6K **Privately Held**
SIC: 3357 Nonferrous wiredrawing & insulating

(G-5928)
TRIUMPH HOSIERY CORP
4624 Hollywood Blvd # 205 (33021-6526)
PHONE..................................954 929-6021
Ed Solomon, *President*
Ann Solomon, *Chairman*
Scott Solomon, *Vice Pres*
Gloria Herrera, *Executive Asst*
▲ **EMP:** 8 **EST:** 1990
SALES (est): 1MM **Privately Held**
WEB: www.triumphhosiery.com
SIC: 2251 2252 Women's hosiery, except socks; hosiery

(G-5929)
TROPICAL DVRSONS MRINA MGT INC
3200 N 29th Ave (33020-1313)
PHONE..................................954 922-0387
Douglas Sherron, *Principal*
EMP: 7 **EST:** 2010
SALES (est): 225.7K **Privately Held**
SIC: 3732 Yachts, building & repairing

(G-5930)
TRUTH NUTRITION LLC
4302 Hollywood Blvd # 16 (33021-6635)
PHONE..................................754 400-0382
EMP: 8 **EST:** 2014
SALES (est): 873.7K **Privately Held**
WEB: www.truthnutrition.com
SIC: 2834 Vitamin, nutrient & hematinic preparations for human use

(G-5931)
TURBINE KINETICS INC
3000 Taft St (33021-4441)
PHONE..................................954 744-7526
Victor Mendelson, *President*
Kevin Keating, *Engineer*
EMP: 51 **EST:** 2001
SALES (est): 10.5MM **Publicly Held**
WEB: www.heico.com
SIC: 3724 Aircraft engines & engine parts
HQ: Heico Aerospace Holdings Corp.
3000 Taft St
Hollywood FL 33021
954 987-4000

(G-5932)
UMA HOLDINGS INC
601 S 21st Ave (33020-6905)
PHONE..................................786 587-1349
Juan Villegas, *CEO*
EMP: 20 **EST:** 2005
SALES (est): 346.3K **Privately Held**
SIC: 3711 5012 Automobile assembly, including specialty automobiles; automotive brokers

(G-5933)
UNIVERSALMS INC
711 S 20th Ave Apt 7 (33020-6984)
PHONE..................................786 285-7531
Dennis P Bost, *President*
EMP: 5
SALES (est): 500K **Privately Held**
WEB: www.universalms.com
SIC: 7372 Application computer software

(G-5934)
URBAN EXTREME LLC
4303 Hayes St (33021-5363)
PHONE..................................954 248-9007
Daniel Shnader, *Manager*
EMP: 10 **EST:** 2015
SALES (est): 876.9K **Privately Held**
SIC: 3949 Playground equipment

(G-5935)
USA CORP AIRPLANE
4601 Sheridan St (33021-3440)
PHONE..................................954 399-8472
Natasha Chipiga, *Principal*
EMP: 6 **EST:** 2016
SALES (est): 142K **Privately Held**
SIC: 3714 Motor vehicle parts & accessories

(G-5936)
VENCO MARINE INC
2012 Hayes St (33020-3552)
P.O. Box 222526 (33022-2526)
PHONE..................................954 923-0036
Magnar Venoy, *President*
Gabriel Molina, *Office Mgr*
▲ **EMP:** 8 **EST:** 1997
SALES (est): 588.8K **Privately Held**
WEB: www.vencomarine.com
SIC: 2842 3699 Specialty cleaning, polishes & sanitation goods; security control equipment & systems

(G-5937)
VIVE CREOLE LLC
Also Called: Haitian Community Yellow Pages
2500 Hollywood Blvd (33020-6615)
PHONE..................................954 607-1925
Luna Clerveaux, *Exec Officer*
Jose Bonny,
Monette Salnave,
EMP: 6
SQ FT: 1,200
SALES (est): 27K **Privately Held**
SIC: 2721 Magazines: publishing & printing

(G-5938)
VOLVOX INC HOLLYWOOD
Also Called: Erwad Real Estate
537 N Rainbow Dr (33021-6021)
PHONE..................................954 961-4942
Ron Stanish, *President*
Alan Stanish, *President*
Dane Stanish, *Production*
Jean Stanish, *Treasurer*
Andrew Stanish, *Sales Mgr*
EMP: 8
SALES (est): 400K **Privately Held**
SIC: 3949 6531 Fishing equipment; real estate agent, residential

(G-5939)
WALKER GRAPHICS INC
2039 Coolidge St B (33020-2427)
PHONE..................................954 964-1688
Michaell P Walker, *President*
Michael P Walker, *President*
EMP: 9 **EST:** 1982
SALES (est): 801.6K **Privately Held**
WEB: www.walker-graphics.co.uk
SIC: 2796 2791 Platemaking services; typesetting

(G-5940)
WILLIAM LAROQUE INSTALLERS INC
Also Called: W.L. Installers
5820 Sheridan St (33021-3244)
PHONE..................................305 769-1717
William Laroque, *President*
Claudia Laroque, *Vice Pres*
Jorge Barco, *Manager*
▼ **EMP:** 23 **EST:** 1992
SQ FT: 7,000
SALES (est): 2.9MM **Privately Held**
WEB: www.wlinstallers.com
SIC: 3535 5084 Conveyors & conveying equipment; industrial machinery & equipment

(G-5941)
WORLD EMBLEM INTERNATIONAL INC (PA)
4601 Sheridan St Ste 300 (33021-3433)
PHONE..................................305 899-9006
Randy Carr, *President*
Jamie Carr, *Vice Pres*
Moran Idith, *Vice Pres*
Tony Morando, *Vice Pres*
Nicolas Restrepo, *Vice Pres*
EMP: 225 **EST:** 1993
SQ FT: 35,000
SALES (est): 36.5MM **Privately Held**
WEB: www.worldemblem.com
SIC: 2395 Emblems, embroidered

(G-5942)
WORLDWIDE AUTO SYSTEMS CORP
900 Tallwood Ave Apt 307 (33021-7918)
PHONE..................................954 439-6332
Ana Diaz Duenas, *President*
EMP: 10 **EST:** 2012
SALES (est): 871.8K **Privately Held**
SIC: 3711 8011 Ambulances (motor vehicles), assembly of; freestanding emergency medical center

(G-5943)
WORLDWIDE INTL TRADE LLC
601 S 21st Ave (33020-6905)
PHONE..................................305 414-9774
Mary Sangio, *CFO*
Juan Villegas, *Mng Member*
EMP: 47 **EST:** 2018
SALES (est): 1.6MM **Privately Held**
SIC: 3751 5012 Motorcycles & related parts; motorcycles

(G-5944)
Z HAYDU MANUFACTURING CORP
1980 Grant St (33020-3544)
P.O. Box 223596 (33022-3596)
PHONE..................................954 925-1779
James Haydu, *President*
John Haydu, *Vice Pres*
Shannon Sease, *Admin Sec*
EMP: 9 **EST:** 1975
SQ FT: 7,500
SALES (est): 662K **Privately Held**
WEB: www.zhaydumfg.com
SIC: 3841 3495 Surgical & medical instruments; wire springs

(G-5945)
ZACHEY DESIGN MARBLE INC
1649 Moffett St 4 (33020-6544)
PHONE..................................754 367-6261
Dumitru Marginean, *President*
EMP: 7 **EST:** 2005
SALES (est): 130.8K **Privately Held**
SIC: 3281 Marble, building: cut & shaped

Holmes Beach
Manatee County

(G-5946)
MACBONNER INC
Also Called: Macbonner Computer Services
315 58th St Unit J (34217-1555)
PHONE..................................941 778-7978
Bonner Joy, *President*
EMP: 11 **EST:** 1992
SALES (est): 770.7K **Privately Held**
WEB: www.islander.org
SIC: 2711 Newspapers: publishing only, not printed on site

(G-5947)
TORTILLA BAY
5318 Marina Dr (34217-1709)
PHONE..................................941 778-3663
Perry Pittman, *Owner*
EMP: 9 **EST:** 2007
SALES (est): 239.8K **Privately Held**
WEB: www.tortilla-bay.com
SIC: 2099 Tortillas, fresh or refrigerated

Holt
Okaloosa County

(G-5948)
CERTIFIED MANUFACTURING INC
583 Armistead Blvd (32564-9166)
PHONE..................................850 537-3777
Pamela B Bechtold, *President*
John Bailie, *President*
Robert W Bechtold, *Vice Pres*
Robert Bechtold, *Vice Pres*
Marliyn Rogers, *CFO*
EMP: 40 **EST:** 1998
SQ FT: 32,000
SALES (est): 7.8MM **Privately Held**
WEB: www.certifiedmfg.com
SIC: 3643 3677 3672 Current-carrying wiring devices; electronic coils, transformers & other inductors; printed circuit boards

(G-5949)
PRESTON WORKS INC
Also Called: Creative Metal Works
599 Armistead Blvd (32564-9166)
PHONE..................................850 932-0888
Robert Preston, *Owner*
Michelle Preston, *Office Mgr*
EMP: 8 **EST:** 2006
SALES (est): 800K **Privately Held**
SIC: 3499 Fire- or burglary-resistive products

(G-5950)
TRINITY EXTERIOR SOLUTIONS LLC
4292 Sundance Way (32564-9153)
P.O. Box 4082, Milton (32572-4082)
PHONE..................................850 393-9682
Debra Lorinczy, *Principal*
EMP: 7 **EST:** 2016
SALES (est): 360K **Privately Held**
SIC: 3299 1742 1771 Stucco; exterior insulation & finish (EIFS) applicator; exterior concrete stucco contractor

Homestead
Miami-Dade County

(G-5951)
A BETTER KITCHEN CABINETS INC
28501 Sw 152nd Ave (33033-1456)
PHONE..................................786 234-1897
Mylene J Romero, *President*
EMP: 6 **EST:** 2013
SALES (est): 124.4K **Privately Held**
SIC: 2434 Wood kitchen cabinets

(G-5952)
ACDM-PMS INC
Also Called: Princeton Machine Shop
25331 Sw 142nd Ave (33032-5424)
P.O. Box 924459, Princeton (33092-4459)
PHONE..................................305 258-0347
Dallas McGlothin, *Chairman*
Catherine McGlothlin, *Administration*
Catherine McGlothin, *Admin Sec*
EMP: 5 **EST:** 1974
SQ FT: 4,800
SALES (est): 451.9K **Privately Held**
SIC: 3599 Machine shop, jobbing & repair

(G-5953)
ADDISON METAL ADDITIONS INC
20231 Sw 321st St (33030-5118)
PHONE..................................305 245-9860
Mark Addison, *Principal*
EMP: 8 **EST:** 2007
SALES (est): 256.5K **Privately Held**
WEB: www.addisonmetal.com
SIC: 3442 Shutters, door or window: metal

(G-5954)
AQUA TECHNOLOGIES
815 N Homestead Blvd (33030-5024)
PHONE..................................305 246-2125
Brian Judge, *Principal*
EMP: 7 **EST:** 2010
SALES (est): 156.4K **Privately Held**
SIC: 3089 Plastics products

(G-5955)
ARESSCO TECHNOLOGIES INC
15600 Sw 288th St Ste 307 (33033-1223)
PHONE..................................305 245-5854
Robert Houston, *President*
Michael J Marcus, *Vice Pres*
◆ **EMP:** 8 **EST:** 1998
SALES (est): 87K
SALES (corp-wide): 272K **Privately Held**
SIC: 3699 Security control equipment & systems
PA: Hs Gateway Holdings Inc
15600 Sw 288th St Ste 307
Homestead FL 33033
305 245-5854

(G-5956)
B & K INSTALLATIONS INC
246 Sw 4th Ave (33030-7077)
PHONE..................................305 245-6968
William E Berzowski, *President*
Joseph M Kurilla, *Vice Pres*
▼ **EMP:** 45
SQ FT: 85,000
SALES (est): 7MM **Privately Held**
WEB: www.bkinstall.com
SIC: 3441 3444 3448 3231 Fabricated structural metal; sheet metalwork; greenhouses: prefabricated metal; products of purchased glass

(G-5957)
CEMEX CNSTR MTLS FLA LLC
Also Called: Cx1 Miami Mobile Mix
15900 Sw 408th St (33034)
PHONE..................................305 247-3011
EMP: 19 **Privately Held**
SIC: 3273 Ready-mixed concrete
HQ: Cemex Construction Materials Florida, Llc
1501 Belvedere Rd
West Palm Beach FL 33406

(G-5958)
COMPLETE MOLD REMEDIATORS INC
31800 Sw 195th Ave (33030-5202)
PHONE..................................305 903-8885
Lisa M Brang, *Principal*
EMP: 9 **EST:** 2015
SALES (est): 877.8K **Privately Held**
WEB: www.cmr-moldremoval.com
SIC: 3544 Industrial molds

(G-5959)
CONTENDER BOATS INC
1820 Se 38th Ave (33035-1345)
PHONE..................................305 230-1600
Joseph Neber, *CEO*
Irving Smith, *COO*
Stephen Cunningham, *Vice Pres*
Robert Desantis, *Engineer*
Maria Cordova, *CFO*
◆ **EMP:** 200
SQ FT: 80,000
SALES (est): 75.2MM **Privately Held**
WEB: www.contenderboats.com
SIC: 3732 Boat building & repairing

(G-5960)
CUSTOMFAB INC
23601 Sw 133rd Ave (33032-2306)
PHONE..................................786 339-9158
EMP: 6 **EST:** 2016
SALES (est): 85.6K **Privately Held**
WEB: www.customfabusa.com
SIC: 3498 Fabricated pipe & fittings

(G-5961)
DE TODOS TORTILLAS INC
820 N Krome Ave (33030-4407)
PHONE..................................305 248-4402
Borges Edson G Jr, *Principal*
EMP: 7 **EST:** 2014
SALES (est): 326.8K **Privately Held**
SIC: 2099 Tortillas, fresh or refrigerated

(G-5962)
DECO TRUSS COMPANY INC
13980 Sw 252nd St (33032-5406)
P.O. Box 924868 (33092-4868)
PHONE..................................305 257-1910
Sonia Espineira, *Corp Secy*
Mario R Espineira, *Vice Pres*
Mario Estinera, *Executive*
◆ **EMP:** 50 **EST:** 1983
SQ FT: 45,616
SALES (est): 7.8MM **Privately Held**
WEB: www.decotruss.com
SIC: 2439 5072 Trusses, wooden roof; hardware

(G-5963)
DISCIPLINE MARKETING INC
Also Called: Galileo
21230 Sw 246th St (33031-3653)
PHONE..................................305 793-7358
Michael Whittmeyer, *President*
Mary Whittmeyer, *Vice Pres*
▲ **EMP:** 13 **EST:** 1988
SALES (est): 537.4K **Privately Held**
SIC: 3827 Binoculars

(G-5964)
DUENAS MOBILE APPLICATIONS LLC (PA)
Also Called: Vuziq
15600 Sw 288th St Ste 402 (33033-1223)
PHONE..................................305 851-3397
Carlos Duenas, *Mng Member*
Danny Duenas,
EMP: 44 **EST:** 2012
SALES (est): 455.5K **Privately Held**
SIC: 7372 Application computer software

(G-5965)
GO LATINOS MAGAZINE LLC
13345 Sw 264th Ter (33032-7789)
PHONE..................................786 601-7693
Ervin Palacios, *Principal*
EMP: 7 **EST:** 2015
SALES (est): 132.3K **Privately Held**
WEB: www.golatinos.net
SIC: 2711 Newspapers, publishing & printing

GEOGRAPHIC

(G-5966)
H&K HOME SUPPLIES DISTRS LLC ✪
10818 Sw 240th St (33032-4309)
PHONE....................................786 308-6024
Keniel Pena,
EMP: 10 **EST:** 2020
SALES (est): 283.4K **Privately Held**
SIC: 2051 7389 Bakery: wholesale or wholesale/retail combined;

(G-5967)
HOMESTEAD DIAGNOSTIC CTR INC
650 Ne 22nd Ter Ste 100 (33033-4710)
PHONE....................................305 246-5600
Tomas Gonzales, *President*
EMP: 18 **EST:** 1999
SALES (est): 2.2MM **Privately Held**
WEB: www.homestead-diagnostic.com
SIC: 3829 8071 Medical diagnostic systems, nuclear; testing laboratories

(G-5968)
HOMESTEAD NEWSPAPERS INC
Also Called: South Dade News Leader
125 Ne 8th St Ste 2 (33030-4676)
P.O. Box 900340 (33090-0340)
PHONE....................................305 245-2311
Gary K Shorts, *President*
Charles P Smith, *Exec VP*
Shirley C Ellis, *Vice Pres*
Stanley M Ellis, *Vice Pres*
Glenn A Martin, *Vice Pres*
EMP: 1392 **EST:** 1912
SQ FT: 6,000
SALES (est): 1.5MM
SALES (corp-wide): 114.9MM **Privately Held**
WEB: www.southdadenewsleader.com
SIC: 2711 Newspapers, publishing & printing
PA: Calkins Media Incorporated
8400 Bristol Pike
Levittown PA 19057
215 949-4000

(G-5969)
HORSESHOE PICKING INC
21400 Sw 392nd St (33034-6811)
PHONE....................................305 345-5778
Leonard Talarico, *Principal*
EMP: 11 **EST:** 2007
SALES (est): 213.6K **Privately Held**
SIC: 3462 Horseshoes

(G-5970)
IGS LLC
27901 Sw 129th Ct (33032-8538)
PHONE....................................800 419-3014
EMP: 6 **EST:** 2019
SALES (est): 162.1K **Privately Held**
WEB: www.youronlinepublicist.com
SIC: 2741 Miscellaneous publishing

(G-5971)
INNOVATIVE HEAT CONCEPTS LLC
127 Sw 5th Ave (33030-7035)
PHONE....................................305 248-4971
Michael Valles, *Principal*
EMP: 9 **EST:** 2010
SALES (est): 122.9K **Privately Held**
WEB: www.innovativeheatconcepts.com
SIC: 3433 Heating equipment, except electric

(G-5972)
INSTITUTIONAL PRODUCTS INC
1011 Nw 6th St (33030-5624)
PHONE....................................305 248-4955
Geymonat Ivan, *CEO*
Ingrid L Crespo, *President*
Ana Maria Moran, *CFO*
▲ **EMP:** 25 **EST:** 1971
SQ FT: 15,000
SALES (est): 4.5MM **Privately Held**
WEB: www.institutionalproductsinc.com
SIC: 3083 1751 Plastic finished products, laminated; cabinet building & installation

(G-5973)
INTELLIGENT HEATER LLC
127 Sw 5th Ave (33030-7035)
P.O. Box 2005, Alpharetta GA (30023-2005)
PHONE....................................305 248-4971
Bosonto Gupta, *Mng Member*
▲ **EMP:** 8 **EST:** 1946
SQ FT: 30,000
SALES (est): 1.5MM **Privately Held**
WEB: www.intelligentheater.com
SIC: 3634 3822 3567 3625 Immersion heaters, electric: household; liquid level controls, residential or commercial heating; oven temperature controls, non-industrial type; electrical furnaces, ovens & heating devices, exc. induction; relays & industrial controls

(G-5974)
J & A CUSTOM CABINETRY INC
15825 Sw 285th St (33033-6108)
PHONE....................................786 255-4181
Joseph Siddons, *Principal*
EMP: 8 **EST:** 2008
SALES (est): 884.3K **Privately Held**
WEB: www.jnacabinetry.net
SIC: 2434 Wood kitchen cabinets

(G-5975)
KEYSTONE PRECAST & COLUMNS COR
29630 Sw 183rd Ct (33030-3034)
PHONE....................................305 216-5375
Miguel A Dana Sr, *Principal*
EMP: 5 **EST:** 2005
SALES (est): 332.2K **Privately Held**
WEB: www.keystoneprecast.com
SIC: 3272 Concrete products, precast

(G-5976)
KEYSTONE PRODUCTS INC
1414 Nw 3rd Ave (33034-2225)
PHONE....................................305 245-4716
Peter Joseph Santi, *President*
Doug Santi, *Corp Secy*
Jim Santi, *Treasurer*
Vincenzo Santi, *Treasurer*
◆ **EMP:** 17 **EST:** 1976
SQ FT: 3,000
SALES (est): 2.2MM **Privately Held**
WEB: www.keystonecoralproducts.com
SIC: 3281 1411 Stone, quarrying & processing of own stone products; dimension stone

(G-5977)
KONCEPT SYSTEMS LLC
10755 Sw 244th Ter (33032-4686)
PHONE....................................786 610-0122
Ernesto Blanco, *Branch Mgr*
EMP: 24
SALES (corp-wide): 2.6MM **Privately Held**
WEB: www.konceptsystems.com
SIC: 3646 3651 3648 Commercial indusl & institutional electric lighting fixtures; audio electronic systems; speaker systems; stage lighting equipment; arc lighting fixtures
PA: Koncept Systems Llc
15802 Sylvan Lake Dr
Houston TX 77062
800 773-4910

(G-5978)
L AND TW OODWORK LLC
17420 Sw 236th St (33031-3507)
PHONE....................................305 742-4362
Tommy Jimenez, *Principal*
EMP: 7 **EST:** 2019
SALES (est): 427.7K **Privately Held**
SIC: 2431 Millwork

(G-5979)
LANDMARK PRECAST LLC
438 Nw 10th Ave (33030-5764)
P.O. Box 902033 (33090-2033)
PHONE....................................305 242-8888
Roger Tomasiono,
Steven Sproul,
EMP: 10 **EST:** 2004
SALES (est): 3.1MM **Privately Held**
WEB: www.landmarkprecast.com
SIC: 3272 Concrete products

(G-5980)
LEEWARD TECH
815 N Homestead Blvd # 405 (33030-5024)
PHONE....................................305 215-4526
Carlos Mauro, *Principal*
EMP: 9 **EST:** 2008
SALES (est): 453.9K **Privately Held**
SIC: 3679 4513 Electronic components; package delivery, private air

(G-5981)
LUMO PRINT INC
27750 S Dixie Hwy (33032-8222)
PHONE....................................305 246-0003
Moe Mohammed Hakssa, *President*
EMP: 5 **EST:** 1981
SQ FT: 1,200
SALES (est): 470.3K **Privately Held**
WEB: www.lumoprint.com
SIC: 2752 Commercial printing, offset

(G-5982)
MATTIS AEROSPACE
26085 S Dixie Hwy (33032-6613)
PHONE....................................305 910-2377
Melissa Vega, *President*
Kyle Quintero, *Purchasing*
Robert Mattis, *Info Tech Mgr*
EMP: 7 **EST:** 2013
SALES (est): 129.2K **Privately Held**
WEB: www.mattis.aero
SIC: 3728 Aircraft parts & equipment

(G-5983)
MIAMI TRANSFORMERS CORP
13935 Sw 252nd St (33032-5405)
PHONE....................................305 257-1491
Javier O Vila, *President*
Jorge J Vila, *Treasurer*
◆ **EMP:** 31 **EST:** 1995
SQ FT: 7,480
SALES (est): 2.2MM **Privately Held**
WEB: www.miamitransformers.com
SIC: 3612 Transformers, except electric

(G-5984)
MOORE & BODE GROUP LLC
2221 Se 27th Dr (33035-1329)
P.O. Box 140221, Coral Gables (33114-0221)
PHONE....................................786 615-9389
Sharon Moore Bode, *President*
Roberto E Bode, *Vice Pres*
EMP: 7 **EST:** 1984
SALES (est): 402.7K **Privately Held**
WEB: www.mooreandbode.com
SIC: 2121 Cigars

(G-5985)
NATURAL CRVINGS PET TREATS LLC
1100 Nw 7th St (33030-6695)
PHONE....................................786 404-8099
Patrick Caprez, *President*
▼ **EMP:** 5 **EST:** 2014
SALES (est): 5MM **Privately Held**
WEB: www.naturalcravingsusa.com
SIC: 2047 Dog & cat food

(G-5986)
NEX SOFTWARE LLC
29690 Sw 183rd Ct (33030-3034)
PHONE....................................786 200-3396
Allan Gobin, *Principal*
EMP: 7 **EST:** 2010
SALES (est): 271.5K **Privately Held**
SIC: 7372 Prepackaged software

(G-5987)
PETS2GO INTERNATIONAL INC
Also Called: Conquistador Management Group
2301 Se 23rd Ter (33035-1907)
PHONE....................................404 625-9606
Angelina Cortez, *CEO*
Blair Blacker, *President*
EMP: 49 **EST:** 2015
SALES (est): 2.1MM **Privately Held**
SIC: 3999 2399 Pet supplies; pet collars, leashes, etc.: non-leather

(G-5988)
PLANT SOLUTIONS INC
15901 Sw 272nd St (33031-3103)
PHONE....................................305 242-3103
Lionelt Marquez, *President*
Margaret Marquez, *President*
◆ **EMP:** 21 **EST:** 1993
SQ FT: 720
SALES (est): 4.1MM **Privately Held**
WEB: www.plantsolutionsinc.com
SIC: 2873 2874 Plant foods, mixed: from plants making nitrog. fertilizers; plant foods, mixed: from plants making phosphatic fertilizer

(G-5989)
RAPID SIGNS AND T SHIRTS
27466 S Dixie Hwy (33032-8213)
PHONE....................................786 486-2804
Olga D Lopez, *President*
EMP: 7 **EST:** 2017
SQ FT: 2,000
SALES (est): 432.8K **Privately Held**
WEB: www.rapidsignsandtshirts.com
SIC: 3993 Signs & advertising specialties

(G-5990)
SAM S ACCRSIO SONS PKG PROD IN
1225 Nw 2nd St (33030-5619)
P.O. Box 901767 (33090-1767)
PHONE....................................305 246-3455
Sam S Accursio Jr, *President*
Phyllis Accursio, *Corp Secy*
EMP: 10 **EST:** 1994
SQ FT: 30,923
SALES (est): 454.3K **Privately Held**
SIC: 2033 Vegetables: packaged in cans, jars, etc.

(G-5991)
SATEN LEAF NURSERY INC
13822 Sw 282nd Ter (33033-5725)
PHONE....................................305 216-5340
Elmer Guandique, *President*
EMP: 13 **EST:** 2005
SALES (est): 674.8K **Privately Held**
SIC: 2221 Satins

(G-5992)
SCHNEBLY REDLANDS WINERY INC
30205 Sw 217th Ave (33030-7601)
PHONE....................................786 247-2060
Peter Schnebly, *President*
Milton Montanez, *Facilities Mgr*
Denisse Schnebly, *Manager*
Dewey Losasso, *Director*
▲ **EMP:** 20 **EST:** 2004
SQ FT: 26,440
SALES (est): 2.9MM **Privately Held**
WEB: www.schneblywinery.com
SIC: 2084 Wines

(G-5993)
SMITTYS BOAT TOPS AND MAR EQP
Also Called: Smittys Boat Tops Sndwner Bats
23701 Sw 212th Ave (33031-1072)
PHONE....................................305 245-0229
William P Crowley, *President*
Robin Crowley, *Vice Pres*
▼ **EMP:** 6 **EST:** 1986
SQ FT: 10,000
SALES (est): 188.3K **Privately Held**
SIC: 2394 2426 2221 3548 Canvas & related products; chair seats, hardwood; glass & fiberglass broadwoven fabrics; welding & cutting apparatus & accessories; welding repair; boat building & repairing

(G-5994)
SOLARBEAM INTERNATIONAL INC
15600 Sw 288th St Ste 307 (33033-1223)
PHONE....................................305 248-8400
Robert Houston, *President*
Robin Marcus, *CFO*
EMP: 7 **EST:** 2007
SALES (est): 572.7K **Privately Held**
WEB: www.solarbeam.com
SIC: 3674 Solar cells

(G-5995)
STEELE DEFENSE LLC
480 Se 26th Dr (33033-5279)
PHONE.....786 610-0857
Charles Steele, *Manager*
EMP: 5 **EST:** 2018
SALES (est): 323.3K **Privately Held**
SIC: 3812 Defense systems & equipment

(G-5996)
TES AMERICA LLC
10867 Sw 235th Ln (33032-6318)
P.O. Box 835602, Miami (33283-5602)
PHONE.....786 393-2544
Diego Henao, *Mng Member*
EMP: 6 **EST:** 2016
SALES (est): 292.1K **Privately Held**
WEB: www.tesamerica.wixsite.com
SIC: 7692 Welding repair

(G-5997)
Y C ALUMINUM WELDING CORP
23701 Sw 132nd Ave Unit 2 (33032-2408)
PHONE.....786 255-7186
Carlos M Heredia, *Branch Mgr*
EMP: 7
SALES (corp-wide): 211.1K **Privately Held**
WEB: www.ycweldingpro.com
SIC: 7692 Welding repair
PA: Y C Aluminum Welding Corp
13800 Sw 143rd St Unit D
Miami FL

(G-5998)
YM WELDING SERVICES INC
28715 Sw 132nd Ave (33033-7442)
PHONE.....502 905-4651
Ernesto Mola, *President*
EMP: 6 **EST:** 2019
SALES (est): 27.6K **Privately Held**
SIC: 7692 Welding repair

Homosassa
Citrus County

(G-5999)
AEB TECHNOLOGIES INC
Also Called: Lunasea Lighting
9619 W Yulee Dr (34448-4105)
PHONE.....352 417-0009
Allen Burley, *CEO*
Bill Vengrofski, *Engineer*
Steve Jordan, *Controller*
▲ **EMP:** 7 **EST:** 1982
SQ FT: 12,000
SALES (est): 917.3K **Privately Held**
WEB: www.lunasealighting.com
SIC: 3575 7373 Computer terminals, monitors & components; computer integrated systems design

(G-6000)
CALIBER ELEMENTS LLC
9020 W Veterans Dr (34448-1488)
PHONE.....352 697-1415
Eric Willis,
EMP: 10 **EST:** 2013
SALES (est): 1.8MM **Privately Held**
WEB: www.caliberelements.com
SIC: 2819 Industrial inorganic chemicals

(G-6001)
CAPITAL STEEL INC
6260 S Tex Pt (34448-5922)
PHONE.....352 628-1700
Phil Bailey, *President*
James Gristwood, *Vice Pres*
David A Peters, *Vice Pres*
EMP: 10 **EST:** 2006
SQ FT: 1,000
SALES (est): 2.3MM **Privately Held**
SIC: 3441 Fabricated structural metal

(G-6002)
DIESELSITE INC
7400 W Industrial Ln # 6 (34448-5909)
PHONE.....888 414-3457
Robert T Riley, *Principal*
▲ **EMP:** 7 **EST:** 2012
SALES (est): 907.5K **Privately Held**
WEB: www.dieselsite.com
SIC: 3462 Automotive forgings, ferrous: crankshaft, engine, axle, etc.

(G-6003)
EASY FOAM INC
4 Calendula Ct W (34446-5933)
P.O. Box 4255, Grand Junction CO (81502-4255)
PHONE.....970 927-0209
Gregory Larson, *President*
Donald Cochran, *Vice Pres*
EMP: 12 **EST:** 2010
SQ FT: 8,000
SALES (est): 318.9K **Privately Held**
SIC: 2841 Detergents, synthetic organic or inorganic alkaline

(G-6004)
GULF COAST READY MIX LLC
8778 W Jump Ct (34448-2323)
PHONE.....352 621-3900
Wallace Hindalong,
Crystal Nelson, *Admin Asst*
Pete Nelson, *Admin Asst*
Amber Litle, *Administration*
Lonnie G Gardner,
EMP: 20 **EST:** 2002
SQ FT: 1,700
SALES (est): 4.9MM **Privately Held**
WEB: www.gulfcoastreadymix.com
SIC: 3273 3271 Ready-mixed concrete; concrete block & brick

(G-6005)
SCREEN MONKEY CORP
5841 W Kime Ln (34448-7330)
PHONE.....352 746-7091
Jeffrey P Scott, *President*
Denise A Scott, *Vice Pres*
EMP: 6 **EST:** 2010
SALES (est): 535.3K **Privately Held**
WEB: www.thescreenmonkey.com
SIC: 2759 1799 Commercial printing; screening contractor: window, door, etc.

(G-6006)
SPORTS RADAR LTD
7397 S Suncoast Blvd (34446-3406)
PHONE.....352 503-6825
Nevin C Jenkins, *Mng Member*
Rande Newberry, *Mng Member*
▲ **EMP:** 6 **EST:** 1991
SALES (est): 786.2K **Privately Held**
WEB: www.sportsradargun.com
SIC: 3663 3949 3812 Radio broadcasting & communications equipment; sporting & athletic goods; search & navigation equipment

Horseshoe Beach
Dixie County

(G-6007)
HORSESHOE SHRIMP BOAT LLC
77 Main St (32648-2100)
P.O. Box 383 (32648-0383)
PHONE.....352 356-1982
Donna J Futch, *Manager*
EMP: 7 **EST:** 2016
SALES (est): 472.9K **Privately Held**
SIC: 3462 Horseshoes

Hosford
Liberty County

(G-6008)
CP LOGGING INC
20688 Ne Burlington Rd (32334-2709)
PHONE.....850 379-8698
Gilford E Pullam, *President*
Anne Pullam, *Admin Sec*
EMP: 10 **EST:** 1999
SALES (est): 953.7K **Privately Held**
SIC: 2411 7389 Logging camps & contractors;

(G-6009)
G BLACK LOGGING LLC
15698 Ne Moore St (32334-2432)
P.O. Box 106 (32334-0106)
PHONE.....850 379-8747
Gary E Black, *Mng Member*
EMP: 6 **EST:** 2013
SALES (est): 739.8K **Privately Held**
SIC: 2411 Logging

(G-6010)
PAUL WHITE LOGGING INC
65 South (32334)
P.O. Box 113 (32334-0113)
PHONE.....850 379-8651
Kenneth P King, *President*
EMP: 5 **EST:** 1950
SALES (est): 483.4K **Privately Held**
SIC: 2411 4212 Timber, cut at logging camp; timber trucking, local

(G-6011)
RICHARD BROWN LOGGING INC
18534 Ne State Road 65 (32334-2849)
P.O. Box 298 (32334-0298)
PHONE.....850 379-8674
Richard G Brown Sr, *President*
EMP: 10 **EST:** 1987
SALES (est): 374.1K **Privately Held**
SIC: 2411 4212 Logging camps & contractors; lumber & timber trucking

Howey In The Hills
Lake County

(G-6012)
SILVER SPRINGS CITRUS INC
25411 N Mare Ave (34737-3124)
P.O. Box 155 (34737-0155)
PHONE.....352 324-2101
Kenny Sadai, *Ch of Bd*
James O'Toole, *President*
Vince Petrucci, *Vice Pres*
Thomas Kolb, *CFO*
Dennis Parker, *Sales Mgr*
◆ **EMP:** 220 **EST:** 1921
SQ FT: 1,260
SALES (est): 29.6MM **Privately Held**
SIC: 2086 2037 Pasteurized & mineral waters, bottled & canned; fruit juices, frozen

(G-6013)
SILVER SPRINGS CITRUS LLC
25411 N Mare Ave (34737-3124)
PHONE.....352 324-2101
Sadai Kenichiro, *Manager*
EMP: 23 **EST:** 2017
SALES (est): 747.3K **Privately Held**
SIC: 2086 Pasteurized & mineral waters, bottled & canned

Hudson
Pasco County

(G-6014)
ADDTAD PARTNERS INC
Also Called: P&L Machine and Tool Co
9704 Katy Dr Ste 2 (34667-4397)
PHONE.....727 863-0847
Alan Dorval, *President*
Trudy Dorval, *Treasurer*
EMP: 6 **EST:** 2014
SQ FT: 4,500
SALES (est): 518.9K **Privately Held**
SIC: 3599 Machine & other job shop work

(G-6015)
ALL ISLAND SIGNS
14803 Us Highway 19 (34667-3354)
PHONE.....631 676-3498
Ruth Clayton, *Owner*
EMP: 6 **EST:** 2008
SALES (est): 205.9K **Privately Held**
SIC: 3993 Signs, not made in custom sign painting shops

(G-6016)
BETTER MIX
9301 Denton Ave (34667-4340)
PHONE.....800 232-6833
Chuck Jackson, *Manager*
EMP: 16 **EST:** 2014
SALES (est): 2MM **Privately Held**
WEB: www.betermix.com
SIC: 3273 Ready-mixed concrete

(G-6017)
CABINET DREAMS & THINGS INC
13954 Sand Oak Ct (34669-1367)
PHONE.....727 514-0847
Debra Barker-Sudnik, *Principal*
EMP: 6 **EST:** 2014
SALES (est): 282.8K **Privately Held**
WEB: www.cabinetdreamsandthings.com
SIC: 2434 Wood kitchen cabinets

(G-6018)
CLEAR HORIZON VENTURES COMPANY
Also Called: Petersen Metals
9410 Eden Ave (34667-5202)
PHONE.....727 372-1100
Paul Schoettelkotte, *President*
Matt Palmer, *Vice Pres*
Shannon Wilson, *Vice Pres*
EMP: 21 **EST:** 2010
SALES (est): 3MM **Privately Held**
WEB: www.grecorailings.com
SIC: 3446 Balconies, metal

(G-6019)
COASTAL CRAFTSMEN ALUMINUM INC (PA)
15046 Labor Pl (34667-3477)
P.O. Box 5606 (34674-5606)
PHONE.....727 868-8802
Bill Woodard, *President*
▲ **EMP:** 30 **EST:** 1980
SQ FT: 7,200
SALES (est): 4.7MM **Privately Held**
WEB: www.coastalcraftsmen.com
SIC: 3448 1799 Screen enclosures; fence construction

(G-6020)
D & I CARBIDE TOOL CO INC
12104 Parkwood St (34669-3790)
PHONE.....727 848-3356
Fax: 727 848-3374
EMP: 10
SQ FT: 5,000
SALES (est): 800K **Privately Held**
SIC: 3441 Mfg Fabricated Structural Metal Specializing In Carbide Wear Parts

(G-6021)
DONE RIGHT FIRE GEAR REPR INC
7621 Maryland Ave (34667-3290)
PHONE.....727 848-9019
Pat Gansert, *President*
Anna Collins, *COO*
Teri Moulton, *CFO*
Renee Costanzo, *Office Mgr*
EMP: 7 **EST:** 2005
SALES (est): 603K **Privately Held**
WEB: www.gearwash.com
SIC: 3569 7699 Firefighting apparatus & related equipment; fire control (military) equipment repair

(G-6022)
DONS CABINETS AND WOODWORKING
Also Called: General Cabinets Pasco County
15801 Archer St (34667-3817)
PHONE.....727 863-3404
Donald J Josephik, *President*
EMP: 10 **EST:** 1999
SQ FT: 15,000
SALES (est): 2MM **Privately Held**
WEB: www.generalcabinets.com
SIC: 2434 2542 2522 2521 Wood kitchen cabinets; partitions & fixtures, except wood; office furniture, except wood; wood office furniture; wood television & radio cabinets

(G-6023)
FIESTA MARINE PRODUCTS INC
Also Called: Fiesta Pontoon Boats
11016 State Road 52 (34669-3047)
PHONE..................................727 856-6900
Carl Morahan, *President*
EMP: 12 **EST:** 1996
SQ FT: 10,000
SALES (est): 876.4K **Privately Held**
WEB: www.fiestaboats.com
SIC: 3732 Pontoons, except aircraft & inflatable

(G-6024)
FLORIDA ENGINEERED CONSTRU
Also Called: Castcrete
16835 Us Highway 19 (34667-4318)
PHONE..................................727 863-7451
Mike Hardy, *Manager*
EMP: 8
SALES (corp-wide): 28.5MM **Privately Held**
WEB: www.castcrete.com
SIC: 3272 Concrete products
PA: Florida Engineered Construction Products Corporation
6324 County Road 579
Seffner FL 33584
813 621-4641

(G-6025)
FLOWERS BKG CO BRADENTON LLC
Also Called: Flowers Baking Company
16721 Us Highway 19 (34667-4316)
PHONE..................................941 758-5656
Chris Peer, *Manager*
EMP: 25
SALES (corp-wide): 4.3B **Publicly Held**
WEB: www.flobradconf.com
SIC: 2051 Bread, cake & related products
HQ: Flowers Baking Co. Of Bradenton, Llc
6490 Parkland Dr
Sarasota FL 34243

(G-6026)
GRECO ALUM RAILINGS USA INC
9410 Eden Ave (34667-5202)
PHONE..................................727 372-4545
EMP: 24 **EST:** 2002
SALES (est): 4.9MM
SALES (corp-wide): 419.2MM **Publicly Held**
WEB: www.grecorailings.com
SIC: 3446 Railings, prefabricated metal
PA: Csw Industrials, Inc.
5420 Lyndon B Johnson Fwy
Dallas TX 75240
214 884-3777

(G-6027)
GREENWOOD LAKE NEWS INC (PA)
Also Called: Greenwood Lk & W Milford News
13032 Pinnacle Ln (34669-2403)
PHONE..................................845 477-2575
Ann Chaimowitz, *President*
EMP: 10
SQ FT: 1,000
SALES (est): 782.3K **Privately Held**
SIC: 2711 Newspapers: publishing only, not printed on site

(G-6028)
GULF VIEW PLASTICS INC
18816 Oak Way Dr (34667-5139)
PHONE..................................727 379-3072
Donna Boyle, *Principal*
Russ Boyle, *Accounts Mgr*
EMP: 5 **EST:** 2010
SALES (est): 416.9K **Privately Held**
WEB: www.gulfviewplastics.com
SIC: 3089 Injection molding of plastics

(G-6029)
INNEVAPE LLC
9718 Katy Dr Ste 2 (34667-5207)
PHONE..................................631 957-6500
Thomas Klingensmith, *Principal*
EMP: 7 **EST:** 2016
SALES (est): 761.2K **Privately Held**
WEB: www.innevape.com
SIC: 3999 Cigar & cigarette holders

(G-6030)
K L DISTRIBUTING INC
7425 Sailfish Dr (34667-3250)
PHONE..................................415 800-2158
Lola Lindon, *Manager*
EMP: 9 **EST:** 1995
SALES (est): 46.5K **Privately Held**
WEB: www.kldistributing.com
SIC: 2211 Bandages, gauzes & surgical fabrics, cotton

(G-6031)
KINGSTON AUTOMOTIVE & WLDG LLC
8039 Palatine Dr (34667-3545)
PHONE..................................727 378-4881
Edwin Kingston, *Principal*
EMP: 9 **EST:** 2019
SALES (est): 661.4K **Privately Held**
WEB: www.kingston-automotive-and-welding.business.site
SIC: 7692 Automotive welding

(G-6032)
MADE FUR YOU INC (PA)
18112 Thomas Blvd (34667-5848)
PHONE..................................813 444-7707
Joanna D Silva, *President*
EMP: 6 **EST:** 2012
SALES (est): 116.6K **Privately Held**
WEB: www.madefuryou.com
SIC: 3999 Furs

(G-6033)
MADE FUR YOU INC
12121 Little Rd (34667-2924)
PHONE..................................813 444-7707
Joanna D Lee, *Branch Mgr*
EMP: 7
SALES (corp-wide): 116.6K **Privately Held**
WEB: www.madefuryou.com
SIC: 3999 Furs
PA: Made Fur You Inc.
18112 Thomas Blvd
Hudson FL 34667
813 444-7707

(G-6034)
MARINE ENGINE CONTROLS INC
Also Called: M E C I
9035 Wister Ln (34669-1948)
PHONE..................................727 518-8080
Patricia J Smith, *President*
John Smith, *Vice Pres*
EMP: 10 **EST:** 1991
SALES (est): 730.7K **Privately Held**
WEB: www.mecicontrols.com
SIC: 3625 Marine & navy auxiliary controls

(G-6035)
P&L MACHINE & TOOL COMPANY INC
9704 Katy Dr Ste 2 (34667-4397)
PHONE..................................727 863-0847
Paul Pataki, *President*
Malinda Pataki, *Corp Secy*
EMP: 5 **EST:** 1974
SQ FT: 3,500
SALES (est): 780K **Privately Held**
WEB: www.plmachineinc.com
SIC: 3599 Machine shop, jobbing & repair

(G-6036)
RACHEL ALLY ✪
9437 Debbie Ln (34669-1832)
PHONE..................................727 804-9596
Rachel Ally, *Owner*
EMP: 10 **EST:** 2021
SALES (est): 600K **Privately Held**
SIC: 1389 Construction, repair & dismantling services

(G-6037)
SARASOTA LEATHER GALLERY INC (PA)
15941 Us Highway 19 (34667-3654)
PHONE..................................800 741-4336
Bruce Weintraub, *President*
EMP: 5 **EST:** 2014
SALES (est): 800K **Privately Held**
WEB: www.leathergallerysarasota.com
SIC: 3199 Boxes, leather

(G-6038)
STAINLESS STEEL GUIDE RODS
9347 Denton Ave Ste C12 (34667-4394)
PHONE..................................813 240-7616
Martin Wanyo, *Principal*
EMP: 6 **EST:** 2017
SALES (est): 99.9K **Privately Held**
WEB: www.ssguiderods.com
SIC: 3312 Stainless steel

(G-6039)
TD TRA -DIX SUPPLY INC
Also Called: Hudson Do It Best Hardware
14196 Us Highway 19 (34667-1167)
PHONE..................................727 869-8662
EMP: 9 **EST:** 2013
SALES (est): 648.5K **Privately Held**
SIC: 3429 Builders' hardware

(G-6040)
TOM WATSON ENTERPRISES INC
Also Called: Spring Hill Newsletter
9629 Amilia Dr Ste 4 (34667-4371)
PHONE..................................352 683-5097
Tom Watson, *President*
Kathryn Watson, *Vice Pres*
EMP: 8 **EST:** 1978
SQ FT: 1,500
SALES (est): 732.2K **Privately Held**
SIC: 2711 7948 7299 1611 Newspapers: publishing only, not printed on site; stock car racing; massage parlor; concrete construction: roads, highways, sidewalks, etc.

(G-6041)
TPI ENGINEERED SYSTEMS INC
17726 Meridian Blvd (34667-5860)
PHONE..................................727 233-2810
EMP: 6 **EST:** 2017
SALES (est): 90.5K **Privately Held**
WEB: www.tpies.com
SIC: 3535 Conveyors & conveying equipment

(G-6042)
TRI COUNTY ALUMINUM SPC
16201 Us Highway 19 (34667-4306)
PHONE..................................727 848-4523
Kathleen Bocchetti, *Principal*
EMP: 8 **EST:** 2011
SALES (est): 290.3K **Privately Held**
WEB: www.tricountyaluminum.net
SIC: 3448 Screen enclosures

(G-6043)
VINEYARD 101 LLC
12930 Us Highway 19 (34667-1745)
PHONE..................................727 819-5300
Anita Castriota, *Principal*
EMP: 6 **EST:** 2015
SALES (est): 99K **Privately Held**
SIC: 2084 Wines, brandy & brandy spirits

Hurlburt Field
Okaloosa County

(G-6044)
L C INDUSTRIES INC
Also Called: LCI-leu
125 Bennett Ave (32544-5705)
PHONE..................................850 581-0117
Jim March, *Branch Mgr*
EMP: 40
SALES (corp-wide): 119MM **Privately Held**
WEB: www.lcindustries.com
SIC: 2311 Military uniforms, men's & youths': purchased materials
PA: L C Industries Inc.
4500 Emperor Blvd
Durham NC 27703
919 596-8277

(G-6045)
LOCKHEED MARTIN CORPORATION
945 Tully St Bldg 90028 (32544-5751)
PHONE..................................850 581-1427
Dennis Andrews, *Branch Mgr*
Steve Pojar, *Technical Staff*
EMP: 6 **Publicly Held**
WEB: www.lockheedmartin.com
SIC: 3812 Defense systems & equipment
PA: Lockheed Martin Corporation
6801 Rockledge Dr
Bethesda MD 20817

(G-6046)
LOCKHEED MARTIN CORPORATION
589 Independence Rd (32544-5604)
PHONE..................................850 581-5710
Tim Shaffer, *Manager*
EMP: 6 **Publicly Held**
WEB: www.lockheedmartin.com
SIC: 3812 Search & navigation equipment
PA: Lockheed Martin Corporation
6801 Rockledge Dr
Bethesda MD 20817

Hutchinson Island
St. Lucie County

(G-6047)
RAILTEC CONSTRUCTIONS COMPANY
Also Called: Railtech Construction
4949 N Hwy A1a Apt 182 (34949-8242)
P.O. Box 314, Sykesville MD (21784-0314)
PHONE..................................410 795-0712
Bill Kirchoff, *Owner*
EMP: 6 **EST:** 1996
SALES (est): 307K **Privately Held**
WEB: www.railtecrailings.com
SIC: 3446 Stairs, staircases, stair treads: prefabricated metal

Hypoluxo
Palm Beach County

(G-6048)
APOLLO WORLDWIDE INC
158 Las Brisas Cir (33462-7072)
PHONE..................................561 585-3865
Michael Mc Davitt, *President*
▲ **EMP:** 9 **EST:** 1997
SALES (est): 595.2K **Privately Held**
WEB: www.kirkmorris.com
SIC: 3589 5064 3631 Microwave ovens (cooking equipment), commercial; refrigerators & freezers; microwave ovens, including portable: household

Immokalee
Collier County

(G-6049)
GLOBAL MANUFACTURING TECH INC
160 Airpark Blvd Unit 101 (34142-3806)
PHONE..................................239 657-3720
Larry Fox, *President*
EMP: 6 **EST:** 1997
SALES (est): 565.6K **Privately Held**
SIC: 3559 Degreasing machines, automotive & industrial

(G-6050)
GULF CONNECTORS INC
160 Airpark Blvd Unit 104 (34142-3806)
PHONE..................................239 657-2986
Adrian Michelle, *CEO*
Minette Langston, *Admin Sec*
EMP: 5 **EST:** 2005
SALES (est): 444.1K **Privately Held**
SIC: 3643 Electric connectors

(G-6051)
IMMOKALEE FABRICATION AND WLDG
891 Arthur Ct (34142-2787)
PHONE..................................239 675-8299
Francisco Juan Enrique, *Owner*
EMP: 7 **EST:** 2016
SALES (est): 363.7K **Privately Held**
SIC: 7692 Automotive welding

(G-6052)
IMMOKALEE RANCH
4451 County Road 846 (34142-9659)
PHONE..................................239 657-2000
Collier Enterprises, *Partner*
Ronnie Raulerson, *Manager*
EMP: 7 **EST:** 1951
SALES (est): 420.5K **Privately Held**
WEB: www.immokaleecra.com
SIC: 2013 Calf's foot jelly from purchased meat

(G-6053)
MAVERICK NATURAL RESOURCES LLC
909 County Road 846 (34142-9724)
P.O. Box 3236 (34143-3236)
PHONE..................................239 657-2171
EMP: 34
SALES (corp-wide): 295.4MM **Privately Held**
WEB: www.mavresources.com
SIC: 1311 Crude petroleum production
PA: Maverick Natural Resources, Llc
1111 Bagby St Ste 1600
Houston TX 77002
713 437-8000

(G-6054)
WESTROCK CP LLC
815 E Main St (34142-3898)
PHONE..................................239 658-8221
Stuart Erwin, *Manager*
EMP: 6
SALES (corp-wide): 17.5B **Publicly Held**
WEB: www.westrock.com
SIC: 2653 Boxes, corrugated: made from purchased materials
HQ: Westrock Cp, Llc
1000 Abernathy Rd Ste 125
Atlanta GA 30328

Indialantic
Brevard County

(G-6055)
A1A RAW LLC
Also Called: Bunkys Raw Bar
2372 N Hwy A1a (32903-2509)
P.O. Box 361017, Melbourne (32936-1017)
PHONE..................................321 777-2526
Douglas F Walker,
EMP: 9 **EST:** 2014
SALES (est): 688.8K **Privately Held**
WEB: www.bunkysrawbar.com
SIC: 2599 Bar, restaurant & cafeteria furniture

(G-6056)
C-NOTE SOLUTIONS INC
334 4th Ave (32903-4214)
PHONE..................................321 952-2490
Gary Parish, *CEO*
Derek Ford, *Technical Staff*
EMP: 10 **EST:** 2013
SALES (est): 208.7K **Privately Held**
WEB: www.c-note-solutions.myshopify.com
SIC: 3699 Security devices

(G-6057)
CATHARINE E ARMSTRONG
137 1st Ave (32903-3101)
PHONE..................................321 704-5042
Michael Armstrong, *Principal*
EMP: 6 **EST:** 2010
SALES (est): 239.3K **Privately Held**
SIC: 2431 Millwork

(G-6058)
DIVERSIFIED WOODWORKS LLC
26 North Ct (32903-2002)
PHONE..................................321 591-9935
Joan C Sparkman, *Manager*
EMP: 6 **EST:** 2015
SALES (est): 179.3K **Privately Held**
SIC: 2431 Millwork

(G-6059)
GLOBAL AEROSPACE
1515 N Hwy A1a Apt 202 (32903-2700)
PHONE..................................407 721-3732
Norman Curran, *Principal*
EMP: 6 **EST:** 2016
SALES (est): 221K **Privately Held**
SIC: 3721 Aircraft

(G-6060)
GOLF SHAFT DEALS INC
529 Franklyn Ave (32903-4109)
PHONE..................................321 591-7824
Lee Sanford, *Principal*
EMP: 6 **EST:** 2010
SALES (est): 112.3K **Privately Held**
SIC: 3949 Shafts, golf club

(G-6061)
VIPER DRONES INC ✪
409 5th Ave (32903-4240)
PHONE..................................321 427-5837
Leon Shivamber, *Principal*
Leslie Jones, *Principal*
Loretta McKeefery, *Principal*
Tom McKeefery, *Principal*
EMP: 12 **EST:** 2020
SALES (est): 800.6K **Privately Held**
WEB: www.viper-drones.com
SIC: 3728 Aircraft parts & equipment

(G-6062)
VIPER DRONES LLC
Also Called: My Drone Services
409 5th Ave (32903-4240)
PHONE..................................205 677-3700
Leon Shivamber, *Principal*
EMP: 6 **EST:** 2016
SALES (est): 439.9K **Privately Held**
WEB: www.viper-drones.com
SIC: 3721 Aircraft

Indian Harbour Beach
Brevard County

(G-6063)
BULLION INTERNATIONAL INC
Also Called: Highland Mint
4100 N Riverside Dr (32937-4834)
PHONE..................................321 773-2727
Michael Kott, *President*
Monica Scroggie, *Vice Pres*
Traci Bruner, *Art Dir*
EMP: 120 **EST:** 1989
SQ FT: 38,000
SALES (est): 40MM **Privately Held**
WEB: www.highlandmint.com
SIC: 3911 Jewelry, precious metal

(G-6064)
ORCOM LABS INC
131 Tomahawk Dr Ste 9b (32937-1814)
PHONE..................................321 773-0741
Teresa Doherty, *President*
Bob Kime, *Vice Pres*
EMP: 8 **EST:** 1991
SQ FT: 600
SALES (est): 321.7K **Privately Held**
WEB: www.orcomtechnologies.com
SIC: 3842 Foot appliances, orthopedic

(G-6065)
PAXEN PUBLISHING LLC (PA)
2194 Highway A1a Ste 208 (32937-4931)
PHONE..................................321 425-3030
Herbert Hilderley, *Principal*
Richard Semancik, *Principal*
Deanna Crosson, *Vice Pres*
Lindsey Alf, *CFO*
Emily Mitchell, *Accountant*
EMP: 11 **EST:** 2017
SALES (est): 1.4MM **Privately Held**
WEB: www.paxenpublishing.com
SIC: 2741 Miscellaneous publishing

(G-6066)
RTA CABINETS & MORE LLC
222 E Eau Gallie Blvd (32937-4874)
PHONE..................................321 288-3068
Robert F Erario, *President*
EMP: 6 **EST:** 2015
SALES (est): 1.2MM **Privately Held**
WEB: www.cabinetsonthecoast.com
SIC: 2434 5211 Wood kitchen cabinets; cabinets, kitchen

(G-6067)
SNAPSPEED LLC
131 Tomahawk Dr Ste 19a (32937-1815)
PHONE..................................321 441-3797
John A Goodman, *Manager*
EMP: 6 **EST:** 2010
SALES (est): 120.1K **Privately Held**
WEB: www.snapspeed.com
SIC: 3433 Stokers, mechanical: domestic or industrial

(G-6068)
STEVEN M ROESSLER LLC
Also Called: Printfast & Office Supplies
1859 South Patrick Dr (32937-4377)
PHONE..................................321 773-2300
Steven Roessler,
EMP: 5 **EST:** 1986
SQ FT: 3,000
SALES (est): 386.9K **Privately Held**
SIC: 2752 5943 Commercial printing, offset; office forms & supplies

Indian Rocks Beach
Pinellas County

(G-6069)
SLYCE INC
311 Gulf Blvd Ste 2 (33785-2548)
PHONE..................................727 408-5272
Suzanne Brown, *General Mgr*
Ken W Gillespie, *Principal*
Christopher Derry, *Manager*
Hank Donnay, *Software Engr*
EMP: 8 **EST:** 2010
SALES (est): 1MM **Privately Held**
WEB: www.slycepizzabar.com
SIC: 3421 Table & food cutlery, including butchers'

Indian Shores
Pinellas County

(G-6070)
INSIGHT RISK TECHNOLOGIES LLC
19455 Gulf Blvd Ste 5 (33785-2000)
PHONE..................................863 804-6038
EMP: 6 **EST:** 2018
SALES (est): 152.3K **Privately Held**
WEB: www.insightrisktech.com
SIC: 7372 Prepackaged software

Indiantown
Martin County

(G-6071)
BAY STATE MILLING COMPANY
19150 Sw Warfield Blvd (34956-9766)
P.O. Box 1280 (34956-1280)
PHONE..................................772 597-2056
Dan Collins, *Exec VP*
Doug J Dewitt, *Vice Pres*
Walker Humphries, *Vice Pres*
Sean Costello, *Plant Mgr*
Bill Raiola, *Plant Mgr*
EMP: 26
SALES (corp-wide): 131.8MM **Privately Held**
WEB: www.baystatemilling.com
SIC: 2041 Flour mills, cereal (except rice)
PA: Bay State Milling Company
100 Congress St Ste 2
Quincy MA 02169
617 328-4423

(G-6072)
GILIBERTI INC
16015 Sw Farm Rd (34956-3526)
PHONE..................................772 597-1870
John F Giliberti Sr, *President*
John F Giliberti Jr, *Vice Pres*
▼ **EMP:** 14 **EST:** 1986
SQ FT: 10,000
SALES (est): 2MM **Privately Held**
WEB: www.giliberti.com
SIC: 3711 Automobile assembly, including specialty automobiles

(G-6073)
GUYTON INDUSTRIES LLC
Also Called: Guyton's Custom Design
14601 Sw 168th Ave (34956-3836)
PHONE..................................772 208-3019
Guyton Stone, *President*
EMP: 20 **EST:** 2017
SALES (est): 1.3MM **Privately Held**
SIC: 2599 2211 2541 5211 Cabinets, factory; furniture denim; cabinets, lockers & shelving; cabinets, kitchen; cabinet work, custom; cabinet building & installation

(G-6074)
SCARB INDUSTRIES INC
15845 Sw Warfield Blvd (34956-3502)
PHONE..................................772 597-3898
Stephen Blake, *President*
EMP: 9 **EST:** 2003
SALES (est): 330.7K **Privately Held**
SIC: 3999 Barber & beauty shop equipment

Inglis
Levy County

(G-6075)
BUILT RITE CABINETS INC
438 Highway 40 E (34449-9432)
PHONE..................................352 447-2238
Tom Thomas, *President*
EMP: 8 **EST:** 1977
SQ FT: 11,300
SALES (est): 908.5K **Privately Held**
WEB: www.builtriteinc.org
SIC: 2434 Wood kitchen cabinets

(G-6076)
GENTEEL COATINGS LLC
10151 Se 195th St (34449-3760)
PHONE..................................772 708-1781
William A Scott III, *Principal*
EMP: 6 **EST:** 2008
SALES (est): 94.3K **Privately Held**
SIC: 3479 Metal coating & allied service

Inlet Beach
Walton County

(G-6077)
OLIVE 30A OIL INC
12805 Us Highway 98 E N1 (32461-9630)
PHONE..................................850 909-0099
EMP: 6 **EST:** 2019
SALES (est): 197.9K **Privately Held**
WEB: www.30aoliveoil.com
SIC: 2079 Olive oil

(G-6078)
OUTPOST 30A LLC
11 N Castle Harbour Dr F (32461-8248)
PHONE..................................850 909-0138
Caitlin Bloodwlorth, *Office Mgr*
Mary Clark, *Mng Member*
EMP: 10 **EST:** 2014
SALES (est): 855K **Privately Held**
SIC: 2519 5812 Household furniture, except wood or metal: upholstered; coffee shop

Interlachen
Putnam County

(G-6079)
ROYAL MANOR VINEYARD & WINERY
224 Royal Ave (32148-7267)
PHONE..................................386 684-6270
Thomas J Pasco, *Principal*
EMP: 7 **EST:** 2008
SALES (est): 207.2K **Privately Held**
WEB: www.royalmanormeadery.com
SIC: 2084 Wines

Inverness
Citrus County

(G-6080)
AAWARENESS MKTG PRTG & PUBG
2659 E Gulf To Lake Hwy (34453-3216)
P.O. Box 1253 (34451-1253)
PHONE..................................352 422-3953
Frederick Clark, *Principal*
EMP: 6 **EST:** 2012
SALES (est): 153.3K **Privately Held**
SIC: 2752 Commercial printing, offset

(G-6081)
ADVANCE GREEN ENERGY INC
523 S Us Highway 41 (34450-6027)
PHONE..................................352 765-3850
Peter M Barbee, *President*
Bradley Dye, *Vice Pres*
Debra Davis, *Executive Asst*
EMP: 6 **EST:** 2017
SALES (est): 453.2K **Privately Held**
WEB: www.advancegreenenergy.us
SIC: 1389 Oil consultants

(G-6082)
CMI MICROCLIMATES INC
1720 S Tranquil Ave (34450-5138)
PHONE..................................607 569-2738
Carmen Kramer, *Principal*
EMP: 8 **EST:** 2018
SALES (est): 316.8K **Privately Held**
SIC: 2655 Fiber cans, drums & similar products

(G-6083)
CONSULTANT MGT GROUP LLC
200 W Main St (34450-4855)
PHONE..................................352 344-4001
Giraldo Alfonso, *Owner*
Chad W Waller, *Mng Member*
Shannon Wallen, *Manager*
Ryan G Waller,
EMP: 6 **EST:** 2011
SQ FT: 1,500
SALES (est): 529.8K **Privately Held**
WEB: www.cmgutilities.com
SIC: 3568 8741 Power transmission equipment; business management

(G-6084)
CUSTOM MANUFACTURING INC
Also Called: CMI Microclimates
1720 S Tranquil Ave (34450-5138)
PHONE..................................607 569-2738
Carmen J Waters, *President*
Michael Waters, *Vice Pres*
▲ **EMP:** 5 **EST:** 1990
SALES (est): 700K **Privately Held**
SIC: 2655 Containers, liquid tight fiber: from purchased material

(G-6085)
DAN FRAME & TRIM INC
7770 E Rustic Trl (34453-1391)
PHONE..................................352 726-4567
EMP: 8
SALES (est): 343.7K **Privately Held**
SIC: 1442 Construction Sand/Gravel

(G-6086)
DLZ HOLDINGS SOUTH INC (PA)
956 S Us Highway 41 (34450-6861)
PHONE..................................352 344-8741
David Ziebarth, *President*
Keven Fults, *Plant Mgr*
Karen Wood, *Controller*
Eric Wood, *Marketing Staff*
Jimmy Russell, *Director*
▼ **EMP:** 12 **EST:** 1985
SALES (est): 7.8MM **Privately Held**
SIC: 2851 Lacquers, varnishes, enamels & other coatings

(G-6087)
FLORAL CITY AIRBOAT CO INC (PA)
5098 S Florida Ave (34450-7258)
PHONE..................................352 637-4390
Michael Emrich, *CEO*
Terrie Emrich, *President*
Lisa Calderone, *Manager*
EMP: 11 **EST:** 1986
SQ FT: 13,500
SALES (est): 1.5MM **Privately Held**
WEB: www.airboatfl.com
SIC: 3732 Boat building & repairing

(G-6088)
GALAXY CUSTOM GRANITE INC
5388 E Jasmine Ln (34453-1069)
PHONE..................................352 220-2822
Jesse O Butzer, *Principal*
Daniel Negrin, *Accounts Mgr*
Ben Negrin, *Regl Sales Mgr*
EMP: 9 **EST:** 2007
SALES (est): 115.3K **Privately Held**
SIC: 3281 Table tops, marble

(G-6089)
GREEN FOREST PRODUCTS LLC
105 N Apopka Ave (34450-4237)
PHONE..................................352 341-5500
Jeffrey Barnes, *President*
Chay Barnes, *Vice Pres*
▲ **EMP:** 7 **EST:** 2000
SQ FT: 1,800
SALES (est): 1MM **Privately Held**
WEB: www.greenforestprod.com
SIC: 2621 Towels, tissues & napkins: paper & stock

(G-6090)
JANS VENTURES LLC ✪
Also Called: Hemp Pantry
2044 Highway 44 W (34453-3858)
PHONE..................................352 341-1710
Rebekah Potter, *Mng Member*
EMP: 10 **EST:** 2020
SALES (est): 250K **Privately Held**
SIC: 3999

(G-6091)
JPS DIGITAL LLC
4860 S Marsh Hawk Ter (34452-7847)
PHONE..................................813 501-6040
Susan Janicki, *Branch Mgr*
EMP: 19
SALES (corp-wide): 149.3K **Privately Held**
WEB: www.picturemystamp.com
SIC: 2752 Commercial printing, lithographic
PA: Jps Digital Llc
2231 Elizabeth Dr
Brandon FL
813 600-3077

(G-6092)
KOMMANDER SOFTWARE LLC
2271 E Steven St (34453-9561)
PHONE..................................407 906-2121
William Kicklighter, *CEO*
EMP: 8 **EST:** 2015
SALES (est): 390.7K **Privately Held**
WEB: www.detailkommander.com
SIC: 7372 Prepackaged software

(G-6093)
ON A ROLL DISTRIBUTORS INC
1626 E Saint James Loop (34453-3679)
PHONE..................................352 726-3420
Peter Bockiaro, *Owner*
EMP: 6 **EST:** 1997
SALES (est): 77.6K **Privately Held**
SIC: 2051 Bread, cake & related products

(G-6094)
PEMBERTON CUSTOM AIRBOATS
8009 E Pemberton Path (34450-3436)
PHONE..................................352 422-5597
EMP: 7 **EST:** 2019
SALES (est): 137.4K **Privately Held**
SIC: 3732 Boat building & repairing

(G-6095)
PERL INC
Also Called: La Perle Memorials
5009 S Florida Ave (34450-7257)
P.O. Box 447 (34451-0447)
PHONE..................................352 726-2483
David La Perle, *President*
EMP: 10 **EST:** 1955
SQ FT: 2,000
SALES (est): 1.3MM **Privately Held**
SIC: 3272 7389 Tombstones, precast terrazzo or concrete; crane & aerial lift service

(G-6096)
SINCERE SENTIMENTS INC
8001 E Shannon Ct (34450-2711)
PHONE..................................352 287-1232
Anthony Caponigro, *Principal*
EMP: 8 **EST:** 2008
SALES (est): 223.6K **Privately Held**
SIC: 2771 Greeting cards

(G-6097)
TIMES PUBLISHING COMPANY
Also Called: Citrus Times Edition
301 W Main St (34450-4743)
PHONE..................................352 567-6660
Andrew Barnes, *Ch of Bd*
EMP: 148
SALES (corp-wide): 14.9MM **Privately Held**
WEB: www.tampabay.com
SIC: 2711 Newspapers, publishing & printing
HQ: Times Publishing Company
490 1st Ave S
Saint Petersburg FL 33701
727 893-8111

Islamorada
Monroe County

(G-6098)
LARGO ALUMINUM INC
86500 Overseas Hwy (33036-3201)
P.O. Box 659, Tavernier (33070-0659)
PHONE..................................305 852-2390
John Kasianowicz, *President*
Michael Powell, *Vice Pres*
EMP: 14 **EST:** 1978
SQ FT: 6,042
SALES (est): 363.1K **Privately Held**
SIC: 3355 1761 5211 3446 Rails, rolled & drawn, aluminum; roofing contractor; lumber & other building materials; architectural metalwork; sheet metalwork; aluminum extruded products

(G-6099)
S & S PERFORMANCE INC
Also Called: S&S Performance Marine
80460 Overseas Hwy (33036-3750)
PHONE..................................305 951-9846
Erik W Shisler, *President*
EMP: 5 **EST:** 2015
SALES (est): 316.4K **Privately Held**
WEB: www.ssperformancemarine.com
SIC: 3732 5541 Boat building & repairing; marine service station

Jacksonville
Duval County

(G-6100)
1425 N WASHINGTON STREET LLC
12808 Gran Bay Pkwy W (32258-4468)
PHONE..................................904 680-6600
EMP: 5 **EST:** 2015
SALES (est): 7MM
SALES (corp-wide): 749.2MM **Privately Held**
WEB: www.web.com
SIC: 7372 Prepackaged software
HQ: Web.Com Group, Inc.
5335 Gate Pkwy
Jacksonville FL 32256

(G-6101)
3TISSUE LLC
8286 Wstn Way Cir C9 C10 (32256)
PHONE..................................904 540-4335
Hector Hurtado, *Manager*
Hector Hurtado Sr,
Mario A Hurtado,
▲ **EMP:** 5 **EST:** 2015
SQ FT: 6,000
SALES (est): 400K **Privately Held**
SIC: 2621 Tissue paper

(G-6102)
4303 SILVERWOOD LLC
4401 San Jose Ln (32207-6236)
PHONE..................................904 900-1702
Jubeen Vaghefi, *Principal*
EMP: 8 **EST:** 2016
SALES (est): 257.4K **Privately Held**
SIC: 2499 Wood products

(G-6103)
525 PRNTING PRMTIONAL PDTS INC
3107 Spring Glen Rd # 211 (32207-5916)
PHONE..................................904 580-5943
Jeree Solomon, *Principal*
EMP: 6 **EST:** 2016
SALES (est): 70K **Privately Held**
SIC: 2752 Commercial printing, lithographic

(G-6104)
904 POWDERWORX LLC
4208 Reservoir Ln S (32223-4027)
PHONE..................................904 290-6383
EMP: 5 **EST:** 2019
SALES (est): 476.1K **Privately Held**
WEB: www.904powderworx.com
SIC: 3479 Coating of metals & formed products

(G-6105)
904 SWEET TREATZ STREET LLC
7643 Gate Pkwy Ste 104 (32256-2893)
PHONE..................................800 889-3298
Marcia Brown, *President*
EMP: 6 **EST:** 2017
SALES (est): 307.5K **Privately Held**
SIC: 2051 5963 Bakery: wholesale or wholesale/retail combined; bakery goods, house-to-house

(G-6106)
9T TECHNOLOGY LLC
3125 Double Oaks Dr (32226-2086)
PHONE..................................904 703-9214
Charlene Dennis, *Owner*
EMP: 7 **EST:** 2013
SALES (est): 456.1K **Privately Held**
WEB: www.9ttech.com
SIC: 3571 7389 Electronic computers;

(G-6107)
A & K MACHINE & FAB SHOP INC
3451 W Beaver St (32254-3709)
P.O. Box 14942 (32238-1942)
PHONE..................................904 388-7772
Alice M Stine, *President*
Cynthia L Rhoden, *Corp Secy*
Jenny Smith, *Corp Secy*
Kenneth D Stine, *Vice Pres*
Mary S Horning, *Director*
EMP: 17 **EST:** 1989
SQ FT: 10,000
SALES (est): 4.9MM **Privately Held**
WEB: www.aandkmachineandfab.com
SIC: 3441 Fabricated structural metal

(G-6108)
A B & B MANUFACTURING INC
2141 Lane Ave N (32254-1531)
P.O. Box 6456 (32236-6456)
PHONE..................................904 378-3350
James T Brooks, *President*
EMP: 14 **EST:** 1999
SALES (est): 3.1MM **Privately Held**
WEB: www.abandbmachineandfab.com
SIC: 3545 Machine tool accessories

(G-6109)
A CLEAN FINISH INC
Also Called: Property Solutions and Cnstr
8848 Quail Roost Ct (32220-1400)
P.O. Box 6236 (32236-6236)
PHONE..................................407 516-1311
Aleya Wolfla, *President*
Charles Wolfla, *Vice Pres*
EMP: 6 **EST:** 2015
SQ FT: 1,500

▲ = Import ▼=Export
◆ =Import/Export

SALES (est): 958.4K Privately Held
SIC: 3589 1721 3069 1752 High pressure cleaning equipment; painting & paper hanging; flooring, rubber: tile or sheet; access flooring system installation; surfacers, concrete grinding

(G-6110)
A M COPLAN ASSOCIATES
Also Called: Coplan Composition Service
4251 University Blvd S # 201 (32216-4981)
P.O. Box 5545 (32247-5545)
PHONE.................................904 737-6996
Alvin M Coplan, *Owner*
Al Copeland, *Web Proj Mgr*
EMP: 5 EST: 1961
SQ FT: 2,000
SALES (est): 1MM Privately Held
SIC: 2711 6162 6163 6512 Newspapers: publishing only, not printed on site; mortgage brokers, using own money; mortgage brokers arranging for loans, using money of others; commercial & industrial building operation

(G-6111)
A PLUS CONSTRUCTION SVCS INC
165 Oakhill St (32227-1817)
PHONE.................................904 612-0597
Chasidy Grubbs, *President*
EMP: 25 EST: 2012
SALES (est): 1.9MM Privately Held
SIC: 1389 1521 1542 1541 Construction, repair & dismantling services; single-family housing construction; nonresidential construction; industrial buildings, new construction

(G-6112)
A-1 DOOR SYSTEMS INC
11555 Central Pkwy # 804 (32224-2700)
PHONE.................................904 327-7206
David Eckes, *President*
Doug Stanford, *Vice Pres*
EMP: 11 EST: 2004
SALES (est): 273.7K Privately Held
SIC: 2431 1751 Garage doors, overhead: wood; garage door, installation or erection

(G-6113)
AA FIBERGLASS INC
9378 Arlington Expy 358 (32225-8213)
PHONE.................................904 355-5511
Michael A Jackson, *Principal*
EMP: 8 EST: 1985
SALES (est): 122.7K Privately Held
WEB: www.aacustomfiberglass.com
SIC: 3083 Laminated plastics plate & sheet

(G-6114)
AA FIBERGLASS INC
521 Copeland St (32204-2721)
PHONE.................................904 355-5511
Michael Jackson, *Owner*
EMP: 8 EST: 2016
SALES (est): 56.3K Privately Held
WEB: www.aacustomfiberglass.com
SIC: 2221 Fiberglass fabrics

(G-6115)
AACECORP INC
Also Called: American Assn Clncal Endcrnlgs
245 Riverside Ave Ste 200 (32202-4933)
PHONE.................................904 353-7878
Donald C Jones, *CEO*
EMP: 9 EST: 1996
SQ FT: 3,700
SALES (est): 1.8MM Privately Held
WEB: www.aace.com
SIC: 2721 2759 Periodicals; advertising literature: printing
PA: American Association Of Clinical Endocrinologists, Inc.
245 Riverside Ave Ste 200
Jacksonville FL 32202

(G-6116)
AAR GOVERNMENT SERVICES INC
Also Called: AAR Defense Systems Logistics
8001 Westside Indus Dr (32219-3238)
PHONE.................................904 693-7260
Michael Lile, *Manager*
EMP: 21
SALES (corp-wide): 1.6B Publicly Held
WEB: www.aarcorp.com
SIC: 3728 Aircraft parts & equipment
HQ: Aar Government Services, Inc.
1100 N Wood Dale Rd
Wood Dale IL 60191
630 227-2000

(G-6117)
ACE FABRICATORS INC
1705 E 30th St (32206-1703)
PHONE.................................904 355-3724
Henry Smith, *President*
Joyce Smith, *Treasurer*
EMP: 18 EST: 1988
SQ FT: 25,000
SALES (est): 4.3MM Privately Held
SIC: 3441 Fabricated structural metal

(G-6118)
AD AMERICA
8679 W Beaver St (32220-2203)
PHONE.................................904 781-5900
G Brett Railey, *Owner*
EMP: 7 EST: 1972
SQ FT: 2,000
SALES (est): 316.8K Privately Held
SIC: 3993 7382 Signs, not made in custom sign painting shops; security systems services

(G-6119)
ADAMS STREET STATION
1738 E Adams St (32202-1220)
PHONE.................................904 304-7222
Linda L Daniels, *Principal*
EMP: 7 EST: 2011
SALES (est): 171K Privately Held
WEB: www.adamstreetstation.com
SIC: 3743 Railway maintenance cars

(G-6120)
ADTEC PRODUCTIONS INCORPORATED
Also Called: Adtec Digital
2231 Corporate Sq Blvd (32216-1921)
PHONE.................................904 720-2003
Kevin Ancelin, *President*
Anderson Brown, *Engineer*
Danny Dresdner, *Engineer*
Jeremy Thien, *Engineer*
Nick Ancelin, *Electrical Engi*
EMP: 8 Privately Held
WEB: www.adtecdigital.com
SIC: 3679 3621 Video triggers, except remote control TV devices; generating apparatus & parts, electrical
PA: Adtec Productions, Incorporated
408 Russell St
Nashville TN 37206

(G-6121)
ADVANCED AWNING & DESIGN LLC
2155 Corp Sq Blvd Ste 100 (32216-0323)
PHONE.................................904 724-5567
Jackie Smith, *Mng Member*
Todd Smith, *Mng Member*
EMP: 8 EST: 1994
SQ FT: 7,500
SALES (est): 898.6K Privately Held
WEB: www.advanced-awning.com
SIC: 2394 Awnings, fabric: made from purchased materials

(G-6122)
ADVANCED COMPOSITE SYSTEMS
10615 New Kings Rd (32219-2129)
PHONE.................................904 765-6502
Henry Happy, *President*
Mark L Jones, *President*
Lorraine Happy, *Corp Secy*
Michael Happy, *Vice Pres*
EMP: 15 EST: 1997
SQ FT: 20,414
SALES (est): 2.5MM Privately Held
WEB: www.teccomposites.com
SIC: 2821 Plastics materials & resins

(G-6123)
ADVANCED DESIGN & PACKG INC
2212 N Pearl St (32206-3647)
PHONE.................................904 356-6063
Doug Johnson, *CEO*
EMP: 15 Privately Held
WEB: www.hoodcontainer.com
SIC: 2653 Boxes, corrugated: made from purchased materials
HQ: Advanced Design & Packaging, Inc.
5090 Mcdougall Dr Sw
Atlanta GA 30336
404 699-1952

(G-6124)
ADVANTAGE PRTG LMNTING FLA INC
Also Called: Advantage Prtg Lminating Signs
4618 Sunbeam Rd (32257-6110)
P.O. Box 24140 (32241-4140)
PHONE.................................904 737-1613
Troy McGee, *President*
Leanne McGee, *Vice Pres*
Debbie Rittenger, *Graphic Designe*
EMP: 7 EST: 2000
SALES (est): 995.7K Privately Held
WEB: www.advantageprintingonline.com
SIC: 2759 Commercial printing

(G-6125)
AEI INTERNATIONAL CORP
7709 Alton Ave (32211-7801)
PHONE.................................904 724-9771
Lewis Spradlin Jr, *President*
Belinda Spradlin, *Vice Pres*
EMP: 5 EST: 1992
SALES (est): 875.6K Privately Held
SIC: 3084 5084 1623 Plastics pipe; propane conversion equipment; oil & gas pipeline construction

(G-6126)
AERIAL PRODUCTS CORPORATION
Also Called: Southern Balloon Works
11653 Central Pkwy # 209 (32224-2711)
PHONE.................................800 973-9110
Kevin M Hess, *President*
EMP: 13 EST: 2007
SALES (est): 681.4K Privately Held
WEB: www.aerialproducts.com
SIC: 3721 3069 Aircraft; balloons, advertising & toy: rubber

(G-6127)
AGILE CARGO TRANSPORTATION LLC ✪
1601-1 N Main St (32206-4453)
PHONE.................................407 747-0812
Richard F Tavarez,
EMP: 10 EST: 2020
SALES (est): 677K Privately Held
SIC: 3799 Transportation equipment

(G-6128)
AGILITY PRESS INC
3060 Mercury Rd (32207-7915)
PHONE.................................904 731-8989
Ray Farah, *President*
Damon Mattheus, *Manager*
EMP: 16 EST: 1999
SQ FT: 10,000
SALES (est): 3.8MM Privately Held
WEB: www.agilitypress.net
SIC: 2759 Commercial printing

(G-6129)
AGR FABRICATORS INC
4879 Clydo Rd S Ste 1 (32207-7974)
P.O. Box 10158 (32247-0158)
PHONE.................................904 733-9393
George Shami, *President*
Charlie J Shami, *Vice Pres*
Charlie Shami, *Vice Pres*
Emile Shami, *Treasurer*
▲ EMP: 17 EST: 1996
SALES (est): 2.5MM Privately Held
WEB: www.agrfabricators.com
SIC: 2541 Counter & sink tops

(G-6130)
AGR OF FLORIDA INC
4879 Clydo Rd S (32207-7957)
PHONE.................................904 733-9393
George Shami, *President*
Emile Shami, *Treasurer*
Peter Shami, *Director*
◆ EMP: 35 EST: 1969
SQ FT: 22,000
SALES (est): 1.4MM Privately Held
WEB: www.agrfabricators.com
SIC: 2541 3821 Counter & sink tops; worktables, laboratory

(G-6131)
AIRPRO DIAGNOSTICS LLC
6873 Phillips Ind Blvd (32256-3029)
PHONE.................................904 717-1711
Lonnie E Margol, *Principal*
Steve Casella, *Vice Pres*
Frank Laviola, *Vice Pres*
Mark McCahill, *Human Res Dir*
Rachel Spell, *Manager*
EMP: 16 EST: 2016
SALES (est): 2.8MM Privately Held
WEB: www.airprodiagnostics.com
SIC: 3829 Measuring & controlling devices

(G-6132)
AKUA RAGE ENTERTAINMENT INC
10960 Beach Blvd Lot 494 (32246-4862)
PHONE.................................904 627-5312
Shaun Santos, *CEO*
Peter Whipple, *COO*
EMP: 7 EST: 2016
SALES (est): 720K Privately Held
SIC: 2741

(G-6133)
ALL METAL FAB INC
2021 Dennis St (32204-1901)
PHONE.................................904 570-9772
Dustin W Workman, *President*
Jessica L Workman, *Vice Pres*
EMP: 22 EST: 2016
SALES (est): 2.6MM Privately Held
WEB: www.allmetalfabinc.com
SIC: 3444 Sheet metalwork

(G-6134)
ALL METALS FABRICATION LLC
4235 Saint Augustine Rd (32207-6643)
PHONE.................................904 862-6885
Michael S Dickens,
Brian H Vick,
EMP: 9 EST: 2017
SALES (est): 1.2MM Privately Held
WEB: www.amfllc.net
SIC: 3341 Secondary nonferrous metals

(G-6135)
ALL PURPOSE PRTG GRAPHICS INC
3521 Saint Augustine Rd (32207-5526)
P.O. Box 5733 (32247-5733)
PHONE.................................904 346-0999
Michael G Amason, *President*
Pamela Woodworth, *Sales Staff*
Sandra Amason, *Admin Sec*
EMP: 10 EST: 1999
SQ FT: 10,000
SALES (est): 1.7MM Privately Held
WEB: www.appagi.com
SIC: 2759 Screen printing

(G-6136)
ALL SIGNS
5277 Alloaks Ct (32258-2299)
PHONE.................................904 262-3795
Dewayne Conner, *Owner*
EMP: 5 EST: 1998
SALES (est): 300K Privately Held
SIC: 3993 Signs & advertising specialties

(G-6137)
ALL-STAR SALES INC
Also Called: Raintree Graphics
5921 Richard St (32216-5926)
P.O. Box 5967 (32247-5967)
PHONE.................................904 396-1653
Michael J Seethler, *President*
Michael Seethaler Sr, *Vice Pres*
Manuel Granados, *Project Mgr*
David Harkness, *Accounts Exec*
Bob Petty, *Manager*
EMP: 35 EST: 1980
SQ FT: 17,000
SALES (est): 7.5MM Privately Held
WEB: www.raintreegraphics.com
SIC: 2759 2752 2796 2789 Commercial printing; commercial printing, lithographic; platemaking services; bookbinding & related work

(G-6138)
ALLIED PLASTICS CO INC
2001 Walnut St (32206-3843)
P.O. Box 3125 (32206-0125)
PHONE..................................904 359-0386
Gregory Berger, *President*
Dennis Berger, *Vice Pres*
◆ **EMP:** 45 **EST:** 1943
SQ FT: 50,000
SALES (est): 10.8MM **Privately Held**
WEB: www.alliedusa.com
SIC: 2511 2493 2531 2522 Tables, household: wood; particleboard, plastic laminated; public building & related furniture; office furniture, except wood; wood office furniture

(G-6139)
ALLIED PRINTING INC
Also Called: Allied Graphics
7403 Philips Hwy (32256-6807)
P.O. Box 11063, Birmingham AL (35202-1063)
PHONE..................................800 749-7683
Dorsey B Thomas Jr, *President*
Richard Muller, *Vice Pres*
EMP: 97 **EST:** 1958
SQ FT: 15,000
SALES (est): 1.6MM **Privately Held**
WEB: www.alliedprinting.com
SIC: 2752 Commercial printing, offset

(G-6140)
ALTEC INDUSTRIES INC
2750 Imeson Rd (32220-2458)
PHONE..................................904 647-5219
EMP: 11
SALES (corp-wide): 1.2B **Privately Held**
WEB: www.altec.com
SIC: 3531 Construction machinery
HQ: Altec Industries, Inc.
210 Inverness Center Dr
Birmingham AL 35242
205 991-7733

(G-6141)
ALTERNATIVE VISION LLC
2915 Anniston Rd (32246-3437)
PHONE..................................904 642-3566
Jim Stanford, *Mng Member*
Annette Stanford, *Mng Member*
EMP: 6 **EST:** 2013
SALES (est): 228.3K **Privately Held**
WEB: www.shufflebowl300.net
SIC: 3949 Ping-pong tables

(G-6142)
ALTERNTIVE REPR MCHNING SVCS L
Also Called: Arms
6555 Trade Center Dr (32254-2248)
PHONE..................................904 861-3040
Pafford Aimee, *Mfg Staff*
Pafford Jason, *Mfg Staff*
Kevin Hillman, *Engineer*
Aimee D Pafford, *Mng Member*
Aimee Pafford, *Manager*
▼ **EMP:** 20 **EST:** 2011
SALES (est): 6.9MM **Privately Held**
WEB: www.armservicesusa.com
SIC: 3511 Turbines & turbine generator sets

(G-6143)
ALUMINATION LLC
2718 Townsend Blvd (32211-4200)
PHONE..................................904 361-8174
Jay T Kish, *Manager*
EMP: 8 **EST:** 2005
SALES (est): 106.7K **Privately Held**
SIC: 3646 Commercial indusl & institutional electric lighting fixtures

(G-6144)
ALUMINUM PRODUCTS WHL INC
Also Called: Apw Wholesale
6963 Bus Pk Blvd N Ste 2 (32256-2736)
PHONE..................................904 268-4895
Mitchell B Shepherd, *President*
EMP: 6 **EST:** 2001
SALES (est): 1.1MM **Privately Held**
WEB: www.aluminum-product-manufacturers.cmac.ws
SIC: 3354 Aluminum extruded products

(G-6145)
AMERAPARTS INTERNATIONAL LLC
103 Century 21 Dr Ste 201 (32216-9295)
PHONE..................................904 725-9700
James R Johnson, *CEO*
Patricia D Smith, *Treasurer*
John E Graham Jr, *Manager*
C P Orantes, *Director*
Padraic E Mulvhill, *Admin Sec*
EMP: 300 **EST:** 1997
SALES (est): 23.9MM **Privately Held**
SIC: 3714 Motor vehicle parts & accessories

(G-6146)
AMERICAN BOTTLING COMPANY
Also Called: Seven-Up Snapple Southeast
6001 Bowdendale Ave (32216-6041)
PHONE..................................904 739-1000
Robert H Paul III, *Branch Mgr*
EMP: 17 **Publicly Held**
WEB: www.keurigdrpepper.com
SIC: 2086 Soft drinks: packaged in cans, bottles, etc.
HQ: The American Bottling Company
6425 Hall Of Fame Ln
Frisco TX 75034

(G-6147)
AMERICAN CABINET WORKS INC
863 Duskin Dr (32216-1550)
PHONE..................................904 672-6649
Daniel Cox, *Principal*
EMP: 6 **EST:** 2013
SALES (est): 70.2K **Privately Held**
WEB: www.americancabinetworks.com
SIC: 2434 Wood kitchen cabinets

(G-6148)
AMERICAN COMMODITY EXCH CORP (HQ)
Also Called: Acec
7825 Baymeadows Way No (32256-7557)
PHONE..................................904 687-0588
Paul Cambria, *CEO*
EMP: 7 **EST:** 2004
SQ FT: 1,200
SALES: 19MM
SALES (corp-wide): 28MM **Privately Held**
WEB: www.pcec1896.com
SIC: 3199 Boxes, leather
PA: Pcec (Latin America) Llc
33 E Main St Ste 500
Madison WI 53703
904 687-0588

(G-6149)
AMERICAN SCREEN PRINT INC
4122 Spring Park Rd (32207-5744)
PHONE..................................904 443-0071
Sara Housend, *President*
EMP: 5 **EST:** 1990
SQ FT: 900
SALES (est): 607.1K **Privately Held**
WEB: www.americanscreenprinting.com
SIC: 2759 Screen printing

(G-6150)
AMERICAN STANDARDS INC
4744 Kingsbury St (32205-5160)
PHONE..................................904 683-2189
Travis Goodale, *Principal*
EMP: 8 **EST:** 2011
SALES (est): 113.7K **Privately Held**
WEB: www.americanstandardair.com
SIC: 3585 Refrigeration & heating equipment

(G-6151)
AMERICAN STOCK LLC
3225 Anniston Rd (32246-4605)
PHONE..................................904 641-2055
A J Johns, *Principal*
EMP: 8 **EST:** 2007
SALES (est): 216.3K **Privately Held**
SIC: 2252 Socks

(G-6152)
AMERICAN TCHNCAL CRMICS FLA IN
2201 Corporate Sq Blvd (32216-1921)
PHONE..................................904 724-2000
Richard Monsorno, *Vice Pres*
Jay Infield, *Vice Pres*
Steve Rabe, *Vice Pres*
Kurt P Cummings, *CFO*
Evan Slavitt, *Admin Sec*
EMP: 55 **EST:** 1979
SALES (est): 2.6MM **Privately Held**
WEB: www.atceramics.com
SIC: 3675 Electronic capacitors
HQ: Kyocera Avx Components Corporation
1 Avx Blvd
Fountain Inn SC 29644
864 967-2150

(G-6153)
ANCHOR GLASS CONTAINER CORP
2121 Huron St (32254-2089)
P.O. Box 6932 (32236-6932)
PHONE..................................904 786-1010
John Rehrer, *General Mgr*
Jerry Brewer, *Warehouse Mgr*
John Burns, *Engineer*
Carrie Dodds, *Manager*
Mike Lane, *Manager*
EMP: 163 **Privately Held**
WEB: www.anchorglass.com
SIC: 3229 3221 Tableware, glass or glass ceramic; glass containers
PA: Anchor Glass Container Corporation
3001 N Rocky Point Dr E # 300
Tampa FL 33607

(G-6154)
AND TEES LLC
7272 Crescent Oaks Ct (32277-9719)
PHONE..................................904 745-0773
Thomas Frank Novak, *Principal*
EMP: 6 **EST:** 2011
SALES (est): 239.2K **Privately Held**
SIC: 2759 Screen printing

(G-6155)
ANDERSON BACKHOE SERVICE INC
5715 Cisco Dr W (32219-2787)
PHONE..................................904 759-9084
Richard Anderson, *Principal*
EMP: 7 **EST:** 2016
SALES (est): 246.6K **Privately Held**
WEB: www.anderson-backhoe-service.business.site
SIC: 3531 Backhoes

(G-6156)
ANDREWS 1ST CHOICE TRCKG LLC ✪
4532 Lane Ave S (32210-6824)
PHONE..................................205 703-5717
Rhonda Singleton,
EMP: 6 **EST:** 2021
SALES (est): 75K **Privately Held**
SIC: 3799 Transportation equipment

(G-6157)
ANJON INC
4801 Dawin Rd (32207-9512)
PHONE..................................904 730-9373
John Knapik, *President*
Janice Knapik, *Vice Pres*
EMP: 20 **EST:** 1989
SQ FT: 14,500
SALES (est): 3.4MM **Privately Held**
WEB: www.anjonholdings.com
SIC: 3842 Braces, orthopedic

(G-6158)
ANTIQUE & MODERN CABINETS INC
2384 Vans Ave (32207-6769)
PHONE..................................904 393-9055
Bill Patterson, *President*
Cindy Patterson, *Corp Secy*
David Greene, *Project Mgr*
Keri Taylor, *Manager*
EMP: 32 **EST:** 1951
SQ FT: 40,000
SALES (est): 2.8MM **Privately Held**
WEB: www.antiqueandmoderncabinets.com
SIC: 2521 2531 2541 7641 Wood office furniture; public building & related furniture; school furniture; office fixtures, wood; cabinets, except refrigerated: show, display, etc.: wood; shelving, office & store, wood; counters or counter display cases, wood; reupholstery & furniture repair; wood kitchen cabinets

(G-6159)
ANTONYO DENARD LLC ✪
1408 San Marco Blvd (32207-8536)
P.O. Box 9627 (32208-0627)
PHONE..................................904 290-1579
Antonyo Sanders, *CEO*
EMP: 10 **EST:** 2021
SALES (est): 180K **Privately Held**
SIC: 2389 Apparel & accessories

(G-6160)
APPLE SPICE - JAX
3061 Philips Hwy Unit 102 (32207-4303)
PHONE..................................904 328-6542
EMP: 7 **EST:** 2019
SALES (est): 342.2K **Privately Held**
WEB: www.applespice.com
SIC: 3571 Personal computers (microcomputers)

(G-6161)
APS PROMOTIONAL SOLUTIONS INC
7121 Beach Blvd (32216-2832)
PHONE..................................904 721-4977
Ronald Roelse, *President*
EMP: 18 **EST:** 1991
SQ FT: 10,000
SALES (est): 2.8MM **Privately Held**
WEB: www.apstitch.com
SIC: 2759 Screen printing

(G-6162)
APYELEN CURVES LLC ✪
13000 City Station Dr (32218-7224)
PHONE..................................904 434-8768
Patrinya Jordan, *Principal*
EMP: 10 **EST:** 2021
SALES (est): 331.8K **Privately Held**
SIC: 2331 Women's & misses' blouses & shirts

(G-6163)
ARB OPTIMAL INC
13783 Devan Lee Dr E (32226-5867)
PHONE..................................904 487-6874
Andre R Brown, *Principal*
EMP: 9 **EST:** 2014
SALES (est): 634.2K **Privately Held**
SIC: 3714 Motor vehicle parts & accessories

(G-6164)
ARC CREATIVE INC
Also Called: Image 360
2683 St Jhns Bluff Rd S S (32246-3763)
PHONE..................................904 996-7773
Ryan Rippel, *President*
EMP: 6 **EST:** 2008
SQ FT: 2,500
SALES (est): 1MM **Privately Held**
WEB: www.image360.com
SIC: 3993 Signs & advertising specialties

(G-6165)
ARC-RITE INC
569 Edgewood Ave S (32205-5332)
PHONE..................................386 325-3523
George Battle, *President*
John L Jones, *Vice Pres*
EMP: 22 **EST:** 1982
SQ FT: 16,000
SALES (est): 935.5K **Privately Held**
WEB: www.arc-riteinc.com
SIC: 3441 7692 3498 3443 Fabricated structural metal; welding repair; fabricated pipe & fittings; tanks, standard or custom fabricated: metal plate; pipe, large diameter: metal plate

(G-6166)
AREA RUGS MFG INC
3674 Saint Augustine Rd (32207-5572)
PHONE..................................904 398-5481

Kathleen Thomson, *President*
Kimberly Crisp, *Vice Pres*
EMP: 5 **EST:** 1966
SQ FT: 3,250
SALES (est): 450K **Privately Held**
SIC: 2273 7389 Rugs, hand & machine made; rug binding

(G-6167)
ARGOS
700 Palmetto St (32202-2406)
PHONE..................................678 368-4300
EMP: 20 **EST:** 2015
SALES (est): 1MM **Privately Held**
WEB: www.argos-us.com
SIC: 3273 Ready-mixed concrete

(G-6168)
ARLINGTON PRTG STATIONERS INC
Also Called: Apex Color
200 N Lee St (32204-1134)
PHONE..................................904 358-2928
Richard Ghelerter, *President*
Allan Ghelerter, *Vice Pres*
John Vega, *Representative*
EMP: 105 **EST:** 1971
SQ FT: 30,000
SALES (est): 15.1MM **Privately Held**
SIC: 2761 Strip forms (manifold business forms); unit sets (manifold business forms); computer forms, manifold or continuous

(G-6169)
ARMOR HOLDINGS FORENSICS LLC
Also Called: Nik Public Safety
13386 International Pkwy (32218-2383)
PHONE..................................904 485-1836
Steve Croskey, *CEO*
Jim Seidel, *Vice Pres*
▲ **EMP:** 29 **EST:** 1976
SQ FT: 16,000
SALES (est): 1.1MM **Privately Held**
WEB: www.forensics-intl.com
SIC: 3999 Fingerprint equipment

(G-6170)
ASH SIGNS INC
Also Called: Fastsigns
2141 St Johns Bluff Rd S (32246-2307)
PHONE..................................904 724-7446
Ann K Helfer, *President*
Todd J Helfer, *Vice Pres*
EMP: 8 **EST:** 1995
SALES (est): 1.2MM **Privately Held**
WEB: www.fastsigns.com
SIC: 3993 Signs & advertising specialties

(G-6171)
ATI2 INC
10448 Atlantic Blvd (32225-6771)
PHONE..................................904 396-3766
Edwin Segars, *President*
EMP: 9 **EST:** 2011
SALES (est): 260.9K **Privately Held**
SIC: 3312 Stainless steel

(G-6172)
ATLANTIC COAST ASPHALT CO
10382 Florida Min Blvd E (32257)
PHONE..................................904 268-0274
Randall Bristol, *Principal*
EMP: 20 **EST:** 2009
SALES (est): 112.4K **Privately Held**
WEB: www.hubbard.com
SIC: 2951 1622 Asphalt paving blocks (not from refineries); bridge construction

(G-6173)
ATLANTIC DRY DOCK
8500 Heckscher Dr (32226-2434)
PHONE..................................904 251-1545
EMP: 37 **EST:** 2019
SALES (est): 316.6K **Privately Held**
WEB: www.crandalldrydock.com
SIC: 3731 Shipbuilding & repairing

(G-6174)
ATLANTIC INSULATION INC
Also Called: Eagle Insulation Fabrication
325 Dennard Ave (32254-3401)
P.O. Box 37332 (32236-7332)
PHONE..................................904 354-2217
Richard K Whitlock, *President*
Mike Chapman, *Vice Pres*
Shane Whitlock, *Manager*
▲ **EMP:** 85 **EST:** 1985
SQ FT: 12,500
SALES (est): 9.3MM **Privately Held**
SIC: 3086 5082 Insulation or cushioning material, foamed plastic; ladders

(G-6175)
ATLANTIC INTL DISTRS INC
Also Called: Atlantic Quality Parts
5061 Shawland Rd Ste A (32254-1649)
PHONE..................................904 725-5202
Ken Maszy, *President*
◆ **EMP:** 139 **EST:** 1998
SALES (est): 2.4MM
SALES (corp-wide): 176.7MM **Privately Held**
SIC: 3559 5085 Semiconductor manufacturing machinery; cans for fruits & vegetables
PA: Arrowhead Engineered Products, Inc.
3705 95th Ave Ne
Circle Pines MN 55014
763 255-2555

(G-6176)
ATLANTIC MARBLE COMPANY INC
11303 Bus Pk Blvd Ste 100 (32256-2783)
PHONE..................................904 262-6262
Ronald A Brown, *Ch of Bd*
Robert A Booth, *President*
EMP: 26 **EST:** 1987
SQ FT: 11,000
SALES (est): 1.4MM **Privately Held**
WEB: www.atlanticmarbleco.com
SIC: 3281 2821 Marble, building: cut & shaped; plastics materials & resins

(G-6177)
ATLANTIC MARINE INC
8500 Heckscher Dr (32226-2434)
PHONE..................................904 251-1580
Edward J Fleming Jr, *President*
Byron N Thompson Jr, *Corp Secy*
EMP: 5 **EST:** 1964
SALES (est): 868.9K **Privately Held**
WEB: www.atlanticmarinefl.com
SIC: 3731 Shipbuilding & repairing

(G-6178)
ATLANTIC TACTICAL INC
13386 International Pkwy (32218-2383)
PHONE..................................909 923-7300
EMP: 5 **EST:** 2018
SALES (est): 336.4K **Privately Held**
WEB: www.safariland.com
SIC: 3842 Surgical appliances & supplies

(G-6179)
ATSG LOGISTIC SUPPORT SERVICE
10142 103rd St Ste 102 (32210-9252)
PHONE..................................904 579-4596
Wesley A Doty, *Principal*
Rodney Housand, *Principal*
EMP: 10 **EST:** 2011
SALES (est): 1.3MM **Privately Held**
WEB: www.atsgsupport.com
SIC: 3769 8711 8741 8744 Airframe assemblies, guided missiles; engineering services; personnel management; facilities support services

(G-6180)
AUTOMATED PRINTING SERVICES
7124 Glendyne Dr N (32216-5789)
PHONE..................................904 731-3244
Jeffrey D Day, *General Mgr*
Jodi Day, *Vice Pres*
EMP: 5 **EST:** 1971
SALES (est): 384K **Privately Held**
WEB: www.sdn.com
SIC: 2752 Commercial printing, offset

(G-6181)
AVK INDUSTRIES INC
2052 St Johns Bluff Rd S (32246-8783)
PHONE..................................904 998-8400
Andrew J Cherinka, *President*
▼ **EMP:** 10 **EST:** 1990
SQ FT: 3,600
SALES (est): 897.2K **Privately Held**
WEB: www.avkinc.com
SIC: 3829 Testing equipment: abrasion, shearing strength, etc.

(G-6182)
AVON COMPANY
11757 Beach Blvd Ste 14 (32246-6633)
PHONE..................................386 405-7208
Barilynn Goldstein, *Manager*
EMP: 6 **Privately Held**
WEB: www.avon.com
SIC: 2844 Cosmetic preparations
HQ: The Avon Company
1 Liberty Plz
New York NY 10006
212 282-6000

(G-6183)
AZ CHEM HOLDINGS LP
4600 Touchton Rd E # 1200 (32246-8299)
PHONE..................................800 526-5294
Kevin M Fogarty, *President*
Kellie D Hardee, *Treasurer*
EMP: 112 **EST:** 2010
SALES (est): 14.1MM **Publicly Held**
WEB: www.kraton.com
SIC: 2861 2911 Gum & wood chemicals; petroleum refining
HQ: Kraton Polymers Llc
15710 John F Kennedy Blvd # 300
Houston TX 77032

(G-6184)
AZAR INDUSTRIES INC
Also Called: Azar & Company
719 E Union St (32206-5606)
P.O. Box 5662 (32247-5662)
PHONE..................................904 358-2354
Sandra Azar, *President*
Philip Azar, *Treasurer*
EMP: 34 **EST:** 1991
SQ FT: 3,800
SALES (est): 3.3MM **Privately Held**
WEB: www.azarsausage.com
SIC: 2011 Meat packing plants

(G-6185)
B & J ATLANTIC INC
5164 Shawland Rd (32254-1651)
PHONE..................................904 338-0088
Minh-Trang Dang, *President*
Thai Q Nguyen, *Vice Pres*
EMP: 32 **EST:** 1998
SQ FT: 15,000
SALES (est): 5.7MM **Privately Held**
WEB: www.bjatlantic.com
SIC: 3613 3728 Cubicles (electric switchboard equipment); aircraft parts & equipment

(G-6186)
B R EXPRESS
221 Arlington Rd N (32211-7806)
P.O. Box 351081 (32235-1081)
PHONE..................................904 881-2556
Rick Madsen, *Owner*
EMP: 6 **EST:** 2010
SALES (est): 208.7K **Privately Held**
SIC: 3537 Trucks: freight, baggage, etc.: industrial, except mining

(G-6187)
BACARDI BOTTLING CORPORATION
12200 N Main St (32218-3819)
PHONE..................................904 757-1290
Mahesh Madhavan, *CEO*
Cheryl Argamasilla, *Opers Staff*
Alan Horton, *Purch Mgr*
Walter Rios, *Treasurer*
Manuel Andreu, *Controller*
◆ **EMP:** 250 **EST:** 1969
SQ FT: 200,000
SALES (est): 48.4MM **Privately Held**
WEB: www.bacardi.com
SIC: 2085 2086 Rum (alcoholic beverage); bottled & canned soft drinks
HQ: Bacardi International Limited
Bacardi Building
Hamilton

(G-6188)
BAD FISH POWDER COAT
2071 Emerson St (32207-5597)
PHONE..................................904 465-8888
Ron Doherty, *Manager*
EMP: 6 **EST:** 2014
SALES (est): 122.5K **Privately Held**
WEB: www.badfishcoatings.com
SIC: 3479 Coating of metals & formed products

(G-6189)
BAE SYSTEMS STHAST SHPYRDS AMH (DH)
8500 Heckscher Dr (32226-2434)
PHONE..................................904 251-3111
Linda Hudson, *CEO*
John Carter, *Superintendent*
Paul W Cobb Jr, *Vice Pres*
Douglas Coleman, *Vice Pres*
John Marinucci, *Vice Pres*
◆ **EMP:** 100 **EST:** 1986
SALES (est): 175.5MM
SALES (corp-wide): 25.6B **Privately Held**
WEB: www.baesystems.com
SIC: 3731 Cargo vessels, building & repairing; barges, building & repairing; tankers, building & repairing; tugboats, building & repairing

GEOGRAPHIC

(G-6190)
BAE SYSTEMS TECH SOL SRVC INC
2292 Mayport Rd (32233-2707)
PHONE..................................904 241-1631
Michael Cetnarowski, *Superintendent*
Jeff Salvie, *Project Mgr*
Leon Woody, *Manager*
Norma Corsetti, *Products*
EMP: 6
SALES (corp-wide): 25.6B **Privately Held**
SIC: 3812 Navigational systems & instruments
HQ: Bae Systems Technology Solutions & Services Inc.
520 Gaither Rd
Rockville MD 20850
703 847-5820

(G-6191)
BAG-A-NUT LLC
Also Called: Ammo-Up
10601 Theresa Dr (32246-8758)
PHONE..................................904 641-3934
Caleb Dudley, *Managing Prtnr*
Caleb L Dudley, *Managing Prtnr*
Annie Rodriguez, *General Mgr*
Shama Dudley, *Marketing Mgr*
▼ **EMP:** 8 **EST:** 1990
SQ FT: 20,000
SALES (est): 1.3MM **Privately Held**
WEB: www.baganut.com
SIC: 3523 3949 Harvesters, fruit, vegetable, tobacco, etc.; shooting equipment & supplies, general

(G-6192)
BAKERS SPORTS INC (PA)
Also Called: Baker's Sporting Goods
3600 Beachwood Ct (32224-5705)
PHONE..................................904 388-8126
Josh Baker, *President*
Tiffany Baker, *Vice Pres*
Jaime Simmons, *Director*
Jesse Schultz, *Art Dir*
▲ **EMP:** 44 **EST:** 1997
SQ FT: 10,000
SALES (est): 10.9MM **Privately Held**
WEB: www.bakerssport.com
SIC: 2396 2395 5941 2329 Screen printing on fabric articles; emblems, embroidered; sporting goods & bicycle shops; men's & boys' athletic uniforms

(G-6193)
BALLARD PRINTING INC
Also Called: Best Choice Printing
1233 Lane Ave S Ste 11 (32205-6254)
PHONE..................................904 783-4430
Jody Ballard, *President*
Diane Ballard, *Treasurer*
EMP: 6 **EST:** 1983
SALES (est): 491.2K **Privately Held**
WEB: www.ballardprinting.com
SIC: 2752 Commercial printing, offset

(G-6194)
BARBES PUBLISHING INC
Also Called: Beson 4 Media Group
13500 Sutton Park Dr S # 105
(32224-5291)
PHONE..................................904 992-9945
Aj Beson, *President*
Mike Hicks, *Exec VP*
Courtney Cooper, *Opers Staff*
Jason Grim, *Graphic Designe*
EMP: 10 **EST:** 1998
SQ FT: 2,200
SALES (est): 1.6MM **Privately Held**
WEB: www.beson4.com
SIC: 2741 Miscellaneous publishing

(G-6195)
BASTECH INC
3211 Powers Ave (32207-8013)
PHONE..................................904 737-1722
Raymond Basso, *Owner*
Bruce Kissel, *Plant Mgr*
Theresa Freeman, *Purch Mgr*
EMP: 15 **EST:** 2007
SALES (est): 2.5MM **Privately Held**
WEB: www.bastechllc.com
SIC: 2874 Phosphates

(G-6196)
BASTECH LLC
3035 Powers Ave Ste 3 (32207-8033)
PHONE..................................904 737-1722
Thomas S Schafer, *CEO*
Thomas Schafer, *CEO*
Bob Closs, *President*
Bill Graves, *Business Mgr*
John Hines, *Vice Pres*
▲ **EMP:** 32 **EST:** 2007
SQ FT: 8,370
SALES (est): 18.2MM **Privately Held**
WEB: www.bastechllc.com
SIC: 2869 Industrial organic chemicals

(G-6197)
BATEH NETWORKING SOLUTIONS LLC
1107 Montego Rd W (32216-3210)
PHONE..................................904 725-2282
Tyler Bateh, *Admin Sec*
EMP: 6 **EST:** 2011
SALES (est): 99.2K **Privately Held**
SIC: 3589 High pressure cleaning equipment

(G-6198)
BCR ENVIRONMENTAL CORPORATION (PA)
4063 Salisbury Rd Ste 203 (32216-6199)
PHONE..................................904 819-9170
Joshua Scott, *CEO*
Joshua R Scott, *CEO*
Aaron F Zahn, *President*
Jim Flanary, *COO*
Kevin F Dunlap, *Vice Pres*
EMP: 44 **EST:** 2011
SALES (est): 8.3MM **Privately Held**
WEB: www.bcrinc.com
SIC: 3567 3589 8744 Driers & redriers, industrial process; commercial cooking & foodwarming equipment;

(G-6199)
BDT CONCEPTS INC
5105 Philips Hwy Ste 205 (32207-1709)
P.O. Box 600128 (32260-0128)
PHONE..................................904 730-2590
Beverly Williams, *President*
Dan Williams, *Treasurer*
EMP: 9 **EST:** 1991
SALES (est): 1.4MM **Privately Held**
WEB: www.bdtconcepts.com
SIC: 3861 5734 Toners, prepared photographic (not made in chemical plants); computer & software stores

(G-6200)
BEACH NEON & SIGN CO
1940 Spearing St (32206-3942)
PHONE..................................904 479-3599
EMP: 6 **EST:** 2018
SALES (est): 46K **Privately Held**
WEB: www.generalsignservice.com
SIC: 3993 Neon signs

(G-6201)
BEAUTYGE BRANDS USA INC
5344 Overmyer Dr (32254-3645)
PHONE..................................904 693-1200
Lemoyne Metlock, *Branch Mgr*
EMP: 193 **Publicly Held**
SIC: 2844 Hair coloring preparations
HQ: Beautyge Brands Usa, Inc.
1515 Wazee St Ste 200
Denver CO 80202

(G-6202)
BELETS MILLWORK INC
505 N Myrtle Ave (32204-1317)
PHONE..................................904 353-8600
Jacques Stewart Belet, *President*
Bruce W Belet, *Vice Pres*
Matt Geoghegan, *Vice Pres*
EMP: 15 **EST:** 2001
SQ FT: 20,000
SALES (est): 269K **Privately Held**
WEB: www.beletsmillwork.com
SIC: 2431 1751 2541 Doors, wood; cabinet & finish carpentry; store & office display cases & fixtures; display fixtures, wood; store fixtures, wood; table or counter tops, plastic laminated

(G-6203)
BEN JAMMIN ISLAND JERKY LLC
12424 Gately Rd S (32225-3948)
PHONE..................................904 220-2067
Reanee Aranas, *Principal*
EMP: 6 **EST:** 2014
SALES (est): 239.4K **Privately Held**
WEB: www.benjamminislandjerky.com
SIC: 2013 Snack sticks, including jerky: from purchased meat

(G-6204)
BENCHMARK QUALITY GUTTERS INC
9526 Argyle Frest Blvd St (32222)
PHONE..................................904 759-9800
Michael A Katrinic, *President*
EMP: 8 **EST:** 2008
SALES (est): 863.3K **Privately Held**
WEB: www.benchmarkqualitygutters.com
SIC: 3444 Gutters, sheet metal

(G-6205)
BENNER CHINA AND GLWR OF FLA
Also Called: Odyssey
5329 Powers Ave (32207-8013)
PHONE..................................904 733-4620
James Y Wang, *President*
Karin Baisden, *Vice Pres*
Scott Mills, *Vice Pres*
Scott Wrazin, *Bookkeeper*
Deanna Austin, *Cust Mgr*
▲ **EMP:** 50
SQ FT: 90,000
SALES (est): 8.7MM **Privately Held**
WEB: www.odysseyfl.com
SIC: 2759 Screen printing

(G-6206)
BENNETTS CUSTOM CABINETS INC
9897 Sisson Dr (32218-5542)
PHONE..................................904 751-1455
Brenda A Bennett, *President*
Wesley D Bennett, *Vice Pres*
Barbara Corzo, *Accounts Exec*
Carlos Mitchell, *Manager*
Jairo Serrano, *Supervisor*
EMP: 27 **EST:** 1984
SQ FT: 6,500
SALES (est): 4.1MM **Privately Held**
WEB: www.bennettscustomcabinets.com
SIC: 2434 Wood kitchen cabinets

(G-6207)
BENTON MACHINE WORKS INC
740 Carlton St (32208-4404)
PHONE..................................904 768-9161
Connie Lee, *President*
Connie Evans, *President*
Donna Stallard, *Exec VP*
James E Stallard, *Exec VP*
Alan Stallard, *Accounts Mgr*
EMP: 8 **EST:** 1963
SQ FT: 7,500
SALES: 1MM **Privately Held**
WEB: www.bmw-cnc.com
SIC: 3599 3469 Machine shop, jobbing & repair; machine parts, stamped or pressed metal

(G-6208)
BIG OS STUMP GRINDING
101 Baisden Rd Apt 2 (32218-4193)
PHONE..................................904 945-5900
Phillip R Robinson, *Principal*
EMP: 9 **EST:** 2007
SALES (est): 459.9K **Privately Held**
SIC: 3599 Grinding castings for the trade

(G-6209)
BLACK CREEK PRECISION LLC
5151 Sunbeam Rd Ste 10 (32257-6135)
PHONE..................................888 426-6624
Darin Phipps, *President*
Jeff Stewart, *General Mgr*
Alm Palmer, *Vice Pres*
EMP: 12 **EST:** 2016
SALES (est): 2.1MM **Privately Held**
WEB: www.blackcreekprecision.com
SIC: 3999 Manufacturing industries

(G-6210)
BLACK KNIGHT INC (PA)
601 Riverside Ave (32204-2946)
PHONE..................................904 854-5100
Anthony M Jabbour, *Ch of Bd*
Joseph M Nackashi, *President*
Lori Fletcher, *Exec VP*
Michael L Gravelle, *Exec VP*
Richard Lombardi, *Senior VP*
EMP: 462 **EST:** 2013
SALES: 1.2B **Publicly Held**
WEB: www.blackknightinc.com
SIC: 7372 7373 Prepackaged software; computer integrated systems design

(G-6211)
BLACK KNIGHT FINCL SVCS INC (HQ)
601 Riverside Ave (32204-2946)
PHONE..................................904 854-5100
Tom Sanzone, *President*
Maria Vivas, *Counsel*
Willie Anderson, *Senior VP*
Andrew Barr, *Vice Pres*
Ann Collins, *Vice Pres*
EMP: 2735 **EST:** 2014
SALES: 1.2B **Publicly Held**
WEB: www.blackknightinc.com
SIC: 7372 Prepackaged software
PA: Black Knight, Inc.
601 Riverside Ave
Jacksonville FL 32204
904 854-5100

(G-6212)
BLAIR MACHINE & TOOL INC
1301 Riverplace Blvd # 800 (32207-9047)
PHONE..................................904 731-4377
Grover Blair, *President*
Pearl Blair, *Corp Secy*
Edward Blair, *Vice Pres*
Glen Blair, *Vice Pres*
Janice Mc Dowell, *Vice Pres*
EMP: 18
SQ FT: 35,000
SALES (est): 3.3MM **Privately Held**
WEB: www.blairmachine.com
SIC: 3599 Custom machinery

(G-6213)
BLUE EAGLE ALLIANCE INC
4651 Salisbury Rd # 4028 (32256-6107)
PHONE..................................904 322-8067
Carl Thomas, *CEO*
EMP: 8 **EST:** 2010
SALES (est): 250K **Privately Held**
SIC: 3578 Calculating & accounting equipment

(G-6214)
BLUE SKY LABS LLC
3811 University Blvd W # 4 (32217-1210)
PHONE..................................901 268-6988
Garland Sullivan, *Owner*
Shane Campbell, *Opers Mgr*
Alex Kiss, *Development*
Max Abre, *Manager*
EMP: 5 **EST:** 2018
SALES (est): 464.7K **Privately Held**
SIC: 2023 Dietary supplements, dairy & non-dairy based

(G-6215)
BLUE WATER INDUSTRIES LLC (PA)
Also Called: Blue Water Industries - FL LLC
200 W Forsyth St Ste 1200 (32202-4326)
PHONE..................................904 512-7706
Ted Baker, *CEO*
Charlie Wodehouse, *CFO*
EMP: 8 **EST:** 2016
SALES (est): 32.1MM **Privately Held**
WEB: www.bluewaterindustriesdotcom.wordpress.com
SIC: 3532 Washers, aggregate & sand

(G-6216)
BLUEGRASS MATERIALS CO LLC (HQ)
200 W Forsyth St Ste 1200 (32202-4326)
P.O. Box 30013, Raleigh NC (27622-0013)
PHONE..................................919 781-4550
C Howard Nye, *President*
Roselyn R Bar, *Exec VP*
James A J Nickolas, *CFO*
Jeremy Goad, *Sales Mgr*
Edward L Baker, *Mng Member*
EMP: 26 **EST:** 2010
SALES (est): 200MM **Publicly Held**
WEB: www.martinmarietta.com
SIC: 3271 3532 5032 Concrete block & brick; washers, aggregate & sand; concrete & cinder block; aggregate

(G-6217)
BOAT WORKS
1282 Belmont Ter (32207-3218)
PHONE..................................904 389-0090
Jonathan Barron L, *Principal*
EMP: 7 **EST:** 2001
SALES (est): 171.5K **Privately Held**
SIC: 3732 Boat building & repairing

(G-6218)
BOATSWAINS LOCKER INC
4565 Lakeside Dr (32210-3392)
PHONE..................................904 388-0231
Bill J Bransford, *President*
William J Bransford, *President*
Jeanne A Bransford, *Treasurer*
▼ **EMP:** 22 **EST:** 1965
SQ FT: 4,800
SALES (est): 1.2MM **Privately Held**
WEB: www.boatswains-locker.com
SIC: 2394 Convertible tops, canvas or boat: from purchased materials

(G-6219)
BOBS BACKFLOW & PLUMBING CO
4640 Sub Chaser Ct # 113 (32244-3319)
PHONE..................................904 268-8009
Patricia Novak, *President*
Robert A Novak, *Vice Pres*
EMP: 5 **EST:** 1987
SALES (est): 690.7K **Privately Held**
WEB: www.bobsbackflow.com
SIC: 3432 Plumbing fixture fittings & trim

(G-6220)
BOEING COMPANY
6222 Pow Mia Memorial Pkw (32221-8138)
PHONE..................................904 772-1273
Jon Fleming, *Prdtn Mgr*
Eli Bekkum, *Engineer*
John Herald, *Engineer*
Karen Trotter, *Manager*
William Zeigler, *Software Dev*
EMP: 6
SALES (corp-wide): 58.1B **Publicly Held**
WEB: www.boeing.com
SIC: 3721 Airplanes, fixed or rotary wing
PA: The Boeing Company
100 N Riverside Plz
Chicago IL 60606
312 544-2000

(G-6221)
BOEING COMPANY
6211 Aviation Ave (32221-8113)
P.O. Box 150844 (32215)
PHONE..................................904 317-2490

Dee Burcham, *Manager*
Atchison Louis, *Manager*
EMP: 6
SALES (corp-wide): 58.1B **Publicly Held**
WEB: www.boeing.com
SIC: 3721 Aircraft
PA: The Boeing Company
100 N Riverside Plz
Chicago IL 60606
312 544-2000

(G-6222)
BOGGY CREEK BOAT CO LLC
14476 Duval Pl W Ste 203 (32218-9414)
PHONE..................................904 707-0952
Richard Dewiggins, *Manager*
EMP: 7 **EST:** 2012
SALES (est): 89.5K **Privately Held**
WEB: www.boggycreekboats.com
SIC: 3732 Boat building & repairing

(G-6223)
BOLD CITY BRAVES LLC
3385 Intl Vlg Dr W (32277-0997)
PHONE..................................904 545-3480
Eric Owen, *Principal*
EMP: 13 **EST:** 2017
SALES (est): 57.2K **Privately Held**
WEB: www.boldcitybrewery.com
SIC: 2082 Malt beverages

(G-6224)
BOLD CITY SPRAY COATINGS LLC
2612 Arlex Dr E (32211-4002)
PHONE..................................904 655-0825
Holly D Califano, *Principal*
EMP: 6 **EST:** 2017
SALES (est): 224.3K **Privately Held**
SIC: 3479 Metal coating & allied service

(G-6225)
BONSAL AMERICAN INC
6659 Highway Ave (32254-3549)
PHONE..................................904 783-0605
Craig Delicato, *Manager*
EMP: 6
SQ FT: 20,040
SALES (corp-wide): 27.5B **Privately Held**
SIC: 3272 Concrete products
HQ: Bonsal American, Inc.
625 Griffith Rd Ste 100
Charlotte NC 28217
704 525-1621

(G-6226)
BORE TECH INC
5333 Skylark Ct (32257-1227)
PHONE..................................904 262-0752
EMP: 5 **EST:** 1995
SALES: 580K **Privately Held**
SIC: 1381 Oil/Gas Well Drilling

(G-6227)
BOX SEAT CLOTHING COMPANY
5555 W 1st St (32254-1670)
PHONE..................................800 787-7792
Heather Cornelius, *Manager*
▲ **EMP:** 5 **EST:** 2011
SALES (est): 318K **Privately Held**
SIC: 2326 Work shirts: men's, youths' & boys'

(G-6228)
BOXSEAT INC
5245 Commonwealth Ave (32254-1629)
PHONE..................................850 656-1223
Michael Rupp, *President*
EMP: 17 **EST:** 1973
SQ FT: 13,000
SALES (est): 326.7K **Privately Held**
SIC: 2326 Work apparel, except uniforms

(G-6229)
BRADDOCK METALLURGICAL INC (HQ)
14600 Duval Pl W (32218-9417)
PHONE..................................386 267-0955
Steve Braddock, *CEO*
George Gieger, *President*
Stephen R Braddock, *Principal*
Bill Braddock, *Exec VP*
William K Braddock, *Exec VP*
EMP: 11 **EST:** 1986
SQ FT: 12,500
SALES (est): 27.4MM **Privately Held**
WEB: www.braddockmt.com
SIC: 3398 Metal heat treating
PA: Braddock Metallurgical Holding Company, Inc.
400 Fentress Blvd
Daytona Beach FL 32114
386 323-1500

(G-6230)
BRAKE-FUNDERBURK ENTPS INC
Also Called: B F E
8383 Baycenter Rd (32256-7415)
PHONE..................................904 730-6788
Eric Nord, *President*
Hoang Votran, *Design Engr*
EMP: 25 **EST:** 1971
SQ FT: 30,000
SALES (est): 4.6MM **Privately Held**
WEB: www.bfeinc.net
SIC: 3589 Commercial cooking & foodwarming equipment

(G-6231)
BRAND LABEL INC
8295 Western Way Cir (32256-8302)
PHONE..................................904 737-6433
Lemoyne F Matlock, *President*
Robert J Metzger, *Corp Secy*
Ray Hamilton, *Plant Mgr*
Leann Metzger, *CFO*
Nancy Metzger, *Shareholder*
EMP: 35 **EST:** 1970
SQ FT: 16,000
SALES: 7.1MM **Privately Held**
WEB: www.brandlabelinc.com
SIC: 2672 Labels (unprinted), gummed: made from purchased materials

(G-6232)
BRANTLEY MACHINE & FABRICATION
4003 N Canal St (32209-3623)
P.O. Box 12268 (32209-0268)
PHONE..................................904 359-0554
William E Taylor, *President*
Pam Walker, *Corp Secy*
EMP: 10 **EST:** 1986
SQ FT: 8,000
SALES (est): 790K **Privately Held**
SIC: 3441 3599 Fabricated structural metal; machine shop, jobbing & repair

(G-6233)
BRC SPORTS LLC
Also Called: Burbank Sports Nets
3600 Beachwood Ct (32224-5705)
PHONE..................................904 388-8126
Lacey Nell, *Principal*
EMP: 10 **EST:** 2016
SALES (est): 387K **Privately Held**
WEB: www.burbanksportnets.com
SIC: 3949 Sporting & athletic goods

(G-6234)
BREAK-FREE INC
13386 International Pkwy (32218-2383)
PHONE..................................800 347-1200
Jonathan M Spiller, *President*
EMP: 21 **EST:** 1989
SALES (est): 565.1K **Privately Held**
WEB: www.safariland.com
SIC: 2992 3489 Lubricating oils & greases; ordnance & accessories

(G-6235)
BREMER GROUP COMPANY INC
11243-5 Saint Johns (32246)
PHONE..................................904 645-0004
Ross Bremer, *President*
EMP: 10 **EST:** 1994
SQ FT: 4,500
SALES (est): 1.5MM **Privately Held**
WEB: www.bremergroup.com
SIC: 3842 Braces, orthopedic

(G-6236)
BREW CENTRAL LLC
1024 Park St (32204-3908)
PHONE..................................936 714-3402
Jack Twachtman, *Administration*
EMP: 11 **EST:** 2015
SALES (est): 85.8K **Privately Held**
SIC: 2082 Malt beverages

(G-6237)
BRITE LITE SERVICE COMPANY
Also Called: Brite Lite Signs
5300 Shad Rd (32257-2006)
PHONE..................................904 398-5305
Michael Moore, *President*
Bonnie Moore, *Vice Pres*
▲ **EMP:** 14 **EST:** 1972
SQ FT: 35,000
SALES (est): 287.3K **Privately Held**
SIC: 3993 Electric signs

(G-6238)
BROWN DOG PUBLISHING INC
8802 Corporate Square Ct (32216-1984)
PHONE..................................904 262-2114
EMP: 6 **EST:** 2018
SALES (est): 256.9K **Privately Held**
WEB: www.browndogpressllc.com
SIC: 2741 Miscellaneous publishing

(G-6239)
BRT OAKLEAF PET INC
Also Called: Pet & Feed Store
1619 Leon Rd (32246-8649)
PHONE..................................904 563-1212
Kelong Shi, *President*
Xiaodan Shi, *Principal*
EMP: 9 **EST:** 2013
SALES (est): 882.4K **Privately Held**
SIC: 2048 Prepared feeds

(G-6240)
BRUSS COMPANY
5441 W 5th St (32254-1664)
PHONE..................................904 693-0688
EMP: 34
SALES (corp-wide): 43.1B **Publicly Held**
WEB: www.tysonfreshmeats.com
SIC: 2011 Beef products from beef slaughtered on site
HQ: The Bruss Company
3548 N Kostner Ave
Chicago IL 60641
773 282-2900

(G-6241)
BRUT PRINTING CO INC
503 Parker St (32202-1199)
PHONE..................................904 354-5055
Adam H Brut Sr, *Ch of Bd*
Adam H Brut Jr, *President*
Dianne Brut, *Corp Secy*
Cliff Summerville, *COO*
Lissley Maddox, *Bookkeeper*
EMP: 38 **EST:** 1966
SQ FT: 20,000
SALES (est): 4.3MM **Privately Held**
WEB: www.brutprinting.com
SIC: 2752 2754 Commercial printing, offset; job printing, gravure

(G-6242)
BUBBA FOODS LLC (PA)
4339 Roosevelt Blvd # 400 (32210-2004)
P.O. Box 2823 (32203-2823)
PHONE..................................904 482-1900
Thomas Pirkle, *Regional Mgr*
William Morris, *Mng Member*
Steven L Coon, *Mng Member*
Clark Schaffer, *Mng Member*
EMP: 128 **EST:** 1993
SQ FT: 55,000
SALES (est): 23.4MM **Privately Held**
WEB: www.bubbafoods.com
SIC: 2011 Meat packing plants

(G-6243)
BUCHANAN SIGNS SCREEN PROCESS
Also Called: Buchanan Sign & Flag
6755 Beach Blvd (32216-2818)
PHONE..................................904 725-5500
Barbara Buchanan, *President*
Harold G Buchanan, *Vice Pres*
Michael Cross, *CFO*
EMP: 24 **EST:** 1960
SQ FT: 15,000
SALES (est): 1.8MM **Privately Held**
WEB: www.signandflag.com
SIC: 2399 3993 5999 3446 Flags, fabric; signs & advertising specialties; banners, flags, decals & posters; flags; architectural metalwork; automotive & apparel trimmings

(G-6244)
BURBANK TRAWL MAKERS INC
Also Called: Burbank Sport Nets
13913 Duval Rd Ste 100 (32218-0200)
P.O. Box 16198, Fernandina Beach (32035-3120)
PHONE..................................904 321-0976
Josh Baker, *President*
Hunt Er, *Vice Pres*
Josh Kubala, *Project Mgr*
Lacey Nell, *Office Mgr*
EMP: 31 **EST:** 1958
SALES (est): 9.5MM **Privately Held**
WEB: www.bakerssport.com
SIC: 2258 2399 Net & netting products; fishing nets
PA: Baker's Sports, Inc.
3600 Beachwood Ct
Jacksonville FL 32224

(G-6245)
BURCH WELDING & FABRICATION
2324 Phoenix Ave (32206-3139)
P.O. Box 28239 (32226-8239)
PHONE..................................904 353-6513
Kenith Burch, *President*
Larry Burch, *Vice Pres*
EMP: 9 **EST:** 1989
SQ FT: 15,000
SALES (est): 884.7K **Privately Held**
WEB: www.burchwelding.com
SIC: 3441 Fabricated structural metal

(G-6246)
BUSINESS JRNL PUBLICATIONS INC
Also Called: Jacksonville Business Journal
112 W Adams St Ste 200 (32202-3861)
PHONE..................................904 396-3502
David Sillick, *President*
Justin Fowler, *Opers Staff*
Sharon Oliver, *Research*
Jeff Blumenthal, *Finance*
Thomas Sander, *Accounts Exec*
EMP: 20 **EST:** 2010
SALES (est): 2MM **Privately Held**
SIC: 2711 Newspapers, publishing & printing

(G-6247)
C & H PRINTING INC
11315-1 St Jhns Indus Pkw (32246-6606)
PHONE..................................904 620-8444
Patrick Calder, *President*
Winston Horton, *Vice Pres*
Jon Thrasher, *Sales Staff*
Jill Cavin,
EMP: 8 **EST:** 1998
SQ FT: 5,200
SALES (est): 1MM **Privately Held**
WEB: www.candhprinting.com
SIC: 2752 Commercial printing, offset

(G-6248)
CABINETRY MASTERS LLC
4193 Oldfield Crossing Dr (32223-7807)
PHONE..................................954 549-8646
Matthew Herman, *Principal*
EMP: 8 **EST:** 2015
SALES (est): 390.7K **Privately Held**
WEB: www.cabinetrymasters.com
SIC: 2434 Wood kitchen cabinets

(G-6249)
CADRE HOLDINGS INC (PA)
Also Called: Safariland Group, The
13386 International Pkwy (32218-2383)
PHONE..................................904 741-5400
Warren B Kanders, *CEO*
Brad Williams, *President*
Blaine Browers, *CFO*
JD Devine, *VP Sales*
Jeffrey Bridi, *Manager*
EMP: 112 **EST:** 2012
SQ FT: 132,224
SALES (est): 1B **Privately Held**
SIC: 2311 3842 3199 3069 Military uniforms, men's & youths': purchased materials; personal safety equipment; holsters, leather; life jackets, inflatable: rubberized fabric

(G-6250)
CAMPEN COMPANIES
2160 Park St (32204-3812)
PHONE..................................904 388-6000
Ben Campen, *Principal*
EMP: 6 **EST:** 2005
SALES (est): 633.2K **Privately Held**
WEB: www.campenproperties.com
SIC: 2952 Asphalt felts & coatings

(G-6251)
CANAM STEEL CORPORATION
140 Ellis Rd S (32254-3547)
PHONE..................................904 781-0898
Russ Rocco, *General Mgr*
EMP: 7
SALES (corp-wide): 586.3MM **Privately Held**
WEB: www.cscsteelusa.com
SIC: 3441 Building components, structural steel
PA: Canam Steel Corporation
4010 Clay St
Point Of Rocks MD 21777
301 874-5141

(G-6252)
CANDLE FOR YOU LLC
6190 Riviera Ln (32216-1214)
PHONE..................................920 883-7900
Mariya Chepurko, *Branch Mgr*
EMP: 7
SALES (corp-wide): 30.6K **Privately Held**
SIC: 3999 Candles
PA: Candle For You Llc
5800 Beach Blvd 203-106
Jacksonville FL

(G-6253)
CANNONS OF JACK LLC
6150 Richard St (32216-6052)
PHONE..................................904 733-3524
Orren K Phillips, *President*
EMP: 6 **EST:** 1958
SQ FT: 6,000
SALES (est): 809.6K **Privately Held**
WEB: www.cannonsofjax.net
SIC: 7692 Welding repair

(G-6254)
CARIB ENERGY (USA) LLC
9487 Regency Square Blvd (32225-8183)
PHONE..................................904 727-2559
Greg Buffington, *President*
Rebecca Hamrick, *Director*
EMP: 1582 **EST:** 2012
SALES (est): 5.4MM **Privately Held**
WEB: www.crowley.com
SIC: 3533 Gas field machinery & equipment
HQ: Crowley Petroleum Services, Inc.
9487 Regency Square Blvd
Jacksonville FL 32225
904 727-2200

(G-6255)
CARPENTREE CREATION
11058 Percheron Dr (32257-4724)
PHONE..................................904 300-4008
Michael Gooch, *Owner*
EMP: 7 **EST:** 2017
SALES (est): 140K **Privately Held**
SIC: 2499 Applicators, wood

(G-6256)
CASEWORK OF AMERICA INC (PA)
1030 Ellis Rd N (32254-2250)
PHONE..................................904 695-0996
Shahid Kahn, *President*
Thomas Clarkson, *Director*
EMP: 8 **EST:** 2013
SALES (est): 175K **Privately Held**
SIC: 2431 Millwork

(G-6257)
CEMEX CNSTR MTLS FLA LLC
Also Called: South Jacksonville - R/M, B/M
14770 Old St Augustine Rd (32258-2464)
PHONE..................................904 880-4958
Steve Kester, *Plant Mgr*
Brian Bussell, *Branch Mgr*
EMP: 10 **Privately Held**
SIC: 3273 Ready-mixed concrete
HQ: Cemex Construction Materials Florida, Llc
1501 Belvedere Rd
West Palm Beach FL 33406

(G-6258)
CEMEX MATERIALS LLC
4807 Collins Rd (32244-9508)
PHONE..................................904 296-2400
Mike Divano, *Branch Mgr*
EMP: 73 **Privately Held**
SIC: 3273 Ready-mixed concrete
HQ: Cemex Materials Llc
1501 Belvedere Rd
West Palm Beach FL 33406
561 833-5555

(G-6259)
CENTRAL STEEL FABRICATORS LLC
2144 Soutel Dr (32208-2177)
P.O. Box 9839 (32208-0839)
PHONE..................................904 503-1660
Ernest Raynor, *Mng Member*
EMP: 5 **EST:** 2014
SALES (est): 949.5K **Privately Held**
SIC: 3441 Fabricated structural metal

(G-6260)
CHAMPAGNE WELDING INC
2910 W Beaver St (32254-3170)
PHONE..................................585 738-8611
Thomas Champagne, *Principal*
EMP: 6 **EST:** 2010
SALES (est): 92.5K **Privately Held**
SIC: 7692 Welding repair

(G-6261)
CHANCEY METAL PRODUCTS INC
5130 Sunbeam Rd (32257-6132)
PHONE..................................904 260-6880
Chancey Joseph L Jr, *President*
Mary G Chancey, *Corp Secy*
Travis Smith, *Project Mgr*
EMP: 40 **EST:** 1986
SQ FT: 24,500
SALES (est): 14MM **Privately Held**
WEB: www.chanceymetals.com
SIC: 3446 Architectural metalwork

(G-6262)
CHEEZEBALLS LLC
3759 Cascade Ct (32207-5707)
PHONE..................................904 716-3709
Zachary A Johnson, *Manager*
EMP: 6 **EST:** 2011
SALES (est): 195K **Privately Held**
WEB: www.cheezeballs.com
SIC: 3949 Skates & parts, roller

(G-6263)
CHILLER MEDIC INC
8933 Western Way Ste 18 (32256-8388)
PHONE..................................904 814-9446
David Lampp, *President*
EMP: 8 **EST:** 2012
SALES (est): 750K **Privately Held**
WEB: www.chillermedic.com
SIC: 3585 1711 7623 Air conditioning equipment, complete; air conditioning units, complete: domestic or industrial; heating & air conditioning contractors; air conditioning repair

(G-6264)
CHILLY WILLYS HEATING & A INC
8006 Renault Dr (32244-1393)
PHONE..................................904 772-1164
William E Hester, *President*
EMP: 9 **EST:** 2009
SALES (est): 275.6K **Privately Held**
WEB: www.chillywillys.co
SIC: 3564 3823 Air cleaning systems; temperature measurement instruments, industrial

(G-6265)
CLARIOS LLC
Also Called: Johnson Controls
6973 Highway Ave Ste 301 (32254-3430)
PHONE..................................904 786-9161
Shawn Mudd, *Division Mgr*
Lindsay Gowan, *Vice Pres*
Mark Kemler, *Opers Staff*
Robert Riggs, *Opers Staff*
Jennifer Warren, *Buyer*
EMP: 6
SALES (corp-wide): 47.9B **Publicly Held**
WEB: www.clarios.com
SIC: 3691 Storage batteries
HQ: Clarios, Llc
5757 N Green Bay Ave
Milwaukee WI 53209

(G-6266)
CLAWSON CUSTOM CUES INC
Also Called: Predator Products
7255 Salisbury Rd Ste 1 (32256-6980)
PHONE..................................904 448-8748
John Foster, *President*
Allan McCarty, *President*
John Riley, *General Mgr*
Martha Hakes, *Analyst*
▲ **EMP:** 20 **EST:** 1994
SQ FT: 1,200
SALES (est): 3.8MM **Privately Held**
SIC: 3949 Sporting & athletic goods

(G-6267)
CLEAR DISTRIBUTION INC
6611 Sthpint Pkwy Ste C30 (32216)
PHONE..................................904 330-5624
Clifford Martin Jr, *CEO*
EMP: 6 **EST:** 2019
SALES (est): 400K **Privately Held**
SIC: 2051 Bakery: wholesale or whole-sale/retail combined

(G-6268)
CLEVELAND DIABETES CARE INC (PA)
10752 Deerwood Park Blvd (32256-4849)
PHONE..................................904 394-2620
Elsa Kerpi, *President*
EMP: 3 **EST:** 2018
SALES (est): 11.7MM **Privately Held**
SIC: 2834 Pharmaceutical preparations

(G-6269)
CLJ INDUSTRIES INC
6015 Chester Cir Ste 213 (32217-2277)
PHONE..................................562 688-0508
Coridale L Jackson, *President*
EMP: 6 **EST:** 2014
SALES (est): 91.9K **Privately Held**
WEB: www.clj-industries-inc.reservio.com
SIC: 3999 Barber & beauty shop equipment

(G-6270)
CLOROX HEALTHCARE HOLDINGS LLC
Also Called: Healthlink
3611 Saint Johns Ave 1 (32205-9025)
PHONE..................................904 996-7758
Chris Temmons, *Branch Mgr*
EMP: 25
SALES (corp-wide): 7.3B **Publicly Held**
WEB: www.thecloroxcompany.com
SIC: 2842 Specialty cleaning, polishes & sanitation goods
HQ: Clorox Healthcare Holdings, Llc
1221 Broadway
Oakland CA

(G-6271)
CLOTHING WAREHOUSE
1010 Park St (32204-3908)
PHONE..................................904 354-9002
Peter A Amador, *Principal*
EMP: 6 **EST:** 2007
SALES (est): 80K **Privately Held**
SIC: 2759 Screen printing

(G-6272)
CMC STEEL US LLC
Also Called: CMC Steel Florida
16770 Rebar Rd (32234-4100)
PHONE..................................904 266-4261
Barbara Smith, *Branch Mgr*
EMP: 30
SALES (corp-wide): 6.7B **Publicly Held**
WEB: www.cmc.com
SIC: 3399 Staples, nonferrous metal or wire
HQ: Cmc Steel Us, Llc
6565 N Macarthur Blvd # 8
Irving TX 75039
214 689-4300

(G-6273)
CMF MEDICON SURGICAL INC
11200 St Jhns Indus Pkwy (32246)
PHONE..................................904 642-7500
Joachim Schmid, *President*
Michael Marsiglia, *Sales Staff*
Barbara Davidson, *CIO*
◆ **EMP:** 6 **EST:** 2006
SALES (est): 834.1K **Privately Held**
WEB: www.medicon.de
SIC: 3841 5047 Surgical & medical instruments; medical equipment & supplies

(G-6274)
CNS SIGNS INC
3539 W Beaver St (32254-3711)
PHONE..................................904 733-4806
Jeanne Bringle, *President*
Ken Bringle, *Vice Pres*
Ernest Hammond, *Treasurer*
EMP: 7 **EST:** 1990
SALES (est): 890.3K **Privately Held**
WEB: www.cnssign.com
SIC: 3993 Signs & advertising specialties

(G-6275)
COASTAL CUSTOM WOODWORK LLC
1435 W Church St Ofc C (32204-1324)
PHONE..................................904 945-2299
Michael Tilgar, *Owner*
EMP: 6 **EST:** 2014
SALES (est): 450K **Privately Held**
WEB: www.coastalcustomwoodwork.com
SIC: 2434 Wood kitchen cabinets

(G-6276)
COASTAL FILMS OF FLORIDA
627 Lane Ave N (32254-2822)
PHONE..................................904 786-2031
Robert Barlanti, *President*
EMP: 95 **EST:** 1989
SALES (est): 17.3MM **Privately Held**
WEB: www.sigmaplasticsgroup.com
SIC: 2673 Bags: plastic, laminated & coated
PA: Alpha Industries Management, Inc.
808 Page Ave
Lyndhurst NJ 07071

(G-6277)
COASTAL INDUSTRIES INC (PA)
3700 St Jhns Indus Pkwy W (32246-7655)
P.O. Box 16091 (32245-6091)
PHONE..................................904 642-3970
Martin Ray Adams, *President*
William M Cobb, *Owner*
Michele Ford, *Principal*
William Cobb Jr, *Vice Pres*
Sue Rosenbaum, *Facilities Mgr*
◆ **EMP:** 167 **EST:** 1972
SQ FT: 250,000
SALES (est): 32.9MM **Privately Held**
WEB: www.coastalshowerdoors.com
SIC: 3231 Doors, glass: made from purchased glass

(G-6278)
COCA-COLA BEVERAGES FLA LLC
1411 Huron St (32254-2026)
PHONE..................................904 786-2720
Jerry Reaves, *Branch Mgr*
EMP: 450
SALES (corp-wide): 366.5MM **Privately Held**
WEB: www.cocacolaflorida.com
SIC: 2086 5149 Bottled & canned soft drinks; soft drinks
PA: Coca-Cola Beverages Florida, Llc
10117 Princess Palm Ave # 100
Tampa FL 33610
800 438-2653

(G-6279)
COM PAC FILTRATION INC
2020 W Beaver St (32209-7533)
P.O. Box 40071 (32203-0071)
PHONE..................................904 356-4003
Dean Atkinson, *President*
Dale Trask, *Warehouse Mgr*
Valerie Atkinson, *Admin Sec*
▲ **EMP:** 35 **EST:** 1987
SQ FT: 8,000

SALES (est): 7.8MM Privately Held
WEB: www.com-pac.net
SIC: 3589 3272 Swimming pool filter & water conditioning systems; fountains, concrete

(G-6280)
COMMERCIAL CASEWORK INC (PA)
1030 Ellis Rd N (32254-2250)
PHONE..................................904 264-4222
Scott T Gay, *President*
EMP: 52 EST: 1992
SQ FT: 42,500
SALES (est): 7.4MM Privately Held
WEB: www.commercialcasework.com
SIC: 2599 2491 5211 Cabinets, factory; millwork, treated wood; millwork & lumber

(G-6281)
COMMERCIAL METALS COMPANY
Also Called: CMC Steel Fabricators
10483 General Ave (32220-2103)
P.O. Box 37979 (32236-7979)
PHONE..................................904 781-4780
Rodney Powell, *Branch Mgr*
EMP: 8
SALES (corp-wide): 6.7B Publicly Held
WEB: www.cmc.com
SIC: 3312 Blast furnaces & steel mills
PA: Commercial Metals Company
6565 N Macarthur Blvd # 800
Irving TX 75039
214 689-4300

(G-6282)
CONCEALMENT EXPRESS LLC
10066 103rd St Ste 103 (32210-9258)
PHONE..................................888 904-2722
Pablo Conde, *Chief Mktg Ofcr*
Benedict Jimenez, *Mng Member*
Sang Cho, *Mng Member*
EMP: 51 EST: 2014
SALES (est): 5.1MM Privately Held
WEB: www.concealmentexpress.com
SIC: 3089 5699 Molding primary plastic; sports apparel

(G-6283)
CONRAD MARKLE BLDR & CBNT
1120 Romney St (32211-5663)
PHONE..................................904 744-4569
Conrad Markle, *Owner*
EMP: 8 EST: 1994
SALES (est): 167.4K Privately Held
SIC: 2431 Millwork

(G-6284)
CONSTRUCTION BULLETIN INC
7033 Commwl Ave Ste 1 (32220)
PHONE..................................904 388-0336
Kenneth Heatherman, *CEO*
EMP: 10 EST: 1972
SQ FT: 2,500
SALES (est): 753.2K Privately Held
WEB: www.cbids.com
SIC: 2741 2721 Business service newsletters: publishing & printing; periodicals

(G-6285)
CONTINENTAL CONCRETE PRODUCTS
2251 Urban Rd (32210-4239)
PHONE..................................904 388-1390
EMP: 5
SQ FT: 2,500
SALES (est): 370K Privately Held
SIC: 3272 1771 Mfg Concrete Products & Concrete & Foundation Work

(G-6286)
CONTINENTAL PRINTING SVCS INC
4929 Toproyal Ln (32277-1044)
PHONE..................................904 743-6718
James L Duduit, *President*
Shirley Duduit, *Admin Sec*
▼ EMP: 9 EST: 1972
SQ FT: 9,200
SALES (est): 239.6K Privately Held
SIC: 2752 7336 Commercial printing, offset; commercial art & graphic design; graphic arts & related design

(G-6287)
CONTROL SOUTHERN INC
4133 N Canal St (32209-3623)
PHONE..................................904 353-0004
Larry Young, *President*
EMP: 56
SALES (corp-wide): 68MM Privately Held
WEB: www.controlsouthern.com
SIC: 3592 Valves
PA: Control Southern Inc.
3850 Lakefield Dr
Suwanee GA 30024
770 495-3100

(G-6288)
COOPERS HAWK INTRMDATE HLDG LL
4850 Big Island Dr (32246-7490)
PHONE..................................904 996-2466
EMP: 6
SALES (corp-wide): 258.3MM Privately Held
SIC: 2084 Mfg Wines/Brandy/Spirits
PA: Cooper's Hawk Intermediate Holding, Llc
3500 Lacey Rd Ste 1000
Downers Grove IL 60515
708 839-2920

(G-6289)
COOSA LLC
12811 Helm Dr (32258-2221)
PHONE..................................904 268-1187
Elise P Jones, *Manager*
EMP: 8 EST: 2005
SALES (est): 146.6K Privately Held
WEB: www.coosacomposites.com
SIC: 2821 Plastics materials & resins

(G-6290)
COPELAND WELDING & MUFFLER SP
484 Lime St (32204-2777)
PHONE..................................904 355-6383
Raymond R Copeland Jr, *President*
Randy Copeland, *Treasurer*
DOT Copeland, *Admin Sec*
EMP: 6 EST: 1933
SALES (est): 380.5K Privately Held
WEB: www.copelandwelding.com
SIC: 7692 Welding repair

(G-6291)
COPY RIGHT BGMD INC
5569 Bowden Rd Ste 6 (32216-0915)
PHONE..................................904 680-0343
Shawn Bass, *President*
Keith Fallon, *Vice Pres*
Kelly Marshall, *Office Mgr*
Ward Huntley, *Director*
Ron Carney, *Graphic Designe*
EMP: 10 EST: 2003
SQ FT: 3,600
SALES (est): 1.2MM Privately Held
WEB: www.copyrightjax.com
SIC: 2752 Commercial printing, offset

(G-6292)
CORK INDUSTRIES INC
5555 W Beaver St (32254-2916)
PHONE..................................904 695-2400
Jeff Moore, *Plant Mgr*
Stephen Foy, *Sales Staff*
Gerald Clauss, *Marketing Staff*
Mike Cox, *Marketing Staff*
Diana Alexander, *Manager*
EMP: 22
SALES (corp-wide): 10MM Privately Held
WEB: www.corkind.com
SIC: 2851 Paints & allied products
PA: Cork Industries, Inc.
500 Kaiser Dr
Folcroft PA 19032
610 522-9550

(G-6293)
CORRIGAN & COMPANY
Also Called: Nu-Trend Container
119 Sewald St (32204-1731)
P.O. Box 2883 (32203-2883)
PHONE..................................904 353-5936
Michael L Corrigan Jr, *President*
Caroline S Corrigan, *Admin Sec*
EMP: 8 EST: 1949
SQ FT: 15,000
SALES (est): 1.8MM Privately Held
WEB: www.ntplastics.com
SIC: 3089 5199 Plastic kitchenware, tableware & houseware; plastic containers, except foam; packaging materials

(G-6294)
CORROCOAT USA INC
6525 Greenland Rd (32258-2439)
PHONE..................................904 268-4559
Josh Tankersley, *General Mgr*
Ed Cilli, *Project Mgr*
Clive A Harper, *CFO*
Charles J Watkinson, *Director*
Philip J Watkinson, *Director*
▲ EMP: 12 EST: 2007
SALES (est): 1.2MM
SALES (corp-wide): 19.2MM Privately Held
WEB: www.corrocoatusa.com
SIC: 3479 Coating of metals & formed products
PA: Corrosioneering Group Limited
Forster Street
Leeds LS10
113 276-0760

(G-6295)
COSTAL FUELS MARKETING
3425 Talleyrand Ave (32206-2649)
PHONE..................................904 358-6725
Cathy Sims, *Principal*
Kevin Brooks, *Plant Mgr*
Mark Olenski, *Terminal Mgr*
EMP: 7 EST: 2010
SALES (est): 152.2K Privately Held
SIC: 2869 Fuels

(G-6296)
CREATIVE COUNTERTOPS INC
Also Called: Creative Counters
4768 Highway Ave (32254-3788)
PHONE..................................904 387-2800
Ronald Moore, *President*
Jason Rebman, *General Mgr*
Louis Gonzalez, *Vice Pres*
Leslie Deaton, *Sales Staff*
Randy Lackey, *Manager*
EMP: 12 EST: 1994
SQ FT: 10,000
SALES (est): 1.7MM Privately Held
WEB: www.creativecountertops.biz
SIC: 3131 2821 2541 Counters; plastics materials & resins; wood partitions & fixtures

(G-6297)
CREATIVE GLASSWORKS
2062 Saint Martins Dr W (32246-7051)
PHONE..................................904 860-0865
Kirk Reber, *Owner*
▲ EMP: 9 EST: 1993
SALES (est): 453.7K Privately Held
SIC: 3231 5231 Stained glass: made from purchased glass; glass

(G-6298)
CREATIVE IMAGES EMBRODIERY
2989 Philips Hwy (32207-4484)
PHONE..................................904 730-5660
Paul Hahn, *President*
EMP: 8 EST: 1988
SALES (est): 553.1K Privately Held
SIC: 2395 Embroidery & art needlework

(G-6299)
CROWN PLATING INC
5285 Ramona Blvd (32205-4414)
P.O. Box 37675 (32236-7675)
PHONE..................................904 783-6640
Robert E Little, *President*
EMP: 50 EST: 1970
SQ FT: 20,000
SALES (est): 3.1MM Privately Held
SIC: 3471 Electroplating of metals or formed products

(G-6300)
CROWN PRODUCTS COMPANY INC (PA)
6390 Philips Hwy (32216-6092)
PHONE..................................904 737-7144
Peter Tuggle, *Principal*
Linda Hardy, *Principal*
Charles Foster, *Sales Staff*
John Gay, *Manager*
Donald Socks, *Executive*
▲ EMP: 180 EST: 1964
SQ FT: 90,000
SALES (est): 41.7MM Privately Held
WEB: www.crownproductsco.com
SIC: 3444 Flues & pipes, stove or furnace: sheet metal; ducts, sheet metal

(G-6301)
CROWN PRODUCTS COMPANY INC
Also Called: Crown Building Systems
3545 New Kings Rd (32209-3349)
PHONE..................................904 924-8340
Lisa McGann, *Human Res Dir*
Tad Dalton, *Sales Staff*
Peter S Tuggle, *Manager*
EMP: 55
SALES (corp-wide): 41.7MM Privately Held
WEB: www.crownproductsco.com
SIC: 3444 3585 Sheet metal specialties, not stamped; refrigeration & heating equipment
PA: Crown Products Company, Inc.
6390 Philips Hwy
Jacksonville FL 32216
904 737-7144

GEOGRAPHIC

(G-6302)
CU HOLDINGS LLC
Also Called: Cardinal Straws
5515 W 5th St (32254-1669)
PHONE..................................904 483-5700
Michael Houle, *President*
▲ EMP: 92 EST: 2006
SALES (est): 18.3MM
SALES (corp-wide): 317MM Privately Held
WEB: www.wincup.com
SIC: 2656 Straws, drinking: made from purchased material
PA: Wincup, Inc.
4640 Lewis Rd
Stone Mountain GA 30083
770 771-5861

(G-6303)
CUSTOM MARINE COMPONENTS INC
13755 Atlantic Blvd (32225-3236)
PHONE..................................904 221-6412
Louis E Leidecker, *President*
John T Quinlan, *Vice Pres*
EMP: 14 EST: 1984
SQ FT: 5,000
SALES (est): 4MM Privately Held
WEB: www.custommarinejax.com
SIC: 3441 5551 3732 Boat & barge sections, prefabricated metal; boat dealers; boat building & repairing

(G-6304)
CUSTOM WOOD PRODUCTS INC
3811 University Blvd W # 10 (32217-2234)
PHONE..................................904 737-6906
Danny Hall, *Principal*
EMP: 7 EST: 2002
SALES (est): 991.5K Privately Held
WEB: www.customwoodjacksonville.com
SIC: 2434 Wood kitchen cabinets

(G-6305)
D J CAMCO CORPORATION
2426 Dennis St (32204-1712)
PHONE..................................904 355-5995
Dennis J Cameron, *President*
EMP: 6 EST: 1988
SQ FT: 1,000
SALES (est): 2MM Privately Held
WEB: www.djcamco.com
SIC: 3451 Screw machine products

(G-6306)
D W ALLEN MARINE SVCS INC
1841 Wambolt St (32202-1026)
P.O. Box 3804 (32206-0804)
PHONE..................................904 358-1933
Dan Allen, *President*
Gretchen Williams, *Director*
EMP: 36 EST: 1985

SQ FT: 15,000
SALES (est): 6.1MM **Privately Held**
WEB: www.dwallenmarine.com
SIC: 3731 3441 Shipbuilding & repairing; ship sections, prefabricated metal

(G-6307)
DAGHER & SONS INC
Also Called: DAGHER PRINTING
11775 Marco Beach Dr (32224-7616)
PHONE..................................904 998-0911
Joseph G Dagher, *President*
Salem Dagher, *Vice Pres*
Mouna Khoury, *Treasurer*
Andy Weldirick, *Office Mgr*
EMP: 16 **EST:** 1976
SQ FT: 20,000
SALES (est): 1.6MM **Privately Held**
WEB: www.dagherprintingonline.com
SIC: 2752 Commercial printing, offset

(G-6308)
DAILYS
9143 Baymeadows Rd (32256-7705)
PHONE..................................904 448-0562
EMP: 11 **EST:** 2014
SALES (est): 171.4K **Privately Held**
WEB: www.dailys.com
SIC: 2711 Newspapers, publishing & printing

(G-6309)
DAILYS
13800 Old St Augustine Rd (32258-2448)
PHONE..................................904 880-4784
EMP: 10 **EST:** 2015
SALES (est): 174.9K **Privately Held**
WEB: www.dailysplace.com
SIC: 2711 Newspapers, publishing & printing

(G-6310)
DAR INDUSTRIES INC
5570 Fl Min Blvd S (32257-3246)
PHONE..................................904 327-9689
David A Ricks, *Principal*
EMP: 6 **EST:** 2014
SALES (est): 135.6K **Privately Held**
SIC: 3999 Manufacturing industries

(G-6311)
DARIFAIR FOODS INC
4131 Sunbeam Rd (32257-6027)
PHONE..................................904 268-8999
Max Block, *Ch of Bd*
Andrew M Block, *President*
Jeffery Block, *Exec VP*
Mark Rones, *Research*
William Block, *CFO*
EMP: 32 **EST:** 1981
SQ FT: 7,000
SALES (est): 14.5MM **Privately Held**
WEB: www.darifair.com
SIC: 2024 5143 2026 Ice cream & frozen desserts; dairy products, except dried or canned; fermented & cultured milk products

(G-6312)
DAUNTLESS USA INC
9995 Gate Pkwy N Ste 400 (32246-1898)
PHONE..................................904 996-8800
Steven C Koegler, *President*
Lazar S Finker, *Vice Pres*
William E Chattin, *Treasurer*
Lisa M Kavalieros, *Admin Sec*
EMP: 19 **EST:** 1994
SALES (est): 3.3MM **Privately Held**
SIC: 1382 Oil & gas exploration services

(G-6313)
DAVID B CASE
10358 Sylvan Ln W (32257-6240)
PHONE..................................904 262-6224
David B Case, *Principal*
EMP: 6 **EST:** 2012
SALES (est): 167.7K **Privately Held**
SIC: 3523 Farm machinery & equipment

(G-6314)
DAVIS MAIL SERVICES INC
13464 Grover Rd (32226-1944)
PHONE..................................904 477-7970
Tony E Davis, *President*
Patricia M Davis, *Vice Pres*
Josh Sudduth, *Opers Staff*
EMP: 150
SALES (est): 12MM **Privately Held**
SIC: 2542 Locker boxes, postal service: except wood

(G-6315)
DEALER IT GROUP LLC
5220 Belfort Rd Ste 400 (32256-6018)
PHONE..................................904 518-3379
EMP: 12 **EST:** 2018
SALES (est): 1MM **Privately Held**
SIC: 7372 Business oriented computer software

(G-6316)
DESIGN CONTAINERS INC
Also Called: Design Cores and Tubes
2913 Westside Blvd (32209-2714)
PHONE..................................904 764-6541
Samuel H Vickers, *CEO*
Samuel Vickers, *Info Tech Dir*
Thomas W Talbot, *Director*
◆ **EMP:** 58 **EST:** 1960
SQ FT: 150,000
SALES (est): 11.2MM **Privately Held**
WEB: www.designcontainers.com
SIC: 2655 1761 2631 Drums, fiber: made from purchased material; roofing, siding & sheet metal work; paperboard mills

(G-6317)
DESIGNER LIFESTYLES LLC
619 Cassat Ave (32205-4716)
PHONE..................................904 631-8954
Christopher Mayer, *President*
Christopher J Mayer, *Principal*
EMP: 16 **EST:** 2006
SALES (est): 2.4MM **Privately Held**
WEB: www.designerlifestyles.com
SIC: 2426 5211 1752 1743 Flooring, hardwood; parquet flooring, hardwood; flooring, wood; ceramic floor tile installation; tile installation, ceramic; tiles, cork; wood flooring

(G-6318)
DFA DAIRY BRANDS FLUID LLC
11231 Phillips Ind Blvd E (32256-3016)
PHONE..................................386 775-6700
Randy Vick, *Branch Mgr*
EMP: 15
SALES (corp-wide): 17.8B **Privately Held**
SIC: 2026 Fluid milk
HQ: Dfa Dairy Brands Fluid, Llc
1405 N 98th St
Kansas City KS 66111
816 801-6455

(G-6319)
DIRECT MEDIA SOLUTIONS INC
11555 Central Pkwy # 804 (32224-2691)
PHONE..................................904 419-3675
David Eckes, *President*
Robert Willis, *COO*
Scott Feely, *CFO*
EMP: 7 **EST:** 2012
SQ FT: 2,200
SALES (est): 58K **Privately Held**
WEB: www.directmediasolutions.us
SIC: 2741

(G-6320)
DIRTRBAGS CHOPPER ✪
2426 Mayport Rd Ste 5 (32233-6818)
PHONE..................................904 725-7600
Jeff Gordon, *CEO*
EMP: 8 **EST:** 2020
SALES (est): 400K **Privately Held**
WEB: www.dirtbagchoppers.business.site
SIC: 3751 Motorcycle accessories

(G-6321)
DIVERSIFIED PERFORMANCE SYSTEM
6800 N Main St (32208-4726)
PHONE..................................904 765-7181
James Walter Newbold, *Owner*
▲ **EMP:** 10 **EST:** 2002
SALES (est): 243.3K **Privately Held**
WEB: www.onediversified.com
SIC: 3579 Embossing machines for store & office use

(G-6322)
DIXIE TANK COMPANY
5349 Highway Ave (32254-3634)
PHONE..................................904 781-9500
Chris Eidson, *President*
Chris Crosby, *Superintendent*
Marty Higdon, *Foreman/Supr*
Carson Wright, *Controller*
Dane Pawela, *Sales Staff*
▼ **EMP:** 50 **EST:** 1943
SQ FT: 59,000
SALES (est): 10.1MM **Privately Held**
WEB: www.dixietank.com
SIC: 3443 Water tanks, metal plate

(G-6323)
DKM MACHINE MANUFACTURING
3811 University Blvd W # 26 (32217-1210)
PHONE..................................904 733-0103
David Kennedy, *Director*
▲ **EMP:** 16 **EST:** 2012
SALES (est): 1MM **Privately Held**
WEB: www.dkmpulpmachines.com
SIC: 3999 Manufacturing industries

(G-6324)
DOCTORXS ALLERGY FORMULA
Also Called: Drs Allergy
2375 St Johns Bluff Rd S (32246-2333)
PHONE..................................904 758-2088
Howard Loff, *Mng Member*
EMP: 6 **EST:** 2013
SALES (est): 254.9K **Privately Held**
SIC: 2835 In vitro & in vivo diagnostic substances

(G-6325)
DORADO GRAPHIX LLC ✪
10592 Balmoral Cir E # 9 (32218-5581)
PHONE..................................904 751-4500
EMP: 7 **EST:** 2020
SALES (est): 465.5K **Privately Held**
WEB: www.doradographix.com
SIC: 2759 Screen printing

(G-6326)
DORAN MANUFACTURING CORP FLA
6261 Powers Ave (32217-2215)
PHONE..................................904 731-3313
Richard Gross, *President*
▲ **EMP:** 7 **EST:** 1975
SQ FT: 36,000
SALES (est): 1MM **Privately Held**
WEB: www.collarstays.com
SIC: 3089 5162 Injection molding of plastics; thermoformed finished plastic products; plastics products

(G-6327)
DPF SOLUTIONS GROUP LLC
6100 Philips Hwy (32216-5980)
PHONE..................................904 580-5343
Samuel Dean Prince, *Manager*
EMP: 7 **EST:** 2016
SALES (est): 299.8K **Privately Held**
WEB: www.dpfsolutionsgroup.com
SIC: 2752 Commercial printing, offset

(G-6328)
DRESSER INC
12970 Normandy Blvd (32221-2110)
PHONE..................................318 640-2250
Fax: 318 640-6222
▲ **EMP:** 21 **EST:** 1999
SALES (est): 3MM **Privately Held**
SIC: 3491 Mfg Industrial Valves

(G-6329)
DRESSER LLC
Dresser Equipment Group
12970 Normandy Blvd (32221-2110)
PHONE..................................904 781-7071
Richard Fentum, *CEO*
EMP: 300
SALES (corp-wide): 432.9MM **Privately Held**
WEB: www.dresserutility.com
SIC: 3491 Industrial valves
PA: Dresser, Llc
4425 Westway Park Blvd
Houston TX 77041
262 549-2626

(G-6330)
DRUMMOND PRESS INC (PA)
2472 Dennis St (32204-1757)
P.O. Box 2421 (32203-2421)
PHONE..................................904 354-2818
Robert J Falconetti, *Ch of Bd*
Diane Falconetti, *President*
Andrew Harrow, *Business Mgr*
Stephen Horne, *Business Mgr*
Brad Little, *Business Mgr*
▲ **EMP:** 53 **EST:** 1939
SQ FT: 40,000
SALES (est): 31.2MM **Privately Held**
WEB: www.drummond.com
SIC: 2752 Commercial printing, offset

(G-6331)
DSX PRODUCTS INC
4430 Palmetto Inlt W (32277-1123)
PHONE..................................904 744-3400
Lee Lippert, *Principal*
Mark Dreksler, *Regional Mgr*
Greg Olson, *Design Engr*
Scott Bennett, *Sales Staff*
EMP: 10 **EST:** 2007
SALES (est): 146K **Privately Held**
WEB: www.dsxinc.com
SIC: 3714 Motor vehicle parts & accessories

(G-6332)
DUDLEY BLAKE LLC
4141 Spring Park Cir (32207-5729)
PHONE..................................904 866-2829
Douglas Blake, *Principal*
David Bahr, *Manager*
EMP: 7 **EST:** 2012
SALES (est): 237.4K **Privately Held**
SIC: 2842 7389 Specialty cleaning preparations;

(G-6333)
DUKEMANS CUSTOM WOODWORKING
Also Called: Dukeman Custom Woodwork
141 N Myrtle Ave Fl 2 (32204-1309)
PHONE..................................904 355-5188
Stan Dukeman, *President*
Kenny Ranpersad, *Principal*
Philip Stein, *Principal*
EMP: 6 **EST:** 1998
SQ FT: 7,000
SALES (est): 824.3K **Privately Held**
WEB: www.dukemancustomwoodworking.com
SIC: 2434 Wood kitchen cabinets

(G-6334)
DUMPSTERME LLC
13255 Lanier Rd (32226-4505)
PHONE..................................904 647-1945
John J Arwood R, *President*
EMP: 6 **EST:** 2017
SALES (est): 142.3K **Privately Held**
SIC: 3443 Dumpsters, garbage

(G-6335)
DUOS TECHNOLOGIES INC (PA)
6622 Sthpint Dr S Ste 310 (32216)
PHONE..................................904 652-1601
Chuck Ferry, *CEO*
Gianni B Arcaini, *President*
Larry Strach, *Vice Pres*
Connie L Weeks, *Vice Pres*
Scott Hill, *Electrical Engi*
EMP: 53 **EST:** 1990
SQ FT: 13,000
SALES (est): 13.7MM **Privately Held**
WEB: www.ir.duostechnologies.com
SIC: 7372 Prepackaged software

(G-6336)
DUOS TECHNOLOGIES GROUP INC (PA)
Also Called: DUOSTECH
6622 Sthpint Dr S Ste 310 (32216)
PHONE..................................904 652-1616
Charles Ferry, *CEO*
Connie L Weeks, *Exec VP*
Adrian G Goldfarb, *CFO*
EMP: 0 **EST:** 1990
SQ FT: 8,308

▲ = Import ▼=Export
◆ =Import/Export

SALES: 8MM **Publicly Held**
WEB: www.duostechnologies.com
SIC: 7372 Business oriented computer software

(G-6337)
DUPUY SILO FACILITY LLC (PA)
1520 Edgewood Ave N (32254-1748)
PHONE..................................904 899-7200
Jeff Hernandez, *Vice Pres*
Joe Waryold, *Vice Pres*
Michael James, *Warehouse Mgr*
Alston Bellflower, *Maint Spvr*
Lane Windham, *Maint Spvr*
EMP: 125 **EST:** 1999
SALES (est): 11.4MM **Privately Held**
WEB: www.dupuygroup.com
SIC: 2095 Coffee extracts

(G-6338)
DUSTSTOP FILTERS INC
Also Called: Duststop Air Filters
165 Tresca Rd (32225-6596)
PHONE..................................904 725-1001
Ovenie Rodriguez, *President*
EMP: 9 **EST:** 1991
SQ FT: 25,000
SALES (est): 1MM **Privately Held**
WEB: www.duststopfilters.com
SIC: 3564 3585 3433 Filters, air: furnaces, air conditioning equipment, etc.; refrigeration & heating equipment; heating equipment, except electric

(G-6339)
DUVAL BAKERY PRODUCTS INC
1733 Evergreen Ave (32206-4730)
PHONE..................................904 354-7878
Robert Gorsuch, *President*
Richard Mc Cullough, *Corp Secy*
EMP: 5 **EST:** 1972
SQ FT: 6,000
SALES (est): 415K **Privately Held**
WEB: www.duvalbakery.com
SIC: 2051 Bread, cake & related products

(G-6340)
DUVAL FIXTURES INC
3600 Saint Augustine Rd (32207-5527)
PHONE..................................904 757-3964
Duane Yoder, *President*
Corey Dawson, *Vice Pres*
Rickie Pittman, *Prdtn Mgr*
Trisha Ziemba, *Executive Asst*
EMP: 21 **EST:** 1965
SALES (est): 2.7MM **Privately Held**
WEB: www.duvalfixtures.com
SIC: 2541 Office fixtures, wood; store fixtures, wood

(G-6341)
DWYER PRECISION PRODUCTS INC
266 20th St N (32250-2727)
PHONE..................................904 249-3545
James E Lineberger Jr, *President*
Bert Wechtenhiser, *Vice Pres*
▲ **EMP:** 11 **EST:** 1966
SQ FT: 7,000
SALES (est): 1.2MM **Privately Held**
WEB: www.dwyerprecisionproducts.com
SIC: 3841 Surgical & medical instruments

(G-6342)
DXM MARKETING GROUP LLC
9485 Rgncy Sq Blvd # 460 (32225-8156)
PHONE..................................904 332-6490
David Matchett,
John Brophy,
Ray Owens,
Dencho Vassilev,
EMP: 16 **EST:** 2010
SQ FT: 16,500
SALES (est): 1.2MM **Privately Held**
WEB: www.dxmgp.com
SIC: 2759 7331 Advertising literature: printing; direct mail advertising services

(G-6343)
E 3 MAINTENANCE ✪
13720 Old St Agstine Rd S (32258-7414)
PHONE..................................904 708-7208
Edward E Murray, *Owner*
EMP: 23 **EST:** 2021
SALES (est): 1.2MM **Privately Held**
SIC: 1389 Construction, repair & dismantling services

(G-6344)
E G PUMP CONTROLS INC
Also Called: E G Controls
11790 Philips Hwy (32256-1642)
PHONE..................................904 292-0110
Brian Dail, *President*
Samuel Jacobson, *Principal*
Tim Howard, *Vice Pres*
Jarret Shuler, *Engineer*
EMP: 25 **EST:** 1988
SQ FT: 22,000
SALES (est): 7.6MM **Privately Held**
WEB: www.egcontrols.com
SIC: 3625 Relays & industrial controls

(G-6345)
EAGLE EYE ANESTHESIA INC
Also Called: Anesthesia Service & Equipment
11233 St Jhns Indus Pkwy (32246-6676)
PHONE..................................817 999-9830
Karen Gustafson, *President*
Kenneth Decray, *President*
Nancy Decray, *Vice Pres*
Larry Laporte, *Technician*
EMP: 5 **EST:** 1991
SALES (est): 1MM **Privately Held**
WEB: www.eagleeyeanesthesia.com
SIC: 3841 Anesthesia apparatus

(G-6346)
EAGLE VIEW WINDOWS INC
13340 International Pkwy (32218-2383)
PHONE..................................904 647-8221
William Meyers, *CEO*
Terry Tuten, *COO*
David Detuccio, *Vice Pres*
Derek Neal, *Vice Pres*
Mike Lane, *VP Mfg*
EMP: 14 **EST:** 2013
SALES (est): 1.4MM **Privately Held**
WEB: www.eagleviewwindows.com
SIC: 2431 Window screens, wood frame

(G-6347)
EARTHCORE INDUSTRIES LLC (PA)
6899 Phillips Ind Blvd (32256-3029)
PHONE..................................904 363-3417
Carl R Spadaro, *CEO*
EMP: 44 **EST:** 2006
SALES (est): 8.9MM **Privately Held**
WEB: www.earthcore.com
SIC: 3272 Fireplace & chimney material: concrete

(G-6348)
EAST COAST COOLING TOWER INC
9850 Interstate Center Dr (32218-5526)
PHONE..................................904 551-5527
Jim Adams, *President*
John Frietz, *Opers Mgr*
John Frietze, *Opers Mgr*
Trish Waters, *Office Mgr*
Terra Strickland, *Manager*
EMP: 12 **EST:** 2008
SQ FT: 11,000
SALES (est): 1.5MM **Privately Held**
WEB: www.eastcoastcoolingtower.com
SIC: 2499 8742 Cooling towers, wood or wood & sheet metal combination; management consulting services

(G-6349)
EAST COAST FIXTURES & MLLWK CO
4880 Clydo Rd S (32207-7956)
PHONE..................................904 733-9711
Clyde Knowles, *President*
John Rappold, *Sales Staff*
Elaine Knowles, *Admin Sec*
Shawn McMenis, *Technician*
Melvin Martinez, *Internal Med*
EMP: 7 **EST:** 1966
SQ FT: 7,000
SALES (est): 965K **Privately Held**
WEB: www.eacoproducts.com
SIC: 2541 2542 3431 3088 Partitions for floor attachment, prefabricated: wood; counters or counter display cases: except wood; metal sanitary ware; plastics plumbing fixtures; wood kitchen cabinets

(G-6350)
EASTERN WIRE PRODUCTS INC
5301 W 5th St (32254-1623)
PHONE..................................904 781-6775
Robert T Yates Jr, *President*
Mark W Yates, *President*
Mark Yates, *Vice Pres*
Scott T Yates, *Vice Pres*
Scott Yates, *Vice Pres*
◆ **EMP:** 38 **EST:** 1971
SQ FT: 80,000
SALES (est): 9.6MM **Privately Held**
WEB: www.eastern-wire.com
SIC: 3496 Miscellaneous fabricated wire products

(G-6351)
EASY RENT INC
Also Called: Fastsigns
8535 Baymeadows Rd Ste 7 (32256-7445)
PHONE..................................904 443-7446
John Ansel, *Owner*
Shawn Layton, *Accounts Mgr*
EMP: 7 **EST:** 1985
SALES (est): 775.4K **Privately Held**
WEB: www.fastsigns.com
SIC: 3993 2759 Signs & advertising specialties; business forms: printing

(G-6352)
ECO SOLAR TECHNOLOGY
12334 Hidden Hills Ln (32225-1702)
PHONE..................................904 219-0807
David Jolicoeur, *Principal*
EMP: 6 **EST:** 2010
SALES (est): 103.3K **Privately Held**
SIC: 3433 Solar heaters & collectors

(G-6353)
ECONOMY DNTRES JCKSONVILLE LLC
1680 Dunn Ave Ste 6 (32218-4788)
PHONE..................................904 696-6767
Leroy R Polite, *President*
Leroy Polite, *President*
Helen Polite, *Vice Pres*
Harold Polite,
EMP: 17 **EST:** 2008
SALES (est): 480.7K **Privately Held**
SIC: 3843 Dental equipment & supplies

(G-6354)
ECONOMY PRINTING CO
14413 Christen Dr S (32218-0854)
P.O. Box 2281 (32203-2281)
PHONE..................................904 786-4070
Robert D Strickland Jr, *President*
Tim Strickland, *Corp Secy*
Joseph Strickland, *Vice Pres*
EMP: 10 **EST:** 1932
SALES (est): 683.8K **Privately Held**
WEB: www.economyprinting.net
SIC: 2761 2752 Manifold business forms; commercial printing, lithographic

(G-6355)
EDWARDS ORNAMENTAL IRON INC
Also Called: Gate Access Systems
1252 W Beaver St (32204-1410)
PHONE..................................904 354-4282
Michael Thurman, *President*
James Thurman, *President*
EMP: 15 **EST:** 1947
SQ FT: 30,000
SALES (est): 2.1MM **Privately Held**
WEB: www.edwardsornamental.com
SIC: 3446 Ornamental metalwork

(G-6356)
EF ENTERPRISES OF NORTH FLA
4381 Gadsden Ct (32207-6218)
P.O. Box 550987 (32255-0987)
PHONE..................................904 739-5995
Frank Wallmeyer, *President*
EMP: 7 **EST:** 2007
SALES (est): 155.4K **Privately Held**
SIC: 2754 2759 Business forms: gravure printing; business forms: printing

(G-6357)
EHUD INDUSTRIES INC
9782 Nimitz Ct S (32246-3608)
PHONE..................................904 803-0873
Rebekah Hudnall, *President*
Brenda Hudnall, *Vice Pres*
EMP: 7 **EST:** 2014
SALES (est): 360.1K **Privately Held**
WEB: www.taxcheckinc.com
SIC: 3089 Injection molded finished plastic products; injection molding of plastics; molding primary plastic

(G-6358)
ELEMENTAL MOBILE SERVICES LLC
3435 Japonica Rd N (32209-2056)
PHONE..................................904 768-9840
Letecia Newman, *Principal*
EMP: 5 **EST:** 2018
SALES (est): 326.7K **Privately Held**
SIC: 2819 Industrial inorganic chemicals

(G-6359)
ELTON FOIL EMBOSSING INC
3414 Galilee Rd (32207-4718)
PHONE..................................904 399-1510
Floyd Houser, *Principal*
EMP: 9 **EST:** 2001
SALES (est): 280.9K **Privately Held**
SIC: 2759 Embossing on paper

(G-6360)
ELYSE INSTALLATIONS LLC ✪
1848 Ector Rd (32211-4705)
PHONE..................................904 322-4754
Joshua Harvey,
EMP: 20 **EST:** 2020
SALES (est): 420K **Privately Held**
SIC: 1389 Construction, repair & dismantling services

(G-6361)
EMB WHOLESALE
7749 Normandy Blvd 145-408
(32221-7657)
PHONE..................................904 452-4362
Allum S Williams, *Principal*
EMP: 6 **EST:** 2010
SALES (est): 164.1K **Privately Held**
SIC: 2396 5961 5199 Screen printing on fabric articles; gift items, mail order; gifts & novelties

(G-6362)
EMERSON ELECTRIC CO
Also Called: Emerson Process Management
13350 International Pkwy # 102
(32218-2397)
PHONE..................................904 741-6800
EMP: 43
SALES (corp-wide): 24.6B **Publicly Held**
SIC: 3823 Mfg Process Control Instruments
PA: Emerson Electric Co.
8000 W Florissant Ave
Saint Louis MO 63136
314 553-2000

(G-6363)
ENDURIS EXTRUSIONS INC (PA)
7167 Old Kings Rd (32219-3727)
PHONE..................................904 421-3304
John Forbis, *CEO*
John Polidan, *President*
Brad Hillman, *CFO*
▲ **EMP:** 85 **EST:** 1998
SQ FT: 68,000
SALES (est): 20MM **Privately Held**
WEB: www.enduris.com
SIC: 3083 Plastic finished products, laminated

(G-6364)
ENGINEER SERVICE CORPORATION
2950 Halcyon Ln Ste 601 (32223-6691)
P.O. Box 23511 (32241-3511)
PHONE..................................904 268-0482
Alva C Atkins Jr, *President*
Charlene Atkins, *Admin Sec*

EMP: 6 EST: 1974
SQ FT: 1,000
SALES (est): 1MM Privately Held
WEB: www.escscada.com
SIC: 3823 Water quality monitoring & control systems

(G-6365)
ENGLAND TRADING COMPANY LLC
Also Called: Industry West
1407 Atlantic Blvd (32207-3205)
PHONE..................................888 969-4190
Shannon Stewart, *Chairman*
Amy Reese, *COO*
Brian Doll, *Sales Staff*
Rocco Paone, *Sales Staff*
Jordan England, *Mng Member*
▲ EMP: 34 EST: 2013
SALES (est): 9.9MM Privately Held
SIC: 2599 Factory furniture & fixtures

(G-6366)
ENTERPRISE SLLING SLUTIONS LLC
12627 San Jose Blvd Ste 1 (32223-2662)
PHONE..................................904 655-9410
Christine Crane, *Principal*
EMP: 7 EST: 2010
SALES (est): 127.3K Privately Held
SIC: 3652 Pre-recorded records & tapes

(G-6367)
ENVIROSAFE TECHNOLOGIES INC
11201 St Johns Indstrl Pk (32246)
PHONE..................................904 646-3456
John Wing, *Principal*
EMP: 7 EST: 2016
SALES (est): 152.9K Privately Held
SIC: 3089 Plastics products

(G-6368)
ENVIROVAULT LLC
Also Called: Phoenix Tanks
1727 Bennett St (32206-5415)
PHONE..................................904 354-1858
Doug Aiosa,
EMP: 13 EST: 2004
SALES (est): 188.7K Privately Held
WEB: www.phoenixprods.com
SIC: 3443 Fuel tanks (oil, gas, etc.): metal plate

(G-6369)
EPIC HARVESTS LLC
5215 Philips Hwy Ste 3 (32207-7990)
PHONE..................................904 503-5143
EMP: 25
SALES: 3MM Privately Held
SIC: 2053 Mfg Frozen Bakery Products

(G-6370)
ESTHER WILSON ENTERPRISES LLC
2303 Rogero Rd (32211-4007)
PHONE..................................904 634-7463
Esther Wilson, *Principal*
EMP: 8 EST: 2015
SALES (est): 188.4K Privately Held
SIC: 3599 Machine shop, jobbing & repair

(G-6371)
EVOLUTION SIGNS AND PRINT INC
11672 Philips Hwy Ste 3 (32256-2782)
PHONE..................................904 634-5666
EMP: 8 EST: 2018
SALES (est): 576.9K Privately Held
SIC: 2752 Commercial printing, lithographic

(G-6372)
EXACT INC
5285 Ramona Blvd (32205-4414)
P.O. Box 61087 (32236-1087)
PHONE..................................904 783-6640
W Wallace Buzz Allen III, *President*
Frank Hajosch, *President*
William W Allen IV, *Vice Pres*
Dale Sanders, *QC Mgr*
Peter Esimaje, *Engineer*
EMP: 115 EST: 1964
SQ FT: 112,000
SALES (est): 14MM Privately Held
WEB: www.exactinc.com
SIC: 7692 3471 3469 3444 Welding repair; plating & polishing; metal stampings; sheet metal specialties, not stamped

(G-6373)
EXIDE BATTERY
600 Suemac Rd Ste 1 (32254-2796)
PHONE..................................904 783-1224
Ron Johnson, *Principal*
EMP: 5 EST: 2007
SALES (est): 352K Privately Held
SIC: 3691 5063 Storage batteries; batteries

(G-6374)
EXPERT TS OF JACKSONVILLE
711 Cassat Ave (32205-4859)
PHONE..................................904 387-2500
Denise Fisher, *President*
Steven Fisher, *Vice Pres*
EMP: 10 EST: 1991
SQ FT: 4,300
SALES (est): 1MM Privately Held
WEB: www.experttsjax.com
SIC: 2396 5699 Screen printing on fabric articles; T-shirts, custom printed

(G-6375)
EXPRESS FUEL SYSTEMS INC
8351 Highgate Dr (32216-1480)
PHONE..................................904 525-4052
Julian L Wilburn, *Principal*
EMP: 7 EST: 2007
SALES (est): 225.2K Privately Held
SIC: 2869 Fuels

(G-6376)
EXPRESS PRINTING & OFFICE SUPS
9840 Interstate Center Dr (32218-5528)
PHONE..................................904 765-9696
Michael Benso, *President*
John Benso, *Vice Pres*
EMP: 6 EST: 1983
SQ FT: 7,000
SALES (est): 729.1K Privately Held
WEB: www.expressprintingjax.com
SIC: 2752 5943 2791 Commercial printing, offset; office forms & supplies; typesetting

(G-6377)
FAM INDUSTRIES INC
7039 Mirabelle Dr (32258-8466)
PHONE..................................281 779-0650
Frank D Mays, *Principal*
EMP: 10 EST: 2007
SALES (est): 448.3K Privately Held
SIC: 3999 Barber & beauty shop equipment

(G-6378)
FANATICS MOUNTED MEMORIES INC
8100 Nations Way (32256-4405)
PHONE..................................866 578-9115
Ross Tannenbaum, *President*
David M Greene, *Senior VP*
Scott Widelitz, *Vice Pres*
Mark Cassuto, *Sales Staff*
Jeff Rabinowitz, *Sales Staff*
EMP: 44 EST: 1998
SALES (est): 5.1MM Privately Held
WEB: www.sportsmemorabilia.com
SIC: 2499 5199 Novelties, wood fiber; gifts & novelties

(G-6379)
FAST LABELS
8680 Bandera Cir S (32244-5947)
PHONE..................................904 626-0508
Susan Sermons, *General Mgr*
Michael Sermons, *Exec Dir*
EMP: 7 EST: 2001
SALES (est): 404.6K Privately Held
SIC: 2759 Labels & seals: printing

(G-6380)
FASTGLAS
Also Called: Island Tops
4226 Spring Grove Rd (32209)
PHONE..................................904 765-2222
Gary Crull, *Owner*
EMP: 8 EST: 1998
SQ FT: 18,446
SALES (est): 887K Privately Held
SIC: 2221 Fiberglass fabrics

(G-6381)
FINNS BRASS AND SILVER POLSG
2025 Hamilton St (32210-2045)
PHONE..................................904 387-1165
Michael R Finn, *President*
Kathy Finn, *Vice Pres*
EMP: 6 EST: 1972
SQ FT: 6,151
SALES (est): 632.5K Privately Held
WEB: www.finnsbrass.com
SIC: 3479 5932 3471 Coating of metals & formed products; antiques; plating & polishing

(G-6382)
FIRE DEFENSE CENTERS INC
3919 Morton St (32217-2260)
PHONE..................................904 731-1833
Ivy A Larusso, *Principal*
EMP: 7 EST: 2011
SALES (est): 298.4K Privately Held
SIC: 3812 Defense systems & equipment

(G-6383)
FIRST CAST STRPPING MBL SNDBLS
4846 Philips Hwy (32207-7270)
PHONE..................................904 733-5915
R Jay Miller, *President*
Lisa Miller, *Vice Pres*
EMP: 5 EST: 1992
SALES (est): 581.1K Privately Held
SIC: 3471 Sand blasting of metal parts

(G-6384)
FIRST COAST CARGO INC
7643 Gate Pkwy 104-31 (32256-3092)
PHONE..................................844 774-7711
Kyle Bailey, *CEO*
Ashley Bailey, *CEO*
EMP: 10 EST: 2019
SALES (est): 659.3K Privately Held
SIC: 3537 Trucks: freight, baggage, etc.: industrial, except mining

(G-6385)
FIRST COAST CONCRETE PUMPING
6115 Earline Cir N (32258-1645)
PHONE..................................904 262-6488
Tammy A McDaniels, *President*
EMP: 8 EST: 2001
SALES (est): 87.7K Privately Held
SIC: 3272 Concrete products

(G-6386)
FIRST COAST GRANITE & MBL INC
6860 Phillips Ind Blvd (32256-3028)
PHONE..................................904 388-1217
Timothy Deck, *President*
EMP: 20 EST: 2001
SALES (est): 607.2K Privately Held
WEB: www.fcsjax.com
SIC: 3281 Cut stone & stone products

(G-6387)
FIRST COAST TEE SHIRT CO INC
5971 Powers Ave Ste 104 (32217-2246)
PHONE..................................904 737-1985
Michael D Arthur, *President*
Craig L Melton, *Vice Pres*
EMP: 9 EST: 1994
SQ FT: 6,000
SALES (est): 780K Privately Held
WEB: www.firstcoasttees.com
SIC: 2759 Screen printing

(G-6388)
FIS AVANTGARD LLC (DH)
Also Called: Sungard
601 Riverside Ave (32204-2946)
PHONE..................................484 582-2000
Jl Alarcon, *General Mgr*
Judy Cho, *Manager*
Alain Fraiberger,
Thomas McDugall,
Karen Mullane,
EMP: 42 EST: 2006
SQ FT: 22,000
SALES (est): 77.1MM
SALES (corp-wide): 12.5B Publicly Held
SIC: 7372 7378 7379 Business oriented computer software; computer maintenance & repair; computer related consulting services
HQ: Fis Capital Markets Us Llc
601 Riverside Ave
Jacksonville FL 32204
877 776-3706

(G-6389)
FIS KIODEX LLC
601 Riverside Ave (32204-2946)
PHONE..................................904 438-6000
EMP: 19 EST: 2000
SALES (est): 2.6MM
SALES (corp-wide): 12.5B Publicly Held
WEB: www.fisglobal.com
SIC: 7372 Business oriented computer software
PA: Fidelity National Information Services, Inc.
601 Riverside Ave
Jacksonville FL 32204
904 438-6000

(G-6390)
FITZLORD INC
Also Called: Vulcan Steel
650 E 27th St (32206-2347)
PHONE..................................904 731-2041
Thomas E Fitzpatrick, *CEO*
Davis H Hopper, *President*
Nancy M Fitzpatrick, *Principal*
EMP: 63 EST: 1974
SQ FT: 55,000
SALES (est): 3.1MM Privately Held
SIC: 3441 1791 Fabricated structural metal; structural steel erection

(G-6391)
FLAGSHIPMD LLC
7800 Belfort Pkwy Ste 230 (32256-6983)
PHONE..................................904 302-6160
Aishwarya Nallapillai, *Vice Pres*
Manivannan M Nallapillai,
EMP: 8 EST: 2007
SALES (est): 285.1K Privately Held
WEB: www.flagshipmd.com
SIC: 7372 Business oriented computer software

(G-6392)
FLAMCO OF TEXAS LLC (HQ)
6940 Stuart Ave (32254-3426)
P.O. Box 6310 (32236-6310)
PHONE..................................904 783-8400
Lee B Jones, *CEO*
Steven C Jones, *Vice Pres*
Gordie Klys, *Sales Staff*
John J Klarfeld, *Admin Sec*
EMP: 22 EST: 2002
SQ FT: 70,000
SALES (est): 6.8MM
SALES (corp-wide): 508MM Privately Held
WEB: www.flamco.com
SIC: 3444 Sheet metalwork
PA: Omnimax International, Llc
30 Technology Pkwy S # 400
Peachtree Corners GA 30092
770 449-7066

(G-6393)
FLAMM INDUSTRIES INC
Also Called: Wco Enterprises
1313 Haines St (32206-6035)
PHONE..................................904 356-2876
Martin Flamm, *President*
Roger McCoy, *Plant Mgr*
EMP: 5 EST: 1978
SQ FT: 28,000
SALES (est): 861.7K Privately Held
WEB: www.flammindustries.com
SIC: 2653 Boxes, corrugated: made from purchased materials

(G-6394)
FLAT GLASS DISTRIBUTORS LLC
5355 Shawland Rd (32254-1649)
P.O. Box 41146 (32203-1146)
PHONE..................................904 354-5413

Thomas Lee, *General Mgr*
Wanda Williamson, *Manager*
Rusty Melcom,
JD Moeller,
Ron Rein,
EMP: 23 **EST:** 2016
SALES (est): 7.1MM **Privately Held**
WEB: www.flatglassdistributors.com
SIC: 3229 1793 Glassware, industrial; glass fiber products; glass & glazing work

(G-6395)
FLORIDA CMC REBAR
1395 Chaffee Rd S 2 (32221-1117)
PHONE..................................407 518-5101
Tania Murciano, *Principal*
EMP: 9 **EST:** 2016
SALES (est): 114.3K **Privately Held**
WEB: www.cmc.com
SIC: 3441 Fabricated structural metal

(G-6396)
FLORIDA E COAST HOLDINGS CORP
Also Called: Florida East Coast Railway
6140 Philips Hwy (32216-5921)
PHONE..................................904 279-3152
Linda Horn, *Opers Staff*
Alonso Rodriguez, *Manager*
EMP: 25 **Publicly Held**
WEB: www.fecrwy.com
SIC: 3531 Railway track equipment
HQ: Florida East Coast Holdings Corp.
7150 Philips Hwy
Jacksonville FL 32256

(G-6397)
FLORIDA EMBROIDME JACKSONVILLE
540 Commerce Center Dr # 1
(32225-8804)
PHONE..................................904 309-9535
Philip Mobley, *Owner*
EMP: 6 **EST:** 2017
SALES (est): 56.8K **Privately Held**
SIC: 2395 Embroidery & art needlework

(G-6398)
FLORIDA FLOATS INC (HQ)
Also Called: B M I Properties
1813 Dennis St (32204-2009)
P.O. Box 8, Bellingham WA (98227-0008)
PHONE..................................904 358-3362
J Everett Babbitt, *President*
J Everett Babbit, *President*
Paul Chapman, *Vice Pres*
Stan Reimer, *Vice Pres*
Kevin Thompson, *Senior Mgr*
▲ **EMP:** 25 **EST:** 1969
SQ FT: 5,000
SALES (est): 11.2MM
SALES (corp-wide): 70.2MM **Privately Held**
WEB: www.bellingham-marine.com
SIC: 3448 1629 Docks: prefabricated metal; marine construction
PA: Bellingham Marine Industries Acquisition, Inc.
1323 Lincoln St
Bellingham WA 98229
360 676-2800

(G-6399)
FLORIDA JACKSONVILLE FORKLIFT
1063 Haines St (32206-6029)
PHONE..................................904 674-6898
EMP: 8 **EST:** 2017
SALES (est): 139.5K **Privately Held**
WEB: www.floridaforklift.com
SIC: 3537 Forklift trucks

(G-6400)
FLORIDA METAL PRODUCTS LLC (HQ)
6940 Stuart Ave (32254-3426)
P.O. Box 6310 (32236-6310)
PHONE..................................904 783-8400
Lee B Jones IV, *President*
John J Klarfeld, *Corp Secy*
Steven C Jones, *Vice Pres*
▼ **EMP:** 100 **EST:** 1923
SQ FT: 100,000
SALES (est): 14MM
SALES (corp-wide): 508MM **Privately Held**
WEB: www.flamco.com
SIC: 3444 Metal roofing & roof drainage equipment
PA: Omnimax International, Llc
30 Technology Pkwy S # 400
Peachtree Corners GA 30092
770 449-7066

(G-6401)
FLORIDA ROCK CONCRETE INC
700 Palmetto St (32202-2406)
PHONE..................................904 355-1781
EMP: 0
SALES (est): 14.4MM
SALES (corp-wide): 2.9B **Publicly Held**
SIC: 3273 Stone Clay Glass Products
HQ: Legacy Vulcan, Llc
1200 Urban Center Dr
Shoal Creek AL 35242
205 298-3000

(G-6402)
FLORIDA ROCK INDUSTRIES (HQ)
Also Called: Vulcan Mtls Co Vestavia Al
4707 Gordon St (32216-4037)
P.O. Box 4667 (32201-4667)
PHONE..................................904 355-1781
Thompson Baker II, *President*
Hill J T, *President*
Michael P Oates, *Vice Pres*
Wallace A Patzke Jr, *Vice Pres*
John D Milton Jr, *CFO*
◆ **EMP:** 140 **EST:** 1931
SQ FT: 60,000
SALES (est): 391.4MM **Publicly Held**
WEB: www.flarock.com
SIC: 1422 Lime rock, ground

(G-6403)
FLORIDA STAR INC
Also Called: Florida Star & News
1257 Edgewood Ave W (32208-2741)
P.O. Box 40629 (32203-0629)
PHONE..................................904 766-8834
Clara Criswell, *President*
EMP: 10 **EST:** 1951
SQ FT: 1,300
SALES (est): 730.6K **Privately Held**
WEB: www.thefloridastar.com
SIC: 2711 Newspapers, publishing & printing

(G-6404)
FLORIDA TRAILER RANCH LLC
14770 Normandy Blvd (32234-2400)
PHONE..................................904 289-7710
Harry Horton, *President*
Shane McKeel, *Vice Pres*
Larry Petrozi, *Treasurer*
Carl Frankich, *Admin Sec*
▼ **EMP:** 10
SALES (est): 781.7K **Privately Held**
WEB: www.florida-trailer.com
SIC: 3799 Horse trailers, except fifth-wheel type

(G-6405)
FLORIDA WILBERT INC (PA)
5050 New Kings Rd (32209-2737)
P.O. Box 40485 (32203-0485)
PHONE..................................904 765-2641
William H Maddox Jr, *President*
▼ **EMP:** 5 **EST:** 1945
SQ FT: 8,000
SALES (est): 3MM **Privately Held**
WEB: www.floridawilbert.com
SIC: 3272 1791 Burial vaults, concrete or precast terrazzo; concrete reinforcement, placing of

(G-6406)
FLOTECH INC (PA)
Also Called: Tube Services-Division
136 Eastport Rd (32218-3906)
P.O. Box 26829 (32226-6829)
PHONE..................................904 358-1849
Richard E Bazar, *President*
Thomas C Goelz, *Corp Secy*
Joe Ferranti, *VP Opers*
Earl Traugott, *Safety Mgr*
Randy Tallman, *Foreman/Supr*
◆ **EMP:** 100 **EST:** 1982
SQ FT: 26,000
SALES (est): 25.7MM **Privately Held**
WEB: www.flotechinc.com
SIC: 3494 7699 3339 3341 Valves & pipe fittings; valve repair, industrial; primary nonferrous metals; secondary nonferrous metals; sheet metalwork; nonferrous foundries

(G-6407)
FLOWERS BKG JACKSONVILLE LLC (DH)
Also Called: Sunbeam Bread
2261 W 30th St (32209-3606)
P.O. Box 12579 (32209-0579)
PHONE..................................904 354-3771
Rick McCombs, *President*
Robert White, *Vice Pres*
▼ **EMP:** 80 **EST:** 1944
SQ FT: 100,000
SALES (est): 13MM
SALES (corp-wide): 4.3B **Publicly Held**
SIC: 2051 Bakery: wholesale or wholesale/retail combined
HQ: Flowers Baking Co. Of Thomasville, Inc.
1919 Flowers Cir
Thomasville GA 31757
229 226-9110

(G-6408)
FLUID DESIGNS INC
4357 Habana Ave (32217-4050)
PHONE..................................904 737-1557
EMP: 6
SQ FT: 3,300
SALES (est): 275K **Privately Held**
SIC: 2759 Letterpress Printing

(G-6409)
FLUIDRA USA LLC (PA)
8525 Mallory Rd (32220-2358)
PHONE..................................904 378-0999
Eloy P Corts, *Ch of Bd*
Pere Ballart, *Ch of Bd*
Stephen B De Bever, *President*
Claudi Sala, *Opers Mgr*
Dustin Borg, *Engineer*
▲ **EMP:** 34 **EST:** 1993
SQ FT: 43,000
SALES (est): 7.9MM **Privately Held**
WEB: www.fluidrausa.com
SIC: 3589 3561 5091 Swimming pool filter & water conditioning systems; pumps & pumping equipment; sporting & recreation goods

(G-6410)
FLYING W PLASTICS FL INC ✪
109 Stevens St (32254-3656)
PHONE..................................904 800-2451
EMP: 14 **EST:** 2020
SALES (est): 1.9MM **Privately Held**
WEB: www.fwplastics.com
SIC: 2821 Polyethylene resins

(G-6411)
FOLEY AIR LLC ✪
Also Called: Air2 G2 Machine
136 Ellis Rd N (32254-2835)
PHONE..................................904 379-2243
Glen Black, *President*
EMP: 11 **EST:** 2020
SALES (est): 3.2MM
SALES (corp-wide): 12.1MM **Privately Held**
WEB: www.foleyco.com
SIC: 3523 Farm machinery & equipment
PA: Foley Company, Llc
1750 Ryden Rd
Prescott WI 54021
800 225-9810

(G-6412)
FRASCOLD USA CORPORATION
5343 Bowden Rd 2 (32216-5945)
PHONE..................................855 547-5600
Kristian Ellefsen, *CEO*
Bina Ellefsen, *Human Res Mgr*
▲ **EMP:** 6 **EST:** 2014
SALES (est): 1.8MM **Privately Held**
WEB: www.frascold.it
SIC: 3585 Compressors for refrigeration & air conditioning equipment

(G-6413)
FRASER MILLWORKS INC
9424 Sisson Dr (32218-6064)
PHONE..................................904 768-7710
Chris M Fraser, *President*
Sharon Fraser, *Treasurer*
EMP: 7 **EST:** 1978
SQ FT: 10,000
SALES (est): 849.7K **Privately Held**
WEB: www.frasermillworks.com
SIC: 2431 Millwork

(G-6414)
FRASER WEST INC
6640 County Road 218 (32234-3047)
PHONE..................................901 620-4200
Chip Osteen, *Manager*
EMP: 74
SALES (corp-wide): 3.6B **Privately Held**
SIC: 2426 2421 2621 Hardwood dimension & flooring mills; sawmills & planing mills, general; paper mills
HQ: West Fraser, Inc.
1900 Exeter Rd Ste 105
Germantown TN 38138
901 620-4200

(G-6415)
FRATTLE STAIRS & RAILS INC
465 Tresca Rd (32225-6566)
PHONE..................................904 384-3495
Don Frattle, *President*
Troy Pagnotto, *Opers Mgr*
EMP: 17 **EST:** 2000
SQ FT: 40,000
SALES (est): 5.7MM **Privately Held**
WEB: www.frattle.com
SIC: 3446 Balconies, metal; railings, banisters, guards, etc.: made from metal pipe; railings, prefabricated metal; stairs, staircases, stair treads: prefabricated metal

(G-6416)
FRESH THREAD LLC
2823 State Road A1a (32233-2843)
PHONE..................................904 677-9505
Jerry Rodriguez, *Principal*
EMP: 11 **EST:** 2012
SALES (est): 273.3K **Privately Held**
SIC: 2752 5136 Commercial printing, lithographic; men's & boys' clothing

(G-6417)
FT ACQUISITION COMPANY LLC
Also Called: Fabtech Supply
11315 Distribution Ave E (32256-2738)
P.O. Box 23325 (32241-3325)
PHONE..................................904 367-0095
Alan Ennis, *CEO*
Scott Lapierre, *Engineer*
EMP: 30 **EST:** 1992
SQ FT: 10,000
SALES (est): 6.4MM **Privately Held**
SIC: 3444 Metal housings, enclosures, casings & other containers

(G-6418)
FUTCH PRINTING & MAILING INC
4606 Shirley Ave (32210-1934)
PHONE..................................904 388-3995
Shuford M Futch III, *President*
Agata Futch, *Vice Pres*
EMP: 12 **EST:** 1922
SQ FT: 10,000
SALES (est): 1MM **Privately Held**
WEB: www.futchprint.net
SIC: 2759 7331 Letterpress printing; direct mail advertising services

(G-6419)
G6 EMBROIDERY LLC
6001 Argyle Frest Blvd St (32244)
PHONE..................................904 729-1191
EMP: 6 **EST:** 2018
SALES (est): 444K **Privately Held**
WEB: www.g6promo.com
SIC: 2395 Embroidery products, except schiffli machine

(G-6420)
GATE PETROLEUM COMPANY
11040 Mccormick Rd (32225-1821)
PHONE..................................904 998-7126

GEOGRAPHIC

EMP: 7
SALES (corp-wide): 708.1K **Privately Held**
WEB: www.gatepetro.com
SIC: 3052 Rubber belting
PA: Gate Petroleum Company
9540 San Jose Blvd
Jacksonville FL 32257
904 737-7220

(G-6421)
GATE PETROLEUM COMPANY
4100 Heckscher Dr (32226-3030)
PHONE..................................904 396-0517
Earl Shimp, *President*
EMP: 7
SQ FT: 5,984
SALES (corp-wide): 708.1K **Privately Held**
WEB: www.gatepetro.com
SIC: 3272 Concrete products
PA: Gate Petroleum Company
9540 San Jose Blvd
Jacksonville FL 32257
904 737-7220

(G-6422)
GATE PRECAST COMPANY
402 Zoo Pkwy (32226-2604)
PHONE..................................904 520-5795
Donald Davis, *Vice Pres*
Todd Petty, *Vice Pres*
Lisa Neuman, *Purch Agent*
Billy Craig, *Sales Executive*
Michael Trosset, *Marketing Staff*
EMP: 107
SALES (corp-wide): 708.1K **Privately Held**
WEB: www.gateprecast.com
SIC: 3272 Precast terrazo or concrete products
HQ: Gate Precast Company
9540 San Jose Blvd
Jacksonville FL 32257
904 732-7668

(G-6423)
GATE PRECAST COMPANY (HQ)
9540 San Jose Blvd (32257-5432)
P.O. Box 23627 (32241-3627)
PHONE..................................904 732-7668
Dean Gwin, *CEO*
Earl N Shimp, *Senior VP*
Mark Ledkins, *Vice Pres*
Joseph Luke, *Vice Pres*
Michael Ryan, *VP Opers*
◆ **EMP:** 9
SALES (est): 221.3K
SALES (corp-wide): 708.1K **Privately Held**
WEB: www.gateprecast.com
SIC: 3272 Concrete stuctural support & building material
PA: Gate Petroleum Company
9540 San Jose Blvd
Jacksonville FL 32257
904 737-7220

(G-6424)
GATE PRECAST ERECTION CO
9540 San Jose Blvd (32257-5432)
P.O. Box 23627 (32241-3627)
PHONE..................................904 737-7220
Joseph C Luke, *Director*
Jack C Lueders Jr, *Director*
Jeremy P Smith Jr, *Director*
EMP: 87 **EST:** 1978
SALES (est): 5.6MM
SALES (corp-wide): 708.1K **Privately Held**
WEB: www.gateprecast.com
SIC: 3272 Concrete stuctural support & building material
PA: Gate Petroleum Company
9540 San Jose Blvd
Jacksonville FL 32257
904 737-7220

(G-6425)
GATER CUSTOM CABINET & DOORS
4621 Wesconnett Blvd (32210-7349)
PHONE..................................904 778-2300
Debra Tucker, *Owner*
Micheal Tucker, *Manager*
EMP: 6 **EST:** 1998
SALES (est): 25.7K **Privately Held**
SIC: 2434 Wood kitchen cabinets

(G-6426)
GAUKAUPA RACEWAY
8405 Beach Blvd (32216-3130)
PHONE..................................904 483-3473
Raj Patel, *Principal*
EMP: 6 **EST:** 2009
SALES (est): 145.3K **Privately Held**
SIC: 3644 Raceways

(G-6427)
GC ELECTRIC LLC
9101 Tobias Rd E (32234-3099)
PHONE..................................386 842-7066
Gregory C Tompkins, *Owner*
EMP: 6 **EST:** 2016
SALES (est): 125.6K **Privately Held**
SIC: 3699 1731 Electrical equipment & supplies; electrical work

(G-6428)
GE
12079 Normandy Blvd (32221-1820)
PHONE..................................904 570-3151
Lisa Marchand, *Manager*
EMP: 9 **EST:** 2015
SALES (est): 104.8K **Privately Held**
WEB: www.ge.jobs
SIC: 3511 Turbines & turbine generator sets

(G-6429)
GE CONSUMER CORPORATION
Also Called: GE Consumer Distribution
600 Whittaker Rd (32218-5781)
PHONE..................................904 696-9775
Steve Holton, *General Mgr*
EMP: 98
SALES (corp-wide): 79.6B **Publicly Held**
WEB: www.geconsumerandindustrial.com
SIC: 3632 Household refrigerators & freezers
HQ: Ge Consumer Corporation
140 Whittington Pkwy
Louisville KY 40222
203 373-2211

(G-6430)
GEM ASSET ACQUISITION LLC
Also Called: Gemseal Pvments Pdts - Jackson
9556 Historic Kings Rd S (32257-2009)
PHONE..................................904 268-6063
Jason Adair, *Store Mgr*
EMP: 17
SALES (corp-wide): 31.7MM **Privately Held**
SIC: 2951 Asphalt paving mixtures & blocks
PA: Gem Asset Acquisition Llc
1855 Lindbergh St Ste 500
Charlotte NC 28208
704 225-3321

(G-6431)
GENERAL BUSINESS SERVICES
12412 San Jose Blvd # 101 (32223-8620)
PHONE..................................904 260-1099
Tom Carroll, *Owner*
EMP: 6 **EST:** 2000
SALES (est): 470.9K **Privately Held**
SIC: 3578 Calculating & accounting equipment

(G-6432)
GENERAL METALS & PLASTICS INC
2727 Waller St (32205-5631)
PHONE..................................904 354-8224
Fred Broadwell Jr, *President*
Joyce Broadwell, *Vice Pres*
EMP: 5 **EST:** 1965
SQ FT: 5,500
SALES (est): 780.9K **Privately Held**
WEB: www.generalmetalsandplastics.com
SIC: 3444 3448 Awnings & canopies; screen enclosures; carports: prefabricated metal

(G-6433)
GENERAL SIGN SERVICE INC
1940 Spearing St (32206-3942)
PHONE..................................904 355-5630
Randall Ginzig, *President*
Carol Ginzig, *Admin Sec*
EMP: 10 **EST:** 1973
SALES (est): 831K **Privately Held**
WEB: www.generalsignservice.com
SIC: 3993 1731 Electric signs; general electrical contractor

(G-6434)
GILSON INC
730 Trinidad Rd (32216-9342)
PHONE..................................904 725-7612
Curtis Carter, *Principal*
EMP: 6 **EST:** 2009
SALES (est): 87.2K **Privately Held**
WEB: www.gilson.com
SIC: 3826 Analytical instruments

(G-6435)
GLASFLOSS INDUSTRIES INC
1310 Tradeport Dr (32218-2485)
PHONE..................................904 741-9922
Doug Lange, *District Mgr*
Mark Filewood, *Vice Pres*
Cheryl Manrique, *Vice Pres*
Bill McKnight, *Vice Pres*
Charles Watts, *Vice Pres*
EMP: 17
SQ FT: 74,952
SALES (corp-wide): 49.5MM **Privately Held**
WEB: www.glasfloss.com
SIC: 3564 Filters, air: furnaces, air conditioning equipment, etc.
PA: Glasfloss Industries, Inc.
420 E Danieldale Rd
Desoto TX 75115
740 687-1100

(G-6436)
GLASSFLAKE INTERNATIONAL INC
6525 Greenland Rd (32258-2439)
PHONE..................................904 268-4000
Clive Harper, *President*
▲ **EMP:** 6 **EST:** 1972
SQ FT: 10,000
SALES (est): 623.3K **Privately Held**
WEB: www.glassflake.com
SIC: 3479 2273 Coating of metals & formed products; floor coverings, textile fiber

(G-6437)
GLOBAL PUBLISHING INC
9799 Old St Augustine Rd (32257-8974)
PHONE..................................904 262-0491
Ronald Legrand, *President*
Debbie Waters, *Mktg Dir*
Nicholas Kouvatsos, *Marketing Staff*
Jon Duck, *Manager*
Karen Raynor, *Info Tech Mgr*
EMP: 35
SQ FT: 25,000
SALES (est): 4.2MM **Privately Held**
WEB: www.ronlegrand.com
SIC: 2741 Miscellaneous publishing

(G-6438)
GLOBAL TISSUE GROUP JAX
11801 Central Pkwy (32224-2637)
PHONE..................................904 861-3290
EMP: 11 **EST:** 2009
SALES (est): 676.5K **Privately Held**
WEB: www.globaltissuegroup.com
SIC: 2621 Paper mills

(G-6439)
GLODEA STORE CORP
Also Called: Glodea Kitchens
521 Copeland St (32204-2721)
PHONE..................................888 400-4937
Ignacio L Santos, *President*
Santos Jose Ignacio L, *President*
Patrick Cherix, *Vice Pres*
▲ **EMP:** 5 **EST:** 2013
SQ FT: 800
SALES (est): 614.4K **Privately Held**
WEB: www.glodea.com
SIC: 2511 5021 Wood household furniture; household furniture

(G-6440)
GOODMAN MANUFACTURING CO LP
Also Called: Pioneer Metals
1934 W Beaver St (32209-7531)
PHONE..................................904 355-4520
Rick Rivas, *Manager*
EMP: 9 **Privately Held**
WEB: www.goodmanmfg.com
SIC: 3694 Distributors, motor vehicle engine; alternators, automotive
HQ: Goodman Manufacturing Company, Lp
19001 Kermier Rd
Waller TX 77484
713 861-2500

(G-6441)
GOODRICH CORPORATION
Engineered Polymer Products
6061 Goodrich Blvd (32226-3402)
PHONE..................................904 757-3660
Mike Smith, *General Mgr*
Keith Reed, *Plant Mgr*
Tom Lynn, *Purchasing*
EMP: 120
SALES (corp-wide): 56.5B **Publicly Held**
WEB: www.collinsaerospace.com
SIC: 3812 8711 3429 3493 Sonar systems & equipment; engineering services; manufactured hardware (general); steel springs, except wire; wire springs; synthetic rubber
HQ: Goodrich Corporation
2730 W Tyvola Rd
Charlotte NC 28217
704 423-7000

(G-6442)
GOSAN USA INC
1926 Spearing St (32206-3942)
P.O. Box 600920 (32260-0920)
PHONE..................................904 356-4181
Rocio Santin, *President*
Francisco Javi Esteban, *Managing Dir*
▲ **EMP:** 12 **EST:** 2007
SALES (est): 703.7K **Privately Held**
WEB: www.jcrenfroe.com
SIC: 3537 Trucks, tractors, loaders, carriers & similar equipment

(G-6443)
GOSPEL JOURNAL
3491 Pall Mall Dr Ste 125 (32257-4410)
PHONE..................................904 389-9635
Johnie Scaggs, *Principal*
EMP: 7 **EST:** 2012
SALES (est): 172.2K **Privately Held**
WEB: www.thegospeljournal.com
SIC: 2711 Newspapers, publishing & printing

(G-6444)
GRAHAM & COMPANY LLC
9440 Philips Hwy Ste 1 (32256-1339)
PHONE..................................904 281-0003
Leslie Williamson, *Chief Engr*
Thomas Michael, *Engineer*
Tana Welch, *Accountant*
EMP: 7
SALES (corp-wide): 11.2MM **Privately Held**
WEB: www.grahamcompany.com
SIC: 3563 Vacuum pumps, except laboratory
PA: Graham & Company, Llc
1801 5th Ave N Ste 300
Birmingham AL 35203
205 871-7100

(G-6445)
GREAT ATLANTIC OUTFITTERS
803 North St (32211-5727)
PHONE..................................904 722-0196
Bob Morris, *CEO*
Andrew Lassiter, *Info Tech Mgr*
EMP: 5 **EST:** 2005
SALES (est): 509.2K **Privately Held**
WEB: www.greatatlanticoutfitters.com
SIC: 2759 Screen printing

▲ = Import ▼=Export
◆ =Import/Export

(G-6446)
GREAT NORTHERN CORPORATION
Also Called: Laminations Southeast
1420 Vantage Way S # 100 (32218-2398)
PHONE..................................920 739-3671
Warren Bobyk, *Business Mgr*
Tim Richardson, *VP Sales*
Chris Sauceda, *Branch Mgr*
EMP: 25
SALES (corp-wide): 406.9MM **Privately Held**
WEB: www.greatnortherncorp.com
SIC: 2631 2671 Container, packaging & boxboard; packaging paper & plastics film, coated & laminated
PA: Great Northern Corporation
395 Stroebe Rd
Appleton WI 54914
920 739-3671

(G-6447)
GREEN ENERGY ENTERPRISES INC (PA)
9300 Normandy Blvd # 511 (32221-5562)
PHONE..................................904 309-8993
Jeffrey Landreth, *CEO*
Joshua Henderson, *President*
Lisa Betros, *COO*
Gene Johnson, *CFO*
EMP: 26 **EST:** 2004
SALES (est): 6.3MM **Privately Held**
SIC: 3812 Aircraft/aerospace flight instruments & guidance systems

(G-6448)
GREEN POWER SYSTEMS LLC
4155 Lakeside Dr (32210-3303)
PHONE..................................904 545-1311
Ingo Krieg,
Dick Basford,
Richard Breitmoser,
EMP: 6 **EST:** 2004
SQ FT: 6,500
SALES (est): 373.9K **Privately Held**
WEB: www.greenpowersystems.com
SIC: 7372 Utility computer software

(G-6449)
GREEN SHADES SOFTWARE INC
7020 A C Skinner Pkwy (32256-6961)
PHONE..................................904 807-0160
David Rosas, *President*
Welles Housh, *Owner*
Howard Tarnoff, *Senior VP*
Matthew Kane, *Vice Pres*
Andrea Potvin, *Controller*
EMP: 10 **EST:** 1985
SALES (est): 2.2MM **Privately Held**
WEB: www.greenshades.com
SIC: 7372 Business oriented computer software

(G-6450)
GREG ALLENS INC (PA)
7071 Davis Creek Rd (32256-3027)
PHONE..................................904 262-8912
Gregory J Allen Jr, *President*
Cynthia J Allen, *Admin Sec*
EMP: 33 **EST:** 1986
SQ FT: 18,000
SALES (est): 5.7MM **Privately Held**
WEB: www.gregallens.com
SIC: 2759 5112 Commercial printing; stationery & office supplies

(G-6451)
GREG CLARK WELDING INC
6108 Arlington Rd (32211-5420)
PHONE..................................904 226-2952
Gregory A Clark, *Principal*
EMP: 5 **EST:** 2008
SALES (est): 363.4K **Privately Held**
SIC: 7692 Welding repair

(G-6452)
GRIFFIN & HOLMAN INC
1855 Cassat Ave Ste 8 (32210-1635)
P.O. Box 60332 (32236-0332)
PHONE..................................904 781-4531
Pam Holman, *President*
EMP: 7 **EST:** 1984
SALES (est): 158K **Privately Held**
WEB: www.holman-inc.com
SIC: 2531 School furniture

(G-6453)
GRISWOLD READY MIX CON INC
11660 Camden Rd (32218-3902)
P.O. Box 28310 (32226-8310)
PHONE..................................904 751-3796
Sherry Griswold, *President*
Larry Griswold Jr, *Vice Pres*
Mabrine H Griswold, *Admin Sec*
EMP: 17 **EST:** 1989
SQ FT: 300
SALES (est): 1.5MM **Privately Held**
WEB: www.griswoldconcrete.com
SIC: 3273 Ready-mixed concrete

(G-6454)
GTG-JAX LLC
Also Called: Global Tissue Group Jax
11801 Central Pkwy (32224-2637)
PHONE..................................904 861-3290
Steven Catalfamo, *Vice Pres*
Phillip Shaoul, *Mng Member*
Vincent Tria, *Manager*
Ehsan Elnaghave,
EMP: 30 **EST:** 2007
SALES (est): 16.6MM
SALES (corp-wide): 28.9MM **Privately Held**
WEB: www.gtgtissue.com
SIC: 2621 Tissue paper
PA: Global Tissue Group, Inc.
870 Expressway Dr S
Medford NY 11763
631 924-3019

(G-6455)
GTGJFE LLC
Also Called: Joint Force Enterprises
5570 Fl Min Blvd S Ste 1 (32257-3246)
PHONE..................................904 800-6333
Robert Bright, *President*
EMP: 6 **EST:** 2015
SQ FT: 4,500
SALES (est): 696.8K **Privately Held**
SIC: 3484 Small arms

(G-6456)
GUANABANA & CO LLC
Also Called: Guanabana Artisan Ice Pops
8802 Corporate Square Ct # 306 (32216-1984)
PHONE..................................904 891-5256
Oliver Mosqueda,
EMP: 11 **EST:** 2014
SALES (est): 270.5K **Privately Held**
SIC: 2024 Juice pops, frozen

(G-6457)
GYRX LLC
11222 St Johns Indus Pkwy (32246-6675)
PHONE..................................904 641-2599
EMP: 12
SALES (est): 930K **Privately Held**
SIC: 3841 Mfg Surgical/Medical Instruments

(G-6458)
H & M STEEL
9843 Evans Rd (32208-7512)
PHONE..................................904 765-3465
Rudolph Murray, *Owner*
EMP: 5 **EST:** 1974
SALES (est): 301.8K **Privately Held**
SIC: 3312 Pipes, iron & steel

(G-6459)
H2 HOME COLLECTION INC ✪
1601-1 N Main St # 3159 (32206-4453)
PHONE..................................714 916-9513
Deanna Hodges, *President*
EMP: 19 **EST:** 2020
SALES (est): 1MM **Privately Held**
SIC: 2299 Broadwoven fabrics: linen, jute, hemp & ramie

(G-6460)
HANS-MILL CORP
5406 W 1st St (32254-1648)
P.O. Box 660, New Vernon NJ (07976-0660)
PHONE..................................904 395-2288
Hong Yuan Han, *President*
Todd Beasley, *Opers Staff*
Xiao Yang, *CFO*
Miki Schau, *Human Res Dir*
David Detuccio, *Planning*
▲ **EMP:** 70 **EST:** 2016
SQ FT: 125,000
SALES (est): 16.1MM **Privately Held**
SIC: 3089 Plastic kitchenware, tableware & houseware

(G-6461)
HARRIS MANUFACTURING INC
Also Called: Harris Lighting
9143 Philips Hwy Ste 420 (32256-1381)
PHONE..................................877 204-7540
Bertha Calkins, *Vice Pres*
George Wilson, *Vice Pres*
Scott Green, *CFO*
Greg Green, *Manager*
◆ **EMP:** 18 **EST:** 1968
SQ FT: 106,000
SALES (est): 700.9K
SALES (corp-wide): 116.8MM **Publicly Held**
WEB: www.orionlighting.com
SIC: 3646 Commercial indusl & institutional electric lighting fixtures
PA: Orion Energy Systems, Inc.
2210 Woodland Dr
Manitowoc WI 54220
920 892-9340

(G-6462)
HARTCO INC
Also Called: Sir Speedy
25 E Beaver St (32202-3020)
PHONE..................................904 353-5259
Michael A Hartley, *President*
Susan Hartley, *Vice Pres*
EMP: 8 **EST:** 1974
SQ FT: 4,000
SALES (est): 2.2MM **Privately Held**
WEB: www.sirspeedy.com
SIC: 2752 2791 Commercial printing, lithographic; typesetting

(G-6463)
HARTLEY PRESS INC
4250 Saint Augustine Rd (32207-6694)
PHONE..................................904 398-5141
Mike Hartley, *President*
Diane McConaughey, *Vice Pres*
Don Patton, *Warehouse Mgr*
Annette Watson, *Sales Staff*
Jim Klusmeyer, *Manager*
▲ **EMP:** 100
SQ FT: 50,000
SALES: 16.6MM **Privately Held**
WEB: www.thehartleypress.com
SIC: 2752 Commercial printing, offset

(G-6464)
HCR SOFTWARE SOLUTIONS INC
13400 Sutton Park Dr S # 1101 (32224-0235)
PHONE..................................904 638-6177
James B Davis, *CEO*
Matt Davis, *Managing Dir*
Cindy Peterson, *Vice Pres*
Caleb Hardy, *Sales Staff*
Susan Keith, *Administration*
EMP: 25 **EST:** 2007
SQ FT: 2,400
SALES (est): 4.2MM **Privately Held**
WEB: www.compensationxl.com
SIC: 7372 Application computer software

(G-6465)
HEALTHY SCHOOLS LLC
3546 Saint Johns Bluff Rd (32224-2714)
PHONE..................................904 887-4540
Tony Boselli, *Mng Member*
EMP: 106 **EST:** 2013
SQ FT: 2,200
SALES (est): 10.7MM **Privately Held**
SIC: 2836 Vaccines & other immunizing products

(G-6466)
HECHT RUBBER CORPORATION
6161 Philips Hwy (32216-5982)
PHONE..................................904 731-3401
Larry Hecht, *President*
Sylvia Hecht, *Corp Secy*
Jacob Hecht, *Vice Pres*
Stuart Hecht, *CFO*
Ric Fleming, *Manager*
EMP: 37 **EST:** 1944
SQ FT: 75,000
SALES (est): 4.6MM **Privately Held**
WEB: www.hechtrubber.com
SIC: 3052 Rubber & plastics hose & beltings

(G-6467)
HEMP CBD DAILY INC
13724 Shady Woods St N (32224-4822)
PHONE..................................904 672-7623
Jason Brandner, *Principal*
EMP: 7 **EST:** 2018
SALES (est): 115.4K **Privately Held**
SIC: 3999

(G-6468)
HENLEY METAL LLC
Also Called: Eligius Metal Works
6593 Powers Ave Ste 23 (32217-2853)
PHONE..................................904 353-4770
Melody Henley,
George Henley,
EMP: 12 **EST:** 2009
SQ FT: 10,000
SALES (est): 1.8MM **Privately Held**
SIC: 3441 Fabricated structural metal

(G-6469)
HENRYS HICKORY HOUSE INC
249 Copeland St (32204-1836)
P.O. Box 2823 (32203-2823)
PHONE..................................904 493-4420
William Morris, *President*
EMP: 53 **EST:** 1966
SQ FT: 40,000
SALES (est): 1MM **Privately Held**
WEB: www.leisurecare.teleflora.com
SIC: 2011 2013 Pork products from pork slaughtered on site; sausages & other prepared meats

(G-6470)
HERFF JONES LLC
12086 Fort Caroline Rd # 201 (32225-2689)
PHONE..................................904 641-4060
Kevin Whitlow, *Owner*
EMP: 8
SALES (corp-wide): 1.1B **Privately Held**
WEB: www.yearbookdiscoveries.com
SIC: 2752 Commercial printing, lithographic
HQ: Herff Jones, Llc
4501 W 62nd St
Indianapolis IN 46268
800 419-5462

(G-6471)
HERITAGE PUBLISHING INC
6620 Sthpint Dr S Ste 310 (32216)
PHONE..................................904 296-1304
Marzoug Al-Amad, *President*
Zeng Hua Lu, *Vice Pres*
Judeh Handoush, *CFO*
Theresamae Teri Ortega, *Manager*
Nour Matrahji, *Graphic Designe*
EMP: 49 **EST:** 1995
SQ FT: 7,000
SALES (est): 4.7MM **Privately Held**
WEB: www.heritagepublishinginc.com
SIC: 2741 Telephone & other directory publishing

(G-6472)
HISCO PUMP SOUTH LLC
2664 Robert St (32207-9500)
PHONE..................................904 786-4488
Julie Dubois, *Owner*
Cato Rogers, *Sales Mgr*
Matthew J Montineri,
Joseph M Montineri,
Joseph A Montineri,
EMP: 16 **EST:** 2007
SALES (est): 2.9MM **Privately Held**
WEB: www.hiscopumpsouth.com
SIC: 3561 3563 5085 Pumps & pumping equipment; vacuum pumps, except laboratory; gaskets

GEOGRAPHIC

(G-6473)
HOGAN ASSESSMENT SYSTEMS INC
13500 Sutton Park Dr S # 401 (32224-5291)
PHONE..................................904 992-0302
EMP: 7
SALES (est): 490.9K **Privately Held**
SIC: 2741 8742 Job Training Services
PA: Hogan Assessment Systems, Inc.
11 S Greenwood Ave
Tulsa OK 74120

(G-6474)
HOGG WILD FABRICATION
5737 Arlington Rd (32211-5317)
PHONE..................................904 214-3453
Joyce B Foston, *Principal*
EMP: 6 **EST:** 2010
SALES (est): 74.8K **Privately Held**
SIC: 3842 Welders' hoods

(G-6475)
HOLLAND PUMP COMPANY
2720 Lane Ave N (32254-1228)
PHONE..................................904 880-0010
William W Blodgett, *Principal*
EMP: 7
SALES (corp-wide): 20.1MM **Privately Held**
WEB: www.hollandpump.com
SIC: 3561 7359 Pumps & pumping equipment; equipment rental & leasing
PA: Holland Pump Company
7312 Westport Pl
West Palm Beach FL 33413
561 697-3333

(G-6476)
HOLMES STAMP COMPANY (PA)
Also Called: Hsc
2021 Saint Augustine Rd E (32207-4144)
P.O. Box 5274 (32247-5274)
PHONE..................................904 396-2291
Bryan Croft, *CEO*
Bob Croft, *President*
Steve Fernandez, *Vice Pres*
Coleman Lisa, *Vice Pres*
Alice Viego, *Opers Staff*
EMP: 26 **EST:** 1954
SQ FT: 3,000
SALES (est): 6.9MM **Privately Held**
WEB: www.hcbrands.com
SIC: 3089 3953 3993 2759 Engraving of plastic; cancelling stamps, hand: rubber or metal; signs & advertising specialties; commercial printing; packaging paper & plastics film, coated & laminated

(G-6477)
HONEYWELL INTERNATIONAL INC
6200 Flagship Cir N (32226-4030)
PHONE..................................904 696-5222
Martin Rosenfield, *Branch Mgr*
EMP: 6
SALES (corp-wide): 32.6B **Publicly Held**
WEB: www.honeywell.com
SIC: 3724 Aircraft engines & engine parts
PA: Honeywell International Inc.
300 S Tryon St
Charlotte NC 28202
704 627-6200

(G-6478)
HONEYWELL INTERNATIONAL INC
9440 Philips Hwy Ste 4 (32256-1339)
PHONE..................................904 260-5900
Roger Parsons, *Branch Mgr*
EMP: 6
SALES (corp-wide): 32.6B **Publicly Held**
WEB: www.honeywell.com
SIC: 3724 Aircraft engines & engine parts
PA: Honeywell International Inc.
300 S Tryon St
Charlotte NC 28202
704 627-6200

(G-6479)
HOPPIN POP KETTLE STOP LLC (PA)
Also Called: Nutty Scoopz
1850 Emerson St (32207-6108)
PHONE..................................502 220-2372
Tina Parks, *Mng Member*
EMP: 5 **EST:** 2018
SALES (est): 548.6K **Privately Held**
SIC: 3556 Food products machinery

(G-6480)
HOWARD PUBLICATIONS INC (HQ)
Also Called: American Shipper
501 W Bay St Ste 200 (32202-4418)
PHONE..................................904 355-2601
Craig Fuller, *CEO*
EMP: 9 **EST:** 1954
SALES (est): 5.6MM
SALES (corp-wide): 12.9MM **Privately Held**
WEB: www.freightwaves.com
SIC: 2721 Magazines: publishing only, not printed on site
PA: Freightwaves, Inc.
405 Cherry St
Chattanooga TN 37402
423 205-3001

(G-6481)
HUCKINS YACHT CORPORATION
3482 Lake Shore Blvd (32210-5391)
PHONE..................................904 389-1125
Dale B Purcell, *President*
Margaret C Purcell, *Corp Secy*
Ricardo Lopez, *Purch Mgr*
Randy Marchman, *Purch Mgr*
▲ **EMP:** 30 **EST:** 1928
SQ FT: 32,000
SALES (est): 4.6MM **Privately Held**
WEB: www.huckinsyacht.com
SIC: 3732 Yachts, building & repairing

(G-6482)
HUGHES CONSOLIDATED SERVICES
4712 Royal Ave (32205-4954)
PHONE..................................904 438-5710
David Hughes, *Partner*
Glenda Hughes, *Partner*
EMP: 5 **EST:** 1988
SQ FT: 3,800
SALES (est): 322.8K **Privately Held**
SIC: 2752 Commercial printing, offset

(G-6483)
HUMIC GROWTH SOLUTIONS INC (PA)
709 Eastport Rd (32218-3915)
PHONE..................................904 392-7201
Kevin Merritt, *President*
Ryan Merritt, *Exec VP*
Ryan S Merritt, *Vice Pres*
▼ **EMP:** 15 **EST:** 2013
SQ FT: 60,000
SALES (est): 10MM **Privately Held**
SIC: 2879 Soil conditioners

(G-6484)
HYDROLEC INC
5050 Stepp Ave (32216-6054)
PHONE..................................904 730-3766
Kim Kawasaki, *President*
Khoa Le, *Production*
Joe Grooms, *Purchasing*
▲ **EMP:** 30 **EST:** 1978
SQ FT: 100,000
SALES (est): 8.4MM **Privately Held**
WEB: www.hydrolecinc.com
SIC: 3561 3594 Pumps & pumping equipment; motors: hydraulic, fluid power or air

(G-6485)
HYPERION MANAGING LLC
2751-2 Larsen Rd (32207-7233)
PHONE..................................904 612-3987
EMP: 9
SALES (est): 400K **Privately Held**
SIC: 2044 Brewing Company

(G-6486)
I ABC CORP
11711 Marco Beach Dr (32224-7616)
PHONE..................................904 645-6000
EMP: 6 **EST:** 2013
SALES (est): 173K **Privately Held**
SIC: 2381 Fabric dress & work gloves

(G-6487)
ICECAPADE FROZEN TREATS INC
1833 N Pearl St (32206-3663)
PHONE..................................904 314-4190
Leonie Wellington, *President*
EMP: 7 **EST:** 2017
SALES (est): 278K **Privately Held**
WEB: www.icecapadefrozentreats.com
SIC: 2024 Ice cream & frozen desserts

(G-6488)
IFF CHEMICAL HOLDINGS INC
2051 Lane Ave N (32254-1529)
PHONE..................................904 783-2180
Richard O'Leary, *President*
Anne Chwat, *Vice Pres*
Tom Rollins, *Engineer*
Robert Anderson, *Treasurer*
▲ **EMP:** 131 **EST:** 2002
SQ FT: 76,890
SALES (est): 57.9MM
SALES (corp-wide): 5B **Publicly Held**
WEB: www.ir.iff.com
SIC: 2869 Industrial organic chemicals
PA: International Flavors & Fragrances Inc.
521 W 57th St
New York NY 10019
212 765-5500

(G-6489)
IMMUDYNE NUTRITIONAL LLC
1301 Riverplace Blvd # 80 (32207-9047)
PHONE..................................914 714-8901
Mark McLaughlin, *CEO*
Dr Arun Bahl, *CEO*
Anthony Bruzzese, *Ch of Bd*
James Wethington, *General Mgr*
Aaron Gruelle, *Vice Pres*
EMP: 7 **EST:** 1986
SALES (est): 1MM **Privately Held**
WEB: www.immudyne.com
SIC: 2833 Medicinals & botanicals

(G-6490)
IMPACT DESIGN GROUP INC
Also Called: Quality Images
4613 Philips Hwy Ste 207 (32207-7290)
PHONE..................................904 636-8989
Alex Pecci Jr, *President*
Chris Brunner, *Vice Pres*
Kate Donalson, *Art Dir*
EMP: 15 **EST:** 1986
SQ FT: 11,000
SALES (est): 1.8MM **Privately Held**
WEB: www.qualityimages.com
SIC: 2791 2796 2759 Typesetting; platemaking services; commercial printing

(G-6491)
IMPULSE AIR INC
2126 W 21st St (32209-4110)
P.O. Box 12273 (32209-0273)
PHONE..................................904 475-1822
Bruce R Hampton, *President*
Edward Guertin, *Vice Pres*
Bruce Hampton, *Executive*
EMP: 22 **EST:** 1991
SQ FT: 26,000
SALES (est): 4.8MM **Privately Held**
WEB: www.impulseairspiral.com
SIC: 3444 Ducts, sheet metal

(G-6492)
INDUSTRIAL CONVEYOR BELT
2475 Lloyd Rd (32254-1214)
PHONE..................................904 345-3046
F Alexander Jr, *Owner*
▲ **EMP:** 8 **EST:** 2013
SALES (est): 149.2K **Privately Held**
WEB: www.macaljon.com
SIC: 3496 Conveyor belts

(G-6493)
INDUSTRIAL MARINE INC
7259 Old Plank Rd (32254-2754)
P.O. Box 37292 (32236-7292)
PHONE..................................904 781-4707
Charles Hawkins Jr, *President*
Vincent French, *Manager*
EMP: 10 **EST:** 1976
SQ FT: 25,000
SALES (est): 2.1MM **Privately Held**
WEB: www.industrialmarineinc.com
SIC: 3471 3599 1721 3589 Sand blasting of metal parts; machine shop, jobbing & repair; industrial painting; ship painting; sandblasting equipment; painting of metal products

(G-6494)
INDUSTRIAL MOBILE HYDRAULICS
Also Called: Imh
1180 Lane Ave N (32254-2228)
P.O. Box 65518, Orange Park (32065-0009)
PHONE..................................904 866-7592
Brian G Sowers, *President*
Donald Presley, *Principal*
Laura Presley, *Principal*
Trudy T Sowers, *Vice Pres*
EMP: 9 **EST:** 2008
SQ FT: 6,000
SALES (est): 1MM **Privately Held**
WEB: www.imhinc.com
SIC: 3492 Control valves, fluid power: hydraulic & pneumatic

(G-6495)
INKY FINGERS PRINTING INC
2752 Park St (32205-7608)
PHONE..................................904 384-1900
Randy Madison, *President*
Melissa Russell, *Vice Pres*
EMP: 8 **EST:** 1990
SQ FT: 2,000
SALES (est): 635.5K **Privately Held**
WEB: www.inkyfingers.biz
SIC: 2752 Commercial printing, offset

(G-6496)
INNOVATIVE CNSTR GROUP LLC (HQ)
Also Called: Innovative Acquisition Co LLC
5216 Shad Rd (32257-2006)
PHONE..................................904 398-5690
Ryan Melin, *President*
Todd Sheldon, *Mng Member*
EMP: 169 **EST:** 2019
SALES (est): 52.7MM
SALES (corp-wide): 11B **Publicly Held**
WEB: www.icgbuilds.com
SIC: 2421 Building & structural materials, wood
PA: Pultegroup, Inc.
3350 Peachtree Rd Ne # 15
Atlanta GA 30326
404 978-6400

(G-6497)
INNOVATIVE MFG SOLUTIONS LLC
7949 Atl Blvd Unit 209 (32211)
PHONE..................................904 647-5300
Randall Bahr,
Linda Wade-Bahr,
EMP: 5 **EST:** 2008
SALES (est): 621.5K **Privately Held**
WEB: www.imfgsol.com
SIC: 3841 3842 Surgical & medical instruments; fixation appliances, internal; bone plates & screws; implants, surgical

(G-6498)
INNOVTIVE CABINETS CLOSETS INC
5772 Mining Ter (32257-3227)
PHONE..................................904 475-2336
David Brent, *President*
Richard Stobe, *CFO*
EMP: 14 **EST:** 2017
SALES (est): 8.5MM **Privately Held**
SIC: 2434 Wood kitchen cabinets

(G-6499)
INSTRUMENT & VALVE SERVICES CO
Also Called: Emerson Instr & Valve Svcs
13350 Intl Pkwy Ste 102 (32218-2395)
PHONE..................................904 741-6800
Greg Dawes, *Manager*
EMP: 8
SALES (corp-wide): 16.7B **Publicly Held**
SIC: 3823 Industrial instrmnts msrmnt display/control process variable

HQ: Instrument & Valve Services Company
205 S Center St
Marshalltown IA 50158

(G-6500)
INTERNATIONAL BALER CORP
5400 Rio Grande Ave (32254-1352)
PHONE....................................904 358-3812
Ronald L McDaniel, *Ch of Bd*
Victor W Biazis, *President*
Jessica Hart, *General Mgr*
Brenda Miller, *Purch Mgr*
William E Nielsen, *CFO*
EMP: 49 **EST:** 1945
SQ FT: 62,000
SALES: 8.9MM **Privately Held**
WEB: www.intl-baler.com
SIC: 3569 5084 Baling machines, for scrap metal, paper or similar material; industrial machinery & equipment

(G-6501)
INTERRAIL ENGINEERING INC
12443 San Jose Blvd # 1103 (32223-8657)
PHONE....................................904 268-6411
Chryol A Kelley, *President*
Brad Slover, *Vice Pres*
Dee IEM, *Engineer*
Jim Doolittle, *Info Tech Dir*
EMP: 50 **EST:** 2001
SALES (est): 5.5MM **Privately Held**
WEB: www.interrail-signal.com
SIC: 3669 Railroad signaling devices, electric

(G-6502)
INTERRAIL POWER INC
12443 San Jose Blvd (32223-8646)
PHONE....................................904 268-6411
Leta Kelley, *Finance Dir*
Jessica Anderson, *Admin Sec*
EMP: 10 **EST:** 2016
SALES (est): 1MM **Privately Held**
WEB: www.interrail-signal.com
SIC: 3699 Electrical equipment & supplies

(G-6503)
ISLAND DREAM ITLN ICE DSSRTS L
9501 Arlington Expy Fc4 (32225-8200)
PHONE....................................904 778-6839
Brittany Sinclair, *Mng Member*
EMP: 10 **EST:** 2019
SALES (est): 200K **Privately Held**
SIC: 2024 Ice cream & frozen desserts

(G-6504)
IT SMELLS GOOD
1705 W 4th St (32209-6002)
PHONE....................................904 899-2818
Lesley Redmond, *Principal*
EMP: 7 **EST:** 2010
SALES (est): 121.7K **Privately Held**
SIC: 2844 Perfumes, natural or synthetic

(G-6505)
ITS TECHNOLOGIES LOGISTICS LLC
Also Called: Conglobal Industries
8831 Moncrief Dinsmore Rd (32219-2464)
P.O. Box 7092, Lawrence KS (66044-7092)
PHONE....................................904 751-1300
Allen Dutra, *Principal*
EMP: 114 **Privately Held**
SIC: 3999 Barber & beauty shop equipment
PA: Intermodal Acquisition, Llc
8205 Cass Ave Ste 115
Darien IL 60561

(G-6506)
J2B INDUSTRIAL LLC
1134 Ovington Rd S (32216-2667)
PHONE....................................904 805-0745
Scott C Baldwin, *Principal*
EMP: 6 **EST:** 2018
SALES (est): 89.7K **Privately Held**
WEB: www.j2bindustrial.com
SIC: 3441 Fabricated structural metal

(G-6507)
J2B INDUSTRIAL LLC
5941 Richard St Unit 19 (32216-5926)
PHONE....................................904 574-8919
Scott Baldwin, *President*
EMP: 15 **EST:** 2018
SALES (est): 2.4MM **Privately Held**
WEB: www.j2bindustrial.com
SIC: 3441 Fabricated structural metal

(G-6508)
JACKSNVLLE ADVNCED MCHNING LLC
9655 Fl Min Blvd W (32257-2031)
PHONE....................................904 292-2999
EMP: 8
SQ FT: 6,800
SALES: 1.1MM **Privately Held**
SIC: 3545 Mfg Machine Tool Accessories

(G-6509)
JACKSON EQUIPMENT INC
2310 Shipwreck Cir W (32224-1126)
PHONE....................................904 845-3696
Bill Schuetz, *President*
EMP: 8 **EST:** 1971
SALES (est): 829.9K **Privately Held**
WEB: www.jacksonequipmentinc.com
SIC: 7692 Welding repair

(G-6510)
JACKSONVILLE BOX & WOODWORK CO
5011 Buffalo Ave (32206-1573)
P.O. Box 3447 (32206-0447)
PHONE....................................904 354-1441
Jennings B King Jr, *President*
Jason Kittrell, *General Mgr*
Ernie Stuckey, *Opers Mgr*
Chip King, *Manager*
◆ **EMP:** 10 **EST:** 1948
SQ FT: 1,700
SALES (est): 2.7MM **Privately Held**
WEB: www.jaxbox.com
SIC: 2448 Pallets, wood

(G-6511)
JACKSONVILLE FREE PRESS
1122 Edgewood Ave W (32208-3419)
P.O. Box 43580 (32203-3580)
PHONE....................................904 634-1993
Rita Perry, *Owner*
EMP: 10 **EST:** 1986
SQ FT: 1,276
SALES (est): 702K **Privately Held**
WEB: www.jacksonvillefreepress.com
SIC: 2711 Newspapers, publishing & printing

(G-6512)
JACKSONVILLE STEEL PDTS INC
6085 Greenland Rd (32258-2405)
PHONE....................................904 268-3364
Janie Vonhofen, *President*
Christopher Roblow, *Vice Pres*
EMP: 9 **EST:** 1996
SQ FT: 2,000
SALES (est): 1.9MM **Privately Held**
SIC: 3443 3441 Fabricated plate work (boiler shop); fabricated structural metal

(G-6513)
JACKSONVILLE TIRE RESCUE INC
Also Called: Jax Tire Rescue
7010 Lenox Ave (32205-6866)
P.O. Box 6931 (32236-6931)
PHONE....................................904 783-1296
Maryalice Lundy, *President*
EMP: 13 **EST:** 2005
SALES (est): 568.9K **Privately Held**
WEB: www.jaxtirerescue.com
SIC: 3011 7534 Tires & inner tubes; tire repair shop

(G-6514)
JADE SOFTWARE CORPORATION USA
10151 Deerwood Park Blvd (32256-0566)
PHONE....................................904 677-5133
Mark Cadman, *Software Dev*
EMP: 9 **EST:** 2016
SALES (est): 3.3MM
SALES (corp-wide): 1.2B **Privately Held**
WEB: www.jadeworld.com
SIC: 7372 Prepackaged software
HQ: Jade Software Corporation Limited
5 Sir Gil Simpson Drive
Christchurch 8053

(G-6515)
JAMES HINES PRINTING
1650 Art Museum Dr Ste 18 (32207-2188)
PHONE....................................904 398-5110
James Hines, *Owner*
EMP: 6 **EST:** 2007
SALES (est): 315.5K **Privately Held**
WEB: www.hinesprinting.com
SIC: 2759 Screen printing

(G-6516)
JAMES R KONTORCHIK LLC
3265 Net Ct (32277-2734)
PHONE....................................904 962-0597
James R Kontorchik, *Manager*
EMP: 6 **EST:** 2005
SALES (est): 65.7K **Privately Held**
WEB: www.3dl-meters-loggers.com
SIC: 2844 Toilet preparations

(G-6517)
JAX EMBROIDERY
8110 Cypress Plaza Dr # 203 (32256-4467)
PHONE....................................904 367-4335
EMP: 6 **EST:** 2019
SALES (est): 89.9K **Privately Held**
WEB: www.saveonstitches.com
SIC: 2395 Embroidery products, except schiffli machine

(G-6518)
JAX ENTERPRISES LLC
Also Called: Metal Building Erection
7042 Wiley Rd (32210-2736)
P.O. Box 37064 (32236-7064)
PHONE....................................904 786-6909
John R Collins, *Mng Member*
EMP: 8 **EST:** 2007
SALES: 525.1K **Privately Held**
SIC: 3448 7389 Prefabricated metal buildings;

(G-6519)
JAX METALS LLC
3740 Morton St (32217-2206)
PHONE....................................904 731-4655
Alan T Ennis, *Manager*
EMP: 7 **EST:** 2018
SALES (est): 442.4K **Privately Held**
SIC: 3444 Sheet metalwork

(G-6520)
JCI JONES CHEMICALS INC
1433 Talleyrand Ave (32206-5435)
PHONE....................................904 355-0779
Ken Lucas, *Vice Pres*
EMP: 18
SALES (corp-wide): 196.9MM **Privately Held**
WEB: www.jcichem.com
SIC: 2812 2819 Chlorine, compressed or liquefied; industrial inorganic chemicals
PA: Jci Jones Chemicals, Inc.
1765 Ringling Blvd # 200
Sarasota FL 34236
941 330-1537

(G-6521)
JEPSEN TOOL COMPANY INC
6864 Phillips Pkwy Dr S (32256-1564)
PHONE....................................904 262-2793
Henry D Speckhahn, *President*
Michael Speckhahn, *Vice Pres*
Ingeborg S Speckhahn, *Treasurer*
EMP: 10 **EST:** 1979
SALES (est): 1MM **Privately Held**
WEB: www.jepsentool.com
SIC: 3841 3535 Surgical & medical instruments; conveyors & conveying equipment

(G-6522)
JJJ & H INC
Also Called: Vizergy
4237 Salisbury Rd Ste 200 (32216-0906)
P.O. Box 551459 (32255-1459)
PHONE....................................904 389-1130
Joseph R Hyman, *President*
Steve E Million,
Michael D Murray, *Admin Sec*
EMP: 41 **EST:** 1996
SQ FT: 10,800
SALES (est): 6MM **Privately Held**
WEB: www.vizergy.com
SIC: 2741

(G-6523)
JMG COUNTERS LLC
5120 W Beaver St (32254-2909)
PHONE....................................904 551-7006
Jose M Garcia, *Mng Member*
EMP: 16 **EST:** 2011
SALES (est): 1.4MM **Privately Held**
WEB: www.jmgcountersllc.com
SIC: 3131 Counters

(G-6524)
JOB NEWS
Also Called: United Metro Media
6620 S Sthpint Dr Ste 300 (32256)
PHONE....................................904 296-3006
Michael Talbot, *CEO*
Leonilda Jamieson, *CFO*
Ruth Razee, *Manager*
EMP: 20 **EST:** 1994
SALES (est): 401.5K **Privately Held**
WEB: www.jobnewsusa.com
SIC: 2711 Newspapers, publishing & printing

(G-6525)
JOHN STEWART ENTERPRISES INC
Also Called: River Printing
502 N Hogan St (32202-4106)
PHONE....................................904 356-9392
Van Stewart, *President*
Van Janet Stewart, *President*
John Stewart, *Vice Pres*
EMP: 10 **EST:** 1977
SQ FT: 8,000
SALES (est): 902.6K **Privately Held**
WEB: www.riverprinting.com
SIC: 2761 2752 Computer forms, manifold or continuous; lithographing on metal

(G-6526)
JOHNSON JHNSON VISION CARE INC (HQ)
Also Called: Vistakon
7500 Centurion Pkwy (32256-0517)
P.O. Box 10157 (32247-0157)
PHONE....................................904 443-1000
Ashley McEvoy, *Ch of Bd*
Jay Rodriguez, *Partner*
Madonna M Malin, *Vice Pres*
James Cowart, *Opers Staff*
Charles Chavers, *Mfg Staff*
◆ **EMP:** 1200 **EST:** 1962
SQ FT: 150,000
SALES (est): 663.4MM
SALES (corp-wide): 82.5B **Publicly Held**
WEB: www.jnjvisioncareinfo.com
SIC: 3851 Contact lenses; eyes, glass & plastic
PA: Johnson & Johnson
1 Johnson And Johnson Plz
New Brunswick NJ 08933
732 524-0400

(G-6527)
JOHNSTON ARCHTCTRAL SYSTEMS IN
Also Called: Delta Fountains
11494 Columbia Park Dr W (32258-1742)
PHONE....................................904 886-9030
Joseph W Petry, *President*
Dixon Scott Johnston, *Corp Secy*
James W J Turner, *Vice Pres*
James Turner, *Vice Pres*
Tyson Newkirk, *Project Mgr*
EMP: 35 **EST:** 1994
SQ FT: 53,100
SALES (est): 6.5MM **Privately Held**
WEB: www.deltafountains.com
SIC: 3499 3641 3561 3432 Fountains (except drinking), metal; electric lamps; pumps & pumping equipment; plumbing fixture fittings & trim

(G-6528)
JT ENTERPRISES GROUP LLC
6100 Philips Hwy (32216-5980)
PHONE....................................904 551-2680
EMP: 10
SALES (corp-wide): 3.9MM **Privately Held**
WEB: www.jturner.com
SIC: 2519 Furniture, household: glass, fiberglass & plastic

PA: Jt Enterprises Group Llc
280 Village Main St
Ponte Vedra Beach FL 32082
904 803-9338

(G-6529)
K & G BOX INC
Also Called: Stronghaven
2212 N Pearl St (32206-3647)
P.O. Box 40104 (32203-0104)
PHONE....................................904 356-6063
Doug Johnson, *CEO*
Rob Macpherson, *Vice Pres*
Charrie Henderson, *Admin Asst*
EMP: 55 **EST:** 1957
SQ FT: 92,000
SALES (est): 8.9MM **Privately Held**
SIC: 2653 Boxes, corrugated: made from purchased materials

(G-6530)
K & I CREATIVE PLAS & WD LLC
582 Nixon St (32204-3010)
PHONE....................................904 923-0409
Albert R Trotter,
EMP: 8 **EST:** 2013
SALES (est): 569.5K **Privately Held**
SIC: 3089 Injection molding of plastics

(G-6531)
K & I PLASTICS INC
582 Nixon St (32204-3010)
PHONE....................................904 387-0438
Bonnie Osterman, *President*
EMP: 7 **EST:** 1958
SQ FT: 11,000
SALES (est): 400K **Privately Held**
SIC: 3089 3993 Plastic containers, except foam; signs & advertising specialties

(G-6532)
KAMAN AEROSPACE CORPORATION
9410 Parker Ave (32218-5764)
PHONE....................................904 751-5369
EMP: 26
SALES (corp-wide): 784.4MM **Publicly Held**
WEB: www.kaman.com
SIC: 3721 3728 Aircraft; aircraft parts & equipment
HQ: Kaman Aerospace Corporation
1332 Blue Hills Ave
Bloomfield CT 06002
860 242-4461

(G-6533)
KARRY INDUSTRIES INC
4007 Saint Augustine Rd (32207-6640)
P.O. Box 5810 (32247-5810)
PHONE....................................904 398-4007
Brice R Holladay, *President*
EMP: 7 **EST:** 1987
SQ FT: 5,300
SALES (est): 300K **Privately Held**
WEB: www.karryindustries.com
SIC: 3599 Machine shop, jobbing & repair

(G-6534)
KELLY FOODS
2240 Dennis St (32204-1808)
PHONE....................................904 354-7600
Kenneth Kelly, *Vice Pres*
Cammie J Lane, *Executive*
EMP: 7 **EST:** 2014
SALES (est): 534.1K **Privately Held**
WEB: www.kellysfoods.com
SIC: 2011 Meat packing plants

(G-6535)
KEYSTONE INDUSTRIES LLC (PA)
Also Called: Keystone Development
1915 Wigmore St (32206-1732)
PHONE....................................239 337-7474
Philip Hetzner, *Finance*
Tom L Scholl, *Mng Member*
Tony L Scholl, *Mng Member*
◆ **EMP:** 17 **EST:** 1864
SALES (est): 17.8MM **Privately Held**
WEB: www.keystoneindustriesllc.com
SIC: 1241 5052 Coal mining exploration & test boring; coal

(G-6536)
KGB KITEBOARDING INC (PA)
9378 Arlington Expy (32225-8213)
PHONE....................................904 705-9235
Mitchell Woodall, *Principal*
EMP: 16 **EST:** 2008
SALES (est): 115.8K **Privately Held**
WEB: www.kgbkiteboarding.com
SIC: 3944 Kites

(G-6537)
KIGHTS PRINTING & OFFICE PDTS
8505-1 Baymeadows Rd (32256-7421)
PHONE....................................904 731-7990
William E Kight, *President*
David Kight, *President*
Arlene S Kight, *Vice Pres*
Sue Harms, *Admin Sec*
EMP: 8 **EST:** 1968
SQ FT: 17,000
SALES (est): 248.3K **Privately Held**
WEB: www.kights-printing.com
SIC: 2752 2791 2789 2759 Commercial printing, offset; typesetting; bookbinding & related work; commercial printing

(G-6538)
KINCO LTD (DH)
5245 Old Kings Rd (32254-1191)
P.O. Box 6429 (32236-6429)
PHONE....................................904 355-1476
Dearen Gates, *Manager*
EMP: 325 **EST:** 1971
SALES (est): 27.5MM
SALES (corp-wide): 4.6B **Publicly Held**
WEB: www.kinco.com
SIC: 3442 Metal doors, sash & trim
HQ: Atrium Windows And Doors, Inc.
9001 Ambassador Row
Dallas TX 75247
214 583-1840

(G-6539)
KITCHEN USA INC
6965 Philips Hwy (32216-6037)
PHONE....................................904 714-1970
Kai Zheng, *President*
▲ **EMP:** 7 **EST:** 2008
SALES (est): 961.7K **Privately Held**
WEB: www.kitchenusa.net
SIC: 2434 Wood kitchen cabinets

(G-6540)
KLEENBORE INC
13386 International Pkwy (32218-2383)
PHONE....................................800 347-1200
Paul Judd, *President*
EMP: 6 **EST:** 2008
SALES (est): 120K **Privately Held**
SIC: 3991 Brooms & brushes

(G-6541)
KME AMRICA MAR TUBE FTTING LLC
3440 Evergreen Ave (32206-2327)
PHONE....................................904 265-4001
John Shay, *President*
Curt Jackson, *Exec Dir*
EMP: 85 **EST:** 2014
SALES (est): 9.7MM **Privately Held**
WEB: www.kme.com
SIC: 3351 Copper & copper alloy pipe & tube

(G-6542)
KNOPF & SONS BINDERY INC (PA)
Also Called: Atlantic Book Bindery
1817 Florida Ave (32206-3971)
PHONE....................................904 353-5115
R Ed Knopf Jr, *President*
Ronald Knopf, *Vice Pres*
Ralph Knopf, *Treasurer*
Cynthia Knopf, *Admin Asst*
EMP: 30 **EST:** 1964
SQ FT: 55,000
SALES (est): 3.5MM **Privately Held**
WEB: www.knopfbindery.com
SIC: 2789 Binding only: books, pamphlets, magazines, etc.

(G-6543)
KNOPF & SONS BINDERY INC
Atlantic East Coast Bindery
1817 Florida Ave (32206-3971)
PHONE....................................904 355-4411
Ronald Knopf, *Manager*
EMP: 13
SQ FT: 18,850
SALES (corp-wide): 3.5MM **Privately Held**
WEB: www.knopfbindery.com
SIC: 2789 2759 2675 Rebinding books, magazines or pamphlets; commercial printing; die-cut paper & board
PA: Knopf & Sons Bindery, Inc.
1817 Florida Ave
Jacksonville FL 32206
904 353-5115

(G-6544)
KRAFT HEINZ FOODS COMPANY
Kraft Foods
735 E Bay St (32202-2303)
PHONE....................................904 632-3400
Darrell Larsen, *Sales Mgr*
Joe Waryold, *Manager*
Lisa Buzby, *Supervisor*
John Wingard, *Maintence Staff*
EMP: 6
SALES (corp-wide): 26.1B **Publicly Held**
WEB: www.kraftheinzcompany.com
SIC: 2095 Coffee roasting (except by wholesale grocers); coffee, ground: mixed with grain or chicory
HQ: Kraft Heinz Foods Company
1 Ppg Pl Ste 3400
Pittsburgh PA 15222
412 456-5700

(G-6545)
KRAFT HEINZ FOODS COMPANY
Portion Pac
7500 Forshee Dr (32219-5303)
PHONE....................................904 695-1300
Ryan Baker, *Plant Mgr*
Robert Lopez, *Mfg Mgr*
EMP: 7
SALES (corp-wide): 26.1B **Publicly Held**
WEB: www.kraftheinzcompany.com
SIC: 2035 2033 Pickles, sauces & salad dressings; jams, jellies & preserves: packaged in cans, jars, etc.
HQ: Kraft Heinz Foods Company
1 Ppg Pl Ste 3400
Pittsburgh PA 15222
412 456-5700

(G-6546)
KRATON CHEMICAL LLC (DH)
Also Called: Arizona Chemical
4600 Touchton Rd E # 1200 (32246-8299)
PHONE....................................904 928-8700
Kevin M Fogarty, *President*
April Cullen, *Business Mgr*
Charles Nelson, *Senior VP*
Carl Bilgrien, *Vice Pres*
Joe Chan, *Vice Pres*
◆ **EMP:** 106 **EST:** 1930
SQ FT: 29,000
SALES (est): 300.3MM **Publicly Held**
WEB: www.kraton.com
SIC: 2861 2911 Wood distillation products; fractionation products of crude petroleum, hydrocarbons

(G-6547)
KWIKPRINT MANUFACTURING CO INC
4868 Victor St (32207-1702)
P.O. Box 23055 (32241-3055)
PHONE....................................904 737-3755
Jay D Cann Jr, *President*
Michael Bulger, *COO*
Nancy Cann, *Treasurer*
Lynn R Cann, *Admin Sec*
▼ **EMP:** 9 **EST:** 1926
SQ FT: 12,000
SALES (est): 950K **Privately Held**
WEB: www.kwik-print.com
SIC: 3469 Stamping metal for the trade

(G-6548)
L C ACME BARRICADES (PA)
9800 Normandy Blvd (32221-2038)
PHONE....................................904 781-1950
Christian Cummings, *General Mgr*
Jimmy Pitts, *Opers Mgr*
Caleb Golson, *Foreman/Supr*
Bucky Wright, *QC Mgr*
Cheryl Asher, *Human Res Mgr*
▲ **EMP:** 57 **EST:** 1993
SALES (est): 23.9MM **Privately Held**
WEB: www.acmebarricades.com
SIC: 3499 7389 Barricades, metal; flagging service (traffic control)

(G-6549)
LAUNCHER SOLUTIONS LLC
10752 Deerwood Park Blvd # 100 (32256-4846)
PHONE....................................904 479-0762
Mark Gainor, *Ch of Bd*
John Deighan, *Manager*
EMP: 12 **EST:** 2017
SALES (est): 515.2K **Privately Held**
WEB: www.launcher.solutions
SIC: 7372 Prepackaged software

(G-6550)
LAWKO INC
5126 Ortega Blvd (32210-8306)
PHONE....................................904 389-2850
Dan Lawless, *President*
Kelly Culber, *Vice Pres*
EMP: 7 **EST:** 1980
SQ FT: 18,500
SALES (est): 198.4K **Privately Held**
SIC: 2511 Unassembled or unfinished furniture, household: wood

(G-6551)
LEE LOWSKY
4651 Salisbury Rd (32256-6107)
PHONE....................................904 470-4110
Lee Lowsky, *Owner*
EMP: 6 **EST:** 2010
SQ FT: 9,000
SALES (est): 241.2K **Privately Held**
SIC: 2325 Jeans: men's, youths' & boys'

(G-6552)
LEE NET SERVICES INC
8216 Cheryl Ann Ln (32244-1224)
PHONE....................................904 777-4833
Jimmie Smith, *Principal*
EMP: 7 **EST:** 2005
SALES (est): 435.9K **Privately Held**
SIC: 3825 Network analyzers

(G-6553)
LEGEND PRINTING COMPANY LLC
9816 Beach Blvd (32246-4704)
PHONE....................................904 268-7079
Christopher Cantillo, *Principal*
EMP: 6 **EST:** 2014
SALES (est): 99.4K **Privately Held**
SIC: 2752 Commercial printing, lithographic

(G-6554)
LERA PLASTICS INC
9216 Haydon Rd (32218-5722)
PHONE....................................904 716-5421
Kurt D Wullenweber, *Principal*
EMP: 6 **EST:** 2019
SALES (est): 240.7K **Privately Held**
SIC: 3089 Injection molding of plastics

(G-6555)
LFTD PARTNERS INC (PA)
4227 Habana Ave (32217-4048)
PHONE....................................847 915-2446
Gerard M Jacobs, *Ch of Bd*
William Carlo Jacobs, *President*
Joshua A Bloom, *Director*
James S Jacobs, *Director*
Richard E Morrissy, *Director*
EMP: 18 **EST:** 2004
SALES: 5.3MM **Publicly Held**
WEB: www.acquiredsalescorp.com
SIC: 3999

(G-6556)
LIDDYS MACHINE SHOP INC
Also Called: Industrial Repair
7621 Holiday Rd S (32216-3247)
PHONE....................................904 354-0134
Ted Gollnick, *President*
Chris Gollnick, *Vice Pres*
Douglas Gollnick, *Vice Pres*
Keith Yake, *Foreman/Supr*

▲ = Import ▼=Export
◆ =Import/Export

EMP: 20 **EST:** 1929
SALES (est): 5MM **Privately Held**
WEB: www.liddysmachineshop.com
SIC: 3599 Machine shop, jobbing & repair

(G-6557)
LIGHTER THAN AIR SYSTEMS CORP (HQ)
Also Called: Drone Aviation
11651 Central Pkwy # 118 (32224-2708)
PHONE..................................904 834-4400
EMP: 16 **EST:** 2009
SALES (est): 1.1MM
SALES (corp-wide): 9.4MM **Publicly Held**
WEB: www.ltascorp.com
SIC: 3721 Aircraft
PA: Comsovereign Holding Corp.
5000 Quorum Dr Ste 400
Dallas TX 75254
904 834-4400

(G-6558)
LIQUID FORCE
3921 Hickory Grove Dr S (32277-1322)
PHONE..................................904 813-1490
Casey Geiger, *Principal*
EMP: 8 **EST:** 2010
SALES (est): 123.9K **Privately Held**
WEB: www.liquidforce.com
SIC: 3949 Water sports equipment

(G-6559)
LOAD KING MANUFACTURING
14001 Atlantic Blvd (32225-3242)
PHONE..................................904 633-7352
Marlena Sopira, *Project Mgr*
Carella Ken, *Mfg Staff*
Alicia Hackney, *Buyer*
Sharon Oliver, *Sr Project Mgr*
Kim Highsmith, *Manager*
EMP: 8 **EST:** 2016
SALES (est): 114K **Privately Held**
WEB: www.loadking.com
SIC: 3999 Manufacturing industries

(G-6560)
LOAD KING MANUFACTURING CO (PA)
Also Called: Lk Industries
1357 W Beaver St (32209-7694)
PHONE..................................904 354-8882
Charles O Chupp, *President*
James M Chupp Sr, *Founder*
Bill Cromity, *Plant Mgr*
Leila Noth, *Project Mgr*
Richard Regnier, *Project Mgr*
EMP: 199 **EST:** 1972
SQ FT: 280,000
SALES (est): 63.7MM **Privately Held**
WEB: www.loadking.com
SIC: 2542 2541 3569 3496 Counters or counter display cases: except wood; racks, merchandise display or storage: except wood; store fixtures, wood; baling machines, for scrap metal, paper or similar material; grocery carts, made from purchased wire; carts, restaurant equipment

(G-6561)
LOCKHEED MARTIN CORPORATION
2629 Port Industrial Dr # 311 (32226-2551)
PHONE..................................904 660-6917
EMP: 6 **Publicly Held**
WEB: www.lockheedmartin.com
SIC: 3721 Aircraft
PA: Lockheed Martin Corporation
6801 Rockledge Dr
Bethesda MD 20817

(G-6562)
LOCKHEED MARTIN CORPORATION
13618 Lake Fretwell St (32221-8130)
PHONE..................................904 392-9779
EMP: 6 **Publicly Held**
WEB: www.lockheedmartin.com
SIC: 3812 Search & navigation equipment
PA: Lockheed Martin Corporation
6801 Rockledge Dr
Bethesda MD 20817

(G-6563)
LOGS GROUP LLC
7785 Bymadows Way Ste 104 (32256)
PHONE..................................904 733-6594
Gerald M Shapiro,
David S Kreisman,
Jamie G Zelvin,
EMP: 6 **EST:** 2005
SALES (est): 72.1K **Privately Held**
SIC: 7372 Prepackaged software

(G-6564)
LONGS WHEEL & RIM INC
Also Called: Otr Wheel Engineering
940 Eastport Rd (32218-3920)
PHONE..................................904 757-3710
Roger W Brodt Jr, *President*
Ann Brodt, *Admin Sec*
▲ **EMP:** 71 **EST:** 1968
SQ FT: 30,000
SALES (est): 2MM **Privately Held**
WEB: www.otrwheel.com
SIC: 3714 5082 5014 Wheels, motor vehicle; tractor-mounting equipment; truck tires & tubes
PA: Otr Wheel Engineering, Inc.
6 Riverside Indus Park Ne
Rome GA 30161

(G-6565)
LOUIS SHERRY COMPANY LLC
Also Called: Louis Chocolates
4339 Rosevlt Blvd Ste 400 (32210-2000)
PHONE..................................904 482-1900
William Morris, *CEO*
Timothy Tippin, *President*
Jeffery Smith, *COO*
EMP: 5 **EST:** 2013
SQ FT: 500
SALES (est): 311.3K **Privately Held**
WEB: www.louis-sherry.com
SIC: 2026 2064 Milk, chocolate; candy bars, including chocolate covered bars; chocolate candy, except solid chocolate

(G-6566)
LUCAS 5135 INC
Also Called: Cue & Case
8130 Bymdws Way W Ste 10 (32256-4409)
P.O. Box 889, Evansville IN (47706-0889)
PHONE..................................800 835-7665
James O Lucas III, *President*
Dorothea Lucas, *Corp Secy*
Cavin Kubala, *Sales Mgr*
◆ **EMP:** 21 **EST:** 1990
SALES (est): 6.9MM
SALES (corp-wide): 273.6MM **Publicly Held**
WEB: www.escaladeinc.com
SIC: 3949 Sporting & athletic goods
PA: Escalade, Incorporated
817 Maxwell Ave
Evansville IN 47711
812 467-1358

(G-6567)
LYRIC CHOIR GOWN COMPANY
6801 Beach Blvd (32216-2820)
P.O. Box 10990 (32247-0990)
PHONE..................................904 725-7977
Fax: 904 725-7924
EMP: 7 **EST:** 1960
SQ FT: 1,000
SALES (est): 600K **Privately Held**
SIC: 2384 Mfg Choir Gowns

(G-6568)
M & M SIGNS
524 Stockton St (32204-2535)
PHONE..................................904 381-7353
Ww Gay, *President*
Andy Patrick, *Manager*
EMP: 27 **EST:** 1994
SALES (est): 1.1MM **Privately Held**
WEB: www.wwgmc.com
SIC: 3993 Signs & advertising specialties

(G-6569)
M/V MARINE INC
609 Talleyrand Ave (32202-1032)
PHONE..................................904 633-7992
Michael Gurliaccio, *President*
Vicki Gurliaccio, *Vice Pres*
EMP: 19 **EST:** 1997
SQ FT: 12,000
SALES (est): 4MM **Privately Held**
WEB: www.mvmarine.com
SIC: 3731 5699 Shipbuilding & repairing; military goods & regalia

(G-6570)
MAC PAPER CONVERTERS LLC
Also Called: Mac Papers Envelope Converters
8370 Philips Hwy (32256-8204)
P.O. Box 5369 (32247-5369)
PHONE..................................800 334-7026
David S McGehee, *CEO*
Sutton McGehee, *President*
Thomas R McGehee, *Senior VP*
Darnell M Babbit, *Vice Pres*
Robert Tees, *Vice Pres*
EMP: 213 **EST:** 1971
SQ FT: 156,000
SALES (est): 34.4MM **Privately Held**
WEB: www.macenvelopes.com
SIC: 2677 Envelopes

(G-6571)
MACHINE ENGINEERS INC
651 E 8th St (32206-3976)
PHONE..................................904 353-8289
Earl Sarrells, *President*
Jacey Sarrells, *Corp Secy*
Jt Nobels, *Vice Pres*
EMP: 11 **EST:** 1953
SQ FT: 10,000
SALES (est): 1.6MM **Privately Held**
WEB: www.machineengineersinc.com
SIC: 3599 Machine shop, jobbing & repair

(G-6572)
MACKAY COMMUNICATIONS INC
Also Called: Mackay Marine
9655 Florida Mining Blvd (32257-2032)
PHONE..................................904 724-6101
Ron Fertgus, *Sales Staff*
Terry Croutharmel, *Director*
EMP: 6
SQ FT: 8,500
SALES (corp-wide): 48.8MM **Privately Held**
WEB: www.mackaycomm.com
SIC: 3663 Radio & TV communications equipment
PA: Mackay Communications, Inc.
3691 Trust Dr
Raleigh NC 27616
919 850-3000

(G-6573)
MADDEN MILLWORKS
1650 Margaret St 116 (32204-3868)
PHONE..................................310 514-2640
EMP: 5
SALES (est): 539.2K **Privately Held**
SIC: 2499 Mfg Wood Products

(G-6574)
MAESTRO WINERY
8241 Pelican Landing Rd (32256-3224)
PHONE..................................308 627-6436
Christopher Gugel, *Principal*
EMP: 5 **EST:** 2019
SALES (est): 338.4K **Privately Held**
WEB: www.maestrowinery.com
SIC: 2084 Wines

(G-6575)
MAIN & SIX BREWING COMPANY LLC
1636 N Main St (32206-4402)
PHONE..................................904 673-0144
Dennis Espinosa, *Mng Member*
Cindy Lasky,
EMP: 7 **EST:** 2016
SALES (est): 781.1K **Privately Held**
WEB: www.mainandsixbrewing.com
SIC: 2082 Malt beverages

(G-6576)
MAJESTIC MACHINE & ENGRG INC
570 Us Highway 90 E (32234-1908)
P.O. Box 4 (32234-0004)
PHONE..................................904 257-9115
Linda G Nettles, *President*
Thomas L Nettles, *Vice Pres*
EMP: 10 **EST:** 2004
SQ FT: 8,000
SALES (est): 2.6MM **Privately Held**
WEB: www.majesticmachine.com
SIC: 3599 Machine shop, jobbing & repair

(G-6577)
MANIFEST DISTILLING LLC
960 E Forsyth St (32202-2222)
PHONE..................................904 619-1479
Jim Webb, *General Mgr*
Hana Ferguson, *Manager*
EMP: 10 **EST:** 2019
SALES (est): 617.9K **Privately Held**
WEB: www.manifestdistilling.com
SIC: 2085 Distilled & blended liquors

(G-6578)
MANUFACTURING MARTIN LLC KLS
11228 St Jhns Indus Pkwy (32246-7651)
PHONE..................................904 641-0421
Thomas S Johnston Jr, *President*
EMP: 10 **EST:** 2017
SALES (est): 1.1MM **Privately Held**
SIC: 3999 Atomizers, toiletry

(G-6579)
MARTIN L MATTHEWS
120 Velvet Dr (32220-1730)
PHONE..................................904 881-3550
Martin Matthews, *Principal*
EMP: 6 **EST:** 2011
SALES (est): 135.9K **Privately Held**
SIC: 3448 Screen enclosures

(G-6580)
MASTER MARINE
14255 Beach Blvd (32250-1576)
PHONE..................................904 329-1541
Morris Hackett, *Owner*
Candice Macvicar, *Purch Mgr*
EMP: 7 **EST:** 2009
SALES (est): 350K **Privately Held**
SIC: 3732 Boat building & repairing

(G-6581)
MASTERCRAFT SHTTERS BLINDS LLC
1700 E Church St (32202-1120)
PHONE..................................904 379-7544
Ivan Dusevic, *Principal*
EMP: 9 **EST:** 2019
SALES (est): 438.2K **Privately Held**
WEB: www.mastercraftshuttersandblinds.com
SIC: 2591 Window blinds

(G-6582)
MAXVILLE LLC
Also Called: Gilman Building Products
6640 County Road 218 (32234-3047)
PHONE..................................904 289-7261
William H Davis, *President*
Bernard D Bergreen, *Chairman*
Dominick Sorrentino, *Senior VP*
Victor Garrett, *Vice Pres*
Natalie P Moody, *Vice Pres*
EMP: 185 **EST:** 1973
SALES (est): 18.2MM
SALES (corp-wide): 3.6B **Privately Held**
SIC: 2421 Building & structural materials, wood
HQ: Gilman Building Products, Llc
2900 Saint Marys Rd
Saint Marys GA 31558
912 576-0300

(G-6583)
MAYO CLINIC
Also Called: Mayo Clnic Pet Rdchmstry Fclty
14225 Zumbro Dr (32224-8803)
PHONE..................................904 953-2000
Jeff Brunette, *Administration*
EMP: 8
SALES (corp-wide): 12.6B **Privately Held**
WEB: www.drmanpreetgrewal.wordpress.com
SIC: 2834 Pharmaceutical preparations
HQ: Mayo Clinic Jacksonville (A Nonprofit Corporation)
4500 San Pablo Rd S
Jacksonville FL 32224
904 953-2000

GEOGRAPHIC

(G-6584)
MAYO CLINIC
Also Called: Mayo Clnic Pet Rdchmstry Fclty
4500 San Pablo Rd S (32224-1865)
PHONE....................................904 953-2000
Hancheng Cai, *Branch Mgr*
EMP: 8
SALES (corp-wide): 12.6B **Privately Held**
WEB:
www.drmanpreetgrewal.wordpress.com
SIC: 2834 Pharmaceutical preparations
HQ: Mayo Clinic Jacksonville (A Nonprofit Corporation)
4500 San Pablo Rd S
Jacksonville FL 32224
904 953-2000

(G-6585)
MCGEE ENTERPRISES INC
8535 Baymeadows Rd Ste 28
(32256-7445)
PHONE....................................904 328-3226
Ryan McGee, *President*
EMP: 7 **EST:** 2015
SQ FT: 2,000
SALES (est): 177K **Privately Held**
SIC: 2396 2732 2752 Fabric printing & stamping; pamphlets: printing only, not published on site; commercial printing, lithographic; business form & card printing, lithographic; calendar & card printing, lithographic

(G-6586)
MDK ENTERPISES INC
Also Called: Premiere Plastering
11623 Columbia Park Dr E (32258-2491)
PHONE....................................904 288-6855
Mark D Kozak, *President*
Mark Kozak, *President*
Linda Hanna, *Manager*
EMP: 11 **EST:** 2005
SQ FT: 4,873
SALES (est): 298.8K **Privately Held**
SIC: 3299 Stucco

(G-6587)
ME THOMPSON INC (PA)
Also Called: Dandee Sandwich
2178 W 21st St (32209-4110)
PHONE....................................904 356-6258
Jerry A Thompson, *President*
EMP: 1 **EST:** 1956
SQ FT: 10,000
SALES (est): 10.2MM **Privately Held**
SIC: 2099 Sandwiches, assembled & packaged: for wholesale market

(G-6588)
MEDIA WORKS INC
Also Called: Printing.com
1451 Louisa St (32207-8317)
PHONE....................................904 398-5518
Fax: 904 398-6747
EMP: 17
SQ FT: 8,000
SALES (est): 2.1MM **Privately Held**
SIC: 2759 Commercial Printing

(G-6589)
MEDIWARE INFO SYSTEMS INC
Also Called: Mediware BCT
7800 Belfort Pkwy Ste 291 (32256-6969)
PHONE....................................904 281-0467
EMP: 10
SALES (corp-wide): 113.5MM **Privately Held**
SIC: 7372 8742 Prepackaged Software Services Management Consulting Services
PA: Mediware Information Systems, Inc.
11711 W 79th St
Lenexa KS 66210
913 307-1000

(G-6590)
MEDTRNIC SOFAMOR DANEK USA INC
10245 Centurion Pkwy N (32256-2808)
PHONE....................................904 645-6925
Kevin Porter, *Branch Mgr*
EMP: 8 **Privately Held**
WEB: www.medtronic.com
SIC: 3841 Surgical & medical instruments
HQ: Medtronic Sofamor Danek Usa, Inc.
1800 Pyramid Pl
Memphis TN 38132
901 396-3133

(G-6591)
MEDTRONIC USA INC
6743 Southpoint Dr N (32216-6218)
PHONE....................................702 308-1302
Brian L Banks, *Director*
EMP: 2026 **Privately Held**
WEB: www.medtronic.com
SIC: 3841 3842 Surgical & medical instruments; surgical appliances & supplies
HQ: Medtronic Usa, Inc.
710 Medtronic Pkwy
Minneapolis MN 55432
763 514-4000

(G-6592)
MEDTRONIC XOMED INC (DH)
6743 Southpoint Dr N (32216-6218)
PHONE....................................904 296-9600
Mark J Fletcher, *President*
Bob Blankemeyer, *Principal*
Nathan Fowler, *District Mgr*
Mike Darragh, *Vice Pres*
Gary L Ellis, *Vice Pres*
EMP: 650 **EST:** 1996
SALES (est): 120.2MM **Privately Held**
WEB: www.solan.com
SIC: 3842 3841 Implants, surgical; instruments, microsurgical: except electromedical
HQ: Medtronic, Inc.
710 Medtronic Pkwy
Minneapolis MN 55432
763 514-4000

(G-6593)
MEDTRONIC XOMED INC
4102 Southpoint Blvd (32216-0929)
PHONE....................................904 296-9600
EMP: 282 **Privately Held**
WEB: www.solan.com
SIC: 3842 3841 Implants, surgical; instruments, microsurgical: except electromedical
HQ: Medtronic Xomed, Inc.
6743 Southpoint Dr N
Jacksonville FL 32216

(G-6594)
MEDWAY HALL DEV GROUP INC (PA)
Also Called: Ejcon
590 Beautyrest Ave (32254-3605)
P.O. Box 61266 (32236-1266)
PHONE....................................904 786-0622
J Franklin Stallwood, *President*
Randy Sheppard, *VP Sales*
EMP: 15 **EST:** 1991
SQ FT: 12,000
SALES (est): 5.4MM **Privately Held**
WEB: www.ejcon.com
SIC: 3499 Aerosol valves, metal

(G-6595)
MERCHANTS METALS LLC
5918-1 Lane Cir S (32254-2244)
PHONE....................................904 781-3920
Matt Jansen, *Manager*
EMP: 10 **Privately Held**
WEB: www.merchantsmetals.com
SIC: 3496 Miscellaneous fabricated wire products
HQ: Merchants Metals Llc
211 Perimeter Center Pkwy
Atlanta GA 30346
770 741-0300

(G-6596)
METAL CONTAINER CORPORATION
1100 Ellis Rd N (32254-2200)
PHONE....................................904 695-7600
Dave Olecki, *Opers-Prdtn-Mfg*
Cesar Vargas, *Officer*
EMP: 158
SALES (corp-wide): 1.2B **Privately Held**
WEB: www.metal-containers.com
SIC: 3411 3354 Metal cans; aluminum extruded products
HQ: Metal Container Corporation
3636 S Geyer Rd Ste 100
Saint Louis MO 63127
314 577-2000

(G-6597)
METAL SALES MANUFACTURING CORP
7110 Stuart Ave (32254-3421)
PHONE....................................904 783-3660
Rick Edwards, *Sales Staff*
Eric Leonetti, *Branch Mgr*
EMP: 10
SQ FT: 68,866
SALES (corp-wide): 347.3MM **Privately Held**
WEB: www.metalsales.us.com
SIC: 3444 Sheet metalwork
HQ: Metal Sales Manufacturing Corporation
545 S 3rd St Ste 200
Louisville KY 40202
502 855-4300

(G-6598)
METALCRAFTERS LLC
10759 Grayson St (32220-1890)
PHONE....................................904 257-9036
Christopher Goodman, *Administration*
EMP: 8 **EST:** 2017
SALES (est): 526.8K **Privately Held**
SIC: 3444 Sheet metalwork

(G-6599)
METALPLATE GALVANIZING LP
7123 Moncrief Rd W (32219-3313)
PHONE....................................904 768-6330
Grant Hauth, *Plant Mgr*
Melanie Gamble, *Info Tech Mgr*
EMP: 60
SQ FT: 14,172
SALES (corp-wide): 95.2MM **Privately Held**
WEB: www.metalplate.com
SIC: 3479 3547 Galvanizing of iron, steel or end-formed products; galvanizing lines (rolling mill equipment)
PA: Metalplate Galvanizing, L.P.
1120 39th St N
Birmingham AL 35234
205 595-4700

(G-6600)
METAVANTE HOLDINGS LLC (HQ)
601 Riverside Ave (32204-2946)
PHONE....................................904 438-6000
Gary Norcross, *President*
Michael Gravelle, *Vice Pres*
Keneitha Gross, *Project Mgr*
Gail Duran, *Manager*
Amy Klapper, *Manager*
▼ **EMP:** 4 **EST:** 2007
SALES (est): 249.3MM
SALES (corp-wide): 12.5B **Publicly Held**
WEB: www.fisglobal.com
SIC: 3578 5049 7374 Banking machines; bank equipment & supplies; data processing & preparation
PA: Fidelity National Information Services, Inc.
601 Riverside Ave
Jacksonville FL 32204
904 438-6000

(G-6601)
METRO MACHINE CORP
Also Called: General Dynmics Nassco Mayport
599 Wonderwood Dr (32233-4613)
PHONE....................................904 249-7772
Karl Haroldsonn, *Branch Mgr*
Andrea Tanner, *Info Tech Mgr*
EMP: 59
SALES (corp-wide): 37.9B **Publicly Held**
WEB: www.nassconorfolk.com
SIC: 3731 Shipbuilding & repairing
HQ: Metro Machine Corp.
200 Ligon St
Norfolk VA 23523
757 543-6801

(G-6602)
MICRO-ANT LLC
4722 Wesconnett Blvd (32210-7315)
PHONE....................................904 683-8394
Michael Blefko, *General Mgr*
James Messink, *Engineer*
Tess Relampagos, *CFO*
James Francis, *Mng Member*
Charles McCarrick, *Mng Member*
◆ **EMP:** 75 **EST:** 2008
SQ FT: 10,000
SALES (est): 25MM **Privately Held**
WEB: www.micro-ant.com
SIC: 3679 Antennas, satellite: household use

(G-6603)
MICROTEK MEDICAL INC
Also Called: Isolyser
13500 Tradeport Cir E (32218-2504)
PHONE....................................904 741-2964
J M Mabry, *Exec VP*
Joe Carr, *Branch Mgr*
EMP: 213
SALES (corp-wide): 11.7B **Publicly Held**
SIC: 3841 Surgical & medical instruments
HQ: Microtek Medical Inc.
512 N Lehmberg Rd
Columbus MS 39702
662 327-1863

(G-6604)
MIKE AND VAL TUPPER IND
14171 Denton Rd (32226-4827)
PHONE....................................904 757-7566
Val Tupper, *Principal*
EMP: 6 **EST:** 2007
SALES (est): 110.9K **Privately Held**
SIC: 2656 Sanitary food containers

(G-6605)
MILITARY ONE CLICK LLC
815 S Main St (32207-9050)
PHONE....................................904 390-7100
Jennifer Pilcher, *President*
EMP: 6 **EST:** 2015
SQ FT: 114,128
SALES (est): 206.3K **Privately Held**
SIC: 2741 7336 8742 8743 ; commercial art & graphic design; marketing consulting services; construction project management consultant; public relations services

(G-6606)
MILLENNIUM METALS INC
10200 Eastport Rd (32218-2229)
PHONE....................................904 358-8366
Scott Gramling, *CEO*
Tanya Cogan, *Vice Pres*
Tonya Steele, *Vice Pres*
Jeff Cruz, *Warehouse Mgr*
Becky Fitchett, *Human Res Dir*
▼ **EMP:** 41 **EST:** 1999
SQ FT: 32,500
SALES (est): 9.9MM **Privately Held**
WEB: www.mmi2000.net
SIC: 3444 Siding, sheet metal

(G-6607)
MILLER CREATIVE GRAPHICS
Also Called: Printing.com
8725 Youngerman Ct # 101 (32244-6692)
PHONE....................................904 771-5855
David Miller, *CEO*
Mike Lear, *Project Mgr*
EMP: 6 **EST:** 2005
SALES (est): 500.4K **Privately Held**
WEB: www.mcg247.com
SIC: 2759 Commercial printing

(G-6608)
MILLER CREATIVE WORKS INC
710 9th Ave N (32250-4652)
PHONE....................................904 504-3212
Brian J Miller, *President*
EMP: 5
SALES (est): 422.5K **Privately Held**
WEB: www.millercreative.com
SIC: 2335 Wedding gowns & dresses

(G-6609)
MINUTEMAN PRESS
1370 Marsh Harbor Dr (32225-2643)
PHONE....................................904 733-5578
Philip Barnes, *Technician*
Brandon Mata, *Graphic Designe*
EMP: 7 **EST:** 2012
SALES (est): 192.1K **Privately Held**
WEB: www.mmpjax.com
SIC: 2752 Commercial printing, lithographic

▲ = Import ▼=Export
◆ =Import/Export

(G-6610)
MLXL PRODUCTIONS INX
2935 Dawn Rd (32207-7903)
P.O. Box 60428 (32236-0428)
PHONE....................................904 350-0048
Michael Brown, *CEO*
Peter Malloy, *Vice Pres*
Elizabeth Yates, *Vice Pres*
▲ **EMP:** 7 **EST:** 2004
SQ FT: 11,329
SALES (est): 574.2K **Privately Held**
WEB: www.mlxlpro.com
SIC: 2759 Screen printing

(G-6611)
MODULAR LIFE SOLUTIONS LLC
6622 Sthpint Dr S Ste 250 (32216)
PHONE....................................904 900-7965
Doug Recker,
EMP: 8 **EST:** 2017
SALES (est): 609.2K **Privately Held**
WEB: www.modularlifesolutions.com
SIC: 3448 Prefabricated metal buildings

(G-6612)
MOLD REMEDIATION SERVICES INC
Also Called: All US Mold Rmval Jcksnvlle FL
7643 Gate Pkwy 104-57 (32256-3092)
PHONE....................................904 574-5266
EMP: 7 **EST:** 2001
SALES (est): 79.9K **Privately Held**
WEB: www.moldremovaljacksonvillefl.info
SIC: 3589 Asbestos removal equipment

(G-6613)
MOLONEY DIE COMPANY
Also Called: Moloney Wire Dies
5002 Palmer Ave (32210-3245)
PHONE....................................904 388-3654
Tom Moloney, *President*
Becky Moloney, *President*
Ruth Ann Moloney, *Treasurer*
EMP: 6 **EST:** 1985
SQ FT: 1,019
SALES (est): 446.6K **Privately Held**
SIC: 3544 Special dies & tools

(G-6614)
MONISON PALLETS INC
3160 W 45th St (32209-2726)
PHONE....................................904 359-0235
Joe Brown, *Principal*
EMP: 15 **EST:** 2009
SALES (est): 813.4K **Privately Held**
WEB: www.monisonpallets.net
SIC: 2448 Pallets, wood

(G-6615)
MONTGOMERY INDUSTRIES INTL
2017 Thelma St (32206-4240)
P.O. Box 3687 (32206-0687)
PHONE....................................904 355-4055
Robert C Montgomery, *President*
Jonathan Montgomery, *Exec VP*
Jonathan C Montgomery, *Vice Pres*
Robert C Montgomrey Jr, *Treasurer*
▼ **EMP:** 20 **EST:** 1925
SQ FT: 36,600
SALES (est): 3.2MM **Privately Held**
WEB: www.montgomeryindustries.com
SIC: 3532 Crushing, pulverizing & screening equipment

(G-6616)
MS MOBILE WLDG & FABRICATION
1929 Logging Ln (32221-2071)
PHONE....................................904 591-1488
Gary M Suggs, *Principal*
EMP: 10 **EST:** 2009
SALES (est): 216.9K **Privately Held**
WEB: www.msmobilewelding.com
SIC: 7692 Welding repair

(G-6617)
N-VIRO INC
7259 Old Plank Rd (32254-2754)
PHONE....................................904 781-4707
Charles Hawkins Jr, *President*
Jr C Hawkins, *Admin Sec*
EMP: 5 **EST:** 1994
SQ FT: 15,000
SALES (est): 468.3K **Privately Held**
SIC: 3589 Sandblasting equipment

(G-6618)
NATIONAL CARBURETORS INC
2461 Rolac Rd (32207-7916)
PHONE....................................904 636-9400
Edward L Obi Jr, *President*
▼ **EMP:** 25 **EST:** 1996
SALES (est): 3.9MM **Privately Held**
WEB: www.nationalcarburetors.com
SIC: 3714 5013 Fuel systems & parts, motor vehicle; motor vehicle supplies & new parts

(G-6619)
NATUREFORM HATCHERY TECH LLC
2550 Cabot Commerce Dr # 22 (32226-5608)
PHONE....................................904 358-0355
Steve Warren, *President*
Sharon Allen, *Controller*
Maria Moreno, *Assistant*
EMP: 19 **EST:** 2013
SALES (est): 2.3MM **Privately Held**
WEB: www.pasreform.com
SIC: 3523 Incubators & brooders, farm

(G-6620)
NAVMAR APPLIED SCIENCES CORP
7254 Golden Wings Rd (32244-3321)
PHONE....................................904 423-0927
William Bensch, *Research*
Charles Lee, *Engineer*
Tiffany Penge, *Engineer*
Erick Leiss, *Electrical Engi*
Kevin Hyland, *Manager*
EMP: 105
SALES (corp-wide): 56.8MM **Privately Held**
WEB: www.nasc.com
SIC: 3721 Motorized aircraft
PA: Navmar Applied Sciences Corporation
65 W Street Rd Ste C
Warminster PA 18974
215 675-4900

(G-6621)
NB PRODUCTS INC
1551 Atl Blvd Ste 105 (32207)
PHONE....................................904 807-0140
Arthur Wotiz, *President*
EMP: 30 **EST:** 2012
SALES (est): 2MM **Privately Held**
SIC: 3841 Surgical & medical instruments

(G-6622)
NC PRINTING & ACCOUNTING CO
6110 Powers Ave Ste 11 (32217-2256)
PHONE....................................904 327-7701
Nada F Chehab, *Principal*
EMP: 6 **EST:** 2007
SALES (est): 161.2K **Privately Held**
WEB: www.nc-accounting.com
SIC: 2752 Commercial printing, lithographic

(G-6623)
NCP SOLUTIONS LLC
841 Prudential Dr # 1200 (32207-8329)
PHONE....................................205 849-5200
Bobby Helms, *President*
Jeffrey Booker, *Vice Pres*
Joseph Tetstone, *Vice Pres*
Robin Harper, *Production*
Jeff England, *Inv Control Mgr*
EMP: 60
SALES (corp-wide): 341.1MM **Privately Held**
WEB: www.ncpsolutions.com
SIC: 2752 7331 Business form & card printing, lithographic; direct mail advertising services
HQ: Ncp Solutions, Llc
5200 E Lake Blvd
Birmingham AL 35217
205 849-5200

(G-6624)
NEPTUNE TECH SERVICES INC (PA)
Also Called: Neptune Precision Composites
11657 Central Pkwy # 405 (32224-2661)
PHONE....................................904 646-2700
Joseph Rocchi, *President*
Marge Pitts, *Human Res Mgr*
EMP: 35 **EST:** 1994
SQ FT: 21,000
SALES (est): 5.2MM **Privately Held**
WEB: www.neptuneprecision.com
SIC: 3083 8711 7374 Plastic finished products, laminated; engineering services; data processing & preparation

(G-6625)
NESSMITH DYE CUTTING & FINSHG
536 E 4th St (32206-4657)
P.O. Box 10527 (32247-0527)
PHONE....................................904 353-6317
Wayne Elton, *President*
EMP: 7 **EST:** 1963
SQ FT: 3,128
SALES (est): 750K **Privately Held**
SIC: 3423 Cutting dies, except metal cutting

(G-6626)
NEW IEM POWER SYSTEMS LLC (DH)
11902 Central Pkwy (32224-2657)
PHONE....................................904 365-4444
Edward Herman, *CEO*
Clayton Such, *COO*
Dan O'Callaghan, *Vice Pres*
Aaron Hargraves, *Project Mgr*
Mike Peterson, *Electrical Engi*
EMP: 180 **EST:** 2014
SALES (est): 44.3MM
SALES (corp-wide): 220.5MM **Privately Held**
WEB: www.iemfg.com
SIC: 3699 Electrical equipment & supplies
HQ: Abd El & Jake Holdings, Llc
11902 Central Pkwy
Jacksonville FL 32224
904 365-4393

(G-6627)
NEW IMAGE PRINTING PROMOTION
9556 Historic Kings Rd S (32257-2009)
PHONE....................................904 240-1516
Melinda Anchel, *CEO*
EMP: 8 **EST:** 2012
SALES (est): 865K **Privately Held**
WEB: www.newimageppd.com
SIC: 2759 Promotional printing

(G-6628)
NEW MIX PRODUCTS
4465 Crooked Oak Ct (32257-6482)
PHONE....................................904 292-1920
George Pannell, *Owner*
EMP: 7 **EST:** 2013
SALES (est): 286.4K **Privately Held**
SIC: 2844 Shampoos, rinses, conditioners: hair

(G-6629)
NEW VBB LLC
Also Called: Village Bread & Bagells
3044 Mercury Rd S (32207-7976)
PHONE....................................904 631-5978
L Ward Huntley, *Mng Member*
▲ **EMP:** 45 **EST:** 2014
SQ FT: 18,000
SALES (est): 3.7MM **Privately Held**
SIC: 2051 Bakery: wholesale or wholesale/retail combined

(G-6630)
NEW WORLD PUBLICATIONS INC
1861 Cornell Rd (32207-7780)
PHONE....................................904 737-6558
Edward L Deloach, *President*
Eric Riesch, *Managing Dir*
Paul H Humann, *Vice Pres*
Paul Humann, *Author*
James P Dalle Pazze, *Asst Sec*
◆ **EMP:** 6 **EST:** 1989
SALES (est): 750K **Privately Held**
WEB: www.fishid.com
SIC: 2731 Books: publishing only

(G-6631)
NEW YORK NAILS
5869 University Blvd W (32216-0804)
PHONE....................................904 448-6040
Tommy Lopez, *Manager*
EMP: 5 **EST:** 2002
SALES (est): 372.9K **Privately Held**
SIC: 3399 7231 Nails: aluminum, brass or other nonferrous metal or wire; beauty shops

(G-6632)
NEWMANS TRUCK BODY AND EQP INC
6880 W 12th St (32254-1545)
P.O. Box 61723 (32236-1723)
PHONE....................................904 695-9589
Don Pierce, *President*
Michael Deniston, *Vice Pres*
EMP: 14 **EST:** 1990
SQ FT: 9,000
SALES (est): 1.7MM **Privately Held**
WEB: www.newmanstruckbody.com
SIC: 3599 Machine shop, jobbing & repair

(G-6633)
NGWEB SOLUTIONS LLC
Also Called: Next Gen Web Solutions
6821 Sthpint Dr N Ste 220 (32216)
PHONE....................................904 332-9001
Jim Grace, *Manager*
Taige Haines,
EMP: 7 **EST:** 2008
SQ FT: 660
SALES (est): 1.2MM
SALES (corp-wide): 1.7B **Publicly Held**
WEB: www.ngwebsolutions.com
SIC: 7372 Educational computer software
PA: Nelnet, Inc.
121 S 13th St Ste 201
Lincoln NE 68508
402 458-2370

(G-6634)
NICHOLS TRUCK BODIES LLC
1168 Cahoon Rd S (32221-6166)
PHONE....................................904 781-5080
Clarence Suggs, *General Mgr*
Kevin Bachhofer, *General Mgr*
EMP: 21 **EST:** 2016
SALES (est): 1.2MM **Privately Held**
WEB: www.nicholstruckbodies.com
SIC: 3713 3446 7699 Dump truck bodies; stake, platform truck bodies; utility truck bodies; lintels light gauge steel; industrial truck repair

(G-6635)
NINE ENTERPRISES INC
3633 Southside Blvd (32216-4635)
PHONE....................................904 998-8880
Laura J Ninesling, *Principal*
EMP: 7 **EST:** 2018
SALES (est): 599.4K **Privately Held**
SIC: 3993 Signs & advertising specialties

(G-6636)
NIVEL HOLDINGS LLC (PA)
Also Called: Nivel Parts Manufacturing
3510 Pt Jacksonville Park (32226)
PHONE....................................904 741-6161
William Bugg, *Mng Member*
▲ **EMP:** 1 **EST:** 2004
SALES (est): 78.8MM **Privately Held**
WEB: www.nivelparts.com
SIC: 3799 5088 Golf carts, powered; golf carts

(G-6637)
NIVEL PARTS & MFG CO LLC (HQ)
3510-1 Port Jcksnvlle Pkw (32226)
PHONE....................................904 741-6161
Alina Alvarez, *Vice Pres*
Walter Woodruff, *IT/INT Sup*
William Bugg,
◆ **EMP:** 50 **EST:** 1968
SQ FT: 30,348
SALES (est): 27.7MM **Privately Held**
WEB: www.nivelparts.com
SIC: 3799 5088 Golf carts, powered; golf carts

(G-6638)
NOAHS MBL TIRE AUTO SOLUTIONS
5119 Cemetery Rd (32210-6835)
PHONE....................................904 250-1502
Corey Lundy, *CEO*
EMP: 6 **EST:** 2017
SALES (est): 30K **Privately Held**
SIC: 3011 Tire & inner tube materials & related products

(G-6639)
NORTH FL CUSTOM COATINGS INC
2896 Cortez Rd (32246-3718)
PHONE....................................904 251-4462
Kyle L Tibbetts, *Principal*
EMP: 9 **EST:** 2015
SALES (est): 258.3K **Privately Held**
WEB: www.homepaintinginjacksonvillefl.com
SIC: 3479 Metal coating & allied service

(G-6640)
NOVALUX SIGNS
8550 Argyle Business Loop (32244-8905)
PHONE....................................904 329-9607
Mario Armando Torres, *Owner*
EMP: 7 **EST:** 2012
SALES (est): 112.5K **Privately Held**
WEB: www.novaluxsigns.com
SIC: 3993 Signs & advertising specialties

(G-6641)
NPACT AMERICA INC
14476 Duval Pl W Ste 109 (32218-9404)
PHONE....................................904 755-6259
Sigmund C Mayerlen, *President*
Harold White, *Vice Pres*
Tommie J Hall, *Admin Sec*
EMP: 5 **EST:** 2010
SALES (est): 457.3K **Privately Held**
WEB: www.npactamerica.org
SIC: 3826 Analytical instruments

(G-6642)
NUFLO INC
3440 Evergreen Ave Ste 1 (32206-2327)
P.O. Box 3251 (32206-0251)
PHONE....................................904 265-4001
John Licausi, *President*
John Conderman, *CFO*
Ann Eadie, *Controller*
Thomas C Goelz, *Director*
William T Goelz, *Director*
▲ **EMP:** 50 **EST:** 2002
SQ FT: 15,000
SALES (est): 8.2MM **Privately Held**
WEB: www.nufloinc.com
SIC: 3494 3356 3272 Pipe fittings; nickel & nickel alloy pipe, plates, sheets, etc.; cylinder pipe, prestressed or pretensioned concrete

(G-6643)
OBITX INC
4720 Salisbury Rd (32256-6101)
PHONE....................................904 748-9750
Eric Jaffe, *CEO*
Michael Hawkins, *Ch of Bd*
EMP: 6
SALES (est): 222.5K **Privately Held**
WEB: www.obitx.com
SIC: 7372 Prepackaged software

(G-6644)
ONE NUGGET LLC
2206 Osprey Point Dr W (32224-3024)
PHONE....................................904 527-3218
David B Hobbing, *Principal*
EMP: 6 **EST:** 2017
SALES (est): 141.7K **Privately Held**
SIC: 2752 Commercial printing, lithographic

(G-6645)
ONESOURCE OF FLORIDA INC
6720 Arlington Expy (32211-7234)
PHONE....................................904 620-0003
Paul Lepore, *President*
EMP: 6 **EST:** 2004
SALES (est): 407.5K **Privately Held**
WEB: www.onesourcecomm.net
SIC: 2752 Commercial printing, lithographic

(G-6646)
ORACLE BALLOON DECOR INC
9951 Atl Blvd Ste 429 (32225-6553)
PHONE....................................386 866-0878
Meagan Branon, *Principal*
EMP: 6 **EST:** 2019
SALES (est): 68.4K **Privately Held**
WEB: www.oracleballoondecor.com
SIC: 7372 Prepackaged software

(G-6647)
ORATTAC INDUSTRIES LLC
15501 Shellcracker Rd (32226-1589)
P.O. Box 17154 (32245-7154)
PHONE....................................904 415-2162
Michael F Cattaro, *Principal*
EMP: 6 **EST:** 2007
SALES (est): 158.4K **Privately Held**
SIC: 3999 Manufacturing industries

(G-6648)
ORION POWER SYSTEMS INC (PA)
2939 W Beaver St (32254-3169)
PHONE....................................877 385-1654
Robert E Bridenbaugh, *President*
Ivette Bridenbaugh, *Vice Pres*
Conne Bridenbaugh, *Treasurer*
Richard Shaw, *Manager*
▲ **EMP:** 8 **EST:** 2011
SALES (est): 2MM **Privately Held**
WEB: www.orionpowersystems.com
SIC: 3568 Chain, power transmission

(G-6649)
OUR SENIORS GUIDECOM INC
14286-19 Bch Blvd Ste 335 (32246)
PHONE....................................904 655-2130
Brenda Elizabeth Badger, *President*
EMP: 9 **EST:** 2018
SALES (est): 191.7K **Privately Held**
WEB: www.ourseniorsguide.com
SIC: 2721 Periodicals: publishing only

(G-6650)
OUTLINE TECHNOLOGIES INC
Also Called: Renovation Concrete
9920 Blakeford Mill Rd (32256-3434)
PHONE....................................904 858-9933
Richard S Still, *President*
Chuck Pitman, *Vice Pres*
EMP: 6 **EST:** 2000
SALES (est): 700K **Privately Held**
SIC: 3545 Scales, measuring (machinists' precision tools)

(G-6651)
P3 FLEET LLC
11950 New Kings Rd (32219-1714)
PHONE....................................904 549-5500
Mark Padgtte, *President*
EMP: 14 **EST:** 2016
SALES (est): 3MM **Privately Held**
WEB: www.p3fleet.com
SIC: 3531 Construction machinery

(G-6652)
PAL-KING INC
1300 W Beaver St (32209-7633)
P.O. Box 442264 (32222-0051)
PHONE....................................904 334-8797
Bonnie Quasnick, *General Mgr*
Dan Quasnick, *Vice Pres*
EMP: 27 **EST:** 1977
SQ FT: 12,000
SALES (est): 2.1MM **Privately Held**
WEB: www.palking.com
SIC: 2448 Pallets, wood

(G-6653)
PALLET DOCTOR INC
221 N Hogan St Ste 371 (32202-4201)
PHONE....................................904 444-2514
Eric Andrews, *President*
EMP: 6 **EST:** 2001
SQ FT: 5,000
SALES (est): 509.4K **Privately Held**
SIC: 2448 Pallets, wood

(G-6654)
PALLET EX JACKSONVILLE INC
7779 Hammond Blvd (32220-3379)
PHONE....................................904 781-2500
Michael Oliveira, *CEO*
Matthew Oliveira, *President*
Brian Keegan, *Vice Pres*
EMP: 34 **EST:** 2006
SQ FT: 50,000
SALES (est): 625.3K **Privately Held**
WEB: www.palletexpressinc.com
SIC: 2448 5031 7699 Pallets, wood; pallets, wood; pallet repair

(G-6655)
PALLET EXPRESS OF JKVL INC
7779 Hammond Blvd (32220-3379)
PHONE....................................904 781-2500
Michael Oliveira, *CEO*
EMP: 15 **EST:** 2012
SALES (est): 263.3K **Privately Held**
WEB: www.palletexpressinc.com
SIC: 2448 Pallets, wood

(G-6656)
PAPA JOHNS PEANUTS INC
2555 W Beaver St (32254-3242)
PHONE....................................904 389-2511
Dwight Champion, *President*
EMP: 32 **EST:** 1998
SQ FT: 7,000
SALES (est): 1.4MM **Privately Held**
WEB: www.papajohnspeanuts.biz
SIC: 2068 Salted & roasted nuts & seeds

(G-6657)
PARKER MACHINERY CO INC
424 Copeland St (32204-2720)
PHONE....................................904 356-5038
Hugh Parker III, *President*
EMP: 5 **EST:** 1981
SQ FT: 3,500
SALES (est): 437.2K **Privately Held**
WEB: www.parkermachinery.net
SIC: 3599 Machine shop, jobbing & repair

(G-6658)
PARKERVISION INC (PA)
9446 Philips Hwy Ste 5a (32256-1349)
PHONE....................................904 732-6100
Jeffrey L Parker, *Ch of Bd*
David Jacobs, *Engineer*
Cynthia L Poehlman, *CFO*
Richard Harlan, *Marketing Staff*
Gregory Rawlins, *CTO*
EMP: 11 **EST:** 1989
SQ FT: 3,000
SALES (est): 5.8MM **Publicly Held**
WEB: www.parkervision.com
SIC: 3663 3674 3825 Radio broadcasting & communications equipment; semiconductors & related devices; radio frequency measuring equipment

(G-6659)
PAS REFORM NORTH AMERICA LLC
Also Called: Natureform Hatchery Systems
2550 Cabot Commerce Dr (32226-5607)
PHONE....................................904 358-0355
Ellis R Warren, *Corp Secy*
Scott Conley, *Vice Pres*
Terry Doss, *Vice Pres*
Jack Hubbell, *Vice Pres*
Cliff Maycott, *Plant Mgr*
◆ **EMP:** 25
SQ FT: 40,000
SALES (est): 3MM **Privately Held**
WEB: www.pasreform.com
SIC: 3523 Incubators & brooders, farm

(G-6660)
PAVERS PROFESSIONAL INC
4086 Stillwood Dr (32257-8919)
PHONE....................................239 878-6989
Fabiano R De Souza, *Principal*
EMP: 6 **EST:** 2012
SALES (est): 197.8K **Privately Held**
WEB: www.paversprofessionaljax.com
SIC: 2951 Asphalt paving mixtures & blocks

(G-6661)
PAW INC
Also Called: Diversified Products Mfg
8330 Atlantic Blvd (32211-8736)
PHONE....................................904 724-0310
Daniel Beilfuss, *President*
Paw II Lc, *Shareholder*
Claudia Beilfuss, *Admin Sec*
EMP: 36 **EST:** 1963
SALES (est): 7.8MM **Privately Held**
SIC: 3714 Motor vehicle parts & accessories

(G-6662)
PAYLESS BRICK PAVERS LLC
6873 Plum Lake Ln E (32222-1570)
PHONE....................................904 629-7436
Renato Machado, *Principal*
EMP: 6 **EST:** 2012
SALES (est): 506.3K **Privately Held**
WEB: www.plbpavers.com
SIC: 3531 Pavers

(G-6663)
PEARL ACADEMY LLC
450 Busch Dr Unit 6 (32218-8543)
PHONE....................................904 619-6419
Nacole Guyton, *Director*
Andre Baker,
Nefferteri Baker,
EMP: 5 **EST:** 2011
SALES (est): 392.4K **Privately Held**
WEB: www.pearlacademykids.com
SIC: 3641 Electric lamps

(G-6664)
PEDANO CUSTOM FURNITURE INC
10617 Coleman Rd (32257-1199)
PHONE....................................904 704-9329
Thomas Pedano Jr, *President*
EMP: 5 **EST:** 2003
SQ FT: 8,000
SALES (est): 323.8K **Privately Held**
SIC: 2434 Wood kitchen cabinets

(G-6665)
PEDICRAFT INC
4134 Saint Augustine Rd (32207-6600)
P.O. Box 5969 (32247-5969)
PHONE....................................904 348-3170
Doug Maynard, *President*
Myers Margaret, *Vice Pres*
Rita Freeman, *Mfg Dir*
Patty Langone, *Mktg Dir*
Bobbie Nord, *Admin Sec*
EMP: 13 **EST:** 1966
SQ FT: 10,000
SALES (est): 1.9MM **Privately Held**
WEB: www.pedicraft.com
SIC: 3841 Surgical & medical instruments

(G-6666)
PEDRONIS CAST STONE INC
5169 Edgewood Ct (32254-3601)
PHONE....................................904 783-1690
Craig Pedroni, *President*
Pat Pedroni, *Vice Pres*
EMP: 32 **EST:** 1984
SQ FT: 850
SALES (est): 2.2MM **Privately Held**
SIC: 3272 Cast stone, concrete

(G-6667)
PENSTRIPE GRAPHICS
4251 University Blvd S # 402 (32216-4923)
PHONE....................................904 726-0200
Sid Stiles, *Owner*
Jackie Stiles, *Co-Owner*
EMP: 7 **EST:** 1988
SALES (est): 400.6K **Privately Held**
WEB: www.penstripe.com
SIC: 2752 Commercial printing, offset

(G-6668)
PEPSI-COLA METRO BTLG CO INC
Also Called: Pepsico
5829 Pepsi Pl (32216-6162)
PHONE....................................904 733-1627
Letitia Griffin, *Regional Mgr*
Ron Cobb, *Sales Staff*
Laurinda Demi, *Sales Staff*
Kevin Munder, *Sales Staff*
Jennifer Stenson, *Marketing Staff*
EMP: 250
SALES (corp-wide): 70.3B **Publicly Held**
WEB: www.pepsico.com
SIC: 2086 5149 Carbonated soft drinks, bottled & canned; groceries & related products

HQ: Pepsi-Cola Metropolitan Bottling Company, Inc.
1111 Westchester Ave
White Plains NY 10604
914 767-6000

(G-6669)
PETROLEUM CONTAINMENT INC
8873 Western Way (32256-0367)
PHONE.................................904 358-1700
Robert W Arn, *President*
Samuel J Arn, *Vice Pres*
Janet Arn, *Treasurer*
Janet L Arn, *Treasurer*
Donna J Arn, *Admin Sec*
EMP: 23 **EST:** 1984
SQ FT: 20,000
SALES (est): 5.8MM **Privately Held**
WEB: www.petroleum-containment.com
SIC: 3089 2655 Synthetic resin finished products; fiber cans, drums & containers

(G-6670)
PHASE INTEGRATION LLC ✪
815 S Main St (32207-9050)
PHONE.................................877 778-8885
Barbara S Strickland, *Manager*
Stephen M Suddath,
Barry S Vaughn,
EMP: 5 **EST:** 2020
SALES (est): 326.2K **Privately Held**
SIC: 7372 Application computer software

(G-6671)
PHIL BUCKNER WOODWORKS INC
118 Jackson Rd Ste 4 (32225-6640)
PHONE.................................904 339-4475
Phil Buckner, *Principal*
EMP: 7 **EST:** 2010
SALES (est): 102.2K **Privately Held**
SIC: 2431 Millwork

(G-6672)
PILLAR INC
2232 Corporate Sq Blvd (32216-1922)
PHONE.................................904 545-4993
Griffith Michael S, *Principal*
EMP: 7 **EST:** 2014
SALES (est): 336.5K **Privately Held**
SIC: 3567 Industrial furnaces & ovens

(G-6673)
PINNACLE CENTRAL COMPANY INC (PA)
103 Bryan St (32202-1307)
PHONE.................................904 354-5746
Toll Free:..888 -
Steve Archibald, *President*
Rick Asbury, *Sales Staff*
▼ **EMP:** 11 **EST:** 1999
SQ FT: 4,000
SALES (est): 9MM **Privately Held**
WEB: www.pinnaclecentral.com
SIC: 3621 7629 Generator sets: gasoline, diesel or dual-fuel; generator repair

(G-6674)
PINNACLE CMMNCATIONS GROUP LLC ✪
Also Called: Pcg
10151 Deerwood Park Blvd (32256-0566)
PHONE.................................904 910-0444
Sonya Morales, *CEO*
Marissa Marchisillo, *COO*
Amara Marchisillo, *Mktg Dir*
EMP: 11 **EST:** 2020
SALES (est): 1.2MM **Privately Held**
WEB: www.pincomgroup.com
SIC: 3663 3825 3812 Radio broadcasting & communications equipment; radio frequency measuring equipment; antennas, radar or communications

(G-6675)
PIONEER DREDGE INC
8515 Baymeadows Way # 201 (32256-1214)
PHONE.................................904 732-2151
Tom H Kroeger, *Opers Staff*
Ken Graves, *Engineer*
Suzette Allen, *Finance Dir*
Michel Allen, *Director*
EMP: 9 **EST:** 2013
SALES (est): 749K **Privately Held**
WEB: www.pioneerdredge.com
SIC: 3561 Industrial pumps & parts

(G-6676)
PLASTIC CONCEPTS & DESIGNS INC
880 Us Highway 301 S # 1 (32234-2902)
PHONE.................................904 396-7500
Carl A Ackerman, *President*
EMP: 5 **EST:** 1989
SQ FT: 4,000
SALES (est): 1MM **Privately Held**
WEB: www.plasticconcepts.com
SIC: 3089 Injection molded finished plastic products; injection molding of plastics

(G-6677)
POLYHISTOR INTERNATIONAL INC
11200 Saint Johns (32246)
PHONE.................................904 646-5666
Peter Schonning, *President*
Michelle Forwood, *Admin Asst*
EMP: 5 **EST:** 1999
SALES (est): 1MM **Privately Held**
WEB: www.phi2.com
SIC: 3841 8711 3069 3812 Surgical & medical instruments; engineering services; rubber automotive products; defense systems & equipment

(G-6678)
POLYTECH INTERNATIONAL LLC
6635 Highway Ave (32254-3519)
PHONE.................................904 354-9355
James Velliky, *President*
John Richards, *COO*
EMP: 10 **EST:** 2012
SQ FT: 1,600
SALES (est): 1.7MM **Privately Held**
WEB: www.danalysis.com
SIC: 3353 Coils, sheet aluminum

(G-6679)
POSITIVE SCREENPRINT
2808 W Beaver St (32254-3168)
PHONE.................................904 381-0963
Cheyenne Mizell, *Principal*
EMP: 6 **EST:** 2005
SALES (est): 100K **Privately Held**
SIC: 2759 Screen printing

(G-6680)
PRECIOUS METAL GROUP LLC
5410 Blanding Blvd (32244-1901)
PHONE.................................904 219-8358
EMP: 8 **EST:** 2011
SALES (est): 476.3K **Privately Held**
SIC: 3339 Precious metals

(G-6681)
PRECISION LEAK DETECTION INC
84 Autumn Springs Ct W (32225-3164)
PHONE.................................904 996-9290
Scott R Monnoyer, *President*
EMP: 7 **EST:** 2007
SALES (est): 470.8K **Privately Held**
SIC: 3829 Liquid leak detection equipment

(G-6682)
PRECISION SVCS JCKSONVILLE INC
5201 W Beaver St (32254-2910)
PHONE.................................904 781-3770
Robert B Coleman, *President*
EMP: 10 **EST:** 2007
SQ FT: 500
SALES (est): 3MM **Privately Held**
WEB: www.precisionjax.com
SIC: 7692 Welding repair

(G-6683)
PREMIER CORPORATE PRINTING
3414 Galilee Rd (32207-4718)
PHONE.................................305 378-8480
Isaac R Camargo, *President*
Joseph Hammond, *Principal*
Shirley Camargo, *Vice Pres*
EMP: 5 **EST:** 2014
SALES (est): 717K **Privately Held**
WEB: www.premiercorporateprinting.com
SIC: 2752 Commercial printing, offset

(G-6684)
PREMIER CORPORATE PRINTING LLC ✪
3414 Galilee Rd (32207-4718)
PHONE.................................305 378-8480
Blake Houser,
EMP: 10 **EST:** 2020
SALES (est): 400K **Privately Held**
SIC: 2752 Commercial printing, lithographic

(G-6685)
PREMIER WATER & ENRGY TECH INC
11481 Columbia Park Dr W (32258-4404)
PHONE.................................904 268-1152
Thomas F Brandvold, *President*
Amanda Geist, *Accountant*
Chuck Brandvold, *Sales Dir*
Danielle Sayre, *Manager*
Tyler Cooper, *Consultant*
◆ **EMP:** 28 **EST:** 1973
SQ FT: 9,500
SALES (est): 7MM **Privately Held**
WEB: www.premierwater.com
SIC: 3589 2899 Water treatment equipment, industrial; water treating compounds

(G-6686)
PRINT EXPRESS
1889 Southampton Rd (32207-8777)
PHONE.................................904 737-6641
Bill Weaver, *Partner*
Debby K Weaver, *Partner*
EMP: 8 **EST:** 1988
SALES (est): 649.7K **Privately Held**
WEB: www.printexpressjacksonville.wordpress.com
SIC: 2752 Commercial printing, offset

(G-6687)
PRINTED SYSTEMS INC
Also Called: PSI Printing
1309 Saint Johns Bluff Rd (32225-8396)
PHONE.................................904 281-0909
Michael Lee Dunaway, *President*
EMP: 8 **EST:** 1986
SQ FT: 1,500
SALES (est): 938.8K **Privately Held**
SIC: 2752 5112 Commercial printing, offset; business forms

(G-6688)
PRINTING EDGE INC
2205 Emerson St (32207-9208)
PHONE.................................904 399-3343
Ruth A Murr, *President*
EMP: 6 **EST:** 1994
SQ FT: 2,880
SALES (est): 907.1K **Privately Held**
WEB: www.eprintingedge.com
SIC: 2752 Commercial printing, offset

(G-6689)
PRINTING IMPRESSIONS PROM
1762 Singing Bird Ln (32223-0861)
PHONE.................................904 465-2223
EMP: 6 **EST:** 2018
SALES (est): 207.7K **Privately Held**
WEB: www.printingimpressions.biz
SIC: 2752 Commercial printing, offset

(G-6690)
PROCORP LLC
8535 Baymeadows Rd Ste 58 (32256-7445)
PHONE.................................904 477-6762
Fred Ewan,
Bob Ozmik,
EMP: 8 **EST:** 2005
SALES (est): 622.7K **Privately Held**
SIC: 2759 Commercial printing

(G-6691)
PROFESSNAL REPRODUCTION OF JAX
Also Called: Rapid Print
7029 Commonwealth Ave (32220-2859)
PHONE.................................904 389-4141
Beverly Aldridge, *President*
Kent Aldridge, *Vice Pres*
EMP: 5 **EST:** 1975
SALES (est): 480.2K **Privately Held**
SIC: 2752 Commercial printing, offset

(G-6692)
PROGRESS RAIL SERVICES CORP
420 Agmac Ave (32254-2863)
PHONE.................................904 783-1143
Del King, *Manager*
EMP: 10
SQ FT: 25,282
SALES (corp-wide): 41.7B **Publicly Held**
WEB: www.progressrail.com
SIC: 3743 Railroad equipment
HQ: Progress Rail Services Corporation
1600 Progress Dr
Albertville AL 35950
256 505-6421

(G-6693)
PROGRESSIVE POWER PRODUCTS INC
4062 N Liberty St (32206-1410)
P.O. Box 24905 (32241-4905)
PHONE.................................904 354-1819
Nancy Kates, *President*
Larry Kates, *Vice Pres*
▲ **EMP:** 8 **EST:** 1989
SQ FT: 9,000
SALES (est): 1.2MM **Privately Held**
WEB: www.pppallison.com
SIC: 3714 Power transmission equipment, motor vehicle

(G-6694)
PROGRESSIVE PRINTING CO INC
4505 Lexington Ave (32210-2037)
PHONE.................................904 388-0746
Fax: 904 388-1330
EMP: 15 **EST:** 1977
SQ FT: 7,113
SALES: 1.2MM **Privately Held**
SIC: 2752 Offset Printing

(G-6695)
PROLIFIC CABINETRY & MORE INC
7660 Philips Hwy Ste 5 (32256-6819)
PHONE.................................904 448-6575
Steven E Brust, *President*
EMP: 5 **EST:** 2006
SALES (est): 876.9K **Privately Held**
WEB: www.prolificcabinetry.com
SIC: 2434 Wood kitchen cabinets

(G-6696)
PROSERVICES SUPPLY LLC
12620 Beach Blvd Ste 3304 (32246-7131)
PHONE.................................858 254-4415
Gary Phillips, *Mng Member*
EMP: 12
SALES (est): 510.6K **Privately Held**
SIC: 3585 Air conditioning equipment, complete

(G-6697)
PUZZLED CATERPILLARS INC
5230 Anisa Ct (32209-3058)
PHONE.................................904 379-9219
Frances McMiller, *Principal*
EMP: 6 **EST:** 2017
SALES (est): 253.7K **Privately Held**
SIC: 3531 Construction machinery

(G-6698)
QUALITY DOOR SERVICE LLC
4223 Key Largo Dr (32218-4448)
PHONE.................................904 588-4817
Peter Snavley, *Mng Member*
EMP: 6 **EST:** 2009
SALES (est): 68.3K **Privately Held**
SIC: 3699 Door opening & closing devices, electrical

(G-6699)
QUALITY NEON SIGN COMPANY (PA)
Also Called: Harbinger
5300 Shad Rd (32257-2006)
PHONE.................................904 268-4681
Roger S Williams II, *CEO*
Roger S Williams, *Ch of Bd*

Sherry Bishop, *Vice Pres*
Julie Bain, *Project Mgr*
Sheila Williams, *Admin Sec*
EMP: 76 **EST:** 1963
SQ FT: 25,000
SALES (est): 15MM **Privately Held**
WEB: www.harbingersign.com
SIC: 3993 Electric signs; neon signs

(G-6700)
QUALITY STONES R US LLC
10475 Fortune Pkwy St (32256-3585)
PHONE..................................904 551-5619
Pratik Shah, *President*
EMP: 9 **EST:** 2008
SALES (est): 566.1K **Privately Held**
WEB: www.qualitystones.com
SIC: 1411 Granite dimension stone

(G-6701)
R & K MARKETING INC
Also Called: Aim
11657 Central Pkwy # 401 (32224-2661)
P.O. Box 350489 (32235-0489)
PHONE..................................904 745-0022
David Harrison, *President*
Julie Harrison, *Vice Pres*
EMP: 7 **EST:** 1991
SQ FT: 2,000
SALES (est): 1.4MM **Privately Held**
WEB: www.aimhere.net
SIC: 3579 5044 Duplicating machines; photocopy machines

(G-6702)
R T PUBLISHING INC
12443 San Jose Blvd # 403 (32223-8646)
PHONE..................................904 886-4919
David L Taus, *Treasurer*
EMP: 5 **EST:** 2001
SALES (est): 463.5K **Privately Held**
WEB: www.rtpublishinginc.com
SIC: 2721 Magazines: publishing only, not printed on site

(G-6703)
RA PRINTING INC
Also Called: Minuteman Press
4185 Sunbeam Rd Ste 100 (32257-2424)
PHONE..................................904 733-5578
Arch Copeland, *President*
Rosemary Copeland, *Vice Pres*
EMP: 7 **EST:** 1994
SQ FT: 4,000
SALES (est): 866.5K **Privately Held**
WEB: www.chanhassen-mn.minuteman-press.com
SIC: 2752 Commercial printing, lithographic

(G-6704)
RAND M RAWLS
4495 Glen Kernan Pkwy E (32224-5629)
PHONE..................................904 382-4844
Renard Rawls, *Principal*
EMP: 7 **EST:** 2011
SALES (est): 233.7K **Privately Held**
SIC: 3131 Rands

(G-6705)
RAPID GENOMICS LLC
5 W Forsyth St Ste 200 (32202-3676)
PHONE..................................352 213-4741
EMP: 6 **EST:** 2014
SALES (est): 139.5K **Privately Held**
SIC: 2835 Microbiology & virology diagnostic products

(G-6706)
RAYONIER A M PRODUCTS INC (HQ)
1301 Riverplace Blvd (32207-9047)
PHONE..................................904 357-9100
Paul Gerard Boynton, *President*
Michael R Herman, *Senior VP*
Charles H Hood, *Senior VP*
Frank A Ruperto, *Senior VP*
Erin M Byers, *Vice Pres*
EMP: 100 **EST:** 2008
SALES (est): 183.4MM
SALES (corp-wide): 1.7B **Publicly Held**
WEB: www.rayonieram.com
SIC: 2821 Plastics materials & resins
PA: Rayonier Advanced Materials Inc.
1301 Riverplace Blvd # 23
Jacksonville FL 32207
904 357-4600

(G-6707)
RAYONIER ADVANCED MTLS INC (PA)
1301 Riverplace Blvd # 23 (32207-9047)
PHONE..................................904 357-4600
Paul G Boynton, *Ch of Bd*
De Lyle Bloomquist, *Ch of Bd*
Stacey Williams, *Superintendent*
Nathan Moore, *Area Mgr*
Caleb Spires, *Area Mgr*
EMP: 2212 **EST:** 1926
SALES: 1.7B **Publicly Held**
WEB: www.rayonieram.com
SIC: 2823 2821 Cellulosic manmade fibers; cellulose derivative materials

(G-6708)
RAYONIER AM SALES AND TECH INC (DH)
Also Called: Rayonier Advanced Materials
1301 Riverplace Blvd # 23 (32207-9047)
PHONE..................................904 357-4600
Paul G Boynton, *President*
◆ **EMP:** 5 **EST:** 2013
SALES (est): 9.8MM
SALES (corp-wide): 1.7B **Publicly Held**
WEB: www.rayonieram.com
SIC: 2821 2822 Cellulose derivative materials; ethylene-propylene rubbers, EPDM polymers
HQ: Rayonier A.M. Products Inc.
1301 Riverplace Blvd
Jacksonville FL 32207
904 357-9100

(G-6709)
REDDI SIGN CORPORATION
107 Mott St (32254-4030)
P.O. Box 28846 (32226-8846)
PHONE..................................904 757-0680
Wendy J Dobson, *Principal*
EMP: 8 **EST:** 2010
SALES (est): 309.4K **Privately Held**
WEB: www.reddi-sign.com
SIC: 3993 Signs, not made in custom sign painting shops

(G-6710)
REDDY ICE CORPORATION
5849 Commonwealth Ave (32254-2205)
P.O. Box 60099 (32236-0099)
PHONE..................................904 388-2653
Fred Day, *Division Mgr*
Alendwa Mallya, *General Mgr*
Lee Hatch, *Manager*
Lorna Williams, *Senior Mgr*
Robert Pierce, *Executive*
EMP: 12 **Privately Held**
WEB: www.reddyice.com
SIC: 2097 Manufactured ice
HQ: Reddy Ice Corporation
5710 Lbj Fwy Ste 300
Dallas TX 75240
214 526-6740

(G-6711)
REDWIRE CORPORATION (PA)
8226 Philips Hwy Ste 101 (32256-1230)
PHONE..................................650 701-7722
Peter Cannito, *Ch of Bd*
Andrew Rush, *President*
Nathan O'Konek, *Exec VP*
William Read, *CFO*
EMP: 0 **EST:** 2010
SALES (est): 34.2MM **Publicly Held**
WEB: www.genesis-park.com
SIC: 3761 Guided missiles & space vehicles

(G-6712)
REFRESHING SMOOTHIE
9550 Baymeadows Rd (32256-0710)
PHONE..................................904 549-5366
Ming Hui Yang, *Principal*
EMP: 6 **EST:** 2015
SALES (est): 146.1K **Privately Held**
SIC: 2037 Frozen fruits & vegetables

(G-6713)
REGENCY CAP & GOWN COMPANY
Also Called: De La Mer Originals
7534 Atlantic Blvd (32211-8714)
P.O. Box 8988 (32239-0988)
PHONE..................................904 724-3500
David K Crisp, *President*
Bob Walkord, *Owner*
Robert E Walkord, *Treasurer*
EMP: 20 **EST:** 1981
SQ FT: 36,000
SALES (est): 875.6K **Privately Held**
WEB: www.rcgown.com
SIC: 2389 2339 Academic vestments (caps & gowns); bathing suits: women's, misses' & juniors'

(G-6714)
REGIONAL TRAILER REPAIR INC
1048 Escambia St (32208-4319)
P.O. Box 3158 (32206-0158)
PHONE..................................912 484-7729
William Brantley, *President*
Marc Scheurer, *Vice Pres*
Samuel Adams, *Shareholder*
EMP: 14 **EST:** 2003
SQ FT: 10,000
SALES (est): 157.8K **Privately Held**
WEB: www.regional-trailer-repair.business.site
SIC: 2448 Pallets, wood

(G-6715)
RELIOX CORPORATION
8475 Western Way Ste 155 (32256-0351)
PHONE..................................904 729-5097
Eric Johnson, *CEO*
Sam McConnell, *Director*
Cristina Knapp, *Admin Sec*
EMP: 5 **EST:** 2012
SALES (est): 855.8K **Privately Held**
WEB: www.reliox-clo2.com
SIC: 2842 Disinfectants, household or industrial plant; industrial plant disinfectants or deodorants

(G-6716)
RESIDENT CMNTY NEWS GROUP INC
1650 Margaret St 31 (32204-3868)
PHONE..................................904 962-6876
Percy Rosenbloom Jr, *Principal*
Kate Hallock, *Manager*
EMP: 17 **EST:** 2009
SALES (est): 846.9K **Privately Held**
WEB: www.residentnews.net
SIC: 2711 Newspapers, publishing & printing

(G-6717)
RESIDENT COMMUNITY NEWS
2973 Fitzgerald St (32254-4068)
PHONE..................................904 388-8839
Pedro Merded, *Principal*
EMP: 8 **EST:** 2007
SALES (est): 81.2K **Privately Held**
SIC: 2711 Newspapers, publishing & printing

(G-6718)
RESILIENT GROUP INC
3114 Double Oaks Dr (32226-2085)
PHONE..................................518 434-4414
EMP: 14
SALES (corp-wide): 94.4K **Privately Held**
WEB: www.resilientpma.com
SIC: 3732 Boat building & repairing
PA: The Resilient Group Inc
3408 Foxmeadow Ct
Longwood FL
800 604-2443

(G-6719)
REVERE MANUFACTURED PDTS INC
323 Hwy Ave (32254)
PHONE..................................904 503-9733
Andrew C Kaufmann, *President*
Howard Kaufmann, *Vice Pres*
Howard W Kaufmann, *Vice Pres*
EMP: 9 **EST:** 2005
SALES (est): 153.1K **Privately Held**
SIC: 3069 Hard rubber & molded rubber products

(G-6720)
REVERE SURVIVAL INC
5323 Highway Ave (32254-3634)
PHONE..................................904 503-9733
Andrew Richards, *CEO*
Nicholas Howland, *President*
Kini Bowers, *Vice Pres*
Thomas Mastrella, *Vice Pres*
Michelle Snow, *Opers Staff*
EMP: 18 **EST:** 2014
SQ FT: 35,000
SALES (est): 3.9MM **Privately Held**
WEB: www.reveresurvival.com
SIC: 3732 Boat kits, not models

(G-6721)
REVLON INC
540 Beautyrest Ave (32254-3605)
PHONE..................................904 693-1254
George Adams, *Engineer*
Karen Wigley, *Manager*
EMP: 7 **Publicly Held**
WEB: www.revloninc.com
SIC: 2844 Cosmetic preparations
HQ: Revlon, Inc.
1 New York Plz Fl 49
New York NY 10004

(G-6722)
REVLON CONSUMER PRODUCTS CORP
5344 Overmyer Dr (32254-3645)
PHONE..................................904 378-4167
Brian Kalch, *Opers Staff*
Sean Dupuis, *Manager*
Henrique Vianna, *Manager*
EMP: 7 **Publicly Held**
WEB: www.revlon.com
SIC: 2844 Cosmetic preparations
HQ: Revlon Consumer Products Corporation
1 New York Plz
New York NY 10004

(G-6723)
RFL & FIGLIO LLC
Also Called: US Body Source
4226 Spring Grove Ave (32209)
PHONE..................................904 765-2222
Christine Zoyhofski,
EMP: 10 **EST:** 2014
SALES (est): 548.8K **Privately Held**
SIC: 2221 Broadwoven fabric mills, manmade

(G-6724)
RIDE LIKE BESSIE INC ✪
7643 Gate Pkwy Unit 104-1 (32256-2893)
PHONE..................................904 580-3631
Susie Hill, *CEO*
EMP: 6 **EST:** 2021
SALES (est): 282.2K **Privately Held**
SIC: 3751 Motorcycle accessories

(G-6725)
RING POWER CORPORATION
Phoenix Products
1727 Bennett St (32206-5415)
PHONE..................................904 354-1858
Ron Roy, *Manager*
EMP: 41
SALES (corp-wide): 1B **Privately Held**
WEB: www.ringpower.com
SIC: 3443 3448 3613 Tanks, standard or custom fabricated: metal plate; panels for prefabricated metal buildings; regulators, power
HQ: Ring Power Corporation
500 World Commerce Pkwy
Saint Augustine FL 32092
904 201-7400

(G-6726)
RIVER CITY ADVG OBJECTIONAL
3514 Morton St (32217-2547)
PHONE..................................904 731-3452
John Wondracek, *President*
Theresa Wondracek, *Admin Sec*
EMP: 8 **EST:** 1992
SQ FT: 2,000

SALES (est): 753.3K **Privately Held**
WEB: www.rcajax.com
SIC: 3993 5099 Signs & advertising specialties; signs, except electric

(G-6727)
RIVER CITY CSTM CABINETRY INC
1863 Mayport Rd (32233-1919)
PHONE..................................904 247-0807
Damon Rebhahn, *President*
EMP: 17 **EST:** 1994
SQ FT: 7,954
SALES (est): 2.2MM **Privately Held**
WEB: www.rivercitycustomcabinetry.com
SIC: 2434 1751 Wood kitchen cabinets; cabinet & finish carpentry

(G-6728)
RIVER CITY STUCCO INC
117 Magnolia Ave (32218-2606)
PHONE..................................904 234-9526
Vance Fiedler, *Principal*
EMP: 7 **EST:** 2008
SALES (est): 108.3K **Privately Held**
WEB: www.rivercitystucco.business.site
SIC: 3299 Stucco

(G-6729)
RIVERVIEW MILLWORKS INC
9157 Lem Turner Rd (32208-2293)
PHONE..................................904 764-9571
Charles A Nichols Jr, *President*
Danny R Raulerson, *Vice Pres*
Danny Raulerson, *Vice Pres*
Garry Du'bois, *Project Mgr*
Bryon Nobles, *Manager*
EMP: 6 **EST:** 1936
SQ FT: 27,000
SALES (est): 906.3K **Privately Held**
WEB: www.riverviewmillworks.com
SIC: 2431 Millwork

(G-6730)
RIW OF JACKSONVILLE INC
608 Carmen St (32206-3951)
PHONE..................................904 356-5635
EMP: 10 **EST:** 1919
SQ FT: 23,000
SALES (est): 950K **Privately Held**
SIC: 3443 3599 Mfg Fabricated Plate Work Mfg Industrial Machinery

(G-6731)
RLC BUILDING INC
11190 Hendon Dr (32246-7125)
PHONE..................................904 704-5614
Riley L Chancey Jr, *Principal*
EMP: 6 **EST:** 2013
SALES (est): 107.8K **Privately Held**
SIC: 7692 7389 Welding repair;

(G-6732)
RM BRANDS INC
Also Called: Property Armor
2910 W Beaver St (32254-3170)
PHONE..................................904 356-0092
Robert Michell, *President*
Robert F Michell, *President*
EMP: 9 **EST:** 2003
SALES (est): 1.2MM **Privately Held**
WEB: www.hapcohvac.com
SIC: 3441 3699 Fabricated structural metal; security devices

(G-6733)
ROBERT JAMES CUSTOM METAL FABR
2900 N Canal St (32209-4630)
PHONE..................................772 214-0996
James R Reitz, *Manager*
EMP: 16 **EST:** 2005
SALES (est): 1.1MM **Privately Held**
SIC: 3499 Fabricated metal products

(G-6734)
ROMEROS PALLETS OF JAX
3151 W Beaver St (32254-3173)
PHONE..................................904 329-2962
Mauricio Romero, *Principal*
EMP: 7 **EST:** 2018
SALES (est): 249.3K **Privately Held**
SIC: 2448 Pallets, wood

(G-6735)
RONCO MACHINE INC
2100 Dennis St (32204-1806)
P.O. Box 31, Lake Winola PA (18625-0031)
PHONE..................................904 827-9795
Bradley Reeves, *President*
Gina L Polseno, *Admin Sec*
EMP: 8 **EST:** 2013
SQ FT: 30,000
SALES (est): 796K **Privately Held**
WEB: www.roncomachine.com
SIC: 3554 Paper industries machinery

(G-6736)
ROUX LABORATORIES INC (DH)
5344 Overmyer Dr (32254-3645)
PHONE..................................904 366-2602
Mike Powell, *President*
Timothy Buckingham, *Vice Pres*
Henry Wernars, *CFO*
Etta Milner, *Treasurer*
Dan D Angelo, *Controller*
◆ **EMP:** 325 **EST:** 1946
SQ FT: 360,000
SALES (est): 131.1MM **Publicly Held**
WEB: www.rouxbeauty.com
SIC: 2844 Cosmetic preparations

(G-6737)
ROUX LABORATORIES INC
Also Called: Revlon Professional Products
5344 Overmyer Dr (32254-3645)
PHONE..................................904 378-4167
Daniel Angelo, *Controller*
EMP: 7 **Publicly Held**
WEB: www.rouxbeauty.com
SIC: 2844 Hair preparations, including shampoos
HQ: Roux Laboratories, Inc.
5344 Overmyer Dr
Jacksonville FL 32254
904 366-2602

(G-6738)
RPD MANAGEMENT LLC
Also Called: Intuition Ale Works
720 King St (32204-3440)
PHONE..................................904 710-8911
▲ **EMP:** 7
SALES (est): 969.6K **Privately Held**
SIC: 2082 Malt Beverages, Nsk

(G-6739)
RUBIN IRON WORKS LLC
608 Carmen St (32206-3951)
P.O. Box 3333 (32206-0333)
PHONE..................................904 356-5635
Charles P Berman, *CEO*
Rochelle B Stoddard, *Admin Sec*
Eric Berman,
▼ **EMP:** 25 **EST:** 2004
SALES (est): 2.8MM **Privately Held**
WEB: www.bermanbros.com
SIC: 3441 Fabricated structural metal

(G-6740)
RUSH TO EXCELLENCE PRTG INC
4204 Spring Park Rd (32207-6956)
PHONE..................................904 367-0100
William Poarch Sr, *President*
EMP: 6 **EST:** 1992
SQ FT: 2,000
SALES (est): 474.4K **Privately Held**
WEB: www.rushtoexcellenceprinting.com
SIC: 2752 Commercial printing, offset

(G-6741)
RZ SERVICE GROUP LLC
12574 Flagler Center Blvd (32258-2614)
PHONE..................................904 402-2313
Joseph Newkirk, *CEO*
Wali Murphy, *COO*
Joseph R Newkirk,
EMP: 6 **EST:** 2015
SALES (est): 794.2K **Privately Held**
WEB: www.recoveryz.com
SIC: 3569 1799 8742 1629 Generators: steam, liquid oxygen or nitrogen; construction site cleanup; materials mgmt. (purchasing, handling, inventory) consultant; dams, waterways, docks & other marine construction; waste water & sewage treatment plant construction; water treatment equipment, industrial; nitrogen

(G-6742)
S & S METAL AND PLASTICS INC
3740 Morton St (32217-2206)
PHONE..................................904 731-4655
Cynthia L Strickland, *President*
Nancy Dearmas, *Corp Secy*
EMP: 32 **EST:** 1962
SQ FT: 17,000
SALES (est): 6.3MM **Privately Held**
WEB: www.ssmetal.com
SIC: 3993 3499 Signs, not made in custom sign painting shops; furniture parts, metal

(G-6743)
S GAGER INDUSTRIES INC
11436 Philips Hwy (32256-1636)
PHONE..................................904 268-6727
Forest Gager, *President*
George Gager, *Vice Pres*
Linda Gager, *Treasurer*
EMP: 31 **EST:** 1969
SQ FT: 20,000
SALES (est): 2.7MM **Privately Held**
WEB: www.sgagerindustries.wixsite.com
SIC: 3089 Injection molding of plastics

(G-6744)
S&P USA VNTILATION SYSTEMS LLC
6393 Powers Ave (32217-2217)
PHONE..................................904 731-4711
Mark Bojarzin, *CEO*
Eugene Scotcher, *CEO*
Patrick Williams III, *President*
Patrick M Williams, *President*
Patrick Williams Jr, *Chairman*
◆ **EMP:** 86 **EST:** 1974
SQ FT: 65,000
SALES (est): 30.3MM **Privately Held**
WEB: www.solerpalau-usa.com
SIC: 3564 Blowing fans: industrial or commercial; exhaust fans: industrial or commercial; ventilating fans: industrial or commercial

(G-6745)
SAFARI PROGRAMS INC
8010 Westside Indus Dr (32219-3290)
PHONE..................................305 621-1000
Alexandre M Pariente, *CEO*
Christina Pariente, *President*
Jorge Alvarado, *Managing Prtnr*
Elizabeth Cruz, *Accountant*
Christina Hartman, *Sales Mgr*
◆ **EMP:** 58 **EST:** 1981
SALES (est): 13.1MM **Privately Held**
WEB: www.safariltd.com
SIC: 3944 5092 Craft & hobby kits & sets; toys & games

(G-6746)
SAFARILAND LLC
3041 Faye Rd (32226-2336)
PHONE..................................904 741-5400
EMP: 17 **EST:** 2016
SALES (est): 3.6MM **Privately Held**
WEB: www.safariland.com
SIC: 3842 Surgical appliances & supplies

(G-6747)
SAFARILAND LLC
Also Called: Rogers Holster Co
3041 Faye Rd (32226-2336)
PHONE..................................904 646-0141
Warren Kanders, *CEO*
Tim West, *Manager*
EMP: 46
SALES (corp-wide): 1B **Privately Held**
WEB: www.safariland.com
SIC: 3089 Blow molded finished plastic products
HQ: Safariland, Llc
13386 International Pkwy
Jacksonville FL 32218
904 741-5400

(G-6748)
SAFARILAND LLC (HQ)
Also Called: Safariland Group
13386 International Pkwy (32218-2383)
PHONE..................................904 741-5400
Warren Kanders, *CEO*
Scott T O'Brien, *President*
Mary Patterson, *COO*
Bryan Lee, *Vice Pres*
Mike Harbison, *Plant Mgr*
▲ **EMP:** 420 **EST:** 1997
SALES (est): 863.6MM
SALES (corp-wide): 1B **Privately Held**
WEB: www.safariland.com
SIC: 3842 Surgical appliances & supplies
PA: Cadre Holdings, Inc.
13386 International Pkwy
Jacksonville FL 32218
904 741-5400

(G-6749)
SAFETY CLAMPS INC
233 Santa Barbara Ave (32254-3589)
PHONE..................................904 781-2809
Scott Griffin, *President*
EMP: 12 **EST:** 1962
SQ FT: 9,000
SALES (est): 2.2MM **Privately Held**
WEB: www.safetyclamps.com
SIC: 3429 Clamps, metal

(G-6750)
SAN MARCO PLACE CONDO ASSN
1478 Riverplace Blvd (32207-1831)
PHONE..................................504 812-0352
Jim Ralph, *Vice Pres*
EMP: 8 **EST:** 2015
SALES (est): 541.5K **Privately Held**
WEB: www.riverplacerealtyjacksonville.com
SIC: 2752 Commercial printing, lithographic

(G-6751)
SAPUTO DAIRY FOODS USA LLC
2198 W Beaver St (32209-7405)
PHONE..................................904 354-0406
Hassan Malih, *Manager*
EMP: 8 **Privately Held**
WEB: www.saputo.com
SIC: 2023 Cream substitutes
HQ: Saputo Dairy Foods Usa, Llc
2711 N Haskell Ave # 370
Dallas TX 75204
214 863-2300

(G-6752)
SARGENT SEAT COVER CO INC
Also Called: Sargent Auto Upholstery
44 E 1st St (32206-5006)
PHONE..................................904 355-2529
Marion E Todd, *CEO*
Mike Todd, *President*
Margaret Todd, *Corp Secy*
Mark Todd, *Vice Pres*
▲ **EMP:** 25 **EST:** 1955
SQ FT: 20,000
SALES (est): 2.4MM **Privately Held**
WEB: www.sargentupholstery.com
SIC: 2399 7532 Seat covers, automobile; top & body repair & paint shops

(G-6753)
SAWGRASS NUTRA LABS LLC
7018 A C Skinner Pkwy # 230 (32256-6935)
PHONE..................................844 688-7244
Scott Teagle, *CEO*
John Devries,
EMP: 35 **EST:** 2018
SALES (est): 3MM **Privately Held**
WEB: www.sawgrassnutralabs.com
SIC: 2023 Dietary supplements, dairy & non-dairy based

(G-6754)
SCHUR & COMPANY LLC
Also Called: Schurco Slurry Pumps
9410 Florida Min Blvd E (32257)
P.O. Box 2369 (32203-2369)
PHONE..................................904 353-8075
Lisa S Schur, *President*
Nicholas J Schur, *Corp Secy*
◆ **EMP:** 51 **EST:** 2002
SQ FT: 25,000
SALES (est): 10.4MM **Privately Held**
WEB: www.schurco.com
SIC: 3599 3568 Custom machinery; shafts, flexible

(G-6755)
SCIF SOLUTIONS INC (PA)
11518 Normandy Blvd (32221-1811)
PHONE.................................904 298-0631
Bruce Paquin Sr, *CEO*
Bruce Paquin Jr, *COO*
Rebecca Manuel, *CFO*
Joel McDaniel, *Sales Staff*
Lauren Scott, *Officer*
EMP: 10 **EST:** 2004
SQ FT: 15,000
SALES (est): 2.5MM **Privately Held**
WEB: www.scifsolutions.com
SIC: 3448 Prefabricated metal buildings; buildings, portable: prefabricated metal; panels for prefabricated metal buildings

(G-6756)
SCOTT INDUSTRIAL SYSTEMS INC
4130 N Canal St (32209-3668)
PHONE.................................904 693-3318
EMP: 18
SALES (corp-wide): 53MM **Privately Held**
WEB: www.scottindustrialsystems.com
SIC: 3594 Fluid power pumps & motors
PA: Scott Industrial Systems Inc
4433 Interpoint Blvd
Dayton OH 45424
937 233-8146

(G-6757)
SCREEN PROCESS PRINTERS INC
101 S Myrtle Ave (32204-2174)
P.O. Box 2511 (32203-2511)
PHONE.................................904 354-8708
Smith Easton, *CEO*
James M Sullivan, *President*
EMP: 5 **EST:** 1979
SALES (est): 500K **Privately Held**
WEB: www.screenprocessprinters.com
SIC: 2759 3993 Screen printing; signs & advertising specialties

(G-6758)
SEA PRODUCTS INC (PA)
Also Called: Southeastern Aluminum
4925 Bulls Bay Hwy (32219-3250)
P.O. Box 6427 (32236-6427)
PHONE.................................904 781-8200
Patrick Dussinger, *President*
William K Jackson Jr, *President*
Jeffrey E Dowd, *Vice Pres*
Joseph T Jackson, *Vice Pres*
John R Jr Wright, *Vice Pres*
◆ **EMP:** 95 **EST:** 1952
SALES (est): 27MM **Privately Held**
WEB: www.southeasternaluminum.com
SIC: 3442 3231 3088 Sash, door or window: metal; doors, glass: made from purchased glass; shower stalls, fiberglass & plastic

(G-6759)
SEACURE INC
9485 Regency Square Blvd # 110 (32225-8156)
PHONE.................................904 353-5353
Warren P Powers, *Principal*
EMP: 10 **EST:** 2006
SALES (est): 740.4K **Privately Held**
SIC: 3089 Plastic boats & other marine equipment

(G-6760)
SEF AMERICAS LLC
14476 Duval Pl W (32218-9403)
PHONE.................................904 423-0211
David P Coleman, *Mng Member*
EMP: 6 **EST:** 2014
SALES (est): 205.2K **Privately Held**
WEB: www.seftextile.com
SIC: 2759 Screen printing

(G-6761)
SENTRY FOOD SOLUTIONS LLC
4339 Roosevelt Blvd # 400 (32210-2004)
PHONE.................................904 482-1900
William Morris, *President*
EMP: 9 **EST:** 2014
SQ FT: 55,000
SALES (est): 459.8K **Privately Held**
SIC: 2099 Food preparations

(G-6762)
SHARK SIGNS OF NE FL INC
5317 Shen Ave (32205-4757)
PHONE.................................904 766-6222
Donny Cagle, *President*
Christopher Miller, *General Mgr*
EMP: 9 **EST:** 2014
SALES (est): 869.9K **Privately Held**
WEB: www.sharksignsofnefl.com
SIC: 3993 Electric signs

(G-6763)
SHAWS STHERN BLLE FRZ FODS IN
821 Virginia St (32208-4950)
P.O. Box 28620 (32226-8620)
PHONE.................................904 768-1591
Howard Shaw, *President*
John R Shaw Jr, *Exec VP*
Joanne Zimmerman, *CFO*
▲ **EMP:** 100 **EST:** 1934
SQ FT: 105,000
SALES (est): 29.2MM
SALES (corp-wide): 51.9MM **Privately Held**
WEB: www.shawsouthernbelle.com
SIC: 2092 5963 8742 Seafoods, fresh: prepared; direct selling establishments; management consulting services
PA: Southern Belle Frozen Foods Inc
821 Virginia St
Jacksonville FL 32208
904 768-1591

(G-6764)
SHERMANS WELDING & MAINTENCE
6299 Powers Ave Ste 3 (32217-2287)
PHONE.................................904 731-3460
Art Sherman, *President*
Alice Sherman, *President*
Craig Sherman, *Vice Pres*
EMP: 10 **EST:** 1981
SALES (est): 461.4K **Privately Held**
WEB: www.swm.inc.angelfire.com
SIC: 7692 Welding repair

(G-6765)
SHIPPING + BUSINESS SVCS LLC
Also Called: SBS Promotional Solutions
12627 San Jose Blvd Ste 5 (32223-2662)
P.O. Box 54593 (32245-4593)
PHONE.................................904 240-1737
Randall Smith,
EMP: 7 **EST:** 2008
SALES (est): 198.4K **Privately Held**
WEB: www.rsstores.net
SIC: 3993 7389 7313 7319 Signs & advertising specialties; embroidering of advertising on shirts, etc.; printed media advertising representatives; poster advertising service, except outdoor; poster advertising, outdoor

(G-6766)
SHORELINE PLASTICS LLC
7167 Old Kings Rd (32219-3727)
PHONE.................................904 696-2981
Mark A Porter,
Mark Porter,
▼ **EMP:** 20 **EST:** 2006
SQ FT: 30,000
SALES (est): 5.5MM **Privately Held**
WEB: www.shorelineplastics.com
SIC: 3089 Extruded finished plastic products

(G-6767)
SHRIJI SWAMI LLC
Also Called: Monument Pharmacy
1301 Monument Rd Ste 22 (32225-6462)
PHONE.................................904 727-3434
M Patel,
EMP: 12 **EST:** 2010
SALES (est): 1.1MM **Privately Held**
WEB: www.monumentrx.com
SIC: 2834 5122 Pharmaceutical preparations; pharmaceuticals

(G-6768)
SHUTTERS WHOLESALE
9440 Philips Hwy Ste 12 (32256-1339)
PHONE.................................770 410-9525
Jennifer Wright, *Manager*
EMP: 6 **EST:** 2012
SALES (est): 75.3K **Privately Held**
SIC: 2431 Door shutters, wood

(G-6769)
SIGMA EXTRUDING CORP
Also Called: Coastal Films of Florida
627 Lane Ave N (32254-2822)
PHONE.................................904 786-2031
EMP: 6 **Privately Held**
SIC: 2673 Mfg Bags-Plastic/Coated Paper
HQ: Sigma Extruding Corp.
808 Page Ave Bldg 8
Lyndhurst NJ 07071
201 933-5353

(G-6770)
SIGN A RAMA INC
Also Called: Sign-A-Rama
3633 Southside Blvd (32216-4635)
PHONE.................................904 998-8880
Cheri Vianello, *Owner*
▲ **EMP:** 5 **EST:** 2008
SALES (est): 402.9K **Privately Held**
WEB: www.signarama.com
SIC: 3993 Signs & advertising specialties

(G-6771)
SIGN PRO AMERICA
3811 University Blvd W # 37 (32217-1210)
PHONE.................................412 908-9832
EMP: 10 **EST:** 2011
SALES (est): 554.7K **Privately Held**
WEB: www.signproamerica.com
SIC: 3993 Signs & advertising specialties

(G-6772)
SIGNLINE SIGNS & ELECTRICAL
562 King St (32204-3006)
PHONE.................................904 388-9474
Sameul Storey, *President*
Debbie Rizer, *Corp Secy*
EMP: 5 **EST:** 1993
SQ FT: 6,500
SALES (est): 973.1K **Privately Held**
SIC: 3993 Neon signs; signs, not made in custom sign painting shops

(G-6773)
SIGNSHARKS SIGN SERVICE
7030 N Main St (32208-4730)
PHONE.................................904 766-6222
Donny Cagle, *President*
Christopher Miller, *General Mgr*
Amber Raulerson, *Info Tech Mgr*
EMP: 9 **EST:** 1997
SQ FT: 2,282
SALES (est): 551K **Privately Held**
WEB: www.sharksignsofnefl.com
SIC: 3993 Electric signs

(G-6774)
SILVERMAN FENCE MFG INC
4698 Dusk Ct (32207-7951)
PHONE.................................904 730-0882
Lynda Silverman, *President*
EMP: 8 **EST:** 1984
SQ FT: 10,000
SALES (est): 650K **Privately Held**
WEB: www.silvermanfence.net
SIC: 2499 1799 Fencing, wood; fence construction

(G-6775)
SILVERSHORE PARTNERS LLC
Also Called: Profilegorilla
10175 Fortune Pkwy # 60 (32256-6746)
PHONE.................................904 562-0812
Edward Baldwin, *Partner*
Edward B Baldwin, *Principal*
Davis Joel, *Manager*
EMP: 10 **EST:** 2012
SALES (est): 1.2MM **Privately Held**
SIC: 7372 Business oriented computer software

(G-6776)
SIMMONDS PRECISION PDTS INC
Also Called: UTC Aerospace Systems
6061 Goodrich Blvd (32226-3402)
PHONE.................................904 757-3660
Justin Robert Keppy, *President*
Thomas Pollack, *Engineer*
Colleen Lott, *Treasurer*
Candace A Kronholm, *Director*
Alexandra McHugh, *Admin Sec*
EMP: 23 **EST:** 2013
SALES (est): 6.3MM **Privately Held**
SIC: 3728 3724 Aircraft assemblies, subassemblies & parts; engine mount parts, aircraft

(G-6777)
SIMPSON SCREENS INC
11458 Harlan Dr (32218-4052)
PHONE.................................904 757-1498
EMP: 10
SALES (est): 976.4K **Privately Held**
SIC: 3442 Mfg Metal Doors/Sash/Trim

(G-6778)
SIPP TECHNOLOGIES LLC
5245 Old Kings Rd (32254-1126)
PHONE.................................904 374-5606
Hector Colon, *Senior Engr*
Brian Augustine, *CFO*
Kent Weisenberg,
James Tadtman,
EMP: 30 **EST:** 2016
SQ FT: 140,000
SALES (est): 4.5MM **Privately Held**
WEB: www.sipptech.com
SIC: 3531 Construction machinery

(G-6779)
SKIPPER WRIGHT INC
Also Called: I R Bowen & Sons
634 Dyal St (32206-3916)
PHONE.................................904 354-4381
Benjamin W Wright, *President*
▲ **EMP:** 16 **EST:** 1992
SQ FT: 10,000
SALES (est): 622K **Privately Held**
WEB: www.irbowen.com
SIC: 3312 Wheels, locomotive & car: iron & steel

(G-6780)
SMART STREAM INC
13500 Sutton Park Dr S # 7 (32224-5251)
PHONE.................................904 223-1511
John Thompson, *Officer*
EMP: 13 **EST:** 1999
SALES (est): 64.3K **Privately Held**
SIC: 2024 Ice cream & frozen desserts

(G-6781)
SMOKERS VIDEO IV (PA)
10150 Beach Blvd (32246-4700)
PHONE.................................904 646-1324
Stephen Bridges, *Principal*
EMP: 6 **EST:** 2009
SALES (est): 722.4K **Privately Held**
WEB: www.mysmokecity.com
SIC: 3999 Cigarette & cigar products & accessories

(G-6782)
SOFT PLASTICS FLORIDA INC
2148 Ellis Rd N (32254-1618)
PHONE.................................904 338-9680
Wayne Smith, *Managing Prtnr*
Mark Nichols, *Partner*
EMP: 6 **EST:** 2003
SALES (est): 633K **Privately Held**
SIC: 3089 Injection molding of plastics

(G-6783)
SOLAR ENTERPRISES INC
Also Called: Brown Enterprises
8841 Corporate Square Ct (32216-1981)
P.O. Box 8241 (32239-0241)
PHONE.................................904 724-2262
Ed Brown, *President*
Nancy R Brown, *Corp Secy*
Linda J Brown, *Vice Pres*
Pam Ricard, *Vice Pres*
Lauren Coghlan, *Project Mgr*
EMP: 34 **EST:** 1969
SQ FT: 10,000
SALES (est): 3.1MM **Privately Held**
SIC: 3993 Signs & advertising specialties

(G-6784)
SONSHINE DIGITAL GRAPHICS INC
Also Called: Minuteman Press
2752 Park St (32205-7608)
PHONE.................................904 858-1000
M Lee Curtis, *President*
Jon Curtis, *Vice Pres*

▲ = Import ▼=Export
◆ =Import/Export

Jonathan D Curtis, *Vice Pres*
EMP: 17 **EST:** 2013
SQ FT: 4,500
SALES (est): 1.2MM **Privately Held**
WEB: www.minutemanjax.com
SIC: 2752 7336 Commercial printing, lithographic; commercial art & graphic design

(G-6785)
SOUTHEAST ATLANTIC BEV CORP
6001 Bowdendale Ave (32216-6041)
PHONE..................................904 731-3644
Robert H Paul III, *Ch of Bd*
Christpher Y Paul, *President*
Guy Jackson, *CFO*
◆ **EMP:** 301 **EST:** 1939
SQ FT: 4,200
SALES (est): 6.9MM **Publicly Held**
WEB: www.seabev.com
SIC: 2086 Soft drinks: packaged in cans, bottles, etc.
HQ: Dr Pepper/Seven Up, Inc.
6425 Hall Of Fame Ln
Frisco TX 75034
972 673-7000

(G-6786)
SOUTHEAST CLINICAL RES LLC
6817 Sthpint Pkwy Ste 902 (32216)
PHONE..................................904 296-3260
Tammy Parrott,
Karen Johnson,
EMP: 10 **EST:** 2006
SALES (est): 877.4K **Privately Held**
WEB: www.southeastclinical.webpropulsion.com
SIC: 3821 Clinical laboratory instruments, except medical & dental

(G-6787)
SOUTHEAST INTL CHEM CO INC
221 N Hogan St 230 (32202-4201)
PHONE..................................904 992-4007
Ken Mattiace, *President*
◆ **EMP:** 6 **EST:** 2014
SALES (est): 652.1K **Privately Held**
SIC: 2899 Insulating compounds

(G-6788)
SOUTHEAST WINDOW COVERINGS
6900 Philips Hwy Ste 46 (32216-6060)
PHONE..................................904 372-0326
Chase Sams, *Executive*
EMP: 8 **EST:** 2009
SALES (est): 63.1K **Privately Held**
SIC: 2591 Drapery hardware & blinds & shades

(G-6789)
SOUTHEASTERN ALUMINUM PDTS LLC
4925 Bulls Bay Hwy (32219-3250)
P.O. Box 6427 (32236-6427)
PHONE..................................800 243-8200
Patrick Dussinger, *Mng Member*
EMP: 6 **EST:** 1952
SALES (est): 96.9K **Privately Held**
WEB: www.southeasternaluminum.com
SIC: 3231 Doors, glass: made from purchased glass

(G-6790)
SOUTHEASTERN ORNAMENTAL IRON
11307 Distribution Ave E (32256-2738)
PHONE..................................904 292-0933
James Green, *President*
Bobby Green, *Vice Pres*
Judy Rhodes, *Admin Sec*
▼ **EMP:** 33 **EST:** 1971
SQ FT: 7,000
SALES (est): 5.6MM **Privately Held**
WEB: www.southeasternornamental.com
SIC: 3446 Architectural metalwork

(G-6791)
SOUTHEASTERN PALLETS INC
2203 W Beaver St (32209-7404)
P.O. Box 92 (32234-0092)
PHONE..................................904 783-8363
Brett Griffis, *Vice Pres*
EMP: 7 **EST:** 2004
SQ FT: 2,474
SALES (est): 500K **Privately Held**
SIC: 2448 Pallets, wood

(G-6792)
SOUTHEASTERN PEGBOARD PRINTERS
Also Called: Pegbroad Data System
2750 Dawn Rd (32207-7904)
PHONE..................................904 731-0357
Steve Edenfield, *President*
EMP: 5 **EST:** 1971
SQ FT: 14,000
SALES (est): 665.5K **Privately Held**
SIC: 2761 5044 Unit sets (manifold business forms); accounting machines, excluding machine program readable type

(G-6793)
SOUTHERN BALLOON WORKS INC
11653 Central Pkwy # 209 (32224-2710)
PHONE..................................727 388-8360
Tom Macnaughton, *President*
EMP: 5
SQ FT: 1,800
SALES (est): 450K **Privately Held**
WEB: www.southernballoonworks.com
SIC: 2211 Balloon cloth, cotton

(G-6794)
SOUTHERN FIBERGLASS INC
41 Spring St (32254-4087)
PHONE..................................904 387-2246
James R Rowand, *President*
James Rowand, *President*
Don A Rowand, *Vice Pres*
EMP: 10 **EST:** 1971
SQ FT: 7,000
SALES (est): 693.9K **Privately Held**
WEB: www.southernfiberglass.com
SIC: 3599 3732 3728 3523 Machine shop, jobbing & repair; boat building & repairing; aircraft parts & equipment; farm machinery & equipment; laminated plastics plate & sheet

(G-6795)
SOUTHERN LBR & TREATING CO INC
1433 Lane Cir E (32254-2239)
P.O. Box 7450 (32238-0450)
PHONE..................................904 695-0784
William Sumner, *President*
Eddy Bryan, *Chief Mktg Ofcr*
EMP: 11 **EST:** 1988
SQ FT: 7,000
SALES (est): 1.7MM **Privately Held**
WEB: www.southern-lumber.com
SIC: 2491 Wood preserving

(G-6796)
SOUTHERN RECREATION INC
4060 Edison Ave (32254-4108)
PHONE..................................904 387-4390
Terry Rogers, *President*
Tim Norton, *Vice Pres*
Sue Box, *Office Mgr*
EMP: 10 **EST:** 1985
SQ FT: 4,000
SALES (est): 1MM **Privately Held**
WEB: www.southernrecreation.com
SIC: 3949 1799 Playground equipment; playground construction & equipment installation

(G-6797)
SOUTHERN SURGICAL CONSULTANTS
11653 Central Pkwy # 201 (32224-2711)
PHONE..................................904 296-7828
Kent Adams, *President*
EMP: 5 **EST:** 1996
SALES (est): 362.5K **Privately Held**
SIC: 3842 Foot appliances, orthopedic

(G-6798)
SOUTHERN TECHNOLOGIES
Also Called: Honeywell Authorized Dealer
270 Us Highway 90 E (32234-1902)
PHONE..................................904 266-2100
Marty Hanks, *Owner*
EMP: 24 **EST:** 2009
SALES (est): 7.1MM **Privately Held**
SIC: 3585 Parts for heating, cooling & refrigerating equipment

(G-6799)
SOUTHERN WHEEL & RIM INC
1044 Lane Ave S (32205-4709)
P.O. Box 37028 (32236-7028)
PHONE..................................904 786-7542
Olin P Joiner, *President*
Roy Hawkins, *Treasurer*
Mike Wilson, *Consultant*
▲ **EMP:** 18 **EST:** 1979
SQ FT: 15,000
SALES (est): 2.6MM **Privately Held**
WEB: www.southernwheel-rim.com
SIC: 3714 Wheels, motor vehicle

(G-6800)
SOUTHSTERN STNLESS FABRICATORS
Also Called: Florida Georgia Welding Supply
634 Dyal St (32206-3916)
PHONE..................................904 354-4381
Teresa Moore, *President*
Douglas Moore, *Director*
Larry Rolfe, *Director*
EMP: 10 **EST:** 2004
SQ FT: 10,000
SALES (est): 1.7MM **Privately Held**
WEB: www.irbowen.com
SIC: 3441 Fabricated structural metal

(G-6801)
SPACELABS HEALTHCARE INC
Also Called: Statcorp Medical
14476 Duval Pl W Ste 303 (32218-9414)
PHONE..................................904 786-5113
EMP: 35
SALES (corp-wide): 906.7MM **Publicly Held**
SIC: 3841 Surgical And Medical Instruments
HQ: Spacelabs Healthcare, Inc.
35301 Se Center St
Snoqualmie WA 98065
425 396-3302

(G-6802)
SPAULDING CUSTOM CABINETS
11857 Duval Rd (32218-3333)
PHONE..................................904 768-4640
Kenneth Spaulding Sr, *Owner*
EMP: 5 **EST:** 2000
SALES (est): 400K **Privately Held**
SIC: 2434 Wood kitchen cabinets

(G-6803)
SPECIAL TOOL SOLUTIONS INC
11699 Camden Rd (32218-3901)
P.O. Box 40585 (32203-0585)
PHONE..................................904 356-5671
John Snead, *President*
EMP: 47 **EST:** 2000
SQ FT: 10,000
SALES (est): 7MM **Privately Held**
SIC: 3599 Custom machinery

(G-6804)
SPECIALTY TANK AND EQP CO
857 Robinson Ave (32209-7559)
P.O. Box 2370 (32203-2370)
PHONE..................................904 353-8761
▼ **EMP:** 7 **EST:** 1940
SQ FT: 30,000
SALES (est): 1.2MM **Privately Held**
SIC: 3443 Mfg Fabricated Plate Work

(G-6805)
SPLASH OF COLOR LLC
2885 Starshire Cv (32257-5801)
PHONE..................................732 735-3090
Natalie Dayan, *Branch Mgr*
EMP: 17
SALES (corp-wide): 73.2K **Privately Held**
SIC: 2759 Screen printing
PA: Splash Of Color Llc
14701 Bartrm Pk Blvd
Jacksonville FL

(G-6806)
ST JOHNS BKY & GOURMET FD CO (PA)
Also Called: Truffles Coffee House & Bakery
6301 Powers Ave (32217-2217)
PHONE..................................813 727-3528
Peter A Podes, *President*
Angelo P Podes, *Principal*
Susan W Podes, *Exec VP*
EMP: 17
SQ FT: 4,800
SALES (est): 1.1MM **Privately Held**
SIC: 2051 Bakery: wholesale or wholesale/retail combined

(G-6807)
STAMPCO INC
2930 Mercury Rd (32207-7913)
PHONE..................................904 737-6144
Kenneth L Parmenter, *President*
Dorothy Decker, *Corp Secy*
James A Parmenter, *Vice Pres*
EMP: 10 **EST:** 1973
SQ FT: 18,000
SALES (est): 1.7MM **Privately Held**
SIC: 3444 5063 Sheet metalwork; wire & cable

(G-6808)
STANDARD PRECAST INC
12300 Presidents Ct (32220-3225)
P.O. Box 61839 (32236-1839)
PHONE..................................904 268-0466
Barbara L Peterson, *President*
Roger Cole, *General Mgr*
Russell A Smith, *Vice Pres*
▲ **EMP:** 80 **EST:** 1965
SALES (est): 17.2MM
SALES (corp-wide): 27.5B **Privately Held**
WEB: www.standardprecast.com
SIC: 3272 Manhole covers or frames, concrete; sewer pipe, concrete
HQ: Oldcastle Infrastructure, Inc.
7000 Central Pkwy Ste 800
Atlanta GA 30328
770 270-5000

(G-6809)
STAR FABRICATORS
989 Imeson Park Blvd (32218-4903)
PHONE..................................904 899-6569
Peter Wu, *Principal*
EMP: 6 **EST:** 2010
SALES (est): 120.4K **Privately Held**
SIC: 3441 Fabricated structural metal

(G-6810)
STATCORP INC
7037 Commonwealth Ave (32220-2857)
PHONE..................................904 786-5113
EMP: 8 **EST:** 2015
SALES (est): 173.7K **Privately Held**
WEB: www.statcorpinc.com
SIC: 3841 Surgical & medical instruments

(G-6811)
STENNER PUMP COMPANY INC (PA)
3174 Desalvo Rd (32246-3733)
PHONE..................................904 641-1666
Ben Ware, *Partner*
Michael Kincid, *CFO*
Jimmy Draughn, *Manager*
Angela Galane, *Manager*
Randy Dorsey, *Technical Staff*
▲ **EMP:** 103 **EST:** 1957
SQ FT: 55,000
SALES (est): 28MM **Privately Held**
WEB: www.stenner.com
SIC: 3561 3586 Pump jacks & other pumping equipment; measuring & dispensing pumps

(G-6812)
STEPHENS ADVERTISING INC
7029 Commwl Ave Ste 9 (32220)
PHONE..................................904 354-7004
Ruth Ann Hicks, *President*
EMP: 5 **EST:** 1978
SQ FT: 15,000
SALES (est): 491K **Privately Held**
WEB: www.stephensjax.com
SIC: 3993 Electric signs

(G-6813)
STERITOOL INC
2376 Lake Shore Blvd (32210-4026)
PHONE..................................904 388-3672
Stephen Rountree, *President*
Adam Rountree, *Vice Pres*
◆ **EMP:** 10 **EST:** 2005
SQ FT: 30,000
SALES (est): 995.8K **Privately Held**
WEB: www.steritool.com
SIC: 3423 Hand & edge tools

(G-6814)
STINNER PUMP COMPANY
11201 St Johns Indstrl Pa (32246-7443)
PHONE..................................904 329-2098
EMP: 7 **EST:** 2013
SALES (est): 151.3K **Privately Held**
WEB: www.stenner.com
SIC: 3561 Pumps & pumping equipment

(G-6815)
STITCHEZ LLC
13714 Longs Landing Rd W (32225-5423)
PHONE..................................904 221-9148
Sebastian Stanciu, *Principal*
EMP: 6 **EST:** 2016
SALES (est): 95.5K **Privately Held**
SIC: 2395 Embroidery & art needlework

(G-6816)
STITCHING HEART LLC
8174 Lexington Dr (32208-2843)
PHONE..................................904 379-7990
Chris Davis, *Principal*
EMP: 6 **EST:** 2013
SALES (est): 57.1K **Privately Held**
SIC: 2395 Embroidery & art needlework

(G-6817)
STORMFORCE JACKSONVILLE LLC
3030 Hartley Rd Ste 210 (32257-8208)
PHONE..................................904 288-6639
Becky Manderson, *CFO*
Keith Manderson, *Sales Staff*
Dillon Mavrich, *Sales Staff*
Rebecca Manderson, *Mng Member*
Debbie Barket, *Recruiter*
EMP: 6 **EST:** 2011
SALES (est): 1.8MM **Privately Held**
WEB: www.stormforce.com
SIC: 2952 Roofing felts, cements or coatings

(G-6818)
STRATTON INC DM
7653 Bayard Blvd (32256-2406)
PHONE..................................904 268-6052
Dillon M Stratton, *President*
EMP: 6 **EST:** 1988
SALES (est): 597.9K **Privately Held**
WEB: www.retirementteam.com
SIC: 2411 Pulpwood contractors engaged in cutting

(G-6819)
STRYKER ORTHOPEDICS
7014 A C Skinner Pkwy (32256-6959)
PHONE..................................904 296-6000
John Bowers, *President*
M Kathryn Kat Fink, *Vice Pres*
Dana McMahon, *Vice Pres*
George Knoblach, *Regl Sales Mgr*
David Dubish, *Sales Staff*
EMP: 7 **EST:** 1986
SQ FT: 1,600
SALES (est): 742.3K **Privately Held**
SIC: 3841 Surgical & medical instruments

(G-6820)
STYLORS INC
640 W 41st St (32206-6235)
PHONE..................................904 765-4453
Michael A Kersun, *President*
Sam Kersun, *Corp Secy*
Mirian Kersun, *Vice Pres*
EMP: 19 **EST:** 1935
SQ FT: 29,000
SALES (est): 1.2MM **Privately Held**
WEB: www.stylors.com
SIC: 2844 3999 2221 Home permanent kits; hair curlers, designed for beauty parlors; broadwoven fabric mills, manmade

(G-6821)
SUN SCREEN PRINT INC
4849 Dawin Rd Ste 3 (32207-9528)
PHONE..................................904 674-0520
David E Fitzsimmons, *President*
Melissa Long, *Vice Pres*
EMP: 6 **EST:** 2005
SALES (est): 509.5K **Privately Held**
WEB: www.sunscreenprint.com
SIC: 2752 Commercial printing, offset

(G-6822)
SUNOPTIC TECHNOLOGIES LLC (PA)
6018 Bowdendale Ave (32216-6042)
PHONE..................................877 677-2832
Craig Stevens, *Vice Pres*
Bryant Thigpen, *Opers Mgr*
Closson Brandon, *Purch Agent*
Jose Galarza, *Engineer*
Rick Mahoney, *Engineer*
◆ **EMP:** 98
SALES (est): 11.7MM **Privately Held**
WEB: www.sunopticsurgical.com
SIC: 3827 3841 3823 3843 Optical instruments & lenses; surgical & medical instruments; industrial instrmnts msrmnt display/control process variable; dental equipment & supplies; products of purchased glass; medical & hospital equipment

(G-6823)
SUNRISE FOODS LLC
4520 Swilcan Bridge Ln N (32224-5617)
PHONE..................................904 613-4756
Bradley R Dermond, *Principal*
EMP: 6 **EST:** 2012
SALES (est): 592.4K **Privately Held**
SIC: 2099 Food preparations

(G-6824)
SUNSET POWER INC
Also Called: Solarenergy.com
5191 Shawland Rd (32254-1649)
PHONE..................................866 485-2757
◆ **EMP:** 16
SQ FT: 25,000
SALES (est): 2.4MM **Privately Held**
SIC: 3433 5074 Mfg Heating Equipment-Nonelectric Whol Plumbing Equipment/Supplies

(G-6825)
SUNSHINE ORGANICS COMPOST LLC
Also Called: Compost Jax
6478 Buffalo Ave (32208-4810)
PHONE..................................904 900-3072
Mike Kelcourse, *Principal*
Michael Kelcourse, *Principal*
EMP: 5 **EST:** 2019
SALES (est): 437.7K **Privately Held**
SIC: 2875 Fertilizers, mixing only

(G-6826)
SUNSHINE PACKING & NOODLE CO
Also Called: Chen, Chao Ming Company.
57 Cantee St (32204-1701)
PHONE..................................904 355-7561
Chao Chen, *President*
Bill H Chen, *Vice Pres*
EMP: 8 **EST:** 1982
SALES (est): 848.5K **Privately Held**
SIC: 2099 Sauces: dry mixes; spices, including grinding

(G-6827)
SUNWYRE INC
4251 Monument Rd Apt 203 (32225-4622)
PHONE..................................904 631-6961
Victor Dorsten, *President*
EMP: 12 **EST:** 2005
SALES (est): 207.2K **Privately Held**
WEB: www.sunwyre.com
SIC: 3674 Magnetohydrodynamic (MHD) devices

(G-6828)
SUPERIOR MILLWORK COMPANY INC
501 E 27th St (32206-2212)
P.O. Box 3321 (32206-0321)
PHONE..................................904 355-5676
Francis Polly III, *President*
Jennifer Polly, *Admin Sec*
EMP: 15 **EST:** 1941
SQ FT: 16,560
SALES (est): 2.2MM **Privately Held**
WEB: www.superiormillworkcompany.com
SIC: 2431 Woodwork, interior & ornamental

(G-6829)
SUPERIOR PAVERS AND STONE LLC
731 Duval Station Rd # 107 (32218-0800)
PHONE..................................904 887-7831
Rex Williams, *Principal*
EMP: 6 **EST:** 2008
SALES (est): 461.3K **Privately Held**
SIC: 3531 Pavers

(G-6830)
SWISHER INTERNATIONAL INC (DH)
459 E 16th St (32206-3025)
P.O. Box 2230 (32203-2230)
PHONE..................................904 353-4311
Peter J Ghiloni, *President*
Kyle Nugent, *Regional Mgr*
Tim Neas, *Dept Chairman*
Lou Caldropoli, *Vice Pres*
Louis A Caldropoli, *Vice Pres*
◆ **EMP:** 1 **EST:** 1966
SALES (est): 37.1MM **Privately Held**
WEB: www.swisher.com
SIC: 2121 Cigars
HQ: Swisher International Group Inc.
20 Thorndal Cir
Darien CT 06820
203 656-8000

(G-6831)
SWISHER INTL GROUP INC
14425 Duval Rd (32218-2473)
PHONE..................................904 353-4311
Carl Trammell, *Branch Mgr*
EMP: 608 **Privately Held**
WEB: www.swisher.com
SIC: 2131 Smoking tobacco
HQ: Swisher International Group Inc.
20 Thorndal Cir
Darien CT 06820
203 656-8000

(G-6832)
SY-KLONE COMPANY LLC
Also Called: Sy-Klone International
4390 Imeson Rd (32219-5314)
PHONE..................................904 448-6563
Dana Cain, *Purchasing*
Rich Uhrie, *Engineer*
Courtney Levine, *Accountant*
Robert Hair, *Human Resources*
Bonalyn Boyd, *Marketing Staff*
EMP: 44 **EST:** 2017
SQ FT: 62,587
SALES (est): 5MM **Privately Held**
WEB: www.sy-klone.com
SIC: 3599 3564 Machine & other job shop work; blowers & fans
PA: Sy-Klone Holdings Incorporated
4390 Imeson Rd
Jacksonville FL 32219

(G-6833)
SYMRISE INC
Also Called: Aroma Chemicals
601 Crestwood St (32208-4476)
PHONE..................................904 768-5800
Michael Klamm, *Branch Mgr*
EMP: 150 **Privately Held**
WEB: www.symrise.com
SIC: 2869 Industrial organic chemicals
HQ: Symrise Inc.
300 North St
Teterboro NJ 07608
201 288-3200

(G-6834)
TAKERIA MIX INC
6680 Powers Ave Ste 108 (32217-8807)
PHONE..................................904 338-9157
Martha L Navarro, *Vice Pres*
EMP: 12 **EST:** 2005
SALES (est): 525.6K **Privately Held**
WEB: www.takeria-mix-jacksonville.business.site
SIC: 3273 Ready-mixed concrete

(G-6835)
TALENT ASSESSMENT INC
Also Called: Borden, Ben Talent Assessment
6838 Phillips Pkwy Dr S (32256-1564)
P.O. Box 5087 (32247-5087)
PHONE..................................904 260-4102
Ben P Borden, *President*
Rebekkah Swisher, *Sales Staff*
Lori Groos, *Creative Dir*
Jamie Coker, *Representative*
Wendy Juenger, *Representative*
EMP: 7 **EST:** 1980
SQ FT: 8,100
SALES (est): 600K **Privately Held**
WEB: www.talentassessment.com
SIC: 3999 Education aids, devices & supplies

(G-6836)
TAMPA ARMATURE WORKS INC
Also Called: Taw Jacksonville Service Ctr
10520 Busch Dr N (32218-5604)
PHONE..................................904 757-7790
Caroline Turner, *Vice Pres*
Rocco Day, *Project Mgr*
George Guillen, *Opers Mgr*
Colin Smith, *Production*
Juan Hernandez, *Engineer*
EMP: 80
SQ FT: 66,788
SALES (corp-wide): 169.6MM **Privately Held**
WEB: www.tawinc.com
SIC: 7694 5063 Electric motor repair; motors, electric
PA: Tampa Armature Works, Inc.
6312 S 78th St
Riverview FL 33578
813 621-5661

(G-6837)
TAMPA FORK LIFT INC
7033 Commonwealth Ave (32220-2851)
PHONE..................................904 674-6899
EMP: 10
SALES (corp-wide): 14.1MM **Privately Held**
WEB: www.floridaforklift.com
SIC: 3537 Forklift trucks
PA: Tampa Fork Lift, Inc.
3221 N 40th St
Tampa FL 33605
813 623-5251

(G-6838)
TANDJTEESANDCUSTOMIZATIONS
13475 Atlantic Blvd Ste 8 (32225-3290)
PHONE..................................904 901-9227
Tarsha Copeland, *CEO*
EMP: 6 **EST:** 2018
SALES (est): 80K **Privately Held**
SIC: 2759 Screen printing

(G-6839)
TAYLOR SIGN & DESIGN INC
4162 Saint Augustine Rd (32207-6618)
PHONE..................................904 396-4652
Randy Taylor, *President*
Ken May, *General Mgr*
Damon Katsikas, *Sales Staff*
Chris Taylor, *Sales Associate*
Tom Brannon, *Marketing Staff*
EMP: 19 **EST:** 1928
SQ FT: 2,500
SALES (est): 3.5MM **Privately Held**
WEB: www.taylorsignco.com
SIC: 3993 Electric signs

(G-6840)
TAYLOR-COTTON-RIDLEY INC
4873 Victor St (32207-7971)
PHONE..................................904 733-8373
James L Ridley Jr, *Branch Mgr*
Julie Rich, *Admin Asst*
EMP: 58
SQ FT: 10,080
SALES (corp-wide): 15.6MM **Privately Held**
WEB: www.taylorcottonridley.com
SIC: 2431 Door frames, wood
PA: Taylor-Cotton-Ridley, Inc.
4410 Sw 35th Ter
Gainesville FL 32608
352 378-1608

(G-6841)
TEC COMPOSITES INC
10615 New Kings Rd (32219-2129)
PHONE..................................904 765-6502
EMP: 10 **EST:** 2019

SALES (est): 546K Privately Held
WEB: www.teccomposites.com
SIC: 2821 Plastics materials & resins

(G-6842)
TECHNCAL PNTG JACKSONVILLE INC
1401 Wheels Rd Bldg 3 (32218-9408)
PHONE..................................904 652-1129
Shoji Mori, *Principal*
Toshiji Yamanaka, *Vice Pres*
Takanori Mori, *Admin Sec*
EMP: 37 EST: 2003
SQ FT: 23,000
SALES (est): 4.1MM Privately Held
WEB: www.totsuka-ltd.com
SIC: 2851 Undercoatings, paint
PA: Totsuka Sogyo Co.,Ltd.
6400-15, Nishiobuchi
Kakegawa SZO 437-1

(G-6843)
TECHNLOGY INTEGRATION SVCS LLC
4600 Touchton Rd E # 1150 (32246-8299)
PHONE..................................904 565-4050
Tim Stickelmaier, *Mng Member*
EMP: 6 EST: 2010
SALES (est): 635.1K Privately Held
WEB: www.tecisusa.com
SIC: 3357 Building wire & cable, nonferrous

(G-6844)
TECTRON
546 Ellis Rd S (32254-3555)
PHONE..................................904 355-5512
Michael Jackson, *Owner*
EMP: 12 EST: 2007
SALES (est): 406.1K Privately Held
WEB: www.tectron.net
SIC: 3599 Bellows, industrial: metal

(G-6845)
TECTRON ENGINEERING COMPANY (PA)
Also Called: Tectron Metal Detection
5820 Commonwealth Ave (32254-2206)
PHONE..................................904 394-0683
Michael Jackson, *President*
Michael A Jackson, *President*
▲ EMP: 10 EST: 1968
SQ FT: 11,200
SALES (est): 1.6MM Privately Held
WEB: www.tectron.net
SIC: 3669 3829 Metal detectors; measuring & controlling devices

(G-6846)
TELEIOS MANUFACTURING INC
8940 Western Way Ste 15 (32256-0329)
PHONE..................................904 490-0600
EMP: 8 EST: 2019
SALES (est): 809.4K Privately Held
WEB: www.teleiosmfg.com
SIC: 3812 Aircraft/aerospace flight instruments & guidance systems

(G-6847)
TERRA NOVA PVERS HRDSCAPE SLTO
7095 Stonelion Cir (32256-6048)
PHONE..................................904 662-2999
Rodrigo C Herreros, *President*
EMP: 7 EST: 2012
SALES (est): 247.8K Privately Held
SIC: 2951 Asphalt paving mixtures & blocks

(G-6848)
THERMAL CONVERSION TECH INC
101 Copeland St (32204-1803)
PHONE..................................904 358-3720
Steven K Gorman, *CEO*
▼ EMP: 26 EST: 1979
SALES (est): 562.5K Privately Held
SIC: 3433 Solar heaters & collectors

(G-6849)
THOMPSON AWNING & SHUTTER CO
2036 Evergreen Ave (32206-3978)
P.O. Box 3478 (32206-0478)
PHONE..................................904 355-1616
Bob O'Brien, *President*
Carol O'Brien, *Vice Pres*
EMP: 24 EST: 1920
SQ FT: 7,000
SALES (est): 1.2MM Privately Held
WEB: www.thompsonawning.com
SIC: 2591 2394 3444 Blinds vertical; awnings, fabric: made from purchased materials; awnings, sheet metal

(G-6850)
THOMPSON REPAIRS INC
4857 Dignan St (32254-3791)
P.O. Box 37922 (32236-7922)
PHONE..................................904 384-5175
Stephen Thompson III, *President*
Nina L Thompson, *Corp Secy*
EMP: 7 EST: 1987
SQ FT: 12,000
SALES (est): 912.9K Privately Held
WEB: www.thompsonrepairs.com
SIC: 3599 Machine shop, jobbing & repair

(G-6851)
THREAD AND INK
4629 Trevor Creek Dr N (32257-8673)
PHONE..................................904 568-9688
Paul Whittaker, *Principal*
EMP: 6 EST: 2001
SQ FT: 2,143
SALES (est): 98.1K Privately Held
WEB: www.threadandink.net
SIC: 2759 Screen printing

(G-6852)
THREE CAY G LLC
5121 Bowden Rd Ste 107 (32216-5929)
PHONE..................................904 930-4554
Barbara Johnson, *Principal*
EMP: 5 EST: 2018
SALES (est): 368.4K Privately Held
WEB: www.3cayg.com
SIC: 2844 Toilet preparations

(G-6853)
THREEZ COMPANY LLC (PA)
1225 W Beaver St Ste 123 (32204-1415)
PHONE..................................904 422-9224
Hanan Furqan, *CEO*
Zakee Furqan, *COO*
▼ EMP: 5 EST: 2011
SQ FT: 1,000
SALES: 3.9MM Privately Held
WEB: www.threezsupplies.com
SIC: 2676 5099 5087 Towels, napkins & tissue paper products; safety equipment & supplies; cleaning & maintenance equipment & supplies; restaurant supplies

(G-6854)
THREEZ COMPANY LLC
7232 Smyrna St (32208-3343)
PHONE..................................904 651-1444
Hanan Furqan, *CEO*
EMP: 6
SALES (corp-wide): 3.9MM Privately Held
WEB: www.threezsupplies.com
SIC: 2676 5087 5099 Towels, napkins & tissue paper products; cleaning & maintenance equipment & supplies; restaurant supplies; safety equipment & supplies
PA: Threez Company Llc
1225 W Beaver St Ste 123
Jacksonville FL 32204
904 422-9224

(G-6855)
TIER5 TECHNICAL SERVICES
Also Called: Jacksonville Cyber Defense
16167 Kayla Cove Ct (32218-0109)
PHONE..................................904 435-3484
Christopher Boyle,
EMP: 7 EST: 2016
SALES (est): 445.7K Privately Held
WEB: www.tier5-tech.com
SIC: 3661 5064 7371 1731 Telephones & telephone apparatus; multiplex equipment, telephone & telegraph; answering machines, telephone; custom computer programming services; telephone & telephone equipment installation

(G-6856)
TIME PRINTING CO INC
Also Called: Ink Master Graphics
3504 Saint Augustine Rd (32207-5525)
P.O. Box 5643 (32247-5643)
PHONE..................................904 396-9967
Ronald Smith, *President*
Hazel E Smith, *Corp Secy*
EMP: 5 EST: 1965
SQ FT: 7,500
SALES (est): 493.7K Privately Held
WEB: www.timeprintingco.com
SIC: 2752 Commercial printing, offset

(G-6857)
TIMUS INC
8131 Baymeadows Cir (32256-2012)
PHONE..................................904 614-4342
Russell E Cain Jr, *President*
EMP: 5 EST: 1999
SALES (est): 594.2K Privately Held
WEB: www.timus.com
SIC: 7372 Business oriented computer software

(G-6858)
TITAN METALWORKS INC ✪
8350 Arlington Expy (32211-8001)
PHONE..................................904 503-2941
EMP: 6 EST: 2020
SALES (est): 88.1K Privately Held
WEB: www.titanjax.com
SIC: 3599 Machine shop, jobbing & repair

(G-6859)
TITAN METALWORKS LLC
8531 Alton Ave (32211-7980)
PHONE..................................904 574-9828
Vincent Urbank, *Principal*
EMP: 7 EST: 2016
SALES (est): 153.4K Privately Held
WEB: www.titanjax.com
SIC: 7692 Welding repair

(G-6860)
TKS PRINTING & PROMO PRODUCTS
3107 Spring Glen Rd Ste 2 (32207-5916)
PHONE..................................904 469-0968
Zachary Robinson, *CEO*
EMP: 84 EST: 2017
SALES (est): 2.8MM Privately Held
SIC: 2752 Commercial printing, lithographic

(G-6861)
TOMS INSTANT PRINTING INC
Also Called: Tom's Instant Printing
3100 Beach Blvd (32207-3796)
PHONE..................................904 396-0686
Tom Tomaski, *President*
Suzanne Tomaski, *Vice Pres*
EMP: 7 EST: 1971
SQ FT: 1,500
SALES (est): 554.5K Privately Held
SIC: 2752 2791 8743 Commercial printing, offset; typesetting; promotion service

(G-6862)
TOO MANY IDEAS INC
Also Called: TMI
1712 Hendricks Ave (32207-3112)
PHONE..................................904 396-9245
Guy Beard, *President*
Linda Beard, *Corp Secy*
EMP: 8 EST: 1992
SQ FT: 10,000
SALES (est): 522K Privately Held
SIC: 3911 Jewelry apparel

(G-6863)
TOP NOTCH DIECUTTING FOIL STA
4246 Saint Augustine Rd (32207-6644)
PHONE..................................904 346-3511
Michael D Hartley, *President*
Clint McConnaughey, *General Mgr*
Diane M McConnaughey, *Vice Pres*
EMP: 5 EST: 1999
SQ FT: 9,000
SALES (est): 553.9K Privately Held
SIC: 3469 2675 Metal stampings; paper die-cutting

(G-6864)
TOP SPEC US INC
1650 Margaret St (32204-3868)
PHONE..................................904 345-0814
Ronald Shinall, *Principal*
EMP: 7 EST: 2010
SALES (est): 203.8K Privately Held
WEB: www.topspecus.com
SIC: 3949 Sporting & athletic goods

(G-6865)
TRAFFIC CONTROL PDTS FLA INC
5639 Witten Rd (32254-1534)
PHONE..................................352 372-7088
Robert Stone, *Manager*
EMP: 16
SALES (corp-wide): 15.5MM Privately Held
WEB: www.trafficcontrolproducts.org
SIC: 3499 3669 1799 3993 Barricades, metal; transportation signaling devices; parking lot maintenance; signs & advertising specialties
PA: Traffic Control Products Of Florida, Inc.
5514 Carmack Rd
Tampa FL 33610
813 621-8484

(G-6866)
TRAILMATE INC
6600 Suemac Pl (32254-2773)
PHONE..................................941 739-5743
Harry Bakker, *President*
▲ EMP: 22 EST: 1977
SALES (est): 3.1MM Privately Held
WEB: www.trailmate.com
SIC: 3524 3751 Lawnmowers, residential: hand or power; bicycles & related parts

(G-6867)
TREBOL FLORIDA LLC
11400 New Berlin Rd (32226-2279)
PHONE..................................904 751-2828
Bill Castleberry, *CEO*
William P Castleberry, *President*
Stephen O'Toole, *CFO*
Naila Cummings, *Controller*
▲ EMP: 10 EST: 2006
SQ FT: 16,000
SALES (est): 3MM Privately Held
SIC: 3299 Ceramic fiber
HQ: Trebol U.S.A. Llc
641 S Rosemary Ave
Andrews SC 29510
843 520-1111

(G-6868)
TREMRON LLC (PA)
Also Called: Tremron Group
2885 Saint Clair St (32254-1863)
PHONE..................................904 359-5900
EMP: 161 EST: 2016
SALES (est): 7MM Privately Held
WEB: www.tremron.com
SIC: 3531 Pavers

(G-6869)
TREND OFFSET PRINTING SVCS INC
Also Called: Mittera
10301 Busch Dr N (32218-5635)
PHONE..................................562 598-2446
Ricky Carter, *President*
Steven Poliks, *General Mgr*
Rich Clark, *Regional Mgr*
Lewis Story, *COO*
Steve Furlong, *Vice Pres*
EMP: 100
SALES (corp-wide): 742.8MM Privately Held
WEB: www.mittera.com
SIC: 2752 Commercial printing, offset
HQ: Trend Offset Printing Services, Inc.
3701 Catalina St
Los Alamitos CA 90720
562 598-2446

GEOGRAPHIC

(G-6870)
TRUE HOUSE INC (PA)
Also Called: True Truss
4745 Sutton Park Ct # 501 (32224-0251)
PHONE....................................904 757-7500
Barry E Dixon, *President*
Rebecca Harrison, *COO*
Oliver L Dixon, *Vice Pres*
Edie D Dixon, *Admin Sec*
EMP: 10 **EST:** 1997
SQ FT: 20,000
SALES (est): 13.6MM **Privately Held**
WEB: www.apextechnology.com
SIC: 2439 Trusses, except roof: laminated lumber

(G-6871)
TURNING POINT PROPELLERS INC
11762 Marco Beach Dr # 2 (32224-5677)
P.O. Box 59299, Schaumburg IL (60159-0299)
PHONE....................................904 900-7739
Eben Chen, *President*
Liheng Chen, *COO*
Dickson Kendall, *Vice Pres*
▲ **EMP:** 6 **EST:** 1997
SALES (est): 577.3K **Privately Held**
WEB: www.turningpointpropellers.com
SIC: 3366 5551 5088 Propellers; boat dealers; marine crafts & supplies

(G-6872)
TURTLE PUBLISHING CO
1034 Hendricks Ave (32207-8308)
PHONE....................................904 568-1484
Katherine Lee, *Principal*
EMP: 7 **EST:** 2016
SALES (est): 222.7K **Privately Held**
SIC: 2741 Miscellaneous publishing

(G-6873)
TYSON FOODS INC
5441 W 5th St (32254-1664)
PHONE....................................904 693-0688
EMP: 6
SALES (corp-wide): 43.1B **Publicly Held**
WEB: www.tysonfoods.com
SIC: 2011 Meat packing plants
PA: Tyson Foods, Inc.
2200 W Don Tyson Pkwy
Springdale AR 72762
479 290-4000

(G-6874)
U S A COATINGS INC
2361 Edwards Ave (32254-4071)
PHONE....................................904 477-0916
Steven Tyrrel, *Principal*
EMP: 11 **EST:** 2009
SALES (est): 94.3K **Privately Held**
SIC: 3479 Metal coating & allied service

(G-6875)
ULTIMATE CARGO SERVICES LLC
10752 Deerwood Park Blvd (32256-4849)
PHONE....................................954 251-1680
EMP: 13
SALES (est): 2MM **Privately Held**
SIC: 3715 4424 5088 Mfg Truck Trailers Domestic Sea Freight Transportation Whol Transportation Equipment

(G-6876)
ULTRATECH INTERNATIONAL INC (PA)
11542 Davis Creek Ct (32256-3003)
PHONE....................................904 292-9019
Mark D Shaw, *CEO*
J Tad Heyman, *President*
Dale Shaw, *Vice Pres*
Matt Clancy, *Engineer*
Sonja Day, *Cust Mgr*
◆ **EMP:** 20 **EST:** 1987
SQ FT: 9,000
SALES (est): 5.7MM **Privately Held**
WEB: www.spillcontainment.com
SIC: 3089 Plastic containers, except foam

(G-6877)
UNDERWOOD BUTCHER BLOCK CO INC
51 Nitram St Ste 500 (32211-7686)
PHONE....................................904 338-2348
Ken O Underwood, *President*
Kristina Underwood, *Vice Pres*
EMP: 10 **EST:** 2012
SALES (est): 909.8K **Privately Held**
WEB: www.underwoodbutcherblock.com
SIC: 2434 2411 Wood kitchen cabinets; wooden logs

(G-6878)
UNILEVER
12200 Presidents Ct (32220-3220)
PHONE....................................904 378-0298
Sara Bertram, *Business Mgr*
Melissa Witsil, *Counsel*
Doug Banes, *Opers Staff*
Willie Eaton, *Opers Staff*
Amanda Resnik, *QC Mgr*
▼ **EMP:** 12 **EST:** 2013
SALES (est): 8.9MM **Privately Held**
WEB: www.unileverusa.com
SIC: 2844 Toilet preparations

(G-6879)
UNISON INDUSTRIES LLC (DH)
7575 Baymeadows Way (32256-7525)
PHONE....................................904 739-4000
Tom Hoferer, *President*
Michael Grunza, *President*
Andi Bartz, *General Mgr*
Barbara A Cameron, *Vice Pres*
Jason Swinny, *Opers Staff*
EMP: 600
SQ FT: 135,000
SALES (est): 390.9MM
SALES (corp-wide): 79.6B **Publicly Held**
WEB: www.unisonindustries.com
SIC: 3728 Aircraft parts & equipment
HQ: Ge Engine Services, Llc
1 Aviation Way
Cincinnati OH 45215
513 243-2000

(G-6880)
UNITED ENERGY CORPORATION
855-21 St Johns Bluff Rd (32225-8398)
PHONE....................................904 296-1168
Richard Phelan, *Branch Mgr*
EMP: 8 **Privately Held**
WEB: www.uecorporation.com
SIC: 1311 Natural gas production
PA: United Energy Corporation
919 S 7th St Ste 405
Bismarck ND 58504

(G-6881)
UNITED RAIL INC
13500 Sutton Park Dr S # 601 (32224-5290)
P.O. Box 1162, Ponte Vedra Beach (32004-1162)
PHONE....................................904 503-9757
Norwin K Voegeli, *CEO*
Paul Campbell, *Principal*
Bob Walker, *Vice Pres*
Brad McLelland, *Director*
EMP: 11 **EST:** 2012
SALES (est): 2.4MM **Privately Held**
WEB: www.global-ingress.com
SIC: 3669 5051 8711 Railroad signaling devices, electric; rails & accessories; engineering services

(G-6882)
UNITED STATE POSTAL SERVICE
1815 Silver St (32206-3665)
P.O. Box 40005 (32203-0005)
PHONE....................................904 783-7145
P Dobbins MD, *Principal*
◆ **EMP:** 17 **EST:** 2014
SALES (est): 1.1MM **Privately Held**
SIC: 2542 Mail racks & lock boxes, postal service: except wood

(G-6883)
UNITED STATES GYPSUM COMPANY
6825 Evergreen Ave (32208-4996)
P.O. Box 9579 (32208-0579)
PHONE....................................904 768-2501
Jim Parnell, *Plant Engr*
Darrell Denmark, *Supervisor*
Kenneth Jenkins, *Supervisor*
Hugh McMillan, *Supervisor*
Tommy Miller, *Supervisor*
EMP: 70
SALES (corp-wide): 10.7B **Privately Held**
WEB: www.usg.com
SIC: 3275 Gypsum products
HQ: United States Gypsum Company
550 W Adams St Ste 1300
Chicago IL 60661
312 606-4000

(G-6884)
UNITED WORLD IMPORTS LLC
2542 Carriage Lamp Dr (32246-0563)
PHONE....................................904 208-1252
Ahmad Bashiti, *Administration*
EMP: 10 **EST:** 2016
SALES (est): 109.2K **Privately Held**
SIC: 2844 Toilet preparations

(G-6885)
UNIVERSAL CNTACT LENSES OF FLA
3840 Williamsburg Pk Blvd (32257-9227)
PHONE....................................904 731-3410
Juanita Padgett, *President*
James F Beeler, *President*
EMP: 7 **EST:** 1982
SQ FT: 2,000
SALES (est): 929.4K **Privately Held**
SIC: 3851 Contact lenses

(G-6886)
UNIVERSAL METAL WORKS INC
14600 Duval Pl W Ste 52 (32218-9418)
PHONE....................................904 765-2600
Larry C Bruce, *President*
Shelia Peters, *Treasurer*
EMP: 7 **EST:** 1993
SQ FT: 22,000
SALES (est): 550K **Privately Held**
WEB: www.umw.comcastbiz.net
SIC: 3443 Fabricated plate work (boiler shop)

(G-6887)
UNIVERSAL PAVERSCAPES LLC
3760 University Blvd S # 1033 (32216-4372)
PHONE....................................904 428-2010
Jorge A Acosta, *Principal*
EMP: 6 **EST:** 2013
SALES (est): 74.1K **Privately Held**
SIC: 2951 Asphalt paving mixtures & blocks

(G-6888)
UP - N - ATOM
3443 Maiden Voyage Cir S (32257-6318)
PHONE....................................904 716-5431
Steven A Kerwick, *Principal*
EMP: 7 **EST:** 2006
SALES (est): 383.2K **Privately Held**
WEB: www.up-n-atom.com
SIC: 3553 Cabinet makers' machinery

(G-6889)
US 1 TRUCK SALES LLC
10126 New Kings Rd (32219-2412)
PHONE....................................904 545-1233
Dagmar K Cvek, *Principal*
Alois Cvek, *Principal*
▼ **EMP:** 6 **EST:** 2011
SALES (est): 158.2K **Privately Held**
WEB: www.us1trucksales.com
SIC: 3596 Truck (motor vehicle) scales

(G-6890)
V-BLOX CORPORATION
Also Called: Florida Power Systems
3653 Regent Blvd Ste 408 (32224-6511)
PHONE....................................904 425-4908
David T Mulvaney, *President*
Scott Hartley, *Vice Pres*
Paul Dubriske, *Regl Sales Mgr*
Brett Lindelof, *Consultant*
Elizabeth Mulvaney, *Admin Sec*
▲ **EMP:** 9 **EST:** 1998
SQ FT: 35,000
SALES (est): 10MM **Privately Held**
WEB: www.v-blox.com
SIC: 3679 Electronic crystals

(G-6891)
VALLEY PROTEINS (DE) INC
6142 Old Soutel Ct (32219-3793)
PHONE....................................704 718-6568
EMP: 89
SALES (corp-wide): 473.5MM **Privately Held**
WEB: www.valleyproteins.com
SIC: 2077 Animal & marine fats & oils
PA: Valley Proteins (De), Inc.
151 Valpro Dr
Winchester VA 22603
540 877-2533

(G-6892)
VANITY FAIR BRANDS LP
10300 Southside Blvd (32256-0770)
PHONE....................................904 538-0288
John Turner, *Branch Mgr*
EMP: 9
SALES (corp-wide): 245.5B **Publicly Held**
WEB: www.fotlinc.com
SIC: 2341 Nightgowns & negligees: women's & children's
HQ: Vanity Fair Brands, Lp
1 Fruit Of The Loom Dr
Bowling Green KY 42103
270 781-6400

(G-6893)
VANITY FURS OF AVONDALE LLC
4555 Saint Johns Ave # 6 (32210-1858)
PHONE....................................904 387-9900
Dawn M Parker, *Principal*
EMP: 8 **EST:** 2010
SALES (est): 339.6K **Privately Held**
SIC: 3999 Furs

(G-6894)
VEGAN SUCKERS LLC ✪
11111 San Jose Blvd Ste 5 (32223-7274)
PHONE....................................904 265-5263
Adrien Ham, *CEO*
EMP: 10 **EST:** 2021
SALES (est): 748.5K **Privately Held**
SIC: 2024 Ice cream & frozen desserts

(G-6895)
VENUS MANUFACTURING CO INC
Also Called: Vm
11711 Marco Beach Dr (32224-7616)
PHONE....................................904 645-3187
Patricia Reifensnyder, *General Mgr*
George Christ Mavrantzas, *Vice Pres*
Kerstin Pittman, *Project Mgr*
Robin Sheffler, *Controller*
Henry Ferris, *Marketing Staff*
EMP: 60 **Privately Held**
WEB: www.venusmanufacturing.com
SIC: 2339 Bathing suits: women's, misses' & juniors'
PA: Venus Manufacturing Co Inc
349 Lakeview Dr
Dexter NY 13634

(G-6896)
VEVYAN HANANIA INC
10415 Beach Blvd (32246-3679)
PHONE....................................800 297-8485
EMP: 7 **EST:** 2017
SALES (est): 264K **Privately Held**
WEB: www.hemoband.net
SIC: 3845 Electromedical equipment

(G-6897)
VICTORY VALET SERVICES LLC
5549 Fort Caroline Rd # 107 (32277-1748)
PHONE....................................904 521-6517
Wylie Watkins, *President*
EMP: 10
SALES (est): 409.5K **Privately Held**
SIC: 2842 Sanitation preparations, disinfectants & deodorants

(G-6898)
VIDEOLINQ STREAMING SVCS LLC
Also Called: Streaming Store, The
4651 Salisbury Rd (32256-6107)
PHONE....................................904 330-1026
Eyal Menin, *Mng Member*
EMP: 7 **EST:** 2019

SALES (est): 213.1K **Privately Held**
SIC: 2741

(G-6899)
VINBILLINGCOM LLC
540 Phelps St (32206-5609)
PHONE..................................904 549-5461
EMP: 6 **EST:** 2016
SALES (est): 114.8K **Privately Held**
WEB: www.vinbilling.com
SIC: 7372 Business oriented computer software

(G-6900)
VISTA PRODUCTS INC (DH)
8801 Corporate Square Ct (32216-1981)
PHONE..................................904 725-2242
Marv Hopkins, *CEO*
Jim Singer, *President*
James E Singer, *President*
Carmen Singer, *Corp Secy*
Ajit Mehra, *Exec VP*
▲ **EMP:** 100 **EST:** 1980
SQ FT: 40,000
SALES (est): 28.6MM **Privately Held**
WEB: www.vistaproducts.com
SIC: 2591 Blinds vertical
HQ: Hunter Douglas Inc.
1 Blue Hill Plz Ste 1569
Pearl River NY 10965
845 664-7000

(G-6901)
VISTAKON PHARMACEUTICALS LLC
7500 Centurion Pkwy # 100 (32256-0517)
PHONE..................................904 443-1000
EMP: 5 **EST:** 2004
SALES (est): 5.2MM
SALES (corp-wide): 82.5B **Publicly Held**
WEB: www.jnjvisioncareinfo.com
SIC: 2834 Pharmaceutical preparations
HQ: Johnson & Johnson Vision Care, Inc.
7500 Centurion Pkwy
Jacksonville FL 32256
904 443-1000

(G-6902)
VIVID IMAGES USA INC
1730 E Duval St (32202-1122)
PHONE..................................904 620-0303
Kenneth D Tapper, *President*
Karen Tapper, *Vice Pres*
EMP: 10 **EST:** 1997
SQ FT: 6,500
SALES (est): 900K **Privately Held**
WEB: www.vividimagesusa.com
SIC: 2759 3993 2396 2395 Screen printing; signs & advertising specialties; automotive & apparel trimmings; pleating & stitching

(G-6903)
VIZTEK INC
6491 Powers Ave (32217-2821)
PHONE..................................904 448-9936
EMP: 13 **EST:** 2019
SALES (est): 1.1MM **Privately Held**
SIC: 3841 Surgical & medical instruments

(G-6904)
VOSS BINDERY INC
2565 Philips Hwy (32207-3553)
PHONE..................................904 396-3330
Alan Weaver, *President*
EMP: 6 **EST:** 2006
SQ FT: 2,970
SALES (est): 174.8K **Privately Held**
SIC: 2789 Binding only: books, pamphlets, magazines, etc.

(G-6905)
WALKER WOOD PRODUCTS INC
6112 Quattlebaum Rd (32217-2233)
PHONE..................................904 448-5202
John Walker, *President*
EMP: 5 **EST:** 1986
SQ FT: 4,000
SALES (est): 386.8K **Privately Held**
SIC: 2434 Wood kitchen cabinets

(G-6906)
WCCM-USA LTD CORPORATION
2024 River Rd (32207-3906)
PHONE..................................904 346-3816
Eugene Bebeau, *Principal*
EMP: 6 **EST:** 2012
SALES: 273.7K **Privately Held**
WEB: www.wccm-usa.org
SIC: 2731 Book publishing

(G-6907)
WEBCOM GROUP INC (HQ)
5335 Gate Pkwy (32256-3070)
PHONE..................................904 680-6600
David L Brown, *President*
Roseann Duran, *Exec VP*
Helen Rowan, *Senior VP*
Kent Warren, *Vice Pres*
Mike Young, *Vice Pres*
▲ **EMP:** 1021 **EST:** 1999
SQ FT: 112,306
SALES (est): 749.2MM **Privately Held**
WEB: www.web.com
SIC: 7372 7374 Prepackaged software; computer graphics service
PA: Parker Private Holdings Ii, Llc
601 Lexington Ave Fl 59
New York NY 10022
212 231-0095

(G-6908)
WEDDINGS BY TINA
4720 Salisbury Rd (32256-6101)
PHONE..................................904 235-3740
Tina M Payne, *Principal*
EMP: 7 **EST:** 2008
SALES (est): 430.4K **Privately Held**
WEB: www.weddingsbytina.com
SIC: 2335 Wedding gowns & dresses

(G-6909)
WELLS LEGAL SUPPLY INC
Also Called: Wells & Drew Companies, The
3414 Galilee Rd (32207-4718)
P.O. Box 10554 (32247-0554)
PHONE..................................904 399-1510
Steven R Houser, *President*
Linda Wells Houser, *Corp Secy*
Kim Pfaff, *Vice Pres*
Roger Davis, *Accounts Exec*
Robyn Owens, *Manager*
EMP: 41 **EST:** 1982
SQ FT: 12,000
SALES (est): 5.6MM **Privately Held**
WEB: www.wellsdrew.com
SIC: 2754 2752 5943 Seals: gravure printing; commercial printing, offset; office forms & supplies

(G-6910)
WEST FRASER INC
109 Halsema Rd S (32220-1657)
PHONE..................................904 786-4155
Hardy Maloch, *Branch Mgr*
Don Pattee, *Manager*
EMP: 74
SALES (corp-wide): 3.6B **Privately Held**
SIC: 2421 2426 2411 Sawmills & planing mills, general; hardwood dimension & flooring mills; logging
HQ: West Fraser, Inc.
1900 Exeter Rd Ste 105
Germantown TN 38138
901 620-4200

(G-6911)
WEST TEXAS PROTEIN INC
601 Riverside Ave (32204-2946)
PHONE..................................806 250-5959
Gary Norcross, *CEO*
Charles Toledo, *President*
Manuel Toledo, *General Mgr*
James Woody, *CFO*
EMP: 10 **EST:** 2009
SQ FT: 125,000
SALES (est): 10MM **Privately Held**
SIC: 3999 4222 7389 8999 Pet supplies; warehousing, cold storage or refrigerated; business services; scientific consulting; banking school, training

(G-6912)
WESTERN MICROSYSTEMS INC (PA)
Also Called: Desert Micro
4230 Pablo Pro Ct Ste 200 (32224-3223)
PHONE..................................800 547-7082
Barry J Grahek, *President*
Evan Schwartz, *CTO*
EMP: 20 **EST:** 1988
SALES (est): 2.5MM **Privately Held**
SIC: 3577 7371 7372 Computer peripheral equipment; custom computer programming services; prepackaged software

(G-6913)
WESTROCK CP LLC
2002 E 18th St (32206-3419)
PHONE..................................904 356-5611
Fax: 904 798-0238
EMP: 112
SALES (corp-wide): 14.1B **Publicly Held**
SIC: 2653 Corrugated Container Plant
HQ: Westrock Cp, Llc
504 Thrasher St
Norcross GA 30328

(G-6914)
WESTROCK CP LLC
9469 Eastport Rd (32218-2261)
P.O. Box 26998 (32226-6998)
PHONE..................................904 714-7151
Del Brooks, *Manager*
EMP: 200
SALES (corp-wide): 17.5B **Publicly Held**
WEB: www.westrock.com
SIC: 2631 Container board; boxboard
HQ: Westrock Cp, Llc
1000 Abernathy Rd Ste 125
Atlanta GA 30328

(G-6915)
WESTROCK RKT LLC
1660 Prudential Dr # 202 (32207-8197)
P.O. Box 100084, Duluth GA (30096-9373)
PHONE..................................904 714-1643
Art Renfro, *Controller*
Paul Powers, *Maintence Staff*
EMP: 161
SALES (corp-wide): 17.5B **Publicly Held**
WEB: www.westrock.com
SIC: 2653 Boxes, corrugated: made from purchased materials
HQ: Westrock Rkt, Llc
1000 Abernathy Rd Ste 125
Atlanta GA 30328
770 448-2193

(G-6916)
WHATS WRONG PUBLISHING CO
2641 Park St (32204-4519)
PHONE..................................904 388-3494
John V Rossi, *Principal*
EMP: 6 **EST:** 2008
SALES (est): 56K **Privately Held**
SIC: 2741 Miscellaneous publishing

(G-6917)
WHERTEC INC (DH)
Also Called: Boiler Inspection Services
5409 Highway Ave (32254-3636)
PHONE..................................904 278-6503
Pete Castiglione, *President*
Ed Lloyd, *General Mgr*
Robert Barlow, *Vice Pres*
Mark Smith, *Vice Pres*
Rodney Bolton, *Project Mgr*
▼ **EMP:** 99 **EST:** 1996
SQ FT: 2,700
SALES (est): 13MM
SALES (corp-wide): 339MM **Privately Held**
WEB: www.castolin.com
SIC: 3398 Metal heat treating
HQ: Eutectic Corporation
N94w14355 Garwin Mace Dr
Menomonee Falls WI 53051
262 532-4677

(G-6918)
WHERTEC TECHNOLOGIES INC
5409 Highway Ave (32254-3636)
PHONE..................................866 207-6503
EMP: 5
SALES (est): 494.1K **Privately Held**
SIC: 3822 Mfg Environmental Controls

(G-6919)
WHITE PUBLISHING CO INC
Also Called: Jacksonville Magazine
1531 Osceola St (32204-4305)
PHONE..................................904 389-3622
James L White III, *President*
Amy Robertson, *Publisher*
Debbie Fewell, *Principal*
Mandy Niesen, *Advt Staff*
Jennifer L Curry, *Director*
EMP: 13 **EST:** 1985
SALES (est): 1.6MM **Privately Held**
WEB: www.jacksonvillemag.com
SIC: 2721 5812 Magazines: publishing only, not printed on site; eating places

(G-6920)
WILKINSON STEEL SUPPLY LLC
3210 Faye Rd (32226-2383)
PHONE..................................904 757-1522
Mike Zipp, *Sales Staff*
Charles H Denny IV, *Mng Member*
Rhonda Dunn, *Mng Member*
Dan Dunn,
EMP: 8 **EST:** 2009
SALES (est): 2.1MM **Privately Held**
WEB: www.bestrebar.com
SIC: 3441 Fabricated structural metal

(G-6921)
WILLIAM FSTER ENTP EMBRDME JCK
2266 Mission Creek Dr (32218-8821)
PHONE..................................904 329-1549
William A Foster, *Manager*
EMP: 6 **EST:** 2016
SALES (est): 118.1K **Privately Held**
SIC: 2395 Embroidery & art needlework

(G-6922)
WILLIAMS INDUSTRIAL SVCS LLC
11380 Island Dr 1 (32226-4484)
PHONE..................................904 696-9994
Herb Deaton, *Regional Mgr*
Megan Horgan, *Counsel*
Loren Monty, *Vice Pres*
Jeremy Williams, *Project Dir*
Alvin Young, *Project Mgr*
EMP: 43
SALES (corp-wide): 269MM **Publicly Held**
WEB: www.wisgrp.com
SIC: 1389 Construction, repair & dismantling services
HQ: Williams Industrial Services, Llc
100 Cres Ctr Pkwy # 1240
Tucker GA 30084
770 879-4165

(G-6923)
WINGARD LLC
Also Called: Printing.com 5point
76 S Laura St Ste 1501 (32202-3420)
PHONE..................................904 387-2570
EMP: 13
SALES (est): 1.8MM **Privately Held**
SIC: 2759 8742 Commercial Printing Management Consulting Services

(G-6924)
WIRE MESH CORP
4034 Faye Rd (32226-2347)
PHONE..................................706 922-5179
Luis Barrenechea, *CEO*
Hector Lopez, *Plant Mgr*
Joaquin Hernandez, *Opers Staff*
Jose Aguirre, *Credit Staff*
Rusty Smith, *Regl Sales Mgr*
EMP: 29 **EST:** 2002
SALES (est): 8.7MM
SALES (corp-wide): 201.4MM **Privately Held**
WEB: www.wmc-us.com
SIC: 3496 Wire winding
HQ: Wmc Holdings, Lp
25219 Kuykendahl Rd Ste 2
The Woodlands TX 77375
904 751-4301

(G-6925)
WJS PRINTING PARTNERS INC
Also Called: Complete Printing Solutions
2750 Dawn Rd (32207-7904)
PHONE....904 731-0357
William S Edenfield, *Principal*
EMP: 8 **EST:** 2014
SALES (est): 240K **Privately Held**
WEB: www.completeprintingsolutionsjax.com
SIC: 2752 Commercial printing, offset

(G-6926)
WOGANS CSTM CBNETS RFACING LLC
9344 Lockheed Ln (32221-8019)
PHONE....904 343-8917
Rosemary Wogan, *Principal*
EMP: 6 **EST:** 2008
SALES (est): 112K **Privately Held**
SIC: 2434 Wood kitchen cabinets

(G-6927)
WONDERLAND PRODUCTS INC
5772 Lenox Ave (32205-6374)
P.O. Box 6074 (32236-6074)
PHONE....904 786-0144
Robert L Ponsler Jr, *President*
James A Ponsler, *Vice Pres*
Joseph Ponsler, *Vice Pres*
Robert Ponsler III, *Vice Pres*
EMP: 7 **EST:** 1950
SQ FT: 5,000
SALES (est): 644.6K **Privately Held**
WEB: www.wonderlandproducts.com
SIC: 3446 Ornamental metalwork

(G-6928)
WOODWORKS CABINETRY INC
4541 Saint Augustine Rd (32207-9524)
PHONE....904 924-5300
Arron Ramroop, *Principal*
EMP: 9 **EST:** 2014
SALES (est): 218.8K **Privately Held**
WEB: www.woodworksjax.com
SIC: 2434 Wood kitchen cabinets

(G-6929)
WORKING DRONES INC
Also Called: Apellix
2180 Emerson St (32207-5544)
PHONE....904 647-4511
Robert Dahlstrom, *CEO*
Jeff McCutcheon, *CFO*
◆ **EMP:** 9 **EST:** 2017
SALES (est): 1.5MM **Privately Held**
WEB: www.apellix.com
SIC: 3728 Target drones

(G-6930)
WWF OPERATING COMPANY LLC
Also Called: Whitewave Foods
2198 W Beaver St (32209-7405)
P.O. Box 2768 (32203-2768)
PHONE....904 354-0406
Bobby Hayden, *Controller*
Nick Dobransky, *Manager*
Erquail Collier, *CIO*
Sidney Rath, *Technician*
EMP: 25
SALES (corp-wide): 735.6MM **Privately Held**
WEB: www.danonenorthamerica.com
SIC: 2026 Milk processing (pasteurizing, homogenizing, bottling)
HQ: Wwf Operating Company, Llc
12002 Airport Way
Broomfield CO 80021

(G-6931)
WYLA INC (PA)
Also Called: Wyla Laces
6920 Phillips Ind Blvd (32256-3007)
P.O. Box 600549 (32260-0549)
PHONE....904 886-4338
Joseph D Wiener, *President*
John G Benis, *Corp Secy*
Charlene C Wilkins, *Vice Pres*
Bruce Walls, *Opers Mgr*
Michael Agner, *Purch Dir*
▲ **EMP:** 26 **EST:** 1971
SQ FT: 40,000
SALES (est): 2.6MM **Privately Held**
WEB: www.wyla.com
SIC: 2258 Lace & lace products

(G-6932)
XYLEM DEWATERING SOLUTIONS
240 Hammond Blvd (32254-3405)
PHONE....904 695-2131
EMP: 7 **EST:** 2019
SALES (est): 189.2K **Privately Held**
WEB: www.xylem.com
SIC: 3561 Pumps & pumping equipment

(G-6933)
YOUR ID GUARD
4417 Beach Blvd Ste 204 (32207-9410)
PHONE....904 354-8989
Laurence F Lee III, *Principal*
EMP: 7 **EST:** 2008
SALES (est): 126.5K **Privately Held**
WEB: www.yigadmin.com
SIC: 3089 Identification cards, plastic

(G-6934)
ZIMMER BIOMET CMF THORACIC LLC
1520 Tradeport Dr (32218-2480)
P.O. Box 708, Warsaw IN (46581-0708)
PHONE....574 267-6639
Adam Johnson, *President*
David Joseph, *President*
Gary Blackall, *Vice Pres*
Aure Bruneau, *Vice Pres*
Gary Maingot, *Vice Pres*
EMP: 235 **EST:** 1991
SQ FT: 82,000
SALES (est): 57.2MM
SALES (corp-wide): 7B **Publicly Held**
WEB: www.zimmerbiomet.com
SIC: 3841 5047 Surgical instruments & apparatus; surgical equipment & supplies
HQ: Biomet, Inc.
345 E Main St
Warsaw IN 46580
574 267-6639

Jacksonville
St. Johns County

(G-6935)
ABC BOOK PUBLISHERS INC
4940 Blackhawk Dr (32259-2170)
PHONE....904 230-0737
Kimberly S Benton, *Principal*
EMP: 6 **EST:** 2010
SALES (est): 70.5K **Privately Held**
WEB: www.abcbookpublishers.com
SIC: 2741 Miscellaneous publishing

(G-6936)
TORRES & TAVARA COATING LLC
705 Putters Green Way S (32259-4338)
PHONE....904 520-9910
Sigifredo Torres, *Principal*
EMP: 6 **EST:** 2013
SALES (est): 117.4K **Privately Held**
SIC: 3479 Metal coating & allied service

Jacksonville Beach
Duval County

(G-6937)
ADVANCED SOFTWARE INC
1902 2nd Ave N (32250-2734)
PHONE....215 369-7800
Joseph Hentz, *President*
Julie Hentz, *Treasurer*
Paul Evenson, *Director*
John Loeb, *Administration*
EMP: 15 **EST:** 1991
SALES (est): 857.8K **Privately Held**
SIC: 7372 5734 5045 Business oriented computer software; computer software & accessories; computers

(G-6938)
AMXS CORP ✪
524 Patricia Ln (32250-4760)
PHONE....904 568-1416
Kenneth Mangione, *Exec Dir*
EMP: 21 **EST:** 2020
SALES (est): 1MM **Privately Held**
SIC: 3721 Aircraft

(G-6939)
BENCHMARK DESIGN GROUP INC (PA)
Also Called: Benchmark Contract Furniture
456 Osceola Ave (32250-4078)
PHONE....904 246-5060
Mark Carroll, *President*
Melissa A Compton, *Principal*
Paul H Haser, *Vice Pres*
Melissa Compton, *Marketing Staff*
Karen Schindler, *Manager*
▲ **EMP:** 19 **EST:** 1996
SALES (est): 5.2MM **Privately Held**
WEB: www.benchmarkcontractfurniture.com
SIC: 2531 Public building & related furniture

(G-6940)
CLASSIC IRON DECOR INC
1004 10th Ave S (32250-3306)
PHONE....904 241-5022
Slade Richardson, *President*
EMP: 10 **EST:** 1994
SQ FT: 10,000
SALES (est): 1.5MM **Privately Held**
WEB: www.classicirondecor.com
SIC: 3446 Architectural metalwork

(G-6941)
CUPCAKE GIRLS DESSERT COMPANY
1516 3rd St N (32250-7352)
PHONE....904 372-4579
Behrouz Y Arabi, *Principal*
EMP: 8 **EST:** 2009
SALES (est): 469.7K **Privately Held**
WEB: www.cupcakegirlsdessert.com
SIC: 2051 Cakes, bakery: except frozen

(G-6942)
DRAGON GLASSING LLC
Also Called: Dragon Factory
1378 Eastwind Dr (32250-3101)
PHONE....904 509-1860
Todd Kirshenbaum, *President*
EMP: 6 **EST:** 2017
SALES (est): 158.8K **Privately Held**
WEB: www.dragonfactoryusa.com
SIC: 3999 Manufacturing industries

(G-6943)
ELECTRONICS FOR IMAGING INC
1902 2nd Ave N (32250-2734)
PHONE....800 624-5999
EMP: 6 **EST:** 2019
SALES (est): 94.5K **Privately Held**
SIC: 3577 Computer peripheral equipment

(G-6944)
GORUCK LLC (HQ)
415 Pablo Ave Ste 140 (32250-5530)
PHONE....904 708-2081
Christian Sbailo, *Opers Mgr*
Jason McCarthy, *Mng Member*
Andy Nelson, *Director*
▲ **EMP:** 23 **EST:** 2008
SQ FT: 3,000
SALES (est): 9.4MM **Privately Held**
WEB: www.goruck.com
SIC: 2389 Costumes
PA: Goruck Holdings, Llc
415 Pablo Ave Ste 140
Jacksonville Beach FL 32250
904 708-2081

(G-6945)
GORUCK HOLDINGS LLC (PA)
415 Pablo Ave Ste 140 (32250-5530)
PHONE....904 708-2081
Jason J McCarthy, *Manager*
EMP: 11 **EST:** 2011
SALES (est): 9.4MM **Privately Held**
WEB: www.goruck.com
SIC: 2389 Costumes

(G-6946)
JD PAVERS INC
1304 8th St N (32250-4739)
PHONE....904 245-9183
Joshua Dubberly, *Principal*
EMP: 7 **EST:** 2012
SALES (est): 202.7K **Privately Held**
WEB: www.jdpaversjax.com
SIC: 2951 Asphalt paving mixtures & blocks

(G-6947)
LEADER GROUP (PA)
Also Called: Beaches Leader, The
1372 Beach Blvd (32250-3447)
P.O. Box 50129 (32240-0129)
PHONE....904 249-7475
Thomas H Wood, *Owner*
Kathleen Bailey, *Editor*
Chelsea Wiggs, *Business Mgr*
EMP: 50 **EST:** 1963
SQ FT: 10,000
SALES (est): 5.3MM **Privately Held**
WEB: www.beachesleader.com
SIC: 2711 Newspapers, publishing & printing

(G-6948)
LEE PRINTING INC (PA)
2653 Isabella Blvd Unit 4 (32250-3841)
PHONE....904 396-5715
Darral Lee, *President*
Andrew Lee, *Vice Pres*
Donald Lee, *Treasurer*
Brad Robinson, *Manager*
June Lee, *Admin Sec*
EMP: 12 **EST:** 1964
SQ FT: 38,000
SALES (est): 2.1MM **Privately Held**
WEB: www.leeprinting.com
SIC: 2752 Commercial printing, offset

(G-6949)
LEVITECH SERVICES LLC ✪
Also Called: Onnow.fm
112 5th Ave S Apt 301 (32250-6795)
PHONE....904 576-0562
John Fasciana, *Mng Member*
EMP: 7 **EST:** 2020
SALES (est): 78.2K **Privately Held**
SIC: 7372 7379 Business oriented computer software; computer related consulting services

(G-6950)
MCCORMICK & COMPANY INC
1020 10th St N (32250-3604)
PHONE....904 247-7773
R Kimener, *Manager*
EMP: 7
SALES (corp-wide): 5.6B **Publicly Held**
WEB: www.mccormick.com
SIC: 2099 Spices, including grinding
PA: Mccormick & Company Incorporated
24 Schilling Rd Ste 1
Hunt Valley MD 21031
410 771-7301

(G-6951)
MOFFITT CORPORATION INC (PA)
1351 13th Ave S Ste 130 (32250-3237)
PHONE....904 241-9944
John D Moffitt, *President*
Kimberly Dove, *Vice Pres*
Taylor Harrington, *Project Mgr*
Jeremy Slater, *Project Mgr*
Curtis Sorensen, *Engineer*
EMP: 13 **EST:** 1961
SQ FT: 7,000
SALES (est): 10MM **Privately Held**
WEB: www.moffittcorp.com
SIC: 3564 Blowers & fans

(G-6952)
MOFFITT FAN CORPORATION
1351 13th Ave S Ste 130 (32250-3237)
PHONE....585 768-7010
John Moffitt, *Ch of Bd*
Terence R Wirth II, *President*
EMP: 19 **EST:** 1993
SALES (est): 610.7K **Privately Held**
WEB: www.moffittcorp.com
SIC: 3564 Blowers & fans

(G-6953)
OCEAN WAVES INC
525 3rd St N Ste 105 (32250-7042)
PHONE..................................904 372-4743
Kevin Carlson, *President*
Kelly Carlson, *General Mgr*
Dale Moore, *Accounts Mgr*
Brad Corwin, *Admin Sec*
EMP: 12 **EST:** 1980
SQ FT: 6,400
SALES (est): 548K **Privately Held**
WEB: www.oceanwaves.com
SIC: 3851 2339 Glasses, sun or glare; women's & misses' outerwear

(G-6954)
PINK INC PUBLISHING
124 Mills Ln (32250-5820)
PHONE..................................904 834-3118
Sherry Sampson, *President*
EMP: 7 **EST:** 1989
SALES (est): 80.6K **Privately Held**
WEB: www.springdalegolf.com
SIC: 2741 Miscellaneous publishing

(G-6955)
R S S PARTNERS INC
1301 1st St S Apt 1501 (32250-6434)
PHONE..................................904 241-6144
Edward A Oertli, *President*
Denise Oertli, *Treasurer*
▲ **EMP:** 9 **EST:** 2000
SALES (est): 305.5K **Privately Held**
SIC: 3578 3824 7389 Calculating & accounting equipment; tally counters; business services

(G-6956)
REEF PAVERS INC
604 Barbara Ln (32250-4758)
PHONE..................................904 471-0859
Charles S Jones III, *Principal*
EMP: 6 **EST:** 2011
SALES (est): 493.4K **Privately Held**
WEB: www.reefpavers.com
SIC: 3531 Pavers

(G-6957)
SALT LIFE LLC
240 3rd St S (32250-6717)
PHONE..................................904 595-5370
Brad Abbott, *Vice Pres*
Edward Steelmon, *Vice Pres*
Parker Hussong, *Store Mgr*
Iris Davis, *Purchasing*
Roger Combs, *Branch Mgr*
EMP: 6
SALES (corp-wide): 381MM **Publicly Held**
WEB: www.saltlife.com
SIC: 3949 2353 2339 5091 Sporting & athletic goods; hats, caps & millinery; women's & misses' outerwear; sporting & recreation goods
HQ: Salt Life, Llc
16 Downing Dr
Phenix City AL 36869

(G-6958)
SCREEN ENCLOSURE LIGHTING
64 Evans Dr (32250-2627)
PHONE..................................904 838-9786
EMP: 6 **EST:** 2017
SALES (est): 146.1K **Privately Held**
SIC: 3448 Screen enclosures

Jasper
Hamilton County

(G-6959)
ASCENT PRECISION GEAR CORP
12180 Se County Road 137 (32052-3803)
PHONE..................................386 792-3215
Debbie Murray, *President*
Chuck Murray, *Vice Pres*
EMP: 6 **EST:** 1998
SQ FT: 4,000
SALES (est): 486.7K **Privately Held**
WEB: www.ascentgear.com
SIC: 3599 Machine shop, jobbing & repair

(G-6960)
PACKAGING CORPORATION AMERICA
Also Called: Pca/Valdosta 645a
5939 Se Us Highway 41 (32052-3816)
P.O. Box 248 (32052-0248)
PHONE..................................386 792-0810
David Allie, *Accounts Exec*
David George, *Manager*
EMP: 8
SALES (corp-wide): 6.6B **Publicly Held**
WEB: www.packagingcorp.com
SIC: 2653 Boxes, corrugated: made from purchased materials
PA: Packaging Corporation Of America
1 N Field Ct
Lake Forest IL 60045
847 482-3000

Jay
Santa Rosa County

(G-6961)
AIRPLANE SERVICES INC
1817 Mineral Springs Rd (32565-9571)
PHONE..................................850 675-1252
Ellis Stuart, *President*
▼ **EMP:** 5 **EST:** 1982
SALES (est): 350K **Privately Held**
SIC: 3728 Aircraft assemblies, subassemblies & parts

(G-6962)
BAXLEY SERVICES INC
13451 Highway 89 (32565-9131)
P.O. Box 828 (32565-0828)
PHONE..................................850 675-4459
Larry Baxley, *President*
Joyce Baxley, *Vice Pres*
EMP: 5 **EST:** 1972
SQ FT: 2,000
SALES (est): 894.4K **Privately Held**
SIC: 7692 Welding repair

(G-6963)
BREITBURN OPERATING LP
5415 Oil Plant Rd (32565-1683)
PHONE..................................713 452-2266
EMP: 81 **EST:** 2014
SALES (est): 6MM
SALES (corp-wide): 295.4MM **Privately Held**
WEB: www.mavresources.com
SIC: 1311 Crude petroleum & natural gas production
PA: Maverick Natural Resources, Llc
1111 Bagby St Ste 1600
Houston TX 77002
713 437-8000

Jennings
Hamilton County

(G-6964)
FKA RACING INC
Also Called: Sims Promotions
3994 Nw 36th Loop (32053-2670)
PHONE..................................386 938-4211
Jimmy Sims, *President*
Judy Sims, *Vice Pres*
▲ **EMP:** 9 **EST:** 1982
SQ FT: 5,000
SALES (est): 725.3K **Privately Held**
SIC: 3519 Gasoline engines

Jensen Beach
Martin County

(G-6965)
AMERICAN RECYCLING SYSTEMS INC
1125 Ne Savannah Oaks Way
(34957-3737)
PHONE..................................772 225-8072
EMP: 8
SQ FT: 3,000
SALES (est): 520K **Privately Held**
SIC: 3569 Mfg General Industrial Machinery

(G-6966)
AQUATIC TECHNOLOGIES INC
1820 Ne Jensen Beach Blvd (34957-7212)
PHONE..................................772 225-4389
Dennis Hardy, *President*
Sean Hardy, *Vice Pres*
EMP: 15 **EST:** 1996
SALES (est): 1.2MM **Privately Held**
SIC: 2851 Epoxy coatings

(G-6967)
DUCK IN THE TRUCK PUPPETS INC
1649 Ne Sunview Ter (34957-3908)
PHONE..................................772 334-3022
David Opasik, *President*
EMP: 7 **EST:** 1997
SALES (est): 1.2MM **Privately Held**
SIC: 3999 Puppets & marionettes

(G-6968)
ENVIRO PETROLEUM INC
10072 S Ocean Dr Apt 7n (34957-2556)
PHONE..................................713 896-6996
Roger Sahni, *President*
▲ **EMP:** 8 **EST:** 1995
SALES (est): 202.3K **Privately Held**
SIC: 3533 5172 Oil & gas field machinery; petroleum products

(G-6969)
FRY TRIM WORKS INC
4626 Ne Dudley Cir (34957-4003)
PHONE..................................772 260-8486
Steven W Fry, *Principal*
EMP: 6 **EST:** 2008
SALES (est): 70.1K **Privately Held**
SIC: 2431 Millwork

(G-6970)
HAMILTON PRINTING INC
779 Ne Dixie Hwy (34957-6176)
P.O. Box 376 (34958-0376)
PHONE..................................772 334-0151
Leonard A Hamilton, *President*
Vince Hamilton, *Vice Pres*
Tiffany Linch, *Vice Pres*
Nancy Hamilton, *Treasurer*
EMP: 5 **EST:** 1985
SQ FT: 1,700
SALES (est): 420.9K **Privately Held**
SIC: 2752 Commercial printing, offset

(G-6971)
MORNING STAR INDUSTRIES INC
630 Ne Jensen Beach Blvd (34957-4750)
P.O. Box 1266 (34958-1266)
PHONE..................................800 440-6050
Kathleen Peruski, *President*
Steven J Peruski, *Vice Pres*
Kelly A Brill, *Treasurer*
Casey J Peruski, *Admin Sec*
EMP: 25 **EST:** 1996
SQ FT: 120,000
SALES (est): 5MM **Privately Held**
WEB: www.morningstarusa.com
SIC: 3646 5169 5063 Commercial indusl & institutional electric lighting fixtures; industrial chemicals; electrical apparatus & equipment

(G-6972)
ONAN GENERATORS & ENGINES
883 Ne Dixie Hwy (34957-6187)
PHONE..................................772 334-8282
George Dietz, *Owner*
EMP: 5 **EST:** 2005
SALES (est): 362.2K **Privately Held**
SIC: 3569 Generators: steam, liquid oxygen or nitrogen

(G-6973)
SAILFISH WOODWORKS LLC
3061 Ne Heather Ct (34957-5071)
PHONE..................................772 708-2791
James H Platt, *Manager*
EMP: 6 **EST:** 2018
SALES (est): 54.1K **Privately Held**
SIC: 2431 Millwork

(G-6974)
WILL SHUTTER U INC
2087 Nw Marsh Rabbit Ln (34957-3524)
PHONE..................................772 285-3600
Cameron Corn, *Principal*
EMP: 6 **EST:** 2005
SALES (est): 86K **Privately Held**
SIC: 3442 Shutters, door or window: metal

Juno Beach
Palm Beach County

(G-6975)
BLUE SUMMIT WIND LLC (DH)
700 Universe Blvd (33408-2657)
PHONE..................................561 691-7171
Tj Tuscai, *Principal*
▲ **EMP:** 4 **EST:** 2012
SALES (est): 23.9MM
SALES (corp-wide): 18B **Publicly Held**
SIC: 3621 6719 Windmills, electric generating; investment holding companies, except banks
HQ: Esi Energy, Llc
700 Universe Blvd
Juno Beach FL 33408
561 691-7171

(G-6976)
BRADY WIND LLC
700 Universe Blvd (33408-2657)
PHONE..................................561 304-5136
EMP: 6 **EST:** 2016
SALES (est): 329.4K **Privately Held**
SIC: 3511 Hydraulic turbines

(G-6977)
BRU BOTTLING INC
1507 Villa Juno Dr N (33408-2258)
PHONE..................................561 324-5053
Gerard George, *Principal*
EMP: 8 **EST:** 2016
SALES (est): 296.1K **Privately Held**
SIC: 2037 Fruit juices

(G-6978)
CLEAN CUT INTL LLC
14255 Us Highway 1 (33408-1490)
PHONE..................................866 599-7066
Winfield S Anderson Jr, *Mng Member*
Sharon Haas, *Manager*
Tom Little,
▲ **EMP:** 10 **EST:** 2009
SQ FT: 1,000
SALES (est): 1.3MM **Privately Held**
SIC: 3634 3639 Electric housewares & fans; major kitchen appliances, except refrigerators & stoves

(G-6979)
EIQ MOBILITY INC
700 Universe Blvd (33408-2657)
PHONE..................................561 691-7171
John Ketchum, *CEO*
EMP: 9 **EST:** 2018
SALES: 283.6K
SALES (corp-wide): 18B **Publicly Held**
WEB: www.eiqmobility.com
SIC: 2451 Mobile homes
HQ: Nextera Energy Resources, Llc
700 Universe Blvd
Juno Beach FL 33408
561 691-7171

(G-6980)
FPL ENERGY OKLAHOMA WIND LLC
700 Universe Blvd (33408-2657)
PHONE..................................561 691-7171
Tj Tuscai, *Principal*
EMP: 1 **EST:** 2012
SALES (est): 11.1MM
SALES (corp-wide): 18B **Publicly Held**
SIC: 3621 4911 Windmills, electric generating; distribution, electric power
HQ: Fpl Energy National Wind, Llc
700 Universe Blvd
Juno Beach FL 33408

(G-6981)
NEXTERA FIBERNET LLC
700 Universe Blvd (33408-2657)
PHONE..................................866 787-2637

GEOGRAPHIC

Carmen Perez, *President*
EMP: 72 **EST:** 2010
SALES (est): 4.7MM
SALES (corp-wide): 18B **Publicly Held**
WEB: www.nexteraenergy.com
SIC: 3661 Fiber optics communications equipment
HQ: Nextera Energy Capital Holdings, Inc.
700 Universe Blvd
Juno Beach FL 33408
561 694-6311

(G-6982)
PHEASANT RUN WIND LLC
700 Universe Blvd (33408-2657)
PHONE..................................561 691-7171
John W Ketchum, *Principal*
EMP: 1 **EST:** 2013
SALES (est): 4.2MM
SALES (corp-wide): 18B **Publicly Held**
SIC: 3621 Windmills, electric generating
HQ: Pheasant Run Wind Holdings, Llc
700 Universe Blvd
Juno Beach FL 33408
561 691-7171

(G-6983)
PHEASANT RUN WIND HOLDINGS II (DH)
700 Universe Blvd (33408-2657)
PHONE..................................561 691-7171
John W Ketchum, *Mng Member*
EMP: 49 **EST:** 2013
SALES (est): 4.4MM
SALES (corp-wide): 18B **Publicly Held**
SIC: 3621 Windmills, electric generating
HQ: Esi Energy, Llc
700 Universe Blvd
Juno Beach FL 33408
561 691-7171

(G-6984)
TBC RETAIL GROUP INC
Also Called: Big O Tires
823 Donald Ross Rd (33408-1605)
PHONE..................................702 395-2100
EMP: 8
SALES (corp-wide): 35.1B **Privately Held**
SIC: 3011 7538 Mfg Tires/Inner Tubes General Auto Repair
HQ: Tbc Retail Group, Inc.
4280 Prof Ctr Dr Ste 400
Palm Beach Gardens FL 33410
561 383-3000

(G-6985)
TUSCOLA WIND II LLC
700 Universe Blvd (33408-2657)
PHONE..................................561 691-7171
Tj Tuscai, *Principal*
EMP: 1 **EST:** 2012
SALES (est): 33.7MM
SALES (corp-wide): 18B **Publicly Held**
SIC: 3621 4911 Windmills, electric generating; distribution, electric power
HQ: Esi Energy, Llc
700 Universe Blvd
Juno Beach FL 33408
561 691-7171

(G-6986)
VASCO WINDS LLC
700 Universe Blvd (33408-2657)
PHONE..................................561 691-7171
Tj Tuscai, *Principal*
EMP: 1 **EST:** 2011
SALES (est): 9.4MM
SALES (corp-wide): 18B **Publicly Held**
SIC: 3621 4911 Windmills, electric generating; electric services
HQ: Esi Energy, Llc
700 Universe Blvd
Juno Beach FL 33408
561 691-7171

(G-6987)
WHITE OAK ENERGY BACKLEVERAGE (DH)
700 Universe Blvd (33408-2657)
PHONE..................................561 691-7171
T J Tuscai, *Mng Member*
EMP: 38 **EST:** 2011
SALES (est): 14.8MM
SALES (corp-wide): 18B **Publicly Held**
WEB: www.whiteoakenergy.com
SIC: 3621 4911 Windmills, electric generating; electric services
HQ: Esi Energy, Llc
700 Universe Blvd
Juno Beach FL 33408
561 691-7171

(G-6988)
WHITE OAK ENERGY HOLDINGS LLC
700 Universe Blvd (33408-2657)
PHONE..................................561 691-7171
T J Tuscai, *President*
Ryan Jones, *Manager*
EMP: 1 **EST:** 2010
SALES (est): 7.6MM
SALES (corp-wide): 18B **Publicly Held**
WEB: www.whiteoakenergy.com
SIC: 3621 Windmills, electric generating
HQ: Esi Energy, Llc
700 Universe Blvd
Juno Beach FL 33408
561 691-7171

(G-6989)
WILTON WIND II LLC
700 Universe Blvd (33408-2657)
PHONE..................................561 691-7171
T J Tuscai, *President*
Dean Gosselin, *Vice Pres*
Charles S Schultz, *Admin Sec*
EMP: 1 **EST:** 2008
SALES (est): 3.8MM
SALES (corp-wide): 18B **Publicly Held**
SIC: 3621 4911 Windmills, electric generating; electric services
HQ: Esi Energy, Llc
700 Universe Blvd
Juno Beach FL 33408
561 691-7171

Jupiter
Palm Beach County

(G-6990)
6 PORTS LLC
Also Called: In-O-Vate Technologies
250 S Central Blvd # 207 (33458-8812)
PHONE..................................561 743-8696
James Ortiz, *Vice Pres*
Todd Peach, *Vice Pres*
Richard J Harpenau,
Karen A Harpenau,
◆ **EMP:** 12 **EST:** 2019
SQ FT: 1,000
SALES (est): 2.7MM **Privately Held**
WEB: www.dryerbox.com
SIC: 3499 Metal household articles

(G-6991)
A AND J SHEET METAL INC
1567 Cypress Dr (33469-3137)
PHONE..................................561 746-4048
Kari E Neville, *CEO*
Suki Atwal, *Vice Pres*
Zenelia Aguilar, *Manager*
EMP: 6 **EST:** 1997
SQ FT: 5,900
SALES (est): 1.1MM **Privately Held**
WEB: www.ajsheetmetals.com
SIC: 3699 1761 1531 Laser welding, drilling & cutting equipment; roofing, siding & sheet metal work;

(G-6992)
A TEK STEEL INDUSTRIES INC
3 Turtle Creek Dr (33469-1593)
PHONE..................................561 745-2858
Bryan McIntyre, *Principal*
EMP: 7 **EST:** 2004
SALES (est): 212.7K **Privately Held**
SIC: 3479 Metal coating & allied service

(G-6993)
ADVANCED FUEL INJECTION
211 S Hampton Dr (33458-8112)
PHONE..................................561 248-6793
Fran Sirico, *Principal*
EMP: 6 **EST:** 2012
SALES (est): 171.5K **Privately Held**
WEB: www.fuelinjectorclinic.com
SIC: 2869 Fuels

(G-6994)
AERO-FLEX CORP
3147 Jupiter Park Cir # 2 (33458-6027)
PHONE..................................561 745-2534
Joshua Deakter, *Principal*
Eric Hobart, *Program Mgr*
EMP: 20 **EST:** 2008
SALES (est): 3.9MM **Privately Held**
WEB: www.aero-flex.aero
SIC: 3728 Aircraft parts & equipment

(G-6995)
AEROJET ROCKETDYNE INC
15270 Endeavor Dr (33478-6447)
P.O. Box 109680, Palm Beach Gardens (33410-9680)
PHONE..................................561 796-2000
Andrew Haas, *Engineer*
George Prueger, *Senior Mgr*
James Maus, *Exec Dir*
Natalie Schilling, *Officer*
Brent Bonar, *Technician*
EMP: 400 **EST:** 2013
SALES (est): 43.1MM **Privately Held**
WEB: www.rocket.com
SIC: 3764 Guided missile & space vehicle propulsion unit parts

(G-6996)
AEROJET ROCKETDYNE DE INC
Pratt & Whitney
17900 Bee Line Hwy (33478-6414)
P.O. Box 109600, West Palm Beach (33410-9600)
PHONE..................................561 882-5150
Gary Halker, *Project Mgr*
Roger Lawrence, *Senior Buyer*
Kevin Hopwood, *Engineer*
Stephen Ogburn, *Engineer*
Oreste Giusti, *Senior Engr*
EMP: 200
SALES (corp-wide): 2B **Publicly Held**
WEB: www.rocket.com
SIC: 2869 3724 Rocket engine fuel, organic; aircraft engines & engine parts
HQ: Inc Aerojet Rocketdyne Of De
8900 De Soto Ave
Canoga Park CA 91304
818 586-1000

(G-6997)
AGPB LLC
Also Called: AlphaGraphics
800 W Indiantown Rd (33458-7501)
PHONE..................................561 935-4147
Timothy J Kerbs, *Mng Member*
Jenn Kerbs,
EMP: 12 **EST:** 2006
SALES (est): 2.9MM **Privately Held**
WEB: www.alphagraphics.com
SIC: 2752 Commercial printing, lithographic

(G-6998)
AGROSOURCE INC
166 Beacon Ln (33469-3504)
P.O. Box 3091, Tequesta (33469-1000)
PHONE..................................908 251-3500
Taw Richardson, *President*
Rene Amundson, *Opers Staff*
EMP: 12 **EST:** 2015
SALES (est): 1.1MM **Privately Held**
SIC: 2879 Insecticides, agricultural or household; pesticides, agricultural or household

(G-6999)
ALLOY CLADDING
15850 Guild Ct (33478-6436)
PHONE..................................561 625-4550
Robert Burns, *Principal*
Robert Macdonald, *Vice Pres*
David Wiggin, *CFO*
Cecil Feagin, *Supervisor*
EMP: 42 **EST:** 2008
SALES (est): 5.8MM **Privately Held**
WEB: www.alloycladding.com
SIC: 3842 Welders' hoods

(G-7000)
ANDREW MJ INC
10152 Indiantown Rd (33478-4707)
PHONE..................................561 575-6032
Jane Miller, *Principal*
EMP: 8 **EST:** 2008
SALES (est): 188K **Privately Held**
SIC: 3651 Household audio & video equipment

(G-7001)
ASSOCATE CBINETMAKERS PALM BCH
134 Toney Penna Dr (33458-5751)
PHONE..................................561 743-9566
Michael Odell, *President*
EMP: 5 **EST:** 1992
SQ FT: 1,250
SALES (est): 439.6K **Privately Held**
WEB: www.associatedcabinetspalm-beach.com
SIC: 2434 Wood kitchen cabinets

(G-7002)
AVSTAR FUEL SYSTEMS INC
1365 Park Ln S (33458-8042)
PHONE..................................561 575-1560
Ronald Weaver, *President*
Henry Hildebrandt, *Opers Staff*
Katia Fuentes, *Buyer*
Jacqueline Weaver, *Human Resources*
Eric Weaver, *Director*
EMP: 8 **EST:** 2007
SALES (est): 2.1MM **Privately Held**
WEB: www.avstardirect.com
SIC: 3724 Aircraft engines & engine parts

(G-7003)
BARON INTERNATIONAL LLC
Also Called: Baron Sign Manufacturing
17180 Innovation Dr (33478-6445)
PHONE..................................800 531-9558
Kimberly G Nemic,
Tom Nemic,
EMP: 11 **EST:** 2018
SALES (est): 997.1K **Privately Held**
WEB: www.baronsign.com
SIC: 3993 Signs & advertising specialties

(G-7004)
BASHERS RC RACEWAY LLC
155 Galicia Way Apt 103 (33458-2742)
PHONE..................................561 889-9386
Brian Buckley, *Principal*
EMP: 6 **EST:** 2009
SALES (est): 100.1K **Privately Held**
SIC: 3644 Raceways

(G-7005)
BEACON PHRM JUPITER LLC
210 Military Trl (33458-5786)
PHONE..................................212 991-8988
Philippe Gastone, *CEO*
Nancy Torres Kaufman, *Ch of Bd*
Martin Weisberg,
EMP: 50 **EST:** 2019
SALES (est): 1.8MM **Privately Held**
WEB: www.beaconpharmaceutical.com
SIC: 2834 8731 Pharmaceutical preparations; commercial physical research

(G-7006)
BERMAN PRODUCTS LLC
19558 Red Gum Trl (33458-2473)
PHONE..................................561 743-5197
Robert S Berman MD,
EMP: 10 **EST:** 2009
SALES (est): 843.6K **Privately Held**
WEB: www.bermanresearch.org
SIC: 2834 Pharmaceutical preparations

(G-7007)
BEVERLY ACQUISITIONS INC (PA)
Also Called: Schrappers Fine Cabinetry
240 W Indiantown Rd # 101 (33458-3548)
PHONE..................................561 746-3827
Beverly Levine, *President*
Keith Levine, *Vice Pres*
EMP: 11 **EST:** 1976
SQ FT: 8,000
SALES (est): 3MM **Privately Held**
SIC: 2434 Vanities, bathroom: wood

(G-7008)
BEYONDCLEAN LLC
601 Heritage Dr Ste 422 (33458-2777)
PHONE.................................561 799-5710
Helen P Troup, *Mng Member*
Lloyd Hanson, *CTO*
EMP: 10 **EST:** 2004
SALES (est): 696.7K **Privately Held**
WEB: www.gobeyondclean.com
SIC: 2842 Specialty cleaning preparations

(G-7009)
BIO-REVIVAL LLC
661 Maplewood Dr Ste 21 (33458-5569)
PHONE.................................561 667-3990
Liudmila Karimova, *President*
Eugene Richter, *Vice Pres*
EMP: 10 **EST:** 2015
SQ FT: 1,800
SALES (est): 540K **Privately Held**
WEB: www.bio-revival.com
SIC: 2099 Food preparations

(G-7010)
BIOCHEM MANUFACTURING INC
15074 Pk Of Commerce Blvd
(33478-6424)
PHONE.................................561 799-1590
Jorge Cepeda, *President*
Nely Cepeda, *Vice Pres*
Violeta Cepeda, *Vice Pres*
▲ **EMP:** 21 **EST:** 2012
SALES (est): 1.5MM **Privately Held**
SIC: 2879 Agricultural disinfectants

(G-7011)
BIOCHEMICAL MANUFACTURING INC
15074 Pk Of Commerce Blvd
(33478-6424)
PHONE.................................561 799-1590
George Cepeda, *President*
EMP: 7 **EST:** 2011
SALES (est): 363.8K **Privately Held**
SIC: 3999 Manufacturing industries

(G-7012)
BLUE HOLE HELICOPTERS INC
3161 Se Chandelle Rd (33478-1909)
PHONE.................................561 723-0378
Brian T Parker Sr, *Principal*
EMP: 10 **EST:** 2007
SALES (est): 121.2K **Privately Held**
SIC: 3721 Helicopters

(G-7013)
BOCA SMOOTHIES LLC
935 Military Trl Ste 102 (33458-7009)
PHONE.................................772 323-2117
Brian F Labovick, *Principal*
EMP: 6 **EST:** 2005
SALES (est): 97.8K **Privately Held**
SIC: 2037 Frozen fruits & vegetables

(G-7014)
CAMCO CORP
1829 Park Ln S Ste 9 (33458-8086)
PHONE.................................561 427-0433
Barbara Roginski, *Principal*
EMP: 8 **EST:** 2004
SALES (est): 168K **Privately Held**
WEB: www.camcohealthcare.com
SIC: 3442 Shutters, door or window: metal

(G-7015)
CARLING TECHNOLOGIES INC
120 Intracoastal Cir # 100 (33469-2709)
PHONE.................................561 745-0405
Richard Sorenson, *Principal*
EMP: 8
SALES (corp-wide): 1.5MM **Privately Held**
WEB: www.carlingtech.com
SIC: 3699 Electrical equipment & supplies
PA: Carling Technologies, Inc.
60 Johnson Ave
Plainville CT 06062
860 793-9281

(G-7016)
CBD BRANDS INC
725 N Highway A1a C106 (33477-4565)
PHONE.................................561 325-0482
EMP: 7
SALES (est): 81.8K **Privately Held**
SIC: 2844 Toilet preparations

(G-7017)
CEMEX CNSTR MTLS FLA LLC
Also Called: Materials Div-Jupiter Lab
1557 Jupiter Park Dr # 1 (33458-8083)
PHONE.................................561 745-5240
Mike Epifano, *Manager*
EMP: 10 **Privately Held**
SIC: 3273 Ready-mixed concrete
HQ: Cemex Construction Materials Florida, Llc
1501 Belvedere Rd
West Palm Beach FL 33406

(G-7018)
CEMEX MATERIALS LLC
282 Old Dixie Hwy (33469-2753)
P.O. Box 3331 (33469-1005)
PHONE.................................561 746-4556
Floyd Gallow, *Branch Mgr*
EMP: 73 **Privately Held**
SIC: 3271 3273 3272 3444 Concrete block & brick; ready-mixed concrete; concrete products; sheet metalwork; cut stone & stone products
HQ: Cemex Materials Llc
1501 Belvedere Rd
West Palm Beach FL 33406
561 833-5555

(G-7019)
CEMEX MATERIALS LLC
1001 Jupiter Park Dr # 108 (33458-6002)
PHONE.................................561 743-4039
Jesse Deurer, *Branch Mgr*
EMP: 73 **Privately Held**
SIC: 3271 3273 3272 1422 Blocks, concrete or cinder: standard; ready-mixed concrete; concrete products used to facilitate drainage; crushed & broken limestone
HQ: Cemex Materials Llc
1501 Belvedere Rd
West Palm Beach FL 33406
561 833-5555

(G-7020)
CSA INTERNATIONAL INC
759 Parkway (33477-4505)
PHONE.................................561 746-7946
EMP: 30
SALES (est): 3.2MM **Privately Held**
SIC: 3531 Mfg Construction Machinery

(G-7021)
CSC RACING CORPORATION
Also Called: Rjs Racing Equipment
15819 Guild Ct B (33478-6436)
PHONE.................................248 548-5727
Robert Farmer, *President*
Cheryl Pemberton, *Vice Pres*
▲ **EMP:** 15 **EST:** 1959
SQ FT: 15,000
SALES (est): 1.2MM **Privately Held**
WEB: www.rjsracing.com
SIC: 2399 2326 Seat belts, automobile & aircraft; men's & boys' work clothing

(G-7022)
CV TECHNOLOGY INC
15852 Mercantile Ct # 100 (33478-6437)
PHONE.................................561 694-9588
David Cvetas, *CEO*
Marty Cvetas, *President*
Bob Cudnik, *Vice Pres*
Jillian Gruss, *Engineer*
Nicholas Licht, *Engineer*
EMP: 36 **EST:** 1994
SQ FT: 29,000
SALES (est): 9.7MM **Privately Held**
WEB: www.cvtechnology.com
SIC: 3823 8748 1731 Infrared instruments, industrial process type; industrial process control instruments; environmental consultant; fire detection & burglar alarm systems specialization

(G-7023)
DB TUCKER LLC
126 S Village Way (33458-7828)
PHONE.................................561 301-4974
Dolores Dioguardi, *President*
EMP: 7 **EST:** 2015
SALES (est): 190.9K **Privately Held**
SIC: 3634 5072 Housewares, excluding cooking appliances & utensils; hand tools

(G-7024)
DL MYERS CORP
5500 Military Trl Ste 22 (33458-2871)
PHONE.................................609 698-8800
Darren L Myers, *President*
EMP: 10
SALES (est): 900K **Privately Held**
SIC: 3443 Fuel tanks (oil, gas, etc.): metal plate

(G-7025)
DOLPHIN SHEET METAL INC
142 Jupiter St (33458-4929)
PHONE.................................561 744-0242
Rachelle Wood, *President*
Bradley Wood, *Contractor*
EMP: 18 **EST:** 1987
SQ FT: 3,900
SALES: 343.9K **Privately Held**
WEB: www.dolphinsheetmetal.com
SIC: 3444 Awnings, sheet metal

(G-7026)
DONALD ROSS GAS INC
225 Skylark Pt (33458-8307)
PHONE.................................561 776-1324
Jay Goldwasser, *President*
EMP: 9 **EST:** 2005
SALES (est): 328.8K **Privately Held**
SIC: 2911 Gases & liquefied petroleum gases

(G-7027)
DYADIC INTERNATIONAL INC (PA)
140 Intrcostal Pt Dr # 404 (33477-5094)
PHONE.................................561 743-8333
Michael P Tarnok, *Ch of Bd*
Mark A Emalfarb, *President*
Ronen Tchelet, *Vice Pres*
Ping W Rawson, *CFO*
Heidi Zosiak, *Executive Asst*
▲ **EMP:** 5 **EST:** 1979
SQ FT: 2,000
SALES: 1.6MM **Publicly Held**
WEB: www.dyadic.com
SIC: 2836 Biological products, except diagnostic

(G-7028)
DYADIC INTERNATIONAL USA INC (HQ)
Also Called: Dyadic Industries Intl
140 Intrcostal Pt Dr # 404 (33477-5094)
PHONE.................................561 743-8333
Harry Rosengart, *Ch of Bd*
David Hooper, *COO*
◆ **EMP:** 5 **EST:** 1979
SALES (est): 592.2K
SALES (corp-wide): 1.6MM **Publicly Held**
WEB: www.dyadic.com
SIC: 2842 2899 5169 5032 Fabric softeners; chemical preparations; industrial chemicals; stone, crushed or broken; cut stone & stone products; brick & structural clay tile
PA: Dyadic International, Inc.
140 Intrcostal Pt Dr # 404
Jupiter FL 33477
561 743-8333

(G-7029)
DYN-O-MAT INC
1201 Jupiter Park Dr # 1 (33458-8084)
PHONE.................................561 747-2301
Mike Yourwicz, *Sales Mgr*
EMP: 6 **EST:** 2017
SALES (est): 46.5K **Privately Held**
SIC: 2273 Carpets & rugs

(G-7030)
DYNOMAT INC
Also Called: Environmental Aborbent Pdts
1201 Jupiter Park Dr (33458-8084)
PHONE.................................561 747-2301
Peter Cordani, *CEO*
Michael Cordani, *COO*
EMP: 35 **EST:** 1994
SQ FT: 1,450
SALES (est): 2MM **Privately Held**
SIC: 2273 Carpets & rugs

(G-7031)
ECOLAB INC
1201 Jupiter Park Dr # 1 (33458-8084)
PHONE.................................800 931-8911
EMP: 15
SALES (corp-wide): 11.7B **Publicly Held**
SIC: 3999 2841 3432 Mfg Misc Products Mfg Soap/Other Detergents Mfg Plumbing Fixture Fittings
PA: Ecolab Inc.
1 Ecolab Pl
Saint Paul MN 55102
800 232-6522

(G-7032)
EDWARD THOMAS COMPANY
Also Called: Smartcolor Graphics
185 E Indiantown Rd # 114 (33477-5071)
PHONE.................................561 746-1441
Tom Beckett, *President*
EMP: 7 **EST:** 1987
SQ FT: 2,700
SALES (est): 869K **Privately Held**
SIC: 2752 2791 Commercial printing, offset; typesetting

(G-7033)
ELK CREEK WINE
4392 Nicole Cir (33469-2572)
PHONE.................................561 529-2822
Curtis Sigretto, *Principal*
EMP: 8 **EST:** 2013
SALES (est): 209.9K **Privately Held**
WEB: www.elkcreekvineyards.com
SIC: 2084 Wines

(G-7034)
ELLISON GRAPHICS CORP
1400 W Indiantown Rd (33458-7998)
P.O. Box 937 (33468-0937)
PHONE.................................561 746-9256
Nicholas E Litwin, *President*
Robert Herlin, *Vice Pres*
EMP: 15 **EST:** 1972
SQ FT: 21,000
SALES (est): 500.8K **Privately Held**
WEB: www.ellisongraphics.com
SIC: 2752 Commercial printing, offset

(G-7035)
ENVOY THERAPEUTICS INC
555 Heritage Dr Ste 150 (33458-5290)
PHONE.................................561 210-7705
EMP: 6 **EST:** 2019
SALES (est): 266.1K **Privately Held**
SIC: 2834 Pharmaceutical preparations

(G-7036)
ERRICO CUSTOM WOODWORKS INC
11637 153rd Ct N (33478-3564)
PHONE.................................561 306-0046
E Joseph Errico, *Principal*
EMP: 6 **EST:** 2019
SALES (est): 59.5K **Privately Held**
SIC: 2431 Millwork

(G-7037)
EXHAUST TECHNOLOGIES INC
851 Jupiter Park Ln (33458-8959)
PHONE.................................561 744-9500
Barton Swank, *President*
Robert E Sterling, *President*
William A Sutherland, *Corp Secy*
▲ **EMP:** 8 **EST:** 1998
SALES (est): 3MM
SALES (corp-wide): 49.1MM **Publicly Held**
WEB: www.florida-pneumatic.com
SIC: 3714 Motor vehicle parts & accessories
HQ: Florida Pneumatic Manufacturing Corporation
851 Jupiter Park Ln Ste A
Jupiter FL 33458
561 744-9500

(G-7038)
EZ NEON INC
12179 179th Ct N (33478-4610)
PHONE.................................561 262-7813
James Mackey, *President*
EMP: 7 **EST:** 2011
SALES (est): 98.6K **Privately Held**
SIC: 2813 Neon

GEOGRAPHIC

(G-7039)
F L F CORP
810 Saturn St Ste 28 (33477-4456)
PHONE....................................561 747-7077
Richard Reina, *Principal*
EMP: 7 **EST:** 2008
SALES (est): 192.1K **Privately Held**
SIC: 2741 Miscellaneous publishing

(G-7040)
FASHION POOL USA INC
6111 Linton St (33458-6745)
PHONE....................................970 367-4797
Hans Taubenberger, *President*
EMP: 5 **EST:** 2009
SALES (est): 907K
SALES (corp-wide): 2.2MM **Privately Held**
WEB: www.tonisailer.com
SIC: 2339 2329 5136 5137 Women's & misses' outerwear; men's & boys' leather, wool & down-filled outerwear; men's & boys' outerwear; women's & children's outerwear
PA: Fashion Pool Gmbh Textilagentur & Vertrieb
St.-Ottilien-Weg 11
Grasbrunn 85630
810 637-7883

(G-7041)
FASULO GRANITE & MARBLE INC
368 River Edge Rd (33477-9344)
PHONE....................................561 371-5410
Laura Fasulo, *President*
John Fasulo, *Vice Pres*
EMP: 8 **EST:** 2004
SALES (est): 79.7K **Privately Held**
SIC: 3281 Granite, cut & shaped

(G-7042)
FIMCO MANUFACTURING INC
15795 Corporate Rd N (33478-6421)
P.O. Box 300 (33468-0300)
PHONE....................................561 624-3308
Roger D Slagel, *President*
Donna Slagel, *Corp Secy*
Gunther Albert, *Vice Pres*
Janet Albert, *Admin Sec*
EMP: 7 **EST:** 1962
SQ FT: 10,000
SALES (est): 986.4K **Privately Held**
WEB: www.fimcomfg.com
SIC: 3089 Injection molding of plastics

(G-7043)
FIRST CLASS MEDIA INC
1003 Jupiter Park Ln # 5 (33458-8909)
PHONE....................................561 719-3433
Daniel Moody, *Principal*
EMP: 6 **EST:** 2007
SALES (est): 900K **Privately Held**
SIC: 2711 Newspapers

(G-7044)
FLORIDA EMBROIDERED PATCH &
1095 Jupiter Park Dr # 8 (33458-8972)
PHONE....................................561 748-9356
▲ **EMP:** 18
SALES (est): 891.3K **Privately Held**
SIC: 2395 Pleating/Stitching Services

(G-7045)
FLORIDA TURBINE TECH INC (HQ)
1701 Military Trl Ste 110 (33458-6331)
PHONE....................................561 427-6400
Shirley Brostmeyer, *President*
Dean Johnson, *Dean*
Jesse Eng, *Chief Engr*
Wm Plank, *Chief Engr*
Dan Davies, *Engineer*
EMP: 5 **EST:** 1998
SQ FT: 63,000
SALES (est): 44.9MM **Publicly Held**
WEB: www.kratosdefense.com
SIC: 3724 8711 Aircraft engines & engine parts; consulting engineer

(G-7046)
FLOTTEC LLC (PA)
19100 Se Reach Island Ln (33458-1125)
PHONE....................................973 588-4717
Frank Cappuccitti,
◆ **EMP:** 3 **EST:** 2006
SALES (est): 4MM **Privately Held**
WEB: www.flottec.com
SIC: 2879 Trace elements (agricultural chemicals)

(G-7047)
GATOR WELDING INC
201 Jupiter St (33458-4997)
PHONE....................................561 746-0049
Kenneth Nogal, *President*
Carey Nogal, *Vice Pres*
Alayne Nogal, *Treasurer*
EMP: 15 **EST:** 1967
SQ FT: 3,800
SALES (est): 1.1MM **Privately Held**
WEB: www.gatorwelding.com
SIC: 7692 Welding repair

(G-7048)
GELTECH SOLUTIONS INC
1460 Park Ln S Ste 1 (33458-8079)
PHONE....................................561 427-6144
Michael Reger, *Ch of Bd*
Gerry Kaiser, *Vice Pres*
Matthew Struzziero, *Vice Pres*
Michael Hull, *CFO*
Matt Struzziero, *Sales Staff*
EMP: 20 **EST:** 2006
SALES (est): 4.9MM **Privately Held**
WEB: www.geltechsolutions.com
SIC: 2899 Fire retardant chemicals

(G-7049)
GLOBAL PHARMA ANALYTICS LLC
225 Chimney Corner Ln # 30 (33458-4803)
PHONE....................................701 491-7770
Theresa Crawford, *Controller*
S Chandrasekhar,
EMP: 15 **EST:** 2013
SALES (est): 1.1MM **Privately Held**
WEB: www.somahlution.com
SIC: 2834 Pharmaceutical preparations

(G-7050)
GOLD COFFEE ROASTERS INC
1425 Park Ln S (33458-8081)
P.O. Box 719 (33468-0719)
PHONE....................................561 746-8110
John Parry, *President*
Jessie Parry, *Treasurer*
EMP: 12 **EST:** 1999
SQ FT: 2,000
SALES (est): 430.3K **Privately Held**
SIC: 2095 Coffee roasting (except by wholesale grocers); instant coffee; coffee extracts

(G-7051)
GRAFLEX INC
15855 Assembly Loop # 100 (33478-6431)
PHONE....................................561 691-5959
Paul Ganther, *President*
HB Brad Ganther, *President*
Jennifer Ganther, *Vice Pres*
Angela C Ganther, *Treasurer*
Jaimie Heard, *Info Tech Mgr*
EMP: 6 **EST:** 1993
SQ FT: 6,000
SALES (est): 1.4MM **Privately Held**
WEB: www.graflex.com
SIC: 3827 Lenses, optical: all types except ophthalmic; sighting & fire control equipment, optical

(G-7052)
HEMARUS LLC-JCKSNVLE PLSMA CTR
601 Heritage Dr 118 (33458-2777)
PHONE....................................904 642-1005
Chigurupati Jayaram, *Manager*
EMP: 5 **EST:** 2010
SALES (est): 319.4K **Privately Held**
SIC: 2836 Plasmas

(G-7053)
HOLTEC INTERNATIONAL (PA)
1001 N Us Highway 1 (33477-4482)
PHONE....................................561 745-7772
Kris Singh, *President*
Pankaj Chaudry, *Senior VP*
Pierre Paul Oneid, *Senior VP*
Robert R Galvin, *CFO*
Matthew Ogrinc, *Sales Staff*
◆ **EMP:** 100 **EST:** 1986
SQ FT: 38,000
SALES (est): 848.3MM **Privately Held**
WEB: www.holtecinternational.com
SIC: 2819 8711 Nuclear fuel scrap, reprocessing; engineering services

(G-7054)
HOWARD SCRIPTS INC
Also Called: Jupiter Courier
800 W Indiantown Rd (33458-7501)
P.O. Box 9009, Stuart (34995-9009)
PHONE....................................561 746-5111
Ken Lowe, *President*
EMP: 9 **EST:** 2001
SALES (est): 508.3K **Privately Held**
SIC: 2711 2741 Newspapers: publishing only, not printed on site; miscellaneous publishing

(G-7055)
IMAGINATION CREATIONS INC
2895 Jupiter Park Dr # 300 (33458-6038)
PHONE....................................561 744-7802
Kathy K Link, *President*
Donna Kurtz, *Vice Pres*
Jackie Link, *Opers Mgr*
EMP: 22 **EST:** 1992
SQ FT: 3,800
SALES (est): 701.4K **Privately Held**
WEB: www.imaginationcreationsinc.com
SIC: 2353 Hats, caps & millinery

(G-7056)
IN THE BITE
342 Toney Penna Dr (33458-5774)
PHONE....................................561 529-3940
Dale Wills, *Principal*
EMP: 12 **EST:** 2016
SALES (est): 279K **Privately Held**
WEB: www.inthebite.com
SIC: 2721 Periodicals: publishing only

(G-7057)
INTEGRITY TECHNOLOGIES LLC
Also Called: Integrity Medical
5270 Pennock Point Rd (33458-3446)
PHONE....................................561 768-9023
Christopher Walsh, *President*
EMP: 8 **EST:** 2010
SALES (est): 372.1K **Privately Held**
SIC: 3069 Medical & laboratory rubber sundries & related products

(G-7058)
INTER CELL TECHNOLOGIES INC
Also Called: Art and Orchid Gallery, The
6671 W Indiantown Rd # 56439 (33458-3991)
PHONE....................................561 575-6868
EMP: 8
SQ FT: 1,400
SALES: 100K **Privately Held**
SIC: 2836 2865 2835 2834 Mfg Biological Products Mfg Cyclic Crudes/Intrmd Mfg Diagnostic Substance

(G-7059)
J-COAST WOODWORKS LLC
1312 Commerce Ln (33458-5685)
PHONE....................................561 262-6144
EMP: 7 **EST:** 2019
SALES (est): 512K **Privately Held**
SIC: 2431 Millwork

(G-7060)
JENOPTIK NORTH AMERICA INC (HQ)
16490 Innovation Dr (33478-6449)
PHONE....................................561 881-7400
Jay Kumler, *President*
Desiree R Yacko, *Export Mgr*
Jonathan Braun, *Engineer*
Amir Tal, *Engineer*
Hubertus Moller, *Controller*
EMP: 250 **EST:** 2009
SQ FT: 80,000
SALES (est): 191.8MM
SALES (corp-wide): 907.3MM **Privately Held**
WEB: www.jenoptik.com
SIC: 3827 Optical instruments & lenses
PA: Jenoptik Ag
Carl-Zeiss-Str. 1
Jena 07743
364 165-0

(G-7061)
JENOPTIK OPTICAL SYSTEMS LLC (DH)
16490 Innovation Dr Ste A (33478-6449)
PHONE....................................561 881-7400
Ralf Kuschnereit, *Ch of Bd*
Lorna Carson, *President*
James Kumler, *President*
Marvin Loveless, *General Mgr*
Marc Himel, *Business Mgr*
▲ **EMP:** 166 **EST:** 1991
SQ FT: 45,000
SALES (est): 40.3MM
SALES (corp-wide): 907.3MM **Privately Held**
WEB: www.jenoptik.us
SIC: 3827 Optical instruments & lenses

(G-7062)
JUPITER PETROLEUM INC
5490 Military Trl (33458-2862)
PHONE....................................561 622-1276
Nuruddin Sheikh, *Manager*
EMP: 7 **EST:** 2017
SALES (est): 205.4K **Privately Held**
SIC: 2911 Petroleum refining

(G-7063)
JUPITER WELLNESS INC
1061 E Indiantown Rd # 110 (33477-5143)
PHONE....................................561 462-2700
Brian John, *CEO*
Rich Miller, *Principal*
EMP: 9 **EST:** 2018
SALES (est): 4MM **Privately Held**
SIC: 2844 7389 Face creams or lotions;

(G-7064)
JUST ENGINES
209 Circle W (33458-7517)
PHONE....................................561 575-2681
Stephen P Gropp, *Owner*
EMP: 6 **EST:** 2013
SALES (est): 169.5K **Privately Held**
SIC: 3519 Internal combustion engines

(G-7065)
KN MACHINE & TOOLS INC
3125 Jupiter Park Cir # 4 (33458-6028)
PHONE....................................561 748-3035
Khoa V Nguyen, *President*
EMP: 13 **EST:** 2000
SQ FT: 5,000
SALES (est): 2MM **Privately Held**
WEB: www.knmachine.com
SIC: 3599 Machine shop, jobbing & repair

(G-7066)
LARTER & SONS
83 River Dr (33469-1950)
PHONE....................................732 290-1515
Stephen G Schutz, *CEO*
EMP: 85 **EST:** 1865
SALES (est): 6.5MM **Privately Held**
SIC: 3911 Medals, precious or semiprecious metal; jewel settings & mountings, precious metal; earrings, precious metal; rings, finger: precious metal

(G-7067)
LIGHTHOUSE BOATWORKS INC
512 N Hepburn Ave (33458-4956)
PHONE....................................561 667-7382
Thomas Land, *Principal*
EMP: 6 **EST:** 2016
SALES (est): 99K **Privately Held**
SIC: 3732 Boat building & repairing

(G-7068)
LIONHEART PRINTERS LLC
1312 Commerce Ln Ste A15 (33458-5640)
PHONE....................................561 781-8300
Enrique Sasson, *Mng Member*
Sasha Dash, *Mng Member*
EMP: 6 **EST:** 2018
SALES (est): 574.8K **Privately Held**
WEB: www.lhprinters.com
SIC: 2752 Commercial printing, lithographic

▲ = Import ▼=Export
◆ =Import/Export

(G-7069)
M Z MACHINE INC
3046 Jupiter Park Cir (33458-6011)
PHONE..................................561 744-2791
Mario Zola, *President*
Linda Zola, *Vice Pres*
EMP: 9 **EST:** 1987
SQ FT: 6,000
SALES (est): 1.3MM **Privately Held**
WEB: www.mzmachine.com
SIC: 3599 Machine shop, jobbing & repair

(G-7070)
M&M STUDIOS INC
1445 Jupiter Park Dr # 1 (33458-8936)
PHONE..................................561 744-2754
Marilyn Welch, *President*
EMP: 6 **EST:** 1972
SQ FT: 3,000
SALES (est): 442.9K **Privately Held**
WEB: www.mandmstudios.com
SIC: 3952 2759 Frames for artists' canvases; business forms: printing

(G-7071)
MADDOX INDUSTRIES INC
16401 134th Ter N (33478-6520)
PHONE..................................561 529-2165
Stephan Maddox, *President*
EMP: 7 **EST:** 2013
SALES (est): 194.6K **Privately Held**
WEB: www.maddoxindustriesinc.com
SIC: 3999 Manufacturing industries

(G-7072)
MAR-CO GAS SERVICES INC
11138 161st St N (33478-6188)
PHONE..................................561 745-0085
Mark Scoville, *President*
EMP: 6 **EST:** 2004
SALES (est): 527.6K **Privately Held**
WEB: www.marcogasservices.com
SIC: 1321 Natural gas liquids

(G-7073)
MARIZYME INC (PA)
555 Heritage Dr Ste 205 (33458-5290)
PHONE..................................561 935-9955
Vithalbhai Dhaduk, *Ch of Bd*
Amy Chandler, *Exec VP*
Roger Schaller, *Exec VP*
Donald Very, *Exec VP*
Bradley Richmond, *Vice Pres*
EMP: 6 **EST:** 2007
SALES (est): 197.1K **Publicly Held**
WEB: www.myprotectall.com
SIC: 2834 Pharmaceutical preparations

(G-7074)
MARLIN GRAPHICS INC
1251 Jupiter Park Dr # 7 (33458-8074)
PHONE..................................561 743-5220
Joseph Gonzalez Jr, *President*
EMP: 7 **EST:** 1991
SQ FT: 2,500
SALES (est): 797.2K **Privately Held**
WEB: www.marlingraphics.com
SIC: 2759 5943 5699 Commercial printing; office forms & supplies; customized clothing & apparel

(G-7075)
MAVERICK COMPOSITES INC
6105 Francis St (33458-6750)
PHONE..................................561 601-3393
Philip La Spina, *Principal*
EMP: 5 **EST:** 2014
SALES (est): 544.4K **Privately Held**
WEB: www.maverickcomposites.com
SIC: 3728 Aircraft parts & equipment

(G-7076)
MMATS INC
Also Called: Mmats Professional Audio
15132 Pk Of Commerce Blvd
(33478-6438)
PHONE..................................561 842-0600
Kathryn Speranza, *President*
Suzanne Hoffman, *Vice Pres*
▲ **EMP:** 24 **EST:** 1976
SQ FT: 15,000
SALES (est): 3.9MM **Privately Held**
WEB: www.mmatsproaudio.com
SIC: 3823 Computer interface equipment for industrial process control

(G-7077)
MODE MARIMBA INC
19960 Earlwood Dr (33458-1867)
PHONE..................................561 512-5001
EMP: 8 **EST:** 2016
SALES (est): 253.9K **Privately Held**
WEB: www.modemarimba.com
SIC: 3931 Marimbas

(G-7078)
MULTI PARTS SUPPLY USA INC
Also Called: Multiparts
1649 Park Ln S (33458-8076)
PHONE..................................561 748-1515
Brian S Cohn, *President*
Jeff Stankard, *President*
Barry Cohn, *Chairman*
Todd Wilson, *Engineer*
Nannette Cassidy, *CFO*
▲ **EMP:** 24 **EST:** 2005
SQ FT: 15,000
SALES (est): 4.7MM **Privately Held**
WEB: www.multiparts.net
SIC: 3714 Brake drums, motor vehicle; clutches, motor vehicle

(G-7079)
NANO SAFE COATINGS INC
5500 Military Trl Ste 22 (33458-2871)
PHONE..................................561 747-5758
Joseph Raich, *Vice Pres*
EMP: 8 **EST:** 2014
SALES (est): 502.1K **Privately Held**
SIC: 3479 Metal coating & allied service

(G-7080)
NEW TECHNOLOGY PRECISION MACHI
15300 Pk Of Commerce Blvd
(33478-6407)
PHONE..................................561 624-3830
Kateryna Larsen, *CEO*
John Larsen, *President*
EMP: 12 **EST:** 1977
SALES (est): 2.4MM **Privately Held**
WEB: www.newtechprecision.com
SIC: 3599 Machine shop, jobbing & repair

(G-7081)
NICHE DIGITAL MEDIA CORP
900 E Indiantown Rd # 312 (33477-5153)
P.O. Box 3214 (33469-1003)
PHONE..................................561 768-9793
Douglas S Commette, *Principal*
Margo Commette, *Principal*
EMP: 6 **EST:** 2016
SALES (est): 138.2K **Privately Held**
WEB: www.nichedigitalmedia.com
SIC: 2621 Magazine paper

(G-7082)
NITEO PRODUCTS LLC
Also Called: Cyclo Industries
902 S Us Highway 1 (33477-6404)
PHONE..................................561 745-1812
Doug Salazar, *Vice Pres*
EMP: 10
SALES (corp-wide): 194MM **Privately Held**
WEB: www.niteoproducts.com
SIC: 3523 Farm machinery & equipment
HQ: Niteo Products, Llc
5949 Sherry Ln Ste 540
Dallas TX 75225
214 245-5000

(G-7083)
NITROGEN JUPITER LLC
6779 W Indiantown Rd (33458-4654)
PHONE..................................561 662-2150
John Ford, *Principal*
EMP: 6 **EST:** 2015
SALES (est): 650.1K **Privately Held**
SIC: 2813 Nitrogen

(G-7084)
NORTH ERIE ELECTRONICS INC
Also Called: Western Reserve Tool Machine
1001 N Us Highway 1 # 506 (33477-4305)
PHONE..................................561 839-8127
William Anderson, *President*
EMP: 11 **Privately Held**
WEB: www.northerie.com
SIC: 3679 Power supplies, all types: static
PA: Erie North Electronics Inc
1001 N Us Highway 1 # 506
Jupiter FL 33477

(G-7085)
NUTRAMEDIX LLC
2885 Jupiter Park Dr # 1600 (33458-6045)
PHONE..................................561 745-2917
Timothy J Eaton, *President*
Mark Toothman, *General Mgr*
Bruce Hodge, *Vice Pres*
Jon Gaydosh, *Sales Staff*
Alena Khadakova, *Mktg Coord*
▲ **EMP:** 14 **EST:** 1994
SQ FT: 6,700
SALES (est): 2.9MM **Privately Held**
WEB: www.nutramedix.com
SIC: 2834 5122 Vitamin, nutrient & hematinic preparations for human use; drugs, proprietaries & sundries

(G-7086)
ODYSSEY FASTENING SYSTEMS INC
516 Commerce Way Ste 5 (33458-8866)
PHONE..................................561 436-5570
Stephen Karaga, *CEO*
Thomas McGuinness, *President*
James McGuinness, *Vice Pres*
Paul McGuinness, *Vice Pres*
EMP: 4 **EST:** 2010
SQ FT: 2,400
SALES (est): 4MM **Privately Held**
SIC: 3541 Machine tools, metal cutting type

(G-7087)
OMNI DSGNS LDSCP MNGEMENTS LLC
18155 Jupiter Landings Dr (33458-3315)
PHONE..................................561 339-4800
Charles Marshall, *Principal*
EMP: 6 **EST:** 2010
SALES (est): 80.2K **Privately Held**
SIC: 2511 Storage chests, household: wood

(G-7088)
OPREME BEVERAGE CORP
5151 Corporate Way (33458-3101)
PHONE..................................954 699-0669
Ryan El-Hosseiny, *President*
Adam El-Hosseiny, *Director*
EMP: 8 **EST:** 2012
SALES (est): 525.9K **Privately Held**
SIC: 2086 Bottled & canned soft drinks

(G-7089)
P&G PAVERS INC
6671 W Indiantown Rd 50-2 (33458-3991)
PHONE..................................561 716-5113
Nathalie Gelinas, *Principal*
EMP: 9 **EST:** 2013
SALES (est): 2.4MM **Privately Held**
WEB: www.pandgpavers.com
SIC: 2951 Asphalt paving mixtures & blocks

(G-7090)
PECKY CYPRESS & MORE LLC
5500 Military Trl 22-12 (33458-2869)
PHONE..................................772 215-0430
Michael A Barone, *Principal*
EMP: 6 **EST:** 2015
SALES (est): 226.6K **Privately Held**
WEB: www.peckycypressandmore.com
SIC: 2431 Millwork

(G-7091)
PEGASUS RESOURCES CORP
224 Commodore Dr (33477-4008)
PHONE..................................561 575-2393
Lisa M Strahl, *Director*
EMP: 6 **EST:** 2005
SALES (est): 164.9K **Privately Held**
WEB: www.pegasusresources.com
SIC: 1382 Oil & gas exploration services

(G-7092)
PERIODIC ELEMENTS LLC
19115 Se Coral Reef Ln (33458-1051)
PHONE..................................561 972-7791
Deborah Carrington, *Principal*
EMP: 6 **EST:** 2014
SALES (est): 158.8K **Privately Held**
SIC: 2819 Industrial inorganic chemicals

(G-7093)
PIXOTINE PRODUCTS INC
1095 Jupiter Park Dr # 12 (33458-8972)
PHONE..................................305 479-1335
Evan Grossman, *CEO*
Melissa Grossman, *President*
Justin Merrell, *Principal*
Chris Miquel, *Principal*
EMP: 6 **EST:** 2013
SQ FT: 1,500
SALES (est): 1MM **Privately Held**
WEB: www.pixotine.com
SIC: 2499 Toothpicks, wood

(G-7094)
POWER SYSTEMS INC
1440 W Indiantown Rd # 200 (33458-7925)
PHONE..................................561 354-1100
Valerie Slagle, *Human Res Mgr*
Jason Eason, *Sales Mgr*
Fergus Ahern, *Sales Staff*
Christy Browning, *Marketing Staff*
Andrew Hunt, *Manager*
EMP: 36 **EST:** 2001
SALES (est): 1.1MM **Privately Held**
WEB: www.psm.com
SIC: 3511 Gas turbine generator set units, complete

(G-7095)
POWER SYSTEMS MFG LLC
Also Called: PSM
1440 W Indiantown Rd # 200 (33458-7925)
PHONE..................................561 354-1100
Alexander Hoffs, *CEO*
Brandy Mahaney, *Principal*
Charles M Biondo, *Vice Pres*
Chuck Biondo, *Vice Pres*
Tim Te Riele, *Vice Pres*
◆ **EMP:** 350 **EST:** 1999
SQ FT: 200,000
SALES (est): 119.8MM **Privately Held**
WEB: www.psm.com
SIC: 3511 8711 Gas turbines, mechanical drive; hydraulic turbines; steam engines; engineering services
HQ: Ansaldo Energia Spa
Via Nicola Lorenzi 8
Genova GE 16152
064 201-3584

(G-7096)
POWERPHASE LLC
1001 N Us Highway 1 # 206 (33477-4482)
PHONE..................................561 299-3970
Plazi Ricklin, *Engineer*
Bob Kraft,
James Kraft,
Peter Perr,
EMP: 12 **EST:** 2012
SQ FT: 2,400
SALES (est): 1.5MM **Privately Held**
WEB: www.powerphase.com
SIC: 3511 Gas turbine generator set units, complete

(G-7097)
PRATT & WHITNEY
15270 Endeavor Dr (33478-6447)
PHONE..................................561 796-6701
Jayne Nye, *President*
Michael Williams, *Engineer*
Antonio Bazemore, *Analyst*
EMP: 21 **EST:** 2014
SALES (est): 4.9MM **Privately Held**
WEB: www.rtx.com
SIC: 3812 Aircraft/aerospace flight instruments & guidance systems

(G-7098)
PRISM VENTURE PARTNERS LLC
675 W Indiantown Rd # 103 (33458-7555)
PHONE..................................561 427-6565
Timothy Anderson, *Principal*
EMP: 10 **EST:** 2006
SALES (est): 386.7K **Privately Held**
SIC: 7372 Prepackaged software

(G-7099)
PROFESSOR SOFTWARE COMPANY
268 Barbados Dr (33458-2917)
PHONE..................................561 691-5455
R F McDonough, *Principal*
EMP: 7 **EST:** 2008
SALES (est): 163.6K **Privately Held**
SIC: 7372 Prepackaged software

(G-7100)
PSI MNFACTURING OPERATIONS LLC (PA)
831 Jupiter Park Dr (33458-8946)
PHONE..................................561 747-6107
Gary P Prus,
Mary Catherine Haas Barre,
David M Cusano,
Joel C Haas,
Daryl H Michaelian,
EMP: 6 **EST:** 2017
SQ FT: 30,000
SALES (est): 1MM **Privately Held**
WEB: www.psi-manufacturing.com
SIC: 3724 Aircraft engines & engine parts

(G-7101)
QUIK SHRED
1070 E Indiantown Rd # 308 (33477-5148)
PHONE..................................561 841-1822
Louise Sacco, *CEO*
EMP: 9 **EST:** 2008
SALES (est): 780K **Privately Held**
SIC: 3559 Tire shredding machinery

(G-7102)
RAYTHEON TECHNOLOGIES CORP
Also Called: Pratt Whitney Rockettdyne
17900 Bee Line Hwy (33478-6414)
PHONE..................................561 796-2000
Joe Sylvestro, *Vice Pres*
Steven Bouley, *Manager*
EMP: 6
SALES (corp-wide): 56.5B **Publicly Held**
WEB: www.rtx.com
SIC: 3764 Guided missile & space vehicle propulsion unit parts
PA: Raytheon Technologies Corporation
870 Winter St
Waltham MA 02451
781 522-3000

(G-7103)
RAYTHEON TECHNOLOGIES CORP
Pratt & Whitney
17900 Bee Line Hwy (33478-6414)
P.O. Box 109600, Palm Beach Gardens (33410-9600)
PHONE..................................858 277-7639
Joaquin Lopez, *Project Mgr*
EMP: 650
SALES (corp-wide): 56.5B **Publicly Held**
WEB: www.rtx.com
SIC: 3511 8611 3812 3728 Gas turbines, mechanical drive; business associations; search & navigation equipment; aircraft parts & equipment; aircraft engines & engine parts; blowers & fans
PA: Raytheon Technologies Corporation
870 Winter St
Waltham MA 02451
781 522-3000

(G-7104)
RIGRAP LLC
2818 28th Ct (33477-9366)
P.O. Box 8464 (33468-8464)
PHONE..................................561 200-5958
Glen Oberacker, *CEO*
▼ **EMP:** 6 **EST:** 2011
SQ FT: 5,000
SALES (est): 223.2K **Privately Held**
WEB: www.rigrap.com
SIC: 3949 Fishing tackle, general

(G-7105)
ROEBIC LABORATORIES INC
1213 Ocean Dunes Cir (33477-9130)
PHONE..................................561 799-3380
Hedy Bush, *COO*
Dale Schmidt, *Vice Pres*
John Peters, *Branch Mgr*
EMP: 13
SALES (corp-wide): 6.8MM **Privately Held**
WEB: www.roebic.com
SIC: 2842 Specialty cleaning, polishes & sanitation goods
PA: Roebic Laboratories, Inc.
25 Connair Rd
Orange CT 06477
203 795-1283

(G-7106)
ROYAL CONCRETE CONCEPTS INC (PA)
1410 Park Ln S Ste 2 (33458-8078)
P.O. Box 2486, Greenville SC (29602-2486)
PHONE..................................561 689-5398
Wallace D Sanger, *CEO*
Dean Locke, *Chairman*
Dean J Locke, *COO*
Eric R Engstrom, *CFO*
Ronald Moffett, *Manager*
▼ **EMP:** 50 **EST:** 1997
SQ FT: 11,000
SALES (est): 7.4MM **Privately Held**
WEB: www.royalconcreteconcepts.com
SIC: 3272 3271 Concrete products, precast; concrete block & brick

(G-7107)
S P SHEET METAL CO INC
5500 Military Trl Ste 22 (33458-2871)
PHONE..................................609 698-8800
Darren Myers, *President*
Clara Dominguez, *Principal*
EMP: 18 **EST:** 1962
SALES (est): 723.2K **Privately Held**
SIC: 3444 Sheet metal specialties, not stamped

(G-7108)
SASCO MACHINING INC
904 Penn Trl (33458-4330)
PHONE..................................561 746-8233
Gregory E Stephen, *President*
Libby Van Deusen, *Vice Pres*
Louis Vandeusen, *Vice Pres*
EMP: 10 **EST:** 1978
SALES (est): 722.2K **Privately Held**
WEB: www.100dollarclub.com
SIC: 3599 Machine shop, jobbing & repair

(G-7109)
SCHRAPPERS FINE CABINETRY INC
240 W Indiantown Rd # 101 (33458-3548)
PHONE..................................561 746-3827
Keith Levine, *President*
Beverly Levine, *Vice Pres*
Brad Rosenberg, *Prdtn Mgr*
Michelle Egan, *Production*
EMP: 10 **EST:** 2008
SALES (est): 751.4K **Privately Held**
WEB: www.schrappers.com
SIC: 2541 5712 Cabinets, lockers & shelving; cabinet work, custom

(G-7110)
SEABREEZE PUBLICATION CENTL FL
Also Called: Seabreeze Publications
1102 W Indiantown Rd # 5 (33458-6813)
PHONE..................................561 741-7770
Sean Reid, *President*
EMP: 6 **EST:** 1990
SALES (est): 458.5K **Privately Held**
WEB: www.seabreezepublications.com
SIC: 2759 Commercial printing

(G-7111)
SEATBELT SOLUTIONS LLC
15835 Corporate Rd N (33478-6422)
PHONE..................................855 642-3964
Glenn Davis, *Manager*
Jeffery L Biegun,
▲ **EMP:** 28 **EST:** 2006
SQ FT: 10,000
SALES (est): 7MM **Privately Held**
WEB: www.seatbeltsolutions.com
SIC: 2399 Seat belts, automobile & aircraft

(G-7112)
SHINY PRINTS
143 Juno St (33458-4941)
PHONE..................................561 200-2872
William George Heinitz, *Principal*
EMP: 10 **EST:** 2016
SALES (est): 597K **Privately Held**
WEB: www.shinyprints.com
SIC: 2752 Commercial printing, lithographic

(G-7113)
SHUTTER LUBRICATION & SERVICE
1821 W 10th St Ste 3 (33469)
P.O. Box 32474, West Palm Beach (33420-2474)
PHONE..................................561 745-8956
Tracy Trefzer, *President*
Paul Trefzer, *Vice Pres*
EMP: 7 **EST:** 2003
SALES (est): 325K **Privately Held**
SIC: 3442 Shutters, door or window: metal

(G-7114)
SHYFT GROUP INC
15335 Pk Of Commerce Blvd (33478-6452)
PHONE..................................954 946-9955
EMP: 26
SALES (corp-wide): 146.2MM **Publicly Held**
WEB: www.spartanmotors.com
SIC: 3711 Chassis, motor vehicle
PA: The Shyft Group Inc
41280 Bridge St
Novi MI 48375
517 543-6400

(G-7115)
SIGNATURE ATHLETICS INC
1025 W Indiantown Rd # 10 (33458-6852)
PHONE..................................561 212-9284
Daniel Soviero, *CEO*
Madeline Lewis, *Manager*
Lance Stone, *Director*
EMP: 6 **EST:** 2016
SALES (est): 2.5MM **Privately Held**
WEB: www.signaturelacrosse.com
SIC: 3949 Baseball, softball & cricket sports equipment

(G-7116)
SNEAKZ LLC
Also Called: Sneakz Organic
2895 Jupiter Park Dr # 500 (33458-6038)
PHONE..................................201 693-5695
Jeff Robbins, *Mng Member*
Jim Costa,
EMP: 6 **EST:** 2012
SQ FT: 3,000
SALES (est): 3MM **Privately Held**
WEB: www.sneakz.com
SIC: 2026 Milk drinks, flavored

(G-7117)
SOFTWARE TEACHER INC
300 N Highway A1a H104 (33477-9510)
PHONE..................................954 593-3333
David Reid, *Principal*
EMP: 6 **EST:** 2001
SALES (est): 284.5K **Privately Held**
SIC: 7372 Prepackaged software

(G-7118)
SOUTHEAST MARKETING CONCEPTS
Also Called: Country Tees
801 Maplewood Dr Ste 11 (33458-8800)
PHONE..................................561 747-7010
Greg Olson, *President*
Gregg Olson, *COO*
EMP: 8 **EST:** 1988
SQ FT: 3,500
SALES (est): 808.1K **Privately Held**
SIC: 2759 3953 Screen printing; screens, textile printing

(G-7119)
SOUTHEASTERN DOOR COMPANY LLC
1505 Commerce Ln (33458-8837)
P.O. Box 794 (33468-0794)
PHONE..................................561 746-5493
Charles Austin, *Purchasing*
William Weizer,
▼ **EMP:** 12 **EST:** 1970
SQ FT: 10,500
SALES (est): 2.4MM **Privately Held**
WEB: www.southeasterndoor.com
SIC: 3442 Screen doors, metal; screens, window, metal

(G-7120)
SPECIALTY SCREEN PRINTING INC
6065 Wolfe St (33458-6760)
PHONE..................................561 758-4944
Jacqueline A Strode, *Principal*
EMP: 8 **EST:** 2013
SALES (est): 255.1K **Privately Held**
SIC: 2752 Commercial printing, lithographic

(G-7121)
SPRING LOADED INC
Also Called: J & R Metal Fabrications
315 Commerce Way Ste 1 (33458-8841)
PHONE..................................561 747-8785
Karen B Kinberger, *President*
Charles R Kinberger, *Vice Pres*
EMP: 5 **EST:** 1987
SQ FT: 2,000
SALES (est): 650.9K **Privately Held**
WEB: www.springloadedtechnology.com
SIC: 3441 Fabricated structural metal

(G-7122)
STEALTH INDUSTRIES
10782 N Dogwood Trl (33478-5322)
PHONE..................................561 747-1471
James Pezzuti, *Principal*
EMP: 6 **EST:** 2001
SALES (est): 118.5K **Privately Held**
WEB: www.stealth.industries
SIC: 3999 Manufacturing industries

(G-7123)
STEWART MATERIALS INC (PA)
2875 Jupiter Park Dr # 1100 (33458-6058)
PHONE..................................561 972-4517
Nick T Stewart, *President*
Oneil Gardner, *Safety Mgr*
Laura Perham, *Finance Dir*
EMP: 3 **EST:** 1981
SQ FT: 400
SALES (est): 12.2MM **Privately Held**
WEB: www.stewartmaterials.com
SIC: 1442 Construction sand & gravel

(G-7124)
STRATGIC TRBINE INVNTORY GROUP
1330 W Indiantown Rd (33458-3908)
PHONE..................................561 427-2007
James La Spina, *Manager*
EMP: 9 **EST:** 2017
SALES (est): 247.1K **Privately Held**
WEB: www.th4.64f.myftpupload.com
SIC: 3511 Gas turbine generator set units, complete

(G-7125)
TECHTRAN LENSES INC
601 Heritage Dr Ste 118 (33458-2777)
PHONE..................................561 623-5490
Chigurupati Jayaram, *Principal*
EMP: 9 **EST:** 2012
SALES (est): 467.8K **Privately Held**
WEB: www.techtranindia.com
SIC: 3851 Ophthalmic goods
PA: Techtran Polylenses Limited
S -7 Ida Technocrat Industrial Estate
Hyderabad TG

(G-7126)
TEQUESTA COMMUNITY HEALTH CTR
470 Tequesta Dr (33469-2585)
PHONE..................................561 713-0798
Leticia Arroyo, *CEO*
EMP: 9
SALES (est): 500K **Privately Held**
WEB: www.tequesta.org
SIC: 3841 Surgical & medical instruments

(G-7127)
THERMAL BRAZE INC
231 Venus St (33458-4967)
PHONE..................................561 746-6640
Ivan Batchelder, *President*
David Wise, *Vice Pres*
EMP: 7 **EST:** 1980

▲ = Import ▼=Export
◆ =Import/Export

SQ FT: 1,500
SALES (est): 1MM **Privately Held**
WEB: www.thermalbraze.com
SIC: 7692 3398 Brazing; metal heat treating

(G-7128)
TIBA ENTERPRISES INC
Also Called: Minuteman Press
1601 Commerce Ln Ste 102 (33458-8818)
PHONE..................................561 575-3037
Barbara Watson, *President*
Timothy R Watson, *Vice Pres*
EMP: 6 **EST:** 2000
SQ FT: 1,500
SALES (est): 815.5K **Privately Held**
WEB: www.chanhassen-mn.minuteman-press.com
SIC: 2752 Commercial printing, lithographic

(G-7129)
TITANS PROTECTIVE COATINGS LLC
150 Evernia St (33458-4954)
PHONE..................................561 370-2085
Andrea Taslidzic, *Manager*
EMP: 10 **EST:** 2016
SALES (est): 1.2MM **Privately Held**
SIC: 3479 Metal coating & allied service

(G-7130)
TRACY PUBLISHING LLC
4025 Community Dr (33458-8758)
PHONE..................................561 799-4690
Tracy Plauche, *Principal*
EMP: 6 **EST:** 2015
SALES (est): 53.2K **Privately Held**
SIC: 2741 Miscellaneous publishing

(G-7131)
TRAFFIPAX LLC
16490 Innovation Dr (33478-6449)
PHONE..................................561 881-7400
Stewart Mackiernan, *CEO*
Albert Miranda, *President*
Jeri Anderson, *Treasurer*
▲ **EMP:** 412 **EST:** 1999
SQ FT: 6,000
SALES (est): 3.6MM
SALES (corp-wide): 907.3MM **Privately Held**
WEB: www.jenoptik.com
SIC: 3669 Traffic signals, electric
HQ: Jenoptik North America, Inc.
16490 Innovation Dr
Jupiter FL 33478

(G-7132)
TRIATOMIC ENVIRONMENTAL INC
1838 Park Ln S (33458-8077)
P.O. Box 1867 (33468-1867)
PHONE..................................561 748-4864
Christopher Willette, *President*
Ron Saunders, *Vice Pres*
Chad Knapp, *VP Opers*
Marissa Granados, *Train & Dev Mgr*
Tim Steinmetz, *Sales Mgr*
▼ **EMP:** 10 **EST:** 1996
SQ FT: 1,500
SALES (est): 2.3MM **Privately Held**
WEB: www.freshaireuv.com
SIC: 3564 Air cleaning systems

(G-7133)
TROPICAL STENCIL PCB INC
1530 Cypress Dr Ste E (33469-3184)
PHONE..................................561 972-5133
Barbara McGlynn, *President*
James McGlynn, *Vice Pres*
William Bishop, *Sales Staff*
EMP: 12 **EST:** 2010
SALES (est): 3MM **Privately Held**
WEB: www.tropicalstencil.com
SIC: 3672 Printed circuit boards

(G-7134)
TROPICHEM RESEARCH LABS LLC
Also Called: Vetio Dev't & Mfg Plant
15843 Guild Ct (33478-6436)
PHONE..................................561 804-7603
Christine Marriott, *Controller*
Ivaldo Pacheco, *Manager*
EMP: 90 **Privately Held**
WEB: www.vetio.com
SIC: 2844 2834 3999 Shampoos, rinses, conditioners: hair; pharmaceutical preparations; pet supplies
PA: Tropichem Research Labs, Llc
2705 Doghrty Frry Rd # 202
Saint Louis MO 63122

(G-7135)
TRUE LINE INDUSTRIES INC
13841 151st Ln N (33478-3541)
PHONE..................................561 745-4828
Randall C Chew, *Principal*
EMP: 8 **EST:** 2003
SALES (est): 616.2K **Privately Held**
WEB: www.trueline.ca
SIC: 3999 Manufacturing industries

(G-7136)
ULTRACLENZ LLC
1201 Jupiter Park Dr # 1 (33458-8084)
PHONE..................................800 931-8911
▲ **EMP:** 15
SQ FT: 8,500
SALES (est): 1.5MM **Privately Held**
SIC: 3999 2841 3432 Mfg Misc Products Mfg Soap/Other Detergents Mfg Plumbing Fixture Fittings

(G-7137)
UNITED TECHNOLOGIES CORP
Also Called: Pratt & Whitney Military Engs
17900 Bee Line Hwy (33478-6414)
P.O. Box 109600, Palm Beach Gardens (33410-9600)
PHONE..................................860 565-4321
Louis Chenevert, *CEO*
Yancey Blanchard, *Administration*
George Dalrymple,
EMP: 25 **EST:** 2013
SALES (est): 9.8MM **Privately Held**
SIC: 3724 Aircraft engines & engine parts

(G-7138)
US MOLD INC
612 N Orange Ave Ste A4 (33458-5021)
PHONE..................................561 748-2223
Mike Fadell, *Manager*
EMP: 5 **EST:** 2007
SALES (est): 512.9K **Privately Held**
WEB: www.usmold.com
SIC: 3544 Industrial molds

(G-7139)
VENTEX TECHNOLOGY INC (PA)
1201 Jupiter Park Dr (33458-8084)
PHONE..................................561 354-6300
John S Boyd, *President*
Morgan Crook, *General Mgr*
Jim Sloan, *Vice Pres*
Richard Ogden, *CFO*
◆ **EMP:** 12 **EST:** 1993
SQ FT: 14,924
SALES (est): 1MM **Privately Held**
WEB: www.ventextech.com
SIC: 3612 Specialty transformers

(G-7140)
VENUE ADVERTISING INC
Also Called: Venue Marketing Group
815 S Us Highway 1 103 (33477-5923)
PHONE..................................561 844-1778
Denise Carter, *Editor*
Mike Albanese, *Chairman*
Shelli Lockhart, *Pub Rel Mgr*
Adam Rosmarin, *Marketing Staff*
Cameron Crotts, *Creative Dir*
EMP: 21 **EST:** 1984
SALES (est): 1.9MM **Privately Held**
WEB: www.venueadv.com
SIC: 2796 7311 2759 Color separations for printing; advertising agencies; commercial printing

(G-7141)
VITSUR INDUSTRIES INC
130 Evernia St Ste 3 (33458-4913)
PHONE..................................561 744-1290
John Vitsur, *President*
EMP: 5 **EST:** 1982
SQ FT: 2,000
SALES (est): 2MM **Privately Held**
WEB: www.motivateddesign.com
SIC: 3429 Marine hardware

(G-7142)
VULCAN STEEL
326 Jupiter Lakes Blvd # 2 (33458-7102)
PHONE..................................561 945-1259
EMP: 6 **EST:** 2017
SALES (est): 175.6K **Privately Held**
WEB: www.vulcansteel.com
SIC: 3441 Fabricated structural metal

(G-7143)
WASTE ADVANTAGE CORPORATION
Also Called: Waste Advantage Magazine
230 Tresana Blvd Unit 64 (33478-5438)
P.O. Box 30126, Palm Beach Gardens (33420-0126)
PHONE..................................800 358-2873
Angelina Ruiz, *Publisher*
Heidi Jensen, *Production*
Noreen Cocron, *Sales Mgr*
Sean Earley, *Accounts Exec*
EMP: 8 **EST:** 2017
SALES (est): 1MM **Privately Held**
WEB: www.wasteadvantagemag.com
SIC: 2721 Periodicals: publishing only

(G-7144)
WATER BAGEL BOCA EAST LLLP
201 N Us Highway 1 Ste C5 (33477-5106)
PHONE..................................347 661-7171
Anne Dangelo, *Principal*
EMP: 6 **EST:** 2013
SALES (est): 103K **Privately Held**
WEB: www.brooklynwaterbagel.com
SIC: 3589 Water treatment equipment, industrial

(G-7145)
WEISS GROUP LLC (PA)
15430 Endeavor Dr Ste 101 (33478-6402)
PHONE..................................561 627-3300
Thomas J Clarke Jr, *CEO*
Cynthia Canterberry, *President*
Jeffrey Rano, *CFO*
Ionel Roiban, *Manager*
Italo Silveria, *Prgrmr*
EMP: 150 **EST:** 1994
SQ FT: 54,000
SALES (est): 29.2MM **Privately Held**
WEB: www.weissinc.com
SIC: 2721 Magazines: publishing only, not printed on site

(G-7146)
WEISS RESEARCH INC
Also Called: Safe Money Report
15430 Endeavor Dr Ste 101 (33478-6400)
PHONE..................................561 627-3300
Tracey L Butz, *President*
Sharon A Daniels, *Vice Pres*
Jeffrey Rano, *CFO*
Martin Weiss, *Director*
EMP: 150 **EST:** 1971
SQ FT: 190,000
SALES (est): 15.4MM **Privately Held**
WEB: www.weissinc.com
SIC: 2721 6282 Magazines: publishing only, not printed on site; investment advice
PA: Weiss Group, Llc
15430 Endeavor Dr Ste 101
Jupiter FL 33478

(G-7147)
WELDCORP INDUSTRIES ✪
15188 Pk Of Cmmrce Blvd S (33478-6406)
PHONE..................................561 339-7713
Alfredo Nicholas, *Principal*
EMP: 40 **EST:** 2020
SALES (est): 1MM **Privately Held**
WEB: www.weldcorpindustries.com
SIC: 1389 Construction, repair & dismantling services

(G-7148)
XTREME ELECTRONIC DESIGNS INC
352 Legare Ct (33458-2901)
PHONE..................................561 557-3667
John C McKeeman, *President*
Owen Dewar, *Engineer*
EMP: 5 **EST:** 2005
SALES (est): 479.1K **Privately Held**
WEB: www.xedi.us
SIC: 3672 Printed circuit boards

(G-7149)
ZEROC INC
4425 Military Trl Ste 209 (33458-4817)
PHONE..................................561 283-1480
Marc Laukien, *President*
Benard Normier, *Vice Pres*
Bernard Nornier, *Vice Pres*
Benoit Foucher, *Software Engr*
Joe George, *Software Dev*
EMP: 5 **EST:** 2002
SALES (est): 687.4K **Privately Held**
WEB: www.zeroc.com
SIC: 7372 Application computer software

Kennedy Space Center
Brevard County

(G-7150)
ASRC AEROSPACE CORP
Bldg M6-744 (32899-0001)
PHONE..................................321 867-1462
EMP: 232
SALES (corp-wide): 2.7B **Privately Held**
WEB: www.asrcfederal.com
SIC: 3812 7371 7373 5088 Search & navigation equipment; custom computer programming services; computer integrated systems design; transportation equipment & supplies
HQ: Asrc Aerospace Corp
7000 Muirkirk Meadows Dr # 100
Beltsville MD 20705
301 837-5500

(G-7151)
BOEING COMPANY
O & C Building Rm 1090 (32815)
PHONE..................................321 867-6005
John Plowden, *Branch Mgr*
EMP: 6
SALES (corp-wide): 58.1B **Publicly Held**
WEB: www.boeing.com
SIC: 3721 Aircraft
PA: The Boeing Company
100 N Riverside Plz
Chicago IL 60606
312 544-2000

(G-7152)
BOEING COMPANY
Nasa Cswy (32815)
P.O. Box 21233 (32815-0233)
PHONE..................................321 867-7380
Bruce Melnik, *Manager*
EMP: 6
SALES (corp-wide): 58.1B **Publicly Held**
WEB: www.boeing.com
SIC: 3721 Aircraft
PA: The Boeing Company
100 N Riverside Plz
Chicago IL 60606
312 544-2000

Kenneth City
Pinellas County

(G-7153)
OLAS FOODS SPECIALTY MKT INC
5791 54th Ave N (33709-2005)
PHONE..................................813 447-5127
Ola Yusuf, *Branch Mgr*
EMP: 20
SALES (corp-wide): 146.8K **Privately Held**
WEB: www.olasfoods.com
SIC: 2032 Canned specialties
PA: Ola's Foods Specialty Market, Inc.
1908 W Dr Mrtn Lther King
Tampa FL 33607
813 200-7202

Key Biscayne
Miami-Dade County

(G-7154)
BUENA CEPA WINES LLC
951 Crandon Blvd (33149-3400)
PHONE..................................310 621-2566
Sebastian E Bustamante, *Mng Member*
Joseph A Foley,
Lisa D Weeks,
▲ **EMP:** 8 **EST:** 2008
SALES (est): 399.2K **Privately Held**
SIC: 2084 Wines

(G-7155)
FEMMESCIENCE LLC
280 Woodcrest Rd (33149-1320)
PHONE..................................305 361-0994
EMP: 6 **EST:** 2009
SALES (est): 117.4K **Privately Held**
SIC: 2844 Toilet preparations

(G-7156)
GEIGEL MARBLE & DESIGN LLC
199 Ocean Lane Dr # 1202 (33149-1400)
PHONE..................................305 301-0399
Mariela Geigel,
EMP: 6 **EST:** 2016
SALES (est): 161.8K **Privately Held**
WEB: www.geigelmarble.com
SIC: 3272 Art marble, concrete

(G-7157)
GROUP 32 DEV & ENGRG INC (PA)
200 Ocean Lane Dr Apt 806 (33149-1447)
PHONE..................................305 361-0463
Frederick Perkins, *President*
EMP: 10 **EST:** 1995
SALES (est): 957.6K **Privately Held**
SIC: 3556 Roasting machinery: coffee, peanut, etc.

(G-7158)
GT SCALE MODELS INC
166 Harbor Dr (33149-1306)
PHONE..................................305 310-8998
Guillermo A Tinoco, *Principal*
EMP: 6 **EST:** 2017
SALES (est): 136.2K **Privately Held**
WEB: www.gtscalemodels.com
SIC: 3944 Games, toys & children's vehicles

(G-7159)
LINKPOINT LLC
137 E Enid Dr (33149-2204)
PHONE..................................305 903-9191
Peter Hoffmann, *Mng Member*
Erika Hoffmann,
▼ **EMP:** 17 **EST:** 2009
SALES (est): 2.1MM **Privately Held**
SIC: 2821 Plastics materials & resins

(G-7160)
MILCA BOTTLING COMPANY
620 Harbor Cir (33149-1703)
PHONE..................................305 365-0044
Ramiro Cardenal, *Principal*
EMP: 10 **EST:** 2010
SALES (est): 543.7K **Privately Held**
SIC: 2086 Bottled & canned soft drinks

(G-7161)
ORGANIC AMAZON CORP
Also Called: Acai To Go
104 Crandon Blvd (33149-1526)
PHONE..................................305 365-7811
Michael Simon, *CEO*
Jayson Fittipaldi,
Rodrigo Lima,
EMP: 9 **EST:** 2013
SALES (est): 593.9K **Privately Held**
WEB: www.acaitogo.com
SIC: 2099 5499 Food preparations; health foods

(G-7162)
SAMARA PUBLISHING
Also Called: Islander
104 Crandon Blvd Ste 301 (33149-1556)
PHONE..................................305 361-3333
Anne Owens, *President*
Justo Rey, *Publisher*
◆ **EMP:** 7 **EST:** 1966
SQ FT: 1,400
SALES (est): 1.6MM **Privately Held**
SIC: 2711 Newspapers: publishing only, not printed on site

(G-7163)
WAU USA CORP
240 Crandon Blvd Ste 278 (33149-1623)
PHONE..................................305 361-6110
Edmond Saade, *President*
Reynaldo Acosta, *President*
EMP: 13 **EST:** 2008
SALES (est): 608.7K **Privately Held**
SIC: 3577 Data conversion equipment, media-to-media: computer

Key Largo
Monroe County

(G-7164)
AUTOMATED PRODUCTION EQP APE
Also Called: A P E
2 N Blackwater Ln (33037-2900)
PHONE..................................631 654-1197
William Scheu, *Ch of Bd*
Jose Vilar, *Opers Mgr*
Barbara Scheu, *Admin Sec*
EMP: 10 **EST:** 1969
SQ FT: 24,200
SALES (est): 500K **Privately Held**
WEB: www.ape.com
SIC: 3559 3548 3423 Electronic component making machinery; welding apparatus; hand & edge tools

(G-7165)
AUTOMATED PRODUCTION EQP APE
Also Called: Ape South
2 N Blackwater Ln (33037-2900)
PHONE..................................305 451-4722
Casey Scheu, *President*
Bobbie Scheu, *Vice Pres*
Casey K Scheu, *Information Mgr*
EMP: 8 **EST:** 1991
SQ FT: 13,000
SALES (est): 1.9MM **Privately Held**
WEB: www.ape.com
SIC: 3599 Machine & other job shop work

(G-7166)
BOSWORTH MILLWORK LLC
329 Mahogany Dr (33037-4561)
PHONE..................................305 942-9017
Dean A Bosworth, *Manager*
EMP: 7 **EST:** 2019
SALES (est): 222.5K **Privately Held**
SIC: 2431 Millwork

(G-7167)
CROSS KEY MARINE CANVAS INC
Also Called: Key Largo Canvas
103761 Overseas Hwy (33037-2832)
P.O. Box 371865 (33037-1865)
PHONE..................................305 451-1302
Robert A Cullin, *President*
Deborah Cullin, *Admin Sec*
EMP: 7 **EST:** 1980
SQ FT: 5,000
SALES (est): 997.5K **Privately Held**
WEB: www.keylargocanvas.com
SIC: 2394 3354 Awnings, fabric: made from purchased materials; aluminum extruded products

(G-7168)
DEGRAAFF INC
99264 Overseas Hwy (33037-2457)
PHONE..................................305 451-4460
Wayne A Degraaff, *Principal*
EMP: 9 **EST:** 2016
SALES (est): 304.2K **Privately Held**
WEB: www.alscarpet.com
SIC: 3482 Small arms ammunition

(G-7169)
FLORIDA KEYS KEYLIME PRODUCTS
95231 Overseas Hwy (33037-3897)
P.O. Box 9305, Fort Myers (33902-9305)
PHONE..................................305 853-0378
John McCarthy, *President*
▲ **EMP:** 6 **EST:** 1995
SQ FT: 1,800
SALES (est): 666K **Privately Held**
WEB: www.keylimeproducts.com
SIC: 2844 5947 7231 Face creams or lotions; gift, novelty & souvenir shop; facial salons

(G-7170)
FLORIDA PHOSPHORUS
6 Abaco Rd (33037-5002)
PHONE..................................561 983-3208
Eva Tuttle, *Owner*
EMP: 5 **EST:** 2009
SALES (est): 406.9K **Privately Held**
SIC: 2873 Nitrogenous fertilizers

(G-7171)
FREE PRESS
100430 Overseas Hwy # 300 (33037-2504)
PHONE..................................305 853-7277
Paul Clarin, *Principal*
EMP: 6 **EST:** 2008
SALES (est): 77.5K **Privately Held**
SIC: 2711 Newspapers, publishing & printing

(G-7172)
KEYS DECK & DOCK SUPPLIES INC
100151 Overseas Hwy (33037-4422)
PHONE..................................305 451-8001
Daniel Hoffman, *President*
EMP: 8 **EST:** 2012
SALES (est): 135.2K **Privately Held**
WEB: www.keysdecksanddocks.com
SIC: 3999 Dock equipment & supplies, industrial

(G-7173)
SINCLAIR INDUSTRIES LLC (PA)
101691 Overseas Hwy (33037-4585)
PHONE..................................305 215-0990
Ronald A Skrumbellos, *Manager*
EMP: 18 **EST:** 2017
SALES (est): 304.7K **Privately Held**
SIC: 3999 Manufacturing industries

(G-7174)
SPEEDSOURCE INC
4 South Dr (33037-2921)
PHONE..................................954 578-7071
EMP: 8
SQ FT: 12,000
SALES (est): 1.6MM **Privately Held**
SIC: 3711 Motor Vehicles And Car Bodies

(G-7175)
TIKI WATER SPORTS INC
94.5 Ocean Side (33037)
PHONE..................................305 852-9298
Robert Chester, *President*
Ted Tumbale, *Vice Pres*
Chip Short, *Sales Staff*
Daniel Delo, *Director*
▼ **EMP:** 8 **EST:** 1983
SQ FT: 7,000
SALES (est): 1.3MM **Privately Held**
WEB: www.tikiwatersports.com
SIC: 3089 5999 Plastic & fiberglass tanks; fiberglass materials, except insulation

Key West
Monroe County

(G-7176)
ALL SAFE OF BIG PINE KEY
1301 1st St (33040-3613)
PHONE..................................305 872-7233
Charles Wicht, *Owner*
EMP: 6 **EST:** 2005
SALES (est): 162.3K **Privately Held**
WEB: www.bigpinekey.com
SIC: 3949 Swimming pools, plastic

(G-7177)
ANCHOR ALUMINUM PRODUCTS SOUTH
2807 Staples Ave (33040-4040)
PHONE..................................305 293-7965
EMP: 5
SALES (est): 557.7K **Privately Held**
SIC: 3446 3442 3354 Mfg Architectural Metalwork Mfg Metal Doors/Sash/Trim Mfg Aluminum Extruded Products

(G-7178)
BABYS COFFEE LLC
3178 Us Highway 1 (33040-6124)
P.O. Box 6558 (33041-6558)
PHONE..................................305 744-9866
Gary Teplitsky, *President*
Mary Broman, *General Mgr*
Olga Teplitsky, *Admin Sec*
EMP: 5 **EST:** 1991
SQ FT: 2,800
SALES (est): 563.2K **Privately Held**
WEB: www.babyscoffee.com
SIC: 2095 5499 5149 Roasted coffee; beverage stores; coffee & tea

(G-7179)
BARRETT & COMPANY
3201 Flagler Ave Ste 501 (33040-4693)
PHONE..................................305 293-4501
EMP: 6
SALES (est): 895.6K **Privately Held**
SIC: 3577 Mfg Computer Peripheral Equipment
PA: Local Enterprises, Inc.
3201 Flagler Ave Ste 501
Key West FL 33040

(G-7180)
CARPE DIEM ICE CREAM LLC
Also Called: Carpe Diem Ice Cream Key West
300 Front St (33040-6629)
PHONE..................................305 504-4469
Julie Cruchet, *Principal*
Patrick Cruchet, *Principal*
EMP: 6 **EST:** 2014
SALES (est): 248K **Privately Held**
SIC: 2024 2052 Ice cream & frozen desserts; cones, ice cream

(G-7181)
CAYO HUESO ENTERPRISES INC
Also Called: Hanson and Bringle Cabinets
5750 2nd Ave (33040-5950)
PHONE..................................305 747-0020
Steve Bringle, *President*
Norma Bringle, *Treasurer*
Ross Brown, *Admin Sec*
EMP: 30 **EST:** 1978
SQ FT: 2,700
SALES (est): 1.7MM **Privately Held**
WEB: www.hansenandbringle.com
SIC: 2434 Wood kitchen cabinets

(G-7182)
CHEF DISTILLED LLC
107 Simonton St (33040-6626)
PHONE..................................305 747-8236
William P Cormack, *Director*
EMP: 8 **EST:** 2013
SALES (est): 427K **Privately Held**
WEB: www.keywestlegalrum.com
SIC: 2085 Distilled & blended liquors

(G-7183)
CLOSET PROS
1103 Truman Ave (33040-3371)
PHONE..................................305 240-7775
George R Newman, *Owner*
EMP: 6 **EST:** 2016
SALES (est): 97.8K **Privately Held**
SIC: 2434 Wood kitchen cabinets

(G-7184)
COOKE COMMUNICATIONS FLA LLC (PA)
Also Called: Key West Citizen
3140 Flagler Ave (33040-4602)
P.O. Box 1800 (33041-1800)
PHONE..................................305 292-7777
John Cooke Jr, *Publisher*
Kevin Downey, *Adv Dir*
Ernestine Balin, *Advt Staff*
Melissa Fernandez, *Advt Staff*

Richard Tamborrino, *Advt Staff*
EMP: 100 **EST:** 2000
SALES (est): 16.5MM **Privately Held**
WEB: www.twooceansdigital.com
SIC: 2711 Commercial printing & newspaper publishing combined

(G-7185)
CURRY & SONS INC
Also Called: Curry & Sons Prtg & Off Sup
3201 Flagler Ave Ste 504 (33040-4693)
PHONE..................................305 296-8781
Scott Curry, *President*
EMP: 5 **EST:** 1972
SQ FT: 2,800
SALES (est): 350K **Privately Held**
WEB: www.curryandsonsprinting.com
SIC: 2752 Commercial printing, offset; lithographing on metal; visiting cards, lithographed; business forms, lithographed

(G-7186)
DION FUELS LLC (PA)
5300 Overseas Hwy 2 (33040-4327)
PHONE..................................305 296-2000
Steven M Uphoff, *CEO*
John J Cary, *President*
Linda Uphoff, *Corp Secy*
EMP: 15 **EST:** 2016
SALES (est): 2MM **Privately Held**
SIC: 2911 Gasoline blending plants

(G-7187)
FURY SURF SHACK
201 Front St Ste 109 (33040-8346)
PHONE..................................305 747-0799
Peter Norquoy, *President*
EMP: 8 **EST:** 2007
SALES (est): 174K **Privately Held**
SIC: 2211 Apparel & outerwear fabrics, cotton

(G-7188)
GOAL LINE EMBROIDERY
3255 Flagler Ave Ste 301 (33040-4646)
PHONE..................................305 295-7585
Patrick Labrada, *Partner*
EMP: 7 **EST:** 1991
SALES (est): 623.1K **Privately Held**
WEB: www.goallineembroidery.com
SIC: 2395 Embroidery products, except schiffli machine

(G-7189)
HEMINGWAY RUM COMPANY LLC (PA)
201 Simonton St (33040-6628)
P.O. Box 783486, Winter Garden (34778-3486)
PHONE..................................305 414-8754
Eric Lear, *Mng Member*
EMP: 19 **EST:** 2012
SALES (est): 2.8MM **Privately Held**
WEB: www.papaspilar.com
SIC: 2085 Rum (alcoholic beverage)

(G-7190)
KEY WEST PRINTING LLC
5585 2nd Ave Ste 1 (33040-5932)
P.O. Box 809 (33041-0809)
PHONE..................................305 517-6711
Richard C Davis,
EMP: 5 **EST:** 2017
SALES (est): 650K **Privately Held**
WEB: www.keywestprinting.net
SIC: 2752 2711 2621 Commercial printing, offset; newspapers, publishing & printing; book, bond & printing papers; printing paper

(G-7191)
KEY WEST SMUGGLER CO
1107 Key Plz (33040-4077)
PHONE..................................916 995-1873
James Martin, *President*
Sarah Bixby, *Admin Sec*
EMP: 5 **EST:** 2017
SALES (est): 314.3K **Privately Held**
WEB: www.jewsofkeywest.com
SIC: 2085 Bourbon whiskey

(G-7192)
KEY WEST WLDG FABRICATION INC
5650 1st Ave (33040-5999)
P.O. Box 2658 (33045-2658)
PHONE..................................305 296-5555
Steve Condella, *President*
EMP: 6 **EST:** 1970
SQ FT: 15,000
SALES (est): 670K **Privately Held**
WEB: www.keywestweldingandcraneservices.com
SIC: 7692 7353 Welding repair; cranes & aerial lift equipment, rental or leasing

(G-7193)
KINO SANDALS INC
Also Called: Kino Shoe Factory
107 Fitzpatrick St (33040-6514)
PHONE..................................305 294-5044
Robert Lopez Jr, *President*
Christina Ruiz, *Vice Pres*
Anna Sariegl, *Vice Pres*
Magot Lopez, *Shareholder*
EMP: 18 **EST:** 1966
SALES (est): 1.7MM **Privately Held**
WEB: www.kinosandals.com
SIC: 3089 3144 3143 Boot or shoe products, plastic; women's footwear, except athletic; men's footwear, except athletic

(G-7194)
LANDMARK AVIATION
3471 S Roosevelt Blvd (33040-5234)
PHONE..................................305 296-5422
EMP: 7 **EST:** 2016
SALES (est): 252K **Privately Held**
SIC: 3721 Aircraft

(G-7195)
MATTHEESSONS
106 Duval St (33040-6506)
PHONE..................................305 296-1616
Yakov Blives, *Principal*
EMP: 7 **EST:** 2010
SALES (est): 104.5K **Privately Held**
SIC: 2024 Ice cream, bulk

(G-7196)
MCCONNELL CORP
Also Called: Flamingo Crossing
1107 Duval St (33040-3127)
PHONE..................................305 296-6124
Eleanor McConnell, *President*
Daniel McConnell, *Treasurer*
EMP: 5 **EST:** 1987
SALES (est): 563.2K **Privately Held**
SIC: 2024 5451 Ice cream, bulk; ice cream (packaged)

(G-7197)
MONROE CONCRETE PRODUCTS
Mile Mark 8 5 # 85 (33040)
P.O. Box 1149 (33041-1149)
PHONE..................................305 296-5606
Frank P Toppino, *President*
Edward Toppino Sr, *Corp Secy*
EMP: 70 **EST:** 1997
SQ FT: 4,000
SALES (est): 5MM **Privately Held**
WEB: www.charleytoppinoandsons.com
SIC: 3272 Concrete products

(G-7198)
MULTIHULL TECHNOLOGIES INC
Also Called: Key West Multihull
6811 Shrimp Rd (33040-5481)
P.O. Box 5372 (33045-5372)
PHONE..................................305 296-2773
Walter Schurtenberger, *President*
Sara C Smiley, *Vice Pres*
EMP: 7 **EST:** 1993
SQ FT: 5,400
SALES (est): 688.3K **Privately Held**
WEB: www.constellationyachts.com
SIC: 3732 5551 Yachts, building & repairing; boat dealers

(G-7199)
NEPTUNE DESIGNS INC
301 Duval St (33040-6509)
PHONE..................................305 294-8131
Jay Pfahl, *President*
Carmenza Pfahl, *Vice Pres*
EMP: 6 **EST:** 1976
SQ FT: 1,400
SALES (est): 530.5K **Privately Held**
WEB: www.neptunedesignskeywest.com
SIC: 3911 5944 Jewelry, precious metal; jewelry, precious stones & precious metals

(G-7200)
OVERSEAS RADIO LLC
Also Called: Mile Marker News
3732 Flagler Ave (33040-4529)
PHONE..................................305 296-1630
Guy Deboer, *President*
EMP: 8 **EST:** 2009
SALES (est): 282.3K **Privately Held**
WEB: www.konkam.com
SIC: 2711 7383 Newspapers, publishing & printing; news reporting services for newspapers & periodicals

(G-7201)
PEPPER SHARK LLC (PA)
6 Havana Ln (33040-3362)
PHONE..................................305 849-0104
Patricia K Coyne, *Principal*
EMP: 15 **EST:** 2015
SALES (est): 226.7K **Privately Held**
SIC: 3999 Manufacturing industries

(G-7202)
SANTIAGO OF KEY WEST INC
1301 United St (33040-3411)
PHONE..................................305 304-6063
Ramona L Santiago, *Principal*
EMP: 6 **EST:** 2014
SALES (est): 103.9K **Privately Held**
WEB: www.keysnews.com
SIC: 2711 Commercial printing & newspaper publishing combined

(G-7203)
SPIRES EMPIRE LLC
1106 Grinnell St (33040-3206)
PHONE..................................305 797-0622
Angelo Morrison,
EMP: 5 **EST:** 2017
SALES (est): 300K **Privately Held**
SIC: 3161 Clothing & apparel carrying cases

(G-7204)
WHIZ BANG LLC
Also Called: Absolutely Amazing Ebooks
926 Truman Ave (33040-6431)
PHONE..................................305 296-0160
Albert L Kelley, *Manager*
EMP: 6 **EST:** 2010
SALES (est): 134.2K **Privately Held**
SIC: 2741 Miscellaneous publishing

Keystone Heights
Clay County

(G-7205)
AAT OMEGA LLC
6670 Spring Lake Rd (32656-8684)
PHONE..................................352 473-6673
EMP: 45 **EST:** 2014
SALES (est): 7.7MM **Privately Held**
WEB: www.aatomega.com
SIC: 3441 Fabricated structural metal

(G-7206)
CROFT PUBLISHING INC
5006 County Road 214 (32656-9796)
PHONE..................................352 473-3159
Sylvia Croft, *Principal*
EMP: 6 **EST:** 2002
SALES (est): 77.2K **Privately Held**
SIC: 2741 Miscellaneous publishing

(G-7207)
FABRICATING TECHNOLOGIES LLC
6670 Spring Lake Rd (32656-8684)
PHONE..................................352 473-6673
EMP: 9 **EST:** 2014
SALES (est): 445.4K **Privately Held**
SIC: 3441 Fabricated structural metal

(G-7208)
G & A MANUFACTURING INC
6587 State Road 21 (32656-6934)
PHONE..................................352 473-6882
Deborah Hoffman, *President*
John Hoffman, *Director*
EMP: 18 **EST:** 2005
SALES (est): 2.2MM **Privately Held**
WEB: www.gamanufacturing.com
SIC: 3441 Fabricated structural metal

(G-7209)
LEGACY VULCAN LLC
6547 State Road 21 (32656-6917)
P.O. Box 546 (32656-0546)
PHONE..................................352 473-4258
Bill Wood, *Manager*
EMP: 6 **Publicly Held**
WEB: www.vulcanmaterials.com
SIC: 3273 Ready-mixed concrete
HQ: Legacy Vulcan, Llc
1200 Urban Center Dr
Vestavia AL 35242
205 298-3000

(G-7210)
MANUFACTURERS INV GROUP LLC
Also Called: Mrl Industries
6670 Spring Lake Rd (32656-8684)
PHONE..................................630 285-0800
Andrew Sandberg, *CEO*
James Soderquist, *President*
▼ **EMP:** 11 **EST:** 1964
SQ FT: 40,000
SALES (est): 522K **Privately Held**
SIC: 3499 Magnetic shields, metal

(G-7211)
S & J CUSTOM FABRICATION INC
5955 Indian Trl (32656-9775)
PHONE..................................352 246-1462
Shane F Baker, *Principal*
EMP: 10 **EST:** 2012
SALES (est): 919.7K **Privately Held**
SIC: 3499 Novelties & giftware, including trophies

(G-7212)
VULCAN MATERIALS COMPANY
6547 State Road 21 (32656-6917)
P.O. Box 546 (32656-0546)
PHONE..................................352 473-4258
Thompson Baker, *Branch Mgr*
EMP: 6 **Publicly Held**
WEB: www.vulcanmaterials.com
SIC: 3273 Ready-mixed concrete
PA: Vulcan Materials Company
1200 Urban Center Dr
Vestavia AL 35242

Kinard
Calhoun County

(G-7213)
FLOWERS LOGGING CO INC
5644 Sw Odeen Flowers Rd (32449-2506)
PHONE..................................850 639-2856
EMP: 8
SALES (est): 689.6K **Privately Held**
SIC: 2411 Logging

Kissimmee
Osceola County

(G-7214)
5TH ELEMENT INC
3848 Shoreview Dr (34744-0001)
PHONE..................................321 331-7028
Berith Nielsen, *Principal*
EMP: 6 **EST:** 2012
SALES (est): 146.4K **Privately Held**
WEB: www.my5thelement.com
SIC: 2819 Industrial inorganic chemicals

(G-7215)
A FINE AFFAIR DJ
1007 Celebration Ave # 304 (34747-4862)
PHONE..................................319 899-2071
Timothy Olson, *Principal*

EMP: 6 **EST:** 2009
SALES (est): 82.6K **Privately Held**
SIC: 2335 Wedding gowns & dresses

(G-7216)
ABBY PRESS INC
Also Called: PIP Printing
929 W Oak St (34741-4941)
PHONE..................................407 847-5565
Jacqueline Bohman, *President*
Frank Petrellis, *President*
Clarice Petrellis, *Corp Secy*
EMP: 23 **EST:** 1984
SQ FT: 4,800
SALES (est): 2.8MM **Privately Held**
WEB: www.pip.com
SIC: 2791 2789 2759 2752 Typesetting; bookbinding & related work; commercial printing; commercial printing, offset; signs & advertising specialties

(G-7217)
ACCURATE METAL FABRICATORS
3718 Grissom Ln (34741-4602)
PHONE..................................407 933-2666
Roger N Shorey, *President*
Brenda Shorey, *Treasurer*
EMP: 14 **EST:** 1985
SQ FT: 20,000
SALES (est): 500.4K **Privately Held**
WEB: www.accuratemetal.net
SIC: 3469 Kitchen fixtures & equipment: metal, except cast aluminum

(G-7218)
AJL FABRICATION LLC (PA)
1436 Wendy Ct (34744-2703)
PHONE..................................407 654-1950
John Maxwell,
EMP: 12 **EST:** 2005
SALES (est): 284.1K **Privately Held**
WEB: www.ajlfabrication.com
SIC: 3441 Fabricated structural metal

(G-7219)
AMERICAN STAINLESS & ALUM PDTS
315 Industrial Way (34746)
PHONE..................................423 472-4832
Michael Gray, *President*
Linda Gray, *Vice Pres*
EMP: 8 **EST:** 1969
SQ FT: 5,000
SALES (est): 580.9K **Privately Held**
WEB: www.americanstainless.net
SIC: 3443 Tanks, standard or custom fabricated: metal plate

(G-7220)
BARSTOOL COMFORTS LLC
623 Front St Apt 5305 (34747-5467)
PHONE..................................610 737-5856
Stephanie Bertha, *Mng Member*
EMP: 8 **EST:** 2018
SALES (est): 1.3MM **Privately Held**
WEB: www.barstoolcomforts.com
SIC: 2521 Wood office chairs, benches & stools

(G-7221)
BASTINELLI CREATIONS LLC
109 Hangar Rd (34741-4505)
PHONE..................................407 572-8073
France Coves, *Principal*
EMP: 10 **EST:** 2017
SALES (est): 630K **Privately Held**
WEB: www.bastinelliknives.com
SIC: 3914 Cutlery, stainless steel

(G-7222)
BATISTA CABINETS INC
2747 Portchester Ct (34744-8551)
PHONE..................................407 922-3459
Roman Batista, *Principal*
EMP: 6 **EST:** 2019
SALES (est): 104K **Privately Held**
SIC: 2434 Wood kitchen cabinets

(G-7223)
BEST ENGINEERED SURFC TECH LLC (PA)
Also Called: Windsor Metal Finishing
1820 Avenue A (34758-2001)
P.O. Box 421210 (34742-1210)
PHONE..................................407 932-0008
William Faucett,
▲ **EMP:** 65
SQ FT: 33,000
SALES (est): 14.8MM **Privately Held**
WEB: www.1stchoicewindsor.com
SIC: 3479 3471 Coating of metals & formed products; finishing, metals or formed products

(G-7224)
BEST PRICE MOBILITY INC
941 Armstrong Blvd Ste B (34741-4619)
PHONE..................................321 402-5955
Robert Odell, *President*
Konni Odell, *Admin Sec*
EMP: 17 **EST:** 2008
SQ FT: 4,200
SALES (est): 1.6MM **Privately Held**
WEB: www.bpmobility.com
SIC: 3842 5012 5999 Wheelchairs; motor scooters; baby carriages & strollers

(G-7225)
BRIAN BELITZ
3130 Winding Trl (34746-2807)
P.O. Box 1345, Geneva (32732-1345)
PHONE..................................407 924-5543
Brian Belitz, *Principal*
Brian L Belitz, *Principal*
EMP: 7 **EST:** 2012
SALES (est): 259.9K **Privately Held**
WEB: www.propertyclean.net
SIC: 3088 Shower stalls, fiberglass & plastic

(G-7226)
BUILDING BLOCKS GFRC LLC
1150 Joelson Rd Fl 3 (34744-1400)
PHONE..................................312 243-9960
Kevin Miske,
EMP: 60 **EST:** 2017
SALES (est): 5.8MM **Privately Held**
WEB: www.buildingblocks.com
SIC: 3272 Concrete products, precast

(G-7227)
BUILDING BLOCKS MANAGEMENT INC
1150 Joelson Rd (34744-1400)
PHONE..................................214 289-9737
EMP: 17 **EST:** 2017
SALES (est): 6.3MM **Privately Held**
WEB: www.buildingblocks.com
SIC: 3089 Spouting, plastic & glass fiber reinforced

(G-7228)
C & J CSTM WLDG FBRICATION LLC
2784 East Lake Rd (34744-9312)
PHONE..................................407 414-1739
Tarawatee Seekaran, *Manager*
EMP: 6 **EST:** 2015
SALES (est): 125.8K **Privately Held**
SIC: 3499 2899 Fabricated metal products; fluxes: brazing, soldering, galvanizing & welding

(G-7229)
CAM BROC SPORTS INC
Also Called: Cambroc Sports
3726 Grissom Ln (34741-4615)
PHONE..................................407 933-6524
Roger Paul Jones, *President*
Betty Ann Jones, *Vice Pres*
EMP: 6 **EST:** 1991
SQ FT: 3,500
SALES (est): 656.7K **Privately Held**
SIC: 2759 Screen printing

(G-7230)
CHEMLINE INC
Also Called: SCI-Chem
1662 Broad St (34746-4282)
P.O. Box 422352 (34742-2352)
PHONE..................................407 847-4181
Greg Livingston, *Principal*
Cheryl Ann Livingston, *Principal*
EMP: 7 **EST:** 1985
SQ FT: 6,000
SALES (est): 895K **Privately Held**
WEB: www.chemlineinc.com
SIC: 2899 Water treating compounds

(G-7231)
CHHAYA CORPORATION
Also Called: Ventura Cleaners
1988 E Osceola Pkwy (34743-8600)
PHONE..................................407 348-9400
Sonal S Patel, *President*
EMP: 9 **EST:** 2004
SALES (est): 385.8K **Privately Held**
WEB: www.chhayacdc.org
SIC: 2842 Laundry cleaning preparations

(G-7232)
CONWAY BLDG CSTM WOODWORKS LLC
3001 Viscount Cir (34747-1620)
PHONE..................................407 738-9266
Peter R Conway, *Manager*
EMP: 6 **EST:** 2010
SALES (est): 11.1K **Privately Held**
WEB: www.cbcw.us
SIC: 2431 Millwork

(G-7233)
CRAIN VENTURES INC
Also Called: Osceola Press
2775 Old Dixie Hwy Ste C (34744-1470)
P.O. Box 450245 (34745-0245)
PHONE..................................407 933-1820
Kevin Crain, *President*
Melanie Crain, *Treasurer*
EMP: 5 **EST:** 1993
SQ FT: 2,400
SALES (est): 795.6K **Privately Held**
WEB: www.osceolapress.com
SIC: 2759 2752 Letterpress printing; screen printing; commercial printing, offset

(G-7234)
CREATIVE COATING LLC
1058 Soaring Eagle Ln (34746-6701)
PHONE..................................407 346-5725
Claudia I Melendez, *Principal*
EMP: 6 **EST:** 2012
SALES (est): 169.2K **Privately Held**
SIC: 3479 Metal coating & allied service

(G-7235)
CUSTOM PLASTIC DEVELOPMENTS
2710 N John Young Pkwy (34741-1266)
P.O. Box 422406 (34742-2406)
PHONE..................................407 847-3054
Richard L Hord, *President*
Louise Hord, *Treasurer*
▲ **EMP:** 58 **EST:** 1962
SQ FT: 52,000
SALES (est): 9.2MM **Privately Held**
WEB: www.cpdfl.com
SIC: 3089 Injection molding of plastics

(G-7236)
CWAC CUSTOM WOODWORKING & CABI
2420 Smith St Ste I (34744-2487)
PHONE..................................407 343-7774
Carlos G Lagos, *Manager*
EMP: 6 **EST:** 2005
SALES (est): 126K **Privately Held**
SIC: 2431 Millwork

(G-7237)
DEEJA FOODS INC
1770 Business Center Ln (34758-1800)
PHONE..................................321 402-8300
Hefazul Hakh, *CEO*
Ikbal Samad, *Director*
Mohamed S Mohamad, *Admin Sec*
◆ **EMP:** 9 **EST:** 2011
SALES (est): 875.3K **Privately Held**
SIC: 2044 Rice milling

(G-7238)
DEVCLAN INC
808 N Main St (34744-4564)
PHONE..................................407 933-8212
Joshua Peters, *President*
Phillip Jackson, *Vice Pres*
Ray Peters, *Admin Sec*
Michael J Barber,
EMP: 8 **EST:** 2012
SALES (est): 401.7K **Privately Held**
SIC: 7372 Educational computer software

(G-7239)
DRAPERY MASTERS LLC
3718 Grissom Ln (34741-4602)
PHONE..................................407 448-6898
William D Phillips,
EMP: 6 **EST:** 2019
SALES (est): 64.5K **Privately Held**
SIC: 2391 Curtains & draperies

(G-7240)
E G COATINGS LLC
1751 Covey Ct (34744-4082)
PHONE..................................407 624-2615
Esteban J Guzman, *Manager*
EMP: 10 **EST:** 2013
SALES (est): 586.5K **Privately Held**
WEB: www.egcoatings.com
SIC: 3479 Metal coating & allied service

(G-7241)
EASY FOODS INC
1965 Avenue A (34758-2003)
PHONE..................................321 300-1104
Juan Pablo Viejo, *Branch Mgr*
Lisa Govind, *Manager*
EMP: 177 **Privately Held**
WEB: www.easyfoodsinc.com
SIC: 2099 Food preparations
PA: Easy Foods Inc.
5900 Nw 97th Ave Unit 14
Doral FL 33178

(G-7242)
EDEN FAST FROZEN DESSERT LLC
107 Broadway (34741-5713)
PHONE..................................787 375-0826
Janette Alvarez, *Mng Member*
EMP: 10 **EST:** 2018
SALES (est): 675.3K **Privately Held**
SIC: 2024 Ice cream & frozen desserts

(G-7243)
EVEREST AIR CORP
3830 Golden Feather Way (34746-1918)
PHONE..................................407 319-6204
Bibi Rahim, *Principal*
EMP: 13 **EST:** 2010
SALES (est): 537.1K **Privately Held**
SIC: 3585 1711 7623 Air conditioning equipment, complete; air conditioning units, complete: domestic or industrial; heating & air conditioning contractors; air conditioning repair

(G-7244)
FLORIDA CHRISTN CONFERENCE INC
1500 E Vine St (34744-3720)
PHONE..................................407 460-8259
James A Estrella, *Principal*
EMP: 7 **EST:** 2010
SALES (est): 70.7K **Privately Held**
WEB: www.fccsports.net
SIC: 2369 Girls' & children's outerwear

(G-7245)
FLORIDA GOLD FOODS LLC
1770 Business Center Ln (34758-1800)
PHONE..................................347 595-1983
Ashishkumar Khandge, *Principal*
EMP: 10 **EST:** 2019
SALES (est): 1.1MM **Privately Held**
WEB: www.floridagoldfoods.com
SIC: 2044 Rice milling

(G-7246)
FLOWERS BKG CO BRADENTON LLC
Also Called: Flowers Baking Company
4990 S Orange Blossom Trl (34758-2039)
PHONE..................................941 758-5656
Chris Peer, *Manager*
EMP: 25
SALES (corp-wide): 4.3B **Publicly Held**
WEB: www.flobradconf.com
SIC: 2051 Bread, cake & related products
HQ: Flowers Baking Co. Of Bradenton, Llc
6490 Parkland Dr
Sarasota FL 34243

(G-7247)
FRESH AIRE SANITIZATION
1107 Mabbette St (34741-5161)
PHONE..................................407 301-9831
EMP: 6 **EST:** 2010
SALES (est): 86.2K **Privately Held**
SIC: 3564 Air cleaning systems

(G-7248)
FUSION SIGNS
Also Called: Fusion Signs & Graphics
720 N John Young Pkwy (34741-4916)
PHONE..................................407 715-6439
Henry L Ritter, *Principal*
EMP: 6 **EST:** 2010
SALES (est): 120.8K **Privately Held**
WEB: www.fusionsigns.biz
SIC: 3993 Signs & advertising specialties

(G-7249)
GATE PRECAST COMPANY
Also Called: Gate Precast Concrete
1018 Sawdust Trl (34744-1418)
PHONE..................................407 847-5285
Bryant Luke, *Vice Pres*
Lisa Neuman, *Purch Agent*
Alexander Perez, *Sales Staff*
Hagan Lambert, *Manager*
EMP: 150
SALES (corp-wide): 708.1K **Privately Held**
WEB: www.gateprecast.com
SIC: 3272 Concrete products, precast
HQ: Gate Precast Company
9540 San Jose Blvd
Jacksonville FL 32257
904 732-7668

(G-7250)
GLOBAL CUSTOM CABINETS LLC
289 Beckenham Dr (34758-4213)
PHONE..................................407 738-0146
Leon Cheong, *Principal*
EMP: 6 **EST:** 2011
SALES (est): 218.7K **Privately Held**
SIC: 2434 Wood kitchen cabinets

(G-7251)
HYDROGEN DIESEL PRFMCE INC
2410 Sabra Ct (34744-2784)
PHONE..................................407 847-6064
Charlene Birch, *CFO*
EMP: 5 **EST:** 2009
SALES (est): 310K **Privately Held**
SIC: 3621 Motors & generators

(G-7252)
ICAMR INC
Also Called: Bridg
200 Neocity Way (34744-4430)
PHONE..................................407 742-4253
Chester Kennedy, *CEO*
Dan Holladay, *President*
John J Callahan, *Vice Pres*
Steve Follis, *Engineer*
Jessica Filter, *Manager*
EMP: 3 **EST:** 2014
SQ FT: 109,000
SALES (est): 3.8MM **Privately Held**
WEB: www.gobridg.com
SIC: 3674 Microcircuits, integrated (semiconductor); wafers (semiconductor devices)

(G-7253)
IFOXX LLC
3051 Greystone Loop # 302 (34741-7740)
PHONE..................................305 785-7130
Dean Hooker,
EMP: 6 **EST:** 2015
SALES (est): 156.5K **Privately Held**
SIC: 3993 Signs & advertising specialties

(G-7254)
INNOVATIVE PDT SOLUTIONS LLC
2710 N John Young Pkwy (34741-1266)
P.O. Box 421265 (34742-1265)
PHONE..................................407 933-2029
Richard W Hord,
Michael Bloemker,
EMP: 11 **EST:** 2002
SALES (est): 918.1K **Privately Held**
WEB: www.gotohmg.com
SIC: 3089 Air mattresses, plastic

(G-7255)
INSPIRATION FOAM INC
2860 Nicole Ave (34744-3808)
PHONE..................................407 498-0040
Linda C Fuest, *Principal*
EMP: 8 **EST:** 2006
SALES (est): 162.1K **Privately Held**
SIC: 3069 Foam rubber

(G-7256)
J HERBERT CORPORATION
1751 S John Young Pkwy (34741-6392)
PHONE..................................407 846-0588
Mary M Selbach, *President*
John Selbach, *Exec VP*
Tyler Bouchard, *Sales Staff*
◆ **EMP:** 17 **EST:** 1978
SQ FT: 9,200
SALES (est): 3.9MM **Privately Held**
WEB: www.jherbertcorp.com
SIC: 3536 Cranes & monorail systems

(G-7257)
JC SANTOS EMBROIDERY
3557 Forest Park Dr (34746-2803)
PHONE..................................407 201-8617
Juan Santos, *Principal*
EMP: 6 **EST:** 2011
SALES (est): 87K **Privately Held**
SIC: 2395 Embroidery & art needlework

(G-7258)
JCS CONTRACTING INC
731 Duncan Ave (34744-1916)
PHONE..................................407 348-4555
Eric Litteral, *Admin Sec*
EMP: 5 **EST:** 2008
SALES (est): 450K **Privately Held**
SIC: 3271 Concrete block & brick

(G-7259)
JUAN ALEMANY WOODWORK
2108 Winding Ridge Ave S (34741-1304)
PHONE..................................407 350-4072
John Alemany, *Principal*
EMP: 6 **EST:** 2010
SALES (est): 107.5K **Privately Held**
SIC: 2431 Millwork

(G-7260)
JULIO GARCIA SATELLITE
1248 S John Young Pkwy (34741-6389)
PHONE..................................407 414-3223
Julio Garcia, *President*
EMP: 8 **EST:** 2009
SALES (est): 160.3K **Privately Held**
SIC: 3663 Space satellite communications equipment

(G-7261)
KING CONSTRUCTION & GLASS LLC
1414 Grandview Blvd (34744-6689)
PHONE..................................407 508-6286
James R Arneson, *Manager*
EMP: 6 **EST:** 2015
SALES (est): 250.4K **Privately Held**
SIC: 3211 Construction glass

(G-7262)
KISSIMMEE IRON WORKS INC
2741 Old Dixie Hwy (34744-1411)
PHONE..................................407 870-8872
Alberto Vega, *President*
Wanda Vega, *Vice Pres*
EMP: 5 **EST:** 1998
SQ FT: 5,000
SALES (est): 809.5K **Privately Held**
SIC: 3312 Rods, iron & steel: made in steel mills

(G-7263)
KISSIMMEE POLISHING
805 Prkway Plz Blvd Ste A (34744)
PHONE..................................407 923-9446
Greg Staker, *Vice Pres*
EMP: 6 **EST:** 2011
SALES (est): 71.4K **Privately Held**
SIC: 3471 Polishing, metals or formed products

(G-7264)
KISSIMMEE PRINTING
1230 Simpson Rd (34744-4602)
PHONE..................................407 518-2514
Fredy Peralta, *President*
EMP: 8 **EST:** 2011
SALES (est): 92.2K **Privately Held**
WEB: www.osceolapress.com
SIC: 2752 Commercial printing, offset

(G-7265)
KISSIMMEE SMOKE SHOP
7551 W Irlo Brnsn Mem Hwy (34747-1725)
PHONE..................................407 952-6181
Cindy Bekkach, *Principal*
EMP: 6 **EST:** 2016
SALES (est): 268.6K **Privately Held**
SIC: 2024 Ice cream & frozen desserts

(G-7266)
KITE TECHNOLOGY GROUP LLC
2642 Michigan Ave Ste C (34744-1911)
PHONE..................................407 557-0512
Rafael Perez, *Principal*
EMP: 10 **EST:** 2015
SALES (est): 490.7K **Privately Held**
SIC: 3944 Kites

(G-7267)
LEADAIR INC
113 Hangar Rd (34741-4505)
PHONE..................................407 343-7571
Jean P Barriere, *President*
Steve Swenson, *Marketing Mgr*
Shirley Meyers, *Admin Mgr*
James Burditt, *Technician*
EMP: 21 **EST:** 2001
SALES (est): 5MM **Privately Held**
WEB: www.trackair.us
SIC: 3829 Surveying instruments & accessories

(G-7268)
LENTUS PRODUCTS LLC
215 Celebration Pl # 520 (34747-5400)
PHONE..................................203 913-7600
Dennis Walls, *CEO*
EMP: 7
SALES (est): 616.4K **Privately Held**
WEB: www.lentusllc.com
SIC: 3531 Pavers

(G-7269)
LOCKHEED MARTIN CORPORATION
4909 Fells Cove Ave (34744-9237)
PHONE..................................407 356-7424
Bryan Bowen, *Engineer*
Manuel Lozada, *Sr Software Eng*
EMP: 6 **Publicly Held**
WEB: www.lockheedmartin.com
SIC: 3812 Search & navigation equipment
PA: Lockheed Martin Corporation
6801 Rockledge Dr
Bethesda MD 20817

(G-7270)
LOGIC ILLUMINATION LLC
Also Called: Led Supply, The
3600 Commerce Blvd 102b (34741-4678)
PHONE..................................407 906-0126
Carlos Torres, *President*
Frank Veliz, *COO*
Christian Torres, *Vice Pres*
EMP: 10 **EST:** 2016
SALES (est): 828.2K **Privately Held**
WEB: www.logicillumination.com
SIC: 3648 3645 Outdoor lighting equipment; public lighting fixtures; residential lighting fixtures

(G-7271)
LOS COQUITOS
1319 E Vine St (34744-3642)
PHONE..................................407 289-9315
Elizabeth Braunschneider, *Principal*
EMP: 7 **EST:** 2007
SALES (est): 152.4K **Privately Held**
SIC: 2024 Ice cream & frozen desserts

(G-7272)
LOV INDUSTRIES INC
742 Royal Palm Dr (34743-9517)
PHONE..................................407 406-8221
Vanessa Gonzalez, *Branch Mgr*
EMP: 9
SALES (corp-wide): 71K **Privately Held**
SIC: 3999 Atomizers, toiletry
PA: Lov Industries Inc
14200 Avonlea Ct
Orlando FL

(G-7273)
MARTIN GALLAGHER LLC
4443 Philadelphia Cir (34746-6734)
PHONE..................................407 453-1027
Martin J Gallagher, *Principal*
Martin Gallagher, *Manager*
EMP: 6 **EST:** 2011
SALES (est): 68.3K **Privately Held**
SIC: 3296 Acoustical board & tile, mineral wool

(G-7274)
METAL BUILDING SUPPLIES LLC
800 E Donegan Ave (34744-1939)
PHONE..................................407 935-9714
Scott J Prossen, *Mng Member*
EMP: 12 **EST:** 2000
SQ FT: 10,000
SALES (est): 1.6MM **Privately Held**
WEB: www.mbsmetals.com
SIC: 3448 Panels for prefabricated metal buildings

(G-7275)
MINUTEMAN PRESS
3 S John Young Pkwy # 17 (34741-3601)
PHONE..................................503 789-5741
EMP: 6 **EST:** 2019
SALES (est): 105.6K **Privately Held**
WEB: www.minutemanpress.com
SIC: 2752 Commercial printing, lithographic

(G-7276)
MIX IT AT LOOP
2617 W Osceola Pkwy (34741-0766)
PHONE..................................407 201-8948
Brian Melaney, *Vice Pres*
EMP: 8 **EST:** 2010
SALES (est): 601.8K **Privately Held**
SIC: 2024 Ice cream, bulk

(G-7277)
MK BROTHERS INC
2790 Michigan Ave Ste 318 (34744-1558)
PHONE..................................407 847-9547
Mohammad Khan, *Principal*
EMP: 6 **EST:** 2008
SALES (est): 639.1K **Privately Held**
SIC: 2253 T-shirts & tops, knit

(G-7278)
NURSERY SUPPLIES INC
2050 Avenue A (34758-2407)
PHONE..................................407 846-9750
Audrey Schultz, *Buyer*
Michelle Boudreau, *Sales Staff*
Cory Butler, *Sales Staff*
Skye Sawyer, *Sales Staff*
Andy Zimlich, *Sales Staff*
EMP: 360
SALES (corp-wide): 61.1MM **Privately Held**
WEB: www.nurserysupplies.com
SIC: 3089 Flower pots, plastic
PA: Nursery Supplies, Inc.
1415 Orchard Dr
Chambersburg PA 17201
717 263-7780

(G-7279)
ORGANIZACION MARKETING MIX LLC
1006 Verona St (34741-5453)
PHONE..................................407 924-2709
Maria T Story, *Principal*
EMP: 10 **EST:** 2010
SALES (est): 306.4K **Privately Held**
SIC: 3273 Ready-mixed concrete

(G-7280)
ORION DNTL SLS TRNING REPR LLC
Also Called: Orion Repair
4721 Rockvale Dr (34758-3361)
PHONE..................................888 674-6657
Amanda Laird, *Principal*

GEOGRAPHIC

EMP: 6 **EST:** 1995
SALES (est): 453.7K **Privately Held**
WEB: www.orionrepair.com
SIC: 3843 Autoclaves, dental; burs, dental; drills, dental; hand pieces & parts, dental

(G-7281)
ORLANDO DONUT MFG LLC
Also Called: Orlando Doughnut Mfg Co
2550 Michigan Ave Ste G (34744-1934)
PHONE..................................407 933-7111
John Rodriguez,
Randy Kopelman,
EMP: 11 **EST:** 2000
SALES (est): 332.4K **Privately Held**
WEB: www.orlandoweekly.com
SIC: 2051 Doughnuts, except frozen

(G-7282)
OSCEOLA STAR
921 Emmett St (34741-5435)
PHONE..................................407 933-0174
Bill Hansen, *Owner*
EMP: 6 **EST:** 1993
SALES (est): 493.6K **Privately Held**
WEB: www.elosceolastar.com
SIC: 2711 Newspapers: publishing only, not printed on site

(G-7283)
OSCEOLA WOMAN NEWSPAPER LLC
111 E Monu Ave Unit 401 (34741)
PHONE..................................407 891-9771
Gregg Blain, *Owner*
EMP: 6 **EST:** 2007
SALES (est): 508.1K **Privately Held**
WEB: www.osceolawoman.com
SIC: 2711 Commercial printing & newspaper publishing combined; newspapers, publishing & printing

(G-7284)
PEEKS MOBILE APP CORP
3955 Golden Finch Way (34746-2007)
PHONE..................................407 931-3878
Estefania Tejada, *Branch Mgr*
EMP: 17
SALES (corp-wide): 94.4K **Privately Held**
SIC: 7372 Application computer software
PA: Peeks Mobile App Corp
611 N Mills Ave
Orlando FL

(G-7285)
PENCIL PRINTING
3004 Michigan Ave (34744-1542)
PHONE..................................407 346-4952
Adriana Gomez, *Principal*
EMP: 6 **EST:** 2017
SALES (est): 418.6K **Privately Held**
WEB: www.pencilprinting.com
SIC: 2752 Commercial printing, lithographic

(G-7286)
PEPSICO INC
1650 S Poinciana Blvd (34758-2046)
PHONE..................................407 933-5542
Matthew Pierson, *Finance*
Samantha Weyant, *Finance*
Ricardo Vazquez, *Sales Staff*
Sheila Cappel, *Manager*
Roy Dedmon, *Manager*
EMP: 7
SALES (corp-wide): 70.3B **Publicly Held**
WEB: www.pepsico.com
SIC: 2033 2086 Fruit juices: packaged in cans, jars, etc.; bottled & canned soft drinks
PA: Pepsico, Inc.
700 Anderson Hill Rd
Purchase NY 10577
914 253-2000

(G-7287)
PK WELDING INC ✪
830 N John Young Pkwy (34741-4912)
PHONE..................................407 694-9403
Karynes Class, *President*
EMP: 6 **EST:** 2020
SALES (est): 100.6K **Privately Held**
WEB: www.pk-welding-inc.business.site
SIC: 7692 1799 Welding repair; welding on site

(G-7288)
PM ENTERPRISES HOLDINGS LLC
1751 S John Young Pkwy (34741-6392)
PHONE..................................407 846-0588
Peter A Scheckenhofer, *CEO*
EMP: 20 **EST:** 2019
SALES (est): 1MM **Privately Held**
SIC: 3536 Cranes & monorail systems

(G-7289)
PNC MANUFACTURING LEATHER
4107 S Orange Blossom Trl (34746-7265)
PHONE..................................407 201-2069
Jose Guzman, *Principal*
EMP: 8 **EST:** 2014
SALES (est): 329.6K **Privately Held**
SIC: 3999 Manufacturing industries

(G-7290)
PRECISION MOLD & TOOL INC
2780 N John Young Pkwy (34741-1222)
PHONE..................................407 847-5687
Jerry Longbrake, *President*
Joseph W Longbrake, *Corp Secy*
Mark E Longbrake, *Vice Pres*
Jennifer Dipaula, *Office Mgr*
▼ **EMP:** 33 **EST:** 1961
SQ FT: 20,000
SALES (est): 7.2MM **Privately Held**
SIC: 3089 Injection molding of plastics

(G-7291)
PRO DUMPSTERS INC
3864 Wood Thrush Dr (34744-9156)
PHONE..................................407 910-6341
Freddy Pena, *Principal*
EMP: 11 **EST:** 2017
SALES (est): 604.8K **Privately Held**
WEB: www.produmpsterorlando.com
SIC: 3443 Dumpsters, garbage

(G-7292)
QUAKER OATS COMPANY
1650 S Poinciana Blvd (34758-2046)
PHONE..................................407 846-5926
Roger Dicky, *General Mgr*
EMP: 107
SALES (corp-wide): 70.3B **Publicly Held**
WEB: www.quakeroats.com
SIC: 2086 Bottled & canned soft drinks
HQ: The Quaker Oats Company
555 W Monroe St Fl 1
Chicago IL 60661
312 821-1000

(G-7293)
QUANTEM FBO GROUP KSSIMMEE LLC
3950 Merlin Dr (34741-4551)
PHONE..................................407 846-8001
Frank Pisano, *Principal*
EMP: 8 **EST:** 2015
SALES (est): 563.5K **Privately Held**
WEB: www.quantemfbo.com
SIC: 3572 Computer storage devices

(G-7294)
SANDPIPER TURBINE LLC
3955 Merlin Dr (34741-4551)
PHONE..................................407 377-7220
William M Whelan,
EMP: 10 **EST:** 2018
SALES (est): 901.8K **Privately Held**
WEB: www.sandpiperturbine.com
SIC: 3511 Turbines & turbine generator sets & parts

(G-7295)
SANTONIS JEWELRY INC
3191 Waterbridge Ln (34744-9238)
PHONE..................................407 298-4994
David Molina, *Owner*
EMP: 7 **EST:** 2009
SALES (est): 204.2K **Privately Held**
WEB: www.santonis.com
SIC: 3911 Jewelry, precious metal

(G-7296)
SCHIMMBROS INC
3726 Grissom Ln (34741-4615)
PHONE..................................407 796-8361
Randy E Schimmelpfennig, *Principal*
EMP: 7 **EST:** 2015
SALES (est): 252.8K **Privately Held**
WEB: www.schimmbros.com
SIC: 2759 Screen printing

(G-7297)
SEARCHLIGHT INC
1970 E Osceola Pkwy 327 (34743-8629)
PHONE..................................407 965-2649
E Dygert, *Principal*
EMP: 6 **EST:** 2010
SALES (est): 132.7K **Privately Held**
SIC: 3648 Searchlights

(G-7298)
SHAVERS PAVERS
4015 Sunny Day Way (34744-9154)
PHONE..................................407 350-3538
Julie A Shaver, *Principal*
EMP: 6 **EST:** 2008
SALES (est): 277.1K **Privately Held**
SIC: 3531 Pavers

(G-7299)
SUN PUBLICATIONS FLORIDA INC
Also Called: Osceola Shopper
108 Church St (34741-5055)
PHONE..................................321 402-0257
Jim Zajas, *General Mgr*
Angelique Priore, *Prdtn Mgr*
Paula Stark, *Manager*
Kathy Beckham, *Manager*
Gary Lugo, *Web Dvlpr*
EMP: 90
SALES (corp-wide): 13.7MM **Privately Held**
WEB: www.sunpubfla.com
SIC: 2741 6531 Guides: publishing only, not printed on site; shopping news: publishing only, not printed on site; real estate agents & managers
HQ: Sun Publications Of Florida, Inc.
7060 Havertys Way
Lakeland FL 33805

(G-7300)
SUNRISE PRINTING & SIGNS
1218 Dyer Blvd (34741-3723)
PHONE..................................321 284-3803
EMP: 8 **EST:** 2016
SALES (est): 141.9K **Privately Held**
SIC: 2752 Commercial printing, lithographic

(G-7301)
SUNSHINE PRINTING AND BUSINESS
2583 N Orange Blossom Trl (34744-1887)
PHONE..................................407 846-0126
Dao Lei Ll, *President*
EMP: 6 **EST:** 2013
SALES (est): 145.7K **Privately Held**
SIC: 2759 Commercial printing

(G-7302)
SYMBOL MATTRESS FLORIDA INC
5000 Mercantile Ln (34758-2401)
P.O. Box 6689, Richmond VA (23230-0689)
PHONE..................................407 343-4626
Charles H Neal, *Ch of Bd*
Ronald L Clevenger, *President*
Michael J McQuiston, *Exec VP*
George Coffey, *Manager*
Richard A Urban, *Admin Sec*
▼ **EMP:** 8 **EST:** 2005
SALES (est): 510.2K **Privately Held**
SIC: 2515 Sleep furniture

(G-7303)
TECHTRONICS LLC
Also Called: 12 Volt USA
2450 Smith St Ste A (34744-2301)
PHONE..................................407 738-4680
Anthony S Marasco, *CEO*
EMP: 7 **EST:** 2007
SALES (est): 190.1K **Privately Held**
SIC: 3679 Electronic circuits

(G-7304)
TF DEFENSE LLC
147 Toluca Dr (34743-7027)
PHONE..................................321 961-7596
EMP: 5 **EST:** 2018
SALES (est): 410.8K **Privately Held**
SIC: 3812 Defense systems & equipment

(G-7305)
U GOT RECOVERY INC
3406 W Vine St (34741-4637)
P.O. Box 420627 (34742-0627)
PHONE..................................407 343-9919
Eric R Escobales, *Principal*
EMP: 12 **EST:** 2006
SALES (est): 410.4K **Privately Held**
SIC: 3531 Automobile wrecker hoists

(G-7306)
UFP TECHNOLOGIES INC
United Foam Plastic
2175 Partin Settlement Rd (34744-4956)
PHONE..................................407 933-4880
John Waddington, *Plant Mgr*
Gwenael Busnel, *Plant Mgr*
Tony Johnson, *Mfg Mgr*
Jose Paguada, *Mfg Spvr*
EMP: 40
SALES (corp-wide): 179.3MM **Publicly Held**
WEB: www.ufpmedtech.com
SIC: 3086 Packaging & shipping materials, foamed plastic
PA: Ufp Technologies, Inc.
100 Hale St
Newburyport MA 01950
978 352-2200

(G-7307)
UNIVERSAL KIT CABINETS CLOSETS
2905 Welcome Cir (34746-3007)
PHONE..................................305 406-9096
Jorge Escobar, *Principal*
EMP: 6 **EST:** 2016
SALES (est): 210.4K **Privately Held**
WEB: www.universalcabinetsfl.com
SIC: 2434 Wood kitchen cabinets

(G-7308)
UTILYTECH COMPANY
630 Baldwin Dr (34758-4100)
PHONE..................................813 778-6952
Kenneth Leff, *Owner*
EMP: 10 **EST:** 2000
SALES (est): 504.5K **Privately Held**
SIC: 3823 Industrial instrmnts msrmnt display/control process variable

(G-7309)
VEATIC
2450 Smith St Ste P (34744-2305)
PHONE..................................888 474-2999
Dario Camacho, *President*
EMP: 6 **EST:** 2014
SALES (est): 490.4K **Privately Held**
WEB: www.veatic.com
SIC: 3441 Fabricated structural metal

(G-7310)
WELSHMAN INVESTMENT CORP
Also Called: Specialty Wood Manufacturing
1570 Kelley Ave Ste 2 (34744-3305)
PHONE..................................407 933-4444
David Wood, *President*
▼ **EMP:** 8 **EST:** 1989
SQ FT: 8,000
SALES (est): 1MM **Privately Held**
SIC: 2434 2499 1751 Wood kitchen cabinets; decorative wood & woodwork; cabinet & finish carpentry

(G-7311)
WHOLESALE SIGNS FABRICATORS
2968 Michigan Ave Ste C (34744-1213)
PHONE..................................407 729-5599
Ariel Inastrilla, *President*
EMP: 8 **EST:** 2016
SALES (est): 256.3K **Privately Held**
WEB: www.wsfsign.com
SIC: 3993 Signs & advertising specialties

(G-7312)
YESCO ORLANDO SOUTH
929 W Oak St (34741-4941)
PHONE..................................407 922-5856
EMP: 8 **EST:** 2019

▲ = Import ▼=Export
◆ =Import/Export

SALES (est): 140.6K Privately Held
WEB: www.yesco.com
SIC: 3993 Signs & advertising specialties

(G-7313)
Z & N MANUFACTURING CORP
1732 Kelley Ave (34744-3300)
PHONE..................................407 518-1114
Yolanda Zambrano, *Principal*
EMP: 8 EST: 2007
SALES (est): 265.9K Privately Held
SIC: 3999 Manufacturing industries

Kissimmee
Polk County

(G-7314)
MATRY GROUP LLC ✪
10 S Flag Dr (34759-3319)
PHONE..................................407 461-9797
Jeff R Bernal, *CEO*
EMP: 10 EST: 2021
SALES (est): 423.7K Privately Held
SIC: 3999 Pet supplies

(G-7315)
WILLIE MAES PIES LLC
843 Cypress Pkwy 253 (34759-3408)
P.O. Box 581329 (34758-0017)
PHONE..................................407 655-9360
Sophia Brown, *Principal*
EMP: 8 EST: 2008
SALES (est): 400K Privately Held
SIC: 2051 Bakery: wholesale or whole-sale/retail combined

La Belle
Hendry County

(G-7316)
ER JAHNA INDUSTRIES INC
Ortona Sand Company
Highway 78 E (33935)
P.O. Box 786, Labelle (33975-0786)
PHONE..................................863 675-3942
Giddel Gallardo, *Branch Mgr*
EMP: 10
SALES (corp-wide): 70.5MM Privately Held
WEB: www.jahna.com
SIC: 1442 Common sand mining
PA: E.R. Jahna Industries, Inc.
202 E Stuart Ave
Lake Wales FL 33853
863 676-9431

Labelle
Hendry County

(G-7317)
CENTERLINE DRCTNAL DRLG SVC IN
Also Called: Centerline Drctnal Drlg Srvcin
900 S Elm St (33935-4620)
P.O. Box 2705 (33975-2705)
PHONE..................................863 674-0913
Lauro Aceveado, *President*
EMP: 42 EST: 2011
SALES (est): 6.2MM Privately Held
SIC: 1381 Directional drilling oil & gas wells

(G-7318)
KENTON INDUSTRIES LLC
1477 Forestry Division Rd (33935-3001)
PHONE..................................863 675-8233
Robert Spencer, *Treasurer*
Kenneth A Wallace,
EMP: 5 EST: 2007
SALES (est): 420.9K Privately Held
WEB: www.kentonindustries.com
SIC: 3271 Concrete block & brick

(G-7319)
LABELLE BRICK PAVERS TILE LLC
Also Called: Gulf Coast Pavers
1515 Forestry Division Rd (33935-3003)
PHONE..................................863 230-3100
Daniel Hinthorn,
Dan Hinthorn,
▲ EMP: 15 EST: 2006
SALES (est): 1.2MM Privately Held
WEB: www.gulfcoastpaversflorida.com
SIC: 3271 3531 Blocks, concrete: drystack interlocking; pavers

(G-7320)
MIMS WELDING INCORPORATED
90 Evans Rd (33935-9135)
P.O. Box 3235, Immokalee (34143-3235)
PHONE..................................863 612-9819
Alton L Mims, *President*
Preston T Mims, *Vice Pres*
EMP: 9 EST: 1962
SQ FT: 13,000
SALES (est): 603.5K Privately Held
SIC: 7692 Automotive welding

(G-7321)
NEW ENERGY FUELS LLC
259 Ford Ave (33935-4642)
PHONE..................................281 205-0153
Nick Dunbar, *Mng Member*
Robert Dascal,
EMP: 7 EST: 2008
SALES (est): 139.7K Privately Held
SIC: 2911 Diesel fuels

(G-7322)
OVIPOST INC
635 A Rd (33935-9454)
PHONE..................................707 776-6108
Trina Chiasson, *CEO*
EMP: 10 EST: 2017
SALES (est): 889.6K Privately Held
WEB: www.ovipost.com
SIC: 3523 Farm machinery & equipment

(G-7323)
SOUTH WEST ADVENTURE TEAM LLC
Also Called: Pool Cleaning Service
505 W Hickpochee Ave # 2001 (33935-4735)
PHONE..................................903 288-4739
James Beecham, *CEO*
EMP: 5 EST: 2017
SALES (est): 318.1K Privately Held
SIC: 3589 1799 5091 5999 Swimming pool filter & water conditioning systems; swimming pool construction; swimming pools, equipment & supplies; swimming pool chemicals, equipment & supplies; swimming pool & hot tub service & maintenance; swimming pool, non-membership

(G-7324)
SUNCREST SHEDS INC (PA)
1451 Commerce Dr (33935-3002)
PHONE..................................863 675-8600
Brian Quinn, *President*
▼ EMP: 14 EST: 1999
SALES (est): 2.4MM Privately Held
WEB: www.suncrestsheds.com
SIC: 2452 Prefabricated buildings, wood

Lady Lake
Lake County

(G-7325)
DOUG BLOODWORTH ENTERPRISES
3211 Lake Griffin Rd (32159-3432)
PHONE..................................407 247-9728
Doug Bloodworth, *President*
EMP: 6 EST: 1993
SALES (est): 373.8K Privately Held
SIC: 3993 7532 Signs & advertising specialties; lettering & painting services

(G-7326)
HARTSOCK SAWMILL INC
2939 Hartsock Sawmill Rd (32159-5249)
PHONE..................................352 753-3581
Diane L Murray, *Principal*
EMP: 9 EST: 2010
SALES (est): 138.5K Privately Held
WEB: www.crane-mats.com
SIC: 2421 Lumber: rough, sawed or planed

(G-7327)
LATHING BY ESTABAN M PEREZ INC
38321 Groveview Ave (32159-4450)
PHONE..................................352 302-8791
Estaban Morales Perez, *Principal*
EMP: 6 EST: 2012
SALES (est): 127.9K Privately Held
SIC: 3541 Lathes

(G-7328)
LOR-ED ENTERPRISES LLC
309 Lagrande Blvd (32159-2386)
PHONE..................................352 750-1999
Francis Neuzil Jr,
EMP: 10 EST: 2008
SQ FT: 3,500
SALES (est): 176.2K Privately Held
SIC: 3841 5047 Inhalators, surgical & medical; oxygen therapy equipment

(G-7329)
TOTAL NTRTN & THERAPEUTICS PA
809 Highway 466 Ste 202c (32159-3909)
PHONE..................................352 259-5190
Lori Esarey, *President*
EMP: 9 EST: 2007
SALES (est): 1MM Privately Held
WEB: www.totalnutritionandtherapeutics.com
SIC: 2834 Vitamin, nutrient & hematinic preparations for human use

Lady Lake
Sumter County

(G-7330)
ATLANTECH PROCESS TECHNOLOGY
1953 Lake Miona Dr (32162-6404)
PHONE..................................352 751-4286
Hans H Thiemann, *President*
Karen L Thiemann, *Admin Sec*
EMP: 9 EST: 2017
SALES (est): 334.1K Privately Held
WEB: www.atlantechprocess.com
SIC: 3069 Brushes, rubber

Lake Alfred
Polk County

(G-7331)
EXTREME IRON & WOOD WORK INC
535 Sellars Dr (33850-3325)
PHONE..................................407 925-2448
Mario Aguirre, *Principal*
EMP: 6 EST: 2008
SALES (est): 125.3K Privately Held
SIC: 2431 Millwork

(G-7332)
GROWERS FERTILIZER CORPORATION (PA)
312 N Buena Vista Dr (33850-2006)
P.O. Box 1407 (33850-1407)
PHONE..................................863 956-1101
Brent W Sutton, *President*
Rick O Steen, *Corp Secy*
Harvey B Snively, *Vice Pres*
John Strang, *Vice Pres*
David White, *Sales Staff*
EMP: 48
SQ FT: 30,000
SALES: 27.7MM Privately Held
WEB: www.growersfertilizer.com
SIC: 2874 2879 2873 Phosphatic fertilizers; insecticides, agricultural or household; nitrogenous fertilizers

(G-7333)
MIZKAN AMERICA INC
445 N Dakota Ave (33850-2127)
PHONE..................................863 956-0391
Jack Kichura, *Business Mgr*
Tim Carrigan, *Vice Pres*
Shen Chang, *Vice Pres*
Michael Allen, *Prdtn Mgr*
Susan Fiscus, *Production*
EMP: 18 Privately Held
WEB: www.mizkan.com
SIC: 2099 2035 Vinegar; dressings, salad: raw & cooked (except dry mixes); mustard, prepared (wet)
HQ: Mizkan America, Inc.
1661 Feehanville Dr 100a
Mount Prospect IL 60056
847 590-0059

(G-7334)
THE FORKLIFT COMPANY INC
290 W Harbord St (33850-3339)
PHONE..................................863 595-8156
EMP: 15
SALES: 266K Privately Held
SIC: 3537 Mfg Industrial Trucks/Tractors

Lake Buena Vista
Orange County

(G-7335)
BUENA VISTA CONSTRUCTION CO
3291 Wed Way (32830)
PHONE..................................407 828-2104
Greg Ruse, *Vice Pres*
Rolando Ortiz, *Opers Mgr*
Douglas Schroeder, *Opers Mgr*
EMP: 45 EST: 1972
SALES (est): 15.2MM
SALES (corp-wide): 65.3B Publicly Held
WEB: www.dpep.disney.com
SIC: 1389 Construction, repair & dismantling services
HQ: Walt Disney Parks And Resorts U.S., Inc.
1375 E Buena Vista Dr
Lake Buena Vista FL 32830
407 824-2222

(G-7336)
JFH TECHNOLOGIES LLC
Also Called: Field Service Office
1500 W Buena Vista Dr (32830)
PHONE..................................407 938-9336
Julie Fantauzzo, *Branch Mgr*
EMP: 23
SALES (corp-wide): 1.8MM Privately Held
WEB: www.proparksmanagement.com
SIC: 3679 Power supplies, all types: static
PA: Jfh Technologies, Llc
13506 Smmrport Vlg Pkwy
Windermere FL 34786
407 938-9336

Lake Butler
Union County

(G-7337)
HYPER-SUB PLATFORM TECH INC
4661 W State Road 238 (32054-5353)
P.O. Box 471, Lake City (32056-0471)
PHONE..................................386 365-6021
Reynolds Marion, *Ch of Bd*
EMP: 10 EST: 2018
SALES (est): 319.5K Privately Held
WEB: www.hypersub.com
SIC: 3812 1629 Defense systems & equipment; marine construction

(G-7338)
JOHN L SHADD ENTERPRISES
Us Hwy 121 (32054)
P.O. Box 506 (32054-0506)
PHONE..................................386 496-3989
John L Shadd, *Owner*
EMP: 15 EST: 1956
SQ FT: 5,000
SALES (est): 130.4K Privately Held
WEB: www.shaddtrucking.us
SIC: 2411 Logging

(G-7339)
KIRKLAND INDUSTRIES LLC
4638 Sw 150th Rd (32054-8102)
PHONE..................................386 496-3491
Amy Kirkland, *Principal*
EMP: 7 EST: 2014

GEOGRAPHIC

SALES (est): 163.4K **Privately Held**
SIC: 3999 Barber & beauty shop equipment

(G-7340)
PEARCE LOGGING LLC
9335 Nw 148th Trl (32054-4159)
PHONE..................................386 365-1880
Nathan Pearce, *Principal*
EMP: 6 **EST:** 2016
SALES (est): 328K **Privately Held**
SIC: 2411 Logging

(G-7341)
SAPHIRE SERVICES LLC
Also Called: Saphire Disinfection Products
250 Sw 9th Ave (32054-1415)
PHONE..................................386 247-1048
Jody Read, *CEO*
Francis Read, *Principal*
EMP: 5 **EST:** 2016
SALES (est): 400.8K **Privately Held**
WEB: www.simpleelementsclean.com
SIC: 2842 Sanitation preparations, disinfectants & deodorants

(G-7342)
SOUTHERN DOOR TECHNOLOGIES
9124 S County Road 231 (32054-7736)
PHONE..................................386 496-3844
Ezra Eugene Mock, *President*
Ezra Mock, *Vice Pres*
EMP: 5 **EST:** 2000
SQ FT: 2,400
SALES (est): 309.4K **Privately Held**
SIC: 2431 Door frames, wood

Lake City
Columbia County

(G-7343)
A 2 Z OF LAKE CITY INC
628 Se Allison Ct (32025-6101)
PHONE..................................386 755-0235
Dave Mangrum, *Principal*
EMP: 10 **EST:** 2010
SALES (est): 64.7K **Privately Held**
WEB: www.ccseniors.com
SIC: 2899 Salt

(G-7344)
A MATERIALS GROUP INC (PA)
871 Nw Guerdon St (32055-4346)
PHONE..................................386 758-3164
Brian P Schreiber, *CEO*
Joe H Anderson Jr, *Ch of Bd*
Jim Maples, *President*
Douglas M Anderson, *Vice Pres*
Cindy Childers, *Treasurer*
EMP: 77 **EST:** 2002
SALES (est): 6.3MM **Privately Held**
SIC: 3273 Ready-mixed concrete

(G-7345)
A MINING GROUP LLC
871 Nw Guerdon St (32055-4346)
P.O. Box 1829 (32056-1829)
PHONE..................................386 752-7585
Joe H Anderson III,
Dan Johnson,
Brian P Schreiber,
Shawn Snyder,
EMP: 28 **EST:** 2004
SALES (est): 1.1MM **Privately Held**
SIC: 1422 Crushed & broken limestone

(G-7346)
ACTION SIGNS & GRAPHICS INC
4180 S Us Highway 441 (32025-0304)
PHONE..................................386 752-0121
Lindsay Laxton, *President*
Lashaun Perry, *President*
Larry Perry Jr, *Vice Pres*
EMP: 6 **EST:** 1998
SQ FT: 5,000
SALES (est): 637.5K **Privately Held**
WEB: www.actionsignsfl.com
SIC: 3993 Signs & advertising specialties

(G-7347)
AMERICAN METAL PROCESSORS INC
186 Se Newell Dr (32025-1985)
PHONE..................................386 754-9367
James Prevatt, *President*
Jessica Langley, *Admin Sec*
EMP: 12 **EST:** 2000
SALES (est): 343K **Privately Held**
SIC: 3398 Tempering of metal

(G-7348)
ANDERSON TRUSS LLC
1730 Nw Oakland Ave (32055-4318)
PHONE..................................386 752-3103
Shawn Anderson,
EMP: 25 **EST:** 1985
SQ FT: 6,000
SALES (est): 438.1K **Privately Held**
SIC: 2439 Trusses, wooden roof

(G-7349)
BRIGHTMAN
417 Sw Aloe Ct (32024-3805)
PHONE..................................386 752-4883
Susan F Brightman, *Principal*
EMP: 6 **EST:** 2010
SALES (est): 156.5K **Privately Held**
SIC: 2451 Mobile homes

(G-7350)
COLUMBIA READY MIX CONCRETE (PA)
516 Nw Waldo St (32055-4357)
P.O. Box 2101 (32056-2101)
PHONE..................................386 755-2458
Renny B Eadie III, *President*
Theda Eadie, *Corp Secy*
Robert M Eadie, *Vice Pres*
EMP: 14 **EST:** 1977
SQ FT: 2,000
SALES (est): 4.8MM **Privately Held**
WEB: www.crmconcrete.com
SIC: 3273 Ready-mixed concrete

(G-7351)
COMMUNITY NEWS PAPERS INC
Also Called: Lake City Reporter
180 E Duval St (32055-4085)
P.O. Box 1709 (32056-1709)
PHONE..................................386 752-1293
Tom Wood, *Ch of Bd*
W H Dink Ne Smith, *President*
Jordan Kroeger, *Editor*
Vince Brown, *Prdtn Dir*
Sharlyn Elmore, *Sales Staff*
EMP: 1 **EST:** 1874
SQ FT: 18,000
SALES (est): 6MM
SALES (corp-wide): 61.5MM **Privately Held**
WEB: www.lakecityreporter.com
SIC: 2711 Newspapers, publishing & printing
PA: Community Newspapers, Inc.
2365 Prince Ave A
Athens GA 30606
706 548-0010

(G-7352)
CUSTOM POWDER COATING LLC
1129 Se Ormond Witt Rd (32025-2750)
PHONE..................................386 758-3973
Mary Witt T, *Principal*
EMP: 6 **EST:** 2010
SALES (est): 93K **Privately Held**
SIC: 3479 Metal coating & allied service

(G-7353)
D R NICKELSON & COMPANY INC
229 Nw Wilks Ln Ste 1 (32055-8373)
P.O. Box 1744 (32056-1744)
PHONE..................................386 755-6565
Dale R Nickelson, *President*
Mark Nickelson, *General Mgr*
David Schlimmer, *Project Mgr*
Scott Nickelson, *Opers Staff*
Diane Steele, *Office Mgr*
EMP: 15 **EST:** 2001
SQ FT: 35,000
SALES (est): 2.8MM **Privately Held**
WEB: www.drnickelson.com
SIC: 2431 2434 Doors, wood; wood kitchen cabinets

(G-7354)
FEAGLE LOGGING LLC
805 Ne Indigo Dr (32055-6858)
PHONE..................................386 365-2689
EMP: 8 **EST:** 2019
SALES (est): 346K **Privately Held**
SIC: 2411 Logging

(G-7355)
FURST-MCNESS COMPANY
3830 Nw Brown Rd (32055-7508)
P.O. Box 168, Wellborn (32094-0168)
PHONE..................................386 755-5605
Mike Casey, *Manager*
Ted Ladue, *Manager*
EMP: 8 **Privately Held**
WEB: www.mcness.com
SIC: 2048 Prepared feeds
HQ: Furst-Mcness Company
120 E Clark St
Freeport IL 61032
800 435-5100

(G-7356)
GRAYS PORTABLE BUILDINGS INC
Also Called: Bam Building and More
792 Sw Bascom Norris Dr (32025-1365)
PHONE..................................386 755-6449
Kevin Gray, *President*
EMP: 6 **EST:** 2011
SALES (est): 768.9K **Privately Held**
WEB: www.buildingsandmore.com
SIC: 3448 Prefabricated metal buildings

(G-7357)
GREAT SOUTH TIMBER & LBR INC
1135 Se State Road 100 (32025-1463)
P.O. Box 2249 (32056-2249)
PHONE..................................386 752-3774
Roland Bales, *Manager*
EMP: 43
SALES (corp-wide): 10.3MM **Privately Held**
WEB: www.gstl.us
SIC: 2421 Lumber: rough, sawed or planed
PA: Great South Timber & Lumber, Inc.
517 Se Baya Dr
Lake City FL 32025
386 755-3046

(G-7358)
GREAT SOUTH TIMBER & LBR INC (PA)
517 Se Baya Dr (32025-6031)
P.O. Box 2249 (32056-2249)
PHONE..................................386 755-3046
W K Cook, *Ch of Bd*
Roland Stern, *President*
Mike Dennard, *General Mgr*
Chad Stalnaker, *Mill Mgr*
Robert Cook, *Treasurer*
EMP: 15 **EST:** 1985
SQ FT: 3,000
SALES (est): 10.3MM **Privately Held**
WEB: www.gstl.us
SIC: 2421 Sawmills & planing mills, general

(G-7359)
GRECIAN & COMPANY INC
2988 Nw Us Highway 41 (32055-8189)
P.O. Box 2947 (32056-2947)
PHONE..................................386 344-1967
Grecian Paul, *President*
EMP: 8 **EST:** 2010
SALES (est): 523.7K **Privately Held**
SIC: 3421 Table & food cutlery, including butchers'

(G-7360)
GRIZZLY MANUFACTURING INC
Also Called: Quality Mills
174 Ne Cortez Ter (32055-1439)
PHONE..................................386 755-0220
Jeff Stotrz, *CEO*
Floyd Messer, *President*
EMP: 25 **EST:** 1972
SQ FT: 19,000
SALES (est): 4.8MM
SALES (corp-wide): 13.6MM **Privately Held**
WEB: www.grizzlysprockets.com
SIC: 3568 3541 3462 Sprockets (power transmission equipment); machine tools, metal cutting type; iron & steel forgings
PA: Quality Industries Of America, Inc.
3631 E Us Highway 90
Lake City FL 32055
386 755-0220

(G-7361)
IDAHO TIMBER LLC
176 Sw Midtown Pl Ste 101 (32025-0782)
PHONE..................................386 758-8111
Chris McSwain, *Branch Mgr*
EMP: 111
SALES (corp-wide): 6B **Publicly Held**
WEB: www.idahofb.org
SIC: 2421 Planing mills
HQ: Idaho Timber, Llc
3540 E Longwing Ln # 270
Meridian ID 83646
208 377-3000

(G-7362)
JACOBSEN FACTORY OUTLET
3973 W Us Highway 90 (32055-4875)
PHONE..................................386 438-8458
Robert C Linton,
EMP: 5 **EST:** 2013
SALES (est): 470.8K **Privately Held**
WEB: www.jacobsenfactoryoutlet.com
SIC: 2451 5271 Mobile homes; mobile homes

(G-7363)
LAKE CITY MEDIPLEX LLC
162 Nw Birdie Pl (32055-8665)
PHONE..................................386 752-2209
Minesh Patel, *Owner*
EMP: 10 **EST:** 2009
SALES (est): 354.7K **Privately Held**
WEB: www.lakecitymedical.com
SIC: 2899 Salt

(G-7364)
LAMARTEK INC
Also Called: Dive Rite
175 Nw Washington St (32055-2862)
PHONE..................................386 752-1087
Lamar Hires, *President*
Debbie Harris, *Manager*
Lee Ann Hires, *Admin Sec*
◆ **EMP:** 25 **EST:** 1980
SQ FT: 4,500
SALES (est): 4.4MM **Privately Held**
WEB: www.diverite.com
SIC: 3949 5091 Skin diving equipment, scuba type; diving equipment & supplies

(G-7365)
LINMAN INC
Also Called: Clayton Industries
Us Hwy 100 (32055)
P.O. Box 1059 (32056-1059)
PHONE..................................904 755-6800
Robert Chaplin III, *President*
Barbara Chaplin, *Vice Pres*
Milburn E Rich, *Vice Pres*
Debra R Williams, *Admin Sec*
EMP: 267
SQ FT: 95,000
SALES (est): 20MM **Privately Held**
SIC: 2451 Mobile homes, except recreational

(G-7366)
LOLLIPOP CHILDREN CENTER INC
416 Se Ermine Ave (32025-0801)
PHONE..................................386 755-3953
Joanne George, *President*
EMP: 8 **EST:** 2017
SALES (est): 518.9K **Privately Held**
SIC: 2064 Lollipops & other hard candy

(G-7367)
MARTINS FMOUS PSTRY SHOPPE INC
297 Nw Brown Rd (32055-7500)
PHONE..................................800 548-1200
EMP: 6

▲ = Import ▼=Export
◆ =Import/Export

SALES (corp-wide): 123.7MM **Privately Held**
WEB: www.potatorolls.com
SIC: 2015 Poultry slaughtering & processing
PA: Martin's Famous Pastry Shoppe, Inc.
1000 Potato Roll Ln
Chambersburg PA 17202
800 548-1200

(G-7368)
NATION SIGNS
162 Sw Spencer Ct Ste 101 (32024-0366)
PHONE..................................386 466-0043
Shane Willems, *Principal*
EMP: 6 **EST:** 2009
SALES (est): 69.7K **Privately Held**
SIC: 3993 Signs & advertising specialties

(G-7369)
NEW MLLENNIUM BLDG SYSTEMS LLC
1992 Nw Bascom Norris Dr (32055-4888)
PHONE..................................386 466-1300
Jeff Coker, *General Mgr*
Francisco Sanchez, *General Mgr*
Chris Graham, *Vice Pres*
Jason Kight, *Maint Spvr*
Doug Rees-Evans, *QC Mgr*
EMP: 148 **Publicly Held**
WEB: www.newmill.com
SIC: 3441 Joists, open web steel: long-span series
HQ: New Millennium Building Systems Llc
7575 W Jefferson Blvd
Fort Wayne IN 46804
260 969-3500

(G-7370)
NORTH CENTRAL ADVERTISER INC
358 Nw Main Blvd (32055-3309)
PHONE..................................386 755-2917
Thomas J Ricketson, *Principal*
EMP: 7 **EST:** 2009
SALES (est): 677.2K **Privately Held**
WEB: www.allthingsvisual.com
SIC: 2711 Newspapers

(G-7371)
NORTH FLORIDA AG SERVICES INC
3151 Sw Custom Made Cir (32024-1372)
PHONE..................................352 494-3978
Michael Emery, *President*
Cindy A Payne, *Principal*
Austin Emory, *Vice Pres*
Austin Ty Hiers, *Vice Pres*
EMP: 6 **EST:** 2017
SALES (est): 882.4K **Privately Held**
SIC: 2879 Pesticides, agricultural or household

(G-7372)
NORTH FLORIDA VAULT LLC
561 Nw Hilton Ave (32055-2710)
PHONE..................................386 303-2267
Christopher M Charles, *Principal*
EMP: 10 **EST:** 2015
SALES (est): 1.3MM **Privately Held**
SIC: 3272 Concrete products

(G-7373)
OMI OF LAKE CITY LLC
4066 Nw Wisteria Dr (32055-4889)
PHONE..................................386 288-5632
Darshana Patel, *Principal*
EMP: 9 **EST:** 2010
SALES (est): 88.5K **Privately Held**
WEB: www.lakecitymedical.com
SIC: 2899 Salt

(G-7374)
OPTIMA ASSOCIATES INC
Also Called: Bag of Ice
2469 W Us Highway 90 # 130
(32055-4740)
PHONE..................................877 371-1555
Michelle Dedeo, *President*
Michelle R Dedeo, *President*
EMP: 10 **EST:** 2009
SQ FT: 6,960
SALES (est): 1.9MM **Privately Held**
SIC: 3581 Automatic vending machines

(G-7375)
PEPSI-COLA METRO BTLG CO INC
619 Sw Arrowhead Ter (32024-3374)
PHONE..................................386 752-8956
Nile Bryant, *Manager*
EMP: 6
SALES (corp-wide): 70.3B **Publicly Held**
WEB: www.pepsico.com
SIC: 2086 Carbonated soft drinks, bottled & canned
HQ: Pepsi-Cola Metropolitan Bottling Company, Inc.
1111 Westchester Ave
White Plains NY 10604
914 767-6000

(G-7376)
PRINT THIS AND THAT LLC (PA)
167 Sw Mossy Oak Way (32024-2908)
PHONE..................................386 752-5905
Ted Whitcomb, *Principal*
EMP: 10 **EST:** 2010
SALES (est): 96.4K **Privately Held**
SIC: 2752 Commercial printing, lithographic

(G-7377)
PRINT THIS AND THAT LLC
231 Nw Burk Ave Ste 101 (32055-3704)
PHONE..................................386 344-4420
Joshua Johnson, *Principal*
EMP: 15
SALES (corp-wide): 96.4K **Privately Held**
SIC: 2752 Commercial printing, lithographic
PA: Print This And That, Llc
167 Sw Mossy Oak Way
Lake City FL 32024
386 752-5905

(G-7378)
QUAIL HEIGHT GOLF CLUB
161 Sw Quail Heights Ter (32025-1427)
PHONE..................................386 752-3339
Chet Carter, *General Mgr*
Todd Carter, *Superintendent*
Carter Robert, *Principal*
EMP: 15 **EST:** 2012
SALES (est): 571.7K **Privately Held**
WEB: www.quailheightscc.com
SIC: 3949 Shafts, golf club

(G-7379)
QUALITY FBRCTION MCH WORKS INC
3631 E Us Highway 90 (32055-1436)
PHONE..................................386 755-0220
Dale Dryden, *President*
Jeffery Stortz, *President*
Guy Musser, *Vice Pres*
James Brown III, *CFO*
EMP: 11 **EST:** 1972
SQ FT: 22,000
SALES (est): 2.1MM
SALES (corp-wide): 13.6MM **Privately Held**
WEB: www.qiagroup.com
SIC: 3443 3441 3553 3535 Fabricated plate work (boiler shop); fabricated structural metal; woodworking machinery; conveyors & conveying equipment; mining machinery
PA: Quality Industries Of America, Inc.
3631 E Us Highway 90
Lake City FL 32055
386 755-0220

(G-7380)
QUALITY INDUSTRIES AMERICA INC (PA)
Also Called: Quality Fabrication Mch Works
3631 E Us Highway 90 (32055-1436)
PHONE..................................386 755-0220
Edward D Dryden, *Ch of Bd*
Jeffery Stortz, *President*
Guy D Messer, *Principal*
James Brown III, *Corp Secy*
Dale N Dryden, *Vice Pres*
EMP: 4 **EST:** 1972
SQ FT: 78,000
SALES (est): 13.6MM **Privately Held**
WEB: www.qiagroup.com
SIC: 3568 3441 1791 5085 Sprockets (power transmission equipment); fabricated structural metal; structural steel erection; mill supplies; steel

(G-7381)
RED BUD ENTERPRISES INC
1435 Nw County Road 25a (32055-4955)
P.O. Box 1118 (32056-1118)
PHONE..................................386 752-5696
Warren E Nail, *President*
Steve Nail, *Vice Pres*
EMP: 29 **EST:** 1976
SQ FT: 17,000
SALES (est): 4.6MM **Privately Held**
SIC: 3083 Plastic finished products, laminated

(G-7382)
ROADSAFE TRAFFIC SYSTEMS INC
2118 Nw County Road 25a (32055-4904)
P.O. Box 2027 (32056-2027)
PHONE..................................386 755-0140
Jack R Keiter, *Manager*
EMP: 22
SQ FT: 11,250 **Privately Held**
WEB: www.roadsafetraffic.com
SIC: 3531 Construction machinery
PA: Roadsafe Traffic Systems, Inc.
8750 W Bryn Mawr Ave
Chicago IL 60631

(G-7383)
SEPHORA INSIDE JCPENNEY
2427 W Us Highway 90 (32055-4727)
PHONE..................................386 752-2822
EMP: 8 **EST:** 2019
SALES (est): 72K **Privately Held**
WEB: www.sephora.com
SIC: 2844 Toilet preparations

(G-7384)
SIGNCRAFT & MORE INC
1554 E Duval St (32055-4118)
PHONE..................................386 755-4754
James E Frazier, *President*
EMP: 7 **EST:** 2017
SALES (est): 285K **Privately Held**
SIC: 3993 Signs & advertising specialties

(G-7385)
SIGNSITECOM INC
Also Called: Speedysignsusa.com,
162 Sw Spencer Ct Ste 106 (32024-0366)
PHONE..................................386 487-0265
Laura A Willems, *President*
Shane D Willems, *Vice Pres*
Tyler Rolfe, *Manager*
Willems Laura, *Director*
Danielle Bullock, *Representative*
EMP: 5 **EST:** 2006
SALES (est): 543.8K **Privately Held**
WEB: www.signsite.com
SIC: 3993 Signs & advertising specialties

(G-7386)
SPEEDYSIGNSCOM INC
Also Called: Speedy Sign
162 Sw Spencer Ct Ste 101 (32024-0366)
PHONE..................................386 755-2006
Shane D Willems, *President*
Laura A Willems, *Corp Secy*
Alex Kirsch, *Vice Pres*
EMP: 35 **EST:** 1996
SQ FT: 12,000
SALES (est): 1MM **Privately Held**
WEB: www.speedysigns.com
SIC: 3993 Signs & advertising specialties

(G-7387)
STARTECH LAKE CITY INC
109 Nw Spring Hill Ct (32055-7512)
PHONE..................................386 466-1969
Bryant Jennings, *Principal*
EMP: 12 **EST:** 2009
SALES (est): 932.5K **Privately Held**
WEB: www.computerserviceslakecity.com
SIC: 2899 Salt

(G-7388)
STOP-N-GO 12
801 Nw Lake Jeffery Rd (32055-1832)
PHONE..................................386 344-5494
EMP: 6 **EST:** 2017
SALES (est): 90.7K **Privately Held**
SIC: 2911 Petroleum refining

(G-7389)
TEEKO GRAPHICS INC
2018 Sw Main Blvd (32025-0025)
PHONE..................................386 754-5600
Rob Summerall, *President*
Milas Summerall, *Principal*
Katie Moore, *Sales Staff*
EMP: 5 **EST:** 1999
SALES (est): 500K **Privately Held**
WEB: www.teeko.com
SIC: 2759 Screen printing

Lake Hamilton
Polk County

(G-7390)
GOLD GRANITE & MARBLE
930 Robert Rd Unit 47 (33851)
PHONE..................................863 439-9794
Luis Mondragon, *Principal*
EMP: 18 **EST:** 2006
SALES (est): 268.6K **Privately Held**
WEB: www.goldenmarblegranite.com
SIC: 3281 Marble, building: cut & shaped

(G-7391)
NWL INC
4701 Crump Rd (33851)
PHONE..................................800 742-5695
EMP: 84
SALES (corp-wide): 101.3MM **Privately Held**
WEB: www.nwl.com
SIC: 3612 Power transformers, electric
HQ: Nwl, Inc.
312 Rising Sun Rd
Bordentown NJ 08505
609 298-7300

(G-7392)
R & K WELDING AND FABRICATION
4709 Crump Rd (33851)
P.O. Box 912 (33851-0912)
PHONE..................................863 422-8728
Kevin Giles, *President*
EMP: 5 **EST:** 2005
SALES (est): 490K **Privately Held**
WEB: www.rkwelding.com
SIC: 7692 Welding repair

(G-7393)
WOODYS HEDGING LLC
225 Water Tank Rd (33851)
P.O. Box 885 (33851-0885)
PHONE..................................863 557-4525
Calvin Ford,
EMP: 6 **EST:** 2010
SALES (est): 241K **Privately Held**
SIC: 3524 Hedge trimmers, electric

Lake Harbor
Palm Beach County

(G-7394)
CALCIUM SILICATE CORP INC
601 Watson Farm Rd (33459)
P.O. Box 405 (33459-0405)
PHONE..................................863 902-0217
Mark Elizer, *President*
EMP: 11 **Privately Held**
WEB: www.calsil.com
SIC: 3295 5191 Slag, crushed or ground; fertilizers & agricultural chemicals
PA: Calcium Silicate Corp., Inc.
2656 Harlan Farm Rd
Columbia TN

Lake Helen
Volusia County

(G-7395)
TST INDUSTRIES LLC
623 Pleasant St (32744-3523)
PHONE..................................386 868-2011

Steven Fox, *Officer*
Bart P Rogowski, *Administration*
EMP: 9 **EST:** 2017
SALES (est): 943.1K **Privately Held**
WEB: www.tstindustries.com
SIC: 3999 Manufacturing industries

Lake Mary
Seminole County

(G-7396)
ABB INC
Also Called: ABB Power Distribution
680 Century Pt (32746-2136)
PHONE..................................407 732-2000
Bruce Wittbrodt, *Manager*
EMP: 63
SALES (corp-wide): 26.1B **Privately Held**
WEB: www.global.abb
SIC: 3613 3625 3675 3612 Switchgear & switchboard apparatus; distribution boards, electric; generator control & metering panels; relays & industrial controls; electronic capacitors; power & distribution transformers
HQ: Abb Inc.
305 Gregson Dr
Cary NC 27511

(G-7397)
AIRFLOWBALANCE LLC
4273 Regal Town Ln (32746-2062)
PHONE..................................386 871-8136
Craig Gordon, *Opers Staff*
Ryan Gordon, *Mng Member*
EMP: 10 **EST:** 2013
SALES (est): 150K **Privately Held**
SIC: 3822 Air flow controllers, air conditioning & refrigeration

(G-7398)
ALACRIANT HOLDINGS LLC
1051 Sand Pond Rd Ste 101 (32746-3341)
PHONE..................................330 233-0523
Nicholas Dvorak, *Principal*
EMP: 25 **EST:** 2008
SALES (est): 12.7MM
SALES (corp-wide): 39.4MM **Privately Held**
WEB: www.alacriant.com
SIC: 3444 Sheet metalwork
PA: Alacriant Inc.
1760 Miller Pkwy
Streetsboro OH 44241
330 562-7191

(G-7399)
AMAG TECHNOLOGY INC
858 Bright Meadow Dr (32746-4861)
PHONE..................................407 549-3882
Gordon Beatty, *Principal*
EMP: 5 **EST:** 2010
SALES (est): 576.8K **Privately Held**
WEB: www.amag.com
SIC: 3577 Computer peripheral equipment
HQ: G4s Technology Limited
International Drive
Tewkesbury GLOS GL20
168 429-9400

(G-7400)
ARCHER ELLISON INC
7025 County Road 46a # 1071
(32746-4721)
PHONE..................................800 449-4095
Allen D'Angelo, *CEO*
Kimberly D'Angelo, *Vice Pres*
EMP: 7 **EST:** 2002
SQ FT: 2,700
SALES (est): 733.5K **Privately Held**
WEB: www.archerellison.com
SIC: 2731 8741 8748 Books: publishing only; management services; business consulting

(G-7401)
AUREL PARTNERS LLC
7025 County Road 46a # 1071380
(32746-4721)
PHONE..................................203 300-7470
William Black,
EMP: 40 **EST:** 2017
SALES (est): 1.1MM **Privately Held**
SIC: 3999 Manufacturing industries

(G-7402)
AXIS PHRM PARTNERS LLC
550 Technology Park (32746-7131)
PHONE..................................407 936-2949
Mark C Montgomery, *Principal*
EMP: 6 **EST:** 2011
SALES (est): 115.1K **Privately Held**
SIC: 2834 Pharmaceutical preparations

(G-7403)
BLACKCLOAK INC
7025 Cty Rd 46a Ste 1071 46 A (32746)
PHONE..................................833 882-5625
Chris Pierson, *CEO*
EMP: 11 **EST:** 2018
SALES (est): 1.4MM **Privately Held**
WEB: www.blackcloak.io
SIC: 7372 Application computer software

(G-7404)
CENTRAL FLORIDA BOX CORP
Also Called: Cfb Display Group
2950 Lake Emma Rd # 1000 (32746-3702)
PHONE..................................407 936-1277
Jeffrey T Ramsey, *President*
Joseph Magliaro, *Opers Staff*
Angela Ramsey, *VP Sls/Mktg*
Alisa Hoskins, *Consultant*
▲ **EMP:** 40 **EST:** 1979
SQ FT: 190,000
SALES (est): 12MM
SALES (corp-wide): 17.5B **Publicly Held**
WEB: www.centralfloridabox.com
SIC: 2653 Boxes, corrugated: made from purchased materials
HQ: Westrock Paper And Packaging, Llc
1000 Abernathy Rd
Atlanta GA 30328

(G-7405)
CHARISMA MEDIA
Also Called: Plus Communication
1051 Sand Pond Rd (32746-3341)
PHONE..................................407 333-0600
Steven Strang, *CEO*
Marcos Perez, *Publisher*
Maureen Eha, *Editor*
Linda Gillotti, *Production*
Joyce Strang, *CFO*
EMP: 84 **EST:** 2012
SALES (est): 6.7MM **Privately Held**
WEB: www.charismamedia.com
SIC: 2711 7311 Newspapers; advertising consultant

(G-7406)
COLONIAL INDUSTRIES CENTL FLA
462 Mohave Ter (32746-7010)
PHONE..................................407 484-5239
John T Davy, *Director*
EMP: 8 **EST:** 2001
SALES (est): 479.5K **Privately Held**
WEB: www.colonialindustriesfl.us
SIC: 3999 Manufacturing industries

(G-7407)
CREATIVE DATA SOLUTIONS INC
1540 Intl Pkwy Ste 2000 (32746)
PHONE..................................407 333-4770
Lisa L Morris, *President*
Rex H Arnold, *Vice Pres*
EMP: 13 **EST:** 1992
SALES (est): 1.2MM **Privately Held**
WEB: www.cdscourts.com
SIC: 7372 Prepackaged software

(G-7408)
DEALERUPS INC
4185 W Lake Mary Blvd # 2 (32746-2400)
PHONE..................................407 557-5368
Theodore Rubin, *President*
David Lampert, *Vice Pres*
EMP: 12 **EST:** 2000
SQ FT: 2,000
SALES (est): 300K **Privately Held**
SIC: 7372 Prepackaged software

(G-7409)
DIXON TICONDEROGA COMPANY (DH)
615 Crscent Exec Ct Ste 5 (32746)
PHONE..................................407 829-9000
James Schmitz, *CEO*
Massimo Candela, *President*
Cody Agaard, *Exec VP*
Luis Pedro, *Exec VP*
Tony Rufo, *Exec VP*
◆ **EMP:** 90 **EST:** 1978
SALES (est): 154.5MM **Privately Held**
WEB: www.dixonwriting.com
SIC: 3952 3951 Pencils & leads, including artists'; artists' materials, except pencils & leads; crayons: chalk, gypsum, charcoal, fusains, pastel, wax, etc.; pencils & pencil parts, mechanical; ball point pens & parts; markers, soft tip (felt, fabric, plastic, etc.)
HQ: F.I.L.A Fabbrica Italiana Lapis Ed Affini Spa
Via Xxv Aprile 5
Pero MI 20016
023 810-51

(G-7410)
EMERGING MFG TECH INC
108 Commerce St Ste 102 (32746-6218)
P.O. Box 952828 (32795-2828)
PHONE..................................407 341-3476
EMP: 7 **EST:** 2011
SALES (est): 84.7K **Privately Held**
SIC: 3999 Manufacturing industries

(G-7411)
EVOLUTION ORTHOTICS INC
156 Harston Ct (32746-6973)
PHONE..................................407 688-2860
▲ **EMP:** 22
SALES (est): 1.3MM **Privately Held**
SIC: 3842 Mfg Surgical Appliances/Supplies

(G-7412)
EXPLORATION RESOURCES INTN GEO
1130 Business Center Dr (32746-7617)
PHONE..................................601 747-0726
Seth Broadfoot, *Mng Member*
EMP: 5 **EST:** 2012
SALES (est): 11.7MM **Privately Held**
SIC: 3699 8711 3829 7389 Electrical equipment & supplies; engineering services; measuring & controlling devices; business services

(G-7413)
FARO TECHNOLOGIES INC
125 Technology Park (32746-6230)
PHONE..................................800 736-0234
Jennifer Young, *Human Resources*
Ronald Benesch, *Accounts Mgr*
Matt Cordato, *Accounts Mgr*
Hasan Bal, *Info Tech Dir*
Enrique Enriquez, *Info Tech Dir*
EMP: 21 **Publicly Held**
WEB: www.faro.com
SIC: 3699 Laser systems & equipment
PA: Faro Technologies, Inc.
250 Technology Park
Lake Mary FL 32746

(G-7414)
FARO TECHNOLOGIES INC (PA)
250 Technology Park (32746-7115)
PHONE..................................407 333-9911
John Donofrio, *Ch of Bd*
Michael D Burger, *President*
Kevin Beadle, *Senior VP*
Christine Friend, *Production*
Allen Muhich, *CFO*
▲ **EMP:** 1047 **EST:** 1982
SQ FT: 46,500
SALES: 303.7MM **Publicly Held**
WEB: www.faro.com
SIC: 3829 Medical diagnostic systems, nuclear

(G-7415)
FICAP
705 Remington Oak Dr (32746-5710)
P.O. Box 4075, Milton (32572-4075)
PHONE..................................407 302-3316
Tony Nguyenthang, *Opers Dir*
Brad Coolidge, *Treasurer*
Michael Smith, *Manager*
Michele Stropoli, *Exec Dir*
Jeff Campbell, *Director*
EMP: 10 **EST:** 2008
SALES (est): 177.9K **Privately Held**
WEB: www.ficap.org
SIC: 3531 Mixers, concrete

(G-7416)
FINASTRA USA CORPORATION
744 Primera Blvd Ste 2000 (32746-2230)
PHONE..................................800 989-9009
Ryan Hengehold, *Partner*
Travis Benn, *Counsel*
Danica Pettit, *Project Mgr*
Brad Blust, *Opers Staff*
Sheri Williams, *Opers Staff*
EMP: 173
SALES (corp-wide): 1.6B **Privately Held**
WEB: www.finastra.com
SIC: 7372 Prepackaged software
HQ: Finastra Usa Corporation
555 Sw Morrison St # 300
Portland OR 97204
407 804-6600

(G-7417)
FLORIDA FROYO INC
725 Primera Blvd (32746-2125)
PHONE..................................407 977-4911
Brian K Linden, *Principal*
EMP: 6
SALES (est): 226.2K **Privately Held**
SIC: 2024 Yogurt desserts, frozen

(G-7418)
FLORIDA MEDIA INC
Also Called: Florida Monthly
1888 Brackenhurst Pl (32746-4611)
PHONE..................................407 816-9596
Doug Cifers, *President*
Kristen Cifers, *Vice Pres*
EMP: 10 **EST:** 1997
SQ FT: 3,000
SALES (est): 725.3K **Privately Held**
WEB: www.floridamagazine.com
SIC: 2721 Magazines: publishing only, not printed on site

(G-7419)
FLORIDA PRTCTIVE COATINGS CONS
482 Cardinal Oaks Ct (32746-3972)
PHONE..................................407 322-1243
Michael R Kendig, *President*
Michael R Stensrud, *Vice Pres*
EMP: 7 **EST:** 1986
SALES (est): 824.9K **Privately Held**
SIC: 2851 Paints & allied products

(G-7420)
HALLDALE MEDIA INC
735 Primera Blvd Ste 220 (32746-2150)
PHONE..................................407 322-5605
Andy Smith, *President*
Lori Ponoroff, *Editor*
Amanda Towner, *Editor*
Holly Foster, *Business Mgr*
David Malley, *Prdtn Mgr*
EMP: 20 **EST:** 2002
SALES (est): 3.5MM **Privately Held**
WEB: www.halldale.com
SIC: 2741 Miscellaneous publishing

(G-7421)
HAZMAT SOFTWARE LLC
760 Heather Glen Cir (32746-6128)
PHONE..................................407 416-5434
Luis Zambrana,
EMP: 19 **EST:** 2001
SALES (est): 1MM **Privately Held**
WEB: www.hazmatsoftware.com
SIC: 7372 Prepackaged software

(G-7422)
HIGH YIELD AG SOLUTIONS LLC
Also Called: Hyas
735 Primera Blvd Ste 200 (32746-2150)
PHONE..................................407 592-8089
EMP: 6 **EST:** 2014
SALES (est): 132.8K **Privately Held**
WEB: www.highyieldag.com
SIC: 3825 Network analyzers

(G-7423)
IGOVSOLUTIONS LLC
1307 S Intl Pkwy Ste 2061 (32746)
PHONE..................................407 574-3056
Prasad Valay,
EMP: 27 **EST:** 2014

▲ = Import ▼=Export
◆ =Import/Export

SALES (est): 2.7MM **Privately Held**
WEB: www.igovsolution.com
SIC: 7372 7371 Business oriented computer software; computer software development & applications; computer software systems analysis & design, custom; computer software development

(G-7424)
INFORMATION BUILDERS INC
300 Primera Blvd Ste 300 (32746-2145)
PHONE..................................407 804-8000
Fax: 407 804-8023
EMP: 25
SALES (corp-wide): 575.4MM **Privately Held**
SIC: 7372 7371 Prepackaged Software Services Custom Computer Programing
PA: Information Builders, Inc.
2 Penn Plz Fl 28
New York NY 10001
212 736-4433

(G-7425)
INTERNATIONAL GUIDELINES CTR
Also Called: Guideline Central
106 Commerce St Ste 105 (32746-6217)
PHONE..................................407 878-7606
Charles Kennedy, *President*
Vickie Reyes, *Director*
Kristie Wise, *Director*
EMP: 6 **EST**: 2002
SALES (est): 1.3MM **Privately Held**
WEB: www.guidelinecentral.com
SIC: 2721 Magazines: publishing only, not printed on site

(G-7426)
INTGRATED AROSPC ALIANCE LLC
188 E Crystal Lake Ave # 132
(32746-3204)
PHONE..................................469 703-7093
Ahmed Yousif Yasin, *Mng Member*
EMP: 6 **EST**: 2014
SALES (est): 194.6K **Privately Held**
SIC: 3728 Aircraft parts & equipment

(G-7427)
JJAZ ENTERPRISES INC
Also Called: AlphaGraphics
1061 S Sun Dr Ste 1033 (32746-6170)
PHONE..................................407 330-0245
Joshua A Field, *President*
EMP: 5 **EST**: 2018
SALES (est): 694.3K **Privately Held**
WEB: www.alphagraphics.com
SIC: 2752 Commercial printing, lithographic

(G-7428)
KENEXA LEARNING INC
100 Colonial Center Pkwy # 1
(32746-4767)
PHONE..................................407 548-0434
John Alonso, *Senior Partner*
Roger Surprenant, *Regional Mgr*
EMP: 9
SALES (corp-wide): 73.6B **Publicly Held**
WEB: www.outstart.com
SIC: 7372 7379 4813 Business oriented computer software; computer related consulting services;
HQ: Kenexa Learning, Inc.
650 E Swedesford Rd 2nd
Wayne PA 19087
610 971-9171

(G-7429)
LOCKHEED MARTIN CORPORATION
1190 Gatwick Loop (32746-1947)
PHONE..................................407 356-5715
Dan Stoppenbach, *Principal*
EMP: 6 **Publicly Held**
WEB: www.lockheedmartin.com
SIC: 3812 Search & navigation equipment
PA: Lockheed Martin Corporation
6801 Rockledge Dr
Bethesda MD 20817

(G-7430)
MAGICAL CREAMERY LLC
965 Helmsley Ct Apt 101 (32746-2010)
PHONE..................................407 719-6866
Abdiel De Jesus, *Principal*
EMP: 6 **EST**: 2010
SALES (est): 94.1K **Privately Held**
SIC: 2021 Creamery butter

(G-7431)
MARY LAKE LIFE MAG INC
881 Silversmith Cir (32746-4975)
PHONE..................................407 324-2644
Chip Colandreo, *Publisher*
Dennie Heidemann, *Principal*
EMP: 9 **EST**: 2011
SALES (est): 167.1K **Privately Held**
WEB: www.lakemarylife.com
SIC: 2721 Magazines: publishing only, not printed on site

(G-7432)
MARY LAKE LIFE MAGAZINE INC
3232 W Lake Mary Blvd # 1420
(32746-3582)
PHONE..................................407 324-2644
Sheila Kramer, *President*
Judith Topper, *Vice Pres*
Michael Kramer, *Admin Sec*
EMP: 16 **EST**: 2003
SALES (est): 4MM **Privately Held**
WEB: www.lakemarylife.com
SIC: 2721 Magazines: publishing only, not printed on site

(G-7433)
MEASUREMENTS INTERNATIONAL INC
343 Clermont Ave (32746-3629)
PHONE..................................315 393-1323
Duane Brown, *President*
Mike Frisz, *Sales Mgr*
EMP: 25 **EST**: 1998
SALES (est): 1.3MM **Privately Held**
WEB: www.mintl.com
SIC: 3825 Instruments to measure electricity

(G-7434)
MICROSEMI CORP
Also Called: Rfis Security Solutions
1064 Greenwood Blvd # 124 (32746-5419)
PHONE..................................407 965-5687
EMP: 12
SALES (est): 1.9MM
SALES (corp-wide): 1.1B **Publicly Held**
SIC: 3699 Mfg Electrical Equipment/Supplies
PA: Microsemi Corporation
1 Enterprise
Aliso Viejo CA 92841
949 380-6100

(G-7435)
MICROVISION TECHNOLOGY CORP
Also Called: Logic Springs Technologies
43 Skyline Dr Ste 3051 (32746-7117)
P.O. Box 950728 (32795-0728)
PHONE..................................407 333-2943
Efren Yero, *President*
William Lefebvre, *Software Engr*
Susan Long, *Analyst*
EMP: 16 **EST**: 1993
SQ FT: 8,500
SALES (est): 3MM **Privately Held**
WEB: www.logicsprings.com
SIC: 7372 7379 Business oriented computer software; computer related consulting services

(G-7436)
MITSUBISHI POWER AMERICAS INC (DH)
Also Called: Mitsubshi Htchi Pwr Systems Am
400 Colonial Center Pkwy # 500
(32746-7683)
PHONE..................................407 688-6100
Paul Browning, *President*
Sam Suttle, *General Mgr*
Bill Newsom, *Exec VP*
Rick Inskeep, *Senior VP*
Sean Joshi, *Vice Pres*
◆ **EMP**: 100 **EST**: 2001
SALES (est): 870.1MM **Privately Held**
WEB: www.power.mhi.com
SIC: 3511 3629 7389 Gas turbines, mechanical drive; steam turbines; thermoelectric generators; patrol of electric transmission or gas lines

(G-7437)
MOTOROLA SOLUTIONS INC
1064 Greenwood Blvd # 400 (32746-5419)
PHONE..................................407 562-4000
Pamela Benke, *Marketing Mgr*
Brian Tomooka, *Marketing Mgr*
Richard Licursi, *Branch Mgr*
Singhee Lim, *Software Engr*
EMP: 6
SALES (corp-wide): 7.4B **Publicly Held**
WEB: www.motorolasolutions.com
SIC: 3663 3674 3571 3812 Radio broadcasting & communications equipment; mobile communication equipment; pagers (one-way); cellular radio telephone; semiconductors & related devices; metal oxide silicon (MOS) devices; random access memory (RAM); microprocessors; personal computers (microcomputers); search & navigation equipment; position indicators for aircraft equipment; navigational systems & instruments; warfare counter-measure equipment; modems; multiplex equipment, telephone & telegraph; ignition apparatus, internal combustion engines
PA: Motorola Solutions, Inc.
500 W Monroe St Ste 4400
Chicago IL 60661
847 576-5000

(G-7438)
NATIONAL NEWSPAPER PLACEM
766 N Sun Dr Ste 2090 (32746-2566)
PHONE..................................866 404-5913
EMP: 8
SALES (est): 650.3K **Privately Held**
SIC: 2711 Newspapers-Publishing/Printing

(G-7439)
NEMEC
1534 Cherry Lake Way (32746-1905)
PHONE..................................407 829-2679
EMP: 7 **EST**: 2010
SALES (est): 103.3K **Privately Held**
SIC: 2851 Paints & allied products

(G-7440)
ORLANDO SHUTTERS LLC (PA)
Also Called: Orlando Shutters Blinds & More
4300 W Lake Mary Blvd # 1 (32746-2060)
PHONE..................................407 495-5250
Lala Beals, *Manager*
EMP: 24 **EST**: 2018
SALES (est): 722.5K **Privately Held**
WEB: www.orlandoshuttersblindsand-more.com
SIC: 3442 2591 2431 Shutters, door or window: metal; drapery hardware & blinds & shades; window shutters, wood

(G-7441)
PAPER BOX
500 Amethyst Way (32746-3769)
PHONE..................................407 415-7262
Kathy Toms, *Principal*
EMP: 6 **EST**: 2014
SALES (est): 63.8K **Privately Held**
SIC: 2652 Setup paperboard boxes

(G-7442)
PAVER KING
1472 Farrindon Cir (32746-4358)
P.O. Box 952452 (32795-2452)
PHONE..................................407 221-1718
Rick Friend, *Principal*
Tiffany King, *Advisor*
EMP: 6 **EST**: 2008
SALES (est): 112.4K **Privately Held**
WEB: www.paver-king.com
SIC: 3531 Pavers

(G-7443)
PLUS COMMUNICATIONS INC (PA)
Also Called: Strang Communications
600 Rinehart Rd (32746-4803)
P.O. Box 951420 (32795-1420)
PHONE..................................407 333-0600
Stephen E Strang, *CEO*
Joy F Strang, *Corp Secy*
Marcos Perez, *Vice Pres*
Rebecca McInnis, *Human Res Dir*
Ruth Whitfield, *Human Resources*
▲ **EMP**: 83 **EST**: 1975
SQ FT: 60,000
SALES (est): 34.9MM **Privately Held**
WEB: www.charismamedia.com
SIC: 2731 2721 Books: publishing & printing; magazines: publishing & printing

(G-7444)
PLUS COMMUNICATIONS INC
Casa Creacion
600 Rinehart Rd (32746-4803)
PHONE..................................407 333-0600
Steve Strang, *Branch Mgr*
EMP: 14
SALES (corp-wide): 34.9MM **Privately Held**
WEB: www.charismamedia.com
SIC: 2731 Book publishing
PA: Plus Communications, Inc.
600 Rinehart Rd
Lake Mary FL 32746
407 333-0600

(G-7445)
PREMIERETRADE FOREX LLC
103 Commerce St Ste 140 (32746-6237)
PHONE..................................407 287-4149
Ralph J Brunton, *Mng Member*
Tyler Benzel, *Manager*
EMP: 5 **EST**: 2004
SALES (est): 646.9K **Privately Held**
WEB: www.premieretrade.com
SIC: 7372 Business oriented computer software

(G-7446)
PROJSTREAM LLC
1540 Intl Pkwy 2000 (32746)
PHONE..................................407 476-1084
James Spear, *COO*
Jim Speer, *COO*
Rory Parkinson, *Project Mgr*
Paul Zecchini, *CTO*
Andrew Smith, *Director*
EMP: 11 **EST**: 2009
SQ FT: 1,000
SALES (est): 1.7MM **Privately Held**
WEB: www.projstream.com
SIC: 7372 Business oriented computer software

(G-7447)
QUALITY MANUFACTURING SVCS INC
400 Caring Dr Ste 1010 (32746-2558)
PHONE..................................407 531-6000
Jeffrey Cox, *CEO*
Sam Hanna, *President*
David Deborde, *Principal*
Josh King, *Production*
Carol Maxey, *Production*
▲ **EMP**: 98 **EST**: 1995
SQ FT: 45,000
SALES (est): 21MM **Privately Held**
WEB: www.qmscfl.com
SIC: 3672 Printed circuit boards

(G-7448)
QUANTUM TECHNOLOGY INC
108 Commerce St Ste 101 (32746-6225)
PHONE..................................407 333-9348
Sanjay R Adhav, *President*
EMP: 5 **EST**: 1968
SALES (est): 693.8K **Privately Held**
WEB: www.quantumtech.com
SIC: 3674 Semiconductors & related devices

(G-7449)
SMART ACCESS INC
2950 Lake Emma Rd # 1030 (32746-3702)
PHONE..................................407 331-4724
M Mehdi Daryadel, *President*

GEOGRAPHIC

Hadi Daryadel, *Vice Pres*
EMP: 9 **EST:** 1985
SQ FT: 3,000
SALES (est): 315.5K **Privately Held**
SIC: 3699 Security control equipment & systems

(G-7450)
SPECTRUM BRIDGE INC
110 Timberlachen Cir # 1012 (32746-3339)
PHONE..................................407 792-1570
Rod Dir, *President*
Peter Stanforth, *Vice Pres*
EMP: 11 **EST:** 2007
SALES (est): 303.7K **Privately Held**
WEB: www.192168ll.onl
SIC: 3825 Spectrum analyzers

(G-7451)
STOCKDALE TECHNOLOGIES INC
104 Commerce St (32746-6206)
PHONE..................................407 323-5121
Blake Guiles, *President*
EMP: 66 **EST:** 1983
SQ FT: 14,900
SALES (est): 4.3MM **Privately Held**
SIC: 3089 Thermoformed finished plastic products

(G-7452)
SUPERION LLC
Also Called: Centralsquare Technologies
1000 Business Center Dr (32746-5585)
PHONE..................................407 304-3235
Todd Schulte, *COO*
Robert Valvano, *CFO*
Lisa Neumann, *Controller*
Dale Loyd, *Accounts Mgr*
Teri Crockett, *Sales Staff*
EMP: 800 **EST:** 2017
SQ FT: 90,000
SALES (est): 136MM
SALES (corp-wide): 272.3MM **Privately Held**
WEB: www.centralsquare.com
SIC: 7372 Prepackaged software
PA: Centralsquare Technologies, Llc
1000 Business Center Dr
Lake Mary FL 32746
800 727-8088

(G-7453)
SWAMI FOODS LLC ✪
1617 Kersley Cir (32746-1925)
PHONE..................................888 697-9264
Graeme Duncan,
EMP: 10 **EST:** 2021
SALES (est): 570.9K **Privately Held**
SIC: 2051 Bakery: wholesale or wholesale/retail combined

(G-7454)
TEAM CYMRU INC
901 Intrntl Pkwy Ste 30 (32746-4703)
PHONE..................................847 378-3300
Robert Thomas, *CEO*
Courtney Auchter, *Business Mgr*
Scott Fisher, *Engineer*
Sina Rabbani, *Engineer*
Bounds Darren, *CFO*
EMP: 105 **EST:** 2011
SALES (est): 10.5MM **Privately Held**
WEB: www.team-cymru.com
SIC: 7372 Prepackaged software

(G-7455)
TOTALLY STORAGE INC
Also Called: Micro Design International
59 Skyline Dr Ste 1550 (32746-7113)
PHONE..................................407 472-6000
M Geoffrey Legat, *President*
EMP: 15 **EST:** 1999
SQ FT: 6,000
SALES (est): 690.8K **Privately Held**
WEB: www.mdi.com
SIC: 3572 Computer storage devices

(G-7456)
TREASURED PHOTO GIFTS LLC
Also Called: Printerpix
107 Commerce St (32746-6206)
PHONE..................................407 324-4816
Roshanali Daya, *Mng Member*
▲ **EMP:** 23 **EST:** 2011
SALES (est): 7.8MM **Privately Held**
WEB: www.printerpix.com
SIC: 2759 Commercial printing

(G-7457)
UNITED BIOSOURCE LLC (UBC)
680 Century Pt (32746-2136)
PHONE..................................877 599-7748
Patricia Mosher, *Vice Pres*
Ellen Baty, *Analyst*
EMP: 8 **EST:** 2019
SALES (est): 403.5K **Privately Held**
WEB: www.ubc.com
SIC: 2834 Pharmaceutical preparations

(G-7458)
VANDEPLAS PUBLISHING
801 International Pkwy # 500 (32746-4762)
PHONE..................................407 562-1947
Anton C Van De Plas, *Principal*
EMP: 5 **EST:** 2006
SALES (est): 318.3K **Privately Held**
WEB: www.vandeplaspublishing.com
SIC: 2741 Miscellaneous publishing

(G-7459)
VISHAY AMERICAS INC
735 Primera Blvd (32746-2112)
PHONE..................................407 804-2567
David Valletta, *Exec VP*
EMP: 460
SALES (corp-wide): 2.5B **Publicly Held**
WEB: www.vishay.com
SIC: 3676 Electronic resistors
HQ: Vishay Americas, Inc.
1 Greenwich Pl
Shelton CT 06484
203 452-5648

(G-7460)
VISUAL COMM SPECIALISTS INC
707 Platinum Pt Ste 2001 (32746-5702)
PHONE..................................407 936-7300
Cheryl Walker, *CEO*
EMP: 5 **EST:** 1996
SALES (est): 374.7K **Privately Held**
WEB: www.viscomspec.com
SIC: 3663 Radio & TV communications equipment

(G-7461)
WESTROCK LAKE MARY
2950 Lake Emma Rd (32746-3702)
PHONE..................................407 936-1277
EMP: 7 **EST:** 2019
SALES (est): 453.5K **Privately Held**
SIC: 3999 Manufacturing industries

(G-7462)
ZENIT SERVICE LLC
309 Grand Valley Dr (32746-6287)
PHONE..................................407 878-7840
Ivan Stoyanov, *Manager*
EMP: 9 **EST:** 2012
SALES (est): 2.4MM **Privately Held**
WEB: www.zenitservice.com
SIC: 3585 Air conditioning units, complete: domestic or industrial

Lake Panasoffkee
Sumter County

(G-7463)
GREAT SOUTHERN WOOD PRSV INC
194 Cr 527a (33538-6504)
P.O. Box 759 (33538-0759)
PHONE..................................352 793-9410
Danny Trabue, *Sales Staff*
Linda Thornton, *Office Mgr*
Mike French, *Branch Mgr*
Mark Callender, *Manager*
EMP: 27
SALES (corp-wide): 337.5MM **Privately Held**
WEB: www.yellawood.com
SIC: 2491 Wood preserving
PA: Great Southern Wood Preserving, Incorporated
1100 Us Highway 431 S
Abbeville AL 36310
334 585-2291

(G-7464)
UNITED AG SVCS AMER INC
534 Cr 529a (33538-6505)
PHONE..................................352 793-1682
Mark Pecsenka, *President*
Lajos Pecsenka, *Vice Pres*
Hilda Pecsenka, *Admin Sec*
▲ **EMP:** 13 **EST:** 1994
SQ FT: 10,000
SALES (est): 3.6MM **Privately Held**
WEB: www.uas-cropmaster.com
SIC: 2875 2873 Potting soil, mixed; fertilizers: natural (organic), except compost

Lake Park
Palm Beach County

(G-7465)
ALL TENNIS LLC
1434 10th St (33403-2037)
PHONE..................................561 842-0070
Perry E Carrell, *Principal*
EMP: 6 **EST:** 2009
SALES (est): 444.9K **Privately Held**
WEB: www.alltennisstore.com
SIC: 3949 Tennis equipment & supplies

(G-7466)
BIG DIGITAL GRAPHICS LLC
1335 Old Dixie Hwy Unit 4 (33403-1967)
PHONE..................................561 844-4708
Cat Estes, *Office Mgr*
Patrick Ward,
EMP: 6 **EST:** 2007
SALES (est): 671.6K **Privately Held**
WEB: www.bigdigitalgraphics.com
SIC: 3993 Signs & advertising specialties

(G-7467)
CAPTAIN CANVAS & MORE
700 Old Dixie Hwy Ste 109 (33403-2321)
PHONE..................................561 881-2278
Susan Benson, *Principal*
EMP: 7 **EST:** 2007
SALES (est): 128.9K **Privately Held**
SIC: 2211 Canvas

(G-7468)
ECOSMART
1313 S Killian Dr (33403-1918)
PHONE..................................561 328-6488
Brian Ireland, *Principal*
Micki Malone, *Controller*
EMP: 11 **EST:** 2012
SALES (est): 406.9K **Privately Held**
SIC: 2851 Paints & allied products

(G-7469)
EMERGENCY VEHICLES INC (PA)
705 13th St (33403-2303)
PHONE..................................561 848-6652
Ernst E Temme, *President*
Barbara Temme, *Principal*
Dave M Taliercio, *Vice Pres*
Chris Temme, *Prdtn Mgr*
Randy Wahl, *Regl Sales Mgr*
◆ **EMP:** 26 **EST:** 1988
SQ FT: 35,000
SALES (est): 6.9MM **Privately Held**
WEB: www.evi-fl.com
SIC: 3711 Automobile assembly, including specialty automobiles

(G-7470)
FINDEXCOM INC (PA)
1313 S Killian Dr (33403-1918)
PHONE..................................561 328-6488
Steven Malone, *Ch of Bd*
EMP: 5 **EST:** 1999
SQ FT: 8,560
SALES: 334.3K **Publicly Held**
WEB: www.findex.com
SIC: 2851 Lacquers, varnishes, enamels & other coatings; removers & cleaners

(G-7471)
FLORIDA AERO PRECISION INC (HQ)
120 Reed Rd (33403-3015)
PHONE..................................561 848-6248
James K Rice, *Principal*
Scott Burfield, *Personnel Exec*
Linda Graham, *Office Mgr*
Gary Bishop, *Prgrmr*
EMP: 30 **EST:** 1981
SQ FT: 10,000
SALES (est): 9.6MM
SALES (corp-wide): 344.8MM **Privately Held**
WEB: www.floridaaeroprecisioninc.com
SIC: 3724 4581 Aircraft engines & engine parts; aircraft servicing & repairing
PA: Meyer Tool, Inc.
3055 Colerain Ave
Cincinnati OH 45225
513 681-7362

(G-7472)
FLORIDA ROADWAY SIGNS INC
1137 Silver Beach Rd (33403-3025)
PHONE..................................561 722-4067
Debra Ricci, *President*
Brittani Ricci, *Vice Pres*
EMP: 9 **EST:** 2018
SALES (est): 302K **Privately Held**
WEB: www.floridaroadway.com
SIC: 3993 Signs & advertising specialties

(G-7473)
GC CABINET EXPRESS LLC
1335 Old Dixie Hwy # 20 (33403-1966)
PHONE..................................561 662-0369
Ronald M Conner, *Manager*
EMP: 6 **EST:** 2016
SALES (est): 665.5K **Privately Held**
WEB: www.gc-cabinet-express-llc.business.site
SIC: 2434 Wood kitchen cabinets

(G-7474)
HARD CHROME ENTERPRISES INC
220 10th St (33403-3150)
PHONE..................................561 844-2529
William Onuska, *President*
William M Onuska Jr, *Vice Pres*
EMP: 9 **EST:** 1971
SQ FT: 5,000
SALES (est): 1.1MM **Privately Held**
WEB: www.hardchromeenterprises.com
SIC: 3471 Electroplating of metals or formed products

(G-7475)
JUNO IRONCRAFT
1233 Old Dixie Hwy (33403-2347)
PHONE..................................561 352-0471
Shea John, *Principal*
EMP: 5 **EST:** 2016
SALES (est): 780.5K **Privately Held**
WEB: www.junoironcraft.com
SIC: 3441 Fabricated structural metal

(G-7476)
MASCHMEYER CONCRETE CO FLA (PA)
1142 Watertower Rd (33403-2397)
PHONE..................................561 848-9112
Troy W Maschmeyer Jr, *President*
Jessie James, *General Mgr*
Jeffrey A Bishop, *COO*
Steven Bishop, *COO*
Mark Arbuckle, *Vice Pres*
▲ **EMP:** 46 **EST:** 1985
SQ FT: 1,800
SALES (est): 136.2MM **Privately Held**
WEB: www.maschmeyer.com
SIC: 3273 3312 Ready-mixed concrete; wire products, steel or iron

(G-7477)
PALM BEACH BTRY VENTURES LLC (PA)
Also Called: Batteries Plus
1250 Northlake Blvd (33403-2050)
PHONE..................................561 881-8900
Brenda Phipps, *Vice Pres*
Richard L Phipps Jr,
EMP: 14 **EST:** 2012
SQ FT: 1,600
SALES (est): 2.4MM **Privately Held**
WEB: www.batteriesplus.com
SIC: 3691 5531 Storage batteries; batteries, automotive & truck

(G-7478)
PRESSURE WASHERS USA
1440 10th Ct Bay A (33403-2007)
PHONE...................................561 848-7970
Lewis Paul, *Director*
EMP: 6 **EST:** 2011
SALES (est): 209.7K **Privately Held**
WEB: www.pressurewashersusa.com
SIC: 3452 Washers

(G-7479)
REXPRO SERVICES
1313 S Killian Dr (33403-1918)
PHONE...................................561 328-6488
Steven Malone, *Principal*
John Kuehne, *Principal*
Micki Malone, *Principal*
Michael Membrado, *Principal*
Donald Schoenfeld, *Principal*
EMP: 6 **EST:** 2019
SALES (est): 576.7K **Privately Held**
SIC: 2851 Paints & allied products

(G-7480)
STREET SIGNS USA INC
1137 Silver Beach Rd (33403-3025)
PHONE...................................561 848-1411
Alan Weissman, *Principal*
EMP: 5 **EST:** 2007
SALES (est): 453.5K **Privately Held**
SIC: 3993 Signs & advertising specialties

(G-7481)
WEST POINT INDUSTRIES INC
1300 Old Dixie Hwy # 101 (33403-1925)
PHONE...................................561 848-8381
Robert Greaves, *President*
EMP: 6 **EST:** 1988
SQ FT: 5,000
SALES (est): 798.6K **Privately Held**
WEB: www.westpointindustries.com
SIC: 7692 3544 3441 Welding repair; special dies, tools, jigs & fixtures; building components, structural steel

(G-7482)
WOOD DRAMS INC OF PALM BEACHES
1137 Silver Beach Rd (33403-3025)
PHONE...................................561 842-9814
Fax: 561 842-5307
EMP: 6
SQ FT: 6,000
SALES (est): 430K **Privately Held**
SIC: 2511 Mfg Wall Units

(G-7483)
WOODHAM INDUSTRIES INC
1400 Old Dixie Hwy Ste 1 (33403-1964)
PHONE...................................561 863-6666
EMP: 7 **EST:** 2018
SALES (est): 1MM **Privately Held**
SIC: 3999 Manufacturing industries

Lake Placid
Highlands County

(G-7484)
APPLIED DESIGN & FABRICATION
3525 Northern Blvd (33852-7595)
PHONE...................................954 524-6619
Lisa Ludwig, *President*
EMP: 7
SALES (est): 550K **Privately Held**
SIC: 3548 Welding & cutting apparatus & accessories

(G-7485)
C & C TOOL & MOLD
3417 Paso Fino Dr (33852-5204)
PHONE...................................863 699-5337
Harold N Crews, *Owner*
EMP: 5 **EST:** 1983
SQ FT: 2,400
SALES (est): 300K **Privately Held**
SIC: 3599 3544 Machine shop, jobbing & repair; industrial molds

(G-7486)
C C LEAD INC
127 Ranier Dr (33852-2404)
PHONE...................................863 465-6458
Clifton H Canter Jr, *President*
Phyllis Canter, *Admin Sec*
EMP: 14 **EST:** 1981
SQ FT: 4,150
SALES (est): 564.8K **Privately Held**
SIC: 3356 3842 3444 3339 Lead & lead alloy: rolling, drawing or extruding; surgical appliances & supplies; sheet metalwork; primary nonferrous metals; asphalt felts & coatings

(G-7487)
GENPAK LLC
55 Pine Ridge Dr (33852-7095)
PHONE...................................863 243-1068
Paula Neville, *Principal*
EMP: 10 **EST:** 2016
SALES (est): 146.3K **Privately Held**
WEB: www.genpak.com
SIC: 3089 Plastics products

(G-7488)
HEARTLAND METALS INC
Also Called: Pure Lead Products
127 Ranier Dr (33852-2404)
PHONE...................................863 465-7501
Mike P Hoy, *President*
Jack B Edgemon, *Vice Pres*
Jack Edgemon, *Vice Pres*
Kathleen P Edgemon, *Vice Pres*
Troy Ragan, *Sales Mgr*
EMP: 40 **EST:** 2003
SALES (est): 11.1MM **Privately Held**
WEB: www.pureleadproducts.com
SIC: 3356 Nonferrous rolling & drawing

(G-7489)
HENSCRATCH FARMS INC
Also Called: Henscratch Farms Winery
980 Henscratch Rd (33852-8220)
PHONE...................................863 699-2060
Brooke Bundy, *President*
Sylvia Lauchman, *President*
Drew Jones, *Vice Pres*
EMP: 7 **EST:** 1998
SQ FT: 1,391
SALES (est): 400K **Privately Held**
WEB: www.henscratchfarms.com
SIC: 2084 Wines

(G-7490)
KEYSTONE WATER COMPANY LLC
200 Turner Rd (33852-5440)
PHONE...................................863 465-1932
Darren Keller, *Mng Member*
Christopher Rapp,
Ryan Hurlbut,
Chris Rapp,
▼ **EMP:** 19 **EST:** 2008
SQ FT: 86,000
SALES (est): 2.4MM **Privately Held**
WEB: www.keystonewatercompany.com
SIC: 2086 7389 5963 Water, pasteurized: packaged in cans, bottles, etc.; labeling bottles, cans, cartons, etc.; bottled water delivery

(G-7491)
NICKELS AND ASSOCIATES LLC
133 Lavender Ave (33852-6107)
PHONE...................................863 699-0180
Barbara Nickels, *Principal*
EMP: 6 **EST:** 2010
SALES (est): 95K **Privately Held**
SIC: 3356 Nickel

(G-7492)
PAUL WONG
1475 Jersey St Ne (33852-3684)
PHONE...................................863 465-1114
Paul Wong, *Principal*
EMP: 7 **EST:** 2010
SALES (est): 162K **Privately Held**
SIC: 3482 Small arms ammunition

(G-7493)
PERFORMANCE SALES & SERVICE
1130 Us Highway 27 N (33852-5684)
PHONE...................................863 465-2814
Darin L Whitaker, *President*
EMP: 6 **EST:** 1974
SQ FT: 2,400
SALES (est): 805.2K **Privately Held**
WEB: www.mercuryperformance.com
SIC: 3599 5551 4493 3732 Machine shop, jobbing & repair; outboard boats; outboard motors; marine supplies; marinas; boat building & repairing

(G-7494)
RAVENSWOOD IMPORT EXPORT LTD L
204 S Main Ave Ste 5 (33852-1810)
P.O. Box 1849 (33862-1849)
PHONE...................................863 800-0210
Greg Gustum, *President*
Angel R Alonso, *Partner*
Angel Rodriguez Alonso R, *Chairman*
Patricia Savanella, *Exec VP*
Alexander Ferguson, *CTO*
EMP: 5 **EST:** 2013
SQ FT: 900
SALES (est): 779.8K **Privately Held**
WEB: www.ravenswood-usa.com
SIC: 2833 8748 Vegetable oils, medicinal grade: refined or concentrated; business consulting

(G-7495)
WEDGWORTHS INC
211 Sr 70 W (33852-8716)
PHONE...................................561 996-2076
EMP: 11 **EST:** 1952
SALES (est): 71.5K **Privately Held**
WEB: www.wedgworth.com
SIC: 2034 Dried & dehydrated vegetables

Lake Suzy
Desoto County

(G-7496)
BARNES GROUP INC
12144 Sw Egret Cir Apt 13 (34269-8728)
PHONE...................................941 255-0978
G E Barnes, *Branch Mgr*
EMP: 8
SALES (corp-wide): 1.4B **Publicly Held**
WEB: www.barnesgroupinc.com
SIC: 3495 Wire springs
PA: Barnes Group Inc.
123 Main St
Bristol CT 06010
860 583-7070

(G-7497)
WINSLOW MARINE PRODUCTS CORP
Also Called: Winslow Life Raft Co
11700 Sw Winslow Dr (34269-1902)
PHONE...................................941 613-6666
David Gitlin, *President*
▼ **EMP:** 85 **EST:** 1941
SQ FT: 35,000
SALES (est): 10.9MM
SALES (corp-wide): 56.5B **Publicly Held**
WEB: www.winslowliferaft.com
SIC: 3069 Life rafts, rubber
PA: Raytheon Technologies Corporation
870 Winter St
Waltham MA 02451
781 522-3000

Lake Wales
Polk County

(G-7498)
ACCOMMODATING SERVICES INC
19456 State Road 60 E (33898-7185)
PHONE...................................863 528-3231
J R Furko, *President*
EMP: 7
SALES (est): 500K **Privately Held**
SIC: 3589 Microwave ovens (cooking equipment), commercial

(G-7499)
ASI CHEMICAL INC
1901 State Road 60 W (33859-8286)
P.O. Box 712 (33859-0712)
PHONE...................................863 678-1814
Raul J Diaz, *President*
Miguel Diaz, *President*
Felix V Vassallo, *Vice Pres*
Cindy Diaz, *Manager*
◆ **EMP:** 11
SQ FT: 40,000
SALES (est): 114.9MM **Privately Held**
WEB: www.asichemical.com
SIC: 2842 Automobile polish

(G-7500)
AUTOMATED METAL PRODUCTS INC
16070 Hwy 27 (33859-2512)
P.O. Box 3426 (33859-3426)
PHONE...................................863 638-4404
Mary B Kregl, *President*
John Kregl, *Corp Secy*
EMP: 6 **EST:** 1997
SQ FT: 8,000
SALES (est): 883.8K **Privately Held**
WEB: www.automatedmetalproducts.com
SIC: 3441 Fabricated structural metal

(G-7501)
CEMEX MATERIALS LLC
Also Called: Rinker Materials
534 Story Rd (33898-9265)
P.O. Box 24731, West Palm Beach (33416-4731)
PHONE...................................863 678-3945
EMP: 45 **Privately Held**
SIC: 3273 Ready-mixed concrete
HQ: Cemex Materials Llc
1501 Belvedere Rd
West Palm Beach FL 33406
561 833-5555

(G-7502)
CENTRAL FLORIDA TINTING
1827 Canal Rd (33898-9191)
P.O. Box 251, Babson Park (33827-0251)
PHONE...................................863 221-0185
Andrew James Phelps, *Owner*
EMP: 6 **EST:** 2011
SALES (est): 294.5K **Privately Held**
WEB: www.centralfloridatint.com
SIC: 3211 Window glass, clear & colored

(G-7503)
CITRUS WORLD INC (PA)
Also Called: Florida's Natural Growers
20205 Hwy 27 (33853-3080)
P.O. Box 1111 (33859-1111)
PHONE...................................863 676-1411
Stephen M Caruso, *CEO*
Joe L Davis Jr, *Ch of Bd*
Dennis Broadaway, *President*
Ed Hendricks, *Business Mgr*
Todd Jones, *Business Mgr*
◆ **EMP:** 740 **EST:** 1934
SQ FT: 1,000,000
SALES (est): 188.1MM **Privately Held**
WEB: www.floridasnatural.com
SIC: 2037 Fruit juice concentrates, frozen

(G-7504)
CITRUS WORLD ADM SVCS INC
20205 Hwy 27 (33853-3080)
P.O. Box 1111 (33859-1111)
PHONE...................................863 676-1411
Richard A Fort Jr, *President*
EMP: 9 **EST:** 2013
SALES (est): 373.5K **Privately Held**
WEB: www.citrusworldinc.com
SIC: 2037 Frozen fruits & vegetables

(G-7505)
CITRUS WORLD SERVICES INC
20205 Hwy 27 (33853-3080)
PHONE...................................863 676-1411
Stephen Caruso, *Principal*
EMP: 10 **EST:** 2011
SALES (est): 385.7K **Privately Held**
WEB: www.citrusworldinc.com
SIC: 2037 Citrus pulp, dried

(G-7506)
COSNER MANUFACTURING LLC
511 N Scenic Hwy (33853-3203)
P.O. Box 152 (33859-0152)
PHONE...................................863 676-2579
Michael Ciferri Jr, *Mng Member*
Michelle Upchurch, *Manager*
EMP: 10 **EST:** 1966
SQ FT: 12,000

SALES (est): 588.1K Privately Held
WEB: www.cosnermfg.com
SIC: 2394 2673 Tarpaulins, fabric: made from purchased materials; bags: plastic, laminated & coated

(G-7507)
DURA-CAST PRODUCTS INC
16160 Hwy 27 (33859-2528)
PHONE....863 638-3200
Bruce Orcutt, *President*
David Orcutt, *Vice Pres*
Peter Villa, *Engineer*
Amber Baldi, *Office Mgr*
Timothy McBride, *Manager*
▼ EMP: 90
SQ FT: 50,000
SALES (est): 16.6MM Privately Held
WEB: www.duracast.com
SIC: 3089 Injection molding of plastics
PA: Tank Holding Corp.
6940 O St Ste 100
Lincoln NE 68510

(G-7508)
ELLISON RBM INC
4865 State Road 60 E (33898-9390)
P.O. Box 2422 (33859-2422)
PHONE....863 679-5283
Woodrow Ellison, *President*
Vicki Ellison, *Manager*
EMP: 5 EST: 2002
SALES (est): 772K Privately Held
WEB: www.designcreations2011.com
SIC: 2911 Road materials, bituminous

(G-7509)
FLINTS WRECKER SERVICE INC
6442 State Road 60 E (33898-9721)
PHONE....863 676-1318
James Flint, *President*
Victoria Flint, *Corp Secy*
EMP: 5 EST: 1958
SQ FT: 1,600
SALES (est): 436.7K Privately Held
SIC: 3711 7539 Wreckers (tow truck), assembly of; automotive sound system service & installation

(G-7510)
FLORIDAS NATURAL FOOD SVC INC
20205 Hwy 27 (33853-2428)
PHONE....888 657-6600
Richard A Fort Jr, *Principal*
Christopher Groom, *Vice Pres*
Tony Durham, *Production*
Terica Turlington, *Production*
Mike Buckland, *QC Mgr*
EMP: 24 EST: 2012
SALES (est): 1MM Privately Held
WEB: www.floridasnaturalfoodservice.com
SIC: 2037 Frozen fruits & vegetables

(G-7511)
FREEDOM BRICK PAVERS LLC
2625 Shiner Dr (33898-8822)
PHONE....863 224-6008
Scott Rian, *Principal*
EMP: 7 EST: 2013
SALES (est): 824.5K Privately Held
WEB: www.freedombrickpaversllc.com
SIC: 2951 Asphalt paving mixtures & blocks

(G-7512)
GRIFFIN SAWMILL & WOODWORKING
845 W Lake Wales Rd N (33859-8272)
PHONE....863 241-5180
Jerrod T Griffin, *President*
EMP: 8 EST: 2014
SALES (est): 101.6K Privately Held
WEB: www.griffinsawmill.com
SIC: 2421 Specialty sawmill products; flitches (veneer stock), made in sawmills

(G-7513)
HEATH CORPORATION
1303 Meyers Rd (33859-2531)
P.O. Box 72 (33859-0072)
PHONE....863 638-1819
Willard Heath Jr, *President*
EMP: 6 EST: 1986
SQ FT: 10,000
SALES (est): 764K Privately Held
SIC: 3541 Machine tools, metal cutting type

(G-7514)
KT FAB INC
1057 Lancelot Dr (33853-2751)
PHONE....863 443-0029
Kenneth Tull, *Principal*
EMP: 8 EST: 2014
SALES (est): 239.7K Privately Held
SIC: 3999 Manufacturing industries

(G-7515)
LTSC LLC
28 W Park Ave (33853-4132)
PHONE....863 678-0011
Mark Warda, *President*
EMP: 6 EST: 2012
SALES (est): 362.5K Privately Held
WEB: www.floridalandtrust.com
SIC: 2741 Miscellaneous publishing

(G-7516)
MIDGARD INC
6402 State Road 60 E (33898-9721)
PHONE....863 696-1224
Brian Byrd, *Vice Pres*
Cheryl Rathbun, *Safety Dir*
Beverly Hediger, *Office Mgr*
Dale Andrew, *Manager*
Debbie Steedley, *Manager*
EMP: 59
SALES (corp-wide): 15MM Privately Held
WEB: www.midgardplastics.com
SIC: 2821 3559 3089 Polycarbonate resins; plastics working machinery; plastic processing
PA: Midgard, Inc
1255 Nursery Rd
Green Lane PA 18054
215 536-3174

(G-7517)
PETERSEN INDUSTRIES INC
4000 State Road 60 W (33859-8201)
PHONE....863 676-1493
Woodrow Casey Hardy, *President*
Bob Beasock, *General Mgr*
Nancy Rathbun, *Trustee*
Sam Petersen, *Vice Pres*
Samuel S Petersen, *Vice Pres*
EMP: 104
SQ FT: 10,000
SALES (est): 26MM Privately Held
WEB: www.petersenind.com
SIC: 3523 Farm machinery & equipment

(G-7518)
PIPELINE FABRICATORS INC
Also Called: Pfi
733 Carlton Ave (33853-4236)
PHONE....863 678-0977
Perry D Batson, *President*
EMP: 10 EST: 1997
SALES (est): 846.2K Privately Held
SIC: 3498 Fabricated pipe & fittings

(G-7519)
SHELLIE BLUM LLC
201 C F Kinney Rd (33859-7545)
PHONE....863 439-3060
Shellie Blum, *Officer*
EMP: 6 EST: 2015
SALES (est): 145.1K Privately Held
WEB: www.waterskigirlwonder.com
SIC: 2731 Books: publishing only

(G-7520)
SPIN MAGNETICS
22501 Us Highway 27 (33859-6863)
P.O. Box 752 (33859-0752)
PHONE....863 676-9333
Howard Spence, *President*
Jim Graham, *Vice Pres*
Deanna Spence, *Opers Staff*
Maya Wiisanen, *CFO*
Margaret Alford, *Admin Sec*
▲ EMP: 29 EST: 1989
SALES (est): 3.4MM Privately Held
WEB: www.spinmagnetics.com
SIC: 3677 3612 5999 Electronic coils, transformers & other inductors; transformers, except electric; electronic parts & equipment

(G-7521)
SPINCONTROL GEARING LLC
4535 Tiger Creek Trl (33898-5552)
PHONE....863 241-9055
Eric Carrier, *General Mgr*
EMP: 7 EST: 2009
SALES (est): 452.3K Privately Held
SIC: 3566 Speed changers, drives & gears

(G-7522)
STORY CITRUS INC
20205 Hwy 27 (33853-2428)
P.O. Box 1221 (33859-1221)
PHONE....863 638-1619
Victor Story, *President*
EMP: 20 EST: 2001
SALES (est): 447.6K Privately Held
WEB: www.storycompanies.com
SIC: 2034 Dehydrated fruits, vegetables, soups

(G-7523)
SUTHERLAND ARMOUR RAND
2426 Lake Front Dr (33898-7203)
PHONE....863 696-3129
Sutherland Armour Rand, *Principal*
EMP: 10 EST: 2010
SALES (est): 87.6K Privately Held
SIC: 3131 Rands

(G-7524)
SUZANNE CHALET FOODS INC
Also Called: Chalet Suzanne Rest Cntry Inn
3800 Chalet Suzanne Dr (33859-7763)
PHONE....863 676-6011
Vita Hinshaw, *President*
Eric Hinshaw, *Treasurer*
EMP: 6 EST: 1956
SALES (est): 540.7K Privately Held
SIC: 2032 5812 2035 Soups, except seafood: packaged in cans, jars, etc.; eating places; pickles, sauces & salad dressings

(G-7525)
TAYLORS INDUS COATINGS INC
108 Drive J A Wltshire Av (33853)
PHONE....800 932-3049
Greg Taylor, *President*
Reamonn McRae, *General Mgr*
Scott Taylor, *Vice Pres*
Tracey Reddick, *Office Mgr*
Ann Taylor, *Admin Sec*
EMP: 19 EST: 1984
SQ FT: 10,000
SALES (est): 3.8MM Privately Held
WEB: www.tic-coatings.com
SIC: 3479 Coating of metals & formed products

Lake Worth
Palm Beach County

(G-7526)
531 EAST INC
712 Lake Ave (33460-3813)
PHONE....561 249-2524
Michele M Bell, *Principal*
EMP: 7 EST: 2007
SALES (est): 131.1K Privately Held
SIC: 3965 Buttons & parts

(G-7527)
A&I ALUMINUM SHUTTERS
4614 Vespasian Ct (33463-7292)
PHONE....561 223-5877
Tzu Ning Liu, *Principal*
EMP: 6 EST: 2018
SALES (est): 57.3K Privately Held
SIC: 2591 Drapery hardware & blinds & shades

(G-7528)
ACCU RIGHT INC
1012 7th Ave S Ste 1 (33460-4973)
PHONE....561 586-5368
William W Vogler Jr, *President*
William W Vogler Sr, *Vice Pres*
EMP: 5 EST: 1987
SALES (est): 437.7K Privately Held
WEB: www.accuright.com
SIC: 3599 Machine shop, jobbing & repair

(G-7529)
ACRYLICO INC
2633 Lantana Rd Ste 6 (33462-2477)
PHONE....561 304-2921
Carlos Cavanagh, *President*
EMP: 5 EST: 2004
SALES (est): 461K Privately Held
WEB: www.acrylico.com
SIC: 3732 Motorized boat, building & repairing

(G-7530)
AERIALIFE INC ✪
1319 S L St Fl 334 (33460-5618)
PHONE....561 990-9299
Bin Liu, *Ch of Bd*
EMP: 8 EST: 2020
SALES (est): 300K Privately Held
SIC: 2869 Silicones

(G-7531)
AFFORDBLE QLTY DRYWALL SCREEN
3841 7th Ave N (33461-2825)
PHONE....561 723-0635
Luisa M Gil, *Principal*
EMP: 6 EST: 2017
SALES (est): 272.4K Privately Held
SIC: 3448 Screen enclosures

(G-7532)
ALERT TOWING INC
Also Called: Alert Manufacturing
331 S H St (33460-4434)
PHONE....561 586-5504
Paul Lobsinger, *President*
Christina Lane, *Vice Pres*
EMP: 20 EST: 1989
SQ FT: 1,596
SALES (est): 1.1MM Privately Held
SIC: 3711 Wreckers (tow truck), assembly of

(G-7533)
ALL AMERICAN LUBE
5865 S State Road 7 (33449-5429)
PHONE....561 432-0476
EMP: 5
SQ FT: 42,186
SALES (est): 340K Privately Held
SIC: 2911 Petroleum Refiner

(G-7534)
ANC SHUTTERS LLC
3386 Pony Run (33449-8005)
PHONE....561 966-8336
Adrian Hernandez, *President*
EMP: 10 EST: 2006
SALES (est): 1.3MM Privately Held
SIC: 3442 Shutters, door or window: metal

(G-7535)
AUSSIE BOOMERANG BAR ON AVE IN
621 Lake Ave (33460-3810)
PHONE....561 436-9741
Rod Regan, *Principal*
EMP: 11 EST: 2011
SALES (est): 478.4K Privately Held
WEB: www.member.qs.4mnw.pw
SIC: 3949 Boomerangs

(G-7536)
BIKEKEEPER LLC
Also Called: Whole Trade
8461 Lake Worth Rd # 173 (33467-2474)
PHONE....561 209-6863
Juho Sillanpaa,
EMP: 5 EST: 2016
SALES (est): 542.5K Privately Held
WEB: www.bikekeeper.com
SIC: 3429 Bicycle racks, automotive

(G-7537)
BILLET TECHNOLOGY
714 S East Coast St (33460-4962)
PHONE....561 582-6171
EMP: 8 EST: 2017
SALES (est): 307.8K Privately Held
WEB: www.billettechnology.com
SIC: 3714 Motor vehicle parts & accessories

▲ = Import ▼=Export
◆ =Import/Export

(G-7538)
CANVAS CLINICAL RESEARCH (PA)
3898 Via Poinciana (33467-2951)
PHONE..................................561 229-0002
Ezequiel Perez, *President*
EMP: 11 **EST:** 2013
SALES (est): 172.5K **Privately Held**
WEB: www.canvascr.com
SIC: 2211 Canvas

(G-7539)
CARAVAGGIO CABINETRY INC
119 S H St (33460-4430)
PHONE..................................561 609-3355
Anthony J Lauria, *Principal*
EMP: 10 **EST:** 2015
SALES (est): 277.8K **Privately Held**
WEB: www.caravaggiocabinetry.com
SIC: 2434 Wood kitchen cabinets

(G-7540)
CATEGORY 5 MANUFACTURING INC
6662 Hillside Ln (33462-4032)
PHONE..................................561 502-4153
Brian Kobosko, *Principal*
EMP: 9 **EST:** 2017
SALES (est): 249.1K **Privately Held**
WEB: www.category5manufacturing.com
SIC: 3999 Manufacturing industries

(G-7541)
CBD DOCS LLC
7343 Lake Worth Rd (33467-2528)
PHONE..................................954 868-5152
EMP: 7 **EST:** 2018
SALES (est): 252.3K **Privately Held**
WEB: www.cbd-docs.com
SIC: 3999

(G-7542)
CLARKS ELECTRICAL SIGNS & SVCS
108 W Cypress Rd (33467-4816)
PHONE..................................561 248-5932
A Clark, *Principal*
EMP: 6 **EST:** 2001
SALES (est): 87.2K **Privately Held**
SIC: 3993 Signs & advertising specialties

(G-7543)
COASTAL SHEET MTALOF S FLA LLC
8927 Hypoluxo Rd Ste A4 (33467-5249)
PHONE..................................561 718-6044
David Wall,
EMP: 20 **EST:** 2012
SALES (est): 1.2MM **Privately Held**
SIC: 3441 Fabricated structural metal

(G-7544)
DOORWAY PROJECTS INC
6484 Kirsten Way (33467-8703)
PHONE..................................561 523-2040
Michael L Schooley, *Principal*
Robert Schooley, *Vice Pres*
Michael Hutchens, *Director*
EMP: 9 **EST:** 2014
SALES (est): 438.3K **Privately Held**
WEB: www.doorwayprojects.com
SIC: 3728 Aircraft parts & equipment

(G-7545)
DPDM INC
10444 White Pinto Ct (33449-5492)
PHONE..................................561 327-4150
Isaac Taylor, *Principal*
EMP: 8 **EST:** 2012
SALES (est): 131.5K **Privately Held**
SIC: 2752 Commercial printing, offset

(G-7546)
DR SPIRITS COMPANY LLC
604 Lake Ave (33460-3811)
PHONE..................................561 349-5005
Daniel De Liege,
EMP: 5 **EST:** 2019
SALES (est): 306.3K **Privately Held**
SIC: 2085 Distilled & blended liquors

(G-7547)
DRIVESHAFT POWER INC
10101 Lantana Rd Ste K (33449-5475)
PHONE..................................561 433-0022
Ollie Jones, *Principal*
EMP: 10 **EST:** 2006
SALES (est): 297.5K **Privately Held**
WEB: www.driveshaftpower.com
SIC: 3317 Tubes, seamless steel

(G-7548)
E & M RECYCLING INC
630 S Palmway (33460-4937)
PHONE..................................561 718-1092
Matthew Pickering, *President*
Elizabeth Pickering, *Admin Sec*
EMP: 7
SALES (est): 983K **Privately Held**
SIC: 2499 Mulch or sawdust products, wood

(G-7549)
EAGLE METAL PRODUCTS INC
100 N Country Club Blvd (33462-1030)
PHONE..................................561 964-4192
Lester W Hensley, *President*
EMP: 5 **EST:** 2008
SALES (est): 785.8K **Privately Held**
WEB: www.eaglemetal.com
SIC: 3441 Fabricated structural metal

(G-7550)
FLORIDA GRASSCHOPPERS
75 Ohio Rd (33467-3846)
PHONE..................................561 718-9346
Ruth Lopez, *Principal*
EMP: 6 **EST:** 2010
SALES (est): 71.4K **Privately Held**
SIC: 3751 Motorcycles & related parts

(G-7551)
FUTURE FOODS LLC
Also Called: Oumph
1005 Lake Ave (33460-3709)
PHONE..................................786 390-5226
Patrik Waxin,
Steve Cohen,
John Resigl,
EMP: 5 **EST:** 2016
SALES (est): 602K **Privately Held**
WEB: www.oumph.us
SIC: 2013 5141 Sausages & other prepared meats; food brokers

(G-7552)
GLO AESTHETIC & LASER INSTITUT
5919 Ithaca Cir W (33463-1517)
PHONE..................................561 704-4565
Alan J Danton Do, *Manager*
EMP: 7 **EST:** 2005
SALES (est): 167.4K **Privately Held**
SIC: 3826 Laser scientific & engineering instruments

(G-7553)
GOLD COAST AERO ACCESSORIES
2633 Lantana Rd Ste 23 (33462-2480)
PHONE..................................561 965-7767
Dorothy E O'Neill, *President*
EMP: 7 **EST:** 2006
SALES (est): 126.2K **Privately Held**
SIC: 3728 Aircraft parts & equipment

(G-7554)
GUERRA UNIVERSAL CABINET I
3324 Sierra Dr Ste A (33461-2870)
PHONE..................................561 317-4079
Jorge Guerra, *Principal*
EMP: 6 **EST:** 2008
SALES (est): 88.2K **Privately Held**
SIC: 2434 Wood kitchen cabinets

(G-7555)
GUY GASKET INC
4446 Carver St (33461-2723)
P.O. Box 31, Ardsley NY (10502-0031)
PHONE..................................561 703-1774
Moshe Schneider, *President*
Avner Harel, *Vice Pres*
Barak Levy, *Vice Pres*
Karen Schneider, *Admin Sec*
▲ **EMP:** 15 **EST:** 2001
SQ FT: 2,500
SALES (est): 569.1K **Privately Held**
WEB: www.gasketguy.com
SIC: 3053 Gaskets & sealing devices

(G-7556)
HYDROFOILS INCORPORATED
4151 Lake Worth Rd (33466-5001)
P.O. Box 6006 (33466-6006)
PHONE..................................561 964-6399
EMP: 7
SALES (est): 460K **Privately Held**
SIC: 3732 Mfg Boats Custom Made

(G-7557)
INSTATECH INDUSTRIES INC
9835 Lake Worth Rd Ste 16 (33467-2370)
PHONE..................................954 415-4392
Aleksandr Fesenko, *Principal*
EMP: 7 **EST:** 2012
SALES (est): 568.4K **Privately Held**
WEB: www.ohio8.vchecks.me
SIC: 3999 Manufacturing industries

(G-7558)
J & H SUPPLY CO INC
825 N Dixie Hwy (33460-2528)
PHONE..................................561 582-3346
Curt R Harvey, *President*
Janice E Harvey, *Vice Pres*
EMP: 5 **EST:** 1962
SQ FT: 3,600
SALES (est): 469.1K **Privately Held**
SIC: 2221 5131 Upholstery fabrics, manmade fiber & silk; upholstery fabrics, woven

(G-7559)
J A CUSTOM FABRICATORS INC
Also Called: A Custom Fabrication
1230 Wingfield St (33460-5586)
PHONE..................................561 615-4680
George Angel, *Owner*
EMP: 10 **EST:** 2007
SALES (est): 800K **Privately Held**
WEB: www.jacustomfab.com
SIC: 3499 8712 8711 Fire- or burglary-resistive products; architectural services; engineering services

(G-7560)
JC 323 MEDIA PUBG GROUP INC
7186 Ontario Shores Pl (33467-7790)
PHONE..................................772 940-3510
Donnetta Alansari, *CEO*
EMP: 7 **EST:** 2017
SALES (est): 252.4K **Privately Held**
SIC: 2741 Miscellaneous publishing

(G-7561)
JODAN TECHNOLOGY INC
7708 Coral Colony Way (33467-6960)
PHONE..................................561 515-5556
Stanley Jasne, *President*
Joe Thoman, *Vice Pres*
EMP: 7 **EST:** 1997
SALES (est): 216.5K **Privately Held**
SIC: 2851 Epoxy coatings

(G-7562)
KMI INTERNATIONAL INC
2501 Park St (33460-6139)
PHONE..................................561 588-5514
Carlos Rodriguez, *President*
◆ **EMP:** 25 **EST:** 1988
SQ FT: 18,200
SALES (est): 2.5MM **Privately Held**
WEB: www.kmiinternational.us
SIC: 2431 1751 Doors, wood; finish & trim carpentry

(G-7563)
LABEL GRAPHICS INC
11298 Roselynn Way (33449-8451)
PHONE..................................561 798-8180
Kathy Robinson, *President*
Robert Robinson, *Vice Pres*
Shannon Reynolds, *Administration*
EMP: 6 **EST:** 1991
SQ FT: 5,000
SALES (est): 460.6K **Privately Held**
WEB: www.labelgraphicsinc.com
SIC: 2759 2671 Labels & seals: printing; packaging paper & plastics film, coated & laminated

(G-7564)
LAKE WORTH HERALD PRESS
Also Called: Coastal Observer
1313 Central Ter (33460-1835)
P.O. Box 191 (33460-0191)
PHONE..................................561 585-9387
Mark J Easton, *President*
Bruce Easton, *Vice Pres*
EMP: 21 **EST:** 1912
SQ FT: 5,200
SALES (est): 678.2K **Privately Held**
WEB: www.lwherald.com
SIC: 2711 2752 2791 2789 Job printing & newspaper publishing combined; lithographing on metal; typesetting; bookbinding & related work

(G-7565)
LEADERINPRINT INC
8927 Hypoluxo Rd Ste A4 (33467-5249)
PHONE..................................561 200-9412
EMP: 6 **EST:** 2019
SALES (est): 109.5K **Privately Held**
WEB: www.leaderinprint.com
SIC: 2752 Commercial printing, offset

(G-7566)
MAGAZINE MORRIS
6108 Royal Birkdale Dr (33463-6526)
PHONE..................................561 963-0231
Morris Magazine, *Principal*
EMP: 6 **EST:** 2001
SALES (est): 189.9K **Privately Held**
SIC: 2721 Magazines: publishing only, not printed on site

(G-7567)
MAGGAC CORPORATION
Also Called: Precision Woodcraft
7629 Santee Ter (33467-7866)
PHONE..................................561 439-2707
Micheal Clark, *President*
Anita Johnson, *Vice Pres*
EMP: 5 **EST:** 1981
SALES (est): 443.2K **Privately Held**
SIC: 2426 2511 2434 Furniture dimension stock, hardwood; wood household furniture; wood kitchen cabinets

(G-7568)
MAJESTIC COATINGS INC
9936 Cross Pine Ct (33467-2313)
PHONE..................................561 722-9593
Sara C Mayo, *Principal*
EMP: 6 **EST:** 2016
SALES (est): 248.3K **Privately Held**
WEB: www.majestic-coatings.com
SIC: 3479 Coating of metals & formed products

(G-7569)
MEZCAL HUB LLC
748 Muirfield Cir (33462-1231)
PHONE..................................561 373-7972
Peter Van Es, *Principal*
EMP: 6 **EST:** 2016
SALES (est): 229.4K **Privately Held**
WEB: www.mezcalhub.com
SIC: 2085 Distilled & blended liquors

(G-7570)
MICROWAVE ELECTRONICS
6314 Dornich Ln (33463-6529)
PHONE..................................561 432-8511
Mitch Kulick, *Owner*
EMP: 5 **EST:** 2007
SALES (est): 337.9K **Privately Held**
SIC: 3679 Microwave components

(G-7571)
MIDDS INC
Also Called: Banyan Printing
128 S Dixie Hwy (33460-4133)
PHONE..................................561 586-6220
Roger B Manning Mr, *Principal*
EMP: 11 **EST:** 1977
SALES (est): 175.5K **Privately Held**
SIC: 2752 Commercial printing, offset

(G-7572)
MILLERS CUSTOM METALS INC
1224 Pope Ln (33460-6146)
PHONE..................................561 540-6263
John Miller, *President*
Gina Miller, *Vice Pres*
◆ **EMP:** 11 **EST:** 1993

SQ FT: 5,000
SALES (est): 1MM **Privately Held**
WEB: www.millerscustommetals.com
SIC: 3446 Stairs, staircases, stair treads: prefabricated metal

(G-7573)
MINUTEMAN PRESS
6677 Lake Worth Rd (33467-1507)
PHONE..................................954 804-8304
EMP: 8 **EST:** 2018
SALES (est): 493.2K **Privately Held**
WEB: www.minutemanpress.com
SIC: 2752 Commercial printing, lithographic

(G-7574)
NATIONAL ASSEMBLERS INC
6586 Hypoluxo Rd Ste 145 (33467-7678)
PHONE..................................877 915-5505
Jeri Castrillon, *Principal*
Jenny Schneider, *Opers Staff*
Nathalie Makepeace, *Business Anlyst*
Debbie Schneider, *Recruiter*
Nancy O'Brien, *Clerk*
EMP: 14 **EST:** 2014
SALES (est): 4.7MM **Privately Held**
SIC: 3732 Boat building & repairing

(G-7575)
NATURES CLEAR LLC ✪
2328 10th Ave N Ste 501d (33461-6615)
PHONE..................................561 503-1751
Anivain Marius, *Principal*
EMP: 5 **EST:** 2020
SALES (est): 332.7K **Privately Held**
SIC: 2833 Medicinals & botanicals

(G-7576)
ORKAN18
9835 Lake Worth Rd Ste 16 (33467-2370)
PHONE..................................855 675-2618
Hanan Assayag, *Principal*
EMP: 6 **EST:** 2015
SALES (est): 365.8K **Privately Held**
SIC: 3565 Packaging machinery

(G-7577)
PALM BEACH CSTM CABINETRY INC
5363 Plains Dr (33463-5813)
PHONE..................................561 859-9071
Robert Gauck, *Principal*
EMP: 6 **EST:** 2008
SALES (est): 66.5K **Privately Held**
SIC: 2434 Wood kitchen cabinets

(G-7578)
PALM BEACH JUNIOR CLG PRNT SHP
4200 S Congress Ave (33461-4705)
PHONE..................................561 969-0122
▼ **EMP:** 15 **EST:** 1988
SALES (est): 179.4K **Privately Held**
WEB: www.palmbeachstate.edu
SIC: 2752 Commercial printing, offset

(G-7579)
PAPER CHASE
6626 Via Rienzo (33467-5915)
PHONE..................................561 641-5319
Steven Askinazi, *Principal*
EMP: 6 **EST:** 2005
SALES (est): 132.2K **Privately Held**
WEB: www.paperchaseboca.net
SIC: 2621 Paper mills

(G-7580)
PLASTIC KINGDOM INC
407 N Dixie Hwy (33460-3037)
PHONE..................................561 586-9300
Eligiusz Baska, *President*
Joanna Baska, *Vice Pres*
EMP: 5 **EST:** 1996
SALES (est): 473.1K **Privately Held**
SIC: 3089 Injection molding of plastics

(G-7581)
POLO PLAYERS EDITION
Also Called: Rizzo Management
9011 Lake Worth Rd B (33467-3617)
PHONE..................................561 968-5208
Gwen Rizzo, *Principal*
Cristina Fernandez, *Marketing Staff*
Maggie Mitchell, *Manager*
Amanda Snow, *Director*
EMP: 5 **EST:** 1996
SALES (est): 420.6K **Privately Held**
WEB: www.poloplayersedition.com
SIC: 2721 Magazines: publishing only, not printed on site

(G-7582)
PRESS BEAUTY FACIAL BAR
3475 Fargo Ave (33467-1015)
PHONE..................................561 281-0631
Patricia Biernat, *Principal*
EMP: 6 **EST:** 2017
SALES (est): 59.2K **Privately Held**
SIC: 2741 Miscellaneous publishing

(G-7583)
PRISON LEGAL NEWS
Also Called: Human Rights Defense Center
1013 Lucerne Ave Ste 206 (33460-3741)
P.O. Box 1151 (33460-1151)
PHONE..................................561 360-2523
Dan Axtell, *Principal*
Paul Wright, *Editor*
EMP: 17 **EST:** 2011
SALES: 1.1MM **Privately Held**
WEB: www.prisonlegalnews.org
SIC: 2711 Newspapers, publishing & printing

(G-7584)
QUALITY SHAVINGS SOUTH FLORIDA
10191 Lantana Rd (33449-5443)
PHONE..................................561 433-9955
Giuseppe J Lebisernia, *Branch Mgr*
EMP: 23
SALES (corp-wide): 162.3K **Privately Held**
SIC: 2399 Horse blankets
PA: Quality Shavings Of South Florida
7800 N University Dr
Tamarac FL

(G-7585)
REBUILD GLOBALLY INC
Also Called: DEUX MAINS
810 S K St (33460-5046)
PHONE..................................407 801-9936
Julie Colombino, *CEO*
Bridget Healy, *President*
Leslie Hielema, *President*
Laurent Prosper, *Vice Pres*
Joshua Johnson, *Treasurer*
EMP: 32 **EST:** 2010
SALES: 213K **Privately Held**
WEB: www.rebuildglobally.org
SIC: 3021 Sandals, rubber

(G-7586)
SFA SYSTEMS INC
Also Called: South Florida Aluminum
1230 Wingfield St (33460-5586)
PHONE..................................561 585-5927
Robert W Miller, *President*
Harry F Leeser Jr, *Vice Pres*
EMP: 23 **EST:** 1965
SQ FT: 15,000
SALES (est): 1.5MM **Privately Held**
WEB: www.southfloridaaluminum.com
SIC: 3444 3312 2851 3446 Canopies, sheet metal; rails, steel or iron; undercoatings, paint; architectural metalwork

(G-7587)
SOUTHERN AWNING INC (PA)
313 S H St (33460-4434)
PHONE..................................561 586-0464
Mitch Lewis, *President*
Richard Trobaugh, *Vice Pres*
Joanne Trobaugh, *Treasurer*
Janice Lewis, *Admin Sec*
EMP: 21 **EST:** 1992
SQ FT: 5,400
SALES (est): 2.7MM **Privately Held**
WEB: www.southernawning.com
SIC: 2394 7692 5999 Canvas awnings & canopies; welding repair; awnings

(G-7588)
STATE LATHINGINC
606 N J St (33460-3036)
PHONE..................................786 357-8404
Edgar Hernandez, *Principal*
EMP: 6 **EST:** 2015
SALES (est): 77K **Privately Held**
SIC: 3541 Lathes

(G-7589)
SWEET AND VICIOUS LLC
1512 N Lakeside Dr (33460-1922)
PHONE..................................772 907-3030
Melba Thompson, *Branch Mgr*
▲ **EMP:** 19
SALES (corp-wide): 632.3K **Privately Held**
WEB: www.sweet-vicious.com
SIC: 2254 Knit underwear mills
PA: Sweet And Vicious Llc
111 Ne 21st St
Miami FL 33137
305 576-0012

(G-7590)
TECHNICO
507 S G St (33460-4370)
PHONE..................................561 588-8300
John Maher, *Manager*
EMP: 11 **EST:** 1985
SALES (est): 324.5K **Privately Held**
WEB: www.technicofl.com
SIC: 3822 Auto controls regulating residntl & coml environmt & applncs

(G-7591)
TIENDA MAYA
6082 S Congress Ave (33462-2318)
PHONE..................................561 965-0900
Juan Tomas, *Principal*
EMP: 7 **EST:** 2009
SALES (est): 365.7K **Privately Held**
WEB: www.krockstarz.com
SIC: 3643 Outlets, electric: convenience

(G-7592)
TORTILLERIA GALLO DE ORO
1302 Lake Ave Ste 2 (33460-3685)
PHONE..................................561 503-3751
Manuel E Perez, *Owner*
EMP: 6 **EST:** 2016
SALES (est): 235.7K **Privately Held**
SIC: 2099 Tortillas, fresh or refrigerated

(G-7593)
TRI-EDGE INDUSTRIES LLC
6586 Hypoluxo Rd (33467-7678)
PHONE..................................561 703-5961
EMP: 6 **EST:** 2016
SALES (est): 211.6K **Privately Held**
WEB: www.tri-edge.com
SIC: 3999 Manufacturing industries

(G-7594)
TRS INDUSTRIES INC
6845 Finamore Cir (33467-8727)
PHONE..................................561 880-0031
Francis Waite, *President*
Brian Waite, *Vice Pres*
▼ **EMP:** 7 **EST:** 2006
SALES (est): 858.2K **Privately Held**
WEB: www.trsindustries.com
SIC: 3951 7389 Markers, soft tip (felt, fabric, plastic, etc.);

(G-7595)
ULTIMATE DOOR OF PALM BEACH
2800 2nd Ave N (33461-4114)
PHONE..................................561 642-2828
Roger Warwick, *President*
Cal Morris, *Vice Pres*
▲ **EMP:** 17 **EST:** 1994
SQ FT: 10,000
SALES (est): 1.1MM **Privately Held**
WEB: www.ultimatedoor.com
SIC: 2431 3442 Doors, wood; metal doors, sash & trim

(G-7596)
UNDERSEA BREATHING SYSTEMS
2565 N Dixie Hwy (33460-6250)
PHONE..................................561 588-7698
William H Delp II, *President*
Dick Rutkowski, *Shareholder*
Morgan J Wells, *Shareholder*
◆ **EMP:** 6 **EST:** 1994
SQ FT: 4,000
SALES (est): 442.3K **Privately Held**
WEB: www.dnax.com
SIC: 3949 5091 Skin diving equipment, scuba type; diving equipment & supplies

(G-7597)
VERTEX PRECISION INC
Also Called: V P I
714 S East Coast St (33460-4962)
PHONE..................................561 582-6171
Heidi Tetzlaff, *President*
EMP: 20 **EST:** 1997
SQ FT: 5,000
SALES (est): 1.5MM **Privately Held**
WEB: www.custombilletstore.net
SIC: 3532 Mining machinery

(G-7598)
WALLACE INDUSTRIES INC
906 N Dixie Hwy (33460-2531)
PHONE..................................561 301-0811
Paul R Kludt, *Principal*
EMP: 10 **EST:** 2012
SALES (est): 255K **Privately Held**
WEB: www.ksmachineinc.com
SIC: 3999 Manufacturing industries

(G-7599)
WEIBEL EQUIPMENT INC
3870 Hidden Cypress Way (33467-2446)
PHONE..................................571 278-1989
Peder Pedersen, *President*
Peter Muller, *Vice Pres*
EMP: 5 **EST:** 1996
SALES (est): 569.7K **Privately Held**
WEB: www.weibelradars.com
SIC: 3812 Navigational systems & instruments

(G-7600)
YOUMOP LLC ✪
714 S Atlantic Dr (33462-1950)
PHONE..................................248 343-2013
Mya Johnson, *CEO*
EMP: 9 **EST:** 2020
SALES (est): 373.4K **Privately Held**
WEB: www.youmop.com
SIC: 2392 5961 Mops, floor & dust;

Lake Worth Beach
Palm Beach County

(G-7601)
ALL COUNTY SHEET METAL INC
1930 7th Ct N (33461-3302)
PHONE..................................561 588-0099
Ronald L Davis, *President*
James Trasport, *Vice Pres*
Kathleen J Davis, *Admin Sec*
EMP: 9 **EST:** 1982
SQ FT: 2,950
SALES (est): 882.3K **Privately Held**
WEB: www.allcountysheetmetal.com
SIC: 3444 Sheet metal specialties, not stamped

(G-7602)
ALL-PRO ACCNTING BKKEEPING LLC
1947 10th Ave N (33461-3309)
PHONE..................................561 212-8418
Rene D Sexton, *Principal*
EMP: 7 **EST:** 2014
SALES (est): 281.7K **Privately Held**
SIC: 2782 Account books

(G-7603)
ARC STONE III LLC
1800 4th Ave N Unit A (33461-3874)
PHONE..................................561 478-8805
Micheal Coiro, *Mng Member*
▲ **EMP:** 10 **EST:** 1998
SQ FT: 50,000
SALES (est): 2.1MM **Privately Held**
WEB: www.arcstonegranite.com
SIC: 1411 Limestone & marble dimension stone

(G-7604)
ARTISTIC DOORS INC
2223 2nd Ave N (33461-3212)
PHONE..................................561 582-0348
Luis E Masson, *President*

EMP: 6 **EST:** 2008
SALES (est): 425.7K **Privately Held**
SIC: 2431 Millwork

(G-7605)
BAXTER ADVENTURES INC
Also Called: Fastsigns
2001 10th Ave N Ste 2 (33461-3362)
PHONE..................................561 439-4700
Ken Baxter, *President*
EMP: 7 **EST:** 1990
SQ FT: 1,600
SALES (est): 940.9K **Privately Held**
WEB: www.fastsigns.com
SIC: 3993 Signs & advertising specialties

(G-7606)
BENCHMARK ENTERTAINMENT LC
Also Called: Benchmark Games
2201 4th Ave N (33461-3835)
PHONE..................................561 588-5200
Ivan Viau, *Purch Mgr*
Alexander F Kress, *Mng Member*
Trevor Gianaris, *Officer*
Paula Rinker, *Merchandising*
◆ **EMP:** 20 **EST:** 1993
SALES (est): 4.9MM **Privately Held**
WEB: www.benchmarkgames.com
SIC: 3944 Electronic games & toys

(G-7607)
BENCHMARK GAMES INTL LLC
2201 4th Ave N (33461-3835)
PHONE..................................561 588-5200
Anthony Maniscalco, *Exec VP*
Joshua Seidel, *Controller*
Tiffany Lomax, *Manager*
Chris Mead, *Manager*
Brian Capellaro, *Director*
EMP: 85 **EST:** 2017
SALES (est): 15MM **Privately Held**
WEB: www.benchmarkgames.com
SIC: 3944 Electronic games & toys

(G-7608)
BLAST CTINGS POWDERCOATING LLC
1847 Aragon Ave Unit 2 (33461-2620)
PHONE..................................561 635-7605
Matias D Sprindys, *Branch Mgr*
EMP: 15 **Privately Held**
SIC: 3479 Etching & engraving
PA: Blast Coatings Powdercoating Llc
1745 Sawgrass Cir
Greenacres FL 33413

(G-7609)
CAPZERPHARMA MANUFACTURING LLC
3677 23rd Ave S Ste B107 (33461-3264)
PHONE..................................561 493-4000
Abdul Naim, *Mng Member*
Mohammad Mamun, *Mng Member*
EMP: 5 **EST:** 2017
SALES (est): 403.9K **Privately Held**
WEB: www.capzerpharmaceuticals.com
SIC: 2834 Tablets, pharmaceutical

(G-7610)
DS POWDER COATING
1800 4th Ave N Unit B (33461-3874)
PHONE..................................561 660-7835
Kristen Dal Santo, *President*
EMP: 7 **EST:** 2017
SALES (est): 453.7K **Privately Held**
WEB: www.dspowdercoating.com
SIC: 3479 Coating of metals & formed products

(G-7611)
DURA-WELD INC
3599 23rd Ave S Ste 9 (33461-3291)
PHONE..................................561 586-0180
Russell Wanser, *President*
Marilyn Prommel, *Office Mgr*
▼ **EMP:** 5 **EST:** 1994
SQ FT: 1,000
SALES (est): 452.8K **Privately Held**
WEB: www.dura-weld.com
SIC: 3089 Plastic & fiberglass tanks; plastic processing

(G-7612)
HE INSTRUMENTS LLC
3677 23rd Ave S Ste B107 (33461-3264)
PHONE..................................561 832-1249
Adrian Mazza, *Principal*
EMP: 6 **EST:** 2011
SALES (est): 169.5K **Privately Held**
WEB: www.heinstruments.com
SIC: 3841 Surgical & medical instruments

(G-7613)
ICE LINK 2018 LLC
1963 10th Ave N (33461-3361)
PHONE..................................305 988-4023
Ash Howell,
EMP: 5 **EST:** 2017
SALES (est): 307.4K **Privately Held**
SIC: 3585 Ice making machinery

(G-7614)
JABS INVESTORS CORP
1815 10th Ave N Ste A (33461-3365)
PHONE..................................561 540-2693
Jaime A Bolivar, *President*
EMP: 11 **EST:** 2003
SALES (est): 208.8K **Privately Held**
SIC: 2493 Marbleboard (stone face hard board)

(G-7615)
MIDDS INC
Also Called: Banyan Printing
1937 10th Ave N (33461-3309)
PHONE..................................561 586-6220
Roger Manning, *President*
Stacie Bailey, *Engineer*
Irene Levine, *Treasurer*
Dawn Roth, *Sales Staff*
EMP: 39 **EST:** 1977
SALES (est): 3.2MM **Privately Held**
SIC: 2752 7389 2789 2672 Commercial printing, offset; printers' services: folding, collating; bookbinding & related work; coated & laminated paper

(G-7616)
MILCOM SERVICES INC
1963 10th Ave N (33461-3361)
PHONE..................................561 907-6816
Ursula White Lemmens, *President*
Kurt Freiter, *Vice Pres*
EMP: 5 **EST:** 1984
SQ FT: 6,000
SALES (est): 520K **Privately Held**
WEB: www.milcomservices.com
SIC: 3199 Harness or harness parts

(G-7617)
MOSCO INC
2200 4th Ave N Ste 10 (33461-3897)
PHONE..................................561 588-3880
Ed Sasso, *President*
EMP: 6
SALES (corp-wide): 1.2MM **Privately Held**
WEB: www.mosco.ru
SIC: 3585 Air conditioning units, complete: domestic or industrial
PA: Mosco Inc
340 S Us Highway 1 # 607
Jupiter FL 33477
561 575-7766

(G-7618)
PATTEN CO INC
Also Called: Patten Group
1803 Madrid Ave (33461-3395)
PHONE..................................707 826-2887
Fred Kaplan, *President*
Tricia Laws, *Controller*
EMP: 38 **EST:** 1974
SQ FT: 38,000
SALES (est): 8.1MM
SALES (corp-wide): 25MM **Privately Held**
WEB: www.pattencompany.com
SIC: 3069 Life rafts, rubber
HQ: Wing Inflatables, Inc.
1220 5th St
Arcata CA 95521

(G-7619)
SOLID PRINT SOLUTIONS INC
1961 10th Ave N (33461-3361)
PHONE..................................561 670-4391
EMP: 6 **EST:** 2019
SALES (est): 111.6K **Privately Held**
WEB: www.solidprintsolutions.com
SIC: 2752 Commercial printing, offset

(G-7620)
SOUTH FLA FORKLIFT DOCTOR CORP
523 Industrial St (33461-3812)
PHONE..................................561 951-6243
Travis A Gonzalez, *Principal*
EMP: 6 **EST:** 2013
SALES (est): 76.2K **Privately Held**
WEB: www.electricforkliftspecialist.com
SIC: 3537 Forklift trucks

(G-7621)
SOUTHERN CUSTOM IRON & ART LLC
3787 Boutwell Rd (33461-3803)
PHONE..................................561 586-8400
Ashleigh R Hernandez, *Mng Member*
EMP: 30 **EST:** 2014
SALES (est): 1.7MM **Privately Held**
WEB: www.southerncustomiron.com
SIC: 3441 Fabricated structural metal

(G-7622)
VAN LINDA IRON WORKS INC
3787 Boutwell Rd (33461-3893)
PHONE..................................561 586-8400
Ashleigh Hernandez, *President*
▼ **EMP:** 30 **EST:** 1949
SQ FT: 47,500
SALES (est): 8.5MM **Privately Held**
WEB: www.vanlinda.com
SIC: 3441 3599 Fabricated structural metal; machine & other job shop work

(G-7623)
VITAL PRINTING CORPORATION
1983 10th Ave N (33461-3361)
PHONE..................................561 659-2367
William J Vitale, *President*
EMP: 10 **EST:** 1980
SALES (est): 1.8MM **Privately Held**
WEB: www.vitalprinting.com
SIC: 2752 Commercial printing, offset

Lakeland
Polk County

(G-7624)
A & J PAVERS INC
1420 Shirley Dr (33810-0560)
PHONE..................................863 559-1920
Joseph B Langley III, *Principal*
EMP: 6 **EST:** 2007
SALES (est): 95.8K **Privately Held**
SIC: 3531 Pavers

(G-7625)
ADEMERO INC
4685 E County Road 540a (33813-4407)
PHONE..................................863 937-0272
Daniel Snell, *Research*
Ian Goodman, *Engineer*
Susana Reilly, *Consultant*
Dustin Baker, *Director*
EMP: 15 **EST:** 2014
SALES (est): 1.6MM **Privately Held**
WEB: www.ademero.com
SIC: 7372 7371 Prepackaged software; custom computer programming services

(G-7626)
ADVANCED ALUM POLK CNTY INC
Also Called: Permatile Roofing
2941 Parkway St (33811-1391)
P.O. Box 5075 (33807-5075)
PHONE..................................863 648-5787
James E Smith, *President*
Marjorie J Smith, *Corp Secy*
EMP: 20 **EST:** 1991
SQ FT: 55,000
SALES (est): 3.5MM **Privately Held**
WEB: www.advaluminum.com
SIC: 3448 3444 Prefabricated metal buildings; sheet metalwork

(G-7627)
ADVANCED OVERHEAD SYSTEMS INC
3510 Craftsman Blvd (33803-7307)
P.O. Box 2645, Eaton Park (33840-2645)
PHONE..................................863 667-3757
Dave Roberts, *General Mgr*
David W Roberts, *General Mgr*
William Y Harrell, *Vice Pres*
Lou Harrell, *Admin Sec*
Mary Harrell, *Admin Sec*
EMP: 23 **EST:** 1993
SALES (est): 7.6MM **Privately Held**
WEB: www.advancedoverheadsystems.com
SIC: 3536 Hoists, cranes & monorails

(G-7628)
ADVANCED SCREEN PRINTING & EMB
Also Called: Sport Section
3635 Ventura Dr W (33811-1294)
PHONE..................................863 648-1268
Daniel J Girata, *President*
Daneil J Girata, *President*
EMP: 9 **EST:** 1994
SALES (est): 134.5K **Privately Held**
WEB: www.advancedscreenprinting.ca
SIC: 2759 Screen printing

(G-7629)
AETHER MEDIA USA INC
Also Called: Sir Speedy
4175 S Pipkin Rd Ste 108 (33811-1699)
PHONE..................................863 647-5500
Julian Robins, *President*
John Robins, *Vice Pres*
Darwin Eicher, *Manager*
EMP: 7 **EST:** 1982
SALES (est): 611.2K **Privately Held**
WEB: www.sirspeedy.com
SIC: 2752 2791 Commercial printing, lithographic; typesetting

(G-7630)
ALABAMA METAL INDUSTRIES CORP
1033 Pine Chase Ave (33815-3139)
PHONE..................................863 688-9256
Robert Poar, *Branch Mgr*
EMP: 70
SQ FT: 86,360
SALES (corp-wide): 1B **Publicly Held**
WEB: www.amicoglobal.com
SIC: 3446 Open flooring & grating for construction
HQ: Alabama Metal Industries Corporation
3245 Fayette Ave
Birmingham AL 35208
205 787-2611

(G-7631)
ALL AMERICAN SIGNS INC
206 N Eastside Dr (33801-2608)
P.O. Box 697, Highland City (33846-0697)
PHONE..................................863 665-7161
Andrew Alach, *President*
EMP: 6 **EST:** 1971
SQ FT: 12,500
SALES (est): 833.9K **Privately Held**
WEB: www.allamericansignsinc.com
SIC: 3993 1799 Neon signs; sign installation & maintenance

(G-7632)
AMEGA SCIENCES INC
6550 New Tampa Hwy Ste A (33815-3146)
PHONE..................................863 937-9792
Julie I Bowey, *President*
David Sparks, *Research*
Gene Baldwin, *Natl Sales Mgr*
▲ **EMP:** 6 **EST:** 2005
SALES (est): 1.3MM **Privately Held**
WEB: www.amegasciencesusa.com
SIC: 3523 Soil preparation machinery, except turf & grounds

(G-7633)
AMERICAN BOTTLING COMPANY
Also Called: Southeast Atlantic
3520 Waterfield Rd (33803-9741)
PHONE..................................863 665-6128
Randy Vaxley, *Manager*
EMP: 17 **Publicly Held**

WEB: www.keurigdrpepper.com
SIC: 2086 Soft drinks: packaged in cans, bottles, etc.
HQ: The American Bottling Company
6425 Hall Of Fame Ln
Frisco TX 75034

(G-7634)
AMERICAN-MARSH PUMPS LLC
2805 Badger Rd (33811-1370)
PHONE..................................863 646-5689
EMP: 9
SALES (corp-wide): 37K Privately Held
SIC: 3561 Pumps And Pumping Equipment, Nsk
HQ: American-Marsh Pumps Llc
550 E South St
Collierville TN 38017
800 888-7167

(G-7635)
AMERICOAT CORPORATION
2935 Barneys Pumps Pl (33812-4209)
P.O. Box 2228, Eaton Park (33840-2228)
PHONE..................................863 667-1035
Shrikant V Desai, *President*
EMP: 5 EST: 1995
SALES (est): 400K Privately Held
WEB: www.ameri-coat.com
SIC: 3479 Coating of metals & formed products

(G-7636)
ANHEUSER-BUSCH INCORPORATED
3907 Aero Pl (33811-1248)
PHONE..................................863 646-7357
Robert Williams, *Manager*
EMP: 6
SALES (corp-wide): 1.2B Privately Held
WEB: www.budweisertours.com
SIC: 2082 Beer (alcoholic beverage)
HQ: Anheuser-Busch, Llc
1 Busch Pl
Saint Louis MO 63118
800 342-5283

(G-7637)
AREA LITHO INC
238 N Wabash Ave (33815-7371)
PHONE..................................863 687-4656
Gerald Winchester, *CEO*
Stanley Sheafer, *Ch of Bd*
EMP: 6 EST: 1981
SQ FT: 4,000
SALES (est): 669.9K Privately Held
WEB: www.unitedlitho.com
SIC: 2752 Promotional printing, lithographic; commercial printing, offset

(G-7638)
ARGENAL CABINETS INC
911 Hammock Shade Dr (33809-4644)
PHONE..................................863 670-7973
Alejandra Argenal, *Owner*
EMP: 8 EST: 2016
SALES (est): 90.6K Privately Held
WEB: www.argenalcabinets.com
SIC: 2434 Wood kitchen cabinets

(G-7639)
ARGOS USA
2300 Mershon St (33815-3532)
PHONE..................................863 687-1898
Dale Jordan, *Plant Mgr*
EMP: 7 EST: 2015
SALES (est): 121.9K Privately Held
WEB: www.argos-us.com
SIC: 3273 Ready-mixed concrete

(G-7640)
AVERETT SEPTIC TANK CO INC
2610 Longhorn Ave (33801-6425)
P.O. Box 266, Eaton Park (33840-0266)
PHONE..................................863 665-1748
Sam A Averett, *President*
Suzanne Britt, *Vice Pres*
Ida Averett, *Shareholder*
EMP: 33 EST: 1958
SQ FT: 1,500
SALES (est): 6.8MM Privately Held
WEB: www.averettseptic.com
SIC: 3272 1711 7699 3432 Septic tanks, concrete; septic system construction; septic tank cleaning service; plumbing fixture fittings & trim

(G-7641)
B H BUNN COMPANY
2730 Drane Field Rd (33811-1325)
PHONE..................................863 647-1555
John R Bunn, *President*
◆ EMP: 15 EST: 1907
SQ FT: 18,000
SALES (est): 2.4MM Privately Held
WEB: www.bunntyco.com
SIC: 3565 Packaging machinery

(G-7642)
BALA INDUSTRIES LLC (PA)
Also Called: McStar Revenue Solutions
7528 Locksley Ln (33809-5028)
PHONE..................................954 243-9804
Althea McLeish Wilson, *President*
EMP: 23 EST: 2005
SALES (est): 112.4K Privately Held
WEB: www.mcstarrs.com
SIC: 3999 Barber & beauty shop equipment

(G-7643)
BATTERY USA INC (PA)
Also Called: Imperial Motor Parts-Division
1840 S Combee Rd (33801-6852)
PHONE..................................863 665-6317
Robert Thomas Standifer II, *President*
Jeff Gray, *Regional Mgr*
James Lawless, *Vice Pres*
Jim Lawless, *Vice Pres*
Byron Smith, *Opers Mgr*
▲ EMP: 40 EST: 1970
SQ FT: 20,000
SALES (est): 19.4MM Privately Held
WEB: www.batteryusa.com
SIC: 3714 5531 5013 7699 Motor vehicle parts & accessories; batteries, automotive & truck; automotive batteries; battery service & repair; motor vehicle parts, used

(G-7644)
BATTERY USA INC
Also Called: Imperial Motor Parts
1930 S Combee Rd (33801-6854)
PHONE..................................863 665-5401
Kevin Layton, *Manager*
EMP: 7
SALES (corp-wide): 19.4MM Privately Held
WEB: www.batteryusa.com
SIC: 3714 Motor vehicle parts & accessories
PA: Battery Usa, Inc.
1840 S Combee Rd
Lakeland FL 33801
863 665-6317

(G-7645)
BEARD BOOZE LLC
5761 Deer Flag Dr (33811-2000)
PHONE..................................352 424-0687
Heather Brown, *Principal*
EMP: 6 EST: 2016
SALES (est): 108.8K Privately Held
WEB: www.beardbooze.com
SIC: 2844 Toilet preparations

(G-7646)
BIO-LAB INC
3125 Drane Field Rd # 10 (33811-1398)
PHONE..................................863 709-1411
Bill Gilberti, *Director*
EMP: 10
SALES (corp-wide): 2B Privately Held
WEB: www.kikcorp.com
SIC: 2819 2869 2812 Industrial inorganic chemicals; alcohols, industrial: denatured (non-beverage); alkalies & chlorine
HQ: Bio-Lab, Inc.
1725 N Brown Rd
Lawrenceville GA 30043
678 502-4000

(G-7647)
BLUE PLANET HOLDINGS LLC (PA)
1738 Clarendon Pl (33803-2567)
PHONE..................................863 559-1236
Scott McBride, *Principal*
EMP: 11 EST: 2013
SALES (est): 14.4MM Privately Held
SIC: 2013 Smoked meats from purchased meat

(G-7648)
BOBS WLDG FBRCATION MAINT INC
542 S Combee Rd (33801-6310)
P.O. Box 1557, Eaton Park (33840-1557)
PHONE..................................863 665-0135
Cameron Honeycutt, *President*
Robert L Honeycutt, *President*
Robert B Honeycutt, *Corp Secy*
Cameron B Honeycutt, *Vice Pres*
EMP: 22 EST: 1986
SALES (est): 627.9K Privately Held
WEB: www.bobs-welding.net
SIC: 3599 7692 Machine shop, jobbing & repair; welding repair

(G-7649)
BRADS INDUSTRIES LLC
5723 Buck Run Dr (33811-2038)
PHONE..................................863 646-0051
EMP: 6
SALES (est): 233.8K Privately Held
SIC: 3999 Mfg Misc Products

(G-7650)
BREW HUB LLC
Also Called: Brew Hub, The
3900 Frontage Rd S (33815-3205)
PHONE..................................863 698-7600
Timothy Schoen, *CEO*
Jerry Mullane, *President*
Jessica Bowey, *Manager*
Paul Farnsworth,
▲ EMP: 52 EST: 2012
SALES (est): 13.5MM Privately Held
WEB: www.brewhub.com
SIC: 2082 Brewers' grain

(G-7651)
BROTHERS PALLETS
2410 Mcjunkin Rd (33803-7318)
P.O. Box 689, Eaton Park (33840-0689)
PHONE..................................863 944-5278
Jose C Garcia, *Owner*
EMP: 6 EST: 2000
SALES (est): 607.3K Privately Held
WEB: www.brotherspallets.doodlekit.com
SIC: 2448 Pallets, wood

(G-7652)
C&D SIGN AND LIGHTING SVCS LLC
Also Called: Sign-A-Rama
2175 E Edgewood Dr (33803-3603)
PHONE..................................863 937-9323
Greg Cameron, *Owner*
EMP: 7 EST: 2008
SALES (est): 883.8K Privately Held
WEB: www.signarama.com
SIC: 3993 2752 2389 5999 Signs & advertising specialties; commercial printing, lithographic; apparel & accessories; banners

(G-7653)
CARLOSS CABINETS INC
120 Fulton Rd (33809)
PHONE..................................863 853-4255
Michele Floyd, *Vice Pres*
EMP: 6 EST: 2010
SALES (est): 64.2K Privately Held
SIC: 2434 Wood kitchen cabinets

(G-7654)
CATAPULT LAKELAND INC
226 N Kentucky Ave (33801-4963)
PHONE..................................863 687-3788
Ira Anderson, *President*
EMP: 9 EST: 2017
SALES: 4.3MM Privately Held
WEB: www.catapultlakeland.com
SIC: 3599 Catapults

(G-7655)
CEMEX MATERIALS LLC
801 Mccue Rd (33815-3236)
PHONE..................................863 688-2306
Jeffrey Toennies, *Accounts Mgr*
Eric Hagerman, *Branch Mgr*
EMP: 10
SQ FT: 3,752 Privately Held
SIC: 3273 Ready-mixed concrete
HQ: Cemex Materials Llc
1501 Belvedere Rd
West Palm Beach FL 33406
561 833-5555

(G-7656)
CHICAGO SOFT LTD
1820 E Edgewood Dr # 105 (33803-3420)
PHONE..................................863 940-2066
Eileen Krause, *President*
Joai Broughton, *Opers Mgr*
Carol Brown, *Accountant*
Mando Reyes, *Natl Sales Mgr*
Stephanie Patterson, *Administration*
EMP: 10 EST: 1982
SQ FT: 800
SALES (est): 1.6MM Privately Held
WEB: www.chicago-soft.com
SIC: 7372 Prepackaged software

(G-7657)
CITY OF LAKELAND
Utilities Finance Div
1140 E Parker St (33801-2066)
PHONE..................................863 834-6780
EMP: 12 Privately Held
SIC: 3087 Custom Compounding-Purchased Resins
PA: City Of Lakeland
228 S Massachusetts Ave
Lakeland FL 33801
863 834-6000

(G-7658)
CO-EDIKIT
Also Called: Advantage Enterprise Ameila Is
307 W Main St Ste 2 (33815-1509)
P.O. Box 1753 (33802-1753)
PHONE..................................863 802-1000
Cheryl Caldwell, *Owner*
EMP: 6 EST: 2000
SQ FT: 1,500
SALES (est): 341.6K Privately Held
WEB: www.co-edikit.com
SIC: 2331 Blouses, women's & juniors': made from purchased material

(G-7659)
COASTAL REIGN INC
2068 Indian Sky Cir (33813-4857)
PHONE..................................863 940-4082
James Massey, *Principal*
EMP: 6 EST: 2016
SALES (est): 92.3K Privately Held
WEB: www.jambre.com
SIC: 2752 Commercial printing, lithographic

(G-7660)
COATINGS SMPLES SLTONS ETC LLC
5515 Summerland Hills Dr (33812-6375)
PHONE..................................863 398-8513
Timothy Franklin, *Mng Member*
EMP: 9 EST: 2016
SALES (est): 780.2K Privately Held
SIC: 2952 Asphalt felts & coatings

(G-7661)
COMPUTATIONAL SYSTEMS INC
5030 Gateway Blvd Ste 11 (33811-2708)
PHONE..................................863 648-9044
Greg Dawes, *Manager*
EMP: 123
SALES (corp-wide): 16.7B Publicly Held
SIC: 3823 Industrial instrmnts msrmnt display/control process variable
HQ: Computational Systems, Incorporated
8000 West Florissant Ave
Saint Louis MO 63136
314 553-2000

(G-7662)
CONIBEAR EQUIPMENT CO INC (PA)
Also Called: Conibear Recreational Vehicles
8910 Us Highway 98 N (33809-1013)
P.O. Box 90215 (33804-0215)
PHONE..................................863 858-4414
Robert Conibear, *President*
Joanne A Conibear, *Corp Secy*
Donald D Mills, *Exec VP*
Dale Burges, *Vice Pres*
Judith C Mills, *Vice Pres*
EMP: 8 EST: 1940
SQ FT: 1,200

SALES (est): 1.5MM **Privately Held**
WEB: www.conibearequipmentinc.com
SIC: 3523 Fertilizing machinery, farm

(G-7663)
CORNERSTONE INTERLOCKING INC
5915 Walt Loop Rd (33809-6637)
PHONE..................................863 944-1609
Keith Davis, *Owner*
EMP: 7 **EST:** 2003
SALES (est): 91.3K **Privately Held**
WEB: www.cornerstoneinterlocking.com
SIC: 3272 Concrete products

(G-7664)
CREATIVE LIGHTING & POWER LLC
Also Called: Creative Lighting & Solar
330 Winston Creek Pkwy G (33810-2856)
PHONE..................................407 967-0957
Richelle Ortiz, *Principal*
Candice Clark, *COO*
EMP: 18 **EST:** 2014
SALES (est): 3.9MM **Privately Held**
WEB: www.commercialelectricianslake-land.com
SIC: 3648 Lighting equipment

(G-7665)
CRH AMERICAS INC
Also Called: Oldcastle Lawn & Garden
500 S Florida Ave Ste 240 (33801-5252)
PHONE..................................843 672-5553
George Driver, *Principal*
EMP: 93
SALES (corp-wide): 27.5B **Privately Held**
WEB: www.crhamericas.com
SIC: 3273 Ready-mixed concrete
HQ: Crh Americas, Inc.
900 Ashwood Pkwy Ste 600
Atlanta GA 30338
770 804-3363

(G-7666)
CRICHLOW DATA SCIENCES INC
2500 Drane Feld Rd Ste 10 (33811)
PHONE..................................863 616-1222
Richard H Crichlow, *Ch of Bd*
Robert C Crichlow III, *President*
◆ **EMP:** 9 **EST:** 1983
SQ FT: 16,000
SALES (est): 1.2MM **Privately Held**
WEB: www.thegeneralstore.com
SIC: 7372 Business oriented computer software

(G-7667)
CROWN PRINTING INC
1303 E Main St (33801-5714)
PHONE..................................863 682-4881
Mark Rust, *President*
Edith Rust, *Vice Pres*
Debbie Gorsuch, *Graphic Designe*
EMP: 18 **EST:** 1967
SQ FT: 17,500
SALES (est): 1.9MM **Privately Held**
WEB: www.crownprint.net
SIC: 2752 Commercial printing, offset

(G-7668)
D E E CUSTOM FABRICATORS INC
3545 Waterfield Pkwy (33803-9735)
P.O. Box 1798, Highland City (33846-1798)
PHONE..................................863 667-1850
Gary Bruce McWhirter, *CEO*
Ethan McWhirter, *Opers Mgr*
Erik McWhirter, *Sales Mgr*
EMP: 20 **EST:** 1999
SALES (est): 2MM **Privately Held**
WEB: www.deecustom.com
SIC: 3993 Signs & advertising specialties

(G-7669)
D I R INC
Also Called: Rob Dinic Interiors
3430 Flightline Dr (33811-2836)
PHONE..................................863 661-5360
Rob Dinicolantonio, *President*
EMP: 9 **EST:** 2004
SQ FT: 6,000
SALES (est): 169.9K **Privately Held**
SIC: 3429 Aircraft hardware

(G-7670)
D J TRUSSES UNLIMITED INC
3125 Reynolds Rd (33803-8328)
PHONE..................................863 687-4796
Gerald B Chipps, *President*
David Snell, *Vice Pres*
Gary Roth, *Sales Mgr*
Dennis Snell, *Manager*
EMP: 16 **EST:** 1993
SQ FT: 2,000
SALES (est): 3.3MM **Privately Held**
WEB: www.djtrussesunlimited.com
SIC: 2439 Trusses, wooden roof

(G-7671)
DAISIES CLOSETS
6720 Bordeaux Blvd (33811-1826)
PHONE..................................863 838-5056
Joan Aldrich, *Principal*
EMP: 6 **EST:** 2012
SALES (est): 76.7K **Privately Held**
SIC: 2673 Wardrobe bags (closet accessories): from purchased materials

(G-7672)
DEC SHEET METAL INC
Also Called: Dec Metals
3015 Waterfield Cir (33803-9733)
P.O. Box 580, Highland City (33846-0580)
PHONE..................................863 669-0707
Cory Maxwell, *CEO*
David Maxwell, *President*
Eric Maxwell, *President*
Karen Maxwell, *Vice Pres*
Doug Petro, *Sales Staff*
EMP: 13 **EST:** 1980
SQ FT: 7,500
SALES (est): 5.2MM **Privately Held**
WEB: www.decmetals.com
SIC: 3441 Fabricated structural metal

(G-7673)
DEMOSS CABINETRY LLC
3003 Brooks St Ste 1 (33803-8386)
PHONE..................................863 738-0080
Thomas E Sharrett, *Mng Member*
EMP: 11 **EST:** 2005
SALES (est): 390.5K **Privately Held**
WEB: www.demosscabinetry.com
SIC: 2434 Wood kitchen cabinets

(G-7674)
DESHAZO LLC
3525 Reynolds Rd Ste 10 (33803-8372)
PHONE..................................863 272-3107
Guy Mitchell, *Branch Mgr*
Terry Ford, *Branch Mgr*
EMP: 9
SALES (corp-wide): 117.3MM **Privately Held**
WEB: www.deshazo.com
SIC: 3536 Cranes, overhead traveling
PA: Deshazo, Llc
200 Kilsby Cir
Bessemer AL 35022
205 664-2006

(G-7675)
DIGITAL TECH OF LAKELAND INC
Also Called: Digitech Graphics Group
3020 Winter Lake Rd (33803-9707)
PHONE..................................863 668-8770
Alfredo Balingit, *President*
Jo Mierzwa, *Accounting Mgr*
David Butfiloski, *Director*
Barbara Balingit, *Admin Sec*
EMP: 10 **EST:** 1990
SALES (est): 1.4MM **Privately Held**
WEB: www.dtechgraphics.com
SIC: 3993 Signs & advertising specialties

(G-7676)
DIXIE SIGNS INC
2930 Drane Field Rd (33811-1329)
PHONE..................................863 644-3521
Roger Snyder, *President*
John R Douglass, *Treasurer*
Keely Chestnut, *Accounting Mgr*
Kathy Agner, *Sales Staff*
EMP: 21 **EST:** 1939
SQ FT: 15,500
SALES (est): 3.2MM **Privately Held**
WEB: www.dixiesignsinc.com
SIC: 3993 Electric signs

(G-7677)
DOUGLASS SCREEN PRINTERS INC
Also Called: Dprint
2710 New Tampa Hwy (33815-3463)
PHONE..................................863 687-8545
Lisa K Hickey, *Ch of Bd*
Lane Hickey-Wiggins, *President*
Michael Hickey, *Vice Pres*
Stephanie McDonald, *Accounts Exec*
Steve Hurley, *Supervisor*
EMP: 25
SQ FT: 28,000
SALES (est): 2.6MM **Privately Held**
WEB: www.dprintworldwide.com
SIC: 2759 Screen printing

(G-7678)
EAGLE PNEUMATIC INC
3902 Industry Blvd (33811-1341)
PHONE..................................863 644-4870
Karl Q Kondolf, *President*
Helen Kondolf, *Corp Secy*
Patrick C Evans, *Vice Pres*
Erik Gardner, *QC Mgr*
David Sirkin, *Electrical Engi*
EMP: 25 **EST:** 1977
SQ FT: 28,000
SALES (est): 3.5MM **Privately Held**
WEB: www.eaglepneumatic.com
SIC: 3535 3494 Pneumatic tube conveyor systems; valves & pipe fittings

(G-7679)
EASTERN METAL SUPPLY INC
4675 Drane Field Rd (33811-1253)
PHONE..................................863 682-6660
James Price, *Opers Mgr*
Norberto Salinas, *Mfg Mgr*
Jesse Cruz, *Mfg Staff*
Larry Hubbard, *Purch Mgr*
Celine Torres, *Purchasing*
EMP: 10
SALES (corp-wide): 162.6MM **Privately Held**
WEB: www.easternmetal.com
SIC: 3334 5051 Primary aluminum; aluminum bars, rods, ingots, sheets, pipes, plates, etc.
PA: Eastern Metal Supply, Inc.
3600 23rd Ave S
Lake Worth Beach FL 33461
561 533-6061

(G-7680)
ECO PRODUCTS LIMITED LLC
3536 Dmg Dr (33811-1039)
PHONE..................................863 337-4918
EMP: 7 **EST:** 2015
SALES (est): 143.9K **Privately Held**
WEB: www.ecoproducts.com
SIC: 3585 Refrigeration & heating equipment

(G-7681)
ESCO INDUSTRIES INC
2001 Lasso Ln (33801-9732)
PHONE..................................863 666-3696
Bill Ellis, *President*
EMP: 12
SALES (corp-wide): 32.1MM **Privately Held**
WEB: www.escoindustries.com
SIC: 2435 Plywood, hardwood or hardwood faced
PA: Esco Industries, Inc.
185 Sink Hole Rd
Douglas GA 31533
912 384-1417

(G-7682)
EVOLUTIONARY SCREEN PRINTING L
3521 Waterfield Pkwy (33803-9735)
PHONE..................................863 248-2692
Michael D Frankow, *Principal*
EMP: 6 **EST:** 2007
SALES (est): 478.3K **Privately Held**
WEB: www.evolutionaryscreenprinting.com
SIC: 2759 Screen printing

(G-7683)
EXCELL SOLUTIONS LLC
5115 N Socrum Loop Rd (33809-4288)
PHONE..................................407 615-9330
Retina Holt, *Principal*
EMP: 7 **EST:** 2018
SALES (est): 148K **Privately Held**
WEB: www.excellsol.com
SIC: 3599 Machine shop, jobbing & repair

(G-7684)
EYE SPECIALISTS MID FLORIDA PA
2004 E County Road 540a (33813-3739)
PHONE..................................863 937-4515
EMP: 10 **EST:** 1960
SALES (est): 164.5K **Privately Held**
WEB: www.eyesfl.com
SIC: 3827 Optical instruments & lenses

(G-7685)
FERRERA TOOLING INC
3960 Air Park Dr (33811-1270)
PHONE..................................863 646-8500
Brian Herrera, *President*
Derrick Fearnow, *President*
Michael Schneider, *Accounts Mgr*
EMP: 12
SALES (est): 3MM **Privately Held**
WEB: www.ferreratooling.com
SIC: 3448 Prefabricated metal components

(G-7686)
FIRMENICH LAKELAND
3919 Kidron Rd (33811-1293)
PHONE..................................863 646-0165
EMP: 9 **EST:** 2017
SALES (est): 264K **Privately Held**
WEB: www.firmenich.com
SIC: 2844 Perfumes & colognes

(G-7687)
FL CENTRAL CNSTR & RMDLG
8120 Timberidge Loop W (33809-2357)
P.O. Box 90044 (33804-0044)
PHONE..................................863 701-3548
Thomas R Hughes, *Mng Member*
EMP: 8 **EST:** 2012
SALES (est): 59.1K **Privately Held**
SIC: 2434 2514 1799 Wood kitchen cabinets; kitchen cabinets: metal; kitchen & bathroom remodeling

(G-7688)
FLARE CLOTHING INC
3800 Us Highway 98 N # 746
(33809-3833)
PHONE..................................863 859-1800
Basheer Alsharif, *Principal*
EMP: 7 **EST:** 2015
SALES (est): 308.2K **Privately Held**
SIC: 2899 Flares

(G-7689)
FLORIDA AMICO
1033 Pine Chase Ave (33815-3139)
PHONE..................................863 688-9256
Ashley Carver, *Branch Mgr*
EMP: 6 **EST:** 2010
SALES (est): 516.2K **Privately Held**
WEB: www.amicoglobal.com
SIC: 3089 3281 5032 Plastic hardware & building products; building stone products; concrete & cinder building products

(G-7690)
FLORIDA CENTAL LOGGING INC
7328 Us Highway 98 N (33809-5323)
P.O. Box 94, Polk City (33868-0094)
PHONE..................................863 272-5364
Teresa White, *Principal*
EMP: 11 **EST:** 2010
SALES (est): 526.4K **Privately Held**
SIC: 2411 Logging

(G-7691)
FLORIDA COOL RING COMPANY
2220 Gator Creek Ranch Rd (33809-0909)
PHONE..................................863 858-2211
Joel F Butler, *Owner*
EMP: 10 **EST:** 2003
SALES (est): 340K **Privately Held**
WEB: www.thecoolring.com
SIC: 3269 Pottery products

(G-7692)
FLORIDA NUTRI LABS LLC
2715 Badger Rd (33811-1348)
PHONE..................................863 607-6708

GEOGRAPHIC

Ron Novak, *Mng Member*
EMP: 10 **EST:** 2002
SALES (est): 1.9MM **Privately Held**
WEB: www.wemakevitamins.com
SIC: 2834 Vitamin preparations

(G-7693)
FLORIDA REFRESCO INC
2090 Bartow Rd (33801-6557)
PHONE..................................863 665-5515
David Moller, *President*
J Michael Grady, *Principal*
John P Grady, *Chairman*
Terry Simmers, *COO*
Keith Bishop, *Vice Pres*
◆ **EMP:** 180 **EST:** 1967
SQ FT: 210,000
SALES (est): 42.2MM
SALES (corp-wide): 1.3B **Privately Held**
WEB: www.refresco-na.com
SIC: 2033 2086 Fruit juices: packaged in cans, jars, etc.; tea, iced: packaged in cans, bottles, etc.
HQ: Refresco Us, Inc.
6655 S Lewis Ave
Tulsa OK 74136

(G-7694)
FLOWERS BAKING CO LAKELAND INC
3355 W Memorial Blvd (33815-1084)
PHONE..................................863 682-1155
Karyl Lauder, *President*
EMP: 34 **EST:** 2019
SALES (est): 1.9MM
SALES (corp-wide): 4.3B **Publicly Held**
WEB: www.flowersfoods.com
SIC: 2051 Bread, cake & related products
PA: Flowers Foods, Inc.
1919 Flowers Cir
Thomasville GA 31757
912 226-9110

(G-7695)
FLOWERS BKG CO BRADENTON LLC
Also Called: Flowers Baking Company
2610 Mine And Mill Rd 4-9 (33801-7002)
PHONE..................................941 758-5656
Chris Peer, *Manager*
EMP: 20
SALES (corp-wide): 4.3B **Publicly Held**
WEB: www.flobradconf.com
SIC: 2051 Bread, cake & related products
HQ: Flowers Baking Co. Of Bradenton, Llc
6490 Parkland Dr
Sarasota FL 34243

(G-7696)
GEA MECHANICAL EQP US INC
4725 Lakeland Commerce Pa (33805-7665)
PHONE..................................863 669-1500
Clim O'Donnel, *Manager*
EMP: 6
SALES (corp-wide): 5.4B **Privately Held**
WEB: www.wsus.com
SIC: 3569 Centrifuges, industrial
HQ: Gea Mechanical Equipment Us, Inc.
100 Fairway Ct
Northvale NJ 07647

(G-7697)
GENIE PUBLISHING
5111 Fernbrook Ln (33811-1653)
PHONE..................................863 937-7769
Gay N Finkelman, *Owner*
EMP: 9 **EST:** 2009
SALES (est): 373.2K **Privately Held**
WEB: www.geniepub.com
SIC: 2741 Miscellaneous publishing

(G-7698)
GIVAUDAN FRAGRANCES CORP
Also Called: Givaudan Roure Flavors
4705 Us Highway 92 E (33801-9584)
PHONE..................................863 667-0821
Chris Rimes, *Maint Spvr*
Steve Cook, *Engineer*
Kristy McKinney, *Human Res Dir*
Mike Taylor, *Branch Mgr*
EMP: 48
SALES (corp-wide): 6.9B **Privately Held**
WEB: www.givaudan.com
SIC: 2869 2087 Industrial organic chemicals; flavoring extracts & syrups
HQ: Givaudan Fragrances Corporation
1199 Edison Dr Ste 1-2
Cincinnati OH 45216
513 948-8000

(G-7699)
GKWF INC
Also Called: Con Serv Manufacturing
520 W Brannen Rd (33813-2726)
P.O. Box 6160 (33807-6160)
PHONE..................................863 644-6925
Dwight Royal, *CEO*
David S Royal Jr, *President*
Kristine Burnett, *Office Mgr*
EMP: 5 **EST:** 1997
SQ FT: 10,000
SALES (est): 1.3MM **Privately Held**
SIC: 3823 Industrial instrmnts msrmnt display/control process variable

(G-7700)
GMF INDUSTRIES INC
Also Called: G M F
4600 Drane Field Rd (33811-1216)
P.O. Box 6688 (33807-6688)
PHONE..................................863 646-5081
Vincent Larry Norman, *President*
Spencer A Norman, *Vice Pres*
Stuart A Norman, *Vice Pres*
Jeremy Turner, *Prdtn Mgr*
Pamela Lsecreta Norman, *Admin Sec*
EMP: 90 **EST:** 1982
SQ FT: 136,000
SALES (est): 13.8MM **Privately Held**
WEB: www.gmfsteel.com
SIC: 3449 3599 Miscellaneous metalwork; machine shop, jobbing & repair

(G-7701)
GRAPHIC INSTALLERS INC
4403 Holden Rd (33811-2849)
P.O. Box 7017 (33807-7017)
PHONE..................................863 646-5543
Andrew Gutentag, *President*
Susan Gutentag, *Vice Pres*
▲ **EMP:** 8 **EST:** 1990
SQ FT: 8,000
SALES (est): 1MM **Privately Held**
WEB: www.graphicinstallers.com
SIC: 3993 Signs & advertising specialties

(G-7702)
GSE AMERICA LLC (PA)
3928 Anchuca Dr Ste 3 (33811-1859)
PHONE..................................863 583-4343
Michael Miner,
EMP: 5 **EST:** 2017
SALES (est): 1MM **Privately Held**
WEB: www.gse-america.com
SIC: 3728 Aircraft parts & equipment

(G-7703)
HARRELLS LLC (HQ)
5105 New Tampa Hwy (33815-3262)
P.O. Box 935358, Atlanta GA (31193-5358)
PHONE..................................863 687-2774
Jack Harrell Jr, *CEO*
David Schermerhorn, *President*
Mike Dukette, *Partner*
Matthew Shook, *COO*
Alex Barcia, *Vice Pres*
◆ **EMP:** 195 **EST:** 2007
SALES (est): 220MM
SALES (corp-wide): 243.4MM **Privately Held**
WEB: www.harrells.com
SIC: 2875 5191 Fertilizers, mixing only; fertilizers & agricultural chemicals
PA: Harrell's Inc.
5105 New Tampa Hwy
Lakeland FL 33815
863 687-2774

(G-7704)
HENDRIX MAINTENANCE & REPR LLC
3705 Century Blvd Ste 6 (33811-1395)
PHONE..................................863 647-3511
Scott Hendrix, *Mng Member*
EMP: 5 **EST:** 1990
SQ FT: 2,000
SALES (est): 450K **Privately Held**
WEB: www.hendrixllc.com
SIC: 3444 Sheet metalwork

(G-7705)
HIGH PERFORMANCE HOLDINGS LTD
Also Called: Createch Machine & Design
625 Mccue Rd Ste 1 (33815-3202)
PHONE..................................815 874-9421
Larry Bull, *President*
Jim Wood, *Sales Dir*
EMP: 20 **EST:** 2007
SALES (est): 2.8MM **Privately Held**
WEB: www.createch-design.com
SIC: 3541 Machine tools, metal cutting type; drilling machine tools (metal cutting)

(G-7706)
HOSE POWER USA
3110 Winter Lake Rd (33803-9708)
PHONE..................................863 669-9333
Jeff Hill, *Manager*
▼ **EMP:** 6 **EST:** 2013
SALES (est): 235.6K **Privately Held**
WEB: www.hosepower.com
SIC: 3492 3491 Fluid power valves & hose fittings; industrial valves

(G-7707)
HUNT ENTERPRISES INC
Also Called: True Bloods Colonial Printing
1224 E Lime St (33801-5754)
PHONE..................................863 682-6187
Charles N Hunt, *President*
Jesse M Thrower, *Vice Pres*
Dorene Hunt, *Treasurer*
▼ **EMP:** 5 **EST:** 1966
SQ FT: 1,320
SALES (est): 454.5K **Privately Held**
WEB: www.truebloods.com
SIC: 2752 Commercial printing, offset

(G-7708)
ILLINOIS TOOL WORKS INC
Also Called: ITW Professional Auto Pdts
3606 Craftsman Blvd (33803-7398)
PHONE..................................863 665-3338
William Crowe, *General Mgr*
Laura Blalock, *Lab Dir*
EMP: 100
SALES (corp-wide): 12.5B **Publicly Held**
WEB: www.itw.com
SIC: 2899 5169 2992 2842 Chemical preparations; chemicals & allied products; lubricating oils & greases; specialty cleaning, polishes & sanitation goods
PA: Illinois Tool Works Inc.
155 Harlem Ave
Glenview IL 60025
847 724-7500

(G-7709)
INDUSTRIAL BRUSH CORPORATION
4000 Drane Field Rd (33811-1208)
PHONE..................................863 647-5643
Tony Jensen, *Purch Agent*
Gary A Messier, *Manager*
Chuck Richardson, *Manager*
EMP: 10
SALES (corp-wide): 11.6MM **Privately Held**
WEB: www.industrialbrush.com
SIC: 3991 Brooms & brushes
PA: Industrial Brush Corporation
763 E Commerce Dr
St George UT 84790
909 591-9341

(G-7710)
INDUSTRIAL CMPSITE SYSTEMS LLC
Also Called: Industrial Plastic Systems
4225 Drane Field Rd (33811-1292)
PHONE..................................863 646-8551
Michael Brown, *President*
EMP: 18 **EST:** 2013
SQ FT: 15,000
SALES (est): 2.4MM **Privately Held**
WEB: www.ips-frp.com
SIC: 3089 Plastic & fiberglass tanks; duct-ing, plastic; fittings for pipe, plastic

(G-7711)
INDUSTRIAL PLASTIC SYSTEMS INC
Also Called: Ips
4225 Drane Field Rd (33811-1292)
P.O. Box 6280 (33807-6280)
PHONE..................................863 646-8551
Barron Burhans, *President*
EMP: 20 **EST:** 1975
SALES (est): 3MM **Privately Held**
WEB: www.ips-frp.com
SIC: 3089 Plastic containers, except foam

(G-7712)
INNOVATIER INC
2769 New Tampa Hwy (33815-3462)
PHONE..................................863 688-4548
Lawrence J Keim, *CFO*
EMP: 6 **EST:** 2004
SALES (est): 470.2K **Privately Held**
WEB: www.innovatier.com
SIC: 3083 Laminated plastics plate & sheet

(G-7713)
INTEGRATED METAL PRODUCTS INC
2923 Old Tampa Hwy (33803-1674)
PHONE..................................863 687-4110
Wayne Albritton, *President*
Eva Albritton, *Vice Pres*
Dewayne Watford, *Controller*
Macel Johnson, *Sales Mgr*
Blair Kinney, *Manager*
EMP: 70
SQ FT: 78,000
SALES (est): 16.5MM **Privately Held**
WEB: www.integratedmetal.com
SIC: 3444 Sheet metalwork

(G-7714)
INTERACTIVE CARDS INC
2787 New Tampa Hwy (33815-3462)
PHONE..................................863 688-4548
Michael Scruggs, *CEO*
David Patterson, *President*
Robert Singleton, *COO*
Lisa Blue, *Mng Member*
Mike Scruggs, *Director*
EMP: 17 **EST:** 2009
SALES (est): 3.1MM **Privately Held**
WEB: www.iacards.com
SIC: 3559 Electronic component making machinery

(G-7715)
INTERCIT INC
4330 Drane Field Rd (33811-1211)
PHONE..................................863 646-0165
Beverly Bateman, *President*
Don Hendrix, *Vice Pres*
Peary Marro, *Vice Pres*
Eric Jorgensen, *Treasurer*
Lisa Alexander, *Admin Sec*
◆ **EMP:** 91 **EST:** 1970
SQ FT: 10,000
SALES (est): 43MM
SALES (corp-wide): 4.7B **Privately Held**
WEB: www.firmenich.com
SIC: 2899 Oils & essential oils
HQ: Firmenich Incorporated
250 Plainsboro Rd
Plainsboro NJ 08536
609 452-1000

(G-7716)
INTERLAKE INDUSTRIES INC
1022 County Line Rd (33815-3177)
PHONE..................................863 688-5665
Jeff Groenstein, *Manager*
EMP: 9
SALES (corp-wide): 28MM **Privately Held**
WEB: www.interlakestamping.com
SIC: 3469 Stamping metal for the trade
PA: Interlake Industries, Inc.
4732 E 355th St
Willoughby OH 44094
440 942-0800

(G-7717)
INTERLAKE STAMPING FLORIDA INC
1022 County Line Rd (33815-3177)
PHONE..................................863 688-5665
Lisa Habe, *Principal*

▲ = Import ▼=Export
◆ =Import/Export

Laura Whitt, *Admin Asst*
EMP: 104 **EST:** 1985
SALES (est): 5.5MM
SALES (corp-wide): 28MM **Privately Held**
WEB: www.interlakestamping.com
SIC: 3469 Stamping metal for the trade
PA: Interlake Industries, Inc.
4732 E 355th St
Willoughby OH 44094
440 942-0800

(G-7718)
INTOUCH GPS LLC
439 S Florida Ave 100b (33801-5212)
PHONE..................................877 593-2981
Jon Jarell, *President*
Rob Case, *Opers Mgr*
Mara Schwartz, *Train & Dev Mgr*
Selina Campbell, *Manager*
EMP: 41 **EST:** 1978
SQ FT: 3,500
SALES (est): 4.8MM
SALES (corp-wide): 10.8MM **Privately Held**
WEB: www.intouchgps.com
SIC: 7372 Prepackaged software
PA: Gpstrackit Holdings, Llc
1080 Holcomb Bridge Rd
Roswell GA 30076
951 296-1316

(G-7719)
J & J DYNAMIC PRODUCTS LLC
2730 Drane Field Rd (33811-1325)
PHONE..................................863 274-5333
John R Bunn, *Principal*
EMP: 6 **EST:** 2011
SALES (est): 155.7K **Privately Held**
WEB: www.balanceyourtires.com
SIC: 3714 Motor vehicle parts & accessories

(G-7720)
JBT FOODTECH CITRUS SYSTEMS
Also Called: Jbt Food Tech
400 Fairway Ave (33801-2468)
PHONE..................................863 683-5411
John T Gremp, *CEO*
Thomas W Giacomini, *President*
Paul Sternlieb, *President*
Bryant Lowery, *Vice Pres*
Younes Benkabbou, *Engineer*
◆ **EMP:** 77 **EST:** 2008
SALES (est): 22.2MM **Privately Held**
WEB: www.jbtc.com
SIC: 3556 Food products machinery

(G-7721)
JC MACHINE INC
Also Called: J C M I
3620 Airport Rd (33811-1002)
P.O. Box 5027 (33807-5027)
PHONE..................................863 644-2815
John Creasy Creasy, *President*
EMP: 10 **EST:** 1984
SQ FT: 4,000
SALES (est): 2.7MM **Privately Held**
WEB: www.jcmi-usa.com
SIC: 3599 Machine shop, jobbing & repair

(G-7722)
JOHN BEAN TECHNOLOGIES CORP
Also Called: Jbt Foodtech
400 Fairway Ave (33801-2468)
PHONE..................................863 683-5411
Halejendro Huidobro, *Principal*
Ian Houston, *Engineer*
Bobbie Spahr, *Engineer*
Sean Casey, *Finance Dir*
Tom Eggleston, *Sales Staff*
EMP: 200 **Publicly Held**
WEB: www.jbtc.com
SIC: 3556 Food products machinery
PA: John Bean Technologies Corporation
70 W Madison St Ste 4400
Chicago IL 60602

(G-7723)
K-TECHNOLOGIES INC
4306 Wallace Rd (33812-6379)
P.O. Box 5377 (33807-5377)
PHONE..................................863 940-4815
Thomas Baroody, *CEO*
Wes Berry, *Vice Pres*
EMP: 8 **EST:** 1987
SQ FT: 12,000
SALES (est): 1.1MM **Privately Held**
WEB: www.ktech-inc.com
SIC: 2819 Industrial inorganic chemicals

(G-7724)
KELLER MANUFACTURING INC
4442 Holden Rd (33811-2850)
PHONE..................................863 937-8928
EMP: 9 **EST:** 2011
SALES (est): 610.3K **Privately Held**
WEB: www.kellermanufacturing.net
SIC: 3999 Manufacturing industries

(G-7725)
KEY AUTOMOTIVE FLORIDA LLC
Also Called: Joyson Safety Systems
5300 Allen K Breed Hwy (33811-1130)
PHONE..................................863 668-6000
Matthew C Cohn, *President*
William McLeod, *Engineer*
Natalia Zarycky, *Treasurer*
Steve Parrish, *Manager*
Marsha A Fershtman, *Admin Sec*
▲ **EMP:** 350 **EST:** 1990
SQ FT: 195,000
SALES (est): 49.2MM
SALES (corp-wide): 7.2B **Privately Held**
WEB: www.joysonsafety.com
SIC: 3714 Motor vehicle parts & accessories
HQ: Joyson Safety Systems Acquisition Llc
2025 Harmon Rd
Auburn Hills MI 48326
248 373-8040

(G-7726)
KEY SAFETY SYSTEMS INC
5300 Allen K Breed Hwy (33811-1130)
PHONE..................................863 668-6000
John Reiss, *President*
EMP: 6
SALES (corp-wide): 7.2B **Privately Held**
WEB: www.joysonsafety.com
SIC: 2399 3714 Seat belts, automobile & aircraft; motor vehicle parts & accessories
HQ: Key Safety Systems, Inc.
2025 Harmon Rd
Auburn Hills MI 48326
248 373-8040

(G-7727)
KEYMARK CORPORATION FLORIDA
2540 Knights Station Rd (33810-2505)
PHONE..................................863 858-5500
William L Keller III, *President*
Joe Crenna, *Vice Pres*
James Keller, *Vice Pres*
Leo Slecton, *Plant Mgr*
Mike Jackman, *Safety Mgr*
▲ **EMP:** 115 **EST:** 1997
SALES (est): 28.5MM **Privately Held**
WEB: www.keymarkcorp.com
SIC: 3354 Aluminum extruded products

(G-7728)
KINGS & QUEENS CABINETS
841 Windsor St (33803-3713)
PHONE..................................863 646-6972
Ronald D Gadd, *Owner*
EMP: 8 **EST:** 1976
SALES (est): 232.1K **Privately Held**
SIC: 2434 2521 Wood kitchen cabinets; wood office furniture

(G-7729)
KNIGHT INDUSTRIAL EQP INC
3701 Airfield Dr W (33811-1244)
PHONE..................................863 646-2997
Bob Knight, *President*
Ray Foucher, *Vice Pres*
Jason Rainboth, *Opers Staff*
Brian Popp, *Engineer*
EMP: 8 **EST:** 1984
SQ FT: 6,000
SALES (est): 1.5MM **Privately Held**
WEB: www.knightindustrial.net
SIC: 3532 5084 Mining machinery; industrial machinery & equipment

(G-7730)
LAKELAND DIGITAL PRINTING CO
3264 Merlot Dr (33811-1810)
PHONE..................................863 509-8049
Kasey Britt, *Principal*
EMP: 9 **EST:** 2018
SALES (est): 101.5K **Privately Held**
SIC: 2752 Commercial printing, lithographic

(G-7731)
LAKELAND LURES INC
955 Oak Ln (33811-2348)
PHONE..................................863 644-3127
Jan Bully, *President*
Vivian Rogers, *General Mgr*
EMP: 9 **EST:** 1981
SQ FT: 3,000
SALES (est): 120.2K **Privately Held**
SIC: 3069 Hard rubber & molded rubber products

(G-7732)
LANE CONSTRUCTION CORPORATION
3350 Reynolds Rd (33803-7325)
P.O. Box 2684, Eaton Park (33840-2684)
PHONE..................................863 665-0457
Gary Jerabeck, *Manager*
EMP: 40
SALES (corp-wide): 2.2B **Privately Held**
WEB: www.laneconstruct.com
SIC: 3272 Building materials, except block or brick: concrete
HQ: The Lane Construction Corporation
90 Fieldstone Ct
Cheshire CT 06410
203 235-3351

(G-7733)
LEDGER (HQ)
Also Called: Ledger Publishing Company
300 W Lime St (33815-4649)
P.O. Box 408 (33802-0408)
PHONE..................................863 802-7000
Toll Free:..................................888 -
Nancy Graham Jump, *Editor*
Arthur Ochs Sulzberger, *Chairman*
Linda Hieber, *Accountant*
Patricia Martin, *Adv Dir*
Don Rothausen, *Adv Dir*
EMP: 353 **EST:** 1989
SALES (est): 42.1MM
SALES (corp-wide): 272.8MM **Privately Held**
WEB: www.theledger.com
SIC: 2759 2711 Commercial printing; newspapers, publishing & printing
PA: Halifax Media Holdings, Llc
901 6th St
Daytona Beach FL 32117
386 681-2404

(G-7734)
LEGACY VULCAN LLC
2300 Mershon St (33815-3532)
PHONE..................................863 687-7625
Harvie Blebins, *Branch Mgr*
EMP: 9 **Publicly Held**
WEB: www.vulcanmaterials.com
SIC: 3273 Ready-mixed concrete
HQ: Legacy Vulcan, Llc
1200 Urban Center Dr
Vestavia AL 35242
205 298-3000

(G-7735)
LINCOLN SMITH VENTURES LLC
Also Called: Minuteman Press
2058 E Edgewood Dr (33803-3632)
PHONE..................................863 337-6670
Patrick L Lincoln,
EMP: 7 **EST:** 2017
SALES (est): 564.8K **Privately Held**
WEB: www.chanhassen-mn.minuteman-press.com
SIC: 2752 Commercial printing, lithographic

(G-7736)
LOCKHEED MARTIN CORPORATION
Also Called: Lockheed Martin Government
1040 S Pkwy Frontage Rd (33813-1400)
PHONE..................................863 647-0100
Shari Foret, *Vice Pres*
Leo S Mackay, *Vice Pres*
Steven Hinchee, *Mfg Spvr*
Josue Barrantes, *Engineer*
Corey Gellis, *Engineer*
EMP: 99 **Publicly Held**
WEB: www.lockheedmartin.com
SIC: 3812 Search & navigation equipment
PA: Lockheed Martin Corporation
6801 Rockledge Dr
Bethesda MD 20817

(G-7737)
LOCKHEED MARTIN CORPORATION
1040 S Pkwy Frontage Rd (33813-1400)
P.O. Box 33064 (33807-3064)
PHONE..................................863 647-0100
Jody Pregent, *Senior Mgr*
EMP: 6 **Publicly Held**
WEB: www.lockheedmartin.com
SIC: 3812 Search & navigation equipment
PA: Lockheed Martin Corporation
6801 Rockledge Dr
Bethesda MD 20817

(G-7738)
LOCKHEED MARTIN CORPORATION
1040 South Blvd (33803-1352)
P.O. Box 33017 (33807-3017)
PHONE..................................863 647-0558
Greg Bosey, *Manager*
EMP: 400 **Publicly Held**
WEB: www.lockheedmartin.com
SIC: 3812 Search & navigation equipment
PA: Lockheed Martin Corporation
6801 Rockledge Dr
Bethesda MD 20817

(G-7739)
LOCKHEED MARTIN CORPORATION
1040 S Pkwy Frontage Rd (33813-1400)
P.O. Box 33037 (33807-3037)
PHONE..................................863 647-0100
EMP: 6 **Publicly Held**
WEB: www.lockheedmartin.com
SIC: 3812 Search & navigation equipment
PA: Lockheed Martin Corporation
6801 Rockledge Dr
Bethesda MD 20817

(G-7740)
LOCKHEED MARTIN CORPORATION
Also Called: Aerontics Customer Support Ctr
1040 S Pkwy Frontage Rd (33813-1400)
PHONE..................................863 647-0303
Hulda Raybon, *Manager*
EMP: 6 **Publicly Held**
WEB: www.lockheedmartin.com
SIC: 3812 Search & navigation equipment
PA: Lockheed Martin Corporation
6801 Rockledge Dr
Bethesda MD 20817

(G-7741)
M P N INC
Also Called: Active Radiator Supply Company
815 Pear St (33815-1333)
PHONE..................................863 606-5999
Monica Rivers, *Branch Mgr*
EMP: 20 **Privately Held**
WEB: www.activeradiator.com
SIC: 3714 Motor vehicle parts & accessories
PA: M. P. N., Inc.
3675 Amber St
Philadelphia PA 19134

(G-7742)
MACLAN CORPORATION INC (PA)
1808 S Combee Rd (33801-6852)
P.O. Box 1906, Eaton Park (33840-1906)
PHONE..................................863 665-4814
Phillip M Lane Sr, *President*

Michael A Lane, *Treasurer*
Wallace Maegan, *Sales Staff*
Sterling Crump, *Analyst*
EMP: 36 **EST:** 1975
SQ FT: 80,000
SALES (est): 6.9MM **Privately Held**
WEB: www.maclan.com
SIC: 2822 3312 Synthetic rubber; blast furnaces & steel mills

(G-7743)
MANGO PUBLICATIONS
715 S New York Ave (33815-4747)
PHONE..................................863 583-4773
EMP: 7
SALES (est): 320K **Privately Held**
SIC: 2759 Commercial Printing

(G-7744)
MAR COR PURIFICATION INC
5001 Gateway Blvd Ste 21 (33811-2715)
PHONE..................................484 991-0220
Patrick Schilling, *Branch Mgr*
EMP: 29 **Privately Held**
WEB: www.mcpur.com
SIC: 3589 Water treatment equipment, industrial
HQ: Mar Cor Purification, Inc.
4450 Township Line Rd
Skippack PA 19474
800 633-3080

(G-7745)
MARK/TRECE INC
Also Called: Mark Trece
5385 Gateway Blvd (33811-1785)
PHONE..................................863 647-4372
EMP: 26
SALES (corp-wide): 33.5MM **Privately Held**
WEB: www.marktrece.com
SIC: 3555 Printing trades machinery
PA: Mark/Trece, Inc.
2001 Stockton Rd
Joppa MD 21085
410 879-0060

(G-7746)
MAX TORQUE LLC
3360 Flightline Dr (33811)
PHONE..................................863 701-8000
EMP: 15
SALES (corp-wide): 12MM **Privately Held**
SIC: 3721 Aircraft, Nsk
PA: Max Torque, Llc
10000 Manchester St Ste H
Houston TX
800 696-7272

(G-7747)
MAX-PAK INC (HQ)
Also Called: Maxpak
2808 New Tampa Hwy (33815-3438)
PHONE..................................863 682-0123
Robert K Beswick, *President*
Scott J McBride, *Vice Pres*
Rhonda G Beswick, *Treasurer*
Julie L McBride, *Admin Sec*
◆ **EMP:** 127 **EST:** 1984
SQ FT: 150,000
SALES (est): 53.8MM
SALES (corp-wide): 215.2MM **Privately Held**
WEB: www.teamtrg.com
SIC: 2653 Boxes, corrugated: made from purchased materials
PA: Schwarz Partners Packaging, Llc
3600 Woodview Trce # 300
Indianapolis IN 46268
317 290-1140

(G-7748)
MCKESSON PHARMACEUTICAL ✪
1515 Kendrick Ln (33805-2501)
PHONE..................................863 616-2973
Douglas Pace, *Principal*
EMP: 13 **EST:** 2020
SALES (est): 835.5K **Privately Held**
SIC: 3841 Surgical & medical instruments

(G-7749)
ME THOMPSON INC
Also Called: Dandee Foods
1840 Fairbanks St (33805-2542)
PHONE..................................863 667-3732
Alan Berry, *Manager*
EMP: 66
SALES (corp-wide): 10.2MM **Privately Held**
SIC: 2099 5149 Sandwiches, assembled & packaged: for wholesale market; groceries & related products
PA: M.E. Thompson, Inc.
2178 W 21st St
Jacksonville FL 32209
904 356-6258

(G-7750)
MGL ENGINEERING INC
2740 Parkway St (33811-1343)
P.O. Box 7701 (33807-7701)
PHONE..................................863 648-0320
Harry Love, *President*
Richard Grant, *Corp Secy*
Barry Mc Keown, *Vice Pres*
Margo Allen, *Office Mgr*
◆ **EMP:** 40 **EST:** 1998
SALES (est): 9.2MM **Privately Held**
WEB: www.mglengineering.com
SIC: 3312 8711 Structural shapes & pilings, steel; engineering services

(G-7751)
MID-STATE MACHINE & FABG CORP (PA)
Also Called: Mid State Machine & Fabg
2730 Mine And Mill Rd (33801-7006)
PHONE..................................863 665-6233
Harold E Kersey, *CEO*
Jeff E Clyne, *President*
Paul Thomassee, *Superintendent*
Mark Freeman, *Business Mgr*
John Hooten, *Vice Pres*
EMP: 354 **EST:** 1972
SQ FT: 60,000
SALES (est): 82.9MM **Privately Held**
WEB: www.midstateindustrialcorp.com
SIC: 3443 3599 7692 3444 Fabricated plate work (boiler shop); machine & other job shop work; welding repair; sheet metalwork

(G-7752)
MINUTEMAN PRESS
2058 E Edgewood Dr Ste C (33803-3632)
PHONE..................................863 337-6670
Patrick Lee Lincoln II, *Principal*
EMP: 6 **EST:** 2016
SALES (est): 128.1K **Privately Held**
WEB: www.minutemanpress.com
SIC: 2752 Commercial printing, lithographic

(G-7753)
MMT TECHNOLOGIES INC
4302 Holden Rd (33811-2854)
PHONE..................................863 619-2926
Otho N Fletcher Jr, *President*
Samantha M Pratt, *Admin Sec*
EMP: 6 **EST:** 1995
SALES (est): 129K **Privately Held**
SIC: 2869 Glycol ethers

(G-7754)
MOSAIC
5810 Deer Flag Dr (33811-4008)
PHONE..................................863 860-1328
Robert Fredere, *General Mgr*
Chris Hagemo, *General Mgr*
Nevin Maga, *General Mgr*
Alex Campbell, *Vice Pres*
Benjamin Lomsak, *Vice Pres*
EMP: 34
SALES (corp-wide): 264.9MM **Privately Held**
WEB: www.mosaicinfo.org
SIC: 1241 Coal mining services
PA: Mosaic
4980 S 118th St
Omaha NE 68137
402 896-3884

(G-7755)
MOTOROLA SOLUTIONS CENTER
2352 Old Combee Rd # 101 (33805-7640)
PHONE..................................863 665-5105
EMP: 5 **EST:** 2019
SALES (est): 429.3K **Privately Held**
WEB: www.motorolasolutionscenter.com
SIC: 3663 Radio & TV communications equipment

(G-7756)
NARRAMORE MACHINE SHOP LLC
2770 Industrial Park Dr (33801-7108)
PHONE..................................863 667-1004
Christopher S Narramore R, *Manager*
EMP: 10 **EST:** 2019
SALES (est): 806.2K **Privately Held**
SIC: 3599 Machine shop, jobbing & repair

(G-7757)
NEXSTAR BROADCASTING INC
Also Called: Tampa Tribune
223 S Florida Ave (33801-4621)
PHONE..................................863 683-6531
EMP: 15
SALES (corp-wide): 2.4B **Publicly Held**
SIC: 2711 7313 Newspapers-Publishing/Printing Advertising Representative
HQ: Wood Television Llc
120 College Ave Se
Grand Rapids MI 49503
616 456-8888

(G-7758)
OMNIA INC
3125 Drane Feld Rd Ste 29 (33811)
PHONE..................................863 619-8100
William Marcy, *Principal*
Christine Buchanan, *Sales Staff*
Keith Wong, *Sales Staff*
EMP: 8 **EST:** 2012
SALES (est): 482.1K **Privately Held**
WEB: www.omniasalesinc.com
SIC: 3728 Aircraft assemblies, subassemblies & parts

(G-7759)
OMNIA INCORPORATED
3125 Drane Feld Rd Ste 29 (33811)
PHONE..................................863 619-8100
Cynthia B Maddox, *President*
Neu A Lawrence, *Vice Pres*
EMP: 23 **EST:** 1984
SALES (est): 2.3MM **Privately Held**
WEB: www.omniainc.com
SIC: 3843 Dental equipment & supplies

(G-7760)
OSHKOSH CORPORATION
4950 Frontage Rd S (33815-3193)
PHONE..................................863 603-4080
Bill Smith, *Branch Mgr*
EMP: 7
SALES (corp-wide): 6.8B **Publicly Held**
WEB: www.oshkoshcorp.com
SIC: 3711 Military motor vehicle assembly
PA: Oshkosh Corporation
1917 Four Wheel Dr
Oshkosh WI 54902
920 502-3009

(G-7761)
PALLET DEPOT LLC
6300 New Tampa Hwy (33815-3144)
PHONE..................................863 686-6245
Brian E O'Donnell,
Bethann O'Donnell,
Mark L Schulcz,
EMP: 22 **EST:** 2008
SALES (est): 1.4MM **Privately Held**
WEB: www.pallet-depot.com
SIC: 2448 Pallets, wood

(G-7762)
PARKINSON ENTERPRISES INC
Also Called: Innovative Ink
1840 Harden Blvd (33803-1827)
PHONE..................................863 688-7900
Charles Parkinson, *President*
Carrie Anderson, *Graphic Designe*
EMP: 16 **EST:** 1985
SQ FT: 4,500
SALES (est): 1.9MM **Privately Held**
SIC: 2752 2791 2789 Commercial printing, offset; typesetting; bookbinding & related work

(G-7763)
PATTERSON PUBLISHING
214 Traders Aly (33801-4986)
P.O. Box 41 (33802-0041)
PHONE..................................863 701-2707
Curtis A Patterson, *Principal*
Annalee Mutz, *Director*
Daniel Barcelo, *Creative Dir*
EMP: 16 **EST:** 2010
SALES (est): 666K **Privately Held**
WEB: www.thelakelander.com
SIC: 2721 Magazines: publishing only, not printed on site

(G-7764)
PATTERSON PUBLISHING LLC
214 Traders Aly (33801-4986)
P.O. Box 41 (33802-0041)
PHONE..................................863 701-2707
Curtis A Patterson, *Principal*
Debra K Patterson, *Vice Pres*
EMP: 9 **EST:** 2003
SALES (est): 372.6K **Privately Held**
SIC: 2741 Miscellaneous publishing

(G-7765)
PEPSI BOTTLING GROUP INC
Also Called: Pepsi-Cola
4100 Frontage Rd S (33815-3201)
PHONE..................................863 687-7605
Eric J Foss, *CEO*
Michael Fichera, *Vice Pres*
Thomas M Lardieri, *Vice Pres*
Steven M Rapp, *Vice Pres*
Alfred H Drewes, *CFO*
EMP: 6 **EST:** 2000
SALES (est): 1.3MM **Privately Held**
WEB: www.pepsico.com
SIC: 2086 Carbonated soft drinks, bottled & canned

(G-7766)
PETLIFT SB MANUFACTURING INC
5301 Gateway Blvd (33811-1735)
PHONE..................................941 346-2211
Nancy Apatow, *Principal*
EMP: 13 **EST:** 2016
SALES (est): 141.1K **Privately Held**
SIC: 3999 Manufacturing industries

(G-7767)
PLASTIC TRADING INTL INC
3612 Ventura Dr E (33811-1229)
PHONE..................................863 688-1983
Brian T Brandt, *President*
Mark Bacon, *Opers Staff*
Jesse Ritter, *Regl Sales Mgr*
Stephanie Fuller, *Marketing Staff*
Nicole Ackerman, *Office Mgr*
EMP: 23 **EST:** 2012
SQ FT: 25,000
SALES (est): 9.2MM **Privately Held**
WEB: www.plastictradingint.org
SIC: 2821 Plastics materials & resins

(G-7768)
PM CRAFTSMAN
Also Called: T & C Creations
3525 Craftsman Blvd (33803-7397)
PHONE..................................863 665-0815
Robert F Schofield Jr, *President*
Linda J Schofield, *Vice Pres*
Linda Schofield, *Vice Pres*
Derek Schofield, *Treasurer*
EMP: 29 **EST:** 1911
SQ FT: 55,000
SALES (est): 2.5MM **Privately Held**
WEB: www.pmcraftsman.com
SIC: 3499 5199 3366 Novelties & giftware, including trophies; gifts & novelties; copper foundries

(G-7769)
POLK AIR FILTER SALES INC
1851 E Gary Rd (33801-2295)
PHONE..................................863 688-4436
Gene Hyman, *President*
Sid Hyman, *Manager*
EMP: 7 **EST:** 1971
SQ FT: 15,000

▲ = Import ▼=Export
◆ =Import/Export

SALES (est): 577K **Privately Held**
SIC: 3564 Filters, air: furnaces, air conditioning equipment, etc.

(G-7770)
PORTER PIZZA BOX FLORIDA INC (PA)
6094 Us Highway 98 S (33812-4347)
P.O. Box 1795, Highland City (33846-1795)
PHONE..................................800 626-0828
Halden L Porter, *President*
Jack Robinson, *Principal*
Linda G Porter, *Vice Pres*
▼ **EMP:** 20 **EST:** 1991
SQ FT: 6,000
SALES (est): 9.9MM **Privately Held**
SIC: 2631 Corrugating medium

(G-7771)
PRO-AD MEDIA INC
115 Allamanda Dr (33803-2925)
P.O. Box 864 (33802-0864)
PHONE..................................863 802-5043
Wes Craven, *President*
James Holloway, *Vice Pres*
EMP: 8 **EST:** 1996
SQ FT: 1,700
SALES (est): 807.1K **Privately Held**
WEB: www.proadmedia.com
SIC: 3993 Displays & cutouts, window & lobby

(G-7772)
PURINA ANIMAL NUTRITION LLC
2815 Drane Field Rd (33811-1851)
PHONE..................................863 262-4332
Kevin Sheridan, *Branch Mgr*
EMP: 13
SALES (corp-wide): 2.8B **Privately Held**
WEB: www.purinamills.com
SIC: 2048 Prepared feeds
HQ: Purina Animal Nutrition Llc
100 Danforth Dr
Gray Summit MO 63039

(G-7773)
QGIV INC
53 Lake Morton Dr (33801-5340)
PHONE..................................888 855-9595
Todd Baylis, *President*
Stephen W Baylis, *Principal*
Abby Jarvis, *Mktg Dir*
Trevor Hillsgrove, *Software Engr*
EMP: 39 **EST:** 2005
SALES (est): 4.8MM **Privately Held**
WEB: www.qgiv.com
SIC: 7372 Business oriented computer software

(G-7774)
QUALITY AEROSPACE COATINGS LLC
3610 Airport Rd (33811-1002)
PHONE..................................863 619-2628
John Creasy, *Principal*
EMP: 7 **EST:** 2008
SALES (est): 500K **Privately Held**
WEB: www.quality-aero.com
SIC: 3479 Coating of metals & formed products

(G-7775)
QUIKRETE COMPANIES LLC
4230 Maine Ave (33801-9785)
P.O. Box 778, Eaton Park (33840-0778)
PHONE..................................863 665-5127
Brian Cronin, *Branch Mgr*
Donald Long, *Director*
EMP: 55
SQ FT: 19,960 **Privately Held**
WEB: www.quikrete.com
SIC: 3272 Concrete products
HQ: The Quikrete Companies Llc
5 Concourse Pkwy Ste 1900
Atlanta GA 30328
404 634-9100

(G-7776)
RAPID METAL PRODUCTS INC
4257 Holden Rd (33811-2837)
PHONE..................................863 701-0058
Kirk D Balliette, *President*
Douglas M Foust, *Vice Pres*
Terry L Wisniewski, *Vice Pres*
Bryan Finch, *Technician*
EMP: 35 **EST:** 1998
SQ FT: 18,000
SALES (est): 6.3MM **Privately Held**
WEB: www.rapidmetalproducts.com
SIC: 3444 Sheet metalwork

(G-7777)
REDEAGLE INTERNATIONAL LLC
Also Called: Redeag Le
5143 S Lakeland Dr Ste 4 (33813-2589)
PHONE..................................863 682-6698
Rhett Atkins, *General Mgr*
Bala Marimuthu, *Business Dir*
Yingxue Yu,
▲ **EMP:** 9 **EST:** 2008
SALES (est): 1.4MM **Privately Held**
WEB: www.redeagleinternational.com
SIC: 2879 Agricultural disinfectants

(G-7778)
RESTORATION MEDICAL LLC
5235 Nichols Dr E (33812-4077)
PHONE..................................863 272-0250
Kurt Stefan,
EMP: 5 **EST:** 2015
SQ FT: 1,200
SALES (est): 1.4MM **Privately Held**
WEB: www.restorationmedical.com
SIC: 3842 Surgical appliances & supplies

(G-7779)
RING POWER CORPORATION
Also Called: Ring Lift
3425 Reynolds Rd (33803-8331)
PHONE..................................863 606-0512
Chris Hobbs, *Branch Mgr*
EMP: 8
SALES (corp-wide): 1B **Privately Held**
WEB: www.ringpower.com
SIC: 3537 5084 Forklift trucks; materials handling machinery
HQ: Ring Power Corporation
500 World Commerce Pkwy
Saint Augustine FL 32092
904 201-7400

(G-7780)
ROBINSON FANS INC
3955 Drane Field Rd (33811-1289)
PHONE..................................724 452-6121
Dustin Moskal, *Editor*
Tim Velte, *Prdtn Mgr*
Jason Welch, *Foreman/Supr*
Vicky Leonberg, *Buyer*
Carol Meeder, *Buyer*
EMP: 35 **Privately Held**
WEB: www.robinsonfans.com
SIC: 3564 Blowers & fans
HQ: Robinson Fans, Inc.
400 Robinson Dr
Zelienople PA 16063
863 646-5270

(G-7781)
ROCKFORD ETTCO PROCUNIER INC
304 Winston Creek Pkwy (33810-2866)
PHONE..................................863 688-0071
Mary Bull, *President*
William S Mele, *Vice Pres*
Ben Hall, *Materials Mgr*
Susan Caldwell, *Admin Sec*
EMP: 16 **EST:** 1917
SQ FT: 30,000
SALES (est): 2.5MM **Privately Held**
WEB: www.rockford-ettco.com
SIC: 3541 Tapping machines

(G-7782)
RUBINGERS MANUFACTURING CO
2626 Mine And Mill Ln (33801-7607)
P.O. Box 1381, Eaton Park (33840-1381)
PHONE..................................863 665-1599
John R Nightlinger Jr, *President*
Ruby Nightlinger, *Corp Secy*
Christopher R Nightlinger, *Vice Pres*
EMP: 10 **EST:** 1979
SQ FT: 21,000
SALES (est): 1.6MM **Privately Held**
WEB: www.rubingers.com
SIC: 3599 Machine shop, jobbing & repair

(G-7783)
S & B METAL PRODUCTS S FLA INC (PA)
5301 Gateway Blvd (33811-1735)
PHONE..................................941 727-3669
Paul R Balliette, *CEO*
Stephen R Campbell, *President*
Ethan Maskolunas, *General Mgr*
Joseph Pateos, *General Mgr*
Philip Skeen, *Accounts Mgr*
EMP: 40 **EST:** 1991
SQ FT: 15,000
SALES (est): 41.5MM **Privately Held**
SIC: 3444 Sheet metalwork

(G-7784)
SAFETY ZONE SPECIALISTS INC
2318 Old Combee Rd 107 (33805-7520)
P.O. Box 90764 (33804-0764)
PHONE..................................863 984-1385
David Vespa, *President*
EMP: 6 **EST:** 1992
SALES (est): 885.7K **Privately Held**
WEB: www.gotchen.com
SIC: 3499 3699 Barricades, metal; trouble lights

(G-7785)
SAMSON METAL AND MACHINE INC (PA)
3225 Us Highway 92 E (33801-9679)
P.O. Box 1586 (33802-1586)
PHONE..................................863 665-0283
Barak Samson, *President*
Nathan Samson, *Vice Pres*
Carolyn S Stewart, *Vice Pres*
Carol Halstead, *Controller*
Carol Lacey, *Human Res Mgr*
EMP: 34 **EST:** 1947
SQ FT: 100,000
SALES (est): 3.7MM **Privately Held**
WEB: www.samsonmetal.com
SIC: 3599 Machine shop, jobbing & repair

(G-7786)
SANDALE UTILITY PRODUCTS
2515 Commerce Point Dr (33801-6803)
PHONE..................................863 937-5208
EMP: 5 **EST:** 2016
SALES (est): 408.7K **Privately Held**
WEB: www.sandale.ca
SIC: 3824 Fluid meters & counting devices

(G-7787)
SANITUBE LLC (PA)
180 Contractors Way (33801-6356)
P.O. Box 2447, Eaton Park (33840-2447)
PHONE..................................863 606-5960
Houston Sigmund, *Prdtn Mgr*
Ronald Pack, *Opers Staff*
Tanya Wilson, *Credit Mgr*
Marty Coggins, *Natl Sales Mgr*
Todd Wilson, *VP Sales*
EMP: 18 **EST:** 2010
SQ FT: 100,000
SALES (est): 10MM **Privately Held**
WEB: www.sanitube.us
SIC: 3317 Steel pipe & tubes

(G-7788)
SCHWARZ PARTNERS PACKAGING LLC
Maxpak
2808 New Tampa Hwy (33815-3438)
PHONE..................................863 682-0123
Kevin Bailey, *General Mgr*
EMP: 135
SALES (corp-wide): 215.2MM **Privately Held**
WEB: www.teamtrg.com
SIC: 2653 Boxes, corrugated: made from purchased materials
PA: Schwarz Partners Packaging, Llc
3600 Woodview Trce # 300
Indianapolis IN 46268
317 290-1140

(G-7789)
SHAIKH RIZWAN
Also Called: Leatherjacket4
316 N Canal Ave (33801-2460)
PHONE..................................202 740-9796
Rizwan Shaikh, *Owner*
EMP: 5 **EST:** 2019
SALES (est): 500K **Privately Held**
WEB: www.leatherjacket4.com
SIC: 2386 Leather & sheep-lined clothing

(G-7790)
SHED4LESS LLC
3147 Us Highway 98 S (33803-7372)
PHONE..................................863 660-7300
Alicia B Wood, *Principal*
EMP: 6 **EST:** 2015
SALES (est): 920.9K **Privately Held**
WEB: www.shed4less.com
SIC: 3448 Prefabricated metal buildings

(G-7791)
SHOWCASE PUBLICATIONS INC
Also Called: Auto Shopper
1211 E Main St (33801-5773)
PHONE..................................863 687-4377
Fax: 863 682-5098
EMP: 50
SALES (est): 5.1MM
SALES (corp-wide): 7.7MM **Privately Held**
SIC: 2721 7313 Periodicals-Publishing/Printing Advertising Representative
PA: Showcase Publications, Inc.
90 Irons St
Toms River NJ
732 349-1134

(G-7792)
SLAPPEY COMMUNICATIONS LLC
Also Called: Presidium
624 Midflorida Dr (33813-4901)
PHONE..................................863 619-5600
EMP: 9
SALES (corp-wide): 4.4MM **Privately Held**
WEB: www.slappey.com
SIC: 7372 Prepackaged software
PA: Slappey Communications, Llc
4260 Cahaba Heights Ct
Vestavia AL 35243
205 970-4209

(G-7793)
SMC DIVERSIFIED SERVICES INC
Also Called: Florida Applied Films
7120 Regent Dr (33810-4710)
PHONE..................................863 698-9696
Shayne Cheney, *President*
EMP: 9 **EST:** 1995
SALES (est): 400K **Privately Held**
WEB: www.floridaappliedfilms.com
SIC: 2752 Decals, lithographed

(G-7794)
SMITH CHALLENGER MFG SVCS INC
3434 Waterfield Rd (33803-9703)
PHONE..................................863 248-2624
Betty J Smith, *President*
Loni Smith, *Treasurer*
EMP: 15 **EST:** 2009
SALES (est): 2.4MM **Privately Held**
WEB: www.smithchallenger.com
SIC: 3531 Construction machinery

(G-7795)
SMITH EQUIPMENT & SUPPLY CO
3825 Maine Ave (33801-9779)
PHONE..................................863 665-4904
James H Smith, *Ch of Bd*
Ginger L Smith, *President*
Keith E Smith, *Senior VP*
Karey J Smith, *Vice Pres*
Dawn Oeters, *Manager*
▲ **EMP:** 37
SQ FT: 26,000
SALES (est): 7.3MM **Privately Held**
WEB: www.smith-equipment.com
SIC: 3991 3589 Brooms & brushes; dirt sweeping units, industrial

(G-7796)
SOLARA INDUSTRIES INC
Also Called: Remodeling Guys, The
4190 Waring Rd (33811-2857)
PHONE..................................863 688-3330

Edward G Bloom, *President*
Charlotte M Bloom, *Corp Secy*
▲ **EMP:** 20 **EST:** 2013
SALES (est): 2.2MM **Privately Held**
WEB: www.solaraindustries.com
SIC: 3446 8748 Balconies, metal; business consulting

(G-7797)
SOLID START INC
2801 Saluda Rd (33801-6335)
PHONE..................................863 937-9297
Amber Lerrall Kossak, *President*
Crystal Matthews, *President*
Fred Pascarella, *Vice Pres*
Freddy Pascarella, *Vice Pres*
Jason Whitaker, *Plant Mgr*
EMP: 20 **EST:** 2010
SALES (est): 2.6MM **Privately Held**
WEB: www.solidstart.com
SIC: 3559 Automotive maintenance equipment

(G-7798)
SOUTHEASTERN PAPER GROUP INC
7080 Havertys Way (33805-1413)
PHONE..................................864 574-0440
Mitchell Harris, *Opers Staff*
Gordon Back, *Sales Staff*
Louis Miller, *Manager*
EMP: 221
SALES (corp-wide): 1.2B **Privately Held**
WEB: www.sepg.com
SIC: 3554 Paper industries machinery
HQ: Southeastern Paper Group, Llc
50 Old Blackstock Rd
Spartanburg SC 29301
800 858-7230

(G-7799)
SOUTHERN AUTOMATED SYSTEMS
3730 N Galloway Rd (33810-0679)
PHONE..................................863 815-7444
George Aycock, *President*
Teresa Aycock, *Treasurer*
EMP: 5 **EST:** 2000
SQ FT: 1,000
SALES (est): 697.9K **Privately Held**
WEB: www.sasoncall.com
SIC: 3625 Electric controls & control accessories, industrial

(G-7800)
SOUTHERN BAKERIES INC (HQ)
Also Called: Butterkrust Bakeries
3355 W Memorial Blvd (33815-1084)
P.O. Box 1707 (33802-1707)
PHONE..................................863 682-1155
Doug Wimberly, *President*
Rob Hancock, *Vice Pres*
Teresa Bass, *Director*
Shea Brock, *Executive*
EMP: 250 **EST:** 1950
SALES (est): 65.8MM
SALES (corp-wide): 4.3B **Publicly Held**
WEB: www.lakelandedc.com
SIC: 2051 5149 Bread, all types (white, wheat, rye, etc): fresh or frozen; bakery products
PA: Flowers Foods, Inc.
1919 Flowers Cir
Thomasville GA 31757
912 226-9110

(G-7801)
SOUTHERN SOFTWOODS INC
2425 Lasso Ln (33801-9733)
PHONE..................................863 666-1404
Shakir Wissa, *President*
Karen Park, *Admin Sec*
▼ **EMP:** 50 **EST:** 1991
SALES (est): 3.4MM **Privately Held**
SIC: 2499 Mulch, wood & bark

(G-7802)
SOUTHERN-BARTLETT INTL LLC
4070 S Pipkin Rd (33811-1849)
PHONE..................................407 374-1613
Christopher Vitito, *President*
EMP: 12 **EST:** 2009
SALES (est): 426.3K **Privately Held**
SIC: 3199 Aprons: welders', blacksmiths', etc.: leather

(G-7803)
SPECIALTY FABRICATION LLC
4015 Drane Field Rd (33811-1290)
PHONE..................................863 683-0708
Samantha Morgan, *Project Mgr*
Earl Hissem, *QC Mgr*
Clayton Cook, *Manager*
Randy Raborn, *Manager*
Hosler L Wall,
EMP: 27 **EST:** 2017
SALES (est): 15.8MM **Privately Held**
WEB: www.specialtyfabllc.com
SIC: 3449 Miscellaneous metalwork

(G-7804)
SPECIALTY MAINTENANCE & CONSTR
4121 Drane Field Rd (33811-1291)
PHONE..................................863 644-8432
EMP: 9 **EST:** 2019
SALES (est): 846.5K **Privately Held**
SIC: 3498 Fabricated pipe & fittings

(G-7805)
STAYSEALED INC
3454 Airfield Dr W (33811-1240)
PHONE..................................866 978-2973
Kenneth H Willaford, *President*
EMP: 9 **EST:** 2012
SALES (est): 141.9K **Privately Held**
SIC: 3443 Fuel tanks (oil, gas, etc.): metal plate

(G-7806)
STEEL TECHNOLOGY & DESIGN
401 Howard Ave Apt C (33815-3400)
PHONE..................................863 665-2525
Daniel Perkins, *President*
Tom Davis, *Vice Pres*
Dave Keen, *Purchasing*
▼ **EMP:** 16 **EST:** 1989
SALES (est): 587.4K **Privately Held**
WEB: www.steeltechnologyanddesign.com
SIC: 3448 Trusses & framing: prefabricated metal

(G-7807)
STERIPACK (USA) LIMITED LLC
4255 S Pipkin Rd (33811-1442)
PHONE..................................863 648-2333
Tony Paolino, *President*
Gary Leonard, *VP Opers*
Aamir Shaikh, *Engineer*
Robert Del Mastro, *CFO*
Ana Williams, *Human Res Mgr*
◆ **EMP:** 50 **EST:** 2012
SQ FT: 40,000
SALES (est): 13.7MM
SALES (corp-wide): 2.2MM **Privately Held**
WEB: www.steripackgroup.com
SIC: 3841 5047 Medical instruments & equipment, blood & bone work; hospital equipment & supplies
HQ: Nelipak Healthcare Packaging Ireland Limited
Kilbeggan Road
Clara R35 F

(G-7808)
STONE CENTER INC
2205 E Edgewood Dr (33803-3605)
P.O. Box 1115, Eaton Park (33840-1115)
PHONE..................................863 669-0292
David Beck, *President*
EMP: 10 **EST:** 1991
SALES (est): 1.5MM **Privately Held**
WEB: www.stonecenterinc.vpweb.com
SIC: 1411 Dimension stone

(G-7809)
STYLE CREST PRODUCTS
5001 Gateway Blvd Ste 14 (33811-2715)
PHONE..................................863 709-8735
Tom Kern, *President*
EMP: 7 **EST:** 1986
SALES (est): 706.8K **Privately Held**
WEB: www.stylecrestinc.com
SIC: 3714 Transmission housings or parts, motor vehicle

(G-7810)
SUN PUBLICATIONS FLORIDA INC (HQ)
Also Called: Osceola Shopper
7060 Havertys Way (33805-1413)
PHONE..................................863 583-1202
Dennis Wilkinson, *COO*
Maurice Maisonville, *Plant Mgr*
Chris A Tiffer, *CFO*
Roger Vanegas, *Manager*
EMP: 50 **EST:** 2003
SQ FT: 40,000
SALES (est): 13.7MM **Privately Held**
WEB: www.sunpubfla.com
SIC: 2741 Miscellaneous publishing
PA: Lakeway Publishers Of Florida, Inc
1609 W 1st North St
Morristown TN 37814
423 581-5630

(G-7811)
SUNCOAST WELDING & FABRICATION
900 Old Combee Rd (33805-9508)
PHONE..................................254 537-3611
Matt Langston, *Principal*
EMP: 7 **EST:** 2016
SALES (est): 77K **Privately Held**
SIC: 7692 Welding repair

(G-7812)
SUNSHINE CAP COMPANY
1142 W Main St (33815-4362)
PHONE..................................863 688-8147
Jordan Cokee, *President*
Matthew Cokee, *Vice Pres*
EMP: 10 **EST:** 1977
SQ FT: 14,000
SALES (est): 291.6K **Privately Held**
SIC: 2353 Caps: cloth, straw & felt

(G-7813)
SUREWELD WELDING INC
3050 W Socrum Loop Rd (33810-0328)
PHONE..................................813 918-1857
Melissa Coe, *CEO*
EMP: 20 **EST:** 1998
SALES (est): 1.1MM **Privately Held**
SIC: 7692 Welding repair

(G-7814)
SWEET & SALTSY SCRUBS
1854 Kinsman Way (33809-5087)
PHONE..................................863 853-8874
Jessica Rouleau, *Principal*
EMP: 6 **EST:** 2013
SALES (est): 143.8K **Privately Held**
SIC: 2844 Toilet preparations

(G-7815)
T&S KITCHEN AND BBQ LLC ✪
4798 S Florida Ave 235 (33813-2181)
PHONE..................................863 608-6223
Terrance Howell, *CEO*
Sonja F Howel, *Mng Member*
EMP: 6 **EST:** 2020
SALES (est): 185.1K **Privately Held**
SIC: 2099 Food preparations

(G-7816)
TASTE ADVANTAGE LLC
3135 Drane Feld Rd Ste 22 (33811)
PHONE..................................863 619-8101
Donald Dawson, *Office Mgr*
Tony Willard,
Henry Todd Sr,
EMP: 6 **EST:** 2006
SALES (est): 1.1MM
SALES (corp-wide): 9.4MM **Privately Held**
WEB: www.natadv.com
SIC: 2087 Flavoring extracts & syrups
PA: Natural Advantage, Llc
1050 Cypress Creek Rd
Oakdale LA 71463
318 215-1456

(G-7817)
TASTEFUL DELIGHT LLC ✪
1919 W 10th St Apt 43 (33805-3389)
PHONE..................................305 879-6487
Tanisha Hobbs,
EMP: 10 **EST:** 2021
SALES (est): 90K **Privately Held**
SIC: 2099 Food preparations

(G-7818)
TEAM HAMMER SCREEN PRINTING
2328 E Main St (33801-2666)
PHONE..................................863 666-1108
Ed Hammerbuger, *President*
EMP: 5 **EST:** 1991
SQ FT: 4,500
SALES (est): 500K **Privately Held**
WEB: www.teamhammerfl.com
SIC: 2211 Print cloths, cotton

(G-7819)
TECHNICAL COMPONENTS INC (PA)
3901 Industry Blvd Ste 6 (33811-1387)
P.O. Box 7178 (33807-7178)
PHONE..................................863 646-3253
Robert K Henning, *President*
Robert J Shemansky, *Vice Pres*
EMP: 5 **EST:** 1988
SQ FT: 2,800
SALES (est): 638.5K **Privately Held**
SIC: 3599 Machine shop, jobbing & repair

(G-7820)
THERMO COMPACTION SYSTEMS INC
5001 Gateway Blvd Ste 22 (33811-2715)
PHONE..................................863 370-3799
William C Major, *President*
EMP: 7 **EST:** 2009
SALES (est): 145K **Privately Held**
WEB: www.moose-herring-ffhe.squarespace.com
SIC: 2821 Plastics materials & resins

(G-7821)
THOMAS SMITH & COMPANY INC
3828 Knights Station Rd (33810-2548)
PHONE..................................863 858-2199
Thomas C Smith, *President*
EMP: 19 **EST:** 1953
SQ FT: 760
SALES (est): 1.3MM **Privately Held**
SIC: 3444 1761 1721 Metal roofing & roof drainage equipment; roofing & gutter work; residential painting

(G-7822)
TITANIUM REAL ESTATE LLC
1543 Lakeland Hills Blvd (33805-3246)
PHONE..................................863 808-0445
Kerry J Nice Jr, *Principal*
Kerry Nice, *Broker*
EMP: 5 **EST:** 2018
SALES (est): 409.9K **Privately Held**
WEB: www.titaniumlakeland.com
SIC: 3356 Titanium

(G-7823)
TOM BURKE SERVICES
6244 Troi Ln (33813-3752)
PHONE..................................863 940-4504
Thomas Burke, *Principal*
EMP: 6 **EST:** 2006
SALES (est): 294.5K **Privately Held**
SIC: 3545 Drilling machine attachments & accessories

(G-7824)
TOOGLE INDUSTRIES LLC
127 N Lake Parker Ave (33801-2164)
PHONE..................................863 688-8975
Anthony Escapa, *Mng Member*
EMP: 5 **EST:** 2019
SALES (est): 395.7K **Privately Held**
WEB: www.toggle.is
SIC: 3999 7539 Manufacturing industries; automotive repair shops

(G-7825)
TRENWA INC
1920 Longhorn Ave (33801-9770)
PHONE..................................863 666-1680
Kim Greene, *Project Mgr*
Austin Riggs, *Project Mgr*
Elliott Schurr, *Project Mgr*
Dan Key, *Opers-Prdtn-Mfg*
Rebecca Whitaker, *QC Mgr*
EMP: 16

SALES (corp-wide): 19.2MM **Privately Held**
WEB: www.trenwa.com
SIC: 3272 5211 Concrete products, pre-cast; masonry materials & supplies
PA: Trenwa, Inc.
1419 Alexandria Pike
Fort Thomas KY 41075
859 781-0831

(G-7826)
TRIUMPH TRANSPORT INC
1104 Bartow Rd Apt 173 (33801-5866)
PHONE..................................863 226-7276
Young Laster Jr, *Owner*
EMP: 8 **EST:** 2019
SALES (est): 263.9K **Privately Held**
SIC: 3799 Transportation equipment

(G-7827)
TWS CABINETS LLC
2947 Vermont Ave (33803-8348)
PHONE..................................863 614-4693
Timmy W Sanquenetti, *Branch Mgr*
EMP: 10
SALES (corp-wide): 72.1K **Privately Held**
SIC: 2434 Wood kitchen cabinets
PA: Tws Cabinets Llc
910 E Memorial Blvd # 1303
Lakeland FL 33801
812 201-3201

(G-7828)
UNIVERSAL DIE SERVICES INC
2646 Lasso Ln (33801-9769)
PHONE..................................863 665-6092
Scott A Farrington, *President*
▼ **EMP:** 5 **EST:** 2005
SALES (est): 410.3K **Privately Held**
SIC: 3544 Special dies & tools

(G-7829)
VALIANT PRODUCTS INC
939 Quincy St (33815-1337)
P.O. Box 405 (33802-0405)
PHONE..................................863 688-7998
Robert F English, *CEO*
Jason Turner, *General Mgr*
John Harris, *Engineer*
Joel Watkins, *Engineer*
Stephen Maxey, *Design Engr*
EMP: 32
SQ FT: 20,000
SALES (est): 4.1MM **Privately Held**
WEB: www.valiantproductsinc.com
SIC: 3443 2542 3442 Chutes, metal plate; lockers (not refrigerated): except wood; shutters, door or window: metal

(G-7830)
VIP SOFTWARE CORPORATION
6000 S Florida Ave # 6832 (33807-8001)
P.O. Box 531826, Saint Petersburg (33747-1826)
PHONE..................................813 837-4347
James Makris, *President*
Michael Battis, *Sales Executive*
EMP: 11 **EST:** 2013
SQ FT: 2,500
SALES (est): 555.6K **Privately Held**
WEB: www.vipsoftware.com
SIC: 7372 7371 Business oriented computer software; computer software development & applications

(G-7831)
WALLER PAVERS INC
4909 Tradition Dr (33812-3157)
PHONE..................................863 644-8187
David R Waller, *Principal*
EMP: 6 **EST:** 2009
SALES (est): 751.7K **Privately Held**
WEB: www.wallerpavers.com
SIC: 3531 Pavers

(G-7832)
WASTEQUIP MANUFACTURING CO LLC
2624 Mine And Mill Ln (33801-7607)
PHONE..................................863 665-6507
Bill Haynes, *Vice Pres*
Thomas Kaltenbaugn, *Manager*
EMP: 20
SQ FT: 8,000 **Privately Held**
WEB: www.wastequip.com
SIC: 3443 3469 3411 5064 Dumpsters, garbage; metal stampings; metal cans; garbage disposals; garbage disposers & compactors, commercial
HQ: Wastequip Manufacturing Company Llc
6525 Morrison Blvd # 300
Charlotte NC 28211

(G-7833)
WE MAKE VITAMINS LLC
2715 Badger Rd (33811-1348)
PHONE..................................863 607-6708
Cameron Novak, *CEO*
EMP: 8 **EST:** 2018
SALES (est): 1.2MM **Privately Held**
WEB: www.wemakevitamins.com
SIC: 2833 Vitamins, natural or synthetic: bulk, uncompounded

(G-7834)
WILKERSON INSTRUMENT CO INC
2915 Parkway St (33811-1391)
P.O. Box 6986 (33807-6986)
PHONE..................................863 647-2000
Rick Huffman, *President*
Bill Wilkerson, *President*
Ted Marshall, *Accounting Mgr*
Leslie Cox, *Manager*
EMP: 16 **EST:** 1983
SQ FT: 14,000
SALES (est): 2.3MM **Privately Held**
WEB: www.wici.com
SIC: 3823 Industrial instrmnts msrmnt display/control process variable

(G-7835)
WILLIAM BURNS
Also Called: Radiant Printing
1800 Via Lago Dr (33810-2341)
PHONE..................................877 462-5872
William Burns, *Owner*
Jonathan Reyes, *Creative Dir*
EMP: 8 **EST:** 2015
SALES (est): 661K **Privately Held**
SIC: 2752 Commercial printing, offset

Lakewood Ranch
Manatee County

(G-7836)
AMERICAN ACCOUNTING ASSN
9009 Town Center Pkwy # 104 (34202-4257)
PHONE..................................941 921-7747
Susan Crosson, *Vice Chairman*
Ginger White, *COO*
Connie O 'brien, *Accountant*
Michelle Russak, *Accountant*
Stephanie Austin, *Manager*
▼ **EMP:** 25
SQ FT: 5,000
SALES: 10.3MM **Privately Held**
WEB: www.aaahq.org
SIC: 2721 2731 Magazines: publishing only, not printed on site; books: publishing only

(G-7837)
BIG MAN FRIENDLY TRNSP LLC ✪
11161 State Road 70 E # 1 (34202-9407)
PHONE..................................941 229-3454
George Hegamin,
EMP: 7 **EST:** 2021
SALES (est): 305.4K **Privately Held**
SIC: 3537 Trucks: freight, baggage, etc.: industrial, except mining

(G-7838)
ENOZO TECHNOLOGIES INC ✪
8470 Enterprise Cir (34202-4102)
PHONE..................................512 944-7772
Wayne Lieberman, *CEO*
EMP: 8 **EST:** 2020
SALES (est): 646.9K **Privately Held**
WEB: www.enozo.com
SIC: 2842 Specialty cleaning, polishes & sanitation goods

(G-7839)
INTERNATIONAL VAULT INC
16227 Daysailor Trl (34202-5617)
PHONE..................................941 390-4505
Stephen G Lask, *CEO*
EMP: 40 **EST:** 2018
SALES (est): 2MM **Privately Held**
WEB: www.internationalvault.com
SIC: 3499 Fabricated metal products

(G-7840)
MANATEE SMOOTHIES LLC
1161 E State Road 70 (34202)
PHONE..................................985 640-3088
Christopher A Thomas, *Principal*
EMP: 8 **EST:** 2012
SALES (est): 373K **Privately Held**
SIC: 2037 Frozen fruits & vegetables

(G-7841)
SMR AGGREGATES INC
14400 Covenant Way (34202-8900)
PHONE..................................941 907-0041
Eugene Henshaw, *President*
EMP: 34 **EST:** 1982
SALES (est): 3.6MM **Privately Held**
WEB: www.lakewoodranch.com
SIC: 1442 1499 Construction sand mining; shell mining

Lakewood Ranch
Sarasota County

(G-7842)
CAPTAINS CUSTOM TEES INC
2417 Lkwood Rnch Blvd N U (34240-7035)
PHONE..................................239 424-8206
EMP: 6 **EST:** 2019
SALES (est): 399.3K **Privately Held**
SIC: 2759 Screen printing

(G-7843)
DISCOVERY TECHNOLOGY INTL INC (HQ)
6700 Professional Pkwy (34240-8444)
PHONE..................................941 907-4444
Mark Broderick, *President*
Nic Copley, *VP Bus Dvlpt*
Valentin Zhelyaskov, *Development*
EMP: 19 **EST:** 2004
SALES (est): 3.4MM **Privately Held**
WEB: www.discovtech.com
SIC: 3621 Motors, electric
PA: Piezo Motion Corp.
6700 Professional Pkwy
Lakewood Ranch FL 34240
941 907-4444

(G-7844)
INVO BIOSCIENCE INC
5582 Broadcast Ct (34240-8471)
PHONE..................................978 878-9505
Steven Shum, *CEO*
Kathleen Karloff, *Ch of Bd*
Michael J Campbell, *COO*
Inger B Carlsson, *Vice Pres*
Andrea Goren, *CFO*
EMP: 5 **EST:** 2005
SQ FT: 1,223
SALES: 1MM **Privately Held**
WEB: www.invobioscience.com
SIC: 3841 Surgical & medical instruments

(G-7845)
LUMOS DIAGNOSTICS INC
7040 Prof Pkwy Ste B (34240)
PHONE..................................941 556-1850
Sacha Dopheide, *CEO*
Randall Ross, *Finance*
Thao Phillips, *Senior Mgr*
James Lulo, *Director*
Huan Tran, *Director*
EMP: 31 **Privately Held**
WEB: www.lumosdiagnostics.com
SIC: 2835 In vitro diagnostics
HQ: Lumos Diagnostics, Inc.
2724 Loker Ave W
Carlsbad CA 92010
760 683-5374

(G-7846)
SASQUATCH CABINET COMPANY
6841 Energy Ct (34240-8523)
PHONE..................................941 365-4950
Lawrence M Hankin, *President*
EMP: 9 **EST:** 2001
SALES (est): 118.3K **Privately Held**
SIC: 2434 Wood kitchen cabinets

(G-7847)
STEWART-HEDRICK INC
Also Called: Palm Printing
6001 Business Blvd (34240-8410)
PHONE..................................941 907-0090
Randy J Hedrick, *President*
Nicole Hedrick, *CFO*
Renee Phinney, *VP Sales*
Charles Zweil, *VP Sales*
▲ **EMP:** 26 **EST:** 1988
SQ FT: 15,000
SALES (est): 4.8MM **Privately Held**
SIC: 2752 Commercial printing, offset

Lanark Village
Franklin County

(G-7848)
AMERICAN SHIELD LLC
644 Oak St (32323)
P.O. Box 1359 (32323-1359)
PHONE..................................850 697-3066
Paul Rohrs, *Principal*
EMP: 7 **EST:** 2004
SALES (est): 164K **Privately Held**
SIC: 3211 Window glass, clear & colored

Land O Lakes
Pasco County

(G-7849)
ARCHITCTRAL SGNAGE SYSTEMS INC
6812 Land O Lakes Blvd (34638-3227)
PHONE..................................813 996-6777
Jonathan Fischer, *Principal*
Heather Kearney, *Production*
EMP: 5 **EST:** 1984
SQ FT: 3,551
SALES (est): 496.9K **Privately Held**
WEB: www.signsbyasap.com
SIC: 3993 Signs & advertising specialties

(G-7850)
BLACK BEAN SOFTWARE LLC
21652 Cormorant Cove Dr (34637-7531)
PHONE..................................727 420-6916
Vicki Kammeier, *Manager*
EMP: 6 **EST:** 2010
SALES (est): 201.7K **Privately Held**
WEB: www.blackbeansoftware.com
SIC: 7372 Prepackaged software

(G-7851)
COLLIER PARKWAY FUEL LLC
3402 Sheehan Dr (34638-8038)
PHONE..................................732 492-4791
Joanne Krepela, *Principal*
EMP: 6 **EST:** 2012
SALES (est): 160.9K **Privately Held**
SIC: 2869 Fuels

(G-7852)
DESIGN SERVICES INC
2200 Knight Rd (34639-5107)
P.O. Box 1789 (34639-1789)
PHONE..................................813 949-4748
Jane Cetrangolo, *President*
Dave Cetrangolo, *Vice Pres*
Liberty Puckett, *Asst Sec*
▲ **EMP:** 8 **EST:** 1984
SQ FT: 4,000
SALES (est): 1.1MM **Privately Held**
WEB: www.industrialgeneralstore.com
SIC: 3953 5131 Stencils, painting & marking; ribbons

(G-7853)
EMC TICKETING LLC
8409 Land O Lakes Blvd (34638-5810)
PHONE..................................813 792-1234

Miriam Kent, *Principal*
EMP: 6 **EST:** 2013
SALES (est): 152.5K **Privately Held**
WEB: www.emctickets.com
SIC: 3572 Computer storage devices

(G-7854)
EXPRESS PRINTING CENTER INC
2355 Raden Dr (34639-5137)
PHONE..................................813 909-1085
John Towson, *President*
Betty Whitaker, *Officer*
EMP: 10 **EST:** 1983
SQ FT: 5,000
SALES (est): 1.8MM **Privately Held**
WEB: www.expprinting.com
SIC: 2752 2759 Commercial printing, offset; business forms: printing

(G-7855)
FIND A FRIEND LLC
Also Called: Qrpetcodes.com
3318 Russett Pl (34638-7725)
PHONE..................................813 293-1584
William Ashby, *Mng Member*
EMP: 6 **EST:** 2012
SALES (est): 10K **Privately Held**
SIC: 2399 7389 Pet collars, leashes, etc.: non-leather; business services

(G-7856)
IN THE LOOP BREWING INC
3338 Land O Lakes Blvd (34639-4408)
PHONE..................................813 857-0111
Peter Abreut, *Principal*
EMP: 8 **EST:** 2016
SALES (est): 372.7K **Privately Held**
WEB: www.intheloopbrewingcompany.com
SIC: 2082 Malt beverages

(G-7857)
IT IS FINISHED INC
24851 Ravello St (34639-6316)
PHONE..................................813 598-9585
Vernon Butler, *Vice Pres*
EMP: 5 **EST:** 2005
SALES (est): 503.1K **Privately Held**
WEB: www.itisfinishednow.com
SIC: 2426 Flooring, hardwood

(G-7858)
JAG STUCCO INC
4047 Marlow Loop (34639-4071)
PHONE..................................813 210-6577
Kimberly Orr, *Principal*
EMP: 6 **EST:** 2009
SALES (est): 242.4K **Privately Held**
SIC: 3299 Stucco

(G-7859)
LAND O LAKES WINERY LLC
3901 Land O Lakes Blvd (34639-4421)
PHONE..................................813 995-9463
Susan Hardy,
Corey Kempton,
EMP: 6 **EST:** 2015
SQ FT: 3,200
SALES (est): 354.3K **Privately Held**
WEB: www.landolakeswinery.com
SIC: 2084 Wines

(G-7860)
M30 FREEDOM INC
Also Called: Real Producers
4018 Stornoway Dr (34638-7801)
PHONE..................................813 433-1776
Donald Hill, *Principal*
EMP: 6 **EST:** 2017
SALES (est): 267.4K **Privately Held**
WEB: www.realproducersmag.com
SIC: 2741 Miscellaneous publishing

(G-7861)
MANATEE MEDIA INC
Also Called: Community News Publications
3632 Land O Lakes Blvd (34639-4405)
P.O. Box 479, Lutz (33548-0479)
PHONE..................................813 909-2800
Diane Kortus, *President*
Diane Mathes, *President*
Mark Mathes, *Vice Pres*
EMP: 12 **EST:** 1999
SALES (est): 784.4K **Privately Held**
WEB: www.manateemedia.com
SIC: 2741 Miscellaneous publishing

(G-7862)
MERRITT MFG LLC
2347 Foggy Ridge Pkwy (34639-5414)
PHONE..................................407 481-1074
Al Erturk, *President*
Deborah Erturk, *Admin Sec*
EMP: 7 **EST:** 2007
SALES (est): 132.6K **Privately Held**
WEB: www.merrittmfg.com
SIC: 3564 Blowers & fans

(G-7863)
PRODUCT MAX GROUP INC
Also Called: Body Action Products
8011 Land O Lakes Blvd (34638-5802)
P.O. Box 1188 (34639-1188)
PHONE..................................813 949-5061
Joey L Jennings, *President*
Christine A Altigilbers, *Vice Pres*
EMP: 5 **EST:** 1999
SALES (est): 494.7K **Privately Held**
WEB: www.pinkprivates.org
SIC: 2844 Face creams or lotions

(G-7864)
PROSHOWMAKER INC
2310 Foggy Ridge Pkwy (34639-5411)
PHONE..................................813 765-2676
Tim Pickens, *Principal*
EMP: 8 **EST:** 2010
SALES (est): 123.7K **Privately Held**
SIC: 3088 Tubs (bath, shower & laundry), plastic

(G-7865)
SANDS MOLDING INC
23324 Gracewood Cir (34639-4947)
PHONE..................................813 345-8646
Jacqueline M Campbell, *Principal*
EMP: 6 **EST:** 2008
SALES (est): 82.6K **Privately Held**
SIC: 3089 Molding primary plastic

(G-7866)
SGF INC
3018 Joan Ct (34639-4608)
P.O. Box 1999 (34639-1999)
PHONE..................................813 996-2528
William Fotopoulos, *President*
EMP: 6 **EST:** 1992
SQ FT: 2,800
SALES (est): 104.3K **Privately Held**
SIC: 3949 Bows, archery

(G-7867)
TEAREPAIR INC
2223 Knight Rd (34639-5111)
P.O. Box 1879 (34639-1879)
PHONE..................................813 948-6898
David Cetrangolo, *President*
Jane Cetrangolo, *Vice Pres*
EMP: 27 **EST:** 1998
SALES (est): 4.2MM **Privately Held**
WEB: www.tearepair.openfos.com
SIC: 3089 Kits, plastic

(G-7868)
TRXADE INC
3840 Land O Lakes Blvd (34639-4418)
P.O. Box 1186 (34639-1186)
PHONE..................................727 230-1915
Suren Ajjarapu, *Principal*
Christy Justi, *Human Resources*
Kelsey Wesley, *Manager*
Heidy Gonzalez, *Bd of Directors*
Dean Olson, *Associate*
EMP: 9 **EST:** 2013
SALES (est): 13.3MM
SALES (corp-wide): 17.1MM **Publicly Held**
WEB: www.rx.trxade.com
SIC: 2834 Pharmaceutical preparations
PA: Trxade Group, Inc.
3840 Land O Lakes Blvd
Land O Lakes FL 34639
800 261-0281

Lantana
Palm Beach County

(G-7869)
CATEGORY 5 MANUFACTURING INC
7150 Seacrest Blvd (33462-5190)
PHONE..................................561 777-2491
EMP: 15 **EST:** 2010
SALES (est): 1MM **Privately Held**
WEB: www.category5manufacturing.com
SIC: 3999 Manufacturing industries

(G-7870)
EAST COAST MEDAL
860 N 8th St (33462-1637)
PHONE..................................561 619-6753
EMP: 8 **EST:** 2013
SALES (est): 131.7K **Privately Held**
WEB: www.eastcoastmetals.net
SIC: 3441 Fabricated structural metal

(G-7871)
EAST COAST METAL DECKS INC
620 Whitney Ave (33462-1642)
PHONE..................................561 433-8259
Tami Allmon, *President*
Daymon Allmon, *Vice Pres*
Chip Post, *Vice Pres*
Dean Allmon, *Project Mgr*
Scott Carmichael, *Project Mgr*
▼ **EMP:** 49 **EST:** 1984
SQ FT: 2,000
SALES (est): 8.9MM **Privately Held**
WEB: www.eastcoastmetals.net
SIC: 3441 Fabricated structural metal

(G-7872)
EMBROIDERY PLUS
824 W Lantana Rd (33462-1509)
PHONE..................................561 439-8943
Tom Fazor, *Owner*
EMP: 9 **EST:** 2015
SALES (est): 273.1K **Privately Held**
SIC: 2395 Embroidery products, except schiffli machine

(G-7873)
EVERY THING ALUMINUM
615 Whitney Ave Ste 15 (33462-1645)
P.O. Box 542002, Lake Worth (33454-2002)
PHONE..................................561 202-9900
Clifton Duckworth, *Owner*
EMP: 6 **EST:** 2005
SALES (est): 409.4K **Privately Held**
SIC: 3479 Aluminum coating of metal products

(G-7874)
FLORIDA PWDR CTING SHTTERS INC
854 N Dixie Hwy (33462-1817)
PHONE..................................561 588-2410
EMP: 12
SQ FT: 47,000
SALES (est): 940K **Privately Held**
SIC: 3479 5023 Powder Coating And Whol Shutters

(G-7875)
LAWRENCEVILLE PRESS INC
820 N 8th St (33462-1666)
PHONE..................................609 737-1148
EMP: 10 **EST:** 2019
SALES (est): 100.5K **Privately Held**
SIC: 2741 Miscellaneous publishing

(G-7876)
SUNDOWN LIGHTING
417 Se Atlantic Dr (33462-1905)
PHONE..................................561 254-3738
Andrej Benesz, *Officer*
EMP: 6 **EST:** 2005
SALES (est): 76.6K **Privately Held**
SIC: 3648 Lighting equipment

(G-7877)
TAGALONG INC
5485 Old Spanish Trl (33462-5121)
PHONE..................................561 585-7400
EMP: 5 **EST:** 1993
SALES (est): 662.5K **Privately Held**
SIC: 2824 Mfg Nylon Products

(G-7878)
THUNDER ENERGIES CORPORATION (HQ)
Also Called: MINA MAR GROUP
111 Moorings Dr (33462-8019)
PHONE..................................561 560-4302
Andrea Zecevic, *President*
Margaret Haberlin-Currey, *CFO*
Irina Veselinovic, *Admin Sec*
EMP: 6 **EST:** 2011
SALES (est): 1.5MM **Publicly Held**
WEB: www.natureconsulting.com
SIC: 3827 Optical instruments & lenses; telescopes: elbow, panoramic, sighting, fire control, etc.
PA: Mina Mar Corporation
111 Moorings Dr
Lantana FL 33462
561 560-4302

Largo
Pinellas County

(G-7879)
3FDM INC
10600 Endeavour Way (33777-1621)
PHONE..................................727 877-3336
S Pres Parvataneni, *Owner*
Philip Berg, *Marketing Staff*
EMP: 12 **EST:** 2017
SALES (est): 1.9MM **Privately Held**
WEB: www.3fdm.com
SIC: 3999 Manufacturing industries

(G-7880)
4K CABINETS
13565 65th St (33771-4967)
PHONE..................................727 507-0444
EMP: 6 **EST:** 2016
SALES (est): 184.7K **Privately Held**
WEB: www.4kcabinets.com
SIC: 2434 Wood kitchen cabinets

(G-7881)
5 DAY PLANTATION SHUTTERS
1876 Lake Ave Se Ste G (33771-3799)
PHONE..................................727 474-6130
Larry T Dickinson, *President*
EMP: 6 **EST:** 2017
SALES (est): 90.5K **Privately Held**
WEB: www.5dayplantationshutters.com
SIC: 3442 Shutters, door or window: metal

(G-7882)
AABC INC
Also Called: Roll-A-Guard
12722 62nd St Ste 206 (33773-1818)
PHONE..................................727 434-4444
Andrew J Ayers, *President*
EMP: 16 **EST:** 2006
SALES (est): 1,000K **Privately Held**
WEB: www.rollaguard.com
SIC: 3442 Shutters, door or window: metal

(G-7883)
ACCENT WOODWORKING INC
2233 34th Way (33771-3902)
PHONE..................................727 522-2700
Richard P Carnevali, *President*
Janet L Carnevali, *Vice Pres*
EMP: 7 **EST:** 1990
SQ FT: 6,000
SALES (est): 753.1K **Privately Held**
WEB: www.accentwoodworking.com
SIC: 2431 Millwork

(G-7884)
ACE MECHANICAL INC
6801 114th Ave Ste C (33773-5308)
PHONE..................................727 304-6277
Pamela Thompson, *Controller*
EMP: 6
SQ FT: 10,000
SALES (est): 405.5K **Privately Held**
SIC: 3317 Tubing, mechanical or hypodermic sizes: cold drawn stainless

(G-7885)
ACH LLC
12318 Keyridge Loop (33778-2551)
PHONE.....727 586-4930
EMP: 6 **EST:** 2018
SALES (est): 170K **Privately Held**
SIC: 3714 Motor vehicle parts & accessories

(G-7886)
ADVANCED IMPACT TECH INC
Also Called: Ait Group
2310 Starkey Rd (33771-3852)
PHONE.....727 287-4620
Jeffrey E Besse, *President*
Christopher Kapiloff, *Vice Pres*
Christine Besse, *Office Mgr*
Jeffrey Wilson, *Director*
Peter Kapiloff, *Admin Sec*
EMP: 27 **EST:** 2017
SALES (est): 1.6MM **Privately Held**
WEB: www.advanced-impact.com
SIC: 3211 Laminated glass

(G-7887)
ADVENT AEROSPACE INC (PA)
11221 69th St (33773-5504)
PHONE.....727 549-9600
Steve Jourdenais, *President*
EMP: 39 **EST:** 2006
SALES (est): 11.5MM **Privately Held**
WEB: www.jormac.com
SIC: 3728 Aircraft parts & equipment

(G-7888)
AFC CABLE SYSTEMS INC
2000 Tall Pines Dr (33771-3845)
PHONE.....813 539-0588
EMP: 7 **EST:** 2017
SALES (est): 262.1K **Privately Held**
WEB: www.afcweb.com
SIC: 3644 Noncurrent-carrying wiring services

(G-7889)
AL STEIN INDUSTRIES LLC
Also Called: Asieei
6911 Bryan Dairy Rd # 280 (33777-1641)
PHONE.....727 329-8755
Allen Stein, *President*
▼ **EMP:** 16 **EST:** 2008
SQ FT: 10,000
SALES (est): 1.6MM **Privately Held**
WEB: www.asieei.com
SIC: 3559 Anodizing equipment; electroplating machinery & equipment; metal finishing equipment for plating, etc.; metal pickling equipment

(G-7890)
ALAKAI DEFENSE SYSTEMS INC
8285 Bryan Dairy Rd # 125 (33777-1350)
P.O. Box 10405 (33773-0405)
PHONE.....727 541-1600
Ed Dottery, *President*
Edwin Dottery, *General Mgr*
Timothy Molner, *Electrical Engi*
Paul Ferreira, *Finance Dir*
Robert Babnick, *IT/INT Sup*
EMP: 18 **EST:** 2009
SALES (est): 2.9MM **Privately Held**
WEB: www.alakaidefense.com
SIC: 3812 Search & navigation equipment

(G-7891)
ALPINE TOOL INC
13070 90th St (33773-1327)
PHONE.....727 587-0407
Norma Lopez, *President*
Mario Lopez, *Vice Pres*
Antonio Diaz, *Mfg Staff*
EMP: 5 **EST:** 1996
SQ FT: 3,000
SALES (est): 550K **Privately Held**
WEB: www.alpineprecisiontools.com
SIC: 3312 Tool & die steel & alloys

(G-7892)
AMERI FOOD & FUEL INC
790 East Bay Dr (33770-3724)
PHONE.....727 584-0120
Zyad Qusini, *Principal*
EMP: 9 **EST:** 2010
SALES (est): 638K **Privately Held**
SIC: 2869 Fuels

(G-7893)
AMERICAN ACRYLIC ADHESIVES LLC
2020 Wild Acres Rd Unit D (33771-3885)
PHONE.....877 422-4583
Jeffrey Smith, *Principal*
EMP: 12 **EST:** 2017
SALES (est): 2.9MM **Privately Held**
WEB: www.aaaglue.com
SIC: 2891 Adhesives

(G-7894)
AMERICAN ADHESIVES LLC
12350 Belcher Rd S 1b (33773-3045)
PHONE.....877 422-4583
Stuart Young, *Manager*
EMP: 8 **EST:** 2017
SALES (est): 575.5K **Privately Held**
WEB: www.aaaglue.com
SIC: 2891 Adhesives

(G-7895)
AMERICAN VET SCIENCES LLC
6911 Bryan Dairy Rd (33777-1641)
PHONE.....727 471-0850
Mihir Taneja, *Vice Pres*
EMP: 5
SQ FT: 40,000
SALES (est): 393.2K **Privately Held**
SIC: 2834 Veterinary pharmaceutical preparations

(G-7896)
AMETEK INC
Ametek Msrment Clibration Tech
8600 Somerset Dr (33773-2700)
PHONE.....727 536-7831
Lisa Simpson, *Buyer*
Jimmy Kane, *Engineer*
Chris Elliott, *Design Engr*
Mike Kern, *Branch Mgr*
Ev Musselman, *Manager*
EMP: 90
SALES (corp-wide): 4.5B **Publicly Held**
WEB: www.ametek.com
SIC: 3823 Industrial instrmnts msrmnt display/control process variable
PA: Ametek, Inc.
1100 Cassatt Rd
Berwyn PA 19312
610 647-2121

(G-7897)
ANVIL PAINTS & COATINGS INC
Also Called: Anvil Paints and Coating
1255 Starkey Rd Ste A (33771-3198)
PHONE.....727 535-1411
Thomas Saeli, *President*
Shawn Sny, *President*
Cory Gergar, *CFO*
Tom Sampson, *Natl Sales Mgr*
John Skinner, *Natl Sales Mgr*
▼ **EMP:** 19 **EST:** 1967
SQ FT: 55,000
SALES (est): 5.3MM **Privately Held**
WEB: www.anvilpaints.com
SIC: 2851 5231 Paints & paint additives; coating, air curing; paint

(G-7898)
ARC DIMENSIONS INC
7545 124th Ave Unit Stef (33773-3016)
P.O. Box 10204 (33773-0204)
PHONE.....727 524-6139
Robert E Pope, *President*
David E Kulak, *Vice Pres*
Paul K Boucher, *Treasurer*
EMP: 5 **EST:** 1995
SALES (est): 392.8K **Privately Held**
WEB: www.arcdimensionsinc.com
SIC: 7692 Welding repair

(G-7899)
ARCHITCTRAL MLLWK SLUTIONS INC
Also Called: Doors and Hardware Tampa Bay
13090 Starkey Rd (33773-1415)
PHONE.....727 441-1409
Daniel J Nash, *CEO*
Richard Souza, *Vice Pres*
EMP: 5 **EST:** 2008
SQ FT: 5,000
SALES (est): 488.5K **Privately Held**
WEB: www.doorsandhardwareoftampabay.com
SIC: 2431 5211 5251 Doors & door parts & trim, wood; door & window products; door locks & lock sets

(G-7900)
ARMSTRONG ELEVATOR COMPANY
9225 Ulmerton Rd Ste 318 (33771-3708)
PHONE.....727 323-3800
Armstrong Roy, *President*
Linda Armstrong, *Vice Pres*
EMP: 8 **EST:** 1990
SQ FT: 2,500
SALES (est): 2.5MM **Privately Held**
WEB: www.armstrong-elevator-company.sbcontract.com
SIC: 3534 Automobile elevators

(G-7901)
ATLANTIC MEDICAL PRODUCTS LLC
Also Called: Scar Heal
13191 Starkey Rd Ste 11 (33773-1438)
P.O. Box 1351, Tampa (33601-1351)
PHONE.....727 535-0022
Thomas Christenberry, *CEO*
Darwin Jre, *General Mgr*
Darwin Salls, *General Mgr*
John Eshleman, *Sales Staff*
EMP: 10 **EST:** 1989
SQ FT: 2,000
SALES (est): 1.6MM **Privately Held**
SIC: 2833 Medicinals & botanicals

(G-7902)
AUTEK SPRAY BOOTHS
6145 126th Ave Unit E (33773-1855)
PHONE.....727 709-4373
EMP: 6
SALES (est): 900K **Privately Held**
SIC: 2851 Mfg Paints/Allied Products

(G-7903)
B & L CREMATION SYSTEMS INC
7205 114th Ave Ste A (33773-5140)
PHONE.....727 541-4666
Steve Looker, *President*
John Rawl, *COO*
Gary Ruhlman, *Purch Agent*
Tabitha Watts, *Human Resources*
Jeff Herman, *Regl Sales Mgr*
▼ **EMP:** 55 **EST:** 1985
SQ FT: 30,000
SALES (est): 16.1MM **Privately Held**
WEB: www.blcremationsystems.com
SIC: 3569 Cremating ovens

(G-7904)
BARE BOARD GROUP INC (PA)
8565 Somerset Dr Ste B (33773-2723)
PHONE.....727 549-2200
Kelsen W Liu, *Opers Staff*
Jason Liu, *Mng Member*
Adrienne Ridley, *Mng Member*
Leah Johnson, *Associate*
▲ **EMP:** 26 **EST:** 2002
SQ FT: 9,600
SALES (est): 3.1MM **Privately Held**
WEB: www.ncabgroup.com
SIC: 3672 Circuit boards, television & radio printed

(G-7905)
BECKWITH ELECTRIC CO INC
11811 62nd St (33773-3704)
PHONE.....727 544-2326
Thomas R Beckwith, *CEO*
EMP: 6
SALES (corp-wide): 4.1B **Publicly Held**
WEB: www.beckwithelectric.com
SIC: 3625 8711 Relays & industrial controls; electrical or electronic engineering
HQ: Beckwith Electric Co., Inc.
6190 118th Ave
Largo FL 33773
727 544-2326

(G-7906)
BELCHER HOLDINGS INC (PA)
Also Called: Belcher Pharm Acquisition
12393 Belcher Rd S # 420 (33773-3097)
PHONE.....727 530-1585
George Stuart, *CEO*
Joseph Mastronardy, *President*
▲ **EMP:** 133 **EST:** 2001
SALES (est): 12.6MM **Privately Held**
SIC: 2834 Pharmaceutical preparations

(G-7907)
BELCHER HOLDINGS INC
6911 Bryan Dairy Rd (33777-1641)
PHONE.....727 471-0850
Prejith Jayakumar, *Engineer*
Brian Neuman, *Engineer*
Kotha Sekharam, *Branch Mgr*
Harry Bedi, *CIO*
Chandra Kasireddy, *Technical Staff*
EMP: 17
SALES (corp-wide): 12.6MM **Privately Held**
WEB: www.belcherpharma.com
SIC: 2834 Pharmaceutical preparations
PA: Belcher Holdings, Inc.
12393 Belcher Rd S # 420
Largo FL 33773
727 530-1585

(G-7908)
BELCHER PHARMACEUTICALS LLC (PA)
6911 Bryan Dairy Rd # 210 (33777-1641)
PHONE.....727 471-0850
Jugal Taneja, *Chairman*
Shyam Busireddy, *COO*
Mandeep Taneja, *Vice Pres*
Mihir Taneja, *Vice Pres*
Brian Neuman, *Engineer*
EMP: 38 **EST:** 2010
SQ FT: 25,000
SALES (est): 31.4MM **Privately Held**
WEB: www.belcherpharma.com
SIC: 2834 Pharmaceutical preparations

(G-7909)
BIODERM INC
12320 73rd Ct (33773-3011)
PHONE.....727 507-7655
Gary Damkoehler, *Ch of Bd*
Gaet Tyranski, *President*
John Debella, *COO*
Shawn Stone, *VP Opers*
Marc Garofani, *CFO*
▲ **EMP:** 54
SQ FT: 8,500
SALES (est): 8.8MM **Privately Held**
WEB: www.biodermincc.com
SIC: 3841 Surgical & medical instruments

(G-7910)
BLUE HAWAIIAN PRODUCTS INC (PA)
Also Called: Blue Hawaiian Fiberglass Pools
2055 Blue Hawaiian Dr (33771)
PHONE.....727 535-5677
Roger W Erdelac, *President*
▼ **EMP:** 40 **EST:** 1988
SQ FT: 36,000
SALES (est): 10.2MM **Privately Held**
WEB: www.lathampool.com
SIC: 3949 Swimming pools, plastic

(G-7911)
BLUESKY MAST INC
2080 Wild Acres Rd (33771-3818)
PHONE.....877 411-6278
Scott Vanover, *President*
Crystal Freund, *Accountant*
◆ **EMP:** 11
SALES (est): 900K **Privately Held**
WEB: www.blueskymast.com
SIC: 3812 Antennas, radar or communications

(G-7912)
BPI LABS LLC
12393 Belcher Rd S # 450 (33773-3097)
PHONE.....727 471-0850
Jugal Taneja, *CEO*
Shyam Busireddy, *COO*
Mandeep Taneja, *Vice Pres*
Lana Radowick, *CFO*
Mihir Taneja, *VP Sales*

EMP: 106 **EST:** 2012
SALES (est): 24.2MM **Privately Held**
WEB: www.belcherpharma.com
SIC: 2834 Pharmaceutical preparations
PA: Belcher Pharmaceuticals, Llc
6911 Bryan Dairy Rd # 210
Largo FL 33777

(G-7913)
BRAWLEY DISTRIBUTING CO INC
Also Called: National Saw Company
7162 123rd Cir (33773-3041)
PHONE..................................727 539-8500
Terrance Brawley, *President*
Tom Lewis, *Vice Pres*
Annett Brawley, *Treasurer*
▲ **EMP:** 11 **EST:** 1945
SQ FT: 6,000
SALES (est): 2.1MM **Privately Held**
WEB: www.brawleydistributing.com
SIC: 3991 Paint brushes; paint rollers

(G-7914)
BREEZE PRODUCTS INC
7207 114th Ave Ste B (33773-5132)
PHONE..................................727 521-4482
Mike Lemle, *President*
Robert Dowdell, *Vice Pres*
Sandy Akl, *Treasurer*
EMP: 33 **EST:** 1999
SQ FT: 11,000
SALES (est): 4.5MM **Privately Held**
WEB: www.breezeproducts.com
SIC: 2844 Suntan lotions & oils

(G-7915)
BT-TWISS TRANSPORT LLC (HQ)
1501 Lake Ave Se (33771-3747)
PHONE..................................866 584-1585
Francis Taylor, *President*
Stephen Gurba, *Mng Member*
Craig Schnee, *Admin Sec*
EMP: 9 **EST:** 2015
SALES (est): 8.7MM
SALES (corp-wide): 25.1MM **Publicly Held**
WEB: www.twisstransport.com
SIC: 3715 4214 Truck trailers; local trucking with storage
PA: Bulova Technologies Group, Inc.
1501 Lake Ave Se
Largo FL 33771
727 536-6666

(G-7916)
BUCKEYE USED OFFICE FURN INC
Also Called: Buckeye Office Intrors Instllt
6166 126th Ave (33773-1854)
PHONE..................................727 457-5287
Dominic J De Marte, *President*
Nicholas Pasquine, *Principal*
EMP: 6 **EST:** 1995
SQ FT: 10,000
SALES (est): 500K **Privately Held**
WEB: www.buckeyeoffices.com
SIC: 2522 Office furniture, except wood

(G-7917)
BUILDERS AUTOMTN MCHY CO LLC
12775 Starkey Rd Ste B (33773-1436)
PHONE..................................727 538-2180
Robert J Mitvalsky, *Mng Member*
Thomas Schusser,
EMP: 25 **EST:** 1992
SQ FT: 10,500
SALES (est): 4.5MM **Privately Held**
WEB: www.buildersautomation.com
SIC: 3599 Custom machinery

(G-7918)
CABINET MASTERS INC
7168 123rd Cir (33773-3041)
PHONE..................................727 535-0020
David Ogden, *President*
Scott Ellis, *Vice Pres*
EMP: 8 **EST:** 1982
SQ FT: 4,000
SALES (est): 670K **Privately Held**
WEB: www.cabinetmastersfl.com
SIC: 2521 2434 Wood office furniture; wood kitchen cabinets

(G-7919)
CATALINA YACHTS INC
7200 Bryan Dairy Rd (33777-1504)
PHONE..................................727 544-6681
Gerry Douglas, *Vice Pres*
EMP: 150
SALES (corp-wide): 29.4MM **Privately Held**
WEB: www.catalinayachts.com
SIC: 3732 Sailboats, building & repairing
PA: Catalina Yachts, Inc.
21200 Victory Blvd
Woodland Hills CA 91367
818 884-7700

(G-7920)
CAYO CUSTOM BOATS LLC
2055 34th Way (33771-3952)
PHONE..................................727 698-7201
EMP: 6 **EST:** 2019
SALES (est): 379.9K **Privately Held**
WEB: www.cayocustomboats.com
SIC: 3732 Boat building & repairing

(G-7921)
CBD BIOCARE
7381 114th Ave Ste 406 (33773-5125)
PHONE..................................813 380-4376
EMP: 7 **EST:** 2018
SALES (est): 268.1K **Privately Held**
WEB: www.cbdbiocare.com
SIC: 3999

(G-7922)
CLARIOS LLC
Johnson Controls
8575 Largo Lakes Dr (33773-4909)
PHONE..................................727 541-3531
Bob Holoms, *Branch Mgr*
Nancy Freshcorn, *IT/INT Sup*
EMP: 444
SALES (corp-wide): 47.9B **Publicly Held**
WEB: www.clarios.com
SIC: 3585 3567 Parts for heating, cooling & refrigerating equipment; industrial furnaces & ovens
HQ: Clarios, Llc
5757 N Green Bay Ave
Milwaukee WI 53209

(G-7923)
CLASSIC CABINETS AND MORE LLC
8187 Wild Oaks Cir (33773-2835)
PHONE..................................727 239-8869
Andy Van Nguyen, *Principal*
EMP: 5 **EST:** 2016
SALES (est): 304.3K **Privately Held**
SIC: 2434 Wood kitchen cabinets

(G-7924)
CLEARWATER ENVIRO TECH INC
8767 115th Ave (33773-4904)
PHONE..................................727 209-6400
Jeffrey M Conway, *President*
Ryan Duksa, *Sales Executive*
EMP: 22 **EST:** 1994
SQ FT: 12,000
SALES (est): 4.1MM **Privately Held**
WEB: www.clearwaterenviro.com
SIC: 3589 Water purification equipment, household type; water treatment equipment, industrial

(G-7925)
CLONDALKIN LLC
Also Called: Llc, Clondalkin
10950 Belcher Rd S (33777-1438)
PHONE..................................866 545-8703
Aaron Weltz, *General Mgr*
Christine Urdiales, *Vice Pres*
Jerry Mangan, *Purch Mgr*
Kevin Kenjarski, *VP Sales*
Denis Thellab, *Accounts Exec*
◆ **EMP:** 35 **EST:** 2013
SALES (est): 344K **Privately Held**
WEB: www.clondalkingroup.com
SIC: 2024 Ice cream, packaged: molded, on sticks, etc.

(G-7926)
COMPUTER FORMS & SUPPLIES
Also Called: One Source Technology
1198 Hickory Dr (33770-4211)
P.O. Box 1830, Pinellas Park (33780-1830)
PHONE..................................727 535-0422
EMP: 7
SQ FT: 3,500
SALES (est): 1MM **Privately Held**
SIC: 3955 5112 Carbon Paper And Inked Ribbons

(G-7927)
CONMED CORPORATION (PA)
11311 Concept Blvd (33773-4908)
PHONE..................................727 392-6464
Curt R Hartman, *Ch of Bd*
Sarah M Oliker, *Counsel*
Heather L Cohen, *Exec VP*
Shanna Cotti-Osmanski, *Exec VP*
Daniel S Jonas, *Exec VP*
◆ **EMP:** 943 **EST:** 1970
SQ FT: 278,000
SALES: 862.4MM **Publicly Held**
WEB: www.conmed.com
SIC: 3845 3841 Electromedical apparatus; electrocardiographs; patient monitoring apparatus; surgical instruments & apparatus; trocars; suction therapy apparatus; probes, surgical

(G-7928)
CONTAGIOUS FISHING CHARTERS
14481 Starboard Ln (33774-2804)
PHONE..................................727 595-6277
Michael Irwin, *Owner*
EMP: 7 **EST:** 2003
SALES (est): 127.5K **Privately Held**
WEB: www.patronsbuckeye.com
SIC: 3949 Fishing equipment

(G-7929)
CUSTOM GRAFIX INDUSTRIES INC
Also Called: Aerial Flags
12571 66th St (33773-3440)
PHONE..................................727 530-7300
Stephen C Foster, *President*
EMP: 6 **EST:** 1972
SALES (est): 738.9K **Privately Held**
WEB: www.customgrafixindustries.com
SIC: 2396 Automotive & apparel trimmings

(G-7930)
DANCO MACHINE INC
13131 92nd St Ste 608a (33773-1331)
PHONE..................................727 501-0460
Daniel B Mothena, *President*
EMP: 6 **EST:** 2002
SQ FT: 5,000
SALES (est): 500K **Privately Held**
WEB: www.dancomachineinc.com
SIC: 3599 3451 Machine shop, jobbing & repair; screw machine products

(G-7931)
DARLY FILTRATION INC
8094 118th Ave (33773-5011)
PHONE..................................727 318-7064
EMP: 8
SALES (corp-wide): 2.4MM **Privately Held**
WEB: www.darlyfilter.com
SIC: 3569 Filters, general line: industrial
PA: Darly Filtration Inc
14225 Telephone Ave
Chino CA 91710
909 591-7999

(G-7932)
DIRECT OPTICAL RESEARCH CO
8725 115th Ave (33773-4904)
PHONE..................................727 319-9000
James T Chivers, *CEO*
EMP: 8 **EST:** 1992
SQ FT: 8,000
SALES (est): 784.7K **Privately Held**
WEB: www.dorc.com
SIC: 3827 Optical test & inspection equipment

(G-7933)
DISCOUNT BOAT TOPS INC
Also Called: Dbt Marine Products
14000 66th St Ste A (33771-4776)
PHONE..................................727 536-4412
Richard Moyse, *President*
EMP: 8 **EST:** 1973
SQ FT: 10,500
SALES (est): 486.3K **Privately Held**
WEB: www.discountboattops.com
SIC: 2394 3732 Convertible tops, canvas or boat: from purchased materials; boat building & repairing

(G-7934)
DISTINCT DSGNS CSTM COML CASE
1135 Starkey Rd (33771-3185)
PHONE..................................727 530-0119
Bill Kratimenos, *President*
Pete Kratimenos, *Director*
EMP: 5 **EST:** 2003
SALES (est): 412.2K **Privately Held**
WEB: www.distinctdesignsfl.com
SIC: 2599 Cabinets, factory

(G-7935)
DOK SOLUTION INC
12253 62nd St (33773-3707)
PHONE..................................727 209-1313
John Strauser, *CEO*
Jeanie Strauser, *Vice Pres*
Edwin Young, *Vice Pres*
EMP: 10 **EST:** 2012
SALES (est): 887.1K **Privately Held**
WEB: www.doksolution.com
SIC: 3931 Musical instruments, electric & electronic

(G-7936)
DRS LAUREL TECHNOLOGIES (DH)
6200 118th Ave (33773-3726)
PHONE..................................727 541-6681
Larry Butera, *General Mgr*
Bob Sleppy, *Technical Staff*
Daniel Skaling, *Director*
EMP: 25 **EST:** 2001
SALES (est): 15.7MM
SALES (corp-wide): 10.2B **Privately Held**
WEB: www.leonardodrs.com
SIC: 3861 Cameras & related equipment
HQ: Leonardo Drs, Inc.
2345 Crystal Dr Ste 1000
Arlington VA 22202
703 416-8000

(G-7937)
DVC SIGNS LLC
12350 Belcher Rd S 14b (33773-3009)
PHONE..................................727 524-8543
Ralph Kay, *Vice Pres*
Kristopher Kay, *Vice Pres*
EMP: 8 **EST:** 2014
SALES (est): 340K **Privately Held**
WEB: www.dvcsigns.com
SIC: 3993 Electric signs

(G-7938)
E T I INCORPORATED
10610 75th St (33777-1420)
PHONE..................................727 546-6472
Jim Smith, *President*
EMP: 28 **EST:** 1987
SQ FT: 11,000
SALES (est): 646.8K
SALES (corp-wide): 28MM **Privately Held**
WEB: www.etiincorporated.com
SIC: 2869 Silicones
PA: Molded Rubber & Plastic Corporation
13161 W Glendale Ave
Butler WI 53007
262 781-7122

(G-7939)
E3 FLUID RECOVERY ENG (PA)
13517 65th St (33771-4967)
P.O. Box 41802, Saint Petersburg (33743-1802)
PHONE..................................727 754-9792
EMP: 6 **EST:** 2011
SQ FT: 4,000

SALES (est): 1MM **Privately Held**
SIC: 3677 8711 Mfg Electronic Coils/Transformers Engineering Services

(G-7940)
ELDER & JENKS LLC
12595 71st Ct (33773-3254)
PHONE..................................727 538-5545
Thomas G Typrowicz,
Thomas F Typrowicz,
Stacy Zumwalt,
EMP: 8 **EST:** 2015
SALES (est): 489.2K **Privately Held**
SIC: 3991 Paint & varnish brushes; paint rollers; paint brushes; varnish brushes

(G-7941)
ENGINEERED MTLS & MFG INTL LLC
Also Called: Emmi
10860 76th Ct Ste A (33777-1409)
PHONE..................................727 546-5580
Robert Brown, *Mng Member*
William Butler,
EMP: 6 **EST:** 2006
SQ FT: 8,000
SALES (est): 545.8K **Privately Held**
SIC: 3492 Fluid power valves & hose fittings

(G-7942)
FASHIONABLE CANES
7381 114th Ave Ste 402b (33773-5105)
PHONE..................................727 547-8866
Stephen Carroll, *Owner*
Elizabeth Carroll, *Co-Owner*
EMP: 10 **EST:** 2010
SALES (est): 473.6K **Privately Held**
WEB: www.fashionablecanes.com
SIC: 3999 Canes & cane trimmings, except precious metal

(G-7943)
FAST FRONTIER PRINTING
7360 Ulmerton Rd Apt 19d (33771-4543)
PHONE..................................407 538-5621
EMP: 10 **EST:** 2016
SALES (est): 589.1K **Privately Held**
WEB: www.fastfrontier.co
SIC: 2752 Commercial printing, lithographic

(G-7944)
FDM OF CLEARWATER INC
Also Called: Florida Discharge Machine
10850 75th St (33777-1424)
PHONE..................................727 544-8801
Michael Conte, *President*
Mike Conte, *Executive*
EMP: 10 **EST:** 1971
SQ FT: 10,000
SALES (est): 1.4MM **Privately Held**
WEB: www.fdmofclearwater.com
SIC: 3544 Special dies & tools

(G-7945)
FIBRE TECH INC
2323 34th Way (33771-3978)
PHONE..................................727 539-0844
Andrew Morris, *President*
▼ **EMP:** 32 **EST:** 1987
SQ FT: 9,000
SALES (est): 4.6MM **Privately Held**
WEB: www.fibretechinc.com
SIC: 2851 7389 Lacquers, varnishes, enamels & other coatings; swimming pool & hot tub service & maintenance

(G-7946)
FILL TECH SOLUTIONS INC 200
11401 Belcher Rd S # 230 (33773-5102)
PHONE..................................727 572-8550
Stewart Nelson, *President*
Ron Nelson, *Vice Pres*
Ana Nelson, *CFO*
Tim Sinclair, *Sales Mgr*
EMP: 26 **EST:** 2009
SALES (est): 7.8MM **Privately Held**
WEB: www.fill-tech.com
SIC: 3565 Packaging machinery

(G-7947)
FINE WOOD DESIGN INC
12087 62nd St Unit 8 (33773-3709)
PHONE..................................727 531-8000
Mark Winter, *President*
EMP: 8 **EST:** 2004
SALES (est): 915.7K **Privately Held**
WEB: www.finewooddesign.net
SIC: 2434 Wood kitchen cabinets

(G-7948)
FLORIDA ELITE INDUSTRIES LLC
1185 Gooden Xing Bldg B (33778-1224)
PHONE..................................727 223-4233
Tony McCarthy, *Mng Member*
Susan McCarthy,
EMP: 7 **EST:** 2017
SALES (est): 95.6K **Privately Held**
WEB: www.floridaeliteindustries.com
SIC: 3999 Manufacturing industries

(G-7949)
FLORIDA FOREST PRODUCTS LLC
1975 20th Ave Se (33771-3808)
P.O. Box 1345 (33779-1345)
PHONE..................................727 585-2067
Diane Norton, *Controller*
Ralph Valle, *Sales Mgr*
John Goley, *Sales Staff*
Orlando Calvo, *Manager*
Rick Cashman,
EMP: 42 **EST:** 1994
SALES (est): 5MM **Privately Held**
WEB: www.ffptruss.com
SIC: 2439 Structural wood members

(G-7950)
FLORIDA METAL SERVICES INC
6951 108th Ave (33777-1615)
PHONE..................................727 541-6441
John Max Jones, *CEO*
Daryle Jones, *President*
Ray Brown, *Opers Mgr*
Julie Samsel, *Purch Agent*
EMP: 75 **EST:** 1975
SQ FT: 30,500
SALES (est): 16.1MM **Privately Held**
WEB: www.florida-metal.com
SIC: 3469 Stamping metal for the trade

(G-7951)
FLORIDA SNCAST TRISM PRMOTIONS
10750 75th St (33777-1422)
PHONE..................................727 544-1212
Drake A Decker, *President*
EMP: 10 **EST:** 1985
SQ FT: 10,000
SALES (est): 947.9K **Privately Held**
WEB: www.floridatourism.com
SIC: 2731 2759 Pamphlets: publishing & printing; commercial printing

(G-7952)
FLORIDA VEEX INC
Also Called: Digital Lightwave
2100 Tall Pines Dr (33771-3809)
PHONE..................................727 442-6677
Paul Chang, *President*
EMP: 15 **EST:** 2016
SALES (est): 1MM **Privately Held**
WEB: www.lightwave.com
SIC: 3661 3825 Fiber optics communications equipment; digital test equipment, electronic & electrical circuits; test equipment for electronic & electric measurement

(G-7953)
FORMULATED SOLUTIONS LLC (PA)
11775 Starkey Rd (33773-4727)
PHONE..................................727 373-3970
Brian Dann, *President*
Thomas Sharo, *Production*
Jonathan Flink, *Engineer*
Michaela Mutlova, *Program Mgr*
Chirag Mehta, *Info Tech Mgr*
◆ **EMP:** 87 **EST:** 1999
SQ FT: 177,000
SALES (est): 32.8MM **Privately Held**
WEB: www.formulatedsolutions.com
SIC: 2844 Cosmetic preparations

(G-7954)
FURNITURE CONCEPTS INC
2180 34th Way Ste D (33771-4095)
PHONE..................................727 535-0093
Lance Breakwell, *President*
EMP: 5 **EST:** 1997
SALES (est): 658.3K **Privately Held**
WEB: www.furnitureconceptsinc.com
SIC: 2541 Counter & sink tops

(G-7955)
G J V INC
Also Called: Sir Speedy
12509 Ulmerton Rd (33774-3628)
PHONE..................................727 584-7136
Anthony Juliano, *President*
Kelly Kimberlin, *VP Bus Dvlpt*
EMP: 9 **EST:** 1979
SQ FT: 3,800
SALES (est): 900K **Privately Held**
WEB: www.sirspeedy.com
SIC: 2752 2791 2789 7334 Commercial printing, lithographic; typesetting; bookbinding & related work; photocopying & duplicating services

(G-7956)
GARELICK MFG CO
7151 114th Ave (33773-5312)
PHONE..................................727 545-4571
EMP: 83
SQ FT: 70,000
SALES (corp-wide): 4.3B **Publicly Held**
SIC: 3499 3429 Marine Accessories
HQ: Garelick Mfg. Co.
644 2nd St
Saint Paul Park MN 55071
651 459-9795

(G-7957)
GENESIS ELECTRIC MOTORS INC
6330 118th Ave Unit A (33773-3722)
PHONE..................................727 572-1414
David Eskew, *President*
EMP: 6 **EST:** 2000
SQ FT: 4,800
SALES (est): 657.3K **Privately Held**
WEB: www.genesiselectricmotors.com
SIC: 7694 Electric motor repair

(G-7958)
GIOVANNIS BAKERY INC
299 Keene Rd (33771-1729)
PHONE..................................727 536-2253
Roberto A Fanzago, *President*
EMP: 14 **EST:** 2000
SQ FT: 4,800
SALES (est): 1.1MM **Privately Held**
SIC: 2051 Bakery: wholesale or wholesale/retail combined

(G-7959)
GJ FRANCOS STAIR CO INC
1079 Woodbrook Dr S (33770-1626)
PHONE..................................727 510-4102
Gregory J Franco, *President*
EMP: 6 **EST:** 2004
SALES (est): 63K **Privately Held**
SIC: 3446 Stairs, staircases, stair treads: prefabricated metal

(G-7960)
GLASS WORKS OF LARGO INC
2020 Wild Acres Rd Unit D (33771-3885)
PHONE..................................727 535-9808
Kenneth Cruz, *President*
Rhonda Cruz, *Vice Pres*
EMP: 6 **EST:** 1997
SALES (est): 668.2K **Privately Held**
WEB: www.glassworksoflargo.com
SIC: 3089 Molding primary plastic

(G-7961)
GLENNMAR SUPPLY LLC
6265 118th Ave (33773-3727)
PHONE..................................727 536-1955
Glenn-Mar Supply, *Sales Staff*
EMP: 11 **EST:** 2016
SALES (est): 5.5MM **Privately Held**
WEB: www.lewismarine.com
SIC: 3465 Body parts, automobile: stamped metal

(G-7962)
GLOBAL IMPRESSIONS INC
1299 Starkey Rd Ste 103 (33771-3101)
PHONE..................................727 531-1290
Dean L Stevenson, *President*
Patricia Stevenson, *Treasurer*
EMP: 13 **EST:** 1994
SQ FT: 10,000
SALES (est): 519.4K **Privately Held**
WEB: www.globalimp.com
SIC: 2752 Transfers, decalcomania or dry: lithographed

(G-7963)
GOLDEN RIBBON CORPORATION
Also Called: Marathon Ribbon Co
10321 72nd St (33777-1542)
PHONE..................................727 545-4499
Lee Manuel, *President*
EMP: 13 **EST:** 1984
SQ FT: 28,000
SALES (est): 488.5K **Privately Held**
WEB: www.marathon4imaging.com
SIC: 3955 Ribbons, inked: typewriter, adding machine, register, etc.

(G-7964)
GREAT BAY SIGNS INC
7381 114th Ave Ste 403a (33773-5105)
PHONE..................................727 437-1091
Starlyn Fikkert, *Principal*
Joan Marzi, *Administration*
EMP: 8 **EST:** 2015
SALES (est): 313.6K **Privately Held**
WEB: www.greatbaysigns.com
SIC: 3993 Signs & advertising specialties

(G-7965)
GREG HEYEN
8950 131st Ave (33773-1406)
PHONE..................................727 585-8555
Greg Heyen, *Principal*
Bryan Heartz, *Vice Pres*
EMP: 6 **EST:** 2018
SALES (est): 102.7K **Privately Held**
WEB: www.servoproductsco.com
SIC: 3544 Special dies, tools, jigs & fixtures

(G-7966)
GRINDER WEAR PARTS INC
2062 20th Ave Se (33771-3846)
PHONE..................................503 982-0881
Helena Vanderwey, *President*
Wayne Brown, *Exec VP*
Paul Minkler, *Mfg Staff*
Dali Kranzthor, *CFO*
Tom Rice, *CFO*
▲ **EMP:** 32 **EST:** 2010
SALES (est): 5MM **Privately Held**
WEB: www.grinderwearparts.com
SIC: 3599 Machine & other job shop work

(G-7967)
GULF ELECTRONICS
12155 Meadowbrook Ln (33774-3141)
P.O. Box 1241 (33779-1241)
PHONE..................................727 595-3840
Harry Schlenther, *Owner*
EMP: 10 **EST:** 1994
SALES (est): 567.7K **Privately Held**
WEB: www.shopperonline.com
SIC: 3354 7622 Aluminum extruded products; radio & television repair

(G-7968)
GULF PUBLISHING COMPANY INC (PA)
11470 Oakhurst Rd (33774-3994)
PHONE..................................727 596-2863
Edward A Hausdorf, *President*
Karan Hausdorf, *Vice Pres*
EMP: 10 **EST:** 1978
SQ FT: 3,100
SALES (est): 1.1MM **Privately Held**
SIC: 2741 2721 Directories: publishing only, not printed on site; guides: publishing only, not printed on site; periodicals

(G-7969)
HENEFELT PRECISION PRODUCTS
8475 Ulmerton Rd (33771-3841)
P.O. Box 1283 (33779-1283)
PHONE..................................727 531-0406
William N Henefelt Jr, *President*
Christie M Henefelt, *Vice Pres*
Kathy Henefelt, *Admin Sec*
EMP: 16 **EST:** 1944
SQ FT: 30,000

SALES (est): 1.2MM **Privately Held**
WEB: www.henefelt.com
SIC: 3452 5085 3965 3545 Nuts, metal; industrial supplies; fasteners, buttons, needles & pins; machine tool accessories; copper foundries

(G-7970)
HERMAN CABINETS INC
1000 Belcher Rd S (33771-3321)
PHONE..................................727 459-6730
John A Herman, *President*
EMP: 8 **EST:** 2004
SALES (est): 163.8K **Privately Held**
WEB: www.hermancabinetsinc.net
SIC: 2434 Wood kitchen cabinets

(G-7971)
HIT PROMOTIONAL PRODUCTS INC (PA)
7150 Bryan Dairy Rd (33777-1501)
P.O. Box 10200, Saint Petersburg (33733-0200)
PHONE..................................727 541-5561
Elizabeth Schmidt, *CEO*
Farah Flores, *President*
Christopher J Schmidt, *President*
Jane Mary, *Editor*
Jake Gaines, *Vice Pres*
◆ **EMP:** 365 **EST:** 1981
SQ FT: 227,000
SALES (est): 229.6MM **Privately Held**
WEB: www.hitpromo.net
SIC: 2759 3993 Promotional printing; signs & advertising specialties

(G-7972)
HONEYWELL INTERNATIONAL INC
13051 66th St (33773-1810)
PHONE..................................727 539-4451
Kathy Bunton, *Manager*
EMP: 6
SALES (corp-wide): 32.6B **Publicly Held**
WEB: www.honeywell.com
SIC: 3724 Aircraft engines & engine parts
PA: Honeywell International Inc.
300 S Tryon St
Charlotte NC 28202
704 627-6200

(G-7973)
HONEYWELL INTERNATIONAL INC
13051 66th St (33773-1810)
PHONE..................................505 358-0676
Darius Adamczyk, *Ch of Bd*
Randy Snell, *Director*
EMP: 6
SALES (corp-wide): 32.6B **Publicly Held**
WEB: www.honeywell.com
SIC: 3728 3812 Aircraft parts & equipment; search & navigation equipment
PA: Honeywell International Inc.
300 S Tryon St
Charlotte NC 28202
704 627-6200

(G-7974)
HOOK INTERNATIONAL INC
6795 114th Ave (33773-5419)
PHONE..................................727 209-0855
Kamal S Juneja, *President*
▲ **EMP:** 8 **EST:** 1993
SALES (est): 799.2K **Privately Held**
SIC: 3536 Hoists

(G-7975)
HOT SHOT WELDING INC
1135 Starkey Rd Ste 10 (33771-3199)
PHONE..................................727 585-1900
Stephen Aretz, *President*
EMP: 15 **EST:** 1991
SQ FT: 3,000
SALES (est): 2.1MM **Privately Held**
WEB: www.hotshotwelding.com
SIC: 7692 Welding repair

(G-7976)
HOYA LARGO
12345 Starkey Rd Ste E (33773-2611)
PHONE..................................727 531-8964
Donald Behagg, *President*
EMP: 17 **EST:** 1980
SQ FT: 6,000
SALES (est): 1.2MM **Privately Held**
SIC: 3851 3229 Lenses, ophthalmic; pressed & blown glass

(G-7977)
HYPERION MUNITIONS INC
2150 34th Way (33771-3943)
PHONE..................................844 622-8339
Thomas Dane, *Principal*
EMP: 18 **EST:** 2015
SALES (est): 2.4MM **Privately Held**
WEB: www.hyperionmunitions.com
SIC: 3482 Shot, steel (ammunition)

(G-7978)
IMPACT REGISTER INC
1870 Starkey Rd Ste 1 (33771-3105)
PHONE..................................727 585-8572
Brad Schmeiser, *President*
Brent Schmeiser, *Vice Pres*
EMP: 5 **EST:** 1940
SQ FT: 3,500
SALES (est): 800K **Privately Held**
WEB: www.impactregister.com
SIC: 3829 Accelerometers

(G-7979)
INDUSTRIAL MARKING SVCS INC
10830 Canal St Ste C (33777-1635)
PHONE..................................727 541-7622
Charles H Harbold, *President*
Tela Harbold, *Principal*
Carol Davis, *Admin Sec*
EMP: 6 **EST:** 1982
SQ FT: 6,000
SALES (est): 700K **Privately Held**
WEB: www.imsink.net
SIC: 2759 Screen printing

(G-7980)
INFINITY MANUFACTURED INDS
12450 Enterprise Blvd (33773-2709)
P.O. Box 10655 (33773-0655)
PHONE..................................727 532-4453
Fred Weisemann, *President*
David Silverstein, *Manager*
EMP: 10 **EST:** 1994
SQ FT: 33,000
SALES (est): 1MM **Privately Held**
WEB: www.imilaser.com
SIC: 3444 Sheet metalwork

(G-7981)
INTERNATIONAL C & C CORP
Also Called: Sign X-Press
10831 Canal St (33777-1636)
PHONE..................................727 249-0675
Xiaojun Liu, *CEO*
William Griffin, *President*
EMP: 40 **EST:** 1990
SQ FT: 2,000
SALES (est): 4.4MM **Privately Held**
WEB: www.signx-press.com
SIC: 3669 Transportation signaling devices; intercommunication systems, electric

(G-7982)
INTERNATIONAL SIGN DESIGN CORP
10831 Canal St (33777-1636)
PHONE..................................727 541-5573
William Griffin, *CEO*
Eric Sekeres, *Vice Pres*
Seth F Sekeres, *CFO*
Dana Grey, *Accounting Mgr*
Rick Incorvia, *Sales Mgr*
EMP: 38 **EST:** 1972
SQ FT: 54,000
SALES (est): 6.7MM **Privately Held**
WEB: www.intlsign.com
SIC: 3993 Signs & advertising specialties

(G-7983)
INTUITOS LLC
Also Called: Optek International
2300 Tall Pines Dr # 120 (33771-5342)
P.O. Box 1050, Pinellas Park (33780-1050)
PHONE..................................727 522-2301
Alan Hodges,
EMP: 18 **EST:** 2012
SQ FT: 14,000
SALES (est): 4MM **Privately Held**
WEB: www.optekinternational.com
SIC: 3559 Optical lens machinery

(G-7984)
ISLAND PCKET SAWARD YACHTS LLC
1979 Wild Acres Rd (33771-3815)
PHONE..................................727 535-6431
Darrell Allen, *Principal*
EMP: 9 **EST:** 2017
SALES (est): 1.2MM **Privately Held**
WEB: www.ipy.com
SIC: 3732 Yachts, building & repairing

(G-7985)
JACKS MAGIC PRODUCTS INC
Also Called: Jack's Magic
12435 73rd Ct (33773-3047)
PHONE..................................727 536-4500
Jack Beane, *President*
Nadia Beane, *Exec VP*
Bernard Simon Sr, *Vice Pres*
Joel Gray, *Regl Sales Mgr*
Dave Schaffer, *Sales Staff*
EMP: 18 **EST:** 1989
SQ FT: 25,000
SALES (est): 4.2MM **Privately Held**
WEB: www.jacksmagic.com
SIC: 2899 5999 1799 Water treating compounds; swimming pool chemicals, equipment & supplies; swimming pool construction

(G-7986)
JAMES SPEAR DESIGN INC
12253 62nd St Ste A (33773-3707)
PHONE..................................727 592-9600
James Spear, *President*
EMP: 9 **EST:** 1990
SQ FT: 75,000
SALES (est): 298.8K **Privately Held**
SIC: 2599 2542 Cabinets, factory; partitions & fixtures, except wood

(G-7987)
JE TAIME FRAGRANCES (PA)
1299 Starkey Rd Ste 103 (33771-3101)
PHONE..................................727 581-0970
Denise Cassaly, *Owner*
EMP: 8 **EST:** 2004
SALES (est): 147.5K **Privately Held**
WEB: www.jetaimefragrances.com
SIC: 3999 Candles

(G-7988)
JEWISH PRESS GROUP OF TMPA BAY
Also Called: Jewish Press Group Tampa Bay
1101 Belcher Rd S Ste H (33771-3356)
P.O. Box 6970, Clearwater (33758-6970)
PHONE..................................727 535-4400
James Dawkins, *Director*
Karen Dawkins, *Director*
EMP: 7 **EST:** 1984
SALES (est): 662.5K **Privately Held**
SIC: 2711 Commercial printing & newspaper publishing combined; newspapers, publishing & printing

(G-7989)
JORMAC AEROSPACE
11221 69th St (33773-5504)
PHONE..................................727 549-9600
Steve Jourdenais, *President*
Tony Mazzuco, *Prdtn Mgr*
Mike Gallagher, *Production*
Mina Bassaly, *Engineer*
Matt Palmer, *Engineer*
EMP: 85 **EST:** 1995
SQ FT: 38,500
SALES (est): 20.8MM **Privately Held**
WEB: www.jormac.com
SIC: 3728 Aircraft parts & equipment

(G-7990)
KING & GRUBE ADVG & PRTG LLC
1211 10th St Sw (33770-4420)
PHONE..................................727 327-6033
Merrill King, *President*
Karen King, *Vice Pres*
EMP: 5 **EST:** 2015
SALES (est): 360.7K **Privately Held**
WEB: www.printkg.com
SIC: 2752 Commercial printing, offset

(G-7991)
KING & GRUBE INC
1211 10th St Sw (33770-4420)
PHONE..................................727 327-6033
Merrill King, *President*
Karen King, *Corp Secy*
Donald Grube, *Vice Pres*
EMP: 16 **EST:** 1983
SQ FT: 4,400
SALES (est): 534.7K **Privately Held**
WEB: www.customthreads.com
SIC: 2752 7311 Commercial printing, offset; advertising agencies

(G-7992)
KLA INDUSTRIES
801 West Bay Dr Ste 203 (33770-3200)
PHONE..................................727 315-4719
Karen Sturgeon, *Principal*
EMP: 9 **EST:** 2016
SALES (est): 248.6K **Privately Held**
WEB: www.klaindustries.com
SIC: 3999 Manufacturing industries

(G-7993)
KM INDUSTRIAL RACKING INC
8989 Ulmerton Rd (33771-3814)
PHONE..................................813 900-7457
Keith McKee, *Principal*
EMP: 7 **EST:** 2011
SALES (est): 90.1K **Privately Held**
WEB: www.km-industrial-racking.com
SIC: 2542 Pallet racks: except wood

(G-7994)
KMSS PRODUCTS INC
Also Called: Safe Stride
9225 Ulmerton Rd Ste D (33771-3739)
PHONE..................................800 646-3005
Kathleen Mott, *President*
EMP: 5
SQ FT: 6,000
SALES (est): 433.2K **Privately Held**
SIC: 2842 Specialty cleaning preparations

(G-7995)
KRAMSKI NORTH AMERICA INC
8222 118th Ave Ste 650 (33773-5057)
PHONE..................................727 828-1500
Andreas Kramski, *CEO*
Martin Bischoff, *President*
Wiestaw Kramski, *President*
Norm Harbison, *Manager*
Stefanie Perez, *Manager*
◆ **EMP:** 16 **EST:** 2002
SQ FT: 33,600
SALES (est): 9.8MM
SALES (corp-wide): 94.5MM **Privately Held**
WEB: www.kramski.de
SIC: 3089 Injection molding of plastics
PA: Kramski Gmbh
Heilbronner Str. 10
Pforzheim 75179
723 115-4100

(G-7996)
L & D STEEL USA INC
13240 Belcher Rd S (33773-1600)
PHONE..................................727 538-9917
Charles Carre, *President*
Patrick Dunn, *Vice Pres*
Simon Harnois, *Vice Pres*
Troy Herstine, *Opers Mgr*
Louise Talbot, *Purch Mgr*
EMP: 12 **EST:** 2017
SQ FT: 20,000
SALES (est): 3.5MM **Privately Held**
WEB: www.ldsteelusa.com
SIC: 3441 Fabricated structural metal

(G-7997)
L & S BAIT CO INC
Also Called: Mirrolure
1415 E Bay Dr (33771-1099)
PHONE..................................727 584-7691
William H Le Master, *President*
Jerry Spaulding, *Vice Pres*
Beverly Swata, *Manager*
EMP: 25 **EST:** 1937
SQ FT: 2,000
SALES (est): 3MM **Privately Held**
SIC: 3949 5941 Lures, fishing: artificial; sporting goods & bicycle shops

(G-7998)
LED TECHNOLOGIES INCORPORATED
Also Called: Revive Light Therapy
12821 Starkey Rd Ste 4900 (33773-1410)
PHONE..................................800 337-9565
Lloyd Nelson, *President*
John Moretz, *Director*
Tracey Edgerton, *Account Dir*
▲ **EMP:** 18 **EST:** 2004
SQ FT: 5,000
SALES (est): 1.7MM **Privately Held**
WEB: www.ledtechnologies.com
SIC: 3841 Surgical & medical instruments

(G-7999)
LEGENDS FABRICATIONS LLC
10298 110th St (33778-4212)
PHONE..................................727 642-0578
Benjamin Emerson, *Principal*
EMP: 6 **EST:** 2016
SALES (est): 60.1K **Privately Held**
WEB:
www.legendsfabrications.business.site
SIC: 3999 Manufacturing industries

(G-8000)
LILY ANN CABINETS - TAMPA BAY
8601 Somerset Dr Ste C (33773-2719)
PHONE..................................727 877-8180
EMP: 6 **EST:** 2018
SALES (est): 79.9K **Privately Held**
SIC: 2434 Wood kitchen cabinets

(G-8001)
LINVATEC CORPORATION (HQ)
Also Called: Conmed Linvatec
11311 Concept Blvd (33773-4908)
PHONE..................................727 392-6464
Curt Hartman, *CEO*
Joseph Darling, *President*
Pam Triplett, *President*
Gingerlee Haas, *General Mgr*
Ken Robinson, *General Mgr*
◆ **EMP:** 835 **EST:** 1963
SQ FT: 120,000
SALES (est): 160MM
SALES (corp-wide): 862.4MM **Publicly Held**
WEB: www.conmed.com
SIC: 3842 3841 2821 Surgical appliances & supplies; surgical instruments & apparatus; elastomers, nonvulcanizable (plastics)
PA: Conmed Corporation
11311 Concept Blvd
Largo FL 33773
727 392-6464

(G-8002)
LITE CART CORP
1950 Lake Ave Se Unit A (33771-3719)
P.O. Box 4316, Seminole (33775-4316)
PHONE..................................727 584-7364
Henry A Stavinga, *President*
EMP: 8 **EST:** 1975
SQ FT: 16,000
SALES (est): 1.2MM **Privately Held**
WEB: www.litecart.com
SIC: 3537 Industrial trucks & tractors

(G-8003)
LUNDY ENTERPRISES INC
Also Called: Gun Drilling of Florida
6951 114th Ave (33773-5302)
PHONE..................................727 549-1292
David Lundy, *President*
Richard Lundy, *Vice Pres*
EMP: 11 **EST:** 1996
SQ FT: 7,500
SALES (est): 750K **Privately Held**
SIC: 3541 Machine tool replacement & repair parts, metal cutting types

(G-8004)
LUXURABLE KITCHEN & BATH LLC
11601 66th St (33773-5412)
PHONE..................................727 286-8927
Zhong Cao, *Principal*
EMP: 8 **EST:** 2015
SALES (est): 575.5K **Privately Held**
WEB: www.luxurablekitchen.com
SIC: 2434 Wood kitchen cabinets

(G-8005)
MARTIN-WESTON CO
10860 76th Ct Ste B (33777-1409)
PHONE..................................727 545-8877
Jeff Hunter, *President*
EMP: 10 **EST:** 1989
SQ FT: 5,000
SALES (est): 566.7K **Privately Held**
SIC: 3841 Surgical & medical instruments

(G-8006)
MAVEN MEDICAL MFG INC
2250 Lake Ave Se (33771-3740)
PHONE..................................727 518-0555
Paul Vaughan, *President*
EMP: 39 **EST:** 1992
SQ FT: 12,700
SALES (est): 3.2MM **Privately Held**
WEB: www.mavenmedical.us
SIC: 3841 3842 Surgical & medical instruments; surgical appliances & supplies

(G-8007)
MCCABINET INC (PA)
7273 112th Ave N (33773-3146)
PHONE..................................727 608-5929
Kevin McKenzie, *President*
Russell D Drevitson, *Vice Pres*
Meaghan Gonzalez, *Manager*
Brian McKenzie, *Director*
Eric McKenzie, *Director*
EMP: 12 **EST:** 2003
SQ FT: 9,000
SALES (est): 2.5MM **Privately Held**
WEB: www.mccabinet.com
SIC: 2521 5712 Cabinets, office: wood; cabinet work, custom

(G-8008)
MEDRX INC
1200 Starkey Rd Ste 105 (33771-3167)
PHONE..................................727 584-9600
Ronald Buck, *President*
Pete Covert, *Chairman*
Jennifer Heckman, *Opers Staff*
EMP: 29 **EST:** 1994
SQ FT: 18,500
SALES (est): 5.1MM **Privately Held**
WEB: www.medrx-diagnostics.com
SIC: 3841 2836 Surgical & medical instruments; veterinary biological products

(G-8009)
MEGA POWER
211 Violet St Ste 100 (33773)
PHONE..................................813 855-6664
▲ **EMP:** 13
SQ FT: 28,000
SALES (est): 2.2MM **Privately Held**
SIC: 2911 Petroleum Refiner

(G-8010)
MERRITT HOLLOW METAL INC
10822 124th Ave (33778-2716)
PHONE..................................727 656-4380
Randy Merritt, *Principal*
EMP: 6 **EST:** 2001
SALES (est): 276.2K **Privately Held**
SIC: 3499 Fabricated metal products

(G-8011)
MINUTEMAN PRESS
2475 E Bay Dr Ste A (33771-2472)
PHONE..................................727 535-3800
Corol Polakovich, *Principal*
EMP: 14 **EST:** 2008
SALES (est): 326.3K **Privately Held**
WEB: www.minutemanpress.com
SIC: 2752 Commercial printing, lithographic

(G-8012)
MIRANDA ELDORADO MFG CO
1744 12th St Se Ofc Ofc (33771-3754)
PHONE..................................727 586-0707
Andrew Miranda Jr, *President*
Cora Miranda, *Corp Secy*
▼ **EMP:** 5
SQ FT: 7,000
SALES (est): 500K **Privately Held**
WEB: www.eldoradomfg.com
SIC: 2599 Restaurant furniture, wood or metal

(G-8013)
MONT KREST STONE INC (PA)
6795 114th Ave (33773-5419)
PHONE..................................727 209-0864
Kamal S Juneja, *President*
◆ **EMP:** 7 **EST:** 2004
SALES (est): 1.5MM **Privately Held**
WEB: www.montkrest.com
SIC: 3281 Marble, building: cut & shaped; granite, cut & shaped

(G-8014)
MOTION INDUSTRIES INC
6480 126th Ave (33773-1831)
PHONE..................................727 536-5521
EMP: 6 **EST:** 2019
SALES (est): 39.6K **Privately Held**
WEB: www.motionindustries.com
SIC: 3999 Manufacturing industries

(G-8015)
MRO AEROSPACE INC
10530 72nd St Ste 701 (33777-1522)
PHONE..................................727 546-4820
Albert Machtinger, *President*
Sandi Cornett, *General Mgr*
Elaine Thomas, *Controller*
Sue Harrison, *Accounts Mgr*
Ron Zonenblik, *Sales Staff*
EMP: 14 **EST:** 2001
SQ FT: 10,100
SALES: 4.9MM **Privately Held**
WEB: www.mroaerospace.com
SIC: 3728 Aircraft parts & equipment

(G-8016)
MYTEK INDUSTRIES
11910 62nd St (33773-3705)
PHONE..................................727 536-7891
EMP: 10 **EST:** 2013
SALES (est): 1MM **Privately Held**
WEB: www.mitek-us.com
SIC: 3999 Manufacturing industries

(G-8017)
NAUTICAL ACQUISITIONS CORP
Also Called: Nautical Structures
7301 114th Ave (33773-5104)
PHONE..................................727 541-6664
James Glen, *President*
Stuart Pavir, *Chairman*
Joseph Distefano, *Vice Pres*
▼ **EMP:** 107 **EST:** 1999
SALES (est): 8.7MM
SALES (corp-wide): 57.8MM **Privately Held**
WEB: www.nautical-structures.com
SIC: 3536 5551 5091 Cranes, overhead traveling; boat dealers; boats, canoes, watercrafts & equipment
PA: County Plastics Corp
361 Neptune Ave
West Babylon NY 11704
631 422-8300

(G-8018)
NAUTICAL STRUCTURES INDS INC (PA)
7301 114th Ave (33773-5104)
PHONE..................................727 541-6664
Robert E Bolline, *President*
Rick Thomas, *Vice Pres*
Richard Thomas, *Enginr/R&D Asst*
▲ **EMP:** 69 **EST:** 1987
SALES (est): 16.3MM **Privately Held**
WEB: www.nautical-structures.com
SIC: 3441 3443 3444 Fabricated structural metal; metal parts; sheet metalwork

(G-8019)
OHANRAHAN CONSULTANTS INC
Also Called: Ohmac Chemical Group
6414 125th Ave (33773-3601)
P.O. Box 5301, Clearwater (33758-5301)
PHONE..................................727 531-3375
Edward J O'Hanrahan Jr, *President*
Sandra M Pisano, *Vice Pres*
Sandi Subrize, *Accountant*
Ed O'Hanrahan, *Manager*
Ed O 'hanrahan, *Manager*
EMP: 40 **EST:** 1960
SQ FT: 9,000
SALES (est): 3.4MM **Privately Held**
WEB: www.sunseal.com
SIC: 2841 5087 2842 Detergents, synthetic organic or inorganic alkaline; carwash equipment & supplies; deodorants, nonpersonal

(G-8020)
OMEGA PROF BRICK PAVERS INC
3679 141st Ave Apt B (33771-4022)
PHONE..................................727 243-4659
Josafa S Alves, *Principal*
EMP: 9 **EST:** 2015
SALES (est): 300K **Privately Held**
SIC: 2951 Asphalt paving mixtures & blocks

(G-8021)
ONICON INCORPORATED (HQ)
11451 Belcher Rd S (33773-5110)
PHONE..................................727 447-6140
Marvin J Feldman, *President*
Bowen Ierna, *Exec VP*
Linda Feldman, *Vice Pres*
Ian McKenzie, *Buyer*
Vince Stanziani, *Engineer*
◆ **EMP:** 45 **EST:** 1987
SALES (est): 43.5MM
SALES (corp-wide): 1.2B **Privately Held**
WEB: www.onicon.com
SIC: 3823 Industrial instrmnts msrmnt display/control process variable
PA: Harbour Group Ltd.
7733 Forsyth Blvd Fl 23
Saint Louis MO 63105
314 727-5550

(G-8022)
PANISH CONTROLS
12553 66th St (33773-3440)
PHONE..................................203 333-7371
Robert P Panish Jr, *President*
EMP: 6 **EST:** 1960
SALES (est): 174.2K **Privately Held**
SIC: 3625 Marine & navy auxiliary controls

(G-8023)
PARTI LINE INTERNATIONAL INC
Also Called: Ffutter Fetti
9219 133rd Ave Unit 1e (33773-1314)
PHONE..................................504 522-0300
Ronee Holmes, *CEO*
◆ **EMP:** 10 **EST:** 2007
SALES (est): 1.6MM **Privately Held**
WEB: www.flutterfetti.com
SIC: 2679 Confetti: made from purchased material

(G-8024)
PCM AND S L PLOTA CO LLC
8016 118th Ave (33773-5044)
PHONE..................................727 547-6277
Larry Earl,
Mike Penhallegon,
EMP: 10 **EST:** 2008
SQ FT: 3,000
SALES (est): 289.9K **Privately Held**
SIC: 3845 3694 3559 3089 Medical cleaning equipment, ultrasonic; generators, automotive & aircraft; automotive related machinery; automotive parts, plastic

(G-8025)
PHARMALINK INC
8285 Bryan Dairy Rd # 200 (33777-1350)
PHONE..................................800 257-3527
Hilmer Beckers, *Ch of Bd*
Thierry C Beckers, *President*
Patricia Fitzgerald, *Vice Pres*
Bill Kuypers, *Marketing Staff*
Shannon Erickson, *Manager*
EMP: 150 **EST:** 2000
SQ FT: 50,000
SALES (est): 27MM **Privately Held**
WEB: www.pharmalinkinc.com
SIC: 2834 Pharmaceutical preparations

(G-8026)
PHILLIP ROY INC
13064 Indian Rocks Rd (33774-2001)
P.O. Box 130, Indian Rocks Beach (33785-0130)
PHONE..................................727 593-2700
Ruth Bragman, *President*
Phil Tadol, *Vice Pres*

GEOGRAPHIC

EMP: 6 **EST:** 1988
SQ FT: 5,000
SALES (est): 681.5K **Privately Held**
WEB: www.philliproy.com
SIC: 2731 Textbooks: publishing only, not printed on site

(G-8027)
PINELLAS CUSTOM CABINETS INC
8800 126th Ave (33773-1508)
PHONE..................................727 864-4263
William A Clore, *President*
Linda L Clore, *Vice Pres*
EMP: 8 **EST:** 1974
SQ FT: 6,000
SALES (est): 678.7K **Privately Held**
WEB: www.pinellascustomcabinets.com
SIC: 2434 2521 2511 Wood kitchen cabinets; wood office furniture; wood household furniture

(G-8028)
PLASTIC SOLUTIONS INC
801 West Bay Dr Ste 308 (33770-3264)
PHONE..................................727 202-6815
EMP: 7 **EST:** 2016
SALES (est): 81.8K **Privately Held**
WEB: www.psimp.com
SIC: 3089 Injection molding of plastics

(G-8029)
PMC NORTH AMERICA INC
2060 34th Way (33771-3960)
PHONE..................................727 530-0714
EMP: 14
SQ FT: 12,000
SALES: 2MM **Privately Held**
SIC: 3566 3519 Mfg Speed Changers/Drives Mfg Internal Combustion Engines

(G-8030)
PRECISE TECHNOLOGIES INC
12395 75th St (33773-3033)
PHONE..................................727 535-5594
David Schwanke, *President*
Jim Lyngholm, *General Mgr*
Jeff Messick, *Vice Pres*
Tara M Schwanke, *Admin Sec*
EMP: 15 **EST:** 1999
SQ FT: 6,000
SALES (est): 4.1MM **Privately Held**
WEB: www.precisetechnologies.net
SIC: 3599 3769 3429 Machine shop, jobbing & repair; guided missile & space vehicle parts & auxiliary equipment; manufactured hardware (general)

(G-8031)
PRICE RITE ENGINES LLC
8152 Candlewoode Dr (33773-2910)
PHONE..................................727 600-8206
Joseph Price, *Principal*
EMP: 6 **EST:** 2010
SALES (est): 82.2K **Privately Held**
SIC: 3519 Internal combustion engines

(G-8032)
PULSAR PROCESS MEASUREMENT INC
11451 Belcher Rd S (33773-5110)
P.O. Box 5177, Niceville (32578-5177)
PHONE..................................850 279-4882
Jeffrey Roberts, *President*
Stephen Burton, *Admin Sec*
EMP: 6 **EST:** 2009
SALES (est): 2MM
SALES (corp-wide): 1.2B **Privately Held**
WEB: www.pulsarmeasurement.com
SIC: 3823 Industrial process measurement equipment
HQ: Pulsar Process Measurement Limited
Cardinal Building
Malvern WORCS WR14

(G-8033)
QEM INC
Also Called: Pharmacy Automation Systems
6513 116th Ave (33773-3735)
PHONE..................................727 545-8833
Norman Knoth, *President*
Linda Knoth, *Vice Pres*
▲ **EMP:** 32 **EST:** 1989
SQ FT: 7,000
SALES (est): 6.2MM **Privately Held**
WEB: www.qem.biz
SIC: 3599 Machine shop, jobbing & repair

(G-8034)
QUALITY CMPNENTS TAMPA BAY LLC
6801 114th Ave (33773-5308)
PHONE..................................727 623-4909
Ivan Dotzinski,
◆ **EMP:** 9 **EST:** 1997
SQ FT: 10,000
SALES (est): 2.5MM **Privately Held**
SIC: 2452 Prefabricated wood buildings

(G-8035)
RAYOVAC CORP
7636 91st St (33777-4028)
PHONE..................................727 393-0966
EMP: 6
SALES (est): 641.5K **Privately Held**
SIC: 3692 5063 5531 Mfg Primary Batteries Whol Electrical Equipment Ret Auto/Home Supplies

(G-8036)
RAYTHEON COMPANY
7887 Bryan Dairy Rd # 110 (33777-1455)
P.O. Box 2920 (33779-2920)
PHONE..................................310 647-9438
Mitchell Lee, *Principal*
Hiram Legrand, *Principal*
Julio Lozada, *Opers Staff*
Evenel Bonhomme, *Engineer*
Jim Holder, *Engineer*
EMP: 200
SALES (corp-wide): 56.5B **Publicly Held**
WEB: www.rtx.com
SIC: 3812 3674 3661 3651 Sonar systems & equipment; semiconductors & related devices; telephone & telegraph apparatus; household audio & video equipment
HQ: Raytheon Company
870 Winter St
Waltham MA 02451
781 522-3000

(G-8037)
RAYTHEON COMPANY
7887 Bryan Dairy Rd # 110 (33777-1455)
P.O. Box 2920 (33779-2920)
PHONE..................................727 768-8468
Cesar Bueno, *Engineer*
John Beach, *Manager*
Luis Izquierdo, *Exec Dir*
Michael Campisi, *Director*
EMP: 6
SALES (corp-wide): 56.5B **Publicly Held**
WEB: www.rtx.com
SIC: 3812 3663 3651 Radar systems & equipment; sonar systems & equipment; radio & TV communications equipment; household audio & video equipment
HQ: Raytheon Company
870 Winter St
Waltham MA 02451
781 522-3000

(G-8038)
RAYTHEON COMPANY
7887 Bryan Dairy Rd # 110 (33777-1455)
PHONE..................................310 647-9438
Donna Mc Cullough, *Manager*
Mitchell Lee, *Executive*
EMP: 6
SALES (corp-wide): 56.5B **Publicly Held**
WEB: www.rtx.com
SIC: 3663 Radio & TV communications equipment
HQ: Raytheon Company
870 Winter St
Waltham MA 02451
781 522-3000

(G-8039)
REFTEC INTL SYSTEMS LLC
6950 112th Cir (33773-5209)
PHONE..................................727 290-9830
Jeff Moore, *President*
Tim Naylor, *VP Sales*
Greg D Veltman,
Rick Roland, *Admin Sec*
William G Buckles,
EMP: 12 **EST:** 2008
SQ FT: 9,000
SALES (est): 3MM **Privately Held**
WEB: www.reftec.com
SIC: 3585 Refrigeration & heating equipment

(G-8040)
RENOS LED SLEDS
14548 Sioux Ave (33774-4417)
PHONE..................................727 593-0340
Frederick A Scalf, *Manager*
EMP: 6 **EST:** 2010
SALES (est): 107.1K **Privately Held**
SIC: 3648 Lighting equipment

(G-8041)
REPCO EQUIPMENT LEASING INC
1550 Starkey Rd (33771-3116)
P.O. Box 607, Ozona (34660-0607)
PHONE..................................727 584-3329
Raymond E Purcell, *President*
EMP: 13 **EST:** 1994
SALES (est): 675.1K **Privately Held**
SIC: 2911 7353 Asphalt or asphaltic materials, made in refineries; heavy construction equipment rental

(G-8042)
ROUZBEH INC
Also Called: Frida's Bakery and Cafe
9700 Ulmerton Rd (33771-3603)
PHONE..................................727 587-7077
Jafar Alipour, *President*
Frida Alipour, *Treasurer*
EMP: 24 **EST:** 1991
SQ FT: 5,955
SALES (est): 1.2MM **Privately Held**
WEB: www.fridascafe.com
SIC: 2051 Bakery: wholesale or wholesale/retail combined

(G-8043)
ROYAL CANES
12399 Belcher Rd S # 160 (33773-3053)
PHONE..................................727 474-0792
EMP: 6 **EST:** 2017
SALES (est): 99.8K **Privately Held**
WEB: www.royalcanes.com
SIC: 3999 Manufacturing industries

(G-8044)
RYTEX INDUSTRIES INC
12855 Belcher Rd S (33773-1657)
PHONE..................................727 557-7450
Patrick J McBride, *President*
EMP: 12 **EST:** 2013
SQ FT: 10,000
SALES (est): 415.7K **Privately Held**
WEB: www.rytexindustries.com
SIC: 3999 Barber & beauty shop equipment

(G-8045)
SCHOONER PRINTS INC
8632 115th Ave (33773-4901)
PHONE..................................727 397-8572
Patrick Bluett, *President*
Chris Arrison,
◆ **EMP:** 52 **EST:** 1979
SQ FT: 70,000
SALES (est): 6MM **Privately Held**
WEB: www.schoonerprints.com
SIC: 2759 2789 2221 Screen printing; bookbinding & related work; upholstery, tapestry & wall covering fabrics

(G-8046)
SCOTT-DOUGLAS DESIGN INC
6275 147th Ave (33770)
PHONE..................................727 535-7900
Scott Garrison, *President*
Page Garrison, *Vice Pres*
EMP: 6 **EST:** 1975
SALES (est): 450.2K **Privately Held**
WEB: www.scott-douglasdesign.com
SIC: 2431 Staircases & stairs, wood

(G-8047)
SEA LINK HOLDINGS LLC
13151 66th St (33773-1812)
PHONE..................................727 523-8660
Tara Dunfield, *VP Sls/Mktg*
Victor Saab, *Program Mgr*
Seth Weisberg, *Director*
EMP: 11 **EST:** 2018
SALES (est): 186.5K **Privately Held**
WEB: www.sealinkinternational.com
SIC: 3089 Automotive parts, plastic

(G-8048)
SEA LINK INTERNATIONAL IRB INC (PA)
13151 66th St (33773-1812)
PHONE..................................727 523-8660
Eric Showalter, *President*
Susan McFarland, *Vice Pres*
Melody Brown, *Purchasing*
Jonathan Willis, *Purchasing*
John Newton, *CFO*
◆ **EMP:** 17 **EST:** 1992
SQ FT: 5,300
SALES (est): 49.3MM **Privately Held**
WEB: www.sealinkinternational.com
SIC: 3647 3172 Automotive lighting fixtures; sewing cases

(G-8049)
SEA SYSTEMS GROUP INC
10631 Whittington Ct (33773-1870)
PHONE..................................434 374-9553
Barbara McKinney, *President*
Richard McKinney, *Treasurer*
EMP: 9 **EST:** 1995
SALES (est): 4MM **Privately Held**
SIC: 3714 Motor vehicle parts & accessories

(G-8050)
SECO SOUTH II INC
2111 34th Way (33771-3952)
PHONE..................................727 536-1924
John Edwards, *President*
Kenneth Brown, *Treasurer*
Steve Hope, *Sales Staff*
▼ **EMP:** 15 **EST:** 2007
SALES (est): 3.1MM **Privately Held**
WEB: www.secosouth.com
SIC: 2431 Staircases, stairs & railings

(G-8051)
SIGLO HOLDINGS LLC
8285 Bryan Dairy Rd (33777-1350)
PHONE..................................727 369-5220
EMP: 175
SALES (est): 12.3MM **Privately Held**
SIC: 3648 Mfg Lighting Equipment

(G-8052)
SIGNS NOW
12350 Belcher Rd S 14a (33773-3009)
PHONE..................................727 524-8500
Travis R Masters, *President*
Kris Kay, *Vice Pres*
EMP: 10 **EST:** 1991
SQ FT: 3,000
SALES (est): 1.6MM **Privately Held**
WEB: www.signsnow.com
SIC: 3993 Signs & advertising specialties

(G-8053)
SILLY DANDELIONS INC
Also Called: Missing Galaxy Publishing
525 Oakwood Dr (33771-1433)
PHONE..................................727 400-6590
Jojo Zawawi, *Principal*
EMP: 7 **EST:** 2016
SALES (est): 112K **Privately Held**
SIC: 2741 Miscellaneous publishing

(G-8054)
SKINGEN USA INC
1258 West Bay Dr Ste F (33770-2240)
PHONE..................................727 586-3751
Paul Guilbaud, *Principal*
Alena Voloboeva, *CPA*
EMP: 7 **EST:** 2016
SALES (est): 164K **Privately Held**
WEB: www.skingeninternational.com
SIC: 2834 Pharmaceutical preparations

(G-8055)
SMARTSAT INC
8222 118th Ave Ste 600 (33773-5054)
PHONE..................................727 535-6880
David Akers, *President*
Heidi Akers, *CFO*
Richard Barnes, *CIO*
▼ **EMP:** 15 **EST:** 1996
SQ FT: 5,000

SALES (est): 1.6MM Privately Held
WEB: www.smartsat.com
SIC: 3825 8711 Instruments to measure electricity; electrical or electronic engineering

(G-8056)
SMOKERSVAPORCOM INCORPORATED
1129 Woodbrook Dr (33770-1625)
PHONE....727 258-4942
Barry D Gray, *Principal*
EMP: 6 EST: 2011
SALES (est): 122.3K Privately Held
SIC: 3911 Cigar & cigarette accessories

(G-8057)
SODA SERVICE OF FLORIDA LLC
14184 Mark Dr (33774-5112)
PHONE....727 595-7632
Lisa A Bialaski, *Manager*
EMP: 6 EST: 2006
SALES (est): 928.2K Privately Held
WEB: www.floridasodaservice.com
SIC: 3585 Refrigeration & heating equipment

(G-8058)
SOLIDAR EXPRESS COATINGS LLC
12912 91st St N (33773-1313)
PHONE....727 585-2192
Daniel Plante, *President*
Abe Azar, *Vice Pres*
▲ EMP: 8 EST: 2009
SALES (est): 984K Privately Held
WEB: www.solidarexpress.com
SIC: 3851 Ophthalmic goods

(G-8059)
SOUTHWIRE COMPANY LLC
Also Called: Technology RES A Southwire Co
11211 69th St (33773-5504)
PHONE....727 535-0572
EMP: 39 EST: 2014
SALES (est): 9.2MM Privately Held
SIC: 3613 Power circuit breakers

(G-8060)
ST MARY PHARMACY LLC
Also Called: Good Neighbor Pharmacy
1290 West Bay Dr (33770-2204)
PHONE....727 585-1333
Albert Shaker,
John Shaker,
Marko Shaker,
EMP: 12 EST: 2009
SALES (est): 1MM Privately Held
WEB: www.mygnp.com
SIC: 2834 5912 Pharmaceutical preparations; drug stores

(G-8061)
STRAIGHT POLARITY WELDING INC
Also Called: Honeywell Authorized Dealer
12855 Belcher Rd S Ste 19 (33773-1638)
PHONE....727 530-7224
EMP: 5
SQ FT: 3,500
SALES (est): 350K Privately Held
SIC: 7692 Welding Shop

(G-8062)
SUN COAST PAPER & ENVELOPE INC
Also Called: Gulf Coast Printing
2050 Tall Pines Dr Ste A (33771-3813)
PHONE....727 545-9566
Elaine M Lewis, *President*
Lori A Wardell, *Corp Secy*
Denise Vanmeter, *Manager*
EMP: 21 EST: 1986
SQ FT: 32,000
SALES (est): 426.9K Privately Held
WEB: www.gulfcoastimprinting.com
SIC: 2754 Envelopes: gravure printing

(G-8063)
SUNCOAST MOLDERS INC
Also Called: S M I
10760 76th Ct (33777-1440)
PHONE....727 546-0041
William E Simmers, *President*
EMP: 15 EST: 1990
SQ FT: 20,000
SALES (est): 3.3MM Privately Held
SIC: 3089 Injection molding of plastics

(G-8064)
SUNSHINE FILTERS OF PINELLAS
12415 73rd Ct (33773-3047)
PHONE....727 530-3884
Fred Cooklin, *President*
Mike Terpstra, *Managing Dir*
Horace Baker, *Vice Pres*
Carmine Cardone, *Vice Pres*
EMP: 21 EST: 1985
SQ FT: 21,000
SALES (est): 3.8MM Privately Held
WEB: www.sunshinefilters.com
SIC: 3599 3564 Air intake filters, internal combustion engine, except auto; blowers & fans

(G-8065)
T W A SPORTS INC
10522 75th St (33777-1418)
PHONE....727 541-9831
Thomas W Acker, *Principal*
EMP: 6 EST: 2012
SALES (est): 67.6K Privately Held
WEB: www.quadcamford.com
SIC: 3949 Fishing tackle, general

(G-8066)
THAT SOFTWARE GUY INC
12825 Pineforest Way W (33773-1723)
PHONE....727 533-8109
Scott C Wilson, *Principal*
EMP: 5 EST: 2003
SALES (est): 350.9K Privately Held
WEB: www.thatsoftwareguy.com
SIC: 7372 Prepackaged software

(G-8067)
TIMBERLAND DOOR LLC
12555 Entp Blvd Ste 102 (33773)
PHONE....727 539-8600
Gregory Reynolds, *Opers Staff*
Keith Norder,
Sal Alfaqeer, *Analyst*
Kevin Conkel,
EMP: 30 EST: 2006
SQ FT: 46,000
SALES (est): 8MM Privately Held
WEB: www.timberlanddoor.com
SIC: 2431 Doors & door parts & trim, wood

(G-8068)
TROLLEY BOATS
9470 Ulmerton Rd Ste 6b (33771-3700)
PHONE....727 588-1100
David Beagle, *Manager*
▲ EMP: 9 EST: 2014
SALES (est): 264K Privately Held
WEB: www.trolleyboats.net
SIC: 3732 Boat building & repairing

(G-8069)
TTC-THE TRADING COMPANY INC (PA)
Also Called: Trading Company, The
2062 20th Ave Se (33771-3846)
PHONE....503 982-0880
Helena Vanderwey, *President*
▲ EMP: 21 EST: 2004
SALES (est): 4.6MM Privately Held
WEB: www.grinderwearparts.com
SIC: 3599 Machine & other job shop work

(G-8070)
TUBOS INC
718 4th Ave Ne (33770-5020)
PHONE....727 504-0633
Kevin M Morris, *Vice Pres*
EMP: 7 EST: 2008
SALES (est): 173.3K Privately Held
WEB: www.tubos.biz
SIC: 3296 Mineral wool

(G-8071)
UNIVERSAL PRECISION INDS INC
1876 Lake Ave Se Ste A (33771-3799)
PHONE....727 581-7097
John Sessa, *President*
Frank Dressel, *Vice Pres*
EMP: 6 EST: 1997
SQ FT: 4,000
SALES (est): 420.9K Privately Held
WEB: www.upi-largo.com
SIC: 3625 Motor controls, electric

(G-8072)
VETBIOTEK INC
11401 Belcher Rd S # 260 (33773-5102)
PHONE....727 308-2030
Thomas Bell, *President*
Brian Bell, *Vice Pres*
Kyle Kerley, *Regl Sales Mgr*
EMP: 11 EST: 2014
SQ FT: 6,800
SALES (est): 1.5MM Privately Held
WEB: www.vetbiotek.com
SIC: 2834 Veterinary pharmaceutical preparations

(G-8073)
VGI MEDICAL LLC
Also Called: V G I
11651 87th St (33773-4917)
PHONE....727 565-1235
Dan Grayson, *CEO*
Tony Capute, *Manager*
Scott Ely, *Manager*
Lori Longo, *Manager*
Tov Vestgaarden, *CTO*
EMP: 12 EST: 2007
SALES (est): 1.4MM Privately Held
WEB: www.vgimedical.com
SIC: 3841 Surgical & medical instruments

(G-8074)
VILLAGE SCRIBE PRINTING CO
Also Called: Monthly Media
1548 Shirley Pl (33770-2218)
PHONE....727 585-7388
Kurt E Beard, *President*
Catherine L Beard, *Admin Sec*
EMP: 10 EST: 1975
SQ FT: 1,400
SALES (est): 992K Privately Held
WEB: www.monthly-media.com
SIC: 2752 Commercial printing, offset; publication printing, lithographic

(G-8075)
VISION ENGINEERING LABS
Also Called: Amglo Halogen
8787 Enterprise Blvd (33773-2702)
PHONE....727 812-2000
Larry A Kerchenfaut, *Principal*
EMP: 23
SALES (corp-wide): 180.9K Privately Held
WEB: www.amglo.com
SIC: 3641 Electric lamps
PA: Vision Engineering Laboratories, Inc
215 Gateway Rd
Bensenville IL 60106
630 350-9470

(G-8076)
VISION ENGINEERING LABS
Also Called: Amglo Kemlite Laboratories
8787 Enterprise Blvd (33773-2702)
PHONE....727 812-2035
James Hyland, *President*
Isabela Veigel, *Vice Pres*
Calvin Zhu, *CFO*
Larry A Kerchenfaut, *Treasurer*
Cathy De Carli, *Sales Associate*
▲ EMP: 56 EST: 1985
SQ FT: 3,000
SALES (est): 8.8MM
SALES (corp-wide): 33.3MM Privately Held
WEB: www.amglo.com
SIC: 3677 3679 3646 Electronic transformers; power supplies, all types: static; commercial indusl & institutional electric lighting fixtures
PA: Amglo Kemlite Laboratories, Inc.
215 Gateway Rd
Bensenville IL 60106
630 238-3031

(G-8077)
VISTAPHARM INC
7265 Ulmerton Rd (33771-4809)
PHONE....727 530-1633
Pam Gerber, *Branch Mgr*
Juan Bosch, *Manager*
Valerie Reyes, *Director*
EMP: 25
SQ FT: 34,016
SALES (corp-wide): 57.4MM Privately Held
WEB: www.vistapharm.com
SIC: 2834 Pharmaceutical preparations
HQ: Vistapharm, Inc.
630 Central Ave
New Providence NJ 07974
908 376-1622

(G-8078)
VISTAPHARM INC
13707 66th St (33771-4902)
PHONE....727 530-1633
Francisco Cosme, *Project Mgr*
Jacob Shafer, *Research*
Erin Casto, *Finance*
Brett Johns, *Manager*
Stacey Cypherd, *Supervisor*
EMP: 20
SQ FT: 55,220
SALES (corp-wide): 57.4MM Privately Held
WEB: www.vistapharm.com
SIC: 2834 2833 Proprietary drug products; drugs & herbs: grading, grinding & milling
HQ: Vistapharm, Inc.
630 Central Ave
New Providence NJ 07974
908 376-1622

(G-8079)
WEBB-MASON INC
12397 Belcher Rd S # 240 (33773-3054)
PHONE....727 531-1112
Mark Smith, *Vice Pres*
EMP: 7 Privately Held
WEB: www.webbmason.com
SIC: 2752 Commercial printing, offset; business form & card printing, lithographic
PA: Webb-Mason, Inc.
10830 Gilroy Rd
Hunt Valley MD 21031

(G-8080)
WINDWARD COMMUNICATIONS INC
2401 West Bay Dr Ste 414 (33770-1941)
P.O. Box 1750 (33779-1750)
PHONE....727 584-7191
William Vanbeuning, *President*
Andria Vanbeuning, *General Mgr*
EMP: 8 EST: 1989
SQ FT: 1,500
SALES (est): 702.7K Privately Held
SIC: 2741 Miscellaneous publishing

(G-8081)
ZEUS INDUSTRIES
12545 Creekside Dr (33773-2708)
PHONE....727 530-4373
Franco Fraine, *Manager*
EMP: 7 EST: 2002
SALES (est): 185.8K Privately Held
SIC: 3089 Plastics products

(G-8082)
ZPS POWDERCOATING
6225 118th Ave (33773-3727)
PHONE....727 465-8131
Mike Seibel, *Principal*
EMP: 7 EST: 2017
SALES (est): 292.2K Privately Held
WEB: www.zpspowdercoatings.com
SIC: 3479 Coating of metals & formed products

Laud By Sea
Broward County

(G-8083)
REFLECTIONS BEACH & RESORTWEAR
104 Commercial Blvd (33308-3681)
PHONE....954 776-1230
Elli Mordoch Sr, *Principal*
EMP: 6 EST: 2010
SALES (est): 92.6K Privately Held
SIC: 2253 Bathing suits & swimwear, knit

Lauderdale By The SE
Broward County

(G-8084)
DNA BRANDS INC (PA)
275 E Coml Blvd Ste 208 (33308)
PHONE..................................561 654-5722
Adrian McKenzie-Patasar, *CEO*
Howard Ullman, *President*
EMP: 1 **EST:** 2007
SALES (est): 11.1MM **Publicly Held**
WEB: www.dnabrandsinc.com
SIC: 2086 2095 Carbonated beverages, nonalcoholic: bottled & canned; instant coffee

Lauderdale Lakes
Broward County

(G-8085)
DELAROSA REAL FOODS LLC
Also Called: De La Rosa
2648 Nw 31st Ave (33311-2708)
PHONE..................................718 333-0333
EMP: 54
SALES (est): 4MM **Privately Held**
SIC: 2032 2099 5411 Mfg Canned Specialties Mfg Food Preparations Ret Groceries

(G-8086)
DRINKABLE AIR INC
2944 Nw 27th St Bldg 14 (33311-2039)
PHONE..................................954 533-6415
Steven J Kairis, *President*
Jeff Szur, *Project Mgr*
Reece Carvalho, *Production*
Japheth Grayson, *Sales Dir*
Joseph Mule, *Mktg Dir*
▲ **EMP:** 22 **EST:** 2010
SQ FT: 15,000
SALES (est): 2.9MM **Privately Held**
WEB: www.drinkableair.tech
SIC: 3585 Refrigeration & heating equipment

(G-8087)
DSAS AIR INC
4509 Nw 39th St (33319-4759)
PHONE..................................954 673-5385
Daniel R Silburn, *Principal*
EMP: 11 **EST:** 2011
SALES (est): 3MM **Privately Held**
WEB: www.dsasair.com
SIC: 3822 Air conditioning & refrigeration controls

(G-8088)
HUGH ROBINSON INC
2718 Nw 31st Ave (33311-2034)
P.O. Box 5543, Fort Lauderdale (33310-5543)
PHONE..................................954 484-0660
John S Robinson, *President*
Richard Robinson, *Vice Pres*
Thomas Robinson, *Vice Pres*
EMP: 6 **EST:** 1975
SQ FT: 13,000
SALES (est): 868.9K **Privately Held**
WEB: www.robinsonwalls.com
SIC: 2541 Partitions for floor attachment, prefabricated: wood

(G-8089)
KAMTEX USA INCORPORATED
2916 Nw 28th St (33311-2028)
PHONE..................................954 733-1044
▲ **EMP:** 8 **EST:** 2007
SALES (est): 1MM **Privately Held**
SIC: 2331 2341 2342 5137 Mfg Women/Misses Blouses Mfg Women/Miss Underwear Mfg Bra/Girdles Whol Women/Child Clothng

(G-8090)
KOOKIE KLLECTION KOSMETICS LLC
Also Called: Cosmetics
3601 Nw 44th Ave (33319-5517)
PHONE..................................954 218-4302
Franshetta Sisney, *President*
EMP: 10 **EST:** 2019
SALES (est): 377.1K **Privately Held**
WEB: www.thekookiekollection.returnscenter.com
SIC: 2844 Cosmetic preparations

(G-8091)
MOBILE 1 INC
3680 W Oakland Park Blvd (33311-1148)
PHONE..................................954 283-8100
Mustafa Natour, *Principal*
EMP: 12 **EST:** 2010
SALES (est): 293.2K **Privately Held**
WEB: www.t-mobile.com
SIC: 2911 Oils, lubricating

(G-8092)
RIKS CABINETRY INC
5011 W Oakland Park Blvd (33313-1595)
PHONE..................................561 929-5260
Natalia Sotelos, *Principal*
EMP: 6 **EST:** 2018
SALES (est): 59.1K **Privately Held**
SIC: 2434 Wood kitchen cabinets

(G-8093)
SHORR ENTERPRISES INC
Also Called: New Design Furniture Mfg
3033 Nw 28th St (33311-2029)
PHONE..................................954 733-9840
Linda Shorr, *President*
EMP: 16 **EST:** 2001
SQ FT: 12,000
SALES (est): 1.5MM **Privately Held**
SIC: 3429 7641 Furniture builders' & other household hardware; reupholstery

(G-8094)
STITCH INK INC
2668 Nw 31st Ave (33311-2708)
PHONE..................................954 203-0868
Maria V Laverde Alvarez, *Principal*
EMP: 6 **EST:** 2017
SALES (est): 202.8K **Privately Held**
SIC: 2395 Embroidery & art needlework

(G-8095)
TROPIC SHIELD INC
Also Called: Exotic Interiors
3031 Nw 28th St (33311-2029)
PHONE..................................954 731-5553
William Holiday, *President*
Jeffrey Holiday, *Vice Pres*
Michael Holiday, *Vice Pres*
EMP: 15 **EST:** 1977
SQ FT: 10,000
SALES (est): 408.1K **Privately Held**
SIC: 3442 5211 2591 5719 Shutters, door or window: metal; windows, storm: wood or metal; blinds vertical; vertical blinds; carpets; home improvement & renovation contractor agency

(G-8096)
WEST HARBOUR WOODWORKING LLC
2543 Nw 49th Ave Apt 203 (33313-3347)
PHONE..................................954 822-7543
Vaughan McKenzie, *Principal*
EMP: 6 **EST:** 2013
SALES (est): 270.2K **Privately Held**
SIC: 2431 Millwork

Lauderhill
Broward County

(G-8097)
24HOUR PRINTING INC
7431 Nw 57th St (33319-2101)
PHONE..................................954 247-9575
EMP: 9 **EST:** 2018
SALES (est): 349K **Privately Held**
SIC: 2752 Commercial printing, offset

(G-8098)
A PLUS KITCHEN & BATH
4432 N University Dr (33351-5738)
PHONE..................................754 200-4207
Mary MA, *Principal*
EMP: 6 **EST:** 2007
SALES (est): 114.1K **Privately Held**
WEB: www.apremodel.com
SIC: 2499 Kitchen, bathroom & household ware: wood

(G-8099)
ADD-V LLC
Also Called: Sugart
1801 Nw 38th Ave Ste H (33311-4144)
PHONE..................................305 496-2445
Valeria Garavaglia, *Manager*
Julian Baluk,
EMP: 5 **EST:** 2015
SQ FT: 2,000
SALES (est): 500K **Privately Held**
SIC: 2061 Dry cane sugar products, except refining

(G-8100)
ALLURE SHADES INC
3714 Nw 16th St (33311-4132)
PHONE..................................954 543-6259
Mark Vanwettering, *President*
Sofia V Sanchez, *Vice Pres*
▲ **EMP:** 14 **EST:** 2008
SALES (est): 1.5MM **Privately Held**
WEB: www.allureshadesinc.com
SIC: 3645 Lamp & light shades

(G-8101)
ANNELLIES CAR WASH LLC
6420 Nw 50th St (33319-7252)
PHONE..................................954 990-8436
Rene L Moreno, *Principal*
EMP: 7 **EST:** 2015
SALES (est): 300.6K **Privately Held**
SIC: 3589 Car washing machinery

(G-8102)
BIG STAR SYSTEMS LLC
2061 Nw 47th Ter Apt 200 (33313-4159)
PHONE..................................954 243-7209
Rebecca Castanon,
EMP: 5 **EST:** 2017
SALES (est): 300K **Privately Held**
WEB: www.bigstarsystems.com
SIC: 7372 7389 Prepackaged software;

(G-8103)
BLACKSTONE LEGAL SUPPLIES INC (PA)
Also Called: Blackstone Legal Supply
3732 Nw 16th St (33311-4148)
PHONE..................................305 945-3450
Leslie Heyman, *President*
EMP: 10 **EST:** 1978
SALES (est): 1MM **Privately Held**
WEB: www.blackstonelegal.com
SIC: 2752 2761 Commercial printing, offset; manifold business forms

(G-8104)
COLOR TOUCH INC
3701 Nw 16th St (33311-4135)
PHONE..................................954 444-1999
Nathan Kurliker, *President*
Moshe Kurliker, *Vice Pres*
EMP: 10 **EST:** 1997
SQ FT: 15,000
SALES (est): 3MM **Privately Held**
SIC: 2253 Dyeing & finishing knit outerwear, excl. hosiery & glove

(G-8105)
COMPASS SERVICE
7822 Nw 44th St (33351-6206)
PHONE..................................954 900-4462
EMP: 6 **EST:** 2019
SALES (est): 74.4K **Privately Held**
WEB: www.compass.com
SIC: 2899 Chemical preparations

(G-8106)
CREATIVE BIZ CENTER INC
7860 W Commercial Blvd (33351-4324)
PHONE..................................954 918-7322
Apolonio I Cedeno, *Vice Pres*
EMP: 6 **EST:** 2016
SALES (est): 355.9K **Privately Held**
SIC: 2752 Commercial printing, lithographic

(G-8107)
DAILY THERAPY SERVICES INC
8040 Nw 54th St (33351-5069)
PHONE..................................954 649-3620
Albert J Daley, *Principal*
EMP: 8 **EST:** 2008
SALES (est): 96.2K **Privately Held**
SIC: 2711 Newspapers, publishing & printing

(G-8108)
DINNER BELLE INC ✪
4214 Inverrary Blvd # 89 (33319-4143)
PHONE..................................747 210-6284
Bassey Ironbar, *CEO*
EMP: 7 **EST:** 2021 **Privately Held**
SIC: 2099 7389 Food preparations;

(G-8109)
FASSMER SERVICE AMERICA LLC (HQ)
3650 Nw 15th St (33311-4133)
PHONE..................................305 557-8875
Timothy Klaybor, *Managing Dir*
Kathy Villalba, *Opers Mgr*
Daniel Ramirez, *Senior Engr*
Cannon Schramm, *Senior Engr*
Nelson Figueroa, *Manager*
◆ **EMP:** 21 **EST:** 2008
SALES (est): 16MM
SALES (corp-wide): 262.4MM **Privately Held**
WEB: www.fassmerusa.com
SIC: 3731 Shipbuilding & repairing
PA: Gebr. Fassmer Ag
Industriestr. 2
Berne 27804
440 694-20

(G-8110)
GRAPHIC DIFFERENCE INC A
Also Called: Image360 - Lauderhill
7362 W Commercial Blvd (33319-2128)
PHONE..................................954 748-6990
Brian Meister, *President*
Susan Meister, *Vice Pres*
▼ **EMP:** 12 **EST:** 2004
SQ FT: 4,000
SALES (est): 1.9MM **Privately Held**
SIC: 3993 Signs & advertising specialties

(G-8111)
HAPPY KIDS FOR KIDS INC
3722 Nw 16th St (33311-4132)
PHONE..................................954 730-7922
Bella Ahoron, *President*
Shmaul Ahoron, *Vice Pres*
Eddie Glikc, *Prdtn Mgr*
◆ **EMP:** 15 **EST:** 1997
SQ FT: 16,000
SALES (est): 3.8MM **Privately Held**
WEB: www.happykidsforkids.com
SIC: 2339 Women's & misses' outerwear

(G-8112)
JJC WOODWORKS INC
4796 Nw 67th Ave (33319-7213)
PHONE..................................954 461-0088
James Ciesla, *Principal*
EMP: 6 **EST:** 2016
SALES (est): 87.6K **Privately Held**
SIC: 2431 Millwork

(G-8113)
KEE KREATIVE LLC
3405 Nw 14th Ct (33311-8447)
PHONE..................................954 931-2579
Kurtis Eiben, *Principal*
EMP: 8 **EST:** 2016
SALES (est): 316.5K **Privately Held**
SIC: 2752 Commercial printing, lithographic

(G-8114)
MACIAS GABIONS INC
3801 Environ Blvd Apt 519 (33319-4292)
PHONE..................................850 910-8000
Jorge Macias, *President*
Olga L Quintero, *Vice Pres*
EMP: 6 **EST:** 2013
SALES (est): 79.7K **Privately Held**
SIC: 3315 Steel wire & related products

▲ = Import ▼=Export
◆ =Import/Export

(G-8115)
MIRANDAS WOODCRAFT LLC
3764 Nw 16th St (33311-4132)
PHONE..................................954 306-3568
EMP: 6
SALES (est): 382.1K **Privately Held**
SIC: 2491 1751 Wood Preserving Carpentry Contractor

(G-8116)
MT DISTRIBUTORS LLC
7818 Nw 44th St (33351-6206)
PHONE..................................954 802-2161
Eli Tal,
EMP: 6 **EST:** 2018
SALES (est): 294.4K **Privately Held**
SIC: 3999 Manufacturing industries

(G-8117)
NEW YORK DELI EXPRESS
4630 N University Dr (33351-5753)
PHONE..................................954 572-1442
EMP: 6 **EST:** 2006
SALES (est): 97.8K **Privately Held**
SIC: 2741 Miscellaneous publishing

(G-8118)
OPIF- OUR PLSTIC IS FNTSTIC
698 1/2 Nw 16 Stunits E F (33311)
PHONE..................................954 636-4228
Esther Tepper Barak, *Mng Member*
Zevi Barak,
EMP: 6 **EST:** 2012
SALES (est): 193.6K **Privately Held**
SIC: 3089 Plastic containers, except foam

(G-8119)
P S RESEARCH CORP
3702 Nw 16th St (33311-4132)
PHONE..................................954 558-8727
Gary Mandel, *President*
Dean Koslofsky, *Vice Pres*
Mel Mandel, *Shareholder*
EMP: 9 **EST:** 1989
SQ FT: 5,000
SALES (est): 567.1K **Privately Held**
SIC: 2819 2899 2891 2851 Industrial inorganic chemicals; chemical preparations; adhesives & sealants; paints & allied products

(G-8120)
SPARKLES AND SUSPENDERS FL
5405 Nw 67th Ave (33319-7298)
PHONE..................................754 701-4528
Samuel Y Andrusier, *Principal*
EMP: 5 **EST:** 2018
SALES (est): 359K **Privately Held**
WEB: www.sparklesandsuspenders.com
SIC: 2389 Suspenders

(G-8121)
STONE SYSTEMS SOUTH FLA LLC
3501 Nw 16th St (33311-4157)
PHONE..................................954 584-4058
Kurt Thiemer,
▼ **EMP:** 16 **EST:** 2006
SQ FT: 4,000
SALES (est): 3.5MM **Privately Held**
WEB: www.silestone.com
SIC: 1411 Dimension stone

(G-8122)
THALERS PRINTING CENTER INC
Also Called: Thaler's Printing Cetner
4970 N University Dr (33351-5748)
PHONE..................................954 741-6522
Gary Thaler, *President*
Morton Thaler, *Trustee*
Warren Thaler, *Vice Pres*
EMP: 8 **EST:** 1979
SQ FT: 3,700
SALES (est): 729.1K **Privately Held**
SIC: 2752 5943 2791 2789 Commercial printing, offset; office forms & supplies; typesetting; bookbinding & related work

(G-8123)
VARIANCE REYNOLDS MTC
3810 Nw 7th St (33311-6314)
PHONE..................................954 765-6320
Nicolas Hernandez, *Owner*
EMP: 6 **EST:** 2010
SALES (est): 91.5K **Privately Held**
SIC: 3931 Mouthpieces for musical instruments

Lawtey
Bradford County

(G-8124)
CRAWFORDS CUSTOM WOODWORK
21535 Us Highway 301 N (32058-4237)
PHONE..................................904 782-1375
John Crawford, *Principal*
EMP: 6 **EST:** 2017
SALES (est): 59.5K **Privately Held**
WEB: www.crawfordscustomwoodworks.com
SIC: 2431 Millwork

(G-8125)
PROFESSIONAL COATING SYSTEMS
2187 Nw 247th St (32058-3106)
PHONE..................................904 477-7138
William Price, *Principal*
Morgan Price, *Principal*
EMP: 6 **EST:** 2019
SALES (est): 451.4K **Privately Held**
SIC: 3731 Shipbuilding & repairing

(G-8126)
TATUM BROTHERS LUMBER CO INC
22796 Nw County Road 200a (32058-4212)
P.O. Box A (32058-0701)
PHONE..................................904 782-3690
Charles W Tatum, *President*
John Tatum, *Vice Pres*
Thomas W Tatum Jr, *Vice Pres*
Thomas W Tatum III, *Vice Pres*
Linda Tatum, *Treasurer*
EMP: 26 **EST:** 1963
SQ FT: 1,000
SALES (est): 1.1MM **Privately Held**
SIC: 2421 Sawdust & shavings

Lecanto
Citrus County

(G-8127)
ALL-BRITE SIGNS ✪
3376 W Pennington Ct (34461-7425)
PHONE..................................352 628-4910
EMP: 6 **EST:** 2020
SALES (est): 270.9K **Privately Held**
WEB: www.all-britesigns.com
SIC: 3993 Signs & advertising specialties

(G-8128)
BILL EVANS ALUMINUM INC
5831 S Gray Oak Ter (34461-9374)
PHONE..................................352 400-1424
Bill S Evans, *Principal*
EMP: 9 **EST:** 2008
SALES (est): 510.2K **Privately Held**
SIC: 3463 7389 Aluminum forgings; business services

(G-8129)
BRUCE COMPONENT SYSTEMS INC
3409 W Pennington Ct (34461-8854)
P.O. Box 730 (34460-0730)
PHONE..................................352 628-0522
Ret Bruce, *President*
EMP: 14 **EST:** 1985
SALES (est): 1.2MM **Privately Held**
SIC: 2439 Trusses, wooden roof

(G-8130)
CAVALLO ESTATE WINERY LLC
8123 S Lecanto Hwy (34461-9072)
PHONE..................................352 500-9463
Katie Wright, *COO*
Philip J Bomhoff Jr, *Mng Member*
Pien Bomhoff,
EMP: 7 **EST:** 2016
SALES (est): 519K **Privately Held**
WEB: www.cavalloestatewinery.com
SIC: 2084 7389 Wines;

(G-8131)
CEMEX CNSTR MTLS FLA LLC
Also Called: Lecanto Ready Mix Con Plant
2975 S Lecanto Hwy (34461-9022)
PHONE..................................352 746-0136
Jerry Hays, *Branch Mgr*
EMP: 7 **Privately Held**
SIC: 3273 Ready-mixed concrete
HQ: Cemex Construction Materials Florida, Llc
1501 Belvedere Rd
West Palm Beach FL 33406

(G-8132)
CITRUS COUNTY LIFE MAGAZINE
305 S Salisbury Ter (34461-5502)
PHONE..................................352 341-4769
Steve Tallman, *Advt Staff*
Joanne Crowley, *Director*
EMP: 6 **EST:** 2019
SALES (est): 202.4K **Privately Held**
WEB: www.citruscountylife.com
SIC: 2741 Miscellaneous publishing

(G-8133)
DMA CABINETS INC
1653b W Gulf To Lake Hwy (34461-7723)
PHONE..................................352 249-8147
David J Beccia, *Principal*
EMP: 12 **EST:** 2016
SALES (est): 283.3K **Privately Held**
WEB: www.dma-cabinets-inc.business.site
SIC: 2434 Wood kitchen cabinets

(G-8134)
GILMANS CUSTOM FURN & CABINETS
Also Called: Gilman's Cabinets
4625 W Homosassa Trl (34461-9107)
PHONE..................................352 746-3532
Lloyd F Gilman, *President*
Patricia Gilman, *Corp Secy*
EMP: 10 **EST:** 1973
SQ FT: 7,400
SALES (est): 732K **Privately Held**
WEB: www.gilmanscabinets.com
SIC: 2511 2521 2434 Wood household furniture; wood office furniture; wood kitchen cabinets

(G-8135)
JWN FAMILY PARTNERS LP LTD
Also Called: All-Bright Signs
6198 S Lecanto Hwy (34461-9057)
PHONE..................................352 628-4910
John W Nemeth, *Partner*
John T Nemeth, *Partner*
Judy Nemeth, *Partner*
EMP: 5 **EST:** 1983
SALES (est): 410K **Privately Held**
SIC: 3993 Signs & advertising specialties

(G-8136)
KCI
24 S Ponder Ave (34461-8030)
PHONE..................................352 572-2873
EMP: 9 **EST:** 2014
SALES (est): 129.6K **Privately Held**
WEB: www.kci.com
SIC: 2599 Hospital beds

Lee
Madison County

(G-8137)
C F WEBB AND SONS LOGGING LLC
625 Se Old Logging Trl (32059-6264)
PHONE..................................850 971-5565
Coye Webb, *Administration*
EMP: 7 **EST:** 2014
SALES (est): 570.1K **Privately Held**
SIC: 2411 Logging camps & contractors

Leesburg
Lake County

(G-8138)
ADVANCE HYDRAULIC SERVICES
1511 South St (34748-6629)
PHONE..................................352 502-9462
Alexi Alvelo, *Vice Pres*
EMP: 5 **EST:** 2013
SALES (est): 400K **Privately Held**
SIC: 3599 Machine shop, jobbing & repair

(G-8139)
AERO FUEL LLC
9595 Silver Lake Dr (34788-3406)
PHONE..................................352 728-2018
Lester A Coggins Jr, *Principal*
EMP: 7 **EST:** 2009
SALES (est): 160.4K **Privately Held**
WEB: www.umatillaaero.com
SIC: 2869 Fuels

(G-8140)
AKERS MEDIA GROUP INC
108 S 5th St Ste 201 (34748-5856)
P.O. Box 490088 (34749-0088)
PHONE..................................352 787-4112
Michael Akers, *President*
Doug Akers, *Vice Pres*
Tim McRae, *Vice Pres*
Heidi Ressler, *Marketing Staff*
Aubrey Akers, *Office Mgr*
EMP: 19 **EST:** 2008
SALES (est): 3.1MM **Privately Held**
WEB: www.akersmediagroup.com
SIC: 2721 Magazines: publishing & printing

(G-8141)
AMTEX-NMS HOLDINGS INC (PA)
2500 Industrial St (34748-3609)
PHONE..................................352 728-2930
Jim Ginas, *President*
David Meyer, *Chairman*
Les Berczy, *COO*
EMP: 56 **EST:** 1999
SALES (est): 88.3MM **Privately Held**
WEB: www.southeastmodular.net
SIC: 3448 Prefabricated metal buildings

(G-8142)
ANCHOR COATINGS LEESBURG INC
2280 Talley Rd (34748-3316)
PHONE..................................352 728-0777
Gary Tutor, *President*
Amanda Schick, *Vice Pres*
Debbie Tutor, *Treasurer*
EMP: 20 **EST:** 1989
SQ FT: 15,000
SALES (est): 3.1MM **Privately Held**
WEB: www.anchorcoatings.com
SIC: 2851 2891 2821 Paints & paint additives; lacquers, varnishes, enamels & other coatings; adhesives & sealants; plastics materials & resins

(G-8143)
ARCHITECTURAL MASTERS LLC
2319 Griffin Rd (34748-3307)
PHONE..................................239 290-2250
David Ashenbrener, *Principal*
EMP: 6 **EST:** 2016
SALES (est): 267.4K **Privately Held**
SIC: 3272 Concrete products

(G-8144)
BAILEY INDUSTRIES INC (PA)
1107 Thomas Ave (34748-3631)
P.O. Box 490090 (34749-0090)
PHONE..................................352 326-2898
Elijah J Bailey, *President*
▲ **EMP:** 40 **EST:** 1992
SQ FT: 15,000
SALES (est): 42.4MM **Privately Held**
WEB: www.baileyind.com
SIC: 2434 Vanities, bathroom: wood

(G-8145)
BLINDS PLUS SHUTTERS & SHADES
2315 Griffin Rd Ste 8 (34748-3338)
PHONE..................................352 430-7200
EMP: 6 **EST:** 2019
SALES (est): 127.8K **Privately Held**
WEB: www.blindsplus-shutters.com
SIC: 2591 Window blinds

(G-8146)
CENTRAL PROCESSING CORP
304 Richey Rd (34748-7165)
P.O. Box 435, Astatula (34705-0435)
PHONE..................................352 787-3004
John Sonnentag, *Principal*
EMP: 7 **EST:** 2008
SALES (est): 153.5K **Privately Held**
SIC: 3589 Water treatment equipment, industrial

(G-8147)
COLUMBIA PARCAR CORP
2505 Industrial St (34748-3608)
P.O. Box 493744 (34749-3744)
PHONE..................................352 753-0244
Ron Sheldon, *Manager*
EMP: 10 **Privately Held**
WEB: www.columbiavehicles.com
SIC: 3799 Golf carts, powered
HQ: Columbia Vehicle Group, Inc.
1115 Commercial Ave
Reedsburg WI 53959
608 524-8888

(G-8148)
CONSOLIDATED MINERALS INC (PA)
Also Called: CMI
8500 Us Highway 441 (34788-4017)
P.O. Box 490180 (34749-0180)
PHONE..................................352 365-6522
Frederick B Gregg, *Ch of Bd*
Fred J Houton, *President*
Jeff Cherry, *VP Opers*
Clint Young, *Opers Staff*
Gary L Jones, *CFO*
◆ **EMP:** 10 **EST:** 2000
SQ FT: 20,000
SALES (est): 52.2MM **Privately Held**
WEB: www.cmineralsinc.com
SIC: 3272 Concrete products

(G-8149)
CUTRALE CITRUS JUICES USA INC
Also Called: Foods Div
11 Cloud St (34748-5306)
PHONE..................................352 728-7800
Jim Fitzgerald, *Vice Pres*
Cathia Pizetta, *Plant Mgr*
Susan Hudgins, *Purchasing*
Michelle Churchill, *Human Resources*
Omaryliz Colon, *Human Resources*
EMP: 294
SQ FT: 68,840
SALES (corp-wide): 1.2B **Privately Held**
WEB: www.cutrale.com
SIC: 2037 2086 2033 Fruit juices; bottled & canned soft drinks; fruit juices: packaged in cans, jars, etc.
HQ: Cutrale Citrus Juices Usa, Inc.
602 Mckean St
Auburndale FL 33823

(G-8150)
DIP-A-DEE DONUTS
1376 W North Blvd (34748-3900)
PHONE..................................352 460-4266
Kevin J Robson, *President*
Sandy Kurtis, *Principal*
Val Robson, *Vice Pres*
EMP: 20 **EST:** 1986
SQ FT: 1,200
SALES (est): 1.9MM **Privately Held**
SIC: 2051 5461 4225 Doughnuts, except frozen; doughnuts; general warehousing & storage

(G-8151)
DUCKSTEINS SERVICES
3 Morgan Ave (34748-8912)
PHONE..................................352 449-5678
Brittany Duckstein, *Owner*
EMP: 6 **EST:** 2018
SALES (est): 300K **Privately Held**
WEB: www.ducksteins.com
SIC: 1389 Construction, repair & dismantling services

(G-8152)
DURA-STRESS INC (PA)
Also Called: Allendale Hunting Management
11325 County Road 44 (34788-2615)
P.O. Box 490779 (34749-0779)
PHONE..................................352 787-1422
G Kent Fuller, *President*
Tim Morley, *General Mgr*
Ryan Wiles, *Project Mgr*
Charlie Baker, *Chief Engr*
Ken Kepley, *CFO*
▲ **EMP:** 169 **EST:** 1950
SQ FT: 11,970
SALES (est): 45MM **Privately Held**
WEB: www.durastress.com
SIC: 3272 Prestressed concrete products

(G-8153)
DYNAMIC ALLOY
1018 W North Blvd Ste A (34748-5057)
PHONE..................................352 728-7600
EMP: 12
SALES (est): 57.2K **Privately Held**
SIC: 3398 Metal Treating Of Metals

(G-8154)
ELITE ENCLOSURES
2505 Industrial St (34748-3608)
PHONE..................................352 323-6005
William R Sauey, *Principal*
EMP: 13 **EST:** 2012
SALES (est): 394.5K **Privately Held**
WEB: www.eliteenclosuresusa.com
SIC: 3799 3711 Golf carts, powered; personnel carriers (motor vehicles), assembly of
PA: Nordic Group Of Companies Ltd.
715 Lynn Ave Ste 100
Baraboo WI 53913

(G-8155)
FFO LEESBURG LLC
9917 Us Highway 441 (34788-3922)
PHONE..................................352 315-0783
Thomas A Marino, *President*
EMP: 6 **EST:** 2015
SALES (est): 225K **Privately Held**
SIC: 3069 Flooring, rubber: tile or sheet

(G-8156)
FLATWOODS FOREST PRODUCTS INC
240 State Road 44 (34748-9488)
PHONE..................................352 787-1161
Charles K Sellars, *President*
Darrell C Sellars, *Principal*
EMP: 15 **EST:** 2003
SQ FT: 3,500
SALES (est): 330K **Privately Held**
SIC: 2411 Logging camps & contractors; timber, cut at logging camp

(G-8157)
FLC MACHINES INC
8010 Us Highway 441 (34788-8243)
P.O. Box 863, Coffeyville KS (67337-0863)
PHONE..................................352 728-2303
Frederick Froelich, *President*
Onzelle Froelich, *Admin Sec*
EMP: 20 **EST:** 1968
SQ FT: 12,000
SALES (est): 817.5K **Privately Held**
WEB: www.flcmachines.com
SIC: 3599 Custom machinery

(G-8158)
FLYING COLORS AIR PARTS
2727 W Main St (34748-4630)
PHONE..................................352 728-1900
EMP: 10 **EST:** 2016
SALES (est): 679.5K **Privately Held**
WEB: www.flyingcolorsairparts.com
SIC: 3728 Aircraft parts & equipment

(G-8159)
FORD PRESS INC
305 S Canal St (34748-5903)
P.O. Box 490480 (34749-0480)
PHONE..................................352 787-4650
Richard Kelley, *President*
Dean Simmons, *Vice Pres*
Kaylyn Harrell,
EMP: 18 **EST:** 1957
SQ FT: 7,000
SALES (est): 2.4MM **Privately Held**
WEB: www.fordpress.com
SIC: 2752 2791 Commercial printing, offset; typesetting

(G-8160)
HAMMOND ENTERPRISES
1460 William St (34748-3811)
PHONE..................................386 575-2402
Les Hammond, *Principal*
EMP: 7 **EST:** 2000
SALES (est): 115.7K **Privately Held**
SIC: 2711 Newspapers

(G-8161)
HARBORPOINT MEDIA LLC (PA)
Also Called: Daily Commercial
212 E Main St (34748-5227)
P.O. Box 490007 (34749-0007)
PHONE..................................352 365-8200
Michael Redding, *CEO*
Rich Pinder, *CFO*
Jordan Walker, *Accounts Exec*
Liana Davis, *Legal Staff*
Joanne French, *Representative*
EMP: 116 **EST:** 2004
SALES (est): 10.9MM **Privately Held**
WEB: www.dailycommercial.com
SIC: 2711 Newspapers, publishing & printing

(G-8162)
JAY BERRY SIGNS
125 Montclair Rd Ste 1 (34748-9773)
P.O. Box 491620 (34749-1620)
PHONE..................................352 805-4050
EMP: 10 **EST:** 2018
SALES (est): 922.8K **Privately Held**
WEB: www.jayberrysigns.com
SIC: 3993 Signs & advertising specialties

(G-8163)
LEESBURG CONCRETE COMPANY INC
1335 Thomas Ave (34748-3223)
PHONE..................................352 787-4177
Lannie M Thomas, *President*
Shawn Thomas, *Vice Pres*
Rick Groves, *Opers Mgr*
Susan Kindle, *Sales Staff*
Kirk Revse, *Mktg Dir*
EMP: 50 **EST:** 1983
SQ FT: 4,500
SALES (est): 12.9MM **Privately Held**
WEB: www.leesburgconcrete.com
SIC: 3499 3272 Metal ladders; concrete products

(G-8164)
M S AMTEX-N INC
Also Called: Southeast Modular Mfg
2500 Industrial St (34748-3609)
PHONE..................................352 326-9729
Jim Ginas, *President*
David Meyer, *Chairman*
Les Berczy, *COO*
Barbara Hicks, *Sales Staff*
John Marzicola, *Sales Staff*
EMP: 150 **EST:** 1975
SQ FT: 65,000
SALES (est): 49.4MM
SALES (corp-wide): 88.3MM **Privately Held**
WEB: www.southeastmodular.net
SIC: 3448 Buildings, portable: prefabricated metal
PA: Amtex-Nms Holdings, Inc.
2500 Industrial St
Leesburg FL 34748
352 728-2930

(G-8165)
MASON-FLORIDA LLC
2415 Griffin Rd (34748-3201)
P.O. Box 59226, Birmingham AL (35259-9226)
PHONE..................................352 638-9003
Allen Applebee,
EMP: 13 **EST:** 2002
SALES (est): 730K **Privately Held**
SIC: 2394 Canopies, fabric: made from purchased materials

(G-8166)
MINUTEMAN PRESS
1417 E Main St (34748-5377)
PHONE..................................352 728-6333
EMP: 7 **EST:** 2018
SALES (est): 318.6K **Privately Held**
WEB: www.minutemanpress.com
SIC: 2752 Commercial printing, lithographic

(G-8167)
MOBILE POWER GENERATORS LLC
Also Called: Power Technology Southeast
634 State Road 44 (34748-8103)
P.O. Box 490133 (34749-0133)
PHONE..................................352 365-2777
Christopher Gray, *CFO*
EMP: 33
SALES (est): 4.5MM **Privately Held**
WEB: www.powertechgenerators.com
SIC: 3621 Generator sets: gasoline, diesel or dual-fuel

(G-8168)
PTSE HOLDING INC
Also Called: Powertech Generators
634 State Road 44 (34748-8103)
P.O. Box 490133 (34749-0133)
PHONE..................................800 760-0027
Gerald Hayman, *President*
Jim Fudge, *Corp Secy*
Chris Gray, *CFO*
Bill Dauley, *Sales Mgr*
▲ **EMP:** 33 **EST:** 1989
SQ FT: 19,000
SALES (est): 6.6MM **Privately Held**
SIC: 3621 Generator sets: gasoline, diesel or dual-fuel

(G-8169)
QUALITY CUSTOM CABINET DESIGN
2215 Griffin Rd (34748-3305)
P.O. Box 491117 (34749-1117)
PHONE..................................352 728-4292
Mark Daigneau, *President*
EMP: 8 **EST:** 1980
SQ FT: 7,550
SALES (est): 200K **Privately Held**
SIC: 2434 5064 5032 5039 Wood kitchen cabinets; electrical appliances, major; marble building stone; structural assemblies, prefabricated: non-wood

(G-8170)
SEAHILL PRESS INC
214 N 3rd St Ste A (34748-5141)
PHONE..................................805 845-8636
Gregory Sharp, *Principal*
EMP: 7 **EST:** 2018
SALES (est): 286.4K **Privately Held**
WEB: www.seahillpress.com
SIC: 2741 Miscellaneous publishing

(G-8171)
SHAR FAMILY ENTERPRISES LLC
2207 Aitkin Loop (34748-2964)
PHONE..................................352 365-6988
Htun Tin Shar, *Principal*
EMP: 6 **EST:** 2009
SALES (est): 169K **Privately Held**
SIC: 3356 Nonferrous rolling & drawing

(G-8172)
SIGN DESIGN OF FLORIDA INC
Also Called: Mid Florida Signs
3602 Parkway Blvd Ste 2 (34748-8591)
PHONE..................................352 787-3882
Richard Hayes, *President*
Chris Singh, *Opers Mgr*
Keith Chapman, *VP Bus Dvlpt*
Chad Vaneffen, *Accounts Mgr*
EMP: 24 **EST:** 1941
SQ FT: 6,000
SALES (est): 2.9MM **Privately Held**
WEB: www.midflsigns.com
SIC: 3993 7389 Signs & advertising specialties; sign painting & lettering shop

(G-8173)
SIGNCRAFTERS OF CENTRAL FLA
1134 E North Blvd (34748-5350)
PHONE.................................352 323-1862
Dennis Martin, *President*
EMP: 18 **EST:** 2007
SQ FT: 6,000
SALES (est): 2.2MM **Privately Held**
WEB: www.signcraftersflorida.com
SIC: 3993 Electric signs

(G-8174)
SOUTH CAROLINA MINERALS INC (PA)
8500 Us Highway 441 (34788-4017)
P.O. Box 490180 (34749-0180)
PHONE.................................352 365-6522
Fred Horton Jr, *President*
EMP: 81 **EST:** 2012
SALES (est): 1.2MM **Privately Held**
WEB: www.cmineralsinc.com
SIC: 1429 Grits mining (crushed stone)

(G-8175)
SUNSHINE CANVAS INC
240 State Road 44 (34748-9488)
PHONE.................................352 787-4436
Russell D Sellars, *President*
EMP: 8 **EST:** 2017
SALES (est): 284.8K **Privately Held**
SIC: 2211 Canvas

(G-8176)
TECHNICUFF CORP
2525 Industrial St (34748-3608)
PHONE.................................352 326-2833
William L Yandell, *President*
Julie Yandell, *Vice Pres*
Scott Van Dyken, *Marketing Staff*
Jenna Hall, *Manager*
EMP: 10 **EST:** 1992
SQ FT: 5,000
SALES (est): 1.1MM **Privately Held**
WEB: www.technicuff.com
SIC: 3841 5047 Blood pressure apparatus; medical equipment & supplies

(G-8177)
TOP LINE INSTALLATION INC
Also Called: Connectsure
2134 Aitkin Loop (34748-2960)
PHONE.................................352 636-4192
Andre Desforges, *Principal*
EMP: 10 **EST:** 2010
SALES (est): 241.8K **Privately Held**
SIC: 3822 7382 Building services monitoring controls, automatic; security systems services

(G-8178)
TOTAL NUTRITION TECHNOLOGY LLC
Also Called: TNT Supplements
154 Park Center St Ste A (34748-4640)
PHONE.................................352 435-0050
Lourdes McAgy, *President*
Lou Fernandez, *Plant Mgr*
Steve Nault, *Mktg Dir*
▲ **EMP:** 20
SQ FT: 4,000
SALES (est): 6MM **Privately Held**
WEB: www.totalnutritiontech.com
SIC: 2099 Food preparations

(G-8179)
TUCKERS MACHINE & STL SVC INC
400 County Road 468 (34748-8548)
P.O. Box 492810 (34749-2810)
PHONE.................................352 787-3157
B Murraytucker III, *President*
Matthew C Tucker, *Corp Secy*
Bascom M Tucker Jr, *Director*
Charles B Tucker, *Director*
▼ **EMP:** 58 **EST:** 1991
SQ FT: 10,000
SALES (est): 10MM **Privately Held**
WEB: www.tuckerbilt.com
SIC: 3441 3599 Fabricated structural metal; machine shop, jobbing & repair

(G-8180)
WALLING CRATE COMPANY
507 N 14th St (34748-4252)
PHONE.................................352 787-5211
Robert Walling, *President*
Mark Sullivan, *Sales Staff*
EMP: 13 **EST:** 1917
SQ FT: 35,000
SALES (est): 186.2K **Privately Held**
SIC: 2448 2449 Pallets, wood; fruit crates, wood: wirebound

(G-8181)
WOLVERINE ADVANCED MTLS LLC
10825 County Road 44 (34788-2616)
PHONE.................................352 787-3015
Scott Rauwald, *General Mgr*
Remi Riou, *General Mgr*
Peter Knittig, *Managing Dir*
Terry Ray, *Opers-Prdtn-Mfg*
Luiz Felipe, *Sales Mgr*
EMP: 6
SQ FT: 50,000
SALES (corp-wide): 2.4B **Publicly Held**
WEB: www.wamglobal.com
SIC: 3559 3714 Automotive related machinery; motor vehicle parts & accessories
HQ: Wolverine Advanced Materials, Llc
5850 Mercury Dr Ste 250
Dearborn MI 48126

(G-8182)
YOUR CABINET SOURCE INC
2606 South St Ste 4 (34748-8704)
PHONE.................................352 728-3806
Jimmy Griffith, *Director*
EMP: 6 **EST:** 2019
SALES (est): 202.6K **Privately Held**
WEB: www.yourcabinetsourceinc.com
SIC: 2434 Wood kitchen cabinets

Lehigh Acres
Lee County

(G-8183)
A MORRIS INDUSTRIES LLC
3824 23rd St W (33971-7571)
PHONE.................................239 308-2199
Alfredo Morris, *Principal*
EMP: 8 **EST:** 2017
SALES (est): 195.8K **Privately Held**
WEB: www.morris-industries.com
SIC: 3999 Manufacturing industries

(G-8184)
AIR DOCTOR OF SWFL LLC
1020 Jackson Ave (33972-3522)
PHONE.................................239 285-8774
Abraham Cortez, *CEO*
EMP: 6 **EST:** 2017
SALES (est): 208K **Privately Held**
SIC: 3585 7623 Air conditioning units, complete: domestic or industrial; air conditioning repair

(G-8185)
BESCUTTER LLC
2225 Carnaby Ct (33973-6035)
PHONE.................................888 525-2897
Shuming Zhang,
◆ **EMP:** 6 **EST:** 2015
SALES (est): 1MM **Privately Held**
WEB: www.bescutter.com
SIC: 3541 Ultrasonic metal cutting machine tools

(G-8186)
CAHILL CONSTRUCTION SERVICES
212 Lake Dr (33936-7020)
PHONE.................................239 369-9290
Micheal Cahill, *President*
Nemorio Ruiz, *Vice Pres*
EMP: 7 **EST:** 2002
SALES (est): 680.6K **Privately Held**
WEB: www.cahillconstructionservices.com
SIC: 3292 Pipe covering (heat insulating material), except felt

(G-8187)
CHACHO CUSTOMS
2401 Gretchen Ave S F (33973-3713)
PHONE.................................239 369-4664
Ezequiel Garcia, *Principal*
EMP: 6 **EST:** 2005
SALES (est): 116.8K **Privately Held**
SIC: 3089 Tires, plastic

(G-8188)
CHARLES SCREENING & ALUM LLC
848 Theodore Vail St E (33974-9769)
P.O. Box 1648 (33970-1648)
PHONE.................................239 369-0551
Mark Charles, *Owner*
EMP: 5 **EST:** 2002
SALES (est): 410.9K **Privately Held**
WEB: www.charlesscreening.com
SIC: 3448 Screen enclosures

(G-8189)
EAST SIDE PRINTING & PUBG
27 Homestead Rd N Ste 53 (33936-6673)
P.O. Box 1525 (33970-1525)
PHONE.................................239 369-1244
Charles G Hodde Jr, *Principal*
EMP: 6 **EST:** 2007
SALES (est): 109.8K **Privately Held**
WEB: www.eastsideprinting.net
SIC: 2752 Commercial printing, lithographic

(G-8190)
EASY PICKER GOLF PRODUCTS INC
415 Leonard Blvd N (33971-6302)
PHONE.................................239 368-6600
Giles Meyer, *President*
Scott Meyer, *General Mgr*
George Hedlund, *Exec VP*
Brett Graham, *Vice Pres*
Angel Fernandez, *Mfg Mgr*
◆ **EMP:** 33 **EST:** 1984
SQ FT: 45,000
SALES (est): 5.9MM **Privately Held**
WEB: www.easypicker.com
SIC: 3949 Driving ranges, golf, electronic

(G-8191)
GOOD TIMES SPORTS BAR AND GRIL
700 Leeland Hts Blvd W (33936-6660)
PHONE.................................239 369-7000
EMP: 6
SALES (est): 525.1K **Privately Held**
SIC: 2599 Mfg Furniture/Fixtures

(G-8192)
INDUSTRIAL REPAIR INC
551 Westgate Blvd Ste 111 (33971-6315)
P.O. Box 1896 (33970-1896)
PHONE.................................239 368-7435
Jim Miller,
Frank R Miller,
EMP: 12 **EST:** 2004
SALES (est): 538.2K **Privately Held**
SIC: 7692 Welding repair

(G-8193)
JEANIUS PUBLISHING LLC
108 Airview Ave (33936-6972)
P.O. Box 1562 (33970-1562)
PHONE.................................239 560-5229
Pierre Jeanty, *Principal*
EMP: 5 **EST:** 2016
SALES (est): 312.6K **Privately Held**
WEB: www.jeaniuspublishing.com
SIC: 2741 Miscellaneous publishing

(G-8194)
LANAI BRIGHT LLC
200 Waldo Ave Unit 1 (33971-6345)
PHONE.................................239 303-4756
EMP: 6 **EST:** 2016
SALES (est): 119.4K **Privately Held**
WEB: www.lanaibright.com
SIC: 3648 Lighting equipment

(G-8195)
LEALS TIRES & WHEELS
1585 Gretchen Ave S # 1 (33973-2616)
PHONE.................................239 491-2214
Leal Epimenio, *Principal*
EMP: 7 **EST:** 2011
SALES (est): 728.2K **Privately Held**
WEB: www.lealstiresandwheels.webs.com
SIC: 3312 Wheels

(G-8196)
LEHIGH ACRS FRE CNRL & RSCUE
636 Thomas Sherwin Ave S (33974-0555)
PHONE.................................239 303-5300
Donald Adams, *Principal*
Anita Kressel, *Finance Mgr*
Tim Mace, *Technology*
Katie Heck, *Officer*
EMP: 39 **EST:** 2008
SALES (est): 5.3MM **Privately Held**
WEB: www.lehighfd.com
SIC: 3699 Fire control or bombing equipment, electronic

(G-8197)
LIBERTY ALUMINUM CO
5613a 6th St W (33971-6323)
PHONE.................................239 369-3000
James E Lowndes, *President*
James D Guerin, *Vice Pres*
Wayne Rafalski, *Project Mgr*
Yvette Worthington, *Opers Staff*
Maureen Grosso, *Controller*
▲ **EMP:** 50 **EST:** 1993
SQ FT: 7,500
SALES (est): 9MM **Privately Held**
WEB: www.libertyaluminum.com
SIC: 3446 1799 3444 3354 Architectural metalwork; screening contractor: window, door, etc.; sheet metalwork; aluminum extruded products

(G-8198)
MARATHON ENGINEERING CORP
Also Called: Specialty Contractor
5615 2nd St W (33971-6332)
PHONE.................................239 303-7378
George Hrunka, *President*
EMP: 30 **EST:** 1974
SQ FT: 7,800
SALES (est): 7.2MM **Privately Held**
WEB: www.goldmedalsafetypadding.com
SIC: 3069 Rubber floor coverings, mats & wallcoverings; wallcoverings, rubber

(G-8199)
MIL-TEC INCORPORATED
5578 6th St W (33971-6327)
PHONE.................................239 369-2880
David Povich, *Principal*
John Forest, *Vice Pres*
EMP: 22 **EST:** 2003
SALES (est): 1MM **Privately Held**
WEB: www.miltecusa.com
SIC: 3599 Machine shop, jobbing & repair

(G-8200)
MPALACIOS BLINDS INC
810 Hillside St (33936-7012)
PHONE.................................239 601-4864
Marcelo Palacios, *Principal*
EMP: 6 **EST:** 2018
SALES (est): 156K **Privately Held**
WEB: www.mpalaciosblinds.com
SIC: 2591 Window blinds

(G-8201)
ODARA KANVAS COSMETICS
1126 Homer Ave S (33973-2095)
PHONE.................................239 785-8013
James A Laumont, *CEO*
EMP: 10 **EST:** 2017
SALES (est): 326.4K **Privately Held**
SIC: 2844 Toilet preparations

(G-8202)
PAPER FREE TECHNOLOGY INC
10626 Windsmont Ct (33936-7267)
PHONE.................................515 270-1505
Samuel W Warren, *President*
EMP: 8 **EST:** 1994
SALES (est): 702.2K **Privately Held**
SIC: 7372 7338 7389 Prepackaged software; secretarial & typing service;

GEOGRAPHIC

(G-8203)
PREMIER SIGN & SERVICE INC
7716 6th Pl (33936-2241)
PHONE..................................239 258-6979
Abner Altamar, *President*
EMP: 9 **EST:** 2014
SALES (est): 590.6K **Privately Held**
SIC: 3993 Signs & advertising specialties

(G-8204)
PS CABINET WORKS INC
217 Jefferson Ave (33936-1633)
PHONE..................................239 850-2162
Patrick Sakitis, *President*
EMP: 9 **EST:** 2005
SALES (est): 175.6K **Privately Held**
WEB: www.pscabinetworks.com
SIC: 2434 Wood kitchen cabinets

(G-8205)
RICHARDSON FAMILY PRODUCTS LLC ✪
8596 Athena Ct (33971-3752)
PHONE..................................239 896-3595
Demmerick Richardson, *Mng Member*
EMP: 6 **EST:** 2021
SALES (est): 265.3K **Privately Held**
SIC: 2051 Yeast goods, sweet: except frozen

(G-8206)
RPM GRAPHICS INC
508 Owen Ave N (33971-6316)
PHONE..................................239 275-3278
John H Bowman, *President*
Sheila Skeel, *Manager*
EMP: 5 **EST:** 2008
SQ FT: 1,200
SALES (est): 310K **Privately Held**
SIC: 3993 Signs & advertising specialties

(G-8207)
SHOT OF FREON
2911 10th St W (33971-5431)
PHONE..................................305 917-5893
Roger H Rivera, *Owner*
EMP: 6 **EST:** 2008
SALES (est): 239.2K **Privately Held**
SIC: 2869 Freon

Lighthouse Point
Broward County

(G-8208)
COMFORT BRACE LLC
1971 Ne 31st St (33064-7643)
PHONE..................................954 899-1563
William Diedwardo,
EMP: 7 **EST:** 2009
SALES (est): 409K **Privately Held**
SIC: 3842 Surgical appliances & supplies

(G-8209)
KMA PHARMA LLC
4151 Ne 30th Ter (33064-8426)
PHONE..................................754 220-6936
Lucio Giambattista, *Owner*
EMP: 6 **EST:** 2014
SALES (est): 168.8K **Privately Held**
SIC: 2834 Pharmaceutical preparations

(G-8210)
NORTH COAST MACHINING INC
2311 Ne 26th St (33064-8350)
PHONE..................................954 942-6943
Paul Maloney, *President*
Deborah Maloney, *Treasurer*
EMP: 6 **EST:** 1983
SQ FT: 20,000
SALES (est): 419.2K **Privately Held**
SIC: 3599 Machine shop, jobbing & repair

(G-8211)
NORTH SHORE HLDNGS LGHTHUSE PT
4130 Ne 24th Ave (33064-8028)
PHONE..................................954 785-1055
Joseph Giaquinto, *CEO*
Colin Hall, *Exec VP*
Lee Epstein, *Vice Pres*
Gil Harmon, *VP Sales*
◆ **EMP:** 30 **EST:** 1994
SALES (est): 9.9MM **Privately Held**
WEB: www.lifeweartechnologies.com
SIC: 3842 Abdominal supporters, braces & trusses
PA: Modular Thermal Technologies, Llc
1520 Sw 5th Ct
Pompano Beach FL 33069
954 785-1055

(G-8212)
PERRY NORTH AEROSPACE INC
2764 Ne 25th St (33064-8308)
PHONE..................................954 295-9520
Lois B Cotton, *Principal*
EMP: 6 **EST:** 2009
SALES (est): 102K **Privately Held**
SIC: 3721 Aircraft

(G-8213)
TRUSTED DAILY SOLUTIONS
3431 Ne 27th Ave (33064-8113)
PHONE..................................954 461-5131
Jeffrey Johnson, *Principal*
EMP: 7 **EST:** 2014
SALES (est): 91.8K **Privately Held**
WEB: www.trusteddailysolutions.com
SIC: 2711 Newspapers, publishing & printing

(G-8214)
ZAHN BUILDERS INC
4628 N Federal Hwy (33064-6511)
PHONE..................................718 885-2202
Suzy Zahn, *Assistant*
EMP: 8 **EST:** 2019
SALES (est): 964.6K **Privately Held**
WEB: www.zahnbuilders.net
SIC: 3443 Fabricated plate work (boiler shop)

Lithia
Hillsborough County

(G-8215)
AMERICAN SPERIOR COMPOUNDS INC
17409 Chelsea Downs Cir (33547-4942)
PHONE..................................716 873-1209
▲ **EMP:** 8
SQ FT: 500
SALES (est): 520K **Privately Held**
SIC: 2821 Mfg Plastic Materials/Resins

(G-8216)
CENTRAL MAINTENANCE & WLDG INC (PA)
Also Called: C M W
2620 E Keysville Rd (33547-1605)
PHONE..................................813 229-0012
Conrad Varnum, *President*
Scott M Varnum, *Corp Secy*
Randy Coates, *COO*
Kathy Gillen, *Controller*
EMP: 322 **EST:** 1966
SQ FT: 4,100
SALES (est): 70.8MM **Privately Held**
WEB: www.cmw.cc
SIC: 3443 1791 7692 Heat exchangers, condensers & components; structural steel erection; welding repair

(G-8217)
COMPLETE INSTRMNTTION CNTRLS I
11524 Hammock Oaks Ct (33547-1947)
PHONE..................................813 340-8545
David L Harris, *Principal*
EMP: 6 **EST:** 2014
SALES (est): 277.6K **Privately Held**
WEB: www.completeiandc.com
SIC: 3823 Industrial instrmnts msrmnt display/control process variable

(G-8218)
DYNAMIC PRINTING OF BRANDON
6014 Tealside Ct (33547-3872)
PHONE..................................813 664-6880
David Waring, *President*
Charles H Moore, *Vice Pres*
EMP: 7 **EST:** 1979
SQ FT: 6,100
SALES (est): 331.2K **Privately Held**
SIC: 2752 Commercial printing, offset

(G-8219)
FLORIDA OIL SERVICE INC
16220 Ternglade Dr (33547-5845)
PHONE..................................813 655-4753
Layne Williams, *Principal*
EMP: 15 **EST:** 2002
SALES (est): 546.7K **Privately Held**
SIC: 3559 7549 Automotive maintenance equipment; automotive services

(G-8220)
MOSAIC CROP NUTRITION LLC
13830 Circa Crossing Dr (33547-3953)
PHONE..................................813 500-6800
Linda D Weber, *Branch Mgr*
EMP: 74 **Publicly Held**
SIC: 2874 Phosphatic fertilizers
HQ: Mosaic Crop Nutrition, Llc
3033 Campus Dr
Minneapolis MN 55441
763 577-2700

(G-8221)
MOSAIC FERTILIZER LLC (HQ)
13830 Circa Crossing Dr (33547-3953)
PHONE..................................813 500-6300
James T Prokopanko, *CEO*
Jason Vanvleet, *Principal*
Richard L Mack, *Exec VP*
Gary Bo Davis, *Senior VP*
Mark E Kaplan, *Vice Pres*
◆ **EMP:** 700 **EST:** 2004
SQ FT: 8,288
SALES (est): 876.1MM **Publicly Held**
WEB: www.mosaicco.com
SIC: 2874 Phosphatic fertilizers

(G-8222)
PREFERRED STITCHING INC
10552 Lithia Pinecrest Rd (33547-2679)
PHONE..................................813 737-3996
Damon E Hunter, *Principal*
EMP: 8 **EST:** 2010
SALES (est): 109.1K **Privately Held**
SIC: 2395 Embroidery & art needlework

(G-8223)
SOUTHERN FABRICATING MACHINERY
10417 S County Road 39 (33547-2864)
PHONE..................................813 966-3983
Scott Courneya, *Sales Staff*
EMP: 7 **EST:** 2019
SALES (est): 853K **Privately Held**
WEB: www.southernfabsales.com
SIC: 3559 Special industry machinery

(G-8224)
TITANIUM GYNMASTICS & CHEER
7017 Lithia Pinecrest Rd (33547-1885)
PHONE..................................813 689-2200
Jessica Charbonneau, *President*
EMP: 7 **EST:** 2014
SALES (est): 399.9K **Privately Held**
WEB: www.titaniumgymandcheer.com
SIC: 3356 Titanium

(G-8225)
UNIVERSAL ERECTORS INC
5668 Fshhawk Crssing Blvd (33547)
PHONE..................................813 621-8111
Jonathan W Hobbs, *Principal*
EMP: 7 **EST:** 2015
SALES (est): 386.1K **Privately Held**
WEB: www.universalerectorsinc.com
SIC: 3441 Fabricated structural metal

Live Oak
Suwannee County

(G-8226)
ADVANTA ASPHALT INC
Also Called: Anderson Advanta Asphalt
1400 Howard St E (32064-3505)
PHONE..................................386 362-5580
Samuel Skierski, *President*
EMP: 8 **EST:** 2011
SALES (est): 963.8K **Privately Held**
WEB: www.advantaasphalt.com
SIC: 2951 Concrete, asphaltic (not from refineries)

(G-8227)
BOWEN MEDICAL SERVICES INC
709 Industrial Ave Sw (32064-4997)
PHONE..................................386 362-1345
Tom Bowen, *President*
Teresa Bowen, *Vice Pres*
EMP: 6 **EST:** 1985
SQ FT: 1,000
SALES (est): 200K **Privately Held**
WEB: www.yc.dev
SIC: 3089 Casting of plastic

(G-8228)
CHECKS YOUR WAY INC
621 Ohio Ave N (32064-1853)
PHONE..................................386 362-4044
Miles Peaven, *Manager*
EMP: 5 **EST:** 2000
SALES (est): 329.4K **Privately Held**
WEB: www.checksyourway.com
SIC: 3579 Check writing, endorsing or signing machines

(G-8229)
CUSTOM ILLUSIONZ
319 Howard St E (32064-3237)
PHONE..................................386 330-5245
Diane Allen, *Owner*
EMP: 6 **EST:** 2002
SALES (est): 335.3K **Privately Held**
WEB: www.custom-illusionz.com
SIC: 3993 Signs, not made in custom sign painting shops

(G-8230)
DENALI INVESTMENTS INC
140 Palm St Ne (32064-4823)
P.O. Box 327 (32064-0327)
PHONE..................................386 364-2979
Wayne Beaver, *President*
Susan Beaver, *Vice Pres*
EMP: 8 **EST:** 1998
SALES (est): 1MM **Privately Held**
SIC: 1411 Limestone, dimension-quarrying

(G-8231)
ELITE OUTDOOR BUILDINGS LLC
2008 Ohio Ave N (32064-4858)
PHONE..................................386 364-1364
Kevin B Greene, *Mng Member*
EMP: 7 **EST:** 2016
SALES (est): 799K **Privately Held**
WEB: www.eliteoutdoorbuildings.com
SIC: 3448 Prefabricated metal buildings

(G-8232)
FARMERS COOPERATIVE INC (PA)
1841 Howard St W (32064-4326)
P.O. Box 610 (32064-0610)
PHONE..................................386 362-1459
William T Carte, *President*
Barry Long, *Division Mgr*
Todd Lawrence, *Treasurer*
Robert Sap, *Manager*
EMP: 22
SQ FT: 42,500
SALES: 13.3MM **Privately Held**
WEB: www.farmerscooperative.org
SIC: 2875 5191 5984 5699 Fertilizers, mixing only; farm supplies; animal feeds; liquefied petroleum gas dealers; western apparel

(G-8233)
J&J SUWANNEE ENTERPRISES LLC
6835 River Rd (32060-7885)
PHONE..................................386 658-1721
Jeremy W Steinbach, *Principal*
EMP: 6 **EST:** 2018
SALES (est): 206.8K **Privately Held**
SIC: 2711 Newspapers, publishing & printing

(G-8234)
KEENS PORTABLE BUILDINGS INC
620 Howard St W (32064-2211)
PHONE....................................386 364-7995
Kevin Keen, *President*
EMP: 10 **EST:** 2000
SQ FT: 600
SALES (est): 1MM **Privately Held**
WEB: www.keensbuildings.com
SIC: 3448 Buildings, portable: prefabricated metal

(G-8235)
NORTH FLORIDA PRINTING INC
109 Tuxedo Ave Ne (32064-2469)
P.O. Box 850 (32064-0850)
PHONE....................................386 362-1080
Edward Howell, *President*
Coy Howell, *General Mgr*
Joanne Howell, *Treasurer*
EMP: 9 **EST:** 1967
SQ FT: 5,000
SALES (est): 500K **Privately Held**
WEB: www.nfpci.com
SIC: 2752 Commercial printing, offset

(G-8236)
PILGRIMS PRIDE CORPORATION
Also Called: Live Oak Feed Mill
1306 Howard St W (32064-2005)
P.O. Box 789 (32064-0789)
PHONE....................................386 362-4171
Hyman Frier, *Purchasing*
Ali Perry, *Sales Mgr*
Doug Chezma, *Manager*
EMP: 6 **Publicly Held**
WEB: www.pilgrims.com
SIC: 2015 Poultry slaughtering & processing
HQ: Pilgrim's Pride Corporation
1770 Promontory Cir
Greeley CO 80634
970 506-8000

(G-8237)
PRECISION TURNING CORPORATION
715 Goldkist Blvd Sw (32064-4995)
PHONE....................................386 364-5788
Cindy W Swann, *Corp Secy*
Charles L Swann, *Administration*
EMP: 19 **EST:** 1996
SQ FT: 9,000
SALES (est): 3.1MM **Privately Held**
WEB: www.precisionturning.net
SIC: 3451 3541 Screw machine products; screw machines, automatic

(G-8238)
RAINBOW STORAGE
7434 County Road 795 (32060-8486)
PHONE....................................386 362-1171
Jack Flowers, *President*
EMP: 10 **EST:** 2005
SALES (est): 560.1K **Privately Held**
SIC: 3691 Storage batteries

(G-8239)
RECYCLING CENTER
700 Houston Ave Nw (32064-4702)
PHONE....................................386 364-5865
Alfred Linton, *President*
EMP: 6 **EST:** 2008
SALES (est): 785.1K **Privately Held**
WEB: www.biggreenball.org
SIC: 3559 Metal finishing equipment for plating, etc.

(G-8240)
SHEDS GALORE AND MORE LLC
1410 Howard St E (32064-3505)
PHONE....................................386 362-1786
EMP: 6 **EST:** 2016
SALES (est): 201.4K **Privately Held**
WEB: www.shedsgaloreandmore.com
SIC: 3448 Prefabricated metal buildings

(G-8241)
SMITH STEPS INC
Also Called: Manufacturer
6944 Us Highway 90 (32060-7155)
P.O. Box 1210 (32064-1210)
PHONE....................................386 963-5655
Lynn Ward, *President*
William Ward, *President*
EMP: 6 **EST:** 2003
SALES (est): 485.6K **Privately Held**
WEB: www.smithsteps.com
SIC: 3272 Steps, prefabricated concrete

(G-8242)
SUWANNEE FUND LLC
5790 98th Ter (32060-7223)
PHONE....................................386 963-1149
Russell S Pope, *Manager*
EMP: 7 **EST:** 2015
SALES (est): 140.5K **Privately Held**
SIC: 2711 Newspapers, publishing & printing

(G-8243)
SUWANNEEARC
617 Ontario Ave Sw (32064-2947)
PHONE....................................386 362-1796
EMP: 7 **EST:** 2016
SALES (est): 127.7K **Privately Held**
SIC: 2711 Newspapers, publishing & printing

Lloyd
Jefferson County

(G-8244)
LEGACY VULCAN LLC
2792 Gamble Rd (32337)
P.O. Box 305 (32337-0305)
PHONE....................................850 997-1490
Dennis Smith, *Manager*
EMP: 7 **Publicly Held**
WEB: www.vulcanmaterials.com
SIC: 3273 Ready-mixed concrete
HQ: Legacy Vulcan, Llc
1200 Urban Center Dr
Vestavia AL 35242
205 298-3000

Longboat Key
Manatee County

(G-8245)
LONGBOAT KEY NEWS INC
5370 Gulf Of Mexico Dr (34228-2070)
P.O. Box 8001 (34228-8001)
PHONE....................................941 387-2200
Stephen L Reid, *President*
Melissa L Reid, *Vice Pres*
EMP: 14 **EST:** 2003
SALES (est): 217.9K **Privately Held**
WEB: www.lbknews.com
SIC: 2711 Newspapers, publishing & printing

(G-8246)
RESOLVER GROUP INC
20 Lighthouse Point Dr (34228-3917)
PHONE....................................941 387-7410
Peter M Simonson, *Principal*
Kevin Vani, *Consultant*
EMP: 9 **EST:** 2008
SALES (est): 360.4K **Privately Held**
SIC: 3621 Resolvers

(G-8247)
SPECIALTY FIN CONSULTING CORP (PA)
5541 Gulf Of Mexico Dr (34228-1903)
PHONE....................................717 246-1661
Carl W Cheek, *CEO*
John Forrey Jr, *President*
EMP: 450 **EST:** 2000
SALES (est): 48.7MM **Privately Held**
SIC: 2653 2679 3672 2675 Sheets, corrugated: made from purchased materials; boxes, corrugated: made from purchased materials; paper products, converted; printed circuit boards; die-cut paper & board

Longwood
Seminole County

(G-8248)
35 TECHNOLOGIES GROUP INC
2280 N Ronald Reagan Blvd (32750-3519)
PHONE....................................407 402-2119
Ann Norelli, *President*
Joseph Norelli, *Vice Pres*
Judith Norelli, *Director*
Nicholas Norelli, *Director*
▼ **EMP:** 33 **EST:** 2007
SQ FT: 15,500
SALES (est): 2.6MM **Privately Held**
SIC: 3699 Electric sound equipment

(G-8249)
7 PLASTICS INC
1680 Timocuan Way (32750-3729)
PHONE....................................407 321-5441
Eduardo Gomez, *President*
Bill Morgan, *Engineer*
Oswald Guzman, *Manager*
EMP: 14 **EST:** 2001
SALES (est): 1MM **Privately Held**
WEB: www.7plastics.com
SIC: 3089 Injection molding of plastics

(G-8250)
ACCU-SPAN TRUSS CO
1891 High St (32750-3721)
PHONE....................................407 321-1440
Emile W Skura, *President*
Gary Pierpont, *General Mgr*
Gerald Mackall, *Corp Secy*
Walter McCall, *Vice Pres*
Linda McCall, *Manager*
EMP: 50 **EST:** 1982
SQ FT: 30,000
SALES (est): 7.3MM **Privately Held**
WEB: www.accuspan.com
SIC: 2439 5039 Trusses, wooden roof; joists

(G-8251)
ALL ELEMENTS MECHANICAL CORP (PA)
776 Bennett Dr Unit 101 (32750-6392)
PHONE....................................866 306-0359
Ronald K Haupt, *President*
Gary Carmack, *Principal*
EMP: 46 **EST:** 2008
SALES (est): 901K **Privately Held**
WEB: www.allelementsmechanical.com
SIC: 2819 Industrial inorganic chemicals

(G-8252)
ALLSTAR LIGHTING & SOUND INC
Also Called: Advanced Powder Coating Fla
754 Fleet Fin Ct Ste 102 (32750-2610)
PHONE....................................407 767-0111
Sandra L Krieger-Bond, *President*
Paula Masselli, *Office Mgr*
Michelle Le Leux, *Manager*
EMP: 10 **EST:** 1991
SQ FT: 10,000
SALES (est): 1.1MM **Privately Held**
SIC: 3479 Painting of metal products; painting, coating & hot dipping

(G-8253)
ALTAMONTE OFFICE SUPPLY INC
1983 Corporate Sq # 101 (32750-3627)
PHONE....................................407 339-6911
EMP: 9
SQ FT: 9,000
SALES (est): 1.5MM **Privately Held**
SIC: 3555 5712 Mfg Printing Trades Machinery Ret Furniture

(G-8254)
AMERICAN MENTALITY INC
Also Called: Ugp
210 E Palmetto Ave (32750-4241)
PHONE....................................407 599-7255
Ronald Bonner Jr, *President*
Ronald Bonner Sr, *Vice Pres*
▲ **EMP:** 9 **EST:** 1986
SQ FT: 5,000
SALES (est): 1MM **Privately Held**
WEB: www.sparkysdistribution.com
SIC: 2261 2759 Screen printing of cotton broadwoven fabrics; screen printing

(G-8255)
ANALOG MODULES INC
126 Baywood Ave (32750-3416)
PHONE....................................407 339-4355
Ian Drummond Crawford, *President*
Elizabeth R Letendre, *Principal*
Carlos L Macau, *CFO*
Judith W Vetter, *Admin Sec*
EMP: 70
SQ FT: 21,000
SALES (est): 13.7MM **Publicly Held**
WEB: www.analogmodules.com
SIC: 3663 3674 Amplifiers, RF power & IF; modules, solid state
HQ: Heico Electronic Technologies Corp.
3000 Taft St
Hollywood FL 33021
954 987-6101

(G-8256)
ARCHITECTURAL OPENINGS INC
1975 Corporate Sq (32750-3536)
PHONE....................................407 260-7110
Robert Bussart, *President*
Chris Bussart, *Director*
EMP: 19 **EST:** 1976
SQ FT: 13,600
SALES (est): 1MM **Privately Held**
WEB: www.architecturalopeningsinc.com
SIC: 3442 Metal doors; window & door frames

(G-8257)
ARGOTEC INC
225 Pineda St Unit 103 (32750-6452)
P.O. Box 520760 (32752-0760)
PHONE....................................407 331-9372
EMP: 7
SALES (corp-wide): 2.2MM **Privately Held**
SIC: 3699 Mfg Electrical Equipment/Supplies
PA: Argotec Inc
4750 N Dixie Hwy Ste 4
Oakland Park FL 33305
954 491-6550

(G-8258)
ATLANTIC STEEL INC
131 Sheridan Ct (32750-3956)
PHONE....................................407 599-3822
Barry McCullen, *President*
John W Grant, *Vice Pres*
EMP: 43 **EST:** 2000
SQ FT: 12,000
SALES (est): 7.1MM **Privately Held**
SIC: 3441 5039 Fabricated structural metal; structural assemblies, prefabricated: non-wood

(G-8259)
AUDINA HEARING INSTRUMENTS
165 E Wildmere Ave (32750-5455)
PHONE....................................407 331-0077
Marc McLarnon, *President*
Frank J Robilotta, *Vice Pres*
EMP: 85 **EST:** 1989
SQ FT: 12,000
SALES (est): 8.9MM **Privately Held**
WEB: www.audina.net
SIC: 3842 5999 5047 Hearing aids; hearing aids; hearing aids

(G-8260)
AXON CIRCUIT INC
155 National Pl Unit 105 (32750-6432)
PHONE....................................407 265-7980
Manish Patel, *Manager*
James Thomas, *Manager*
EMP: 15 **Privately Held**
WEB: www.axoncircuit.com
SIC: 3672 5063 Printed circuit boards; switchboards
PA: Axon Circuit, Inc.
424 S Ware Blvd Ste A
Tampa FL 33619

(G-8261)
BAY MEADOW ARCHITECTURAL MLLWK
400 Bay Meadow Rd (32750-3430)
PHONE..................................407 332-7992
Edgar Fernandez, *President*
Pedro Fernandez, *Vice Pres*
▼ **EMP:** 25 **EST:** 1992
SQ FT: 9,600
SALES (est): 2.3MM **Privately Held**
WEB: www.baymeadowmillwork.com
SIC: 2431 5211 Millwork; millwork & lumber

(G-8262)
BELL PERFORMANCE INC
1340 Bennett Dr (32750-7503)
PHONE..................................407 831-5021
Ola R Williams, *President*
Dan Bordui, *Partner*
Glenn Williams, *Vice Pres*
Scott Shumaker, *Manager*
James Parry, *Info Tech Dir*
EMP: 16 **EST:** 1909
SQ FT: 3,000
SALES (est): 2.8MM **Privately Held**
WEB: www.bellperformance.com
SIC: 2992 2899 Oils & greases, blending & compounding; fuel treating compounds

(G-8263)
CANVAS LAND SURVEYING LLC
1650 Oak Valley Dr (32750-6263)
PHONE..................................321 689-5330
Roxanna Fulford, *Principal*
EMP: 6 **EST:** 2019
SALES (est): 46.5K **Privately Held**
WEB: www.canvaslandsurveying.com
SIC: 2211 Canvas

(G-8264)
CB PRECIOUS METALS LLC
1237 Bella Vista Cir (32779-5867)
PHONE..................................407 790-1585
Dipak Parekh, *Principal*
EMP: 10 **EST:** 2011
SALES (est): 1MM **Privately Held**
SIC: 3339 Precious metals

(G-8265)
CENVEO WORLDWIDE LIMITED
1955 Corporate Sq (32750-3503)
PHONE..................................321 207-0403
EMP: 251
SALES (corp-wide): 1B **Privately Held**
WEB: www.cenveo.com
SIC: 2677 Envelopes
HQ: Cenveo Worldwide Limited
200 First Stamford Pl
Stamford CT 06902
203 595-3000

(G-8266)
COINWEEK LLC
306 N Swetwater Cove Blvd (32779-2318)
P.O. Box 916909 (32791-6909)
PHONE..................................407 786-5555
Scott Purvis,
EMP: 10 **EST:** 2010
SALES (est): 277.5K **Privately Held**
WEB: www.coinweek.com
SIC: 2711 Commercial printing & newspaper publishing combined

(G-8267)
CONSOLIDATED FOREST PDTS INC (PA)
375 Commerce Way (32750-7633)
PHONE..................................407 830-7723
William Stlaurent, *President*
EMP: 19 **EST:** 1982
SQ FT: 200
SALES (est): 2.7MM **Privately Held**
WEB: www.americanmulch.net
SIC: 2869 2499 Fuels; fencing, wood

(G-8268)
CREATIVE CONCEPTS ORLANDO INC
1650 Forest Ave Ste 100 (32750-6423)
PHONE..................................407 260-1435
Wayne Bishop, *President*
Joann Arndt, *Director*
Timothy Arndt, *Director*
EMP: 50 **EST:** 1997
SQ FT: 35,000
SALES (est): 7.5MM **Privately Held**
WEB: www.creativeconceptsorl.com
SIC: 2434 2521 2431 Wood kitchen cabinets; wood office furniture; millwork

(G-8269)
CUSTOM GRAPHICS AND PLATES INC
782 Big Tree Dr Unit 100 (32750-3528)
PHONE..................................407 696-5448
Robert Spering, *President*
Anthony Spering, *Vice Pres*
Robert Spring, *Manager*
EMP: 23 **EST:** 1997
SQ FT: 7,000
SALES (est): 522.2K **Privately Held**
WEB: www.platecrafters.com
SIC: 2752 Commercial printing, offset

(G-8270)
CUSTOM MASTERS INC
Also Called: Flo King Filter Systems
401 Lake Bennett Ct (32750-7670)
PHONE..................................407 331-4634
Allen Horvath, *President*
Valerie Parks, *Vice Pres*
EMP: 20 **EST:** 1985
SQ FT: 8,000
SALES (est): 4.2MM **Privately Held**
WEB: www.floking.com
SIC: 3561 3569 8742 3564 Pumps & pumping equipment; filters, general line: industrial; management consulting services; blowers & fans

(G-8271)
CYBORTRACK SOLUTIONS INC
657 Florida Central Pkwy (32750-6345)
PHONE..................................805 904-5677
EMP: 5
SQ FT: 1,000
SALES: 3MM **Privately Held**
SIC: 3674 Mfg Semiconductors/Related Devices

(G-8272)
DAPP EMBROIDERY INC
1075 Fla Cntl Pkwy Ste 25 (32750)
PHONE..................................407 260-1600
Stephen Sutphin, *CEO*
Kathy Stephens, *General Mgr*
EMP: 5 **EST:** 2006
SQ FT: 2,300
SALES (est): 516K **Privately Held**
WEB: www.dappembroidery.com
SIC: 2395 Embroidery products, except schiffli machine; embroidery & art needlework

(G-8273)
DESIGN PRO SCREENS INC
1287 S Oleander St (32750-5424)
PHONE..................................407 831-6541
Jeffrey Cheffer, *Owner*
EMP: 6 **EST:** 1991
SALES (est): 413.1K **Privately Held**
WEB: www.designproscreensinc.com
SIC: 3448 Screen enclosures

(G-8274)
DONALD ART COMPANY INC
713 Industry Rd (32750-3629)
PHONE..................................407 831-2525
Andrea Wallace, *President*
EMP: 7 **EST:** 2001
SALES (est): 76.8K **Privately Held**
WEB: www.donaldartco.com
SIC: 2752 Commercial printing, lithographic

(G-8275)
DYNAMIC MANUFACTURING INC
2280 N Ronald Reagan Blvd (32750-3519)
PHONE..................................727 639-8633
Nicholas Norelli, *President*
EMP: 6 **EST:** 2017
SALES (est): 80K **Privately Held**
WEB: www.dynamicmanufacturinginc.com
SIC: 3999 Manufacturing industries

(G-8276)
ERIC LEMOINE
Also Called: Black Aces Tactical
1355 Bennett Dr Unit 129 (32750-7587)
PHONE..................................407 919-9783
Eric Lemoine, *Owner*
EMP: 5 **EST:** 2016
SALES (est): 706K **Privately Held**
SIC: 3484 Small arms

(G-8277)
EXIT TEN INC
Also Called: Southern Ordnance
100 Highline Dr Unit 116 (32750-5192)
PHONE..................................407 574-2433
Larry Newberry, *President*
Megan Simara, *Director*
Vladimir Simara, *Director*
▲ **EMP:** 7 **EST:** 2002
SQ FT: 2,300
SALES (est): 1.2MM **Privately Held**
WEB: www.southord.com
SIC: 3423 Masons' hand tools

(G-8278)
EXPRESS LABEL CO INC
1955 Corp Sq Ste 1001 (32750)
PHONE..................................407 332-4774
Michael Sisinni, *President*
EMP: 20 **EST:** 1987
SQ FT: 10,000
SALES (est): 3.6MM **Privately Held**
WEB: www.expresslabel.net
SIC: 2672 2679 2241 Labels (unprinted), gummed: made from purchased materials; labels, paper: made from purchased material; labels, woven

(G-8279)
EXXELIA USA INC (PA)
1221 N Us Highway 17 92 (32750-3739)
PHONE..................................407 695-6562
Paul Massioner, *CEO*
Lynn Hartley, *Buyer*
EMP: 49 **EST:** 2019
SALES (est): 25.3MM **Privately Held**
SIC: 3612 3677 3675 5063 Transformers, except electric; electronic coils, transformers & other inductors; filtration devices, electronic; electronic capacitors; transformers, electric

(G-8280)
F W I INC
Also Called: Florida Wood
1388 S Ronald Reagan Blvd (32750-6419)
PHONE..................................407 509-9739
Charles D Poole, *President*
James Piegls, *General Mgr*
EMP: 12 **EST:** 1974
SQ FT: 11,000
SALES (est): 353.8K **Privately Held**
SIC: 2431 Millwork

(G-8281)
FALCO INDUSTRIES INC
1550 Dixon Rd (32779-2759)
PHONE..................................407 956-0045
Ileana Dimario, *President*
▲ **EMP:** 8 **EST:** 2007
SQ FT: 1,200
SALES (est): 382.9K **Privately Held**
SIC: 3999 Manufacturing industries

(G-8282)
FIRST IMPRSSONS PRTG CMMNCTONS
851 E State Road 434 (32750-5386)
PHONE..................................407 831-6100
Erika Williams, *President*
EMP: 6 **EST:** 1982
SALES (est): 419.5K **Privately Held**
SIC: 2752 2791 2789 Commercial printing, offset; typesetting; bookbinding & related work

(G-8283)
FLORIDA MARKING PRODUCTS LLC
1205 Sarah Ave Ste 171 (32750-6564)
PHONE..................................407 834-3000
John Totten, *IT/INT Sup*
Bertram Kennedy,
Sandra Balsamo, *Administration*
Joel Vanluven, *Graphic Designe*
Michael Kennedy,
EMP: 22 **EST:** 2010
SALES (est): 3.4MM
SALES (corp-wide): 27.4MM **Privately Held**
WEB: www.kennedygrp.com
SIC: 2269 Labels, cotton: printed
PA: The Kennedy Group Incorporated
38601 Kennedy Pkwy
Willoughby OH 44094
440 951-7660

(G-8284)
FOUR G ENTERPRISES INC
Also Called: BCT
1150 Florida Central Pkwy (32750-6348)
PHONE..................................407 834-4143
Gary A Grieger, *President*
Martha Grieger, *Vice Pres*
Caroline Lavender, *Accounting Mgr*
Carolyn Lavender, *Executive*
Justin Crain, *Technician*
EMP: 45 **EST:** 1981
SALES (est): 7.5MM **Privately Held**
WEB: www.evoprint.com
SIC: 2752 3953 2791 2759 Commercial printing, lithographic; marking devices; typesetting; commercial printing; packaging paper & plastics film, coated & laminated

(G-8285)
GOOD REP INC
100 Bay Hammock Ln (32779-3401)
PHONE..................................407 869-6531
Mary E Gary, *Director*
EMP: 6 **EST:** 2001
SALES (est): 77.2K **Privately Held**
SIC: 2451 Mobile homes

(G-8286)
GREYSON CORP
Also Called: Sign King
726 N Us Highway 17 92 (32750-3293)
PHONE..................................407 830-7443
Micheal Gray, *President*
Scott M Grey, *Vice Pres*
Carla Grey, *Treasurer*
Stephanie Tolles, *Sales Associate*
EMP: 13 **EST:** 1976
SALES (est): 1.1MM **Privately Held**
SIC: 3993 Signs & advertising specialties

(G-8287)
HOLIDAY ICE INC
Also Called: Arctic-Temp Ice Makers
204 Short Ave (32750-5130)
P.O. Box 520606 (32752-0606)
PHONE..................................407 831-2077
Raymond Armstrong, *President*
Ray Armstrong, *General Mgr*
Walter Nicholas, *Purchasing*
Nick Creanza, *Sales Staff*
Rich Bush, *CIO*
◆ **EMP:** 22 **EST:** 1959
SQ FT: 7,000
SALES (est): 4.8MM **Privately Held**
WEB: www.holiday-ice.com
SIC: 3585 7359 Ice making machinery; equipment rental & leasing

(G-8288)
I C PROBOTICS INC
122 E Lake Ave (32750-5441)
P.O. Box 520669 (32752-0669)
PHONE..................................407 339-8298
EMP: 60
SQ FT: 4,000
SALES (est): 551.6K **Privately Held**
SIC: 3825 3823 3643 Mfg Electrical Measuring Instruments Mfg Process Control Instruments Mfg Conductive Wiring Devices

(G-8289)
IMPREMEDIA LLC
Also Called: La Prensa
685 S Ronald Reagan Blvd (32750-6435)
PHONE..................................407 767-0070
Dora Detoro, *Manager*
EMP: 8
SALES (corp-wide): 94.2MM **Privately Held**
WEB: www.impremedia.com
SIC: 2711 Newspapers, publishing & printing

PA: Impremedia, Llc
1 Metrotech Ctr Fl 18
Brooklyn NY 11201
212 807-4600

(G-8290)
INK BROS PRINTING LLC
1372 Bennett Dr Unit 164 (32750-7564)
PHONE..................................407 494-9585
Diego R Milan, *Manager*
EMP: 7 **EST:** 2019
SALES (est): 384.1K **Privately Held**
WEB: www.inkbros.com
SIC: 2752 Commercial printing, lithographic

(G-8291)
INSTANT CALL CENTER LLC
126 Ingram Cir (32779-5753)
PHONE..................................321 356-1587
John W Baker, *Manager*
EMP: 7 **EST:** 2015
SALES (est): 171.2K **Privately Held**
SIC: 2752 Commercial printing, lithographic

(G-8292)
INTERNATIONAL SIGNS & LTG INC
714 Commerce Cir (32750-3608)
PHONE..................................407 332-9663
Morgan Voke, *President*
Paul C Riccard, *President*
Maria L Riccard, *Treasurer*
EMP: 16 **EST:** 2008
SALES (est): 2.2MM **Privately Held**
WEB: www.islsigns.com
SIC: 3993 Electric signs

(G-8293)
IRON-ART & FENCE INC
731 N Us Highway 17 92 # 201
(32750-3639)
PHONE..................................407 699-1734
Lou Guglielmello, *President*
Marilyn Guglielmello, *Director*
EMP: 10 **EST:** 1989
SQ FT: 6,000
SALES (est): 776.7K **Privately Held**
SIC: 3446 Fences or posts, ornamental iron or steel; gates, ornamental metal

(G-8294)
IT BUSNESS SOLUTIONS GROUP INC
Also Called: Minuteman Press
800 Waterway Pl (32750-3535)
PHONE..................................407 260-0116
Michael Wise, *President*
Bill Potter, *President*
EMP: 18 **EST:** 2000
SQ FT: 5,800
SALES (est): 2.4MM **Privately Held**
WEB: www.itbsg.com
SIC: 2752 Commercial printing, lithographic

(G-8295)
JD TOOLS LLC
786 Big Tree Dr (32750-3539)
PHONE..................................407 767-5175
John Deac, *Mng Member*
EMP: 18 **EST:** 2007
SALES (est): 1.3MM **Privately Held**
WEB: www.jdtoolshop.com
SIC: 3599 Machine shop, jobbing & repair

(G-8296)
JESSUPS SPECIALTY PRODUCTS
910 Waterway Pl (32750-3545)
PHONE..................................407 332-7574
Clarence Jessup, *President*
EMP: 7 **EST:** 2017
SALES (est): 213.5K **Privately Held**
SIC: 2844 Toilet preparations

(G-8297)
JM COATINGS INC
1910 Longwood Lk Mary Rd (32750-4619)
PHONE..................................407 312-1115
Miguel Marzcuk, *Principal*
EMP: 7 **EST:** 2007
SALES (est): 182K **Privately Held**
SIC: 3479 Metal coating & allied service

(G-8298)
JQ INDUSTRIES INC
2070 Terrace Blvd (32779-4859)
PHONE..................................407 509-3880
Quinn James, *President*
EMP: 8 **EST:** 2014
SALES (est): 289.1K **Privately Held**
SIC: 3999 Manufacturing industries

(G-8299)
KIDS WOOD
714 Commerce Cir (32750-3608)
PHONE..................................407 332-9663
Kevin Webb, *President*
Julie Webb, *Vice Pres*
EMP: 9 **EST:** 1995
SALES (est): 380.6K **Privately Held**
SIC: 3993 Signs & advertising specialties

(G-8300)
KITCHENS CRAFTERS INC
302 Black Gum Trl (32779-2529)
PHONE..................................407 788-0560
James Knowles Jr, *President*
EMP: 6 **EST:** 1989
SQ FT: 1,800
SALES (est): 708.5K **Privately Held**
WEB: www.kitchencrafters.net
SIC: 2434 Wood kitchen cabinets

(G-8301)
KRAFT HEINZ FOODS COMPANY
2180 W State Road 434 # 2112
(32779-5041)
PHONE..................................407 786-8157
Mark Matthews, *Principal*
EMP: 7
SALES (corp-wide): 26.1B **Publicly Held**
WEB: www.kraftheinzcompany.com
SIC: 2032 Canned specialties
HQ: Kraft Heinz Foods Company
1 Ppg Pl Ste 3400
Pittsburgh PA 15222
412 456-5700

(G-8302)
KUSTOM INDUSTRIAL FABRICATORS
265 Hunt Park Cv (32750-7567)
PHONE..................................407 965-1940
Andrew Zavodney, *President*
Jim Guenther, *Project Mgr*
Jim Howell, *Project Mgr*
Dan Noyce, *Project Mgr*
Kirk Zachrich, *Project Mgr*
EMP: 17 **EST:** 2008
SALES (est): 1.4MM **Privately Held**
WEB: www.kustom.us
SIC: 3444 Sheet metalwork

(G-8303)
KUSTOM US INC (PA)
640 E State Road 434 # 1000
(32750-5389)
PHONE..................................407 965-1940
Andrew L Zavodney Jr, *President*
Donnie Jordan, *Managing Prtnr*
Travis Christensen, *General Mgr*
Sarah Try, *Exec VP*
Peter Demains, *Vice Pres*
EMP: 18 **EST:** 1968
SALES (est): 34.3MM **Privately Held**
WEB: www.kustom.us
SIC: 3444 1761 1799 Sheet metalwork; roofing, siding & sheet metal work; post-disaster renovations

(G-8304)
LA PARADA CRIOLLA INC
254 W State Road 434 (32750-5114)
PHONE..................................321 207-7100
Elizabeth Ocasio, *Principal*
EMP: 8 **EST:** 2011
SALES (est): 453.9K **Privately Held**
SIC: 3421 Table & food cutlery, including butchers'

(G-8305)
LDS VACUUM PRODUCTS INC (PA)
773 Big Tree Dr (32750-3513)
PHONE..................................407 862-4643
Greer Russo, *President*
Cindy Reed, *Sales Staff*
Charles Price, *Manager*
▲ **EMP:** 25 **EST:** 1973
SQ FT: 11,000
SALES (est): 4.8MM **Privately Held**
WEB: www.ldsvacuumshopper.com
SIC: 3589 3829 Vacuum cleaners & sweepers, electric: industrial; gas detectors

(G-8306)
LIBERTY CRTIVE - COML PRTG PRM
800 Waterway Pl (32750-3535)
PHONE..................................407 960-4270
Lee Tyndall, *Production*
EMP: 7 **EST:** 2013
SALES (est): 140.6K **Privately Held**
WEB: www.liberty-creative.com
SIC: 2752 Commercial printing, offset

(G-8307)
LIGHT INTEGRATION INC
477 Commerce Way Ste 105 (32750-7571)
P.O. Box 141503, Orlando (32814-1503)
PHONE..................................407 681-0072
Robert Temple, *President*
Gary Gunter, *Treasurer*
◆ **EMP:** 6 **EST:** 2000
SQ FT: 3,000
SALES (est): 683.6K **Privately Held**
WEB: www.namestore.com
SIC: 3647 Vehicular lighting equipment

(G-8308)
MACROCAP LABS INC (PA)
975 Bennett Dr (32750-6352)
PHONE..................................321 234-6282
Chris Wagner, *President*
Troy Weyman, *Vice Pres*
David Castro, *Supervisor*
EMP: 48 **EST:** 2010
SALES (est): 14.7MM **Privately Held**
WEB: www.macrocaplabs.com
SIC: 2833 Medicinals & botanicals

(G-8309)
MARK WAYNE ADAMS INC
490 Wekiva Cove Rd (32779-5666)
P.O. Box 916392 (32791-6392)
PHONE..................................407 756-5862
Mark Adams, *Principal*
EMP: 9 **EST:** 2007
SALES (est): 561.5K **Privately Held**
WEB: www.markwayneadams.com
SIC: 2741 Miscellaneous publishing

(G-8310)
MASCHMEYER CONCRETE CO FLA
1601 S Ronald Reagan Blvd (32750-6420)
PHONE..................................407 339-5311
Jessie James, *General Mgr*
Mike Merrell, *Controller*
Suzy Wittman, *Manager*
Jerri J Harris, *Director*
EMP: 15
SALES (corp-wide): 136.2MM **Privately Held**
WEB: www.maschmeyer.com
SIC: 3273 Ready-mixed concrete
PA: Maschmeyer Concrete Company Of Florida
1142 Watertower Rd
Lake Park FL 33403
561 848-9112

(G-8311)
MERIT FASTENER CORPORATION (PA)
2510 N Ronald Reagan Blvd (32750-3703)
PHONE..................................407 331-4815
Gene Romagna, *CEO*
Donna J Best, *President*
Ritch Stevens, *Corp Secy*
Linda Sprinkle Anderson, *Vice Pres*
Laura Napoleon, *Vice Pres*
◆ **EMP:** 20 **EST:** 1977
SQ FT: 15,000
SALES (est): 5.6MM **Privately Held**
WEB: www.meritfasteners.com
SIC: 3599 5085 Machine & other job shop work; fasteners, industrial: nuts, bolts, screws, etc.

(G-8312)
METAL ESSENCE INC
910 Waterway Pl (32750-3545)
PHONE..................................407 478-8480
Yvonne Stimac, *President*
Alfredo Stimac, *Vice Pres*
▼ **EMP:** 6
SQ FT: 7,800
SALES (est): 660K **Privately Held**
WEB: www.metalessence.com
SIC: 3444 3599 Sheet metalwork; machine shop, jobbing & repair

(G-8313)
MOHAWK MANUFACTURING COMPANY
963 N Ronald Reagan Blvd (32750-3011)
PHONE..................................407 849-0333
Darrell Leidigh, *President*
Betty S Leidigh, *Corp Secy*
EMP: 14 **EST:** 1964
SALES (est): 662.9K **Privately Held**
WEB: www.mohawk-mfg.com
SIC: 3469 Stamping metal for the trade

(G-8314)
MRI DEPOT INC
1075 Fla Cntl Pkwy Ste 20 (32750)
PHONE..................................407 696-9822
Richard J Henderson, *President*
Mark R Henderson, *Vice Pres*
Mark Henderson, *Vice Pres*
Rick Henderson, *Finance Mgr*
EMP: 7 **EST:** 1996
SQ FT: 5,200
SALES (est): 1.1MM **Privately Held**
SIC: 3845 3829 Ultrasonic scanning devices, medical; ultrasonic testing equipment

(G-8315)
NAVA PETS INC
400 North St Unit 184 (32750-7566)
P.O. Box 679226, Orlando (32867-9226)
PHONE..................................407 982-7256
Janel Young, *Principal*
EMP: 10 **EST:** 2013
SALES (est): 741.4K **Privately Held**
WEB: www.navapets.com
SIC: 3999 Pet supplies

(G-8316)
NELSON PLASTICS INC
578 North St (32750-7646)
PHONE..................................407 339-3570
Richard Bradford, *President*
Becky Kesselring, *Vice Pres*
Rebecca Kesselring, *Office Mgr*
EMP: 37 **EST:** 1992
SQ FT: 12,000
SALES (est): 3.6MM **Privately Held**
WEB: www.nelsonplastics.com
SIC: 3089 Injection molding of plastics; plastic processing

(G-8317)
NEXUS ALLIANCE CORP
160 Vista Oak Dr (32779-3009)
PHONE..................................321 945-4283
George Habash, *Principal*
EMP: 9 **EST:** 2012
SALES (est): 132.3K **Privately Held**
SIC: 2834 Pharmaceutical preparations

(G-8318)
NUTRAKEY LLC
975 Bennett Dr (32750-6352)
PHONE..................................321 234-6282
Christopher Wagner, *CEO*
Troy Weyman, *COO*
EMP: 52 **EST:** 2016
SALES (est): 14.7MM **Privately Held**
WEB: www.nutrakeyhealth.com
SIC: 2834 Medicines, capsuled or ampuled
PA: Macrocap Labs, Inc.
975 Bennett Dr
Longwood FL 32750
321 234-6282

(G-8319)
PAGEANTRY TLENT ENTRMT SVCS IN
Also Called: Pageantry Magazine
1855 W State Road 434 (32750-5069)
P.O. Box 160307, Altamonte Springs (32716-0307)
PHONE..................................407 260-2262
Carl Dunn, *CEO*
Betty W Dunn, *President*
Charles Dunn, *Publisher*
EMP: 6 **EST:** 1992
SQ FT: 1,300
SALES (est): 1.1MM **Privately Held**
WEB: www.pageantrymagazine.com
SIC: 2721 8111 Magazines: publishing only, not printed on site; legal services

(G-8320)
PANEL ARMOR PRODUCTS LLC
1970 Corporate Sq Unit B (32750-3520)
PHONE..................................407 960-5946
Gene Piscopo, *Principal*
EMP: 8 **EST:** 2014
SALES (est): 261K **Privately Held**
WEB: www.panelarmorproducts.com
SIC: 3999 Manufacturing industries

(G-8321)
PAVERSEALINGCOM CORP
1225 Windsor Ave (32750-6825)
PHONE..................................407 951-6437
George T Sandland, *Principal*
EMP: 8 **EST:** 2010
SALES (est): 106.4K **Privately Held**
WEB: www.paversealing.com
SIC: 2951 Asphalt paving mixtures & blocks

(G-8322)
PEMBERTON INC
103 Highline Dr (32750-4939)
P.O. Box 521000 (32752-1000)
PHONE..................................407 831-6688
Todd N Pemberton, *President*
John Kinney, *Sales Associate*
W Bruce Pemberton, *Shareholder*
▲ **EMP:** 50 **EST:** 1968
SQ FT: 4,000
SALES (est): 14.2MM **Privately Held**
WEB: www.pembertonattachments.com
SIC: 3531 Construction machinery attachments

(G-8323)
PERFORMANCE POWDER COATING
416 Commerce Way (32750-7659)
PHONE..................................407 339-4000
Heath Walters, *Mng Member*
Robert Hiii Bledsoe, *Manager*
EMP: 13 **EST:** 2013
SALES (est): 1.4MM **Privately Held**
WEB: www.performancepowdercoating.com
SIC: 3479 Coating of metals & formed products

(G-8324)
PFI INC
607 Savage Ct (32750-5151)
PHONE..................................407 822-4499
Joseph Gurley, *President*
James C Gurley, *President*
Ruth Ann Gurley, *Vice Pres*
John Sullivan, *Manager*
◆ **EMP:** 9 **EST:** 1980
SALES (est): 1.9MM **Privately Held**
WEB: www.pfipcb.com
SIC: 3699 Electrical equipment & supplies

(G-8325)
PHANTOM TECHNOLOGIES INC
2280 N Ronald Reagan Blvd # 103 (32750-3519)
PHONE..................................407 265-2567
Joseph Norelli, *President*
EMP: 32 **EST:** 2000
SALES (est): 4.4MM **Privately Held**
WEB: www.phantomtec.com
SIC: 3679 Electronic circuits

(G-8326)
PLATECRAFTERS CORPORATION
782 Big Tree Dr (32750-3528)
PHONE..................................215 997-1990
Robert Spering, *President*
EMP: 14 **EST:** 2018
SALES (est): 276.7K **Privately Held**
WEB: www.platecrafters.com
SIC: 2759 Commercial printing

(G-8327)
POROUS METAL FILTERS INC
112 Wheatland Ct (32779-4615)
PHONE..................................407 682-1494
Rick Kenney, *Manager*
Danny Wilhelm, *Manager*
EMP: 7 **EST:** 2015
SALES (est): 107.2K **Privately Held**
WEB: www.pmfilter.net
SIC: 3569 Filters

(G-8328)
PRECISION LABORATORIES INC
165 E Wildmere Ave (32750-5455)
P.O. Box 609500, Orlando (32860-9500)
PHONE..................................407 774-4261
William V Lassiter, *President*
Donna Lassiter, *Vice Pres*
EMP: 21 **EST:** 1991
SALES (est): 5.4MM **Privately Held**
WEB: www.precisionweb.com
SIC: 3842 Hearing aids

(G-8329)
RANGER ASSOCIATES INC
Also Called: Ranger Prtg & Promotional Pdts
688 Florida Central Pkwy (32750-6344)
PHONE..................................407 869-0024
Sharon Lane, *CEO*
William Lane, *President*
Rob Lane, *CFO*
EMP: 6 **EST:** 1979
SQ FT: 2,400
SALES (est): 1MM **Privately Held**
WEB: www.rangeronline.com
SIC: 2759 2752 Screen printing; commercial printing, lithographic

(G-8330)
RELIABLE BUSINESS TECHNOLOGIES
285 W Pine Ave (32750-4138)
PHONE..................................386 561-9944
Chris Mitchell, *Principal*
EMP: 6 **EST:** 2016
SALES (est): 94.4K **Privately Held**
SIC: 7372 Application computer software

(G-8331)
RELIABLE CUSTOM IMPRINTS CORP
448 Commerce Way Unit 100 (32750-6384)
PHONE..................................407 834-0571
Bill Melise, *President*
EMP: 6 **EST:** 2000
SALES (est): 416.7K **Privately Held**
WEB: www.rciapparel.com
SIC: 2395 2396 Embroidery & art needlework; screen printing on fabric articles

(G-8332)
ROLLADEN INC
1328 Bennett Dr (32750-7503)
PHONE..................................954 454-4114
Robert Hoffman, *President*
EMP: 10
SALES (corp-wide): 15.9MM **Privately Held**
WEB: www.rolladen.com
SIC: 3442 5211 Storm doors or windows, metal; door & window products
PA: Rolladen, Inc.
3146 John P Curci Dr # 5
Hallandale Beach FL 33009
954 454-4114

(G-8333)
SAMJAY MEDIA GROUP ORLANDO LLC
Also Called: Home Mag, The
187 Sabal Palm Dr Ste 200 (32779-2595)
PHONE..................................407 865-7526
John Jericiau,
EMP: 6 **EST:** 2008
SALES (est): 491.6K **Privately Held**
SIC: 2731 Book publishing

(G-8334)
SELECTWO MACHINE COMPANY INC
1695 Ee Williamson Rd (32779-2839)
PHONE..................................407 788-3102
Katherine Skrobiak, *President*
Gary Skrobiak, *Principal*
EMP: 6 **EST:** 1978
SQ FT: 2,000
SALES (est): 884.5K **Privately Held**
WEB: www.selectwo.com
SIC: 3599 Machine shop, jobbing & repair

(G-8335)
SENTINEL CMMNCTONS NEWS VNTRES
210 Pembrook Pl (32779-4523)
PHONE..................................407 420-6229
Mike Griffin, *Principal*
EMP: 9
SALES (corp-wide): 4.5B **Publicly Held**
WEB: www.orlandosentinel.com
SIC: 2711 Newspapers, publishing & printing
HQ: Sentinel Communications News Ventures Inc.
633 N Orange Ave
Orlando FL 32801
407 420-5000

(G-8336)
SERVOS AND SIMULATION INC
Also Called: Engineering
421 Meadowridge Cv (32750-7126)
PHONE..................................407 807-0208
Rachel Baker, *President*
Phil Hutchings, *Executive*
EMP: 5 **EST:** 1980
SALES (est): 554.9K **Privately Held**
WEB: www.servosandsimulation.com
SIC: 3699 3825 8748 7371 Flight simulators (training aids), electronic; test equipment for electronic & electrical circuits; systems analysis or design; computer software development; computer software systems analysis & design, custom

(G-8337)
SOURGLASS BREWING
480 S Ronald Reagan Blvd (32750-5498)
PHONE..................................407 262-0056
EMP: 8 **EST:** 2019
SALES (est): 122.8K **Privately Held**
WEB: www.hourglassbrewing.com
SIC: 2082 Malt beverages

(G-8338)
SOUTHEASTERN FASTENERS
955 Charles St Unit 105 (32750-5496)
PHONE..................................407 790-4888
Billy L Willier, *President*
EMP: 6 **EST:** 2016
SALES (est): 232.3K **Privately Held**
SIC: 3965 Fasteners

(G-8339)
SPRAY-TECH STAINING INC
569 Darby Way (32779-3389)
PHONE..................................407 443-4239
Martin Feinen IV, *President*
Rosalie Feinen, *Admin Sec*
EMP: 10 **EST:** 2000
SALES (est): 900K **Privately Held**
SIC: 2499 Fencing, wood

(G-8340)
STARBOARD CONSULTING LLC
2170 W State Road 434 # 3 (32779-4957)
PHONE..................................407 622-6414
Amy Tatum, *Vice Pres*
Alicia Hilliard, *Office Mgr*
Doug Carrington, *Manager*
James Smith, *Software Dev*
Karen A Buck,
EMP: 22 **EST:** 2007
SALES (est): 3.5MM **Privately Held**
WEB: www.starboard-consulting.com
SIC: 7372 7371 Application computer software; computer software development & applications

(G-8341)
SUN BARRIER PRODUCTS INC
159 Baywood Ave (32750-3449)
PHONE..................................407 830-9085
Charles T Donaldson, *President*
Charles Donaldson, *Med Doctor*
▼ **EMP:** 15 **EST:** 1988
SQ FT: 3,500
SALES (est): 2.6MM **Privately Held**
WEB: www.sunbarrierproducts.com
SIC: 3442 5211 Shutters, door or window: metal; door & window products

(G-8342)
TIFCO INDUSTRIES FREEDOM ALLOY
651 Fox Hunt Cir (32750-3350)
PHONE..................................407 474-6747
EMP: 6 **EST:** 2017
SALES (est): 79.9K **Privately Held**
WEB: www.tifco.com
SIC: 3999 Manufacturing industries

(G-8343)
TIFFANY QUILTING & DRAPERY
206 E Palmetto Ave (32750-4241)
PHONE..................................407 834-6386
Benjamin Magaldino, *President*
Michael P Magaldino, *Vice Pres*
EMP: 11 **EST:** 1977
SQ FT: 7,000
SALES (est): 420.2K **Privately Held**
SIC: 2392 2391 2395 Bedspreads & bed sets: made from purchased materials; comforters & quilts: made from purchased materials; draperies, plastic & textile: from purchased materials; pleating & stitching

(G-8344)
TREASURE CHEST OF SWEETWATER
2901 W State Road 434 # 121 (32779-4883)
P.O. Box 915102 (32791-5102)
PHONE..................................407 788-0020
Ginny Ellison, *President*
EMP: 5 **EST:** 1979
SALES (est): 380.6K **Privately Held**
WEB: www.treasurechestsw.com
SIC: 2711 Newspapers, publishing & printing

(G-8345)
TRU DIMENSIONS PRINTING INC
2100 N R Reagan Blvd 10 (32750)
PHONE..................................407 339-3410
Mary E Jett, *President*
Charles Jett, *Treasurer*
EMP: 9 **EST:** 1985
SQ FT: 4,000
SALES (est): 667.4K **Privately Held**
WEB: www.allinonemediaandprinting.com
SIC: 2759 7334 5199 Commercial printing; photocopying & duplicating services; advertising specialties

(G-8346)
UNI-PAK CORP
1015 N Ronald Reagan Blvd (32750-3013)
P.O. Box 522168 (32752-2168)
PHONE..................................407 830-9300
Jeffrey A Coutant, *President*
Christopher T Coutant, *Vice Pres*
Stephen J Coutant, *Vice Pres*
John Garvis, *Cust Mgr*
Jean Olsen, *Info Tech Dir*
◆ **EMP:** 30 **EST:** 1970
SQ FT: 40,000
SALES (est): 4MM **Privately Held**
WEB: www.unipak.com
SIC: 3535 Unit handling conveying systems

(G-8347)
VJ PUBLICATIONS INC
1551 W Marvin St (32750-6761)
P.O. Box 915804 (32791-5804)
PHONE..................................407 461-0707
EMP: 7 **EST:** 2006
SALES (est): 201K **Privately Held**
WEB: www.vjpinc.com
SIC: 2741 Miscellaneous publishing

▲ = Import ▼=Export
◆ =Import/Export

(G-8348)
VMAK CORP
Also Called: Sir Speedy
131 Applewood Dr (32750-3450)
PHONE..................................407 260-1199
Patricia Brown, *President*
Betty Chesser, *Vice Pres*
Vicente Cruz, *Director*
EMP: 10 **EST:** 1999
SALES (est): 2MM **Privately Held**
WEB: www.sirspeedy.com
SIC: 2752 2791 2789 Commercial printing, lithographic; typesetting; bookbinding & related work

(G-8349)
WATERBOX USA LLC (PA)
Also Called: Waterbox Aquariums
320 W Sabal Palm Pl # 10 (32779-3639)
PHONE..................................800 674-2608
Richard Gilliland, *President*
EMP: 6 **EST:** 2018
SALES (est): 1.2MM **Privately Held**
SIC: 3231 5999 Aquariums & reflectors, glass; aquarium supplies

(G-8350)
WESTON PARK AT LONGWOOD STA
100 Wax Myrtle Ln (32779-4926)
PHONE..................................321 422-3546
EMP: 7 **EST:** 2016
SALES (est): 128K **Privately Held**
WEB: www.westonparkapts.com
SIC: 2499 Wood products

(G-8351)
WINTEL
1051 Bennett Dr Ste 101 (32750-7588)
PHONE..................................407 834-1188
Angie Rivera, *General Mgr*
John Zeh, *Foreman/Supr*
EMP: 16 **EST:** 1971
SQ FT: 18,000
SALES (est): 3.4MM **Privately Held**
WEB: www.wintelphones.com
SIC: 3661 7629 Telephone & telegraph apparatus; telecommunication equipment repair (except telephones)

(G-8352)
XOTHERMIC INC
311 Riverbend Blvd (32779-2307)
PHONE..................................407 951-8008
James Nabors, *Principal*
EMP: 7 **EST:** 2016
SALES (est): 1.2MM **Privately Held**
WEB: www.xothermicinc.com
SIC: 3823 Industrial instrmnts msrmnt display/control process variable

(G-8353)
XPERIENT LLC
250 W Church Ave Ste 100 (32750-5900)
PHONE..................................407 265-8000
Jason McCormick, *Mng Member*
▼ **EMP:** 8 **EST:** 2003
SALES (est): 818.4K **Privately Held**
WEB: www.xperient.com
SIC: 2752 Commercial printing, offset

Lorida
Highlands County

(G-8354)
CAPTAIN RUSTYS
Also Called: Captain Rustys Smoked Fish Dip
1958 Us Highway 98 (33857-9724)
PHONE..................................813 244-2799
Rusty West, *Principal*
EMP: 8 **EST:** 2015
SALES (est): 202.8K **Privately Held**
WEB: www.captainrustysseafood.com
SIC: 2091 5421 Fish, smoked; fish & seafood markets; seafood markets

Loxahatchee
Palm Beach County

(G-8355)
ACE MIRROR & GLASS WORKS INC
Also Called: Ace Window & Door
14083 85th Rd N (33470-4353)
PHONE..................................561 792-7478
Jason Louis Higgins, *President*
EMP: 9 **EST:** 2002
SALES (est): 667.4K **Privately Held**
SIC: 3231 Ornamental glass: cut, engraved or otherwise decorated

(G-8356)
AMERICAN ALL
16079 70th St N (33470-3445)
PHONE..................................561 401-0885
EMP: 6 **EST:** 2013
SALES (est): 153.9K **Privately Held**
WEB: www.allamericanlandclearing.net
SIC: 3674 Semiconductors & related devices

(G-8357)
AMERICAN MOLD REMOVAL INC
17462 37th Pl N (33470-5408)
PHONE..................................561 575-7757
Donal Dillon, *Principal*
EMP: 7 **EST:** 2012
SALES (est): 148.6K **Privately Held**
SIC: 3544 Industrial molds

(G-8358)
BLACK PEARL WOODWORKS LLC
16142 E Burns Dr (33470-4115)
PHONE..................................954 214-0899
Tammy Nugent, *Manager*
EMP: 6 **EST:** 2019
SALES (est): 65.4K **Privately Held**
WEB: www.blackpearlwoodworks.com
SIC: 2431 Millwork

(G-8359)
FLOWMASTER INC
14231 83rd Ln N (33470-4377)
PHONE..................................561 249-1145
Joseph T Hennessey Vp, *Principal*
EMP: 9 **EST:** 2014
SALES (est): 103.8K **Privately Held**
SIC: 3714 Motor vehicle parts & accessories

(G-8360)
JMG TOOL LLC
14282 76th Rd N (33470-5217)
PHONE..................................805 532-1631
Gill M Jeremy, *Principal*
EMP: 9 **EST:** 2016
SALES (est): 457.1K **Privately Held**
WEB: www.tiborsmachineshop.com
SIC: 3599 Machine shop, jobbing & repair

(G-8361)
LOXAHATCHEE SHUTTER & ALUM INC
16758 67th Ct N (33470-3331)
PHONE..................................561 513-9581
Sidney Garcia, *President*
EMP: 9 **EST:** 2018
SALES (est): 745.8K **Privately Held**
SIC: 3442 Shutters, door or window: metal

(G-8362)
PALM BEACH AGGREGATES LLC
20125 Southern Blvd (33470-9259)
P.O. Box 700 (33470-0700)
PHONE..................................561 795-6550
Sam Klein, *Ch of Bd*
Enrique Tomeu, *President*
Ben R Turner, *Exec VP*
Johnathan Bates, *Opers Mgr*
R Patrick McMullen, *CFO*
▲ **EMP:** 43 **EST:** 1900
SQ FT: 12,000
SALES (est): 17MM **Privately Held**
WEB: www.palmbeachag.com
SIC: 3281 0181 0133 Stone, quarrying & processing of own stone products; sod farms; sugarcane farm

(G-8363)
ROY SMITH S SCREEN
16648 71st Ln N (33470-3382)
PHONE..................................561 792-3381
Roy Smith, *Principal*
EMP: 17 **EST:** 2009
SALES (est): 2.1MM **Privately Held**
WEB:
www.roysmithscreensandshutters.yolasite.com
SIC: 2431 Door shutters, wood

(G-8364)
SOPHISTCTED PLLET WOODWORX LLC
7119 Apache Blvd (33470-3154)
PHONE..................................561 795-0739
Christopher M Burgio, *Manager*
EMP: 6 **EST:** 2015
SALES (est): 206.8K **Privately Held**
SIC: 2448 Pallets, wood

(G-8365)
SOUTHERN POWER WASHING
16931 W Burns Dr (33470-4170)
PHONE..................................561 644-2237
Andrea Ronga, *Principal*
EMP: 6 **EST:** 2007
SALES (est): 81.3K **Privately Held**
WEB: www.southernpowerwashing.com
SIC: 3589 High pressure cleaning equipment

(G-8366)
TROPICAL PCB DESIGN SERVICES
7960 Banyan Blvd (33470-3030)
PHONE..................................561 784-9536
Sam Burton, *President*
Gloyd Dearth, *Engineer*
EMP: 11 **EST:** 1998
SQ FT: 500
SALES (est): 423.4K **Privately Held**
WEB: www.tropicalpcb.com
SIC: 3577 8711 Computer peripheral equipment; engineering services

Loxahatchee Groves
Palm Beach County

(G-8367)
PERFORMNCE NTRTN SOLUTIONS LLC
14895 22nd Rd N (33470-4638)
PHONE..................................310 435-2995
Justin Hickey, *President*
EMP: 6
SALES (est): 298.6K **Privately Held**
WEB: www.nutritionsolutions.com
SIC: 3523 Farm machinery & equipment

Lulu
Columbia County

(G-8368)
CASONS QUALITY CARE SVCS LLC
226 Se Lee Dr (32061-7548)
PHONE..................................386 365-1016
Erin Cason, *Principal*
EMP: 6 **EST:** 2013
SALES (est): 419K **Privately Held**
SIC: 2431 Millwork

Lutz
Hillsborough County

(G-8369)
A A A SIGNS INC
1911 Passero Ave (33559-7352)
PHONE..................................813 949-8397
David M Smith, *President*
EMP: 8 **EST:** 1991
SQ FT: 4,000
SALES (est): 1MM **Privately Held**
SIC: 3993 Electric signs

(G-8370)
A C REPAIRS INC
1519 Camphor Cove Dr (33549-5831)
PHONE..................................813 909-0809
John Daniel, *Principal*
EMP: 8 **EST:** 2006
SALES (est): 789.4K **Privately Held**
WEB: www.acrepairstampa.com
SIC: 3585 Air conditioning equipment, complete

(G-8371)
ABOUT FACE CABINETRY & REFACIN
110 Crenshaw Lake Rd (33548-6101)
PHONE..................................813 777-4088
Christopher C Robinson, *President*
EMP: 14 **EST:** 2008
SALES (est): 493.1K **Privately Held**
WEB:
www.kitchencabinetrefacingtampa.com
SIC: 2434 Wood kitchen cabinets

(G-8372)
ACCESS WRLESS DATA SLTIONS LLC
21756 State Road 54 # 101 (33549-2905)
PHONE..................................813 751-2039
Becky Messenger, *Project Mgr*
Loretta Lau, *Purchasing*
Clara Mas-Zayas, *Accounting Mgr*
Michelle Hart, *Accounts Mgr*
Megan Lynch, *Accounts Mgr*
EMP: 8 **EST:** 2008
SQ FT: 1,000
SALES (est): 1.7MM **Privately Held**
WEB: www.accesswds.com
SIC: 3669 Intercommunication systems, electric

(G-8373)
ADVANCED COMPONENTS SOLUTIONS
22652 Laureldale Dr (33549-8787)
PHONE..................................813 884-1600
Eric Levenson, *President*
EMP: 5 **EST:** 2003
SALES (est): 330K **Privately Held**
SIC: 3089 Lamp bases & shades, plastic

(G-8374)
ADVANCED DRAINAGE & HYDRO INC
19805 Deer Lake Rd (33548-4273)
PHONE..................................813 957-3162
Donald E Kipp Jr, *President*
EMP: 7 **EST:** 2012
SALES (est): 470.3K **Privately Held**
SIC: 3089 Plastic hardware & building products

(G-8375)
APPLE SIGN & AWNING LLC
1635 Dale Mabry Hwy Ste 7 (33548-3000)
PHONE..................................813 948-2220
Madeline C Rogers, *Mng Member*
EMP: 10 **EST:** 1991
SALES (est): 794.2K **Privately Held**
WEB: www.applesignandawning.info
SIC: 3993 Electric signs

(G-8376)
COAST TO COAST SOLAR INC
19209 N Us Highway 41 (33549-4262)
PHONE..................................813 406-6501
Jeff Saitta, *Owner*
Coast Melissa, *Med Doctor*
EMP: 16 **EST:** 2012
SALES (est): 3.3MM **Privately Held**
WEB: www.coasttocoastsolar.com
SIC: 3433 Solar heaters & collectors

(G-8377)
COLORPROOF SOFTWARE INC
Also Called: Colorbyte Software
234 Crystal Grove Blvd (33548-6460)
PHONE..................................813 963-0241
Mark M Dale, *CEO*
John Pannozzo, *President*
Sergiy Murashkin, *Software Engr*

GEOGRAPHIC

EMP: 5 **EST:** 1994
SQ FT: 3,000
SALES (est): 564.4K **Privately Held**
WEB: www.colorbytesoftware.com
SIC: 7372 Application computer software

(G-8378)
COMMUNITY NEWS PUBLICATIONS
Also Called: Riverview Community News
3632 Land O Lkes Blvd Ste (33549)
P.O. Box 479 (33548-0479)
PHONE..................................813 909-2800
Diane Kortus, *Owner*
B Manion, *Editor*
EMP: 14 **EST:** 1999
SALES (est): 118.5K **Privately Held**
WEB: www.lakerlutznews.com
SIC: 2721 2711 Periodicals; newspapers

(G-8379)
CROSS CONSTRUCTION SVCS INC
25221 Wesley Chapel Blvd (33559-7201)
PHONE..................................813 907-1013
Russell E Arney, *President*
Tony Hanson, *Senior VP*
Pete Swyryd, *Project Mgr*
Skip Johnson, *Sales Staff*
EMP: 69 **EST:** 1978
SALES (est): 7.8MM **Privately Held**
WEB: www.crossconstructionservices.net
SIC: 3531 Construction machinery

(G-8380)
DOORKNOB DISCOUNT CENTER LLC
18404 Bittern Ave (33558-2738)
PHONE..................................813 963-3104
Bob Bardel, *CEO*
EMP: 7 **EST:** 2010
SALES (est): 231K **Privately Held**
SIC: 3429 5961 Builders' hardware; tools & hardware, mail order

(G-8381)
DOWN SHIFT LLC
4504 Scott Rd (33558-4804)
P.O. Box 340442, Tampa (33694-0442)
PHONE..................................813 431-2389
Robert W Maddrey, *Partner*
Shaun Robinson, *Manager*
Laura Seymour, *Director*
EMP: 5 **EST:** 2002
SALES (est): 312.8K **Privately Held**
WEB: www.downshiftmagazine.com
SIC: 2741 Miscellaneous publishing

(G-8382)
EMBROIDERTOO LLC
17230 Chinaberry Rd (33558-5225)
PHONE..................................813 909-0239
Young Won, *Principal*
EMP: 6 **EST:** 2011
SALES (est): 164.9K **Privately Held**
SIC: 2395 Embroidery products, except schiffli machine

(G-8383)
FRESH PRINTS
19514 French Lace Dr (33558-9244)
PHONE..................................813 992-1655
Lewis Paul Bellaire, *Principal*
EMP: 6 **EST:** 2018
SALES (est): 182.6K **Privately Held**
WEB: www.freshprints.com
SIC: 2752 Commercial printing, lithographic

(G-8384)
GIBBONS INDUSTRIES INC
Also Called: Comprehensive Grants MGT
1927 Passero Ave (33559-7352)
PHONE..................................352 330-0294
Cereta M Gibbons, *President*
EMP: 9 **EST:** 2017
SALES (est): 273K **Privately Held**
SIC: 3999 Barber & beauty shop equipment

(G-8385)
GMA-FOOD LLC
24756 State Road 54 (33559-6245)
PHONE..................................646 469-8599
Mohamed Ismail,
Abdelrahman Abdaltattah,
Sherif Ismail,
Mahamed Masoud,
EMP: 7 **EST:** 2019
SALES (est): 100K **Privately Held**
WEB: www.gmafood.com
SIC: 2033 Canned fruits & specialties

(G-8386)
GRIND IT LLC
17002 Hanna Rd (33549-5665)
PHONE..................................813 310-9710
Dillon J Harris, *Owner*
EMP: 7 **EST:** 2014
SALES (est): 1MM **Privately Held**
WEB: www.grinditstumpremoval.com
SIC: 3599 Grinding castings for the trade

(G-8387)
HANNA PHARMACEUTICALS LLC
1451 Kensington Woods Dr (33549-3882)
PHONE..................................813 409-9327
Mazen Hanna, *President*
EMP: 6 **EST:** 2016
SALES (est): 148.9K **Privately Held**
SIC: 2834 Pharmaceutical preparations

(G-8388)
HANTERI ENTERPRISES CORP
Also Called: Designs In Rugs
1915 Vandervort Rd (33549-5758)
PHONE..................................813 949-8729
Henry J Molesky, *President*
EMP: 11 **EST:** 2004
SALES (est): 311.5K **Privately Held**
SIC: 2273 Carpets & rugs

(G-8389)
HIGHWAY SYSTEMS INCORPORATED
4450 Pet Ln (33559-6307)
PHONE..................................813 907-7512
EMP: 10 **EST:** 2013
SALES (est): 199.3K **Privately Held**
WEB: www.highwaysystemsinc.com
SIC: 3441 Fabricated structural metal

(G-8390)
IN DIVERSIFIED PLANT SERVICES
22528 Laureldale Dr (33549-8785)
P.O. Box 931 (33548-0931)
PHONE..................................813 453-7025
Denny Langworthy, *President*
Mark A Ogden, *Treasurer*
Steve Boleyn, *Shareholder*
Dante Dalere, *Shareholder*
Joy Vallieril, *Shareholder*
EMP: 12 **EST:** 2008
SALES (est): 1.4MM **Privately Held**
WEB: www.dpsfla.com
SIC: 1446 Blast sand mining

(G-8391)
INTEC PRINTING SOLUTIONS CORP
16011 N Nebraska Ave (33549-6158)
PHONE..................................813 949-7799
Ian Melville, *President*
Michael Sparbeck, *COO*
Helen Sims, *Purchasing*
Steve Duff, *Technical Mgr*
Todd Tedesco, *Engineer*
▲ **EMP:** 6 **EST:** 2011
SALES (est): 1MM **Privately Held**
WEB: www.intecprinters.com
SIC: 2752 Commercial printing, offset

(G-8392)
INTERNATIONAL SPECIALISTS INC (PA)
15424 N Nebraska Ave (33549-6150)
P.O. Box 271430, Tampa (33688-1430)
PHONE..................................813 631-8643
Philip K Lau, *President*
Donald K Lau, *Principal*
◆ **EMP:** 6 **EST:** 1971
SQ FT: 3,400
SALES (est): 1MM **Privately Held**
WEB: www.internationalspecialists.com
SIC: 3625 Switches, electronic applications

(G-8393)
JAB-B-INC
18125 N Us Highway 41 # 104
(33549-6455)
PHONE..................................813 803-3995
Marie L Blaxton, *President*
Bill Falin, *Vice Pres*
EMP: 5 **EST:** 2016
SQ FT: 1,200
SALES (est): 5.6MM **Privately Held**
SIC: 1389 1522 Construction, repair & dismantling services; remodeling, multi-family dwellings

(G-8394)
JDT SERVICING LLC
24310 Breezy Oak Ct (33559-7924)
PHONE..................................813 909-8640
Ashley Wilhelm, *Principal*
EMP: 7 **EST:** 2015
SALES (est): 501.9K **Privately Held**
WEB: www.jdtservicing.com
SIC: 1389 Roustabout service

(G-8395)
LEAN DESIGN & MFG INC
19412 Livingston Ave (33559-4011)
PHONE..................................727 415-3504
Tarek Chbeir, *CEO*
Michael Bacher, *President*
EMP: 12 **EST:** 2013
SALES (est): 634K **Privately Held**
SIC: 3089 Engraving of plastic

(G-8396)
LOWE GEAR PRINTING
15510 N Nebraska Ave B (33549-6107)
PHONE..................................866 714-9965
Cotton Lowe, *Principal*
▲ **EMP:** 6 **EST:** 2011
SALES (est): 724.5K **Privately Held**
WEB: www.lowegear.com
SIC: 2759 Screen printing

(G-8397)
MAILING & BINDERY SYSTEMS INC
3959 Van Dyke Rd (33558-8025)
PHONE..................................813 416-8965
Brian Walders, *Principal*
EMP: 5 **EST:** 2010
SALES (est): 351.6K **Privately Held**
WEB: www.mailingandbinderysystems.com
SIC: 2789 Bookbinding & related work

(G-8398)
MEDITEK-ICOT INC
Also Called: Lutz Radiology
1916 Highland Oaks Blvd (33559-7323)
PHONE..................................813 909-7476
Thomas G Winter, *President*
David E Six, *Vice Pres*
Richard R Six, *Med Doctor*
EMP: 10 **EST:** 1992
SQ FT: 3,600
SALES (est): 194K **Privately Held**
SIC: 3845 Laser systems & equipment, medical

(G-8399)
METTLER TOLEDO
1571 Northpointe Pkwy (33558-5522)
PHONE..................................607 257-6000
EMP: 12 **EST:** 2018
SALES (est): 880.4K **Privately Held**
WEB: www.mt.com
SIC: 3596 Scales & balances, except laboratory

(G-8400)
METTLER-TOLEDO INC
1571 Northpointe Pkwy (33558-5522)
PHONE..................................607 257-6000
Olivier Filliol, *CEO*
William P Donnelly, *Ch of Bd*
Gerald Liswoski, *General Mgr*
Rob Phillips, *Technology*
EMP: 135 **EST:** 1987
SQ FT: 45,000
SALES (est): 39.2MM
SALES (corp-wide): 3B **Publicly Held**
WEB: www.mt.com
SIC: 3596 3537 Weighing machines & apparatus; industrial trucks & tractors
HQ: Mettler-Toledo, Llc
1900 Polaris Pkwy Fl 6
Columbus OH 43240
614 438-4511

(G-8401)
MHMS CORP
142 Whitaker Rd Ste A (33549-5767)
PHONE..................................813 948-0504
Vincent Menendez, *President*
EMP: 45 **EST:** 1986
SALES (est): 2.2MM **Privately Held**
SIC: 2389 2673 Disposable garments & accessories; plastic bags: made from purchased materials

(G-8402)
MONADNOCK PAPER MILLS INC
1439 Kensington Woods Dr (33549-3882)
PHONE..................................603 588-8672
Randy Norris, *Sales Staff*
EMP: 6 **EST:** 2018
SALES (est): 90.7K **Privately Held**
SIC: 2621 Paper mills

(G-8403)
MORGAN CABINET RESTYLERS LLC
15915 N Florida Ave (33549-8109)
PHONE..................................813 931-4663
Kirk C Morgan, *President*
EMP: 7 **EST:** 2017
SALES (est): 259.8K **Privately Held**
WEB: www.morganexteriorsinc.com
SIC: 2434 Wood kitchen cabinets

(G-8404)
NANO LIQUITEC LLC
5627 Terrain De Golf Dr (33558-2864)
PHONE..................................813 447-1742
Julie Manley, *Branch Mgr*
EMP: 11
SALES (corp-wide): 133.1K **Privately Held**
WEB: www.nanoliquitec.com
SIC: 2819 Catalysts, chemical
PA: Nano Liquitec, Llc
2202 N West Shore Blvd # 2
Tampa FL

(G-8405)
NEW TAMPA EMBROIDME OF
1917 Passero Ave (33559-7352)
PHONE..................................813 994-0118
EMP: 7 **EST:** 2015
SALES (est): 79.4K **Privately Held**
WEB: www.fullypromoted.com
SIC: 2395 Embroidery & art needlework

(G-8406)
NOWVISION TECHNOLOGIES INC
618 De Buel Rd Bldng A (33549)
PHONE..................................813 943-4639
Dan S Lawrence, *COO*
EMP: 9 **EST:** 2000
SQ FT: 3,000
SALES (est): 499K **Privately Held**
WEB: www.nowvision.com
SIC: 3651 Household audio & video equipment

(G-8407)
OPINICUS TEXTRON INC
1827 Northpointe Pkwy (33558-0101)
PHONE..................................813 792-9300
Mark G Budd, *CEO*
James R Takats, *President*
Patricia Elmer, *Vice Pres*
Troy Fey, *Vice Pres*
Jodi Noah, *CFO*
▲ **EMP:** 75 **EST:** 1988
SALES (est): 22MM
SALES (corp-wide): 11.6B **Publicly Held**
WEB: www.trusimulation.com
SIC: 3699 Flight simulators (training aids), electronic
PA: Textron Inc.
40 Westminster St
Providence RI 02903
401 421-2800

(G-8408)
PERPETUAL MARKETING ASSOC INC (PA)
25126 State Road 54 (33559-6256)
PHONE..................................813 949-9385
Jaime Wood, *President*
Diane Putt, *CFO*
EMP: 5 **EST:** 1981
SALES (est): 510.4K **Privately Held**
SIC: 3651 5099 Household audio & video equipment; video & audio equipment

(G-8409)
PIERGATE LLC
4450 Pet Ln Ste 105 (33559-6308)
PHONE..................................813 938-9170
Sameh A Hassan, *Principal*
EMP: 7 **EST:** 2016
SALES (est): 1MM **Privately Held**
WEB: www.piergate.com
SIC: 3652 Pre-recorded records & tapes

(G-8410)
POLKS MEAT PRODUCTS INC
18104 Muncie Pl (33558-2753)
PHONE..................................813 961-2881
EMP: 6 **EST:** 2017
SALES (est): 79.4K **Privately Held**
WEB: www.polksmeat.com
SIC: 2011 Meat packing plants

(G-8411)
PRECISE PRINT FLORIDA
410 W Chapman Rd (33548-6100)
PHONE..................................813 960-4958
Donna Christine Sutton, *Principal*
EMP: 7 **EST:** 2009
SALES (est): 192.2K **Privately Held**
SIC: 2752 Commercial printing, lithographic

(G-8412)
PREFERRED MATERIALS INC (DH)
4636 Scarborough Dr (33559-8506)
PHONE..................................904 288-0244
Darryl Fales, *President*
Sherman Matt, *Area Mgr*
Matthew Saenz, *Project Mgr*
William Sullivan, *Project Mgr*
Paul Sweet, *Production*
EMP: 25 **EST:** 2007
SALES (est): 103.1MM
SALES (corp-wide): 27.5B **Privately Held**
WEB: www.preferredmaterials.com
SIC: 3273 Ready-mixed concrete

(G-8413)
PSYCHLGCAL ASSSSMENT RSRCES IN (PA)
Also Called: Par
16204 N Florida Ave (33549-8119)
PHONE..................................813 968-3003
R Bob I Smith, *Chairman*
Travis G White, *Exec VP*
Serje Seminoff, *Vice Pres*
Catherine Smith, *Vice Pres*
Carrie Morera, *Project Dir*
EMP: 61 **EST:** 1978
SQ FT: 15,000
SALES (est): 63MM **Privately Held**
WEB: www.parinc.com
SIC: 2741 Miscellaneous publishing

(G-8414)
ROOF HUGGER INC
142 Whitaker Rd Ste B (33549-5767)
P.O. Box 1027, Odessa (33556-1027)
PHONE..................................813 909-4424
Dale Nelson, *President*
Janet Nelson, *Director*
EMP: 3 **EST:** 1991
SQ FT: 500
SALES (est): 3MM **Privately Held**
WEB: www.roofhugger.com
SIC: 3441 Fabricated structural metal

(G-8415)
S + L MILLWORKS INC
18631 Avenue Capri (33558-5346)
PHONE..................................813 413-6260
Ronald Sato, *Principal*
Ron Sato, *Opers Mgr*
EMP: 6 **EST:** 2012
SALES (est): 459.4K **Privately Held**
SIC: 2431 Millwork

(G-8416)
SAFECRAFT RSTRAINT SYSTEMS INC
3959 Van Dyke Rd (33558-8025)
PHONE..................................813 758-3571
Charles Espenlaub, *Branch Mgr*
EMP: 10
SALES (corp-wide): 287.7K **Privately Held**
WEB: www.safecraftracing.com
SIC: 3799 Automobile trailer chassis
PA: Safecraft Restraint Systems, Inc.
304 S Plant Ave
Tampa FL
813 758-3571

(G-8417)
SAR WHOLESALE SIGN FACTORY
1903 Passero Ave (33559-7352)
PHONE..................................813 949-8397
Roberto Hiller, *Principal*
EMP: 17 **EST:** 2013
SALES (est): 1.5MM **Privately Held**
SIC: 3993 Electric signs

(G-8418)
SIGNS OF TAMPA BAY LLC
Also Called: Sign-A-Rama
1903 Passero Ave (33559-7352)
PHONE..................................813 526-0484
James Charos, *General Mgr*
Roberto Hiller, *COO*
Beatriz E Cardona,
EMP: 31 **EST:** 2010
SQ FT: 15,000
SALES (est): 2.5MM **Privately Held**
WEB: www.signarama.com
SIC: 3993 Signs & advertising specialties

(G-8419)
SOUND CONNECTIONS INTL
Also Called: Vampire Wire
611 Chancellar Dr (33548-4510)
PHONE..................................813 948-2707
Stuart Marcus, *President*
▲ **EMP:** 6 **EST:** 1979
SALES (est): 960.3K **Privately Held**
SIC: 3679 Harness assemblies for electronic use: wire or cable

(G-8420)
SYMMETRY PAVERS INC
2407 Vandervort Rd (33549-5706)
PHONE..................................813 340-0724
Robert Counts, *Principal*
EMP: 8 **EST:** 2014
SALES (est): 147.9K **Privately Held**
SIC: 2951 Asphalt paving mixtures & blocks

(G-8421)
TRADEMARK COMPONENTS INC
21432 Keating Way (33549-8757)
PHONE..................................813 948-2233
Debra Coslov, *President*
Arlyn Shane, *Vice Pres*
EMP: 8 **EST:** 2004
SALES (est): 528.1K **Privately Held**
WEB: www.trademarkcomponents.com
SIC: 3679 Electronic components

(G-8422)
VALIDSOFT
19103 Centre Rose Blvd (33558-9015)
PHONE..................................813 334-9745
Steven Gersten, *Vice Pres*
Andre Davis, *Vice Pres*
Tom Hohman, *Vice Pres*
EMP: 7 **EST:** 2009
SALES (est): 222.9K **Privately Held**
WEB: www.validsoft.com
SIC: 3699 Security control equipment & systems

(G-8423)
VOLT LIGHTING
16011 N Nebraska Ave # 102 (33549-6158)
PHONE..................................813 978-3700
Alan Brynjolfsson, *Principal*
Josh Barter, *Marketing Mgr*
Peyton Fox, *Marketing Staff*
Michael Casalinuovo, *Director*
Andrew Krasner, *Director*
◆ **EMP:** 16 **EST:** 2010
SALES (est): 5.6MM **Privately Held**
WEB: www.voltlighting.com
SIC: 3648 Lighting equipment

(G-8424)
WINTER QARTERS PASCO RV RESORT
21632 State Road 54 (33549-6914)
PHONE..................................800 879-2131
EMP: 6 **EST:** 1969
SALES (est): 183.3K **Privately Held**
SIC: 3131 Quarters

(G-8425)
XCAPE SOLUTIONS INC (PA)
207 Crystal Grove Blvd # 101 (33548-6409)
P.O. Box 213, Odessa (33556-0213)
PHONE..................................813 369-5261
David Ellis, *President*
Leslie Ellis, *Vice Pres*
EMP: 45 **EST:** 2004
SQ FT: 3,500
SALES (est): 2.9MM **Privately Held**
WEB: www.xcapesolutions.net
SIC: 7372 Prepackaged software

(G-8426)
YORK BRIDGE CONCEPTS INC
2420 Brunello Trce (33558-7800)
PHONE..................................813 482-0613
James York, *President*
Brian Bullock, *Project Mgr*
Vivian Lenoble, *Controller*
Lelia Preiser, *Controller*
Anthony Tricarico, *Sales Staff*
EMP: 40 **EST:** 1985
SQ FT: 4,000
SALES (est): 7MM **Privately Held**
WEB: www.ybc.com
SIC: 2491 Bridges & trestles, treated wood

Lynn Haven
Bay County

(G-8427)
ACMT SOUTH LLC
Also Called: Aerospace Manufacturing
1006 Arthur Dr (32444-1683)
PHONE..................................860 645-0592
Michael Polo, *CEO*
EMP: 13 **EST:** 2015
SQ FT: 14,000
SALES (est): 1.4MM **Privately Held**
WEB: www.acmt.aero
SIC: 3724 3728 Aircraft engines & engine parts; roto-blades for helicopters

(G-8428)
AMERICAN CARBONS INC
104 New York Ave (32444-1347)
PHONE..................................850 265-4214
M D Bowen, *President*
Eric A Newsom, *Corp Secy*
EMP: 5 **EST:** 1978
SALES (est): 301.1K **Privately Held**
SIC: 2869 2819 Fuels; charcoal (carbon), activated

(G-8429)
B AND B ROOF AND FLOOR TRUSSES
1808 Tennessee Ave (32444-4223)
PHONE..................................850 265-4119
James Barnhill, *President*
EMP: 6 **EST:** 1989
SQ FT: 7,000
SALES (est): 750.3K **Privately Held**
SIC: 2439 Trusses, wooden roof

(G-8430)
BOARDWALK DESIGNS INC
1312 Louisiana Ave (32444-2742)
P.O. Box 747 (32444-0747)
PHONE..................................850 265-0988
Joseph Paffoon, *President*
Sandy Paffoon, *Vice Pres*
Jo Maxhimer, *Office Mgr*
Cassandra Paffoon, *Admin Sec*
EMP: 9 **EST:** 1992
SQ FT: 3,600
SALES (est): 1.3MM **Privately Held**
WEB: www.boardwalkdesigns.com
SIC: 3993 Signs, not made in custom sign painting shops

(G-8431)
CAMERA2CANVAS LLC
2500 Minnesota Ave (32444-4801)
PHONE..................................850 276-6990
Chris Moseley, *Principal*
EMP: 10 **EST:** 2015
SALES (est): 315.7K **Privately Held**
WEB: www.mycamera2canvas.com
SIC: 2211 Canvas

(G-8432)
EXOTIC CUSTOM COATINGS
605 New York Ave (32444-1749)
PHONE..................................850 358-1492
Brandi L Davis, *Owner*
EMP: 6 **EST:** 2015
SALES (est): 122.8K **Privately Held**
SIC: 3479 Metal coating & allied service

(G-8433)
HARLEN S WOODWORKING
1709 Tennessee Ave (32444-4220)
PHONE..................................850 774-2224
Lawrence A Harlen, *Principal*
EMP: 7 **EST:** 2009
SALES (est): 77.5K **Privately Held**
SIC: 2431 Millwork

(G-8434)
MARTINS FMOUS PSTRY SHOPPE INC
3000 S Highway 77 (32444-5623)
PHONE..................................800 548-1200
EMP: 6
SALES (corp-wide): 123.7MM **Privately Held**
WEB: www.potatorolls.com
SIC: 2015 Poultry slaughtering & processing
PA: Martin's Famous Pastry Shoppe, Inc.
1000 Potato Roll Ln
Chambersburg PA 17202
800 548-1200

(G-8435)
MEDELITE SOLUTIONS
1804 Scarlett Blvd (32444-8326)
PHONE..................................850 348-0468
Tina L Kelley, *Principal*
EMP: 6 **EST:** 2016
SALES (est): 115.2K **Privately Held**
WEB: www.medelitesolutions.com
SIC: 7372 Prepackaged software

(G-8436)
MERRICK INDUSTRIES INC
10 Arthur Dr (32444-1685)
PHONE..................................850 265-3611
Joseph K Tannehill Jr, *CEO*
Kathy Gower, *President*
Erik Nolte, *General Mgr*
Grady W McDaniel, *Vice Pres*
Kerri Powell, *Project Mgr*
▲ **EMP:** 115 **EST:** 1977
SQ FT: 40,000
SALES (est): 23.5MM **Privately Held**
WEB: www.merrick-inc.com
SIC: 3596 Weighing machines & apparatus
PA: Tannehill International Industries, Inc.
10 Arthur Dr
Lynn Haven FL 32444

(G-8437)
RINEHART CORP
Also Called: Off The Wall Screen Printing
1515 Ohio Ave (32444-3744)
PHONE..................................850 271-5600
Bronze Lee Rinehart, *President*
Rielly Rinehart, *Vice Pres*
EMP: 5 **EST:** 1994
SQ FT: 3,500
SALES (est): 548.6K **Privately Held**
SIC: 2759 Screen printing

GEOGRAPHIC

(G-8438)
SHWINCO INDUSTRIES INC
400 Aberdeen Loop (32444)
P.O. Box 1496 (32444-6296)
PHONE..................................850 271-8900
Fax: 850 271-3050
EMP: 40 **EST:** 1989
SQ FT: 11,000
SALES (est): 4.2MM **Privately Held**
SIC: 3089 Mfg Plastic Products

(G-8439)
TANNEHILL INTL INDS INC (PA)
10 Arthur Dr (32444-1685)
PHONE..................................850 265-3611
Jack Dehner, *General Mgr*
Joe K Tannehill Sr, *Chairman*
Grady W McDaniel, *Vice Pres*
Jene Roberson, *Foreman/Supr*
A Giridhar, *Opers Staff*
EMP: 120 **EST:** 1991
SQ FT: 57,000
SALES (est): 26.8MM **Privately Held**
WEB: www.merrick-inc.com
SIC: 3596 Weighing machines & apparatus

(G-8440)
THE NATURAL LIGHT INC
Also Called: Natural Light, The
1020 Arthur Dr (32444-1683)
P.O. Box 16449, Panama City (32406-6449)
PHONE..................................850 265-0800
Harvey Hollingsworth, *President*
Joann Hollingsworth, *Admin Sec*
◆ **EMP:** 50 **EST:** 1978
SQ FT: 40,000
SALES (est): 8.9MM **Privately Held**
WEB: www.thenaturallight.com
SIC: 3645 5712 Table lamps; chandeliers, residential; furniture stores

Macclenny
Baker County

(G-8441)
APEX FABRICATION INC
710 Griffin Ct (32063-4629)
P.O. Box 366 (32063-0366)
PHONE..................................904 259-4666
Kirby L O'Steen III, *President*
John Linsley, *Vice Pres*
EMP: 19 **EST:** 1999
SQ FT: 3,638
SALES (est): 2.4MM **Privately Held**
SIC: 3441 Fabricated structural metal

(G-8442)
BAKER COUNTY PRESS INC
104 S 5th St (32063-2304)
P.O. Box 598 (32063-0598)
PHONE..................................904 259-2400
James Charles Mc Gauley, *President*
James Mc Gauley, *Publisher*
Joel Addington, *Editor*
Brianna Bartlett, *Editor*
Margaret E Mc Gauley, *Vice Pres*
EMP: 5 **EST:** 1968
SQ FT: 1,800
SALES (est): 994.1K **Privately Held**
WEB: www.bakercountypress.com
SIC: 2711 5112 5943 2752 Newspapers: publishing only, not printed on site; office supplies; office forms & supplies; commercial printing, lithographic; gift shop

(G-8443)
L & J CBD LLC
14176 Camelot Pl (32063-3724)
PHONE..................................904 305-9700
Jeremy S Pietrowski Jr, *Principal*
EMP: 6 **EST:** 2018
SALES (est): 192.2K **Privately Held**
SIC: 3999

(G-8444)
RACE WAY 6800
1651 S 6th St (32063-5041)
PHONE..................................904 329-2961
EMP: 6 **EST:** 2013
SALES (est): 219.6K **Privately Held**
SIC: 3644 Raceways

Madeira Beach
Pinellas County

(G-8445)
A SANBORN CORPORATION
Also Called: Sanbornwebdesigns.com
15019 Madeira Way (33708-1900)
P.O. Box 86747, Saint Petersburg (33738-6747)
PHONE..................................727 397-3073
Ann Sanborn, *President*
EMP: 21 **EST:** 2000
SALES (est): 1MM **Privately Held**
WEB: www.sanbornwebdesigns.com
SIC: 3229 7374 Art, decorative & novelty glassware; glassware, art or decorative; computer graphics service

(G-8446)
FLORIDA WINERY INC
12945 Village Blvd (33708-2656)
PHONE..................................727 362-0008
Matt Powers, *President*
EMP: 6 **EST:** 2010
SALES (est): 144.3K **Privately Held**
WEB: www.thefloridawinery.com
SIC: 2084 Wines

(G-8447)
JOHNS PASS WINERY
12945 Village Blvd (33708-2656)
PHONE..................................727 362-0008
Diane Downs, *Manager*
EMP: 7 **EST:** 2004
SALES (est): 474K **Privately Held**
WEB: www.thefloridawinery.com
SIC: 2084 Wines

(G-8448)
SPORT AMERICA MAGAZINE
248 144th Ave (33708-2108)
PHONE..................................727 391-3099
Allan Dill, *President*
EMP: 8 **EST:** 1978
SALES (est): 395.9K **Privately Held**
SIC: 2721 Magazines: publishing only, not printed on site

Madison
Madison County

(G-8449)
GRAY LOGGING LLC
811 Ne Oats Ave (32340-3648)
PHONE..................................850 973-3863
Jerry Gray, *Mng Member*
EMP: 8 **EST:** 2002
SQ FT: 800
SALES (est): 535.3K **Privately Held**
WEB: www.graylogging.com
SIC: 2411 Logging camps & contractors

(G-8450)
GRAY LOGGING LLC
665 Sw Harvey Greene Dr (32340-4429)
PHONE..................................850 973-3863
Jerry Gray, *Mng Member*
EMP: 7 **EST:** 2012
SALES (est): 763K **Privately Held**
WEB: www.graylogging.com
SIC: 2411 Logging camps & contractors

(G-8451)
GREENE PUBLISHING INC
1695 S State Road 53 (32340-3331)
P.O. Box 772 (32341-0772)
PHONE..................................850 973-6397
Emerald Greene, *President*
Emerald Kinsley, *President*
Cheltsie Holbrook, *Office Mgr*
Mary E Greene, *Admin Sec*
EMP: 17 **EST:** 1964
SQ FT: 1,000
SALES (est): 2.2MM **Privately Held**
WEB: www.greenepublishing.com
SIC: 2711 Newspapers, publishing & printing

(G-8452)
JIMBOB PRINTING INC
482 Sw Range Ave (32340-2209)
P.O. Box 633 (32341-0633)
PHONE..................................850 973-2633
James Williams, *President*
Sylvia Williams, *Treasurer*
EMP: 10 **EST:** 1968
SQ FT: 2,100
SALES (est): 668.2K **Privately Held**
SIC: 2752 Commercial printing, offset

(G-8453)
PRG PACKING CORP (PA)
Also Called: Ferris Stahl-Meyers Packing
294 Sw Harvey Greene Dr (32340-4266)
P.O. Box 1538, Fort Lee NJ (07024-8038)
PHONE..................................201 242-5500
Guillermo Gonzalez, *Ch of Bd*
Ana Gonzalez, *Controller*
Louie Miller, *Manager*
EMP: 46 **EST:** 1997
SALES (est): 24.9MM **Privately Held**
WEB: www.stahlmeyer.com
SIC: 2011 Meat packing plants

(G-8454)
SWAPPER
115 Se Madison St (32340-2715)
P.O. Box 422 (32341-0422)
PHONE..................................850 973-6653
Wilmer Strickland, *Owner*
EMP: 6 **EST:** 1986
SALES (est): 370.5K **Privately Held**
WEB: www.madisonswapper.com
SIC: 2721 2711 Magazines: publishing only, not printed on site; newspapers: publishing only, not printed on site

Maitland
Orange County

(G-8455)
3N2 LLC
Also Called: 3n2 Sports
111 Atlantic Annex Pt # 1 (32751-3369)
PHONE..................................407 862-3622
Sean Murphy, *CEO*
Marty Graham, *Vice Pres*
Judita GA, *Opers-Prdtn-Mfg*
Derek Hemingway, *Accounts Mgr*
▲ **EMP:** 6 **EST:** 2007
SALES (est): 1MM **Privately Held**
WEB: www.3n2sports.com
SIC: 3949 Sporting & athletic goods

(G-8456)
ABBOTT PRINTING CO
Also Called: Abbott Communications Group
110 Atlantic Dr Ste 110 # 110 (32751-3300)
PHONE..................................407 831-2999
Arthur R Abbott, *President*
Kathy Trail, *Assistant VP*
David W Abbott, *Vice Pres*
Larry Germain, *Accounts Exec*
Steve Abbott, *Sales Staff*
EMP: 54 **EST:** 1977
SQ FT: 23,000
SALES (est): 14.8MM **Privately Held**
WEB: www.abbottcg.com
SIC: 2752 Commercial printing, offset

(G-8457)
BAYSHORE CON PRDCTS/CHSPAKE IN
2600 Mtland Ctr Pkwy Ste (32751)
P.O. Box 230, Cape Charles VA (23310-0230)
PHONE..................................757 331-2300
John Gray, *President*
John Chandler, *Vice Pres*
EMP: 88 **EST:** 1989
SALES (est): 1.5MM
SALES (corp-wide): 18.5B **Privately Held**
SIC: 3272 Concrete products
HQ: Bayshore Concrete Products Corporation
2600 Mtland Ctr Pkwy Ste
Maitland FL 32751
757 331-2300

(G-8458)
BAYSHORE CONCRETE PDTS CORP (DH)
2600 Mtland Ctr Pkwy Ste (32751)
PHONE..................................757 331-2300
John Gray, *President*
John D Chandler, *Corp Secy*
Wayne Bell, *Safety Mgr*
▲ **EMP:** 250 **EST:** 1961
SALES (est): 94.1MM
SALES (corp-wide): 18.5B **Privately Held**
SIC: 3272 Prestressed concrete products; concrete products, precast; poles & posts, concrete
HQ: Skanska Usa Civil Southeast Inc.
2600 Mtland Ctr Pkwy Ste
Maitland FL 32751
757 420-4140

(G-8459)
BCA TECHNOLOGIES INC
1051 Winderley Pl Ste 310 (32751-7266)
PHONE..................................407 659-0653
Brian Cumming, *President*
Lollie Marcelin, *Sales Executive*
Danny Sala-Diakanda, *Manager*
Keith Szirmay, *Software Dev*
Kelsey Cumming, *Admin Asst*
EMP: 12 **EST:** 1997
SALES (est): 2MM **Privately Held**
WEB: www.bcatech.com
SIC: 7372 8711 7373 7371 Business oriented computer software; engineering services; systems software development services; computer software development & applications; computer software development

(G-8460)
BOTANICAL INNOVATIONS INC
Also Called: Tree Innovations
100 Candace Dr Unit 120 (32751-3359)
PHONE..................................407 332-8733
James N Wilke, *President*
EMP: 7 **EST:** 1982
SQ FT: 5,000
SALES (est): 123.1K **Privately Held**
SIC: 3999 Artificial trees & flowers

(G-8461)
BUILDERS PUBLISHING GROUP LLC
Also Called: Bpg
500 N Maitland Ave # 313 (32751-4482)
PHONE..................................407 539-2938
David A Konkol, *Mng Member*
EMP: 8 **EST:** 2010
SALES (est): 309.1K **Privately Held**
WEB: www.builderspublishinggroup.com
SIC: 2741 2731 Miscellaneous publishing; book publishing

(G-8462)
COMP U NETCOM INC
331 N Maitland Ave D10 (32751-4762)
PHONE..................................407 539-1800
Edgar Aya, *Principal*
EMP: 11 **EST:** 2001
SALES (est): 470.9K **Privately Held**
WEB: www.comp-u-floor.com
SIC: 7372 Prepackaged software

(G-8463)
CREATIVE VTRAN PRODUCTIONS LLC
2400 Mtland Ctr Pkwy Ste (32751)
PHONE..................................407 656-2743
Joshua Lively, *Principal*
James Noble, *Principal*
Randy Noble, *Vice Pres*
David Wellons, *Manager*
EMP: 18 **EST:** 2007
SALES (est): 1.4MM **Privately Held**
WEB: www.creativevet.com
SIC: 7372 Prepackaged software

(G-8464)
CUPCAKE INC
105 Candace Dr Unit 109 (32751-3327)
PHONE..................................407 644-7800
William J Murphy, *President*
EMP: 6 **EST:** 2010
SALES (est): 215.4K **Privately Held**
SIC: 2051 Bread, cake & related products

(G-8465)
FIREHOUSE PROMOTIONS INC
2450 Maitland Center Pkwy (32751-4140)
PHONE..................................407 990-1600
Sylvanio Perino, *President*
Anthony Perino, *Vice Pres*
Lee Drayton, *Director*
Sarah Morrison, *Admin Sec*
EMP: 9 **EST:** 2013
SALES (est): 208K **Privately Held**
SIC: 2752 Advertising posters, lithographed

(G-8466)
GLUCORELL INC
Also Called: Insulow
130 White Oak Cir (32751-4827)
PHONE..................................407 384-3388
Laurence Berube, *President*
Jerel Scott Ferguson, *Vice Pres*
Ursula Berube, *Treasurer*
EMP: 10 **EST:** 2000
SALES (est): 770.9K **Privately Held**
WEB: www.glucorell.com
SIC: 2834 Vitamin preparations

(G-8467)
GRAND CYPRESS GROUP INC
Also Called: Brandcomet
151 N Maitland Ave (32751-5515)
P.O. Box 947819 (32794-7819)
PHONE..................................407 622-1993
Sandal Scarborough, *CEO*
James Esch, *President*
EMP: 6 **EST:** 2001
SQ FT: 1,000
SALES (est): 671.7K **Privately Held**
WEB: www.brandcomet.com
SIC: 2759 8743 8742 Screen printing; promotion service; marketing consulting services

(G-8468)
JAYCO SIGNS INC
149 Atlantic Dr (32751-3323)
PHONE..................................407 339-5252
Gregory Yoder, *President*
Gregory L Yoder, *President*
▲ **EMP:** 12 **EST:** 1972
SQ FT: 100,000
SALES (est): 551K **Privately Held**
WEB: www.jaycosigns.net
SIC: 3993 7389 1799 Electric signs; crane & aerial lift service; sign installation & maintenance

(G-8469)
KBF DESIGN GALLERY INC
1295 S Orlando Ave (32751-6412)
PHONE..................................407 830-7703
Keith J Vellequette, *President*
Meredith Barnes, *Consultant*
EMP: 5 **EST:** 2003
SALES (est): 3MM **Privately Held**
WEB: www.kbfdesigngallery.com
SIC: 2434 Wood kitchen cabinets

(G-8470)
KENEXA LEARNING INC
601 S Lake Destiny Rd # 30 (32751-7226)
PHONE..................................407 562-1905
Masood Zarrabian, *Branch Mgr*
EMP: 9
SALES (corp-wide): 73.6B **Publicly Held**
WEB: www.outstart.com
SIC: 7372 7379 Business oriented computer software; computer related consulting services
HQ: Kenexa Learning, Inc.
650 E Swedesford Rd 2nd
Wayne PA 19087
610 971-9171

(G-8471)
L4 DESIGN LLC (PA)
Also Called: Oakley Signs
2701 Mtland Ctr Pkwy Ste (32751)
PHONE..................................407 262-8200
Kenneth D Levitt, *President*
Tom Symonanis, *COO*
Brett M Levitt, *Vice Pres*
Brett Levitt, *Vice Pres*
Keith R Levitt, *Vice Pres*
▼ **EMP:** 20 **EST:** 2003
SALES (est): 14.7MM **Privately Held**
WEB: www.oakleysign.com
SIC: 3993 Signs, not made in custom sign painting shops

(G-8472)
L4 DESIGN LLC
2701 Mtland Ctr Pkwy Ste (32751)
PHONE..................................224 612-5045
Tom Symonanis, *COO*
Kenneth D Levitt, *Branch Mgr*
Jason Vetter, *Supervisor*
EMP: 15
SALES (corp-wide): 14.7MM **Privately Held**
WEB: www.oakleysign.com
SIC: 3993 Signs & advertising specialties
PA: L4 Design, Llc
2701 Mtland Ctr Pkwy Ste
Maitland FL 32751
407 262-8200

(G-8473)
MAP & GLOBE LLC (PA)
Also Called: Map and Globe Store, The
113 Candace Dr Ste 3 (32751-3330)
PHONE..................................407 898-0757
Jane Bond,
Greg Bond,
EMP: 10 **EST:** 1989
SQ FT: 4,677
SALES (est): 1.2MM **Privately Held**
WEB: www.mgstore.com
SIC: 2741 5999 Maps: publishing only, not printed on site; maps & charts

(G-8474)
PHOCAS SOFTWARE
235 S Maitland Ave (32751-5677)
PHONE..................................863 738-9107
Myles Glashier, *Principal*
Evan Tennyson, *Business Mgr*
Peter Jenkins, *Sales Executive*
Andrea Hilleary, *Marketing Staff*
Tom Falter, *Manager*
EMP: 14 **EST:** 2014
SALES (est): 260K **Privately Held**
WEB: www.phocassoftware.com
SIC: 7372 Business oriented computer software

(G-8475)
PROPEL BUILDERS INC
111 S Maitland Ave # 200 (32751-5637)
PHONE..................................407 960-5116
Walter Olejarski, *Production*
Ashley Cornell, *Office Mgr*
EMP: 16 **EST:** 2016
SALES (est): 2.4MM **Privately Held**
WEB: www.propelbuilders.com
SIC: 3731 Shipbuilding & repairing

(G-8476)
SAINT-GOBAIN VETROTEX AMER INC
110 Atlantic Annex Pt (32751-3314)
PHONE..................................407 834-8968
EMP: 148
SALES (corp-wide): 332.4MM **Privately Held**
WEB: www.saint-gobain-northamerica.com
SIC: 3089 Spouting, plastic & glass fiber reinforced
HQ: Saint-Gobain Vetrotex America, Inc.
20 Moores Rd
Valley Forge PA 19482

(G-8477)
SIGNPOST LLC
Also Called: Signposts
1236 Trust Ln (32751-4258)
PHONE..................................813 334-7678
Randall Chan-A-Shing, *Manager*
EMP: 7 **EST:** 2014
SALES (est): 185.5K **Privately Held**
WEB: www.signpost.com
SIC: 3993 Signs & advertising specialties

(G-8478)
SILLY GRAPE INC
1720 Fennell St Ste 5 (32751-8672)
PHONE..................................407 790-7999
Cesar Da Costa, *Principal*
EMP: 6 **EST:** 2011
SALES (est): 97.3K **Privately Held**
WEB: www.thesillygrape.com
SIC: 3421 Table & food cutlery, including butchers'

(G-8479)
SOUTHERN HVAC CORPORATION (PA)
Also Called: Honeywell Authorized Dealer
485 N Keller Rd Ste 515 (32751-7506)
PHONE..................................407 917-1800
Bryan Benak, *President*
Dena Jalbert, *CFO*
EMP: 5 **EST:** 2016
SALES (est): 7.6MM **Privately Held**
WEB: www.southernhvac.com
SIC: 3585 Air conditioning units, complete: domestic or industrial

(G-8480)
TEKTRONIX INC
151 Southhall Ln Ste 170 (32751-7486)
PHONE..................................407 660-2727
EMP: 14
SALES (corp-wide): 19.1B **Publicly Held**
SIC: 3825 Mfg Computers And Computer Software & Service Center
HQ: Tektronix, Inc.
14150 Sw Karl Braun Dr
Beaverton OR 97005
800 833-9200

(G-8481)
THE NANOSTEEL COMPANY LLC (HQ)
485 N Keller Rd Ste 100 (32751-7507)
PHONE..................................407 838-1427
Harald Lemke, *Vice Pres*
Robert C Marini Jr, *Vice Pres*
David Paratore,
EMP: 100 **EST:** 2002
SQ FT: 3,600
SALES (est): 1MM
SALES (corp-wide): 4MM **Privately Held**
WEB: www.milcomtech.com
SIC: 3479 Galvanizing of iron, steel or end-formed products
PA: Military Commercial Technologies Inc
750 S Orlando Ave Ste 200
Winter Park FL 32789
407 659-0443

(G-8482)
UNITIME SYSTEMS INC (PA)
Also Called: Empower Software Solutions
2600 Lake Lucien Dr # 200 (32751-7275)
PHONE..................................407 233-2050
Bill Korstad, *CEO*
Doug Peterman, *President*
Amir Ghobrial, *Vice Pres*
Tab Arnold, *Analyst*
EMP: 3 **EST:** 1993
SALES (est): 3.5MM **Privately Held**
SIC: 7372 Business oriented computer software

(G-8483)
US IMPLANT SOLUTIONS LLC
Also Called: I.T.S. USA
1778 N Park Ave Ste 200 (32751-6504)
PHONE..................................407 971-8054
Dustin Dittmer, *COO*
EMP: 9 **EST:** 2004
SALES (est): 5.3MM **Privately Held**
WEB: www.its-implant.com
SIC: 3842 Implants, surgical

(G-8484)
VIADIEM LLC
555 Winderley Pl Ste 300 (32751-7133)
PHONE..................................407 571-6845
EMP: 6
SQ FT: 1,800
SALES: 150K **Privately Held**
SIC: 2834 Mfg Pharmaceutical Preparations

(G-8485)
VMAX VISION INC
2600 Mtland Ctr Pkwy Ste (32751)
PHONE..................................321 972-1823
Xantha Real, *Director*
EMP: 5 **EST:** 2007
SQ FT: 2,500
SALES (est): 1.2MM **Privately Held**
WEB: www.vmaxvision.com
SIC: 3841 Eye examining instruments & apparatus

(G-8486)
WESTCOAST BRACE & LIMB INC
341 N Maitland Ave # 210 (32751-4783)
PHONE..................................407 502-0024
Greg Bauer, *Principal*
EMP: 75 **EST:** 1981
SALES (est): 2MM **Privately Held**
SIC: 3842 Surgical appliances & supplies

(G-8487)
ZERION GROUP LLC
235 S Maitland Ave # 100 (32751-5677)
P.O. Box 940411 (32794-0411)
PHONE..................................877 872-1726
Joel Gordon, *Marketing Staff*
Jef Nordstrom, *Consultant*
Tony King,
EMP: 9 **EST:** 2005
SALES (est): 693.2K **Privately Held**
WEB: www.zeriongroup.com
SIC: 7372 Business oriented computer software

Malabar
Brevard County

(G-8488)
DWI INC
1960 Howell Ln (32950-7017)
P.O. Box 500283 (32950-0283)
PHONE..................................321 508-9833
Douglas E Weaver, *Principal*
EMP: 10 **EST:** 2008
SALES (est): 408.5K **Privately Held**
SIC: 3443 Industrial vessels, tanks & containers

(G-8489)
HALO FISHING LLC
520 Atz Rd (32950-3625)
PHONE..................................321 373-2055
Lionel Botha, *CEO*
Lesley Botha,
▲ **EMP:** 6
SALES (est): 1MM **Privately Held**
WEB: www.americanbaitworks.com
SIC: 3949 Rods & rod parts, fishing

(G-8490)
JOHNSON WOODWORKING
3470 Leghorn Rd (32950-4017)
PHONE..................................772 473-1404
Craig Johnson, *Owner*
EMP: 9 **EST:** 1983
SALES (est): 458.8K **Privately Held**
SIC: 2431 Millwork

(G-8491)
K K WOODWORKING
2300 Kahler Ln (32950-4009)
PHONE..................................321 724-1298
Kim Kahler, *Owner*
EMP: 8 **EST:** 2000
SALES (est): 546.4K **Privately Held**
WEB: www.k-kwoodworking.com
SIC: 2499 Decorative wood & woodwork

(G-8492)
KNIGHTMARE SURFBOARDS LLC
3525 Corey Rd (32950-4006)
PHONE..................................321 720-4157
Kane Barrie, *Principal*
EMP: 7 **EST:** 2008
SALES (est): 147.5K **Privately Held**
WEB: www.eriesurfboards.com
SIC: 3949 Surfboards

(G-8493)
KRIEGER PUBLISHING CO INC
1725 Krieger Ln (32950-3323)
PHONE..................................321 724-9542
Robert E Krieger, *CEO*
Donald Krieger, *President*
Maxine D Krieger, *Vice Pres*
Shel Cohen, *Sales Dir*
Carol Krieger, *Manager*

▲ **EMP:** 16 **EST:** 1969
SQ FT: 40,000
SALES (est): 2MM **Privately Held**
WEB: www.krieger-publishing.com
SIC: 2741 Miscellaneous publishing

(G-8494)
L3HARRIS TECHNOLOGIES INC
2800 Jordan Blvd (32950-4536)
PHONE..................................321 768-4660
Bill Brown, *CEO*
Brian Warkentine, *Manager*
EMP: 57
SALES (corp-wide): 3.7B **Publicly Held**
WEB: www.l3harris.com
SIC: 3812 3663 Search & navigation equipment; radio & TV communications equipment
PA: L3harris Technologies, Inc.
1025 W Nasa Blvd
Melbourne FL 32919
321 727-9100

(G-8495)
LURE COURSE BREVARD LLC
2955 Lett Ln (32950-5014)
PHONE..................................321 412-7143
Meghan Wolfgram, *Principal*
EMP: 7 **EST:** 2016
SALES (est): 269.8K **Privately Held**
SIC: 3949 Sporting & athletic goods

(G-8496)
NORTHROP GRUMMAN CORPORATION
2880 Pomello Rd (32950-4746)
PHONE..................................321 951-5529
Johnny Marshall, *Principal*
Kai Brix, *Engineer*
Dale Carter, *Engineer*
William Chambers, *Engineer*
Kelly Fanto, *Engineer*
EMP: 6 **Publicly Held**
WEB: www.northropgrumman.com
SIC: 3812 Search & navigation equipment
PA: Northrop Grumman Corporation
2980 Fairview Park Dr
Falls Church VA 22042

Mangonia Park
Palm Beach County

(G-8497)
AMERICAN METAL FABRICATORS INC
Also Called: AMF Building Products
1501 53rd St (33407-2210)
PHONE..................................561 790-5799
David T Zajac, *President*
◆ **EMP:** 40 **EST:** 2008
SALES (est): 9.1MM **Privately Held**
WEB: www.amfbuildingproducts.com
SIC: 3444 Sheet metalwork

(G-8498)
AUTOMATED MFG SYSTEMS INC
5700 Columbia Cir (33407-2217)
P.O. Box 31731, West Palm Beach (33420-1731)
PHONE..................................561 833-9898
Richard Bell, *President*
Brandon Bell, *Sales Executive*
EMP: 7 **EST:** 1993
SALES (est): 1.7MM **Privately Held**
WEB: www.ams-plasticextrusions.com
SIC: 3089 Injection molding of plastics

(G-8499)
BAHAMA BOAT WORKS LLC
5490 Dexter Way (33407-2219)
PHONE..................................561 882-4069
Amy Kirk, *Purchasing*
John Mooney, *Purchasing*
Scott Henley, *Sales Staff*
Robert Sparks, *Mng Member*
EMP: 10 **EST:** 2005
SALES (est): 1.8MM **Privately Held**
WEB: www.bahamaboatworks.com
SIC: 3732 Boats, fiberglass: building & repairing

(G-8500)
BRICK MARKERS USA INC
4430 W Tiffany Dr Ste 2 (33407-3239)
PHONE..................................561 842-1338
Sharon Rieck, *President*
Albert S Rieck, *Vice Pres*
Kellie Wallace, *Sales Staff*
Stephenie Standish, *Consultant*
EMP: 14 **EST:** 1996
SQ FT: 7,500
SALES (est): 1.9MM **Privately Held**
WEB: www.brickmarkers.com
SIC: 3251 Brick & structural clay tile

(G-8501)
HOOK FISH & CHKN - MANGONIA PK
5701 N Australian Ave (33407-2325)
PHONE..................................561 855-6385
EMP: 6 **EST:** 2019
SALES (est): 106.4K **Privately Held**
WEB: www.hookmangoniapark.com
SIC: 3949 Hooks, fishing

(G-8502)
HOOVER CANVAS PRODUCTS CO
Also Called: Datum Metal Products
5107 N Australian Ave (33407-2313)
PHONE..................................954 541-9745
EMP: 13
SALES (corp-wide): 9.4MM **Privately Held**
WEB: www.hooverap.com
SIC: 2394 Awnings, fabric: made from purchased materials
PA: Hoover Canvas Products, Co.
4351 Ne 12th Ter
Oakland Park FL 33334
954 764-1711

(G-8503)
HOOVER CANVAS PRODUCTS CO
5107 N Australian Ave (33407-2313)
PHONE..................................561 844-4444
Eric Garey, *Prdtn Mgr*
Chad Zimmermann, *Engineer*
Jennifer Walter, *Manager*
Tim Whipps, *Director*
EMP: 13
SALES (corp-wide): 9.4MM **Privately Held**
WEB: www.hooverap.com
SIC: 2394 Awnings, fabric: made from purchased materials
PA: Hoover Canvas Products, Co.
4351 Ne 12th Ter
Oakland Park FL 33334
954 764-1711

(G-8504)
JC IRON OMAMENTAL WORKS INC
1213 50th St (33407-2201)
PHONE..................................561 508-5966
Juan Castro, *President*
EMP: 6 **EST:** 2018
SALES (est): 97.8K **Privately Held**
WEB: www.jcornamental.com
SIC: 3446 Architectural metalwork

(G-8505)
JM CUSTOM MILLWORKS INC
1113 48th St Ste 2 (33407-2367)
PHONE..................................561 582-5600
Jeremy J Mulligan, *Principal*
EMP: 19 **EST:** 2012
SALES (est): 1.2MM **Privately Held**
SIC: 2431 Millwork

(G-8506)
JM CUSTOM WOODWORKING
1113 48th St Ste 2 (33407-2367)
PHONE..................................561 582-5600
Jeremy J Mulligan, *President*
EMP: 17 **EST:** 2008
SALES (est): 2.4MM **Privately Held**
SIC: 2431 Millwork

(G-8507)
KEMP SIGNS INC
1740 Hill Ave (33407-2237)
PHONE..................................561 840-6382
Steven Kemp, *President*
Stephen Kemp, *President*
Gilbert Strelec Jr, *Vice Pres*
▼ **EMP:** 10 **EST:** 1995
SQ FT: 2,000
SALES (est): 1.5MM **Privately Held**
WEB: www.kempsigns.net
SIC: 3993 Signs, not made in custom sign painting shops

(G-8508)
PALM BEACH CSTM WOODWORKS LLC
Also Called: Pbcw Shutters and More
1315 53rd St Ste 5 (33407-2245)
PHONE..................................561 575-5335
Perez Victor, *Mng Member*
EMP: 18 **EST:** 2013
SALES (est): 1.7MM **Privately Held**
WEB: www.palmbeachcustomwoodworks.com
SIC: 2431 Millwork

(G-8509)
PALM BEACH WOODWORK CO INC
1101 53rd Ct S Ste B (33407-2384)
PHONE..................................561 844-8818
Bradley T Haylett, *President*
Tom Haylett, *Senior VP*
Bartley R Haylett, *Vice Pres*
Thomas D Haylett, *Vice Pres*
EMP: 6 **EST:** 1934
SQ FT: 8,000
SALES (est): 999.5K **Privately Held**
WEB: www.palmbeachwoodwork.com
SIC: 2431 Ornamental woodwork: cornices, mantels, etc.

(G-8510)
PRIME TECH COATINGS INC
Also Called: Prime Technical Coatings
1135 53rd Ct N (33407-2347)
PHONE..................................561 844-2312
Pete J Luther, *President*
Sherry M Luther, *Vice Pres*
Tim Olmetti, *Manager*
▼ **EMP:** 7 **EST:** 1971
SQ FT: 10,000
SALES (est): 984.5K **Privately Held**
WEB: www.primetechcoatings.com
SIC: 3479 Coating of metals & formed products

(G-8511)
SCIENTIFIC INSTRUMENTS INC
4400 W Tiffany Dr (33407-3294)
PHONE..................................561 881-8500
Leigh Ann Hoey, *President*
Joan Hoey, *Principal*
Deanna Szpendyk, *Purch Mgr*
Romeo Cuvin, *QC Mgr*
Kevin Nussair Pe, *Engineer*
▼ **EMP:** 40
SQ FT: 12,000
SALES (est): 10.2MM **Privately Held**
WEB: www.scientificinstruments.com
SIC: 3829 3823 3674 3625 Measuring & controlling devices; industrial instrmnts msrmnt display/control process variable; semiconductors & related devices; relays & industrial controls

(G-8512)
STERLING STEEL FABRICATIONS
1139 53rd Ct N (33407-2347)
PHONE..................................561 366-8600
Patricia A Fye, *President*
Allen Auman, *Opers Mgr*
EMP: 20 **EST:** 2004
SQ FT: 16,200
SALES (est): 3.8MM **Privately Held**
WEB: www.sterlingsteelfabrications.com
SIC: 3441 Fabricated structural metal

(G-8513)
TERRY D TRIPLETT INC
Also Called: House of Wood
1103 53rd Ct S Ste B (33407-2329)
P.O. Box 17559, West Palm Beach (33416-7559)
PHONE..................................561 251-3641
Terry D Triplett, *President*
EMP: 7 **EST:** 1993
SALES (est): 698.9K **Privately Held**
SIC: 2431 Moldings, wood: unfinished & prefinished

(G-8514)
TITAN AMERICA LLC
1453 53rd St (33407-2208)
PHONE..................................561 842-5309
Tyron Roberson, *General Mgr*
EMP: 10
SQ FT: 28,794
SALES (corp-wide): 177.9K **Privately Held**
WEB: www.titanamerica.com
SIC: 3273 Ready-mixed concrete
HQ: Titan America Llc
5700 Lake Wright Dr # 300
Norfolk VA 23502
757 858-6500

(G-8515)
ZELLERMAYER SUPPLY CORP (PA)
1231 52nd St Ste B (33407-2267)
P.O. Box 13026, West Palm Beach (33408-7026)
PHONE..................................561 848-0057
Gerald Singer, *President*
Myrna Singer, *Vice Pres*
David Singer, *Treasurer*
Eric Singer, *Admin Sec*
EMP: 12 **EST:** 1938 **Privately Held**
SIC: 2211 Bags & bagging, cotton

Marathon
Monroe County

(G-8516)
AIR ALLIANCE INC ✪
13369 Overseas Hwy (33050-3550)
PHONE..................................305 735-4864
Michael Moore, *CEO*
Lynn Moore, *CFO*
EMP: 7 **EST:** 2020
SALES (est): 800.1K **Privately Held**
WEB: www.airalliance.co
SIC: 3724 Aircraft engines & engine parts

(G-8517)
ALL KEYS DIESEL REPAIR INC
531 107th Street Gulf (33050-3021)
PHONE..................................305 289-2070
Neil Gonzalez, *President*
EMP: 7 **EST:** 1994
SQ FT: 1,000
SALES (est): 908.8K **Privately Held**
WEB: www.allkeysdiesel.com
SIC: 3519 Diesel, semi-diesel or duel-fuel engines, including marine

(G-8518)
JONES MEDIAAMERICA INC
11399 Overseas Hwy 5sw (33050-3403)
PHONE..................................305 289-4524
Gwen Jones, *President*
Robert W Hampton, *Vice Pres*
Gary Schonfeld, *Vice Pres*
Lorri Ellis, *Treasurer*
Mark Lane, *Admin Sec*
EMP: 267 **EST:** 1987
SALES (est): 324.7K **Privately Held**
WEB: www.tritonmedia.com
SIC: 3825 Network analyzers
PA: Triton Media Group, Llc
15303 Ventura Blvd # 1500
Sherman Oaks CA 91403

(G-8519)
KEYNOTER PUBLISHING CO INC
Also Called: Florida Keys Keynoter
3015 Overseas Hwy (33050-2236)
P.O. Box 500158 (33050-0158)
PHONE..................................305 743-5551
Wayne Markem, *Vice Pres*
Robert Singleton, *Vice Pres*
Larry Levin, *Treasurer*
Mary Lou Sollberger, *Finance Dir*
EMP: 15 **EST:** 1953
SQ FT: 4,000

SALES (est): 3.8MM
SALES (corp-wide): 709.5MM **Privately Held**
WEB: www.keysinfonet.com
SIC: 2711 Newspapers, publishing & printing
HQ: Jck Legacy Company
1601 Alhambra Blvd # 100
Sacramento CA 95816
916 321-1844

(G-8520)
MATLOCKS WELDING & FAB
799 106th Street Ocean (33050-3346)
PHONE..................................305 942-9201
Kenny Matlock, *Owner*
EMP: 6 **EST:** 2017
SALES (est): 251K **Privately Held**
SIC: 7692 Welding repair

(G-8521)
WEEKLY NEWSPAPER
9709 Overseas Hwy (33050-3342)
PHONE..................................305 743-0844
Jason Koler, *Owner*
Lesley Aaron, *Marketing Staff*
EMP: 10 **EST:** 2007
SALES (est): 837.1K **Privately Held**
WEB: www.keysweekly.com
SIC: 2711 5994 Newspapers, publishing & printing; newsstand

(G-8522)
WOHLERS PUBLISHING INC
10701 6th Avenue Gulf (33050-2919)
P.O. Box 504462 (33050-4462)
PHONE..................................305 289-1644
Tressa L Wohlers, *President*
EMP: 8 **EST:** 2010
SALES (est): 175.4K **Privately Held**
WEB: www.wohlerspublishing.com
SIC: 2741 Miscellaneous publishing

Marco Island
Collier County

(G-8523)
AMIZETTA VINEYARDS
525 Hernando Dr (34145-2411)
PHONE..................................707 963-1460
EMP: 6 **EST:** 2014
SALES (est): 178.3K **Privately Held**
WEB: www.amizetta.com
SIC: 2084 Wines

(G-8524)
EVOLVE TECHNOLOGIES INC
Also Called: Evolve E-Learning Solutions
950 N Collier Blvd # 400 (34145-2722)
PHONE..................................239 963-8037
Preston Stiner, *President*
Jeanine Delaney, *Sales Staff*
EMP: 5 **EST:** 2001
SALES (est): 600K **Privately Held**
WEB: www.evolveelearning.com
SIC: 7372 Prepackaged software

(G-8525)
HYDRAPOWER INTERNATIONAL INC
950 N Collier Blvd # 202 (34145-2725)
P.O. Box 2649 (34146-2649)
PHONE..................................239 642-5379
Robin F Wissing, *President*
Carol A Wissing, *Admin Sec*
▲ **EMP:** 1100 **EST:** 1973
SQ FT: 3,100
SALES (est): 37.7MM **Privately Held**
WEB: www.hydrapower-intl.com
SIC: 3542 Shearing machines, power; press brakes; presses: hydraulic & pneumatic, mechanical & manual

(G-8526)
ROBERT DUFFY CABINETS INC
161 Tahiti Rd (34145-3945)
PHONE..................................239 777-0372
Robert Duffy, *Principal*
EMP: 6 **EST:** 2008
SALES (est): 180.4K **Privately Held**
SIC: 2434 Wood kitchen cabinets

(G-8527)
TEAM SERVICE CORP NEW YORK
1040 Coronado Ct (34145-4520)
PHONE..................................410 365-1574
James Huber, *Branch Mgr*
EMP: 30
SALES (corp-wide): 12.2MM **Privately Held**
SIC: 7694 5063 Electric motor repair; motors, electric
PA: T.E.A.M. Service Corporation Of New York
1401 Angela Ave
Baltimore MD 21227
410 536-4488

(G-8528)
WHITMAN INDUSTRIES LLC
1825 Dogwood Dr (34145-6718)
PHONE..................................239 216-6171
Robert J Whitman, *Principal*
EMP: 8 **EST:** 2008
SALES (est): 860.9K **Privately Held**
WEB: www.whitmanindustries.com
SIC: 3999 Manufacturing industries

Margate
Broward County

(G-8529)
AC PHARMA CORP
3241 Holiday Springs Blvd (33063-5468)
PHONE..................................954 773-9735
Mohamed Shafeek, *President*
Naeema Lodhi, *Exec Sec*
EMP: 5 **EST:** 2013
SQ FT: 3,000
SALES (est): 500K **Privately Held**
WEB: www.acpharmacorp.com
SIC: 2834 Pharmaceutical preparations

(G-8530)
ADVANCED CNC MACHINING INC
6135 Nw 20th Ct (33063-2346)
PHONE..................................954 478-8369
Peter Paulovich, *President*
EMP: 6 **EST:** 1996
SQ FT: 4,000
SALES (est): 450K **Privately Held**
WEB: www.advmach.com
SIC: 3599 Machine shop, jobbing & repair

(G-8531)
ADVANCED PALLETS INC
2151 N State Road 7 (33063-5713)
P.O. Box 51629, Lighthouse Point (33074-1629)
PHONE..................................954 785-1215
Michael K McBride, *President*
EMP: 29 **EST:** 1996
SALES (est): 1.4MM **Privately Held**
SIC: 2448 Pallets, wood

(G-8532)
AEROUNO LLC
3090 Holiday Springs Blvd (33063-5420)
PHONE..................................561 767-5597
Lucio Montenegro, *CEO*
EMP: 18 **EST:** 2016
SALES (est): 1.2MM **Privately Held**
WEB: www.aerouno.com
SIC: 3674 5065 Solid state electronic devices; capacitors, electronic

(G-8533)
AHC VENTURES CORP
Also Called: Cryoderm
5415 Nw 24th St Ste 103 (33063-7730)
PHONE..................................954 978-9290
Lloyd List, *CEO*
Laura Allen, *Vice Pres*
Alyse M List, *CFO*
▼ **EMP:** 11 **EST:** 2000
SQ FT: 10,000
SALES (est): 1.7MM **Privately Held**
SIC: 3841 Surgical & medical instruments

(G-8534)
AJ AZ WOODWORK INC
1917 Mears Pkwy (33063-3702)
PHONE..................................561 859-4963
Everton Reid, *Principal*
EMP: 8 **EST:** 2010
SALES (est): 209.8K **Privately Held**
SIC: 2431 Millwork

(G-8535)
AMERICAN COATINGS CORPORATION
1457 Banks Rd (33063-3960)
PHONE..................................954 970-7820
Herbert Weisberg, *President*
EMP: 5 **EST:** 1979
SQ FT: 6,300
SALES (est): 930.7K **Privately Held**
WEB: www.goamerco.com
SIC: 3292 2842 2851 5085 Asbestos products; specialty cleaning preparations; lacquers, varnishes, enamels & other coatings; industrial supplies; chemicals, industrial & heavy

(G-8536)
AVW INC
Also Called: Blow Off
541 S State Road 7 Ste 2 (33068-1711)
P.O. Box 9962, Fort Lauderdale (33310-0962)
PHONE..................................954 972-3338
Michael Fishman, *President*
▼ **EMP:** 24 **EST:** 1992
SQ FT: 4,000
SALES (est): 25MM **Privately Held**
SIC: 2813 5065 3822 Aerosols; electronic parts & equipment; auto controls regulating residntl & coml environmt & applncs

(G-8537)
BRANDANO DISPLAYS INC (PA)
1473 Banks Rd (33063-3960)
PHONE..................................954 956-7266
John D Brandano, *Principal*
Patrick Brandano, *Exec VP*
EMP: 20 **EST:** 1976
SQ FT: 50,000
SALES (est): 2.5MM **Privately Held**
WEB: www.brandano.com
SIC: 3496 3999 Miscellaneous fabricated wire products; advertising display products

(G-8538)
COLLINS MEDIA & ADVG LLC
5453 Nw 24th St Ste 2 (33063-7776)
PHONE..................................954 688-9758
Elitsa Hristova,
EMP: 10 **EST:** 2015
SALES (est): 1.2MM **Privately Held**
WEB: www.collinscompletemedia.com
SIC: 3993 7812 2754 7313 Signs & advertising specialties; video production; commercial printing, gravure; printed media advertising representatives

(G-8539)
COMPASS PRINTING AND MARKETING
5218 Nw 15th St (33063-3783)
PHONE..................................954 856-8331
Jose Vasquez, *Principal*
EMP: 7 **EST:** 2015
SALES (est): 148.6K **Privately Held**
SIC: 2752 Commercial printing, lithographic

(G-8540)
CONTRACTORS CABINET COMPANY
5512 W Sample Rd (33073-3468)
PHONE..................................786 492-7118
Hal Berner, *President*
Jan Hoffman, *Vice Pres*
EMP: 7 **EST:** 1993
SQ FT: 1,400
SALES (est): 801K **Privately Held**
WEB: www.cabinetsmargatefl.com
SIC: 2434 5211 Wood kitchen cabinets; cabinets, kitchen

(G-8541)
DAVIS-WICK TALENT MGT LLC
5400 Nw 27th Ct (33063-1602)
PHONE..................................407 369-1614
Janelle Brice, *CEO*
Brian Brice, *Director*
EMP: 36 **EST:** 2013
SALES (est): 1.1MM **Privately Held**
SIC: 2389 8741 7922 7929 Men's miscellaneous accessories; business management; entertainment promotion; entertainment group

(G-8542)
EXCELL WOODWORK CORP
1917 Mears Pkwy (33063-3702)
PHONE..................................954 461-0465
Yngrid Silva, *Principal*
EMP: 7 **EST:** 2017
SALES (est): 59.5K **Privately Held**
SIC: 2431 Millwork

(G-8543)
EXECUTIVE LABEL INC
5447 Nw 24th St Ste 5 (33063-7773)
PHONE..................................954 978-6983
Richard Preiser, *President*
Kevin Longuiel, *Vice Pres*
Peggy Preiser, *Production*
Preiser Peggy, *Treasurer*
Samuel Montero, *Sales Staff*
◆ **EMP:** 12 **EST:** 1989
SQ FT: 10,000
SALES (est): 3.7MM **Privately Held**
WEB: www.executivelabel.com
SIC: 2759 Labels & seals: printing

(G-8544)
FIT CANVAS INC
870 Sw 50th Ave (33068-3135)
PHONE..................................954 258-9352
Valencia Jiovani, *Principal*
EMP: 12 **EST:** 2014
SALES (est): 89.7K **Privately Held**
WEB: www.fit-canvas.com
SIC: 2211 Canvas

(G-8545)
GOLD COAST PLST & STUCCO INC
1815 Nw 64th Way (33063-2326)
PHONE..................................954 275-9132
Jim A Kriz, *President*
EMP: 14 **EST:** 2001
SALES (est): 365.5K **Privately Held**
SIC: 3299 Stucco

(G-8546)
GOLDEN CENTURY INC
1935 Banks Rd (33063-7716)
PHONE..................................954 933-2911
Hwan K Yoon, *President*
EMP: 5 **EST:** 1984
SQ FT: 1,600
SALES (est): 685.1K **Privately Held**
WEB: www.goldencenturycasting.com
SIC: 3911 Jewelry, precious metal

(G-8547)
GRAPHIC DATA INC
7378 W Atlantic Blvd (33063-4214)
PHONE..................................954 493-8003
David Tomlin, *President*
EMP: 5 **EST:** 1995
SQ FT: 4,260
SALES (est): 597.5K **Privately Held**
SIC: 3577 5045 Computer peripheral equipment; computers, peripherals & software

(G-8548)
GRASS RIVER PUBLSHING
5510 Sw 7th St (33068-2906)
PHONE..................................954 974-7383
William G Slager, *Principal*
EMP: 6 **EST:** 2006
SALES (est): 209.6K **Privately Held**
WEB: www.grassriver.com
SIC: 2711 Newspapers

(G-8549)
HURRICANE ROOFING & SHTMTL INC
1905 Mears Pkwy (33063-3702)
PHONE..................................954 968-8155
Eduardo B Valle Sr, *President*
EMP: 9 **EST:** 2012
SALES (est): 94.5K **Privately Held**
SIC: 3444 Sheet metalwork

GEOGRAPHIC

(G-8550)
INTERNATIONAL DRAPERIES INC
1471 Banks Rd (33063-3960)
PHONE..................................954 590-3897
Tom Turner, *President*
EMP: 7 **EST:** 2004
SALES (est): 112.1K **Privately Held**
WEB: www.internationaldrapercontractors.com
SIC: 2211 Broadwoven fabric mills, cotton

(G-8551)
JAMBCO MILLWORK INC
101 S State Road 7 (33068-5722)
PHONE..................................954 977-4998
Don Gladis, *President*
Jane Jolliff, *Administration*
EMP: 12 **EST:** 1989
SQ FT: 22,000
SALES (est): 1.3MM **Privately Held**
WEB: www.jambcomillwork.com
SIC: 2431 3442 3431 3231 Doors, wood; metal doors, sash & trim; metal sanitary ware; products of purchased glass

(G-8552)
JAWIL ENTERPRISES CORPS
205 S State Road 7 (33068-5702)
PHONE..................................954 366-4212
EMP: 6 **EST:** 2009
SALES (est): 235.1K **Privately Held**
SIC: 3949 Bowling alleys & accessories

(G-8553)
JPM IMPORT LLC
7350 Nw 1st St Apt 207 (33063-7519)
PHONE..................................800 753-3009
Joseph Maas, *President*
EMP: 13
SALES (corp-wide): 128.4K **Privately Held**
SIC: 3714 Wheels, motor vehicle
PA: Jpm Import Llc
5935 W Park Rd
Hollywood FL 33021
800 753-3009

(G-8554)
KAY PEAK GROUP INC
6510 W Atlantic Blvd (33063-5135)
PHONE..................................754 307-5400
Yves Laurent, *President*
EMP: 6 **EST:** 2017
SALES (est): 300K **Privately Held**
SIC: 2066 Chocolate

(G-8555)
KOVA LABORATORIES INC
1711 Banks Rd (33063-7744)
PHONE..................................954 978-8730
Kirk Sakai, *President*
EMP: 8 **EST:** 1986
SQ FT: 2,000
SALES (est): 966.8K **Privately Held**
SIC: 2834 Pharmaceutical preparations

(G-8556)
LOCAL WOODWORK LLC
5491 Nw 15th St (33063-3779)
PHONE..................................954 551-1515
EMP: 7 **EST:** 2018
SALES (est): 426.4K **Privately Held**
WEB: www.localwoodwork.com
SIC: 2431 Millwork

(G-8557)
MAX AVW PROFESSIONAL LLC
441 S State Road 7 Ste 4 (33068-1967)
P.O. Box 5501, Fort Lauderdale (33310-5501)
PHONE..................................954 972-3338
Michael Fishman, *Mng Member*
Niel Markus,
EMP: 10 **EST:** 2010
SQ FT: 10,000
SALES (est): 348.2K **Privately Held**
SIC: 2834 5122 Pharmaceutical preparations; pharmaceuticals

(G-8558)
MYERS ENGINEERING INTL INC
Also Called: Antennas.us
5425 Nw 24th St Ste 202 (33063-7731)
PHONE..................................954 975-2712
Steven Myers, *President*
EMP: 30 **EST:** 1990
SQ FT: 6,000
SALES (est): 3.1MM **Privately Held**
WEB: www.antennas.us
SIC: 3663 7373 Antennas, transmitting & communications; computer integrated systems design

(G-8559)
P & G PRINTING GROUP INC
Also Called: Yovino Printing
2034 Mears Pkwy (33063-3753)
PHONE..................................954 971-2511
George Paparelli, *President*
Patricia Paparelli, *Vice Pres*
EMP: 10 **EST:** 1985
SQ FT: 1,600
SALES (est): 170K **Privately Held**
SIC: 2752 Commercial printing, offset

(G-8560)
PHI CHI FOUNDATION INC
740 Sw 50th Ter (33068-3042)
PHONE..................................561 526-3401
Nzinga N Myton, *President*
Neville Myton, *Publisher*
William Myton, *Vice Pres*
Nastassia Myton, *Treasurer*
Paulette Myton, *Admin Sec*
EMP: 6 **EST:** 2013
SALES (est): 99.3K **Privately Held**
WEB: www.studentmarketing.net
SIC: 2759 2396 5111 2269 Fashion plates: printing; printing & embossing on plastics fabric articles; printing paper; printing of narrow fabrics; community service employment training program

(G-8561)
PLASTIC PARTS INC
6222 Flores Del Mar (33063-9306)
PHONE..................................954 974-3051
Todd Pores, *President*
EMP: 6 **EST:** 2018
SALES (est): 107.6K **Privately Held**
WEB: www.plasticpartsinc.com
SIC: 3089 Injection molding of plastics

(G-8562)
POMS ENTERPRISES INC
5425 Nw 24th St Ste 210 (33063-7731)
PHONE..................................954 358-1359
Carol Musto, *President*
Anthony Musto, *Vice Pres*
Donna Hicks, *Admin Sec*
EMP: 6 **EST:** 1992
SQ FT: 6,000
SALES (est): 584.7K **Privately Held**
WEB: www.datahorse.net
SIC: 2759 Commercial printing

(G-8563)
PRINCETON INDUSTRIES INC (PA)
Also Called: Princeton Custom Cabinetry
1790 Mears Pkwy (33063-3749)
PHONE..................................954 344-9155
Brad W Brewster, *President*
Marc B Kaye, *Corp Secy*
Mona Fleri, *Sales Staff*
Brent Brewster, *Director*
Sue Kaye, *Director*
EMP: 30 **EST:** 1987
SQ FT: 7,200
SALES (est): 1.8MM **Privately Held**
WEB: www.princetonkb.com
SIC: 2511 2541 5211 1751 Wood household furniture; wood partitions & fixtures; cabinets, kitchen; cabinet & finish carpentry; vanities, bathroom: wood

(G-8564)
PRO WATER TREATMENT INC
1935 Mears Pkwy Frnt (33063-3702)
PHONE..................................954 650-1955
William Avellanet Sr, *Manager*
EMP: 6 **EST:** 2002
SALES (est): 773.4K **Privately Held**
WEB: www.prowaterfl.net
SIC: 3589 Water treatment equipment, industrial

(G-8565)
PRO WELD OF SOUTH FLORIDA INC
3101 Vista Del Mar (33063-9304)
PHONE..................................954 984-0104
Effie Darshan, *President*
EMP: 6 **EST:** 1999
SALES (est): 175.3K **Privately Held**
SIC: 7692 Welding repair

(G-8566)
SAM WEISS WOODWORKING INC
5195 Nw 15th St (33063-3714)
PHONE..................................954 975-8158
Sam Weiss, *President*
Linda Weiss, *Vice Pres*
Kevin Weiss, *Treasurer*
EMP: 5 **EST:** 1981
SQ FT: 11,000
SALES (est): 818.4K **Privately Held**
WEB: www.samweisswoodwork.com
SIC: 2541 3993 2542 Store & office display cases & fixtures; signs & advertising specialties; partitions & fixtures, except wood

(G-8567)
SIGN DESIGN AND CREATIONS
5000 Nw 17th St Ste 3 (33063-3707)
PHONE..................................954 724-2884
Regis M Sassaki, *President*
EMP: 8 **EST:** 2013
SALES (est): 598.7K **Privately Held**
WEB: www.signdesignandcreations.com
SIC: 3993 Signs & advertising specialties

(G-8568)
THEBESTCANDLESCOM
5453 Nw 24th St Ste 1 (33063-7776)
PHONE..................................732 608-5081
EMP: 6 **EST:** 2015
SALES (est): 116.8K **Privately Held**
SIC: 3999 Candles

(G-8569)
THINKTECH CORPORATION
1840 Vista Way (33063-1206)
PHONE..................................954 501-3034
Antonio Mendez, *President*
Cliff Toma, *Engineer*
EMP: 10 **EST:** 2003
SALES (est): 641.4K **Privately Held**
WEB: www.thinktech.us
SIC: 3577 Computer peripheral equipment

(G-8570)
TRADING POST OF CENTRAL FLA
Also Called: Orlando Post
7626 Nw 25th St (33063-8132)
PHONE..................................954 675-2149
Robert Ericson, *President*
Mary Lowerey, *Admin Sec*
EMP: 6 **EST:** 1985
SQ FT: 2,000
SALES (est): 187.2K **Privately Held**
SIC: 2741 Shopping news: publishing & printing

(G-8571)
VINYLOT OF FLORIDA INC
Also Called: Vinylot Signs & Graphics
2048 Mears Pkwy (33063-3753)
PHONE..................................954 978-8424
Albert L Scungio, *President*
Gwendolyn Scungio, *Vice Pres*
EMP: 5 **EST:** 1983
SALES (est): 652.3K **Privately Held**
WEB: www.vinylot.com
SIC: 2752 Commercial printing, lithographic

(G-8572)
WILLSON & SON INDUSTRY INC
Also Called: W.S.I.
2000 Banks Rd Ste H1 (33063-7732)
PHONE..................................954 972-5073
Les Willson Jr, *President*
Hannelore Willson, *Vice Pres*
EMP: 7 **EST:** 1975
SQ FT: 7,000
SALES (est): 828.1K **Privately Held**
WEB: www.willson-son-industry-inc.business.site
SIC: 2511 Wood household furniture

(G-8573)
WOODWORK IN NOVA ARCHITECTURAL
2242 Mears Pkwy (33063-3758)
PHONE..................................954 448-2962
Mauricio Calek, *Owner*
EMP: 6 **EST:** 2018
SALES (est): 216.5K **Privately Held**
SIC: 2431 Millwork

Marianna
Jackson County

(G-8574)
ACG MATERIALS
5160 Vermont Rd (32448-7473)
PHONE..................................405 366-9500
EMP: 5 **EST:** 2019
SALES (est): 323.2K **Privately Held**
WEB: www.acgmaterials.com
SIC: 1499 Miscellaneous nonmetallic minerals

(G-8575)
CATALYST FABRIC SOLUTIONS LLC
3595 Industrial Park Dr (32446-8092)
PHONE..................................850 396-4325
Charles Smith,
EMP: 50 **EST:** 2016
SQ FT: 235,000
SALES (est): 7.4MM **Privately Held**
WEB: www.catalystfabricsolutions.com
SIC: 2396 Apparel & other linings, except millinery

(G-8576)
DOLOMITE INC
1321 Highway 71 (32448-5399)
P.O. Box 1568 (32447-5568)
PHONE..................................850 482-4962
David Sloan, *President*
Kathy Sloan, *Vice Pres*
EMP: 23 **EST:** 1972
SQ FT: 1,000
SALES (est): 10.4MM **Privately Held**
WEB: www.dolomitefl.com
SIC: 1422 Dolomite, crushed & broken-quarrying
PA: Baxter's Asphalt And Concrete, Inc.
4049 Lafayette St
Marianna FL 32446
850 482-4621

(G-8577)
E M A C INC (PA)
Also Called: Emac
4518 Lafayette St (32446-3418)
PHONE..................................850 526-4111
Timothy Mowrey, *President*
Nolan Coumbe, *Vice Pres*
Laura Mowrey, *Treasurer*
EMP: 40 **EST:** 1976
SQ FT: 480,000
SALES (est): 4.9MM **Privately Held**
SIC: 3534 Elevators & equipment

(G-8578)
HARRISON GYPSUM LLC
5160 Vermont Rd (32448-7473)
PHONE..................................850 762-4315
Fred Webb, *Branch Mgr*
EMP: 30
SALES (corp-wide): 1.9B **Publicly Held**
WEB: www.arcosaspecialtymaterials.com
SIC: 1499 4213 Gypsum mining; trucking, except local
HQ: Harrison Gypsum, Llc
1550 Double C Dr
Norman OK 73069
405 366-9500

(G-8579)
HOME SOURCE MANUFACTURING INC
3595 Industrial Park Dr (32446-8092)
PHONE..................................404 663-0647
Keith Sorgeloos, *CEO*

Mike Beard, *CFO*
EMP: 20 **EST:** 1995
SQ FT: 275,000
SALES (est): 583K **Privately Held**
SIC: 2392 Household furnishings

(G-8580)
LMS MANUFACTURING LLC
4430 Magnolia Rd (32448-7410)
P.O. Box 189 (32447-0189)
PHONE..................................850 526-0121
Leslie Linton, *Finance Dir*
Kenneth Linton,
Greg Self,
EMP: 10 **EST:** 1982
SALES (est): 992.7K **Privately Held**
WEB: www.lmsmanufacturing.com
SIC: 3599 Machine shop, jobbing & repair

(G-8581)
MARIANNA LIME PRODUCTS INC
3333 Valley View Rd (32446-5664)
P.O. Box 1505 (32447-5505)
PHONE..................................850 526-3580
Leon Brooks, *President*
EMP: 8 **EST:** 1979
SQ FT: 20,000
SALES (est): 678.1K **Privately Held**
WEB: www.southfieldcarton.com
SIC: 1422 3274 Agricultural limestone, ground; lime

(G-8582)
MARIANNA LIMESTONE LLC
3333 Valley View Rd (32446-5664)
PHONE..................................954 581-1220
M Austin Forman, *Mng Member*
Leon Brooks,
Gilbert Spenser,
EMP: 10 **EST:** 2005
SQ FT: 12,000
SALES (est): 1.4MM **Privately Held**
SIC: 1422 3274 Agricultural limestone, ground; agricultural lime

(G-8583)
MARIANNA TRUSS INC
3644 Highway 71 (32446-8074)
P.O. Box 833 (32447-0833)
PHONE..................................850 594-5420
Garry Gochenaur, *President*
Debra Gochenaur, *Corp Secy*
EMP: 21 **EST:** 1985
SQ FT: 21,000
SALES (est): 526.5K **Privately Held**
WEB: www.mariannatruss.com
SIC: 2439 2448 Trusses, wooden roof; trusses, except roof: laminated lumber; wood pallets & skids

(G-8584)
METAL PRODUCTS COMPANY LC
3787 Industrial Park Dr (32446-8096)
P.O. Box 6429 (32447-6429)
PHONE..................................850 526-5593
Gary Pinson,
Marcie Pinson,
EMP: 16 **EST:** 2000
SALES (est): 1MM **Privately Held**
SIC: 3469 3444 Metal stampings; sheet metalwork

(G-8585)
ROLLS RITE TRAILERS INC
3741 Industrial Park Dr (32446-8096)
PHONE..................................850 526-2290
Richard Dunlap, *President*
EMP: 16 **EST:** 1998
SQ FT: 21,000
SALES (est): 4.2MM **Privately Held**
WEB: www.rollsrite.com
SIC: 3715 3537 Truck trailers; industrial trucks & tractors

(G-8586)
SPANISH TRAIL LUMBER CO LLC
6112 Old Spanish Trl (32448-7598)
PHONE..................................850 592-8512
Ross Jackson, *General Mgr*
Jay Rees, *General Mgr*
Ross D Jackson, *Mng Member*
EMP: 126
SALES (est): 19.2MM **Privately Held**
WEB: www.spanishtraillumber.com
SIC: 2421 Lumber: rough, sawed or planed

(G-8587)
WHEELER EMERGENCY MANAGEMENT C
Also Called: Wheeler EMC
2954 Highway 71 (32446-8197)
PHONE..................................850 372-4174
EMP: 6 **EST:** 2017
SALES (est): 287.4K **Privately Held**
SIC: 3572 Computer storage devices

(G-8588)
WOODY HATCHER
Also Called: Jackson County Times
2866 Madison St (32448-4610)
PHONE..................................850 526-1501
Linda Hatcher, *President*
EMP: 8 **EST:** 2005
SALES (est): 111.6K **Privately Held**
WEB: www.jacksoncountytimes.net
SIC: 2711 Newspapers, publishing & printing

Mary Esther
Okaloosa County

(G-8589)
IMAGE PRTG & DIGITAL SVCS INC
Also Called: Insty-Prints
315 E Hollywood Blvd # 3 (32569-1915)
PHONE..................................850 244-3380
McCain J Young, *President*
Gill McLane, *Vice Pres*
EMP: 8 **EST:** 1986
SQ FT: 2,000
SALES (est): 633K **Privately Held**
WEB: www.imagepds.com
SIC: 2752 2791 Commercial printing, offset; typesetting

(G-8590)
KJS HOT CHOPPERS
1652 W Highway 98 (32569-1548)
PHONE..................................850 200-4860
Krystal Jackson, *Manager*
EMP: 6 **EST:** 2015
SALES (est): 136.6K **Privately Held**
SIC: 3751 Motorcycles & related parts

(G-8591)
KOCHAN CASES
740 Bryn Mawr Blvd (32569-1726)
PHONE..................................850 533-4190
Michael Kochan, *Principal*
EMP: 6 **EST:** 2019
SALES (est): 262.7K **Privately Held**
WEB: www.kochancases.com
SIC: 3523 Farm machinery & equipment

(G-8592)
TRIO ENVMTL SOLUTIONS LLC
301 Friar Tuck Rd (32569-2213)
PHONE..................................850 543-9125
Deborah R Hammett, *CEO*
Caren Schau, *Controller*
EMP: 15 **EST:** 2009
SALES (est): 1.9MM **Privately Held**
WEB: www.trioenvironmentalsolutions.com
SIC: 2655 4213 Wastebaskets, fiber: made from purchased material; automobiles, transport & delivery

Mascotte
Lake County

(G-8593)
ALL MODULAR SERVICE INC
861 W Myers Blvd (34753-9727)
P.O. Box 516, Groveland (34736-0516)
PHONE..................................352 429-0868
Kevin J Pearson, *President*
EMP: 17 **EST:** 1987
SQ FT: 1,000
SALES (est): 1.1MM **Privately Held**
SIC: 2452 Modular homes, prefabricated, wood

Mayo
Lafayette County

(G-8594)
AGRI METAL SUPPLY INC
232 Se Indus Pk Cir Ste C (32066-5629)
PHONE..................................386 294-1720
Moises Rodriguez, *President*
EMP: 7 **EST:** 2005
SALES (est): 826.3K **Privately Held**
SIC: 3446 Architectural metalwork

(G-8595)
MAYO PLASTICS MFG INC
232 Se Indus Cir S B (32066)
P.O. Box 248 (32066-0248)
PHONE..................................386 294-1049
Robin C Shiver Sr, *President*
Robin C Shiver Jr, *Corp Secy*
Vera L Shiver, *Vice Pres*
EMP: 10 **EST:** 1991
SQ FT: 40,000
SALES (est): 406.2K **Privately Held**
SIC: 3949 Lures, fishing: artificial

(G-8596)
MAYO TRUSS CO INC
845 E Us 27 (32066-5730)
PHONE..................................386 294-3988
Wayne Hamlin, *President*
EMP: 11 **EST:** 1996
SALES (est): 993.1K **Privately Held**
SIC: 2439 Trusses, wooden roof

(G-8597)
PERRY PRECAST INC
232 Se Industrial Pk Cir (32066-5200)
PHONE..................................386 294-2710
EMP: 5
SALES (est): 509.5K **Privately Held**
SIC: 3272 Mfg Concrete Products

Mc Alpin
Suwannee County

(G-8598)
BUBBLEMAC INDUSTRIES INC
11932 156th St (32062-2242)
P.O. Box 51 (32062-0051)
PHONE..................................352 396-8043
Mach Cathie L, *Principal*
EMP: 7 **EST:** 2014
SALES (est): 525.8K **Privately Held**
WEB: www.bubblemacairdiffusers.com
SIC: 3999 Manufacturing industries

(G-8599)
COMPETITION SPECIALTIES INC
Also Called: Csr Performance Products
16936 County Road 252 (32062-2048)
PHONE..................................386 776-1476
Rowland W Wood, *President*
Kim Wood, *Principal*
EMP: 15 **EST:** 1989
SQ FT: 22,000
SALES (est): 1.6MM **Privately Held**
WEB: www.csr-performance.com
SIC: 3714 3694 Motor vehicle parts & accessories; engine electrical equipment

(G-8600)
PETERSON ENTERPRISES LLC
12502 158th Ter (32062-2333)
PHONE..................................386 456-3400
Douglas Peterson, *Principal*
EMP: 7 **EST:** 2011
SALES (est): 106.9K **Privately Held**
SIC: 3524 5261 7699 Lawn & garden tractors & equipment; lawn & garden mowers & accessories; lawn & garden equipment; lawn mower repair shop

Mc David
Escambia County

(G-8601)
LANE SHARK USA LLC
4600 Highway 97a (32568-1439)
PHONE..................................864 382-6892
Travis Odom, *Principal*
EMP: 6 **EST:** 2017
SALES (est): 222.1K **Privately Held**
WEB: www.lanesharkusa.com
SIC: 3999 Atomizers, toiletry

(G-8602)
WEST FRASER INC
401 Champion (32568-2676)
PHONE..................................850 587-1000
Allen Smith, *Manager*
EMP: 74
SALES (corp-wide): 3.6B **Privately Held**
SIC: 2426 2421 2621 Hardwood dimension & flooring mills; sawmills & planing mills, general; paper mills
HQ: West Fraser, Inc.
1900 Exeter Rd Ste 105
Germantown TN 38138
901 620-4200

Medley
Miami-Dade County

(G-8603)
AA FLORIDA PALLETS
7611 Nw 74th Ave (33166-2424)
PHONE..................................305 805-1522
Scott Lattiere, *Principal*
◆ **EMP:** 8 **EST:** 2007
SALES (est): 359.4K **Privately Held**
WEB: www.aafloridapallets.com
SIC: 2448 Pallets, wood

(G-8604)
AAR CORP
Also Called: AAR Wheel & Brake Services
9270 Nw 100th St (33178-1423)
PHONE..................................786 337-4000
Maggie Ibarlucea, *Business Mgr*
Alex Lara, *Branch Mgr*
Richard Fortner, *Manager*
German Lara, *Supervisor*
Vanry Tyler, *Info Tech Mgr*
EMP: 6
SALES (corp-wide): 1.6B **Publicly Held**
WEB: www.aarcorp.com
SIC: 3728 Aircraft parts & equipment
PA: Aar Corp.
1100 N Wood Dale Rd
Wood Dale IL 60191
630 227-2000

(G-8605)
AAR LANDING GEAR LLC
Also Called: AAR Landing Gear Services
9371 Nw 100th St (33178-1420)
PHONE..................................305 883-1511
Mike Kritch, *Vice Pres*
Shane Laakso, *Mfg Staff*
Sheldon Smith, *Engineer*
Kyle Young, *Accountant*
▲ **EMP:** 27 **EST:** 2011
SALES (est): 9.8MM
SALES (corp-wide): 1.6B **Publicly Held**
WEB: www.aarcorp.com
SIC: 3728 Aircraft parts & equipment
HQ: Aar Airlift Group, Inc.
2301 Commerce Park Dr Ne # 11
Palm Bay FL 32905
321 837-2345

(G-8606)
ACCURATE METALS SPINNING INC
9001 Nw 97th Ter Ste K (33178-1460)
PHONE..................................305 885-9988
Alfredo Perez, *President*
Teresa Perez, *Vice Pres*
EMP: 7 **EST:** 1995
SQ FT: 7,250

SALES (est): 673.7K **Privately Held**
WEB: www.accuratemetalspinning.com
SIC: 3443 3469 Heat exchangers, condensers & components; spinning metal for the trade

(G-8607)
ALLSTONE CASTING
6900 Nw 77th Ter (33166-2540)
PHONE.................................305 528-1677
EMP: 15 **EST:** 2015
SALES (est): 287K **Privately Held**
WEB: www.allstonecasting.com
SIC: 3272 Concrete products

(G-8608)
ALPINE SYSTEMS ASSOCIATES INC
11725 Nw 100th Rd Ste 1 (33178-1013)
PHONE.................................305 262-3263
Petra Peters, *President*
EMP: 8
SALES (est): 1.6MM **Privately Held**
WEB: www.alpinehandlingsystems.com
SIC: 3537 Containers (metal), air cargo

(G-8609)
AMIGO PALLETS INC
7650 Nw 69th Ave (33166-2521)
PHONE.................................305 631-2452
Raul Alfonso, *CEO*
David Lopez, *CFO*
EMP: 6 **EST:** 2018
SALES (est): 803.8K **Privately Held**
WEB: www.amigopallets.com
SIC: 2448 Pallets, wood

(G-8610)
ANTHEM SOUTH LLC
9710 Nw 110th Ave Unit 10 (33178-2549)
PHONE.................................973 779-1982
Raj Prakash, *Mng Member*
◆ **EMP:** 36 **EST:** 2018
SALES (est): 15MM
SALES (corp-wide): 108.2MM **Privately Held**
WEB: www.anthemusb.com
SIC: 2676 Cleansing tissues: made from purchased paper
PA: Disposable Hygiene Llc
60 Page Rd
Clifton NJ 07012
973 779-1982

(G-8611)
ARCTIC INDUSTRIES LLC
9731 Nw 114th Way (33178-1178)
PHONE.................................305 883-5581
Brian Murphy, *CEO*
Donald Goodstein, *President*
Everardo Hern Sagarnaga, *General Mgr*
David Grife, *COO*
Lucy Deltoro, *Vice Pres*
◆ **EMP:** 85
SQ FT: 50,000
SALES (est): 17.1MM **Privately Held**
WEB: www.arcticwalkins.com
SIC: 3585 Refrigeration equipment, complete

(G-8612)
ARGEN FOODS
9220 Nw 102nd St (33178-1315)
PHONE.................................305 884-0037
EMP: 6
SALES (est): 415.3K **Privately Held**
SIC: 2099 Mfg Food Preparations

(G-8613)
ARMOR SUPPLY METALS LLC
Also Called: Amb Trucks
12690 Nw South River Dr (33178-1198)
PHONE.................................305 640-9901
Jimmy Dos Reis, *Mng Member*
EMP: 6 **EST:** 2016
SALES (est): 436.5K **Privately Held**
SIC: 3713 7692 Dump truck bodies; welding repair

(G-8614)
ARTE BRONCE MONUMENTS INC
Also Called: AB Transportation
8600 Nw S Rver Dr Ste 109 (33166)
PHONE.................................305 477-0813
Miguel Lozano Pampillon, *President*
Maria Josefa Espinosa, *Vice Pres*
EMP: 9 **EST:** 2002
SALES (est): 402.6K **Privately Held**
WEB: www.artebroncemonuments.com
SIC: 3366 Bronze foundry

(G-8615)
ARTEMISA LUXURY MILL WORK
10147 Nw 87th Ave (33178-1343)
PHONE.................................305 439-3246
EMP: 6 **EST:** 2017
SALES (est): 219.5K **Privately Held**
SIC: 2431 Millwork

(G-8616)
ASSOCIATED PAINT INC
10160 Nw South River Dr (33178-1324)
PHONE.................................305 885-1964
Lee Hackmeyer, *Vice Pres*
Mark Hackmeyer, *Treasurer*
◆ **EMP:** 14 **EST:** 1953
SQ FT: 10,000
SALES (est): 1.9MM **Privately Held**
WEB: www.associatedpaint.com
SIC: 2851 Paints & paint additives

(G-8617)
ATLANTIC MODELS INC
10631 Nw 123rd Street Rd (33178-3166)
PHONE.................................305 883-2012
Carol Jarman, *President*
Roger Jarman, *Vice Pres*
Betsy Jarman, *Mktg Dir*
EMP: 18 **EST:** 1982
SALES (est): 871.5K **Privately Held**
WEB: www.atlantic-models.com
SIC: 3944 Airplane models, toy & hobby

(G-8618)
AZTLAN FOODS CORP
9110 Nw 106th St (33178-1204)
PHONE.................................786 202-8301
Mariana Saul, *President*
EMP: 23 **EST:** 2010
SALES (est): 1.4MM **Privately Held**
WEB: www.aztlanfoods.com
SIC: 2099 Food preparations

(G-8619)
B E AEROSPACE
9100 Nw 105th Cir (33178-1305)
PHONE.................................305 459-7000
Kevin K Kim, *President*
Kristin Longmire, *Buyer*
Alex Micu, *Engineer*
Raynaldo Licea, *Manager*
Theresa Henry, *Software Dev*
EMP: 30 **EST:** 1995
SQ FT: 23,000
SALES (est): 8.4MM
SALES (corp-wide): 56.5B **Publicly Held**
WEB: www.beaerospace.com
SIC: 3728 Aircraft parts & equipment
HQ: B/E Aerospace, Inc.
1400 Corporate Center Way
Wellington FL 33414
410 266-2048

(G-8620)
BARJO PRINTING AND SIGN
7911 Nw 72nd Ave (33166-2227)
PHONE.................................786 332-2661
Renny Gamez, *Administration*
EMP: 6 **EST:** 2016
SALES (est): 285.9K **Privately Held**
WEB: www.barjoprintshop.com
SIC: 2759 Commercial printing

(G-8621)
BEN KAUFMAN SALES CO INC
10025 Nw 116th Way Ste 14 (33178-1173)
PHONE.................................305 688-2144
Benjamin Kaufman, *President*
EMP: 27
SALES (corp-wide): 13.3MM **Privately Held**
WEB: www.benkaufmancatalog.com
SIC: 2395 5023 Embroidery products, except schiffli machine; home furnishings
PA: Ben Kaufman Sales Co., Inc.
9265 Nw 101st St
Medley FL 33178
305 688-2144

(G-8622)
BERRY GLOBAL INC
9016 Nw 105th Way (33178-1218)
PHONE.................................305 887-2040
Tony Iannazzone, *Manager*
EMP: 8 **Publicly Held**
WEB: www.berryplastics.com
SIC: 3089 Bottle caps, molded plastic
HQ: Berry Global, Inc.
101 Oakley St
Evansville IN 47710

(G-8623)
BETTY DAIN CREATIONS LLC
9701 Nw 112th Ave Ste 10 (33178-1335)
PHONE.................................305 769-3451
Gerald Leebow, *President*
Leebow Alex, *Business Mgr*
Alex Leebow, *Business Mgr*
Donald Leebow, *Vice Pres*
Richard Leebow, *Vice Pres*
◆ **EMP:** 88 **EST:** 1946
SQ FT: 62,000
SALES (est): 9.8MM **Privately Held**
WEB: www.bettydain.com
SIC: 3999 5087 Barber & beauty shop equipment; beauty salon & barber shop equipment & supplies

(G-8624)
BONUS AEROSPACE INC
8545 Nw 79th Ave (33166-2166)
P.O. Box 669203, Miami (33166-9429)
PHONE.................................305 887-6778
Vincent Benoit, *CEO*
Jeffrey Kuhn, *Principal*
Vladimir V Pereira, *Principal*
▲ **EMP:** 5 **EST:** 2002
SALES (est): 713.2K **Privately Held**
SIC: 3724 Aircraft engines & engine parts

(G-8625)
BONUS TECH INC
8575 Nw 79th Ave Ste 4d (33166-2188)
PHONE.................................786 251-4232
Jeffrey Kuhn, *President*
Vladimir Pereira, *Vice Pres*
EMP: 12 **EST:** 2000
SQ FT: 6,400
SALES (est): 672.3K **Privately Held**
WEB: www.bonusaero.com
SIC: 3724 Aircraft engines & engine parts

(G-8626)
BROADBAND INTERNATIONAL INC (PA)
11650 Nw 102nd Rd (33178-1026)
PHONE.................................305 882-0505
Edward Perez, *President*
Lynn Newsom, *Vice Pres*
Angela Spyredes, *Purchasing*
Jennifer Tyrrel, *Sales Staff*
Amira Alvarez, *Manager*
◆ **EMP:** 7 **EST:** 1997
SALES (est): 3.2MM **Privately Held**
WEB: www.broadbandinternational.com
SIC: 3643 Plugs, electric

(G-8627)
BROADCAST TECH INC (PA)
10100 Nw 116th Way Ste 6 (33178-1154)
PHONE.................................786 351-4227
Roquel Garcia, *President*
EMP: 25 **EST:** 2004
SALES (est): 159.1K **Privately Held**
WEB: www.broadcast-tech.com
SIC: 2741

(G-8628)
CEMEX CONCRETE COMPANY
11100 Nw 138th St (33178-3110)
PHONE.................................305 558-0255
Ramiro Lanzis, *Principal*
EMP: 12 **EST:** 2010
SALES (est): 690.4K **Privately Held**
WEB: www.cemexusa.com
SIC: 3273 Ready-mixed concrete

(G-8629)
CEMEX MATERIALS LLC
13292 Nw 118th Ave (33178-3106)
PHONE.................................305 821-5661
Frank Prieto, *Sales Staff*
Danny Blomme, *Branch Mgr*
EMP: 73 **Privately Held**
SIC: 3273 Ready-mixed concrete
HQ: Cemex Materials Llc
1501 Belvedere Rd
West Palm Beach FL 33406
561 833-5555

(G-8630)
CEMEX MATERIALS LLC
FEC Quary
13292 Nw 118th Ave (33178-3106)
PHONE.................................305 818-4941
Roderick B Martin, *Branch Mgr*
EMP: 73 **Privately Held**
WEB: www.cemex.com
SIC: 3273 Ready-mixed concrete
HQ: Cemex Materials Llc
1501 Belvedere Rd
West Palm Beach FL 33406
561 833-5555

(G-8631)
CIENFUEGOS PALLETS CORP
7781 Nw 73rd Ct (33166-2201)
PHONE.................................786 703-3686
Zoila Hernandez, *President*
EMP: 8 **EST:** 2016
SALES (est): 415.1K **Privately Held**
WEB: www.cienfuegospallet.com
SIC: 2448 Pallets, wood

(G-8632)
CLIMB YOUR MOUNTAIN INC
11345 Nw 122nd St (33178-3176)
PHONE.................................571 571-8623
Ana Marma Duque, *Ch of Bd*
▲ **EMP:** 50 **EST:** 2011
SQ FT: 3,400
SALES (est): 8.6MM **Privately Held**
SIC: 2023 Dry, condensed, evaporated dairy products

(G-8633)
CONCHITA FOODS INC (PA)
10051 Nw 99th Ave Ste 3 (33178-1161)
P.O. Box 520156, Miami (33152-0156)
PHONE.................................305 888-9703
Sixto L Ferro, *President*
Teresita F Menendez, *Vice Pres*
Gaetano Costantino, *Sales Staff*
Jorge Rodriguez, *Sales Staff*
◆ **EMP:** 55 **EST:** 1987
SQ FT: 45,000
SALES (est): 8.6MM **Privately Held**
WEB: www.conchita-foods.com
SIC: 2033 2032 5149 2077 Fruits: packaged in cans, jars, etc.; beans, with meat: packaged in cans, jars, etc.; groceries & related products; animal & marine fats & oils; rice milling; dehydrated fruits, vegetables, soups

(G-8634)
CONVERPACK INC
9230 9250 Nw 102nd St 9 (33178)
PHONE.................................786 304-1680
Guillermo Roversi, *President*
Luis G Roversi, *Vice Pres*
Ranza Armas, *Accountant*
◆ **EMP:** 6 **EST:** 2010
SALES (est): 2.7MM **Privately Held**
WEB: www.conver-pack.com
SIC: 2656 Paper cups, plates, dishes & utensils

(G-8635)
CORESLAB STRUCTURES MIAMI INC
10501 Nw 121st Way (33178-1011)
PHONE.................................305 823-8950
Mario Francisosa, *President*
Luigi Franciosa, *President*
Ted Wolfsthal, *General Mgr*
Sidney Speigel, *Corp Secy*
Frank Franciosa, *Vice Pres*
▼ **EMP:** 280 **EST:** 1955
SQ FT: 10,000
SALES (est): 68.3MM
SALES (corp-wide): 27.3MM **Privately Held**
WEB: www.coreslab.com
SIC: 3272 Concrete products, precast; prestressed concrete products
HQ: Coreslab Holdings U S Inc
332 Jones Rd Suite 1
Stoney Creek ON
905 643-0220

(G-8636)
COSMETIC CORP OF AMERICA INC
9750 Nw 91st Ct (33178-1427)
PHONE..............................305 883-8434
Jesus Rodriguez, *President*
Eric Bedenbaugh, *CFO*
EMP: 21 **EST:** 1996
SALES (est): 2.4MM **Privately Held**
WEB: www.gabriellas-garden.com
SIC: 2844 Cosmetic preparations

(G-8637)
CREACTION INDUSTRY LLC
Also Called: Creaction Organize
8710 Nw 100th St (33178-1454)
PHONE..............................305 779-4851
Pierre Amezcua, *CEO*
EMP: 12 **EST:** 2011
SQ FT: 17,500
SALES (est): 1.7MM **Privately Held**
WEB: www.creaction.co
SIC: 2541 Store & office display cases & fixtures

(G-8638)
CROSSTAC CORPORATION
12605 Nw 115th Ave B-104 (33178-3190)
PHONE..............................406 522-9300
Sean Osman, *Manager*
EMP: 7
SALES (corp-wide): 1.1MM **Privately Held**
WEB: www.crosstac.com
SIC: 3484 Small arms
PA: Crosstac Corporation
1010 S Lincoln Ave # 100
Loveland CO 80537
406 522-9300

(G-8639)
CUSTOM MANUFACTURING CORP
9324 Nw 102nd St (33178-1334)
PHONE..............................305 863-1001
David Wilpon, *President*
Sharon L Wilpon, *Vice Pres*
EMP: 18
SQ FT: 15,000
SALES (est): 3.7MM **Privately Held**
WEB: www.custom-mfg.com
SIC: 2844 Cosmetic preparations

(G-8640)
DAUER MANUFACTURING CORP
10100 Nw 116th Way U (33178-1154)
PHONE..............................800 883-2590
Craig Klomparens, *President*
Joaquin Obeso, *Vice Pres*
▲ **EMP:** 8 **EST:** 2012
SALES (est): 953.5K **Privately Held**
WEB: www.dauermanufacturing.com
SIC: 3646 3645 Commercial indusl & institutional electric lighting fixtures; residential lighting fixtures

(G-8641)
DAWN FOODS INC
8035 Nw 84th St (33166-2109)
PHONE..............................866 218-3801
EMP: 7
SALES (corp-wide): 1.7B **Privately Held**
WEB: www.dawnfoods.com
SIC: 2053 Cakes, bakery: frozen
PA: Dawn Foods, Inc.
3333 Sargent Rd
Jackson MI 49201
517 789-4400

(G-8642)
DEL ROSARIO ENTERPRISES INC
7339 Nw 79th Ter (33166-2211)
PHONE..............................786 547-6812
Emanuel Fernandez, *President*
EMP: 12 **EST:** 2019
SALES (est): 1.2MM **Privately Held**
WEB: www.delrosariomiami.com
SIC: 2092 5147 Fresh or frozen packaged fish; meats & meat products

(G-8643)
DOORS 4 U INC
7322 Nw 79th Ter (33166-2212)
PHONE..............................786 400-2298
Sardinas S Gendry, *Principal*
EMP: 9 **EST:** 2014
SALES (est): 313.3K **Privately Held**
SIC: 2431 Door frames, wood

(G-8644)
DOR A LUM CORPORATION
Also Called: Doralum
7040 Nw 77th Ter (33166-2542)
PHONE..............................305 884-3922
Victorina Pino, *President*
Vicky Pino, *Office Mgr*
Richard Gallart, *Manager*
▼ **EMP:** 12 **EST:** 1996
SALES (est): 250K **Privately Held**
WEB: www.doralum.com
SIC: 3442 Metal doors; store fronts, prefabricated, metal

(G-8645)
ECO WINDOW SYSTEMS LLC
8502 Nw 80th St Unit 100 (33166-2137)
PHONE..............................305 885-5299
Paola Gomez, *Sales Mgr*
Frank E Mata, *Mng Member*
Mike Vilarino, *Manager*
Ricardo E Suarez,
▼ **EMP:** 439 **EST:** 2009
SALES (est): 23MM
SALES (corp-wide): 882.6MM **Publicly Held**
WEB: www.ecowindowsystems.com
SIC: 2431 Storm windows, wood; window frames, wood; window sashes, wood; windows, wood
PA: Pgt Innovations, Inc.
1070 Technology Dr
North Venice FL 34275
941 480-1600

(G-8646)
EL TRIGAL INTERNATIONAL
10740 Nw 74th St (33178-1504)
PHONE..............................305 594-6610
EMP: 7 **EST:** 2010
SALES (est): 234.3K **Privately Held**
SIC: 2051 Cakes, bakery: except frozen

(G-8647)
ELECTRONIC SIGN SUPPLY CORP
12601 Nw 115th Ave 106a (33178-3184)
PHONE..............................305 477-0555
Marcela Veloz, *Principal*
◆ **EMP:** 6 **EST:** 2009
SALES (est): 1.3MM **Privately Held**
WEB: www.electrosignsupply.com
SIC: 3993 Signs & advertising specialties
PA: Sign Solution S A S
Via Parque Agroindustrial De La Sabana Bg 35 Km 18
Mosquera

(G-8648)
EUROPE COATING INDUSTRIES LLC
8213 Nw 74th Ave (33166-7403)
PHONE..............................786 535-4143
EMP: 6 **EST:** 2017
SALES (est): 255.1K **Privately Held**
SIC: 3999 Manufacturing industries

(G-8649)
EUSA GLOBAL LLC
Also Called: Ecleris
11801 Nw 100th Rd Ste 17 (33178-1046)
PHONE..............................786 483-7490
Henry E Sand Casali, *Mng Member*
EMP: 9 **EST:** 2013
SALES (est): 896.6K **Privately Held**
SIC: 3841 Surgical & medical instruments

(G-8650)
EXPRESSWAY OIL CORP
7391 Nw 78th St (33166-2207)
PHONE..............................786 302-9534
Jose Ochoa, *Owner*
EMP: 6 **EST:** 2012
SALES (est): 404K **Privately Held**
SIC: 1389 Oil & gas field services

(G-8651)
FLORIDA AA PALLETS INC
7611 Nw 74th Ave (33166-2424)
PHONE..............................305 805-1522
Leonardo Acosta, *President*
EMP: 7 **EST:** 2007
SQ FT: 10,000
SALES (est): 922.7K **Privately Held**
WEB: www.aafloridapallets.com
SIC: 2448 Pallets, wood; pallets, wood & wood with metal

(G-8652)
FLORIDA LIFT STATIONS CORP
9498 Nw South River Dr (33166-2004)
PHONE..............................305 887-8485
Alex De Bogory Jr, *President*
David Brunswick, *CFO*
EMP: 7 **EST:** 1976
SQ FT: 5,000
SALES (est): 578.5K **Privately Held**
SIC: 3272 Concrete products

(G-8653)
FRIEDMAN BROS DCRTIVE ARTS INC
9015 Nw 105th Way (33178-1217)
PHONE..............................800 327-1065
Bernard Singer, *President*
Marilyn Singer, *Vice Pres*
Clifford Poole, *Exec Dir*
◆ **EMP:** 70 **EST:** 1903
SQ FT: 30,000
SALES (est): 7.7MM **Privately Held**
WEB: www.friedmanmirrors.com
SIC: 3231 Mirrored glass; ornamental glass: cut, engraved or otherwise decorated

(G-8654)
G & S MACHINE SHOP CORP
7715 Nw 74th Ave (33166-7501)
PHONE..............................305 863-7866
Gregorio Martin, *President*
Nelsey Perez, *Vice Pres*
Alberto D Armas, *Admin Sec*
EMP: 9 **EST:** 1996
SALES (est): 646.7K **Privately Held**
SIC: 3599 Machine shop, jobbing & repair

(G-8655)
GAR-P INDUSTRIES INC
10890 Nw South River Dr (33178-1129)
PHONE..............................305 888-7252
Peter Garcia Jr, *President*
Jorge J Garcia, *Vice Pres*
Brenda Ortiz, *CFO*
◆ **EMP:** 45 **EST:** 1975
SALES (est): 5.5MM **Privately Held**
WEB: www.gar-p.com
SIC: 3713 5013 7532 3711 Truck bodies (motor vehicles); truck parts & accessories; body shop, trucks; motor vehicles & car bodies

(G-8656)
GEM PAVER SYSTEMS INC (PA)
9845 Nw 118th Way (33178-1043)
PHONE..............................305 805-0000
Jorge Fernandez, *President*
Jurek Kocik, *Corp Secy*
◆ **EMP:** 26 **EST:** 1989
SQ FT: 20,000
SALES (est): 8.8MM **Privately Held**
WEB: www.gempavers.com
SIC: 3255 Brick, clay refractory

(G-8657)
GENERAL MRO AEROSPACE INC
10990 Nw 92nd Ter (33178-2515)
PHONE..............................305 482-9903
Cristian Munoz, *President*
Lester Kamberger, *President*
Fabiola Ortega, *Business Mgr*
Sebastian Nardo, *Purch Agent*
Irene Fernandez, *Finance*
EMP: 3 **EST:** 2006
SALES (est): 3.5MM **Privately Held**
WEB: www.generalmroaerospace.com
SIC: 3728 Aircraft parts & equipment

(G-8658)
GEORGES WELDING SERVICES INC
Also Called: George's Metal Fab
11400 Nw 134th St (33178-3113)
PHONE..............................305 822-2445
Jorge Amador Sr, *CEO*
Angelica Amador, *Vice Pres*
Jorge Amador Jr, *Vice Pres*
Luz Amador, *Treasurer*
Luz M Amador, *Treasurer*
EMP: 60 **EST:** 1984
SQ FT: 32,000
SALES (est): 12.6MM **Privately Held**
WEB: www.georgeswelding.com
SIC: 3441 Fabricated structural metal

(G-8659)
GLOBAL TURBINE SERVICES INC
9374 Nw 102nd St (33178-1334)
PHONE..............................786 476-2166
Jack A Tanner, *President*
David Rodriguez, *Vice Pres*
Wally Azzam, *Opers Staff*
Matthew Anderson, *Director*
EMP: 12 **EST:** 2012
SQ FT: 25,000
SALES (est): 1.9MM **Privately Held**
WEB: www.gtsaviation.com
SIC: 3724 Aircraft engines & engine parts

(G-8660)
GONDIA MACHINE SHOP INC
9452 Nw 109th St (33178-1223)
PHONE..............................305 763-7494
Louis Diaz, *President*
EMP: 9 **EST:** 1989
SALES (est): 604K **Privately Held**
WEB: www.medleymachine.com
SIC: 3599 Machine shop, jobbing & repair

(G-8661)
HARBOR LINEN LLC (HQ)
Also Called: 1concier
10800 Nw 106th St Ste 12 (33178-1261)
PHONE..............................305 805-8085
Chris Nelson, *CEO*
Ron Brozo, *Vice Pres*
Gary Geiger, *Vice Pres*
Lou Gostino, *Vice Pres*
Lamar Tomlin, *Vice Pres*
◆ **EMP:** 100 **EST:** 1973
SQ FT: 87,000
SALES (est): 50.6MM
SALES (corp-wide): 193MM **Privately Held**
WEB: www.1concier.com
SIC: 2299 5023 Linen fabrics; linens & towels
PA: Lion Equity Holdings Ii, Llc
3 E 3rd Ave Ste 201
Denver CO 80203
303 847-4100

(G-8662)
HITACHI RAIL STS USA INC
11150 Nw 122nd St (33178-3456)
PHONE..............................415 397-7010
Giancarlo Fantappie, *Branch Mgr*
EMP: 60 **Privately Held**
SIC: 3743 Train cars & equipment, freight or passenger
HQ: Hitachi Rail Sts Usa, Inc.
1000 Technology Dr
Pittsburgh PA 15219
412 688-2400

(G-8663)
HITACHI RAIL USA INC (PA)
11150 Nw 122nd St (33178-3456)
PHONE..............................415 397-7010
▲ **EMP:** 14
SALES (est): 23.4MM **Privately Held**
SIC: 3743 Mfg Railroad Equipment

(G-8664)
HOBBY PRESS INC
Also Called: Executive Printers of Florida
8001 Nw 74th Ave (33166-7507)
PHONE..............................305 887-4333
Jo A Gardner, *CEO*
David Gardner, *President*
Ryan Gardner, *Vice Pres*
Elena Gardner, *Opers Staff*
Carly Gardner, *CFO*
▼ **EMP:** 34
SQ FT: 11,000
SALES (est): 3.6MM **Privately Held**
WEB: www.executiveprinters.com
SIC: 2752 7334 Commercial printing, offset; photocopying & duplicating services

(G-8665)
HOMETOWN FOODS USA LLC
11800 Nw 102nd Rd Ste 6 (33178-1030)
PHONE..................................305 887-5200
Troy Schwartzberg, *President*
Ed Eberts, *COO*
Gary J Schwartzberg, *Exec VP*
Janet Martin, *Vice Pres*
Bryan Schwartzberg, *Vice Pres*
◆ **EMP:** 200 **EST:** 1931
SQ FT: 85,000
SALES (est): 30MM **Privately Held**
WEB: www.hometownfoodsusa.com
SIC: 2053 2051 Frozen bakery products, except bread; bagels, fresh or frozen

(G-8666)
HONTUS LTD (PA)
Also Called: Hontus, Ltd., Inc.
11450 Nw 122nd St Ste 100 (33178-3259)
PHONE..................................786 322-3022
Haroon Sheikh, *President*
Kayla Crawford, *Sales Staff*
EMP: 15 **EST:** 2014
SALES (est): 2MM **Privately Held**
WEB: www.hontus.com
SIC: 3161 Wardrobe bags (luggage)

(G-8667)
IDSOLUTION INC ✪
Also Called: Marvelous Mushrooms
10302 Nw S Rver Dr Ste 15 (33178)
PHONE..................................305 603-9835
Alessandro Farana, *CEO*
EMP: 8 **EST:** 2021
SALES (est): 351.2K **Privately Held**
SIC: 2033 Mushrooms: packaged in cans, jars, etc.

(G-8668)
IESC DIESEL CORP
Also Called: Hd Kit
7817 Nw 72nd Ave (33166-2215)
PHONE..................................305 470-9306
Laura Paret, *President*
Jose Paret, *Vice Pres*
Stan Rodriguez, *Sales Staff*
◆ **EMP:** 5 **EST:** 2003
SQ FT: 2,000
SALES (est): 1.3MM **Privately Held**
WEB: www.heavydutykits.com
SIC: 3714 Motor vehicle parts & accessories

(G-8669)
IMPEX OF DORAL INC
7850 Nw 80th St (33166-2104)
PHONE..................................305 470-0041
Giancarlo Di Mella, *CEO*
Giovanni Di Mella, *Ch of Bd*
◆ **EMP:** 50 **EST:** 1994
SQ FT: 80,000
SALES (est): 13.2MM **Privately Held**
WEB: www.impexofdoral.com
SIC: 2676 Diapers, paper (disposable): made from purchased paper
PA: Zaimella Del Ecuador S.A.
Ave Juan De Dios Morales Lt.1
Quito

(G-8670)
INTERNATIONAL CLOSET CENTER
7330 Nw 79th Ter (33166-2212)
PHONE..................................305 883-6551
Paola I Frewa, *President*
Elia Frewa, *Admin Sec*
▼ **EMP:** 6 **EST:** 2006
SALES (est): 874.4K **Privately Held**
WEB: www.internationalcabinetcontractors.com
SIC: 2421 Sawmills & planing mills, general

(G-8671)
INTRADECO APPAREL INC (HQ)
9500 Nw 108th Ave (33178-2517)
PHONE..................................305 264-8888
Felix Siman, *CEO*
Jaime Miguel, *President*
Jose Siman, *CFO*
Eti Ashkenazi, *Controller*
Jay Boyett, *VP Sales*
◆ **EMP:** 134 **EST:** 1982
SQ FT: 15,000
SALES (est): 75.5MM
SALES (corp-wide): 96.1MM **Privately Held**
WEB: www.intradecoapparel.com
SIC: 2254 3161 Underwear, knit; clothing & apparel carrying cases
PA: Intradeco, Inc.
9500 Nw 108th Ave
Medley FL 33178
305 264-6022

(G-8672)
IVORY INTERNATIONAL INC (DH)
9500 Nw 108th Ave (33178-2517)
P.O. Box 569, Waynesville NC (28786-0569)
PHONE..................................305 687-2244
Robert J Lodge, *CEO*
Sandy Lipson, *President*
Wilbur O Hopper, *CFO*
Joseph I J Lodge, *Shareholder*
◆ **EMP:** 102 **EST:** 1976
SQ FT: 60,000
SALES (est): 16.5MM
SALES (corp-wide): 96.1MM **Privately Held**
WEB: www.intradecoapparel.com
SIC: 2326 2339 2369 Service apparel (baker, barber, lab, etc.), washable: men's; women's & misses' outerwear; girls' & children's outerwear
HQ: Intradeco Apparel, Inc.
9500 Nw 108th Ave
Medley FL 33178
305 264-8888

(G-8673)
J & J STEEL SERVICES CORP
9401 Nw 109th St Unit 5 (33178-1226)
PHONE..................................305 878-8929
EMP: 8 **EST:** 2014
SALES (est): 483.5K **Privately Held**
SIC: 3441 3444 Fabricated structural metal; sheet metalwork

(G-8674)
J M SMUCKER COMPANY
Also Called: CAF Bustelo
9290 Nw 112th Ave Ste 15 (33178-2783)
PHONE..................................305 594-2886
Angel Souto, *Manager*
EMP: 6
SALES (corp-wide): 8B **Publicly Held**
WEB: www.jmsmucker.com
SIC: 2095 Coffee roasting (except by wholesale grocers)
PA: The J M Smucker Company
1 Strawberry Ln
Orrville OH 44667
330 682-3000

(G-8675)
J&N KEYSTONE OF FLORIDA
6900 Nw 77th Ter (33166-2540)
PHONE..................................305 528-1677
Jose Delgado, *Principal*
EMP: 7 **EST:** 2008
SALES (est): 885K **Privately Held**
SIC: 3369 Nonferrous foundries

(G-8676)
JAMO INC
8850 Nw 79th Ave (33166-2197)
PHONE..................................305 885-3444
Thomas R Peck Sr, *President*
Michael Bilek, *Vice Pres*
◆ **EMP:** 55 **EST:** 1967
SQ FT: 17,000
SALES (est): 7.1MM **Privately Held**
WEB: www.jamoproducts.com
SIC: 3273 3255 2899 2891 Ready-mixed concrete; clay refractories; chemical preparations; adhesives & sealants
HQ: Custom Building Products Llc
7711 Center Ave Ste 500
Huntington Beach CA 92647
800 272-8786

(G-8677)
KONUS USA CORPORATION
7530 Nw 79th St (33166-7537)
PHONE..................................305 884-7618
Giuseppe Alberti, *President*
Stefano Alberti, *Vice Pres*
Patricia Torres, *Bookkeeper*
Patricia L Torres, *Comptroller*
▲ **EMP:** 6 **EST:** 1998
SALES (est): 999.6K **Privately Held**
WEB: www.konuscopes.com
SIC: 3827 Aiming circles (fire control equipment)

(G-8678)
LAWSON INDUSTRIES INC (PA)
8501 Nw 90th St (33166-2187)
PHONE..................................305 696-8660
Harold Bailey, *President*
Ronald Bailey, *Vice Pres*
Joe Thiry, *Opers Staff*
Carolina Campillo, *Purch Mgr*
Erick Martinez, *Purch Mgr*
◆ **EMP:** 300 **EST:** 1965
SQ FT: 300,000
SALES (est): 31.1MM **Privately Held**
WEB: www.lawson-industries.com
SIC: 3231 3442 Doors, glass: made from purchased glass; metal doors, sash & trim

(G-8679)
LOCUST USA INC
Also Called: Locust Power
8312 Nw 74th Ave (33166-7406)
PHONE..................................305 889-5410
Kirk Warshaw, *President*
Rene Borroto, *Mfg Staff*
EMP: 18 **EST:** 1999
SALES (est): 1.9MM **Privately Held**
WEB: www.locustusa.com
SIC: 3511 Turbines & turbine generator sets

(G-8680)
MADE IN AMERICA PLASTIC INC
9949 Nw 89th Ave Unit 11 (33178-1466)
PHONE..................................786 310-7816
Elda S Liberatore, *Principal*
EMP: 6 **EST:** 2015
SALES (est): 229K **Privately Held**
SIC: 2821 Molding compounds, plastics

(G-8681)
MADSON INC
Also Called: Madson Meat
10925 Nw South River Dr (33178-1132)
PHONE..................................305 863-7390
John Maderal, *President*
Stacy Maderal, *Corp Secy*
Francisco Maderal, *Vice Pres*
EMP: 10 **EST:** 1974
SQ FT: 8,000
SALES (est): 896.6K **Privately Held**
SIC: 2011 7692 3599 Meat packing plants; welding repair; machine & other job shop work

(G-8682)
MANN+HUMMEL FILTRATION TECHNOL
10505 Nw 112th Ave Ste 22 (33178-1000)
PHONE..................................305 499-5100
EMP: 7
SALES (corp-wide): 4.6B **Privately Held**
SIC: 3714 Motor vehicle brake systems & parts
HQ: Mann+Hummel Filtration Technology Group Inc.
1 Wix Way
Gastonia NC 28054
704 869-3300

(G-8683)
MARQUEZ BROTHERS INC
9115 Nw 93rd St (33178-1440)
PHONE..................................305 888-0090
Andres A Marquez, *Ch of Bd*
Lidia Marquez, *President*
Olga Lidia Marquez, *Vice Pres*
Olga Marquez, *Admin Sec*
▼ **EMP:** 12 **EST:** 1987
SQ FT: 9,000
SALES (est): 2.4MM **Privately Held**
WEB: www.mbrothersdumpbody.com
SIC: 3465 Body parts, automobile: stamped metal

(G-8684)
MARTINEZ TRUSS COMPANY INC
9280 Nw S River Dr (33166-2110)
PHONE..................................305 883-6261
Jorge L Martinez, *President*
Marta C Martinez, *Vice Pres*
▼ **EMP:** 18 **EST:** 1984
SQ FT: 7,000
SALES (est): 2.2MM **Privately Held**
WEB: www.martineztruss.net
SIC: 2439 Trusses, wooden roof

(G-8685)
MCM FOOD CORP
7385 Nw 78th St (33166-2207)
PHONE..................................305 885-9254
Clara I Lenis, *President*
Adeliks Villareal, *Vice Pres*
EMP: 6 **EST:** 2004
SALES (est): 1MM **Privately Held**
WEB: www.mcmfoodcorp.com
SIC: 2099 Food preparations

(G-8686)
MDT TECHNOLOGIES INC
10619 Nw 122nd St (33178-3186)
PHONE..................................305 308-2902
EMP: 6 **EST:** 2005
SALES (est): 528.1K **Privately Held**
WEB: www.mdttechnologiesfl.com
SIC: 3651 Household audio & video equipment

(G-8687)
MEDLEY MACHINE SHOP INC
Also Called: Gondia Machine Shop
9452 Nw 109th St (33178-1223)
PHONE..................................305 884-3200
Luis Diaz, *President*
Luis Alaniz, *VP Sales*
Raquel Ball, *Asst Mgr*
EMP: 10 **EST:** 1994
SALES (est): 1.4MM **Privately Held**
WEB: www.medleymachine.com
SIC: 3599 Machine shop, jobbing & repair

(G-8688)
MELT-TECH POLYMERS INC
7570 Nw 79th St (33166-7537)
PHONE..................................305 887-6148
Juan A Bravo, *Director*
EMP: 7 **EST:** 2015
SALES (est): 105.5K **Privately Held**
SIC: 3089 5162 Extruded finished plastic products; plastics materials

(G-8689)
MELTPOINT PLASTICS INTL INC
7570 Nw 79th St (33166-7537)
PHONE..................................305 887-8020
Carlos Bravo, *President*
◆ **EMP:** 27 **EST:** 2000
SQ FT: 13,000
SALES (est): 6.4MM **Privately Held**
WEB: www.meltpointplastics.com
SIC: 3089 Injection molding of plastics

(G-8690)
METRO ROOF TILE INC
9845 Nw 118th Way (33178-1043)
PHONE..................................863 467-0042
Fernando Arias, *President*
Arias Fernando M, *Principal*
James Bertelson, *Sales Staff*
◆ **EMP:** 15 **EST:** 1984
SQ FT: 2,000
SALES (est): 177.5K **Privately Held**
WEB: www.crownrooftiles.com
SIC: 3259 3272 2952 Roofing tile, clay; concrete products; asphalt felts & coatings

(G-8691)
MIAMI NDT INC
8050 Nw 90th St (33166-2114)
P.O. Box 668528, Miami (33166-9418)
PHONE..................................305 599-9393
Jose Perez, *President*
Jessie Cardena, *Vice Pres*
Victor Campos, *Technical Staff*
▼ **EMP:** 10 **EST:** 2008
SALES (est): 2.3MM **Privately Held**
WEB: www.miamindt.aero
SIC: 3724 Aircraft engines & engine parts

(G-8692)
MOTORS PUMPS AND ACCESSORIES
7530 Nw 77th St (33166-7525)
PHONE..................................305 883-3181
Fernando Higuera, *Principal*

▲ = Import ▼=Export
◆ =Import/Export

EMP: 8 **EST:** 2001
SALES (est): 252.9K **Privately Held**
SIC: 3594 Fluid power pumps & motors

(G-8693)
MR WINTER INC
Also Called: ISO Panel
8800 Nw 77th Ct (33166-2105)
P.O. Box 126460, Hialeah (33012-1607)
PHONE..................................800 327-3371
Manny Mijares, *President*
Manuel Mijares, *President*
David Mijares, *Vice Pres*
Jennifer Ghacham, *Sales Staff*
Robert Triana, *Sales Executive*
◆ **EMP:** 48 **EST:** 1976
SQ FT: 54,000
SALES (est): 6.5MM **Privately Held**
WEB: www.mrwinterinc.net
SIC: 3585 Refrigeration equipment, complete

(G-8694)
NETS DEPOT INC
9949 Nw 89th Ave Unit 13 (33178-1466)
PHONE..................................305 215-5579
Jean-Michel Fethiere, *President*
Antonio Suergiu, *Vice Pres*
Ralph Rouzier, *Admin Sec*
EMP: 10 **EST:** 2015
SALES (est): 508.6K **Privately Held**
WEB: www.netsdepot.com
SIC: 2298 Blasting mats, rope

(G-8695)
NEW AGE WINDOWS & DOORS CORP
7196 Nw 77th Ter (33166-2544)
PHONE..................................305 889-0703
Jose Bosch, *President*
◆ **EMP:** 10 **EST:** 1994
SQ FT: 16,150
SALES (est): 1.5MM **Privately Held**
WEB: www.newagewindow.com
SIC: 2431 3442 Doors & door parts & trim, wood; windows & window parts & trim, wood; metal doors, sash & trim

(G-8696)
NEW GENERATION AEROSPACE INC
8004 Nw 90th St (33166-2114)
PHONE..................................305 882-1410
Orlando Fernandez, *President*
Amauri Izquierdo, *Vice Pres*
Ivon Fernandez, *Accounting Dir*
EMP: 6 **EST:** 2010
SALES (est): 1MM **Privately Held**
WEB: www.ngaerospace.com
SIC: 3812 7694 Aircraft/aerospace flight instruments & guidance systems; armature rewinding shops; rewinding services; coil winding service; rewinding stators

(G-8697)
NEWLINK CABLING SYSTEMS INC (PA)
11701 Nw 102nd Rd Ste 21 (33178-1016)
PHONE..................................305 477-8063
Jorge Villegas, *President*
Fernando Pacheco, *Vice Pres*
◆ **EMP:** 12 **EST:** 1994
SQ FT: 10,000
SALES (est): 2.3MM **Privately Held**
WEB: www.newlink-usa.com
SIC: 3357 2298 Fiber optic cable (insulated); cable, fiber

(G-8698)
NORTH AMERICAN MINING
10025 Nw 116th Way Ste 1 (33178-1197)
PHONE..................................305 824-3181
EMP: 7 **EST:** 2019
SALES (est): 3.1MM **Privately Held**
WEB: www.nacoal.com
SIC: 1241 Coal mining services

(G-8699)
OSKO INC
8085 Nw 90th St (33166-2113)
PHONE..................................305 599-7161
Jinsu Do, *President*
Jeonghoon Hyun, *Director*
Kukchin Yang, *Director*
EMP: 17 **EST:** 2013
SALES (est): 10.3MM **Privately Held**
WEB: www.oskomedical.com
SIC: 3844 X-ray apparatus & tubes
PA: Rayence Co., Ltd.
14 Samsung 1-Ro 1-Gil
Hwaseong 18449

(G-8700)
PACIFIC SCIENTIFIC COMPANY
Also Called: Meggitt Aftermarket Services
11700 Nw 102nd Rd Ste 6 (33178-1029)
PHONE..................................305 477-4711
Albert Figueroa, *Principal*
Edwin Afshalimi, *Director*
EMP: 50
SALES (corp-wide): 2.2B **Privately Held**
WEB: www.hachultra.com
SIC: 3728 Aircraft parts & equipment
HQ: Pacific Scientific Company Inc
1785 Voyager Ave
Simi Valley CA 93063
805 526-5700

(G-8701)
PAN AMERICAN CNSTR PLANT
8000 Nw 74th St (33166-2318)
PHONE..................................305 477-5058
Bob Pritchard, *Principal*
EMP: 9 **EST:** 2001
SALES (est): 24.2K **Privately Held**
SIC: 2951 Asphalt paving mixtures & blocks

(G-8702)
PANAPASTRY LLC
9001 Nw 97th Ter Ste M (33178-1460)
PHONE..................................305 883-1557
Maria E Del Rio,
EMP: 5 **EST:** 2007
SALES (est): 480.6K **Privately Held**
WEB: www.panapastry.com
SIC: 2051 Pastries, e.g. danish: except frozen

(G-8703)
PEPSICO INC
Also Called: Pepsi-Cola
8701 Nw 93rd St (33178-2103)
PHONE..................................305 593-7500
John Nickels, *Branch Mgr*
Vivian Fajardo, *Manager*
Ed Gonzalez, *Manager*
Andrea Lopera, *Analyst*
EMP: 6
SALES (corp-wide): 70.3B **Publicly Held**
WEB: www.pepsico.com
SIC: 2086 5149 3565 Carbonated soft drinks, bottled & canned; soft drinks; packaging machinery
PA: Pepsico, Inc.
700 Anderson Hill Rd
Purchase NY 10577
914 253-2000

(G-8704)
PERRI BROTHERS AND ASSOCIATES
9001 Nw 97th Ter (33178-1460)
PHONE..................................305 887-8686
EMP: 6 **EST:** 2019
SALES (est): 359.4K **Privately Held**
WEB: www.perribros.com
SIC: 2511 Wood household furniture

(G-8705)
PHARMA FORMULATIONS LABS INC
12601 Nw 115th Ave # 103 (33178-3184)
PHONE..................................786 985-1254
Maria Jerez, *Principal*
EMP: 6 **EST:** 2013
SALES (est): 232.3K **Privately Held**
SIC: 2834 Pharmaceutical preparations

(G-8706)
PINOS WINDOW CORPORATION
6860 Nw 75th St (33166-2549)
PHONE..................................305 888-9903
Mario Pino, *President*
Mercy Blanco, *Vice Pres*
George Pino, *Vice Pres*
Julio Rodriguez, *CFO*
▼ **EMP:** 18 **EST:** 1965
SQ FT: 26,000
SALES (est): 2.9MM **Privately Held**
WEB: www.pinoswindow.com
SIC: 3442 1751 Window & door frames; window & door installation & erection

(G-8707)
PLASTIC COMPONENTS INC (PA)
Also Called: Plastic International
9051 Nw 97th Ter (33178-1430)
PHONE..................................305 885-0561
Thomas Stark, *President*
Audrey English, *Accountant*
Eugene Stark Jr, *Director*
Patricia Stark, *Director*
Ray Barnes, *Executive*
◆ **EMP:** 35 **EST:** 1976
SQ FT: 40,000
SALES: 6.7MM **Privately Held**
WEB: www.plasticomponents.com
SIC: 3089 Plastic hardware & building products

(G-8708)
POLIMIX USA LLC
11750 Nw South River Dr (33178-1117)
PHONE..................................305 888-4752
Tarik Andrade, *President*
Luis Gabriel Munoz, *General Mgr*
EMP: 16 **EST:** 2014
SQ FT: 174,240
SALES (est): 6.6MM **Privately Held**
WEB: www.polimixusa.com
SIC: 3273 Ready-mixed concrete

(G-8709)
PREMIUM AUTO SEALANT USA LLC
12450 Nw South River Dr (33178-1155)
PHONE..................................786 637-2573
Roberto C Fernandez, *President*
EMP: 6 **EST:** 2017
SALES (est): 171K **Privately Held**
SIC: 2891 Sealants

(G-8710)
PRO-CHEMICALS USA CORP
7575 Nw 82nd St (33166-7412)
PHONE..................................305 885-7922
Enrique Herrero, *President*
Gabriel Herrero, *Corp Secy*
Bibiana Herrero, *Vice Pres*
EMP: 5 **EST:** 1998
SALES (est): 1MM **Privately Held**
SIC: 3471 Cleaning, polishing & finishing

(G-8711)
PRO-MIX INC
11405 Nw 138th St (33178-3111)
PHONE..................................305 556-6699
Emilio R Vega, *President*
EMP: 7 **EST:** 2005
SALES (est): 322.9K **Privately Held**
WEB: www.promixconcrete.com
SIC: 3273 Ready-mixed concrete

(G-8712)
PROBAG INC
9955 Nw 88th Ave (33178-1450)
PHONE..................................305 883-3266
Ignacio Rivero, *President*
Paul La Fontaine, *Vice Pres*
Sergio Jilmnez, *Treasurer*
EMP: 15 **EST:** 2010
SALES (est): 1.9MM **Privately Held**
WEB: www.probag.biz
SIC: 2621 Bag paper

(G-8713)
QUEST MANUFACTURING CORP
11200 Nw 138th St (33178-3157)
PHONE..................................305 513-8583
Armando Ujueta, *President*
Nestor Novo, *Vice Pres*
Hernan Salcedo, *Treasurer*
Michael Convissar, *Admin Sec*
EMP: 18 **EST:** 2001
SALES (est): 175.7K **Privately Held**
WEB: www.questtechnologyintl.com
SIC: 3399 1731 Iron ore recovery from open hearth slag; voice, data & video wiring contractor

(G-8714)
RAM INVESTMENTS SOUTH FLA INC (PA)
Also Called: Sea Enterprise Adventures
11102 Nw South River Dr (33178-1135)
PHONE..................................305 759-6419
Ariel Parad, *President*
Elizabeth Gomez, *Business Mgr*
Lizeth Monserrat, *Purchasing*
Moises Rodrigues, *Treasurer*
Juan Diaz, *Executive*
▼ **EMP:** 103 **EST:** 1993
SALES (est): 27.1MM **Privately Held**
SIC: 3732 5551 Motorized boat, building & repairing; boat dealers

GEOGRAPHIC

(G-8715)
RAVIC TECHNOLOGIES LLC
7939 Nw 84th St Ste 101 (33166-2107)
PHONE..................................954 237-3241
Alberto Ravachi Arza,
Sandra Victoria,
▼ **EMP:** 6 **EST:** 2000
SQ FT: 5,000
SALES (est): 600.2K **Privately Held**
WEB: www.stumplaw.net
SIC: 3663 Cable television equipment

(G-8716)
RED HOT TRENDS INC
7911 Nw 72nd Ave Ste 107 (33166-2221)
PHONE..................................305 888-6951
John A McAlister, *President*
Albert Zamora, *Vice Pres*
Dalila Gomez, *Admin Sec*
▼ **EMP:** 6 **EST:** 1989
SQ FT: 3,500
SALES (est): 400K **Privately Held**
WEB: www.redhottrends.com
SIC: 2759 Screen printing

(G-8717)
RINKER MATERIALS
13100 Nw 118th Ave (33178-3105)
PHONE..................................305 345-4127
David Clarke, *CEO*
EMP: 11 **EST:** 2015
SALES (est): 941.7K **Privately Held**
WEB: www.rinkermaterials.com
SIC: 3272 Concrete products

(G-8718)
RIOS CON PMPG & RENTL INC
Also Called: Rio's Concrete Equipment
8750 Nw 93rd St (33178-1412)
PHONE..................................305 888-7909
Serafin Del Rio, *President*
Olga Del Rio, *Vice Pres*
Barbara Delrio, *Opers Staff*
Amado Del Rio, *Human Resources*
Bargo Del Rio, *Manager*
▼ **EMP:** 40 **EST:** 1975
SQ FT: 5,000
SALES (est): 4.3MM **Privately Held**
WEB: www.riosequipmentsales.com
SIC: 3273 5084 Ready-mixed concrete; industrial machinery & equipment

(G-8719)
ROCKWELL COLLINS INC
9100 Nw 105th Cir (33178-1305)
PHONE..................................305 459-7000
George Evans, *Branch Mgr*
EMP: 6
SALES (corp-wide): 56.5B **Publicly Held**
WEB: www.rockwellcollins.com
SIC: 3728 Aircraft parts & equipment
HQ: Rockwell Collins, Inc.
400 Collins Rd Ne
Cedar Rapids IA 52498

(G-8720)
ROYAL HEADWEAR & EMB INC
7675 Nw 80th Ter (33166-7538)
PHONE..................................305 889-8480
Dominic Amendolia, *President*
◆ **EMP:** 8 **EST:** 1987
SQ FT: 15,000
SALES (est): 410.6K **Privately Held**
SIC: 2353 5136 5137 2395 Hats: cloth, straw & felt; hats, men's & boys'; hats: women's, children's & infants'; embroidery products, except schiffli machine; schiffli machine embroideries

(G-8721)
ROYAL TRUSS CORP
10900 Nw South River Dr (33178-1131)
PHONE..................................786 222-1100
Edward J Davies, *President*
Hector Llado, *Corp Secy*
EMP: 10 **EST:** 1978
SALES (est): 933.6K **Privately Held**
WEB: www.royaltrusscorp.com
SIC: 2439 Trusses, wooden roof

(G-8722)
SAUL SIGNS INC
10631 Nw 123rd Street Rd (33178-3166)
PHONE..................................305 266-8484
Jose Hernandez, *President*
Leida Hernandez, *Vice Pres*
EMP: 14 **EST:** 1981
SQ FT: 20,000
SALES (est): 405.9K **Privately Held**
WEB: www.saulsigns.com
SIC: 3993 Signs & advertising specialties

(G-8723)
SEVEN DEFENSES CORPORATION
10550 Nw 74th St Unit 202 (33178-2475)
PHONE..................................786 448-5701
Suarez Diaz, *Principal*
EMP: 13 **EST:** 2015
SALES (est): 130.7K **Privately Held**
WEB: www.defense.gov
SIC: 3812 Defense systems & equipment

(G-8724)
SOLAR ERECTORS US INC
10501 Nw 121st Way (33178-1028)
PHONE..................................305 823-8950
Luiqi Francisosa, *President*
Robert Spiegel, *Principal*
Sidney Spiegel, *Principal*
Mario Franciosa, *Vice Pres*
EMP: 12 **EST:** 2003
SALES (est): 177.9K **Privately Held**
WEB: www.solarerectors.com
SIC: 3272 Concrete stuctural support & building material

(G-8725)
SOUTH FLORIDA CONCRETE & RDYMX
Also Called: S F C
9500 Nw 109th St (33178-1230)
PHONE..................................305 888-0420
Neida Suarez, *President*
Sergio Suarez, *General Mgr*
Lily Verde, *Office Mgr*
EMP: 41 **EST:** 1981
SQ FT: 1,190
SALES (est): 5.7MM **Privately Held**
WEB: www.sfcrmix.com
SIC: 3273 Ready-mixed concrete

(G-8726)
SOUTHAST AUTO ACQUISITION CORP
Also Called: Southeast Worldwide
7575 Nw 74th Ave (33166-2422)
PHONE..................................305 885-8689
Bernardo Davila, *CEO*
◆ **EMP:** 25 **EST:** 1981
SQ FT: 49,500
SALES (est): 2.7MM **Privately Held**
WEB: www.unagota.com
SIC: 3089 5013 Automotive parts, plastic; automotive supplies & parts

(G-8727)
SOUTHPOINT SPORTSWEAR LLC
11525 Nw 124th St (33178-3193)
PHONE..................................305 885-3045
Branko Zunjic, *Mng Member*
Allison Rosen, *Manager*
Gale S Crawford,
◆ **EMP:** 5 **EST:** 2002
SALES (est): 884.2K **Privately Held**
WEB: www.southpointsportswear.com
SIC: 2339 Sportswear, women's

(G-8728)
SPANISH HOUSE INC
Also Called: Editorial Unilit
8167 Nw 84th St (33166-2111)
PHONE..................................305 503-1191
David Ecklebarger, *President*
Catherine Ecklebarger, *Vice Pres*
Myriam Macri, *Sales Dir*
Adriana Santacruz, *Marketing Staff*
◆ **EMP:** 42 **EST:** 1977
SQ FT: 16,000
SALES (est): 4.8MM **Privately Held**
WEB: www.expolit.com
SIC: 2731 5192 7812 2721 Books: publishing only; books; music video production; periodicals

(G-8729)
STANDARD KEGS LLC
Also Called: Standard Kegs & Equipment
9106 Nw 106th St (33178-1204)
PHONE..................................305 454-9721
Zhi Yang, *General Mgr*
Zhilong Yang,
▲ **EMP:** 11 **EST:** 2015
SALES (est): 2MM **Privately Held**
WEB: www.standardkegs.com
SIC: 3412 Metal barrels, drums & pails

(G-8730)
STORE IT COLD LLC
9731 Nw 114th Way (33178-1178)
PHONE..................................720 456-1178
Brian Murphy, *Mng Member*
Ryan Berk, *Manager*
Michael Dworkis, *Manager*
EMP: 8 **EST:** 2015
SALES (est): 865.2K **Privately Held**
WEB: www.storeitcold.com
SIC: 3585 Refrigeration & heating equipment

(G-8731)
STOROPACK INC
11825 Nw 100th Rd Ste 5 (33178-1034)
PHONE..................................305 805-9696
Mike Osgood, *Owner*
EMP: 9
SALES (corp-wide): 530.1MM **Privately Held**
WEB: www.storopack.us
SIC: 3086 5199 2671 Packaging & shipping materials, foamed plastic; packaging materials; packaging paper & plastics film, coated & laminated
HQ: Storopack, Inc.
4758 Devitt Dr
West Chester OH 45246
513 874-0314

(G-8732)
SUINPLA LLC
12605 Nw 115th Ave # 106 (33178-3191)
PHONE..................................786 747-4829
Maria C Toro,
Jaime M Ferreira,
EMP: 10 **EST:** 2016
SALES (est): 2.3MM **Privately Held**
WEB: www.suinpla.com
SIC: 3569 3599 Filters; filters, general line: industrial; gasoline filters, internal combustion engine, except auto; air intake filters, internal combustion engine, except auto

(G-8733)
SUNSHINE MARINE TANKS INC
8045 Nw 90th St (33166-2113)
PHONE..................................305 805-9898
Lucy Maciaz, *President*
▼ **EMP:** 8 **EST:** 1984
SQ FT: 7,190
SALES (est): 1.2MM **Privately Held**
WEB: www.sunshinemarinetanks.com
SIC: 3443 Tanks, standard or custom fabricated: metal plate

(G-8734)
TECHSHOP INT
9372 Nw 101st St (33178-1314)
PHONE..................................713 589-3559
EMP: 6 **EST:** 2018
SALES (est): 180.4K **Privately Held**
SIC: 3599 Machine shop, jobbing & repair

(G-8735)
TIRE EXPERTS LLC
10903 Nw 122nd St (33178-3168)
PHONE..................................305 663-3508
Silvano Buttaci,
Carlos A Buttaci,
Tiberio Buttaci,
Nunzia Costanzo De Buttaci,
▲ **EMP:** 7 **EST:** 2011
SALES (est): 528.4K **Privately Held**
SIC: 3011 Tire & inner tube materials & related products

(G-8736)
TITAN AMERICA LLC
11955 Nw 102nd Rd (33178-1014)
PHONE..................................305 761-1944
John Taut, *Branch Mgr*
EMP: 32
SALES (corp-wide): 177.9K **Privately Held**
WEB: www.titanamerica.com
SIC: 3273 Ready-mixed concrete
HQ: Titan America Llc
5700 Lake Wright Dr # 300
Norfolk VA 23502
757 858-6500

(G-8737)
TITAN AMERICA LLC
Tarmac Block Division
10100 Nw 121st Way (33178-1010)
PHONE..................................954 481-2800
George Pantaz, *Vice Pres*
Terry Merrion, *Branch Mgr*
Carlos Odriozola, *Supervisor*
Frank Alonso, *Maintence Staff*
EMP: 10
SALES (corp-wide): 177.9K **Privately Held**
WEB: www.titanamerica.com
SIC: 3273 Ready-mixed concrete
HQ: Titan America Llc
5700 Lake Wright Dr # 300
Norfolk VA 23502
757 858-6500

(G-8738)
TITAN AMERICA LLC
Also Called: Titan Florida
10100 Nw 121st Way (33178-1010)
PHONE..................................305 364-2200
Alberto Hernandez, *Principal*
Carlos Gonzalez, *Project Mgr*
Curtis Leonard, *Manager*
EMP: 180
SALES (corp-wide): 177.9K **Privately Held**
WEB: www.titanamerica.com
SIC: 3241 3273 3271 4213 Cement, hydraulic; ready-mixed concrete; blocks, concrete or cinder: standard; trucking, except local
HQ: Titan America Llc
5700 Lake Wright Dr # 300
Norfolk VA 23502
757 858-6500

(G-8739)
TITAN FLORIDA LLC
10100 Nw 121st Way (33178-1010)
PHONE..................................800 588-3939
Aris Papadopoulos, *Mng Member*
◆ **EMP:** 774 **EST:** 2000
SALES (est): 83.7MM
SALES (corp-wide): 177.9K **Privately Held**
WEB: www.titanamerica.com
SIC: 3273 Ready-mixed concrete
HQ: Titan America Llc
5700 Lake Wright Dr # 300
Norfolk VA 23502
757 858-6500

(G-8740)
TOP KITCHEN CABINETS
12650 Nw 107th Ave (33178-3127)
PHONE..................................305 392-9938
Gilbert Cover, *Principal*
▼ **EMP:** 8 **EST:** 2013
SALES (est): 322.9K **Privately Held**
WEB: www.topskitchen.com
SIC: 2434 Wood kitchen cabinets

(G-8741)
TREMRON INC (DH)
11321 Nw 138th St (33178-3101)
PHONE..................................305 825-9000
Michelle Caron, *President*
Jacques Tremblay, *Vice Pres*
Edilio Pacitti, *Manager*
Francisco Leite, *Supervisor*
◆ **EMP:** 16 **EST:** 1990
SQ FT: 2,000
SALES (est): 7.9MM
SALES (corp-wide): 2.1MM **Privately Held**
WEB: www.tremron.com
SIC: 3271 Blocks, concrete: drystack interlocking
HQ: Groupe Caron & Caron Inc
800 Boul Pierre-Tremblay
Saint-Jean-Sur-Richelieu QC J2X 4
450 545-7174

(G-8742)
TRITON SEAFOOD CO
7301 Nw 77th St (33166-2205)
PHONE..................................305 888-8999
Alfredo Alvarez, *CEO*
Yvonne M Conde, *President*
Rady M Alvarez, *Treasurer*
EMP: 16 **EST:** 1987
SALES (est): 2.2MM **Privately Held**
WEB: www.tritonsfd.com
SIC: 2099 Food preparations

(G-8743)
TROPICAL BOTTLING CORPORATION (PA)
8074 Nw 74th Ave (33166-7542)
PHONE..................................786 636-6169
Mario Rodriguez, *Principal*
Erik Brito, *Manager*
Ana Brito, *Assistant*
EMP: 8 **EST:** 2017
SALES (est): 1.5MM **Privately Held**
WEB: www.tropicalbottling.com
SIC: 2086 Bottled & canned soft drinks

(G-8744)
TRUSSCORP INTERNATIONAL INC
9590 Nw 89th Ave (33178-1406)
PHONE..................................305 882-8826
Oscar Tabares, *President*
EMP: 34 **EST:** 1991
SQ FT: 2,500
SALES (est): 1.8MM **Privately Held**
WEB: www.trusscorp-international-inc.business.site
SIC: 2439 Trusses, wooden roof

(G-8745)
TST IMPRESO INC
9114 Nw 106th St (33178-1204)
PHONE..................................305 381-5153
EMP: 9 **EST:** 2018
SALES (est): 375.3K **Privately Held**
WEB: www.tstimpreso.com
SIC: 2752 Commercial printing, offset

(G-8746)
ULTIMA DESIGN SOUTH FLA INC
11305 Nw 128th St (33178-3118)
PHONE..................................305 477-9300
Victoria Hallett, *President*
Vicky Hallett, *Vice Pres*
◆ **EMP:** 14 **EST:** 1993
SQ FT: 15,000
SALES (est): 4.6MM **Privately Held**
WEB: www.ultimadesign.com
SIC: 2599 Factory furniture & fixtures

(G-8747)
UNITED CONCRETE PRODUCTS LLC (HQ)
8351 Nw 93rd St (33166-2025)
PHONE..................................786 402-3536
Alex L Debugory Jr,
Thomas Bond,
▼ **EMP:** 4 **EST:** 2012
SALES (est): 4.6MM
SALES (corp-wide): 157.6MM **Privately Held**
WEB: www.frsprestress.com
SIC: 3272 Precast terrazo or concrete products
PA: U. S. Holdings, Inc.
3200 W 84th St
Hialeah FL 33018
305 885-0301

▲ = Import ▼=Export
◆ =Import/Export

(G-8748)
UNITED STATES FNDRY & MFG CORP (HQ)
Also Called: US Foundry
8351 Nw 93rd St (33166-2025)
PHONE..................................305 885-0301
Alex Lane De Bogory, *Ch of Bd*
Alex Debogory Jr, *President*
Lee Fortney, *General Mgr*
Robert Marr, *General Mgr*
Bill Vanness, *General Mgr*
▼ **EMP:** 200 **EST:** 1916
SALES (est): 62.2MM
SALES (corp-wide): 157.6MM **Privately Held**
WEB: www.usfoundry.com
SIC: 3321 3441 3322 Gray iron castings; fabricated structural metal; malleable iron foundries
PA: U. S. Holdings, Inc.
3200 W 84th St
Hialeah FL 33018
305 885-0301

(G-8749)
UNIVERSAL CONCRETE & READY MIX
11790 Nw South River Dr (33178-1117)
PHONE..................................305 888-4101
Juan Alvarez, *President*
EMP: 10 **EST:** 1986
SQ FT: 6,140
SALES (est): 208.8K **Privately Held**
SIC: 3273 Ready-mixed concrete

(G-8750)
UNIVERSAL TRANSACTIONS INC
Also Called: Universal Packaging Co
12870 Nw South River Dr (33178-1108)
PHONE..................................305 887-4677
Larry Epstein, *President*
◆ **EMP:** 20 **EST:** 1979
SQ FT: 6,000
SALES (est): 2.5MM **Privately Held**
SIC: 2812 2899 Alkalies & chlorine; chemical preparations

(G-8751)
US DEFIB MEDICAL TECH LLC (PA)
7831 Nw 72nd Ave (33166-2215)
PHONE..................................305 887-7552
Amanda Felix, *CEO*
Guilherme Oliveira, *Sales Mgr*
Marco Aurelio M Felix, *Mng Member*
▲ **EMP:** 6 **EST:** 2011
SQ FT: 5,000
SALES (est): 862.3K **Privately Held**
WEB: www.usdefib.com
SIC: 3845 Defibrillator

(G-8752)
US PRECAST CORPORATION
8351 Nw 93rd St (33166-2096)
P.O. Box 918720, Orlando (32891-0001)
PHONE..................................305 885-8471
Alexander De Bogory Jr, *President*
Barbara Degregory, *Principal*
Carl Frumenti, *Opers Mgr*
David Brunswick, *CFO*
Alex S Debogory, *Treasurer*
▼ **EMP:** 1 **EST:** 1965
SALES (est): 12.1MM
SALES (corp-wide): 157.6MM **Privately Held**
SIC: 3272 Concrete products
PA: U. S. Holdings, Inc.
3200 W 84th St
Hialeah FL 33018
305 885-0301

(G-8753)
VIDCO INDUSTRIES INC
Also Called: Delta Doors
7500 Nw 69th Ave Frnt Ste (33166-2525)
PHONE..................................305 888-0077
Jesus Martinez, *President*
◆ **EMP:** 37 **EST:** 1996
SQ FT: 40,000
SALES (est): 527.6K **Privately Held**
SIC: 3442 Metal doors; store fronts, prefabricated, metal

(G-8754)
WALL WAY CORPORATION
Also Called: Wall Way USA of Florida
9001 Nw 97th Ter Ste F (33178-1460)
PHONE..................................305 484-7600
Amir Massoumi, *President*
Mohammed Dadullah, *Treasurer*
▲ **EMP:** 19 **EST:** 1988
SQ FT: 10,000
SALES (est): 3MM **Privately Held**
WEB: www.wallwayusa.com
SIC: 3272 Concrete products

Melbourne
Brevard County

(G-8755)
321WEBPRINT
2788 Algonquin Dr (32935-8808)
PHONE..................................321 285-6771
C Robert Saunders, *Owner*
EMP: 6 **EST:** 2015
SALES (est): 137.4K **Privately Held**
WEB: www.321webprint.com
SIC: 2752 Commercial printing, offset

(G-8756)
ABS STRUCTURAL CORP
700 E Melbourne Ave (32901-5507)
PHONE..................................321 768-2067
Frank Kingston, *President*
Helen Kingston, *Corp Secy*
Heather Chambers, *Vice Pres*
EMP: 11 **EST:** 1985
SQ FT: 4,653
SALES (est): 1.9MM **Privately Held**
WEB: www.abs-structural.com
SIC: 3312 Structural shapes & pilings, steel

(G-8757)
ACT USA INTERNATIONAL LLC
Also Called: Act USA Int'l
3962 W Eau Gallie Blvd C (32934-3294)
PHONE..................................321 725-4200
Jerry Gerard, *President*
Sharlene Edlin, *Vice Pres*
Jack Gemmell, *Opers Mgr*
Adam Tennant, *Accounts Mgr*
Dajim Delgado, *Manager*
▲ **EMP:** 16 **EST:** 1994
SALES (est): 3.2MM **Privately Held**
WEB: www.act-usa.com
SIC: 3672 Printed circuit boards

(G-8758)
ADVANCED MAGNET LAB INC
1604 S Hbr Cy Blvd Ste 10 (32901)
PHONE..................................321 728-7543
Rainer Meinka, *President*
Mark Senti, *Vice Pres*
Matthew McDowell, *Research*
EMP: 12 **EST:** 1995
SALES (est): 2.4MM **Privately Held**
WEB: www.magnetlab.com
SIC: 3357 Magnet wire, nonferrous

(G-8759)
AEROBASE GROUP INC
Also Called: A B G
145 East Dr Ste B (32904-1007)
PHONE..................................321 802-5889
Lisette Corrao, *Principal*
Thomas Corrao, *Principal*
Alexina Cyr, *Accounts Mgr*
Robert Frungillo, *Accounts Mgr*
Brittany Kronebusch, *Accounts Mgr*
EMP: 23 **EST:** 2013
SALES (est): 5.3MM **Privately Held**
WEB: www.aerobasegroup.com
SIC: 3728 Aircraft parts & equipment

(G-8760)
AIRCRAFT TBULAR COMPONENTS INC
3939 Dow Rd (32934-9221)
PHONE..................................321 757-9020
Rodney Simon, *President*
Jeffrey Simon, *Vice Pres*
Jeffrey W Simon, *Vice Pres*
Jeff Simon, *VP Mfg*
Luis Aynat, *Purchasing*
EMP: 27 **EST:** 1991
SQ FT: 23,000
SALES (est): 6.7MM **Privately Held**
WEB: www.airtube.net
SIC: 3469 Machine parts, stamped or pressed metal

(G-8761)
AIRON CORPORATION
751 North Dr Ste 6 (32934-9289)
PHONE..................................321 821-9433
G Eric Gjerde, *President*
Pamela Kay Fry, *Vice Pres*
◆ **EMP:** 8 **EST:** 1997
SQ FT: 2,300
SALES (est): 1.3MM **Privately Held**
WEB: www.aironusa.com
SIC: 3841 Surgical & medical instruments

(G-8762)
ALERTGY INC
2401 S Harbor City Blvd (32901-5530)
PHONE..................................321 914-3199
Marc Rippen, *President*
John Hubert, *Vice Pres*
Craig Nelson, *Officer*
EMP: 5 **EST:** 2017
SALES (est): 669.9K **Privately Held**
WEB: www.alertgy.com
SIC: 3829 Measuring & controlling devices

(G-8763)
ALL SERVICE GRAPHICS INC
1020 W Eau Gallie Blvd I (32935-5874)
PHONE..................................321 259-8957
William Smith, *President*
Donald E Gust, *Vice Pres*
Linda Finley, *Comptroller*
Cheryl Lamp, *Sales Staff*
Lori Gust, *Marketing Staff*
EMP: 17 **EST:** 1987
SQ FT: 11,500
SALES (est): 3.1MM **Privately Held**
WEB: www.asgprinting.com
SIC: 2752 Commercial printing, offset

(G-8764)
ALLGEO & YERKES ENTPS INC
Also Called: Tropical Designs
397 Pineda Ct (32940-7508)
PHONE..................................321 255-9030
William Yerkes, *President*
William Allgeo, *Vice Pres*
▲ **EMP:** 10 **EST:** 1990
SQ FT: 10,000
SALES (est): 1.4MM **Privately Held**
SIC: 2759 Screen printing

(G-8765)
ALSTOM SIGNALING OPERATION LLC
Also Called: Real Solutions
1990 W Nasa Blvd (32904-2309)
PHONE 781 740-8111
EMP: 200
SALES (corp-wide): 1.6B **Privately Held**
SIC: 3669 Mfg Electronic Systems
PA: Alstom Signaling Operation, Llc
2901 E Lake Rd Bldg 122
Erie PA 64029
800 825-3178

(G-8766)
AMERICAN MOULDING CORPORATION
710 Atlantis Rd (32904-2317)
PHONE..................................321 676-8929
Robert Sicoli, *President*
Chris Bryant, *Owner*
John Sicoli, *Admin Sec*
EMP: 16 **EST:** 2002
SALES (est): 3.5MM **Privately Held**
WEB: www.americanmouldingllc.com
SIC: 3089 Molding primary plastic

(G-8767)
ANDREW MARTIN SWIFT
Also Called: Sgmc Microwave
620 Atlantis Rd Ste A (32904-2341)
PHONE..................................321 409-0509
Andrew Swift, *Owner*
EMP: 6 **EST:** 2000
SALES (est): 573.7K **Privately Held**
SIC: 3559 Electronic component making machinery

(G-8768)
ANUVA MANUFACTURING SVCS INC
7801 Ellis Rd Ste 101 (32904-1190)
PHONE..................................321 821-4900
Vinu Patel, *CEO*
Jim Davis, *Vice Pres*
EMP: 25 **EST:** 2010
SALES (est): 4.3MM **Privately Held**
WEB: www.anuva.com
SIC: 3661 5063 Telephone sets, all types except cellular radio; electrical apparatus & equipment

(G-8769)
APIS COR INC
3060 Venture Ln Ste 101 (32934-8103)
PHONE..................................347 404-1481
Anna Cheniutai, *CEO*
Nikita Cheniutai, *Director*
EMP: 12 **EST:** 2019
SALES (est): 254.4K **Privately Held**
SIC: 2759 Commercial printing

(G-8770)
APPLIED SYSTEMS INTEGRATOR INC
746 North Dr Ste B (32934-9252)
P.O. Box 411471 (32941-1471)
PHONE..................................321 259-6106
Kanitha Hay, *President*
EMP: 6 **EST:** 1997
SQ FT: 10,000
SALES (est): 970.1K **Privately Held**
WEB: www.asinetlink.com
SIC: 3663 7373 Satellites, communications; computer systems analysis & design

(G-8771)
ATLANTIC JET CENTER INC
1401 Gen Avi Dr (32935)
PHONE..................................321 255-7111
Spence Edwards, *President*
EMP: 6 **EST:** 1990
SQ FT: 40,000
SALES (est): 670K **Privately Held**
WEB: www.atlanticjetcenter.com
SIC: 2911 5172 6512 5599 Jet fuels; gasoline; aircraft fueling services; commercial & industrial building operation; aircraft, self-propelled

(G-8772)
AURORA STONE & GRAVEL LLC
2699 Aurora Rd (32935-2854)
PHONE..................................321 253-4808
Saul Ventura, *Mng Member*
EMP: 6 **EST:** 2009
SALES (est): 548K **Privately Held**
WEB: www.aurorastoneandgravel.com
SIC: 1442 Construction sand & gravel

(G-8773)
AVASAR CORP
435 West Dr (32904-1035)
PHONE..................................321 723-3456
EMP: 30
SQ FT: 11,000
SALES (est): 3.6MM **Privately Held**
SIC: 3489 Mfg Ordnance & Accessories

(G-8774)
AVIDYNE CORPORATION (PA)
710 North Dr (32934-9286)
PHONE..................................321 751-8520
Dan Schwinn, *CEO*
Steve Jacobson, *Senior VP*
Roger Mitchell, *Senior VP*
Steve Rosker, *VP Engrg*
WEI Guo, *Engineer*
EMP: 95 **EST:** 1994
SQ FT: 30,000
SALES (est): 32MM **Privately Held**
WEB: www.avidyne.com
SIC: 3812 Aircraft/aerospace flight instruments & guidance systems

(G-8775)
B & K DISCOUNT CABINETS LLC (PA)
Also Called: Bk Cabinets
280 N Wickham Rd (32935-8650)
PHONE..................................321 254-2322
Karen Livingood,

Dina Mae Whipple,
EMP: 14 **EST:** 2018
SALES (est): 293.7K **Privately Held**
WEB: www.melbournecabinets.com
SIC: 2434 Wood kitchen cabinets

(G-8776)
BARRETT CUSTOM DESIGNS LLC
6430 Anderson Way Ste A (32940-7407)
PHONE..................................321 242-2002
Jeffrey G Barrett, *Mng Member*
▼ **EMP:** 5 **EST:** 2011
SALES (est): 776.8K **Privately Held**
WEB: www.barrettcustomdesigns.com
SIC: 3441 1799 3444 Fabricated structural metal; ornamental metal work; sheet metalwork

(G-8777)
BARTMAN ENTERPRISES INC
2735 Center Pl Ste 101 (32940-7181)
PHONE..................................321 259-4898
Dave Bartman, *President*
Gloria Jeanne Bartman, *Vice Pres*
EMP: 5 **EST:** 1986
SQ FT: 40,000
SALES (est): 561.1K **Privately Held**
WEB: www.bartmanenterprises.com
SIC: 2395 Embroidery products, except schiffli machine; embroidery & art needlework

(G-8778)
BEST CIRCUITS INC
300 North Dr Ste 106 (32934-9273)
PHONE..................................321 425-6725
Daniel Dina, *President*
EMP: 22 **EST:** 2001
SALES (est): 1.7MM **Privately Held**
WEB: www.bestcircuits.com
SIC: 3679 Electronic circuits

(G-8779)
BEST LIDAR CORPORATION ✪
300 North Dr Ste 106 (32934-9273)
PHONE..................................321 425-6725
Daniel Dina, *President*
EMP: 50 **EST:** 2021
SALES (est): 1.7MM **Privately Held**
SIC: 3571 Computers, digital, analog or hybrid

(G-8780)
BIOFUSE MEDICAL TECH INC
200 S Hbr Cy Blvd Ste 402 (32901)
PHONE..................................877 466-2434
Ralph Zipper MD Facog, *CEO*
Vik Malik, *CEO*
Ralph Zipper, *President*
Guy Hoagland, *Principal*
Charles Federico, *Director*
EMP: 6 **EST:** 2014
SALES (est): 508.3K **Privately Held**
WEB: www.biofusemedical.com
SIC: 3845 Electromedical equipment

(G-8781)
BLACKBIRD ARMAMENT LLC
150 East Dr Ste B (32904-1082)
PHONE..................................833 255-2473
Michael Lewis, *CEO*
Jair Lahens, *Principal*
Charles Vanepps, *Principal*
EMP: 13 **EST:** 2019
SALES (est): 677.3K **Privately Held**
SIC: 3484 Small arms

(G-8782)
BLUE SIREN INC
3030 Venture Ln Ste 103 (32934-8172)
PHONE..................................321 242-0300
Janet Stile, *President*
EMP: 50 **EST:** 2010
SALES (est): 3.1MM **Privately Held**
WEB: www.blue-siren.com
SIC: 3823 Industrial process control instruments

(G-8783)
BMS-TEK LLC
2896 Harper Rd (32904-1196)
PHONE..................................321 727-7800
Ron Buanno, *CEO*
Ken Mitchell, *Senior VP*
Joe Mac Donald,
EMP: 6 **EST:** 2013
SALES (est): 225.3K **Privately Held**
WEB: www.bms-tek.com
SIC: 3519 Parts & accessories, internal combustion engines

(G-8784)
BRADY BUILT TECHNOLOGIES INC
Also Called: Brady Builders
3661 Waynesboro Way (32934-8396)
PHONE..................................270 692-6866
Joseph Brady, *President*
EMP: 6 **EST:** 1989
SALES (est): 574.2K **Privately Held**
SIC: 3499 Machine bases, metal

(G-8785)
BRAID SALES AND MARKETING INC (PA)
Also Called: Full House
320 North Dr (32934-9206)
PHONE..................................321 752-8180
Fred Braid, *CEO*
Todd W Braid, *President*
Beau Braid, *Vice Pres*
Chad Braid, *Vice Pres*
Jeff Paine, *Purchasing*
◆ **EMP:** 31 **EST:** 1982
SQ FT: 40,000
SALES (est): 5MM **Privately Held**
WEB: www.full-house.com
SIC: 3553 Woodworking machinery

(G-8786)
BREVARD BUSINESS NEWS
4300 Fortune Pl Ste D (32904-1527)
PHONE..................................321 951-7777
Adrienne Roth, *President*
EMP: 10 **EST:** 1988
SALES (est): 550K **Privately Held**
WEB: www.brevardbusinessnews.com
SIC: 2711 Newspapers, publishing & printing

(G-8787)
CENTRAL FLA PRTG GRAPHICS LLC
772 Washburn Rd Ste A (32934-7329)
PHONE..................................321 752-8753
Mark Liles, *Owner*
EMP: 6 **EST:** 2011
SALES (est): 433.8K **Privately Held**
WEB: www.centralflprinting.com
SIC: 2752 Commercial printing, offset

(G-8788)
CHEM-TEK METAL FINISHING CORP
Also Called: Chem-Tek Plating Industries
636 Atlantis Rd (32904-2315)
PHONE..................................321 722-2227
Robert G Galligan Jr, *President*
EMP: 11 **EST:** 2006
SALES (est): 400.1K **Privately Held**
WEB: www.chem-tekplating.com
SIC: 3471 Finishing, metals or formed products; electroplating of metals or formed products

(G-8789)
CIRCLE REDMONT INC
2760 Business Center Blvd (32940-7101)
PHONE..................................321 259-7374
Frederick J Sandor, *President*
Virginia Hughes, *Vice Pres*
▲ **EMP:** 28 **EST:** 1966
SQ FT: 12,000
SALES (est): 5MM **Privately Held**
WEB: www.circleredmont.com
SIC: 3444 3231 Skylights, sheet metal; furniture tops, glass: cut, beveled or polished

(G-8790)
CLASSIC KITCHENS BREVARD INC
670 S Wickham Rd (32904-1645)
PHONE..................................321 327-5972
Christopher L Hampson, *President*
EMP: 7 **EST:** 2008
SALES (est): 869.3K **Privately Held**
WEB: www.classickitchensofbrevard.com
SIC: 2434 Wood kitchen cabinets

(G-8791)
CNC CABINET COMPONENTS INC
560 Distribution Dr (32904-1183)
PHONE..................................321 956-3470
Earl Matthews, *President*
▲ **EMP:** 16 **EST:** 1998
SALES (est): 1.8MM **Privately Held**
WEB: www.cnccabinetcomponents.com
SIC: 2434 Wood kitchen cabinets

(G-8792)
COASTAL DIRECTORY COMPANY
1900 S Hbr Cy Blvd Ste 30 (32901)
P.O. Box 33665, Indialantic (32903-0665)
PHONE..................................321 777-7076
Wilson Sims, *President*
Dave Fishburne, *Principal*
David K Fishburne, *Director*
Walter W Sims, *Director*
EMP: 10 **EST:** 2003
SALES (est): 941.3K **Privately Held**
WEB: www.coastaldirectoryco.com
SIC: 2741 Telephone & other directory publishing

(G-8793)
COASTAL IMPRINTING
3091 Ohio St (32904-9046)
PHONE..................................321 543-4169
Karen Margaret Sexton, *Principal*
EMP: 6 **EST:** 2008
SALES (est): 122.9K **Privately Held**
SIC: 2759 Imprinting

(G-8794)
COMMUNICATIONS LABS INC
Also Called: Comlabs
4005 Opportunity Dr (32934-9296)
PHONE..................................321 701-9000
Roland Lussier, *President*
Avis Lussier, *Vice Pres*
Scott Hawksley, *Purchasing*
Tom Restivo, *Engineer*
Gary R Gorthe, *CFO*
EMP: 16 **EST:** 1985
SQ FT: 9,800
SALES (est): 3.6MM **Privately Held**
WEB: www.comlabs.com
SIC: 3661 Telephone & telegraph apparatus

(G-8795)
COMPSYS INC
4255 Dow Rd (32934-9218)
PHONE..................................321 255-0399
Scott M Lewit, *President*
Ronnal P Reichard, *Chairman*
Charolette Greaves, *Office Mgr*
EMP: 56 **EST:** 1992
SQ FT: 40,000
SALES (est): 7.2MM **Privately Held**
WEB: www.preforms.com
SIC: 3086 Insulation or cushioning material, foamed plastic

(G-8796)
CONTEC AMERICAS INC
3991 Sarno Rd (32934-7239)
PHONE..................................321 728-0172
Alex Blochtein, *CEO*
Daniel Butler, *General Mgr*
Randall Poliner, *Chairman*
Ryan Legg, *Vice Pres*
Phyllis Foix, *Senior Buyer*
▲ **EMP:** 95 **EST:** 1991
SQ FT: 31,000
SALES (est): 57.6MM **Privately Held**
WEB: www.contec.com
SIC: 3571 7373 Electronic computers; computer integrated systems design
HQ: Contec Co., Ltd.
3-9-31, Himesato, Nishiyodogawa-Ku
Osaka OSK 555-0

(G-8797)
COOPER CROUSE-HINDS MTL INC (DH)
4325 Wdlnd Pk Dr Ste 101 (32904)
PHONE..................................321 725-8000
Grant Gawronski, *President*
▲ **EMP:** 101 **EST:** 1978
SQ FT: 24,000
SALES (est): 4.3MM **Privately Held**
WEB: www.mtl-inst.com
SIC: 3643 Lightning protection equipment

(G-8798)
CRUCIAL COLLISION PROD LLC ✪
3334 Henry St (32901-8041)
P.O. Box 120071 (32912-0071)
PHONE..................................321 501-1722
Terry Lynn Howard II, *Mng Member*
EMP: 10 **EST:** 2020
SALES (est): 460K **Privately Held**
SIC: 3577 Data conversion equipment, media-to-media: computer

(G-8799)
D R S OPTRONICS INC
100 N Babcock St (32935-6715)
PHONE..................................321 309-1500
EMP: 12 **EST:** 2019
SALES (est): 1.6MM **Privately Held**
WEB: www.leonardodrs.com
SIC: 3827 Optical instruments & lenses

(G-8800)
DATA FLOW SYSTEMS INC
Also Called: D F S
605 N John Rodes Blvd (32934-9105)
PHONE..................................321 259-5009
Thomas F Smaidris, *President*
Colleen Reilly, *General Mgr*
Tom Hogeland, *Business Mgr*
Ryan Arnold, *Vice Pres*
Brent Saunders, *Vice Pres*
EMP: 80 **EST:** 1981
SQ FT: 18,100
SALES (est): 17.6MM **Privately Held**
WEB: www.dataflowsys.com
SIC: 3825 Electrical energy measuring equipment

(G-8801)
DEFRANCISCI MACHINE CO LLC
Also Called: Demaco
2681 Aurora Rd (32935-2854)
PHONE..................................321 952-6600
Joseph Defrancisci, *Mng Member*
Leonard J Defrancisci,
EMP: 15 **EST:** 1914
SQ FT: 30,000
SALES (est): 2.9MM **Privately Held**
WEB: www.demaco.com
SIC: 3556 Pasta machinery

(G-8802)
DENTAL PARTNERS ALLIANCE LLC (PA)
7341 Office Park Pl # 101 (32940-8369)
PHONE..................................321 574-8003
Kelly England, *Regional Mgr*
Bryan T Marshall, *Mng Member*
Emma Hayes, *IT Specialist*
Ashley Reimiller, *Director*
EMP: 7 **EST:** 2011
SALES (est): 689.6K **Privately Held**
WEB: www.puredentalbrands.com
SIC: 3843 Enamels, dentists'

(G-8803)
DFA DAIRY BRANDS FLUID LLC
650 S Wickham Rd (32904-1645)
PHONE..................................386 775-6700
Randy Vick, *Branch Mgr*
EMP: 9
SALES (corp-wide): 17.8B **Privately Held**
SIC: 2026 Fluid milk
HQ: Dfa Dairy Brands Fluid, Llc
1405 N 98th St
Kansas City KS 66111
816 801-6455

(G-8804)
DIAMOND MT INC
Also Called: Diamond-Mt
4200 Dow Rd Ste Cd (32934-9295)
PHONE..................................321 339-3377
EMP: 10 **Privately Held**
SIC: 3672 Printed Circuit Boards

(G-8805)
DICTAPHONE CORPORATION
3984 Pepsi Cola Dr (32934-9299)
P.O. Box 36814 (32934)
PHONE..................................321 255-8668

Janice Evans, *Sales Staff*
Laine E Howell, *Architect*
Joe Delaney, *Manager*
EMP: 65 **Publicly Held**
WEB: www.dictaphone.com
SIC: 3579 Dictating machines
HQ: Dictaphone Corporation
3191 Broadbridge Ave
Stratford CT 06614
203 381-7000

(G-8806)
DISCOVERY AVIATION INC
100 Aerospace Dr Unit 4 (32901-1811)
PHONE....................................321 752-0332
Paul Barlett, *COO*
CJ Corman, *Vice Pres*
Mark Miller, *VP Opers*
EMP: 25 **EST:** 2011
SALES (est): 2.2MM **Privately Held**
WEB: www.discovery-aviation.com
SIC: 3728 3721 Aircraft parts & equipment; aircraft

(G-8807)
DRS ADVANCED ISR LLC
100 N Babcock St (32935-6715)
PHONE....................................321 622-1202
Aaron Hankins, *Mng Member*
EMP: 14
SALES (corp-wide): 10.2B **Privately Held**
WEB: www.leonardodrs.com
SIC: 3812 Cabin environment indicators
HQ: Drs Icas, Llc
2601 Mssion Pt Blvd Ste 2
Beavercreek OH 45431

(G-8808)
DRS CENGEN LLC (DH)
100 Babcock St Melbourne (32935)
PHONE....................................321 622-1500
Terry Murphy, *VP Admin*
EMP: 268 **EST:** 2011
SALES (est): 55.2MM
SALES (corp-wide): 10.2B **Privately Held**
WEB: www.leonardodrs.com
SIC: 3812 Search & navigation equipment
HQ: Leonardo Drs, Inc.
2345 Crystal Dr Ste 1000
Arlington VA 22202
703 416-8000

(G-8809)
DRS LAND ELECTRONICS
100 N Babcock St (32935-6715)
PHONE....................................321 622-1435
EMP: 7 **EST:** 2017
SALES (est): 189.8K **Privately Held**
WEB: www.leonardodrs.com
SIC: 3812 Search & navigation equipment

(G-8810)
DRS NTWORK IMAGING SYSTEMS LLC (DH)
100 N Babcock St (32935-6715)
PHONE....................................321 309-1500
Michael Sarrica, *President*
Toby Mannheimer, *Vice Pres*
Thomas P Crimmins, *Treasurer*
▲ **EMP:** 500 **EST:** 1995
SQ FT: 225,000
SALES (est): 343.3MM
SALES (corp-wide): 10.2B **Privately Held**
WEB: www.leonardodrs.com
SIC: 3812 Search & navigation equipment
HQ: Leonardo Drs, Inc.
2345 Crystal Dr Ste 1000
Arlington VA 22202
703 416-8000

(G-8811)
DRS S AND T OPTRONICS DIV
100 N Babcock St (32935-6715)
PHONE....................................321 309-1500
EMP: 12
SALES (est): 1.8MM **Privately Held**
SIC: 3812 Mfg Search/Navigation Equipment

(G-8812)
DRS SENSORS TARGETING SYSTEMS
100 N Babcock St (32935-6715)
PHONE....................................321 309-1500
Sally Wallace, *Principal*
EMP: 29 **EST:** 2009
SALES (est): 3.5MM **Privately Held**
WEB: www.leonardodrs.com
SIC: 3812 Search & navigation equipment

(G-8813)
DRS SONETICOM INC
Also Called: Drs Technology
100 N Babcock St (32935-6715)
PHONE....................................321 733-0400
Timothy Reynolds, *CEO*
James Kingsley, *Vice Pres*
Wendi-Lynn Reeves, *Vice Pres*
Melissa Zimak, *Opers Staff*
Leo Torres, *Engineer*
▲ **EMP:** 30 **EST:** 1998
SQ FT: 26,600
SALES (est): 16.1MM
SALES (corp-wide): 10.2B **Privately Held**
WEB: www.leonardodrs.com
SIC: 3812 Search & navigation equipment
HQ: Drs Signal Solutions, Inc.
1 Milestone Center Ct
Germantown MD 20876
301 948-7550

(G-8814)
DRS SYSTEMS INC
100 N Babcock St (32935-6715)
PHONE....................................973 451-3525
Terence Murphy, *President*
EMP: 4 **EST:** 2001
SQ FT: 400
SALES (est): 5.3MM
SALES (corp-wide): 10.2B **Privately Held**
WEB: www.leonardodrs.com
SIC: 3812 Search & navigation equipment
HQ: Leonardo Drs, Inc.
2345 Crystal Dr Ste 1000
Arlington VA 22202
703 416-8000

(G-8815)
DRS TACTICAL SYSTEMS INC
100 N Babcock St (32935-6715)
PHONE....................................321 727-3672
Sally Wallace, *President*
Jason I Rinsky II, *Vice Pres*
Russ Marsh, *Vice Pres*
Wayne Grimes, *Engineer*
W Christopher Durborow, *Treasurer*
EMP: 112 **EST:** 1998
SALES (est): 27.1MM
SALES (corp-wide): 10.2B **Privately Held**
WEB: www.leonardodrs.com
SIC: 3812 Search & navigation equipment
HQ: Leonardo Drs, Inc.
2345 Crystal Dr Ste 1000
Arlington VA 22202
703 416-8000

(G-8816)
DYNASYSTEMS LLC
3445 Spring Branch Trl # 360
(32935-0001)
PHONE....................................410 343-7759
EMP: 7
SQ FT: 1,800
SALES (est): 507.7K **Privately Held**
SIC: 3669 Mfg Communications Equipment

(G-8817)
E QUALITY CABLES INC
4450 Enterprise Ct Ste G (32934-9203)
PHONE....................................321 242-4820
Darla L Smith, *President*
Allan Boone, *VP Opers*
Bill Sanford, *Marketing Staff*
Robert Hutchins, *Department Mgr*
EMP: 14 **EST:** 2007
SALES (est): 629.7K **Privately Held**
SIC: 2298 3199 Cable, fiber; harness or harness parts

(G-8818)
E&T HORIZONS LTD LIABILITY CO
2623 Chapel Bridge Ln (32940-7992)
PHONE....................................321 704-1244
Terri Gelman, *Principal*
Eric Gelman, *Principal*
Jeff Moore, *Principal*
▲ **EMP:** 11 **EST:** 2012
SALES (est): 1MM **Privately Held**
SIC: 2599 Stools, factory

(G-8819)
EASYLIFT N BANSBACH AMER INC
50 West Dr (32904-1074)
PHONE....................................321 253-1999
Robert Rose, *CEO*
Thomas Weiss, *President*
John Blackledge, *Vice Pres*
Vickery David, *Engineer*
Edgar Hahn-Bansbach, *CFO*
▲ **EMP:** 46 **EST:** 2007
SALES (est): 5.3MM **Privately Held**
WEB: www.bansbach.com
SIC: 3493 Steel springs, except wire

(G-8820)
EDAK INC (DH)
630 Distribution Dr (32904-1179)
PHONE....................................321 674-6804
Gregg T Benoit, *President*
Susan M Denyer, *President*
Hans F Kaeser, *Admin Sec*
▲ **EMP:** 15 **EST:** 1986
SQ FT: 25,000
SALES (est): 13.9MM
SALES (corp-wide): 11.5B **Privately Held**
WEB: www.edak.com
SIC: 3499 Boxes for packing & shipping, metal
HQ: Edak Ag
Rheinauerweg 17
Dachsen ZH 8447
526 472-200

(G-8821)
EDGE POWER SOLUTIONS INC
Also Called: Manufacturer
5131 Industry Dr Ste 107 (32940-7198)
PHONE....................................321 499-1919
Jeromy Kendall, *CEO*
EMP: 10 **EST:** 2016
SALES (est): 971.3K **Privately Held**
WEB: www.edgepowersolutions.net
SIC: 3679 Electronic loads & power supplies

(G-8822)
ELECTRIC PCTURE DSPLAY SYSTEMS
6425 Anderson Way (32940-7467)
PHONE....................................321 757-8484
Robert Higgins, *President*
Pam Higgins, *Vice Pres*
EMP: 5
SQ FT: 2,500
SALES (est): 2.3MM **Privately Held**
WEB: www.electricpicture.com
SIC: 3823 Digital displays of process variables

(G-8823)
ELECTRNIC SHTMTAL CRFTSMEN FLA
3675 W New Haven Ave (32904-3556)
PHONE....................................321 727-0633
Ricky W Miller, *President*
Chris Miller, *Purch Mgr*
Valerie Froelich, *Admin Sec*
EMP: 30 **EST:** 1973
SQ FT: 25,000
SALES (est): 4.8MM **Privately Held**
WEB: www.esc-of-fl.com
SIC: 3444 Sheet metal specialties, not stamped

(G-8824)
EMBRAER EXECUTIVE AIRCRAFT INC (DH)
Also Called: Embraer Executive Jets
1111 General Aviation Dr (32935-6316)
PHONE....................................321 751-5050
Ernie Edwards, *President*
Philip Krull, *COO*
Phillip Krull, *COO*
Christian Zinn, *Counsel*
Peter Griffith, *Vice Pres*
EMP: 100 **EST:** 2012
SALES (est): 66.6MM **Privately Held**
SIC: 3721 Aircraft

(G-8825)
ENDURIS EXTRUSIONS INC
605 Distribution Dr Ste 1 (32904-1185)
PHONE....................................321 914-0897
Dan Whitson, *Principal*
EMP: 20
SALES (corp-wide): 20MM **Privately Held**
WEB: www.enduris.com
SIC: 3999 Atomizers, toiletry
PA: Enduris Extrusions, Inc.
7167 Old Kings Rd
Jacksonville FL 32219
904 421-3304

(G-8826)
ENVIRNMENTAL MFG SOLUTIONS LLC (PA)
Also Called: E M S
7705 Progress Cir (32904-1657)
PHONE....................................321 837-0050
Kimber Jensen, *Vice Pres*
John Macdonald, *Executive*
Charlene Macdonald,
EMP: 12
SQ FT: 25,000
SALES (est): 8.5MM **Privately Held**
WEB: www.enviromfg.com
SIC: 2869 Industrial organic chemicals

(G-8827)
ERCHONIA CORPORATION LLC
650 Atlantis Rd (32904-2315)
PHONE....................................321 473-1251
Steven C Shanks, *President*
Mark Shanks, *COO*
Charlie Shanks, *Vice Pres*
Kevin Tycek, *Chief Engr*
▲ **EMP:** 38 **EST:** 1996
SQ FT: 18,000
SALES (est): 8.6MM **Privately Held**
WEB: www.erchonia.com
SIC: 3845 5047 Laser systems & equipment, medical; medical equipment & supplies

(G-8828)
EXTANT CMPNNTS GROUP HLDNGS IN
Also Called: Extant Aerospace
1615 W Nasa Blvd (32901-2613)
PHONE....................................321 254-1500
Jim Gerwien, *CEO*
Gary Boekenkamp, *Exec VP*
Michael Donlan, *Vice Pres*
Charles Mitchell, *VP Opers*
Edward Dietze, *CFO*
EMP: 5 **EST:** 2010
SALES (est): 4.1MM
SALES (corp-wide): 5.1B **Publicly Held**
WEB: www.extantaerospace.com
SIC: 3324 Aerospace investment castings, ferrous
PA: Transdigm Group Incorporated
1301 E 9th St Ste 3000
Cleveland OH 44114
216 706-2960

(G-8829)
EXTANT CMPNNTS GROUP INTRMDATE (PA)
1615 W Nasa Blvd (32901-2613)
PHONE....................................321 254-1500
James Gerwien, *CEO*
Edward Dietze, *CFO*
EMP: 112 **EST:** 2016
SALES (est): 21.4MM **Privately Held**
WEB: www.extantaerospace.com
SIC: 3324 Aerospace investment castings, ferrous

(G-8830)
EYEDEAL VISION CARE INC
5500 Stadium Pkwy Ste 102 (32940-8095)
PHONE....................................321 631-2811
Jacqueline Tran-Pastore, *President*
EMP: 7 **EST:** 2017
SALES (est): 72.9K **Privately Held**
SIC: 3851 Eyeglasses, lenses & frames

(G-8831)
FASTSIGNS 176101
Also Called: McCord Holding
7640 N Wickham Rd (32940-8146)
PHONE....................................321 307-2400
EMP: 13 **EST:** 2017
SALES (est): 1.6MM **Privately Held**
WEB: www.fastsigns.com
SIC: 3993 Signs & advertising specialties

(G-8832)
FIBERTRONICS INC
2900 Dusa Dr (32934-8102)
PHONE..................................321 473-8933
Barbara A Larson, *President*
Mitchel Larson, *QC Mgr*
EMP: 33 **EST:** 2009
SALES (est): 3MM **Privately Held**
WEB: www.fibertronics.com
SIC: 3357 Communication wire

(G-8833)
FLAMINGO PRINTING OF BREVARD
1785 Waverly Pl (32901-4641)
PHONE..................................321 723-2771
Stacey Norman, *President*
Lisa Norman, *Admin Sec*
EMP: 8 **EST:** 1969
SQ FT: 2,000
SALES (est): 646.3K **Privately Held**
WEB: www.flamingoprinting.com
SIC: 2752 Commercial printing, offset

(G-8834)
FLORIDA SPCIALTY COATINGS CORP
3270 Suntree Blvd Ste 214 (32940-7505)
PHONE..................................727 224-6883
Jessica Walker, *Principal*
EMP: 8 **EST:** 2016
SALES (est): 69.9K **Privately Held**
SIC: 3479 Metal coating & allied service

(G-8835)
GEODETIC SERVICES INC
1511 Riverview Dr (32901-4694)
PHONE..................................321 724-6831
John Brown, *President*
Gary Johanning, *General Mgr*
Theresa Brown, *Treasurer*
John Vehec, *Manager*
Christos Stamatopoulos, *CTO*
EMP: 16 **EST:** 1977
SQ FT: 4,600
SALES (est): 2.3MM **Privately Held**
WEB: www.geodetic.com
SIC: 3829 Photogrammetrical instruments

(G-8836)
GEORGIA USSSA BASEBALL
5610 Rusack Dr (32940-8014)
PHONE..................................678 794-1630
Wally Fortuna, *Principal*
EMP: 6 **EST:** 2010
SALES (est): 181.2K **Privately Held**
WEB: www.gausssabaseball.com
SIC: 3949 Sporting & athletic goods

(G-8837)
GOLDFIELD CNSLD MINES CO (DH)
100 Rialto Pl Ste 500 (32901-3015)
PHONE..................................321 724-1700
Patrick Freeman, *President*
John Sottile, *Vice Pres*
Stephen Wherry, *Treasurer*
John Starling, *Admin Sec*
EMP: 100 **EST:** 1971
SALES (est): 7.4MM
SALES (corp-wide): 180.6MM **Privately Held**
WEB: www.goldfieldcorp.com
SIC: 1021 1041 1044 Copper ores; gold ores; silver ores
HQ: The Goldfield Corporation Del
1684 W Hibiscus Blvd
Melbourne FL 32901
321 724-1700

(G-8838)
HALLIDAY INDUSTRIES LLC
7715 Ellis Rd Ste A (32904-1159)
PHONE..................................321 288-3979
David J Halliday, *Principal*
EMP: 9 **EST:** 2018
SALES (est): 907.1K **Privately Held**
SIC: 3999 Manufacturing industries

(G-8839)
HAMANT AIRBOATS LLC
108 E Hibiscus Blvd (32901-3103)
PHONE..................................321 259-6998
Murphy Kevin, *Principal*
EMP: 9 **EST:** 2013
SALES (est): 696.9K **Privately Held**
WEB: www.hamantboats.com
SIC: 3732 Boat building & repairing

(G-8840)
HAMMOND KITCHENS & BATH LLC
7618 Silver Sands Rd (32904-1128)
PHONE..................................321 768-9549
Nathan A Hammond, *President*
EMP: 15 **EST:** 1983
SQ FT: 10,000
SALES (est): 5MM **Privately Held**
WEB: www.hammondkitchens.com
SIC: 2434 Wood kitchen cabinets

(G-8841)
HELICOPTER HELMET LLC (PA)
Also Called: Helicopter Helmets.com
274 West Dr (32904-1042)
PHONE..................................843 556-0405
Ron Abbott, *Owner*
Gloria Abbott,
▲ **EMP:** 5 **EST:** 2000
SQ FT: 2,000
SALES (est): 3.1MM **Privately Held**
WEB: www.helicopterhelmet.com
SIC: 3469 7363 Helmets, steel; pilot service, aviation

(G-8842)
HELLER CABINETRY INC
415 Stan Dr (32904-1046)
PHONE..................................321 729-9690
Kristen S Heller, *President*
Stephen M Heller, *Vice Pres*
EMP: 13 **EST:** 2002
SALES (est): 1.7MM **Privately Held**
WEB: www.hellercabinetry.com
SIC: 2434 1799 Wood kitchen cabinets; counter top installation

(G-8843)
HIGH TECH HOIST CORP
3682 N Wickham Rd 225 (32935-2334)
PHONE..................................321 733-3387
Henry M Powers Jr, *President*
EMP: 9 **EST:** 1987
SQ FT: 11,000
SALES (est): 791K **Privately Held**
WEB: www.betamaxhoist.com
SIC: 3536 Hoists

(G-8844)
HILLS INC
7785 Ellis Rd (32904-1105)
PHONE..................................321 723-5560
Arnold Wilkie, *President*
Wilkie Arnold E Jr, *President*
Kevin Regan, *General Mgr*
Penny Wilkie, *Corp Secy*
Shirley Hill, *Shareholder*
◆ **EMP:** 53
SALES (est): 14MM **Privately Held**
WEB: www.hillsinc.net
SIC: 3552 Fabric forming machinery & equipment

(G-8845)
HOMES DEVOTED INC
694 Hammock Rd (32904-2210)
PHONE..................................321 473-8567
Carrie Cronkhite, *Principal*
EMP: 6 **EST:** 2012
SALES: 54.5K **Privately Held**
WEB: www.homesdevoted.com
SIC: 2741 Miscellaneous publishing

(G-8846)
HOMETOWN NEWS LC
380 N Wickham Rd Ste F (32935-8646)
PHONE..................................321 242-1013
Katie Brousse, *Advt Staff*
Lisa Henderson, *Advt Staff*
Catherine Cawthon, *Office Mgr*
Tammy Raits, *Manager*
EMP: 9
SALES (corp-wide): 16MM **Privately Held**
WEB: www.hometowngiftcertificates.com
SIC: 2711 Newspapers, publishing & printing
PA: Hometown News, L.C.
1102 S Us Highway 1
Fort Pierce FL 34950
772 465-5656

(G-8847)
HOUSMANS ALUM & SCREENING INC
2911 Dusa Dr Ste E (32934-8100)
PHONE..................................321 255-2778
Mark J Housman, *President*
EMP: 13 **EST:** 2009
SALES (est): 1.7MM **Privately Held**
WEB: www.housmansaluminum.com
SIC: 3448 Screen enclosures

(G-8848)
HY-TECH THERMAL SOLUTIONS LLC
159 Park Hill Blvd (32904-5115)
P.O. Box 216 (32902-0216)
PHONE..................................321 984-9777
Tony Abruzzese, *Manager*
Anthony Abruzzese,
EMP: 9 **EST:** 1996
SALES (est): 1.6MM **Privately Held**
WEB: www.hytechsales.com
SIC: 2851 5231 5198 Paints & paint additives; paint; paints

(G-8849)
ILS MANAGEMENT LLC
Also Called: Interactive Legal
930 S Hbr Cy Blvd Ste 505 (32901)
PHONE..................................321 252-0100
Deanne McDougall, *Opers Staff*
James McLelland, *Controller*
Lisa Briley, *Sales Staff*
Steve Palumbo, *Sales Staff*
Michael L Graham, *Mng Member*
EMP: 20 **EST:** 2003
SQ FT: 2,600
SALES (est): 6.4MM **Privately Held**
WEB: www.interactivelegal.com
SIC: 7372 Business oriented computer software

(G-8850)
IMPRINT PROMOTIONS LLC
Also Called: Custom Engraving Company
405 N Wickham Rd Ste A (32935-8628)
PHONE..................................321 622-8946
▲ **EMP:** 8
SQ FT: 1,800
SALES (est): 1.1MM **Privately Held**
SIC: 2759 2399 3993 Commercial Printing Mfg Fabricated Textile Products Mfg Signs/Advertising Specialties

(G-8851)
IQ VALVES CO
425 West Dr (32904-1035)
PHONE..................................321 729-9634
V Sampath Kumar, *Principal*
Raju Kumar, *Assistant VP*
John Lee, *Purchasing*
Brad Mohr, *QC Mgr*
Hung Ho, *Engineer*
EMP: 32 **EST:** 2007
SALES (est): 4.2MM **Privately Held**
WEB: www.iqvalves.com
SIC: 3491 Industrial valves

(G-8852)
IVENGO SOFTWARE INC
1378 Tipperary Dr (32940-6030)
PHONE..................................321 480-3155
Michael S Keels, *President*
EMP: 6 **EST:** 2008
SALES (est): 150K **Privately Held**
WEB: www.ivengosoft.com
SIC: 7372 7379 7389 Prepackaged software; computer related consulting services;

(G-8853)
J W AUSTIN INDUSTRIES INC
7713 Ellis Rd (32904-1119)
P.O. Box 511058, Melbourne Beach (32951-1058)
PHONE..................................321 723-2422
James W Austin, *CEO*
Lucy A Murphy, *President*
Steve Austin, *Admin Sec*
EMP: 7 **EST:** 1975
SQ FT: 10,000
SALES (est): 963.2K **Privately Held**
WEB: www.jwaustin.com
SIC: 3089 Plastic processing

(G-8854)
JOSEPH J TAYLOR TRUSS
2599 Larry Ct (32935-2835)
PHONE..................................321 482-4039
Joseph J Taylor, *Principal*
EMP: 8 **EST:** 2010
SALES (est): 102.2K **Privately Held**
WEB: www.jjtaylor.com
SIC: 2439 Structural wood members

(G-8855)
JOYS INTERNATIONAL FOODS INC
Also Called: Joy's Gourmet
2600 Aurora Rd Ste Q (32935-2884)
PHONE..................................321 242-6520
Jean F Najjar, *President*
Eugenie K Najjar, *Vice Pres*
Jean Najjar, *Opers Staff*
EMP: 6 **EST:** 2004
SQ FT: 3,000
SALES (est): 500K **Privately Held**
WEB: www.joyofgarlic.com
SIC: 2035 5149 Spreads, garlic; sauces

(G-8856)
JUNIORS BAIT AND SEAFOOD INC
1500 Maple Ave (32935-5962)
PHONE..................................321 480-5492
Mark B Maynard Jr, *President*
EMP: 20 **EST:** 2010
SQ FT: 22,000
SALES (est): 1.5MM **Privately Held**
WEB: www.sinisterballyhoo.com
SIC: 2092 Shellfish, fresh: shucked & packed in nonsealed containers

(G-8857)
JUST-IN-TIME MFG CORP
3153 Skyway Cir Ste 101 (32934-7369)
PHONE..................................321 752-7552
Patricia Scardino, *President*
George Scardino, *Vice Pres*
EMP: 15 **EST:** 1995
SALES (est): 2MM **Privately Held**
WEB: www.justintimemanufacturing.com
SIC: 3679 3441 Electronic circuits; fabricated structural metal

(G-8858)
KIINDE LLC
6300 N Wickham Rd Ste 130 (32940-2029)
PHONE..................................404 368-5382
Vijay Brihmadesam, *Mng Member*
Kailas Narendran,
Barbara Roth,
▼ **EMP:** 6 **EST:** 2017
SQ FT: 300
SALES (est): 3.1MM **Privately Held**
WEB: www.kiinde.com
SIC: 3221 3565 Milk bottles, glass; bottle washing & sterilizing machines
PA: Kiinde Holdings, Llc
2060 Highway A1a Ste 303
Indian Harbour Beach FL 32937
617 216-7719

(G-8859)
KINSHIP PRECISION LLC
Also Called: Freedom Fittings
435 West Dr (32904-1035)
PHONE..................................321 765-3531
Raju Kumar, *Manager*
EMP: 16 **EST:** 2017
SQ FT: 11,000
SALES (est): 2.6MM **Privately Held**
WEB: www.kinshipprecision.com
SIC: 3444 1531 3599 Sheet metalwork; ; crankshafts & camshafts, machining

(G-8860)
KITCHEN DSGNS BY JOAN E RBBINS
7690 Industrial Rd (32904-1629)
PHONE..................................321 727-0012
Joan E Robbins, *Owner*
Jeff Hochadel, *Sales Staff*
EMP: 6 **EST:** 1983
SQ FT: 6,000
SALES (est): 498.6K **Privately Held**
SIC: 2541 Cabinets, except refrigerated: show, display, etc.: wood

▲ = Import ▼=Export
◆ =Import/Export

(G-8861)
KONA GOLD LLC
746 North Dr Ste A (32934-9252)
PHONE..................................844 714-2224
Jazmin Gonzalez, *Office Mgr*
EMP: 10 **EST:** 2019
SALES (est): 719.9K **Privately Held**
WEB: www.konagoldhemp.com
SIC: 2369 2086 Girls' & children's outerwear; bottled & canned soft drinks

(G-8862)
L & L AUTOMOTIVE ELECTRIC INC
4575 Carolwood Dr (32934-7182)
PHONE..................................631 471-5230
Lawrence Holmes, *President*
Linda Holmes, *Vice Pres*
EMP: 11 **EST:** 1987
SQ FT: 3,000
SALES (est): 606.5K **Privately Held**
WEB: www.larrysae.com
SIC: 3694 7539 Engine electrical equipment; electrical services

(G-8863)
L-3 CMMNCTONS NTRONIX HOLDINGS
1025 W Nasa Blvd (32919-0001)
PHONE..................................212 697-1111
Michael T Strianese, *President*
Anthony Flynn, *General Mgr*
Steven M Post, *Senior VP*
Curtis Brunson, *Vice Pres*
Jerry Barofsky, *Engineer*
EMP: 65 **EST:** 2003
SALES (est): 28.3MM
SALES (corp-wide): 3.7B **Publicly Held**
WEB: www.l3harris.com
SIC: 3625 3699 8711 Marine & navy auxiliary controls; underwater sound equipment; marine engineering
HQ: L3 Technologies, Inc.
600 3rd Ave Fl 34
New York NY 10016
321 727-9100

(G-8864)
L3 TECHNOLOGIES INC
Communction Systms-Wst/Lnkabit
1200 Woody Burke Rd (32901-2757)
PHONE..................................321 409-6122
Marla Bartel, *General Mgr*
Mace Lund, *General Mgr*
Allison Carberry, *Finance*
David Lynn, *Finance*
Amy Scheerens, *Finance*
EMP: 6
SALES (corp-wide): 3.7B **Publicly Held**
WEB: www.l3harris.com
SIC: 3812 3577 Search & navigation equipment; computer peripheral equipment
HQ: L3 Technologies, Inc.
600 3rd Ave Fl 34
New York NY 10016
321 727-9100

(G-8865)
L3HARRIS TECHNOLOGIES INC (PA)
1025 W Nasa Blvd (32919-0001)
PHONE..................................321 727-9100
Christopher E Kubasik, *CEO*
William M Brown, *Ch of Bd*
Todd W Gautier, *President*
Dana A Mehnert, *President*
Sean J Stackley, *President*
▲ **EMP:** 269 **EST:** 1890
SALES (est): 3.7B **Publicly Held**
WEB: www.l3harris.com
SIC: 3812 3663 3699 3661 Search & navigation equipment; radio & TV communications equipment; satellites, communications; microwave communication equipment; receiver-transmitter units (transceiver); security control equipment & systems; telephones & telephone apparatus; switching equipment, telephone; PBX equipment, manual or automatic; integrated circuits, semiconductor networks, etc.

(G-8866)
L3HARRIS TECHNOLOGIES INC
407 N John Rodes Blvd (32934-8059)
P.O. Box 37 (32902-0037)
PHONE..................................321 309-7848
Stephen Bolze, *Owner*
Barbara Widerman, *Marketing Staff*
EMP: 6
SALES (corp-wide): 3.7B **Publicly Held**
WEB: www.l3harris.com
SIC: 3663 3699 Radio & TV communications equipment; electrical equipment & supplies
PA: L3harris Technologies, Inc.
1025 W Nasa Blvd
Melbourne FL 32919
321 727-9100

(G-8867)
L3HARRIS TECHNOLOGIES INC
2571 Kirby Cir Ne (32905-3401)
PHONE..................................321 729-2186
Bruce Pielow, *Manager*
EMP: 8
SALES (corp-wide): 3.7B **Publicly Held**
WEB: www.l3harris.com
SIC: 3699 Electrical equipment & supplies
PA: L3harris Technologies, Inc.
1025 W Nasa Blvd
Melbourne FL 32919
321 727-9100

(G-8868)
L3HARRIS TECHNOLOGIES INC
Harris Corporation
150 S Wickham Rd (32904-1132)
P.O. Box 37 (32902-0037)
PHONE..................................321 984-0782
John Yates, *Project Mgr*
Ronda R Henning, *Engineer*
James A Proctor, *Branch Mgr*
Keith Hayes, *Sr Project Mgr*
Kenneth Luan, *Manager*
EMP: 20
SALES (corp-wide): 3.7B **Publicly Held**
WEB: www.l3harris.com
SIC: 3661 Telephone & telegraph apparatus
PA: L3harris Technologies, Inc.
1025 W Nasa Blvd
Melbourne FL 32919
321 727-9100

(G-8869)
L3HARRIS TECHNOLOGIES INC
Also Called: Harris Corporation, Gcsd
1025 W Nasa Blvd (32902)
P.O. Box 9002 (32902-9002)
PHONE..................................321 727-4000
Pete Olavarria, *Manager*
EMP: 6
SALES (corp-wide): 3.7B **Publicly Held**
WEB: www.l3harris.com
SIC: 3812 5088 Search & navigation equipment; navigation equipment & supplies
PA: L3harris Technologies, Inc.
1025 W Nasa Blvd
Melbourne FL 32919
321 727-9100

(G-8870)
L3HARRIS TECHNOLOGIES INC
Rf Communications
1025 W Nasa Blvd (32919-0001)
P.O. Box 9001 (32902-9001)
PHONE..................................321 727-9100
Allen Greathouse, *Vice Pres*
Leon Shivamber, *Vice Pres*
Steve Wallick, *Branch Mgr*
Thomas Dattilo, *Bd of Directors*
EMP: 6
SALES (corp-wide): 3.7B **Publicly Held**
WEB: www.l3harris.com
SIC: 3661 3671 Telephone & telegraph apparatus; electron tubes
PA: L3harris Technologies, Inc.
1025 W Nasa Blvd
Melbourne FL 32919
321 727-9100

(G-8871)
L3HARRIS TECHNOLOGIES INC
1025 W Nasa Blvd D11d (32919-0001)
PHONE..................................321 674-4589
Carl D Dalessandro, *President*
EMP: 6
SALES (corp-wide): 3.7B **Publicly Held**
WEB: www.l3harris.com
SIC: 3812 Search & navigation equipment
PA: L3harris Technologies, Inc.
1025 W Nasa Blvd
Melbourne FL 32919
321 727-9100

(G-8872)
LIFDEK CORPORATION
1620 Tangerine St Ste 1 (32901-4685)
PHONE..................................321 759-3422
EMP: 8 **EST:** 2017
SALES (est): 82.3K **Privately Held**
WEB: www.lifdek.com
SIC: 2448 Pallets, wood

(G-8873)
LIFETIME WELLNESS CENTERS INC
618 Washburn Rd Ste A (32934-7320)
PHONE..................................321 693-8698
Kathy Pihlaja Lacina, *President*
EMP: 10 **EST:** 2003
SALES (est): 900K **Privately Held**
WEB: www.lifetimewellnesscenters.com
SIC: 3949 Exercise equipment

(G-8874)
LIGHTING SCIENCE GROUP CORP (HQ)
3905 W Eau Gallie Blvd # 101 (32934-7232)
PHONE..................................321 779-5520
Khim Lee, *President*
David Friedman, *President*
Wayne Nesbit, *COO*
Jonathan Pale, *VP Engrg*
David Quigley, *CFO*
▲ **EMP:** 1 **EST:** 1988
SALES: 52.7MM **Publicly Held**
WEB: www.pcalp.com
SIC: 3646 3648 Commercial indusl & institutional electric lighting fixtures; street lighting fixtures

(G-8875)
LIGHTNING PRTG & GRAPHICS INC
2330 N Wickham Rd Ste 12 (32935-8184)
PHONE..................................321 242-7766
Robert Palumbo, *President*
Joanne Palumbo, *Corp Secy*
EMP: 6 **EST:** 2004
SALES (est): 460.3K **Privately Held**
SIC: 2752 Commercial printing, offset

(G-8876)
LIVETV
1333 Gateway Dr Ste 1007 (32901-2646)
PHONE..................................321 722-0783
Karen Hawkins, *Finance*
EMP: 14 **EST:** 1938
SALES (est): 288.5K **Privately Held**
SIC: 3769 Guided missile & space vehicle parts & auxiliary equipment

(G-8877)
LOCUS DIAGNOSTICS LLC
Also Called: Locususa
1055 S John Rodes Blvd (32904-2005)
PHONE..................................321 727-3077
Joseph Rey,
Susan Jaramillo,
EMP: 15 **EST:** 2009
SQ FT: 6,000
SALES (est): 950K **Privately Held**
WEB: www.locususa.com
SIC: 3825 Radio frequency measuring equipment

(G-8878)
LOCUS LOCATION SYSTEMS LLC
1055 S John Rodes Blvd (32904-2005)
PHONE..................................321 727-3077
Susan Jaramillo, *President*
Joseph Rey, *Managing Prtnr*
Jesus Barrios, *Opers Staff*
Stephen Perrone, *CFO*
Heather Weightman, *Administration*
EMP: 34 **EST:** 2001
SALES (est): 6.7MM **Privately Held**
WEB: www.locususa.com
SIC: 3441 Tower sections, radio & television transmission

(G-8879)
M C TEST SERVICE INC (DH)
Also Called: M C Assembly
425 North Dr (32934-9209)
PHONE..................................321 253-0541
George W Moore, *President*
Mark McReynolds, *Vice Pres*
Raul Irizarry, *Opers Staff*
Donna Meurett, *Mfg Staff*
Mitchell Phillips, *Mfg Staff*
▲ **EMP:** 738 **EST:** 1984
SQ FT: 135,000
SALES (est): 313.6MM
SALES (corp-wide): 386.4MM **Privately Held**
WEB: www.smtc.com
SIC: 3663 3672 Radio & TV communications equipment; printed circuit boards

(G-8880)
MACHINE TECHNOLOGY INC
Also Called: Machine Tech Services
2495 Jen Dr Ste 1 (32940-7495)
PHONE..................................321 254-3886
Andria Sandora, *Vice Pres*
Dick Sawyer, *Engineer*
James Briddy, *Manager*
Jeanne Boutton, *Manager*
EMP: 6 **Privately Held**
WEB: www.mtipowerservices.com
SIC: 3541 Machine tools, metal cutting type
PA: Machine Technology Inc.
1020 Broadway St
Marseilles IL 61341

(G-8881)
MACK TECHNOLOGIES FLORIDA INC
7505 Technology Dr (32904-1574)
PHONE..................................321 725-6993
John Kovach, *President*
Larry Walk, *President*
Randy Boduch, *Treasurer*
▲ **EMP:** 103 **EST:** 2000
SQ FT: 141,000
SALES (est): 78.2MM
SALES (corp-wide): 856.4MM **Privately Held**
WEB: www.macktech.com
SIC: 3672 Printed circuit boards
HQ: Mack Technologies, Inc.
27 Carlisle Rd
Westford MA 01886

(G-8882)
MAGNUS HITECH INDUSTRIES INC
1605 Lake St (32901-4697)
PHONE..................................321 724-9731
Frank Bonarrigo, *General Mgr*
David Farris, *Opers Mgr*
Kathy Montagnino, *Purch Mgr*
Melanie Sechrist, *Purch Agent*
Bonarrigo Angelo, *Engineer*
EMP: 48 **EST:** 1984
SQ FT: 50,000
SALES (est): 11.1MM
SALES (corp-wide): 34.6MM **Privately Held**
WEB: www.micorind.com
SIC: 3599 3444 Machine shop, jobbing & repair; sheet metal specialties, not stamped
HQ: Micor Industries, Llc
1314 State Docks Rd
Decatur AL 35601
256 560-0770

(G-8883)
MARK HOUSMAN SCREEN RPS INC
2911 Dusa Dr Ste E (32934-8100)
PHONE..................................321 255-2778
Mark J Housman, *President*
▲ **EMP:** 45 **EST:** 1995
SALES (est): 3.6MM **Privately Held**
SIC: 3448 Screen enclosures

(G-8884)
MC ASSEMBLY HOLDINGS INC (HQ)
425 North Dr (32934-9209)
PHONE..................................321 253-0541
George W Moore, *President*
Jorge Benedito, *Vice Pres*
Vicki Cooke, *Vice Pres*
Thomas Hansen, *Vice Pres*
Richard Kelly, *Vice Pres*
▲ **EMP:** 5 **EST:** 1984
SALES (est): 319.9MM
SALES (corp-wide): 386.4MM **Privately Held**
WEB: www.smtc.com
SIC: 3672 8734 Printed circuit boards; testing laboratories
PA: Smtc Corporation
7050 Woodbine Ave
Markham ON L3R 4
905 479-1810

(G-8885)
MC ASSEMBLY INTERNATIONAL LLC (DH)
425 North Dr (32934-9209)
PHONE..................................321 253-0541
George Moore,
EMP: 10 **EST:** 2004
SALES (est): 57.2MM
SALES (corp-wide): 386.4MM **Privately Held**
WEB: www.smtc.com
SIC: 3825 1389 Test equipment for electronic & electrical circuits; testing, measuring, surveying & analysis services
HQ: M C Test Service, Inc.
425 North Dr
Melbourne FL 32934
321 253-0541

(G-8886)
MEDICOMP INC (PA)
600 Atlantis Rd (32904-2315)
PHONE..................................321 676-0010
Tony Balda, *CEO*
Michael Thomas, *President*
Daniel Balda, *Principal*
David Gibson, *Vice Pres*
Manogna Ghali, *Engineer*
EMP: 144 **EST:** 1981
SQ FT: 25,000
SALES (est): 34.1MM **Privately Held**
WEB: www.medicompinc.com
SIC: 3845 Cardiographs

(G-8887)
MELBOURNE ARCHITECTURAL MLLWK
325 East Dr (32904-1030)
PHONE..................................321 308-3297
Thomas W Soyk, *President*
Fran Walker, *Manager*
Donna D Soyk, *Admin Sec*
EMP: 11 **EST:** 1998
SQ FT: 6,900
SALES (est): 3MM **Privately Held**
WEB: www.mamillwork.com
SIC: 2431 1751 Millwork; carpentry work

(G-8888)
MGI USA INC
Also Called: M G I USA Inc Mastercarte
3143 Skyway Cir (32934-7334)
PHONE..................................321 751-6755
Michael Abergel, *Exec VP*
Micheal Abergel, *Exec VP*
Kevin Abergel, *Vice Pres*
Steve Bruno, *Natl Sales Mgr*
Peter Lim, *Sales Staff*
▲ **EMP:** 14 **EST:** 1995
SQ FT: 10,000
SALES (est): 3.2MM
SALES (corp-wide): 441.2K **Privately Held**
WEB: www.mgi-fr.com
SIC: 3555 Printing trades machinery
PA: M.G.I
19 A Rue De Chatillon
Rennes

(G-8889)
MICRO TECHNOLOGY OF BREVARD
255 West Dr (32904-1043)
PHONE..................................321 733-1766
Fred Rech, *President*
Charlotte Rech, *Vice Pres*
EMP: 8 **EST:** 1978
SQ FT: 4,000
SALES (est): 848.2K **Privately Held**
SIC: 3679 Electronic circuits

(G-8890)
MILPRO PUBLICATIONS LLC
559 Edward Rd (32904-7403)
PHONE..................................321 613-2250
William M Laderer Sr, *President*
EMP: 6 **EST:** 2016
SALES (est): 42K **Privately Held**
SIC: 2741 Miscellaneous publishing

(G-8891)
MOTION MACHINING LLC
1568 Maeve Cir (32904-7346)
PHONE..................................321 693-0999
James M Canitano, *Principal*
EMP: 6 **EST:** 2008
SALES (est): 129.9K **Privately Held**
SIC: 3599 Machine shop, jobbing & repair

(G-8892)
NCH FL FUNDING LLC
525 N Harbor City Blvd (32935-6837)
PHONE..................................321 777-7777
James H Nance, *Manager*
EMP: 6 **EST:** 2001
SALES (est): 139.7K **Privately Held**
SIC: 2842 Specialty cleaning, polishes & sanitation goods

(G-8893)
NEOS TECHNOLOGIES INC (PA)
4300 Fortune Pl Ste C (32904-1527)
PHONE..................................321 242-7818
William P Shannonhouse, *President*
Huey-Chin Ho, *Vice Pres*
EMP: 9 **EST:** 2010
SALES (est): 1.2MM **Privately Held**
SIC: 3674 Semiconductors & related devices

(G-8894)
NIDA CORPORATION (PA)
300 S John Rodes Blvd (32904-1052)
PHONE..................................321 727-2265
Joseph Beauseigneur, *CEO*
Lydia Beauseigneur, *President*
Katie Beauseigneur, *Business Mgr*
Jay Buckman, *Vice Pres*
Bob Burk, *Purchasing*
◆ **EMP:** 45 **EST:** 1972
SQ FT: 22,000
SALES (est): 9.2MM **Privately Held**
WEB: www.nida.com
SIC: 3699 Electronic training devices

(G-8895)
NORTHROP GRMMAN TCHNCAL SVCS I
1235 Evans Rd (32904-2314)
PHONE..................................321 837-7000
Craig Donnelly, *President*
EMP: 8 **Publicly Held**
SIC: 3812 Search & navigation equipment
HQ: Northrop Grumman Technical Services, Inc.
7575 Colshire Dr
Mc Lean VA 22102
703 556-1144

(G-8896)
NORTHROP GRUMMAN CORPORATION
2000 W Nasa Blvd (32904-2322)
PHONE..................................321 951-5000
Thomas Boyle, *Counsel*
Victor Carrion, *Project Mgr*
Christopher Isaacs, *Project Mgr*
Anthony Calabro, *Opers Staff*
Dave Huddleston, *Technical Mgr*
EMP: 2000 **Publicly Held**
WEB: www.northropgrumman.com
SIC: 3812 Search & detection systems & instruments
PA: Northrop Grumman Corporation
2980 Fairview Park Dr
Falls Church VA 22042

(G-8897)
NORTHROP GRUMMAN SYSTEMS CORP
Also Called: Northrop Grumman Corporation
2000 W Nasa Blvd (32904-2322)
P.O. Box 9650 (32902-9650)
PHONE..................................321 951-5000
John Saunders, *Engineer*
Dianne Farrar, *Accountant*
Allen Doshier, *Manager*
Carol Hansen, *Manager*
Antonio Wright, *Planning*
EMP: 1719 **Publicly Held**
WEB: www.northropgrumman.com
SIC: 3812 Radar systems & equipment
HQ: Northrop Grumman Systems Corporation
2980 Fairview Park Dr
Falls Church VA 22042
703 280-2900

(G-8898)
NORTHSTAR AVIATION USA LLC
1431 General Aviation Dr (32935-6332)
PHONE..................................321 600-4557
Lyle Becka, *Vice Pres*
Amy Styers, *Officer*
EMP: 23 **EST:** 2012
SQ FT: 8,000
SALES (est): 2.1MM **Privately Held**
WEB: www.usanstar.com
SIC: 3721 3728 Aircraft; aircraft parts & equipment

(G-8899)
O I INC
295 North Dr Ste A (32934-9261)
PHONE..................................321 499-3800
Ulrich Wiegand, *President*
Richard Wade, *Manager*
◆ **EMP:** 24 **EST:** 1995
SQ FT: 60,000
SALES (est): 4.6MM **Privately Held**
SIC: 3484 Guns (firearms) or gun parts, 30 mm. & below

(G-8900)
OGRE CUSTOM FABRICATIONS LLC
2495 Jen Dr Ste 10 (32940-7495)
PHONE..................................321 544-2142
Paul M Stewart, *Principal*
▼ **EMP:** 5 **EST:** 2011
SALES (est): 484.3K **Privately Held**
WEB: www.ogrecustomfab.com
SIC: 3399 Primary metal products

(G-8901)
OMEGA GARAGE DOORS INC
7751 Industrial Rd (32904-1630)
PHONE..................................352 620-8830
Darrell Wright, *Sales Mgr*
Duane Wright, *Manager*
EMP: 10
SALES (corp-wide): 6.1MM **Privately Held**
WEB: www.omegadoorsflorida.com
SIC: 2431 3442 3231 Door screens, metal covered wood; fire doors, metal; insulating glass: made from purchased glass
PA: Omega Garage Doors, Inc.
328 Seaboard Ave
Venice FL 34285
941 627-0150

(G-8902)
OSTRICH MARKET INC
381 Dayton Blvd (32904-3715)
PHONE..................................954 873-1957
Henry G Slaughter, *President*
EMP: 5 **EST:** 2005
SALES (est): 373.4K **Privately Held**
WEB: www.ostrichmarket.com
SIC: 3172 Personal leather goods

(G-8903)
PALM BAY COML COATINGS INC
615 Palmetto Ave (32901-4723)
PHONE..................................321 266-2467
Josh M Denton, *President*
EMP: 6 **EST:** 2017
SALES (est): 129.9K **Privately Held**
WEB: www.pbccoatings.com
SIC: 3479 Coating of metals & formed products

(G-8904)
PALMAS PRINTING INC (PA)
200 East Dr (32904-1027)
PHONE..................................321 984-4451
J Robert Gunther, *Principal*
James Love, *Vice Pres*
Jean Chapman, *CFO*
Dean Dettore, *Sales Mgr*
Terry Popeck, *Manager*
◆ **EMP:** 20 **EST:** 1998
SQ FT: 30,000
SALES (est): 7.6MM **Privately Held**
WEB: www.palmasprinting.com
SIC: 2759 2679 Screen printing; labels, paper: made from purchased material

(G-8905)
PARABEL INC
Also Called: (A DEVELOPMENT STAGE COMPANY)
1901 S Hbr Cy Blvd Ste 60 (32901)
PHONE..................................321 409-7415
Anthony John Phipps Tiarks, *Ch of Bd*
Lucille Forbes, *Purchasing*
Syed Naqvi, *CFO*
Simon Magnay, *Manager*
EMP: 38
SALES: 650K **Privately Held**
WEB: www.parabel.com
SIC: 2869 6794 Industrial organic chemicals; patent buying, licensing, leasing

(G-8906)
PEPSI-COLA METRO BTLG CO INC
3951 Sarno Rd (32934-7275)
PHONE..................................321 242-2984
Jim Harrington, *Sales/Mktg Mgr*
Anthony Munroe, *Manager*
EMP: 6
SALES (corp-wide): 70.3B **Publicly Held**
WEB: www.pepsico.com
SIC: 2086 Carbonated soft drinks, bottled & canned
HQ: Pepsi-Cola Metropolitan Bottling Company, Inc.
1111 Westchester Ave
White Plains NY 10604
914 767-6000

(G-8907)
PHLEXAPEEL LLC
100 Rialto Pl Ste 743 (32901-3072)
P.O. Box 410250 (32941-0250)
PHONE..................................407 990-1854
George D Sergio, *Owner*
EMP: 5 **EST:** 2014
SALES (est): 502.1K **Privately Held**
WEB: www.phlexapeel.com
SIC: 2869 Industrial organic chemicals

(G-8908)
PHOTOTELESIS LP
1615 W Nasa Blvd (32901-2613)
PHONE..................................321 254-1500
Deon Harkey, *Partner*
Judi Padilla, *Partner*
▲ **EMP:** 25 **EST:** 2005
SALES (est): 293.8K **Privately Held**
WEB: www.extantaerospace.com
SIC: 3663 5065 Radio & TV communications equipment; electronic parts & equipment

(G-8909)
PLANET INHOUSE INC
3000 N Wickham Rd (32935-2303)
P.O. Box 411306 (32941-1306)
PHONE..................................321 216-2189
Todd Hillhouse, *CEO*
Brandon Riley, *Vice Pres*
EMP: 10 **EST:** 2013
SALES (est): 1MM **Privately Held**
WEB: www.planetinhouse.com
SIC: 3861 Motion picture film

(G-8910)
PRECISION TECH MACHINING LLC
1421 Albert Dr (32935-2807)
PHONE..................................321 693-3469

Kevin S Walker, *Mng Member*
Wanda G Walker,
EMP: 8 **EST:** 2007
SALES (est): 537.9K **Privately Held**
SIC: 3599 Machine shop, jobbing & repair

(G-8911)
PRESTIGE/AB READY MIX LLC
Also Called: Prestige Concrete
2585 Avocado Ave (32935-5586)
PHONE..................................321 751-2566
Bryan Moffit, *Branch Mgr*
EMP: 43
SALES (corp-wide): 11.2MM **Privately Held**
SIC: 3273 Ready-mixed concrete
PA: Prestige/Ab Ready Mix, Llc
7228 Westport Pl Ste C
West Palm Beach FL 33413
561 478-9980

(G-8912)
PROCESSING AND PACKG SUPS CO
Also Called: Papsco
700 S John Rodes Blvd (32904-1507)
PHONE..................................321 723-2723
Bryan Russell, *President*
◆ **EMP:** 23 **EST:** 1986
SQ FT: 30,000
SALES (est): 1.9MM **Privately Held**
SIC: 3082 3081 Tubes, unsupported plastic; packing materials, plastic sheet

(G-8913)
PROMO DADDY LLC
812 N Apollo Blvd (32935-5068)
PHONE..................................877 557-2336
Bill Stevens, *Branch Mgr*
EMP: 11
SALES (corp-wide): 1.1MM **Privately Held**
WEB: www.custombuttonco.com
SIC: 3993 2396 2399 3999 Advertising novelties; screen printing on fabric articles; emblems, badges & insignia; coins & tokens, non-currency; buttons
PA: Promo Daddy Llc
800 N Apollo Blvd
Melbourne FL 32935
352 390-3081

(G-8914)
PROMO DADDY LLC (PA)
Also Called: Custom Button Company
800 N Apollo Blvd (32935-5068)
PHONE..................................352 390-3081
Ian McRoberts, *CEO*
▲ **EMP:** 11 **EST:** 2015
SALES (est): 1.1MM **Privately Held**
WEB: www.custombuttonco.com
SIC: 3993 Advertising novelties

(G-8915)
PURE WAVE ORGANICS INC
Also Called: Laughing Mermaid The
2861 Saint James Ln (32935-3602)
PHONE..................................321 368-7002
John McElhinny, *President*
EMP: 6 **EST:** 2013
SALES (est): 86.3K **Privately Held**
SIC: 2834 7389 5169 Dermatologicals; ; organic chemicals, synthetic

(G-8916)
Q P CONSULTING INC
Also Called: Paragon Printers
2110 Dairy Rd Ste 102 (32904-5200)
PHONE..................................321 727-2442
John Stewart, *President*
Mary Stewart, *Vice Pres*
EMP: 6 **EST:** 1983
SQ FT: 8,000
SALES (est): 763.7K **Privately Held**
SIC: 2752 Commercial printing, offset

(G-8917)
QUEST ENVIRONMENTAL PRODUCTS
6928 Sonny Dale Dr Ste A (32904-2200)
PHONE..................................321 984-4423
Fred K Ungerer, *President*
Lynda Ungerer, *Admin Sec*
EMP: 9 **EST:** 1994
SQ FT: 8,500
SALES (est): 1.7MM **Privately Held**
WEB: www.questenvironmentalproducts.com
SIC: 2819 Industrial inorganic chemicals

(G-8918)
RELIABLE FINISHES
7730 Industrial Rd (32904-1631)
PHONE..................................321 723-3334
Greg Becker, *Owner*
EMP: 8 **EST:** 2007
SALES (est): 551.2K **Privately Held**
WEB: www.reliablefinishes.com
SIC: 3479 Painting of metal products

(G-8919)
RELM COMMUNICATIONS INC
Also Called: Bk Technologies
7100 Technology Dr (32904-1521)
PHONE..................................321 953-7800
D Kyle Cerminara, *Ch of Bd*
Timothy A Vitou, *President*
Lewis Johnson, *Chairman*
Henry R Willis, *COO*
Tina Boucher, *Vice Pres*
▲ **EMP:** 114 **EST:** 1945
SQ FT: 54,000
SALES (est): 20.4MM
SALES (corp-wide): 49.3MM **Publicly Held**
WEB: www.bktechnologies.com
SIC: 3825 3663 Power measuring equipment, electrical; mobile communication equipment; cellular radio telephone; receiver-transmitter units (transceiver)
HQ: Bk Technologies, Inc.
7100 Technology Dr
West Melbourne FL 32904

(G-8920)
ROCKWELL COLLINS INC
795 W Nasa Blvd (32901-1815)
PHONE..................................321 768-7492
James Lombardy, *Senior Buyer*
Amy Leonard, *Engineer*
Ted Peterson, *Engineer*
William Zakaluk, *Engineer*
Patricia Osborne, *Branch Mgr*
EMP: 6
SALES (corp-wide): 56.5B **Publicly Held**
WEB: www.rockwellcollins.com
SIC: 3728 Aircraft parts & equipment
HQ: Rockwell Collins, Inc.
400 Collins Rd Ne
Cedar Rapids IA 52498

(G-8921)
ROCKWELL COLLINS INC
1100 W Hibiscus Blvd (32901-2704)
P.O. Box 1060 (32902-1060)
PHONE..................................321 768-7303
Jeff Moore, *Principal*
Frank Joslin, *Prdtn Mgr*
Clara Centeno, *Mfg Staff*
Eldredge Don, *Engineer*
Dave Foy, *Engineer*
EMP: 100
SALES (corp-wide): 56.5B **Publicly Held**
WEB: www.rockwellcollins.com
SIC: 3663 3812 Radio & TV communications equipment; search & navigation equipment
HQ: Rockwell Collins, Inc.
400 Collins Rd Ne
Cedar Rapids IA 52498

(G-8922)
RTI DONOR SERVICES INC
401 N Wickham Rd Ste 143 (32935-8667)
PHONE..................................321 431-2464
Tom Cannan, *Manager*
EMP: 25
SALES (corp-wide): 101.7MM **Publicly Held**
WEB: www.rtix.com
SIC: 3841 Surgical & medical instruments
HQ: Rti Donor Services, Inc.
11621 Research Cir
Alachua FL 32615

(G-8923)
SAGRAD INC
202 West Dr (32904-1042)
PHONE..................................321 726-9400
Adam K Harriman, *President*
Michael Graff, *President*
Martha J Harriman, *Vice Pres*
Tony Crosthwaite, *Opers Mgr*
Dawn Harris, *QC Mgr*
◆ **EMP:** 15 **EST:** 2004
SQ FT: 1,200
SALES (est): 4.4MM **Privately Held**
WEB: www.sagrad.com
SIC: 3629 5065 Electronic generation equipment; electronic parts & equipment

(G-8924)
SAILOR MADE CUSTOM WOODWORKS L
4260 Dow Rd Ste 401 (32934-9294)
PHONE..................................805 587-1197
EMP: 5 **EST:** 2019
SALES (est): 303.5K **Privately Held**
SIC: 2431 Millwork

(G-8925)
SATCOM DIRECT INC
1421 General Aviation Dr (32935-6332)
PHONE..................................321 242-6665
Stefan Tilliard, *General Mgr*
Anna Sellart, *Business Mgr*
Rich Pilock, *Vice Pres*
Gerry Connell, *Opers Staff*
Sonya Griffin, *Opers Staff*
EMP: 6
SALES (corp-wide): 167.9MM **Privately Held**
WEB: www.satcomdirect.com
SIC: 3663 Satellites, communications
PA: Satcom Direct, Inc.
1050 Satcom Ln
Melbourne FL 32940
321 777-3000

(G-8926)
SATCOM DIRECT CMMUNICATIONS INC (PA)
1050 Satcom Ln (32940-7010)
P.O. Box 372667, Satellite Beach (32937-0667)
PHONE..................................321 777-3000
James Jensen, *President*
David Greenhill, *President*
Alexandrea Simser, *Principal*
Darlene Ciarcia, *Vice Pres*
Zachary Cotner, *CFO*
EMP: 10 **EST:** 2003
SQ FT: 3,500
SALES (est): 68MM **Privately Held**
WEB: www.satcomdirect.com
SIC: 3663 Satellites, communications

(G-8927)
SBS PRECISION SHTMTL INC
Also Called: SBS
615 Distribution Dr (32904-1178)
PHONE..................................321 951-7411
Don Morse, *President*
EMP: 20 **EST:** 1985
SQ FT: 11,000
SALES (est): 4.3MM **Privately Held**
WEB: www.sbspre.net
SIC: 3441 3429 3444 3469 Fabricated structural metal; manufactured hardware (general); sheet metal specialties, not stamped; machine parts, stamped or pressed metal

(G-8928)
SDI INDUSTRIES INC
1216 Prospect Ave 101 (32901-7330)
PHONE..................................321 733-1128
Cristian Ahumada, *COO*
Jim Suggs, *VP Engrg*
Alejandro Deluca, *CFO*
Carol Soltys, *Branch Mgr*
Dave Bodenheimer, *Manager*
EMP: 25
SALES (corp-wide): 49.5MM **Privately Held**
WEB: www.sdi.systems
SIC: 3535 3537 8748 8711 Conveyors & conveying equipment; industrial trucks & tractors; business consulting; engineering services; machinery installation
PA: Sdi Industries, Inc.
13000 Pierce St
Pacoima CA 91331
818 890-6002

(G-8929)
SEA GEAR CORPORATION
700 S John Rodes Blvd B1 (32904-1508)
PHONE..................................321 728-9116
Bobbie Lee Seigler, *President*
EMP: 5 **EST:** 1975
SQ FT: 3,500
SALES (est): 664.9K **Privately Held**
WEB: www.sea-gear.net
SIC: 3826 8731 Water testing apparatus; biological research

(G-8930)
SENIOR LIFE OF FLORIDA
7350 Shoppes Dr Ste 102 (32940-6076)
PHONE..................................321 242-1235
Jill Gaines, *President*
EMP: 10 **EST:** 2010
SALES (est): 348.6K **Privately Held**
WEB: www.vieravoice.com
SIC: 2711 Newspapers, publishing & printing

(G-8931)
SHELTON GROUP LLC
Also Called: Homes & Land Magazine
1333 Gateway Dr Ste 1013 (32901-2647)
PHONE..................................321 676-8981
Tom Shelton, *Manager*
EMP: 7 **EST:** 1999
SALES (est): 545.8K **Privately Held**
SIC: 2721 Magazines: publishing & printing

(G-8932)
SIGN MAN INC
4580 N Us Highway 1 (32935-7202)
PHONE..................................321 259-1703
Patrick L Neve, *President*
Colleen Jones, *Corp Secy*
Anna Neve, *Vice Pres*
EMP: 8 **EST:** 1979
SQ FT: 2,600
SALES (est): 400K **Privately Held**
WEB: www.signmaninc.com
SIC: 3993 Signs & advertising specialties

(G-8933)
SILVERHORSE RACING LLC
700 S John Rodes Blvd (32904-1507)
PHONE..................................321 722-2813
Joseph Marcello Canitano, *Principal*
▼ **EMP:** 7 **EST:** 2004
SQ FT: 3,000
SALES (est): 1.3MM **Privately Held**
WEB: www.silverhorseracing.com
SIC: 3714 Motor vehicle parts & accessories

(G-8934)
SINGER HOLDINGS INC
Also Called: Florida Sheet Metal
7791 Industrial Rd (32904-1630)
PHONE..................................321 724-0900
Deeon Singer, *President*
Henry L Singer II, *Vice Pres*
EMP: 12 **EST:** 2003
SALES (est): 1MM **Privately Held**
WEB: www.floridasheetmetal.com
SIC: 3444 Sheet metal specialties, not stamped

(G-8935)
SMITTYS WELDING SHOP
2526 S Harbor City Blvd (32901-7206)
PHONE..................................321 723-4533
Jonathon David Bauer, *Owner*
EMP: 6 **EST:** 1978
SQ FT: 2,400
SALES (est): 477.2K **Privately Held**
SIC: 7692 Welding repair

(G-8936)
SOUTHERN DUMPSTERS INC
380 Sagamore St (32904-4851)
PHONE..................................772 413-1228
Terry Dourth, *Principal*
EMP: 7 **EST:** 2017
SALES (est): 456.6K **Privately Held**
WEB: www.southerndumpsters.com
SIC: 3443 Dumpsters, garbage

(G-8937)
SPACE CAST INTLLGENT SLTONS IN
770 North Dr Ste B (32934-9270)
PHONE..................................321 622-6858
Brian J Jaskiewicz, *President*
Bill Anderson, *General Mgr*
James A Ralph, *Vice Pres*
Todd Flato, *Software Engr*
EMP: 11 **EST:** 2008
SALES (est): 500K **Privately Held**
WEB: www.goscis.com
SIC: 3812 Defense systems & equipment

(G-8938)
SPACE COAST MAP LLC
1359 Richmond Dr (32935-5325)
P.O. Box 361893 (32936-1893)
PHONE..................................321 242-4538
Julia Perian, *Principal*
EMP: 8 **EST:** 2012
SALES (est): 320.6K **Privately Held**
SIC: 3471 Plating of metals or formed products

(G-8939)
SPACECAST PLTG MET RFNSHING IN
975 Aurora Rd (32935-5968)
PHONE..................................321 254-2880
David P Pratt, *President*
Sandra Pratt, *Vice Pres*
EMP: 17 **EST:** 1996
SQ FT: 15,000
SALES (est): 1.1MM **Privately Held**
WEB: www.spacecoast-plating.com
SIC: 3471 Plating of metals or formed products

(G-8940)
SPECIALTY PHARMACY SERVICES
800 E Melbourne Ave (32901-5549)
PHONE..................................321 953-2004
Barbara Switzler, *President*
Thomas Switzler, *Vice Pres*
Joy Leffler, *Manager*
EMP: 7 **EST:** 1996
SQ FT: 900
SALES (est): 400K **Privately Held**
WEB: www.specialty-pharmacy.com
SIC: 2834 5122 Pharmaceutical preparations; pharmaceuticals

(G-8941)
SPECTRUM MICROWAVE INC
API Technologies
1335 Gateway Dr Ste 2016 (32901-2644)
PHONE..................................321 727-1838
Richard Graham, *Manager*
Scott Spangenberg, *Technology*
EMP: 148 **Privately Held**
WEB: www.apitech.com
SIC: 3679 Microwave components
HQ: Spectrum Microwave, Inc.
1900 W College Ave
State College PA 16801
814 272-2700

(G-8942)
SPIRIT CONNECTION
Also Called: Spiritualist Chapel Melbourne
588 Waveside Dr (32934-8057)
P.O. Box 1052 (32902-1052)
PHONE..................................321 327-3804
John Rogers, *Owner*
Trish Rogers, *Co-Owner*
EMP: 6 **EST:** 2001
SALES (est): 96K **Privately Held**
SIC: 2731 7311 Book publishing; advertising agencies

(G-8943)
SPOONS CHILLY
4980 N Wickham Rd Ste 106 (32940-7320)
PHONE..................................321 610-8966
EMP: 6
SALES (est): 417K **Privately Held**
SIC: 2026 Mfg Fluid Milk

(G-8944)
SS & S INDUSTRIES INC
620 Di Lido St Ne (32907-2029)
PHONE..................................321 327-2500
EMP: 11 **EST:** 2017
SALES (est): 568.6K **Privately Held**
SIC: 3999 Manufacturing industries

(G-8945)
STRATEGIC PRODUCTS INC
5100 Laguna Vista Dr (32934-7837)
PHONE..................................321 752-0441
Art Markuson, *President*
Jeff Markuson, *Vice Pres*
Joe Giusti, *Manager*
EMP: 9 **EST:** 1984
SQ FT: 9,000
SALES (est): 292.9K **Privately Held**
WEB: www.accuheat2.com
SIC: 3631 Convection ovens, including portable: household

(G-8946)
STRATOS LIGHT WAVE INC
Also Called: Stratos Optical
1333 Gateway Dr Ste 1007 (32901-2646)
PHONE..................................321 308-4100
Brian Mason, *President*
Dale Reed, *VP Sales*
Mike Nipper, *Regl Sales Mgr*
EMP: 1 **EST:** 2000
SQ FT: 13,000
SALES (est): 5.3MM
SALES (corp-wide): 465.7MM **Publicly Held**
WEB: www.stratosoptical.com
SIC: 3678 Electronic connectors
HQ: Stratos International, Inc.
299 Johnson Ave Sw
Waseca MN 56093
507 833-8822

(G-8947)
STRUCTURAL COMPOSITES INC
360 East Dr (32904-1029)
PHONE..................................321 951-9464
Ronnal P Reichard, *Ch of Bd*
Scott M Lewit, *President*
Michael Nichols, *Vice Pres*
Morgan Herring, *Opers Mgr*
Codrington Barzey, *Engineer*
EMP: 14 **EST:** 1987
SQ FT: 13,000
SALES (est): 2.5MM **Privately Held**
WEB: www.structuralcomposites.com
SIC: 3089 8711 Plastic boats & other marine equipment; marine engineering

(G-8948)
STRUCTURAL STEEL OF BREVARD
6951 Vickie Cir Ste A (32904-2203)
PHONE..................................321 726-0271
EMP: 8 **EST:** 2017
SALES (est): 885.7K **Privately Held**
SIC: 3441 Fabricated structural metal

(G-8949)
SUMMATION RESEARCH INC
305 East Dr Ste D (32904-1033)
PHONE..................................321 254-2580
Thomas A Drago, *President*
Tom Drago, *Vice Pres*
EMP: 36 **EST:** 1989
SQ FT: 14,700
SALES (est): 3.1MM **Privately Held**
WEB: www.summationresearch.com
SIC: 3663 7371 Receivers, radio communications; computer software development

(G-8950)
SUN NUCLEAR CORP (HQ)
3275 Suntree Blvd (32940-7514)
PHONE..................................321 259-6862
Jeffery A Simon, *CEO*
William E Simon, *President*
EMP: 116 **EST:** 1984
SQ FT: 13,000
SALES (est): 63.4MM **Privately Held**
WEB: www.sunnuclear.com
SIC: 3829 8734 7699 Nuclear radiation & testing apparatus; testing laboratories; professional instrument repair services

(G-8951)
SUNTREE DIAGNOSTIC CENTER
7970 N Wickham Rd Ste 102 (32940-8299)
PHONE..................................321 259-8800
Thomas Foster, *Director*
EMP: 7 **EST:** 1991
SQ FT: 4,800
SALES (est): 757.2K **Privately Held**
WEB: www.vieradiagnosticcenter.com
SIC: 2835 In vitro & in vivo diagnostic substances

(G-8952)
SUPPORT SYSTEMS ASSOCIATES INC
700 S John Rodes Blvd (32904-1507)
PHONE..................................321 724-5566
John P Zoltak, *Branch Mgr*
EMP: 30
SALES (corp-wide): 25MM **Privately Held**
WEB: www.ssai.org
SIC: 3728 Aircraft parts & equipment
PA: Support Systems Associates, Inc.
304 S Hbr Cy Blvd Ste 100
Melbourne FL 32901
321 724-5566

(G-8953)
SWISS COMPONENTS INC
405 West Dr Ste A (32904-1084)
PHONE..................................321 723-6729
Abner Telebrico, *President*
Bernice O Morris, *Treasurer*
Bernice Morris, *Treasurer*
Angela Carter, *Manager*
Terri S Telebrico, *Admin Sec*
EMP: 12 **EST:** 2000
SQ FT: 6,000
SALES (est): 1MM **Privately Held**
WEB: www.swisscomponents.com
SIC: 3599 3443 Machine shop, jobbing & repair; fabricated plate work (boiler shop)

(G-8954)
SYMETRICS INDUSTRIES LLC
Also Called: Extant Aerospace
1615 W Nasa Blvd (32901-2613)
PHONE..................................321 254-1500
James Gerwien, *CEO*
Henry Abele, *President*
David Minton, *General Mgr*
Bill White, *Business Mgr*
Thomas Deasy, *Vice Pres*
▲ **EMP:** 145 **EST:** 1998
SQ FT: 40,000
SALES (est): 43MM
SALES (corp-wide): 5.1B **Publicly Held**
WEB: www.symetrics.com
SIC: 3699 Electrical equipment & supplies
PA: Transdigm Group Incorporated
1301 E 9th St Ste 3000
Cleveland OH 44114
216 706-2960

(G-8955)
SYMETRICS TECHNOLOGY GROUP LLC
1615 W Nasa Blvd (32901-2613)
PHONE..................................321 254-1500
James Gerwien, *CEO*
D Mitchell Garner, *Principal*
Dudley Garner, *Principal*
EMP: 23 **EST:** 2013
SALES (est): 5.1MM
SALES (corp-wide): 5.1B **Publicly Held**
WEB: www.extantaerospace.com
SIC: 3699 Security devices
PA: Transdigm Group Incorporated
1301 E 9th St Ste 3000
Cleveland OH 44114
216 706-2960

(G-8956)
TECORE GOVERNMENT SERVICES LLC
295 North Dr Ste G (32934-9261)
PHONE..................................410 872-6000
Joseph F Gerrity, *CFO*
Joseph Gerrity, *Manager*
Deniz Hardy, *General Counsel*
EMP: 9 **EST:** 2015
SQ FT: 48,000
SALES (est): 128.5K **Privately Held**
WEB: www.tecore.com
SIC: 3663 Radio broadcasting & communications equipment

(G-8957)
TEK-LITE INC
1279 Tipperary Dr (32940-6029)
PHONE..................................410 775-7123
Kevin F McDermott, *President*
EMP: 8 **EST:** 1978
SQ FT: 9,000
SALES (est): 829.7K **Privately Held**
WEB: www.teklite.com
SIC: 3646 Commercial indusl & institutional electric lighting fixtures

(G-8958)
TEKNIFAB INDUSTRIES INC
179 Park Hill Blvd (32904-5115)
PHONE..................................321 722-1922
Sean Makowsky, *President*
Rebecca Makowsky, *Vice Pres*
EMP: 6 **EST:** 1995
SALES (est): 770K **Privately Held**
WEB: www.teknifab.com
SIC: 3441 Fabricated structural metal

(G-8959)
TEKNOCRAFT INC
425 West Dr (32904-1035)
PHONE..................................321 729-9634
Sampath V Kumar, *President*
EMP: 29 **EST:** 1983
SQ FT: 52,000
SALES (est): 4.5MM **Privately Held**
WEB: www.iqvalves.com
SIC: 3599 5084 3494 3492 Machine shop, jobbing & repair; industrial machinery & equipment; valves & pipe fittings; fluid power valves & hose fittings

(G-8960)
TERRY LABORATORIES LLC
7005 Technology Dr (32904-1512)
PHONE..................................321 259-1630
Jim Gambino, *General Mgr*
Zachary Gault, *Sales Staff*
James A Gambino, *Manager*
Rex Maughan,
◆ **EMP:** 13
SQ FT: 19,000
SALES (est): 3.2MM **Privately Held**
WEB: www.terrylabs.com
SIC: 2833 2844 2869 Medicinals & botanicals; toilet preparations; industrial organic chemicals

(G-8961)
THOMPSON ENVRMNTAL MNTRING CTR
444 Oleander Ln (32935-6945)
PHONE..................................321 591-7300
William E Thompson, *Partner*
David Thompson, *Partner*
William Thompson, *Analyst*
EMP: 6 **EST:** 2001
SALES (est): 110.9K **Privately Held**
WEB: www.envlink.net
SIC: 3822 Auto controls regulating residntl & coml environmt & applncs

(G-8962)
TIME INDUSTRIES INC
709 Silver Palm Ave Ste J (32901-4803)
PHONE..................................321 676-2080
Fred Zeit, *President*
EMP: 5 **EST:** 2002
SQ FT: 1,600
SALES (est): 461.4K **Privately Held**
WEB: www.timeind.com
SIC: 3545 Precision measuring tools

(G-8963)
TITANIUM ENDEAVORS LLC
2205 Botanica Cir (32904-7340)
PHONE..................................321 728-9732
Justin M Lauer, *Principal*
EMP: 7 **EST:** 2012
SALES (est): 293.4K **Privately Held**
SIC: 3356 Titanium

(G-8964)
TK TIRES & WHEELS INC
2400 S Harbor City Blvd (32901-5531)
PHONE..................................321 473-8945
Timothy Fitzwater, *Director*
EMP: 6 **EST:** 2011
SALES (est): 109.5K **Privately Held**
SIC: 3312 Wheels

(G-8965)
TOM & COMPANY LLC
1101 W Hibiscus Blvd # 10 (32901-2718)
PHONE..................................321 917-0760
EMP: 6 **EST:** 2019
SALES (est): 63.3K **Privately Held**
SIC: 3489 Ordnance & accessories

(G-8966)
TRIPLE PLAY CMMUNICATIONS CORP
250 East Dr Ste F (32904-1031)
PHONE..................................321 327-8997
Keith Riffee, *President*
Jim Wernlund, *VP Engrg*
EMP: 6 **EST:** 2006
SQ FT: 3,050
SALES (est): 840.3K **Privately Held**
WEB: www.macom.com
SIC: 3674 Semiconductors & related devices

(G-8967)
TRU MENSION MFG SOLUTIONS
3900 Dow Rd Ste C (32934-9255)
PHONE..................................321 255-4665
Kenneth J Sheehan, *President*
Kenneth Sheehan, *Vice Pres*
EMP: 8 **EST:** 1986
SALES (est): 827.6K **Privately Held**
SIC: 3499 3334 Machine bases, metal; pigs, aluminum

(G-8968)
UROSHAPE LLC
Also Called: Sola Therapy
1130 S Harbor City Blvd (32901-1947)
PHONE..................................321 960-2484
Ralph Zipper, *CEO*
Steve Bowers, *Vice Pres*
EMP: 10 **EST:** 2010
SALES (est): 1.2MM **Privately Held**
SIC: 3841 5047 Surgical & medical instruments; medical instruments & equipment, blood & bone work; instruments, surgical & medical

(G-8969)
US BLANKS LLC
282 N Wickham Rd (32935-8650)
PHONE..................................321 253-3626
EMP: 48
SALES (corp-wide): 7.8MM **Privately Held**
WEB: www.usblanks.com
SIC: 2821 Plastics materials & resins
PA: Us Blanks, Llc
14700 S San Pedro St
Gardena CA 90248
310 225-6774

(G-8970)
VERTICAL FLIGHT TECHNOLOGY INC
3385 Shady Run Rd (32934-8567)
PHONE..................................407 687-3126
Laura Rvtd Melnik, *Principal*
EMP: 12 **EST:** 2012
SALES (est): 690.8K **Privately Held**
WEB: www.demonheli.com
SIC: 2591 Blinds vertical

(G-8971)
VIATECH OF DELAWARE INC
Also Called: Skycross
7341 Office Park Pl # 102 (32940-8280)
PHONE..................................321 308-6600
EMP: 24
SQ FT: 10,000
SALES (est): 1.9MM **Privately Held**
SIC: 3663 Design/Mfg Wireless Antennas

(G-8972)
VISION BLOCKS INC
1634 Cypress Ave (32935-5931)
PHONE..................................321 254-7478
Judy Pollard, *President*
Allan Pollard, *General Mgr*
EMP: 10 **EST:** 1979
SQ FT: 6,000
SALES (est): 500K **Privately Held**
WEB: www.visionblocks.com
SIC: 3231 Safety glass: made from purchased glass

(G-8973)
VISION SYSTEMS NORTH AMERICA
1801 Penn St Ste 104 (32901-2693)
PHONE..................................321 265-5110
Carl Putman, *President*
Catherine Robin, *President*
Robin Bokilo, *COO*
EMP: 14 **EST:** 2013
SALES (est): 3.5MM
SALES (corp-wide): 1.3MM **Privately Held**
WEB: www.vision-systems.fr
SIC: 3728 Aircraft parts & equipment
HQ: Vision Systems Corporate
Zone Industrielle
Brignais 69530
953 522-056

(G-8974)
WHITTINGTON ENERGY CO
730 E Strawbridge Ave # 205 (32901-4912)
PHONE..................................321 984-2128
Richard A Whittington, *President*
Barbara C Whittington, *Vice Pres*
EMP: 7 **EST:** 1996
SALES (est): 484.4K **Privately Held**
SIC: 1382 Oil & gas exploration services

(G-8975)
WINCHSTER INTERCONNECT RF CORP
3950 Dow Rd (32934-8902)
PHONE..................................800 881-9689
EMP: 30
SALES (corp-wide): 14.3B **Privately Held**
SIC: 3678 Electronic connectors
HQ: Winchester Interconnect Rf Corporation
245 Lynnfield St
Peabody MA 01960
978 532-0775

(G-8976)
WINCHSTER INTRCNNECT HRMTICS L (HQ)
3950 Dow Rd (32934-8901)
PHONE..................................321 254-4067
Kevin Perhamus, *CEO*
Tom Drago, *Vice Pres*
Vincent Garrett, *Vice Pres*
▲ **EMP:** 65 **EST:** 2003
SQ FT: 25,000
SALES (est): 24.5MM **Privately Held**
WEB: www.snowphipps.com
SIC: 3679 Hermetic seals for electronic equipment

(G-8977)
WIND RIVER SYSTEMS INC
100 Rialto Pl Ste 525 (32901-3007)
PHONE..................................321 726-9463
Brian Donaldson, *Manager*
EMP: 9 **Privately Held**
WEB: www.windriver.com
SIC: 7372 Application computer software
HQ: Wind River Systems, Inc.
500 Wind River Way
Alameda CA 94501
510 748-4100

(G-8978)
YP ADVRTISING PUBG LLC NOT LLC
Also Called: BellSouth
100 Rialto Pl Ste 300 (32901-3073)
PHONE..................................321 956-5400
Jim Watkins, *Director*
EMP: 90
SALES (corp-wide): 1.4B **Publicly Held**
SIC: 2741 Directories: publishing only, not printed on site
HQ: Yp Advertising & Publishing Llc (Not Llc)
2247 Northlake Pkwy
Tucker GA 30084

Melbourne Beach
Brevard County

(G-8979)
INFINTY GENOME SCIENCES INC
301 Riverside Dr (32951-2141)
PHONE..................................321 327-7365
John Detter, *Principal*
EMP: 6 **EST:** 2017
SALES (est): 195.8K **Privately Held**
SIC: 2835 Microbiology & virology diagnostic products

(G-8980)
INSPIRED THERAPEUTICS LLC
7309 S Highway A1a (32951-3514)
PHONE..................................339 222-0847
Kurt Dasse, *CEO*
Priscilla Petit, *Principal*
Barry Gellman, *COO*
John Whiting, *CFO*
EMP: 7 **EST:** 2017
SALES (est): 104.8K **Privately Held**
SIC: 3841 Surgical & medical instruments

(G-8981)
PINNACLE FOODS INC
5905 S Highway A1a (32951-3704)
PHONE..................................321 952-7926
Mohammed Elguindy, *President*
Alice Elguindy, *Vice Pres*
EMP: 5 **EST:** 1991
SQ FT: 8,000
SALES (est): 503.4K **Privately Held**
SIC: 2066 Chocolate & cocoa products

(G-8982)
QUANTUM PHARMACEUTICALS LLC
429 Riverview Ln (32951-2716)
PHONE..................................321 724-0625
Steven Strauss,
Mark Steele,
Valerie Strauss,
EMP: 5 **EST:** 2004
SALES (est): 446.5K **Privately Held**
SIC: 2834 Proprietary drug products

(G-8983)
RAPID REPRODUCTIONS LLC
108 Seagrape Rd (32951-4029)
PHONE..................................607 843-2221
Bryant Latourette, *Mng Member*
EMP: 8 **EST:** 1977
SALES (est): 680K **Privately Held**
WEB: www.waterproofcopies.com
SIC: 2752 Commercial printing, offset

(G-8984)
SALTY INDUSTRIES LLC
231 6th Ave (32951-2322)
PHONE..................................321 626-6331
George D Hirst, *Principal*
EMP: 5 **EST:** 2016
SALES (est): 395.3K **Privately Held**
WEB: www.saltyindustriesllc.com
SIC: 3999 Manufacturing industries

Melrose
Putnam County

(G-8985)
GINGHAM GATOR LLC
8136 Alderman Rd (32666-8818)
PHONE..................................352 475-1985
Beth Frost, *Principal*
EMP: 6 **EST:** 2017
SALES (est): 85.4K **Privately Held**
SIC: 2211 Ginghams

(G-8986)
LAKE AREA WATERSPORTS LLC
Also Called: Pro Water Sports
829 N State Road 21 (32666-4162)
PHONE..................................352 475-3434
Scott Diley, *Manager*
Chad Hovsepian,
EMP: 8 **EST:** 2004
SQ FT: 2,000
SALES (est): 1.2MM **Privately Held**
WEB: www.lakeareawatersports.com
SIC: 3949 5091 Water sports equipment; boats, canoes, watercrafts & equipment

Merritt Island
Brevard County

(G-8987)
AIR LIQUIDE LARGE INDS US LP
7007 N Courtenay Pkwy (32953-7112)
PHONE..................................321 452-2214
Rudy Strickland, *Manager*
EMP: 7
SQ FT: 7,320
SALES (corp-wide): 102.6MM **Privately Held**
WEB: www.airliquide.com
SIC: 2813 Industrial gases
HQ: Air Liquide Large Industries U.S. Lp
9811 Katy Fwy Ste 100
Houston TX 77024
713 624-8000

(G-8988)
AIRBUS ONEWEB SATELLITES LLC (PA)
8301 Newspace Dr (32953-6700)
PHONE..................................321 735-8446
Anthony Gingiss, *CEO*
James Hinds, *COO*
Roman Winzelle, *CFO*
Kai Schmidt, *Persnl Dir*
Laura Kraus, *Director*
EMP: 143 **EST:** 2017
SALES (est): 51.2MM **Privately Held**
WEB: www.onewebsatellites.com
SIC: 3721 Aircraft

(G-8989)
AIRBUS ONWEB STLLTES N AMER LL (HQ)
8301 Newspace Dr (32953-6700)
PHONE..................................321 522-6645
James Hinds, *CEO*
Anthony Gingiss, *CEO*
Roman Winzelle, *CFO*
Kai Schmidt, *Persnl Dir*
Laura Kraus, *Director*
EMP: 190 **EST:** 2015
SALES (est): 51.2MM **Privately Held**
WEB: www.onewebsatellites.com
SIC: 3663 Space satellite communications equipment
PA: Airbus Oneweb Satellites Llc
8301 Newspace Dr
Merritt Island FL 32953
321 735-8446

(G-8990)
AIRBUS ONWEB STLLTES N AMER LL
8301 Newspace Dr (32953-6700)
PHONE..................................321 522-6645
John Timmermann, *Principal*
EMP: 100
SALES (corp-wide): 51.2MM **Privately Held**
SIC: 3663 Space satellite communications equipment
HQ: Airbus Oneweb Satellites North America Llc
8301 Newspace Dr
Merritt Island FL 32953
321 522-6645

(G-8991)
ATLANTIC COAST ROOFING & METAL
350 Myrtice Ave Ste 201 (32953-4720)
PHONE..................................321 449-9494
David R Lightholder Jr, *Principal*
EMP: 7 **EST:** 2009
SALES (est): 655.6K **Privately Held**
SIC: 3499 Fabricated metal products

(G-8992)
AUTOCRAFT MANUFACTURING CO
810 Kemp St (32952-3768)
P.O. Box 540475 (32954-0475)
PHONE..................................321 453-1850

Martha Mc Leod, *President*
▲ **EMP:** 28 **EST:** 1964
SQ FT: 65,000
SALES (est): 1.1MM **Privately Held**
WEB: www.autocraftmfg.com
SIC: 3714 3732 3647 Motor vehicle parts & accessories; boat building & repairing; vehicular lighting equipment

(G-8993)
BILL & RENEE ENTERPRISES
Also Called: PIP Printing
275 Magnolia Ave Ste 2 (32952-4839)
PHONE.................................321 452-2800
Renee Frederick, *President*
Bill Frederick, *Vice Pres*
EMP: 9 **EST:** 1996
SQ FT: 1,300
SALES (est): 1MM **Privately Held**
WEB: www.pip.com
SIC: 2789 2752 Bookbinding & related work; commercial printing, lithographic

(G-8994)
BLUE ORIGIN FLORIDA LLC (HQ)
8082 Space Commerce Way (32953-8703)
PHONE.................................253 437-9300
Bob Smith, *President*
EMP: 100 **EST:** 2015
SALES (est): 64.5MM **Privately Held**
WEB: www.blueorigin.com
SIC: 3761 Guided missiles & space vehicles

(G-8995)
BREVARD SOFTBALL MAGAZINE INC
400 Nora Ave (32952-5123)
PHONE.................................321 453-3711
Gene Smith, *President*
EMP: 10 **EST:** 1996
SALES (est): 845.9K **Privately Held**
WEB: www.softballmag.com
SIC: 2721 8641 Magazines: publishing & printing; civic social & fraternal associations

(G-8996)
BRUNSWICK BOAT GROUP
100 Sea Ray Dr (32953-4104)
PHONE.................................321 449-8754
EMP: 7 **EST:** 2019
SALES (est): 258.6K **Privately Held**
WEB: www.jerseygirlcleaning.com
SIC: 3732 Boat building & repairing

(G-8997)
CAPTIVATED COATINGS LLC
310 Manor Dr (32952-3739)
PHONE.................................321 446-6619
Thomas Williams, *Principal*
EMP: 6 **EST:** 2017
SALES (est): 95.7K **Privately Held**
SIC: 3479 Metal coating & allied service

(G-8998)
CENTRAL FLORIDA PLATING INC
675 Cypress Dr (32952-3719)
PHONE.................................321 452-7234
Tibor Menyhart, *President*
Barbara Menyhart, *Vice Pres*
Cal Dixon, *Human Res Dir*
Davis Joan, *Admin Sec*
EMP: 5 **EST:** 1986
SQ FT: 4,000
SALES (est): 500K **Privately Held**
WEB: www.centralfloridaplating.com
SIC: 3471 Electroplating of metals or formed products

(G-8999)
DARK STORM MANUFACTURING LLC ✪
3390 N Courtenay Pkwy (32953-8310)
PHONE.................................516 983-3473
Edward Newman, *Mng Member*
EMP: 5 **EST:** 2021
SALES (est): 332.1K **Privately Held**
SIC: 3484 Small arms

(G-9000)
EMF INC
Also Called: Engineering & Met Fabrication
124 Imperial St (32952-3630)
PHONE.................................321 453-3670
David W Clark, *President*
Jeff Flick, *Vice Pres*
James Hoskins, *Project Mgr*
Jim Lacey, *Engineer*
Jorge Parra, *Design Engr*
EMP: 117 **EST:** 1971
SQ FT: 25,000
SALES (est): 25.1MM **Privately Held**
WEB: www.emfinc.net
SIC: 3441 7692 Fabricated structural metal; welding repair

(G-9001)
FINE INDUSTRIES CORPORATION
1591 Stafford Ave (32952-5453)
PHONE.................................321 452-6956
James Finerfrock, *Principal*
EMP: 6 **EST:** 2010
SALES (est): 59.6K **Privately Held**
SIC: 3999 Manufacturing industries

(G-9002)
HEALTH STAR INC
625 E Merritt Ave Ste I (32953-3483)
PHONE.................................321 914-6012
Bryan Sylver, *President*
Bryan B Sylver, *Principal*
EMP: 8 **EST:** 2015
SALES (est): 398.4K **Privately Held**
SIC: 3841 Surgical & medical instruments

(G-9003)
MERRITT PRECISION TECH INC
3425 N Courtenay Pkwy (32953-8315)
PHONE.................................321 453-2334
Douglas Keehn, *President*
Ben Ousley, *Vice Pres*
EMP: 7 **EST:** 2002
SQ FT: 7,500
SALES (est): 643.4K **Privately Held**
WEB: www.merrittprecision.com
SIC: 3229 2221 Glass fiber products; fiberglass fabrics

(G-9004)
MIGRANDY CORP
675 Cypress Dr (32952-3719)
PHONE.................................321 459-0044
Tibor Menyhart, *President*
Barbara Menyhart, *Vice Pres*
Mike Menyhart, *Plant Mgr*
EMP: 38 **EST:** 1981
SQ FT: 15,000
SALES (est): 2.2MM **Privately Held**
WEB: www.migrandy.com
SIC: 3452 3412 Screws, metal; barrels, shipping: metal

(G-9005)
ORBITAL SCIENCES LLC
5335 N Courtenay Pkwy (32953-7327)
PHONE.................................703 406-5474
Blake Larson, *Principal*
EMP: 343 **Publicly Held**
WEB: www.northropgrumman.com
SIC: 3812 Defense systems & equipment; aircraft control instruments; navigational systems & instruments
HQ: Orbital Sciences Llc
2980 Fairview Park Dr
Falls Church VA 22042

(G-9006)
PERII INC
Also Called: Perii Software
2755 N Bnana Rver Dr Ste (32952)
PHONE.................................321 253-2269
James E Witcher, *President*
EMP: 7 **EST:** 2003
SALES (est): 200K **Privately Held**
SIC: 7372 Prepackaged software

(G-9007)
REDSTONE CORPORATION
606 Gladiola St Hngr 255 (32952-3728)
PHONE.................................321 213-2135
Michael Kruse, *President*
Thorwald Eide, *Vice Pres*
Dominic Gilbert, *CFO*
EMP: 7 **EST:** 2008
SQ FT: 10,000
SALES (est): 463.2K **Privately Held**
SIC: 3728 8711 8742 Aircraft parts & equipment; engineering services; aviation &/or aeronautical engineering; management consulting services

(G-9008)
SCREEN TECH
1501 Bermuda Ave (32952-5740)
PHONE.................................321 536-6091
Douglas Buford, *Principal*
EMP: 6 **EST:** 2005
SALES (est): 427.4K **Privately Held**
SIC: 2759 Screen printing

(G-9009)
SEA RAY BOATS INC
Also Called: Merritt Island Plant
350 Sea Ray Dr (32953-4194)
PHONE.................................321 459-9463
Jim Barclay, *Manager*
Jason Brown, *Supervisor*
Jim Walden, *Supervisor*
EMP: 120
SALES (corp-wide): 4.3B **Publicly Held**
WEB: www.searay.com
SIC: 3732 Boats, fiberglass: building & repairing
HQ: Sea Ray Boats, Inc.
800 S Gay St Ste 1200
Knoxville TN 37929
865 522-4181

(G-9010)
SEA RAY BOATS INC
Sykes Creek Division
350 Sea Ray Dr (32953-4194)
PHONE.................................321 459-2930
Steve Fielder, *Manager*
EMP: 120
SALES (corp-wide): 4.3B **Publicly Held**
WEB: www.searay.com
SIC: 3732 Boats, fiberglass: building & repairing
HQ: Sea Ray Boats, Inc.
800 S Gay St Ste 1200
Knoxville TN 37929
865 522-4181

(G-9011)
SEA RAY BOATS INC
Also Called: Sea Ray PD&e
200 Sea Ray Dr (32953-4195)
PHONE.................................321 452-9876
Robert Macias, *Electrical Engi*
Terry McNew, *Manager*
EMP: 120
SALES (corp-wide): 4.3B **Publicly Held**
WEB: www.searay.com
SIC: 3732 Boats, fiberglass: building & repairing
HQ: Sea Ray Boats, Inc.
800 S Gay St Ste 1200
Knoxville TN 37929
865 522-4181

(G-9012)
SEALIFT LLC
3390 N Courtenay Pkwy A (32953-8341)
PHONE.................................321 638-0301
Stephen Johns, *Owner*
▼ **EMP:** 13 **EST:** 2005
SALES (est): 285K **Privately Held**
WEB: www.sealiftusa.com
SIC: 3569 Jacks, hydraulic

(G-9013)
SEASIDE STITCHING
1505 Martin Blvd (32952-5515)
PHONE.................................321 455-6427
Lynda Jean Brill, *Owner*
EMP: 6 **EST:** 2011
SALES (est): 59.2K **Privately Held**
SIC: 2395 Embroidery & art needlework

(G-9014)
STAMP CONCRETE & PAVERS INC
230 Cherry Ave (32953-4310)
PHONE.................................561 880-1527
Denise A Spiva, *Principal*
EMP: 9 **EST:** 2012
SALES (est): 231.9K **Privately Held**
SIC: 3531 Pavers

(G-9015)
SUNDOG SOFTWARE LLC
Also Called: Sundog Education
4022 Tradewinds Trl (32953-8077)
PHONE.................................425 635-8683
Frank Kane,
EMP: 5 **EST:** 2009
SALES (est): 414K **Privately Held**
WEB: www.sundog-soft.com
SIC: 7372 Business oriented computer software

(G-9016)
TRASPORT JOHN
Also Called: American Cabinet Mill & Supply
645 S Plumosa St Ste 5 (32952-3108)
PHONE.................................321 452-6789
John Trasport, *Owner*
EMP: 7 **EST:** 1992
SALES (est): 573.1K **Privately Held**
SIC: 2541 Cabinets, except refrigerated: show, display, etc.: wood

(G-9017)
TROPICAL SIGNS & GRAPHICS
425 Deb Ln (32952-4915)
PHONE.................................321 458-7742
Maria G Christel, *Principal*
EMP: 6 **EST:** 2016
SALES (est): 214.4K **Privately Held**
WEB: www.tropicalsignsmerrittisland.com
SIC: 3993 Signs & advertising specialties

(G-9018)
TUA SYSTEMS INC
Also Called: AMS
3645 N Courtenay Pkwy (32953-8104)
PHONE.................................321 453-3200
Ted Unkel Jr, *President*
EMP: 9 **EST:** 1988
SQ FT: 7,500
SALES (est): 945.5K **Privately Held**
WEB: www.tua-systems.com
SIC: 3479 Coating of metals & formed products

(G-9019)
TWINOXIDE-USA INC
3700 N Courtenay Pkwy (32953-8193)
PHONE.................................321 207-8524
Donald Lenci, *CEO*
Johannes G Verwater, *President*
EMP: 9 **EST:** 2015
SALES (est): 261.2K **Privately Held**
WEB: www.twinoxide.us
SIC: 3589 Water treatment equipment, industrial

Miami
Miami-Dade County

(G-9020)
123 DOLLAR PLUS INC
7181 Sw 8th St (33144-4659)
PHONE.................................305 456-4561
Jazmin G Martinez, *Principal*
EMP: 6 **EST:** 2010
SALES (est): 122K **Privately Held**
SIC: 3643 Outlets, electric: convenience

(G-9021)
1600 LENOX LLC
7350 Biscayne Blvd (33138-5151)
PHONE.................................786 360-2553
EMP: 6 **EST:** 2018
SALES (est): 437.9K **Privately Held**
SIC: 3585 Refrigeration & heating equipment

(G-9022)
1SOURCE BIOTECHNOLOGY LLC
4300 Sw 73rd Ave (33155-4512)
PHONE.................................305 668-5888
Robert Dicrisci, *Principal*
EMP: 8 **EST:** 2011
SALES (est): 312.6K **Privately Held**
SIC: 2834 Pharmaceutical preparations

(G-9023)
2 GUYS COMPANY
9315 Sw 77th Ave Apt 228 (33156-7922)
PHONE.................................786 970-9275

Daniel Avalos, *Vice Pres*
EMP: 6 **EST:** 2016
SALES (est): 281.4K **Privately Held**
SIC: 3999 Candles

(G-9024)
2U SERVICE CORP
7255 Nw 68th St Ste 1 (33166-3015)
PHONE..................................786 219-6564
Maria G Molina, *Principal*
EMP: 8 **EST:** 2017
SALES (est): 96.2K **Privately Held**
SIC: 3993 Signs & advertising specialties

(G-9025)
360 ENERGY SOLUTIONS LLC
7650 Nw 50th St (33166-4700)
PHONE..................................786 348-2156
Antonio Noa, *President*
Bryan Garcia, *Principal*
EMP: 22 **EST:** 2013
SALES: 4.7MM **Privately Held**
WEB: www.360energysolutions.net
SIC: 3519 3621 Gas engine rebuilding; motors & generators; power generators

(G-9026)
3LMETALS INC
12987 Sw 19th Ter (33175-1309)
PHONE..................................305 497-4038
Erick Arce Zubizarreta, *Principal*
EMP: 7 **EST:** 2018
SALES (est): 323.6K **Privately Held**
SIC: 3441 Fabricated structural metal

(G-9027)
4 OVER LLC
16500 Nw 15th Ave (33169-5620)
PHONE..................................818 246-1170
Zarik Megerdichian, *CEO*
EMP: 10
SALES (corp-wide): 172.3MM **Privately Held**
WEB: www.4over.com
SIC: 2759 Commercial printing
HQ: 4 Over, Llc
5900 San Fernando Rd D
Glendale CA 91202
818 246-1170

(G-9028)
4ELEMENTUM LLC
9149 Sw 157th Ct (33196-1167)
PHONE..................................305 989-1106
Jennifer Pinillos, *Chairman*
EMP: 7 **EST:** 2013
SALES (est): 250.8K **Privately Held**
WEB: www.4elementum.com
SIC: 2844 Toilet preparations

(G-9029)
A & A ORTHOPEDICS MFG
12250 Sw 129th Ct Ste 101 (33186-6492)
PHONE..................................305 256-8119
Migdalia Ugarte, *President*
EMP: 6 **EST:** 2016
SQ FT: 1,500
SALES (est): 387.9K **Privately Held**
WEB: www.aaorthopedics.com
SIC: 3842 Abdominal supporters, braces & trusses; cervical collars; braces, orthopedic; braces, elastic

(G-9030)
A & C CONCRETE PRODUCTS INC
9741 Sw 168th Ter (33157-4325)
P.O. Box 561094 (33256-1094)
PHONE..................................305 232-1631
David E Cunningham, *President*
EMP: 5 **EST:** 2001
SQ FT: 1,566
SALES (est): 345K **Privately Held**
SIC: 3272 Concrete products

(G-9031)
A & J AEROSPACE CORP
8356 Nw 66th St (33166-2674)
PHONE..................................786 564-9986
Mayra Martin, *Principal*
EMP: 10 **EST:** 2018
SALES (est): 270.4K **Privately Held**
SIC: 3599 Machine shop, jobbing & repair

(G-9032)
A & S ENTERTAINMENT LLC
Also Called: Office, The
250 Ne 183rd St (33179-4507)
PHONE..................................305 627-3456
Alix Beaubrun, *Mng Member*
Claudette M Pierre,
▼ **EMP:** 10 **EST:** 2010
SALES (est): 958.9K **Privately Held**
SIC: 2253 Lounge, bed & leisurewear

(G-9033)
A 1 A SIGNS & SERVICE INC
Also Called: A 1a Displays
8965 Ne 10th Ave (33138-3337)
PHONE..................................305 757-6950
Ira Knigin, *President*
Paula Knigin, *Vice Pres*
EMP: 10 **EST:** 1968
SQ FT: 8,000
SALES (est): 410.4K **Privately Held**
WEB: www.a1asigns.com
SIC: 3993 Electric signs

(G-9034)
A AND A CONCRETE BLOCK INC
4410 Sw 115th Ave (33165-5526)
PHONE..................................305 986-5128
Jose Atanay, *Principal*
EMP: 6 **EST:** 2006
SALES (est): 130.6K **Privately Held**
SIC: 3271 Blocks, concrete or cinder: standard

(G-9035)
A AND A ORTHOPEDICS INC
12250 Sw 129th Ct Ste 101 (33186-6492)
P.O. Box 441645 (33144-1645)
PHONE..................................305 256-8119
Migdalia Ugarte, *President*
EMP: 7 **EST:** 2000
SALES (est): 520K **Privately Held**
WEB: www.aaorthopedics.com
SIC: 3842 Prosthetic appliances

(G-9036)
A D COACHES CORNER INC
13365 Sw 135th Ave # 102 (33186-6220)
PHONE..................................786 242-2229
Alexander Diaz, *President*
EMP: 7 **EST:** 2005
SQ FT: 2,340
SALES (est): 252.9K **Privately Held**
WEB: www.coachscornermiami.com
SIC: 2759 Screen printing

(G-9037)
A FINE PRINT OF MIAMI LLC
Also Called: Lucy Print
2420 Sw 27th Ave (33145-3655)
PHONE..................................305 441-5263
Lucia Landsberg, *Mng Member*
EMP: 5 **EST:** 2008
SALES (est): 305.4K **Privately Held**
SIC: 2752 Commercial printing, offset

(G-9038)
A G A ELECTRONICS CORP
Also Called: AGA
7209 Nw 41st St (33166-6711)
PHONE..................................305 592-1860
Andre M Apaid, *President*
Renaldo Perez, *General Mgr*
Gerald Apaid, *Vice Pres*
Carlos Perez, *Treasurer*
◆ **EMP:** 12 **EST:** 1977
SQ FT: 13,000
SALES (est): 2.8MM **Privately Held**
WEB: www.agacorp.com
SIC: 2321 2361 2311 Men's & boys' sports & polo shirts; t-shirts & tops: girls', children's & infants'; men's & boys' uniforms

(G-9039)
A H WOODCRAFTER
7313 Nw 56th St (33166-4203)
PHONE..................................305 885-2136
Alcides Hernandez, *Principal*
EMP: 5 **EST:** 2008
SALES (est): 430.1K **Privately Held**
SIC: 3553 Bandsaws, woodworking

(G-9040)
A IZQUIERDO ENTERPRISES LLC
12691 Nw 9th Way (33182-2061)
PHONE..................................786 558-6657
Jesus Izquierdo, *Principal*
EMP: 6 **EST:** 2016
SALES (est): 120.3K **Privately Held**
SIC: 2431 Millwork

(G-9041)
A PLUS LAMINATION & FINSHG INC
5559 Nw 36th Ave (33142-2709)
PHONE..................................305 636-9888
Nubia Marcela Perez, *Owner*
EMP: 11 **EST:** 2006
SALES (est): 1MM **Privately Held**
WEB: www.apluslam.com
SIC: 2671 Paper coated or laminated for packaging

(G-9042)
A R COMPONENTS CORP
8544 Nw 66th St (33166-2635)
PHONE..................................786 703-8456
Ana Maria Soto Quintana, *President*
EMP: 15 **EST:** 2016
SALES (est): 1.2MM **Privately Held**
WEB: www.aarcorp.com
SIC: 3728 Aircraft parts & equipment

(G-9043)
A SOTOLONGO POLISHING MARBLE C
5435 Sw 99th Ct (33165-7138)
PHONE..................................305 271-7957
Adolfo Sotolongo, *Principal*
EMP: 5 **EST:** 2002
SALES (est): 326K **Privately Held**
SIC: 3471 Polishing, metals or formed products

(G-9044)
A&K SHEET METAL LLC
9720 Nw 4th Ln (33172-4002)
PHONE..................................786 351-8313
Alvaro Luquez, *Principal*
EMP: 6 **EST:** 2018
SALES (est): 322.2K **Privately Held**
WEB: www.ak-sheet-metal.business.site
SIC: 3444 Sheet metalwork

(G-9045)
A-MARI-MIX LLC
9700 Sw 24th St (33165-7500)
PHONE..................................305 603-9134
Mariela Reyes, *Principal*
EMP: 11 **EST:** 2014
SALES (est): 1.2MM **Privately Held**
WEB: www.amarimix.com
SIC: 3273 Ready-mixed concrete

(G-9046)
A-N-L HOME SOLUTIONS LLC ✪
1000 Ne 196th St (33179-3514)
PHONE..................................954 648-2623
Nahum Gabriel,
EMP: 10 **EST:** 2020
SALES (est): 419K **Privately Held**
SIC: 3651 Home entertainment equipment, electronic

(G-9047)
A1CM
5521 Nw 7th Ave (33127-1401)
PHONE..................................954 716-3216
EMP: 5 **EST:** 2018
SALES (est): 483.3K **Privately Held**
WEB: www.a1-cm.com
SIC: 2591 Window blinds

(G-9048)
A2F LLC
Also Called: COMPOUND MIAMI THE
2010 Nw Miami Ct Unit A (33127-4920)
PHONE..................................305 984-9205
Bewille Datelma, *CEO*
EMP: 9 **EST:** 2016
SALES (est): 447.4K **Privately Held**
SIC: 2741 7999 7922 Miscellaneous publishing; night club, not serving alcoholic beverages; entertainment promotion

(G-9049)
AAW PRODUCTS INC
Also Called: Mdg Tools
825 Brckhllday Dr Ste 246 (33130)
PHONE..................................305 330-6863
Andre Woolery, *President*
▲ **EMP:** 5 **EST:** 2005
SALES (est): 485.1K **Privately Held**
WEB: www.magnogrip.com
SIC: 3545 Tool holders

(G-9050)
AB USED PALLETS INC
6350 Nw 72nd Ave (33166-3626)
P.O. Box 667930 (33166-9408)
PHONE..................................305 594-2776
Anna Lesteiro, *Owner*
EMP: 12 **EST:** 2001
SQ FT: 1,080
SALES (est): 198K **Privately Held**
WEB: www.premier-pallets.com
SIC: 2448 3999 Pallets, wood; manufacturing industries

(G-9051)
AB WOOD WORK INC
13365 Sw 135th Ave Ste 10 (33186-8116)
PHONE..................................786 701-3611
Alexander Briceno, *Principal*
EMP: 6 **EST:** 2016
SALES (est): 93.8K **Privately Held**
SIC: 2431 Millwork

(G-9052)
ABAKAN INC (PA)
2665 S Byshr Dr Ste 450 (33133-5410)
PHONE..................................786 206-5368
Robert H Miller, *President*
Stephen Goss, *COO*
EMP: 8 **EST:** 2009
SQ FT: 800
SALES (est): 4.1MM **Privately Held**
WEB: www.abakaninc.com
SIC: 3479 Coating of metals & formed products

(G-9053)
ABB INC
Also Called: A B B Power Technolgies Div
8785 Sw 165th Ave Ste 302 (33193-5828)
PHONE..................................305 471-0844
Rafael Cortes, *Engineer*
Guillermo Rodriguez, *Manager*
Billy Martinez, *Manager*
EMP: 63
SALES (corp-wide): 26.1B **Privately Held**
WEB: www.global.abb
SIC: 3613 3625 3675 3612 Switchgear & switchboard apparatus; distribution boards, electric; generator control & metering panels; relays & industrial controls; electronic capacitors; power & distribution transformers
HQ: Abb Inc.
305 Gregson Dr
Cary NC 27511

(G-9054)
ABC SHUTTERS PROTECTION CORP
7420 Sw 38th St (33155-6612)
PHONE..................................785 547-9527
Alberto Quile, *Principal*
EMP: 6 **EST:** 2018
SALES (est): 203K **Privately Held**
SIC: 3442 Shutters, door or window: metal

(G-9055)
ABCO PRODUCTS INC
6800 Nw 36th Ave (33147-6504)
PHONE..................................888 694-2226
Carlos Albir Jr, *President*
Isacio Albir, *Vice Pres*
Christopher Meaney, *Vice Pres*
◆ **EMP:** 22 **EST:** 1979
SQ FT: 5,000
SALES (est): 8.9MM **Privately Held**
WEB: www.abcoproducts.com
SIC: 3069 5199 Floor coverings, rubber; broom, mop & paint handles

(G-9056)
ABOVE GROUND LEVEL AEROSPACE
Also Called: Agl Aerospace
13420 Sw 131st St (33186-5817)
PHONE..............................305 713-2629
Francisco A Aracena, *President*
Dorys Acena, *General Mgr*
EMP: 12 **EST:** 2018
SALES (est): 1MM **Privately Held**
WEB: www.aglaerospace.com
SIC: 3721 Aircraft

(G-9057)
ABRACOL NORTH AMERICA CORP
5220 Nw 72nd Ave Ste 22 (33166-4858)
PHONE..............................305 431-5596
Peter Chirdaris, *President*
EMP: 5 **EST:** 2015
SALES (est): 494.6K **Privately Held**
SIC: 3291 Aluminum oxide (fused) abrasives

(G-9058)
ACASI MACHINERY INC
7085 Nw 46th St (33166-5605)
PHONE..............................305 805-8533
Isaac Possin, *President*
Fermin Diaz, *Sales Dir*
Maria Brenes, *Office Mgr*
◆ **EMP:** 15 **EST:** 2002
SQ FT: 8,000
SALES (est): 4.5MM **Privately Held**
WEB: www.acasi.com
SIC: 3565 Packaging machinery

(G-9059)
ACCAR LTD INC
Also Called: Bezels For Watches
56 Ne 1st St (33132-2412)
PHONE..............................305 375-0620
Joseph Akar, *President*
EMP: 5 **EST:** 1993
SQ FT: 3,400
SALES (est): 659.1K **Privately Held**
WEB: www.accarjewelry.com
SIC: 3911 5094 Jewelry, precious metal; jewelry & precious stones

(G-9060)
ACCENDO TOBACCO LLC
7575 Nw 70th St (33166-2815)
PHONE..............................305 407-2222
William Hill, *Mng Member*
EMP: 5 **EST:** 2013
SALES (est): 1.1MM **Privately Held**
SIC: 2131 Smoking tobacco
PA: Ignis Group Inc.
7575 Nw 70th St
Miami FL 33166
305 407-2222

(G-9061)
ACE PRINTING INC
Also Called: Ace Industries
2846 Nw 79th Ave (33122-1033)
PHONE..............................305 358-2572
Mario Cerratto, *President*
Andrea Ferreti, *Sales Staff*
▼ **EMP:** 12 **EST:** 1958
SQ FT: 12,000
SALES (est): 382.2K **Privately Held**
WEB: www.ace-printing.net
SIC: 2752 2796 3953 Commercial printing, offset; platemaking services; marking devices

(G-9062)
ACE RESTORATION SERVICES LLC
11921 Sw 130th St Ste 402 (33186-5256)
PHONE..............................786 487-1870
Juan Cabrera,
EMP: 15 **EST:** 2010
SALES (est): 1.6MM **Privately Held**
WEB: www.ace2restore.com
SIC: 3842 Cosmetic restorations

(G-9063)
ACE SALES CORP
Also Called: Sanacare
8085 Nw 68th St (33166-2794)
P.O. Box 561126 (33256-1126)
PHONE..............................305 835-0310
Frank A Maresma, *President*
Tony Falcon, *Director*
▼ **EMP:** 10 **EST:** 1957
SALES (est): 2.7MM **Privately Held**
WEB: www.sanacare.com
SIC: 3842 Linemen's safety belts

(G-9064)
ACM SCREEN PRINTING INC
2106 Nw 22nd Ct (33142-7346)
PHONE..............................305 547-1552
Luis Gutierrez, *President*
▼ **EMP:** 8 **EST:** 1996
SALES (est): 656.6K **Privately Held**
WEB: www.acmscreenprinting.com
SIC: 2759 7389 Screen printing; embroidering of advertising on shirts, etc.

(G-9065)
ACME SERVICE CORP
Also Called: Acme Miami
1290 Nw 74th St (33147-6428)
P.O. Box 380876 (33238-0876)
PHONE..............................305 836-4800
Chuck Levine, *President*
Gloria Levine, *Advt Staff*
▼ **EMP:** 10 **EST:** 1965
SQ FT: 14,400
SALES (est): 1.7MM **Privately Held**
WEB: www.acmemiami.com
SIC: 3585 3632 3621 7539 Refrigeration equipment, complete; household refrigerators & freezers; motors & generators; powertrain components repair services; pumps & pumping equipment

(G-9066)
ACRYPLEX INC
2380 Nw 21st Ter Unit A (33142-7206)
PHONE..............................305 633-7636
Aileen Lastra, *President*
Tomas Lastra, *President*
Mayra E Lastra, *Corp Secy*
Aileen I Lastra, *Vice Pres*
EMP: 6 **EST:** 1987
SQ FT: 3,500
SALES (est): 940.7K **Privately Held**
WEB: www.acryplexmiami.com
SIC: 3083 3732 1751 2542 Plastic finished products, laminated; boats, rigid: plastics; cabinet & finish carpentry; office & store showcases & display fixtures; marine hardware; doors, glass: made from purchased glass

(G-9067)
ACTION PRINTING INC
612 Nw 134th Ave (33182-1669)
PHONE..............................305 592-4646
William Tamayo, *President*
EMP: 5 **EST:** 1998
SALES (est): 344.8K **Privately Held**
WEB: www.actionprintinginc.com
SIC: 2752 Commercial printing, offset

(G-9068)
ADELMAN STEEL CORP
12040 Sw 113th Ave (33176-4402)
PHONE..............................305 691-7740
Marty Adelman, *President*
▼ **EMP:** 14 **EST:** 1927
SQ FT: 6,500
SALES (est): 1.4MM **Privately Held**
SIC: 3441 Fabricated structural metal

(G-9069)
ADMIRAL
1690 Ne 205th Ter (33179-2117)
PHONE..............................305 493-4355
Warren Copper, *Owner*
EMP: 9 **EST:** 2006
SALES (est): 570.7K **Privately Held**
SIC: 3732 Yachts, building & repairing

(G-9070)
ADONEL BLOCK MFG CORP
2101 Nw 110th Ave (33172-1904)
PHONE..............................561 615-9500
EMP: 12 **EST:** 2019
SALES (est): 159.9K **Privately Held**
WEB: www.adonelconcrete.com
SIC: 3999 Manufacturing industries

(G-9071)
ADONEL CON PMPG FNSHG S FLA IN (PA)
2101 Nw 110th Ave (33172-1904)
P.O. Box 226950 (33222-6950)
PHONE..............................305 392-5416
Gerardo L Garcia, *President*
Yessica Morillo, *Purch Agent*
Irvyn Rivas, *Purch Agent*
Alan Silverman, *Controller*
Alexander Sarite, *Bookkeeper*
▼ **EMP:** 82
SALES (est): 28.6MM **Privately Held**
WEB: www.adonelconcrete.com
SIC: 3273 1771 Ready-mixed concrete; concrete pumping

(G-9072)
ADORGRAF CORP
7770 Nw 64th St (33166-2705)
PHONE..............................786 752-1680
Ruben Valladares, *President*
EMP: 8 **EST:** 2019
SALES (est): 409.3K **Privately Held**
SIC: 2752 Commercial printing, lithographic

(G-9073)
ADTECH ELECTRIC ADVERTISING
1840 Coral Way (33145-2748)
PHONE..............................786 533-3210
Robert Isakof, *President*
EMP: 89 **EST:** 1980
SALES (est): 2.8MM **Privately Held**
WEB: www.adtechadv.com
SIC: 3993 1799 Signs & advertising specialties; sign installation & maintenance

(G-9074)
ADVANCE ONE WHEELS INC
Also Called: Adv1
14397 Sw 143rd Ct Ste 105 (33186-6730)
PHONE..............................305 238-5833
Jordan Swerdloff, *President*
Mike Burroughs, *CFO*
Michael Espinel, *Admin Sec*
▲ **EMP:** 18 **EST:** 2010
SQ FT: 15,000
SALES (est): 1.7MM **Privately Held**
WEB: www.adv1wheels.com
SIC: 3312 Wheels

(G-9075)
ADVANCED BIOPROCESS LLC
3200 Nw 67th Ave Bldg 3 (33166-2239)
PHONE..............................305 927-3661
EMP: 6 **EST:** 2017
SALES (est): 125.4K **Privately Held**
SIC: 2835 Microbiology & virology diagnostic products

(G-9076)
ADVANCED PROF SURGICAL SVCS
2237 Sw 63rd Ave (33155-2066)
PHONE..............................786 326-0576
Jorge C Gamoneda, *Mng Member*
Claudia C Facchinelli, *Mng Member*
EMP: 6 **EST:** 2015
SALES (est): 254.5K **Privately Held**
SIC: 3842 8099 Adhesive tape & plasters, medicated or non-medicated; childbirth preparation clinic

(G-9077)
ADVANCED SOFTWARE ENGINEERING
9601 Sw 142nd Ave (33186-7327)
P.O. Box 836142 (33283-6142)
PHONE..............................305 387-0112
Robertfortunato, *Principal*
EMP: 6 **EST:** 2004
SALES (est): 139.3K **Privately Held**
WEB:
www.advancedsoftwareengineering.com
SIC: 7372 Prepackaged software

(G-9078)
ADWAVE GRAPHICS INC ✪
35 Nw 27th Ave (33125-5111)
PHONE..............................305 643-8020
EMP: 7 **EST:** 2020
SALES (est): 647.2K **Privately Held**
WEB: www.adwavesigns.com
SIC: 3993 Signs & advertising specialties

(G-9079)
AE TENT LLC
Also Called: Economy Tent International
2995 Nw 75th St (33147-5943)
PHONE..............................305 691-0191
Hal Paul Lapping, *Manager*
EMP: 40 **EST:** 2011
SALES (est): 8.3MM
SALES (corp-wide): 45.7MM **Privately Held**
WEB: www.economytent.com
SIC: 2394 Tents: made from purchased materials; tarpaulins, fabric: made from purchased materials
PA: Anchor Industries Inc.
1100 Burch Dr
Evansville IN 47725
812 867-2421

(G-9080)
AEGLE THERAPEUTICS CORPORATION
1951 Nw 7th Ave Fl 3 (33136-1104)
PHONE..............................305 608-9705
Robert Williamson, *President*
Bob Williamson, *Director*
EMP: 5 **EST:** 2013
SALES (est): 794.7K **Privately Held**
WEB: www.aegletherapeutics.com
SIC: 2834 Pharmaceutical preparations

(G-9081)
AERO STITCH INC
18264 Sw 143rd Pl (33177-7644)
PHONE..............................305 978-3446
Luz P Leguizamo, *Principal*
EMP: 6 **EST:** 2010
SALES (est): 62.6K **Privately Held**
SIC: 2395 Embroidery & art needlework

(G-9082)
AERO TECHNOLOGY MFG INC
7735 Nw 64th St Ste 1 (33166-3501)
PHONE..............................305 345-7747
Claudia Diaz, *Principal*
EMP: 10 **EST:** 2016
SQ FT: 5,550
SALES (est): 1.2MM **Privately Held**
WEB: www.atmcorp.net
SIC: 3469 7539 3599 Machine parts, stamped or pressed metal; machine shop, automotive; machine & other job shop work

(G-9083)
AEROTOOLS CONNECTION LLC
12625 Sw 134th Ct Ste 208 (33186-6423)
PHONE..............................305 234-3034
Dino Armetta, *President*
EMP: 7 **EST:** 2015
SALES (est): 598.2K **Privately Held**
WEB: www.aerotoolsconnection.com
SIC: 3728 5599 5088 Aircraft parts & equipment; aircraft instruments, equipment or parts; aircraft equipment & supplies

(G-9084)
AEROTOOLS USA INC
12591 Sw 134th Ct Ste 105 (33186-6496)
PHONE..............................305 432-4258
Nelson Urbay, *Principal*
EMP: 8 **EST:** 2019
SALES (est): 173.3K **Privately Held**
WEB: www.aerotoolsconnection.com
SIC: 3728 Aircraft parts & equipment

(G-9085)
AFFORDABLE AT HOME HAS INC
8870 Sw 40th St Ste 7 (33165-5465)
PHONE..............................786 200-0484
Diaz Jesus, *Principal*
EMP: 5 **EST:** 2016
SALES (est): 374.6K **Privately Held**
SIC: 3842 Hearing aids

(G-9086)
AFFORDABLE MED SCRUBS LLC (PA)
Also Called: AMS Uniforms
888 Brickell Ave Ste 100 (33131-2913)
PHONE..................................419 222-1088
Ted Ralston, *President*
▲ **EMP:** 17 **EST:** 2003
SQ FT: 15,000
SALES (est): 9.7MM **Privately Held**
SIC: 2326 Medical & hospital uniforms, men's

(G-9087)
AFFORDABLE QUALITY BLINDS INC
7345 Sw 32nd St (33155-2724)
PHONE..................................786 412-4840
Andres H Sabogal, *Principal*
EMP: 6 **EST:** 2019
SALES (est): 57.3K **Privately Held**
SIC: 2591 Window blinds

(G-9088)
AGAPE GRAPHICS & PRINTING INC
14255 Sw 119th Ave (33186-6008)
PHONE..................................305 252-9147
Robert Winant Jr, *President*
Barbara B Winant, *Director*
EMP: 6 **EST:** 1989
SQ FT: 3,200
SALES (est): 800K **Privately Held**
WEB: www.agapegraphicsandprinting.com
SIC: 2752 Commercial printing, offset

(G-9089)
AGROTEK SERVICES INCORPORATED
Also Called: Industrias De Aslntes Y Acero
6414 Nw 82nd Ave (33166-2734)
PHONE..................................305 599-3818
Yuri J Fernandez Camacho, *President*
Lisbeth 4 Cols De Fernandez, *Vice Pres*
▲ **EMP:** 8 **EST:** 2009
SALES (est): 2.3MM **Privately Held**
WEB: www.agrotekservices.com
SIC: 2999 Coke

(G-9090)
AIOLOS GROUP INC
2529 Nw 74th Ave (33122-1417)
PHONE..................................305 496-7674
Alejandro Nasio, *Principal*
EMP: 5 **EST:** 2010
SALES (est): 941.5K **Privately Held**
WEB: www.aiolos-group.com
SIC: 3841 Surgical & medical instruments

(G-9091)
AIR ESSCENTIALS INC
Also Called: Air Essentials
7055 Sw 47th St (33155-4651)
PHONE..................................305 446-1670
Spence Levy, *President*
Marc Levy, *Exec VP*
Walter Nunez, *Controller*
EMP: 32 **EST:** 2007
SQ FT: 8,500
SALES (est): 5.5MM **Privately Held**
WEB: www.airesscentials.com
SIC: 2869 Perfume materials, synthetic

(G-9092)
AIR OPERATIONS
4000 Nw 28th St (33142-5612)
PHONE..................................305 871-5449
Mario La Torre, *Principal*
EMP: 11 **EST:** 2010
SALES (est): 260K **Privately Held**
SIC: 3728 Aircraft parts & equipment

(G-9093)
AIR PURIFYING SYSTEMS INC
3750 Nw 28th St Unit 206 (33142-6204)
PHONE..................................954 962-0450
Carlos Jimenez, *President*
EMP: 6 **EST:** 1999
SQ FT: 1,500
SALES (est): 459.4K **Privately Held**
WEB: www.pure-air.com
SIC: 3564 Air purification equipment

(G-9094)
AIRAM STONE DESIGNS INC
8900 Sw 104th St (33176-3714)
PHONE..................................305 477-8009
Maria Garcia, *President*
Freddy Castillo, *Vice Pres*
▼ **EMP:** 7 **EST:** 2001
SALES (est): 777.5K **Privately Held**
WEB: www.airamstonedesigns.com
SIC: 3281 Curbing, granite or stone; marble, building: cut & shaped

(G-9095)
AIRCO PLATING COMPANY INC
3650 Nw 46th St (33142-3944)
PHONE..................................305 633-2476
Michael King, *President*
George L King, *President*
I Stanley Levine, *Treasurer*
Cynthia Randall, *Office Mgr*
Sherry Morris, *Director*
EMP: 42 **EST:** 1955
SQ FT: 30,000
SALES (est): 4.9MM **Privately Held**
WEB: www.aircoplating.com
SIC: 3471 Electroplating of metals or formed products

(G-9096)
AIRE-TECH ROTORCRAFT SVCS LLC
6270 Nw 37th Ave (33147-7522)
PHONE..................................305 696-8001
EMP: 12
SALES (est): 734.6K **Privately Held**
SIC: 3728 Mfg Aircraft Parts/Equipment

(G-9097)
AIRFREE USA LLC
25 Se 2nd Ave Ste 1235 (33131-1606)
PHONE..................................305 772-6577
Carlos Matias, *Manager*
EMP: 10 **EST:** 2017
SALES (est): 982.6K
SALES (corp-wide): 9.5MM **Privately Held**
WEB: www.airfree.com
SIC: 3634 Air purifiers, portable
PA: Airfree - Produtos ElectrOnicos, S.A.
Rua Julieta FerrAo, Torre 10 9o
Lisboa 1600-
213 156-222

(G-9098)
AIT USA CORP
Also Called: Atlantic Island Trading
8485 Nw 74th St (33166-2325)
PHONE..................................786 953-5918
Jose A Paradiso, *CEO*
Jose C De Faria, *Director*
Alexander Fernandes, *Director*
EMP: 6 **EST:** 2015
SQ FT: 6,500
SALES (est): 967.3K **Privately Held**
SIC: 2032 5141 Italian foods: packaged in cans, jars, etc.; food brokers

(G-9099)
AL-RITE FRUITS AND SYRUPS INC
Also Called: Master Syrup Makers
18524 Ne 2nd Ave (33179-4427)
PHONE..................................305 652-2540
Steve Bragg, *President*
William M S Bragg, *President*
Clifford Spring, *Controller*
Anne Efros, *Admin Sec*
▲ **EMP:** 9 **EST:** 1964
SQ FT: 8,500
SALES (est): 1.1MM **Privately Held**
WEB: www.al-rite.com
SIC: 2087 2099 2086 Beverage bases; concentrates, drink; syrups, drink; cocktail mixes, nonalcoholic; food preparations; bottled & canned soft drinks

(G-9100)
ALBASOL LLC
325 S Biscayne Blvd (33131-2306)
PHONE..................................830 334-3280
Alejandro Solis, *Principal*
EMP: 6 **EST:** 2012
SALES (est): 345.9K **Privately Held**
WEB: www.harvestmidstream.com
SIC: 1382 Oil & gas exploration services

(G-9101)
ALDANAS PAVERS INC
3281 Nw 18th St (33125-1837)
PHONE..................................305 970-5339
Ingrid M Aldana, *President*
EMP: 7 **EST:** 2005
SALES (est): 109.9K **Privately Held**
SIC: 2951 Asphalt paving mixtures & blocks

(G-9102)
ALFA MANUFACTURING LLC
4701 Nw 77th Ave (33166-5521)
PHONE..................................305 436-8150
Alejandro Valdes Mana, *Principal*
▲ **EMP:** 11 **EST:** 2013
SALES (est): 1.7MM **Privately Held**
WEB: www.alfavitamins.com
SIC: 2833 Vitamins, natural or synthetic: bulk, uncompounded

(G-9103)
ALFRESCO AIR
690 Sw 1st Ct Unit Cui (33130-2991)
PHONE..................................786 275-5111
Fabricio Cordoba, *President*
EMP: 14 **EST:** 2017
SALES (est): 1.3MM **Privately Held**
WEB: www.alfresco-air.business.site
SIC: 1389 Oil & gas field services

(G-9104)
ALGY TRIMMINGS CO INC
Also Called: Algy Dance Costumes
7478 Nw 54th St (33166-4811)
PHONE..................................954 457-8100
Herbert Lieberman, *Ch of Bd*
Susan Gordon, *President*
Laurie Godbout, *Corp Secy*
Paola Stewart, *Purch Mgr*
Shannon Berkstresser, *Marketing Staff*
EMP: 60 **EST:** 1926
SALES (est): 12.6MM **Privately Held**
WEB: www.starstyled.com
SIC: 2389 2339 Theatrical costumes; women's & misses' outerwear

(G-9105)
ALIENWARE CORP
13462 Sw 131st St (33186-5891)
PHONE..................................786 260-9625
John Beekley, *VP Mktg*
Claudina Lopez, *Marketing Mgr*
Patrick Theodore, *Manager*
Christophe Maire, *Director*
Frank Azor, *Officer*
EMP: 5 **EST:** 2018
SALES (est): 447.7K **Privately Held**
SIC: 3571 Electronic computers

(G-9106)
ALIGN KPITAL USA LLC
2500 Sw 107th Ave Ste 8 (33165-2491)
PHONE..................................305 423-7100
Juan Ramon R Bandera, *Manager*
EMP: 6 **EST:** 2011
SALES (est): 129.6K **Privately Held**
WEB: www.alignkpital.com
SIC: 2752 Commercial printing, lithographic

(G-9107)
ALIGNED GLOBAL
8370 W Flagler St Ste 125 (33144-2047)
PHONE..................................305 731-2117
Scott Durgun, *Chairman*
EMP: 6 **EST:** 2016
SALES (est): 144K **Privately Held**
WEB: www.alignedglobal.com
SIC: 2741 Miscellaneous publishing

(G-9108)
ALL AMERICAN SEALCOATING LLC
1200 Brickell Ave # 1950 (33131-3214)
PHONE..................................305 961-1655
EMP: 6 **EST:** 2019
SALES (est): 768.4K **Privately Held**
WEB: www.allasco.com
SIC: 2952 Asphalt felts & coatings

(G-9109)
ALL FLRIDA HRRCANE PRTCTION CO
22840 S Dixie Hwy Ste 2 (33170-6358)
PHONE..................................305 305-9177
EMP: 8 **EST:** 2012
SALES (est): 548.9K **Privately Held**
WEB: www.floridahurricanedepot.com
SIC: 3442 Metal doors, sash & trim

(G-9110)
ALL IN ONE MAIL SHOP INC
Also Called: All In One Drect Mktg Slutions
11950 Sw 128th St (33186-5207)
PHONE..................................305 233-6100
Shelley Jacoby, *President*
Resnick Holly, *Accounts Exec*
▲ **EMP:** 10 **EST:** 1989
SQ FT: 16,000
SALES (est): 1MM **Privately Held**
WEB: www.allinonedirectms.com
SIC: 2752 Commercial printing, offset

(G-9111)
ALL LIFT SOLUTIONS INC
261 Sw 63rd Ct (33144-3141)
PHONE..................................786 295-3946
Jorge L Toste, *Principal*
EMP: 6 **EST:** 2009
SALES (est): 113K **Privately Held**
WEB: www.allliftsolutions.com
SIC: 3537 Forklift trucks

(G-9112)
ALL MIAMI SIGNS INC
7508 Nw 55th St (33166-4220)
PHONE..................................305 406-2420
Gregory Perdomo, *Principal*
EMP: 11 **EST:** 2010
SALES (est): 401.4K **Privately Held**
SIC: 3993 Signs & advertising specialties

(G-9113)
ALL THINGS DIGITAL INC
Also Called: Atdsat
7213 Nw 54th St (33166-4807)
PHONE..................................305 887-9464
▼ **EMP:** 20
SQ FT: 10,000
SALES (est): 2.5MM **Privately Held**
SIC: 3679 Mfg Electronic Components

(G-9114)
ALL-JER CONSTRUCTION USA INC
12225 Sw 217th St (33170-2830)
PHONE..................................305 257-0225
EMP: 6 **EST:** 2008
SALES (est): 400K **Privately Held**
SIC: 1389 Oil/Gas Field Services

(G-9115)
ALLAPATTAH ELECTRIC MOTOR REPR
1746 Nw 21st Ter (33142-7438)
PHONE..................................305 325-0330
David Galdona, *President*
Miguel Betancourt, *President*
Gregory Gonzales, *President*
EMP: 7 **EST:** 1973
SQ FT: 4,000
SALES (est): 458.5K **Privately Held**
WEB: www.allapattahelectric.com
SIC: 7694 Electric motor repair

(G-9116)
ALLAPATTAH INDUSTRIES INC
Also Called: Lakewood Juices
1035 Nw 21st Ter (33127-4517)
P.O. Box 12311, Gainesville (32604-0311)
PHONE..................................305 324-5900
Thomas R Fuhrman, *CEO*
Vivian Calzadilla, *President*
Scott P Fuhrman, *COO*
Carmen Delgado, *Purch Agent*
Cathy Garcia, *Controller*
◆ **EMP:** 50 **EST:** 1956
SQ FT: 105,000
SALES (est): 15.3MM **Privately Held**
WEB: www.lakewoodorganic.com
SIC: 2037 5142 2033 Fruit juices; packaged frozen goods; canned fruits & specialties

(G-9117)
ALLIED METALS LLC
2902 Nw 32nd Ave (33142-6316)
PHONE..................................305 635-3360
Tom Egan, *CFO*
EMP: 10 **EST:** 2012
SALES (est): 1.4MM **Privately Held**
WEB: www.alliedmetalsllc.com
SIC: 1081 Test boring, metal mining

(G-9118)
ALLIED USA INCORPORATED
2824 Sw 138th Path (33175-6663)
PHONE..................................305 235-3950
Rodolfo Martinez, *President*
Ernesto Vila, *Vice Pres*
◆ **EMP:** 7 **EST:** 2000
SQ FT: 6,000
SALES (est): 1.6MM **Privately Held**
WEB: www.alliedusainc.com
SIC: 2865 5169 Food dyes or colors, synthetic; chemicals & allied products
PA: Allied Industrial Corp., Ltd.
12f, No. 76, Dunhua S. Rd., Sec. 2
Taipei City TAP 10683

(G-9119)
ALMANAC LLC (PA)
1457 Sw 14th Ter (33145-1542)
PHONE..................................415 310-5143
Estibaliz Brooks, *Principal*
EMP: 19 **EST:** 2013
SALES (est): 129.6K **Privately Held**
WEB: www.almanac.com
SIC: 2711 Newspapers, publishing & printing

(G-9120)
ALMAR INDUSTRIES INC
6301 Sw 157th Pl (33193-3684)
PHONE..................................305 385-8284
Alberto Gonzalez Jr, *Vice Pres*
EMP: 12 **EST:** 2012
SALES (est): 158.8K **Privately Held**
WEB: www.almarindustries.com
SIC: 3999 Manufacturing industries

(G-9121)
ALONSO DEFENSE GROUP LLC
5076 Nw 74th Ave (33166-5550)
PHONE..................................305 989-0927
Alonso F Juan, *Principal*
EMP: 6 **EST:** 2013
SALES (est): 470.1K **Privately Held**
WEB: www.ciguera.com
SIC: 3812 Defense systems & equipment

(G-9122)
ALTA INDUSTRIES LLC
9930 Sw 164th Ter (33157-3282)
PHONE..................................305 343-6091
Indra Gupta, *Principal*
EMP: 6 **EST:** 2016
SALES (est): 176.3K **Privately Held**
WEB: www.altaindustries.com
SIC: 3999 Manufacturing industries

(G-9123)
ALTANET CORPORATION
7950 Nw 53rd St Ste 337 (33166-4791)
PHONE..................................786 228-5758
Lorena Altamirano, *Vice Pres*
EMP: 8 **EST:** 2012
SALES (est): 2.5MM **Privately Held**
WEB: www.altanet-corp.com
SIC: 3661 Telephone station equipment & parts, wire
PA: Altielectronica Cia. Ltda.
Republica 89125 Amazonas
Quito

(G-9124)
ALTIRA INC
3225 Nw 112th St (33167-3330)
PHONE..................................305 687-8074
Ramon E Poo, *CEO*
Tino Poo, *General Mgr*
Ramon E Poo Jr, *Senior VP*
Anthony L Poo, *Vice Pres*
Cristina M Poo, *Vice Pres*
▲ **EMP:** 85 **EST:** 1984
SQ FT: 50,000
SALES (est): 24.9MM **Privately Held**
WEB: www.altira.com
SIC: 3085 2759 Plastics bottles; commercial printing

(G-9125)
ALTIS AJU KINGWOOD LLC
175 Sw 7th St Ste 1106 (33130-2951)
PHONE..................................305 338-5232
Frank Guerra, *Principal*
EMP: 6 **EST:** 2012
SALES (est): 198.1K **Privately Held**
SIC: 3369 Nonferrous foundries

(G-9126)
ALTON MANUFACTURING INC
9511 Fontnbleau Blvd # 402 (33172-6824)
PHONE..................................305 821-0701
Moshe Engel, *President*
◆ **EMP:** 7 **EST:** 1980
SALES (est): 578.2K **Privately Held**
SIC: 3634 Personal electrical appliances

(G-9127)
ALUTECH CORPORATION
8548 Nw 64th St (33166-2627)
PHONE..................................305 593-2080
▼ **EMP:** 9
SQ FT: 6,000
SALES (est): 1.3MM **Privately Held**
SIC: 3442 Mfg Metal Doors/Sash/Trim

(G-9128)
ALWAYS FLOWERS INC
6955 Nw 52nd St (33166-4844)
PHONE..................................305 572-1122
Karen J Cohen, *President*
Elaine Chehebar, *Vice Pres*
Julie Dixson, *Opers Staff*
Raquel Pena, *Manager*
Irma Hernandez, *Director*
▲ **EMP:** 12 **EST:** 1996
SALES (est): 1.1MM **Privately Held**
SIC: 3999 5992 Flowers, artificial & preserved; florists

(G-9129)
AMA WATERS LLC
Also Called: Amazonia Beverages
6701 Nw 7th St Ste 175 (33126-6033)
PHONE..................................786 400-1630
Gabriel Filassi, *CEO*
▲ **EMP:** 9 **EST:** 2010
SQ FT: 1,000
SALES (est): 2.6MM **Privately Held**
SIC: 2086 Pasteurized & mineral waters, bottled & canned

(G-9130)
AMADO WHEEL FINISHING
15050 Sw 137th St (33196-5747)
PHONE..................................786 732-6249
Amado A Fernandez, *President*
EMP: 6 **EST:** 2017
SALES (est): 293.7K **Privately Held**
SIC: 3471 Polishing, metals or formed products

(G-9131)
AMAYA LATHING & PLASPERING
2301 Nw 7th St (33125-3299)
PHONE..................................786 953-6420
EMP: 7 **EST:** 2018
SALES (est): 1MM **Privately Held**
SIC: 3541 Lathes

(G-9132)
AMAYA LATHING & PLASTERING LLC
3475 W Flagler St (33135-1025)
PHONE..................................305 216-4247
Victor Amaya, *Principal*
EMP: 6 **EST:** 2018
SALES (est): 376.3K **Privately Held**
SIC: 3541 Lathes

(G-9133)
AMAZON SERVICES INC
Also Called: Amazon Printers
7186 Sw 47th St (33155-4656)
PHONE..................................305 663-0585
Cristina Serralta, *President*
Linda Uriarte, *Marketing Staff*
Hector Medina, *Technician*
▼ **EMP:** 17 **EST:** 1987
SQ FT: 2,800
SALES (est): 1MM **Privately Held**
WEB: www.amazonprinters.com
SIC: 2752 Commercial printing, offset

(G-9134)
AMBA HAM COMPANY INC
6863 Ne 3rd Ave (33138-5510)
PHONE..................................305 754-0001
Ricardo Navarro, *President*
EMP: 6 **EST:** 1981
SALES (est): 691.6K **Privately Held**
WEB: www.ambaham.com
SIC: 2013 Ham, boiled: from purchased meat; ham, boneless: from purchased meat; ham, roasted: from purchased meat; ham, smoked: from purchased meat

(G-9135)
AMBER JEWELERS CORP
Also Called: Rafael Moreaun
36 Ne 1st St Ste 1002 (33132-2492)
PHONE..................................305 373-8089
Walter Suarez, *President*
EMP: 8 **EST:** 1968
SQ FT: 2,000
SALES (est): 450K **Privately Held**
SIC: 3911 7631 Jewel settings & mountings, precious metal; jewelry repair services

(G-9136)
AMBIANCE INTERIORS MFG CORP
7456 Sw 48th St (33155-4469)
PHONE..................................305 668-4995
Enrique Beltran, *Manager*
EMP: 9 **EST:** 2012
SALES (est): 1MM **Privately Held**
WEB: www.ambinter.net
SIC: 3446 Architectural metalwork

(G-9137)
AMENDAR PRINTING INC
10207 Nw 10th St (33172-5701)
PHONE..................................786 287-5189
Rocco Amendolara, *Principal*
EMP: 10 **EST:** 2014
SALES (est): 129.3K **Privately Held**
WEB: www.amendar.com
SIC: 2752 Commercial printing, offset

(G-9138)
AMERICA SOLUTIONS FOR BUSINESS
12943 Sw 133rd Ct (33186-5853)
PHONE..................................305 971-5400
EMP: 6 **EST:** 2019
SALES (est): 166.3K **Privately Held**
WEB: www.business.toshiba.com
SIC: 2761 Manifold business forms

(G-9139)
AMERICA TRADING INC
9355 Sw 144th St (33176-6820)
PHONE..................................305 256-0101
Fabio Chazyn, *President*
◆ **EMP:** 11 **EST:** 2001
SALES (est): 451.9K **Privately Held**
SIC: 2451 Mobile homes

(G-9140)
AMERICAN BLIND CORPORATION
4232 Sw 75th Ave (33155-4425)
PHONE..................................305 262-2009
Rolando Rodrigiuz, *President*
Jesus Sanchez, *Vice Pres*
Regino Rodriguez, *Director*
▼ **EMP:** 18 **EST:** 1982
SQ FT: 10,000
SALES (est): 574.2K **Privately Held**
SIC: 2591 Blinds vertical

(G-9141)
AMERICAN CHIROPRACTOR
8619 Nw 68th St Ste C0138 (33166-2685)
P.O. Box 527948 (33152-7948)
PHONE..................................305 434-8865
Richard Busch Jr, *Ch of Bd*
Tracy Pate, *Publisher*
Jaclyn Busch Touzard, *Publisher*
James Busch, *Director*
EMP: 10
SALES (est): 1MM **Privately Held**
WEB: www.theamericanchiropractor.com
SIC: 2721 Magazines: publishing & printing

(G-9142)
AMERICAN FRAME FURNITURE INC
1857 Nw 21st Ter (33142-7439)
PHONE..................................305 548-3018
Zoila Diaz, *President*
EMP: 6 **EST:** 1999
SQ FT: 10,000
SALES (est): 328K **Privately Held**
WEB: www.americanframe.com
SIC: 2511 Wood household furniture

(G-9143)
AMERICAN HERMETICS GEORGIA INC
7478 Nw 55th St (33166-4218)
PHONE..................................305 592-8958
Albert Lamelas, *President*
EMP: 6
SALES (corp-wide): 4.2MM **Privately Held**
WEB: www.americanhermeticsga.com
SIC: 3585 Air conditioning units, complete: domestic or industrial
PA: American Hermetics Of Georgia, Inc.
2935 E Ponce De Leon Ave
Decatur GA 30030
404 373-8782

(G-9144)
AMERICAN HYGENIC LABORATORIES
Also Called: D' Lanerg
1800 Ne 114th St Ste J (33181-3415)
PHONE..................................305 891-9518
EMP: 10 **EST:** 1946
SQ FT: 5,000
SALES: 250K **Privately Held**
SIC: 2844 Mfg Toilet Preparations

(G-9145)
AMERICAN LED DISPLAY SOLUTIONS
8060 Nw 71st St (33166-2350)
PHONE..................................561 227-8048
Orlando Pavon, *President*
Guillermo Hanger, *Vice Pres*
EMP: 8 **EST:** 2015
SALES (est): 928.7K **Privately Held**
WEB: www.americanledisplays.com
SIC: 3674 Light emitting diodes

(G-9146)
AMERICAN NATURAL PDTS LAB INC
7350 Nw 7th St Ste 101 (33126-2976)
PHONE..................................305 261-5152
Rodolfo Cruz, *President*
▲ **EMP:** 8 **EST:** 2000
SQ FT: 7,000
SALES (est): 1.5MM **Privately Held**
SIC: 2833 Vitamins, natural or synthetic: bulk, uncompounded

(G-9147)
AMERICAN STAINLESS MFRS (PA)
8390 Nw 68th St (33166-2655)
PHONE..................................786 275-4458
Jorge A Sanders, *President*
EMP: 54 **EST:** 2016
SALES (est): 560.8K **Privately Held**
SIC: 3312 Stainless steel

(G-9148)
AMERICAN WLDG & INSTALLATION
4851 Nw 36th Ave (33142-3909)
PHONE..................................786 391-4800
Jose M Carballo, *President*
EMP: 8 **EST:** 2011
SALES (est): 159.3K **Privately Held**
SIC: 7692 Welding repair

(G-9149)
AMERIFOOD CORP
1717 Nw 22nd St 6 (33142-7441)
P.O. Box 421852 (33242-1852)
PHONE..................................305 305-5951
Victor Angulo, *President*
EMP: 5 **EST:** 2015
SALES (est): 380.7K **Privately Held**
SIC: 2075 Soybean oil mills

(G-9150)
AMIGO PALLETS INC
10251 Sw 109th St (33176-3464)
PHONE..................................305 302-9751
Olga L Alfonso, *Principal*
EMP: 11 **EST:** 2010
SALES (est): 220.8K **Privately Held**
WEB: www.amigopallets.com
SIC: 2448 Pallets, wood & wood with metal

(G-9151)
AMP AERO SERVICES LLC
13806 Sw 145th Ct (33186-6710)
PHONE..................................833 267-2376
Natasha Marie Pinder, *Manager*
EMP: 8 **EST:** 2019
SALES (est): 1MM **Privately Held**
WEB: www.amp-aero.com
SIC: 3728 Aircraft body & wing assemblies & parts

(G-9152)
AMS GLOBAL SUPPLIERS GROUP LLC
200 S Biscayne Blvd (33131-2310)
PHONE..................................305 714-9441
Jose D Lacayo Vindas, *Mng Member*
EMP: 5 **EST:** 2015
SALES (est): 307.2K **Privately Held**
WEB: www.amsledsolutions.com
SIC: 3641 Electric light bulbs, complete

(G-9153)
AMTEC SALES INC
Also Called: Print Media
1594 Nw 159th St (33169-5635)
PHONE..................................800 994-3318
Robert Gonzalez, *President*
Mary Comas, *CFO*
Arturo Comas, *Controller*
Adrian Mandreanu, *Sales Mgr*
Jim Kiah, *Sales Staff*
▲ **EMP:** 17 **EST:** 1993
SALES (est): 2MM **Privately Held**
SIC: 2754 2752 2759 2679 Business form & card printing, gravure; business form & card printing, lithographic; tag, ticket & schedule printing: lithographic; schedule, ticket & tag printing & engraving; pin tickets, paper: made from purchased paper

(G-9154)
ANMAPEC CORPORATION
5210 Nw 5th St (33126-5034)
PHONE..................................786 897-5389
Maria Clemente, *President*
Tito Clemente, *Vice Pres*
Angel Clemente, *Treasurer*
EMP: 14 **EST:** 1978
SQ FT: 5,000
SALES (est): 264K **Privately Held**
SIC: 2329 2339 2326 Men's & boys' sportswear & athletic clothing; sportswear, women's; men's & boys' work clothing

(G-9155)
ANUE LIGNE INC
Also Called: A' Nue Miami
3300 Nw 41st St (33142-4306)
P.O. Box 520549 (33152-0549)
PHONE..................................305 638-7979
Lois Varat, *President*
Carlos Torres, *Sales Staff*
EMP: 5 **EST:** 1990
SALES (est): 677.8K **Privately Held**
WEB: www.anuemiami.com
SIC: 2339 Women's & misses' outerwear

(G-9156)
APEX AVIATION GROUP LLC
801 Brickell Ave Ste 900 (33131-2979)
PHONE..................................305 789-6695
Eduardo Palma,
EMP: 7
SALES (est): 2.1MM **Privately Held**
WEB: www.apexaviationgroupllc.com
SIC: 3728 Aircraft parts & equipment

(G-9157)
APPAREL IMPORTS INC
Also Called: Formal Wear International
10893 Nw 17th St Unit 126 (33172-2059)
PHONE..................................800 428-6849
Esperanza Campo, *President*
Arturo Alcantara, *Vice Pres*
Sandra P Vallejo, *Treasurer*
◆ **EMP:** 30 **EST:** 1989
SQ FT: 15,000
SALES (est): 6.3MM **Privately Held**
SIC: 2311 5137 5136 Formal jackets, men's & youths': from purchased materials; tuxedos: made from purchased materials; women's & children's clothing; men's & boys' clothing

(G-9158)
APPROVED PERFORMANCE TOOLING
Also Called: APT
8405 Nw 66th St (33166-2630)
PHONE..................................305 592-7775
Hyman Ash, *President*
Peter Field, *Corp Secy*
Richard Kandarian, *Vice Pres*
◆ **EMP:** 33 **EST:** 1971
SQ FT: 38,000
SALES (est): 1.2MM **Privately Held**
SIC: 3545 Drill bits, metalworking

(G-9159)
APURE DISTRIBUTION LLC
5555 Biscayne Blvd Fl 3 (33137-2656)
PHONE..................................305 351-1025
Uli Petzold, *CEO*
EMP: 15 **EST:** 2010
SQ FT: 6,000
SALES (est): 1.1MM **Privately Held**
SIC: 3674 7349 Light emitting diodes; lighting maintenance service

(G-9160)
ARA FOOD CORPORATION
8001 Nw 60th St (33166-3412)
PHONE..................................305 592-5558
Alberto R Abrante, *Vice Pres*
Rick Samudio, *Plant Mgr*
Marta Devarona, *Purch Dir*
Marta E De Varona, *Treasurer*
Alberto Abrante, *VP Sales*
◆ **EMP:** 60 **EST:** 1975
SQ FT: 7,000
SALES (est): 14.4MM **Privately Held**
WEB: www.arafood.com
SIC: 2099 Food preparations

(G-9161)
ARAYA INC
9582 Sw 40th St Ste 5 (33165-4064)
PHONE..................................305 229-6868
Adelys C Marquez, *Principal*
EMP: 9 **EST:** 2012
SALES (est): 256.4K **Privately Held**
SIC: 2066 Chocolate

(G-9162)
ARCA LLC
1220 Nw 7th St (33125-3702)
PHONE..................................305 470-1430
John Irvin, *Manager*
EMP: 14 **EST:** 2006
SALES (est): 646.1K **Privately Held**
WEB: www.arca.com
SIC: 3423 Jewelers' hand tools

(G-9163)
ARCHITCTRAL MLDING MLLWRKS INC
3545 Nw 50th St (33142-3931)
PHONE..................................305 638-8900
Shanon Siegfried, *President*
Scott Gumora, *Vice Pres*
Eric Siegfried, *Vice Pres*
Shanon Smith, *Info Tech Mgr*
▼ **EMP:** 24 **EST:** 1996
SQ FT: 42,000
SALES (est): 2.3MM **Privately Held**
WEB: www.millworks.biz
SIC: 2431 2439 Moldings, wood: unfinished & prefinished; structural wood members

(G-9164)
ARCHITECTURAL SIGNS INC
14200 Sw 161st Pl (33196-6553)
PHONE..................................305 282-4427
EMP: 7 **EST:** 2008
SALES (est): 175.8K **Privately Held**
WEB: www.architecturalsigns.com
SIC: 3993 Signs & advertising specialties

(G-9165)
ARD PRINTING SOLUTIONS LL
14016 Sw 140th St (33186-5547)
PHONE..................................305 785-7200
EMP: 8 **EST:** 2018
SALES (est): 723.1K **Privately Held**
SIC: 2752 Commercial printing, lithographic

(G-9166)
ARDE APPAREL INC
Also Called: Denise Marie
1852 Nw 21st St (33142-7436)
PHONE..................................305 326-0861
Arturo A Dopazo, *President*
Hilda Dopazo, *Vice Pres*
EMP: 25 **EST:** 1981
SALES (est): 1.9MM **Privately Held**
SIC: 2335 Women's, juniors' & misses' dresses

(G-9167)
ARES DISTRIBUTORS INC
2601 S Bayshore Dr # 1150 (33133-5431)
PHONE..................................305 858-0163
Eduardo Rodriguez, *President*
Olga Michel, *Partner*
Giancarlo Orlando, *Vice Pres*
Jackelyne Rodriguez, *Vice Pres*
Felix Menendez, *Credit Staff*
EMP: 8 **EST:** 2009
SALES (est): 1.1MM **Privately Held**
WEB: www.aresdistributors.com
SIC: 2911 Gasoline blending plants

(G-9168)
ARGOS
12201 Nw 25th St (33182-1504)
PHONE..................................305 592-3501
EMP: 7 **EST:** 2015
SALES (est): 1.1MM **Privately Held**
WEB: www.argos-us.com
SIC: 1422 Crushed & broken limestone

(G-9169)
ARMADILLO SOUNDS INC
Also Called: Apara Productions
4246 Nw 37th Ave (33142-4224)
PHONE..................................305 801-7906
Enrique O Vega, *President*
Jeany Oliva, *Vice Pres*
EMP: 8 **EST:** 2001
SALES (est): 889.2K **Privately Held**
WEB: www.armadillosoundandstaging.net
SIC: 3648 5099 Stage lighting equipment; video & audio equipment

(G-9170)
ARMSTRONG POWER SYSTEMS LLC (PA)
5100 Nw 72nd Ave (33166-5607)
PHONE..................................305 470-0058
Enrique Villacrez,
◆ **EMP:** 15 **EST:** 1990
SQ FT: 13,000
SALES (est): 2.9MM **Privately Held**
WEB: www.armstrongpower.com
SIC: 3621 5063 Generators & sets, electric; generators

(G-9171)
ART PRINTING MIAMI
13234 Sw 131st St (33186-5888)
PHONE..................................786 581-9889
Luis G Hernandez, *President*
EMP: 6 **EST:** 2017
SALES (est): 230K **Privately Held**
WEB: www.miamigiclee.com
SIC: 2759 Screen printing

(G-9172)
ARTCO GROUP INC
5851 Nw 35th Ave (33142-2001)
PHONE..................................305 638-1785
Dan Romeu, *President*
Mickey Minagorri, *Exec VP*
Luis Victoria, *Exec VP*
Manuel Romero, *Vice Pres*
Martha Robles, *Buyer*
◆ **EMP:** 90
SQ FT: 65,000
SALES (est): 10.4MM **Privately Held**
WEB: www.artcogroup.com
SIC: 2541 Store fixtures, wood; cabinets, lockers & shelving

(G-9173)
ARTEX COMPUTER LLC
4737 Nw 72nd Ave (33166-5616)
PHONE..................................407 844-2253
Angel Ramirez, *Mng Member*
Iriana Urdaneta,
EMP: 5 **EST:** 2015
SQ FT: 2,800
SALES (est): 2MM **Privately Held**
WEB: www.artexcomputer.com
SIC: 3571 3663 Minicomputers; mobile communication equipment

(G-9174)
ARTISTIC PAVER MFG INC
120 Ne 179th St Ste 1 (33162-1002)
PHONE..................................305 653-7283
Daniel Essig, *President*
Sandy Llorenty, *Accounting Mgr*
Sal Franco, *Sales Executive*
Eduardo Sznajderman, *Manager*
Rubens Defaria, *Officer*
◆ **EMP:** 50 **EST:** 2000
SQ FT: 60,000
SALES (est): 10MM **Privately Held**
WEB: www.artisticpavers.com
SIC: 2951 3271 3251 Asphalt paving mixtures & blocks; concrete block & brick; brick & structural clay tile

(G-9175)
ARTS WORK UNLIMITED INC
22150 Sw 154th Ave (33170-4002)
P.O. Box 700513 (33170-0513)
PHONE..................................305 247-9257
Arthur Ballard, *President*
Phil Heermance, *Vice Pres*
Mary Peterson, *Manager*
Kathleen Ballard, *Admin Sec*
▼ **EMP:** 7 **EST:** 1972
SALES (est): 1MM **Privately Held**
WEB: www.artsworkunlimited.com
SIC: 3446 1799 Ornamental metalwork; gates, ornamental metal; fences or posts, ornamental iron or steel; fence construction

(G-9176)
ASB SPORTS GROUP LLC
Also Called: Storngerrx
801 Brickell Bay Dr (33131-2952)
PHONE..................................305 775-4689
Omar Cordero, *Mng Member*
EMP: 10 **EST:** 2005
SQ FT: 5,000
SALES (est): 900K **Privately Held**
WEB: www.asbsports.com
SIC: 3949 Sporting & athletic goods

(G-9177)
ASG AEROSPACE LLC
12906 Sw 139th Ave (33186-5348)
PHONE..................................305 253-0802
Arthur Thompson, *Principal*
Art Thompson, *Maintence Staff*
Mariana Thompson, *Maintence Staff*
EMP: 8 **EST:** 2013
SALES (est): 519.8K **Privately Held**
WEB: www.asgaerospace.com
SIC: 3721 Aircraft

(G-9178)
ASKA COMMUNICATION CORP
2020 Nw 129th Ave Ste 205 (33182-2438)
PHONE..................................954 708-2387
Toshi Nigorikawa, *President*
Sagie Subramoney, *Manager*
Debbie Okamoto, *Admin Sec*
◆ **EMP:** 7 **EST:** 1992
SALES (est): 988.1K **Privately Held**
WEB: www.askacom.com
SIC: 3663 Radio & TV communications equipment

(G-9179)
ASPEN ELECTRONICS INC
7288 Nw 54th St (33166-4808)
PHONE..................................305 863-2151
Edwardo A Trelles, *President*
EMP: 26 **EST:** 1985
SALES (est): 1.5MM **Privately Held**
WEB: www.aspenelectronics.us
SIC: 3679 Electronic circuits

GEOGRAPHIC

(G-9180)
ASSOCIATED MACHINE COMPANY INC
6540 Nw 35th Ave (33147-7563)
PHONE..................................305 836-6163
Jesse A Jones, *President*
Ellen M Smith, *Admin Sec*
EMP: 90
SQ FT: 13,000
SALES (est): 15MM **Privately Held**
WEB: www.assocmachine.com
SIC: 3599 Machine shop, jobbing & repair

(G-9181)
ASTRUM TRAVEL INTL LTD
Also Called: Astrum Helicopters
1 Aeropost Way 12658 (33206-3206)
PHONE..................................917 779-9462
Gustavo Giron, *President*
EMP: 15 **EST:** 2019
SALES (est): 416.1K **Privately Held**
SIC: 3721 Helicopters

(G-9182)
ATLANTIC DRY ICE CORPORTION
6950 Nw 12th St (33126-1336)
PHONE..................................305 592-7000
Kenia Montejo, *President*
▼ **EMP:** 18 **EST:** 1988
SALES (est): 2.8MM **Privately Held**
SIC: 2813 5169 2097 Dry ice, carbon dioxide (solid); dry ice; manufactured ice

(G-9183)
ATLANTIC SAILS MAKERS
Also Called: Uk Sails Makers
2801 Sw 31st Ave Ste 2a (33133-3540)
PHONE..................................305 567-1773
Mark Wood, *President*
EMP: 5 **EST:** 1977
SQ FT: 3,200
SALES (est): 383.4K **Privately Held**
SIC: 2394 Sails: made from purchased materials

(G-9184)
ATLANTIC STEEL CNSTR LLC
18851 Ne 29th Ave Ste 700 (33180-2845)
PHONE..................................419 236-2200
Brooke A Emrick, *Principal*
EMP: 5 **EST:** 2011
SALES (est): 428.2K **Privately Held**
WEB: www.atlantic-steel.com
SIC: 3449 Bars, concrete reinforcing: fabricated steel

(G-9185)
ATLANTIS PORCELAIN ART CORP
4241 Sw 154th Ct (33185-4259)
PHONE..................................305 582-8663
Jorge Martinez, *Principal*
Roberto Lodeiro, *Sales Mgr*
▲ **EMP:** 6 **EST:** 2008
SALES (est): 600.6K **Privately Held**
WEB: www.atlantisporcelainsink.com
SIC: 3431 Bathroom fixtures, including sinks

(G-9186)
ATLAS METAL INDUSTRIES INC
1135 Nw 159th Dr (33169-5882)
PHONE..................................305 625-2451
Joseph F Meade, *Ch of Bd*
David C Meade, *President*
Joseph F Meade III, *Vice Pres*
Mark Siegfriedt, *Vice Pres*
Tito Orozco, *Plant Mgr*
EMP: 120 **EST:** 1948
SQ FT: 52,253
SALES (est): 24.5MM
SALES (corp-wide): 94.5MM **Privately Held**
WEB: www.atlasfoodserv.com
SIC: 3589 3523 3535 Commercial cooking & foodwarming equipment; driers (farm): grain, hay & seed; conveyors & conveying equipment
PA: Mercury Aircraft Inc.
8126 Cty Rd Rte 88
Hammondsport NY 14840
607 569-4200

(G-9187)
ATLAS PAPER MILLS LLC (DH)
3301 Nw 107th St (33167-3714)
PHONE..................................800 562-2860
Jim Brown, *President*
Greg Englert, *Sales Staff*
◆ **EMP:** 16 **EST:** 1979
SQ FT: 240,000
SALES (est): 86.6MM
SALES (corp-wide): 2.9B **Privately Held**
WEB: www.resolutetissue.com
SIC: 2621 Toilet tissue stock; absorbent paper
HQ: Resolute Fp Florida Inc.
3301 Nw 107th St
Miami FL 33167
800 562-2860

(G-9188)
ATLAS POLYMERS CORP
1809 Micanopy Ave (33133-3329)
PHONE..................................786 312-2131
Adolfo S Rosendo R, *Vice Pres*
EMP: 15 **EST:** 2013
SALES (est): 1.4MM **Privately Held**
WEB: www.atlas-polymers.com
SIC: 2821 Plastics materials & resins

(G-9189)
ATLAS RENEWABLE ENERGY USA LLC
1221 Brickell Ave # 1400 (33131-3224)
PHONE..................................786 358-5614
Carlos Barrera, *CEO*
Alfredo Solar, *General Mgr*
Javier Barajas, *CFO*
Diana Castellanos, *Marketing Staff*
Renato Valdivia, *Director*
EMP: 11 **EST:** 2016
SALES (est): 1MM **Privately Held**
WEB: www.atlasrenewableenergy.com
SIC: 3674 Solar cells

(G-9190)
ATTESA HOLDINGS GROUP LLC
2949 Coconut Ave Unit 20 (33133-3795)
P.O. Box 972330 (33197-2330)
PHONE..................................305 777-3567
Salvador J Juncadella III, *Principal*
Angel R Kerkado,
◆ **EMP:** 3 **EST:** 2012
SQ FT: 1,200
SALES (est): 5MM **Privately Held**
SIC: 2671 Plastic film, coated or laminated for packaging

(G-9191)
ATTILA SERVICES CORP
12250 Sw 129th Ct Ste 108 (33186-6492)
PHONE..................................305 255-6776
Charles Lema, *Owner*
EMP: 6 **EST:** 2006
SALES (est): 208K **Privately Held**
SIC: 7692 Welding repair

(G-9192)
AURUM CHEMICALS CORP
9485 Sw 72nd St Ste A190 (33173-5417)
PHONE..................................305 412-4141
Rodrigo A Castellanos, *President*
▲ **EMP:** 5 **EST:** 1997
SALES (est): 401.3K **Privately Held**
WEB: www.aurum-chemicals.co
SIC: 2899 Chemical preparations

(G-9193)
AVAYA INC
1000 Nw 57th Ct Ste 100 (33126-3284)
PHONE..................................305 264-7021
Fax: 813 655-2088
EMP: 111
SALES (corp-wide): 4.3B **Privately Held**
SIC: 3661 Mfg Telephone/Telegraph Apparatus
HQ: Avaya Inc.
4655 Great America Pkwy
Santa Clara CA 27713
908 953-6000

(G-9194)
AVBORNE ACCESORY GROUP LLC (HQ)
Also Called: Sargent Aerospace and Defense
7500 Nw 26th St (33122-1404)
PHONE..................................305 593-6038
Scott Wargo, *General Mgr*
Gary Johnson, *Director*
EMP: 119 **EST:** 2015
SQ FT: 150,000
SALES (est): 40MM
SALES (corp-wide): 608.9MM **Publicly Held**
WEB: www.rbcbearings.com
SIC: 3728 Aircraft parts & equipment
PA: Rbc Bearings Incorporated
102 Willenbrock Rd Bldg B
Oxford CT 06478
203 267-7001

(G-9195)
AVBORNE ACCESSORY GROUP INC (DH)
Also Called: Aersale Component Solutions
7600 Nw 26th St (33122-1416)
P.O. Box 522537 (33152-2537)
PHONE..................................305 593-6038
Nicolas Finazzo, *CEO*
Scott Wargo, *General Mgr*
Daniel Bergeron, *COO*
Harold Labbe, *Opers Staff*
Pedro Cabezas, *Buyer*
▲ **EMP:** 38 **EST:** 2004
SQ FT: 150,000
SALES (est): 35.6MM **Privately Held**
WEB: www.aersale.com
SIC: 3728 Aircraft parts & equipment

(G-9196)
AVENTURA JEWELRY & COIN
19275 Biscayne Blvd # 22 (33180-2308)
PHONE..................................305 933-2646
Michael Freiman, *Owner*
EMP: 2 **EST:** 1996
SALES (est): 3MM **Privately Held**
WEB: www.worldofcoins.com
SIC: 3961 5094 Costume jewelry; coins, medals & trophies

(G-9197)
AVERY DENNISON CORPORATION
5200 Blue Lagoon Dr # 130 (33126-7006)
PHONE..................................305 228-8740
EMP: 115
SALES (corp-wide): 6.3B **Publicly Held**
SIC: 2672 Mfg Coated/Laminated Paper
PA: Avery Dennison Corporation
207 N Goode Ave Fl 6
Glendale CA 91203
626 304-2000

(G-9198)
AVIACOL USA CORP
2299 Nw 108th Ave (33172-2022)
PHONE..................................786 701-2152
Hugo Francisco Fajardo, *President*
Harold Giovanny Bocanegra, *Vice Pres*
Antanas Jurksaitis, *Admin Sec*
EMP: 10 **EST:** 2014
SALES (est): 291.3K **Privately Held**
WEB: www.aviacolusacorp.com
SIC: 3728 Aircraft parts & equipment

(G-9199)
AVIONICS SUPPORT GROUP INC
13155 Sw 132nd Ave # 200 (33186-6148)
PHONE..................................305 378-9786
Armand Wong, *President*
Hugo Fortes, *General Mgr*
Hugo L Fortes, *Vice Pres*
Alex Rodrigo, *Vice Pres*
Amy Marquez, *Purchasing*
EMP: 20 **EST:** 1996
SQ FT: 2,400
SALES: 6.2MM **Privately Held**
WEB: www.asginc.net
SIC: 3728 Aircraft parts & equipment

(G-9200)
AVON CORRUGATED/FLORIDA CORP
15600 Nw 15th Ave (33169-5604)
PHONE..................................305 770-3439
Selwyn Cain, *President*
Robert Farbish, *Vice Pres*
▼ **EMP:** 16 **EST:** 1989
SQ FT: 60,000
SALES (est): 432.6K **Privately Held**
SIC: 2653 Boxes, corrugated: made from purchased materials

(G-9201)
AW PUBLISHING
3135 Sw 3rd Ave (33129-2711)
PHONE..................................305 856-7000
Anthony G Aguirre, *President*
Veronica Wolman, *Vice Pres*
EMP: 10 **EST:** 1995
SQ FT: 1,200
SALES (est): 911.5K **Privately Held**
SIC: 2759 2711 Schedules, transportation: printing; newspapers

(G-9202)
AW-TRONICS LLC
100 Biscayne Blvd # 1315 (33132-2309)
PHONE..................................786 228-7835
Arash Caby, *Mng Member*
Catherine Caby, *Mng Member*
Marco Gutierrez, *Manager*
EMP: 20 **EST:** 2010
SALES (est): 3.6MM **Privately Held**
SIC: 3672 Circuit boards, television & radio printed

(G-9203)
AWE DIAGNOSTICS LLC ✪
3401 N Miami Ave Ste 230 (33127-3546)
PHONE..................................786 285-0755
Luis A Urrea, *Principal*
Dr Pablo Guzman, *Principal*
Leon Levy, *Principal*
Joaquin Sabaris, *Principal*
EMP: 25 **EST:** 2020
SALES (est): 1.2MM **Privately Held**
SIC: 3829 Measuring & controlling devices

(G-9204)
AXXIUM ENGINEERING LLC
14032 Sw 140th St 16 (33186-5548)
PHONE..................................786 573-9808
Paul H Lopez, *Principal*
EMP: 5 **EST:** 2006
SALES (est): 365.8K **Privately Held**
WEB: www.axxiumengineering.com
SIC: 3715 Truck trailers

(G-9205)
AYURDEVAS NATURAL PRODUCTS LLC
2076 Nw 21st St (33142-7316)
PHONE..................................786 322-0909
Jordi Verite, *Managing Prtnr*
Leonardo Gutter, *Managing Prtnr*
EMP: 9 **EST:** 2011
SQ FT: 3,000
SALES (est): 371.2K **Privately Held**
SIC: 2844 Toilet preparations

(G-9206)
AZEX FLOW TECHNOLOGIES INC
Also Called: A F T
13431 Nw 19th Ln (33182-1909)
PHONE..................................305 393-8037
Carlos M Garcia, *Director*
Alvaro P Diaz, *Director*
▼ **EMP:** 8 **EST:** 2003
SQ FT: 800
SALES (est): 1MM **Privately Held**
SIC: 3491 3494 7363 5085 Automatic regulating & control valves; pipe fittings; industrial help service; valves & fittings

(G-9207)
B & G INSTRUMENTS INC
5000 Nw 36th St Bldg 875 (33166-2763)
P.O. Box 661073, Miami Springs (33266-1073)
PHONE..................................305 871-4445
Robert L Brown, *President*
Pablo Gonzalez, *Vice Pres*
Ady Lebrija, *Purch Mgr*

EMP: 12 **EST:** 1982
SQ FT: 3,600
SALES (est): 1.3MM **Privately Held**
WEB: www.bginstruments.net
SIC: 3829 Measuring & controlling devices

(G-9208)
B AND M SUGAR PRODUCTS LLC
Also Called: B&M
936 Sw 1st Ave 345 (33130-4520)
PHONE.................................305 897-8427
Jurgen Murrle, *Mng Member*
Ana Maria Borrero, *Director*
▲ **EMP:** 2 **EST:** 2010
SALES (est): 16.7MM **Privately Held**
SIC: 2062 Cane sugar refining

(G-9209)
B D D INTERNATIONAL CORP
Also Called: Sir Speedy
203 Nw 36th St Ste 2 (33127-3128)
PHONE.................................305 573-2416
Julio Bielich, *President*
Logo Bielich, *Vice Pres*
Martha Bielich, *Director*
Miguel Bielich, *Director*
Luis Bielich, *Admin Sec*
EMP: 8 **EST:** 1980
SQ FT: 2,100
SALES (est): 1.6MM **Privately Held**
WEB: www.sirspeedy.com
SIC: 2752 Commercial printing, lithographic

(G-9210)
B&C PUBLISHING INC
13010 N Calusa Club Dr (33186-1704)
PHONE.................................305 385-8216
Maria Christina, *President*
EMP: 7 **EST:** 2000
SALES (est): 130K **Privately Held**
SIC: 2741 Miscellaneous publishing

(G-9211)
B&C SHEET METAL DUCT CORP
Also Called: Little Steps Daycare
1025 Sw 82nd Ave (33144-4241)
PHONE.................................305 316-9212
Arleny Barruelo, *Principal*
EMP: 8 **EST:** 2008
SALES (est): 793K **Privately Held**
WEB: www.bcsheetmetal.com
SIC: 3444 Sheet metalwork

(G-9212)
BABY ABUELITA PRODUCTIONS LLC
6619 S Dixie Hwy Ste 139 (33143-7919)
PHONE.................................305 662-7320
Carol Fenster, *CEO*
EMP: 6 **EST:** 2007
SQ FT: 1,250
SALES (est): 303.4K **Privately Held**
SIC: 3942 Dolls & stuffed toys

(G-9213)
BACHILLER IRON WORKS INC
Also Called: BIW
295 Ne 71st St (33138-5527)
PHONE.................................305 751-7773
Felix Bachiller, *President*
Gypsy Bachiller, *Vice Pres*
EMP: 20 **EST:** 1993
SQ FT: 9,000
SALES (est): 2.6MM **Privately Held**
WEB: www.biwiron.com
SIC: 3446 Architectural metalwork

(G-9214)
BAHAMAS UPHL & MAR CANVAS INC
4782 Sw 75th Ave (33155-4435)
PHONE.................................305 992-4346
William Lanzas, *Principal*
EMP: 10 **EST:** 2018
SALES (est): 370.2K **Privately Held**
WEB: www.bahamasupholsterymiami.com
SIC: 2211 Canvas

(G-9215)
BAKER NORTON US INC
74 Nw 176th St (33169-5043)
PHONE.................................305 575-6000
Thomas Beier, *President*
RAO Uppaluri, *Treasurer*
Steven D Rubin, *Admin Sec*
Marianne Hurd-Nation, *Asst Sec*
EMP: 60 **EST:** 1986
SALES (est): 5.6MM **Privately Held**
WEB: www.tevapharm.com
SIC: 2834 Pharmaceutical preparations
HQ: Ivax Corporation
4400 Biscayne Blvd
Miami FL 33137
305 329-3795

(G-9216)
BALLA DE RODRIGUEZ MIGDALIA M
14493 Sw 27th St (33175-7449)
PHONE.................................305 228-6566
Migdalia De Rodriguez, *Principal*
▲ **EMP:** 6 **EST:** 2004
SALES (est): 194K **Privately Held**
SIC: 3634 Dryers, electric: hand & face

(G-9217)
BARBECUE SUPERSTORE
Also Called: Weeks Gas Hme of The Brbc Sprs
3800 Nw 59th St (33142-2032)
PHONE.................................305 635-4427
Jeffrey Miller, *President*
Freddy Royero, *Vice Pres*
Steve Kenorr, *CFO*
EMP: 7 **EST:** 2001
SQ FT: 30,000
SALES (est): 736K **Privately Held**
WEB: www.thebbqsuperstore.com
SIC: 2033 Barbecue sauce: packaged in cans, jars, etc.

(G-9218)
BARCLAYS BUSINESS CENTER LLC
555 Ne 15th St Ste 200 (33132-1455)
PHONE.................................786 260-0080
Mathieu Rochette, *Principal*
EMP: 7 **EST:** 2010
SALES (est): 200.8K **Privately Held**
WEB: www.barclaysbusinesscenter.com
SIC: 3579 Typing & word processing machines

(G-9219)
BARCO LLC
475 Brickell Ave (33131-2498)
PHONE.................................305 677-9600
Victor Barroso, *Principal*
▼ **EMP:** 7 **EST:** 2010
SALES (est): 203.6K **Privately Held**
SIC: 3663 Radio & TV communications equipment

(G-9220)
BARD SPORTS CORP (PA)
Also Called: Gold Eagle
14516 Sw 119th Ave (33186-6100)
PHONE.................................305 233-2200
Mitchel M Lombard, *President*
EMP: 9 **EST:** 1986
SALES (est): 750.3K **Privately Held**
WEB: www.bard.edu
SIC: 3949 Rackets & frames: tennis, badminton, squash, lacrosse, etc

(G-9221)
BARNARD NUT COMPANY INC
Also Called: Nuts About Florida
2801 Nw 125th St (33167-2514)
P.O. Box 453636 (33245-3636)
PHONE.................................305 836-9999
Julio J Rosa, *President*
Jennifer Rosa, *Vice Pres*
Dinora Rosa, *Admin Sec*
▼ **EMP:** 60 **EST:** 1942
SQ FT: 30,500
SALES (est): 7.5MM **Privately Held**
WEB: www.nutsaboutflorida.com
SIC: 2099 2064 5145 Popcorn, packaged: except already popped; nuts, candy covered; popcorn & supplies

(G-9222)
BARON PAVERS CORP
3281 Nw 18th St (33125-1837)
PHONE.................................786 389-2894
Jorge Aldana, *Principal*
EMP: 8 **EST:** 2009
SALES (est): 453.4K **Privately Held**
SIC: 3531 Pavers

(G-9223)
BARRAU & COIRIN INC
Also Called: Sign-A-Rama
250 Ne 61st St (33137-2127)
PHONE.................................305 571-5051
Christine Barrau, *Vice Pres*
Lucien Barrau, *Director*
▼ **EMP:** 5 **EST:** 2005
SQ FT: 1,500
SALES (est): 527.6K **Privately Held**
WEB: www.signarama.com
SIC: 3993 Signs & advertising specialties

(G-9224)
BARTON & GUESTIER USA INC
4700 Biscayne Blvd # 503 (33137-3200)
PHONE.................................305 895-9757
Phillippe T Marion, *CEO*
Jean-Luc G Noel, *CEO*
Hubert D Surville, *COO*
Laurent P Prada, *Vice Pres*
▲ **EMP:** 7 **EST:** 2011
SALES (est): 1.4MM
SALES (corp-wide): 84.4K **Privately Held**
WEB: www.barton-guestier.com
SIC: 2084 Wines
HQ: Barton & Guestier
Chateau Magnol
Blanquefort 33290
556 954-800

(G-9225)
BAUDUCCO MANUFACTURING INC
1705 Nw 133rd Ave Ste 101 (33182-2293)
PHONE.................................305 477-9270
Stefano L Mozzi, *President*
Leonardo T Dib, *Treasurer*
Ricardo Yuki, *Admin Sec*
Magdalena Lopez, *Asst Sec*
EMP: 12 **EST:** 2019
SALES (est): 3MM **Privately Held**
SIC: 2051 Bread, cake & related products; breads, rolls & buns
HQ: Bauducco Usa Holding Company
1705 Nw 133rd Ave Ste 101
Miami FL 33182
305 477-9270

(G-9226)
BAUDUCCO USA HOLDING COMPANY (DH)
1705 Nw 133rd Ave Ste 101 (33182-2293)
PHONE.................................305 477-9270
Stefano L Mozzi, *President*
Leonardo T Dib, *Treasurer*
Ricardo Yuki, *Admin Sec*
Magdelena A Lopez, *Asst Sec*
EMP: 4 **EST:** 2018
SALES (est): 5.9MM **Privately Held**
WEB: www.bauducco.com.br
SIC: 2051 5149 Bread, cake & related products; crackers, cookies & bakery products

(G-9227)
BAYSIDE SMALL CAP SENIOR LOAN
1450 Brickell Ave Fl 31 (33131-3460)
PHONE.................................305 381-4100
EMP: 11 **EST:** 2016
SALES (est): 8.3MM **Privately Held**
WEB: www.whitehorsecapital.com
SIC: 3313 Electrometallurgical products
HQ: H.I.G. Capital, L.L.C.
1450 Brickell Ave Fl 31
Miami FL 33131
305 379-2322

(G-9228)
BCC-BGLE CMMNCTONS CRP-CLRIN L
Also Called: El Clarin
8900 Sw 107th Ave Ste 30 (33176-1451)
PHONE.................................305 270-3333
Jose Noboa, *President*
▼ **EMP:** 12 **EST:** 1979
SALES (est): 1.1MM **Privately Held**
WEB: www.elclarin.com
SIC: 2711 Newspapers, publishing & printing

(G-9229)
BCDIRECT CORP
Also Called: Robotray
15625 Nw 15th Ave (33169-5601)
PHONE.................................305 623-3838
Luis A Lacal, *President*
Juan Lacal, *Vice Pres*
EMP: 12 **EST:** 2000
SALES (est): 2.2MM **Privately Held**
SIC: 3569 Robots, assembly line: industrial & commercial

(G-9230)
BDNZ ASSOCIATES INC
Also Called: Fastsigns
9481 Sw 134th St (33176-5749)
PHONE.................................305 379-7993
Susan Chai-Onn, *President*
Roger D Chai-Onn, *Vice Pres*
EMP: 7
SQ FT: 1,800
SALES (est): 1MM **Privately Held**
WEB: www.fastsigns.com
SIC: 3993 Signs & advertising specialties

(G-9231)
BECKMAN COULTER INC
Also Called: Iris Diagnostics
11800 Sw 147th Ave (33196-2500)
PHONE.................................305 380-2175
Jorge Fernandez, *Engineer*
Luis Gamarra, *Engineer*
Jose Rabade, *Engineer*
Victor Rodriguez, *Engineer*
Eric Statler, *Engineer*
EMP: 15
SALES (corp-wide): 22.2B **Publicly Held**
WEB: www.beckmancoulter.com
SIC: 3826 Analytical instruments
HQ: Beckman Coulter, Inc.
250 S Kraemer Blvd
Brea CA 92821
714 993-5321

(G-9232)
BERKANT CORP
6370 Nw 82nd Ave (33166-3427)
PHONE.................................305 771-5578
Rapahel Diaz, *Vice Pres*
EMP: 10 **EST:** 2017
SALES (est): 449.5K **Privately Held**
SIC: 2844 Toilet preparations

(G-9233)
BERKSHIRE MANAGMENT ASSOCIATES
Also Called: Techcrete Architectural Precast
12841 Sw 117th St (33186-4653)
PHONE.................................305 883-3277
Tom Ban, *Owner*
EMP: 7 **EST:** 2002
SALES (est): 105.3K **Privately Held**
SIC: 3273 Ready-mixed concrete

(G-9234)
BEST FINISHER
2780 Nw 122nd St (33167-2508)
PHONE.................................305 688-8174
Casimiro Saboya, *Owner*
EMP: 18 **EST:** 1978
SQ FT: 20,000
SALES (est): 1.1MM **Privately Held**
WEB: www.bestfinishers.com
SIC: 3479 Coating of metals & formed products

(G-9235)
BEST TRUSS COMPANY (PA)
7035 Sw 44th St (33155-4643)
PHONE.................................305 667-6797
Antonio Sierra, *President*
Carlos Blume, *Vice Pres*
▼ **EMP:** 59 **EST:** 1987
SQ FT: 52,000
SALES (est): 8MM **Privately Held**
WEB: www.besttruss.com
SIC: 2439 Trusses, wooden roof; trusses, except roof: laminated lumber

(G-9236)
BESTCANVAS INC
3343 Nw 107th St (33167-3714)
PHONE.................................305 759-7800
Daniel Muehlbauer, *President*
Philipp Muehlbauer, *Vice Pres*

▲ **EMP:** 11 **EST:** 2010
SQ FT: 5,000
SALES (est): 1.4MM **Privately Held**
WEB: www.canvasdiscount.com
SIC: 2211 Canvas

(G-9237)
BETTY ENGINES MACHINE SHOP INC
7120 Sw 44th St Ste A (33155-4638)
PHONE..................................305 458-1467
Marco Valcarcel, *Principal*
EMP: 7 **EST:** 2015
SALES (est): 155.7K **Privately Held**
WEB: www.birdroadmachine.com
SIC: 3599 Machine shop, jobbing & repair

(G-9238)
BEV-CO ENTERPRISES INC (PA)
2761 Nw 82nd Ave (33122-1041)
PHONE..................................786 362-6368
Enoc Martinez, *Principal*
EMP: 22 **EST:** 2009
SALES (est): 320.1K **Privately Held**
SIC: 2087 Beverage bases

(G-9239)
BEVERAGE CANNERS INC
3550 Nw 110th St (33167-3724)
PHONE..................................305 714-7000
EMP: 8 **EST:** 2016
SALES (est): 103.1K **Privately Held**
WEB: www.bcibeverages.com
SIC: 2086 Soft drinks: packaged in cans, bottles, etc.

(G-9240)
BEVERAGE CANNERS INTERNATIONAL
Also Called: BCI
3505 Nw 107th St (33167-3794)
PHONE..................................305 714-7000
Nick Cabrella, *President*
▼ **EMP:** 26 **EST:** 2002
SALES (est): 503.1K **Privately Held**
WEB: www.bcibeverages.com
SIC: 2086 Soft drinks: packaged in cans, bottles, etc.

(G-9241)
BEVERAGE CORP INTL INC
3505 Nw 107th St (33167-3716)
PHONE..................................305 714-7000
Joseph Caporella, *President*
Nick Caporella, *Chairman*
George Bracken, *Vice Pres*
Alan Domzalski, *Vice Pres*
Dean McCoy, *Vice Pres*
◆ **EMP:** 100 **EST:** 1985
SALES (est): 13.4MM
SALES (corp-wide): 1B **Publicly Held**
WEB: www.bcibeverages.com
SIC: 2086 Soft drinks: packaged in cans, bottles, etc.; water, pasteurized: packaged in cans, bottles, etc.; fruit drinks (less than 100% juice): packaged in cans, etc.
PA: National Beverage Corp.
8100 Sw 10th St Ste 4000
Plantation FL 33324
954 581-0922

(G-9242)
BEYOND WHITE SPA LLC
Also Called: Ezywipe of America
3200 Nw 67th Ave Unit 600 (33166-2256)
PHONE..................................866 399-8867
Alex Munoz, *Mng Member*
Carmelina Natale,
Cesar Sordo,
◆ **EMP:** 6 **EST:** 2014
SQ FT: 2,014
SALES (est): 486K **Privately Held**
SIC: 2392 Towels, fabric & nonwoven: made from purchased materials

(G-9243)
BID EXCELLENCE CO LLC
Also Called: Bid Uniforms.com
20404 Ne 16th Pl (33179-2704)
PHONE..................................609 929-9019
Michael Ryba, *President*
EMP: 7 **EST:** 2011
SQ FT: 2,000
SALES (est): 325.8K **Privately Held**
WEB: www.bid-excellence-co-llc.business.site
SIC: 2311 2326 5136 Men's & boys' uniforms; work apparel, except uniforms; men's & boys' sportswear & work clothing

(G-9244)
BIG CYPRESS DISTILLERY LLC
13995 Sw 144th Ave # 207 (33186-8656)
PHONE..................................786 228-9740
Fernando Plata, *Mng Member*
Danny Garo,
Mark A Graham,
▼ **EMP:** 6 **EST:** 2015
SQ FT: 1,900
SALES (est): 499.3K **Privately Held**
WEB: www.bigcypressdistillery.com
SIC: 2085 Distilled & blended liquors

(G-9245)
BIJOL AND SPICES INC
Also Called: Bijol & Spices
2154 Nw 22nd Ct (33142-7346)
P.O. Box 420189 (33242-0189)
PHONE..................................305 634-9030
Ida M Borges, *President*
Iliat M Llamozas, *COO*
Diego Borges, *Vice Pres*
Ivette V Borges, *Admin Sec*
▲ **EMP:** 8 **EST:** 1962
SQ FT: 4,000
SALES (est): 879.1K **Privately Held**
WEB: www.bijol.com
SIC: 2099 5499 Spices, including grinding; spices & herbs

(G-9246)
BINGO BAKERY INC
2125 Nw 8th Ave (33127-4609)
PHONE..................................305 545-9993
Joel Gali, *President*
Ann Gali, *Corp Secy*
▲ **EMP:** 10 **EST:** 1975
SQ FT: 8,000
SALES (est): 238.3K **Privately Held**
WEB: www.bingobakery.com
SIC: 2052 Bakery products, dry

(G-9247)
BIO-NUCLEONICS PHARMA INC
Also Called: Bio Nucleonics
1 Ne 19th St (33132-1030)
PHONE..................................305 576-0996
Stanley Satz, *President*
Rosanne Satz, *Vice Pres*
EMP: 17 **EST:** 2002
SALES (est): 301.2K **Privately Held**
SIC: 2834 Pharmaceutical preparations

(G-9248)
BIOCHEM MANUFACTURING INC
7300 N Kendall Dr Ste 640 (33156-7840)
PHONE..................................786 210-1290
EMP: 7 **EST:** 2019
SALES (est): 153.6K **Privately Held**
WEB: www.bmichem.com
SIC: 3999 Manufacturing industries

(G-9249)
BIRDIEBOX LLC
2129 Nw 86th Ave (33122-1527)
PHONE..................................786 762-2975
Pat Depirro, *CEO*
Kristine Reeder, *Vice Pres*
Brooke Evans, *Buyer*
Frances Gulick, *Marketing Staff*
Esme Flynn, *Manager*
EMP: 27 **EST:** 2014
SQ FT: 1,500
SALES: 5.8MM **Privately Held**
WEB: www.birdiebox.com
SIC: 2653 5199 7389 Boxes, corrugated: made from purchased materials; gifts & novelties; packaging & labeling services

(G-9250)
BISCAYNE AWNING & SHADE CO
2333 Nw 8th Ave (33127-4216)
PHONE..................................305 638-7933
Conrado Perez, *President*
Alicia Perez, *Corp Secy*
▼ **EMP:** 28 **EST:** 1924
SQ FT: 8,000
SALES (est): 663.4K **Privately Held**
WEB: www.biscayneawning.com
SIC: 2394 2591 Awnings, fabric: made from purchased materials; canvas covers & drop cloths; drapery hardware & blinds & shades

(G-9251)
BISCAYNE ELECTRIC MOTOR & PUMP
830 Nw 144th St (33168-3024)
PHONE..................................305 681-8171
Peter Ross, *President*
John Birri, *President*
Sheila Birri, *Vice Pres*
▼ **EMP:** 5 **EST:** 1963
SQ FT: 1,500
SALES (est): 919.2K **Privately Held**
WEB: www.biscayneelectricmotor.com
SIC: 7694 5063 5999 Electric motor repair; motors, electric; motors, electric

(G-9252)
BISCAYNE TENNIS LLC
19021 Biscayne Blvd (33180-2819)
PHONE..................................786 231-8372
Alexander Pinto, *Mng Member*
Alberto Acosta, *Mng Member*
Horacio Pinto, *Mng Member*
EMP: 6 **EST:** 2012
SALES (est): 336.9K **Privately Held**
WEB: www.biscaynetennis.com
SIC: 3949 Tennis equipment & supplies; fencing equipment (sporting goods)

(G-9253)
BK STAINLESS INC
13899 Sw 140th St (33186-5522)
PHONE..................................786 474-0203
EMP: 6 **EST:** 2019
SALES (est): 126.9K **Privately Held**
WEB: www.bkstainlessinc.com
SIC: 2434 Wood kitchen cabinets

(G-9254)
BKN INTERNATIONAL INC
Also Called: Izzycue
1100 Biscayne Blvd # 290 (33132-1717)
PHONE..................................301 518-7153
Kenneth Tan, *President*
Felecia Tan, *CFO*
EMP: 8 **EST:** 1997
SALES (est): 451K **Privately Held**
SIC: 2051 0181 2023 Pastries, e.g. danish: except frozen; seeds, vegetable: growing of; dietary supplements, dairy & non-dairy based

(G-9255)
BLACKFIST MAGAZINE LLC (PA)
382 Ne 191st St Ste 73388 (33179-3899)
PHONE..................................904 864-8695
Nicole Teamer,
EMP: 14 **EST:** 2018
SALES (est): 957.8K **Privately Held**
SIC: 2721 Magazines: publishing only, not printed on site

(G-9256)
BLIND BROTHERS INC
7038 Sw 46th St (33155-4614)
PHONE..................................786 518-8938
Regino Rodriguez, *Principal*
EMP: 8 **EST:** 2016
SALES (est): 161.3K **Privately Held**
WEB: www.blindbrosinc.com
SIC: 3442 Metal doors, sash & trim

(G-9257)
BLINDS 321 INC
12335 Nw 7th St (33182-2048)
PHONE..................................305 336-9221
EMP: 7 **EST:** 2019
SALES (est): 108.2K **Privately Held**
WEB: www.myblinds321.com
SIC: 2591 Window blinds

(G-9258)
BLINDS DR LLC
2220 Sw 84th Ave (33155-1151)
PHONE..................................305 394-4808
Tomas Carrillo, *Principal*
EMP: 6 **EST:** 2019
SALES (est): 81K **Privately Held**
SIC: 2591 Window blinds

(G-9259)
BLINDS R US CORP
5946 Sw 162nd Path (33193-5666)
PHONE..................................305 303-2072
Jorge Perez, *President*
EMP: 7 **EST:** 2010
SALES (est): 59.6K **Privately Held**
WEB: www.blindsr-us.com
SIC: 2591 Venetian blinds

(G-9260)
BLINDS SHADES INDUSTRIES CORP
245 Ne 183rd St Ste 2b (33179-4500)
PHONE..................................786 445-2144
EMP: 6 **EST:** 2019
SALES (est): 93.1K **Privately Held**
SIC: 2591 Window blinds

(G-9261)
BLUE LEAF HOSPITALITY INC
4405 Sw 74th Ave (33155-4407)
PHONE..................................305 668-3000
Stan C Shockley, *President*
Anamaria Jimenez, *Project Mgr*
Rachel Penabella, *Sr Project Mgr*
Solanch Mejia, *Manager*
Salima Ramlakan, *Manager*
▲ **EMP:** 10 **EST:** 2002
SQ FT: 4,500
SALES (est): 1.6MM **Privately Held**
WEB: www.blueleafmiami.com
SIC: 2599 Hotel furniture

(G-9262)
BLUES DESIGN GROUP LLC
Also Called: Green Surfaces
3724 Nw 43rd St (33142-4238)
PHONE..................................305 586-3630
Ricardo Mucenic, *Mng Member*
▲ **EMP:** 10 **EST:** 2010
SQ FT: 8,000
SALES (est): 295.5K **Privately Held**
WEB: www.greensurfacesgroup.com
SIC: 2541 Counter & sink tops

(G-9263)
BMG AEROSPACE
245 Ne 14th St Apt 3701 (33132-1639)
P.O. Box 371558 (33137-1558)
PHONE..................................786 725-4959
Brian Gordillo, *Principal*
EMP: 10 **EST:** 2016
SALES (est): 496.7K **Privately Held**
SIC: 3721 Aircraft

(G-9264)
BOHNERT SHEET METAL & ROOFG CO
2225 Nw 76th St (33147-6092)
PHONE..................................305 696-6851
William Marvel Jr, *President*
Christopher Marvel, *Corp Secy*
▼ **EMP:** 12 **EST:** 1912
SQ FT: 17,400
SALES (est): 2MM **Privately Held**
WEB: www.bohnertsheetmetal.com
SIC: 3444 Sheet metal specialties, not stamped

(G-9265)
BOLD LOOK INC
6721 Nw 36th Ave (33147-6501)
PHONE..................................305 687-8725
Kenneth Bold, *President*
Madelin Castillo, *General Mgr*
Janet Bold, *Principal*
Carol Dipietro, *Vice Pres*
Michelle Padilla, *Sales Staff*
▲ **EMP:** 29 **EST:** 1989
SALES (est): 6MM **Privately Held**
WEB: www.boldlook.net
SIC: 2389 Uniforms & vestments

(G-9266)
BOLLOU TRANSPORTATION LLC ✪
11626 Ne 2nd Ave (33161-6104)
PHONE..................................800 548-1768
Kevin Lecsaint, *Mng Member*
EMP: 10 **EST:** 2021
SALES (est): 360.4K **Privately Held**
SIC: 3799 Transportation equipment

(G-9267)
BOOSTAN INC
Also Called: Minuteman Press
8300 W Flagler St Ste 155 (33144-2098)
PHONE....................................305 223-5981
Ray Dehbozorgi, *President*
Hamid Zolfaghari, *Vice Pres*
EMP: 5 **EST:** 1989
SQ FT: 1,200
SALES (est): 500K **Privately Held**
WEB: www.chanhassen-mn.minuteman-press.com
SIC: 2752 2759 Commercial printing, lithographic; thermography

(G-9268)
BORGESFS INC
14920 Sw 137th St Unit 2 (33196-5623)
PHONE....................................786 210-0327
Amaury Borges, *Principal*
EMP: 9 **EST:** 2014
SALES (est): 117.7K **Privately Held**
WEB: www.aerospaceconnectionsinc.com
SIC: 3728 Aircraft parts & equipment

(G-9269)
BORIS SKATEBOARDS MFG INC
695 Ne 77th St (33138-5105)
PHONE....................................305 519-3544
Matthew McNertney, *Principal*
EMP: 7 **EST:** 2010
SALES (est): 157K **Privately Held**
WEB: www.centurycarecherryville.com
SIC: 3949 Skateboards

(G-9270)
BOSTON NTRCEUTICAL SCIENCE LLC
801 Brickell Ave (33131-2951)
PHONE....................................617 848-4560
Daniel Shina, *Mng Member*
EMP: 10 **EST:** 2015
SALES (est): 778.5K **Privately Held**
SIC: 2833 5122 Vitamins, natural or synthetic: bulk, uncompounded; vitamins & minerals

(G-9271)
BOULDER BLIMP COMPANY INC
13350 Sw 131st St # 106 (33186-6187)
PHONE....................................303 664-1122
Loni Gilfedder, *CEO*
Frank Rider, *President*
Ben Azadi, *Accounts Exec*
Dan Pagano, *Sales Staff*
Jessica Lila, *Office Mgr*
◆ **EMP:** 12 **EST:** 1980
SALES (est): 1.1MM **Privately Held**
WEB: www.boulderblimp.com
SIC: 3069 2399 Balloons, advertising & toy: rubber; banners, made from fabric

(G-9272)
BPC LLC
1717 N Byshore Dr Apt 313 (33132)
PHONE....................................305 987-9517
Ivan Bonvini, *Mng Member*
EMP: 11
SQ FT: 1,800
SALES (est): 200K **Privately Held**
SIC: 2511 Wood household furniture

(G-9273)
BRAIN POWER INCORPORATED
Also Called: B P I
4470 Sw 74th Ave (33155-4495)
P.O. Box 559501 (33255-9501)
PHONE....................................305 264-4465
Herbert A Wertheim MD, *President*
Laurent Hage, *Business Mgr*
William Moore, *COO*
Yelena Marrero, *Design Engr*
Jean Brill, *CFO*
▲ **EMP:** 46 **EST:** 1971
SQ FT: 85,000
SALES (est): 10.6MM **Privately Held**
WEB: www.callbpi.com
SIC: 3827 3841 Optical instruments & lenses; ophthalmic instruments & apparatus

(G-9274)
BRAZILIAN WOOD WORKS INC
3000 Sw 3rd Ave (33129-2777)
PHONE....................................786 468-5712
Marcos M Freitas, *Principal*
EMP: 6 **EST:** 2017
SALES (est): 58.4K **Privately Held**
SIC: 2431 Millwork

(G-9275)
BREEZY SWIMWEAR
8762 Sw 133rd St (33176-5929)
PHONE....................................305 763-9570
Kristofer Izquierdo, *Principal*
EMP: 6 **EST:** 2018
SALES (est): 261.4K **Privately Held**
WEB: www.breezyswimwear.com
SIC: 2323 Men's & boys' neckwear

(G-9276)
BRICKMED LLC
1800 Sw 27th Ave Ste 505 (33145-2400)
PHONE....................................305 774-0081
Jewel D Lambert, *Vice Pres*
Peter Legor, *Vice Pres*
Roland J Millas, *Treasurer*
Peter Legorburu, *Mng Member*
EMP: 5 **EST:** 1991
SQ FT: 2,200
SALES (est): 500K **Privately Held**
WEB: www.brickmed.com
SIC: 3695 5045 5734 8741 Computer software tape & disks: blank, rigid & floppy; computer software; computer & software stores; management services

(G-9277)
BRITISH BOYS & ASSOCIATES
14480 Sw 151st Ter (33186-5666)
PHONE....................................305 278-1790
Stuart Hinde, *President*
Mohannad Iqbal, *Corp Secy*
EMP: 5
SALES (est): 383.2K **Privately Held**
WEB: www.britishboysmiami.com
SIC: 3448 1799 1521 Screen enclosures; screening contractor: window, door, etc.; general remodeling, single-family houses

(G-9278)
BRITVIC NORTH AMERICA LLC
360 Nw 27th St (33127-4158)
PHONE....................................786 641-5041
Olivier Mercier, *Managing Dir*
John Daly, *Principal*
Elaine McCague, *Controller*
Rebecca Sutton, *Credit Mgr*
Michelle Hunter, *Manager*
EMP: 19 **EST:** 2011
SALES (est): 12.3MM
SALES (corp-wide): 1.8B **Privately Held**
WEB: www.britvic.com
SIC: 2834 Pharmaceutical preparations
PA: Britvic Plc
Breakspear Park
Hemel Hempstead HERTS HP2 4
121 711-1102

(G-9279)
BROOKLYN STITCH INC
20213 Ne 16th Pl (33179-2719)
PHONE....................................786 280-1730
David Douenias, *Ch of Bd*
EMP: 7 **EST:** 2017
SALES (est): 426.1K **Privately Held**
WEB: www.brooklynstitch.com
SIC: 2395 Embroidery & art needlework

(G-9280)
BROWN (USA) INC
2245 Nw 72nd Ave (33122-1825)
PHONE....................................305 593-9228
Peter Browne, *CEO*
Michael Browne, *President*
Stephano Annicchiarico, *Regional Mgr*
Peter Braley, *COO*
Dawn Johnson, *Vice Pres*
◆ **EMP:** 12 **EST:** 2012
SALES (est): 1.1MM **Privately Held**
WEB: www.brown-usa.com
SIC: 3429 3272 5961 Manufactured hardware (general); building materials, except block or brick: concrete; tools & hardware, mail order

(G-9281)
BRUNSTEEL CORP
14065 Sw 142nd St (33186-5565)
PHONE....................................305 251-7607
EMP: 6
SQ FT: 8,000
SALES (est): 1.3MM **Privately Held**
SIC: 3449 Mfg Fabricated Steel Concrete Reinforcing Bars

(G-9282)
BUCKET COMPANY LLC
641 Nw 7th Street Rd (33136-3021)
P.O. Box 560989 (33256-0989)
PHONE....................................786 473-6484
Frank Escobedo, *Mng Member*
EMP: 6 **EST:** 2016
SALES (est): 150K **Privately Held**
WEB: www.thebucketcompany.com
SIC: 3089 5113 5961 Plastic & fiberglass tanks; containers, paper & disposable plastic;

(G-9283)
BUILT STORY LLC
1581 Brickell Ave # 2207 (33129-1215)
PHONE....................................305 671-3890
Brian Alonso,
EMP: 9 **EST:** 2018
SALES (est): 592.6K **Privately Held**
WEB: www.builtstory.com
SIC: 3679 3999 8322 Electronic circuits; education aids, devices & supplies; travelers' aid

(G-9284)
BULLDOG NEON SIGN COMPANY INC
5728 Ne 4th Ave (33137-2528)
PHONE....................................786 277-6366
EMP: 7 **EST:** 2019
SALES (est): 230.3K **Privately Held**
WEB: www.bulldogneon.com
SIC: 3993 Neon signs

(G-9285)
BURKE BRANDS LLC
Also Called: Cafe Don Pablo
521 Ne 189th St (33179-3909)
PHONE....................................305 249-5628
Darron J Burke, *CEO*
Jonson Ll, *Managing Prtnr*
Hernan Cabrera, *General Mgr*
Tracy Walsh, *COO*
Eliana Burke, *Vice Pres*
▲ **EMP:** 19 **EST:** 2004
SQ FT: 12,000
SALES (est): 3.1MM **Privately Held**
WEB: www.donpablocoffee.com
SIC: 2095 Coffee roasting (except by wholesale grocers)

(G-9286)
BURN PROOF GEAR LLC
7121 N Miami Ave (33150-3717)
PHONE....................................786 634-7406
Alceu R Aragao Jr, *CEO*
EMP: 6 **EST:** 2015
SALES (est): 359.9K **Privately Held**
WEB: www.burnproofgear.com
SIC: 3949 2311 Sporting & athletic goods; men's & boys' uniforms

(G-9287)
BUSINESS CENTER & PRINTSHOP
815 Nw 119th St (33168-2336)
PHONE....................................786 547-6681
Susana Sanchez, *Principal*
EMP: 6 **EST:** 2015
SALES (est): 111.2K **Privately Held**
SIC: 2752 Commercial printing, offset

(G-9288)
BUSINESS WORLD TRADING INC
Also Called: Best Buy Awnings
13275 Sw 136th St Unit 22 (33186-5832)
PHONE....................................305 238-0724
EMP: 16
SQ FT: 3,000
SALES (est): 117.4K **Privately Held**
SIC: 2211 5039 5999 Mfg Whol And Ret Awnings

(G-9289)
BUTLER GRAPHICS INC
Also Called: Alta Graphics
5055 Nw 74th Ave Unit 5 (33166-5505)
PHONE....................................305 477-1344
Kathy Butler, *President*
John Butler, *Corp Secy*
▼ **EMP:** 6 **EST:** 1991
SALES (est): 943.6K **Privately Held**
WEB: www.alta-graphics.com
SIC: 2752 Commercial printing, offset

(G-9290)
BUVIN JEWELRY OF FLORIDA INC
36 Ne 1st St Ste 217 (33132-2474)
PHONE....................................305 358-0170
Stanislas Sowinski, *President*
Anna Maria De Sowinski, *Principal*
EMP: 10 **EST:** 1980
SQ FT: 800
SALES (est): 772.3K **Privately Held**
WEB: www.buvinjewelry.com
SIC: 3911 5094 Jewelry, precious metal; jewelry & precious stones

(G-9291)
BYBLOS GROUP INC
7175 Sw 47th St Ste 210 (33155-4637)
PHONE....................................305 662-6666
Kamal T Farah, *President*
Leila Farah, *Vice Pres*
▲ **EMP:** 8 **EST:** 2000
SQ FT: 1,300
SALES (est): 645.5K **Privately Held**
WEB: www.byblosgroup.com
SIC: 2599 2541 Cabinets, factory; counter & sink tops

(G-9292)
C & C MULTISERVICES CORP
2849 Nw 7th St (33125-4303)
PHONE....................................305 200-5851
Milagros Campos, *President*
EMP: 11 **EST:** 2000
SALES (est): 462.7K **Privately Held**
SIC: 3661 Communication headgear, telephone

(G-9293)
C L F ENTERPRISES
Also Called: General Sign
111 Sw 17th Ave (33135-2126)
PHONE....................................305 643-3222
Eddy Lopez, *President*
EMP: 8 **EST:** 1973
SQ FT: 3,000
SALES (est): 618.8K **Privately Held**
SIC: 3993 Signs & advertising specialties

(G-9294)
C&D PURVEYORS INC
7274 Nw 70th St (33166-2900)
PHONE....................................305 562-8541
Horacio Zapata, *President*
EMP: 7 **EST:** 2014
SALES (est): 308.7K **Privately Held**
WEB: www.lasmercedes.com.co
SIC: 2095 Roasted coffee

(G-9295)
C1 AEROSPACE LLC
14519 Sw 138th Pl (33186-7215)
PHONE....................................786 712-9949
Chris J Annoual, *President*
EMP: 7 **EST:** 2017
SALES (est): 406.4K **Privately Held**
SIC: 3721 Aircraft

(G-9296)
CA INC
15298 Sw 17th Ter (33185-5873)
PHONE....................................305 559-4640
EMP: 142
SALES (corp-wide): 4.6B **Publicly Held**
SIC: 7372 Prepackaged Software Svcs
PA: Ca, Inc.
1 Ca Plz Ste 100
Islandia NY 10022
800 225-5224

(G-9297)
CA PIPELINE INC
15621 Sw 209th Ave (33187-5677)
PHONE....................................305 969-4655

EMP: 8 **EST:** 2019
SALES (est): 735.6K **Privately Held**
SIC: 1389 Oil field services

(G-9298)
CABALLERO METALS CORP
7315 Sw 45th St (33155-4534)
PHONE..................................305 266-9085
Jose A Caballero, *President*
Pedro Caballero, *Vice Pres*
EMP: 6 **EST:** 2012
SALES (est): 140.4K **Privately Held**
SIC: 3446 Architectural metalwork

(G-9299)
CABALLERO METALS CORP
7315 Sw 45th St Ste 4 (33155-4534)
PHONE..................................305 266-9085
Pedro J Caballero, *President*
Jose Caballero, *Vice Pres*
EMP: 10 **EST:** 1982
SQ FT: 3,000
SALES (est): 979.8K **Privately Held**
SIC: 3446 Architectural metalwork

(G-9300)
CAF USA INC
9400 Nw 37th Ave (33147-2703)
PHONE..................................305 753-5371
EMP: 6 **EST:** 2017
SALES (est): 182.6K **Privately Held**
WEB: www.cafusa.com
SIC: 3743 Railroad equipment

(G-9301)
CAFCO LLC
Also Called: Pawtitas
3370 Ne 190th St Apt 2206 (33180-2418)
PHONE..................................240 848-5574
Francisco Hoheb, *Mng Member*
Ingrid Randolf, *Mng Member*
EMP: 6 **EST:** 2017
SALES (est): 1.6MM **Privately Held**
SIC: 3999 Pet supplies

(G-9302)
CAL AIR FORWARDING
3000 Nw 74th Ave (33122-1428)
PHONE..................................305 871-4552
Jeff Cac, *General Mgr*
Brandon Rounds, *Marketing Staff*
Jeff Higdon, *Branch Mgr*
EMP: 6 **Privately Held**
WEB: www.calaircargo.com
SIC: 2448 Cargo containers, wood & wood with metal
PA: Cal Air Forwarding
6830 Via Del Oro Ste 210
San Jose CA 95119

(G-9303)
CAMBRIDGE AERONAUTICAL LLC
4890 Sw 74th Ct (33155-4454)
PHONE..................................305 987-3851
Emilio J Dirube, *Manager*
EMP: 6 **EST:** 2017
SALES (est): 125.7K **Privately Held**
WEB: www.cambridgeaeronautical.com
SIC: 3728 Aircraft parts & equipment

(G-9304)
CAMEL ENTERPRISES CORP
Also Called: Camel Power Drinks
2120 Ne 203rd Ter (33179-2217)
P.O. Box 3691, Hallandale (33008-3691)
PHONE..................................954 234-2559
Tarek Hamandi, *Principal*
EMP: 10 **EST:** 2010
SALES (est): 530.4K **Privately Held**
SIC: 2086 0781 5047 Soft drinks: packaged in cans, bottles, etc.; landscape services; instruments, surgical & medical

(G-9305)
CAMILO OFFICE FURNITURE INC (PA)
Also Called: Camilo Muebles
7344 Sw 48th St Ste 202 (33155-5521)
P.O. Box 560147 (33256-0147)
PHONE..................................305 261-5366
Camilo Lopez Jr, *President*
Camilo Lopez III, *Vice Pres*
Luis Lopez, *Treasurer*
Ricardo Lopez, *Treasurer*
Jose Lopez, *Admin Sec*
▲ **EMP:** 84 **EST:** 1963
SQ FT: 74,000
SALES (est): 7.5MM **Privately Held**
SIC: 2521 Chairs, office: padded, upholstered or plain: wood

(G-9306)
CAMILO OFFICE FURNITURE INC
18360 Sw 224th St (33170-3507)
PHONE..................................305 261-5366
Jose Lopez, *Admin Sec*
EMP: 6 **EST:** 2010
SALES (est): 90.4K **Privately Held**
WEB: www.camilo.com
SIC: 2521 Wood office furniture

(G-9307)
CAMPEONES MARINA CORP
600 Nw 7th Ave (33136-3104)
PHONE..................................305 491-5738
Mario Hernandez Sr, *President*
EMP: 8 **EST:** 2007
SALES (est): 149K **Privately Held**
WEB: www.campeonesmarina.com
SIC: 3732 Yachts, building & repairing

(G-9308)
CANSORTIUM CHARITIES INC
82 Ne 26th St (33137-4428)
PHONE..................................305 902-2720
Jose Hidalgo, *CEO*
EMP: 9 **EST:** 2017
SALES (est): 347.6K **Privately Held**
WEB: www.investors.getfluent.com
SIC: 2833 Medicinals & botanicals

(G-9309)
CAPITOL RENTAL BLDG EQP INC
Also Called: Capital Steel Structures
2188 Nw 25th Ave (33142-7121)
PHONE..................................305 633-5008
Ruben Diaz, *President*
Alicia Diaz, *Vice Pres*
EMP: 15 **EST:** 1973
SQ FT: 8,700
SALES (est): 5.4MM **Privately Held**
WEB: www.capitolsteelstructures.com
SIC: 3441 Fabricated structural metal

(G-9310)
CAPTIVA CONTAINERS LLC
95 Ne 179th St (33162-1021)
PHONE..................................800 861-3868
Adriana Aponte, *Supervisor*
Alan Katz, *Exec Dir*
Daniela Morgenstern, *Exec Dir*
Freddy Morgenstern,
Freddy Morganstern,
▲ **EMP:** 70 **EST:** 2013
SQ FT: 35,000
SALES (est): 9.4MM **Privately Held**
WEB: www.captivaco.com
SIC: 3085 Plastics bottles

(G-9311)
CAQ INTERNATIONAL LLC
900 Biscayne Blvd # 4906 (33132-1574)
PHONE..................................305 744-1472
Victor Samama Jr, *Mng Member*
EMP: 5 **EST:** 2011
SQ FT: 260
SALES (est): 452.9K **Privately Held**
SIC: 2834 Adrenal pharmaceutical preparations

(G-9312)
CARDENAS ROBERTO BLINDS OF FLA ✪
13301 Sw 132nd Ave Unit 2 (33186-6188)
PHONE..................................315 807-6878
Roberto Rodriguez Guerra, *Principal*
EMP: 6 **EST:** 2020
SALES (est): 57.3K **Privately Held**
SIC: 2591 Window blinds

(G-9313)
CARIBBEAN BOX COMPANY
3123 Nw 73rd St (33147-5947)
PHONE..................................305 667-4900
Miguel Garcia Armengol, *President*
EMP: 15 **EST:** 1987
SQ FT: 45,000
SALES (est): 250.3K **Privately Held**
SIC: 2657 Folding paperboard boxes

(G-9314)
CARIBBEAN CANVAS AND MARI
7296 Sw 42nd Ter (33155-4532)
PHONE..................................786 972-6377
EMP: 6 **EST:** 2018
SALES (est): 407.4K **Privately Held**
SIC: 2211 Canvas

(G-9315)
CARIBBEAN FIBERGLASS PRODUCTS
5445 Nw 72nd Ave (33166-4246)
PHONE..................................305 888-0774
Cirilo F Padron, *President*
Elvis Padron, *Owner*
Everardo E Padron, *Treasurer*
▼ **EMP:** 10 **EST:** 1977
SQ FT: 30,000
SALES (est): 586.4K **Privately Held**
SIC: 2519 Furniture, household: glass, fiberglass & plastic

(G-9316)
CARIBBEAN FUELS INC
15001 Sw 141st Ter (33196-4691)
PHONE..................................305 233-3016
Bernando Sanchez, *Vice Pres*
EMP: 8 **EST:** 2005
SALES (est): 272.3K **Privately Held**
WEB: www.caribbeanfuels.com
SIC: 2869 Fuels

(G-9317)
CARIBBEAN TRAILERS CORP
12240 Sw 130th St (33186-6217)
PHONE..................................305 256-1505
Carlos Colunga, *President*
▼ **EMP:** 5 **EST:** 2004
SALES (est): 427.7K **Privately Held**
WEB: www.caribbeantrailer.com
SIC: 3799 Boat trailers

(G-9318)
CARIBE EXPRESS ASSOCIATES INC
7320 Nw 12th St Ste 111 (33126-1913)
PHONE..................................305 222-9057
Rosario Dieguez, *President*
Alberto Dieguez, *Vice Pres*
EMP: 10
SALES (corp-wide): 523.3K **Privately Held**
SIC: 2819 Carbides
PA: Caribe Express Associates, Inc.
6710 Bergenline Ave
Guttenberg NJ 07093
201 869-2822

(G-9319)
CARLEES CREATIONS INC
Also Called: I Wed Today
12275 Sw 129th Ct (33186-6435)
P.O. Box 971144 (33197-1144)
PHONE..................................786 232-0050
Ka'sandra Bryant-Jones, *CEO*
EMP: 8 **EST:** 2007
SQ FT: 1,500
SALES (est): 420K **Privately Held**
WEB: www.carleescreations.com
SIC: 2051 5461 7371 5999 Cakes, pies & pastries; cakes; computer software development & applications; cake decorating supplies; notary publics; wedding chapel, privately operated

(G-9320)
CARLOS ABASCAL
3640 Yacht Club Dr # 1703 (33180-3558)
PHONE..................................973 696-1971
Carlos Abascal, *Executive*
EMP: 6 **EST:** 2000
SALES (est): 85.9K **Privately Held**
WEB: www.zalta.com
SIC: 3577 Computer peripheral equipment

(G-9321)
CARNE ASADA TORTILLERIA NICAS
10404 W Flagler St Ste 5 (33174-1669)
PHONE..................................305 221-7001
Jacqueline Garcia, *Principal*
EMP: 8 **EST:** 2007
SALES (est): 459.4K **Privately Held**
SIC: 2099 Tortillas, fresh or refrigerated

(G-9322)
CASA DEL MARINERO CORP
288 Ne 2nd St (33132-2213)
PHONE..................................305 374-5386
Wilson Ramirez, *President*
▼ **EMP:** 8 **EST:** 1993
SALES (est): 953.5K **Privately Held**
SIC: 3676 5731 Electronic resistors; radio, television & electronic stores

(G-9323)
CASTILLOS FARMS INC
Also Called: Castillo's Farm Equipment
19744 Sw 177th Ave (33187-2600)
PHONE..................................305 232-0771
Manuel Del Castillo, *President*
EMP: 8 **EST:** 1999
SALES (est): 636.9K **Privately Held**
SIC: 3523 Sprayers & spraying machines, agricultural

(G-9324)
CATAPULT 13 CRTIVE STUDIOS LLC
5 Nw 39th St Street1 (33127-2944)
PHONE..................................305 788-6948
Rodrigo Londono, *Principal*
EMP: 8 **EST:** 2010
SALES (est): 1.2MM **Privately Held**
WEB: www.catapult13.com
SIC: 3599 Catapults

(G-9325)
CATERPILLAR 2 BUTTERFLY CORP
1153 Nw 47th Ter (33127-2221)
PHONE..................................786 540-4191
Tiquanna Taylor, *Principal*
EMP: 18 **EST:** 2015
SALES (est): 66K **Privately Held**
WEB: www.caterpillar.com
SIC: 3531 Construction machinery

(G-9326)
CAVEAT
448 Nw 28th St (33127-4136)
PHONE..................................305 501-4646
Stacy Glover, *President*
EMP: 6 **EST:** 2016
SALES (est): 69K **Privately Held**
WEB: www.caveatmiami.com
SIC: 2323 Men's & boys' neckwear

(G-9327)
CAVO DEVELOPMENT INC
16380 Sw 137th Ave (33177-1904)
PHONE..................................305 255-7465
James C Cavo, *President*
Martin O Stelling, *CFO*
Volker Meldner, *Admin Sec*
EMP: 9 **EST:** 1989
SQ FT: 1,800
SALES (est): 262.1K **Privately Held**
SIC: 3531 Dredging machinery

(G-9328)
CAWY BOTTLING CO INC
2440 Nw 21st Ter (33142-7182)
PHONE..................................305 634-8669
Vincent Cossio, *President*
Frank Garcia, *Vice Pres*
Ramon Rodriguez, *Purchasing*
Alex Garcia, *Treasurer*
Domingo Villalba, *Treasurer*
▼ **EMP:** 50 **EST:** 1964
SQ FT: 50,000
SALES (est): 6.7MM **Privately Held**
WEB: www.cawy.net
SIC: 2086 Soft drinks: packaged in cans, bottles, etc.

(G-9329)
CBI INDUSTRIES INC
Also Called: Seagear Performance Apparel
13225 Sw 95th Ave (33176-5732)
PHONE..................................305 796-9346
Robert Francis, *President*
▲ **EMP:** 9 **EST:** 1998
SALES (est): 800K **Privately Held**
SIC: 2221 5699 5136 Shirting fabrics, manmade fiber & silk; shirts, custom made; shirts, men's & boys'

(G-9330)
CC KITCHEN CABINETS CORP
521 Sw 127th Ave (33184-1318)
PHONE..................................786 457-1494
Antonio Campos, *Treasurer*
EMP: 6 **EST:** 2012
SALES (est): 79.1K **Privately Held**
SIC: 2434 Wood kitchen cabinets

(G-9331)
CCP OF MIAMI INC
13601 Sw 143rd Ct (33186-5604)
PHONE..................................305 233-6534
Seudial Paul Ramsingh, *Principal*
EMP: 9 **EST:** 2005
SALES (est): 285.2K **Privately Held**
SIC: 2542 Partitions & fixtures, except wood

(G-9332)
CEDAR FRESH HOME PRODUCTS LLC (PA)
4207 University Dr (33146-1140)
PHONE..................................305 975-8524
Howard J Goldman, *Mng Member*
Kanas Fisher,
Steven Gerson,
William Grossman,
AVI Weinpraub,
▲ **EMP:** 8 **EST:** 2003
SQ FT: 2,000 **Privately Held**
SIC: 2511 Cedar chests

(G-9333)
CELLULAR MASTERS INC
Also Called: Fifo Wireless
10900 Nw 21st St Ste 210 (33172-2006)
PHONE..................................305 592-7906
Abderrahim McHatet, *President*
Hamid McHatet, *Vice Pres*
Abraham Mekki, *Sales Associate*
▲ **EMP:** 25 **EST:** 2000
SQ FT: 10,000
SALES (est): 4.8MM **Privately Held**
SIC: 3661 Telephone cords, jacks, adapters, etc.

(G-9334)
CEMENT MIAMI TERMINAL
1200 Nw 137th Ave (33182-1803)
PHONE..................................305 221-2502
▲ **EMP:** 6 **EST:** 2005
SALES (est): 1MM **Privately Held**
SIC: 3273 Ready-mixed concrete

(G-9335)
CEMEX CORP
1200 Nw 137th Ave (33182-1803)
PHONE..................................561 820-8613
EMP: 62 **EST:** 1988
SALES (est): 7.7MM **Privately Held**
WEB: www.cemexusa.com
SIC: 3273 Ready-mixed concrete

(G-9336)
CEMEX MATERIALS LLC
Also Called: Rinker Portland Cement
1200 Nw 137th Ave (33182-1803)
PHONE..................................305 223-6934
EMP: 73 **Privately Held**
SIC: 3273 Ready-mixed concrete
HQ: Cemex Materials Llc
1501 Belvedere Rd
West Palm Beach FL 33406
561 833-5555

(G-9337)
CEMEX MATERIALS LLC
2201 Nw 38th Ct (33142-6749)
PHONE..................................305 558-0315
Robert Suarez, *Branch Mgr*
EMP: 73 **Privately Held**
SIC: 3271 3273 3272 1422 Blocks, concrete or cinder: standard; ready-mixed concrete; pipe, concrete or lined with concrete; crushed & broken limestone
HQ: Cemex Materials Llc
1501 Belvedere Rd
West Palm Beach FL 33406
561 833-5555

(G-9338)
CENTER AMERICAN LONGEVITY
2627 Ne 203rd St Ste 118 (33180-1945)
PHONE..................................305 777-1667
John Graner, *Principal*
EMP: 8 **EST:** 2012
SALES (est): 163.7K **Privately Held**
WEB: www.americanlongevitycenter.com
SIC: 3295 Minerals, ground or treated

(G-9339)
CENTRAL METAL FABRICATORS INC
900 Sw 70th Ave (33144-4614)
PHONE..................................305 261-6262
Harold Baskin, *President*
Raul J Cossio, *Vice Pres*
Beth Colacurto, *Office Mgr*
Joshua Baskin, *Technology*
Raul Cossio, *Assistant*
EMP: 45 **EST:** 1948
SQ FT: 32,000
SALES (est): 5.6MM **Privately Held**
WEB: www.cmf-co.com
SIC: 3443 3444 3441 Fabricated plate work (boiler shop); sheet metalwork; fabricated structural metal

(G-9340)
CENTRALUM USA LLC
175 Sw 7th St Ste 1706 (33130-2957)
PHONE..................................786 646-9756
Carlos Zuluaga,
EMP: 5
SALES (est): 500K **Privately Held**
WEB: www.centralumusa.com
SIC: 3442 Metal doors, sash & trim

(G-9341)
CEPERO REMODELING INC
6972 Sw 4th St (33144-3642)
PHONE..................................305 265-1888
Maria Cepero, *President*
EMP: 6 **EST:** 1998
SQ FT: 2,500
SALES (est): 919.4K **Privately Held**
WEB:
www.ceperoremodelinganddesign.com
SIC: 2434 Wood kitchen cabinets

(G-9342)
CERAMICA VEREA USA CORP
7035 Sw 44th St (33155-4643)
PHONE..................................305 665-3923
Manuel Menendez, *Principal*
▼ **EMP:** 12 **EST:** 2010
SALES (est): 200.4K **Privately Held**
WEB: www.comacastcorp.com
SIC: 3259 Roofing tile, clay

(G-9343)
CERNO PHARMACEUTICALS LLC
6714 Nw 72nd Ave (33166-3045)
PHONE..................................786 763-2766
Pedro Paz, *Principal*
Juan J Hernandez, *Mng Member*
EMP: 7 **EST:** 2013
SALES (est): 321.6K **Privately Held**
WEB: www.cernopharma.com
SIC: 2023 2834 Dietary supplements, dairy & non-dairy based; pharmaceutical preparations

(G-9344)
CEW LLC
14008 Sw 140th St (33186-5547)
PHONE..................................305 232-8892
Christopher Wilson, *President*
John Hawk, *Mng Member*
▼ **EMP:** 5 **EST:** 2006
SALES (est): 708.5K **Privately Held**
WEB: www.miamiwaterjet.com
SIC: 3599 Machine shop, jobbing & repair

(G-9345)
CEW TECHNOLOGIES INC
14008 Sw 140th St (33186-5547)
PHONE..................................305 232-8892
Christopher Wilson, *President*
EMP: 6 **EST:** 2016
SQ FT: 7,000
SALES (est): 897.6K **Privately Held**
WEB: www.cewtechnologies.com
SIC: 3599 Machine shop, jobbing & repair

(G-9346)
CFUEL ENERGY CORP
2601 Biscayne Blvd (33137-4532)
PHONE..................................561 336-4084
Stuart Cooper, *President*
EMP: 7 **EST:** 2013
SALES (est): 168.7K **Privately Held**
SIC: 2869 Fuels

(G-9347)
CHANNEL LETTER NETWORK CORP
7204 Nw 31st St (33122-1216)
PHONE..................................305 594-3360
Alvaro Brito, *President*
▼ **EMP:** 24 **EST:** 2009
SALES (est): 1MM **Privately Held**
WEB: www.dcsigns.com
SIC: 3993 Electric signs

(G-9348)
CHANNEL LOGISTICS LLC
Also Called: Space-Eyes
888 Biscayne Blvd Ste 505 (33132-1509)
PHONE..................................856 614-5441
Brian Breck, *Architect*
Jatin S Bains, *Mng Member*
Christine Atherholt, *Administration*
EMP: 20 **EST:** 2001
SQ FT: 2,500
SALES (est): 1.5MM **Privately Held**
WEB: www.space-eyes.com
SIC: 7372 7371 Business oriented computer software; software programming applications

(G-9349)
CHARCOAL CHEF USA LLC
Also Called: Josper Chef USA
680 Ne 50th Ter (33137-3023)
PHONE..................................786 273-6511
Agusti Comabella, *Mng Member*
EMP: 7 **EST:** 2016
SALES (est): 1.4MM **Privately Held**
SIC: 3634 Broilers, electric

(G-9350)
CHELLY COSMETICS MANUFACTURING
7172 Sw 30th Rd (33155-2844)
P.O. Box 559062 (33255-9062)
PHONE..................................305 471-9608
Juan C Granado, *President*
Carlos V Granado, *Vice Pres*
◆ **EMP:** 9 **EST:** 1993
SQ FT: 6,000
SALES (est): 921.7K **Privately Held**
WEB: www.chellycosmetics.com
SIC: 3999 5122 2844 Fingernails, artificial; cosmetics; toilet preparations

(G-9351)
CHRISTIAN L INTERNATIONAL INC
2297 Ne 164th St (33160-3703)
PHONE..................................305 947-1722
▲ **EMP:** 7
SALES (est): 990.5K **Privately Held**
SIC: 2844 Mfg Toilet Preparations

(G-9352)
CHROME PLATING SHOP
18680 Ne 2nd Ave Ste 1 (33179-4452)
PHONE..................................786 527-5357
Eugenio Rojas, *Principal*
EMP: 6 **EST:** 2016
SALES (est): 233.6K **Privately Held**
WEB: www.thechromeplatingshop.com
SIC: 3471 Plating of metals or formed products

(G-9353)
CHUCULU LLC
9455 Sw 78th St (33173-3395)
PHONE..................................305 595-4577
Daniel Agruelles, *Mng Member*
Linda Arguelles,
▲ **EMP:** 10 **EST:** 2003
SALES (est): 250K **Privately Held**
SIC: 2952 1761 1521 Roofing materials; roofing contractor; single-family housing construction

(G-9354)
CINEVISE INC
12457 Sw 130th St (33186-6238)
PHONE..................................305 232-8182
Alexander Younger, *President*
EMP: 6 **EST:** 2010
SALES (est): 49.1K **Privately Held**
WEB: www.cinevise.com
SIC: 3861 Motion picture apparatus & equipment

(G-9355)
CITILUBE INC
3300 Nw 112th St (33167-3313)
PHONE..................................305 681-6064
Gregory Bass, *President*
Alexander Bass, *Vice Pres*
▼ **EMP:** 17 **EST:** 2004
SQ FT: 45,000
SALES (est): 4.7MM **Privately Held**
WEB: www.citilube.com
SIC: 2911 Oils, lubricating

(G-9356)
CITY ELEVATOR SERVICE CORP
15107 Sw 138th Pl (33186-5795)
PHONE..................................305 345-1951
Elsie Mercado Sanchez, *Director*
EMP: 6 **EST:** 2005
SALES (est): 412.2K **Privately Held**
WEB: www.southfloridaelevatorservice.com
SIC: 3534 Elevators & moving stairways

(G-9357)
CITY LABS INC
12491 Sw 134th Ct Ste 23 (33186-6416)
PHONE..................................305 909-7593
Peter Cabauy, *CEO*
Denset Serralta, *Vice Pres*
EMP: 7 **EST:** 2005
SALES (est): 735.3K **Privately Held**
WEB: www.citylabs.net
SIC: 3674 Microcircuits, integrated (semiconductor)

(G-9358)
CITYGRADER LLC
2990 Nw 40th Street Miami (33142)
PHONE..................................305 635-2686
Paola Newell, *Principal*
Norman Newell,
EMP: 6 **EST:** 2017
SALES (est): 83.6K **Privately Held**
WEB: www.citygrader.com
SIC: 2741

(G-9359)
CJ LABS INC
12245 Sw 128th St Unit 30 (33186-5999)
PHONE..................................305 234-9644
Carlos Alvarez, *President*
Odalys Gonzalez, *Vice Pres*
Andy Alvarez, *Manager*
EMP: 13 **EST:** 2004
SQ FT: 1,000
SALES (est): 2.7MM **Privately Held**
WEB: www.cjlabs.com
SIC: 2833 Vitamins, natural or synthetic: bulk, uncompounded

(G-9360)
CJL BRICKS & PAVERS INC
9301 Nw 33rd Ct (33147-2945)
PHONE..................................305 527-4240
Jose L Torres, *Director*
EMP: 7 **EST:** 2001
SALES (est): 303.9K **Privately Held**
SIC: 2951 Asphalt paving mixtures & blocks

(G-9361)
CL DADELAND LLC
Dadeland Mall 7535 N Kend (33156)
PHONE..................................305 712-6825
Edward W Beiner,
EMP: 6 **EST:** 2011
SALES (est): 295.3K **Privately Held**
SIC: 3851 Ophthalmic goods

(G-9362)
CLASSIC STARS INC
2355 Nw 35th Ave (33142-6825)
PHONE..................................305 871-6767
Carlos Padrino, *Principal*
EMP: 7 **EST:** 2010

GEOGRAPHIC

SALES (est): 91.5K Privately Held
SIC: 2335 Wedding gowns & dresses

(G-9363)
CLOSEUP INC
8400 Nw 25th St (33198-1503)
PHONE..................................650 284-8831
Oliver Hausler, *CEO*
EMP: 6 EST: 2015
SALES (est): 44.9K Privately Held
SIC: 2741 7389 ;

(G-9364)
CLOUD VENEER LLC
1001 Brickell Bay Dr # 2700 (33131-4900)
PHONE..................................305 230-7379
Anthony Richardson,
EMP: 7 EST: 2019
SQ FT: 8,000
SALES (est): 475.4K Privately Held
SIC: 7372 4813 7379 Business oriented computer software; ; ; computer related consulting services

(G-9365)
CLR ROASTERS LLC
2131 Nw 72nd Ave (33122-1823)
PHONE..................................305 591-0040
Sonia Aguila, *Vice Pres*
Lidier Reyes, *Production*
Kathleen Ruiz, *Controller*
David Briskie, *Mng Member*
▲ EMP: 21 EST: 2007
SQ FT: 34,000
SALES (est): 14.5MM
SALES (corp-wide): 147.4MM Publicly Held
WEB: www.clrroasters.com
SIC: 2095 Roasted coffee
HQ: Al Global Corporation
2400 Boswell Rd
Chula Vista CA 91914

(G-9366)
CME ARMA INC
4500 Nw 36th Ave (33142-4220)
PHONE..................................305 633-1524
Katherine Yasgar, *President*
Howard Yasgar, *Vice Pres*
Vannessa Jimenez, *Sales Staff*
Colin Joao, *Director*
◆ EMP: 22 EST: 1991
SQ FT: 14,500
SALES (est): 5.6MM Privately Held
WEB: www.cmearma.com
SIC: 3531 5088 Construction machinery; transportation equipment & supplies

(G-9367)
CMN STEEL FABRICATORS INC
7993 Nw 60th St (33166-3410)
PHONE..................................305 592-5466
Timothy P Kressly, *President*
Carlos Perez, *Engineer*
Marisa M Nunez, *Admin Sec*
EMP: 58 EST: 2016
SALES (est): 7MM Privately Held
WEB: www.cmnsteel.com
SIC: 3317 3448 Steel pipe & tubes; trusses & framing: prefabricated metal

(G-9368)
COASTAL SHUTTERS ONLINE LLC
1300 S Miami Ave # 3907 (33130-4467)
PHONE..................................786 509-2093
EMP: 7 EST: 2017
SALES (est): 134K Privately Held
WEB: www.coastalshuttersonline.com
SIC: 3442 Shutters, door or window: metal

(G-9369)
COCA COLA ENTERPRISES INC
Also Called: Coca-Cola
16569 Sw 117th Ave (33177-2183)
PHONE..................................305 256-3628
EMP: 9 EST: 2018
SALES (est): 410.5K Privately Held
WEB: www.coca-cola.com
SIC: 2086 Bottled & canned soft drinks

(G-9370)
COCA-COLA BOTTLING CO
16569 Sw 117th Ave (33177-2183)
PHONE..................................305 378-1073
Scott Turner, *Manager*
EMP: 19 EST: 2010
SALES (est): 96.5K Privately Held
WEB: www.ccbcc.com
SIC: 2086 Bottled & canned soft drinks

(G-9371)
COCO COSMETICS INC
20325 Ne 15th Ct (33179-2709)
PHONE..................................305 622-3488
Anna P Hua, *President*
Tien Lowe, *Vice Pres*
▼ EMP: 11 EST: 2009
SALES (est): 622.7K Privately Held
WEB: www.coco-cosmetics.com
SIC: 2844 Cosmetic preparations

(G-9372)
COCO GELATO CORP (PA)
3514 Nw 36th St (33142-5040)
PHONE..................................786 621-2444
Gustavo Sidelnik, *President*
EMP: 45 EST: 1994
SQ FT: 1,000
SALES (est): 3.2MM Privately Held
WEB: www.cocogelato.com
SIC: 2024 5812 Ice cream & ice milk; ice cream stands or dairy bars

(G-9373)
COCRYSTAL PHARMA INC ✪
4400 Biscayne Blvd (33137-3212)
PHONE..................................877 262-7123
EMP: 7 EST: 2020
SALES (est): 702.8K Privately Held
SIC: 2834 Pharmaceutical preparations

(G-9374)
CODMAN & SHURTLEFF INC
Also Called: Johnson and Johnson
6303 Blue Lagoon Dr (33126-6002)
PHONE..................................908 704-4024
EMP: 12
SALES (corp-wide): 82.5B Publicly Held
SIC: 3841 Surgical & medical instruments
HQ: Codman & Shurtleff, Inc.
325 Paramount Dr
Raynham MA 02767

(G-9375)
COFFEE CLLLOID PRODUCTIONS LLC
12240 Sw 132nd Ct (33186-6476)
PHONE..................................305 424-8900
Joseph A Daoud, *CEO*
EMP: 10 EST: 2010
SALES (est): 155.9K Privately Held
WEB: www.newterritory.media
SIC: 3089 Celluloid products

(G-9376)
COIN-O-MATIC INC
3950 Nw 31st Ave (33142-5123)
PHONE..................................305 635-4141
Stephen Cohen, *President*
▼ EMP: 37 EST: 1984
SQ FT: 20,500
SALES (est): 3MM Privately Held
WEB: www.wash.com
SIC: 3582 Washing machines, laundry: commercial, incl. coin-operated; commercial laundry equipment

(G-9377)
COLD STORAGE ENGINEERING CO (PA)
703 Nw 62nd Ave Ste 650 (33126-4680)
PHONE..................................305 448-0099
Fred Garcia, *President*
▼ EMP: 9 EST: 1981
SALES (est): 1MM Privately Held
SIC: 3585 Refrigeration equipment, complete

(G-9378)
COLDFLO INC
Also Called: J & J Refregrator
1050 Nw 21st St (33127-4514)
PHONE..................................305 324-8555
Elan Feldman, *President*
Nancy Feldman, *Treasurer*
◆ EMP: 8 EST: 1987
SQ FT: 16,000
SALES (est): 1MM Privately Held
WEB: www.coldflow.com
SIC: 3585 Parts for heating, cooling & refrigerating equipment

(G-9379)
COLONIAL PRESS INTL INC
3690 Nw 50th St (33142-3987)
PHONE..................................305 633-1581
Jorge Gomez, *President*
Dan Michels, *General Mgr*
Jose A Gomez, *Corp Secy*
Henry Hernandez, *Exec VP*
Jeff Statler, *Exec VP*
◆ EMP: 200
SQ FT: 120,000
SALES (est): 64.8MM Privately Held
WEB: www.colonialpressintl.com
SIC: 2752 2789 Commercial printing, offset; lithographing on metal; bookbinding & related work

(G-9380)
COLOR PRESS CORP
1835 Nw 112th Ave Ste 184 (33172-1839)
PHONE..................................786 621-8491
EMP: 8 EST: 2008
SALES (est): 797.9K Privately Held
SIC: 2741 Misc Publishing

(G-9381)
COLORAMAX PRINTING INC
3215 Nw 7th St (33125-4101)
PHONE..................................305 541-0322
Xiomara Romero, *President*
EMP: 10 EST: 1963
SQ FT: 6,945
SALES (est): 688K Privately Held
WEB: www.coloramaxprinting.com
SIC: 2752 2791 2789 Commercial printing, offset; typesetting; bookbinding & related work

(G-9382)
COLORMET FOODS LLC
3610 Ne 1st Ave (33137-3602)
P.O. Box 613114 (33261-3114)
PHONE..................................888 775-3966
Eva Colmenares, *Principal*
EMP: 12 EST: 2015
SQ FT: 1,200
SALES (est): 2.1MM Privately Held
WEB: www.seriouscow.com
SIC: 2026 5143 Yogurt; yogurt

(G-9383)
COLORPRINT DESIGN
1220 Sw 78th Ct (33144-4310)
PHONE..................................305 229-8880
Mathew Jordan, *CEO*
EMP: 7 EST: 2008
SALES (est): 237.3K Privately Held
SIC: 2752 Color lithography

(G-9384)
COM MIAMI CORPORATION
3832 Ne 199th Ter (33180-3402)
PHONE..................................305 376-5040
Giuseppe Naim, *Principal*
EMP: 6 EST: 2010
SALES (est): 97K Privately Held
SIC: 2711 Newspapers, publishing & printing

(G-9385)
COMA CAST CORP
4383 Sw 70th Ct (33155-4622)
P.O. Box 557044 (33255-7044)
PHONE..................................305 667-6797
Carlos Blume, *President*
◆ EMP: 22 EST: 1971
SALES (est): 3.8MM Privately Held
WEB: www.comacastcorp.com
SIC: 3272 5032 2952 Roofing tile & slabs, concrete; tile & clay products; asphalt felts & coatings

(G-9386)
COMEP USA INC (PA)
1301 Ne 13th Ct Ste 220 (33172)
PHONE..................................786 554-2211
Hector D Escobar, *President*
Juan J Escobar, *Vice Pres*
▲ EMP: 34 EST: 2000
SALES (est): 167.2K Privately Held
WEB: www.canoa.us
SIC: 2032 Ethnic foods: canned, jarred, etc.

(G-9387)
COMIMPEX GROUP LLC
Also Called: Comimpex Flooring and Finishes
844 Sw 154th Ct (33194-2757)
PHONE..................................786 306-3204
David O Diaz, *President*
Richard Hernandez, *Sales Mgr*
▲ EMP: 5 EST: 2014
SALES (est): 1.2MM Privately Held
WEB: www.comimpexgroup.com
SIC: 3255 Fire clay blocks, bricks, tile or special shapes

(G-9388)
COMM DOTS LLC CONNECTING
3890 Coco Grove Ave (33133-6120)
PHONE..................................305 505-6009
Emilia Burbano, *President*
Margarita Gomez, *Vice Pres*
Maria Clara Burbano, *Manager*
EMP: 12 EST: 2013
SALES (est): 80K Privately Held
SIC: 2741 8742 7389 ; marketing consulting services;

(G-9389)
COMPLIANCE MEDS TECH LLC
20855 Ne 16th Ave Ste C13 (33179-2140)
PHONE..................................786 319-9826
Moses Zonana, *CEO*
Daniel E Dosoretz, *Principal*
Moses A Zonana, *Controller*
EMP: 9 EST: 2010
SALES (est): 1MM Privately Held
WEB: www.cmtcares.com
SIC: 3845 7389 3085 7352 Patient monitoring apparatus; packaging & labeling services; design services; plastics bottles; medical equipment rental

(G-9390)
CONCEPT ELEVATOR GROUP LLC (PA)
8027 Nw 71st St (33166-2303)
PHONE..................................786 845-8955
Rolando M Nieves, *CEO*
Gabriel Garcia, *Engineer*
Adrian Rodriguez, *Controller*
Randy Jimenez, *Mktg Coord*
Bill Swanson, *Mng Member*
◆ EMP: 52 EST: 2003
SQ FT: 60,000
SALES (est): 10.3MM Privately Held
WEB: www.conceptelevator.com
SIC: 3534 Elevators & equipment

(G-9391)
CONCORDIA PHARMACEUTICALS INC
2600 Sw 3rd Ave Ste 950 (33129-2355)
PHONE..................................786 304-2083
Reginald Hardy, *President*
Andrew Sklawer, *Opers Staff*
EMP: 5 EST: 2005
SALES (est): 378.3K Privately Held
WEB: www.concordiapharma.com
SIC: 2834 Pharmaceutical preparations

(G-9392)
CONCRETE STRUCTURES INC
12100 Nw 58th St (33010)
PHONE..................................305 597-9393
Dick Salonia, *President*
EMP: 13 EST: 1991
SQ FT: 230
SALES (est): 344.2K Privately Held
SIC: 3272 Precast terrazo or concrete products

(G-9393)
CONQUEST FINANCIAL MANAGEMENT
Also Called: Source Outdoor
11451 Nw 36th Ave (33167-2910)
PHONE..................................305 630-8950
Gerald Shvartsman, *CEO*
Candice McCarthy, *Vice Pres*
Jeniffer Bello, *Marketing Mgr*
Patrick Survilas, *Marketing Mgr*
Maggie Carrero, *Office Mgr*

▲ = Import ▼=Export
◆ =Import/Export

◆ **EMP:** 75 **EST:** 2009
SQ FT: 70,000
SALES (est): 8.6MM **Privately Held**
WEB: www.sourcefurniture.com
SIC: 2519 Wicker & rattan furniture

(G-9394)
CONTACT CENTER SOLUTIONS INC
66 W Flagler St (33130-1807)
PHONE..................................305 499-0163
Jeff Entel, *President*
EMP: 20 **EST:** 2014
SALES (est): 984.9K **Privately Held**
WEB: www.genesys.com
SIC: 7372 Business oriented computer software

(G-9395)
CONTINENTAL BELT CORP
Also Called: Continental Belt & Tie
2267 Nw 20th St (33142-7371)
PHONE..................................305 573-8871
Eli Bick, *President*
Linda Bick, *Treasurer*
▲ **EMP:** 6 **EST:** 1974
SQ FT: 5,000
SALES (est): 383.3K **Privately Held**
WEB: www.continentalbelt.com
SIC: 3172 5136 Personal leather goods; apparel belts, men's & boys'

(G-9396)
CONTINENTAL SERVICES GROUP (PA)
Also Called: Continental Blood Bank
1300 Nw 36th St (33142-5556)
P.O. Box 420950 (33242-0950)
PHONE..................................305 633-7700
Cherry D Wheeler-Capik, *CEO*
Richard W Capik, *President*
Chris Stroup, *Opers Mgr*
Christopher Stroup, *Opers Mgr*
Paul Wilson, *Administration*
◆ **EMP:** 30 **EST:** 1970
SQ FT: 15,500
SALES (est): 6.4MM **Privately Held**
WEB: www.continentalbloodbank.com
SIC: 2835 In vitro & in vivo diagnostic substances

(G-9397)
CONVIVIUM PRESS INC
7661 Nw 68th St Unit 108 (33166-2840)
PHONE..................................305 889-0489
Rafael F Luciani Rivero, *President*
Maria Rosa Malave Carrasco, *CFO*
Manuel Polanco, *Admin Sec*
EMP: 5 **EST:** 2007
SALES (est): 524.3K **Privately Held**
WEB: www.conviviumpress.com
SIC: 2741 Miscellaneous publishing

(G-9398)
COOKIE APP LLC
2 S Biscayne Blvd # 2680 (33131-1806)
PHONE..................................305 330-5099
Alex Pereira,
EMP: 5 **EST:** 2017
SALES (est): 309.3K **Privately Held**
SIC: 7372 Educational computer software

(G-9399)
COOLHEAD HELMET LLC
999 Brickell Bay Dr (33131-2934)
PHONE..................................786 292-4829
Sergejs Zelinskis,
EMP: 7 **EST:** 2018
SALES (est): 286.7K **Privately Held**
WEB: www.coolheadhelmet.com
SIC: 2353 Helmets, jungle cloth: wool lined

(G-9400)
CORAL CABINET INC
14378 Sw 98th Ter (33186-1146)
PHONE..................................305 484-8702
Eduardo Ricci, *Vice Pres*
EMP: 7 **EST:** 2018
SALES (est): 180.2K **Privately Held**
SIC: 2434 Wood kitchen cabinets

(G-9401)
CORAL GABLES CUSTOM DESIGN INC
4038 Nw 32nd Ave (33142-5002)
PHONE..................................305 591-7575
Leandro Morris, *President*
EMP: 14 **EST:** 2008
SALES (est): 846.6K **Privately Held**
WEB: www.leandromorastudio.com
SIC: 2499 Decorative wood & woodwork

(G-9402)
CORALDOM USA LLC
4434 Nw 74th Ave (33166-6443)
PHONE..................................305 716-0200
Gustavo G Cruz,
◆ **EMP:** 5 **EST:** 2010
SALES (est): 900K **Privately Held**
WEB: www.coraldom.com
SIC: 1499 Asphalt mining & bituminous stone quarrying

(G-9403)
CORESYSTEMS SOFTWARE USA INC
Also Called: Coresystems USA
801 Brickell Ave Ste 1400 (33131-2945)
PHONE..................................786 497-4477
Manuel Grenacher, *CEO*
Arti Sahgal, *Executive*
EMP: 11 **EST:** 2014
SALES (est): 289.4K **Privately Held**
SIC: 7372 Business oriented computer software

(G-9404)
CORPDESIGN
6695 Nw 36th Ave (33147-7519)
PHONE..................................866 323-6055
Steve Baricko, *Sales Staff*
EMP: 12 **EST:** 2015
SALES (est): 374.3K **Privately Held**
WEB: www.corpdesign.com
SIC: 2521 Wood office furniture

(G-9405)
CORPORATE PRINTING & ADVG INC
13515 Sw 99th St (33186-2805)
PHONE..................................305 273-6000
Robert Distillator, *President*
Susana Araya, *Vice Pres*
EMP: 10 **EST:** 2000
SQ FT: 3,700
SALES (est): 3.4MM **Privately Held**
SIC: 2759 Advertising literature: printing

(G-9406)
CORPORATE PRINTING SVCS INC
13288 Sw 114th Ter (33186-7918)
P.O. Box 526900 (33152-6900)
PHONE..................................305 273-6000
Robert Distillator, *President*
EMP: 6 **EST:** 1989
SQ FT: 2,500
SALES (est): 606.3K **Privately Held**
SIC: 2752 Commercial printing, offset

(G-9407)
COSTEX CORPORATION (PA)
Also Called: Costex Tractor Parts
5800 Nw 74th Ave (33166-3740)
PHONE..................................305 592-9769
Gilberto C Uribe, *President*
Nabil Sagbini, *Regional Mgr*
Teresa Uribe, *Corp Secy*
Gonzalo Gonzalez, *Purch Mgr*
Paulette Dubuc, *Purch Agent*
◆ **EMP:** 130 **EST:** 1980
SALES (est): 62.4MM **Privately Held**
WEB: www.costex.com
SIC: 3531 5084 Construction machinery; industrial machinery & equipment

(G-9408)
COUNTRY FRITS JUICES NURS CORP
12100 Sw 177th Ave (33196-3046)
PHONE..................................786 302-8487
Felix Calle, *Principal*
EMP: 6 **EST:** 2016
SALES (est): 68.6K **Privately Held**
SIC: 2037 Fruit juices

(G-9409)
CRAMCO INC
5600 Nw 36th Ave (33142-2712)
PHONE..................................305 634-7500
Paul Cramer, *Owner*
Beth Wiegand, *Sales Staff*
Zuelma Calle, *Manager*
EMP: 8
SALES (corp-wide): 30.1MM **Privately Held**
WEB: www.cramco.net
SIC: 2514 2511 Metal household furniture; wood household furniture
PA: Cramco Inc
2200 E Ann St
Philadelphia PA 19134
215 427-9500

(G-9410)
CREAPRINT USA CORP
8950 Sw 74th Ct Ste 1406 (33156-3173)
P.O. Box 560668 (33256-0668)
PHONE..................................786 369-7398
Ignacio Guillem Pico, *President*
Vanessa Guillem Pico, *General Mgr*
Jose V Guillem Pico, *Vice Pres*
EMP: 6 **EST:** 2013
SALES (est): 73.2K **Privately Held**
WEB: www.creaprintusa.com
SIC: 2759 Labels & seals: printing

(G-9411)
CREATIVE WOODWORK MIAMI INC
6001 Nw 37th Ave (33142-2013)
PHONE..................................305 634-3100
Luis Sanchez, *President*
EMP: 18 **EST:** 1993
SQ FT: 23,000
SALES (est): 2.7MM **Privately Held**
SIC: 2511 Wood household furniture

(G-9412)
CROSSROADS INDUSTRIES LLC
12807 Sw 42nd St (33175-3424)
PHONE..................................305 967-8116
Flor M Quiroz, *Principal*
Lisa Morse, *Director*
EMP: 6 **EST:** 2016
SALES (est): 114.4K **Privately Held**
SIC: 3999 Manufacturing industries

(G-9413)
CROWN CASTLE INTL CORP
9250 W Flagler St (33174-3415)
PHONE..................................305 552-3675
Sharon Belizaire-Stewa, *Project Mgr*
Nicholas Campos, *Project Mgr*
Dianna Cardoza, *Project Mgr*
Cynthia Baez, *Manager*
EMP: 12
SALES (corp-wide): 5.7B **Publicly Held**
WEB: www.crowncastle.com
SIC: 3663 Satellites, communications
PA: Crown Castle International Corp.
1220 Augusta Dr Ste 600
Houston TX 77057
713 570-3000

(G-9414)
CRUSELLAS & CO INC
7014 Sw 4th St (33144-2707)
P.O. Box 440814 (33144-0814)
PHONE..................................305 261-9580
Luis R Santeiro, *President*
Juan Santalla, *Vice Pres*
Maria Santeiro, *Treasurer*
Maria Santalla, *Asst Treas*
▲ **EMP:** 10 **EST:** 1967
SQ FT: 3,500
SALES (est): 1.1MM **Privately Held**
WEB: www.crusellasandcompany.com
SIC: 2844 Perfumes, natural or synthetic

(G-9415)
CST USA INC
20533 Biscayne Blvd # 565 (33180-1529)
PHONE..................................404 695-2249
Peter Kesper, *President*
Toni Sims, *Acting CEO*
EMP: 15 **EST:** 2014
SALES (est): 500K
SALES (corp-wide): 0 **Privately Held**
WEB: www.c-s-t.de
SIC: 3555 Printing trades machinery
HQ: Cst Colour Scanner Technology Gmbh
Konigsberger Str. 117
Krefeld 47809
215 115-9226

(G-9416)
CTM BIOMEDICAL LLC
78 Sw 7th St Ste 500 (33130-3782)
P.O. Box 231, Lake Worth (33460-0231)
PHONE..................................561 650-4027
Bryan Banman, *CEO*
EMP: 16 **EST:** 2018
SALES (est): 797.8K **Privately Held**
SIC: 3842 Implants, surgical

(G-9417)
CUBAN PRESS
526 Sw 98th Ct (33174-1964)
PHONE..................................305 304-9419
EMP: 6 **EST:** 2013
SALES (est): 187.5K **Privately Held**
SIC: 2741 Miscellaneous publishing

(G-9418)
CUBOS LLC
13832 Sw 142nd Ave (33186-6772)
PHONE..................................786 299-2671
Juan Carlos Gonzalez,
EMP: 6 **EST:** 2013
SALES (est): 350K **Privately Held**
WEB: www.cubosllc.com
SIC: 2499 2431 Decorative wood & woodwork; woodwork, interior & ornamental

(G-9419)
CUSTOM STAINLESS STL EQP INC
16215 Nw 15th Ave (33169-5613)
PHONE..................................305 627-6049
Antonio Carnero, *CEO*
Robin Carnero, *Office Mgr*
Craig Dubov, *Manager*
Jordan Morales, *Data Proc Exec*
▼ **EMP:** 40 **EST:** 1991
SQ FT: 64,000
SALES (est): 8MM **Privately Held**
WEB: www.customstainless.com
SIC: 3312 Stainless steel

(G-9420)
CUSTOM WD ARCHITECTURAL MLLWK
13119 Sw 122nd Ave (33186-6231)
PHONE..................................786 290-5412
EMP: 6 **EST:** 2019
SALES (est): 65.1K **Privately Held**
WEB: www.millworks.biz
SIC: 2431 Millwork

(G-9421)
CVG AEROSPACE LLC
13500 Sw 134th Ave Ste 6 (33186-4553)
PHONE..................................786 293-9923
EMP: 8 **EST:** 2019
SALES (est): 658.5K **Privately Held**
WEB: www.cvgaerospace.com
SIC: 3728 Aircraft parts & equipment

(G-9422)
CYBER MANUFACTURING INC
14440 Sw 110th St (33186-6624)
PHONE..................................786 457-1973
Chin-Sheng Chen, *Principal*
EMP: 6 **EST:** 2000
SALES (est): 105K **Privately Held**
SIC: 7372 Prepackaged software

(G-9423)
CZARNIKOW GROUP LTD
333 Se 2nd Ave Ste 3410 (33131-2182)
PHONE..................................786 476-0000
Mario Bolival, *Partner*
Debra Proenza, *Office Mgr*
Luis Felipe Trindade, *Associate Dir*
EMP: 6 **EST:** 2013
SALES (est): 411.2K **Privately Held**
WEB: www.czarnikow.com
SIC: 3556 Sugar plant machinery

(G-9424)
D & G MILLWORK & CABINETRY LLC
2618 Ne 191st St (33180-2632)
PHONE..................................305 830-3000
Eli Ran, *Mng Member*

GEOGRAPHIC

Carpenter Grushka, *Master*
EMP: 5 **EST:** 2008
SALES (est): 611.9K **Privately Held**
WEB: www.dgmillwork.com
SIC: 2434 Wood kitchen cabinets

(G-9425)
D AND I TRUCKING EXPRESS INC
21009 Nw 14th Pl Apt 353 (33169-2887)
PHONE..................................786 443-3320
Nadine Andrews, *Vice Pres*
EMP: 6 **EST:** 2012
SALES (est): 76.9K **Privately Held**
SIC: 3479 Metal coating & allied service

(G-9426)
D D B CORPORATION
Also Called: Sundrinks
7340 Nw 35th Ave (33147-5808)
PHONE..................................305 721-9506
Carlo Darbouze, *President*
Maryse Bateau, *Vice Pres*
▼ **EMP:** 5 **EST:** 1999
SQ FT: 6,000
SALES (est): 379.9K **Privately Held**
SIC: 2086 Carbonated beverages, nonalcoholic: bottled & canned

(G-9427)
D1 LOCKER LLC
4880 Nw 4th St (33126-2168)
PHONE..................................305 446-9041
EMP: 6
SALES (est): 376.4K **Privately Held**
SIC: 2741 Internet Publishing And Broadcasting

(G-9428)
DACCORD SHIRTS & GUAYABERAS
7320 Nw 12th St (33126-1912)
PHONE..................................305 576-0926
Contreras Rafael, *Principal*
EMP: 6 **EST:** 2015
SALES (est): 285.9K **Privately Held**
WEB: www.daccordshirts.com
SIC: 2759 Screen printing

(G-9429)
DADE ENGINEERING GROUP LLC
7700 Nw 37th Ave (33147-4423)
PHONE..................................305 885-2766
Donald M Pittsley, *Mng Member*
EMP: 12 **EST:** 2014
SQ FT: 30,000
SALES (est): 3MM **Privately Held**
WEB: www.dadecoolers.com
SIC: 3441 3585 Building components, structural steel; refrigeration & heating equipment

(G-9430)
DADE PUMP & SUPPLY CO
Also Called: De Ruiter Electric Motor
14261 S Dixie Hwy (33176-7224)
PHONE..................................305 235-5000
John K Delaney, *President*
Marilyn Delaney, *Corp Secy*
Mary Hernandez, *Manager*
◆ **EMP:** 9 **EST:** 1960
SQ FT: 4,000
SALES: 2.4MM **Privately Held**
WEB: www.dadepump.com
SIC: 7694 7699 5063 5084 Electric motor repair; pumps & pumping equipment repair; motors, electric; pumps & pumping equipment

(G-9431)
DADE TRUSS COMPANY INC
Also Called: Dtc Stairs
6401 Nw 74th Ave (33166-3634)
PHONE..................................305 592-8245
Salvador A Jurado, *President*
Mike Toyota, *General Mgr*
Jose Alonso Jurado Jr, *Corp Secy*
Manuel Alegre, *Sales Staff*
▼ **EMP:** 130 **EST:** 1978
SQ FT: 900
SALES (est): 19.3MM **Privately Held**
WEB: www.bcg.bz
SIC: 2439 2431 Trusses, wooden roof; millwork

(G-9432)
DAILY MELT
3401 N Miami Ave (33127-3525)
PHONE..................................305 519-2585
Gregg Lurie, *Principal*
EMP: 7 **EST:** 2011
SALES (est): 387.1K **Privately Held**
SIC: 2711 Newspapers, publishing & printing

(G-9433)
DAILY MELT
98 Ne 2nd Ave (33132-2508)
PHONE..................................305 573-9700
EMP: 6 **EST:** 2015
SALES (est): 124.1K **Privately Held**
SIC: 2711 Newspapers, publishing & printing

(G-9434)
DANLY CORPORATION (PA)
3121 Commodore Plz Ph 5 (33133-5846)
PHONE..................................305 285-0111
James C Danly Jr, *President*
Michael D Danly, *Corp Secy*
EMP: 2
SALES (est): 13MM **Privately Held**
SIC: 3544 Industrial molds

(G-9435)
DANNYS PRTG SVC SUPS & EQP INC
7233 Biscayne Blvd (33138-5118)
PHONE..................................305 757-2282
Elvia Alvarenga, *President*
Jose D Alvarenga, *Vice Pres*
EMP: 5 **EST:** 1991
SQ FT: 1,200
SALES (est): 457.4K **Privately Held**
WEB: www.dannysprinting.com
SIC: 2752 5112 2791 2789 Commercial printing, offset; business forms; typesetting; bookbinding & related work; commercial printing

(G-9436)
DASAN ZHONE SOLUTIONS INC
801 Brickell Ave Fl 9 (33131-2945)
PHONE..................................305 789-6680
Antonio Jonusas, *Branch Mgr*
EMP: 6
SALES (corp-wide): 300.6MM **Publicly Held**
WEB: www.dzsi.com
SIC: 3661 Telephone & telegraph apparatus
PA: Dzs Inc.
5700 Tennyson Pkwy # 400
Plano TX 75024
469 327-1531

(G-9437)
DATA ACCESS INTERNATIONAL INC
14000 Sw 119th Ave (33186-6017)
P.O. Box 770970 (33177-0017)
PHONE..................................305 238-0012
Charles L Casanave III, *President*
Stephen W Meely, *Vice Pres*
Charles L Casanave Jr, *CFO*
EMP: 55 **EST:** 1993
SQ FT: 25,000
SALES (est): 740.7K
SALES (corp-wide): 7.6MM **Privately Held**
WEB: www.dataaccess.com
SIC: 7372 Prepackaged software
PA: Data Access Corporation
14000 Sw 119th Ave
Miami FL 33186
305 238-0012

(G-9438)
DAVIE FASTSIGNS
40 Nw 3rd St Ste 1 (33128-1838)
PHONE..................................305 423-2332
Alberto Reyes, *Manager*
EMP: 6 **EST:** 2017
SALES (est): 151.3K **Privately Held**
WEB: www.fastsigns.com
SIC: 3993 Signs & advertising specialties

(G-9439)
DB MOTORING GROUP INC
6834 Nw 77th Ct (33166-2713)
PHONE..................................305 685-0707
Gustavo Baldor, *President*
Carlos Don, *Vice Pres*
◆ **EMP:** 6 **EST:** 2009
SALES (est): 889.2K **Privately Held**
WEB: www.dbmotoringgroup.com
SIC: 3011 Tires & inner tubes

(G-9440)
DC STYLE CORP
1835 Nw 112th Ave (33172-1817)
PHONE..................................786 391-3780
EMP: 8 **EST:** 2019
SALES (est): 644.2K **Privately Held**
WEB: www.dcstyle.espwebsite.com
SIC: 2752 Commercial printing, lithographic

(G-9441)
DCS PHARMA USA LLC
801 Brickell Ave Ste 900 (33131-2979)
PHONE..................................248 979-8866
EMP: 6 **EST:** 2016
SALES (est): 281.6K **Privately Held**
SIC: 2834 Pharmaceutical preparations

(G-9442)
DEAKO COATING & CHEMICAL INC
2540 Nw 29th Ave Ste 105 (33142-6438)
PHONE..................................305 634-5162
Rocio Fernandez, *President*
▼ **EMP:** 8 **EST:** 1973
SQ FT: 5,000
SALES (est): 651.1K **Privately Held**
SIC: 2851 Paints: oil or alkyd vehicle or water thinned

(G-9443)
DECOY INC
Also Called: Decoy Next Level In Apparel
2480 Nw 20th St Unit D (33142-7116)
PHONE..................................305 633-6384
Yaron Gilboa, *Principal*
▲ **EMP:** 10 **EST:** 2007
SALES (est): 568K **Privately Held**
WEB: www.etzo.com
SIC: 2331 2341 5137 Women's & misses' blouses & shirts; women's & children's underwear; women's & children's clothing

(G-9444)
DEEPSTREAM DESIGNS INC
2699 Tigertail Ave Apt 54 (33133-4662)
PHONE..................................305 857-0466
Sheila K Boyce, *President*
Thomas H Boyce, *Vice Pres*
EMP: 5 **EST:** 2009
SQ FT: 9,400
SALES (est): 795.2K **Privately Held**
WEB: www.deepstreamdesign.com
SIC: 2599 Hotel furniture

(G-9445)
DELET DOORS INC
9250 Sw 117th Ter (33176-4234)
PHONE..................................786 250-4506
Marlene Harris, *President*
E M Harris, *President*
Ronit Moll, *Vice Pres*
Ana Y Santos, *Vice Pres*
Jeronimo Pineda, *Director*
▼ **EMP:** 10 **EST:** 2006
SQ FT: 3,500
SALES (est): 817.9K **Privately Held**
WEB: www.nationaltradersinc.com
SIC: 2431 2499 Windows, wood; wooden-ware, kitchen & household

(G-9446)
DELI FRESH FOODS INC
Also Called: Mak Food Service
18630 Ne 2nd Ave (33179-4452)
PHONE..................................305 652-2848
Charles Chmelir, *President*
EMP: 10 **EST:** 2008
SALES (est): 1.2MM **Privately Held**
WEB: www.boxedlunchexpress.com
SIC: 2099 Sandwiches, assembled & packaged: for wholesale market

(G-9447)
DELICATE DESIGNS EVENT PLG INC
12080 Ne 16th Ave Apt 201 (33161-6514)
PHONE..................................305 833-8725
Regina Bryant, *CEO*
EMP: 5
SALES (est): 300K **Privately Held**
SIC: 2752 Business form & card printing, lithographic

(G-9448)
DELICIOSA FOOD GROUP INC
1177 Nw 81st St (33150-2739)
PHONE..................................954 492-6131
Jorge A Bravo, *CEO*
EMP: 10 **EST:** 2018
SALES (est): 2.9MM **Privately Held**
WEB: www.deliciosafoodgroup.com
SIC: 2024 Ice cream & frozen desserts

(G-9449)
DELISSER ENTERPRISES INC
Also Called: Banks Sails
3470 Nw 7th St (33125-4014)
PHONE..................................305 649-6001
Emonn Delisser, *President*
Heidi Delisser, *Vice Pres*
EMP: 5 **EST:** 1994
SQ FT: 3,000
SALES (est): 337.2K **Privately Held**
SIC: 2394 Sails: made from purchased materials

(G-9450)
DELL USA LP
14591 Sw 120th St (33186-8638)
PHONE..................................512 728-8391
Rich Rothberg, *General Counsel*
EMP: 12 **EST:** 2015
SALES (est): 941.8K **Privately Held**
WEB: www.dell.com
SIC: 3571 Personal computers (microcomputers)

(G-9451)
DELTA INTERNATIONAL INC
4856 Sw 72nd Ave (33155-5526)
PHONE..................................305 665-6573
Elena De La Torre, *President*
Claudia De La Torre, *QC Mgr*
◆ **EMP:** 10 **EST:** 1976
SQ FT: 4,000
SALES (est): 2.9MM **Privately Held**
WEB: www.deltaintl.com
SIC: 3545 3546 3444 Machine tool accessories; drills & drilling tools; sheet metalwork

(G-9452)
DELUXE CLSETS CABINETS STN LLC
15290 Sw 36th Ter (33185-4795)
PHONE..................................786 879-3371
Rigoberto Arias Sala, *Manager*
EMP: 8 **EST:** 2018
SALES (est): 351.8K **Privately Held**
SIC: 2434 Wood kitchen cabinets

(G-9453)
DEMACO LLC
121 Sw 109th Ave Apt M2 (33174-1230)
PHONE..................................321 952-6600
Roberth E Gomez, *Principal*
EMP: 9 **EST:** 2010
SALES (est): 125.9K **Privately Held**
WEB: www.demaco.com
SIC: 3559 Special industry machinery

(G-9454)
DEMERX INC
1951 Nw 7th Ave Ste 300 (33136-1112)
PHONE..................................954 607-3670
Holger Weis, *President*
Steve Gorlin, *Principal*
Elizabeth Yager, *Admin Asst*
EMP: 9 **EST:** 2010
SALES (est): 1.7MM **Privately Held**
WEB: www.demerx.com
SIC: 2836 Biological products, except diagnostic

(G-9455)
DEPUY INC
6303 Blue Lagoon Dr (33126-6002)
PHONE....305 412-8010
EMP: 42
SALES (corp-wide): 71.3B **Publicly Held**
SIC: 3842 Mfg Surgical Appliances/Supplies
HQ: Depuy Synthes Inc.
1 Johnson And Johnson Plz
New Brunswick NJ 08901
732 524-0400

(G-9456)
DEPUY SYNTHES PRODUCTS INC
Also Called: Cerenovus
6303 Blue Lagoon Dr (33126-6002)
PHONE....305 265-6842
EMP: 192
SALES (corp-wide): 82.5B **Publicly Held**
SIC: 3841 Surgical & medical instruments
HQ: Depuy Synthes Products, Inc.
325 Paramount Dr
Raynham MA 02767
508 880-8100

(G-9457)
DESCO INDUSTRIES
13937 Sw 119th Ave (33186-6202)
PHONE....305 255-7744
▼ **EMP:** 8
SALES (est): 612.3K **Privately Held**
SIC: 3999 Mfg Misc Products

(G-9458)
DESIGN YOUR KIT CLSET MORE INC
13400 Sw 134th Ave Ste 5 (33186-4523)
PHONE....786 227-6412
Shaukat Ali, *President*
Monica Ali-Gordon, *CFO*
EMP: 7 **EST:** 2017
SALES (est): 364.6K **Privately Held**
SIC: 2434 5031 Wood kitchen cabinets; kitchen cabinets

(G-9459)
DESIGNER DOOR PRODUCTS INC
17852 State Road 9 (33162-1008)
PHONE....786 800-3855
Pavel Pojidaev, *President*
EMP: 8 **EST:** 2014
SALES (est): 133.1K **Privately Held**
WEB: www.designerdoorproducts.com
SIC: 2431 Door frames, wood

(G-9460)
DESIGNERS SPECIALTY CAB CO INC
Also Called: Designer Speciality Millwork
1730 Biscayne Blvd 201g (33132-1124)
PHONE....954 776-4500
EMP: 23 **Privately Held**
SIC: 2431 Mfg Millwork
PA: Designer's Specialty Cabinet Company, Inc.
1320 Nw 65th Pl
Fort Lauderdale FL 33309

(G-9461)
DESIGNERS TOPS INC
4725 Nw 36th Ave (33142-3907)
PHONE....305 599-9973
Tony Pino, *CEO*
Erlinda Pino, *President*
Pablo Pino, *Vice Pres*
Roberto Pino, *Treasurer*
◆ **EMP:** 18 **EST:** 1984
SALES (est): 2MM **Privately Held**
WEB: www.designerstops.com
SIC: 2541 3281 2821 Counter & sink tops; cut stone & stone products; plastics materials & resins

(G-9462)
DEXTRUM LABORATORIES INC
Also Called: Agnus Distributors
6993 Nw 82nd Ave Ste 20 (33166-2782)
PHONE....305 594-4020
Rabames Riesgo, *President*
▲ **EMP:** 8 **EST:** 2000
SALES (est): 1.1MM **Privately Held**
WEB: www.dextrumlabs.com
SIC: 2834 Vitamin preparations

(G-9463)
DHS POWER CORP
8061 Nw 67th St (33166-2750)
PHONE....305 599-1022
Danny Hernandez, *President*
◆ **EMP:** 6 **EST:** 2010
SALES (est): 897.6K **Privately Held**
WEB: www.dhspower.com
SIC: 3537 5531 Industrial trucks & tractors; automotive parts

(G-9464)
DIANTHUS MIAMI INC (PA)
7635 Nw 27th Ave (33147-5503)
PHONE....786 800-8365
Johannes Kornman, *President*
Dianthus Miami, *Creative Dir*
Jan Kornman, *Master*
EMP: 8 **EST:** 2010
SALES (est): 553.7K **Privately Held**
WEB: www.dianthusmiami.com
SIC: 3999 Artificial flower arrangements

(G-9465)
DIATOMITE CORP OF AMERICA
19925 Ne 39th Pl (33180-3088)
PHONE....305 466-0075
Allan Applestein, *President*
EMP: 9 **EST:** 1956
SQ FT: 2,500
SALES (est): 222.4K **Privately Held**
SIC: 1481 0811 6552 3295 Mine development, nonmetallic minerals; timber tracts; subdividers & developers; minerals, ground or treated

(G-9466)
DIESEL MACHINERY INTL USA
4121 Sw 90th Ct (33165-5367)
PHONE....305 551-4424
Franco Giangradi, *President*
Charles Matuszak, *Vice Pres*
▼ **EMP:** 5 **EST:** 1991
SALES (est): 933.5K **Privately Held**
WEB: www.dmi-usa.com
SIC: 3519 Diesel engine rebuilding

(G-9467)
DIESEL PRO POWER INC
Also Called: Diesel Pro Power USA
760 Nw 4th St Ste 100 (33128-1464)
PHONE....305 545-5588
Luis Uva, *President*
Cesar Flores, *Sales Mgr*
◆ **EMP:** 15
SQ FT: 11,000
SALES (est): 5MM **Privately Held**
WEB: www.dieselpro.com
SIC: 3519 5084 Parts & accessories, internal combustion engines; engines & parts, diesel

(G-9468)
DIGITAL LIGHTING SYSTEMS INC
Also Called: D L S Electronics
7588 Nw 8th St Fl 2 (33126-2915)
PHONE....305 264-8391
Alif Khawand, *President*
Elias Khawand, *Vice Pres*
EMP: 7 **EST:** 1978
SQ FT: 6,000
SALES (est): 800K **Privately Held**
WEB: www.digitallighting.com
SIC: 3648 8711 Lighting equipment; electrical or electronic engineering

(G-9469)
DISCOS Y EMPANADAS ARGENTINA
2181 Nw 10th Ave (33127-4635)
PHONE....305 326-9300
Albert Muniz, *President*
Jesus Guerra, *Corp Secy*
▼ **EMP:** 10 **EST:** 1986
SQ FT: 3,000
SALES (est): 1.1MM **Privately Held**
WEB: www.empanadawholesale.com
SIC: 2038 2013 Frozen specialties; sausages & other prepared meats

(G-9470)
DISCOUNT WELDS LLC
2745 Nw 21st St (33142-7015)
PHONE....305 637-3939
Silvio Fernandez, *Principal*
EMP: 8 **EST:** 2017
SALES (est): 1.1MM **Privately Held**
WEB: www.discountwelds.com
SIC: 7692 Welding repair

(G-9471)
DISCOVERY CANVAS EAST COAST CO
1386 Nw 54th St (33142-3859)
PHONE....786 487-8897
Mercedes Abreut, *Principal*
Juan C Sarmento, *Principal*
EMP: 8 **EST:** 2010
SALES (est): 10.5K **Privately Held**
SIC: 2211 Canvas

(G-9472)
DIVAS FASHION
8382 Bird Rd (33155-3355)
PHONE....786 717-7039
Sirlhey Guerrero Nunez, *Principal*
EMP: 6 **EST:** 2016
SALES (est): 121.3K **Privately Held**
SIC: 2299 Jute & flax textile products

(G-9473)
DK EVENTS LLC
1565 Ne 150th St (33161-2642)
PHONE....305 760-2963
Ketia Salvador, *Principal*
EMP: 6 **EST:** 2012
SALES (est): 95K **Privately Held**
WEB: www.eventsbydk.com
SIC: 2754 Stationery & invitation printing, gravure

(G-9474)
DOCUPRINT CORPORATION
7950 Nw 53rd St Ste 337 (33166-4791)
PHONE....305 639-8618
Antonio Analia, *Principal*
EMP: 12 **EST:** 2000
SALES (est): 455.2K **Privately Held**
WEB: www.docuprint.us
SIC: 2752 Commercial printing, offset

(G-9475)
DOLCI PECCATI LLC
1900 N Bayshore Dr (33132-3001)
PHONE....954 632-8551
Natalie Yepes Lasprilla, *Principal*
EMP: 7 **EST:** 2010
SALES (est): 393.4K **Privately Held**
WEB: www.dolcipeccatigelato.com
SIC: 2024 Ice cream & frozen desserts

(G-9476)
DOLPHIN KITCHEN & BATH
2051 Nw 112th Ave Ste 123 (33172-1835)
PHONE....305 482-9486
Roberto Colatosti, *President*
EMP: 7 **EST:** 2007
SALES (est): 120K **Privately Held**
SIC: 2499 Kitchen, bathroom & household ware: wood

(G-9477)
DON AND KATHY KESLER
3897 Kumquat Ave (33133-5609)
PHONE....305 793-9216
Kenneth Kesler, *Vice Pres*
EMP: 6 **EST:** 1985
SALES (est): 66.3K **Privately Held**
WEB: www.interspacedesign.net
SIC: 2759 Commercial printing

(G-9478)
DONICA INTERNATIONAL INC
7500 Nw 52nd St (33166-5511)
PHONE....954 217-7616
Guanglu Wang, *President*
Guy Kennett, *Principal*
EMP: 10 **EST:** 2011
SALES (est): 558.2K **Privately Held**
SIC: 3728 Aircraft assemblies, subassemblies & parts

(G-9479)
DONNELLEY FINANCIAL LLC
200 S Biscayne Blvd # 1750 (33131-2310)
PHONE....305 371-3900
Paul Nuttaol, *Manager*
EMP: 10
SQ FT: 3,500
SALES (corp-wide): 894.5MM **Publicly Held**
WEB: www.rrd.com
SIC: 2752 7373 Commercial printing, offset; computer integrated systems design
HQ: Donnelley Financial, Llc
35 W Wacker Dr
Chicago IL 60601
844 866-4337

(G-9480)
DOOR STYLES INC
1178 Nw 163rd Dr (33169-5816)
PHONE....305 653-4447
Eduardo Zegarra, *President*
▼ **EMP:** 25 **EST:** 1995
SQ FT: 5,000
SALES (est): 1.9MM **Privately Held**
SIC: 2431 Door frames, wood; window frames, wood

(G-9481)
DORAL IMAGING INSTITUTE LLC
2760 Sw 97th Ave Apt 101 (33165-2685)
PHONE....305 594-2881
Amy Dusee, *Mktg Dir*
Viana Vivar,
EMP: 9 **EST:** 2007
SALES (est): 825.1K **Privately Held**
SIC: 3841 Diagnostic apparatus, medical

(G-9482)
DOT BLUE TRADING INC
3100 Nw 72nd Ave Ste 126 (33122-1336)
PHONE....954 646-0448
Pedro E Quinteros, *Principal*
EMP: 9 **EST:** 2016
SALES (est): 1MM **Privately Held**
WEB: www.bluedot-trading.com
SIC: 3564 Filters, air: furnaces, air conditioning equipment, etc.

(G-9483)
DOTCHI LLC
Also Called: Crescent Garden
6807 Biscayne Blvd (33138-6214)
PHONE....305 477-0024
Harry Tchira, *President*
Paula Douer, *Vice Pres*
Andrea Cepero, *Controller*
EMP: 15 **EST:** 2014
SALES (est): 7.3MM **Privately Held**
SIC: 3089 Air mattresses, plastic

(G-9484)
DOUBLE DOWN BOAT WORKS INC
8204 Sw 103rd Ave (33173-3906)
PHONE....305 984-3000
Brill Arielle, *Principal*
EMP: 7 **EST:** 2015
SALES (est): 249.9K **Privately Held**
SIC: 3732 Boat building & repairing

(G-9485)
DREW ESTATE LLC (PA)
12415 Sw 136th Ave Ste 7 (33186-6488)
PHONE....786 581-1800
John Hazard, *Partner*
David Lazarus, *Vice Pres*
William Gentry, *Opers Mgr*
Michael Garcia, *Purchasing*
Gustavo Jaramillo, *CFO*
◆ **EMP:** 24 **EST:** 1996
SALES (est): 14MM **Privately Held**
WEB: www.drewestate.com
SIC: 2131 Chewing & smoking tobacco

(G-9486)
DRINKS ON ME 305 LLC
6118 Nw 7th Ave (33127-1112)
PHONE....786 488-2356
Chazemon Fenderson,
EMP: 10 **EST:** 2018
SALES (est): 160K **Privately Held**
SIC: 2599 Food wagons, restaurant

GEOGRAPHIC

(G-9487)
DRONE PICS AND VIDS CORP
13237 Sw 45th Ln (33175-3932)
PHONE....................................786 558-4027
Christian Mirabal, *Principal*
EMP: 7 **EST:** 2016
SALES (est): 80K **Privately Held**
SIC: 3721 Motorized aircraft

(G-9488)
DUTCH PACKING CO INC
74 Sw Coral Ter Ste 101 (33155)
P.O. Box 143518, Coral Gables (33114-3518)
PHONE....................................305 871-3640
Victor Rodriguez, *President*
Raul Rodriguez, *President*
William Rodriguez, *Vice Pres*
EMP: 6 **EST:** 1961
SQ FT: 10,000
SALES (est): 7MM **Privately Held**
WEB: www.garciasausagebrand.com
SIC: 2013 2011 Sausages & other prepared meats; meat packing plants

(G-9489)
E & P PRINTING CORP
7882 Nw 64th St (33166-2706)
PHONE....................................305 715-9545
Cesar Casamayor, *President*
▼ **EMP:** 7 **EST:** 1977
SQ FT: 1,300
SALES (est): 1MM **Privately Held**
WEB: www.eandpgroup.com
SIC: 2752 Commercial printing, offset

(G-9490)
E T C R INC
3181 Nw 36th Ave (33142-4921)
PHONE....................................305 637-0999
Milagros Espinosa, *President*
◆ **EMP:** 25 **EST:** 2005
SALES (est): 5.9MM **Privately Held**
SIC: 3272 Floor slabs & tiles, precast concrete

(G-9491)
E&P SOLUTIONS AND SERVICES INC
7884 Nw 64th St (33166-2706)
PHONE....................................305 715-9545
Cesar Casamayor, *President*
EMP: 6 **EST:** 2009
SALES (est): 359.5K **Privately Held**
WEB: www.eandpgroup.com
SIC: 2759 8742 Commercial printing; transportation consultant

(G-9492)
E-STONE USA CORPORATION (HQ)
1565 Nw 36th St (33142-5559)
PHONE....................................863 214-8281
Andrea Di Giuseppe, *President*
Giuseppe Bisazza, *Vice Pres*
James A Gorsuch, *Vice Pres*
Cristiano Tonini, *CFO*
Tino Biszza, *Treasurer*
▲ **EMP:** 100 **EST:** 2005
SQ FT: 150,000
SALES (est): 23.9MM
SALES (corp-wide): 29MM **Privately Held**
WEB: www.granitetransformations.com
SIC: 3272 Floor slabs & tiles, precast concrete
PA: Trend Usa Ltd.
10306 Usa Today Way
Miramar FL 33025
954 435-5538

(G-9493)
EAGLE ATHLETICA LLC ✪
1000 Brickell Ave Ste 715 (33131-3047)
PHONE....................................305 209-7002
Oguzhan Avcioglu, *Mng Member*
EMP: 9 **EST:** 2021
SALES (est): 900K **Privately Held**
SIC: 3949 Sporting & athletic goods

(G-9494)
EAGLELITHOCOM INC
2725 Nw 17th Ave (33142-6639)
PHONE....................................786 521-7211
EMP: 7 **EST:** 2010
SALES (est): 57.1K **Privately Held**
WEB: www.eaglelitho.com
SIC: 2732 Book printing

(G-9495)
EASTERN AERO MARINE INC
Also Called: Eam Worldwide
5502 Nw 37th Ave (33142-2718)
P.O. Box 660067, Miami Springs (33266-0067)
PHONE....................................305 871-4050
Miriam Oroshnik, *President*
Lorena Galarza, *Purchasing*
Judith Gallo, *QC Mgr*
George Quirk, *Engineer*
Ken Diaz, *Accounting Mgr*
◆ **EMP:** 185
SQ FT: 62,000
SALES (est): 41.5MM **Privately Held**
WEB: www.eamworldwide.com
SIC: 3069 7699 Life rafts, rubber; life saving & survival equipment, non-medical: repair

(G-9496)
EATON & WOLK
2665 S Byshr Dr Ste 609 (33133-5401)
PHONE....................................305 249-1640
EMP: 9 **EST:** 2019
SALES (est): 1.2MM **Privately Held**
WEB: www.eatonwolk.com
SIC: 3625 Motor controls & accessories

(G-9497)
EBS QUALITY SERVICE INC
Also Called: Kings Creek Flowers
13210 Sw 132nd Ave Ste 1 (33186-6136)
PHONE....................................305 595-4048
Aristides Borrell, *CEO*
Aristides H Borrell, *CEO*
Emma Borrell, *Vice Pres*
EMP: 12 **EST:** 2000
SQ FT: 1,400
SALES (est): 1.3MM **Privately Held**
WEB: www.ebsqualityserviceinc.com
SIC: 2051 5193 5992 7379 Bakery: wholesale or wholesale/retail combined; flowers & florists' supplies; florists' supplies; florists;

(G-9498)
ECLIPSE SCREEN AND SHUTTERS
3120 Sw 114th Ave (33165-2116)
PHONE....................................305 216-4716
Carlos Fernando Saavedra, *Principal*
EMP: 6 **EST:** 2016
SALES (est): 159.1K **Privately Held**
SIC: 3442 Shutters, door or window: metal

(G-9499)
ECO INFORMATIVO
1901 Brickell Ave B201 (33129-1724)
PHONE....................................786 362-6789
Jose A Aybar, *Principal*
EMP: 6 **EST:** 2012
SALES (est): 109.3K **Privately Held**
SIC: 2711 Newspapers

(G-9500)
ECONOMY TENT INTERNATIONAL INC
2995 Nw 75th St (33147-5943)
PHONE....................................305 691-0191
Hal Paul Lapping, *President*
H Steven Mishket, *Vice Pres*
Rebecca C Mishket, *Treasurer*
Erika Hernandez, *Sales Staff*
Linda Lapping, *Admin Sec*
◆ **EMP:** 53 **EST:** 1948
SQ FT: 25,000
SALES (est): 1MM **Privately Held**
WEB: www.economytent.com
SIC: 2394 Tents: made from purchased materials; tarpaulins, fabric: made from purchased materials

(G-9501)
ECS AMERICA LLC
Also Called: Locksmith Killers
7253 Nw 12th St (33126-1908)
PHONE....................................305 629-9599
Jose Romero, *Mng Member*
EMP: 5 **EST:** 2015
SALES (est): 1MM **Privately Held**
WEB: www.locksmithkeyless.com
SIC: 3429 Keys, locks & related hardware

(G-9502)
EDIGITALPRINTINGCOM INC
11950 Sw 128th St (33186-5207)
PHONE....................................305 378-2325
Michael Stoyanovich, *President*
EMP: 8 **EST:** 2000
SQ FT: 2,000
SALES (est): 1MM **Privately Held**
WEB: www.theprintingcrew.com
SIC: 2752 Commercial printing, offset

(G-9503)
EFFEARREDI USA INC
123 Nw 23rd St (33127-4409)
PHONE....................................786 725-4948
Fabio Giovanni Allievi, *Principal*
▲ **EMP:** 17 **EST:** 2012
SALES (est): 748.1K
SALES (corp-wide): 4.5MM **Privately Held**
WEB: www.effearredi.it
SIC: 2431 Millwork
PA: Effearredi Srl
Viale Industria 37
Castelli Calepio BG
035 442-5460

(G-9504)
EGEA FOOD LLC
4313 Sw 75th Ave (33155-4474)
PHONE....................................833 353-6637
Tufan Aycicek, *Principal*
EMP: 15 **EST:** 2017
SALES (est): 1.8MM **Privately Held**
WEB: www.egeafood.com
SIC: 2011 Meat packing plants

(G-9505)
EL COLUSA NEWS
2550 Nw 72nd Ave Ste 308 (33122-1348)
P.O. Box 165739 (33116-5739)
PHONE....................................786 845-6868
Gabrael Martinez, *Owner*
EMP: 7 **EST:** 2001
SALES (est): 399K **Privately Held**
WEB: www.elcolusa.com
SIC: 2711 Newspapers, publishing & printing

(G-9506)
EL RINKON
3105 Nw 27th Ave (33142-5819)
PHONE....................................786 332-3125
German A Rached, *Principal*
EMP: 6 **EST:** 2011
SALES (est): 228.5K **Privately Held**
SIC: 3421 Table & food cutlery, including butchers'

(G-9507)
EL SABOR SPICES INC
3501 Nw 67th St (33147-7554)
PHONE....................................305 691-2300
Ercida Echemendia, *President*
EMP: 12 **EST:** 2012
SALES (est): 911.5K **Privately Held**
WEB: www.elsaborspices.com
SIC: 2099 5149 5499 Spices, including grinding; spices & seasonings; spices & herbs

(G-9508)
EL TEIDE NORTH INDUSTRIES
7763 Nw 64th St Ste 4 (33166-3503)
PHONE....................................786 830-7506
Nicolas Mesa, *Principal*
EMP: 7 **EST:** 2016
SALES (est): 276.6K **Privately Held**
WEB: www.elteidenorth.com
SIC: 3999 Manufacturing industries

(G-9509)
EL TORO MEAT PACKING CORP
Also Called: Morrison Meat Packers
738 Nw 72nd St (33150-3613)
PHONE....................................305 836-4461
Claudio Rodriguez, *President*
Gilda M Rodriguez, *Admin Sec*
▲ **EMP:** 56 **EST:** 1966
SQ FT: 14,000
SALES (est): 5.6MM **Privately Held**
WEB: www.morrisonmeat.com
SIC: 2011 Meat packing plants

(G-9510)
ELECTROLYTIC TECHNOLOGIES CORP (PA)
19597 Ne 10th Ave Ste G (33179-3578)
PHONE....................................305 655-2755
Edmund M Cudworth, *CEO*
Derek B Lubie, *President*
Derick Oubie, *President*
Manuel EE, *Engrg Dir*
Manuel Gonzalez, *Engrg Dir*
▲ **EMP:** 16 **EST:** 2001
SQ FT: 13,179
SALES (est): 3.9MM **Privately Held**
WEB: www.electrolytictech.com
SIC: 3589 Water treatment equipment, industrial

(G-9511)
ELECTROSTATIC INDUSTRIAL PNTG
6801 Nw 25th Ave (33147-6803)
PHONE....................................305 696-4556
Guillermo Lugo, *President*
Jose Lugo, *Vice Pres*
▲ **EMP:** 8 **EST:** 1979
SQ FT: 10,000
SALES (est): 568.9K **Privately Held**
SIC: 3479 Painting of metal products

(G-9512)
ELEMENT INC CO
6606 Sw 52nd Ter (33155-6406)
PHONE....................................786 208-5693
Christian Ortiz, *Principal*
EMP: 7 **EST:** 2012
SALES (est): 152.7K **Privately Held**
WEB: www.netelement.com
SIC: 2819 Industrial inorganic chemicals

(G-9513)
ELEMENTS ACCOUNTING INC
7344 Sw 48th St Ste 301 (33155-5521)
P.O. Box 347875 (33234-7875)
PHONE....................................305 662-4448
Eillen Aguirre, *President*
EMP: 9 **EST:** 2005
SALES (est): 255.4K **Privately Held**
WEB: www.elementsaccounting.com
SIC: 2819 8721 Industrial inorganic chemicals; billing & bookkeeping service; auditing services

(G-9514)
ELICAR PRINTING
1929 Nw 22nd St (33142-7331)
PHONE....................................305 324-5252
Roberto Valverde, *Principal*
EMP: 7 **EST:** 2001
SALES (est): 145.3K **Privately Held**
SIC: 2796 Lithographic plates, positives or negatives

(G-9515)
ELITE FLOWER SERVICES INC
6755 Nw 36th St Unit 180 (33166-6813)
PHONE....................................305 436-7400
Lorena Amaya, *Sales Staff*
Pamela Duperly, *Sales Staff*
Angela Fajardo, *Sales Staff*
Claudia Guevara, *Sales Staff*
Andres Pinto, *Sales Staff*
EMP: 36
SALES (corp-wide): 102.5MM **Privately Held**
WEB: www.eliteflower.com
SIC: 3999 Barber & beauty shop equipment
PA: Elite Flower Services, Inc.
6745 Nw 36th St Unit 290
Miami FL 33166
305 436-7400

(G-9516)
ELITE INTL GROUP LLC
Also Called: E L I T E Intergroup
7950 Nw 53rd St Ste 337 (33166-4791)
PHONE....................................305 901-5005
Alvin Zacarias, *CEO*
EMP: 15 **EST:** 2014

SALES (est): 1.7MM **Privately Held**
SIC: 3728 7363 8249 3721 Aircraft training equipment; pilot service, aviation; aviation school; aircraft; aircraft engines & engine parts

(G-9517)
ELITE POWDER COATING
8298 Nw 64th St (33166-2740)
PHONE..................................786 616-8084
Isidro F Suarez, *Principal*
EMP: 9 **EST:** 2016
SALES (est): 407.4K **Privately Held**
WEB: www.elitecoating.com
SIC: 3479 Coating of metals & formed products

(G-9518)
ELITE POWER PRTG SOLUTIONS INC
10103 Sw 166th Ct (33196-1043)
PHONE..................................786 387-7164
Markus Kahlig, *Director*
EMP: 9 **EST:** 2014
SALES (est): 340.1K **Privately Held**
SIC: 2752 Commercial printing, lithographic

(G-9519)
ELORE ENTERPRISES LLC
1055 Nw 159th Dr (33169-5805)
PHONE..................................305 477-1650
Maylin Fojo, *CFO*
Philippe Pinel,
Jesus Elejabarrieta,
Juan A Elejabarrieta,
Elore Holdings,
◆ **EMP:** 28 **EST:** 2007
SALES (est): 9.7MM
SALES (corp-wide): 305.7K **Privately Held**
WEB: www.palacios.us
SIC: 2013 Sausages from purchased meat
HQ: Elore Holdings, Inc.
1055 Nw 159th Dr
Miami FL 33169
305 477-1650

(G-9520)
ELORE HOLDINGS INC (DH)
Also Called: El Quijote
1055 Nw 159th Dr (33169-5805)
PHONE..................................305 477-1650
Francisco J Palacios, *President*
Angel P Palacios, *Vice Pres*
Maylin Fojo, *CFO*
▲ **EMP:** 7 **EST:** 1986
SQ FT: 12,000
SALES (est): 19.3MM
SALES (corp-wide): 305.7K **Privately Held**
SIC: 2013 Sausages from purchased meat
HQ: Palacios Alimentacion Sl.
Carretera Logrolo, S/N
Albelda De Iregua 26120
941 443-032

(G-9521)
EMBROIDERY USA INC
6900 Nw 50th St (33166-5632)
PHONE..................................305 477-9973
Jorge Murcia, *President*
Carol Yidi, *Admin Sec*
EMP: 6 **EST:** 1992
SQ FT: 5,000
SALES (est): 436.9K **Privately Held**
SIC: 2395 Embroidery & art needlework

(G-9522)
EMBROSERVICE LLC
7003 N Waterway Dr # 222 (33155-2897)
PHONE..................................305 267-2323
Miguel Marmol, *Partner*
EMP: 15 **EST:** 1999
SALES (est): 545.9K **Privately Held**
WEB: www.embroservice.com
SIC: 2395 Embroidery & art needlework

(G-9523)
EMC MANUFACTURING
3032 Nw 72nd Ave (33122-1314)
PHONE..................................305 613-9546
EMP: 7 **EST:** 2019
SALES (est): 288.8K **Privately Held**
SIC: 3999 Manufacturing industries

(G-9524)
EMMANUEL HOLDINGS INC
Also Called: USA Plastic Industry
2190 Nw 46th St (33142-4017)
PHONE..................................305 558-3088
Miguel Ruiz, *President*
Albert Marryschow, *General Mgr*
Maria Ruiz, *Admin Sec*
▼ **EMP:** 17 **EST:** 2005
SQ FT: 41,171
SALES (est): 788.6K **Privately Held**
SIC: 3089 Extruded finished plastic products

(G-9525)
EMPANADA LADY CO
6732 Ne 4th Ave (33138-5515)
PHONE..................................786 271-6460
Boris Marinovic, *President*
EMP: 10 **EST:** 2015
SALES (est): 391K **Privately Held**
WEB: www.artpieusa.com
SIC: 2051 Pies, bakery: except frozen

(G-9526)
ENDO-GEAR LLC
Also Called: Zag Medical
4390 Sw 74th Ave (33155-4406)
PHONE..................................305 710-6662
John Zabalo, *Mng Member*
Alvaro Angulo, *Mng Member*
Carlos Gonzalez, *Mng Member*
EMP: 10 **EST:** 2013
SQ FT: 3,500
SALES (est): 663.5K **Privately Held**
WEB: www.endogear.com
SIC: 3845 3841 Endoscopic equipment, electromedical; gastroscopes, except electromedical

(G-9527)
ENERGY SVING SOLUTIONS USA LLC
1031 Ives Dairy Rd # 228 (33179-2538)
PHONE..................................305 735-2878
Peter J Stein, *Managing Dir*
Andrew Nestra, *Vice Pres*
▲ **EMP:** 11 **EST:** 2010
SALES (est): 2MM **Privately Held**
WEB: www.energysavingindustry.com
SIC: 3646 Commercial indusl & institutional electric lighting fixtures

(G-9528)
ENTECH CONTROLS CORP
1031 Ives Dairy Rd Bldg 4 (33179-2538)
PHONE..................................954 613-2971
Alan D Jorczak, *President*
Cecelia L Jorczak, *Corp Secy*
EMP: 7 **EST:** 1980
SQ FT: 10,000
SALES (est): 1.2MM **Privately Held**
WEB: www.entechcontrolscorp.com
SIC: 3613 5065 3625 Switches, electric power except snap, push button, etc.; electronic parts & equipment; relays & industrial controls

(G-9529)
ENVIRALUM INDUSTRIES INC
5100 Nw 72nd Ave Unit C (33166-5608)
PHONE..................................305 752-4411
Frank Messa, *President*
EMP: 11 **EST:** 2010
SALES (est): 2MM **Privately Held**
WEB: www.enviralum.net
SIC: 3231 Doors, glass: made from purchased glass

(G-9530)
ENVISION GRAPHICS INC
7335 Nw 35th St (33122-1268)
PHONE..................................305 470-0083
Janoy Fuentes, *President*
Edilberto Fuentes, *Vice Pres*
EMP: 37 **EST:** 1999
SQ FT: 3,700
SALES (est): 2.5MM **Privately Held**
SIC: 2759 2752 Commercial printing; commercial printing, lithographic

(G-9531)
EPARE LLC
117 Ne 1st Ave (33132-2125)
PHONE..................................347 682-5121
Yevgeniy Khayman, *President*
Eugene Khayman, *Vice Pres*
EMP: 10 **EST:** 2012
SALES (est): 874K **Privately Held**
WEB: www.epare.com
SIC: 3469 Household cooking & kitchen utensils, metal

(G-9532)
EPITOMI INC
12201 Sw 128th Ct Ste 108 (33186-6425)
P.O. Box 561564 (33256-1564)
PHONE..................................305 971-5370
▼ **EMP:** 20
SALES (est): 3.3MM **Privately Held**
SIC: 2844 Mfg Toiletry Preparations

(G-9533)
EPOWER 360 LLC (PA)
7780 Sw 71st Ave (33143-4313)
PHONE..................................305 330-6684
Saied Hussaini, *CEO*
Iliana Hussaini, *Office Mgr*
▲ **EMP:** 11 **EST:** 2014
SQ FT: 1,500
SALES (est): 1.1MM **Privately Held**
WEB: www.epower360.com
SIC: 3714 Booster (jump-start) cables, automotive

(G-9534)
EQUIGRAPH TRADING CORP
13331 Sw 132nd Ave (33186-6197)
PHONE..................................786 237-5665
Natalia E Polla, *President*
Joan M Zuniga, *Vice Pres*
Pablo M Zuniga, *Vice Pres*
EMP: 8 **EST:** 2016
SALES (est): 800K **Privately Held**
WEB: www.equigraf.com
SIC: 3555 Printing trade parts & attachments

(G-9535)
ES TUDIOS CORP
5483 Nw 72nd Ave (33166-4223)
PHONE..................................305 300-9262
Enrique A Sarubbi, *Principal*
EMP: 7 **EST:** 2012
SALES (est): 193.6K **Privately Held**
SIC: 3691 Storage batteries

(G-9536)
ESPRESSO DISPOSITION CORP 1 (HQ)
6262 Bird Rd Ste 2i (33155-4882)
PHONE..................................305 594-9062
Angel L Souto, *CEO*
Jose Enrique Souto, *CEO*
Jose A Souto Jr, *President*
◆ **EMP:** 84 **EST:** 1961
SQ FT: 53,000
SALES (est): 34.8MM
SALES (corp-wide): 8B **Publicly Held**
WEB: www.jmsmucker.com
SIC: 2095 Coffee roasting (except by wholesale grocers)
PA: The J M Smucker Company
1 Strawberry Ln
Orrville OH 44667
330 682-3000

(G-9537)
ESTAL USA INC
150 Se 2nd Ave (33131-1518)
PHONE..................................305 728-3272
Frederic Alberti, *Director*
EMP: 9 **EST:** 2013
SALES (est): 996.3K
SALES (corp-wide): 41.2MM **Privately Held**
WEB: www.estal.com
SIC: 2656 2671 Sanitary food containers; packaging paper & plastics film, coated & laminated
PA: Estal Packaging Sa
Calle Taper (Pol Industrial Bujonis) 23
Sant Feliu De Guixols 17220
972 821-676

(G-9538)
ETI-LABEL INC
Also Called: Aetiquetas Araragua
6961 Nw 82nd Ave (33166-2774)
PHONE..................................305 716-0094
Carlo Damas, *President*
Carlo Lina Damas, *Manager*
EMP: 5 **EST:** 2006
SALES (est): 450.3K **Privately Held**
WEB: www.etilabels.net
SIC: 2754 Commercial printing, gravure

(G-9539)
EURO GEAR (USA) INC (PA)
1395 Brickell Ave Ste 800 (33131-3302)
PHONE..................................518 578-1775
Greg Gohrt, *President*
Eloise Gohrt, *Vice Pres*
EMP: 20 **EST:** 2001
SQ FT: 15,000
SALES (est): 5.4MM **Privately Held**
WEB: www.eurogearinc.com
SIC: 3241 3599 Natural cement; machine & other job shop work

(G-9540)
EVERGLADES PRO PAINTERS CORP
2200 Sw 59th Ave (33155-2257)
PHONE..................................786 444-5024
Nelson R Romero, *Principal*
EMP: 7 **EST:** 2007
SALES (est): 156.3K **Privately Held**
WEB: www.evergladespainters.com
SIC: 2752 Commercial printing, lithographic

(G-9541)
EVERGREEN SWEETENERS INC
3601 Nw 62nd St (33147-7539)
PHONE..................................305 835-6907
EMP: 15
SALES (corp-wide): 10.3MM **Privately Held**
WEB: www.esweeteners.com
SIC: 2099 Food preparations
PA: Evergreen Sweeteners, Inc.
1936 Hollywood Blvd # 20
Hollywood FL 33020
954 381-7776

(G-9542)
EXCEL CONVERTING INC
6950 Nw 37th Ct (33147-6533)
P.O. Box 668826 (33166-9423)
PHONE..................................786 318-2222
Rafael A Marin, *President*
▼ **EMP:** 10 **EST:** 2000
SALES (est): 1.5MM **Privately Held**
SIC: 2621 Paper mills

(G-9543)
EXCEL HANDBAGS CO INC
3651 Nw 81st St (33147-4444)
PHONE..................................305 836-8800
Brian D Fink, *President*
▲ **EMP:** 10 **EST:** 1941
SQ FT: 30,000
SALES (est): 5MM **Privately Held**
WEB: www.excelhandbags.com
SIC: 3171 5137 Handbags, women's; handbags

(G-9544)
EXCELAG CORP (PA)
7300 N Kendall Dr Ste 640 (33156-7840)
PHONE..................................305 670-0145
Jorge Cepeda, *President*
Nely V Cepeda, *Vice Pres*
Violeta Cepeda, *Vice Pres*
David L Miles, *Treasurer*
◆ **EMP:** 5 **EST:** 2001
SQ FT: 1,500
SALES (est): 2MM **Privately Held**
WEB: www.excelag.com
SIC: 2879 Agricultural chemicals

(G-9545)
EXOTICS CAR WRAPS
245 Ne 183rd St Ste 3a (33179-4500)
PHONE..................................786 768-6798
EMP: 7 **EST:** 2018
SALES (est): 504.1K **Privately Held**
WEB: www.exoticscarwraps.com
SIC: 3993 Signs & advertising specialties

(G-9546)
EXPERT SUBJECTS LLC
4775 Collins Ave (33140-3262)
PHONE..................................786 877-8531
William Suddah,
EMP: 7 **EST:** 2010

SALES (est): 134.9K **Privately Held**
SIC: 2741 Miscellaneous publishing

(G-9547)
EXPORT DIESEL LLC (PA)
1835 Nw 112th Ave Ste 173 (33172-1819)
PHONE..................................305 396-1943
Miguel A Figueroa, *Principal*
Catalina Figueroa, *Principal*
German A Figueroa Jr, *Principal*
Miguel Figueroa, *Vice Pres*
Carlos Figueroa, *Manager*
▲ **EMP:** 18 **EST:** 2009
SALES (est): 19.5MM **Privately Held**
WEB: www.exportdiesel.com
SIC: 2911 Diesel fuels

(G-9548)
EXPRESS IRONING INC
Also Called: Express Ironing of Miami
4707 Sw 75th Ave (33155-4436)
PHONE..................................305 261-1072
Alina Perez, *Principal*
EMP: 9 **EST:** 2005
SALES (est): 861.5K **Privately Held**
WEB: www.expressironing.co.uk
SIC: 2741 Miscellaneous publishing

(G-9549)
EXPRESS PRINTING CORPORATION
7024 Sw 46th St (33155-4614)
PHONE..................................305 546-6369
Susan Muci, *Principal*
EMP: 6 **EST:** 2009
SALES (est): 101.2K **Privately Held**
WEB: www.express-printing-inc.com
SIC: 2752 Commercial printing, offset

(G-9550)
EYEDOSE INC
Also Called: Leisurelay365
66 W Flagler St Ste 900 (33130-1807)
PHONE..................................786 853-6194
Zettie Jones, *President*
EMP: 6 **EST:** 2010
SALES (est): 358.7K **Privately Held**
SIC: 2254 Shirts & t-shirts (underwear), knit

(G-9551)
EYESON DGTAL SRVLLNCE MGT SYST
64 Ne 1st St (33132-2412)
PHONE..................................305 808-3344
Raphael Adouth, *Principal*
EMP: 5 **EST:** 2004
SALES (est): 1.3MM **Privately Held**
WEB: www.eyeson.biz
SIC: 3861 7382 Cameras & related equipment; security systems services

(G-9552)
F P GENERAL WELDING
3131 Sw 120th Ct (33175-3144)
PHONE..................................786 812-6673
Filemon Perez, *Principal*
EMP: 6 **EST:** 2016
SALES (est): 25K **Privately Held**
SIC: 7692 Welding repair

(G-9553)
FABIS GROUP CORPORATION
8025 Nw 68th St (33166-2794)
PHONE..................................305 718-3638
Jose Latella, *President*
Juana Pelosi, *Vice Pres*
▲ **EMP:** 7 **EST:** 2011
SALES (est): 153.4K **Privately Held**
WEB: www.fabis.us
SIC: 2394 Canvas awnings & canopies

(G-9554)
FABIS GROUP CORPORATION
8231 Nw 66th St (33166-2721)
PHONE..................................305 718-3638
Jose Latella, *President*
EMP: 6 **EST:** 2016
SALES (est): 118.6K **Privately Held**
WEB: www.fabis.us
SIC: 2394 Canvas & related products

(G-9555)
FABRIC INNOVATIONS INC
7318 Sw 48th St (33155-5523)
PHONE..................................305 860-5757
Deborah Herman, *President*
Alison Goldman, *Vice Pres*
Gonzalo Leon, *Vice Pres*
Mayling Jaramillo, *Finance Dir*
Anita Khullar, *Sales Staff*
▲ **EMP:** 24 **EST:** 1997
SALES (est): 19MM **Privately Held**
WEB: www.fabricinnovations.com
SIC: 2391 5023 5719 Curtains & draperies; pillowcases; beddings & linens

(G-9556)
FACELOVE COSMETICS INC (PA)
18202 Homestead Ave (33157-5532)
PHONE..................................786 346-7357
Alona Naylor, *President*
EMP: 8 **EST:** 2015
SQ FT: 4,500
SALES (est): 1.6MM **Privately Held**
SIC: 2844 Toilet preparations; face creams or lotions; cosmetic preparations

(G-9557)
FACTORFOX SOFTWARE LLC
14221 Sw 120th St (33186-7236)
PHONE..................................305 671-9526
Kayla Miller, *Cust Mgr*
Robert Vasquez, *CTO*
Atul Kumar, *CTO*
EMP: 5 **EST:** 2014
SALES (est): 634.2K **Privately Held**
WEB: www.factorfox.com
SIC: 7372 Prepackaged software

(G-9558)
FALCON COMMERCIAL AVIATION LLC
13500 Sw 134th Ave Ste 3 (33186-4553)
PHONE..................................786 340-9464
Civa Civarajah, *CEO*
Thanushan Sivothayan, *President*
EMP: 12 **EST:** 2007
SALES (est): 1.7MM **Privately Held**
SIC: 3724 Aircraft engines & engine parts

(G-9559)
FARARTIS LLC
Also Called: Pagnifique
12050 Nw 28th Ave (33167-2518)
PHONE..................................305 594-5704
Pablo De Leon, *Opers Staff*
Julia Palacio, *Sales Staff*
Marcelo Picasso, *Sales Staff*
Luis Abella, *Mng Member*
Heidy Noda, *Administration*
EMP: 4
SQ FT: 29,965
SALES: 7.6MM **Privately Held**
SIC: 2051 Bakery: wholesale or wholesale/retail combined; bakery products, partially cooked (except frozen)

(G-9560)
FARMA INTERNATIONAL INC
9400 S Ddland Blvd Ste 60 (33156)
PHONE..................................305 670-4416
Maria E Medina, *President*
Michael Milgrom, *Vice Pres*
Victor Medellin, *Opers Staff*
◆ **EMP:** 13 **EST:** 1966
SALES (est): 7.5MM **Privately Held**
WEB: www.farmainternational.com
SIC: 2834 Pharmaceutical preparations

(G-9561)
FEICK CORPORATION
8869 Sw 131st St (33176-5944)
PHONE..................................305 271-8550
EMP: 65
SQ FT: 800
SALES (est): 3.4MM **Privately Held**
SIC: 7372 6531 Prepackaged Software Services

(G-9562)
FENIX WESTER CORP
2006 Nw 20th St (33142-7308)
PHONE..................................305 324-9105
Noria Cordova, *President*
EMP: 6 **EST:** 2007
SALES (est): 136.1K **Privately Held**
SIC: 2341 Women's & children's underwear

(G-9563)
FERRARI EXPRESS INC
36 Ne 1st St Ste 1049 (33132-2494)
PHONE..................................305 374-5003
Andrea Deldotto, *Branch Mgr*
EMP: 27 **Privately Held**
WEB: www.ferrarigroup.net
SIC: 2741 Miscellaneous publishing
PA: Ferrari Express Inc.
215 Mill St
Lawrence NY 11559

(G-9564)
FERRERA EMBROIDERY & PRTG SER
331 Ne 167th St (33162-2304)
PHONE..................................786 667-2680
Lenin Ferrera, *Principal*
EMP: 6 **EST:** 2016
SALES (est): 393.3K **Privately Held**
WEB: www.ferreraembroideryandprinting.com
SIC: 2752 Commercial printing, lithographic

(G-9565)
FI AEROSPACE SOLUTIONS INC
7938 Nw 66th St (33166-2726)
PHONE..................................786 395-3289
Francisco Ramirez, *President*
EMP: 7 **EST:** 2018
SALES (est): 222K **Privately Held**
WEB: www.fiaerospace.com
SIC: 3721 Aircraft

(G-9566)
FIBERFLON USA INC
1835 Nw 112th Ave (33172-1817)
PHONE..................................786 953-7329
EMP: 8 **EST:** 2017
SALES (est): 747.8K **Privately Held**
WEB: www.fiberflon.de
SIC: 2821 Plastics materials & resins

(G-9567)
FILTHY FOOD LLC
16500 Nw 15th Ave (33169-5620)
PHONE..................................786 916-5556
Daniel Singer, *CEO*
Charlie Hart, *COO*
Jennifer Hughes, *Senior VP*
Robert Shell, *Vice Pres*
Ralph Singer,
EMP: 60 **EST:** 2009
SQ FT: 50,000
SALES (est): 7.8MM **Privately Held**
WEB: www.filthyfood.com
SIC: 2035 Olives, brined: bulk

(G-9568)
FINE SURFACES AND MORE INC
8860 Nw 15th Ave (33147-3602)
PHONE..................................305 691-5752
Gabriel Segret, *President*
Pablo Lorenzo, *Vice Pres*
EMP: 8 **EST:** 2009
SALES (est): 1MM **Privately Held**
WEB: www.finesurfacesandmore.com
SIC: 3281 Granite, cut & shaped

(G-9569)
FINESTA INC
12650 Nw 25th St Ste 112 (33182-1512)
PHONE..................................786 439-1647
Henry Waissmann, *President*
Hugo Beltran, *Finance Dir*
▲ **EMP:** 6 **EST:** 2009
SQ FT: 3,000
SALES (est): 1MM **Privately Held**
SIC: 2339 Women's & misses' accessories

(G-9570)
FINOTEX USA CORP (PA)
6942 Nw 50th St (33166-5632)
PHONE..................................305 593-1102
Carlos Yidi, *President*
Carlos Yidi Jr, *Vice Pres*
William Yidi, *Vice Pres*
Andres Yidi, *Treasurer*
Caridad Hernandez, *Accountant*
◆ **EMP:** 40 **EST:** 1989
SQ FT: 18,500
SALES (est): 11.3MM **Privately Held**
WEB: www.finotex.com
SIC: 2269 Labels, cotton: printed

(G-9571)
FIRST AMERICA PRODUCTS LLC
9710 E Indigo St Ste 203 (33157-5613)
PHONE..................................904 215-8075
Arjun Saluja,
Suraj Saluja,
EMP: 5 **EST:** 2010
SALES (est): 2.4MM **Privately Held**
WEB: www.firstamericaproducts.com
SIC: 3585 Air conditioning units, complete: domestic or industrial

(G-9572)
FIRST TEE MIAMI DAGA
1802 Nw 37th Ave (33125-1052)
PHONE..................................305 633-4583
Lucca Charles III, *Principal*
Carlos Rodriguez, *Adv Board Mem*
John Reed, *Vice Pres*
John Moscoso, *Director*
Stephanie Peareth, *Program Dir*
EMP: 13 **EST:** 2011
SALES (est): 554.2K **Privately Held**
WEB: www.thefirstteemiami.org
SIC: 3949 Shafts, golf club

(G-9573)
FIRSTCUT
3030 Virginia St (33133-4524)
PHONE..................................786 740-3683
Jorge Soto, *Principal*
EMP: 7 **EST:** 2017
SALES (est): 100.4K **Privately Held**
WEB: www.protolabs.com
SIC: 3089 Molding primary plastic

(G-9574)
FLASH ROOFING AND SHTMTL LLC
17425 Sw 109th Ct (33157-4046)
PHONE..................................786 237-9440
EMP: 8 **EST:** 2019
SALES (est): 779.6K **Privately Held**
WEB: www.flashroofingmiami.com
SIC: 3444 Sheet metalwork

(G-9575)
FLEURISSIMA INC (PA)
Also Called: Robba, Emilio
4242 Ne 2nd Ave (33137-3520)
PHONE..................................305 572-0203
Emilio Robba, *President*
Antoine G Lamarche, *General Mgr*
Michel Robba, *Vice Pres*
Jean-Pierre De Regaini, *Treasurer*
Iris Cheng, *Consultant*
◆ **EMP:** 13 **EST:** 1999
SQ FT: 5,000
SALES (est): 2.8MM **Privately Held**
WEB: www.emiliorobba.com
SIC: 3299 5023 5999 7389 Non-metallic mineral statuary & other decorative products; decorating supplies; art, picture frames & decorations; interior decorating

(G-9576)
FLEXO CONCEPTS MANUFACTURING
13552 Sw 129th St (33186-6276)
PHONE..................................305 233-7075
Raul Ford, *President*
Jorge Ford, *Principal*
Luis Rodriguez, *Vice Pres*
EMP: 5 **EST:** 2002
SALES (est): 508.2K **Privately Held**
WEB: www.flexoconcepts.com
SIC: 3565 Labeling machines, industrial

(G-9577)
FLEXOFFERSCOM INC
990 Biscayne Blvd (33132-1557)
P.O. Box 7520, Fort Lauderdale (33338-7520)
PHONE..................................305 999-9940
Alexander Daskaloff, *President*
Louise Forbes, *Marketing Staff*
Fillipe Oliveira, *Marketing Staff*
David Boostrom, *Manager*

Gus Brito, *Director*
EMP: 5 **EST:** 2010
SALES (est): 2.7MM **Privately Held**
WEB: www.flexoffers.com
SIC: 3993 7311 Signs & advertising specialties; advertising agencies

(G-9578)
FLIGHT AEROTECH LLC
7241 Nw 54th St (33166-4807)
PHONE..................................305 901-6001
Luis F Rodriguez Sr, *Principal*
Luis Rodriguez, *Manager*
EMP: 10 **EST:** 2015
SALES (est): 1.5MM **Privately Held**
WEB: www.flightaerotech.com
SIC: 3728 Aircraft parts & equipment

(G-9579)
FLORIBBEAN INC
6800 Bird Rd (33155-3708)
PHONE..................................844 282-8459
Mary Jo Mellinger, *Principal*
EMP: 8 **EST:** 2010
SALES (est): 111.4K **Privately Held**
SIC: 2099 Food preparations

(G-9580)
FLORIDA BREWERY INC
6303 Blue Lagoon Dr # 280 (33126-6002)
PHONE..................................305 621-0099
Jose M Carballo, *Principal*
EMP: 7 **EST:** 2015
SALES (est): 222.8K **Privately Held**
SIC: 2082 Malt beverages

(G-9581)
FLORIDA ELC MTR CO MIAMI INC
6350 Ne 4th Ct (33138-6108)
PHONE..................................305 759-3835
Vicky Assalone, *President*
John Assalone, *Vice Pres*
Lisa Assalone, *Admin Sec*
▲ **EMP:** 26 **EST:** 1951
SQ FT: 23,000
SALES (est): 1.6MM **Privately Held**
SIC: 7694 5063 7349 Electric motor repair; motors, electric; cleaning service, industrial or commercial

(G-9582)
FLORIDA ENGINE REBUILDERS CORP
12500 Sw 130th St Ste 13 (33186-6206)
PHONE..................................305 232-8784
Miguel D Gonzalez, *President*
Teresita Gonzalez, *Vice Pres*
EMP: 5 **EST:** 1990
SQ FT: 900
SALES (est): 481.6K **Privately Held**
WEB: www.miamiferco.com
SIC: 3599 Machine shop, jobbing & repair

(G-9583)
FLORIDA FRESH SEAFOOD CORP
7337 Nw 37th Ave Unit 7 (33147-5806)
PHONE..................................305 694-1733
Carlos E Tabora, *President*
Leuis Alonso, *Vice Pres*
◆ **EMP:** 11 **EST:** 1985
SQ FT: 10,000
SALES (est): 1MM **Privately Held**
WEB: www.flafreshseafood.com
SIC: 2092 5146 Seafoods, fresh: prepared; seafoods

(G-9584)
FLORIDA HOSE & HYDRAULICS INC
7128 Nw 72nd Ave Ste 336 (33166-2932)
PHONE..................................305 887-9577
E F Mendia, *President*
Gloria Mendia, *Corp Secy*
▼ **EMP:** 5 **EST:** 1981
SQ FT: 5,000
SALES (est): 461.1K **Privately Held**
WEB: www.floridahose.com
SIC: 3492 Hose & tube couplings, hydraulic/pneumatic

(G-9585)
FLORIDA MOTORS INC
1515 Nw 167th St Ste 300 (33169-5106)
PHONE..................................786 524-9001
EMP: 6 **EST:** 2018
SALES (est): 623.8K **Privately Held**
WEB: www.myfloridamotors.com
SIC: 3714 Motor vehicle parts & accessories

(G-9586)
FLORIDA PRSTHTICS ORTHTICS INC
9981 Sw 12th St (33174-2808)
PHONE..................................305 553-1217
Rolando Torres, *Principal*
EMP: 7 **EST:** 2008
SALES (est): 151.6K **Privately Held**
SIC: 3842 Prosthetic appliances

(G-9587)
FLORIDIAN BLINDS LLC
10735 Sw 216th St Unit 40 (33170-3151)
PHONE..................................786 250-4697
EMP: 8 **EST:** 2019
SALES (est): 536.2K **Privately Held**
WEB: www.floridianblinds.com
SIC: 2591 Window blinds

(G-9588)
FLORIDIAN TITLE GROUP INC
20801 Biscayne Blvd # 306 (33180-1430)
PHONE..................................305 792-4911
Oscar Grisales Racini, *Principal*
EMP: 5 **EST:** 2005
SALES (est): 460.5K **Privately Held**
WEB: www.floridatitlegroupinc.com
SIC: 3469 Tile, floor or wall: stamped metal

(G-9589)
FLOWERS BAKING CO MIAMI LLC (DH)
17800 Nw Miami Ct (33169-5092)
P.O. Box 693483 (33269-0483)
PHONE..................................305 652-3416
Ken Redd, *Opers Staff*
Andrew Herrin, *Engineer*
Danna Jones, *Treasurer*
Peter Chao, *VP Sales*
John M Deleu, *Mng Member*
◆ **EMP:** 98
SQ FT: 40,000
SALES (est): 100MM
SALES (corp-wide): 4.3B **Publicly Held**
SIC: 2051 5461 Breads, rolls & buns; bakeries
HQ: Flowers Baking Co. Of Thomasville, Inc.
1919 Flowers Cir
Thomasville GA 31757
229 226-9110

(G-9590)
FLOWHANCE INC
1951 Nw 7th Ave (33136-1104)
PHONE..................................305 690-0784
Davis Nunez, *CEO*
EMP: 11 **EST:** 2018
SALES (est): 496.4K **Privately Held**
WEB: www.flowhance.com
SIC: 2741

(G-9591)
FOAM DECORATION INC
13800 Sw 142nd Ave (33186-7309)
PHONE..................................786 293-8813
Noel Garcia, *President*
EMP: 5 **EST:** 2002
SALES (est): 515.3K **Privately Held**
SIC: 3086 Plastics foam products

(G-9592)
FOH INC
Also Called: Front of House Rm 360 By Foh
7630 Biscayne Blvd (33138-5136)
PHONE..................................305 757-7940
Simone Mayer, *President*
Mayda Perez, *Treasurer*
◆ **EMP:** 120 **EST:** 2013
SALES (est): 13.7MM **Privately Held**
WEB: www.frontofthehouse.com
SIC: 3229 Barware

(G-9593)
FOR-A LATIN AMERICA INC
5200 Blue Lagoon Dr # 130 (33126-7006)
PHONE..................................305 261-2345
EMP: 6
SALES (est): 683K **Privately Held**
SIC: 3823 Mfg Process Control Instruments

(G-9594)
FORKLIFT
2365 Nw 70th Ave (33122-1819)
PHONE..................................305 468-1824
EMP: 6 **EST:** 2014
SALES (est): 120.6K **Privately Held**
WEB: www.miamidadeforklift.com
SIC: 3537 Forklift trucks

(G-9595)
FORWARD EXPRESS ONE LLC
Also Called: Aerotools Connection
12625 Sw 134th Ct Ste 208 (33186-6423)
PHONE..................................305 234-3034
Lorenzo Locurcio,
EMP: 14 **EST:** 2011
SQ FT: 4,500
SALES (est): 846.9K **Privately Held**
SIC: 3728 Aircraft parts & equipment

(G-9596)
FRAGRANCE EXPRESSCOM LLC
Also Called: Fragrance Health and Buty Aids
1221 Nw 165th St (33169-5809)
PHONE..................................800 372-4726
Jose M Norona, *Mng Member*
John Alexander, *Mng Member*
Ernesto Erdmann, *Mng Member*
Mary Barnes,
Bob Bartlett,
EMP: 9 **EST:** 2007
SQ FT: 50,000
SALES (est): 421.5K **Privately Held**
WEB: www.fragranceexpress.com
SIC: 2844 Toilet preparations

(G-9597)
FRAKO CONCRETE SERVICES INC
10312 Sw 3rd St (33174-1709)
P.O. Box 440541 (33144-0541)
PHONE..................................305 551-8196
EMP: 5
SALES (est): 348.3K **Privately Held**
SIC: 3273 Mfg Ready-Mixed Concrete

(G-9598)
FRITANGA Y TORTILLA MODRA
1885 W Flagler St (33135-1939)
PHONE..................................305 649-9377
Teofilo C Mondragon, *Principal*
EMP: 9 **EST:** 2009
SALES (est): 236.6K **Privately Held**
SIC: 2099 Tortillas, fresh or refrigerated

(G-9599)
FRONT OF HOUSE INC
7630 Biscayne Blvd # 105 (33138-5136)
PHONE..................................305 757-7940
Simone Mayer, *President*
◆ **EMP:** 20
SALES (est): 3.6MM **Privately Held**
WEB: www.frontofthehouse.com
SIC: 2541 Table or counter tops, plastic laminated

(G-9600)
FROSTBITE NITROGEN ICE CREAM
2305 Ne 197th St (33180-2150)
PHONE..................................305 933-5482
Jeffrey Saunders, *Principal*
EMP: 8 **EST:** 2016
SALES (est): 153.6K **Privately Held**
SIC: 2813 Nitrogen

(G-9601)
FROZEN WHEELS LLC
Also Called: B H Med Supplies
16565 Nw 15th Ave (33169-5619)
PHONE..................................305 799-2258
Isaac Halwani,
EMP: 17 **EST:** 2010
SALES (est): 10.3MM **Privately Held**
WEB: www.frozenwheels.com
SIC: 3312 Wheels

(G-9602)
FRUSELVA USA LLC
801 Brickell Ave Ste 800 (33131-2978)
PHONE..................................949 798-0061
Javier Hernandez, *CEO*
◆ **EMP:** 10 **EST:** 2017
SALES (est): 1.3MM **Privately Held**
WEB: www.fruselva.com
SIC: 2033 Fruits: packaged in cans, jars, etc.

(G-9603)
FUN ELECTRONICS INC
2999 Ne 191st St Ph 2 (33180-3117)
PHONE..................................305 933-4646
David Levy, *CEO*
Eyal Levy, *Vice Pres*
Yizhak Toledano, *CFO*
▲ **EMP:** 14 **EST:** 2009
SQ FT: 20,000
SALES (est): 581.2K **Privately Held**
SIC: 3571 3651 5731 Personal computers (microcomputers); audio electronic systems; consumer electronic equipment

(G-9604)
FUNDACION EDUCATIVA CARLOS M
1925 Brickell Ave D1108 (33129-1737)
PHONE..................................305 859-9617
Lillian Castaneda, *President*
EMP: 6 **EST:** 2004
SALES: 7.7K **Privately Held**
WEB: www.fecmc.org
SIC: 2721 Trade journals: publishing & printing

(G-9605)
FUTURE MODES INC
1910 Ne 206th St (33179-2254)
PHONE..................................305 654-9995
Michael Fischer, *President*
Mindy Fischer, *Corp Secy*
▼ **EMP:** 7 **EST:** 1984
SQ FT: 5,000
SALES (est): 1MM **Privately Held**
WEB: www.futuremodes.com
SIC: 2431 3089 3442 Door shutters, wood; window shutters, wood; shutters, plastic; shutters, door or window: metal

(G-9606)
FWS DISTRIBUTORS LLC (PA)
Also Called: Progress Wine Group
14501 Nw 57th Ave Ste 113 (33014)
PHONE..................................561 312-3318
Hunter Seidel, *Sales Staff*
Carolyn Corey, *Mng Member*
Proal Perry, *Consultant*
EMP: 8 **EST:** 2017
SALES (est): 2.3MM **Privately Held**
SIC: 2084 Wines

(G-9607)
G METAL INDUSTRIES INC
3670 Nw 49th St (33142-3928)
PHONE..................................305 633-0300
Omar Valdez, *President*
EMP: 11 **EST:** 2000
SALES (est): 1MM **Privately Held**
WEB: www.gmetalcorporation.com
SIC: 3443 Metal parts

(G-9608)
GABRIELAS MEMOIRS INC
5750 Sw 45th Ter (33155-6002)
PHONE..................................305 666-9991
Diana M De Los Reyes, *President*
EMP: 6 **EST:** 2004
SALES (est): 72.5K **Privately Held**
SIC: 2759 Commercial printing

(G-9609)
GADAL LABORATORIES INC
12178 Sw 128th St (33186-5230)
PHONE..................................786 732-2571
Giodardo Del Campo, *President*
EMP: 6
SQ FT: 5,000
SALES (est): 700K **Privately Held**
WEB: www.gadallaboratories.com
SIC: 2834 Pharmaceutical preparations

(G-9610)
GALAN EXPRESS INC
1150 Sw 154th Ave (33194-2676)
PHONE..................................305 438-8738
Maikel Galan, *President*
EMP: 7 **EST:** 2005
SALES (est): 172K **Privately Held**
SIC: 2741 Miscellaneous publishing

(G-9611)
GALEA CORPORATION
Also Called: Instant Signs of South Florida
4679 Sw 72nd Ave (33155-4540)
PHONE..................................305 663-0244
Alejandro A Handal, *Vice Pres*
Louis Latorre, *Vice Pres*
Giancarla Latorre, *Treasurer*
Lissette Handal, *Admin Sec*
▼ **EMP:** 9 **EST:** 1984
SQ FT: 1,800
SALES (est): 879K **Privately Held**
SIC: 3993 Signs & advertising specialties

(G-9612)
GARBO SPORT INTERNATIONAL INC
11231 Nw 20th St Unit 122 (33172-1857)
PHONE..................................305 599-8797
▲ **EMP:** 6
SALES (est): 650.1K **Privately Held**
SIC: 3949 Mfg Sporting/Athletic Goods

(G-9613)
GARCIA ARMANDO CUSTOM CABINETS
220 Sw 30th Rd (33129-2726)
PHONE..................................305 775-5674
Armando R Garcia Jr, *Principal*
EMP: 7 **EST:** 2010
SALES (est): 283.8K **Privately Held**
WEB: www.agcustomcabinets.com
SIC: 2434 Wood kitchen cabinets

(G-9614)
GARCIA DOOR & WINDOW INC
2787 Nw 34th St (33142-5216)
PHONE..................................305 635-0644
Leonardo Garcia, *President*
◆ **EMP:** 6 **EST:** 1974
SQ FT: 5,000
SALES (est): 971.8K **Privately Held**
WEB: www.garciadoorandwindow.com
SIC: 3442 Window & door frames

(G-9615)
GAUMARD SCIENTIFIC COMPANY INC
14700 Sw 136th St (33196-5691)
P.O. Box 140098 (33114-0098)
PHONE..................................305 971-3790
Daphne Eggert, *President*
David Cohen, *Vice Pres*
John S Eggert, *Vice Pres*
Peter A Eggert, *Vice Pres*
Peter Eggert, *Vice Pres*
EMP: 40 **EST:** 1961
SQ FT: 15,000
SALES (est): 11.1MM **Privately Held**
WEB: www.gaumard.com
SIC: 3841 Surgical & medical instruments

(G-9616)
GB ENERGY MANAGEMENT LLC
2875 Ne 191st St Ste 901 (33180-2842)
PHONE..................................305 792-4650
Edwin Marcano, *CFO*
Reuven Bigio, *Mng Member*
EMP: 7 **EST:** 2013
SALES (est): 4.4MM **Privately Held**
WEB: www.gbgroup.com
SIC: 2992 Lubricating oils & greases
HQ: Gulfstream Petroleum Dominicana S De Rl
Av Abraham Lincoln #1057
Santo Domingo

(G-9617)
GBIG CORPORATION
Also Called: Continental Marketing Group
8744 Sw 133rd St (33176-5929)
PHONE..................................866 998-8466
Sandra L Gordon, *President*
EMP: 8 **EST:** 1978
SQ FT: 3,800
SALES (est): 660.4K **Privately Held**
SIC: 3953 Marking devices

(G-9618)
GE GLASS INC
4455 Nw 73rd Ave (33166-6436)
PHONE..................................305 599-7725
Eugenio M Benitez, *President*
EMP: 8 **EST:** 2005
SALES (est): 246.4K **Privately Held**
SIC: 3231 Products of purchased glass

(G-9619)
GEAR DYNAMICS INC
Also Called: Southern Gear
3685 Nw 106th St (33147-1030)
PHONE..................................305 691-0151
Alex Perdomo, *President*
Patricia Nader, *Purch Agent*
Lou Torchetti, *Shareholder*
Chris Turnau, *Shareholder*
Allan S Arch, *Admin Sec*
EMP: 5 **EST:** 1988
SALES (est): 796.4K **Privately Held**
WEB: www.southerngear.com
SIC: 3714 5531 Gears, motor vehicle; automotive parts

(G-9620)
GEEKSHIVE INC
9100 S Ddland Blvd Ste 15 (33156)
PHONE..................................888 797-4335
Borras J Sebastian, *Principal*
Claudio S Martinez, *Vice Pres*
Juan Ferreira, *Purch Mgr*
Jorge Sebastian Borras, *Director*
Mara Sanfilippo, *Executive*
EMP: 19 **EST:** 2010
SALES (est): 4.7MM **Privately Held**
WEB: www.geekshive.com
SIC: 2389 3571 Apparel for handicapped; electronic computers

(G-9621)
GEM 360 LLC
7650 Nw 50th St (33166-4700)
PHONE..................................800 436-1932
Michael Mathon,
EMP: 25 **EST:** 2018
SALES (est): 3MM **Privately Held**
WEB: www.gem360.net
SIC: 3585 Air conditioning equipment, complete

(G-9622)
GENEFORCE INCORPORATED
2635 Nw 20th St (33142-7105)
PHONE..................................786 823-0700
Nemer Ahmad, *CEO*
Zarina Ahmad, *COO*
▼ **EMP:** 5 **EST:** 2012
SQ FT: 3,000
SALES (est): 600.9K **Privately Held**
WEB: www.geneforcepower.com
SIC: 3621 3691 Frequency converters (electric generators); power generators; storage battery chargers, motor & engine generator type; storage batteries; lead acid batteries (storage batteries)

(G-9623)
GENERAL & DUPLICATING SERVICES
Also Called: Sir Speedy
2057 Nw 27th Ave (33142-7126)
PHONE..................................305 541-2116
Leonel Ley, *President*
Rene Ley, *Vice Pres*
▼ **EMP:** 7 **EST:** 1981
SQ FT: 2,500
SALES (est): 500K **Privately Held**
WEB: www.sirspeedy.com
SIC: 2752 Commercial printing, lithographic

(G-9624)
GENERAL ASPHALT CO INC
4850 Nw 72nd Ave (33166-5642)
P.O. Box 522306 (33152-2306)
PHONE..................................305 592-6005
Robert A Lopez, *President*
Albert J Lopez, *Vice Pres*
Royal Webster Jr, *Vice Pres*
Gabriel Martinez, *Project Mgr*
Emilio Zamora, *Project Mgr*
EMP: 150 **EST:** 1966
SQ FT: 10,000
SALES (est): 21.8MM **Privately Held**
WEB: www.generalasphalt.com
SIC: 2951 Asphalt paving mixtures & blocks

(G-9625)
GENERAL OCEANICS INC
Also Called: Geo Environmental
1295 Nw 163rd St (33169-5830)
PHONE..................................305 621-2882
Regis Cook, *CEO*
Sylvia Martin, *Vice Pres*
▲ **EMP:** 17
SQ FT: 12,000
SALES (est): 2.4MM **Privately Held**
WEB: www.generaloceanics.com
SIC: 3829 8731 Measuring & controlling devices; commercial research laboratory

(G-9626)
GENERAL SCREEN SERVICE CO
5033 Sw 151st Pl (33185-4002)
PHONE..................................305 226-0741
Zoe Alberto Rodiguez, *Owner*
EMP: 5 **EST:** 1972
SALES (est): 347.3K **Privately Held**
SIC: 3861 Screens, projection

(G-9627)
GENIE SHELF
10935 Sw 138th Ct (33186-3231)
PHONE..................................305 213-4382
Pauline Hamian, *President*
EMP: 7 **EST:** 2011
SALES (est): 141.7K **Privately Held**
WEB: www.shelfgenie.com
SIC: 2511 Wood household furniture

(G-9628)
GENZYME CORPORATION
Also Called: Genzyme Genetics
1031 Ives Dairy Rd # 228 (33179-2538)
PHONE..................................800 245-4363
EMP: 93
SALES (corp-wide): 400.4MM **Privately Held**
SIC: 2835 Mfg Diagnostic Substances
HQ: Genzyme Corporation
500 Kendall St
Cambridge MA 02142
617 252-7500

(G-9629)
GEORGIAN AMERICAN ALLOYS INC (PA)
200 Suth Bscyne Blvd Ste (33131)
PHONE..................................305 375-7560
Mordechai Korf, *President*
Barry Nuss, *CFO*
Diane Hill, *Controller*
Zakaria Zalikashvili, *Pub Rel Dir*
EKA Kiria, *Manager*
▲ **EMP:** 40 **EST:** 2012
SALES (est): 108.8MM **Privately Held**
WEB: www.delivery-plan-fact.com
SIC: 1061 Manganese ores mining

(G-9630)
GERBER COBURN OPTICAL INC
Coburn Technologies
2585 Nw 74th Ave (33122-1417)
PHONE..................................305 592-4705
Pedro Parra, *Sales/Mktg Mgr*
Jesus Rodriguez, *Sales Staff*
EMP: 30 **Privately Held**
WEB: www.coburntechnologies.com
SIC: 3851 Ophthalmic goods
HQ: Coburn Gerber Optical Inc
55 Gerber Rd E
South Windsor CT 06074

(G-9631)
GERMAIN CANVAS & AWNING CO
Also Called: Germain Awning Center
921 Belle Meade Island Dr (33138-5249)
PHONE..................................305 751-4963
Milton Hughs, *President*
Rita Hughs, *Corp Secy*
EMP: 6 **EST:** 1977
SQ FT: 3,300
SALES (est): 310.1K **Privately Held**
SIC: 2394 1799 Canvas & related products; awning installation

(G-9632)
GEROGARI DISPLAY MANUFACTURE
5517 Nw 72nd Ave (33166-4205)
PHONE..................................305 888-0993
German Galvin, *President*
Jeshica Miedda, *Vice Pres*
EMP: 7 **EST:** 1992
SALES (est): 512.9K **Privately Held**
WEB: www.gerogaridisplay.com
SIC: 3089 Injection molding of plastics

(G-9633)
GETABSTRACT INC
20900 Ne 30th Ave Ste 315 (33180-2163)
PHONE..................................305 936-2626
Thomas Bergen, *CEO*
Michel Cootman, *CEO*
Manuela Nieth, *President*
Carey Halpern, *Vice Pres*
Arnhild Walz-Rasilier, *Vice Pres*
EMP: 33 **EST:** 1999
SALES (est): 7.1MM **Privately Held**
WEB: www.getabstract.com
SIC: 2731 Book publishing

(G-9634)
GFX INC (PA)
4810 Nw 74th Ave (33166-5512)
P.O. Box 668440 (33166-9416)
PHONE..................................305 499-9789
George Feldenkreis, *President*
Fanny Hanono, *President*
Gabriela Hanono, *Treasurer*
Diego Garcia, *Accounts Exec*
Evan Hanono, *Accounts Exec*
▲ **EMP:** 36 **EST:** 1961
SQ FT: 32,000
SALES (est): 5MM **Privately Held**
WEB: www.gfxcorp.com
SIC: 3568 3714 5063 5023 Power transmission equipment; transmission housings or parts, motor vehicle; electrical apparatus & equipment; home furnishings

(G-9635)
GG PROFESSIONAL PAINTING CORP
2001 Ludlam Rd Apt 317 (33155-1897)
PHONE..................................786 716-8972
Ronnie Saldana, *President*
EMP: 10
SALES (est): 280K **Privately Held**
SIC: 3479 Painting, coating & hot dipping

(G-9636)
GGB1 LLC
9828 Sw 146th Pl (33186-8404)
PHONE..................................305 387-5334
Edgard R Kamel, *Principal*
EMP: 8 **EST:** 2007
SALES (est): 198.6K **Privately Held**
SIC: 3568 Power transmission equipment

(G-9637)
GIZ STUDIO INC
601 Nw 11th St (33136-2414)
PHONE..................................305 416-5001
Fax: 305 663-0975
▼ **EMP:** 16
SQ FT: 22,000
SALES (est): 1.3MM **Privately Held**
SIC: 3211 Mfg Flat Glass

(G-9638)
GLASS TECH CORP
3103 Nw 20th St (33142-6935)
PHONE..................................305 633-6491
Nelson Fernandez Jr, *President*
◆ **EMP:** 35 **EST:** 1984
SQ FT: 90,000
SALES (est): 4.8MM **Privately Held**
WEB: www.glass-tech.com
SIC: 3732 Yachts, building & repairing

(G-9639)
GLASSARIUM LLC
444 Ne 30th St Unit 804 (33137-4312)
PHONE..................................786 631-7080
Sergij Zelinsky, *Partner*
EMP: 50

SALES (est): 2.1MM **Privately Held**
WEB: www.glassarium.com
SIC: 3334 3259 3446 Primary aluminum; architectural clay products; architectural metalwork

(G-9640)
GLOBAL MIND USA LLC
250 Nw 23rd St Unit 212 (33127-4308)
PHONE..................................305 402-2190
Scott Hughes, *Director*
David Mark Wein, *Director*
EMP: 100 **EST:** 2009
SALES (est): 1MM **Privately Held**
WEB: www.iprospect.com
SIC: 3577 Data conversion equipment, media-to-media: computer
HQ: Iprospect.Com Inc.
85 Devonshire St
Boston MA 02109
617 449-4300

(G-9641)
GLOBAL SOURCE IMPORTS LLC
175 Sw 7th St Ste 1518 (33130-2955)
PHONE..................................917 213-6891
Diego Ostos,
EMP: 7 **EST:** 2013
SALES (est): 295.7K **Privately Held**
WEB: www.globalsources.com
SIC: 3085 Plastics bottles

(G-9642)
GLOBAL TRADING INC (PA)
7500 Nw 25th St Unit 12 (33122-1700)
PHONE..................................305 471-4455
Viraj S Wikramanayake, *President*
◆ **EMP:** 18 **EST:** 1991
SQ FT: 11,000
SALES (est): 2.7MM **Privately Held**
WEB: www.gtim.com
SIC: 3021 2311 2326 Protective footwear, rubber or plastic; men's & boys' uniforms; policemen's uniforms: made from purchased materials; work uniforms

(G-9643)
GLOBE BOYZ INTERNATIONAL LLC ✪
1365 Nw 84th Ter (33147-4337)
PHONE..................................305 308-8160
Bremond Harris,
EMP: 10 **EST:** 2021
SALES (est): 600.1K **Privately Held**
SIC: 2741 Music books: publishing & printing

(G-9644)
GLOBE SPECIALTY METALS INC (HQ)
600 Brickell Ave Ste 3100 (33131-3089)
P.O. Box 157, Beverly OH (45715-0157)
PHONE..................................786 509-6900
Alan Kestenbaum, *Chairman*
Jeff Watson, *Vice Pres*
Joseph Ragan, *CFO*
J M Perkins, *VP Sales*
Timothy Ogrady, *Supervisor*
EMP: 16 **EST:** 2006
SQ FT: 10,566
SALES (est): 489.1MM
SALES (corp-wide): 1.1B **Privately Held**
WEB: www.ferroglobe.com
SIC: 3313 3339 Ferrosilicon, not made in blast furnaces; silicon refining (primary, over 99% pure)
PA: Ferroglobe Plc
5 Fleet Place
London EC4M
203 129-2420

(G-9645)
GOLD BANNER USA INC
2660 Nw 3rd Ave (33127-4103)
PHONE..................................305 576-2215
▲ **EMP:** 11
SQ FT: 6,000
SALES (est): 1MM **Privately Held**
SIC: 3021 Mfg Rubber/Plastic Footwear

(G-9646)
GOLDEN BOAR PRODUCT CORP
Also Called: Lucky Pig
7224 Nw 25th St (33122-1701)
P.O. Box 521094 (33152-1094)
PHONE..................................305 500-9392
Felix Martinez, *President*
Oscar Martinez, *Vice Pres*
EMP: 6 **EST:** 2012
SQ FT: 4,000
SALES (est): 1.5MM **Privately Held**
SIC: 2013 Ham, boiled: from purchased meat; ham, boneless: from purchased meat

(G-9647)
GONTECH CUSTOM WOOD CORP
2005 Sw 129th Ct (33175-1327)
PHONE..................................305 323-0765
Gilfredo Gonzalez, *President*
EMP: 8 **EST:** 2005
SALES (est): 200.2K **Privately Held**
WEB: www.gontechcustomcabinetry.com
SIC: 2434 Wood kitchen cabinets

(G-9648)
GOOD CATCH INC
6713 Ne 3rd Ave (33138-5509)
P.O. Box 370366 (33137-0366)
PHONE..................................305 757-7700
David Bloom, *President*
EMP: 5 **EST:** 1992
SQ FT: 2,400
SALES (est): 500K **Privately Held**
WEB: www.goodcatch.com
SIC: 2395 2759 Embroidery products, except schiffli machine; screen printing

(G-9649)
GOOD IMPRESSIONS
12434 Sw 27th St (33175-2107)
P.O. Box 942468 (33194-2468)
PHONE..................................305 336-0318
Antonio Barnuevo, *Principal*
EMP: 6 **EST:** 2008
SALES (est): 87.3K **Privately Held**
SIC: 2752 Commercial printing, lithographic

(G-9650)
GOPI GLASS SALES & SVCS CORP
7450 Nw 41st St (33166-6716)
PHONE..................................305 592-2089
Marlen De Varona, *President*
Rafael De Varona, *Vice Pres*
◆ **EMP:** 29 **EST:** 1971
SQ FT: 20,000
SALES (est): 2.2MM **Privately Held**
WEB: www.gopiglass.com
SIC: 3442 5039 Store fronts, prefabricated, metal; window & door frames; exterior flat glass: plate or window

(G-9651)
GOVPAY NETWORK LLC
12855 Sw 132nd St Ste 204 (33186-7221)
PHONE..................................866 893-9678
Anthony J Garay,
EMP: 6 **EST:** 2010
SALES (est): 797.4K **Privately Held**
WEB: www.govpaynetwork.com
SIC: 7372 Business oriented computer software

(G-9652)
GRADUATE PLASTICS INC (PA)
Also Called: Quantum Storage Systems
15800 Nw 15th Ave (33169-5606)
PHONE..................................305 687-0405
Laurent Groll, *President*
Anthony Cohen, *Vice Pres*
Scott Frobese, *Sales Staff*
Rick Diaz, *Manager*
Dean Cohen, *Admin Sec*
◆ **EMP:** 200 **EST:** 1973
SQ FT: 30,000
SALES (est): 48.8MM **Privately Held**
WEB: www.quantumstorage.com
SIC: 3089 Injection molding of plastics

(G-9653)
GRAFTON FURNITURE COMPANY
3401 Nw 71st St (33147-6652)
PHONE..................................305 696-3811
Steve Grafton Jr, *President*
Ryan Grafton, *Analyst*
Grafton Steve,
EMP: 25 **EST:** 1963
SQ FT: 20,000
SALES (est): 2.7MM **Privately Held**
WEB: www.graftonfurniture.com
SIC: 2512 7641 Upholstered household furniture; reupholstery

(G-9654)
GRAIN MACHINERY MFG CORP
Also Called: Grainman
1130 Nw 163rd Dr (33169-5816)
PHONE..................................305 620-2525
Octavio Castellanos, *President*
Clemente Dieguez, *Vice Pres*
◆ **EMP:** 14 **EST:** 1975
SQ FT: 13,000
SALES (est): 2.4MM **Privately Held**
WEB: www.grainman.com
SIC: 3523 3565 Driers (farm): grain, hay & seed; bag opening, filling & closing machines

(G-9655)
GRANADA PRTG & GRAPHICS CORP
Also Called: Granada Art Service
8693 Nw 66th St (33166-2670)
P.O. Box 668106 (33166-9411)
PHONE..................................305 593-5266
EMP: 13
SQ FT: 10,000
SALES (est): 1.4MM **Privately Held**
SIC: 2759 Graphic Designer

(G-9656)
GRAPHIC MASTERS INC
801 Brickell Ave Ste 300 (33131-2900)
Drawer 2600 S, League City TX (77573)
PHONE..................................800 230-3873
EMP: 60
SALES (est): 6.5MM **Privately Held**
SIC: 2752 8742 7336 Lithographic Commercial Printing Management Consulting Services Commercial Art/Graphic Design

(G-9657)
GRAPHICA SERVICES INC
12943 Sw 133rd Ct (33186-5853)
P.O. Box 160322 (33116-0322)
PHONE..................................305 232-5333
Eloy Delvalle, *President*
Eloy Valle, *Sales Staff*
EMP: 6 **EST:** 1990
SQ FT: 15,000
SALES (est): 793.6K **Privately Held**
WEB: www.graphicaservices.com
SIC: 2752 Commercial printing, offset

(G-9658)
GRAPHICS TYPE COLOR ENTPS INC
Also Called: GTC Media
2300 Nw 7th Ave (33127-4204)
PHONE..................................305 591-7600
Manuel Perez, *President*
Mark Quetgles, *COO*
Carlos M Perez, *Vice Pres*
Ralph Matos, *Prdtn Mgr*
Leo Rivera, *Sales Staff*
▼ **EMP:** 45 **EST:** 1990
SQ FT: 15,563
SALES (est): 7.1MM **Privately Held**
WEB: www.clubflyers.com
SIC: 2759 7336 2791 2752 Commercial printing; commercial art & graphic design; typesetting; commercial printing, lithographic

(G-9659)
GRASS CHOPPERS
11861 Sw 180th St (33177-2412)
PHONE..................................305 253-1217
Reinaldo Fernandez, *Principal*
EMP: 6 **EST:** 2006
SALES (est): 146.9K **Privately Held**
SIC: 3751 Motorcycles & related parts

(G-9660)
GRASS CHOPPERS SOUTH FLA CORP
.9240 Sw 16th St (33165-7714)
PHONE..................................786 586-2767
Mathieu Zimmerman, *Principal*
EMP: 7 **EST:** 2008
SALES (est): 127.3K **Privately Held**
SIC: 3751 Motorcycles & related parts

(G-9661)
GREAT AMERICAN IMPORTS LLC ✪
3758 Nw 54th St (33142-3215)
PHONE..................................786 524-4120
Paul Groll, *Mng Member*
Theresa Grace, *Manager*
EMP: 6 **EST:** 2020
SALES (est): 294.3K **Privately Held**
SIC: 2434 Wood kitchen cabinets

(G-9662)
GREATER 7TH DIGITAL PRESS INC
14627 Nw 7th Ave (33168-3029)
PHONE..................................305 681-2412
Wisly Lefevre, *Principal*
EMP: 8 **EST:** 2011
SALES (est): 855K **Privately Held**
SIC: 2759 Commercial printing

(G-9663)
GREATER MIAMI ELKS LODGE INC
5150 Nw 2nd Ave (33127-2127)
PHONE..................................305 754-5899
EMP: 14
SQ FT: 3,869
SALES (est): 967.7K **Privately Held**
SIC: 2389 Mfg Apparel/Accessories

(G-9664)
GREEN BIOFUELS LLC
3123 Nw 73rd St (33147-5947)
PHONE..................................305 639-3030
Jose Bergonsi, *Mng Member*
Sara Sanchez, *Admin Sec*
▲ **EMP:** 16 **EST:** 2009
SALES (est): 1.9MM **Privately Held**
WEB: www.gbcorp.biz
SIC: 2869 Fuels

(G-9665)
GREEN BIOFUELS MIAMI LLC
3123 Nw 73rd St Ste A-C (33147-5947)
PHONE..................................305 639-3030
Fabio Santos, *CEO*
Edilson Bianconi, *Principal*
Guilherme Cirino, *Principal*
Sandra Daza, *Principal*
EMP: 13
SQ FT: 26,500
SALES (est): 2.2MM **Privately Held**
WEB: www.gbcorp.biz
SIC: 2869 Industrial organic chemicals

(G-9666)
GREEN ESSENTIALS LLC ✪
7480 Bird Rd Ste 810 (33155-6660)
PHONE..................................786 584-4377
Gerardo Mujica,
EMP: 20 **EST:** 2020
SALES (est): 860K **Privately Held**
SIC: 2023 Dietary supplements, dairy & non-dairy based

(G-9667)
GREEN LIGHT PRINTING INC
151 Nw 36th St (33127-3107)
PHONE..................................305 576-5858
Mercedes Quanch, *President*
Andro Mateu, *Vice Pres*
EMP: 6 **EST:** 1994
SALES (est): 69.5K **Privately Held**
WEB: www.leonarts.com
SIC: 2752 Commercial printing, offset

(G-9668)
GREEN MARINE FUELS INC
3220 S Dixie Hwy Ste 201 (33133-3672)
PHONE..................................305 775-3546
James Doddo, *Principal*
EMP: 10 **EST:** 2010

GEOGRAPHIC

SALES (est): 410.5K **Privately Held**
SIC: 2869 Fuels

(G-9669)
GREEN PLANT LLC
3600 Nw 59th St (33142-2030)
PHONE..................................305 397-9394
Federico Intriago, *CEO*
EMP: 35 **EST:** 2015
SALES (est): 3.2MM **Privately Held**
WEB: www.greenplant.com
SIC: 2037 Frozen fruits & vegetables

(G-9670)
GREGOMARC LLC
Also Called: La Sin Rival
9772 Sw 8th St (33174-2902)
PHONE..................................305 559-9777
Rodrigues Pereira Jose G, *Mng Member*
Cafe Metro Plaza CA, *Mng Member*
EMP: 8 **EST:** 2010
SALES (est): 561.8K **Privately Held**
SIC: 2051 Cakes, bakery: except frozen

(G-9671)
GRESSO LLC
495 Brickell Ave Apt 3902 (33131-2859)
PHONE..................................305 515-8677
Andrey Kalashnikov, *Mng Member*
EMP: 7 **EST:** 2011
SALES (est): 1.6MM
SALES (corp-wide): 3.5MM **Privately Held**
WEB: www.gresso.com
SIC: 3669 Intercommunication systems, electric
PA: Alan-Abris, Ooo
22 Ul. Bogdanova
Penza 44005
841 245-2380

(G-9672)
GRILLE TECH INC
5101 Nw 36th Ave (33142-3226)
PHONE..................................305 537-0053
Isidro Gonzalez, *President*
◆ **EMP:** 30 **EST:** 2002
SALES (est): 5.1MM **Privately Held**
WEB: www.grilletechinc.com
SIC: 3496 Grilles & grillework, woven wire

(G-9673)
GRIZZLY PRINTING PARLOUR LLC
14244 Sw 90th Ter (33186-7800)
PHONE..................................786 416-2494
Christopher Algaze, *Principal*
EMP: 6 **EST:** 2012
SALES (est): 156.3K **Privately Held**
WEB: www.grizzly.com
SIC: 2752 Commercial printing, lithographic

(G-9674)
GROBARTY INC (PA)
10891 Nw 17th St Unit 133 (33172-2053)
PHONE..................................786 398-5530
Teresa M Haouilou, *President*
Badui Haouilou, *Vice Pres*
EMP: 13 **EST:** 2016
SALES (est): 240.5K **Privately Held**
SIC: 3842 Gloves, safety

(G-9675)
GROUP HEROS INC
Also Called: Victores Machine Shop
5720 Nw 35th Ave (33142-2708)
PHONE..................................305 635-0219
Jesus Victores, *President*
EMP: 5 **EST:** 1990
SQ FT: 35,000
SALES (est): 539.2K **Privately Held**
WEB: www.victoresmachineshop.com
SIC: 3599 Machine shop, jobbing & repair

(G-9676)
GROUP STEEL INC
2437 Sw 138th Ave (33175-6367)
PHONE..................................305 965-0614
Erick Gonzalez, *President*
EMP: 7
SALES (corp-wide): 1.5MM **Privately Held**
SIC: 3441 Fabricated structural metal
PA: Group Steel Inc.
3492 W 84th St
Hialeah FL 33018
786 319-1222

(G-9677)
GROVE MEDICAL LLC
11926 Sw 8th St (33184-1671)
PHONE..................................305 903-6402
Art Miller, *Mng Member*
Robert Beau,
Josh Glick,
EMP: 5 **EST:** 2005
SQ FT: 1,500
SALES (est): 375.9K **Privately Held**
SIC: 3069 Birth control devices, rubber

(G-9678)
GRUNENTHAL SERVICES INC
1005 Sw 87th Ave (33174-3208)
PHONE..................................786 364-6308
Jan Van Ruymbeke, *CEO*
Victor Barbosa, *Vice Pres*
Karina Salazar, *Vice Pres*
Joao Simoes, *Treasurer*
EMP: 19 **EST:** 2011
SALES (est): 9.1MM
SALES (corp-wide): 1.5B **Privately Held**
WEB: www.grunenthal.com
SIC: 2834 Analgesics
HQ: Grunenthal Gmbh
Zieglerstr. 6
Aachen 52078
241 569-0

(G-9679)
GRUPO DE DIARIOS AMERICA LLC
848 Brickell Ave Ste 600 (33131-2946)
PHONE..................................305 577-0094
Jose Romano, *Executive*
EMP: 6 **EST:** 1991
SALES (est): 814.2K **Privately Held**
WEB: www.gda.com
SIC: 2711 Newspapers: publishing only, not printed on site

(G-9680)
GRUPO PHOENIX CORP SVCS LLC (PA)
2980 Ne 207th St Ste 705 (33180-1465)
PHONE..................................954 241-0023
Monica Peisach, *CEO*
Alberto Peisach, *President*
Jaime Lederman, *COO*
Ed Kopetman, *Vice Pres*
Jesus Villaverde, *Plant Mgr*
◆ **EMP:** 30 **EST:** 2004
SALES (est): 215.2MM **Privately Held**
WEB: www.grupophoenix.com
SIC: 3089 Cups, plastic, except foam

(G-9681)
GS CABINETS INC
3054b Nw 15th St (33125-1924)
PHONE..................................305 986-4768
Gerardo Sotolongo, *Principal*
EMP: 6 **EST:** 2004
SALES (est): 69.6K **Privately Held**
SIC: 2434 Wood kitchen cabinets

(G-9682)
GT PALLETS LLC
958 Nw 73rd St (33150-3627)
PHONE..................................786 541-6532
EMP: 6
SALES (est): 363.3K **Privately Held**
SIC: 2448 Mfg Wood Pallets/Skids

(G-9683)
GVJ CORP
15120 Sw 159th Ct (33196-5765)
PHONE..................................786 224-2808
Johnson P Charuvila, *President*
EMP: 6 **EST:** 2012
SALES (est): 53.5K **Privately Held**
WEB: www.gvjcorp.com
SIC: 2299 Batting, wadding, padding & fillings

(G-9684)
H & J ASPHALT INC
Also Called: H&J Asphalt Plant
4310 Nw 35th Ave (33142-4323)
PHONE..................................305 635-8110
Lorenzo J Humberto, *President*
Jorge Lorenzo, *Vice Pres*
EMP: 8 **EST:** 1987
SQ FT: 1,000
SALES (est): 4.3MM **Privately Held**
WEB: www.hjasphaltinc.com
SIC: 2951 Asphalt paving mixtures & blocks

(G-9685)
HAMMOCKS PLAZA
11735 Sw 147th Ave (33196-3321)
PHONE..................................305 380-0961
EMP: 6 **EST:** 2008
SALES (est): 166K **Privately Held**
WEB: www.hammockplaza.com
SIC: 3421 Table & food cutlery, including butchers'

(G-9686)
HAPPY ENDINGS OF MIAMI INC
651 Nw 106th St (33150-1124)
PHONE..................................305 759-4467
Martin F Marotta, *President*
Maria Walker, *Vice Pres*
▼ **EMP:** 9 **EST:** 1976
SQ FT: 1,350
SALES (est): 931.2K **Privately Held**
WEB: www.happyendingstshirts.com
SIC: 2261 2759 Screen printing of cotton broadwoven fabrics; screen printing

(G-9687)
HARDWARE CONCEPTS INC
3758 Nw 54th St (33142-3215)
PHONE..................................305 685-1337
Paul Groll, *President*
Phil Rodriguez, *General Mgr*
Henry Sanchez, *Vice Pres*
Michael Yanez, *Executive*
◆ **EMP:** 9 **EST:** 1988
SALES (est): 1.1MM **Privately Held**
WEB: www.hardwareconcepts.com
SIC: 3089 3429 Injection molded finished plastic products; manufactured hardware (general)

(G-9688)
HASBRO LATIN AMERICA INC (DH)
5200 Blue Lagoon Dr Fl 10 (33126-2089)
PHONE..................................305 931-3180
Brian Goldner, *CEO*
Augusto Brambilla, *General Mgr*
◆ **EMP:** 47 **EST:** 1998
SQ FT: 9,000
SALES (est): 2.7MM
SALES (corp-wide): 5.4B **Publicly Held**
SIC: 3944 5092 Board games, children's & adults'; toys & hobby goods & supplies

(G-9689)
HAUTE LIVING INC
999 Brickell Ave Ste 520 (33131-3041)
PHONE..................................305 798-1373
Seth Semilof, *President*
Andres Caceres, *Editor*
Colin Daniels, *Editor*
▼ **EMP:** 24 **EST:** 2005
SALES (est): 2.4MM **Privately Held**
WEB: www.hauteliving.com
SIC: 2721 Magazines: publishing only, not printed on site

(G-9690)
HAVANA DREAMS LLC
Also Called: Havana Dream Cigars
2621 Sw 132nd Ave (33175-1110)
PHONE..................................305 322-7599
Ivette Carreno, *Mng Member*
EMP: 8 **EST:** 2009
SALES (est): 111.5K **Privately Held**
SIC: 2121 Cigars

(G-9691)
HEALTH & MUSCLES
14144 Sw 8th St (33184-3105)
PHONE..................................305 225-2929
EMP: 6
SALES (est): 438K **Privately Held**
SIC: 2023 Mfg Dry/Evaporated Dairy Products

(G-9692)
HEALTH ROBOTICS CANADA LLC
6303 Blue Lagoon Dr # 310 (33126-6068)
PHONE..................................786 388-5339
EMP: 10
SALES (est): 1.1MM **Privately Held**
SIC: 3569 Mfg General Industrial Machinery

(G-9693)
HEALTHEINTENTIONS INC (PA)
Also Called: Juicera
500 Ne 185th St Unit 8 (33179-4541)
PHONE..................................954 394-8867
Stephanie C De Filippo, *President*
Natalie Alazrathi, *Principal*
Richard Epstein, *Principal*
Jennifer Rozman, *Principal*
Lori S Robinson, *Vice Pres*
EMP: 6 **EST:** 2011
SQ FT: 2,500
SALES (est): 760K **Privately Held**
SIC: 2037 5499 Fruit juices; juices, fruit or vegetable

(G-9694)
HEARA INC
19595 Ne 10th Ave Ste H (33179-3580)
PHONE..................................305 651-5200
Yaeli Merenfeld, *President*
EMP: 8 **EST:** 2012
SALES (est): 738.7K **Privately Held**
SIC: 2051 Bread, cake & related products

(G-9695)
HEC AMERICA INC
Also Called: Kitchenpro
4919 Sw 147th Pl (33185-4055)
PHONE..................................786 543-9238
Regla Jimene-Gomez, *President*
EMP: 6 **EST:** 2011
SALES (est): 285.2K **Privately Held**
WEB: www.hec.usace.army.mil
SIC: 3843 Dental equipment & supplies

(G-9696)
HECTOR & HECTOR INC
6790 Nw 84th Ave (33166-2615)
PHONE..................................305 629-8864
Hector Sardinas Sr, *President*
Hector Sardinas Jr, *Vice Pres*
▼ **EMP:** 18 **EST:** 1985
SALES (est): 1.8MM **Privately Held**
WEB: www.hectorandhector.com
SIC: 2434 Wood kitchen cabinets

(G-9697)
HECTOR CORPORATION
2127 Nw 88th St (33147-4215)
PHONE..................................786 308-5853
Hector Rodriguez, *Principal*
EMP: 6 **EST:** 2005
SALES (est): 508.9K **Privately Held**
WEB: www.hectorsalon.weebly.com
SIC: 1442 Construction sand & gravel

(G-9698)
HEICO AEROSPACE HOLDINGS CORP
7875 Nw 64th St (33166-2718)
PHONE..................................305 463-0455
EMP: 6 **Publicly Held**
WEB: www.heico.com
SIC: 3724 Aircraft engines & engine parts
HQ: Heico Aerospace Holdings Corp.
3000 Taft St
Hollywood FL 33021
954 987-4000

(G-9699)
HEICO CORPORATION
825 Brickell Bay Dr # 1643 (33131-2920)
PHONE..................................305 374-1745
Pedro Alvarez, *Engineer*
Isabel Fernandez, *Branch Mgr*
Mark Sorensen, *Director*
Vivian Machado, *Admin Asst*
Jorge Rodriguez, *Technician*
EMP: 7 **Publicly Held**
WEB: www.heico.com
SIC: 3724 Aircraft engines & engine parts
PA: Heico Corporation
3000 Taft St
Hollywood FL 33021

(G-9700)
HEICO CORPORATION
7900 Nw 64th St (33166-2722)
PHONE..................................305 463-0455
Laurans A Mendelson, *Ch of Bd*
Paul Belisle, *General Mgr*
Bill Fenne, *General Mgr*
Barbara N Williams, *Principal*
Keith Coleman, *Vice Pres*
EMP: 6 **Publicly Held**
WEB: www.heico.com
SIC: 3724 Aircraft engines & engine parts
PA: Heico Corporation
3000 Taft St
Hollywood FL 33021

(G-9701)
HENJATY PUBLISHING CO
3824 Nw 15th Ave (33142-4822)
PHONE..................................305 633-9993
James Bush, *Principal*
EMP: 6 **EST:** 2014
SALES (est): 110.1K **Privately Held**
SIC: 2741 Miscellaneous publishing

(G-9702)
HEPBURN INDUSTRIES INC
300 Ne 59th St (33137-2114)
PHONE..................................305 757-6688
Timothy Klink, *President*
◆ **EMP:** 7 **EST:** 1995
SQ FT: 13,210
SALES (est): 990.2K **Privately Held**
WEB: www.hepburnsuperior.com
SIC: 2869 Embalming fluids

(G-9703)
HERA CASES LLC
10 Nw 42nd Ave Ste 700 (33126-5473)
PHONE..................................305 714-2274
Fabiana Bond, *Manager*
EMP: 5 **EST:** 2018
SALES (est): 643.8K **Privately Held**
WEB: www.heracases.com
SIC: 3523 5065 Farm machinery & equipment; electronic parts & equipment

(G-9704)
HERNANDEZ METAL FABRICATORS
15062 Sw 9th Way (33194-2770)
PHONE..................................305 970-4145
Andre Hernandez, *President*
EMP: 7 **EST:** 2008
SALES (est): 910K **Privately Held**
WEB: www.hernandezmetalfab.net
SIC: 3441 Fabricated structural metal

(G-9705)
HERNANDEZ PRINTING SERVICE
Also Called: Hps
1771 W Flagler St (33135-2015)
PHONE..................................305 642-0483
Modesto Hernandez, *President*
Maria Hernandez, *Admin Sec*
EMP: 10 **EST:** 1976
SQ FT: 8,000
SALES (est): 1.1MM **Privately Held**
SIC: 2752 2789 2759 Commercial printing, offset; bookbinding & related work; commercial printing

(G-9706)
HEXSKIN LLC
1901 Brickell Ave B201 (33129-1724)
PHONE..................................305 901-1573
David Villegas, *President*
EMP: 5 **EST:** 2014
SALES (est): 357.9K **Privately Held**
WEB: www.hexskin.com
SIC: 2329 5699 Bathing suits & swimwear: men's & boys'; marine apparel

(G-9707)
HI TECH AVIATION WELDING LLC
Also Called: HI Tech Welding
8060 Nw 67th St (33166-2730)
PHONE..................................305 591-3393
Wayne Amodie,
EMP: 7 **EST:** 1988
SALES (est): 700K **Privately Held**
WEB: www.hitechweldingfl.com
SIC: 7692 Welding repair

(G-9708)
HIDALGO CORP
Also Called: Hidalgo Jewelry
14 Ne 1st Ave Ste 805 (33132-2411)
PHONE..................................305 379-0110
◆ **EMP:** 6
SQ FT: 4,000
SALES: 1MM **Privately Held**
SIC: 3911 5094 Mfg Precious Metal Jewelry Whol Jewelry/Precious Stones

(G-9709)
HIGGINS GROUP CORP
3198 Nw 125th St (33167-2516)
PHONE..................................305 681-4444
Andres D Perea, *President*
Andres Perea, *Owner*
Suzanne Perea, *Vice Pres*
Maggie Mosquera, *Sales Staff*
Magaly Bustamante, *Administration*
◆ **EMP:** 40 **EST:** 1972
SQ FT: 15,000
SALES (est): 15.1MM
SALES (corp-wide): 1.4MM **Privately Held**
WEB: www.higginspremium.com
SIC: 3999 2048 Pet supplies; prepared feeds
HQ: Versele-Laga
Kapellestraat 70
Deinze 9800
938 132-00

(G-9710)
HIGH TOP PRODUCTS CORP
8187 Nw 8th St Apt 108 (33126-2894)
PHONE..................................305 633-3287
Mariano Vazquez, *President*
Charles Vazquez, *Owner*
Marilyn Vazquez, *Corp Secy*
Eloy Vazquez, *Vice Pres*
EMP: 100 **EST:** 1965
SQ FT: 31,000
SALES (est): 4.8MM **Privately Held**
WEB: www.hightop-products.com
SIC: 2013 2011 Ham, boneless: from purchased meat; sausages from purchased meat; variety meats, fresh edible organs

(G-9711)
HILCRAFT ENGRAVING INC
3960 Nw 26th St (33142-6728)
P.O. Box 110687, Hialeah (33011-0687)
PHONE..................................305 871-6100
Edel Lopez, *President*
Frances Morales, *Vice Pres*
EMP: 9 **EST:** 1945
SQ FT: 10,000
SALES (est): 747.3K **Privately Held**
WEB: www.hilcraft.com
SIC: 2796 2752 2791 2759 Engraving platemaking services; commercial printing, offset; typesetting; commercial printing

(G-9712)
HIRE AUTHORITY
8445 Miller Dr (33155-5426)
PHONE..................................561 477-6663
Peter Brown, *Principal*
EMP: 10 **EST:** 2007
SALES (est): 517K **Privately Held**
WEB: www.hireauthoritygaragedoors.com
SIC: 2431 Garage doors, overhead: wood

(G-9713)
HITEX MARKETING GROUP INC
1566 Nw 108th Ave (33172-2052)
PHONE..................................305 406-1150
Enrique Perez, *President*
Peter Perez, *Vice Pres*
Catalina Gonzalez, *Sales Executive*
Richely Lopez, *Marketing Staff*
Marlo Byrne, *Consultant*
◆ **EMP:** 5 **EST:** 1996
SQ FT: 12,000
SALES (est): 2.8MM **Privately Held**
WEB: www.hitexmarketingsolutions.com
SIC: 2653 5099 Display items, corrugated: made from purchased materials; video & audio equipment

(G-9714)
HM FACTORY LLC
2952 Nw 72nd Ave (33122-1312)
PHONE..................................305 897-0004
Adolfo Heller, *Mng Member*
Alejandro Carboni,
EMP: 8 **EST:** 2017
SALES (est): 830K **Privately Held**
SIC: 2024 Ice cream & frozen desserts

(G-9715)
HNM STAINLESS LLC
Also Called: Hnm Medical
20855 Ne 16th Ave Ste C15 (33179-2140)
PHONE..................................866 291-8498
Noe Roitman, *Partner*
Noah Ritman, *Vice Pres*
Dominique Camacho, *Sales Staff*
Christian Rolon, *Sales Staff*
Todd Sapp, *Sales Staff*
▲ **EMP:** 20 **EST:** 2004
SALES (est): 2.6MM **Privately Held**
WEB: www.hnmmedical.com
SIC: 3841 Surgical & medical instruments

(G-9716)
HOME & GARDEN INDUSTRIES INC
5700 Nw 32nd Ave (33142-2193)
PHONE..................................305 634-0681
Theodore F Moczik, *President*
EMP: 16 **EST:** 1967
SQ FT: 10,000
SALES (est): 2.5MM **Privately Held**
WEB: www.homeandgardenind.com
SIC: 3444 3432 3088 3523 Irrigation pipe, sheet metal; plumbing fixture fittings & trim; plastics plumbing fixtures; farm machinery & equipment; blast furnaces & steel mills

(G-9717)
HOME EXAMINER INC
1690 Ne 191st St Apt 308 (33179-4191)
PHONE..................................786 897-8349
Richard H McMonagle, *Principal*
EMP: 6 **EST:** 2008
SALES (est): 150.3K **Privately Held**
SIC: 2711 Newspapers, publishing & printing

(G-9718)
HOMYN ENTERPRISES CORP
Also Called: Secure Wrap
4050 Nw 29th St (33142-5616)
PHONE..................................305 870-9720
Radames Villalon, *President*
Minet Villalon, *Vice Pres*
Anthony Vega, *Financial Analy*
▲ **EMP:** 100 **EST:** 1996
SQ FT: 10,000
SALES (est): 16.1MM **Privately Held**
WEB: www.securewrap.com
SIC: 3089 4581 4783 Cases, plastic; airports, flying fields & services; packing & crating

(G-9719)
HONEYWELL INTERNATIONAL INC
5783 Sw 40th St 308 (33155-5301)
PHONE..................................305 525-1950
Maria Martel, *Branch Mgr*
Santos Oquendo, *Manager*
EMP: 6
SALES (corp-wide): 32.6B **Publicly Held**
WEB: www.honeywell.com
SIC: 3724 Aircraft engines & engine parts
PA: Honeywell International Inc.
300 S Tryon St
Charlotte NC 28202
704 627-6200

(G-9720)
HOUSE OF LLULL ATLIER
13850 Sw 143rd Ct Ste 19 (33186-6123)
PHONE..................................305 964-7921
Carla Llull, *Owner*
EMP: 7 **EST:** 2015
SALES (est): 470.1K **Privately Held**
WEB: www.houseofllull.com
SIC: 2253 Bathing suits & swimwear, knit

(G-9721)
HURRICANE SHUTTER & PLUS INC
8004 Sw 149th Ave (33193-3145)
PHONE..................................786 287-0007
Rodolfo Rizo, *President*
EMP: 9 **EST:** 2005
SALES (est): 128K **Privately Held**
SIC: 3442 Shutters, door or window: metal

(G-9722)
HYDRO INDUSTRIES-USA LLC
3401 Ne 1st Ave (33137-3981)
PHONE..................................305 440-0893
EMP: 7 **EST:** 2019
SALES (est): 130.2K **Privately Held**
WEB: www.hydro.aero
SIC: 3999 Manufacturing industries

(G-9723)
HYGENATOR PILLOW SERVICE INC
10100 E Calusa Club Dr (33186-2344)
PHONE..................................305 325-0250
Tomiko Erickson, *President*
Young Soong, *Vice Pres*
Ellen Erickson, *Admin Sec*
EMP: 5 **EST:** 1955
SQ FT: 27,000
SALES (est): 470.5K **Privately Held**
SIC: 2392 7389 Pillows, bed: made from purchased materials; interior design services

(G-9724)
I J PRECIOUS METALS INC
22 Ne 1st St (33132-2459)
PHONE..................................305 371-3009
Igor Alishayev, *Principal*
EMP: 7 **EST:** 2012
SALES (est): 140.3K **Privately Held**
SIC: 3339 Precious metals

(G-9725)
I2K DIGITAL SOLUTIONS LLC
7884 Nw 64th St (33166-2706)
PHONE..................................305 507-0707
Humberto Santana, *Manager*
Cesar Casamayor, *Manager*
EMP: 12 **EST:** 2017
SALES (est): 993.1K **Privately Held**
WEB: www.i2kdigital.com
SIC: 3993 Signs & advertising specialties

(G-9726)
IAG ENGINE CENTER LLC
6929 Nw 46th St (33166-5603)
PHONE..................................305 591-0643
Mauricio Luna, *CEO*
Alex Alonso, *Controller*
EMP: 40 **EST:** 2012
SALES (est): 7.5MM **Privately Held**
WEB: www.iagaerogroup.com
SIC: 3724 Aircraft engines & engine parts

(G-9727)
ICHOSEN1 INC
1441 Brickell Ave Ste 17 (33131-3362)
PHONE..................................844 403-4055
Christopher Rogers, *President*
Genevieve Bassett, *Principal*
EMP: 10 **EST:** 2018
SALES (est): 269.2K **Privately Held**
SIC: 7372 Prepackaged software

(G-9728)
ICOME2FIX LLC
400 Nw 26th St (33127-4120)
PHONE..................................954 789-4102
Juvonal Allen,
EMP: 11 **EST:** 2019
SALES (est): 325K **Privately Held**
WEB: www.icome2fix.com
SIC: 2741

(G-9729)
IDEAL FASTENER CORPORATION
10800 Biscayne Blvd (33161-7482)
PHONE..................................201 207-6722
EMP: 61
SALES (corp-wide): 40.3MM **Privately Held**
WEB: www.idealfastener.com
SIC: 3965 Zipper
PA: Ideal Fastener Corporation
603 W Industry Dr
Oxford NC 27565
919 693-3115

(G-9730)
IDEASGT CORP
7510 Sw 153rd Pl Apt 101 (33193-1726)
PHONE.................................786 370-7767
Ernesto Torrez, *Principal*
EMP: 6 **EST:** 2010
SALES (est): 68.7K **Privately Held**
WEB: www.ideasgt.com
SIC: 3825 Network analyzers

(G-9731)
IES SALES AND SERVICE LLC
2233 Nw 77th Ter (33147-5531)
PHONE.................................305 525-6079
Janet Sanchez, *Mng Member*
EMP: 7 **EST:** 2016
SALES (est): 950K **Privately Held**
WEB: www.refusewastequip.com
SIC: 2611 Pulp mills, mechanical & recycling processing

(G-9732)
IL NUTS INC
19098 W Dixie Hwy (33180-2638)
PHONE.................................786 366-4536
Joseph Hagby, *President*
EMP: 5 **EST:** 2013
SALES (est): 620K **Privately Held**
WEB: www.yossef-roasting.com
SIC: 2068 Nuts: dried, dehydrated, salted or roasted

(G-9733)
IMAGICLE INC
66 W Flagler St Ste 1002 (33130-1809)
PHONE.................................206 201-2042
Christian Bongiovanni, *President*
Massimo Di Puccio, *Vice Pres*
Giorgio Barsacchi, *Manager*
EMP: 16 **EST:** 2017
SALES (est): 162.7K **Privately Held**
WEB: www.imagicle.com
SIC: 7372 Application computer software

(G-9734)
IMC LIGHTING INC
Also Called: Space Lighting
2915 Biscayne Blvd # 301 (33137-4197)
PHONE.................................305 373-4422
Jean L Raphael, *President*
▲ **EMP:** 7 **EST:** 2010
SQ FT: 10,000
SALES (est): 834.3K **Privately Held**
WEB: www.spacelighting.com
SIC: 3648 Lighting equipment

(G-9735)
IMPRESSIONS OF MIAMI INC
6960 Sw 47th St (33155-4645)
PHONE.................................305 666-0277
Jose Segrera, *President*
Dannaliz Segrera, *Vice Pres*
EMP: 5 **EST:** 1985
SQ FT: 4,700
SALES (est): 411.9K **Privately Held**
SIC: 2759 Commercial printing

(G-9736)
INBIGVMYSHOPIFY LLC ✪
12030 Sw 129th Ct Ste 105 (33186-4584)
PHONE.................................844 689-9033
Dr Leslie V McMillan, *Principal*
Leslie McMillan, *Principal*
EMP: 19 **EST:** 2021
SALES (est): 674.5K **Privately Held**
SIC: 3873 Watches, clocks, watchcases & parts

(G-9737)
INCLAN MACHINE SHOP
4401 Sw 75th Ave (33155-4445)
PHONE.................................305 846-9675
Raul Aroix, *Principal*
EMP: 6 **EST:** 2016
SALES (est): 165.4K **Privately Held**
SIC: 3599 Machine shop, jobbing & repair

(G-9738)
INDUSTRIAL GALVANIZERS MIAMI
3350 Nw 119th St (33167-2902)
PHONE.................................305 681-8844
Sandy Robertson, *President*
◆ **EMP:** 26 **EST:** 1999
SALES (est): 582.7K **Privately Held**
WEB: www.valmontcoatings.com
SIC: 3547 3312 Galvanizing lines (rolling mill equipment); blast furnaces & steel mills

(G-9739)
INDUSTRIAL GLVANIZERS AMER INC
Also Called: Industrial Galvanizers Miami
3350 Nw 119th St (33167-2902)
PHONE.................................305 681-8844
Javier Dela Vega, *Branch Mgr*
EMP: 43
SQ FT: 25,496 **Privately Held**
WEB: www.valmontcoatings.com
SIC: 3479 Galvanizing of iron, steel or end-formed products
HQ: Industrial Galvanizers America, Inc.
3535 Halifax Rd Ste A
Petersburg VA 23805

(G-9740)
INDUSTRIAL GLVNZERS STHEASTERN
Also Called: Valmont Stheastern Galvanizing
3350 Nw 119th St (33167-2902)
PHONE.................................813 621-8990
Todd G Atkinson, *President*
Mark Mellon, *Marketing Staff*
Maria Elena Albo, *Manager*
Shaun G Sheppard, *Admin Sec*
▲ **EMP:** 70 **EST:** 1995
SALES (est): 10.2MM
SALES (corp-wide): 2.9B **Publicly Held**
WEB: www.valmontmiami.com
SIC: 3479 Galvanizing of iron, steel or end-formed products
PA: Valmont Industries, Inc.
1 Valmont Plz Ste 500
Omaha NE 68154
402 963-1000

(G-9741)
INFINITE RET DESIGN & MFG CORP
7320 Nw 36th Ave (33147-5810)
PHONE.................................305 967-8339
Hector Gonzalez, *CEO*
▼ **EMP:** 10 **EST:** 2013
SALES (est): 516.7K **Privately Held**
WEB: www.infiniterdm.com
SIC: 2511 2431 2491 1751 Wood household furniture; millwork; millwork, treated wood; cabinet & finish carpentry; wood kitchen cabinets

(G-9742)
INFLATABLE DESIGN WORKS CORP
13350 Sw 131st St Unit 10 (33186-6186)
PHONE.................................786 242-1049
Alejandro S Handal, *Owner*
Lissette R Caras, *CFO*
Richard Desaulniers, *VP Sales*
▼ **EMP:** 15 **EST:** 2002
SALES (est): 543.5K **Privately Held**
WEB: www.idwcorp.com
SIC: 2759 3993 Promotional printing; advertising novelties

(G-9743)
INKLAB SIGNS INC
12324 Sw 117th Ct (33186-3919)
PHONE.................................786 430-8100
Carlos J Parets, *President*
EMP: 7 **EST:** 2013
SALES (est): 266.1K **Privately Held**
SIC: 3993 Signs & advertising specialties

(G-9744)
INNFOCUS INC
12415 Sw 136th Ave Ste 3 (33186-6488)
PHONE.................................305 378-2651
Randy Lindholm, *Ch of Bd*
Russ Trenary, *President*
Leonard Pinchuk, *Founder*
Yasushi Kato, *Vice Pres*
Yasushi P Kato, *Vice Pres*
EMP: 12 **EST:** 2006
SQ FT: 10,000
SALES (est): 6.4MM **Privately Held**
WEB: www.innfocusinc.com
SIC: 3841 Surgical & medical instruments
PA: Santen Pharmaceutical Co., Ltd.
4-20, Ofukacho, Kita-Ku
Osaka OSK 530-0

(G-9745)
INNOCOR FOAM TECH - ACP INC
3225 Nw 107th St (33167-3713)
PHONE.................................305 685-6341
Michele Boyd, *Office Mgr*
Hermann Leopold, *Branch Mgr*
EMP: 100 **Privately Held**
WEB: www.fxi.com
SIC: 3086 Plastics foam products
HQ: Innocor Foam Technologies - Acp, Inc.
200 Schulz Dr Ste 2
Red Bank NJ 07701
732 945-6222

(G-9746)
INNOVA ECO BLDG SYSTEMS LLC
Also Called: Mgo America
3300 Nw 110th St (33167-3720)
PHONE.................................305 455-7707
Jerry Gillman, *CEO*
◆ **EMP:** 41 **EST:** 2012
SALES (est): 7.1MM **Privately Held**
WEB: www.innovapanel.com
SIC: 2452 Panels & sections, prefabricated, wood

(G-9747)
INNOVA SOFTGEL LLC
Also Called: Innova Gel
14193 Sw 119th Ave (33186-6013)
PHONE.................................855 536-8872
Francisco Tafoya, *Warehouse Mgr*
Adriana Martinez, *Purch Agent*
Rodrigo Mera, *Controller*
Raciel Martin, *Accountant*
Olav Sandnes, *Mng Member*
◆ **EMP:** 153 **EST:** 2015
SALES (est): 57.2MM
SALES (corp-wide): 355.8K **Privately Held**
WEB: www.kdpharmagroup.com
SIC: 2834 Pharmaceutical preparations
HQ: Marine Ingredients, Llc
794 Sunrise Blvd
Mount Bethel PA 18343
570 260-6900

(G-9748)
INNOVATIONS CABINETS CORP
8887 Fontainebleau Blvd # 406
(33172-6407)
PHONE.................................305 458-9395
Ana M Aguado, *Principal*
EMP: 6 **EST:** 2017
SALES (est): 101.3K **Privately Held**
SIC: 2434 Wood kitchen cabinets

(G-9749)
INOVINOX USA LLC
7875 Sw 104th St (33156-2677)
PHONE.................................800 780-1017
EMP: 5 **EST:** 2017
SALES (est): 390.6K **Privately Held**
WEB: www.inovinox.com
SIC: 3491 Industrial valves

(G-9750)
INSIGHTEC INC (HQ)
801 Brickell Ave Ste 1600 (33131-4901)
PHONE.................................786 534-3849
Maurice Ferre, *President*
Debra Luckey, *General Mgr*
Oded Tamir, *COO*
Achal Achrol, *Vice Pres*
Xen M Aderka, *Vice Pres*
EMP: 3 **EST:** 2010
SQ FT: 8,400
SALES (est): 4.4MM **Privately Held**
WEB: www.insightec.com
SIC: 3845 Medical cleaning equipment, ultrasonic

(G-9751)
INSTANT PS LLC
8415 Sw 107th Ave (33173-4393)
PHONE.................................786 278-5007
Carlos A Calderon, *Principal*
EMP: 6 **EST:** 2015
SALES (est): 126K **Privately Held**
SIC: 2752 Commercial printing, lithographic

(G-9752)
INTELLGENT HARING SYSTEMS CORP (PA)
6860 Sw 81st St (33143-7708)
PHONE.................................305 668-6102
Edward Miskiel, *President*
Ozcan Ozdamar, *COO*
Rafael Delgato, *Exec VP*
Rafael E Delgado, *Vice Pres*
Ozdamar Ozcan, *Vice Pres*
EMP: 15 **EST:** 1983
SQ FT: 3,000
SALES (est): 6MM **Privately Held**
WEB: www.ihsys.com
SIC: 3841 5734 5045 8731 Diagnostic apparatus, medical; computer & software stores; computer software; commercial physical research

(G-9753)
INTELLICLEAN SOLUTIONS LLC (PA)
444 Brickell Ave Ste 800 (33131-2442)
PHONE.................................615 293-2299
Amanda Harrington, *Marketing Mgr*
Larry York, *Mng Member*
Tim Harrington, *Mng Member*
Randy Spencer, *Mng Member*
EMP: 5 **EST:** 2016
SQ FT: 2,000
SALES (est): 2.8MM **Privately Held**
SIC: 3635 Household vacuum cleaners

(G-9754)
INTERBEVERAGE LLC
3100 Nw 74th Ave (33122-1226)
PHONE.................................305 961-1110
Juan Vaamonde Gomez, *Mng Member*
Andrea R Taddei Dennett,
Claudio P Taddei Dennett,
Luis E Osorio Pedauga,
▲ **EMP:** 6 **EST:** 2011
SALES (est): 455.2K **Privately Held**
WEB: www.rwbmd.com
SIC: 2086 Carbonated beverages, nonalcoholic: bottled & canned

(G-9755)
INTERFRIES INC (PA)
18800 Ne 29th Ave Apt 426 (33180-2863)
PHONE.................................786 427-1427
David Winiarz, *President*
▲ **EMP:** 3 **EST:** 2010
SALES: 3.5MM **Privately Held**
WEB: www.interfries.com
SIC: 2037 Potato products, quick frozen & cold pack

(G-9756)
INTERNATIONAL CLOTHIERS INC
Also Called: Uniform Authority, The
4000 Twrside Ter Ste 2412 (33138)
PHONE.................................914 715-5600
Steven M Singer, *President*
Elizabeth M Singer, *Vice Pres*
Matthew Singer, *Vice Pres*
▲ **EMP:** 14 **EST:** 2015
SQ FT: 2,000
SALES (est): 8MM **Privately Held**
WEB: www.inclothiers.com
SIC: 2326 2337 Work uniforms; uniforms, except athletic: women's, misses' & juniors'

(G-9757)
INTERNATIONAL CNSTR PUBG
Also Called: Construccion-Pan Americana
4913 Sw 75th Ave (33155-4440)
PHONE.................................305 668-4999
Luis Suao, *President*
Adriana Suao, *Corp Secy*
EMP: 8 **EST:** 1972
SQ FT: 3,800
SALES (est): 550K **Privately Held**
SIC: 2721 Magazines: publishing & printing

(G-9758)
INTERNATIONAL GREENSCAPES LLC
Also Called: International Treescapes
20855 Ne 16th Ave Ste C4 (33179-2125)
PHONE..................................760 631-6789
Juan Ascencio, *Branch Mgr*
EMP: 75
SALES (corp-wide): 596.1K **Privately Held**
SIC: 3999 Artificial trees & flowers; flowers, artificial & preserved; foliage, artificial & preserved; plants, artificial & preserved
PA: International Greenscapes, Llc
180 Vallecitos De Oro
San Marcos CA 92069
760 631-6789

(G-9759)
INTERNATIONAL MACHINE WORKS
Also Called: International Machine Shop
3631 Nw 48th Ter (33142-3923)
PHONE..................................305 635-3585
James Patterson, *President*
Marie Patterson, *Vice Pres*
▼ **EMP:** 11 **EST:** 1981
SQ FT: 30,000
SALES (est): 2.4MM **Privately Held**
SIC: 3534 7699 Elevators & equipment; elevators: inspection, service & repair

(G-9760)
INTERNATIONAL POWER USA LLC
2091 Nw 139th St (33015)
PHONE..................................305 534-7993
Chain Carlos, *Mng Member*
EMP: 7 **EST:** 2008
SALES (est): 942.3K **Privately Held**
WEB: www.internationalpower.com
SIC: 3089 Automotive parts, plastic
PA: Industria De Servicios Tecnicos Inseteca, Ca
Ave. Michelena, C.C.Arpe, Local 15 Nave B
Valencia

(G-9761)
INTERNTNAL EXPORT UNIFORMS INC
Also Called: International Uniform
4000 Nw 29th St (33142-5616)
PHONE..................................305 869-9900
Roger Gorwitz, *President*
Maria T Garcia, *Vice Pres*
Richard Barnes, *CIO*
Yumis Rodriguez, *Administration*
◆ **EMP:** 22 **EST:** 1981
SQ FT: 5,500
SALES (est): 2.8MM **Privately Held**
WEB: www.intluniforms.com
SIC: 2337 5136 Uniforms, except athletic: women's, misses' & juniors'; uniforms, men's & boys'

(G-9762)
INTERTECH SUPPLY INC
13334 Sw 9th Ter (33184-1934)
PHONE..................................786 200-0561
Carlos Hierro, *Vice Pres*
◆ **EMP:** 7 **EST:** 2009
SALES (est): 262.1K **Privately Held**
WEB: www.intertechus.com
SIC: 3674 Semiconductors & related devices

(G-9763)
INTERTEX MIAMI LLC
50 Ne 179th St Bay 1-2 (33162-1014)
PHONE..................................305 627-3536
David Ojalvo, *Mng Member*
Jessica Gonzales,
Sonia Klainbaum,
Jose Mugrabi,
EMP: 9 **EST:** 2012
SALES (est): 732K **Privately Held**
WEB: www.intertexmiami.com
SIC: 2211 Denims

(G-9764)
INVERSNES WLLDEL ASOCIADOS INC (PA)
4700 Nw 72nd Ave (33166-5617)
PHONE..................................305 591-0118
William A Delgado Sr, *President*
William Delgado, *Owner*
Rafael Palomino, *Sales Staff*
▼ **EMP:** 78 **EST:** 2006
SALES (est): 1.1MM **Privately Held**
WEB: www.inversioneswilldel.net
SIC: 3441 Railroad car racks, for transporting vehicles: steel

(G-9765)
INVOINET INC (HQ)
1111 Brickell Ave # 1860 (33131-3112)
PHONE..................................305 432-5366
Pablo Sanucci, *CEO*
Martin Almirall, *Vice Pres*
EMP: 55 **EST:** 2004
SQ FT: 10,752
SALES (corp-wide): 806.6K **Privately Held**
SIC: 2782 Receipt, invoice & memorandum books
PA: Invoinet Holdings, Llc
1111 Brickell Ave # 1100
Miami FL 33131
305 913-7149

(G-9766)
IPG NETWORK CORP
3155 Nw 40th St (33142-5109)
PHONE..................................305 681-4001
Adeniyi Oyegunle, *President*
EMP: 10 **EST:** 2005
SALES (est): 521.5K **Privately Held**
WEB: www.ipgnetwork.net
SIC: 3299 Gravel painting

(G-9767)
IPLINE LLC
18152 Sw 144th Ct (33177-3308)
PHONE..................................305 675-4235
Joaquin Cabada, *Principal*
EMP: 10 **EST:** 2015
SALES (est): 395.9K **Privately Held**
SIC: 3429 Manufactured hardware (general)

(G-9768)
IPQ TRADE CORP
488 Ne 18th St Ste Cu1 (33132-1120)
PHONE..................................786 522-2310
Paolo Fontanot, *Owner*
EMP: 12 **EST:** 2016
SALES (est): 540K **Privately Held**
SIC: 2051 Bakery: wholesale or wholesale/retail combined

(G-9769)
IQ DOMINOES CORP
11740 Sw 14th St (33184-2513)
PHONE..................................305 967-8583
Alberto Hernandez, *President*
EMP: 1 **EST:** 2011
SALES (est): 3MM **Privately Held**
WEB: www.dominoker.com
SIC: 3944 Electronic games & toys

(G-9770)
IRIS INTERNATIONAL INC (DH)
11800 Sw 147th Ave (33196-2500)
PHONE..................................818 709-1244
Cesar M Garcia, *Ch of Bd*
Bernard M Alfano, *President*
Robert A Mello, *President*
Lawrence J Blecka, *Vice Pres*
David W Gates, *Vice Pres*
◆ **EMP:** 100 **EST:** 1979
SQ FT: 98,446
SALES (est): 130.7MM
SALES (corp-wide): 22.2B **Publicly Held**
WEB: www.beckmancoulter.com
SIC: 3841 3845 Surgical & medical instruments; electromedical equipment
HQ: Beckman Coulter, Inc.
250 S Kraemer Blvd
Brea CA 92821
714 993-5321

(G-9771)
IRON CONTAINER LLC (PA)
8505 Nw 74th St (33166-2327)
PHONE..................................305 726-2150
Stephanie L Irons, *Mng Member*
Jonathan S Leoniff, *Mng Member*
John Martorana, *Mng Member*
Rodney C Walters, *Mng Member*
▼ **EMP:** 20 **EST:** 2009
SALES (est): 23.7MM **Privately Held**
WEB: www.ironcontainer.com
SIC: 3469 Metal stampings

(G-9772)
IRON STRENGTH CORP
Also Called: Jr Electronics
9568 Sw 40th St (33165-4036)
PHONE..................................305 226-6866
Espinel Guadarrama, *President*
Francisco Espinel, *Vice Pres*
Ricardo Rodriguez, *Vice Pres*
EMP: 11 **EST:** 2016
SALES (est): 621.5K **Privately Held**
SIC: 3714 Automotive wiring harness sets

(G-9773)
ISA GROUP CORP
2665 S Byshr Dr Ste 710 (33133-5406)
PHONE..................................305 748-1578
Veruska Chalbaud, *Vice Pres*
EMP: 10 **EST:** 2013
SALES (est): 257.5K **Privately Held**
WEB: www.isagroupca.com
SIC: 3552 3565 3535 Textile machinery; packaging machinery; conveyors & conveying equipment

(G-9774)
ITALIAN CABINETRY INC
Also Called: Mirrors 2 Go
3250 Ne 1st Ave Ste 305 (33137-4295)
PHONE..................................786 534-2742
Rodrigo Mattevi, *CEO*
EMP: 13
SQ FT: 15,000
SALES (est): 4MM **Privately Held**
WEB: www.italiancabinetry-usa.com
SIC: 2434 2599 Wood kitchen cabinets; hotel furniture

(G-9775)
IVAX CORPORATION (HQ)
4400 Biscayne Blvd (33137-3212)
PHONE..................................305 329-3795
Phillip Frost MD, *Ch of Bd*
Jane Hsiao PHD, *Vice Ch Bd*
Neil W Flanzraich, *President*
William Marth, *President*
Richard Daniell, *Exec VP*
◆ **EMP:** 175 **EST:** 1985
SALES (est): 390.8MM **Privately Held**
WEB: www.tevapharm.com
SIC: 2834 Drugs acting on the cardiovascular system, except diagnostic

(G-9776)
IVAX PHARMACEUTICALS LLC (DH)
74 Nw 176th St (33169-5043)
PHONE..................................305 575-6000
Rafick Henein,
▲ **EMP:** 200 **EST:** 1995
SALES (est): 107.9MM **Privately Held**
WEB: www.tevapharm.com
SIC: 2834 Pharmaceutical preparations
HQ: Ivax Corporation
4400 Biscayne Blvd
Miami FL 33137
305 329-3795

(G-9777)
IVAX RESEARCH INC (DH)
4400 Biscayne Blvd (33137-3212)
PHONE..................................305 668-7688
Neil Flanzraich, *President*
Jane Hsiao, *Vice Pres*
EMP: 70 **EST:** 1986
SQ FT: 74,200
SALES (est): 60MM **Privately Held**
WEB: www.tevapharm.com
SIC: 2834 Pharmaceutical preparations
HQ: Ivax Corporation
4400 Biscayne Blvd
Miami FL 33137
305 329-3795

(G-9778)
IVM USA INC
800 Brickell Ave Ste 550 (33131-2970)
PHONE..................................786 693-2755
Pietro Iemmolo, *President*
▲ **EMP:** 23 **EST:** 2009
SALES (est): 678.8K **Privately Held**
SIC: 3732 Yachts, building & repairing
PA: Ivm Spa
Via Toscana 2/A
Padova PD 35127

(G-9779)
J & V PAVERSCORP
2614 Sw 36th Ave (33133-2722)
PHONE..................................786 510-4389
Jorge Cardoza, *Principal*
EMP: 8 **EST:** 2012
SALES (est): 617K **Privately Held**
WEB: www.jvpaverscorporation.com
SIC: 2951 Asphalt paving mixtures & blocks

(G-9780)
J C & A OF SOUTH FLORIDA INC
3109 Grand Ave (33133-5103)
PHONE..................................305 445-6665
Jeff Capanach, *Owner*
EMP: 5 **EST:** 1984
SALES (est): 650K **Privately Held**
SIC: 3086 Packaging & shipping materials, foamed plastic

(G-9781)
J F AEROSPACE INC
12242 Sw 132nd Ct (33186-6476)
PHONE..................................786 242-6686
Joe Balleste, *President*
EMP: 8 **EST:** 1998
SALES (est): 755.4K **Privately Held**
WEB: www.amcohenlaw.com
SIC: 3728 Aircraft parts & equipment

(G-9782)
J J CABINETS APPLIANCES
8833 Sw 129th St (33176-5918)
PHONE..................................786 573-0300
John Villoria, *Principal*
EMP: 8 **EST:** 2010
SALES (est): 537.3K **Privately Held**
WEB: www.jandjcabinets.com
SIC: 2434 Wood kitchen cabinets

(G-9783)
J W DAWSON CO INC
3739 Nw 43rd St (33142-4237)
P.O. Box 554, Eaton Park (33840-0554)
PHONE..................................305 634-8618
Earl S Heatherdale, *President*
Beverly Heatherdale, *Corp Secy*
EMP: 24 **EST:** 1971
SQ FT: 2,000
SALES (est): 709.1K **Privately Held**
SIC: 2421 Sawdust & shavings

(G-9784)
JA UNIFORMS INC
12323 Sw 132nd Ct (33186-6477)
PHONE..................................305 234-1231
Alexander Arencibia, *President*
Menchu Dominicis, *Vice Pres*
Ulysses Garcia, *Sales Executive*
Mario Nunez, *Manager*
▲ **EMP:** 12 **EST:** 1997
SQ FT: 6,000
SALES (est): 2.3MM **Privately Held**
WEB: www.jauniforms.com
SIC: 2326 5137 Work uniforms; uniforms, women's & children's

(G-9785)
JABBERWOCKY LLC
2 S Biscayne Blvd # 2680 (33131-1806)
PHONE..................................310 717-3343
Alex Pereira,
EMP: 5 **EST:** 2016
SALES (est): 324.1K **Privately Held**
WEB: www.jabberwockyapp.com
SIC: 2731 Book publishing

(G-9786)
JAMMIN JAMS USA LLC
9351 Sw 56th St (33165-6558)
PHONE..................................305 494-5617
Taharaa P Wong, *Manager*
EMP: 6 **EST:** 2014

SALES (est): 131.1K **Privately Held**
SIC: 2033 Jams, jellies & preserves: packaged in cans, jars, etc.

(G-9787)
JANUSZ ART STONE INC
7025 Ne 2nd Ave (33138-5507)
PHONE..................................305 754-7171
Janusz Niedbala, *Principal*
EMP: 8 **EST:** 2016
SALES (est): 223.5K **Privately Held**
WEB: www.urbanstoneworks.com
SIC: 3272 Concrete products

(G-9788)
JC BEST FINISH CABINET INC
2150 Nw 35th St (33142-5428)
PHONE..................................786 216-5571
Julio C Letran, *President*
EMP: 6 **EST:** 2010
SALES (est): 161.9K **Privately Held**
SIC: 2434 Wood kitchen cabinets

(G-9789)
JC INDUSTRIAL MFG CORP
Also Called: J C Machine Shop
5700 Nw 32nd Ct (33142-2141)
PHONE..................................305 634-5280
Pedro L Amador, *President*
Francis Chester, *Business Mgr*
Jorge Amador, *Vice Pres*
Annabelle Amador, *Treasurer*
Richard Nardone, *Sales Staff*
◆ **EMP:** 36 **EST:** 1980
SQ FT: 40,000
SALES (est): 2MM **Privately Held**
WEB: www.jcmachineshop.com
SIC: 3599 7692 3444 Machine shop, jobbing & repair; welding repair; sheet metalwork

(G-9790)
JC MACHINE WORKS CORP
Also Called: J. C. Mch Sp & Met Fabrication
5700 Nw 32nd Ct (33142-2141)
PHONE..................................305 634-5280
Pedro L Amador, *President*
Jorge L Amador, *Vice Pres*
Guillermo Arnold, *Supervisor*
▲ **EMP:** 30 **EST:** 2010
SQ FT: 27,575
SALES (est): 5.3MM **Privately Held**
WEB: www.jcmachineshop.com
SIC: 3599 Machine shop, jobbing & repair

(G-9791)
JCP SIGNS INC
20483 Sw 127th Pl (33177-5102)
PHONE..................................305 790-5336
Jon Pineiro, *President*
EMP: 8 **EST:** 2007
SALES (est): 224.8K **Privately Held**
SIC: 3993 Signs & advertising specialties

(G-9792)
JDM OF MIAMI LLC
14195 Sw 139th Ct (33186-5599)
PHONE..................................305 253-4650
Carlos Montealegre, *Principal*
▼ **EMP:** 8 **EST:** 2005
SALES (est): 1MM **Privately Held**
WEB: www.jdmofmiami.com
SIC: 3621 Motors & generators

(G-9793)
JEAN RICHARD KITCHEN CABINETS
18342 Ne 2nd Ave (33179-4424)
PHONE..................................786 285-5506
Jean Henry, *Vice Pres*
EMP: 6 **EST:** 2018
SALES (est): 53.7K **Privately Held**
SIC: 2434 Wood kitchen cabinets

(G-9794)
JEFFERSON SOLENOID VALVES USA
20225 Ne 15th Ct (33179-2710)
PHONE..................................305 249-8120
Jose Dadin, *Principal*
Maria Castro, *Opers Mgr*
▲ **EMP:** 100 **EST:** 1999
SALES (est): 8.1MM **Privately Held**
WEB: www.jeffersonvalves.com
SIC: 3491 Solenoid valves

(G-9795)
JESUS CABINETS CORP
10641 Sw 20th Ter (33165-7920)
PHONE..................................786 237-6299
Jesus C Rodriguez, *Principal*
EMP: 6 **EST:** 2018
SALES (est): 59.1K **Privately Held**
SIC: 2434 Wood kitchen cabinets

(G-9796)
JET GRAPHICS INC
4101 Sw 73rd Ave (33155-4520)
PHONE..................................305 264-4333
Teresita Garcia Calvo, *President*
Isabel M Garcia, *Vice Pres*
EMP: 19 **EST:** 1994
SQ FT: 8,000
SALES (est): 2.1MM **Privately Held**
WEB: www.jetgraphics.com
SIC: 2752 2791 2789 Commercial printing, offset; typesetting; bookbinding & related work

(G-9797)
JHK LLC
7950 Nw 53rd St Ste 215 (33166-4638)
PHONE..................................786 871-0150
▲ **EMP:** 5
SALES: 950K **Privately Held**
SIC: 3499 Mfg Misc Fabricated Metal Products

(G-9798)
JIREH AC & RFRGN INC
5001 Sw 142nd Pl (33175-5027)
PHONE..................................305 216-2774
Jose Acosta, *President*
Jorge Pinto, *Vice Pres*
Jose Luis Rodriguez, *Treasurer*
EMP: 16 **EST:** 1984
SALES (est): 2.4MM **Privately Held**
WEB: www.miamihvac.org
SIC: 3822 Air conditioning & refrigeration controls

(G-9799)
JMP FASHION INC (PA)
2199 Nw 20th St Unit 2 (33142-7399)
PHONE..................................305 633-9920
Jorge Perez, *President*
Maritza Perez, *Corp Secy*
Telmo Perez, *Vice Pres*
◆ **EMP:** 19 **EST:** 1985
SALES (est): 2.5MM **Privately Held**
WEB: www.jmpwarehouse.com
SIC: 2339 2329 5621 Sportswear, women's; men's & boys' sportswear & athletic clothing; women's sportswear

(G-9800)
JOHNNY DEVIL INC
Also Called: Johnny Heaven
7301 Nw 36th Ct (33147-5811)
PHONE..................................305 634-0700
Mario Frati, *President*
EMP: 7 **EST:** 1993
SALES (est): 258.7K **Privately Held**
SIC: 2331 2339 Blouses, women's & juniors': made from purchased material; shirts, women's & juniors': made from purchased materials; slacks: women's, misses' & juniors'

(G-9801)
JOHNSON & JOHNSON
6303 Blue Lagoon Dr # 450 (33126-6029)
P.O. Box 25323 (33102-5323)
PHONE..................................305 261-3500
Hannah Foley, *General Mgr*
Judy Jimenez, *Project Mgr*
Lisa Snellen, *Opers Staff*
Meredith Bishop, *Research*
Pei-Yu Chung, *Engineer*
EMP: 36
SALES (corp-wide): 82.5B **Publicly Held**
WEB: www.jnj.com
SIC: 3842 Surgical appliances & supplies
PA: Johnson & Johnson
1 Johnson And Johnson Plz
New Brunswick NJ 08933
732 524-0400

(G-9802)
JORGES FINEST WOODWORKS INC
2471 Nw 95th St (33147-2417)
PHONE..................................305 491-4380
Jorge L Herrera, *Principal*
EMP: 7 **EST:** 2013
SALES (est): 109.2K **Privately Held**
SIC: 2431 Millwork

(G-9803)
JOSE MORALES HURRICANE SHUTTER
13271 Sw 17th Ln (33175-7650)
PHONE..................................786 315-1835
Jose Morales, *Principal*
EMP: 7 **EST:** 2008
SALES (est): 255.3K **Privately Held**
SIC: 3442 Shutters, door or window: metal

(G-9804)
JOSE POLANCO
Also Called: T-Shirt Florida
614 Sw 22nd Ave (33135-3119)
PHONE..................................305 631-1784
Jose Polanco, *Owner*
EMP: 5 **EST:** 2013
SALES (est): 348.1K **Privately Held**
WEB: www.tshirtsflorida.com
SIC: 2759 Screen printing

(G-9805)
JOSE RODRIGUEZ MET FABRICATION
2451 Brickell Ave (33129-2436)
PHONE..................................305 305-6110
Jose Rodriguez, *Principal*
▼ **EMP:** 7 **EST:** 2012
SALES (est): 182.5K **Privately Held**
SIC: 3499 Fabricated metal products

(G-9806)
JP CUSTOM METALS
7200 Nw 29th Ct (33147-5960)
PHONE..................................786 318-2855
George Peron, *President*
Stephanie Peron, *Office Mgr*
◆ **EMP:** 10 **EST:** 1998
SALES (est): 1.2MM **Privately Held**
WEB: www.jpcustommetals.net
SIC: 3444 Sheet metalwork

(G-9807)
JR EMBROIDERY INC
12321 Sw 133rd Ct (33186-6434)
PHONE..................................305 253-6968
Fax: 305 251-7353
EMP: 5
SQ FT: 2,000
SALES (est): 432.1K **Privately Held**
SIC: 2395 Embroidery Work

(G-9808)
JR WOOD WORKS INC
7954 Ne 4th Ave (33138-4408)
PHONE..................................305 401-6056
Jose A Rodriguez, *President*
EMP: 6 **EST:** 2005
SALES (est): 124.5K **Privately Held**
SIC: 2431 Millwork

(G-9809)
JSN BLUE THUNDER LLC
1876 Nw 7th St (33125-3504)
PHONE..................................786 398-5222
Jeffrey S Nunberg, *Principal*
EMP: 6 **EST:** 2011
SALES (est): 252K **Privately Held**
SIC: 3482 Small arms ammunition

(G-9810)
JTI DUTY-FREE USA INC
501 Brickell Dr Ste 402 (33131)
PHONE..................................305 377-3922
Ignacio Luthessa, *CEO*
EMP: 5 **EST:** 2000
SALES (est): 2.7MM **Privately Held**
SIC: 2131 Chewing & smoking tobacco
HQ: Japan Tobacco International U.S.A., Inc.
Glenpnte Ctr E 300 Frank
Teaneck NJ 07666
201 871-1210

(G-9811)
JUAN F MONTANO
7895 Sw 57th Ter (33143-1622)
PHONE..................................305 274-0512
Juan Montano, *President*
Juan F Montano, *Owner*
Olga Montana, *Vice Pres*
EMP: 8 **EST:** 2004
SALES (est): 227.1K **Privately Held**
SIC: 2051 Cakes, bakery: except frozen

(G-9812)
JUAN PAMPANAS DESIGNS INC
32 Nw 20th St (33127-4908)
PHONE..................................305 573-7550
Juan Pampanas, *President*
Daniel Pampanas, *Associate Dir*
EMP: 7 **EST:** 1984
SQ FT: 10,000
SALES (est): 300K **Privately Held**
WEB: www.pampanas.com
SIC: 2426 1751 Carvings, furniture: wood; cabinet & finish carpentry

(G-9813)
K COLOR CORP
Also Called: Color K Graphics
7255 Nw 68th St Ste 1 (33166-3015)
PHONE..................................305 579-2290
Fax: 305 882-8353
▼ **EMP:** 14
SALES (est): 1.7MM **Privately Held**
SIC: 2752 Lithographic Commercial Printing

(G-9814)
KALUZ LLC
Also Called: Decocandles
7105 Nw 41st St (33166-6818)
PHONE..................................786 991-2260
Karen Lawrence, *Mng Member*
▼ **EMP:** 49 **EST:** 2001
SALES (est): 3.2MM **Privately Held**
SIC: 3999 5199 Candles; candles

(G-9815)
KARIGAM ENTERPRISES INC
1110 Brickell Ave Ste 702 (33131-3136)
PHONE..................................305 358-7755
EMP: 9
SALES (est): 1MM **Privately Held**
SIC: 2339 Mfg Women's/Misses' Outerwear

(G-9816)
KASH CORPORATION
7450 Sw 82nd Ave (33143-3805)
PHONE..................................786 368-7747
Rajnish Kashyap, *President*
EMP: 6 **EST:** 2001
SALES (est): 164.2K **Privately Held**
WEB: www.kashcorp.com
SIC: 3691 Storage batteries

(G-9817)
KD-PHARMA USA INC
14193 Sw 119th Ave Ste 10 (33186-6013)
PHONE..................................786 345-5500
Peter Lembke, *President*
EMP: 7 **EST:** 2018
SALES (est): 378.6K **Privately Held**
WEB: www.kdpharmagroup.com
SIC: 2834 Pharmaceutical preparations

(G-9818)
KEL GLO CORP
54 Ne 73rd St (33138-5350)
PHONE..................................305 751-5641
Ron Smalzer, *Ch of Bd*
▼ **EMP:** 7 **EST:** 1952
SQ FT: 10,000
SALES (est): 1.2MM **Privately Held**
WEB: www.kel-glo.com
SIC: 2851 Paints: oil or alkyd vehicle or water thinned; plastics base paints & varnishes

(G-9819)
KENDALL FUEL INC
9949 N Kendall Dr (33176-1720)
PHONE..................................305 270-7735
Ehsan U Haq, *President*
EMP: 5 **EST:** 2009
SALES (est): 10MM **Privately Held**
SIC: 2869 5541 Fuels;

(G-9820)
KENDALL SIGN AND DESIGN INC
Also Called: Sign-A-Rama
12558 Sw 88th St (33186-1850)
PHONE..................................305 595-2000
Paul Klugerman, *President*
EMP: 5 **EST:** 1995
SQ FT: 900
SALES (est): 531.3K **Privately Held**
WEB: www.signarama.com
SIC: 3993 Signs & advertising specialties

(G-9821)
KERALIS INTER INC (PA)
2539 S Byshr Dr Apt 117 (33133-4733)
PHONE..................................305 345-0849
Alhai Eng, *Principal*
EMP: 17 **EST:** 2008
SALES (est): 101.7K **Privately Held**
WEB: www.keralisprofessional.com
SIC: 2844 Toilet preparations

(G-9822)
KING TECH PRINT LLC
7205 Nw 44th St (33166-6418)
PHONE..................................786 362-6249
Pablo E Fernandez, *Principal*
EMP: 7 **EST:** 2014
SALES (est): 163.8K **Privately Held**
SIC: 2752 Commercial printing, lithographic

(G-9823)
KISKEYA MINERALS USA LLC
Also Called: White Cliff
8249 Nw 70th St (33166-2743)
PHONE..................................305 328-5082
Douglas Lofland,
James Cole,
EMP: 8 **EST:** 2009
SQ FT: 5,500
SALES (est): 419K **Privately Held**
SIC: 1481 Mine & quarry services, nonmetallic minerals

(G-9824)
KITE RUNNER LLC
6031 Sw 85th St (33143-8143)
PHONE..................................305 785-5056
Thomas E Byrne Jr, *Manager*
EMP: 6 **EST:** 2016
SALES (est): 213K **Privately Held**
SIC: 3944 Kites

(G-9825)
KLA AVENTURA LLC
600 Sw 1st Ave (33130-3002)
PHONE..................................305 931-2322
Roberto X Ortega, *Principal*
EMP: 9 **EST:** 2010
SALES (est): 167.1K **Privately Held**
WEB: www.klaschoolsaventura.com
SIC: 3825 Instruments to measure electricity

(G-9826)
KLASMANN-DEILMANN AMERICAS INC
1300 S Miami Ave # 1905 (33130-4475)
PHONE..................................305 397-8498
Marinus Nugteren, *Managing Dir*
Martin Nugteren, *Area Mgr*
Deyanira Knight, *Office Mgr*
▲ **EMP:** 2 **EST:** 2011
SALES (est): 3.7MM **Privately Held**
WEB: www.klasmann-deilmann.com
SIC: 2875 Potting soil, mixed

(G-9827)
KMS MEDICAL LLC
13755 Sw 119th Ave (33186-6265)
PHONE..................................305 266-3388
Sean McBrayer,
Matt Palmer,
Kevin W Smith,
EMP: 10 **EST:** 2004
SALES (est): 954.7K **Privately Held**
WEB: www.kms-medical.com
SIC: 3841 8731 Surgical & medical instruments; medical research, commercial

(G-9828)
KNIGHT-RDDR/MIAMI HERALD CR UN
1 Herald Plz Fl 2 (33132-1609)
PHONE..................................305 376-2181
Debra Touhey, *Manager*
▲ **EMP:** 10 **EST:** 1966
SQ FT: 745
SALES (est): 304.7K **Privately Held**
SIC: 2711 Newspapers, publishing & printing

(G-9829)
KORANGY PUBLISHING INC
6318 Biscayne Blvd (33138-6226)
PHONE..................................786 334-5052
EMP: 60
SALES (corp-wide): 20.1MM **Privately Held**
WEB: www.therealdeal.com
SIC: 2741 Miscellaneous publishing
PA: Korangy Publishing Inc
450 W 31st St Fl 4
New York NY 10001
212 260-1332

(G-9830)
KRAMER PHARMACAL INC
8900 Sw 24th St (33165-2075)
PHONE..................................305 226-0641
Juan Ruiz, *President*
EMP: 13 **EST:** 2000
SALES (est): 198.1K **Privately Held**
SIC: 2834 Pharmaceutical preparations

(G-9831)
KREYOL ESSENCE LLC
8325 Ne 2nd Ave Ste 117 (33138-3815)
PHONE..................................786 453-8287
Stephane Jean-Baptiste, *COO*
EMP: 15 **EST:** 2013
SALES (est): 826K **Privately Held**
WEB: www.kreyolessence.com
SIC: 2844 Toilet preparations

(G-9832)
KROME BREWING COMPANY LLC
17480 Sw 232nd St (33170-5504)
PHONE..................................786 601-9337
Gustavo Fernandez, *Manager*
EMP: 8 **EST:** 2016
SALES (est): 514.9K **Privately Held**
SIC: 2082 Beer (alcoholic beverage)

(G-9833)
KUANDO TRADING CORP
1001 Brickell Bay Dr (33131-4900)
PHONE..................................786 603-3772
Reddy Stehlin, *President*
◆ **EMP:** 10 **EST:** 2017
SALES (est): 632.3K **Privately Held**
SIC: 2013 Frozen meats from purchased meat

(G-9834)
L & A QUALITY PRODUCTS INC
2181 Nw 10th Ave (33127-4635)
PHONE..................................305 326-9300
Albert Muniz, *President*
Olga Gaugrra, *Owner*
Jesus Guerra, *Admin Sec*
EMP: 9 **EST:** 1999
SALES (est): 550.9K **Privately Held**
WEB: www.laqualityproducts.com
SIC: 2099 Food preparations

(G-9835)
L A ORNAMENTAL & RACK CORP
3708 Nw 82nd St (33147-4457)
PHONE..................................305 696-0419
Jesus Velunza, *President*
Aleida Velunza, *Vice Pres*
▼ **EMP:** 5 **EST:** 1978
SQ FT: 17,500
SALES (est): 1.2MM **Privately Held**
WEB: www.laornamental.com
SIC: 3315 1731 3446 2411 Fence gates posts & fittings: steel; access control systems specialization; fences or posts, ornamental iron or steel; gates, ornamental metal; rails, fence: round or split

(G-9836)
L AND I DIAMONDS
36 Ne 1st St (33132-2403)
PHONE..................................305 603-7727
Israel Abramov, *Principal*
EMP: 6 **EST:** 2011
SALES (est): 371.3K **Privately Held**
SIC: 3915 Jewel cutting, drilling, polishing, recutting or setting

(G-9837)
L3HARRIS TECHNOLOGIES INC
7508 Nw 54th St (33166-4871)
PHONE..................................305 542-5441
Stephen Brown, *Software Dev*
EMP: 6
SALES (corp-wide): 3.7B **Publicly Held**
WEB: www.l3harris.com
SIC: 3812 Search & navigation equipment
PA: L3harris Technologies, Inc.
1025 W Nasa Blvd
Melbourne FL 32919
321 727-9100

(G-9838)
LA CORONELLA MEAT PROCESSING
9566 Nw 7th Ave (33150-1844)
PHONE..................................305 691-2630
Isidoro Fernandez, *President*
Ramona Fernandez, *Vice Pres*
Margarita Garcia, *Admin Sec*
EMP: 10 **EST:** 1973
SQ FT: 2,400
SALES (est): 1.1MM **Privately Held**
SIC: 2013 Prepared pork products from purchased pork; sausages from purchased meat

(G-9839)
LA CUISINE INTL DISTRS INC
Also Called: LCI DISTRIBUTORS
2005 Nw 115th Ave (33172-4919)
PHONE..................................305 418-0010
Josu Gaubeka, *President*
Rafael Guerrero, *COO*
Lissett Lopez, *Opers Mgr*
Cynthia Carneiro, *Purchasing*
Jaime Miranda, *Technical Mgr*
◆ **EMP:** 24 **EST:** 2004
SALES (est): 11.1MM **Privately Held**
WEB: www.lacuisineinternational.com
SIC: 3639 5023 5064 Major kitchen appliances, except refrigerators & stoves; kitchenware; electrical appliances, television & radio

(G-9840)
LA FABRIKA RETAIL SERVICES LLC
6303 Blue Lagoon Dr Ste 4 (33126-6002)
PHONE..................................786 525-4491
Salomon Amador,
EMP: 5 **EST:** 2015
SQ FT: 700
SALES (est): 413.4K **Privately Held**
SIC: 2542 7319 Stands, merchandise display: except wood; display advertising service

(G-9841)
LA LECHONERA PRODUCTS INC
Also Called: La Lechonera Media
2161 Nw 22nd Ct (33142-7301)
PHONE..................................305 635-2303
Luis Mejuto, *President*
Ernesto Sobalvarro, *General Mgr*
EMP: 15 **EST:** 1974
SALES (est): 924.6K **Privately Held**
WEB: www.lalechoneraproducts.com
SIC: 2035 Seasonings, meat sauces (except tomato & dry)

(G-9842)
LA LUNA LTD
1638 Sw 8th St (33135-5220)
PHONE..................................305 644-0444
Gael Decourtivron, *President*
EMP: 5 **EST:** 1997
SALES (est): 493K **Privately Held**
WEB: www.lalunacigars.com
SIC: 2121 Cigars

(G-9843)
LA MANSION LATINA LLC
Also Called: Biscotti Gourment Bakery
9183 Sw 152nd Path (33196-1262)
PHONE..................................305 406-1606
EMP: 6
SALES (est): 390K **Privately Held**
SIC: 2051 Mfg Bread/Related Products

(G-9844)
LA MONTINA INC
Also Called: Tiger Meat & Provisions
1445 Nw 22nd St (33142-7741)
P.O. Box 14260 (33101-4260)
PHONE..................................305 324-0083
Manuel Alonso, *President*
Luis Requejo, *Vice Pres*
EMP: 21 **EST:** 1975
SQ FT: 6,000
SALES (est): 2.8MM **Privately Held**
SIC: 2013 2011 Ham, canned: from purchased meat; sausages from purchased meat; meat packing plants

(G-9845)
LA MOTI ROOF & TILE INC
1360 Nw 29th St (33142-6620)
PHONE..................................305 635-2641
Ruben Bernal, *President*
Elizabeth Bernal, *Corp Secy*
▼ **EMP:** 7
SQ FT: 1,200
SALES (est): 906K **Privately Held**
WEB: www.lamotirooftile.com
SIC: 3272 Roofing tile & slabs, concrete

(G-9846)
LA PROVIDENCIA EXPRESS CO
Also Called: Anavini
4728 Sw 74th Ave (33155-4417)
P.O. Box 559048 (33255-9048)
PHONE..................................305 409-9894
Ana Del Velasquez, *President*
Jose Velasquez, *Vice Pres*
EMP: 7 **EST:** 1990
SQ FT: 1,200
SALES (est): 811.4K **Privately Held**
SIC: 2361 2321 2325 5137 Dresses: girls', children's & infants'; men's & boys' furnishings; shorts (outerwear): men's, youths' & boys'; women's & children's clothing

(G-9847)
LA PROVINCE INC
2106 Nw 13th Ave (33142-7704)
PHONE..................................305 538-2406
EMP: 18
SQ FT: 8,485
SALES (est): 1.5MM **Privately Held**
SIC: 2051 5149 Mfg Bread/Related Products Whol Groceries

(G-9848)
LA REAL FOODS INC
Also Called: La Real Tortillas
13013 Sw 122nd Ave (33186-6240)
PHONE..................................305 232-6449
Yair Rosemberg, *CEO*
▼ **EMP:** 25 **EST:** 1991
SQ FT: 6,500
SALES (est): 2.9MM **Privately Held**
WEB: www.larealfoods.com
SIC: 2099 Tortillas, fresh or refrigerated

(G-9849)
LA VILLARENA MEAT & PORK INC (PA)
6455 Ne 3rd Ave (33138-6096)
PHONE..................................305 759-0555
Osvaldo Castillo, *President*
Candelario Rodriguez, *Vice Pres*
Teresa Garcia, *Admin Sec*
EMP: 11 **EST:** 1968
SQ FT: 8,898
SALES (est): 6MM **Privately Held**
WEB: www.lavillarena.com
SIC: 2013 5144 5147 Frozen meats from purchased meat; smoked meats from purchased meat; poultry & poultry products; meats, cured or smoked; meats, fresh

(G-9850)
LAAL MANUFACTURING INC
55 Ne 1st St Ste 55 # 55 (33132-2484)
PHONE..................................786 859-3613
Otero Garcia, *Principal*
EMP: 8 **EST:** 2013
SALES (est): 233.5K **Privately Held**
SIC: 3999 Manufacturing industries

(G-9851)
LAHIA AMERICA CORP
12401 Sw 134th Ct (33186-6413)
PHONE..................................305 254-6212
George Vithayathil, *President*
▲ **EMP:** 10 **EST:** 2009
SALES (est): 810K **Privately Held**
SIC: 2299 Textile goods

(G-9852)
LAKEWOOD ORGANICS LLC
2125 Nw 10th Ct (33127-4501)
PHONE..................................305 324-5900
Aaron L Peterson, *Branch Mgr*
EMP: 76
SALES (corp-wide): 15.3MM **Privately Held**
SIC: 2033 Fruit juices: fresh
PA: Lakewood Organics, Llc
3104 W Baseline Rd
Shelby MI 49455
231 861-6333

(G-9853)
LAN DESIGNS INC
Also Called: By Dancers For Dancers
7169 Sw 44th St (33155-4636)
PHONE..................................305 661-7878
Liz Nieves, *President*
EMP: 6 **EST:** 2004
SALES (est): 519.4K **Privately Held**
SIC: 2339 5621 Athletic clothing: women's, misses' & juniors'; women's sportswear

(G-9854)
LAN INDUSTRIES LLC
Also Called: Life All Natural
5413 Nw 74th Ave (33166-4225)
PHONE..................................305 889-2087
Alejandro Meneses, *CEO*
Matthew Guccione, *Accountant*
EMP: 16 **EST:** 2019
SALES (est): 1.4MM **Privately Held**
SIC: 2833 Vitamins, natural or synthetic: bulk, uncompounded

(G-9855)
LAN MUSIC CORP
13611 S Dixie Hwy (33176-7258)
PHONE..................................305 722-5842
Ricardo Boevri, *President*
▼ **EMP:** 3 **EST:** 2005
SALES (est): 30MM **Privately Held**
WEB: www.lanmusicusa.com
SIC: 3931 Musical instruments

(G-9856)
LANCE PRINTERS SERVICE INC
13934 Sw 154th St (33177-0937)
PHONE..................................305 256-7982
EMP: 6 **EST:** 2008
SALES (est): 79.4K **Privately Held**
SIC: 2752 Commercial printing, lithographic

(G-9857)
LAND LEATHER INC
1927 Nw 135th Ave (33182-1925)
PHONE..................................305 594-2260
Susie Iszler, *CEO*
Karl Iszler, *Admin Sec*
EMP: 5 **EST:** 1969
SALES (est): 2.5MM **Privately Held**
WEB: www.landleather.com
SIC: 3199 5199 5948 Leather goods; leather goods, except footwear, gloves, luggage, belting; leather goods, except luggage & shoes

(G-9858)
LANZAS DISTRIBUTOR INC
Also Called: Lanzas Foods
7251 Nw 54th St (33166-4807)
PHONE..................................305 885-5966
Antonio M Lanzas, *President*
Maria S Lanzas, *Vice Pres*
▲ **EMP:** 5 **EST:** 1992
SQ FT: 25,000
SALES (est): 1.6MM **Privately Held**
WEB: www.lanzasfoods.com
SIC: 2022 Natural cheese

(G-9859)
LARGENT FUELS USA LLC
1200 Brickell Ave Ste 240 (33131-3373)
PHONE..................................786 431-5981
Jennifer Ahumada, *Sales Mgr*
Pablo Condeza,
Raul Condeza,
Luisa Solorzano,
EMP: 6 **EST:** 2015
SALES (est): 1MM **Privately Held**
WEB: www.largentfuels.com
SIC: 2869 Fuels

(G-9860)
LARSEN CABINETMAKER CO
14374 Sw 142nd Ave (33186-6769)
PHONE..................................305 252-1212
Ivan Larsen, *Owner*
EMP: 7 **EST:** 1981
SALES (est): 293.4K **Privately Held**
SIC: 2599 2541 2434 Bar, restaurant & cafeteria furniture; wood partitions & fixtures; wood kitchen cabinets

(G-9861)
LAS AMRCAS MLTIMEDIA GROUP LLC
Also Called: Diario Las Americas
888 Brickell Ave Ste 500 (33131-2913)
PHONE..................................305 633-3341
Tulio Casal, *Editor*
Beatriz Mendoza, *Editor*
Aquiles Presilla, *COO*
Ann Fernandez, *Accounts Exec*
Kairy Franco, *Accounts Exec*
EMP: 26 **EST:** 2012
SALES (est): 8.4MM **Privately Held**
WEB: www.diariolasamericas.com
SIC: 2711 8999 Newspapers: publishing only, not printed on site; advertising copy writing

(G-9862)
LAS ZIRH AMERICAS INC
2792 Nw 24th St (33142-7006)
PHONE..................................305 942-7597
Burak P Yolga, *President*
EMP: 7 **EST:** 2017
SALES (est): 148.6K **Privately Held**
WEB: www.laszirhusa.com
SIC: 3496 Tire chains

(G-9863)
LASER SURGICAL FLORIDA INC
900 Biscayne Blvd # 2001 (33132-1563)
PHONE..................................954 609-7639
Russell Wright, *CEO*
Gerald Wright, *President*
EMP: 6 **EST:** 2009
SALES (est): 435.8K **Privately Held**
WEB: www.lasersurgicalofflorida.com
SIC: 3841 Surgical & medical instruments

(G-9864)
LATAM GROUP CORP
12453 Sw 124th Ter (33186-5497)
PHONE..................................305 793-8961
Gabriel Sebastian, *President*
Angel Mendez, *Vice Pres*
EMP: 6 **EST:** 2012
SALES (est): 91K **Privately Held**
SIC: 2822 5113 5169 Synthetic rubber; industrial & personal service paper; chemicals & allied products

(G-9865)
LATAM OPTICAL LLC
2585 Nw 74th Ave (33122-1417)
PHONE..................................786 275-3284
Nestor A Descarso, *Principal*
Mauricio Paez, *Opers Mgr*
◆ **EMP:** 6 **EST:** 2014
SALES (est): 235.5K **Privately Held**
WEB: www.latamoptical.com
SIC: 3089 Lenses, except optical: plastic

(G-9866)
LATELIER PRIS HUTE DESIGN LLC
6151 Biscayne Blvd (33137-2226)
PHONE..................................800 792-3550
Victoria Lane, *VP Sales*
Elisa Waysenson, *VP Sales*
Ricardo Moraes,
Maria Moraes,
EMP: 11 **EST:** 2019
SALES (est): 1.7MM **Privately Held**
WEB: www.leatelierparis.com
SIC: 3469 Kitchen fixtures & equipment: metal, except cast aluminum

(G-9867)
LATIN AMERCN MEATS & FOODS USA (PA)
Also Called: Baby Beef USA
6939 Nw 82nd Ave (33166-2766)
PHONE..................................305 477-2700
Jose Azuaje, *President*
Juan J Tamayo, *Director*
EMP: 8 **EST:** 2015
SALES (est): 400K **Privately Held**
SIC: 2013 5147 5142 5143 Sausages & other prepared meats; meats, fresh; meat, frozen: packaged; cheese

(G-9868)
LATIN AMRCN FNCL PBLCTIONS INC (HQ)
Also Called: Latinfinance
1101 Brickell Ave # 1200 (33131-3105)
PHONE..................................305 416-5261
Stuart Allen, *CEO*
Robert Chandler, *Partner*
Mick Bowen, *Editor*
Richard Ensor, *Chairman*
Karah Niemann, *Regional Mgr*
▲ **EMP:** 14 **EST:** 1988
SQ FT: 3,441
SALES (est): 7.9MM
SALES (corp-wide): 438.1MM **Privately Held**
WEB: www.latinfinance.com
SIC: 2721 Magazines: publishing only, not printed on site
PA: Euromoney Institutional Investor Plc
6-8 Bouverie Street
London EC4Y
207 779-8888

(G-9869)
LATIN DAIRY FOODS LLC
Also Called: Jls Dairy Holdings
2175 Nw 24th Ave (33142-7279)
PHONE..................................305 888-1788
Jose Salazar, *CEO*
EMP: 18 **EST:** 2010
SQ FT: 5,000
SALES (est): 554.9K **Privately Held**
SIC: 2024 5143 Dairy based frozen desserts; frozen dairy desserts

(G-9870)
LATIN PRESS INC
600 Sw 22nd Ave (33135-3119)
PHONE..................................305 285-3133
Max Jaramillo, *CEO*
Duvan Chaverra, *Editor*
Sandra Camacho, *Project Mgr*
Manuela Jaramillo, *CFO*
Amparo Ramirez, *Sales Associate*
EMP: 15 **EST:** 1993
SALES (est): 2.2MM **Privately Held**
WEB: www.latinpressinc.com
SIC: 2721 Magazines: publishing only, not printed on site

(G-9871)
LAU INTERNATIONAL INC
Also Called: Ojm
36 Ne 1st St Ste 438 (33132-2493)
PHONE..................................305 381-9855
Fax: 305 539-0794
▲ **EMP:** 8
SQ FT: 1,500
SALES (est): 954.7K **Privately Held**
SIC: 3911 Mfg Precious Jewelry

(G-9872)
LAZA IRON WORKS INC
7251 N Miami Ave (33150-3719)
PHONE..................................305 754-8200
Israel Laza, *President*
Estrella Moussawel, *Vice Pres*
▼ **EMP:** 12 **EST:** 1980
SQ FT: 4,500
SALES (est): 1.9MM **Privately Held**
WEB: www.lazairon.com
SIC: 3446 Architectural metalwork

(G-9873)
LCN INCORPORATED
Also Called: Consolidated Parking Equipment
6949 Nw 82nd Ave (33166-2766)
PHONE..................................305 461-2770
Alexandre Oliva, *CEO*
Iris Del, *Vice Pres*
Anthony D'Ambrosio, *Treasurer*
Jerry Acosta, *Sales Staff*
Robbie Mancl, *Technician*
EMP: 25 **EST:** 2006
SALES (est): 3.3MM **Privately Held**
WEB: www.consolidatedparking.com
SIC: 3559 Parking facility equipment & supplies

(G-9874)
LDM INDUSTRIES INC
12904 Sw 132nd Ct (33186-5819)
PHONE..................................305 216-1545
Elizabeth Murialdo, *Principal*
EMP: 8 **EST:** 2008
SALES (est): 361.9K **Privately Held**
WEB: www.ldmindustries.com
SIC: 3999 Manufacturing industries

(G-9875)
LE MUNDO VINO LLC
12323 Sw 130th St (33186-6208)
PHONE..................................786 369-5232
Lazara Villalobos,
Juan Cabrales,
▲ **EMP:** 10 **EST:** 2010
SALES (est): 769.2K **Privately Held**
WEB: www.lemundovino.com
SIC: 2082 Beer (alcoholic beverage)

(G-9876)
LEAD ENTERPRISES INC
3300 Nw 29th St (33142-6310)
PHONE..................................305 635-8644
Thomas Taylor, *CEO*
Juan Betancourt, *Controller*
Joaquin Velazquez, *Sales Staff*
◆ **EMP:** 18 **EST:** 1961
SQ FT: 6,600
SALES (est): 1.7MM **Privately Held**
WEB: www.leadenterprises.com
SIC: 3949 3844 Fishing tackle, general; X-ray apparatus & tubes

(G-9877)
LEADEX
4731 Sw 75th Ave (33155-4436)
PHONE..................................305 266-2028
Cary Rogirguez, *Manager*
EMP: 8 **EST:** 1977
SALES (est): 399.3K **Privately Held**
WEB: www.leadexcorp.com
SIC: 3356 Nonferrous rolling & drawing

(G-9878)
LEBLON LLC
Also Called: Leblon Cachaca
2701 S Le Jeune Rd (33134-5809)
PHONE..................................954 649-0148
Eric Goldman, *President*
▲ **EMP:** 8 **EST:** 2005
SALES (est): 149K **Privately Held**
SIC: 2085 Distilled & blended liquors

(G-9879)
LEE CABINETS CORP
11260 Sw 50th St (33165-6038)
PHONE..................................786 291-5871
Jose A Lee, *Principal*
EMP: 6 **EST:** 2016
SALES (est): 92.3K **Privately Held**
SIC: 2434 Wood kitchen cabinets

(G-9880)
LEEDER GROUP INC
8508 Nw 66th St (33166-2635)
PHONE..................................305 436-5030
Mark Webster, *President*
◆ **EMP:** 30 **EST:** 1996
SQ FT: 13,000

SALES (est): 2.8MM **Privately Held**
WEB: www.leedergroup.com
SIC: 3842 Orthopedic appliances

(G-9881)
LEGEND DESIGN AND PRODUCTION
9765 Sw 84th St (33173-4046)
PHONE.................................305 270-1156
Robert Egan, *Owner*
EMP: 6
SALES (est): 410K **Privately Held**
SIC: 2431 1751 Ornamental woodwork: cornices, mantels, etc.; carpentry work

(G-9882)
LEITON DECOR & DESIGN
4237 Nw 37th Ct (33142-4233)
PHONE.................................786 286-4776
Dennis Leiton, *President*
EMP: 6 **EST:** 2008
SALES (est): 100K **Privately Held**
WEB: www.leitondecor.com
SIC: 2434 Wood kitchen cabinets

(G-9883)
LEMON LIME CATERING LLC
425 Nw 100th Ter (33150-1441)
PHONE.................................786 332-3636
Maime Okur, *Principal*
EMP: 7 **EST:** 2012
SALES (est): 124.6K **Privately Held**
WEB: www.lemonlimecatering.com
SIC: 3274 Lime

(G-9884)
LENNOX NATIONAL ACCOUNT S
4418 Sw 74th Ave (33155-4408)
PHONE.................................954 745-3482
EMP: 7 **EST:** 2018
SALES (est): 156K **Privately Held**
WEB: www.lennoxnas.com
SIC: 3585 Refrigeration & heating equipment

(G-9885)
LERNESS SHOE CORP
2155 Sw 8th St (33135-3319)
Rural Route 2155 Sw 8t (33135)
PHONE.................................305 643-6525
Mark Saracino, *Manager*
EMP: 8 **EST:** 1967
SQ FT: 2,700
SALES (est): 745.6K **Privately Held**
WEB: www.lernesshoes.com
SIC: 3144 3143 5661 Women's footwear, except athletic; men's footwear, except athletic; women's shoes; men's shoes

(G-9886)
LESS FRTNATE MUS PUBG LTD LBLT ✪
10724 Nw 18th Ave (33167-3902)
PHONE.................................786 663-0385
Stanislas Pierre,
EMP: 6 **EST:** 2020
SALES (est): 186.6K **Privately Held**
SIC: 2741 Miscellaneous publishing

(G-9887)
LEXMARK INTERNATIONAL INC
5201 Blue Lagoon Dr # 87 (33126-2064)
PHONE.................................305 467-2200
Carlota Blom, *Managing Dir*
Jose Cantor, *Manager*
EMP: 15 **Privately Held**
WEB: www.lexmark.com
SIC: 3577 5065 Printers, computer; electronic parts & equipment
HQ: Lexmark International Inc.
740 W New Circle Rd
Lexington KY 40511

(G-9888)
LEXPRINT LLC
4255 Sw 72nd Ave (33155-4527)
PHONE.................................305 661-2424
Ernesto Rodriguez, *Principal*
EMP: 6 **EST:** 2007
SALES (est): 418.2K **Privately Held**
WEB: www.lexprintusa.com
SIC: 2752 Commercial printing, offset

(G-9889)
LIBRE
2700 Sw 8th St (33135-4619)
PHONE.................................305 267-2000
Demetrio Perez, *Principal*
EMP: 6 **EST:** 2015
SALES (est): 140.2K **Privately Held**
WEB: www.libreonline.com
SIC: 2711 Newspapers

(G-9890)
LIFT AEROSPACE CORP
6960 Nw 50th St (33166-5632)
PHONE.................................305 851-5237
Reinaldo Barroso, *Partner*
Michael Jaramillo, *Business Mgr*
Jonathan Cruz, *Sales Mgr*
Maria Rojas, *Director*
EMP: 14 **EST:** 2013
SALES (est): 2.6MM **Privately Held**
WEB: www.liftaerospace.com
SIC: 3721 5088 5046 5065 Aircraft; transportation equipment & supplies; commercial equipment; electronic parts & equipment; airports, flying fields & services; freight transportation arrangement

(G-9891)
LIGHTNET USA INC
123 Nw 23rd St (33127-4409)
PHONE.................................305 260-6444
Christoph Rosslenbroich, *President*
EMP: 10 **EST:** 2013
SALES (est): 1MM **Privately Held**
SIC: 3648 8748 8712 Area & sports luminaries; lighting consultant; architectural services

(G-9892)
LIGHTWORKS INC
7035 Sw 47th St Ste A (33155-4625)
PHONE.................................305 456-3520
Mainnor Pino, *President*
Solange P Boiangin, *Principal*
Fabrice Pellegrino, *Vice Pres*
Manfred Koberg, *Project Mgr*
EMP: 6 **EST:** 2017
SQ FT: 35,000
SALES (est): 506.6K **Privately Held**
WEB: www.lightworksflorida.com
SIC: 3699 Electrical equipment & supplies

(G-9893)
LILAS DESSERTS INC
12309 Sw 130th St (33186-6208)
PHONE.................................305 252-1441
Reinaldo Navarro Jr, *President*
Sara Navarro, *Manager*
EMP: 19 **EST:** 1989
SQ FT: 10,000
SALES (est): 2.8MM **Privately Held**
WEB: www.lilasdesserts.com
SIC: 2024 Custard, frozen

(G-9894)
LIMITED DESIGNS LLC
382 Ne 191st St 87394 (33179-3899)
PHONE.................................305 547-9909
Elizabeta Dimkova,
EMP: 6 **EST:** 2018
SALES (est): 189.8K **Privately Held**
SIC: 2759 Commercial printing

(G-9895)
LINCOLN-MARTI CMNTY AGCY INC (PA)
2700 Sw 8th St (33135-4619)
PHONE.................................305 643-4888
Martin Anorga, *President*
Dominica Alcantara, *Vice Pres*
EMP: 597 **EST:** 1990
SQ FT: 13,009
SALES: 32.8MM **Privately Held**
WEB: www.lincoln-marti.com
SIC: 2732 8211 5812 8351 Book printing; specialty education; contract food services; child day care services

(G-9896)
LINCOLN-MARTI CMNTY AGCY INC
Also Called: Marti Lincoln Community Agency
450 Sw 16th Ave (33135-3625)
PHONE.................................646 463-6120
EMP: 19
SALES (corp-wide): 32.8MM **Privately Held**
WEB: www.lincoln-marti.com
SIC: 2732 Book printing
PA: Lincoln-Marti Community Agency, Inc.
2700 Sw 8th St
Miami FL 33135
305 643-4888

(G-9897)
LISA TODD INTERNATIONAL LLC
1441 Nw N River Dr 3a (33125-2601)
PHONE.................................305 445-2632
Lisa A Shapiro, *Mng Member*
Coralia J Rodriguez,
EMP: 6 **EST:** 2013
SALES (est): 317.3K **Privately Held**
SIC: 2339 Women's & misses' outerwear

(G-9898)
LIST + BEISLER CORP
200 Suth Bscyne Blvd Lvel Level (33131)
PHONE.................................646 866-6960
Robert Heuveldop, *Managing Prtnr*
Jan Walter, *Managing Prtnr*
Philip Von Der Goltz, *Principal*
EMP: 30 **EST:** 2018
SALES (est): 2.7MM **Privately Held**
WEB: www.list-beisler.coffee
SIC: 2095 Roasted coffee

(G-9899)
LIT LIGHTING & GRIP LLC
19599 Ne 10th Ave (33179-3579)
PHONE.................................305 770-0272
Antal Steinbach, *Principal*
EMP: 6 **EST:** 2013
SALES (est): 156.7K **Privately Held**
SIC: 3648 Lighting equipment

(G-9900)
LIT PRINTS INC
2181 Sw 1st St (33135-1636)
PHONE.................................305 456-0150
EMP: 7 **EST:** 2014
SALES (est): 246K **Privately Held**
WEB: www.litprints.com
SIC: 2752 Commercial printing, lithographic

(G-9901)
LITECRETE INC
Also Called: Lite Crete Insulated Concrete
8095 Nw 64th St (33166-2747)
PHONE.................................305 500-9373
Bernardo Duran, *President*
Eugenio Fernandez, *Vice Pres*
Lina Vidales, *Manager*
▼ **EMP:** 35 **EST:** 1997
SALES (est): 8.4MM **Privately Held**
WEB: www.litecrete.com
SIC: 3273 3446 Ready-mixed concrete; architectural metalwork

(G-9902)
LITHO ART INC
Also Called: Lithographing Art
12190 Sw 131st Ave (33186-6446)
PHONE.................................305 232-7098
Edwardo Valdes, *President*
Berta Huerta, *Director*
Isidro Huerta, *Director*
Ada E Valdes, *Director*
EMP: 7 **EST:** 1990
SALES (est): 837.2K **Privately Held**
WEB: www.printnmore.com
SIC: 2752 Commercial printing, offset

(G-9903)
LIVE AEROSPACE INC
7205 Nw 68th St Ste 11 (33166-3016)
PHONE.................................305 910-0091
Janet Ayo, *President*
EMP: 9 **EST:** 2010
SALES (est): 740.6K **Privately Held**
WEB: www.liveaerospace.com
SIC: 3728 Aircraft parts & equipment

(G-9904)
LLORENS PHRM INTL DIV INC
7080 Nw 37th Ct (33147-6531)
P.O. Box 720008 (33172-0001)
PHONE.................................305 716-0595
Jose Llorens, *President*
Jose Hernadez, *Director*
EMP: 12 **EST:** 2001
SQ FT: 18,000
SALES (est): 3.5MM **Privately Held**
WEB: www.llorenspharm.com
SIC: 2834 Pharmaceutical preparations

(G-9905)
LOGISCENTER LLC
Also Called: Barcode Distributor
5201 Blue Lagoon Dr Fl 8 (33126-7050)
PHONE.................................800 729-0236
Manuel Campos Galvan, *Manager*
Juan L Manaute Lopez, *Manager*
EMP: 6
SALES (est): 409.4K **Privately Held**
WEB: www.logiscenter.us
SIC: 3577 Bar code (magnetic ink) printers

(G-9906)
LOGISTIC SYSTEMS INC (PA)
Also Called: L S I
2175 Nw 115th Ave (33172-4920)
PHONE.................................305 477-4999
Francisco Casanova, *President*
Carlos R Villarreal, *Treasurer*
▼ **EMP:** 5 **EST:** 1992
SQ FT: 2,325
SALES (est): 1.1MM **Privately Held**
WEB: www.lsi-logistics.com
SIC: 3533 3559 Oil & gas drilling rigs & equipment; oil field machinery & equipment; petroleum refinery equipment

(G-9907)
LOGOI INC
12900 Sw 128th St Ste 204 (33186-6274)
P.O. Box 770128 (33177-0003)
PHONE.................................305 232-5880
Joseph Linn, *Ch of Bd*
Leslie Thompson, *President*
Angie Moure, *Editor*
Edward Thompson, *Vice Pres*
Oscar Oglieve, *Treasurer*
EMP: 7 **EST:** 1959
SQ FT: 5,000
SALES: 331.7K **Privately Held**
WEB: www.logoi.org
SIC: 2731 Textbooks: publishing only, not printed on site

(G-9908)
LONGCHAMP USA INC
1450 Brickell Ave # 2140 (33131-3444)
PHONE.................................305 372-1628
Kenneth Thomas, *Sales Staff*
Christine Auclir, *Manager*
Jennifer Hoang, *Manager*
Joshua Kokeny, *Store Dir*
EMP: 36 **Privately Held**
WEB: www.longchamp.com
SIC: 3199 Equestrian related leather articles
PA: Longchamp Usa, Inc.
4 Applegate Dr B
Robbinsville NJ 08691

(G-9909)
LONGEVERON INC
1951 Nw 7th Ave Ste 520 (33136-1121)
PHONE.................................305 909-0840
Joshua M Hare, *Ch of Bd*
Geoff Green, *President*
Dan Gincel, *Senior VP*
Anthony Oliva, *Senior VP*
James Clavijo, *CFO*
EMP: 12 **EST:** 2014
SQ FT: 15,000
SALES: 5.6MM **Privately Held**
WEB: www.longeveron.com
SIC: 2834 2836 Pharmaceutical preparations; biological products, except diagnostic

(G-9910)
LOOK WORLDWIDE INC
6851 Sw 31st St (33155-3823)
PHONE.................................305 662-1287
William Sancho, *President*
Vincent Sancho, *Vice Pres*
EMP: 6 **EST:** 1996
SQ FT: 1,500
SALES (est): 389.6K **Privately Held**
SIC: 3999 Advertising display products

(G-9911)
LOPEZ & COMPANY INC (PA)
Also Called: Lopco Aviation
2221 Ne 164th St (33160-3703)
PHONE..................................305 302-3045
Jose E Lopez, *President*
EMP: 32 **EST:** 2008
SALES (est): 3MM **Privately Held**
SIC: 3728 Military aircraft equipment & armament

(G-9912)
LOS PRIMOS EXPRESS SERVICE
Also Called: LP Express Services
12039 Sw 132nd Ct (33186-4783)
PHONE..................................786 701-3297
Judith Cruz, *President*
EMP: 6 **EST:** 2016
SALES (est): 615.9K **Privately Held**
WEB: www.losprimosexpress.com
SIC: 1389 1799 7299 1522 Construction, repair & dismantling services; cleaning new buildings after construction; home/office interiors finishing, furnishing & remodeling; handyman service; remodeling, multi-family dwellings; moving services

(G-9913)
LOTUS CONTAINERS INC
1000 Brickell Ave Ste 640 (33131-3033)
PHONE..................................786 590-1056
Willem-Alexander Dous, *CEO*
Marcus Rocha, *President*
Tracey Qu, *Managing Dir*
Eva Partsch, *Opers Dir*
Joanna Alruzzi, *Opers Mgr*
EMP: 9 **EST:** 2018
SALES (est): 2.9MM **Privately Held**
WEB: www.lotus-containers.com
SIC: 3499 7359 3799 Boxes for packing & shipping, metal; rental store, general; transportation equipment

(G-9914)
LRVS BARRICADES LLC
8461 Nw 61st St (33166-3307)
PHONE..................................305 343-6101
Jack Lurvey, *Principal*
EMP: 7 **EST:** 2016
SALES (est): 339.9K **Privately Held**
WEB: www.ssbarricades.com
SIC: 3499 Barricades, metal

(G-9915)
LUDACA PRINTING CORP
13339 Sw 42nd St (33175-3270)
PHONE..................................305 300-4355
Luz Orellana, *Principal*
EMP: 6 **EST:** 2017
SALES (est): 82.8K **Privately Held**
WEB: www.ludacaprinting.com
SIC: 2752 Commercial printing, offset

(G-9916)
LUGLOC LLC
550 Nw 29th St (33127-3918)
PHONE..................................305 961-1765
EMP: 10
SQ FT: 6,000
SALES: 700K **Privately Held**
SIC: 3669 8748 Mfg Communications Equipment Business Consulting Services

(G-9917)
LUMENIS LTD
6800 Sw 40th St Ste 102 (33155-3708)
PHONE..................................305 508-5052
EMP: 15
SALES (est): 920K **Privately Held**
SIC: 3841 Business Services

(G-9918)
LUMILUM LLC
12400 Sw 134th Ct Ste 1 (33186-6499)
PHONE..................................305 233-2844
Michael Meiser, *President*
▲ **EMP:** 12 **EST:** 2012
SQ FT: 2,500
SALES (est): 1.2MM **Privately Held**
WEB: www.lumilum.com
SIC: 3646 5063 5719 Commercial indusl & institutional electric lighting fixtures; lighting fixtures, commercial & industrial; lighting fixtures

(G-9919)
LUMIRON INC
20725 Ne 16th Ave Ste A33 (33179-2126)
PHONE..................................305 652-2599
Shai Dinari, *President*
Laura Dinari, *Vice Pres*
EMP: 5 **EST:** 2002
SALES (est): 1MM **Privately Held**
WEB: www.lumiron.com
SIC: 3674 Light emitting diodes

(G-9920)
LUNA NEGRA PRODUCTIONS INC
3110 Sw 129th Ave (33175-2508)
PHONE..................................786 247-1215
EMP: 7 **EST:** 1999
SALES (est): 258.1K **Privately Held**
WEB: www.reyruiz.com
SIC: 2741 Music book & sheet music publishing

(G-9921)
LUSA SUPPLIER LLC
7339 Nw 66th St (33166-3009)
PHONE..................................305 885-7634
Carlos Sousa,
◆ **EMP:** 9 **EST:** 2009
SALES (est): 1.2MM **Privately Held**
WEB: www.lusasupplier.com
SIC: 3714 Water pump, motor vehicle

(G-9922)
LUX UNLIMITED INC
Also Called: Future Designs By Lahijani
4121 Nw 27th St (33142-5605)
P.O. Box 144979, Coral Gables (33114-4979)
PHONE..................................305 871-8774
Mike Lahijani, *President*
Elsa Lahijani, *Admin Sec*
◆ **EMP:** 7 **EST:** 1979
SQ FT: 15,000
SALES (est): 834.3K **Privately Held**
WEB: www.luxunlimited.com
SIC: 3648 Lighting equipment

(G-9923)
M & M PLASTICS INC
15800 Nw 15th Ave (33169-5606)
PHONE..................................305 688-4335
Anthony Cohen, *President*
▲ **EMP:** 32 **EST:** 2009
SALES (est): 1.4MM **Privately Held**
WEB: www.mandmplastics.net
SIC: 3089 Injection molding of plastics

(G-9924)
M CABINETS
18955 Ne 4th Ct (33179-3901)
PHONE..................................305 968-8188
EMP: 6 **EST:** 2018
SALES (est): 271.4K **Privately Held**
SIC: 2434 Wood kitchen cabinets

(G-9925)
M F B INTERNATIONAL INC
Also Called: Magic Faucet Bidet
8323 Nw 64th St (33166-2601)
PHONE..................................305 436-6601
Roger Mora, *President*
Jose Romeu, *Sales Mgr*
▲ **EMP:** 5 **EST:** 1981
SALES (est): 394.3K **Privately Held**
SIC: 3261 3432 Bidets, vitreous china; plumbing fixture fittings & trim

(G-9926)
M L SOLUTIONS INC
1395 Brckwell Ave Ste 800 (33132)
PHONE..................................305 506-5113
Michelle Lynn Adderley, *President*
Vicki Drane, *Admin Sec*
EMP: 5 **EST:** 2010
SQ FT: 1,000
SALES (est): 300K **Privately Held**
SIC: 2752 Commercial printing, lithographic

(G-9927)
M R M S INC
Also Called: Priority Manufacturing
571 Nw 29th St (33127-3917)
PHONE..................................305 576-3000
Fax: 305 576-2672
▼ **EMP:** 6
SQ FT: 3,800
SALES (est): 500K **Privately Held**
SIC: 2326 Mfg Men's/Boy's Suits/Coats Mfg Women's/Misses' Suits/Coats Mfg Men's/Boy's Work Clothing

(G-9928)
M&C HARDWARE LLC
13720 Sw 152nd St (33177-1161)
PHONE..................................305 971-9444
Luis F Trabucco,
EMP: 7 **EST:** 2015
SALES (est): 314.7K **Privately Held**
SIC: 3429 Builders' hardware

(G-9929)
MA FINE FOODS LLC
13280 Sw 131st St Ste 106 (33186-6286)
PHONE..................................305 878-6277
Marcelo Aviles Martirene,
EMP: 6 **EST:** 2014
SALES (est): 135.2K **Privately Held**
WEB: www.mafinefoods.com
SIC: 2032 Ethnic foods: canned, jarred, etc.

(G-9930)
MA GLASS & MIRROR LLC
Also Called: La Glass
7116 Nw 42nd St (33166-6825)
PHONE..................................305 593-8555
Nelson Morelo,
Roger Abdo,
EMP: 15 **EST:** 2014
SQ FT: 20,000
SALES (est): 1MM **Privately Held**
WEB: www.la-glass.com
SIC: 3231 1793 Products of purchased glass; glass & glazing work

(G-9931)
MA METAL FABRICATORS INC
937 Nw 97th Ave Apt 104 (33172-2383)
PHONE..................................786 343-0268
Marco A Perez, *President*
EMP: 7 **EST:** 2012
SALES (est): 587.8K **Privately Held**
WEB: www.metal-fabricators.org
SIC: 3499 Furniture parts, metal

(G-9932)
MACHIN SIGNS INC
2530 Nw 77th St (33147-5506)
PHONE..................................305 694-0464
Jose Machin, *President*
EMP: 8 **EST:** 2007
SALES (est): 996.1K **Privately Held**
WEB: www.machinsigns.com
SIC: 3993 Electric signs

(G-9933)
MAGNETO SPORTS LLC
360 Nw 27th St (33127-4158)
PHONE..................................760 593-4589
Andrew Curtis, *President*
EMP: 6 **EST:** 2017
SALES (est): 383.3K **Privately Held**
SIC: 3949 Skateboards

(G-9934)
MAGNUM MARINE CORPORATION
2900 Ne 188th St (33180-2998)
PHONE..................................305 931-4292
Katrin Theodoli, *President*
▼ **EMP:** 20 **EST:** 1975
SQ FT: 10,000
SALES (est): 1.1MM **Privately Held**
WEB: www.magnummarine.com
SIC: 3732 Boats, fiberglass: building & repairing; boats, rigid: plastics

(G-9935)
MAHNKES ORTHTICS PRSTHTICS OF (PA)
Also Called: Sun Coast Orthotics Assn
4990 Sw 72nd Ave Ste 107 (33155-5524)
PHONE..................................954 772-1299
Silvio Martinez, *President*
EMP: 8 **EST:** 1975
SQ FT: 3,000
SALES (est): 1.1MM **Privately Held**
WEB: www.mahnkesop.com
SIC: 3842 5047 Prosthetic appliances; medical & hospital equipment

(G-9936)
MAIN PACKAGING SUPPLY
7317 Nw 61st St (33166-3703)
P.O. Box 1148, Coshocton OH (43812-6148)
PHONE..................................305 863-7176
Adianes Piloto, *President*
Betty Rodriguez, *Vice Pres*
Ramon Perez, *Treasurer*
▼ **EMP:** 23 **EST:** 2001
SQ FT: 7,000
SALES (est): 2.8MM **Privately Held**
WEB: www.mainpackagingsupply.net
SIC: 2621 5131 Wrapping & packaging papers; labels

(G-9937)
MAIN USA CORP
Also Called: Voda USA
8549 Nw 68th St (33166-2664)
PHONE..................................305 499-4994
Dario Boyortnik, *President*
Albert Serge, *Vice Pres*
▲ **EMP:** 6 **EST:** 2002
SQ FT: 5,000
SALES (est): 752.1K **Privately Held**
WEB: www.watermainusa.com
SIC: 3589 Water purification equipment, household type

(G-9938)
MALETA IMPORT
6928 Nw 12th St (33126-1336)
PHONE..................................305 592-2410
Hsiu-MEI Chang, *President*
Chih-Cheng Chen, *Vice Pres*
Lisa Chen, *Treasurer*
Anna Vasquez, *Manager*
▲ **EMP:** 6 **EST:** 1999
SQ FT: 10,000
SALES (est): 494.6K **Privately Held**
WEB: www.cyluggageinc.com
SIC: 3161 Luggage

(G-9939)
MAMALU WOOD LLC
7003 N Waterway Dr # 207 (33155-2842)
PHONE..................................305 261-6332
EMP: 8
SALES (est): 44K **Privately Held**
SIC: 2499 Mfg Wood Products

(G-9940)
MAMBI CHEESE COMPANY INC
Also Called: Sanchelima Dairy Products
2151 Nw 10th Ave (33127-4635)
PHONE..................................305 324-5282
Juan A Sanchelima, *President*
Victoria Wedmeyer, *Treasurer*
Maximo Cuesta, *Controller*
Jenny Romney, *Director*
Chris Sanchelima, *Patent Law*
▲ **EMP:** 18 **EST:** 1975
SQ FT: 1,824
SALES (est): 484.7K **Privately Held**
SIC: 2022 Natural cheese

(G-9941)
MANDALA TOOL COMPANY INC
18588 Ne 2nd Ave (33179-4427)
PHONE..................................305 652-4575
James Power, *President*
Karen Power, *Vice Pres*
EMP: 5 **EST:** 1979
SQ FT: 2,500
SALES (est): 474.6K **Privately Held**
WEB: www.mandalatool.com
SIC: 3599 Machine shop, jobbing & repair

(G-9942)
MANUTECH ASSEMBLY INC (PA)
7901 Nw 67th St (33166-2632)
PHONE..................................305 888-2800
Lance P Durban, *President*
Nadia Durban, *Chairman*
Sam Seyfi, *Vice Pres*
Laila Durban, *Opers Mgr*
Bernadette Villagracia, *Engineer*
◆ **EMP:** 3 **EST:** 2010
SQ FT: 25,000

▲ = Import ▼=Export
◆ =Import/Export

SALES (est): 52.8MM **Privately Held**
WEB: www.manutech.us
SIC: **3612** 3677 Power transformers, electric; inductors, electronic

(G-9943)
MAR COMPANY DISTRIBUTORS LLC
Also Called: AROMAR
6750 Nw 79th Ave (33166-2779)
PHONE..................................786 477-4174
Marcelo Moreno, *Mng Member*
Mauricio Garcia, *Products*
EMP: 48 **EST**: 2013
SALES: 12.3MM **Privately Held**
WEB: www.aromar.com
SIC: **2844** Concentrates, perfume

(G-9944)
MARES SERVICES CORP
14758 Sw 56th St (33185-4067)
PHONE..................................305 752-0093
Jany De La Nuez, *Principal*
EMP: 11 **EST**: 2013
SALES (est): 288.6K **Privately Held**
SIC: **3441** Fabricated structural metal

(G-9945)
MAREY INTERNATIONAL LLC
8113 Nw 68th St (33166-2757)
P.O. Box 6281, San Juan PR (00914-6281)
PHONE..................................787 727-0277
Victor Yanguas, *Mng Member*
Lourdes Yanguas,
EMP: 7 **EST**: 2014
SALES (est): 733.1K **Privately Held**
WEB: www.marey.com
SIC: **3639** 5074 Hot water heaters, household; water heaters, except electric

(G-9946)
MARGARITA INTERNL TRADING INC
Also Called: Margarita International
5601 Nw 72nd Ave (33166-4207)
PHONE..................................305 688-1300
▲ **EMP**: 12
SQ FT: 20,000
SALES (est): 1.5MM **Privately Held**
SIC: **3142** Mfg House Slippers

(G-9947)
MARIA FUENTES LLC
10130 Sw 32nd St (33165-2915)
PHONE..................................305 717-3404
Maria Fuentes,
EMP: 7 **EST**: 2013
SALES (est): 292.5K **Privately Held**
SIC: **2339** 7389 Women's & misses' accessories; business services

(G-9948)
MARINE CANVAS INC
471 Ne 79th St (33138-4514)
PHONE..................................305 325-1830
Kim Waesnir, *Principal*
EMP: 6 **EST**: 2012
SALES (est): 98.8K **Privately Held**
WEB: www.marinecanvasmiami.com
SIC: **2211** Canvas

(G-9949)
MARIO KENNY
Also Called: Cosmo Leather Co
789 Ne 83rd St (33138-4119)
PHONE..................................786 274-0527
Mario Kenny, *Partner*
EMP: 5 **EST**: 1999
SALES (est): 348.1K **Privately Held**
SIC: **2326** 4725 2311 2299 Men's & boys' work clothing; arrangement of travel tour packages, wholesale; men's & boys' suits & coats; batting, wadding, padding & fillings

(G-9950)
MARIOS CASTING JEWELRY INC
36 Ne 1st St Ste 851 (33132-2467)
PHONE..................................305 374-2894
Martha Camero, *President*
Elsa Martinez, *Corp Secy*
▼ **EMP**: 9 **EST**: 1968
SQ FT: 420
SALES (est): 714.4K **Privately Held**
WEB: www.marioscasting.com
SIC: **3915** 5944 3911 Jewelers' materials & lapidary work; jewelry, precious stones & precious metals; jewelry, precious metal

(G-9951)
MARTELL GLASS
7246 Nw 25th St (33122-1701)
PHONE..................................786 336-0142
Luis Miduel, *Principal*
▼ **EMP**: 8 **EST**: 2007
SALES (est): 164.5K **Privately Held**
WEB: www.martellgallery.com
SIC: **3088** 3231 3431 Shower stalls, fiberglass & plastic; doors, glass: made from purchased glass; shower stalls, metal

(G-9952)
MARTINEZ DISTRIBUTORS CORP
3081 Nw 74th Ave (33122-1427)
P.O. Box 526368 (33152-6368)
PHONE..................................305 882-8282
Fabian J Martinez, *Branch Mgr*
EMP: 20
SALES (corp-wide): 58.3MM **Privately Held**
WEB: www.mdist.us
SIC: **2011** Meat packing plants
PA: Martinez Distributors Corp.
7379 Nw 31st St
Miami FL 33122
305 882-8282

(G-9953)
MASSIMO ROMA LLC
1395 Brickell Ave Ste 900 (33131-3302)
PHONE..................................561 302-5998
Massimiliano Mattetti, *Mng Member*
EMP: 6 **EST**: 2014
SALES (est): 549.5K **Privately Held**
WEB: www.massimoroma.com
SIC: **3999** Atomizers, toiletry

(G-9954)
MASTER FABRICATORS INC
12101 Sw 114th Pl (33176-4492)
PHONE..................................786 537-7440
Heriberto Rosales, *President*
Mayra Sixto, *Partner*
Myra Rosales, *Vice Pres*
▲ **EMP**: 10 **EST**: 1997
SQ FT: 5,000
SALES (est): 962.6K **Privately Held**
WEB: www.masterfabricatorsinc.com
SIC: **3441** Fabricated structural metal

(G-9955)
MASTER PAINTING & SEALANTS LLC
480 Ne 112th St (33161-7160)
PHONE..................................305 910-5104
Manuel Turcios, *Principal*
EMP: 6 **EST**: 2008
SALES (est): 191.7K **Privately Held**
SIC: **2891** Sealants

(G-9956)
MATRIX PACKAGING OF FLORIDA (DH)
1001 Brickell Bay Dr (33131-4900)
PHONE..................................305 358-9696
Joseph Artiga, *President*
Joaquin Vinas, *Corp Secy*
◆ **EMP**: 8 **EST**: 1989
SQ FT: 2,300
SALES (est): 51.2MM **Privately Held**
SIC: **2655** 2631 6794 5087 Fiber cans, drums & similar products; paperboard mills; franchises, selling or licensing; beauty parlor equipment & supplies; cosmetics
HQ: Conitex Sonoco Holding B.V.
Prinses Margrietplnts 88 Wtc Toren E,
's-Gravenhage
850 700-300

(G-9957)
MATSU IMAGING LLC
2125 Nw 115th Ave (33172-4920)
PHONE..................................305 503-2906
Ana M Garcia, *Administration*
EMP: 10 **EST**: 2014
SALES (est): 209.7K **Privately Held**
WEB: www.matsullc.com
SIC: **3861** Photographic equipment & supplies

(G-9958)
MAXAM GROUP LLC
Also Called: Brainchild Nutritionals
20725 Ne 16th Ave Ste A1 (33179-2123)
PHONE..................................305 952-3227
Samuel Swerdlow, *President*
EMP: 10 **EST**: 1999
SALES (est): 1MM **Privately Held**
SIC: **2023** Dietary supplements, dairy & non-dairy based

(G-9959)
MC INTL TRANSPORTATION
8321 Nw 68th St (33166-2662)
P.O. Box 526661 (33152-6661)
PHONE..................................305 805-8228
Franceseo Monetti, *Principal*
Fulvio Monetti, *Manager*
EMP: 14 **EST**: 2007
SALES (est): 869.9K **Privately Held**
WEB: www.mcitransport.com
SIC: **3537** Trucks: freight, baggage, etc.: industrial, except mining

(G-9960)
MD AUDIO ENGINEERING INC
6941 Nw 42nd St (33166-6800)
PHONE..................................305 593-8361
Jose L Telle, *President*
Maryelin Cedeno, *President*
▲ **EMP**: 8 **EST**: 2011
SQ FT: 27,000
SALES (est): 1MM **Privately Held**
WEB: www.orioncaraudio.com
SIC: **3651** Audio electronic systems

(G-9961)
MDINTOUCH US INC
11735 Sw 103rd Ave (33176-4000)
P.O. Box 562916 (33256-2916)
PHONE..................................786 268-1161
Kent Wreder, *President*
Karen Wreder, *Admin Sec*
EMP: 8 **EST**: 1999
SALES (est): 1.4MM **Privately Held**
WEB: www.mdintouch.com
SIC: **7372** 7338 Business oriented computer software; secretarial & typing service

(G-9962)
MECOL OIL TOOLS CORP
1741 Nw 21st St (33142-7433)
PHONE..................................305 638-7686
Claudio Pietrobelli, *Principal*
Alejandro Pietrobelli, *Principal*
Fausto Pietrobelli, *Principal*
EMP: 14 **EST**: 2009
SALES (est): 3.8MM **Privately Held**
WEB: www.mecol.com
SIC: **1389** Running, cutting & pulling casings, tubes & rods
PA: Mecol Americas Colombia S A
Calle 88 30 74
Bogota 820

(G-9963)
MED DENTAL EQUIPMENT (IMPORT)
7795 Sw 161st Ave (33193-3405)
PHONE..................................786 417-8486
Victor Bernal, *Principal*
EMP: 6 **EST**: 2008
SALES (est): 85.8K **Privately Held**
SIC: **3843** Dental equipment

(G-9964)
MEDALLION LEISURE FURNITURE
800 Nw 166th St (33169-5820)
PHONE..................................305 626-0000
Robert L Gass Jr, *President*
Albert Careaga, *Sales Staff*
▼ **EMP**: 25 **EST**: 1972
SQ FT: 20,000
SALES (est): 483.1K **Privately Held**
WEB: www.medallionfurniture.com
SIC: **2514** Lawn furniture: metal

(G-9965)
MEDEIROS CUSTOM WOOD WORK
8000 Nw 37th Ave (33147-4465)
PHONE..................................305 970-0472
EMP: 6 **EST**: 2007
SALES (est): 23K **Privately Held**
SIC: **2431** Millwork

(G-9966)
MEDICAL OUTFITTERS INC (PA)
8062 Nw 66th St (33166-2728)
PHONE..................................305 885-4045
Miguel Machuca, *President*
Viviana Machuca, *Vice Pres*
Zelinsky Mark, *Engineer*
Susan Traino, *Exec Dir*
EMP: 3 **EST**: 2010
SALES: 6.9MM **Privately Held**
WEB: www.medicaloutfitter.net
SIC: **3826** 5047 Magnetic resonance imaging apparatus; medical & hospital equipment

(G-9967)
MEDIPHARMA INC (PA)
2001 Sw 27th Ave (33145-2540)
PHONE..................................305 858-7332
Carlos M Siblesz, *President*
George Siblesz, *Business Mgr*
George L Siblesz, *Vice Pres*
Magali A Siblesz, *Vice Pres*
Enrique G Garcia, *Treasurer*
▼ **EMP**: 6 **EST**: 1977
SQ FT: 17,050
SALES (est): 1.2MM **Privately Held**
WEB: www.medipharmainc.com
SIC: **2834** Pharmaceutical preparations

(G-9968)
MEDTEK MEDICAL SOLUTIONS LLC
6961 Nw 82nd Ave (33166-2774)
PHONE..................................786 458-8080
Felix M Zuniga, *President*
Arnie Appell, *COO*
Jeffrey S Appell, *Vice Pres*
Roxanne Zuniga, *Opers Staff*
EMP: 13 **EST**: 2007
SALES (est): 1MM **Privately Held**
WEB: www.medtek-ms.com
SIC: **2599** 7363 Hospital beds; medical help service

(G-9969)
MEDTRONIC
8501 Sw 84th Ct (33143-6913)
PHONE..................................305 206-8487
Jesus Azan, *Principal*
Erin Keller, *Sales Staff*
Mark Aeschleman, *Manager*
EMP: 16 **EST**: 2017
SALES (est): 287K **Privately Held**
WEB: www.medtronic.com
SIC: **3841** Surgical & medical instruments

(G-9970)
MEEKTEES LLC
3606 Nw 5th Ave (33127-3160)
PHONE..................................786 424-8491
Tamika L Denson, *President*
EMP: 6 **EST**: 2014
SALES (est): 86.6K **Privately Held**
SIC: **2759** Screen printing

(G-9971)
MEGA 4S BOTTLING COMPANY LLC
5144 Sw 163rd Pl (33185-5165)
PHONE..................................305 815-3775
Henri Chaumin, *Principal*
EMP: 6 **EST**: 2013
SALES (est): 218.4K **Privately Held**
WEB: www.mega4s.com
SIC: **2086** Bottled & canned soft drinks

(G-9972)
MEGATRON EQUITY PARTNERS INC
801 Brickell Ave Ste 900 (33131-2979)
PHONE..................................305 789-6688
John B Schmidt, *President*
EMP: 11 **EST**: 2007
SQ FT: 10,000

SALES (est): 245.7K **Privately Held**
SIC: 2052 Bakery products, dry

(G-9973)
MENDEZ FUEL
11870 Sw 40th St (33175-3532)
PHONE..................................305 227-0470
Michael Mendez, *Principal*
EMP: 7 **EST:** 2013
SALES (est): 812.2K **Privately Held**
WEB: www.mendez-fuel.com
SIC: 2869 Fuels

(G-9974)
MENDOZA PAVERS CORP
1137 Nw 2nd St Apt 3 (33128-1026)
PHONE..................................305 494-6794
Luis A Mendoza, *Principal*
EMP: 7 **EST:** 2004
SALES (est): 187.7K **Privately Held**
WEB: www.mendozapavers.com
SIC: 2951 Asphalt paving mixtures & blocks

(G-9975)
MENSCIENCE-MK
2199 Nw 22nd Ct (33142-7301)
PHONE..................................305 361-0994
Christian Sannia, *CFO*
Albert Hexson, *Manager*
EMP: 8 **EST:** 2016
SALES (est): 341.4K **Privately Held**
WEB: www.menscience.com
SIC: 2844 Cosmetic preparations

(G-9976)
MENU MEN INC
1301 Nw 27th Ave (33125-2509)
PHONE..................................305 633-7925
Walter Baker Sr, *President*
Donald Baker, *Vice Pres*
Michele Benesch, *Vice Pres*
Aracelys Pena, *Office Mgr*
Don Baker, *CIO*
▼ **EMP:** 21 **EST:** 1968
SQ FT: 13,000
SALES (est): 3.1MM **Privately Held**
WEB: www.menumen.com
SIC: 2752 2791 Commercial printing, offset; typesetting

(G-9977)
MERCED INDUSTRIAL CORP
230 Nw 107th Ave Apt 106 (33172-3887)
PHONE..................................908 309-0170
Oscar Merced, *President*
Nancy M Eman, *Vice Pres*
EMP: 6 **EST:** 2007
SQ FT: 3,000
SALES (est): 313K **Privately Held**
SIC: 3731 Landing ships, building & repairing

(G-9978)
MERCOFRAMES OPTICAL CORP
Also Called: Merco Frame
5555 Nw 74th Ave (33166-4200)
PHONE..................................305 882-0120
Alejandro Gutman, *President*
Marina Gonzalez Ugarte, *Vice Pres*
◆ **EMP:** 5 **EST:** 1999
SQ FT: 3,500
SALES (est): 952K **Privately Held**
WEB: www.mercoframes.com
SIC: 3827 Optical instruments & lenses

(G-9979)
MERCURY AIRCRAFT
1135 Nw 159th Dr (33169-5807)
PHONE..................................607 776-7002
Richard Bussmann, *Engineer*
Claudio Funes, *Engineer*
Bob Cooper, *Executive*
EMP: 7 **EST:** 2019
SALES (est): 258.2K **Privately Held**
WEB: www.mercuryaircraft.com
SIC: 3444 Sheet metalwork

(G-9980)
MERIT INTERNATIONAL ENTPS INC
Also Called: Access Tools
1628 Nw 28th St (33142-6668)
PHONE..................................305 635-1011
Aurelio A Vigil, *President*
◆ **EMP:** 20 **EST:** 1984
SQ FT: 26,000
SALES: 3MM **Privately Held**
WEB: www.accesstoolsusa.com
SIC: 3423 Hand & edge tools

(G-9981)
MERKAVAH INTERNATIONAL INC
201 S Biscayne Blvd (33131-4332)
PHONE..................................305 909-6798
Barry Schneer, *CEO*
Claudia Mesa, *President*
Oscar Gonzalez, *Corp Secy*
Chad Altieri, *COO*
Leo Snari, *Vice Pres*
EMP: 7 **EST:** 2008
SALES (est): 115.7K **Privately Held**
WEB: www.merkavahsugar.com
SIC: 2062 Cane sugar refining

(G-9982)
MERLOLA INDUSTRIES LLC ✪
7950 Nw 53rd St Ste 341 (33166-4791)
PHONE..................................888 418-0408
Cery Perle,
EMP: 8 **EST:** 2020
SALES (est): 856.7K **Privately Held**
SIC: 3841 Surgical & medical instruments

(G-9983)
MERRILL-STEVENS DRY DOCK CO (PA)
Also Called: Merrill-Stevens Yachts
1270 Nw 11th St (33125-1680)
PHONE..................................305 640-5676
Fred W Kirtland, *CEO*
Hugh Westbrook, *Ch of Bd*
Ron Baker, *President*
Carole Shields Westbrook, *Chairman*
Brent Allsop, *Project Mgr*
▲ **EMP:** 90 **EST:** 1923
SQ FT: 60,000
SALES (est): 9MM **Privately Held**
SIC: 3732 7389 Boat building & repairing; yacht brokers

(G-9984)
METAL IMPROVEMENT COMPANY LLC
1940 Nw 70th Ave (33126-1326)
PHONE..................................305 592-5960
Jose Lapuerta, *Manager*
Jose Puerta, *Manager*
Yvonne Engle, *Administration*
EMP: 7
SQ FT: 8,000
SALES (corp-wide): 2.3B **Publicly Held**
WEB: www.cwst.com
SIC: 3398 Shot peening (treating steel to reduce fatigue)
HQ: Metal Improvement Company, Llc
80 E Rte 4 Ste 310
Paramus NJ 07652
201 843-7800

(G-9985)
METAL SPINNING SYSTEMS INC
14250 Sw 136th St Ste 2 (33186-6718)
PHONE..................................305 252-7778
Manuel Rocafort, *Principal*
EMP: 7 **EST:** 2010
SALES (est): 79.4K **Privately Held**
SIC: 3469 Spinning metal for the trade

(G-9986)
METRO DOOR BRICKELL LLC
2660 Ne 189th St (33180-2628)
PHONE..................................786 326-4748
Jose Alter, *Principal*
EMP: 7 **EST:** 2014
SALES (est): 358.7K **Privately Held**
WEB: www.metrodooraventura.com
SIC: 2434 Wood kitchen cabinets

(G-9987)
MIA AEROSPACE LLC
12560 Nw 11th Ln (33182-2476)
PHONE..................................786 973-4118
Alvaro Vera, *Principal*
EMP: 6 **EST:** 2018
SALES (est): 195.6K **Privately Held**
WEB: www.aerospaceasset.com
SIC: 3721 Aircraft

(G-9988)
MIA APPLIANCES LLC
3650 N Miami Ave Fl 2 (33127-3114)
PHONE..................................866 670-4860
EMP: 6
SALES (est): 56K **Privately Held**
WEB: www.mia-appliances.com
SIC: 3639 Household appliances

(G-9989)
MIA CONSULTING & TRADING INC
Also Called: Performance USA Battery
7806 Nw 71st St Ste 209 (33166-2345)
P.O. Box 2423 Sw 147 Ave (33185)
PHONE..................................305 640-9677
EMP: 6
SQ FT: 4,500
SALES (est): 686.9K **Privately Held**
SIC: 3625 Mfg Relays/Industrial Controls

(G-9990)
MIACUCINA LLC
3650 N Miami Ave (33127-3114)
PHONE..................................305 792-9494
Sandhya Murphy, *Office Mgr*
Reynaldo Rouco,
Mark Murphy,
Ariel Wainer,
◆ **EMP:** 7 **EST:** 2001
SALES (est): 1.2MM **Privately Held**
WEB: www.miacucina.com
SIC: 2434 Wood kitchen cabinets

(G-9991)
MIAMI
3661 S Miami Ave Ste 407 (33133-4230)
PHONE..................................954 874-7707
Julie Nida, *Owner*
EMP: 11 **EST:** 2011
SALES (est): 598.7K **Privately Held**
WEB: www.greatermiamiaudiology.com
SIC: 3842 5999 5047 Hearing aids; hearing aids; hearing aids

(G-9992)
MIAMI BANNERS & SIGNS INC
Also Called: Miami Balloons & Signs
6335 Nw 74th Ave (33166-3632)
PHONE..................................305 262-4460
Edwin Pagan, *CEO*
EMP: 9 **EST:** 2011
SALES (est): 1MM **Privately Held**
WEB: www.mbssigns.com
SIC: 3993 Signs & advertising specialties

(G-9993)
MIAMI BEACH AWNING CO
Also Called: Miami Awning
3905 Nw 31st Ave (33142-5122)
PHONE..................................305 576-2029
Michael Reilly, *Ch of Bd*
Joseph Riley, *General Mgr*
Joan R Garvey, *Corp Secy*
William Garvey, *Vice Pres*
Federico Bordignon, *Project Mgr*
◆ **EMP:** 45 **EST:** 1929
SQ FT: 12,000
SALES (est): 9.1MM **Privately Held**
WEB: www.miamiawning.com
SIC: 2394 1799 Awnings, fabric: made from purchased materials; awning installation

(G-9994)
MIAMI COCKTAIL COMPANY INC
2750 Nw 3rd Ave Ste 14 (33127-4143)
PHONE..................................305 482-1974
Ross Graham, *CEO*
EMP: 10 **EST:** 2016
SALES (est): 564K **Privately Held**
WEB: www.miamicocktail.com
SIC: 2085 Cocktails, alcoholic

(G-9995)
MIAMI COMPRESSOR RBLDRS INC
Also Called: Usacompressors.com
3230 Nw 38th St (33142-5032)
PHONE..................................305 303-2251
Robert G Gonzalez, *President*
Alex Fernandez, *Controller*
▼ **EMP:** 10 **EST:** 1975
SQ FT: 5,500
SALES (est): 659.3K **Privately Held**
WEB:
www.miamicompressorrebuilders.com
SIC: 7694 Rebuilding motors, except automotive

(G-9996)
MIAMI CORDAGE LLC
Also Called: Florida Wire and Rigging Works
2475 Nw 38th St (33142-5369)
PHONE..................................305 636-3000
Jason Hoffman, *CEO*
Audrey Stirman, *President*
Fran Hoffman, *COO*
Hermi Recio, *CFO*
Herminia Recio, *Controller*
◆ **EMP:** 32 **EST:** 1960
SQ FT: 40,000
SALES (est): 8.3MM **Privately Held**
WEB: www.miamicordage.com
SIC: 2298 5088 3496 Cable, fiber; rope, except asbestos & wire; slings, rope; wire rope centers; marine crafts & supplies; miscellaneous fabricated wire products

(G-9997)
MIAMI DADE TRUCK & EQP SVC
3294 Nw 69th St (33147-6640)
PHONE..................................305 691-2932
Onelio Cruz Sr, *President*
▼ **EMP:** 10 **EST:** 1980
SQ FT: 12,000
SALES (est): 576.5K **Privately Held**
SIC: 3713 5521 Truck beds; trucks, tractors & trailers: used

(G-9998)
MIAMI DECOR INC
7351 Nw 61st St (33166-3703)
PHONE..................................800 235-2197
Faber Aristizabal, *President*
Piedad Aristizabal, *Vice Pres*
Melida Aristizabal, *Shareholder*
▼ **EMP:** 10 **EST:** 1979
SQ FT: 12,000
SALES (est): 293.9K **Privately Held**
SIC: 2499 Picture & mirror frames, wood

(G-9999)
MIAMI ENGRV CO-OXFORD PRTG CO
Also Called: Oxford Acquisition
54 Nw 11th St (33136-2803)
PHONE..................................305 371-9595
Mario Cerratto, *President*
Richard Freeman, *President*
EMP: 8 **EST:** 1957
SQ FT: 10,250
SALES (est): 453.8K **Privately Held**
SIC: 2759 2754 Invitation & stationery printing & engraving; commercial printing, gravure

(G-10000)
MIAMI FABRICATOR INC
5323 Sw 159th Ct (33185-5058)
PHONE..................................305 505-1908
Laisy Martinez, *Principal*
EMP: 7 **EST:** 2011
SALES (est): 109.7K **Privately Held**
WEB: www.miamifabricators.com
SIC: 3441 Fabricated structural metal

(G-10001)
MIAMI FABRICATOR INC
2235 Nw 41st St (33142-4623)
PHONE..................................305 505-1908
Laisy Martinez, *President*
EMP: 8 **EST:** 2017
SALES (est): 314K **Privately Held**
WEB: www.miamifabricators.com
SIC: 3441 Fabricated structural metal

(G-10002)
MIAMI HERALD
4302 Sw 73rd Ave (33155-4550)
PHONE..................................305 269-7768
EMP: 13 **EST:** 2009
SALES (est): 700K **Privately Held**
SIC: 2711 Newspapers, publishing & printing

(G-10003)
MIAMI LEASING INC
14532 Sw 129th St (33186-5305)
PHONE..................................786 431-1215

Maria Mikluscak, *Vice Pres*
EMP: 7 **EST:** 2004
SALES (est): 12MM **Privately Held**
SIC: 3724 Aircraft engines & engine parts

(G-10004)
MIAMI POWER WHEELS
9500 Sw 40th St Ste 305 (33165-4036)
PHONE..................................305 553-1888
Manuel Estrada, *Owner*
▼ **EMP:** 8 **EST:** 2004
SALES (est): 624.1K **Privately Held**
WEB: www.miamipowerwheel.com
SIC: 3312 Wheels

(G-10005)
MIAMI PRESTIGE INTERIORS INC
3000 Nw 125th St Unit C (33167-2515)
PHONE..................................305 685-3343
Reinier Lopez, *CEO*
Rogelio Delarosa, *President*
Richard Delarosa, *Vice Pres*
Cathy Dela Rosa, *Admin Sec*
◆ **EMP:** 45 **EST:** 1971
SALES (est): 4.2MM **Privately Held**
WEB: www.miamiprestige.com
SIC: 2392 2221 Boat cushions; upholstery fabrics, manmade fiber & silk

(G-10006)
MIAMI PUBLICITY LLC
8300 Sw 8th St Ste 101 (33144-4100)
P.O. Box 442861 (33144-7861)
PHONE..................................561 215-5189
Luis Safonts, *Principal*
EMP: 6 **EST:** 2015
SALES (est): 58.5K **Privately Held**
SIC: 2741 Miscellaneous publishing

(G-10007)
MIAMI QUALITY GRAPHICS INC
3701 Nw 51st St (33142-3240)
PHONE..................................305 634-9506
Rafael Farah, *President*
Lesley Acosta, *VP Opers*
Carlos Hernandez, *Plant Mgr*
Mariluz Suero, *Office Mgr*
EMP: 50
SQ FT: 37,000
SALES (est): 7.5MM **Privately Held**
WEB: www.miamiquality.com
SIC: 2752 2759 3544 Trading stamps, lithographed; embossing on paper; die sets for metal stamping (presses)

(G-10008)
MIAMI QUALITY PAVERS CORP
5800 Sw 177th Ave Ste 101 (33193-5302)
PHONE..................................305 408-3444
Jorge A Rinaldi, *President*
EMP: 6 **EST:** 2006
SALES (est): 499.9K **Privately Held**
WEB: www.mqpavers.com
SIC: 3271 Concrete block & brick

(G-10009)
MIAMI RAILING DESIGN CORP
4401 Sw 75th Ave Ste 10 (33155-4445)
PHONE..................................305 926-0062
Kalet Suarez, *Principal*
EMP: 7 **EST:** 2017
SALES (est): 388.7K **Privately Held**
WEB: www.miamirailingdesign.com
SIC: 3446 Architectural metalwork

(G-10010)
MIAMI SIGNAGE LLC
8311 Sw 157th Ave (33193-5040)
PHONE..................................305 877-3924
Karla Portal, *Principal*
EMP: 7 **EST:** 2017
SALES (est): 232K **Privately Held**
WEB: www.miasignage.com
SIC: 3993 Signs & advertising specialties

(G-10011)
MIAMI SLICE LLC
3177 Nw 7th Ave (33127-3669)
PHONE..................................786 200-2723
EMP: 6 **EST:** 2017
SALES (est): 98.1K **Privately Held**
SIC: 2711 Newspapers, publishing & printing

(G-10012)
MIAMI STITCH AND PRINT CENTER
20213 Ne 16th Pl (33179-2719)
PHONE..................................305 770-4285
EMP: 6 **EST:** 2015
SALES (est): 92.3K **Privately Held**
SIC: 2752 Commercial printing, lithographic

(G-10013)
MIAMI SWITCHGEAR COMPANY
7060 Nw 52nd St (33166-4845)
PHONE..................................786 336-5783
Federico Anselmetti, *President*
◆ **EMP:** 7 **EST:** 2012
SALES (est): 880.2K **Privately Held**
WEB: www.miamiswitchgear.com
SIC: 3613 Time switches, electrical switchgear apparatus; switchgear & switchgear accessories

(G-10014)
MIAMI TECH INC (PA)
3611 Nw 74th St (33147-5827)
PHONE..................................305 693-7054
Isidro J Gonzalez, *President*
Christopher Gonzalez, *Opers Mgr*
Chris Gonzalez, *Manager*
Maria Ventriere, *Admin Sec*
◆ **EMP:** 20
SQ FT: 1,000
SALES (est): 14.9MM **Privately Held**
WEB: www.miamitech.com
SIC: 3444 Sheet metal specialties, not stamped

(G-10015)
MIAMI TIMES
900 Nw 54th St (33127-1897)
PHONE..................................305 694-6210
Rachel R Reeves, *President*
Karen Franklin, *Opers Mgr*
EMP: 39 **EST:** 1921
SALES (est): 4.6MM **Privately Held**
WEB: www.miamitimesonline.com
SIC: 2711 Newspapers, publishing & printing

(G-10016)
MICHELLE LYNN SOLUTIONS INC
1395 Brickell Ave Ste 800 (33131-3302)
PHONE..................................786 413-0455
Michelle Adderley, *President*
Dwight Drane, *Vice Pres*
EMP: 6 **EST:** 2003
SALES (est): 500K **Privately Held**
WEB: www.naacp100store.com
SIC: 2261 Screen printing of cotton broadwoven fabrics

(G-10017)
MICHELSONS TROPHIES INC
14730 Nw 7th Ave (33168-3104)
PHONE..................................305 687-9898
Keith Stunson, *President*
James L Michelson, *Corp Secy*
Efraim Lapscher, *Manager*
Bruno Valle, *Asst Mgr*
▼ **EMP:** 8 **EST:** 1958
SQ FT: 6,000
SALES (est): 850K **Privately Held**
WEB: www.michelsonstrophies.com
SIC: 3914 5947 Trophies; gift, novelty & souvenir shop

(G-10018)
MIDNIGHT EXPRESS PWR BOATS INC
351 Ne 185th St (33179-4510)
PHONE..................................954 745-8284
Bert M Glaser, *President*
Eric Glaser, *Vice Pres*
Harris Glaser, *Vice Pres*
▼ **EMP:** 41 **EST:** 1998
SALES (est): 6.6MM **Privately Held**
WEB: www.midnightboats.com
SIC: 3732 5551 Boats, fiberglass: building & repairing; boat dealers

(G-10019)
MIKES TRCK PRTS MCH SP PLUS I
7337 Nw 54th St (33166-4831)
PHONE..................................786 534-9608
Miguel Morejon, *Principal*
EMP: 6 **EST:** 2015
SALES (est): 104.7K **Privately Held**
SIC: 3599 Machine shop, jobbing & repair

(G-10020)
MILENIUM PUBLISHING LLC
12742 Sw 103rd Ct (33176-4769)
PHONE..................................786 573-9974
Juan J Wong, *Manager*
EMP: 6 **EST:** 2010
SALES (est): 4.2K **Privately Held**
WEB: www.milenium.group
SIC: 2741 Miscellaneous publishing

(G-10021)
MILES OF WOOD INC
5951 Sw 44th Ter (33155-5216)
PHONE..................................305 300-6370
Miles Black, *Principal*
EMP: 5 **EST:** 2004
SALES (est): 414.6K **Privately Held**
WEB: www.milesofwood.com
SIC: 2431 Millwork

(G-10022)
MILLENIUM OIL & GAS DISTRS INC
Also Called: Food Spot 59
12801 Sw 42nd St (33175-3424)
PHONE..................................305 220-3669
Elena G Hasan, *President*
Allan Hasan, *Owner*
EMP: 14 **EST:** 2001
SALES (est): 1.4MM **Privately Held**
WEB: www.sunshinegasoline.com
SIC: 1389 Testing, measuring, surveying & analysis services

(G-10023)
MILLENIUM WOOD BOXES INC
13139 Sw 122nd Ave (33186-6232)
PHONE..................................305 969-5510
Miguel Cabrera, *Manager*
EMP: 5 **EST:** 2001
SALES (est): 456.8K **Privately Held**
WEB: www.mwoodboxes.com
SIC: 2449 Rectangular boxes & crates, wood

(G-10024)
MILLENNIUM GLASS INC
5851 Nw 35th Ave (33142-2001)
PHONE..................................305 638-1785
Luis Victoria, *Principal*
EMP: 8 **EST:** 2007
SALES (est): 231.7K **Privately Held**
WEB: www.millenniumglassinc.com
SIC: 2431 Millwork

(G-10025)
MIND&MELODY INC
12905 Sw 132nd St (33186-6293)
PHONE..................................305 582-1006
Cristina Rodriguez, *President*
EMP: 7 **EST:** 2014
SALES: 324.7K **Privately Held**
WEB: www.mindandmelody.org
SIC: 3931 Musical instruments

(G-10026)
MINERAL LIFE INTL INC
6732 Sw 71st Ct (33143-3022)
PHONE..................................305 661-9854
David L Shankman, *President*
Marlon J Garcia, *COO*
◆ **EMP:** 9 **EST:** 1976
SQ FT: 1,200
SALES (est): 350K **Privately Held**
WEB: www.minerallife.com
SIC: 3274 3479 Lime; coating of metals & formed products

(G-10027)
MISHAAL AEROSPACE CORPORATION
31 Se 5th St Apt 3415 (33131-2526)
PHONE..................................786 353-2685
Mishaal Ashemimry, *President*
EMP: 7 **EST:** 2010
SALES (est): 204.1K **Privately Held**
WEB: www.mishaalaerospace.com
SIC: 3761 Guided missiles & space vehicles

(G-10028)
MISHAS CUPCAKES INC (PA)
5616 Sunset Dr (33143-5611)
PHONE..................................786 200-6153
Misha Kuryla, *President*
Michelle Gomez, *Principal*
EMP: 32 **EST:** 2007
SALES (est): 4.2MM **Privately Held**
WEB: www.mishascupcakes.com
SIC: 2051 5812 Bakery: wholesale or wholesale/retail combined; restaurant, family: independent

(G-10029)
MK MONOMERS LLC
905 Brickell Bay Dr # 23 (33131-2935)
PHONE..................................732 928-5800
James Kronenthal, *President*
Edward Kronenthal, *Vice Pres*
Theresa Romano, *Accountant*
Mirela Fabreti, *Manager*
EMP: 7 **EST:** 2013
SALES (est): 151.8K **Privately Held**
SIC: 2899 Chemical preparations

(G-10030)
MMX MANUFACTURING LLC ✪
6508 Nw 77th Ct (33166-2710)
PHONE..................................786 456-5072
Jaime Gomez,
EMP: 10 **EST:** 2020
SALES (est): 556.3K **Privately Held**
WEB: www.mmxusa.com
SIC: 3999 5047 Manufacturing industries; medical equipment & supplies

(G-10031)
MO STEEL FBRICATOR ERECTOR INC
353 Ne 185th St (33179-4510)
PHONE..................................305 945-4855
Maurice Sutton, *Owner*
Miguel Gutierrez, *Opers Staff*
◆ **EMP:** 8 **EST:** 2004
SALES (est): 1.7MM **Privately Held**
WEB: www.mosteel.com
SIC: 3441 Fabricated structural metal

(G-10032)
MOBVIOUS CORP
2100 Coral Way Ste 200 (33145-2657)
PHONE..................................786 497-6620
Giuliano Stiglitz, *Principal*
EMP: 8 **EST:** 2016
SALES (est): 164.8K **Privately Held**
WEB: www.prisabrandsolutions.us
SIC: 7372 Prepackaged software

(G-10033)
MODERN COATING SYSTEM LLC
3201 Nw 13th Ave (33142-6105)
PHONE..................................786 326-3652
Walter Noel Ulloa, *Manager*
EMP: 6 **EST:** 2016
SALES (est): 118K **Privately Held**
WEB: www.moderncoatingsystem.com
SIC: 3479 Metal coating & allied service

(G-10034)
MODULEX AMERICA LLC
14 Ne 1st Ave Ste 707 (33132-2411)
PHONE..................................786 424-0857
Ketil M Staalesen, *General Mgr*
Ketil Molbach, *Principal*
Andres Becerra, *Project Mgr*
Nathan Brenneman, *Project Mgr*
EMP: 11 **EST:** 2013
SALES (est): 2.1MM **Privately Held**
WEB: www.modulex.com
SIC: 3993 Electric signs; neon signs; letters for signs, metal

(G-10035)
MODULEX AMERICAS GROUP CORP
14 Ne 1st Ave Ste 707 (33132-2411)
PHONE..................................877 808-8049
EMP: 7

SALES (est): 396.6K **Privately Held**
WEB: www.modulex.com
SIC: 3993 Electric signs

(G-10036)
MOLD BUSTERS LLC
12900 Sw 80th St (33183-4213)
PHONE....................................786 360-6464
Yvette C Blanco, *Manager*
EMP: 7 **EST:** 2018
SALES (est): 534.2K **Privately Held**
SIC: 3544 Industrial molds

(G-10037)
MOLSON COORS BREWING COMPANY
5200 Blue Lagoon Dr # 220 (33126-7006)
PHONE....................................305 792-6620
Gavin Hattersley, *COO*
Kristina Viduka, *Marketing Mgr*
Aaron Smith, *Manager*
Amy Jacquemard, *IT/INT Sup*
EMP: 6
SALES (corp-wide): 9.6B **Publicly Held**
WEB: www.molsoncoors.com
SIC: 2082 Beer (alcoholic beverage)
PA: Molson Coors Beverage Company
311 10th St
Golden CO 80401
303 279-6565

(G-10038)
MOMENTUM COMFORT GEAR INC
470 Ne 185th St (33179-4511)
PHONE....................................305 653-5050
Yariv Shaked, *President*
EMP: 9 **EST:** 2017
SALES (est): 198.8K **Privately Held**
SIC: 2339 Service apparel, washable: women's

(G-10039)
MONCADA BACKHOE SERVICES LLC
11427 Nw 4th Ter (33172-4933)
PHONE....................................786 269-5427
Gilberto D Moncada, *Manager*
EMP: 6 **EST:** 2010
SALES (est): 167.5K **Privately Held**
SIC: 3531 Backhoes

(G-10040)
MONISON PALLETS INC (PA)
5420 Nw 37th Ave (33142-2716)
PHONE....................................305 637-1600
Victor Carrascal, *President*
Gem Vasquez, *Vice Pres*
Mavila Vasquez, *Vice Pres*
Barbara Miguel, *Manager*
EMP: 17 **EST:** 1986
SQ FT: 115,000
SALES (est): 5.6MM **Privately Held**
WEB: www.monisonpallets.net
SIC: 2448 Pallets, wood

(G-10041)
MORLEE LAMPSHADE CO INC
6915 Nw 43rd St (33166-6844)
PHONE....................................305 500-9310
EMP: 26
SQ FT: 6,500
SALES: 820K **Privately Held**
SIC: 3645 Manufactures Lamp Shades

(G-10042)
MORSE ENTERPRISES LIMITED INC
Also Called: Keyplex
400 N Ny Ave Ste 200 (33129)
PHONE....................................407 682-6500
Gerald C O'Connor, *President*
Steven Bessette, *President*
Gerald O'Connor, *Vice Pres*
Shannon Newman, *Sales Staff*
EMP: 6 **EST:** 1980
SALES (est): 603.3K **Privately Held**
SIC: 2879 5191 Agricultural chemicals; farm supplies

(G-10043)
MOSCH INTERNATIONAL CORP
6400 Nw 72nd Ave (33166-3627)
PHONE....................................786 616-9108
Socors E Perez- Rodriguez, *President*
Juan Pablo Vergara, *Vice Pres*
EMP: 7 **EST:** 2014
SALES (est): 123.2K **Privately Held**
SIC: 3253 5032 Ceramic wall & floor tile; ceramic wall & floor tile

(G-10044)
MOTOR SERVICE GROUP LLC
6600 Nw 77th Ct (33166-2795)
PHONE....................................305 592-2440
Robert Valdes, *Mng Member*
EMP: 8 **EST:** 2015
SQ FT: 10,000
SALES (est): 800K **Privately Held**
WEB: www.motorservicegroup.com
SIC: 3599 5013 Machine shop, jobbing & repair; automotive supplies & parts

(G-10045)
MOTOR SERVICE INC
6600 Nw 77th Ct (33166-2795)
PHONE....................................305 592-2440
Fax: 305 592-2443
EMP: 8
SQ FT: 12,000
SALES: 1MM **Privately Held**
SIC: 3599 5013 Mfg Industrial Machinery Whol Auto Parts/Supplies

(G-10046)
MOTORSPORT GAMES INC (HQ)
5972 Ne 4th Ave (33137-2134)
PHONE....................................305 507-8799
Dmitry Kozko, *Ch of Bd*
Stephen Hood, *President*
Jonathan New, *CFO*
EMP: 75 **EST:** 2018
SQ FT: 2,000
SALES: 19MM
SALES (corp-wide): 1.2MM **Publicly Held**
WEB: www.motorsport.com
SIC: 7372 Prepackaged software
PA: Motorsport Network, Llc
5972 Ne 4th Ave
Miami FL 33137
305 507-8799

(G-10047)
MPR AUDIO SYSTEM LLC
3465 Nw 71st Ter (33147-6667)
PHONE....................................305 988-8524
Rebeca Lange, *Mng Member*
EMP: 7 **EST:** 2015
SALES (est): 544.7K **Privately Held**
SIC: 3651 Audio electronic systems

(G-10048)
MR COOL WATERS INC (PA)
12009 Sw 129th Ct Unit 5 (33186-6918)
PHONE....................................305 234-6311
EMP: 16
SALES (est): 2.2MM **Privately Held**
SIC: 2671 Mfg Packaging Paper/Film

(G-10049)
MRKT DEUX
140 Ne 39th St (33137-3614)
PHONE....................................305 603-9682
EMP: 6 **EST:** 2016
SALES (est): 210.8K **Privately Held**
WEB: www.shop-mrkt.com
SIC: 3171 5632 Women's handbags & purses; handbags

(G-10050)
MSQUARED PUBLISHING
3200 Mary St (33133-5290)
PHONE....................................786 399-0607
Joseph Grant, *Principal*
EMP: 6 **EST:** 2011
SALES (est): 80.2K **Privately Held**
SIC: 2741 Miscellaneous publishing

(G-10051)
MTNG USA CORP
11334 Sw 157th Pl (33196-3129)
P.O. Box 560668 (33256-0668)
PHONE....................................305 670-0979
Pascual Ros, *President*
Santiago Ros, *Vice Pres*
Sergio Ros, *Director*
▲ **EMP:** 6 **EST:** 2010
SALES (est): 105.6K **Privately Held**
SIC: 3089 Molding primary plastic

(G-10052)
MULLER FIRE PROTECTION INC
2311 Sw 98th Pl (33165-7526)
PHONE....................................305 636-9780
Carlos S Muller, *President*
Carlos A Muller, *President*
EMP: 23 **EST:** 1995
SALES (est): 3.3MM **Privately Held**
WEB: www.mullerfireprotection.com
SIC: 3569 Sprinkler systems, fire: automatic

(G-10053)
MULTI SOFT II INC
4400 Biscayne Blvd Fl 10 (33137-3212)
PHONE....................................305 579-8000
Charles J Lombardo, *Ch of Bd*
Miriam G Jarney, *Exec VP*
EMP: 10 **EST:** 1985
SQ FT: 4,200
SALES (est): 304.2K **Privately Held**
SIC: 7372 Application computer software

(G-10054)
MULTI-COMMERCIAL SERVICES CORP
Also Called: Turbo Rotating Spare US
15420 Sw 136th St Unit 26 (33196-2673)
PHONE....................................305 235-1373
Enrique D Rasch, *CEO*
Freddy E Barcena, *President*
▼ **EMP:** 5 **EST:** 2008
SQ FT: 2,800
SALES (est): 1MM **Privately Held**
WEB: www.turborots.com
SIC: 3621 Inverters, rotating: electrical

(G-10055)
MUNICIPAL LIGHTING SYSTEMS INC (PA)
Also Called: Florida Coast Lighting Systems
7035 Sw 47th St Ste A (33155-4625)
P.O. Box 140134, Coral Gables (33114-0134)
PHONE....................................305 666-4210
Roy Bustillo, *President*
Scott Stefan, *Treasurer*
Rosa Zampieri, *Accountant*
EMP: 5 **EST:** 1995
SQ FT: 4,000
SALES (est): 1.5MM **Privately Held**
SIC: 3646 Commercial indusl & institutional electric lighting fixtures

(G-10056)
MY GLAM CHOICE INC
6910 Nw 84th Ave (33166-2619)
PHONE....................................786 586-7927
Rhona Tatiana Hernandez, *President*
Jeremias Martorell, *Principal*
Josue Emilio Bravo Hernandez, *Vice Pres*
EMP: 6 **EST:** 2017
SALES (est): 218.3K **Privately Held**
SIC: 2389 5137 5611 Apparel & accessories; women's & children's clothing; men's & boys' clothing stores

(G-10057)
N V TEXPACK GROUP
3225 Aviation Ave Ste 303 (33133-4741)
PHONE....................................305 358-9696
Joseph Artiga, *President*
Joaquin Vinas, *Treasurer*
Miguel Domingo, *Director*
EMP: 12 **EST:** 2004
SALES (est): 512K **Privately Held**
WEB: www.conitex.com
SIC: 2621 Paper mills

(G-10058)
NAC USA CORPORATION
Also Called: Dermaccina Dossier
9000 Sw 137th Ave (33186-1411)
PHONE....................................800 396-0149
Diego Ariza, *Principal*
EMP: 6 **EST:** 2015
SALES (est): 231.2K **Privately Held**
WEB: www.cremadermanac.com
SIC: 2844 Face creams or lotions

(G-10059)
NAHUEL TRADING CORP
17838 State Road 9 (33162-1008)
PHONE....................................305 999-9944
Oscar A Mouras, *President*
Natalia C Mouras, *Treasurer*
Hugo D Mouras, *Director*
Elisa B De Mouras, *Admin Sec*
EMP: 11 **EST:** 1993
SQ FT: 3,800
SALES (est): 503.7K **Privately Held**
SIC: 3663 Television broadcasting & communications equipment

(G-10060)
NAKASAWA MINING AND ENERGY LLC
175 Sw 7th St Ste 1812 (33130-2959)
PHONE....................................305 302-4980
Jose W Molina, *President*
EMP: 8 **EST:** 2016
SALES (est): 460.4K **Privately Held**
SIC: 1382 Oil & gas exploration services

(G-10061)
NAKED WHEY INC
382 Ne 191st St (33179-3899)
P.O. Box 348634, Coral Gables (33234-8634)
PHONE....................................352 246-7294
Stephen E Zieminski, *President*
EMP: 8 **EST:** 2014
SALES (est): 1MM **Privately Held**
WEB: www.nakednutrition.com
SIC: 2023 Powdered whey

(G-10062)
NATIONAL PALLETS
2160 Nw 8th Ave (33127-4638)
PHONE....................................305 324-1021
Norma R Garcia, *President*
Raul N Garcia Jr, *Vice Pres*
EMP: 23 **EST:** 1973
SQ FT: 30,000
SALES (est): 1.3MM **Privately Held**
WEB: www.nationalpallets.net
SIC: 2448 Pallets, wood

(G-10063)
NEGLEX INC
300 Sw 107th Ave Ste 114 (33174-3601)
PHONE....................................305 551-4177
Jose M Negrin, *President*
EMP: 15 **EST:** 1999
SALES (est): 366.6K **Privately Held**
SIC: 2834 Pharmaceutical preparations

(G-10064)
NELVER AIRPARTS INC
12360 Sw 132nd Ct Ste 205 (33186-6461)
PHONE....................................305 378-0072
Nelson Pacheco, *Manager*
EMP: 5 **EST:** 2006
SALES (est): 375.4K **Privately Held**
WEB: www.nelver.com
SIC: 3812 Aircraft/aerospace flight instruments & guidance systems

(G-10065)
NEOCIS INC
2800 Biscayne Blvd # 600 (33137-4523)
PHONE....................................855 963-6247
Alon Mozes, *CEO*
Dennis Moses, *Vice Pres*
Christopher Sells, *Vice Pres*
Manan Shah, *Engineer*
Jason Carl, *Sales Staff*
EMP: 75 **EST:** 2012
SALES (est): 10.7MM **Privately Held**
WEB: www.neocis.com
SIC: 3841 Surgical & medical instruments

(G-10066)
NEW CENTURY
7950 Sunset Dr (33143-3944)
PHONE....................................305 670-3510
Alex De La Cruz, *Principal*
EMP: 9 **EST:** 2010
SALES (est): 476.1K **Privately Held**
WEB: www.ncirgroup.com
SIC: 2121 Cigars

(G-10067)
NEW VISION SIGNS CORP
15446 Sw 25th Ter (33185-5761)
PHONE....................................786 514-6822
Juan Carlos Garcia, *President*
EMP: 6 **EST:** 2014
SALES (est): 249.6K **Privately Held**
WEB: www.newvisionsigns.net
SIC: 3993 Signs & advertising specialties

▲ = Import ▼=Export
◆ =Import/Export

(G-10068)
NEXTSOURCE BIOTECHNOLOGY LLC
80 Sw 8th St (33130-3003)
PHONE..................................305 753-6360
Mohamed Osman, *Mng Member*
Steve Schafer,
Christopher Yankana,
EMP: 5 **EST:** 2011
SQ FT: 2,000
SALES (est): 892.7K
SALES (corp-wide): 1.9MM **Privately Held**
WEB: www.nextsourcepharma.com
SIC: 2834 Pharmaceutical preparations
PA: Tri-Source Pharma, Llc
80 Sw 8th St Ste 2660
Miami FL 33130
844 696-4667

(G-10069)
NFK CORPORATION
8150 Sw 118th Pl (33183-3832)
PHONE..................................305 791-2044
Farissa Khan, *President*
◆ **EMP:** 11 **EST:** 2012
SALES (est): 625.3K **Privately Held**
SIC: 2891 Adhesives, plastic

(G-10070)
NFK CORPORATION
13456 Sw 131st St (33186-5891)
PHONE..................................305 378-2116
Farissa Khan, *President*
EMP: 12
SALES (est): 1.5MM **Privately Held**
SIC: 3089 Boxes, plastic

(G-10071)
NIAGARA INDUSTRIES INC
4120 Nw 28th St (33142-5614)
PHONE..................................305 876-9010
Louis Bolivar, *President*
Alejandro Bolivar, *President*
Sergio Pino, *Vice Pres*
Israel Laitano, *Accounts Exec*
Carlos Linchenat, *Manager*
◆ **EMP:** 10 **EST:** 1985
SQ FT: 10,000
SALES (est): 1.6MM **Privately Held**
WEB: www.tanklesswaterheater.com
SIC: 3822 5064 Auto controls regulating residntl & coml environmt & applncs; water heaters, electric

(G-10072)
NIAGRATECH INDUSTRIES INC
2540 Nw 38th Ct (33142-6746)
PHONE..................................305 876-9010
Alejandro Bolivar, *Principal*
▼ **EMP:** 8 **EST:** 2009
SALES (est): 314.6K **Privately Held**
SIC: 3999 Manufacturing industries

(G-10073)
NIFTYS INC ✪
78 Sw 7th St (33130-3402)
PHONE..................................786 878-4725
Jeff Marsilio, *CEO*
EMP: 15 **EST:** 2021
SALES (est): 1MM **Privately Held**
SIC: 7372 3679 Application computer software; antennas, receiving

(G-10074)
NO EQUAL DESIGN INC
6995 Nw 46th St A (33166-5603)
PHONE..................................305 971-5177
Casparus D Otto, *President*
EMP: 5 **EST:** 2008
SALES (est): 760.1K **Privately Held**
WEB: www.shadeports.com
SIC: 3444 Awnings & canopies

(G-10075)
NOODLE TIME INC
8685 Nw 53rd Ter (33166)
PHONE..................................305 593-0770
Joel Schwartz, *President*
EMP: 79 **EST:** 2005
SALES (est): 974.6K
SALES (corp-wide): 2.1B **Privately Held**
WEB: www.benihana.com
SIC: 2098 Noodles (e.g. egg, plain & water), dry
HQ: Benihana Inc.
21500 Biscayne Blvd # 100
Miami FL 33180
305 593-0770

(G-10076)
NORSEMAN SHIPBUILDING CORP
437 Nw South River Dr (33128-1496)
PHONE..................................305 545-6815
Richard A Herron, *President*
Jane J Herron, *Vice Pres*
Warren M Salomon, *Admin Sec*
▼ **EMP:** 30 **EST:** 1969
SQ FT: 50,000
SALES (est): 4.3MM **Privately Held**
WEB: www.norsemanshipbuilding.com
SIC: 3731 Shipbuilding & repairing

(G-10077)
NORTH AMERICAN COAL CORP
Also Called: Florida Dragline Operations
18300 Sw 122nd St (33196-1954)
PHONE..................................305 824-9018
Ted Duna, *General Mgr*
EMP: 8
SALES (corp-wide): 128.4MM **Publicly Held**
WEB: www.nacoal.com
SIC: 1221 Bituminous coal & lignite-surface mining
HQ: The North American Coal Corporation
5340 Legacy Dr Ste 300
Plano TX 75024
972 448-5400

(G-10078)
NORTHWINGS ACCESSORIES CORP (DH)
Also Called: Heico Component Repair Group
7875 Nw 64th St (33166-2718)
PHONE..................................305 463-0455
Luis J Morell, *President*
Javier Diaz, *Vice Pres*
Laurans Mendelson, *Vice Pres*
Regieleime Albea, *Engineer*
Alexa Merrifield, *Accounts Mgr*
EMP: 138 **EST:** 1991
SQ FT: 1,000
SALES (est): 43.3MM **Publicly Held**
WEB: www.heico.com
SIC: 3724 Aircraft engines & engine parts
HQ: Heico Aerospace Corporation
3000 Taft St
Hollywood FL 33021
954 987-6101

(G-10079)
NOSTA INC
Also Called: Nosta Carpenter Shop
1235 Nw 29th St (33142-6617)
PHONE..................................305 634-1435
Emilio Nosta, *President*
Jorge Noste, *Vice Pres*
Emilio Noste Jr, *Treasurer*
▼ **EMP:** 8 **EST:** 1970
SQ FT: 5,000
SALES (est): 500K **Privately Held**
WEB: www.nostainc.com
SIC: 2434 2511 Wood kitchen cabinets; wood household furniture

(G-10080)
NOVA SIDERA METAL FORMING CORP
14341 Sw 120th St Ste 105 (33186-7032)
PHONE..................................786 717-7149
Gianfranco Pirastu, *Sales Mgr*
EMP: 6 **EST:** 2018
SALES (est): 235.6K **Privately Held**
WEB: www.novasidera.com
SIC: 3444 Sheet metalwork

(G-10081)
NOVEN PHARMACEUTICALS INC (HQ)
11960 Sw 144th St (33186-6109)
PHONE..................................305 964-3393
Naruhito Higo, *CEO*
Jay Kolman, *Counsel*
Joel Lippman, *Exec VP*
Peter Amanatides, *Vice Pres*
Brian J Board, *Vice Pres*
▲ **EMP:** 150
SQ FT: 20,000
SALES (est): 127.7MM **Privately Held**
WEB: www.noven.com
SIC: 2834 Pharmaceutical preparations

(G-10082)
NOVEN THERAPEUTICS LLC
11960 Sw 144th St (33186-6109)
PHONE..................................212 682-4420
Naruhito Higo, *Director*
Arthur Besteman, *Director*
EMP: 371 **EST:** 2004
SQ FT: 31,000
SALES (est): 10.7MM **Privately Held**
WEB: www.noven.com
SIC: 2834 Pharmaceutical preparations
HQ: Noven Pharmaceuticals, Inc.
11960 Sw 144th St
Miami FL 33186
305 964-3393

(G-10083)
NSK LATIN AMERICA INC (DH)
11601 Nw 107th St Ste 200 (33178-3386)
PHONE..................................305 477-0605
Marco Rodriguez, *President*
Angel Salgado, *Sales Executive*
◆ **EMP:** 39 **EST:** 1995
SALES (est): 6.1MM **Privately Held**
WEB: www.nskamericas.com
SIC: 3562 5085 3568 Ball & roller bearings; industrial supplies; power transmission equipment

(G-10084)
NU-ART SIGNS INC
3343 Nw 7th Ave (33127-3303)
PHONE..................................305 531-9850
David Burnard, *President*
Maria Burnard, *Treasurer*
Wayne Grabein, *Office Mgr*
EMP: 5 **EST:** 1956
SQ FT: 1,200
SALES (est): 551.5K **Privately Held**
WEB: www.nuartsigns.net
SIC: 3993 Signs & advertising specialties

(G-10085)
NUEVO MUNDO COMPANY
9702 Sw 40th St (33165-4075)
PHONE..................................305 207-8155
Pedro Lopez, *Principal*
EMP: 10 **EST:** 2007
SALES (est): 362.8K **Privately Held**
WEB: www.nuevomundousa.com
SIC: 7372 Home entertainment computer software

(G-10086)
NUTRASOURCE LLC (PA)
1395 Brickell Ave Ste 800 (33131-3302)
PHONE..................................786 427-4305
Luis Gonzalez, *Manager*
EMP: 30 **EST:** 2010
SALES (est): 679.6K **Privately Held**
WEB: www.nutravive.org
SIC: 2834 Vitamin, nutrient & hematinic preparations for human use

(G-10087)
OBSOLETE GAMER INC
13501 Sw 80th St (33183-4111)
PHONE..................................305 388-3372
Ignacio Rodriguez-Trelles, *Principal*
EMP: 6 **EST:** 2010
SALES (est): 58.6K **Privately Held**
WEB: www.obsoletegamer.com
SIC: 3652 Pre-recorded records & tapes

(G-10088)
OCEAN DYNAMICS USA INC
18377 Ne 4th Ct (33179-4531)
PHONE..................................305 770-1800
Ron Kaplan, *President*
Ron Kappy, *Director*
◆ **EMP:** 6 **EST:** 1993
SQ FT: 5,000
SALES (est): 991.6K **Privately Held**
WEB: www.oceandynamics.com
SIC: 3429 3231 Furniture builders' & other household hardware; products of purchased glass

(G-10089)
OCEAN MARINE LLC
3109 Grand Ave 408 (33133-5103)
PHONE..................................305 549-6092
Tony Bordignon, *Manager*
EMP: 10 **EST:** 2005
SALES (est): 230.7K **Privately Held**
SIC: 3731 Shipbuilding & repairing

(G-10090)
OFFICE EXPRESS CORP
1835 Nw 112th Ave Ste 174 (33172-1819)
PHONE..................................786 503-6800
Noslen A Anaya, *Principal*
◆ **EMP:** 12 **EST:** 2015
SALES (est): 1.5MM **Privately Held**
WEB: www.officexpress-us.com
SIC: 2522 Office furniture, except wood

(G-10091)
OFFICINE GULLO USA LLC
Also Called: Le Atelier Paris Haute Design
6151 Biscayne Blvd (33137-2226)
PHONE..................................800 781-7125
Ricardo Moraes,
▲ **EMP:** 11 **EST:** 2012
SALES (est): 506.5K **Privately Held**
WEB: www.officinegullo.com
SIC: 3469 Kitchen fixtures & equipment: metal, except cast aluminum

(G-10092)
OH CATERING INC
3006 Sw 155th Ave (33185-5908)
PHONE..................................305 903-9271
EMP: 6
SALES (est): 421.4K **Privately Held**
SIC: 2099 Mfg Food Preparations

(G-10093)
OILS R US 1 800
3300 Nw 112th St (33167-3313)
PHONE..................................305 681-0909
Gregory Bass, *Owner*
EMP: 7 **EST:** 2015
SALES (est): 707.8K **Privately Held**
WEB: www.1800oilsrus.com
SIC: 1389 Oil field services

(G-10094)
OLIAN INC
Also Called: Analili Analili
13011 Sw 132nd St (33186-7197)
PHONE..................................305 233-9116
Liliana A Delcueto, *President*
Adriana Gonzalez, *General Mgr*
Ricardo A Delcueto, *Vice Pres*
Conchita N Alentado, *Treasurer*
Conchita Alentado, *Treasurer*
◆ **EMP:** 34 **EST:** 1984
SQ FT: 44,000
SALES (est): 3MM **Privately Held**
WEB: www.olianmaternity.com
SIC: 2339 Maternity clothing

(G-10095)
OLMEDO PRINTING CORP
710 Sw 73rd Ct (33144-2642)
PHONE..................................305 262-4666
Manuel Olmedo Jr, *President*
Carlos Olmedo, *Vice Pres*
EMP: 5 **EST:** 1973
SQ FT: 2,800
SALES (est): 747.2K **Privately Held**
WEB: www.olmedoprinting.com
SIC: 2752 Commercial printing, offset

(G-10096)
OLY CUSTOM CABINETS MIAMI INC
13285 Sw 39th St (33175-3223)
PHONE..................................305 216-3947
Leon Eduardo, *President*
EMP: 6 **EST:** 2001
SALES (est): 189.7K **Privately Held**
SIC: 2434 Wood kitchen cabinets

(G-10097)
OMEGA ENERGY USA LLC
600 Brickell Ave Ste 1530 (33131-3068)
PHONE..................................786 245-0642
Omar Leal, *CEO*
Sofia Santo Domingo, *Vice Pres*
Brandon Banks, *Mng Member*
EMP: 7 **EST:** 2010
SQ FT: 5,000
SALES (est): 14MM **Privately Held**
WEB: www.omegaenergyusa.com
SIC: 2869 Ethyl alcohol, ethanol

GEOGRAPHIC

PA: Omega Energy Colombia
Carrera 9 Nol 115 06 P 1 B Of 1808
Bogota

(G-10098)
OMEGA GAS INC
18401 Sw 115th Ave (33157-6513)
PHONE..................................786 277-2176
Pablo Moncada, *Principal*
EMP: 7 **EST:** 2006
SALES (est): 213.1K **Privately Held**
SIC: 2911 Gases & liquefied petroleum gases

(G-10099)
ON TIME LOADING ✪
4300 Biscayne Blvd (33137-3255)
PHONE..................................877 668-4630
Frankie King, *President*
EMP: 12 **EST:** 2021
SALES (est): 482K **Privately Held**
SIC: 3537 Trucks, tractors, loaders, carriers & similar equipment

(G-10100)
ON-Q SOFTWARE INC
13764 Sw 11th St (33184-2771)
PHONE..................................305 553-6566
Terry Cajigas, *President*
EMP: 5 **EST:** 2001
SALES (est): 443.6K **Privately Held**
WEB: www.on-qsoftware.com
SIC: 7372 Application computer software

(G-10101)
ONARIS
14 Ne 1st Ave Ste 607 (33132-2431)
PHONE..................................305 579-0056
Michael Pezua, *President*
Edgar Pezua, *Vice Pres*
▼ **EMP:** 10 **EST:** 2008
SQ FT: 3,500
SALES (est): 435.3K **Privately Held**
SIC: 3714 Acceleration equipment, motor vehicle

(G-10102)
ONE MILO INC
1010 Brickell Ave # 2709 (33131-3757)
PHONE..................................305 804-0266
Russell Leigh,
EMP: 10 **EST:** 2018
SQ FT: 4,000
SALES (est): 1.2MM **Privately Held**
WEB: www.onemilo.com
SIC: 3841 7371 Surgical & medical instruments; computer software development & applications

(G-10103)
ONE STEP PAPERS LLC (PA)
12105 Sw 130th St Ste 202 (33186-5260)
PHONE..................................305 238-2296
Carey Kummelman, *Mng Member*
Rodney Croes,
Rick Hess,
◆ **EMP:** 8 **EST:** 1996
SQ FT: 10,000
SALES (est): 1.7MM **Privately Held**
WEB: www.onesteppapers.com
SIC: 2672 2893 Transfer paper, gold or silver: from purchased materials; printing ink

(G-10104)
ONE WORLD MEDIA LLC
3390 Mary St Ste 116 (33133-5255)
PHONE..................................786 762-3030
Pablo Alvarez,
EMP: 6 **EST:** 2013
SALES (est): 287.6K **Privately Held**
WEB: www.oneworldmediacorp.com
SIC: 2711 Commercial printing & newspaper publishing combined

(G-10105)
ONE WORLD RESOURCE LLC
Also Called: Coast To Coast Designs
4608 Sw 74th Ave (33155-4422)
PHONE..................................305 445-9199
Claudia Parra, *Project Mgr*
Nick Hammond, *Sales Staff*
Vanessa Garcia, *Manager*
Douglas H Olson,
▲ **EMP:** 32 **EST:** 2003
SQ FT: 4,000
SALES (est): 1.2MM **Privately Held**
WEB: www.c2cdesigns.com
SIC: 2599 Hotel furniture

(G-10106)
ONETOWN BOARDS
580 Nw 120th St (33168-3529)
P.O. Box 680940 (33168-0940)
PHONE..................................786 704-5921
Felix Ernesto Puello, *Owner*
Socrates Elie, *Principal*
EMP: 7
SALES (est): 94.4K **Privately Held**
SIC: 3949 5961 Skateboards; fitness & sporting goods, mail order

(G-10107)
ONPOINT GLOBAL
8325 Ne 2nd Ave Ste 100 (33138-3815)
PHONE..................................651 788-1274
Leyanis Martinez, *Manager*
EMP: 26 **EST:** 2018
SALES (est): 9.3MM **Privately Held**
WEB: www.onpointglobal.com
SIC: 2782 Ledger, inventory & account books

(G-10108)
ONYX PROTECTIVE GROUP INC
Also Called: Onyx Armor
7359 Nw 34th St (33122-1272)
PHONE..................................305 282-4455
Ana Maria Cuartas, *President*
Juan Gutierrez, *Principal*
Javier Rocha, *Director*
▼ **EMP:** 10 **EST:** 2012
SQ FT: 20,000
SALES (est): 1.8MM **Privately Held**
WEB: www.onyxarmor.com
SIC: 3842 2311 Bulletproof vests; policemen's uniforms: made from purchased materials

(G-10109)
OPEN HOUSE MAGAZINE INC
505 Ne 30th St Apt 405 (33137-4303)
PHONE..................................305 576-6011
Patricia G Ernst, *President*
EMP: 7 **EST:** 1989
SQ FT: 1,500
SALES (est): 271K **Privately Held**
WEB: www.openhousemagazineinc.com
SIC: 2721 Magazines: publishing only, not printed on site

(G-10110)
OPKO CURNA LLC
4400 Biscayne Blvd (33137-3212)
PHONE..................................305 575-4100
Allyson Parker, *Vice Pres*
EMP: 9 **EST:** 2011
SALES (est): 427.8K **Privately Held**
WEB: www.opko.com
SIC: 3841 Surgical & medical instruments

(G-10111)
OPKO HEALTH INC (PA)
4400 Biscayne Blvd (33137-3212)
PHONE..................................305 575-4100
Phillip Frost, *Ch of Bd*
Jane H Hsiao, *Vice Ch Bd*
Steven D Rubin, *Exec VP*
Jon R Cohen, *Senior VP*
Harvey Felman, *Senior VP*
EMP: 1019 **EST:** 2007
SQ FT: 29,500
SALES: 1.4B **Publicly Held**
WEB: www.opko.com
SIC: 2834 2835 8731 Pharmaceutical preparations; in vitro & in vivo diagnostic substances; biotechnical research, commercial

(G-10112)
ORACLE AMERICA INC
6505 Blue Lagoon Dr # 40 (33126-6009)
PHONE..................................305 260-7200
EMP: 6 **EST:** 2019
SALES (est): 903.1K
SALES (corp-wide): 40.4B **Publicly Held**
WEB: www.oracle.com
SIC: 7372 Prepackaged software
PA: Oracle Corporation
2300 Oracle Way
Austin TX 78741
737 867-1000

(G-10113)
ORACLE ELEVATOR COMPANY
8000 Nw 25th St Ste 400 (33122-1609)
PHONE..................................954 391-5835
EMP: 6 **EST:** 2019
SALES (est): 303K **Privately Held**
WEB: www.oracleelevator.com
SIC: 7372 Prepackaged software

(G-10114)
ORELLANA COATINGS INC
9447 Fontainebleau Blvd (33172-7520)
PHONE..................................305 389-4610
Rafael A Orellana, *Principal*
EMP: 8 **EST:** 2010
SALES (est): 112.7K **Privately Held**
SIC: 3479 Metal coating & allied service

(G-10115)
ORELLANA INVESTMENTS INC
Also Called: Minuteman Press
2818 Nw 79th Ave (33122-1033)
PHONE..................................305 477-2817
Luz M Orellana, *President*
Daniel Orellana, *CFO*
▼ **EMP:** 8 **EST:** 2007
SALES (est): 996.9K **Privately Held**
WEB: www.chanhassen-mn.minutemanpress.com
SIC: 2752 Commercial printing, lithographic

(G-10116)
ORIA LAB LLC
7064 Sw 44th St (33155-4609)
PHONE..................................888 329-4298
Michael Oria,
EMP: 20 **EST:** 2019
SALES (est): 1MM **Privately Held**
SIC: 3999

(G-10117)
ORIENTAL PACKING COMPANY INC
12221 Sw 104th Ter (33186-3612)
PHONE..................................305 235-1829
Herman D Lue, *President*
Lillas Lue, *Principal*
Deborah L Lue, *Vice Pres*
Natalie A Lue, *Vice Pres*
▼ **EMP:** 10 **EST:** 1981
SALES (est): 825.4K **Privately Held**
WEB: www.orientalpacking.com
SIC: 2099 Spices, including grinding

(G-10118)
ORIENTAL RED APPLE LLC
255 Park Blvd (33126-8009)
PHONE..................................646 853-1468
Liya Liu, *Principal*
EMP: 8 **EST:** 2016
SALES (est): 408.7K **Privately Held**
SIC: 3571 Electronic computers

(G-10119)
ORIGIN PC LLC
12400 Sw 134th Ct Ste 8 (33186-6499)
PHONE..................................305 971-1000
Kevin Wasielewski, *CEO*
Richard Cary, *COO*
Linda Rodriguez, *Vice Pres*
Mike Wall, *Manager*
▲ **EMP:** 30 **EST:** 2009
SQ FT: 2,000
SALES (est): 8.9MM
SALES (corp-wide): 1.7B **Publicly Held**
WEB: www.originpc.com
SIC: 3571 5734 Computers, digital, analog or hybrid; software, computer games
PA: Corsair Gaming, Inc.
47100 Bayside Pkwy
Fremont CA 94538
510 657-8747

(G-10120)
ORLANDO FLORES
3841 Sw 92nd Ave (33165-4154)
PHONE..................................305 898-2111
Orlando Flores, *Principal*
EMP: 6 **EST:** 2010
SALES (est): 111.2K **Privately Held**
SIC: 3844 X-ray apparatus & tubes

(G-10121)
ORTEGA & VELAZCO CABINET INC
8346 Nw D South River Dr (33116)
PHONE..................................305 726-9097
Bernardo Velazco, *Principal*
EMP: 6 **EST:** 2008
SALES (est): 65.1K **Privately Held**
SIC: 2434 Wood kitchen cabinets

(G-10122)
OTUS CORP INTL LLC
8306 Mills Dr 222 (33183-4838)
PHONE..................................305 833-6078
Joel Mateu, *Mng Member*
Yolanda Fischer,
EMP: 9 **EST:** 2010
SALES (est): 1.6MM **Privately Held**
WEB: www.us100548355.trustpass.alibaba.com
SIC: 2911 2992 Oils, fuel; lubricating oils & greases

(G-10123)
OUTFORM INC (DH)
82 Ne 26th St Unit 103 (33137-4442)
PHONE..................................800 204-0524
Ariel Haroush, *CEO*
James Wu, *General Mgr*
Ben Chanoch, *Senior VP*
Lorraine McNicholas, *Opers Staff*
Batia Shaham, *CFO*
▲ **EMP:** 9 **EST:** 2008
SALES (est): 11.2MM **Privately Held**
WEB: www.outform.com
SIC: 3823 Digital displays of process variables

(G-10124)
OXPECKER ENTERPRISE INC
Also Called: Hunting Report The
12182 Sw 128th St (33186-5230)
P.O. Box 972682 (33197-2682)
PHONE..................................305 253-5301
Donald Causey, *President*
EMP: 6 **EST:** 1991
SQ FT: 961
SALES (est): 628.8K **Privately Held**
SIC: 2721 Magazines: publishing only, not printed on site

(G-10125)
P4RTS LLC
Also Called: A V E Parts & Accesories
11601 Nw 107th St Ste 300 (33178-3386)
PHONE..................................305 396-4879
Felix E Beaujon Wulff, *Principal*
EMP: 6 **EST:** 2014
SALES (est): 124.6K **Privately Held**
SIC: 3714 Motor vehicle parts & accessories

(G-10126)
PACHECO CREATIVE GROUP INC
Also Called: Evolutions - Graphics Designs-
2164 Nw 19th Ave (33142-7452)
PHONE..................................305 541-1400
Manriquel Pacheco, *President*
EMP: 10 **EST:** 2010
SALES (est): 666.8K **Privately Held**
WEB: www.evolutionsgraphics.com
SIC: 3993 Signs & advertising specialties

(G-10127)
PACIFIC
8526 Nw 70th St (33166-2652)
PHONE..................................305 785-9068
Victor Sales, *CEO*
EMP: 9 **EST:** 2015
SALES (est): 172K **Privately Held**
WEB: www.pacificblowers.com
SIC: 3531 Scrapers, graders, rollers & similar equipment

(G-10128)
PACIFIC LIMITED INTL CORP
825 Brickell Bay Dr # 17 (33131-2936)
PHONE..................................305 358-1900
Jose Massuh, *President*
EMP: 5 **EST:** 2019
SALES: 11.1MM **Privately Held**
WEB: www.pacific-ltd.com
SIC: 2821 5162 Plastics materials & resins; resins

(G-10129)
PACIFIC LTD CORP
Also Called: Pacific Limited
825 Brickell Bay Dr # 17 (33131-2936)
PHONE..................................305 358-1900
Jose Massuh, *President*
▼ **EMP:** 7 **EST:** 1982
SQ FT: 3,000
SALES (est): 3.3MM **Privately Held**
WEB: www.pacific-ltd.com
SIC: 2821 Plastics materials & resins

(G-10130)
PAINTS N COCKTAILS INC
14710 Ne 2nd Ct (33161-2013)
PHONE..................................954 514-7383
Lynn Smith Clyne, *CEO*
EMP: 14 **EST:** 2011
SALES (est): 985.1K **Privately Held**
WEB: www.paintsncocktails.com
SIC: 3993 5199 Signs & advertising specialties; advertising specialties

(G-10131)
PALLET ENTERPRISES OF FLORIDA
7525 Nw 37th Ave Unit D (33147-5802)
PHONE..................................305 836-3204
Pepe Lopez, *President*
▲ **EMP:** 8 **EST:** 2004
SALES (est): 286.7K **Privately Held**
SIC: 2448 Pallets, wood

(G-10132)
PALLET SOLUTIONS INC
7525 Nw 37th Ave Unit D (33147-5802)
P.O. Box 138717, Hialeah (33013-8717)
PHONE..................................305 801-8314
Rene Mendoza, *Principal*
EMP: 6 **EST:** 2012
SALES (est): 292.5K **Privately Held**
SIC: 2448 Pallets, wood

(G-10133)
PALLETS TO GO INC
1691 Nw 23rd St (33142-7625)
PHONE..................................305 654-0303
Rigoberto Lesceiro, *President*
Susie Ayerdis, *Admin Sec*
EMP: 10 **EST:** 1997
SALES (est): 848.4K **Privately Held**
WEB: www.sfpallets.com
SIC: 2448 Pallets, wood

(G-10134)
PALMETTO PRINTING INC
3065 Ohio St (33133-4418)
PHONE..................................305 253-2444
Eduardo Rivas, *President*
Joaquin Rivas, *Production*
Wendy Miranda, *Finance*
Linda Salisbury, *Admin Sec*
▼ **EMP:** 10 **EST:** 1974
SALES (est): 762.8K **Privately Held**
WEB: www.palmettoprinting.com
SIC: 2752 7334 Commercial printing, offset; photocopying & duplicating services

(G-10135)
PAMPLONA FOODS INC
9600 Sw 122nd Ct (33186-2538)
PHONE..................................305 970-4120
Carlos M Garcia, *President*
Juan G Guerra, *Vice Pres*
Jesus Garcia, *Admin Sec*
EMP: 8 **EST:** 1995
SALES (est): 131.9K **Privately Held**
SIC: 2013 Canned meats (except baby food) from purchased meat

(G-10136)
PANAGENICS INC
10711 Sw 216th St Unit 10 (33170-3139)
P.O. Box 972195 (33197-2195)
PHONE..................................888 773-0700
Scott Collman, *President*
Christina Amengual, *Vice Pres*
EMP: 6 **EST:** 2014
SQ FT: 1,000
SALES (est): 566.1K **Privately Held**
WEB: www.panagenics.com
SIC: 3999 5199 Pet supplies; pet supplies

(G-10137)
PANAMCO LLC
701 Nw 62nd Ave Ste 800 (33126-4684)
PHONE..................................305 856-7100
Francisco Sanchez,
EMP: 10 **EST:** 2000
SALES (est): 226.9K **Privately Held**
SIC: 2086 Bottled & canned soft drinks

(G-10138)
PANELFOLD INC
10700 Nw 36th Ave (33167-3785)
P.O. Box 680130 (33168-0130)
PHONE..................................305 688-3501
Guy E Dixon III, *President*
Dale Gurley, *Vice Pres*
Marsha A Kallstrom, *Vice Pres*
Marsha Kallstroms, *Vice Pres*
James Lyons, *Vice Pres*
◆ **EMP:** 165 **EST:** 1953
SQ FT: 140,000
SALES (est): 22.9MM **Privately Held**
WEB: www.panelfold.com
SIC: 2679 3442 Wallboard, decorated: made from purchased material; sash, door or window: metal

(G-10139)
PANTALEON COMMODITIES CORP
601 Brickell Key Dr # 60 (33131-2662)
PHONE..................................786 542-6333
Diego Herrera, *President*
EMP: 16 **EST:** 2018
SALES (est): 1.7MM **Privately Held**
SIC: 2099 Sugar

(G-10140)
PANTHER SOFTWARE INC
Also Called: Practicepanther
10800 Biscayne Blvd # 201 (33161-7482)
PHONE..................................800 856-8729
Sam Alkoubey, *Sales Mgr*
Eytan Haddad, *Manager*
Richard Barnes, *CIO*
Soumya Nettimi, *CIO*
Ori Tamuz, *CTO*
EMP: 19 **EST:** 2015
SALES (est): 569.8K **Privately Held**
WEB: www.practicepanther.com
SIC: 7372 Prepackaged software

(G-10141)
PARADISE AWNINGS CORPORATION
Also Called: Paradise Archtctral Panels Stl
4310 Nw 36th Ave (33142-4220)
PHONE..................................305 597-5714
Juan Chaviano, *President*
Manny Alcibar, *Vice Pres*
▼ **EMP:** 23 **EST:** 1998
SQ FT: 18,000
SALES (est): 4MM **Privately Held**
WEB: www.paradiseawnings.com
SIC: 2394 1799 Awnings, fabric: made from purchased materials; awning installation

(G-10142)
PARADISE EMB & SILKSCREEN INC
8801 Sw 129th St (33176-5918)
PHONE..................................305 595-6441
Cheryl Vihlen, *President*
EMP: 6 **EST:** 1998
SALES (est): 386.8K **Privately Held**
WEB: www.logofactory.com
SIC: 2395 Embroidery products, except schiffli machine

(G-10143)
PARRAS PLASTIC INC
13894 Sw 139th Ct (33186-5512)
PHONE..................................305 972-9537
EMP: 5
SALES (est): 569.3K **Privately Held**
SIC: 3089 Mfg Plastic Products

(G-10144)
PATLON INDUSTRIES INC
13913 Sw 119th Ave (33186-6202)
PHONE..................................305 255-7744
Michael J Mann, *President*
Stephen Mann, *Exec VP*
Mike Little, *Vice Pres*
Lisa Mann, *Vice Pres*
Walter F Pettit, *Vice Pres*
EMP: 5 **EST:** 1985
SQ FT: 7,500
SALES (est): 726.3K **Privately Held**
WEB: www.patlon.com
SIC: 3629 Static elimination equipment, industrial

(G-10145)
PAWS OFF PRIME K9 CUISINE LLC
7415 Nw 54th St (33166-4810)
PHONE..................................305 546-7475
Lisa Delasotta,
EMP: 7 **EST:** 2017
SALES (est): 165.7K **Privately Held**
WEB: www.k9cuisine.com
SIC: 2048 Rolled oats, prepared as animal feed

(G-10146)
PAX CATHOLIC COMMUNICATIONS
Also Called: Radio Paz
1779 Nw 28th St (33142-6016)
PHONE..................................305 638-9729
Father Federico Capdebon, *Principal*
Jenny Gamito, *Opers Staff*
Jorge Diaz-Diaz, *Corp Comm Staff*
EMP: 21 **EST:** 1994
SALES (est): 5.2MM **Privately Held**
WEB: www.paxcc.org
SIC: 3663 Radio broadcasting & communications equipment

(G-10147)
PEACE MILLWORK CO INC
3535 Nw 50th St (33142-3931)
PHONE..................................305 573-6222
George W Peace, *President*
Tomi Peace, *Admin Sec*
EMP: 49 **EST:** 1990
SQ FT: 20,000
SALES (est): 1.2MM **Privately Held**
WEB: www.peacemillwork.com
SIC: 2431 2434 Interior & ornamental woodwork & trim; panel work, wood; wood kitchen cabinets

(G-10148)
PEAK ELECTRONICS INC
7255 Nw 68th St Ste 8 (33166-3015)
PHONE..................................305 888-1588
Jose Alvarez, *President*
EMP: 8 **EST:** 1993
SQ FT: 2,500
SALES (est): 696.1K **Privately Held**
WEB: www.peakelectronics.com
SIC: 3825 Test equipment for electronic & electric measurement

(G-10149)
PEDRO TRUCK PARTS & TRAILERS
9140 Fontnbleau Blvd # 5 (33172-4379)
PHONE..................................786 439-8652
Pedro E Castrillon, *Principal*
EMP: 6 **EST:** 2019
SALES (est): 87.2K **Privately Held**
SIC: 3715 Truck trailers

(G-10150)
PENA GENERAL WELDING INC
4788 Sw 75th Ave (33155-4435)
PHONE..................................786 255-2153
Medardo Pena, *President*
EMP: 9 **EST:** 2004
SALES (est): 457.1K **Privately Held**
SIC: 7692 Welding repair

(G-10151)
PENINSULA TISSUE CORPORATION
2630 Nw 72nd Ave (33122-1306)
PHONE..................................305 863-0704
Hermelice Tineo, *Principal*
◆ **EMP:** 5 **EST:** 2011
SALES (est): 847.2K **Privately Held**
WEB: www.peninsulatissue.com
SIC: 2621 Paper mills

(G-10152)
PEPSICO BEVERAGE DISTRIBUTORS
1000 Nw 57th Ct (33126-3274)
PHONE..................................305 537-4477
EMP: 8 **EST:** 2014
SALES (est): 278.4K **Privately Held**
WEB: www.pepsico.com
SIC: 2086 Carbonated soft drinks, bottled & canned

(G-10153)
PEPSICO LATIN AMERICA BEVERAGE
1000 Nw 57th Ct Ste 800 (33126-3288)
PHONE..................................305 537-4477
EMP: 12 **EST:** 2015
SALES (est): 516.5K **Privately Held**
WEB: www.pepsico.com
SIC: 2086 Carbonated soft drinks, bottled & canned

(G-10154)
PERFORMNCE GLZING SLUTIONS LLC
7239 Nw 54th St (33166-4807)
PHONE..................................305 975-3717
Victor F Rosado, *Managing Prtnr*
Eduardo A Recio, *Managing Prtnr*
EMP: 7 **EST:** 2016
SALES (est): 134K **Privately Held**
WEB: www.performanceglazing.com
SIC: 2431 3442 Windows & window parts & trim, wood; metal doors, sash & trim

(G-10155)
PESTANOS WOODWORKING LLC
15332 Sw 53rd Ln (33185-4179)
PHONE..................................954 448-3932
Roberto Pestano, *Principal*
EMP: 6 **EST:** 2008
SALES (est): 163.9K **Privately Held**
SIC: 2431 Millwork

(G-10156)
PETAINER MANUFACTURING US
5901 Sw 74th St 311 (33143-5165)
PHONE..................................786 999-2019
EMP: 10 **EST:** 2019
SALES (est): 628.6K **Privately Held**
WEB: www.petainer.com
SIC: 3999 Manufacturing industries

(G-10157)
PETROSOL PROCESSING & REFINING
2655 S Le Jeune Rd # 1003 (33134-5803)
PHONE..................................305 442-7400
EMP: 10
SALES (est): 1.2MM **Privately Held**
SIC: 2911 Petroleum Refining

(G-10158)
PHILIPS NORTH AMERICA LLC
13305 Sw 106th Ave (33176-6053)
PHONE..................................305 969-7447
Sinforiano Echeverria, *Director*
EMP: 99
SALES (corp-wide): 133.6MM **Privately Held**
WEB: www.usa.philips.com
SIC: 3651 Household audio & video equipment
HQ: Philips North America Llc
222 Jacobs St Fl 3
Cambridge MA 02141
978 659-3000

(G-10159)
PHOTO OFFSET INC
4824 Sw 72nd Ave (33155-5526)
PHONE..................................305 666-1067
John Knowles, *President*
Mindy Knowles, *Production*
Anne Knowles, *Admin Sec*
EMP: 18 **EST:** 1952
SQ FT: 2,000
SALES (est): 1.4MM **Privately Held**
WEB: www.photooffset.com
SIC: 2752 Commercial printing, offset

(G-10160)
PHOTON TOWERS INC
17290 Sw 192nd St (33187-5101)
PHONE..................................305 235-7337
Sergio Cabrera, *Principal*
EMP: 6 **EST:** 2016
SALES (est): 77.5K **Privately Held**
SIC: 3661 Fiber optics communications equipment

(G-10161)
PHXTREME CORP
1835 Nw 112th Ave Ste 166 (33172-1819)
PHONE..................................305 594-2284
Pablo Holgado, *Principal*
Pablo R Holgado, *Vice Pres*
EMP: 6 **EST:** 2008
SALES (est): 251.6K **Privately Held**
WEB: www.phxtreme.com
SIC: 3751 Motorcycle accessories

(G-10162)
PHY-MED
8905 Sw 87th Ave Ste 200 (33176-2214)
PHONE..................................305 925-0141
Diego Cordova, *Administration*
EMP: 6 **EST:** 2018
SALES (est): 104.2K **Privately Held**
SIC: 3821 Laboratory apparatus & furniture

(G-10163)
PILLOW PLUS MANUFACTURING INC
515 Ne 189th St (33179-3909)
PHONE..................................305 652-2218
Raymond Alemany, *President*
EMP: 7 **EST:** 2001
SQ FT: 4,000
SALES (est): 558K **Privately Held**
WEB: www.pillowplusmfrs.com
SIC: 2392 Mattress pads; pillows, bed: made from purchased materials

(G-10164)
PILOTO MUSIC PUBLISHER CORP
13660 Sw 32nd St (33175-6607)
PHONE..................................321 348-0638
Jorge Piloto, *President*
EMP: 7 **EST:** 2008
SALES (est): 150.6K **Privately Held**
SIC: 2741 Miscellaneous publishing

(G-10165)
PINZON CARAMEL SYRUP
6937 Nw 52nd St (33166-4844)
PHONE..................................305 591-2472
Florentino Fernandez, *President*
Carlo Fernandez, *Senior VP*
▲ **EMP:** 5 **EST:** 2006
SALES (est): 404.1K **Privately Held**
WEB: www.pinzoncaramel.com
SIC: 2087 Syrups, flavoring (except drink)

(G-10166)
PIONEER ANNOUNCEMENTS INC
20324 Ne 16th Pl (33179-2706)
PHONE..................................305 573-7000
Gregory Schenker, *President*
Laurie Schenker, *Vice Pres*
EMP: 13 **EST:** 1950
SQ FT: 17,000
SALES (est): 1.5MM **Privately Held**
WEB: www.pioneerannouncements.com
SIC: 2759 2752 Invitation & stationery printing & engraving; thermography; commercial printing, lithographic

(G-10167)
PKOLINO LLC
Also Called: P'Kolino Studio
7300 Nw 35th Ave (33147-5808)
PHONE..................................888 403-8992
Antonio Turco-Rivas, *Mng Member*
JB Schneider,
▲ **EMP:** 8 **EST:** 2004
SQ FT: 2,500
SALES (est): 1.4MM **Privately Held**
WEB: www.pkolino.com
SIC: 2511 Wood household furniture

(G-10168)
PLANTAIN PRODUCTS COMPANY (PA)
2440 Nw 116th St Ste 100 (33167-0005)
PHONE..................................800 477-2447
Antonio Rivas, *President*
Maria Aguilar, *Accounts Mgr*
Liam Clarke, *Manager*
Margarita Guillen, *Admin Mgr*
◆ **EMP:** 26 **EST:** 1963
SQ FT: 22,000
SALES (est): 3.7MM **Privately Held**
WEB: www.chifleschips.com
SIC: 2099 Food preparations

(G-10169)
PLAYBILL SOUTHERN PUBLISHING
Also Called: Playbill Magazine
10001 Sw 54th St (33165-7117)
PHONE..................................305 595-1984
Leslie Feldman, *President*
EMP: 10 **EST:** 1975
SALES (est): 241.7K **Privately Held**
SIC: 2721 Magazines: publishing & printing

(G-10170)
PLD ACQUISITIONS LLC
Also Called: Avema Pharma Solutions
10400 Nw 29th Ter Miami (33172)
PHONE..................................305 463-2270
Mitchel Singer, *CEO*
EMP: 99 **EST:** 2007
SQ FT: 63,000
SALES (est): 19.8MM **Privately Held**
WEB: www.pldevelopments.com
SIC: 2834 Pharmaceutical preparations
PA: P & L Development, Llc
609 Cantiague Rock Rd 2a
Westbury NY 11590

(G-10171)
PM ENGRAVING CORP
18425 Sw 200th St (33187-2506)
PHONE..................................786 573-5292
Mary Castellanos, *President*
EMP: 10 **EST:** 2000
SALES (est): 856.6K **Privately Held**
SIC: 3271 7389 Blocks, concrete or cinder: standard; engraving service

(G-10172)
POD CRANE SERVICES AND RENTALS
5203 Sw 159th Ct (33185-5056)
PHONE..................................805 291-2675
Olga Orrino, *Principal*
EMP: 6 **EST:** 2019
SALES (est): 73.2K **Privately Held**
SIC: 2759 Commercial printing

(G-10173)
POGI BEAUTY LLC
3800 Ne 1st Ave (33137-3604)
PHONE..................................305 600-1305
Erica Han,
EMP: 7 **EST:** 2018
SALES (est): 226.7K **Privately Held**
SIC: 7372 Educational computer software

(G-10174)
POLI GROUP INTERNATIONAL INC
Also Called: Poli Sign Supplies
1574 Nw 108th Ave (33172-2052)
PHONE..................................305 468-8986
Miguel Chiting, *CEO*
Polly Ng, *Admin Sec*
◆ **EMP:** 10 **EST:** 2001
SQ FT: 1,100
SALES (est): 1.4MM **Privately Held**
WEB: www.polisigns.com
SIC: 3993 5085 Signs & advertising specialties; signmaker equipment & supplies

(G-10175)
POLICRETE LLC
3399 Nw 72nd Ave Ste 108 (33122-1339)
PHONE..................................305 552-7026
Romel Pana, *Mng Member*
EMP: 6 **EST:** 2011
SALES (est): 139.8K **Privately Held**
WEB: www.policrete.com
SIC: 3471 Cleaning, polishing & finishing

(G-10176)
POLY-CHEM CORP
3039 Ne Quayside Ln (33138-2258)
PHONE..................................305 593-1928
Carlos Diaz, *Owner*
EMP: 6 **EST:** 1989
SALES (est): 139.3K **Privately Held**
WEB: www.pcipcc.com
SIC: 2821 Plastics materials & resins

(G-10177)
POLYGRAMA INC
245 Se 1st St Ste 234 (33131-1904)
PHONE..................................305 577-9716
Andre Jacobovitz, *President*
Joao Lambert, *Vice Pres*
EMP: 6 **EST:** 2013
SALES (est): 119.5K **Privately Held**
SIC: 3826 Photomicrographic apparatus

(G-10178)
PONCE DE LEON CONSTRUCTION
440 Nw 132nd Ave (33182-1152)
PHONE..................................786 554-3685
Maria J Ponce De Leon, *Vice Pres*
EMP: 8 **EST:** 1997
SALES (est): 263.4K **Privately Held**
WEB: www.newportpropertyconstruction.com
SIC: 3272 Concrete products

(G-10179)
POSEIDON SERVICES INC
12685 Nw 11th Ln (33182-2453)
PHONE..................................786 294-8529
Alexei Diaz, *Principal*
EMP: 7 **EST:** 2018
SALES (est): 200.7K **Privately Held**
SIC: 3589 Water treatment equipment, industrial

(G-10180)
POTENZA SERVICES INC
Also Called: Potenza Hrc
10711 Sw 216th St (33170-3139)
PHONE..................................305 400-4938
Cesar Giraldo, *President*
EMP: 6 **EST:** 2016
SALES (est): 519.5K **Privately Held**
SIC: 3829 3842 Thermometers, including digital: clinical; orthopedic appliances

(G-10181)
PPA MIAMI CORP
8620 Nw 64th St Ste 10 (33166-2672)
PHONE..................................305 436-0460
Sebastian R Barbosa, *President*
▲ **EMP:** 7 **EST:** 2000
SALES (est): 493.5K **Privately Held**
WEB: www.miamicorp.com
SIC: 3441 Dam gates, metal plate

(G-10182)
PRECHECK HEALTH SERVICES INC (PA)
848 Brickell Ave Ph 5 (33131-3180)
PHONE..................................305 203-4711
Natalia A Lopera, *President*
Doug Samuelson, *CFO*
EMP: 26 **EST:** 2014
SALES: 70K **Privately Held**
SIC: 3841 Surgical & medical instruments

(G-10183)
PRECIOUS PRINTS INC
7670 Sw 82nd Ave (33143-3809)
PHONE..................................786 346-7740
Nancy Macias, *Principal*
EMP: 6 **EST:** 2012
SALES (est): 74.7K **Privately Held**
SIC: 2752 Commercial printing, lithographic

(G-10184)
PRECISION MANUFACTURING I
8760 Sw 131st St (33176-5908)
PHONE..................................786 547-2683
Adam Garabello, *Principal*
EMP: 6 **EST:** 2013
SALES (est): 154.5K **Privately Held**
SIC: 3999 Manufacturing industries

(G-10185)
PREMIUM LATIN MUSIC INC
1545 Sw 14th Ter (33145-1544)
PHONE..................................212 873-1472
Franklin Jr Romero, *Branch Mgr*
EMP: 16
SALES (corp-wide): 94.4K **Privately Held**
SIC: 2741 Miscellaneous publishing
PA: Premium Latin Music Inc.
601 Ne 36th St Apt 2802
Miami FL

(G-10186)
PREMIUM MARINE INC
777 Brickell Ave Ste 500 (33131-2803)
PHONE..................................786 903-0851
Charles Lee, *President*
Chip Hampton, *Vice Pres*
Dick Bramer, *Engineer*
EMP: 21 **EST:** 2000
SQ FT: 10,000
SALES (est): 761.2K **Privately Held**
WEB: www.premiummarine.com
SIC: 3732 Boat building & repairing

(G-10187)
PREMIUM RUBBER BANDS INC
9430 Sw 136th St (33176-6802)
PHONE..................................305 321-0333
Christian Chamizo, *Principal*
EMP: 7 **EST:** 2016
SALES (est): 83.5K **Privately Held**
WEB: www.rubberband.com
SIC: 3069 Rubber bands

(G-10188)
PREPAID SOLUTIONS LLC
601 Brickell Key Dr # 70 (33131-2662)
PHONE..................................786 257-2714
Edward Madera, *CEO*
EMP: 15 **EST:** 2010
SQ FT: 5,000
SALES (est): 1.6MM **Privately Held**
WEB: www.prepaid.solutions
SIC: 3661 8748 Telephone sets, all types except cellular radio; telecommunications consultant

(G-10189)
PRESSNET CORP
Also Called: Calle Ocho News
321 Nw 63rd Ct (33126-4542)
P.O. Box 260011 (33126-0002)
PHONE..................................786 728-1369
Marta Rosell, *Principal*
EMP: 8 **EST:** 1998
SALES (est): 250K **Privately Held**
WEB: www.pressnetcorp.com
SIC: 2711 Newspapers, publishing & printing

(G-10190)
PRESTASHOP INC
1001 Brickell Bay Dr # 2502 (33131-4900)
PHONE..................................888 947-6543
Bruno Leveque, *Principal*
Charlotte Clement, *Human Resources*
Denis Severe, *Technical Staff*
EMP: 15 **EST:** 2010
SALES (est): 539.1K **Privately Held**
WEB: www.prestashop.com
SIC: 7372 Application computer software

(G-10191)
PRESYS INSTRUMENTS INC
14453 Sw 84th St (33183-3906)
PHONE..................................305 495-3335
William F Charles, *Principal*
Marc Vantournhoudt, *Sales Mgr*
EMP: 7 **EST:** 2016
SALES (est): 1MM **Privately Held**
WEB: www.presyscorp.com
SIC: 3823 Industrial instrmnts msrmnt display/control process variable

(G-10192)
PRIDE STRAWS LLC
3246 N Miami Ave (33127-3555)
P.O. Box 371507 (33137-1507)
PHONE..................................407 754-5833
Kevin Corp,
EMP: 6 **EST:** 2019
SALES (est): 90.7K **Privately Held**
SIC: 2656 Straws, drinking: made from purchased material

▲ = Import ▼=Export
◆ =Import/Export

(G-10193)
PRINT BOLD CORP
Also Called: Orion Press
13995 Sw 144th Ave Ste 20 (33186-8655)
PHONE..................................305 517-1281
Hernandez Sandra, *Principal*
EMP: 13 **EST:** 2010
SALES (est): 1MM **Privately Held**
SIC: 2752 Commercial printing, offset

(G-10194)
PRINT FARM INC (PA)
Also Called: Printfarm
3511 Nw 74th Ave (33122-1233)
PHONE..................................305 592-2895
Albert Alvarez, *President*
Mike Depaz, *Vice Pres*
EMP: 22 **EST:** 2000
SQ FT: 3,500
SALES (est): 3.2MM **Privately Held**
WEB: www.pf-solutions.com
SIC: 2752 Commercial printing, offset

(G-10195)
PRINT MOTION INC (PA)
1501 Sw 118th Ct (33184-2538)
PHONE..................................305 851-7206
Yudith Cordon, *Principal*
EMP: 16 **EST:** 2014
SALES (est): 164.4K **Privately Held**
WEB: www.printmotion.us
SIC: 2752 Commercial printing, offset

(G-10196)
PRINT PRO SHOP INC
Also Called: Orion Visual Group
660 Nw 85th St (33150-2560)
PHONE..................................305 859-8282
Alex Peysakhovich, *President*
Mike Peysakhovich, *Vice Pres*
EMP: 13 **EST:** 2012
SALES (est): 2.3MM **Privately Held**
WEB: www.pps.printproshop.com
SIC: 2752 Commercial printing, lithographic

(G-10197)
PRINT RITE CO
748 Ne 79th St (33138-4752)
PHONE..................................305 757-0611
Benjamin Kram, *Owner*
EMP: 6 **EST:** 1953
SQ FT: 2,500
SALES (est): 520.8K **Privately Held**
SIC: 2752 Letters, circular or form: lithographed; lithographing on metal

(G-10198)
PRINT SIGNS & BANNERS
4244 Sw 73rd Ave (33155-4545)
PHONE..................................305 600-1349
EMP: 6 **EST:** 2016
SALES (est): 175.6K **Privately Held**
WEB: www.psbmiami.com
SIC: 3993 Signs & advertising specialties

(G-10199)
PRINTERBAZAAR USA INC
15321 S Dixie Hwy Ste 309 (33157-1873)
PHONE..................................954 730-3473
Shyama P Mukerjee, *Principal*
EMP: 6 **EST:** 2010
SALES (est): 117K **Privately Held**
WEB: www.printerbazaar.com
SIC: 2752 Commercial printing, lithographic

(G-10200)
PRINTING CENTER LLC
6740 Sw 155th Ave (33193-2115)
PHONE..................................305 513-9114
Dianne Coe, *Principal*
EMP: 6 **EST:** 2009
SALES (est): 153.2K **Privately Held**
SIC: 2752 Commercial printing, offset

(G-10201)
PRINTING GRPHICS CNNECTION INC
823 Nw 133rd Ct (33182-2205)
PHONE..................................305 222-6144
Octavio J Del Castillo, *President*
Catherine Del Castillo, *Vice Pres*
EMP: 5 **EST:** 1985
SQ FT: 3,300
SALES (est): 482.6K **Privately Held**
WEB: www.store.pgcprinting.com
SIC: 2752 Commercial printing, offset

(G-10202)
PRISNA LATINO
7455 Nw 50th St (33166-5538)
PHONE..................................305 525-9292
Victor M Fernandez Jr, *President*
Victor M Fernandez Sr, *Vice Pres*
Sofia Fernandez, *Admin Sec*
EMP: 5 **EST:** 2009
SQ FT: 1,700
SALES (est): 319.5K **Privately Held**
SIC: 2732 Book printing

(G-10203)
PRO FUSE
11231 Nw 20th St (33172-1856)
PHONE..................................305 982-8457
Jonathan Borges, *Principal*
EMP: 7 **EST:** 2016
SALES (est): 158.8K **Privately Held**
SIC: 3679 Electronic components

(G-10204)
PROANDRE HYGIENE SYSTEMS INC
1200 Brickell Ave # 1950 (33131-3214)
PHONE..................................305 433-3493
Enrique Cerezalez, *President*
▲ **EMP:** 19 **EST:** 2007
SALES (est): 721.3K
SALES (corp-wide): 1.7MM **Privately Held**
WEB: www.proandre.com
SIC: 3089 Tops: dispenser, shaker, etc.: plastic
PA: Proandre Sl
Calle Conestable De Portugal, 43 - 45
3
Granollers 08402
938 600-341

(G-10205)
PROFESSIONAL BINDERY INC
3668 Nw 48th Ter (33142-3924)
PHONE..................................305 633-3761
Fax: 305 633-3762
EMP: 12
SQ FT: 4,500
SALES (est): 670K **Privately Held**
SIC: 2789 Bookbinding And Related Work

(G-10206)
PROFESSIONAL OFFICE SVCS INC
176 Ne 82nd St (33138-3708)
PHONE..................................305 756-8632
Lucie Casthely, *Branch Mgr*
EMP: 7
SALES (corp-wide): 75.4MM **Privately Held**
WEB: www.poscorp.com
SIC: 2761 Manifold business forms
PA: Professional Office Services, Inc.
2757 Burton Ave
Waterloo IA 50703
319 235-6777

(G-10207)
PROFESSIONAL SIGNS
6460 Sw 35th St (33155-3960)
PHONE..................................305 662-5957
Maria J Bertot, *Principal*
EMP: 5 **EST:** 1997
SALES (est): 391.5K **Privately Held**
WEB: www.welovesun.com
SIC: 3993 Signs & advertising specialties

(G-10208)
PROFORM SYSTEM INC
2665 S Bayshore Dr (33133-5448)
PHONE..................................305 854-2800
James Deane, *Principal*
EMP: 6 **EST:** 2009
SALES (est): 208.5K **Privately Held**
WEB: www.proform.com
SIC: 3069 Fabricated rubber products

(G-10209)
PROMOITALIA LLC
1221 Brickell Ave (33131-3224)
PHONE..................................305 347-5178
Valerio Matano,
EMP: 5 **EST:** 2018
SALES (est): 388.8K **Privately Held**
WEB: www.us.webpromoitalia.com
SIC: 2844 Cosmetic preparations

(G-10210)
PROPGLIDE USA CORP
4769 Nw 72nd Ave (33166-5616)
PHONE..................................305 520-0150
Rola Zaki, *Vice Pres*
Jason Revie, *Director*
EMP: 5 **EST:** 2017
SALES (est): 378.8K **Privately Held**
WEB: www.propglide.com
SIC: 3714 Motor vehicle parts & accessories

(G-10211)
PROSOLUS INC (HQ)
6701 Nw 7th St Ste 165 (33126-6032)
PHONE..................................305 514-0270
Alex Moreno, *CEO*
Juan Mantelle, *COO*
Rod L Hartwig, *Vice Pres*
David Houze, *Research*
Arturo Serrano-Batista, *Senior Mgr*
EMP: 9 **EST:** 2015
SALES (est): 4.9MM **Privately Held**
WEB: www.prosoluspharma.com
SIC: 2834 Pharmaceutical preparations

(G-10212)
PROUD TSHIRTS CORP
62 Ne 167th St (33162-3401)
PHONE..................................305 769-3300
Eline Stgeorges, *Principal*
EMP: 6 **EST:** 2017
SALES (est): 355.1K **Privately Held**
WEB: www.proudtshirts.com
SIC: 2759 Screen printing

(G-10213)
PUBLISHERS DIRECT CHOICE LLC
1440 Sw 78th Ave (33144-5210)
PHONE..................................305 264-5998
Alvvaro Uribe, *Principal*
EMP: 7 **EST:** 2010
SALES (est): 133.2K **Privately Held**
WEB: www.publishersdirectchoice.com
SIC: 2741 Miscellaneous publishing

(G-10214)
PUMA MARBLE CO INC
5445 Nw 2nd Ave (33127-1794)
PHONE..................................305 758-6461
Theresa Puma, *President*
Robert Seitz, *Vice Pres*
Mary Seitz, *Vice Pres*
Maryellen Seitz, *Treasurer*
Melissa B Mestre, *Admin Sec*
◆ **EMP:** 15 **EST:** 1969
SQ FT: 1,500
SALES (est): 1.6MM **Privately Held**
WEB: www.pumamarble.com
SIC: 3281 1743 Marble, building: cut & shaped; marble installation, interior

(G-10215)
PUPPET WORKSHOP INC
7040 Sw 47th St Fl 2 (33155-4647)
PHONE..................................305 666-2655
EMP: 30
SALES (corp-wide): 21.7MM **Privately Held**
SIC: 3999 Mfg Puppets
PA: The Puppet Workshop Inc
295 E 10th Ct
Hialeah FL 33010
305 666-2655

(G-10216)
PURE LIFE PRODUCTS LLC
Also Called: Pure Life Soap Company
3380 Nw 114th St Bldg C (33167-3321)
PHONE..................................321 578-2060
Mark P Sawyer, *Manager*
EMP: 6 **EST:** 2006
SALES (est): 97.9K **Privately Held**
SIC: 2844 Hair preparations, including shampoos; cosmetic preparations; face creams or lotions

(G-10217)
PUROVITE INC
7347 Sw 45th St (33155-4509)
PHONE..................................305 364-5727
Momin Dowlah, *President*
Tarif Gaffar, *Vice Pres*
EMP: 9 **EST:** 2016
SALES (est): 741.9K **Privately Held**
WEB: www.purovite.com
SIC: 2833 Medicinals & botanicals

(G-10218)
QUALITY WOOD MACHINE INC
8410 Sw 33rd Ter (33155-3248)
PHONE..................................305 221-0218
Rogerio Pereira, *Director*
EMP: 7 **EST:** 2001
SALES (est): 175.3K **Privately Held**
SIC: 3599 Machine shop, jobbing & repair

(G-10219)
QUALITYSAT CORP
13355 Sw 135th Ave (33186-6268)
PHONE..................................305 232-4211
Ana M Obregon, *Principal*
EMP: 7 **EST:** 2008
SALES (est): 179K **Privately Held**
SIC: 3663 Satellites, communications

(G-10220)
QUANTUM ASSETS LLC
638 Nw 11th St (33136-2404)
PHONE..................................786 484-1187
Adam A Avhad, *Principal*
EMP: 6 **EST:** 2010
SALES (est): 144.8K **Privately Held**
SIC: 3572 Computer storage devices

(G-10221)
QUANTUM SAFETY SERVICES INC
20280 Sw 190th St (33187-1871)
PHONE..................................786 420-0735
Javier Duran, *Principal*
EMP: 7 **EST:** 2016
SALES (est): 85.9K **Privately Held**
SIC: 3572 Computer storage devices

(G-10222)
QUANTUM SERVICING CORPORATION
790 Nw 107th Ave Ste 400 (33172-3159)
PHONE..................................305 229-6675
EMP: 7 **EST:** 2019
SALES (est): 454K **Privately Held**
SIC: 3572 Computer storage devices

(G-10223)
QUANTURO PUBLISHING INC
Also Called: Quantoro Publishing
4141 Ne 2nd Ave Ste 202 (33137-3539)
PHONE..................................305 373-3700
EMP: 23
SALES: 300K **Privately Held**
SIC: 2721 Magazine Publisher

(G-10224)
QUEEN B HAIR COLLECTION LLC
17111 Nw 10th Ct (33169-5240)
PHONE..................................954 393-2791
Reigna Booker, *President*
EMP: 10 **EST:** 2019
SALES (est): 565.4K **Privately Held**
WEB: www.qbhaircollection.com
SIC: 3999 Hair, dressing of, for the trade

(G-10225)
QUEST INTERNATIONAL INC
8127 Nw 29th St (33122-1051)
PHONE..................................305 592-6991
Oscar Compain, *President*
Robert Cort, *Vice Pres*
David J Kiefer, *Vice Pres*
EMP: 10 **EST:** 1994
SQ FT: 2,000
SALES (est): 670.2K **Privately Held**
WEB: www.jimcharltonphotography.com
SIC: 3825 Instruments to measure electricity

(G-10226)
QUIKRETE COMPANIES LLC
3700 Nw 123rd St (33167-2035)
PHONE..................................305 681-8664

Sylvia Salazar, *Branch Mgr*
EMP: 6 **Privately Held**
WEB: www.quikrete.com
SIC: 3272 Concrete products
HQ: The Quikrete Companies Llc
5 Concourse Pkwy Ste 1900
Atlanta GA 30328
404 634-9100

(G-10227)
QUIRANTES ORTHOPEDICS INC
5840 W Flagler St (33144-3399)
PHONE..................................305 261-1382
Tulio Quirantes, *President*
EMP: 6 **EST:** 1983
SQ FT: 1,500
SALES (est): 663.5K **Privately Held**
WEB: www.quirantesortho.com
SIC: 3842 5999 Orthopedic appliances; orthopedic & prosthesis applications

(G-10228)
R & R AMERICAN CORPORATION (PA)
Also Called: American R&R
7222 Nw 56th St (33166-4247)
PHONE..................................786 497-8898
Raul Brand, *President*
Pilar Brand, *Vice Pres*
Edilma Brand, *Director*
EMP: 6 **EST:** 2008
SALES (est): 1MM **Privately Held**
WEB: www.americanrr.com
SIC: 3646 Ceiling systems, luminous

(G-10229)
R & R STONE INDUSTRIES INC
7941 Nw 67th St (33166-2694)
PHONE..................................888 999-4921
Ramos A Diego, *Principal*
▲ **EMP:** 5 **EST:** 2015
SALES (est): 833K **Privately Held**
WEB: www.rrstoneind.com
SIC: 3589 Shredders, industrial & commercial

(G-10230)
R AND D KITCHEN CABINETS CORP
14863 Sw 139th St (33196-4679)
PHONE..................................305 305-2390
Ricardo Valdes, *Principal*
EMP: 6 **EST:** 2018
SALES (est): 111.5K **Privately Held**
SIC: 2434 Wood kitchen cabinets

(G-10231)
R C R MANUFACTURING INC
9279 Sw 38th St (33165-4143)
PHONE..................................786 499-9245
Raidy Concepcion Gomez, *Principal*
EMP: 9 **EST:** 2016
SALES (est): 450.7K **Privately Held**
SIC: 3999 Manufacturing industries

(G-10232)
R M EQUIPMENT INC
6975 Nw 43rd St (33166-6844)
PHONE..................................305 477-9312
Ronald Martin, *President*
Todd Griffin, *Vice Pres*
EMP: 20 **EST:** 1972
SQ FT: 6,000
SALES (est): 1.2MM **Privately Held**
WEB: www.rm-equipment.com
SIC: 3484 Guns (firearms) or gun parts, 30 mm. & below

(G-10233)
R Y D ENTERPRISES INC
Also Called: Ryd Enterprises
20815 Ne 16th Ave Ste B7 (33179-2124)
PHONE..................................305 655-1045
Ronen Dagan, *President*
◆ **EMP:** 26 **EST:** 1991
SQ FT: 6,000
SALES (est): 367.2K **Privately Held**
WEB: www.rydembroidery.com
SIC: 2395 Embroidery products, except schiffli machine

(G-10234)
R&S INTRNATIONAL INV GROUP LLC
571 Nw 29th St (33127-3917)
PHONE..................................305 576-3000
Leonardo Roa, *President*
EMP: 10 **EST:** 2014
SALES (est): 375.6K **Privately Held**
SIC: 2326 2331 Work uniforms; medical & hospital uniforms, men's; aprons, work, except rubberized & plastic: men's; jackets, overall & work; women's & misses' blouses & shirts

(G-10235)
RAINBOW EB BUENAVISTA
8554 Sw 8th St (33144-4053)
PHONE..................................305 982-8153
Ernesto Borges, *President*
EMP: 6 **EST:** 2010
SALES (est): 225.8K **Privately Held**
SIC: 3564 Air cleaning systems

(G-10236)
RALLY MANUFACTURING INC
7200 Nw 19th St Ste 308 (33126-1212)
PHONE..................................305 628-2886
Christian Iacovelli, *President*
David Kraus, *CFO*
Acacia Lopez, *Manager*
◆ **EMP:** 150
SQ FT: 17,000
SALES (est): 22MM **Privately Held**
WEB: www.rallymfg.com
SIC: 3714 Motor vehicle parts & accessories

(G-10237)
RAM SALES LLC
Also Called: Ram Steel Framing
7400 Nw 37th Ave (33147-5816)
PHONE..................................844 726-6382
Andy Redmond, *CEO*
Roberto Colina, *Vice Pres*
Michael Barker, *CFO*
Eduardo Gracia, *Mng Member*
Andrew Redmond,
◆ **EMP:** 80 **EST:** 2001
SQ FT: 105,000
SALES (est): 24MM **Privately Held**
WEB: www.ramsteelframing.com
SIC: 3442 Window & door frames

(G-10238)
RAMPMASTER INC
11098 Biscayne Blvd # 401 (33161-7429)
P.O. Box 530176 (33153-0176)
PHONE..................................305 691-9090
Robert Davis, *President*
Ron Bowser, *Mfg Staff*
Hunt Davis, *Manager*
EMP: 18 **EST:** 1968
SQ FT: 35,000
SALES (est): 1.1MM **Privately Held**
WEB: www.rampsonline.com
SIC: 3448 3446 3537 3429 Ramps: prefabricated metal; ladders, for permanent installation: metal; industrial trucks & tractors; manufactured hardware (general)

(G-10239)
RAP SNACKS INC
150 Se 2nd Ave Ph 6 (33131-1516)
PHONE..................................305 926-9594
James Lindsay, *CEO*
Taylor McCain, *COO*
EMP: 4 **EST:** 2018
SALES (est): 13MM **Privately Held**
WEB: www.rapsnacks.net
SIC: 2096 Potato chips & similar snacks; potato chips & other potato-based snacks; corn chips & other corn-based snacks; tortilla chips

(G-10240)
RAPTOR WEAR PRODUCTS USA INC
7842 Nw 71st St (33166-2344)
PHONE..................................786 972-0326
Robin Miller, *General Mgr*
EMP: 13 **EST:** 2013
SALES (est): 3.1MM **Privately Held**
WEB: www.raptormining.com
SIC: 3599 Machine shop, jobbing & repair

(G-10241)
RASS FAST PALLET INC
4214 Nw 11th Pl (33127-2711)
PHONE..................................786 877-2854
Raquel Sebastian, *President*
EMP: 8 **EST:** 2006
SALES (est): 454.1K **Privately Held**
SIC: 2448 Pallets, wood

(G-10242)
RAZIENT LLC
990 Biscayne Blvd Ste 503 (33132-1556)
PHONE..................................855 747-5911
EMP: 7
SALES (est): 430K **Privately Held**
SIC: 7372 Prepackaged Software Services

(G-10243)
RECON GROUP LLP
Also Called: Gotrg
20200 W Dixie Hwy # 1005 (33180-1926)
PHONE..................................855 874-8741
EMP: 8 **EST:** 2014
SALES (est): 219.4K **Privately Held**
SIC: 7372 Prepackaged software

(G-10244)
RED MICROPHONE
3312 N Miami Ave (33127-3524)
PHONE..................................818 806-8545
Robert Zuniga, *Admin Sec*
EMP: 6 **EST:** 2016
SALES (est): 81.4K **Privately Held**
SIC: 3651 Microphones

(G-10245)
REDERICK METAL INDUSTRIES (PA)
1933 Nw 21st Ter (33142-7325)
PHONE..................................305 396-3396
Guillermo R Thomas, *Principal*
EMP: 23 **EST:** 2007
SALES (est): 147.3K **Privately Held**
WEB: www.yardbeast.com
SIC: 3999 Manufacturing industries

(G-10246)
REFLY OF MIAMI INC
7360 Nw 35th St (33122-1267)
PHONE..................................786 762-2748
Oscar Molina Jr, *President*
EMP: 10 **EST:** 1995
SQ FT: 11,000
SALES (est): 1.6MM **Privately Held**
SIC: 3572 3571 Computer storage devices; electronic computers

(G-10247)
REFRIGERATION PANELS INC
7215 Nw 36th Ave (33147-5876)
PHONE..................................305 836-6900
Juan Hernandez, *President*
Mercedes Hernandez, *Corp Secy*
▼ **EMP:** 18 **EST:** 1969
SQ FT: 30,000
SALES (est): 1.8MM **Privately Held**
SIC: 3585 Refrigeration equipment, complete

(G-10248)
REFRIGRTION ENGNRED SYSTEMS IN
Also Called: Refrigeration Panels
7215 Nw 36th Ave (33147-5835)
PHONE..................................305 836-6900
Juan J Hernandez, *President*
Aurea Rodriguez, *Corp Secy*
Maria E Gestido, *Vice Pres*
Maggie Suarez, *Admin Asst*
◆ **EMP:** 46 **EST:** 1969
SQ FT: 30,000
SALES (est): 3.9MM **Privately Held**
SIC: 3585 Refrigeration equipment, complete

(G-10249)
RELA USA LLC
Also Called: Best Custom Tape
8398 Nw 70th St (33166-2623)
PHONE..................................786 656-5069
EMP: 6 **EST:** 2018
SALES (est): 499.2K **Privately Held**
WEB: www.relabrand.com
SIC: 3572 Computer storage devices

(G-10250)
REMIOR INDUSTRIES INC
9165 Nw 96th St (33178-1407)
PHONE..................................305 883-8722
Lazaro Rolando Remior, *President*
Marta Remior, *Vice Pres*
Silvia Remior, *Vice Pres*
Epifeania Remior, *Treasurer*
Rolando Remior, *Shareholder*
EMP: 40 **EST:** 1975
SQ FT: 21,000
SALES (est): 4.8MM **Privately Held**
WEB: www.remiorindustries.com
SIC: 3446 2431 Railings, bannisters, guards, etc.: made from metal pipe; staircases & stairs, wood; stair railings, wood

(G-10251)
RENACER BROS LLC
18839 Biscayne Blvd # 150 (33180-3397)
PHONE..................................305 935-6777
Leonardo Ring, *Owner*
EMP: 6 **EST:** 2016
SALES (est): 403.5K **Privately Held**
SIC: 2024 Ice cream & frozen desserts

(G-10252)
RENCO USA INC
5959 Blue Lagoon Dr (33126-2039)
PHONE..................................321 637-1000
Kenneth A Smuts, *President*
Vedat Kalkuz, *CFO*
EMP: 15 **EST:** 2011
SALES (est): 261.6K **Privately Held**
WEB: www.rencousa.com
SIC: 3677 5065 Electronic transformers; electronic tubes: receiving & transmitting or industrial

(G-10253)
RENEWABLE FUELS GROUP LLC
15184 Sw 111th St (33196-2502)
PHONE..................................305 388-3028
Octavio B Castillo, *Principal*
EMP: 6 **EST:** 2008
SALES (est): 301.8K **Privately Held**
WEB: www.regi.com
SIC: 2869 Fuels

(G-10254)
REPLENISH INK INC
701 Brickell Ave Key Blvd (33131-2813)
P.O. Box 310070 (33231-0070)
PHONE..................................818 206-2424
Hector Erquiaga, *President*
▼ **EMP:** 5 **EST:** 2006
SQ FT: 1,300
SALES (est): 850K **Privately Held**
WEB: www.replenishink.com
SIC: 3955 5112 Print cartridges for laser & other computer printers; office supplies

(G-10255)
REPROGRAPHIC SERVICES INC
1036 Sw 8th St (33130-3602)
PHONE..................................305 859-8282
Alex Poysakhovich, *President*
Joe Pulik, *Vice Pres*
EMP: 10 **EST:** 2002
SQ FT: 3,000
SALES (est): 300K **Privately Held**
SIC: 2754 Job printing, gravure

(G-10256)
REPUBLIC DRILL/APT CORP (PA)
Also Called: Michigan Drill
7840 Nw 62nd St (33166-3539)
PHONE..................................305 592-7777
Cloys Arnett, *General Mgr*
Mark Linari, *General Mgr*
Marc Zeitlin, *Vice Pres*
Noel Rivera, *Opers Mgr*
Irene Garcia, *Purchasing*
▲ **EMP:** 80 **EST:** 1974
SQ FT: 40,000
SALES (est): 28.7MM **Privately Held**
WEB: www.michigandrill.com
SIC: 3541 Machine tools, metal cutting type

(G-10257)
RESOLUTE FP FLORIDA INC (HQ)
3301 Nw 107th St (33167-3714)
PHONE..................................800 562-2860
Jim Brown, *CEO*
Lester Martino, *Research*
Kim Orozco, *Manager*
EMP: 100 **EST:** 2014
SALES (est): 107.9MM
SALES (corp-wide): 2.9B **Privately Held**
WEB: www.pfresolu.com
SIC: 2621 Toilet tissue stock
PA: Resolute Forest Products Inc
111 Boul Robert-Bourassa Bureau 5000
Montreal QC H3C 2
514 875-2160

(G-10258)
RESOLUTE TISSUE LLC
Also Called: Atlas Tissue A Resolute Bus
3301 Nw 107th St (33167-3714)
PHONE..................................305 636-5741
Tim Loughrey, *Sales Staff*
Marvin Cabrera, *Manager*
Enrique Llorente, *Manager*
Michael Shaughnessy, *Director*
EMP: 12 **EST:** 2017
SALES (est): 1MM **Privately Held**
WEB: www.resolutetissue.com
SIC: 2621 Paper mills

(G-10259)
REYES GRANITE & MARBLE CORP
7905 Nw 60th St (33166-3410)
PHONE..................................305 599-7330
Pedro Reyes, *President*
EMP: 10 **EST:** 1994
SALES (est): 1.4MM **Privately Held**
WEB: www.reyesgranitemarble.com
SIC: 3281 1411 Granite, cut & shaped; statuary, marble; dimension stone

(G-10260)
REYES JEWELERS CORP
36 Ne 1st St Ste 734 (33132-2481)
PHONE..................................305 431-8303
Jonathan Reyes, *Principal*
EMP: 7 **EST:** 2014
SALES (est): 516K **Privately Held**
WEB: www.reyes-jewelers-corp.business.site
SIC: 3911 Jewelry, precious metal

(G-10261)
RFG CONSULTING SERVICES INC
801 Brickell Ave Ste 900 (33131-2979)
PHONE..................................786 498-2177
Jose G Guevara, *President*
EMP: 5 **EST:** 2011
SALES (est): 417.7K **Privately Held**
WEB: www.rfgconsultingservices.com
SIC: 3599 Machine & other job shop work

(G-10262)
RIBBON WHOLESALE CORP
219 Sw 21st Ct (33135-1712)
PHONE..................................786 457-0555
Luis Bravo, *Manager*
EMP: 11 **EST:** 2001
SALES (est): 156.3K **Privately Held**
WEB: www.jkmribbon.com
SIC: 3955 Ribbons, inked: typewriter, adding machine, register, etc.

(G-10263)
RICE MACHINERY SUPPLY CO INC
1130 Nw 163rd Dr (33169-5816)
PHONE..................................305 620-2274
Maria Dieguez, *President*
▲ **EMP:** 10 **EST:** 1990
SALES (est): 739.2K **Privately Held**
WEB: www.rimacusa.com
SIC: 3556 Food products machinery

(G-10264)
RIMA CARGO LLC
8375 Nw 68th St (33166-2663)
PHONE..................................305 477-8002
Ricardo Gutierrez, *Mng Member*
Maryori Berrueta, *Mng Member*
▼ **EMP:** 8 **EST:** 2009
SALES (est): 798.4K **Privately Held**
WEB: www.rimacargo.com
SIC: 2448 Cargo containers, wood & metal combination

(G-10265)
RINKER MATERIALS CORP
8800 Sw 177th Ave (33196-2904)
P.O. Box 960700 (33296-0700)
PHONE..................................305 386-0078
Haim Pillosof, *Manager*
EMP: 6 **EST:** 2014
SALES (est): 93.5K **Privately Held**
WEB: www.wallingcos.com
SIC: 3273 Ready-mixed concrete

(G-10266)
RJ FORKLIFT SERVICES INC
8567 Coral Way (33155-2335)
PHONE..................................786 539-6613
Jabier Alfonso Alba, *President*
EMP: 6 **EST:** 2012
SALES (est): 301.8K **Privately Held**
WEB: www.rjforkliftservices.com
SIC: 3537 Forklift trucks

(G-10267)
RM CUSTOM WOODCRAFT INC
10400 Nw 36th Ct (33147-1034)
PHONE..................................786 355-7387
Ricardo Malaver, *President*
EMP: 7 **EST:** 2013
SALES (est): 178.6K **Privately Held**
SIC: 2511 Wood household furniture

(G-10268)
RME STUDIO INC
Also Called: Peixoto
7245 Ne 4th Ave Ste 102 (33138-5371)
PHONE..................................305 409-0856
Rafael M Esquenazi, *Principal*
EMP: 6 **EST:** 2010
SALES (est): 230.2K **Privately Held**
SIC: 2369 Bathing suits & swimwear: girls', children's & infants'

(G-10269)
RMF PRINTING TECHNOLOGIES INC
21200 Ne 38th Ave # 1501 (33180-4060)
PHONE..................................716 683-7500
EMP: 6 **EST:** 2019
SALES (est): 89.4K **Privately Held**
WEB: www.rmfprinting.com
SIC: 2752 Commercial printing, lithographic

(G-10270)
RNN PRODUCTIONS LLC
7700 Biscayne Blvd # 200 (33138-5132)
PHONE..................................437 238-9501
Ezra Levant, *Principal*
EMP: 15
SALES (est): 1.5MM **Privately Held**
SIC: 2741

(G-10271)
ROBERTO VALVERDE
1929 Nw 22nd St (33142-7331)
PHONE..................................305 324-5252
Roberto Valverde, *Principal*
EMP: 7 **EST:** 2006
SALES (est): 101.9K **Privately Held**
SIC: 3577 Printers & plotters

(G-10272)
ROCK INTL DISTRIBUTORS INC
8279 Nw 66th St (33166-2721)
PHONE..................................305 513-3314
Maria C Ortiz, *President*
Amado L Ortiz, *Treasurer*
EMP: 35 **EST:** 2006
SALES (est): 2.2MM **Privately Held**
SIC: 3264 Porcelain electrical supplies

(G-10273)
ROCKERS STONE INC
3615 Plaza St (33133-6222)
PHONE..................................305 447-1231
Josh Billig, *President*
Michelle McGonigal, *Admin Sec*
EMP: 6 **EST:** 1978
SALES (est): 200K **Privately Held**
WEB: www.rockersstone.com
SIC: 1411 Dimension stone

(G-10274)
RODES PRINTING CORP
8369 Bird Rd (33155-3353)
PHONE..................................305 559-5263
Roberto Escobar, *President*
◆ **EMP:** 5 **EST:** 1984
SQ FT: 1,800
SALES (est): 637.3K **Privately Held**
SIC: 2752 Commercial printing, offset

(G-10275)
RODRIGUEZ WELDING
220 Sw 6th St (33130-2911)
PHONE..................................305 856-3749
Gilberto Rodriguez, *Owner*
▲ **EMP:** 5 **EST:** 1975
SQ FT: 2,000
SALES (est): 321.6K **Privately Held**
SIC: 3599 7692 Machine & other job shop work; welding repair

(G-10276)
ROLLING DOOR PARTS INC
8187 Nw 71st St (33166-2341)
PHONE..................................305 888-5020
Vincent Giatonia, *President*
◆ **EMP:** 5 **EST:** 1997
SALES (est): 837K **Privately Held**
WEB: www.rollingdoorparts.com
SIC: 3442 Rolling doors for industrial buildings or warehouses, metal

(G-10277)
ROMA CASTING INC
14 Ne 1st Ave Ste 306 (33132-2404)
PHONE..................................305 577-0289
Luis Reyes, *President*
EMP: 7 **EST:** 1983
SQ FT: 1,700
SALES (est): 437K **Privately Held**
SIC: 3915 3911 Jewelers' castings; jewelry, precious metal

(G-10278)
ROMANO GROUP LLC
12253 Sw 130th St (33186-6218)
PHONE..................................305 255-4242
Ricardo Romano, *Principal*
Ricardo Robaina, *Manager*
▲ **EMP:** 18 **EST:** 2011
SALES (est): 1.3MM **Privately Held**
WEB: www.romanogrp.com
SIC: 2844 Cosmetic preparations

(G-10279)
RON MATUSALEM & MATUSA FLA INC
Also Called: Matusalem & Company
1205 Sw 37th Ave Ste 300 (33135-4226)
PHONE..................................305 448-8255
Claudio Alvarez MD, *President*
EMP: 14 **EST:** 1961
SALES (est): 613.6K **Privately Held**
SIC: 2085 Rum (alcoholic beverage)

(G-10280)
RONNIE & MOES ITALIAN ICE LLC
7900 Nw 27th Ave Ste 602a (33147-4911)
P.O. Box 813124, Hollywood (33081-3124)
PHONE..................................786 970-1805
Ronnie Melton, *Principal*
EMP: 6 **EST:** 2016
SALES (est): 328.9K **Privately Held**
SIC: 2024 5812 Ice cream & frozen desserts; eating places

(G-10281)
ROQUE BROTHERS CORP
5646 Nw 35th Ct (33142-2730)
PHONE..................................305 885-6995
Roberto F Roque Sr, *President*
Marina Roque, *Corp Secy*
Raul Roque, *Vice Pres*
Roberto A Roque Jr, *Vice Pres*
EMP: 15 **EST:** 1972
SQ FT: 30,000
SALES (est): 429.8K **Privately Held**
SIC: 2521 Wood office furniture

(G-10282)
ROSS PIVNIK
9380 Sw 125th Ter (33176-5034)
PHONE..................................305 254-1635
Ross Pivnik, *Owner*
EMP: 6 **EST:** 2010
SALES (est): 103K **Privately Held**
SIC: 3271 Blocks, concrete: landscape or retaining wall

(G-10283)
ROYAL BLINDS LLC
13006 Sw 50th St (33175-5314)
PHONE..................................786 253-8126
Julio Rodriguez, *Manager*
EMP: 13 **EST:** 2016
SALES (est): 605.1K **Privately Held**
WEB: www.royalblinds.com
SIC: 2591 Window blinds

(G-10284)
RQ WELDING INC
6011 Sw 109th Ave (33173-1246)
PHONE..................................786 609-3384
Roger Quesada, *President*
EMP: 7 **EST:** 2015
SALES (est): 155.6K **Privately Held**
WEB: www.rqweldinginc.com
SIC: 3315 3312 Fence gates posts & fittings: steel; rails, steel or iron

(G-10285)
RRHILL PRINTING SOLUTIONS INC
16637 Sw 81st Ter (33193-5755)
PHONE..................................786 897-2432
Randolph R Hill, *Principal*
EMP: 6 **EST:** 2010
SALES (est): 66.4K **Privately Held**
SIC: 2752 Commercial printing, lithographic

(G-10286)
RUBBER 2 GO LLC
Also Called: Leader Mulch
3551 Nw 116th St (33167-2923)
PHONE..................................305 688-8566
Alfredo Reviati, *Mng Member*
EMP: 8 **EST:** 2013
SALES (est): 1.6MM **Privately Held**
WEB: www.leadermulch.com
SIC: 3069 Medical & laboratory rubber sundries & related products

(G-10287)
RUDYS READY MIX
5800 Sw 122nd Ave (33183-1510)
PHONE..................................305 382-9283
Rudy Delamora, *Owner*
EMP: 5 **EST:** 1994
SALES (est): 462.9K **Privately Held**
WEB: www.concrete-readymix.com
SIC: 3273 Ready-mixed concrete

(G-10288)
RUIZ INDUSTRIES
10752 Sw 143rd Ave (33186-3069)
PHONE..................................305 218-6258
Albert Ruiz, *Principal*
EMP: 6 **EST:** 2010
SALES (est): 87.1K **Privately Held**
SIC: 3999 Manufacturing industries

(G-10289)
RUNN-IT LLC ✪
66 W Flagler St Ste 900 (33130-1807)
PHONE..................................800 932-8052
John Dieurestil,
EMP: 9 **EST:** 2021
SALES (est): 250K **Privately Held**
SIC: 3537 Trucks: freight, baggage, etc.: industrial, except mining

(G-10290)
RXGENESYS LLC
175 Sw 7th St Ste 2417 (33130-2966)
PHONE..................................786 220-8366
Kirsty Barany, *Mng Member*
EMP: 5 **EST:** 2015
SALES (est): 500K **Privately Held**
WEB: www.rxgenesys.com
SIC: 2844 Cosmetic preparations

(G-10291)
S & B INDUSTRIES INC
11052 Sw 162nd Ter (33157-2845)
PHONE..................................305 367-1068
Scott Lyn, *Principal*
EMP: 6 **EST:** 2010
SALES (est): 81.8K **Privately Held**
SIC: 3999 Manufacturing industries

(G-10292)
S PRINTING INC
2207 Nw 23rd Ave (33142-7355)
PHONE..................................305 633-3343
Ofelia Fern, *President*
▼ **EMP:** 5 **EST:** 1970
SQ FT: 12,000
SALES (est): 703.8K **Privately Held**
SIC: 2752 2791 Commercial printing, offset; typesetting

(G-10293)
S&B PALLET CORP
14765 Sw 36th Ter (33185-3913)
PHONE..................................305 525-0872
Pedro A Yero, *President*
EMP: 6 **EST:** 2005
SALES (est): 161.6K **Privately Held**
WEB: www.sbpallet.com
SIC: 2448 Pallets, wood & wood with metal

(G-10294)
SACYR ENVIRONMENT USA LLC
3191 Coral Way Ste 510 (33145-3227)
PHONE..................................202 361-4568
Brian Kirby, *General Mgr*
Laurenia Augustin, *Director*
EMP: 18 **EST:** 2014
SALES (est): 2.8MM
SALES (corp-wide): 88.1MM **Privately Held**
WEB: www.sacyr.com
SIC: 3822 Auto controls regulating residntl & coml environmt & applncs
HQ: Valoriza Servicios Medioambientales Sa
Calle Juan Esplandiu, 11 - 13 Planta 13
Madrid 28007
915 455-000

(G-10295)
SAFEGUARD AMERICA INC (PA)
3935 Nw 26th St (33142-6727)
PHONE..................................305 859-9000
Steven Masdeu, *President*
EMP: 19 **EST:** 1998
SALES (est): 3.1MM **Privately Held**
WEB: www.americastransportation.com
SIC: 3699 Security devices; security control equipment & systems

(G-10296)
SAFEPRINTS LLC
9155 S Dadeland Blvd # 1504 (33156-2737)
PHONE..................................305 960-7391
Luis A Rojas, *President*
EMP: 6
SALES (est): 724.7K **Privately Held**
WEB: www.safeprints.com
SIC: 2759 Flexographic printing

(G-10297)
SAFILO USA INC
703 Nw 62nd Ave Ste 100 (33126-4686)
PHONE..................................305 262-5727
Ana Crola, *Manager*
Max Beaubrun, *Manager*
Loredana Galli, *Manager*
Lidia Autuori, *Regional*
EMP: 24
SALES (corp-wide): 1.2MM **Privately Held**
WEB: www.safilogroup.com
SIC: 3229 Optical glass
HQ: Safilo Usa, Inc.
300 Lighting Way 4
Secaucus NJ 07094
973 952-2800

(G-10298)
SAINT GEORGE INDUSTRIES LLC
9130 S Dadelnd Blvd 180 (33156)
PHONE..................................786 212-1176
Patrick Stallings,
Karan Cerutti,
EMP: 25 **EST:** 2012
SQ FT: 7,988
SALES (est): 2.2MM **Privately Held**
WEB: www.stgeorgeindustries.com
SIC: 2326 2339 2396 Work apparel, except uniforms; service apparel, washable: women's; linings, apparel: made from purchased materials

(G-10299)
SAL AEROSPACE ENGINEERING LLC
11990 Sw 128th St (33186-5207)
PHONE..................................305 791-0593
Michael Salomon, *President*
Jonathan Martinez, *Purchasing*
Joel Navarro, *Engineer*
EMP: 10 **EST:** 2010
SQ FT: 4,500
SALES (est): 2MM **Privately Held**
WEB: www.salaerospace.com
SIC: 3728 Aircraft parts & equipment

(G-10300)
SALTEX GROUP CORP
7509 Nw 36th St (33166-6708)
PHONE..................................305 477-3187
Mauricio Salmon, *President*
Nicholas Salmon, *Project Mgr*
Gladys Yera, *Sales Staff*
EMP: 8 **EST:** 1997
SALES (est): 2.5MM **Privately Held**
WEB: www.saltexgroup.com
SIC: 3699 Security control equipment & systems

(G-10301)
SAMEDAY PRINTING INC
6815 Biscayne Blvd (33138-6292)
PHONE..................................800 411-3106
Kevin Henao, *President*
▼ **EMP:** 6
SALES (est): 619.7K **Privately Held**
WEB: www.samedayprinting.com
SIC: 2752 Commercial printing, offset

(G-10302)
SANIFLOW CORPORATION
3325 Nw 70th Ave (33122-1332)
PHONE..................................305 424-2433
Luis Sau, *President*
David Ruiz, *Vice Pres*
▲ **EMP:** 5 **EST:** 2004
SQ FT: 3,000
SALES (est): 704K **Privately Held**
WEB: www.saniflowcorp.com
SIC: 3634 Dryers, electric: hand & face

(G-10303)
SANTILLANA USA PUBG CO INC (DH)
8333 Nw 53rd St Ste 402 (33166-4787)
PHONE..................................305 591-9522
Miguel Tapia, *CEO*
Marta Moldes, *COO*
Stephen Marban, *Vice Pres*
Hector Miralles, *CFO*
Efrain Santa, *CFO*
▲ **EMP:** 65 **EST:** 1972
SALES (est): 16.2MM
SALES (corp-wide): 137.2MM **Privately Held**
WEB: www.santillanausa.com
SIC: 2731 Books: publishing only
HQ: Grupo Santillana Educacion Global Slu
Avenida De Los Artesanos 6
Tres Cantos 28760
917 449-060

(G-10304)
SANZAY CORPORATION
Also Called: Integrated Diagnostics Group
1080 Nw 163rd Dr (33169-5818)
PHONE..................................305 826-9886
Maria R Sanchez, *President*
Franciso J Perez, *COO*
▲ **EMP:** 25 **EST:** 2005
SALES (est): 1.5MM **Privately Held**
WEB: www.idgone.com
SIC: 2835 8071 In vitro & in vivo diagnostic substances; medical laboratories; testing laboratories

(G-10305)
SAPORE DI VINO INC
6905 Nw 51st St (33166-5627)
PHONE..................................561 818-8411
Medici Francesco, *President*
EMP: 10 **EST:** 2018
SALES (est): 551.7K **Privately Held**
WEB: www.saporedicasamiami.com
SIC: 2084 Wines

(G-10306)
SATIN SENSATION CO
16657 Sw 79th Ter (33193-5776)
PHONE..................................786 290-4114
Di Paolo Juan, *Principal*
EMP: 6 **EST:** 2013
SALES (est): 91.5K **Privately Held**
WEB: www.sensationsatin.com
SIC: 2221 Satins

(G-10307)
SAVING FOR COLLEGE LLC
444 Brickell Ave Ste 820 (33131-2407)
PHONE..................................954 770-5136
Marcos Cordero, *CEO*
EMP: 12 **EST:** 2012
SQ FT: 1,700
SALES (est): 1MM **Privately Held**
WEB: www.savingforcollege.com
SIC: 2741

(G-10308)
SC PARENT CORPORATION
1450 Brickell Ave Fl 31 (33131-3460)
PHONE..................................703 351-0200
Matthew Small, *CEO*
Keval Patel, *Ch of Bd*
Justin Tan, *COO*
Ryan Geary, *Vice Pres*
Ryan Kaplan, *Vice Pres*
EMP: 99
SQ FT: 15,000
SALES (est): 3.4MM **Privately Held**
SIC: 7372 7371 Application computer software; computer software development & applications

(G-10309)
SC PURCHASER CORPORATION
1450 Brickell Ave Fl 31 (33131-3460)
PHONE..................................703 351-0200
Matthew Small, *CEO*
Keval Patel, *Ch of Bd*
Justin Tan, *COO*
Ryan Geary, *Vice Pres*
Ryan Kaplan, *Vice Pres*
EMP: 99
SQ FT: 15,000
SALES (est): 2.4MM **Privately Held**
SIC: 7372 7371 Application computer software; computer software development & applications

(G-10310)
SCANID INC
444 Brickell Ave (33131-2403)
PHONE..................................305 607-3523
Nicolas Nicolaou, *CEO*
EMP: 5
SALES (est): 500K **Privately Held**
SIC: 7372 Prepackaged software

(G-10311)
SCHICK LLC
20412 Ne 15th Ct (33179-2708)
PHONE..................................718 810-3804
EMP: 14 **EST:** 2011
SALES (est): 397.9K **Privately Held**
WEB: www.schick.com
SIC: 3944 Games, toys & children's vehicles

(G-10312)
SCHNUPP MANUFACTURING CO INC
2113 Nw 17th Ave (33142-7477)
PHONE..................................305 325-0520
Leo E Schnupp Jr, *President*
◆ **EMP:** 6 **EST:** 1948
SQ FT: 5,000
SALES (est): 560.1K **Privately Held**
WEB: www.schnuppumbrellas.com
SIC: 3999 2394 Garden umbrellas; canvas & related products

(G-10313)
SCOPE WORKER LLC
2121 Nw 2nd Ave Ste 203 (33127-4830)
PHONE..................................917 855-5379
Justin Duval, *CEO*
Joshua Mangerson,
John Rafferty,
Sean Yazbeck,
EMP: 20 **EST:** 2017
SALES (est): 1.4MM **Privately Held**
WEB: www.scopeworker.com
SIC: 7372 Prepackaged software

(G-10314)
SCOTT SLIDE FASTENERS INC
Also Called: Notions
545 Nw 26th St (33127-4367)
PHONE..................................305 576-3328
Maria Srebnick, *President*
Ben Horstein, *Vice Pres*
Rene Gutierrez, *Controller*
Ivette Barros, *Technology*
EMP: 11 **EST:** 1966
SQ FT: 10,000
SALES (est): 163.6K **Privately Held**
SIC: 3965 5072 Fasteners, buttons, needles & pins; miscellaneous fasteners

(G-10315)
SEA SITE INC
1180 Nw 163rd Dr (33169-5816)
PHONE..................................305 403-3002
Murray Ginsberg, *Principal*
EMP: 8 **EST:** 2010
SALES (est): 102.9K **Privately Held**
SIC: 3479 Etching & engraving

(G-10316)
SEAL-TITE PLASTIC PACKG CO INC
4655 Sw 74th Ave (33155-4411)
P.O. Box 558748 (33255-8748)
PHONE..................................305 264-9015
James B Black Jr, *President*
Sheri Jude, *Controller*
▼ **EMP:** 90
SQ FT: 20,000
SALES (est): 20.4MM **Privately Held**
WEB: www.seal-tite.us
SIC: 2673 3083 3081 Food storage & frozen food bags, plastic; laminated plastics plate & sheet; unsupported plastics film & sheet

(G-10317)
SEAQUEST MARINE LLC
777 Brickell Ave (33131-2809)
PHONE..................................781 888-8850
Antonios Sikolas,
EMP: 5 **EST:** 2018
SALES (est): 352.4K **Privately Held**
WEB: www.seaquest.co
SIC: 3731 Shipbuilding & repairing

(G-10318)
SEAT SAVERS PLUS INC
Also Called: Supreme Seat Covers
12105 Sw 129th Ct Bay 10 (33186-6845)
PHONE..................................305 256-7863
Juan Alfonso, *President*
Carmen Alfonso, *Vice Pres*
EMP: 6 **EST:** 1994
SALES (est): 704.5K **Privately Held**
WEB: www.seatsavers.com
SIC: 2399 Seat covers, automobile

(G-10319)
SECOND 2 NONE WOOD WORK INC
10141 Sw 40th Ter (33165-5028)
PHONE..................................786 299-3580
Javier Jimenez, *President*
EMP: 6 **EST:** 2012
SALES (est): 64.9K **Privately Held**
WEB:
www.second2noneconsignments.com
SIC: 2431 Millwork

(G-10320)
SECURITY TECH GROUP INC
Also Called: Home Protection Team
9425 Sw 72nd St Ste 100 (33173-3295)
P.O. Box 560243 (33256-0243)
PHONE..................................305 631-2228
Sandra Di Mara, *President*

EMP: 7 **EST:** 2011
SALES (est): 833.9K **Privately Held**
WEB: www.securitytechfl.com
SIC: 3669 Burglar alarm apparatus, electric

(G-10321)
SELLINK AVIATION FUEL DIV LLC
Also Called: Sellinkafs
4019 Nw 28th St (33142-5611)
PHONE..................................305 336-6627
EMP: 8
SALES (est): 783.9K **Privately Held**
SIC: 2911 Petroleum Refiner

(G-10322)
SEMINOLE PAPER & PRINTING CO
60 Nw 3rd St (33128)
PHONE..................................305 379-8481
Sidney Goldston, *President*
EMP: 6 **EST:** 1953
SQ FT: 10,000
SALES (est): 113.1K **Privately Held**
SIC: 2752 Commercial printing, offset

(G-10323)
SENDA DE VIDA PUBLISHERS
14320 Sw 143rd Ct # 705 (33186-7612)
P.O. Box 559055 (33255-9055)
PHONE..................................305 262-2627
Marco Calderon, *President*
▼ **EMP:** 31 **EST:** 1997
SALES (est): 3.7MM **Privately Held**
WEB: www.sendadevida.us
SIC: 2731 Books: publishing only

(G-10324)
SENIORS VENT MGMT INC
6100 Blue Lagoon Dr # 110 (33126-7036)
PHONE..................................305 266-0988
Felix Martin, *Principal*
EMP: 5 **EST:** 2010
SALES (est): 365.1K **Privately Held**
SIC: 7372 Prepackaged software

(G-10325)
SEPAC CORP
5201 Blue Lagoon Dr (33126-2064)
PHONE..................................305 718-3379
Louis Lechevalier, *President*
Silvia Lechevalier, *Vice Pres*
Fernando Barilari, *VP Sales*
EMP: 12 **EST:** 2010
SALES (est): 314.8K **Privately Held**
WEB: www.sepaccorp.com
SIC: 3674 3625 4911 3629 Semiconductors & related devices; relays & industrial controls; ; electronic generation equipment; measuring & controlling devices; industrial process control instruments

(G-10326)
SERGIOS PRINTING INC
14265 Sw 140th St (33186-6760)
PHONE..................................305 971-4112
Sergio Fernandez, *President*
Miriam Fernandez, *Vice Pres*
EMP: 10 **EST:** 1998
SALES (est): 1.5MM **Privately Held**
WEB: www.sergiosprinting.com
SIC: 2791 2752 Typesetting; commercial printing, lithographic

(G-10327)
SERIES USA LLC
20900 Ne 30th Ave Ste 901 (33180-2166)
PHONE..................................305 932-4626
Maria Breton, *Accounting Mgr*
Roberto Gomez, *Manager*
EMP: 9 **EST:** 2008
SALES (est): 661.4K **Privately Held**
WEB: www.seriesseating.com
SIC: 2531 School furniture

(G-10328)
SEYER - TECH INDUSTRIES INC
1420 Sw 152nd Pl (33194-2663)
PHONE..................................305 233-2672
Adrian Reyes, *Principal*
▲ **EMP:** 9 **EST:** 2010
SALES (est): 157.1K **Privately Held**
WEB: www.seyer-tech.com
SIC: 3999 Manufacturing industries

(G-10329)
SG GLOBAL LLC (PA)
Also Called: Velgen Wheels
12192 Sw 128th St (33186-5231)
PHONE..................................305 726-3439
Scott Gibson, *Mng Member*
EMP: 2 **EST:** 2013
SQ FT: 4,000
SALES (est): 3MM **Privately Held**
SIC: 3312 Wheels

(G-10330)
SGS US EAST COAST LLC
Also Called: Miami Diver
12062 Nw 27th Ave (33167-2651)
PHONE..................................305 571-9700
Thomas Zels, *CEO*
Paul Peters, *President*
◆ **EMP:** 35 **EST:** 1981
SALES (est): 4.6MM **Privately Held**
SIC: 3731 Shipbuilding & repairing

(G-10331)
SH SHOWER & TUB ENCLOSURES LLC
4101 Sw 74th Ct (33155-4423)
PHONE..................................786 229-2529
Manuel Monteagudo, *Manager*
EMP: 6 **EST:** 2017
SALES (est): 150K **Privately Held**
SIC: 3088 Plastics plumbing fixtures

(G-10332)
SH SIGNS
215 Sw 17th Ave Ste 203 (33135-3628)
PHONE..................................305 967-8964
Shirley Hernandez, *Principal*
EMP: 7 **EST:** 2008
SALES (est): 196.2K **Privately Held**
SIC: 3993 Signs & advertising specialties

(G-10333)
SHADES BY ANA INC
12240 Sw 128th St (33186-5419)
PHONE..................................305 238-4858
Ana Lerin, *President*
EMP: 6
SALES (est): 490K **Privately Held**
WEB: www.shadesbyana.com
SIC: 2391 Draperies, plastic & textile: from purchased materials

(G-10334)
SHANTUI AMERICA CORP
5201 Nw 77th Ave Ste 600 (33166-4838)
PHONE..................................786 491-9114
Zhi Zhu, *President*
WEI Cheng, *Vice Pres*
EMP: 15 **EST:** 2015
SALES (est): 2.6MM
SALES (corp-wide): 47.3B **Privately Held**
WEB: www.en.shantui.com
SIC: 3531 Construction machinery
HQ: Shandong Shantui Machinery Co., Ltd.
No.6, Jiejia Road, High-Tech Zone
Jining 27210

(G-10335)
SHEILA SHINE INC
Also Called: Pan American Chemical Co.
1201 Nw 1st Pl (33136-2609)
P.O. Box 4784, Hialeah (33014-0784)
PHONE..................................305 557-1729
William Wallach, *President*
James G Wallach, *Principal*
David J Wallach, *Principal*
David Wallach, *Vice Pres*
Rita Wallach, *Vice Pres*
▼ **EMP:** 29 **EST:** 1961
SQ FT: 26,000
SALES (est): 3.4MM **Privately Held**
WEB: www.sheilashineinc.com
SIC: 2842 3291 Cleaning or polishing preparations; abrasive products

(G-10336)
SHELL AEROSPACE LLC
7500 Nw 25th St Unit 1a (33122-1729)
PHONE..................................786 400-2660
Vittorio Rivalta, *Purch Mgr*
Carlos A Suito, *Mng Member*
EMP: 8 **EST:** 2017
SALES (est): 1.1MM **Privately Held**
SIC: 3369 Aerospace castings, nonferrous: except aluminum

(G-10337)
SHELLEYS CUSHIONS MFG INC
Also Called: Shelleys Cshions Umbrellas Mfg
3640 Nw 52nd St (33142-3245)
PHONE..................................305 633-1790
Raul M Mollera, *President*
Aracelia Mollera, *Vice Pres*
EMP: 22 **EST:** 1973
SALES (est): 1MM **Privately Held**
SIC: 3999 2393 Garden umbrellas; cushions, except spring & carpet: purchased materials

(G-10338)
SHERRY MANUFACTURING CO INC
3287 Nw 65th St (33147-7590)
PHONE..................................305 693-7000
Quentin H Sandler, *Ch of Bd*
Scott Coltune, *President*
Sherry Zimand, *Vice Pres*
Jayne Walker, *Executive*
◆ **EMP:** 150 **EST:** 1948
SQ FT: 220,000
SALES (est): 25.4MM **Privately Held**
WEB: www.sherrymfg.com
SIC: 2261 Screen printing of cotton broadwoven fabrics

(G-10339)
SHISEIDO AMERICAS CORPORATION
1221 Brickell Ave Fl 26 (33131-3224)
PHONE..................................305 416-6021
Michael Gebrael, *Manager*
EMP: 10 **Privately Held**
WEB: www.jobs.shiseidoamericas.com
SIC: 2844 5122 Cosmetic preparations; toilet preparations; cosmetics; toilet preparations
HQ: Shiseido Americas Corporation
900 3rd Ave Fl 15
New York NY 10022
212 805-2300

(G-10340)
SHORES GLOBAL LLC
2440 Nw 116th St Ste 600 (33167-0009)
PHONE..................................305 716-0848
Antonia Eggers, *Project Mgr*
Karina Baban, *Purch Mgr*
Jose Cordero, *Manager*
William Schuitema, *Manager*
Susan Sadolin,
EMP: 9 **EST:** 2016
SALES: 2.4MM **Privately Held**
WEB: www.shoresglobal.com
SIC: 2512 5021 Upholstered household furniture; furniture

(G-10341)
SIBLING GROUP HOLDINGS INC (PA)
Also Called: Global Personalized Academics
6340 Sunset Dr (33143-4836)
PHONE..................................786 618-1472
Julie E Young, *CEO*
Angelle Judice, *CFO*
EMP: 63 **EST:** 1988
SALES (est): 5.2MM **Privately Held**
WEB: www.gpaed.com
SIC: 7372 8299 Educational computer software; educational services

(G-10342)
SIGN DEVELOPMENT CORPORATION
Also Called: Fastsigns
8240 W Flagler St (33144-2028)
PHONE..................................305 227-6250
Burt Poppeliers, *President*
Arthur Zalduondo, *Corp Secy*
EMP: 8 **EST:** 1990
SQ FT: 900
SALES (est): 780.9K **Privately Held**
WEB: www.fastsigns.com
SIC: 3993 Signs & advertising specialties

(G-10343)
SIGN ROCKERS LLC
12485 Sw 137th Ave # 206 (33186-4216)
PHONE..................................866 212-9697
Carlos Bethencourt,
EMP: 20 **EST:** 2017
SALES (est): 116K **Privately Held**
WEB: www.signrockers.com
SIC: 3993 Signs & advertising specialties

(G-10344)
SIGN SPACE
2365 Nw 70th Ave (33122-1819)
PHONE..................................786 360-2670
Adrian Gonzalez, *President*
EMP: 6 **EST:** 2017
SALES (est): 397K **Privately Held**
WEB: www.thesignspace.com
SIC: 3993 Signs & advertising specialties

(G-10345)
SIGNS 2 U INC
Also Called: Fastsigns
8240 W Flagler St (33144-2028)
PHONE..................................305 227-6250
Walter Prio, *President*
EMP: 8 **EST:** 2013
SALES (est): 766.2K **Privately Held**
WEB: www.signs2uboise.com
SIC: 3993 Signs & advertising specialties

(G-10346)
SIGNS CONNECTION INC
600 Ne 36th St Apt 807 (33137-3933)
PHONE..................................305 978-5777
Armando Santacruz, *Principal*
EMP: 5 **EST:** 2008
SALES (est): 307.4K **Privately Held**
WEB: www.signsconnection.com
SIC: 3993 Signs & advertising specialties

(G-10347)
SIGNS FOR YOU INC
2401 Nw 34th Ave (33142-6931)
PHONE..................................305 635-6662
Anthony Yazbek, *President*
Constantine Stavro, *Vice Pres*
Haroutiun Jlinkrian, *Prdtn Mgr*
▼ **EMP:** 21 **EST:** 1997
SQ FT: 10,000
SALES (est): 1.6MM **Privately Held**
WEB: www.signsforyou.com
SIC: 3993 Electric signs

(G-10348)
SIGNS INTERNATIONAL DISTR CORP
Also Called: Sid Signs
8461 Nw 61st St (33166-3307)
PHONE..................................305 715-0017
Antonio De Fonseca Nadais, *President*
Sidney T Dos Santos, *Director*
◆ **EMP:** 5 **EST:** 2006
SALES (est): 986.3K **Privately Held**
WEB: www.signsfy.com
SIC: 3993 Signs & advertising specialties

(G-10349)
SILVERLINE FURNITURE CORP
15940 Sw 60th St (33193-5810)
PHONE..................................305 663-9560
Roger Silverio, *President*
Regina Morais, *Controller*
▲ **EMP:** 8 **EST:** 2000
SQ FT: 7,500
SALES (est): 569.9K **Privately Held**
SIC: 2511 Wood household furniture

(G-10350)
SIMKINS INDUSTRIES INC (PA)
5080 Biscayne Blvd Ste A (33137-3218)
PHONE..................................305 899-8184
David Simkins, *CEO*
Barbara P Camera, *Corp Secy*
Anthony Battaglia, *CFO*
Tony Battaglia, *CFO*
David M Fanesi, *Controller*
▲ **EMP:** 16 **EST:** 1901
SALES (est): 5.5MM **Privately Held**
WEB: www.simkinsindustries.com
SIC: 2652 Setup paperboard boxes

(G-10351)
SIMONS HALLANDALE INC
850 Ives Dairy Rd Ste T9 (33179-2412)
PHONE..................................561 468-1174
Dani Shimon, *CEO*
Ilan Shimon, *Vice Pres*
EMP: 50 **EST:** 2013
SALES (est): 4.3MM **Privately Held**
SIC: 3949 5651 Sporting & athletic goods; family clothing stores

GEOGRAPHIC

(G-10352)
SIMPLESHOW USA CORP
7300 Biscayne Blvd # 100 (33138-5182)
PHONE....................................844 468-5447
Susanne Schmidt, *President*
Daniel Pichardo, *Project Mgr*
Monica Pimienta, *Project Mgr*
Elizabeth Yanez, *Opers Mgr*
Rachel Barash, *Sales Mgr*
EMP: 20 **EST:** 2014
SALES (est): 2MM **Privately Held**
WEB: www.simpleshow.com
SIC: 2741 7373 ; computer integrated systems design

(G-10353)
SINERGIE PRINTING INC
1717 N Bayshore Dr (33132-1180)
PHONE....................................786 493-6167
Paul Sainz, *President*
EMP: 8 **EST:** 2013
SQ FT: 1,000
SALES (est): 254.1K **Privately Held**
SIC: 2621 2741 Book, bond & printing papers; art copy & poster publishing

(G-10354)
SIPPERS BY DESIGN
555 Ne 15th St (33132-1451)
PHONE....................................305 371-5087
Lisa Dominique, *Principal*
Edgard Lequerique, *Vice Pres*
Andriene Johnson, *Sales Staff*
EMP: 5 **EST:** 2011
SALES (est): 716.2K **Privately Held**
WEB: www.sippersbydesign.com
SIC: 3089 Plastic processing

(G-10355)
SIR WINSTON GARMENTS INC
Also Called: Sea Suns
13428 Sw 131st St (33186-5817)
PHONE....................................305 499-3144
Valentina Lozada, *President*
Jacqueline Chaleff, *President*
Marguerite Domville, *Treasurer*
EMP: 12 **EST:** 1979
SQ FT: 5,000
SALES (est): 282.3K **Privately Held**
WEB: www.seasuns.net
SIC: 2339 Sportswear, women's

(G-10356)
SKIDE LLC
6303 Blue Lagoon Dr (33126-6002)
PHONE....................................305 537-4275
Jorge Abuim,
Edgar Bermudez,
Ricardo Nunez,
EMP: 10 **EST:** 2007
SALES (est): 885.1K **Privately Held**
WEB: www.skidenet.com
SIC: 3533 8742 Oil & gas field machinery; industry specialist consultants

(G-10357)
SKINMETICS INC
Also Called: Wilma Schumann Skin Care Pdts
4850 Sw 72nd Ave (33155-5526)
PHONE....................................305 663-5750
Pedro Ortega, *President*
Barbara Ortega, *Vice Pres*
Jorge Tapanes, *Finance*
▲ **EMP:** 15 **EST:** 1997
SALES (est): 1.8MM **Privately Held**
WEB: www.wilmaschumann.com
SIC: 2844 5122 Cosmetic preparations; cosmetics, perfumes & hair products

(G-10358)
SKWHOLESALENET
62 Ne 1st St (33132-2412)
PHONE....................................305 372-3751
Jack Dannon, *President*
EMP: 11 **EST:** 2016
SALES (est): 92.3K **Privately Held**
WEB: www.skwholesale.net
SIC: 2326 Men's & boys' work clothing

(G-10359)
SKY CAPITAL PARTNERS INC
2900 Sw 28th Ter Ste 401 (33133-3768)
PHONE....................................305 934-8259
EMP: 5 **EST:** 2018
SALES (est): 318.2K **Privately Held**
SIC: 3728 Aircraft parts & equipment

(G-10360)
SKY TECHNICS AVIATION SLS INC
6732 Nw 72nd Ave (33166-3047)
PHONE....................................305 885-7499
Manuel Castaneda, *President*
Milton Aguilera, *Vice Pres*
EMP: 9 **EST:** 2014
SALES (est): 525.5K **Privately Held**
WEB: www.sta-repairs.com
SIC: 3728 5088 Aircraft parts & equipment; aeronautical equipment & supplies

(G-10361)
SLATE GROUP LLC
9357 Sw 77th Ave (33156-7900)
PHONE....................................786 484-9408
Robert Inguanzo, *Principal*
EMP: 8 **EST:** 2012
SALES (est): 274.3K
SALES (corp-wide): 2.8B **Publicly Held**
WEB: www.slate.com
SIC: 2741
PA: Graham Holdings Company
1300 17th St N Fl 17
Arlington VA 22209
703 345-6300

(G-10362)
SLTONS ENVIRNMNTAL GROUP ASSOC
Also Called: Ecopod
2950 Sw 27th Ave Ste 2 (33133-3765)
PHONE....................................305 665-5594
Henry Pino, *President*
Gabriela Pino, *Co-Founder*
Matt Gawne, *COO*
EMP: 15 **EST:** 2016
SALES (est): 552.2K **Privately Held**
WEB: www.ecopod.us
SIC: 2842 Specialty cleaning, polishes & sanitation goods; laundry cleaning preparations

(G-10363)
SMART FOR LIFE INC (PA)
Also Called: Bonne Sante Group
990 Biscayne Blvd # 1203 (33132-1559)
PHONE....................................786 749-1221
Ryan Zackon, *CEO*
Darren Minton, *President*
Alfonso J Cervantes, *Chairman*
Alan Bergman, *CFO*
EMP: 9 **EST:** 2017
SALES (est): 41MM **Privately Held**
WEB: www.bonnesantegroup.com
SIC: 2834 Vitamin, nutrient & hematinic preparations for human use

(G-10364)
SMART SHUTTERS INC
3070 Nw 72nd Ave (33122-1314)
PHONE....................................786 391-1100
Anwar Ladhani, *President*
EMP: 8 **EST:** 2017
SALES (est): 149.1K **Privately Held**
WEB: www.thesmartshutter.com
SIC: 3442 Shutters, door or window: metal

(G-10365)
SMOOTHIE CORP
10211 Sw 137th Ct (33186-6896)
PHONE....................................305 588-0867
Antonio De La Maza, *Branch Mgr*
EMP: 46
SALES (corp-wide): 540.9K **Privately Held**
WEB: www.smoothiespotmiami.com
SIC: 2037 Frozen fruits & vegetables
PA: Smoothie, Corp
12520 Sw 88th St
Miami FL 33186
305 598-7004

(G-10366)
SMOOTHIE OPERATOR BY JC INC
13727 Sw 152nd St (33177-1106)
PHONE....................................786 367-4245
Yvette C Lopez, *President*
EMP: 6 **EST:** 2011
SALES (est): 122.8K **Privately Held**
SIC: 2037 Frozen fruits & vegetables

(G-10367)
SMX-US INC
Also Called: Socialmetrix
80 Sw 8th St Ste 2000 (33130-3038)
PHONE....................................914 840-5631
Martin Enriquez, *CEO*
Walter Ciffer, *CFO*
EMP: 30 **EST:** 2014
SQ FT: 3,300
SALES (est): 2MM **Privately Held**
WEB: www.socialmetrix.com
SIC: 7372 8732 Application computer software; business oriented computer software; business research service

(G-10368)
SNIF-SNAX LTD
540 Brickell Key Dr C2 (33131-3827)
PHONE....................................786 613-7007
Jonathan Brown, *CEO*
Hannah Brown, *Vice Pres*
Marja Machado, *Opers Staff*
Aaron Brown, *Production*
Karen Gumpel, *Director*
EMP: 10
SALES (est): 1.5MM **Privately Held**
WEB: www.snifsnax.com
SIC: 2047 Dog food

(G-10369)
SOFTECH INTERNATIONAL INC
1421 Sw 107th Ave (33174-2526)
PHONE....................................305 233-4813
EMP: 14
SQ FT: 3,500
SALES (est): 1.9MM **Privately Held**
SIC: 7372 Prepackaged Software Services

(G-10370)
SOLAR TURBINES INCORPORATED
701 Nw 62nd Ave Ste 600 (33126-4683)
PHONE....................................305 476-6855
Jamie Saldarriago, *Director*
EMP: 10
SALES (corp-wide): 41.7B **Publicly Held**
WEB: www.solarturbines.com
SIC: 3511 Gas turbine generator set units, complete
HQ: Solar Turbines Incorporated
2200 Pacific Hwy
San Diego CA 92101
619 544-5000

(G-10371)
SOLAR VENETIAN BLINDS INC
3639 Nw 47th St (33142-3947)
PHONE....................................305 634-4553
Kenneth Gordon, *President*
Betty Gordon, *Treasurer*
▼ **EMP:** 5 **EST:** 1947
SQ FT: 5,000
SALES (est): 545.8K **Privately Held**
SIC: 2591 Window shade rollers & fittings; blinds vertical; venetian blinds

(G-10372)
SOLO PRINTING LLC
7860 Nw 66th St (33166-2708)
PHONE....................................305 594-8699
Luis Fiallos, *General Mgr*
Robert Hernandez, *Principal*
Jorge Hernandez, *Vice Pres*
Liz Valdez, *Accounts Mgr*
Viviana Rauseo, *Accounts Exec*
◆ **EMP:** 152
SQ FT: 100,000
SALES: 44MM **Privately Held**
WEB: www.soloprinting.com
SIC: 2752 Commercial printing, offset

(G-10373)
SOLUCNES ELCTRCAS INTGRLES LLC
2609 Ne 189th St (33180-2627)
PHONE....................................305 804-4201
Juan Araujo, *Principal*
▲ **EMP:** 8 **EST:** 2009
SQ FT: 2,000
SALES (est): 161.2K **Privately Held**
SIC: 3612 Electric furnace transformers; electronic meter transformers

(G-10374)
SOMAY MANUFACTURING INC (PA)
4301 Nw 35th Ave (33142-4382)
PHONE....................................305 637-4757
Dario Echeverry, *President*
Josephine Garcia, *General Mgr*
Russell Lewis, *Treasurer*
Francisco J Guerra, *Admin Sec*
EMP: 6 **EST:** 2015
SALES (est): 5.9MM **Privately Held**
WEB: www.somay.com
SIC: 2851 Paints & allied products

(G-10375)
SOMETHING IN A TIN INC
2401 Ne 199th St (33180-1829)
PHONE....................................305 785-6891
Linda S Pierre, *Principal*
Linda Pierre, *Principal*
▼ **EMP:** 9 **EST:** 2009
SALES (est): 152.4K **Privately Held**
SIC: 3356 Tin

(G-10376)
SONOBRANDS LLC (PA)
Also Called: Chiptronics
1970 Nw 129th Ave Ste 108 (33182-2399)
PHONE....................................305 418-9367
Melissa C Cuartero,
Angelica Paranzino-Cedeno,
EMP: 19 **EST:** 2015
SALES (est): 465.5K **Privately Held**
SIC: 3651 Audio electronic systems

(G-10377)
SONY DISCOS
3390 Mary St Ste 220 (33133-5282)
PHONE....................................305 420-4540
Luis Rodriguez, *President*
EMP: 9 **EST:** 2009
SALES (est): 988.3K **Privately Held**
WEB: www.sony.com
SIC: 2741 Miscellaneous publishing
PA: Sony Group Corporation
1-7-1, Konan
Minato-Ku TKY 108-0

(G-10378)
SOS SOFTWARE CORP
950 Brickell Bay Dr # 53 (33131-3931)
PHONE....................................786 237-4903
Juan Basanez, *Principal*
EMP: 7 **EST:** 2015
SALES (est): 678.7K **Privately Held**
SIC: 7372 Prepackaged software

(G-10379)
SOTO METAL FABRICATION INC (PA)
7025 Sw 16th Ter (33155-1668)
PHONE....................................786 486-7125
Angel Soto, *Principal*
EMP: 24 **EST:** 2018
SALES (est): 335.4K **Privately Held**
SIC: 3499 Fabricated metal products

(G-10380)
SOURCE CONTRACT LLC
11451 Nw 36th Ave (33167-2910)
PHONE....................................305 630-8950
Candice McCarthy, *Opers Dir*
Iveta Dunn, *Sales Staff*
Golan Rabin, *Mng Member*
EMP: 15 **EST:** 2010
SALES (est): 2.8MM **Privately Held**
WEB: www.sourcefurniture.com
SIC: 2519 Wicker & rattan furniture

(G-10381)
SOUTH AMERCN LBR & TIMBER LLC
78 Sw 7th St Ste 500 (33130-3782)
PHONE....................................786 280-8326
Mario Auvert,
EMP: 8 **EST:** 2019
SALES (est): 252.9K **Privately Held**
WEB: www.southamericalumber.com
SIC: 2411 Wooden logs

(G-10382)
SOUTH FLORIDA CON BLOCK LLC
5800 Sw 177th Ave Ste 101 (33193-5302)
PHONE..................................305 408-3444
Jorge Rinaldi, *Mng Member*
Sergio Rinaldi,
EMP: 6 **EST:** 2007
SALES (est): 958.2K **Privately Held**
WEB: www.sfcblocks.com
SIC: 3273 Ready-mixed concrete

(G-10383)
SOUTH FLORIDA PALLET INC
224 Nw 136th Pl (33182-1942)
PHONE..................................305 330-7663
EMP: 7 **EST:** 2011
SALES (est): 95.3K **Privately Held**
WEB: www.sfpallets.com
SIC: 2448 Pallets, wood

(G-10384)
SOUTHEAST ATLANTIC BEVERA
5900 Nw 72nd Ave (33166-3736)
PHONE..................................904 739-1000
Bob Vargos, *CEO*
▼ **EMP:** 7 **EST:** 2009
SALES (est): 147.4K **Privately Held**
SIC: 2086 Bottled & canned soft drinks

(G-10385)
SOUTHERN DIE CASTING CORP
3560 Nw 59th St (33142-2022)
PHONE..................................305 635-6571
Allan F Hippler, *President*
◆ **EMP:** 42 **EST:** 1962
SQ FT: 40,000
SALES (est): 813.4K **Privately Held**
WEB: www.thesdccorp.com
SIC: 3364 3089 3363 3429 Zinc & zinc-base alloy die-castings; window frames & sash, plastic; aluminum die-castings; manufactured hardware (general); nonferrous foundries; aluminum foundries

(G-10386)
SOUTHERN GEAR & MACHINE INC
3685 Nw 106th St (33147-1099)
PHONE..................................305 691-6300
Allan Arch, *President*
Susan Arch, *Corp Secy*
Alex Perdomo, *Vice Pres*
Lihn Tran, *Plant Mgr*
Margarita Anico, *Purch Mgr*
EMP: 82
SQ FT: 30,000
SALES (est): 10.6MM **Privately Held**
WEB: www.southerngear.com
SIC: 3728 3568 Gears, aircraft power transmission; sprockets (power transmission equipment)

(G-10387)
SOUTHERN INTERNATIONAL SVCS
18970 Ne 4th Ct (33179-3902)
PHONE..................................954 349-7321
Robert Mercado, *President*
Anahi Mercado, *Vice Pres*
◆ **EMP:** 10 **EST:** 1993
SQ FT: 2,000
SALES (est): 300.6K **Privately Held**
SIC: 2395 7219 2396 Embroidery products, except schiffli machine; laundry, except power & coin-operated; automotive & apparel trimmings

(G-10388)
SOUTHERN MANUFACTURING INC
7064 Sw 10th St (33144-4608)
PHONE..................................305 267-1943
Isaac Canteli, *President*
Bernardo Yepes, *Vice Pres*
Hermes Rivas, *Opers Mgr*
Gabriel Cabrera, *Engineer*
EMP: 15 **EST:** 1992
SQ FT: 50,000
SALES (est): 2.5MM **Privately Held**
WEB: www.southernmanufacturing.com
SIC: 3599 Machine shop, jobbing & repair

(G-10389)
SOUTHERNUNDERGROUND INDUSTRIES
10621 Sw 139th St (33176-6683)
PHONE..................................954 650-4699
Belseri L Comerford, *Principal*
EMP: 6 **EST:** 2014
SALES (est): 169.1K **Privately Held**
SIC: 3999 Manufacturing industries

(G-10390)
SPA WORLD CORPORATION (PA)
Also Called: SW
5701 Nw 35th Ave (33142-2707)
PHONE..................................866 588-8008
Joseph Schwartz, *President*
Kris Tatur, *Vice Pres*
Eduardo Perez, *Plant Mgr*
Michelle Ceglarek, *Finance*
Aimee Sullivan, *Marketing Staff*
▲ **EMP:** 71 **EST:** 1996
SALES (est): 19.4MM **Privately Held**
WEB: www.swcorp.com
SIC: 3088 Bathroom fixtures, plastic

(G-10391)
SPACE X DESIGN LLC
13022 Sw 142nd Ter (33186-8941)
PHONE..................................407 592-5147
Jesse Medina, *Principal*
Will Riddle, *Officer*
Wesley Massey, *Technician*
EMP: 8 **EST:** 2010
SALES (est): 135.2K **Privately Held**
SIC: 3761 Guided missiles & space vehicles

(G-10392)
SPACEPORT CORPORATION
Also Called: Laser Productions Network
20209 Ne 15th Ave (33179-5103)
PHONE..................................305 690-6885
T H Harman, *Manager*
EMP: 6
SALES (corp-wide): 450.3K **Privately Held**
SIC: 3699 5063 Laser systems & equipment; electrical apparatus & equipment
PA: The Spaceport Corporation
941 Abbot Rd
East Lansing MI

(G-10393)
SPACIOS DESIGN GROUP INC
7370 Nw 36th Ave (33147-5810)
PHONE..................................305 696-1766
Carlos Lopez, *President*
Luiz Gonzales, *President*
EMP: 16 **EST:** 2001
SALES (est): 270.9K **Privately Held**
SIC: 2511 Wood household furniture

(G-10394)
SPANCRETE INC
7907 Nw 53rd St 347 (33166-4603)
PHONE..................................305 599-8885
Gary Schmidt, *President*
EMP: 35 **EST:** 1986
SQ FT: 3,000
SALES (est): 2.3MM **Privately Held**
WEB: www.spancrete.com
SIC: 3272 Prestressed concrete products

(G-10395)
SPANGLISH ADVERTISING COR
6857 Ne 3rd Ave (33138-5510)
PHONE..................................305 244-0918
EMP: 5 **EST:** 2018
SALES (est): 310K **Privately Held**
SIC: 2752 Commercial printing, lithographic

(G-10396)
SPANISH PUBG VENTURES INC
9385 Sw 21st St (33165-8107)
PHONE..................................305 220-8044
Jose Bohorques, *Principal*
EMP: 6 **EST:** 2009
SALES (est): 225.1K **Privately Held**
SIC: 2741 Miscellaneous publishing

(G-10397)
SPANISH PUBLISHERS LLC
8871 Sw 129th St (33176-5918)
PHONE..................................305 233-3365
Lucia Laratelli, *Principal*
Lucialaratell Ucia, *Manager*
▲ **EMP:** 9 **EST:** 2009
SALES (est): 1.1MM **Privately Held**
WEB: www.spanishpublishers.net
SIC: 2741 Miscellaneous publishing

(G-10398)
SPARKLEAN
11401 Nw 12th St (33172-6904)
PHONE..................................305 599-8479
Daniel Sanchez, *Owner*
EMP: 5 **EST:** 2009
SALES (est): 359.2K **Privately Held**
WEB: www.sparklean.com
SIC: 2842 Specialty cleaning preparations

(G-10399)
SPECIAL AMERICAS BBQ INC
Also Called: Mr Tango Sausages
11411 Nw 107th St Ste 1 (33178-4063)
P.O. Box 960458 (33296-0458)
PHONE..................................305 637-7377
Maria Ruiz, *President*
Ricardo Presa, *Manager*
EMP: 36 **EST:** 1995
SQ FT: 10,000
SALES (est): 5.6MM **Privately Held**
WEB: www.mrtangosausages.com
SIC: 2011 2013 Meat packing plants; sausages & other prepared meats

(G-10400)
SPECIALTY FORGED WHEELS INC
12146 Sw 114th Pl (33176-4473)
PHONE..................................786 332-5925
Carlos Gonzalez, *President*
EMP: 6 **EST:** 2014
SALES (est): 790.7K **Privately Held**
WEB: www.specialtyforged.com
SIC: 3312 Wheels

(G-10401)
SPECIALTY PRODUCTIONS INC
2476 Sw 25th Ter (33133-2217)
PHONE..................................786 399-1393
Henry Benavides, *President*
EMP: 6 **EST:** 2010
SALES (est): 390.8K **Privately Held**
SIC: 2771 Greeting cards

(G-10402)
SPECIALTY STEEL HOLDCO INC ✪
200 Biscayne Blvd (33132-2219)
PHONE..................................305 375-7560
EMP: 7 **EST:** 2020
SALES (est): 564.9K **Privately Held**
SIC: 3317 Steel pipe & tubes

(G-10403)
SPEED PRINT ONE INC
1 Biscayne Tower Ste 1 # 1 (33131-1846)
PHONE..................................305 374-5936
Guillermo Bru, *President*
Maria Bru, *Vice Pres*
EMP: 8 **EST:** 1971
SQ FT: 780
SALES (est): 692.2K **Privately Held**
WEB: www.speedprintone.com
SIC: 2752 Commercial printing, offset

(G-10404)
SPENCER BOAT CO LLC
881 Nw 13th Ave (33125-3713)
PHONE..................................305 324-5211
John Spencer,
EMP: 6 **EST:** 2009
SALES (est): 164.8K **Privately Held**
SIC: 3732 Boat building & repairing

(G-10405)
SPI LLC
11200 Nw 107th St Ste 8 (33178-3298)
PHONE..................................786 907-4022
EMP: 102
SALES (corp-wide): 144.6MM **Privately Held**
SIC: 3339 Precious metals
PA: Spi Llc
2101 Rexford Rd Ste 300e
Charlotte NC 28211
704 336-9555

(G-10406)
SPORTAILOR INC
6501 Ne 2nd Ct (33138-6093)
PHONE..................................305 754-3255
Frank Rudman, *President*
Albert Rudman, *Vice Pres*
Terry Alfonso, *Comptroller*
Miriam Rudman, *Admin Sec*
Marisela Collazo, *Admin Asst*
◆ **EMP:** 52 **EST:** 1962
SQ FT: 50,000
SALES (est): 6.6MM **Privately Held**
WEB: www.sportailor.com
SIC: 2329 5136 5137 Men's & boys' sportswear & athletic clothing; men's & boys' sportswear & work clothing; women's & children's sportswear & swimsuits

(G-10407)
SQUARE ONE ARMORING SVCS CO
12370 Sw 130th St (33186-6229)
PHONE..................................305 477-1109
Maria Elena Cardenal, *President*
Julio C Cardenal, *Vice Pres*
Martin Cardenal, *Vice Pres*
Julio Cardenal, *Prdtn Mgr*
Luis Lago, *Engineer*
◆ **EMP:** 70 **EST:** 1991
SQ FT: 10,800
SALES (est): 24.2MM **Privately Held**
WEB: www.sq1armor.com
SIC: 3711 3714 3231 Cars, armored, assembly of; motor vehicle parts & accessories; products of purchased glass

(G-10408)
STALO MODULARS LLC ✪
Also Called: Stalo Group
5400 Nw 32nd Ave Bay B (33142-2121)
PHONE..................................786 713-2410
Jose Cueva, *Mng Member*
Victoriya Strilets, *Administration*
EMP: 10 **EST:** 2020
SALES (est): 733.3K **Privately Held**
WEB: www.stalo-us.com
SIC: 2452 Modular homes, prefabricated, wood

(G-10409)
STAR BAKERY INC
Also Called: Galletas La Unica
3914 Nw 32nd Ave (33142-5010)
PHONE..................................305 633-4284
Manuel Sendina, *President*
Ana Gloria Sendina, *Vice Pres*
Ana Sendina, *Manager*
▲ **EMP:** 18 **EST:** 1966
SQ FT: 10,000
SALES (est): 3.4MM **Privately Held**
WEB: www.sbmia.com
SIC: 2052 2051 Bakery products, dry; bread, cake & related products

(G-10410)
STAYFILM INC
2234 Sw 8th St (33135-4914)
PHONE..................................786 961-1007
Douglas Almeida, *CEO*
Daniel Almeida, *Security Dir*
EMP: 7 **EST:** 2017
SALES (est): 3.1MM **Privately Held**
WEB: www.stayfilm.com
SIC: 7372 Application computer software

(G-10411)
STEEL MONKEY DREAM SHOP LLC
1369 Nw 74th St (33147-6429)
PHONE..................................786 356-1077
Vincent Revollon, *Principal*
EMP: 6 **EST:** 2011
SALES (est): 446.4K **Privately Held**
WEB: www.steelmonkeydreamshop.com
SIC: 3441 Fabricated structural metal

(G-10412)
STEERING & SUSPENSION PARTS
Also Called: SSP
2740 Nw 35th St (33142-5238)
PHONE..................................786 523-3726
Laura Torres, *Principal*
EMP: 7 **EST:** 2016
SALES (est): 348.2K **Privately Held**
WEB: www.sspparts.net
SIC: 3714 Motor vehicle parts & accessories

(G-10413)
STEPINCORP AUTO SOLUTIONS LLC
12480 Nw 25th St Ste 115 (33182-1535)
PHONE..................................786 864-3222
Igor Borisov, *Mng Member*
EMP: 7 **EST:** 2019
SALES (est): 50K **Privately Held**
SIC: 3069 Bushings, rubber

(G-10414)
STERN BLOOM MEDIA INC
Also Called: Aventura Magazine
20454 Ne 34th Ct (33180-1650)
PHONE..................................954 454-8522
Michael Stern, *President*
Amit Bloom, *Vice Pres*
Mike Pariso, *Prdtn Dir*
David Bloom, *Treasurer*
EMP: 24 **EST:** 1998
SALES (est): 2.3MM **Privately Held**
WEB: www.sternbloom.com
SIC: 2721 Magazines: publishing only, not printed on site

(G-10415)
STITCHING AROUND INC
4862 Sw 72nd Ave (33155-5526)
PHONE..................................305 665-1600
Claudia C Kitchens, *President*
▼ **EMP:** 5 **EST:** 2005
SALES (est): 416.6K **Privately Held**
WEB: www.stitchingaround.com
SIC: 3999 Embroidery kits

(G-10416)
STONE AND EQUIPMENT INC
4681 Sw 72nd Ave Ste 104 (33155-4540)
PHONE..................................305 665-0002
Lissette Rodriguez, *CEO*
Daniel Tormo, *CFO*
EMP: 20 **EST:** 1999
SALES (est): 1.2MM **Privately Held**
WEB: www.stoneandequipment.com
SIC: 3281 5032 Table tops, marble; marble building stone

(G-10417)
STONEWORKS INC
Also Called: Stoneworks of Art
6840 Sw 81st Ter (33143-7712)
PHONE..................................305 666-6676
Clement Zanzuri, *President*
Kim Thorn, *Sales Staff*
Kelly Young, *Sales Staff*
Victor Colon,
◆ **EMP:** 16 **EST:** 1984
SQ FT: 27,000
SALES (est): 2.9MM **Privately Held**
WEB: www.trimstonepanels.com
SIC: 3281 Marble, building: cut & shaped; granite, cut & shaped

(G-10418)
STRANDS INC (PA)
3390 Mary St Ste 116 (33133-5255)
PHONE..................................415 398-4333
Erik Brieva, *CEO*
Cesar Richardson, *General Mgr*
Jordi Teixido, *COO*
Pablo De La Concepcion, *Manager*
Mark Torrens, *CIO*
EMP: 7
SALES (est): 2.8MM **Privately Held**
WEB: www.strands.com
SIC: 7372 Business oriented computer software

(G-10419)
STRASSE FORGED LLC
13979 Sw 140th St (33186-5528)
PHONE..................................786 701-3649
Christian Carrillo, *Mng Member*
Eriana Blanco, *Manager*
EMP: 12 **EST:** 2009
SALES (est): 555.8K **Privately Held**
WEB: www.strassewheels.com
SIC: 3714 Motor vehicle parts & accessories

(G-10420)
STRATUS PHARMACEUTICALS INC
12379 Sw 130th St (33186-6208)
PHONE..................................305 254-6793
Alberto Hoyo, *President*
John Billoch, *Treasurer*
Carlos Hoyo, *Admin Sec*
EMP: 36 **EST:** 1988
SQ FT: 26,000
SALES (est): 14.8MM **Privately Held**
WEB: www.stratuspharmaceuticals.com
SIC: 2834 Pharmaceutical preparations

(G-10421)
STRONG HURRICANE SHUTTER
6406 Nw 82nd Ave (33166-2734)
PHONE..................................786 587-3990
Steve Silguero, *Principal*
EMP: 6 **EST:** 2007
SALES (est): 100.5K **Privately Held**
WEB: www.strongshutters.com
SIC: 3442 Shutters, door or window: metal

(G-10422)
STRUCTURAL METAL FABRICATORS
3182 Nw 75th St (33147-5914)
PHONE..................................786 253-8012
Rolando Sanchez, *Principal*
EMP: 5 **EST:** 2018
SALES (est): 301.2K **Privately Held**
WEB: www.masterfabricatorsinc.com
SIC: 3499 Fabricated metal products

(G-10423)
STRUMBA MEDIA LLC (PA)
Also Called: Miracle Noodle
382 Ne 191st St Ste 6920 (33179-3899)
PHONE..................................800 948-4205
Jonathan Carp, *CEO*
Susan Carp, *Vice Pres*
Jill Goldstein, *Vice Pres*
◆ **EMP:** 5 **EST:** 2006
SALES (est): 4.5MM **Privately Held**
SIC: 2099 Noodles, uncooked: packaged with other ingredients

(G-10424)
STUART COMPOSITES LLC
6900 Nw 77th Ct (33166-2714)
PHONE..................................772 266-4285
Moises Rodriguez,
EMP: 40 **EST:** 2014
SALES (est): 4.6MM **Privately Held**
WEB: www.stuartcomposites.com
SIC: 3732 Boat building & repairing

(G-10425)
STUART INDUSTRIES INC
526 Ne 190th St (33179-3919)
PHONE..................................305 651-3474
Stuart Collins, *President*
Marsha Collins, *Corp Secy*
Sheldon Collins, *Vice Pres*
EMP: 15 **EST:** 1982
SQ FT: 20,000
SALES (est): 1.3MM **Privately Held**
WEB: www.stuartfishingtackle.com
SIC: 3949 3429 3769 Lures, fishing: artificial; marine hardware; guided missile & space vehicle parts & auxiliary equipment

(G-10426)
STYLE-VIEW PRODUCTS INC
Also Called: Aluma Craft Products
1800 N Byshore Dr Apt 400 (33132)
PHONE..................................305 634-9688
Mark A Caplan, *President*
Albert M Caplan, *Vice Pres*
▼ **EMP:** 19 **EST:** 1964
SQ FT: 80,000
SALES (est): 1MM **Privately Held**
WEB: www.aluma-craft.com
SIC: 3442 3444 3443 3354 Storm doors or windows, metal; awnings, sheet metal; canopies, sheet metal; fabricated plate work (boiler shop); aluminum extruded products

(G-10427)
SUGAR FANCIES LLC
1091 Sw 134th Ct (33184-3318)
PHONE..................................786 558-9087
Sandra Rios Monsante, *Principal*
EMP: 8 **EST:** 2011
SALES (est): 477.5K **Privately Held**
SIC: 2053 Cakes, bakery: frozen

(G-10428)
SUN ORCHARD LLC (PA)
1198 W Frmont Dr Ste 2350 (33131)
PHONE..................................786 646-9200
Marc Isaacs, *President*
Jean-Marc Rotsaert, *Chairman*
Deena Pitzele, *Vice Pres*
Kevin Mason, *Purch Mgr*
Kim Hansen, *QC Mgr*
▲ **EMP:** 35 **EST:** 1988
SQ FT: 40,000
SALES (est): 65.2MM **Privately Held**
WEB: www.sunorchard.com
SIC: 2033 2037 Fruit juices: fresh; fruit juices, frozen

(G-10429)
SUNCO PLASTICS INC
8501 Nw 90th St (33166-2187)
PHONE..................................305 238-2864
Harold Bailey, *President*
Kurt Maree, *Manager*
▼ **EMP:** 16 **EST:** 1966
SQ FT: 35,000
SALES (est): 325.9K **Privately Held**
WEB: www.suncoplastics.com
SIC: 3089 3544 Injection molding of plastics; special dies, tools, jigs & fixtures

(G-10430)
SUNCOAST POST-TENSION LTD
7223 Nw 46th St 29 (33166-6422)
PHONE..................................305 592-5075
Phil Arana, *Manager*
EMP: 25
SALES (corp-wide): 2.7B **Privately Held**
WEB: www.suncoast-pt.com
SIC: 3315 3316 5072 Cable, steel: insulated or armored; cold finishing of steel shapes; builders' hardware
HQ: Suncoast Post-Tension, Ltd.
509 N Sam Houston Pkwy E # 300
Houston TX 77060
281 445-8886

(G-10431)
SUNILAND PRESS INC
7379 Nw 31st St (33122-1240)
P.O. Box 561108 (33256-1108)
PHONE..................................305 235-8811
Peter Rood, *President*
Florence Rood, *Corp Secy*
▲ **EMP:** 39 **EST:** 1972
SQ FT: 65,000
SALES (est): 709K **Privately Held**
WEB: www.sunilandpress.com
SIC: 2752 Commercial printing, offset

(G-10432)
SUNRISE FIBERGLASS INC
3280 Nw 29th St (33142-6308)
PHONE..................................305 636-4111
Gervacia Minerva Tapanes, *President*
Jesus Mesa, *Vice Pres*
EMP: 6 **EST:** 1983
SALES (est): 400K **Privately Held**
WEB: www.sunrisefiberglass.com
SIC: 3089 Injection molding of plastics

(G-10433)
SUNSHINE
15198 Sw 56th St (33185-4073)
PHONE..................................305 382-6677
EMP: 6 **EST:** 2011
SALES (est): 157.1K **Privately Held**
WEB: www.sunshinegasoline.com
SIC: 1499 Peat grinding

(G-10434)
SUNSHINE CORDAGE CORPORATION
7190 Nw 12th St (33126-1304)
PHONE..................................305 592-3750
Joel Ellison, *President*
Guillermo Carranza, *Vice Pres*
Ellison Joel, *CFO*
◆ **EMP:** 6 **EST:** 1969
SALES (est): 983.9K **Privately Held**
WEB: www.sunshinecordage.com
SIC: 2298 Rope, except asbestos & wire; twine

(G-10435)
SUNSHINE OIL AND GAS INC (PA)
Also Called: Sunshine Oil and Gas Fla Inc
13230 Sw 132nd Ave Ste 22 (33186-6144)
PHONE..................................305 367-3100
Rishi Burke, *President*
EMP: 5 **EST:** 2013
SALES (est): 666.3K **Privately Held**
WEB: www.sunshinegasoline.com
SIC: 1389 Oil & gas wells: building, repairing & dismantling

(G-10436)
SUPER BRITE SCREW CORP
16 Sw 1st Ave (33130-1606)
PHONE..................................305 822-6560
Carlos Hernandez, *Vice Pres*
EMP: 10 **EST:** 1977
SALES (est): 365.9K **Privately Held**
SIC: 3452 Bolts, nuts, rivets & washers

(G-10437)
SUPERIOR OIL 2016 INC
5477 Nw 72nd Ave (33166-4223)
PHONE..................................305 851-5140
Ronald Brio, *Principal*
EMP: 6 **EST:** 2016
SALES (est): 402.1K **Privately Held**
SIC: 1382 Oil & gas exploration services

(G-10438)
SUPERIOR STORM SOLUTIONS ✪
1501 Nw 79th St (33147-5343)
PHONE..................................305 638-8420
Jorg Rios, *Owner*
EMP: 6 **EST:** 2020
SALES (est): 632.1K **Privately Held**
SIC: 3442 Metal doors, sash & trim

(G-10439)
SUPERMIX CONCRETE (PA)
Also Called: Continental Concrete
4300 Sw 74th Ave (33155-4406)
P.O. Box 13128, Fort Lauderdale (33316-0100)
PHONE..................................954 858-0780
Frank Anderson, *President*
Robert Cordone, *Exec VP*
Martin Bodg, *Vice Pres*
▲ **EMP:** 25 **EST:** 1975
SQ FT: 13,500
SALES (est): 12.3MM **Privately Held**
SIC: 3273 5032 Ready-mixed concrete; concrete & cinder block

(G-10440)
SUPPER ON WHEELS INC
2423 Sw 147th Ave (33185-4082)
PHONE..................................305 205-8999
Eunice Gibson, *Exec Dir*
EMP: 5 **EST:** 2019
SALES (est): 500K **Privately Held**
SIC: 2099 Ready-to-eat meals, salads & sandwiches

(G-10441)
SUPPORT AIRCRAFT PARTS INC
13034 Sw 133rd Ct (33186-5855)
PHONE..................................305 975-3767
Ricardo L Cerioni, *Principal*
EMP: 13 **EST:** 2015
SALES (est): 1.3MM **Privately Held**
SIC: 3728 Aircraft parts & equipment

(G-10442)
SUREFIRE LASER LLC
9611 Sw 130th St (33176-5741)
PHONE..................................305 720-7118
Robert E Schurr, *Principal*

EMP: 6 **EST:** 2011
SALES (est): 154.8K **Privately Held**
WEB: www.surefire.com
SIC: 3842 Surgical appliances & supplies

(G-10443)
SUTTON DRAPERIES INC
1762 Ne 205th Ter (33179-2112)
PHONE..................................305 653-7738
Steven Barg, *President*
Vicki Colenzo, *Vice Pres*
EMP: 10 **EST:** 1971
SQ FT: 7,000
SALES (est): 605.7K **Privately Held**
WEB: www.suttondraperies.com
SIC: 2391 2591 5023 Draperies, plastic & textile: from purchased materials; window blinds; window shades; vertical blinds

(G-10444)
SUVILLAGA CONSTRUCTION MGT LLC
11411 Nw 7th St Apt 206 (33172-3566)
PHONE..................................305 323-8380
Juan Carlos Gonzalez,
EMP: 10 **EST:** 2019
SALES (est): 276.1K **Privately Held**
SIC: 1389 Construction, repair & dismantling services

(G-10445)
SWATCH GROUP CARIBBEAN
5301 Blue Lagoon Dr # 620 (33126-2098)
PHONE..................................877 839-5224
Nick Hayek, *President*
EMP: 10 **EST:** 2015
SALES (est): 144.9K **Privately Held**
WEB: www.swatchgroup.com
SIC: 3961 Costume jewelry

(G-10446)
SWEET AND VICIOUS LLC (PA)
Also Called: Bubbles Body Wear
111 Ne 21st St (33137-4820)
PHONE..................................305 576-0012
Karen E Jones, *Principal*
EMP: 6 **EST:** 2003
SALES (est): 632.3K **Privately Held**
WEB: www.sweet-vicious.com
SIC: 2341 Women's & children's underwear

(G-10447)
SWEETWATER TODAY INC
35 Sw 114th Ave (33174-1002)
PHONE..................................305 456-4724
Doug Mayorga, *Principal*
EMP: 6 **EST:** 2013
SALES (est): 92.9K **Privately Held**
WEB: www.sweetwater.com
SIC: 2711 Newspapers

(G-10448)
SWIRE PACIFIC HOLDINGS INC
Coca-Cola
98 Se 7th St Ste 601 (33131-3530)
PHONE..................................305 371-3877
J Megan Kelly, *Senior VP*
Tina Chan, *Marketing Mgr*
Stephen L Owens, *Branch Mgr*
EMP: 12
SALES (corp-wide): 14.2B **Privately Held**
WEB: www.swirecc.com
SIC: 2086 Bottled & canned soft drinks
HQ: Swire Pacific Holdings Inc.
12634 S 265 W Bldg A
Draper UT 84020
801 816-5300

(G-10449)
SWISS CAPS USA INC
14193 Sw 119th Ave (33186-6013)
PHONE..................................786 345-5505
Markus Nussbaumer, *President*
Brad Carlson, *Vice Pres*
EMP: 31 **EST:** 1994
SALES (est): 4.4MM **Privately Held**
SIC: 2834 Pharmaceutical preparations

(G-10450)
SYNKT GAMES INC
1820 Micanopy Ave (33133-3330)
PHONE..................................305 779-5611
Bryan Abboud, *CEO*
EMP: 12 **EST:** 2013
SALES (est): 152.4K **Privately Held**
WEB: www.synktgames.miami
SIC: 7372 Prepackaged software

(G-10451)
SYNTHEON LLC
13755 Sw 119th Ave (33186-6265)
PHONE..................................305 255-1745
Derek Deville, *Vice Pres*
Michael Kirk, *Engineer*
Eric Petersen, *Engineer*
Jorge Pinos, *Engineer*
Jake Pistiner, *Engineer*
EMP: 5 **EST:** 2008
SALES (est): 2.1MM **Privately Held**
WEB: www.syntheon.com
SIC: 3841 Surgical & medical instruments

(G-10452)
T & M ATLANTIC INC
436 Sw 8th St (33130-2814)
PHONE..................................786 332-4773
Alexander Afonskiy, *President*
▲ **EMP:** 7 **EST:** 2010
SALES (est): 606.8K **Privately Held**
WEB: www.tmatlantic.com
SIC: 3825 Instruments to measure electricity

(G-10453)
T & R STORE FIXTURES INC
2700 N Miami Ave (33127-4466)
PHONE..................................305 751-0377
Reynaldo Hechavarria, *President*
Antonio Hechevarria Sr, *Treasurer*
▼ **EMP:** 23 **EST:** 1972
SQ FT: 16,000
SALES (est): 442.4K **Privately Held**
SIC: 2541 2542 Store fixtures, wood; partitions & fixtures, except wood

(G-10454)
T A C ARMATURES & PUMPS CORP
800 Nw 73rd St (33150-3625)
PHONE..................................305 835-8845
Jorge F Martinez, *President*
▲ **EMP:** 15 **EST:** 1973
SQ FT: 3,000
SALES (est): 932.9K **Privately Held**
WEB: www.tacarmature.com
SIC: 7694 5551 Electric motor repair; boat dealers

(G-10455)
T SHIRT CENTER INC
Also Called: Vivid Sportwear
19900 Ne 15th Ct (33179-2715)
PHONE..................................305 655-1955
Sasson Jacoby, *President*
▲ **EMP:** 8 **EST:** 2015
SALES (est): 1MM **Privately Held**
SIC: 2339 2329 5136 5137 Sportswear, women's; men's & boys' sportswear & athletic clothing; sportswear, men's & boys'; sportswear, women's & children's

(G-10456)
T-SHIRTS PLUS COLOR INC
4156 Sw 74th Ct (33155-4414)
PHONE..................................305 267-7664
Susana Grossen, *President*
Wilhem Boulay, *General Mgr*
▼ **EMP:** 7 **EST:** 1991
SQ FT: 4,500
SALES (est): 880.4K **Privately Held**
WEB: www.tshirtspluscolor.com
SIC: 2759 Screen printing

(G-10457)
TAG & LABEL OF FLORIDA INC
Also Called: Printing Online
13375 Sw 128th St Ste 106 (33186-6288)
PHONE..................................305 255-1050
Ralph Perez, *Manager*
EMP: 5 **EST:** 1981
SQ FT: 2,500
SALES (est): 378.3K **Privately Held**
WEB: www.tagsandlabelsofflorida.com
SIC: 2752 Commercial printing, offset

(G-10458)
TAGUA LEATHER CORPORATION
2047 Nw 24th Ave (33142-7237)
PHONE..................................305 637-3014
Luis Kellemen, *Principal*
Miguel Coronel, *Opers Mgr*
Juan Valdez, *Sales Staff*
EMP: 7 **EST:** 2015
SALES (est): 75.8K **Privately Held**
WEB: www.taguagunleather.com
SIC: 2386 2387 Coats & jackets, leather & sheep-lined; garments, leather; apparel belts

(G-10459)
TAN GROUP USA LLC
31 Se 5th St (33131-2503)
PHONE..................................954 600-8697
EMP: 5 **EST:** 2018
SALES (est): 367K **Privately Held**
SIC: 3851 Eyeglasses, lenses & frames

(G-10460)
TARGET MANUFACTURING INC
Also Called: Guardian Fire Equipment
3430 Nw 38th St (33142-5034)
PHONE..................................305 633-0361
Richard H Childress, *President*
Lisa C Petersen, *Treasurer*
▲ **EMP:** 7 **EST:** 1984
SQ FT: 13,500
SALES (est): 495K **Privately Held**
WEB: www.guardianfire.com
SIC: 3569 3494 3491 3432 Firefighting apparatus & related equipment; valves & pipe fittings; industrial valves; plumbing fixture fittings & trim; nonferrous die-castings except aluminum

(G-10461)
TAVAREZ SPORTING GOODS INC
1840 Coral Way (33145-2748)
PHONE..................................347 441-9690
Manuel Tavarez, *CEO*
EMP: 5 **EST:** 2014
SALES (est): 309.2K **Privately Held**
SIC: 3949 Helmets, athletic; balls: baseball, football, basketball, etc.; polo equipment & supplies, general; gloves, sport & athletic: boxing, handball, etc.

(G-10462)
TECHNICAL INTERNATIONAL CORP
1000 Brickell Ave Ste 625 (33131-3047)
PHONE..................................305 374-1054
Albertina Genghini, *President*
Donald A McGregor Jr, *Vice Pres*
Donald McGregor, *Vice Pres*
Anita M Wong, *Treasurer*
Albertina McGregor, *Sales Staff*
◆ **EMP:** 8
SQ FT: 1,028
SALES: 4.5MM **Privately Held**
WEB: www.tic-usa.com
SIC: 3589 3825 3532 Water treatment equipment, industrial; electrical energy measuring equipment; mining machinery

(G-10463)
TECHNISYS LLC
701 Brickell Ave Ste 1550 (33131-2824)
PHONE..................................305 728-5372
Miguel Santos, *CEO*
Adrian Iglesias, *COO*
Liliana Ferreiro, *CFO*
Francisco Sanz, *CFO*
Marcelo Blanco, *Manager*
EMP: 500 **EST:** 2003
SALES (est): 44.7MM **Privately Held**
WEB: www.technisys.com
SIC: 7372 Prepackaged software

(G-10464)
TECHNOMARINE USA INC
7600 Corp Ctr Dr Ste 4 (33126)
PHONE..................................305 438-0880
Jacques P Auriol, *CEO*
Pedro Fernandez, *Manager*
▲ **EMP:** 18 **EST:** 1998
SALES (est): 1.3MM **Privately Held**
SIC: 3873 Watches, clocks, watchcases & parts

(G-10465)
TEES BY BO INC
13220 Sw 66th St (33183-2361)
PHONE..................................305 382-8551
Dan Bowersox, *President*
EMP: 9 **EST:** 1989
SQ FT: 1,500
SALES (est): 275K **Privately Held**
SIC: 2326 Men's & boys' work clothing

(G-10466)
TEKMATIC CORP
7522 Sw 143rd Ave (33183-2920)
PHONE..................................305 972-1300
Gregg Tekerman, *Principal*
EMP: 16 **EST:** 2012
SALES (est): 335.1K **Privately Held**
WEB: www.tekmatic.com
SIC: 3552 Textile machinery

(G-10467)
TENTECH CORPORATION
7330 Nw 66th St (33166-3010)
PHONE..................................305 938-0389
Andres Hernandez, *President*
▲ **EMP:** 13 **EST:** 2009
SALES (est): 4.6MM **Privately Held**
WEB: www.tentech.com
SIC: 3625 Control equipment, electric

(G-10468)
TERRACASSA LLC
950 Nw 72nd St Unit 102 (33150-3618)
PHONE..................................786 581-7741
Jordi Trulla, *Mng Member*
EMP: 7 **EST:** 2017
SALES (est): 159.2K **Privately Held**
WEB: www.terracassa.com
SIC: 2299 3643 3261 Batting, wadding, padding & fillings; power outlets & sockets; bathroom accessories/fittings, vitreous china or earthenware

(G-10469)
TERRASTONE INC
8747 Sw 134th St (33176-5930)
PHONE..................................305 234-8384
Rolando Cabezas, *President*
◆ **EMP:** 5 **EST:** 1984
SALES (est): 350K **Privately Held**
WEB: www.terra-stone.com
SIC: 3281 Curbing, granite or stone

(G-10470)
TESLA INC
3851 Bird Rd Ste 100 (33146-1572)
PHONE..................................305 774-5965
EMP: 7
SALES (corp-wide): 31.5B **Publicly Held**
WEB: www.tesla.com
SIC: 3711 Motor vehicles & car bodies
PA: Tesla, Inc.
3500 Deer Creek Rd
Palo Alto CA 94304
650 681-5000

(G-10471)
TEVA PHARMACEUTICALS USA INC
74 Nw 176th St (33169-5043)
PHONE..................................305 575-6000
William M Marth, *President*
Brendan O 'grady, *Exec VP*
David Stark, *Exec VP*
Lori Queisser, *Senior VP*
Gary Cockroft, *Opers Mgr*
EMP: 23 **EST:** 2008
SALES (est): 1.4MM **Privately Held**
WEB: www.tevapharm.com
SIC: 2834 Pharmaceutical preparations

(G-10472)
THALES INFLIGHT ENTERTAIMENT
6101 Blue Lagoon Dr (33126-2055)
PHONE..................................786 777-9031
EMP: 6 **EST:** 2015
SALES (est): 132.3K **Privately Held**
SIC: 3728 Aircraft parts & equipment

(G-10473)
THIDA THAI JEWELRY
47 E Flagler St (33131-1003)
PHONE..................................561 455-4249
Salvatore S Esposito, *Principal*

GEOGRAPHIC

EMP: 9 **EST:** 2008
SALES (est): 182.7K **Privately Held**
WEB: www.thidathai.com
SIC: 3423 Jewelers' hand tools

(G-10474)
THINKING FOODS INC
123 Nw 23rd St (33127-4409)
PHONE..................................305 433-8287
Roberto Brisciani, *President*
Julia G De La Morena, *Admin Sec*
◆ **EMP:** 8 **EST:** 2011
SALES (est): 756.8K **Privately Held**
SIC: 3556 Food products machinery

(G-10475)
TI-PAGOS USA INC
20200 W Dixie Hwy Ste 603 (33180-1925)
PHONE..................................786 310-7423
Anderson Cicotoste, *Principal*
EMP: 9 **EST:** 2017
SALES (est): 624K **Privately Held**
WEB: www.ti-pagos.com.br
SIC: 3111 Leather tanning & finishing
PA: Pinbank Brasil - Pagamentos Inteligentes S/A
Al. Rio Negro 503
Barueri SP 06454

(G-10476)
TIC LIGHT ELECTRICAL CORP
11519 Sw 172nd Ter (33157-3976)
PHONE..................................305 712-3499
Sameh Tadros, *President*
EMP: 8 **EST:** 2014
SALES (est): 327.5K **Privately Held**
SIC: 3625 5063 Industrial electrical relays & switches; boxes & fittings, electrical; hanging & fastening devices, electrical; receptacles, electrical; service entrance equipment, electrical

(G-10477)
TICKET DROP TRAFFIC DEFENSE
20137 Ne 16th Pl (33179-2720)
PHONE..................................305 332-3186
Carlos Saltz, *Principal*
EMP: 6 **EST:** 2016
SALES (est): 241.7K **Privately Held**
SIC: 3812 Defense systems & equipment

(G-10478)
TIKORE INDUSTRIES LLC
14397 Sw 143rd Ct Ste 106 (33186-6730)
PHONE..................................954 616-5902
Joshua A Montagna, *Principal*
Elliot Evelyn, *Engineer*
EMP: 8 **EST:** 2010
SALES (est): 340.5K **Privately Held**
SIC: 3999 Manufacturing industries

(G-10479)
TINFOIL HATS LLC
11858 Sw 100th Ter (33186-2744)
PHONE..................................407 844-0578
Don Montes, *Principal*
EMP: 5 **EST:** 2018
SALES (est): 463.9K **Privately Held**
SIC: 2353 Hats, caps & millinery

(G-10480)
TITA ITLN IMPORT & EXPORT LLC
1408 Nw 23rd St (33142-7624)
PHONE..................................305 608-4258
Gianluca Vietti, *Opers Staff*
Nicolo Tita,
◆ **EMP:** 5 **EST:** 2009
SALES (est): 421.3K **Privately Held**
WEB: www.titaitalia.com
SIC: 2084 Wines

(G-10481)
TLC FOOD TRUCK LLC
8602 Nw 22nd Ave (33147-4108)
PHONE..................................305 879-2488
Katrina Toles,
EMP: 17 **EST:** 2015
SALES (est): 580K **Privately Held**
SIC: 2599 Food wagons, restaurant

(G-10482)
TNT CUSTOM MARINE INC (PA)
3030 Ne 188th St (33180-2856)
PHONE..................................305 931-3157
John Tomlinson, *President*
Mike Thomas, *Vice Pres*
▼ **EMP:** 6 **EST:** 1986
SQ FT: 30,000
SALES (est): 1.2MM **Privately Held**
WEB: www.tntcustommarine.com
SIC: 3731 Marine rigging

(G-10483)
TNT PACKAGING INC
Also Called: Coale Industries
17375 Ne 7th Ave (33162-2037)
P.O. Box 402883, Miami Beach (33140-0883)
PHONE..................................305 769-0616
Harold Tokayer, *CEO*
Barry J Tokayer, *President*
Marilyn Tokayer, *Corp Secy*
Jeffrey Tokayer, *Vice Pres*
EMP: 10 **EST:** 1981
SALES (est): 686.5K **Privately Held**
SIC: 3053 Packing materials

(G-10484)
TOBRUK INTERNATIONAL CORP
Also Called: Tic Logistics
6970 Nw 50th St (33166-5632)
PHONE..................................305 406-0263
Silvia Gutierrez, *President*
Manuel Polo, *Vice Pres*
Andres Torres, *Vice Pres*
▼ **EMP:** 7 **EST:** 1991
SQ FT: 3,532
SALES (est): 921.8K **Privately Held**
SIC: 3728 5088 Aircraft parts & equipment; aircraft equipment & supplies

(G-10485)
TODAYS FROZEN DESSERTS INC
7156 Nw 50th St (33166-5636)
PHONE..................................305 994-9940
Ely Cukierman, *President*
▼ **EMP:** 10 **EST:** 1987
SQ FT: 5,000
SALES (est): 1.2MM **Privately Held**
WEB: www.ice-cream-wholesalers.cmac.ws
SIC: 2024 Dairy based frozen desserts

(G-10486)
TODO EN UNO
6601 W Flagler St (33144-2921)
PHONE..................................305 263-6934
Carlos R Fernandez, *Principal*
EMP: 7 **EST:** 2009
SALES (est): 237K **Privately Held**
SIC: 2051 Cakes, bakery: except frozen

(G-10487)
TOLEDO DOORS INC
Also Called: Toledo Iron Works
4710 Nw 37th Ave (33142-3914)
PHONE..................................305 633-4352
Bill Suarez, *President*
Guillermo Suarez, *Shareholder*
▲ **EMP:** 10 **EST:** 1969
SALES (est): 1.9MM **Privately Held**
WEB: www.toledoironworks.com
SIC: 3446 3442 Architectural metalwork; metal doors, sash & trim

(G-10488)
TOLEDO SALES INC
835 Nw 7th Street Rd (33136-3024)
PHONE..................................305 389-3441
Manuel Toledo, *President*
Silvio J Toledo, *Vice Pres*
◆ **EMP:** 5 **EST:** 2004
SALES (est): 419.4K **Privately Held**
WEB: www.toledosalesinc.com
SIC: 3732 5941 Boat building & repairing; fishing equipment

(G-10489)
TONE PRINTING LLC (PA)
1221 Brickell Ave Fl 9 (33131-3800)
PHONE..................................855 505-8663
Steven Thompson,
EMP: 5 **EST:** 2005
SQ FT: 4,000
SALES (est): 742.8K **Privately Held**
SIC: 3993 2752 2732 2759 Signs & advertising specialties; offset & photolithographic printing; pamphlets: printing & binding, not published on site; advertising literature: printing; commercial printing, gravure

(G-10490)
TOP DRINKS USA CORP
3550 Biscayne Blvd # 507 (33137-3841)
PHONE..................................305 407-3514
Antonio Regojo, *Principal*
EMP: 7 **EST:** 2016
SALES (est): 68.6K **Privately Held**
SIC: 2087 Beverage bases

(G-10491)
TOP NOTCH WOOD WORKS INC
526 Nw 43rd Pl (33126-5412)
PHONE..................................954 445-7861
Yunia Dieguez Jomarron, *Principal*
EMP: 7 **EST:** 2015
SALES (est): 215.8K **Privately Held**
WEB: www.tnwworks.com
SIC: 2431 Millwork

(G-10492)
TOP OPTICAL LAB
4444 Sw 71st Ave Ste 111 (33155-4658)
PHONE..................................305 662-2893
Angel Pardinas, *President*
Carlos Pardinas, *Vice Pres*
EMP: 10 **EST:** 1975
SQ FT: 1,313
SALES (est): 606.6K **Privately Held**
SIC: 3851 Ophthalmic goods

(G-10493)
TOP QUALITY FINISHERS INC
2780 Nw 122nd St (33167-2508)
PHONE..................................305 688-8174
Casimiro An Saboya, *Principal*
EMP: 6 **EST:** 2019
SALES (est): 196.6K **Privately Held**
SIC: 3479 Coating of metals & formed products

(G-10494)
TOPFLITE MANUFACTURING INC
Also Called: Topflite Components
14262 Sw 140th St Ste 108 (33186-7365)
PHONE..................................800 219-2601
Bruce Price, *President*
Jonathan Falco, *Vice Pres*
Brenda Lola, *Purchasing*
EMP: 16 **EST:** 2008
SALES (est): 2.4MM **Privately Held**
WEB: www.topflitecomponents.com
SIC: 3643 Connectors & terminals for electrical devices; caps & plugs, electric: attachment

(G-10495)
TOUCHE SOFTWARE LLC
15616 Sw 62nd St (33193-2572)
PHONE..................................786 241-9907
Ruben Dorrego, *President*
EMP: 7 **EST:** 2010
SALES (est): 361.4K **Privately Held**
WEB: www.touchesoftware.com
SIC: 7372 Prepackaged software

(G-10496)
TOUCHPOINT GROUP HOLDINGS INC
4300 Biscayne Blvd # 203 (33137-3255)
PHONE..................................305 420-6640
EMP: 6
SALES (est): 234.8K **Privately Held**
WEB: www.touchpointgh.com
SIC: 3661 Telephone & telegraph apparatus

(G-10497)
TOYS FOR BOYS MIAMI LLC
1924 N Miami Ave (33136-1314)
PHONE..................................786 464-0160
Rafael E Gill, *Principal*
Jilian Sanz, *Chief*
EMP: 8 **EST:** 2013
SALES (est): 383.1K **Privately Held**
WEB: www.toysforboysmagazine.com
SIC: 2741 Miscellaneous publishing

(G-10498)
TRA PUBLISHING LLP
245 Ne 37th St (33137-3710)
PHONE..................................305 424-6468
Andrea Gollin, *Manager*
Ilona Oppenheim, *Director*
Raul Lira, *Director*
Rita Delcarmen Martin, *Director*
Rita Martin, *Account Dir*
EMP: 10 **EST:** 2016
SALES (est): 473.7K **Privately Held**
WEB: www.trapublishing.com
SIC: 2731 Books: publishing & printing

(G-10499)
TRACTO PARTS CORP
7401 Nw 68th St Ste 122 (33166-2807)
PHONE..................................305 972-1357
Hernan Alvarez, *President*
◆ **EMP:** 6 **EST:** 2000
SALES (est): 190.6K **Privately Held**
WEB: www.foxtracto.com
SIC: 3523 Farm machinery & equipment

(G-10500)
TRADEPAK INC
4041 Nw 25th St A (33142-6723)
PHONE..................................305 871-2247
Peter A Hoffmann Jr, *President*
Erika Hoffmann, *Shareholder*
Paul E Hoffmann, *Shareholder*
◆ **EMP:** 6 **EST:** 2003
SALES (est): 996.2K **Privately Held**
WEB: www.tradepak.net
SIC: 2821 Plastics materials & resins

(G-10501)
TRADINGFLEX INC
Also Called: Labelflex
1395 Brickell Ave Ste 800 (33131-3302)
PHONE..................................877 522-3535
Kevin Blanco-Uribe, *President*
EMP: 10 **EST:** 2014
SQ FT: 2,400
SALES (est): 1MM **Privately Held**
WEB: www.tradingflex.com
SIC: 2759 Labels & seals: printing

(G-10502)
TRANE CENTRAL AMERICA INC
7650 Nw 19th St Ste 270 (33126-1220)
PHONE..................................305 592-8646
William Sekkel, *CEO*
◆ **EMP:** 50 **EST:** 2008
SALES (est): 13.6MM **Privately Held**
WEB: www.trane.com
SIC: 3585 Air conditioning equipment, complete
HQ: The Trane Company
3600 Pammel Creek Rd
La Crosse WI 54601
608 787-2000

(G-10503)
TRANSAMERICA INTL BRDCSTG
Also Called: Omb America
3100 Nw 72nd Ave Ste 112 (33122-1336)
PHONE..................................305 477-0973
Antonia Ormab, *President*
Julian Muro, *President*
Rafael Arreaz, *Principal*
◆ **EMP:** 6 **EST:** 1991
SQ FT: 2,500
SALES (est): 830.4K **Privately Held**
SIC: 3663 Radio & TV communications equipment

(G-10504)
TRAP WORLD LLC
2125 Biscayne Blvd # 400 (33137-5031)
PHONE..................................305 517-5676
Mike Upton, *Principal*
EMP: 76 **EST:** 2014
SQ FT: 7,000
SALES (est): 5MM **Privately Held**
SIC: 3861 Motion picture film

(G-10505)
TREND AT LLC
2627 S Bayshore Dr (33133-5438)
PHONE..................................786 300-2550
Andres E Toro, *President*
John H Schulte, *Principal*
Juan Valencia, *CFO*
EMP: 12 **EST:** 2018

▲ = Import ▼=Export
◆ =Import/Export

SALES (est): 2.8MM Privately Held
SIC: 2759 5111 5999 2671 Commercial printing; printing paper; packaging materials: boxes, padding, etc.; packaging paper & plastics film, coated & laminated; bags: uncoated paper & multiwall

(G-10506)
TRIDOR GROUP INC
Also Called: TGI
10118 W Flagler St (33174-1897)
PHONE.................................786 707-2241
Joseph Rosa, *President*
EMP: 10 EST: 2015
SALES (est): 407.1K Privately Held
WEB: www.tridorgroup.com
SIC: 3663 2451 7629 Mobile communication equipment; mobile homes, industrial or commercial use; telecommunication equipment repair (except telephones)

(G-10507)
TROPICAL CEILING FAN COMPANY
13110 S Dixie Hwy (33156-6510)
PHONE.................................877 921-3267
EMP: 7 EST: 2011
SALES (est): 417.5K Privately Held
WEB: www.tropicalfancompany.com
SIC: 3634 Ceiling fans

(G-10508)
TROPICAL PALLETS INC (PA)
1500 Nw 23rd St (33142-7626)
PHONE.................................305 634-0346
Rigoberto Lesteiro, *President*
Rigoberto Lesteiro Jr, *Vice Pres*
EMP: 7 EST: 1984
SQ FT: 33,000
SALES (est): 1MM Privately Held
WEB: www.tropicalpalletsinc.com
SIC: 2448 Pallets, wood; pallets, wood & wood with metal

(G-10509)
TROPICAL PRINTS INC A CORP
4401 Sw 75th Ave Ste 2 (33155-4445)
PHONE.................................305 261-9926
George Sanchez, *Principal*
EMP: 6 EST: 2008
SALES (est): 172K Privately Held
SIC: 2752 Commercial printing, lithographic

(G-10510)
TRUJILLO OIL PLANT INC
3325 Nw 62nd St (33147-7533)
PHONE.................................305 696-8701
Lucas Trujillo Jr, *President*
Alberto Trujillo, *Vice Pres*
Joseph Murphy, *Plant Engr Mgr*
◆ EMP: 15 EST: 1996
SQ FT: 5,000
SALES (est): 2.4MM Privately Held
WEB: www.trujilloandsons.com
SIC: 2076 Vegetable oil mills

(G-10511)
TUKA IMPORTS LLC
3729 Nw 71st St (33147-6521)
PHONE.................................305 640-8336
Michael Kuper, *Mng Member*
▲ EMP: 9 EST: 2011
SALES (est): 444.9K Privately Held
WEB: www.tukaimports.com
SIC: 2392 Blankets, comforters & beddings

(G-10512)
TULY CORPORATION
Also Called: Galletas Yeya
3820 Nw 32nd Ave (33142-5008)
PHONE.................................305 633-0710
EMP: 16 EST: 1974
SQ FT: 5,000
SALES (est): 1.1MM Privately Held
SIC: 2052 2051 Mfg Cookies/Crackers Mfg Bread/Related Products

(G-10513)
TUTTI HOGAR INTERNATIONAL LLC
19472 Diplomat Dr (33179-6434)
PHONE.................................305 705-4735
Johnny Dejman,
EMP: 7 EST: 2017
SALES (est): 180.4K Privately Held
SIC: 2671 Packaging paper & plastics film, coated & laminated

(G-10514)
TUUCI WORLDWIDE LLC (PA)
2900 Nw 35th St (33142-5240)
PHONE.................................305 634-5116
Tammy Lenham, *Sales Staff*
Dougan H Clarke,
◆ EMP: 145 EST: 2008
SALES (est): 29.5MM Privately Held
WEB: www.tuuci.com
SIC: 2514 Metal household furniture

(G-10515)
TV FILM INTERNATIONAL INC
2600 Sw 3rd Ave Ste 850 (33129-2329)
PHONE.................................305 671-3265
Pamela D Argandona, *Director*
EMP: 6 EST: 2000
SALES (est): 800K Privately Held
WEB: www.tvfilminternational.com
SIC: 3663 Radio & TV communications equipment

(G-10516)
TWINS & MARTIN EQUIPMENT CORP
80 Sw 8th St Ste 2056 (33130-3003)
PHONE.................................954 802-0345
Mauro Levinton, *President*
Tomas Levinton, *COO*
Alejandro Levinton, *CFO*
Martin Levinton, *Marketing Staff*
EMP: 5 EST: 2004
SALES (est): 477.8K Privately Held
WEB: www.twinsandmartin.com
SIC: 3841 Diagnostic apparatus, medical

(G-10517)
TWO LITTLE FISHIES INC
Also Called: Ricordea Publishing
15801 Nw 15th Ave (33169-5605)
PHONE.................................305 623-7695
Julian Sprung, *President*
Ines Betancourt, *Office Mgr*
▲ EMP: 9 EST: 1991
SALES (est): 1.3MM Privately Held
WEB: www.twolittlefishies.com
SIC: 2731 2899 3677 Books: publishing only; chemical preparations; filtration devices, electronic

(G-10518)
TX TRADING INC
20355 Ne 34th Ct Apt 427 (33180-3311)
PHONE.................................786 303-9950
Beny Ichilevici, *President*
EMP: 5 EST: 2013
SALES (est): 5.2MM Privately Held
WEB: www.txtradings.com
SIC: 3663 Mobile communication equipment

(G-10519)
TYCOON TUTTI INC
1361 Nw 155th Dr (33169-5723)
P.O. Box 546375, Miami Beach (33154-0375)
PHONE.................................305 624-7811
▼ EMP: 45
SQ FT: 16,000
SALES (est): 2.5MM Privately Held
SIC: 2321 2311 Mfg Children' Apparel

(G-10520)
TYREX ORE & MINERALS COMPANY
8950 Sw 74th Ct Fl 22 (33156-3171)
PHONE.................................305 333-5288
Maurice Hoo, *Principal*
EMP: 7 EST: 2018
SALES (est): 75MM Privately Held
SIC: 1011 3291 Iron ore mining; abrasive metal & steel products

(G-10521)
TYS HOMETOWN CAFE BISTRO LLC ✪
1847 Nw 1st Ct (33136-1707)
PHONE.................................786 208-1163
Tywanda Dupont,
EMP: 6 EST: 2021 Privately Held
SIC: 2099 Food preparations

(G-10522)
U M P
6262 Bird Rd (33155-4882)
PHONE.................................305 740-4996
Carmen Ferrida, *Principal*
EMP: 7 EST: 2008
SALES (est): 124.6K Privately Held
SIC: 3568 Bearings, bushings & blocks

(G-10523)
UFP PALM BCH LLC DBA UFP MAMI ✪
11400 Nw 32nd Ave (33167-2905)
PHONE.................................786 837-0552
Michael Nuclo, *Principal*
EMP: 54 EST: 2020
SALES (est): 2.4MM
SALES (corp-wide): 5.1B Publicly Held
WEB: www.ufpi.com
SIC: 2421 Outdoor wood structural products
PA: Ufp Industries, Inc.
2801 E Beltline Ave Ne
Grand Rapids MI 49525
616 364-6161

(G-10524)
ULTIMATE SOFTWARE
11900 Sw 46th St (33175-4736)
PHONE.................................305 559-3052
Debby Sessions, *Principal*
Erik Kusins, *Sales Mgr*
Anderson Denise, *Prgrmr*
EMP: 18 EST: 2010
SALES (est): 286K Privately Held
WEB: www.ultimatesoftware.com
SIC: 7372 Prepackaged software

(G-10525)
ULTRA AEROSPACE INC
12235 Sw 128th St (33186-5993)
PHONE.................................305 728-6361
Michael Naranjo, *President*
EMP: 11 EST: 2015
SALES (est): 1.2MM Privately Held
WEB: www.ultra-aero.com
SIC: 3728 Aircraft parts & equipment

(G-10526)
ULTRA GRAPHICS CORP
132 Sw 96th Ave (33174-2009)
PHONE.................................305 593-0202
Humberto Luis Sr, *President*
Ceneira Luis, *Corp Secy*
Bertha Luis, *Vice Pres*
Humberto Luis Jr, *Vice Pres*
◆ EMP: 5 EST: 1972
SQ FT: 4,000
SALES (est): 328.8K Privately Held
WEB: www.ultragraphics.homestead.com
SIC: 2752 Commercial printing, offset

(G-10527)
ULTRAPANEL MARINE INC
2665 S Byshr Dr Ste 220 (33133-5402)
PHONE.................................772 285-4258
Ivo Gomis, *President*
Amarilis Gomis, *Vice Pres*
◆ EMP: 30 EST: 1987
SALES (est): 6.2MM Privately Held
WEB: www.ultrapanel.net
SIC: 3613 3732 3625 Panelboards & distribution boards, electric; boat building & repairing; relays & industrial controls

(G-10528)
UNICRAFT CORP
3640 Nw 52nd St (33142-3245)
PHONE.................................305 633-4945
Martin Gopman, *President*
◆ EMP: 10 EST: 1983
SQ FT: 10,000
SALES (est): 1.9MM Privately Held
WEB: www.unicraftcorp.com
SIC: 3552 Cloth spreading machines

(G-10529)
UNIFORM AUTHORITY INC (PA)
Also Called: Ibiley School Uniforms
2263 Sw 12th St (33135-5016)
PHONE.................................305 625-8050
Eduardo Barea, *President*
Lelaine Barea, *Sales Mgr*
◆ EMP: 81 EST: 1988
SQ FT: 11,000
SALES (est): 6.1MM Privately Held
WEB: www.the-uniform-authority.business.site
SIC: 2311 2337 5699 5621 Men's & boys' uniforms; uniforms, except athletic: women's, misses' & juniors'; uniforms; women's clothing stores; men's & boys' work clothing

(G-10530)
UNIMAT INDUSTRIES LLC
6980 Nw 43rd St (33166-6826)
PHONE.................................305 716-0358
Masaru Ceja, *Principal*
◆ EMP: 6 EST: 2010
SALES (est): 885K Privately Held
WEB: www.unimatindustries.com
SIC: 2512 Upholstered household furniture
HQ: Unimat De Mexico, S.A. De C.V.
Calle 4 No. 25-D
Naucalpan EDOMEX. 53370

(G-10531)
UNIQUE CUSTOM TRUCK & TRLR LLC
Also Called: Uct2
7248 Sw 42nd Ter (33155-4531)
PHONE.................................305 403-7042
Michael Frank,
Ana Frank,
EMP: 10 EST: 2004
SQ FT: 20,000
SALES (est): 1MM Privately Held
SIC: 3715 Truck trailers

(G-10532)
UNIQUE MARBLE POLISHING INC
18093 Sw 135th Ave (33177-7117)
PHONE.................................305 969-1554
Pablo Perez, *President*
Johanni Ravel, *Vice Pres*
EMP: 5 EST: 2000
SALES (est): 437.1K Privately Held
SIC: 3471 Polishing, metals or formed products

(G-10533)
UNITECH INDUSTRIES CORP
7525 Nw 37th Ave (33147-5800)
PHONE.................................305 691-0330
Dan Carmona, *President*
Orlando Nieves, *VP Opers*
Carmelo Villegas, *CFO*
Sara Carmona, *Admin Sec*
EMP: 18 EST: 1996
SQ FT: 52,000
SALES (est): 536.5K Privately Held
SIC: 3534 Elevators & moving stairways

(G-10534)
UNITED ELECTRONICS CORPORATION
1 Se 3rd Ave Ste 158 (33131-1714)
PHONE.................................954 888-1024
Shane Scanlon, *CEO*
Dave York, *President*
Mario Alvarez, *Vice Pres*
Gavriel Meidar, *Director*
Hanna Meidar, *Director*
▲ EMP: 78 EST: 2003
SQ FT: 20,000
SALES (est): 12.8MM Privately Held
WEB: www.lextm3.com
SIC: 3643 Current-carrying wiring devices

(G-10535)
UNITED EXPRESS INTL CORP
7302 Nw 34th St (33122-1262)
PHONE.................................305 591-3292
Sharon Asrillion, *President*
EMP: 7
SALES (corp-wide): 2.3MM Privately Held
WEB: www.unitedexpressintl.com
SIC: 3444 Mail (post office) collection or storage boxes, sheet metal
PA: United Express International, Corp.
7300 Nw 34th St
Miami FL 33122
305 591-3292

GEOGRAPHIC

(G-10536)
UNITED FUEL
6900 Sw 8th St (33144-4744)
PHONE..................................305 992-2923
Joel Costantino, *Principal*
EMP: 6 **EST:** 2010
SALES (est): 223.5K **Privately Held**
WEB: www.unitedfuel.net
SIC: 2869 Fuels

(G-10537)
UNITED OIL PACKERS INC
Also Called: Uo Packers
3200 Nw 125th St Stop 4 (33167-2403)
PHONE..................................305 687-6457
Henry Hamersmith, *President*
Minda Hamersmith, *Admin Sec*
◆ **EMP:** 28 **EST:** 1981
SQ FT: 280,000
SALES (est): 17.6MM
SALES (corp-wide): 22MM **Privately Held**
WEB: www.unitedoilcompany.com
SIC: 2079 Olive oil
PA: Hamersmith, Inc.
3200 Nw 125th St Stop 4
Miami FL 33167
305 685-7451

(G-10538)
UNITED PILLOW MFG INC
5646 Nw 35th Ct (33142-2730)
PHONE..................................305 636-9747
Miguel Angel Rodriguez, *President*
Juan Roddriguez, *Vice Pres*
▼ **EMP:** 19 **EST:** 2004
SQ FT: 11,000
SALES (est): 2MM **Privately Held**
WEB: www.unitedpillow.com
SIC: 2392 Pillows, bed: made from purchased materials

(G-10539)
UNITED VERTICAL BLINDS LLC
1261 Nw 175th St (33169-4656)
PHONE..................................786 348-8000
Desmond Patten, *Principal*
EMP: 10 **EST:** 2019
SALES (est): 654.6K **Privately Held**
SIC: 2591 Blinds vertical

(G-10540)
UNIVERSAL CRGO DOORS & SVC LLC
8490 Nw 68th St (33166-2661)
P.O. Box 660460, Miami Springs (33266-0460)
PHONE..................................305 594-9175
David Sandri, *President*
Roy Sandri, *COO*
Marli Sandri, *Treasurer*
EMP: 34 **EST:** 1988
SQ FT: 22,000
SALES (est): 10.3MM **Privately Held**
WEB: www.universalcargodoors.com
SIC: 3728 Aircraft parts & equipment

(G-10541)
UNIVERSAL PRINTING COMPANY
3100 Nw 74th Ave (33122-1226)
PHONE..................................305 592-5387
Jack Nicol, *President*
Gloria Bechtel, *Corp Secy*
▼ **EMP:** 18 **EST:** 1961
SQ FT: 57,000
SALES (est): 479.6K **Privately Held**
WEB: www.universalprintingco.com
SIC: 2752 Commercial printing, offset

(G-10542)
UNIVERSAL RIBBON CORPORATION
8111 Nw 68th St (33166-2757)
PHONE..................................305 471-0828
Juan Rios, *President*
Irene Rios, *Vice Pres*
David Rios, *Admin Sec*
◆ **EMP:** 23 **EST:** 1988
SQ FT: 6,000
SALES (est): 1.1MM **Privately Held**
WEB: www.universalribbon.com
SIC: 3955 Print cartridges for laser & other computer printers

(G-10543)
UNIVERSAL SEAT COVERS AUTO ACC (PA)
2370 Ludlam Rd (33155-1846)
PHONE..................................305 262-3955
Isora Del Cristo, *President*
▼ **EMP:** 5 **EST:** 1986
SQ FT: 5,000
SALES (est): 1.3MM **Privately Held**
WEB: www.universalseatcovers.com
SIC: 2399 Seat covers, automobile

(G-10544)
UNIVERSAL SURGICAL APPLIANCE
400 Ne 191st St (33179-3986)
P.O. Box 693099 (33269-0099)
PHONE..................................305 652-0810
Ira S Lehman, *President*
Shirley Lehman, *Corp Secy*
David Lehman, *Vice Pres*
Lisa Lehman, *Vice Pres*
EMP: 11 **EST:** 1962
SQ FT: 8,000
SALES (est): 259.3K **Privately Held**
SIC: 3842 3841 Surgical appliances & supplies; abdominal supporters, braces & trusses; belts: surgical, sanitary & corrective; braces, orthopedic; surgical & medical instruments

(G-10545)
UNIVERSAL TECH INC
3042 Nw 72nd Ave (33122-1314)
PHONE..................................786 220-8032
Ling Chen, *President*
EMP: 8 **EST:** 2013
SALES (est): 279.5K **Privately Held**
SIC: 2678 Stationery products

(G-10546)
UNLIMITED INPRESSIONS INC
1424 Mw 82nd Ave (33176)
PHONE..................................305 606-2699
Benito H Rodriguez, *President*
EMP: 6 **EST:** 2008
SALES (est): 68.7K **Privately Held**
SIC: 2754 Color printing, gravure

(G-10547)
UPTON HOUSE COOLER CORPORATION
2490 Nw 7th Ave (33127-4206)
PHONE..................................305 633-2531
Dimas Beret, *President*
EMP: 5 **EST:** 1952
SQ FT: 15,000
SALES (est): 467.9K **Privately Held**
SIC: 3564 3444 Ventilating fans: industrial or commercial; blowing fans: industrial or commercial; exhaust fans: industrial or commercial; sheet metalwork

(G-10548)
URANO PUBLISHING INC
8871 Sw 129th Ter (33176-5905)
PHONE..................................305 233-3365
Lucia Laratelli, *President*
◆ **EMP:** 7 **EST:** 2000
SALES (est): 245.2K **Privately Held**
WEB: www.edicionesuranousa.com
SIC: 2741 Miscellaneous publishing

(G-10549)
URBAN STONE WORKS
7025 Ne 2nd Ave (33138-5507)
PHONE..................................305 754-7171
Janusz Niedbala, *President*
◆ **EMP:** 10 **EST:** 1988
SQ FT: 5,000
SALES (est): 1.6MM **Privately Held**
WEB: www.urbanstoneworks.com
SIC: 3272 Concrete products, precast

(G-10550)
URIBEMONICA
2127 Sw 16th Ter (33145-2111)
PHONE..................................305 856-3857
Monica Uribe, *Principal*
EMP: 6 **EST:** 2018
SALES (est): 110.6K **Privately Held**
SIC: 3861 Photographic equipment & supplies

(G-10551)
US AMERICAN PLASTIC CORP
2164 Nw 22nd Ct (33142-7346)
PHONE..................................305 200-3683
Hector Pino, *President*
Adrian Alfonso, *Vice Pres*
Ulises Cruz, *Vice Pres*
EMP: 10 **EST:** 2016
SALES (est): 760.7K **Privately Held**
SIC: 2673 Bags: plastic, laminated & coated

(G-10552)
US GLOBAL GLASS LLC
Also Called: Florida Laminated Tempered GL
220 Ne 187th St (33179-4516)
PHONE..................................305 651-6630
Frank Wilson, *President*
John Parell, *Chairman*
Patrick Tschrin, *COO*
J Randy Beard, *Finance*
EMP: 14 **EST:** 2001
SQ FT: 75,000
SALES (est): 289.6K **Privately Held**
SIC: 3211 Window glass, clear & colored

(G-10553)
US SHEET METAL INC
7333 Nw 66th St (33166-3009)
PHONE..................................305 884-7705
Francisco M Valdes, *President*
Barbara Valdes, *Vice Pres*
◆ **EMP:** 19 **EST:** 1997
SQ FT: 5,798
SALES (est): 1.8MM **Privately Held**
SIC: 3444 Ducts, sheet metal

(G-10554)
USA EXPRESS PALLETS CORP
4655 Nw 36th Ave (33142-3938)
PHONE..................................786 251-9543
Raul Gomez, *Principal*
EMP: 8 **EST:** 2005
SALES (est): 502.6K **Privately Held**
SIC: 2448 Pallets, wood

(G-10555)
USA RECMAR CORP
918 Nw 106th Avenue Cir (33172-3123)
PHONE..................................786 554-3505
Amadeo N Roig, *President*
Martiza Gonzalez, *General Mgr*
EMP: 7 **EST:** 2018
SALES (est): 120.2K **Privately Held**
SIC: 2591 Drapery hardware & blinds & shades

(G-10556)
USA SIGNS INC
7230 Nw 46th St (33166-6423)
PHONE..................................305 470-2333
Jose Pacheco, *President*
Katya Caceres, *Sales Staff*
EMP: 8 **EST:** 2001
SALES (est): 500K **Privately Held**
WEB: www.usasigns.us
SIC: 3993 Electric signs

(G-10557)
USG INTERNATIONAL LTD
3001 Nw 125th St (33167-2524)
PHONE..................................305 688-8744
EMP: 11 **EST:** 2014
SALES (est): 2.2MM **Privately Held**
SIC: 3272 Wall & ceiling squares, concrete

(G-10558)
V & C SUPPLY ORNAMENTAL CORP
6400 Nw 72nd Ave (33166-3627)
PHONE..................................305 634-9040
Maria V Solano, *President*
Ronald Solano, *Vice Pres*
Jose Solano, *Director*
◆ **EMP:** 6 **EST:** 2002
SALES (est): 832K **Privately Held**
WEB: www.vcmetalsupply.com
SIC: 3548 3089 Welding apparatus; fences, gates & accessories: plastic

(G-10559)
V & F AIR CONDITIONING SUP LLC
7320 Nw 12th St Ste 107 (33126-1913)
PHONE..................................305 477-1040
Dainel D Fuentes, *Mng Member*
Rolando Vento,
EMP: 14 **EST:** 2014
SALES (est): 4.4MM **Privately Held**
WEB: www.vfacsupply.com
SIC: 3585 Air conditioning equipment, complete

(G-10560)
V M VISUAL MDSG DCTR GROUP INC
600 Nw 62nd St (33150-4330)
PHONE..................................305 759-9910
Rafael Velazquez, *President*
EMP: 10 **EST:** 2001
SALES (est): 636.6K **Privately Held**
SIC: 2392 Cushions & pillows; blankets, comforters & beddings; tablecloths & table settings; sheets, fabric: made from purchased materials

(G-10561)
V2 CIGS
3050 Biscayne Blvd # 700 (33137-4184)
PHONE..................................305 240-6387
David Turner, *Branch Mgr*
EMP: 25
SALES (corp-wide): 569K **Privately Held**
WEB: www.v2.com
SIC: 2111 Cigarettes
PA: V2 Cigs
1521 Alton Rd Ste 275
Miami Beach FL 33139
305 517-1149

(G-10562)
VALENTINA SIGNA INC
Also Called: G & B Trading Imports
7343 Nw 56th St (33166-4203)
PHONE..................................305 264-0673
Gun Gilgim, *President*
EMP: 5 **EST:** 1991
SALES (est): 309K **Privately Held**
WEB: www.valentinagb.com
SIC: 2339 Neckwear & ties: women's, misses' & juniors'

(G-10563)
VALENTINI ITALIAN SPC CO
4290 Nw 37th Ct (33142-4234)
PHONE..................................305 638-0822
Lislei Gamarra, *Branch Mgr*
EMP: 6
SALES (corp-wide): 3.6MM **Privately Held**
WEB: www.valentiniicecream.com
SIC: 2024 Ice cream, bulk
PA: Valentini Italian Specialties, Co.
11700 Nw 102nd Rd Ste 2
Medley FL
305 638-3177

(G-10564)
VAMPA TIRES SUPPLIES INC
7243 Nw 54th St (33166-4807)
PHONE..................................305 888-1001
Emilio Perez, *President*
Lazaro Perez, *Vice Pres*
◆ **EMP:** 5 **EST:** 1999
SQ FT: 600
SALES (est): 939.2K **Privately Held**
WEB: www.vampa.net
SIC: 3559 Tire retreading machinery & equipment

(G-10565)
VAN TEAL HOSPITALITY INC ✪
13480 Sw 131st St (33186-5891)
PHONE..................................305 751-6767
Eduardo Gonzalez Sr, *Principal*
EMP: 7 **EST:** 2020
SALES (est): 166.4K **Privately Held**
WEB: www.vanteal.com
SIC: 3646 Commercial indusl & institutional electric lighting fixtures

(G-10566)
VAN TEAL INC
Also Called: Bb & T
7240 Ne 4th Ave (33138-5316)
PHONE..................................305 751-6767
Hivo Gonzalez, *CEO*
Estella Van Teal, *President*
Eduardo Vanteal, *Exec VP*
Eddie Gonzalez, *Vice Pres*
Jorge Morales, *Sales Mgr*

▲ = Import ▼=Export
◆ =Import/Export

▲ **EMP:** 30 **EST:** 1974
SQ FT: 50,000
SALES (est): 4.1MM **Privately Held**
WEB: www.vanteal.com
SIC: 3645 3221 3648 Residential lighting fixtures; glass containers; lighting equipment

(G-10567)
VAPOR GROUP INC (PA)
20725 Ne 16th Ave Ste A4 (33179-2123)
PHONE.................................954 792-8450
David Zinger, *President*
Yaniv Nahon, *COO*
Jorge Schcolnik, *CFO*
Dror Svorai, *Treasurer*
EMP: 16 **EST:** 1990
SQ FT: 500
SALES: 1.9MM **Publicly Held**
WEB: www.vaporgroup.com
SIC: 2111 5571 Cigarettes; motor scooters

(G-10568)
VAPOR GROUP INC (PA)
20200 W Dixie Hwy Ste 906 (33180-1926)
PHONE.................................954 792-8450
Yaniv Nahon, *President*
Jorge Schcolnik, *CFO*
EMP: 10 **EST:** 2012
SALES (est): 1.3MM **Privately Held**
SIC: 3634 Cigarette lighters, electric

(G-10569)
VARIBELT INCORPORATED ✪
13216 Sw 45th Ln (33175-3931)
PHONE.................................305 775-1568
Davut Ozdemir, *President*
Nazlican Ozdemir Serin, *Vice Pres*
EMP: 5 **EST:** 2020
SALES (est): 304.7K **Privately Held**
WEB: www.myvbelt.com
SIC: 3052 Rubber & plastics hose & beltings

(G-10570)
VC SERUM LLC
425 Ne 22nd St Apt 2505 (33137-5192)
PHONE.................................305 778-2190
Teresa Ramirez, *Principal*
EMP: 6 **EST:** 2014
SALES (est): 209.9K **Privately Held**
WEB: www.vcserum.com
SIC: 2836 Serums

(G-10571)
VECTOR GROUP LTD (PA)
4400 Biscayne Blvd (33137-3212)
PHONE.................................305 579-8000
Bennett S Lebow, *Ch of Bd*
Howard M Lorber, *President*
Nicholas P Anson, *President*
Richard J Lampen, *COO*
J David Ballard, *Senior VP*
EMP: 173 **EST:** 1873
SQ FT: 12,390
SALES: 2B **Publicly Held**
WEB: www.vectorgroupltd.com
SIC: 2111 6552 Cigarettes; subdividers & developers

(G-10572)
VENCHI US INC
1111 Brickell Ave # 2650 (33131-3112)
PHONE.................................646 448-8663
Paolo Dellamora, *Principal*
EMP: 6 **EST:** 2015
SALES (est): 118.9K **Privately Held**
SIC: 2066 Chocolate

(G-10573)
VENSOFT CORP
2530 Ne 208th Ter (33180-1316)
PHONE.................................786 991-2080
Moises Romero, *President*
◆ **EMP:** 13 **EST:** 1999
SALES (est): 139.4K **Privately Held**
WEB: www.vensoft.com
SIC: 7372 5734 Prepackaged software; computer & software stores

(G-10574)
VERU INC (PA)
Also Called: Veru Healthcare
48 Nw 25th St Ste 102 (33127-4442)
PHONE.................................305 509-6897
Mitchell S Steiner, *Ch of Bd*
Harry Fisch, *Vice Ch Bd*
Rachel Steiner, *General Mgr*
Sam Fisch, *Investment Ofcr*
K Gary Barnette, *Security Dir*
EMP: 292 **EST:** 1971
SQ FT: 4,640
SALES: 42.5MM **Publicly Held**
WEB: www.verupharma.com
SIC: 2834 3069 Pharmaceutical preparations; birth control devices, rubber

(G-10575)
VERY TASTY LLC
2177 Nw 24th Ct (33142-7114)
PHONE.................................305 636-4140
Pedro A Cardenas, *Principal*
EMP: 10 **EST:** 2011
SQ FT: 4,500
SALES (est): 978.4K **Privately Held**
WEB: www.very-tasty.com
SIC: 2038 Ethnic foods, frozen

(G-10576)
VGR HOLDING LLC (HQ)
4400 S Biscayne Blvd # 10 (33131-2303)
PHONE.................................305 579-8000
Richard J Lampen, *Manager*
Marc N Bell, *Manager*
EMP: 100 **EST:** 1999
SALES (est): 172.6MM **Publicly Held**
WEB: www.vectorgroupltd.com
SIC: 2111 6552 Cigarettes; subdividers & developers

(G-10577)
VIBRANT SIGN STUDIO LLC
8890 Sw 129th Ter (33176-5945)
PHONE.................................305 363-2181
Julio C Novoa, *President*
EMP: 6 **EST:** 2015
SALES (est): 278.5K **Privately Held**
WEB: www.vibrantsignstudio.com
SIC: 3993 Signs & advertising specialties

(G-10578)
VICBAG LLC
80 Sw 8th St Ste 2000 (33130-3038)
PHONE.................................305 423-7042
Djamal Bellechilli, *Mng Member*
◆ **EMP:** 5 **EST:** 2005
SQ FT: 371
SALES (est): 1.1MM
SALES (corp-wide): 401.6K **Privately Held**
WEB: www.vicbag.com
SIC: 2759 Bags, plastic: printing
HQ: Vicbag
23 Rue Du Depart
Paris 75014
143 259-111

(G-10579)
VICCARBE INC
8950 Sw 74th Ct Ste 1406 (33156-3173)
PHONE.................................305 670-0979
Rodrigo Roche Silvia, *QC Dir*
Benedito Gonzalez Daniel, *Comms Dir*
Carrasco Berlanga Victor Manue, *Manager*
EMP: 27 **EST:** 2013
SALES (est): 2.5MM
SALES (corp-wide): 76.2K **Privately Held**
WEB: www.viccarbe.com
SIC: 2521 2522 Wood office furniture; office chairs, benches & stools, except wood
HQ: Viccarbe Habitat Sl
Camino Raco (Pg Ind Norte) 23
Beniparrell 46469
961 201-010

(G-10580)
VICENTE GANDIA PLA
Also Called: Vicente Gandia USA
7300 N Kendall Dr Ste 470 (33156-7854)
P.O. Box 560668 (33256-0668)
PHONE.................................310 699-8559
▲ **EMP:** 120
SALES: 44.5MM **Privately Held**
SIC: 2084 5182 Mfg Wines/Brandy/Spirits Whol Wine/Distilled Beverages

(G-10581)
VICENTE GANDIA USA INC
7300 N Kendall Dr Ste 470 (33156-7854)
PHONE.................................310 699-8559
Jose Maria Gandia, *President*
Laura Gordon, *Vice Pres*
EMP: 8 **EST:** 2011
SALES (est): 102.8K **Privately Held**
WEB: www.vicentegandiausa.com
SIC: 2084 Wines

(G-10582)
VICTUS LLC (PA)
4918 Sw 74th Ct (33155-4400)
PHONE.................................305 663-2129
Victor Garcia, *Vice Pres*
Carlos Fernandez, *CFO*
Arturo Celis, *Finance*
Armando Triana, *Marketing Staff*
Enrique J Lopez,
◆ **EMP:** 30 **EST:** 1999
SQ FT: 14,000
SALES (est): 3.7MM **Privately Held**
WEB: www.victus.com
SIC: 2834 3069 Vitamin, nutrient & hematinic preparations for human use; medical & laboratory rubber sundries & related products

(G-10583)
VIDA 18COM LLC
7499 Nw 31st St (33122-1221)
PHONE.................................305 935-6657
EMP: 6 **EST:** 2019
SALES (est): 47.7K **Privately Held**
WEB: www.vida18.com
SIC: 2741 Miscellaneous publishing

(G-10584)
VIDREPUR OF AMERICA LLC
2301 Nw 84th Ave (33122-1531)
PHONE.................................305 468-9008
June Rodgers, *Comptroller*
Darren Caraway, *Manager*
Eduardo Sanchez,
Jose Santapou,
◆ **EMP:** 15 **EST:** 2001
SQ FT: 45,000
SALES (est): 2.1MM **Privately Held**
WEB: www.vidrepur.us
SIC: 3253 Mosaic tile, glazed & unglazed: ceramic

(G-10585)
VINITA USA CO
3250 Ne 1st Ave Ste 305 (33137-4295)
PHONE.................................650 260-5161
Ariel Casali, *CEO*
EMP: 6 **EST:** 2014
SALES (est): 107.6K **Privately Held**
WEB: www.vinitausa.com
SIC: 2084 Wines

(G-10586)
VINYL CORP (DH)
8000 Nw 79th Pl Ste 4 (33166-2181)
PHONE.................................305 477-6464
Garden W Smith, *President*
Ernie Reyes, *General Mgr*
Arthur L Whitman, *Vice Pres*
Nick Apan, *VP Sales*
Angelic Colon, *Sales Staff*
▼ **EMP:** 14 **EST:** 1987
SQ FT: 84,000
SALES (est): 5.2MM **Privately Held**
WEB: www.clarkdietrich.com
SIC: 3089 Plastic hardware & building products

(G-10587)
VIOLETTAS LLC (PA)
Also Called: Sync Footwear
145 Sw 8th St Unit 1901 (33130-3663)
PHONE.................................305 301-3351
David Panettiere, *Mng Member*
Angelica Llamas,
EMP: 4 **EST:** 2015
SQ FT: 2,000
SALES (est): 5MM **Privately Held**
WEB: www.syncfootwear.com
SIC: 3131 Boot & shoe accessories

(G-10588)
VISION ANALYTICAL INC (PA)
4444 Sw 71st Ave Ste 112 (33155-4658)
PHONE.................................305 801-7140
Pedro Bouza, *President*
Peter Bouza, *General Mgr*
EMP: 5 **EST:** 2005
SQ FT: 500
SALES (est): 459.6K **Privately Held**
WEB: www.particleshape.com
SIC: 3826 Analytical instruments

(G-10589)
VISION CANDLES INC
7363 Nw 36th Ave (33147-5809)
PHONE.................................305 836-8650
Jose E Garcia, *President*
◆ **EMP:** 5 **EST:** 2004
SALES (est): 414.7K **Privately Held**
WEB: www.tuvisioncandles.com
SIC: 3999 Candles

(G-10590)
VISUAL ACOUSTICS LLC
591 Nw 35th St (33127-3436)
PHONE.................................786 390-6128
Marc Lewin, *Mng Member*
Enrique Alfonso, *Technician*
EMP: 5 **EST:** 2003
SALES (est): 1MM **Privately Held**
WEB: www.visualacoustics.net
SIC: 3651 7622 Home entertainment equipment, electronic; home entertainment repair services

(G-10591)
VS CARBONICS INC
3491 Nw 79th St (33147-4532)
PHONE.................................305 903-6501
Dios Vazquez, *President*
EMP: 12 **EST:** 2009
SALES (est): 2.6MM **Privately Held**
WEB: www.vscarbonics.com
SIC: 2813 Industrial gases

(G-10592)
VS COATINGS LLC
3491 Nw 79th St (33147-4532)
PHONE.................................305 677-6224
Carlos Alvarez, *Principal*
EMP: 10 **EST:** 2018
SALES (est): 619.1K **Privately Held**
SIC: 3423 Hand & edge tools

(G-10593)
VSF CORP
Also Called: Infinity Embroidery
2800 Nw 125th St (33167-2513)
PHONE.................................305 769-2202
Joseph Friedman, *President*
Lior Friedman, *Vice Pres*
Orit Olshansky, *Controller*
▲ **EMP:** 30 **EST:** 1999
SQ FT: 40,000
SALES (est): 3.2MM **Privately Held**
WEB: www.infinityapparelgroup.com
SIC: 2395 Embroidery products, except schiffli machine

(G-10594)
VTRONIX LLC
7900 Nw 68th St (33166-2796)
P.O. Box 267096, Weston (33326-7096)
PHONE.................................305 471-7600
Anil Gowda,
Nina Birnbach,
Jorge Cosio,
Chaiyasit Thampeera,
▲ **EMP:** 5 **EST:** 2001
SQ FT: 3,000
SALES (est): 891.9K **Privately Held**
WEB: www.vtronix.com
SIC: 3822 Thermostats, except built-in

(G-10595)
WAR CHEST RIVER LLC
675 Nw 97th St (33150-1652)
PHONE.................................954 736-7704
Chapman Ducote, *Principal*
EMP: 7 **EST:** 2015
SALES (est): 398.1K **Privately Held**
SIC: 2741 Miscellaneous publishing

(G-10596)
WATERHUSE ARCHTCTRAL WDWRK LLC
4261 Nw 36th Ave (33142-4217)
PHONE.................................786 534-4943
Carlos E De Leon, *Mng Member*
EMP: 10 **EST:** 2018
SALES (est): 773.8K **Privately Held**
WEB: www.waterhousewoodwork.com
SIC: 2431 Millwork

(G-10597)
WATSON STEEL PRODUCTS
8067 Nw 66th St (33166-2729)
PHONE..................................716 853-2233
Jeff Watson, *President*
EMP: 8 **EST:** 2007
SALES (est): 613.5K **Privately Held**
WEB: www.watsonsteelandiron.com
SIC: 3599 Machine shop, jobbing & repair

(G-10598)
WESTIME
701 S Miami Ave Unit 168c (33130-1951)
PHONE..................................310 205-5555
EMP: 6 **EST:** 2015
SALES (est): 95K **Privately Held**
WEB: www.westime.com
SIC: 3873 Watches, clocks, watchcases & parts

(G-10599)
WHATEVER LO QUE SEA LLC
2087 Nw 135th Ave (33182-1926)
PHONE..................................786 429-3462
Fede Annito, *CEO*
EMP: 6 **EST:** 2018
SALES (est): 300K **Privately Held**
WEB: www.whateverloquesea.com
SIC: 2711 Commercial printing & newspaper publishing combined

(G-10600)
WHITE CARDBOARD CORP
3671 Nw 81st St (33147-4444)
PHONE..................................786 260-4692
Oscar Fidalgo, *Principal*
▲ **EMP:** 8 **EST:** 2013
SALES (est): 188.5K **Privately Held**
SIC: 2631 Cardboard

(G-10601)
WHITE MIAMI LLC
117 Ne 1st Ave Apt 1301 (33132-2112)
PHONE..................................305 579-9115
Monica Slodarz, *Principal*
EMP: 6 **EST:** 2013
SALES (est): 118.6K **Privately Held**
WEB: www.miaminewtimes.com
SIC: 2711 Newspapers, publishing & printing

(G-10602)
WHITE STARR PUBLISHING
12031 Sw 107th St (33186-3832)
PHONE..................................305 322-5788
Sandra Richardson, *Principal*
EMP: 6 **EST:** 2005
SALES (est): 110.7K **Privately Held**
SIC: 2741 Miscellaneous publishing

(G-10603)
WHITEWATER BOAT CORP
280 Nw 73rd St (33150-3427)
PHONE..................................305 756-9191
Norman Collins, *President*
Shane Collins, *Vice Pres*
EMP: 6 **EST:** 1980
SQ FT: 12,000
SALES (est): 880.6K **Privately Held**
WEB: www.whitewaterboat.com
SIC: 3732 1799 Boats, fiberglass: building & repairing; rigging & scaffolding

(G-10604)
WHOLE COFFEE COMPANY LLC
Also Called: TN Cruz
1130 Nw 159th Dr (33169-5808)
PHONE..................................786 364-4444
David Burke, *CEO*
Wilmar Guasti, *Opers Mgr*
Liza Norona, *VP Sales*
Tony Farias, *Accounts Mgr*
▲ **EMP:** 80 **EST:** 2007
SQ FT: 42,000
SALES (est): 27.9MM **Privately Held**
SIC: 2066 2095 Chocolate; roasted coffee

(G-10605)
WHYTE POWER INDUSTRIES CORP
Also Called: Animal Agrclture Advrsries Ame
22524 Sw 110th Ct (33170-3068)
PHONE..................................786 200-6033
Geovanny Calero, *Principal*
EMP: 5 **EST:** 2017
SALES (est): 365.9K **Privately Held**
SIC: 3999 Manufacturing industries

(G-10606)
WILCOX AND RAY MUSIC PUBG INC
1275 Nw 50th St (33142-4159)
PHONE..................................786 220-1362
Jimmie Wilcox, *Director*
EMP: 6 **EST:** 2018
SALES (est): 87.1K **Privately Held**
SIC: 2741 Miscellaneous publishing

(G-10607)
WILL & MIA CORP
1250 Ne 207th Ter (33179-2021)
PHONE..................................617 943-6914
Mia Zabala, *Principal*
EMP: 11 **EST:** 2016
SALES (est): 78.8K **Privately Held**
SIC: 2711 Newspapers, publishing & printing

(G-10608)
WILLIE D WOOD WORKS INC
14185 Sw 142nd St (33186-5574)
PHONE..................................305 969-6522
William Diaz, *Director*
EMP: 6 **EST:** 2005
SALES (est): 150K **Privately Held**
SIC: 2431 Millwork

(G-10609)
WINDSTAR EXPRESS INC
19499 Ne 10th Ave (33179-5732)
PHONE..................................786 252-1569
Yoandy Navarro, *Principal*
EMP: 6 **EST:** 2012
SALES (est): 101.2K **Privately Held**
SIC: 3537 Industrial trucks & tractors

(G-10610)
WINE WORLD INC
12650 Nw 25th St Ste 112 (33182-1512)
PHONE..................................786 348-8780
Modesto Gil, *President*
Aldo Neyra, *Vice Pres*
EMP: 9 **EST:** 2014
SALES (est): 141.7K **Privately Held**
SIC: 2084 Wines

(G-10611)
WINK STREAMING LLC
6703 Nw 7th St 87872 (33126-6070)
PHONE..................................312 281-5444
Michael McConnell, *Mng Member*
EMP: 7 **EST:** 2013
SALES (est): 78.8K **Privately Held**
WEB: www.winkstreaming.com
SIC: 3825 5072 Network analyzers; hardware

(G-10612)
WINSLOW MICROPLASTICS CORP
20257 Ne 15th Ct (33179-2710)
PHONE..................................305 493-3501
Adolfo Saul, *President*
Nora Saul, *President*
Jose Abadia, *Principal*
Gabriel E Saul, *Director*
Sebastian E Saul, *Director*
EMP: 6 **EST:** 1986
SALES (est): 551.3K **Privately Held**
SIC: 3089 Injection molding of plastics

(G-10613)
WINWOOD PRINT
591 Nw 29th St (33127-3917)
PHONE..................................786 615-3188
EMP: 6 **EST:** 2017
SALES (est): 163K **Privately Held**
WEB: www.wynwoodprint.com
SIC: 2752 Commercial printing, lithographic

(G-10614)
WIRELESS LATIN ENTRMT INC
Also Called: Wilaen
5301 Blue Lagoon Dr # 180 (33126-2093)
PHONE..................................305 858-7740
Gabriel Abaroa, *CEO*
Luis Samra, *COO*
Gustavo Falkenhagen, *Opers Staff*
Alberto Espana, *CFO*
Maria Gonzalez, *Sr Project Mgr*
EMP: 5 **EST:** 2002
SALES (est): 782.7K **Privately Held**
WEB: www.make-mo.com
SIC: 3357 Communication wire

(G-10615)
WONDER HOLDINGS ACQUISITION
1450 Brickell Ave # 3100 (33131-3444)
PHONE..................................305 379-2322
Anthony A Tamer, *CEO*
EMP: 11 **EST:** 2010
SALES (est): 159.8K **Privately Held**
SIC: 2834 Drugs acting on the respiratory system

(G-10616)
WOOD SPLINTER CORP
15451 Sw 60th St (33193-2811)
PHONE..................................305 721-7215
Armando Agustin, *Principal*
EMP: 6 **EST:** 2015
SALES (est): 45.6K **Privately Held**
SIC: 2499 Wood products

(G-10617)
WOOD ZONE INC
13751 Sw 147th Ave (33196-2884)
PHONE..................................305 971-5550
Francisco Ormaza, *Owner*
▲ **EMP:** 6 **EST:** 1987
SALES (est): 427.3K **Privately Held**
WEB: www.roswellsskateboards.com
SIC: 2434 Wood kitchen cabinets

(G-10618)
WOODIES INC
2041 Sw 82nd Pl (33155-1213)
PHONE..................................305 266-9209
Augusto G Perez, *President*
Sandra C Figuerola, *Vice Pres*
EMP: 7 **EST:** 1996
SALES (est): 464.9K **Privately Held**
SIC: 3429 Cabinet hardware

(G-10619)
WORLD EVENT PROMOTIONS LLC
Also Called: Wep Sourcing
4302 Sw 73rd Ave (33155-4550)
PHONE..................................800 214-3408
Patrick Lowenthal, *CEO*
EMP: 30 **EST:** 2015
SALES (est): 3.3MM **Privately Held**
WEB: www.wepsourcing.com
SIC: 2396 2759 7389 8742 Apparel & other linings, except millinery; promotional printing; advertising, promotional & trade show services; embroidering of advertising on shirts, etc.; marketing consulting services

(G-10620)
WORLD FROST INC
14853 Sw 152nd Ter (33187-5544)
PHONE..................................786 439-4445
◆ **EMP:** 8
SQ FT: 4,000
SALES: 3.3MM **Privately Held**
SIC: 2085 Mfg Distilled/Blended Liquor

(G-10621)
WORLDBOX CORPORATION
Also Called: Bolbox
8333 Nw 66th St (33166-2626)
PHONE..................................305 253-8800
Patricia A Ortiz, *Principal*
EMP: 7 **EST:** 2012
SALES (est): 201.3K **Privately Held**
WEB: www.worldbox.net
SIC: 2711 Newspapers

(G-10622)
WORLDWIDE BUILDING INTL INC
1840 Coral Way (33145-2748)
PHONE..................................786 744-7076
Kevin Goldstein, *CEO*
EMP: 248 **EST:** 2008
SALES (est): 500K **Privately Held**
WEB: www.worldbuildingprods.com
SIC: 3999 Manufacturing industries

(G-10623)
WPP GROUP USA INC
Also Called: Muv
601 Brickell Key Dr # 700 (33131-2649)
PHONE..................................305 341-8132
Spencer Aleman, *Accounts Mgr*
Taylor Devost, *Accounts Mgr*
Alexis Quintal, *Accounts Mgr*
Devin Zampaglione, *Accounts Mgr*
Sarah Bowyer, *Accounts Exec*
EMP: 6
SALES (corp-wide): 15.9B **Privately Held**
WEB: www.wpp.com
SIC: 3663 7311 Mobile communication equipment; advertising agencies
HQ: Wpp Group Usa, Inc.
3 World Trade Ctr Grnwich
New York NY 10007
212 632-2200

(G-10624)
YAM MACHINE SHOP AND IRON WORK
3710 Nw 50th St (33142-3936)
PHONE..................................786 246-4174
Barbaro Y Abreu, *Manager*
EMP: 6 **EST:** 2011
SALES (est): 240.7K **Privately Held**
WEB: www.iron-work-services.cmac.ws
SIC: 3599 Machine shop, jobbing & repair

(G-10625)
YATFL INC
19425 Sw 188th St (33187-1948)
PHONE..................................786 643-8660
Yuliet Martinez, *President*
Yosvany Acosta, *Vice Pres*
EMP: 5 **EST:** 2009
SALES (est): 974.4K **Privately Held**
SIC: 1389 8711 Construction, repair & dismantling services; consulting engineer

(G-10626)
YIPPY INC (PA)
999 Brickell Ave Ste 610 (33131-3043)
PHONE..................................877 947-7901
Richard Granville, *CEO*
John Macartney, *President*
John Routhier, *Exec VP*
Emily Parker, *Software Dev*
EMP: 8 **EST:** 2006 **Privately Held**
WEB: www.yippyinc.com
SIC: 7372 Business oriented computer software

(G-10627)
YOLY MUNOZ CORP
102 Se 1st St (33131-1402)
PHONE..................................305 860-3839
Yolanda Munoz, *President*
Carlos Munoz, *Treasurer*
EMP: 6 **EST:** 1978
SQ FT: 2,500
SALES (est): 194K **Privately Held**
WEB: www.yolymunozcouture.com
SIC: 2335 5621 Dresses, paper: cut & sewn; ready-to-wear apparel, women's

(G-10628)
YP GENERAL WORK & CABINETS
600 Nw 111th St (33168-3307)
PHONE..................................786 317-0973
Yusmar Pena, *Principal*
EMP: 6 **EST:** 2012
SALES (est): 146.8K **Privately Held**
SIC: 2434 Wood kitchen cabinets

(G-10629)
ZEN DISTRIBUTORS GROUP II LLC
Also Called: Tagua Gun Leather
2047 Nw 24th Ave (33142-7237)
PHONE..................................305 637-3014
Jose Kellemen,
EMP: 10 **EST:** 2008
SALES (est): 1.1MM **Privately Held**
SIC: 3199 Holsters, leather

(G-10630)
ZETA KITCHEN & BATH INC
6905 Nw 82nd Ave (33166-2766)
PHONE..................................786 552-2322
Jorge F Zamora, *President*
Malena Mercedes Zamora, *Vice Pres*

Marilin Fuentes, *Admin Sec*
EMP: 8 **EST:** 2013
SALES (est): 168.4K **Privately Held**
WEB: www.global.dopa.com
SIC: 2499 Kitchen, bathroom & household ware: wood

(G-10631)
ZHYNO INC
20815 Ne 16th Ave Ste B22 (33179-2136)
PHONE..................................844 313-1900
Liliana Ramirez, *President*
EMP: 7 **EST:** 2016
SALES (est): 695.5K **Privately Held**
SIC: 3578 Point-of-sale devices

(G-10632)
ZONDERVAN CORPORATION LLC
Vida Publishers
8333 Nw 53rd St Ste 450 (33166-4837)
PHONE..................................616 698-3437
David Alarcon, *Manager*
Michael Lautenbach, *Manager*
Helen Schmitt, *Director*
Matthew Saganski, *Senior Editor*
EMP: 7
SALES (corp-wide): 9.3B **Publicly Held**
WEB: www.zondervan.com
SIC: 2731 Books: publishing only
HQ: The Zondervan Corporation L L C
3900 Sparks Dr Se
Grand Rapids MI 49546
616 698-6900

(G-10633)
ZURIGO TRADING INC
5077 Nw 7th St Apt 1118 (33126-3465)
PHONE..................................305 244-4681
Alfredo Puglia, *President*
EMP: 7 **EST:** 2004
SALES (est): 89.1K **Privately Held**
SIC: 2851 Paints & allied products

Miami Beach
Miami-Dade County

(G-10634)
AAA CUSTOM POWDER COATING INC
2625 Collins Ave Apt 803 (33140-4749)
PHONE..................................305 531-5983
Jose A Benitez Jr, *President*
EMP: 6 **EST:** 2005
SALES (est): 227.3K **Privately Held**
WEB: www.westcoastpowdercoating.com
SIC: 3479 Coating of metals & formed products

(G-10635)
ACCUWARE INC
235 Lincoln Rd Ste 306 (33139-3157)
PHONE..................................305 894-6874
Cyril Houri, *Principal*
Gianni Giorgetti, *Research*
EMP: 8 **EST:** 2015
SALES (est): 139.5K **Privately Held**
WEB: www.accuware.com
SIC: 7372 Prepackaged software

(G-10636)
ADIR SCOOTERS INC
Also Called: VIP Scooter Rental
739 5th St (33139-6517)
PHONE..................................305 532-0019
Gitai Levi, *Principal*
EMP: 6 **EST:** 2005
SALES (est): 375.5K **Privately Held**
WEB: www.hotwheelsrentals.com
SIC: 3751 Motor scooters & parts

(G-10637)
AGUA VIVA LLC
1111 Lincoln Rd (33139-2452)
PHONE..................................954 802-3255
Fernando Olivera,
Rafaela Porcaro,
EMP: 6 **EST:** 2012
SALES (est): 137.8K **Privately Held**
SIC: 2369 Bathing suits & swimwear: girls', children's & infants'

(G-10638)
AICON YACHTS AMERICAS LLC
1801 West Ave (33139-1431)
PHONE..................................910 583-5299
Anton A Speciale, *President*
EMP: 7 **EST:** 2008
SALES (est): 141.2K **Privately Held**
WEB: www.aiconyachts.com
SIC: 3732 Boat building & repairing

(G-10639)
AMAMI UNITED FLAVOURS OF WORLD
224 Espanola Way (33139-4106)
PHONE..................................305 397-8577
Cataldo Dell Anno, *Principal*
EMP: 8 **EST:** 2011
SALES (est): 436.9K **Privately Held**
WEB: www.amamius.com
SIC: 3421 Table & food cutlery, including butchers'

(G-10640)
AMERICAN COMPUTER & TECH CORP
Also Called: Mac Directory
1775 Washington Ave 3f (33139-7538)
PHONE..................................786 738-3220
Markin Abras, *President*
EMP: 5 **EST:** 1993
SQ FT: 750
SALES (est): 418.2K **Privately Held**
SIC: 2741 Directories: publishing & printing

(G-10641)
AMERICAN SCIENCE AND TECH CORP
1330 West Ave Apt 3305 (33139-0913)
PHONE..................................312 898-3333
Mohammad A Manesh, *Principal*
EMP: 6 **EST:** 2016
SALES (est): 95.5K **Privately Held**
WEB: www.amsnt.com
SIC: 3728 Aircraft parts & equipment

(G-10642)
ANTI-GING ASTHTIC LSER CTR INC
4401 Collins Ave (33140-3227)
PHONE..................................786 539-4901
Oleg Rybak, *President*
Sergey Rybak, *Vice Pres*
EMP: 7 **EST:** 2007
SALES (est): 169.7K **Privately Held**
SIC: 3845 Laser systems & equipment, medical

(G-10643)
APPEL 26 CORP
4101 Pine Tree Dr Apt 111 (33140-3628)
PHONE..................................305 672-8645
Barry Appel, *President*
EMP: 6 **EST:** 2004
SALES (est): 165.8K **Privately Held**
SIC: 3571 Personal computers (microcomputers)

(G-10644)
ARKUP LLC
2100 Park Ave Apt 211s (33139-1757)
PHONE..................................786 448-8635
Nicolas Derouin,
Arnaud Luguet,
EMP: 5 **EST:** 2016
SALES (est): 399.9K **Privately Held**
WEB: www.arkup.com
SIC: 3732 7011 4499 Yachts, building & repairing; resort hotel; boathouses, commercial

(G-10645)
ASG CORP
5235 N Bay Rd (33140-2010)
PHONE..................................718 641-4500
EMP: 8 **EST:** 2018
SALES (est): 67K **Privately Held**
WEB: www.asg.com
SIC: 3999 Manufacturing industries

(G-10646)
AURUM ENTERPRISES LLC
5601 Collins Ave Apt 515 (33140-2407)
PHONE..................................561 921-5119
EMP: 8 **EST:** 2018
SALES (est): 110.1K **Privately Held**
WEB: www.volumecases.com
SIC: 3131 Footwear cut stock

(G-10647)
BIGHILL CORPORATION
Also Called: Mangiamo
1111 Lincoln Rd Fl 4 (33139-2439)
PHONE..................................786 497-1875
EMP: 3
SALES: 5MM **Privately Held**
SIC: 2086 Mfg And Export Of Soft Drinks And Fruit Juices

(G-10648)
BROOKLANDS NEW MEDIA LLC
1000 5th St Ste 200 (33139-6510)
PHONE..................................305 901-9674
Davanand Lall, *Managing Prtnr*
Vesta Lall, *Mng Member*
EMP: 5 **EST:** 2013
SALES (est): 589.6K **Privately Held**
WEB: www.brooklandsnewmedia.com
SIC: 2721 Magazines: publishing only, not printed on site

(G-10649)
BRUSH CASES LLC
Also Called: Custom Bag Designs
1007 Meridian Ave Apt 9 (33139-8319)
PHONE..................................305 340-7214
Anca Barbu, *Principal*
EMP: 6 **EST:** 2015
SALES (est): 244.1K **Privately Held**
WEB: www.brushcases.com
SIC: 3523 Farm machinery & equipment

(G-10650)
BUFALINDA USA LLC
2000 Bay Dr (33141-4554)
PHONE..................................305 979-9258
Alberto Enrique Duhau, *Manager*
EMP: 6 **EST:** 2017
SALES (est): 186.6K **Privately Held**
SIC: 2022 Natural cheese

(G-10651)
CANAM ELECTRIC
4835 Collins Ave (33140-2751)
PHONE..................................305 534-7903
EMP: 8 **EST:** 2007
SALES (est): 14.7K **Privately Held**
SIC: 3699 Electrical equipment & supplies

(G-10652)
CAXTON NEWSPAPERS INC
Also Called: Sunpost
1688 Meridian Ave Ste 404 (33139-2715)
P.O. Box 191870 (33119-1870)
PHONE..................................305 538-9700
Jeannette Stark, *President*
EMP: 38 **EST:** 1985
SALES (est): 800K **Privately Held**
WEB: www.miamisunpost.com
SIC: 2711 2791 2752 Newspapers: publishing only, not printed on site; typesetting; commercial printing, lithographic

(G-10653)
CDA VENTURES INC
Also Called: Cda Group
270 N Shore Dr (33141-2426)
P.O. Box 414002 (33141-0002)
PHONE..................................305 428-2857
Ivan Alvarez, *Principal*
EMP: 10 **EST:** 2006
SALES (est): 500K **Privately Held**
WEB: www.cdaventures.com
SIC: 2741 Miscellaneous publishing

(G-10654)
CEPODS LLC
1348 Washington Ave # 257 (33139-4212)
PHONE..................................786 520-1412
Timothy Dunlap,
EMP: 5 **EST:** 2011
SALES (est): 388.3K **Privately Held**
WEB: www.cepods.com
SIC: 3715 Demountable cargo containers

(G-10655)
CHROME AEROSPACE INC
345 85th St (33141-4865)
PHONE..................................305 506-8182
Nonato Arcila, *President*
EMP: 6 **EST:** 2001
SALES (est): 143.7K **Privately Held**
WEB: www.chromeaerospace.com
SIC: 3229 Pressed & blown glass

(G-10656)
CITY DEBATE PUBLISHING COMPANY
6538 Collins Ave (33141-4694)
PHONE..................................305 868-1161
J P Morgan, *Admin Sec*
EMP: 6 **EST:** 2001
SALES (est): 37.5K **Privately Held**
SIC: 2741 Miscellaneous publishing

(G-10657)
COLA CONSTRUCTION INC
1111 Lincoln Rd Ste 800 (33139-2451)
PHONE..................................305 218-3985
Alan Cote, *President*
◆ **EMP:** 7 **EST:** 2001
SALES (est): 121K **Privately Held**
SIC: 2086 Soft drinks: packaged in cans, bottles, etc.

(G-10658)
CORVATSCH CORP
Also Called: True Loaf
1894 Bay Rd (33139-1416)
PHONE..................................305 775-2831
Tomas Strulovic, *President*
EMP: 14 **EST:** 2009
SALES (est): 661.2K **Privately Held**
SIC: 2051 Bread, cake & related products

(G-10659)
COZY BAR
500 S Pointe Dr (33139-7302)
PHONE..................................305 532-2699
Jean-Alexandre Maufroy, *Principal*
EMP: 10
SALES (est): 270K **Privately Held**
WEB: www.thecozybar.com
SIC: 2064 Candy bars, including chocolate covered bars

(G-10660)
CRAIG ARMSTRONG
Also Called: Glu
1770 Normandy Dr Apt 2 (33141-4749)
PHONE..................................786 319-6514
Craig Armstrong, *Principal*
EMP: 10 **EST:** 2006
SALES (est): 484.8K **Privately Held**
SIC: 2891 Glue

(G-10661)
DEL MAR HOLLYWOOD LLC
1680 Michigan Ave Ste 910 (33139-2550)
PHONE..................................786 325-8335
Cinzia Zanella, *Principal*
EMP: 6 **EST:** 2017
SALES (est): 169.5K **Privately Held**
SIC: 2499 Wood products

(G-10662)
DELICIO BAKING COMPANY INC
300 71st St Ste 450 (33141-3088)
PHONE..................................305 865-5664
Ana Maria H De Alba, *Principal*
Celeste De Armas, *Manager*
Cody Smith, *Director*
EMP: 7 **EST:** 2013
SALES (est): 92.1K **Privately Held**
SIC: 2051 Bread, cake & related products

(G-10663)
DO YOU REMEMBER INC
36 Island Ave Apt 45 (33139-1312)
PHONE..................................305 987-9111
Michael Gitter, *Principal*
EMP: 6 **EST:** 2018
SALES (est): 116.1K **Privately Held**
WEB: www.doyouremember.com
SIC: 2741

(G-10664)
ELITE FITFOREVER LLC
4302 Alton Rd Ste 300 (33140-2818)
PHONE..................................305 902-2358
EMP: 7 **EST:** 2019
SALES (est): 572K **Privately Held**
WEB: www.elitefitforever.com
SIC: 2834 Pharmaceutical preparations

(G-10665)
EXTRALINK CORPORATION
6538 Collins Ave (33141-4694)
PHONE..................................305 804-1100
Daniel Estrada, *Principal*
EMP: 7 **EST:** 2008
SALES (est): 121K **Privately Held**
WEB: www.danestra.com
SIC: 7372 Prepackaged software

(G-10666)
F&J USA LLC
Also Called: Dr. Botanicals
1111 Lincoln Rd Ste 500 (33139-2439)
PHONE..................................800 406-6190
Richard Walker, *President*
David Ledezma, *Vice Pres*
EMP: 40 **EST:** 2017
SALES (est): 7MM **Privately Held**
SIC: 2844 Cosmetic preparations

(G-10667)
FILORGA AMERICAS INC
429 Lenox Ave (33139-6532)
PHONE..................................786 266-7429
Didier Tabary, *President*
Emmanuel Calvo, *Vice Pres*
EMP: 17 **EST:** 1999
SALES (est): 737.8K
SALES (corp-wide): 3.3MM **Privately Held**
SIC: 2844 Toilet preparations
PA: Laboratoires Fill-Med
2 4
Paris 75008
142 939-400

(G-10668)
FLUENZ INC
1000 5th St Ste 200 (33139-6510)
PHONE..................................305 209-1695
Carlos Lizarralde, *Chairman*
Sonia Gil,
EMP: 7
SQ FT: 1,100
SALES (est): 751.1K **Privately Held**
WEB: www.fluenz.com
SIC: 7372 Educational computer software

(G-10669)
FRESH ON FIFTH
Also Called: Jafar On Fifth
448 Ocean Dr Ste 2 (33139-6614)
PHONE..................................305 234-5678
Safaaldin A Majeed, *Principal*
EMP: 8 **EST:** 2007
SALES (est): 326.2K **Privately Held**
WEB: www.freshonfifth.com
SIC: 2051 Bread, cake & related products

(G-10670)
GAND INC
119 Wshington Ave Ste 618 (33139)
PHONE..................................240 575-0622
George Sing, *CEO*
David Steed, *Vice Pres*
Douglas Tadaki, *Admin Sec*
EMP: 5 **EST:** 2017
SALES (est): 521K **Privately Held**
SIC: 2834 Solutions, pharmaceutical

(G-10671)
GDE LLC
430 W 37th St (33140-3912)
PHONE..................................305 458-3025
Eugene F Gant, *Principal*
EMP: 8 **EST:** 2016
SALES (est): 98.3K **Privately Held**
SIC: 3731 Shipbuilding & repairing

(G-10672)
GELATERIA MILANI LLC
436 Espanola Way (33139-8123)
PHONE..................................305 532-8562
EMP: 10
SALES (est): 775.6K **Privately Held**
SIC: 2024 Mfg Ice Cream/Frozen Desert

(G-10673)
GOCASE LLC
125 Jefferson Ave Apt 121 (33139-7032)
PHONE..................................415 341-6248
Eli M Blatt, *Mng Member*
EMP: 6 **EST:** 2013
SALES (est): 169.8K **Privately Held**
WEB: www.gocase.com
SIC: 3651 Household audio & video equipment

(G-10674)
GRAND HAVANA INC
407 Lincoln Rd Ste 2a (33139-3018)
PHONE..................................305 297-2207
Robert Rico, *CEO*
Tanya Bredemeier, *Ch of Bd*
Louis Bustello, *COO*
Jorge Moreno, *Chief Mktg Ofcr*
EMP: 7 **EST:** 2009
SALES: 169.9K **Privately Held**
WEB: www.grandhavanacoffee.com
SIC: 2095 2099 5149 Roasted coffee; tea blending; coffee & tea

(G-10675)
GULFSTREAM MSES INVSTMNTS GROU
1535 Biarritz Dr (33141-4721)
PHONE..................................305 975-6186
Jorge M Lopez, *Principal*
Ada O Lopez, *Principal*
EMP: 5 **EST:** 2001
SALES (est): 580.1K **Privately Held**
SIC: 3721 Aircraft

(G-10676)
GYROTONIC MFG INC
1370 Washington Ave # 307 (33139-4261)
PHONE..................................305 397-8070
EMP: 6 **EST:** 2004
SALES (est): 141.3K **Privately Held**
WEB: www.marikasich.com
SIC: 3999 Manufacturing industries

(G-10677)
HEY DAY
1825 West Ave (33139-1441)
PHONE..................................305 763-8660
Peter Hey, *Principal*
EMP: 7 **EST:** 2012
SALES (est): 195.4K **Privately Held**
SIC: 2759 Invitation & stationery printing & engraving

(G-10678)
HILLIARD BRUCE VINEYARDS LLC
1521 Alton Rd Ste 842 (33139-3301)
PHONE..................................305 979-2601
John C Hilliard, *Principal*
EMP: 7 **EST:** 2015
SALES (est): 338.3K **Privately Held**
SIC: 2084 Wines, brandy & brandy spirits

(G-10679)
HOME BISTRO INC (PA)
4014 Chase Ave Ste 212 (33140-3446)
PHONE..................................561 227-2727
Roy G Warren, *Ch of Bd*
Andy Schamisso, *President*
EMP: 9 **EST:** 2006
SALES: 1.3MM **Publicly Held**
SIC: 2086 Iced tea & fruit drinks, bottled & canned

(G-10680)
HUMMINGBIRDS AI INC ✪
8140 Hawthorne Ave (33141-1009)
PHONE..................................305 432-2787
Nima Schei, *CEO*
EMP: 15 **EST:** 2020
SALES (est): 800K **Privately Held**
WEB: www.hummingbirds.ai
SIC: 3699 7371 Security devices; software programming applications

(G-10681)
HYDROGEN TECHNOLOGY CORP
900 West Ave Apt 501 (33139-5210)
PHONE..................................800 315-9554
Matthew Kane, *Vice Pres*
EMP: 27 **EST:** 2017
SALES (est): 3MM **Privately Held**
WEB: www.hydrogenplatform.com
SIC: 7372 Application computer software

(G-10682)
INDUSTRIAL OVIEDO LLC
7601 E Trsore Dr Unit 121 (33141)
PHONE..................................786 350-8153
Alam Oviedo, *Manager*
EMP: 7 **EST:** 2015
SALES (est): 348.1K **Privately Held**
SIC: 3599 Machine shop, jobbing & repair

(G-10683)
INPERIUM CORP
1111 Lincoln Rd Ste 760 (33139-2402)
PHONE..................................305 901-5650
Christian Ehrenthal, *CEO*
EMP: 37 **EST:** 2018
SALES (est): 1MM **Privately Held**
SIC: 7372 Business oriented computer software

(G-10684)
JAZANIQUE WICKSON
Also Called: Sheeituuuu
8135 Crespi Blvd Apt 4 (33141-1544)
PHONE..................................815 221-7155
Jazanique Wickson, *Owner*
EMP: 6 **EST:** 2019
SALES (est): 216.7K **Privately Held**
SIC: 2339 Women's & misses' accessories

(G-10685)
JEAN LA FRITE
1520 Washington Ave (33139-7801)
PHONE..................................305 397-8747
Jean La Frite, *Principal*
EMP: 8 **EST:** 2010
SALES (est): 59.3K **Privately Held**
SIC: 3421 Table & food cutlery, including butchers'

(G-10686)
JMG STRATEGIES LLC
300 S Pointe Dr Apt 907 (33139-7353)
PHONE..................................305 606-2117
J Mark Goode, *Manager*
EMP: 6 **EST:** 2018
SALES (est): 393.7K **Privately Held**
SIC: 3462 Horseshoes

(G-10687)
LENNOX MIAMI CORP
1900 Collins Ave (33139-1912)
PHONE..................................305 763-8655
Diego Agnelli, *Principal*
Eddie Rivera, *Chief Engr*
Jack Jernstrom, *Sales Mgr*
EMP: 21 **EST:** 2010
SALES (est): 2.6MM **Privately Held**
WEB: www.lennoxmiamibeach.com
SIC: 3585 Refrigeration & heating equipment

(G-10688)
LIVE ULTIMATE INC
1691 Michigan Ave (33139-2520)
PHONE..................................305 532-6882
Marc S Wachter, *CEO*
EMP: 6 **EST:** 2011
SALES (est): 811.7K **Privately Held**
WEB: www.liveultimate.com
SIC: 2741 Miscellaneous publishing

(G-10689)
LOUIS DI RMNDO WRLDWIDE INVSTM
Also Called: All Amercian Hot Dog Cart Co
2410 N Shore Ter (33141-2448)
PHONE..................................786 536-7578
Louis D Raimondo, *President*
Louis Di Raimondo, *President*
▼ **EMP:** 10 **EST:** 1972
SQ FT: 5,500
SALES (est): 1MM **Privately Held**
SIC: 3589 Commercial cooking & foodwarming equipment

(G-10690)
MASKCO TECHNOLOGIES INC ✪
1348 Washington Ave (33139-4212)
PHONE..................................877 261-6405
Scott Weissman, *CEO*
EMP: 10 **EST:** 2020
SALES (est): 283.1K **Privately Held**
WEB: www.maskcotech.com
SIC: 3999 Manufacturing industries

(G-10691)
MAU MAU CORPORATION
555 Jefferson Ave (33139-6302)
PHONE..................................305 440-5203
Frank Amadeo, *President*
EMP: 26 **EST:** 2001
SALES (est): 518.5K **Privately Held**
WEB: www.mau.com
SIC: 7372 Prepackaged software

(G-10692)
MEGACOLOR PRINT LLC
221 Meridian Ave Apt 413 (33139-7071)
PHONE..................................305 499-9395
Marcello Cabrier,
EMP: 10 **EST:** 2002
SALES (est): 740.5K **Privately Held**
WEB: www.megacolorprint.com
SIC: 2752 Commercial printing, offset

(G-10693)
MILLIONAIRE PUBLISHING LLC
110 Wshngton Ave Apt 1524 (33139)
PHONE..................................305 763-8184
EMP: 9 **EST:** 2018
SALES (est): 282.9K **Privately Held**
SIC: 2741 Miscellaneous publishing

(G-10694)
MIRAMAR PUBLISHING INC
1030 14th St (33139-3816)
PHONE..................................305 695-0639
Carolina G Hamshaw, *Principal*
EMP: 8 **EST:** 2010
SALES (est): 108.6K **Privately Held**
SIC: 2741 Miscellaneous publishing

(G-10695)
MOHAMED LAMRANA JALLOH
Also Called: Palama
811 Jefferson Ave Apt 205 (33139-5634)
PHONE..................................347 305-5556
Mohamed Jalloh, *Owner*
EMP: 6
SALES (est): 170.2K **Privately Held**
SIC: 2431 Entertainers; millwork; artist

(G-10696)
NATIONAL BIDET CORP
7150 Indian Creek Dr # 404 (33141-3083)
PHONE..................................786 325-6593
Karel Giron-Milan, *Principal*
EMP: 6 **EST:** 2007
SALES (est): 146.2K **Privately Held**
SIC: 3261 Bathroom accessories/fittings, vitreous china or earthenware

(G-10697)
NAVIZON INC
235 Lincoln Rd Ste 306 (33139-3157)
PHONE..................................305 501-2409
Thomas Kramer, *President*
Gianni Giorgetti, *Research*
EMP: 6 **EST:** 2010
SALES (est): 158.5K **Privately Held**
WEB: www.navizon.com
SIC: 7372 Prepackaged software

(G-10698)
NEWS FEATURES USA INC
6301 Collins Ave (33141-4627)
PHONE..................................305 298-5313
Christopher M Bott, *Director*
EMP: 7 **EST:** 2005
SALES (est): 143.2K **Privately Held**
SIC: 2711 Newspapers, publishing & printing

(G-10699)
OCEANSTYLE LLC
Also Called: Oceanstyle By Burgess
390 Alton Rd Ste 2 (33139-8902)
PHONE..................................305 672-9400
Alexander G Wheatley, *Mng Member*
EMP: 8 **EST:** 2005
SALES (est): 608.7K **Privately Held**
SIC: 2386 Garments, leather

(G-10700)
ONE GROUP
2311 Collins Ave (33139-1608)
PHONE..................................305 604-6999
Harley Demeiers, *General Mgr*
Caroline Mahony, *General Mgr*
Jay Law, *Principal*

Frederick Contini, *Vice Pres*
Fred Contini, *Project Mgr*
EMP: 93 **EST:** 2009
SQ FT: 10,000
SALES (est): 832.2K **Publicly Held**
WEB: www.togrp.com
SIC: 2599 Bar, restaurant & cafeteria furniture
PA: The One Group Hospitality Inc
411 W 14th St Fl 2
New York NY 10014

(G-10701)
PLAN AUTOMATION LLC
350 Lincoln Rd (33139-3154)
PHONE..................................786 502-1812
Brendan Clery, *Mng Member*
EMP: 1 **EST:** 2019
SALES (est): 5MM **Privately Held**
SIC: 3565 Packaging machinery

(G-10702)
PLANT THEORY LLC
Also Called: Plant Theory Botanical CAF
1525 Meridian Ave Apt 210 (33139-3471)
PHONE..................................305 672-5785
Sheryn Abalos,
EMP: 7 **EST:** 2014
SALES (est): 358.5K **Privately Held**
WEB: www.plant-theory.com
SIC: 2046 5499 Wheat gluten; gourmet food stores

(G-10703)
PLATINIUM ROSIS INC
1602 Alton Rd 602 (33139-2421)
PHONE..................................786 617-9973
David Gardoqui, *President*
Romano Silvia, *Principal*
Greg Davis, *Principal*
Clara Romano De Feo, *Principal*
Silvia Romano, *Principal*
EMP: 6 **EST:** 2013
SALES (est): 83.9K **Privately Held**
SIC: 3443 2611 9511 1795 Dumpsters, garbage; pulp mills, mechanical & recycling processing; air, water & solid waste management; wrecking & demolition work; parking lot construction

(G-10704)
PREKCOM LLC
429 Lenox Ave (33139-6532)
PHONE..................................877 773-5669
Ben Mayer, *Mng Member*
EMP: 9 **EST:** 2019
SALES (est): 465.3K **Privately Held**
WEB: www.prek.com
SIC: 7372 Educational computer software

(G-10705)
PRESTIGE PUBLICATION GROUP
Also Called: Sunpost Newspaper Group
1688 Meridian Ave Ste 404 (33139-2715)
P.O. Box 191870 (33119-1870)
PHONE..................................305 538-9700
Janet Stark, *President*
EMP: 25 **EST:** 1985
SALES (est): 1.2MM **Privately Held**
SIC: 2711 Newspapers, publishing & printing

(G-10706)
ROYALTY ENTERPRISES LLC
221 Meridian Ave Apt 508 (33139-7087)
Rural Route 221 Meridian Ave (33139)
PHONE..................................786 380-7774
Oscar Pyzyk, *Branch Mgr*
EMP: 9
SALES (corp-wide): 94.4K **Privately Held**
SIC: 2252 Socks
PA: Royalty Enterprises Llc
2565 Nw 49th Ave Apt 108
Lauderdale Lakes FL

(G-10707)
RUBBER B LLC
605 Lincoln Rd Ste 210 (33139-2934)
PHONE..................................305 771-2369
Arnaud B Tibi, *Mng Member*
Jean-Jacques G Sarkissian,
EMP: 5 **EST:** 2010
SALES (est): 443K **Privately Held**
WEB: www.rubberb.com
SIC: 3172 Watch straps, except metal

(G-10708)
SCRIPT CENTRAL LLC
1680 Michigan Ave Ste 800 (33139-2519)
PHONE..................................954 805-8581
EMP: 12 **EST:** 2015
SALES (est): 151.5K **Privately Held**
WEB: www.scriptcentral.com
SIC: 2834 Pharmaceutical preparations

(G-10709)
SHANGRI-LA ENTERPRISES
4101 Pine Tree Dr # 1704 (33140-3628)
PHONE..................................305 672-6683
Scott Shane, *President*
EMP: 6 **EST:** 1999
SALES (est): 241.2K **Privately Held**
SIC: 2339 Scarves, hoods, headbands, etc.: women's

(G-10710)
SIMPLIFIED SYSTEMS INC
4014 Chase Ave Ph (33140-3490)
PHONE..................................305 672-7676
Paula Turk, *President*
Bernardo Cano, *President*
EMP: 10 **EST:** 1971
SQ FT: 3,000
SALES (est): 625.9K **Privately Held**
WEB: www.thecommunicatorfl.com
SIC: 3843 3841 Ultrasonic dental equipment; surgical & medical instruments

(G-10711)
SKY PHONE LLC (PA)
Also Called: Sky Device
1348 Washington Ave # 350 (33139-4212)
PHONE..................................305 531-5218
Enrique Quimper, *Mng Member*
Raffael Attar,
▲ **EMP:** 18 **EST:** 2013
SQ FT: 4,000
SALES (est): 42MM **Privately Held**
SIC: 3663 5065 5999 Cellular radio telephone; mobile telephone equipment; mobile telephones & equipment

(G-10712)
SOBE EXPRESS
1205 Lincoln Rd Ste 209 (33139-2365)
PHONE..................................305 674-4454
Wilfredo Lugo, *President*
EMP: 5 **EST:** 2016
SALES (est): 335.3K **Privately Held**
WEB: www.sobeexpress.com
SIC: 2752 Commercial printing, offset

(G-10713)
SONY/ATV MUSIC PUBLISHING LLC
1111 Lincoln Rd Ste 803 (33139-2451)
PHONE..................................305 532-9064
EMP: 7 **Privately Held**
WEB: www.sonymusic.com
SIC: 2741 Catalogs: publishing & printing
HQ: Sony/Atv Music Publishing Llc
25 Madison Ave Fl 24
New York NY 10010
212 833-7730

(G-10714)
SOUTH BEACH CIGAR FACTORY LLC
1059 Collins Ave Ste 108 (33139-5036)
PHONE..................................786 216-7475
Mireya Mayor, *Principal*
EMP: 7 **EST:** 2012
SALES (est): 191K **Privately Held**
SIC: 2121 Cigars

(G-10715)
SPORTS STRUCTURE INTL LLC
Also Called: Kiddidoo USA
1680 Michigan Ave Ste 700 (33139-2551)
PHONE..................................305 777-2225
Johan Bos, *Managing Dir*
EMP: 5
SQ FT: 1,000
SALES (est): 1MM **Privately Held**
SIC: 2329 Men's & boys' sportswear & athletic clothing

(G-10716)
STADIUM 1 SOFTWARE LLC
7115 Rue Notre Dame (33141-3618)
PHONE..................................561 498-8356
Tim McDulin, *Exec VP*
Kathy Shea, *Sales Staff*
Alan Cables, *Technology*
Lewis Gordon,
EMP: 23 **EST:** 2011
SALES (est): 1.7MM **Privately Held**
WEB: www.stadium1.com
SIC: 7372 Prepackaged software

(G-10717)
STRIPPING ALPACA LLC
900 West Ave Apt 713 (33139-5212)
PHONE..................................207 208-9687
Corvalan Bruno,
EMP: 15 **EST:** 2019
SALES (est): 553.3K **Privately Held**
SIC: 2099 Vegetables, peeled for the trade

(G-10718)
STUNTWEAR LLC
Also Called: Cold Fire Direct
6538 Collins Ave Unit 414 (33141-4694)
PHONE..................................305 842-2115
Lars Mohlin, *Owner*
EMP: 8 **EST:** 2010
SQ FT: 2,000
SALES (est): 250K **Privately Held**
SIC: 2389 Apparel for handicapped

(G-10719)
TESLA INC
513 Lincoln Rd (33139-2913)
PHONE..................................305 535-7596
EMP: 7
SALES (corp-wide): 31.5B **Publicly Held**
WEB: www.tesla.com
SIC: 3711 Motor vehicles & car bodies
PA: Tesla, Inc.
3500 Deer Creek Rd
Palo Alto CA 94304
650 681-5000

(G-10720)
TITANIUM 22 PRODUCTIONS
800 W 42nd St Apt 1b (33140-2873)
PHONE..................................310 962-0937
Graciella Creazzo, *President*
EMP: 7 **EST:** 2012
SALES (est): 241.9K **Privately Held**
SIC: 3356 Titanium

(G-10721)
TROPICOLOR PHOTO SERVICE INC
Also Called: Tropicolor Display Graphics
1442 Alton Rd (33139-3828)
PHONE..................................305 672-3720
Tom Chien, *President*
John Chien, *Vice Pres*
TSE-Dao Chien, *Vice Pres*
EMP: 8 **EST:** 1986
SQ FT: 4,000
SALES (est): 1.3MM **Privately Held**
WEB: www.tropicolor.com
SIC: 2759 Posters, including billboards: printing; security certificates: engraved

(G-10722)
UMG RECORDINGS INC
Also Called: Universal Recording
404 Wshington Ave Ste 800 (33139)
PHONE..................................305 532-4754
Jesus Lopez, *Chairman*
EMP: 224
SALES (corp-wide): 108MM **Privately Held**
SIC: 2782 Record albums
HQ: Umg Recordings, Inc.
5822 Haverford Ave
Philadelphia PA 19131
310 865-0000

(G-10723)
UPROXX MEDIA INC
1602 Alton Rd Ste 447 (33139-2421)
PHONE..................................917 603-2374
Jarret Myer, *CEO*
Brian Brater, *President*
EMP: 10 **EST:** 2008
SALES (est): 1.3MM **Publicly Held**
WEB: www.uproxx.com
SIC: 2721 Trade journals: publishing only, not printed on site
HQ: Wovexx Holdings, Inc.
10381 Jefferson Blvd
Culver City CA 90232

(G-10724)
URBAN CHARGE LLC
1330 West Ave Apt 1411 (33139-0906)
PHONE..................................305 809-6625
EMP: 5
SALES: 1,000K **Privately Held**
SIC: 3714 Mfg Motor Vehicle Parts/Accessories

(G-10725)
V2 CIGS (PA)
1521 Alton Rd Ste 275 (33139-3301)
PHONE..................................305 517-1149
David Turner, *Manager*
EMP: 16 **EST:** 2011
SALES (est): 569K **Privately Held**
WEB: www.v2.com
SIC: 2111 Cigarettes

(G-10726)
VENTI GROUP LLC
1521 Alton Rd Ste 697 (33139-3301)
PHONE..................................949 264-3185
Henry Adamany, *Managing Dir*
Dow A Eichenlaub, *Managing Dir*
Ludovic Bainvel, *Principal*
Robert Mark, *Vice Pres*
Tony Eichenlaub, *Engineer*
EMP: 7 **EST:** 2009
SALES (est): 121.6K **Privately Held**
WEB: www.ventigroup.com
SIC: 3663 Antennas, transmitting & communications

(G-10727)
VENTUM LLC
1100 14th St (33139-3818)
P.O. Box 460, Heber City UT (84032-0460)
PHONE..................................786 838-1113
Diaa Nour, *Mng Member*
Justin Diamond, *Director*
EMP: 8 **EST:** 2015
SALES (est): 466.4K **Privately Held**
WEB: www.ventumracing.com
SIC: 3751 5961 Bicycles & related parts; fitness & sporting goods, mail order

(G-10728)
VISTA PUBLISHING CORPORATION
Also Called: Vista Magazine
6538 Collins Ave (33141-4694)
PHONE..................................305 416-4644
EMP: 10
SQ FT: 2,850
SALES (est): 710K **Privately Held**
SIC: 2721 Periodicals-Publishing/Printing

(G-10729)
WESTON MAGAZINE INC
6103 Aqua Ave Ph 2 (33141-5878)
P.O. Box 1006, Weston CT (06883-0006)
PHONE..................................203 451-1967
Eric S Meadow, *President*
Eric Meadow, *Publisher*
Susan Engel, *Editor*
Mark Goldenberg, *Editor*
Celia R Meadow, *Admin Sec*
EMP: 6 **EST:** 2003
SALES (est): 173.7K **Privately Held**
WEB: www.wellesleywestonmagazine.com
SIC: 2721 Periodicals

(G-10730)
WORLDS GREATEST ICE CREAM INC
Also Called: Frieze, The
1626 Michigan Ave (33139-2504)
P.O. Box 190646, Miami (33119-0646)
PHONE..................................305 538-0207
Lisa Warren, *President*
Robert Warren, *Vice Pres*
EMP: 10 **EST:** 1987
SQ FT: 1,200
SALES (est): 949.1K **Privately Held**
WEB: www.thefrieze.com
SIC: 2024 5451 Ice cream, bulk; ice cream (packaged)

Miami Gardens
Miami-Dade County

(G-10731)
ADNAN ENTERPRISES
4699 Nw 183rd St (33055-3051)
PHONE..................................305 430-9752
Kishwar Khan, *Principal*
EMP: 5 **EST:** 2008
SALES (est): 353.2K **Privately Held**
SIC: 3578 Automatic teller machines (ATM)

(G-10732)
AHUS INC
Also Called: Adriana Hoyos
3371 Nw 168th St (33056-4229)
PHONE..................................305 572-9052
Eduardo Perez, *President*
Diana Mejia, *Chairman*
Eduardo Perez Darquea, *Vice Pres*
Adriana Hoyos, *Vice Pres*
Angela Hoyos, *Vice Pres*
▲ **EMP:** 25 **EST:** 2001
SALES (est): 4MM **Privately Held**
SIC: 2511 Wood household furniture

(G-10733)
ALFA MANUFACTURING GROUP LLC ✪
17401 Nw 2nd Ave Ste 7 (33169-5039)
PHONE..................................305 979-7344
Alexandros Kyritsis,
EMP: 6 **EST:** 2020
SALES (est): 454.7K **Privately Held**
SIC: 2844 Cosmetic preparations

(G-10734)
ALSE INDUSTRIES LLC ✪
Also Called: American Architectural Mtls GL
16201 Nw 49th Ave (33014-6314)
PHONE..................................305 688-8778
Francisco A Serrano, *Mng Member*
EMP: 19 **EST:** 2020
SALES (est): 1.1MM **Privately Held**
WEB: www.aamg.us
SIC: 3441 3446 Fabricated structural metal; architectural metalwork

(G-10735)
BLINDS BY RANDY LLC
3274 Nw 181st St (33056-3432)
PHONE..................................305 300-1147
Randolph White, *Principal*
EMP: 7 **EST:** 2013
SALES (est): 158.1K **Privately Held**
SIC: 2591 7389 Window blinds;

(G-10736)
BLUEGATE INC
16409 Nw 8th Ave (33169-5812)
PHONE..................................305 628-8391
Alizera Haghayegh, *President*
▲ **EMP:** 12 **EST:** 1998
SQ FT: 75,000
SALES (est): 600K **Privately Held**
WEB: www.glowbackledstore.com
SIC: 3648 Decorative area lighting fixtures

(G-10737)
DOUGLAS FUEL II INC
3701 Nw 167th St (33055-4510)
PHONE..................................305 620-0707
Eden Herrera, *Principal*
EMP: 9 **EST:** 2013
SALES (est): 395.1K **Privately Held**
SIC: 2869 Fuels

(G-10738)
DUNCAN AND SONS CNSTR EQP INC ✪
2750 Nw 209th Ter (33056-1443)
PHONE..................................305 216-3115
Adrian M Duncan, *President*
EMP: 10 **EST:** 2020
SALES (est): 528.5K **Privately Held**
SIC: 3531 Graders, road (construction machinery)

(G-10739)
EXPRESS REMOVAL SERVICE LLC
15950 Bunche Park Schl Dr (33054-6962)
PHONE..................................305 303-8249
Todd Hodge,
EMP: 6
SALES (est): 152.7K **Privately Held**
SIC: 1481 Overburden removal, nonmetallic minerals

(G-10740)
FLASH PRINTS LLC
19401 Nw 23rd Ave (33056-2638)
PHONE..................................786 422-3195
Antoinette Payne,
Lamott Croom,
EMP: 5 **EST:** 2019
SALES (est): 308.8K **Privately Held**
SIC: 2752 Commercial printing, lithographic

(G-10741)
FLASH SALES INC
4401 Nw 167th St (33055-4311)
PHONE..................................954 914-2689
Jacob Levy, *President*
Barry Rub, *Vice Pres*
◆ **EMP:** 5 **EST:** 2003
SQ FT: 10,000
SALES (est): 759.7K **Privately Held**
WEB: www.flashsales.com
SIC: 3634 5064 Electric housewares & fans; electrical appliances, television & radio

(G-10742)
GLOVAL DISPLAYS INC
1100 Nw 159th Dr (33169-5808)
PHONE..................................800 972-0353
Joan Barrientos, *President*
Bernardo Botero, *Engineer*
EMP: 20 **EST:** 2008
SALES (est): 2.3MM **Privately Held**
WEB: www.glovaldisplays.com
SIC: 2431 2541 2789 3999 Millwork; store & office display cases & fixtures; display fixtures, wood; counters or counter display cases, wood; display mounting; preparation of slides & exhibits

(G-10743)
GOLDEN GLADES RACEWAY LLC
17021 Nw 27th Ave (33056-4407)
P.O. Box 560962, Miami (33256-0962)
PHONE..................................305 321-9627
Jorge Almirall, *Principal*
EMP: 6 **EST:** 2015
SALES (est): 117.6K **Privately Held**
SIC: 3644 Raceways

(G-10744)
GOODRICH CORPORATION
Also Called: UTC Aerospace Systems
3201 Nw 167th St (33056-4253)
PHONE..................................305 622-4500
Greg Watson, *President*
Donald Dass, *Materials Mgr*
EMP: 6
SALES (corp-wide): 56.5B **Publicly Held**
WEB: www.collinsaerospace.com
SIC: 3724 3728 7372 Aircraft engines & engine parts; aircraft parts & equipment; prepackaged software
HQ: Goodrich Corporation
2730 W Tyvola Rd
Charlotte NC 28217
704 423-7000

(G-10745)
GOODRICH CORPORATION
Also Called: Collins Aerospace
3201 Nw 167th St (33056-4253)
PHONE..................................305 622-4565
EMP: 6
SALES (corp-wide): 56.5B **Publicly Held**
WEB: www.collinsaerospace.com
SIC: 3728 Aircraft parts & equipment
HQ: Goodrich Corporation
2730 W Tyvola Rd
Charlotte NC 28217
704 423-7000

(G-10746)
HURRICANE GRAPHICS INC
Also Called: Printing Sensations
3331 Nw 168th St (33056-4229)
PHONE..................................305 760-9154
Michael Gherman, *President*
Jeff Shapiro, *Production*
EMP: 20 **EST:** 1989
SQ FT: 7,500
SALES (est): 3.9MM **Privately Held**
WEB: www.printingsensations.com
SIC: 2752 Commercial printing, offset

(G-10747)
IN GEAR FASHIONS INC (PA)
Also Called: Ingear
4401 Nw 167th St (33055-4311)
PHONE..................................305 830-2900
Kevin N Frija, *President*
Jacob D Levy, *Vice Pres*
Jacob Levy, *Vice Pres*
Alyx Fisten, *Sales Staff*
Christine Vitale, *Sales Executive*
◆ **EMP:** 75 **EST:** 1990
SQ FT: 30,000
SALES (est): 20.4MM **Privately Held**
WEB: www.ingear.com
SIC: 2339 2329 Sportswear, women's; beachwear: women's, misses' & juniors'; men's & boys' sportswear & athletic clothing

(G-10748)
ISCAR GSE CORP
1182 Nw 159th Dr (33169-5808)
PHONE..................................305 364-8886
EMP: 30
SALES (est): 1.7MM **Privately Held**
SIC: 3537 Mfg Industrial Trucks/Tractors

(G-10749)
ISCAR GSE CORP
Also Called: Iscar Ground Services Eqp
1180 Nw 159th Dr (33169-5808)
PHONE..................................305 364-8886
Israel S Carruyo, *President*
Victor M Carruyo, *Vice Pres*
Victor Carruyo, *Mng Member*
Israel J Carruyo, *Admin Sec*
EMP: 30 **EST:** 2010
SQ FT: 70,000
SALES (est): 2.7MM **Privately Held**
WEB: www.iscar-gse.com
SIC: 3537 Trucks: freight, baggage, etc.: industrial, except mining

(G-10750)
LEADING EDGE AEROSPACE LLC
16115 Nw 52nd Ave (33014-6205)
PHONE..................................305 608-6826
Mark Schenck, *Director*
Steven A Server,
Marbel Izquierdo,
EMP: 7 **EST:** 2014
SALES (est): 737.7K **Privately Held**
WEB: www.leadingedgeaero.com
SIC: 3594 Pumps, hydraulic, aircraft

(G-10751)
NEW GENERATION PACKAGING LLC
16542 Nw 54th Ave (33014-6113)
P.O. Box 5705, Hialeah (33014-1705)
PHONE..................................786 259-6670
Tam Muk Chan,
Sze Y Chan,
Szeon Chan,
EMP: 7 **EST:** 2016
SALES (est): 465.6K **Privately Held**
WEB: www.newgenpack.com
SIC: 3089 Boxes, plastic

(G-10752)
QUANTUM CREATIONS LLC
15705 Nw 13th Ave (33169-5703)
PHONE..................................786 233-6769
Arthur V Rodriguez,
EMP: 11 **EST:** 2013
SALES (est): 3.3MM **Privately Held**
WEB: www.azulle.com
SIC: 3572 Computer storage devices

(G-10753)
RESTORATION ARTS
15301 Nw 34th Ave (33054-2459)
P.O. Box 541601, Opa Locka (33054-1601)
PHONE..................................305 953-9755
Micheal Minor, *President*
EMP: 8 **EST:** 1992
SALES (est): 953.5K **Privately Held**
WEB: www.restorationartsandlighting.com
SIC: 3646 Commercial indusl & institutional electric lighting fixtures

(G-10754)
SECURITY WORLD ELECTRONICS
19704 Nw 48th Ct (33055-1720)
PHONE..................................786 285-5303
Raul Fernandez, *President*
Maria E Fernandez, *Admin Sec*
EMP: 6
SQ FT: 3,000
SALES (est): 588.4K **Privately Held**
SIC: 2431 Millwork

(G-10755)
SPIRIT LLC
Also Called: Ds18
1400 Nw 159th St Ste 101 (33169-5704)
PHONE..................................954 592-0227
Robert Chin, *Sales Staff*
Jonathan Garber, *Marketing Staff*
Alberto Susterman, *Mng Member*
Etti Susterman, *Graphic Designe*
◆ **EMP:** 45 **EST:** 2007
SQ FT: 15,000
SALES (est): 35MM **Privately Held**
SIC: 3651 Audio electronic systems

(G-10756)
STEINER-ATLANTIC LLC ✪
1714 Nw 215th St (33056-1153)
PHONE..................................305 754-4551
Zachary Mangones, *Principal*
Diane Nino, *Principal*
Richard O'Connell Jr, *Principal*
Robert Lazar, *Mng Member*
EMP: 33 **EST:** 2020
SALES (est): 2.5MM **Privately Held**
WEB: www.steineratlantic.com
SIC: 3582 Drycleaning equipment & machinery, commercial

(G-10757)
ULTIMATE CONTAINERS PRO LLC
355 Nw 171st St (33169-5908)
PHONE..................................786 241-4306
Bladimir Parra, *Mng Member*
EMP: 10 **EST:** 2019
SALES (est): 1.1MM **Privately Held**
WEB: www.ultimatecontainerspro.com
SIC: 3089 Garbage containers, plastic

(G-10758)
VENAIR INC
16713 Park Centre Blvd (33169-5300)
PHONE..................................305 362-8920
Miguel Fernandez, *CEO*
Nicholas Bechtel, *Vice Pres*
Joseph Vattimo, *Sales Executive*
◆ **EMP:** 7 **EST:** 2005
SQ FT: 20,000
SALES (est): 5.1MM
SALES (corp-wide): 316K **Privately Held**
WEB: www.venair.com
SIC: 2822 Silicone rubbers
HQ: Venair Iberica Sa
Calle Cerdanya 26
Terrassa 08226
937 364-860

Miami Lakes
Miami-Dade County

(G-10759)
ADVANCE PANEL CORP
7877 Nw 165th Ter (33016-3485)
PHONE..................................347 399-6732
Amarilis Gomis, *Vice Pres*
EMP: 6 **EST:** 2014
SALES (est): 80.8K **Privately Held**
WEB: www.bes2buy.net
SIC: 3429 Manufactured hardware (general)

(G-10760)
ADVENTRY CORP
Also Called: Goodyear Belts
8190 Commerce Way (33016-1645)
PHONE..................................305 582-2977

▲ = Import ▼=Export
◆ =Import/Export

Tara Cevallos, *CEO*
Jorge Gomariz, *Ch of Bd*
EMP: 12 **EST:** 2018
SALES (est): 1MM **Privately Held**
SIC: 3052 Rubber belting

(G-10761)
AIRCRAFT ELECTRIC MOTORS INC
5800 Nw 163rd St (33014-5600)
PHONE..................................305 885-9476
William A Clot, *Ch of Bd*
Stephen J Clot, *President*
Lester R Johnson, *Vice Pres*
Rocco Campione, *Engineer*
Darrin Avick, *Sales Staff*
EMP: 100 **EST:** 1972
SQ FT: 30,000
SALES (est): 15.8MM **Privately Held**
WEB: www.aem.us
SIC: 7694 Rewinding services; rebuilding motors, except automotive

(G-10762)
AMERICAN AUTOMTN SYSTEMS INC
Also Called: Aas
5471 Nw 159th St (33014-6723)
PHONE..................................305 620-0077
Fax: 305 558-9082
EMP: 5
SQ FT: 4,000
SALES (est): 922.3K **Privately Held**
SIC: 3535 Mfg Conveyors/Equipment

(G-10763)
ASSOCATED PRTG PRODUCTIONS INC
Also Called: Appi
13925 Nw 60th Ave (33014-3126)
PHONE..................................305 623-7600
Jjohn P Beadel, *President*
John P Beadel, *President*
Marni Bauman, *General Mgr*
Linda Beadel, *Vice Pres*
Jimmie Davis, *Production*
▼ **EMP:** 50 **EST:** 1991
SQ FT: 20,000
SALES (est): 5.2MM **Privately Held**
WEB: www.appi1.com
SIC: 2796 2791 2789 Platemaking services; typesetting; bookbinding & related work

(G-10764)
AVANTI NUTRITIONAL LABS LLC
14101 Commerce Way (33016-1513)
PHONE..................................305 822-3880
Adolfo Gomez, *President*
Leydilian Carrera, *Manager*
EMP: 185 **EST:** 2014
SALES (est): 25.7MM **Privately Held**
SIC: 2834 Vitamin preparations

(G-10765)
BENGIS SIGNS INC
9821 Nw 80th Ave Unit 5t (33016-2366)
PHONE..................................305 592-3860
Joel Serkes, *President*
Janet Serkes, *Vice Pres*
EMP: 13 **EST:** 1991
SQ FT: 14,500
SALES (est): 337.2K **Privately Held**
SIC: 3993 Electric signs; neon signs

(G-10766)
BEST CLOSURES INC
9780 Nw 79th Ave (33016-2514)
PHONE..................................305 821-6607
Santiago A Suarez, *President*
Brian E Santore, *Vice Pres*
EMP: 8 **EST:** 2013
SALES (est): 133.2K **Privately Held**
SIC: 3549 Coilers (metalworking machines)

(G-10767)
BEST ROLLING MANUFACTURER INC
Also Called: Best Door
9780 Nw 79th Ave (33016-2514)
PHONE..................................305 821-4276
Santiago Suarez, *President*
▼ **EMP:** 60 **EST:** 1999
SALES (est): 11.3MM **Privately Held**
WEB: www.bestdoor.us
SIC: 3442 Garage doors, overhead: metal; rolling doors for industrial buildings or warehouses, metal; hangar doors, metal

(G-10768)
BETANCOURT SPORTS NTRTN LLC (HQ)
14700 Nw 60th Ave (33014-2813)
PHONE..................................305 593-9296
Colin Watts, *CEO*
Michael Beardall, *President*
Jason Reiser, *COO*
Brenda Galgano, *CFO*
EMP: 5 **EST:** 2009
SALES (est): 1.4MM
SALES (corp-wide): 2.1B **Publicly Held**
WEB: www.franchisegrp.com
SIC: 2023 Dietary supplements, dairy & non-dairy based
PA: Franchise Group, Inc.
2387 Liberty Way
Virginia Beach VA 23456
757 493-8855

(G-10769)
BIODEGRADABLE PACKAGING CORP
9775 Nw 80th Ave (33016-2315)
PHONE..................................305 824-1164
Frades Sanchez Sr, *President*
Frades Sanchez Jr, *Vice Pres*
Diane Sanchezm, *Manager*
EMP: 26 **EST:** 1989
SQ FT: 14,000
SALES (est): 5.2MM **Privately Held**
SIC: 2631 2653 Paperboard mills; corrugated & solid fiber boxes

(G-10770)
BIOREP TECHNOLOGIES INC
15804 Nw 57th Ave (33014-6702)
PHONE..................................305 330-4449
Ramon E Poo, *President*
Alexander Orozco, *Business Dir*
EMP: 18
SQ FT: 6,000
SALES (est): 4MM **Privately Held**
WEB: www.biorep.com
SIC: 3841 8733 Anesthesia apparatus; medical research

(G-10771)
BREFAROS NOBILE FOOD LLC
Also Called: Fiori Bruna Pasta Products
5340 Nw 163rd St (33014-6228)
PHONE..................................305 621-0074
Jose Yamin, *CEO*
Mayid Yamin, *Vice Pres*
◆ **EMP:** 30 **EST:** 1985
SQ FT: 8,000
SALES (est): 5.4MM **Privately Held**
SIC: 2099 Pasta, uncooked: packaged with other ingredients

(G-10772)
CALIFORNIA SHUTTERS INC
16480 Nw 48th Ave (33014-6419)
PHONE..................................305 827-9333
Ana Salomon, *Ch of Bd*
Edmond Salomon, *Vice Pres*
Marlise Cummings, *Treasurer*
George Cummings, *Admin Sec*
▼ **EMP:** 5 **EST:** 1987
SQ FT: 16,000
SALES (est): 700K **Privately Held**
WEB: www.californiashutters.com
SIC: 3442 Shutters, door or window: metal

(G-10773)
CAME AMERICAS AUTOMATION LLC
5863 Nw 159th St (33014-6717)
PHONE..................................305 433-3307
Winslow Wise, *Managing Dir*
H Gonzalez, *Business Mgr*
◆ **EMP:** 13 **EST:** 2007
SALES (est): 2.1MM **Privately Held**
WEB: www.came.com
SIC: 3699 Security devices

(G-10774)
CANDIES AND BEYOND INC
Also Called: Coffee Candy Store, The
14100 Nw 60th Ave (33014-3131)
PHONE..................................954 828-2255
Carlos Simao, *President*
EMP: 6 **EST:** 2014
SALES (est): 107.8K **Privately Held**
SIC: 2064 5149 Lollipops & other hard candy; beverages, except coffee & tea

(G-10775)
CHAMPION WELDING SERVICES LLC
5608 Nw 161st St (33014-6129)
PHONE..................................786 262-5727
Victor Tuckler,
EMP: 5 **EST:** 2008
SALES (est): 509.9K **Privately Held**
WEB: www.championweldingservices.com
SIC: 7692 Welding repair

(G-10776)
CHEMCO CORP
4920 Nw 165th St (33014-6323)
PHONE..................................305 623-4445
Eitelberg G Montarroyos, *CEO*
Jack Wang, *Purch Agent*
Amy S Montarroyos, *CFO*
◆ **EMP:** 50 **EST:** 1957
SQ FT: 60,000
SALES (est): 22.2MM **Privately Held**
WEB: www.echemco.com
SIC: 2844 2842 Shampoos, rinses, conditioners: hair; manicure preparations; cleaning or polishing preparations

(G-10777)
CORDIS CORPORATION
Cordis Cardiology
14201 Nw 60th Ave (33014-2894)
PHONE..................................786 313-2000
Brian Bowen, *Division Mgr*
Jorge Dowling, *Principal*
Alexander Perez, *Mfg Staff*
Magaly Ferguson, *Buyer*
Dax Stewart, *QC Mgr*
EMP: 280
SALES (corp-wide): 728.4MM **Privately Held**
SIC: 3841 Surgical & medical instruments
PA: Cordis Corporation
7000 Cardinal Pl
Dublin OH 43017
408 273-3700

(G-10778)
DARMAR CABINETS INC
5273 Nw 161st St (33014-6221)
PHONE..................................786 556-5784
Norberto Ricardo, *President*
EMP: 7 **EST:** 2010
SALES (est): 188.4K **Privately Held**
SIC: 2434 Wood kitchen cabinets

(G-10779)
DASH AIR PARTS LLC
6625 Mami Lkes Dr Ste 525 (33014)
PHONE..................................786 659-5013
Jose Farias, *Principal*
EMP: 6 **EST:** 2019
SALES (est): 465.5K **Privately Held**
WEB: www.dashairparts.net
SIC: 3825 Instruments to measure electricity

(G-10780)
DEGGY CORP
15485 Eagle Nest Ln # 100 (33014-2221)
PHONE..................................305 377-2233
▼ **EMP:** 6
SALES (est): 610K **Privately Held**
SIC: 3699 Mfg Electrical Equipment/Supplies

(G-10781)
DEMETECH CORPORATION (PA)
14175 Nw 60th Ave (33014-3130)
PHONE..................................305 824-1048
Luis H Arguello, *President*
Karla V Arguello, *Vice Pres*
Karla Arguello, *Vice Pres*
Luis M Arguello, *Vice Pres*
Luis H Arguello Jr, *Vice Pres*
◆ **EMP:** 74 **EST:** 2000
SQ FT: 5,000
SALES (est): 24.4MM **Privately Held**
WEB: www.demetech.us
SIC: 3842 Sutures, absorbable & non-absorbable

(G-10782)
DONOSO PRINTING CORP
9811 Nw 80th Ave (33016-2347)
PHONE..................................786 508-9426
Carlos Donoso, *Principal*
EMP: 5 **EST:** 2014
SALES (est): 364.4K **Privately Held**
WEB: www.donosoprinting.com
SIC: 2752 Commercial printing, offset

(G-10783)
DREW SCIENTIFIC INC (DH)
Also Called: Danam Electronics
14100 Nw 57th Ct (33014-3107)
PHONE..................................305 418-2320
Richard J Depiano Jr, *CEO*
Douglas P Nickols, *President*
Jim Acock, *Principal*
Dr Andrew Kinney, *Senior VP*
Francis Matuszak Jr, *Vice Pres*
◆ **EMP:** 17 **EST:** 1985
SALES (est): 15.9MM **Publicly Held**
WEB: www.drew-scientific.com
SIC: 3829 3841 Geophysical or meteorological electronic equipment; medical instruments & equipment, blood & bone work; blood transfusion equipment
HQ: Erba Diagnostics, Inc.
14100 Nw 57th Ct
Miami Lakes FL 33014
305 324-2300

(G-10784)
ECOPRINTQ INC
14261 Commerce Way # 101
(33016-1647)
PHONE..................................305 681-7445
Alfredo Milanes, *President*
Ever Milanes, *Vice Pres*
Joseph Pelino, *Sales Staff*
Anibal Rivera, *Sales Staff*
David Rodriguez, *Sales Staff*
EMP: 10 **EST:** 2011
SQ FT: 3,500
SALES: 4MM **Privately Held**
WEB: www.ecoprintq.com
SIC: 7372 Operating systems computer software

(G-10785)
EMC QUALITY GROUP CORP
6625 Mami Lkes Dr E Ste 2 (33014)
PHONE..................................786 501-5891
Elder Maldonado, *President*
EMP: 8 **EST:** 2017
SALES (est): 326K **Privately Held**
SIC: 3572 Computer storage devices

(G-10786)
ERBA DIAGNOSTICS INC (DH)
14100 Nw 57th Ct (33014-3107)
PHONE..................................305 324-2300
Hayden Jeffreys, *CEO*
Suresh Vazirani, *Ch of Bd*
Jonathan Arauz, *Production*
Aidan Rivero, *Production*
Yami Athenesaw, *Technical Mgr*
▲ **EMP:** 100 **EST:** 1980
SALES (est): 32.5MM **Publicly Held**
WEB: www.erbadiagnostics.com
SIC: 2834 3841 Pharmaceutical preparations; diagnostic apparatus, medical

(G-10787)
EXPRESS PAPER COMPANY INC
Also Called: South Florida Tissue Paper Co
5590 Nw 163rd St (33014-6132)
PHONE..................................305 685-4929
Juan E Corzo, *President*
Alfredo Cortes, *CFO*
Clara V Crocker-Morales, *Treasurer*
◆ **EMP:** 15 **EST:** 1998
SQ FT: 40,000
SALES (est): 6.4MM **Privately Held**
WEB: www.southfloridatissuepaper.com
SIC: 2679 Paper products, converted

GEOGRAPHIC

(G-10788)
FASTSIGNS
15925 Nw 57th Ave (33014-6703)
PHONE..................................305 628-3278
Sergio Smith, *Owner*
EMP: 14 **EST:** 2009
SALES (est): 978.9K **Privately Held**
WEB: www.fastsigns.com
SIC: 3993 Signs & advertising specialties

(G-10789)
FDC VITAMINS LLC (DH)
Also Called: Nutri-Force Nutrition
14620 Nw 60th Ave (33014-2811)
PHONE..................................305 468-1600
Colin Watts, *CEO*
Dan Alhadeff, *COO*
◆ **EMP:** 398 **EST:** 2001
SQ FT: 120,000
SALES (est): 40.2MM
SALES (corp-wide): 2.1B **Publicly Held**
SIC: 2833 Vitamins, natural or synthetic: bulk, uncompounded

(G-10790)
FLA PROPERTY HOLDINGS INC
13980 Nw 58th Ct (33014-3115)
PHONE..................................813 888-8796
Jennifer Bly, *President*
Mitch Rotberg, *CFO*
EMP: 20 **EST:** 1936
SQ FT: 22,000
SALES (est): 605.2K **Privately Held**
SIC: 2759 Screen printing

(G-10791)
FLORIDA KOLMIAMI CORPORATION
6491 Cow Pen Rd Apt H102 (33014-6641)
PHONE..................................305 582-0114
Julian Orozco, *President*
EMP: 9 **EST:** 2001
SQ FT: 500
SALES (est): 507.4K **Privately Held**
SIC: 2899 Oils & essential oils

(G-10792)
FRUITFUL LLC
Also Called: Fruitful International
10030 Nw 79th Ave Hleahg (33016-2408)
PHONE..................................954 534-9828
Angel Rodriguez, *CEO*
Mario Arrue, *President*
EMP: 5 **EST:** 2018
SALES (est): 498.4K **Privately Held**
SIC: 2844 Toilet preparations

(G-10793)
G WELDING CONTRACTOR CORP
10226 Nw 80th Ave (33016-2308)
PHONE..................................305 896-0311
Roberlay Romero, *President*
EMP: 7 **EST:** 2016
SALES (est): 115K **Privately Held**
WEB: www.gwelding.com
SIC: 7692 Welding repair

(G-10794)
GENERAL MACHINE SHOP
9820 Nw 80th Ave (33016-2346)
PHONE..................................305 558-2409
Jose R Rodriguez, *President*
▼ **EMP:** 6 **EST:** 2010
SALES (est): 119.2K **Privately Held**
SIC: 3599 Machine shop, jobbing & repair

(G-10795)
GLOBAL CABINET DISTRIBUTORS
16355 Nw 48th Ave (33014-6416)
PHONE..................................305 625-9814
Terri Reeves, *Principal*
▲ **EMP:** 7 **EST:** 2009
SALES (est): 346K **Privately Held**
SIC: 2434 Wood kitchen cabinets

(G-10796)
GUARDIAN HURRICANE PROTECTION
5729 Nw 159th St (33014-6750)
PHONE..................................305 805-7050
Pablo J Ramos, *CEO*
Andrea Ramos, *President*
▼ **EMP:** 13 **EST:** 2000
SALES (est): 2.8MM **Privately Held**
WEB: www.guardian-shutters.com
SIC: 3442 2431 Shutters, door or window: metal; door shutters, wood

(G-10797)
INDUSTRIAL PLASTIC PDTS INC
14025 Nw 58th Ct (33014-3116)
PHONE..................................305 822-3223
Veronika Thorne, *President*
George Thorne, *Exec VP*
Tania Ortiz, *Vice Pres*
▲ **EMP:** 50 **EST:** 1975
SQ FT: 35,000
SALES (est): 3.8MM **Privately Held**
WEB: www.ipprod.com
SIC: 3089 2821 Injection molding of plastics; plastics materials & resins

(G-10798)
INTERNATIONAL CASTING CORP
Also Called: ICC
6187 Miami Lakes Dr E (33014-2407)
PHONE..................................305 558-3515
Walter Alvarez, *Owner*
Jesus Marrero, *Manager*
EMP: 30 **EST:** 1998
SALES (est): 2.6MM **Privately Held**
SIC: 3272 Concrete products, precast

(G-10799)
INTERNATIONAL VAPOR GROUP LLC (DH)
14300 Commerce Way (33016-1501)
PHONE..................................305 824-4027
Marc Waxman, *COO*
Nichele Thompson, *Mktg Coord*
Nick Rucci, *IT/INT Sup*
Xiomara Restrepo, *Graphic Designe*
EMP: 72 **EST:** 2009
SALES (est): 50MM
SALES (corp-wide): 405.1MM **Publicly Held**
WEB: www.turningpointbrands.com
SIC: 3999 5194 5993 Cigarette & cigar products & accessories; cigarettes;
HQ: Turning Point Brands, Llc
5201 Interchange Way
Louisville KY 40229
502 778-4421

(G-10800)
JTF VENTURES LLC
Also Called: Advak Techologies
7889 Nw 98th St (33016-2428)
P.O. Box 171034, Hialeah (33017-1034)
PHONE..................................305 556-5156
Tania Garza, *CEO*
Erik Purne, *Project Engr*
EMP: 7 **EST:** 1994
SQ FT: 10,000
SALES (est): 520K **Privately Held**
WEB: www.advak.com
SIC: 3089 Injection molding of plastics

(G-10801)
KELLSTROM COML AROSPC INC
14400 Nw 77th Ct Ste 306 (33016-1592)
PHONE..................................305 818-5400
Jeff Lund, *Manager*
EMP: 47
SALES (corp-wide): 1B **Privately Held**
SIC: 3728 Aircraft parts & equipment
HQ: Kellstrom Commercial Aerospace, Inc.
450 Medinah Rd
Roselle IL 60172
847 233-5800

(G-10802)
LA EXPERIENCIA CRANKSHAFT
9910 Nw 80th Ave Unit 2m (33016-2322)
PHONE..................................305 823-6161
Jacobo Ulloa, *President*
EMP: 7 **EST:** 2000
SALES (est): 506.5K **Privately Held**
SIC: 3714 Crankshaft assemblies, motor vehicle

(G-10803)
LADOVE INC
Also Called: Headwear International
5701 Miami Lakes Dr E (33014-2417)
P.O. Box 5169, Hialeah (33014-1169)
PHONE..................................305 823-8051
Sheree Kent, *President*
Michael Bass, *Exec VP*
Jorge Loaiza, *Production*
Jeanette Reneau, *Purch Mgr*
Stephanie Bleyer, *Purch Agent*
▲ **EMP:** 55 **EST:** 1977
SQ FT: 20,000
SALES (est): 16.3MM **Privately Held**
WEB: www.ladove.com
SIC: 2844 Shampoos, rinses, conditioners: hair

(G-10804)
LADOVE INDUSTRIES INC
5701 Miami Lakes Dr E (33014-2417)
P.O. Box 5169, Hialeah (33014-1169)
PHONE..................................305 624-2456
Sheree Lacove, *President*
EMP: 9 **EST:** 1977
SALES (est): 240.3K **Privately Held**
WEB: www.ladove.com
SIC: 2844 Hair preparations, including shampoos

(G-10805)
LAWRENCE FACTOR INC
4740 Nw 157th St (33014-6421)
PHONE..................................305 430-9152
Lawrence Kaplan, *President*
Judy Cummings, *Corp Secy*
Michael Casey, *Vice Pres*
John S Kostick, *Vice Pres*
Robert Laughlin, *Vice Pres*
◆ **EMP:** 30 **EST:** 1981
SQ FT: 23,000
SALES (est): 5.9MM **Privately Held**
WEB: www.lawrence-factor.com
SIC: 3599 Air intake filters, internal combustion engine, except auto

(G-10806)
LEWA GROUP CORP
Also Called: Sunshine Ready Technologies
6001 Nw 153rd St (33014-2419)
PHONE..................................305 407-9500
Federico A Velazco, *Principal*
EMP: 6 **EST:** 2014
SALES (est): 197.2K **Privately Held**
SIC: 3559 Special industry machinery

(G-10807)
LIOHER ENTERPRISE CORP
13939 Nw 60th Ave (33014-3126)
PHONE..................................305 685-0005
Armando R Gonzalez-Diaz, *President*
Raul Gonzalez Lio, *Vice Pres*
Reynaldo Ruiz, *Treasurer*
Matias Cobo, *Director*
▲ **EMP:** 5 **EST:** 2010
SALES (est): 1MM **Privately Held**
WEB: www.lioher.com
SIC: 3553 5712 Woodworking machinery; customized furniture & cabinets

(G-10808)
LIV LLC
Also Called: Smart Foods
8004 Nw 154th St Ste 261 (33016-5814)
PHONE..................................321 276-5302
Deviree Vallejo, *Broker*
Manoj Srivastava, *Mng Member*
EMP: 25 **EST:** 2017
SALES (est): 5MM **Privately Held**
SIC: 2833 5122 Vitamins, natural or synthetic: bulk, uncompounded; vitamins & minerals

(G-10809)
LPS PRODUCTION LLC
Also Called: Lps Lighting Sound Video Prod
15915 Nw 59th Ave (33014-6718)
PHONE..................................786 208-6217
Jose Laria, *President*
EMP: 10 **EST:** 2015
SALES (est): 710K **Privately Held**
WEB: www.lpsproduction.com
SIC: 3648 Lighting equipment

(G-10810)
LUMINOSO LLC
Also Called: Led Lighting
9800 Nw 78th Ave (33016-2402)
PHONE..................................305 364-8099
James Knips, *Mng Member*
EMP: 9 **EST:** 2013
SALES (est): 1.1MM **Privately Held**
WEB: www.luminosoled.com
SIC: 3674 Light emitting diodes

(G-10811)
MAQ INVESTMENTS GROUP INC
Also Called: D G Steel Rule Die Mfg
14312 Commerce Way (33016-1501)
PHONE..................................305 691-1468
Daniel Ziadi, *President*
▲ **EMP:** 25 **EST:** 1937
SALES (est): 3.6MM **Privately Held**
SIC: 2675 Die-cut paper & board

(G-10812)
MARBLE LITE PRODUCTS CORP
9920 Nw 79th Ave (33016-2406)
PHONE..................................305 557-8766
Nestor Perez, *President*
Juan Miguel Blanco, *Vice Pres*
Magda Larrauri, *Vice Pres*
Gustavo Perez, *Vice Pres*
Tony Riestra, *Vice Pres*
◆ **EMP:** 34 **EST:** 1978
SQ FT: 16,000
SALES (est): 5.1MM **Privately Held**
WEB: www.marblelite.com
SIC: 3281 Marble, building: cut & shaped

(G-10813)
MARGOTH MANUFACTURING CO
9910 Nw 80th Ave Unit 2u (33016-2365)
PHONE..................................954 200-3894
Elcie Lanza, *Principal*
EMP: 6 **EST:** 2015
SALES (est): 47.3K **Privately Held**
SIC: 3999 Manufacturing industries

(G-10814)
MASON VITAMINS INC
15750 Nw 59th Ave (33014-6716)
PHONE..................................800 327-6005
Yosuke Honjo, *CEO*
Ofelia Perez, *President*
Garcia Richard, *Vice Pres*
SEI Shimizu, *Controller*
Gary Pigott, *VP Sales*
▼ **EMP:** 100 **EST:** 1967
SQ FT: 40,000
SALES (est): 20.7MM **Privately Held**
WEB: www.masonvitamins.com
SIC: 2834 Vitamin, nutrient & hematinic preparations for human use; vitamin preparations

(G-10815)
MASTER TOOL CO INC
6115 Nw 153rd St (33014-2480)
PHONE..................................305 557-1020
Paul Roos, *President*
Paul Kevin Roos, *President*
Julie Estock, *Vice Pres*
Zack Estock, *Opers Staff*
EMP: 35
SQ FT: 17,500
SALES (est): 1.2MM **Privately Held**
WEB: www.mastertoolusa.com
SIC: 3089 Injection molding of plastics

(G-10816)
MEDTRONIC
14420 Nw 60th Ave (33014-2807)
PHONE..................................305 458-7260
Sacha Hall, *Engineer*
Arismely Duverge, *Auditor*
Randy Krueger, *Branch Mgr*
Ventura Martha, *Technician*
EMP: 23 **Privately Held**
WEB: www.heartware.com
SIC: 3841 Medical instruments & equipment, blood & bone work
HQ: Medtronic
14400 Nw 60th Ave
Miami Lakes FL 33014
305 818-4100

(G-10817)
MEDTRONIC (DH)
14400 Nw 60th Ave (33014-2807)
PHONE..................................305 818-4100
Douglas Godshall, *President*
Larry Knopf, *Senior VP*
Peter McAree, *Senior VP*
Jim Schuermann, *Senior VP*
Lauren Farrell, *Vice Pres*
EMP: 70 **EST:** 1998
SQ FT: 59,000
SALES (est): 158.2MM **Privately Held**
WEB: www.heartware.com
SIC: 3841 Surgical & medical instruments

(G-10818)
MERCK SHARP & DOHME CORP
14240 Plmetto Frontage Rd (33016-1533)
PHONE..................................305 512-6062
EMP: 78
SALES (corp-wide): 39.8B **Publicly Held**
SIC: 2834 Mfg Pharmaceuticals
HQ: Merck Sharp & Dohme Corp.
2000 Galloping Hill Rd
Kenilworth NJ 07033
908 740-4000

(G-10819)
MIAMI SCREENPRINT SUPPLY
5566 Nw 161st St (33014-6127)
PHONE..................................305 622-7532
Kevin Flury, *President*
Maureen Alvarez, *Vice Pres*
▼ **EMP:** 6 **EST:** 2006
SALES (est): 330K **Privately Held**
WEB: www.miamiscreenprintsupply.com
SIC: 2759 Screen printing

(G-10820)
MIAMI TEES INC
5120 Nw 165th St Ste 101 (33014-6340)
PHONE..................................305 623-3908
Michael Chavez, *President*
▲ **EMP:** 65 **EST:** 1988
SALES (est): 5.3MM **Privately Held**
WEB: www.miamitees.us
SIC: 2759 Screen printing

(G-10821)
MILTECHNOLOGIES INC
13980 Nw 58th Ct (33014-3115)
PHONE..................................305 817-4244
Jorge Mejia, *President*
▼ **EMP:** 5 **EST:** 2004
SQ FT: 5,500
SALES (est): 800K **Privately Held**
WEB: www.miltechnologies.com
SIC: 3724 Aircraft engines & engine parts

(G-10822)
MIY CERAMIC
7000 Gleneagle Dr (33014-6510)
PHONE..................................305 823-5758
Denise Mendez, *Principal*
EMP: 6 **EST:** 2010
SALES (est): 135.1K **Privately Held**
WEB: www.miyceramics.com
SIC: 3269 Pottery products

(G-10823)
MJM MANUFACTURING INC
5205 Nw 161st St (33014-6221)
P.O. Box 5427, Miami (33101-5427)
PHONE..................................305 620-2020
Michael J Mijares, *President*
Renard Amaro, *Vice Pres*
Maria Perez, *Finance*
Alexander Mijares, *Marketing Staff*
EMP: 60 **EST:** 1979
SQ FT: 57,000
SALES (est): 13.3MM **Privately Held**
WEB: www.mjmmfg.com
SIC: 3444 Sheet metal specialties, not stamped

(G-10824)
MTSERVICER LLC
8140 Nw 155th St (33016-5999)
PHONE..................................305 200-1254
Jorge Barreto, *Principal*
EMP: 7 **EST:** 2011
SALES (est): 259.1K **Privately Held**
SIC: 3621 Generators & sets, electric

(G-10825)
MUNDY KITCHEN CABINET INC
9921 Nw 80th Ave Unit 1p (33016-2321)
PHONE..................................786 298-0131
Raymundo Parrado, *Principal*
EMP: 6 **EST:** 2013
SALES (est): 165K **Privately Held**
SIC: 2434 Wood kitchen cabinets

(G-10826)
MY FOCUS INC
5395 Nw 165th St Ste 102 (33014-6218)
PHONE..................................305 826-4480
Chenny WEI Chen, *President*
◆ **EMP:** 7 **EST:** 2004
SALES (est): 1.5MM **Privately Held**
SIC: 3161 Traveling bags

(G-10827)
NATIONAL MOLDING LLC (PA)
Also Called: Security Plastics
14427 Nw 60th Ave (33014-2806)
PHONE..................................305 823-5440
John Johnson, *CEO*
Mike Curran, *General Mgr*
Richard L Baum, *Vice Pres*
Tony Wong, *Vice Pres*
Gerardo Palmer, *Engineer*
◆ **EMP:** 140 **EST:** 1965
SQ FT: 7,700
SALES (est): 50.9MM **Privately Held**
WEB: www.nationalmolding.com
SIC: 3089 Injection molding of plastics

(G-10828)
NEW GENERATION COMPUTING INC (HQ)
14900 Nw 79th Ct Ste 100 (33016-5791)
PHONE..................................800 690-0642
Alan Brooks, *Chairman*
Lilly Sabin, *Controller*
Lilian Sadin, *Human Res Mgr*
Marisol Gomez, *Marketing Staff*
Damion Thompson, *Manager*
EMP: 60 **EST:** 1982
SQ FT: 5,000
SALES (est): 28.9MM
SALES (corp-wide): 111.4MM **Publicly Held**
WEB: www.ngcsoftware.com
SIC: 7372 Business oriented computer software
PA: American Software, Inc.
470 E Paces Ferry Rd Ne
Atlanta GA 30305
404 261-4381

(G-10829)
NEW LASER TECH INC
7003 Greentree Ln (33014-2077)
PHONE..................................305 450-0456
Mark Chariff, *Principal*
EMP: 6 **EST:** 2007
SALES (est): 90.6K **Privately Held**
SIC: 3699 Laser systems & equipment

(G-10830)
NEW UNDERGROUND RR PUBG CO
14411 Commerce Way # 320 (33016-1596)
PHONE..................................305 825-1444
EMP: 15
SALES (est): 1.1MM **Privately Held**
SIC: 2731 4011 Books-Publishing/Printing Railroad Line-Haul Operator

(G-10831)
NUNEZ MACHINE SHOP INC
9809 Nw 80th Ave (33016-2333)
PHONE..................................786 615-4261
Eugene Nunez, *President*
EMP: 14 **EST:** 2015
SALES (est): 1MM **Privately Held**
SIC: 3599 Machine shop, jobbing & repair

(G-10832)
OCC MY STONE LLC
10090 Nw 80th Ct Apt 1238 (33016-2239)
PHONE..................................786 352-1567
Oscar Castillo, *Mng Member*
EMP: 9 **EST:** 2013
SALES (est): 2.3MM **Privately Held**
SIC: 1411 Granite dimension stone

(G-10833)
OUTDOOR AMERICA IMAGES INC
Also Called: Rose Poster Printing
13982 Nw 58th Ct (33014-3115)
PHONE..................................813 888-8796
Mick Taylor, *General Mgr*
John Wurster, *General Mgr*
Eric Blanc, *Business Mgr*
Whitney Jude, *Accounts Mgr*
Kristina Lausier, *Manager*
EMP: 31 **Privately Held**
SIC: 2759 Screen printing
PA: Outdoor America Images, Inc.
4545 W Hillsborough Ave
Tampa FL 33614

(G-10834)
PAN AMERICAN GRAPHIC INC
9745 Nw 80th Ave (33016-2315)
P.O. Box 524149, Miami (33152-4149)
PHONE..................................305 885-1962
Martin Roca, *President*
Elba Roca, *Vice Pres*
Danielle Roca, *Sales Staff*
Magda Luna, *Admin Asst*
◆ **EMP:** 36 **EST:** 1976
SQ FT: 4,000
SALES (est): 5.1MM **Privately Held**
WEB: www.panamgraphic.com
SIC: 2752 Commercial printing, offset

(G-10835)
PC MASTERS CORP
5951 Nw 151st St Ste 35 (33014-2423)
PHONE..................................305 582-5595
Will Angel, *General Mgr*
EMP: 6
SALES (est): 370K **Privately Held**
WEB: www.mastercorp.com
SIC: 3571 Electronic computers

(G-10836)
PETRUJ CHEMICAL CORP
8055 Nw 98th St (33016-2319)
PHONE..................................305 556-1271
Raul Perez-Trujillo, *President*
Casandra Perez-Trujillo, *Vice Pres*
Adrian Garcia, *Manager*
Al Morgan, *Software Dev*
◆ **EMP:** 10 **EST:** 1979
SQ FT: 5,000
SALES (est): 1.9MM **Privately Held**
WEB: www.formula88.com
SIC: 2842 Degreasing solvent

(G-10837)
PFAFFCO INC
Also Called: Pfaff Engraving
14329 Commerce Way (33016-1502)
PHONE..................................305 635-0986
Daniel Pfaff, *President*
Kimberly E Pfaff, *Vice Pres*
Kathleen N Pfaff, *Admin Sec*
◆ **EMP:** 14 **EST:** 1970
SQ FT: 2,500
SALES (est): 447.9K **Privately Held**
SIC: 2759 2752 2796 Stationery: printing; thermography; commercial printing, lithographic; platemaking services

(G-10838)
PHARMALAB ENTERPRISES INC (PA)
14501 Nw 60th Ave (33014-2808)
PHONE..................................305 821-4002
Alberto J Perez, *President*
Ramona Perez, *Admin Sec*
EMP: 20 **EST:** 2004
SALES (est): 8.4MM **Privately Held**
WEB: www.pharmalabenterprises.com
SIC: 2834 Vitamin preparations

(G-10839)
PIONEER LED LIGHTING CORP
Also Called: Zollan
4980 Nw 165th St Unit A1 (33014-6304)
P.O. Box 823691, Pembroke Pines (33082-3691)
PHONE..................................305 620-5300
Robert Behnejad, *President*
Mitra K Behnejad, *Vice Pres*
EMP: 7 **EST:** 2009
SALES (est): 596.1K **Privately Held**
WEB: www.zollan.com
SIC: 3646 Commercial indusl & institutional electric lighting fixtures

(G-10840)
POINT BLANK ENTERPRISES INC
Also Called: Protective Group A Pt Blank Co
14100 Nw 58th Ct (33014-3119)
PHONE..................................305 820-4270
Jorge Bernal, *Engineer*
Denise Garib, *IT/INT Sup*
Elizabeth Serrania, *Director*
Ashley Reynolds,
EMP: 67 **Privately Held**
WEB: www.pointblankenterprises.com
SIC: 3699 3842 Security devices; bullet-proof vests
HQ: Point Blank Enterprises, Inc.
2102 Sw 2nd St
Pompano Beach FL 33069
954 630-0900

(G-10841)
PRATT & WHITNEY ENG SVCS INC
14100 Palmetto Frntg Rd (33016-1569)
PHONE..................................305 512-9882
Feilding T Dameron, *Branch Mgr*
EMP: 6
SALES (corp-wide): 56.5B **Publicly Held**
WEB: www.prattwhitney.com
SIC: 3724 3728 Aircraft engines & engine parts; aircraft parts & equipment
HQ: Pratt & Whitney Engine Services, Inc.
1525 Midway Park Rd
Bridgeport WV 26330
304 842-5421

(G-10842)
PRECISION TECH AERO INC
6051 Nw 153rd St (33014-2413)
PHONE..................................305 603-8347
Taves Luiz M, *Principal*
Maickel Vazquez, *Supervisor*
EMP: 14 **EST:** 2013
SALES (est): 2.3MM **Privately Held**
WEB: www.ptaero.com
SIC: 3728 Aircraft parts & equipment

(G-10843)
PRIKO CORP
16500 Nw 86th Ct (33016-6144)
PHONE..................................305 556-3558
Humberto Gomez, *Principal*
Julia A Gomez, *Principal*
EMP: 14 **EST:** 2007
SALES (est): 334.1K **Privately Held**
SIC: 3465 Body parts, automobile: stamped metal

(G-10844)
PROFAST CORPORATION
5854 Miami Lakes Dr E (33014-2402)
PHONE..................................305 827-7801
Joel Asseraf, *President*
Laurence Asseraf, *Vice Pres*
◆ **EMP:** 25 **EST:** 1983
SQ FT: 12,000
SALES (est): 914.3K **Privately Held**
WEB: www.profastusa.com
SIC: 3089 Boxes, plastic; plastic hardware & building products

(G-10845)
PROFAST USA INC
5854 Miami Lakes Dr E (33014-2402)
PHONE..................................305 827-7801
Marcos M Drobiner, *President*
Beatrice R Drobiner, *Vice Pres*
Oscar Gutierrez, *Sales Staff*
◆ **EMP:** 17 **EST:** 2006
SALES (est): 2.5MM **Privately Held**
WEB: www.profastusa.com
SIC: 3462 Anchors, forged

(G-10846)
PROTECTIVE GROUP INC
14100 Nw 58th Ct (33014-3119)
PHONE..................................305 820-4266
EMP: 30 **Privately Held**
SIC: 3699 3842 Electrical Equipment And Supplies, Nec, N

GEOGRAPHIC

PA: The Protective Group Inc
14100 Nw 58th Ct
Miami Lakes FL 33014
305 820-4270

(G-10847)
R & R MICA WORKS INC
6541 Lake Blue Dr (33014-3003)
PHONE..................................305 231-1887
Rigo Malpica, *President*
EMP: 6 **EST:** 1988
SQ FT: 5,000
SALES (est): 482.3K **Privately Held**
SIC: 2511 Tables, household: wood

(G-10848)
RAINBOW MANUFACTURING COMPANY
Also Called: Rainbow Irrigation
16541 Nw 84th Ave (33016-6143)
PHONE..................................305 477-5541
Paul Gannom, *Manager*
EMP: 6
SALES (corp-wide): 4.9MM **Privately Held**
WEB: www.rainbowirrigation.com
SIC: 3523 Irrigation equipment, self-propelled
PA: Rainbow Manufacturing Company
101 Rainbow Rd
Fitzgerald GA 31750
229 423-4341

(G-10849)
RECOMMEND TRAVEL PUBLICATIONS
5979 Nw 151st St Ste 120 (33014-2448)
P.O. Box 171070, Hialeah (33017-1070)
PHONE..................................305 826-4763
EMP: 17
SQ FT: 7,000
SALES (est): 1.5MM
SALES (corp-wide): 7.9MM **Privately Held**
SIC: 2721 Periodicals-Publishing/Printing
PA: Worth International Media Group
5979 Nw 151st St Ste 120
Miami Lakes FL 33014
305 826-4763

(G-10850)
RENNAK INC
Also Called: Sir Speedy
6161 Miami Lakes Dr E (33014-2408)
PHONE..................................305 558-0144
Reuven Kanner, *President*
Susanne Kanner, *Corp Secy*
Manny Pose, *Sales Staff*
▼ **EMP:** 6 **EST:** 1979
SQ FT: 3,000
SALES (est): 990K **Privately Held**
WEB: www.sirspeedymiamilakes.com
SIC: 2752 Commercial printing, lithographic

(G-10851)
RICH WOODTURNING INC
5626 Nw 161st St (33014-6129)
PHONE..................................305 573-9142
Richard Rocard, *President*
▼ **EMP:** 10 **EST:** 1952
SQ FT: 8,000
SALES (est): 677.9K **Privately Held**
WEB: www.richwoodturning.com
SIC: 2499 2431 Carved & turned wood; millwork

(G-10852)
ROLLING SHIELD INCORPORATED
9875 Nw 79th Ave (33016-2424)
PHONE..................................305 436-6661
Jose A Delgado, *President*
Daniel Hazinski, *Production*
Yaris Ovalles, *Clerk*
◆ **EMP:** 23 **EST:** 1993
SQ FT: 50,000
SALES (est): 4.6MM **Privately Held**
WEB: www.rollingshield.com
SIC: 3442 3354 3444 Shutters, door or window: metal; aluminum extruded products; awnings, sheet metal

(G-10853)
ROLLING SHIELD PARTS INC
9875 Nw 79th Ave (33016-2424)
PHONE..................................305 436-6661
Jose Delgado, *President*
◆ **EMP:** 17 **EST:** 1995
SALES (est): 3.3MM **Privately Held**
WEB: www.rollingshield.com
SIC: 3442 3444 5999 Shutters, door or window: metal; awnings, sheet metal; awnings

(G-10854)
SCENTS NATURE ENTERPRISES CORP
Also Called: Botanical Scents Nature Entps
7850 Nw 98th St (33016-2429)
PHONE..................................305 547-2334
◆ **EMP:** 15
SQ FT: 20,000
SALES: 2.5MM **Privately Held**
SIC: 2899 Mfg Chemical Preparations

(G-10855)
SCENTS OF NATURE ENTERPRISES
Also Called: Sonec
7850 Nw 98th St (33016-2429)
PHONE..................................305 547-2334
EMP: 20
SALES: 5MM **Privately Held**
SIC: 3999 Mfg Misc Products

(G-10856)
SCIENTIFIC PLASTICS LTD
5852 Miami Lakes Dr E (33014-2402)
PHONE..................................305 557-3737
Bernardo Perafan, *Manager*
James Handzo, *Manager*
◆ **EMP:** 10 **EST:** 2001
SALES (est): 629.8K **Privately Held**
WEB: www.sciplastics.com
SIC: 3089 Injection molded finished plastic products

(G-10857)
SIGNATURE PRINTING INC
5725 Nw 151st St (33014-2481)
P.O. Box 820021, Pembroke Pines (33082-0021)
PHONE..................................305 828-9992
Jaime Prada, *President*
Maria Prada, *Corp Secy*
Jose Prada, *Vice Pres*
Maria Watson, *Admin Sec*
EMP: 10 **EST:** 1982
SQ FT: 2,000
SALES (est): 843.1K **Privately Held**
WEB: www.signature-printing.com
SIC: 2752 Commercial printing, offset

(G-10858)
SOLARA INC
Also Called: Solara Labs
5105 Nw 159th St (33014-6336)
PHONE..................................305 592-4748
Jose Rocca, *CEO*
Jeff Powlowsky, *President*
Maria Bolivar, *Project Mgr*
Alex Wagner, *Marketing Staff*
▼ **EMP:** 18 **EST:** 2007
SQ FT: 7,200
SALES (est): 2.5MM **Privately Held**
WEB: www.barimelts.com
SIC: 2834 Vitamin, nutrient & hematinic preparations for human use

(G-10859)
SOUTHEAST ID LLC
5830 Nw 163rd St (33014-5600)
PHONE..................................954 571-6665
Alan Mendelson, *CEO*
Jacob Brafman, *CFO*
Albert Villacampa, *Info Tech Mgr*
Michael Smith, *Administration*
EMP: 13 **EST:** 2015
SALES (est): 1.9MM **Privately Held**
WEB: www.southeastid.com
SIC: 3089 2672 Identification cards, plastic; coated & laminated paper

(G-10860)
SOUTHEAST OFFSET INC
4880 Nw 157th St (33014-6434)
PHONE..................................305 623-7788
Troy Clowdus, *President*
▼ **EMP:** 24 **EST:** 1995
SQ FT: 36,000
SALES (est): 1.2MM **Privately Held**
WEB: www.productionworkflow.southeast-offset.com
SIC: 2711 Commercial printing & newspaper publishing combined

(G-10861)
SOUTHERN FIBER INC
4715 Nw 157th St Ste 104 (33014-6433)
PHONE..................................786 916-3052
Robert Ruberti, *Branch Mgr*
EMP: 11
SQ FT: 22,900
SALES (corp-wide): 8.5MM **Privately Held**
WEB: www.southernfiberinc.com
SIC: 2281 Manmade & synthetic fiber yarns, spun
PA: Southern Fiber, Inc.
1041 S Grove Ext
Lincolnton NC 28093
704 736-0011

(G-10862)
SOUTHERN UNDERGROUND INDS
5979 Nw 151st St Ste 223 (33014-2467)
PHONE..................................954 226-3865
John Brady, *Principal*
EMP: 10 **EST:** 2017
SALES (est): 4.7MM **Privately Held**
WEB: www.southernui.com
SIC: 1389 Oil field services

(G-10863)
SOUTHWINGS AVIONICS AND ACC
5429 Nw 161st St (33014-6124)
PHONE..................................305 825-6755
Manuel Lopez, *Principal*
EMP: 8 **EST:** 2010
SALES (est): 810.8K **Privately Held**
SIC: 3721 Aircraft

(G-10864)
SUN CATALINA HOLDINGS LLC
16200 Nw 59th Ave Ste 101 (33014-7541)
PHONE..................................305 558-4777
Dorothy Ardito, *Vice Pres*
Dennis Poppe, *Vice Pres*
Sandra Roy, *Controller*
David Garcia, *Sales Staff*
Joe Kitchel, *Director*
EMP: 25 **EST:** 2001
SALES (est): 2MM
SALES (corp-wide): 3.4B **Privately Held**
WEB: www.suncappart.com
SIC: 3645 3646 3648 3641 Residential lighting fixtures; commercial indusl & institutional electric lighting fixtures; lighting equipment; electric lamps
PA: Sun Capital Partners, Inc.
5200 Town Center Cir # 600
Boca Raton FL 33486
561 962-3400

(G-10865)
SUNCREST SHEDS OF SOUTH FLA
9600 Nw 77th Ave (33016-2501)
PHONE..................................305 231-1990
Juan Carlos Zamora, *President*
Javier Parra, *Sales Mgr*
EMP: 10
SALES (est): 1.7MM **Privately Held**
WEB: www.sheddepotsheds.com
SIC: 3448 1542 Buildings, portable: prefabricated metal; commercial & office building contractors

(G-10866)
SWEEPY GROUP PRODUCTS LLC
14501 Nw 60th Ave Unit 37 (33014-2808)
PHONE..................................305 556-3450
EMP: 5
SALES: 4.5MM **Privately Held**
SIC: 3565 Mfg Packaging Machinery

(G-10867)
TEXENE LLC
Also Called: Manufacturer
5860 Miami Lakes Dr E (33014-2402)
PHONE..................................305 200-5001
Carlos Echeverria, *CEO*
Dee Glowa, *Accountant*
▼ **EMP:** 12 **EST:** 2007
SALES (est): 923.8K **Privately Held**
WEB: www.texene.com
SIC: 2394 2869 5131 Tarpaulins, fabric: made from purchased materials; olefins; synthetic fabrics

(G-10868)
TONER CARTRIDGE RECHARGE INC
7923 Nw 163rd Ter (33016-6105)
PHONE..................................305 968-1045
Nino Clares-Prieto, *President*
Marcia Clares, *Admin Sec*
EMP: 5 **EST:** 1997
SALES (est): 623.9K **Privately Held**
SIC: 3955 Print cartridges for laser & other computer printers

(G-10869)
TOP DRAWER INC
5190 Nw 165th St (33014-6303)
PHONE..................................305 620-1102
Richard Herman, *President*
Adam Herman, *COO*
Craig Herman, *Vice Pres*
Catalina Bermudez, *Office Mgr*
EMP: 10 **EST:** 1974
SQ FT: 10,000
SALES (est): 1MM **Privately Held**
WEB: www.topdrawermediasolutions.com
SIC: 2752 Commercial printing, offset

(G-10870)
TOP DRAWER PRINTERS INC
5190 Nw 165th St (33014-6303)
PHONE..................................305 620-1102
Richard E Herman, *President*
Adam Herman, *COO*
Craig F Herman, *Vice Pres*
Marilyn Herman, *Treasurer*
Catalina Bermudez, *Office Mgr*
EMP: 21 **EST:** 1974
SQ FT: 10,000
SALES (est): 1.5MM **Privately Held**
SIC: 2752 Commercial printing, offset

(G-10871)
TORRO FOODS LLC
6725 Main St (33014-2071)
PHONE..................................305 558-3212
Hector F Rodriguez, *Principal*
EMP: 6 **EST:** 2009
SALES (est): 495.6K **Privately Held**
SIC: 2099 Food preparations

(G-10872)
UNIK DESIGN & PRINT INC
10220 Nw 80th Ave (33016-2308)
PHONE..................................786 355-6877
Beatriz Cobena, *Principal*
EMP: 7 **EST:** 2018
SALES (est): 92.3K **Privately Held**
SIC: 2752 Commercial printing, lithographic

(G-10873)
UNITED SIERRA GROUP CORP
8200 Commerce Way (33016-1536)
PHONE..................................305 297-5835
Bernadett Csillag, *President*
David Khan, *Vice Pres*
Nasir M Khan, *Director*
Alicia Anderson, *Creative Dir*
EMP: 65 **EST:** 2018
SALES (est): 4.3MM **Privately Held**
SIC: 2842 Bleaches, household: dry or liquid

(G-10874)
UNIVERSAL WELDING SERVICE CO
9921 Nw 80th Ave Unit 1u (33016-2363)
PHONE..................................305 898-9130
EMP: 6 **EST:** 2018
SALES (est): 546.9K **Privately Held**
SIC: 3441 Fabricated structural metal

(G-10875)
UNIWARE HOUSEWARE CORP
5275 Nw 163rd St (33014-6225)
PHONE..................................305 952-4958
Lily Dong, *President*
EMP: 33 **Privately Held**
WEB: www.uniwarehouseware.com
SIC: 3634 Electric housewares & fans
PA: Uniware Houseware Corp.
120 Wilshire Blvd Ste B
Brentwood NY 11717

(G-10876)
US BINDERY INC
5330 Nw 161st St (33014-6224)
PHONE..................................305 622-7070
Celestino Carballo Sr, *President*
Celestino A Carballo Jr, *Vice Pres*
Nayza Hernandez, *Vice Pres*
Ron Dearing, *Executive*
EMP: 28 **EST:** 1977
SQ FT: 18,000
SALES (est): 2.2MM **Privately Held**
SIC: 2789 Binding only: books, pamphlets, magazines, etc.

(G-10877)
USPHARMA LTD
13900 Nw 57th Ct (33014-3103)
PHONE..................................954 817-4418
Dr Manesh A Dixit, *CEO*
Manoharan Govindaraj, *CFO*
William Franco, *Manager*
Diego Martini, *Manager*
Ariel Robelo, *Technology*
EMP: 78 **EST:** 2017
SQ FT: 150,000
SALES (est): 12.7MM **Privately Held**
WEB: www.uspharmaltd.com
SIC: 2834 5122 Pharmaceutical preparations; pharmaceuticals

(G-10878)
VANLEX CLOTHING INC
5850 Miami Lakes Dr E (33014-2402)
PHONE..................................305 431-4669
Ish Gonzalez, *President*
EMP: 20 **EST:** 2009
SALES (est): 1.1MM **Privately Held**
WEB: www.vanlexclothing.com
SIC: 2396 2759 3953 Screen printing on fabric articles; screen printing; screens, textile printing

(G-10879)
VISION WEB OFFSET LLC
13930 Nw 60th Ave (33014-3127)
PHONE..................................305 433-6188
Mohamed Sadik, *President*
EMP: 10 **EST:** 2013
SALES (est): 571.6K **Privately Held**
SIC: 2759 Magazines: printing

(G-10880)
WHEELER TRADING INC
5851 Nw 159th St (33014-6717)
PHONE..................................305 430-7100
Emanuel Daskos, *President*
▲ **EMP:** 13 **EST:** 2001
SALES (est): 363.8K **Privately Held**
SIC: 2395 Tucking, for the trade

(G-10881)
WORTH INTL MEDIA GROUP (PA)
Also Called: Recommend Magazine
5979 Nw 151st St Ste 120 (33014-2448)
P.O. Box 171070, Hialeah (33017-1070)
PHONE..................................305 826-4763
Harold Herman, *President*
Laurel A Herman, *Exec VP*
Geraldine Ellis, *Vice Pres*
Terrence Murphy, *Vice Pres*
Marcia Bayer, *VP Sales*
◆ **EMP:** 40 **EST:** 1970
SQ FT: 6,500
SALES (est): 12.7MM **Privately Held**
WEB: www.recommend.com
SIC: 2721 Magazines: publishing only, not printed on site

(G-10882)
XCESSIVE INC
Also Called: Xcessive Engines
8714 Nw 153rd Ter (33018-1353)
PHONE..................................866 919-9527
Rick Malaga, *President*
◆ **EMP:** 5 **EST:** 2007
SQ FT: 3,000
SALES (est): 568.6K **Privately Held**
WEB: www.xcessiveinc.com
SIC: 3462 3519 Automotive & internal combustion engine forgings; marine engines

(G-10883)
YFAN LLC
5340 Nw 163rd St (33014-6228)
PHONE..................................786 453-3724
Jose A Yamin, *Principal*
EMP: 8 **EST:** 2015
SALES (est): 94.1K **Privately Held**
SIC: 2099 Food preparations

Miami Shores
Miami-Dade County

(G-10884)
ENCHANTING CREATIONS
210 Ne 98th St (33138-2408)
PHONE..................................305 978-2828
Alex Darnel Matamoros, *Owner*
EMP: 8 **EST:** 2011
SALES (est): 492.9K **Privately Held**
WEB: www.midisparate.design
SIC: 2051 Bakery: wholesale or wholesale/retail combined

(G-10885)
HERITAGE SKIN CARE INC
180 Ne 99th St (33138-2341)
PHONE..................................305 757-9264
Fax: 305 757-9267
▲ **EMP:** 11
SALES (est): 1.4MM **Privately Held**
SIC: 2834 Mfg Pharmaceutical Preparations

(G-10886)
UNITED STATES GYPSUM COMPANY
3301 Nw 125th St (33167-2409)
PHONE..................................305 688-8744
Mike Falcon, *Branch Mgr*
EMP: 70
SALES (corp-wide): 10.7B **Privately Held**
WEB: www.usg.com
SIC: 3275 Gypsum board
HQ: United States Gypsum Company
550 W Adams St Ste 1300
Chicago IL 60661
312 606-4000

Miami Springs
Miami-Dade County

(G-10887)
AIRLOCK USA LLC
145 Curtiss Pkwy (33166-5220)
PHONE..................................305 888-6454
Linda Carlson, *Principal*
EMP: 11 **EST:** 2007
SQ FT: 1,933
SALES (est): 378.1K **Privately Held**
SIC: 3443 Airlocks

(G-10888)
CALEV SYSTEMS INC (PA)
5575 Nw 36th St (33166-5812)
PHONE..................................786 837-2343
Mark Calev, *CEO*
Christine Palermo, *Chief*
Rick De Armas, *COO*
Loyd Walker, *Exec VP*
Carlos Cueto, *Vice Pres*
◆ **EMP:** 26 **EST:** 2000
SQ FT: 4,600
SALES (est): 18.5MM **Privately Held**
WEB: www.calevsystems.com
SIC: 2752 8748 Commercial printing, offset; business consulting

(G-10889)
CARIBBEAN SHUTTER LLC
633 De Soto Dr (33166-6012)
PHONE..................................305 202-0501
Gil A Rodriguez, *Manager*
EMP: 6 **EST:** 2017
SALES (est): 163.2K **Privately Held**
SIC: 3442 Shutters, door or window: metal

(G-10890)
DOLPHIN/CURTIS PUBLISHING CO (PA)
Also Called: Dolphin Publishing
53 Curtiss Pkwy (33166-5218)
P.O. Box 526600, Miami (33152-6600)
PHONE..................................305 594-0508
Thomas Curtis, *President*
Debrah Curtis, *Vice Pres*
Tammi Curtis, *Treasurer*
Andrew Cohen, *Admin Sec*
EMP: 8 **EST:** 1974
SQ FT: 2,000
SALES (est): 1.1MM **Privately Held**
SIC: 2721 Magazines: publishing only, not printed on site

(G-10891)
INTERNATIONAL FOOD EQP INC
1280 Partridge Ave (33166-3128)
PHONE..................................305 785-5100
Robert Klopfenstein, *President*
Bruce D Barrington, *Director*
Richard L Owens, *Director*
Charles E Verkler, *Admin Sec*
EMP: 8 **EST:** 1980
SALES (est): 274.4K **Privately Held**
SIC: 3589 Food warming equipment, commercial

(G-10892)
INTRATAB LABS INC
424 Hunting Lodge Dr (33166-5742)
PHONE..................................305 887-5850
Rudy Emmelot, *CEO*
John McCarty, *President*
John A McCarty, *Principal*
EMP: 13 **EST:** 2012
SALES (est): 750K **Privately Held**
SIC: 2834 Pharmaceutical preparations

(G-10893)
LINDORM INC
601 Plover Ave (33166-3928)
PHONE..................................305 888-0762
Ulf Erlingsson, *CEO*
EMP: 10 **EST:** 2006
SALES (est): 711.6K **Privately Held**
WEB: www.lindorm.com
SIC: 3826 Environmental testing equipment

(G-10894)
LOMBARDIS WOODWORKING
1000 Oriole Ave (33166-3847)
PHONE..................................305 439-7208
Paul Christopher Lombardi, *President*
Lizette Martinez, *CIO*
EMP: 7 **EST:** 2009
SALES (est): 86.5K **Privately Held**
WEB: www.lombardiswoodworking.net
SIC: 2431 Millwork

(G-10895)
MUCHOCHOS SAW MILL & PALLETS ✪
356 Palmetto Dr A (33166-5824)
PHONE..................................786 899-0535
EMP: 9 **EST:** 2020
SALES (est): 391.3K **Privately Held**
SIC: 2448 Pallets, wood

(G-10896)
OBEM FOODS INC
Also Called: Cheesecake Etc Desserts
400 Swallow Dr (33166-4432)
PHONE..................................305 887-0258
Orlando Irsula, *President*
Belinda Irsula, *Vice Pres*
EMP: 5 **EST:** 2011
SALES (est): 474.9K **Privately Held**
WEB: www.obemfoods.com
SIC: 2051 Bread, cake & related products

(G-10897)
RHODES BROTHERS MIAMI INC
37 Deer Run (33166-5785)
PHONE..................................305 456-9682
John Rhodes, *Principal*
EMP: 6 **EST:** 2010
SALES (est): 104.3K **Privately Held**
SIC: 2869 Fuels

(G-10898)
T & W INC
Also Called: Cheesecake, Etc
400 Swallow Dr (33166-4432)
PHONE..................................305 887-0258
William J Wolar, *President*
Suzanne Conlon Wolar, *Vice Pres*
Terry Wolar, *Director*
William Wolar Sr, *Director*
EMP: 7 **EST:** 1974
SQ FT: 10,000
SALES (est): 690.6K **Privately Held**
SIC: 2051 Bread, cake & related products

Micanopy
Alachua County

(G-10899)
ANALYTICAL RESEARCH SYSTEMS
Also Called: ARS
12109 Highway 441 S (32667-5310)
P.O. Box 140218, Gainesville (32614-0218)
PHONE..................................352 466-0051
ARA Manukian, *President*
Lloyde Manukian, *Principal*
Rudy Strohschein, *Vice Pres*
EMP: 10 **EST:** 1994
SQ FT: 7,000
SALES (est): 902.4K **Privately Held**
WEB: www.ars-fla.com
SIC: 3826 8732 8711 8748 Analytical instruments; business research service; engineering services; business consulting; scientific instruments

(G-10900)
FRONTIER ELECTRONICS
Also Called: Frontier Communications
255 W Smith Ave (32667-4025)
PHONE..................................954 255-0911
Robert Mance, *President*
Jesse Falto, *Education*
EMP: 8 **EST:** 1998
SALES (est): 148K **Privately Held**
SIC: 3812 Antennas, radar or communications

(G-10901)
GOODWIN LUMBER COMPANY INC
Also Called: Goodwin Heart Pine Company
106 Sw 109th Pl (32667-3441)
PHONE..................................352 466-0339
George Goodwin, *President*
Carol Goodwin, *President*
Andrew Stjames, *General Mgr*
Jeffrey L Forbes, *Marketing Mgr*
Jeffrey Forbes, *Mktg Coord*
EMP: 13 **EST:** 1984
SQ FT: 35,000
SALES (est): 3.1MM **Privately Held**
WEB: www.tantumandhumphrey.com
SIC: 2426 2435 2431 Flooring, hardwood; hardwood veneer & plywood; millwork

(G-10902)
JER-AIR MANUFACTURING INC
22750 Highway 441 N (32667-7529)
P.O. Box 656, Mc Intosh (32664-0656)
PHONE..................................352 591-2674
C Jerry Philman, *President*
Janice Philman, *Vice Pres*
EMP: 37 **EST:** 1974
SQ FT: 10,000
SALES (est): 3.5MM **Privately Held**
WEB: www.jerair.com
SIC: 3444 3585 3433 Ducts, sheet metal; refrigeration & heating equipment; heating equipment, except electric

(G-10903)
JPT-TECH LLC
11094 Nw 188th Street Rd (32667-8030)
PHONE..................................352 219-7860
Jacques Patrick Thimote,
EMP: 6 **EST:** 2012
SALES (est): 157K **Privately Held**
WEB: www.jpttech.com
SIC: 3571 Computers, digital, analog or hybrid

Middleburg
Clay County

(G-10904)
BLACK CREEK LOGGING
4159 County Road 218 (32068-4846)
P.O. Box 520 (32050-0520)
PHONE..................................904 591-9681
EMP: 6 **EST:** 2010
SALES (est): 254.2K **Privately Held**
SIC: 2411 Logging

(G-10905)
GREENES WLDG & FABRICATION LLC
32 Mink Ave (32068-4835)
PHONE..................................904 773-3101
Kelsie M Greene, *Manager*
Raymond M Greene,
EMP: 6 **EST:** 2016
SALES (est): 233.4K **Privately Held**
WEB: www.greeneswelding.com
SIC: 3441 7692 Fabricated structural metal; welding repair

(G-10906)
HUNTLEY STEMWOOD INC
2785 Black Creek Dr (32068-5713)
PHONE..................................904 237-4005
John Huntley Jr, *President*
EMP: 7 **EST:** 1978
SALES (est): 928K **Privately Held**
SIC: 2411 Pulpwood contractors engaged in cutting

(G-10907)
IRONWORKS INC OF ORANGE PARK
1701 Blanding Blvd (32068-4095)
P.O. Box 65849, Orange Park (32065-0015)
PHONE..................................904 291-9330
Michael A Vallencourt, *President*
EMP: 22 **EST:** 1998
SALES (est): 725.6K **Privately Held**
SIC: 3446 Architectural metalwork

(G-10908)
KINGDOM COATINGS INC
2779 Indigo Cir (32068-6083)
PHONE..................................904 600-1424
Nicholas C Oliver, *President*
EMP: 6 **EST:** 2016
SALES (est): 71.8K **Privately Held**
SIC: 3479 Metal coating & allied service

(G-10909)
MY CUSTOM CART LLC
2581 Blanding Blvd (32068-5177)
PHONE..................................904 214-3723
EMP: 7 **EST:** 2016
SALES (est): 220.9K **Privately Held**
WEB: www.my-custom-cart.business.site
SIC: 3799 5599 5088 Golf carts, powered; golf cart, powered; golf carts

(G-10910)
N & H CONSTRUCTION INC
1708 Nolan Rd (32068-3054)
PHONE..................................904 282-2224
EMP: 15
SALES (est): 2.1MM **Privately Held**
SIC: 3669 Mfg Communications Equipment

(G-10911)
PADGETTS PULPWOOD INC
3745 Old Jennings Rd (32068-3733)
PHONE..................................904 282-5112
Jerry A Padgett, *President*
Anita Paggett, *Admin Sec*
EMP: 7 **EST:** 1959
SALES (est): 845.6K **Privately Held**
SIC: 2411 Pulpwood contractors engaged in cutting

(G-10912)
REILEY TOOL COMPANY LLC
3950 Equestrian Ct (32068-3296)
PHONE..................................360 929-0350
Jonathon Reiley, *Manager*
EMP: 7 **EST:** 2018
SALES (est): 471.2K **Privately Held**
SIC: 3541 Machine tools, metal cutting type

(G-10913)
UNIVERSAL PROF COATINGS INC
2125 Candlewood Ct (32068-3618)
PHONE..................................954 294-5236
Brian Wherry, *Principal*
EMP: 7 **EST:** 2011
SALES (est): 98.9K **Privately Held**
SIC: 3479 Metal coating & allied service

(G-10914)
US INK A DIV SUN CHEM CORP
Also Called: US Ink A Division Sun Chemical
4725 Javeline Cir (32068-6431)
PHONE..................................904 786-1474
Mike Dodd, *President*
◆ **EMP:** 6 **EST:** 2010
SALES (est): 124.4K **Privately Held**
SIC: 2893 Printing ink

(G-10915)
WHITLEY WELDING COMPANY L
4280 Chokeberry Rd (32068-7003)
PHONE..................................904 576-3410
EMP: 6 **EST:** 2018
SALES (est): 520.8K **Privately Held**
SIC: 7692 Welding repair

(G-10916)
XCALIBUR ARCFT SOLUTIONS LLC
2859 Longleaf Ranch Cir (32068-6353)
PHONE..................................305 744-2830
Gray Rivera, *Manager*
EMP: 8 **EST:** 2018
SALES (est): 452.4K **Privately Held**
WEB: www.xcaliburaircraftsolutions.com
SIC: 3728 Aircraft parts & equipment

Midway
Gadsden County

(G-10917)
EXCEL MILLWORK & MOULDING INC
7001 Fortune Blvd (32343-6520)
P.O. Box 1086, Leavenworth WA (98826-1586)
PHONE..................................850 576-7228
Scott Campbell, *President*
Jerry W Ruis, *President*
Donald Ray Ruis, *Vice Pres*
EMP: 26 **EST:** 1989
SQ FT: 35,000
SALES (est): 1.2MM **Privately Held**
WEB: www.woodindustry.com
SIC: 2431 5031 2499 Moldings, wood: unfinished & prefinished; woodwork, interior & ornamental; molding, all materials; decorative wood & woodwork

(G-10918)
SUPERIOR REDI-MIX
61 Commerce Ln (32343-6608)
PHONE..................................850 575-1532
Danny Colins, *Owner*
EMP: 11 **EST:** 2004
SALES (est): 542.4K **Privately Held**
SIC: 3273 Ready-mixed concrete

(G-10919)
T-FORMATION INC TALLAHASSEE
864 Commerce Blvd (32343-6618)
PHONE..................................850 574-0122
Alan H Gentry, *President*
Edwin D Mitchell, *Assistant VP*
Barton R Mitchell, *Vice Pres*
Philip Brown, *CFO*
Melanie D Mitchell, *Controller*
EMP: 100
SQ FT: 42,000
SALES (est): 13MM **Privately Held**
WEB: www.tformation.com
SIC: 2399 Emblems, badges & insignia

Milton
Santa Rosa County

(G-10920)
AEROSYNC ENGRG CONSULTING INC
Also Called: Aerosync Support
5848 Moors Oaks Dr (32583-2807)
PHONE..................................316 208-3367
Greg F Bartlett, *President*
Diana Bartlett, *Vice Pres*
EMP: 6 **EST:** 2012
SQ FT: 2,500
SALES (est): 1MM **Privately Held**
WEB: www.aerosyncsupport.com
SIC: 3724 Aircraft engines & engine parts

(G-10921)
ANDREWS CABINET
4025 Bell Ln (32571-2755)
PHONE..................................850 994-0836
Dearl Andrews Jr, *President*
Paul S Andrews, *Principal*
Oliver Scott, *Principal*
Donald W Andrews, *Vice Pres*
EMP: 10 **EST:** 1982
SQ FT: 4,000
SALES (est): 602.1K **Privately Held**
SIC: 2434 Wood kitchen cabinets

(G-10922)
BLACKWATER FOLK ART INC
4917 Glover Ln (32570-4528)
P.O. Box 488, Bagdad (32530-0488)
PHONE..................................850 623-3470
Pam Mitchell, *President*
EMP: 6 **EST:** 1990
SALES (est): 250K **Privately Held**
WEB: www.blackwaterfolkart.com
SIC: 2499 3469 3444 Kitchen, bathroom & household ware: wood; metal stampings; sheet metalwork

(G-10923)
BLACKWATER TRUSS SYSTEMS LLC
6603 Old Bagdad Hwy (32583-7603)
P.O. Box 186, Bagdad (32530-0186)
PHONE..................................850 623-1414
Kenneth J Smith, *Mng Member*
Faye E Smith,
K David Smith,
Meredith J Smith,
EMP: 6 **EST:** 2009
SQ FT: 3,000
SALES (est): 600K **Privately Held**
WEB: www.blackwatertruss.com
SIC: 3443 Truss plates, metal

(G-10924)
BLACKWTER METAL SLS NW FLA LLC
8736 Highway 87 N (32570-9035)
PHONE..................................850 622-1414
Ken Smith, *Manager*
EMP: 6 **EST:** 2017
SALES (est): 108.2K **Privately Held**
WEB: www.blackwatertruss.com
SIC: 3999 Manufacturing industries

(G-10925)
C & S SIGNS INC
8895 S Lynn Rd (32583-2581)
PHONE..................................850 983-9540
Jessica Wilbourn, *President*
Stanley Wilbourn, *President*
EMP: 7 **EST:** 1987
SQ FT: 38,000
SALES (est): 681.2K **Privately Held**
WEB: www.cssigns.com
SIC: 3993 Electric signs

(G-10926)
CENTRAL WIRE INDUSTRIES LLC
Also Called: Strand Core
5881 Commerce Rd (32583-2318)
PHONE..................................850 983-9926
Paul From, *President*
Tommy Leonard, *Maint Spvr*
Chris Charron, *CFO*
▲ **EMP:** 35 **EST:** 2014
SALES (est): 4.6MM **Privately Held**
WEB: www.strandcore.com
SIC: 3496 Miscellaneous fabricated wire products

(G-10927)
EMERALD COAST TRUSS LLC
Also Called: Milton Truss Company
5817 Commerce Rd (32583-2318)
P.O. Box 888 (32572-0888)
PHONE..................................850 623-1967
Charles Smith, *Mng Member*
Deanna D Smith,
EMP: 49 **EST:** 1980
SQ FT: 9,000
SALES (est): 1MM **Privately Held**
WEB: www.miltontruss.com
SIC: 2439 Trusses, wooden roof

(G-10928)
FORMWELD FITTING INC
8118 Progress Dr (32583-7700)
PHONE..................................850 626-4888
Charles Hartwig, *President*
Clint Dinwiddie, *Sales Staff*
Dennis Hudson, *Manager*
EMP: 27 **EST:** 1989
SQ FT: 30,000
SALES (est): 4.1MM **Privately Held**
WEB: www.formweldfitting.us
SIC: 3498 3443 3494 Fabricated pipe & fittings; fabricated plate work (boiler shop); valves & pipe fittings

(G-10929)
FOSSCO INC
3948 Garcon Point Rd (32583-9035)
PHONE..................................850 983-1330
Scott Foss, *President*
EMP: 7 **EST:** 2005
SQ FT: 12,500
SALES (est): 1.4MM **Privately Held**
WEB: www.fosscoinc.com
SIC: 3724 Aircraft engines & engine parts

(G-10930)
GRACE BIBLE CHURCH
6331 Chestnut St (32570-8794)
P.O. Box 643 (32572-0643)
PHONE..................................850 623-4671
Tod Brainard, *Pastor*
EMP: 9 **EST:** 1999
SALES (est): 140.7K **Privately Held**
WEB: www.gracebiblechurchmilton.com
SIC: 2759 8661 Commercial printing; miscellaneous denomination church

(G-10931)
GROUP III ASPHALT INC
6108 Wastle Rd (32583-8941)
P.O. Box 3687, Pensacola (32516-3687)
PHONE..................................850 983-0611
Johnnie Long, *President*
Jerry Long, *Vice Pres*
Donald Long, *Treasurer*
EMP: 10 **EST:** 1995
SALES (est): 1.7MM **Privately Held**
WEB: www.panhandlegradingandpaving.com
SIC: 2951 5032 Asphalt & asphaltic paving mixtures (not from refineries); paving materials

(G-10932)
GULF CABLE LLC
5700 Industrial Blvd (32583-8736)
PHONE..................................201 720-2417
Orin Singh, *Branch Mgr*
EMP: 150
SALES (corp-wide): 100.3MM **Privately Held**
WEB: www.wtecenergy.com
SIC: 2298 Cable, fiber

PA: Gulf Cable, Llc
777 Terrace Ave Ste 101
Hasbrouck Heights NJ 07604
201 242-9906

(G-10933)
JOINERS ENTERPRISES INC
4973 Joiner Cir (32583-2781)
PHONE..................................850 623-5593
William Joiner, *President*
Kimberly Jerenigan, *Corp Secy*
EMP: 14 **EST:** 1973
SALES (est): 667.3K **Privately Held**
SIC: 2411 Logging

(G-10934)
KOTTLER RESEARCH CORP
Also Called: K R C
2000 Garcon Point Rd (32583-7453)
PHONE..................................850 776-7021
Daniel N Kottler, *President*
Pamela Kottler, *Corp Secy*
▲ **EMP:** 7 **EST:** 1986
SQ FT: 7,000
SALES (est): 497.1K **Privately Held**
SIC: 3843 Impression material, dental

(G-10935)
MILTON NEWSPAPERS INC
Also Called: The Press Gazette
6576 Caroline St (32570-4778)
PHONE..................................850 623-2120
Jim Fletcher, *Principal*
EMP: 1195 **EST:** 1907
SQ FT: 10,000
SALES (est): 1.6MM
SALES (corp-wide): 3.4B **Publicly Held**
WEB: www.srpressgazette.com
SIC: 2711 2752 Newspapers, publishing & printing; commercial printing, lithographic
HQ: Panama City News Herald
501 W 11th St
Panama City FL 32401
850 747-5000

(G-10936)
PIONEER AEROSPACE CORPORATION
Airlift Technologies Intl
8101 Opportunity Dr (32583-8728)
PHONE..................................850 623-3330
Bryon Woram, *President*
EMP: 10
SQ FT: 11,907
SALES (corp-wide): 639.8MM **Privately Held**
WEB: www.pioneeraero.com
SIC: 3728 Aircraft assemblies, subassemblies & parts
HQ: Pioneer Aerospace Corporation
131 Phoenix Xing
Bloomfield CT 06002
860 528-0092

(G-10937)
PRODAIR CORPORATION (HQ)
4575 Highway 90 (32571-2043)
PHONE..................................850 994-5511
Jessica J Holliday, *CEO*
James T Christy, *President*
Richard L Sutton, *Vice Pres*
Tom Van Dorp, *Vice Pres*
Margaret Pulgini, *Treasurer*
EMP: 5 **EST:** 1972
SALES (est): 110.1MM
SALES (corp-wide): 8.8B **Publicly Held**
WEB: www.airproducts.com
SIC: 2813 Industrial gases
PA: Air Products And Chemicals, Inc.
7201 Hamilton Blvd
Allentown PA 18195
610 481-4911

(G-10938)
PRODUCTION METAL STAMPINGS
8133 Opportunity Dr (32583-8728)
PHONE..................................850 981-8240
T Barry Fulford, *President*
Meriel C Fulford, *Vice Pres*
EMP: 10 **EST:** 1988
SQ FT: 8,000
SALES (est): 1.4MM **Privately Held**
WEB: www.productionmetalstampings.com
SIC: 3599 3469 7692 3542 Machine & other job shop work; custom machinery; metal stampings; welding repair; machine tools, metal forming type; sheet metalwork

(G-10939)
R & K BUILDINGS INC
Also Called: R & K Portable Builders
4213 Avalon Blvd (32583-2810)
PHONE..................................850 995-9525
Glennon Russell, *President*
Toby Russell, *Vice Pres*
Ashley Russell, *Admin Sec*
EMP: 38 **EST:** 1981
SQ FT: 1,408
SALES (est): 2.6MM **Privately Held**
WEB: www.rnkbuildings.com
SIC: 3448 Prefabricated metal buildings

(G-10940)
STEP ZONE LLC
6674 Elva St (32570-4723)
PHONE..................................850 983-3758
Fax: 850 983-3358
EMP: 5
SALES (est): 705.4K **Privately Held**
SIC: 2451 Mfg Mobile Homes

(G-10941)
STERLING FIBERS INC
5005 Sterling Way (32571-2799)
PHONE..................................850 994-5311
James Hagerott, *President*
Susan Allender, *Vice Pres*
Brian Hagerott, *Production*
◆ **EMP:** 70
SALES (est): 13.6MM **Privately Held**
WEB: www.sterlingfibers.com
SIC: 2824 Acrylic fibers

(G-10942)
SYSTEMATIX INC
5953 Commerce Rd (32583-2320)
PHONE..................................850 983-2213
James S Hogan, *President*
Linda B Hogan, *Treasurer*
EMP: 21 **EST:** 1989
SQ FT: 11,000
SALES (est): 3MM **Privately Held**
WEB: www.systematix.org
SIC: 3646 2522 Desk lamps, commercial; chairs, office: padded or plain, except wood

(G-10943)
TITAN SPECIALTY CNSTR INC
Also Called: Titan Sunrooms
8188 Armstrong Rd (32583-8738)
PHONE..................................850 916-7660
Fred D Genkin, *President*
▲ **EMP:** 45 **EST:** 2002
SALES (est): 5.3MM **Privately Held**
WEB: www.titansunrooms.com
SIC: 3448 1761 3471 3354 Sunrooms, prefabricated metal; gutter & downspout contractor; coloring & finishing of aluminum or formed products; aluminum extruded products

(G-10944)
TPR SYSTEMS INC
8100 Armstrong Rd (32583-8738)
PHONE..................................850 983-8600
Richard Todd, *Principal*
EMP: 13 **EST:** 2014
SALES (est): 764.8K **Privately Held**
WEB: www.tpr-systems.com
SIC: 3599 Machine shop, jobbing & repair

(G-10945)
TURBINE PARTS REPAIR INC
8100 Armstrong Rd (32583-8738)
PHONE..................................850 983-8600
Chuck Pyritz, *Principal*
EMP: 6 **EST:** 2006
SALES (est): 813.9K **Privately Held**
WEB: www.turbinepartsrepair.com
SIC: 3599 Machine shop, jobbing & repair

(G-10946)
WHEEL WRIGHT
6899 Deception Rd (32583-8187)
PHONE..................................850 626-2662
George Pilling, *Principal*
EMP: 6 **EST:** 2008
SALES (est): 91.7K **Privately Held**
SIC: 3312 Blast furnaces & steel mills

(G-10947)
WHIP-IT INVENTIONS INC (PA)
5946 Commerce Rd (32583-2319)
PHONE..................................850 626-6300
John Alessi, *CEO*
Joann Watson, *COO*
Mark Kreisler, *CFO*
EMP: 27 **EST:** 2010
SQ FT: 12,000
SALES (est): 3MM **Privately Held**
WEB: www.amazingwhipit.com
SIC: 2841 Soap & other detergents

(G-10948)
WPR INC
4175 Briarglen Rd (32583-2884)
PHONE..................................850 626-7713
D Pete Russell, *President*
Lauren Coogle, *Controller*
Lauren C Coogle, *Controller*
EMP: 36 **EST:** 1973
SQ FT: 22,784
SALES (est): 6.5MM **Privately Held**
WEB: www.wprincfl.com
SIC: 3272 3273 Septic tanks, concrete; ready-mixed concrete

Mims
Brevard County

(G-10949)
ARI SPECIALTIES LLC
3660 Us Highway 1 (32754-5505)
P.O. Box 765 (32754-0765)
PHONE..................................321 269-2244
Eric A Anderson,
EMP: 6 **EST:** 2008
SALES (est): 337.9K **Privately Held**
SIC: 3999 Manufacturing industries

(G-10950)
CTR INDUSTRIES
3980 Hammock Rd (32754-5693)
P.O. Box 171 (32754-0171)
PHONE..................................321 264-1458
George L Newman, *Principal*
EMP: 8 **EST:** 2007
SALES (est): 433K **Privately Held**
SIC: 3999 Manufacturing industries

(G-10951)
INDUSTRIAL FILTER PUMP MFG CO
2680 Us Highway 1 (32754-3804)
P.O. Box 1079 (32754-1079)
PHONE..................................708 656-7800
John Keegan, *CEO*
Zubin Mehta, *Director*
Gregory Shalov, *Director*
▲ **EMP:** 7 **EST:** 2004
SALES (est): 862.9K **Privately Held**
WEB: www.industrialfilter.com
SIC: 3569 Filters, general line: industrial; filters

(G-10952)
S AJ CABINETS INC
4950 Harrison Rd (32754-4617)
PHONE..................................321 264-2872
Andrew Johnson, *Principal*
EMP: 6 **EST:** 2012
SALES (est): 145.7K **Privately Held**
SIC: 2434 Wood kitchen cabinets

(G-10953)
STAT BIOMEDICAL LLC
2865 Night Heron Dr (32754-6508)
PHONE..................................210 365-1495
Troy Richie, *Principal*
EMP: 6 **EST:** 2016
SALES (est): 506.5K **Privately Held**
WEB: www.stat-biomedical.com
SIC: 2836 Biological products, except diagnostic

Minneola
Lake County

(G-10954)
GUERRILLA PRTG SOLUTIONS LLC
Also Called: Minuteman Press
304 Mohawk Rd (34715-7434)
PHONE..................................352 394-7770
Kenneth S Rose, *Principal*
EMP: 6 **EST:** 2005
SALES (est): 551.8K **Privately Held**
WEB: www.chanhassen-mn.minuteman-press.com
SIC: 2752 Commercial printing, lithographic

(G-10955)
JUAN DIAZ STUCCO SPC INC
825 High Pointe Cir (34715-7417)
PHONE..................................407 402-1912
William Marquet, *Principal*
EMP: 6 **EST:** 2008
SALES (est): 70.2K **Privately Held**
SIC: 3299 Stucco

(G-10956)
SYNERGISTIC OFFICE SOLUTIONS
Also Called: SOS Software
11350 Tuscarora Ln (34715-7914)
PHONE..................................352 242-9100
Seth Krieger, *President*
Katherine Peres, *Vice Pres*
Stephane Tessier, *Prgrmr*
Linda Crosby, *Executive*
Manon Faucher, *Representative*
EMP: 10 **EST:** 1985
SALES (est): 1MM **Privately Held**
WEB: www.sosoft.com
SIC: 7372 Application computer software

(G-10957)
TREADWAY INDUSTRIES LLC
Also Called: Elega Fam FL More Drect Axic
410 Virginia St (34715-7496)
PHONE..................................352 326-3313
Steve Vanderwall, *Project Mgr*
Lyonel Nichols, *Opers Staff*
Chip Robart, *Engineer*
Coral Nolan, *Marketing Staff*
Paul C Whitehouse,
▼ **EMP:** 20 **EST:** 1983
SALES (est): 2.6MM **Privately Held**
WEB: www.treadwayindustries.com
SIC: 3069 Foam rubber

Miramar
Broward County

(G-10958)
3A PRODUCTS LLC
2737 N Commerce Pkwy (33025-3955)
PHONE..................................754 263-2968
Preeti Singh, *President*
Rohit Singh, *Agent*
EMP: 5 **EST:** 2014
SQ FT: 1,500
SALES (est): 800K **Privately Held**
WEB: www.3aproducts.com
SIC: 3086 Packaging & shipping materials, foamed plastic

(G-10959)
A&R XPRESS INC
9997 Nandina St (33025-3229)
PHONE..................................954 744-4343
Alberto Ruiz, *President*
EMP: 6 **EST:** 2013
SALES (est): 181.2K **Privately Held**
SIC: 3799 Automobile trailer chassis

(G-10960)
ABB INC
A B B Marine &TUrbo Charger
10004 Premier Pkwy (33025-3210)
PHONE..................................954 450-9544
EMP: 50
SALES (corp-wide): 34.3B **Privately Held**
SIC: 3519 Mfg Internal Combustion Engines

HQ: Abb Inc.
305 Gregson Dr
Cary NC 27511

(G-10961)
ADVANCED SERVICES INTL INC
3600 Caldwell Rd Ste 406 (33027)
PHONE....................................954 889-1366
Glory Manolo, *Office Mgr*
EMP: 6 **EST:** 2011
SALES (est): 836.7K **Privately Held**
WEB: www.adsintl.net
SIC: 7372 Prepackaged software

(G-10962)
AFINA SYSTEMS INC (DH)
3350 Sw 148th Ave Ste 401 (33027-3259)
PHONE....................................305 261-1433
Pedro Galatas, *President*
Fernando Rivera, *Treasurer*
Javier San Juan, *Executive*
◆ **EMP:** 9 **EST:** 2000
SALES (est): 2.5MM
SALES (corp-wide): 24.6B **Publicly Held**
WEB: www.westconcomstor.com
SIC: 7372 Prepackaged software
HQ: Westcon Group, Inc.
520 White Plains Rd # 200
Tarrytown NY 10591
914 829-7000

(G-10963)
ALCO SERVICES INC
15501 Sw 29th St (33027-5255)
PHONE....................................954 538-2189
Christopher R Celtruda, *President*
Nathan A Skop, *Exec VP*
Jikun Kim, *CFO*
EMP: 47 **EST:** 2013
SQ FT: 35,000
SALES (est): 1MM
SALES (corp-wide): 178.4MM **Privately Held**
WEB: www.goallclear.com
SIC: 3728 Aircraft parts & equipment
PA: Kellstrom Holding Corporation
100 N Pcf Cast Hwy Ste 19
El Segundo CA 90245
561 222-7455

(G-10964)
ALFA LAVAL AALBORG INC (DH)
3118 Commerce Pkwy (33025-3943)
PHONE....................................954 435-5999
Holger Nielsen, *President*
Kristen Langkj, *Vice Pres*
Olga Uresti, *Admin Sec*
▲ **EMP:** 100 **EST:** 1999
SQ FT: 3,000
SALES (est): 12.9MM **Privately Held**
WEB: www.alfalaval.us
SIC: 3443 Boilers: industrial, power, or marine

(G-10965)
ALL POLISHING SOLUTIONS
3056 S State Road 7 (33023-5285)
PHONE....................................954 505-4041
Antonio Rios, *Principal*
▼ **EMP:** 5 **EST:** 2012
SALES (est): 514.7K **Privately Held**
SIC: 3291 Abrasive products

(G-10966)
ALLCLEAR AEROSPACE & DEF INC (HQ)
Also Called: Kellstrom Defense Arospc Inc
15501 Sw 29th St Ste 101 (33027-5257)
PHONE....................................954 200-9195
Greg Beason, *CEO*
Michael Farmer, *Vice Pres*
Juan Forero, *Vice Pres*
Diamy Dunton, *Opers Staff*
Alfredo Serantes, *Purchasing*
▲ **EMP:** 10 **EST:** 2002
SQ FT: 75,860
SALES (est): 48.4MM **Privately Held**
WEB: www.goallclear.com
SIC: 3728 Aircraft parts & equipment

(G-10967)
ALUMICENTER INC
3160 Sw 176th Way (33029-5610)
PHONE....................................954 674-2631
Juan Cohen, *President*
Ivonne Cohen, *Vice Pres*
EMP: 5 **EST:** 2009
SQ FT: 2,200
SALES (est): 648.5K **Privately Held**
WEB: www.alumcenter.net
SIC: 3448 Screen enclosures

(G-10968)
ARTECHE USA INC
3401 Sw 160th Ave Ste 430 (33027-6306)
PHONE....................................954 438-9499
Juan Pablo Estrada, *Chairman*
Enrique Hurtado Aguado, *Finance*
Nadia Contreras, *Finance*
Charbel Saliba, *Sales Staff*
EMP: 10 **EST:** 2010
SALES (est): 4.5MM
SALES (corp-wide): 266K **Privately Held**
WEB: www.arteche.com
SIC: 3612 Instrument transformers (except portable)
HQ: Arteche Lantegi Elkartea, Sa
Camino Derio 28
Mungia 48100

(G-10969)
ARTISTIC PAVER MFG
10111 Business Dr (33025-3942)
PHONE....................................305 949-0000
Carmen Parisenti, *Principal*
EMP: 6 **EST:** 2019
SALES (est): 169.2K **Privately Held**
SIC: 3999 Manufacturing industries

(G-10970)
AVEVA DRUG DLVRY SYSTEMS INC
3250 Commerce Pkwy (33025-3907)
PHONE....................................954 430-3340
Jeremy B Desai, *President*
Pere Paton, *President*
Jeff Watson, *President*
Steven Liberty, *Exec VP*
Jose Diaz, *Production*
▲ **EMP:** 80 **EST:** 1991
SQ FT: 74,000
SALES (est): 52.6MM
SALES (corp-wide): 1.1B **Privately Held**
WEB: www.apotex.com
SIC: 2834 Pharmaceutical preparations
HQ: Apotex Corp.
2400 N Commerce Pkwy # 400
Weston FL 33326

(G-10971)
AZOPHARMA INC
6137 Sw 19th St (33023-2914)
PHONE....................................954 536-4738
Ed Kuper, *Principal*
EMP: 7 **EST:** 2010
SALES (est): 109.5K **Privately Held**
SIC: 2834 Pharmaceutical preparations

(G-10972)
BAA LLC
16482 Sw 18th St (33027-4470)
PHONE....................................954 292-9449
Barbara M Sharief, *Principal*
EMP: 12 **EST:** 2009
SALES (est): 388K **Privately Held**
SIC: 2869 Fuels

(G-10973)
BEAUTY AWAITS COSMETICS LLC ✪
13021 Sw 20th St (33027-3407)
PHONE....................................754 226-5800
Melissa Alonzo,
EMP: 6 **EST:** 2020
SALES (est): 60K **Privately Held**
SIC: 2844 Cosmetic preparations

(G-10974)
BECKER AVIONICS INC
Also Called: Becker USA
10376 Usa Today Way (33025-3901)
PHONE....................................954 450-3137
Roland Becker, *CEO*
Arturo Garcia, *Sales Mgr*
Brett Gardner, *Marketing Staff*
Virginia Gomez, *Manager*
Paulette Morgenstein, *CIO*
EMP: 13 **EST:** 1975
SQ FT: 7,000
SALES: 5.7MM **Privately Held**
WEB: www.becker-avionics.com
SIC: 3663 3812 Airborne radio communications equipment; aircraft flight instruments

(G-10975)
BLUESTAR LATIN AMERICA INC
3541-3561 Enterprise Way (33025)
PHONE....................................800 354-9776
Albert B Vivet, *President*
Stephen G Cuntz, *President*
Luis Fernando Proano, *Vice Pres*
Javier Ramirez, *Finance*
Doug J Bivins, *Admin Sec*
◆ **EMP:** 50 **EST:** 1994
SQ FT: 50,000
SALES (est): 26.3MM
SALES (corp-wide): 253.9MM **Privately Held**
WEB: www.bluestarinc.com
SIC: 3578 5045 Point-of-sale devices; printers, computer
PA: United Radio Incorporated
3345 Point Pleasant Rd
Hebron KY 41048
859 371-4423

(G-10976)
CAPTAIN MAX
3700 S State Road 7 (33023-6158)
PHONE....................................954 987-8552
Wisam Faoor, *Principal*
EMP: 6 **EST:** 2005
SALES (est): 178.5K **Privately Held**
WEB: www.captainmaxseafood.com
SIC: 2599 Food wagons, restaurant

(G-10977)
CARIBBEAN DISCOUNT PTG INC
6314 Pembroke Rd Ste A (33023-2222)
PHONE....................................954 961-5015
Jose Ballero, *Manager*
EMP: 6 **EST:** 2005
SALES (est): 67.8K **Privately Held**
WEB:
www.caribbeandiscountprintingusa.com
SIC: 2752 Commercial printing, lithographic

(G-10978)
CASTLE DISTRIBUTING INDUSTRIES
6506 Sw 19th St (33023-2119)
PHONE....................................305 336-0855
James V Colbert, *President*
EMP: 8 **EST:** 2001
SALES (est): 469.1K **Privately Held**
SIC: 3999 Manufacturing industries

(G-10979)
CITEL AMERICA INC
10108 Usa Today Way (33025-3903)
PHONE....................................954 430-6310
Patrick Coyle, *CEO*
Francois Guichard, *President*
Vincent Crevenat, *Engineer*
Brandon Jefferson, *Engineer*
David McClellan, *Engineer*
▲ **EMP:** 10 **EST:** 1983
SQ FT: 4,000
SALES (est): 3.3MM
SALES (corp-wide): 3.9MM **Privately Held**
WEB: www.citel.us
SIC: 3671 5063 Electron tubes; electrical fittings & construction materials
HQ: Citel 2 C P
2 Rue Troyon
Sevres 92310
141 235-033

(G-10980)
COCO LOPEZ INC (PA)
3401 Sw 160th Ave Ste 350 (33027-6306)
PHONE....................................954 450-3100
Leonardo Vargas, *President*
Jake Jacobsen, *Regional Mgr*
Gisela Alexander, *Vice Pres*
Luis Martinez, *Controller*
Jose L Suarez, *Sales Mgr*
◆ **EMP:** 7
SQ FT: 2,500
SALES (est): 15MM **Privately Held**
WEB: www.cocolopez.com
SIC: 2033 2099 Fruit juices: packaged in cans, jars, etc.; food preparations

(G-10981)
CPS PRODUCTS INC (HQ)
3600 Enterprise Way (33025-6616)
PHONE....................................305 687-4121
Paul Baldetti, *President*
Edward Jeffers, *President*
John D Jeffers, *Vice Pres*
Trina King, *Vice Pres*
Damon Butler, *CFO*
◆ **EMP:** 1 **EST:** 1989
SALES (est): 8MM
SALES (corp-wide): 1.2B **Privately Held**
WEB: www.cpsproducts.com
SIC: 3585 3825 3823 3812 Refrigeration & heating equipment; instruments to measure electricity; industrial instrmnts msrmnt display/control process variable; search & navigation equipment
PA: Harbour Group Ltd.
7733 Forsyth Blvd Fl 23
Saint Louis MO 63105
314 727-5550

(G-10982)
DAYORIS DOORS
2114 Sw 60th Ter (33023-2934)
PHONE....................................954 374-8538
Dan Benica, *Owner*
EMP: 9 **EST:** 2015
SALES (est): 147.4K **Privately Held**
WEB: www.dayoris.com
SIC: 2431 Door frames, wood

(G-10983)
DERMATONUS
5262 Sw 158th Ave (33027-4989)
PHONE....................................305 229-3923
Patricia Erazo, *Treasurer*
EMP: 7 **EST:** 2008
SALES (est): 228.7K **Privately Held**
WEB: www.dermatonusglobal.com
SIC: 2834 Pharmaceutical preparations

(G-10984)
DIGITAL COMPOSITING SYSTEMS
Also Called: Moore Computer Consultants
3309 Onyx Rd (33025-2820)
P.O. Box 245746, Pembroke Pines (33024-0112)
PHONE....................................954 432-4988
John L Moore, *President*
EMP: 5 **EST:** 1992
SALES (est): 300.8K **Privately Held**
SIC: 3695 Computer software tape & disks: blank, rigid & floppy

(G-10985)
DIVATTI & CO LLC
1050 E 17th St (33027)
PHONE....................................786 354-1888
Henry Orellana, *Mng Member*
EMP: 6 **EST:** 2015
SQ FT: 8,000
SALES (est): 600K **Privately Held**
SIC: 2531 Public building & related furniture

(G-10986)
DREAMS INC
15701 Sw 29th St (33027-5260)
PHONE....................................954 377-0002
EMP: 6 **EST:** 2019
SALES (est): 47K **Privately Held**
SIC: 3949 Sporting & athletic goods

(G-10987)
DURABODY USA LLC
12068 Miramar Pkwy (33025-7003)
PHONE....................................954 357-2333
Teddy Teixeira, *Sales Mgr*
Teodoro Teixeira, *Manager*
EMP: 8 **EST:** 2015
SALES (est): 302.5K **Privately Held**
WEB: www.durabodysports.com
SIC: 3949 Sporting & athletic goods

▲ = Import ▼=Export
◆ =Import/Export

(G-10988)
ELEMENT ELIQUID LLC
Also Called: Element E-Liquid
11411 Interchange Cir S (33025-6009)
PHONE..................................754 260-5500
David Botton,
▲ **EMP:** 12 **EST:** 2014
SALES (est): 2.7MM **Privately Held**
WEB: www.elementeliquids.com
SIC: 2046 Liquid starch

(G-10989)
ENERGY SERVICES PROVIDERS INC (DH)
3700 Lakeside Dr 6 (33027-3264)
PHONE..................................305 947-7880
Douglas W Marcille, *CEO*
Brian Rose, *Vice Pres*
David Weinberg, *Treasurer*
EMP: 12 **EST:** 2006
SQ FT: 7,500
SALES (est): 13.6MM
SALES (corp-wide): 11.4B **Publicly Held**
WEB: www.usgande.com
SIC: 2211 Broadwoven fabric mills, cotton
HQ: U.S. Gas & Electric, Inc.
6555 Sierra Dr
Irving TX 75039
954 947-7880

(G-10990)
ESTEEMED BRANDS INC
3450 Lakeside Dr Ste 120 (33027-3262)
PHONE..................................954 442-3923
Leslie Almond, *President*
Craig Mansfield, *CFO*
◆ **EMP:** 12 **EST:** 2012
SQ FT: 2,000
SALES (est): 3MM **Privately Held**
WEB: www.esteemed-brands.com
SIC: 2676 2844 Feminine hygiene paper products; toilet preparations

(G-10991)
FIVE STAR BAKERY
6847 Miramar Pkwy (33023-6023)
PHONE..................................954 983-6133
Bernard Brown, *President*
EMP: 8 **EST:** 2003
SALES (est): 258.6K **Privately Held**
SIC: 2051 Bread, cake & related products

(G-10992)
FOOD MARKETING CONSULTANTS INC
Also Called: San Bernardo Ice Cream
2805 N Commerce Pkwy (33025-3956)
PHONE..................................954 322-2668
Robert Tammara, *President*
Jonathan Tammara, *Principal*
Robyn Bofshever, *Marketing Staff*
Stacey Schrager, *Marketing Staff*
▼ **EMP:** 7 **EST:** 1979
SQ FT: 13,500
SALES (est): 2.3MM **Privately Held**
WEB: www.sanbernardofoods.com
SIC: 2024 Ice cream, bulk; sorbets, non-dairy based; ice cream, packaged: molded, on sticks, etc.; sherbets, dairy based

(G-10993)
FOR EYES OPTCAL CCNUT GROVE IN (DH)
3601 Sw 160th Ave Ste 400 (33027-6312)
PHONE..................................305 557-9004
Phillip Wolman, *President*
Robert Messa, *Vice Pres*
Johnny Ampuero, *Software Dev*
EMP: 200 **EST:** 1975
SALES (est): 119.7MM
SALES (corp-wide): 1.7MM **Privately Held**
WEB: www.foreyes.com
SIC: 3851 5995 Eyeglasses, lenses & frames; opticians
HQ: Grandvision N.V.
Evert Van De Beekstraat 1 6th Floor-ruimte
Luchthaven Schiphol
888 870-100

(G-10994)
FOR LIFE PRODUCTS LLC
2301 Sw 145th Ave Ste 301 (33027-6602)
PHONE..................................954 747-3300
Joseph Mc Donell, *President*
Scott Bettencourt, *Vice Pres*
Julie Ebbert, *Vice Pres*
Beth McDonnell, *Vice Pres*
Victoria Paredes, *Project Mgr*
▲ **EMP:** 60 **EST:** 1998
SQ FT: 37,000
SALES (est): 19.5MM **Privately Held**
WEB: www.forlifeproducts.com
SIC: 2842 Specialty cleaning, polishes & sanitation goods

(G-10995)
FRED INTERNATIONAL LLC
3350 Sw 148th Ave Ste 120 (33027-3258)
PHONE..................................786 539-1600
Rodolfo Martnez, *Vice Pres*
Moises Gonto, *Sales Staff*
Francisco Diaz, *Mng Member*
Flor Brito, *Manager*
▼ **EMP:** 12 **EST:** 2003
SQ FT: 2,900
SALES: 1.5MM **Privately Held**
WEB: www.jellybellyjelly2017.com
SIC: 3533 Oil & gas field machinery

(G-10996)
GAR INTERNATIONAL
3315 Commerce Pkwy (33025-3954)
PHONE..................................954 704-9590
Peter Voigt, *Manager*
EMP: 7 **EST:** 2017
SALES (est): 270.5K **Privately Held**
SIC: 3531 Construction machinery

(G-10997)
GENERAL METAL INTL INC
Also Called: Sun Light Products
13580 Sw 51st St (33027-5937)
PHONE..................................305 628-2052
Zhihua Deng, *President*
Albert Deng, *Manager*
EMP: 7 **EST:** 1995
SALES (est): 331.1K **Privately Held**
SIC: 3645 Lamp & light shades

(G-10998)
GLOBAL FORCE ENTERPRISES LLC
2331 W Lake Miramar Cir (33025-4807)
PHONE..................................786 317-8197
Kim Griffith, *President*
EMP: 5 **EST:** 2010
SALES (est): 500K **Privately Held**
WEB: www.globalforceenterprises.com
SIC: 3069 Fabricated rubber products

(G-10999)
GLOBAL GALAN LOGISTICS INC
3132 Sw 173rd Ter (33029-5581)
PHONE..................................754 263-2708
George Galan, *President*
Carmen Caino, *Vice Pres*
Carmen Galan, *Vice Pres*
▼ **EMP:** 6 **EST:** 2005
SALES (est): 696.6K **Privately Held**
WEB: www.gglusa.com
SIC: 2448 Cargo containers, wood & metal combination

(G-11000)
GOODRICH CORPORATION
3601 S Flamingo Rd (33027-2936)
PHONE..................................954 538-8900
Jean Philippe, *Branch Mgr*
EMP: 6
SALES (corp-wide): 56.5B **Publicly Held**
WEB: www.collinsaerospace.com
SIC: 3728 Aircraft parts & equipment
HQ: Goodrich Corporation
2730 W Tyvola Rd
Charlotte NC 28217
704 423-7000

(G-11001)
GREEN LEAF FOODS LLC
4050 Sw 145th Ter (33027-3775)
Rural Route 4050 Sw 145 Ter (33027)
PHONE..................................305 308-9167
Brandy Chappell, *CEO*
Fernando Siman,
EMP: 6 **EST:** 2013
SALES (est): 810K **Privately Held**
WEB: www.rawwraps.org
SIC: 2034 2676 Dehydrated fruits, vegetables, soups; towels, napkins & tissue paper products

(G-11002)
HCW BIOLOGICS INC
Also Called: HCW Therapeutics
2929 N Commerce Pkwy (33025-3957)
PHONE..................................954 842-2024
Hing C Wong, *CEO*
Lee Flowers, *Senior VP*
Jin-An Jiao, *Vice Pres*
Peter Rhode, *Vice Pres*
Rebecca Byam, *CFO*
EMP: 40 **EST:** 2018
SQ FT: 12,250
SALES (est): 4.8MM **Privately Held**
SIC: 2836 Biological products, except diagnostic

(G-11003)
IN FOCUS INTERACTIVE MAGAZINE
3001 Sw 64th Ter (33023-3847)
P.O. Box 4492, Hollywood (33083-4492)
PHONE..................................954 966-1233
Fax: 954 989-2993
EMP: 6
SALES (est): 410K **Privately Held**
SIC: 2721 Periodicals-Publishing/Printing

(G-11004)
INGERSOLL RAND
2884 Corporate Way (33025-6546)
PHONE..................................954 391-4500
Shawn Chambers, *Vice Pres*
Mark Tillinghast, *Opers Mgr*
Tom Mikulich, *Mfg Staff*
Theresa Stremlau, *Accounts Mgr*
Peter Wong, *Sales Staff*
EMP: 18 **EST:** 2009
SALES (est): 585K **Privately Held**
WEB: www.irco.com
SIC: 3131 Rands

(G-11005)
IT MANEX LLC
16140 Sw 51st St (33027-4963)
PHONE..................................954 442-4465
Alberto Garcia-Angeles,
EMP: 6 **EST:** 2012
SALES (est): 179.5K **Privately Held**
WEB: www.itmanex.com
SIC: 3577 7359 5112 Printers & plotters; office machine rental, except computers; laserjet supplies

(G-11006)
IVA PARTS BROKER LLC
2708 Sw 165th Ave (33027-5241)
PHONE..................................239 222-2604
Igor Villalobos, *Principal*
◆ **EMP:** 7 **EST:** 2010
SALES (est): 1MM **Privately Held**
WEB: www.ivapartsbroker.com
SIC: 3469 Machine parts, stamped or pressed metal

(G-11007)
J J M SERVICES INC
Also Called: Minuteman Press
12004 Miramar Pkwy (33025-7000)
PHONE..................................954 437-1880
Joanne Miner, *President*
EMP: 5 **EST:** 1988
SQ FT: 2,500
SALES (est): 711.8K **Privately Held**
WEB: www.chanhassen-mn.minuteman-press.com
SIC: 2752 2791 2789 2759 Commercial printing, lithographic; typesetting; bookbinding & related work; commercial printing

(G-11008)
K P KITCHENS CORP
6412 Pembroke Rd (33023-2138)
PHONE..................................954 322-9087
David I Arias, *President*
EMP: 6 **EST:** 2014
SALES (est): 112.5K **Privately Held**
SIC: 2434 5211 Wood kitchen cabinets; lumber products

(G-11009)
KERMA MEDICAL PRODUCTS INC
3371 Executive Way (33025-3935)
PHONE..................................954 744-3480
Danielle Reubel, *Vice Pres*
Cindy Gonzalez, *Purch Mgr*
Earl G Reubel, *Branch Mgr*
EMP: 6 **Privately Held**
WEB: www.kermamedical.com
SIC: 3841 Surgical & medical instruments
PA: Kerma Medical Products, Inc.
215 Suburban Dr
Suffolk VA 23434

(G-11010)
LODEX ENTERPRISES CORP
17048 Sw 38th Dr (33027-4601)
PHONE..................................954 442-3843
Luis I Gutierrez, *President*
EMP: 7
SQ FT: 10,000
SALES (est): 900.7K **Privately Held**
SIC: 3569 3561 3589 5085 Separators for steam, gas, vapor or air (machinery); pumps & pumping equipment; water treatment equipment, industrial; industrial supplies

(G-11011)
LUJOTEX LLC
Also Called: UPS Store 4332, The
14359 Miramar Pkwy # 290 (33027-4134)
PHONE..................................954 322-1001
Luis J Delgado Pda,
EMP: 7 **EST:** 2011
SALES (est): 466.3K **Privately Held**
SIC: 2759 Commercial printing

(G-11012)
LUTIMI NR CORP
3190 S State Road 7 # 18 (33023-5280)
PHONE..................................954 245-7986
Miguel Angel S Noriega R, *President*
EMP: 8 **EST:** 2015
SALES (est): 443.6K **Privately Held**
SIC: 2752 Photolithographic printing

(G-11013)
MACTECH POWER LINE AND CABLE
15120 Sw 49th St (33027-3644)
PHONE..................................954 895-9966
Dale A Dunkley, *Principal*
EMP: 8 **EST:** 2019
SALES (est): 162.4K **Privately Held**
WEB: www.mactechonsite.com
SIC: 3643 Power line cable

(G-11014)
MARVELLETH INDUSTRIES CORP
6661 Sw 26th St (33023-3805)
PHONE..................................754 263-7197
Rosario Molleturo, *Principal*
EMP: 6 **EST:** 2018
SALES (est): 108.5K **Privately Held**
SIC: 3999 Manufacturing industries

(G-11015)
MAX GLOBAL NORTH AMERICA LLC
6137 Sw 33rd St (33023-5123)
PHONE..................................954 727-6656
Ozge Aytekin, *Principal*
EMP: 7 **EST:** 2017
SALES (est): 173.6K **Privately Held**
WEB: www.hyperenergyusa.com
SIC: 3691 Storage batteries

(G-11016)
MIAMI MIX CORP
15014 Sw 21st St (33027-4366)
PHONE..................................954 704-9682
Hector Neciosup, *Principal*
EMP: 8 **EST:** 2008
SALES (est): 114.2K **Privately Held**
SIC: 3273 Ready-mixed concrete

(G-11017)
MIRAMAR MRMIDS SYNCHRO TEAM LL
4944 Sw 164th Ave (33027-4947)
PHONE..................................954 646-6350

GEOGRAPHIC

Mayra Cartagena, *President*
EMP: 6 **EST:** 2013
SALES (est): 240.2K **Privately Held**
WEB: www.miramarmermaids.com
SIC: 3621 Synchros

(G-11018)
MOUNTED MEMORIES INC
15701 Sw 29th St (33027-5260)
PHONE..................................866 236-2541
Mitch Adelstein, *President*
Scott Widelitz, *Vice Pres*
Ross Tannenbaum, *CFO*
EMP: 14 **EST:** 1993
SQ FT: 22,000
SALES (est): 508.8K **Privately Held**
SIC: 2499 5199 Novelties, wood fiber; gifts & novelties

(G-11019)
MTN GOVERNMENT SERVICES INC
3044 N Commerce Pkwy (33025-3969)
PHONE..................................954 538-4000
Errol Olivier, *Principal*
EMP: 15 **EST:** 2014
SALES (est): 922.9K **Privately Held**
SIC: 3679 Quartz crystals, for electronic application

(G-11020)
NAP IMPEX LLC
18592 Sw 55th St (33029-6294)
PHONE..................................954 589-2861
Noman A Paracha, *Principal*
EMP: 6 **EST:** 2012
SALES (est): 113.5K **Privately Held**
WEB: www.napimpex.com
SIC: 2911 Liquefied petroleum gases, LPG

(G-11021)
NEXPUB INC
3820 Executive Way (33025-3947)
PHONE..................................954 392-5889
Robert Edgman, *Acting CFO*
EMP: 16 **EST:** 1999
SQ FT: 18,000
SALES (est): 375.6K **Privately Held**
WEB: www.nexpub.com
SIC: 2752 Commercial printing, offset

(G-11022)
OFFENSIVE DEFENSE INC
5444 Sw 186th Way (33029-6258)
PHONE..................................786 306-8162
Thomas Stuebe, *Principal*
EMP: 6 **EST:** 2005
SALES (est): 79K **Privately Held**
WEB: www.ebmasflorida.com
SIC: 3812 Defense systems & equipment

(G-11023)
OLEVIN COMPOUNDS LLC
12758 Sw 47th St (33027-6031)
PHONE..................................954 993-5148
Farhat Syed, *Mng Member*
EMP: 7 **EST:** 2017
SALES (est): 378.3K **Privately Held**
WEB: www.olevincompounds.com
SIC: 2821 Plastics materials & resins

(G-11024)
ON THE RUN PRINTING
7141 Dilido Blvd (33023-6513)
PHONE..................................305 733-2619
Walter Joseph, *Principal*
EMP: 6 **EST:** 2010
SALES (est): 86.1K **Privately Held**
SIC: 2752 Commercial printing, offset

(G-11025)
ONE NURSING CARE LLC
3351 Executive Way (33025-3935)
PHONE..................................954 441-6644
Guillermo Salazar, *CEO*
EMP: 9 **EST:** 2013
SALES (est): 867.5K **Privately Held**
WEB: www.onehome.health
SIC: 2834 Pharmaceutical preparations

(G-11026)
PANAMERICAN FOOD LLC (PA)
Also Called: Pagnifique USA
10491 N Commerce Pkwy (33025-3971)
PHONE..................................305 594-5704
Fernando Abella, *Managing Dir*
Pablo De Leon, *Opers Staff*
Erika Perez-Espinosa, *Controller*
Veronica Pereira, *Sales Staff*
Marcelo Picasso, *Sales Staff*
◆ **EMP:** 37 **EST:** 2002
SQ FT: 29,397
SALES (est): 7.4MM **Privately Held**
WEB: www.pagnifique.com
SIC: 2051 Bread, all types (white, wheat, rye, etc): fresh or frozen

(G-11027)
PATTERN GRADING & MARKER SVCS
Also Called: Pgms
3650 Sw 141st Ave (33027-3240)
PHONE..................................305 495-9963
Regina Gottlieb, *Vice Pres*
Saul Gottlieb, *Director*
EMP: 6 **EST:** 2001
SALES (est): 737.5K **Privately Held**
WEB: www.pattern-maker.com
SIC: 3543 5136 5137 Industrial patterns; men's & boys' clothing; women's & children's clothing

(G-11028)
PENIEL INC
11844 Sw 27th St (33025-0783)
PHONE..................................305 594-2739
Sergio D Daldi, *President*
EMP: 7 **EST:** 2000
SALES (est): 352.5K **Privately Held**
SIC: 2741 Miscellaneous publishing

(G-11029)
PREMIUM QUALITY MEATS INC
7979 Riviera Blvd (33023-6440)
PHONE..................................239 309-4418
Timothy Mooti Persad, *President*
Ivan Mooti Persad, *Vice Pres*
EMP: 9 **EST:** 2019
SALES (est): 526K **Privately Held**
WEB: www.pqmfl.com
SIC: 2015 5142 Poultry sausage, luncheon meats & other poultry products; frozen fish, meat & poultry

(G-11030)
PRESS-RITE INC
Also Called: Dlp Industries
2125 Sw 60th Way (33023-2941)
PHONE..................................954 963-7373
Dave Phipps, *President*
EMP: 9
SALES (corp-wide): 1.2MM **Privately Held**
WEB: www.pressritehardware.com
SIC: 3469 3429 Metal stampings; manufactured hardware (general)
PA: Press-Rite, Inc.
2125 Sw 60th Way
Miramar FL 33023
954 963-7373

(G-11031)
PRINT FACTORY LLC
Also Called: Nexpub
3820 Executive Way (33025-3947)
PHONE..................................954 392-5889
Laurie Edgman, *Mng Member*
Robert Edgman,
Neal Polan,
EMP: 7 **EST:** 2002
SQ FT: 9,800
SALES (est): 1.3MM **Privately Held**
WEB: www.nexpub.com
SIC: 2752 Commercial printing, offset

(G-11032)
PRINTS HOPE INTERNATIONAL INC
2353 Sw 130th Ter (33027-2658)
P.O. Box 278435 (33027-8435)
PHONE..................................305 528-1593
David Rivera, *Principal*
EMP: 6 **EST:** 2011
SALES (est): 69.3K **Privately Held**
WEB: www.printsofhope.org
SIC: 2752 Commercial printing, lithographic

(G-11033)
PROFESSNAL KIT INSTLLER GROUP
Also Called: Pki Group
1892 Sw 152nd Ter (33027-4312)
PHONE..................................954 436-1513
Benjamin Colon, *President*
EMP: 13 **EST:** 2004
SQ FT: 3,400
SALES (est): 2.6MM **Privately Held**
WEB: www.thepkigroup.com
SIC: 3469 1799 Kitchen fixtures & equipment: metal, except cast aluminum; kitchen cabinet installation

(G-11034)
PROPULSION TECH INTL LLC
Also Called: P T I
15301 Sw 29th St Ste 100 (33027-5248)
PHONE..................................954 874-0274
Michael Mitchell, *CEO*
Michael Tucker, *Production*
Tom Gowen, *Engineer*
Gregory Miller, *Engineer*
Michel Fiot, *CFO*
EMP: 300 **EST:** 2001
SQ FT: 40,000
SALES (est): 37.7MM **Privately Held**
WEB: www.ptechi.com
SIC: 3724 Engine mount parts, aircraft

(G-11035)
REGINA BEHAR ENTERPRISES INC
Also Called: Ike Behar
11440 Interchange Cir N (33025-6005)
PHONE..................................305 557-5212
Ike Behar, *CEO*
Regina Behar, *President*
Lawrence Behar, *Vice Pres*
Steve Behar, *Admin Sec*
▲ **EMP:** 26 **EST:** 1957
SALES (est): 1.9MM **Privately Held**
WEB: www.ikebehar.com
SIC: 2321 Men's & boys' dress shirts; men's & boys' sports & polo shirts

(G-11036)
RENOVA LAND AND SEA LLC
4954 Sw 128th Ave (33027-5828)
PHONE..................................786 916-2695
Dennis Rodriguez, *Mng Member*
EMP: 5 **EST:** 2015
SALES (est): 322.6K **Privately Held**
SIC: 3441 Fabricated structural metal

(G-11037)
RUSSELL HOBBS INC (DH)
3633 S Flamingo Rd (33027-2936)
PHONE..................................954 883-1000
Terry L Polistina, *President*
Ivan R Habibe, *CFO*
▲ **EMP:** 100 **EST:** 1991
SQ FT: 110,000
SALES (est): 101.1MM
SALES (corp-wide): 3.9B **Publicly Held**
SIC: 3634 3873 3648 2499 Electric household cooking appliances; watches, clocks, watchcases & parts; lighting equipment; picture & mirror frames, wood; picture frames, metal
HQ: Spectrum Brands, Inc.
3001 Deming Way
Middleton WI 53562
608 275-3340

(G-11038)
SAFETY COMPLIANCE PUBL INC
3600 S State Road 7 # 204 (33023-5200)
PHONE..................................844 556-3149
Valle Patricia, *Principal*
EMP: 8 **EST:** 2017
SALES (est): 89.2K **Privately Held**
WEB: www.safetypub.net
SIC: 2741 Miscellaneous publishing

(G-11039)
SAS R & D SERVICES INC
2371 Sw 195th Ave (33029-5917)
PHONE..................................954 432-2345
Ted Sas, *CEO*
▼ **EMP:** 15 **EST:** 1988
SQ FT: 7,000
SALES (est): 5MM **Privately Held**
WEB: www.sasrad.com
SIC: 3812 Defense systems & equipment

(G-11040)
SDMO GENERATING SETS INC
Also Called: Kohler Sdmo
3801 Commerce Pkwy (33025-3940)
PHONE..................................305 863-0012
Jacky Pluchon, *President*
Roberto Piccolo, *Regl Sales Mgr*
Lucile Bonal, *Marketing Mgr*
Nicolas Lahera, *Director*
Jackie Pluchon, *Director*
◆ **EMP:** 26 **EST:** 2000
SQ FT: 14,000
SALES (est): 8.8MM
SALES (corp-wide): 1.4B **Privately Held**
WEB: www.us.sdmo.com
SIC: 3621 Generator sets: gasoline, diesel or dual-fuel
HQ: S.D.M.O. Industries
270 Rue De Kerervern
Guipavas 29490
298 411-388

(G-11041)
SECURUS BROT LLC
2400 Sw 132nd Ter (33027-2684)
PHONE..................................954 532-8065
Gregory St Fort,
EMP: 9 **EST:** 2011
SALES (est): 751.4K **Privately Held**
SIC: 2752 Commercial printing, lithographic

(G-11042)
SIGNS & STRIPES LLC
2371 Dunhill Ave (33025-3815)
PHONE..................................305 775-1174
EMP: 6 **EST:** 2017
SALES (est): 133.3K **Privately Held**
WEB: www.signsstripes.com
SIC: 3993 Signs & advertising specialties

(G-11043)
SIMTEC SILICONE PARTS LLC
9658 Premier Pkwy (33025-3203)
PHONE..................................954 656-4212
Frank Dilly, *Managing Dir*
Franz Dilly, *Managing Dir*
Zeno Weidenthaler, *Vice Pres*
Craig Templen, *Info Tech Mgr*
Enrique Camacho,
▼ **EMP:** 22 **EST:** 2002
SQ FT: 10,000
SALES (est): 14.9MM
SALES (corp-wide): 355.8K **Privately Held**
WEB: www.simtec-silicone.com
SIC: 3089 Injection molding of plastics
PA: Rico Group Gmbh
Am Thalbach 8
Thalheim Bei Wels
724 276-460

(G-11044)
SINCERE FUEL INC
16100 Sw 51st St (33027-4963)
PHONE..................................954 433-3577
Ward George, *Principal*
EMP: 7 **EST:** 2010
SALES (est): 138.2K **Privately Held**
SIC: 2869 Fuels

(G-11045)
SPEED PRO MIAMI
11341 Interchange Cir S (33025-6008)
PHONE..................................954 534-9503
EMP: 6 **EST:** 2014
SALES (est): 130.7K **Privately Held**
WEB: www.speedpro.com
SIC: 3993 Signs & advertising specialties

(G-11046)
STATESIDE INDUS SOLUTIONS LLC
14900 Sw 30th St # 278663 (33027-7329)
PHONE..................................305 301-4052
Rochy J Rodriguez,
EMP: 8 **EST:** 2017
SALES (est): 1MM **Privately Held**
WEB: www.statesideindustrial.com
SIC: 3645 Lamp & light shades

(G-11047)
STEMTECH HEALTHSCIENCES CORP ✪
10370 Usa Today Way (33025-3901)
PHONE..................................954 715-6000
Ray C Carter Jr, *Principal*
Marge Berger, *Director*
EMP: 25 **EST:** 2021
SALES (est): 9.9MM **Privately Held**
WEB: www.stemtech.com
SIC: **2834** Pharmaceutical preparations

(G-11048)
STS DISTRIBUTION SOLUTIONS LLC
Also Called: STS Air-Pro
11650 Miramar Pkwy # 500 (33025-5823)
PHONE..................................844 359-4673
Thomas Covella, *President*
EMP: 15 **EST:** 2015
SALES (est): 7MM **Privately Held**
WEB: www.stsaviationgroup.com
SIC: **3492** Hose & tube couplings, hydraulic/pneumatic; hose & tube fittings & assemblies, hydraulic/pneumatic

(G-11049)
SUNTYX LLC
Also Called: Poggesi USA
11550 Interchange Cir N (33025-6006)
PHONE..................................786 558-2233
Danny Tuaty, *Mng Member*
David Bensadon, *Senior Mgr*
EMP: 14 **EST:** 2016
SALES (est): 2.6MM **Privately Held**
SIC: **3999** Garden umbrellas

(G-11050)
SURVITEC SURVIVOR CFT MAR INC
9640 Premier Pkwy (33025-3203)
PHONE..................................954 374-4276
Issac Ancona, *General Mgr*
Mike Glover, *Fire Chief*
Steve Blair, *Manager*
▲ **EMP:** 7 **EST:** 2012
SQ FT: 1,500
SALES (est): 661.6K **Privately Held**
SIC: **3732** 5091 Lifeboats, building & repairing; boats, canoes, watercrafts & equipment

(G-11051)
THE ALLURING GROUP INC
Also Called: Belladonna Hair Bar
7451 Riviera Blvd Ste 112 (33023-6567)
PHONE..................................800 731-2280
Utonia Lloyd, *CEO*
EMP: 12 **EST:** 2017
SALES (est): 657.1K **Privately Held**
SIC: **2389** Apparel & accessories

(G-11052)
TRANE US INC
Also Called: South Florida Trane
2884 Corporate Way (33025-6546)
PHONE..................................954 499-6900
Roberto Masson, *Accounts Mgr*
Lou Zaccone, *Branch Mgr*
Harry Torres, *Technician*
EMP: 85 **Privately Held**
WEB: www.trane.com
SIC: **3585** Refrigeration & heating equipment
HQ: Trane U.S. Inc.
3600 Pammel Creek Rd
La Crosse WI 54601
608 787-2000

(G-11053)
TROPICAL SKOOPS LLC
11635 Red Rd (33025-7810)
PHONE..................................954 440-8736
Shanillia Forbes, *CEO*
EMP: 6 **EST:** 2013
SALES (est): 340.2K **Privately Held**
WEB: www.tropical-skoops.weebly.com
SIC: **2024** Ice cream & frozen desserts

(G-11054)
TURBINE CONTROLS LLC
3501 Enterprise Way (33025-6545)
PHONE..................................954 517-1706
Glen Greenberg, *President*
Eric Fraher, *Vice Pres*
EMP: 97 **EST:** 2012
SALES (est): 17.6MM
SALES (corp-wide): 24.1MM **Privately Held**
WEB: www.tcimro.com
SIC: **3728** Aircraft parts & equipment
PA: Turbine Controls, Inc.
5 Old Windsor Rd
Bloomfield CT 06002
860 242-0448

(G-11055)
UNITED AEROSPACE CORPORATION
9800 Premier Pkwy (33025-3211)
PHONE..................................954 364-0085
Manuel Martinez, *President*
Abelardo Cantillo, *Vice Pres*
Martin Cantillo, *Controller*
Ana Munoz, *VP Sales*
Marlene Cardenas, *Sales Staff*
EMP: 26 **EST:** 1972
SQ FT: 35,000
SALES (est): 5.8MM **Privately Held**
WEB: www.unitedaerospace.com
SIC: **3728** Aircraft parts & equipment

(G-11056)
UNITED TECHNOLOGIES CORP
Also Called: Collins Aerospace
3601 S Flamingo Rd (33027-2936)
PHONE..................................954 538-8900
Michael Zall, *President*
EMP: 52 **EST:** 1934
SALES (est): 3.7MM **Privately Held**
SIC: **3728** Aircraft parts & equipment

(G-11057)
UTC AEROSPACE SYSTEMS ✪
3601 S Flamingo Rd (33027-2936)
PHONE..................................954 538-8971
EMP: 8 **EST:** 2020
SALES (est): 627.2K **Privately Held**
WEB: www.utcaerospacesystems.com
SIC: **3728** Aircraft parts & equipment

(G-11058)
VSI & PARTNERS INC
Also Called: Lake Aerospace Services
14501 Sw 39th St (33027-3794)
PHONE..................................954 205-8653
Antonio Valdes, *CEO*
EMP: 10 **EST:** 2000
SALES (est): 689.1K **Privately Held**
SIC: **3721** Aircraft

(G-11059)
WATSON THERAPEUTICS INC
3400 Enterprise Way (33025-3941)
PHONE..................................954 266-1000
Andrew Boyer, *President*
Brian Shanahan, *Vice Pres*
EMP: 20 **EST:** 2013
SALES (est): 3.7MM **Privately Held**
WEB: www.actavis.com
SIC: **2834** Pharmaceutical preparations
HQ: Actavis Llc
5 Giralda Farms
Madison NJ 07940
862 261-7000

(G-11060)
WETHERILL ASSOCIATES INC (PA)
Also Called: Wai Corporate - USA
3300 Corporate Way (33025-3945)
PHONE..................................800 773-0005
Jeffery W Sween, *CEO*
Earl Proud, *President*
Douglas Moul, *COO*
Jordan Siegel, *COO*
Blake Deavers, *Vice Pres*
◆ **EMP:** 200 **EST:** 1978
SQ FT: 100,000
SALES (est): 70.6MM **Privately Held**
SIC: **3714** 5013 4731 Motor vehicle parts & accessories; automotive supplies & parts; freight forwarding

(G-11061)
WINRISE ENTERPRISES LLC
15701 Sw 29th St 100 (33027-5260)
PHONE..................................786 621-6705
Peter Loucks, *Mng Member*
▲ **EMP:** 11 **EST:** 2008
SQ FT: 4,000
SALES (est): 1.6MM **Privately Held**
WEB: www.manufactureraluminumfences.com
SIC: **3355** Aluminum rod & bar

(G-11062)
ZSNO FT LAUDERDALE
3801 Commerce Pkwy (33025-3940)
PHONE..................................954 792-2223
Ginger Dairsaw, *Owner*
EMP: 6 **EST:** 2010
SALES (est): 116.8K **Privately Held**
SIC: **3577** Printers & plotters

Miramar Beach
Walton County

(G-11063)
BILLABONG DESTIN
500 Grand Blvd Ste 102 (32550-1899)
PHONE..................................850 424-3553
Frank Sims, *Owner*
Jacki Sitarik, *Regional Mgr*
EMP: 5 **EST:** 2007
SALES (est): 324.8K **Privately Held**
WEB: www.billabongdestin.com
SIC: **3949** Surfboards

(G-11064)
BOTE LLC
Also Called: Bote Boards
12598 Emerald Coast Pkwy (32550-2103)
PHONE..................................888 855-4450
Corey M Cooper, *Mng Member*
Magdalena Cooper, *Mng Member*
EMP: 12 **EST:** 2010
SQ FT: 800
SALES (est): 1.3MM **Privately Held**
WEB: www.boteboard.com
SIC: **3949** 5941 5551 5091 Surfboards; surfing equipment & supplies; canoe & kayak dealers; sporting & recreation goods

(G-11065)
COASTAL CABINETS & COUNTERTOPS
12889 Us Highway 98 W 109a (32550-3241)
PHONE..................................850 424-3940
Wayne Martin, *Owner*
Sharon Martin, *Co-Owner*
EMP: 7 **EST:** 2008
SALES (est): 424.2K **Privately Held**
WEB: www.coastalcabinetsandcounters.com
SIC: **2434** Wood kitchen cabinets

(G-11066)
GULF COAST BEACH CAMS LLC
12273 Us Highway 98 W (32550-6963)
PHONE..................................850 792-4617
Charles Steeg, *Principal*
EMP: 6 **EST:** 2015
SALES (est): 87.7K **Privately Held**
WEB: www.gulfcoastbeachcams.com
SIC: **3651** Household audio & video equipment

(G-11067)
PAVERSCAPE SOLUTIONS LLC
21 Professional Ct (32550-6821)
PHONE..................................850 497-5557
Joshua Fleming, *Principal*
EMP: 7 **EST:** 2015
SALES (est): 193.4K **Privately Held**
WEB: www.uspaverscape.com
SIC: **2951** Asphalt paving mixtures & blocks

(G-11068)
PVH CORP
10746 Us Highway 98 W # 158 (32550-7119)
PHONE..................................850 269-0482
Harlen Ozoria, *Branch Mgr*
Polina Bess, *Technology*
EMP: 10
SALES (corp-wide): 7.1B **Publicly Held**
WEB: www.pvh.com
SIC: **2321** Men's & boys' dress shirts
PA: Pvh Corp.
200 Madison Ave
New York NY 10016
212 381-3500

(G-11069)
SP PUBLICATIONS LLC
495 Grand Blvd Ste 206 (32550-1897)
PHONE..................................239 595-9040
Stephane Perrin,
EMP: 7 **EST:** 2009
SALES (est): 362.6K **Privately Held**
WEB: www.patriciacreativecakes.com
SIC: **2741** Miscellaneous publishing

(G-11070)
US IRON LLC
755 Grand Blvd Ste 105b (32550-1839)
PHONE..................................765 210-4111
Mark Miller, *President*
Cathy Howard, *Executive Asst*
EMP: 15 **EST:** 2005
SALES (est): 1.4MM **Privately Held**
WEB: www.usmagnetite.com
SIC: **1011** Iron ore mining

Miromar Lakes
Lee County

(G-11071)
POWERCASES INC
18281 Via Caprini Dr (33913-7611)
PHONE..................................239 415-3846
Jeff Mason, *Director*
EMP: 7 **EST:** 2014
SALES (est): 375.1K **Privately Held**
WEB: www.usa.powercases.com
SIC: **3523** Farm machinery & equipment

(G-11072)
WIZTEL USA INC
18281 Via Caprini Dr (33913-7611)
PHONE..................................416 457-5513
Jeff Mason, *CEO*
EMP: 7 **EST:** 2005
SALES (est): 549.9K **Privately Held**
WEB: www.wiztelusainc.com
SIC: **3663** 7389 Citizens' band (CB) radio;

Molino
Escambia County

(G-11073)
CLASSIC HARDWOOD DESIGN
3895 Highway 97 (32577-5062)
PHONE..................................850 232-6473
Van Deese, *Owner*
EMP: 7 **EST:** 2002
SALES (est): 600K **Privately Held**
SIC: **3999** Furniture, barber & beauty shop

(G-11074)
SOUL KASS BOUTIQUE LLC
1218 Bet Raines Rd (32577-7125)
PHONE..................................682 429-4323
Angel Ross, *Branch Mgr*
EMP: 10
SALES (corp-wide): 362.1K **Privately Held**
SIC: **3172** Personal leather goods
PA: Soul Kass Boutique Llc
212 S Chickasaw St
Webb MS 38966
682 429-4323

Monticello
Jefferson County

(G-11075)
BBTS LOGGING LLC
2182 S Jefferson Hwy (32344-5136)
P.O. Box 15 (32345-0015)
PHONE..................................850 997-2436
Benjamin D Walton, *Principal*
EMP: 8 **EST:** 2014
SALES (est): 454K **Privately Held**
SIC: **2411** Logging camps & contractors

(G-11076)
HEALTHQUEST TECHNOLOGIES LLC
1817 W Capps Hwy (32344-7109)
PHONE..................................850 997-6300
Tim Kerr, *Partner*
EMP: 7
SALES (corp-wide): 1.8MM **Privately Held**
WEB: www.pionair.net
SIC: 3634 Air purifiers, portable
PA: Healthquest Technologies, L.L.C.
1819 Meredith Park Dr
Mcdonough GA 30253
770 320-9900

(G-11077)
JOHN P COOKSEY LLC
205 Oma Rd (32344-0885)
PHONE..................................850 997-8426
Carolyn Cooksey, *Manager*
EMP: 7 **EST:** 2012
SALES (est): 365.8K **Privately Held**
SIC: 2899 Fluxes: brazing, soldering, galvanizing & welding

(G-11078)
JOINER LAND CLEARING LLC
1417 Government Farm Rd (32344-5163)
PHONE..................................850 997-5729
Donald F Joiner, *Principal*
Linda Joiner, *Co-Owner*
EMP: 8 **EST:** 1972
SALES (est): 491.8K **Privately Held**
SIC: 2411 Pulpwood contractors engaged in cutting

(G-11079)
MONTICELLO MILLING CO INC
500 S Jefferson St (32344-1822)
PHONE..................................850 997-5521
Gerald Miller, *President*
Sara L Mc Call, *Treasurer*
EMP: 7 **EST:** 1964
SQ FT: 900
SALES (est): 665.8K **Privately Held**
SIC: 2048 Livestock feeds

(G-11080)
MONTICELLO NEWS
Also Called: ECB Publishing
180 W Washington St (32344-1954)
P.O. Box 428 (32345-0428)
PHONE..................................850 997-3568
Emerald Greene, *Owner*
Ron Cichon, *Owner*
EMP: 10 **EST:** 1971
SQ FT: 2,500
SALES (est): 2.2MM **Privately Held**
WEB: www.ecbpublishing.com
SIC: 2711 Newspapers, publishing & printing

(G-11081)
RANDY WHEELER
Also Called: Georgia-Florida Bark and Mulch
1560 Spring Hollow Dr (32344-1662)
PHONE..................................850 997-1248
Randy Wheeler, *Owner*
EMP: 8 **EST:** 1971
SQ FT: 10,000
SALES (est): 1MM **Privately Held**
SIC: 2499 0783 Mulch, wood & bark; ornamental shrub & tree services

(G-11082)
RIGHT WAY WLDG FABRICATION LLC
1605 Cherry Tree Rd (32344-6919)
PHONE..................................850 212-9672
Cody Tatum, *Manager*
EMP: 7 **EST:** 2014
SALES (est): 211.4K **Privately Held**
SIC: 7692 Welding repair

(G-11083)
WESTERN GRAPHITE INC (PA)
1045 E Washington St (32344-3022)
PHONE..................................850 270-2808
David Wimberly, *CEO*
EMP: 10 **EST:** 2006
SQ FT: 2,000
SALES (est): 1.6MM **Privately Held**
WEB: www.westerngraphite.com
SIC: 1499 Graphite mining

(G-11084)
WHARTON PEPPER CO
2873a St Augustine Rd (32344-6945)
PHONE..................................850 997-4359
William Wharton, *President*
EMP: 6 **EST:** 1987
SALES (est): 373.8K **Privately Held**
SIC: 2033 2035 Chili sauce, tomato: packaged in cans, jars, etc.; pickles, sauces & salad dressings

Moore Haven
Glades County

(G-11085)
BURMA SPICE INC
133 Florida Ave Nw (33471-2701)
PHONE..................................863 254-0960
Edward Brakus Jr, *President*
EMP: 6 **EST:** 2014
SALES (est): 565.8K **Privately Held**
WEB: www.burmaspice.com
SIC: 2099 Seasonings & spices

(G-11086)
CEMEX CNSTR MTLS FLA LLC
Also Called: Readymix - Moore Haven Rm
1290 Foxmoor St (33471-9201)
PHONE..................................800 992-3639
Paul Alt, *Branch Mgr*
EMP: 12 **Privately Held**
SIC: 1442 Construction sand & gravel
HQ: Cemex Construction Materials Florida, Llc
1501 Belvedere Rd
West Palm Beach FL 33406

(G-11087)
LEGEND MOTO LLC
1100 Us Highway 27 (33471-5517)
PHONE..................................863 946-2002
Odalis Remedios, *Principal*
EMP: 5 **EST:** 2017
SALES (est): 375.9K **Privately Held**
WEB: www.legendmoto.net
SIC: 2221 Broadwoven fabric mills, manmade

(G-11088)
MAXANT BUTTONS LLC
213 Florida Ave Nw (33471-2723)
PHONE..................................770 460-2227
Stephen Reed,
EMP: 5 **EST:** 2015
SALES (est): 366K **Privately Held**
WEB: www.coverbuttons.com
SIC: 3965 Fasteners, buttons, needles & pins

(G-11089)
SCOTT SAFETY LLC
13999 W Sr 78 (33471)
PHONE..................................239 340-8695
John Scott,
EMP: 32 **EST:** 2018
SALES (est): 1.5MM **Privately Held**
WEB: www.scottsafetyfl.com
SIC: 3444 1611 Guard rails, highway: sheet metal; highway signs & guardrails; highway & street sign installation; highway reflector installation

(G-11090)
VULCAN MATERIALS COMPANY
7425 W State Road 78 (33471-8452)
PHONE..................................863 675-5866
Carl Manning, *Manager*
EMP: 6 **Publicly Held**
WEB: www.vulcanmaterials.com
SIC: 3273 Ready-mixed concrete
PA: Vulcan Materials Company
1200 Urban Center Dr
Vestavia AL 35242

Morriston
Levy County

(G-11091)
A&H LOGGING INC
2752 Se 174th Ct (32668)
P.O. Box 277 (32668-0277)
PHONE..................................352 528-3868
Art Nussel, *Owner*
EMP: 7 **EST:** 1988
SALES (est): 396.7K **Privately Held**
SIC: 2411 Logging camps & contractors

(G-11092)
FIELD SPECIALTIES
4750 Se 220th Ave (32668-4142)
PHONE..................................440 635-0282
David Fry, *President*
EMP: 5 **EST:** 2019
SALES (est): 328.5K **Privately Held**
WEB: www.fieldspecialties.com
SIC: 3999 Manufacturing industries

(G-11093)
NORTON MANUFACTURING & SVC INC
11590 Se 30th St (32668-3296)
PHONE..................................352 225-1225
Norton Scott R, *Principal*
EMP: 6 **EST:** 2014
SALES (est): 116.1K **Privately Held**
SIC: 3999 Manufacturing industries

Mossy Head
Walton County

(G-11094)
TRANN TECHNOLOGIES INC
12526 Us Hwy 90 (32434)
P.O. Box 1221 (32434-1221)
PHONE..................................888 668-6700
Charity Prescott, *General Mgr*
Bryan E Kilbey, *Director*
EMP: 6 **EST:** 2002
SALES (est): 138.7K **Privately Held**
WEB: www.tranntech.com
SIC: 2295 Laminating of fabrics

Mount Dora
Lake County

(G-11095)
AMERICRAFT COOKWARE LLC
4129 United Ave (32757-2016)
P.O. Box 347 (32756-0347)
PHONE..................................352 483-7600
Bryan D Hurley, *Principal*
Craig Weinand, *VP Opers*
EMP: 22 **EST:** 2008
SALES (est): 2MM **Privately Held**
WEB: www.americraft.myshopify.com
SIC: 3269 Vases, pottery

(G-11096)
ANUVIA FLORIDA LLC
6751 Jones Ave (32757)
P.O. Box 220, Zellwood (32798-0220)
PHONE..................................352 720-7070
Amy Yoder, *Mng Member*
Gary Dahms,
Ed Zughaft,
EMP: 12 **EST:** 2009
SALES: 12.2MM **Privately Held**
WEB: www.anuviaplantnutrients.com
SIC: 2873 Fertilizers: natural (organic), except compost

(G-11097)
ATA GROUP OF COMPANIES INC
Also Called: Aishwarya Tari Apparels
8020 Arcadian Ct (32757-9122)
PHONE..................................352 735-1588
Rajesh S Tari, *President*
EMP: 7 **EST:** 2000
SQ FT: 2,100
SALES (est): 196.9K **Privately Held**
WEB: www.mimiseafood.com
SIC: 2211 2411 2037 0751 Apparel & outerwear fabrics, cotton; timber, cut at logging camp; frozen fruits & vegetables; frozen fruits & vegetables; fruit juices; cattle services; timber tracts, hardwood

(G-11098)
C P ENTERPRISES OF APOPKA INC
Also Called: V J Pro Fabrics
3351 Laughlin Rd (32757-7322)
PHONE..................................407 886-3321
Charles Poillion, *President*
EMP: 7
SQ FT: 15,000
SALES (est): 954.2K **Privately Held**
SIC: 3448 3523 Greenhouses: prefabricated metal; trailers & wagons, farm

(G-11099)
CASMIN INC
2255 Crescent Dr (32757-4708)
P.O. Box 895250, Leesburg (34789-5250)
PHONE..................................352 253-5000
Valerie Burleigh, *Manager*
EMP: 9 **Privately Held**
SIC: 2439 Trusses, wooden roof
PA: Casmin, Inc.
32506 County Road 473
Leesburg FL
352 343-0680

(G-11100)
DATA GRAPHICS INC
Also Called: Dg Promotions
3800 Progress Blvd (32757-2214)
PHONE..................................352 589-1312
Brad Butterstein, *President*
Tim Shephard, *President*
Robert K Welter III, *Owner*
Buffy Carroll, *Vice Pres*
Steve Salvo, *Production*
EMP: 54 **EST:** 1984
SQ FT: 22,000
SALES (est): 11MM **Privately Held**
WEB: www.datagraphicsinc.com
SIC: 3993 Signs & advertising specialties

(G-11101)
EDUCATIONAL PUBG CENTL FLA LLC
1551 Cobble Ln (32757-6215)
PHONE..................................407 234-4401
Derek W Berge, *Principal*
EMP: 6 **EST:** 2010
SALES (est): 127.5K **Privately Held**
SIC: 2741 Miscellaneous publishing

(G-11102)
ELEMENTAL ENERGY INC
4400 N Highway 19a Ste 5 (32757-2022)
PHONE..................................352 589-5703
Jamie Barrett, *Principal*
EMP: 6 **EST:** 2018
SALES (est): 226.8K **Privately Held**
WEB: www.elementalenergy.net
SIC: 2819 Industrial inorganic chemicals

(G-11103)
HALLMARK NAMEPLATE INC
1717 Lincoln Ave (32757-4108)
PHONE..................................352 383-8142
Daniel Fortuna, *CEO*
Gary A Stura, *President*
John Santiago, *Vice Pres*
EMP: 100
SQ FT: 32,000
SALES (est): 23.1MM **Privately Held**
WEB: www.hallmarknameplate.com
SIC: 3613 3993 Panel & distribution boards & other related apparatus; name plates: except engraved, etched, etc.: metal

(G-11104)
HEDRICK-WALKER & ASSOCIATES
3425 Lake Center Dr Ste 2 (32757-2345)
PHONE..................................352 735-2600
Edgar J Hedrick, *President*
Scott Coffield, *Managing Prtnr*
Robert S Walker, *Vice Pres*
EMP: 5 **EST:** 1970

SALES (est): 467.9K **Privately Held**
WEB: www.hedrick-walker.com
SIC: 3824 Mechanical & electromechanical counters & devices

(G-11105)
INTERNATIONAL OZONE SVCS LLC
320924 Sunnygo Dr Ste 210 (32757)
PHONE..................................352 978-9785
John Gaudaur, *Mng Member*
EMP: 5 **EST:** 2014
SALES (est): 469.1K **Privately Held**
WEB: www.io3services.com
SIC: 3559 7629 Ozone machines; electrical measuring instrument repair & calibration

(G-11106)
KWIK KERB BY 3D
814 Liberty Ave (32757-6013)
P.O. Box 288 (32756-0288)
PHONE..................................352 383-1123
Jim Revell, *Vice Pres*
EMP: 7 **EST:** 2012
SALES (est): 343.5K **Privately Held**
WEB: www.kwik-kerb-atwater.com
SIC: 3281 Curbing, paving & walkway stone

(G-11107)
MID-FLORIDA PUBLICATIONS INC (PA)
Also Called: Triangle Shopping Guide
4645 N Highway 19a (32757-2039)
PHONE..................................352 589-8811
Donna Covert, *Manager*
EMP: 6
SQ FT: 20,000
SALES (est): 2.3MM **Privately Held**
SIC: 2711 Newspapers, publishing & printing

(G-11108)
NATURAL ORGANIC PRODUCTS INTL
Also Called: Nopi
710 S Rossiter St (32757-6139)
PHONE..................................352 383-8252
Fax: 352 383-7307
EMP: 5
SQ FT: 60,000
SALES (est): 510K **Privately Held**
SIC: 2899 2873 2869 Mfg Chemical Preparations Mfg Nitrogenous Fertilizers Mfg Industrial Organic Chemicals

(G-11109)
PANDIA PRESS INC
312 Forest Rd (32757-9503)
PHONE..................................352 789-8156
Karen Gann, *Mktg Dir*
EMP: 10 **EST:** 2019
SALES (est): 299.9K **Privately Held**
WEB: www.pandiapress.com
SIC: 2741 Miscellaneous publishing

(G-11110)
PHYSICIANS IMAGING LLC (PA)
3615 Lake Center Dr (32757-2364)
P.O. Box 8723, Coral Springs (33075-8723)
PHONE..................................352 383-3716
Elias J Gerth, *Principal*
Tiffany McDonald, *Manager*
EMP: 6 **EST:** 2007
SALES (est): 2MM **Privately Held**
WEB: www.physiciansimagingllc.com
SIC: 2835 In vitro & in vivo diagnostic substances

(G-11111)
PRINCE MINERALS INC
710 S Rossiter St (32757-6139)
PHONE..................................832 241-2169
EMP: 9 **EST:** 2015
SALES (est): 1.1MM **Privately Held**
WEB: www.princecorp.com
SIC: 2819 Industrial inorganic chemicals

(G-11112)
SERENITY SLID SRFACES AMER LLC
3795 Codding Pl (32757-2217)
P.O. Box 2054 (32756-2054)
PHONE..................................352 459-1561
Sherrie L Knop, *Principal*
EMP: 6 **EST:** 2016
SALES (est): 192.2K **Privately Held**
SIC: 2434 Wood kitchen cabinets

(G-11113)
SERONIX CORPORATION
27109 Oak Shadow Ln (32757-7142)
PHONE..................................352 406-1698
Scott Morrell, *CEO*
Scott Russell, *President*
Kerrie Russell, *CFO*
Christopher Straut, *Shareholder*
Marie Straut, *Shareholder*
EMP: 7 **EST:** 2003
SALES (est): 675.1K **Privately Held**
WEB: www.seronix.com
SIC: 7372 Application computer software

(G-11114)
SIMPLEX INC
4085 N Highway 19a (32757-2005)
PHONE..................................352 357-2828
Tom Burkett, *President*
Beau Burkett, *Project Mgr*
David Pfister, *Sales Staff*
Dustin Williams, *Manager*
EMP: 20 **EST:** 1982
SQ FT: 8,000
SALES (est): 4.2MM **Privately Held**
WEB: www.simplexglass.net
SIC: 3442 5231 Screen doors, metal; screens, window, metal; glass

(G-11115)
TCT MANUFACTURING
21911 Us Highway 441 (32757-9737)
P.O. Box 1659, Sorrento (32776-1659)
PHONE..................................352 735-5070
James Urmson, *President*
Shirley Urmson, *Vice Pres*
EMP: 24 **EST:** 1997
SQ FT: 20,000
SALES (est): 2MM **Privately Held**
WEB: www.tctautomation.com
SIC: 3546 Saws & sawing equipment

(G-11116)
TRIANGLE SHOPPING GUIDE INC
Also Called: Lake News
4645 N Highway 19a (32757-2039)
PHONE..................................352 589-8811
William Matthews, *Chairman*
EMP: 5 **EST:** 1964
SQ FT: 2,300
SALES (est): 708.3K
SALES (corp-wide): 2.3MM **Privately Held**
WEB: www.midfloridanewspapers.com
SIC: 2711 Newspapers, publishing & printing
PA: Mid-Florida Publications Inc
4645 N Highway 19a
Mount Dora FL 32757
352 589-8811

(G-11117)
TRUEAR INC
18997 Us Highway 441 (32757-6735)
PHONE..................................352 314-8805
Adam Woodard, *CEO*
Catherine B Rathbun, *CPA*
EMP: 14 **EST:** 2017
SALES (est): 2.1MM **Privately Held**
WEB: www.truearhearing.com
SIC: 3842 Hearing aids

Mulberry
Polk County

(G-11118)
ACC HOLDCO INC
4800 State Road 60 E (33860-7905)
PHONE..................................863 578-1206
Glen Varnadoe, *President*
Robert Brinkman, *CFO*
EMP: 129 **EST:** 1998
SALES (est): 11.2MM **Privately Held**
SIC: 2899 Acid resist for etching

(G-11119)
ARRMAZ PRODUCTS INC (HQ)
Also Called: Arr-Maz Products, L.P.
4800 State Road 60 E (33860-7905)
PHONE..................................863 578-1206
William Cook, *Partner*
Patrick Lavin, *Partner*
Ronald S Lueptow, *Partner*
Martin Poveda, *Partner*
Doug Vanorsdall, *Partner*
▲ **EMP:** 100 **EST:** 1994
SQ FT: 125,000
SALES (est): 51.9MM
SALES (corp-wide): 117MM **Privately Held**
WEB: www.arrmaz.com
SIC: 2899 2869 Chemical preparations; industrial organic chemicals
PA: Arkema
420 Rue D Estienne D Orves
Colombes 92700
149 008-080

(G-11120)
BBH GENERAL PARTNERSHIP
610 N Industrial Park Rd (33860)
P.O. Box 826 (33860-0826)
PHONE..................................863 425-5626
Stan Hobby, *Partner*
Ronnie Bashlor, *Partner*
EMP: 8 **EST:** 2002
SQ FT: 10,142
SALES (est): 162.2K **Privately Held**
SIC: 3559 Rubber working machinery, including tires

(G-11121)
DANIELLE FENCE MFG CO INC
4855 State Road 60 W (33860-7820)
P.O. Box 1019 (33860-1019)
PHONE..................................863 425-3182
Marc Jeffrey Glogower, *President*
Paul Robert Glogower, *Vice Pres*
Celeste Thornton, *Comptroller*
▼ **EMP:** 75 **EST:** 1976
SALES (est): 16MM **Privately Held**
WEB: www.daniellefence.com
SIC: 2499 3699 1799 1521 Fencing, wood; security devices; fence construction; patio & deck construction & repair

(G-11122)
DEL MONTE FRESH PRODUCTION INC
5050 State Rte 60w (33860)
PHONE..................................863 844-5836
Bruce A Jordan, *Senior VP*
EMP: 7 **EST:** 2015
SALES (est): 140.5K **Privately Held**
WEB: www.freshdelmonte.com
SIC: 3824 Production counters

(G-11123)
DIVERSE CO
Also Called: Diverse Transport Systems
1950 Industrial Park Rd (33860-6610)
P.O. Box 975 (33860-0975)
PHONE..................................863 425-4251
C A Williams, *President*
Adele Williams, *Admin Sec*
EMP: 18 **EST:** 1985
SQ FT: 13,000
SALES (est): 1.2MM **Privately Held**
WEB: www.diverseco.com
SIC: 3312 1796 7699 Blast furnaces & steel mills; millwright; industrial machinery & equipment repair

(G-11124)
FLORIDA METALLIZING SVC INC
1810 State Road 37 S (33860-6915)
P.O. Box 585 (33860-0585)
PHONE..................................863 425-1143
Thomas Crews, *President*
Ismael Garcia, *Foreman/Supr*
Becky Kerber, *Office Mgr*
EMP: 32 **EST:** 1955
SQ FT: 26,562
SALES (est): 3.4MM **Privately Held**
WEB: www.fmsmulberry.com
SIC: 3599 Machine shop, jobbing & repair

(G-11125)
HICKS INDUSTRIES INC (PA)
Also Called: Carlton Funeral Service
2005 Industrial Park Rd (33860-9619)
P.O. Box 1303 (33860-1303)
PHONE..................................863 425-4155
Daniel Hicks, *President*
Stephen Hatfield, *Exec VP*
EMP: 41 **EST:** 1998
SALES (est): 8.7MM **Privately Held**
WEB: www.hicksindustries.com
SIC: 3273 Ready-mixed concrete

(G-11126)
JKS INDUSTRIES INC
2701 Cozart Rd (33860-8966)
PHONE..................................863 425-1745
Ken Shin, *Branch Mgr*
EMP: 50 **Privately Held**
WEB: www.jksindustries.net
SIC: 3499 Strapping, metal
PA: Jks Industries, Inc.
4644 W Gandy Blvd
Tampa FL 33611

(G-11127)
K C INDUSTRIES LLC
2420 Old Highway 60 (33860-7212)
P.O. Box 646 (33860-0646)
PHONE..................................863 425-1195
Steve McCarter, *Vice Pres*
Steven McCarter, *Mng Member*
◆ **EMP:** 8 **EST:** 1999
SQ FT: 1,600
SALES (est): 3MM **Privately Held**
WEB: www.kcindustries.com
SIC: 2819 Industrial inorganic chemicals

(G-11128)
LANGSTONS UTILITY BUILDINGS
4298 State Road 60 W (33860-6663)
PHONE..................................813 659-0141
Lloyd Langston, *Owner*
Brent McKinney, *Manager*
EMP: 5 **EST:** 1982
SALES (est): 382.5K **Privately Held**
WEB: www.langstonsutilitybuildings.com
SIC: 3448 5039 Buildings, portable: prefabricated metal; prefabricated structures

(G-11129)
MASTER MACHINE & TOOL CO II
2010 Moores Ln (33860-6666)
P.O. Box 495 (33860-0495)
PHONE..................................863 425-4902
Joseph Nemechek, *President*
▼ **EMP:** 17 **EST:** 1965
SQ FT: 15,000
SALES (est): 1MM **Privately Held**
WEB: www.mmt-llc.com
SIC: 3599 Machine shop, jobbing & repair

(G-11130)
METPRO SUPPLY INC
5070 State Road 60 E (33860-7907)
PHONE..................................863 425-7155
Jay Hazen, *President*
James Hazen, *Vice Pres*
Julie Wells, *Vice Pres*
Chuck Bromley, *Sales Staff*
EMP: 24 **EST:** 1985
SQ FT: 13,000
SALES (est): 4MM **Privately Held**
WEB: www.metprosupply.com
SIC: 3441 Fabricated structural metal

(G-11131)
MOS HOLDINGS INC
Also Called: IMC Agrico
5000 Old Highway 37 (33860-8863)
P.O. Box 2000 (33860-1100)
PHONE..................................763 577-2700
Mr Willie Timms, *Safety Mgr*
Levi Buzzell, *Engineer*
Steven Garcia, *Branch Mgr*
EMP: 22 **Publicly Held**
SIC: 2874 Phosphatic fertilizers
HQ: Mos Holdings Inc.
3033 Campus Dr Ste E490
Plymouth MN 55441
763 577-2700

GEOGRAPHIC

(G-11132)
P & A WELDING AND MACHINE INC
2811 State Road 60 W (33860-8866)
PHONE..................................863 425-3198
Randall Boggess, *President*
Velma Cooprider, *Vice Pres*
Dustin Ervin, *Foreman/Supr*
Faith Stegall, *Treasurer*
Timothy Cooprider, *Admin Sec*
EMP: 6 **EST:** 1990
SQ FT: 3,500
SALES (est): 1MM **Privately Held**
WEB: www.pandawelding.com
SIC: 7692 3599 1799 Welding repair; machine shop, jobbing & repair; welding on site

(G-11133)
QUALITY BLOCK & SUPPLY INC
Also Called: Quality Precast
1590 Industrial Park Rd (33860-9504)
P.O. Box 247, Seffner (33583-0247)
PHONE..................................863 425-3070
Richard Phelps, *Vice Pres*
Preston Sparkman, *VP Sales*
Tim Garlock, *Sales Staff*
Jake Rayos, *Manager*
EMP: 6 **EST:** 1987
SALES (est): 1MM **Privately Held**
WEB: www.qualityblocksupply.com
SIC: 3273 Ready-mixed concrete

(G-11134)
RJ FOODS
104 N Church Ave (33860-2497)
PHONE..................................863 425-3282
Ricky Joe Jackson, *Principal*
EMP: 6 **EST:** 2013
SALES (est): 345.3K **Privately Held**
WEB: www.rjfoods.us
SIC: 2099 Food preparations

(G-11135)
SAINT-GOBAIN CORPORATION
Also Called: Phoenix Coating Resources
2377 State Road 37 S (33860-6920)
PHONE..................................863 425-3299
EMP: 119
SALES (corp-wide): 332.4MM **Privately Held**
WEB: www.saint-gobain-northamerica.com
SIC: 3728 Aircraft parts & equipment
HQ: Saint-Gobain Corporation
20 Moores Rd
Malvern PA 19355

(G-11136)
SHAWS FIBERGLASS INC
6925b State Road 60 W (33860-7803)
PHONE..................................863 425-9176
Charles Shaw, *President*
Conchita Shaw, *Admin Sec*
EMP: 6 **EST:** 1998
SALES (est): 300K **Privately Held**
WEB: www.shawfiberglass.net
SIC: 3441 3312 Fabricated structural metal; stainless steel

(G-11137)
SOUTHERN AIR COMPRSR SVC INC
2260 Peerless Rd (33860-4448)
P.O. Box 468 (33860-0468)
PHONE..................................863 425-9111
Charles T Caveney Sr, *President*
Charles T Caveney Jr, *Vice Pres*
Edna Caveney, *Admin Sec*
EMP: 5 **EST:** 1992
SQ FT: 1,800
SALES (est): 998.2K **Privately Held**
WEB: www.sacs-fla.com
SIC: 3563 Air & gas compressors

(G-11138)
SOUTHSTERN RAIL SVCS MLBRRY FL
Also Called: Mulberry Railcar
1200 Prairie Mine Rd (33860-8168)
P.O. Box 1038 (33860-1038)
PHONE..................................863 425-4986
Stephen Howell, *President*
Thomas Reichert, *General Mgr*
Josh Conley, *Accounting Mgr*
David Howell,
EMP: 13 **EST:** 2014
SQ FT: 4,000
SALES (est): 3.1MM **Privately Held**
WEB: www.mulberryrailcar.com
SIC: 3743 Railroad car rebuilding

(G-11139)
TIDAL WAVE TANKS FABRICATIONS
3275 Mulford Rd (33860-8667)
P.O. Box 252 (33860-0252)
PHONE..................................863 425-7795
Martha E Jennings, *President*
Kelly Hahn, *Project Mgr*
EMP: 7 **EST:** 2016
SALES (est): 1.3MM **Privately Held**
WEB: www.tidalwavetanks.com
SIC: 3441 Fabricated structural metal

(G-11140)
VALLEY PROTEINS (DE) INC
465 Caboose Pl (33860-9165)
PHONE..................................910 282-7900
Duane Royal, *Branch Mgr*
EMP: 89
SALES (corp-wide): 473.5MM **Privately Held**
WEB: www.valleyproteins.com
SIC: 2077 Animal & marine fats & oils
PA: Valley Proteins (De), Inc.
151 Valpro Dr
Winchester VA 22603
540 877-2533

Myakka City
Manatee County

(G-11141)
COASTAL MARINE POWER INC
30710 Saddlebag Trl (34251-8415)
PHONE..................................941 322-8182
Richard B Stem, *President*
EMP: 9 **EST:** 2005
SALES (est): 161.4K **Privately Held**
WEB: www.coastalmarinecenterinc.com
SIC: 3443 Boilers: industrial, power, or marine

(G-11142)
CROWN WELDING & FABG INC
6030 Wauchula Rd (34251-9027)
P.O. Box 293 (34251-0293)
PHONE..................................941 737-6844
Travis L Barfield, *Principal*
EMP: 7 **EST:** 2016
SALES (est): 317.1K **Privately Held**
SIC: 7692 Welding repair

(G-11143)
STONY CORAL INVESTMENTS LLC
Also Called: Nextreef Systems
23410 78th Ave E (34251-6064)
PHONE..................................941 704-5391
EMP: 11
SQ FT: 5,500
SALES (est): 1.3MM **Privately Held**
SIC: 3231 Products Of Purchased Glass

(G-11144)
TANKS INCORPORATED
5150 Wauchula Rd (34251-9217)
PHONE..................................941 320-4371
Patricia A McCollough, *Principal*
EMP: 6 **EST:** 2018
SALES (est): 299.7K **Privately Held**
WEB: www.tanksinc.com
SIC: 3714 Motor vehicle parts & accessories

Naples
Collier County

(G-11145)
ABC RECYCLERS COLLIER CNTY INC
Also Called: Wholesale Trade
4930 21st Pl Sw (34116-5726)
PHONE..................................239 643-2302
Don Dunmire, *President*
Viola Dunmire, *Vice Pres*
EMP: 5 **EST:** 1999
SQ FT: 14,000
SALES (est): 565.8K **Privately Held**
WEB: www.colliercountyfl.gov
SIC: 2611 Pulp manufactured from waste or recycled paper

(G-11146)
ABOVE PROPERTY LLC
3555 Kraft Rd Unit 400 (34105-5079)
PHONE..................................239 263-7406
Aaron Shepherd, *CEO*
Steve Lapekas, *COO*
Karen Shepherd, *Vice Pres*
Robert Smyth, *Office Mgr*
Don Collins, *CIO*
EMP: 23 **EST:** 2012
SQ FT: 15,310
SALES (est): 2.7MM **Privately Held**
WEB: www.aboveproperty.com
SIC: 7372 5045 Prepackaged software; computer software

(G-11147)
ACI WORLDWIDE INC (PA)
3520 Kraft Rd Ste 300 (34105-4957)
PHONE..................................239 403-4600
Odilon Almeida, *President*
Glenn Wolff, *General Mgr*
Kenneth Larsen, *Chief*
Hannes Van Rensburg, *Senior VP*
Nicole Antonneau, *Vice Pres*
EMP: 1207 **EST:** 1993
SALES: 1.2B **Publicly Held**
WEB: www.aciworldwide.com
SIC: 7372 5045 Business oriented computer software; computer software

(G-11148)
ACTUAL WOODWORKING INC
668 104th Ave N (34108-3227)
PHONE..................................305 606-7849
Duvan E Pineda, *President*
EMP: 8 **EST:** 2013
SALES (est): 155.7K **Privately Held**
SIC: 2431 Millwork

(G-11149)
ADELHEIDIS COMMERCIAL INC
3847 Tamiami Trl E (34112-6201)
PHONE..................................239 384-8642
David Hoffman, *President*
Marion Scheuppenhauer, *Vice Pres*
Jens C Schuppenhauer, *Vice Pres*
EMP: 5 **EST:** 2018
SALES (est): 800K **Privately Held**
SIC: 2099 Food preparations

(G-11150)
ADVANCED SHEET METAL & WELDING
4443 Arnold Ave (34104-3339)
PHONE..................................239 430-1155
Steven Trapasso, *Principal*
EMP: 8 **EST:** 2001
SALES (est): 931.7K **Privately Held**
WEB: www.advanced-sheet-metal-welding.business.site
SIC: 3444 Sheet metalwork

(G-11151)
AGM KITCHEN & BATH LLC ✪
4384 Progress Ave (34104-7045)
PHONE..................................239 300-4739
Raybert Hernandez Ortis,
EMP: 7 **EST:** 2020
SALES (est): 295.9K **Privately Held**
WEB: www.agmkitchenandbath.com
SIC: 3131 Counters

(G-11152)
AIRCEL LLC
3033 Riviera Dr Ste 101 (34103-2746)
PHONE..................................865 681-7066
Steven E Moellers, *CEO*
▲ **EMP:** 35 **EST:** 1994
SQ FT: 30,000
SALES (est): 4.3MM **Privately Held**
WEB: www.airceldryers.com
SIC: 3563 5084 Air & gas compressors; processing & packaging equipment

(G-11153)
ALBERTOS ON FIFTH
868 5th Ave S (34102-6630)
PHONE..................................239 430-1060
Alberto Varetto, *Principal*
EMP: 8 **EST:** 2011
SALES (est): 533.2K **Privately Held**
WEB: www.albertosonfifth.com
SIC: 3421 Table & food cutlery, including butchers'

(G-11154)
ALL WELD INC
4416 18th Pl Sw (34116-5920)
PHONE..................................239 348-9550
Javier Betancourt, *Principal*
EMP: 6 **EST:** 2015
SALES (est): 54.2K **Privately Held**
SIC: 7692 Welding repair

(G-11155)
ALLIED CIRCUITS LLC
18018 Royal Tree Pkwy (34114-8941)
PHONE..................................239 970-2299
Ralph Bayer, *Principal*
EMP: 8 **EST:** 2015
SALES (est): 129.6K **Privately Held**
WEB: www.alliedcircuits.com
SIC: 3679 Electronic circuits

(G-11156)
ALTERNATIVE COATINGS OF SW FLA
3411 1st Ave Nw (34120-2705)
PHONE..................................239 537-6153
Clint R Cox, *Principal*
EMP: 9 **EST:** 2012
SALES (est): 97.3K **Privately Held**
WEB: www.lawtondentalandimplants.com
SIC: 3479 Metal coating & allied service

(G-11157)
ALUMINUM DESIGNS LLC
3573 Entp Ave Ste 75 (34104)
PHONE..................................239 289-3388
Vernon Hanks,
Nancy Hanks,
EMP: 6 **EST:** 1999
SALES (est): 539.2K **Privately Held**
SIC: 3441 Fabricated structural metal

(G-11158)
AMAZON CLEANING & MORE INC
2015 Morning Sun Ln (34119-3326)
PHONE..................................239 594-1733
Deborah Ward, *Manager*
EMP: 10 **EST:** 2007
SALES (est): 319.1K **Privately Held**
SIC: 2842 Specialty cleaning preparations

(G-11159)
AMAZON ORIGINS INC
5911 Livermore Ln (34119-4626)
PHONE..................................239 404-1818
Jeffrey A Moats, *Principal*
▲ **EMP:** 6 **EST:** 1998
SALES (est): 422.7K **Privately Held**
WEB: www.amazonorigins.com
SIC: 2064 Candy & other confectionery products

(G-11160)
AMERICA MARINE & FUEL INC
895 10th St S Ste 100 (34102-6956)
PHONE..................................239 261-3715
EMP: 7 **EST:** 2008
SALES (est): 650K **Privately Held**
SIC: 2869 Mfg Industrial Organic Chemicals

(G-11161)
AMERICAN BUSINESS CARDS INC
Also Called: Print Avenue
16475 Seneca Way (34110-3280)
P.O. Box 1378, Maryland Heights MO (63043-0378)
PHONE..................................314 739-0800
Mark B Zimmer, *President*
Kaitlin Miller, *Marketing Staff*
Shane Styker, *Manager*
Janice Zimmer, *Admin Sec*
EMP: 40 **EST:** 1981
SALES (est): 4.7MM **Privately Held**
SIC: 2759 2796 2791 2789 Thermography; platemaking services; typesetting; bookbinding & related work; commercial printing, lithographic

(G-11162)
AMERICAN LED TECHNOLOGY INC
1210 Wildwood Lakes Blvd # 202 (34104-5807)
PHONE.....850 863-8777
EMP: 12
SALES (est): 1.8MM **Privately Held**
SIC: 3993 1799 Mfg Signs/Advertising Specialties Trade Contractor

(G-11163)
ANNAT INC
Also Called: Municipal Supply & Sign
6203 Janes Ln Ste D (34109-6208)
P.O. Box 1765 (34106-1765)
PHONE.....239 262-4639
Leonard Ciarrocchi, *President*
Sandy Steinkopf, *Controller*
◆ **EMP:** 11 **EST:** 1962
SALES (est): 1.6MM **Privately Held**
SIC: 3993 Signs, not made in custom sign painting shops

(G-11164)
AP RICHTER HOLDING CO LLC
1617 Gulfstar Dr S (34112-6407)
PHONE.....239 732-9440
August P Richter, *Principal*
EMP: 9 **EST:** 2009
SALES (est): 495.5K **Privately Held**
SIC: 3399 Primary metal products

(G-11165)
APOLLO METRO SOLUTIONS INC
2975 Horseshoe Dr S # 500 (34104-6103)
PHONE.....239 444-6934
Ulrich Altvater, *CEO*
Michael Shoaff, *COO*
Craig Henning, *Engineer*
▲ **EMP:** 8 **EST:** 2012
SALES (est): 318.3K **Privately Held**
WEB: www.apollometro.com
SIC: 3646 3648 3674 Commercial indusl & institutional electric lighting fixtures; lighting equipment; street lighting fixtures; light emitting diodes

(G-11166)
ARCHITCTRAL WDWKG CONCEPTS INC
3863 Entp Ave Unit 2 (34104)
PHONE.....239 434-0549
Nelson Badilio, *President*
Eulalia Badilio, *Corp Secy*
EMP: 5 **EST:** 1998
SQ FT: 3,000
SALES (est): 400K **Privately Held**
WEB: www.awci.company
SIC: 2512 Upholstered household furniture

(G-11167)
ARCHITCTURAL WD PDTS OF NAPLES
Also Called: Architecture Wood Products
2154 J And C Blvd (34109-2052)
PHONE.....239 260-7156
Aaron Johnson, *President*
EMP: 5 **EST:** 1978
SQ FT: 4,000
SALES (est): 760.8K **Privately Held**
WEB: www.archwoodproducts.com
SIC: 2431 5211 Millwork; millwork & lumber

(G-11168)
ARTCRAFT STONE INC
2806 Aintree Ln Apt H101 (34112-5315)
PHONE.....239 253-6696
Jack Goodwin, *President*
EMP: 6 **EST:** 2005
SALES (est): 76.7K **Privately Held**
WEB: www.exiletruckwash.com
SIC: 3499 Fabricated metal products

(G-11169)
ARTHREX INC (PA)
1370 Creekside Blvd (34108-1945)
PHONE.....239 643-5553
Reinhold D Schmieding, *President*
Luc Peeters, *General Mgr*
Christopher Corwin, *Counsel*
Tricia Couto, *Vice Pres*
Kevin Grieff, *Vice Pres*
◆ **EMP:** 150 **EST:** 1991
SQ FT: 90,000
SALES (est): 616MM **Privately Held**
WEB: www.arthrex.com
SIC: 3841 Surgical & medical instruments

(G-11170)
ARTHREX MANUFACTURING INC
1370 Creekside Blvd (34108-1945)
PHONE.....239 643-5553
Reinhold Schmieding, *CEO*
Bryan King, *Opers Staff*
Kyle Armstrong, *Engineer*
Jon W Cheek, *Treasurer*
John Taylor, *Director*
EMP: 115 **EST:** 2002
SALES (est): 34.6MM
SALES (corp-wide): 616MM **Privately Held**
WEB: www.arthrex.com
SIC: 3841 Surgical instruments & apparatus
PA: Arthrex, Inc.
1370 Creekside Blvd
Naples FL 34108
239 643-5553

(G-11171)
ARTHREX TRAUMA INC ✪
1370 Creekside Blvd (34108-1945)
PHONE.....239 643-5553
Reinhold D Schmieding, *President*
EMP: 13 **EST:** 2020
SALES (est): 662.6K
SALES (corp-wide): 616MM **Privately Held**
WEB: www.arthrex.com
SIC: 3841 Surgical & medical instruments
PA: Arthrex, Inc.
1370 Creekside Blvd
Naples FL 34108
239 643-5553

(G-11172)
ARTISAN WOOD WORKS INC
701 Grove Dr (34120-1420)
PHONE.....239 321-9122
Yorky Rodriguez, *Branch Mgr*
EMP: 32
SALES (corp-wide): 81.5K **Privately Held**
SIC: 2431 Millwork
PA: Artisan Wood Works Inc
10501 Regent Cir
Naples FL

(G-11173)
ARTISANIS GUILD
1510 Rail Head Blvd (34110-8402)
PHONE.....239 591-3203
Doug Poe, *General Mgr*
John Pomeroy, *Principal*
Les Faircloth, *Vice Pres*
Mark Bolton, *Project Mgr*
Jennifer Paiva, *Accountant*
EMP: 11 **EST:** 2013
SALES (est): 601.2K **Privately Held**
WEB: www.artisansguild.net
SIC: 2431 Millwork

(G-11174)
ASG FEDERAL INC
708 Goodlette-Frank Rd N (34102-5644)
PHONE.....239 435-2200
Arthur L Allen, *President*
EMP: 9
SALES (est): 750.6K **Privately Held**
WEB: www.asg.com
SIC: 7372 Prepackaged software

(G-11175)
ATLANTIC WEST MOLDING & MLLWK
4530 Arnold Ave Ste 3 (34104-3344)
PHONE.....239 261-2874
Kevin Sperry, *Principal*
EMP: 10 **EST:** 2008
SALES (est): 481.9K **Privately Held**
WEB: www.atlanticwestmoldingandmillwork.com
SIC: 2431 Millwork

(G-11176)
ATOMIC MACHINE & EDM INC
9950 Business Cir Ste 13 (34112-3441)
PHONE.....239 353-9100
John Neader, *President*
Maxwell Lowther, *Opers Staff*
Max Lowther, *Engineer*
Bill Colburn, *CFO*
Jay Minarcin, *CFO*
EMP: 9 **EST:** 1994
SQ FT: 3,575
SALES (est): 2.6MM
SALES (corp-wide): 4.7MM **Privately Held**
WEB: www.atomicmachine.com
SIC: 3599 Machine shop, jobbing & repair
PA: Technical Ordnance Solutions, Llc
9495 Puckett Rd
Perry FL 32348
850 223-2393

(G-11177)
AVSTAR SYSTEMS LLC
4025 Skyway Dr (34112-2926)
PHONE.....239 793-5511
Dale Mohrbacher, *Principal*
EMP: 9 **EST:** 2004
SALES (est): 489.8K **Privately Held**
SIC: 3634 Electric housewares & fans

(G-11178)
AWL MANUFACTURING INC
4406 Exchange Ave Ste 109 (34104-7024)
PHONE.....239 643-5780
Ralph Shaw, *President*
Dan Shaw, *Vice Pres*
EMP: 7 **EST:** 1983
SQ FT: 3,500
SALES (est): 642.5K **Privately Held**
SIC: 3561 3825 Pumps, domestic: water or sump; spark plug testing equipment, electric

(G-11179)
AZT TECHNOLOGY LLC
10130 Market St Ste 7 (34112-3444)
PHONE.....239 352-0600
Len Zaiser IV, *CEO*
Emeric Robert, *CFO*
EMP: 120 **EST:** 2017
SQ FT: 45,000
SALES (est): 123.3MM **Privately Held**
WEB: www.azimuthtechnology.com
SIC: 3541 Machine tools, metal cutting type
PA: Azt Holdings, Llc
10130 Market St Ste 7
Naples FL 34112
239 352-0600

(G-11180)
BALISTIC 2400 LLC
2338 Immokalee Rd Ste 177 (34110-1445)
PHONE.....407 955-0065
Charles Hager,
EMP: 10
SALES (est): 348.9K **Privately Held**
SIC: 3999 Manufacturing industries

(G-11181)
BALZARANO JOHN
781 14th St Se (34117-3698)
PHONE.....239 455-1231
Balzarano John, *Principal*
EMP: 11 **EST:** 2005
SALES (est): 352K **Privately Held**
SIC: 2253 T-shirts & tops, knit

(G-11182)
BAR BEVERAGE CTRL SYSTEMS FLA
3427 Exchange Ave Ste 7 (34104-3731)
PHONE.....239 213-3301
Daniel Richman, *Owner*
EMP: 6 **EST:** 1999
SALES (est): 422.1K **Privately Held**
SIC: 3823 Fluidic devices, circuits & systems for process control

(G-11183)
BARJOR BAKING GROUP LLC
6215 Taylor Rd (34109-1959)
PHONE.....239 325-8591
Antonio Jordan, *Principal*
EMP: 8 **EST:** 2011
SALES (est): 233.6K **Privately Held**
SIC: 2052 Bakery products, dry

(G-11184)
BAY DESIGN MARINE GROUP INC
2319 J And C Blvd Ste 1 (34109-2009)
PHONE.....239 825-8094
Joel Arvilla, *Director*
EMP: 6 **EST:** 2005
SALES (est): 172.3K **Privately Held**
SIC: 3669 Sirens, electric: vehicle, marine, industrial & air raid

(G-11185)
BELATRIX SOFTWARE INC
9128 Strada Pl Ste 10115 (34108-2937)
PHONE.....801 673-8331
Silvana Gaia, *Vice Pres*
Pablo Lecea, *Vice Pres*
Ariel Seoane, *Vice Pres*
Mart N Alfieri, *Manager*
Mauricio Besse, *Manager*
EMP: 31 **EST:** 2014
SALES (est): 3.6MM **Privately Held**
WEB: www.globant.com
SIC: 7372 Prepackaged software

(G-11186)
BESTPRINTINGONLINECOM LLC
4408 Corporate Sq (34104-4755)
PHONE.....239 263-2106
EMP: 30
SALES (est): 2.2MM **Privately Held**
SIC: 2752 Lithographic Commercial Printing

(G-11187)
BGT HOLDINGS LLC
200 Aviation Dr N Ste 5 (34104-3501)
PHONE.....239 643-9949
Bill Bond, *CEO*
EMP: 6 **EST:** 2011
SALES (est): 379.1K **Privately Held**
WEB: www.bgtholdings.com
SIC: 3621 Generators & sets, electric

(G-11188)
BIO FUEL PROFESSIONALS
25 Mentor Dr (34110-1353)
PHONE.....239 591-3835
Jesse T Goges, *Principal*
EMP: 8 **EST:** 2008
SALES (est): 253.3K **Privately Held**
SIC: 2869 Fuels

(G-11189)
BIOMECH GOLF EQUIPMENT LLC
711 5th Ave S Ste 212 (34102-6628)
PHONE.....401 932-0479
Frank Fornari, *Principal*
EMP: 10
SQ FT: 2,000
SALES (est): 353.1K **Privately Held**
SIC: 3949 Golf equipment

(G-11190)
BODMAN OIL & GAS LLC
3007 Rum Row (34102-7851)
PHONE.....239 430-8545
Richard S Bodman, *Manager*
EMP: 9 **EST:** 2005
SALES (est): 904.2K **Privately Held**
SIC: 1389 Oil & gas field services

(G-11191)
BONITA DAILY NEWS
Also Called: Naple Daily News, The
1100 Immokalee Rd (34110-4811)
PHONE.....239 213-6060
Corbin Wyant, *Principal*
EMP: 20 **EST:** 1990
SALES (est): 1.4MM **Privately Held**
WEB: www.enzosofbonita.com
SIC: 2711 2741 Newspapers, publishing & printing; miscellaneous publishing

(G-11192)
BONITA GENTE MAGAZINE
2840 29th Ave Ne (34120-7414)
PHONE.....239 331-7952
Maria Alvarez, *Principal*
EMP: 6 **EST:** 2005

SALES (est): 139.8K **Privately Held**
SIC: 2721 Periodicals

(G-11193)
BRAINCHILD CORP
3050 Horseshoe Dr N # 210 (34104-7909)
PHONE..................................239 263-0100
Jeffrey Cameron, *President*
Joey Gamble, *COO*
Robert Winslow, *Database Admin*
EMP: 25 **EST:** 1991
SQ FT: 5,000
SALES (est): 5.3MM **Privately Held**
WEB: www.brainchild.com
SIC: 7372 3999 5734 Educational computer software; publishers' computer software; education aids, devices & supplies; computer & software stores

(G-11194)
BRIGHTSKY LLC
Also Called: Simplify
1004 Collier Center Way # 2 (34110-8468)
PHONE..................................239 919-8551
Matthew Miller, *Exec VP*
Tod Williams, *Chief Mktg Ofcr*
John Shevillo, *Mng Member*
Mark Hedstrom, *CTO*
EMP: 15 **EST:** 2004
SALES (est): 2MM **Privately Held**
WEB: www.simplifi.io
SIC: 3663 Mobile communication equipment

(G-11195)
BROIT BUILDERS INC
Also Called: Broit Lifting
1588 Vizcaya Ln (34113-8638)
PHONE..................................239 300-6900
Troy Broitzman, *President*
Quenby A Broitzman, *President*
EMP: 20 **EST:** 2015
SALES (est): 1.8MM **Privately Held**
WEB: www.broit.com
SIC: 1389 Construction, repair & dismantling services

(G-11196)
BUONAVENTURA BAG AND CASES LLC
Also Called: Burkley Case
4795 Enterprise Ave (34104-7042)
PHONE..................................212 960-3442
Serkan Demiray,
EMP: 5 **EST:** 2014
SALES (est): 303.6K **Privately Held**
WEB: www.burkleycase.com
SIC: 3111 Handbag leather

(G-11197)
BURN BY ROCKY PATEL
9110 Strada Pl Ste 6160 (34108-2396)
PHONE..................................239 653-9013
Rocky Patel, *President*
Richie Constancia, *Principal*
Kenneth Staudt, *Manager*
Brett Harrington, *Director*
EMP: 9 **EST:** 2012
SALES (est): 525.8K **Privately Held**
WEB: www.burnbyrockypatel.com
SIC: 3911 5813 Cigar & cigarette accessories; bars & lounges

(G-11198)
CABINET SPECIALIST INC
1520 21st St Sw (34117-4342)
PHONE..................................239 641-6931
James W Archer, *Principal*
EMP: 6 **EST:** 2008
SALES (est): 134.2K **Privately Held**
WEB: www.cabinetspecialist.net
SIC: 2434 Wood kitchen cabinets

(G-11199)
CARTER DAY HOLDING INC (PA)
27 Casa Mar Ln (34103-3685)
PHONE..................................239 280-0361
Paul W Ernst, *President*
Tim Ryan, *Treasurer*
Tim Cummings, *Sales Staff*
◆ **EMP:** 80
SALES (est): 21.8MM **Privately Held**
SIC: 3569 3556 Assembly machines, nonmetalworking; dairy & milk machinery

(G-11200)
CASEY WESTON LLC
4754 1st Ave Sw (34119-2629)
PHONE..................................239 229-8375
David E Weston, *Principal*
EMP: 6 **EST:** 2014
SALES (est): 133.5K **Privately Held**
WEB: www.caseyweston.com
SIC: 2741 Miscellaneous publishing

(G-11201)
CATALYST ORTHOSCIENCE INC
14710 Tamiami Trl N # 102 (34110-6208)
PHONE..................................239 325-9976
Brian Hutchison, *CEO*
Steven Goldberg, *Founder*
Denise Holt, *CFO*
Greg Rainey, *Sales Staff*
Michael Steuer, *Sales Staff*
EMP: 16 **EST:** 2014
SQ FT: 2,400
SALES (est): 1.7MM **Privately Held**
WEB: www.catalystortho.com
SIC: 3842 Implants, surgical

(G-11202)
CBG BIOTECH LTD CO (PA)
100 Glenview Pl Apt 1003 (34108-3132)
PHONE..................................239 514-1148
Camiener Gerald W, *Mng Member*
Gerald W Camiener, *Mng Member*
EMP: 1 **EST:** 1995
SQ FT: 4,000
SALES (est): 7.3MM **Privately Held**
WEB: www.cbgbiotech.com
SIC: 3821 Laboratory apparatus, except heating & measuring

(G-11203)
CEMEX CNSTR MTLS FLA LLC
Also Called: Prospect Avenue Rm
3728 Prospect Ave (34104-3712)
PHONE..................................855 292-8453
Warren Anderson, *Branch Mgr*
EMP: 18 **Privately Held**
SIC: 1422 Crushed & broken limestone
HQ: Cemex Construction Materials Florida, Llc
1501 Belvedere Rd
West Palm Beach FL 33406

(G-11204)
CENTER FOR BUSINESS OWNERSHIP
956 Glen Lake Cir (34119-2313)
PHONE..................................239 455-9393
Paul Willax, *Owner*
EMP: 5
SALES (est): 900K **Privately Held**
SIC: 2731 Books: publishing only

(G-11205)
CENTER FOR VITAL LIVING DBA
2132 Tamiami Trl N (34102-4807)
PHONE..................................239 213-2222
Francis A Oakes, *Principal*
EMP: 12 **EST:** 2010
SALES (est): 571.9K **Privately Held**
WEB: www.thecenterforvitalliving.com
SIC: 2082 Malt beverage products

(G-11206)
CESIBON
8807 Tamiami Trl N (34108-2525)
PHONE..................................239 682-5028
Mohammad Rahman, *Owner*
EMP: 6 **EST:** 2008
SALES (est): 260.1K **Privately Held**
SIC: 2024 Ice cream, bulk

(G-11207)
CHARLES GABLE INC
18511 Royal Hammock Blvd (34114-8947)
PHONE..................................239 300-0220
Charles Gable, *President*
EMP: 6 **EST:** 2008
SALES (est): 381.7K **Privately Held**
WEB: www.cgableinc.com
SIC: 3589 High pressure cleaning equipment

(G-11208)
CINCINNATI PRINTING SERVICE
174 Via Perignon (34119-4733)
PHONE..................................239 455-0960
James C Tosti, *President*
EMP: 6 **EST:** 1997
SALES (est): 87.2K **Privately Held**
SIC: 2752 Commercial printing, lithographic

(G-11209)
CL WATERSIDE NAPLES LLC
5455 Tamiami Trl N (34108-2870)
PHONE..................................239 734-8534
Edward W Beiner,
EMP: 11 **EST:** 2006
SALES (est): 261.7K **Privately Held**
WEB: www.watersideshops.com
SIC: 3851 Ophthalmic goods

(G-11210)
CLASSICA & TELECARD CORP
Also Called: Classica Tlcard Comm Srervices
12355 Collier Blvd Ste C (34116-6027)
PHONE..................................239 354-3727
Inirida Sandoval, *President*
Orlando E Primera, *Vice Pres*
EMP: 8 **EST:** 2001
SALES (est): 468.9K **Privately Held**
WEB: www.classicatelecard.com
SIC: 3089 5023 5499 Kitchenware, plastic; kitchen tools & utensils; gourmet food stores

(G-11211)
CLEAN & SHINE AUTO MARINE
4451 Gulf Shore Blvd N (34103-2690)
PHONE..................................239 261-6563
James Williams, *Owner*
EMP: 7 **EST:** 2006
SALES (est): 145.2K **Privately Held**
SIC: 2842 Automobile polish

(G-11212)
COATING HUES INC
747 Pine Crest Ln (34104-9520)
PHONE..................................786 626-9241
Daniel Lopera, *Principal*
EMP: 6 **EST:** 2017
SALES (est): 152K **Privately Held**
SIC: 3471 Plating & polishing

(G-11213)
COBHAM SLIP RINGS NAPLES INC (DH)
3030 Horseshoe Dr S (34104-6143)
PHONE..................................239 263-3102
Bernard Meynet, *President*
Gary Bucholtz, *Treasurer*
Miguel Torres, *Info Tech Mgr*
Todd Marshke, *Admin Sec*
EMP: 100 **EST:** 2015
SALES (est): 26.8MM
SALES (corp-wide): 177.9K **Privately Held**
WEB: www.cobham.com
SIC: 3674 Semiconductors & related devices
HQ: Cobham Holdings Inc.
10 Cobham Dr
Orchard Park NY 14127
716 662-0006

(G-11214)
COLE MACHINE LLC
Also Called: Cole Machine Naples
5740 Shirley St (34109-1814)
PHONE..................................239 571-4364
Lawrence W Cole, *Mng Member*
EMP: 8 **EST:** 2015
SALES (est): 528.2K **Privately Held**
WEB: www.colemachinenaples.com
SIC: 3599 Custom machinery

(G-11215)
COLLIER BUSINESS SYSTEMS
2280 Linwood Ave (34112-4738)
PHONE..................................239 649-5554
EMP: 6 **EST:** 2011
SALES (est): 111.7K **Privately Held**
WEB: www.colliertaxcollector.com
SIC: 2754 Business form & card printing, gravure

(G-11216)
COUNTER
9110 Strada Pl Ste 6130 (34108-2396)
PHONE..................................239 566-0644
EMP: 9 **Privately Held**
WEB: www.thecounter.com
SIC: 3131 Counters
PA: The Counter
2901 Ocean Park Blvd # 102
Santa Monica CA 90405

(G-11217)
COUNTERTOP SOLUTIONS INC
3930 Domestic Ave Ste B (34104-3674)
PHONE..................................239 961-0663
Blanca Sauceda, *Principal*
EMP: 5 **EST:** 2010
SALES (est): 497.5K **Privately Held**
WEB: www.countertopsolutionsfl.com
SIC: 2541 Counter & sink tops

(G-11218)
CREATIVE DESIGN AND PRINT
809 Walkerbilt Rd Ste 4 (34110-1511)
PHONE..................................239 325-9163
Jennifer C Betterman, *Principal*
EMP: 6 **EST:** 2016
SALES (est): 143.4K **Privately Held**
WEB: www.creativedesignandprint.co
SIC: 2752 Commercial printing, offset

(G-11219)
CRONUS LITHO LLC
9010 Strada Stell Ct # 103 (34109-4424)
PHONE..................................239 325-4846
Kathleen Conley, *Principal*
EMP: 11 **EST:** 2015
SALES (est): 269.5K **Privately Held**
WEB: www.northernlitho.com
SIC: 2752 Commercial printing, lithographic

(G-11220)
DANNY BRAWLEY
5790 Waxmyrtle Way (34109-5931)
PHONE..................................239 597-0084
Danny Brawley, *President*
EMP: 6 **EST:** 2002
SALES (est): 201.8K **Privately Held**
SIC: 1381 Service well drilling

(G-11221)
DANS CUSTOM SHEET METAL INC
Also Called: Dcsm
5700 Washington St (34109-1930)
PHONE..................................239 594-0530
Dan Osborne, *President*
Amy Beeall, *Office Mgr*
▼ **EMP:** 25 **EST:** 1993
SQ FT: 15,000
SALES (est): 3.4MM **Privately Held**
WEB: www.dcsm.net
SIC: 3444 Metal roofing & roof drainage equipment

(G-11222)
DAVE SILER TRANSPORT
111 14th St Se (34117-3686)
PHONE..................................239 348-3283
David Siler, *Principal*
EMP: 8 **EST:** 2004
SALES (est): 619.1K **Privately Held**
SIC: 3531 Construction machinery

(G-11223)
DC KERCKHOFF COMPANY
1901 Elsa St (34109-6219)
P.O. Box 9053 (34101-9053)
PHONE..................................239 597-7218
Daniel C Kerckhoff, *President*
Laura Kerckhoff, *Vice Pres*
Laura H Kerckhoff, *VP Sales*
▼ **EMP:** 18
SQ FT: 5,000
SALES (est): 2.3MM **Privately Held**
WEB: www.kerckhoffstone.com
SIC: 3272 Concrete products, precast

(G-11224)
DEBANIE INC
Also Called: Marble Designs
5450 Taylor Rd (34109-1845)
PHONE..................................239 254-1222
Enrico Piccaluga, *President*
Cathy Piccaluga, *Vice Pres*
▲ **EMP:** 18 **EST:** 1984
SQ FT: 67,000
SALES (est): 2.4MM **Privately Held**
SIC: 3281 Marble, building: cut & shaped

▲ = Import ▼=Export
◆ =Import/Export

(G-11225)
DECORATIVE PRECAST LLC
420 Sharwood Dr (34110-5726)
PHONE....................................239 566-9503
EMP: 10
SALES (est): 1.1MM **Privately Held**
SIC: 3272 Mfg Concrete Products

(G-11226)
DESIGNERS WHOLESALE WORKROOM
1035 Industrial Blvd (34104-3613)
PHONE....................................239 434-7633
Joe Pla, *President*
Norma Pla, *Vice Pres*
Tammi Chaffee, *Bookkeeper*
Angela Pla, *Executive*
EMP: 10 **EST:** 1997
SALES (est): 1.1MM **Privately Held**
WEB: www.dwworkroom.com
SIC: 2211 2591 Draperies & drapery fabrics, cotton; drapery hardware & blinds & shades

(G-11227)
DION MONEY MANAGEMENT LLC
3101 Green Dolphin Ln (34102-7915)
PHONE....................................413 458-4700
Donald R Dion Jr, *Chairman*
EMP: 19 **EST:** 1995
SQ FT: 12,000
SALES (est): 754.2K **Privately Held**
SIC: 2741 8742 Miscellaneous publishing; financial consultant

(G-11228)
DISTINCTIVE CABINET DESIGNS
5556 Yahl St Ste A (34109-1944)
PHONE....................................239 641-5165
Renee K Boyce, *President*
EMP: 7 **EST:** 1993
SQ FT: 4,020
SALES (est): 545.3K **Privately Held**
WEB: www.distinctivecabinet.com
SIC: 2434 Wood kitchen cabinets

(G-11229)
DIVERSIFIED PUBG & DESIGN
975 Imperl Golf Cours Bld (34110)
PHONE....................................239 598-4826
Anthony Spano, *Owner*
EMP: 9 **EST:** 2004
SALES (est): 758.3K **Privately Held**
SIC: 2741 Miscellaneous publishing

(G-11230)
DOLL MAKER LLC
Also Called: Doll Maker, The
11330 Tamiami Trl E (34113-8614)
PHONE....................................800 851-5183
Craig Schoenhals, *Engineer*
Whitney Sties, *Manager*
Linda Rick,
▲ **EMP:** 6 **EST:** 1992
SQ FT: 11,000
SALES (est): 609.2K **Privately Held**
WEB: www.thedollmakerdolls.com
SIC: 3942 Dolls, except stuffed toy animals

(G-11231)
DOMESTIC CUSTOM METALS COMPANY
Also Called: Domestic Metals
4275 Progress Ave (34104-7044)
PHONE....................................239 643-2422
Thomas H Grandy, *President*
EMP: 6 **EST:** 1985
SQ FT: 7,410
SALES (est): 1.1MM **Privately Held**
SIC: 3441 Fabricated structural metal

(G-11232)
E-DIRECT OIL INC
1675 Persimmon Dr (34109-0307)
PHONE....................................518 366-2208
Kenneth Sommerville, *Principal*
EMP: 6 **EST:** 2016
SALES (est): 105.3K **Privately Held**
SIC: 1311 Crude petroleum & natural gas

(G-11233)
EAGLE READY MIX
9210 Collier Blvd (34114-2541)
PHONE....................................239 732-9333
EMP: 6 **EST:** 2015
SALES (est): 133.7K **Privately Held**
SIC: 3273 Ready-mixed concrete

(G-11234)
EBELLA MAGAZINE
5647 Naples Blvd (34109-2023)
PHONE....................................239 431-7231
Sharon L Hood, *Principal*
EMP: 7 **EST:** 2015
SALES (est): 250.5K **Privately Held**
WEB: www.ebellamag.com
SIC: 2721 Magazines: publishing only, not printed on site

(G-11235)
ELITE CABINETRY INC
5435 Jaeger Rd Ste 100 (34109-5802)
PHONE....................................239 262-1144
Amy Rogers, *Owner*
EMP: 8 **EST:** 2006
SALES (est): 854.8K **Privately Held**
WEB: www.elitecabinetrynaples.com
SIC: 2434 Wood kitchen cabinets

(G-11236)
EMERGENCY MOLD SPECIALIST LLC
1344 Park Lake Dr (34110-1064)
PHONE....................................239 691-3157
Stacey L Peterson, *Principal*
EMP: 6 **EST:** 2013
SALES (est): 134.3K **Privately Held**
WEB: www.emergencyandmold.com
SIC: 3544 Industrial molds

(G-11237)
ENCHANTING ELEMENTS ✪
8261 Lucello Ter W (34114-2879)
PHONE....................................321 663-9521
Anthony Schanna Jr, *Partner*
EMP: 6 **EST:** 2020
SALES (est): 74.4K **Privately Held**
SIC: 2819 Elements

(G-11238)
ENERGENICS CORPORATION
1470 Don St (34104-3366)
PHONE....................................239 643-1711
John T Hutterly, *President*
Ingrid Naranjo, *Purch Mgr*
Tim Dunigan, *Executive*
EMP: 25 **EST:** 1974
SQ FT: 12,000
SALES (est): 6.7MM **Privately Held**
WEB: www.energenics.com
SIC: 3564 Filters, air: furnaces, air conditioning equipment, etc.; air purification equipment

(G-11239)
ENGITORK INDUSTRIES LLC
222 Industrial Blvd # 13 (34104-3704)
PHONE....................................239 877-8499
Jasmin Beslija, *Principal*
EMP: 6 **EST:** 2012
SALES (est): 166.9K **Privately Held**
SIC: 3999 Manufacturing industries

(G-11240)
ENVERIC BIOSCIENCES INC (PA)
4851 Tamiami Trl N # 200 (34103-3096)
PHONE....................................239 302-1707
David Johnson, *Ch of Bd*
Avani Kanubaddi, *COO*
Carter J Ward, *CFO*
Robert Wilkins, *Chief Mktg Ofcr*
Raj Aiyer, *Technology*
EMP: 12 **EST:** 1994
SALES (est): 41.1MM **Publicly Held**
WEB: www.enveric.com
SIC: 2834 Pharmaceutical preparations

(G-11241)
EVAMPED LLC
13751 Luna Dr (34109-0571)
PHONE....................................614 205-4467
Scott Klabunde, *Principal*
EMP: 7 **EST:** 2017
SALES (est): 422.4K **Privately Held**
WEB: www.evamped.com
SIC: 3714 Motor vehicle parts & accessories

(G-11242)
F & J WOODWORKING INC
1311 Wildwood Lakes Blvd (34104-6447)
PHONE....................................239 455-8823
Frank M Paoletta, *Principal*
EMP: 6 **EST:** 2012
SALES (est): 60.7K **Privately Held**
SIC: 2431 Millwork

(G-11243)
F I B US CORP
3966 Arnold Ave (34104-3302)
PHONE....................................239 262-6070
Ricardo Arias, *President*
EMP: 5 **EST:** 1999
SALES (est): 430.1K **Privately Held**
SIC: 3711 Cars, armored, assembly of

(G-11244)
FANTASY BREWMASTERS LLC
Also Called: FB Beer Company
950 Commercial Blvd (34104-7096)
PHONE....................................239 206-3247
Christopher Guerra, *Manager*
Chris D Guerra, *Manager*
EMP: 7 **EST:** 2009
SALES (est): 108.2K **Privately Held**
WEB: www.fantasy-brewmasters.myshopify.com
SIC: 2082 Malt beverages

(G-11245)
FEKEL STUCCO PLASTERING INC
3780 29th Ave Sw (34117-8428)
PHONE....................................239 571-5464
Fekel Altimeaux, *President*
EMP: 7 **EST:** 2003
SALES (est): 79.3K **Privately Held**
SIC: 3299 Stucco

(G-11246)
FIVE STAR GURMET FOODS FLA INC
3600 Shaw Blvd (34117-8408)
PHONE....................................239 280-0336
Tal Shoshan, *CEO*
Michelle Eoff, *Exec VP*
Masha Simonian, *CFO*
Carl Shigenaga, *Controller*
EMP: 125 **EST:** 2015
SALES (est): 9.7MM **Privately Held**
SIC: 2099 Ready-to-eat meals, salads & sandwiches

(G-11247)
FLEXIINTERNATIONAL SFTWR INC
856 3rd Ave S Ste 200 (34102-6336)
PHONE....................................239 298-5700
Stefan R Bothe, *Manager*
Spencer Kuo, *Manager*
EMP: 8 **Publicly Held**
WEB: www.flexi.com
SIC: 7372 Application computer software
PA: Flexiinternational Software, Inc.
2 Trap Falls Rd Ste 501
Shelton CT 06484

(G-11248)
FOAM MASTERS INC
4506 Mercantile Ave (34104-3361)
PHONE....................................239 403-0755
David Ashenbrener, *President*
Cheryl Ashenbrener, *Vice Pres*
EMP: 22 **EST:** 1996
SQ FT: 23,000
SALES (est): 639.2K **Privately Held**
WEB: www.foammasters.net
SIC: 3086 Insulation or cushioning material, foamed plastic

(G-11249)
FOX INDUSTRIES OF SWFL INC
Also Called: Gutters Unlimited Plus
3951 Mercantile Ave (34104-3303)
PHONE....................................239 732-6199
Brent Fox, *President*
EMP: 14 **EST:** 2011
SALES (est): 365.3K **Privately Held**
SIC: 3999 Manufacturing industries

(G-11250)
FREDERIC THOMAS USA INC
5621 Strand Blvd Ste 301 (34110-7307)
PHONE....................................239 593-8000
Frederic Reimer, *President*
Brian Michalowski, *Vice Pres*
Todd Reimer, *Vice Pres*
Carl Greene, *Engineer*
▲ **EMP:** 10 **EST:** 1998
SALES (est): 1.1MM **Privately Held**
WEB: www.fredericthomasusa.com
SIC: 2731 Books: publishing only

(G-11251)
FRUIT DYNAMICS LLC
4206 Mercantile Ave (34104-3346)
PHONE....................................239 643-7373
Robert Eddy,
EMP: 136 **EST:** 2000
SQ FT: 2,200
SALES (est): 11MM **Privately Held**
WEB: www.incrediblefresh.com
SIC: 2033 Vegetables & vegetable products in cans, jars, etc.

(G-11252)
FUEL AIR SPARK TECHNOLOGY
160 10th St N (34102-6219)
PHONE....................................901 260-3278
Chris Hoffmann, *Controller*
EMP: 10 **EST:** 2005
SALES (est): 478.6K **Privately Held**
WEB: www.fuelairspark.com
SIC: 3089 Automotive parts, plastic

(G-11253)
FULLY PROMOTED
1410 Pine Ridge Rd Ste 9 (34108-8905)
PHONE....................................239 593-2193
EMP: 6 **EST:** 2018
SALES (est): 44.8K **Privately Held**
WEB: www.fullypromoted.com
SIC: 2395 Embroidery & art needlework

(G-11254)
FUSION INDUSTRIES
1998 Trade Center Way (34109-6260)
PHONE....................................239 592-7070
Trevor Johnson, *Project Mgr*
Phillip Miller, *Purchasing*
Scotta Ens, *Engineer*
EMP: 9 **EST:** 2011
SALES (est): 149.6K **Privately Held**
WEB: www.fusionindustriesllc.com
SIC: 3999 Manufacturing industries

(G-11255)
FYI SOFTWARE INC
4850 Tamiami Trl N # 301 (34103-3029)
PHONE....................................239 272-6016
Stefan Bothe, *President*
Terry Timmins, *Partner*
Jim Van Riper, *Vice Pres*
Dan Lyons, *Sales Staff*
Marc Meyer, *Marketing Staff*
EMP: 20 **EST:** 2016
SALES (est): 612.1K **Privately Held**
WEB: www.fyisoft.com
SIC: 7372 Prepackaged software

(G-11256)
G AND W CRAFTSMAN LLC
2249 Kirkwood Ave (34112-4713)
PHONE....................................440 453-2770
Warren Hunsicker, *Mng Member*
EMP: 7 **EST:** 2014
SALES (est): 368.5K **Privately Held**
WEB: www.gandwcraftsman.com
SIC: 2499 Decorative wood & woodwork

(G-11257)
GALACTIC NEWS SERVICE
6809 Wellington Dr (34109-7207)
PHONE....................................239 431-7470
Jeffrey Bruce, *Principal*
EMP: 7 **EST:** 2010
SALES (est): 123.3K **Privately Held**
SIC: 2711 Newspapers

(G-11258)
GANNON CHARLES BERCHMAN III
Also Called: Accurate Cabinet Refacing Co
1290 Oakes Blvd (34119-1304)
PHONE....................................239 514-0243

GEOGRAPHIC

Charles Gannon III, *Principal*
EMP: 6 **EST:** 2010
SALES (est): 199.3K **Privately Held**
SIC: 2434 Wood kitchen cabinets

(G-11259)
GEM REMOTES INC
Also Called: Gem Inc of Capri
3527 Plover Ave Unit 2 (34117-8439)
PHONE....................................239 642-0873
Jim Muth, *General Mgr*
Richard Shanahan, *Principal*
EMP: 10 **EST:** 1985
SQ FT: 3,000
SALES (est): 2.2MM **Privately Held**
WEB: www.gemremotes.com
SIC: 3519 5084 Controls, remote, for boats; industrial machinery & equipment

(G-11260)
GENEREX LABORATORIES LLC
Also Called: Generex Labs
1915 Trade Center Way (34109-6220)
PHONE....................................239 592-7255
Robert Riess, *CEO*
Megan Galler, *Vice Pres*
EMP: 5 **EST:** 2007
SALES (est): 789.3K **Privately Held**
WEB: www.generexlabs.com
SIC: 2833 Medicinals & botanicals

(G-11261)
GETITCLEANED
3520 6th Ave Ne (34120-4983)
PHONE....................................239 331-2891
Christopher Felts, *Principal*
EMP: 11 **EST:** 2010
SALES (est): 1.2MM **Privately Held**
SIC: 3589 High pressure cleaning equipment

(G-11262)
GLOBAL INTRCNNECT SLUTIONS LLC
4522 Executive Dr Ste 103 (34119-9013)
PHONE....................................239 254-0326
Alfredo Ronca,
EMP: 2 **EST:** 2009
SQ FT: 1,500
SALES (est): 5MM **Privately Held**
WEB: www.globalinterconnectsolutions.com
SIC: 3672 Printed circuit boards

(G-11263)
GLOBALINK MFG SOLUTIONS
3893 Mannix Dr Ste 514 (34114-5417)
PHONE....................................239 455-5166
Jorge Barreto, *Principal*
Byron Chestnut, *Production*
Timothy O 'meara, *Marketing Staff*
▲ **EMP:** 13 **EST:** 2006
SALES (est): 844.3K **Privately Held**
WEB: www.globalinkmfg.com
SIC: 3841 Surgical & medical instruments

(G-11264)
GOODCAT LLC
1440 Rail Head Blvd Ste 5 (34110-8442)
PHONE....................................239 254-8288
Shawn Hall, *General Mgr*
Brandy Irons, *Production*
Raymond M Keller, *Mng Member*
▲ **EMP:** 37 **EST:** 2009
SQ FT: 34,000
SALES (est): 5MM **Privately Held**
WEB: www.goodcatlabs.com
SIC: 3999 Cigarette & cigar products & accessories

(G-11265)
GOT RESIDUALS INC
2614 Tamiami Trl N # 704 (34103-4409)
PHONE....................................775 343-9240
Lily Boone, *Admin Sec*
EMP: 6 **EST:** 2018
SALES (est): 99.8K **Privately Held**
SIC: 2911 Residues

(G-11266)
GRAND WOODWORKING LLC
663 Hickory Rd (34108-2638)
PHONE....................................239 594-9663
EMP: 10
SALES (est): 1.6MM **Privately Held**
SIC: 2431 Mfg Millwork

(G-11267)
GREAT LAKES WTR TRTMNT SYSTEMS
Also Called: Geat Lakes Water Cond Systems
1000 Wiggins Pass Rd (34110-6300)
PHONE....................................269 381-0210
Glenn Rockafellow, *Owner*
EMP: 6 **EST:** 1970
SALES (est): 473.8K **Privately Held**
WEB: www.greatlakesintl.com
SIC: 3589 Water purification equipment, household type

(G-11268)
GREGORYS CABINETS INC
3470 27th Ave Sw (34117-7138)
PHONE....................................239 450-8840
Gregory Weppner, *Principal*
EMP: 6 **EST:** 2012
SALES (est): 125.2K **Privately Held**
SIC: 2434 Wood kitchen cabinets

(G-11269)
GUARD DOG VALVES INC
14500 Tamiami Trl E (34114-8428)
PHONE....................................239 793-6886
Jerome Guidish, *President*
EMP: 6 **EST:** 2015
SALES (est): 276.3K **Privately Held**
WEB: www.guarddogvalves.com
SIC: 3491 Automatic regulating & control valves

(G-11270)
GULF COAST AIRWAYS INC
526 Terminal Dr (34104-3570)
PHONE....................................239 403-3020
Joel Johnson, *President*
EMP: 5 **EST:** 1998
SQ FT: 1,000
SALES (est): 419.8K **Privately Held**
WEB: www.gulfcoastairways.com
SIC: 3721 Aircraft

(G-11271)
GULF SHORE PRESS LLC
1997 Timberline Dr (34109-7125)
PHONE....................................727 641-2920
Richard Conrath, *Principal*
EMP: 6 **EST:** 2017
SALES (est): 41.3K **Privately Held**
SIC: 2741 Miscellaneous publishing

(G-11272)
GULFSHORE BUSINESS
1421 Pine Ridge Rd # 100 (34109-2116)
PHONE....................................239 887-1930
Shannon Quinn, *Principal*
Phil Borchmann, *Manager*
EMP: 6 **EST:** 2018
SALES (est): 266.3K **Privately Held**
WEB: www.gulfshorebusiness.com
SIC: 2721 Magazines: publishing only, not printed on site

(G-11273)
GULFSHORE CLOTHIER LLC
201 8th St S Ste 101 (34102-6141)
PHONE....................................239 450-8437
Joseph Genta,
EMP: 5 **EST:** 2005
SALES (est): 334.1K **Privately Held**
WEB: www.joegenta.com
SIC: 2326 Men's & boys' work clothing

(G-11274)
H H TERRY CO INC
4445 Dunlin Ct (34119-8905)
PHONE....................................239 593-0132
John Bobela, *President*
Thomas G Settineri, *Vice Pres*
EMP: 10 **EST:** 1968
SQ FT: 10,000
SALES (est): 135.8K **Privately Held**
SIC: 3724 3769 Aircraft engines & engine parts; guided missile & space vehicle parts & aux eqpt, rsch & dev

(G-11275)
HALEX CORPORATION
2059 Trade Center Way (34109-6244)
PHONE....................................239 216-4444
Lauren Maxwell, *Principal*
EMP: 8 **EST:** 2008
SALES (est): 218.3K **Privately Held**
WEB: www.halexco.com
SIC: 3423 Hand & edge tools

(G-11276)
HIGH FIVE PRODUCTS INC
7361 Lantana Way (34119-9814)
PHONE....................................239 449-9268
Donna Smith, *Principal*
EMP: 8 **EST:** 2015
SALES (est): 171.7K **Privately Held**
SIC: 2834 Pharmaceutical preparations

(G-11277)
HINCKLEY
535 5th Ave S (34102-6613)
PHONE....................................239 919-8142
EMP: 6 **EST:** 2012
SALES (est): 114.9K **Privately Held**
WEB: www.hinckleyyachts.com
SIC: 3732 Boat building & repairing

(G-11278)
HIPAAT INTERNATIONAL INC
340 9th St N (34102-5803)
PHONE....................................905 405-6299
Terry Callahan, *Managing Dir*
Christine Callahan, *Principal*
Kelly Callahan, *Vice Pres*
EMP: 10 **EST:** 2010
SALES (est): 113.4K **Privately Held**
WEB: www.hipaat.com
SIC: 7372 Application computer software

(G-11279)
HOERNDLER INC
4165 Corporate Sq (34104-4754)
PHONE....................................239 643-2008
Georg Hoerndler, *Principal*
EMP: 6 **EST:** 2007
SALES (est): 403K **Privately Held**
SIC: 2035 Seasonings, meat sauces (except tomato & dry)

(G-11280)
HOME AND DESIGN MAGAZINE
809 Walkerbilt Rd Ste 4 (34110-1511)
PHONE....................................239 598-4826
Tony Spano, *Principal*
EMP: 5 **EST:** 2008
SALES (est): 607.7K **Privately Held**
WEB: www.homeanddesign.net
SIC: 2721 Magazines: publishing only, not printed on site

(G-11281)
HOUSE OF MARBLE & GRANITE INC (PA)
440 Tamiami Trl N (34102-5805)
PHONE....................................239 261-0099
Lewis G Soriero, *President*
Raisa Soriero, *Vice Pres*
EMP: 6 **EST:** 1964
SQ FT: 4,500
SALES (est): 555K **Privately Held**
SIC: 3281 Cut stone & stone products

(G-11282)
HYDROGEN INC
383 Harbour Dr Apt 111 (34103-4015)
PHONE....................................239 436-6668
Erik Monostory, *President*
EMP: 6 **EST:** 2012
SALES (est): 173.7K **Privately Held**
WEB: www.hydrogenadvertising.com
SIC: 2813 Hydrogen

(G-11283)
I M I PUBLISHING INC
425 Cove Twr Dr Apt 1204 (34110)
PHONE....................................615 957-9288
Annie Stivers, *Principal*
EMP: 7 **EST:** 2012
SALES (est): 286.4K **Privately Held**
WEB: www.imipublishing.com
SIC: 2741 Miscellaneous publishing

(G-11284)
IMI PUBLISHING INC
640 21st St Nw (34120-1812)
PHONE....................................239 529-5081
Angel Jarvis, *Director*
EMP: 9 **EST:** 2012
SALES (est): 1MM **Privately Held**
SIC: 2741 Miscellaneous publishing

(G-11285)
INDIGO MOUNTAIN INC
4280 Mourning Dove Dr (34119-8867)
PHONE....................................239 947-0023
Yatin Shelar, *President*
Alanna Shelar, *Vice Pres*
◆ **EMP:** 5 **EST:** 1996
SALES (est): 3MM **Privately Held**
SIC: 2211 5136 Apparel & outerwear fabrics, cotton; men's & boys' clothing

(G-11286)
INDUSTRIAL NANOTECH INC
1415 Panther Ln (34109-7874)
PHONE....................................800 767-3998
George S Burchill, *President*
Francesca Crolley, *President*
Laurie Burchill, *Vice Pres*
EMP: 8 **EST:** 2005
SQ FT: 2,000
SALES (est): 1.3MM **Privately Held**
WEB: www.industrial-nanotech.com
SIC: 3479 Coating of metals with silicon

(G-11287)
INSTORESCREEN LLC
2338 Immokalee Rd (34110-1445)
PHONE....................................646 301-4690
EMP: 6 **EST:** 2012
SALES (est): 372K **Privately Held**
WEB: www.instorescreen.com
SIC: 2893 Screen process ink

(G-11288)
INTELLGENT INSTRUMENTATION INC (PA)
Also Called: I3
1421 Pine Ridge Rd # 120 (34109-2116)
PHONE....................................520 573-0887
Richard Daniel, *President*
Robert M Auman, *President*
Paul Liska, *Vice Pres*
Darshan Phillips, *Director*
EMP: 10 **EST:** 1984
SALES (est): 2.1MM **Privately Held**
WEB: www.lanpoint.com
SIC: 3823 Computer interface equipment for industrial process control

(G-11289)
INTERNATIONAL MDSE SOURCES INC (PA)
4551 Gulf Shore Blvd N (34103-2219)
PHONE....................................239 430-9993
John Brooking, *President*
Dennis R Back, *Vice Pres*
▲ **EMP:** 126 **EST:** 2006
SALES (est): 10.9MM **Privately Held**
SIC: 2273 Carpets & rugs

(G-11290)
INTERNATIONAL PACKAGING MCHS
Also Called: I P M
3963 Enterprise Ave (34104-3640)
PHONE....................................239 643-2020
J R Humphrey, *President*
Eileen Curran Lagan, *Vice Pres*
EMP: 8 **EST:** 1962
SQ FT: 21,000
SALES (est): 471.5K **Privately Held**
SIC: 3565 3523 Wrapping machines; farm machinery & equipment

(G-11291)
IPEG CORPORATION
5400 Jaeger Rd Ste 2 (34109-5807)
PHONE....................................239 963-1470
Alan Haddy, *Owner*
Annie Burns, *Manager*
EMP: 13 **EST:** 2012
SALES (est): 2.8MM **Privately Held**
WEB: www.utto.com
SIC: 3823 Temperature measurement instruments, industrial

(G-11292)
IRECO INC
9929 Clear Lake Cir (34109-0788)
PHONE....................................239 593-3749
Peter F Fagan Ptd, *Principal*
EMP: 11 **EST:** 2010
SALES (est): 104.1K **Privately Held**
WEB: www.ireco.com
SIC: 2892 Explosives

(G-11293)
ISLAND PRINT SHOP
3888 Mannix Dr Ste 301 (34114-5408)
P.O. Box 1363, Marco Island (34146-1363)
PHONE..................................239 642-0077
Jeffrey J Biden, *Owner*
EMP: 5 **EST:** 1988
SALES (est): 465.5K **Privately Held**
SIC: 2752 Commercial printing, offset

(G-11294)
JB CUSTOM MARINE
3461 18th Ave Ne (34120-5564)
PHONE..................................239 877-2784
Brett Sheldon, *Principal*
EMP: 5 **EST:** 2011
SALES (est): 380.6K **Privately Held**
WEB: www.jbcustommarine.com
SIC: 3669 Sirens, electric: vehicle, marine, industrial & air raid

(G-11295)
JBT LLC
2875 Citrus Lake Dr # 205 (34109-7640)
PHONE..................................513 238-4218
Joseph R Nugent, *Branch Mgr*
EMP: 16
SALES (corp-wide): 106.1K **Privately Held**
WEB: www.jbtc.com
SIC: 3556 Food products machinery
PA: Jbt Llc
528 W Yale St
Orlando FL 32804
407 463-2045

(G-11296)
JFAURE LLC
Also Called: Coastal Kitchen Interiors
22758 J&C Blvd (34109)
PHONE..................................239 631-5324
Shelly Benfield, *Office Mgr*
Stephen Kilchenstein, *Manager*
EMP: 9 **EST:** 2014
SALES (est): 359.4K **Privately Held**
SIC: 2434 Wood kitchen cabinets

(G-11297)
JMC COATINGS LLC
2025 J And C Blvd (34109-6204)
PHONE..................................239 260-5451
EMP: 6 **EST:** 2016
SALES (est): 156.3K **Privately Held**
SIC: 3479 Metal coating & allied service

(G-11298)
JOHN A PULLING JR
5610 Yahl St Ste 6 (34109-1921)
PHONE..................................239 593-5247
John A Pulling, *Principal*
EMP: 5 **EST:** 2017
SALES (est): 450.7K **Privately Held**
SIC: 1389 Construction, repair & dismantling services

(G-11299)
JOHN S WILSON INC
6222 Parkers Hammock Rd (34112-2992)
PHONE..................................410 442-2400
John S Wilson, *President*
Jacquelyn Mongelli, *Credit Mgr*
EMP: 10
SALES (est): 803K **Privately Held**
WEB: www.johnswilson.com
SIC: 2431 Millwork

(G-11300)
JSI SCIENTIFIC INC
862 105th Ave N Ste 18 (34108-1844)
PHONE..................................732 845-1925
Kathleen V Kuchinski, *President*
EMP: 8 **EST:** 2013
SALES (est): 435K **Privately Held**
WEB: www.jsiscientific.com
SIC: 3823 7389 Chromatographs, industrial process type;

(G-11301)
JUST NOW JENNINGS LLC
Also Called: Minuteman Press
6542 Chestnut Cir (34109-7810)
PHONE..................................239 331-0315
Anthony Jennings, *Manager*
EMP: 6 **EST:** 2016
SALES (est): 722.6K **Privately Held**
WEB: www.chanhassen-mn.minutemanpress.com
SIC: 2024 Ice cream & frozen desserts

(G-11302)
K R O ENTERPRISES LTD
Also Called: Printing Unlimited
7950 Preserve Cir Apt 816 (34119-6743)
PHONE..................................309 797-2213
Karen Osterhaus, *President*
EMP: 6 **EST:** 1984
SQ FT: 1,500
SALES (est): 936.6K **Privately Held**
SIC: 2752 3993 2791 2789 Commercial printing, offset; signs & advertising specialties; typesetting; bookbinding & related work; manifold business forms

(G-11303)
KEITH DENNIS MARKHAM
Also Called: Aqua Pure of SW Florida Lc
220 24th Ave Ne (34120-2386)
PHONE..................................239 353-4122
Keith Markham, *Owner*
EMP: 8 **EST:** 2006
SALES (est): 775.2K **Privately Held**
SIC: 7372 Application computer software

(G-11304)
KENNEDY CRAFT CABINETS INC
5790 Washington St (34109-1930)
PHONE..................................239 598-1566
Mike Kennedy, *President*
EMP: 6 **EST:** 1985
SQ FT: 3,300
SALES (est): 584.8K **Privately Held**
SIC: 2439 5712 Timbers, structural: laminated lumber; customized furniture & cabinets

(G-11305)
KENNETH E KELLER
4110 Entp Ave Ste 116 (34116)
PHONE..................................239 649-7579
Kenneth E Keller, *President*
EMP: 7 **EST:** 2010
SALES (est): 700K **Privately Held**
SIC: 2431 Awnings, blinds & shutters, wood

(G-11306)
KM PRECAST INC
7701 Gardner Dr Unit 101 (34109-0639)
PHONE..................................239 438-2146
Kelly R Montgomery, *President*
EMP: 12 **EST:** 2005
SALES (est): 220.3K **Privately Held**
SIC: 3272 Precast terrazo or concrete products

(G-11307)
LAKE & BAY BOATS LLC
5770 Shirley St (34109-1814)
PHONE..................................813 949-7300
Michael A Del Duca, *Principal*
EMP: 8 **EST:** 2008
SALES (est): 144.2K **Privately Held**
WEB: www.lakeandbay.com
SIC: 3732 Boat building & repairing

(G-11308)
LAW OFFCES RBECCA A BEDDOW LLC
2500 Airport Rd S Ste 208 (34112-4803)
PHONE..................................516 671-6566
Rebecca Beddow, *CEO*
EMP: 6 **EST:** 2019
SALES (est): 45.1K **Privately Held**
WEB: www.rebeccabeddow.com
SIC: 3944 Games, toys & children's vehicles

(G-11309)
LED SURF LIGHTING INC
3425 Radio Rd Ste 202 (34104-3758)
PHONE..................................239 687-4458
Felliciano Leonard, *Principal*
▲ **EMP:** 6 **EST:** 2013
SALES (est): 401.6K **Privately Held**
WEB: www.ledsurf.com
SIC: 3648 Lighting equipment

(G-11310)
LEISURE FURNITURE POWDER CT
1076 Business Ln Ste 7 (34110-8466)
PHONE..................................239 597-4343
EMP: 12 **EST:** 2019
SALES (est): 776.1K **Privately Held**
WEB: www.leisurefurniture.net
SIC: 3479 Metal coating & allied service

(G-11311)
LENKBAR LLC
2705 Corporate Flight Dr (34104-3524)
PHONE..................................239 732-5915
Louis Lauch, *Principal*
James Magee, *Prdtn Mgr*
Erik Papenfuss, *Mng Member*
Vicki Dedio, *Manager*
Nola Gastineau, *Director*
EMP: 60 **EST:** 2011
SALES (est): 7.8MM **Privately Held**
WEB: www.lenkbar.com
SIC: 3841 Surgical & medical instruments

(G-11312)
LIGHTNING PRTCTION SYSTEMS INC
38818 Exchange Ave (34104)
PHONE..................................239 643-4323
Lance Fleming, *President*
Sandy Langley, *Corp Secy*
EMP: 10 **EST:** 1974
SQ FT: 1,500
SALES (est): 1.9MM **Privately Held**
WEB: www.lightningprotectionsystemsinc.com
SIC: 3643 Lightning protection equipment

(G-11313)
LIME STREET DEVELOPMENT LLC
808 Wiggins Pass Rd # 201 (34110-6138)
PHONE..................................239 594-7777
Joseph McHarris, *Principal*
EMP: 8 **EST:** 2008
SALES (est): 176.2K **Privately Held**
SIC: 3274 Lime

(G-11314)
LINGA POS LLC (PA)
4501 Tamiami Trl N # 400 (34103-3023)
PHONE..................................800 619-5931
Onur Haytac, *President*
Oscar Fandino, *Manager*
Bob Frazier, *Officer*
EMP: 44 **EST:** 2004
SALES (est): 3MM **Privately Held**
WEB: www.lingaros.com
SIC: 7372 Prepackaged software

(G-11315)
LOKSAK INC
6507 Marbella Dr (34105-5045)
P.O. Box 7127 (34101-7127)
PHONE..................................239 331-5550
Ottavio Cinelli, *Sales Staff*
Ryan Zvibleman, *Executive*
EMP: 7 **EST:** 1992
SALES (est): 908.2K **Privately Held**
WEB: www.loksak.com
SIC: 2385 Waterproof outerwear

(G-11316)
LOOS & CO INC
Also Called: Cableware Technology Division
901 Industrial Blvd (34104-3715)
PHONE..................................239 643-5667
Tony Carminati, *Materials Mgr*
Chris Albury, *Purch Mgr*
Charlie Hill, *Engineer*
Anthony Rondeau, *Engineer*
Curtis Schopfer, *Engineer*
EMP: 80
SQ FT: 100,000
SALES (corp-wide): 79.1MM **Privately Held**
WEB: www.loosco.com
SIC: 3728 3812 3429 Aircraft parts & equipment; search & navigation equipment; manufactured hardware (general)
PA: Loos & Co., Inc.
16b Mashamoquet Rd
Pomfret CT 06258
860 928-7981

(G-11317)
M-BIOLABS INC
Also Called: MBL
1415 Panther Ln (34109-7874)
PHONE..................................239 571-0435
Corey Sandmann, *Principal*
Bria Thamarus, *Exec VP*
EMP: 9 **EST:** 2016
SALES (est): 202K **Privately Held**
WEB: www.mbiolabs.com
SIC: 2836 Biological products, except diagnostic

(G-11318)
MANLEY FARMS INC (PA)
Also Called: Manley Farms North
1040 Collier Center Way # 12 (34110-8480)
PHONE..................................239 597-6416
Kent Manley, *President*
Judy Manley, *Treasurer*
▲ **EMP:** 5 **EST:** 1972
SQ FT: 20,000
SALES (est): 6.7MM **Privately Held**
SIC: 3523 Soil preparation machinery, except turf & grounds

(G-11319)
MARBLE BRIDGE INC
3827 Arnold Ave (34104-3301)
PHONE..................................239 213-1411
Onelio Caballero, *Owner*
EMP: 12 **EST:** 2004
SALES (est): 1.1MM **Privately Held**
SIC: 3499 Fabricated metal products

(G-11320)
MARCH INC
Also Called: March Performance
16160 Performance Way (34110-2224)
PHONE..................................239 593-4074
Kim March, *President*
Craig J March, *Vice Pres*
▲ **EMP:** 40 **EST:** 1973
SQ FT: 27,000
SALES (est): 4.9MM **Privately Held**
WEB: www.marchperformance.com
SIC: 3714 Motor vehicle parts & accessories

(G-11321)
MARIOS METALCRAFT
Also Called: Marios Mtalcraft Powdr Coating
4227 Mercantile Ave Ste A (34104-3389)
PHONE..................................239 649-0085
David Heinemann, *Owner*
Wayde Cargill, *Vice Pres*
EMP: 5 **EST:** 1985
SQ FT: 14,000
SALES (est): 805.8K **Privately Held**
WEB: www.mariosmetalcraft.com
SIC: 3645 3471 Table lamps; chandeliers, residential; plating & polishing

(G-11322)
MARMON AEROSPACE & DEFENSE LLC
Also Called: Cable USA
2584 Horseshoe Dr S (34104-6131)
PHONE..................................239 643-6400
Tim Grass, *President*
EMP: 70
SALES (corp-wide): 245.5B **Publicly Held**
WEB: www.marmon-ad.com
SIC: 3496 Miscellaneous fabricated wire products
HQ: Marmon Aerospace & Defense Llc
680 Hayward St
Manchester NH 03103
603 622-3500

(G-11323)
MAVERICK PRESS INC
975 6th Ave S Ste 200 (34102-6753)
PHONE..................................239 331-8379
Debra K Horner, *Principal*
EMP: 7 **EST:** 2015
SALES (est): 41.3K **Privately Held**
SIC: 2741 Miscellaneous publishing

(G-11324)
MC JOHNSON CO
2037 J And C Blvd (34109-6213)
PHONE..................................239 293-0901

GEOGRAPHIC

Richard Ballo, *Principal*
EMP: 13 **EST:** 2010
SALES (est): 212.3K **Privately Held**
WEB: www.mcjohnson.com
SIC: 3841 Surgical & medical instruments

(G-11325)
MEADOWBROOK INC
Also Called: Meadowbrook Press
970 Egrets Run Apt 102 (34108-2480)
PHONE..................................800 338-2232
▲ **EMP:** 22
SQ FT: 16,000
SALES (est): 2.3MM **Privately Held**
SIC: 2731 Books-Publishing/Printing

(G-11326)
MEG SYSTEMS INC
2030 River Reach Dr # 138 (34104-5257)
PHONE..................................239 263-5833
Elena Gracia, *President*
Charles Harris, *Vice Pres*
EMP: 5 **EST:** 1998
SALES (est): 1MM **Privately Held**
WEB: www.pcmakers.org
SIC: 3825 Network analyzers

(G-11327)
MHKAP LLC
2059 Tamiami Trl E (34112-4636)
PHONE..................................239 919-0786
Matthew Kragh, *Owner*
EMP: 5 **EST:** 2018
SALES (est): 517.8K **Privately Held**
WEB: www.mhkap.com
SIC: 2599 Hospital beds

(G-11328)
MOLD PROS FRANCHISING INC
3428 Runaway Ln Ste 106 (34114-8440)
PHONE..................................239 262-6653
John Bohde, *President*
EMP: 15 **EST:** 2016
SALES (est): 1.2MM **Privately Held**
SIC: 3544 Industrial molds

(G-11329)
MOLLYS MARINE SERVICE LLC
895 10th St S (34102-6949)
PHONE..................................239 262-2628
Danny Commers, *Principal*
EMP: 6 **EST:** 2009
SALES (est): 896.1K **Privately Held**
WEB: www.mollysmarineservice.com
SIC: 2211 Canvas

(G-11330)
MONTAGUE ENTERPRISES INC
Also Called: Activedata
1004 Collier Center Way # 206
(34110-8484)
PHONE..................................239 631-5292
James Montague, *President*
Valerie Montague, *Vice Pres*
EMP: 5 **EST:** 2010
SALES (est): 407.4K **Privately Held**
WEB: www.m.activedatamobile.com
SIC: 7372 7371 Prepackaged software; custom computer programming services

(G-11331)
MONTALVOS RACEWAY LLC
280 35th Ave Ne (34120-1874)
PHONE..................................239 289-6931
Oscar Montalvo, *Principal*
EMP: 8 **EST:** 2013
SALES (est): 748.1K **Privately Held**
SIC: 3644 Raceways

(G-11332)
MONTY SANITATION INC
5545 Shirley St (34109-1809)
PHONE..................................239 597-2486
Robert M Montgomery, *President*
EMP: 5 **EST:** 1974
SALES (est): 704K **Privately Held**
WEB: www.montysanitationsws.com
SIC: 3272 7699 7359 Septic tanks, concrete; septic tank cleaning service; portable toilet rental

(G-11333)
N MEDIA GROUP LLC (PA)
4500 Executive Dr Ste 320 (34119-8908)
PHONE..................................239 594-1322
Thomas Brown, *Mng Member*
EMP: 25 **EST:** 1999
SQ FT: 4,000
SALES (est): 3.6MM **Privately Held**
SIC: 2721 Periodicals: publishing & printing

(G-11334)
NAPLES HOTRODS & PRFMCE LLC
6122 Janes Ln (34109-6224)
PHONE..................................239 653-9076
James Hurd, *Principal*
EMP: 6 **EST:** 2011
SALES (est): 126.9K **Privately Held**
SIC: 3711 Motor vehicles & car bodies

(G-11335)
NAPLES ILLUSTRATED
3066 Tamiami Trl Mre 10 Moore Ste 102
(34102)
PHONE..................................239 434-6966
Fax: 239 435-0409
EMP: 7
SALES (est): 590.6K **Privately Held**
SIC: 2721 Periodicals-Publishing/Printing

(G-11336)
NAPLES IRON WORKS INC
4551 Arnold Ave (34104-3339)
PHONE..................................239 649-7265
James W Sauerwald, *President*
EMP: 28 **EST:** 1997
SALES (est): 3.7MM **Privately Held**
WEB: www.naplesironworks.com
SIC: 3441 3446 3444 3354 Fabricated structural metal; architectural metalwork; sheet metalwork; aluminum extruded products

(G-11337)
NAPLES POWDER COATING LLC
3960 Domestic Ave Ste A (34104-3609)
PHONE..................................239 352-3500
Terry L Kelly, *Manager*
EMP: 5 **EST:** 2019
SALES (est): 840.4K **Privately Held**
WEB: www.naplespowdercoating.com
SIC: 3479 Coating of metals & formed products

(G-11338)
NAPLES PRINTING INC
1100 Coml Blvd Ste 114 (34104)
PHONE..................................239 643-2442
Michael Couture, *Principal*
EMP: 10 **EST:** 2009
SALES (est): 161.3K **Privately Held**
WEB: www.allegramarketingprint.com
SIC: 2752 Commercial printing, offset

(G-11339)
NAPLES STONE CONSULTING LLC
1881 Trade Center Way (34109-1863)
PHONE..................................239 325-8653
Michael Gonzales, *President*
EMP: 11 **EST:** 2016
SALES (est): 818.3K **Privately Held**
SIC: 3281 Granite, cut & shaped

(G-11340)
NAPLES WOODWORKS INC
6080 Golden Oaks Ln (34119-1214)
PHONE..................................239 287-1632
Theresa M Martin, *Principal*
EMP: 7 **EST:** 2016
SALES (est): 67.1K **Privately Held**
SIC: 2431 Millwork

(G-11341)
NATIONAL CUSTOM TABLE PADS
6030 English Oaks Ln (34119-1328)
PHONE..................................239 596-6805
Jerry Goldberg, *Principal*
EMP: 7 **EST:** 2001
SALES (est): 160K **Privately Held**
SIC: 2392 Pads & padding, table: except asbestos, felt or rattan

(G-11342)
NATIONAL SCIENTIFIC INC
3838 Tamiami Trl N Ste 31 (34103-3590)
PHONE..................................239 262-4047
J Burton, *Principal*
EMP: 8 **EST:** 2016
SALES (est): 129.3K **Privately Held**
SIC: 3826 Analytical instruments

(G-11343)
NATIONAL SUBSCRIPTION BUREAU
Also Called: Coding Institute, The
2272 Airport Rd S Ste 301 (34112-4837)
PHONE..................................800 508-1311
Leslie Norins, *Ch of Bd*
Sylvia Albert, *Cust Mgr*
EMP: 31 **EST:** 1990
SQ FT: 1,500
SALES (est): 2.1MM **Privately Held**
WEB: www.eliresearch.com
SIC: 2741 Newsletter publishing

(G-11344)
NEON SLEEVZ LLC
4437 54th Ave Ne (34120-3205)
PHONE..................................239 348-0520
Pierre Borgela, *Principal*
EMP: 6 **EST:** 2017
SALES (est): 214K **Privately Held**
SIC: 2813 Neon

(G-11345)
NGP CORPORATE SQUARE INC
Also Called: Intech Graphics
4408 Corporate Sq (34104-4755)
PHONE..................................239 643-3430
David Wacker, *President*
Dan Fitzgerald, *Accounts Exec*
Bob Greenhalgh, *Accounts Exec*
Steve Bello, *Manager*
EMP: 26 **EST:** 1991
SQ FT: 10,000
SALES (est): 3.9MM **Privately Held**
WEB: www.intechprinting.com
SIC: 2752 2791 2789 Commercial printing, offset; typesetting; bookbinding & related work

(G-11346)
NORTHERN LITHO INC
9486 Gulf Shore Dr (34108-2077)
PHONE..................................239 653-9645
EMP: 6 **EST:** 2017
SALES (est): 191.1K **Privately Held**
SIC: 2752 Commercial printing, lithographic

(G-11347)
NUTRIFUSION LLC
10641 Airport Pulling Rd (34109-7330)
PHONE..................................404 240-0030
Myra Grand,
EMP: 11 **EST:** 2017
SALES (est): 1.1MM **Privately Held**
WEB: www.nutrifusion.com
SIC: 2099 Food preparations

(G-11348)
NVIP LLC ✪
2231 Linwood Ave (34112-4737)
PHONE..................................972 435-4097
Tony Gaines,
EMP: 8 **EST:** 2020
SALES (est): 574.7K **Privately Held**
WEB: www.nvipllc.com
SIC: 2842 Sanitation preparations, disinfectants & deodorants

(G-11349)
OBSERVER GROUP AND GULF COAST
2960 Immokalee Rd (34110-1439)
PHONE..................................239 263-0122
EMP: 8 **EST:** 2017
SALES (est): 106.5K **Privately Held**
WEB: www.businessobserverfl.com
SIC: 2711 Job printing & newspaper publishing combined

(G-11350)
OLD WORLD MARBLE AND GRAN INC
1998 Trade Center Way # 1 (34109-6260)
PHONE..................................239 596-4777
Marc Beaudet, *President*
▲ **EMP:** 9 **EST:** 1998
SALES (est): 527.6K **Privately Held**
SIC: 1411 3281 Dimension stone; marble, building: cut & shaped

(G-11351)
OLIVE NAPLES OIL COMPANY (PA)
2368 Immokalee Rd (34110-1446)
PHONE..................................239 596-3000
Marilyn J McGinty, *Principal*
EMP: 20 **EST:** 2005
SALES (est): 533.1K **Privately Held**
WEB: www.naplesoliveoilcompany.com
SIC: 2079 Olive oil

(G-11352)
OLIVE OIL CO OF FORT MYERS
2960 39th St Sw (34117-8462)
PHONE..................................239 821-4630
Crystal Hollingsworth, *Principal*
EMP: 6 **EST:** 2017
SALES (est): 107.1K **Privately Held**
SIC: 2079 Olive oil

(G-11353)
PALERMO PAVERS INC
4001 Estey Ave (34104-4460)
PHONE..................................239 263-0593
Anthony Palermo, *President*
EMP: 5 **EST:** 2005
SALES (est): 461.5K **Privately Held**
WEB: www.palermopavers.com
SIC: 2951 Asphalt paving mixtures & blocks

(G-11354)
PALLET DIRECT INC
5660 Cypress Hollow Way (34109-5907)
PHONE..................................888 433-1727
Ann Stillwell, *President*
EMP: 5 **EST:** 1997
SALES (est): 6MM **Privately Held**
SIC: 2448 7389 Pallets, wood;

(G-11355)
PALM BEACH MEDIA GROUP INC
Also Called: Naples Illustrated
3066 Tamiami Trl N # 102 (34103-2757)
PHONE..................................239 434-6966
Loretta Grantham, *Chief*
Todd Schmidt, *Opers Dir*
Kathy Beuttel, *Accounts Mgr*
Melissa Schwartz, *Accounts Mgr*
Linda Sciuto, *Mktg Dir*
EMP: 8 **Privately Held**
WEB: www.palmbeachmedia.com
SIC: 2721 Magazines: publishing only, not printed on site
PA: Palm Beach Liquidation Company
1000 N Dixie Hwy Ste C
West Palm Beach FL 33401

(G-11356)
PAPENFUSS HOLDINGS INC
11430 Tamiami Trl E (34113-7915)
PHONE..................................239 775-9090
Hans Papenfuss, *President*
Erik Papan, *Vice Pres*
EMP: 6 **EST:** 1984
SQ FT: 3,000
SALES (est): 775.9K **Privately Held**
SIC: 3544 Industrial molds; special dies & tools

(G-11357)
PARADISE WLDG CSTM FABRICATION
3888 Mannix Dr Ste 310 (34114-5408)
PHONE..................................239 961-8864
Kenneth J Marino, *Principal*
EMP: 5 **EST:** 2009
SALES (est): 508.4K **Privately Held**
WEB: www.paradiseweldinginc.com
SIC: 7692 Welding repair

(G-11358)
PARKER-HANNIFIN CORPORATION
Fluid Systems Division
3580 Shaw Blvd (34117-8408)
PHONE..................................239 304-1000
Stephen Adams, *Opers Staff*
Michael Dill, *Branch Mgr*
EMP: 6

SALES (corp-wide): 13.7B **Publicly Held**
WEB: www.parker.com
SIC: 3728 3724 Aircraft assemblies, subassemblies & parts; aircraft engines & engine parts
PA: Parker-Hannifin Corporation
6035 Parkland Blvd
Cleveland OH 44124
216 896-3000

(G-11359)
PARTSVU LLC
829 Airport Pulling Rd N (34104-6106)
PHONE..................................239 643-2292
Philip Osborne, *Principal*
EMP: 239 **EST:** 2015
SALES (est): 2.2MM
SALES (corp-wide): 1B **Publicly Held**
WEB: www.onewatermarine.com
SIC: 3714 5571 Motor vehicle parts & accessories; all terrain vehicle parts and accessories
PA: Onewater Marine Inc.
6275 Lanier Islands Pkwy
Buford GA 30518
678 541-6300

(G-11360)
PEPSI-COLA BOTTLING CO TAMPA
Also Called: Pepsico
1171 Industrial Blvd (34104-3630)
PHONE..................................239 643-4642
Matt Edwards, *Branch Mgr*
EMP: 224
SALES (corp-wide): 70.3B **Publicly Held**
WEB: www.pepsico.com
SIC: 2086 Carbonated soft drinks, bottled & canned
HQ: Pepsi-Cola Bottling Company Of Tampa
11315 N 30th St
Tampa FL 33612
813 971-2550

(G-11361)
PFCI LLC
Also Called: Precast Keystone
4610 Enterprise Ave (34104-7014)
PHONE..................................239 435-3575
Elio Jacome, *Project Mgr*
William Towers, *Mng Member*
Ed Towers,
Gretchen Towers,
EMP: 25 **EST:** 2010
SALES (est): 2.9MM **Privately Held**
SIC: 3272 Concrete products

(G-11362)
PHELPS MOTORSPORTS LLC
2255 Linwood Ave (34112-4737)
PHONE..................................239 417-2042
Robert J Phelps,
EMP: 7 **EST:** 2001
SALES (est): 124.3K **Privately Held**
WEB: www.phelps-motorsports.com
SIC: 3711 Automobile assembly, including specialty automobiles

(G-11363)
PHOTO FINISHING NEWS INC
Also Called: Photofinishing News
11618 Quail Village Way (34119-8872)
PHONE..................................239 992-4421
Don Franz, *President*
George Gamaz, *Vice Pres*
EMP: 6 **EST:** 1983
SQ FT: 1,000
SALES (est): 400K **Privately Held**
SIC: 2711 Newspapers: publishing only, not printed on site

(G-11364)
PHYSICIAN HEARING CARE
11121 Health Park Blvd # 700 (34110-5739)
PHONE..................................239 261-7722
William Laswski, *Owner*
Taite Seals, *Owner*
EMP: 10 **EST:** 2002
SALES (est): 490.9K **Privately Held**
SIC: 3842 Hearing aids

(G-11365)
PICKLE PRO LLC
3527 Plover Ave Unit 2 (34117-8439)
PHONE..................................844 332-7069
Todd Pree,
EMP: 7 **EST:** 2013
SQ FT: 4,500
SALES (est): 352K **Privately Held**
SIC: 3949 Rackets & frames: tennis, badminton, squash, lacrosse, etc

(G-11366)
PINSTRIPE MAGAZINE LLC
3770 58th Ave Ne (34120-2780)
PHONE..................................201 310-5398
Marvin Valladares, *Chief*
EMP: 6 **EST:** 2017
SALES (est): 96K **Privately Held**
WEB: www.pinstripemag.com
SIC: 2721 Magazines: publishing only, not printed on site

(G-11367)
PIONEER DEVELOPMENT ENTPS INC
5901 Shirley St (34109-1817)
PHONE..................................239 592-0001
Robert Hunter, *President*
Matthew Hunter, *Principal*
Bryan Hunter, *Vice Pres*
EMP: 15 **EST:** 1999
SQ FT: 7,500
SALES (est): 919.3K **Privately Held**
SIC: 3448 3444 1761 Screen enclosures; sheet metalwork; roofing, siding & sheet metal work

(G-11368)
PK GROUP INC
Also Called: ALLEGRA NAPLES
3930 Domestic Ave Ste A (34104-3674)
PHONE..................................239 643-2442
Paul J Kessen, *President*
Pamela L Kessen, *Vice Pres*
Randy Bailey, *Accounts Mgr*
EMP: 18 **EST:** 2009
SALES: 2.7MM **Privately Held**
SIC: 2752 8742 3993 Commercial printing, offset; marketing consulting services; signs & advertising specialties

(G-11369)
PLASTIC SPECIALTIES INC
3573 Arnold Ave Ste B (34104-3372)
PHONE..................................239 643-0933
Steven Gnerre, *President*
EMP: 17 **EST:** 2004
SALES (est): 500K **Privately Held**
WEB: www.plasticspecialtiesofflorida.com
SIC: 2821 Plastics materials & resins

(G-11370)
PLC CABINETS INSTALLED LTD
1408 Rail Head Blvd (34110-8421)
PHONE..................................239 641-7565
EMP: 8 **EST:** 2018
SALES (est): 714.6K **Privately Held**
WEB: www.plcclosets.com
SIC: 2434 Wood kitchen cabinets

(G-11371)
PMC ENTERPRISES MGMT DIVISION
11216 Tamiami Trl N (34110-1640)
PHONE..................................239 949-6566
Patrick F McHugh Jr, *President*
EMP: 18 **EST:** 2004
SALES (est): 2.6MM **Privately Held**
SIC: 3544 Industrial molds

(G-11372)
POPCORN CELLAR LLC
651 5th Ave S (34102-6601)
PHONE..................................239 272-8494
Jeremy Domin,
Patricia Fortune,
▲ **EMP:** 7 **EST:** 2012
SQ FT: 1,400
SALES (est): 239.4K **Privately Held**
WEB: www.bestpopcorncompany.com
SIC: 2051 Bakery: wholesale or wholesale/retail combined

(G-11373)
PORTALP USA INC
1030 Collier Center Way # 10 (34110-8477)
PHONE..................................800 474-3667
◆ **EMP:** 17
SALES (est): 3.1MM **Privately Held**
SIC: 3699 3822 Mfg Electrical Equipment/Supplies Mfg Environmental Controls

(G-11374)
PRO EDGE CUTLERY LLC
Also Called: Pro Edge Paper
4484 Arnold Ave (34104-3340)
PHONE..................................239 304-8000
Rudy Ambrosi, *Mng Member*
▲ **EMP:** 8 **EST:** 2005
SALES (est): 1.5MM **Privately Held**
WEB: www.proedgepaper.com
SIC: 2621 Art paper

(G-11375)
PRO TRIM MILLWORK INC
3995 Upolo Ln (34119-7510)
PHONE..................................239 592-5454
Michael Cannivet, *Director*
EMP: 9 **EST:** 2005
SALES (est): 316.6K **Privately Held**
WEB: www.protrimmillwork.com
SIC: 2431 Millwork

(G-11376)
PROGRESS RAIL SERVICES CORP
3581 Mercantile Ave (34104-3309)
PHONE..................................239 643-3013
Marty Haycraft, *Senior VP*
EMP: 75
SALES (corp-wide): 41.7B **Publicly Held**
WEB: www.progressrail.com
SIC: 3519 5084 3714 Internal combustion engines; fuel injection systems; fuel pumps, motor vehicle
HQ: Progress Rail Services Corporation
1600 Progress Dr
Albertville AL 35950
256 505-6421

(G-11377)
PROLINK SOFTWARE CORPORATION
999 Vanderbilt Beach Rd (34108-3508)
PHONE..................................860 659-5928
Bruce Brigham, *Principal*
EMP: 9 **EST:** 2013
SALES (est): 867.1K **Privately Held**
WEB: www.prolinksoftware.com
SIC: 7372 Prepackaged software

(G-11378)
Q PLASTERING AND STUCCO INC
5422 Texas Ave (34113-7859)
PHONE..................................239 530-1712
Gerard Pierre, *Principal*
EMP: 6 **EST:** 2011
SALES (est): 68.4K **Privately Held**
SIC: 3299 Stucco

(G-11379)
QUALITY LIFE PUBLISHING CO
6210 Shirley St Ste 112 (34109-6258)
PHONE..................................239 513-9907
Karla Wheeler, *President*
Mary K Grimaldi, *Editor*
Anthony Perez, *Production*
Michelle Pulley, *Sales Staff*
Katie Jensen, *Assistant*
EMP: 9 **EST:** 1999
SALES (est): 1.2MM **Privately Held**
WEB: www.qolpublishing.com
SIC: 2741 8743 8322 Miscellaneous publishing; public relations services; outreach program

(G-11380)
RACING SHELL COVERS LLC
3899 Mannix Dr Ste 409 (34114-5414)
PHONE..................................732 236-0435
Alex Grigoriev, *Principal*
EMP: 5 **EST:** 2018
SALES (est): 664.8K **Privately Held**
WEB: www.racingshellcovers.com
SIC: 3069 Fabricated rubber products

(G-11381)
RAS CONCRETE CONSTRUCTION INC
5501 Cynthia Ln (34112-5455)
PHONE..................................239 775-3709
Susan G Smith, *President*
Roger Smith, *Vice Pres*
EMP: 24 **EST:** 1976
SQ FT: 7,000
SALES (est): 3.4MM **Privately Held**
SIC: 3272 Concrete products

(G-11382)
RECORDSONE LLC
10641 Airport Pulling R (34109-7334)
PHONE..................................301 440-8119
Steve Bonney, *Exec VP*
Steven Bonney, *Exec VP*
Charles Neuenberger, *Mng Member*
Brent Smith, *Director*
Jason Vitz, *Director*
EMP: 16 **EST:** 2014
SALES (est): 1.4MM **Privately Held**
WEB: www.recordsone.com
SIC: 7372 Business oriented computer software

(G-11383)
RICHARD WAGNER LLC
9601 Campbell Cir (34109-4506)
PHONE..................................239 450-1721
Richard L Wagner, *Principal*
Richard Wagner, *Principal*
EMP: 5 **EST:** 2010
SALES (est): 320.7K **Privately Held**
SIC: 2679 Wallpaper

(G-11384)
RICHTER INDUSTRIES INC
1617 Gulfstar Dr S (34112-6407)
PHONE..................................239 732-9440
August Richter, *Principal*
EMP: 7
SALES (corp-wide): 3.9MM **Privately Held**
WEB: www.richterindustries.net
SIC: 3999 Atomizers, toiletry
PA: Richter Industries, Inc.
4910 70th Ave
Kenosha WI 53144
262 656-0097

(G-11385)
RITTER KIT BATH & CLOSET LLC
4870 Tallowood Way (34116-5002)
PHONE..................................239 272-4551
Chuck Ritter,
EMP: 8 **EST:** 2007
SALES (est): 343.5K **Privately Held**
WEB: www.kbcnaples.com
SIC: 2434 Wood kitchen cabinets

(G-11386)
RMMJ INC
Also Called: Monty Sanitation
5545 Shirley St (34109-1809)
PHONE..................................239 597-2486
Robert M Montgomery Jr, *Principal*
EMP: 20 **EST:** 2002
SALES (est): 1MM **Privately Held**
SIC: 3272 Precast terrazo or concrete products

(G-11387)
ROBERT E WEISSENBORN SR (PA)
Also Called: Naples Armature Works
1101 5th Ave S (34102-6415)
PHONE..................................239 262-1771
R E Weissenborn Jr, *Co-Owner*
Janet Blumert, *Co-Owner*
Irene Weissenborn, *Co-Owner*
Robert E Weissenborn Jr, *Co-Owner*
EMP: 6 **EST:** 1948
SQ FT: 11,400
SALES (est): 912.9K **Privately Held**
WEB: www.naplesarmature.com
SIC: 7694 5083 5063 7699 Electric motor repair; irrigation equipment; motors, electric; pumps & pumping equipment repair; power transmission equipment & apparatus

(G-11388)
SAFEBOOT CORP
2640 Golden Gate Pkwy # 1 (34105-3220)
PHONE..................................239 298-7000
Gerhard Watzinger, *CEO*
Frank Jorissen, *Vice Pres*
Eric Sommerton, *Vice Pres*
Piet Weijers, *CFO*
Simon Hunt, *CTO*
EMP: 42 **EST:** 1991
SQ FT: 100,000
SALES (est): 4.8MM
SALES (corp-wide): 2.9B **Publicly Held**
WEB: www.mcafee.com
SIC: 7372 Prepackaged software
HQ: Mcafee, Llc
6220 America Center Dr
San Jose CA 95002

(G-11389)
SALVIA TILE & STONE INC
303 Airport Pulling Rd N (34104-3507)
PHONE..................................239 643-7770
Gerardo Salvia, *President*
David Wood, *Vice Pres*
Steve Cushing, *Treasurer*
Joann Salvia, *Admin Sec*
◆ **EMP:** 12 **EST:** 2005
SQ FT: 16,000
SALES (est): 558K **Privately Held**
WEB: www.salviastone.com
SIC: 2541 5032 Counter & sink tops; ceramic wall & floor tile

(G-11390)
SAMARIAN PRODUCTS LLC
780 Fifth Ave S Ste 200 (34102-6632)
PHONE..................................212 781-2121
Alfred Zaccagnino, *Mng Member*
Mark Schneider, *Mng Member*
EMP: 20
SALES (est): 40MM **Privately Held**
SIC: 2842 2326 Sanitation preparations, disinfectants & deodorants; medical & hospital uniforms, men's

(G-11391)
SANO ASSOCIATES INC
Also Called: High Velocity
3827 Progress Ave (34104-3647)
PHONE..................................239 403-2650
Steven Camposano, *President*
Jean Camposano, *Treasurer*
EMP: 34 **EST:** 1994
SQ FT: 30,000
SALES (est): 2.7MM **Privately Held**
WEB: www.category5.com
SIC: 3442 Shutters, door or window: metal

(G-11392)
SARA GLOVE COMPANY INC
7935 Airprt Pulling N Ste (34109)
PHONE..................................866 664-7272
Sara Delio, *President*
Joseph Delio, *COO*
EMP: 8 **EST:** 2018
SQ FT: 1,500
SALES (est): 6.4MM **Privately Held**
WEB: www.saraglove.com
SIC: 2385 3151 5099 Waterproof outerwear; gloves, leather: work; safety equipment & supplies

(G-11393)
SAVOR SLEEP LLC
8805 Tamiami Trl N (34108-2525)
PHONE..................................860 577-2867
Taylor Smith, *Administration*
EMP: 7 **EST:** 2019
SALES (est): 286.8K **Privately Held**
WEB: www.savorsleep.com
SIC: 2515 Mattresses & bedsprings

(G-11394)
SAW PALMETTO BERRIES COOPERATI
7440 Friendship Ln (34120-2459)
PHONE..................................239 775-4286
EMP: 7 **EST:** 2015
SALES (est): 346.6K **Privately Held**
WEB: www.sawpalmettoflorida.com
SIC: 2834 Vitamin, nutrient & hematinic preparations for human use

(G-11395)
SAW PALMETTO FLORIDA LLC
7440 Friendship Ln (34120-2459)
PHONE..................................239 775-4286
Zlatko Altiparmakov,
EMP: 13 **EST:** 2017
SALES (est): 1MM **Privately Held**
WEB: www.sawpalmettoflorida.com
SIC: 2834 Vitamin, nutrient & hematinic preparations for human use

(G-11396)
SCHOOL-ON-WHEELS
13520 Tamiami Trl E (34114-8703)
PHONE..................................239 530-8522
Patricia Brennan, *Manager*
EMP: 8 **EST:** 2011
SALES (est): 150K **Privately Held**
WEB: www.schoolonwheels.org
SIC: 3312 Wheels

(G-11397)
SENTINEL INC
Also Called: Sentinel Storm Protection
3673 Exchange Ave Ste 1 (34104-3743)
PHONE..................................239 263-9888
Mike Marczak, *President*
Reed Fearheiley, *Sales Staff*
EMP: 16 **EST:** 2002
SALES (est): 2.7MM **Privately Held**
WEB: www.sentinelstormprotection.com
SIC: 3442 Shutters, door or window: metal

(G-11398)
SHELFGENIE
16422 Carrara Way # 102 (34110-3286)
PHONE..................................877 814-3643
EMP: 7 **EST:** 2013
SALES (est): 109.6K **Privately Held**
WEB: www.shelfgenie.com
SIC: 2511 Wood household furniture

(G-11399)
SHOW PUBLISHING LLC
1540 Clermont Dr Unit 102 (34109-0336)
PHONE..................................239 272-8477
David Stewart, *Principal*
EMP: 6 **EST:** 2008
SALES (est): 114.5K **Privately Held**
WEB: www.wedshow.net
SIC: 2741 Miscellaneous publishing

(G-11400)
SHUTTERMAN STORM & SECURITY
4186 Domestic Ave (34104-7019)
PHONE..................................239 455-9166
Curt Barnicle, *President*
Carol Barnicle, *Office Mgr*
Dennis Barnicle, *Admin Sec*
EMP: 15 **EST:** 1998
SALES (est): 1.1MM **Privately Held**
WEB: www.myshutterman.com
SIC: 2431 7699 Door shutters, wood; door & window repair

(G-11401)
SIC PRODUCTS LLC
5130 Kristin Ct (34105-2113)
PHONE..................................904 374-2639
Erik D Howe, *Mng Member*
Robert Harrington,
EMP: 7 **EST:** 2015
SALES (est): 875.2K **Privately Held**
SIC: 2656 Paper cups, plates, dishes & utensils

(G-11402)
SICK RIDE LLC
6355 Naples Blvd Ste 5 (34109-2070)
PHONE..................................239 300-5995
Richard V Leli,
EMP: 6 **EST:** 2011
SALES (est): 91.4K **Privately Held**
WEB: www.sickridenaples.com
SIC: 3211 Window glass, clear & colored

(G-11403)
SIGNARAMA NAPLES
Also Called: Sign-A-Rama
1095 5th Ave N (34102-5818)
PHONE..................................239 330-3737
Marc Estes, *Principal*
EMP: 6 **EST:** 2015
SALES (est): 139.1K **Privately Held**
WEB: www.signarama.com
SIC: 3993 Signs & advertising specialties

(G-11404)
SIMPLY CUPCAKES
2490 Outrigger Ln (34104-6905)
PHONE..................................239 262-5184
Kenneth Glasgow, *Principal*
EMP: 7 **EST:** 2007
SALES (est): 164.3K **Privately Held**
SIC: 2051 Bread, cake & related products

(G-11405)
SMART FLOORS LLC
4365 Tamiami Trl N (34103-3106)
PHONE..................................239 500-1234
George Smart, *Mng Member*
EMP: 6 **EST:** 2018
SALES (est): 55K **Privately Held**
SIC: 2426 Flooring, hardwood

(G-11406)
SMDK CORP
4802 Kittiwake Ct (34119-8864)
PHONE..................................239 444-1736
Addison M Fischer, *Ch of Bd*
Michael S Battaglia, *President*
Steve Armfield, *Vice Pres*
Charles Klinker, *Vice Pres*
Anderw Warner, *CFO*
▲ **EMP:** 26 **EST:** 1997
SQ FT: 27,000
SALES (est): 615.8K **Privately Held**
WEB: www.smdkcorp.com
SIC: 3577 7372 Computer peripheral equipment; prepackaged software

(G-11407)
SOSUMI HOLDINGS INC
Also Called: Intech Printing & Direct Mail
4408 Corporate Sq (34104-4755)
PHONE..................................239 634-3430
Rodney Held, *CEO*
Dale Haddad, *CFO*
EMP: 23 **EST:** 2015
SQ FT: 15,000
SALES (est): 1.3MM **Privately Held**
WEB: www.intechprinting.com
SIC: 2732 2752 Books: printing & binding; commercial printing, offset

(G-11408)
SOUTHEAST PUBLISHING CO INC (PA)
Also Called: Southeast Food Service News
2539 Avila Ln (34105-3059)
PHONE..................................239 213-1277
Dal Rasmussen, *President*
Elliott Fischer, *Admin Sec*
EMP: 6
SALES (est): 683.5K **Privately Held**
WEB: www.sfsn.com
SIC: 2711 Newspapers

(G-11409)
SOUTHERN LITHO II LLC
9010 Strada Stell Ct # 103 (34109-4425)
PHONE..................................724 394-3693
Conley Daniel J, *Principal*
EMP: 24 **EST:** 2012
SALES (est): 3.5MM **Privately Held**
WEB: www.northernlitho.com
SIC: 2752 Commercial printing, lithographic

(G-11410)
SOUTHWEST CUSTOM COATINGS INC
4498 22nd Ave Se (34117-9277)
PHONE..................................239 682-9462
Stone Vance H, *Principal*
EMP: 7 **EST:** 2014
SALES (est): 252.3K **Privately Held**
SIC: 3479 Metal coating & allied service

(G-11411)
SOUTHWEST WOODWORK INC
429 Production Blvd (34104-4724)
PHONE..................................239 213-0126
Sherrad Reites, *President*
Sherrad J Reites, *President*
EMP: 17 **EST:** 1980
SQ FT: 10,000
SALES (est): 724.3K **Privately Held**
WEB: www.southwestwoodwork.com
SIC: 2431 1751 5712 8712 Millwork; cabinet building & installation; custom made furniture, except cabinets; architectural services

(G-11412)
SOUVAY CABINETRY INC
4292 Corporate Sq Ste C (34104-4801)
PHONE..................................239 273-5947
Herve Souvay, *Principal*
EMP: 7 **EST:** 2018
SALES (est): 53.7K **Privately Held**
SIC: 2434 Wood kitchen cabinets

(G-11413)
SPACEMAKERS CLOSETS SW FLA INC
2044 J And C Blvd (34109-6214)
PHONE..................................239 598-0222
Mark A Delashmet, *Vice Pres*
EMP: 8 **EST:** 2011
SALES (est): 382.6K **Privately Held**
WEB: www.spacemakerscustomcabinetry-naples.com
SIC: 2434 Wood kitchen cabinets

(G-11414)
SPECIAL COATINGS INC
6210 Shirley St Ste 105 (34109-6258)
PHONE..................................239 301-2714
Douglas A Treadwell, *President*
EMP: 7 **EST:** 2015
SALES (est): 152.5K **Privately Held**
WEB: www.special-coatings.com
SIC: 3479 Coating of metals & formed products

(G-11415)
SPECTRUM SIGNWORKS LLC
1474 Rail Head Blvd (34110-8421)
PHONE..................................239 908-0505
Scott Levy, *CEO*
EMP: 6 **EST:** 2014
SALES (est): 545.5K **Privately Held**
WEB: www.spectrumsignworks.com
SIC: 3993 Signs & advertising specialties

(G-11416)
SPOT-ON WLDG MET FBRCATION LLC
2365 14th Ave Ne (34120-4015)
PHONE..................................239 825-7452
Helvaci Armahan, *Principal*
EMP: 7 **EST:** 2016
SALES (est): 807.7K **Privately Held**
SIC: 3499 Fabricated metal products

(G-11417)
STEVE UNSER CABINETRY INC
5550 Shirley St (34109-1869)
PHONE..................................239 631-2951
Steve M Unser, *Principal*
EMP: 11 **EST:** 2015
SALES (est): 358.8K **Privately Held**
WEB: www.steveunsercabinetry.com
SIC: 2434 Wood kitchen cabinets

(G-11418)
STONELIGHT LLC
4775 Aston Gardens Way # 205
(34109-3574)
PHONE..................................239 514-3272
Dick Metchear, *CEO*
Betsy Piper, *CFO*
Elizabeth Piper, *CFO*
EMP: 7 **EST:** 2009
SALES (est): 628.3K **Privately Held**
WEB: www.stonelight.com
SIC: 3648 Lighting equipment

(G-11419)
STRUCTURE MEDICAL LLC (HQ)
9935 Business Cir (34112-3317)
PHONE..................................239 262-5551
Paul Goldman, *Vice Pres*
Dean McCann, *Vice Pres*
Mark Gilbert, *Prdtn Mgr*
Victor Georgiev, *Opers Staff*
Vadim Babinov, *Engineer*
▼ **EMP:** 70 **EST:** 2008
SQ FT: 30,000

SALES (est): 50.7MM Privately Held
WEB: www.structuremedical.com
SIC: 3842 Orthopedic appliances

(G-11420)
SUMMIT ORTHOPEDIC TECH INC
2975 Horseshoe Dr S # 100 (34104-6153)
PHONE..................................203 693-2727
Adam Ferrell, *President*
Jason Blake, *COO*
Ron Dunn, *Vice Pres*
EMP: 45 EST: 2014
SALES (est): 2.5MM Privately Held
WEB: www.summit.tech
SIC: 3841 Surgical & medical instruments

(G-11421)
SUNBELT USA INC
132 Vista Ln (34119-4666)
PHONE..................................239 353-5519
S John Conti, *President*
Ryan J Conti, *Director*
Randi C Ordetx, *Director*
EMP: 9 EST: 2007
SALES (est): 501K Privately Held
WEB: www.sunbeltusa.net
SIC: 2752 Commercial printing, offset

(G-11422)
SUNCOAST FABRICS INC
Also Called: Suncoast Window Fashion
5400 Yahl St Ste A (34109-1910)
PHONE..................................239 566-3313
Barbara M Minkler, *President*
Allen M Minkler, *Vice Pres*
EMP: 9 EST: 1981
SALES (est): 255.8K Privately Held
SIC: 2391 Draperies, plastic & textile: from purchased materials

(G-11423)
SUNFLEX
4120 Enterprise Ave # 120 (34104-7087)
PHONE..................................800 606-0756
Malte Schneider, *Principal*
Todd Hoffman, *Business Mgr*
▲ EMP: 6 EST: 2015
SALES (est): 233.6K Privately Held
WEB: www.sunflex-aluminiumsystems.com
SIC: 3089 Plastics products

(G-11424)
SUNFLEX WALL SYSTEMS LP
1494 Pacaya Cv (34119-3367)
PHONE..................................239 220-1570
▲ EMP: 9 EST: 2008
SALES (est): 388.2K Privately Held
WEB: www.sunflex-aluminiumsystems.com
SIC: 3089 Fiberglass doors

(G-11425)
SUNLUVER SMOOTHIES INC
160 12th Ave Nw (34120-2305)
PHONE..................................239 331-5431
Krista Lefchak, *Principal*
EMP: 6 EST: 2007
SALES (est): 94.9K Privately Held
SIC: 2037 Frozen fruits & vegetables

(G-11426)
SUNMASTER OF NAPLES INC
900 Industrial Blvd (34104-3612)
PHONE..................................239 261-3581
John H Wilkinson, *President*
David J Rinker, *Vice Pres*
Tom Napierkowski, *Purch Mgr*
John Knapp, *Treasurer*
EMP: 40 EST: 1969
SQ FT: 23,000
SALES (est): 6.4MM Privately Held
WEB: www.sunmasterinc.com
SIC: 3357 5999 5031 Aircraft wire & cable, nonferrous; awnings; doors, combination, screen-storm

(G-11427)
SUPERIOR CHROME PLATING INC
861 101st Ave N (34108-3208)
PHONE..................................832 659-0873
Robert L Baker, *President*
EMP: 10 EST: 2002
SALES (est): 622.9K Privately Held
WEB: www.justchromeit.com
SIC: 3471 Plating of metals or formed products

(G-11428)
SUPERIOR SWIM SYSTEMS INC
2340 Vanderbilt Beach Rd (34109-2763)
PHONE..................................239 566-2060
Donna Koenig, *CEO*
Michael Koenig, *President*
Mike Koenig, *Vice Pres*
EMP: 5 EST: 1987
SQ FT: 2,000
SALES (est): 900K Privately Held
WEB: www.superiorswimsystems.com
SIC: 3441 5091 Fabricated structural metal; swimming pools, equipment & supplies

(G-11429)
SUSTAINABLE PROJECTS GROUP INC
2316 Pine Ridge Rd # 383 (34109-2006)
PHONE..................................239 316-4593
Christian Winzenried, *President*
EMP: 5 EST: 2018
SALES (est): 447.8K Privately Held
WEB: www.spgroupe.com
SIC: 1311 Crude petroleum & natural gas

(G-11430)
SWEET TREATS
7935 Airprt Plng Rd N 1 Ste 11 (34109)
PHONE..................................239 598-3311
EMP: 7
SALES (est): 458.9K Privately Held
SIC: 2024 Mfg Ice Cream/Frozen Desert

(G-11431)
SWEETREATS OF NAPLES INC
7935 Airport Pulling Rd N (34109-1732)
PHONE..................................239 598-3311
EMP: 8
SALES (est): 310K Privately Held
SIC: 2024 Mfg Ice Cream/Frozen Desert

(G-11432)
SYNERGY SPORTS LLC
Also Called: Naples Team Sports Center
6300 Taylor Rd (34109-1841)
PHONE..................................239 593-9374
Kurt Swiderski,
Beth Swiderski,
EMP: 7 EST: 1984
SQ FT: 10,200
SALES (est): 744.5K Privately Held
SIC: 2396 5941 Screen printing on fabric articles; sporting goods & bicycle shops

(G-11433)
TACO MIX CORP
1740 Wilson Blvd N (34120-2339)
PHONE..................................239 498-9448
Yadil Caceres, *Principal*
EMP: 8 EST: 2007
SALES (est): 84.5K Privately Held
WEB: www.tacomix.co
SIC: 3273 Ready-mixed concrete

(G-11434)
TAILORED LLC
603 Cypress Way E (34110-1163)
PHONE..................................239 249-9636
Dave Desmarais, *Principal*
EMP: 7 EST: 2016
SALES (est): 130.5K Privately Held
WEB: www.thetailoredco.com
SIC: 2323 Men's & boys' neckwear

(G-11435)
TALARIA COMPANY LLC
3450 Westview Dr Unit 11 (34104-4293)
PHONE..................................239 261-2870
Jack Erbes, *Branch Mgr*
EMP: 90
SALES (corp-wide): 209.7MM Privately Held
WEB: www.hinckleyyachts.com
SIC: 3732 Yachts, building & repairing
PA: The Talaria Company Llc
1 Lil Hrbr Landing Prt
Portsmouth RI 02871
401 683-7100

(G-11436)
TE OLDE FOUNDRY SHOPPE INC
4573 Exchange Ave Ste 7 (34104-7027)
PHONE..................................239 261-3911
Doug Howard, *President*
EMP: 6 EST: 2004
SALES (est): 120.9K Privately Held
WEB: www.yeoldefoundryshoppeoffla.com
SIC: 3354 Aluminum extruded products

(G-11437)
TECHTRON CORPORATION
1400 Rail Head Blvd (34110-8421)
PHONE..................................239 513-0800
Samuel Freedland, *President*
EMP: 11 EST: 1989
SALES (est): 379K Privately Held
WEB: www.techtroncorporation.com
SIC: 3825 Instruments to measure electricity

(G-11438)
TESCO OF SWFL INC
Also Called: American Led Technology
3992 Prospect Ave Ste C (34104-3725)
PHONE..................................239 234-6490
Steven Pursley, *President*
Ken Machuta, *Director*
EMP: 9 EST: 2017
SALES (est): 720.8K Privately Held
SIC: 3674 Light emitting diodes

(G-11439)
THOMAS A GLASSMAN LLC
3840 7th Ave Nw (34120-1614)
PHONE..................................239 822-2219
Thomas A Glassman, *Manager*
EMP: 7 EST: 2010
SALES (est): 206.8K Privately Held
SIC: 3423 Carpenters' hand tools, except saws: levels, chisels, etc.

(G-11440)
THOMAS RLEY ARTISANS GUILD INC (PA)
Also Called: Hyland Custom Cabinetry
1510 Rail Head Blvd (34110-8402)
PHONE..................................239 591-3203
Thomas S Riley III, *CEO*
Benjamin T Riley, *President*
Ben Riley, *COO*
Les Faircloth, *Vice Pres*
Mark Bolton, *Project Mgr*
EMP: 49 EST: 1989
SQ FT: 21,000
SALES: 13.6MM Privately Held
WEB: www.thomasriley.net
SIC: 2431 2434 2435 2436 Millwork; wood kitchen cabinets; hardwood veneer & plywood; softwood veneer & plywood; wood household furniture

(G-11441)
TIM HARDY PLASTER MOLDINGS LLC
232 Palm Dr Apt 2 (34112-4943)
PHONE..................................239 877-8434
Timothy C Hardy, *Manager*
EMP: 6 EST: 2013
SALES (est): 104.2K Privately Held
WEB: www.hardyplastering.com
SIC: 3299 7389 Moldings, architectural: plaster of paris;

(G-11442)
TIMBERCRAFT OF NAPLES INC
802 Tallow Tree Ct (34108-8207)
PHONE..................................239 566-2559
Richard Daniel, *President*
EMP: 9 EST: 1991
SALES (est): 880.1K Privately Held
WEB: www.naplescabinets.com
SIC: 2431 1799 Blinds (shutters), wood; window treatment installation

(G-11443)
TIN MAN MOBILE WELDING LLC
830 93rd Ave N (34108-2443)
PHONE..................................239 465-9058
Ryan D Paige, *Manager*
EMP: 6 EST: 2013
SALES (est): 64.2K Privately Held
WEB: www.tin-man-welding.com
SIC: 7692 Welding repair

(G-11444)
TOPHET-BLYTH LLC
1415 Panther Ln Ste 402 (34109-7874)
PHONE..................................239 594-5477
Kenneth D Mac Alpine, *Principal*
▲ EMP: 12 EST: 2008
SALES (est): 803K Privately Held
WEB: www.tophet.com
SIC: 3549 Marking machines, metalworking

(G-11445)
TROPICAL TAFFY NAPLES INC
2655 64th St Sw (34105-7305)
PHONE..................................239 571-3761
Sharon M Kurgis, *Principal*
EMP: 6 EST: 2015
SALES (est): 102.1K Privately Held
WEB: www.tropicaltaffynaples.com
SIC: 2064 Candy & other confectionery products

(G-11446)
UNITED ABRASIVES INC
3551 Westview Dr (34104-4045)
PHONE..................................239 300-0033
Eric Marcialli, *President*
EMP: 16
SALES (corp-wide): 32.5MM Privately Held
WEB: www.unitedabrasives.com
SIC: 3291 Abrasive products
PA: United Abrasives, Inc.
185 Boston Post Rd
North Windham CT 06256
860 456-7131

(G-11447)
UNITED DRONES LLC
9146 Quartz Ln (34120-4368)
PHONE..................................305 978-1480
Harrison Hubschman, *Principal*
Gary Brecka, *Principal*
Chris Knott, *Principal*
Curt Winter, *Principal*
EMP: 8 EST: 2012
SALES (est): 200.4K Privately Held
WEB: www.uniteddrones.com
SIC: 3761 Rockets, space & military, complete

(G-11448)
UPTOWN CSTM CABINETS OF NAPLES
6260 Shirley St Ste 603 (34109-6257)
PHONE..................................239 825-8432
Aaron Elbe, *President*
EMP: 8 EST: 2007
SALES (est): 575.7K Privately Held
WEB: www.uptowncustomcabinets.com
SIC: 2434 Wood kitchen cabinets

(G-11449)
VET-EQUIP LLC
999 Vanderbilt Beach Rd # 200
(34108-3508)
PHONE..................................239 537-3402
Robert Gibbs,
Courtney McCoy, *Administration*
EMP: 5 EST: 2013
SQ FT: 400
SALES (est): 420K Privately Held
WEB: www.vetequip.com
SIC: 3751 7352 Bicycles & related parts; medical equipment rental

(G-11450)
VFINITY INC
837 5th Ave S Ste 200 (34102-6660)
P.O. Box 1949 (34106-1949)
PHONE..................................239 244-2555
Murray Polischuk, *Principal*
EMP: 10 EST: 2014
SALES (est): 688.5K Privately Held
WEB: www.vfinity.com
SIC: 7372 Prepackaged software

(G-11451)
VIENNA BEAUTY PRODUCTS CO (PA)
Also Called: White Cross Supply Co
222 Harbour Dr Apt 100 (34103-4071)
PHONE..................................937 228-7109
Timothy K Miller, *President*
Robert H Miller Sr, *Treasurer*

GEOGRAPHIC

EMP: 13 EST: 1956
SQ FT: 20,000
SALES (est): 1MM Privately Held
SIC: 2844 Face creams or lotions

(G-11452)
VISTA SEMANAL
1100 Immokalee Rd (34110-4810)
PHONE..................................239 263-4785
Albert Sabina, Manager
EMP: 6 EST: 2018
SALES (est): 128.8K Privately Held
WEB: www.nexstardigital.com
SIC: 2711 Newspapers

(G-11453)
VOGUE AEROSPACE & DEFENSE INC
1712 Commercial Dr (34112-4752)
PHONE..................................321 289-0872
Michael Ressa, Principal
Travis Matthew, Principal
Giuseppe Ressa, Principal
EMP: 5 EST: 2019
SALES (est): 337K Privately Held
WEB: www.vogueaerospace.com
SIC: 3721 Aircraft

(G-11454)
WESTVIEW CORP INC
Also Called: Screen Printing Unlimited
3419 Westview Dr (34104-4042)
PHONE..................................239 643-5699
John D Dick, President
Nancy J Dick, Vice Pres
EMP: 6 EST: 1994
SQ FT: 3,200
SALES (est): 791.8K Privately Held
WEB: www.screenprintingunlimited.com
SIC: 2759 Screen printing

(G-11455)
WHOLESALE SCREEN PRTG OF NPLES
3584 Mercantile Ave Ste B (34104-3381)
PHONE..................................239 263-7061
Dustin Goeggle, President
Steve Esarey, Sales Staff
Perrin Kelley, Tech Recruiter
CAM Demay, Graphic Designe
EMP: 5 EST: 1989
SQ FT: 2,000
SALES (est): 1MM Privately Held
WEB: www.wholesalescreenprinting.com
SIC: 2759 3953 Screen printing; screens, textile printing

(G-11456)
WILLS PRESTRESS INC
680 31st St Sw (34117-3112)
PHONE..................................239 417-9117
David V Will, President
EMP: 14 EST: 1999
SALES (est): 818.8K Privately Held
SIC: 3272 Piling, prefabricated concrete

(G-11457)
WINE TASTERS OF NAPLES INC
2021 Painted Palm Dr (34119-3373)
PHONE..................................239 961-1522
Rosemarie Woodbridge, President
EMP: 6 EST: 2015
SALES (est): 108.9K Privately Held
WEB: www.winetastersofnaples.org
SIC: 2084 Wines, brandy & brandy spirits

(G-11458)
WIRE EXPERTS GROUP INC (PA)
Also Called: Pelican Wire
3650 Shaw Blvd (34117-8408)
PHONE..................................239 597-8555
Theodore Bill, President
John Niggle, Business Mgr
Robert Ferris, Vice Pres
Paul Snapp, Mfg Mgr
Brinson White, Engrg Dir
EMP: 80 EST: 1977
SQ FT: 35,000
SALES (est): 38.8MM Privately Held
WEB: www.pelicanwire.com
SIC: 3496 Miscellaneous fabricated wire products

(G-11459)
WISHBONE WOODWORKING INC
121 Pinehurst Cir (34113-8330)
PHONE..................................239 262-7230
Gregory Beall, Director
EMP: 8 EST: 2005
SALES (est): 129.3K Privately Held
WEB: www.wishbonewoodworking.com
SIC: 2431 Millwork

(G-11460)
WOODWORKERS CABINET INC
6189 Taylor Rd Ste 2 (34109-2301)
PHONE..................................239 593-1718
Gary Fusco, President
EMP: 10 EST: 2006
SALES (est): 505.9K Privately Held
WEB: www.woodworkersnaples.com
SIC: 2431 Millwork

(G-11461)
WOODWORKERS CABINET NAPLES INC
6189 Taylor Rd (34109-2301)
PHONE..................................239 593-1718
Daniel Fusco, Principal
EMP: 6 EST: 2012
SALES (est): 53.7K Privately Held
WEB: www.woodworkersnaples.blogspot.com
SIC: 2434 Wood kitchen cabinets

(G-11462)
YAHL MULCHING & RECYCLING INC
Also Called: Naples C&D Recycling Facility
2250 Washburn Ave (34117-4032)
PHONE..................................239 352-7888
Theresa Filmore, President
John Filmore, Vice Pres
EMP: 15 EST: 1997
SQ FT: 2,000
SALES (est): 2.5MM Privately Held
WEB: www.yahl.us
SIC: 2499 4953 4212 Mulch, wood & bark; recycling, waste materials; local trucking, without storage

(G-11463)
YOUTHFUL INNOVATIONS LLC
Also Called: Original Seat Sack Company.
3066 Tamiami Trl N # 101 (34103-2758)
PHONE..................................239 596-2200
Timothy Mullins, Principal
EMP: 9 EST: 2018
SALES (est): 742.1K Privately Held
SIC: 2393 Textile bags

(G-11464)
ZMH PUBLISHERS INC
340 15th St Nw (34120-1906)
PHONE..................................239 404-9259
Kimberly Todd, Principal
Kim Todd, Author
EMP: 6 EST: 2009
SALES (est): 83K Privately Held
WEB: www.heavenspostcards.com
SIC: 2741 Miscellaneous publishing

Navarre
Santa Rosa County

(G-11465)
CONSOLIDATED ACE HDWR SUP INC
Also Called: Benjamin Moore Authorized Ret
8188 Navarre Pkwy (32566-6906)
P.O. Box 1449, Defuniak Springs (32435-7449)
PHONE..................................850 939-9800
EMP: 9 EST: 2018
SALES (est): 366.2K Privately Held
WEB: www.benjaminmoore.com
SIC: 3429 5231 Manufactured hardware (general); paint, glass & wallpaper

(G-11466)
INTEGRITRUST SOLUTIONS LLC
2078 Bahama Dr (32566-7696)
PHONE..................................850 685-9801
Greg Britton, President
EMP: 7 EST: 2016
SALES (est): 507.9K Privately Held
WEB: www.integritrustsolutions.com
SIC: 3728 3599 8742 Aircraft body & wing assemblies & parts; machine & other job shop work; management consulting services

(G-11467)
K & N INDUSTRIES INC
9218 Navarre Pkwy (32566-2936)
PHONE..................................850 939-7722
Isaac T Newlin, Principal
EMP: 6 EST: 2013
SALES (est): 342.9K Privately Held
SIC: 3999 Manufacturing industries

(G-11468)
KOBETRON LLC
1778 Sea Lark Ln (32566-7472)
PHONE..................................850 939-5222
Greg Kobe, President
Grant Stousland, Engineer
Paul Magno,
James Maida,
EMP: 16 EST: 1984
SALES (est): 229.3K Privately Held
WEB: www.kobetron.com
SIC: 3825 Test equipment for electronic & electrical circuits

(G-11469)
LASER ASSAULT
9863 Creet Cir (32566-3347)
PHONE..................................801 374-3400
Jim Degroot, Mng Member
Jim De Groot, Mng Member
EMP: 6 EST: 2004
SALES (est): 336.5K Privately Held
WEB: www.laserassault.net
SIC: 3699 Laser systems & equipment

(G-11470)
NAVARRE BEACH WOODWORKS
1713 Shellfish Dr (32566-7432)
PHONE..................................850 781-7884
David Doss, Principal
EMP: 6 EST: 2017
SALES (est): 95.6K Privately Held
SIC: 2431 Millwork

(G-11471)
NAVARRE INDUSTRIES INC
2056 Sundown Dr (32566-8245)
PHONE..................................850 554-6682
Randall M Seltzer, Principal
EMP: 6 EST: 2008
SALES (est): 88.5K Privately Held
SIC: 3999 Manufacturing industries

(G-11472)
PREMIER BUILDINGS OF NAVARRE
2617 Hidden Creek Dr (32566-6704)
PHONE..................................850 684-3639
Jeff A Richardson, Owner
EMP: 6 EST: 2016
SALES (est): 84.1K Privately Held
WEB: www.buildingsbypremier.com
SIC: 3448 Prefabricated metal buildings

(G-11473)
REAL PRO WELDING INC
Also Called: R P Welding
8285 East Bay Blvd (32566-9388)
PHONE..................................850 939-3469
Randal L Patton, President
Randall Patton, President
EMP: 7 EST: 2004
SALES (est): 305K Privately Held
WEB: www.rpwelding.net
SIC: 7692 Welding repair

(G-11474)
SALMI AND COMPANY INC
8328 Randall Dr (32566-9419)
PHONE..................................443 243-8537
Steven Salmi, President
Kimberly Adams, Corp Secy
Marva Salmi, Vice Pres
EMP: 6 EST: 1997
SALES (est): 400K Privately Held
SIC: 3731 Shipbuilding & repairing

(G-11475)
SANDPAPER MARKETING INC
Also Called: Navarre Fishing Rodeo
7502 Harvest Village Ct (32566-7319)
PHONE..................................850 939-8040
Sandra F Kemp, Principal
EMP: 6 EST: 2016
SALES (est): 83.3K Privately Held
WEB: www.sandpapermarketing.com
SIC: 3291 Sandpaper

(G-11476)
WOODCRAFT LLC
2218 Avenida De Sol (32566-9206)
PHONE..................................850 217-7757
Harold J Comalander, Manager
EMP: 6 EST: 2011
SALES (est): 237.1K Privately Held
WEB: www.woodcraft.com
SIC: 2511 Wood household furniture

Neptune Beach
Duval County

(G-11477)
SAAVY NATURALS
241 Atlantic Blvd (32266-5282)
PHONE..................................904 372-0002
EMP: 7 EST: 2016
SALES (est): 143K Privately Held
WEB: www.saavynaturals.com
SIC: 2844 Toilet preparations

(G-11478)
TSB EMULSIONS LLC
1306 Big Tree Rd (32266-3197)
PHONE..................................904 249-5115
Thomas S Bloodworth, Manager
EMP: 6 EST: 2015
SALES (est): 101.6K Privately Held
SIC: 2951 Asphalt paving mixtures & blocks

(G-11479)
VITALLEO LLC
Also Called: Vitalleo Health
2300 Marsh Point Rd 302c (32266-1646)
PHONE..................................904 474-5330
John M McGuire, Mng Member
EMP: 7 EST: 2017
SALES (est): 440.9K Privately Held
WEB: www.vitalleohealth.com
SIC: 2833 Vitamins, natural or synthetic: bulk, uncompounded

New Port Richey
Pasco County

(G-11480)
AQUINAS INC
Also Called: Printing Place, The
4936 Us Highway 19 (34652-4251)
PHONE..................................727 842-2254
Angie Burke, President
Thomas A Burke, Vice Pres
Kimberly M Burke, Admin Sec
▼ EMP: 5 EST: 1988
SQ FT: 2,400
SALES (est): 532.9K Privately Held
WEB: www.printnowdigital.com
SIC: 2752 Commercial printing, offset

(G-11481)
AUTO GARD QMI INC
5318 Lemon St (34652-3731)
PHONE..................................727 847-5441
John H Nicholson, President
Shane Willis, Vice Pres
EMP: 10 EST: 1996
SQ FT: 1,000
SALES (est): 291.3K Privately Held
SIC: 2819 5169 Industrial inorganic chemicals; chemicals & allied products

(G-11482)
BALKAN INDUSTRIES LLC (PA)
7100 Maclura Dr (34653-1935)
PHONE..................................727 485-3357
Peter Banic, Manager
EMP: 13 EST: 2014

SALES (est): 236.2K Privately Held
SIC: 3999 Manufacturing industries

(G-11483)
BROACH PROCESS SERVING
4720 Wolfram Ln (34653-5655)
PHONE....727 385-9467
Barry Roach, *Principal*
EMP: 8 EST: 2016
SALES (est): 176.3K Privately Held
SIC: 3443 Fabricated plate work (boiler shop)

(G-11484)
BROTHERS POWDER COATING INC
7721 Rutillio Ct Ste D (34653-1134)
PHONE....727 846-0717
Steve Burton, *President*
Michael Burton, *Treasurer*
EMP: 5 EST: 2006
SALES (est): 600K Privately Held
WEB: www.brotherspowdercoating.com
SIC: 3479 Coating of metals & formed products

(G-11485)
BURTON SIGNS INC
7349 Walnut St (34652-1445)
PHONE....727 841-8927
Bill Burton, *CEO*
EMP: 6 EST: 2006
SALES (est): 250K Privately Held
SIC: 3993 Signs & advertising specialties

(G-11486)
CANNON INDUSTRIES INC
5349 Seafoam Dr (34652-6040)
PHONE....727 320-5040
Diana L Perez, *Principal*
EMP: 13 EST: 2016
SALES (est): 50.5K Privately Held
WEB: www.cannonind.com
SIC: 3999 Manufacturing industries

(G-11487)
CLASSICS REBORN PUBLISHING LLC
9954 Sweet Bay Ct (34654-5702)
PHONE....727 232-6739
Stanley Singer, *Principal*
EMP: 7 EST: 2012
SALES (est): 235.7K Privately Held
SIC: 2741 Miscellaneous publishing

(G-11488)
DANIFER PRINTING INC
Also Called: Minuteman Press
7117 Us Highway 19 (34652-1638)
PHONE....727 849-5883
James Curtin, *President*
Dorothy Curtin, *Corp Secy*
Bonnie J Howard, *Director*
EMP: 5 EST: 2002
SALES (est): 1MM Privately Held
WEB: www.chanhassen-mn.minuteman-press.com
SIC: 2752 Commercial printing, lithographic

(G-11489)
DR BAINS PREMIER CBD OIL
6121 Fjord Way (34652-2025)
PHONE....727 992-5289
Russell T Bain, *Principal*
EMP: 6 EST: 2018
SALES (est): 73.5K Privately Held
SIC: 3999

(G-11490)
EVERETT PUBG - TAMPA BAY LLC
6044 Grand Blvd (34652-2606)
PHONE....727 534-3425
E J Miller, *Principal*
EMP: 6 EST: 2015
SALES (est): 177K Privately Held
WEB: www.thmtampa.com
SIC: 2741 Miscellaneous publishing

(G-11491)
GRACE PRSTHTIC FABRICATION INC
7928 Rutillio Ct (34653-1103)
PHONE....727 842-2265
Anthony Culver, *President*
William Edward Grace, *President*
Tony Culver, *Vice Pres*
▲ EMP: 8 EST: 1990
SQ FT: 5,000
SALES (est): 1.2MM Privately Held
WEB: www.gpfinc.com
SIC: 3842 Limbs, artificial; prosthetic appliances

(G-11492)
HOLIDAY CLEANERS INC
3640 Calera Dr (34652-6416)
PHONE....727 842-6989
Joseph J Cinquemano, *President*
Catherine Cinquemano, *Corp Secy*
EMP: 6 EST: 1992
SQ FT: 1,500
SALES (est): 864.2K Privately Held
WEB: www.holidaycleaners.biz
SIC: 2842 7212 Drycleaning preparations; polishing preparations & related products; laundry & drycleaner agents

(G-11493)
ICEBLOX INC
7436 Evesborough Ln (34655-4209)
PHONE....717 697-1900
Brion P McMullen, *CEO*
EMP: 11 EST: 2010
SALES (est): 442.1K Privately Held
SIC: 3524 Lawn & garden equipment

(G-11494)
JAMES FRNCISCO BACKHOE SVC INC
7833 Griswold Loop (34655-2735)
PHONE....727 514-1968
James Francisco, *Principal*
EMP: 6 EST: 2008
SALES (est): 75.5K Privately Held
SIC: 3531 Backhoes

(G-11495)
JEFFREY BOWDEN CABINETS LLC
12437 Banbury Ave (34654-4156)
PHONE....727 992-9187
Jeffrey D Bowden, *Principal*
EMP: 6 EST: 2008
SALES (est): 164.5K Privately Held
SIC: 2434 Wood kitchen cabinets

(G-11496)
JOHN S SMITH STUCCO INC
10041 Orland St (34654-3851)
PHONE....813 928-4320
John S Smith, *Principal*
EMP: 6 EST: 2009
SALES (est): 170K Privately Held
WEB: www.john-s-smith-stucco-inc.business.site
SIC: 3299 Stucco

(G-11497)
KRS MSA LLC
1324 Seven Springs Blvd (34655-5635)
PHONE....727 264-7605
Aaron Hunziker, *Exec VP*
Karen Cofield,
EMP: 7 EST: 2005
SALES (est): 493.1K Privately Held
SIC: 2834 Pharmaceutical preparations

(G-11498)
LORIS 1 INC
3544 Grand Blvd (34652-6407)
PHONE....727 847-4499
Eleftheria Mougros, *President*
EMP: 6 EST: 2014
SALES (est): 204.7K Privately Held
SIC: 2841 Soap & other detergents

(G-11499)
MAC ENTPS TAMPA BAY INC
4928 Ladyfish Ct (34652-1015)
PHONE....813 363-2601
Joseph M Doyne, *Principal*
EMP: 7 EST: 2008
SALES (est): 174.9K Privately Held
WEB: www.macenterprisesrenovations.com
SIC: 2434 Wood kitchen cabinets

(G-11500)
MARK 1 CONTRACTING INC
10656 Casey Dr (34654-3514)
PHONE....727 894-3600
Mark Sulkowski, *Principal*
EMP: 10 EST: 2000
SQ FT: 1,600
SALES (est): 1.2MM Privately Held
SIC: 3272 Building materials, except block or brick: concrete

(G-11501)
MILLWORK MASTERS LLC
7013 Us Highway 19 (34652-1636)
PHONE....727 807-6221
Joseph Gatto, *President*
Crystal Marcoux, *Principal*
EMP: 15 EST: 2007
SALES (est): 1.3MM Privately Held
WEB: www.woodburysupply.com
SIC: 2431 Millwork

(G-11502)
MORGANNAS ALCHEMY LLC
10347 Palladio Dr (34655-2196)
PHONE....727 505-8376
Maya Williams,
EMP: 5 EST: 2006
SALES (est): 491.3K Privately Held
WEB: www.morgannasalchemy.com
SIC: 2833 7389 Medicinals & botanicals;

(G-11503)
OCEAN GLOBAL INC
Also Called: Alta Labs
4925 Southshore Dr (34652-3029)
P.O. Box 901, Victor ID (83455-0901)
PHONE....727 842-7544
Jamie Petersen, *President*
EMP: 5 EST: 2004
SQ FT: 10,000
SALES (est): 514.8K Privately Held
WEB: www.motioneaze.com
SIC: 2833 Drugs & herbs: grading, grinding & milling

(G-11504)
OMEGA PUBLISHING
6014 Us Highway 19 # 305 (34652-2505)
PHONE....727 815-0402
Carolyn Greenwood, *President*
EMP: 6
SALES (est): 400K Privately Held
SIC: 2741 Miscellaneous publishing

(G-11505)
OMEGA SIGN SERVICE CORPORATION
11301 Biddeford Pl (34654-4496)
PHONE....727 505-7833
Anthony Garcia, *President*
EMP: 9 EST: 2009
SALES (est): 836.2K Privately Held
WEB: www.omegasignservice.com
SIC: 3993 Signs & advertising specialties

(G-11506)
ON THE GO FOOD & FUEL INC
6444 Massachusetts Ave (34653-2532)
PHONE....727 815-0823
Masood Sial, *President*
EMP: 11 EST: 2010
SALES (est): 754.8K Privately Held
SIC: 2869 Fuels

(G-11507)
PALL AEROPOWER CORPORATION (DH)
10540 Ridge Rd Ste 100 (34654-5111)
PHONE....727 849-9999
Lawrence Mr Kingsley, *President*
Matt May, *Engineer*
John Adamovich, *Treasurer*
Christina Confer, *Controller*
Kimberly Kester, *Cust Mgr*
◆ EMP: 500 EST: 1981
SALES (est): 170.8MM
SALES (corp-wide): 22.2B Publicly Held
WEB: www.pall.com
SIC: 3569 Filters, general line: industrial
HQ: Pall Corporation
25 Harbor Park Dr
Port Washington NY 11050
516 484-5400

(G-11508)
POINT DISTILLERY LLC
11807 Little Rd (34654-1012)
PHONE....727 269-5588
Spencer Wolf, *Mng Member*
EMP: 12 EST: 2018
SALES (est): 2.9MM Privately Held
WEB: www.thepointdistillery.com
SIC: 3556 Distillery machinery

(G-11509)
RUSSELL ASSOCIATES INC (DH)
10540 Ridge Rd Ste 300 (34654-5111)
PHONE....727 815-3100
Don Stevens, *President*
Godwin Abele, *Senior VP*
Gregory Horne, *Vice Pres*
EMP: 6 EST: 1942
SQ FT: 1,800
SALES (est): 13.9MM
SALES (corp-wide): 22.2B Publicly Held
WEB: www.russellassociatesinc.com
SIC: 3812 Acceleration indicators & systems components, aerospace
HQ: Pall Corporation
25 Harbor Park Dr
Port Washington NY 11050
516 484-5400

(G-11510)
SOUTHERN LIGHTS
3822 Grayton Dr (34652-5711)
PHONE....727 849-4442
EMP: 7
SALES (est): 160K Privately Held
SIC: 3229 Fiber Optics/Assembly

(G-11511)
STATEWIDE BLNDS SHTTERS MORE I
3030 Starkey Blvd (34655-2175)
PHONE....813 480-8638
Larry M Vanderhoof, *President*
EMP: 7 EST: 2017
SALES (est): 378.3K Privately Held
SIC: 2591 Window blinds

(G-11512)
SUNYBELL LLC ✪
4344 Cold Harbor Dr (34653-6117)
PHONE....727 301-2832
Eyal Gamili Holtzeker,
EMP: 10 EST: 2020
SALES (est): 334.8K Privately Held
SIC: 2759 Imprinting

(G-11513)
SUPERIOR SEALERS COATINGS INC
7849 Riverdale Dr (34653-5036)
PHONE....727 807-7851
Matthew Kurnat, *Principal*
EMP: 6 EST: 2017
SALES (est): 78.2K Privately Held
SIC: 3479 Metal coating & allied service

(G-11514)
SWISSCOSMET CORP
5540 Rowan Rd (34653-4551)
PHONE....727 842-9419
Roland C Pfister, *President*
Gene Galianese, *Vice Pres*
▲ EMP: 7 EST: 2008
SALES (est): 658.4K Privately Held
WEB: www.cellcosmet-cellmen.us
SIC: 2844 5122 Cosmetic preparations; cosmetics

(G-11515)
SYRAC ORDNANCE INC
6626 Osteen Rd Ste 331 (34653-3665)
PHONE....727 612-6090
Jason M Adams, *President*
EMP: 5 EST: 2011
SALES (est): 461.5K Privately Held
WEB: www.syracordnance.com
SIC: 3489 3483 Guns or gun parts, over 30 mm.; ammunition components

(G-11516)
TRI TECH METAL INC
6925 Daubon Ct (34655-5605)
PHONE....727 946-1229
Carlo Parente, *President*
Thomas Parente, *Vice Pres*

GEOGRAPHIC

EMP: 5 **EST:** 2005
SALES (est): 450.9K **Privately Held**
SIC: 3449 Miscellaneous metalwork

(G-11517)
TRINITY MOBILITY
8343 Royal Hart Dr (34653-7004)
PHONE..................................727 389-1438
Gerald Gluck, *President*
EMP: 8 **EST:** 2010
SALES (est): 233.7K **Privately Held**
WEB: www.trinitymobility.com
SIC: 3842 Wheelchairs

(G-11518)
UTOPIA GRILLING LLC
3511 Cockatoo Dr (34652-6415)
PHONE..................................727 488-1355
Derek Joseph, *Mng Member*
EMP: 7 **EST:** 2019
SALES (est): 1MM **Privately Held**
SIC: 2511 Kitchen & dining room furniture

(G-11519)
VISUAL MAGIC
8255 Tanglewood Dr (34654-5737)
PHONE..................................727 271-2702
David Evangelista, *President*
EMP: 6 **EST:** 2001
SALES (est): 165.1K **Privately Held**
WEB: www.visualmagicshop.com
SIC: 3999 Magic equipment, supplies & props

(G-11520)
VONWIDMAN DESIGNS LLC
9246 Hilltop Dr (34654-3433)
PHONE..................................727 862-5303
Alex Widman, *Owner*
EMP: 6 **EST:** 2015
SALES (est): 87.3K **Privately Held**
SIC: 3511 Turbines & turbine generator sets

(G-11521)
WOOD TELEVISION LLC
Also Called: Sun Coast Newspaper
6214 Us Highway 19 (34652-2528)
PHONE..................................727 815-1000
Dwayne Chichester, *Principal*
EMP: 6
SQ FT: 24,143
SALES (corp-wide): 4.5B **Publicly Held**
WEB: www.woodtv.com
SIC: 2711 Newspapers, publishing & printing
HQ: Wood Television Llc
120 College Ave Se
Grand Rapids MI 49503
616 456-8888

New Smyrna
Volusia County

(G-11522)
GREEN BULL PRODUCTS INC
310 Washington St (32168-7070)
PHONE..................................386 402-0409
Michael McNerney, *CEO*
▲ **EMP:** 5 **EST:** 2008
SALES (est): 350K **Privately Held**
WEB: www.greenbull.us
SIC: 2842 Specialty cleaning preparations

(G-11523)
RM INDUSTRIES
424 Luna Bella Ln Apt 318 (32168-4683)
PHONE..................................386 428-4454
Richard Mistarz, *Principal*
EMP: 6 **EST:** 2009
SALES (est): 114.5K **Privately Held**
SIC: 3999 Manufacturing industries

New Smyrna Beach
Volusia County

(G-11524)
ADVANCED MACHINING INC
1500 Airway Cir (32168-5929)
PHONE..................................386 424-7333
Robert E Kayat, *President*
EMP: 9 **EST:** 1995
SQ FT: 7,000
SALES (est): 1.1MM **Privately Held**
WEB: www.advmach.com
SIC: 3599 Machine shop, jobbing & repair

(G-11525)
ATLANTIC GAS SERVICES LLC
2948 Meleto Blvd (32168-6479)
P.O. Box 2301 (32170-2301)
PHONE..................................386 957-3668
Donald Fitzgerald Jr, *Principal*
EMP: 5 **EST:** 2012
SALES (est): 407.4K **Privately Held**
WEB: www.atlanticgasservices.com
SIC: 1382 Aerial geophysical exploration oil & gas

(G-11526)
BAILEY SIGLER INC
1050 Fremont St (32168-6239)
P.O. Box 393 (32170-0393)
PHONE..................................386 428-5566
Dean Sigler, *President*
Jack Schafer, *Vice Pres*
Charlie Sigler, *Vice Pres*
Caroline Sigler, *Treasurer*
Hugh Sigler, *Shareholder*
EMP: 7 **EST:** 1962
SQ FT: 1,500
SALES (est): 796K **Privately Held**
WEB: www.baileysigler.com
SIC: 3272 Concrete products, precast

(G-11527)
BAJIO INC ◆
1674 Tionia Rd (32168-9289)
PHONE..................................630 461-0915
Alvin P Perkinson III, *CEO*
EMP: 8 **EST:** 2020
SALES (est): 2.5MM **Privately Held**
SIC: 3851 Eyeglasses, lenses & frames

(G-11528)
BEACH EMBROIDERY & SCREEN PTG
806 E 3rd Ave (32169-3136)
PHONE..................................386 478-3931
Laura Wooley, *Owner*
EMP: 7 **EST:** 2014
SALES (est): 60.7K **Privately Held**
WEB: www.beachembroidery.com
SIC: 2759 Screen printing; card printing & engraving, except greeting

(G-11529)
CANAL CREAMERY
323 Canal St (32168-7007)
PHONE..................................386 410-4703
EMP: 6 **EST:** 2014
SALES (est): 162.2K **Privately Held**
SIC: 2021 Creamery butter

(G-11530)
CAPTAIN FOODS INC
207 Sapphire Rd (32169-2325)
PHONE..................................386 428-5833
Douglas Feindt, *President*
Kathryn Feindt, *Vice Pres*
Chris Feindt, *VP Sales*
Andrew Feindt, *Manager*
▼ **EMP:** 7 **EST:** 1994
SALES (est): 880K **Privately Held**
WEB: www.house-autry.com
SIC: 2099 Food preparations

(G-11531)
DAVIS KWIK KERB LLC
656 S State Road 415 (32168-9175)
PHONE..................................386 690-0058
EMP: 6 **EST:** 2009
SALES (est): 340K **Privately Held**
SIC: 3281 Mfg Cut Stone/Products

(G-11532)
DAYTONA PARTS COMPANY
1191 Turnbull Bay Rd (32168-6001)
P.O. Box 247 (32170-0247)
PHONE..................................386 427-7108
Ron Hewitt, *Owner*
▲ **EMP:** 8 **EST:** 1972
SQ FT: 6,000
SALES (est): 867.9K **Privately Held**
WEB: www.daytonaparts.com
SIC: 3592 3714 Carburetors; motor vehicle electrical equipment

(G-11533)
FLORIDA E COAST SUPERSONICS TC
712 Cherry St (32168-6515)
PHONE..................................386 689-2367
Wonzel Morris, *President*
EMP: 7 **EST:** 2015
SALES (est): 119.7K **Privately Held**
WEB: www.daytonatimes.com
SIC: 2711 Newspapers, publishing & printing

(G-11534)
GOSS INC
1419 Industrial Dr (32168-5957)
PHONE..................................386 423-0311
Herb Schubert, *Manager*
Ken Goss, *Info Tech Mgr*
EMP: 20
SQ FT: 20,292
SALES (corp-wide): 9.8MM **Privately Held**
WEB: www.gossonline.com
SIC: 3545 3548 Precision tools, machinists'; welding apparatus
PA: Goss, Inc.
1511 Route 8
Glenshaw PA 15116
412 486-6100

(G-11535)
HORIZON PUBLICATIONS INC
Also Called: Observer, The
508 Tanal St (32168)
PHONE..................................386 427-1000
EMP: 9
SQ FT: 2,400
SALES (corp-wide): 72.1MM **Privately Held**
SIC: 2711 Mfg Newspapers
PA: Horizon Publications Inc.
1120 N Carbon St Ste 100
Marion IL 62959
618 993-1711

(G-11536)
JL OPTICAL INC
Also Called: Jl Optical Microscopes
2908 Palma Ln (32168-6362)
PHONE..................................386 428-6928
George Walker, *President*
EMP: 5 **EST:** 1992
SALES (est): 647.9K **Privately Held**
WEB: www.secure28.securewebsession.com
SIC: 3826 5999 Microscopes, electron & proton; binoculars & telescopes

(G-11537)
LIFESTYLE MAGAZINE
1210 S Riverside Dr (32168-7768)
P.O. Box 1251 (32170-1251)
PHONE..................................386 423-2772
W Reed, *Owner*
EMP: 5 **EST:** 1985
SALES (est): 334.7K **Privately Held**
WEB: www.lifestylemagazineflorida.com
SIC: 2721 Periodicals

(G-11538)
MEDICAL WASTE INDUSTRIES INC
612 Downing St (32168-6909)
PHONE..................................407 325-4832
Ron Kroll, *Principal*
EMP: 20 **EST:** 2016
SALES (est): 95.7K **Privately Held**
WEB: www.medicalwasteindustries.com
SIC: 3999 Manufacturing industries

(G-11539)
NOR EAST MATERIALS INC
3459 Velona Ave (32168-4675)
PHONE..................................386 478-0087
John J Enterkin, *President*
EMP: 11 **EST:** 2006
SALES (est): 238.8K **Privately Held**
WEB: www.noreast-materials.com
SIC: 3674 Semiconductors & related devices

(G-11540)
OHANA LIQUIDS LLC
900 N Atlantic Ave (32169-2312)
PHONE..................................888 642-6244
Joseph Savas, *CEO*
Joseph N Savas, *Manager*
EMP: 7
SQ FT: 37,000
SALES (est): 648.4K **Privately Held**
WEB: www.ohanaliquids.com
SIC: 2023 Dietary supplements, dairy & non-dairy based

(G-11541)
SABIC INNOVATIVE PLASTICS
703 South St (32168-5867)
PHONE..................................386 409-5540
Richard Moeller, *Principal*
EMP: 7 **EST:** 2010
SALES (est): 1.1MM **Privately Held**
SIC: 2295 Resin or plastic coated fabrics

(G-11542)
SAND DOLLAR CHARTERS LLC
147 Middle Way (32169-5212)
PHONE..................................903 734-5376
Donald Owens,
EMP: 6 **EST:** 2019
SALES (est): 448.8K **Privately Held**
WEB: www.sanddollarboatrentals.com
SIC: 2541 Wood partitions & fixtures

(G-11543)
SEN-PACK INC
820 Rasley Rd (32168-5219)
PHONE..................................386 763-3312
Adam Vinoskey, *President*
Mark Brogan, *General Mgr*
Dave Cooley, *Vice Pres*
Gert Gast, *Buyer*
Pete Connor, *Electrical Engi*
EMP: 42 **EST:** 2007
SALES (est): 6.3MM **Privately Held**
WEB: www.sentryequipment.com
SIC: 3556 Food products machinery

(G-11544)
SO NAPA
3406 S Atlantic Ave (32169-3626)
PHONE..................................407 782-0459
Adam R Barringer, *Principal*
EMP: 6 **EST:** 2010
SALES (est): 241.4K **Privately Held**
SIC: 2084 Wines

(G-11545)
SONOCO PRODUCTS COMPANY
Also Called: New Smyrna Beach Plas Plant
1601 Tionia Rd (32168-9290)
PHONE..................................386 424-0970
Cathy Cottle, *Manager*
EMP: 30
SALES (corp-wide): 5.2B **Publicly Held**
WEB: www.sonoco.com
SIC: 2631 Paperboard mills
PA: Sonoco Products Company
1 N 2nd St
Hartsville SC 29550
843 383-7000

(G-11546)
SUGAR WORKS DISTILLERY LLC
1714 State Road 44 (32168-8339)
PHONE..................................386 463-0120
Thomas McPeek, *Mng Member*
Danay McPeek, *Mng Member*
EMP: 6 **EST:** 2017
SALES (est): 258.1K **Privately Held**
WEB: www.sugarworksdistillery.com
SIC: 2085 Distilled & blended liquors

(G-11547)
TIGER COMPOSITES INC
1531 Airway Cir (32168-5929)
P.O. Box 730125, Ormond Beach (32173-0125)
PHONE..................................386 334-0941
Aaron Duncan, *President*
Colleen Duncan, *Shareholder*
EMP: 14 **EST:** 2014
SQ FT: 32,000
SALES (est): 411.1K **Privately Held**
WEB: www.tigercomposites.com
SIC: 3721 3732 Motorized aircraft; gliders (aircraft); boats, fiberglass: building & repairing

▲ = Import ▼=Export
◆ =Import/Export

Newberry
Alachua County

(G-11548)
3522091611 (PA)
Also Called: Citrus Industry Magazine
27206 Sw 22nd Pl (32669-4302)
PHONE....................................352 671-1909
Robin Loftin, *President*
Tacy Callies, *Editor*
Ernie Neff, *Editor*
Ron Linkous, *Business Mgr*
Taylor Hillman, *Opers Staff*
EMP: 13 **EST:** 1984
SQ FT: 5,414
SALES (est): 1.3MM **Privately Held**
WEB: www.southeastagnet.com
SIC: 2721 Magazines: publishing only, not printed on site

(G-11549)
AAA EVENT SERVICES LLC
Also Called: AAA Porta Serve
25370 Nw 8th Ln (32669-2538)
P.O. Box 907, High Springs (32655-0907)
PHONE....................................386 454-0929
Ross Ambrose, *Managing Prtnr*
Steven Carson,
Thomas Hewlett,
James Wood,
EMP: 12 **EST:** 2014
SALES (est): 2.2MM **Privately Held**
WEB: www.aaaportaserve.com
SIC: 3431 7342 7359 Portable chemical toilets, metal; washroom sanitation service (industrial locations); portable toilet rental

(G-11550)
ALL STITCHED UP LLC
1909 Sw 186th St (32669-4720)
PHONE....................................352 316-4859
Christine Simmons, *Principal*
EMP: 6
SALES (corp-wide): 94.4K **Privately Held**
WEB: www.allstitchedupbyangela.com
SIC: 2395 Embroidery & art needlework
PA: All Stitched Up Llc
4850 Wellbrook Dr
New Port Richey FL

(G-11551)
ARGOS USA LLC
Also Called: Cement Plant
4000 Nw County Road 235 (32669-2380)
PHONE....................................678 368-4300
EMP: 35 **Privately Held**
WEB: www.argos-us.com
SIC: 3272 Concrete products
HQ: Argos Usa Llc
3015 Windward Plz Ste 300
Alpharetta GA 30005
678 368-4300

(G-11552)
ARGOS USA LLC
4000 Nw County Road 235 (32669-2380)
PHONE....................................352 472-4722
Eric Flesch, *Mng Member*
EMP: 35 **EST:** 2011
SALES (est): 3.1MM **Privately Held**
WEB: www.argos-us.com
SIC: 3241 5032 Masonry cement; cement

(G-11553)
EASTERN IRRIGATION SUPPLY
5328 Nw State Road 45 (32669-2523)
P.O. Box 1089 (32669-1089)
PHONE....................................352 472-3323
Cliff Brown, *President*
Nona H Brown, *Treasurer*
Bob Jocens, *Shareholder*
Clifton A Brown, *Admin Sec*
▲ **EMP:** 7 **EST:** 1999
SQ FT: 13,000
SALES (est): 1MM **Privately Held**
WEB: www.irrigationdistributors.com
SIC: 3523 Irrigation equipment, self-propelled

(G-11554)
ENDOSCOPY RPLACEMENT PARTS INC
25430 Nw 8th Ln (32669-3518)
PHONE....................................352 472-5120
David Bello, *President*
Nelly Gomez, *Sales Staff*
EMP: 6 **EST:** 1997
SALES (est): 841.6K **Privately Held**
WEB: www.endoscopeparts.com
SIC: 3599 Machine shop, jobbing & repair

(G-11555)
EVREN TECHNOLOGIES INC
404 Sw 140th Ter Ste 50 (32669-3655)
PHONE....................................352 494-0950
Weaver Gaines, *CEO*
EMP: 5 **EST:** 2018
SALES (est): 533.8K **Privately Held**
WEB: www.evrenvns.com
SIC: 3845 3841 Electromedical equipment; surgical & medical instruments

(G-11556)
FLORIDA ROCK
4000 Nw County Road 235 (32669-2380)
PHONE....................................352 472-4722
Fred Cohrs, *Principal*
Kip Rouse, *Consultant*
Lisa Penney, *Cashier*
Mike Waldrep, *Cashier*
◆ **EMP:** 15 **EST:** 2010
SALES (est): 1.1MM **Privately Held**
SIC: 3273 Ready-mixed concrete

(G-11557)
INSPIRED ENERGY LLC
25440 Nw 8th Pl (32669-2539)
PHONE....................................352 472-4855
Lori Brewster, *Finance Mgr*
Richard A Hudson, *Mng Member*
Samantha Smith, *Manager*
Ariel Leggett, *Supervisor*
Alexander I Jacobs,
◆ **EMP:** 129 **EST:** 2001
SQ FT: 29,855
SALES: 34.2MM **Privately Held**
WEB: www.inspired-energy.com
SIC: 3691 Alkaline cell storage batteries

(G-11558)
LIMESTONE PRODUCTS COMPANY
3107 Nw County Road 235 (32669-2384)
P.O. Box 177 (32669-0177)
PHONE....................................352 472-2116
James Downing, *Branch Mgr*
EMP: 6
SALES (corp-wide): 3.9MM **Privately Held**
WEB: www.limestoneproductsinc.com
SIC: 1422 Crushed & broken limestone
PA: Limestone Products Company Inc
3302b W Highway 74
Monroe NC 28110
704 283-9492

(G-11559)
PRECON CORPORATION
115 Sw 140th Ter (32669-3026)
PHONE....................................352 332-1200
Richard G Moore, *President*
Colin Tenney, *Superintendent*
Patrick J Wheeler, *Vice Pres*
Kurt Linebarger, *Project Mgr*
Pete Miner, *Project Mgr*
EMP: 150 **EST:** 1980
SQ FT: 3,200
SALES (est): 34.1MM **Privately Held**
WEB: www.precontanks.com
SIC: 3272 Tanks, concrete; prestressed concrete products

(G-11560)
RG GROUNDWORKS LLC ✪
5915 Nw 210th St (32669-2342)
PHONE....................................352 474-7949
Renato S Gomez Gonzalez R, *Principal*
EMP: 5 **EST:** 2020
SALES (est): 374.9K **Privately Held**
WEB: www.rggroundworksfl.com
SIC: 3561 2951 1771 Pumps & pumping equipment; asphalt paving mixtures & blocks; concrete work

(G-11561)
SOUTHERN FUELWOOD INC
28826 W Newberry Rd (32669-2674)
P.O. Box 1319 (32669-1319)
PHONE....................................352 472-4324
Patrick M Post, *Owner*
Rudy Davis, *Principal*
Keith Oliver, *Principal*
Joan Feuston, *Manager*
EMP: 40 **EST:** 1985
SQ FT: 1,000
SALES (est): 4.4MM **Privately Held**
WEB: www.southernfuelwood.com
SIC: 2421 5211 5031 Sawdust, shavings & wood chips; lumber & other building materials; lumber, plywood & millwork

Niceville
Okaloosa County

(G-11562)
ALDA STEVENS WOODWORKING
1537 Catmar Rd (32578-9744)
PHONE....................................850 897-4967
Alda Stevens, *Principal*
EMP: 6 **EST:** 2006
SALES (est): 68.3K **Privately Held**
SIC: 2431 Millwork

(G-11563)
BEEZ WORX BOATS LLC
1000 Coral Dr (32578-3506)
PHONE....................................850 678-6548
Brenda Karlek,
EMP: 6 **EST:** 2011
SALES (est): 117.5K **Privately Held**
SIC: 3732 7389 Boat building & repairing;

(G-11564)
CLJP INC
Also Called: Legacy Cabinet Company, The
200 Hart St (32578-1037)
P.O. Box 191 (32588-0191)
PHONE....................................850 678-8819
Charles R Agnew, *President*
John Agnew, *Vice Pres*
Jenna Sheely, *Controller*
Zach Witmyer, *Sales Staff*
Jon Reimer, *Info Tech Mgr*
EMP: 30
SALES (est): 10.9MM **Privately Held**
WEB: www.thelegacycabinetcompany.com
SIC: 2434 Wood kitchen cabinets

(G-11565)
EGLIN FLYER
1181 John Sims Pkwy E (32578-2752)
PHONE....................................850 678-4581
Ellie Clark, *Principal*
EMP: 6 **EST:** 2010
SALES (est): 17.2K **Privately Held**
WEB: www.baybeacon.com
SIC: 2711 Newspapers, publishing & printing

(G-11566)
EMERALD PRINTS LLC
1169 John Sims Pkwy E (32578-2752)
PHONE....................................850 460-5532
Kent Nguyen, *President*
EMP: 7 **EST:** 2017
SALES (est): 553.9K **Privately Held**
WEB: www.emeraldprints.com
SIC: 2752 Commercial printing, lithographic

(G-11567)
GENERAL DYNAMICS CORPORATION
115 Hart St (32578-1040)
PHONE....................................850 897-9700
Edward Lawrence, *Engineer*
Rosemary Hillyer, *Branch Mgr*
EMP: 6
SALES (corp-wide): 37.9B **Publicly Held**
WEB: www.gd.com
SIC: 3721 Aircraft
PA: General Dynamics Corporation
11011 Sunset Hills Rd
Reston VA 20190
703 876-3000

(G-11568)
GR DYNAMICS LLC
115 Hart St (32578-1040)
PHONE....................................850 897-9700
Ken Morgan, *Principal*
EMP: 18 **EST:** 2008
SALES (est): 2.3MM
SALES (corp-wide): 37.9B **Publicly Held**
WEB: www.gd-ots.com
SIC: 3489 Ordnance & accessories
PA: General Dynamics Corporation
11011 Sunset Hills Rd
Reston VA 20190
703 876-3000

(G-11569)
HELMS HAULING & MATERIALS LLC
Also Called: Helms Hauling and Materials
1423 Pine St (32578-9780)
PHONE....................................850 218-6895
Scott Michael Helms,
Lauren Helms,
EMP: 10 **EST:** 2012
SQ FT: 600
SALES (est): 1.8MM **Privately Held**
WEB: www.helmshauling.com
SIC: 1442 1422 5211 5032 Construction sand & gravel; crushed & broken limestone; sand & gravel; limestone; mulching services, lawn

(G-11570)
LEGACY BUILDING SUPPLY COMPANY
109 Kelly Rd (32578-1824)
PHONE....................................850 729-5901
Charles Agnew, *President*
EMP: 6 **EST:** 2014
SALES (est): 75.8K **Privately Held**
WEB: www.thelegacycabinetcompany.com
SIC: 2434 Wood kitchen cabinets

(G-11571)
POLLY CONCRETE PRODUCTS CO
1495 Cedar St (32578-9748)
PHONE....................................850 897-3314
Sherrie Venghaus, *Owner*
EMP: 10 **EST:** 1963
SQ FT: 3,850
SALES (est): 793.4K **Privately Held**
SIC: 3272 Concrete products, precast

(G-11572)
POPE ENTERPRISES INC
Also Called: Accent Signs
516 John Sims Pkwy E (32578-2028)
PHONE....................................850 729-7446
Greg Pope, *President*
Victoria Pope, *Corp Secy*
Patti Checkler, *Bookkeeper*
Michael Depoorter, *Information Mgr*
EMP: 11 **EST:** 1984
SQ FT: 5,000
SALES (est): 1.1MM **Privately Held**
SIC: 3993 Signs, not made in custom sign painting shops

(G-11573)
RMC EWELL INC
16040 State Highway 20 (32578-8215)
PHONE....................................850 879-0959
EMP: 21
SALES (corp-wide): 13.3B **Privately Held**
SIC: 3273 3272 Manufactures Ready Mix Concrete And Concrete Pipe
HQ: Ewell Rmc Inc
801 Mccue Rd
Lakeland FL
863 688-5787

(G-11574)
S&S CONSULTING PARTNERS LLC
139 Bayside Dr (32578-8257)
PHONE....................................850 803-8379
Benjamin Schladenhauffen, *Manager*
EMP: 6 **EST:** 2016
SALES (est): 323.1K **Privately Held**
SIC: 3629 Series capacitors

(G-11575)
TITANIUM LASER TECH INC
4463 Kingslynn Rd (32578-2389)
PHONE....................................956 279-0638
EMP: 5 **EST:** 2017
SALES (est): 350.9K **Privately Held**
WEB: www.titaniumlaser.com
SIC: 3356 Titanium

(G-11576)
VINTAGE ART AND SIGN LLC
1419 29th St 3 (32578-2724)
PHONE....................................770 815-7887
Kim M Sutton, *Principal*
EMP: 9 **EST:** 2013
SALES (est): 629K **Privately Held**
WEB: www.vintagesignandlight.com
SIC: 3993 Signs & advertising specialties

(G-11577)
ZITEC INC
1031 Partin Dr N (32578-1419)
PHONE....................................850 678-9747
Daniel T Mank, *President*
EMP: 5 **EST:** 2000
SALES (est): 668K **Privately Held**
WEB: www.zitecusa.com
SIC: 3728 Military aircraft equipment & armament

Nokomis
Sarasota County

(G-11578)
BUDDY BRIDGE INC (PA)
350 Sorrento Ranches Dr (34275-2468)
PHONE....................................941 488-0799
James F Gordon, *President*
EMP: 24 **EST:** 2010
SALES (est): 350.9K **Privately Held**
WEB: www.bridgebuddy.net
SIC: 2759 Playing cards: printing

(G-11579)
CARIBBEAN BASIN INDUSTRIES INC
2407 Casey Key Rd (34275-3384)
PHONE....................................941 726-7272
Diane K McNeer, *Principal*
EMP: 6 **EST:** 2012
SALES (est): 184.3K **Privately Held**
SIC: 3999 Manufacturing industries

(G-11580)
CLOVER INTERIOR SYSTEMS INC
505 Lyons Bay Rd (34275-3074)
P.O. Box 508 (34274-0508)
PHONE....................................941 484-1300
Joseph De Falco, *President*
Mary Ann De Falco, *Vice Pres*
EMP: 11 **EST:** 1971
SQ FT: 15,000
SALES (est): 1MM **Privately Held**
SIC: 2434 Vanities, bathroom: wood

(G-11581)
IMPRINT
3449 Tech Dr Unit 212 (34275)
PHONE....................................941 484-5151
Walter Rossmann, *Owner*
Brad Murray, *Director*
Brad Prepress, *Director*
EMP: 5 **EST:** 2006
SALES (est): 344.4K **Privately Held**
WEB: www.iloveimprint.com
SIC: 2752 Commercial printing, offset

(G-11582)
INNOVATIVE FABRICATORS FLA INC
Also Called: Innovative Contractors
104 Palmetto Rd W (34275-2035)
P.O. Box 1545, Osprey (34229-1545)
PHONE....................................941 375-8668
Jason Tison, *President*
EMP: 6 **EST:** 2002
SALES (est): 863.4K **Privately Held**
WEB: www.innovative-contractors.com
SIC: 3441 Fabricated structural metal

(G-11583)
JAZZY DOGS PUBLISHING
204 Millet Pl (34275-1332)
PHONE....................................941 726-0343
Jeffrey Johnson, *Principal*
EMP: 6 **EST:** 2016
SALES (est): 171.2K **Privately Held**
WEB: www.swflplacemats.com
SIC: 2741 Miscellaneous publishing

(G-11584)
KENT MANUFACTURING VENICE INC
155 Toscavilla Blvd (34275-1013)
PHONE....................................941 485-8871
Kent Drobisch, *President*
Chad Drobisch, *Vice Pres*
EMP: 15
SALES (est): 2.4MM **Privately Held**
WEB: www.kentmfg.com
SIC: 3949 Golf equipment

(G-11585)
METALEX LLC
3816 Cutlass Byu (34275-3343)
PHONE....................................941 918-4431
Robert Metzger, *President*
EMP: 100 **EST:** 2017
SALES (est): 3.6MM **Privately Held**
WEB: www.metlx.com
SIC: 2295 Metallizing of fabrics

(G-11586)
NIELSEN PUBLISHING
2504 Tamiami Trl N (34275-3482)
P.O. Box 866, Osprey (34229-0866)
PHONE....................................941 539-7579
EMP: 6 **EST:** 2017
SALES (est): 175.6K **Privately Held**
SIC: 2741 Miscellaneous publishing

(G-11587)
PRECISION FABRICATION CORP
510 Church St (34275-2723)
P.O. Box 666 (34274-0666)
PHONE....................................941 488-2474
Christopher Van Pelt, *President*
Deborah Van Pelt, *Vice Pres*
EMP: 20 **EST:** 1983
SQ FT: 10,500
SALES (est): 4MM **Privately Held**
WEB: www.precisionfabricationfl.com
SIC: 3444 Sheet metal specialties, not stamped

(G-11588)
STEPHEN J AUSTIN
120 Gulf Ave (34275-1323)
PHONE....................................941 780-7842
Stephen J Austin, *Principal*
EMP: 7 **EST:** 2013
SALES (est): 232.9K **Privately Held**
SIC: 3556 Food products machinery

(G-11589)
TEN4 SOLUTIONS LLC ✪
2342 Laurel Rd E # 7308 (34275-3594)
PHONE....................................302 544-1120
Barry McMonigle,
EMP: 8 **EST:** 2020
SALES (est): 260.5K **Privately Held**
SIC: 1389 Construction, repair & dismantling services

(G-11590)
UNIHOLD INC
2307 Tamiami Trl N (34275-3474)
PHONE....................................941 966-7440
Brian Dumas, *President*
EMP: 6 **EST:** 2018
SALES (est): 135.1K **Privately Held**
SIC: 3589 Service industry machinery

(G-11591)
VENICE CUSTOM CABINETS INC
510 Colonia Ln E (34275-2607)
PHONE....................................941 488-5000
Paul R Willhite, *Owner*
EMP: 8 **EST:** 1983
SQ FT: 5,000
SALES (est): 600K **Privately Held**
SIC: 2434 Wood kitchen cabinets

North Bay Village
Miami-Dade County

(G-11592)
ADVANCED CABINETRY INVENTIONS
7601 E Treasure Dr # 2120 (33141-4391)
PHONE....................................305 866-1160
Francisco Irace, *Principal*
EMP: 9 **EST:** 2013
SALES (est): 180.4K **Privately Held**
WEB: www.kitchencabinetscorp.com
SIC: 2434 Wood kitchen cabinets

(G-11593)
MEDICAL OUTFITTERS INC
1666 J F Kennedy Cswy # 409
(33141-4169)
PHONE....................................305 332-9103
Mark Zelinsky, *President*
Carlos Naya, *Vice Pres*
EMP: 22
SALES (corp-wide): 6.9MM **Privately Held**
WEB: www.medicaloutfitter.net
SIC: 3826 Magnetic resonance imaging apparatus
PA: Medical Outfitters Inc.
8062 Nw 66th St
Miami FL 33166
305 885-4045

(G-11594)
OMNIAELECTRONICS LLC
Also Called: Syxa Enterprise
7945 East Dr Apt 204 (33141-3304)
PHONE....................................631 742-5719
Gianluca Aprea, *CEO*
EMP: 8 **EST:** 2016
SALES (est): 717.3K **Privately Held**
SIC: 3629 Electronic generation equipment

(G-11595)
QUIANTUM CREATIVE GROUP INC
7935 East Dr (33141-3682)
PHONE....................................954 557-6777
Luis F Duarte, *Principal*
EMP: 6 **EST:** 2014
SALES (est): 175.8K **Privately Held**
SIC: 3572 Computer storage devices

(G-11596)
STAINLESS STEEL KITCHENS CORP
7601 E Treasure Dr # 2120 (33141-4391)
PHONE....................................305 999-1543
Klische Mirta, *Principal*
EMP: 10 **EST:** 2010
SALES (est): 268.1K **Privately Held**
WEB: www.steelkitchenweb.com
SIC: 3312 Stainless steel

North Fort Myers
Lee County

(G-11597)
CHVIEK
6650 Rich Rd (33917-4516)
PHONE....................................239 567-1511
William Chviek, *Principal*
EMP: 7 **EST:** 2010
SALES (est): 86.8K **Privately Held**
SIC: 7692 Welding repair

(G-11598)
GOLDEN MANUFACTURING INC
Also Called: Golden Boatlifts
17611 East St Unit B (33917-2138)
PHONE....................................239 337-4141
William Golden, *CEO*
Ken Felty, *Vice Pres*
Tom Flynn, *Sales Staff*
Tommy Fryer, *Manager*
Liz Travis, *Manager*
◆ **EMP:** 23 **EST:** 1997
SQ FT: 29,000
SALES (est): 6.9MM **Privately Held**
WEB: www.goldenboatlifts.com
SIC: 3536 Boat lifts

(G-11599)
MIDWEST MTAL FBRCTION CSTM RLL
13331 Seaside Harbour Dr (33903-7119)
PHONE....................................317 769-6489
Thomas Riddle, *President*
Mike Nickels, *Vice Pres*
EMP: 20 **EST:** 1989
SQ FT: 35,000
SALES (est): 1MM **Privately Held**
WEB: www.midwestmetalfabandrolling.com
SIC: 3443 3449 Fuel tanks (oil, gas, etc.): metal plate; miscellaneous metalwork

(G-11600)
NORTH FORT MYERS PRESCR SP
16251 N Cleveland Ave # 13 (33903-2176)
PHONE....................................239 599-4120
Lawrence Lisa, *President*
EMP: 8 **EST:** 2011
SALES (est): 162.4K **Privately Held**
WEB: www.therxshops.com
SIC: 2834 Dermatologicals; hormone preparations; medicines, capsuled or ampuled

(G-11601)
PAINTS & COATINGS INC
17660 East St (33917-2120)
PHONE....................................239 997-6645
Carl Laguidara, *President*
Jeff Yingling, *Vice Pres*
Melissa Giustina, *Office Mgr*
EMP: 30 **EST:** 1995
SALES (est): 3.8MM **Privately Held**
WEB: www.paintsandcoatings.net
SIC: 2851 Undercoatings, paint

(G-11602)
PELLICCIONE BUILDERS SUP INC
17056 Wayzata Ct (33917-3816)
PHONE....................................941 334-3014
Larry Pelliccione, *President*
EMP: 14 **EST:** 1973
SQ FT: 3,200
SALES (est): 664.6K **Privately Held**
SIC: 2439 Trusses, wooden roof

(G-11603)
PRECISION ECONOWIND LLC
8940 N Fork Dr (33903-1421)
PHONE....................................239 997-3860
Loyal Tingley III, *President*
Jeremy Krenzelak, *Accounting Mgr*
EMP: 17 **EST:** 2007
SALES (est): 7MM **Privately Held**
WEB: www.precisioneconowind.com
SIC: 3677 Coil windings, electronic

(G-11604)
SCOTTIES CANVAS & MAR SUP LLC
2211 N Tamiami Trl (33903-2806)
PHONE....................................239 995-7479
Mike Lueneburg, *General Mgr*
Patricia A Givens, *Principal*
EMP: 8 **EST:** 2016
SALES (est): 304.2K **Privately Held**
WEB: www.scottiescanvas.com
SIC: 2394 Canvas & related products

(G-11605)
SIGN AND DESIGN DEPOT LLC
960 Pondella Rd Ste C (33903-3514)
PHONE....................................239 995-7446
Greg Bullock, *Mng Member*
Margaret Wolter, *Graphic Designe*
Mary Bullock,
EMP: 9 **EST:** 2010
SQ FT: 1,800
SALES (est): 400K **Privately Held**
WEB: www.signanddesigndepot.com
SIC: 3993 Signs & advertising specialties

(G-11606)
SIGNARAMA
Also Called: Sign-A-Rama
4621 Bayshore Rd (33917-3986)
PHONE....................................239 997-1644
EMP: 6 **EST:** 2014

SALES (est): 171.6K Privately Held
WEB: www.signarama.com
SIC: 3993 5999 2759 Signs & advertising specialties; banners, flags, decals & posters; commercial printing

(G-11607)
TELEMATIC SYSTEMS INC
2029 Club House Rd (33917-2519)
PHONE..................................239 217-0629
William P Tassic, *President*
Don Tassic, *Manager*
EMP: 9 EST: 1978
SALES (est): 646.9K Privately Held
SIC: 3679 Electronic circuits

(G-11608)
UPRIGHT ALUMINUM INC
7908 Interstate Ct (33917-2112)
PHONE..................................239 731-6644
EMP: 6 EST: 2013
SALES (est): 530.4K Privately Held
WEB: www.uprightaluminum.com
SIC: 3442 Metal doors, sash & trim

(G-11609)
WANTED DEAD OR ALIVE INC
1011 April Ln (33903-5206)
PHONE..................................239 633-5080
Christopher Oncken, *Principal*
EMP: 8 EST: 2007
SALES (est): 295.1K Privately Held
SIC: 3531 Automobile wrecker hoists

North Lauderdale
Broward County

(G-11610)
A1 ELEVATORS LLC
8185 S Coral Cir (33068-4119)
PHONE..................................954 773-4443
Tracy Louis, *Co-Owner*
Ebony Louis, *Co-Owner*
EMP: 7 EST: 2014
SALES (est): 488.8K Privately Held
WEB: www.a1elevator.net
SIC: 3534 Stair elevators, motor powered

(G-11611)
AMERICAN PAYMENT SYSTEMS
1655 S State Road 7 (33068-4694)
PHONE..................................954 968-6920
EMP: 9 EST: 2006
SALES (est): 88.5K Privately Held
WEB: www.americanpaymentsystems.com
SIC: 3812 Defense systems & equipment

(G-11612)
BURNHAM WOODS UNTD CIVIC GROUP
8211 Sw 19th St (33068-4702)
PHONE..................................954 532-2675
Hallam Batson, *Principal*
EMP: 6 EST: 2015
SALES (est): 99.7K Privately Held
SIC: 2499 Wood products

(G-11613)
DMONEY365 LOGISTIC LLC ✪
1331 S State Road 7 (33068-4023)
PHONE..................................954 529-8202
Davens Deville,
EMP: 10 EST: 2021
SALES (est): 516.5K Privately Held
SIC: 3537 Trucks: freight, baggage, etc.: industrial, except mining

(G-11614)
EVM WOODWORK CORP
971 Sw 70th Way (33068-2557)
PHONE..................................954 970-4352
EMP: 6 EST: 2019
SALES (est): 165.5K Privately Held
SIC: 2431 Millwork

(G-11615)
EVM WOODWORKS CORP
7542 W Mcnab Rd (33068-5487)
PHONE..................................954 655-6414
EMP: 6 EST: 2017
SALES (est): 300.5K Privately Held
SIC: 2431 Millwork

(G-11616)
J L FINISH WOODWORK INC
2003 Sw 70th Way (33068-4803)
PHONE..................................954 609-4387
Juan E Lopez, *Principal*
EMP: 6 EST: 2016
SALES (est): 80.2K Privately Held
SIC: 2431 Millwork

(G-11617)
KDAVID WOODWORK & DESIGN INC
7546 W Mcnab Rd (33068-5484)
PHONE..................................754 205-2433
Diego A Cadavid, *Principal*
EMP: 12 EST: 2013
SALES (est): 491.8K Privately Held
SIC: 2431 Millwork

(G-11618)
MY PASSION ON A PLATE LLC ✪
7901 Southgate Blvd C3 (33068-1161)
PHONE..................................954 857-6382
EMP: 10 EST: 2020
SALES (est): 105K Privately Held
SIC: 2599 Food wagons, restaurant

(G-11619)
PAIRE JR WELD INC
7540 W Mcnab Rd Ste E13 (33068-5459)
PHONE..................................754 281-1803
Jeffrey Toussaint, *Vice Pres*
EMP: 6 EST: 2016
SALES (est): 128.9K Privately Held
SIC: 7692 Welding repair

(G-11620)
RICHARD LYN
7944 Forest Blvd (33068-1115)
PHONE..................................954 326-1017
Richard Lyn, *Principal*
EMP: 6 EST: 2007
SALES (est): 502.2K Privately Held
SIC: 3589 High pressure cleaning equipment

(G-11621)
SAP ENTERPRISES INC
309 Sw 77th Ave (33068-1220)
PHONE..................................954 871-8688
Shaun Allaham, *President*
EMP: 10 EST: 2008
SALES (est): 250K Privately Held
SIC: 3581 Automatic vending machines

North Miami
Miami-Dade County

(G-11622)
ADVANCED PHARMACEUTICAL INC
1065 Ne 125th St Ste 211 (33161-5832)
PHONE..................................866 259-7122
Ronel L Pierre, *President*
EMP: 9 EST: 2004
SALES (est): 164.3K Privately Held
SIC: 2834 Pharmaceutical preparations

(G-11623)
AJF SHEET METALS INC
7495 Nw 7th St Ste 10 (33181)
PHONE..................................305 970-6359
Alejo Fernandez, *President*
EMP: 7 EST: 2010
SALES (est): 653.8K Privately Held
SIC: 3444 Sheet metalwork

(G-11624)
AMERICAN SPECIALTY SALES CORP
Also Called: K & C The Printer
14286 Biscayne Blvd (33181-1204)
PHONE..................................305 947-9700
Robert K Minick, *President*
EMP: 8 EST: 1987
SQ FT: 4,000
SALES (est): 642.3K Privately Held
SIC: 2752 Commercial printing, offset

(G-11625)
ARTNEXUS ONLINE INC
12500 Ne 8th Ave (33161-4963)
PHONE..................................305 891-7270
Celia S Birbragher, *President*
Zulema Roca, *Sales Mgr*
Mercedes Guerrero, *Sales Staff*
EMP: 22 EST: 2001
SALES (est): 1.3MM Privately Held
WEB: www.artnexus.com
SIC: 2721 Magazines: publishing & printing

(G-11626)
AVENTURA CUSTOM WOODWORK
1450 Ne 130th St (33161-4411)
PHONE..................................305 891-9093
Isaiah Frometa, *Principal*
EMP: 6 EST: 2010
SALES (est): 71K Privately Held
SIC: 2431 Millwork

(G-11627)
BANKINGLY INC
1942 Ne 148th St (33181-1161)
PHONE..................................734 201-0007
Martin Naor, *CEO*
EMP: 20 EST: 2015
SQ FT: 1,000
SALES (est): 1MM Privately Held
SIC: 7372 Prepackaged software

(G-11628)
BOBBIE WEINER ENTERPRISES LLC
12355 Ne 13th Ave Unit 40 (33161-5972)
PHONE..................................817 615-8610
Bobbie Weiner, *Owner*
▲ EMP: 6 EST: 1997
SALES (est): 465.7K Privately Held
SIC: 2844 5122 Cosmetic preparations; cosmetics

(G-11629)
BORDERS & ACCENTS INC
1890 Ne 144th St (33181-1420)
PHONE..................................305 947-6200
Ignacio Paz, *President*
EMP: 10 EST: 1995
SQ FT: 16,000
SALES (est): 893.2K Privately Held
SIC: 3281 Building stone products

(G-11630)
BYOMED LLC
1555 Ne 123rd St (33161-6029)
PHONE..................................305 634-6763
Tarek Hamandi, *Mng Member*
EMP: 10 EST: 2016
SALES (est): 510.2K Privately Held
SIC: 3841 Medical instruments & equipment, blood & bone work

(G-11631)
CABUS USA INC
Also Called: Professional Engrv & Trophy
12300 Nw 7th Ave (33168-2604)
PHONE..................................305 681-0872
Pierre Dubose, *President*
Roselis Dubose, *Vice Pres*
◆ EMP: 5 EST: 1964
SQ FT: 1,500
SALES (est): 440.2K Privately Held
SIC: 3499 5944 Trophies, metal, except silver; jewelry, precious stones & precious metals; watches; silverware

(G-11632)
CINEMA CRAFTERS INC
Also Called: First Impression Design MGT
12564 Ne 14th Ave (33161-4439)
PHONE..................................305 891-6121
Jeffrey Smith, *CEO*
Mohni Kundnani, *Exec VP*
EMP: 7 EST: 1999
SQ FT: 15,000
SALES (est): 225K Privately Held
WEB: www.cineloungers.com
SIC: 2531 5049 Theater furniture; theatrical equipment & supplies

(G-11633)
COBRA POWER CORPORATION
13353 Ne 17th Ave (33181-1714)
PHONE..................................305 893-5018
Randy Garciga, *President*
Albert Levey, *Technical Staff*
◆ EMP: 5 EST: 1981
SQ FT: 11,000
SALES (est): 915.5K Privately Held
WEB: www.cobrapower.com
SIC: 3519 7699 Marine engines; marine engine repair

(G-11634)
CODSWORTH INDUSTRIES INC
Also Called: Prestige Entertainment
12864 Biscayne Blvd Ste 3 (33181-2007)
PHONE..................................203 622-5151
Steven Lichtman, *President*
EMP: 7 EST: 2016
SALES (est): 179.5K Privately Held
SIC: 3999 Manufacturing industries

(G-11635)
CSR ENTERPRISE LTD
370 Nw 123rd St (33168-3543)
PHONE..................................954 624-2284
Cranston Rolle, *CEO*
EMP: 7 EST: 2018
SALES (est): 129K Privately Held
SIC: 2673 Plastic bags: made from purchased materials

(G-11636)
ECSTATIC NAILS INC
13224 W Dixie Hwy (33161-4133)
PHONE..................................305 328-9554
Pauline Paul, *CEO*
Jenny Casamir, *COO*
Whitney Taylor, *CFO*
EMP: 5 EST: 2015
SALES (est): 323.9K Privately Held
WEB: www.ecstatic-nails.business.site
SIC: 3999 7231 Sterilizers, barber & beauty shop; fingernails, artificial; cosmetology & personal hygiene salons

(G-11637)
ENERGETICO INC
2260 Ne 123rd St (33181-2904)
PHONE..................................213 550-5211
Abe Sher, *CEO*
EMP: 4 EST: 2019
SALES (est): 10MM Privately Held
WEB: www.energetico.com
SIC: 3585 Air conditioning equipment, complete

(G-11638)
EXOTIC MARBLE POLISHING INC
12325 Ne 9th Ave Apt 4 (33161-5733)
PHONE..................................786 318-6568
Jose R Hidalgo, *Principal*
EMP: 7 EST: 2009
SALES (est): 50.6K Privately Held
SIC: 3471 Polishing, metals or formed products

(G-11639)
FUEL CONNECTION
14290 W Dixie Hwy (33161-2533)
PHONE..................................305 354-8115
EMP: 5 EST: 2008
SALES (est): 733.4K Privately Held
SIC: 2869 Mfg Industrial Organic Chemicals

(G-11640)
GDS
11900 Biscayne Blvd # 262 (33181-2743)
PHONE..................................305 764-0920
Todd Fisch, *Principal*
EMP: 6 EST: 2016
SALES (est): 90.4K Privately Held
WEB: www.myfavoriteaddress.com
SIC: 2541 Wood partitions & fixtures

(G-11641)
HEMCO INDUSTRIES INC (PA)
2500 Ne 135th St Ph 5 (33181-3616)
PHONE..................................305 769-0606
Aurelio F Hernandez Jr, *President*
Aida Hernandez, *Treasurer*
EMP: 19
SALES (est): 1.5MM Privately Held
SIC: 3661 3699 Telephone & telegraph apparatus; security devices

GEOGRAPHIC

(G-11642)
J M INTERIORS INC
Also Called: First Impressions Industries
12564 Ne 14th Ave (33161-4439)
PHONE..................................305 891-6121
Jeffrey W Smith, *President*
EMP: 8 **EST:** 1990
SQ FT: 9,000
SALES (est): 323.7K **Privately Held**
WEB: www.cineloungers.com
SIC: 2434 2511 2514 2541 Wood kitchen cabinets; wood household furniture; metal household furniture; wood partitions & fixtures

(G-11643)
LASER LIGHT LITHO CORP
1440 Ne 131st St (33161-4424)
PHONE..................................305 899-0713
Clifford Warren, *President*
Armando Bacigalupi, *Treasurer*
Doug Bressler, *Sales Mgr*
Hal Lieberman, *Technology*
Brian Pringle, *Technology*
EMP: 10 **EST:** 1980
SQ FT: 4,000
SALES (est): 1.6MM **Privately Held**
WEB: www.imageplusgraphics.com
SIC: 2752 Commercial printing, offset

(G-11644)
M D R INTERNATIONAL INC
14861 Ne 20th Ave (33181-1143)
PHONE..................................305 944-5335
Bernard Ghelbendorf, *President*
Jeana Ghelbendorf, *Treasurer*
EMP: 12 **EST:** 1973
SQ FT: 20,000
SALES (est): 517.9K **Privately Held**
WEB: www.mdrinternational.com
SIC: 3089 3965 3914 Injection molding of plastics; buttons & parts; trophies

(G-11645)
MAJESTICS BUSINESS USA LLC
Also Called: Tropic Spa
11077 Biscayne Blvd # 201 (33161-7419)
PHONE..................................305 713-9773
Jeremy C Faligand, *Mng Member*
Cindy D Navarro,
EMP: 5 **EST:** 2017
SQ FT: 800
SALES (est): 396.5K **Privately Held**
WEB: www.tropicspa.com
SIC: 2013 Sausages & other prepared meats

(G-11646)
MG COATING AND SEALANTSLLC
1280 Ne 137th Ter (33161-3421)
PHONE..................................305 409-0915
Miguel Reyes, *Principal*
EMP: 7 **EST:** 2014
SALES (est): 586.1K **Privately Held**
SIC: 2891 Sealants

(G-11647)
MVP GROUP LLC
2175 Ne 120th St (33181-2912)
PHONE..................................786 600-4687
Fabrizio Busso-Campana, *Vice Pres*
Michael Bromberg, *Mng Member*
◆ **EMP:** 12 **EST:** 2012
SALES: 15.4MM
SALES (corp-wide): 6.1MM **Privately Held**
WEB: www.mvpgroupcorp.com
SIC: 3556 Food products machinery
HQ: Mvp Group Corporation
5659 Av Royalmount
Mont-Royal QC H4P 2
514 737-9701

(G-11648)
NEMAL ELECTRONICS INTL INC (PA)
12240 Ne 14th Ave (33161-6521)
PHONE..................................305 899-0900
Benjamin L Nemser, *President*
Robert Larish, *Natl Sales Mgr*
Valber Mascarenhas, *VP Sales*
Madelene Torres, *Sales Mgr*
Ketty Inguanzo, *Supervisor*
▼ **EMP:** 20 **EST:** 1975
SQ FT: 40,000
SALES (est): 6.5MM **Privately Held**
WEB: www.nemal.com
SIC: 3577 5065 Computer peripheral equipment; electronic parts & equipment

(G-11649)
OSBORN PUBLICATIONS
2365 Biscayne Bay Dr (33181-2411)
PHONE..................................305 899-0501
Kenneth R Osborn, *Principal*
Tania Sutton, *Director*
EMP: 7 **EST:** 2007
SALES (est): 146.2K **Privately Held**
WEB: www.osborn.com
SIC: 2741 Miscellaneous publishing

(G-11650)
PARKER PROTECTIVE PRODUCTS LLC ✪
1965 Ne 148th St (33181-1136)
PHONE..................................800 879-0329
Ian Parker,
EMP: 10 **EST:** 2020
SALES (est): 391.5K **Privately Held**
SIC: 2381 Fabric dress & work gloves

(G-11651)
PUBLISHING RESEARCH INC
1313 Ne 125th St (33161-5975)
PHONE..................................954 921-4026
Benjamin R Jacobi, *President*
EMP: 9 **EST:** 2011
SALES (est): 171.4K **Privately Held**
WEB: www.kmgnet.com
SIC: 2741 Miscellaneous publishing

(G-11652)
PVC WINDOORS INC
1815 Ne 144th St (33181-1419)
PHONE..................................305 940-3608
Gaston Boudreau, *President*
▼ **EMP:** 17 **EST:** 1996
SQ FT: 33,000
SALES (est): 591.7K **Privately Held**
WEB: www.pvcwindoors.com
SIC: 3089 Window frames & sash, plastic

(G-11653)
SABROSOL LABORATORIES LLC
12585 Ne 7th Ave (33161-4811)
PHONE..................................305 290-4038
EMP: 8 **EST:** 2014
SALES (est): 181.8K **Privately Held**
SIC: 2844 Hair preparations, including shampoos; cosmetic preparations

(G-11654)
SFADA TAG AGENCY INC
625 Ne 124th St (33161-5522)
PHONE..................................305 981-1077
Richard A Baker, *President*
EMP: 18 **EST:** 1962
SALES (est): 1.3MM **Privately Held**
SIC: 2631 5511 Tagboard; new & used car dealers

(G-11655)
SKYWAYS TECHNICS AMERICAS LLC
13447 Ne 17th Ave (33181-1716)
PHONE..................................786 615-2443
Lucas Ansinelli, *Sales Staff*
Hernan Morales, *Sales Staff*
Juan Pablo Dorrejo, *Manager*
EMP: 7 **EST:** 2019
SALES (est): 1MM **Privately Held**
WEB: www.skywaystechnics.com
SIC: 3728 Aircraft parts & equipment

(G-11656)
SLIM AND SOFT BREAD LLC
15051 Royal Oaks Ln # 2105
(33181-2457)
PHONE..................................305 759-2126
Robert D Retondaro,
Eduardo E Jimenez,
▲ **EMP:** 10 **EST:** 2002
SQ FT: 15,000
SALES (est): 550K **Privately Held**
WEB: www.slimandsoft.com
SIC: 2051 Breads, rolls & buns

(G-11657)
SYKLEB INC
455 Ne 144th St (33161-2942)
PHONE..................................305 303-9391
Belkys Estrada, *Principal*
EMP: 6 **EST:** 2009
SALES (est): 100K **Privately Held**
SIC: 3423 Carpenters' hand tools, except saws: levels, chisels, etc.

(G-11658)
TD COATING INC
12420 Nw 5th Ave (33168-3608)
PHONE..................................786 325-4211
Tamara Diaz, *President*
EMP: 6 **EST:** 2015
SALES (est): 150.8K **Privately Held**
SIC: 3479 Coating of metals & formed products

(G-11659)
TECHNO-COATINGS INC
Also Called: Techno Aerospace
1865 Ne 144th St (33181-1419)
PHONE..................................305 945-2220
Juan P Camargo, *CEO*
Saul Camargo, *Chairman*
Rosario Camargo, *Corp Secy*
Carlos Camargo, *Engineer*
Paola Suarez, *CFO*
EMP: 250 **EST:** 1978
SQ FT: 25,000
SALES (est): 23.6MM **Privately Held**
WEB: www.techno-coatings.com
SIC: 3471 Plating of metals or formed products

(G-11660)
ULTRA-PURE BOTTLED WATER INC
1801 Ne 123rd St Ste 314 (33181-2883)
PHONE..................................281 731-0258
Sharon Smith, *President*
Lawrence Cacciatore, *President*
Gary Dukes, *Sales Staff*
Domenick V Traina, *Admin Sec*
◆ **EMP:** 15 **EST:** 1998
SQ FT: 18,500
SALES (est): 4.5MM **Privately Held**
WEB: www.nameyourbottle.com
SIC: 2086 5149 5499 5963 Water, pasteurized: packaged in cans, bottles, etc.; water, distilled; water: distilled mineral or spring; bottled water delivery

(G-11661)
UNITED METAL FABRICATIONS INC
1635 Ne 133rd St (33181-1704)
P.O. Box 611844, Miami (33261-1844)
PHONE..................................305 962-1608
Tomas Casal, *Principal*
Tomas M Casal, *Principal*
▲ **EMP:** 8 **EST:** 2009
SALES (est): 292.7K **Privately Held**
SIC: 3499 Fabricated metal products

(G-11662)
VINES WORLDWIDE LLC
13300 Biscayne Island Ter (33181-2248)
PHONE..................................786 353-2102
Judith Rodriguez, *Manager*
EMP: 6 **EST:** 2006
SALES (est): 104.4K **Privately Held**
SIC: 2084 Wines

(G-11663)
WBT APPAREL INC
1175 Ne 125th St Ste 102 (33161-5009)
PHONE..................................305 891-1107
Kenneth J Tate, *President*
Howard Posner, *COO*
James D Tate, *Vice Pres*
Steven Lieberman, *CFO*
EMP: 7 **EST:** 2007
SALES (est): 261.7K **Privately Held**
SIC: 2331 Women's & misses' blouses & shirts

(G-11664)
WILD DIAMOND VINEYARDS LLC
1680 Ne 135th St (33181-1725)
PHONE..................................305 892-8699
Robert C Bowling, *Principal*
EMP: 5 **EST:** 2014
SALES (est): 326.8K **Privately Held**
SIC: 2084 Wines, brandy & brandy spirits

(G-11665)
WORKEP INC
11930 N Bayshore Dr (33181-2900)
PHONE..................................787 634-1115
EMP: 7 **EST:** 2018
SALES (est): 198.7K **Privately Held**
WEB: www.workep.com
SIC: 3652 Pre-recorded records & tapes

North Miami Beach
Miami-Dade County

(G-11666)
AMERICAN INDUSTRIAL GROUP INC ✪
3363 Ne 163rd St Ste 611 (33160-4436)
PHONE..................................703 757-7683
Yan Aronov, *CEO*
EMP: 10 **EST:** 2020
SALES (est): 500K **Privately Held**
SIC: 2869 Alcohols, non-beverage

(G-11667)
ARCHANGEL TABLETS LLC
15421 W Dixie Hwy Unit 11 (33162-6060)
PHONE..................................703 981-7732
Josh Weinberg, *Manager*
EMP: 14 **EST:** 2017
SALES (est): 6MM **Privately Held**
WEB: www.archangeltablets.com
SIC: 7372 Prepackaged software

(G-11668)
ATTILAS MACHINE & WELDING
2143 Ne 161st St (33162-4919)
PHONE..................................305 947-0953
Ference Madar, *Principal*
EMP: 6 **EST:** 2016
SALES (est): 108.4K **Privately Held**
SIC: 3599 Machine shop, jobbing & repair

(G-11669)
CHROME CONNECTION CORP
15405 W Dixie Hwy (33162-6093)
PHONE..................................305 947-9191
Natalio Zaglul, *President*
Newlove Tone, *Vice Pres*
▲ **EMP:** 9 **EST:** 2002
SALES (est): 133.1K **Privately Held**
SIC: 2211 5137 Apparel & outerwear fabrics, cotton; women's & children's clothing

(G-11670)
DHSS LLC
Also Called: Sleep Group Solutions
16830 Ne 19th Ave (33162-3108)
PHONE..................................305 405-4001
Ran Ben-David, *Principal*
John Nadeau, *Vice Pres*
Jim Arden, *Regl Sales Mgr*
Donna Davidovitch, *Manager*
Raymond Champ, *Representative*
EMP: 15 **EST:** 2007
SALES (est): 5MM **Privately Held**
SIC: 3841 5047 Surgical & medical instruments; medical & hospital equipment

(G-11671)
DIY BLINDS INC
19515 Presidential Way (33179-6406)
PHONE..................................305 692-8877
Arnold S Goldin, *Principal*
EMP: 7 **EST:** 2018
SALES (est): 207.7K **Privately Held**
SIC: 2591 Window blinds

(G-11672)
EDS DELIGHT LLC
2080 Ne 186th Dr (33179-4387)
PHONE..................................305 632-3051
Edward Sthilaire,
EMP: 8 **EST:** 2009
SALES (est): 250K **Privately Held**
SIC: 2024 Ice cream & frozen desserts

(G-11673)
ELECTROLYTIC TECH SVCS LLC
19501 Ne 10th Ave Ste 203 (33179-3576)
PHONE..................................305 655-2755

Derek Lubie, *Mng Member*
EMP: 9 **EST:** 2019
SALES (est): 524.4K **Privately Held**
WEB: www.electrolytictech.com
SIC: 3589 Water treatment equipment, industrial

(G-11674)
EMC AEROSPACE INC
570 Ne 185th St (33179-4513)
PHONE..................................954 316-6015
Edward Monserrat, *CEO*
Christine Monserrat, *CFO*
EMP: 20
SALES (est): 1MM **Privately Held**
WEB: www.emcaerospace.com
SIC: 3721 Aircraft

(G-11675)
FASTSIGNS
15405 W Dixie Hwy (33162-6093)
PHONE..................................305 945-4700
Rudolf Bauer, *Principal*
EMP: 16 **EST:** 2010
SALES (est): 408.9K **Privately Held**
WEB: www.fastsigns.com
SIC: 3993 Signs & advertising specialties

(G-11676)
FBR 1804 INC
18320 Ne 21st Ct (33179-5022)
PHONE..................................305 340-3114
Irvin Pean, *CEO*
EMP: 11 **EST:** 2018
SALES (est): 250K **Privately Held**
SIC: 2741

(G-11677)
FERRELLI INDUSTRIES INC
2058 Ne 183rd St (33179-5045)
PHONE..................................305 792-0100
Joseph D Ferrelli, *Vice Pres*
EMP: 6 **EST:** 2010
SALES (est): 103.1K **Privately Held**
SIC: 3999 Manufacturing industries

(G-11678)
FRESH PRESS
15334 W Dixie Hwy (33162-6030)
PHONE..................................305 942-8571
Jovanni Garofolo, *Administration*
EMP: 10 **EST:** 2014
SALES (est): 536.9K **Privately Held**
WEB: www.freshpressmiami.com
SIC: 2741 Miscellaneous publishing

(G-11679)
FUEL SOLUTIONS DISTRS LLC
Also Called: Fuel Medics
3777 Ne 163rd St Pmb 148 (33160-4104)
PHONE..................................305 528-3758
David E Suaya, *Mng Member*
David Suaya, *Mng Member*
Samantha Suaya,
◆ **EMP:** 6 **EST:** 2008
SALES (est): 1MM **Privately Held**
SIC: 2911 5169 Fuel additives; oil additives

(G-11680)
GENUINE DENIM
851 Ne 182nd Ter (33162-1156)
PHONE..................................305 491-1326
Ovadia Tamir, *Principal*
EMP: 6 **EST:** 2016
SALES (est): 83.9K **Privately Held**
SIC: 2211 Denims

(G-11681)
GREEN PAPERS INC
Also Called: Green Toad Printers
15660 W Dixie Hwy (33162-6036)
PHONE..................................305 956-3535
Carlos A Girlando, *President*
EMP: 5 **EST:** 2009
SALES (est): 647.1K **Privately Held**
WEB: www.crossmediamg.com
SIC: 2752 Publication printing, lithographic

(G-11682)
HONEYWELL US CORP
3545 Ne 166th St Apt 304 (33160-3824)
PHONE..................................617 955-4031
EMP: 12 **EST:** 2018
SALES (est): 111.8K **Privately Held**
WEB: www.honeywell.com
SIC: 3724 Aircraft engines & engine parts

(G-11683)
INTERNATIONAL H20 INC
18387 Ne 4th Ct (33179-4531)
PHONE..................................954 854-1638
Juhani C Defazio, *President*
EMP: 7 **EST:** 2013
SQ FT: 6,000
SALES (est): 933.4K **Privately Held**
WEB: www.internationalh2o.com
SIC: 3585 Coolers, milk & water: electric

(G-11684)
IVER SERVICES
2381 Ne 135th Ter (33181-1847)
PHONE..................................786 329-3018
EMP: 12
SALES (est): 329.6K **Privately Held**
SIC: 3999 Mfg Misc Products

(G-11685)
J&S INKS LLC
1212 Ne 176th Ter (33162-1208)
PHONE..................................305 999-0304
Shlomo Friedman, *Principal*
EMP: 8 **EST:** 2006
SALES (est): 319.1K **Privately Held**
SIC: 2893 Printing ink

(G-11686)
JESS BY INCHES LLC ✪
2185 Ne 169th St (33162-6214)
PHONE..................................305 731-1387
Kathy Augustin,
EMP: 6 **EST:** 2021
SALES (est): 282.2K **Privately Held**
SIC: 3999 7389 Hair & hair-based products;

(G-11687)
JNR INTERNATIONAL METALS INC
17071 W Dixie Hwy Ste 301 (33160-3773)
PHONE..................................305 671-3509
David Aronson, *President*
EMP: 5
SALES (est): 346K **Privately Held**
WEB: www.jnrmetals.com
SIC: 3479 Aluminum coating of metal products

(G-11688)
KOLLSUT INTERNATIONAL INC
1763 Ne 162nd St (33162-4757)
PHONE..................................305 438-6877
Arkady Teplitsky, *President*
Enrique Berrios, *President*
Mingze Chen,
Binoy Joese,
Jing Wang,
EMP: 8 **EST:** 2006
SALES (est): 317.2K **Privately Held**
WEB: www.kollsut.com
SIC: 3841 5047 Surgical & medical instruments; surgical equipment & supplies

(G-11689)
LATINO CABINET CENTER PLUS LLC
487 Ne 167th St (33162-3909)
PHONE..................................786 663-0909
Merilien R Jean, *Manager*
EMP: 5 **EST:** 2018
SALES (est): 483.1K **Privately Held**
SIC: 2434 Wood kitchen cabinets

(G-11690)
LAURA KNIT COLLECTION INC (PA)
3224 Ne 167th St (33160-3848)
PHONE..................................305 945-8222
Joseph Feuer, *President*
Linda Feuer, *Corp Secy*
▲ **EMP:** 152 **EST:** 1979
SQ FT: 40,000
SALES (est): 10.2MM **Privately Held**
SIC: 2337 2335 Suits: women's, misses' & juniors'; women's, juniors' & misses' dresses

(G-11691)
MC MONUMENTAL GROUP INC
281 Ne 168th Ter (33162-2323)
PHONE..................................305 651-9113
Jean Casimir, *President*
EMP: 7 **EST:** 2017
SALES (est): 203.9K **Privately Held**
SIC: 3272 Monuments & grave markers, except terrazo

(G-11692)
MISS BS INC
13899 Biscayne Blvd # 309 (33181-1600)
PHONE..................................305 981-9900
Brenda Bontarii, *President*
Emmanouil Alevropoulos, *Manager*
EMP: 6 **EST:** 1991
SALES (est): 892.8K **Privately Held**
WEB: www.missbs.com
SIC: 2389 Costumes

(G-11693)
MUSCLE FX LLC
2221 Ne 164th St Ste 1267 (33160-3703)
PHONE..................................305 514-0061
Akshat Bhatia, *CEO*
EMP: 5 **EST:** 2008
SALES (est): 760K **Privately Held**
WEB: www.getmusclefx.com
SIC: 2834 Vitamin, nutrient & hematinic preparations for human use

(G-11694)
NEW DAIRY OPCO LLC
501 Ne 181st St (33162-1006)
PHONE..................................305 652-3720
EMP: 251
SALES (corp-wide): 660.3MM **Privately Held**
SIC: 2023 Dry, condensed, evaporated dairy products
PA: New Dairy Opco, Llc
8750 N Central Expy # 400
Dallas TX 75231
972 619-1535

(G-11695)
ONELID LLC
2100 Ne 211th Ter (33179-1639)
PHONE..................................305 335-9730
Stuart Frankel, *Principal*
EMP: 7 **EST:** 2015
SALES (est): 212K **Privately Held**
SIC: 3089 Plastics products

(G-11696)
PALM PHEON MUSIC PUBLISHING
Also Called: Bay Eight Studios
15421 W Dixie Hwy (33162-6059)
PHONE..................................305 705-2405
Matthew P Defreitas, *President*
EMP: 6 **EST:** 2016
SALES (est): 389.3K **Privately Held**
SIC: 2741 Miscellaneous publishing

(G-11697)
PERFORMANCE BOATS INC
2050 Ne 153rd St (33162-6020)
PHONE..................................305 956-9549
Bob Cetrealt, *President*
Debbie Divich, *Vice Pres*
◆ **EMP:** 10 **EST:** 2001
SQ FT: 7,889
SALES (est): 1MM **Privately Held**
WEB: www.performancepowerboats.com
SIC: 3732 Motorized boat, building & repairing

(G-11698)
PRIVE INTERNATIONAL INC
19597 Ne 10th Ave Ste F (33179-3578)
PHONE..................................888 750-5850
Valentina Cohen, *President*
EMP: 20 **EST:** 2013
SALES (est): 1.3MM **Privately Held**
WEB: www.prive-international.com
SIC: 2844 Cosmetic preparations

(G-11699)
PROFBOX OF AMERICA INC
17071 W Dixie Hwy Ste 116 (33160-3773)
PHONE..................................786 454-8148
Tatiana Sokolova, *Vice Pres*
EMP: 6 **EST:** 2012
SALES (est): 438.8K **Privately Held**
WEB: www.amprofbox.com
SIC: 3089 Plastics products

(G-11700)
R & Y AUTOMOTIVE AC CMPSR
15315 Ne 21st Ave (33162-6005)
PHONE..................................305 919-9232
Jacob Shaked, *Exec VP*
Prosper Mamane, *Manager*
EMP: 20 **Privately Held**
WEB: www.rycompressors.com
SIC: 3585 Compressors for refrigeration & air conditioning equipment
PA: R & Y Automotive Air Conditioning Compressors, Inc
15315 Ne 21st Ave
North Miami Beach FL 33162

(G-11701)
R & Y AUTOMOTIVE AC CMPSR (PA)
15315 Ne 21st Ave (33162-6005)
PHONE..................................305 947-1173
Prosper Mamane, *President*
▼ **EMP:** 17 **EST:** 1988
SQ FT: 19,495
SALES (est): 3.4MM **Privately Held**
WEB: www.rycompressors.com
SIC: 3585 Compressors for refrigeration & air conditioning equipment

(G-11702)
RADWAG USA LLC
19599 Ne 10th Ave Ste E (33179-3579)
PHONE..................................305 651-3522
Pawel Gorzalczynski, *Export Mgr*
Adrian Casanova, *Sales Mgr*
Alfonso Romero, *Sales Executive*
Maciej Lewandowski, *Mng Member*
Ernesto Garcia, *Manager*
▲ **EMP:** 9 **EST:** 2006
SALES (est): 1.2MM **Privately Held**
WEB: www.balances.shop
SIC: 3596 Weighing machines & apparatus

(G-11703)
RANGEVIDEO LAAP
15101 Ne 21st Ave (33162-6001)
PHONE..................................404 421-2574
Vladimir Reznik, *Principal*
Arkady Reznik, *Accountant*
EMP: 5 **EST:** 2015
SALES (est): 645.6K **Privately Held**
SIC: 3663 Radio & TV communications equipment

(G-11704)
SCALE MODELS ARTS & TECH
Also Called: Smartt
15455 W Dixie Hwy Ste G (33162-6067)
P.O. Box 600505 (33160-0505)
PHONE..................................305 949-1706
Michael Hart, *President*
Tom Kapatelis, *Manager*
Raymond Potter, *Director*
EMP: 12 **EST:** 1995
SALES (est): 1MM **Privately Held**
WEB: www.smarttinc.com
SIC: 3999 3944 Models, general, except toy; games, toys & children's vehicles

(G-11705)
SUNNY SKIES ENTERPRISES INC
570 Ne 185th St (33179-4513)
PHONE..................................954 316-6015
Edward J Monserrat, *CEO*
Mike Lopez, *Manager*
Edward Lee Morgan, *Manager*
EMP: 30 **EST:** 1997
SQ FT: 10,000
SALES (est): 6.8MM
SALES (corp-wide): 65.3MM **Privately Held**
WEB: www.velocityaero.com
SIC: 3728 Aircraft parts & equipment
PA: Velocity Aerospace Group, Inc.
7460 Warren Pkwy Ste 180
Frisco TX 75034
214 988-9898

(G-11706)
SWEET TOOTH INC
18435 Ne 19th Ave (33179-5033)
PHONE..................................305 682-1400

GEOGRAPHIC

Leigh Kersh, *President*
Johnny Berman, *Principal*
▼ **EMP:** 6 **EST:** 1983
SALES (est): 1MM **Privately Held**
WEB: www.thesweettooth.com
SIC: 2064 5812 5441 2066 Chocolate candy, except solid chocolate; caterers; candy; chocolate & cocoa products

(G-11707)
SWIM BY CHUCK HANDY INC
15415 Ne 21st Ave (33162-6007)
PHONE....305 519-4946
Charles J Handy, *President*
Mary Lou Handy, *Vice Pres*
◆ **EMP:** 6 **EST:** 2010
SALES (est): 342.3K **Privately Held**
WEB: www.buychuckhandy.com
SIC: 2253 5137 Bathing suits & swimwear, knit; swimsuits: women's, children's & infants'

(G-11708)
VELOCITY AEROSPACE - NMB INC
570 Ne 185th St (33179-4513)
PHONE....214 396-9030
Dale Gabel, *CEO*
Dennis Lainez, *General Mgr*
Vilma Figueroa, *Accountant*
EMP: 40 **EST:** 2015
SQ FT: 39,000
SALES (est): 8MM
SALES (corp-wide): 65.3MM **Privately Held**
WEB: www.velocityaero.com
SIC: 3728 Aircraft parts & equipment
PA: Velocity Aerospace Group, Inc.
7460 Warren Pkwy Ste 180
Frisco TX 75034
214 988-9898

(G-11709)
VENETA CUCINE INC
2020 Ne 163rd St Ste 100 (33162-4927)
PHONE....305 949-5223
Corrado Bonanno, *Manager*
EMP: 7 **EST:** 2007
SALES (est): 140.1K **Privately Held**
WEB: www.venetacucine.us
SIC: 2434 Wood kitchen cabinets

(G-11710)
VONN LLC
Also Called: Vonn Lighting
3323 Ne 163rd St Ph 706 (33160-5599)
PHONE....888 604-8666
Sergio Magarik, *CEO*
Lenny Valdberg, *President*
EMP: 18 **EST:** 2015
SQ FT: 7,000
SALES (est): 10MM **Privately Held**
WEB: www.vonn.com
SIC: 3646 3645 Commercial indusl & institutional electric lighting fixtures; residential lighting fixtures

(G-11711)
WE LOVE TEC LLC
2032 Ne 155th St (33162-6058)
PHONE....305 433-4453
Nicolas Massri, *Mng Member*
EMP: 5 **EST:** 2016
SALES (est): 805.3K **Privately Held**
WEB: www.welovetec.com
SIC: 3812 Electronic field detection apparatus (aeronautical)

(G-11712)
WHITE SANDS DMG INC
Also Called: Sign-A-Rama
1798 Ne 163rd St (33162-4733)
PHONE....305 947-7731
Roger Maxfield, *President*
Marisol Maxfield, *Vice Pres*
EMP: 5 **EST:** 1988
SQ FT: 1,550
SALES (est): 587.6K **Privately Held**
WEB: www.signarama.com
SIC: 3993 Signs & advertising specialties

(G-11713)
WISH INC
33 Nw 168th St (33169-6027)
PHONE....305 653-9474
Allan Moiseyev, *President*
▲ **EMP:** 13 **EST:** 2010
SALES (est): 1.2MM **Privately Held**
SIC: 3465 Body parts, automobile: stamped metal

(G-11714)
Y F LEUNG INC (PA)
1155 Ne 177th Ter (33162-1211)
PHONE....305 651-6851
Man Chung Leung, *President*
Yuen Cheung Leung, *Vice Pres*
EMP: 8 **EST:** 1978
SQ FT: 15,000
SALES (est): 568.2K **Privately Held**
SIC: 2431 1799 2541 2517 Millwork; home/office interiors finishing, furnishing & remodeling; wood partitions & fixtures; wood television & radio cabinets; wood household furniture; wood kitchen cabinets

North Palm Beach
Palm Beach County

(G-11715)
ACUCALL LLC
824 Us Highway 1 Ste 335 (33408-3860)
PHONE....855 799-7905
Rafael Egiazarian, *Chief Engr*
Kurt Goodridge, *CIO*
Stephen Ward, *Executive*
EMP: 11 **EST:** 2011
SALES (est): 1.3MM **Privately Held**
WEB: www.acucall.com
SIC: 7372 Application computer software

(G-11716)
ALPHA COMMERCIAL PRINTING
838 Northlake Blvd (33408-5210)
PHONE....561 841-1415
Panos Antonio, *Owner*
Catherine Antonio, *Co-Owner*
EMP: 5 **EST:** 1997
SALES (est): 328.3K **Privately Held**
WEB: www.alphacommercialcards.com
SIC: 2752 Commercial printing, offset

(G-11717)
ATTITUDE DRINKS INCORPORATED (PA)
712 Us Highway 1 Ste 200 (33408-4521)
PHONE....561 227-2727
Roy Warren, *Ch of Bd*
Tommy Kee, *CFO*
EMP: 4 **EST:** 2007
SALES (est): 5.4MM **Publicly Held**
WEB: www.attitudedrinks.com
SIC: 2026 Milk drinks, flavored

(G-11718)
BEACON PUBLISHING INC
631 Us Highway 1 Ste 201 (33408-4614)
PHONE....888 618-5253
Matthew Kelly, *President*
EMP: 9 **EST:** 2003
SALES (est): 176.8K **Privately Held**
WEB: www.bluesparrowbooks.org
SIC: 2731 Books: publishing & printing

(G-11719)
BEST PUBLISHING COMPANY
631 Us Highway 1 Ste 307 (33408-4618)
PHONE....561 776-6066
John S Peters, *Owner*
John Peters, *Sales Mgr*
EMP: 14 **EST:** 2009
SALES (est): 538K **Privately Held**
WEB: www.bestpub.com
SIC: 2741 Miscellaneous publishing

(G-11720)
CALKINS HARBOR PUBLISHING INC
441 Marlin Rd (33408-4321)
PHONE....561 906-4642
Joseph A Tringali, *Principal*
EMP: 8 **EST:** 2015
SALES (est): 45.4K **Privately Held**
WEB: www.calkinsharbor.com
SIC: 2741 Miscellaneous publishing

(G-11721)
CHERVO USA INC
1201 Us Highway 1 Ste 435 (33408-8509)
PHONE....561 510-2458
Marianne Strelec, *Principal*
EMP: 7 **EST:** 2017
SALES (est): 74.5K **Privately Held**
WEB: www.chervo.com
SIC: 2323 Men's & boys' neckwear

(G-11722)
LOCAL WOOD INC
336 Golfview Rd Apt 810 (33408-3512)
PHONE....561 410-2113
Danijel Antolovic, *President*
EMP: 6 **EST:** 2018
SALES (est): 124.6K **Privately Held**
WEB: www.localwoodva.com
SIC: 2431 Millwork

(G-11723)
MUELBY CONSTRUCTION SERVICES ✪
378 Northlake Blvd (33408-5421)
PHONE....561 376-7614
Michael Moss, *President*
EMP: 50 **EST:** 2020
SALES (est): 3.3MM **Privately Held**
SIC: 1389 Construction, repair & dismantling services

(G-11724)
PATIENT PORTAL TECH INC (PA)
2000 Pga Blvd Ste 4440 (33408-2738)
PHONE....877 779-6627
Brian Kelly, *CEO*
John O'Mara, *President*
Thomas Hagan, *CFO*
EMP: 37 **EST:** 2003
SALES (est): 5.1MM **Publicly Held**
WEB: www.medxgo.com
SIC: 7372 Prepackaged software

(G-11725)
PROFESSIONAL PRINTING
120 Us Highway 1 Ste 1 (33408-5404)
PHONE....561 845-0514
Gary Brown, *Principal*
EMP: 7 **EST:** 2007
SALES (est): 72.8K **Privately Held**
WEB: www.preferredprinting.net
SIC: 2752 Commercial printing, offset

(G-11726)
PURAGEN LLC
11300 Us Highway 1 # 203 (33408-3217)
PHONE....760 630-5724
Mark McCormick, *Vice Pres*
EMP: 50
SALES (corp-wide): 633.2MM **Privately Held**
WEB: www.puragen.com
SIC: 2819 Charcoal (carbon), activated
HQ: Puragen Llc
1601 Forum Pl Ste 1400
West Palm Beach FL 33401
561 907-5400

(G-11727)
TRANSDERMAL TECHNOLOGIES INC
521 Northlake Blvd Ste B (33408-5418)
PHONE....561 848-2345
Kenneth B Kirby, *President*
Bruce Crawford, *Exec VP*
EMP: 7
SQ FT: 9,000
SALES (est): 929.8K **Privately Held**
SIC: 2834 Ointments

(G-11728)
TURTLEHUE LLC
11231 Us Highway 1 170 (33408-3216)
PHONE....561 775-6614
Robert Maciejko, *Principal*
EMP: 6 **EST:** 2012
SALES (est): 310.5K **Privately Held**
SIC: 2711 Newspapers, publishing & printing

(G-11729)
UNIVERSAL GRAPHICS & PRTG INC
Also Called: Minuteman Press
120 Us Highway 1 Ste 1 (33408-5404)
PHONE....561 845-6404
Dennis Beck, *President*
Phyllis Beck, *Vice Pres*
EMP: 5 **EST:** 1991
SQ FT: 1,300
SALES (est): 749.8K **Privately Held**
WEB: www.chanhassen-mn.minutemanpress.com
SIC: 2752 2791 2789 Commercial printing, offset; typesetting; bookbinding & related work

(G-11730)
WOOD STILE INC
644 Marbella Ln (33403-1239)
PHONE....561 329-4671
Andrew Hanbury, *President*
EMP: 5
SALES (est): 750K **Privately Held**
SIC: 2599 Cabinets, factory

North Port
Sarasota County

(G-11731)
ADAMS BROS CABINETRY INC
Also Called: Adams Group
2221 Murphy Ct (34289-9314)
PHONE....941 639-7188
Ethan M Adams, *President*
Maria Adams, *Vice Pres*
Josh Underdown, *Project Mgr*
Ron Schmitt, *Mfg Staff*
Susan J Adams, *Treasurer*
EMP: 89 **EST:** 1978
SQ FT: 50,000
SALES (est): 17MM **Privately Held**
SIC: 2431 8071 Millwork; medical laboratories

(G-11732)
BIMBO BAKERIES USA
2625 Commerce Pkwy # 112 (34289-9347)
PHONE....941 875-5945
EMP: 6 **EST:** 2011
SALES (est): 116.5K **Privately Held**
WEB: www.bakeries.cmac.ws
SIC: 2051 Bakery: wholesale or wholesale/retail combined

(G-11733)
BINDELS CUSTOM WOODWORK INC
7514 Tasco Dr (34291-5312)
PHONE....727 776-5233
Joshua Bindel, *President*
EMP: 6 **EST:** 2012
SALES (est): 63.6K **Privately Held**
SIC: 2431 Millwork

(G-11734)
BUSY BEE CABINETS INC
2845 Commerce Pkwy (34289-9303)
PHONE....941 628-2025
Matthew M Uebelacker, *President*
Glenn Miller, *General Mgr*
Diana R Uebelacker, *Vice Pres*
Kenny Midgett, *Sales Mgr*
Nancy Dietzman, *Sales Executive*
EMP: 80 **EST:** 1982
SQ FT: 27,000
SALES (est): 9.7MM **Privately Held**
WEB: www.busybeecabinets.com
SIC: 2434 Wood kitchen cabinets

(G-11735)
BUTLER PAVERS INC
6862 Van Camp St (34291-4026)
PHONE....941 423-3977
EMP: 9 **EST:** 2004
SALES (est): 114.1K **Privately Held**
WEB: www.butlerpavers.com
SIC: 2951 Asphalt paving mixtures & blocks

(G-11736)
C&S OSTOMY POUCH COVERS INC
2214 Cloras St (34287-5174)
PHONE....................................941 423-8542
Bonnie Coker, *President*
EMP: 5 **EST:** 2010
SALES (est): 327.8K **Privately Held**
WEB: www.cspouchcovers.com
SIC: 2258 Covers, lace: chair, dresser, piano & table

(G-11737)
DEVINE CABINETRY LLC
6315 Ruff St (34291-2005)
PHONE....................................941 716-0339
Mark J Devine, *Principal*
EMP: 6 **EST:** 2016
SALES (est): 147.3K **Privately Held**
SIC: 2434 Wood kitchen cabinets

(G-11738)
EURO-WALL SYSTEMS LLC
2200 Murphy Ct (34289-9302)
PHONE....................................941 979-5316
Lori Langfang, *Controller*
Michael Zurbrigen, *Mng Member*
Carolina Zurbrigen,
◆ **EMP:** 27 **EST:** 2012
SALES (est): 15.9MM **Privately Held**
WEB: www.euro-wall.com
SIC: 3442 Metal doors, sash & trim

(G-11739)
G & R STUCCO INC
7234 Belcrest Ct (34287-1705)
PHONE....................................941 780-1561
Eugene J Spencer, *Principal*
EMP: 6 **EST:** 2012
SALES (est): 64K **Privately Held**
SIC: 3299 Stucco

(G-11740)
GEMSTONE CABINETRY LLC
2845 Commerce Pkwy (34289-9303)
PHONE....................................941 426-5656
Matt Uebelacker, *Principal*
EMP: 7 **EST:** 2016
SALES (est): 115.7K **Privately Held**
WEB: www.gemstonecabinetry.com
SIC: 2434 Wood kitchen cabinets

(G-11741)
HOT SAUCE HARRYS INC
1077 Innovation Ave # 10 (34289-9345)
PHONE....................................941 423-7092
Dianne P Harris, *President*
Bob Harris, *Vice Pres*
EMP: 6 **EST:** 1994
SALES (est): 770K **Privately Held**
WEB: www.hotsauceharrys.com
SIC: 2033 5149 Barbecue sauce: packaged in cans, jars, etc.; groceries & related products

(G-11742)
KING PLASTIC CORPORATION
1100 N Toledo Blade Blvd (34288-8694)
PHONE....................................941 423-8666
Jeff King, *CEO*
Thomas M King, *Chairman*
Diane Charest, *Buyer*
Craig Calhoun, *CFO*
Judith King, *Treasurer*
EMP: 120 **EST:** 1968
SQ FT: 150,000
SALES (est): 79.8MM **Privately Held**
WEB: www.kingplastic.com
SIC: 3081 3082 Plastic film & sheet; rods, unsupported plastic

(G-11743)
MCR COMPRESSION SERVICES LLC (PA)
1261 S Haberland Blvd (34288-8164)
P.O. Box 13180, Odessa TX (79768-3180)
PHONE....................................432 552-8720
Pamela Trout,
EMP: 17 **EST:** 2012
SALES (est): 4MM **Privately Held**
SIC: 1389 Gas field services

(G-11744)
MONROE CABLE LLC
Also Called: ATI
2529 Commerce Pkwy (34289-9355)
PHONE....................................941 429-8484
Richard Samuels, *General Mgr*
Robin Nichols, *Finance*
EMP: 70 **EST:** 1989
SQ FT: 17,000
SALES (est): 20.6MM
SALES (corp-wide): 64.1MM **Privately Held**
WEB: www.monroeengineering.com
SIC: 3679 3661 3663 3357 Electronic circuits; telephone & telegraph apparatus; television monitors; nonferrous wiredrawing & insulating
PA: Monroe Engineering, Llc
2990 Technology Dr
Rochester Hills MI 48309
877 740-1077

(G-11745)
NORTH PORT PAVERS INC
6099 Estates Dr (34291-4600)
PHONE....................................941 391-7557
Adeleimar Figueiredo, *Principal*
EMP: 7 **EST:** 2010
SALES (est): 198.4K **Privately Held**
SIC: 3531 Pavers

(G-11746)
PET SUPPLIES PLUS ✪
1045 Front Pl (34287-7001)
PHONE....................................248 824-4676
EMP: 6 **EST:** 2020
SALES (est): 43.6K **Privately Held**
WEB: www.petsuppliesplus.com
SIC: 3999 Pet supplies

(G-11747)
PICKLES PLUS
6196 Tidwell St (34291-2003)
PHONE....................................941 661-6139
Denise Proper, *Owner*
EMP: 8 **EST:** 2006
SALES (est): 129K **Privately Held**
WEB: www.picklesplus.com
SIC: 2035 Pickled fruits & vegetables

(G-11748)
ROTARY MANUFACTURING LLC
3276 Commerce Pkwy (34289-9339)
PHONE....................................941 564-8038
McAloon Scott, *Mng Member*
EMP: 11 **EST:** 2012
SALES (est): 259.8K **Privately Held**
WEB: www.rotarymfg.com
SIC: 2679 Pipes & fittings, fiber: made from purchased material

(G-11749)
SHELDON SIGN COMPANY INC
1236 Webster St (34288-8601)
PHONE....................................941 321-6313
Sheldon L Raymond, *Principal*
EMP: 6 **EST:** 2014
SALES (est): 196.5K **Privately Held**
WEB: www.sheldonsigncompany.com
SIC: 3993 Signs & advertising specialties

(G-11750)
SHUTTER SOUTHERN CROSS
1401 Henning St (34288-8971)
PHONE....................................941 276-7064
Brant Smith, *Principal*
EMP: 6 **EST:** 2016
SALES (est): 108.3K **Privately Held**
WEB: www.southerncrossstorm.com
SIC: 3442 Shutters, door or window: metal

(G-11751)
TROPICALCREATION
1310 Atwater Dr (34288-8404)
PHONE....................................941 580-8465
Teddy James Hettich, *Owner*
EMP: 6 **EST:** 2011
SALES (est): 200.3K **Privately Held**
SIC: 3081 Floor or wall covering, unsupported plastic

(G-11752)
UNIQUE LED PRODUCTS LLC
408 Madonna (34287-2536)
PHONE....................................440 520-4959
Linda Frycz, *General Mgr*
Darrell Frycz, *Mng Member*
EMP: 6 **EST:** 2012
SALES (est): 291.8K **Privately Held**
WEB: www.uniqueledproducts.com
SIC: 3993 Signs & advertising specialties

North Venice
Sarasota County

(G-11753)
B G INSTRUMENT CORP
112 Morse Ct (34275-3635)
PHONE....................................941 485-7700
Robert Gredick, *President*
EMP: 10 **EST:** 1946
SQ FT: 5,000
SALES (est): 217.9K **Privately Held**
SIC: 3599 Machine shop, jobbing & repair

(G-11754)
BOAT STEERING SOLUTIONS LLC
1070 Endeavor Ct (34275-3623)
PHONE....................................727 400-4746
EMP: 5 **EST:** 2019
SALES (est): 540.2K **Privately Held**
WEB: www.boatsteer.com
SIC: 3714 Motor vehicle parts & accessories

(G-11755)
COYOTE ACQUISITION CO (HQ)
1070 Technology Dr (34275-3617)
PHONE....................................941 480-1600
Rodney Hershberger, *Principal*
EMP: 100 **EST:** 2018
SALES (est): 39.4MM
SALES (corp-wide): 882.6MM **Publicly Held**
WEB: www.pgtwindows.com
SIC: 3442 Window & door frames
PA: Pgt Innovations, Inc.
1070 Technology Dr
North Venice FL 34275
941 480-1600

(G-11756)
DENNYS ELECTRONICS INC
1044 Endeavor Ct (34275-3623)
PHONE....................................941 485-5400
Dennis Bartosik, *President*
EMP: 23 **EST:** 1977
SQ FT: 16,000
SALES (est): 1.6MM **Privately Held**
WEB: www.dennyselectronics.com
SIC: 3944 Games, toys & children's vehicles

(G-11757)
DIVERSFIED MTL SPECIALISTS INC
Also Called: D M S I
105 Triple Dmd Blvd Ste 1 (34275-3646)
PHONE....................................941 244-0935
Jeff Dalonzo, *President*
Brandon Woodward, *Vice Pres*
Dustin Hall, *Regl Sales Mgr*
Nick Berg, *Director*
Tyler Blakeslee, *Director*
▲ **EMP:** 5 **EST:** 1996
SALES (est): 1.2MM **Privately Held**
WEB: www.dmsimfg.com
SIC: 3678 8742 7373 3357 Electronic connectors; management consulting services; systems integration services; communication wire; engineering services; computer (hardware) development

(G-11758)
GAUTIER FABRICATION INC
1049 Endeavor Ct (34275-3622)
PHONE....................................941 485-2464
Michael Gautier, *President*
Sonya Murphy, *Office Admin*
EMP: 20 **EST:** 1994
SALES (est): 5.1MM **Privately Held**
WEB: www.gautierfabrication.com
SIC: 3444 Sheet metalwork

(G-11759)
JANSEN SHUTTERS & SPC LTD
115 Morse Ct (34275-3636)
PHONE....................................941 484-4700
Travis Jansen, *Sales Executive*
Phillip Jansen, *Executive*
Susan Jansen,
EMP: 8 **EST:** 2002
SALES (est): 2.4MM **Privately Held**
WEB: www.jansenshutters.com
SIC: 3442 Shutters, door or window: metal

(G-11760)
MASTER MOLD CORP
123 Morse Ct (34275-3636)
PHONE....................................941 486-0000
Danny Davis, *President*
EMP: 7 **EST:** 2000
SQ FT: 2,000
SALES (est): 755.7K **Privately Held**
WEB: www.master-mold.net
SIC: 3089 3944 Injection molding of plastics; dice & dice cups

(G-11761)
PGT INDUSTRIES INC (HQ)
Also Called: PGT Custom Windows Doors
1070 Technology Dr (34275-3617)
P.O. Box 1529, Nokomis (34274-1529)
PHONE....................................941 480-1600
Rodney Hershberger, *President*
Benji Hershberger, *Vice Pres*
Jeffrey Jackson, *CFO*
Brad West, *CFO*
Sharon Pind, *Sales Staff*
◆ **EMP:** 900 **EST:** 1980
SQ FT: 420,000
SALES (est): 511.3MM
SALES (corp-wide): 882.6MM **Publicly Held**
WEB: www.pgtwindows.com
SIC: 3442 2431 3231 Window & door frames; windows & window parts & trim, wood; doors & door parts & trim, wood; products of purchased glass
PA: Pgt Innovations, Inc.
1070 Technology Dr
North Venice FL 34275
941 480-1600

(G-11762)
PGT INNOVATIONS INC (PA)
1070 Technology Dr (34275-3617)
PHONE....................................941 480-1600
Rodney Hershberger, *Ch of Bd*
Jeffrey T Jackson, *President*
Robert A Keller, *President*
Mike Wothe, *President*
Gary Greksa, *Regional Mgr*
▼ **EMP:** 830 **EST:** 1980
SQ FT: 363,000
SALES: 882.6MM **Publicly Held**
WEB: www.pgtwindows.com
SIC: 3442 2431 3211 Window & door frames; windows & window parts & trim, wood; doors & door parts & trim, wood; laminated glass

(G-11763)
TERVIS TUMBLER COMPANY (PA)
201 Triple Diamond Blvd (34275-3634)
PHONE....................................941 966-2114
John P Redmond Jr, *CEO*
Dorothy Lierman, *President*
Joshua Quillen, *General Mgr*
Norbert Donnelly, *Chairman*
Norbert Donelly, *Vice Pres*
◆ **EMP:** 200 **EST:** 1946
SQ FT: 55,830
SALES (est): 80.5MM **Privately Held**
WEB: www.tervis.com
SIC: 3089 Cups, plastic, except foam

(G-11764)
WEBER MFG & SUPPLIES INC
Also Called: Weber Manufacturing
3430 Technology Dr (34275-3618)
PHONE....................................941 488-5185
Pamela J Prost, *CEO*
Louis Samuel Prost, *President*
Patrick C Smith, *Vice Pres*
Aaron Prost, *Sales Staff*
Lynda Hayes, *Office Admin*
EMP: 17 **EST:** 1963
SQ FT: 15,000
SALES (est): 3.8MM **Privately Held**
WEB: www.webermfg.com
SIC: 3451 3599 Screw machine products; machine & other job shop work

(G-11765)
WINDOOR INCORPORATED
1070 Technology Dr (34275-3617)
PHONE....................................407 481-8400
Frank R Lukens Jr, *President*
Lizmarie Torres, *Production*
George Hanus, *Marketing Mgr*
Kristy L Thacker, *Admin Sec*
◆ **EMP:** 105 **EST:** 2001
SALES (est): 24.1MM
SALES (corp-wide): 882.6MM **Publicly Held**
WEB: www.windoorinc.com
SIC: 3231 3211 Doors, glass: made from purchased glass; window glass, clear & colored
HQ: Pgt Industries, Inc.
1070 Technology Dr
North Venice FL 34275

O Brien
Suwannee County

(G-11766)
STRAW LIFE INC
25434 87th Dr (32071-3911)
PHONE....................................386 935-2850
Verlin R Sherrell, *President*
Millicent Perry, *Vice Pres*
EMP: 7 **EST:** 2015
SALES (est): 218.1K **Privately Held**
SIC: 3999 Straw goods

Oakland
Orange County

(G-11767)
ABC ENTERPRISES
16274 Lake Johns Cir (34787-9426)
P.O. Box 218 (34760-0218)
PHONE....................................407 656-6503
Andrew Arsenio, *Owner*
Tammy Steen, *Vice Pres*
EMP: 7 **EST:** 1987
SQ FT: 1,008
SALES (est): 580K **Privately Held**
SIC: 3841 Surgical & medical instruments

(G-11768)
CREATIVE AUTO BOUTIQUE LLC
17949 W Colonial Dr (34787-9768)
PHONE....................................407 654-7300
Omar I Alli, *Mng Member*
Brian Jankuhn,
EMP: 8 **EST:** 2009
SALES (est): 1.4MM **Privately Held**
WEB: www.creativeautoboutique.com
SIC: 3714 Acceleration equipment, motor vehicle

(G-11769)
CUSTOM METAL DESIGNS INC
921 W Oakland Ave (34760-8855)
P.O. Box 783037, Winter Garden (34778-3037)
PHONE....................................407 656-7771
Saul Grimes, *Ch of Bd*
Steven Grimes, *President*
Ann Grimes, *Corp Secy*
H T Lucas Jr, *Vice Pres*
Wesley Kolpin, *Bookkeeper*
EMP: 55 **EST:** 1972
SQ FT: 25,000
SALES (est): 13.4MM **Privately Held**
WEB: www.custommetaldesigns.com
SIC: 3535 Conveyors & conveying equipment

(G-11770)
MPACT SALES SOLUTIONS
622 Largovista Dr (34787-8973)
PHONE....................................630 669-5937
EMP: 9
SALES: 50K **Privately Held**
SIC: 2834 Mfg Pharmaceutical Preparations

(G-11771)
SOUTHWIND AVIATION SUPPLY LLC
752 Strihal Loop (34787-8957)
P.O. Box 1256 (34760-1256)
PHONE....................................405 491-0500
Gary P Henricksen, *Vice Pres*
Sandi Chuck, *Controller*
George S Andrews,
Justin Nalley,
Ronald O Shrum,
EMP: 12 **EST:** 2004
SALES (est): 2.7MM **Privately Held**
WEB: www.southwindaviation.com
SIC: 3728 Aircraft parts & equipment

Oakland Park
Broward County

(G-11772)
A MEANS TO A VEND INC
4700 N Dixie Hwy (33334-3915)
PHONE....................................954 533-8330
Bary J Bass, *President*
EMP: 12 **EST:** 2012
SALES (est): 1.3MM **Privately Held**
WEB: www.ameanstoavend.com
SIC: 2024 Ice cream, bulk

(G-11773)
ACRYLIC IMAGES INC
2011 Nw 29th St (33311-2128)
PHONE....................................954 484-6633
Donald V Potter Jr, *President*
Jackie Potter, *Admin Sec*
EMP: 10 **EST:** 1992
SQ FT: 5,000
SALES (est): 998.1K **Privately Held**
SIC: 3089 Injection molding of plastics

(G-11774)
AIGEAN NETWORKS
3496 Ne 12th Ter (33334-4565)
PHONE....................................754 223-2240
Richard McLaughlin, *Principal*
EMP: 7 **EST:** 2015
SALES (est): 644.5K **Privately Held**
WEB: www.aigean.com
SIC: 3861 Photographic equipment & supplies

(G-11775)
ALL STAR GRAPHIX INC
5055 Ne 12th Ave (33334-4916)
PHONE....................................954 772-1972
Joshua Gorelick, *President*
EMP: 7 **EST:** 2019
SALES (est): 348.8K **Privately Held**
WEB: www.allstargraphix.com
SIC: 2759 Screen printing

(G-11776)
AMS FABRICATIONS INC
2816 Nw 30th Ave (33311-2003)
PHONE....................................813 420-0784
EMP: 10 **EST:** 2017
SALES (est): 428.6K **Privately Held**
WEB: www.amsfabrications.com
SIC: 3444 Sheet metalwork

(G-11777)
APA WIRELESS TECHNOLOGIES INC
4066 Ne 5th Ave (33334-2202)
PHONE....................................954 563-8833
Eliot Fenton, *President*
Eliot D Fenton, *President*
William W Dietz, *Vice Pres*
Stefan Babulal, *Engineer*
Kim London, *Manager*
EMP: 10 **EST:** 1993
SALES (est): 1.8MM **Privately Held**
WEB: www.apawireless.com
SIC: 3679 Oscillators

(G-11778)
APEX MACHINE COMPANY (PA)
3000 Ne 12th Ter (33334-4497)
PHONE....................................954 563-0209
A Robert Coningsby III, *Ch of Bd*
Todd D Coningsby, *President*
Russell W Coningsby, *Corp Secy*
Gregg O Coningsby, *Vice Pres*
Nicole Hamlin, *Purchasing*
◆ **EMP:** 71 **EST:** 1906
SQ FT: 25,000
SALES (est): 27MM **Privately Held**
WEB: www.apexmachine.com
SIC: 3555 Printing trades machinery

(G-11779)
ARCCO INC
Also Called: Sealites
939 Nw 35th Ct (33309-5906)
PHONE....................................954 564-0827
Fax: 954 564-0827
EMP: 9
SALES: 400K **Privately Held**
SIC: 3679 Mfg Electronic Components

(G-11780)
ARTISTIC COLUMNS INC
533 Ne 33rd St (33334-2139)
PHONE....................................954 530-5537
Arthur C Harold, *President*
Joanne B Harold, *Treasurer*
EMP: 6 **EST:** 1970
SALES (est): 839.6K **Privately Held**
WEB: www.artisticcolumnsfl.com
SIC: 3272 3281 Columns, concrete; cut stone & stone products

(G-11781)
ARTISTIC GATE RAILING
5100 Ne 12th Ave (33334-4919)
PHONE....................................954 348-9752
Carlton A Dwyer Sr, *Principal*
EMP: 9 **EST:** 2011
SALES (est): 963.5K **Privately Held**
WEB: www.southfloridarailings.com
SIC: 3441 Fabricated structural metal

(G-11782)
ARTISTIC WELDING INC
802 Ne 40th Ct (33334-3018)
PHONE....................................954 563-3098
Joseph Uskert IV, *President*
EMP: 6 **EST:** 1979
SQ FT: 2,500
SALES (est): 774.8K **Privately Held**
SIC: 3446 Ornamental metalwork

(G-11783)
ATLANTIC CAST PRCAST S FLA LLC
533 Ne 33rd St (33334-2139)
PHONE....................................954 564-6245
James A Rushton,
Anthony M Rushton,
EMP: 25 **EST:** 1965
SALES (est): 3.6MM **Privately Held**
WEB: www.atlanticcoastprecast.com
SIC: 3272 Concrete products, precast

(G-11784)
BARCO SALES & MFG INC
4201 Ne 6th Ave (33334-3107)
PHONE....................................954 563-3922
Richard L Kellogg, *President*
Bob Behrendt, *Corp Secy*
Toni Kellogg, *Vice Pres*
Chris Kellogg, *Prdtn Dir*
EMP: 10 **EST:** 1995
SQ FT: 10,000
SALES (est): 1.5MM **Privately Held**
WEB: www.ebarco.com
SIC: 3081 3086 2653 Packing materials, plastic sheet; plastics foam products; corrugated & solid fiber boxes

(G-11785)
BATHROOM WORLD MANUFACTURING
4160 Ne 6th Ave (33334-2211)
PHONE....................................954 566-0451
Wesley G Masterson, *President*
Michael Masterson, *Vice Pres*
Carol Masterson, *Admin Sec*
▼ **EMP:** 6
SQ FT: 10,000
SALES (est): 710.2K **Privately Held**
WEB: www.bathroomworld.com
SIC: 3842 3431 3281 3088 Whirlpool baths, hydrotherapy equipment; metal sanitary ware; cut stone & stone products; plastics plumbing fixtures

(G-11786)
BLINDS EXPRESS
3000 Ne 16th Ave Apt D105 (33334-5213)
PHONE....................................954 826-6185
James Obrien, *Principal*
EMP: 6 **EST:** 2018
SALES (est): 107.8K **Privately Held**
WEB: www.blindsexpress.com
SIC: 2591 Window blinds

(G-11787)
BRIGHTWATTS INC
1967 Nw 22nd St (33311-2938)
PHONE....................................954 513-3352
Shih Tza Wu, *President*
Tsai Hui Wu, *Admin Sec*
▲ **EMP:** 19 **EST:** 2006
SALES (est): 208.1K **Privately Held**
WEB: www.brightwatts.com
SIC: 3674 Solar cells

(G-11788)
CABINETS BY DESIGN
4815 Ne 12th Ave (33334-4803)
PHONE....................................954 829-2923
EMP: 6 **EST:** 2015
SALES (est): 150K **Privately Held**
WEB: www.cabinetsbydesign.com
SIC: 2434 Wood kitchen cabinets

(G-11789)
CADILLAC GRAPHICS INC
Also Called: Classic Architecutal
4521 Ne 5th Ter (33334-2307)
PHONE....................................954 772-2440
David Braden, *President*
Larry Braden, *Treasurer*
EMP: 9 **EST:** 1959
SQ FT: 50,000
SALES (est): 857.4K **Privately Held**
WEB: www.cadillacgraphics.com
SIC: 3993 Electric signs

(G-11790)
CAREGIVERCOM INC
1871e W Oakland Park Blvd (33311-1517)
PHONE....................................954 893-0550
Gary E Barg, *CEO*
Steven C Barg, *COO*
EMP: 8 **EST:** 2011
SALES (est): 1.3MM **Privately Held**
WEB: www.caregiver.com
SIC: 2836 Culture media

(G-11791)
COASTAL WLDG FABRICATIONS INC
740 Ne 45th St (33334-3250)
PHONE....................................954 938-7933
Scott Thompson, *President*
Mark Thompson, *Vice Pres*
Rj Forsythe, *Prdtn Mgr*
EMP: 14 **EST:** 1988
SQ FT: 35,000
SALES (est): 3.1MM **Privately Held**
WEB: www.coastalweldfab.com
SIC: 7692 Welding repair

(G-11792)
CREATIVE SHIRTS INTL INC
5214 Ne 12th Ave (33334-4921)
PHONE....................................954 351-0909
Joel McCall, *President*
EMP: 14 **EST:** 1990
SQ FT: 7,000
SALES (est): 1.4MM **Privately Held**
WEB: www.creativeshirts.com
SIC: 2395 2262 Embroidery & art needlework; screen printing: manmade fiber & silk broadwoven fabrics

(G-11793)
CUSTOM MARINE JOINERY INC
4032 Ne 5th Ter (33334-2213)
PHONE....................................954 822-6057
Jose Almiron, *Principal*
EMP: 8 **EST:** 2015
SALES (est): 65.4K **Privately Held**
SIC: 2431 Millwork

(G-11794)
CYIPCOM INC
300 E Oakland Park Blvd # 358 (33334-2148)
PHONE....................................954 727-2500

Nolan Fleishman, *CEO*
EMP: 6 **EST:** 1992
SALES (est): 850K **Privately Held**
WEB: www.cyipcom.com
SIC: 3661 3577 5065 5999 Telephones & telephone apparatus; data conversion equipment, media-to-media: computer; telephone equipment; telephone & communication equipment; telephone services; computer related consulting services

(G-11795)
DALEO FUELS INC
Also Called: Oakland Park Exxon
2901 W Oakland Park Blvd (33311-1243)
PHONE..................................954 931-3331
EMP: 6 **EST:** 2014
SALES (est): 281.9K **Privately Held**
SIC: 2869 Fuels

(G-11796)
DEAL TO WIN INC
Also Called: Monogram Online
4050 Ne 9th Ave (33334-3006)
PHONE..................................718 609-1165
Shlomi Matalon, *President*
EMP: 30 **EST:** 2015
SALES (est): 2.4MM **Privately Held**
WEB: www.monogramonline.com
SIC: 3999 Barber & beauty shop equipment

(G-11797)
DENNIS BOATWORKS
2207 Nw 29th St (33311-2145)
PHONE..................................954 260-6855
Denis F Page, *Principal*
EMP: 6 **EST:** 2006
SALES (est): 576.5K **Privately Held**
WEB: www.dennisboatworks.com
SIC: 3732 Boat building & repairing

(G-11798)
DESCO MACHINE COMPANY LLC
3000 Ne 12th Ter (33334-4403)
PHONE..................................954 565-2739
A Robert I Coningsby II,
Gregg O Coningsby,
Russell W Coningsby III,
EMP: 8 **EST:** 2015
SALES (est): 2.7MM
SALES (corp-wide): 27MM **Privately Held**
WEB: www.apexmachine.com
SIC: 3714 Motor vehicle parts & accessories
PA: Apex Machine Company
3000 Ne 12th Ter
Oakland Park FL 33334
954 563-0209

(G-11799)
DOLPH MAP COMPANY INC
1600 E Commercial Blvd (33334-5719)
P.O. Box 11207, Fort Lauderdale (33339-1207)
PHONE..................................954 763-4732
Ryan H Dolph, *President*
Patrick O Loughlin, *Treasurer*
Maggie Davis, *Manager*
EMP: 18 **EST:** 1959
SQ FT: 5,000
SALES (est): 599.5K **Privately Held**
WEB: www.dolphmap.com
SIC: 2741 Miscellaneous publishing

(G-11800)
DON SCHICK LLC
4741 Ne 13th Ave (33334-4811)
PHONE..................................954 491-9042
Don Schick, *Owner*
EMP: 8 **EST:** 2005
SALES (est): 1MM **Privately Held**
SIC: 1446 Blast sand mining

(G-11801)
EASY SIGNS INC
4860 N Dixie Hwy (33334-3929)
PHONE..................................954 673-0118
Isreal Mike Gedj, *President*
Alex Vernaza, *Creative Dir*
▲ **EMP:** 9 **EST:** 2006
SQ FT: 1,700
SALES (est): 507.3K **Privately Held**
WEB: www.easysignsinc.com
SIC: 3993 Signs & advertising specialties

(G-11802)
ECO WOODWORK AND DESIGN INC
3761 Ne 4th Ave (33334-2230)
PHONE..................................954 326-8806
Gustavo Mendez, *President*
EMP: 5 **EST:** 2010
SQ FT: 3,000
SALES (est): 350K **Privately Held**
SIC: 2434 Wood kitchen cabinets

(G-11803)
ESSE SALES INC
2725 Nw 30th Ave (33311-2030)
PHONE..................................954 368-3900
Shalom Edelkopf, *President*
▲ **EMP:** 8 **EST:** 2013
SALES (est): 469.2K **Privately Held**
SIC: 3589 Swimming pool filter & water conditioning systems

(G-11804)
FABSOUTH LLC (HQ)
721 Ne 44th St (33334-3150)
PHONE..................................954 938-5800
Craig Cape, *Project Mgr*
Marshall Cayll, *Project Mgr*
Timothy Burns, *CFO*
Aaron McKee, *Controller*
Kurt Langsenkamp,
EMP: 100 **EST:** 2004
SALES (est): 404.6MM
SALES (corp-wide): 586.3MM **Privately Held**
WEB: www.fabsouthllc.com
SIC: 3441 Fabricated structural metal
PA: Canam Steel Corporation
4010 Clay St
Point Of Rocks MD 21777
301 874-5141

(G-11805)
FELIX REYNOSO
Also Called: R & H Platting
3062 Nw 23rd Ter (33311-1403)
PHONE..................................954 497-2330
Felix Reynoso, *Owner*
EMP: 7 **EST:** 1995
SQ FT: 17,000
SALES (est): 670.7K **Privately Held**
SIC: 2899 Bluing

(G-11806)
FLORIDAS HOTSPOTS PUBLISHING
5090 Ne 12th Ave (33334-4917)
PHONE..................................954 928-1862
Jason Bell, *President*
EMP: 10 **EST:** 1986
SQ FT: 8,000
SALES (est): 1.5MM **Privately Held**
WEB: www.hotspotsmediagroup.com
SIC: 2721 Magazines: publishing only, not printed on site

(G-11807)
GARCIA WOODWORK ENTPS INC
1961 Nw 29th St (33311-2126)
PHONE..................................954 226-3906
EMP: 7 **EST:** 2017
SALES (est): 600.7K **Privately Held**
WEB: www.garciawoodwork.com
SIC: 2431 Millwork

(G-11808)
GIBBONS ADVG DBA GAI EXHIBITS
4050 Ne 6th Ave (33334-2231)
PHONE..................................954 395-2397
EMP: 7 **EST:** 2018
SALES (est): 123.7K **Privately Held**
WEB: www.gaiexhibits.com
SIC: 3993 Signs & advertising specialties

(G-11809)
GRAPHIC BANNER LLP
1330 E Commercial Blvd (33334-5723)
PHONE..................................954 491-9441
Wayne Shim, *Managing Prtnr*
Richard Vilissov, *Managing Prtnr*
EMP: 6 **EST:** 2003
SQ FT: 1,400
SALES (est): 400K **Privately Held**
WEB: www.signshopoaklandparkfl.com
SIC: 3993 Signs & advertising specialties

(G-11810)
H LAMM INDUSTRIES INC
4425 Ne 6th Ter (33334-3253)
PHONE..................................954 491-8929
Helmut Lamm, *President*
Julie Lamm, *Corp Secy*
Jefery Hawk, *Vice Pres*
Robert A Tolleson, *Vice Pres*
Don Curtis, *Sales Mgr*
▲ **EMP:** 120 **EST:** 1974
SQ FT: 7,000
SALES (est): 23.8MM **Privately Held**
WEB: www.hlamm.com
SIC: 3444 Sheet metalwork

(G-11811)
HOOVER CANVAS PRODUCTS CO (PA)
4351 Ne 12th Ter (33334-4724)
PHONE..................................954 764-1711
James E Carroll Jr, *President*
Lucie Fabien, *Corp Secy*
Matt Carroll, *Vice Pres*
Justin Hagelberg, *Prdtn Mgr*
Lucie Spratlin, *Controller*
▼ **EMP:** 35 **EST:** 1960
SALES (est): 9.4MM **Privately Held**
WEB: www.hooverap.com
SIC: 2394 Awnings, fabric: made from purchased materials

(G-11812)
ILLUMINATED LIGHTPANELS INC
2011 Nw 29th St (33311-2128)
PHONE..................................954 484-6633
Donald V Potter Jr, *President*
▲ **EMP:** 8 **EST:** 2012
SALES (est): 524K **Privately Held**
WEB: www.lightpanelsled.com
SIC: 3648 Lighting equipment

(G-11813)
INNOVATIVE POWDER COATING INC
550 Ne 33rd St (33334-2140)
PHONE..................................954 537-2558
Tom Bates, *Owner*
EMP: 9 **EST:** 2009
SALES (est): 646K **Privately Held**
WEB: www.innovativepowdercoating.com
SIC: 3479 Coating of metals & formed products

(G-11814)
INTERNATIONAL JEWELRY DESIGNS
Also Called: Diwi Jewelry
4750 N Dixie Hwy Ste 3 (33334-3948)
PHONE..................................954 577-9099
Larry Goldberg, *President*
Claudia Zambrano, *Purch Agent*
Robert Goldberg, *Treasurer*
Marilyn Pagni, *Accounting Mgr*
Toni Viera, *Office Mgr*
◆ **EMP:** 9 **EST:** 1984
SALES (est): 2MM **Privately Held**
WEB: www.ijdi.net
SIC: 3961 5094 Costume jewelry; jewelry

(G-11815)
INZIRILLO
2051 Nw 29th St (33311-2127)
PHONE..................................954 486-0055
Patrick Robinson, *Owner*
EMP: 5 **EST:** 2007
SALES (est): 534K **Privately Held**
WEB: www.inzirillocompany.com
SIC: 3553 Bandsaws, woodworking

(G-11816)
JAY ROBINSON CABINET SALES INC
683 Ne 42nd St (33334-3140)
PHONE..................................954 298-3009
Jay Robinson, *Principal*
Jay S Robinson, *Principal*
EMP: 7 **EST:** 2008
SALES (est): 140.7K **Privately Held**
SIC: 2434 Wood kitchen cabinets

(G-11817)
KICKIN IT LLC
3560 Lloyd Dr (33309-5013)
PHONE..................................954 648-1405
Rachael Dubois,
EMP: 6 **EST:** 2010
SALES (est): 274.8K **Privately Held**
WEB: www.kitnwelding.com
SIC: 7692 Welding repair

(G-11818)
LAKES METAL FABRICATION INC
2350 Nw 30th Ct (33311-1416)
PHONE..................................954 731-2010
Reddy Thiagarajan, *Principal*
EMP: 7 **EST:** 2007
SQ FT: 3,566
SALES (est): 615.4K **Privately Held**
SIC: 3499 Fabricated metal products

(G-11819)
MAGNAPRINT CORP
1522 E Commercial Blvd (33334-5751)
PHONE..................................954 376-8416
EMP: 7 **EST:** 2019
SALES (est): 327.3K **Privately Held**
SIC: 2752 Commercial printing, offset

(G-11820)
MAJESTIC ULTIMATE DESIGN INC
4431 Ne 6th Ave (33334-2309)
PHONE..................................954 533-8677
Dora Russo, *Office Mgr*
EMP: 10 **EST:** 2010
SALES (est): 755.3K **Privately Held**
WEB: www.majesticultimate.weebly.com
SIC: 3442 Window & door frames

(G-11821)
MAJOR CANVAS PRODUCTS INC
Also Called: Hoover Canvas Products
4351 Ne 12th Ter (33334-4724)
PHONE..................................954 764-1711
James Caroll Jr, *President*
Jim Carroll, *Vice Pres*
Lucy Spratlin, *Treasurer*
EMP: 17 **EST:** 1963
SALES (est): 195.9K **Privately Held**
SIC: 2394 Awnings, fabric: made from purchased materials; canopies, fabric: made from purchased materials

(G-11822)
MARK V PRINTING LLC
140 Ne 32nd Ct (33334-1136)
PHONE..................................954 563-2505
Gustavo Baner,
EMP: 8 **EST:** 1972
SQ FT: 1,600
SALES (est): 1.2MM **Privately Held**
WEB: www.m5p.net
SIC: 2752 Commercial printing, offset

(G-11823)
NE MEDIA GROUP INC
2880 W Oklnd Prk Blvd # 207 (33311-1354)
PHONE..................................954 733-8393
Jack O'Neill, *Principal*
EMP: 8
SALES (corp-wide): 453.3MM **Privately Held**
SIC: 2711 Newspapers, publishing & printing
PA: Ne Media Group Inc.
1 Exchange Pl Ste 201
Boston MA 02109
617 929-2000

(G-11824)
NEW WOODWORKS INC
4140 Ne 5th Ave (33334-2203)
PHONE..................................954 520-4812
Levinson William D, *Principal*
EMP: 6 **EST:** 2014
SALES (est): 121.3K **Privately Held**
SIC: 2431 Millwork

GEOGRAPHIC

(G-11825)
NO 1 BEAUTY SALON FURNITURE
Also Called: No. 1 Bsf
4712 Ne 12th Ave (33334-4802)
P.O. Box 190706, Fort Lauderdale (33319-0706)
PHONE....................................954 981-0403
Hripsime Carocatsanis, *President*
◆ **EMP:** 5
SQ FT: 6,000
SALES (est): 1.5MM **Privately Held**
WEB: www.3dcartstores.com
SIC: 3999 5087 Barber & beauty shop equipment; beauty parlor equipment & supplies

(G-11826)
OPEN MAGNETIC SCANNING LTD
Also Called: Windsor Imaging
4805 N Dixie Hwy (33334-3928)
PHONE....................................954 202-5097
Raymond M Windsor, *Partner*
Scott Windsor, *Mktg Dir*
EMP: 9 **EST:** 2002
SQ FT: 4,000
SALES (est): 1.9MM **Privately Held**
SIC: 3826 Magnetic resonance imaging apparatus

(G-11827)
ORBE INC
2310 Nw 30th Ct (33311-1416)
PHONE....................................954 534-2264
Orlando Ortiz, *Principal*
EMP: 6 **EST:** 2009
SALES (est): 369.6K **Privately Held**
WEB: www.orbeinc.com
SIC: 3429 Marine hardware

(G-11828)
PLASTICS DYNAMICS INC
4301 Ne 11th Ave (33334-3801)
PHONE....................................954 565-7122
▲ **EMP:** 6
SQ FT: 10,000
SALES (est): 500K **Privately Held**
SIC: 3089 Plastics Products, Nec, Nsk

(G-11829)
POMPER SHEET METAL INC
4444 Ne 11th Ave (33334-3883)
PHONE....................................954 492-9717
Keith Pomper, *President*
Kenneth Pomper, *Vice Pres*
EMP: 5 **EST:** 1977
SQ FT: 6,000
SALES (est): 772.3K **Privately Held**
SIC: 3444 Sheet metal specialties, not stamped

(G-11830)
POWER VAC CORPORATION
4811 Ne 12th Ave (33334-4803)
PHONE....................................954 491-0188
Daniel Boeckler, *President*
▲ **EMP:** 5 **EST:** 1995
SQ FT: 1,600
SALES (est): 650.8K **Privately Held**
WEB: www.powervac.com
SIC: 3699 Cleaning equipment, ultrasonic, except medical & dental

(G-11831)
POWLESS DRAPERY SERVICE INC
Also Called: P D Services
4029 Ne 10th Ave (33334-3009)
PHONE....................................954 566-7863
Joseph Materdomini, *President*
Richard Materdomini, *Vice Pres*
▼ **EMP:** 24 **EST:** 1962
SALES (est): 1.9MM **Privately Held**
WEB: www.powless.net
SIC: 2391 Draperies, plastic & textile: from purchased materials

(G-11832)
PRINTMASTER INC
5220 Ne 12th Ave (33334-4921)
PHONE....................................954 771-6104
John W Snyder Jr, *President*
Matthew Snyder, *Vice Pres*
EMP: 6 **EST:** 1971
SQ FT: 4,000
SALES (est): 700K **Privately Held**
WEB: www.printmaster.net
SIC: 2752 Commercial printing, offset

(G-11833)
PROSPECT PLASTICS INC
Also Called: Prospects Plastics
836 Ne 44th St (33334-3131)
PHONE....................................954 564-7282
Lawrence Million Jr, *President*
Robert Jennings, *Vice Pres*
Marci Million, *Vice Pres*
Misty Sammons, *Vice Pres*
EMP: 8 **EST:** 1974
SQ FT: 6,000
SALES (est): 1MM **Privately Held**
WEB: www.prospectplastics.com
SIC: 3089 Injection molding of plastics

(G-11834)
R & R DESIGNER CABINETS INC
3063 Nw 23rd Way (33311-1404)
PHONE....................................954 735-6435
Reynaldo Miranda, *President*
EMP: 6 **EST:** 1976
SALES (est): 637.7K **Privately Held**
WEB: www.randrdesignercabinets.com
SIC: 2434 5712 Wood kitchen cabinets; cabinets, except custom made: kitchen

(G-11835)
RACEWAY TOWING LLC
Also Called: Junk Cars Broward County
480 Ne 35th Ct Unit 4 (33334-2170)
PHONE....................................754 244-9597
Nisan Tamir, *President*
EMP: 7 **EST:** 2016
SALES (est): 741.9K **Privately Held**
SIC: 3644 Raceways

(G-11836)
SANASTAR INC
5079 N Dixie Hwy Ste 303 (33334-4000)
PHONE....................................954 323-2485
Jeffrey S Crevier, *President*
Nate Ellwitz, *Vice Pres*
EMP: 10 **EST:** 2004
SALES (est): 281.9K **Privately Held**
SIC: 3431 Urinals: enameled iron, cast iron or pressed metal

(G-11837)
SEBCO INDUSTRIES INC
Also Called: Fastsigns
211 E Oakland Park Blvd (33334-1155)
PHONE....................................954 566-8500
Sebastian Spada, *President*
EMP: 8 **EST:** 1993
SQ FT: 2,400
SALES (est): 1.2MM **Privately Held**
WEB: www.fastsigns.com
SIC: 3993 Signs & advertising specialties

(G-11838)
SHARP MARKETING LLC
655 W Prospect Rd (33309-3948)
PHONE....................................954 565-2711
Nestor Villalobos,
◆ **EMP:** 9 **EST:** 1989
SALES (est): 1.1MM **Privately Held**
WEB: www.sharppromo.com
SIC: 2395 5199 3951 5137 Embroidery products, except schiffli machine; carnival supplies; pens & mechanical pencils; women's & children's clothing; uniforms

(G-11839)
SHORELINE PRINTING COMPANY
5100 Ne 12th Ave A (33334-4919)
PHONE....................................954 491-0311
Carlos Pasos, *President*
EMP: 6 **EST:** 1985
SQ FT: 5,000
SALES (est): 519.5K **Privately Held**
WEB: www.tfaccounting.com
SIC: 2752 Commercial printing, offset

(G-11840)
SIGNATURE CABINETS
1034 Ne 44th Ct (33334-3824)
PHONE....................................954 563-8584
Brandon Crookes, *Owner*
EMP: 8 **EST:** 2017
SALES (est): 518.7K **Privately Held**
WEB: www.signaturecontractingpm.com
SIC: 2434 Wood kitchen cabinets

(G-11841)
SOTA MANUFACTURING LLC
124 Ne 32nd Ct (33334-1136)
PHONE....................................561 251-3389
Brian Burke, *Branch Mgr*
EMP: 32
SALES (corp-wide): 3MM **Privately Held**
SIC: 3999 Barber & beauty shop equipment
PA: Sota Manufacturing, Inc.
1561 Sw 6th Ave
Boca Raton FL 33486
561 368-8007

(G-11842)
SPYDER GRAPHICS INC
3601 Ne 5th Ave (33334-2214)
PHONE....................................954 561-9725
Michael Gorelick,
EMP: 8 **EST:** 2002
SALES (est): 724.5K **Privately Held**
WEB: www.spydergraphicsinc.com
SIC: 2752 Commercial printing, offset

(G-11843)
STEEL FABRICATORS LLC (DH)
721 Ne 44th St (33334-3150)
PHONE....................................954 772-0440
Sidney Blaauw, *Vice Pres*
Ron Alix, *Project Mgr*
Marshall Cayll, *Project Mgr*
Steven Potts, *Project Mgr*
Joe Olexo, *Foreman/Supr*
◆ **EMP:** 200 **EST:** 1962
SQ FT: 14,000
SALES (est): 50.2MM
SALES (corp-wide): 586.3MM **Privately Held**
WEB: www.sfab.com
SIC: 3441 Fabricated structural metal
HQ: Fabsouth Llc
721 Ne 44th St
Oakland Park FL 33334
954 938-5800

(G-11844)
STEVEN R DURANTE
Also Called: Acrylic Fabrication
1056 Ne 44th Pl (33334-3827)
PHONE....................................954 564-9913
Steven R Durante, *Owner*
EMP: 6 **EST:** 2015
SALES (est): 508.8K **Privately Held**
WEB: www.acrylicparts.com
SIC: 3089 Injection molding of plastics

(G-11845)
SUNGLASS HEAVEN
3161 W Oakland Park Blvd (33311-1229)
PHONE....................................305 302-7285
Mike Israel, *Principal*
EMP: 6 **EST:** 2017
SALES (est): 96.3K **Privately Held**
WEB: www.sunglass-heaven.business.site
SIC: 3851 Glasses, sun or glare

(G-11846)
TAURUS CHUTES INC
3030 Nw 23rd Ave (33311-1428)
P.O. Box 221907, Hollywood (33022-1907)
PHONE....................................954 445-0146
Jose S Calderon, *Principal*
EMP: 7 **EST:** 2017
SALES (est): 2.2MM **Privately Held**
WEB: www.tauruschutesinc.com
SIC: 3444 Sheet metalwork

(G-11847)
TRITECH INDUSTRIES LLC
5204 Ne 12th Ave (33334-4921)
PHONE....................................954 383-3545
Donna Carey, *Engineer*
Dan Hosley, *Natl Sales Mgr*
Don Applegate, *Regl Sales Mgr*
Barry Barrett, *Manager*
Anis Buonpensiere,
EMP: 10 **EST:** 2004
SQ FT: 6,000
SALES (est): 305.1K **Privately Held**
SIC: 3728 Aircraft parts & equipment

(G-11848)
TROPICAL ASSEMBLIES INC
4066 Ne 5th Ave (33334-2202)
PHONE....................................954 396-9999
Randall A Dietz, *President*
Sofia Contoral, *Purchasing*
Fred Manfredonia, *Treasurer*
Fred Manfrdonia, *Marketing Mgr*
Mark Goddard, *Info Tech Mgr*
EMP: 55 **EST:** 1994
SALES (est): 14.1MM **Privately Held**
WEB: www.tropicalassemblies.com
SIC: 3672 Printed circuit boards

(G-11849)
TURBO AEROSPACE CORP
2920 Nw 17th Ter (33311-1502)
PHONE....................................786 218-8990
Ramiro Luna, *President*
EMP: 7 **EST:** 2017
SALES (est): 265.4K **Privately Held**
WEB: www.turboaerospacecorp.com
SIC: 3728 Aircraft parts & equipment

(G-11850)
TURBOUSA INC
1867 Ne 33rd St (33306-1003)
PHONE....................................954 767-8631
Willem Franken, *President*
EMP: 13 **EST:** 1994
SALES (est): 14MM **Privately Held**
WEB: www.mshsturbousa.com
SIC: 3519 Diesel, semi-diesel or duel-fuel engines, including marine

(G-11851)
TWO B PRINTING INC
625 Ne 42nd St (33334-3140)
PHONE....................................954 566-4886
William T Schenden, *Principal*
EMP: 6 **EST:** 1996
SQ FT: 2,000
SALES (est): 1.5MM **Privately Held**
SIC: 2752 7336 Commercial printing, offset; commercial art & graphic design

(G-11852)
ULTIMATE SIGN MFG LLC
4080 Ne 8th Ave (33334-3004)
PHONE....................................954 864-7776
Rodolfo Quispe, *Principal*
EMP: 6 **EST:** 2015
SALES (est): 150.8K **Privately Held**
SIC: 3993 Signs & advertising specialties

(G-11853)
ULTIMATE TOOL INC
5105 Ne 12th Ave (33334-4918)
PHONE....................................954 489-9996
Maxine Moore, *Owner*
EMP: 11 **EST:** 1995
SALES (est): 172.5K **Privately Held**
SIC: 3599 Machine shop, jobbing & repair

(G-11854)
ULTIMATE WDWKG & DESIGN INC
1881 Nw 29th St (33311-2123)
PHONE....................................754 223-4004
Bilecki Robert S, *Principal*
EMP: 6 **EST:** 2013
SALES (est): 105.8K **Privately Held**
SIC: 2431 Millwork

(G-11855)
UNI-BOX INC
Also Called: Unifab Co
1700 Nw 27th St (33311-2106)
P.O. Box 8083, Fort Lauderdale (33310-8083)
PHONE....................................954 733-3550
David S Pearl, *President*
▲ **EMP:** 28 **EST:** 1979
SQ FT: 24,000
SALES (est): 1.7MM **Privately Held**
WEB: www.uni-box.biz
SIC: 2653 Boxes, corrugated: made from purchased materials

(G-11856)
US BULLNOSING
216 Ne 33rd St (33334-1144)
PHONE....................................954 567-0404
Ozgur Avsar, *Principal*
▲ **EMP:** 15 **EST:** 2007

▲ = Import ▼=Export
◆ =Import/Export

SALES (est): 2.7MM **Privately Held**
WEB: www.usbullnosing.com
SIC: 3272 Floor slabs & tiles, precast concrete

(G-11857)
VAN CHARLES INC
4794 Ne 11th Ave (33334-3908)
PHONE..................................954 394-3242
Peter Whittington, *CEO*
Vanessa Whittington, *President*
Paul Skyers, *CFO*
Vincent Brown, *Director*
Marguerite Deal, *Admin Sec*
EMP: 7 **EST:** 2015
SALES (est): 293.5K **Privately Held**
WEB: www.vancharles.com
SIC: 2752 Commercial printing, lithographic

(G-11858)
VERSACOMP INC
4021 Ne 5th Ter (33334-2228)
PHONE..................................954 561-8778
Richard Ulrich, *Principal*
EMP: 11 **EST:** 2005
SALES (est): 351.5K **Privately Held**
SIC: 3544 5571 Special dies & tools; motorcycle dealers

(G-11859)
VERSATILE MANUFACTURING INC (PA)
Also Called: Versatile Water Jet
4021 Ne 5th Ter (33334-2228)
PHONE..................................954 561-8083
Dick Ulrich, *President*
EMP: 20 **EST:** 1971
SQ FT: 18,000
SALES (est): 2.7MM **Privately Held**
SIC: 3444 3544 Sheet metalwork; die sets for metal stamping (presses)

(G-11860)
VERSATILE MANUFACTURING INC
4020 Ne 5th Ter (33334-2213)
PHONE..................................954 561-8083
Dick Ulrich, *President*
EMP: 10
SALES (corp-wide): 2.7MM **Privately Held**
SIC: 3444 3544 Sheet metalwork; die sets for metal stamping (presses)
PA: Versatile Manufacturing, Inc.
4021 Ne 5th Ter
Oakland Park FL 33334
954 561-8083

(G-11861)
WILSON MANIFOLDS INC
4700 Ne 11th Ave (33334-3952)
PHONE..................................954 771-6216
Keith D Wilson, *President*
Keith Wilson, *President*
Frederick Chapman, *Sales Associate*
David Secunda, *Marketing Staff*
EMP: 20 **EST:** 1985
SQ FT: 3,400
SALES (est): 4.5MM **Privately Held**
WEB: www.wilsonmanifolds.com
SIC: 3714 Manifolds, motor vehicle

(G-11862)
WOOD U LLC
4321 Nw 19th Ave (33309-3610)
PHONE..................................954 560-2000
Richard Curry, *Principal*
EMP: 6 **EST:** 2016
SALES (est): 55.2K **Privately Held**
SIC: 2499 Wood products

Ocala
Marion County

(G-11863)
A & F PAVING LLC
4802 Sw 44th Cir (34474-9652)
P.O. Box 357413, Gainesville (32635-7413)
PHONE..................................352 359-2282
◆ **EMP:** 6
SALES (est): 426.7K **Privately Held**
SIC: 2951 Mfg Asphalt Mixtures/Blocks

(G-11864)
ADVANCED MANUFACTURING & ENGRG
Also Called: AME
3220 Ne 24th St (34470-3926)
PHONE..................................352 629-1494
Michael Dyess, *CEO*
EMP: 7 **EST:** 2007
SALES (est): 1MM **Privately Held**
WEB: www.advancedamecorp.com
SIC: 3441 Fabricated structural metal

(G-11865)
ADVTRAVL INC
Also Called: Ocoos
116 S Magnolia Ave Ste 2 (34471-1178)
P.O. Box 6078 (34478-6078)
PHONE..................................978 549-5013
Rahul Razdan, *CEO*
Robert Powers, *Business Mgr*
WEI Song, *Marketing Staff*
EMP: 8 **EST:** 2012
SQ FT: 1,200
SALES (est): 1.1MM **Privately Held**
SIC: 7372 Application computer software

(G-11866)
AGRI-SOURCE INC
4001 Ne 35th St (34479-3128)
P.O. Box 879, Fruitland Park (34731-0879)
PHONE..................................352 351-2700
Ralph T Spencer, *President*
Mark Browne, *Executive*
EMP: 24 **EST:** 1994
SALES (est): 2.8MM **Privately Held**
SIC: 2499 Mulch or sawdust products, wood

(G-11867)
AIM IMMUNOTECH INC (PA)
2117 Sw Highway 484 (34473-7949)
PHONE..................................352 448-7797
Thomas K Equels, *CEO*
William M Mitchell, *Ch of Bd*
Wayne S Springate, *Senior VP*
Ellen Lintal, *CFO*
Carol Smith, *Chief Mktg Ofcr*
EMP: 13 **EST:** 1966
SALES: 163K **Publicly Held**
WEB: www.aimimmuno.com
SIC: 2834 Pharmaceutical preparations

(G-11868)
AKEYMA BRODEN
10 Sw 49th Ave Bldg 100 (34474-1825)
PHONE..................................309 428-5938
EMP: 6 **EST:** 2016
SALES (est): 152.9K **Privately Held**
SIC: 3825 Instruments to measure electricity

(G-11869)
ALL STAR MATERIALS LLC
6760 Nw 27th Avenue Rd (34475-7417)
PHONE..................................352 598-7590
Scott Ritchey,
EMP: 10 **EST:** 2018
SALES (est): 450.7K **Privately Held**
WEB: www.allstarmaterialsfl.com
SIC: 3273 Ready-mixed concrete

(G-11870)
ALUMA TEC ALUMINUN
4412 Ne 2nd St (34470-1491)
PHONE..................................352 732-7362
Rick Mixson, *President*
Emelio Canganelli, *Partner*
EMP: 9 **EST:** 1995
SQ FT: 1,500
SALES (est): 620.3K **Privately Held**
WEB: www.aluma-tec.com
SIC: 3448 5211 Screen enclosures; lumber & other building materials

(G-11871)
AMERICAN PANEL CORPORATION
5800 Se 78th St (34472-3412)
PHONE..................................352 245-7055
Danny E Duncan, *President*
Laura G Duncan, *Corp Secy*
Harmon Lewis, *Exec VP*
R Kevin Graham, *Vice Pres*
Chris Haan, *Vice Pres*
▲ **EMP:** 135
SQ FT: 100,000
SALES (est): 39.7MM **Privately Held**
WEB: www.americanpanel.com
SIC: 3585 Refrigeration equipment, complete

(G-11872)
AMERICAN POLYLACTIDE INDS
3666 Ne 25th St (34470-3143)
PHONE..................................352 653-5963
Adel Arami, *President*
EMP: 9 **EST:** 2000
SALES (est): 124.4K **Privately Held**
WEB: www.americanpolylactide.com
SIC: 3999 Barber & beauty shop equipment

(G-11873)
AMI GRAPHICS INC
Also Called: Quality Banner Company
1302 Sw 42nd Ave (34474-8592)
PHONE..................................352 629-4455
Peter Wensberg, *President*
Isaiah Tamblingson, *Prdtn Mgr*
Claire Trepanier, *Purchasing*
Ernesto Bagasan, *Marketing Mgr*
Stacey Mackinnon, *Manager*
EMP: 45 **Privately Held**
WEB: www.amigraphics.com
SIC: 2399 Banners, made from fabric; pennants; flags, fabric
PA: Ami Graphics, Inc.
223 Drake Hill Rd
Strafford NH 03884

(G-11874)
AMINO CELL INC
5640 Sw 6th Pl Ste 500 (34474-8591)
PHONE..................................352 291-0200
Analissa Benedetti, *President*
Cesar Nieves, *Principal*
EMP: 10 **EST:** 2001
SQ FT: 3,000
SALES (est): 600K **Privately Held**
WEB: www.chondropaw.com
SIC: 2834 2836 2023 Veterinary pharmaceutical preparations; veterinary biological products; dietary supplements, dairy & non-dairy based

(G-11875)
ANTEBELLUM MANUFACTURING LLC
1120 N Magnolia Ave (34475-5106)
PHONE..................................352 877-3888
Chris Boyd, *Mng Member*
Robby Bray,
EMP: 35 **EST:** 2014
SALES (est): 5MM **Privately Held**
WEB: www.antebellumdecorativefences.com
SIC: 3315 Fence gates posts & fittings: steel

(G-11876)
ANTENNAS FOR CMMNCTONS OCALA F
2499 Sw 60th Ave (34474-4324)
PHONE..................................352 687-4121
Ronald S Posner, *President*
Jill Posner, *Admin Sec*
▲ **EMP:** 44 **EST:** 1972
SQ FT: 40,000
SALES (est): 4.7MM **Privately Held**
WEB: www.afcsat.com
SIC: 3661 3663 5731 Telephone & telegraph apparatus; satellites, communications; radio, television & electronic stores

(G-11877)
ANTYLIA SCIENTIFIC
Also Called: Zefon International
5350 Sw 1st Ln (34474-9303)
PHONE..................................352 854-8080
Jeffrey Mantz, *General Mgr*
Luc Belec, *Engineer*
Martin Harper, *Director*
EMP: 95
SALES (corp-wide): 466.5MM **Privately Held**
WEB: www.coleparmer.com
SIC: 3826 Analytical instruments
HQ: Cole-Parmer Instrument Company Llc
625 Bunker Ct
Vernon Hills IL 60061
847 549-7600

(G-11878)
APOLLO RENAL THERAPEUTICS LLC
Also Called: Artemis Plastics
2811 Ne 14th St (34470-4819)
PHONE..................................202 413-0963
Gary Mishki, *President*
EMP: 21 **EST:** 2011
SQ FT: 31,500
SALES (est): 4.9MM **Privately Held**
WEB: www.artemisplastics.com
SIC: 3841 3089 Surgical & medical instruments; injection molded finished plastic products

(G-11879)
ARNOLD INDUSTRIES SOUTH INC
1601 Ne 6th Ave (34470-3642)
PHONE..................................352 867-0190
George Arnold, *President*
Kathie Arnold, *Vice Pres*
EMP: 6 **EST:** 1987
SQ FT: 6,700
SALES (est): 653.6K **Privately Held**
SIC: 7692 3599 Welding repair; machine & other job shop work

(G-11880)
ASHTIN INC
Also Called: Tin Cup Catering
1800 Sw College Rd (34471-1622)
PHONE..................................352 867-1900
Teresa Vadney, *Principal*
Ramy Tarawneh, *Sales Mgr*
EMP: 9 **EST:** 2010
SALES (est): 724.3K **Privately Held**
SIC: 3356 Tin

(G-11881)
ATLANTIC PUBLISHING GROUP INC (PA)
1396 Ne 20th Ave Ste 300 (34470-7737)
PHONE..................................352 622-6220
Bob Montgomery, *CEO*
Douglas R Brown, *Vice Pres*
Sherry Frazier, *Vice Pres*
Jack Bussell, *Consultant*
▲ **EMP:** 63 **EST:** 1981
SQ FT: 40,000
SALES (est): 8.8MM **Privately Held**
WEB: www.atlantic-pub.com
SIC: 2741 Miscellaneous publishing

(G-11882)
AVL SYSTEMS INC
5540 Sw 6th Pl (34474-9372)
PHONE..................................352 854-1170
Philip Hale, *President*
Michelle Weeks, *Opers Staff*
▼ **EMP:** 50 **EST:** 1983
SQ FT: 36,000
SALES (est): 8.3MM **Privately Held**
WEB: www.avlonline.com
SIC: 2522 Panel systems & partitions, office: except wood

(G-11883)
B & E RV SERVICE & REPAIR LLC
6028 Ne 26th Ave (34479-1840)
PHONE..................................352 401-7930
Bobby Sumter, *Principal*
EMP: 7 **EST:** 2006
SALES (est): 540.5K **Privately Held**
WEB: www.bandervservicerepair.com
SIC: 3799 Recreational vehicles

(G-11884)
B & T METALWORKS INC
4630 Ne 35th St (34479-3230)
PHONE..................................352 236-6000
Wade G Tackett, *President*
Jeffrey E Tackett, *Vice Pres*
EMP: 29 **EST:** 1987
SQ FT: 4,800
SALES (est): 4.7MM **Privately Held**
WEB: www.btmetalworksocala.com
SIC: 3444 Sheet metal specialties, not stamped

(G-11885)
BEDROCK RESOURCES LLC
Also Called: Ocala Bedrock
2441 E Fort King St 202 (34471-2558)
PHONE..................................352 369-8600
Darryl C Lanker, *President*
Lee Madsen, *Administration*
EMP: 30 **EST:** 1984
SQ FT: 2,700
SALES (est): 6.1MM **Privately Held**
WEB: www.bedrockresources.com
SIC: 1422 Limestones, ground

(G-11886)
BIG SUN EQUINE PRODUCTS INC (PA)
Also Called: Big Sun Products
2001 Nw 1st Ave (34475-9125)
PHONE..................................352 629-9645
Marilyn Kenworthy, *President*
Steve Kenworthy, *Corp Secy*
Ken Aldrich, *Vice Pres*
▼ **EMP:** 6 **EST:** 1989
SQ FT: 12,500
SALES (est): 1.3MM **Privately Held**
WEB: www.bigsunproducts.com
SIC: 3363 Aluminum die-castings

(G-11887)
BIG SUN PLASTICS INC
2615 Nw Old Blitchton Rd (34475-5256)
PHONE..................................352 671-1844
William Boothby, *President*
EMP: 15 **EST:** 1999
SQ FT: 10,000
SALES (est): 750K **Privately Held**
SIC: 3089 Injection molding of plastics

(G-11888)
BMW & ASSOCIATES INC
Also Called: BMW Window Coverings
4380 Se 53rd Ave (34480-7404)
P.O. Box 291 (34478-0291)
PHONE..................................352 694-2300
Katherine Mullis, *President*
EMP: 7 **EST:** 1992
SQ FT: 5,000
SALES (est): 1MM **Privately Held**
SIC: 2211 5023 2591 Upholstery, tapestry & wall coverings: cotton; window furnishings; window blinds

(G-11889)
BOYD WELDING LLC
802 Nw 27th Ave (34475-5620)
PHONE..................................352 447-2405
David E Boyd III,
EMP: 9 **EST:** 1998
SQ FT: 6,500
SALES (est): 950K **Privately Held**
WEB: www.boydwelding.com
SIC: 3443 7692 Boiler shop products: boilers, smokestacks, steel tanks; welding repair

(G-11890)
BRANCH PROPERTIES INC (PA)
Also Called: Seminole Marico Fertilizer Div
335 Ne Watula Ave (34470-5806)
P.O. Box 940 (34478-0940)
PHONE..................................352 732-4143
Greg Branch, *President*
Greg Allen, *Vice Pres*
Gregory S Allen, *Vice Pres*
Richard De Simone, *Vice Pres*
Richard Simone, *Vice Pres*
EMP: 71
SQ FT: 120,000
SALES (est): 15.8MM **Privately Held**
WEB: www.seminolefeed.com
SIC: 2048 5999 5191 Livestock feeds; feed & farm supply; farm supplies

(G-11891)
BURLAKOFF MANUFACTURING CO
826 Se 9th Ter (34471-3969)
PHONE..................................972 889-2502
Jim Burlakoff, *Vice Pres*
EMP: 5 **EST:** 2018
SALES (est): 424.7K **Privately Held**
SIC: 3629 Electrical industrial apparatus

(G-11892)
C W MACHINING INC
2820 Nw 8th Pl (34475-5660)
PHONE..................................352 732-5824
Paul Cox, *President*
Emily Cox, *Vice Pres*
EMP: 6 **EST:** 1988
SQ FT: 8,000
SALES (est): 682.3K **Privately Held**
SIC: 3599 Machine shop, jobbing & repair

(G-11893)
CAPRIS FURNITURE INDS INC
1401 Nw 27th Ave (34475-4723)
PHONE..................................352 629-8889
Pedro R Interian, *President*
C A Stubbs, *Vice Pres*
Donald R Beaudet, *CFO*
William Ingram, *Director*
◆ **EMP:** 140 **EST:** 1986
SQ FT: 180,000
SALES (est): 22.9MM **Privately Held**
WEB: www.beachcraftrattan.com
SIC: 2512 2519 Wood upholstered chairs & couches; rattan furniture: padded or plain; wicker furniture: padded or plain

(G-11894)
CAR WASH SOLUTIONS FLORIDA INC
3310 Sw 7th St Unit 2 (34474-1911)
P.O. Box 15285, Sarasota (34277-1285)
PHONE..................................941 323-8817
John Hamill, *CEO*
EMP: 32 **EST:** 2015
SALES (est): 862.6K **Privately Held**
SIC: 3589 Car washing machinery

(G-11895)
CARDINAL LG COMPANY
1300 Sw 44th Ave (34474-8747)
PHONE..................................352 237-4410
Kyle Petersen, *Plant Mgr*
Yvonne Roach, *Human Resources*
Ted Paget, *Sales Mgr*
Steve Brown, *Info Tech Mgr*
Ralph Emminger, *Director*
EMP: 60
SALES (corp-wide): 1B **Privately Held**
WEB: www.cardinalcorp.com
SIC: 3211 Laminated glass
HQ: Cardinal Lg Company
250 Griffin St E
Amery WI 54001

(G-11896)
CARPORT SOLUTION LLC
8975 Sw Highway 200 (34481-7704)
PHONE..................................352 789-1149
William C Simmons, *Mng Member*
Javier Urdaneta, *Mng Member*
EMP: 11 **EST:** 2010
SQ FT: 700
SALES (est): 765.4K **Privately Held**
WEB: www.carportsolution.com
SIC: 3448 1541 Prefabricated metal buildings; steel building construction; truck & automobile assembly plant construction

(G-11897)
CEMEX CEMENT INC
619 Sw 17th Loop (34471-3610)
PHONE..................................352 867-5794
EMP: 214 **Privately Held**
WEB: www.cemexusa.com
SIC: 3273 Ready-mixed concrete
HQ: Cemex Cement, Inc.
10100 Katy Fwy Ste 300
Houston TX 77043
713 650-6200

(G-11898)
CENTRAL FLA KIT BATH SRFCES IN
2800 Se 62nd St (34480-8038)
P.O. Box 137, Summerfield (34492-0137)
PHONE..................................352 307-2333
Decnis Villeda, *President*
EMP: 18 **EST:** 2007
SQ FT: 5,280
SALES (est): 853.1K **Privately Held**
WEB: www.centralfloridakitchenbath.com
SIC: 3088 2541 Shower stalls, fiberglass & plastic; wood partitions & fixtures

(G-11899)
CENTRAL FLA STL BLDG & SUP LLC
4750 S Pine Ave (34480-9104)
PHONE..................................352 266-6795
William White, *Mng Member*
Mike Martin,
Bruce Pritchet,
EMP: 7 **EST:** 2016
SALES (est): 1.5MM **Privately Held**
WEB: www.cfsteelbuildings.com
SIC: 3441 5051 Building components, structural steel; steel

(G-11900)
CFU PLATING
7575 S Us Highway 441 # 118
(34480-8079)
PHONE..................................386 795-5198
David Hellmuth, *Principal*
EMP: 7 **EST:** 2010
SALES (est): 212.8K **Privately Held**
SIC: 3471 Plating of metals or formed products

(G-11901)
CHARIOT EAGLE INC (PA)
931 Nw 37th Ave (34475-5683)
PHONE..................................623 936-7545
Robert Holliday, *President*
Elaine Morris, *Human Res Dir*
Dale Frisbie, *Director*
▼ **EMP:** 104 **EST:** 1984
SQ FT: 31,000
SALES (est): 13.7MM **Privately Held**
WEB: www.charioteagle.com
SIC: 3792 2452 2451 House trailers, except as permanent dwellings; prefabricated wood buildings; mobile homes

(G-11902)
CHOICE CABINETS LLC
3826 Nw Gainesville Rd (34475-3478)
PHONE..................................352 629-1556
Kevin L Barlow, *Manager*
Kevin Barlow, *Manager*
EMP: 6 **EST:** 2015
SALES (est): 273K **Privately Held**
WEB: www.choicecabinetsofocala.com
SIC: 2434 Wood kitchen cabinets

(G-11903)
CITY OF OCALA
Also Called: Ocala Engineering-Traffic Div
1307 Nw 4th Ave (34475-5142)
PHONE..................................352 622-6803
Wayne Little, *Director*
EMP: 24
SQ FT: 9,755
SALES (corp-wide): 91.8MM **Privately Held**
WEB: www.ocalafl.org
SIC: 3669 9111 Traffic signals, electric; mayors' offices
PA: City Of Ocala
110 Se Watula Ave
Ocala FL 34471
352 401-3914

(G-11904)
CLARKWESTERN DIETRICH BUILDING
331 Sw 57th Ave (34474-9346)
PHONE..................................800 693-3018
EMP: 52
SALES (corp-wide): 20.2B **Privately Held**
SIC: 3441 Structural Metal Fabrication
HQ: Clarkwestern Dietrich Building Systems Llc
9050 Centre Pointe Dr
West Chester OH 45069

(G-11905)
CLOSETMAID LLC
720 Sw 17th Pl (34471-1233)
PHONE..................................352 351-6100
Dale Debruycker, *Vice Pres*
Mike Williams, *Purch Agent*
Michle Mosher, *Personnel Exec*
Rob Clements, *Manager*
EMP: 29
SQ FT: 100,000
SALES (corp-wide): 2.4B **Publicly Held**
WEB: www.closetmaid.com
SIC: 3496 Shelving, made from purchased wire
HQ: Closetmaid Llc
13485 Veterans Way # 200
Orlando FL 32827
352 401-6000

(G-11906)
COMPACT CONTRACT INC
1822 Sw 34th Ct (34474-2834)
PHONE..................................352 817-8058
Ronnie Jones, *Owner*
EMP: 6 **EST:** 2008
SALES (est): 506K **Privately Held**
SIC: 1389 Construction, repair & dismantling services

(G-11907)
CONTEMPORARY INTERIORS INC
2626 Nw 35th St (34475-3342)
PHONE..................................352 620-8686
David Silk, *President*
Ryan Anderson, *Vice Pres*
EMP: 21 **EST:** 1989
SALES (est): 2.8MM **Privately Held**
WEB: www.contemporaryinteriors.com
SIC: 2512 2521 5712 5021 Upholstered household furniture; wood office furniture; furniture stores; office furniture; furniture; office furniture; public building & related furniture; wood household furniture

(G-11908)
CORDELL INTERNATIONAL INC
1056 Ne 16th St (34470-4204)
PHONE..................................352 694-1800
Kyle P Cordell, *President*
Kyle Cordell, *Principal*
Brad Cordell, *Vice Pres*
▲ **EMP:** 10 **EST:** 2007
SQ FT: 33,000
SALES (est): 2MM **Privately Held**
WEB: www.cordellinternational.com
SIC: 3442 Metal doors, sash & trim

(G-11909)
CORKSCREW WINERY
205 Se Sanchez Ave (34471-2231)
PHONE..................................352 751-1787
Joseph P Carvalho, *Principal*
Kelli Carvalho, *Co-Owner*
EMP: 7 **EST:** 2012
SALES (est): 125.3K **Privately Held**
WEB: www.thecorkscrewwinery.com
SIC: 2084 Wines

(G-11910)
CRANDON ENTERPRISES INC
Also Called: Crandon Electric Co
255 Sw 96th Ln (34476-7615)
PHONE..................................352 873-8400
Gary Crandon, *President*
Greg Artliaff, *Vice Pres*
Paulet Crandon, *Admin Sec*
EMP: 6 **EST:** 1965
SALES (est): 787.3K **Privately Held**
SIC: 3699 1731 Electrical welding equipment; banking machine installation & service
PA: Crandon Enterprises Inc
1731 Se 83rd St
Ocala FL

(G-11911)
CREATIVE ENERGIES INC
1805 Ne 19th Ave (34470-4775)
PHONE..................................352 351-9448
Roxanne Free, *Principal*
EMP: 8 **EST:** 2010
SALES (est): 490K **Privately Held**
WEB: www.lightdomecanopies.com
SIC: 2394 Canvas & related products

(G-11912)
CUMMINS INC
321 Sw 52nd Ave (34474-9365)
PHONE..................................352 861-1122
Richard Boisvert, *General Mgr*
Jess Williams, *Branch Mgr*
Richard Stewart, *Supervisor*
Laura Espinosa, *Planning*
EMP: 7

SALES (corp-wide): 19.8B **Publicly Held**
WEB: www.cummins.com
SIC: **3714** Motor vehicle parts & accessories
PA: Cummins Inc.
500 Jackson St
Columbus IN 47201
812 377-5000

(G-11913)
CURLY GIRLZ CREATIONS
10410 Sw 98th Ter (34481-9059)
PHONE..................................386 960-3536
Nickie Olivier, *Principal*
Darrell Olivier, *Vice Pres*
EMP: 6 **EST**: 2010
SALES (est): 207.3K **Privately Held**
SIC: **3961** Costume jewelry

(G-11914)
CUSTOM WINDOW SYSTEMS INC
1900 Sw 44th Ave (34474-8743)
PHONE..................................352 368-6922
Greg Schorr, *CEO*
Matthew Shaw, *CFO*
◆ **EMP**: 600 **EST**: 1986
SQ FT: 200,000
SALES (est): 81.4MM
SALES (corp-wide): 2B **Privately Held**
WEB: www.cws.cc
SIC: **3442** Window & door frames
PA: Pella Corporation
102 Main St
Pella IA 50219
641 621-1000

(G-11915)
CWS HOLDING COMPANY LLC
Also Called: Custom Window Systems
1900 Sw 44th Ave (34474-8743)
PHONE..................................352 368-6922
Greg Schorr, *CEO*
EMP: 51 **EST**: 2014
SALES (est): 15.6MM **Privately Held**
WEB: www.cws.cc
SIC: **2431** 3211 Window frames, wood; window glass, clear & colored
PA: Nautic Partners, Llc
100 Westminster St # 1220
Providence RI 02903

(G-11916)
D & S PALLET RECYCLE CENTER
2640 Nw 35th St (34475-3342)
PHONE..................................352 351-0070
Steve Wojtaszak, *Owner*
EMP: 8 **EST**: 1982
SQ FT: 5,000
SALES (est): 936.7K **Privately Held**
SIC: **2448** Pallets, wood

(G-11917)
DAVID R NASSIVERA INC
2250 Ne 70th St (34479-1414)
PHONE..................................352 351-1176
David Nassivera, *President*
Susan Nassivera, *Admin Sec*
EMP: 24 **EST**: 1974
SQ FT: 10,500
SALES (est): 1.3MM **Privately Held**
SIC: **2426** Furniture stock & parts, hardwood

(G-11918)
DELTA LABORATORIES INC (PA)
3710 W Highway 326 (34475-2320)
P.O. Box 2258 (34478-2258)
PHONE..................................305 887-4393
Richard E Pesola, *President*
Charles J Pesola, *Vice Pres*
Ray Craig, *Plant Mgr*
◆ **EMP**: 30 **EST**: 1964
SQ FT: 4,500
SALES (est): 8.8MM **Privately Held**
SIC: **2851** Lacquer: bases, dopes, thinner; varnishes; stains: varnish, oil or wax; enamels

(G-11919)
DELZOTTO PRODUCTS FLORIDA INC
4575 W Highway 40 (34482-4042)
PHONE..................................352 351-3834
Laura Del Zotto, *President*
EMP: 100
SQ FT: 4,000
SALES (est): 14.3MM **Privately Held**
WEB: www.delzottoproducts.com
SIC: **3272** Concrete products, precast

(G-11920)
DIXIE LIME ANDSTONE CO
2441 E Fort King St (34471-2558)
PHONE..................................352 512-0180
Darrel Lanker, *President*
William Moore, *Sales Staff*
EMP: 12 **EST**: 2013
SALES (est): 405.9K **Privately Held**
WEB: www.dixielime.com
SIC: **1422** Crushed & broken limestone

(G-11921)
DIXIE METAL PRODUCTS INC (PA)
Also Called: D M P
442 Sw 54th Ct (34474-1893)
PHONE..................................352 873-2554
J Philip Schnorr, *Ch of Bd*
Dave Carroll, *COO*
John Schnorr, *COO*
Keith Holman, *Vice Pres*
Mark Hyzny, *Vice Pres*
EMP: 95 **EST**: 1968
SQ FT: 75,000
SALES (est): 12MM **Privately Held**
WEB: www.dixiemetals.com
SIC: **3441** Fabricated structural metal

(G-11922)
DIXIE WORKSHOP INC
2350 Nw 42nd St (34475-3121)
PHONE..................................352 629-4699
Michael Miller, *President*
EMP: 9 **EST**: 1994
SQ FT: 4,000
SALES (est): 543.6K **Privately Held**
WEB: www.dixieworkshop.net
SIC: **2499** 2511 2434 Decorative wood & woodwork; wood household furniture; wood kitchen cabinets

(G-11923)
DONARRA EXTRUSIONS LLC
Also Called: Bluegator Ground Protection
1811 Sw 42nd Ave (34474-9814)
P.O. Box 770599 (34477-0599)
PHONE..................................352 369-5552
John K Donohue, *Mng Member*
Kevin Donahue,
Maryann G Donohue,
▲ **EMP**: 12 **EST**: 2010
SALES (est): 2.6MM **Privately Held**
WEB: www.donarraextrusions.com
SIC: **3089** Injection molding of plastics; plastic processing

(G-11924)
DOUBLE R MFG OCALA INC
5529 Sw 1st Ln (34474-9308)
PHONE..................................352 873-1441
Richard Moore, *President*
Thomas Moore, *President*
Julia Moore, *Treasurer*
David Anderson, *Consultant*
▲ **EMP**: 19 **EST**: 1992
SQ FT: 7,800
SALES (est): 3.8MM **Privately Held**
WEB: www.doublermfg.com
SIC: **7692** Welding repair

(G-11925)
DR PEPPER/SEVEN UP INC
3337 Sw 7th St (34474-1956)
PHONE..................................352 732-9777
John Scullin, *Branch Mgr*
EMP: 19
SQ FT: 2,400 **Publicly Held**
WEB: www.drpepper.com
SIC: **2086** Soft drinks: packaged in cans, bottles, etc.
HQ: Dr Pepper/Seven Up, Inc.
6425 Hall Of Fame Ln
Frisco TX 75034
972 673-7000

(G-11926)
DRAGGIN TRAILERS INC
3100 Se 50th Pl (34480-5795)
PHONE..................................352 351-8790
Dorothy A Griffin, *President*
Dorothy Driffin, *President*
Kenneth Griffin Jr III, *Vice Pres*
EMP: 6 **EST**: 1997
SQ FT: 1,200
SALES (est): 500K **Privately Held**
WEB: www.draggintrailers.com
SIC: **3715** Truck trailers

(G-11927)
DSM LAKE CITY LLC
8100 Sw 54th Ct (34476-3788)
PHONE..................................352 861-5843
Chandrakant Doshi, *Branch Mgr*
EMP: 6
SALES (corp-wide): 809.8K **Privately Held**
WEB: www.bestwestern.com
SIC: **2899** Salt
PA: Lake Dsm City Llc
3598 W Us Highway 90
Lake City FL 32055
386 752-3801

(G-11928)
E-ONE INC (HQ)
Also Called: E-One Parts Central
1601 Sw 37th Ave (34474-2829)
PHONE..................................352 237-1122
Dan Peters, *President*
Kent Tyler, *President*
James Meyer, *COO*
Dino Cusumano, *Vice Pres*
Davis Neal, *Vice Pres*
◆ **EMP**: 489 **EST**: 1967
SQ FT: 391,750
SALES (est): 184.5MM **Publicly Held**
WEB: www.e-one.com
SIC: **3711** Fire department vehicles (motor vehicles), assembly of

(G-11929)
E-ONE INC
1701 Sw 37th Ave (34474-2827)
P.O. Box 2710 (34478-2710)
PHONE..................................352 237-1122
Frank Carmody, *President*
Steve Savage, *Opers Mgr*
Jason Lemstrom, *Production*
Lemorne Piner, *Production*
Robert Weber, *Production*
EMP: 89 **Publicly Held**
WEB: www.e-one.com
SIC: **3711** Fire department vehicles (motor vehicles), assembly of
HQ: E-One, Inc.
1601 Sw 37th Ave
Ocala FL 34474
352 237-1122

(G-11930)
EHS FLA
3159 Se 6th St (34471-2875)
PHONE..................................352 438-0005
Richard Eyman, *Executive*
EMP: 6 **EST**: 2010
SALES (est): 93.5K **Privately Held**
SIC: **3442** Molding, trim & stripping

(G-11931)
ELSTER AMCO WATER LLC
Also Called: Elster Amco Wtr Mtring Systems
10 Sw 49th Ave Ste 101 (34474-1825)
PHONE..................................352 369-6500
Alex Watson, *President*
◆ **EMP**: 19 **EST**: 1962
SQ FT: 90,000
SALES (est): 20MM
SALES (corp-wide): 32.6B **Publicly Held**
WEB: www.smartenergy.honeywell.com
SIC: **3824** Water meters
PA: Honeywell International Inc.
300 S Tryon St
Charlotte NC 28202
704 627-6200

(G-11932)
ENDEAVOR PUBLICATIONS INC
Also Called: Canine Chronicle, The
4727 Nw 80th Ave (34482-2031)
PHONE..................................352 369-1104
Thomas Grabe, *President*
Amy Grabe, *Admin Sec*
EMP: 7 **EST**: 1997
SQ FT: 1,500
SALES (est): 1.5MM **Privately Held**
SIC: **2721** Magazines: publishing & printing

(G-11933)
ESD WASTE2WATER INC
495 Oak Rd (34472-3005)
PHONE..................................800 277-3279
Jon E Houchens, *President*
Kevin Hawkins, *General Mgr*
Cody Lasley, *Regional Mgr*
Alan Pierce, *Vice Pres*
Barb Schroeder, *Vice Pres*
▼ **EMP**: 85 **EST**: 1993
SQ FT: 170,000
SALES: 115.3MM **Privately Held**
WEB: www.waste2water.com
SIC: **3589** Water treatment equipment, industrial

(G-11934)
EVORA ENTERPRISES INC
Also Called: Tarps and Beyond
2608 Nw 6th St (34475-5794)
P.O. Box 520397, Miami (33152-0397)
PHONE..................................305 261-4522
Brenda Evora, *President*
▲ **EMP**: 10 **EST**: 1974
SQ FT: 8,000
SALES (est): 926K **Privately Held**
WEB: www.evora.com
SIC: **2394** Canvas covers & drop cloths

(G-11935)
EXPRESS AUTO CARRIERS LLC
5551 Se 44th Cir (34480-4929)
PHONE..................................352 541-0040
Miguel A Morales,
EMP: 6 **EST**: 2012
SALES (est): 250.4K **Privately Held**
WEB: www.expressautocarriers.com
SIC: **3713** Car carrier bodies

(G-11936)
EXPRESS BRAKE INTERNATIONAL
4376 Ne 35th St (34479-3236)
PHONE..................................352 304-6263
Drew Larsen, *President*
Branchard Tucker, *CFO*
Pat McLaughlin, *Director*
EMP: 10 **EST**: 1994
SALES (est): 920K **Privately Held**
WEB: www.extremebrake.com
SIC: **3714** Motor vehicle brake systems & parts

(G-11937)
EXTREME BRAKE INTEGRATION INC
5817 Nw 44th Ave (34482-7891)
P.O. Box 216 (34478-0216)
PHONE..................................352 342-9596
Kevin Reed, *President*
EMP: 8 **EST**: 2013
SALES (est): 1.4MM **Privately Held**
WEB: www.extremebrake.com
SIC: **3714** Motor vehicle brake systems & parts

(G-11938)
EXTREME MANUFACTURING LLC
1909 Ne 25th Ave (34470-4848)
PHONE..................................888 844-7734
Valerie Reed, *Mng Member*
Kevin Reed,
EMP: 14 **EST**: 2018
SALES (est): 2.3MM **Privately Held**
WEB: www.extremebrake.com
SIC: **3714** Motor vehicle parts & accessories

(G-11939)
F & J SPECIALTY PRODUCTS INC
404 Cypress Rd (34472-3106)
P.O. Box 2888 (34478-2888)
PHONE..................................352 680-1177
Frank Gavila, *President*
Paul Cheries, *Vice Pres*
Tonda King, *Marketing Staff*
Lisa Brault, *Manager*
Peterson Dean, *Administration*
EMP: 15 **EST**: 1979
SQ FT: 17,000

SALES (est): 3.7MM
SALES (corp-wide): 3.9MM **Privately Held**
WEB: www.fjspecialty.com
SIC: 3826 3822 3829 Environmental testing equipment; auto controls regulating residntl & coml environmt & applncs; measuring & controlling devices
PA: Ga-Ma & Associates, Inc.
404 Cypress Rd
Ocala FL 34472
352 687-8840

(G-11940)
FIDELITY MANUFACTURING LLC
1900 Ne 25th Ave (34470-4849)
PHONE..................................352 414-4700
Loretta Jackson, *Human Res Mgr*
Nathaniel Kitchens, *Sales Engr*
Daniel Stromwall, *Sales Engr*
Bradford Dinkins, *Mng Member*
Nick Davis, *Manager*
EMP: 38 **EST:** 2014
SQ FT: 70,000
SALES (est): 6.6MM **Privately Held**
WEB: www.fidelitymfg.com
SIC: 3795 7538 Tanks & tank components; general automotive repair shops

(G-11941)
FINGER LAKES CUSTOM MFG LLC
1211 Ne 17th Rd (34470-4611)
PHONE..................................315 283-4849
Neal P Purdy, *Principal*
EMP: 7 **EST:** 2019
SALES (est): 328.3K **Privately Held**
SIC: 3999 Manufacturing industries

(G-11942)
FINYL PRODUCTS INC
8657 Nw 80th Ave (34482-1105)
P.O. Box 6241 (34478-6241)
PHONE..................................352 351-4033
Ted L Hagemeyer, *President*
Marilyn Kenworthy, *Owner*
EMP: 8 **EST:** 1997
SALES (est): 118.9K **Privately Held**
WEB: www.finylsales.com
SIC: 2851 5211 5162 Vinyl coatings, strippable; lumber & other building materials; plastics materials & basic shapes

(G-11943)
FIRST IMPRESSIONS PRINTING
1847 Sw 27th Ave (34471-2037)
PHONE..................................352 237-6141
Mike Spontelli, *President*
Dennis Dimatteo, *Vice Pres*
Daniel Opitz, *Vice Pres*
Gail Haile, *Sales Staff*
Terry Steele, *Sales Staff*
EMP: 17 **EST:** 1965
SQ FT: 10,000
SALES (est): 1MM **Privately Held**
WEB: www.fipprinting.com
SIC: 2752 Commercial printing, offset

(G-11944)
FLAIRE CORPORATION
Also Called: Kemp
4647 Sw 40th Ave (34474-5799)
PHONE..................................352 237-1220
James Doherty, *President*
James Daugherty, *President*
Richard Porri, *Vice Pres*
Keith Miller, *CFO*
Cor Stokenborg, *Sales Staff*
▲ **EMP:** 118 **EST:** 1986
SQ FT: 120,000
SALES (est): 10.5MM
SALES (corp-wide): 1.3B **Publicly Held**
SIC: 3564 3594 Blowers & fans; fluid power pumps & motors
HQ: Spx Flow Technology Usa, Inc.
4647 Se 40th Ave
Ocala FL 34474

(G-11945)
FLORIDA EQINE PUBLICATIONS INC
Also Called: Floridahorse, The
801 Sw 60th Ave (34474-8593)
PHONE..................................352 732-8686
J Michael, *General Mgr*
J Michael O'Farrell Jr, *Chairman*
Robert A Cromartie, *Vice Pres*
Richard E Hancock, *Treasurer*
K Behrens, *Manager*
EMP: 16 **EST:** 1957
SQ FT: 3,139
SALES (est): 530.9K **Privately Held**
WEB: www.wiretowire.net
SIC: 2721 0752 Magazines: publishing only, not printed on site; animal specialty services

(G-11946)
FLORIDA GENERAL TRADING INC (PA)
6195 N Us Highway 441 (34475-1519)
P.O. Box 89189, Tampa (33689-0403)
PHONE..................................813 391-2149
Aosama Alatabi, *Principal*
▼ **EMP:** 74 **EST:** 2005
SALES (est): 1MM **Privately Held**
WEB: www.floridageneraltrading.com
SIC: 3531 Construction machinery

(G-11947)
FLORIDA ROCK INDUSTRIES
Also Called: Vulcan Materials
3599 Sw 74th Ave (34474-6452)
PHONE..................................352 854-6468
Kevin Bradbury, *Manager*
EMP: 6 **Publicly Held**
WEB: www.flarock.com
SIC: 3273 Ready-mixed concrete
HQ: Florida Rock Industries
4707 Gordon St
Jacksonville FL 32216
904 355-1781

(G-11948)
FLUID ROUTING SOLUTIONS LLC
3100 Se Maricamp Rd (34471-6250)
PHONE..................................352 732-0222
Gary Franks, *Principal*
Laura Cole, *Engineer*
Tony Stamour, *Engineer*
Brent Scott, *Supervisor*
EMP: 304
SALES (corp-wide): 1.3B **Publicly Held**
WEB: www.pkoh.com
SIC: 3052 3714 Rubber hose; motor vehicle parts & accessories
HQ: Fluid Routing Solutions, Llc
30000 Stephenson Hwy B
Madison Heights MI 48071
248 228-8900

(G-11949)
FLYRITE BANNER MAKERS INC
3459 Sw 74th Ave Ste 100 (34474-7235)
PHONE..................................352 873-7501
Fred Nonnemacher, *CEO*
EMP: 10 **EST:** 1983
SQ FT: 5,500
SALES (est): 1.5MM **Privately Held**
WEB: www.flyritebanners.com
SIC: 2399 Banners, made from fabric; banners, pennants & flags

(G-11950)
FUEL TANKS TO GO LLC
13 Cypress Road Pass (34472-3535)
PHONE..................................865 604-4726
Mark Green, *General Mgr*
Tim Shively, *Production*
EMP: 6 **EST:** 2013
SALES (est): 480K **Privately Held**
WEB: www.fueltankstogo.com
SIC: 3443 Fuel tanks (oil, gas, etc.): metal plate

(G-11951)
FULLER AMUSEMENTS
2250 Se 52nd St (34480-7554)
PHONE..................................352 629-2792
Kurt Folson, *President*
EMP: 5 **EST:** 1960
SQ FT: 7,800
SALES (est): 820K **Privately Held**
WEB: www.fulleramusement.com
SIC: 3999 Coin-operated amusement machines

(G-11952)
FUQUA SAWMILL INC
1751 Nw 33rd Ave (34475-4617)
PHONE..................................352 236-3456
Larry Fuqua, *President*
John Fuqua, *Admin Sec*
EMP: 5 **EST:** 1950
SQ FT: 1,000
SALES (est): 350K **Privately Held**
WEB: www.warfauction.com
SIC: 2421 Custom sawmill

(G-11953)
GA-MA & ASSOCIATES INC (PA)
404 Cypress Rd (34472-3106)
P.O. Box 2918 (34478-2918)
PHONE..................................352 687-8840
Frank M Gavila, *President*
Paul Cheries, *Sales Dir*
Sharon Rodriguez, *Sales Mgr*
Carl Rahbein, *Info Tech Mgr*
David Albury, *Director*
EMP: 7 **EST:** 1975
SQ FT: 8,000
SALES (est): 3.9MM **Privately Held**
WEB: www.ga-maassociates.com
SIC: 3069 3821 Medical & laboratory rubber sundries & related products; laboratory apparatus & furniture

(G-11954)
GATOR BLINDS & SHUTTERS
3035 Se Maricmp Rd104 234 (34471)
PHONE..................................352 375-1995
EMP: 6 **EST:** 2019
SALES (est): 223.5K **Privately Held**
WEB: www.gatorblindsandshutters.com
SIC: 2591 Window blinds

(G-11955)
GATOR CUSTOM BLINDS
1871 Ne 23rd St (34470-4428)
PHONE..................................352 867-0448
Larry S Feenstra, *Owner*
EMP: 8 **EST:** 2010
SALES (est): 139.2K **Privately Held**
WEB: www.gatorblindsandshutters.com
SIC: 2591 Window blinds

(G-11956)
GLOBAL BAMBOO TECHNOLOGIES INC ✪
Also Called: Bam Core
310 Cypress Rd (34472-3102)
PHONE..................................707 730-0288
Hal Hinkle, *CEO*
Zack Zimmerman, *Risk Mgmt Dir*
EMP: 26 **EST:** 2020
SALES (est): 1.3MM **Privately Held**
SIC: 2448 Wood pallets & skids

(G-11957)
GML INDUSTRIES LLC
5542 Sw 6th Pl (34474-9317)
PHONE..................................352 671-7619
Del Lukens, *Managing Prtnr*
Del McGighan Lukens, *Mng Member*
Melinda Freeman,
Gerri McGighan-Lukens,
EMP: 40 **EST:** 2011
SALES (est): 2.8MM **Privately Held**
WEB: www.gmlindustries.com
SIC: 3694 Engine electrical equipment

(G-11958)
GOOD TIME OUTDOORS INC
Also Called: Gto Performance Air Boats
4600 W Highway 326 (34482-1257)
PHONE..................................352 401-9070
Norman P Clifton, *President*
Brad McCullough, *Vice Pres*
▼ **EMP:** 20 **EST:** 1992
SALES (est): 3.5MM **Privately Held**
WEB: www.core15rifles.com
SIC: 3732 5551 Boat building & repairing; boat dealers

(G-11959)
GOOD TIME PRINTING INC
1522 E Silver Sprng Blvd (34470-6818)
PHONE..................................352 629-8838
Butch White, *President*
Marie Green, *Vice Pres*
Robert White, *Admin Sec*
EMP: 7 **EST:** 1984
SQ FT: 3,400
SALES (est): 776.7K **Privately Held**
WEB: www.goodtimeprinting.com
SIC: 2752 Commercial printing, offset

(G-11960)
GREAT NORTHERN REHAB PC (PA)
Also Called: Gnr Orthopedic Designs
2620 Se Merrycamp Rd (34471)
PHONE..................................352 732-8868
Richard W Shutes, *President*
Raymond Brown, *Corp Secy*
EMP: 9 **EST:** 1970
SQ FT: 1,000
SALES (est): 1.9MM **Privately Held**
WEB: www.greatnorthernrehab.com
SIC: 3842 8049 5047 Orthopedic appliances; physical therapist; medical & hospital equipment

(G-11961)
GREAT NORTHERN REHAB PC
2620 Se Maricamp Rd (34471-5582)
PHONE..................................352 732-8868
Rick Shutes, *Branch Mgr*
EMP: 10
SALES (corp-wide): 1.9MM **Privately Held**
WEB: www.greatnorthernrehab.com
SIC: 3842 8049 5047 Orthopedic appliances; physical therapist; medical & hospital equipment
PA: Great Northern Rehab Pc
2620 Se Merrycamp Rd
Ocala FL 34471
352 732-8868

(G-11962)
GREENES RESERVE INC ✪
500 Nw 27th Ave (34475-5626)
PHONE..................................954 304-0791
Jeff Greene, *CEO*
EMP: 19 **EST:** 2020
SALES (est): 1MM **Privately Held**
SIC: 2099 Food preparations

(G-11963)
HALE PRODUCTS INC
Also Called: Class 1
607 Nw 27th Ave (34475-5623)
PHONE..................................352 629-5020
Bill Simmons, *CEO*
Bruce Lear, *Vice Pres*
Palmer Pendleton, *Mfg Staff*
Paula Flinn, *Buyer*
Donna Sharlow, *Buyer*
▲ **EMP:** 240 **EST:** 1991
SQ FT: 70,000
SALES (est): 39.5MM
SALES (corp-wide): 2.3B **Publicly Held**
WEB: www.haleproducts.com
SIC: 3625 3088 3714 3699 Electric controls & control accessories, industrial; plastics plumbing fixtures; motor vehicle parts & accessories; electrical equipment & supplies
PA: Idex Corporation
3100 Sanders Rd Ste 301
Northbrook IL 60062
847 498-7070

(G-11964)
HAMMILL POST
8400 Sw 90th St Unit B (34481-7510)
PHONE..................................352 304-8675
Ellen Hammill, *Principal*
EMP: 6 **EST:** 2012
SALES (est): 128.2K **Privately Held**
WEB: www.hammillpost.com
SIC: 2711 Newspapers, publishing & printing

(G-11965)
HANKISON
4647 Sw 40th Ave (34474-5730)
PHONE..................................352 273-1220
Bill Jenkins, *Plant Mgr*
EMP: 6 **EST:** 2009
SALES (est): 129.9K **Privately Held**
SIC: 3563 Air & gas compressors

(G-11966)
HOSELINE INC
701 Nw 37th Ave (34475-5682)
PHONE..................................541 258-8984
EMP: 16 **EST:** 2019
SALES (est): 2.8MM **Privately Held**
WEB: www.hoselineinc.net
SIC: 3585 Refrigeration & heating equipment

(G-11967)
I-75 INDUSTRIES INC
1466 Nw 38th Ave (34482-8573)
PHONE..................................352 840-3155
Mike L Raney, *Treasurer*
EMP: 6 **EST:** 2017
SALES (est): 43.6K **Privately Held**
SIC: 3999 Manufacturing industries

(G-11968)
IBS MANUFACTURING LLC
18 Ne 16th St (34470-4109)
PHONE..................................352 629-9752
Ivedent Lloyd Sr, *Principal*
EMP: 6 **EST:** 2013
SALES (est): 144.4K **Privately Held**
SIC: 3999 Barber & beauty shop equipment

(G-11969)
ICE CREAM & GIFTS LLC
6160 Sw Highway 200 # 116 (34476-5519)
PHONE..................................352 237-2660
Deborah D Tomashek, *Principal*
EMP: 6 **EST:** 2013
SALES (est): 136.1K **Privately Held**
SIC: 2024 Ice cream & frozen desserts

(G-11970)
INTREPID PRECAST INC
470 Se 123rd Street Rd (34480-8530)
PHONE..................................352 347-7475
R Stem, *Principal*
EMP: 6 **EST:** 2015
SALES (est): 78K **Privately Held**
SIC: 3272 Precast terrazo or concrete products

(G-11971)
ISLAND MILLWORK INC
3621 Ne 36th Ave (34479-2253)
PHONE..................................352 694-5565
EMP: 11 **EST:** 2017
SALES (est): 1MM **Privately Held**
WEB: www.islandmillworkinc.com
SIC: 2431 Millwork

(G-11972)
JR PLASTICS CORPORATION
5111 S Pine Ave Ste G (34480-7176)
PHONE..................................352 401-0880
Rick Diamond, *President*
Robert Ruwitch, *Chairman*
James Wear, *Vice Pres*
◆ **EMP:** 100 **EST:** 1997
SQ FT: 100,000
SALES (est): 21.9MM **Privately Held**
WEB: www.jrplastics.com
SIC: 2671 2673 Plastic film, coated or laminated for packaging; plastic & pliofilm bags

(G-11973)
KAROB INSTRUMENT INC
1644 Ne 22nd Ave (34470-7748)
PHONE..................................352 732-2414
Karl Windischmann, *President*
Robert Windischmann, *Vice Pres*
EMP: 8 **EST:** 1984
SALES (est): 1.2MM **Privately Held**
WEB: www.karobinstrument.com
SIC: 3728 Aircraft parts & equipment

(G-11974)
KAROB MANUFACTURING INC
1644 Ne 22nd Ave Bldg Ste (34470-7748)
PHONE..................................352 732-2414
Karl C Windischmann Jr, *President*
Andrea Wright, *Corp Secy*
Robert Windischmann, *Vice Pres*
EMP: 36 **EST:** 1963
SQ FT: 7,500
SALES (est): 610.8K **Privately Held**
WEB: www.karobinstrument.com
SIC: 3599 Machine shop, jobbing & repair

(G-11975)
KAY ENTERPRISES
2026 Se 3rd Pl (34471-2516)
PHONE..................................352 732-5770
Mary Kay, *Owner*
▲ **EMP:** 6 **EST:** 1991
SALES (est): 340.9K **Privately Held**
SIC: 3993 Signs & advertising specialties

(G-11976)
KEITHCO INC
Also Called: Budget Print Center
1519 S Pine Ave (34471-6547)
PHONE..................................352 351-4741
Stephen M Chancas, *President*
Barbara Chancas, *Owner*
EMP: 9 **EST:** 1982
SQ FT: 6,200
SALES (est): 998.7K **Privately Held**
SIC: 2752 2796 2791 2789 Commercial printing, offset; platemaking services; typesetting; bookbinding & related work; commercial printing; coated & laminated paper

(G-11977)
KRAUSZ USA INC
331 Sw 57th Ave (34474-9346)
P.O. Box 770207 (34477-0207)
PHONE..................................352 509-3600
Dan Krausz, *CEO*
Mary Edwards, *Business Mgr*
Cindy Kransler, *Vice Pres*
Alistair M Vaughan-Edwards, *Vice Pres*
Andy Conger, *Sales Staff*
◆ **EMP:** 16 **EST:** 2013
SQ FT: 50,000
SALES (est): 4.7MM **Privately Held**
WEB: www.hymaxusa.com
SIC: 3443 3533 Water tanks, metal plate; water well drilling equipment

(G-11978)
L C SOUTHWIND MANUFACTURING
415 Cypress Rd (34472-3107)
PHONE..................................352 687-1999
Colleen Jernigan, *Purch Mgr*
Colleen Winchester, *Purchasing*
Denise Tinline, *Bookkeeper*
Melody Schmid, *Executive*
Charles Perry,
▲ **EMP:** 18 **EST:** 1996
SQ FT: 20,000
SALES (est): 2.7MM **Privately Held**
WEB: www.southwindmfg.com
SIC: 3089 Injection molding of plastics

(G-11979)
L M COMPRESSOR LLC
5800 Sw 25th St (34474-9746)
PHONE..................................352 484-0850
EMP: 8 **EST:** 2018
SALES (est): 1.9MM **Privately Held**
WEB: www.lmcompressor.com
SIC: 3563 Air & gas compressors

(G-11980)
LARRY CUBI
9772 Sw 46th Ct (34476-4029)
PHONE..................................352 445-7435
Larry Cubi, *Owner*
EMP: 6 **EST:** 2017
SALES (est): 92.9K **Privately Held**
SIC: 3873 Watches, clocks, watchcases & parts

(G-11981)
LEGACY SPORTS INC
1417 Sw 17th St (34471-1234)
PHONE..................................352 732-6759
Seth McBride, *CEO*
EMP: 30 **EST:** 2006
SALES (est): 1.8MM **Privately Held**
WEB: www.shoplts.com
SIC: 2759 2395 Promotional printing; embroidery & art needlework

(G-11982)
LEWIS VAULT & PRECAST INC
1731 Sw 7th Ave (34471-1315)
P.O. Box 3275 (34478-3275)
PHONE..................................352 351-2992
David Lewis, *President*
John Lewis, *Vice Pres*
Cheryl Cochran, *Treasurer*
EMP: 8 **EST:** 1982
SQ FT: 624
SALES (est): 338.8K **Privately Held**
SIC: 3272 Burial vaults, concrete or precast terrazzo

(G-11983)
LHOIST NORTH AMERICA TENN INC
Also Called: Lowell Plant Usf5
11661 Nw Gainesville Rd (34482-1486)
P.O. Box 10, Lowell (32663-0010)
PHONE..................................352 629-7990
Phillip Curtin, *Plant Mgr*
Stephen Hedrick, *QC Mgr*
EMP: 18
SALES (corp-wide): 2.6MM **Privately Held**
SIC: 1422 5032 Crushed & broken limestone; brick, except refractory
HQ: Lhoist North America Of Tennessee, Inc.
750 Old Hickry Blvd 200-2
Brentwood TN 37027
615 259-4222

(G-11984)
LIFETIME ENVIRONMENTAL DESIGNS
3550 Sw 74th Ave (34474-6451)
P.O. Box 770891 (34477-0891)
PHONE..................................352 237-7177
John K Van Fleet, *President*
Kim Van Fleet, *Vice Pres*
EMP: 6
SQ FT: 5,200
SALES (est): 443K **Privately Held**
SIC: 2511 Lawn furniture: wood

(G-11985)
LILES CUSTOM TRAILERS
Also Called: ACR Custom Trailer Products
4940 N Us Highway 441 (34475-1522)
PHONE..................................352 368-2652
Arthur C Richardson, *Owner*
A C Richardson, *Owner*
EMP: 7 **EST:** 1985
SALES (est): 749K **Privately Held**
SIC: 3799 Trailers & trailer equipment

(G-11986)
LIQUID METAL PRODUCTS INC
901 Sw 73rd Street Rd (34476-6877)
PHONE..................................402 895-4436
Eugene T Harmel, *President*
Janis Silverberg, *Treasurer*
EMP: 6 **EST:** 1984
SALES (est): 628.7K **Privately Held**
WEB: www.liquidmetal.com
SIC: 3291 Abrasive metal & steel products

(G-11987)
LOW VISION AIDS INC (PA)
Also Called: Magnifying America
2125 Sw Highway 484 (34473-7949)
PHONE..................................954 722-1580
John Palmer, *President*
Peggy Palmer, *Vice Pres*
EMP: 9 **EST:** 1991
SALES (est): 3.2MM **Privately Held**
WEB: www.magnifyingamerica.com
SIC: 3827 5049 Optical instruments & apparatus; magnifying instruments, optical; optical goods

(G-11988)
LUV ENTERPRISES INC
Also Called: Adrian Lucas Aluminum
141 Sw 71st Pl (34476-6887)
PHONE..................................352 867-8440
Brian Lucas, *President*
EMP: 12 **EST:** 1989
SQ FT: 15,000
SALES (est): 717K **Privately Held**
SIC: 3365 3231 5211 Aluminum foundries; products of purchased glass; fencing

(G-11989)
M BILT ENTERPRISES INC
Also Called: Well Bilt Industries
1821 Sw 28th St (34471-7732)
PHONE..................................352 528-5566
Carol Bilt, *President*
EMP: 14 **EST:** 1969
SQ FT: 23,500
SALES (est): 1.7MM **Privately Held**
SIC: 3442 5088 Hangar doors, metal; aircraft equipment & supplies

(G-11990)
MAGNOLIAS GURMET BKY ITLN DELI
Also Called: Magnolia Bakery
1412 N Magnolia Ave (34475-9077)
PHONE..................................352 207-2667
Salvatore Castello, *President*
Landa Castello, *Vice Pres*
EMP: 6 **EST:** 1974
SQ FT: 15,000
SALES (est): 426.5K **Privately Held**
WEB: www.magnoliabakery.com
SIC: 2051 5812 2052 Bakery: wholesale or wholesale/retail combined; eating places; cookies & crackers

(G-11991)
MAJIC STAIRS INC (PA)
120 Cypress Rd (34472-5169)
PHONE..................................352 446-6295
John K Liles, *Principal*
EMP: 36 **EST:** 2016
SALES (est): 803.9K **Privately Held**
WEB: www.majicstairsinc.com
SIC: 3446 Stairs, staircases, stair treads: prefabricated metal

(G-11992)
MARION METAL WORKS INC
4750 S Pine Ave (34480-9104)
P.O. Box 830307 (34483-0307)
PHONE..................................352 351-4221
Linda L Bourne, *Manager*
EMP: 20
SQ FT: 18,000
SALES (est): 3.7MM **Privately Held**
WEB: www.mmwcfl.com
SIC: 3444 Sheet metalwork

(G-11993)
MARION PRECISION TOOL INC
1800 Nw 10th St (34475-5331)
PHONE..................................352 867-0080
Barbara Luider, *President*
Edward Luider, *Vice Pres*
EMP: 12 **EST:** 1997
SALES (est): 1.1MM **Privately Held**
WEB: www.marionprecisiontoolinc.com
SIC: 3599 Machine shop, jobbing & repair

(G-11994)
MARION ROCK INC
5979 Se Maricamp Rd (34472-2003)
PHONE..................................352 687-2023
James Boutwell, *President*
John F Boutwell, *Vice Pres*
EMP: 35 **EST:** 1996
SALES (est): 9.9MM **Privately Held**
WEB: www.marionrock.com
SIC: 1499 Mineral abrasives mining

(G-11995)
MATCHLESS MANUFACTURING
10709 Sw 55th Ave (34476-7076)
PHONE..................................352 390-3010
Nathan Yedinak, *Principal*
EMP: 7 **EST:** 2013
SALES (est): 105.9K **Privately Held**
WEB: www.matchlessmetal.com
SIC: 3999 Manufacturing industries

(G-11996)
MAXIMILIAN ZENHO & CO INC
2775 Nw 49th Ave Unit 205 (34482-6213)
PHONE..................................352 875-1190
Pablo Fernandez, *CEO*
EMP: 7 **EST:** 2012
SQ FT: 1,500
SALES (est): 572K **Privately Held**
WEB: www.tattoocyn.net
SIC: 2834 Pharmaceutical preparations

(G-11997)
MEDX CORPORATION
839 Nw 25th Ave (34475-5789)
PHONE..................................352 351-2005
Micheal Dettmers, *President*
David Fleming, *CFO*
◆ **EMP:** 15 **EST:** 1988
SQ FT: 100,000
SALES (est): 1.4MM **Privately Held**
SIC: 3949 Exercise equipment

(G-11998)
MESTIZO FOODS LLC
3031 W Silver Sprng Blvd (34475-5647)
PHONE..................................352 414-4900
Mariellen Cabral, *Manager*
Andy Westervelt,
Lydia Karschner,
Daniel Villanueva,
EMP: 104 **EST:** 2017
SALES (est): 10.5MM **Privately Held**
SIC: 2099 Food preparations

(G-11999)
METALCRAFT INDUSTRIES INC
120 Cypress Rd (34472-5169)
PHONE..................................352 680-3555
Kevin Liles, *President*
EMP: 27 **EST:** 1997
SQ FT: 10,000
SALES (est): 4.1MM **Privately Held**
WEB: www.metalcraftindustries.net
SIC: 3444 Sheet metalwork

(G-12000)
MICHIGAN AVENUE BRIDGE INC
Also Called: Rainbow Cabinets
4690 Ne 35th St (34479-3230)
PHONE..................................352 236-4044
Marilyn J Busse, *President*
Mark S Allin, *Vice Pres*
EMP: 15 **EST:** 2005
SALES (est): 1.2MM **Privately Held**
WEB: www.rainbowcabinets.com
SIC: 2434 Wood kitchen cabinets

(G-12001)
MICKEY TRUCK BODIES INC
601 Nw 24th Ct (34475-5718)
PHONE..................................352 620-0015
Sid Merrill, *Principal*
Scott Whittmier, *Executive*
EMP: 10
SALES (corp-wide): 141.2MM **Privately Held**
WEB: www.mickeybody.com
SIC: 3713 Truck & bus bodies
PA: Mickey Truck Bodies Inc.
1305 Trinity Ave
High Point NC 27260
336 882-6806

(G-12002)
MOYO
6027 Sw 54th St Ste 201 (34474-5547)
PHONE..................................352 208-2770
Christina Harper, *Principal*
EMP: 6 **EST:** 2012
SALES (est): 127.6K **Privately Held**
SIC: 3421 Table & food cutlery, including butchers'

(G-12003)
MULCH & STONE EMPORIUM INC
7699 Sw Highway 200 (34476-7051)
PHONE..................................352 237-7870
Chris Winn, *President*
Lisa Winn, *Office Mgr*
EMP: 5 **EST:** 2008
SALES (est): 327K **Privately Held**
WEB: www.mulchandstonesuperstore.com
SIC: 3524 Lawn & garden equipment

(G-12004)
NANOTECHNOVATION CORPORATION
Also Called: Clairson Plastics
2811 Ne 14th St (34470-4819)
PHONE..................................352 732-3244
Don Sauey, *CEO*
Troy Carswell, *President*
Kelly Jemison, *Controller*
Marcelle West, *Administration*
EMP: 25 **EST:** 2007
SALES (est): 1MM **Privately Held**
SIC: 3089 Injection molded finished plastic products

(G-12005)
NELSONS TRUCK AND TRLR SLS LLC
4131 Nw Blitchton Rd (34482-4058)
PHONE..................................352 732-8908
EMP: 10 **EST:** 2010
SALES (est): 506.4K **Privately Held**
WEB: www.nelsonstrailers.com
SIC: 3715 Truck trailers

(G-12006)
NOBILITY HOMES INC (PA)
3741 Sw 7th St (34474-1945)
PHONE..................................352 732-5157
Terry E Trexler, *Ch of Bd*
Thomas W Trexler, *CFO*
Lynn J Cramer Jr, *Treasurer*
Lj Anderson, *Manager*
Robert P Saltsman, *Director*
EMP: 71 **EST:** 1967
SQ FT: 72,000
SALES: 41.6MM **Publicly Held**
WEB: www.nobilityhomes.com
SIC: 2451 5271 Mobile homes; mobile homes

(G-12007)
OCALA BREEDERS SALES CO INC (PA)
Also Called: Ocala Breeders' Feed & Supply
1701 Sw 60th Ave (34474-1800)
P.O. Box 99 (34478-0099)
PHONE..................................352 237-4667
Thomas Ventura, *President*
EMP: 50 **EST:** 1977
SQ FT: 20,000
SALES (est): 13.2MM **Privately Held**
WEB: www.obssales.com
SIC: 2048 7389 7999 Livestock feeds; auctioneers, fee basis; gambling & lottery services

(G-12008)
OCALA CENTRE 6
3075 Sw 53rd St (34471-5802)
PHONE..................................305 322-7365
EMP: 7 **EST:** 2016
SALES (est): 138K **Privately Held**
WEB: www.ocala.com
SIC: 2711 Newspapers: publishing only, not printed on site

(G-12009)
OCALA CONCRETE SERVICES LLC
3498 W Highway 326 (34475-2464)
PHONE..................................352 694-4300
Gonzalo Pozo Sr, *Mng Member*
EMP: 7 **EST:** 2009
SALES (est): 925.6K **Privately Held**
WEB: www.ocalaconcrete.com
SIC: 3273 Ready-mixed concrete

(G-12010)
OCALA MAGAZINE
Also Called: Gainesville/Ocala Business
743 E Fort King St (34471-2233)
P.O. Box 4649 (34478-4649)
PHONE..................................352 622-2995
Linda Marks, *President*
Ronald Wetherington, *Editor*
Dr William Eyerly, *Vice Pres*
Jean Mc Connell, *Vice Pres*
Randy Woodruff, *CFO*
EMP: 21 **EST:** 1984
SALES (est): 1MM **Privately Held**
WEB: www.ocalamagazine.com
SIC: 2721 Magazines: publishing only, not printed on site; magazines: publishing & printing

(G-12011)
OCALA MANUFACTURING
10245 N Us Highway 27 (34482-1848)
PHONE..................................352 433-6643
Richard Estes, *Principal*
EMP: 8 **EST:** 2010
SALES (est): 179.8K **Privately Held**
SIC: 3999 Manufacturing industries

(G-12012)
OCALA METAL PRODUCTS INC
800 N Pine Ave (34475-8879)
PHONE..................................352 861-4500
Bob E Hatcher, *President*
EMP: 7 **EST:** 2008
SALES (est): 950K **Privately Held**
SIC: 3448 Prefabricated metal buildings

(G-12013)
OCALA PHARMACY LLC
8290 Sw Highway 200 (34481-9677)
PHONE..................................352 509-7890
Rameshbhai S Patel, *Principal*
EMP: 6 **EST:** 2015
SALES (est): 990.7K **Privately Held**
WEB: www.ocalapharmacy.com
SIC: 2834 Pharmaceutical preparations

(G-12014)
OCALA PRINT QUICK INC
Also Called: Concord Print Shops
600 S Magnolia Ave (34471-0976)
PHONE..................................352 629-0736
William Marren, *President*
EMP: 9 **EST:** 1973
SQ FT: 3,575
SALES (est): 881.4K **Privately Held**
WEB: www.concordprintocala.com
SIC: 2752 7334 2791 2789 Commercial printing, offset; photocopying & duplicating services; typesetting; bookbinding & related work

(G-12015)
OCALA PUBLICATION INCORPORTED
Also Called: Ocala Style Magazine
908 Se 16th St (34471-3904)
PHONE..................................352 732-0073
Kathy Johnson, *President*
Melissa Peterson, *Production*
Evelyn Anderson, *Marketing Staff*
EMP: 20 **EST:** 2006
SALES (est): 1.2MM **Privately Held**
WEB: www.ocalastyle.com
SIC: 2721 Magazines: publishing only, not printed on site

(G-12016)
OCALA STAR BANNER CORPORATION
2121 Sw 19th Avenue Rd (34471-7704)
PHONE..................................352 867-4010
Bruce Gaultney, *President*
Reynolds Larry, *Sales Staff*
John Gavel, *Manager*
Craig Pressnell, *Manager*
Gavel John, *Senior Editor*
EMP: 200 **EST:** 1980
SALES (est): 11.7MM
SALES (corp-wide): 272.8MM **Privately Held**
WEB: www.ocala.com
SIC: 2711 Newspapers, publishing & printing
PA: Halifax Media Holdings, Llc
901 6th St
Daytona Beach FL 32117
386 681-2404

(G-12017)
OCALA SWAMP LLC
1900 Se 18th Ave (34471-8312)
PHONE..................................352 732-4260
Jeffery P Crippen, *Principal*
EMP: 7 **EST:** 2010
SALES (est): 146.5K **Privately Held**
WEB: www.ocala.com
SIC: 2711 Newspapers: publishing only, not printed on site

(G-12018)
OCALANOW COM
126 Se 41st Ave (34471-3134)
PHONE..................................352 433-2497
Joshua Cody Gray, *Principal*
EMP: 6 **EST:** 2016
SALES (est): 113.2K **Privately Held**
WEB: www.ocala.com
SIC: 2711 Newspapers, publishing & printing

(G-12019)
OFAB INC
1909 Ne 25th Ave (34470-4848)
PHONE..................................352 629-0040
Larry Amyotte, *President*
Gary Ringo, *Vice Pres*
Jeff Johnson, *Sales Staff*
Melissa Vachon, *Executive*
Ben Davis, *Shareholder*
EMP: 65 **EST:** 1984
SQ FT: 18,000
SALES (est): 15.2MM **Privately Held**
WEB: www.ofab.net
SIC: 3443 3599 4214 Fabricated plate work (boiler shop); machine shop, jobbing & repair; local trucking with storage

(G-12020)
PACIFIC ARCHES CORPORATION
1740 Se 18th St Ste 1302 (34471-5454)
PHONE..................................352 236-7787
Lori Findlay, *Principal*
EMP: 18 **EST:** 2008
SALES (est): 5.2MM **Privately Held**
WEB: www.pacarches.com
SIC: 2439 Structural wood members

(G-12021)
PACKAGING ALTERNATIVES CORP (PA)
4130 Sw 13th St (34474-8589)
P.O. Box 770907 (34477-0907)
PHONE..................................352 867-5050
James F Byrne, *President*
Sandra E Byrne, *Vice Pres*
EMP: 11 **EST:** 1994
SQ FT: 20,000
SALES (est): 4.5MM **Privately Held**
WEB: www.packagingalternatives.com
SIC: 2653 2675 Corrugated & solid fiber boxes; die-cut paper & board

(G-12022)
PARAMOUNT MARKETING INC
138 Juniper Loop Cir (34480-5211)
PHONE..................................352 608-8801
Hronec Sharon D, *Principal*
Miguel Sandoval, *Sales Staff*
Cheryl Valenzuela, *Marketing Staff*
EMP: 12 **EST:** 2014
SALES (est): 152.8K **Privately Held**
WEB: www.paramountmarketing.net
SIC: 2741 Miscellaneous publishing

(G-12023)
PATRICK INDUSTRIES INC
Custom Vinyls Division
1609 Sw 17th St (34471-1224)
PHONE..................................352 732-8841
Chuck Hardyman, *Manager*
EMP: 7
SALES (corp-wide): 2.4B **Publicly Held**
WEB: www.patrickind.com
SIC: 2295 Coated fabrics, not rubberized
PA: Patrick Industries, Inc.
107 W Franklin St
Elkhart IN 46516
574 294-7511

(G-12024)
PEPSI-COLA METRO BTLG CO INC
525 Sw 16th St (34471-0601)
PHONE..................................352 629-8911
Mike McCullough, *Manager*
EMP: 6
SQ FT: 19,400
SALES (corp-wide): 70.3B **Publicly Held**
WEB: www.pepsico.com
SIC: 2086 Carbonated soft drinks, bottled & canned
HQ: Pepsi-Cola Metropolitan Bottling Company, Inc.
1111 Westchester Ave
White Plains NY 10604
914 767-6000

(G-12025)
PHILLIPS GRAPHICS INC
1711 Sw 17th St (34471-1200)
PHONE..................................352 622-1776
Joseph G Phillips Jr, *President*
Jolea S Phillips, *Treasurer*
Jolea Womble, *Finance*
Stacie C Phillips, *Admin Sec*
EMP: 6 **EST:** 1985
SALES (est): 661.6K **Privately Held**
WEB: www.phillipsgraphics.com
SIC: 2752 Commercial printing, offset

(G-12026)
PHOENIX WOOD PRODUCTS INC (PA)
3761 Ne 36th Ave (34479-2251)
PHONE..................................888 304-1131

Brian Knight, *President*
Glenn Ryan, *General Mgr*
Stan Redrick, *Vice Pres*
Steve Redrick, *Treasurer*
Phillip Schuster, *Controller*
EMP: 40 **EST:** 1993
SQ FT: 2,500
SALES (est): 13.3MM **Privately Held**
WEB: www.phoenixwood.com
SIC: 2448 Pallets, wood

(G-12027)
PIP PRINTING
11 Sw 1st Ave (34471-1101)
PHONE..................................352 622-3224
Rich Bierema, *President*
Nancy Bierema, *Treasurer*
EMP: 8 **EST:** 1979
SQ FT: 2,500
SALES (est): 600K **Privately Held**
WEB: www.pip.com
SIC: 2752 2791 2789 Commercial printing, offset; typesetting; bookbinding & related work

(G-12028)
PLASTIC AND PRODUCTS MKTG LLC
3445 Sw 6th St (34474-1916)
PHONE..................................352 867-8078
Jeffrey Stein, *Mng Member*
Eileen Keeler, *Manager*
Liz Troutman, *Manager*
EMP: 14 **EST:** 1986
SALES (est): 2MM **Privately Held**
WEB: www.plasticpm.com
SIC: 2821 3354 2434 3469 Thermoplastic materials; shapes, extruded aluminum; wood kitchen cabinets; metal stampings; plastics sheets & rods

(G-12029)
PNEUMATIC PRODUCTS CORPORATION
Also Called: SPX Flow Technology
4647 Sw 40th Ave (34474-5730)
PHONE..................................352 873-5793
Carl Ruder, *General Mgr*
Keith Lassiter, *Purch Mgr*
George Rogers, *Research*
Harry Derkay, *Sales Mgr*
EMP: 7 **EST:** 2010
SALES (est): 1.7MM **Privately Held**
WEB: www.spxflow.com
SIC: 3569 General industrial machinery

(G-12030)
POWDER SYSTEMS INC
120 Cypress Rd (34472-5169)
PHONE..................................352 680-3558
Michael Murdock, *President*
John Kevin Liles, *Vice Pres*
EMP: 5 **EST:** 1994
SQ FT: 9,600
SALES (est): 422.2K **Privately Held**
SIC: 3599 Chemical milling job shop

(G-12031)
PRIMA FOODS INTERNATIONAL INC
2140 Ne 36th Ave (34470-3183)
P.O. Box 2208, Silver Springs (34489-2208)
PHONE..................................352 732-9148
Hector Viale, *President*
Celeste Viale, *Vice Pres*
EMP: 8 **EST:** 1985
SQ FT: 4,000
SALES (est): 1MM **Privately Held**
WEB: www.primafoodsinc.com
SIC: 2087 Concentrates, drink

(G-12032)
PRO POLY OF AMERICA INC
230 Ne 25th Ave Ste 300 (34470-7075)
PHONE..................................352 629-1414
Tim Dean, *President*
Nick Dean, *Vice Pres*
Chris Smith, *Engineer*
Missy Allen, *Comptroller*
Mollie Miranda, *Marketing Staff*
EMP: 9
SALES (corp-wide): 8.9MM **Privately Held**
WEB: www.propolyamerica.com
SIC: 2821 Thermosetting materials
PA: Pro Poly Of America, Inc.
1821 Nw 57th St
Ocala FL 34475
352 629-1414

(G-12033)
PRO POLY OF AMERICA INC (PA)
1821 Nw 57th St (34475-3031)
PHONE..................................352 629-1414
Tim Dean, *President*
Branden Sharbono, *Design Engr*
Missy Allen, *Comptroller*
EMP: 40 **EST:** 1996
SQ FT: 12,500
SALES (est): 8.9MM **Privately Held**
WEB: www.propolyamerica.com
SIC: 2821 Plastics materials & resins

(G-12034)
PROFAB CORPORATION (PA)
Also Called: Profab Plastics
4901 Nw 5th St (34482-3287)
PHONE..................................352 369-5515
Keith Hoffmann, *CEO*
Ralph Milykovic, *CEO*
Jim Gischia, *Vice Pres*
Alexis Monigal Leitzki, *Vice Pres*
EMP: 30 **EST:** 1996
SQ FT: 10,000
SALES (est): 4.8MM **Privately Held**
WEB: www.profabplastics.net
SIC: 2821 Plastics materials & resins

(G-12035)
RAINBOW CABINETS INC
4690 Ne 35th St (34479-3230)
PHONE..................................352 236-4044
Marilyn Busse, *President*
Mark Allin, *Officer*
EMP: 9 **EST:** 1987
SALES (est): 508.4K **Privately Held**
SIC: 2434 Wood kitchen cabinets

(G-12036)
RELIANCE PETRO HOLDINGS LLC
1820 Se 18th Ave Ste 3 (34471-8303)
PHONE..................................352 390-8039
Neil Patel, *Vice Pres*
Bharat P Patel,
Neel Patel, *Maintence Staff*
Mulka J Patel,
Trupti B Patel,
EMP: 10 **EST:** 2004
SQ FT: 4,000
SALES (est): 1.5MM **Privately Held**
WEB: www.reliancepetroleumllc.wordpress.com
SIC: 1382 5541 Oil & gas exploration services; gasoline service stations

(G-12037)
RESHARP INDUSTRIES
5101 Se 11th Ave (34480-6666)
PHONE..................................352 362-1730
Timothy A Staub, *Principal*
EMP: 9 **EST:** 2002
SALES (est): 258.8K **Privately Held**
WEB: www.resharpindustries.com
SIC: 3999 Manufacturing industries

(G-12038)
RILEY COATINGS & PAVERS LLC
4402 Ne 18th Ter (34479-8616)
PHONE..................................352 598-9520
Jessica L Riley, *Principal*
EMP: 6 **EST:** 2013
SALES (est): 126.5K **Privately Held**
SIC: 2951 Asphalt paving mixtures & blocks

(G-12039)
ROLLING GREENS MOBILE HOME PK
1899 Se 58th Ave (34480-5847)
PHONE..................................352 624-0022
Jim Ford, *Senior VP*
EMP: 8 **EST:** 1995
SALES (est): 170.6K **Privately Held**
WEB: www.covecommunities.com
SIC: 2451 Mobile homes, except recreational

(G-12040)
ROLLING GREENS NEWS
1720 Ne 49th Ave (34470-1178)
P.O. Box 2288, Silver Springs (34489-2288)
PHONE..................................352 236-0007
Donna L Furce, *Owner*
EMP: 8 **EST:** 2010
SALES (est): 182.2K **Privately Held**
WEB: www.rghoa.net
SIC: 2711 Newspapers, publishing & printing

(G-12041)
ROTECH OXYGEN & MEDICAL EQUIP
3300 Sw 34th Ave Ste 116 (34474-4438)
PHONE..................................352 291-1070
Terri Holloway, *Principal*
EMP: 6 **EST:** 2018
SALES (est): 138.6K **Privately Held**
SIC: 3841 Surgical & medical instruments

(G-12042)
SARNIYA ENTERPRISES INC
8140 Se 58th Ave (34480-8257)
PHONE..................................352 347-6030
Nizar N Dhamani, *Principal*
EMP: 10 **EST:** 2009
SALES (est): 288K **Privately Held**
SIC: 3578 Automatic teller machines (ATM)

(G-12043)
SCORPION EQUITY LLC
Also Called: Scorpion Racing Products
5817 Nw 44th Ave (34482-7891)
PHONE..................................352 512-0800
Chuck Layton, *General Mgr*
Kyle Weaver, *Prdtn Mgr*
Zac Collins, *Design Engr*
Jessica Parise, *Comptroller*
Kate Weaver, *Director*
EMP: 33 **EST:** 2016
SALES (est): 3.8MM **Privately Held**
WEB: www.scorpionracingproducts.com
SIC: 3462 Automotive & internal combustion engine forgings

(G-12044)
SEMINOLE STORES INC
Also Called: Seminole Feed Division
335 Ne Watula Ave (34470-5806)
P.O. Box 940 (34478-0940)
PHONE..................................352 732-4143
O C Branch Jr, *Ch of Bd*
Greg Branch, *President*
◆ **EMP:** 15 **EST:** 1987
SQ FT: 120,000
SALES (est): 12.6MM
SALES (corp-wide): 15.8MM **Privately Held**
WEB: www.seminolefeed.com
SIC: 2048 5999 Frozen pet food (except dog & cat); feed & farm supply
PA: Branch Properties, Inc.
335 Ne Watula Ave
Ocala FL 34470
352 732-4143

(G-12045)
SHADE SAVER INC
3330 Nw 95th Avenue Rd (34482-3895)
PHONE..................................850 650-0884
Bryan K Myers, *Director*
EMP: 5 **EST:** 2012
SALES (est): 471.7K **Privately Held**
SIC: 3578 Accounting machines & cash registers

(G-12046)
SHADE SYSTEMS INC
4150 Sw 19th St (34474-2860)
PHONE..................................352 237-0135
Alan A Bayman, *President*
Eric Kinoti, *Managing Dir*
Brad Buzard, *Natl Sales Mgr*
Margo Talbot, *Cust Mgr*
Margo Ross, *Manager*
▲ **EMP:** 30 **EST:** 2003
SQ FT: 50,000
SALES (est): 4.9MM **Privately Held**
WEB: www.shadesystemsinc.com
SIC: 2421 Outdoor wood structural products

(G-12047)
SHASHY ENTERPRISES INC
Also Called: Southern Blade & Supply
1824 N Magnolia Ave (34475-9112)
P.O. Box 2063 (34478-2063)
PHONE..................................352 732-3904
Shashy Marion, *Vice Pres*
EMP: 6 **EST:** 1984
SQ FT: 2,400
SALES (est): 874.3K **Privately Held**
SIC: 3399 5072 Metal fasteners; hardware

(G-12048)
SHEALY REVEL B INC
606 Ne 35th St (34479-2714)
P.O. Box 634 (34478-0634)
PHONE..................................352 629-1552
Preston Shealy, *President*
EMP: 6 **EST:** 1990
SALES (est): 413.8K **Privately Held**
SIC: 3271 Concrete block & brick

(G-12049)
SIBE AUTOMATION LLC
1521 Sw 12th Ave Ste 700 (34471-0541)
PHONE..................................352 690-1741
Simon Gaysinsky,
EMP: 15 **EST:** 2012
SALES (est): 2.3MM **Privately Held**
WEB: www.sibeautomation.com
SIC: 3089 Thermoformed finished plastic products

(G-12050)
SIGNATURE BRANDS LLC (PA)
Also Called: Paas
808 Sw 12th St (34471-0540)
PHONE..................................352 622-3134
Jared Konstanty, *CEO*
Brian Crosby, *Managing Dir*
Jennifer Ellis, *Business Mgr*
Hannah Baderschneider, *Vice Pres*
Michael Garritano, *Safety Mgr*
◆ **EMP:** 452 **EST:** 1951
SQ FT: 240,000
SALES (est): 95.7MM **Privately Held**
WEB: www.signaturebrands.com
SIC: 2064 Cake ornaments, confectionery

(G-12051)
SIGNATURE BRANDS LLC
1930 Sw 38th Ave Ste 300 (34474-4903)
PHONE..................................352 622-3134
Jerry Reardon, *CEO*
Andrew Laudicina, *Creative Dir*
EMP: 56
SALES (corp-wide): 95.7MM **Privately Held**
WEB: www.signaturebrands.com
SIC: 2064 Candy & other confectionery products
PA: Signature Brands, Llc
808 Sw 12th St
Ocala FL 34471
352 622-3134

(G-12052)
SIGNS UNLIMITED SEA INC
618 S Magnolia Ave (34471-0976)
PHONE..................................352 732-7341
Victor Buttermore, *President*
Irma P Buttermore, *Treasurer*
EMP: 14 **EST:** 1991
SQ FT: 4,224
SALES (est): 574.7K **Privately Held**
SIC: 3993 7336 7389 Signs & advertising specialties; silk screen design; embroidering of advertising on shirts, etc.

(G-12053)
SIMAR INDUSTRIES INC
805 Nw 25th Ave (34475-5784)
PHONE..................................352 622-2287
Derek T Evans, *President*
Marlene Evans, *Corp Secy*
Vince Troisi, *Opers Staff*
Robin Phillips, *Purch Mgr*
John Locke, *Supervisor*
EMP: 24
SQ FT: 18,000

SALES (est): 4.7MM **Privately Held**
WEB: www.simarindustries.com
SIC: 3444 Sheet metal specialties, not stamped

(G-12054)
SIYUFY INTERNATIONAL INC
925 Se 17th St Ste D (34471-3900)
PHONE..................................352 512-0658
Lydia A Siyufy, *Principal*
EMP: 6 **EST:** 2012
SALES (est): 116.5K **Privately Held**
WEB: www.siyufyinternational.com
SIC: 2323 Men's & boys' neckwear

(G-12055)
SOKOL VINEYARDS LLC
101 E Silver Springs Blvd (34470-6618)
PHONE..................................352 368-4069
EMP: 6 **EST:** 2017
SALES (est): 155.1K **Privately Held**
WEB: www.katyavineyards.com
SIC: 2084 Wines

(G-12056)
SPECIAL PUBLICATIONS INC
Also Called: Today Magazines Group
743 Se Fort King Rd (34471)
P.O. Box 4649 (34478-4649)
PHONE..................................352 622-2995
Linda Marks, *President*
EMP: 10 **EST:** 1976
SALES (est): 1.2MM **Privately Held**
SIC: 2721 7311 Magazines: publishing & printing; advertising agencies

(G-12057)
SPICER INDUSTRIES INC
840 Nw 24th Ct (34475-5768)
PHONE..................................352 732-5300
Paul J Spicer, *President*
EMP: 10 **EST:** 1953
SQ FT: 9,000
SALES (est): 920K **Privately Held**
SIC: 3465 3469 3499 Body parts, automobile: stamped metal; metal stampings; furniture parts, metal

(G-12058)
SPX FLOW TECHNOLOGY USA INC (HQ)
Also Called: Kemp
4647 Se 40th Ave (34474)
PHONE..................................352 237-1220
Marc Michael, *President*
Dwight Gibson, *President*
David Kowalski, *President*
Tony Renzi, *President*
David J Wilson, *President*
◆ **EMP:** 5 **EST:** 1992
SALES (est): 14.5MM
SALES (corp-wide): 1.3B **Publicly Held**
WEB: www.spxflow.com
SIC: 3443 Fabricated plate work (boiler shop)
PA: Spx Flow, Inc.
13320 Balntyn Corp Pl
Charlotte NC 28277
704 752-4400

(G-12059)
STEVEN CHANCAS
Also Called: Keithco Enterprises
1519 S Pine Ave (34471-6547)
PHONE..................................352 629-5016
Steven Chancas, *Owner*
EMP: 10 **EST:** 1973
SQ FT: 7,500
SALES (est): 215.7K **Privately Held**
SIC: 2759 3993 2752 2396 Letterpress printing; screen printing; signs & advertising specialties; commercial printing, lithographic; automotive & apparel trimmings

(G-12060)
THI E-COMMERCE LLC
Also Called: Running Board Warehouse
4414 Sw College Rd # 14 (34474-4790)
PHONE..................................352 327-4058
William Reminder, *President*
Kelly Kneifl, *COO*
John Eichler, *Engineer*
Jim Bresingham, *CFO*
Donald Wentling, *Consultant*
▲ **EMP:** 98 **EST:** 1997
SQ FT: 18,000
SALES (est): 27.1MM
SALES (corp-wide): 623.9MM **Privately Held**
WEB: www.thiecommerce.com
SIC: 3714 Motor vehicle parts & accessories
HQ: Tectum Holdings, Inc.
5400 Data Ct
Ann Arbor MI 48108
734 677-0444

(G-12061)
TRUE BLUE METAL LLC
14350 Sw 20th Avenue Rd (34473-4016)
PHONE..................................352 444-9596
Tymon Anderson,
EMP: 6 **EST:** 2018
SALES (est): 118K **Privately Held**
WEB: www.trueblue-usa.com
SIC: 3999 Manufacturing industries

(G-12062)
TRUSCO MANUFACTURING COMPANY
545 Nw 68th Ave (34482-8255)
PHONE..................................352 237-0311
Brad Harris, *Vice Pres*
Brandon Harris, *Vice Pres*
Bruce Harris, *Vice Pres*
Daniel Harris, *Vice Pres*
EMP: 6 **EST:** 1965
SQ FT: 9,000
SALES (est): 842.5K **Privately Held**
WEB: www.truscomfg.com
SIC: 3563 Dusting outfits for metals, paints & chemicals

(G-12063)
TRUSS SPANS UNLIMITED LLC
12830 Sw 58th Cir (34473-5255)
PHONE..................................352 274-0306
Paul Charity, *Principal*
EMP: 9 **EST:** 2015
SALES (est): 289.1K **Privately Held**
SIC: 2439 Structural wood members

(G-12064)
TURBO PARTS LLC
810 Nw 25th Ave Ste 102 (34475-5781)
PHONE..................................352 351-4510
EMP: 12
SALES (est): 1.9MM **Privately Held**
SIC: 3599 Mfg Industrial Machinery

(G-12065)
U-DUMP TRAILERS LLC
Also Called: Trailer Source, The
2610 Nw 10th St (34475-5709)
PHONE..................................352 351-8510
Betty Duffy, *General Mgr*
Ken Lenox, *Sales Staff*
Anthony Manna, *Mng Member*
Ken Krismanth, *Mng Member*
◆ **EMP:** 52 **EST:** 1979
SQ FT: 16,000
SALES (est): 10.4MM **Privately Held**
WEB: www.udumptrailers.com
SIC: 3715 Truck trailers

(G-12066)
UNIQUE FBRCTIONS UNLIMITED LLC
12 Pine Trace Ter (34472-2829)
PHONE..................................352 229-8511
Michael Anthony Pitts, *Owner*
EMP: 6 **EST:** 2014
SALES (est): 429.7K **Privately Held**
WEB: www.elevationmarine.com
SIC: 3999 Manufacturing industries

(G-12067)
UNITED PLASTIC FABRICATING INC
5000 Nw 5th St (34482-3286)
PHONE..................................352 291-2477
Ken Vachon, *Design Engr*
Nelson Lateer, *Manager*
David Lovely, *Info Tech Dir*
Robert Cunningham, *Technology*
Katrina Santiago, *Personnel Assit*
EMP: 51
SALES (corp-wide): 41.6MM **Privately Held**
WEB: www.unitedplastic.com
SIC: 3089 Injection molding of plastics; plastic processing
PA: United Plastic Fabricating, Inc.
165 Flagship Dr
North Andover MA 01845
978 975-4520

(G-12068)
US HEMP AND OIL LLC
1010 Ne 16th St (34470-4204)
PHONE..................................352 817-2455
Robert Ergle, *Mng Member*
EMP: 8 **EST:** 2019
SALES (est): 513.3K **Privately Held**
WEB: www.ushempandoil.com
SIC: 3999

(G-12069)
USA SCIENTIFIC INC (DH)
346 Sw 57th Ave (34474-9345)
P.O. Box 3565 (34478-3565)
PHONE..................................352 237-6288
Robert Declerk, *President*
Howard Epstein, *Vice Pres*
Cheri Kreutchic, *Vice Pres*
Debbie Peterson, *Purch Mgr*
Kim Garrett, *Purch Agent*
▲ **EMP:** 33 **EST:** 1982
SALES (est): 25.9MM
SALES (corp-wide): 177.9K **Privately Held**
WEB: www.usascientific.com
SIC: 3826 Analytical instruments
HQ: Eppendorf Ag
Barkhausenweg 1
Hamburg 22339
405 380-10

(G-12070)
VETCON CONSTRUCTION INC
Also Called: Vetcon Construction - Ocala
1825 Ne 17th St (34470-4601)
PHONE..................................352 234-6668
Frederick L Franks, *President*
EMP: 6 **EST:** 2019
SALES (est): 66K **Privately Held**
WEB: www.vetcons.com
SIC: 1442 Construction sand & gravel

(G-12071)
VIKING WOODWORKING
13401 W Highway 328 (34482-7056)
PHONE..................................352 237-5050
Bert Eriksen, *Owner*
EMP: 6 **EST:** 1977
SQ FT: 3,350
SALES (est): 300K **Privately Held**
SIC: 2434 Wood kitchen cabinets

(G-12072)
VIPER COMMUNICATION SYSTEMS (HQ)
4211 Sw 13th St (34474-8595)
PHONE..................................352 694-7030
Jimmy Comont, *President*
Don Jones, *Principal*
James Conant, *Principal*
Preston Spurlin, *Principal*
EMP: 25 **EST:** 1997
SQ FT: 5,000
SALES (est): 23.5MM
SALES (corp-wide): 63.5MM **Privately Held**
WEB: www.mtsi.com
SIC: 3669 3441 1791 Visual communication systems; fabricated structural metal; structural steel erection
PA: Microwave Transmission Systems, Inc
1751 Jay Ell Dr
Richardson TX 75081
972 669-0591

(G-12073)
VISTA-PRO AUTOMOTIVE LLC
2410 Nw 8th Pl (34475-5774)
PHONE..................................352 867-7272
EMP: 16
SALES (corp-wide): 81.4MM **Privately Held**
SIC: 3714 Mfg Motor Vehicle Parts/Accessories
HQ: Vista-Pro Automotive, Llc
15 Century Blvd Ste 600
Nashville TN 37214
888 250-2676

(G-12074)
WELL BILT INDUSTRIES USA LLC
3001 Sw 67th Avenue Rd # 100 (34474-1708)
PHONE..................................352 528-5566
Tim Schendel, *Vice Pres*
Virginia Macdonald, *Marketing Mgr*
Mark Macdonald,
EMP: 19 **EST:** 2009
SQ FT: 25,000
SALES (est): 3MM **Privately Held**
WEB: www.wellbiltdoors.com
SIC: 3442 Hangar doors, metal

(G-12075)
WESTERN IVY
6998 N Us Highway 27 (34482-8906)
PHONE..................................352 622-5767
EMP: 6 **EST:** 2019
SALES (est): 230.7K **Privately Held**
WEB: www.westernivy.com
SIC: 2395 Embroidery & art needlework

(G-12076)
WINCO MFG LLC (PA)
Also Called: Transmotion Medical
5516 Sw 1st Ln (34474-9366)
PHONE..................................352 854-2929
Jim Ankoviak, *CEO*
Justin Camp, *Production*
Richard Burchett, *Engineer*
Jessica Cuebas, *Sales Staff*
Mark Lazzeri, *Marketing Staff*
▲ **EMP:** 93 **EST:** 2010
SALES (est): 30.9MM **Privately Held**
WEB: www.wincomfg.com
SIC: 2599 Hospital furniture, except beds

(G-12077)
WOODS PRINTING OF OCALA INC
1740 Ne 23rd Ter (34470-4790)
PHONE..................................352 629-1665
James Wood, *President*
EMP: 6 **EST:** 1976
SQ FT: 3,000
SALES (est): 872.5K **Privately Held**
WEB: www.woodspfa.com
SIC: 2752 2759 Commercial printing, offset; letterpress printing

(G-12078)
YANDLES QUALITY ROOF TRUSSES
834 N Magnolia Ave (34475-8874)
PHONE..................................352 732-3000
Lanas C Yandle, *President*
EMP: 6 **EST:** 1985
SQ FT: 20,300
SALES (est): 659.3K **Privately Held**
WEB: www.yandles.com
SIC: 2439 5211 Trusses, wooden roof; roofing material

(G-12079)
YES SOLUTIONS GALLERY LLC
Also Called: Yes Ink Solutions
4901 E Slver Sprng Blvd (34470-3228)
PHONE..................................352 622-7937
Ron Corbett,
Sydney B Corbett,
EMP: 8 **EST:** 2007
SQ FT: 3,000
SALES (est): 327.9K **Privately Held**
SIC: 2893 Printing ink

Ocean Ridge
Palm Beach County

(G-12080)
TDK ELECTRONICS INC
6530 N Ocean Blvd (33435-5249)
PHONE..................................561 509-7771
EMP: 10 **Privately Held**

SIC: 3679 5065 3546 Electronic crystals; diskettes, computer; power-driven handtools; grinders, portable: electric or pneumatic
HQ: Tdk Electronics Inc.
485b Us Highway 1 S # 200
Iselin NJ 08830
732 906-4300

Ocklawaha
Marion County

(G-12081)
GRUENEWALD MFG CO INC
9800 Se 176th Court Rd (32179-4526)
PHONE..................................978 777-0200
Thomas Muldoon, *President*
Rickey Schwed, *Sales Staff*
▼ **EMP:** 10 **EST:** 1939
SALES (est): 915.1K **Privately Held**
WEB: www.whipcream.com
SIC: 3556 Food products machinery

Ocoee
Orange County

(G-12082)
AMERICAN SANI PARTITION CORP
300 Enterprise St (34761-3002)
P.O. Box 99 (34761-0099)
PHONE..................................407 656-0611
Ronald Birkenmaier, *President*
Gerald Birkenmaier, *Shareholder*
◆ **EMP:** 45 **EST:** 1934
SQ FT: 75,000
SALES (est): 7.5MM **Privately Held**
WEB: www.am-sanitary-partition.com
SIC: 2542 Partitions for floor attachment, prefabricated: except wood

(G-12083)
ANDRO CORP INDUSTRIES
3496 Meadow Breeze Loop (34761-4479)
PHONE..................................917 287-5294
Dewrell Joshua D, *Principal*
EMP: 7 **EST:** 2014
SALES (est): 222.4K **Privately Held**
WEB: www.androcorpind.com
SIC: 3999 Manufacturing industries

(G-12084)
BACKSTAGE SOFTWARE INC
2582 Maguire Rd Pmb 2 (34761-4749)
PHONE..................................407 925-8751
Louis M Bradley, *President*
EMP: 6 **EST:** 2010
SALES (est): 68.2K **Privately Held**
WEB: www.backstagesoftware.com
SIC: 7372 Prepackaged software

(G-12085)
FCS INDUSTRIES CORP
406 Anessa Rose Loop (34761-4623)
PHONE..................................407 947-3127
Willie D Fisher, *President*
EMP: 6 **EST:** 2014
SALES (est): 159.6K **Privately Held**
SIC: 3999 Manufacturing industries

(G-12086)
KREATIVE CERAMICS INC
2165 Twisted Pine Rd (34761-7671)
PHONE..................................321 278-9889
Christopher Taylor, *Director*
EMP: 6 **EST:** 2005
SALES (est): 60.5K **Privately Held**
SIC: 3269 Pottery products

(G-12087)
LIMITLESS MOBILE WHOLESALE INC (PA)
885 Sedalia St (34761-3164)
PHONE..................................321 710-6936
Jim Croal, *CTO*
EMP: 99 **EST:** 2013
SALES (est): 5.8MM **Privately Held**
SIC: 3663 Mobile communication equipment

(G-12088)
PHYSIORX LLC
2706 Rew Cir (34761-4215)
PHONE..................................407 718-5549
Denise Masson, *Principal*
EMP: 16 **EST:** 2001
SALES (est): 507.7K **Privately Held**
WEB: www.physiorx.com
SIC: 3842 Implants, surgical

(G-12089)
QUALITY VAULTS INC (PA)
751 S Bluford Ave (34761-2942)
PHONE..................................407 656-8781
James Tramonte, *President*
Donna G Bryce, *Corp Secy*
Donna G Butler, *Corp Secy*
Boettcher Joyce, *Vice Pres*
EMP: 13 **EST:** 1970
SALES (est): 2.3MM **Privately Held**
WEB: www.qualityvaults.com
SIC: 3272 5032 Burial vaults, concrete or precast terrazzo; brick, stone & related material

(G-12090)
STONE BRICK PAVERS INC
1699 Cambridge Village Ct (34761-6986)
PHONE..................................407 844-1455
Domingos Oliveira, *Principal*
EMP: 8 **EST:** 2010
SALES (est): 504.9K **Privately Held**
WEB: www.rusticbrickpavers.com
SIC: 3531 Pavers

(G-12091)
TEAK ISLE INC
Also Called: Teak Isle Manufacturing
401 Capitol Ct (34761-3024)
P.O. Box 417 (34761-0417)
PHONE..................................407 656-8885
Patrick H Brown, *President*
David R Brown, *Vice Pres*
Brian Oleary, *Project Mgr*
Justin Brady, *Marketing Staff*
Hector J Brown, *Director*
◆ **EMP:** 225 **EST:** 1980
SALES (est): 45.8MM **Privately Held**
WEB: www.teakisle.com
SIC: 2821 2542 2431 Plastics materials & resins; partitions & fixtures, except wood; millwork

(G-12092)
TMMR HOLDINGS LLC (PA)
Also Called: Verticals Unlimited
301 Enterprise St Unit A (34761-3030)
PHONE..................................407 295-5200
Thomas Mostardi, *General Mgr*
Lois Janofsky, *Bookkeeper*
Ahren Nevins, *Sales Staff*
Tracy Davis, *Office Mgr*
Michelle Mostardi, *Mng Member*
EMP: 22 **EST:** 2010
SALES (est): 3.1MM **Privately Held**
SIC: 2591 1799 Drapery hardware & blinds & shades; window treatment installation

(G-12093)
TRANSACTION DATA SYSTEMS INC
1555 Boren Dr (34761-2989)
PHONE..................................407 295-5050
Charles Hall, *Vice Pres*
EMP: 38 **EST:** 1977
SALES (est): 2.9MM **Privately Held**
WEB: www.rx30.com
SIC: 7372 Business oriented computer software

(G-12094)
U C FAB OF FLORIDA LLC
301 Enterprise St Unit C (34761-3030)
PHONE..................................407 614-4210
Rosa Dalbow, *Mng Member*
EMP: 9 **EST:** 2009
SALES (est): 461.5K **Privately Held**
SIC: 3448 Prefabricated metal components

Odessa
Hills County

(G-12095)
ICOSI MANUFACTURING LLC
11134 Challenger Ave (33556-3436)
PHONE..................................813 854-1333
EMP: 10 **EST:** 2007
SALES (est): 1.1MM **Privately Held**
SIC: 3469 3541 Mfg Metal Stampings Mfg Machine Tools-Cutting

Odessa
Hillsborough County

(G-12096)
3M RESIDENT MONITORING INC
1838 Gunn Hwy (33556-3524)
PHONE..................................813 749-5453
▲ **EMP:** 25
SALES (est): 3.4MM **Privately Held**
SIC: 3845 Mfg Electromedical Equipment

(G-12097)
A M TOOL & ENGINEERING COMPANY
2343 Destiny Way (33556-3411)
PHONE..................................727 375-5002
Jerry Mendik, *President*
EMP: 9 **EST:** 1997
SQ FT: 10,000
SALES (est): 601K **Privately Held**
SIC: 3599 Machine shop, jobbing & repair

(G-12098)
ADVANCED CNC MANUFACTURING
2313 Destiny Way (33556-3411)
P.O. Box 991 (33556-0991)
PHONE..................................727 372-8222
Miguel Carrosso, *President*
Maggie Carrosso, *Vice Pres*
Maria Carrosso, *Director*
EMP: 14 **EST:** 2002
SQ FT: 11,000
SALES (est): 2MM **Privately Held**
WEB: www.advanced-cnc.com
SIC: 3599 Machine shop, jobbing & repair

(G-12099)
AERONAUTICAL SYSTEMS ENGRG INC
2448 Destiny Way (33556-3412)
PHONE..................................727 375-2520
Faiek Zora, *President*
Jeffrey Kuliga, *Exec VP*
Laith Habhab, *Engineer*
James Clary, *Marketing Staff*
Matt Carullo, *Administration*
▲ **EMP:** 8 **EST:** 1994
SQ FT: 7,200
SALES (est): 1.5MM **Privately Held**
WEB: www.aerosyseng.com
SIC: 3699 Electrical equipment & supplies

(G-12100)
AIRCRAFT SYSTEMS GROUP INC
11528 Perpetual Dr (33556-3464)
PHONE..................................727 376-9292
Audrey Gallagher, *President*
Robert Gallagher, *Vice Pres*
EMP: 5 **EST:** 2004
SALES (est): 658.7K **Privately Held**
WEB: www.aircraftsystemsgroup.com
SIC: 3721 Aircraft

(G-12101)
AMROB INCORPORATED
Also Called: Aqueous Concepts
16101 Carden Dr (33556-3314)
PHONE..................................813 237-5891
Robert Pettit, *Owner*
EMP: 6 **EST:** 2001
SALES (est): 137.5K **Privately Held**
SIC: 2893 Lithographic ink

(G-12102)
ANVIL IRON WORKS INC
11607 Perpetual Dr (33556-3467)
PHONE..................................727 375-2884
Dennis Moulton, *President*
William Cheatley, *Vice Pres*
EMP: 21 **EST:** 1991
SQ FT: 14,000
SALES (est): 3.4MM **Privately Held**
SIC: 3444 3449 Sheet metalwork; miscellaneous metalwork

(G-12103)
ATLANTIC CUSTOM WOODCRAFT CORP
11146 Challenger Ave # 101 (33556-3425)
PHONE..................................727 645-6905
Trevor Haughey, *President*
Nichole Haughey, *Corp Secy*
Peter Atkins, *Vice Pres*
James R Haughey, *Vice Pres*
Donald Spence, *Vice Pres*
EMP: 20 **EST:** 1993
SQ FT: 15,000
SALES (est): 2.4MM **Privately Held**
WEB: www.atlanticcustomwoodcraft.com
SIC: 2431 Millwork

(G-12104)
ATTENTI US INC (PA)
Also Called: Electronic Monitoring
1838 Gunn Hwy (33556-3524)
PHONE..................................813 749-5454
Yoaz Reisman, *CEO*
Rachel Semago, *General Mgr*
Arnold Roese, *Vice Pres*
Jeffrey Aspenleiter, *Engineer*
Eyal Sharoni, *CFO*
▲ **EMP:** 160 **EST:** 1999
SQ FT: 10,000
SALES (est): 37.4MM **Privately Held**
WEB: www.attentigroup.com
SIC: 3669 Intercommunication systems, electric

(G-12105)
BAY TECH INDUSTRIES INC
13275 Byrd Dr (33556-5307)
PHONE..................................813 854-1774
Robert P Bourassa, *President*
Rick Seal, *Treasurer*
EMP: 48 **EST:** 1986
SQ FT: 11,800
SALES (est): 5.4MM **Privately Held**
WEB: www.baytechindustries.com
SIC: 3599 Machine shop, jobbing & repair

(G-12106)
BINNEY FAMILY OF FLORIDA INC
Also Called: Environmental Graphics
11232 Challenger Ave (33556-3420)
PHONE..................................727 376-5596
Keith Binney, *President*
Ray Binney, *Vice Pres*
Laura Binney, *Treasurer*
Charisse Clouse, *Manager*
Jan Jansen, *Manager*
EMP: 10 **EST:** 1993
SQ FT: 3,000
SALES (est): 1.6MM **Privately Held**
WEB: www.egisigns.com
SIC: 3993 Signs & advertising specialties

(G-12107)
BK PLASTICS INDUSTRY INC
13414 Byrd Dr (33556-5310)
PHONE..................................813 920-3628
Bruce Knecht, *President*
Robin Knecht, *Vice Pres*
▲ **EMP:** 16 **EST:** 1997
SQ FT: 22,000
SALES (est): 2.6MM **Privately Held**
WEB: www.bkplastics.com
SIC: 3089 Thermoformed finished plastic products; plastic processing

(G-12108)
BONEFISH BOATWORKS LLC
Also Called: Inshore Power Boats
1005 Gunn Hwy (33556-5301)
PHONE..................................727 243-6767
Ronald D Cook, *President*
EMP: 6 **EST:** 2011

GEOGRAPHIC

SALES (est): 224.8K **Privately Held**
WEB: www.bonefishboats.com
SIC: 3732 Boat building & repairing

(G-12109)
CAN CAN CONCEALMENT LLC
2521b Success Dr (33556-3401)
PHONE..................................727 841-6930
Darlene Cahill, *Partner*
Douglas Erickson, *Partner*
EMP: 6 **EST:** 2013
SALES (est): 379.3K **Privately Held**
WEB: www.cancanconcealment.com
SIC: 2389 2339 Men's miscellaneous accessories; garter belts; garters; women's & misses' accessories

(G-12110)
CHRISTIAN PUBLISHING INC
8807 Bys Run (33556-4522)
P.O. Box 128 (33556-0128)
PHONE..................................813 920-5664
Gaile Howell, *Principal*
EMP: 6 **EST:** 2015
SALES (est): 52.5K **Privately Held**
SIC: 2741 Miscellaneous publishing

(G-12111)
COAST WCP
Also Called: Bengal Industries
1806 Gunn Hwy (33556-3524)
PHONE..................................727 572-4249
John Guthrie, *President*
▲ **EMP:** 24 **EST:** 1981
SQ FT: 20,000
SALES (est): 546.6K **Privately Held**
SIC: 3714 3728 Gears, motor vehicle; gears, aircraft power transmission

(G-12112)
COMPONENT GENERAL INC
2445 Success Dr (33556-3429)
PHONE..................................727 376-6655
James A Cook, *President*
▲ **EMP:** 36 **EST:** 1973
SQ FT: 16,000
SALES (est): 4.4MM **Privately Held**
WEB: www.componentgeneral.com
SIC: 3676 5065 3663 3577 Electronic resistors; electronic parts & equipment; radio & TV communications equipment; computer peripheral equipment

(G-12113)
CONVEYOR CONSULTING & RBR CORP
2511 Destiny Way (33556-3473)
PHONE..................................813 385-1254
Ronald D Fernandes, *President*
◆ **EMP:** 7 **EST:** 1997
SQ FT: 12,500
SALES (est): 4MM **Privately Held**
WEB: www.ccrconveyor.com
SIC: 3535 Conveyors & conveying equipment

(G-12114)
D G MORRISON INC (PA)
Also Called: Arete Industries
13209 Byrd Dr (33556-5307)
PHONE..................................813 865-0208
Donald Morrison, *CEO*
Dan Morrison, *Vice Pres*
James Slanina, *Opers Staff*
John Glenzer, *Sales Staff*
▲ **EMP:** 19 **EST:** 2000
SQ FT: 15,000
SALES (est): 2.9MM **Privately Held**
WEB: www.areteindustries.us
SIC: 3281 3993 3949 2759 Granite, cut & shaped; signs & advertising specialties; sporting & athletic goods; commercial printing; bar, restaurant & cafeteria furniture; architectural metalwork

(G-12115)
DAIS CORP
11552 Prosperous Dr (33556-3452)
PHONE..................................727 375-8484
Timothy N Tangredi, *Ch of Bd*
Brian C Johnson, *CTO*
EMP: 10 **EST:** 1993
SQ FT: 7,200
SALES (est): 1MM **Privately Held**
WEB: www.daisanalytic.com
SIC: 3822 3589 Air conditioning & refrigeration controls; air flow controllers, air conditioning & refrigeration; temperature controls, automatic; electric heat controls; sewage & water treatment equipment

(G-12116)
DILO PRODUCTION INC (PA)
Also Called: Dilo Direct
11642 Pyramid Dr (33556-3449)
PHONE..................................727 376-5593
Lukas Rothlisberger, *CEO*
Reinhold Probst, *President*
EMP: 6 **EST:** 2012
SQ FT: 800
SALES (est): 1.5MM **Privately Held**
WEB: www.us.dilo.com
SIC: 1389 5169 Gas field services; compressed gas

(G-12117)
EASTERN RIBBON & ROLL CORP (PA)
Also Called: Paper Converter
1920 Gunn Hwy (33556-3524)
PHONE..................................813 676-8600
▲ **EMP:** 22
SQ FT: 100,000
SALES (est): 5.6MM **Privately Held**
SIC: 3955 5044 5131 Carbon Paper And Inked Ribbons

(G-12118)
ELECTRO MECH SOLUTIONS INC
Also Called: E M S
1555 Gunn Hwy (33556-5308)
PHONE..................................813 792-0400
Venkata Boyanapalli, *President*
Venkat Boyanapalli, *President*
RAO Jupalli, *Finance Mgr*
EMP: 25 **EST:** 2001
SQ FT: 45,000
SALES (est): 3.8MM **Privately Held**
WEB: www.emsinc.net
SIC: 3444 3542 8711 Sheet metalwork; sheet metalworking machines; mechanical engineering

(G-12119)
EUCLID CHEMICAL COMPANY
Also Called: Increte Systems
19215 Redwood Rd (33556)
P.O. Box 196 (33556-0196)
PHONE..................................813 886-8811
Nathan Blackburn, *Technical Staff*
▼ **EMP:** 13 **EST:** 2007
SALES (est): 1.2MM **Privately Held**
WEB: www.euclidchemical.com
SIC: 2899 Chemical preparations

(G-12120)
FLEDA PHARMACEUTICALS CORP
13231 Byrd Legg Dr (33556-5325)
PHONE..................................813 920-9882
Yang Wang, *CEO*
EMP: 5 **EST:** 2018
SALES (est): 333.3K **Privately Held**
WEB: www.fledausa.com
SIC: 2023 Dietary supplements, dairy & non-dairy based

(G-12121)
FLORIDA CUSTOM MOLD INC (PA)
Also Called: Fcm
1806 Gunn Hwy (33556-3524)
PHONE..................................813 343-5080
Michael A Cave, *President*
Joe Duren, *General Mgr*
Gary Krivan, *Plant Mgr*
Austin Cave, *Engineer*
Cynthia Park, *Controller*
◆ **EMP:** 89 **EST:** 1988
SQ FT: 54,000
SALES: 10.1MM **Privately Held**
WEB: www.fla-mold.com
SIC: 3089 Injection molding of plastics

(G-12122)
GATECRAFTERSCOM
13100 State Road 54 (33556-3419)
PHONE..................................800 537-4283
Anthony Gaeto, *President*
EMP: 15 **EST:** 2000
SALES (est): 1.1MM **Privately Held**
WEB: www.gatecrafters.com
SIC: 3699 Security devices

(G-12123)
GFSF INC
Also Called: Power Quality International
2404 Merchant Ave (33556-3460)
P.O. Box 190437, Boise ID (83719-0437)
PHONE..................................727 478-7284
Gregory NC Ferguson, *Ch of Bd*
Shaun D Ferguson, *President*
Doug Dayton, *Marketing Staff*
EMP: 6 **EST:** 1994
SQ FT: 7,500
SALES (est): 2.5MM **Privately Held**
WEB: www.powerqualityinternational.com
SIC: 3612 Transformers, except electric

(G-12124)
GREAT AMERICAN WOODWORKS INC
Also Called: Tables Designs
11445 Pyramid Dr (33556-3455)
PHONE..................................727 375-1212
Jennifer Bilthouse, *President*
Bob Bilthouse, *Corp Secy*
Jakea Cates, *Sales Associate*
EMP: 15 **EST:** 1979
SQ FT: 15,000
SALES (est): 1.9MM **Privately Held**
WEB: www.tabledesigns.com
SIC: 2211 Sheets, bedding & table cloths: cotton

(G-12125)
H&M PHILLIPS INC
Also Called: Liberty Printing
12772 Burns Dr (33556-4071)
PHONE..................................727 797-4600
Mitch Phillips, *President*
EMP: 9 **EST:** 1986
SALES (est): 361.5K **Privately Held**
SIC: 2752 Commercial printing, offset

(G-12126)
INCRETE SYSTEMS
1725 Gunn Hwy (33556-5305)
PHONE..................................813 886-8811
EMP: 9 **EST:** 2015
SALES (est): 599.8K **Privately Held**
WEB: www.euclidchemical.com
SIC: 2899 Chemical preparations

(G-12127)
INTERNATIONAL GRAN & STONE LLC
Also Called: Granite Tampa Bay
1842 Gunn Hwy (33556-3524)
PHONE..................................813 920-6500
Lisa Banks, *Project Mgr*
Melody Haasl, *Project Mgr*
Nate Faiella, *Production*
Ryan Hulsey, *Production*
Bill Stivali, *Controller*
▲ **EMP:** 45 **EST:** 2002
SQ FT: 20,000
SALES (est): 9.9MM **Privately Held**
WEB: www.igscountertops.com
SIC: 3281 1799 Cut stone & stone products; counter top installation

(G-12128)
INTERNATIONAL IMAGING MTLS INC
Also Called: Talon Industries
2300 Destiny Way (33556-3403)
PHONE..................................727 834-8200
EMP: 12
SALES (corp-wide): 133.8MM **Privately Held**
SIC: 2899 Mfg Chemical Preparations
PA: International Imaging Materials, Inc.
310 Commerce Dr
Amherst NY 14228
716 691-6333

(G-12129)
JACORE TECHNOLOGIES
1346 Osceola Hollow Rd (33556-3823)
PHONE..................................813 860-7465
Corman D Jennifer, *Vice Pres*
EMP: 13 **EST:** 2018
SALES (est): 301K **Privately Held**
WEB: www.jacoretechnologies.com
SIC: 3599 Machine shop, jobbing & repair

(G-12130)
KMG MARKETING LLC
Also Called: Abco Graphics & Printing
11515 Pyramid Dr (33556-3457)
PHONE..................................727 376-7200
Kelly McKnight Goelz, *CEO*
Deb Smith, *Production*
Cathy Lange, *Office Mgr*
EMP: 9 **EST:** 2016
SALES (est): 1.1MM **Privately Held**
WEB: www.abcotogo.com
SIC: 2752 Commercial printing, offset

(G-12131)
LIGHTNING SPECIALISTS INC
11498 Prosperous Dr (33556-3519)
PHONE..................................727 938-3560
Charles O Wilson, *President*
EMP: 5 **EST:** 2001
SALES (est): 759.8K **Privately Held**
WEB: www.lsi-fl.com
SIC: 3643 Current-carrying wiring devices

(G-12132)
LINDSEY MACKE BINDERY PRINTING
11626 Prosperous Dr (33556-3458)
PHONE..................................727 514-3570
Edgar Lee Lindsey Jr, *Principal*
EMP: 9 **EST:** 2008
SALES (est): 133.9K **Privately Held**
SIC: 2752 Commercial printing, lithographic

(G-12133)
MASKING SYSTEMS OF AMERICA
13221 Byrd Dr (33556-5307)
PHONE..................................813 920-2271
EMP: 18
SALES (est): 2MM **Privately Held**
SIC: 2891 Mfg Adhesives/Sealants

(G-12134)
MICRON PHARMAWORKS LLC
Also Called: Micron Pharmaworks, Inc.
2346 Success Dr (33556-3430)
PHONE..................................727 232-8200
Peter Buczynsky, *CEO*
Ben Brower, *Vice Pres*
Ingo Federle, *Vice Pres*
Frank Lovetere, *CFO*
Ray Zaccardi, *Sales Staff*
▲ **EMP:** 105 **EST:** 2002
SQ FT: 35,926
SALES: 28.3MM **Privately Held**
WEB: www.pharmaworks.com
SIC: 3565 Packaging machinery
HQ: Pro Mach, Inc.
50 E Rvrcnter Blvd Ste 18
Covington KY 41011
513 831-8778

(G-12135)
NICRAF SOFTWARE & CREATIONS
17413 Equestrian Trl (33556-1847)
PHONE..................................813 842-9648
Nicholas M Gordon, *Principal*
EMP: 7 **EST:** 2007
SALES (est): 372.6K **Privately Held**
WEB: www.nicraf.com
SIC: 7372 Prepackaged software

(G-12136)
NU TREK INC
Also Called: Everett-Morrison Motorcars
16708 Hutchison Rd (33556-2321)
PHONE..................................813 920-4348
Buford R Everett, *President*
Brett Everett, *Vice Pres*
Bruce Everett, *Treasurer*
EMP: 8 **EST:** 1983
SQ FT: 15,000

SALES (est): 146.5K **Privately Held**
SIC: 3711 Cars, armored, assembly of

(G-12137)
O2 DEFENSE LLC
13501 Lunker Ct (33556-4018)
PHONE..................................704 408-7357
Mark Owens, *Branch Mgr*
EMP: 8
SALES (corp-wide): 98.8K **Privately Held**
SIC: 3812 Defense systems & equipment
PA: O2 Defense, Llc
3152 Little Rd
Trinity FL

(G-12138)
PACE LAUNCHER CASINGS LLC
Also Called: Pace Defense
2445 Merchant Ave Unit B (33556-3466)
PHONE..................................813 245-6570
Scot Pace, *Principal*
EMP: 6 **EST:** 2010
SALES (est): 266.1K **Privately Held**
WEB: www.reloadableshells.com
SIC: 3489 Ordnance & accessories

(G-12139)
PLASMA ENERGY GROUP LLC
17402 Isbell Ln (33556-1962)
PHONE..................................813 760-6385
Stacy Y Patrick, *Principal*
EMP: 8 **EST:** 2015
SALES (est): 249.8K **Privately Held**
WEB: www.plasmaenergy-group.com
SIC: 2836 Plasmas

(G-12140)
POLARIS SALES CO INC
Also Called: Polaris Electrical Connectors
11625 Prosperous Dr (33556-3459)
PHONE..................................727 372-1703
Janeen Patten, *President*
Lisaann Armes, *President*
Luke Hill, *Vice Pres*
Troje Zibilich, *Opers Mgr*
Rich Fish, *Engineer*
▲ **EMP:** 112 **EST:** 1973
SQ FT: 48,334
SALES: 21.3MM **Privately Held**
WEB: www.polarisconnectors.com
SIC: 3643 Connectors & terminals for electrical devices

(G-12141)
POWER QUALITY INTL LLC
2404 Merchant Ave (33556-3460)
P.O. Box 190437, Boise ID (83719-0437)
PHONE..................................727 478-7284
Jarrod Dobbs, *Vice Pres*
Jeffrey Turner, *VP Engrg*
Jane Wilhite, *Controller*
Gregory Ferguson,
Shaun Ferguson,
EMP: 8 **EST:** 2013
SALES (est): 1.4MM **Privately Held**
WEB: www.powerqualityinternational.com
SIC: 3612 Power & distribution transformers

(G-12142)
PRECAST SOLUTION SYSTEM INC
2045 Chesapeake Dr Ste 2 (33556-3669)
PHONE..................................813 949-7929
EMP: 10
SALES (est): 1.2MM **Privately Held**
SIC: 3272 Mfg Concrete Products

(G-12143)
PREMIER ARCHTCTURAL SHTMTL INC
8501 Northton Groves Blvd (33556-1402)
PHONE..................................727 373-8937
Angel L Torres Jr, *Vice Pres*
EMP: 9 **EST:** 2019
SALES (est): 321.8K **Privately Held**
SIC: 3444 Sheet metalwork

(G-12144)
PURE 32 LLC
17633 Gunn Hwy Ste 132 (33556-1912)
PHONE..................................813 792-9219
Kristina Goldfield, *Principal*
EMP: 7 **EST:** 2018
SALES (est): 353.8K **Privately Held**
SIC: 2323 Men's & boys' neckwear

(G-12145)
RICHARD APPELBAUM & ASSOCIATES
18412 Keystone Grove Blvd (33556-4812)
P.O. Box 99 (33556-0099)
PHONE..................................813 920-0300
Richard Appelbaum, *President*
Adele Appelbaum, *Admin Sec*
EMP: 4 **EST:** 1976
SALES (est): 4MM **Privately Held**
SIC: 2329 Men's & boys' sportswear & athletic clothing

(G-12146)
ROAN MANUFACTURING INC
1834 Gunn Hwy (33556-3524)
PHONE..................................813 510-4929
Greg Roan, *President*
EMP: 8 **EST:** 2005
SALES (est): 986.4K **Privately Held**
SIC: 3599 Machine shop, jobbing & repair

(G-12147)
ROORDA BUIDERS INC
15115 Race Track Rd (33556-2913)
PHONE..................................727 410-7776
Milt Roorda, *President*
EMP: 6 **EST:** 1994
SALES (est): 233.6K **Privately Held**
WEB: www.roordabuilders.com
SIC: 2426 Frames for upholstered furniture, wood

(G-12148)
SABALO BOATS
1005 Gunn Hwy (33556-5301)
PHONE..................................727 243-6767
EMP: 6 **EST:** 2013
SALES (est): 93K **Privately Held**
WEB: www.sabaloboats.com
SIC: 3732 Boat building & repairing

(G-12149)
SEAL PUBLISHING LLC
14611 Middlefield Ln (33556-3634)
PHONE..................................813 792-5852
Therese C Seal, *Manager*
EMP: 6 **EST:** 2005
SALES (est): 37.5K **Privately Held**
SIC: 2741 Miscellaneous publishing

(G-12150)
SEQUOIA BRANDS INC
13100 State Road 54 (33556-3419)
PHONE..................................813 969-2000
Anthony Gaeto, *President*
EMP: 25 **EST:** 2010
SALES (est): 1.1MM **Privately Held**
WEB: www.sequoiabrands.com
SIC: 3953 Irons, marking or branding

(G-12151)
SILCO SOFTWARE TECHNOLOGY INC
16223 Ivy Lake Dr (33556-6047)
PHONE..................................813 475-4591
Rama Juturu, *President*
Chandra Juturu, *Vice Pres*
EMP: 10 **EST:** 1995
SALES (est): 805K **Privately Held**
WEB: www.ramaonhealthcare.com
SIC: 7372 Prepackaged software

(G-12152)
SITE ESSENTIALS
13209 Byrd Dr (33556-5307)
PHONE..................................813 865-0208
EMP: 8 **EST:** 2019
SALES (est): 46K **Privately Held**
WEB: www.siteessentialscompany.com
SIC: 3993 Signs & advertising specialties

(G-12153)
SOUTHERN CLOSET SYSTEMS INC
13211 Byrd Dr (33556-5307)
PHONE..................................813 926-9348
Wayne Smith, *President*
Joanne Smith, *Treasurer*
EMP: 6 **EST:** 1983
SQ FT: 4,000
SALES (est): 494.1K **Privately Held**
WEB: www.southerncloset.com
SIC: 2449 5211 Wood containers; closets, interiors & accessories

(G-12154)
SPECTRUM ENGINEERING & MFG INC
11609 Pyramid Dr (33556-3450)
PHONE..................................727 376-5510
Nicholas Juranko, *President*
Dan Juranko, *Treasurer*
Anthony Juranko, *Admin Sec*
EMP: 5 **EST:** 1991
SQ FT: 4,200
SALES (est): 814.7K **Privately Held**
SIC: 3444 8711 Sheet metalwork; engineering services

(G-12155)
STAINLESS FABRICATORS INC
11107 Challenger Ave (33556-3439)
PHONE..................................813 926-7113
Keith B Binney, *President*
Diana Binney, *Vice Pres*
Scott J Binney, *Vice Pres*
Scott Binney, *Vice Pres*
Brian Binney, *Project Mgr*
▼ **EMP:** 47
SQ FT: 25,000
SALES (est): 4.5MM **Privately Held**
WEB: www.stainlessfabinc.com
SIC: 3446 3444 3429 3312 Railings, bannisters, guards, etc.: made from metal pipe; fences or posts, ornamental iron or steel; sheet metalwork; manufactured hardware (general); blast furnaces & steel mills

(G-12156)
STRATCO PHARMACEUTICALS LLC
2600 Lakepointe Pkwy (33556-4375)
PHONE..................................813 403-5060
Brian Nugent, *President*
Alexander Sierra, *Manager*
EMP: 12 **EST:** 2011
SALES (est): 4MM
SALES (corp-wide): 27.7MM **Privately Held**
WEB: www.stratfordrx.com
SIC: 2834 Pharmaceutical preparations
HQ: Stratford Care Usa, Inc.
2600 Lakepointe Pkwy
Odessa FL 33556
877 498-2002

(G-12157)
STRATFORD CARE USA INC (HQ) ✪
2600 Lakepointe Pkwy (33556-4375)
PHONE..................................877 498-2002
Brian Nugent, *CEO*
Nicole Ladue, *Vice Pres*
Jenny Graflind, *Director*
Hakan Lagerberg, *Director*
EMP: 3 **EST:** 2020
SALES (est): 4.3MM
SALES (corp-wide): 27.7MM **Privately Held**
WEB: www.stratfordrx.com
SIC: 2048 Mineral feed supplements
PA: Swedencare Ab (Publ)
Per Albin Hanssons Vag 41
Malmo 214 3
408 593-3

(G-12158)
SUNCOAST PAVERS LLC
16544 Ivy Lake Dr (33556-6016)
PHONE..................................813 323-4014
Richard Fernandez, *Principal*
EMP: 6 **EST:** 2008
SALES (est): 257.4K **Privately Held**
WEB: www.suncoastbrickpavers.com
SIC: 3531 Pavers

(G-12159)
TOUCHPOINT MEDICAL INC (PA)
2200 Touchpoint Dr (33556-4435)
PHONE..................................813 854-1905
Brian McNeill, *CEO*
Pascal Testeil, *President*
Michael McCluhan, *Area Mgr*
Mark Harris, *Manager*
Mark Rickert, *Manager*
EMP: 314 **EST:** 2016
SALES (est): 69.5MM **Privately Held**
WEB: www.touchpointmed.com
SIC: 3845 Laser systems & equipment, medical

(G-12160)
TRINITY CREAMERY INC
14167 Wadsworth Dr (33556-4303)
PHONE..................................813 926-2023
Robert J Byrne, *Principal*
EMP: 6 **EST:** 2009
SALES (est): 120.9K **Privately Held**
SIC: 2021 Creamery butter

(G-12161)
TRU SIMULATION + TRAINING INC
1551 Gunn Hwy (33556-5308)
PHONE..................................813 792-9300
Troy Fey, *Vice Pres*
Gerald Messaris, *Vice Pres*
Kristen Samson, *Vice Pres*
Jeff Stewart, *Vice Pres*
Anthony Ackerman, *Project Mgr*
EMP: 100
SALES (corp-wide): 11.6B **Publicly Held**
WEB: www.trusimulation.com
SIC: 3443 3699 Space simulation chambers, metal plate; flight simulators (training aids), electronic
HQ: Tru Simulation + Training Inc.
5 Alliance Dr
Goose Creek SC 29445
843 574-5469

(G-12162)
UNITED CHAIR INDUSTRIES LLC
16442 Ivy Lake Dr (33556-6049)
PHONE..................................386 333-0800
Jalal Chowdhury, *CEO*
Victor Yan, *Managing Dir*
EMP: 6 **EST:** 2015
SQ FT: 60,000
SALES (est): 328K **Privately Held**
WEB: www.unitedofficechair.com
SIC: 2522 5021 Office chairs, benches & stools, except wood; chairs

(G-12163)
USB PLASTICS
11805 State Road 54 (33556-3469)
PHONE..................................727 375-8840
James Bylone, *Principal*
EMP: 7 **EST:** 2013
SALES (est): 238.4K **Privately Held**
WEB: www.usbplastics.com
SIC: 3089 Injection molding of plastics

(G-12164)
USBEV PRODUCTS INC
11805 State Road 54 (33556-3469)
PHONE..................................727 375-8840
Charles Williams, *President*
▼ **EMP:** 12 **EST:** 2011
SALES (est): 337.1K **Privately Held**
WEB: www.usbplastics.com
SIC: 3089 Injection molding of plastics

(G-12165)
VUESSENCE INC
17633 Gunn Hwy Ste 107 (33556-1912)
PHONE..................................813 792-7123
Maha Sallam, *President*
EMP: 5 **EST:** 2010
SALES (est): 318.3K **Privately Held**
WEB: www.vuessence.com
SIC: 3841 Surgical & medical instruments

(G-12166)
WOODWORKS KIT & BATH DESIGNS
8717 Gunn Hwy (33556-3210)
PHONE..................................813 926-0570
Eva D Nesbitt, *Owner*
EMP: 11 **EST:** 2014
SALES (est): 1.3MM **Privately Held**
WEB: www.woodworksdesigns.com
SIC: 2434 Wood kitchen cabinets

(G-12167)
ZEL CUSTOM MANUFACTURING LLC
11419 Challenger Ave (33556-3446)
PHONE..................................303 880-8701
Michael Brendzel, *Principal*
EMP: 8 **EST:** 2010
SALES (est): 415.9K **Privately Held**
WEB: www.zelcustom.com
SIC: 3999 Manufacturing industries

Okahumpka
Lake County

(G-12168)
AMERICAN MFG & MCH INC
Also Called: Vac-Tron Equipment
27137 County Road 33 (34762-3207)
PHONE..................................352 728-2222
Don M Buckner Sr, *President*
Gene M Buckner, *Vice Pres*
EMP: 51 **EST:** 1999
SQ FT: 70,000
SALES (est): 6.2MM **Privately Held**
SIC: 3443 3544 3563 3531 Industrial vessels, tanks & containers; industrial molds; air & gas compressors; construction machinery

(G-12169)
CEMEX MATERIALS LLC
27111 County Road 33 (34762-3209)
PHONE..................................352 435-0783
Rick Rhodes, *Branch Mgr*
EMP: 73
SQ FT: 17,463 **Privately Held**
SIC: 3271 3273 3272 1422 Blocks, concrete or cinder: standard; ready-mixed concrete; pipe, concrete or lined with concrete; crushed & broken limestone
HQ: Cemex Materials Llc
1501 Belvedere Rd
West Palm Beach FL 33406
561 833-5555

(G-12170)
CORESLAB STRCTURES ORLANDO INC
2720 County Road 470 (34762-3117)
PHONE..................................407 855-3191
Sidney Spiegel, *Ch of Bd*
Luigi Franciosa, *President*
Matthew Metz, *President*
Mario Franciosa, *Exec VP*
Dominic Franciosa, *Vice Pres*
◆ **EMP:** 42 **EST:** 1993
SQ FT: 17,000
SALES (est): 15.1MM
SALES (corp-wide): 178.7K **Privately Held**
WEB: www.coreslab.com
SIC: 3272 Concrete products
PA: Arge Umweltzentrum Lauingen
Kastellstr.
Lauingen (Donau)
907 271-0

(G-12171)
FLORIDA WILBERT INC
27439 Hayward Worm Frm Rd (34762)
PHONE..................................352 728-3531
Sam Smart, *Manager*
EMP: 9
SQ FT: 9,600
SALES (corp-wide): 3MM **Privately Held**
WEB: www.floridawilbert.com
SIC: 3272 Burial vaults, concrete or precast terrazzo
PA: Florida Wilbert Inc
5050 New Kings Rd
Jacksonville FL 32209
904 765-2641

Okeechobee
Okeechobee County

(G-12172)
ALLIED WELDING & MAINT INC
2912 Nw 35th Dr (34972-1181)
P.O. Box 1084 (34973-1084)
PHONE..................................863 634-7718
Mike Corwin, *President*
EMP: 5 **EST:** 2002
SALES (est): 500K **Privately Held**
WEB: www.alliedwelding.net
SIC: 7692 Welding repair

(G-12173)
CHARLES COMPOSITES LLC
Also Called: Charles Industries
1252 Ne 12th St (34972-3073)
PHONE..................................863 357-2500
Joseph T Charles, *Mng Member*
EMP: 10 **EST:** 2012
SQ FT: 40,000
SALES (est): 958.5K **Privately Held**
SIC: 3229 Tubing, glass

(G-12174)
COMMUNICATION EQP & ENGRG CO
Also Called: Ceeco
519 Sw Park St (34972-4166)
PHONE..................................863 357-0798
Nancy M Haist, *Chairman*
Mike Freeman, *Administration*
EMP: 15 **EST:** 1930
SALES (est): 2.4MM **Privately Held**
WEB: www.ceeco.net
SIC: 3661 Telephone & telegraph apparatus

(G-12175)
DAIRY FEEDS INC (PA)
1901 Nw 9th St (34972-2074)
P.O. Box 1365 (34973-1365)
PHONE..................................863 763-0258
Louis E Larson Jr, *President*
John Brooks, *Vice Pres*
EMP: 5 **EST:** 1978
SQ FT: 6,000
SALES (est): 6.2MM **Privately Held**
SIC: 2048 Feed premixes

(G-12176)
DIAMOND R FERTILIZER CO INC
Ranch Fertilizer Div
710 Ne 5th Ave (34972-2601)
PHONE..................................863 763-2158
Wayne Prevatt, *Prdtn Mgr*
Kim Johnson, *Human Resources*
Tim McKenna, *Sales Staff*
Pat Hood, *Manager*
Matthew Wilkins, *Manager*
EMP: 19
SALES (corp-wide): 109.3MM **Privately Held**
WEB: www.diamond-r.com
SIC: 2875 2879 Fertilizers, mixing only; agricultural chemicals
HQ: Diamond R Fertilizer Co., Inc.
4100 Glades Cut Off Rd
Fort Pierce FL 34981
772 464-9300

(G-12177)
ECOTEC MANUFACTURING INC
312 Sw 7th Ave (34974-4279)
P.O. Box 5501, Fort Lauderdale (33310-5501)
PHONE..................................863 357-4500
Neal Markus, *President*
Neil Markus, *President*
Michael D Fishman, *Vice Pres*
◆ **EMP:** 22 **EST:** 2001
SALES (est): 3.2MM **Privately Held**
WEB: www.ecotecsolar.com
SIC: 3999 Barber & beauty shop equipment

(G-12178)
GALLEY MAID MARINE PDTS INC
60 Ne 110th St (34972-7507)
PHONE..................................863 467-6070
Laura Tumoszwicz, *President*
Ernie Tumoszwicz, *Vice Pres*
Ronald Tumoszwicz, *Vice Pres*
◆ **EMP:** 10 **EST:** 1967
SQ FT: 75,000
SALES (est): 1.2MM **Privately Held**
WEB: www.galleymaid.com
SIC: 3429 Marine hardware

(G-12179)
GATOR FEED CO INC
1205 Us Highway 98 N (34972-8766)
P.O. Box 756 (34973-0756)
PHONE..................................863 763-3337
Patricia Ziglar, *President*
Tom Ziglar, *Vice Pres*
Larry Davis, *Treasurer*
Jeannie Tindall, *Office Mgr*
Linda Davis, *Admin Sec*
EMP: 15 **EST:** 1958
SQ FT: 8,000
SALES (est): 2.4MM **Privately Held**
WEB: www.gatorfeedco.com
SIC: 2048 Livestock feeds

(G-12180)
GRANNYS CHEESECAKE & MORE INC
17003 Nw 32nd Ave (34972-8430)
PHONE..................................561 847-6599
EMP: 7 **EST:** 2019
SALES (est): 279.6K **Privately Held**
SIC: 2591 Window blinds

(G-12181)
HERNANDEZ MOBILE WELDING INC
20320 Nw 258th St (34972-6993)
PHONE..................................954 347-4071
Estuardo Hernandez, *Principal*
EMP: 6 **EST:** 2002
SALES (est): 58.6K **Privately Held**
WEB: www.hmweld.com
SIC: 7692 Welding repair

(G-12182)
INDEPENDENT NEWSMEDIA INC USA
Also Called: Clewiston News
107 Sw 17th St Ste D (34974-6110)
PHONE..................................863 983-9148
EMP: 8 **Privately Held**
SIC: 2711 Newspapers-Publishing/Printing
HQ: Independent Newsmedia Usa, Inc.
110 Galaxy Dr
Dover DE 19901
302 674-3600

(G-12183)
JFE COMPOST
11000 Red Barn Rd Ne (34974)
PHONE..................................863 532-9629
Gene Lewis, *Principal*
EMP: 11 **EST:** 2015
SALES (est): 879K **Privately Held**
SIC: 2875 Compost

(G-12184)
JW FABRICATIONS INC
32801 Us Highway 441 N # 171
(34972-4402)
PHONE..................................772 201-7097
James W Marshall Sr, *President*
EMP: 6 **EST:** 2004
SALES (est): 88.3K **Privately Held**
SIC: 3999 Manufacturing industries

(G-12185)
LAKESIDE RECREATIONAL INC
4074 Us Highway 441 Se (34974-7213)
PHONE..................................863 467-1530
Gary Ruppert, *Principal*
EMP: 6 **EST:** 2008
SALES (est): 115.5K **Privately Held**
SIC: 3799 Recreational vehicles

(G-12186)
LE POSH PUP
14625 Nw 298th St (34972-5621)
PHONE..................................561 625-6391
Melissa Ayers, *Principal*
EMP: 6 **EST:** 2010
SALES (est): 93.7K **Privately Held**
SIC: 3999 Pet supplies

(G-12187)
OKEECHOBEE ASPHALT & READY MIX
503 Nw 9th St (34972-2123)
P.O. Box 1994 (34973-1994)
PHONE..................................863 763-7373
Christopher M Lynch, *President*
Robert P Gent, *Vice Pres*
Jim Haywood, *Manager*
Raquel M Rodriguez, *Director*
EMP: 9 **EST:** 2007
SALES (est): 560K **Privately Held**
WEB: www.cwrcontracting.com
SIC: 3273 Ready-mixed concrete

(G-12188)
OUR VILLAGE OKEECHOBEE INC
325 Se 15th Ave (34974-4722)
PHONE..................................863 467-0158
Lonnie Kirsch, *Vice Pres*
Kris Schwartz, *Production*
EMP: 7 **EST:** 2015
SALES: 43.9K **Privately Held**
WEB: www.southcentralfloridalife.com
SIC: 2711 Newspapers, publishing & printing

(G-12189)
ROOF TILE ADMINISTRATION INC
1289 Ne 9th Ave (34972-3501)
PHONE..................................863 467-0042
Reinaldo Padron, *Principal*
EMP: 13 **EST:** 2007
SQ FT: 54,976
SALES (est): 847K **Privately Held**
SIC: 3272 Roofing tile & slabs, concrete

(G-12190)
ROOF TILE INC
Also Called: Entegra Roof Tile
1289 Ne 9th Ave (34972-3501)
PHONE..................................863 467-0042
Michael Johnson, *President*
EMP: 37 **EST:** 1997
SALES (est): 5.7MM **Privately Held**
WEB: www.headwaters.com
SIC: 3272 3271 Concrete products; concrete block & brick
HQ: Headwaters Incorporated
10701 S River Front Pkwy # 300
South Jordan UT 84095

(G-12191)
SAND HILL ROCK LLC
7660 Ne 304th St (34972-0329)
P.O. Box 13896, Fort Pierce (34979-3896)
PHONE..................................772 216-4852
J Andrew Murphy, *Mng Member*
EMP: 7 **EST:** 2013
SALES (est): 841.5K **Privately Held**
SIC: 1446 Silica sand mining

(G-12192)
SEMINOLE SIGN COMPANY LLC
16900 Reservation Rd Ne (34974-2803)
PHONE..................................863 623-6600
Laverne D Thomas, *Manager*
EMP: 7 **EST:** 2011
SALES (est): 359.5K **Privately Held**
SIC: 3993 Signs & advertising specialties

(G-12193)
SUPERIOR CAST STONE LLC
6344 Se 30th Pkwy (34974-1171)
PHONE..................................863 634-4771
Jose Nunez, *Principal*
▲ **EMP:** 12 **EST:** 2010
SALES (est): 2.3MM **Privately Held**
SIC: 3272 Concrete products

(G-12194)
WORLD BOAT MANUFACTURING INC
8040 Nw 144th Trl (34972-9678)
PHONE..................................863 824-0015
Stanley White, *President*
EMP: 11 **EST:** 1995
SQ FT: 11,152
SALES (est): 420.2K **Privately Held**
SIC: 3732 Boats, fiberglass: building & repairing

▲ = Import ▼=Export
◆ =Import/Export

Old Town
Dixie County

(G-12195)
ANDERSON MINING CORPORATION (HQ)
624 Ne Highway 349 (32680-5031)
P.O. Box 38 (32680-0038)
PHONE..................................352 542-7942
Rolfe Wall, *President*
Joe Anderson Jr, *Corp Secy*
Joe Anderson III, *Vice Pres*
EMP: 3 **EST:** 1980
SQ FT: 4,000
SALES (est): 9.4MM
SALES (corp-wide): 168.7MM **Privately Held**
WEB: www.andersoncolumbia.com
SIC: **1422** Lime rock, ground
PA: Anderson Columbia Co., Inc.
871 Nw Guerdon St
Lake City FL 32055
386 752-7585

(G-12196)
FANNING SPRINGS ICE COMPANY
3080 Pine Ave (32680)
PHONE..................................352 463-1999
EMP: 6 **EST:** 1997
SALES (est): 210K **Privately Held**
SIC: **2097** Mfg Ice

(G-12197)
HENRY W LONG
Also Called: Long, H W Logging
264 Se 752nd Ave (32680-4520)
PHONE..................................352 542-7068
Henry W Long, *Owner*
EMP: 5 **EST:** 1969
SALES (est): 328.3K **Privately Held**
SIC: **2411** Logging camps & contractors

(G-12198)
INSTRUMENT PUBLICATION
521 Ne 452nd St (32680-3871)
PHONE..................................352 542-7716
Anthony A Zenner, *Principal*
EMP: 6 **EST:** 2010
SALES (est): 77.3K **Privately Held**
SIC: **2741** Miscellaneous publishing

(G-12199)
RPM CO
27908 Se Hwy 19 (32680-4842)
PHONE..................................352 542-3110
Dave Jarnigan, *Principal*
EMP: 5 **EST:** 2010
SALES (est): 351.9K **Privately Held**
WEB: www.rpm-co.com
SIC: **3715** Trailers or vans for transporting horses

Oldsmar
Pinellas County

(G-12200)
ALLCASES REEKSTIN & ASSOC INC
300 Mears Blvd (34677-3047)
PHONE..................................813 891-1313
Deborah A Reekstin, *President*
Joe Weber, *General Mgr*
Karl R Reekstin, *Vice Pres*
Karl Reekstin, *Vice Pres*
Pearlman Ginny, *Engineer*
▼ **EMP:** 12 **EST:** 1985
SQ FT: 7,500
SALES (est): 2.8MM **Privately Held**
WEB: www.allcases.com
SIC: **2449** 2441 3199 Shipping cases, wood: wirebound; shipping cases, wood: nailed or lock corner; boxes, leather

(G-12201)
AMERX HEALTH CARE CORP
164 Douglas Rd E (34677-2939)
PHONE..................................727 443-0530
James B Anderson, *CFO*
Sheri Kempinski, *Sales Mgr*
Stephanie Miron, *Accounts Mgr*
Jennifer Creel, *Manager*
Jennifer Lachtara, *Supervisor*
EMP: 15 **EST:** 1993
SALES (est): 3.2MM **Publicly Held**
WEB: www.amerigel.com
SIC: **2834** Ointments
PA: Procyon Corporation
1300 S Highland Ave
Clearwater FL 33756

(G-12202)
ANDRITZ IGGESUND TOOLS INC (HQ)
220 Scarlet Blvd (34677-3016)
PHONE..................................813 855-6902
John Tillte, *President*
Dawn Fernandez, *Vice Pres*
John E Morphis, *Treasurer*
Luhrman Carl, *Director*
Ann Rahnstron, *Admin Sec*
▲ **EMP:** 20 **EST:** 1983
SQ FT: 16,500
SALES (est): 18.9MM **Privately Held**
SIC: **3423** 3545 3541 3421 Knives, agricultural or industrial; machine tool accessories; machine tools, metal cutting type; cutlery
PA: Ramab Iggesund Ab
Villagatan 19
Stockholm
650 291-01

(G-12203)
ARJ MEDICAL INC
209 State St E (34677-3654)
PHONE..................................813 855-1557
Morris Behar, *Principal*
EMP: 9 **EST:** 1996
SALES (est): 172K **Privately Held**
SIC: **2819** 3821 Chemicals, reagent grade: refined from technical grade; laboratory apparatus, except heating & measuring

(G-12204)
ARJAY PRINTING COMPANY INC
131 Burbank Rd (34677-4900)
PHONE..................................904 764-6070
Andrew Fraser, *President*
Andy Fraser, *Vice Pres*
EMP: 6 **EST:** 1986
SQ FT: 5,000
SALES (est): 916.9K **Privately Held**
SIC: **2752** Commercial printing, offset

(G-12205)
AROMAVALUE INC
Also Called: Scent Fill
720 Brooker Creek Blvd # 210 (34677-2937)
PHONE..................................866 223-7561
Mark Callison, *President*
EMP: 5 **EST:** 2016
SQ FT: 6,450
SALES (est): 600K **Privately Held**
WEB: www.scentfill.com
SIC: **2844** Toilet preparations

(G-12206)
ASTRA PRODUCTS CO INC TAMPA
3675 Tampa Rd (34677-6311)
P.O. Box 711 (34677-0711)
PHONE..................................813 855-3021
Steve Ladoniczki, *President*
Steven Ladoniczki, *General Mgr*
Bill Ladoniczki, *Treasurer*
Clara Ladoniczki, *Admin Sec*
EMP: 32 **EST:** 1967
SQ FT: 40,000
SALES (est): 5.7MM **Privately Held**
WEB: www.astraprodco.com
SIC: **3651** Amplifiers: radio, public address or musical instrument

(G-12207)
BAY CNC MACHINE LLC
305 Scarlet Blvd (34677-3019)
PHONE..................................813 362-9626
EMP: 7 **EST:** 2019
SALES (est): 350.9K **Privately Held**
WEB: www.baycncmachine.com
SIC: **3599** Machine shop, jobbing & repair

(G-12208)
BBULL USA INC
260 Scarlet Blvd (34677-3016)
PHONE..................................813 855-1400
Guido Luis Riveros, *President*
Michael John L Lawn, *Vice Pres*
Berhard Bull, *Director*
Richard J Riveros, *Admin Sec*
EMP: 9 **EST:** 2010
SALES (est): 351.9K **Privately Held**
WEB: www.bbullusa.com
SIC: **3565** Packaging machinery

(G-12209)
BEAM ASSOCIATES LLC (PA)
301 Commerce Blvd Ste 2 (34677-2806)
PHONE..................................813 855-5695
Brook Massey, *Mng Member*
EMP: 30 **EST:** 2012
SALES (est): 85.2MM **Privately Held**
SIC: **3585** Refrigeration & heating equipment

(G-12210)
BELAC LLC
420 Commerce Blvd (34677-2808)
PHONE..................................813 749-3200
Chong Yi, *President*
Dennis Piotrowski, *Vice Pres*
Pete Cirak, *QC Mgr*
Kevin Tuttle, *QC Mgr*
Martin Kley, *Engineer*
EMP: 60 **EST:** 1998
SQ FT: 30,000
SALES (est): 17.1MM **Privately Held**
WEB: www.belac.com
SIC: **3511** Turbines & turbine generator sets

(G-12211)
BELL HEARING INSTRUMENTS INC (PA)
Also Called: Sonus-USA
700 Stevens Ave Ste B (34677-2987)
P.O. Box 1888 (34677-1888)
PHONE..................................813 814-2355
William Bell, *President*
EMP: 27 **EST:** 1988
SQ FT: 15,000
SALES (est): 2.3MM **Privately Held**
WEB: www.bellhearingaids.com
SIC: **3842** 5999 Hearing aids; hearing aids

(G-12212)
BRYCOAT INC
207 Vollmer Ave (34677-2938)
P.O. Box 1976 (34677-6976)
PHONE..................................727 490-1000
Robert A Smith, *CEO*
Michael D Smith, *President*
Mark McDonough, *Vice Pres*
Damon Phelps, *Purch Agent*
Kamiron Brown, *Engineer*
EMP: 40 **EST:** 1990
SQ FT: 22,000
SALES (est): 5.4MM **Privately Held**
WEB: www.brycoat.com
SIC: **3479** Coating of metals & formed products

(G-12213)
CEMEX CNSTR MTLS FLA LLC
Also Called: Oldsmar Ready Mix Con Plant
501 Douglas Rd E (34677-4923)
PHONE..................................800 992-3639
Robert Snook, *Branch Mgr*
EMP: 8
SQ FT: 1,131 **Privately Held**
SIC: **3272** 3273 Pipe, concrete or lined with concrete; ready-mixed concrete
HQ: Cemex Construction Materials Florida, Llc
1501 Belvedere Rd
West Palm Beach FL 33406

(G-12214)
CEVA ANIMAL HEALTH LLC
4027 Tampa Rd Ste 3000 (34677-3215)
PHONE..................................727 548-8345
Karla Barton, *Branch Mgr*
EMP: 12
SALES (corp-wide): 2MM **Privately Held**
WEB: www.ceva.us
SIC: **2833** Animal based products
HQ: Ceva Animal Health, Llc
8735 Rosehill Rd Ste 300
Lenexa KS 66215

(G-12215)
CLEARWATER MANUFACTURING CO
203 Tower Dr (34677-2964)
PHONE..................................813 818-0959
Frank Wenglasz Jr, *President*
Anna Wenglasz, *Corp Secy*
Charles Wenglasz, *Vice Pres*
EMP: 5 **EST:** 1976
SQ FT: 6,000
SALES (est): 500K **Privately Held**
SIC: **3599** Machine shop, jobbing & repair

(G-12216)
COATING TECHNOLOGY INC
360 Scarlet Blvd (34677-3018)
PHONE..................................813 854-3674
Steve Pantle, *President*
EMP: 33 **EST:** 1995
SQ FT: 7,800
SALES (est): 1.8MM **Privately Held**
WEB: www.coatingtechinc.com
SIC: **3471** Electroplating of metals or formed products

(G-12217)
COFFEE NEWS CLEARWATER
160 Lisa Ln (34677-2389)
PHONE..................................727 789-6677
EMP: 7 **EST:** 2014
SALES (est): 86.4K **Privately Held**
WEB: www.coffeenews.com
SIC: **2711** Newspapers, publishing & printing

(G-12218)
COFFMAN SYSTEMS INC
300 Stevens Ave (34677-2919)
PHONE..................................813 891-1300
Dale D Windsor, *President*
Richard Peck, *Vice Pres*
EMP: 13 **EST:** 1995
SQ FT: 22,000
SALES (est): 667.6K **Privately Held**
WEB: www.coffmansystems.com
SIC: **3823** Water quality monitoring & control systems

(G-12219)
COUNTRYSIDE PUBLISHING CO INC
Also Called: Federal Suppliers Guide
477 Commerce Blvd (34677-2809)
P.O. Box 1735 (34677-1735)
PHONE..................................813 925-0195
Yvonne Shawn, *President*
EMP: 15 **EST:** 2001
SQ FT: 20,000
SALES (est): 754K **Privately Held**
WEB: www.gsaapplicationservices.info
SIC: **2741** Miscellaneous publishing

(G-12220)
DIGITAL DIRECT CORPORATION
Also Called: Bay Diecutting
131 Burbank Rd (34677-4900)
PHONE..................................813 448-9071
Kenneth Fraser, *President*
EMP: 6 **EST:** 2002
SQ FT: 10,443
SALES (est): 823.7K **Privately Held**
WEB: www.digitaldirectpress.com
SIC: **2732** 2741 Book printing; technical manual & paper publishing

(G-12221)
DIGITAL PUBLISHING OF FLORIDA
131 Burbank Rd (34677-4900)
PHONE..................................813 749-8640
EMP: 8 **EST:** 2019
SALES (est): 495.3K **Privately Held**
WEB: www.digitaldata-corp.com
SIC: **2741** Miscellaneous publishing

(G-12222)
DSC SALES OF SC INC (PA)
Also Called: Diversified Sales Company
455 Commerce Blvd (34677-2809)
P.O. Box 2123 (34677-7123)
PHONE..................................813 854-3131

Leslie L Lipsey, *President*
L Richard Lipsey, *President*
Lauren Wanzie, *Corp Secy*
Gregory L Shattuck, *Vice Pres*
Dana Z Lipsey, *Director*
▲ **EMP:** 10
SALES (est): 12MM **Privately Held**
WEB: www.dscsales.com
SIC: 2369 Beachwear: girls', children's & infants'

(G-12223)
E-Z FASTENING SOLUTIONS INC
640 Brooker Creek Blvd # 425 (34677-2931)
PHONE..................................813 854-3937
Edgard Zayas, *President*
▲ **EMP:** 5 **EST:** 2010
SALES (est): 1MM **Privately Held**
WEB: www.ez-fastening.com
SIC: 3429 3545 3965 5072 Manufactured hardware (general); precision tools, machinists'; fasteners; hardware

(G-12224)
EDMUND OPTICS INC
Also Called: Edmund Optics Florida
141 Burbank Rd (34677-4900)
PHONE..................................813 855-1900
Sean Cleary, *CFO*
EMP: 33
SALES (corp-wide): 439.7MM **Privately Held**
WEB: www.edmundoptics.com
SIC: 3699 Laser systems & equipment
PA: Edmund Optics, Inc.
101 E Gloucester Pike
Barrington NJ 08007
856 547-3488

(G-12225)
ELECTRO LAB INC
369 Douglas Rd E (34677-2922)
P.O. Box 1135 (34677-1135)
PHONE..................................813 818-7605
William Grady Harder Jr, *President*
Gradey Harder, *COO*
Lonnie Harder, *Mfg Staff*
V J Houston, *Manager*
Shawn Pradaxay, *Manager*
EMP: 15 **EST:** 1956
SQ FT: 12,000
SALES (est): 2.3MM **Privately Held**
WEB: www.electrolab2.com
SIC: 3471 Electroplating of metals or formed products

(G-12226)
ENFORCEMENT ONE INC
Also Called: Fleet Spc An Enforcement One
381 Roberts Rd (34677-4914)
PHONE..................................727 816-9833
Aaron S Watkins, *Principal*
EMP: 13 **EST:** 2011
SALES (est): 3.1MM **Privately Held**
WEB: www.johnsonsecurityservices.com
SIC: 3714 Motor vehicle parts & accessories

(G-12227)
GARDNER-WATSON DECKING INC
305 Scarlet Blvd Ste A (34677-3019)
PHONE..................................813 891-9849
Bruce Nichols, *President*
Geoff Kress, *Vice Pres*
Geoffrey G Kress, *Vice Pres*
Rick Vassallo, *Manager*
Jeremy McAllister, *Director*
EMP: 43 **EST:** 2005
SALES (est): 9MM **Privately Held**
WEB: www.gwdeck.com
SIC: 3441 Fabricated structural metal

(G-12228)
GILCO SPRING OF FLORIDA INC
3991 Tampa Rd (34677-3233)
PHONE..................................813 855-4631
Patrick Gillum, *CEO*
Todd Gaito, *General Mgr*
Jim Danielski, *Materials Mgr*
▲ **EMP:** 20 **EST:** 1987
SQ FT: 3,000
SALES (est): 4.6MM **Privately Held**
WEB: www.gilco.com
SIC: 3495 Wire springs

(G-12229)
GULF FIBEROPTICS INC
448 Commerce Blvd (34677-2808)
PHONE..................................813 891-1993
Christopher Kerns, *President*
Craig Vogeley, *Vice Pres*
Chris Bailey, *Design Engr*
Paige Redditt, *Human Resources*
Connie Derosa, *Supervisor*
EMP: 45 **EST:** 1997
SALES (est): 5MM **Privately Held**
WEB: www.gulffiberoptics.com
SIC: 3229 Fiber optics strands

(G-12230)
GULF MEDICAL FIBEROPTICS INC
448 Commerce Blvd (34677-2808)
PHONE..................................813 855-6618
Patrick Bennetts, *CEO*
Christophe Kerns, *President*
Vogeley Craig, *VP Opers*
Nick Malure, *QC Mgr*
Kim Pilkenton, *Accounts Mgr*
EMP: 8 **EST:** 2002
SQ FT: 15,000
SALES (est): 847.3K **Privately Held**
WEB: www.gulffiberoptics.com
SIC: 3841 Surgical instruments & apparatus

(G-12231)
GULF PHOTONICS INC
448 Commerce Blvd (34677-2808)
PHONE..................................813 855-6618
Patrick Bennetts, *President*
Craig Vogeley, *Vice Pres*
Christopher Kerns, *Treasurer*
EMP: 9 **EST:** 2010
SQ FT: 13,600
SALES (est): 771.6K **Privately Held**
WEB: www.gulffiberoptics.com
SIC: 3357 Fiber optic cable (insulated)

(G-12232)
HUNT RDS INC
Also Called: Fastsigns
3898 Tampa Rd (34677-3137)
PHONE..................................813 249-7551
Robert G Hunt, *Principal*
EMP: 6 **EST:** 2016
SALES (est): 174K **Privately Held**
WEB: www.fastsigns.com
SIC: 3993 Signs & advertising specialties

(G-12233)
HYDRO-DYNE ENGINEERING INC
4750 118th Ave N (34677)
PHONE..................................727 532-0777
Jay R Conroy, *President*
Timothy L Pe Hunt, *Vice Pres*
Christy Walsh, *Vice Pres*
James Ranno, *Project Mgr*
Randall Dow, *Sales Dir*
EMP: 38 **EST:** 1978
SALES (est): 4.1MM **Privately Held**
WEB: www.hydro-dyne.com
SIC: 3589 Water purification equipment, household type

(G-12234)
IN STOCK PRINTERS INC
725 Stevens Ave (34677-2917)
PHONE..................................727 447-2515
Frank Gonzalez, *President*
Morgan Schmid, *Vice Pres*
EMP: 7 **EST:** 2010
SALES (est): 92.1K **Privately Held**
SIC: 2752 Commercial printing, lithographic

(G-12235)
INDUSTRY WEAPON INC
4033 Tampa Rd Ste 103 (34677-3224)
PHONE..................................877 344-8450
David Wible, *CEO*
Brian Pullman, *Business Mgr*
Marcy Long, *Production*
Matthew Polaski, *Production*
Jason Holliday, *Sales Mgr*
EMP: 41 **EST:** 2007
SALES (est): 9.8MM **Privately Held**
WEB: www.spectrio.com
SIC: 7372 Application computer software

(G-12236)
INTEGRATED DEALER SYSTEMS INC
640 Brooker Creek Blvd (34677-2929)
PHONE..................................800 962-7872
Dawn Tillotson, *Branch Mgr*
Lindsey Manders, *Analyst*
EMP: 10
SALES (corp-wide): 3.9B **Privately Held**
WEB: www.ids-astra.com
SIC: 3571 3577 Personal computers (microcomputers); computer peripheral equipment
HQ: Integrated Dealer Systems Inc.
12339 Wake Union Church R
Wake Forest NC 27587
919 790-5442

(G-12237)
J & D MANUFACTURING INC
375 Mears Blvd (34677-3048)
P.O. Box 1945 (34677-6945)
PHONE..................................813 854-1700
James L Villa, *President*
David M Kaercher, *Vice Pres*
EMP: 11 **EST:** 1959
SQ FT: 84,000
SALES (est): 2.3MM **Privately Held**
SIC: 3081 Packing materials, plastic sheet

(G-12238)
JUSTI GROUP INC
Also Called: Specialty Glass
305 Marlborough St (34677-3107)
PHONE..................................813 855-5779
Colleen Morrisette, *President*
EMP: 20 **EST:** 1977
SQ FT: 20,000
SALES (est): 2.5MM **Privately Held**
WEB: www.sgiglass.com
SIC: 3231 Products of purchased glass
PA: Justi Group, Inc.
804 Old Lancaster Rd
Berwyn PA 19312

(G-12239)
KEN R AVERY PAINTING INC
3704 State Road 580 W (34677-5618)
PHONE..................................813 855-5037
Ken R Avery, *President*
EMP: 26
SALES (corp-wide): 2.9MM **Privately Held**
SIC: 2851 1721 Paints & allied products; painting & paper hanging
PA: Ken R Avery Painting Inc
3650 Old Keystone Rd
Tarpon Springs FL 34688
813 855-5037

(G-12240)
KLOPP INTERNATIONAL INC
Also Called: Klopp Coin Counters
237 Dunbar Ct (34677-2956)
P.O. Box 985 (34677-0985)
PHONE..................................813 855-6789
Rick Nelson, *President*
Brian Bump, *Technical Staff*
▲ **EMP:** 19 **EST:** 1930
SQ FT: 12,000
SALES (est): 1MM **Privately Held**
WEB: www.kloppcoin.com
SIC: 3578 3579 Coin counters; coin wrapping machines

(G-12241)
KLOPP OF FLORIDA INC
251 Dunbar Ave (34677-2900)
P.O. Box 1109 (34677-1109)
PHONE..................................813 855-6789
Daniel Nelson, *President*
▲ **EMP:** 8 **EST:** 2006
SALES (est): 137K **Privately Held**
WEB: www.kloppcoin.com
SIC: 3578 Coin counters

(G-12242)
KW PRODUCTS INC
305 Mears Blvd (34677-3048)
PHONE..................................813 855-7817
Carlos Sevillano, *President*
EMP: 13 **EST:** 1986
SALES (est): 1MM **Privately Held**
WEB: www.kwproducts.org
SIC: 3599 Machine shop, jobbing & repair

(G-12243)
LABELCLICK INC
630 Brooker Creek Blvd # 340 (34677-2927)
PHONE..................................727 548-8345
EMP: 8 **EST:** 2004
SALES (est): 116.7K **Privately Held**
WEB: www.vitalityvet.com
SIC: 2834 Pharmaceutical preparations

(G-12244)
LIQUID TECHNOLGY CORP
340 Scarlet Blvd (34677-3018)
PHONE..................................832 804-8650
Dave Cagrise, *President*
Tim Hoeksema,
EMP: 14 **EST:** 2015
SALES (est): 566.5K **Privately Held**
SIC: 2813 5085 Industrial gases; gas equipment, parts & supplies

(G-12245)
LOCKHEED MARTIN CORPORATION
3655 Tampa Rd (34677-6308)
PHONE..................................813 855-5711
Hercules Georgeou, *Design Engr Mgr*
Lamont Gooding, *Engineer*
Barbara Julian, *Finance Mgr*
Courtney Dupree, *Manager*
Lisa Williams, *Manager*
EMP: 450
SQ FT: 198,678 **Publicly Held**
WEB: www.lockheedmartin.com
SIC: 3812 7371 3571 Defense systems & equipment; custom computer programming services; electronic computers
PA: Lockheed Martin Corporation
6801 Rockledge Dr
Bethesda MD 20817

(G-12246)
MARINE SPC CSTM FABRICATOR
360 Mears Blvd (34677-3047)
PHONE..................................813 855-0554
Thomas S Foley, *President*
EMP: 7 **EST:** 1986
SQ FT: 10,000
SALES (est): 350K **Privately Held**
WEB: www.marinespecialties.com
SIC: 3531 5551 Marine related equipment; boat dealers

(G-12247)
MEDFAB CORPORATION
210 Douglas Rd E (34677-2912)
P.O. Box 2366 (34677-2193)
PHONE..................................813 854-2646
Brad Hugus, *President*
Mike Sullivan, *General Mgr*
Mike Curtis, *Vice Pres*
Brad P Hugus, *Vice Pres*
EMP: 7 **EST:** 1994
SALES (est): 1.4MM **Privately Held**
WEB: www.medfabusa.com
SIC: 3086 3069 Plastics foam products; molded rubber products

(G-12248)
MI METALS INC (HQ)
301 Commerce Blvd (34677-2806)
PHONE..................................813 855-5695
Brook Massey, *President*
Sarah Guthrie, *Vice Pres*
Kevin Sponsler, *Vice Pres*
Jim Sebben, *Manager*
EMP: 219 **EST:** 1997
SQ FT: 200,000
SALES (est): 85.2MM **Privately Held**
WEB: www.mimetals.com
SIC: 3585 Refrigeration & heating equipment
PA: Beam Associates, Llc
301 Commerce Blvd Ste 2
Oldsmar FL 34677
813 855-5695

(G-12249)
MICON PACKAGING INC
301 Commerce Blvd Bldg 1 (34677-2806)
P.O. Box 789 (34677-0789)
PHONE..................................813 855-4651
Peter Tracey, *President*
▲ **EMP:** 115 **EST:** 1998
SQ FT: 283,000
SALES (est): 22.9MM **Privately Held**
WEB: www.miconpackaging.com
SIC: 2653 Boxes, corrugated: made from purchased materials
HQ: Stronghaven, Incorporated
2727 Paces Ferry Rd Se 1-1850
Atlanta GA 30339
678 235-2713

(G-12250)
MICROLUMEN INC
1 Microlumen Way (34677-2983)
PHONE..................................813 886-1200
Roger O Roberds, *CEO*
M Scott Roberds, *President*
Rod Peifer, *Vice Pres*
Mark Roberds, *Vice Pres*
Brandon Day, *Project Mgr*
EMP: 80 **EST:** 1987
SQ FT: 59,000
SALES (est): 30.1MM **Privately Held**
WEB: www.microlumen.com
SIC: 3082 3644 Tubes, unsupported plastic; noncurrent-carrying wiring services

(G-12251)
NOVICON INDUSTRIES
400 Roberts Rd (34677-4915)
P.O. Box 2366 (34677-2193)
PHONE..................................813 854-3235
EMP: 7 **EST:** 2018
SALES (est): 85.1K **Privately Held**
WEB: www.noviconusa.com
SIC: 3086 Plastics foam products

(G-12252)
OL PRODUCTS INC
100 Mount Vernon St (34677-3009)
PHONE..................................813 854-3575
George Carollo, *Branch Mgr*
EMP: 90 **Privately Held**
WEB: www.olproducts.com
SIC: 2844 Toilet preparations
PA: O.L. Products, Inc.
3874 Tampa Rd Ste 200
Oldsmar FL 34677

(G-12253)
ONE SOURCE INDUSTRIES INC
200 Pine Ave N Ste A (34677-4646)
PHONE..................................813 855-3440
Gary Woodward, *President*
Philip Gozo, *Accounts Exec*
Lynn Gill, *Office Admin*
EMP: 9 **EST:** 1998
SQ FT: 2,000
SALES (est): 1.3MM **Privately Held**
WEB: www.alphacard.com
SIC: 3999 Identification badges & insignia

(G-12254)
OSGOOD INDUSTRIES LLC
Also Called: Osgood Industries LLC
601 Burbank Rd (34677-4903)
PHONE..................................813 448-9041
Rich Mueller, *Exec VP*
Ed Chicon, *Purch Agent*
Dalibor Bodruzic, *Engineer*
Dave Clift, *Engineer*
Mark Burnard, *Electrical Engi*
▲ **EMP:** 120 **EST:** 1976
SQ FT: 40,043
SALES (est): 35.8MM
SALES (corp-wide): 177.9K **Privately Held**
WEB: www.syntegon.com
SIC: 3444 3561 3565 8711 Sheet metalwork; pumps & pumping equipment; packaging machinery; bag opening, filling & closing machines; engineering services
HQ: Syntegon Technology Gmbh
Stuttgarter Str. 130
Waiblingen 71332
715 114-00

(G-12255)
PA C PUBLISHING INC
Also Called: Nightmoves Magazine
850 Dunbar Ave (34677-2901)
P.O. Box 492, Palm Harbor (34682-0492)
PHONE..................................813 814-1505
Paul A Cianci, *President*
Paul Allen,
EMP: 5 **EST:** 1990
SQ FT: 8,000
SALES (est): 646.6K **Privately Held**
WEB: www.pacpublishing.com
SIC: 2721 Magazines: publishing only, not printed on site

(G-12256)
PERIPHERAL SERVICES INC
Also Called: PSI
103 Pine Ave S (34677-3026)
P.O. Box 1086 (34677-1086)
PHONE..................................813 854-1181
Bill Small, *President*
James Harrington, *General Mgr*
Jim Harrington, *Vice Pres*
William Small, *Executive*
EMP: 28 **EST:** 1987
SQ FT: 6,200
SALES (est): 1.3MM **Privately Held**
WEB: www.periph.net
SIC: 3577 7699 Printers, computer; printing trades machinery & equipment repair

(G-12257)
PLATESMART TECHNOLOGIES
640 Brooker Creek Blvd # 465
(34677-2934)
PHONE..................................813 749-0892
John Chigos, *Owner*
Kenn Campbell, *CFO*
Michael Budz, *Regl Sales Mgr*
Dale Hempel, *Sales Staff*
Tricia Parzuchowski, *Sales Staff*
EMP: 10 **EST:** 2012
SALES (est): 1.4MM **Privately Held**
WEB: www.platesmart.com
SIC: 7372 Prepackaged software

(G-12258)
POWER KLEEN CORPORATION
101 S Bayview Blvd (34677-3101)
PHONE..................................813 854-2648
John Sanders, *President*
Joyce M Sanders, *Corp Secy*
David Huddleston, *Purch Agent*
Doug Dirscherl, *Sales Mgr*
Nancy Harris, *Office Mgr*
▼ **EMP:** 30 **EST:** 1973
SQ FT: 6,000
SALES (est): 4.8MM **Privately Held**
WEB: www.powerkleen.com
SIC: 2842 7699 5087 Cleaning or polishing preparations; industrial machinery & equipment repair; dry cleaning plant equipment & supplies

(G-12259)
PRECISION COATING RODS INC
600 Mount Vernon St (34677-3024)
P.O. Box 10594, Tampa (33679-0594)
PHONE..................................813 855-5054
Fax: 813 891-9904
EMP: 10
SQ FT: 3,000
SALES (est): 890K **Privately Held**
SIC: 3821 Mfg Lab Apparatus/Furniture

(G-12260)
PREMIER FABRICATING LLC
232 Dunbar Ct (34677-2956)
PHONE..................................813 855-4633
Keith Laggett, *Mng Member*
Sandra Usling,
EMP: 22 **EST:** 2008
SQ FT: 19,000
SALES (est): 2.3MM **Privately Held**
WEB: www.premierfabricating.com
SIC: 3444 3469 Sheet metalwork; metal stampings

(G-12261)
PREMIUM DYNAMIC LENS
640 Brooker Creek Blvd # 435
(34677-2929)
PHONE..................................813 891-9912
Cheryl Swartz, *Principal*
Jason McLachlan, *Manager*
Ian Peterson, *Manager*
Mike Jedynak, *Network Tech*
Paul Burgholzer, *Sr Ntwrk Engine*
EMP: 13 **EST:** 2007
SALES (est): 191.1K **Privately Held**
SIC: 3851 5049 5995 Ophthalmic goods; optical goods; optical goods stores

(G-12262)
PRINT ONE INC
Also Called: Unlimited Printing & Copying
3898 Tampa Rd Ste B (34677-3137)
PHONE..................................813 273-0240
William Wilkerson, *President*
Sally Williams, *Vice Pres*
EMP: 6 **EST:** 1986
SALES (est): 773K **Privately Held**
WEB: www.unlimitedprinting.com
SIC: 2752 2791 7334 Commercial printing, offset; typesetting; photocopying & duplicating services

(G-12263)
PRINTEC INC
241 Douglas Rd E Ste 1 (34677-2913)
PHONE..................................813 854-1075
EMP: 8 **EST:** 2019
SALES (est): 73.2K **Privately Held**
WEB: www.printec-ht.com
SIC: 2759 Screen printing

(G-12264)
PRINTING DEPOT INC
3898 Tampa Rd Ste B (34677-3137)
PHONE..................................813 855-6758
Robert Hunt, *President*
Steve Hunt, *General Mgr*
Becky Harness, *Creative Dir*
EMP: 7 **EST:** 1984
SQ FT: 6,000
SALES (est): 946.9K **Privately Held**
WEB: www.goprintingdepot.com
SIC: 2752 Commercial printing, offset

(G-12265)
PROMEDICA INC
114 Douglas Rd E (34677-2933)
PHONE..................................813 854-1905
Edward C Padinske, *CEO*
Ronald J Padinske, *President*
Robert E Wade, *CFO*
EMP: 99 **EST:** 1987
SQ FT: 62,000
SALES (est): 3.2MM
SALES (corp-wide): 69.5MM **Privately Held**
WEB: www.touchpointmed.com
SIC: 3841 Surgical & medical instruments
PA: Touchpoint Medical, Inc.
2200 Touchpoint Dr
Odessa FL 33556
813 854-1905

(G-12266)
QTM INC
300 Stevens Ave (34677-2919)
PHONE..................................813 891-1300
Richard K Peck, *CEO*
Richard Barnes, *CIO*
EMP: 26 **EST:** 1989
SQ FT: 21,000
SALES (est): 7.2MM **Privately Held**
WEB: www.qtminc.com
SIC: 3599 Machine shop, jobbing & repair

(G-12267)
R & D MACHINE AND ENGRG INC
Also Called: R&D
130 Scarlet Blvd (34677-3002)
PHONE..................................813 891-9109
Carl W Whitley, *CEO*
Hilary Whitley, *President*
Carl Whitley, *General Mgr*
EMP: 28 **EST:** 1992
SQ FT: 6,000
SALES (est): 5.8MM **Privately Held**
WEB: www.rdmachine.com
SIC: 3599 Machine shop, jobbing & repair

(G-12268)
RONECKER HOLDINGS LLC
Also Called: On Demand Printing
303 Mears Blvd (34677-3048)
PHONE..................................813 855-5559
EMP: 9
SQ FT: 1,800
SALES (est): 1.4MM **Privately Held**
SIC: 2711 6719 Commercial-Publishing/Printing

(G-12269)
STRUCTALL BUILDING SYSTEMS INC (PA)
Also Called: Oldsmar Service Center
350 Burbank Rd (34677-4906)
PHONE..................................813 855-2627
Steve Meyerson, *President*
Mark Van Dame, *COO*
Jim Forsberg, *Vice Pres*
Ken Matuza, *Project Mgr*
Art McCulley, *Warehouse Mgr*
◆ **EMP:** 30
SQ FT: 54,000
SALES (est): 24.7MM **Privately Held**
WEB: www.structall.com
SIC: 3449 Miscellaneous metalwork

(G-12270)
TAMPA MACHINE PRODUCTS INC
151 Vollmer Ave (34677-2936)
PHONE..................................813 854-3332
James Lyngholm, *President*
EMP: 22 **EST:** 1974
SQ FT: 20,000
SALES (est): 404.2K **Privately Held**
SIC: 3599 Machine shop, jobbing & repair

(G-12271)
THUNDER BAY FOODS CORPORATION
640 Douglas Rd E Ste A (34677-4925)
PHONE..................................727 943-0606
Jonathan D Key, *President*
James B Bond, *Vice Pres*
EMP: 16 **EST:** 2017
SALES (est): 1.7MM **Privately Held**
SIC: 2099 Food preparations

(G-12272)
ULTRA CLEAN SYSTEMS INC
110 Douglas Rd E (34677-2910)
PHONE..................................813 925-1003
Billy O Cale, *President*
Rebecca Cale, *Corp Secy*
Michael Cale, *Vice Pres*
Norman Cale, *Vice Pres*
Becky Cale, *VP Opers*
EMP: 18 **EST:** 1999
SALES (est): 7.3MM **Privately Held**
WEB: www.ultracleansystems.com
SIC: 3841 Surgical & medical instruments

(G-12273)
UNITED ADVANTAGE SIGNS INC
Also Called: United Signs Systems
206 Tower Dr (34677-2964)
PHONE..................................813 855-3300
Steven Higger, *President*
Forrest Massa, *Project Mgr*
Andy Noethen, *Project Mgr*
John Scott, *Purchasing*
Scott Aldridge, *Human Res Dir*
EMP: 66 **EST:** 1984
SQ FT: 40,000
SALES (est): 7.8MM **Privately Held**
WEB: www.uvbrand.com
SIC: 3993 Electric signs

(G-12274)
UNITED VISUAL BRANDING LLC
206 Tower Dr (34677-2964)
PHONE..................................813 855-3300
Tim Kramer, *Purchasing*
Kylee Chlopecki, *Sales Staff*
Ric Everett, *Sales Staff*
Ben Zaccagnino,
EMP: 95 **EST:** 2018
SALES (est): 6.2MM **Privately Held**
WEB: www.uvbrand.com
SIC: 3993 Signs & advertising specialties

(G-12275)
USBEV PLASTICS LLC
3874 Tampa Rd (34677-3126)
PHONE..................................813 855-0700
Santo Carollo, *Mng Member*
EMP: 16 **EST:** 2012
SQ FT: 22,500

SALES (est): 1.1MM **Privately Held**
SIC: 3089 Molding primary plastic

(G-12276)
UVLRX THERAPEUTICS INC
640 Brooker Creek Blvd (34677-2929)
PHONE..................................813 309-1976
Michael Harter, *CEO*
EMP: 16 **EST:** 2016
SALES (est): 1.7MM **Privately Held**
SIC: 2834 Pharmaceutical preparations

(G-12277)
VANGUARD PRODUCTS GROUP INC
Also Called: Vanguard Protex Global
720 Brooker Creek Blvd (34677-2935)
PHONE..................................813 855-9639
Christopher Kelsch, *President*
Rodney Surratt, *COO*
John Obryan, *Vice Pres*
Johnathan Obryan, *Vice Pres*
Bill Hamblin, *Opers Mgr*
▲ **EMP:** 70 **EST:** 2000
SQ FT: 8,000
SALES (est): 25.1MM **Privately Held**
WEB: www.vanguardprotexglobal.com
SIC: 3669 3699 7382 Burglar alarm apparatus, electric; security devices; burglar alarm maintenance & monitoring

(G-12278)
WF BRICK PAVERS INC
213 Lexington St (34677-4331)
PHONE..................................813 506-1941
Wender R Fonseca, *President*
EMP: 6 **EST:** 2012
SALES (est): 766.6K **Privately Held**
WEB: www.wfbrickpavers.com
SIC: 3531 Pavers

(G-12279)
WORLDWIDE TECHNOLOGY INC (PA)
141 Stevens Ave Ste 10 (34677-2954)
P.O. Box 1693 (34677-1693)
PHONE..................................813 855-2443
Edward M Contreras, *President*
Doris A Contreras, *Corp Secy*
Tom Gain, *Vice Pres*
Mike Taylor, *CTO*
EMP: 26 **EST:** 1986
SALES (est): 3.1MM **Privately Held**
SIC: 3564 3589 3559 Air cleaning systems; water purification equipment, household type; ozone machines

Ona
Hardee County

(G-12280)
FLORIDA FENCE POST CO INC (PA)
5251 State Road 64 W (33865-8704)
P.O. Box 645 (33865-0645)
PHONE..................................863 735-1361
F L Revell Jr, *President*
Alice Salas, *Corp Secy*
Oneita Revell, *Vice Pres*
▼ **EMP:** 8 **EST:** 1946
SQ FT: 20,000
SALES (est): 1.5MM **Privately Held**
WEB: www.flfencepost.com
SIC: 2411 5211 5999 Posts, wood: hewn, round or split; fencing; alarm & safety equipment stores

Opa Locka
Miami-Dade County

(G-12281)
AAA SECURITY DEPOT CORP
12815 Nw 45th Ave Ste 2 (33054-5100)
PHONE..................................305 652-8567
Shirley Jacobowitz, *President*
Ron Jacobowitz, *Vice Pres*
▲ **EMP:** 20 **EST:** 2007
SALES (est): 2MM **Privately Held**
WEB: www.aaasecuritydepot.com
SIC: 3699 Security control equipment & systems

(G-12282)
ACTION PLATING CORP
1220 Ali Baba Ave (33054-3613)
PHONE..................................305 685-6313
William J Bain, *President*
EMP: 19 **EST:** 1977
SQ FT: 38,465
SALES (est): 1.9MM **Privately Held**
WEB: www.actionplatingcorp.com
SIC: 3471 Plating of metals or formed products

(G-12283)
AERO PRECISION PRODUCTS INC
Also Called: Appi
14000 Nw 19th Ave (33054-4190)
PHONE..................................305 688-2565
Paul R Fournier, *President*
Robert Fout, *COO*
Vanessa Sao, *Sales Staff*
Sal Rodriguez, *CIO*
▼ **EMP:** 85
SQ FT: 50,000
SALES (est): 15.5MM **Privately Held**
WEB: www.appiusa.com
SIC: 3599 3469 Machine shop, jobbing & repair; stamping metal for the trade

(G-12284)
ALEXIS WELDING EXPRESS CORP
12900 Nw 30th Ave (33054-5011)
PHONE..................................786 626-4090
Alexis Cepero, *Principal*
EMP: 7 **EST:** 2018
SALES (est): 431.5K **Privately Held**
SIC: 7692 Welding repair

(G-12285)
ALLCOFFEE LLC
12815 Nw 45th Ave Ste 6b (33054-5100)
PHONE..................................305 685-6856
Benedetto Mazzucco, *CEO*
Giuseppe Cecinato, *Mktg Dir*
Alexandro Centofanti, *Officer*
EMP: 5 **EST:** 2006
SALES (est): 367K **Privately Held**
WEB: www.allcoffee.com
SIC: 2095 Roasted coffee

(G-12286)
ALLIED GENERAL ENGRV & PLAS
3485 Nw 167th St (33056-4118)
PHONE..................................305 626-6585
Bedros Kazazian, *President*
Berge Kazazian, *Vice Pres*
▲ **EMP:** 10 **EST:** 1978
SALES (est): 789.3K **Privately Held**
SIC: 3089 2759 3544 2789 Injection molding of plastics; engraving; special dies, tools, jigs & fixtures; bookbinding & related work

(G-12287)
AMERICAN THRMPLASTIC EXTRUSION
Also Called: Ateco
4851 Nw 128th Street Rd (33054-5134)
PHONE..................................305 769-9566
Donald P Miller, *Ch of Bd*
Don Gellett, *President*
Mark J Baker, *Treasurer*
Iliana Salum, *Human Res Mgr*
Angela K Gillett, *Admin Sec*
EMP: 150 **EST:** 1959
SQ FT: 61,000
SALES (est): 27.9MM
SALES (corp-wide): 203MM **Privately Held**
WEB: www.roppeholdingcompany.com
SIC: 3089 3083 Extruded finished plastic products; thermoformed finished plastic products; laminated plastics plate & sheet
PA: Roppe Holding Company
1602 N Union St
Fostoria OH 44830
419 435-8546

(G-12288)
ANDRE T JEAN ✪
Also Called: Bubble Bath Detailing Car Wash
2306 Ali Baba Ave (33054-3134)
PHONE..................................305 647-8744
Andre T Jean, *Owner*
EMP: 7 **EST:** 2020
SALES (est): 57.6K **Privately Held**
SIC: 3589 Car washing machinery

(G-12289)
AQUARIUS PRESS INC
13795 Nw 19th Ave (33054-4215)
PHONE..................................305 688-0066
Valerie Doten, *President*
James A Williams, *Vice Pres*
▼ **EMP:** 11 **EST:** 1976
SQ FT: 3,600
SALES (est): 763.2K **Privately Held**
WEB: www.aquariuspress.com
SIC: 2752 Commercial printing, offset

(G-12290)
ARSO ENTERPRISES INC
Also Called: Sol-A-Trol Aluminum Products
4101 Nw 132nd St (33054-4510)
PHONE..................................305 681-2020
Antonio L Soler, *President*
Marie Soler, *Corp Secy*
Anthony M Soler, *Vice Pres*
Anthony Soler, *Vice Pres*
Antonio Soler, *CFO*
◆ **EMP:** 37 **EST:** 1976
SALES (est): 4.9MM **Privately Held**
WEB: www.arsoent.com
SIC: 3442 1751 5031 1793 Window & door frames; window & door (prefabricated) installation; building materials, exterior; building materials, interior; glass & glazing work; products of purchased glass

(G-12291)
B & P MOTOR HEADS INC
1815 Opa Locka Blvd (33054-4223)
PHONE..................................305 769-3183
Pedro Finales, *President*
EMP: 7 **EST:** 1990
SQ FT: 25,000
SALES (est): 200K **Privately Held**
SIC: 3599 5015 Machine shop, jobbing & repair; automotive parts & supplies, used

(G-12292)
B & P MOTORS INC
1815 Opa Locka Blvd (33054-4223)
PHONE..................................305 687-7337
Pedro Finales, *President*
Pedro Finalen, *President*
EMP: 8 **EST:** 2001
SALES (est): 535.6K **Privately Held**
SIC: 3545 Machine tool accessories

(G-12293)
BEAUTY COSMETICA
Also Called: Keratin Cure
3406 Nw 151st Ter (33054-2450)
PHONE..................................305 406-1022
EMP: 15
SALES (est): 799.6K **Privately Held**
SIC: 3999 Mfg Misc Products

(G-12294)
BEAUTY LAB INC
2360 Nw 150th St (33054-2706)
PHONE..................................305 687-0071
▼ **EMP:** 20
SQ FT: 56,000
SALES: 1.5MM **Privately Held**
SIC: 2844 Mfg Toilet Preparations

(G-12295)
BOLIDT CRUISE CONTROL CORP
14501 Nw 57th Ave Ste 111 (33054-2375)
PHONE..................................305 607-4172
Antoine M Dons Mr, *General Mgr*
Overbeek Jacco, *Principal*
Jacco Van Overbeek Mr, *Vice Pres*
Peter Plaisier Mr, *Director*
▲ **EMP:** 9 **EST:** 1999
SALES (est): 2.4MM **Privately Held**
WEB: www.bolidt.com
SIC: 3069 Flooring, rubber: tile or sheet

(G-12296)
BON VIVANT INTERIORS INC
Also Called: Bon Vivant Custom Woodworking
4400 Nw 135th St (33054-4420)
PHONE..................................305 576-8066
Ricardo Rammos, *President*
EMP: 35 **EST:** 1982
SQ FT: 30,000
SALES (est): 4.5MM **Privately Held**
WEB: www.bvmiami.com
SIC: 2512 2517 2511 Upholstered household furniture; wood television & radio cabinets; wood household furniture

(G-12297)
C M I ENTERPRISES INC (PA)
Also Called: CMI
13145 Nw 45th Ave (33054-4305)
P.O. Box 941150, Miami (33194-1150)
PHONE..................................305 622-6410
Michael Novick, *President*
Jorge Canamero, *Vice Pres*
Ricardo Porras, *CFO*
◆ **EMP:** 40 **EST:** 1984
SQ FT: 25,000
SALES: 27.1MM **Privately Held**
WEB: www.cmi-enterprises.com
SIC: 3999 2295 Boat models, except toy; resin or plastic coated fabrics

(G-12298)
CEDENA CARMENN
2310 Nw 150th St (33054-2706)
PHONE..................................305 681-1222
Karla Pena, *President*
EMP: 7 **EST:** 2016
SALES (est): 65.4K **Privately Held**
SIC: 2011 Lamb products from lamb slaughtered on site

(G-12299)
CIGARETTE RACING TEAM LLC
4355 Nw 128th St (33054-5123)
PHONE..................................305 769-4350
Chad Braver, *Engineer*
Mark Belisle, *Sales Staff*
Skip Braver, *Mng Member*
Bud Lorow, *Manager*
▲ **EMP:** 99 **EST:** 2002
SALES (est): 16.1MM **Privately Held**
WEB: www.cigaretteracing.com
SIC: 3732 Motorized boat, building & repairing

(G-12300)
CLERO ENTERPRISES INC
3881 Nw 125th St (33054-4515)
PHONE..................................305 681-4877
Jorge Clero, *President*
Mary Martinez, *Purchasing*
William G Clero, *Admin Sec*
EMP: 6 **EST:** 1998
SALES (est): 1.4MM **Privately Held**
WEB: www.cleroaviation.com
SIC: 3728 Aircraft parts & equipment

(G-12301)
CM2 INDUSTRIES INC
Also Called: SBC Laser
1769 Opa Locka Blvd (33054-4221)
PHONE..................................305 685-4812
Nicholas Caito, *President*
EMP: 6 **EST:** 2018
SALES (est): 50K **Privately Held**
SIC: 3479 Etching on metals

(G-12302)
COFFEE UNLIMITED LLC
Also Called: Allcoffee
12815 Nw 45th Ave Ste 6b (33054-5100)
PHONE..................................305 685-6366
Juan Mendes,
EMP: 10 **EST:** 2019
SALES (est): 632.8K **Privately Held**
WEB: www.coffeeunlimited.com
SIC: 2095 Coffee roasting (except by wholesale grocers)

(G-12303)
CONCEPT BOATS INC
2410 Nw 147th St (33054-3130)
PHONE..................................305 635-8712
Luis Avila, *President*
Susan Patterson, *Vice Pres*
Chris Box, *Sales Dir*
Anay Santos, *Admin Mgr*
▼ **EMP:** 25 **EST:** 1986
SQ FT: 10,000
SALES (est): 5MM **Privately Held**
WEB: www.conceptboats.com
SIC: 3732 5551 Boat building & repairing; boat dealers

▲ = Import ▼=Export
◆ =Import/Export

(G-12304)
CUPCAKES FRSTING SPRINKLES LLC
2301 Nw 155th St (33054-2750)
PHONE..............................305 769-3393
Minerva B Hector, *Manager*
EMP: 8 **EST:** 2013
SALES (est): 146.9K **Privately Held**
WEB: www.sprinkles.com
SIC: 2051 Bread, cake & related products

(G-12305)
D N L PERFORMANCE INC
1797 Opa Locka Blvd (33054-4221)
PHONE..............................786 295-8831
David Rivera, *Principal*
EMP: 6 **EST:** 2012
SALES (est): 437.3K **Privately Held**
SIC: 2992 Lubricating oils

(G-12306)
DI DI DESIGNS INC
Also Called: Elana Kattan
13376 Nw 42nd Ave (33054-4526)
PHONE..............................305 836-0266
Elana Henry, *President*
Richard Henry, *Vice Pres*
Rami Kattan, *Vice Pres*
Abraham Kattan, *Admin Sec*
◆ **EMP:** 19 **EST:** 1982
SALES (est): 2.1MM **Privately Held**
WEB: www.elanakattan.com
SIC: 2339 Leotards: women's, misses' & juniors'; athletic clothing: women's, misses' & juniors'

(G-12307)
DISTRIBUIDORA GIORGIO USA LLC
12815 Nw 45th Ave (33054-5116)
PHONE..............................305 685-6366
Mazzucco Benedetto,
Centofanti Alexandro,
Cecinato Giuseppe,
Taurchini Stefano,
◆ **EMP:** 17 **EST:** 2007
SALES (est): 3.3MM **Privately Held**
SIC: 2095 Roasted coffee

(G-12308)
DONE RITE PUMPS
Also Called: Repair Electrical Motors Ac/DC
4240 Nw 133rd St (33054-4400)
PHONE..............................305 953-3380
Luis Navarro, *President*
EMP: 8 **EST:** 2012
SALES (est): 1MM **Privately Held**
WEB: www.doneritepumps.com
SIC: 7694 7699 Electric motor repair; industrial equipment services

(G-12309)
DOSAL TOBACCO CORPORATION (PA)
4775 Nw 132nd St (33054-4313)
PHONE..............................305 685-2949
Margarita Dosal, *President*
Margarita D Owen, *Exec VP*
George Dosal, *Vice Pres*
Yolanda Snader, *CFO*
Henry Aleman, *Technology*
▲ **EMP:** 22 **EST:** 1962
SALES (est): 31.2MM **Privately Held**
SIC: 2111 2121 Cigarettes; cigars

(G-12310)
DYNASTY APPAREL CORP (PA)
13000 Nw 42nd Ave (33054-4500)
PHONE..............................305 685-3490
Ignacio Mendez, *President*
Caridad Mendez, *Admin Sec*
Ovidio Mendez, *Admin Sec*
◆ **EMP:** 90 **EST:** 1978
SQ FT: 72,000
SALES (est): 26.3MM **Privately Held**
WEB: www.dynastyapparel.com
SIC: 2325 2321 Shorts (outerwear): men's, youths' & boys'; trousers, dress (separate): men's, youths' & boys'; men's & boys' sports & polo shirts; sport shirts, men's & boys': from purchased materials

(G-12311)
DYPLAST PRODUCTS LLC
12501 Nw 38th Ave (33054-4543)
PHONE..............................305 921-0100
Joseph Hughes, *VP Sls/Mktg*
Vincent Fuster, *CFO*
Cristina Mayor, *Credit Mgr*
Ted Berglund, *Mng Member*
Claude Hartdegen, *Manager*
◆ **EMP:** 61 **EST:** 2003
SQ FT: 90,000
SALES (est): 15.9MM **Privately Held**
WEB: www.dyplastproducts.com
SIC: 3086 5033 Insulation or cushioning material, foamed plastic; roofing & siding materials

(G-12312)
EASTERN SHORES PRINTING (PA)
Also Called: Eastern Shres Prtg Woven Label
4476 Nw 128th St (33054-5126)
PHONE..............................305 685-8976
Gladys Marcus, *President*
Laurie Marcus, *Corp Secy*
Steven Marcus, *Vice Pres*
◆ **EMP:** 30 **EST:** 1974
SQ FT: 12,000
SALES (est): 5.6MM **Privately Held**
WEB: www.easternshoresprint.com
SIC: 2752 2396 2241 Lithographing on metal; tags, lithographed; automotive & apparel trimmings; narrow fabric mills

(G-12313)
ENDFLEX LLC
4760 Nw 128th St (33054-5132)
PHONE..............................305 622-4070
Louis Taraborelli, *President*
Frank Milone, *President*
Jorge Perez, *Vice Pres*
Nicholas Taraborelli, *Vice Pres*
Jazmin Aguirrre, *Office Mgr*
▲ **EMP:** 35 **EST:** 2008
SQ FT: 14,475
SALES (est): 2.6MM **Privately Held**
WEB: www.endflex.com
SIC: 3565 Carton packing machines

(G-12314)
EVERGLADES CREATIONS INC
Also Called: Winston Manufacturing
2335 Nw 149th St (33054-3131)
PHONE..............................305 822-3344
William Di Scipio, *President*
EMP: 26 **EST:** 2007
SALES (est): 1.4MM **Privately Held**
SIC: 3172 Personal leather goods

(G-12315)
FIS GROUP INC
3820 Nw 125th St (33054-4541)
PHONE..............................786 622-3308
EMP: 6 **EST:** 2017
SALES (est): 120.1K **Privately Held**
SIC: 3441 Fabricated structural metal

(G-12316)
FLORIDA ICE CORPORATION
13401 Nw 38th Ct (33054-4512)
PHONE..............................305 685-9377
Miguel Angel Guerra, *President*
Maria Rodriguez, *Corp Secy*
EMP: 10 **EST:** 1999
SQ FT: 13,600
SALES (est): 1MM **Privately Held**
WEB: www.floridaice.net
SIC: 2097 Manufactured ice

(G-12317)
FLORIDA POLISHING
2163 Opa Locka Blvd (33054-4229)
PHONE..............................305 688-2988
Evelyn Venerio, *Principal*
EMP: 5 **EST:** 2010
SALES (est): 353.5K **Privately Held**
SIC: 3471 Polishing, metals or formed products

(G-12318)
FLORIDA STORM PANELS INC
14475 Nw 26th Ave (33054-3121)
PHONE..............................305 685-9000
Victor Cruz, *President*
▲ **EMP:** 10 **EST:** 1993
SQ FT: 26,000
SALES (est): 1.2MM **Privately Held**
SIC: 3444 Sheet metal specialties, not stamped

(G-12319)
GABOL SCREEN PRINTING CO
12815 Nw 45th Ave (33054-5116)
PHONE..............................305 681-3882
Ken Curley, *Owner*
EMP: 6 **EST:** 2001
SALES (est): 132.6K **Privately Held**
SIC: 2752 Commercial printing, lithographic

(G-12320)
GLASSPEC CORP
2385 Nw 149th St (33054-3131)
PHONE..............................305 255-8444
Luis Echenique, *Manager*
EMP: 6 **EST:** 2015
SALES (est): 197.6K **Privately Held**
SIC: 3089 Injection molding of plastics

(G-12321)
GSE JETALL INC
4821 Nw 128th St (33054-5134)
PHONE..............................305 688-2111
Marisol G Alvarez, *Administration*
EMP: 8 **EST:** 2014
SALES (est): 257.3K **Privately Held**
WEB: www.jetall.com
SIC: 3728 3511 Aircraft parts & equipment; turbines & turbine generator sets

(G-12322)
H SIXTO DISTRIBUTORS INC
Also Called: Sixto Packaging
13301 Nw 38th Ct (33054-4517)
PHONE..............................305 688-5242
Carmen Sixto, *President*
Andres Sixto, *Vice Pres*
Alan Raines, *Production*
Felipe Humberto Sixto, *Treasurer*
Emilio Sixto, *Admin Sec*
◆ **EMP:** 12 **EST:** 1978
SALES (est): 3.5MM **Privately Held**
WEB: www.sixtopack.com
SIC: 2673 2396 Cellophane bags, unprinted: made from purchased materials; automotive & apparel trimmings

(G-12323)
HIGHLANDER STONE CORP
14105 Nw 19th Ave (33054-4141)
PHONE..............................786 333-1151
Miguel A Garutti, *Principal*
EMP: 8 **EST:** 2012
SALES (est): 654.3K **Privately Held**
SIC: 3281 Cut stone & stone products

(G-12324)
IES SALES AND SERVICE LLC
2340 Nw 147th St (33054-3128)
PHONE..............................305 687-9400
Osniel Sanchez,
Janet Sanchez,
▼ **EMP:** 8
SQ FT: 37,000
SALES (est): 5MM **Privately Held**
WEB: www.refusewastequip.com
SIC: 2631 Container, packaging & boxboard

(G-12325)
INEN USA CORP
12750 Cairo Ln (33054-4611)
PHONE..............................305 343-6666
Jesus A Berrio Ramirez, *Principal*
Lina Arenas, *Manager*
EMP: 6 **EST:** 2008
SALES (est): 367.1K **Privately Held**
SIC: 3549 Metalworking machinery

(G-12326)
INTERNATIONAL PAINT LLC
3489 Nw 167th St (33056-4118)
PHONE..............................305 620-9220
Robert Hall, *Manager*
EMP: 8
SQ FT: 5,013
SALES (corp-wide): 10B **Privately Held**
WEB: www.international-pc.com
SIC: 2851 Paints & allied products
HQ: International Paint Llc
6001 Antoine Dr
Houston TX 77091
713 682-1711

(G-12327)
INVINCIBLE BOAT COMPANY LLC
4700 Nw 132nd St (33054-4314)
PHONE..............................305 685-2704
John Dorton, *CEO*
Ian Birdsall, *Vice Pres*
Jorge Delgado, *Parts Mgr*
Anthony Porben, *Parts Mgr*
Blake Johnson, *QC Mgr*
▼ **EMP:** 30 **EST:** 2005
SALES (est): 7.1MM **Privately Held**
WEB: www.invincibleboats.com
SIC: 3732 Boat building & repairing

(G-12328)
J & J STONE TOPS INC
13760 Nw 19th Ave (33054-4233)
PHONE..............................305 305-8993
Julio Rodriguez, *President*
Jackie Alva, *Vice Pres*
▲ **EMP:** 5 **EST:** 2000
SQ FT: 4,500
SALES (est): 600K **Privately Held**
WEB: www.jjstonetops.com
SIC: 3281 Table tops, marble

(G-12329)
JOHN M CALDWELL DISTRG CO INC
Also Called: Custom Screen Printing Florida
1150 Ali Baba Ave (33054-3611)
PHONE..............................305 685-9822
John M Caldwell, *President*
EMP: 7 **EST:** 1972
SQ FT: 14,000
SALES (est): 710.7K **Privately Held**
SIC: 2339 2329 Sportswear, women's; men's & boys' sportswear & athletic clothing

(G-12330)
KELLYS BAKERY CORP
Also Called: Atlantic Coastal Bakery
3990 Nw 132nd St Unit A (33054-4535)
PHONE..............................305 685-4622
Elango Ellappan, *President*
Brian Hersch, *Principal*
EMP: 14 **EST:** 1998
SALES (est): 1MM **Privately Held**
SIC: 2051 Bakery: wholesale or wholesale/retail combined

(G-12331)
KOHTLER ELEVATOR INDS INC (PA)
4115 Nw 132nd St Unit B (33054-4539)
PHONE..............................305 687-7037
Olga V Diaz, *President*
EMP: 20 **EST:** 2008
SALES (est): 2.9MM **Privately Held**
WEB: www.kohtler.com
SIC: 3534 1761 Elevators & equipment; sheet metalwork

(G-12332)
LANDING AEROSPACE INC
4604 Nw 133rd St (33054-4406)
PHONE..............................305 687-0100
Mery L Ramirez, *Principal*
▲ **EMP:** 9 **EST:** 2013
SALES (est): 528.5K **Privately Held**
WEB: www.landingaerospace.net
SIC: 3728 Aircraft parts & equipment

(G-12333)
LEAR INVESTORS INC (PA)
Also Called: International Trading Company
4154 Nw 132nd St (33054-4511)
PHONE..............................305 681-8582
Leon Bekerman, *President*
Freny Bekerman, *Vice Pres*
▲ **EMP:** 7 **EST:** 1985
SQ FT: 4,200
SALES (est): 1MM **Privately Held**
WEB: www.lear.com
SIC: 2339 5137 Sportswear, women's; sportswear, women's & children's

(G-12334)
LUDLOW FIBC CORP
13260 Nw 45th Ave (33054-4308)
PHONE.................................305 702-5000
Carol Barber, *Manager*
▲ **EMP:** 5
SALES (est): 372.8K **Privately Held**
SIC: 3496 Miscellaneous fabricated wire products

(G-12335)
MARTINSON MICA WOOD PDTS INC
13740 Nw 19th Ave (33054-4211)
PHONE.................................305 688-4445
Martin Del Ray, *President*
EMP: 6 **EST:** 1994
SQ FT: 5,000
SALES (est): 754.3K **Privately Held**
WEB: www.martinsonproducts.com
SIC: 2512 Upholstered household furniture

(G-12336)
MASTER NUTRITION LABS INC
13165 Nw 47th Ave (33054-4309)
PHONE.................................786 847-2000
Solomon Brander, *Principal*
EMP: 7 **EST:** 2016
SALES (est): 90K **Privately Held**
WEB: www.masternutritionlabs.com
SIC: 2834 Vitamin preparations

(G-12337)
MEELKO CO
3890 Nw 132nd St Unit F (33054-4537)
PHONE.................................845 600-3379
Edu Y Cristian Moreno, *CEO*
EMP: 9 **EST:** 2013
SALES (est): 696.4K **Privately Held**
WEB: www.meelko.com
SIC: 1011 Iron ore pelletizing

(G-12338)
MENDEZ BROTHERS LLC
13000 Nw 42nd Ave (33054-4405)
PHONE.................................305 685-3490
Armando Mendez, *Manager*
EMP: 10 **EST:** 2005
SALES (est): 509.4K **Privately Held**
SIC: 2759 Commercial printing

(G-12339)
MIAMI SIGN INDUSTRY
13454 Nw 38th Ct (33054-4506)
PHONE.................................305 418-0673
EMP: 6 **EST:** 2018
SALES (est): 359.2K **Privately Held**
WEB: www.miamisign.net
SIC: 3993 Signs & advertising specialties

(G-12340)
MOLDS AND PLASTIC MACHINERY
13145 Nw 47th Ave (33054-4309)
PHONE.................................305 828-3456
Bruce Miller, *President*
Guillermo Sanchez, *Corp Secy*
Jose Anton, *Vice Pres*
◆ **EMP:** 8 **EST:** 1996
SQ FT: 30,000
SALES (est): 1MM **Privately Held**
WEB: www.moldsplastic.us
SIC: 3089 Injection molding of plastics

(G-12341)
MR GUMMY VITAMINS LLC
12845 Nw 45th Ave (33054-5119)
PHONE.................................855 674-8669
Monica G Suarez, *Mng Member*
EMP: 9 **EST:** 2013
SALES (est): 812.6K **Privately Held**
WEB: www.mrgummyvitamins.com
SIC: 2048 5122 Feed supplements; vitamins & minerals

(G-12342)
MTI AVIATION INC
13150 Nw 45th Ave (33054-4306)
PHONE.................................305 817-4244
Milagros Mejia, *President*
Jorge Mejia, *Vice Pres*
Hector Franco, *Purch Mgr*
Oscar Ramudo, *Cust Mgr*
EMP: 39 **EST:** 2013
SALES (est): 6.2MM **Privately Held**
WEB: www.mtiaviation.com
SIC: 3724 Aircraft engines & engine parts

(G-12343)
NATURAL VITAMINS LAB CORP
12845 Nw 45th Ave (33054-5119)
PHONE.................................305 265-1660
EMP: 136 **Privately Held**
SIC: 2834 Mfg Pharmaceutical Preparations
PA: Natural Vitamins Laboratory Corporation
12845 Nw 45th Ave
Opa Locka FL 33054

(G-12344)
NATURAL VITAMINS LAB CORP
Also Called: Natural Vitamins Labs
12845 Nw 45th Ave (33054-5119)
PHONE.................................305 265-1660
Karan Arora, *President*
Tejas Choksi, *Vice Pres*
Tejus Choski, *Treasurer*
Shruti Shah, *Manager*
◆ **EMP:** 200 **EST:** 1995
SQ FT: 70,000
SALES (est): 40.6MM **Privately Held**
WEB: www.nvlabs.com
SIC: 2834 Vitamin preparations

(G-12345)
NELSON MCH SP WLDG & ENGRG INC
13990 Nw 22nd Ave (33054-4127)
PHONE.................................305 710-5029
Mariuxi Salazar, *Principal*
EMP: 7 **EST:** 2012
SALES (est): 151.7K **Privately Held**
WEB: www.nelsonmachineandwelding.com
SIC: 3599 Machine shop, jobbing & repair

(G-12346)
NEW VISION FURNITURE INC
4115 Nw 132nd St Unit I (33054-4539)
PHONE.................................305 562-9428
Juan Benavente, *President*
EMP: 7 **EST:** 2013
SQ FT: 5,000
SALES (est): 450K **Privately Held**
WEB: www.newvisionfurniture.com
SIC: 2522 5712 Office furniture, except wood; office furniture

(G-12347)
OPA-LOCKA PALLETS INC
3180 Nw 131st St (33054-4921)
PHONE.................................305 681-8212
Jose Almendares, *President*
Maria Almendares, *Vice Pres*
▲ **EMP:** 17 **EST:** 1985
SQ FT: 800
SALES (est): 2MM **Privately Held**
WEB: www.opalockapallets.com
SIC: 2448 Pallets, wood

(G-12348)
ORTEGA INDUSTRIES AND MFG
13281 Nw 43rd Ave (33054-4436)
PHONE.................................305 688-0090
Omar Dube, *President*
Magdalena Dube, *Vice Pres*
Alex Pea, *Accounts Mgr*
◆ **EMP:** 100 **EST:** 1971
SQ FT: 65,000
SALES (est): 8.3MM **Privately Held**
WEB: www.ortegaindustries.com
SIC: 2591 5023 Blinds vertical; window covering parts & accessories

(G-12349)
PAPER BAG MANUFACTURERS INC
4131 Nw 132nd St (33054-4510)
PHONE.................................305 685-1100
Joseph Greenspan, *President*
Susan Hernandez, *Vice Pres*
▲ **EMP:** 17 **EST:** 1994
SALES (est): 1.8MM **Privately Held**
WEB: www.paperbag.com
SIC: 2393 2674 Bags & containers, except sleeping bags: textile; bags: uncoated paper & multiwall

(G-12350)
PASA SERVICES INC
Also Called: Flamingo Graphics
13015 Nw 38th Ave (33054-4501)
PHONE.................................305 594-8662
Blanca Bichara, *CEO*
Tatiana Bautista, *President*
Edwin Mora, *General Mgr*
EMP: 41 **EST:** 1988
SQ FT: 17,000
SALES (est): 11.8MM **Privately Held**
SIC: 2752 2759 Commercial printing, lithographic; security certificates: engraved

(G-12351)
PLASTICS FOR MANKIND INC (PA)
Also Called: Plastiform
13050 Nw 47th Ave (33054-4326)
PHONE.................................305 687-5917
Jorge G Blodek, *President*
George G Blodek, *President*
EMP: 11 **EST:** 1984
SQ FT: 24,000
SALES (est): 1.2MM **Privately Held**
SIC: 3827 3089 Optical instruments & lenses; molding primary plastic

(G-12352)
QUANTUM STORAGE SYSTEMS ✪
4820 Nw 128th St (33054-5133)
PHONE.................................305 687-0405
EMP: 6 **EST:** 2021
SALES (est): 271.3K **Privately Held**
SIC: 3841 Surgical & medical instruments

(G-12353)
REMCRAFT LIGHTING PRODUCTS INC
Also Called: Baci By Remcraft
12870 Nw 45th Ave (33054-5120)
P.O. Box 541487 (33054-1487)
PHONE.................................305 687-9031
Mitchell J Robboy, *CEO*
Jeffrey Robboy, *President*
David Crossley, *Natl Sales Mgr*
◆ **EMP:** 20 **EST:** 1920
SQ FT: 40,000
SALES (est): 3.6MM **Privately Held**
WEB: www.bacihospitality.com
SIC: 3645 3646 Residential lighting fixtures; commercial indusl & institutional electric lighting fixtures

(G-12354)
REPUBLIC METALS CORPORATION
Also Called: RMC
12900 Nw 38th Ave (33054-4527)
PHONE.................................305 685-8505
Jason Rubin, *CEO*
Scott Avila, *Principal*
Rose Rubin, *Vice Pres*
James Snyder, *Vice Pres*
Emre Karalar, *Engineer*
◆ **EMP:** 150 **EST:** 1980
SALES (est): 39.3MM **Privately Held**
WEB: www.republicmetalscorp.com
SIC: 3339 Precious metals

(G-12355)
REPUBLIC PACKAGING FLORIDA INC
4570 Nw 128th St (33054-5128)
PHONE.................................305 685-5175
Charles Wood, *President*
Tommy Briggs, *Business Mgr*
EMP: 43 **EST:** 1961
SQ FT: 45,000
SALES (est): 8.9MM
SALES (corp-wide): 16.4MM **Privately Held**
WEB: www.repco.com
SIC: 3086 2653 Packaging & shipping materials, foamed plastic; corrugated & solid fiber boxes
PA: Republic Packaging Corp.
9160 S Green St Ste 1
Chicago IL 60620
773 233-6530

(G-12356)
ROYAL PRECISION PRODUCTS INC (PA)
13171 Nw 43rd Ave (33054-4424)
PHONE.................................305 685-5490
Scott Lettiere, *CEO*
Albert Stoyanov, *President*
Rick Deleon, *Finance Mgr*
Tatiana Viena, *Comptroller*
Laura Alvarado, *Office Mgr*
EMP: 28 **EST:** 1975
SQ FT: 12,000
SALES (est): 4.7MM **Privately Held**
WEB: www.royalprecisionproducts.com
SIC: 3451 Screw machine products

(G-12357)
RYDER WELDING SERVICE INC
350 Ali Baba Ave (33054-3815)
P.O. Box 540796 (33054-0796)
PHONE.................................305 685-6630
Joel Gaus, *President*
EMP: 12 **EST:** 1971
SQ FT: 10,000
SALES (est): 1.7MM **Privately Held**
SIC: 3599 7692 3441 Machine shop, jobbing & repair; welding repair; fabricated structural metal

(G-12358)
SIGNS ALL SIGNS
14121 Nw 19th Ave (33054-4141)
PHONE.................................786 285-7900
Jorge Acebedo, *Principal*
▲ **EMP:** 7 **EST:** 2013
SALES (est): 200.3K **Privately Held**
WEB: www.signsallsigns.com
SIC: 3993 Electric signs

(G-12359)
SOL-A-TROL ALUMINUM PDTS INC
4101 Nw 132nd St (33054-4510)
PHONE.................................305 681-2020
Anthony M Soler, *President*
Sammy Delahoz, *CFO*
EMP: 25 **EST:** 2006
SALES (est): 1.3MM **Privately Held**
WEB: www.solatrol.com
SIC: 2431 Windows & window parts & trim, wood; louver windows, glass, wood frame

(G-12360)
ST IVES BURRUPS
13449 Nw 42nd Ave (33054-4513)
PHONE.................................305 685-7381
Wayne Angstrom, *CEO*
EMP: 6 **EST:** 2014
SALES (est): 160.1K **Privately Held**
SIC: 2759 Commercial printing

(G-12361)
STAINLESS MARINE INC
13800 Nw 19th Ave (33054-4220)
PHONE.................................305 681-7893
Jerry Schmid, *President*
Leticia Romero, *Principal*
Norris Perez, *Admin Sec*
◆ **EMP:** 20 **EST:** 1978
SQ FT: 24,000
SALES (est): 2.9MM **Privately Held**
WEB: www.stainlessmarine.com
SIC: 3429 Marine hardware

(G-12362)
SUPER STONE INC (PA)
1251 Burlington St (33054-3618)
PHONE.................................305 681-3561
Janine Lutz, *CEO*
◆ **EMP:** 22 **EST:** 1978
SQ FT: 25,500
SALES (est): 4.2MM **Privately Held**
WEB: www.superstone.com
SIC: 2952 Asphalt felts & coatings

(G-12363)
SWIM BUOY
2596 Ali Baba Ave (33054-3138)
PHONE.................................305 953-4101
Decantillon S Brasington, *Principal*
EMP: 6 **EST:** 2010
SALES (est): 470.4K **Privately Held**
WEB: www.swimbuoy.com
SIC: 3949 Sporting & athletic goods

▲ = Import ▼=Export
◆ =Import/Export

(G-12364)
TEX Z-E CORP
12815 Nw 45th Ave (33054-5116)
PHONE..................................305 769-0202
Jorge Zarur, *President*
Edwardo Elias, *Vice Pres*
▲ **EMP:** 5 **EST:** 2002
SQ FT: 42,000
SALES (est): 526.1K **Privately Held**
SIC: 2211 Broadwoven fabric mills, cotton

(G-12365)
TOMMY & GIORDY BUY/SELL
15060 Nw 22nd Ave (33054-2827)
PHONE..................................786 797-6973
Shananya C Santana, *Principal*
EMP: 6 **EST:** 2013
SALES (est): 113.9K **Privately Held**
SIC: 2631 Cardboard

(G-12366)
TSA REWINDS FLORIDA INC
13050 Nw 47th Ave (33054-4326)
PHONE..................................305 681-2030
Mike Cean, *President*
EMP: 7 **EST:** 2010
SALES (est): 329.3K **Privately Held**
WEB: www.tsarewindgroup.com
SIC: 7694 Rewinding services

(G-12367)
UNIVERSAL BAKERY LLC
Also Called: Aaron Best Pita
1050 Ali Baba Ave (33054-3610)
PHONE..................................786 566-3303
Francisco R Lin, *Owner*
EMP: 9 **EST:** 2011
SALES (est): 427.5K **Privately Held**
SIC: 2051 Bakery: wholesale or whole-sale/retail combined

(G-12368)
WARBIRD MARINE HOLDINGS LLC (PA)
4700 Nw 132nd St (33054-4314)
PHONE..................................844 341-2504
John Dorton, *CEO*
Thomas Wieners, *COO*
Jeff Needles, *CFO*
EMP: 3 **EST:** 2019
SALES (est): 20.8MM **Privately Held**
SIC: 3732 Boat building & repairing

(G-12369)
WISE BUSINESS FORMS INC
13015 Nw 38th Ave (33054-4501)
PHONE..................................770 442-1060
Bret Marshal, *Branch Mgr*
EMP: 49
SALES (corp-wide): 78MM **Privately Held**
WEB: www.wbf.com
SIC: 2621 Business form paper
PA: Wise Business Forms Incorporated
555 Mcfarland 400 Dr
Alpharetta GA 30004
770 442-1060

(G-12370)
WORLD PERFUMES INC
Also Called: Pharmachem
2360 Nw 150th St (33054-2706)
PHONE..................................305 822-0004
Saul Rios, *President*
▲ **EMP:** 15 **EST:** 2001
SQ FT: 8,000
SALES (est): 1.5MM **Privately Held**
WEB: www.worldperfumesus.com
SIC: 2844 2833 Toilet preparations; medicinals & botanicals

(G-12371)
XTREME TOOLS INTERNATIONAL INC
Also Called: Okay Pure Naturals
15400 Nw 34th Ave (33054-2461)
PHONE..................................305 622-7474
Ali Mithavayani, *CEO*
Osmani Mithavayan, *Vice Pres*
Mira Mithavayani, *Vice Pres*
Osman Mithavayani, *Vice Pres*
◆ **EMP:** 46 **EST:** 2003
SQ FT: 50,000
SALES (est): 5.3MM **Privately Held**
WEB: www.okaypurenaturals.com
SIC: 2844 5961 Hair coloring preparations; cosmetics & perfumes, mail order

(G-12372)
YALE OGRON MFG CO INC (PA)
Also Called: Florida Screen Enterprise
15201 Nw 34th Ave (33054-2449)
PHONE..................................305 687-0424
Jeffrey Ogron, *President*
Jeffrey D Ogron, *Exec VP*
Sharry Ogron, *Shareholder*
▼ **EMP:** 60 **EST:** 1958
SQ FT: 53,000
SALES (est): 8MM **Privately Held**
SIC: 3442 Screen doors, metal

Orange City
Volusia County

(G-12373)
CENTRAL FLORIDA WELD & FAB LLC
259 N Industrial Dr (32763-7412)
PHONE..................................407 919-8706
Robert J Gingerich, *Principal*
EMP: 1 **EST:** 2007
SALES (est): 45MM **Privately Held**
WEB: www.cfweld.com
SIC: 7692 Welding repair

(G-12374)
COPACO INC
366 E Graves Ave Ste B (32763-5266)
PHONE..................................407 333-3041
J Stephen Dowd, *President*
Micheal Dowd, *Vice Pres*
EMP: 12 **EST:** 1986
SQ FT: 750
SALES (est): 421K **Privately Held**
SIC: 1499 4449 Gypsum & calcite mining; calcite mining; canal & intracoastal freight transportation

(G-12375)
DIXIE SPTIC TANK ORANGE CY LLC
1200 S Leavitt Ave (32763-7114)
PHONE..................................386 775-3051
Eugene M Evans, *President*
EMP: 15 **EST:** 1969
SQ FT: 1,200
SALES (est): 531.1K **Privately Held**
SIC: 3272 1711 4953 3084 Septic tanks, concrete; septic system construction; refuse systems; plastics pipe

(G-12376)
MRM CREATIVE LLC
Also Called: Bizcard Xpress
1209 Saxon Blvd Ste 4 (32763-8402)
PHONE..................................386 218-5940
Michael W Weber, *Principal*
EMP: 9 **EST:** 2014
SALES (est): 374.6K **Privately Held**
WEB: www.mrm.com
SIC: 2752 Commercial printing, lithographic

(G-12377)
PALLET EXCHANGE INC
1219 Doris St (32763-8813)
PHONE..................................386 734-0133
EMP: 10
SQ FT: 1,900
SALES (est): 1.1MM **Privately Held**
SIC: 2448 Mfg Wood Pallets/Skids

(G-12378)
SHENK ENTERPRISES LLC
985 Harley Strcklnd Blvd (32763-7980)
PHONE..................................386 753-1959
EMP: 12
SQ FT: 2,100
SALES (est): 1.3MM **Privately Held**
SIC: 3845 Mfg Electromedical Equipment

(G-12379)
SUPERIOR SHEDS INC (PA)
2323 S Volusia Ave (32763-7615)
PHONE..................................386 774-9861
Alex Martens, *President*
David N Sexton, *Vice Pres*
Bill Zile, *Transptn Dir*
Jorge Gaitan, *Manager*
Raquel Gibson, *Administration*
EMP: 27
SQ FT: 10,000
SALES (est): 13.3MM **Privately Held**
WEB: www.superiorsheds.com
SIC: 3448 Buildings, portable: prefabricated metal

Orange Park
Clay County

(G-12380)
AERO HOSE CORP
1845 Town Center Blvd # 140 (32003-4300)
PHONE..................................904 215-9638
Joseph Lemieux, *President*
Lin Dixson, *Sales Staff*
Tom Carmody, *Marketing Staff*
EMP: 15 **EST:** 2004
SQ FT: 5,500
SALES (est): 6.7MM
SALES (corp-wide): 245.5B **Publicly Held**
WEB: www.aero-hose.com
SIC: 3728 Aircraft parts & equipment
HQ: Marmon Distribution Services, Inc.
225 E Cunningham St
Butler PA 16001

(G-12381)
AMERICAN VLY AVNICS CLBRTION L ✪
Also Called: Avacs
137 Industrial Loop W (32073-2859)
PHONE..................................904 579-5272
Stephen Carlo, *Principal*
EMP: 10 **EST:** 2021
SALES (est): 707K **Privately Held**
SIC: 3728 Aircraft parts & equipment

(G-12382)
BANNERS-N-SIGNS ETC INC
Also Called: Banners & Signs
1970 Solomon St (32073-4735)
PHONE..................................904 272-3395
Bobby Hartley, *President*
Louis Hartley, *Vice Pres*
EMP: 6 **EST:** 1994
SALES (est): 1MM **Privately Held**
WEB: www.bnsigns.com
SIC: 3993 Signs, not made in custom sign painting shops

(G-12383)
BRIDGESTONE HOSEPOWER LLC (HQ)
50 Industrial Loop N (32073-6258)
PHONE..................................904 264-1267
John Clarkson, *President*
Todd Jorgensen, *Vice Pres*
Mike Morris, *Vice Pres*
Mike Watts, *Vice Pres*
Jerry Garcia, *Opers Mgr*
◆ **EMP:** 100 **EST:** 1990
SQ FT: 135,000
SALES (est): 170.1MM **Privately Held**
WEB: www.hosepower.com
SIC: 3542 5085 Crimping machinery, metal; pistons & valves

(G-12384)
CEMEX CEMENT INC
340 Corporate Way Ste 100 (32073-2851)
PHONE..................................904 296-2400
Charlie Buotman, *Branch Mgr*
EMP: 214 **Privately Held**
WEB: www.cemexusa.com
SIC: 3273 Ready-mixed concrete
HQ: Cemex Cement, Inc.
10100 Katy Fwy Ste 300
Houston TX 77043
713 650-6200

(G-12385)
CEMEX CNSTR MTLS FLA LLC
Also Called: Materials Div-Jacksonville ADM
340 Corporate Way Ste 100 (32073-2851)
PHONE..................................904 213-8860
Ryan Chandley, *Branch Mgr*
EMP: 10 **Privately Held**
SIC: 3273 Ready-mixed concrete
HQ: Cemex Construction Materials Florida, Llc
1501 Belvedere Rd
West Palm Beach FL 33406

(G-12386)
CINEGA CUSTOM FRAMING & DESIGN (PA)
490 Hillside Dr (32073-7622)
PHONE..................................904 495-1846
Juan Cinega, *President*
Brian P Anderson, *Director*
EMP: 29 **EST:** 2008
SALES (est): 278.4K **Privately Held**
SIC: 2499 Picture frame molding, finished

(G-12387)
CUSTOM GRAPHICS & SIGN DESIGN
230 Industrial Loop S (32073-2858)
PHONE..................................904 264-7667
Marvin Thole, *President*
Pat Thole, *Vice Pres*
EMP: 8 **EST:** 1988
SALES (est): 1.3MM **Privately Held**
WEB: www.cgsigns.net
SIC: 3993 Electric signs; neon signs

(G-12388)
DHA FILTER LLC
38 Knight Boxx Rd (32065-7327)
PHONE..................................904 269-8701
Darrell Hanna, *Mng Member*
EMP: 7
SALES (corp-wide): 6.1MM **Privately Held**
WEB: www.dhafilter.com
SIC: 3569 Filters
PA: Dha Filter, Llc
38 Knight Boxx Rd
Orange Park FL 32065
904 269-8701

(G-12389)
DOCTOR EASY MEDICAL PDTS LLC
1029 Blanding Blvd # 701 (32065-7753)
P.O. Box 1717 (32067-1717)
PHONE..................................904 276-7200
Marsha Garcia, *President*
Sterling E Price, *Vice Pres*
Charlene Reilly, *Sales Mgr*
Emily Garcia, *Director*
EMP: 8 **EST:** 1993
SQ FT: 1,500
SALES (est): 5MM **Privately Held**
WEB: www.doctor-easy.com
SIC: 3841 Surgical & medical instruments

(G-12390)
DOVER CYLINDER HEAD OF JACKSON
80 Industrial Loop N A (32073-6263)
EMP: 10
SQ FT: 5,000
SALES: 610.2K **Privately Held**
SIC: 3714 Rebuilds Cylinder Heads For Engines

(G-12391)
FAIRING XCHANGE LLC
144 Industrial Loop E (32073-6281)
PHONE..................................904 589-5253
EMP: 6 **EST:** 2016
SALES (est): 93.1K **Privately Held**
SIC: 2821 Plastics materials & resins

(G-12392)
FIREBIRD SCRUBS AND MORE LLC ✪
805 Glendale Ln (32065-5631)
PHONE..................................904 258-7514
Judith Phoenix, *CEO*
EMP: 9 **EST:** 2020
SALES (est): 443.6K **Privately Held**
SIC: 2211 Scrub cloths

(G-12393)
FIRST AMERICA PRODUCTS
153 Industrial Loop S (32073-6259)
PHONE..................................904 683-1253
Garfield West, *Principal*
EMP: 12 **EST:** 2015

GEOGRAPHIC

SALES (est): 626.1K **Privately Held**
WEB: www.firstamericaproducts.com
SIC: 3585 Air conditioning units, complete: domestic or industrial

(G-12394)
FIRST CAST FLA MFG SUPPORT LLC
1884 Chatham Village Dr (32003-8381)
PHONE..................................904 434-4128
James McCord, *Principal*
EMP: 6 **EST:** 2014
SALES (est): 65.5K **Privately Held**
WEB: www.fcmanufacturingsupport.com
SIC: 3999 Manufacturing industries

(G-12395)
FIRST COAST PAVERS CORP
204 Blairmore Blvd (32073-4319)
PHONE..................................904 410-0278
Jason Dugger, *President*
EMP: 15 **EST:** 2010
SALES (est): 973.6K **Privately Held**
WEB: www.firstcoastpaver.com
SIC: 3531 Pavers

(G-12396)
HAWKHEAD INTERNATIONAL INC
90 Industrial Loop N (32073-6258)
PHONE..................................904 264-4295
Russell Ross, *President*
Cheryll Ross, *Vice Pres*
EMP: 8 **EST:** 1983
SQ FT: 10,000
SALES (est): 5MM **Privately Held**
WEB: www.hatcheryequipment.com
SIC: 3523 5083 Incubators & brooders, farm; poultry equipment

(G-12397)
LARMAC DEVELOPMENT CORP
879 Camp Frncis Jhnson Rd (32065-5832)
PHONE..................................904 264-5006
Lawrence D Nichols, *President*
Lawerence D Nichols, *Principal*
EMP: 6 **EST:** 2001
SALES (est): 70.4K **Privately Held**
SIC: 3861 Developing machines & equipment, still or motion picture

(G-12398)
LIQUID EDGE LLC
178 Industrial Loop S (32073-2858)
PHONE..................................904 637-1494
EMP: 5 **EST:** 2019
SALES (est): 627.2K **Privately Held**
WEB: www.liquidedge.us
SIC: 2397 Schiffli machine embroideries

(G-12399)
LLOYD INDUSTRIES INC
138 Industrial Loop W (32073-6221)
PHONE..................................904 541-1655
William Lloyd, *President*
EMP: 66 **EST:** 2004
SQ FT: 55,000
SALES (est): 3.3MM
SALES (corp-wide): 13.5MM **Privately Held**
WEB: www.firedamper.com
SIC: 3444 5084 5051 Sheet metalwork; metalworking machinery; metals service centers & offices
PA: Lloyd Industries, Inc.
231 Commerce Dr
Montgomeryville PA 18936
215 367-5863

(G-12400)
MECK TECH CORP ✪
747 Park Ave Ste 2m (32073-3112)
PHONE..................................888 225-9403
Alex Subirats, *President*
EMP: 6 **EST:** 2020
SALES (est): 90K **Privately Held**
WEB: www.meck-tech.com
SIC: 3679 Liquid crystal displays (LCD)

(G-12401)
ORANGE PARK MACHINE INC
84 Industrial Loop N (32073-6258)
PHONE..................................904 269-1935
Keith F Stoudenmire, *President*
J Palmer Clarkson, *Owner*
Eben Barnes, *Opers Mgr*
▲ **EMP:** 32 **EST:** 1994
SALES (est): 2.6MM **Privately Held**
WEB: www.orangeparkmachine.com
SIC: 3599 Machine shop, jobbing & repair

(G-12402)
PHLINTROCK INDUSTRIES INC
2117 Foxwood Dr (32073-5106)
PHONE..................................904 579-3334
Flint C Anderson, *President*
EMP: 6 **EST:** 2005
SALES (est): 173K **Privately Held**
SIC: 3999 Manufacturing industries

(G-12403)
PIN-N-WIN WRESTLING CLUB INC
117 Suzanne Ave (32073-6425)
PHONE..................................904 276-8038
Christopher L McNealy, *President*
EMP: 7 **EST:** 2011
SALES (est): 138.7K **Privately Held**
WEB: www.pin-n-winwrestling.com
SIC: 3452 Pins

(G-12404)
POWDERTECH PLUS INC
98 Industrial Loop N (32073-6279)
PHONE..................................904 269-1719
Richard Pittman, *President*
Dawn Pittman, *Vice Pres*
EMP: 6 **EST:** 2007
SALES (est): 542K **Privately Held**
WEB: www.powdertechplus.com
SIC: 3479 Coating of metals & formed products

(G-12405)
SIGMA PRESS INC
Also Called: Sigma Marketing
1543 Kingsley Ave Ste 7 (32073-4583)
PHONE..................................904 264-6006
Michael J Sapit, *President*
Deena Lauderdale-Berry, *Vice Pres*
Sherry Dehner, *Marketing Staff*
Donald Sapit, *Shareholder*
EMP: 15
SQ FT: 5,500
SALES: 3MM **Privately Held**
WEB: www.sigmacalendars.com
SIC: 2741 Miscellaneous publishing

(G-12406)
SIGNS N STUFF INC
60 Canterbury Ct (32065-7290)
PHONE..................................904 248-8141
Patrick T Omeara, *Principal*
EMP: 7 **EST:** 2001
SALES (est): 107.5K **Privately Held**
WEB: www.signsnstuff.com
SIC: 3993 Signs & advertising specialties

(G-12407)
STRONGBRIDGE INTERNATIONAL LLC
154 Industrial Loop S (32073-2858)
P.O. Box 58177, Jacksonville (32241-8177)
PHONE..................................904 278-7499
Sandra P Cote, *President*
Andre B Cote, *Vice Pres*
Shelley Tiemann, *Manager*
▲ **EMP:** 50 **EST:** 2006
SALES (est): 6.9MM **Privately Held**
WEB: www.strongbridge.us
SIC: 3498 Fabricated pipe & fittings

(G-12408)
SUN STATE SYSTEMS INC
140 Industrial Loop W (32073-6221)
PHONE..................................904 269-2544
Gary Armbruster, *President*
Michael Anthony Rhodes, *Vice Pres*
Julie Rhodes, *Human Resources*
Donnie Martin, *Sales Staff*
EMP: 11 **EST:** 1991
SQ FT: 8,000
SALES (est): 2.5MM **Privately Held**
WEB: www.sunstatesystems.com
SIC: 3625 Control equipment, electric

(G-12409)
TITAN INDUSTRIES
3470 Peoria Rd (32065-7625)
PHONE..................................904 608-3905
Michael Todd Mathewson, *Owner*
EMP: 6 **EST:** 2012
SALES (est): 134.3K **Privately Held**
WEB: www.titanindustriesinc.com
SIC: 3999 Manufacturing industries

(G-12410)
TUCKER LITHOGRAPHIC CO
661 Blanding Blvd Ste 103 (32073-5066)
PHONE..................................904 276-0568
Eliot P Tucker, *Principal*
EMP: 7 **EST:** 2008
SALES (est): 95.7K **Privately Held**
WEB: www.tuckerlithographic.com
SIC: 2752 Commercial printing, lithographic

(G-12411)
VIKING WELDING AND FABRICATION
835 Camp Frncis Jhnson Rd (32065-5832)
PHONE..................................904 234-5964
Kenneth Ritland, *Principal*
EMP: 6 **EST:** 2016
SALES (est): 90.3K **Privately Held**
SIC: 7692 Welding repair

(G-12412)
VISION MANUFACTURING TECH INC
Also Called: Vision Mt
137 Industrial Loop W (32073-2859)
PHONE..................................904 579-5272
Stephen J Carlo, *President*
Lisa Machel, *President*
EMP: 30 **EST:** 2018
SALES (est): 4.1MM **Privately Held**
SIC: 3728 Aircraft parts & equipment

(G-12413)
VOLPINO CORP
1551 Pine Hammock Trl (32003-7214)
PHONE..................................904 264-8808
Fabrizio Volpino, *President*
▲ **EMP:** 10 **EST:** 2005
SALES (est): 220.2K **Privately Held**
WEB: www.volpino.com
SIC: 3423 Jewelers' hand tools

(G-12414)
ZILLA INC
Also Called: First Coast Continuous Forms
4265 Eldridge Loop (32073-3023)
PHONE..................................904 610-1436
Charles Zilla, *President*
EMP: 10 **EST:** 1984
SQ FT: 10,000
SALES (est): 912.5K **Privately Held**
SIC: 2761 Continuous forms, office & business

Orlando
Orange County

(G-12415)
0ENERGY LIGHTING INC
1110 Sligh Blvd (32806-1031)
PHONE..................................855 955-1055
EMP: 15
SALES (est): 1.7MM
SALES (corp-wide): 29.8MM **Privately Held**
SIC: 3648 Mfg Lighting Equipment
PA: Bulbtronics Inc.
45 Banfi Plz N
Farmingdale NY 11735
631 249-2272

(G-12416)
3 D F X INC
279 N Texas Ave (32805-1231)
PHONE..................................407 237-6249
Wayne Sargeant, *President*
Mark Lamm, *President*
▲ **EMP:** 10 **EST:** 2000
SQ FT: 40,000
SALES (est): 927.1K **Privately Held**
SIC: 3599 3993 3441 5199 Amusement park equipment; signs & advertising specialties; fabricated structural metal; statuary; theme park, amusement; tourist attractions, amusement park concessions & rides

(G-12417)
3 MIRACLES CORPORATION
Also Called: 3miracles
6843 Conway Rd Ste 120 (32812-3605)
PHONE..................................407 796-9292
Daniela Schiming Silva, *CEO*
John Schiming, *Principal*
EMP: 9 **EST:** 2018
SALES (est): 1.6MM **Privately Held**
WEB: www.3miraclesusa.com
SIC: 2821 Plastics materials & resins
PA: Schiming Promocao De Vendas E Transportes Eireli
Av. Rudolf Dafferner 400
Sorocaba SP 18085

(G-12418)
4 POWER INTERNATIONAL STONES
2704 Hazelhurst Ave (32804-2718)
PHONE..................................407 286-4677
Sharif Abu Snaineh, *President*
EMP: 7 **EST:** 2016
SQ FT: 25,000
SALES (est): 660.2K **Privately Held**
SIC: 1499 Gem stones (natural) mining

(G-12419)
4EVER MUSIC LLC
618 E South St Ste 500 (32801-2986)
PHONE..................................407 490-0977
Jamar West, *Manager*
EMP: 27 **EST:** 2019
SALES (est): 1MM **Privately Held**
SIC: 2731 Book music: publishing & printing

(G-12420)
5DT INC
12249 Science Dr Ste 135 (32826-2905)
PHONE..................................407 734-5377
Paul Olckers, *CEO*
Dennis Mayo, *General Mgr*
Jared Baer, *COO*
Ana Vela, *Research*
Frikkie Klopper, *Manager*
EMP: 29 **EST:** 1998
SQ FT: 3,000
SALES (est): 1.2MM **Privately Held**
WEB: www.5dt.com
SIC: 3699 7373 Flight simulators (training aids), electronic; automotive driving simulators (training aids), electronic; systems software development services; value-added resellers, computer systems

(G-12421)
7 UP SNAPPLE SOUTHEAST
1181 Tradeport Dr (32824-6823)
PHONE..................................407 839-1706
EMP: 6 **EST:** 2009
SALES (est): 145.9K **Privately Held**
SIC: 2086 Soft drinks: packaged in cans, bottles, etc.

(G-12422)
A & A ELECTRIC MTRS & PUMP SVC
1320 W Central Blvd (32805-1708)
PHONE..................................407 843-5005
Andy K Maraj, *Vice Pres*
▲ **EMP:** 6 **EST:** 1999
SQ FT: 2,500
SALES (est): 546K **Privately Held**
WEB: www.aaelectricmotors.com
SIC: 7694 Electric motor repair

(G-12423)
A & L SEPTIC TANK PRODUCTS
9304 E Colonial Dr (32817-4130)
P.O. Box 677878 (32867-7878)
PHONE..................................407 273-2149
Roger Anderson, *President*
Patricia Anderson, *Corp Secy*
EMP: 6 **EST:** 1984
SQ FT: 5,000
SALES (est): 896.5K **Privately Held**
WEB: www.alsepticfl.com
SIC: 3272 7699 Septic tanks, concrete; septic tank cleaning service

(G-12424)
A-1 BLOCK CORPORATION
1617 S Division Ave (32805-4797)
PHONE..................................407 422-3768

Adam Freeman, *President*
Gail Freeman, *Corp Secy*
John Freeman, *Vice Pres*
Brad Coolidge, *Admin Sec*
Daryl Gorenflo, *Associate*
EMP: 44 **EST:** 1952
SQ FT: 1,600
SALES (est): 18MM **Privately Held**
WEB: www.a1block.com
SIC: 3271 5032 Blocks, concrete or cinder: standard; brick, stone & related material

(G-12425)
ABBOTT LABS US SBSDRIES ALERE (HQ)
Also Called: Abbott Rapid Dx North Amer LLC
30 S Keller Rd Ste 100 (32810-6297)
PHONE..................................877 441-7440
John Yonkin, *President*
Chris Dejongh, *Principal*
Jon Russell, *Corp Secy*
Cory Courtney, *Exec VP*
Tara Marsan, *Credit Staff*
▲ **EMP:** 96 **EST:** 2007
SALES (est): 36.8MM
SALES (corp-wide): 34.6B **Publicly Held**
WEB: www.abbott.com
SIC: 3841 Surgical & medical instruments
PA: Abbott Laboratories
100 Abbott Park Rd
Abbott Park IL 60064
224 667-6100

(G-12426)
ABSEN INC (HQ)
7120 Lake Ellenor Dr (32809-5721)
PHONE..................................407 203-8870
Yonghong Ren, *CEO*
Chunlin Liu, *President*
Scott Hsu, *Finance*
Drew Zhou, *CIO*
Ruben Rengel, *Director*
▲ **EMP:** 59 **EST:** 2012
SQ FT: 6,000
SALES (est): 13.2MM **Privately Held**
WEB: www.usabsen.com
SIC: 3674 Light emitting diodes

(G-12427)
ACADEMY PUBLISHING INC
Also Called: School New Letter Program
210 S Semoran Blvd (32807-3802)
PHONE..................................407 736-0100
Christopher Kircher, *CEO*
Elizabeth Gentry, *Marketing Mgr*
Rebecca Rivera, *Technology*
Chris Dodgion, *Graphic Designe*
Amanda Horta, *Graphic Designe*
EMP: 34 **EST:** 1992
SQ FT: 3,000
SALES (est): 2.6MM **Privately Held**
WEB: www.academypublishing.com
SIC: 2759 2721 Commercial printing; periodicals

(G-12428)
ACCOUNTING & COMPUTER SYSTEMS
810 Alameda St (32804-7203)
PHONE..................................407 353-1570
Jackelyn Smith, *Principal*
EMP: 5 **EST:** 1988
SALES (est): 366.9K **Privately Held**
SIC: 7372 Prepackaged software

(G-12429)
ACE CONSTRUCTION MANAGEMENT
801 N Pine Hills Rd (32808-7209)
PHONE..................................407 704-7803
Jaja Wade, *CEO*
EMP: 6 **EST:** 2019
SALES (est): 56.4K **Privately Held**
WEB: www.aceconstructionmanagement.com
SIC: 3449 Miscellaneous metalwork

(G-12430)
ADDISON HVAC LLC
7050 Overland Rd (32810-3404)
PHONE..................................407 292-4400
Lisa Galiatsatos, *Cust Mgr*
Charles Brown, *Mng Member*
Leon Folts, *Technician*
▼ **EMP:** 120 **EST:** 2008
SALES (est): 29.3MM
SALES (corp-wide): 907.1MM **Privately Held**
WEB: www.addison-hvac.com
SIC: 3585 Heating & air conditioning combination units
HQ: Roberts-Gordon Llc
1250 William St
Buffalo NY 14206
716 852-4400

(G-12431)
ADIDAS NORTH AMERICA INC
Also Called: Adidas Outlet Store Orlando
8200 Vineland Ave Ste 350 (32821-6824)
PHONE..................................321 677-0078
Fred GM, *Branch Mgr*
EMP: 9
SALES (corp-wide): 23.4B **Privately Held**
SIC: 2329 Athletic (warmup, sweat & jogging) suits: men's & boys'; men's & boys' athletic uniforms; knickers, dress (separate): men's & boys'
HQ: Adidas North America, Inc.
3449 N Anchor St Ste 500
Portland OR 97217
971 234-2300

(G-12432)
ADRIANO GB BRICK PAVERS LLC
9851 Cypress Park Dr (32824-8405)
PHONE..................................407 497-1517
Adriano F De Oliveira, *Principal*
EMP: 8 **EST:** 2012
SALES (est): 634.6K **Privately Held**
SIC: 3531 Pavers

(G-12433)
ADVANCED MILLWORK INC
2645 Regent Ave (32804-3337)
PHONE..................................407 294-1927
Garry Filger, *President*
Thomas McDonald, *General Mgr*
Shea L Figler, *Vice Pres*
Camilo Saravia, *Project Mgr*
Stephen Toland, *Project Mgr*
▲ **EMP:** 35 **EST:** 1992
SQ FT: 32,862
SALES (est): 7.4MM **Privately Held**
WEB: www.advancedmillwork.net
SIC: 2431 Millwork

(G-12434)
ADVANCED XRGRPHICS IMGING SYST
Also Called: Axis
6851 Tpc Dr Ofc Ofc (32822-5141)
PHONE..................................407 351-0232
David R Salazar, *President*
Teresa Salazar, *Corp Secy*
Claudia Alexander, *Controller*
EMP: 48 **EST:** 1991
SQ FT: 45,840
SALES (est): 3.9MM **Privately Held**
SIC: 2759 7331 7374 Laser printing; mailing service; data processing service

(G-12435)
ADVANTAGECARE INC
7081 Grand National Dr # 113 (32819-8385)
PHONE..................................407 345-8877
William Brooks, *President*
Bill Hughes, *Practice Mgr*
Krystle Sauers, *Director*
Rene Shastid,
EMP: 5 **EST:** 1990
SALES (est): 865.4K **Privately Held**
WEB: www.advcare.com
SIC: 2899 8099 8742 ; medical services organization; management consulting services

(G-12436)
ADVANTOR SYSTEMS CORPORATION
12612 Challenger Pkwy # 3 (32826-2759)
PHONE..................................407 859-3350
Richard Clifton, *CEO*
Jeffrey Whirley, *President*
Grant Herring, *Vice Pres*
Mike Ollivier, *Vice Pres*
Kurt Kuenn, *Project Mgr*
EMP: 150 **EST:** 1997
SALES (est): 33.5MM
SALES (corp-wide): 1.4B **Publicly Held**
WEB: www.advantor.com
SIC: 3669 Emergency alarms
PA: Vectrus, Inc.
655 Space Center Dr
Colorado Springs CO 80915
719 591-3600

(G-12437)
ADVENTUROUS ENTERTAINMENT LLC
6424 Milner Blvd 4 (32809-6670)
PHONE..................................407 483-4057
Victor Romero, *Mng Member*
EMP: 13
SQ FT: 7,013
SALES (est): 100K **Privately Held**
WEB: www.adenter.io
SIC: 7372 Prepackaged software

(G-12438)
AERO BRIDGEWORKS INC
1209 E Landstreet Rd (32824-7924)
PHONE..................................321 689-1912
Donald Porper, *Manager*
EMP: 6 **EST:** 2018
SALES (est): 86K **Privately Held**
SIC: 3728 Aircraft parts & equipment

(G-12439)
AERO-TEL WIRE HARNESS CORP
3788 Silver Star Rd (32808-4630)
PHONE..................................407 445-1722
Antoine J Donatto, *President*
Lee Adkison, *Sales Mgr*
EMP: 20
SQ FT: 9,800
SALES (est): 5.5MM **Privately Held**
WEB: www.aerotelwireharness.com
SIC: 3699 Electrical equipment & supplies

(G-12440)
AEROBOTICS TECHNOLOGIES INC
4514 Saddleworth Cir (32826-4124)
PHONE..................................407 658-9864
Steven A Burhoe, *Principal*
EMP: 8 **EST:** 2016
SALES (est): 136.4K **Privately Held**
WEB: www.aerobotics.com
SIC: 2834 Pharmaceutical preparations

(G-12441)
AEROJET RCKTDYNE CLMAN ARSPC I
7675 Municipal Dr (32819-8930)
PHONE..................................407 354-0047
Tyler Evans, *President*
Brendan King, *Principal*
James S Simpson, *Principal*
Arjun L Kampani, *Vice Pres*
Juan Mercado, *Senior Engr*
EMP: 99 **EST:** 2017
SQ FT: 80,000
SALES (est): 12.8MM
SALES (corp-wide): 2B **Publicly Held**
WEB: www.rocket.com
SIC: 3812 Defense systems & equipment
PA: Aerojet Rocketdyne Holdings, Inc.
222 N Pcf Cast Hwy Ste 50
El Segundo CA 90245
310 252-8100

(G-12442)
AGRI MACHINERY & PARTS INC
Also Called: A M P
3489 All American Blvd (32810-4722)
PHONE..................................407 299-1592
Gillian Dobes, *President*
Mark S Dobes, *Vice Pres*
▼ **EMP:** 18 **EST:** 1976
SQ FT: 25,000
SALES (est): 5.5MM **Privately Held**
WEB: www.ouramp.com
SIC: 3523 3535 Farm machinery & equipment; conveyors & conveying equipment

(G-12443)
AIR DUCT SYSTEMS INC
2106 W Central Blvd (32805-2131)
P.O. Box 770038 (32877-0038)
PHONE..................................407 839-3313
EMP: 12 **EST:** 2018
SALES (est): 1MM **Privately Held**
WEB: www.airductsystemsinc.com
SIC: 3441 Fabricated structural metal

(G-12444)
AIR-FLITE CONTAINERS INC
2699 N Forsyth Rd Ste 101 (32807-6497)
PHONE..................................407 679-1200
Kevin E McDonald, *President*
Mark Prince, *General Mgr*
▼ **EMP:** 7 **EST:** 1973
SQ FT: 16,000
SALES (est): 746K **Privately Held**
WEB: www.air-flite.com
SIC: 2441 2653 Nailed wood boxes & shook; boxes, corrugated: made from purchased materials

(G-12445)
AIRCRAFT ENGRG INSTLLTION SVCS
101 W Landstreet Rd (32824-7820)
PHONE..................................407 438-4436
John R Corthell, *President*
Amber Cenci, *Purchasing*
Rafael Rivera, *Supervisor*
EMP: 20 **EST:** 1993
SQ FT: 28,000
SALES (est): 4.4MM **Privately Held**
WEB: www.aei.aero
SIC: 3728 Aircraft parts & equipment

(G-12446)
AIRGAS USA LLC
Also Called: Airgas Puritan Medical
3100 Silver Star Rd (32808-4616)
PHONE..................................407 293-6630
Daniel Murray, *Branch Mgr*
EMP: 9
SALES (corp-wide): 102.6MM **Privately Held**
WEB: www.airgas.com
SIC: 2813 5984 5169 Oxygen, compressed or liquefied; propane gas, bottled; industrial gases
HQ: Airgas Usa, Llc
259 N Radnor Chester Rd
Radnor PA 19087
216 642-6600

(G-12447)
AIRSTAR AMERICA INC (HQ)
Also Called: Airstar Orlando
9603 Satellite Blvd # 150 (32837-8476)
PHONE..................................407 851-7830
Pierre Chabert, *President*
Yan Rigoulot, *Prdtn Mgr*
Dean Pritchard, *Treasurer*
Kristine Maguire, *Accounting Mgr*
Rick Andrews, *Natl Sales Mgr*
▲ **EMP:** 15 **EST:** 1998
SQ FT: 20,000
SALES (est): 12.4MM **Privately Held**
WEB: www.airstar-light.us
SIC: 3648 7359 Outdoor lighting equipment; sound & lighting equipment rental

(G-12448)
ALCEE INDUSTRIES INC
Also Called: Beach King
1701 Acme St 32805 (32805-3603)
PHONE..................................407 468-4573
Ashwin A Mehta, *Director*
J A Mehta, *Director*
▲ **EMP:** 10 **EST:** 1999
SQ FT: 48,000
SALES (est): 277.9K **Privately Held**
SIC: 2211 Towels & toweling, cotton

(G-12449)
ALCOHOL COUNTERMEASURE SYSTEMS (PA)
Also Called: Alcolock USA
5776 Hoffner Ave Ste 303 (32822-4810)
PHONE..................................407 207-3337
Felix Comeau, *President*
Adam Comeau, *Exec VP*
Felix Adam Comeau, *Vice Pres*
EMP: 10 **EST:** 1976
SALES (est): 7.1MM **Privately Held**
WEB: www.alcolock.net
SIC: 3829 Breathalyzers

(G-12450)
ALCOLOCK FL INC
5776 Hoffner Ave Ste 303 (32822-4810)
PHONE..................................407 207-3337
Felix J E Comeau, *President*
Adam Comeau, *Exec VP*
▲ **EMP:** 8 **EST:** 2003
SALES (est): 651.9K **Privately Held**
WEB: www.alcolockusa.com
SIC: 3694 Ignition apparatus & distributors

(G-12451)
ALEAVIA BRANDS LLC
3025 Middlesex Rd (32803-1128)
PHONE..................................407 289-2632
Douglas J Graham, *President*
EMP: 7 **EST:** 2016
SALES (est): 183.8K **Privately Held**
WEB: www.aleavia.com
SIC: 2844 Toilet preparations

(G-12452)
ALEAVIA LLC
3025 Middlesex Rd (32803-1128)
PHONE..................................407 898-5800
Douglas J Graham, *Principal*
EMP: 7 **EST:** 2012
SALES (est): 227.9K **Privately Held**
WEB: www.aleavia.com
SIC: 2844 Toilet preparations

(G-12453)
ALGOMA HARDWOODS INC
7630 Currency Dr (32809-6925)
PHONE..................................865 471-6300
Libby Trivett, *Manager*
EMP: 40
SALES (corp-wide): 2.2B **Publicly Held**
WEB: www.architectural.masonite.com
SIC: 2431 Doors, wood
HQ: Algoma Hardwoods, Inc.
1001 Perry St
Algoma WI 54201
920 487-5221

(G-12454)
ALL STATE PALLETS COMPANY LLC
9801 Recycle Center Rd (32824-8151)
PHONE..................................407 855-8087
Kyle Zuchowski,
EMP: 18 **EST:** 1998
SALES (est): 520.6K **Privately Held**
WEB: www.allstatepallets.com
SIC: 2448 Pallets, wood

(G-12455)
ALL-WEATHER COATINGS LLC
4409 Hoffner Ave (32812-2331)
PHONE..................................888 405-8904
Todd M Hoepker, *Administration*
EMP: 6 **EST:** 2012
SALES (est): 207.1K **Privately Held**
WEB: www.allweathercoatings.com
SIC: 2851 Paints & allied products

(G-12456)
ALLAN INDUSTRIES
1901 Summit Tower Blvd (32810-5904)
PHONE..................................407 875-0897
EMP: 10 **EST:** 2016
SALES (est): 42.8K **Privately Held**
WEB: www.allanindustries.com
SIC: 3999 Manufacturing industries

(G-12457)
ALLEGRA DIRECT - SOUTH INC
2420 Lakemont Ave (32814-6164)
PHONE..................................586 226-1400
Joanne Crispignani, *President*
EMP: 16 **EST:** 2012
SALES (est): 318.4K **Privately Held**
SIC: 2752 Commercial printing, offset

(G-12458)
ALLEGRA PRINT AND IMAGING
6220 Masters Blvd Apt 301 (32819-4852)
PHONE..................................407 246-1567
Fran Schell, *Principal*
EMP: 6 **EST:** 2012
SALES (est): 70K **Privately Held**
WEB: www.allegramarketingprint.com
SIC: 2752 Commercial printing, offset

(G-12459)
ALLIANCE RSRVATIONS NETWRK LLC (DH)
7380 W Sand Lake Rd # 360 (32819-5248)
PHONE..................................602 889-5505
Pete Bertenshaw, *CEO*
Peter Strank, *President*
Kim Andreello, *Vice Pres*
David Friend, *CFO*
EMP: 6 **EST:** 1995
SQ FT: 3,500
SALES (est): 4.8MM **Publicly Held**
WEB: www.alliancereservations.com
SIC: 7372 Business oriented computer software
HQ: Rci, Llc
9998 N Michigan Rd
Carmel IN 46032
317 805-9000

(G-12460)
ALLIED PRECAST PRODUCTS CO
5640 Carder Rd (32810-4704)
P.O. Box 607460 (32860-7460)
PHONE..................................407 745-5605
William P Thomas Sr, *CEO*
Banner Lee Thomas, *President*
Thomas Ellen D, *Corp Secy*
EMP: 27 **EST:** 1957
SQ FT: 40,000
SALES (est): 1.7MM **Privately Held**
WEB: www.alliedprecastinc.net
SIC: 3272 Concrete products, precast; septic tanks, concrete; lintels, concrete; sills, concrete

(G-12461)
ALPHA PRESS INC
4333 Silver Star Rd # 19 (32808-5100)
PHONE..................................407 299-2121
Alex Latorre, *President*
Madeline I Latorre, *Admin Sec*
◆ **EMP:** 10 **EST:** 1998
SQ FT: 2,000
SALES (est): 2.5MM **Privately Held**
WEB: www.apiprint.net
SIC: 2752 Commercial printing, offset

(G-12462)
ALTERNA POWER INC
390 N Orange Ave (32801-1640)
PHONE..................................407 287-9148
Raushan A Murshid, *President*
Claudia L Harris, *Vice Pres*
EMP: 11 **EST:** 2017
SALES (est): 1.1MM **Privately Held**
SIC: 3674 1711 8748 8742 Solar cells; solar energy contractor; systems analysis & engineering consulting services; management consulting services

(G-12463)
ALUMITECH INC
5104 S Orange Ave (32809-3020)
PHONE..................................407 826-5373
Ramon Reel, *President*
EMP: 18 **EST:** 1986
SQ FT: 10,000
SALES (est): 2.5MM **Privately Held**
WEB: www.alumitech.net
SIC: 3732 3354 Hydrofoil boats; aluminum extruded products

(G-12464)
AM METAL FINISHING
Also Called: A. M. Metal Finishing
7594 Chancellor Dr (32809-6919)
PHONE..................................407 843-0182
Toll Free:..888 -
Rick Hunter, *Owner*
Sloane H Hunter, *Managing Dir*
Sloane Hunter, *Vice Pres*
EMP: 25 **EST:** 1984
SQ FT: 21,000
SALES (est): 3.3MM **Privately Held**
WEB: www.ammetal.com
SIC: 3471 Anodizing (plating) of metals or formed products; chromium plating of metals or formed products

(G-12465)
AMAZIN PUBLISHING INC
10810 Waterford Ct (32821-8716)
PHONE..................................954 445-6303
Robert N Hazen, *Principal*
EMP: 6 **EST:** 2015
SALES (est): 59.2K **Privately Held**
SIC: 2741 Miscellaneous publishing

(G-12466)
AMAZING CABINET STORE LLC
4639 Ligustrum Way (32839-3143)
PHONE..................................407 270-7865
Carolina Matehus, *Branch Mgr*
EMP: 14
SALES (corp-wide): 493.3K **Privately Held**
WEB: www.amazingcabinetstore.com
SIC: 2434 Wood kitchen cabinets
PA: Amazing Cabinet Store Llc
6220 S Orange Blossom Trl
Orlando FL 32809
407 437-9856

(G-12467)
AMERICAN ALL SCURE GTES FNCE L
1316 29th St (32805-6116)
PHONE..................................407 423-4962
John Mills,
EMP: 10 **EST:** 2010
SALES (est): 1.1MM **Privately Held**
WEB: www.securitygate.com
SIC: 3446 5039 Fences, gates, posts & flagpoles; wire fence, gates & accessories

(G-12468)
AMERICAN BUFFING SOLID SURFACE
4407 Fairlawn Dr (32809-4409)
PHONE..................................407 625-6837
Francisco Cabrera, *Principal*
EMP: 6 **EST:** 2005
SALES (est): 75.6K **Privately Held**
SIC: 3471 Buffing for the trade

(G-12469)
AMERICAN GIRL BRANDS LLC
8001 S Orange Blossom Trl # 1460 (32809-9169)
PHONE..................................407 852-9771
EMP: 17
SALES (corp-wide): 4.5B **Publicly Held**
WEB: www.americangirl.com
SIC: 3942 Dolls & doll clothing
HQ: American Girl Brands, Llc
8400 Fairway Pl
Middleton WI 53562
608 836-4848

(G-12470)
AMERICAN INCINERATORS CORP
Also Called: US Cremation Equipment
2814 Silver Star Rd # 20 (32808-3941)
PHONE..................................321 282-7357
Luis Llorens, *President*
Randy Bryant, *Production*
Brian Gamage, *Marketing Staff*
EMP: 36 **EST:** 2004
SALES (est): 7.3MM **Privately Held**
WEB: www.uscremationequipment.com
SIC: 3561 Pumps & pumping equipment

(G-12471)
AMERICAN METAL PRODUCTS INC
4026 Silver Star Rd Ste A (32808-4657)
PHONE..................................407 293-0090
Jeanell Pritchett, *President*
Robert Headberg, *Vice Pres*
EMP: 6 **EST:** 1982
SQ FT: 25,000
SALES (est): 1MM **Privately Held**
WEB: www.americanmp.com
SIC: 2599 5046 Carts, restaurant equipment; restaurant equipment & supplies

(G-12472)
AMERICAN PAYMENT SYSTEMS
11500 S Ornge Blossom Trl (32837-9418)
PHONE..................................407 856-8524
Maria P Castano, *Principal*
EMP: 11 **EST:** 2007
SALES (est): 197.3K **Privately Held**
WEB: www.americanpaymentsystems.com
SIC: 3629 Electronic generation equipment

(G-12473)
AMERICAN PHARMACEUTICAL SVCS
6001 Silver Star Rd Ste 2 (32808-8219)
PHONE..................................407 704-5937
Bamidele D Obaitan, *Principal*
EMP: 9 **EST:** 2009
SALES (est): 331.4K **Privately Held**
SIC: 2834 Pharmaceutical preparations

(G-12474)
AMERICAN WTRJET FBRCATION SVCS
5104 S Orange Ave (32809-3020)
PHONE..................................407 826-0497
Raymon Reel, *Owner*
EMP: 7 **EST:** 2017
SALES (est): 112.8K **Privately Held**
SIC: 3441 Fabricated structural metal

(G-12475)
AMES COMPANIES INC (DH)
13485 Veterans Way # 200 (32827-7718)
P.O. Box 8859, Camp Hill PA (17001-8859)
PHONE..................................717 737-1500
Michael A Sarrica, *President*
Jacob Haas, *Opers Staff*
John Sohn, *Purchasing*
Dave Wentzel, *Purchasing*
Mark Pursel, *Engineer*
◆ **EMP:** 412 **EST:** 1981
SQ FT: 400,000
SALES (est): 494MM
SALES (corp-wide): 2.4B **Publicly Held**
WEB: www.griffon.com
SIC: 3423 3799 3524 Garden & farm tools, including shovels; wheelbarrows; lawn & garden equipment

(G-12476)
AMPHENOL CUSTOM CABLE INC
7461 Currency Dr (32809)
PHONE..................................407 393-3886
Jack Freed, *Branch Mgr*
EMP: 20
SALES (corp-wide): 8.6B **Publicly Held**
WEB: www.customcable.com
SIC: 3827 3357 Optical instruments & lenses; fiber optic cable (insulated)
HQ: Amphenol Custom Cable, Inc.
3221 Cherry Palm Dr
Tampa FL 33619
813 623-2232

(G-12477)
ANCIENT LANGUAGE INC
10524 Moss Park Rd # 204 (32832-5898)
PHONE..................................413 344-4042
Annette Kramek, *Mng Member*
EMP: 6 **EST:** 2008
SALES (est): 150.5K **Privately Held**
WEB: www.ancientlanguage97.com
SIC: 2335 Women's, juniors' & misses' dresses

(G-12478)
ANDREW PRATT STUCCO & PLST INC
8048 Bridgestone Dr (32835-8016)
PHONE..................................407 501-2609
Andrew M Pratt, *Principal*
EMP: 11 **EST:** 2012
SALES (est): 191.4K **Privately Held**
WEB: www.andrewprattstucco.com
SIC: 3299 5032 Stucco; stucco

(G-12479)
ANDREWS FILTER AND SUPPLY CORP (PA)
2309 Coolidge Ave (32804-4897)
PHONE..................................407 423-3310
Wallace W Andrews, *President*
Mark D Andrews, *Vice Pres*
W Lee Andrews, *Vice Pres*
Shirley W Andrews, *Treasurer*
Mark Andrews, *Sales Executive*
▼ **EMP:** 30 **EST:** 1971
SQ FT: 34,000

▲ = Import ▼=Export
◆ =Import/Export

SALES (est): 5.5MM Privately Held
WEB: www.andrewsfilter.com
SIC: 3564 5075 3585 Filters, air: furnaces, air conditioning equipment, etc.; air filters; refrigeration & heating equipment

(G-12480)
ANHEUSER-BUSCH COMPANIES LLC
10928 Florida Crown Dr (32824-7031)
P.O. Box 620006 (32862-0006)
PHONE....................................407 251-4049
Ford Kiene, *Branch Mgr*
Daniel Borja, *Manager*
EMP: 55
SALES (corp-wide): 1.2B Privately Held
WEB: www.anheuser-busch.com
SIC: 2082 3411 7996 Beer (alcoholic beverage); near beer; aluminum cans; beer cans, metal; beverage cans, metal: except beer; theme park, amusement
HQ: Anheuser-Busch Companies, Llc
1 Busch Pl
Saint Louis MO 63118
314 632-6777

(G-12481)
ANUPACK LLC
2501 Principal Row (32837-8357)
PHONE....................................407 850-1960
EMP: 7 EST: 2016
SALES (est): 158.7K Privately Held
WEB: www.anupack.com
SIC: 3085 3089 2086 3221 Plastics bottles; bottle caps, molded plastic; soft drinks: packaged in cans, bottles, etc.; bottles for packing, bottling & canning: glass

(G-12482)
AP BUCK INC
7101 Presidents Dr # 110 (32809-5649)
PHONE....................................407 851-8602
Broir Nguyen, *President*
EMP: 15 EST: 1981
SQ FT: 6,600
SALES (est): 1.9MM Privately Held
WEB: www.apbuck.com
SIC: 3823 Primary elements for process flow measurement

(G-12483)
APRU LLC
3125 Lake George Cove Dr (32812-6822)
PHONE....................................888 741-3777
David Anthony Torgerud, *CEO*
EMP: 8 EST: 2016
SALES (est): 1.3MM
SALES (corp-wide): 2.8MM Privately Held
WEB: www.applerush.com
SIC: 2086 Carbonated soft drinks, bottled & canned; iced tea & fruit drinks, bottled & canned
PA: Apple Rush Company, Inc.
1419 Chaffee Dr Ste 4
Titusville FL 32780
888 741-3777

(G-12484)
AQUA PURE LLC
Also Called: Livie Water
6541 N Orange Blossom Trl (32810-4101)
P.O. Box 965, Gotha (34734-0965)
PHONE....................................407 521-3055
Eric Morris,
EMP: 5 EST: 1998
SQ FT: 8,500
SALES (est): 480K Privately Held
WEB: www.liviewater.com
SIC: 2086 5149 Mineral water, carbonated: packaged in cans, bottles, etc.; mineral or spring water bottling

(G-12485)
AQUALLSION DESIGN CONCEPTS LLC
991 Juel St (32814-6037)
PHONE....................................407 440-2972
David C McKnight,
EMP: 5 EST: 2009
SALES (est): 500K Privately Held
SIC: 3648 Lighting equipment

(G-12486)
ARCHITECTURAL METAL SYSTEMS
4881 Distribution Ct (32822-4918)
PHONE....................................407 277-1364
Terry Davis, *President*
EMP: 16 EST: 1979
SALES (est): 1.4MM Privately Held
SIC: 3446 3444 3442 Architectural metalwork; sheet metalwork; store fronts, prefabricated, metal

(G-12487)
ARGOS USA LLC
2858 Sidney Ave (32810-5134)
PHONE....................................407 299-9924
Charlie Kenyon, *Sales Mgr*
Mark Meggison, *Manager*
EMP: 28 Privately Held
WEB: www.argos-us.com
SIC: 3273 Ready-mixed concrete
HQ: Argos Usa Llc
3015 Windward Plz Ste 300
Alpharetta GA 30005
678 368-4300

(G-12488)
ARGOS-US LLC
5109 Carder Rd (32810-5111)
PHONE....................................407 298-1900
EMP: 8 EST: 2014
SALES (est): 233.9K Privately Held
WEB: www.argos-us.com
SIC: 3271 Concrete block & brick

(G-12489)
AROMATECH FLAVORINGS INC
7001 Mccoy Rd Ste 200 (32822-4717)
PHONE....................................407 277-5727
Jaques Martel, *CEO*
Yvan Grattarola, *Director*
David Pujol, *Director*
Regis Baudot, *Administration*
▲ EMP: 5 EST: 2007
SALES (est): 1.2MM
SALES (corp-wide): 25.5MM Privately Held
WEB: www.aromatech.fr
SIC: 2087 Extracts, flavoring
PA: Aromatech
Parc D Activites
Saint Cezaire Sur Siagne 06530
493 608-444

(G-12490)
ARRIVE ALIVE TRAFFIC CTRL LLC
3165 N John Young Pkwy (32804-4128)
PHONE....................................407 578-5431
EMP: 17 EST: 2018
SALES (est): 2.3MM Privately Held
WEB: www.arrivealivetrafficcontrol.com
SIC: 3993 Signs & advertising specialties

(G-12491)
ART & FRAME DIRECT INC (PA)
Also Called: Timeless Reflections
11423 Satellite Blvd (32837-9225)
PHONE....................................407 857-6000
George Eouse, *President*
Corey Craftsman, *Exec VP*
Dorothy A Eouse, *Vice Pres*
John H Esguera, *Vice Pres*
Lexy Bell, *Purch Dir*
◆ EMP: 150 EST: 1991
SQ FT: 500,000
SALES (est): 40.7MM Privately Held
WEB: www.afdhome.com
SIC: 2499 5999 3231 3999 Picture & mirror frames, wood; artists' supplies & materials; mirrored glass; plaques, picture, laminated; frames for artists' canvases

(G-12492)
ART & FRAME DRCT/TIMELESS INDS
11423 Satellite Blvd (32837-9225)
PHONE....................................407 857-6000
▲ EMP: 9 EST: 2013
SALES (est): 255.3K Privately Held
WEB: www.afdhome.com
SIC: 2499 Cork & cork products

(G-12493)
ARTISTIC ADVENTURES INC
2517 Shader Rd Unit 2 (32804-2771)
PHONE....................................407 297-0557
Michael Grenell, *President*
EMP: 6 EST: 1998
SQ FT: 12,000
SALES (est): 502.6K Privately Held
WEB: www.jillandzoe.wix.com
SIC: 3993 Displays & cutouts, window & lobby

(G-12494)
ASOTTU INC ✪
1317 Edgewater Dr # 3455 (32804-6350)
PHONE....................................626 627-6021
Shangguan Jiao, *CEO*
EMP: 15 EST: 2021 Privately Held
SIC: 2542 Office & store showcases & display fixtures

(G-12495)
ASSISTRX INC (PA)
4700 Millenia Blvd # 500 (32839-6013)
PHONE....................................855 421-4607
Jeff Spafford, *President*
Jan Nielsen, *President*
Rich Prest, *Sr Exec VP*
Richard Prest, *Exec VP*
Brian Anderson, *Vice Pres*
EMP: 158 EST: 2009
SALES (est): 54.6MM Privately Held
WEB: www.assistrx.com
SIC: 2834 Medicines, capsuled or ampuled

(G-12496)
ASTRONICS TEST SYSTEMS INC
12889 Ingenuity Dr (32826-3001)
PHONE....................................407 381-6062
Quentin Avery, *Sales Staff*
Lou Salzano, *Manager*
EMP: 130
SQ FT: 50,800 Privately Held
WEB: www.astronics.com
SIC: 3812 3699 Search & navigation equipment; electrical equipment & supplies
HQ: Astronics Test Systems Inc.
4 Goodyear
Irvine CA 92618
800 722-2528

(G-12497)
ATLAS CONCRETE PRODUCTS INC
6452 E Colonial Dr (32807-3651)
PHONE....................................407 277-0841
Michael C Payment, *President*
Adair Payment, *Corp Secy*
Chris C Payment, *Vice Pres*
Joseph C Payment, *Vice Pres*
EMP: 7 EST: 1949
SQ FT: 2,000
SALES (est): 898.5K Privately Held
SIC: 3272 3271 Burial vaults, concrete or precast terrazzo; concrete products, precast; furniture, garden: concrete; brick, concrete

(G-12498)
ATLAS WALLS LLC
10500 Rocket Ct (32824-8567)
P.O. Box 540316 (32854-0316)
PHONE....................................800 951-9201
Michael Madden,
▼ EMP: 8 EST: 2013
SQ FT: 2,000
SALES (est): 766.1K Privately Held
WEB: www.atlaswalls.com
SIC: 3272 Floor slabs & tiles, precast concrete

(G-12499)
ATMFLA INC (PA)
4601 Sw 34th St Ste 100 (32811-6415)
P.O. Box 618346 (32861-8346)
PHONE....................................407 425-7708
Glen Lyon, *President*
Mac Cochran, *Vice Pres*
EMP: 6 EST: 1989
SQ FT: 8,000
SALES (est): 2.8MM Privately Held
WEB: www.atmfla.com
SIC: 3578 Automatic teller machines (ATM)

(G-12500)
AUDIO EXCELLENCE (PA)
477 N Semoran Blvd (32807-3323)
PHONE....................................407 277-8790
Halah Abed, *President*
EMP: 8 EST: 2002
SALES (est): 1.2MM Privately Held
WEB: www.beyond-comparison.com
SIC: 3999 Atomizers, toiletry

(G-12501)
AUTOMATED BUILDINGS INC
5520 Hansel Ave (32809-3464)
PHONE....................................407 857-0140
Mark Zeitler, *President*
Megan Finch-Bates, *Administration*
EMP: 10 EST: 1999
SALES (est): 1.7MM Privately Held
WEB: www.abi-fla.com
SIC: 3822 1711 Building services monitoring controls, automatic; plumbing, heating, air-conditioning contractors

(G-12502)
AXIOM AUTOMOTIVE TECHNOLOGIES
4290 Seaboard Rd (32808-3842)
PHONE....................................407 299-4400
Dwight Sayer, *Owner*
EMP: 6 EST: 2017
SALES (est): 105.2K Privately Held
SIC: 3545 Machine tool accessories

(G-12503)
B-N-J POWDER COATINGS LLC
111 W Pineloch Ave Ste 2 (32806-8563)
PHONE....................................407 999-8448
Steve Bronovitsky, *Principal*
EMP: 6 EST: 2007
SALES (est): 555.2K Privately Held
WEB: www.b-n-jpowdercoating.com
SIC: 3399 Silver powder

(G-12504)
BADGER WELDING ORLANDO LLC
806 W Landstreet Rd (32824-8023)
P.O. Box 593982 (32859-3982)
PHONE....................................407 648-1100
Jennifer Heidenreich,
EMP: 6 EST: 2006
SQ FT: 20,000
SALES (est): 550K Privately Held
WEB: www.badgerwelding.net
SIC: 7692 Welding repair

(G-12505)
BANKER STEEL SOUTH LLC
6635 Edgewater Dr (32810-4205)
P.O. Box 10875, Lynchburg VA (24506-0875)
PHONE....................................407 293-0120
Gregory R Nichols, *Mng Member*
EMP: 10 EST: 2012
SALES (est): 1MM Privately Held
WEB: www.bankersteel.com
SIC: 3441 Building components, structural steel

(G-12506)
BARCELONA DR PHILLIPS LLC
7600 Dr Phillips Blvd (32819-7231)
PHONE....................................407 352-9733
EMP: 8 EST: 2015
SALES (est): 257.4K Privately Held
WEB: www.drphillipsanimalhospital.com
SIC: 2834 Pharmaceutical preparations

(G-12507)
BARRS EQUIPMENT SERVICE INC
2506 Taylor Ave (32806-4428)
PHONE....................................407 999-5214
George D Barr, *President*
Patsy Barr, *Admin Sec*
EMP: 10 EST: 1960
SQ FT: 5,340
SALES (est): 951.6K Privately Held
WEB: www.welderfix.com
SIC: 7692 Welding repair

(G-12508)
BARRY RESNICK
480 27th St (32806-4451)
PHONE....................................407 296-9999

GEOGRAPHIC

Barry Resnick, *Principal*
EMP: 7 **EST:** 2012
SALES (est): 314.7K **Privately Held**
SIC: 3569 Generators: steam, liquid oxygen or nitrogen

(G-12509)
BEDROCK INDUSTRIES INC
10500 Rocket Ct (32824-8567)
PHONE..................................407 859-1300
Lou Deberandinis, *President*
Linda Owens, *Accounts Mgr*
EMP: 19 **EST:** 1998
SQ FT: 9,290
SALES (est): 3.9MM **Privately Held**
WEB: www.bedrockindustries.com
SIC: 3271 Blocks, concrete or cinder: standard

(G-12510)
BEHRS CHOCOLATES BY DESIGN
3450 Vineland Rd Ste B (32811-6421)
PHONE..................................407 648-2020
Glenn Behr, *President*
Debra Behr, *Vice Pres*
Laura David, *Opers Mgr*
Shannon Everhart, *Creative Dir*
▲ **EMP:** 5 **EST:** 1983
SQ FT: 2,500
SALES (est): 1.2MM **Privately Held**
WEB: www.behrschocolates.com
SIC: 2066 2064 Chocolate candy, solid; candy & other confectionery products

(G-12511)
BESPOKE STITCHERY LLC
2437 E Landstreet Rd (32824-7945)
PHONE..................................407 412-9937
Scott Sims, *Managing Prtnr*
EMP: 7 **EST:** 2014
SALES (est): 351.1K **Privately Held**
SIC: 3172 5131 Personal leather goods; piece goods & notions

(G-12512)
BEST PAVERS LLC
8730 Hastings Beach Blvd (32829-8818)
PHONE..................................407 259-9020
Ivonne I Irizarry, *Principal*
EMP: 7 **EST:** 2014
SALES (est): 136K **Privately Held**
SIC: 2951 Asphalt paving mixtures & blocks

(G-12513)
BETTER PLASTICS INC
780 Central Florida Pkwy (32824-8502)
PHONE..................................407 480-2909
W A Messina, *Principal*
EMP: 6 **EST:** 2012
SALES (est): 150.5K **Privately Held**
SIC: 3089 Injection molding of plastics

(G-12514)
BIG IRON INTL INC
3936 S Semoran Blvd Ste 2 (32822-4015)
PHONE..................................407 222-2573
M Vilayath Ali, *President*
EMP: 8 **EST:** 2017
SALES (est): 1MM **Privately Held**
WEB: www.bigironintl.com
SIC: 3441 7353 Fabricated structural metal; cranes & aerial lift equipment, rental or leasing

(G-12515)
BIO-LOGIC SYSTEMS CORP
12301 Lake Underhill Rd # 201 (32828-4511)
PHONE..................................847 949-0456
James B Hawkins, *President*
Frank Mancuso, *Research*
Michael J Hanley, *Controller*
EMP: 82 **EST:** 1979
SALES (est): 11.9MM
SALES (corp-wide): 415.6MM **Publicly Held**
WEB: www.natus.com
SIC: 3845 3571 3841 Electromedical equipment; electronic computers; surgical & medical instruments
PA: Natus Medical Incorporated
6701 Koll Center Pkwy # 12
Pleasanton CA 94566
925 223-6700

(G-12516)
BIOSAFE SUPPLIES LLC
9436 Southridge Park Ct # 400 (32819-8639)
PHONE..................................407 281-6658
Kenneth Ford, *Opers Staff*
Evelyne Cook, *Sales Staff*
Nadine Monico, *Mng Member*
EMP: 15 **EST:** 1999
SQ FT: 6,000
SALES (est): 2.9MM **Privately Held**
WEB: www.biosafesupplies.com
SIC: 3841 Medical instruments & equipment, blood & bone work

(G-12517)
BIOZONE SCIENTIFIC INTL INC (PA)
7616 Southland Blvd # 114 (32809-8513)
PHONE..................................407 876-2000
ARI Ahola, *President*
Paul Morris, *Sales Staff*
Matti Ahola, *Manager*
Adam Anthony, *Director*
Cole Perry, *Executive*
▲ **EMP:** 6 **EST:** 1999
SQ FT: 25,000
SALES (est): 5.3MM **Privately Held**
WEB: www.biozonescientific.com
SIC: 3564 3589 Air purification equipment; water purification equipment, household type

(G-12518)
BLA SOFTWARE INC
10424 Sparkle Ct (32836-6000)
P.O. Box 692005 (32869-2005)
PHONE..................................407 355-0800
Rozalia Deborde, *CFO*
EMP: 5 **EST:** 2006
SALES (est): 346.4K **Privately Held**
WEB: www.blasoftware.com
SIC: 7372 Business oriented computer software

(G-12519)
BLACK & DECKER (US) INC
Also Called: Dewalt Service Center 076
6100 Hanging Moss Rd # 520 (32807-3907)
PHONE..................................407 657-0474
Debbie Arlington, *Branch Mgr*
EMP: 6
SALES (corp-wide): 14.5B **Publicly Held**
WEB: www.dewalt.com
SIC: 3546 Power-driven handtools
HQ: Black & Decker (U.S.) Inc.
1000 Stanley Dr
New Britain CT 06053
860 225-5111

(G-12520)
BLACK BOX CORPORATION
Also Called: Microblack Enterprise
19 Fanfair Ave (32811-3835)
PHONE..................................407 276-3171
Tm Prioleau, *Branch Mgr*
EMP: 6
SALES (corp-wide): 573.9MM **Privately Held**
WEB: www.blackbox.com
SIC: 3661 Telephone & telegraph apparatus
HQ: Black Box Corporation
1000 Park Dr
Lawrence PA 15055
724 746-5500

(G-12521)
BLACK LABEL GROUP LLC
Also Called: Theblklbl Publishing Group
51 E Jefferson St # 1242 (32802-7501)
P.O. Box 1242 (32802-1242)
PHONE..................................407 917-1255
James A Tribue III, *Mng Member*
Jonathan Aleem,
Michael Bright,
Calvin Ellis Ivory Jr,
Bryan Tribue,
EMP: 6 **EST:** 2013
SALES (est): 72.8K **Privately Held**
WEB: www.theblklbl.com
SIC: 2741 Miscellaneous publishing

(G-12522)
BLACKTON FLOORING INC
1714 Alden Rd (32803-1480)
PHONE..................................407 898-2661
Sean Monett, *President*
Agnes Monett, *Manager*
EMP: 8 **EST:** 2010
SALES (est): 20K **Privately Held**
WEB: www.blacktoninc.com
SIC: 3253 Ceramic wall & floor tile

(G-12523)
BLAZER BOATS INC
12001 Res Pkwy Ste 236 (32826)
PHONE..................................321 307-4761
Keith E Craft, *President*
Lonnie G Craft, *Corp Secy*
Kelly Dougherty, *Office Mgr*
Lonnie N Craft, *Shareholder*
◆ **EMP:** 45 **EST:** 1977
SQ FT: 70,000
SALES (est): 8.6MM **Privately Held**
WEB: www.blazerboats.com
SIC: 3732 Boats, fiberglass: building & repairing

(G-12524)
BLP RACING PRODUCTS LLC
1015 W Church St (32805-2215)
PHONE..................................407 422-0394
Joe Hilerio, *Mng Member*
EMP: 19 **EST:** 2016
SALES (est): 2.9MM **Privately Held**
SIC: 3714 Motor vehicle parts & accessories

(G-12525)
BLUE DIAMOND ORTHOPEDIC LLC
6439 Milner Blvd Ste 4 (32809-6692)
PHONE..................................407 613-2001
David J Hendricks, *Principal*
EMP: 7 **EST:** 2015
SALES (est): 366.8K **Privately Held**
WEB: www.bluediamondorthopedic.com
SIC: 3842 Surgical appliances & supplies

(G-12526)
BLUE SHOE SOFTWARE LLC
424 E Central Blvd # 720 (32801-1923)
PHONE..................................321 438-5708
Shana K Small, *Principal*
EMP: 6 **EST:** 2016
SALES (est): 158.9K **Privately Held**
WEB: www.blueshoesoftware.com
SIC: 7372 Prepackaged software

(G-12527)
BLUEDROP USA INC ✪
2603 Challenger Tech Ct (32826-2716)
PHONE..................................407 470-0865
Belinda Lewis, *CEO*
Brett Ulander, *President*
EMP: 8 **EST:** 2020
SALES (est): 524K **Privately Held**
SIC: 3699 8331 Flight simulators (training aids), electronic; job training services

(G-12528)
BLUWORLD INNOVATIONS LLC
635 W Michigan St (32805-6203)
PHONE..................................888 499-5433
Betty Cunnigham, *Vice Pres*
Clint Siddens, *Vice Pres*
Rhea Hernandez, *Opers Staff*
Lewen Rosario, *Engineer*
Betty Cunningham, *Controller*
▲ **EMP:** 100 **EST:** 1999
SQ FT: 7,800
SALES (est): 17.6MM **Privately Held**
WEB: www.bluworldusa.com
SIC: 2899 Water treating compounds

(G-12529)
BLUWORLD OF WATER LLC
3093 Caruso Ct Ste 40-A (32806-8556)
PHONE..................................407 426-7674
Asa Peacock, *Prdtn Mgr*
Dan Gunn, *Design Engr*
Marty Effron, *CFO*
Janet Dorsey, *Controller*
Kelly Hagedorn, *Marketing Staff*
▲ **EMP:** 55 **EST:** 2010
SALES (est): 6.8MM **Privately Held**
WEB: www.bluworldusa.com
SIC: 3648 Fountain lighting fixtures

(G-12530)
BOEING COMPANY
13501 Ingenuity Dr # 204 (32826-3018)
PHONE..................................407 306-8782
EMP: 196
SALES (corp-wide): 58.1B **Publicly Held**
SIC: 3721 Mfg Aircraft
PA: The Boeing Company
100 N Riverside Plz
Chicago IL 60606
312 544-2000

(G-12531)
BOHEMIA INTRCTIVE SMLTIONS INC
3050 Tech Pkwy Ste 110 (32826)
PHONE..................................407 608-7000
John F Givens, *President*
Gregg Owens, *President*
Rusmat Ahmed, *Vice Pres*
Scott Hooper, *Vice Pres*
Peter Morrison, *Vice Pres*
EMP: 10 **EST:** 2010
SALES (est): 3MM **Privately Held**
WEB: www.bisimulations.com
SIC: 7372 Prepackaged software
PA: Bohemia Interactive Simulations K.S.
Pernerova 691/42
Praha 8 - Karlin 186 0

(G-12532)
BOLT SYSTEMS INC
1700 Silver Star Rd (32804-3444)
PHONE..................................407 425-0012
Wallace C Beitl Sr, *President*
Margaret M Beitl, *Vice Pres*
EMP: 9 **EST:** 1992
SALES (est): 283.4K **Privately Held**
WEB: www.boltsystems.com
SIC: 3842 5999 Braces, orthopedic; orthopedic & prosthesis applications

(G-12533)
BOSSA HOSPITALITY
7389 Universal Blvd (32819-8322)
PHONE..................................305 394-3994
EMP: 6 **EST:** 2019
SALES (est): 158.1K **Privately Held**
WEB: www.bossahospitality.com
SIC: 2519 Furniture, household: glass, fiberglass & plastic

(G-12534)
BRASILEIRAS & BRASILEIROS INC
4847 Lake Milly Dr (32839-2075)
PHONE..................................407 855-9541
Eraldo Manes, *Principal*
EMP: 6 **EST:** 2010
SALES (est): 163.7K **Privately Held**
WEB: www.jornalbb.com
SIC: 2711 Newspapers, publishing & printing

(G-12535)
BRICK PVERS DRVEWAY BIG PAVERS
6111 Metrowest Blvd (32835-2958)
PHONE..................................407 928-1217
Edelson Silva, *Administration*
EMP: 6 **EST:** 2015
SALES (est): 976.2K **Privately Held**
WEB: www.bigpavers.com
SIC: 2951 Asphalt paving mixtures & blocks

(G-12536)
BRISTOL VENTURE SERVICE LLC
16121 Bristol Lake Cir (32828-6963)
PHONE..................................407 844-8629
Fu Feng, *Principal*
EMP: 7 **EST:** 2013
SALES (est): 283.7K **Privately Held**
SIC: 2621 Paper mills

(G-12537)
BROWNLEE LIGHTING INC
4600 Dardanelle Dr (32808-3832)
PHONE..................................407 297-3677
Curtis M Brownlee, *President*

Thomas M Brownlee, *Chairman*
Thomas J Brownlee, *Vice Pres*
Stephanie Galbraith, *Mfg Staff*
Charlotte McCree, *Purchasing*
◆ **EMP:** 40
SQ FT: 30,000
SALES (est): 11.5MM **Privately Held**
WEB: www.brownlee.com
SIC: 3646 3645 Commercial indusl & institutional electric lighting fixtures; residential lighting fixtures

(G-12538)
C & H SIGN ENTERPRISES INC
Also Called: Fastsigns
9900 Universal Blvd # 114 (32819-8716)
PHONE..................................407 826-0155
EMP: 7
SQ FT: 2,800
SALES (est): 1MM **Privately Held**
SIC: 3993 Signsadv Specs

(G-12539)
C & S PRESS INC
405 27th St (32806-4452)
PHONE..................................407 841-3000
Frank J Tantillo, *President*
Roxane Alaimo, *General Mgr*
Daniel B Ellis, *Principal*
Raymond G Cody, *Corp Secy*
Sheryl Gray, *Vice Pres*
EMP: 60 **EST:** 1985
SQ FT: 18,500
SALES (est): 8.6MM **Privately Held**
WEB: www.cspressonline.com
SIC: 2752 Lithographing on metal; commercial printing, offset

(G-12540)
C L INDUSTRIES INC
Also Called: LCI
8188 S Orange Ave (32809-6731)
P.O. Box 490180, Leesburg (34749-0180)
PHONE..................................800 333-2660
Fred Horton Jr, *CEO*
Horton Fred Jr, *Principal*
Jones Gary L, *Principal*
Paskiet Sherrie L, *Vice Pres*
Bruce Campagno, *Sales Mgr*
◆ **EMP:** 40 **EST:** 1971
SQ FT: 40,000
SALES (est): 22MM
SALES (corp-wide): 52.2MM **Privately Held**
WEB: www.clindustries.com
SIC: 3281 5032 Pedestals, marble; marble building stone
PA: Consolidated Minerals, Inc.
8500 Us Highway 441
Leesburg FL 34788
352 365-6522

(G-12541)
C4 ADVNCED TCTICAL SYSTEMS LLC
Also Called: C4ats
243 Wetherbee Rd (32824-8623)
PHONE..................................407 206-3886
Theresa Smith, *Exec VP*
Chris Gardner, *Senior Buyer*
Becky McCarthy, *Buyer*
Sam Charlton, *Engineer*
Bob Tortolano, *Manager*
◆ **EMP:** 99 **EST:** 2005
SALES (est): 31.4MM **Privately Held**
WEB: www.c4ats.com
SIC: 3489 3795 3769 Ordnance & accessories; specialized tank components, military; casings, missiles & missile components: storage
HQ: Rafael U.S.A., Inc.
6903 Rockledge Dr Ste 850
Bethesda MD 20817

(G-12542)
CABINETS ONE LLC
4502 Old Winter Garden Rd (32811-1747)
PHONE..................................407 227-1147
Enrique Batista, *Principal*
EMP: 6 **EST:** 2018
SALES (est): 728.8K **Privately Held**
WEB: www.cabinetsone.com
SIC: 2434 Wood kitchen cabinets

(G-12543)
CABLES AND SENSORS LLC
5874 S Semoran Blvd (32822-4817)
PHONE..................................866 373-6767
Kevin Allen, *Vice Pres*
Steve Carpio, *Sales Staff*
Michelle Pignaloso, *Sales Staff*
Lina Salinas, *Sales Staff*
Diego E Orjuela, *Mng Member*
EMP: 15 **EST:** 2010
SALES (est): 2.7MM **Privately Held**
WEB: www.cablesandsensors.com
SIC: 3061 5999 Oil & gas field machinery rubber goods (mechanical); medical apparatus & supplies

(G-12544)
CAMARA INDUSTRIES LLC
9927 Dean Cove Ln (32825-6570)
PHONE..................................407 879-2549
Israel Camara,
EMP: 11 **EST:** 2014
SALES (est): 669.3K **Privately Held**
WEB: www.camaraindustries.com
SIC: 2448 Wood pallets & skids

(G-12545)
CANAM STEEL CORPORATION
2536 Hansrob Rd (32804-3318)
PHONE..................................407 295-3864
EMP: 7
SALES (corp-wide): 586.3MM **Privately Held**
WEB: www.cscsteelusa.com
SIC: 3441 Building components, structural steel
PA: Canam Steel Corporation
4010 Clay St
Point Of Rocks MD 21777
301 874-5141

(G-12546)
CANTOR DESIGN ON GRANITE
Also Called: Cantor Granite & Marble
4180 Player Cir (32808-2245)
PHONE..................................407 230-1568
Gerson Cevallos, *Owner*
Oswaldo Cevallos, *General Mgr*
EMP: 8 **EST:** 1998
SQ FT: 4,600
SALES (est): 559.2K **Privately Held**
SIC: 3281 Granite, cut & shaped

(G-12547)
CANVAS FREAKS LLC
11300 Space Blvd Ste 4 (32837-9209)
PHONE..................................407 978-6224
Atikur Motiwala, *Principal*
EMP: 7 **EST:** 2017
SALES (est): 1.7MM **Privately Held**
WEB: www.canvasfreaks.com
SIC: 2211 Canvas

(G-12548)
CANVAS SHOP INC
635 Wilmer Ave (32808-7635)
PHONE..................................407 898-6001
Boris Roitman, *Principal*
ABI Roitman, *Assistant*
EMP: 9 **EST:** 2010
SALES (est): 364.5K **Privately Held**
WEB: www.horizonenvironmental.com
SIC: 2394 Awnings, fabric: made from purchased materials

(G-12549)
CAPTEL INC
2602 Challenger Tech Ct (32826-2741)
PHONE..................................407 730-3397
Reina Soto, *Owner*
Oliver Dotson, *Assistant*
EMP: 97
SALES (corp-wide): 99.1MM **Privately Held**
WEB: www.captel.com
SIC: 3842 Hearing aids
PA: Captel, Inc.
450 Science Dr Ste 120
Madison WI 53711
608 238-5400

(G-12550)
CARILLON PUBLISHING LLC
9775 Bohart Ct (32836-6329)
PHONE..................................407 363-0375
Lewis Torman, *Principal*
EMP: 6 **EST:** 2016
SALES (est): 62.9K **Privately Held**
SIC: 2711 Newspapers

(G-12551)
CARLOS VELEZ CABINETS & INSTAL
5314 Ira St (32807-1717)
PHONE..................................407 929-3402
Carlos Velez Jr, *Principal*
EMP: 8 **EST:** 2005
SALES (est): 141.1K **Privately Held**
SIC: 2434 Wood kitchen cabinets

(G-12552)
CARPE DIEM SALES & MKTG INC (PA)
4560 36th St (32811-6526)
PHONE..................................407 682-1400
Mike Giordano, *President*
Philip Fry, *Vice Pres*
Amanda Bini, *Purch Mgr*
Rondi Boudreau, *Accounts Mgr*
Kathryn C Mathews, *Accounts Exec*
◆ **EMP:** 33 **EST:** 1993
SQ FT: 22,000
SALES (est): 8.2MM **Privately Held**
WEB: www.thesourcinggroup.com
SIC: 2759 5136 5137 Screen printing; men's & boys' clothing; women's & children's clothing

(G-12553)
CARTER-HEALTH DISPOSABLES LLC
4201 Vinelnd Rd I-13 (32811)
PHONE..................................407 296-6689
Roda Carter, *Mng Member*
▲ **EMP:** 5 **EST:** 2009
SALES (est): 676.2K **Privately Held**
WEB: www.carter-health.com
SIC: 2389 Hospital gowns

(G-12554)
CATAPULT PRINT AND PACKG LLC (PA)
5945 Hazeltine Nat Dr (32822-5019)
PHONE..................................407 717-4323
Mark Cook, *Mng Member*
Ashley Cook,
EMP: 14 **EST:** 2017
SALES (est): 1.9MM **Privately Held**
WEB: www.wearecatapultprint.com
SIC: 2752 Commercial printing, offset

(G-12555)
CAUSEY MACHINE WORKS INC
Also Called: Victoriano Pantoja
12131 Science Dr (32826-3232)
PHONE..................................407 277-7570
Maria Pantoja, *President*
Victoriano Pantoja Sr, *Vice Pres*
EMP: 10 **EST:** 1980
SQ FT: 15,000
SALES (est): 1.6MM **Privately Held**
WEB: www.causeymachine.com
SIC: 3599 Machine shop, jobbing & repair

(G-12556)
CAVADAS RUBEN & TRISHA WAGNER
3125 Crystal Creek Blvd (32837-5072)
PHONE..................................407 248-2659
Eliane Cavadas, *Principal*
EMP: 6 **EST:** 2003
SALES (est): 82.9K **Privately Held**
SIC: 2673 Cellophane bags, unprinted: made from purchased materials

(G-12557)
CB DESIGNING INC
812 Plaza Ct (32803-4225)
PHONE..................................407 927-1808
Christopher A Bertoch, *President*
EMP: 7 **EST:** 2005
SALES (est): 270.8K **Privately Held**
WEB: www.cbdesigning.com
SIC: 1389 Construction, repair & dismantling services

(G-12558)
CCI HAIR BOUTIQUE LLC
400 N Pine Hills Rd Ste C (32811-1652)
PHONE..................................407 408-8649
Cheryl Pickett, *CEO*
EMP: 15 **EST:** 2018
SALES (est): 579.8K **Privately Held**
SIC: 3999 Hair & hair-based products

(G-12559)
CEDARS BAKERY GROUP INC
4704 L B Mcleod Rd (32811-6408)
PHONE..................................407 476-6593
Imad Nasnas, *President*
Issam Sleiman, *Vice Pres*
EMP: 16 **EST:** 2013
SQ FT: 6,800
SALES (est): 2MM **Privately Held**
WEB: www.cedarsbread.com
SIC: 2051 Bread, cake & related products

(G-12560)
CELLOFOAM NORTH AMERICA INC
11237 Astronaut Blvd (32837-9203)
PHONE..................................407 888-4667
Mike Grunnet, *Exec VP*
Ryan J Rutledge, *Sales Staff*
Erika Davila, *Office Mgr*
Greg Bontrager, *Branch Mgr*
EMP: 30
SALES (corp-wide): 143.4MM **Privately Held**
WEB: www.cellofoam.com
SIC: 2821 Plastics materials & resins
PA: Cellofoam North America Inc.
1977 Weaver Ct
Conyers GA 30013
770 929-3688

(G-12561)
CEMI INTERNATIONAL INC
Also Called: Celmark International
2600 Titan Row (32809-5659)
PHONE..................................407 859-7701
Keith Frankel, *President*
EMP: 150 **EST:** 2007
SQ FT: 80,000
SALES (est): 21.4MM **Privately Held**
WEB: www.celmarkint.com
SIC: 2844 Cosmetic preparations

(G-12562)
CENTRAL FLA ATTRNSFSONISTS INC
3791 Half Moon Dr (32812-3819)
PHONE..................................321 299-6019
James M Frank, *Vice Pres*
EMP: 8 **EST:** 2008
SALES (est): 192.8K **Privately Held**
SIC: 3841 Surgical & medical instruments

(G-12563)
CENTRAL FLA REMANUFACTURING
Also Called: Central Florida Remanufactory
2526 W Washington St (32805-1257)
PHONE..................................407 299-9011
Ray Osorio, *President*
Leandra Osorio, *Vice Pres*
Nelson Madruga, *Manager*
EMP: 7 **EST:** 1979
SQ FT: 800
SALES (est): 948.2K **Privately Held**
WEB: www.centralfloridaremanufactory.com
SIC: 3621 3694 Starters, for motors; alternators, automotive

(G-12564)
CENTRAL FLORIDA CENTRAL FLA
4157 Seaboard Rd (32808-3849)
PHONE..................................407 674-2626
Evan John, *Principal*
EMP: 24 **EST:** 2016
SALES (est): 8.9MM **Privately Held**
WEB: www.cf.edu
SIC: 3564 Blowers & fans

(G-12565)
CENTRAL FLORIDA CNSTR WALLS
5923 Bamboo Dr (32807-4405)
PHONE..................................407 448-2350
Manuel Quilli, *President*
EMP: 10 **EST:** 2010

SALES (est): 1.1MM **Privately Held**
WEB: www.cflconstructionwalls.com
SIC: 3271 1742 Concrete block & brick; stucco work, interior

(G-12566)
CENTRAL FLORIDA CSTM TRLRS INC (PA)
Also Called: Ram-Lin
2136 4th St (32824-7709)
PHONE..................................407 851-1144
David McCorkle, *President*
EMP: 34 **EST:** 1993
SQ FT: 30,000
SALES (est): 8.3MM **Privately Held**
WEB: www.ramlin.com
SIC: 3799 Trailers & trailer equipment; boat trailers

(G-12567)
CENTRAL FLORIDA DRIVESHAFT
Also Called: Advance Driveline
5512 Carder Rd (32810-4729)
PHONE..................................407 299-1100
David Crutch, *Manager*
EMP: 8
SQ FT: 5,059
SALES (corp-wide): 1.8MM **Privately Held**
WEB: www.centralfloridadriveshaft.com
SIC: 3714 Drive shafts, motor vehicle
PA: Central Florida Driveshaft
307 S Combee Rd
Lakeland FL 33801
863 666-3874

(G-12568)
CENTRAL FLORIDA ICE SERVICES ✪
410 27th St (32806-4451)
PHONE..................................407 779-0161
Julio Zaldivar, *President*
EMP: 6 **EST:** 2020
SALES (est): 94.4K **Privately Held**
SIC: 2097 Manufactured ice

(G-12569)
CENTRAL FLORIDA LBR & SUP CO
Also Called: Mills & Nebraska
2721 Regent Ave (32804-3337)
P.O. Box 536548 (32853-6548)
PHONE..................................407 298-5600
Thomas Pulsifer, *President*
Bridget A Pulsifer, *Vice Pres*
Susan T Pulsifer, *Treasurer*
▼ **EMP:** 65
SALES (est): 16.2MM **Privately Held**
WEB: www.millsnebraska.com
SIC: 3442 5211 Metal doors; lumber & other building materials

(G-12570)
CENTRAL FLORIDA STONE PAVERS
4560 Saint Brides Ct (32812-5929)
PHONE..................................407 227-3519
Trevor Longmire, *Manager*
EMP: 6 **EST:** 2014
SALES (est): 247.9K **Privately Held**
WEB: www.bedrockorlando.com
SIC: 2951 Asphalt paving mixtures & blocks

(G-12571)
CENTURY METAL PRODUCTS INC
3108 Friendly Ave (32808-3907)
PHONE..................................407 293-8871
Tim Dewald, *President*
EMP: 32 **EST:** 1947
SQ FT: 4,980
SALES (est): 4MM **Privately Held**
SIC: 3444 Sheet metalwork

(G-12572)
CESCO SIGNS INC
6631 E Colonial Dr (32807-5234)
PHONE..................................407 463-6635
Juana Cuevas, *Principal*
EMP: 7 **EST:** 2019
SALES (est): 274.1K **Privately Held**
WEB: www.cescosigns.com
SIC: 3993 Signs & advertising specialties

(G-12573)
CG ROXANE LLC
Also Called: Crystal Geyser
2224 Hazelhurst Ave (32804-2714)
PHONE..................................407 241-1640
EMP: 22 **Privately Held**
WEB: www.crystalgeyserplease.com
SIC: 2086 Water, pasteurized: packaged in cans, bottles, etc.
PA: Cg Roxane Llc
2330 Marinship Way # 190
Sausalito CA 94965

(G-12574)
CHANCE ALUMINUM CORP ✪
11616 Landstar Blvd (32824-9025)
PHONE..................................407 789-1606
Xiangming Cheng, *Director*
EMP: 18 **EST:** 2021
SALES (est): 878.1K **Privately Held**
SIC: 3313 Electrometallurgical products

(G-12575)
CHANGE THIS WORLD
6790 Edgwter Cmmerce Pkwy (32810-4278)
PHONE..................................407 900-8840
Steven Hooper, *Principal*
EMP: 7 **EST:** 2010
SALES (est): 470K **Privately Held**
WEB: www.ushunger.org
SIC: 2041 Flour & other grain mill products

(G-12576)
CHARLES K SEWELL
Also Called: C K S
333 W Michigan St (32806-4422)
PHONE..................................407 423-1870
Charles K Sewell, *Owner*
EMP: 8 **EST:** 2006
SALES (est): 707K **Privately Held**
WEB: www.ckspackaging.com
SIC: 2821 Plastics materials & resins

(G-12577)
CHASE AEROSPACE INC
5342 Greenside Ct (32819-3829)
PHONE..................................407 812-4545
Nick Thomas, *President*
Brenda Thomas, *Admin Sec*
▲ **EMP:** 10 **EST:** 1997
SQ FT: 11,250
SALES (est): 2.1MM **Privately Held**
WEB: www.chaseaerospace.com
SIC: 3728 Aircraft parts & equipment

(G-12578)
CHEFS COMMISSARY LLC
6929 Narcoossee Rd # 509 (32822-5567)
PHONE..................................321 303-2947
Michael J Birnbaum, *Mng Member*
John Brauner,
Warren G Dietel,
Raul Matias,
Daniel E Robinson,
EMP: 65 **EST:** 2013
SQ FT: 15,000
SALES (est): 3MM **Privately Held**
WEB: www.chefscommissary.com
SIC: 2038 Frozen specialties

(G-12579)
CHENEY OFS INC
Also Called: Grand Western
3875 Bengert St (32808-4603)
PHONE..................................407 292-3223
Bill Folwy, *President*
Sean Stout, *Sales Staff*
David Pinna, *Representative*
EMP: 552 **EST:** 2010
SALES (est): 31.7MM
SALES (corp-wide): 1.8B **Privately Held**
WEB: www.cheneybrothers.com
SIC: 2013 5149 Sausages & other prepared meats; spaghetti
PA: Cheney Bros., Inc.
1 Cheney Way
Riviera Beach FL 33404
561 845-4700

(G-12580)
CHIP SUPPLY INC (HQ)
Also Called: Micross Components
7725 N Orange Blossom Trl (32810-2697)
PHONE..................................407 298-7100
Richard Kingdon, *CEO*
Brad Buser, *Vice Pres*
Cyndy Hernandez, *Vice Pres*
Dale Pullis, *Vice Pres*
Michael Pisch, *CFO*
▲ **EMP:** 100 **EST:** 1979
SQ FT: 5,000
SALES (est): 52.2MM
SALES (corp-wide): 191.4MM **Privately Held**
WEB: www.micross.com
SIC: 3674 Microcircuits, integrated (semiconductor)
PA: Micross Components, Inc.
7725 N Orange Blossom Trl
Orlando FL 32810
407 298-7100

(G-12581)
CHRISTIE LITES ENTPS USA LLC (PA)
6990 Lake Ellenor Dr (32809-4604)
PHONE..................................407 856-0016
Jeni Ofarril, *Purch Agent*
Jenn Bodshaug, *Manager*
Glenda Pacheco, *Manager*
Christie Lite,
Mark Broedling, *Representative*
EMP: 125 **EST:** 2013
SALES (est): 20.2MM **Privately Held**
WEB: www.christielites.com
SIC: 3648 Lighting equipment

(G-12582)
CHRISTIE LITES ORLANDO LLC (HQ)
2479 Eunice Ave (32808-4609)
PHONE..................................206 223-7200
Huntly Christie, *CEO*
Jesse Glance, *Opers Mgr*
Todd Hucul, *Opers Mgr*
Dustin Cone, *Transportation*
Shaun Durnin, *Transportation*
▲ **EMP:** 15 **EST:** 1998
SQ FT: 19,200
SALES (est): 13.4MM
SALES (corp-wide): 20.2MM **Privately Held**
WEB: www.christielites.com
SIC: 3648 Lighting equipment
PA: Christie Lites Enterprises Usa, Llc
6990 Lake Ellenor Dr
Orlando FL 32809
407 856-0016

(G-12583)
CHUNKY PLATES LLC
2550 W Colonial Dr (32804-8017)
PHONE..................................321 746-3346
Latisha Nicole Boykin, *Owner*
Pastorq Hepburn, *Director*
Phuong Hepburn, *Administration*
EMP: 6 **EST:** 2016
SALES (est): 298.1K **Privately Held**
SIC: 2037 Frozen fruits & vegetables

(G-12584)
CITORY SOLUTIONS LLC
10524 Moss Park Rd # 204 (32832-5898)
PHONE..................................407 766-6533
Derek Isaacson, *Vice Pres*
Gerald J Leo Connet, *Manager*
EMP: 13 **EST:** 2011
SALES (est): 3.9MM **Privately Held**
WEB: www.citory.com
SIC: 3446 Architectural metalwork

(G-12585)
CITY PRINTS LLC
200 E Colonial Dr (32801-1204)
PHONE..................................407 409-0509
Rodney Thompson, *Manager*
EMP: 6 **EST:** 2016
SALES (est): 147.5K **Privately Held**
WEB: www.instyprints.com
SIC: 2752 Commercial printing, lithographic

(G-12586)
CKS PACKAGING INC
333 W Michigan St (32806-4422)
PHONE..................................407 423-0333
Melvin Brown, *Opers Mgr*
Jim Fouty, *Plant Engr Mgr*
Joseph Murphy, *Plant Engr Mgr*
Brian McClarty Proj, *Engineer*
Sterling Mazza, *Human Resources*
EMP: 53
SALES (corp-wide): 411.1MM **Privately Held**
WEB: www.ckspackaging.com
SIC: 3089 3085 5085 Plastic containers, except foam; plastics bottles; commercial containers
PA: C.K.S. Packaging, Inc.
350 Great Sw Pkwy
Atlanta GA 30336
404 691-8900

(G-12587)
CKS PACKAGING INC
7400 S Orange Ave (32809-6057)
PHONE..................................407 420-9529
EMP: 53
SALES (corp-wide): 411.1MM **Privately Held**
WEB: www.ckspackaging.com
SIC: 3089 Plastic containers, except foam
PA: C.K.S. Packaging, Inc.
350 Great Sw Pkwy
Atlanta GA 30336
404 691-8900

(G-12588)
CLASSIC SCREEN PRTG DESIGN INC
1353 Pine Ave (32824-7939)
PHONE..................................407 850-0112
John W Nanstiel, *President*
EMP: 7 **EST:** 1999
SQ FT: 6,000
SALES (est): 618.3K **Privately Held**
WEB: www.classicscreenprinting.com
SIC: 2759 Screen printing

(G-12589)
CLEARANT INC (PA)
6001 Lexington Park (32819-4433)
PHONE..................................407 876-3134
Jon M Garfield, *CEO*
Michael Bartlett, *Ch of Bd*
Susan E Etzel,
◆ **EMP:** 8
SQ FT: 2,500 **Privately Held**
SIC: 2836 7389 Blood derivatives; product sterilization service

(G-12590)
CLEVER COVERS INC
524 W Winter Park St (32804-4435)
PHONE..................................407 423-5959
John Smith, *President*
EMP: 6 **EST:** 1996
SALES (est): 446.4K **Privately Held**
SIC: 3465 Hub caps, automobile: stamped metal

(G-12591)
CLOSETMAID LLC (HQ)
13485 Veterans Way # 200 (32827-7718)
PHONE..................................352 401-6000
Robert J Clements Jr, *President*
Catherine Beal, *Vice Pres*
Debra M Charles, *Vice Pres*
Craig Moeller, *Vice Pres*
David J Rabe, *Treasurer*
◆ **EMP:** 496 **EST:** 1965
SALES (est): 350.6MM
SALES (corp-wide): 2.4B **Publicly Held**
WEB: www.closetmaid.com
SIC: 2511 5712 Storage chests, household: wood; furniture stores
PA: Griffon Corporation
712 5th Ave Fl 18
New York NY 10019
212 957-5000

(G-12592)
COASTAL AWNGS HRRCANE PRTCTION
14438 Avalon Reserve Blvd (32828-5196)
PHONE..................................407 923-9482
Gracie I Whittaker, *President*

EMP: 5
SALES (est): 417.2K **Privately Held**
WEB: www.crystalcoastawnings.com
SIC: 2394 3444 3089 3442 Canvas awnings & canopies; awnings & canopies; awnings, fiberglass & plastic combination; storm doors or windows, metal; roofing, siding & sheet metal work; millwork

(G-12593)
COATING HEAVEN
2555 N Forsyth Rd Ste E (32807-6463)
PHONE..................................321 300-5464
Nejat Arslaner, *Owner*
EMP: 6 **EST:** 2017
SALES (est): 93K **Privately Held**
WEB: www.coatingheaven.com
SIC: 3479 Coating of metals & formed products

(G-12594)
COBALT LASER
965 W Taft Vineland Rd # 107 (32824-8024)
PHONE..................................407 855-2833
Marvin J Sweers, *Principal*
EMP: 6 **EST:** 2008
SALES (est): 384.5K **Privately Held**
WEB: www.cobaltlaser.com
SIC: 2752 Commercial printing, lithographic

(G-12595)
COCA-COLA BEVERAGES FLA LLC
2900 Mercy Dr (32808-3897)
PHONE..................................407 295-9290
Fax: 407 294-2320
EMP: 150
SALES (corp-wide): 481.3MM **Privately Held**
SIC: 2086 5149 Mfg Bottled/Canned Soft Drinks Whol Groceries
PA: Coca-Cola Beverages Florida, Llc
10117 Princess Palm Ave # 100
Tampa FL 33610
813 327-7294

(G-12596)
COCA-COLA COMPANY
1512 E Buena Vista Dr (32830)
PHONE..................................407 560-0107
EMP: 6
SALES (corp-wide): 33B **Publicly Held**
WEB: www.coca-cola.com
SIC: 2086 Bottled & canned soft drinks
PA: The Coca-Cola Company
1 Coca Cola Plz Nw
Atlanta GA 30313
404 676-2121

(G-12597)
COCA-COLA COMPANY
2900 Mercy Dr (32808-3897)
PHONE..................................407 295-9290
Fax: 407 294-2322
EMP: 112
SALES (corp-wide): 35.4B **Publicly Held**
SIC: 2086 Mfg Bottled/Canned Soft Drinks
PA: The Coca-Cola Company
1 Coca Cola Plz Nw
Atlanta GA 30313
404 676-2121

(G-12598)
CODA OCTOPUS GROUP INC (PA)
3300 S Hiawassee Rd # 104 (32835-6350)
PHONE..................................407 735-2402
Annmarie Gayle, *Ch of Bd*
Blair Cunningham, *President*
Michael Midgley, *CFO*
EMP: 12 **EST:** 1994
SQ FT: 3,000
SALES: 20MM **Publicly Held**
WEB: www.codaoctopusgroup.com
SIC: 3812 Search & navigation equipment; sonar systems & equipment

(G-12599)
COLEMAN AEROSPACE
5950 Lakehurst Dr (32819-8345)
PHONE..................................407 354-0047
Mark Stephen, *Vice Pres*
EMP: 22 **EST:** 2005
SALES (est): 7.1MM **Privately Held**
WEB: www.rocket.com
SIC: 3721 Aircraft

(G-12600)
COLL BUILDERS SUPPLY INC
6663 Narcoossee Rd # 178 (32822-5549)
PHONE..................................407 745-4641
Humberto Collazo, *President*
Collazo Adrian, *President*
Adrian Collazo, *General Mgr*
EMP: 12 **EST:** 2012
SQ FT: 6,300
SALES (est): 8K **Privately Held**
WEB: www.pr1mo.net
SIC: 3965 Fasteners

(G-12601)
COLLEGE HUNKS HLG JUNK & MVG
4484 Sw 34th St (32811-6446)
PHONE..................................407 378-2500
EMP: 6 **EST:** 2015
SALES (est): 184.6K **Privately Held**
WEB: www.collegehunkshaulingjunk.com
SIC: 3443 4953 Dumpsters, garbage; recycling, waste materials

(G-12602)
COLLIDECOM LLC
4700 Mllnia Blvdn Ste 400 (32839)
PHONE..................................407 903-5626
Dan Thresher,
EMP: 10
SALES (est): 347.4K **Privately Held**
SIC: 2741

(G-12603)
COLLINS RESEARCH INC
Also Called: Flame Boss
6790 Edgwter Cmmerce Pkwy (32810-4278)
PHONE..................................321 401-6060
Micheal Collins, *CEO*
Roger Collins, *President*
Bob Hack, *General Mgr*
Robert Hack, *Vice Pres*
EMP: 16 **EST:** 2007
SQ FT: 190,000
SALES (est): 800K **Privately Held**
WEB: www.flameboss.com
SIC: 3829 Measuring & controlling devices

(G-12604)
COMMERCIAL CABINETRY LLC
6135 Cyril Ave (32809-5045)
PHONE..................................407 440-4601
Warren A Skipper,
EMP: 5 **EST:** 2010
SALES (est): 693.7K **Privately Held**
SIC: 3553 Cabinet makers' machinery

(G-12605)
COMMERCIAL METAL PHOTOGRAPHY
Also Called: C M P G
1934a Silver Star Rd (32804-3302)
P.O. Box 547155 (32854-7155)
PHONE..................................407 295-8182
Lawrence Albrecht, *President*
EMP: 6 **EST:** 1983
SQ FT: 3,000
SALES (est): 591.5K **Privately Held**
SIC: 3999 7336 Identification plates; silk screen design

(G-12606)
COMMERCIAL MILLWORKS INC
1120 S Hughey Ave Ste A (32806-1011)
PHONE..................................407 648-2787
Robert Coursey, *President*
Gayle King, *Vice Pres*
EMP: 15
SQ FT: 15,000
SALES: 1.4MM **Privately Held**
WEB: www.commercialmillworksinc.com
SIC: 2431 Millwork

(G-12607)
COMMSCOPE TECHNOLOGIES LLC
11310 Satellite Blvd (32837-9224)
PHONE..................................407 944-9116
Jim Watkins, *Manager*
EMP: 10 **Publicly Held**
SIC: 3663 Radio & TV communications equipment
HQ: Commscope Technologies Llc
4 Westbrook Corp Ctr
Westchester IL 60154

(G-12608)
COMPLEMENTARY COATINGS CORP
Also Called: Insl-X Coronado Lenmar
9592 Parksouth Ct (32837-8383)
PHONE..................................386 428-6461
EMP: 200
SALES (corp-wide): 242.1B **Publicly Held**
SIC: 2851 Mfg Paints & Industrial Coatings
HQ: Complementary Coatings Corp.
101 Paragon Dr
Montvale NJ 07645

(G-12609)
COMTECH ANTENNA SYSTEMS INC
212 Outlook Point Dr # 100 (32809-7200)
PHONE..................................407 854-1950
Tom Christi, *President*
Justin O'Neill, *Marketing Staff*
Bill Parke, *Director*
▼ **EMP:** 98 **EST:** 1984
SQ FT: 35,000
SALES (est): 28MM
SALES (corp-wide): 581.7MM **Publicly Held**
WEB: www.comtechsystems.com
SIC: 3663 Satellites, communications; antennas, transmitting & communications
PA: Comtech Telecommunications Corp.
68 S Service Rd Ste 230
Melville NY 11747
631 962-7000

(G-12610)
COMTECH SYSTEMS INC
212 Outlook Point Dr # 100 (32809-7200)
PHONE..................................407 854-1950
Fred Kornberg, *Ch of Bd*
Richard Luhrs, *President*
Rich Luhrs, *President*
Joe Smith, *Engineer*
Tom Sheehan, *Senior Engr*
▼ **EMP:** 72 **EST:** 1974
SALES (est): 20.5MM
SALES (corp-wide): 581.7MM **Publicly Held**
WEB: www.comtechsystems.com
SIC: 3663 Satellites, communications; microwave communication equipment
PA: Comtech Telecommunications Corp.
68 S Service Rd Ste 230
Melville NY 11747
631 962-7000

(G-12611)
CON-AIR INDUSTRIES INC
4157 Seaboard Rd (32808-3849)
PHONE..................................407 298-5733
Jack Lefort, *CEO*
Robert N Hering Jr, *CEO*
Christina Adkinson, *President*
Michael Cooper, *President*
Charles Adkinson, *Regional Mgr*
EMP: 100 **EST:** 1980
SQ FT: 100,000
SALES (est): 25MM
SALES (corp-wide): 16MM **Privately Held**
WEB: www.conairindustries.com
SIC: 3585 5075 7623 Refrigeration & heating equipment; air filters; air conditioning repair
HQ: Filtration Group Llc
912 E Washington St Ste 1
Joliet IL 60433
803 628-2410

(G-12612)
CONCRETE EDGE COMPANY
1952 Saturn Blvd (32837-9417)
PHONE..................................407 658-2788
Robert Matthias, *President*
▼ **EMP:** 8 **EST:** 1993
SALES (est): 1.2MM **Privately Held**
WEB: www.lilbubba.com
SIC: 3559 5211 5083 0782 Concrete products machinery; masonry materials & supplies; landscaping equipment; landscape contractors; landscape planning services

(G-12613)
CONDUENT IMAGE SOLUTIONS INC
Also Called: ACS
4209 Vineland Rd Ste J2 (32811-6630)
PHONE..................................407 849-0279
G Marino, *Vice Pres*
Amanda Mas, *Controller*
Marty Martinez, *Manager*
EMP: 238
SALES (corp-wide): 4.1B **Publicly Held**
WEB: www.conduent.com
SIC: 3577 Computer peripheral equipment
HQ: Conduent Image Solutions, Inc.
100 Campus Dr Ste 200e
Florham Park NJ 07932

(G-12614)
CONKLIN METAL INDUSTRIES INC
3060 Pennington Dr (32804-3334)
PHONE..................................407 688-0900
Brian Campbell, *Sales Mgr*
Dave Hills, *Branch Mgr*
Angel Sante, *Manager*
EMP: 17
SALES (corp-wide): 56.9MM **Privately Held**
WEB: www.conklinmetal.com
SIC: 3444 Sheet metalwork
PA: Conklin Metal Industries, Inc.
684 Antone St Nw Ste 100
Atlanta GA 30318
404 688-4510

(G-12615)
CONSUMER SOURCE INC
Also Called: Apartment Guide
8026 Sunport Dr Ste 304 (32809-8108)
PHONE..................................407 888-0745
EMP: 9 **Privately Held**
SIC: 2741 Publisher
HQ: Consumer Source Inc.
3585 Engrg Dr Ste 100
Norcross GA 30092
678 421-3000

(G-12616)
CONTINENTAL PROPERTY LLC
901 Central Florida Pkwy A3 (32824-8506)
PHONE..................................817 613-1890
Yitchak Menaged, *Owner*
Isaac Menaged, *Vice Pres*
EMP: 7 **EST:** 1986
SALES (est): 268.8K **Privately Held**
WEB: www.continentalpropertyllc.com
SIC: 3479 Metal coating & allied service

(G-12617)
CONTROL LASER CORPORATION
Also Called: CLC
8251 Presidents Dr # 1688 (32809-7653)
PHONE..................................407 926-3500
Renjie Liu, *President*
Nichole Rice, *Buyer*
Nikki Rice, *Purchasing*
Sumedha Hewagama, *Engineer*
Daniel Giesler, *Sales Mgr*
▲ **EMP:** 40 **EST:** 1965
SQ FT: 80,000
SALES (est): 9.9MM **Privately Held**
WEB: www.controllaser.com
SIC: 3699 Laser systems & equipment
PA: Han's Laser Technology Industry Group Co.,Ltd.
No.9988 Shennan Road, Nanshan District
Shenzhen 51800

(G-12618)
CONVERGENT TECHNOLOGIES
14764 Sapodilla Dr (32828-7321)
PHONE..................................407 482-4381
Scott C Barry, *Principal*
EMP: 12 **EST:** 2008

GEOGRAPHIC

SALES (est): 1.1MM **Privately Held**
SIC: 3674 Semiconductors & related devices

(G-12619)
COOL TREAT
7001 International Dr (32819-8221)
PHONE..................................407 248-0743
Roger Patel, *Principal*
EMP: 8 **EST:** 2007
SALES (est): 595.7K **Privately Held**
SIC: 2024 Ice cream, bulk

(G-12620)
COPERNICCO COATINGS LLC
2624 Pisces Dr (32837-9012)
PHONE..................................407 948-3434
Ismael Perez, *Principal*
EMP: 6 **EST:** 2016
SALES (est): 114.6K **Privately Held**
SIC: 3479 Metal coating & allied service

(G-12621)
CORKCICLE LLC
1300 Brookhaven Dr Ste 2 (32803-2547)
P.O. Box 547965 (32854-7965)
PHONE..................................866 780-0007
Chris McDonough, *CEO*
Sharrie Booker, *Vice Pres*
Cari Davidson, *Human Res Dir*
Brandon Blahnik, *Cust Mgr*
Felecia Benzakan, *Sales Staff*
◆ **EMP:** 28 **EST:** 2010
SALES (est): 2.9MM **Privately Held**
WEB: www.corkcicle.com
SIC: 3089 Plastic kitchenware, tableware & houseware

(G-12622)
CORONADO PAINT CO INC
9592 Parksouth Ct (32837-8383)
P.O. Box 308, Edgewater (32132-0308)
PHONE..................................386 428-6461
James Weil, *President*
▼ **EMP:** 154 **EST:** 1957
SQ FT: 193,000
SALES (est): 30MM
SALES (corp-wide): 245.5B **Publicly Held**
WEB: www.benjaminmoore.com
SIC: 2851 Paints & allied products
HQ: Benjamin Moore & Co.
101 Paragon Dr
Montvale NJ 07645
201 573-9600

(G-12623)
COUNTY OF ORANGE
400 E South St (32801-2816)
PHONE..................................407 649-0076
Scott Hall, *Vice Pres*
John Davis, *Project Mgr*
Eittreim Mark, *Purch Mgr*
Lucia Lettie, *Engineer*
Lanny Wood, *Engineer*
EMP: 6
SALES (corp-wide): 1.9B **Privately Held**
WEB: www.occompt.com
SIC: 2741 Miscellaneous publishing
PA: County Of Orange
201 S Rosalind Ave Fl 5
Orlando FL 32801
407 836-7350

(G-12624)
CRAIG CATAMARAN CORPORATION
4333 Silver Star Rd # 1 (32808-5100)
PHONE..................................407 290-8778
Robert Craig, *President*
Erik Craig, *Vice Pres*
Evana Craig, *Vice Pres*
▼ **EMP:** 7 **EST:** 1970
SQ FT: 5,000
SALES (est): 1MM **Privately Held**
WEB: www.craigcat.com
SIC: 3732 Boat building & repairing

(G-12625)
CREATIVE EVENTS AND EXHIBITS (PA)
Also Called: Zweifel International
405 Fairlane Ave (32809-4104)
PHONE..................................407 851-4754
John Zweifel, *President*
▲ **EMP:** 8 **EST:** 1955
SQ FT: 50,000
SALES (est): 375.1K **Privately Held**
SIC: 3999 Advertising display products

(G-12626)
CREATIVE PROMOTIONAL PRODUCTS
1325 E Harding St (32806-4115)
PHONE..................................407 383-7114
Annie McRae, *Principal*
Judy Elowe, *Vice Pres*
Mike Elowe, *Vice Pres*
Sharon Biernat, *Sales Staff*
Jerry Gleicher, *Sales Staff*
EMP: 8 **EST:** 2008
SALES (est): 135.8K **Privately Held**
WEB: www.creativepromo.net
SIC: 2759 Promotional printing

(G-12627)
CREATIVE PRTG GRPHIC DSIGN INC
1009 Pine St (32824-8342)
PHONE..................................407 855-0202
Rick Pearce, *President*
Randy Pearce, *Vice Pres*
Brandy Bennett, *Sales Staff*
Christy Henderson, *Sales Staff*
Teresa Pearce, *Office Mgr*
EMP: 30 **EST:** 1982
SQ FT: 16,000
SALES (est): 4.1MM **Privately Held**
WEB: www.creativepgm.com
SIC: 2752 2796 2791 2789 Commercial printing, offset; platemaking services; typesetting; bookbinding & related work; commercial printing

(G-12628)
CRESS CHEMICAL & EQUIPMENT CO
519 19th St (32805-4747)
P.O. Box 555649 (32855-5649)
PHONE..................................407 425-2846
Stephen E Cressman, *President*
Stephen Cressman, *Vice Pres*
EMP: 5 **EST:** 1970
SQ FT: 4,000
SALES (est): 500K **Privately Held**
SIC: 2851 5084 Removers & cleaners; cleaning equipment, high pressure, sand or steam

(G-12629)
CSL OF AMERICA INC
1900 S Orange Blossom Trl (32805-4652)
PHONE..................................407 849-7070
Cesar S Leirias, *President*
EMP: 11 **EST:** 2005
SALES (est): 192.2K **Privately Held**
SIC: 2298 Nets, rope

(G-12630)
CSMC INC
Also Called: Allegra Print & Imaging
4498 Vineland Rd (32811-7334)
PHONE..................................407 246-1567
Don Snyder, *President*
EMP: 28 **EST:** 1982
SALES (est): 6.6MM **Privately Held**
WEB: www.allegramarketingprint.com
SIC: 2752 2791 2789 2759 Commercial printing, offset; typesetting; bookbinding & related work; commercial printing

(G-12631)
CTE JV LLC
12802 Science Dr Ste 300 (32826-3021)
PHONE..................................407 894-5575
Sharon Wolford, *President*
Debra Brunetti, *Vice Pres*
EMP: 3 **EST:** 2013
SQ FT: 55,000
SALES (est): 10MM **Privately Held**
SIC: 3728 Aircraft training equipment

(G-12632)
CUBIC ADVNCED LRNG SLTIONS INC
2001 W Oak Ridge Rd (32809-3813)
PHONE..................................407 859-7410
Theresa W Kohl, *President*
Thomas D Echols, *Vice Pres*
Angela L Hartley, *Admin Sec*
EMP: 15 **EST:** 2013
SALES (est): 3.6MM **Privately Held**
WEB: www.cubic.com
SIC: 3699 3812 7372 Flight simulators (training aids), electronic; defense systems & equipment; application computer software
HQ: Cubic Corporation
9333 Balboa Ave
San Diego CA 92123
858 277-6780

(G-12633)
CUBIC CORPORATION
3862 Quadrangle Blvd # 100 (32817-8368)
PHONE..................................407 859-7410
Penny Romano, *Buyer*
Ray Boyles, *Engineer*
Ed Campbell, *Engineer*
Jason Schwartz, *Engineer*
Sonia Scott, *Senior Engr*
EMP: 6 **Privately Held**
WEB: www.cubic.com
SIC: 3812 Defense systems & equipment
HQ: Cubic Corporation
9333 Balboa Ave
San Diego CA 92123
858 277-6780

(G-12634)
CUBIC SIMULATION SYSTEMS INC
Also Called: Cubic Transportation Systems
2001 W Oak Ridge Rd # 100 (32809-3813)
PHONE..................................407 641-2037
Robert L Collins, *CEO*
William W Boyle, *CEO*
Bradley H Feldmann, *President*
Walter C Zable, *Chairman*
Glenn C Andrew, *COO*
◆ **EMP:** 140 **EST:** 1951
SQ FT: 398,086
SALES (est): 33.8MM **Privately Held**
WEB: www.cubic.com
SIC: 3699 Electronic training devices
HQ: Cubic Corporation
9333 Balboa Ave
San Diego CA 92123
858 277-6780

(G-12635)
CULINARY CONCEPTS INC
2215 Tradeport Dr (32824-7005)
P.O. Box 2066, Winter Park (32790-2066)
PHONE..................................407 228-0069
Moorefield Margaret D, *Principal*
Hal Valdes, *Vice Pres*
Manny Garcia, *Vice Pres*
Anthony Pace, *Vice Pres*
Thomas F Gilbertson, *Director*
EMP: 39 **EST:** 1998
SALES (est): 2MM **Privately Held**
SIC: 2099 5812 2035 2034 Food preparations; eating places; pickles, sauces & salad dressings; dehydrated fruits, vegetables, soups

(G-12636)
CUMMINS INC
4820 N Orange Blossom Trl (32810-1605)
PHONE..................................407 298-2080
Larry Fetting, *General Mgr*
Donald Baldwin, *Vice Pres*
Eric Nelson, *Vice Pres*
Joe Wismann, *Opers Mgr*
Prafulla Neema, *Purchasing*
EMP: 7
SALES (corp-wide): 19.8B **Publicly Held**
WEB: www.cummins.com
SIC: 3714 Motor vehicle parts & accessories
PA: Cummins Inc.
500 Jackson St
Columbus IN 47201
812 377-5000

(G-12637)
CUSANOS ITALIAN BAKERY INC
Also Called: Cusano's Baking Co.
1904 Premier Row (32809-6206)
PHONE..................................786 506-4281
EMP: 34
SALES (corp-wide): 28.2MM **Privately Held**
WEB: www.cusanos.com
SIC: 2051 Bakery: wholesale or wholesale/retail combined
PA: Cusano's Italian Bakery, Inc.
5480 W Hillsboro Blvd
Coconut Creek FL 33073
954 458-1010

(G-12638)
CUSTOM CORNHOLE BOARDS INC
Also Called: Wholesale Cornhole Bags
6169 Cyril Ave (32809-5045)
PHONE..................................407 203-6886
Daniel A Jones Sr, *President*
Laurence Ragan, *President*
EMP: 20 **EST:** 2014
SQ FT: 9,000
SALES (est): 3.1MM **Privately Held**
WEB: www.cornholeboards.us
SIC: 2493 Hardboard, tempered

(G-12639)
CUSTOM FAB INC (DH)
109 5th St (32824-8258)
PHONE..................................407 859-3954
Christopher M Comins, *President*
Holly Porter, *General Mgr*
Kevin Larrabee, *Project Mgr*
Henry Herrera, *CFO*
Robin Mitchem, *Asst Controller*
▲ **EMP:** 86 **EST:** 2005
SQ FT: 2,400
SALES (est): 28.6MM
SALES (corp-wide): 1.5B **Publicly Held**
WEB: www.uspipe.com
SIC: 3317 3498 Steel pipe & tubes; coils, pipe: fabricated from purchased pipe
HQ: United States Pipe And Foundry Company Llc
2 Chase Corporate Dr # 200
Hoover AL 35244
205 263-8540

(G-12640)
CUSTOM METAL FABRICATORS INC
1415 Long St (32805-2410)
PHONE..................................407 841-8551
Earl Potts, *President*
Kevin Potts, *Vice Pres*
EMP: 7 **EST:** 1973
SQ FT: 8,162
SALES (est): 997.9K **Privately Held**
SIC: 3444 Sheet metal specialties, not stamped

(G-12641)
CYBERCELLULARS INC
12981 S Ornge Blossom Trl (32837-6592)
PHONE..................................407 608-7888
EMP: 6 **EST:** 2014
SALES (est): 112.5K **Privately Held**
SIC: 3663 Television broadcasting & communications equipment

(G-12642)
D & A MACHINE INC
7220 Old Cheney Hwy (32807-6222)
PHONE..................................407 275-5770
EMP: 9 **EST:** 2019
SALES (est): 345.8K **Privately Held**
WEB: www.damachine.com
SIC: 3469 Stamping metal for the trade

(G-12643)
D&D WOOD WORKING INC
8622 Brackenwood Dr (32829-8628)
PHONE..................................407 427-0106
David A Batista, *President*
EMP: 7 **EST:** 2004
SALES (est): 79.8K **Privately Held**
SIC: 2431 Millwork

(G-12644)
DAHLQUIST ENTERPRISES INC
Also Called: Dahlquists Printing & Graphics
1315 N Mills Ave (32803-2542)
PHONE..................................407 896-2294
George Dahlquist, *President*
EMP: 9 **EST:** 1978
SQ FT: 4,200

SALES (est): 741.1K **Privately Held**
WEB: www.dahlquistprinting.com
SIC: 2752 2791 2789 2759 Commercial printing, offset; typesetting; bookbinding & related work; commercial printing

(G-12645)
DALE SMITH CABINETRY LLC
6598 S Goldenrod Rd (32822-8717)
PHONE..................................407 625-2274
Dale Wii Smith, *Principal*
EMP: 6 **EST:** 2012
SALES (est): 241.4K **Privately Held**
SIC: 2434 Wood kitchen cabinets

(G-12646)
DANIELS MANUFACTURING CORP
526 Thorpe Rd (32824-8133)
P.O. Box 593872 (32859-3872)
PHONE..................................407 855-6161
George G Daniels, *CEO*
James D Vargo, *Corp Secy*
Andre Hulsbosch, *Purch Agent*
John Kokat, *Purchasing*
Tony Dilworth, *Engineer*
▲ **EMP:** 170 **EST:** 1949
SQ FT: 60,000
SALES (est): 42.2MM **Privately Held**
WEB: www.dmctools.com
SIC: 3546 3423 Power-driven handtools; hand & edge tools

(G-12647)
DARKSIDE VAULT LLC
207 N Goldenrod Rd # 200 (32807-8294)
PHONE..................................407 353-3776
Tran Duong B, *Principal*
EMP: 6 **EST:** 2013
SALES (est): 211.9K **Privately Held**
WEB: www.darksidevault.com
SIC: 3272 Burial vaults, concrete or precast terrazzo

(G-12648)
DARLAND BAKERY INC
42 Cardamon Dr (32825-3658)
PHONE..................................407 894-1061
EMP: 15
SQ FT: 8,000
SALES (est): 155.1K **Privately Held**
SIC: 2051 Mfg Pies Cakes & Muffins

(G-12649)
DARLING INGREDIENTS INC
408 W Landstreet Rd (32824-7805)
PHONE..................................407 856-7667
Tony Bell, *Safety Mgr*
EMP: 7
SALES (corp-wide): 3.3B **Publicly Held**
WEB: www.darlingii.com
SIC: 2077 Animal & marine fats & oils
PA: Darling Ingredients Inc.
5601 N Macarthur Blvd
Irving TX 75038
972 717-0300

(G-12650)
DART INDUSTRIES INC (HQ)
14901 S Ornge Blssom Trl (32837-6600)
P.O. Box 2353 (32802-2353)
PHONE..................................407 826-5050
E V Goings, *President*
Richard A Lisec, *Vice Pres*
Shirley Bush, *Purch Agent*
Thomas M Roehlk, *Admin Sec*
▲ **EMP:** 350 **EST:** 1928
SALES (est): 425MM **Publicly Held**
WEB: www.tupperwarebrands.com
SIC: 3089 Plastic containers, except foam; kitchenware, plastic

(G-12651)
DATAMAX INTERNATIONAL CORP (DH)
4501 Pkwy Commerce Blvd (32808-1013)
PHONE..................................407 578-8007
William Bouverie, *President*
David Winder, *Vice Pres*
▲ **EMP:** 349 **EST:** 1991
SQ FT: 90,000
SALES (est): 69.9MM
SALES (corp-wide): 32.6B **Publicly Held**
SIC: 3577 2754 Input/output equipment, computer; labels: gravure printing

(G-12652)
DATAMAX-ONEIL CORPORATION (HQ)
4501 Pkwy Commerce Blvd (32808-1013)
PHONE..................................800 816-9649
Michael Savignac, *President*
John Yuncza, *CFO*
Phillip Pastore, *Controller*
Karl Tao, *Asst Sec*
◆ **EMP:** 160 **EST:** 1984
SQ FT: 70,000
SALES (est): 97.3MM
SALES (corp-wide): 32.6B **Publicly Held**
WEB: www.honeywell.com
SIC: 3577 2754 Input/output equipment, computer; labels: gravure printing
PA: Honeywell International Inc.
300 S Tryon St
Charlotte NC 28202
704 627-6200

(G-12653)
DAVES SUPER SMOOTHIES LLC
2505 Monte Carlo Trl (32805-3528)
PHONE..................................407 293-7334
David L Brewer III, *CEO*
EMP: 6 **EST:** 2014
SALES (est): 102.8K **Privately Held**
WEB: www.davessupersmoothies.com
SIC: 2037 Frozen fruits & vegetables

(G-12654)
DAVID DELIGHTS LLC
4677 L B Mcleod Rd Ste J (32811-5609)
PHONE..................................407 648-2020
Walter David,
EMP: 5 **EST:** 2004
SALES (est): 488.1K **Privately Held**
SIC: 2066 Chocolate & cocoa products

(G-12655)
DAVISON PUBLISHING CO INC
3452 Lake Lynda Dr # 363 (32817-8456)
PHONE..................................407 657-3710
Deborah M Martin, *Principal*
EMP: 6 **EST:** 2017
SALES (est): 37.5K **Privately Held**
WEB: www.davisonpublishing.com
SIC: 2741 Miscellaneous publishing

(G-12656)
DAVISON PUBLISHING COMPANY LLC
2860 Delaney Ave (32806-5413)
PHONE..................................407 380-8900
Art Mc Ginnis, *Partner*
Marie Juma, *Sales Mgr*
EMP: 8 **EST:** 1885
SALES (est): 481.9K **Privately Held**
WEB: www.davisonpublishing.com
SIC: 2741 5112 5045 Catalogs: publishing only, not printed on site; office supplies; computer software

(G-12657)
DAYTON SUPERIOR CORPORATION
7415 Emerald Dunes Dr # 1200 (32822-4710)
PHONE..................................407 859-4541
Scot Perry, *Regional Mgr*
Judy Williams, *Manager*
EMP: 7 **Privately Held**
WEB: www.daytonsuperior.com
SIC: 3429 3444 Builders' hardware; concrete forms, sheet metal
HQ: Dayton Superior Corporation
1125 Byers Rd
Miamisburg OH 45342
937 866-0711

(G-12658)
DBN INVESTMENT LLC
3300 S Hiawassee Rd # 107 (32835-6350)
PHONE..................................407 917-2525
Shahabadeen Khan,
EMP: 14 **EST:** 2013
SALES (est): 509.8K **Privately Held**
SIC: 1389 Construction, repair & dismantling services

(G-12659)
DDCI INC
Also Called: Csg
995 W Kennedy Blvd Ste 35 (32810-6139)
PHONE..................................407 814-0225
Dino Derose, *President*
Howard Sullivan, *General Mgr*
Christopher E Inman, *Vice Pres*
Shane Bowen, *Project Mgr*
Chris Schronski, *Project Mgr*
EMP: 80 **EST:** 1987
SQ FT: 12,000
SALES: 8.4MM
SALES (corp-wide): 1.4B **Privately Held**
WEB: www.convergint.com
SIC: 3669 5063 Burglar alarm apparatus, electric; alarm systems
HQ: Convergint Technologies Llc
1 Commerce Dr
Schaumburg IL 60173
847 620-5000

(G-12660)
DEFENSE FLIGHT AEROSPACE LLC
5448 Hoffner Ave Ste 105 (32812-2506)
PHONE..................................321 442-7255
Stephen Pratt,
EMP: 13
SALES (est): 545.9K **Privately Held**
SIC: 3589 Service industry machinery

(G-12661)
DELIVERY SIGNS LLC
Also Called: Art Signs The
40 W Crystal Lake St # 100 (32806-4404)
PHONE..................................407 362-7896
D A Quiroz Zaiter, *Mng Member*
Daniel A Quiroz Zaiter, *Mng Member*
EMP: 5 **EST:** 2010
SALES (est): 502.8K **Privately Held**
WEB: www.signs247.net
SIC: 3993 Signs, not made in custom sign painting shops

(G-12662)
DESIGN COMMUNICATIONS LTD
10611 Satellite Blvd (32837-8429)
PHONE..................................407 856-9661
Dana Lanasa, *Project Mgr*
Jason Abbatoy, *Prdtn Mgr*
Craig Kutner, *Branch Mgr*
Scott Saccullo, *Manager*
Roger Stone, *Executive*
EMP: 11
SALES (corp-wide): 29.2MM **Privately Held**
WEB: www.designcommunicationsltd.com
SIC: 3993 Signs & advertising specialties
PA: Design Communications, Ltd.
85 Bodwell St Ste 1
Avon MA 02322
617 542-9620

(G-12663)
DESIGN FURNISHINGS INC
3647 All American Blvd (32810-4726)
PHONE..................................407 294-0507
John Follo, *President*
EMP: 31 **EST:** 1986
SQ FT: 30,000
SALES (est): 4.3MM **Privately Held**
WEB: www.designfurnishings.net
SIC: 2599 2512 Bar furniture; chairs: upholstered on wood frames

(G-12664)
DESIGNERS PRESS INC
6305 Chancellor Dr (32809-5609)
PHONE..................................407 843-3141
David R Simons, *CEO*
Gary Leoce, *Vice Pres*
Tina Bean, *Production*
Shelley Manes, *Sales Staff*
Ellen Benton, *Consultant*
EMP: 64
SQ FT: 36,000
SALES (est): 15.1MM
SALES (corp-wide): 111.2MM **Privately Held**
WEB: www.sandyinc.com
SIC: 2759 2752 Commercial printing; commercial printing, lithographic
PA: Sandy Alexander, Inc.
200 Entin Rd
Clifton NJ 07014
973 470-8100

(G-12665)
DESIND INDUSTRIES CORP
150 E Robinson St # 1009 (32801-1695)
PHONE..................................212 729-0192
Brian Desind, *President*
EMP: 8 **EST:** 2014
SALES (est): 240.9K **Privately Held**
SIC: 3999 Barber & beauty shop equipment

(G-12666)
DESYSCA INC
9528 Silver Buttonwood St (32832-5659)
PHONE..................................407 724-4148
Alexis Villamizar, *President*
EMP: 6 **EST:** 2015
SALES (est): 132.3K **Privately Held**
WEB: www.desysca.com
SIC: 3861 Photographic equipment & supplies

(G-12667)
DEVON CHASE & COMPANY
2814 Silver Star Rd # 5 (32808-3941)
P.O. Box 593730 (32859-3730)
PHONE..................................407 438-6466
Thomas M Tedesco, *President*
Sue Tedesco, *Admin Sec*
Tammy Weaver, *Technician*
EMP: 9 **EST:** 1989
SQ FT: 20,000
SALES (est): 601.2K **Privately Held**
WEB: www.devonchase.com
SIC: 2512 2515 Wood upholstered chairs & couches; mattresses & foundations

(G-12668)
DF MULTI SERVICES LLC
845 N Garland Ave (32801-1095)
PHONE..................................407 683-2223
Paulo Fabiano Carneiro, *President*
EMP: 5 **EST:** 2017
SALES (est): 667.5K **Privately Held**
SIC: 3448 1799 1741 Screen enclosures; fence construction; unit paver installation

(G-12669)
DIAGMA U S LLC
255 S Orange Ave Ste 745 (32801-5007)
PHONE..................................407 683-0852
Azat Berdyyev, *Manager*
EMP: 6 **EST:** 2015
SALES (est): 172.4K **Privately Held**
SIC: 3728 Aircraft parts & equipment

(G-12670)
DIAZ GO GREEN INC
413 Brailiff Ct (32824-5970)
PHONE..................................407 501-2724
Maribel Diaz, *Vice Pres*
EMP: 8 **EST:** 2012
SALES (est): 132.8K **Privately Held**
WEB: www.diazgogreen.com
SIC: 3714 Motor vehicle parts & accessories

(G-12671)
DIDNA INC
206 Hillcrest St (32801-1212)
PHONE..................................239 851-0966
Deke Hooper, *CEO*
Dwight Hooper, *Ch of Bd*
Troy Bubley, *President*
William Lutzen, *CFO*
EMP: 7 **EST:** 2016
SALES (est): 527.1K **Privately Held**
WEB: www.didna.io
SIC: 7372 8742 Publishers' computer software; management consulting services

(G-12672)
DIGITAL ANTOMY SMLTONS FOR HLT ✪
1720 S Orange Ave Ste 300 (32806-2967)
PHONE..................................937 623-7377
Jack Stubbs,
EMP: 6 **EST:** 2020
SALES (est): 500K **Privately Held**
SIC: 3842 Models, anatomical

GEOGRAPHIC

(G-12673)
DIGITAL PIXEL DISPLAYS LLC (PA)
111 N Orange Ave (32801-2316)
PHONE..................................321 948-3751
Khaled Khuda, *Mng Member*
EMP: 5 **EST:** 2019
SALES (est): 377.4K **Privately Held**
SIC: 3679 Liquid crystal displays (LCD)

(G-12674)
DIGITAL PRESS
12002 Philbrook Ct (32825-2718)
PHONE..................................407 421-3131
Edward Esquivel, *Principal*
EMP: 6 **EST:** 2010
SALES (est): 143.9K **Privately Held**
SIC: 2741 Miscellaneous publishing

(G-12675)
DIGITAL PROPAGANDA INC
997 W Kennedy Blvd A12 (32810-6140)
PHONE..................................407 644-8444
EMP: 14
SALES (est): 1.7MM **Privately Held**
SIC: 2731 Publishing And Printing

(G-12676)
DISTINGSHED GNTLMAN MBL DTLING ◆
7512 Dr Phillips Blvd 50-1 (32819-5131)
PHONE..................................321 200-4331
Jonathan Brown,
EMP: 6 **EST:** 2020
SALES (est): 300K **Privately Held**
WEB: www.thedgmd.com
SIC: 2842 Automobile polish

(G-12677)
DIVERSIFIED GRAPHICS INC
720 Franklin Ln (32801-3624)
PHONE..................................407 425-9443
Edwin T Stephens, *President*
Norma Stephens, *Treasurer*
Carolyn Sasser, *Office Mgr*
Dean Leatherbarrow, *Analyst*
EMP: 10 **EST:** 1976
SQ FT: 16,000
SALES (est): 715.4K **Privately Held**
WEB: www.diversified-graphics.com
SIC: 2796 2752 Color separations for printing; commercial printing, lithographic

(G-12678)
DIVINITAS DISPLAYS LLC
7598 Currency Dr (32809-6923)
PHONE..................................407 660-6625
Kitt Hancock, *Vice Pres*
Perry J Degregorio,
EMP: 14 **EST:** 2013
SALES (est): 410.8K **Privately Held**
WEB: www.divinitasnow.com
SIC: 3993 Signs & advertising specialties

(G-12679)
DL CABINETRY ORLANDO LLC
7025 W Colonial Dr (32818-6705)
PHONE..................................504 669-7847
Junxiu Ren, *Mng Member*
EMP: 9 **EST:** 2017
SALES (est): 580.7K **Privately Held**
WEB: www.dlcabinetryorlando.com
SIC: 2434 Wood kitchen cabinets

(G-12680)
DOUGLAS ABBOTT
3708 S John Young Pkwy (32839-9204)
PHONE..................................407 422-3597
Douglas Abbott, *Owner*
EMP: 9 **EST:** 2001
SALES (est): 132.7K **Privately Held**
SIC: 3643 Rail bonds, electric: for propulsion & signal circuits

(G-12681)
DP PET PRODUCTS INC
Also Called: Pro Pet Distributors
5340 Young Pine Rd 8 (32829-7415)
PHONE..................................407 888-4627
David Canning, *President*
▲ **EMP:** 10 **EST:** 1991
SALES (est): 953.7K **Privately Held**
WEB: www.propetdistributors.com
SIC: 3199 Dog furnishings: collars, leashes, muzzles, etc.: leather

(G-12682)
DR PEPPER BOTTLING CO
1700 Directors Row (32809-6226)
PHONE..................................407 354-5800
Don Dignan, *CFO*
EMP: 7 **EST:** 2007
SALES (est): 140.8K **Privately Held**
WEB: www.drpepper.com
SIC: 2086 Tea, iced: packaged in cans, bottles, etc.

(G-12683)
DRAGONFIRE INDUSTRIES INC
4065 L B Mcleod Rd Ste G1 (32811-5663)
PHONE..................................407 999-2215
Tim Titus, *President*
Tammy Titus, *Vice Pres*
Doris Titus, *Treasurer*
EMP: 5 **EST:** 1994
SALES (est): 562.6K **Privately Held**
WEB: www.dragonfireindustries.com
SIC: 3993 Signs, not made in custom sign painting shops

(G-12684)
DRAKE TOOL CO INC
10211 General Dr (32824-8529)
PHONE..................................407 859-4221
Lenville G Drake, *President*
Mary Drake, *Corp Secy*
EMP: 8 **EST:** 1985
SQ FT: 5,100
SALES (est): 943.2K **Privately Held**
WEB: www.draketoolco.com
SIC: 3599 Machine shop, jobbing & repair

(G-12685)
DRIP COMMUNICATION LLC
6831 Edgwter Cmmerce Pkwy (32810-4224)
PHONE..................................407 730-5519
Ricardo Rosa,
EMP: 11 **EST:** 2016
SALES (est): 411.7K **Privately Held**
WEB: www.dripcommunications.com
SIC: 2759 Promotional printing

(G-12686)
DRONE CLIPS BY MAJIC
4772 Lonsdale Cir (32817-3144)
PHONE..................................407 619-3704
Majid Heidari, *Principal*
EMP: 6 **EST:** 2017
SALES (est): 99.9K **Privately Held**
SIC: 3721 Motorized aircraft

(G-12687)
DRONE IMAGING SERVICES LLC
8540 Summerville Pl (32819-3928)
PHONE..................................407 620-5258
William Woodard, *Principal*
EMP: 7 **EST:** 2017
SALES (est): 383.7K **Privately Held**
SIC: 3721 Motorized aircraft

(G-12688)
DRONE MASTER SHOTS LLC
3603 N Pine Hills Rd (32808-2837)
PHONE..................................407 295-7715
Humberto Caron, *Principal*
EMP: 6 **EST:** 2016
SALES (est): 100.2K **Privately Held**
SIC: 3721 Motorized aircraft

(G-12689)
DRY COLOR USA LLC
8701 S Ct Skinner (32824)
PHONE..................................407 856-7788
Clovis Filipov, *President*
Eliezer Filipov, *Director*
Silas Filipov, *Director*
Priscila F Silva, *Director*
▲ **EMP:** 5 **EST:** 2012
SQ FT: 39,000
SALES (est): 2.7MM **Privately Held**
WEB: www.drycolor.com
SIC: 2816 Color pigments
PA: Dry Color Especialidades Quimicas Ltda
Rua Pedro Suzan 170
Cosmopolis SP 13150

(G-12690)
DRYWALL ELEMENTS
1700 35th St Ste 110 (32839-8950)
PHONE..................................407 454-7293
Ronald Sisson, *Project Mgr*
EMP: 12 **EST:** 2019
SALES (est): 3.1MM **Privately Held**
SIC: 2819 Elements

(G-12691)
DUCT DYNASTY
465 Mandalay Rd (32809-3015)
PHONE..................................407 730-9081
EMP: 6 **EST:** 2018
SALES (est): 74.4K **Privately Held**
WEB: www.ductdynasty.net
SIC: 2842 Specialty cleaning, polishes & sanitation goods

(G-12692)
DUSOBOX CORPORATION
Also Called: Dusobox Creative Packg Group
2501 Investors Row # 500 (32837-8387)
PHONE..................................407 855-5120
John L Kelley, *President*
Richard J Kelley Sr, *Chairman*
Greg Cetera, *Business Mgr*
Richard J Kelley Jr, *Vice Pres*
Julian Silva, *Manager*
▼ **EMP:** 83 **EST:** 1955
SQ FT: 65,000
SALES (est): 20MM **Privately Held**
WEB: www.dusobox.com
SIC: 2653 Boxes, corrugated: made from purchased materials; display items, corrugated: made from purchased materials

(G-12693)
EAGLE METAL DISTRIBUTORS INC
603 W Landstreet Rd Ste B (32824-7856)
PHONE..................................407 367-0688
Von Plourde, *President*
▲ **EMP:** 9 **EST:** 2003
SQ FT: 36,000
SALES (est): 4.5MM **Privately Held**
WEB: www.eaglemetalsinc.com
SIC: 3354 Aluminum extruded products

(G-12694)
EAST COAST FLOATS LLC
4832 New Broad St (32814-6628)
PHONE..................................407 203-5628
Mark Bowers,
Laurie J Samulonis-Bowers,
EMP: 7 **EST:** 2013
SALES (est): 280.4K **Privately Held**
WEB: www.eastcoastfloats.com
SIC: 2452 Sauna rooms, prefabricated, wood

(G-12695)
ECHODOG INDUSTRIES INC
9350 Bentley Park Cir (32819-5345)
P.O. Box 2568, Windermere (34786-2568)
PHONE..................................407 909-1636
Bobby L Moore, *Principal*
EMP: 8 **EST:** 2007
SALES (est): 128K **Privately Held**
SIC: 3999 Manufacturing industries

(G-12696)
ECO CUPS INTERNATIONAL CORP
2814 Silver Star Rd Apt 4 (32808-3941)
PHONE..................................407 308-1764
Karel P Hartinger, *President*
Stella M Hartinger, *Principal*
Abriela C Granes Alvarez, *Director*
Armando P Valdes Garrido-Lecca, *Director*
Adele E Gobelli, *Director*
EMP: 14 **EST:** 2017
SALES (est): 2.5MM **Privately Held**
WEB: www.ecocupsintl.com
SIC: 2656 3229 Paper cups, plates, dishes & utensils; bowls, glass

(G-12697)
ECX ONLINE INC
11208 Taeda Dr (32832-7019)
PHONE..................................407 442-6834
Scott McKirahan, *Principal*
EMP: 6 **EST:** 2012
SALES (est): 65.4K **Privately Held**
SIC: 3949 Sporting & athletic goods

(G-12698)
EDDYS JEWLELRY
2148 Whisper Lakes Blvd (32837-6761)
PHONE..................................321 236-7887
John E Mosquera, *Owner*
EMP: 6 **EST:** 2016
SALES (est): 72.4K **Privately Held**
SIC: 3961 Costume jewelry

(G-12699)
EDUMATICS INC
7649 W Clnl Dr Ste 120 (32818)
PHONE..................................407 656-0661
Kietta Mayweather Gamble, *President*
Gary Amodt, *Director*
Soraya Smith, *Admin Asst*
EMP: 15 **EST:** 2012
SALES (est): 1.2MM **Privately Held**
WEB: www.edumaticsprogram.com
SIC: 3999 7812 7373 Education aids, devices & supplies; educational motion picture production, television; motion picture production & distribution; computer-aided manufacturing (CAM) systems service

(G-12700)
EI INTERACTIVE LLC
121 S Orange Ave Ste 1400 (32801-3240)
PHONE..................................407 579-0993
Fabio Cardoso, *Mng Member*
EMP: 9 **EST:** 2012
SQ FT: 1,630
SALES (est): 584.4K **Privately Held**
SIC: 7372 Business oriented computer software

(G-12701)
EJM BROADCAST INC
Also Called: Adoracion Visual
12854 Boggy Pointe Dr (32824-4844)
PHONE..................................321 251-5662
John Rodriguez, *Principal*
Martha Camargo, *Vice Pres*
EMP: 5 **EST:** 2015
SALES (est): 486K **Privately Held**
SIC: 3663 Studio equipment, radio & television broadcasting

(G-12702)
EJM COPPER INC
Also Called: E J M Gutter
1911 Ellman St (32804-4201)
PHONE..................................407 447-0074
Edward J Majewski, *CEO*
Angie Majewski, *Vice Pres*
EMP: 14 **EST:** 1999
SQ FT: 5,000
SALES (est): 2.3MM **Privately Held**
WEB: www.ejmcopper.com
SIC: 3331 Primary copper

(G-12703)
ELECTRONIC ARTS INC
1950 Summit Park Dr (32810-5933)
PHONE..................................407 838-8000
Jeff Aho, *Editor*
Scott Forrest, *Senior VP*
Roy Harvey, *Vice Pres*
Daryl Holt, *Vice Pres*
Joel Knutson, *Vice Pres*
EMP: 10
SALES (corp-wide): 5.5B **Publicly Held**
WEB: www.ea.com
SIC: 7372 Home entertainment computer software
PA: Electronic Arts Inc.
209 Redwood Shores Pkwy
Redwood City CA 94065
650 628-1500

(G-12704)
ELEMENTS OF SPACE LLC
10142 Pink Carnation Ct (32825-8814)
PHONE..................................407 718-9690
Wendy J Hilton, *Principal*
EMP: 9 **EST:** 2015
SALES (est): 224.5K **Privately Held**
WEB: www.elementsofspace.com
SIC: 3555 Engraving machinery & equipment, except plates; blocks, wood: engravers'

(G-12705)
ELITE DISTRIBUTORS LLC
1716 Premier Row A (32809-6202)
PHONE..................................407 601-6665

Naushad Manjani, *Manager*
EMP: 11 **EST:** 2017
SALES (est): 1.1MM **Privately Held**
SIC: 3489 Smoke generators (ordnance)

(G-12706)
ELLIOTT CUSTOM COATINGS LLC
14128 Rensselaer Rd (32826-3557)
PHONE..................................407 734-5221
Christopher Elliott, *Principal*
EMP: 6 **EST:** 2016
SALES (est): 78K **Privately Held**
SIC: 2952 Asphalt felts & coatings

(G-12707)
ELLIPSIS BREWING
7500 Tpc Blvd Ste 8 (32822-5181)
PHONE..................................407 556-3241
Robert McKee, *Principal*
EMP: 9 **EST:** 2016
SQ FT: 7,500
SALES (est): 374.2K **Privately Held**
WEB: www.commerce.arryved.com
SIC: 2082 Beer (alcoholic beverage)

(G-12708)
EMBROIDERY SOLUTIONS INC
6001 S Orange Ave (32809-4237)
PHONE..................................407 438-8188
Leo Ambrose, *President*
Andrew Nazareth, *Vice Pres*
EMP: 6 **EST:** 1998
SALES (est): 716.4K **Privately Held**
WEB: www.embroiderysolutions.com
SIC: 2759 Screen printing

(G-12709)
EMINEL CORPORATION INC
Also Called: Tiregraficx
8600 Com Cir Unit 148 (32819)
PHONE..................................407 900-0190
Steven M Mandala, *President*
EMP: 10 **EST:** 2014
SQ FT: 3,000
SALES (est): 3MM **Privately Held**
SIC: 3011 Tire & inner tube materials & related products

(G-12710)
EMS TECHNOLOGIES NA LLC
121 S Orange Ave Ste 1500 (32801-3241)
P.O. Box 162797, Altamonte Springs (32716-2797)
PHONE..................................321 259-5979
Chris Moats, *Mng Member*
EMP: 10 **EST:** 2006
SALES (est): 3MM **Privately Held**
WEB: www.ems-technologies.com
SIC: 3541 Machine tools, metal cutting type

(G-12711)
ENCOMPASS MKTG & DEV GROUP INC
102 Drennen Rd (32806-8511)
PHONE..................................407 420-7777
Gary Schwartz, *President*
EMP: 8 **EST:** 2007
SALES (est): 4.2MM **Privately Held**
SIC: 2099 Food preparations

(G-12712)
ENTERPRISE SYSTEM ASSOC INC (PA)
Also Called: E S A I
3259 Progress Dr (32826-3230)
PHONE..................................407 275-0220
Robert Barbour, *President*
Santiago Tula, *Principal*
EMP: 12 **EST:** 2000
SALES (est): 1.7MM **Privately Held**
WEB: www.esaigroup.com
SIC: 7372 Business oriented computer software

(G-12713)
ENTERPRISE TECH PARTNERS LLC
37 N Orange Ave Ste 616 (32801-2449)
PHONE..................................918 851-3285
Sandra Dennard, *Manager*
EMP: 11 **EST:** 2000
SALES (est): 822.7K **Privately Held**
WEB: www.etpco.com
SIC: 3571 Electronic computers

(G-12714)
ENVIRONMENTAL TECTONICS CORP
Etc
2100 N Alafaya Trl # 900 (32826-4747)
PHONE..................................407 282-3378
Chad Minor, *Project Mgr*
Bob Rubeo, *Project Mgr*
Katarzyna Wrzesinski, *Opers Staff*
Paul Biocic, *QC Mgr*
Richard Turkiewicz, *Engineer*
EMP: 10
SALES (corp-wide): 73.8MM **Publicly Held**
WEB: www.etcusa.com
SIC: 3699 Electronic training devices
PA: Environmental Tectonics Corporation
125 James Way
Southampton PA 18966
215 355-9100

(G-12715)
EPRINT INC
14 E Washington St (32801-2354)
PHONE..................................407 930-5870
Juan C Castaneda, *Principal*
EMP: 6 **EST:** 2016
SALES (est): 135.3K **Privately Held**
WEB: www.eprintcopies.com
SIC: 2752 Commercial printing, lithographic

(G-12716)
ERICSSON INC
360 S Lake Destiny Dr (32810-6226)
PHONE..................................856 230-6268
EMP: 6
SALES (corp-wide): 26.8B **Privately Held**
SIC: 3663 Radio & TV communications equipment
HQ: Ericsson Inc.
6300 Legacy Dr
Plano TX 75024
972 583-0000

(G-12717)
ESTEREL TECHNOLOGIES INC
Also Called: North American Operations
1082 N Alsaya Trl Ste 124 (32826)
PHONE..................................724 746-3304
Chip Downing, *CEO*
Tony Karam, *General Mgr*
EMP: 10 **EST:** 2001
SQ FT: 500
SALES (est): 464.8K **Privately Held**
WEB: www.ansys.com
SIC: 7372 Prepackaged software

(G-12718)
ETERNAL SMOKE INC
1321 Edgewater Dr Ste 1 (32804-6387)
PHONE..................................407 984-5090
Angela Denise Smith, *President*
EMP: 7 **EST:** 2018
SALES (est): 705.8K **Privately Held**
WEB: www.eternalsmoke.com
SIC: 2131 Smoking tobacco

(G-12719)
EUROASIA PRODUCTS INC
3956 W Town Center Blvd # 166 (32837-6103)
PHONE..................................321 221-9398
John Bowers, *President*
▲ **EMP:** 5 **EST:** 1998
SQ FT: 2,000
SALES (est): 708.3K **Privately Held**
WEB: www.euroasiaproducts.com
SIC: 3589 5023 Cooking equipment, commercial; home furnishings

(G-12720)
EUROGAN-USA INC
502 Sunport Ln Ste 350 (32809-8135)
PHONE..................................321 356-5248
Luis Hernandez, *President*
Raul Hernandez, *COO*
▲ **EMP:** 10 **EST:** 2014
SQ FT: 10,000
SALES (est): 2MM **Privately Held**
SIC: 3089 Injection molded finished plastic products

(G-12721)
EVEREST CABINETS INC
6100 Hanging Moss Rd # 5 (32807-3790)
PHONE..................................407 790-7819
Ming Shu Lu, *Principal*
EMP: 8 **EST:** 2018
SALES (est): 65K **Privately Held**
WEB: www.everestcabinetsorlando.com
SIC: 2434 Wood kitchen cabinets

(G-12722)
EVERYTHING COMMUNICATES INC
Also Called: Sign-A-Rama
4380 L B Mcleod Rd (32811-5619)
P.O. Box 1077, Flagler Beach (32136-1077)
PHONE..................................407 578-6616
Amy S Marvin, *President*
Ross M Marvin, *Vice Pres*
EMP: 8 **EST:** 2004
SALES (est): 731.8K **Privately Held**
WEB: www.signarama.com
SIC: 3993 Signs & advertising specialties

(G-12723)
EVOLUTION LINERS INC
40 W Illiana St (32806-4455)
PHONE..................................407 839-6213
Stan Patterson, *CEO*
EMP: 9 **EST:** 2004
SALES (est): 845.1K **Privately Held**
WEB: www.evoii.com
SIC: 3842 Prosthetic appliances

(G-12724)
EVOLUTION VOICE INC
5728 Major Blvd Ste 720 (32819-7973)
PHONE..................................407 204-1614
Neil Tolley, *President*
EMP: 8 **EST:** 2019
SALES (est): 481.9K **Privately Held**
WEB: www.fourteenip.com
SIC: 7372 Business oriented computer software

(G-12725)
EVOQUA WATER TECHNOLOGIES LLC
4506 L B Mcleod Rd (32811-5651)
PHONE..................................407 650-1765
EMP: 6
SALES (corp-wide): 1.4B **Publicly Held**
WEB: www.evoqua.com
SIC: 3589 Water treatment equipment, industrial
HQ: Evoqua Water Technologies Llc
210 6th Ave Ste 3300
Pittsburgh PA 15222
724 772-0044

(G-12726)
EXCELLENT GUARANTD ELCTRCL
1625 Red Clover Ct (32825-8815)
PHONE..................................407 221-6234
William B Gwinn, *Principal*
EMP: 6 **EST:** 2012
SALES (est): 134.7K **Privately Held**
SIC: 3993 Signs & advertising specialties

(G-12727)
EXCELOR LLC
7380 W Sand Lake Rd # 500 (32819-5248)
PHONE..................................321 300-3315
Joseph S Vangala,
EMP: 10 **EST:** 2001
SALES (est): 813.5K **Privately Held**
WEB: www.excelor.com
SIC: 7372 8721 Business oriented computer software; accounting services, except auditing

(G-12728)
EXTRACT DOWNTOWN ORLANDO LLC
101 S Garland Ave (32801-3276)
PHONE..................................407 722-7379
Bryce Rockhill, *Principal*
EMP: 6 **EST:** 2014
SALES (est): 198.5K **Privately Held**
WEB: www.downtownorlando.com
SIC: 2836 Extracts

(G-12729)
EZE CASTLE SOFTWARE LLC
3501 Quadrangle Blvd # 200 (32817-8330)
PHONE..................................407 692-9699
Eric W Noll, *CEO*
EMP: 6 **EST:** 2012
SALES (est): 143.6K **Privately Held**
SIC: 7372 Prepackaged software

(G-12730)
FABBRO MARINE GROUP INC
Also Called: Cape Horn Boats
100 E Pine St Ste 110 (32801-2759)
PHONE..................................321 701-8141
Christopher R Fabbro, *President*
Franklin Davis, *Corp Secy*
Tyler Cesar, *Vice Pres*
EMP: 28 **EST:** 1988
SQ FT: 25,000
SALES (est): 5.9MM **Privately Held**
WEB: www.capehornboats.com
SIC: 3732 Boats, fiberglass: building & repairing

(G-12731)
FABIO NAPOLEONI ARTWORKS
2701 Gretagreen Ct (32835-6159)
PHONE..................................207 952-1561
Fabio Napoleoni, *Principal*
EMP: 7 **EST:** 2014
SALES (est): 263.4K **Privately Held**
WEB: www.fabionapoleoni.com
SIC: 2741 Miscellaneous publishing

(G-12732)
FANTASY CHOCOLATES INC
Also Called: Williams & Bennett
1815 Cypress Lake Dr (32837-8457)
PHONE..................................561 276-9007
Becky Gardner, *President*
William Gardner, *Vice Pres*
EMP: 50 **EST:** 1994
SQ FT: 30,000
SALES (est): 15MM
SALES (corp-wide): 519.4MM **Publicly Held**
WEB: www.williamsandbennett.com
SIC: 2066 Chocolate
HQ: Bbx Capital Corporation
401 E Las Olas Blvd Fl 8
Fort Lauderdale FL 33301

(G-12733)
FANTO GROUP LLC (PA)
7022 Tpc Dr Ste 550 (32822-5174)
PHONE..................................407 857-5101
William Eickenberg, *General Mgr*
Tom Sublette, *Vice Pres*
Sandra Esquivel, *Project Mgr*
Cheryl Henning, *Project Mgr*
Christopher O 'steen, *Project Mgr*
◆ **EMP:** 11 **EST:** 2004
SALES (est): 3.4MM **Privately Held**
WEB: www.fantogroup.com
SIC: 3648 Lighting equipment

(G-12734)
FASTSIGNS
5125 The Oaks Cir (32809-3050)
PHONE..................................903 629-7204
EMP: 6 **EST:** 2018
SALES (est): 91.7K **Privately Held**
WEB: www.fastsigns.com
SIC: 3993 Signs & advertising specialties

(G-12735)
FCS INDUSTRIES CORP
6996 Piazza Grande Ave # 314 (32835-8756)
PHONE..................................407 412-5642
Willie Daniel Fisher, *Owner*
EMP: 7 **EST:** 2015
SALES (est): 798.5K **Privately Held**
WEB: www.palhumanesociety.org
SIC: 3999 Manufacturing industries

(G-12736)
FERMATEX ENTERPRISES INC
Also Called: Royal Press
685 S Rnald Reagan Blvd (32808)
PHONE..................................407 332-8320
Luis Quiroz, *President*
EMP: 7 **EST:** 1983
SQ FT: 2,300

GEOGRAPHIC

SALES (est): 1.1MM **Privately Held**
WEB: www.royalpressonline.com
SIC: 2752 Commercial printing, offset

(G-12737)
FGT CABINETRY LLC
1031 Crews Comm Dr Ste 13 (32837)
PHONE..................................321 800-2036
Jinming Fang,
Xin Jiang,
EMP: 9 **EST:** 2018
SALES (est): 740.8K **Privately Held**
WEB: www.fgtcabinetry.com
SIC: 2434 Wood kitchen cabinets

(G-12738)
FILTA GROUP INC (PA)
7075 Kingspointe Pkwy # 1 (32819-6541)
PHONE..................................407 996-5550
Tom Dunn, *CEO*
Victor Clewes, *President*
Colin Hecht, *General Mgr*
Rob Totten, *COO*
John Lopez, *Vice Pres*
◆ **EMP:** 16 **EST:** 2003
SQ FT: 12,000
SALES (est): 6.5MM **Privately Held**
WEB: www.gofilta.com
SIC: 3677 Filtration devices, electronic

(G-12739)
FINASTRA USA CORPORATION
8010 Sunport Dr Ste 101 (32809-7897)
PHONE..................................800 394-8778
Michelle Willis, *Branch Mgr*
EMP: 75
SALES (corp-wide): 1.6B **Privately Held**
WEB: www.finastra.com
SIC: 7372 Prepackaged software
HQ: Finastra Usa Corporation
555 Sw Morrison St # 300
Portland OR 97204
407 804-6600

(G-12740)
FIRETAINMENT INC
2475 N John Young Pkwy (32804-4123)
PHONE..................................888 552-7897
Shawn Clark, *CEO*
EMP: 9
SALES: 1.1MM **Privately Held**
WEB: www.firetainment.com
SIC: 3631 Barbecues, grills & braziers (outdoor cooking)

(G-12741)
FIRST CHECK DIAGNOSTICS LLC
30 S Keller Rd Ste 100 (32810-6297)
PHONE..................................858 805-2425
EMP: 46 **EST:** 2007
SALES (est): 2.4MM
SALES (corp-wide): 34.6B **Publicly Held**
WEB: www.abbott.com
SIC: 3841 Diagnostic apparatus, medical
PA: Abbott Laboratories
100 Abbott Park Rd
Abbott Park IL 60064
224 667-6100

(G-12742)
FL PRECAST LLC
12679 Maribou Cir (32828-7120)
PHONE..................................321 356-9673
Victor S Vallejo R, *President*
Victor Vallejo,
EMP: 8 **EST:** 2016
SALES (est): 411.8K **Privately Held**
SIC: 3272 Window sills, cast stone

(G-12743)
FLEX BEAUTY LABS LLC
7512 Dr Phillips Blvd (32819-5131)
PHONE..................................646 302-8542
George Mandras,
Christopher Mandras,
Lauren Mandras,
EMP: 13 **EST:** 2017
SALES (est): 3MM **Privately Held**
WEB: www.flexbeautylabs.com
SIC: 3999 Hair & hair-based products

(G-12744)
FLEX PACK USA LLC
1205 Pine Ave (32824-7937)
PHONE..................................407 704-0800
Intaaf Ali, *Mng Member*
EMP: 5 **EST:** 2015
SALES (est): 400K **Privately Held**
WEB: www.flexpackusallc.com
SIC: 2631 Container, packaging & boxboard

(G-12745)
FLOOR TECH LLC
Also Called: All State Pallets
9801 Recycle Center Rd (32824-8151)
PHONE..................................407 855-8087
Robert Zuchowski, *COO*
Kyle Zuchowski, *Mng Member*
Mark Hayes,
EMP: 15 **EST:** 1983
SQ FT: 7,110
SALES (est): 2.4MM **Privately Held**
WEB: www.allstatepallets.com
SIC: 2448 Pallets, wood; pallets, wood & wood with metal

(G-12746)
FLORIDA BUS UNLIMITED INC
1925 W Princeton St (32804-4705)
PHONE..................................407 656-1175
James Bay, *President*
Jeffrey Slack, *Vice Pres*
Michael Stotler, *Vice Pres*
Tod Chapman, *Admin Sec*
EMP: 22 **EST:** 1981
SQ FT: 38,000
SALES (est): 511.1K **Privately Held**
SIC: 3711 5561 Buses, all types, assembly of; recreational vehicle dealers

(G-12747)
FLORIDA CATHOLIC MEDIA INC
50 E Robinson St (32801-1619)
P.O. Box 4993 (32802-4993)
PHONE..................................407 373-0075
Ann B Slade Publisher, *Principal*
Maurice Beaulieu, *Editor*
Susan Hunt, *CFO*
Carolyn Ell, *Accountant*
Valerie Casko, *Advt Staff*
EMP: 6 **EST:** 1939
SALES (est): 1.1MM **Privately Held**
WEB: www.thefloridacatholic.org
SIC: 2711 8661 Newspapers: publishing only, not printed on site; religious organizations

(G-12748)
FLORIDA COPIER CONNECTIONS
Also Called: Green Holness
8022 Office Ct Ste 100 (32809-6768)
PHONE..................................407 844-9690
Green Holness, *President*
EMP: 9 **EST:** 2009
SQ FT: 13,000
SALES (est): 218.2K **Privately Held**
WEB: www.copiersflorida.com
SIC: 3861 Photocopy machines

(G-12749)
FLORIDA HOSPITAL ASSN MGT CORP
Also Called: Park Lake Printers
827 Highland Ave (32803-3919)
PHONE..................................407 841-6230
Frances Owens, *Principal*
John Mines, *Vice Pres*
Rebecca Ryan, *Admin Asst*
EMP: 6
SALES (est): 110K **Privately Held**
WEB: www.fha.org
SIC: 2752 Commercial printing, lithographic

(G-12750)
FLORIDA JERKY ENTERPRISES INC
14025 Budworth Cir (32832-6123)
PHONE..................................256 682-2959
EMP: 6 **EST:** 2019
SALES (est): 93.8K **Privately Held**
SIC: 2013 Snack sticks, including jerky: from purchased meat

(G-12751)
FLORIDA NONWOVENS INC
1111 Central Florida Pkwy (32837-9258)
PHONE..................................407 241-2701
Dan Dobbins, *CEO*
Mike Wood, *Vice Pres*
◆ **EMP:** 18 **EST:** 1998
SALES (est): 466.4K **Privately Held**
SIC: 3299 Ceramic fiber

(G-12752)
FLORIDA PILLOW COMPANY
1012 Sligh Blvd (32806-1029)
PHONE..................................407 648-9121
Chris A Allard, *President*
Christopher Allard, *Owner*
▼ **EMP:** 5 **EST:** 1982
SQ FT: 4,700
SALES (est): 590K **Privately Held**
WEB: www.floridapillow.com
SIC: 2392 Cushions & pillows; pillows, bed: made from purchased materials

(G-12753)
FLORIDA PRNTS BLIND CHLDREN IN
1431 Spring Fest Ln (32828-7454)
PHONE..................................407 257-7637
EMP: 6 **EST:** 2019
SALES (est): 99.4K **Privately Held**
SIC: 2591 Window blinds

(G-12754)
FLORIDA PWRTRAIN HYDRULICS INC
4455 Dardanelle Dr (32808-3850)
PHONE..................................407 291-1441
Tommy Goul, *Manager*
EMP: 6
SALES (corp-wide): 6.2MM **Privately Held**
WEB: www.floridapowertrain.com
SIC: 3714 Motor vehicle parts & accessories
PA: Florida Powertrain & Hydraulics, Inc.
2265 W Beaver St
Jacksonville FL 32209
904 354-5691

(G-12755)
FLORIDA SCREEN SERVICES INC
805 W Central Blvd (32805-1808)
PHONE..................................407 316-0466
Gil Adkins, *President*
Linda Adkins, *Corp Secy*
Steven Adkins, *Vice Pres*
Smith Lawrence W, *Vice Pres*
Heather Adkins, *Manager*
EMP: 10 **EST:** 1980
SQ FT: 6,000
SALES (est): 641.2K **Privately Held**
SIC: 2759 2396 Screen printing; automotive & apparel trimmings

(G-12756)
FLORIDA SIGN SOURCE
505 W Robinson St (32801-1721)
P.O. Box 521135, Longwood (32752-1135)
PHONE..................................407 316-0466
Stephen Adkins, *Principal*
EMP: 5 **EST:** 2011
SALES (est): 407.4K **Privately Held**
WEB: www.floridasignsource.com
SIC: 3993 Signs & advertising specialties

(G-12757)
FLORIDA SUNSHINE STUCCO LLC
9484 Boggy Creek Rd (32824-8720)
PHONE..................................407 947-2088
Milena C Neal, *Principal*
EMP: 6 **EST:** 2008
SALES (est): 85K **Privately Held**
SIC: 3299 Stucco

(G-12758)
FLORIDA TRUSS CORPORATION
1302 Abberton Dr (32837-6520)
PHONE..................................407 438-2553
Carlos A Mendez, *Principal*
EMP: 8 **EST:** 2012
SALES (est): 363.6K **Privately Held**
WEB: www.floridatrusscorp.com
SIC: 2439 Structural wood members

(G-12759)
FLORIDA WIRE & RIGGING SUP INC
4524 36th St (32811-6526)
P.O. Box 180127, Casselberry (32718-0127)
PHONE..................................407 422-6218
Ronald J Worswick, *President*
Scott Battaglia, *General Mgr*
Dennis E Worswick, *Senior VP*
Douglas Worswick, *Senior VP*
Connie Gahnz, *CFO*
▼ **EMP:** 7 **EST:** 1968
SQ FT: 6,180
SALES (est): 1.1MM **Privately Held**
WEB: www.floridawire.com
SIC: 3496 Miscellaneous fabricated wire products

(G-12760)
FLOWERS BKG CO BRADENTON LLC
Also Called: Flowers Baking Company
4301 N Pine Hills Rd (32808-2546)
PHONE..................................941 758-5656
Chris Peer, *Manager*
EMP: 25
SALES (corp-wide): 4.3B **Publicly Held**
WEB: www.flobradconf.com
SIC: 2051 Bread, cake & related products
HQ: Flowers Baking Co. Of Bradenton, Llc
6490 Parkland Dr
Sarasota FL 34243

(G-12761)
FONON TECHNOLOGIES INC (PA)
1101 N Keller Rd Ste G (32810-5917)
PHONE..................................407 477-5618
Dmitri Nikitin, *Vice Pres*
Wayne Tupuola, *Vice Pres*
Arnold Bykov, *Director*
EMP: 24 **EST:** 2013
SQ FT: 45,000
SALES (est): 2.3MM **Publicly Held**
WEB: www.fonon.us
SIC: 3699 Laser welding, drilling & cutting equipment; laser systems & equipment

(G-12762)
FORM-CO INC
2487 Tradeport Dr Ste 200 (32824-7067)
PHONE..................................800 745-3700
Jeffrey D Church, *Principal*
EMP: 6 **EST:** 2010
SALES (est): 123.4K **Privately Held**
SIC: 3531 Construction machinery

(G-12763)
FRESH CHOICE MA RKET
10249 S John Young Pkwy (32837-4022)
PHONE..................................407 448-8956
Amine Harb, *Principal*
EMP: 8 **EST:** 2011
SALES (est): 245.3K **Privately Held**
SIC: 3421 Table & food cutlery, including butchers'

(G-12764)
FRESH INK PRINT LLC
Also Called: Fresh Ink Signs & Graphics
4729 Patch Rd Ste 200 (32822-3579)
PHONE..................................407 412-5905
Carlos A Rivero, *Manager*
Deann Kroeplin, *Manager*
Christian Stanley, *Manager*
EMP: 6 **EST:** 2012
SQ FT: 3,800
SALES (est): 773.2K **Privately Held**
WEB: www.freshinkorlando.com
SIC: 3993 7336 Electric signs; signs, not made in custom sign painting shops; graphic arts & related design

(G-12765)
FRESHETECH LLC
1211 Pine Ave (32824-7937)
PHONE..................................516 519-3453
Mike Pyle, *Vice Pres*
Adam Schwartz, *Mng Member*
Robinson Rob, *Manager*
EMP: 8 **EST:** 2013

SALES (est): 2.7MM **Privately Held**
WEB: www.freshe.tech
SIC: 3651 Home entertainment equipment, electronic

(G-12766)
FRITO-LAY NORTH AMERICA INC
2800 Silver Star Rd (32808-3941)
PHONE..................................407 295-1810
Tamara Kimball, *Sales Staff*
Leslie Starr, *Branch Mgr*
Kristina Casanova, *Manager*
Bob Zak, *Manager*
Angela Jerry, *Technical Staff*
EMP: 6
SQ FT: 175,562
SALES (corp-wide): 70.3B **Publicly Held**
WEB: www.fritolay.com
SIC: 2096 2099 Potato chips & similar snacks; food preparations
HQ: Frito-Lay North America, Inc.
7701 Legacy Dr
Plano TX 75024

(G-12767)
FW SHORING COMPANY
Also Called: Professional Shoring & Supply
11128 Boggy Creek Rd (32824-7415)
PHONE..................................517 676-8800
Wayne Agamie, *Branch Mgr*
EMP: 9
SALES (corp-wide): 23.4MM **Privately Held**
WEB: www.efficiencyproduction.com
SIC: 3531 Construction machinery
PA: Fw Shoring Company
685 Hull Rd
Mason MI 48854
517 676-8800

(G-12768)
FWS DISTRIBUTORS LLC
Also Called: Progress Wine Group
4653 L B Mcleod Rd Ste B (32811-5603)
PHONE..................................305 677-9663
Roberto Camacho, *Branch Mgr*
EMP: 8
SALES (corp-wide): 2.3MM **Privately Held**
SIC: 2084 Wines
PA: Fws Distributors, Llc
14501 Nw 57th Ave Ste 113
Miami FL 33014
561 312-3318

(G-12769)
G J EMBROIDERY INC
6839 Narcoossee Rd Ste 33 (32822-5581)
PHONE..................................407 284-8036
Basem E Farag, *Principal*
EMP: 5 **EST:** 2015
SALES (est): 303.3K **Privately Held**
WEB: www.gjembroidery.com
SIC: 2395 Embroidery products, except schiffli machine

(G-12770)
GAM LASER INC (PA)
7100 Tpc Dr Ste 200 (32822-5125)
PHONE..................................407 851-8999
Gordon A Murray, *President*
Joseph Batcho, *Marketing Mgr*
Ray Lambert, *Manager*
EMP: 10 **EST:** 1986
SQ FT: 8,000
SALES (est): 1.1MM **Privately Held**
WEB: www.gamlaser.com
SIC: 3826 Laser scientific & engineering instruments

(G-12771)
GAS TURBINE EFFICIENCY INC
Also Called: GTE
300 Sunport Ln Ste 100 (32809-8121)
PHONE..................................407 304-5200
Steven Zwolinski, *Principal*
Chris Watson, *Principal*
EMP: 50 **EST:** 2005
SQ FT: 60,000
SALES (est): 27.4MM
SALES (corp-wide): 7.5B **Privately Held**
WEB: www.gtefficiency.com
SIC: 3511 Steam turbines
PA: John Wood Group Plc
15 Justice Mill Lane
Aberdeen AB11
122 485-1000

(G-12772)
GAS TURBINE EFFICIENCY LLC
Also Called: GTE
300 Sunport Ln Ste 100 (32809-8121)
PHONE..................................407 304-5200
Steven Zwolinski, *CEO*
John Brooks, *President*
Jorge Cadena, *President*
Michael Thomas, *President*
Bob Knott, *Vice Pres*
EMP: 50 **EST:** 1999
SQ FT: 60,000
SALES (est): 30.5MM
SALES (corp-wide): 7.5B **Privately Held**
WEB: www.gtefficiency.com
SIC: 3823 8711 5084 3613 Industrial process measurement equipment; petroleum engineering; industrial machinery & equipment; switchgear & switchboard apparatus; steam turbines
PA: John Wood Group Plc
15 Justice Mill Lane
Aberdeen AB11
122 485-1000

(G-12773)
GB BRICK PAVERS INC
4409 S Kirkman Rd Apt 303 (32811-2827)
PHONE..................................407 453-5505
Eraldo J Benedito, *Principal*
EMP: 7 **EST:** 2006
SALES (est): 131.7K **Privately Held**
WEB: www.totalbrickpavers.com
SIC: 2951 Asphalt paving mixtures & blocks

(G-12774)
GELTECH INC
2603 Challenger Tech Ct # 100 (32826-2716)
PHONE..................................407 382-4003
Dr Jean-Luz Nogues, *Vice Pres*
Pamela Hood, *Purchasing*
EMP: 54 **EST:** 1985
SQ FT: 22,000
SALES (est): 1.1MM
SALES (corp-wide): 38.4MM **Publicly Held**
WEB: www.lightpath.com
SIC: 3231 Products of purchased glass
PA: Lightpath Technologies, Inc.
2603 Challenger Tech Ct
Orlando FL 32826
407 382-4003

(G-12775)
GEM ASSET ACQUISITION LLC
Also Called: Gemseal Pvments Pdts - Orlando
6441 Pinecastle Blvd (32809-6673)
PHONE..................................407 888-2080
EMP: 17
SALES (corp-wide): 31.7MM **Privately Held**
SIC: 2951 Asphalt paving mixtures & blocks
PA: Gem Asset Acquisition Llc
1855 Lindbergh St Ste 500
Charlotte NC 28208
704 225-3321

(G-12776)
GENCOR INDUSTRIES INC (PA)
5201 N Orange Blossom Trl (32810-1038)
PHONE..................................407 290-6000
John E Elliott, *CEO*
E J Elliott, *Ch of Bd*
Marc G Elliott, *President*
Dennis B Hunt, *Senior VP*
Eric E Mellen, *CFO*
EMP: 200 **EST:** 1968
SQ FT: 215,000
SALES: 77.4MM **Publicly Held**
WEB: www.gencor.com
SIC: 3531 3823 3443 Asphalt plant, including gravel-mix type; combustion control instruments; heat exchangers, condensers & components

(G-12777)
GENERAL CLAMP INDUSTRIES INC
Also Called: United States Crene
1155 Central Florida Pkwy (32837-9258)
P.O. Box 593290 (32859-3290)
PHONE..................................407 859-6000
Rick Ridley, *CEO*
Linda Ames, *President*
EMP: 11 **EST:** 1994
SALES (est): 558.4K **Privately Held**
WEB: www.superclamp.com
SIC: 3531 3429 Ladder ditchers, vertical boom or wheel; manufactured hardware (general)

(G-12778)
GENERAL DYNAMICS CORPORATION
3275 Progress Dr (32826-2932)
PHONE..................................407 380-9384
EMP: 44
SALES (corp-wide): 31.3B **Publicly Held**
SIC: 3731 Shipbuilding And Repairing
PA: General Dynamics Corporation
2941 Frview Pk Dr Ste 100
Falls Church VA 20190
703 876-3000

(G-12779)
GENERAL DYNMICS MSSION SYSTEMS
12001 Res Pkwy Ste 500 (32826)
PHONE..................................407 823-7000
Robert Parrish, *Chief Engr*
Tom Bates, *Engineer*
Michael Burman, *Engineer*
Paul Cailleteau, *Engineer*
Judd Cheatwood, *Engineer*
EMP: 25
SALES (corp-wide): 37.9B **Publicly Held**
WEB: www.gdmissionsystems.com
SIC: 3571 Electronic computers
HQ: General Dynamics Mission Systems, Inc.
12450 Fair Lakes Cir
Fairfax VA 22033
877 449-0600

(G-12780)
GENERATOR SUPERCENTER ORLANDO
3071 N Orange Blossom Trl (32804-3468)
PHONE..................................407 984-5000
EMP: 6 **EST:** 2019
SALES (est): 539.1K **Privately Held**
SIC: 3621 Motors & generators

(G-12781)
GENESIS REFERENCE LABORATORIES
7924 Forest Cy Rd Ste 210 (32810)
PHONE..................................407 232-7130
Ernest Traynham, *CEO*
Ernest Fisher, *CEO*
Chris Hansen, *Managing Prtnr*
EMP: 100 **EST:** 2015
SALES (est): 13.5MM **Privately Held**
WEB: www.genesisreferencelabs.com
SIC: 3821 8734 Clinical laboratory instruments, except medical & dental; testing laboratories

(G-12782)
GENICON INC
2455 Ridgemoor Dr (32828-7513)
PHONE..................................407 657-4851
Jim Kirchberg, *Vice Pres*
Ken Roger, *Prdtn Mgr*
Nathan Baker, *Production*
Dario N Vitali, *Engineer*
Daniel Doerr, *Design Engr*
EMP: 45 **EST:** 2013
SALES (est): 5.5MM **Privately Held**
WEB: www.geniconendo.com
SIC: 3841 Surgical & medical instruments

(G-12783)
GEORGE BIRNEY JR
6714 Bouganvillea Cres Dr (32809-6615)
PHONE..................................407 851-5604
George Birney, *Principal*
EMP: 7 **EST:** 2007
SALES (est): 172.4K **Privately Held**
SIC: 3423 Jewelers' hand tools

(G-12784)
GLORY SANDBLASTING INC
Also Called: Glory Company
2922 38th St (32839-8631)
PHONE..................................407 422-0078
Linda Marjama, *CEO*
James Marjama, *Vice Pres*
Fernando Ortiz, *Manager*
EMP: 11 **EST:** 1982
SQ FT: 12,000
SALES (est): 1.1MM **Privately Held**
WEB: www.glorysandblasting.com
SIC: 3479 1721 Coating of metals & formed products; exterior commercial painting contractor

(G-12785)
GOEN3 CORPORATION (PA)
Also Called: Invel
6555 Sanger Rd Ste 100 (32827-7585)
PHONE..................................407 601-6000
Carla H Taba, *CEO*
EMP: 9 **EST:** 2015
SALES (est): 654K **Privately Held**
SIC: 2325 2331 Men's & boys' trousers & slacks; blouses, women's & juniors': made from purchased material

(G-12786)
GOLOSO FOOD LLC
Also Called: Gran Savana USA
1700 35th St Ste 107 (32839-8950)
PHONE..................................321 277-2055
Leo Calligaro,
Johanna Bracho,
▼ **EMP:** 9 **EST:** 2012
SALES (est): 2.5MM **Privately Held**
SIC: 2022 5143 Cheese, natural & processed; cheese

(G-12787)
GRANDSTAND PUBLISHING LLC
Also Called: Baseball Digest
390 N Orange Ave Ste 2300 (32801-1684)
PHONE..................................847 491-6440
Norman Jacobs, *Publisher*
EMP: 7 **EST:** 2012
SALES (est): 629.9K **Privately Held**
WEB: www.baseballdigest.com
SIC: 2721 Magazines: publishing only, not printed on site

(G-12788)
GREAT HSE MDIA GROUP OF PBLS I
Also Called: Media Publishing
4449 Riverton Dr (32817-1451)
P.O. Box 780172 (32878-0172)
PHONE..................................407 779-3846
Michael O Lattiboudeaire, *CEO*
EMP: 10 **EST:** 2016
SALES (est): 397.3K **Privately Held**
SIC: 2741 7929 8661 5963 Miscellaneous publishing; entertainment group; Pentecostal Church; encyclopedias & publications, direct sales; book publishing

(G-12789)
GRIFFIN INDUSTRIES LLC
408 W Landstreet Rd (32824-7805)
PHONE..................................407 857-5474
Dennis Griffin, *Chairman*
EMP: 49
SQ FT: 8,728
SALES (corp-wide): 3.3B **Publicly Held**
WEB: www.griffinind.com
SIC: 2077 Animal & marine fats & oils
HQ: Griffin Industries Llc
4221 Alexandria Pike
Cold Spring KY 41076
859 781-2010

(G-12790)
GRIFFITHS CORPORATION
Also Called: Wrico Stamping Co of Florida
10659 Rocket Blvd (32824-8517)
PHONE..................................407 851-8342
Richard Albright, *Principal*
William Krichman, *Info Tech Mgr*
Jerry Wilson, *Executive*
EMP: 87
SQ FT: 34,500

SALES (corp-wide): 147.9MM **Privately Held**
WEB: www.griffithscorp.com
SIC: 3469 7692 Stamping metal for the trade; welding repair
HQ: Griffiths Corporation
2717 Niagara Ln N
Minneapolis MN 55447
763 557-8935

(G-12791)
GWB COATINGS LLC
3612 Danby Ct (32812-6018)
PHONE..................................407 271-7732
Gary Baxter, *Principal*
EMP: 6 **EST:** 2016
SALES (est): 108.8K **Privately Held**
WEB: www.gwbcoatings.com
SIC: 3479 Metal coating & allied service

(G-12792)
H & H PRINTING INC
1406 W Washington St (32805-1738)
P.O. Box 560176 (32856-0176)
PHONE..................................407 422-2932
Ronald Hoevenaar, *CEO*
Chris Hoevenaar, *Vice Pres*
Lucille Hoevenaar, *Vice Pres*
Yvonne Hoevenaar, *Admin Sec*
EMP: 10 **EST:** 1963
SQ FT: 5,400
SALES (est): 435.7K **Privately Held**
WEB: www.hhprintinginc.com
SIC: 2752 2759 2789 Commercial printing, offset; commercial printing; bookbinding & related work

(G-12793)
H & H PRODUCTS COMPANY
6600 Magnolia Homes Rd (32810-4285)
PHONE..................................407 299-5410
Morris L Hartley, *President*
Morris L Hartley Jr, *Vice Pres*
Clayton Morris, *CFO*
Emily Hauptvogel, *Sales Staff*
Nicole Ostrowski, *Sales Staff*
EMP: 26 **EST:** 1964
SQ FT: 40,500
SALES (est): 6.3MM **Privately Held**
WEB: www.hhproductscompany.com
SIC: 2086 2087 Fruit drinks (less than 100% juice): packaged in cans, etc.; syrups, flavoring (except drink); concentrates, drink

(G-12794)
HALLIDAY PRODUCTS INC
6401 Edgewater Dr (32810-4293)
PHONE..................................407 298-4470
Don Ahlberg, *President*
Chris Halliday, *Vice Pres*
Patrick H Hanley, *Plant Supt*
Trey Freeland, *Plant Mgr*
Casey McCoy, *Sales Staff*
▼ **EMP:** 55 **EST:** 1966
SQ FT: 60,000
SALES (est): 8.5MM **Privately Held**
WEB: www.hallidayproducts.com
SIC: 3442 3321 3446 3444 Metal doors, sash & trim; manhole covers, metal; architectural metalwork; sheet metalwork; fabricated plate work (boiler shop); manufactured hardware (general)

(G-12795)
HARVEST MOON DISTRIBUTORS LLC
3450 Parkway Center Ct (32808-1012)
PHONE..................................321 297-7942
Cherie L Rivett, *Principal*
Gloria Richards, *Principal*
Cherie Rivett, *Principal*
David Graeser, *Sales Staff*
▲ **EMP:** 5 **EST:** 2012
SALES (est): 938.8K **Privately Held**
SIC: 2084 Wines, brandy & brandy spirits

(G-12796)
HATALOM CORPORATION
3505 Lake Lynda Dr # 200 (32817-8324)
PHONE..................................407 567-2556
John Hinnant, *CEO*
EMP: 30 **EST:** 2017
SQ FT: 1,000
SALES (est): 2.8MM **Privately Held**
WEB: www.hatalom.com
SIC: 3571 3572 7379 8742 Computers, digital, analog or hybrid; computer storage devices; computer related maintenance services; materials mgmt. (purchasing, handling, inventory) consultant; computer software development; systems engineering consultant, ex. computer or professional

(G-12797)
HELOU REGINO PUBLISHER LLC
7061 Grand National Dr 105b (32819-8395)
PHONE..................................407 370-7300
Garufi Paula, *Principal*
EMP: 6 **EST:** 2014
SALES (est): 112.7K **Privately Held**
WEB: www.lifeseedbooks.com
SIC: 2741 Miscellaneous publishing

(G-12798)
HELPING ADLSCNTS LIVE OPTMSTCL
Also Called: H.A.L.o
4844 Cason Cove Dr # 204 (32811-6309)
PHONE..................................407 257-8221
Amanda Jenkins, *President*
▲ **EMP:** 7 **EST:** 2012
SALES (est): 72K **Privately Held**
SIC: 3272 Furniture, church: concrete

(G-12799)
HEROAL USA INC
7022 Tpc Dr Ste 100 (32822-5139)
PHONE..................................888 437-6257
Sarah Koring, *Vice Pres*
EMP: 800 **EST:** 2016
SALES (est): 18.5MM **Privately Held**
WEB: www.heroal.de
SIC: 3365 Machinery castings, aluminum

(G-12800)
HG BROKERAGE SERVICES INC
2813 S Hiawassee Rd # 301 (32835-6690)
PHONE..................................407 294-3507
Enrique I Gonzalez, *President*
Migdalia S Gonzalez, *Vice Pres*
EMP: 6 **EST:** 2010
SALES (est): 1.1MM **Privately Held**
SIC: 2656 Frozen food containers: made from purchased material

(G-12801)
HG2 EMERGENCY LIGHTING LLC
477 N Semoran Blvd (32807-3323)
PHONE..................................407 426-7700
Monsour Baker, *Principal*
Helen Rosario, *Controller*
Susan Tatum, *Accounts Exec*
Bhojani Ali, *Sales Staff*
Cory Fisher, *Mktg Dir*
EMP: 10 **EST:** 2010
SALES (est): 1.6MM **Privately Held**
WEB: www.hg2lighting.com
SIC: 3647 Vehicular lighting equipment

(G-12802)
HI TECH GRANITE AND MARBLE
11362 Space Blvd (32837-9265)
PHONE..................................407 230-4363
Keith Damario, *Manager*
EMP: 5 **EST:** 2011
SALES (est): 413.1K **Privately Held**
WEB: www.hitechgranite.com
SIC: 3281 Granite, cut & shaped

(G-12803)
HIGHVAC CO LLC
Also Called: Amazonia Marine Products
3842 Commerce Loop (32808-3818)
PHONE..................................407 969-0399
Bob Ghamandi,
EMP: 12 **EST:** 2002
SALES (est): 950K **Privately Held**
WEB: www.highvacco.com
SIC: 3541 Machine tools, metal cutting type

(G-12804)
HM FROYOS LLC
8204 Firenze Blvd (32836-8767)
PHONE..................................561 339-0603
Omar Vaid, *Principal*
EMP: 6 **EST:** 2014
SALES (est): 127.5K **Privately Held**
SIC: 2024 Yogurt desserts, frozen

(G-12805)
HMH PUBLISHING CO INC
9400 Southpark Ctr Loop (32819-8647)
PHONE..................................617 351-5000
Gordon Crovitz, *Director*
EMP: 59 **EST:** 2010
SALES (est): 13.5MM
SALES (corp-wide): 1B **Publicly Held**
WEB: www.ir.hmhco.com
SIC: 2741 Miscellaneous publishing
PA: Houghton Mifflin Harcourt Company
125 High St Ste 900
Boston MA 02110
617 351-5000

(G-12806)
HOLLYWOOD CLLCTIBLES GROUP LLC
11491 Rocket Blvd (32824-8514)
PHONE..................................407 985-4613
Mark Hilliard, *President*
Linda Hiltonv, *Vice Pres*
▲ **EMP:** 6 **EST:** 2005
SALES (est): 537.7K **Privately Held**
WEB: www.hollywood-collectibles.com
SIC: 3999 5961 7389 Models, general, except toy; miniatures; collectibles & antiques, mail order;

(G-12807)
HOLOVIS INTERNA TIONAL
7380 W Sand Lake Rd (32819-5248)
PHONE..................................407 286-3976
EMP: 6 **EST:** 2017
SALES (est): 155.4K **Privately Held**
WEB: www.holovis.com
SIC: 3699 Teaching machines & aids, electronic

(G-12808)
HONE RENOVATION SPECIALISTS
10760 Emerald Chase Dr (32836-5880)
PHONE..................................407 202-3536
Douglas C Pavlic, *President*
EMP: 6 **EST:** 2016
SALES (est): 60.1K **Privately Held**
SIC: 3291 Hones

(G-12809)
HOOSIER LIGHTENING INC
2415 N John Young Pkwy (32804-4105)
PHONE..................................407 290-3323
David Elkins, *Principal*
EMP: 7 **EST:** 2000
SALES (est): 125.7K **Privately Held**
WEB: www.hoosier.aaa.com
SIC: 3648 Lighting equipment

(G-12810)
HOTSPRAY INDUSTRIAL COATINGS
1932 N Goldenrod Rd (32807-8406)
PHONE..................................407 658-5700
Lyle Cummings, *President*
Steve Gibbs, *Manager*
EMP: 10 **EST:** 1997
SQ FT: 3,000
SALES (est): 1MM **Privately Held**
WEB: www.hotspray.com
SIC: 2851 Lacquers, varnishes, enamels & other coatings

(G-12811)
HOUGHTON MIFFLIN HARCOURT
9400 S Park Loop (32819)
PHONE..................................407 345-2000
Diane Lampitt, *President*
Javan Walker, *Financial Analy*
Rudi Ali, *Webmaster*
EMP: 55 **EST:** 2001
SALES (est): 4.8MM **Privately Held**
WEB: www.hmhco.com
SIC: 2731 Book publishing

(G-12812)
HOUSE PLASTICS UNLIMITED INC
2580 S Orange Blossom Trl (32805-5455)
PHONE..................................407 843-3290
John J Davis, *CEO*
Todd Davis, *President*
Jeanne Davis, *Corp Secy*
Victor Velez, *Sales Executive*
EMP: 20 **EST:** 1969
SQ FT: 14,000
SALES (est): 4.7MM **Privately Held**
SIC: 3089 Injection molding of plastics; plastic processing

(G-12813)
HP PREFERRED LTD PARTNERS
Also Called: Halliday Product
6401 Edgewater Dr (32810-4203)
PHONE..................................407 298-4470
Doug Halliday, *Partner*
Tre Freeland, *Vice Pres*
Marc Semones, *Sales Staff*
Earl Sande, *Marketing Staff*
Donna Willis, *Marketing Staff*
EMP: 13 **EST:** 1970
SALES (est): 383K **Privately Held**
WEB: www.hallidayproducts.com
SIC: 3365 Aluminum foundries

(G-12814)
HUGHES TRIM LLC
7613 Currency Dr (32809-6924)
PHONE..................................863 206-6048
Don Pool, *VP Opers*
Benjamin Worth, *Mng Member*
EMP: 75 **EST:** 2008
SALES (est): 3.6MM **Privately Held**
WEB: www.hughestrim.com
SIC: 2431 1751 Moldings, wood: unfinished & prefinished; staircases, stairs & railings; carpentry work

(G-12815)
HYLTON & ASSOC
1449 Sackett Cir (32818-9066)
PHONE..................................321 303-2862
Rohan Hylton, *President*
EMP: 6 **EST:** 1989
SALES (est): 396.1K **Privately Held**
SIC: 3581 Automatic vending machines

(G-12816)
I FIX & CASES LLC
11068 Smmrspring Lakes Dr (32825-7403)
PHONE..................................939 645-5252
David Vazquez, *Principal*
EMP: 6 **EST:** 2018
SALES (est): 385.2K **Privately Held**
SIC: 3523 Farm machinery & equipment

(G-12817)
I-ACRITAS LLC
118 E Jefferson St Fl 3 (32801-1828)
PHONE..................................407 375-5707
Joe Seebach, *Principal*
EMP: 6 **EST:** 2015
SALES (est): 119.6K **Privately Held**
WEB: www.iacritas.com
SIC: 3663 Radio & TV communications equipment

(G-12818)
IAIRE LLC
2100 Consulate Dr Ste 102 (32837-8397)
PHONE..................................407 873-2538
Chuck Eno, *Vice Pres*
EMP: 7
SALES (corp-wide): 5MM **Privately Held**
WEB: www.myiaire.com
SIC: 3564 Air purification equipment
PA: Iaire, Llc
6805 Hillsdale Ct
Indianapolis IN 46250
317 806-2750

(G-12819)
ICE MAGIC-ORLANDO INC (PA)
Also Called: Ice Magic Holdings
9468 American Eagle Way # 100 (32837-8380)
PHONE..................................407 816-1905
William Whidden, *President*
◆ **EMP:** 64 **EST:** 1996

SALES (est): 621.2K **Privately Held**
WEB: www.questevents.com
SIC: 2097 Manufactured ice

(G-12820)
ICLOAK INC
37 N Orange Ave Ste 1025 (32801-2449)
P.O. Box 560474, Montverde (34756-0474)
PHONE..................................407 422-0876
Eric Delisle, *President*
Garrett Clark, *Director*
EMP: 7 **EST:** 2014
SQ FT: 2,000
SALES (est): 278.2K **Privately Held**
WEB: www.icloak.org
SIC: 3577 Input/output equipment, computer

(G-12821)
ID SOLUTIONS INC
9609 Pacific Pines Ct (32832-5928)
PHONE..................................407 823-7710
Tracy Mills, *President*
EMP: 10 **EST:** 2014
SALES (est): 158.6K **Privately Held**
WEB: www.authid.ai
SIC: 3825 Digital panel meters, electricity measuring

(G-12822)
ILSC HOLDINGS LC
Also Called: Katmai Electronic Systems
12001 Science Dr Ste 160 (32826-2916)
PHONE..................................480 935-4230
Melinda Popwell, *Asst Controller*
Don Becker, *Manager*
Lena Delgado, *Administration*
EMP: 8
SALES (corp-wide): 85.3MM **Privately Held**
WEB: www.katmaicorp.com
SIC: 3812 Search & navigation equipment; acceleration indicators & systems components, aerospace
HQ: Ilsc Holdings Lc
11001 Omalley Centre Dr # 204
Anchorage AK 99515

(G-12823)
IMAGINATION ENTERPRISES LLC
Also Called: Magic Candle
7616 Southland Blvd # 102 (32809-6993)
PHONE..................................504 289-9691
Keith Mahne,
EMP: 19 **EST:** 2017
SALES (est): 7MM **Privately Held**
SIC: 3999 5961 Candles; general merchandise, mail order

(G-12824)
IMAGING DIAGNOSTIC SYSTEMS INC
Also Called: (A DEVELOPMENT STAGE COMPANY)
1221 E Robinson St (32801-2115)
PHONE..................................954 581-9800
Linda B Grable, *CEO*
Michael Addley, *COO*
Deborah O'Brien, *Senior VP*
Jose Cisneros, *Research*
David Fong, *CFO*
EMP: 10 **EST:** 1993 **Privately Held**
WEB: www.imds.com
SIC: 3841 Surgical & medical instruments

(G-12825)
IMPRESS INK LLC (PA)
Also Called: Impress Ink Screen Prtg & EMB
540 N Goldenrod Rd Ste A (32807-8295)
PHONE..................................407 982-5646
Michael Cho, *Mng Member*
Xi Guo,
EMP: 15 **EST:** 2009
SALES (est): 350K **Privately Held**
WEB: www.impressink.com
SIC: 2759 Screen printing

(G-12826)
IMPROVED RACING PRODUCTS LLC
4855 Dist Ct Ste 1 (32822)
PHONE..................................407 705-3054
Richard M Ihns,
EMP: 5 **EST:** 2008
SQ FT: 5,500
SALES (est): 779.4K **Privately Held**
WEB: www.improvedracing.com
SIC: 3714 Lubrication systems & parts, motor vehicle

(G-12827)
INDRA SYSTEMS INC
3505 Lake Lynda Dr # 200 (32817-8324)
PHONE..................................407 567-1977
Carlos Acosta, *CEO*
Oznur Vural, *General Mgr*
Eduardo Viaggio, *Senior Engr*
Luis Posada, *Manager*
Pio Cabanillas Alonso, *Director*
▲ **EMP:** 28 **EST:** 2002
SQ FT: 20,000
SALES (est): 18.6MM
SALES (corp-wide): 1.1B **Privately Held**
WEB: www.indracompany.com
SIC: 3825 3699 Test equipment for electronic & electric measurement; flight simulators (training aids), electronic
PA: Indra Sistemas, Sociedad Anonima
Avenida De Bruselas 35
Alcobendas 28108
914 805-000

(G-12828)
INDUSTRIAL SMOKE & MIRRORS INC
Also Called: I S M
3024 Shader Rd (32808-3922)
PHONE..................................407 299-9400
Andrew W Garvis, *President*
Joseph Barnicki, *Opers Staff*
Brian Lynn, *Engineer*
Dennis Wilhelm, *Engineer*
Scott Page, *CFO*
EMP: 42 **EST:** 1995
SQ FT: 35,000
SALES (est): 9.2MM **Privately Held**
WEB: www.industrialsmokeandmirrors.com
SIC: 3699 Security control equipment & systems

(G-12829)
INFINITY SIGNS & GRAPHIX LLC
1887 Central Florida Pkwy (32837-9287)
PHONE..................................407 270-6733
Sal Kalai, *Vice Pres*
EMP: 10 **EST:** 2016
SALES (est): 635.4K **Privately Held**
WEB: www.infinitysignindustries.com
SIC: 3993 Signs & advertising specialties

(G-12830)
INGENUS PHARMACEUTICALS LLC (PA)
4190 Millenia Blvd (32839-6408)
PHONE..................................407 354-5365
Raju Mantena, *CEO*
Andrew Gellman, *President*
Matthew Baumgartner, *CFO*
Brahmaji Valiveti, *Officer*
▲ **EMP:** 10 **EST:** 2009
SALES (est): 18.3MM **Privately Held**
WEB: www.ingenus.com
SIC: 2834 Cough medicines

(G-12831)
INNOVATIVE SVC SOLUTIONS LLC
Also Called: Honeywell Authorized Dealer
3144 N John Young Pkwy (32804-4127)
PHONE..................................407 296-5211
Bart Gedeon, *Opers Staff*
Joe Terry, *Engineer*
Richard A Bodwell, *Mng Member*
Gregory Suarez, *Manager*
Stacie Martucci, *Info Tech Mgr*
EMP: 23 **EST:** 2002
SQ FT: 5,000
SALES (est): 5.1MM **Privately Held**
WEB: www.issmechanical.com
SIC: 3585 7623 Air conditioning equipment, complete; air conditioning repair

(G-12832)
INSTANATURAL LLC
12001 Res Pkwy Ste 244 (32826)
PHONE..................................800 290-6932
Patel Atit, *CEO*
Hannah Balatbat, *Opers Staff*
Ethelbert Williams, *Chief Mktg Ofcr*
Aditya Patel,
Ajay Patel,
EMP: 40 **EST:** 2013
SALES (est): 2.5MM **Privately Held**
WEB: www.instanatural.com
SIC: 2844 5122 Cosmetic preparations; cosmetics

(G-12833)
INSTANT IMPRINTS
1915 Crown Hill Blvd (32828-7430)
PHONE..................................224 764-2198
EMP: 6 **EST:** 2018
SALES (est): 196K **Privately Held**
WEB: www.instantimprints.com
SIC: 2752 Commercial printing, lithographic

(G-12834)
INTEPLAST ENGINEERED FILMS INC
7549 Brokerage Dr (32809-5625)
PHONE..................................407 851-6620
Lee Seidel, *Controller*
Angel Gomez, *Supervisor*
C Bowman, *Maintence Staff*
EMP: 100 **Privately Held**
WEB: www.inteplastef.com
SIC: 2673 Food storage & trash bags (plastic); trash bags (plastic film): made from purchased materials; plastic bags: made from purchased materials
HQ: Inteplast Engineered Films Inc.
2875 Market St Ste 100
Garland TX 75041
800 373-9410

(G-12835)
INTERLINK SOFTWARE INC
8946 Leeland Archer Blvd (32836-8836)
PHONE..................................407 927-0898
Lloyd Hopkins, *President*
Collin Griffiths, *Vice Pres*
Barry Hopkins, *Vice Pres*
David Arrowsmith, *Sales Staff*
Matthew Sweeney, *Consultant*
EMP: 7 **EST:** 2003
SALES (est): 583.5K **Privately Held**
WEB: www.interlinksoftware.com
SIC: 3695 Computer software tape & disks: blank, rigid & floppy

(G-12836)
INTERNATIONAL KEG RENTAL LLC ✪
10450 Trkey Lk Rd Unit 69 (32819)
PHONE..................................407 900-9992
Thadeus Avvampato, *Mng Member*
EMP: 10 **EST:** 2020
SALES (est): 518.7K **Privately Held**
WEB: www.intlkeg.com
SIC: 2082 7359 Beer (alcoholic beverage); business machine & electronic equipment rental services

(G-12837)
INTERNTNAL SYNRGY FOR TCHNCAL
Also Called: Is4ts
12001 Res Pkwy Ste 236 (32826)
PHONE..................................321 305-0863
Abdelhamid Elkheir, *CEO*
EMP: 6 **EST:** 2016
SALES (est): 544.9K **Privately Held**
WEB: www.is4ts.com
SIC: 3724 3728 7699 5999 Aircraft engines & engine parts; research & dev by manuf., aircraft parts & auxiliary equip; aircraft & heavy equipment repair services; electronic parts & equipment; corporate objectives & policies consultant

(G-12838)
INTERSTATE RECYCLING WASTE
5232 Laval Dr (32839-6902)
PHONE..................................407 812-5555
Wanda Santiago, *President*
Saul Ortega, *Vice Pres*
EMP: 19 **EST:** 2004
SALES (est): 2MM **Privately Held**
WEB: www.interstaterecyclingfl.com
SIC: 3443 Dumpsters, garbage

(G-12839)
INTOUCH INC
5036 Dr Phillips Blvd (32819-3310)
PHONE..................................702 572-4786
John Jackson, *Principal*
EMP: 19 **EST:** 2010
SALES (est): 106K **Privately Held**
WEB: www.24-7intouch.com
SIC: 3999 Manufacturing industries

(G-12840)
INVIRO TEK INC
11334 Boggy Creek Rd # 1 (32824-7416)
PHONE..................................215 499-1209
EMP: 8 **EST:** 2015
SALES (est): 601K **Privately Held**
SIC: 3699 Electrical equipment & supplies

(G-12841)
INVISION AUTO SYSTEMS INC
3001 Directors Row (32809-5675)
PHONE..................................407 956-5161
Phillip Prince, *Sales Mgr*
Robert Hughes, *Accounts Mgr*
Lisa Swanson, *Branch Mgr*
EMP: 100
SALES (corp-wide): 563.6MM **Publicly Held**
SIC: 3699 Automotive driving simulators (training aids), electronic
HQ: Invision Automotive Systems Inc.
2351 J Lawson Blvd
Orlando FL 32824

(G-12842)
INVISION AUTO SYSTEMS INC (HQ)
2351 J Lawson Blvd (32824-4386)
PHONE..................................407 956-5161
Thomas C Malone, *President*
Loriann Shelton, *Vice Pres*
Charles M Stoehr, *Vice Pres*
Lisa Swanson, *Director*
Chris Lis Johnson, *Admin Sec*
EMP: 99 **EST:** 2010
SALES (est): 48.2MM
SALES (corp-wide): 563.6MM **Publicly Held**
WEB: www.voxxintl.com
SIC: 3699 Automotive driving simulators (training aids), electronic
PA: Voxx International Corporation
2351 J Lawson Blvd
Orlando FL 32824
800 645-7750

(G-12843)
INVISION INDUSTRIES INC
2351 J Lawson Blvd (32824-4386)
PHONE..................................407 451-8353
EMP: 7 **EST:** 2017
SALES (est): 57.3K **Privately Held**
WEB: www.invisiondirect.com
SIC: 3699 Electrical equipment & supplies

(G-12844)
IRONWIFI LLC
3071 N Orange Blossom Trl C (32804-3455)
PHONE..................................800 963-6221
Martin Benuska, *Principal*
EMP: 10 **EST:** 2014
SALES (est): 665.6K **Privately Held**
WEB: www.ironwifi.com
SIC: 7372 Business oriented computer software

(G-12845)
ISP OPTICS CORPORATION (HQ)
2603 Challenger Tech Ct # 100 (32826-2716)
PHONE..................................914 591-3070
Mark Lifshotz, *CEO*
Joseph Menaker, *President*
▲ **EMP:** 97 **EST:** 1993
SALES (est): 11.4MM
SALES (corp-wide): 38.4MM **Publicly Held**
WEB: www.ispoptics.com
SIC: 3827 Optical instruments & apparatus
PA: Lightpath Technologies, Inc.
2603 Challenger Tech Ct
Orlando FL 32826
407 382-4003

GEOGRAPHIC

(G-12846)
ITYX SOLUTIONS INC
2915 Musselwhite Ave (32804-4549)
P.O. Box 2448 (32802-2448)
PHONE..................................407 474-4383
Joe Radomsky, *General Mgr*
EMP: 15 **EST:** 2014
SALES (est): 172K **Privately Held**
WEB: www.ityxsolutions.com
SIC: 7372 Prepackaged software

(G-12847)
J & A BIG PAVERS LLC
6214 W Robinson St (32835-1362)
PHONE..................................321 948-0019
Jenny Avila, *Principal*
EMP: 7 **EST:** 2014
SALES (est): 179.1K **Privately Held**
SIC: 2951 Asphalt paving mixtures & blocks

(G-12848)
J V INSTALLATIONS CORP
1310 W Central Blvd (32805-1708)
PHONE..................................407 849-0262
James Vargas, *President*
Alicia Vargas, *Manager*
Jennifer Diaz, *Officer*
EMP: 30 **EST:** 2000
SQ FT: 13,500
SALES (est): 4.8MM **Privately Held**
WEB: www.jvinstallationscorp.com
SIC: 3281 2434 Granite, cut & shaped; wood kitchen cabinets

(G-12849)
JAMES A DE FLIPPO CO
4665 Gatlin Oaks Ln (32806-7249)
P.O. Box 560067 (32856-0067)
PHONE..................................407 851-2765
James A Deflippo, *President*
Joyce Deflippo, *Vice Pres*
EMP: 7 **EST:** 1974
SQ FT: 1,000
SALES (est): 474.8K **Privately Held**
SIC: 3961 5094 5099 Costume jewelry, ex. precious metal & semiprecious stones; jewelry; brass goods

(G-12850)
JAMES SIMMONS CABINETS INC
4835 Berrywood Dr (32812-7327)
PHONE..................................407 468-1802
James Simmons, *Principal*
EMP: 8 **EST:** 2008
SALES (est): 409.5K **Privately Held**
SIC: 2434 Wood kitchen cabinets

(G-12851)
JAR ADVERTISING LLC
8601 Commodity Cir (32819-9003)
PHONE..................................844 344-4586
Johnny Pineyro,
Roberto Pineyro,
EMP: 6 **EST:** 2016
SQ FT: 4,500
SALES (est): 298.1K **Privately Held**
SIC: 3993 7312 5199 7311 Signs & advertising specialties; outdoor advertising services; poster advertising, outdoor; advertising specialties; advertising agencies

(G-12852)
JAYCO INTERNATIONAL LLC
7451 Brokerage Dr (32809-5623)
PHONE..................................407 855-8880
James Rutledge, *General Mgr*
James R Rutledge Jr,
Cynthia Arsuaga,
EMP: 53 **EST:** 2005
SQ FT: 24,900
SALES (est): 5.7MM **Privately Held**
WEB: www.jaycointernational.net
SIC: 2258 Bedspreads, lace: made on lace machines

(G-12853)
JBT LLC (PA)
528 W Yale St (32804-5338)
PHONE..................................407 463-2045
Jamieson Thomas, *Principal*
Crystal Morris, *Manager*
EMP: 30 **EST:** 2012
SALES (est): 106.1K **Privately Held**
WEB: www.jbtc.com
SIC: 3556 Food products machinery

(G-12854)
JD WINE CONCEPTS LLC
Also Called: Quantum Leap Winery
1312 Wilfred Dr (32803-2537)
PHONE..................................407 730-3082
Trey Wheeler, *Manager*
Jill Ramsier,
▲ **EMP:** 6 **EST:** 2013
SALES (est): 538.4K **Privately Held**
WEB: www.quantumleapwinery.com
SIC: 2084 Wines

(G-12855)
JENARD FRESH INCORPORATED
Also Called: Spice Worlds
8101 Presidents Dr (32809-7624)
PHONE..................................407 851-9432
Gary R Caneza, *President*
Maria Valentin, *Supervisor*
Kevin Smith, *CIO*
▲ **EMP:** 46 **EST:** 1991
SALES (est): 7.8MM **Privately Held**
SIC: 2099 Food preparations

(G-12856)
JEWELS HANDMADE LLC ✪
2648 Renegade Dr Apt 101 (32818-2622)
PHONE..................................407 283-9951
Emmanuel Hampton,
EMP: 10 **EST:** 2020
SALES (est): 249.3K **Privately Held**
SIC: 2389 Apparel & accessories

(G-12857)
JNE CANDY CO LLC (PA)
11767 Chateaubriand Ave (32836-8803)
PHONE..................................407 622-6292
Julien L Emmanuel, *Principal*
Julien Emmanuel, *Vice Pres*
EMP: 12 **EST:** 2014
SALES (est): 218.7K **Privately Held**
SIC: 2064 Candy & other confectionery products

(G-12858)
JOHN BEAN TECHNOLOGIES CORP
Also Called: Jbt Aerotech-Military Programs
7300 Presidents Dr (32809-5620)
PHONE..................................407 851-3377
Roy Fulcher, *General Mgr*
Josh Parkin, *Plant Mgr*
Terry Brecht, *Project Mgr*
Michael Mulhern, *Project Mgr*
John Thompson, *Project Mgr*
EMP: 25 **Publicly Held**
WEB: www.jbtc.com
SIC: 3556 3585 3537 Food products machinery; refrigeration & heating equipment; containers (metal), air cargo
PA: John Bean Technologies Corporation
70 W Madison St Ste 4400
Chicago IL 60602

(G-12859)
JOMAR METAL FABRICATION INC
1239 Spruce Ave (32824-7935)
PHONE..................................407 857-1259
Marvin Sweers, *President*
John Edmondson, *Vice Pres*
Frances Sweers, *Admin Sec*
EMP: 7 **EST:** 1996
SQ FT: 10,000
SALES (est): 1.2MM **Privately Held**
WEB: www.jomarmetal.com
SIC: 3441 Fabricated structural metal

(G-12860)
JONES AWNINGS & CANVAS INC
372 W Grant St (32806-3934)
PHONE..................................407 845-9400
Robert Greenwood, *Vice Pres*
EMP: 7 **EST:** 2017
SALES (est): 271.7K **Privately Held**
WEB: www.greenwoodawnings.com
SIC: 2211 Canvas

(G-12861)
JORDAN NORRIS INC
997 W Kennedy Blvd Ste A1 (32810-6100)
P.O. Box 421922, Kissimmee (34742-1922)
PHONE..................................407 846-1400
Kathy Groover, *President*
William Groover, *Vice Pres*
EMP: 8 **EST:** 1976
SQ FT: 6,000
SALES (est): 550K **Privately Held**
WEB: www.jordannorris.com
SIC: 2752 Commercial printing, offset

(G-12862)
JOYA ESSENTIALS LLC
9918 Hatton Cir (32832-6172)
PHONE..................................407 865-0880
Steve Aidala, *Principal*
EMP: 8 **EST:** 2015
SALES (est): 133.4K **Privately Held**
WEB: www.joyaessentials.com
SIC: 2844 Toilet preparations

(G-12863)
JTA INDUSTRIES LLC (PA)
9165 Phillips Grove Ter (32836-5058)
PHONE..................................407 352-4255
Peter Anthony Jr, *Principal*
EMP: 9 **EST:** 2018
SALES (est): 44.7K **Privately Held**
SIC: 3999 Manufacturing industries

(G-12864)
JTA INDUSTRIES LLC
3391 S Kirkman Rd # 1223 (32811-1943)
PHONE..................................321 663-4395
Joshua T Anthony, *Branch Mgr*
EMP: 10
SALES (corp-wide): 44.7K **Privately Held**
SIC: 3999 Atomizers, toiletry
PA: Jta Industries Llc
9165 Phillips Grove Ter
Orlando FL 32836
407 352-4255

(G-12865)
KAMAN PRECISION PRODUCTS INC (DH)
6655 E Colonial Dr (32807-5200)
PHONE..................................407 282-1000
Gerald C Ricketts, *President*
Clarence Close, *Vice Pres*
Jeffrey Leeper, *Vice Pres*
Robert Renz, *Vice Pres*
Robert D Starr, *Treasurer*
▼ **EMP:** 200 **EST:** 2002
SQ FT: 90,000
SALES (est): 38.4MM
SALES (corp-wide): 784.4MM **Publicly Held**
WEB: www.kamansensors.com
SIC: 3483 3489 Ammunition, except for small arms; ordnance & accessories

(G-12866)
KASSE CABINETS INC
9781 S Orange Blossom Trl # 8
(32837-8968)
PHONE..................................407 285-2738
Freddy Kasse, *Manager*
EMP: 6 **EST:** 2012
SALES (est): 123.8K **Privately Held**
SIC: 2434 Wood kitchen cabinets

(G-12867)
KAWNEER COMPANY INC
Also Called: Kawneer Architectural Products
4645 L B Mcleod Rd (32811-6405)
PHONE..................................407 648-4511
Brian Norberg, *Manager*
EMP: 116
SALES (corp-wide): 5.6B **Publicly Held**
WEB: www.kawneer.com
SIC: 3446 Architectural metalwork
HQ: Kawneer Company, Inc.
555 Guthridge Ct
Norcross GA 30092
770 449-5555

(G-12868)
KEMET VENTURES LLC
10524 Moss Park Rd (32832-5898)
PHONE..................................407 403-2958
Magued S Sherif, *Principal*
EMP: 6 **EST:** 2015
SALES (est): 400.7K **Privately Held**
WEB: www.kemet.com
SIC: 3675 Electronic capacitors

(G-12869)
KENNEY COMMUNICATIONS INC (PA)
1215 Spruce Ave (32824-7935)
PHONE..................................407 859-3113
Barbara A Kenney, *President*
EMP: 19
SQ FT: 23,600 **Privately Held**
WEB: www.kenneycom.com
SIC: 2721 2741 7319 Magazines: publishing only, not printed on site; miscellaneous publishing; guides: publishing only, not printed on site; distribution of advertising material or sample services

(G-12870)
KENS STUMP GRINDING LLC
3848 Beachman Dr (32810-3649)
PHONE..................................407 948-5031
Kenneth E Faulkner, *Branch Mgr*
EMP: 7
SALES (corp-wide): 25.6K **Privately Held**
SIC: 3599 Grinding castings for the trade
PA: Kens Stump Grinding Llc
6662 82nd Avenue Ct N
Pinellas Park FL 33781
727 289-9968

(G-12871)
KIRCHMAN CORPORATION (PA)
Also Called: Metavante Banking Solutions
2001 Summit Park Dr # 100 (32810-5906)
PHONE..................................877 384-0936
Rachel Landrum, *President*
Paul T Danola, *Chairman*
Michael D Hayford, *Exec VP*
Mark Viselli, *Exec VP*
Jerry White, *Vice Pres*
EMP: 98 **EST:** 2004
SALES (est): 3.6MM **Privately Held**
SIC: 7372 Application computer software

(G-12872)
KITCHENS BY US
4201 L B Mcleod Rd (32811-5616)
PHONE..................................407 745-4923
EMP: 11 **EST:** 2018
SALES (est): 713.3K **Privately Held**
WEB: www.kitchensbyus.com
SIC: 2434 Wood kitchen cabinets

(G-12873)
KITCHENS RTA LLC
2467 N John Young Pkwy (32804-4123)
PHONE..................................407 969-0902
Madison Pruitt, *President*
EMP: 7 **EST:** 2017
SALES (est): 159.7K **Privately Held**
WEB: www.kitchensrta.com
SIC: 2434 Wood kitchen cabinets

(G-12874)
KITEMAN PRODUCTIONS INC
5200 Ridgeway Dr (32819-7431)
PHONE..................................407 943-8480
Bruce Flora, *President*
EMP: 7 **EST:** 1991
SQ FT: 6,000
SALES (est): 401.5K **Privately Held**
WEB: www.kiteman.net
SIC: 2399 Banners, made from fabric

(G-12875)
KOLLSMAN INC
12600 Challenger Pkwy (32826-2754)
PHONE..................................407 312-1384
Jeff Crystal, *Branch Mgr*
EMP: 7
SALES (corp-wide): 4.6B **Privately Held**
SIC: 3812 3629 Search & navigation equipment; electrochemical generators (fuel cells)
HQ: Kollsman, Inc.
220 Daniel Webster Hwy
Merrimack NH 03054

(G-12876)
KONNECTED INC
5718 Old Cheney Hwy (32807-3525)
PHONE..................................407 286-3138
EMP: 10 **EST:** 2019

SALES (est): 1.1MM **Privately Held**
WEB: www.konnected.io
SIC: 3571 7371 Electronic computers; computer software development & applications

(G-12877)
KRATOS DEF & SEC SOLUTIONS INC
8601 Transport Dr (32832-7102)
PHONE....................................866 606-5867
David Laird, *Vice Pres*
Paul Evenson, *Software Engr*
EMP: 6 **Publicly Held**
WEB: www.kratosdefense.com
SIC: 3761 8744 7382 Guided missiles & space vehicles; facilities support services; security systems services
PA: Kratos Defense & Security Solutions, Inc.
10680 Treena St Ste 600
San Diego CA 92131

(G-12878)
L & C METALS LLC
711 Central Florida Pkwy (32824-8501)
PHONE....................................407 859-2600
Michael Steadman, *Mng Member*
Luard Steadman,
Melanie Wright,
EMP: 6 **EST:** 2004
SALES (est): 526.1K **Privately Held**
WEB: www.landcmetals.com
SIC: 7692 Welding repair

(G-12879)
L M INDUSTRIAL INC
1429 Central Florida Pkwy (32837-9405)
PHONE....................................407 240-8911
Lois McGinnis, *President*
Tim McGinnis, *Vice Pres*
EMP: 7 **EST:** 1994
SQ FT: 2,500
SALES (est): 898K **Privately Held**
SIC: 3441 1799 Fabricated structural metal; welding on site

(G-12880)
L R GATOR CORPORATION
4380 L B Mcleod Rd (32811-5619)
PHONE....................................407 578-6616
EMP: 9 **EST:** 2014
SALES (est): 397K **Privately Held**
WEB: www.signaramaorlando.com
SIC: 3993 Signs & advertising specialties

(G-12881)
L-3 CMMNCTONS ADVNCED LSER SYS
Also Called: Advanced Lser Systems Tech Div
2500 N Orange Blossom Trl (32804-4807)
PHONE....................................407 295-5878
Lawrence Van Blerkom, *Vice Pres*
Steve Post, *Admin Sec*
EMP: 66 **EST:** 1987
SQ FT: 40,000
SALES (est): 12.1MM
SALES (corp-wide): 3.7B **Publicly Held**
WEB: www.l3harris.com
SIC: 3699 Laser systems & equipment
HQ: L3 Technologies, Inc.
600 3rd Ave Fl 34
New York NY 10016
321 727-9100

(G-12882)
L3 TECHNOLOGIES INC
Also Called: Advanced Laser Systems
2500 N Orange Blossom Trl (32804-4807)
PHONE....................................407 295-5878
EMP: 89
SALES (corp-wide): 3.7B **Publicly Held**
WEB: www.l3harris.com
SIC: 3699 Laser systems & equipment
HQ: L3 Technologies, Inc.
600 3rd Ave Fl 34
New York NY 10016
321 727-9100

(G-12883)
L3HARRIS TECHNOLOGIES INC
7022 Tpc Dr Ste 500 (32822-5140)
PHONE....................................407 581-3782
Dan Keppel, *Project Mgr*
Curt Jones, *Manager*
EMP: 6
SALES (corp-wide): 3.7B **Publicly Held**
WEB: www.l3harris.com
SIC: 3812 Search & navigation equipment
PA: L3harris Technologies, Inc.
1025 W Nasa Blvd
Melbourne FL 32919
321 727-9100

(G-12884)
LA CHIQUITA TORTILLA MFR
6918 Presidents Dr (32809-5668)
PHONE....................................407 251-8290
Steve Bright, *Director*
EMP: 27 **EST:** 2016
SALES (est): 651.7K **Privately Held**
WEB: www.lachiquitatortilla.com
SIC: 2099 Tortillas, fresh or refrigerated

(G-12885)
LA MAR ORLANDO LLC
Also Called: Sir Speedy
621 Commonwealth Ave (32803-5223)
PHONE....................................407 423-2051
Michael Levangie, *Partner*
Laurence Nye, *Partner*
Belinda Danals, *COO*
Etta Lazarus, *Vice Pres*
Matthew Diehl, *Opers Mgr*
EMP: 30 **EST:** 2008
SALES (est): 6.8MM **Privately Held**
WEB: www.sirspeedy.com
SIC: 2752 Commercial printing, lithographic

(G-12886)
LA PAVERS INC
2349 Lake Debra Dr (32835-6625)
PHONE....................................407 209-9163
Lourival Aguiar, *Principal*
EMP: 8 **EST:** 2005
SALES (est): 203.8K **Privately Held**
WEB: www.lapavers.com
SIC: 2951 Asphalt paving mixtures & blocks

(G-12887)
LACHANCE LEATHERS LLC
4017 Moorings Ln (32810-2859)
PHONE....................................407 790-6712
Joseph B Sallette, *Principal*
EMP: 6 **EST:** 2010
SALES (est): 96.5K **Privately Held**
SIC: 3199 Leather goods

(G-12888)
LAKE NEWS LLC
9836 Sweetleaf St (32827-6812)
PHONE....................................407 251-1314
Allyn Maycumber, *Principal*
EMP: 11 **EST:** 2010
SALES (est): 362.3K **Privately Held**
SIC: 2711 Newspapers, publishing & printing

(G-12889)
LAMBERT CORPORATION FLORIDA
20 Coburn Ave (32805-2198)
PHONE....................................407 841-2940
Matthew L Ledlow, *CEO*
Patrick Enelus, *Production*
Armand Hamilton, *Production*
Tyron Peter, *Production*
Damarcus Johnson, *Research*
◆ **EMP:** 21 **EST:** 1978
SQ FT: 26,000
SALES (est): 15MM **Privately Held**
WEB: www.lambertusa.net
SIC: 2819 2851 2891 3272 Industrial inorganic chemicals; paints & allied products; adhesives & sealants; concrete products; gypsum products
PA: Meyer Ledlow, Llc
20 Coburn Ave
Orlando FL 32805
407 481-2940

(G-12890)
LANCO & HARRIS CORP
600 Mid Florida Dr (32824-7008)
PHONE....................................407 240-4000
Sergio Blanco, *President*
Inrique Blanco, *Vice Pres*
Guillermo Blanco, *Treasurer*
◆ **EMP:** 60
SQ FT: 100,000
SALES (est): 15.8MM **Privately Held**
WEB: www.lancoandharriscorp.cityfos.com
SIC: 2851 Paints & allied products

(G-12891)
LAPEL PIN & BUTTON COMPANY INC (PA)
10151 University Blvd (32817-1904)
PHONE....................................407 677-6144
Carey P Stewart, *President*
EMP: 13 **EST:** 1999
SQ FT: 4,800
SALES (est): 1.3MM **Privately Held**
WEB: www.signaturepatches.com
SIC: 3965 Fasteners, buttons, needles & pins

(G-12892)
LAPIN SHEET METAL COMPANY
3825 Gardenia Ave (32839-9201)
PHONE....................................407 423-9897
Ronald Lapin, *President*
Janet Lapin, *President*
Daniel Lapin, *Vice Pres*
Mary Davis, *Purch Mgr*
Ernest Agustin, *CFO*
EMP: 75 **EST:** 1973
SQ FT: 50,000
SALES (est): 12.6MM **Privately Held**
WEB: www.lapinsm.com
SIC: 3444 Ducts, sheet metal

(G-12893)
LASERSIGHT INCORPORATED (PA)
10244 E Clnl Dr Ste 201 (32817)
PHONE....................................407 678-9900
Xian Ding Weng, *Ch of Bd*
Danghui Liu, *President*
Dorothy M Cipolla, *CFO*
Zhaokai Tang, *Treasurer*
Jeanette Williams, *Accounting Mgr*
EMP: 15 **EST:** 1987
SQ FT: 156,000 **Privately Held**
SIC: 3845 3699 6794 Electromedical equipment; laser systems & equipment; patent owners & lessors

(G-12894)
LASERSIGHT TECHNOLOGIES INC
10244 E Clnl Dr Ste 201 (32817)
PHONE....................................407 678-9900
Michael R Farris, *President*
D Michael Litscher, *COO*
Gregory Wilson, *CFO*
EMP: 5 **EST:** 1991
SALES (est): 1.9MM **Privately Held**
WEB: www.lase.com
SIC: 3845 5049 Electromedical equipment; optical goods
PA: Lasersight Incorporated
10244 E Clnl Dr Ste 201
Orlando FL 32817

(G-12895)
LASERSTAR TECHNOLOGIES CORP
2461 Orlando Central Pkwy (32809-5619)
PHONE....................................401 438-1500
EMP: 9 **EST:** 2019
SALES (est): 4.8MM **Privately Held**
WEB: www.laserstar.net
SIC: 3599 Machine shop, jobbing & repair

(G-12896)
LASERSTAR TECHNOLOGIES CORP
2453 Orlando Central Pkwy (32809-5619)
PHONE....................................407 248-1142
Laurie Akers, *Accountant*
Albert Smith, *Executive*
Richard Hacker, *Planning*
EMP: 8
SALES (corp-wide): 5.6MM **Privately Held**
WEB: www.laserstar.net
SIC: 3559 3699 Jewelers' machines; electrical equipment & supplies
PA: Laserstar Technologies Corporation
1 Industrial Ct
Riverside RI 02915
401 438-1500

(G-12897)
LAWALL PRSTHTICS ORTHOTICS INC
6535 Nemours Pkwy (32827-7884)
PHONE....................................407 567-5190
Harry Lawall, *Principal*
EMP: 6 **EST:** 2013
SALES (est): 212.8K **Privately Held**
WEB: www.lawall.com
SIC: 3842 Prosthetic appliances

(G-12898)
LAWTON PRINTERS INC
Also Called: Lawton Connect
649 Triumph Ct (32805-1276)
PHONE....................................407 260-0400
Kimberly Lawton Koon, *President*
Ty Koon, *Vice Pres*
Tyler Koon, *Vice Pres*
Jim Bissonnette, *Plant Mgr*
Dave Dragan, *Plant Mgr*
▼ **EMP:** 30 **EST:** 1900
SQ FT: 21,000
SALES (est): 7.1MM **Privately Held**
WEB: www.lawtonconnect.com
SIC: 2752 Commercial printing, offset

(G-12899)
LEDGER 2 LEDGER INC
4700 Millenia Blvd # 175 (32839-6013)
PHONE....................................321 961-4017
Jean-Baptiste Marta, *Principal*
EMP: 6 **EST:** 2013
SALES (est): 204.2K **Privately Held**
WEB: www.ledger2ledger.com
SIC: 3648 Lighting equipment

(G-12900)
LEE CHEMICAL CORPORATION
Also Called: Hotsy Cleaning Systems
2800 Taft Ave (32804-4399)
PHONE....................................407 843-6950
Robley Hackley II, *President*
Mary C Hackley, *Corp Secy*
James Dunn, *Mktg Coord*
Jim Dunn, *Mktg Coord*
Sandy Fielding, *Office Mgr*
EMP: 5 **EST:** 1964
SQ FT: 10,000
SALES (est): 422K **Privately Held**
WEB:
www.leechemical.alkotadistributors.com
SIC: 2842 5084 Industrial plant disinfectants or deodorants; industrial machinery & equipment

(G-12901)
LEEDS MACHINING CO
4025 Bibb Ln (32817-1635)
PHONE....................................407 671-3688
William Leeds, *Principal*
EMP: 6 **EST:** 1996
SALES (est): 134.4K **Privately Held**
SIC: 3544 Special dies, tools, jigs & fixtures

(G-12902)
LEGACY PUBLISHING GROUP
3878 N Lake Orlando Pkwy (32808-2203)
PHONE....................................407 290-8414
Saneen R Cochran, *Principal*
EMP: 6 **EST:** 2007
SALES (est): 93K **Privately Held**
WEB: www.legacybookpublishing.com
SIC: 2741 Miscellaneous publishing

(G-12903)
LEGACY VULCAN LLC
8500 Florida Rock Rd (32824-7841)
PHONE....................................407 855-9902
Brad Bushur, *Manager*
EMP: 8
SQ FT: 1,798 **Publicly Held**
WEB: www.vulcanmaterials.com
SIC: 3273 Ready-mixed concrete
HQ: Legacy Vulcan, Llc
1200 Urban Center Dr
Vestavia AL 35242
205 298-3000

(G-12904)
LENSAR INC
2800 Discovery Dr Ste 100 (32826-3010)
PHONE....................................888 536-7271
Nicholas T Curtis, *CEO*

GEOGRAPHIC

William J Link, *Ch of Bd*
Lothar Koob, *COO*
Dara Osuilleabhain, *Mfg Staff*
Greg Smith, *Engineer*
▼ **EMP:** 30 **EST:** 2004
SQ FT: 40,000
SALES: 26.3MM
SALES (corp-wide): 58.3MM **Publicly Held**
WEB: www.lensar.com
SIC: 3841 Surgical lasers
HQ: Alphaeon Corporation
17901 Von Karman Ave # 150
Irvine CA 92614
949 284-4555

(G-12905)
LEWIS-RIGGS CUSTOM GUITARS INC
1001 Lake Sherwood Dr (32818-6612)
PHONE..................................407 538-3710
Barry Lewis, *President*
Leland Riggs, *Vice Pres*
EMP: 6
SQ FT: 2,800
SALES (est): 30K **Privately Held**
SIC: 3931 5099 Guitars & parts, electric & nonelectric; musical instruments

(G-12906)
LEXINGTON DSIGN + FBRCTION E L
Also Called: Caylex
613 Triumph Ct Ste 1 (32805-1248)
PHONE..................................407 578-4720
Tom Hughes, *Mng Member*
▲ **EMP:** 10 **EST:** 1994
SQ FT: 15,000
SALES (est): 6.8MM
SALES (corp-wide): 31.8MM **Privately Held**
WEB: www.companiesofnassal.com
SIC: 3441 Fabricated structural metal
PA: Nassal Company
415 W Kaley St
Orlando FL 32806
407 648-0400

(G-12907)
LGL GROUP INC (PA)
2525 Shader Rd (32804-2721)
PHONE..................................407 298-2000
Ivan Arteaga, *CEO*
Michael J Ferrantino Sr, *Ch of Bd*
Marc J Gabelli, *Ch of Bd*
James W Tivy, *CFO*
James Tivy, *CFO*
EMP: 2 **EST:** 1928
SQ FT: 71,000
SALES: 31.1MM **Publicly Held**
WEB: www.lglgroup.com
SIC: 3679 3559 Electronic circuits; electronic component making machinery

(G-12908)
LIDARIT INC ✪
7208 W Sand Lake Rd (32819-5200)
PHONE..................................407 632-2622
Andres Valencia Vidarte, *President*
Carlos Juri Feghali, *Vice Pres*
EMP: 20 **EST:** 2020
SALES (est): 1.4MM **Privately Held**
WEB: www.lidarit.com
SIC: 7372 Utility computer software

(G-12909)
LIFELINK FOUNDATION INC
1739 S Orange Ave (32806-2935)
PHONE..................................407 218-8783
Dennis Heinricks, *Branch Mgr*
EMP: 32
SALES (corp-wide): 128.9MM **Privately Held**
WEB: www.lifelinkfoundation.org
SIC: 2676 Towels, napkins & tissue paper products
PA: Lifelink Foundation, Inc.
9661 Delaney Creek Blvd
Tampa FL 33619
813 253-2640

(G-12910)
LIFT SPECTRUM TECHNOLOGIES LLC
Also Called: Lst
4700 Millenia Blvd # 175 (32839-6013)
PHONE..................................407 228-8343
Jim Hukill,
EMP: 5
SALES (est): 300K **Privately Held**
SIC: 3577 Computer peripheral equipment

(G-12911)
LIGHTPATH TECHNOLOGIES INC (PA)
2603 Challenger Tech Ct (32826-2716)
PHONE..................................407 382-4003
Chris Morley, *CEO*
Al Symmons, *COO*
Alan Symmons, *Exec VP*
Peter Greif, *Vice Pres*
Mark Palvino, *Vice Pres*
EMP: 67 **EST:** 1985
SQ FT: 38,000
SALES: 38.4MM **Publicly Held**
WEB: www.lightpath.com
SIC: 3827 Optical instruments & lenses

(G-12912)
LIMBITLESS SOLUTIONS INC (PA)
4217 E Plaza Dr (32816-8013)
PHONE..................................407 494-3661
Albert Manero, *CEO*
Albert Francis, *Assistant VP*
Dominique Courbin, *Production*
Angie Carloss, *Admin Sec*
EMP: 27 **EST:** 2014
SALES (est): 761.3K **Privately Held**
WEB: www.limbitless-solutions.org
SIC: 3842 Limbs, artificial

(G-12913)
LINOGRAPHICS INC
Also Called: Digital Graphics
617 N Magnolia Ave (32801-1258)
PHONE..................................407 422-8700
Gary Michael, *President*
EMP: 16 **EST:** 1979
SALES (est): 304.1K **Privately Held**
SIC: 2791 7336 2796 2752 Typesetting; commercial art & graphic design; platemaking services; commercial printing, lithographic

(G-12914)
LION LOCS LLC
1002 Lucerne Ter (32806-1015)
PHONE..................................704 802-2752
Nathan Watson,
EMP: 10 **EST:** 2019
SALES (est): 324.2K **Privately Held**
WEB: www.lionlocs.com
SIC: 3999 Hair & hair-based products

(G-12915)
LIQUID SOUL DGTAL GRAPHICS LLC
Also Called: Specialty Stamp & Sign
3628 E Esther St (32812-5117)
P.O. Box 568444 (32856-8444)
PHONE..................................407 948-6973
Sean McLaughlin, *Technology*
Melanie Lexner,
EMP: 9 **EST:** 2005
SALES (est): 264.8K **Privately Held**
SIC: 3993 Signs & advertising specialties

(G-12916)
LITEWORKS LIGHTING PRODUCTIONS
752 Palm Dr (32803-4221)
PHONE..................................407 888-8677
Dave Eveson, *President*
Andrew Douglas, *Vice Pres*
EMP: 9 **EST:** 2000
SALES (est): 302.9K **Privately Held**
SIC: 3648 7336 Stage lighting equipment; art design services

(G-12917)
LIVING PARABLES
1823 Antigua Dr (32806-1506)
PHONE..................................407 488-6201
Lori Pedonti, *Principal*
EMP: 6 **EST:** 2005
SALES (est): 105.3K **Privately Held**
WEB: www.living-parables.com
SIC: 2731 Book publishing

(G-12918)
LLC BEST BLOCK (PA)
2858 Sidney Ave (32810-5134)
PHONE..................................239 789-3531
Thilo D Best,
EMP: 46 **EST:** 2015
SALES (est): 4.1MM **Privately Held**
SIC: 3251 Paving brick, clay

(G-12919)
LOCKHEED MARTIN CORPORATION
100 Global Innovation Cir (32825-5003)
PHONE..................................407 306-6405
David Tatro, *Opers Staff*
Courtney Netzer, *Mfg Staff*
Patrick Cepek, *Engineer*
Gene Cox, *Engineer*
Neil Gaffin, *Engineer*
EMP: 1332 **Publicly Held**
WEB: www.lockheedmartin.com
SIC: 3812 Search & navigation equipment
PA: Lockheed Martin Corporation
6801 Rockledge Dr
Bethesda MD 20817

(G-12920)
LOCKHEED MARTIN CORPORATION
12506 Lake Underhill Rd (32825-5002)
PHONE..................................407 306-1000
Bob Hunt, *Principal*
Dan Norton, *Vice Pres*
Frank St John, *Vice Pres*
Patricia D Armond, *Senior Buyer*
Dave Keeran, *Buyer*
EMP: 584 **Publicly Held**
WEB: www.lockheedmartin.com
SIC: 3761 3699 Ballistic missiles, complete; guided missiles & space vehicles, research & development; guided missiles, complete; space vehicles, complete; electrical equipment & supplies
PA: Lockheed Martin Corporation
6801 Rockledge Dr
Bethesda MD 20817

(G-12921)
LOCKHEED MARTIN CORPORATION
1700 Tradeport Dr (32824-7018)
PHONE..................................407 517-6627
Monica McManus, *Vice Pres*
Shauna M Ferguson, *Mfg Staff*
Cindy Hampton, *Financial Analy*
Glen Ives, *Manager*
Kenny King, *Software Engr*
EMP: 6 **Publicly Held**
WEB: www.lockheedmartin.com
SIC: 3812 5072 Search & navigation equipment; hardware
PA: Lockheed Martin Corporation
6801 Rockledge Dr
Bethesda MD 20817

(G-12922)
LOCKHEED MARTIN CORPORATION
6429 Marlberry Dr (32819-4132)
PHONE..................................407 306-4758
Robert Garza, *Engineer*
Joseph Defrancisci, *Manager*
Christopher Noble, *Manager*
Thomas Norton, *Manager*
Brad Anderson, *Technician*
EMP: 6 **Publicly Held**
WEB: www.lockheedmartin.com
SIC: 3812 Search & navigation equipment
PA: Lockheed Martin Corporation
6801 Rockledge Dr
Bethesda MD 20817

(G-12923)
LOCKHEED MARTIN CORPORATION
Also Called: Lockheed Martin Mis Fire Ctrl
5600 W Sand Lake Rd (32819-8907)
PHONE..................................407 356-2000
Lauren Douglass, *General Mgr*
Charles Fleming, *General Mgr*
Jed Clear, *Vice Pres*
Mary Sturtevant, *Vice Pres*
Adam Koffler, *Opers Staff*
EMP: 10 **Publicly Held**
WEB: www.lockheedmartin.com
SIC: 3812 Search & navigation equipment
PA: Lockheed Martin Corporation
6801 Rockledge Dr
Bethesda MD 20817

(G-12924)
LOCKHEED MARTIN CORPORATION
100 Global Innovation Cir (32825-5003)
P.O. Box 780547 (32878-0547)
PHONE..................................407 306-2745
Gary Kowatch, *Manager*
EMP: 6 **Publicly Held**
WEB: www.lockheedmartin.com
SIC: 3812 Search & navigation equipment
PA: Lockheed Martin Corporation
6801 Rockledge Dr
Bethesda MD 20817

(G-12925)
LOCKHEED MARTIN CORPORATION
Also Called: Lockheed Martin Mis Fire Ctrl
8751 Lockheed Martin Blvd (32819-8913)
PHONE..................................407 356-1034
Alexander Shuster, *IT/INT Sup*
EMP: 6 **Publicly Held**
WEB: www.lockheedmartin.com
SIC: 3812 Search & navigation equipment
PA: Lockheed Martin Corporation
6801 Rockledge Dr
Bethesda MD 20817

(G-12926)
LOCKHEED MARTIN CORPORATION
5600 W Sand Lake Rd (32819-8907)
PHONE..................................301 240-7500
Denise Leone, *Senior Buyer*
Tony Furnari, *Engineer*
Chris Laughrey, *Engineer*
Robert Bain, *Consultant*
EMP: 6 **Publicly Held**
WEB: www.lockheedmartin.com
SIC: 3812 Search & navigation equipment
PA: Lockheed Martin Corporation
6801 Rockledge Dr
Bethesda MD 20817

(G-12927)
LOCKHEED MARTIN CORPORATION
5600 W Sand Lake Rd (32819-8907)
PHONE..................................407 356-2000
EMP: 6 **Publicly Held**
WEB: www.lockheedmartin.com
SIC: 3721 Motorized aircraft
PA: Lockheed Martin Corporation
6801 Rockledge Dr
Bethesda MD 20817

(G-12928)
LOCKHEED MARTIN CORPORATION
733 Saxby Ave (32835-1811)
PHONE..................................407 356-6423
Sheila R Mayo, *Branch Mgr*
EMP: 6 **Publicly Held**
WEB: www.lockheedmartin.com
SIC: 3812 Search & navigation equipment
PA: Lockheed Martin Corporation
6801 Rockledge Dr
Bethesda MD 20817

(G-12929)
LOCKHEED MARTIN CORPORATION
9556 Turkey Oak Bnd (32817-2773)
PHONE..................................407 356-1947
Jim Arcomone, *Manager*
Ray Ferrel, *Legal Staff*
EMP: 6 **Publicly Held**
WEB: www.lockheedmartin.com
SIC: 3812 Search & navigation equipment
PA: Lockheed Martin Corporation
6801 Rockledge Dr
Bethesda MD 20817

▲ = Import ▼=Export
◆ =Import/Export

(G-12930)
LOCKHEED MRTIN GYRCAM SYSTEMS
5600 W Sand Lake Rd Mp-265 (32819-8907)
PHONE..................................407 356-6500
Jay Pitman, *CEO*
Dan Kiehl, *Opers Mgr*
Al Bryan, *Manager*
Rita Flaherty, *Manager*
David J Huber, *Manager*
EMP: 53 **EST:** 2003
SALES (est): 3MM **Publicly Held**
WEB: www.lockheedmartin.com
SIC: 3812 Search & navigation equipment
PA: Lockheed Martin Corporation
6801 Rockledge Dr
Bethesda MD 20817

(G-12931)
LOCKHEED MRTIN INTGRTED SYSTEM
5600 W Sand Lake Rd (32819-8907)
PHONE..................................407 356-2000
William Boysen, *Manager*
EMP: 118 **Publicly Held**
SIC: 3812 Search & navigation equipment
HQ: Lockheed Martin Integrated Systems, Llc
6801 Rockledge Dr
Bethesda MD 20817

(G-12932)
LOCKHEED MRTIN MLLMTER TECH IN
5600 W Sand Lake Rd (32819-8907)
PHONE..................................407 356-4186
James Sharp, *Principal*
EMP: 22 **EST:** 2007
SALES (est): 6.2MM **Publicly Held**
WEB: www.lockheedmartin.com
SIC: 3721 Aircraft
PA: Lockheed Martin Corporation
6801 Rockledge Dr
Bethesda MD 20817

(G-12933)
LOCKHEED MRTIN TRNING SLTONS I (HQ)
Also Called: Lockheed Mrtin Rtary Mssion Sy
100 Global Innovation Cir (32825-5003)
PHONE..................................856 722-3317
Marillyn A Hewson, *CEO*
Nick Ali, *President*
Harold Browning, *Vice Pres*
Bruce L Tanner, *CFO*
David Cline, *Manager*
◆ **EMP:** 185 **EST:** 1984
SQ FT: 1,200
SALES (est): 165.2MM **Publicly Held**
WEB: www.lockheedmartin.com
SIC: 3812 Search & navigation equipment

(G-12934)
LOGIC CONTROLS INC
Also Called: Bematech
404 Sunport Ln Ste 550 (32809-8115)
PHONE..................................800 576-9647
Juliet Derby, *President*
Wladimir Alvarez, *Principal*
Fabio Romano, *Manager*
▲ **EMP:** 33 **EST:** 1982
SALES (est): 14.5MM **Privately Held**
WEB: www.logiccontrols.com
SIC: 3578 Accounting machines & cash registers; cash registers; point-of-sale devices; registers, credit account
HQ: Totvs Large Enterprise Tecnologia S/A
Av. Rui Barbosa 2529
Sao Jose Dos Pinhais PR 83055

(G-12935)
LOGOS PROMOTE INC
3804 N John Young Pkwy (32804-3201)
PHONE..................................407 447-5646
Gerald Hynes, *Principal*
Leslie Hynes, *Principal*
EMP: 8 **EST:** 2005
SALES (est): 967.8K **Privately Held**
WEB: www.logospromote.com
SIC: 2759 Screen printing

(G-12936)
LOS ATNTCOS SNDWICH CUBAN CAFE
7339 E Colonial Dr Ste 1 (32807-6380)
PHONE..................................407 282-2322
Robert Y Cruz, *Owner*
EMP: 6 **EST:** 2008
SALES (est): 154.8K **Privately Held**
SIC: 2035 2099 5149 Spreads, sandwich: salad dressing base; ready-to-eat meals, salads & sandwiches; sandwiches

(G-12937)
LUG USA LLC
8546 Palm Pkwy Ste 305 (32836-6415)
P.O. Box 91239, Austin TX (78709-1239)
PHONE..................................855 584-5433
Jason Richter, *Partner*
▲ **EMP:** 14 **EST:** 2006
SALES (est): 1MM **Privately Held**
SIC: 3161 Luggage

(G-12938)
LUMINAR TECHNOLOGIES INC (PA)
2603 Discovery Dr Ste 100 (32826-3006)
PHONE..................................407 900-5259
Austin Russell, *Ch of Bd*
Thomas J Fennimore, *CFO*
Matthew Weed, *Technology*
Rich Hicks, *Director*
EMP: 135 **EST:** 2018
SQ FT: 120,716
SALES: 13.9MM **Publicly Held**
WEB: www.luminartech.com
SIC: 3714 Motor vehicle parts & accessories

(G-12939)
LUMINAR TECHNOLOGIES INC
12601 Research Pkwy (32826-3226)
PHONE..................................407 900-5259
EMP: 20
SALES (corp-wide): 13.9MM **Publicly Held**
WEB: www.luminartech.com
SIC: 3714 Motor vehicle parts & accessories
PA: Luminar Technologies, Inc.
2603 Discovery Dr Ste 100
Orlando FL 32826
407 900-5259

(G-12940)
LUXURY MOTOR CARS LLC
420 S Orange Ave Ste 220 (32801-4910)
PHONE..................................407 398-6933
Steve Parmee, *Mng Member*
EMP: 10 **EST:** 2018
SALES (est): 583.8K **Privately Held**
SIC: 3714 Motor vehicle parts & accessories

(G-12941)
M J EMBROIDERY SCREEN PRTG LLC
8651 8th St (32836-6228)
PHONE..................................407 239-0246
Abdul Jabbar Bhangda, *Principal*
EMP: 7 **EST:** 2012
SALES (est): 256.9K **Privately Held**
WEB: www.mjembroideryandprinting.business.site
SIC: 2752 Commercial printing, lithographic

(G-12942)
M&B STEEL FABRICATORS INC
2536 Hansrob Rd (32804-3318)
PHONE..................................407 486-1774
Jose D Mansilla, *President*
Gregory G Baker, *Vice Pres*
Tyler Pelleymounter, *Admin Sec*
EMP: 17 **EST:** 2010
SQ FT: 14,000
SALES (est): 1.2MM **Privately Held**
SIC: 3446 Ornamental metalwork

(G-12943)
MAC GREGOR SMITH BLUEPRINTERS
1500 S Division Ave (32805-4724)
PHONE..................................407 423-5944
Brenda M Smith, *President*
Alexander Smith, *President*
Thomas M Gregor-Smith, *Vice Pres*
Thomas Mac Gregor-Smith Jr, *Vice Pres*
Greg Smith, *Vice Pres*
EMP: 19 **EST:** 1958
SQ FT: 7,500
SALES (est): 1.3MM **Privately Held**
WEB: www.macgregorsmith.com
SIC: 3861 Reproduction machines & equipment

(G-12944)
MACHINE SHOP
11609 Malverns Loop (32832-6026)
PHONE..................................786 991-6959
Clara Calderon, *Principal*
EMP: 6 **EST:** 2016
SALES (est): 92.8K **Privately Held**
SIC: 3599 Machine shop, jobbing & repair

(G-12945)
MAGIC MAGAZINE
633 N Orange Ave (32801-1325)
PHONE..................................407 420-6080
EMP: 8 **EST:** 2017
SALES (est): 120.8K **Privately Held**
WEB: www.magicmagazine.com
SIC: 2721 Magazines: publishing only, not printed on site

(G-12946)
MAHER INDUSTRIES INC
5434 Osprey Isle Ln (32819-4015)
PHONE..................................407 928-5288
Blake A Maher, *Principal*
EMP: 7 **EST:** 2016
SALES (est): 108.4K **Privately Held**
WEB: www.maher.com
SIC: 3999 Manufacturing industries

(G-12947)
MANATEE BAY ENTERPRISES INC
2234 W Taft Vnlnd Rd A (32837-7800)
PHONE..................................407 245-3600
Robert W Palmiero, *Ch of Bd*
Steve Horne, *Vice Pres*
Larrie McCleary, *Vice Pres*
EMP: 11 **EST:** 1990
SQ FT: 10,000
SALES (est): 376.9K **Privately Held**
SIC: 2396 2339 2369 Screen printing on fabric articles; women's & misses' outerwear; girls' & children's outerwear

(G-12948)
MANSCI INC
6925 Lake Ellenor Dr # 136 (32809-4648)
PHONE..................................866 763-2122
Ed Godman, *CEO*
Michael Cauley, *President*
EMP: 11 **EST:** 2005
SALES (est): 1.6MM **Privately Held**
WEB: www.mansci.com
SIC: 3821 Laboratory equipment: fume hoods, distillation racks, etc.

(G-12949)
MARILYN JEFFCOAT
1198 Paladin Ct (32812-1983)
PHONE..................................407 382-1783
Marilyn Jeffcoat, *Principal*
EMP: 6 **EST:** 2017
SALES (est): 85.7K **Privately Held**
SIC: 3312 Blast furnaces & steel mills

(G-12950)
MARUTI TECHNOLOGY INC
Also Called: Maruti Fence
1775 Colton Dr (32822-5909)
PHONE..................................407 704-4775
Ketankumar S Dave, *President*
EMP: 14 **EST:** 2010
SALES (est): 149.3K **Privately Held**
WEB: www.fence4sale.com
SIC: 3084 Plastics pipe

(G-12951)
MARVIN J DERICHO
4618 Dutton Dr (32808-7322)
PHONE..................................407 290-0109
Marvin J Dericho, *Principal*
EMP: 6 **EST:** 2006
SALES (est): 116.9K **Privately Held**
SIC: 2411 Logging

(G-12952)
MASCOT FACTORY INC
4376 L B Mcleod Rd (32811-5619)
PHONE..................................877 250-2244
Benjamin E Lee, *Principal*
EMP: 8 **EST:** 2012
SALES (est): 63.2K **Privately Held**
WEB: www.mascotfactory.com
SIC: 3942 Dolls & stuffed toys

(G-12953)
MASTER CONSTRUCTION PDTS INC (PA)
Also Called: MCP
501 Thorpe Rd (32824-8134)
P.O. Box 593918 (32859-3918)
PHONE..................................407 857-1221
Kevin Decker, *President*
Josh Antrobus, *Opers Mgr*
Steve Sweat, *Accounts Mgr*
Brandon Brown, *Branch Mgr*
EMP: 24 **EST:** 2002
SQ FT: 5,000
SALES (est): 8.1MM **Privately Held**
WEB: www.masterconstructionproducts.com
SIC: 3272 Precast terrazo or concrete products

(G-12954)
MATAO BRICK PAVERS INC
4348 S Kirkman Rd Apt 801 (32811-3123)
PHONE..................................321 663-1978
Adeildo A Nogueira, *Principal*
EMP: 6 **EST:** 2008
SALES (est): 265.7K **Privately Held**
WEB: www.totalbrickpavers.com
SIC: 3531 Pavers

(G-12955)
MAYDONE LTD LIABILITY COMPANY
6233 Westgate Dr Apt 613 (32835-7071)
PHONE..................................407 399-3287
Andrii Khimich, *CEO*
EMP: 7 **EST:** 2014
SALES (est): 224.6K **Privately Held**
SIC: 3541 3542 7371 5085 Machine tools, metal cutting type; machine tools, metal forming type; custom computer programming services; industrial supplies; industrial machinery & equipment;

(G-12956)
MEADS INTERNATIONAL INC (HQ)
5600 W Sand Lake Rd (32819-8907)
PHONE..................................407 356-8400
Jim Cravens, *President*
Volker Weidemann, *Engineer*
James Hanbbery, *Treasurer*
Robert Grubbs, *Director*
▲ **EMP:** 60 **EST:** 1996
SALES (est): 24.8MM **Publicly Held**
WEB: www.meads-amd.com
SIC: 3812 Search & navigation equipment

(G-12957)
MECHANICAL SVCS CENTL FLA INC (HQ)
Also Called: Honeywell Authorized Dealer
9820 Satellite Blvd (32837-8447)
PHONE..................................407 857-3510
Bernard B Horne, *CEO*
David Goerke, *President*
Tim Miles, *Vice Pres*
Steve Patiry, *Vice Pres*
Debbie Alazraki, *CFO*
EMP: 204 **EST:** 1974
SQ FT: 50,000
SALES (est): 57.4MM
SALES (corp-wide): 8.8B **Publicly Held**
WEB: www.msifla.com
SIC: 3444 1761 1711 7623 Pipe, sheet metal; sheet metalwork; mechanical contractor; refrigeration repair service
PA: Emcor Group, Inc.
301 Merritt 7 Fl 6
Norwalk CT 06851
203 849-7800

(G-12958)
MED ALERT RESPONSE INC
6239 Edgewater Dr Ste N1 (32810-4735)
PHONE..................................407 730-3571

GEOGRAPHIC

Dorothy King, *President*
EMP: 5 **EST:** 1987
SALES (est): 489.4K **Privately Held**
WEB: www.getmedalert.com
SIC: 3669 5999 Emergency alarms; hospital equipment & supplies

(G-12959)
MELODON SOFTWARE INC
2813 S Hiawassee Rd # 302 (32835-6690)
PHONE..................................407 654-1234
Faramarz Saberian, *President*
EMP: 8 **EST:** 2010
SALES (est): 250.9K **Privately Held**
WEB: www.melodon.healthcare
SIC: 7372 Prepackaged software

(G-12960)
MERCHSPIN INC
Also Called: Akt Enterprises
6424 Forest City Rd (32810-4322)
PHONE..................................877 306-3651
Alex Tchekmeian, *President*
Grant Tchekmeian, *COO*
Jerred Nenderwicv, *Vice Pres*
Robert Pfeffer, *Opers Mgr*
John Raudebaugh, *Prdtn Mgr*
▼ **EMP:** 50 **EST:** 2005
SALES (est): 10.7MM **Privately Held**
WEB: www.aktenterprises.com
SIC: 2759 8741 Screen printing; management services

(G-12961)
MESSER LLC
Also Called: B O C Industrial Gases Div
1134 Central Florida Pkwy (32837-9253)
PHONE..................................407 851-3311
Jason Chagan, *Branch Mgr*
EMP: 16
SALES (corp-wide): 1.2B **Privately Held**
WEB: www.messeramericas.com
SIC: 2813 Nitrogen; oxygen, compressed or liquefied
HQ: Messer Llc
200 Smrst Corp Blvd # 7000
Bridgewater NJ 08807
800 755-9277

(G-12962)
METALHOUSE LLC
4705 S Apk Vnlnd Rd # 140 (32819-3105)
PHONE..................................407 270-3000
John Unsalan, *Mng Member*
John C Unsalan, *Mng Member*
EMP: 6 **EST:** 2014
SALES (est): 912.7K **Privately Held**
WEB: www.metalhouse.us
SIC: 3547 5051 8742 3315 Rolling mill machinery; reinforcement mesh, wire; marketing consulting services; steel wire & related products

(G-12963)
METALMASTER MACHINE SHOP INC
Also Called: Metalmaster Manufacturing Svcs
4549 L B Mcleod Rd (32811-6405)
PHONE..................................407 423-9049
Joe Skawinski, *President*
▼ **EMP:** 12 **EST:** 1981
SQ FT: 7,000
SALES (est): 1.7MM **Privately Held**
WEB: www.metalmaster.biz
SIC: 3599 Machine shop, jobbing & repair

(G-12964)
METTLER-TOLEDO INC
45 N Magnolia Ave (32801-2427)
PHONE..................................407 423-3856
Floyd Haenson, *Manager*
EMP: 12
SALES (corp-wide): 3B **Publicly Held**
WEB: www.packrite.com
SIC: 3596 Industrial scales
HQ: Mettler-Toledo, Llc
1900 Polaris Pkwy Fl 6
Columbus OH 43240
614 438-4511

(G-12965)
MFX CORP
7065 Westpointe Blvd # 205 (32835-8758)
PHONE..................................407 429-4051
Flavio Boghossian, *President*
Martha Norena, *Principal*
Marcus A El Huaick, *Treasurer*
Adriana B El Huaick, *Admin Sec*
EMP: 10 **EST:** 2013
SALES (est): 4MM **Privately Held**
WEB: www.mfxcorp.com
SIC: 3085 8742 Plastics bottles; marketing consulting services
HQ: Riopet Embalagens S/A
Rua Professor Eduardo Vianna 175
Nova Iguacu RJ 26012

(G-12966)
MGM CARGO LLC
Also Called: Fastsigns
7154 W Colonial Dr (32818-6751)
PHONE..................................407 770-1500
Frank Adam, *Mng Member*
Jose Marin,
EMP: 6 **EST:** 2015
SALES (est): 740.8K **Privately Held**
WEB: www.fastsigns.com
SIC: 3993 7313 7336 Signs & advertising specialties; printed media advertising representatives; commercial art & graphic design

(G-12967)
MICHIGAN PMPS ELC MTRS REPR CO
Also Called: Michigan St Pump & Electric
1210 W Michigan St (32805-5451)
PHONE..................................407 841-6800
Jeff Ramsammy, *President*
Sharmilee Ramsammy, *Vice Pres*
EMP: 8 **EST:** 2002
SQ FT: 5,000
SALES (est): 1MM **Privately Held**
WEB: www.michstpump.com
SIC: 7694 3599 Electric motor repair; machine shop, jobbing & repair

(G-12968)
MICROSS COMPONENTS INC (PA)
7725 N Orange Blossom Trl (32810-2636)
PHONE..................................407 298-7100
Vincent Buffa, *CEO*
John Lannon, *General Mgr*
Jeremy Adams, *Vice Pres*
Dane Ramkalawan, *Vice Pres*
Rex Anderson, *Opers Staff*
EMP: 49 **EST:** 2009
SALES (est): 191.4MM **Privately Held**
WEB: www.micross.com
SIC: 3674 Semiconductors & related devices

(G-12969)
MICROSS MINCO LLC
7725 N Orange Blossom Trl (32810-2636)
PHONE..................................512 339-3422
Richard Kingeon, *President*
David Harrison, *Engineer*
Mellisa Martin, *Finance*
Jeff Weiss, *Sales Staff*
EMP: 55 **EST:** 2010
SQ FT: 3,200
SALES (est): 20.5MM
SALES (corp-wide): 191.4MM **Privately Held**
WEB: www.micross.com
SIC: 3674 Microcircuits, integrated (semiconductor)
PA: Micross Components, Inc.
7725 N Orange Blossom Trl
Orlando FL 32810
407 298-7100

(G-12970)
MID-FLORIDA PLASTICS INC
Also Called: Engineered Plastic Specialists
780 Central Florida Pkwy (32824-8502)
PHONE..................................407 856-1805
James Z Golembski, *President*
Gary Golembeski, *Vice Pres*
EMP: 25 **EST:** 1992
SQ FT: 17,000
SALES (est): 2.5MM **Privately Held**
WEB: www.engineeredplastics.net
SIC: 3089 Injection molded finished plastic products; injection molding of plastics

(G-12971)
MILLS & NEBRASKA DOOR & TRIM
2721 Regent Ave (32804-3358)
P.O. Box 536548 (32853-6548)
PHONE..................................407 472-2742
John M Pulsifer, *President*
Roy Pulsifer, *Treasurer*
Thomas S Pulsifer, *Admin Sec*
EMP: 15 **EST:** 1973
SQ FT: 800
SALES (est): 381.2K **Privately Held**
WEB: www.millsnebraska.com
SIC: 2431 5031 3442 Door frames, wood; doors; metal doors, sash & trim

(G-12972)
MILSAV LLC
Also Called: Metronow
10542 Wittenberg Way (32832-7024)
PHONE..................................407 556-5055
Jorge Bravo,
EMP: 7 **EST:** 2007
SALES (est): 272.7K **Privately Held**
SIC: 3661 Telephone sets, all types except cellular radio

(G-12973)
MIX IT LOOP INC
12517 Greco Dr (32824-5823)
PHONE..................................407 902-9334
Rodney Harter, *Principal*
EMP: 8 **EST:** 2010
SALES (est): 91.9K **Privately Held**
SIC: 3273 Ready-mixed concrete

(G-12974)
MOBILITY FREEDOM INC
7260 Narcoossee Rd (32822-5534)
PHONE..................................407 495-1333
EMP: 8
SALES (corp-wide): 218.5MM **Privately Held**
WEB: www.mobilityworks.com
SIC: 3842 7699 Wheelchairs; hospital equipment repair services
HQ: Mobility Freedom, Inc.
20354 Us Highway 27
Clermont FL 34715
352 322-2256

(G-12975)
MODERN WELDING COMPANY FLA INC
1801 Atlanta Ave (32806-3924)
P.O. Box 568678 (32856-8678)
PHONE..................................407 843-1270
James E Jones, *President*
Vince Pedigo, *Warehouse Mgr*
Karen Bleddyn, *Accounting Dir*
Lee Alexander, *Sales Staff*
Jeff Herter, *Sales Staff*
▼ **EMP:** 54 **EST:** 1948
SQ FT: 2,500
SALES (est): 18.5MM
SALES (corp-wide): 159.6MM **Privately Held**
WEB: www.modweldco.com
SIC: 3443 5051 Tanks, standard or custom fabricated: metal plate; steel
PA: Modern Welding Company, Inc.
2880 New Hartford Rd
Owensboro KY 42303
270 685-4400

(G-12976)
MODEST LOGISTICS LLC ✪
2295 S Hiawassee Rd (32835-8746)
PHONE..................................321 314-2825
David Modeste, *Mng Member*
EMP: 11 **EST:** 2021
SALES (est): 120K **Privately Held**
SIC: 3537 Trucks: freight, baggage, etc.: industrial, except mining

(G-12977)
MONARCH SAFETY PRODUCTS INC
121 S Orange Ave Ste 1500 (32801-3241)
PHONE..................................407 442-0269
Nigel Graham, *President*
EMP: 9 **EST:** 2000
SQ FT: 2,500
SALES (est): 283.2K **Privately Held**
SIC: 2385 Waterproof outerwear

(G-12978)
MOOG-FTS
7455 Emerald Dunes Dr # 2 (32822-5185)
PHONE..................................407 264-0611
James Riedel, *President*
Maureen Athoe, *Vice Pres*
Timothy Balkin, *Treasurer*
John Drenning, *Admin Sec*
EMP: 8 **EST:** 2006
SQ FT: 6,640
SALES (est): 2.5MM
SALES (corp-wide): 2.8B **Publicly Held**
WEB: www.moog.com
SIC: 3812 Acceleration indicators & systems components, aerospace
PA: Moog Inc.
400 Jamison Rd
Elma NY 14059
716 652-2000

(G-12979)
MOOSE TRACTS INC
2325 Ohio Dr (32803-2027)
PHONE..................................407 491-1412
Eric Moose, *Owner*
EMP: 9 **EST:** 2018
SALES (est): 286.8K **Privately Held**
SIC: 2434 Wood kitchen cabinets

(G-12980)
MORNING GLORY LAWN MAINTENANCE
4750 Nantucket Ln (32808-2622)
PHONE..................................407 376-5833
Kelvin Rumph, *CEO*
EMP: 5 **EST:** 2008
SALES (est): 385.4K **Privately Held**
SIC: 3524 Lawn & garden equipment

(G-12981)
MORRIS VISITOR PUBLICATIONS
801 N Magnolia Ave # 201 (32803-3842)
PHONE..................................407 423-0618
John Byrne, *Principal*
EMP: 18 **EST:** 2005
SALES (est): 628.5K **Privately Held**
WEB: www.morris.com
SIC: 2759 Publication printing

(G-12982)
MP 93 SCREEN PRINT AND EMB LLC
3330 Vineland Rd Ste C (32811-6453)
PHONE..................................407 592-3657
Philip Fry, *Administration*
EMP: 10 **EST:** 2017
SALES (est): 578.7K **Privately Held**
SIC: 2752 Commercial printing, lithographic

(G-12983)
MR AMERICAS 2 LLC ✪
15771 State Road 535 K (32821-5605)
PHONE..................................407 217-2282
Matheus Cabral,
EMP: 7 **EST:** 2020
SALES (est): 600K **Privately Held**
SIC: 2099 Ready-to-eat meals, salads & sandwiches

(G-12984)
MULTICORE PHOTONICS INC
5832 N Dean Rd (32817-3249)
PHONE..................................407 325-7800
Darren Engle, *CEO*
Jody Wilson, *COO*
Christian Adams, *Senior VP*
Chris Adams, *Vice Pres*
Son Ho, *Vice Pres*
EMP: 6 **EST:** 2015
SALES (est): 409.2K **Privately Held**
WEB: www.multicore-photonics.com
SIC: 3826 3674 3827 Analytical instruments; semiconductors & related devices; optical instruments & apparatus

(G-12985)
MULTICORE PHOTONICS INC
319 N Crystal Lake Dr (32803-5831)
PHONE..................................407 325-7800
EMP: 11 **EST:** 2016
SALES (est): 824.6K **Privately Held**
SIC: 3661 Fiber optics communications equipment

(G-12986)
MULTICORE TECHNOLOGIES LLC
319 N Crystal Lake Dr (32803-5831)
PHONE..................................407 325-7800
Jody Wilson, *COO*
EMP: 5 **EST:** 2019
SALES (est): 302.2K **Privately Held**
SIC: 3674 Semiconductors & related devices

(G-12987)
MUSCLE MIXES INC
1617 Hillcrest St (32803-4809)
P.O. Box 533967 (32853-3967)
PHONE..................................407 872-7576
Denise Imbesi, *President*
Randi Solomon, *Vice Pres*
Vincent Imbesi, *Production*
EMP: 10 **EST:** 1988
SQ FT: 3,070
SALES (est): 1MM **Privately Held**
WEB: www.musclemixes.com
SIC: 3652 5735 Pre-recorded records & tapes; audio tapes, prerecorded

(G-12988)
MUSE GELATO INC
Also Called: Orlando Ice Cream Company
7362 Futures Dr Ste 20 (32819-9088)
PHONE..................................407 363-1443
Andrea N Moss Davidoff, *President*
EMP: 10 **EST:** 2010
SALES (est): 1.2MM **Privately Held**
WEB: www.musegelato.com
SIC: 2024 5143 Ice cream, bulk; ice cream & ices

(G-12989)
NANA FOODS INC
5219 Timberview Ter (32819-3924)
PHONE..................................407 363-7183
Awad Mubarak, *Principal*
EMP: 9 **EST:** 2012
SALES (est): 311.1K **Privately Held**
SIC: 2099 Food preparations

(G-12990)
NATIONAL CYLINDER SERVICES LLC (PA)
4601 Dardanelle Dr (32808-3833)
PHONE..................................407 299-8454
Harold William Berg Jr,
EMP: 21 **EST:** 2006
SALES (est): 2.8MM **Privately Held**
WEB: www.natcyl.com
SIC: 3714 Cylinder heads, motor vehicle

(G-12991)
NATIONAL TCHNCAL CMMUNICATIONS
Also Called: Florida Specifier
8645 Port Said St (32817-1624)
P.O. Box 2175, Goldenrod (32733-2175)
PHONE..................................407 671-7777
Michael R Eastman, *President*
Michael Eastman, *Publisher*
EMP: 5 **EST:** 1974
SQ FT: 1,500
SALES (est): 391.2K **Privately Held**
SIC: 2711 7389 8742 Newspapers: publishing only, not printed on site; trade show arrangement; industrial & labor consulting services

(G-12992)
NATIONAL WOODWORKS INC
4122 Mercy Industrial Ct (32808-3811)
PHONE..................................407 489-3572
John R Gardner, *Director*
Richard D Reimann, *Director*
EMP: 8 **EST:** 2013
SALES (est): 148.3K **Privately Held**
WEB: www.nationalwoodworks.com
SIC: 2431 Millwork

(G-12993)
NATURES FUEL INC
2254 Saw Palmetto Ln (32828-4650)
PHONE..................................407 808-4272
Kleinberg Alan J Sr, *Principal*
EMP: 7 **EST:** 2014
SALES (est): 316K **Privately Held**
WEB: www.naturesfuelorlando.com
SIC: 2869 Fuels

(G-12994)
NATUS MEDICAL INCORPORATED
12301 Lake Underhill Rd # 201 (32828-4511)
PHONE..................................321 235-8213
Josh Cheuvront, *Accountant*
Jamie Phipps, *Accountant*
Jose Leon, *Manager*
Tina Fernandez, *Manager*
Matthew Tinsley, *Manager*
EMP: 30
SALES (corp-wide): 415.6MM **Publicly Held**
WEB: www.natus.com
SIC: 3845 Electromedical equipment
PA: Natus Medical Incorporated
6701 Koll Center Pkwy # 12
Pleasanton CA 94566
925 223-6700

(G-12995)
NATUS MEDICAL INCORPORATED
Also Called: Bio-Logic Systems
12301 Lake Underhill Rd # 201 (32828-4511)
PHONE..................................847 949-5200
EMP: 14
SALES (corp-wide): 530.8MM **Publicly Held**
SIC: 3845 Mfg Electromedical Equipment
PA: Natus Medical Incorporated
6701 Koll Center Pkwy # 12
Pleasanton CA 94566
925 223-6700

(G-12996)
NCG MEDICAL SYSTEMS INC (PA)
Also Called: Perfect Care
1402 Edgewater Dr Ste 101 (32804-6396)
PHONE..................................407 788-1906
Tony Arias, *President*
Riaz Latib, *Engineer*
Jackie Huasupoma, *Mktg Coord*
John Giddings, *Manager*
EMP: 28 **EST:** 1978
SALES (est): 7.2MM **Privately Held**
WEB: www.ncgmedical.com
SIC: 7372 7371 Business oriented computer software; custom computer programming services

(G-12997)
NEPHRON PHARMACEUTICALS
1162 Bella Vida Blvd (32828-6758)
PHONE..................................407 913-3142
Hieu Pham, *Principal*
Justin Austin, *Opers Staff*
Jon Burgess, *Engineer*
Bridgette Vining, *Personnel*
Phyllis Fox, *Sales Staff*
EMP: 20 **EST:** 2010
SALES (est): 3.4MM **Privately Held**
WEB: www.nephronpharm.com
SIC: 2834 Pharmaceutical preparations

(G-12998)
NEPHRON PHARMACEUTICALS CORP
4121 Sw 34th St (32811-6475)
PHONE..................................407 999-2225
Susan Rucker, *Chief*
Charles Taylor, *Vice Pres*
Jon Burgess, *Engineer*
Michelle Brady, *Human Res Mgr*
Lisa Cox, *Sales Staff*
EMP: 30 **EST:** 2019
SALES (est): 6.8MM **Privately Held**
WEB: www.nephronpharm.com
SIC: 2834 Pharmaceutical preparations

(G-12999)
NEW VISION DISPLAY INC
Also Called: Osd Display
135 W Central Blvd # 330 (32801-2430)
PHONE..................................407 480-5800
Khaled R Khuda, *Branch Mgr*
EMP: 7 **Privately Held**
WEB: www.newvisiondisplay.com
SIC: 3679 Liquid crystal displays (LCD)
HQ: New Vision Display, Inc.
1430 Blue Oaks Blvd # 100
Roseville CA 95747
916 786-8111

(G-13000)
NEW YORK INTL BREAD CO
1500 W Church St (32805-2408)
PHONE..................................407 843-9744
Vincent Masella Jr, *President*
Laura Masella, *Vice Pres*
Craig Amster, *Opers Staff*
Sandy Mobley, *CFO*
Abigail Parks, *Asst Mgr*
EMP: 90
SQ FT: 30,000
SALES (est): 18MM **Privately Held**
WEB: www.nyibco.com
SIC: 2051 Bakery: wholesale or wholesale/retail combined; bread, all types (white, wheat, rye, etc): fresh or frozen; rolls, bread type: fresh or frozen

(G-13001)
NEXT STEP PRODUCTS LLC
9400 Southridge Park Ct # 200 (32819-8643)
PHONE..................................407 857-9900
Mark Masterman, *President*
Kathy Cregan,
Rosa Rodriguez,
EMP: 8 **EST:** 2008
SALES (est): 484.8K **Privately Held**
WEB: www.jandy.com
SIC: 3648 Lighting equipment

(G-13002)
NIGHTHAWK RUNNING LLC
Also Called: Nighthawk Safety
1623 Wycliff Dr (32803-1929)
PHONE..................................407 443-8404
Douglas R Storer, *Manager*
EMP: 10 **EST:** 2013
SALES (est): 295.5K **Privately Held**
WEB: www.nighttechgear.com
SIC: 3949 Sporting & athletic goods

(G-13003)
NINA PLASTIC BAGS INC (PA)
Also Called: Nina Plastics
1903 Cypress Lake Dr (32837-8459)
P.O. Box 2758, Windermere (34786-2758)
PHONE..................................407 802-6828
Satish Sharma, *President*
James Snell, *Vice Pres*
◆ **EMP:** 60 **EST:** 1979
SQ FT: 75,000
SALES (est): 10.7MM **Privately Held**
SIC: 3081 Unsupported plastics film & sheet

(G-13004)
NIS PRINT INC
Also Called: National Indexing Systems
1809 S Division Ave (32805-4729)
PHONE..................................407 423-7575
Sheryl A Batchelder, *President*
Cathy Marques, *Med Doctor*
EMP: 44 **EST:** 1986
SQ FT: 30,000
SALES (est): 4.9MM **Privately Held**
WEB: www.nisprint.com
SIC: 2759 Commercial printing

(G-13005)
NITESOL INC
1831 Tallokas Ave (32805-4735)
PHONE..................................407 557-4042
EMP: 6
SALES (est): 440K **Privately Held**
SIC: 3993 Mfg Signs/Advertising Specialties

(G-13006)
NOMMO INTERNATIONAL LLC
1317 Edgewater Dr (32804-6350)
PHONE..................................866 366-3688
EMP: 6
SALES (est): 75K **Privately Held**
SIC: 3953 Mfg Marking Devices

(G-13007)
NORMAN ENGINEERING CORPORATION
2579 N Orange Blossom Trl (32804-4808)
PHONE..................................407 425-6433
Anne Belderes, *President*
John Belderes, *Vice Pres*
Bill Newsom, *Treasurer*
EMP: 7 **EST:** 1972
SQ FT: 2,400
SALES (est): 589.7K **Privately Held**
SIC: 3599 Machine shop, jobbing & repair

(G-13008)
NORTHROP GRUMMAN SYSTEMS CORP
Also Called: Northrop Grmman Mssion Systems
11474 Corp Blvd Ste 120 (32817)
PHONE..................................407 737-4900
James Harvey, *Division Mgr*
Frank Demauro, *Vice Pres*
Marty Amen, *Branch Mgr*
Derek Batts, *Administration*
EMP: 206 **Publicly Held**
WEB: www.northropgrumman.com
SIC: 3812 Search & navigation equipment
HQ: Northrop Grumman Systems Corporation
2980 Fairview Park Dr
Falls Church VA 22042
703 280-2900

GEOGRAPHIC

(G-13009)
NOUVEAU COSMETIQUE USA INC
189 S Orange Ave Ste 1110 (32801-3257)
PHONE..................................321 332-6976
Armand Hoes, *President*
Robert Waters, *Vice Pres*
Joeren Kluge, *Director*
EMP: 6 **EST:** 2009
SQ FT: 2,000
SALES (est): 504.8K **Privately Held**
WEB: www.nouveaucontourusa.com
SIC: 3841 Surgical & medical instruments

(G-13010)
NOVA LASERLIGHT LLC
7600 Dr Phillips Blvd (32819-7231)
PHONE..................................407 226-0609
Jan V Karlin, *Mng Member*
EMP: 10 **EST:** 2011
SALES (est): 631K **Privately Held**
SIC: 3845 Laser systems & equipment, medical

(G-13011)
NOVENA TEC LLC (PA)
4767 New Broad St (32814-6405)
PHONE..................................407 392-1868
Robby Thirun, *Mng Member*
Thanuja Thevan,
EMP: 22 **EST:** 2014
SQ FT: 4,000
SALES (est): 1.3MM **Privately Held**
WEB: www.novenatec.com
SIC: 3559 3699 Semiconductor manufacturing machinery; high-energy particle physics equipment

(G-13012)
NSCRYPT INC
12151 Res Pkwy Ste 150 (32826)
PHONE..................................407 275-4720
Kenneth H Church, *President*
Beth Dickerson, *General Mgr*
Debra Brownell, *Vice Pres*
Xudong Chen, *Vice Pres*
Mike Newton, *Vice Pres*
EMP: 35 **EST:** 2002
SQ FT: 125,000
SALES (est): 10.2MM **Privately Held**
WEB: www.nscrypt.com
SIC: 3577 Printers, computer
PA: Sciperio, Inc.
12151 Res Pkwy Ste 150
Orlando FL 32826
407 275-4755

(G-13013)
NTS INDUSTRIES INC
1218 W New Hampshire St (32804-5759)
P.O. Box 540602 (32854-0602)
PHONE..................................317 847-6675
Nathan Shanabruch, *Principal*
EMP: 18 **EST:** 2009
SALES (est): 70.7K **Privately Held**
WEB: www.nts.com
SIC: 3999 Manufacturing industries

(G-13014)
NUMBER 1 BRICK PAVERS INC
3406 Soho St Apt 101 (32835-7593)
PHONE....................................321 388-7889
Italo Silva, *Principal*
EMP: 7 **EST:** 2008
SALES (est): 133.3K **Privately Held**
WEB: www.number1pavers.com
SIC: 3531 Pavers

(G-13015)
OBERON INDUSTRIES INC
1900 Stanley St (32803-5531)
PHONE....................................321 245-7338
Randall Krull, *President*
EMP: 8 **EST:** 2017
SALES (est): 62K **Privately Held**
WEB: www.oberoninc.com
SIC: 3999 Manufacturing industries

(G-13016)
OCEAN OPTICS INC (HQ)
Also Called: Ocean Insight
3500 Quadrangle Blvd (32817-8326)
P.O. Box 2249, Dunedin (34697-2249)
PHONE....................................407 673-0041
Michael Edwards, *President*
Lora Allemeier, *President*
Bob Daly, *President*
Steve Buckley, *General Mgr*
Kevin Pate, *Business Mgr*
▲ **EMP:** 50 **EST:** 1989
SQ FT: 20,000
SALES (est): 72.1MM
SALES (corp-wide): 1.8B **Privately Held**
WEB: www.oceaninsight.com
SIC: 3826 3827 Analytical instruments; optical instruments & lenses
PA: Halma Public Limited Company
Misbourne Court Rectory Way
Amersham BUCKS HP7 0
149 472-1111

(G-13017)
OCEAN OPTICS INC
Ocean Thin Films
3500 Quadrangle Blvd (32817-8326)
PHONE....................................727 545-0741
Phillip Buchsbaum, *General Mgr*
EMP: 53
SALES (corp-wide): 1.8B **Privately Held**
WEB: www.oceaninsight.com
SIC: 3826 3827 Analytical instruments; optical instruments & lenses
HQ: Ocean Optics, Inc.
3500 Quadrangle Blvd
Orlando FL 32817

(G-13018)
OCEAN WAY TRANSPORT LLC ✪
4529 Piedmont St (32811-4528)
PHONE....................................407 669-3822
Kervens Ocean, *Mng Member*
EMP: 5 **EST:** 2020
SALES (est): 316.5K **Privately Held**
SIC: 3537 Trucks, tractors, loaders, carriers & similar equipment

(G-13019)
OCOA LLC
800 N Magnolia Ave # 1400 (32803-3248)
PHONE....................................407 898-1961
Dagmar Moore, *Mng Member*
EMP: 20
SALES (est): 859.8K **Privately Held**
WEB: www.ocoa.com
SIC: 3652 Pre-recorded records & tapes

(G-13020)
ODYSSEY MANUFACTURING CO
250 Central Florida Pkwy (32824-7601)
PHONE....................................407 582-9051
Randy Hancock, *Plant Supt*
EMP: 8 **EST:** 2016
SALES (est): 82.3K **Privately Held**
WEB: www.odysseymanufacturing.com
SIC: 3999 Manufacturing industries

(G-13021)
OLYMPUS GROUP INC
2100 Principal Row # 407 (32837-8317)
PHONE....................................407 851-6229
Michelle Moore, *Project Mgr*
Linda Winks, *Opers Staff*
Erica Masters, *Production*
Jalena Hegemann, *QC Mgr*
Alex Greeley, *Engineer*
EMP: 6
SALES (corp-wide): 24MM **Privately Held**
WEB: www.olympusgrp.com
SIC: 2399 Banners, made from fabric
PA: Olympus Group, Inc.
9000 W Heather Ave
Milwaukee WI 53224
414 355-2010

(G-13022)
OMNIMARK ENTERPRISES LLC
6843 Narcoossee Rd (32822-5512)
PHONE....................................516 351-9075
Jason Kilner, *Principal*
EMP: 7 **EST:** 2015
SALES (est): 159.7K **Privately Held**
SIC: 2023 Dietary supplements, dairy & non-dairy based

(G-13023)
ONTIC ENGINEERING & MFG
13485 Veterans Way # 600 (32827-7718)
PHONE....................................407 206-8459
EMP: 6 **EST:** 2019
SALES (est): 177.3K **Privately Held**
SIC: 3999 Manufacturing industries

(G-13024)
OPEN MARKET ENTERPRISES LLC
Also Called: Communicate 360
3461 Parkway Center Ct (32808-1047)
PHONE....................................407 322-5434
Ana Torres, *President*
EMP: 9 **EST:** 2017
SALES (est): 826.5K **Privately Held**
SIC: 2396 2752 Fabric printing & stamping; commercial printing, lithographic; commercial printing, offset; promotional printing, lithographic; business form & card printing, lithographic

(G-13025)
OPENKM USA LLC
1715 Branchwater Trl (32825-8508)
PHONE....................................407 257-2640
Mario Zules,
EMP: 6 **EST:** 2017
SALES (est): 289.2K **Privately Held**
WEB: www.openkm.us
SIC: 7372 Prepackaged software

(G-13026)
OPENWATER SEAFOOD LLC
13435 S Orange Ave (32824-6012)
PHONE....................................407 440-0656
Patrick Nierle, *CEO*
EMP: 4 **EST:** 2017
SALES (est): 4MM **Privately Held**
SIC: 2077 Marine fats, oils & meals

(G-13027)
OPTIMUS-FLEET LLC
7550 Futures Dr (32819-9095)
PHONE....................................407 590-5060
Juan Martinez, *COO*
Sergio Barcellos, *Mng Member*
Richard Barcellos, *Director*
Patricia Martinez, *Director*
EMP: 10 **EST:** 2018
SALES (est): 100K **Privately Held**
WEB: www.optimus-fleet.com
SIC: 7372 Operating systems computer software

(G-13028)
OPTRONIC LABORATORIES LLC
4632 36th St (32811-6532)
PHONE....................................407 422-3171
Jay Silverman, *President*
EMP: 16 **EST:** 2018
SQ FT: 25,000
SALES (est): 2.9MM **Privately Held**
WEB: www.optroniclabs.com
SIC: 3825 Instruments to measure electricity

(G-13029)
ORACLE AMERICA INC
7453 T G Lee Blvd (32822-4416)
PHONE....................................407 458-1200
EMP: 25
SALES (corp-wide): 40.4B **Publicly Held**
WEB: www.oracle.com
SIC: 7372 Prepackaged software
HQ: Oracle America, Inc.
500 Oracle Pkwy
Redwood City CA 94065
650 506-7000

(G-13030)
ORION TECHNOLOGIES LLC
12605 Challenger Pkwy # 130 (32826-2711)
PHONE....................................407 476-2120
Nirav Pandya, *CEO*
Larry Ford, *Vice Pres*
Richard Miller, *Vice Pres*
Jeffrey Van Anda, *Vice Pres*
David Beckman, *CFO*
EMP: 28
SQ FT: 12,000
SALES (est): 7MM
SALES (corp-wide): 745.7MM **Privately Held**
WEB: www.oriontechnologies.com
SIC: 3571 Electronic computers
PA: Phoenix Mecano Ag
Hofwisenstrasse 6
Stein Am Rhein SH 8260
432 554-255

(G-13031)
ORLANDO BLINDS FACTORY
210 N Goldenrod Rd Ste 1 (32807-8222)
PHONE....................................407 697-0521
EMP: 10 **EST:** 2019
SALES (est): 387.8K **Privately Held**
WEB: www.orlandoblindsfactory.com
SIC: 2591 Window blinds

(G-13032)
ORLANDO BREWING PARTNERS
1401 W Gore St Ste 3 (32805-3778)
PHONE....................................407 843-6783
John Cheek, *President*
EMP: 8 **EST:** 2002
SALES (est): 156.2K **Privately Held**
WEB: www.orlandobrewing.com
SIC: 2082 Malt beverages

(G-13033)
ORLANDO ICE SERVIVE CORP
2640 Kunze Ave (32806-4443)
PHONE....................................407 999-4940
Alex Zaldibar, *President*
Carlos Herrera, *Principal*
Eddie Roque, *Vice Pres*
EMP: 6 **EST:** 2007
SALES (est): 800K **Privately Held**
SIC: 2097 Manufactured ice

(G-13034)
ORLANDO METAL FABRICATION INC
11516 Satellite Blvd (32837-9228)
PHONE....................................407 850-4313
Jack Scales, *Vice Pres*
Robert Matthias, *IT/INT Sup*
EMP: 13 **EST:** 2005
SALES (est): 750K **Privately Held**
WEB: www.orlandometalfab.net
SIC: 3441 Fabricated structural metal

(G-13035)
ORLANDO NOVELTY LLC (PA)
Also Called: Orlando Novelty Wholesale
1624 Premier Row (32809-5712)
PHONE....................................407 858-9499
Almi Athraf, *Mng Member*
EMP: 5 **EST:** 2014
SALES (est): 596.1K **Privately Held**
WEB: www.orlandonovelty.com
SIC: 3911 Cigar & cigarette accessories

(G-13036)
ORLANDO PLATING CO
601 N Orange Blossom Trl (32805-1491)
P.O. Box 2609 (32802-2609)
PHONE....................................407 843-1140
Servet Aral, *President*
Gary Hall, *Corp Secy*
Cynthia Scott, *Vice Pres*
Norleen Hilliard, *Bookkeeper*
EMP: 8 **EST:** 1940
SQ FT: 20,000
SALES (est): 720.2K **Privately Held**
WEB: www.orlandoplating.com
SIC: 3471 Finishing, metals or formed products

(G-13037)
ORLANDO TIMES INC
4403 Vineland Rd Ste B5 (32811-7362)
P.O. Box 555339 (32855-5339)
PHONE....................................407 841-3052
Calvin Collins Jr, *President*
Lottie Collins, *Admin Sec*
EMP: 5 **EST:** 1976
SALES (est): 559.3K **Privately Held**
WEB: www.orlando-times.com
SIC: 2711 8661 Newspapers: publishing only, not printed on site; religious organizations

(G-13038)
ORLANDOS FORKLIFT SERVICE LLC
3138 Natoma Way (32825-7183)
PHONE....................................407 761-9104
Orlando Rodriguez, *Principal*
EMP: 5 **EST:** 2016
SALES (est): 354.5K **Privately Held**
SIC: 3537 Forklift trucks

(G-13039)
ORTHOMERICA PRODUCTS INC
6333 N Orange Blossom Trl (32810-4223)
P.O. Box 607129 (32860-7129)
PHONE....................................407 290-6592
David C Kerr, *President*
Peter Spears, *COO*
Shannon Schwenn, *Exec VP*
Vicki Lewis, *Purch Agent*
Robert Tetro, *Research*
▲ **EMP:** 180 **EST:** 1989
SQ FT: 80,000
SALES (est): 31.3MM **Privately Held**
WEB: www.orthomerica.com
SIC: 3842 Orthopedic appliances

(G-13040)
OUTDOOR IMAGES CENTRAL FLA INC
4061 Forrestal Ave Unit 2 (32806-6151)
PHONE....................................407 825-9944
Ken D Luzadder, *President*
David Wood, *Vice Pres*
EMP: 5 **EST:** 1990
SQ FT: 2,400
SALES (est): 441.1K **Privately Held**
WEB: www.outdoorimagesinc.net
SIC: 3993 5046 Signs & advertising specialties; neon signs; signs, electrical

(G-13041)
P B C CENTRAL
Also Called: Behrs
3450 Vineland Rd Ste B (32811-6421)
PHONE....................................407 648-2020
Douglass Davis, *Principal*
EMP: 6 **EST:** 1998
SALES (est): 301.6K **Privately Held**
SIC: 2066 2064 Chocolate candy, solid; candy & other confectionery products

(G-13042)
P&A MACHINE
7220 Old Cheney Hwy (32807-6222)
PHONE....................................407 275-5770
Edward Ditges, *Principal*
EMP: 10 **EST:** 2006
SALES (est): 363.8K **Privately Held**
WEB: www.damachine.com
SIC: 3469 3599 Stamping metal for the trade; machine shop, jobbing & repair

(G-13043)
PACK4U LLC
7531 Currency Dr (32809-6922)
PHONE....................................407 857-2871
Jane Garrison, *General Mgr*
Brent Herman, *Director*
Shane Bishop, *Director*
Barry Hart, *Director*
EMP: 21 **EST:** 2011

SALES (est): 3MM Privately Held
WEB: www.pack4u.com
SIC: 2834 Druggists' preparations (pharmaceuticals)

(G-13044)
PALLET ENTERPRISES ORLANDO INC
10694 Cosmonaut Blvd (32824-7615)
PHONE 407 888-3200
Pepe Lopez, *Principal*
EMP: 8 EST: 2006
SALES (est): 639K Privately Held
SIC: 2448 Pallets, wood

(G-13045)
PALLET RACKS PLUS LLC
20445 Nettleton St (32833-4041)
PHONE 321 203-6634
Lindsay Jenkins, *Principal*
EMP: 6 EST: 2015
SALES (est): 115.4K Privately Held
WEB: www.palletracksplus.net
SIC: 2448 Pallets, wood

(G-13046)
PAMATIAN GROUP INC (PA)
Also Called: Minuteman Press
997 W Kennedy Blvd Ste A1 (32810-6100)
PHONE 407 291-8387
Mark Peeples, *President*
Ken Windsor, *Principal*
Tim Yousef, *Treasurer*
EMP: 4 EST: 1970
SALES (est): 3.5MM Privately Held
WEB: www.chanhassen-mn.minuteman-press.com
SIC: 2752 Commercial printing, lithographic

(G-13047)
PANAMA JACK INC
230 Ernestine St (32801-3622)
PHONE 407 843-8110
Jack Katz, *Ch of Bd*
Kimberly Mana, *President*
Larry Green, *Vice Pres*
Beau Katz, *Project Mgr*
Jeffrey Bowma, *CFO*
▼ EMP: 10 EST: 1974
SQ FT: 27,000
SALES (est): 2.5MM Privately Held
WEB: www.panamajack.com
SIC: 2844 Suntan lotions & oils

(G-13048)
PANOPTEX TECHNOLOGIES INC
6555 Sanger Rd Ste 100 (32827-7585)
PHONE 407 412-0222
EMP: 15 EST: 2017
SALES (est): 605.3K Privately Held
SIC: 3652 Pre-recorded records & tapes

(G-13049)
PAPER PALM LLC
Also Called: Sir Speedy
621 Commonwealth Ave (32803-5223)
PHONE 407 647-3328
EMP: 6
SALES (est): 908.5K Privately Held
SIC: 2752 Comm Prtg Litho

(G-13050)
PAPILA DESIGN INC
701 W Landstreet Rd (32824-8022)
PHONE 407 240-2992
Ayhan Papila, *President*
◆ EMP: 9 EST: 1992
SQ FT: 20,000
SALES (est): 1MM Privately Held
WEB: www.papiladesign.com
SIC: 3645 Table lamps

(G-13051)
PASSUR AEROSPACE INC
5750 Major Blvd Ste 530 (32819-7965)
PHONE 631 589-6800
G S Beckwith Gilbert, *Ch of Bd*
James T Barry, *President*
Renee Alter, *Vice Pres*
John Keller, *Vice Pres*
Bill Leber, *Vice Pres*
EMP: 6 EST: 1978
SALES (est): 3.1MM
SALES (corp-wide): 11.5MM Publicly Held
WEB: www.passur.com
SIC: 3671 Cathode ray tubes, including rebuilt
PA: Passur Aerospace, Inc.
1 Landmark Sq Ste 1905
Stamford CT 06901
203 622-4086

(G-13052)
PASTRANA PRIME LLC ✪
524 Madrigal Ct (32825-3367)
PHONE 407 470-9339
Danny Pastrana, *Owner*
EMP: 10 EST: 2021
SALES (est): 322.9K Privately Held
SIC: 2511 5023 5719 Kitchen & dining room furniture; decorative home furnishings & supplies; kitchen tools & utensils; lighting, lamps & accessories

(G-13053)
PATRIOT PRESS INC
14141 Lake Price Dr (32826-3504)
PHONE 407 625-7516
Arnie B Eastlick, *President*
EMP: 10 EST: 2000
SALES (est): 382.5K Privately Held
WEB: www.patriotpress.net
SIC: 2752 Commercial printing, offset

(G-13054)
PAVEMAX
5401 S Kirkman Rd 310a (32819-7940)
PHONE 407 494-1959
EMP: 6 EST: 2018
SALES (est): 90.7K Privately Held
WEB: www.pavemax.com
SIC: 2951 Asphalt paving mixtures & blocks

(G-13055)
PAVER SYSTEMS LLC
Also Called: Tarmac America
39 E Landstreet Rd (32824-7814)
PHONE 407 859-9117
Rod Ross, *Engrg Mgr*
Nancy Murphy, *Office Mgr*
EMP: 47
SALES (corp-wide): 118.5MM Privately Held
WEB: www.paversystems.com
SIC: 3281 3272 3271 2816 Paving blocks, cut stone; concrete products; concrete block & brick; inorganic pigments; masonry materials & supplies; paving materials
HQ: Paver Systems, Llc
7167 Interpace Rd
Riviera Beach FL 33407
561 844-5202

(G-13056)
PBC PAVERS BORBA CO
1841 S Kirkman Rd # 1311 (32811-2378)
PHONE 407 296-7727
Sidney S Borba, *President*
EMP: 6 EST: 2004
SALES (est): 72.1K Privately Held
SIC: 2951 Asphalt paving mixtures & blocks

(G-13057)
PEI SHORES INC
4100 Silver Star Rd Ste C (32808-4618)
PHONE 407 523-2899
Jack Law, *President*
EMP: 7 EST: 2012
SALES (est): 254.7K Privately Held
WEB: www.embroideryworksplus.com
SIC: 2395 Embroidery & art needlework

(G-13058)
PELLICONI FLORIDA LLC (HQ)
2501 Principal Row (32837-8357)
PHONE 407 855-6984
Pier Nigito, *Opers Mgr*
Dan Breeze, *QC Mgr*
Cristina Casalboni, *Human Resources*
Stephen Donaghy, *Sales Staff*
Massimo Sabattini, *Sales Staff*
◆ EMP: 46 EST: 2009
SALES (est): 15.2MM
SALES (corp-wide): 52.7MM Privately Held
WEB: www.pelliconi.com
SIC: 3565 Packaging machinery
PA: Pelliconi & C. Spa
Via Emilia 314
Ozzano Dell'emilia BO 40064
051 651-2611

(G-13059)
PENINSULA METAL FINISHING INC
2550 Dinneen Ave (32804-4204)
P.O. Box 540899 (32854-0899)
PHONE 407 291-1023
C David Roach, *President*
F Smith Coachman, *Corp Secy*
EMP: 50 EST: 1985
SQ FT: 22,000
SALES (est): 1.3MM Privately Held
WEB: www.pmforlando.com
SIC: 3471 Anodizing (plating) of metals or formed products; plating of metals or formed products

(G-13060)
PEPSI BEVERAGES COMPANY
7701 Southland Blvd (32809-6948)
PHONE 407 241-4110
Bruce Matzner, *Vice Pres*
EMP: 42 EST: 2019
SALES (est): 4.7MM
SALES (corp-wide): 70.3B Publicly Held
WEB: www.pepsico.com
SIC: 2086 Carbonated soft drinks, bottled & canned
PA: Pepsico, Inc.
700 Anderson Hill Rd
Purchase NY 10577
914 253-2000

(G-13061)
PEPSI-COLA BOTTLING CO TAMPA
1700 Directors Row (32809-6299)
P.O. Box 593889 (32859-3889)
PHONE 407 857-3301
Laurence Roethel, *Opers Mgr*
Emmanuel Ige, *Production*
John Williams, *Marketing Staff*
John Nichols, *Manager*
Elizabeth Elrod, *Manager*
EMP: 10
SQ FT: 33,000
SALES (corp-wide): 70.3B Publicly Held
WEB: www.pepsico.com
SIC: 2086 Carbonated soft drinks, bottled & canned
HQ: Pepsi-Cola Bottling Company Of Tampa
11315 N 30th St
Tampa FL 33612
813 971-2550

(G-13062)
PEPSI-COLA BOTTLING CO TAMPA
7501 Monetary Dr (32809-5730)
PHONE 407 826-5929
EMP: 224
SALES (corp-wide): 70.3B Publicly Held
WEB: www.pepsico.com
SIC: 2086 Carbonated soft drinks, bottled & canned
HQ: Pepsi-Cola Bottling Company Of Tampa
11315 N 30th St
Tampa FL 33612
813 971-2550

(G-13063)
PEPSI-COLA METRO BTLG CO INC
7380 W Sand Lake Rd # 230 (32819-5248)
PHONE 407 354-5800
Ben Witten, *Finance*
Rebecca Ross, *Marketing Staff*
Rich Panner, *Manager*
Marc Fantone, *Manager*
Greg Merthie, *Manager*
EMP: 6
SALES (corp-wide): 70.3B Publicly Held
WEB: www.pepsico.com
SIC: 2086 Carbonated soft drinks, bottled & canned
HQ: Pepsi-Cola Metropolitan Bottling Company, Inc.
1111 Westchester Ave
White Plains NY 10604
914 767-6000

(G-13064)
PERFORMANCE AIRCRAFT UNLIMITED
4918 Sudbury Ct (32826-4012)
PHONE 808 782-7171
Herve Lejeune, *Principal*
EMP: 6 EST: 2015
SALES (est): 164.9K Privately Held
WEB: www.carf-models.com
SIC: 3944 Games, toys & children's vehicles

(G-13065)
PERFUMELAND
5216 Vanguard St (32819-8527)
PHONE 407 354-3342
EMP: 13
SALES (est): 3.4MM Privately Held
SIC: 2844 Mfg Toilet Preparations

(G-13066)
PHINTEC LLC
618 E South St Ste 500 (32801-2986)
PHONE 321 214-2500
Todd Ludington,
EMP: 5 EST: 1996
SALES (est): 525.9K Privately Held
WEB: www.phintec.com
SIC: 3571 7373 Electronic computers; value-added resellers, computer systems

(G-13067)
PIEZO TECHNOLOGY INC (HQ)
Also Called: Mtronpti
2525 Shader Rd (32804-2721)
PHONE 407 298-2000
William Drafts, *President*
Luis Romaguera, *General Mgr*
Paul A Dechen, *Vice Pres*
Mike Howard, *Vice Pres*
Luis Delatorre, *Opers Mgr*
EMP: 103 EST: 1967
SQ FT: 75,000
SALES (est): 7.9MM
SALES (corp-wide): 31.1MM Publicly Held
WEB: www.mtronpti.com
SIC: 3679 3677 3825 Oscillators; resonant reed devices, electronic; piezoelectric crystals; filtration devices, electronic; instruments to measure electricity
PA: Lgl Group, Inc.
2525 Shader Rd
Orlando FL 32804
407 298-2000

(G-13068)
PILKINGTON NORTH AMERICA INC
4500 Seaboard Rd Ste A (32808-3846)
PHONE 407 295-8560
Kevin Howel, *Manager*
EMP: 10 Privately Held
WEB: www.pilkington.com
SIC: 3211 Flat glass
HQ: Pilkington North America, Inc.
811 Madison Ave Fl 3
Toledo OH 43604
419 247-3731

(G-13069)
PITBULL TACTICAL LLC
3564 Avalon Park Blvd E (32828-7365)
PHONE 866 452-4708
EMP: 6 EST: 2018
SALES (est): 158.9K Privately Held
WEB: www.pitbulltactical.com
SIC: 3131 Footwear cut stock

(G-13070)
PIXELTEQ INC (DH)
3500 Quadrangle Blvd (32817-8326)
PHONE 727 545-0741
Phil Buchsbaum, *CEO*
Mark Lavelee, *President*
Gordon McPhee, *Vice Pres*

GEOGRAPHIC

Richard Eichholtz, *Mfg Dir*
Brad Bishop, *Mfg Staff*
▲ **EMP:** 9 **EST:** 2009
SALES (est): 9.9MM
SALES (corp-wide): 1.8B **Privately Held**
WEB: www.oceaninsight.com
SIC: 3827 Optical instruments & lenses
HQ: Halma Holdings Inc.
11500 Northlake Dr # 306
Cincinnati OH 45249
513 772-5501

(G-13071)
PLANAR ENERGY DEVICES INC
653 W Michigan St (32805-6203)
PHONE..................................407 459-1440
EMP: 10
SALES (est): 1.5MM **Privately Held**
SIC: 3674 Semiconductors And Related Devices, Nsk

(G-13072)
PLAYLIST LIVE INC
Also Called: Akt
6424 Forest City Rd (32810-4322)
PHONE..................................877 306-3651
Jared Mendelewicz, *Vice Pres*
John Raudebaugh, *Manager*
Rena Tchekmeian, *Director*
EMP: 22 **EST:** 2010
SALES (est): 2.4MM **Privately Held**
WEB: www.new.playlist-live.com
SIC: 2752 Offset & photolithographic printing

(G-13073)
PMA LLC
4646 Patricia Ann Ct (32839-1324)
PHONE..................................407 310-2548
Dean Snyder, *Principal*
EMP: 6 **EST:** 2016
SALES (est): 123.9K **Privately Held**
SIC: 3724 Aircraft engines & engine parts

(G-13074)
POWDER COATING FACTORY LLC
635 Wilmer Ave (32808-7635)
PHONE..................................407 286-4550
Boris Roitman, *Branch Mgr*
EMP: 6
SALES (corp-wide): 1.4MM **Privately Held**
WEB: www.thepowdercoatingfactory.com
SIC: 3479 Coating of metals & formed products
PA: The Powder Coating Factory Llc
1453 Valley Pine Cir
Apopka FL

(G-13075)
POWER EVOLUTION INC
14163 Sapphire Bay Cir (32828-7482)
PHONE..................................305 318-8476
Omar Masri, *President*
EMP: 7 **EST:** 2016
SALES (est): 163.7K **Privately Held**
WEB: www.buypowerevolution.com
SIC: 3651 Audio electronic systems

(G-13076)
POWERDMS INC
Also Called: Innovative Data Solutions
101 S Garland Ave Ste 300 (32801-3277)
P.O. Box 2468 (32802-2468)
PHONE..................................407 992-6000
David Digiacomo, *CEO*
Joshua J Brown, *President*
Christine Goracke, *Partner*
Ryan Robinson, *Partner*
Kelly Kyle, *Regional Mgr*
EMP: 75
SQ FT: 15,506
SALES (est): 11.5MM **Privately Held**
WEB: www.powerdms.com
SIC: 7372 Prepackaged software

(G-13077)
PRAESTO ENTERPRISES LLC
Also Called: JW Machine
2525 Industrial Blvd (32804-4209)
PHONE..................................407 298-9171
Mark Chen, *CEO*
Phyllis Chen, *Mng Member*
EMP: 7 **EST:** 1986
SQ FT: 4,000
SALES (est): 827.9K **Privately Held**
WEB: www.jwmachinecorp.com
SIC: 3599 8711 3451 3452 Machine shop, jobbing & repair; mechanical engineering; screw machine products; bolts, nuts, rivets & washers; acceleration indicators & systems components, aerospace

(G-13078)
PRAXIS SOFTWARE INC
7575 Kingspointe Pkwy # 9 (32819-8593)
PHONE..................................407 226-5691
Rhonda Copley, *President*
Amin Ismail, *Vice Pres*
EMP: 10 **EST:** 1998
SALES (est): 727.8K **Privately Held**
SIC: 7372 7371 Prepackaged software; custom computer programming services

(G-13079)
PRECAST DESIGNS INC
Also Called: T & T Concrete Specialties
10305 Rocket Ct (32824-8559)
PHONE..................................407 856-5444
David E Ford, *President*
EMP: 19 **EST:** 1975
SALES (est): 3.3MM **Privately Held**
WEB: www.precastdesigns.net
SIC: 3272 Concrete products, precast

(G-13080)
PRECISION INFINITY SYSTEMS INC
14569 Jamaica Dogwood Dr (32828-4833)
P.O. Box 781005 (32878-1005)
PHONE..................................407 490-2320
Michael Adamission, *President*
EMP: 5 **EST:** 2006
SALES (est): 348.6K **Privately Held**
SIC: 7372 7389 Application computer software;

(G-13081)
PREFERRED MATERIALS INC
7120 Overland Rd (32810-3422)
PHONE..................................407 578-1200
Paul Eveland, *Plant Mgr*
EMP: 9 **EST:** 2019
SALES (est): 191.3K **Privately Held**
WEB: www.preferredmaterials.com
SIC: 3273 Ready-mixed concrete

(G-13082)
PREFERRED METAL PRODUCTS INC
3614 Princeton Oaks St (32808-5636)
PHONE..................................407 296-4449
Lawrence Bechtold, *President*
Angela Bechtold, *Vice Pres*
Ryan Bechtold, *Treasurer*
EMP: 13 **EST:** 1988
SQ FT: 14,000
SALES (est): 2.2MM **Privately Held**
WEB: www.preferredmetal.com
SIC: 3444 Sheet metalwork

(G-13083)
PRESTIGE FLRG INSTLLATIONS INC
Also Called: Prestige Granite & Marble
3065 Pennington Dr (32804-3333)
PHONE..................................407 291-0609
Mark D'Agostino, *President*
Karen D'Agostino, *Vice Pres*
▲ **EMP:** 14 **EST:** 1989
SQ FT: 8,000
SALES (est): 839.6K **Privately Held**
WEB: www.prestigegranite.net
SIC: 3281 1752 Granite, cut & shaped; floor laying & floor work

(G-13084)
PRESTIGE/AB READY MIX LLC
8529 Suthpark Cir Ste 320 (32819)
PHONE..................................407 847-7229
John Anderson, *Manager*
EMP: 10
SALES (corp-wide): 11.2MM **Privately Held**
SIC: 3273 Ready-mixed concrete
PA: Prestige/Ab Ready Mix, Llc
7228 Westport Pl Ste C
West Palm Beach FL 33413
561 478-9980

(G-13085)
PRICE CHOPPER INC
Also Called: Price Chopper Wristbands
6325 Mccoy Rd (32822-5167)
PHONE..................................407 679-1600
Shara Sooknarine, *President*
Jefferson Sooknarine, *Chairman*
Jennifer Collins, *Vice Pres*
Deven Pathak, *Vice Pres*
Nyla Sooknarine, *CFO*
◆ **EMP:** 40 **EST:** 1997
SQ FT: 43,000
SALES (est): 9.1MM **Privately Held**
WEB: www.pchopper.com
SIC: 2389 Arm bands, elastic

(G-13086)
PRICE CHPPER MED WRSTBANDS INC
Also Called: Medical ID Solutions
6325 Mccoy Rd (32822-5167)
PHONE..................................407 505-5809
Tory Jacobson, *Sales Staff*
Leslie Gray, *Manager*
Ricardo Rivera, *Manager*
Shara Sooknarine, *Director*
EMP: 5 **EST:** 2006
SALES (est): 871.1K **Privately Held**
WEB: www.medicalbands.com
SIC: 3089 Bands, plastic

(G-13087)
PRIMUS STERILIZER COMPANY LLC (HQ)
7936 Forest City Rd (32810-2907)
PHONE..................................402 344-4200
Michael Douglas, *President*
David Counley, *Vice Pres*
Dave Schall, *Vice Pres*
Dan Schenk, *Plant Mgr*
Gary Molacek, *Materials Mgr*
EMP: 15 **EST:** 1990
SALES (est): 14.8MM
SALES (corp-wide): 73.1MM **Privately Held**
WEB: www.spire-is.com
SIC: 3842 Sterilizers, hospital & surgical
PA: K S T Industries Inc
6400 Northam Dr
Mississauga ON L4V 1
905 362-6400

(G-13088)
PRINT MY ATM LLC
100 W Lucerne Cir Ste 200 (32801-3718)
PHONE..................................866 292-6179
William Saunders, *President*
EMP: 6 **EST:** 2014
SALES (est): 260.4K **Privately Held**
WEB: www.printmyuniversity.com
SIC: 2752 Commercial printing, lithographic

(G-13089)
PRINTERS EDGE LLC
6229 Edgewater Dr Ste 400 (32810-4773)
P.O. Box 160602, Altamonte Springs (32716-0602)
PHONE..................................407 294-8542
EMP: 13
SALES (est): 1.5MM **Privately Held**
SIC: 2752 Lithographic Commercial Printing

(G-13090)
PRINTING USA INC
4732 S Orange Blossom Trl (32839-1708)
PHONE..................................407 857-7468
Robert Hill, *President*
Susan Hill, *Sales Staff*
Lance Bell, *Graphic Designe*
EMP: 12 **EST:** 1982
SQ FT: 8,821
SALES (est): 4.2MM **Privately Held**
WEB: www.printingusa.org
SIC: 2752 Commercial printing, offset

(G-13091)
PRO CHEM PRODUCTS INC
1340 W Central Blvd (32805-1754)
PHONE..................................407 425-5533
EMP: 6
SQ FT: 7,500
SALES: 1MM **Privately Held**
SIC: 2842 5064 5013 2841 Mfg Polish/Sanitation Gd Whol Appliances/Tv/Radio Whol Auto Parts/Supplies Mfg Soap/Other Detergent

(G-13092)
PRO DUFFERS ORLANDO
1144 Ballyshannon Pkwy (32828-8682)
PHONE..................................407 641-7626
Otis Windham, *Principal*
EMP: 9 **EST:** 2010
SALES (est): 245.7K **Privately Held**
WEB: www.produffersorlando.com
SIC: 3949 Shafts, golf club

(G-13093)
PRO MACHINE INC
6150 Edgewater Dr Ste H (32810-4861)
PHONE..................................407 296-5031
Roger Bolen, *President*
EMP: 5 **EST:** 1994
SQ FT: 4,000
SALES (est): 400.4K **Privately Held**
SIC: 3599 Machine shop, jobbing & repair

(G-13094)
PRO-CRETE MATERIAL CORPORATION
1617 S Division Ave (32805-4725)
PHONE..................................352 748-1505
Adam Freeman, *President*
EMP: 21 **EST:** 2011
SALES (est): 932K **Privately Held**
SIC: 3272 Concrete products, precast

(G-13095)
PROFITSWORD LLC
7512 Dr Phillips Blvd (32819-5131)
PHONE..................................407 909-8822
Michele Beardsley, *Accounts Mgr*
Dana Ertler, *Accounts Mgr*
Michele Schnieder, *Accounts Mgr*
Michele Mott, *Marketing Staff*
Heather Armstrong, *Manager*
EMP: 50 **EST:** 2001
SALES (est): 6.7MM **Privately Held**
WEB: www.profitsword.com
SIC: 7372 Business oriented computer software

(G-13096)
PROFOUNDA HEALTH & BEAUTY
10501 S Orange Ave # 124 (32824-7749)
PHONE..................................407 270-7792
Todd Maclaughlan, *Principal*
EMP: 10 **EST:** 2019
SALES (est): 957.6K **Privately Held**
WEB: www.profounda.com
SIC: 2834 Pharmaceutical preparations

(G-13097)
PROLOGO BRANDING LLC
5508 Commerce Dr (32839-2975)
PHONE..................................407 730-9831
Bryan Crist, *Principal*
EMP: 7 **EST:** 2014
SALES (est): 368.9K **Privately Held**
WEB: www.prologobranding.com
SIC: 2395 Embroidery products, except schiffli machine

(G-13098)
PRS TACO PLACE
717 W Smith St (32804-5225)
PHONE..................................407 440-2803
EMP: 6 **EST:** 2019
SALES (est): 249.3K **Privately Held**
SIC: 2741 Miscellaneous publishing

(G-13099)
PUCH MANUFACTURING CORPORATION
3701 Saint Valentine Way (32811-6515)
PHONE..................................407 650-9926
Carl Puch, *President*
Dale Puch, *Vice Pres*
Neil Perkins, *Purch Agent*
EMP: 30 **EST:** 1966
SQ FT: 27,000
SALES (est): 3.1MM **Privately Held**
WEB: www.puch.com
SIC: 3599 Machine shop, jobbing & repair

(G-13100)
PURECYCLE TECHNOLOGIES INC (PA)
5950 Hazeltine National D (32822-5035)
PHONE..................................877 648-3565
Michael Otworth, *Ch of Bd*
Michael Dee, *CFO*
David Brenner, *Ch Credit Ofcr*
Dustin Olson, *Chief Mktg Ofcr*
Brad Kalter, *Admin Sec*
EMP: 31 **EST:** 2015
SQ FT: 2,870
SALES (est): 6.2MM **Publicly Held**
SIC: 2821 4953 Polypropylene resins; recycling, waste materials

(G-13101)
PURPLEGLASSBOUTIQUE LLC
6337 W Colonial Dr (32818-6817)
PHONE..................................407 601-2641
Kenisha R Laws, *Mng Member*
Kenisha Laws,
EMP: 6 **EST:** 2013
SALES (est): 505.8K **Privately Held**
WEB: www.purpleglassboutique.com
SIC: 2389 5621 Men's miscellaneous accessories; boutiques

(G-13102)
QUALCOMM ATHEROS INC
5955 T G Lee Blvd Ste 600 (32822-4431)
PHONE..................................407 284-7314
Shu Zhang, *Engineer*
Bob Guarnieri, *Branch Mgr*
EMP: 10
SALES (corp-wide): 23.5B **Publicly Held**
SIC: 3674 Semiconductors & related devices
HQ: Qualcomm Atheros, Inc.
1700 Technology Dr
San Jose CA 95110
408 773-5200

(G-13103)
QUALITY CABLE CONTRACTORS INC
Also Called: Quality Cable & Communications
1936 Premier Row (32809-6206)
PHONE..................................407 246-0606
Jorge Del Rio, *President*
Gabriel Del Rio, *Vice Pres*
Milagros Del Rio, *Vice Pres*
Josh Barajas, *Project Mgr*
EMP: 46 **EST:** 1986
SQ FT: 2,100
SALES (est): 5.7MM **Privately Held**
WEB: www.qccflorida.com
SIC: 3663 1799 1623 5063 Cable television equipment; cable splicing service; cable laying construction; cable conduit; fiber optic cable installation; access control systems specialization; burglar alarm maintenance & monitoring

(G-13104)
QUANTUM-L/S DNA LABS INTL
511 Shady Lane Dr (32804-5812)
PHONE..................................407 246-0484
Charles Badger, *Principal*
EMP: 7 **EST:** 2015
SALES (est): 90.2K **Privately Held**
SIC: 3572 Computer storage devices

(G-13105)
QUEST DRAPE
10003 Satellite Blvd # 210 (32837-8473)
PHONE..................................407 888-8164
Nicole Peters, *Sales Mgr*
Megan Burge, *Office Mgr*
Jim Cundiff, *Director*
EMP: 8 **EST:** 2015
SALES (est): 149.9K **Privately Held**
WEB: www.questevents.com
SIC: 2391 Curtains & draperies

(G-13106)
QWIKPIK GOLF LLC
10096 Tavistock Rd (32827-7053)
PHONE..................................407 505-5546
Mary T Spacone,
EMP: 5 **EST:** 2010
SALES (est): 347.9K **Privately Held**
SIC: 3949 Golf equipment

(G-13107)
R & A POWER GRAPHICS INC
Also Called: Fastsigns
5000 E Colonial Dr (32803-4312)
PHONE..................................407 898-5770
Renee Friedman, *President*
Samir Martinez, *Opers Mgr*
Renee Friedman Codron, *Admin Sec*
EMP: 11 **EST:** 2001
SALES (est): 2.9MM **Privately Held**
WEB: www.fastsigns.com
SIC: 3993 Signs & advertising specialties

(G-13108)
R B CASTING INC
637 22nd St (32805-5311)
PHONE..................................407 648-2005
Randy Beasley, *Principal*
EMP: 8 **EST:** 2004
SALES (est): 72.8K **Privately Held**
SIC: 3324 Steel investment foundries

(G-13109)
R G MANAGEMENT INC
Also Called: Spectrum Packaging
3640 Princeton Oaks St (32808-5636)
PHONE..................................407 889-3100
Michael F Rogers, *President*
Bill Cassese, *Vice Pres*
Mark Mills, *Vice Pres*
Missy Todd, *Manager*
Elizabeth L Cassese, *Representative*
EMP: 47 **EST:** 1996
SQ FT: 26,400
SALES (est): 7.5MM **Privately Held**
WEB: www.thinkspc.com
SIC: 2657 Folding paperboard boxes

(G-13110)
R K CONSTRUCTORS OF CENTL FLA
4630 S Kirkman Rd Ste 221 (32811-2833)
PHONE..................................407 222-5376
Stanton Reich, *President*
EMP: 6 **EST:** 1992
SQ FT: 3,500
SALES (est): 181K **Privately Held**
SIC: 2431 Millwork

(G-13111)
RADIXX SOLUTIONS INTL INC (HQ)
20 N Orange Ave Ste 150 (32801-4604)
PHONE..................................407 856-9009
John Elieson, *President*
Jamie Schulze, *COO*
Ludvik Olason, *Vice Pres*
Blair Morgan, *Sales Staff*
Jamie O'Coin, *Marketing Staff*
EMP: 50 **EST:** 1993
SQ FT: 15,000
SALES (est): 9MM **Publicly Held**
WEB: www.radixx.com
SIC: 7372 Prepackaged software

(G-13112)
RAFAB SPCIALTY FABRICATION INC
2116 W Central Blvd (32805-2131)
P.O. Box 585665 (32858-5665)
PHONE..................................407 422-3750
Rick Arnold, *President*
Scott Campbell, *Vice Pres*
Cindy Hester, *Manager*
EMP: 18 **EST:** 1987
SQ FT: 12,000
SALES (est): 2.4MM **Privately Held**
WEB: www.rafab.com
SIC: 3441 3444 Fabricated structural metal; sheet metalwork

(G-13113)
RAPHA PHARMACEUTICALS INC
7208 W Sand Lake Rd (32819-5200)
PHONE..................................727 946-9444
EMP: 7 **EST:** 2016
SALES (est): 172.3K **Privately Held**
WEB: www.raphapharma.com
SIC: 2834 Pharmaceutical preparations

(G-13114)
RAVAGO AMERICAS LLC (DH)
Also Called: Amco Polymers
1900 Smmit Twr Blvd Ste 9 (32810)
PHONE..................................407 773-7777
James Duffy, *President*
Carl Hill, *General Mgr*
Anthony Segale, *General Mgr*
Oscar Novo, *Senior VP*
John Provost, *Vice Pres*
◆ **EMP:** 520 **EST:** 2003
SALES (est): 814.6MM
SALES (corp-wide): 1.9MM **Privately Held**
WEB: www.rma.ravagomanufacturing.com
SIC: 2821 5162 Plastics materials & resins; plastics resins

(G-13115)
RAVAGO HOLDINGS AMERICA INC (DH)
1900 Smmit Twr Blvd Ste 9 (32810)
PHONE..................................407 875-9595
James Duffy, *President*
Mark Appelbaum, *Vice Pres*
Damian M Mullin, *Vice Pres*
Ronald Nardozzi, *Vice Pres*
John Provost, *Vice Pres*
▲ **EMP:** 75 **EST:** 2006
SALES (est): 1.7B
SALES (corp-wide): 1.9MM **Privately Held**
WEB: www.ravago.com
SIC: 2821 Plastics materials & resins
HQ: Ravago Distribution S.A.
Rue De Merl 76-78
Luxembourg
264 804-35

(G-13116)
RAYTHEON COMPANY
13501 Ingenuity Dr # 100 (32826-3017)
PHONE..................................321 235-6682
Bernard Sacco, *Engineer*
Robert Suarez, *Financial Analy*
Catherine Emerick, *Manager*
David Beltran, *Director*
EMP: 6
SALES (corp-wide): 56.5B **Publicly Held**
WEB: www.rtx.com
SIC: 3812 3663 3761 Defense systems & equipment; space satellite communications equipment; airborne radio communications equipment; guided missiles & space vehicles, research & development; rockets, space & military, complete
HQ: Raytheon Company
870 Winter St
Waltham MA 02451
781 522-3000

(G-13117)
RAYTHEON COMPANY
12792 Research Pkwy # 100 (32826-3245)
PHONE..................................407 207-9223
Donna McCullough, *Accounts Mgr*
Lisa Nguyen, *Branch Mgr*
Yvette Wilde, *Manager*
EMP: 55
SALES (corp-wide): 56.5B **Publicly Held**
WEB: www.rtx.com
SIC: 3812 Search & navigation equipment
HQ: Raytheon Company
870 Winter St
Waltham MA 02451
781 522-3000

(G-13118)
RAYTHEON COMPANY
2603 Challenger Tech Ct (32826-2716)
PHONE..................................321 235-1700
Bishi Das, *Finance*
Mike Edwards, *Branch Mgr*
Douglas Dayton, *Software Engr*
EMP: 6
SALES (corp-wide): 56.5B **Publicly Held**
WEB: www.rtx.com
SIC: 3812 Defense systems & equipment
HQ: Raytheon Company
870 Winter St
Waltham MA 02451
781 522-3000

(G-13119)
REAL THREAD INC
1101 N Keller Rd Ste A (32810-5944)
PHONE..................................407 679-3895
Dru A Dalton, *President*
Senny Luu, *Accounts Exec*
Sheryl Bordenga, *Mktg Dir*
Jordan Schiller, *Director*
EMP: 20 **EST:** 2011
SALES (est): 4.9MM **Privately Held**
WEB: www.realthread.com
SIC: 2759 Screen printing

(G-13120)
REBAH FABRICATION INC
12081 Stone Bark Trl (32824-7394)
PHONE..................................407 857-3232
Pamela L Haber, *President*
Lauren Haber, *Vice Pres*
EMP: 18 **EST:** 1977
SALES (est): 4.6MM **Privately Held**
SIC: 3365 3441 Aluminum foundries; fabricated structural metal

(G-13121)
RED METERS LLC
Also Called: Manufctring Prcess Ctrl Instrs
6520 Pinecastle Blvd (32809-6675)
PHONE..................................407 337-0110
Marion Moth, *COO*
Rosie Moth, *Mktg Dir*
David Moth,
EMP: 13 **EST:** 2016
SALES (est): 3.5MM **Privately Held**
WEB: www.redmeters.com
SIC: 3823 Industrial instrmnts msrmnt display/control process variable

(G-13122)
REDAT OF NORTH AMERICA INC
120 Bonnie Loch Ct (32806-2910)
PHONE..................................407 246-1600
Atillio Cortella, *President*
Raymond Roach, *Vice Pres*
▲ **EMP:** 5 **EST:** 1980
SQ FT: 8,500
SALES (est): 910K **Privately Held**
WEB: www.redatnorthamerica.com
SIC: 3714 Motor vehicle parts & accessories

(G-13123)
REDDY ICE INC
1920 Commerce Oak Ave (32808-5640)
PHONE..................................407 296-8300
Gil Cassagne, *CEO*
Don Plante, *Principal*
Jane Plante, *Admin Sec*
Eileen Paul, *Asst Sec*
Andrew Moxley, *Regional*
EMP: 1 **EST:** 1946
SQ FT: 56,000
SALES (est): 7.7MM **Privately Held**
WEB: www.reddyice.com
SIC: 2097 Manufactured ice
HQ: Reddy Ice Holdings, Inc.
5720 Lbj Fwy Ste 200
Dallas TX 75240
214 526-6740

(G-13124)
REDWOOD CUSTOM WOODWORKING (PA)
1409 Murdock Blvd (32825-5638)
PHONE..................................407 529-9877
Leonid Vyazhevich, *Principal*
EMP: 15 **EST:** 2010
SALES (est): 57.1K **Privately Held**
WEB: www.redwoodcw.com
SIC: 2431 Millwork

(G-13125)
REED BRENNAN MEDIA ASSOCIATES
Also Called: Reed Brenan
628 Virginia Dr (32803-1858)
PHONE..................................407 894-7300
Tim Brennan, *President*
Tony Decarlo, *Prdtn Mgr*
EMP: 43 **EST:** 1993

GEOGRAPHIC

SALES (est): 12MM
SALES (corp-wide): 4.2B **Privately Held**
WEB: www.rbma.com
SIC: **2711** 7311 Newspapers: publishing only, not printed on site; advertising consultant
PA: The Hearst Corporation
300 W 57th St Fl 42
New York NY 10019
212 649-2000

(G-13126)
REFLECTION MANUFACTURING
10336 Pointview Ct (32836-3736)
PHONE..................................407 297-5727
◆ **EMP**: 53
SALES (est): 2.7MM **Privately Held**
SIC: **3999** Mfg Misc Products

(G-13127)
REGAL MARINE INDUSTRIES INC (PA)
Also Called: Regal Boats
2300 Jetport Dr (32809-7895)
PHONE..................................407 851-4360
Duane Kuck, *President*
Mary Geltzer, *President*
Martin Clement, *Vice Pres*
Paul Kuck, *Vice Pres*
Timothy Kuck, *Vice Pres*
◆ **EMP**: 350 **EST**: 1969
SQ FT: 300,000
SALES (est): 87.4MM **Privately Held**
WEB: www.regalboats.com
SIC: **3732** Boats, fiberglass: building & repairing

(G-13128)
REHRIG PACIFIC COMPANY
7452 Presidents Dr (32809-5608)
PHONE..................................407 857-3888
Livan Torres, *Foreman/Supr*
Philana Haumiller, *Purchasing*
Rainey Booker, *Plant Engr*
Andres Guttierrez, *Branch Mgr*
EMP: 10 **Privately Held**
WEB: www.rehrigpacific.com
SIC: **3089** 2821 Cases, plastic; garbage containers, plastic; molding primary plastic; plasticizer/additive based plastic materials
HQ: P M Rehrig Inc
4010 E 26th St
Vernon CA 90058
323 262-5145

(G-13129)
RELIABLE POOL ENCLSRES SCRENS
Also Called: Reliable Pool Enclsres Screens
5558 Force Four Pkwy (32839-2968)
PHONE..................................407 731-3408
EMP: 8 **EST**: 2017
SALES (est): 939.6K **Privately Held**
WEB: www.rpesfl.com
SIC: **3442** Screens, window, metal

(G-13130)
RELION ENTERPRISES LLC
Also Called: Minuteman Press
13526 Village Park Dr # 202 (32837-7685)
PHONE..................................321 287-4225
Javier Santos,
EMP: 9 **EST**: 2017
SALES (est): 609.8K **Privately Held**
WEB: www.chanhassen-mn.minutemanpress.com
SIC: **2752** Commercial printing, lithographic

(G-13131)
REPRO PLUS INC
Also Called: Triangle Reprogressives
850 S Hughey Ave (32801-3630)
PHONE..................................407 843-1492
Roger Garner, *President*
Joanne F Garner, *President*
Thomas Jennie F, *Vice Pres*
J F Thomas, *Vice Pres*
EMP: 11 **EST**: 1975
SQ FT: 1,000
SALES (est): 804.3K **Privately Held**
SIC: **2752** Commercial printing, offset

(G-13132)
RESIDUAL INNOVATIONS LLC
7253 Pleasant Dr (32818-5867)
PHONE..................................407 459-5497
Michael Bridgett, *Principal*
EMP: 8 **EST**: 2015
SALES (est): 140.9K **Privately Held**
SIC: **2911** Residues

(G-13133)
REVOLOGY CARS LLC
6756 Edgwter Cmmrce Pkwy (32810-4200)
PHONE..................................800 974-4463
Thomas Scarpello, *Mng Member*
EMP: 15 **EST**: 2017
SALES (est): 310.4K **Privately Held**
WEB: www.revologycars.com
SIC: **3711** 7549 5511 Automobile assembly, including specialty automobiles; high performance auto repair & service; new & used car dealers

(G-13134)
RHINESTNTRANSFERSDIRECTC OM INC
1821 Verde Way (32835-8174)
PHONE..................................484 254-6410
Christina Demuth, *Principal*
EMP: 6 **EST**: 2013
SALES (est): 177.5K **Privately Held**
WEB: www.dazzling.biz
SIC: **2395** Embroidery & art needlework

(G-13135)
RHINO TIRE USA LLC
11423 Satellite Blvd (32837-9225)
PHONE..................................407 777-5598
Yi Langang, *CEO*
EMP: 18 **EST**: 2016
SALES (est): 2MM **Privately Held**
WEB: www.rhinotiresusa.com
SIC: **3011** 3714 5014 Motorcycle tires, pneumatic; wheels, motor vehicle; tires & tubes

(G-13136)
RIBEIRO STONES LLC
2207 Silver Star Rd (32804-3307)
PHONE..................................407 723-8802
Linholene Ribeiro,
Gabriel V Ribeiro,
Rafael V Ribeiro,
EMP: 7 **EST**: 2015
SALES (est): 734.8K **Privately Held**
WEB: www.ribeirostones.com
SIC: **3281** Granite, cut & shaped

(G-13137)
RICHARD BRYAN INGRAM LLC
Also Called: Artios
2454 N Forsyth Rd (32807-6430)
PHONE..................................407 677-7779
Bryan Ingram, *Mng Member*
EMP: 7 **EST**: 2004
SQ FT: 9,000
SALES (est): 923.3K **Privately Held**
WEB: www.artioscabinetry.com
SIC: **2434** 5031 Wood kitchen cabinets; kitchen cabinets

(G-13138)
RIEKER LLC
5337 Foxshire Ct (32819-3824)
PHONE..................................407 496-1555
Kathleen M Rieker, *Principal*
EMP: 7 **EST**: 2007
SALES (est): 409.3K **Privately Held**
WEB: www.rieker.us
SIC: **3829** Measuring & controlling devices

(G-13139)
RIGHT STUCCO INC
7585 Stidham Dr (32818-3031)
PHONE..................................407 468-6119
Andrew Wright, *Principal*
EMP: 7 **EST**: 2009
SALES (est): 63K **Privately Held**
SIC: **3299** Stucco

(G-13140)
RIO PAVERS INC
7297 Mardell Ct (32835-2672)
PHONE..................................321 388-6757
Paulo Monteiro, *Officer*
EMP: 8 **EST**: 2007
SALES (est): 518.9K **Privately Held**
WEB: www.riopavers.com
SIC: **3531** Pavers

(G-13141)
RIVER CRAFT LLC
2148 Orinoco Dr Ste 356 (32837-8933)
PHONE..................................407 867-0584
Luis D Rivera,
EMP: 15 **EST**: 2017
SALES (est): 1MM **Privately Held**
WEB: www.rivercraftllc.com
SIC: **2431** Millwork

(G-13142)
RLCJC INC
Also Called: Good Feet
4684 Millenia Plaza Way (32839-2434)
P.O. Box 568392 (32856-8392)
PHONE..................................407 370-3338
Rebecca Conner, *President*
EMP: 5 **EST**: 2008
SALES (est): 303.1K **Privately Held**
SIC: **3842** Foot appliances, orthopedic

(G-13143)
RMC EWELL INC
7400 Narcoossee Rd (32822-5586)
PHONE..................................407 282-0984
EMP: 18
SALES (corp-wide): 15.4B **Privately Held**
SIC: **3273** 3272 Manufactures Ready Mix Concrete And Concrete Pipes
HQ: Ewell Rmc Inc
801 Mccue Rd
Lakeland FL
863 688-5787

(G-13144)
ROCK BRICK PAVERS INC
344 S Hart Blvd (32835-1948)
PHONE..................................407 692-6816
Maria Lopez, *Principal*
EMP: 6 **EST**: 2014
SALES (est): 110.9K **Privately Held**
SIC: **2951** Asphalt paving mixtures & blocks

(G-13145)
ROCKWELL COLLINS INC
Also Called: Rockwell Cllins Vsual Dsplay S
12600 Challenger Pkwy # 130
(32826-2755)
PHONE..................................866 786-0290
Thomas Barber, *Sales Staff*
Mike Kochmann, *Program Mgr*
Owen Wynn, *Manager*
EMP: 6
SALES (corp-wide): 56.5B **Publicly Held**
WEB: www.rockwellcollins.com
SIC: **3812** Search & navigation equipment
HQ: Rockwell Collins, Inc.
400 Collins Rd Ne
Cedar Rapids IA 52498

(G-13146)
RONCA INDUSTRIES LLC
719 Peachtree Rd Ste 100 (32804-6821)
PHONE..................................407 839-0440
Brandon Ronca, *Principal*
EMP: 7 **EST**: 2012
SALES (est): 87.7K **Privately Held**
SIC: **3999** Manufacturing industries

(G-13147)
ROYAL BATHS MANUFACTURING CO
1920 Premier Row (32809-6206)
PHONE..................................407 854-1740
Kevin Sommerio, *General Mgr*
Elvin Santana, *Office Mgr*
EMP: 36
SALES (corp-wide): 91.4MM **Privately Held**
WEB: www.royal-mfg.com
SIC: **3842** Whirlpool baths, hydrotherapy equipment
PA: Royal Baths Manufacturing Company
14635 Chrisman Rd
Houston TX 77039
281 442-3400

(G-13148)
ROYAL SPLITS INC (PA)
6633 Voltaire Dr (32809-6465)
PHONE..................................310 935-6699
George A Spurling, *President*
EMP: 7 **EST**: 2013
SALES (est): 442.4K **Privately Held**
SIC: **3911** Cigar & cigarette accessories

(G-13149)
RUSH SIGNS
1612 Prgrine Flcons Way A (32837-8039)
PHONE..................................407 308-6362
N Danny A Morales-Pabo, *Principal*
EMP: 6 **EST**: 2019
SALES (est): 98.9K **Privately Held**
WEB: www.rushsignsfl.com
SIC: **3993** Signs & advertising specialties

(G-13150)
RXPRINTING AND GRAPHICS LLC
4909 S Orange Ave (32806-6932)
PHONE..................................407 965-3039
Raymon Diaz, *Principal*
EMP: 7 **EST**: 2009
SALES (est): 123K **Privately Held**
SIC: **2752** Commercial printing, offset

(G-13151)
S E INC
Also Called: Strong Enterprises
6448 Pinecastle Blvd # 104 (32809-6682)
PHONE..................................407 859-9317
Marcia Lavanway, *President*
Mike Rinaldi, *Vice Pres*
Jessica Hanson, *Admin Sec*
◆ **EMP**: 43 **EST**: 1961
SALES (est): 3.6MM **Privately Held**
WEB: www.seincwy.com
SIC: **2399** 8611 Parachutes; business associations

(G-13152)
S M I CABINETRY INC
Also Called: SMI Cabinetry Stone Millwork
2525 N Orange Blossom Trl (32804-4808)
PHONE..................................407 841-0292
Michelle Hull, *CEO*
William Bergin, *President*
Eileen Bergin, *Corp Secy*
Russell Bergin, *Vice Pres*
EMP: 46 **EST**: 1985
SQ FT: 22,000
SALES (est): 4.5MM **Privately Held**
WEB: www.smi-cabinetry.com
SIC: **2541** 2521 2434 2431 Cabinets, except refrigerated: show, display, etc.: wood; counters or counter display cases, wood; desks, office: wood; wood kitchen cabinets; millwork; cabinet & finish carpentry

(G-13153)
S&L CNSTRCTION SPECIALISTS INC
13412 Heswall Run (32832-6156)
PHONE..................................407 300-5080
Saulo M Laceda, *President*
EMP: 5 **EST**: 2013
SALES (est): 395.8K **Privately Held**
SIC: **2952** 3444 3299 Siding materials; gutters, sheet metal; stucco

(G-13154)
SAFETY SYSTEMS BARRICADES
2513 Industrial Blvd (32804-4209)
PHONE..................................407 674-8440
EMP: 6 **EST**: 2017
SALES (est): 142K **Privately Held**
WEB: www.ssbarricades.com
SIC: **3499** Barricades, metal

(G-13155)
SAGE IMPLEMENTATIONS LLC
Also Called: Flexfield Express
7648 San Remo Pl (32835-2674)
PHONE..................................407 290-6952
Helene Abrams, *CEO*
Chris Busbee,
EMP: 8 **EST**: 2005
SALES (est): 514.1K **Privately Held**
WEB: www.flexfieldexpress.com
SIC: **7372** Application computer software

(G-13156)
SAI SUPER SOFTWARE SOLUTIONS
5230 Cona Reef Ct (32810-4075)
PHONE..................................407 445-2520
Sridhar Rangaswamy, *Principal*
EMP: 5
SALES (est): 1MM **Privately Held**
SIC: 7372 Application computer software; educational computer software

(G-13157)
SAIKOU OPTICS INCORPORATED
3259 Progress Dr Ste 128 (32826-3230)
PHONE..................................407 986-4200
Eric Sanford, *CEO*
EMP: 5 **EST:** 2015
SQ FT: 400
SALES (est): 3.5MM **Privately Held**
WEB: www.saikouoptics.com
SIC: 3827 3823 3812 Optical instruments & lenses; industrial instrmnts msrmnt display/control process variable; search & navigation equipment

(G-13158)
SALON TECHNOLOGIES INTL
8810 Com Cir Ste 20-22 (32819)
P.O. Box 2320, Windermere (34786-2320)
PHONE..................................407 301-3726
Ted A Khoury, *Principal*
Gaston A Khoury, *Principal*
Pascal N Khoury, *Principal*
Henriette Khoury, *Vice Pres*
EMP: 9 **EST:** 1998
SALES (est): 244K **Privately Held**
WEB: www.salontechnologiesint.com
SIC: 2844 Suntan lotions & oils

(G-13159)
SALT 1 TO 1
11221 John Wycliffe Blvd (32832-7013)
PHONE..................................407 538-2134
EMP: 8 **EST:** 2018
SALES (est): 725.2K **Privately Held**
WEB: www.salt1to1.com
SIC: 2752 Commercial printing, offset

(G-13160)
SALT 1TO1 INC
214 N Goldenrod Rd Ste 8 (32807-8220)
PHONE..................................407 721-8107
Anthony W Metcalf, *Principal*
Brenda P Metcalf, *Principal*
Brenda Metcalf, *Vice Pres*
EMP: 10 **EST:** 2007
SALES (est): 315.6K **Privately Held**
WEB: www.salt1to1.com
SIC: 2899 Salt

(G-13161)
SANITARY PRCESS COMPONENTS INC
3711 Vineland Rd (32811-6416)
PHONE..................................407 650-8988
URS Lackner, *Marketing Mgr*
EMP: 6 **EST:** 2018
SALES (est): 124.3K **Privately Held**
WEB: www.spc-fl.com
SIC: 3053 Gaskets, packing & sealing devices

(G-13162)
SANOFI US SERVICES INC
2501 Discovery Dr (32826-3718)
PHONE..................................407 736-0226
Janice Moser, *Director*
EMP: 39 **Privately Held**
WEB: www.sanofi.us
SIC: 2834 Pharmaceutical preparations
HQ: Sanofi Us Services Inc.
55 Corporate Dr
Bridgewater NJ 08807
336 407-4994

(G-13163)
SARDEE INDUSTRIES INC
2211 W Washington St (32805-1254)
PHONE..................................407 295-2114
Raymond E Godwin, *General Mgr*
EMP: 20
SQ FT: 37,000
SALES (corp-wide): 13.5MM **Privately Held**
WEB: www.sardee.com
SIC: 3565 3567 3537 3535 Packaging machinery; industrial furnaces & ovens; industrial trucks & tractors; conveyors & conveying equipment
PA: Sardee Industries, Inc.
5100 Academy Dr Ste 400
Lisle IL 60532
630 824-4200

(G-13164)
SATCOM SCIENTIFIC INC
5644 Commerce Dr Ste G (32839-2962)
PHONE..................................407 856-1050
Angelo J Miceli, *President*
James Abbott, *CFO*
◆ **EMP:** 10 **EST:** 2007
SQ FT: 7,500
SALES (est): 2.1MM **Privately Held**
WEB: www.satcomscientific.com
SIC: 3663 4899 Radio & TV communications equipment; data communication services

(G-13165)
SBR CUSTOM CABINETS INC
4093 Floralwood Ct (32812-7912)
PHONE..................................407 765-8134
Steven B Rumplik Sr, *Principal*
EMP: 6 **EST:** 2010
SALES (est): 70.1K **Privately Held**
SIC: 2434 Wood kitchen cabinets

(G-13166)
SBT RIVER PIP PROJECT
4400 N Alafaya Trl (32826-2301)
PHONE..................................919 469-5095
EMP: 25 **EST:** 2011
SALES (est): 1.1MM **Privately Held**
SIC: 2752 Commercial printing, offset

(G-13167)
SCHERING-PLOUGH CORP
438 E Gore St (32806-1335)
PHONE..................................407 353-2076
Lalania Pividal, *Principal*
EMP: 7 **EST:** 2016
SALES (est): 296.8K **Privately Held**
SIC: 2834 Pharmaceutical preparations

(G-13168)
SCHROE LIGHTS LLC
833 Timber Isle Dr (32828-6912)
PHONE..................................407 748-9300
Angela Schroeder, *Mng Member*
EMP: 5
SQ FT: 5,000
SALES (est): 2MM **Privately Held**
SIC: 3646 Commercial indusl & institutional electric lighting fixtures

(G-13169)
SCHWARTZ ELECTRO-OPTICS INC
8337 Southpark Cir (32819-9049)
PHONE..................................407 297-8988
Jeffrey A Saunders, *President*
EMP: 14 **EST:** 1984
SALES (est): 1MM **Privately Held**
SIC: 3699 Laser systems & equipment

(G-13170)
SCREENWORKS USA INC
2234 W Taft Vineland Rd (32837-7800)
PHONE..................................407 426-9999
Sharad Mehta, *President*
Brian Dezavala, *Exec VP*
Carlos Dezavala, *Shareholder*
Ernie Dezavala, *Shareholder*
◆ **EMP:** 130 **EST:** 1999
SQ FT: 65,000
SALES (est): 24.9MM **Privately Held**
WEB: www.screenworksusa.com
SIC: 2261 Screen printing of cotton broadwoven fabrics

(G-13171)
SEA CREATIONS INC
408 Bif Ct (32809-6668)
PHONE..................................407 857-2000
Diane Dinger, *President*
Robert Dinger, *Vice Pres*
◆ **EMP:** 5 **EST:** 1981
SQ FT: 12,000
SALES (est): 563.9K **Privately Held**
WEB: www.sea-creations.com
SIC: 3999 Novelties: bone, beaded or shell

(G-13172)
SEAL SHIELD LLC (PA)
315 E Robinson St Ste 500 (32801-1983)
PHONE..................................877 325-7443
Andrew McCarthy, *President*
J Andrew McCarthy, *Vice Pres*
Russell Verhovec, *Vice Pres*
Jason Bray, *VP Opers*
Vincent Schreber, *CFO*
◆ **EMP:** 33 **EST:** 2007
SQ FT: 4,000
SALES (est): 24MM **Privately Held**
WEB: www.sealshield.com
SIC: 3575 2842 3641 Keyboards, computer, office machine; disinfectants, household or industrial plant; ultraviolet lamps

(G-13173)
SENTINEL CMMNCTONS NEWS VNTRES
Also Called: Sentinel Direct
75 E Amelia St (32801-1320)
P.O. Box 2833 (32802-2833)
PHONE..................................407 420-5291
Ashley Allen, *CEO*
Sophie Rahimi, *Technology*
EMP: 9
SALES (corp-wide): 4.5B **Publicly Held**
WEB: www.orlandosentinel.com
SIC: 2711 2741 Newspapers, publishing & printing; miscellaneous publishing
HQ: Sentinel Communications News Ventures Inc.
633 N Orange Ave
Orlando FL 32801
407 420-5000

(G-13174)
SENTINEL COMMUNICATNS NEWS VEN (DH)
Also Called: Orlando Sentinnel Media Group
633 N Orange Ave (32801-1325)
P.O. Box 2833 (32802-2833)
PHONE..................................407 420-5000
Howard Greenberg, *CEO*
Chris Hays, *Editor*
Avido Khahaifa, *Senior VP*
Bert Ortiz, *Vice Pres*
Thomas Brown, *CFO*
EMP: 577
SQ FT: 50,000
SALES (est): 153.3MM
SALES (corp-wide): 4.5B **Publicly Held**
WEB: www.orlandosentinel.com
SIC: 2711 Commercial printing & newspaper publishing combined
HQ: Tribune Media Company
515 N State St Ste 2400
Chicago IL 60654
312 222-3394

(G-13175)
SERENITY SCREEN ENCLOSURES LLC
3700 Timber Trl (32808-2343)
PHONE..................................407 692-3031
Ronald Richar, *Manager*
EMP: 6 **EST:** 2015
SALES (est): 105.2K **Privately Held**
WEB: www.builder.pagevamp.com
SIC: 3448 Screen enclosures

(G-13176)
SEXY WINKS LLC
10321 Manderley Way (32829-7343)
PHONE..................................407 949-2981
Sade M Coakley, *Principal*
EMP: 8 **EST:** 2017
SALES (est): 261.7K **Privately Held**
SIC: 3999 Eyelashes, artificial

(G-13177)
SFI INC
1730 N Forsyth Rd (32807-5274)
PHONE..................................407 834-2258
Anthony J Sano Jr, *President*
Mandy D Fuller, *Vice Pres*
EMP: 45 **EST:** 1978
SQ FT: 27,000
SALES (est): 5.9MM **Privately Held**
WEB: www.sfiinc.com
SIC: 3444 3499 Sheet metalwork; coal chutes, prefabricated sheet metal; aerosol valves, metal

(G-13178)
SGM LIGHTING INC
7806 Kingspointe Pkwy (32819-8520)
PHONE..................................407 440-3601
Filippo Frigeri, *Principal*
▲ **EMP:** 6 **EST:** 2015
SALES (est): 1MM **Privately Held**
WEB: www.sgmlight.com
SIC: 3648 Lighting equipment

(G-13179)
SHELBIE PRESS INC
1203 N Mills Ave (32803-2540)
PHONE..................................407 896-4600
Debbie Simmons, *President*
Michelle Murray, *Vice Pres*
EMP: 5 **EST:** 1993
SQ FT: 1,300
SALES (est): 372.5K **Privately Held**
SIC: 2752 Commercial printing, offset

(G-13180)
SHERRY J BERTUCELLI INC
3827 E Kaley Ave (32812-9148)
PHONE..................................407 760-7585
Sherry J Bertucelli, *Owner*
EMP: 6 **EST:** 2006
SALES (est): 76.4K **Privately Held**
SIC: 1389 Construction, repair & dismantling services

(G-13181)
SHGAR KANE COUTURE INC
4900 Silver Oaks Village (32808-2092)
PHONE..................................407 205-8038
Charmaine P Allwood, *Principal*
EMP: 6 **EST:** 2012
SALES (est): 418.4K **Privately Held**
SIC: 2339 7389 Women's & misses' athletic clothing & sportswear; apparel designers, commercial

(G-13182)
SIEMENS CORPORATION
4041 Forest Island Dr (32826-2621)
PHONE..................................407 736-5629
William R Weir, *Principal*
Julia Lopez, *Regional Mgr*
Elvira Anoshkina, *Engineer*
Sundar Raghavan, *Engineer*
Gavin Gaul, *Manager*
EMP: 6
SALES (corp-wide): 67.4B **Privately Held**
WEB: www.siemens.com
SIC: 3661 Telephones & telephone apparatus
HQ: Siemens Corporation
300 New Jersey Ave Nw # 10
Washington DC 20001
202 434-4800

(G-13183)
SIEMENS ENERGY INC
3850 Quadrangle Blvd (32817-8368)
PHONE..................................407 736-1400
Mick McCormic, *Principal*
Steve Auman, *Project Mgr*
Ron Shires, *Project Mgr*
Gregor Braunschweig, *Engineer*
Hunter Buck, *Engineer*
EMP: 77
SALES (corp-wide): 32.3B **Privately Held**
WEB: www.siemens.com
SIC: 3511 Turbines & turbine generator sets
HQ: Siemens Energy, Inc.
4400 N Alafaya Trl
Orlando FL 32826
407 736-2000

(G-13184)
SIEMENS ENERGY INC
11842 Corporate (32817)
PHONE..................................407 206-5008
Randy Zwirn, *President*
Leon Armstrong, *Project Mgr*
Marty Shriner, *Project Mgr*
Dilshan Canagasaby, *Engineer*
George Haas, *Engineer*
EMP: 77

SALES (corp-wide): 32.3B **Privately Held**
WEB: www.siemens.com
SIC: 3511 Turbines & turbine generator sets
HQ: Siemens Energy, Inc.
4400 N Alafaya Trl
Orlando FL 32826
407 736-2000

(G-13185)
SIEMENS ENERGY INC
11950 Corporate Blvd (32817)
PHONE..................................407 736-7957
Seyed Farhid, *Engineer*
David Fortna, *Engineer*
Reinhard Schilp, *Engineer*
Angelique Falkenberg, *Project Engr*
Mario Velasquez, *Financial Analy*
EMP: 77
SALES (corp-wide): 32.3B **Privately Held**
WEB: www.siemens.com
SIC: 3511 Steam turbines
HQ: Siemens Energy, Inc.
4400 N Alafaya Trl
Orlando FL 32826
407 736-2000

(G-13186)
SIEMENS GMESA RNWBLE ENRGY INC (DH)
4400 N Alafaya Trl Q2 (32826-2301)
PHONE..................................407 736-2000
Jose Soto, *President*
Karl Armond, *Project Mgr*
Ron Mixon, *Project Mgr*
George Barkulis, *Opers Staff*
Fred Corraro, *Opers Staff*
EMP: 1543 **EST:** 2016
SALES (est): 477.8MM
SALES (corp-wide): 32.3B **Privately Held**
WEB: www.siemensgamesa.com
SIC: 3511 Turbines & turbine generator sets
HQ: Siemens Gamesa Renewable Energy Sociedad Anonima
Poligono Teknologi Elkartegia, Edif. 222
Zamudio 48170
944 037-352

(G-13187)
SIEMENS GMESA RNWBLE ENRGY INC
11950 Corporate Blvd (32817)
PHONE..................................407 721-3273
EMP: 54
SALES (corp-wide): 32.3B **Privately Held**
WEB: www.siemensgamesa.com
SIC: 3511 Turbines & turbine generator sets
HQ: Siemens Gamesa Renewable Energy, Inc.
4400 N Alafaya Trl Q2
Orlando FL 32826
407 736-2000

(G-13188)
SIEMENS INDUSTRY INC
4506 L B Mcleod Rd Ste C (32811-5665)
PHONE..................................407 650-3570
Craig Cortes, *Engineer*
John Gates, *Engineer*
Jeff Nelson, *Sales Mgr*
Carlos Curti, *Sales Staff*
Amanda Sharma, *Business Anlyst*
EMP: 9
SALES (corp-wide): 67.4B **Privately Held**
WEB: www.siemens.com
SIC: 3569 5999 5074 Filters; water purification equipment; water purification equipment
HQ: Siemens Industry, Inc.
1000 Deerfield Pkwy
Buffalo Grove IL 60089
847 215-1000

(G-13189)
SIGN & VEHICLE WRAPS INC
1011 W Lancaster Rd Ste 7 (32809-5888)
PHONE..................................407 859-8631
Marcos A Diaz Diaz, *Principal*
EMP: 5 **EST:** 2010
SALES (est): 482.6K **Privately Held**
WEB: www.signsvw.com
SIC: 3993 Signs & advertising specialties

(G-13190)
SIGN DEPOT CO
1100 W Colonial Dr Unit 1 (32804-7334)
PHONE..................................407 894-0090
Tuan T MAI, *President*
◆ **EMP:** 12 **EST:** 2006
SALES (est): 2.5MM **Privately Held**
WEB: www.yardsignwholesale.com
SIC: 2759 5099 5999 Screen printing; signs, except electric; banners, flags, decals & posters

(G-13191)
SIGN PRODUCERS INC
Also Called: SPI
555 W Landstreet Rd (32824-7808)
PHONE..................................407 855-8864
Deborah Scime, *President*
▼ **EMP:** 22 **EST:** 1986
SQ FT: 2,500
SALES (est): 1.9MM **Privately Held**
WEB: www.signproducers.com
SIC: 3993 7336 Signs, not made in custom sign painting shops; commercial art & graphic design

(G-13192)
SIGN STAPLER
1969 S Alafaya Trl (32828-8732)
PHONE..................................800 775-3971
EMP: 6 **EST:** 2017
SALES (est): 223.3K **Privately Held**
WEB: www.signstapler.com
SIC: 3993 Signs & advertising specialties

(G-13193)
SIGNATURE AVI US HOLDINGS INC (DH)
Also Called: BBA Aviation Group
13485 Veterans Way # 600 (32827-7719)
PHONE..................................407 648-7230
Joseph I Goldstein, *President*
Steve Bongiorno, *General Mgr*
Lori Golda, *Area Mgr*
Sandy Montalbano, *Area Mgr*
Daniel Marcinik, *Treasurer*
EMP: 14 **EST:** 1994
SALES (est): 146.5MM
SALES (corp-wide): 1.4B **Privately Held**
SIC: 3728 2399 3052 Aircraft parts & equipment; belting, fabric: made from purchased materials; rubber belting

(G-13194)
SINGULAR GRAPE INC
7380 W Sand Lake Rd (32819-5248)
PHONE..................................305 508-4000
Victor Friedman, *CEO*
Einav Raff, *President*
EMP: 8 **EST:** 2007
SALES: 1.2MM **Privately Held**
WEB: www.singulargrape.com
SIC: 7372 Business oriented computer software

(G-13195)
SKY AEROSPACE ENGINEERING ✪
4219 Lindy Cir (32827-5309)
PHONE..................................407 251-7111
EMP: 7 **EST:** 2020
SALES (est): 781.6K **Privately Held**
WEB: www.jetsae.com
SIC: 3728 Aircraft parts & equipment

(G-13196)
SKY AEROSPACE ENGINEERING INC (PA)
Also Called: SAE
9419 Tradeport Dr (32827-5345)
PHONE..................................407 251-7111
Joseph Fernandez, *President*
Monica Fernandez, *Treasurer*
EMP: 9 **EST:** 2008
SALES (est): 1.6MM **Privately Held**
WEB: www.jetsae.com
SIC: 3728 Aircraft parts & equipment

(G-13197)
SKYLINE ATTRACTIONS LLC
5233 Alleman Dr (32809-3026)
PHONE..................................407 587-0080
Jeffrey Pike, *Partner*
Christopher M Gray, *Partner*
Evan Souliere, *Treasurer*
Richard Barnes, *CIO*
Christopher Gray,
EMP: 10 **EST:** 2014
SALES (est): 962K **Privately Held**
WEB: www.skylineattractions.com
SIC: 3599 Amusement park equipment

(G-13198)
SMARTE CARTE INC
9251 Jeff Fuqua Blvd # 1596 (32827-4450)
PHONE..................................407 857-5841
EMP: 7 **EST:** 2019
SALES (est): 152.8K **Privately Held**
WEB: www.smartecarte.com
SIC: 2599 Furniture & fixtures

(G-13199)
SNA SOFTWARE LLC (PA)
1730 Santa Maria Pl (32806-1446)
P.O. Box 531146 (32853-1146)
PHONE..................................866 389-6750
Nicholas Pisano, *Mng Member*
EMP: 12 **EST:** 2007
SALES (est): 1.4MM **Privately Held**
WEB: www.sna-software.com
SIC: 7372 Publishers' computer software

(G-13200)
SOUL FUEL INC
155 S Court Ave Unit 2215 (32801-3215)
PHONE..................................407 448-6533
Amicarelle William, *Principal*
EMP: 6 **EST:** 2014
SALES (est): 191.2K **Privately Held**
SIC: 2869 Fuels

(G-13201)
SOUTH EAST FUEL LLC
5600 Butler National Dr (32812-3000)
PHONE..................................407 392-4668
EMP: 8
SALES (est): 884.4K **Privately Held**
SIC: 2869 Mfg Industrial Organic Chemicals

(G-13202)
SOUTHEAST FINISHING GROUP INC (PA)
2807 Mercy Dr (32808-3807)
PHONE..................................407 299-4620
Robert S Clark Jr, *President*
James R Clark, *Owner*
Julian Malkiewicz, *Plant Mgr*
Dianne Clark, *Admin Sec*
EMP: 50 **EST:** 1970
SQ FT: 24,800
SALES (est): 6.5MM **Privately Held**
WEB: www.southeastfinishing.com
SIC: 2759 2657 2796 2789 Commercial printing; folding paperboard boxes; platemaking services; bookbinding & related work; die-cut paper & board

(G-13203)
SOUTHERN EXHIBITS AND GRAPHICS
4360 36th St Unit 1 (32811-6506)
PHONE..................................407 423-2860
Gary Churchill, *President*
EMP: 9 **EST:** 2017
SALES (est): 382.8K **Privately Held**
WEB: www.southernexhibits.com
SIC: 3993 Signs & advertising specialties

(G-13204)
SOVITA RETAIL INC
1317 Edgewater Dr # 1943 (32804-6350)
PHONE..................................888 871-2408
Talika Moore, *President*
Charlika Stubbs, *Vice Pres*
EMP: 35 **EST:** 2002
SQ FT: 6,500
SALES (est): 1.2MM **Privately Held**
SIC: 2339 Athletic clothing: women's, misses' & juniors'

(G-13205)
SPEED CUSTOM CABINET CORP
6923 Narcoossee Rd (32822-5572)
PHONE..................................407 953-1479
Dani Garcia, *President*
EMP: 9 **EST:** 2006
SALES (est): 157.9K **Privately Held**
WEB: www.speedcustomcabinet.co
SIC: 2434 Wood kitchen cabinets

(G-13206)
SPEEDPRO OF ORLANDO WEST
9032 Della Scala Cir (32836-5401)
PHONE..................................407 509-8956
EMP: 6 **EST:** 2014
SALES (est): 87.2K **Privately Held**
WEB: www.speedpro.com
SIC: 3993 Signs & advertising specialties

(G-13207)
SPICE WORLD LLC (PA)
8101 Presidents Dr (32809-9113)
PHONE..................................407 851-9432
Andrew P Caneza, *CEO*
Gary Caneza, *President*
Susan Whitson, *Corp Secy*
Esteban Arreguin, *Vice Pres*
Mitch Dimarco, *Vice Pres*
◆ **EMP:** 196 **EST:** 1949
SQ FT: 68,000
SALES (est): 30.8MM **Privately Held**
WEB: www.spiceworldinc.com
SIC: 2099 Food preparations

(G-13208)
SPORTS N STUFF SCREEN PRINTING
3975 Forrestal Ave # 600 (32806-8545)
PHONE..................................407 859-0437
Charles R Maxwell,
EMP: 5 **EST:** 1993
SALES (est): 492.3K **Privately Held**
SIC: 2759 Screen printing

(G-13209)
SRM WATERPROOFING SEALANTS INC
2899 Burwood Ave (32837-8557)
PHONE..................................407 963-3619
Falero Alexis, *Principal*
EMP: 6 **EST:** 2014
SALES (est): 81.3K **Privately Held**
SIC: 2891 Sealants

(G-13210)
STAIRWAYS BY ANGEL LLC
5555 Burlwood Dr (32810-6633)
PHONE..................................407 790-7181
Katrina A Gleeson, *Principal*
EMP: 5 **EST:** 2018
SALES (est): 468.3K **Privately Held**
WEB: www.stairwaysbyangel.com
SIC: 2431 Millwork

(G-13211)
STAN WEAVER & CO INC
3663 All American Blvd (32810-4726)
PHONE..................................407 581-6940
Charles Weaver, *President*
Ike Crimm, *Engineer*
Dean Pieper, *Sales Staff*
Joe Winkenwerder, *Sales Staff*
Lance Wooles, *Sales Staff*
EMP: 34 **EST:** 1978
SALES (est): 3.2MM **Privately Held**
WEB: www.stanweaver.com
SIC: 3585 Heating equipment, complete

(G-13212)
STAND VERTICAL INC
983 Bennett Rd Apt 103 (32814-6092)
PHONE..................................407 474-0456
Micheal Morgan, *Principal*
EMP: 6 **EST:** 2008
SALES (est): 62.2K **Privately Held**
SIC: 2591 Blinds vertical

(G-13213)
STANDARD MOTOR PRODUCTS INC
Also Called: Standard Motor Products Elec
170 Sunport Ln Ste 100 (32809-8111)
PHONE..................................718 392-0200
Tom Latimer, *Manager*
EMP: 7
SALES (corp-wide): 1.1B **Publicly Held**
WEB: www.smpcorp.com
SIC: 3714 Motor vehicle parts & accessories

PA: Standard Motor Products, Inc.
3718 Northern Blvd # 600
Long Island City NY 11101
718 392-0200

(G-13214)
STEEL CNSTR SYSTEMS HOLDG CO
11250 Astronaut Blvd (32837-9204)
P.O. Box 3949, Spokane WA (99220-3949)
PHONE..................................407 438-1664
Dan Dry, *General Mgr*
Gerald Hockenberry, *Controller*
EMP: 25 **EST:** 2016
SQ FT: 30,000
SALES (est): 14MM **Privately Held**
SIC: 3444 Studs & joists, sheet metal

(G-13215)
STEWARTS ELC MTR WORKS INC
8951 Trussway Blvd (32824-7812)
PHONE..................................407 859-1837
Michael Joe Stewart, *President*
Helon G Stewart, *Exec VP*
Paul E Stewart, *Vice Pres*
Billy Johns, *Treasurer*
Myra L Williams, *Treasurer*
EMP: 25 **EST:** 1982
SQ FT: 15,400
SALES (est): 4.2MM **Privately Held**
WEB: www.semw.net
SIC: 7694 5999 Electric motor repair; rewinding services; motors, electric

(G-13216)
STONE PALACE
1901 N Orange Ave (32804-5530)
PHONE..................................407 896-0872
EMP: 10
SALES (est): 650K **Privately Held**
SIC: 3281 Mfg Cut Stone/Products

(G-13217)
STR RACING WHEELS
Also Called: Redline Wheels Florida
7558 Brokerage Dr (32809-5650)
PHONE..................................407 251-7171
Tom Luo, *Principal*
EMP: 6 **EST:** 2014
SALES (est): 223.5K **Privately Held**
WEB: www.str-racing.net
SIC: 3312 Wheels

(G-13218)
STRESS NUTS LLC ✪
10715 Bonne Chance Dr (32832-5137)
PHONE..................................787 675-3042
Nelson Diaz, *Mng Member*
EMP: 6 **EST:** 2021
SALES (est): 276.1K **Privately Held**
SIC: 7372 7389 Application computer software;

(G-13219)
SUBLIMATION STATION INC
1656 N Goldenrod Rd (32807-8454)
PHONE..................................407 605-5300
Khrystine Roman, *President*
EMP: 8 **EST:** 2015
SALES (est): 290.4K **Privately Held**
WEB: www.thesublimationstation.com
SIC: 2759 Screen printing

(G-13220)
SULZER EMS INC
7200 Lake Ellenor Dr (32809-5700)
PHONE..................................407 858-9447
EMP: 32 **Privately Held**
SIC: 3599 Mfg Industrial Machinery
HQ: Sulzer Ems Inc.
2412 W Durango St
Phoenix AZ 85009
602 258-8545

(G-13221)
SUMMIT ATL PRODUCTIONS LLC
Also Called: Unconventional Marine
3320 Vineland Rd Ste A (32811-6452)
PHONE..................................407 930-5488
Justin P Massicotte,
EMP: 11 **EST:** 2016
SALES (est): 261.3K **Privately Held**
WEB: www.summitatlantic.com
SIC: 2499 Decorative wood & woodwork

(G-13222)
SUN GRO HORTICULTURE DIST INC
6021 Beggs Rd (32810-2600)
PHONE..................................407 291-1676
EMP: 6 **Privately Held**
WEB: www.sungro.com
SIC: 1499 2875 Peat grinding; peat mining; fertilizers, mixing only
PA: Sun Gro Horticulture Distribution Inc.
770 Silver St
Agawam MA 01001

(G-13223)
SUN-TEK MANUFACTURING INC
Also Called: Sun-Tek Skylights
10303 General Dr (32824-8555)
PHONE..................................407 859-2117
Glen R Sincic, *Director*
▲ **EMP:** 50 **EST:** 1979
SQ FT: 64,400
SALES (est): 6.7MM **Privately Held**
WEB: www.sun-tek.com
SIC: 3089 3211 Windows, plastic; skylight glass

(G-13224)
SUNNYPICS LLC
618 E South St Ste 500 (32801-2986)
PHONE..................................407 992-6210
Dmitriy Toroptsev, *CEO*
EMP: 5 **EST:** 2017
SALES (est): 510.8K **Privately Held**
WEB: www.sunny-pics.com
SIC: 3581 5946 5087 Automatic vending machines; camera & photographic supply stores; vending machines & supplies

(G-13225)
SUNRISE FINANCIAL ASSOC INC
Also Called: Realstargps
14004 Chcora Crssing Blvd (32828-7744)
PHONE..................................321 439-9797
Nadir Dalal, *President*
EMP: 5 **EST:** 2008
SALES (est): 314.4K **Privately Held**
SIC: 3699 Security control equipment & systems

(G-13226)
SUNSHINE SOFTWARE
8043 Sweetgum Loop (32835-5342)
PHONE..................................407 297-6253
Jim Lesher, *Owner*
EMP: 6 **EST:** 1982
SALES (est): 115K **Privately Held**
SIC: 7372 Prepackaged software

(G-13227)
SUNSHINE SUPPLEMENTS INC (PA)
Also Called: What To Drink B4 You Drink
120 E Marks St Ste 250 (32803-3829)
PHONE..................................407 751-4299
John Mansour, *Principal*
David Larue, *Principal*
EMP: 11 **EST:** 2017
SALES (est): 1.6MM **Privately Held**
SIC: 2023 Dietary supplements, dairy & non-dairy based

(G-13228)
SUPER COLOR DIGITAL LLC
3450 Vineland Rd Ste 200 (32811-6421)
PHONE..................................407 240-1660
Pat Pidgeon, *Manager*
EMP: 10 **Privately Held**
WEB: www.supercolor.com
SIC: 2759 Commercial printing
PA: Super Color Digital, Llc
16761 Hale Ave
Irvine CA 92606

(G-13229)
SUPERIOR METAL
Also Called: Laser
2409 N John Young Pkwy (32804-4105)
PHONE..................................407 522-8100
Lyndell N Freeman II, *President*
EMP: 10 **EST:** 1987
SQ FT: 10,000
SALES (est): 906.5K **Privately Held**
WEB: www.superiormetalfab.com
SIC: 3444 Sheet metalwork

(G-13230)
SUPERIOR METAL FABRICATORS INC
Also Called: Superiorlaser
2411 N John Young Pkwy (32804-4105)
PHONE..................................407 295-5772
Lyndell N Freeman II, *President*
Charles T Gross, *Vice Pres*
▼ **EMP:** 23 **EST:** 1987
SQ FT: 10,000
SALES (est): 5MM **Privately Held**
WEB: www.superiormetalfab.com
SIC: 3444 3699 Sheet metalwork; electrical equipment & supplies

(G-13231)
SUPERIOR SIGNS INC
3975 Forrestal Ave # 600 (32806-6198)
PHONE..................................407 601-7964
Daniel Eric Shiman, *Principal*
EMP: 12 **EST:** 2004
SALES (est): 508.4K **Privately Held**
WEB: www.asuperiorsign.com
SIC: 3993 5099 1799 Signs & advertising specialties; signs, except electric; sign installation & maintenance

(G-13232)
SUREPODS LLC
2300 Principal Row # 101 (32837-8810)
PHONE..................................407 859-7034
Bill Seery, *Vice Pres*
Rosa Rodriguez, *Controller*
Eric Lamb, *Mng Member*
▲ **EMP:** 70 **EST:** 2016
SALES (est): 11MM **Privately Held**
WEB: www.surepods.com
SIC: 2452 Prefabricated buildings, wood

(G-13233)
SWISSTECH MACHINERY LLC
8815 Conroy Windermere Rd (32835-3129)
PHONE..................................407 416-2383
Page Spinetti, *Mng Member*
EMP: 5 **EST:** 2007
SALES (est): 408.5K **Privately Held**
WEB: www.swisstechmachinery.com
SIC: 3545 Machine tool accessories

(G-13234)
SYMME3D LLC
1 S Orange Ave Ste 502 (32801-2626)
PHONE..................................321 220-1584
Calin Brandabur, *CEO*
Kennan Clark, *Chairman*
EMP: 12
SQ FT: 1,200
SALES (est): 3.1MM **Privately Held**
SIC: 3549 Metalworking machinery
PA: Symme3d Manufacturing Srl
Calea Sagului Nr. 85 Bl. 11 Sc. G Ap. 30
Timisoara

(G-13235)
SYNAPTIC SPARKS INC
9738 Old Patina Way (32832-5822)
PHONE..................................205 774-8324
Christopher Meyer, *CEO*
Mike Kalaf, *COO*
Jason Lamm, *CFO*
Shannon Heylmun, *Admin Sec*
EMP: 9 **EST:** 2013
SALES (est): 377.1K **Privately Held**
WEB: www.synapticsparks.org
SIC: 3652 Pre-recorded records & tapes

(G-13236)
SYNERON
605 W Yale St (32804-5337)
PHONE..................................407 489-3366
Jennifer Calabrese, *Principal*
EMP: 6 **EST:** 2015
SALES (est): 225.7K **Privately Held**
SIC: 3845 Electromedical equipment

(G-13237)
SYNTHES3D USA INC
1800 Pembrook Dr (32810-6928)
PHONE..................................321 946-1303
Vivien Poujade, *Principal*
EMP: 10 **EST:** 2016
SALES (est): 128.7K **Privately Held**
WEB: www.orthovirtualconvention.com
SIC: 3577 Computer peripheral equipment

(G-13238)
T R S
Also Called: Trs
6330 Silver Star Rd (32818-3119)
PHONE..................................407 298-5490
Carl Summers, *President*
Randy Summers, *Exec VP*
Ardis Summers, *Admin Sec*
EMP: 45 **EST:** 1973
SQ FT: 26,000
SALES (est): 3MM **Privately Held**
WEB: www.trselectric.com
SIC: 3694 3625 5063 5013 Alternators, automotive; starter, electric motor; motor controls, starters & relays: electric; alternators; automotive parts; batteries, automotive & truck

(G-13239)
T&T DETAILING INC
1801 E Clnl Dr Ste 107 (32803)
PHONE..................................407 414-6710
Mark Alston, *Owner*
EMP: 7 **EST:** 2002
SALES (est): 88.3K **Privately Held**
SIC: 2396 Automotive & apparel trimmings

(G-13240)
TAR BUILDING LLC
1155 N Orange Ave (32804-6407)
PHONE..................................407 896-7252
Thomas Rensenhouse, *Principal*
EMP: 6 **EST:** 2011
SALES (est): 160.3K **Privately Held**
SIC: 2865 Tar

(G-13241)
TARPON WOODWORKS LLC
1518 Newbridge Ln (32825-8239)
PHONE..................................407 446-9450
Laszlo Bossanyi, *Principal*
EMP: 6 **EST:** 2011
SALES (est): 94.9K **Privately Held**
SIC: 2431 Millwork

(G-13242)
TAYLOR FARMS FLORIDA INC
7492 Chancellor Dr (32809-6242)
PHONE..................................407 859-3373
Bruce Taylor, *Ch of Bd*
Tim Unick, *President*
Esteban Arreguin, *Vice Pres*
Lewis Swarts, *Opers Mgr*
Terry Kitts, *Purch Mgr*
▲ **EMP:** 480 **EST:** 1983
SQ FT: 66,000
SALES (est): 210.5MM **Privately Held**
WEB: www.taylorfarms.com
SIC: 2099 Ready-to-eat meals, salads & sandwiches
PA: Taylor Fresh Foods, Inc.
150 Main St Ste 400
Salinas CA 93901

(G-13243)
TDR FOOD DISTRIBUTION LLC
7810 Kingspointe Pkwy (32819-8520)
PHONE..................................561 860-7617
Jim Mizak, *Principal*
EMP: 6
SALES (est): 292.8K **Privately Held**
SIC: 2099 Food preparations

(G-13244)
TECPORT OPTICS INC
6457 Hazeltine National D (32822-5162)
PHONE..................................407 855-1212
Tam V Le, *President*
Joseph Kim, *Vice Pres*
Jong Woo, *Engineer*
Dale Flowers, *CFO*
Frank Helmes, *Executive*
▲ **EMP:** 15 **EST:** 1997
SQ FT: 3,300
SALES (est): 3MM **Privately Held**
WEB: www.tecportoptics.com
SIC: 3827 Optical instruments & lenses

(G-13245)
TEE-N-JAY SERVICES LLC
528 Kittredge Dr (32805-1328)
PHONE....................................407 760-7925
Thomas Whitley, *Manager*
EMP: 6 **EST:** 2012
SALES (est): 153.5K **Privately Held**
SIC: 2759 Screen printing

(G-13246)
TEM SYSTEMS INC
4520 Pkwy Commerce Blvd (32808-1014)
PHONE....................................407 251-7114
Scott Roether, *Manager*
EMP: 6
SALES (corp-wide): 18.5MM **Privately Held**
WEB: www.temsystems.com
SIC: 3699 7221 Security devices; passport photographer
PA: Tem Systems, Inc.
15491 Sw 12th St Ste 408
Sunrise FL 33326
954 577-6044

(G-13247)
TEN IN MOTION LLC
8544 Commodity Cir (32819-9001)
PHONE....................................407 226-0204
Marc A Plogstedt, *President*
Itec Entertainment Corp,
EMP: 10 **EST:** 2000
SALES (est): 705.7K **Privately Held**
SIC: 3577 Data conversion equipment, media-to-media: computer

(G-13248)
TERALIFE LLC
5950 Lakehurst Dr Ste 249 (32819-8391)
PHONE....................................407 434-0408
Paulo Miguel Da Silva,
EMP: 8 **EST:** 2018
SALES (est): 175.4K **Privately Held**
SIC: 2515 Mattresses, containing felt, foam rubber, urethane, etc.

(G-13249)
TERANEX SYSTEMS INC
2602 Challenger Tech Ct # 240
(32826-2782)
PHONE....................................407 888-4300
Fax: 407 858-6001
EMP: 30
SALES (est): 4MM
SALES (corp-wide): 30MM **Privately Held**
SIC: 3651 Mfg Home Audio/Video Equipment
PA: Jupiter Systems
31015 Huntwood Ave
Hayward CA 94544
510 675-1000

(G-13250)
TERRY M GRIFFIN WELDING
18290 Hewlett Rd (32820-2105)
PHONE....................................407 209-8317
Terry Griffin, *President*
EMP: 6 **EST:** 2009
SALES (est): 77.7K **Privately Held**
SIC: 7692 Welding repair

(G-13251)
TFL OF ORLANDO
2586 N Orange Blossom Trl (32804-4865)
PHONE....................................407 936-1553
Frank Gulfroy, *Owner*
EMP: 9 **EST:** 2011
SALES (est): 147.6K **Privately Held**
SIC: 3537 Industrial trucks & tractors

(G-13252)
TH CUSTOM PROMO TIONS
102 Drennen Rd (32806-8511)
PHONE....................................407 704-7921
EMP: 6 **EST:** 2019
SALES (est): 168.8K **Privately Held**
SIC: 2752 Commercial printing, lithographic

(G-13253)
THE SCRANTON TIMES L P
Also Called: Orlando Weekly
16 W Pine St (32801-2612)
PHONE....................................407 377-0400
Rich Schreiber, *Manager*
Zackary Rowe, *Director*
Michael Wagner, *Creative Dir*
EMP: 26
SALES (corp-wide): 63.5MM **Privately Held**
WEB: www.thetimes-tribune.com
SIC: 2711 Commercial printing & newspaper publishing combined
PA: The Scranton Times L P
149 Penn Ave Ste 1
Scranton PA 18503
570 348-9100

(G-13254)
THERMOTECH SYSTEMS CORPORATION
Also Called: Gencor Industries
5201 N Orange Blossom Trl (32810-1008)
PHONE....................................407 290-6000
John E Elliott, *Vice Pres*
EMP: 1 **EST:** 1977
SALES (est): 3.2MM
SALES (corp-wide): 77.4MM **Publicly Held**
WEB: www.gencor.com
SIC: 3567 Industrial furnaces & ovens
PA: Gencor Industries, Inc.
5201 N Orange Blossom Trl
Orlando FL 32810
407 290-6000

(G-13255)
THREADBIRD LLC
3715 Vineland Rd (32811-6416)
PHONE....................................407 545-6506
Ilene Appel, *Production*
Martha Christine, *Production*
Nicholas Roccanti, *Mng Member*
Scott Anderson,
EMP: 7 **EST:** 2008
SALES (est): 1.1MM **Privately Held**
WEB: www.threadbird.com
SIC: 2759 Screen printing

(G-13256)
THRIVE FROZEN NUTRITION INC (PA)
4767 New Broad St Ste 325 (32814-6405)
P.O. Box 2186, Winter Park (32790-2186)
PHONE....................................407 960-4883
Robert Wengert, *CEO*
Travis Milks, *Partner*
Bob Wengert, *CFO*
Franklin C Everett, *Mng Member*
Chris Dreska, *Director*
EMP: 11 **EST:** 2011
SQ FT: 1,000
SALES (est): 1.5MM **Privately Held**
WEB: www.thriveicecream.com
SIC: 2038 Frozen specialties

(G-13257)
TITANIUM DEVELOPMENT LLC
Also Called: Titanium Pavers
3209 Prkchster Sq Blvd Ap (32835-7551)
PHONE....................................407 844-8664
Andreia B Piroupo, *Principal*
EMP: 7 **EST:** 2017
SALES (est): 1MM **Privately Held**
WEB: www.titaniumpavers.com
SIC: 3356 Titanium

(G-13258)
TITANIUM FUSION TECH LLC
8501 Amber Oak Dr (32817-1242)
PHONE....................................435 881-5742
Daniel F Justin, *Manager*
EMP: 6 **EST:** 2017
SALES (est): 251K **Privately Held**
SIC: 3356 Titanium

(G-13259)
TITANIUM TECH CORP
6373 Conroy Rd (32835-3510)
PHONE....................................407 912-9126
Erica Miashita, *Vice Pres*
EMP: 6 **EST:** 2018
SALES (est): 99.9K **Privately Held**
WEB: www.titanium.org
SIC: 3356 Titanium

(G-13260)
TJ CABINETRY INC
4333 Silver Star Rd # 14 (32808-5100)
PHONE....................................407 886-8294
David Sabuncu, *President*
EMP: 14 **EST:** 1992
SQ FT: 3,000
SALES (est): 309.1K **Privately Held**
WEB: www.tjcustomcabinets.com
SIC: 2434 Wood kitchen cabinets

(G-13261)
TONERS PLUS LLC
1969 S Alafaya Trl 218 (32828-8732)
PHONE....................................407 756-5787
Jim Novak,
EMP: 7 **EST:** 2010
SALES (est): 250.3K **Privately Held**
WEB: www.tonersplus.biz
SIC: 3861 5045 5112 Toners, prepared photographic (not made in chemical plants); printers, computer; laserjet supplies

(G-13262)
TOP OF THE LINE COATING INC
13209 Briar Forest Ct (32828-4610)
PHONE....................................407 485-8546
Jose Rivera, *Principal*
EMP: 6 **EST:** 2008
SALES (est): 103.5K **Privately Held**
SIC: 3479 Metal coating & allied service

(G-13263)
TOTAL VISION DESIGN GROUP
Also Called: Pictures and Mirrors
7552 10th Chancellor Dr (32809)
PHONE....................................407 438-6933
Arno Heyder, *President*
EMP: 9 **EST:** 2012
SALES (est): 502.7K **Privately Held**
WEB: www.totalvisiondesigngroup.com
SIC: 2499 Picture & mirror frames, wood

(G-13264)
TOTEUM ALL TRCKG TRNSPRTING L
5401 S Kirkman Rd Ste 310 (32819-7937)
PHONE....................................888 506-5890
Eddie McIntosh III, *CEO*
EMP: 50
SALES (est): 2MM **Privately Held**
SIC: 3537 Trucks: freight, baggage, etc.: industrial, except mining

(G-13265)
TOUCHLESS COVER LLC
10150 Central Port Dr (32824-7059)
PHONE....................................407 679-2217
Slate Kirk, *President*
Carlos Cardenas, *Plant Mgr*
Holly Engilis, *Accounting Mgr*
◆ **EMP:** 21 **EST:** 1998
SQ FT: 3,000
SALES (est): 4.4MM **Privately Held**
WEB: www.touchlesscover.com
SIC: 3536 Boat lifts

(G-13266)
TP AEROSPACE TECHNICS LLC (DH)
6470 Narcoossee Rd Ste A (32822-5594)
PHONE....................................407 730-9988
Peter Lyager, *CEO*
Thomas Ibs, *President*
Nikolaj Lei Jacobsen, *COO*
EMP: 2 **EST:** 2014
SALES (est): 10.6MM
SALES (corp-wide): 488.2K **Privately Held**
WEB: www.tpaerospace.com
SIC: 3721 Aircraft

(G-13267)
TRAFFIC CONTROL PDTS FLA INC
249 N Ivey Ln Ste A (32811-4253)
PHONE....................................407 521-6777
Mike Bartlett, *Manager*
EMP: 10
SALES (corp-wide): 15.5MM **Privately Held**
WEB: www.trafficcontrolproducts.org
SIC: 3499 Barricades, metal
PA: Traffic Control Products Of Florida, Inc.
5514 Carmack Rd
Tampa FL 33610
813 621-8484

(G-13268)
TRANSTAT EQUIPMENT INC
510 Thorpe Rd (32824-8133)
P.O. Box 593865 (32859-3865)
PHONE....................................407 857-2040
Otto L Schodorf Jr, *Ch of Bd*
John Reetz, *President*
Paul Schodorf, *Corp Secy*
Leroy Peterson, *Exec VP*
EMP: 14 **EST:** 1900
SQ FT: 17,000
SALES (est): 640.8K **Privately Held**
SIC: 3713 7532 7538 Truck bodies (motor vehicles); body shop, trucks; general automotive repair shops

(G-13269)
TREE STAKE SOLUTIONS LLC
6713 New Hope Rd (32824-8936)
PHONE....................................407 920-0507
Martin B White, *Mng Member*
EMP: 6 **EST:** 2017
SALES (est): 120K **Privately Held**
WEB: www.treestakesolutions.net
SIC: 2499 5211 5099 Handles, poles, dowels & stakes: wood; flooring, wood; wood & wood by-products

(G-13270)
TRI-TECH ELECTRONICS INC
9480 E Colonial Dr (32817-4198)
P.O. Box 678028 (32867-8028)
PHONE....................................407 277-2131
Joseph Gurvich, *President*
John F Zold, *Principal*
Stanton A J Jr, *Corp Secy*
EMP: 60 **EST:** 1957
SQ FT: 27,000
SALES (est): 9.6MM **Privately Held**
WEB: www.tri-techelectronics.com
SIC: 3728 3845 3679 7629 Aircraft body & wing assemblies & parts; electromedical apparatus; electronic circuits; harness assemblies for electronic use: wire or cable; electrical personal use appliance repair; electronic equipment repair; sanitary engineers; electrical or electronic engineering

(G-13271)
TRIAD ISOTOPES INC (PA)
4205 Vineland Rd Ste L13 (32811-6601)
PHONE....................................407 455-6700
Dom Meffe, *President*
William McCormick, *Vice Pres*
Brian Schumer, *Vice Pres*
Shane Scott, *Vice Pres*
Debbie Vanerka, *VP Bus Dvlpt*
◆ **EMP:** 30 **EST:** 2006
SALES (est): 140.4MM **Privately Held**
WEB: www.jdiri.com
SIC: 2834 Pharmaceutical preparations

(G-13272)
TRIKAROO
5525 Commerce Dr Ste 1 (32839-2988)
PHONE....................................800 679-3415
Gina Garcia, *President*
▲ **EMP:** 5 **EST:** 2013
SALES (est): 443K **Privately Held**
WEB: www.trikaroo.com
SIC: 3711 Motor vehicles & car bodies

(G-13273)
TRIM-PAK CORPORATION (PA)
8700 S Orange Ave (32824-7901)
PHONE....................................407 851-8900
David L Smith, *President*
John Shugart, *Vice Pres*
Glenn Trimble, *Sales Staff*
Wayne Boisvert, *Sales Associate*
Tony Wingerter, *Sales Associate*
EMP: 20 **EST:** 1977
SQ FT: 125,000
SALES (est): 10.5MM **Privately Held**
WEB: www.trim-pak.com
SIC: 2434 5031 5072 5211 Wood kitchen cabinets; doors; kitchen cabinets; builders' hardware; doors, storm: wood or metal; builders' hardware

(G-13274)
TRITON II JV LLC
12802 Science Dr Ste 300 (32826-3021)
PHONE....................................407 894-5575
Sharon Wolford, *Principal*

EMP: 8 **EST:** 2017
SALES (est): 182.2K **Privately Held**
SIC: 3699 Electronic training devices; flight simulators (training aids), electronic

(G-13275)
TRIUMVIRATE ENVIRONMENTAL
10100 Rocket Blvd (32824-8565)
PHONE..................................407 859-4441
John McQuillan Jr, *Mng Member*
EMP: 23
SALES (corp-wide): 113MM **Privately Held**
WEB: www.triumvirate.com
SIC: 3822 Auto controls regulating residntl & coml environmt & applncs
PA: Triumvirate Environmental, Inc
200 Innerbelt Rd 4
Somerville MA 02143
617 628-8098

(G-13276)
TROST INDUSTRIES LLC
6300 Parc Corniche Dr (32821-7306)
P.O. Box 690297 (32869-0297)
PHONE..................................407 690-8603
Dennis Trost, *Principal*
EMP: 6 **EST:** 2011
SALES (est): 132.6K **Privately Held**
SIC: 3999 Manufacturing industries

(G-13277)
TRS WIRELESS INC
1711 S Division Ave (32805-4727)
PHONE..................................407 447-7333
John Raga, *CEO*
April Bennett, *Office Mgr*
Jeff Rhea, *Manager*
Tim Bennett, *Info Tech Mgr*
Sterling Tucker, *Executive*
EMP: 23 **EST:** 1969
SALES (est): 1.4MM **Privately Held**
WEB: www.trswireless.com
SIC: 3663 5999 Transmitter-receivers, radio; telephone & communication equipment

(G-13278)
TRUE EAST SURFBOARD INC
3155 Rider Pl (32817-2046)
PHONE..................................407 679-6896
Ricardo D Montilla, *Principal*
EMP: 6 **EST:** 2007
SALES (est): 114.9K **Privately Held**
SIC: 3949 Surfboards

(G-13279)
TRUSSWAY MANUFACTURING INC
8850 Trussway Blvd (32824-7897)
PHONE..................................407 857-2777
Daniel Durski, *Vice Pres*
Dan Eberle, *Plant Mgr*
Jose Ramirez, *Plant Mgr*
Kirk Crowe, *Project Mgr*
Travis Anderson, *Opers Staff*
EMP: 15 **Privately Held**
WEB: www.trussway.com
SIC: 2439 Trusses, wooden roof
HQ: Trussway Manufacturing, Inc.
9411 Alcorn St
Houston TX 77093

(G-13280)
TUPPERWARE BRANDS CORPORATION (PA)
14901 S Ornge Blossom Trl (32837-6600)
P.O. Box 2353 (32802-2353)
PHONE..................................407 826-5050
Susan M Cameron, *Ch of Bd*
Miguel Fernandez, *President*
Hector Lezama, *President*
Deepak Chhabra, *Managing Dir*
Cassandra Harris, *COO*
▲ **EMP:** 9041 **EST:** 1996
SALES: 1.7B **Publicly Held**
WEB: www.tupperwarebrands.com
SIC: 3089 2844 Kitchenware, plastic; toilet preparations; toilet preparations

(G-13281)
TUPPERWARE PRODUCTS INC
14901 S Ornge Blossom Trl (32837-6600)
PHONE..................................407 826-5050
Miguel Fernandez, *President*
Randy Griswold, *Manager*
EMP: 27 **EST:** 1996
SALES (est): 6.1MM **Publicly Held**
WEB: www.tupperware.com
SIC: 2821 Molding compounds, plastics
PA: Tupperware Brands Corporation
14901 S Ornge Blossom Trl
Orlando FL 32837

(G-13282)
TUPPERWARE TURKEY INC
14901 S Orange Blossom Tr (32837-6600)
PHONE..................................407 826-5050
EMP: 56 **EST:** 1996
SALES (est): 262.2K **Privately Held**
WEB: www.tupperwarebrands.com
SIC: 3089 Plastic kitchenware, tableware & houseware

(G-13283)
TUPPERWARE US INC (HQ)
14901 S Ornge Blossom Trl (32837-6600)
P.O. Box 2353 (32802-2353)
PHONE..................................407 826-5050
Thomas M Roehlk, *CEO*
Ev Goings, *Ch of Bd*
Pablo Munoz, *President*
Christian Skr Der, *Vice Pres*
Jos Timmerman, *Vice Pres*
▲ **EMP:** 446 **EST:** 1989
SQ FT: 10,000
SALES (est): 87.4MM **Publicly Held**
WEB: www.tupperware.com
SIC: 3089 Jars, plastic

(G-13284)
TURNSTILE PUBLISHING COMPANY (DH)
Also Called: Golfweek
1500 Park Center Dr (32835-5704)
P.O. Box 783908, Winter Garden (34778-3908)
PHONE..................................407 563-7000
Francis Farrell, *President*
Cindy Crain, *Corp Secy*
Patti Green, *Vice Pres*
Eric Beckson, *CFO*
EMP: 60 **EST:** 1975
SQ FT: 9,740
SALES (est): 32.6MM
SALES (corp-wide): 3.4B **Publicly Held**
SIC: 2721 Magazines: publishing only, not printed on site; periodicals: publishing only
HQ: Usa Today Sports Media Group, Llc
7950 Jones Branch Dr
Mc Lean VA 22102
703 854-6000

(G-13285)
UFP ORLANDO LLC
7205 Rose Ave (32810-3414)
PHONE..................................407 982-3312
Gabe High, *Manager*
EMP: 14 **EST:** 2016
SALES (est): 2.5MM
SALES (corp-wide): 5.1B **Publicly Held**
WEB: www.ufpi.com
SIC: 2491 Millwork, treated wood
PA: Ufp Industries, Inc.
2801 E Beltline Ave Ne
Grand Rapids MI 49525
616 364-6161

(G-13286)
UK US PARTNERS LLC T MCCULOCH
10806 Woodchase Cir (32836-5868)
PHONE..................................407 217-2978
Thomas McCulloch, *Principal*
EMP: 6 **EST:** 2016
SALES (est): 104.2K **Privately Held**
SIC: 3829 Measuring & controlling devices

(G-13287)
ULTIMATE OVERSTOCK LLC
Also Called: VIP Sports Idrive
4967 Intl Dr Ste 3a27 (32819-6213)
PHONE..................................407 851-1017
Javed Iqbal, *Mng Member*
EMP: 20 **EST:** 2018
SALES (est): 1.1MM **Privately Held**
SIC: 2329 Men's & boys' sportswear & athletic clothing

(G-13288)
ULTIMATE STNWRKS CENTL FLA LLC
9220 Boggy Creek Rd # 221 (32824-8382)
PHONE..................................407 412-5981
Patricia Gutierrez, *Mng Member*
EMP: 5 **EST:** 2008
SALES (est): 800K **Privately Held**
SIC: 1499 Gem stones (natural) mining

(G-13289)
UNFOLDINGWORD CORPORATION
Also Called: Distant Shores Media
10524 Moss Park Rd # 204 (32832-5898)
PHONE..................................407 900-3005
David Reeves, *CEO*
Jan Perry, *CFO*
Heather Eastwood, *Human Res Mgr*
EMP: 18 **EST:** 2003
SALES: 4.2MM **Privately Held**
WEB: www.unfoldingword.org
SIC: 7372 Educational computer software

(G-13290)
UNIQUE DESIGNS PROF SVCS INC
Also Called: Dj DK
918 Wooden Blvd (32805-3467)
P.O. Box 561333 (32856-1333)
PHONE..................................407 296-6204
David J Hardrick, *President*
EMP: 13 **EST:** 2008
SALES (est): 320.4K **Privately Held**
SIC: 2752 Commercial printing, lithographic

(G-13291)
UNIQUE ELECTRONICS INC (PA)
1320 26th St (32805-5297)
PHONE..................................407 422-3051
George Singleton, *CEO*
Michael M Klinger, *President*
Penny Huynh, *Materials Mgr*
Jay Cooper, *Engineer*
James T Giuliano, *CFO*
EMP: 129 **EST:** 1980
SQ FT: 25,145
SALES (est): 19.4MM **Privately Held**
WEB: www.uniqueelectronics.com
SIC: 3679 Harness assemblies for electronic use: wire or cable

(G-13292)
UNITED FABRICATION SHTMTL INC
1815 Tallokas Ave (32805-4735)
PHONE..................................407 826-1933
Albert Geluso, *Principal*
EMP: 7 **EST:** 2017
SALES (est): 152.3K **Privately Held**
SIC: 3444 Sheet metalwork

(G-13293)
UNITED MACHINING SERVICE INC
2410 Coolidge Ave (32804-4812)
PHONE..................................407 422-7710
Samuel D Reynolds, *President*
EMP: 5 **EST:** 1995
SALES (est): 400K **Privately Held**
SIC: 3549 Metalworking machinery

(G-13294)
UNITED TROPHY MANUFACTURING (PA)
Also Called: Fleaworld Div
610 N Orange Ave (32801-1398)
PHONE..................................407 841-2525
Sydney Allen Levy, *President*
Marianne Levy, *Corp Secy*
▲ **EMP:** 50 **EST:** 1952
SQ FT: 17,000
SALES (est): 14MM **Privately Held**
WEB: www.unitedtrophy.com
SIC: 3914 7389 7996 Trophies, plated (all metals); flea market; amusement parks

(G-13295)
UNITED WORLD PRINTING INC
236 Outlook Point Dr # 300 (32809-7253)
PHONE..................................407 738-0888
Matthew Harris, *Vice Pres*
EMP: 6 **EST:** 2019
SALES (est): 111.6K **Privately Held**
WEB: www.unitedworldprinting.com
SIC: 2752 Commercial printing, lithographic

(G-13296)
UNIVERSAL PC ORGANIZATION INC
8082 Wellsmere Cir (32835-5360)
PHONE..................................321 285-9206
Mark Wascher, *President*
Joseph Machado, *Director*
EMP: 6 **EST:** 2013
SALES (est): 466.6K **Privately Held**
SIC: 2611 Pulp mills, mechanical & recycling processing

(G-13297)
UNIVERSAL POLISHING SYSTEMS
4333 Silver Star Rd # 175 (32808-5170)
PHONE..................................407 227-9516
Abrasive Xiaoyu, *Principal*
Andrew Knopp, *Sales Mgr*
▲ **EMP:** 5 **EST:** 2010
SALES (est): 335.8K **Privately Held**
WEB: www.universalpolishingsystems.com
SIC: 3471 Polishing, metals or formed products

(G-13298)
US MOBILE PRO LLC
6422 Milner Blvd Ste 103 (32809-6699)
P.O. Box 593531 (32859-3531)
PHONE..................................973 365-1812
Brian Wizniewski, *Principal*
EMP: 8 **EST:** 2017
SALES (est): 810.5K **Privately Held**
SIC: 3663 Mobile communication equipment

(G-13299)
US PIPE FABRICATION LLC
109 5th St (32824-8258)
PHONE..................................860 769-6097
Rob Morris, *Branch Mgr*
EMP: 21
SALES (corp-wide): 1.5B **Publicly Held**
WEB: www.uspipe.com
SIC: 3498 3312 Fabricated pipe & fittings; pipes, iron & steel
HQ: Us Pipe Fabrication, Llc
2 Chase Corporate Dr # 200
Hoover AL 35244

(G-13300)
VESTAGEN TCHNICAL TEXTILES INC
Also Called: Vestex
1301 W Colonial Dr (32804-7133)
PHONE..................................407 781-2570
Bill Bold, *CEO*
Dale Pfost, *Ch of Bd*
Uncas B Favret III, *President*
Stewart B Davis, *Vice Pres*
Stewart Davis, *Vice Pres*
◆ **EMP:** 5 **EST:** 2009
SALES (est): 1.4MM **Privately Held**
WEB: www.vestagen.com
SIC: 2819 2843 5023 8731 Fluorine, elemental; textile finishing agents; sheets, textile; commercial physical research

(G-13301)
VIA CABINETS CORP
3113 Willie Mays Pkwy (32811-5523)
PHONE..................................407 633-1915
Bernardo Das Chagas Viana, *President*
Monica Cristina Viana, *Vice Pres*
EMP: 7 **EST:** 2018
SALES (est): 392.9K **Privately Held**
SIC: 2511 Wood household furniture

(G-13302)
VIA OPTRONICS LLC
6220 Hzltine Nat Dr Ste 1 (32822-5145)
PHONE..................................407 745-5031
Jurgen Eichner, *CEO*
Ed Illingworth, *Manager*
◆ **EMP:** 24 **EST:** 2009
SQ FT: 52,000

SALES (est): 6MM
SALES (corp-wide): 2.6MM **Privately Held**
WEB: www.via-optronics.com
SIC: 3679 Liquid crystal displays (LCD)
HQ: Via Optronics Gmbh
Sieboldstr. 18
Nurnberg 90411
911 597-5750

(G-13303)
VICTORY TAILGATE LLC
2437 E Landstreet Rd (32824-7945)
PHONE..................................407 704-8775
Scott D Sims, *CEO*
Marcos Olivares, *Production*
Pranil Patel, *Accounts Mgr*
James Penedo, *Sales Staff*
Jason Bergman, *Graphic Designe*
◆ **EMP:** 160 **EST:** 2009
SALES (est): 35.2MM
SALES (corp-wide): 273.6MM **Publicly Held**
WEB: www.victorytailgate.com
SIC: 3944 Board games, children's & adults'
HQ: Indian Industries Inc
817 Maxwell Ave
Evansville IN 47711
812 467-1200

(G-13304)
VIOLET DEFENSE LLC
189 S Orange Ave Ste 1400 (32801-3258)
PHONE..................................407 433-1104
Terrance Berland, *CEO*
Richard Brown, *Vice Pres*
Mark Nathan, *Mng Member*
Richard Barnes, *CIO*
EMP: 25 **EST:** 2015
SALES (est): 6.7MM **Privately Held**
WEB: www.violetdefense.com
SIC: 3646 Commercial indusl & institutional electric lighting fixtures

(G-13305)
VISIONS SKY CORP
18154 Cadence St (32820-2728)
PHONE..................................888 788-8609
David Barefoot, *Principal*
EMP: 9 **EST:** 2012
SALES (est): 125.6K **Privately Held**
WEB: www.visionssky.com
SIC: 7372 Prepackaged software

(G-13306)
VISUAL SIGNS LLC
7041 Grand National Dr (32819-8381)
PHONE..................................407 693-0200
EMP: 8 **EST:** 2019
SALES (est): 960.7K **Privately Held**
WEB: www.visualsignsandgraphics.com
SIC: 3993 Signs & advertising specialties

(G-13307)
VITAL HEALTH CORP
6150 Metrowest Blvd # 204 (32835-3290)
PHONE..................................407 522-1125
EMP: 8 **EST:** 2015
SALES (est): 296.1K **Privately Held**
WEB: www.vitalhealthus.com
SIC: 2023 Dry, condensed, evaporated dairy products

(G-13308)
VITAL HEALTH CORPORATION (HQ)
Also Called: Inprovit Vital Health
6000 Metrowest Blvd # 200 (32835-7629)
PHONE..................................407 522-1125
Julio Correa, *President*
Sergio Correa, *Admin Sec*
EMP: 8 **EST:** 2000
SQ FT: 6,000
SALES (est): 14.2MM **Privately Held**
WEB: www.vitalhealthus.com
SIC: 2023 Dietary supplements, dairy & non-dairy based

(G-13309)
VITAL SIGNS OF ORLANDO INC
Also Called: Vso
2111 S Division Ave Ste A (32805-6206)
PHONE..................................407 297-0680
David New, *President*
Gary Stephens, *Research*
EMP: 6 **EST:** 1987
SALES (est): 953.8K **Privately Held**
WEB: www.vitalsignsorlando.com
SIC: 3993 Signs, not made in custom sign painting shops

(G-13310)
VONOS LLC ✪
1317 Edgewater Dr Ste 476 (32804-6350)
PHONE..................................888 698-6667
Anthony Velez, *Mng Member*
EMP: 6 **EST:** 2020
SALES (est): 267.4K **Privately Held**
WEB: www.vonos.com
SIC: 2842 Disinfectants, household or industrial plant

(G-13311)
VOXX AUTOMOTIVE CORP (HQ)
2351 J Lawson Blvd (32824-4386)
PHONE..................................631 231-7750
Patrick M Lavelle, *President*
Patrick Lavelle, *Director*
EMP: 28 **EST:** 2018
SALES (est): 12.9MM
SALES (corp-wide): 563.6MM **Publicly Held**
WEB: www.voxxautomotive.com
SIC: 3699 Automotive driving simulators (training aids), electronic
PA: Voxx International Corporation
2351 J Lawson Blvd
Orlando FL 32824
800 645-7750

(G-13312)
VOXX AUTOMOTIVE CORPORATION
2351 J Lawson Blvd (32824-4386)
PHONE..................................407 842-7000
EMP: 10 **EST:** 2019
SALES (est): 3MM
SALES (corp-wide): 563.6MM **Publicly Held**
WEB: www.voxxautomotive.com
SIC: 3711 Motor vehicles & car bodies
PA: Voxx International Corporation
2351 J Lawson Blvd
Orlando FL 32824
800 645-7750

(G-13313)
VOXX INTERNATIONAL CORPORATION (PA)
2351 J Lawson Blvd (32824-4386)
PHONE..................................800 645-7750
John J Shalam, *Ch of Bd*
Patrick M Lavelle, *President*
Loriann Shelton, *COO*
Richard A Maddia, *Vice Pres*
James Shutowich, *Vice Pres*
◆ **EMP:** 330 **EST:** 1960
SALES: 563.6MM **Publicly Held**
WEB: www.voxxintl.com
SIC: 3711 3651 3663 5013 Motor vehicles & car bodies; household audio & video equipment; audio electronic systems; video camera-audio recorders, household use; radio & TV communications equipment; automotive supplies & parts; electronic parts & equipment

(G-13314)
VOXXHIRSCHMANN CORPORATION
Also Called: Voxx Electronics
2351 J Lawson Blvd (32824-4386)
PHONE..................................866 869-7888
Ludwig Geis, *President*
EMP: 250 **EST:** 2014
SALES (est): 17.9MM **Privately Held**
WEB: www.voxxautomotive.com
SIC: 3714 Motor vehicle parts & accessories

(G-13315)
VPR 4X4
1870 Saturn Blvd (32837-9416)
PHONE..................................305 468-9818
EMP: 9 **EST:** 2019
SALES (est): 577.5K **Privately Held**
WEB: www.vpr4x4.com
SIC: 3714 Motor vehicle parts & accessories

(G-13316)
VUAANT INC (PA)
Also Called: Care.ai
7300 Sandlake Commons Blv (32819-8008)
PHONE..................................407 701-6975
Chakravarthy Toleti, *CEO*
EMP: 11 **EST:** 2018
SALES (est): 961.1K **Privately Held**
SIC: 7372 7389 Application computer software;

(G-13317)
WALDEN CONSULTING LLC
Also Called: Turbo Vacuum
1021 E Robinson St Ste A (32801-2004)
PHONE..................................407 563-3620
Scott E Walden, *Mng Member*
EMP: 5 **EST:** 2004
SQ FT: 1,500
SALES (est): 415.9K **Privately Held**
WEB: www.turbovacuum.com
SIC: 3821 Vacuum pumps, laboratory

(G-13318)
WALKER HOSPITALITY INC
1038 25th St (32805-5474)
PHONE..................................407 927-1871
Jung H Moon, *Principal*
EMP: 6 **EST:** 2010
SALES (est): 211.2K **Privately Held**
WEB: www.walkerhospitalityfl.com
SIC: 3842 Surgical appliances & supplies

(G-13319)
WASHINGTON SHORES ELEMENT
944 W Lake Mann Dr (32805-3435)
PHONE..................................407 250-6260
EMP: 5 **EST:** 2014
SALES (est): 597.6K **Privately Held**
WEB: www.washingtonshoreses.ocps.net
SIC: 2819 Elements

(G-13320)
WE PRINT FLYERS AND SHIRTS
210 N Kirkman Rd (32811-1102)
PHONE..................................407 902-7128
Dave B Howell, *Principal*
EMP: 7 **EST:** 2016
SALES (est): 96K **Privately Held**
SIC: 2752 Commercial printing, lithographic

(G-13321)
WEST COAST WONDERWORKS LLC
9067 International Dr (32819-9316)
PHONE..................................407 351-8800
EMP: 6 **EST:** 2016
SALES (est): 112.3K **Privately Held**
SIC: 3599 Amusement park equipment

(G-13322)
WEST DEVELOPMENT GROUP LLC
Also Called: Floribbean Grill The
4520 Malvern Hill Dr (32818-8296)
PHONE..................................407 308-5020
Dontaye West, *CEO*
Niurka West, *Principal*
EMP: 6 **EST:** 2017
SALES (est): 252.7K **Privately Held**
SIC: 2099 2499 8322 8099 Food preparations; food handling & processing products, wood; meal delivery program; nutrition services; restaurant management; restaurant & food services consultants

(G-13323)
WESTROCK CP LLC
4364 Sw 34th St (32811-6414)
PHONE..................................407 843-1300
Tom Grahan, *Manager*
John Cole, *Manager*
John Conley, *Manager*
EMP: 50
SALES (corp-wide): 17.5B **Publicly Held**
WEB: www.westrock.com
SIC: 2631 Paperboard mills
HQ: Westrock Cp, Llc
1000 Abernathy Rd Ste 125
Atlanta GA 30328

(G-13324)
WESTROCK CP LLC
375 W 7th St (32824-8145)
PHONE..................................407 859-9701
EMP: 20
SALES (corp-wide): 14.1B **Publicly Held**
SIC: 2653 Mfg Corrugated/Solid Fiber Boxes
HQ: Westrock Cp, Llc
504 Thrasher St
Norcross GA 30328

(G-13325)
WILLIAMS AND KING PUBLISHERS
3900 Millenia Blvd (32839-6407)
PHONE..................................407 914-8134
Marcia Richardson, *Principal*
EMP: 6 **EST:** 2016
SALES (est): 37.5K **Privately Held**
WEB: www.williamsandkingpublishers.com
SIC: 2741 Miscellaneous publishing

(G-13326)
WJ BERGIN CABINETRY LLC
1228 28th St (32805-6103)
PHONE..................................407 271-8982
William Bergin, *President*
Christopher Grey, *Sr Project Mgr*
EMP: 24 **EST:** 2009
SALES (est): 2.4MM **Privately Held**
WEB: www.wjbergin.com
SIC: 2599 Cabinets, factory

(G-13327)
WOLF AMERICAS LLC
Also Called: Wolf Rock Drills
3113 Willie Mays Pkwy (32811-5523)
PHONE..................................407 704-2051
Tiago Wolf, *Mng Member*
EMP: 5 **EST:** 2014
SALES (est): 2.8MM **Privately Held**
WEB: www.wolfdrill.com
SIC: 3532 Drills & drilling equipment, mining (except oil & gas)
PA: Wolf Equipamentos De Perfuracao Ltda
Rod. Engenheiro Ermenio De Oliveira 54,5
Indaiatuba SP 13340

(G-13328)
WONDER EMPORIUM MILLWORK FAB
10779 Satellite Blvd (32837-8422)
PHONE..................................407 850-3131
Winnie Abram, *Principal*
James Conner, *Senior VP*
Peter Abram, *Vice Pres*
EMP: 9 **EST:** 2016
SALES (est): 223.1K **Privately Held**
SIC: 2431 2521 2541 Millwork; wood office furniture; wood partitions & fixtures

(G-13329)
WONDERWORLD 100 LLC ✪
2209 S Fern Creek Ave (32806-4185)
PHONE..................................407 618-3207
Keshia Almonor, *CEO*
EMP: 10 **EST:** 2020
SALES (est): 415.5K **Privately Held**
SIC: 2676 7389 Infant & baby paper products;

(G-13330)
WOOD MACHINE CORP
491 Thorpe Rd (32824-8132)
PHONE..................................407 851-8714
Daniel Thomas Wood, *President*
EMP: 8 **EST:** 1982
SQ FT: 10,000
SALES (est): 665.5K **Privately Held**
WEB: www.woodmachinecorp.com
SIC: 3599 Machine shop, jobbing & repair

(G-13331)
WORLDWIDE CHALLENGE MAGAZINE
100 Lake Hart Dr Ste 1600 (32832-0100)
PHONE..................................407 826-2390
Steve Douglas, *President*
Judy Nelson, *Principal*
Dan Willmann, *Vice Pres*
Mike Adamson, *Comms Dir*
Cherry Fields, *Consultant*

EMP: 26 EST: 2002
SALES (est): 373.2K Privately Held
WEB: www.cru.org
SIC: 2721 Magazines: publishing only, not printed on site

(G-13332)
XEROX BUSINESS SERVICES LLC
2290 Premier Row (32809-6212)
PHONE..................................407 926-4228
EMP: 6 EST: 2015
SALES (est): 155.3K Privately Held
SIC: 3861 Photographic equipment & supplies

(G-13333)
XTREME DUMPSTER SERVICES CORP
6142 Buford St (32835-2942)
PHONE..................................407 272-8899
Ricardo M Cabo, *President*
EMP: 7 EST: 2017
SALES (est): 306.8K Privately Held
SIC: 3443 Dumpsters, garbage

(G-13334)
XTREME SIGNS PRINTING INC
4401 Vineland Rd Ste A9 (32811-7361)
PHONE..................................321 438-3954
Lina M Orozco, *Principal*
EMP: 11 EST: 2016
SALES (est): 619.5K Privately Held
WEB: www.xtremeprinting.net
SIC: 3993 Signs & advertising specialties

(G-13335)
XYMOGEN INC (PA)
Also Called: Atlantic Pro-Nutrients
6900 Kingspointe Pkwy (32819-6544)
PHONE..................................407 445-0203
Brian Blackburn, *President*
Stephanie Blackburn, *Vice Pres*
Mike Mahoney, *Vice Pres*
Darrell Parkhill, *Project Mgr*
Luis Vasquez, *Traffic Mgr*
▲ EMP: 358 EST: 1979
SQ FT: 3,500
SALES (est): 94.4MM Privately Held
WEB: www.xymogen.com
SIC: 2833 Adrenal derivatives

(G-13336)
XYMOPRINT LLC
6900 Kingspointe Pkwy (32819-6544)
PHONE..................................407 504-2170
David Perlmutte, *CEO*
EMP: 13 EST: 2012
SALES (est): 534.2K Privately Held
WEB: www.xymoprint.com
SIC: 2752 Commercial printing, lithographic
PA: Xymogen, Inc.
6900 Kingspointe Pkwy
Orlando FL 32819

(G-13337)
YKK AP AMERICA INC
7608 Currency Dr (32809-6925)
PHONE..................................407 856-0660
Barry Wampler, *Manager*
EMP: 15 Privately Held
WEB: www.ykkap.com
SIC: 3442 Sash, door or window: metal
HQ: Ykk Ap America Inc.
270 Rverside Pkwy Ste 100
Austell GA 30168

(G-13338)
YOGURT BREEZE LLC
10727 Narcoossee Rd B4 (32832-6943)
PHONE..................................407 412-5939
Daphny Feria, *Mng Member*
EMP: 8 EST: 2012
SALES (est): 563K Privately Held
WEB: www.yogurtbreeze.com
SIC: 2026 2024 Yogurt; ice cream & frozen desserts

(G-13339)
ZESTY BRANDS LLC
2160 Premier Row (32809-6210)
PHONE..................................954 348-2827
Evgenii Ianchik, *Mng Member*
Mikhail Kogegoe,
Oxana Makarenko,
EMP: 12 EST: 2016
SQ FT: 13,000
SALES (est): 0 Privately Held
SIC: 2038 Snacks, including onion rings, cheese sticks, etc.

(G-13340)
ZESTY PAWS LLC
12124 High Tech Ave Ste 2 (32817-8373)
PHONE..................................407 358-6601
Chris Jaromin, *Senior VP*
Sarah Reinartz, *Manager*
Steven Ball,
EMP: 45 EST: 2019
SALES (est): 3.5MM Privately Held
SIC: 2047 Dog & cat food

(G-13341)
ZETMA LLC
Also Called: Minuteman
901 Indiana St (32805-4535)
P.O. Box 560669 (32856-0669)
PHONE..................................407 237-0233
Ruth Chambers,
Kendall Wilson,
EMP: 6 EST: 2017
SALES (est): 46.4K Privately Held
SIC: 2771 2789 2741 Greeting cards; bookbinding & related work; pamphlets, binding; catalogs: publishing & printing

(G-13342)
ZIEHM IMAGING INC
6280 Hzltine Nat Dr 100 (32822-5114)
PHONE..................................407 615-8560
Nelson Mendes, *CEO*
Dr Jorg Strobel, *President*
Dmitry Makovkin, *Business Mgr*
Bert Parlevliet, *Business Mgr*
Konrad Schaaser, *Opers Staff*
▲ EMP: 50 EST: 2005
SQ FT: 30,000
SALES (est): 11.7MM
SALES (corp-wide): 2.6MM Privately Held
WEB: www.ziehm.com
SIC: 3844 X-ray apparatus & tubes
HQ: Ziehm Imaging Gmbh
Lina-Ammon-Str. 10
Nurnberg 90471
911 660-670

(G-13343)
ZK CABINETS INC
5509 Commerce Dr (32839-2987)
PHONE..................................407 421-7307
Zein Khater, *President*
EMP: 9 EST: 2004
SALES (est): 145.8K Privately Held
SIC: 2434 Wood kitchen cabinets

(G-13344)
ZOM MONTERRA LP
2001 Summit Park Dr # 300 (32810-5945)
PHONE..................................407 644-6300
Steven K Buck, *Manager*
EMP: 9 EST: 2011
SALES: 3.5MM Privately Held
SIC: 3669 Emergency alarms

Ormond Beach
Volusia County

(G-13345)
A CERTIFIED SCREEN SERVICE
560 S Yonge St (32174-7540)
PHONE..................................386 673-0054
Todd Orie, *President*
EMP: 14 EST: 2003
SALES (est): 3.8MM Privately Held
WEB: www.acertifiedscreen.com
SIC: 3444 Metal housings, enclosures, casings & other containers

(G-13346)
ABA ENGINEERING & MFG INC
5 Aviator Way (32174-2982)
PHONE..................................386 672-9665
Winston Tomlinson, *President*
Thomas Bonarrigo, *Vice Pres*
EMP: 12 EST: 1992
SQ FT: 8,500
SALES (est): 500.4K Privately Held
SIC: 3444 3599 Sheet metalwork; machine & other job shop work

(G-13347)
ABB INSTALLATION PRODUCTS INC
Also Called: Homac Manufacturing
12 Southland Rd (32174-3002)
PHONE..................................386 677-9110
Dominic Pileggi, *President*
Janie Barberio, *Human Resources*
EMP: 95
SALES (corp-wide): 26.1B Privately Held
WEB: www.elastimoldswitchgear.com
SIC: 3643 Connectors & terminals for electrical devices
HQ: Abb Installation Products Inc.
860 Ridge Lake Blvd
Memphis TN 38120
901 252-5000

(G-13348)
AMERITECH DIE & MOLD SOUTH INC
Also Called: Ameritech Die & Mold & South
1 E Tower Cir (32174-8760)
PHONE..................................386 677-1770
Rusty Rotman, *Manager*
EMP: 9
SQ FT: 9,152
SALES (corp-wide): 4MM Privately Held
WEB: www.amdiemold.com
SIC: 3544 Industrial molds; dies, plastics forming; dies, steel rule
PA: Ameritech Die & Mold South, Inc.
107 Knob Hill Rd
Mooresville NC 28117
704 664-0801

(G-13349)
ARISTCRETE COATING EXPERTS LLC
1264 Riverbreeze Blvd (32176-4154)
PHONE..................................386 882-3660
Matthew Carolin, *Principal*
EMP: 9 EST: 2016
SALES (est): 426.4K Privately Held
SIC: 2952 Asphalt felts & coatings

(G-13350)
ATLANTIC MOBILE IMAGING SVCS
1400 Hand Ave Ste A (32174-8195)
PHONE..................................386 239-8271
Vernon Thurman, *President*
EMP: 6 EST: 2001
SQ FT: 768
SALES (est): 896.7K Privately Held
WEB: www.atlanticmobileimaging.com
SIC: 3844 X-ray apparatus & tubes

(G-13351)
BASIC ELEMENTS LLC
300 N Nova Rd (32174-9531)
PHONE..................................386 673-3100
Sam Jaffe, *Principal*
EMP: 6 EST: 2012
SALES (est): 174.7K Privately Held
SIC: 2819 Industrial inorganic chemicals

(G-13352)
BELLOWSTECH LLC
1289 N Us Highway 1 (32174-0722)
PHONE..................................386 615-7530
Glenn Weinrich, *President*
Gerard O'Donovan, *CFO*
EMP: 9 EST: 2007
SALES (est): 894.8K Privately Held
WEB: www.bellowstech.com
SIC: 3599 Bellows, industrial: metal

(G-13353)
BELLOWSTECH LLC
115 Business Center Dr (32174-6620)
PHONE..................................386 615-7530
Glenn Weinrich,
Jessica Kempfer, *Admin Asst*
EMP: 28 EST: 1999
SQ FT: 6,000
SALES (est): 5.4MM
SALES (corp-wide): 1B Privately Held
WEB: www.bellowstech.com
SIC: 3599 Bellows, industrial: metal
HQ: Precision Manufacturing Group Llc
501 Little Falls Rd
Cedar Grove NJ 07009
973 785-4630

(G-13354)
BLANE E TAYLOR WELDING INC
1760 N Us Highway 1 (32174-2540)
PHONE..................................386 931-1240
EMP: 8 EST: 2013
SALES (est): 377.5K Privately Held
SIC: 7692 Welding repair

(G-13355)
BLUE COAST BAKERS LLC
1899 N Us Highway 1 (32174-2579)
PHONE..................................386 944-0800
Amber Caballero, *Human Res Mgr*
David Z Lu, *Mng Member*
Ardeshir Asassan,
▲ EMP: 25 EST: 2013
SQ FT: 195,000
SALES (est): 1.3MM Privately Held
WEB: www.bluecoastbakers.com
SIC: 2053 Frozen bakery products, except bread

(G-13356)
C & J INDUSTRIES INC
105 John Anderson Dr (32176-5703)
PHONE..................................386 589-4907
Corina Nesbit, *Principal*
Barry Stainbrook, *Regl Sales Mgr*
Melissa White, *Regl Sales Mgr*
EMP: 13 EST: 2011
SALES (est): 221.8K Privately Held
WEB: www.cjindustries.com
SIC: 3089 Injection molding of plastics

(G-13357)
CARTERS CABINETRY INC
4 Aviator Way (32174-2982)
PHONE..................................386 677-4192
Fred A Carter, *President*
EMP: 20 EST: 1989
SALES (est): 2.7MM Privately Held
WEB: www.carterscabinetry.com
SIC: 2434 Wood kitchen cabinets

(G-13358)
CO2METER INC
131 Business Center Dr A3 (32174-6625)
PHONE..................................386 310-4933
Travis Lenander, *CEO*
Joshua Pringle, *Vice Pres*
Ayaris Rivera, *Mfg Staff*
Ray Hicks, *Engineer*
Melyssia Santiago, *VP Sales*
EMP: 18 EST: 2010
SALES (est): 2.7MM Privately Held
WEB: www.co2meter.com
SIC: 3829 Thermometers & temperature sensors

(G-13359)
COMMAND MEDICAL PRODUCTS INC
15 Signal Ave (32174-2984)
PHONE..................................386 677-7775
David T Slick, *Ch of Bd*
Jim Carnall, *President*
Chad Tremaroli, *Opers Staff*
Rick Smith, *Production*
Miguel Ballesteros, *Engineer*
◆ EMP: 135 EST: 1982
SQ FT: 56,000
SALES (est): 24.7MM Privately Held
WEB: www.commandmedical.com
SIC: 3841 Surgical & medical instruments

(G-13360)
CONCENTRATED ALOE CORP
20 W Tower Cir (32174-8761)
PHONE..................................386 673-7566
Brian Meadows, *Sales Staff*
EMP: 6 EST: 2019
SALES (est): 641.9K Privately Held
WEB: www.conaloe.com
SIC: 2833 Medicinals & botanicals

(G-13361)
DELTA P SYSTEMS INC
3 E Tower Cir (32174-8760)
PHONE..................................386 236-0950
Mark D Blais, *President*
Julia S Blais, *Vice Pres*

Michael Moyer, *Engineer*
EMP: 10 **EST:** 1994
SQ FT: 10,000
SALES (est): 2MM **Privately Held**
WEB: www.deltapcarver.com
SIC: 3561 Pumps & pumping equipment

(G-13362)
DENTERPRISE INTERNATIONAL INC
100 E Granada Blvd # 219 (32176-6660)
P.O. Box 36 (32175-0036)
PHONE..................................386 672-0450
Claude Berthoin, *President*
Ivan Mihajlovik, *Marketing Staff*
Michaelle Berthoin Todd, *Manager*
EMP: 10 **EST:** 1996
SQ FT: 3,200
SALES (est): 1.1MM **Privately Held**
WEB: www.denterpriseintl.com
SIC: 3843 Dental materials

(G-13363)
DIVA STUFF
1368 N Us Highway 1 # 406 (32174-8909)
PHONE..................................386 256-2521
James P Nadeau Jr,
EMP: 7 **EST:** 2014
SALES (est): 1.5MM **Privately Held**
WEB: www.divastuff.com
SIC: 2834 Dermatologicals

(G-13364)
DOUBLE H ENTERPRISES INC
170 Bear Foot Trl (32174-3201)
PHONE..................................972 562-8588
Beth Hobensack, *President*
Yvonne Hensley, *Vice Pres*
EMP: 9 **EST:** 2002
SALES (est): 796.6K **Privately Held**
SIC: 2759 Screen printing

(G-13365)
DUGOUT SPORTSWEAR ✪
488 Parque Dr (32174-7530)
PHONE..................................386 615-0024
EMP: 6 **EST:** 2020
SALES (est): 206.3K **Privately Held**
WEB: www.thedugoutsportswear.com
SIC: 2752 Commercial printing, lithographic

(G-13366)
EAST ORMOND BEACH CROSSFIT
1474 W Granada Blvd (32174-9187)
PHONE..................................386 673-3011
Kevin Broone, *Owner*
EMP: 6 **EST:** 2010
SALES (est): 188.1K **Privately Held**
WEB: www.eobcrossfit.com
SIC: 3851 Frames & parts, eyeglass & spectacle

(G-13367)
EDGEWELL PERSONAL CARE COMPANY
Also Called: Alpha To Omega
1190 N Us Highway 1 (32174-2997)
P.O. Box 265111, Daytona Beach (32126-5111)
PHONE..................................386 673-2024
Marge Frassrand, *Manager*
Sue Craggs, *Administration*
EMP: 400
SALES (corp-wide): 1.9B **Publicly Held**
WEB: www.schick.com
SIC: 2844 Suntan lotions & oils
PA: Edgewell Personal Care Company
6 Research Dr Ste 400
Shelton CT 06484
203 944-5500

(G-13368)
ESSENTIALS
150a W Granada Blvd (32174-6304)
PHONE..................................386 677-7444
Donna Bushara, *Owner*
EMP: 6 **EST:** 2006
SALES (est): 206.7K **Privately Held**
SIC: 3571 5045 Electronic computers; computers, peripherals & software

(G-13369)
EWH PRESS
1796 Ocean Shore Blvd (32176-3237)
P.O. Box 275 (32175-0275)
PHONE..................................386 405-5069
Jeffrey Stoner, *Principal*
EMP: 6 **EST:** 2015
SALES (est): 70.4K **Privately Held**
SIC: 2741 Miscellaneous publishing

(G-13370)
FAB DEFENSE INC
873 Hull Rd Unit 5 (32174-0738)
PHONE..................................386 263-3054
Ido Solomon, *President*
EMP: 7 **EST:** 2018
SALES (est): 1.1MM **Privately Held**
WEB: www.fab-defenseus.com
SIC: 3812 Defense systems & equipment

(G-13371)
FABROX LLC
Also Called: Fitusa Manufacturing
2 Sunshine Blvd (32174-8754)
PHONE..................................904 342-4048
Troy Olson,
EMP: 48 **EST:** 2016
SALES (est): 2.5MM **Privately Held**
SIC: 2329 2326 Men's & boys' sportswear & athletic clothing; men's & boys' athletic uniforms; medical & hospital uniforms, men's

(G-13372)
FLORIDA PRODUCTION ENGRG INC (HQ)
Also Called: Automotive Mfg & Indus PDT
2 E Tower Cir (32174-8759)
PHONE..................................386 677-2566
Larry Jutte, *President*
Brad Gotts, *Principal*
Derrick Redding, *COO*
Vinc E Ellerbrock, *Vice Pres*
Joe Hasson, *Opers Mgr*
▲ **EMP:** 250 **EST:** 1987
SQ FT: 110,000
SALES (est): 122.7MM
SALES (corp-wide): 338.9MM **Privately Held**
WEB: www.fpe-inc.com
SIC: 3465 3089 Moldings or trim, automobile: stamped metal; injection molded finished plastic products; injection molding of plastics; automotive parts, plastic
PA: Ernie Green Industries, Inc.
2030 Dividend Dr
Columbus OH 43228
614 219-1423

(G-13373)
GASLAB
131 Business Center Dr (32174-6625)
PHONE..................................386 872-7668
EMP: 6 **EST:** 2019
SALES (est): 144.8K **Privately Held**
WEB: www.gaslab.com
SIC: 3829 Measuring & controlling devices

(G-13374)
GERMFREE LABORATORIES INC
4 Sunshine Blvd (32174-8754)
PHONE..................................386 265-4300
Keith Landy, *CEO*
Kevin Kyle, *President*
Jeff Serle, *Senior VP*
Lisa Engel, *Buyer*
Zachary Pyle, *Engineer*
◆ **EMP:** 185
SQ FT: 170,000
SALES (est): 36MM **Privately Held**
WEB: www.germfree.com
SIC: 3821 Laboratory equipment: fume hoods, distillation racks, etc.

(G-13375)
GRUB COMPANY
6 Fernwood Trl (32174-4955)
PHONE..................................347 464-9770
Motty Hershkowitz, *CEO*
Shmuel Albukerk, *Director*
Chaya Hershkowit, *Director*
Yehuda Lewis, *Director*
EMP: 11 **EST:** 2018
SALES (est): 381.9K **Privately Held**
SIC: 2013 Snack sticks, including jerky: from purchased meat

(G-13376)
HES PRODUCTS INC
Also Called: Research II
87 Old Wiggins Ln (32174-2616)
PHONE..................................407 834-0741
Ronald E Sarzier, *President*
Ann T Sarzier, *Corp Secy*
EMP: 6 **EST:** 1976
SALES (est): 441K **Privately Held**
SIC: 2759 7389 2396 2395 Screen printing; embroidering of advertising on shirts, etc.; automotive & apparel trimmings; pleating & stitching

(G-13377)
HOT ACTION SPORTSWEAR INC
307 Division Ave (32174-6249)
PHONE..................................386 677-5680
Melissa Penland, *President*
Robert Pomerenke, *Vice Pres*
Kim Jarvis, *Production*
Cheryl Mannocchi, *Buyer*
Irene Lipsey, *Treasurer*
EMP: 45 **EST:** 1990
SQ FT: 13,500
SALES (est): 7.3MM **Privately Held**
WEB: www.hotactionsportswear.com
SIC: 2759 Screen printing

(G-13378)
HUDSON TOOL & DIE COMPANY INC
Also Called: Hudson Technologies
1327 N Us Highway 1 (32174-2900)
PHONE..................................386 672-2000
Bret Schmitz, *President*
Mark Andrews, *President*
John Debone, *VP Bus Dvlpt*
Farley Fitzpatrick, *Sales Mgr*
EMP: 220 **EST:** 1940
SALES (est): 34.3MM
SALES (corp-wide): 1B **Privately Held**
WEB: www.hudson-technologies.com
SIC: 3469 Stamping metal for the trade
PA: Jsj Corporation
700 Robbins Rd
Grand Haven MI 49417
616 842-6350

(G-13379)
IMPERIAL FOAM & INSUL MFG CO
2360 Old Tomoka Rd W (32174-2529)
PHONE..................................386 673-4177
Robert W Ahrens, *President*
Harry Merryday, *President*
Aileen Ahrens, *Vice Pres*
▲ **EMP:** 55 **EST:** 1973
SQ FT: 45,000
SALES (est): 7.3MM **Privately Held**
SIC: 3086 Insulation or cushioning material, foamed plastic

(G-13380)
INFORMATION MGT SVCS INC
Also Called: I M S
107 Sundance Trl (32176-5743)
P.O. Box 1918 (32175-1918)
PHONE..................................386 677-5073
C William Phillips, *President*
EMP: 10 **EST:** 1979
SALES (est): 791.6K **Privately Held**
WEB: www.imsutility.com
SIC: 7372 5734 Business oriented computer software; computer & software stores

(G-13381)
ITA INC
9 W Tower Cir Ste C (32174-0740)
PHONE..................................386 301-5172
Adam Potter, *Principal*
EMP: 17 **EST:** 2013
SALES (est): 1MM **Privately Held**
WEB: www.itainc.net
SIC: 2431 Window shutters, wood

(G-13382)
KITCHEN COUNTER CONNECTIONS
123 N Orchard St Ste 3e (32174-9513)
PHONE..................................386 677-9471
John Pehr, *Partner*
Cong MAI, *Partner*
EMP: 25 **EST:** 1991
SALES (est): 5.1MM **Privately Held**
SIC: 2542 2541 Counters or counter display cases: except wood; wood partitions & fixtures

(G-13383)
LUCAS CONSTRUCTION INC
5 Echo Woods Way (32174-6754)
P.O. Box 730908 (32173-0908)
PHONE..................................386 623-0088
Doug Lucas, *President*
Janet Lucas, *Corp Secy*
EMP: 5 **EST:** 1978
SALES (est): 536.8K **Privately Held**
WEB: www.lucascg.com
SIC: 1389 1531 Construction, repair & dismantling services; speculative builder, single-family houses

(G-13384)
MAJOR PRODUCTS COMPANY
841 Buena Vista Ave (32174-7616)
PHONE..................................386 673-8381
EMP: 26
SALES (corp-wide): 34.8MM **Privately Held**
WEB: www.majorproducts.com
SIC: 2034 Soup mixes
PA: Major Products Co. Inc.
66 Industrial Ave
Little Ferry NJ 07643
201 641-5555

(G-13385)
MAYHEW/BESTWAY LLC
2a Sunshine Blvd (32174-8754)
PHONE..................................631 586-4702
John Lawless,
EMP: 24 **EST:** 2019
SALES (est): 1.3MM **Privately Held**
SIC: 3423 Mechanics' hand tools

(G-13386)
MICROFLEX INC
Also Called: Microflex Automotive
1810 N Us Highway 1 (32174-2578)
P.O. Box 730068 (32173-0068)
PHONE..................................386 672-1945
John Atanasoski, *General Mgr*
Matt Russell, *Materials Mgr*
James Lalanne, *Buyer*
Armando Mustiga, *Med Doctor*
EMP: 20
SALES (corp-wide): 26.6MM **Privately Held**
WEB: www.microflexinc.com
SIC: 3599 3494 Hose, flexible metallic; expansion joints pipe
PA: Microflex, Inc.
1800 N Us Highway 1
Ormond Beach FL 32174
386 677-8100

(G-13387)
OFFICIAL GEAR COMPANY INC
106 Deer Run Lake Dr (32174-8142)
PHONE..................................407 721-9110
Brian Holt, *President*
EMP: 5 **EST:** 2005
SQ FT: 3,000
SALES (est): 500K **Privately Held**
WEB: www.officialgearpromotions.com
SIC: 2211 5136 5699 Apparel & outerwear fabrics, cotton; men's & boys' clothing; uniforms & work clothing

(G-13388)
ORMOND BEACH CLINICAL RES LLC
1400 Hand Ave Ste L (32174-8196)
PHONE..................................386 310-7462
Nicole Morris, *President*
EMP: 9 **EST:** 2016
SALES (est): 544.3K **Privately Held**
WEB: www.ormondbeachobserver.com
SIC: 3821 Clinical laboratory instruments, except medical & dental

(G-13389)
ORMOND BEACH OBSERVER
310 Wilmette Ave Ste 3 (32174-5276)
P.O. Box 353850, Palm Coast (32135-3850)
PHONE..................................386 492-2784
Richard Dichiera, *Principal*

▲ = Import ▼=Export
◆ =Import/Export

Jaclyn Centofanti, *Opers Mgr*
Simmons Jonathan, *Manager*
EMP: 10 **EST:** 2016
SALES (est): 136.4K **Privately Held**
WEB: www.ormondbeachobserver.com
SIC: 2711 Newspapers, publishing & printing

(G-13390)
ORMOND BEACH OLIVE OIL
203 E Granada Blvd (32176-6632)
PHONE..................................386 333-9236
EMP: 6 **EST:** 2017
SALES (est): 352.1K **Privately Held**
WEB: www.shop.theanointedolivellc.com
SIC: 2079 Olive oil

(G-13391)
PLAYTEX MANUFACTURING INC
1190 N Us Highway 1 (32174-2997)
PHONE..................................386 677-9559
Karen Jesse, *Vice Pres*
Jack Surrette, *Vice Pres*
Dennis Lott, *VP Engrg*
Stephanie Mellenberndt, *Marketing Staff*
Mischelle Romesberg, *Branch Mgr*
EMP: 20
SALES (corp-wide): 1.9B **Publicly Held**
WEB: www.ob-tampons.com
SIC: 2676 Sanitary paper products
HQ: Playtex Manufacturing, Inc.
50 N Dupont Hwy
Dover DE 19901
302 678-6000

(G-13392)
POWER PLUS INC
550 Parque Dr (32174-7703)
PHONE..................................386 672-7579
David Tanges, *President*
Andrew Hyldahl, *Manager*
Anita Tanges, *Manager*
EMP: 8 **EST:** 1994
SQ FT: 6,200
SALES (est): 1MM **Privately Held**
WEB: www.power-plus.net
SIC: 3824 Mechanical & electromechanical counters & devices

(G-13393)
PRIME GLOBAL GROUP INC
3 Aviator Way (32174-2982)
P.O. Box 730957 (32173-0957)
PHONE..................................386 676-2200
Maryann Honczarenko, *President*
Stephen J Honczarenko, *Vice Pres*
Stephen Mandarano, *Production*
Jose Colon, *Engineer*
EMP: 23 **EST:** 2015
SALES (est): 2.5MM **Privately Held**
SIC: 3552 3549 Winders, textile machinery; coiling machinery

(G-13394)
PROFESSIONAL HOLIDAY LIGHTING
Also Called: Phl Pool Services
181 Royal Dunes Cir (32176-4744)
PHONE..................................208 709-2968
Scott A Brown, *Principal*
EMP: 7 **EST:** 2010
SALES (est): 180.2K **Privately Held**
SIC: 3648 Lighting equipment

(G-13395)
PROGRESSIVE MACHINE CO INC
3 Aviator Way (32174-2982)
PHONE..................................386 333-6850
Stephen Honczarenko, *Principal*
EMP: 15 **EST:** 2019
SALES (est): 1.2MM **Privately Held**
WEB: www.progressivewinders.com
SIC: 3552 Winders, textile machinery

(G-13396)
REZOLIN LLC
131 Business Center Dr A7 (32174-6624)
PHONE..................................386 677-8238
Carl Dellinger,
Dave Morton,
Jeff Scherer,
EMP: 8 **EST:** 2002
SQ FT: 7,000
SALES (est): 773.6K **Privately Held**
WEB: www.rezolin.com
SIC: 2851 Putty

(G-13397)
SELF INDUSTRIES INCORPORATED
30 Choctaw Trl (32174-4347)
PHONE..................................386 882-3644
Tyler A Self, *Principal*
EMP: 7 **EST:** 2018
SALES (est): 145.4K **Privately Held**
SIC: 3999 Manufacturing industries

(G-13398)
SIGN LANGUAGE INTERPRETING
74 Concord Dr (32176-3200)
PHONE..................................386 681-9784
Kathy Mason, *Principal*
Cynthia Duggan, *Program Mgr*
EMP: 6 **EST:** 2010
SALES (est): 86.7K **Privately Held**
SIC: 3993 Signs & advertising specialties

(G-13399)
SKYO INDUSTRIES INC
2 Sunshine Blvd (32174-8754)
PHONE..................................631 586-4702
Warren Anderson, *President*
Wayne Anderson, *President*
Arleen Anderson Cassutti, *Admin Sec*
◆ **EMP:** 40 **EST:** 1961
SQ FT: 26,000
SALES (est): 3.8MM **Privately Held**
SIC: 3423 3714 Hand & edge tools; motor vehicle parts & accessories

(G-13400)
SOLAR X
Also Called: Solar-X of Daytona
630 S Yonge St Us1 (32174-7654)
PHONE..................................386 673-2111
Howard Smith, *President*
EMP: 2 **EST:** 1973
SQ FT: 2,070
SALES (est): 12MM **Privately Held**
WEB: www.solar-x.com
SIC: 3081 5211 1799 Unsupported plastics film & sheet; door & window products; glass tinting, architectural or automotive

(G-13401)
SOUTHERN PLASTICS & RUBBER CO
565 Parque Dr (32174-7529)
PHONE..................................386 672-1167
Frank Noce Jr, *President*
Sandra Noce, *Admin Sec*
EMP: 29 **EST:** 1958
SQ FT: 14,000
SALES (est): 3MM **Privately Held**
WEB: www.southernplasticandrubber.com
SIC: 3061 2821 Mechanical rubber goods; molding compounds, plastics

(G-13402)
STANDARD TECHNOLOGY INC
1230 N Us Highway 1 # 18 (32174-6637)
PHONE..................................386 671-7406
Anthony J Bilello, *President*
Lisa Beasor, *Admin Mgr*
EMP: 15
SALES (est): 1MM **Privately Held**
WEB: www.standardtechinc.com
SIC: 3699 3677 3625 Automotive driving simulators (training aids), electronic; electronic coils, transformers & other inductors; solenoid switches (industrial controls)

(G-13403)
SUN KRAFTS OF VOLUSIA COUNTY
217 Royal Dunes Cir (32176-4746)
PHONE..................................386 441-1961
Bob Marcinko, *President*
Hariklia Marcinko, *Vice Pres*
Paula L Estridge, *Manager*
EMP: 6 **EST:** 1979
SQ FT: 9,000
SALES (est): 467.5K **Privately Held**
SIC: 3999 5199 Novelties: bone, beaded or shell; seashells

(G-13404)
T-M FABRICATIONS LLC
11 Seaside Dr (32176-3548)
PHONE..................................386 295-5302
Todd McFadden, *Manager*
EMP: 6 **EST:** 2016
SALES (est): 166.6K **Privately Held**
WEB: www.tmfabrications.com
SIC: 2431 Millwork

(G-13405)
TANNING RESEARCH LABS LLC (HQ)
1190 N Us Highway 1 (32174-2997)
PHONE..................................386 677-9559
Amy Williams, *Controller*
EMP: 277 **EST:** 2009
SALES (est): 94.4MM
SALES (corp-wide): 1.9B **Publicly Held**
WEB: www.edgewell.com
SIC: 2844 Cosmetic preparations
PA: Edgewell Personal Care Company
6 Research Dr Ste 400
Shelton CT 06484
203 944-5500

(G-13406)
USAOP INC
578 Sterthaus Dr (32174-5128)
PHONE..................................386 212-9514
Maribel Mejia, *Principal*
EMP: 8 **EST:** 2017
SALES (est): 90.1K **Privately Held**
WEB: www.usaop.us
SIC: 3841 Surgical & medical instruments

(G-13407)
VANGUARDISTAS LLC
564 S Yonge St (32174-7540)
PHONE..................................386 868-2919
Mark Pratt, *Principal*
EMP: 9 **EST:** 2007
SALES (est): 275.1K **Privately Held**
WEB: www.metropublisher.com
SIC: 7372 Prepackaged software

(G-13408)
W R KERSHAW INC
12 Aviator Way (32174-2983)
PHONE..................................386 673-0602
Richard Kershaw, *President*
Richard D Kershaw, *President*
EMP: 7 **EST:** 1982
SQ FT: 4,500
SALES (est): 732K **Privately Held**
WEB: www.kershawinc.com
SIC: 3089 3085 Injection molding of plastics; plastics bottles

(G-13409)
WILTCHER INDUSTRIES INC
1034 Sudbury Ln (32174-2207)
PHONE..................................704 907-9838
EMP: 5 **EST:** 2019
SALES (est): 364.8K **Privately Held**
WEB: www.wiltcherindustries.com
SIC: 3999 Manufacturing industries

Osprey
Sarasota County

(G-13410)
CHICKASHA MANUFACTURING CO INC
277 Saratoga Ct (34229-9386)
PHONE..................................405 224-0229
Larry Lewis, *President*
Glenn McNatt, *Vice Pres*
Jennifer Jones, *QC Mgr*
Linda Freeman, *Info Tech Mgr*
EMP: 36 **EST:** 1946
SALES (est): 3.2MM **Privately Held**
WEB: www.chickashamfg.com
SIC: 3599 Machine shop, jobbing & repair

Oviedo
Seminole County

(G-13411)
AMERIBUILT STL STRUCTURES LLC
1016 Moccasin Run Rd (32765-5646)
P.O. Box 623001 (32762-3001)
PHONE..................................407 340-9401
James D Horgan,
Renee' M Horgan,
EMP: 8 **EST:** 2004
SALES (est): 599.2K **Privately Held**
WEB: www.ameribuiltsteel.com
SIC: 3441 Building components, structural steel

(G-13412)
ARSENEX INC
2229 Blossomwood Dr (32765-6152)
PHONE..................................407 256-3490
Stephen P Arseneault, *Principal*
EMP: 6 **EST:** 2010
SALES (est): 96.4K **Privately Held**
WEB: www.arsenex.com
SIC: 2741 Miscellaneous publishing

(G-13413)
ART EDIBLES INC
428 Wilmington Cir (32765-6186)
PHONE..................................407 603-4043
Paul B Joachim, *President*
EMP: 8 **EST:** 2013
SALES (est): 39.5K **Privately Held**
SIC: 2066 Chocolate

(G-13414)
ASIAN FOOD SOLUTIONS INC
5600 Elmhurst Cir (32765-4100)
PHONE..................................888 499-6888
Lincoln Yee, *President*
Allan Lam, *CFO*
EMP: 22 **EST:** 2008
SQ FT: 1,500
SALES (est): 7.1MM **Privately Held**
WEB: www.internationalfoodsolutions.com
SIC: 2015 2038 Poultry, processed: frozen; ethnic foods, frozen
PA: International Food Solutions, Inc.
5600 Elmhurst Cir
Oviedo FL 32765

(G-13415)
ATTICUS SCREEN PRINTING T
159 N Central Ave Ste I (32765-6334)
PHONE..................................407 365-9911
Donna Rohr, *Manager*
EMP: 6 **EST:** 2005
SALES (est): 504.7K **Privately Held**
WEB: www.atticusprinting.com
SIC: 2759 2395 Screen printing; emblems, embroidered

(G-13416)
AZURE COMPUTING INC
Also Called: Elite Simulation Solutions
5700 Dot Com Ct Ste 1010 (32765-3400)
PHONE..................................407 359-8787
John Dixion, *President*
EMP: 7 **EST:** 1995
SQ FT: 5,000
SALES (est): 1MM **Privately Held**
SIC: 7372 Publishers' computer software

(G-13417)
B & B INDUSTRIES OF ORLANDO
3008 Kananwood Ct Ste 124 (32765-2200)
PHONE..................................407 366-1800
William S Clark, *President*
Michael A Clark, *Corp Secy*
EMP: 9 **EST:** 1980
SQ FT: 15,000
SALES (est): 778.1K **Privately Held**
SIC: 2339 2329 Women's & misses' athletic clothing & sportswear; men's & boys' sportswear & athletic clothing

(G-13418)
BEST QUALITY WATER SYS OF FLA (PA)
2200 Winter Springs Blvd # 106 (32765-9358)
PHONE.................................407 971-2537
Mark Smith, *President*
Monica Smith, *Vice Pres*
Delta Tooney, *Treasurer*
EMP: 113 **EST:** 1985
SALES (est): 5.3MM **Privately Held**
SIC: 3221 Water bottles, glass

(G-13419)
BOT INTERNATIONAL INC
1320 Tall Maple Loop (32765-7785)
PHONE.................................407 366-6547
Mark P Perry, *President*
EMP: 9 **EST:** 1999
SALES (est): 840.9K **Privately Held**
WEB: www.botinternational.com
SIC: 2741 Technical manual & paper publishing

(G-13420)
CLONTS GROVES INC
285 Howard Ave (32765-6840)
PHONE.................................407 359-4103
W Rex Clonts Jr, *President*
EMP: 10 **EST:** 2001
SALES (est): 660.7K **Privately Held**
SIC: 2037 Frozen fruits & vegetables

(G-13421)
COMIDA VIDA INC
5600 Elmhurst Cir (32765-4100)
PHONE.................................855 720-7663
Lincoln Yee, *President*
EMP: 5 **EST:** 2016
SALES (est): 346K **Privately Held**
WEB: www.internationalfoodsolutions.com
SIC: 2038 Ethnic foods, frozen

(G-13422)
CONTINUITY UNLIMITED INC
1750 W Broadway St # 112 (32765-9618)
PHONE.................................561 358-8171
David Bateman, *President*
Bob Becker, *Vice Pres*
James Walker, *VP Sales*
EMP: 15 **EST:** 1986
SQ FT: 5,000
SALES (est): 900K **Privately Held**
SIC: 3679 3672 Electronic circuits; printed circuit boards

(G-13423)
COPY VAN OF FLORIDA INC
Also Called: Copy Van Printing
2224 Andrew Ln (32765-9494)
PHONE.................................407 366-7126
Carol Goad, *President*
EMP: 5 **EST:** 1967
SQ FT: 2,500
SALES (est): 346.4K **Privately Held**
WEB: www.copyvanofflorida.com
SIC: 2752 8721 Commercial printing, offset; accounting services, except auditing

(G-13424)
COULOMBE ENTERPRISES
1293 N County Road 426 # 121 (32765-7363)
PHONE.................................407 366-4387
Bruce F Coulombe, *Principal*
EMP: 6 **EST:** 2011
SALES (est): 209.7K **Privately Held**
SIC: 3743 Freight cars & equipment

(G-13425)
DAN BOUDREAU INC
3325 Red Ash Cir (32766-8105)
PHONE.................................407 491-7611
Dan Boudreau, *Principal*
EMP: 7 **EST:** 2008
SALES (est): 72.2K **Privately Held**
SIC: 2439 Trusses, wooden roof

(G-13426)
DAVES ALL AROUND
3530 Hollow Oak Run (32766-7016)
PHONE.................................407 325-6693
David James, *Principal*
EMP: 6 **EST:** 2008
SALES (est): 167.1K **Privately Held**
SIC: 3423 Carpenters' hand tools, except saws: levels, chisels, etc.

(G-13427)
DYNAMIC MATERIAL SYSTEMS LLC
269 Aulin Ave Ste 1003 (32765-4806)
PHONE.................................407 353-6885
William Easter, *CEO*
Arnold Hill, *Principal*
EMP: 6 **EST:** 2013
SALES (est): 416.5K **Privately Held**
SIC: 2821 Plastics materials & resins

(G-13428)
ENGINEERICA SYSTEMS INC
7250 Red Bug Lake Rd # 1036 (32765-9290)
PHONE.................................407 542-4982
Maan Nassereddeen, *Principal*
Laura Alvarez, *Manager*
EMP: 18 **EST:** 1994
SALES (est): 2MM **Privately Held**
WEB: www.engineerica.com
SIC: 7372 7371 Prepackaged software; custom computer programming services

(G-13429)
EXCESS LIQUIDATOR LLC
Also Called: Shop Munki
3012 Kananwood Ct Ste 132 (32765-2204)
PHONE.................................407 247-9105
Paul SMR Bergeron, *Mng Member*
Yvette Bergeron,
EMP: 7 **EST:** 2014
SALES (est): 552.2K **Privately Held**
WEB: www.shopmunki.com
SIC: 2339 5621 2329 Women's & misses' athletic clothing & sportswear; women's clothing stores; athletic (warmup, sweat & jogging) suits: men's & boys'

(G-13430)
FASTSIGNS
2200 Winter Springs Blvd # 118 (32765-9358)
PHONE.................................407 542-1234
Liz Allen, *Principal*
EMP: 6 **EST:** 2017
SALES (est): 46K **Privately Held**
WEB: www.fastsigns.com
SIC: 3993 Signs & advertising specialties

(G-13431)
FSF MANUFACTURING INC
575 Econ River Pl (32765-7343)
PHONE.................................407 971-8280
Jacqueline M Amrhein, *President*
James A Amrhein, *Vice Pres*
James Amrhein, *Vice Pres*
Guy Clarke, *Project Mgr*
Nick Shepherd, *Project Mgr*
▼ **EMP:** 112
SQ FT: 53,000
SALES (est): 34.2MM **Privately Held**
WEB: www.fsfmfg.com
SIC: 3441 Fabricated structural metal

(G-13432)
GENENSYS LLC
7269 Winding Lake Cir (32765-5664)
PHONE.................................407 701-4158
Murthy Bondada, *Vice Pres*
Francis Cabrera, *Project Mgr*
Farhan Shamsi, *Manager*
Julee Clark, *Manager*
Naveen Dua, *Manager*
EMP: 11 **EST:** 2012
SALES (est): 371.6K **Privately Held**
WEB: www.genensys.com
SIC: 7372 Business oriented computer software

(G-13433)
GUILD MFG SOLUTIONS LLC
1005 Lingo Cir (32765-6435)
PHONE.................................407 366-5165
Michael S Guild, *Principal*
EMP: 8 **EST:** 2019
SALES (est): 368.7K **Privately Held**
SIC: 3999 Manufacturing industries

(G-13434)
HAYMAN SAFE CO INC
1291 N County Road 426 (32765-7102)
PHONE.................................407 365-5434
William Hayman, *CEO*
Gary Hayman, *President*
Carolyn Hayman, *Corp Secy*
Dick Divittorio, *Vice Pres*
◆ **EMP:** 15 **EST:** 1970
SQ FT: 7,500
SALES (est): 2.1MM **Privately Held**
WEB: www.haymansafe.com
SIC: 3499 Safes & vaults, metal

(G-13435)
HOLESHOT RACEWAY INC
434 Terrace Dr (32765-7741)
PHONE.................................407 864-1095
Kristopher B James, *Principal*
EMP: 7 **EST:** 2012
SALES (est): 242.4K **Privately Held**
WEB: www.hsraceway.com
SIC: 3644 Raceways

(G-13436)
HONEYWELL INTERNATIONAL INC
1006 Lingo Ct (32765-6413)
PHONE.................................877 841-2840
EMP: 6
SALES (corp-wide): 32.6B **Publicly Held**
WEB: www.honeywell.com
SIC: 3724 Aircraft engines & engine parts
PA: Honeywell International Inc.
300 S Tryon St
Charlotte NC 28202
704 627-6200

(G-13437)
HOPSCOTCH TECHNOLOGY GROUP INC ✪
1288 Sanctuary Dr (32766-6604)
PHONE.................................305 846-0942
Oliver Von Trapp, *CEO*
EMP: 10 **EST:** 2021
SALES (est): 474.4K **Privately Held**
SIC: 7372 Educational computer software

(G-13438)
I-CON SYSTEMS INC
3100 Camp Rd (32765-7532)
PHONE.................................407 365-6241
Shawn Bush, *President*
Ray Elliott, *Vice Pres*
Dale Haswell, *Prdtn Mgr*
Rich Tomai, *Sales Staff*
Ed Howell, *Manager*
▲ **EMP:** 56 **EST:** 1994
SQ FT: 55,000
SALES (est): 12MM
SALES (corp-wide): 33.7MM **Privately Held**
WEB: www.i-con.com
SIC: 3679 8711 Electronic circuits; professional engineer
PA: I-Con Systems Holdings, Llc
3100 Camp Rd
Oviedo FL 32765
407 365-6241

(G-13439)
INFORMULATE LLC
7437 Winding Lake Cir (32765-5666)
PHONE.................................866 222-2307
Annie Menon, *Managing Prtnr*
Tristan Mills, *Manager*
Jared McGuire, *Web Dvlpr*
EMP: 9 **EST:** 2010
SALES (est): 926.9K **Privately Held**
WEB: www.informulate.com
SIC: 7372 7371 Application computer software; computer software systems analysis & design, custom

(G-13440)
INTERNATIONAL FD SOLUTIONS INC (PA)
Also Called: Asian Food Solutions
5600 Elmhurst Cir (32765-4100)
PHONE.................................888 499-6888
Allan Lam, *President*
Lincoln Yee, *President*
Candy Kitchen, *Regional Mgr*
Gary Vix, *Controller*
Karl Chapman, *Sales Staff*
EMP: 21 **EST:** 2008
SQ FT: 1,500
SALES (est): 7.1MM **Privately Held**
WEB: www.internationalfoodsolutions.com
SIC: 2015 2038 Poultry, processed: frozen; ethnic foods, frozen

(G-13441)
JAPAN FABRICARE INC
Also Called: Motherkin Cleaners
9 Alafaya Woods Blvd (32765-6232)
PHONE.................................407 366-9986
Ung J Park, *President*
Ung Park, *Owner*
EMP: 6 **EST:** 2002
SALES (est): 142.8K **Privately Held**
SIC: 3633 Drycleaning machines, household: including coin-operated

(G-13442)
K C SCREEN
1705 Evans St (32765-9371)
PHONE.................................407 977-9636
Carl Anderson, *President*
Kimberly M Anderson, *Vice Pres*
EMP: 5 **EST:** 2003
SQ FT: 1,300
SALES (est): 674.7K **Privately Held**
WEB: www.kcscreen.com
SIC: 3448 1521 Screen enclosures; patio & deck construction & repair

(G-13443)
KALITEC DIRECT LLC
Also Called: Kalitec Medical
865 Oviedo Blvd Ste 1017 (32765-3523)
PHONE.................................407 545-2063
Scott J Winn, *Manager*
EMP: 8 **EST:** 2011
SALES (est): 347.2K **Privately Held**
SIC: 3841 Surgical & medical instruments

(G-13444)
KAMEL SOFTWARE INC
1809 E Broadway St # 134 (32765-8597)
PHONE.................................407 672-0202
Keith Linn, *President*
Michael Linn, *Vice Pres*
Patti Linn, *Vice Pres*
EMP: 8 **EST:** 1988
SQ FT: 3,000
SALES (est): 982.6K **Privately Held**
WEB: www.kamelsoftware.com
SIC: 7372 7371 Prepackaged software; custom computer programming services

(G-13445)
KELSIES BLINDS
Also Called: KELSIES BLINDS
2464 W State Rd Ste 1028 (32765)
PHONE.................................407 977-0827
David Wright, *CEO*
Nicole Compton, *Admin Sec*
▼ **EMP:** 9 **EST:** 1994
SALES: 2.1MM **Privately Held**
WEB: www.orlandoblinds.com
SIC: 2591 5719 Window blinds; window shades

(G-13446)
LASERPATH TECHNOLOGIES LLC
2789 Wrights Rd Ste 1021 (32765-8528)
PHONE.................................407 247-3930
Robert J Hopkins,
▼ **EMP:** 5 **EST:** 2001
SQ FT: 3,000
SALES (est): 737.7K **Privately Held**
SIC: 3699 Laser systems & equipment

(G-13447)
LEVIL TECHNOLOGY CORP
1704 Kennedy Pt Ste 1124 (32765-5188)
PHONE.................................407 542-3971
Carmen C Diaz, *President*
Ruben D Leon, *Principal*
Carlos Leon, *Prdtn Mgr*
Michelle Leon, *Opers Staff*
EMP: 8 **EST:** 2009
SQ FT: 3,500
SALES (est): 2.4MM **Privately Held**
WEB: www.levil.com
SIC: 3552 3541 Spindles, textile; drilling machine tools (metal cutting)

(G-13448)
LOCKHEED MARTIN CORPORATION
568 Carrigan Ave (32765-6290)
PHONE.................................407 365-4254
EMP: 6 **Publicly Held**
WEB: www.lockheedmartin.com
SIC: 3812 Search & navigation equipment
PA: Lockheed Martin Corporation
6801 Rockledge Dr
Bethesda MD 20817

(G-13449)
NGF DISTRIBUTORS INC
3035 Turkey Ave (32765-7925)
P.O. Box 622062 (32762-2062)
PHONE.................................407 816-7554
Josue Moncata, *President*
Matt Wadsworth, *General Mgr*
EMP: 10 **EST:** 2005
SALES (est): 975K **Privately Held**
WEB: www.ngfdistributors.com
SIC: 3999 Framed artwork

(G-13450)
OPTIGRATE CORPORATION
562 S Econ Cir (32765-4303)
PHONE.................................407 542-7704
Alexei Glebov, *President*
Brian Domian, *Managing Dir*
Vadim Smirnov, *Vice Pres*
Joshua Beharry, *Engineer*
Nelson Nunez, *Engineer*
EMP: 34 **EST:** 1999
SALES (est): 8.4MM
SALES (corp-wide): 1.2B **Publicly Held**
WEB: www.optigrate.com
SIC: 3827 Optical elements & assemblies, except ophthalmic
PA: Ipg Photonics Corporation
50 Old Webster Rd
Oxford MA 01540
508 373-1100

(G-13451)
ORLANDO BRANDING AGENCY LLC
Also Called: Real Producers
1035 Covington St (32765-7037)
PHONE.................................407 692-8868
Aaron Ludin,
EMP: 10 **EST:** 2013
SALES (est): 552.1K **Privately Held**
WEB: www.orlandobranding.com
SIC: 2741 Miscellaneous publishing

(G-13452)
PALM TREE COMPUTER SYSTEMS INC (PA)
19 E Broadway St (32765-7529)
PHONE.................................407 359-3356
Paul Rosarius, *Vice Pres*
EMP: 12 **EST:** 1996
SQ FT: 4,200
SALES (est): 1.5MM **Privately Held**
WEB: www.palmtreetechcenter.com
SIC: 3571 5045 Electronic computers; computers, peripherals & software

(G-13453)
PET DOC FL LLC
1630 Sand Key Cir (32765-6968)
PHONE.................................407 437-6614
Margaret A Martinez, *Principal*
EMP: 5 **EST:** 2009
SALES (est): 346.6K **Privately Held**
WEB: www.petvetcarefl.com
SIC: 2836 Vaccines

(G-13454)
PREMIER CABINETS LLC
3036 Kananwood Ct # 1024 (32765-8830)
PHONE.................................407 760-9060
David Arocho, *Administration*
EMP: 8 **EST:** 2018
SALES (est): 403.1K **Privately Held**
WEB: www.premiercabinets.net
SIC: 2434 Wood kitchen cabinets

(G-13455)
R & A INDUSTRIES INC
306 Aulin Ave (32765-9314)
PHONE.................................352 307-6655
EMP: 16 **EST:** 2013
SALES (est): 1.1MM **Privately Held**
WEB: www.randaindustries.com
SIC: 3999 Manufacturing industries

(G-13456)
SCRATCH OFF STORE
876 Geneva Dr (32765-9605)
PHONE.................................800 584-9937
EMP: 8 **EST:** 2011
SALES (est): 80.1K **Privately Held**
WEB: www.scratchoffstore.com
SIC: 2621 Paper mills

(G-13457)
SEMPLASTICS
269 Aulin Ave Ste 1003 (32765-4806)
PHONE.................................407 353-6885
Wiliam Easter, *Principal*
Sue Easter, *Director*
EMP: 9 **EST:** 2012
SALES (est): 1.5MM **Privately Held**
WEB: www.semplastics.com
SIC: 3089 Plastics products

(G-13458)
STRUCTURAL CNSTR ORLANDO INC
2200 Winter Springs Blvd (32765-9358)
PHONE.................................407 383-9719
James Courtney, *President*
EMP: 30 **EST:** 2001
SQ FT: 1,800
SALES (est): 4MM **Privately Held**
SIC: 3272 Concrete products

(G-13459)
T&T SONS INC
1999 N County Road 426 (32765-8150)
PHONE.................................859 576-3316
Maryanne F Taylor, *Principal*
EMP: 7 **EST:** 2017
SALES (est): 200.6K **Privately Held**
SIC: 3312 Blast furnaces & steel mills

(G-13460)
TACTICAL PHASER CORP
2993 Moore Dr (32765-7632)
PHONE.................................321 262-4140
Lucian Randolph, *CEO*
EMP: 5
SALES (est): 331.4K **Privately Held**
SIC: 3571 Electronic computers

(G-13461)
TAYLOR MADE SYSTEMS BRDNTON IN (PA)
2750 Kansas St (32765-7726)
PHONE.................................941 747-1900
James W Taylor, *Ch of Bd*
Dennis Flint, *President*
John Martin, *General Mgr*
Robert Luxon, *Regl Sales Mgr*
▲ **EMP:** 114 **EST:** 1998
SQ FT: 120,000
SALES (est): 10.9MM **Privately Held**
WEB: www.tmsbradenton.com
SIC: 3429 8742 2394 3732 Manufactured hardware (general); management consulting services; canvas & related products; boat building & repairing

(G-13462)
XILINX INC
3518 Buckingham Ct (32765-5123)
PHONE.................................407 365-8644
EMP: 10
SALES (corp-wide): 3B **Publicly Held**
SIC: 3674 Mfg Semiconductors/Related Devices
PA: Xilinx, Inc.
2100 All Programable
San Jose CA 95124
408 559-7778

(G-13463)
YIHONG SOFTWARE INC
169 Adler Pt (32765-6402)
PHONE.................................407 391-8450
Yihong Qian, *Principal*
EMP: 6 **EST:** 2008
SALES (est): 209.4K **Privately Held**
SIC: 7372 Prepackaged software

Oxford
Sumter County

(G-13464)
MM WILDWOOD LLC
10126 Lake Miona Way (34484-3799)
PHONE.................................917 609-7128
MEI Chen, *Principal*
EMP: 6 **EST:** 2016
SALES (est): 47.1K **Privately Held**
SIC: 2499 Wood products

(G-13465)
WHISPERING OAKS WINERY
10934 County Road 475 (34484-3126)
PHONE.................................352 748-0449
Brent Trela, *Principal*
EMP: 8 **EST:** 2014
SALES (est): 368.9K **Privately Held**
WEB: www.winesofflorida.com
SIC: 2084 Wines

(G-13466)
WOODWORK UNLIMITED INC
4075 County Road 106 (34484-3525)
PHONE.................................352 267-4051
Carlos Balsinde, *President*
Martha A Balsinde, *Manager*
EMP: 10 **EST:** 2010
SALES (est): 139.6K **Privately Held**
SIC: 2431 1771 1611 Millwork; concrete work; general contractor, highway & street construction

Ozona
Pinellas County

(G-13467)
DORADO MARINE INC
270 Hedden Ct (34660)
PHONE.................................727 786-3800
Bob Lickert, *President*
EMP: 13 **EST:** 1987
SQ FT: 22,000
SALES (est): 326.6K **Privately Held**
WEB: www.doradocustomboats.com
SIC: 3732 Boat building & repairing

Pace
Santa Rosa County

(G-13468)
ELEMENT OUTDOORS LLC
5412 Covered Bridge Ln (32571-6420)
PHONE.................................888 589-9589
Christopher R Nallick, *Manager*
EMP: 6 **EST:** 2015
SALES (est): 146.3K **Privately Held**
WEB: www.elementoutdoors.com
SIC: 2323 Men's & boys' neckwear

(G-13469)
HARDY LOGGING COMPANY INC
3901 Willard Norris Rd (32571-9463)
PHONE.................................850 994-1955
Theresa K Hardy, *Principal*
EMP: 8 **EST:** 2018
SALES (est): 883.3K **Privately Held**
SIC: 2411 Logging

Pahokee
Palm Beach County

(G-13470)
OSCEOLA FARMS CO
Us Highway 98 Hatton Hwy (33476)
P.O. Box 679 (33476-0679)
PHONE.................................561 924-7156
Carlos Rionda, *Manager*
EMP: 1545
SALES (corp-wide): 2.1B **Privately Held**
SIC: 2099 2062 Sugar grinding; cane sugar refining
HQ: Osceola Farms Co
340 Royal Poinciana Way # 315
Palm Beach FL 33480
561 655-6303

Palatka
Putnam County

(G-13471)
4 C TIMBER INC
130 Odom Rd (32177-8212)
PHONE.................................386 937-0806
EMP: 8
SQ FT: 2,000
SALES (est): 1MM **Privately Held**
SIC: 2411 Logging & Pulpwood Contractor And Siteprep Work And Road Work

(G-13472)
A J GIAMMANCO & ASSOCIATES
Also Called: Lion Pool Products
115 Rachel Rd (32177-9598)
PHONE.................................386 328-1254
EMP: 19
SQ FT: 25,000
SALES (est): 2.5MM **Privately Held**
SIC: 3648 3991 Mfg Lighting Equipment Mfg Brooms/Brushes

(G-13473)
APEX METAL FABRICATION INC
177 Comfort Rd (32177-8637)
P.O. Box 1421 (32178-1421)
PHONE.................................386 328-2564
Keven Walker, *President*
Walter Walker, *President*
Donald Walker, *Chairman*
EMP: 12
SQ FT: 900
SALES (est): 3MM **Privately Held**
WEB: www.apexmetalfabrication.com
SIC: 3441 Building components, structural steel

(G-13474)
CARAUSTAR INDUS CNSMR PDTS GRO
Also Called: Palatka Tube Plant
188 Comfort Rd (32177-8636)
PHONE.................................386 328-8335
Stacy Robinson, *Opers-Prdtn-Mfg*
Brandi Traxler, *Human Resources*
EMP: 22
SALES (corp-wide): 4.5B **Publicly Held**
SIC: 2655 Tubes, for chemical or electrical uses: paper or fiber; cones, fiber: made from purchased material
HQ: Caraustar Industrial And Consumer Products Group Inc
5000 Austell Powder Ste
Austell GA 30106
803 548-5100

(G-13475)
CONTINENTAL PALATKA LLC
886 N Highway 17 (32177-8647)
PHONE.................................703 480-3800
Ike Preston, *President*
Dennis Romps, *CFO*
EMP: 100 **EST:** 2013
SALES (est): 11.1MM
SALES (corp-wide): 528MM **Privately Held**
WEB: www.certainteed.com
SIC: 2493 3275 2891 Building board & wallboard, except gypsum; building board, gypsum; sealing compounds for pipe threads or joints
HQ: Certainteed Gypsum Products, Inc.
12950 Worldgate Dr # 700
Herndon VA 20170
703 480-3800

(G-13476)
DAILY NEWS INC
Also Called: Palatka Daily News
1825 Saint Johns Ave (32177-4442)
P.O. Box 777 (32178-0777)
PHONE.................................386 312-5200
Wayne Anucales, *President*
Wayne Anucles, *President*
Michael Leonard, *Publisher*
Anthony Clarke, *Principal*
Rusty Starr, *Principal*

GEOGRAPHIC

EMP: 1 **EST:** 1885
SQ FT: 10,000
SALES (est): 5.2MM
SALES (corp-wide): 61.5MM **Privately Held**
WEB: www.palatkadailynews.com
SIC: 2711 Commercial printing & newspaper publishing combined; newspapers, publishing & printing
PA: Community Newspapers, Inc.
2365 Prince Ave A
Athens GA 30606
706 548-0010

(G-13477)
DAVES MACHINE SHOP INC
644 W Peniel Rd (32177-8968)
PHONE..................................386 325-0974
A Dave Daniel Jr, *Principal*
EMP: 6 **EST:** 2018
SALES (est): 100.4K **Privately Held**
SIC: 3599 Machine shop, jobbing & repair

(G-13478)
FLORIDA HYDRO POWER & LIGHT CO
171 Comfort Rd (32177-8637)
PHONE..................................386 328-2470
Herbert L Williams, *President*
EMP: 7 **EST:** 1998
SALES (est): 724.1K **Privately Held**
SIC: 3511 Turbines & turbine generator sets

(G-13479)
FLORIDA NORTH EMULSIONS INC
701 N Moody Rd Ste 151 (32177-2343)
PHONE..................................386 328-1733
Jeffrey King, *President*
EMP: 9 **EST:** 2003
SALES (est): 1.5MM **Privately Held**
WEB: www.northfloridaemulsions.com
SIC: 2951 Asphalt paving mixtures & blocks

(G-13480)
FORTERRA PRESSURE PIPE INC
245 Comfort Rd (32177-8634)
PHONE..................................386 328-8841
Steven M Braxton, *Branch Mgr*
EMP: 171
SQ FT: 10,000
SALES (corp-wide): 42.1MM **Privately Held**
SIC: 3321 3272 Pressure pipe & fittings, cast iron; concrete products
PA: Forterra Pressure Pipe, Inc.
4416 Prairie Hill Rd
South Beloit IL 61080
815 389-4800

(G-13481)
GEORGIA-PACIFIC LLC
County Rd 216 E (32177)
P.O. Box 1040 (32178-1040)
PHONE..................................386 328-8826
Gorman Edison, *Manager*
EMP: 25
SALES (corp-wide): 36.9B **Privately Held**
WEB: www.gp.com
SIC: 2621 Paper mills
HQ: Georgia-Pacific Llc
133 Peachtree St Nw
Atlanta GA 30303
404 652-4000

(G-13482)
H JONES TIMBER LLC
546 W Peniel Rd (32177-8941)
P.O. Box 2246 (32178-2246)
PHONE..................................386 312-0603
EMP: 6
SALES (est): 826.5K **Privately Held**
SIC: 2411 Logging

(G-13483)
HOLBROOK METAL FABRICATION LLC
341 N Highway 17 (32177-8616)
PHONE..................................386 937-5441
EMP: 8 **EST:** 2019
SALES (est): 1.1MM **Privately Held**
WEB: www.holbrookmetalfabrication.com
SIC: 3441 Fabricated structural metal

(G-13484)
LIFES A STITCH
2510 Crill Ave (32177-4272)
PHONE..................................386 385-3079
Laurie Cannon, *Owner*
EMP: 6 **EST:** 2014
SALES (est): 104.5K **Privately Held**
WEB: www.lifesastitch.business.site
SIC: 2395 Embroidery & art needlework

(G-13485)
LJ&J LATHING INC
402 N 16th St B6 (32177-3143)
P.O. Box 277, Bostwick (32007-0277)
PHONE..................................386 325-5040
Sindy Hunt, *Principal*
EMP: 6 **EST:** 2009
SALES (est): 59.4K **Privately Held**
SIC: 3541 Lathes

(G-13486)
LUMBERSTAK INC
125 Underwood Dr (32177-8167)
PHONE..................................386 546-3745
Amy Bennett, *President*
EMP: 7 **EST:** 2012
SALES (est): 162.6K **Privately Held**
WEB: www.lumberstak.com
SIC: 3944 Games, toys & children's vehicles

(G-13487)
NEW BEST PACKERS INC
1122 Bronson St (32177-3362)
PHONE..................................386 328-5127
Michael K Drew, *President*
EMP: 30 **EST:** 1966
SQ FT: 35,000
SALES (est): 7MM **Privately Held**
WEB: www.newbestpackers.com
SIC: 2013 Sausages from purchased meat; smoked meats from purchased meat; frankfurters from purchased meat; roast beef from purchased meat

(G-13488)
PALATKA WELDING SHOP INC
1301 Madison St (32177-3298)
PHONE..................................386 328-1507
John W Buckles, *President*
Ginger Buckles De Loach, *Corp Secy*
Clifford Buckles Jr, *Vice Pres*
EMP: 23 **EST:** 1948
SQ FT: 10,000
SALES (est): 1.9MM **Privately Held**
SIC: 7692 7538 7549 3441 Welding repair; general automotive repair shops; towing services; fabricated structural metal

(G-13489)
PORT OF PALM COLD STORAGE INC
1122 Bronson St (32177-3362)
PHONE..................................386 328-5127
Michael Drew, *Manager*
EMP: 26
SALES (corp-wide): 2MM **Privately Held**
WEB: www.portofpalmcoldstorage.com
SIC: 2013 Sausages & other prepared meats
PA: Port Of Palm Cold Storage Inc
1800 Dr Mrtn Lther King J
Riviera Beach FL 33404
561 743-8001

(G-13490)
PRICE BROTHERS COMPANY
245 Comfort Rd (32177-8634)
P.O. Box 1770 (32178-1770)
PHONE..................................386 328-8841
Steven M Braxton, *Executive*
EMP: 8 **EST:** 2010
SALES (est): 132.3K **Privately Held**
WEB: www.pricebrotherskc.com
SIC: 3498 Fabricated pipe & fittings

(G-13491)
PUTNAM PAPER & PACKAGING INC
109 Jax Ln (32177)
P.O. Box 2068 (32178-2068)
PHONE..................................904 328-5101
John Robinson, *President*
Kay Hood, *Controller*
EMP: 10 **EST:** 1985
SQ FT: 15,000
SALES (est): 979.7K **Privately Held**
SIC: 2679 Paper products, converted

(G-13492)
SMITH PRODUCTS CO INC (PA)
Also Called: Smith Products Kitchens
1005 Kirby St (32177-5157)
P.O. Box 114 (32178-0114)
PHONE..................................386 325-4534
Richard Loosemore, *President*
Steven Rodrigue, *Vice Pres*
EMP: 14 **EST:** 1951
SQ FT: 15,000
SALES (est): 2.6MM **Privately Held**
WEB: www.smith-products.com
SIC: 2511 2434 Wood household furniture; vanities, bathroom: wood

(G-13493)
SMOKEY MOUNTAIN CABINETS INC
103 E Lake St (32177-9198)
PHONE..................................386 325-1677
David Smith, *President*
EMP: 10 **EST:** 2004
SALES (est): 1.3MM **Privately Held**
WEB: www.smokeymountaincabinets.com
SIC: 2434 Wood kitchen cabinets

(G-13494)
SOFTEX PAPER INC (PA)
1400 Reid St (32177-3240)
PHONE..................................386 328-8488
Paul Lucien Lieuw, *President*
Robin Wilkinson, *Human Res Mgr*
Yisel Diaz, *Officer*
Marcel Lieuw, *Admin Sec*
◆ **EMP:** 65 **EST:** 2001
SQ FT: 80,000
SALES (est): 16.2MM **Privately Held**
SIC: 2676 Towels, napkins & tissue paper products

(G-13495)
ST JOHNS SHIP BUILDING INC
560 Stokes Landing Rd (32177-8485)
PHONE..................................386 328-6054
Steven Ganoe, *President*
Bobby Barfield, *General Mgr*
Michael Knecht, *Opers Staff*
Marcia Ganoe, *Production*
Karen Smith, *Purch Agent*
◆ **EMP:** 154 **EST:** 2006
SALES (est): 35.1MM **Privately Held**
WEB: www.stjohnsshipbuilding.com
SIC: 3731 Shipbuilding & repairing

(G-13496)
TK CABINETS
500 N Pine St (32177-2732)
PHONE..................................386 325-6906
Hoyt Knowles, *CEO*
Glenn Thomas, *Vice Pres*
EMP: 7 **EST:** 2004
SALES (est): 792.6K **Privately Held**
WEB: www.tkcabinets.net
SIC: 2434 Wood kitchen cabinets

Palm Bay
Brevard County

(G-13497)
A-BREVARD COATINGS INC
1921 Roc Rosa Dr Ne (32905-3909)
PHONE..................................321 726-0322
Seth R Lee, *CEO*
EMP: 6 **EST:** 2016
SALES (est): 129.7K **Privately Held**
SIC: 3479 Metal coating & allied service

(G-13498)
AAR AIRLIFT GROUP INC (HQ)
2301 Commerce Park Dr Ne # 11 (32905-2611)
PHONE..................................321 837-2345
David P Storch, *CEO*
Randy Martinez, *President*
Timothy J Romenesko, *President*
Michael K Carr, *Vice Pres*
Peter K Chapman, *Vice Pres*
EMP: 29 **EST:** 1998
SALES (est): 35.6MM
SALES (corp-wide): 1.6B **Publicly Held**
WEB: www.aarcorp.com
SIC: 3728 Aircraft parts & equipment
PA: Aar Corp.
1100 N Wood Dale Rd
Wood Dale IL 60191
630 227-2000

(G-13499)
ART-KRAFT SIGN CO INC
2675 Kirby Cir Ne (32905-3403)
PHONE..................................321 727-7324
Donald H Reilly, *President*
Steve Hart, *Vice Pres*
Katie Hart, *Finance*
Don Riley, *Human Res Mgr*
Robert Harper, *Sales Staff*
EMP: 30 **EST:** 1968
SQ FT: 17,500
SALES (est): 3.9MM **Privately Held**
WEB: www.art-kraft.com
SIC: 3993 1799 Electric signs; sign installation & maintenance

(G-13500)
AVIATION WORLDWIDE SVCS LLC (HQ)
Also Called: AAR Airlift Group
2301 Commerce Park Dr Ne (32905-2611)
PHONE..................................321 837-2345
Jeff Schloesser, *Mng Member*
Timothy Childrey,
EMP: 18 **EST:** 2003
SQ FT: 6,000
SALES (est): 15.5MM
SALES (corp-wide): 1.6B **Publicly Held**
WEB: www.aarcorp.com
SIC: 3728 Aircraft parts & equipment
PA: Aar Corp.
1100 N Wood Dale Rd
Wood Dale IL 60191
630 227-2000

(G-13501)
B & D MACHINE AND TOOL INC
1720 Main St Ne Ste 3 (32905-3427)
PHONE..................................321 727-0098
Duard Anzengruber, *President*
EMP: 12 **EST:** 1978
SQ FT: 5,000
SALES (est): 1.9MM **Privately Held**
WEB: www.bndmt.com
SIC: 3599 Machine shop, jobbing & repair

(G-13502)
BETA MAX INC
Also Called: Beta Max Hoist
1895 Rbert J Cnlan Blvd N (32905-3409)
P.O. Box 2750, Melbourne (32902-2750)
PHONE..................................321 727-3737
Tony D Rowell, *President*
◆ **EMP:** 30 **EST:** 1993
SQ FT: 30,000
SALES (est): 7.7MM **Privately Held**
WEB: www.betamaxhoist.com
SIC: 3536 Hoists

(G-13503)
BETA MAX INC
2750 Hudson Ave Ne (32905-3422)
PHONE..................................321 914-0918
EMP: 6 **EST:** 2019
SALES (est): 284.7K **Privately Held**
WEB: www.betamaxhoist.com
SIC: 3536 Hoists, cranes & monorails

(G-13504)
BLACK WIDOW CUSTOM CASES
1720 Main St Ne (32905-3427)
PHONE..................................321 327-8058
EMP: 6 **EST:** 2019
SALES (est): 806.6K **Privately Held**
SIC: 3523 Farm machinery & equipment

(G-13505)
BLUE PLANET ENVMTL SYSTEMS
2600 Kingswood Dr Ne (32905-2508)
P.O. Box 60790 (32906-0790)
PHONE..................................321 255-1931
Craig Allen Smith, *President*
EMP: 6 **EST:** 1997
SALES (est): 1.8MM **Privately Held**
WEB: www.blueplanetenv.com
SIC: 2899 Chemical preparations

(G-13506)
C HORSE SOFTWARE INC
1510 Charles Blvd Ne (32907-2403)
PHONE..................................321 952-0692
Alfredo Padilla, *President*
EMP: 5 **EST:** 2005
SALES (est): 353.1K **Privately Held**
SIC: 7372 Prepackaged software

(G-13507)
CONSUMER ENGINEERING INC
1240 Clearmont St Ne # 1 (32905-4048)
PHONE..................................321 984-8550
Jerrell P Hollaway, *President*
Sharon Hollaway, *Vice Pres*
Charlotte Parker, *Treasurer*
EMP: 18 **EST:** 1986
SQ FT: 16,000
SALES (est): 2.6MM **Privately Held**
WEB: www.consumerengineering.com
SIC: 3613 3589 8711 Control panels, electric; commercial cleaning equipment; water treatment equipment, industrial; professional engineer

(G-13508)
DIAMOND PRECISION MACHINE INC
2300 Commerce Park Dr Ne (32905-2619)
PHONE..................................321 729-8453
Robin Squillante, *CEO*
Michael Squillante, *President*
EMP: 10 **EST:** 1990
SQ FT: 6,450
SALES (est): 1MM **Privately Held**
WEB: www.diamondprecision.net
SIC: 3599 3089 Machine shop, jobbing & repair; injection molded finished plastic products

(G-13509)
DRS NTWORK IMAGING SYSTEMS LLC
3520 Dixie Hwy Ne (32905-2700)
PHONE..................................321 309-1500
Joseph Danielle, *Engineer*
Lou Demore, *Engineer*
Steve Marteney, *Engineer*
Dennis Wills, *Engineer*
Terry Neuhart, *Project Engr*
EMP: 31
SALES (corp-wide): 10.2B **Privately Held**
WEB: www.leonardodrs.com
SIC: 3674 Infrared sensors, solid state
HQ: Drs Network & Imaging Systems, Llc
100 N Babcock St
Melbourne FL 32935

(G-13510)
DRT SERVICES
861 Young Ave Nw (32907-7728)
PHONE..................................321 549-1431
Derek Austin, *Principal*
EMP: 7 **EST:** 2010
SALES (est): 308.5K **Privately Held**
SIC: 3674 Semiconductors & related devices

(G-13511)
FAR RESEARCH INC
Also Called: Far Chemical
2210 Wilhelmina Ct Ne (32905-2548)
PHONE..................................321 723-6160
Joseph Beatty, *CEO*
Joe Beatty, *Vice Pres*
Geoffrey Crook, *Production*
Patricia Wichmann, *Purch Agent*
Zachary Fine, *Engineer*
▲ **EMP:** 25 **EST:** 1982
SALES (est): 9.2MM
SALES (corp-wide): 41.2MM **Privately Held**
WEB: www.far-chemical.com
SIC: 2899 Chemical preparations
HQ: Cyalume Technologies, Inc.
96 Windsor St
West Springfield MA 01089
888 858-7881

(G-13512)
FILTER RESEARCH CORPORATION
1270 Clearmont St Ne # 15 (32905-4016)
P.O. Box 60898 (32906-0898)
PHONE..................................321 802-3444
Ahmed El-Mahdawy, *President*
EMP: 20 **EST:** 1977
SQ FT: 12,000
SALES (est): 2MM **Privately Held**
WEB: www.frccorp.com
SIC: 3677 Electronic transformers

(G-13513)
FLORIDA ENGINEERED CONSTRU
Also Called: Cast-Crete
2590 Kirby Cir Ne (32905-3416)
PHONE..................................321 953-5161
Dustin Hirsch, *Purchasing*
Jeff Roble, *Sales Associate*
Carl Eschmann, *Manager*
EMP: 7
SALES (corp-wide): 28.5MM **Privately Held**
WEB: www.castcrete.com
SIC: 3272 Precast terrazo or concrete products
PA: Florida Engineered Construction Products Corporation
6324 County Road 579
Seffner FL 33584
813 621-4641

(G-13514)
FRC ELECTRICAL INDUSTRIES INC (PA)
1260 Clearmont St Ne (32905-4030)
P.O. Box 60898 (32906-0898)
PHONE..................................321 676-3300
Ahmed El-Mahdawy, *President*
EMP: 1 **EST:** 1994
SALES (est): 4.4MM **Privately Held**
WEB: www.frccorp.com
SIC: 3679 3444 Hermetic seals for electronic equipment; sheet metalwork

(G-13515)
GROUP E HOLDINGS INC
Also Called: Custom Aerospace Machine
2144 Franklin Dr Ne (32905-4021)
PHONE..................................321 724-0127
Evan Cramer, *CEO*
Michael Huber, *Engineer*
Chris Hoffman,
James McCandless,
EMP: 53 **EST:** 2011
SQ FT: 12,500
SALES (est): 6.1MM **Privately Held**
WEB: www.custommoldandtool.com
SIC: 3599 Machine shop, jobbing & repair

(G-13516)
INNOVATIVE TECH BY DESIGN INC
Also Called: Itd Food Safety
2469 Palm Bay Rd Ne 9 (32905-3353)
PHONE..................................321 676-3194
Jason Mobley, *President*
Kelly Mobley, *Vice Pres*
EMP: 10 **EST:** 2005
SALES (est): 1.5MM **Privately Held**
WEB: www.itdfoodsafety.com
SIC: 3829 Measuring & controlling devices

(G-13517)
INSPIRE INC
137 Wishing Well Cir Sw (32908-6415)
PHONE..................................321 557-3247
Michelle Currie, *Principal*
EMP: 6 **EST:** 2017
SALES (est): 184.5K **Privately Held**
SIC: 2834 Pharmaceutical preparations

(G-13518)
L3HARRIS TECHNOLOGIES INC
1282 Roslyn Ave Nw (32907-7811)
PHONE..................................321 412-6601
EMP: 6
SALES (corp-wide): 3.7B **Publicly Held**
WEB: www.l3harris.com
SIC: 3812 Search & navigation equipment
PA: L3harris Technologies, Inc.
1025 W Nasa Blvd
Melbourne FL 32919
321 727-9100

(G-13519)
L3HARRIS TECHNOLOGIES INC
Also Called: Mdso Security Office
Plant 16 Troutman Blvd (32905)
P.O. Box 37, Melbourne (32902-0037)
PHONE..................................321 727-4255
Sheldon J Fox, *Vice Pres*
Joyce Williams, *Manager*
Dayne Barrow, *Manager*
EMP: 20
SALES (corp-wide): 3.7B **Publicly Held**
WEB: www.l3harris.com
SIC: 3661 Telephone & telegraph apparatus
PA: L3harris Technologies, Inc.
1025 W Nasa Blvd
Melbourne FL 32919
321 727-9100

(G-13520)
L3HARRIS TECHNOLOGIES INC
Harris Corporation
1000 Charles J Herbert Dr (32905)
PHONE..................................321 727-4660
K Alaskiewicz, *Branch Mgr*
EMP: 6
SALES (corp-wide): 3.7B **Publicly Held**
WEB: www.l3harris.com
SIC: 3728 Aircraft parts & equipment
PA: L3harris Technologies, Inc.
1025 W Nasa Blvd
Melbourne FL 32919
321 727-9100

(G-13521)
LIGHTHOUSE OF LEESBURG INC
420 Calamondin Ave Nw (32907-1843)
PHONE..................................352 408-6566
Alison K Schmidt, *Principal*
EMP: 6 **EST:** 2012
SALES (est): 138.6K **Privately Held**
SIC: 3452 Pins

(G-13522)
M P I MEDICAL PRODUCTS INC
1631 Elmhurst Cir Se (32909-8883)
PHONE..................................321 676-1299
Sydney Goldstein, *President*
Hildergarde Lore Goldstein, *Vice Pres*
EMP: 6 **EST:** 1996
SALES (est): 441.5K **Privately Held**
SIC: 3674 Radiation sensors

(G-13523)
MC GRAPHIX
1390 Ashboro Cir Se (32909-6551)
PHONE..................................321 725-7243
Fitzgerald Lawrence, *Principal*
EMP: 6 **EST:** 2010
SALES (est): 251.3K **Privately Held**
WEB: www.mcgraphixsigns.com
SIC: 3993 Signs & advertising specialties

(G-13524)
MELBOURNE-TILLMAN WTR CTRL DST
5990 Minton Rd Nw (32907-1977)
PHONE..................................321 723-7233
John Devivo, *President*
Daniel Anderson, *Agent*
EMP: 29 **EST:** 1922
SQ FT: 3,984
SALES (est): 2.6MM **Privately Held**
WEB: www.melbournetillman.org
SIC: 3822 Auto controls regulating residntl & coml environmt & applncs

(G-13525)
NEXGEN FRAMING SYSTEM LLC
2288 Wilhelmina Ct Ne (32905-2536)
PHONE..................................321 508-6763
EMP: 11 **EST:** 2019
SALES (est): 1.7MM **Privately Held**
SIC: 2439 Trusses, wooden roof

(G-13526)
NOHBO LABS LLC
1581 Robert J Conlan Blvd (32905-3563)
PHONE..................................321 345-5319
Melinda Warren, *Mng Member*
Carrie Warren,
EMP: 7 **EST:** 2017
SALES (est): 809K **Privately Held**
WEB: www.nohbo.com
SIC: 2844 Cosmetic preparations

(G-13527)
NORTHROP GRUMMAN CORPORATION
811 Gabriel Ave Ne (32907-1546)
PHONE..................................321 951-5730
David Kverek, *Branch Mgr*
EMP: 6 **Publicly Held**
WEB: www.northropgrumman.com
SIC: 3812 Search & navigation equipment
PA: Northrop Grumman Corporation
2980 Fairview Park Dr
Falls Church VA 22042

(G-13528)
OAKRIDGE GLOBL ENRGY SLTONS IN
3520 Dixie Hwy Ne (32905-2700)
PHONE..................................321 610-7959
Stephen J Barber, *Ch of Bd*
EMP: 42
SALES: 1.6K **Privately Held**
WEB: www.oakridgeglobalenergy.com
SIC: 3692 Primary batteries, dry & wet

(G-13529)
PROGRESS HOUSE
1097 Sandy Ln Ne (32905-4622)
PHONE..................................321 298-4652
EMP: 7 **EST:** 2008
SALES (est): 166.7K **Privately Held**
SIC: 2711 Newspapers, publishing & printing

(G-13530)
RECALL TECHNOLOGIES INC
1651 Seabury Point Rd Nw (32907-6335)
P.O. Box 100546 (32910-0546)
PHONE..................................321 952-4422
Susan Voelkel, *President*
John Voelkel, *Vice Pres*
EMP: 5 **EST:** 1994
SQ FT: 2,000
SALES (est): 463.7K **Privately Held**
WEB: www.recallt3.com
SIC: 3661 Telephone & telegraph apparatus

(G-13531)
RENESAS ELECTRONICS AMER INC
1650 Rbert J Cnlan Blvd N (32905-3406)
P.O. Box 65004 (32906-5004)
PHONE..................................321 724-7000
Vern Kelley, *Vice Pres*
Randy Pitts, *Marketing Staff*
Wayman Aldridge Jr, *Branch Mgr*
Brannon Harris, *Senior Mgr*
Robin Nursey, *Director*
EMP: 600 **Privately Held**
WEB: www.renesas.com
SIC: 3674 Semiconductors & related devices
HQ: Renesas Electronics America Inc.
6024 Silver Creek Vly Rd
San Jose CA 95138
408 432-8888

(G-13532)
RONCO AIRCRAFT AND MARINE INC (PA)
1774 Plantation Cir Se (32909-7111)
PHONE..................................321 220-0209
Ronald A Waddell, *Principal*
EMP: 21 **EST:** 2012
SALES (est): 833.3K **Privately Held**
WEB: www.sgjacobiphd.com
SIC: 3721 Aircraft

(G-13533)
SAILOR MADE CSTM WOODWORKS LLC
190 Wading Bird Cir Sw (32908-6410)
PHONE.................................805 587-1197
William Vega,
EMP: 6 **EST:** 2017
SALES (est): 165.2K **Privately Held**
WEB: www.sailormadecww.com
SIC: 2431 Millwork

(G-13534)
SHAPES GROUP LTD CO
Also Called: Shapes Precision Manufacturing
1415 Fundation Pk Blvd Se (32909-2104)
PHONE.................................321 837-0500
Kyle Benusa, *President*
T Kyle Benusa, *President*
Carman Cicarella, *Purch Agent*
Wayne Elliott, *CFO*
Jason Baran, *Manager*
▲ **EMP:** 83
SQ FT: 65,000
SALES (est): 26.5MM **Privately Held**
WEB: www.shapesmfg.com
SIC: 3441 Fabricated structural metal

(G-13535)
SOD DEPOT & GRAVEL INC
1378 Malabar Rd Se (32907-2553)
PHONE.................................321 728-2766
Saul Ventura, *Principal*
EMP: 6 **EST:** 2015
SALES (est): 66K **Privately Held**
SIC: 1442 Construction sand & gravel

(G-13536)
SOLUNET
1571 Robert J Conlan Blvd (32905-3562)
PHONE.................................321 369-9719
Dan Kinnick, *Sales Executive*
EMP: 7 **EST:** 2015
SALES (est): 138.4K **Privately Held**
SIC: 3579 Office machines

(G-13537)
SOUND ANCHORS INC
2835 Kirby Cir Ne Ste 110 (32905-3411)
PHONE.................................321 724-1237
Robert Worzalla, *President*
Debbie Worzalla, *Vice Pres*
▲ **EMP:** 7 **EST:** 1986
SQ FT: 5,600
SALES (est): 500K **Privately Held**
WEB: www.soundanchors.com
SIC: 3651 5731 Household audio equipment; radio, television & electronic stores

(G-13538)
SOUTHEASTERN ENGINEERING INC
1340 Clearmont St Ne # 304 (32905-4049)
P.O. Box 61442 (32906-1442)
PHONE.................................321 984-2521
Harry Zeek, *President*
EMP: 19 **EST:** 1978
SQ FT: 12,000
SALES (est): 1.2MM **Privately Held**
SIC: 3663 3728 3714 Satellites, communications; aircraft parts & equipment; motor vehicle parts & accessories

(G-13539)
STARTEK SERVICES LLC
920 Almeria Ln Sw (32908-7659)
PHONE.................................631 224-9220
EMP: 8 **EST:** 2014
SALES (est): 82.9K **Privately Held**
WEB: www.startek.com
SIC: 3993 Signs & advertising specialties

(G-13540)
STEEN AERO LAB LLC
1451 Clearmont St Ne (32905-4017)
PHONE.................................321 725-4160
Mike Whaley, *Webmaster*
Paul Goetsch,
Jeri Larson,
EMP: 9 **EST:** 2000
SALES (est): 1.1MM **Privately Held**
WEB: www.steenaero.com
SIC: 3728 Aircraft assemblies, subassemblies & parts

(G-13541)
STONE MOSAICS
1735 Biltz Ave Ne (32905-3413)
PHONE.................................321 773-3635
Roger Sinigoi, *President*
EMP: 8 **EST:** 2015
SALES (est): 1.2MM **Privately Held**
SIC: 1411 Dimension stone

(G-13542)
SYNCRON EMS LLC
2330 Commerce Park Dr Ne # 6 (32905-7721)
PHONE.................................321 409-0025
John Sjolander, *CEO*
Rick Price, *Vice Pres*
Kayla Smiroldo, *Senior Buyer*
Dave Glionna, *Engineer*
Cheri Bia, *Program Mgr*
EMP: 85 **EST:** 2008
SQ FT: 25,000
SALES (est): 21.6MM **Privately Held**
WEB: www.syncron-ems.com
SIC: 3679 Electronic circuits

(G-13543)
TECHNOLOGY PRODUCTS DESIGN INC
3806 Hield Rd Nw (32907-6303)
PHONE.................................321 432-3537
Charles Burr, *Principal*
EMP: 13 **EST:** 2001
SALES (est): 168.3K **Privately Held**
SIC: 3674 Semiconductors & related devices

(G-13544)
TEKQUEST INC
2510 Kirby Cir Ne Ste 106 (32905-3426)
P.O. Box 410165, Melbourne (32941-0165)
PHONE.................................321 768-6069
Basil Pappademetriou, *President*
John Pappademetriou, *Vice Pres*
EMP: 12 **EST:** 1993
SQ FT: 10,000
SALES (est): 2MM **Privately Held**
WEB: www.tekquest-llc.com
SIC: 3679 Electronic circuits

(G-13545)
ULTRA PRCSION MCHNING GRNDING
2870 Kirby Cir Ne Ste 6 (32905-3438)
PHONE.................................321 725-9655
Mike Higley, *President*
Paul Hill, *QC Mgr*
EMP: 17 **EST:** 1995
SQ FT: 2,200
SALES (est): 1.7MM **Privately Held**
WEB: www.ultramachining.com
SIC: 3599 Machine shop, jobbing & repair

(G-13546)
WALTERS TOOLS LLC
Also Called: Cornwell
2998 Hester Ave Se (32909-7600)
PHONE.................................321 537-4788
EMP: 5 **EST:** 2018
SALES (est): 1.6MM **Privately Held**
SIC: 1389 Oil field services

Palm Beach
Palm Beach County

(G-13547)
ABB PARTNERS LLC
340 Royal Poinciana Way # 3 (33480-4048)
PHONE.................................917 843-4430
Matti C Anttila, *CEO*
EMP: 12 **EST:** 2006
SALES (est): 1MM
SALES (corp-wide): 26.1B **Privately Held**
WEB: www.global.abb
SIC: 3612 Transformers, except electric
PA: Abb Ltd
Affolternstrasse 44
ZUrich ZH 8050
433 177-111

(G-13548)
ABSOLUTELY SUITABLE
1 S County Rd (33480-4023)
PHONE.................................561 653-6380
Gabriela Amato Heape, *Manager*
EMP: 6 **EST:** 1996
SALES (est): 266.4K **Privately Held**
SIC: 2253 Bathing suits & swimwear, knit

(G-13549)
BENCHMARK OF PALM BEACH (PA)
205 Worth Ave Ste 315 (33480-4618)
PHONE.................................706 258-3553
Ken Burns, *President*
EMP: 8 **EST:** 2006
SALES (est): 217.6K **Privately Held**
WEB: www.benchmarkofpalmbeach.com
SIC: 3423 Jewelers' hand tools

(G-13550)
CAMPER & NICHOLSONS USA INC (PA)
450 Royal Palm Way # 100 (33480-4144)
PHONE.................................561 655-2121
Russell Preston III, *President*
Paolo Casani, *Managing Dir*
Fabrizio Scerch, *Managing Dir*
Jillian Montgomery, *COO*
Elodie Arnaud, *Opers Staff*
◆ **EMP:** 30 **EST:** 1992
SALES (est): 5.5MM **Privately Held**
WEB: www.camperandnicholsons.com
SIC: 3732 5551 Yachts, building & repairing; boat dealers

(G-13551)
COLLECTORS INTERNATIONAL PUBG
1285 N Lake Way (33480-3145)
PHONE.................................561 845-7156
Vincent J Ricardel, *Director*
EMP: 6 **EST:** 2001
SALES (est): 94.6K **Privately Held**
SIC: 2741 Miscellaneous publishing

(G-13552)
CONNECTRONICS US INC
101 Bradley Pl Ste 202 (33480-3828)
PHONE.................................954 534-3335
Lee Hauradou, *President*
EMP: 5 **EST:** 2011
SQ FT: 1,500
SALES (est): 300K **Privately Held**
WEB: www.customrfconnectors.com
SIC: 3559 Electronic component making machinery

(G-13553)
DIVERSITYINC MEDIA LLC
111 Reef Rd (33480-3058)
P.O. Box 348, Princeton NJ (08542-0348)
PHONE.................................973 494-0539
Carolynn Johnson, *COO*
Lucas J Visconti, *Mng Member*
EMP: 19 **EST:** 2001
SQ FT: 5,500
SALES (est): 2.6MM **Privately Held**
WEB: www.diversityinc.com
SIC: 2721 Magazines: publishing only, not printed on site

(G-13554)
FLO SUN LAND CORPORATION
Also Called: Florida Crystals
340 Royal Poinciana Way # 316 (33480-4048)
PHONE.................................561 655-6303
Alfonso Fanjul Jr, *Ch of Bd*
Jose Fanjul, *President*
Donald W Carson, *Exec VP*
Oscar R Hernandez, *Vice Pres*
Robert Dias, *Opers Staff*
◆ **EMP:** 38 **EST:** 1950
SQ FT: 9,000
SALES (est): 1MM **Privately Held**
SIC: 2099 0133 6552 Sugar grinding; sugarcane farm; subdividers & developers

(G-13555)
GARRISON LICKLE AIRCRAFT
400 S Ocean Blvd Ofc (33480-6715)
PHONE.................................561 833-7111
Garrison Lickle, *Principal*
EMP: 8 **EST:** 2005
SALES (est): 231.8K **Privately Held**
SIC: 3721 Aircraft

(G-13556)
HRF EXPLORATION & PROD LLC (PA)
250 El Dorado Ln (33480-3302)
P.O. Box 160, Gaylord MI (49734-0160)
PHONE.................................561 847-4743
H R Fruehaug III, *President*
EMP: 18 **EST:** 1994
SALES (est): 6.5MM **Privately Held**
SIC: 1382 Oil & gas exploration services

(G-13557)
LIFE SPICE AND INGREDIENTS LLC
300 Cherry Ln (33480-3419)
PHONE.................................708 301-0447
Dawn Pavela, *VP Finance*
Lisa Stern, *Sales Mgr*
Peter Garvy, *Mng Member*
EMP: 26 **EST:** 2009
SQ FT: 5,000
SALES (est): 1.4MM **Privately Held**
WEB: www.lifespiceingredients.com
SIC: 2099 Spices, including grinding

(G-13558)
MAUI HOLDINGS LLC
250 Royal Palm Way # 201 (33480-4319)
PHONE.................................904 741-5400
Nicholas Sokolow, *Manager*
EMP: 2533 **EST:** 2012
SALES (est): 37.4MM **Privately Held**
SIC: 2311 Policemen's uniforms: made from purchased materials

(G-13559)
MECOX GARDENS & POTTERY INC
3900 S Dixie Hwy (33480)
PHONE.................................561 805-8611
Christin Tucker, *Manager*
EMP: 6 **Privately Held**
WEB: www.mecoxgardens.com
SIC: 2392 Household furnishings
PA: Mecox Gardens & Pottery, Inc.
257 County Road 39a
Southampton NY 11968

(G-13560)
OSCEOLA FARMS CO (HQ)
340 Royal Poinciana Way # 315 (33480-4048)
P.O. Box 1059 (33480-1059)
PHONE.................................561 655-6303
Alfonso Fanjul Jr, *Ch of Bd*
Jose Fanjul, *President*
Donald W Carson, *Vice Pres*
Oscar R Hernandez, *VP Finance*
Roland Gonzalez, *Manager*
▲ **EMP:** 35 **EST:** 1960
SQ FT: 9,000
SALES (est): 205.3MM
SALES (corp-wide): 2.1B **Privately Held**
WEB: www.pepefanjul.org
SIC: 2099 Sugar grinding
PA: Fanjul Corp.
1 N Clematis St Ste 200
West Palm Beach FL 33401
561 655-6303

(G-13561)
RAMPELL SOFTWARE
122 N County Rd (33480-3917)
PHONE.................................561 628-5102
Alex Rampell, *Principal*
EMP: 12 **EST:** 2016
SALES (est): 101.7K **Privately Held**
SIC: 2273 Carpets & rugs

(G-13562)
UAS DRONE CORP (PA)
420 Royal Palm Way # 100 (33480-4133)
PHONE.................................561 693-1424
Yossi Balucka, *President*
Chris Leith, *Corp Secy*
Sagiv Aharon, *CTO*
EMP: 8 **EST:** 2015
SALES (est): 833.3K **Privately Held**
WEB: www.uasdronecorp.com
SIC: 3721 Aircraft

▲ = Import ▼=Export
◆ =Import/Export

(G-13563)
Y3K LLC
44 Cocoanut Row Ste T1 (33480-4069)
PHONE..................................561 835-0404
Peter Lester,
EMP: 8 **EST:** 2005
SALES (est): 119.9K **Privately Held**
WEB: www.y3kfoods.com
SIC: 2024 Ice cream & frozen desserts

Palm Beach Gardens
Palm Beach County

(G-13564)
ACE-PIPE WELDING LLC
305 Camellia St (33410-4812)
PHONE..................................561 727-6345
Ronald C Miles, *Principal*
EMP: 8 **EST:** 2013
SALES (est): 589.9K **Privately Held**
SIC: 7692 Welding repair

(G-13565)
ALL AMERICAN PET COMPANY INC
3801 Pga Blvd Ste 600 (33410-2756)
PHONE..................................561 337-5340
Barry Schwartz, *CEO*
EMP: 10 **EST:** 2003
SQ FT: 1,000
SALES (est): 585.8K **Privately Held**
SIC: 2047 Dog & cat food

(G-13566)
ANNONA BIOSCIENCES INC
2401 Pga Blvd Ste 196 (33410-3500)
PHONE..................................888 204-4980
Donna Douglas, *Principal*
EMP: 5 **EST:** 2009
SALES (est): 388.9K **Privately Held**
SIC: 2834 Pharmaceutical preparations

(G-13567)
AQUALOGIX INC (PA)
4440 Pga Blvd Ste 600 (33410-6542)
PHONE..................................858 442-4550
Donald Hofmann, *President*
William Richardson, *Manager*
EMP: 12 **EST:** 2013
SQ FT: 5,000
SALES: 95.5K **Privately Held**
WEB: www.aqualogix.com
SIC: 3823 7389 7371 Water quality monitoring & control systems; water softener service; computer software development & applications

(G-13568)
ARCHITCTRAL WDWRKS CBNETRY INC
219 Coral Cay Ter (33418-4003)
PHONE..................................561 848-8595
Chris Williams, *President*
Jose Montero, *President*
Jason Long, *Vice Pres*
▼ **EMP:** 14 **EST:** 1989
SALES (est): 907.8K **Privately Held**
SIC: 2434 2431 Wood kitchen cabinets; woodwork, interior & ornamental

(G-13569)
BIGGS INDUSTRIES INC
11426 88th Rd N (33412-1348)
PHONE..................................561 775-6944
Sean Harmon, *President*
EMP: 6 **EST:** 2010
SALES (est): 87.8K **Privately Held**
SIC: 3999 Manufacturing industries

(G-13570)
BIOMET 3I LLC
Also Called: 3i Implant Innovations
4555 Riverside Dr (33410-4200)
PHONE..................................561 775-9928
Alex Garcia, *Purch Mgr*
Andrew Hood, *Manager*
Richard Lazzara,
Keith Beaty,
Jeffrey R Binder,
▼ **EMP:** 600 **EST:** 1987
SQ FT: 67,000
SALES (est): 138.6MM
SALES (corp-wide): 7B **Publicly Held**
WEB: www.zimmerbiometdental.com
SIC: 3843 Dental materials
HQ: Biomet, Inc.
345 E Main St
Warsaw IN 46580
574 267-6639

(G-13571)
BLUE BIOFUELS INC
3710 Buckeye St Ste 120 (33410-4290)
PHONE..................................561 693-1943
Benjamin Slager, *CEO*
Anthony Santelli, *COO*
George Bolton,
EMP: 8 **EST:** 2012
SALES (est): 2.9MM **Privately Held**
WEB: www.bluebiofuels.com
SIC: 2869 Fuels

(G-13572)
BRIEMAD INC
Also Called: Nutrition World Health Market
2401 Pga Blvd Ste 136 (33410-3515)
PHONE..................................561 626-4377
Bruce S Cohen, *President*
EMP: 10 **EST:** 2011
SALES (est): 483K **Privately Held**
WEB: www.nutritionworld.com
SIC: 2834 Pharmaceutical preparations

(G-13573)
CARRIER CORPORATION (HQ)
Also Called: United Technologies Carrier
13995 Pasteur Blvd (33418-7231)
P.O. Box 4808, Syracuse NY (13221-4808)
PHONE..................................800 379-6484
David Gitlin, *President*
Ted Amyuni, *Senior VP*
Chuck Balawajder, *Vice Pres*
Ted Fetterman, *Vice Pres*
Robert Galli, *Vice Pres*
◆ **EMP:** 170 **EST:** 1978
SALES (est): 1.4B
SALES (corp-wide): 17.4B **Publicly Held**
WEB: www.rtx.com
SIC: 3585 Air conditioning equipment, complete; heating equipment, complete; room coolers, portable; heat pumps, electric
PA: Carrier Global Corporation
13995 Pasteur Blvd
Palm Beach Gardens FL 33418
561 365-2000

(G-13574)
CARRIER FIRE SEC AMERICAS CORP
Also Called: UTC Fire & Security Lincolnton
13995 Pasteur Blvd (33418-7231)
PHONE..................................828 695-4000
Charlette Teage, *Branch Mgr*
EMP: 6
SALES (corp-wide): 17.4B **Publicly Held**
WEB: www.corporate.carrier.com
SIC: 3669 5065 Burglar alarm apparatus, electric; fire alarm apparatus, electric; fire detection systems, electric; electronic parts & equipment
HQ: Carrier Fire & Security Americas Corporation
13995 Pasteur Blvd
Palm Beach Gardens FL 33418

(G-13575)
CARRIER GLOBAL CORPORATION (PA)
13995 Pasteur Blvd (33418-7231)
PHONE..................................561 365-2000
John V Faraci, *Ch of Bd*
David Gitlin, *President*
David Appel, *President*
Christopher Nelson, *President*
Jurgen Timperman, *President*
EMP: 656 **EST:** 1902
SALES (est): 17.4B **Publicly Held**
WEB: www.corporate.carrier.com
SIC: 3585 Refrigeration & heating equipment

(G-13576)
CERTUSVIEW TECHNOLOGIES LLC
3980 Rca Blvd Ste 8000 (33410-4273)
PHONE..................................844 533-1258
Andrew H Deferrari, *Principal*
EMP: 2 **EST:** 2008
SALES (est): 3MM
SALES (corp-wide): 3.2B **Publicly Held**
WEB: www.dycomind.com
SIC: 7372 Application computer software
PA: Dycom Industries, Inc.
11780 Us Highway 1 # 600
Palm Beach Gardens FL 33408
561 627-7171

(G-13577)
CHROMALLOY CASTINGS TAMPA CORP (DH)
3999 Rca Blvd (33410-4219)
PHONE..................................561 935-3571
Armand F Lauzon, *President*
Carlo Luzzatto, *Principal*
Mike Beffel, *Vice Pres*
Tom Trotter, *Vice Pres*
James P Langelotti, *Treasurer*
▲ **EMP:** 110 **EST:** 1970
SQ FT: 105,000
SALES (est): 27.8MM
SALES (corp-wide): 2.9B **Publicly Held**
WEB: www.chromalloy.com
SIC: 3369 3714 3511 Machinery castings, nonferrous: ex. alum., copper, die, etc.; motor vehicle parts & accessories; turbines & turbine generator sets
HQ: Chromalloy Gas Turbine Llc
4100 Rca Blvd
Palm Beach Gardens FL 33410
561 935-3571

(G-13578)
CHROMALLOY GAS TURBINE LLC (DH)
Also Called: Gemoco Division
4100 Rca Blvd (33410-4251)
PHONE..................................561 935-3571
Mike Harris, *General Mgr*
Jim Adkins, *Vice Pres*
Dan Albert, *Vice Pres*
Michael Boehm, *Vice Pres*
Costa Brian, *Vice Pres*
▲ **EMP:** 1234 **EST:** 1951
SQ FT: 15,000
SALES (est): 1B
SALES (corp-wide): 2.9B **Publicly Held**
WEB: www.chromalloy.com
SIC: 3724 7699 4581 3764 Aircraft engines & engine parts; engine mount parts, aircraft; engine repair & replacement, non-automotive; aircraft servicing & repairing; guided missile & space vehicle propulsion unit parts; propulsion units for guided missiles & space vehicles; guided missile & space vehicle parts & auxiliary equipment; guided missile & space vehicle parts & aux eqpt, rsch & dev; oil & gas field machinery
HQ: Sequa Corporation
3999 Rca Blvd
Palm Beach Gardens FL 33410
561 935-3571

(G-13579)
CL GARDENS LLC
3101 Pga Blvd (33410-2820)
PHONE..................................561 567-0504
Edward W Beiner,
EMP: 9 **EST:** 2006
SALES (est): 395.5K **Privately Held**
SIC: 3851 Ophthalmic goods

(G-13580)
CLINE RESOURCE AND DEV CO (PA)
Also Called: Cline Group
3825 Pga Blvd Ste 1101 (33410-2991)
PHONE..................................561 626-4999
Christopher Cline, *President*
EMP: 96 **EST:** 2006
SALES (est): 4.9MM **Privately Held**
SIC: 1241 Coal mining services

(G-13581)
COMMUNITY MGT SYSTEMS LLC
4650 Donald Ross Rd # 220 (33418-5102)
PHONE..................................561 214-4780
Kirk Kanjian,
EMP: 16 **EST:** 2003
SALES (est): 593.3K **Privately Held**
WEB: www.buildercms.com
SIC: 7372 Application computer software

(G-13582)
CONCEPT GROUP LLC
350 Hiatt Dr Ste 120 (33418-7197)
PHONE..................................856 767-5506
Maryann Tucker, *Owner*
Ricard Riabko, *Manager*
EMP: 11
SALES (corp-wide): 10.1MM **Privately Held**
WEB: www.conceptgroupllc.com
SIC: 3679 3599 Antennas, receiving; machine shop, jobbing & repair
HQ: Concept Group, Llc
380 Cooper Rd
West Berlin NJ 08091
856 767-5506

(G-13583)
CROSS MATCH TECHNOLOGIES INC (DH)
3950 Rca Blvd Ste 5001 (33410-4227)
PHONE..................................561 622-1650
Richard Agostinelli, *CEO*
Donald E Nickelson, *Ch of Bd*
David Buckley, *President*
George McClurg, *Principal*
Don Sutton, *Regional Mgr*
◆ **EMP:** 205 **EST:** 1996
SQ FT: 71,000
SALES (est): 68.4MM
SALES (corp-wide): 10.1B **Privately Held**
WEB: www.hidglobal.com
SIC: 3999 Fingerprint equipment

(G-13584)
DONNA LYNN ENTERPRISES INC
Also Called: PIP Printing
10358 Rverside Dr Ste 130 (33410)
PHONE..................................772 286-2812
Lloyd Blank, *President*
Donna Blank, *Office Mgr*
EMP: 7 **EST:** 1984
SQ FT: 2,000
SALES (est): 973.7K **Privately Held**
WEB: www.pip.com
SIC: 2789 2752 Bookbinding & related work; commercial printing, lithographic

(G-13585)
ECOLAB INC
100 Vllage Sq Xing Ste 10 (33410)
PHONE..................................561 207-6278
Ed Erico, *Manager*
EMP: 6
SALES (corp-wide): 11.7B **Publicly Held**
WEB: www.ecolab.com
SIC: 2841 Soap & other detergents
PA: Ecolab Inc.
1 Ecolab Pl
Saint Paul MN 55102
800 232-6522

(G-13586)
EMBROIDERY CHIMP LLC
3954 Northlake Blvd (33403-1501)
PHONE..................................561 775-9195
EMP: 9
SALES (corp-wide): 230.4K **Privately Held**
WEB: www.fullypromoted.com
SIC: 2395 Embroidery & art needlework
PA: Embroidery Chimp Llc
107 Sycamore Dr
Royal Palm Beach FL

(G-13587)
EMJ PHARMA INC
133 Playa Rienta Way (33418-6210)
PHONE..................................973 600-9087
Elizabeth B Marchese, *Principal*
EMP: 6 **EST:** 2009
SALES (est): 144.8K **Privately Held**
SIC: 2834 Pharmaceutical preparations

GEOGRAPHIC

(G-13588)
EMPOWERED PROSTHETICS CORP
392 Prestwick Cir Apt 4 (33418-8454)
PHONE..................................561 630-9137
Juan Casas, *Principal*
EMP: 6 **EST:** 2017
SALES (est): 65.3K **Privately Held**
WEB: www.empowered-prosthetics.org
SIC: 3842 Prosthetic appliances

(G-13589)
FIRE RESCUE PINS COM
4292 Osha St (33410-5960)
PHONE..................................561 312-8423
Nicholas Gerry, *Owner*
EMP: 6 **EST:** 2010
SALES (est): 63K **Privately Held**
SIC: 3452 Pins

(G-13590)
FITTEAM GLOBAL LLC
4440 Pga Blvd Ste 600 (33410-6542)
PHONE..................................586 260-1487
Christine Madrazo, *Partner*
Christopher S Hummel, *Manager*
Linda Pesonen, *Executive*
Brittanni Raney, *Executive*
Falyn Shilts, *Executive*
EMP: 7 **EST:** 2014
SQ FT: 1,200
SALES (est): 1MM **Privately Held**
WEB: www.fitteam.com
SIC: 2834 Pharmaceutical preparations

(G-13591)
FLORIDA FLVORS CNCENTRATES INC
205 Sedona Way (33418-1718)
PHONE..................................561 775-5714
Didier Hardy, *President*
Gina M Cieri, *Treasurer*
EMP: 8 **EST:** 2010
SALES (est): 115.9K **Privately Held**
SIC: 2087 5148 Flavoring extracts & syrups; fresh fruits & vegetables

(G-13592)
GMV HOLDINGS LLC
4905 Midtown Ln Apt 2414 (33418-3419)
PHONE..................................561 747-7864
Bruce Harris, *Principal*
EMP: 6 **EST:** 2009
SALES (est): 84.2K **Privately Held**
SIC: 2741

(G-13593)
GND PUBLISHING LLC
72 Saint James Ter (33418-4032)
PHONE..................................561 625-1242
George A Bernstein, *Principal*
EMP: 6 **EST:** 2013
SALES (est): 121.2K **Privately Held**
SIC: 2741 Miscellaneous publishing

(G-13594)
HARRIS WOODWORKS LLC
4078 Jonquil Cir S (33410-5531)
PHONE..................................561 543-3265
James C Harris II, *Principal*
EMP: 6 **EST:** 2019
SALES (est): 288.7K **Privately Held**
SIC: 2431 Millwork

(G-13595)
HUNTER INDUSTRIES
10235 Allamanda Cir (33410-5219)
PHONE..................................561 775-3239
Thomas Decavalcanti, *Owner*
EMP: 7 **EST:** 2015
SALES (est): 150.6K **Privately Held**
WEB: www.hunterindustries.com
SIC: 3999 Manufacturing industries

(G-13596)
INDUSTRIAL MARKING EQP CO INC
4152 Lazy Hammock Rd (33410-6114)
PHONE..................................561 626-8520
Gary Samwick, *President*
Marilyn Samwick, *Corp Secy*
EMP: 6 **EST:** 1941
SQ FT: 15,000
SALES (est): 223.7K **Privately Held**
SIC: 3565 Labeling machines, industrial

(G-13597)
INTEGRITY IMPLANTS INC
354 Hiatt Dr Ste 100 (33418-7241)
PHONE..................................800 201-9300
Christopher Walsh, *CEO*
Wyatt Geist, *President*
Lynn Wiley, *General Mgr*
Michele Wilyey, *General Mgr*
Sonia Fanou, *COO*
EMP: 50 **EST:** 2016
SQ FT: 15,000
SALES (est): 5MM **Privately Held**
WEB: www.integrityimplants.com
SIC: 3841 Surgical & medical instruments

(G-13598)
IT LABS LLC
1810 Flower Dr (33410-1700)
PHONE..................................310 490-6142
Branislav Gjorcevski, *CEO*
EMP: 70 **EST:** 2013
SALES (est): 3.1MM **Privately Held**
WEB: www.it-labs.com
SIC: 7372 7371 7373 Application computer software; educational computer software; computer software development; computer software systems analysis & design, custom; systems software development services

(G-13599)
JUPITER COMPASS LLC
600 S Entrada Way Apt 204 (33410-5320)
PHONE..................................561 444-6740
Paul O'Meara, *Principal*
EMP: 6 **EST:** 2016
SALES (est): 127.4K **Privately Held**
WEB: www.jupitercompass.com
SIC: 7372 Prepackaged software

(G-13600)
KAUFFS VENTURES LLC
3587 Northlake Blvd (33403-1625)
PHONE..................................561 775-3278
EMP: 6 **EST:** 2019
SALES (est): 215.1K **Privately Held**
WEB: www.kauffskompanies.com
SIC: 3993 Signs & advertising specialties

(G-13601)
L C CLARK PUBLISHING INC
Also Called: World of Window Coverings
600 Sandtree Dr Ste 107 (33403-1538)
P.O. Box 13079, North Palm Beach (33408-7079)
PHONE..................................561 627-3393
John Clark, *President*
Valerie Cohen, *Vice Pres*
Kelley C Whitt, *Vice Pres*
EMP: 12 **EST:** 1983
SQ FT: 4,800
SALES (est): 645K **Privately Held**
WEB: www.dwcdesignet.com
SIC: 2721 Magazines: publishing only, not printed on site

(G-13602)
LAKESIDE PUBLISHING CO LLC
3180 Burgundy Dr N (33410-1485)
PHONE..................................847 491-6440
Barry Jacobs, *Principal*
Dale Jacobs, *Prdtn Mgr*
EMP: 5 **EST:** 2008
SALES (est): 431.4K **Privately Held**
WEB: www.cruisetravelarchive.com
SIC: 2721 Magazines: publishing only, not printed on site

(G-13603)
LESTER A DINE INC
351 Hiatt Dr (33418-7198)
PHONE..................................561 624-3009
William Glassgold, *President*
Selda Dine, *Corp Secy*
Enid Glassgold, *Vice Pres*
Matt Glassgold, *Vice Pres*
Colleen Glassgold, *Opers Staff*
EMP: 8 **EST:** 1949
SQ FT: 8,000
SALES (est): 1.1MM **Privately Held**
WEB: www.dinecorp.com
SIC: 3861 5946 Photographic equipment & supplies; cameras; photographic supplies

(G-13604)
LEVATAS
11701 Lk Vctr Grdn Ave (33410-2706)
PHONE..................................561 622-4511
Chris Neilsen, *Owner*
Orlando Allgeier, *QC Mgr*
Rick Blalock, *Engineer*
David Newmon, *Engineer*
Santiago Valdarrama, *Engineer*
EMP: 63 **EST:** 2013
SALES (est): 5MM **Privately Held**
WEB: www.levatas.com
SIC: 2741

(G-13605)
LOCUS SOLUTIONS LLC
Also Called: Locus Traxx Worlwide
7121 Fairway Dr Ste 400 (33418-3776)
PHONE..................................561 575-7600
EMP: 65 **EST:** 2006
SQ FT: 60,000
SALES (est): 15MM
SALES (corp-wide): 16.7B **Publicly Held**
WEB: www.emerson.com
SIC: 3663 7374 ; data processing service
PA: Emerson Electric Co.
8000 West Florissant Ave
Saint Louis MO 63136
314 553-2000

(G-13606)
LOGICAL DATA SOLUTIONS INC
31 Windward Isle (33418-8046)
PHONE..................................561 694-9229
Valerie King, *President*
William King, *Vice Pres*
Chuck Partridge, *Technical Staff*
EMP: 10 **EST:** 1983
SQ FT: 1,200
SALES (est): 982.3K **Privately Held**
WEB: www.logicalds.com
SIC: 7372 8748 Prepackaged software; business consulting

(G-13607)
LRP CONFERENCES LLC (HQ)
360 Hiatt Dr (33418-7106)
PHONE..................................215 784-0860
Ken Kahn, *President*
Emanuel Cotronakis, *Exec VP*
EMP: 21 **EST:** 2006
SALES (est): 9.8MM
SALES (corp-wide): 77.6MM **Privately Held**
WEB: www.lrp.com
SIC: 2759 Commercial printing
PA: Lrp Publications, Inc.
360 Hiatt Dr
Palm Beach Gardens FL 33418
215 784-0860

(G-13608)
LRP PUBLICATIONS INC (PA)
Also Called: L R P
360 Hiatt Dr (33418-7106)
PHONE..................................215 784-0860
Kenneth Kahn, *President*
Jennifer Herseim, *Editor*
Jim Sarmiento, *Editor*
Florence Simmons, *Editor*
Emanuel Cotronakis, *Exec VP*
EMP: 150 **EST:** 1975
SQ FT: 60,000
SALES (est): 77.6MM **Privately Held**
WEB: www.lrp.com
SIC: 2721 Magazines: publishing only, not printed on site

(G-13609)
MICHAEL RYBVICH SONS BOAT WRKS
2175 Idlewild Rd (33410-2583)
PHONE..................................561 627-9168
Blake Gill, *Purch Mgr*
David Parchesco, *Broker*
Michael Rybovich, *Sales Staff*
Josee Olsen, *Office Mgr*
Estelle Peacock, *Admin Asst*
EMP: 20 **EST:** 2010
SALES (est): 3.7MM **Privately Held**
WEB: www.michaelrybovichandsons.com
SIC: 3732 Boat building & repairing

(G-13610)
MOLD CONTROL SYSTEMS INC
2000 Pga Blvd Ste 4440 (33408-2738)
PHONE..................................561 316-5412
Shashrul Khan, *President*
Raymon Jabar, *Vice Pres*
Jeff Clark, *Creative Dir*
▲ **EMP:** 8 **EST:** 1991
SQ FT: 10,000
SALES (est): 1.6MM **Privately Held**
SIC: 3822 3559 Thermostats, except built-in; plastics working machinery

(G-13611)
NIGHTINGALE CORP
11380 Prosperity Farms Rd (33410-3474)
PHONE..................................800 363-8954
William R Breen, *CEO*
Edward Breen, *President*
EMP: 7 **EST:** 2017
SQ FT: 2,795
SALES (est): 1MM
SALES (corp-wide): 16.8MM **Privately Held**
WEB: www.nightingalechairs.com
SIC: 2522 Office chairs, benches & stools, except wood
PA: Nightingale Corp
2301 Dixie Rd
Mississauga ON L4Y 1
905 896-3434

(G-13612)
NORTH PALM PRINTING CENTER
4588 Juniper Ln (33418-4521)
PHONE..................................561 622-2839
John Amann, *President*
Cathy Amann, *Corp Secy*
EMP: 6 **EST:** 1985
SALES (est): 444.4K **Privately Held**
SIC: 2752 Commercial printing, offset

(G-13613)
NORTHROP GRUMMAN SYSTEMS CORP
Also Called: Weapons Systems
348 Hiatt Dr Ste 100 (33418-7234)
PHONE..................................561 515-3651
Scott Longshore, *Engineer*
Alicia Howard, *Senior Engr*
Chris Gettinger, *Branch Mgr*
Beth Byrne, *Program Mgr*
Alice Reed, *Analyst*
EMP: 50 **Publicly Held**
WEB: www.northropgrumman.com
SIC: 3812 Search & navigation equipment
HQ: Northrop Grumman Systems Corporation
2980 Fairview Park Dr
Falls Church VA 22042
703 280-2900

(G-13614)
OLDCASTLE APG SOUTH INC
Also Called: Coastal
3801 Pga Blvd Ste 806 (33410-2757)
PHONE..................................813 367-9780
Ian Crabtree, *Ch of Bd*
Tim Ortman, *President*
Jim Coldwell, *Finance*
Keith A Haas, *Director*
Paul R Valentine, *Director*
▲ **EMP:** 1500 **EST:** 1986
SALES (est): 213.1MM
SALES (corp-wide): 27.5B **Privately Held**
WEB: www.oldcastlecoastal.com
SIC: 3272 Concrete products
HQ: Crh Americas, Inc.
900 Ashwood Pkwy Ste 600
Atlanta GA 30338
770 804-3363

(G-13615)
PALM BEACH GARDENS FLA WKLY
11380 Prosperity Farms Rd (33410-3474)
PHONE..................................561 904-6443
Michelle Noga, *Branch Mgr*
EMP: 7 **EST:** 2010
SALES (est): 140.8K **Privately Held**
SIC: 2711 Newspapers, publishing & printing

(G-13616)
PAPERS UNLIMITED PLUS INC (PA) ✪
161 Remo Pl (33418-1740)
PHONE.................................215 947-1155
Dustin Seidman, *President*
EMP: 3 **EST:** 2021
SALES (est): 20MM **Privately Held**
SIC: 2676 2621 Towels, napkins & tissue paper products; packaging paper

(G-13617)
PRET-EE LLC
Also Called: Heet
4440 Pga Blvd Ste 600 (33410-6542)
PHONE.................................561 839-4338
Meredith Devore,
EMP: 5 **EST:** 2009
SALES (est): 466.3K **Privately Held**
WEB: www.shopheet.com
SIC: 3961 Jewelry apparel, non-precious metals

(G-13618)
PRINT HEADQUARTERS
10358 Rverside Dr Ste 130 (33410)
PHONE.................................772 286-2812
Donna Blank, *President*
Lloyd Blank, *Principal*
EMP: 10 **EST:** 2000
SALES (est): 610.9K **Privately Held**
WEB: www.printheadquarters.com
SIC: 2752 Commercial printing, offset

(G-13619)
PROVICTUS INC
4440 Pga Blvd Ste 635 (33410-6539)
PHONE.................................561 437-0232
David Park, *CEO*
EMP: 20 **EST:** 2011
SALES (est): 738.1K **Privately Held**
SIC: 7372 Application computer software

(G-13620)
RA CO AMO INC
4100 Burns Rd (33410-4695)
PHONE.................................561 626-7232
Carl Volk, *Ch of Bd*
Margaret Volk, *President*
EMP: 16 **EST:** 1976
SQ FT: 32,656
SALES (est): 780.7K **Privately Held**
WEB: www.racoamo.net
SIC: 3672 1761 3825 7629 Circuit boards, television & radio printed; sheet metalwork; test equipment for electronic & electrical circuits; electronic equipment repair; electronic computers

(G-13621)
RAINBOW PRECISION MFG CORP
4371 Northlake Blvd (33410-6253)
PHONE.................................561 691-1658
Richard Thew, *President*
EMP: 8 **EST:** 2002
SALES (est): 170.9K **Privately Held**
SIC: 3089 3444 Injection molded finished plastic products; injection molding of plastics; metal housings, enclosures, casings & other containers

(G-13622)
RESPECT FOODS
4731 Cadiz Cir (33418-8981)
PHONE.................................561 557-2832
EMP: 6
SALES (est): 300K **Privately Held**
SIC: 2099 Mfg Food Preparations

(G-13623)
SANTO DOMINGO TIMBER CO LLC
3910 Rca Blvd Ste 1015 (33410-4284)
PHONE.................................561 627-4000
John C Bills,
EMP: 8 **EST:** 2008
SALES (est): 317.7K **Privately Held**
SIC: 2411 Timber, cut at logging camp

(G-13624)
SCREENCO NORTH INC
11211 81st Ct N (33412-1520)
PHONE.................................561 840-3300
Richard Prince, *President*
▲ **EMP:** 26 **EST:** 1960
SQ FT: 30,000
SALES (est): 2.3MM **Privately Held**
WEB: www.screencoinc.com
SIC: 3446 3448 Architectural metalwork; screen enclosures

(G-13625)
SENECA INDUSTRIES
3825 Pga Blvd Ste 1101 (33410-2991)
PHONE.................................561 626-4999
Stacy Blum, *Principal*
EMP: 7 **EST:** 2009
SALES (est): 196.2K **Privately Held**
SIC: 3999 Manufacturing industries

(G-13626)
SEQUA CORPORATION (DH)
Also Called: Kollsman Instrument Division
3999 Rca Blvd (33410-4219)
PHONE.................................561 935-3571
Armand F Lauzon, *CEO*
Martin Weinstein, *CEO*
Gerard M Dombek, *President*
Carlo Luzzatto, *President*
Kathleen Peskens, *President*
◆ **EMP:** 1234 **EST:** 1929
SQ FT: 45,000
SALES (est): 2B
SALES (corp-wide): 2.9B **Publicly Held**
WEB: www.sequa.com
SIC: 3764 3812 3699 3845 Guided missile & space vehicle propulsion unit parts; rocket motors, guided missiles; propulsion units for guided missiles & space vehicles; search & navigation equipment; infrared object detection equipment; missile guidance systems & equipment; aircraft flight instruments; flight simulators (training aids), electronic; electromedical apparatus; automated blood & body fluid analyzers, except laboratory; metal container making machines: cans, etc.; airfoils, aircraft engine
HQ: The Carlyle Group Inc
1001 Pennsylvania Ave Nw 220s
Washington DC 20004
202 729-5626

(G-13627)
SERVICE INDUSTRY CONSULTANT
9123 N Military Trl # 216 (33410-5990)
PHONE.................................561 775-4782
Charles Sollins, *Manager*
EMP: 6 **EST:** 2018
SALES (est): 165.2K **Privately Held**
WEB: www.tsiconsultant.com
SIC: 3999 Manufacturing industries

(G-13628)
SHUTTER2THINK INC
1014 Raintree Ln (33410-5200)
PHONE.................................850 291-8301
Chester I Miller, *Principal*
EMP: 8 **EST:** 2007
SALES (est): 85.3K **Privately Held**
SIC: 3442 Shutters, door or window: metal

(G-13629)
STAREWELL PUBLISHING LLC
200 Bent Tree Dr (33418-3401)
PHONE.................................561 694-0365
David Sidney Kahn, *Principal*
EMP: 6 **EST:** 2015
SALES (est): 132.6K **Privately Held**
SIC: 2741 Miscellaneous publishing

(G-13630)
SWEET ADDITIONS LLC (PA)
4440 Pga Blvd Ste 600 (33410-6542)
PHONE.................................561 472-0178
Carla Davis, *Marketing Mgr*
Kenneth Valdivia, *Mng Member*
EMP: 19 **EST:** 2012
SALES (est): 8.8MM **Privately Held**
WEB: www.sweetadditions.com
SIC: 2099 Food preparations

(G-13631)
TECHDERM LLC
220 Legendary Cir (33418-8485)
PHONE.................................407 795-1517
Richard Johnson, *Chairman*
EMP: 6 **EST:** 2014
SALES (est): 97.8K **Privately Held**
SIC: 3841 7371 Surgical & medical instruments; computer software development & applications

(G-13632)
TITANIUM INTEGRATION LLC
11211 Prosperity Farms Rd (33410-3446)
PHONE.................................561 775-1898
Robert C Vogel, *Manager*
EMP: 6 **EST:** 2010
SALES (est): 1.1MM **Privately Held**
WEB: www.robertvogeldds.com
SIC: 3356 Titanium

(G-13633)
UNIVERSAL BRASS FABRICATION
109 Palm Point Cir (33418-4636)
PHONE.................................561 691-5445
EMP: 10
SALES (est): 989K **Privately Held**
SIC: 2342 Mfg Bras/Girdles

(G-13634)
WATERJET ROBOTICS USA LLC
86 Cayman Pl (33418-8096)
PHONE.................................772 403-2192
EMP: 8
SALES (est): 809.9K **Privately Held**
SIC: 3549 Metalworking Machinery, Nec

(G-13635)
WELDING ANYTHING ANYWHERE LLC
6231 Pga Blvd (33418-4033)
PHONE.................................561 762-1404
Dalton Wiita, *Principal*
EMP: 5 **EST:** 2014
SALES (est): 402.9K **Privately Held**
WEB: www.palmbeachmobilewelding.com
SIC: 7692 Welding repair

(G-13636)
YARD HOUSE HALLANDALE BCH LLC
11701 Lk Vctr Grdn Ave (33410-2706)
PHONE.................................561 691-6901
Harold Herrmann, *Owner*
EMP: 7 **EST:** 2011
SALES (est): 295K **Privately Held**
SIC: 2599 Bar, restaurant & cafeteria furniture

(G-13637)
ZIMMER DENTAL INC
4555 Riverside Dr (33410-4200)
PHONE.................................561 776-6700
Rachel Ellingson, *Vice Pres*
David Kunz, *Vice Pres*
Ivor Reid, *Engineer*
Jonathan Gold, *Finance Dir*
Kristin Cummings, *Sales Staff*
EMP: 76 **EST:** 1990
SALES (est): 13.2MM
SALES (corp-wide): 7B **Publicly Held**
WEB: www.zimmerbiomet.com
SIC: 3842 Orthopedic appliances
PA: Zimmer Biomet Holdings, Inc.
345 E Main St
Warsaw IN 46580
574 267-6131

(G-13638)
ZOAG LLC
102 Alegria Way (33418-1722)
PHONE.................................862 591-2969
Zoltan Hetzer, *Mng Member*
▲ **EMP:** 8 **EST:** 2013
SALES (est): 312.2K **Privately Held**
SIC: 3965 Fasteners, buttons, needles & pins

Palm City
Martin County

(G-13639)
AIR BURNERS INC
4390 Sw Cargo Way (34990-5577)
PHONE.................................772 220-7303
Brian O'Connor, *President*
Michael Schmitt, *Sales Mgr*
EMP: 12 **EST:** 2011
SALES (est): 1.9MM **Privately Held**
WEB: www.airburners.com
SIC: 3567 Industrial furnaces & ovens

(G-13640)
AIR BURNERS LLC
4390 Sw Cargo Way (34990-5577)
PHONE.................................772 220-7303
Michael Schmitt, *Sales Mgr*
Brian O'Connor, *Mng Member*
Gary Ford,
◆ **EMP:** 30 **EST:** 2001
SALES (est): 5.3MM **Privately Held**
WEB: www.airburners.com
SIC: 3567 Incinerators, metal: domestic or commercial

(G-13641)
AQUA PULSAR LLC
Also Called: Clear Water Plasma
3275 Sw 42nd Ave (34990-5540)
PHONE.................................772 320-9691
EMP: 7 **EST:** 2017
SALES (est): 249.2K **Privately Held**
WEB: www.clearwaterplasma.com
SIC: 2836 Plasmas

(G-13642)
AWARENESS TECHNOLOGY INC (PA)
2325 Sw Martin Hwy (34990-3222)
P.O. Box 1679 (34991-6679)
PHONE.................................772 283-6540
Mary Freeman, *CEO*
Gary S Freeman, *Admin Sec*
EMP: 104 **EST:** 1982
SQ FT: 50,000
SALES (est): 13.8MM **Privately Held**
WEB: www.awaretech.com
SIC: 3826 2869 Analytical instruments; laboratory chemicals, organic

(G-13643)
B4C TECHNOLOGIES INC
4306 Sw Cargo Way (34990-5577)
PHONE.................................772 463-1557
Kenneth Hoffman, *CEO*
Ed McComas, *Chairman*
EMP: 6 **EST:** 2010
SQ FT: 10,000
SALES (est): 410K **Privately Held**
WEB: www.b4ctechnologies.com
SIC: 3471 Electroplating of metals or formed products

(G-13644)
CAMERON TEXTILES INC
Also Called: Aresco Manufacturing & Safety
2740 Sw Martin Downs Blvd (34990-6046)
PHONE.................................954 454-6482
Darby Cameron, *President*
Michael Cameron, *Vice Pres*
▲ **EMP:** 9
SQ FT: 6,000
SALES (est): 1MM **Privately Held**
SIC: 2393 2326 2311 2392 Canvas bags; aprons, work, except rubberized & plastic: men's; vests: made from purchased materials; bags, laundry: made from purchased materials; personal safety equipment; industrial safety devices: first aid kits & masks

(G-13645)
CERAMLOCK COATINGS INC
3912 Sw Bruner Ter (34990-5549)
PHONE.................................772 781-2141
Doug Byron, *Principal*
▼ **EMP:** 9 **EST:** 2010
SALES (est): 731.4K **Privately Held**
WEB: www.ceramlock.com
SIC: 3399 Powder, metal

(G-13646)
CHEMPLEX INDUSTRIES INC
2820 Sw 42nd Ave (34990-5573)
PHONE.................................772 283-2700
Monte J Solazzi, *President*
EMP: 12 **EST:** 1971
SQ FT: 22,000
SALES (est): 2MM **Privately Held**
WEB: www.chemplex.com
SIC: 3826 Spectroscopic & other optical properties measuring equipment

(G-13647)
CHITTUM YACHTS LLC (PA)
4577 Sw Cargo Way (34990-5521)
PHONE..................................386 589-7224
Harold Thomas Chittum III,
George Sawley,
EMP: 12 **EST:** 2010
SALES (est): 2.6MM **Privately Held**
SIC: 3732 Yachts, building & repairing

(G-13648)
COASTAL POWDER COATINGS INC
2049 Sw Poma Dr (34990-6602)
PHONE..................................772 283-5311
Frank Poma, *President*
Jason Poma, *Vice Pres*
Kimberly Poma, *Controller*
EMP: 9 **EST:** 2008
SALES (est): 1.1MM **Privately Held**
WEB: www.coastalpowder.com
SIC: 3479 Coating of metals & formed products

(G-13649)
CORE LABEL LLC
4313 Sw Port Way (34990-5584)
PHONE..................................772 287-2141
EMP: 27
SALES (corp-wide): 584.5MM **Privately Held**
SIC: 2759 Commercial printing
HQ: Core Label, Llc
13985 S Eagle Valley Rd
Tyrone PA 16686
814 684-0934

(G-13650)
CUSTOM AGRONOMICS INC
2300 Sw Poma Dr (34990-6611)
PHONE..................................772 223-0775
Michael F Ciferri Sr, *President*
Mike Ciferi, *President*
Brian Scott, *Vice Pres*
Michael Williams, *Vice Pres*
Bryan Scott, *Purchasing*
◆ **EMP:** 10 **EST:** 2009
SQ FT: 20,000
SALES (est): 4.3MM **Privately Held**
WEB: www.customagronomics.com
SIC: 2879 Agricultural chemicals

(G-13651)
EAGLE I TECH INC
Also Called: Florida Rs Technology
4529 Sw Cargo Way (34990-5521)
PHONE..................................772 221-8188
Al Ragl, *President*
Mike Trivison, *Business Mgr*
Tim Spacek, *Vice Pres*
Ken Peters, *Opers Staff*
Valerie Selfe, *Buyer*
◆ **EMP:** 47 **EST:** 1993
SALES (est): 9.7MM **Privately Held**
WEB: www.flrst.com
SIC: 3678 Electronic connectors

(G-13652)
ELECTRON BEAM DEVELOPMENT
3591 Sw Deggeller Ct (34990-5548)
PHONE..................................772 219-4600
James S Bickel, *President*
Edward L Bancroft, *Corp Secy*
EMP: 17 **EST:** 1976
SQ FT: 10,000
SALES (est): 396.5K **Privately Held**
SIC: 7692 Welding repair

(G-13653)
EZ BOATWORKS INC
10602 Sw Corey Pl (34990-7801)
PHONE..................................772 475-8721
Garcia Ester, *Principal*
EMP: 8 **EST:** 2014
SALES (est): 155.6K **Privately Held**
SIC: 3732 Boat building & repairing

(G-13654)
FATOVICH TECHNOLOGIES LLC
2159 Sw Cameron Ln (34990-6225)
PHONE..................................772 597-1326
Bronco Fatovich, *Mng Member*
Kathleen M Fatovich, *Mng Member*
EMP: 7 **EST:** 2008
SALES (est): 530K **Privately Held**
WEB: www.fatovichtechnologies.com
SIC: 2822 Ethylene-propylene rubbers, EPDM polymers

(G-13655)
FIVE OCEANS FLORIDA INC
Also Called: Florida Rs Technology
4529 Sw Cargo Way (34990-5521)
PHONE..................................772 221-8188
Chester Claudon, *President*
Ken Peters, *Opers Staff*
Valerie Selfe, *Purch Mgr*
Raul Castro, *Engineer*
EMP: 34 **EST:** 2016
SALES (est): 3.1MM **Privately Held**
WEB: www.flrst.com
SIC: 3643 Current-carrying wiring devices

(G-13656)
FLORIDA CYPRESS & FENCE CO
3922 Sw Saint Lucie Ln (34990-3826)
PHONE..................................561 392-3011
▼ **EMP:** 8
SQ FT: 8,000
SALES (est): 944.3K **Privately Held**
SIC: 2499 5031 Mfg Wood Products Whol Lumber/Plywood/Millwork

(G-13657)
FLORIDA POLE SETTLERS & CRANE
4157 Sw Moore St (34990-5650)
PHONE..................................772 283-6820
Kenneth A Wieser, *President*
EMP: 9 **EST:** 2006
SQ FT: 3,322
SALES (est): 402.6K **Privately Held**
WEB: www.floridapolesetters.com
SIC: 2411 Pole cutting contractors

(G-13658)
GEN-PRODICS INC
2029 Sw Oak Ridge Rd (34990-2156)
PHONE..................................772 221-8464
EMP: 5
SALES (est): 515.9K **Privately Held**
SIC: 3674 Mfg Semiconductors/Related Devices

(G-13659)
GMS SHEET METAL INC
3377 Sw 42nd Ave Ste D (34990-5595)
PHONE..................................772 221-0585
Michael Mazzilli, *Principal*
EMP: 14 **EST:** 2012
SALES (est): 2.5MM **Privately Held**
SIC: 3444 Sheet metalwork

(G-13660)
GREEN GAS AMERICA INC (PA)
2740 Sw Martin Downs Blvd (34990-6046)
PHONE..................................772 220-0717
Duncan Cox, *President*
EMP: 70 **EST:** 1998
SALES (est): 2.9MM **Privately Held**
SIC: 1382 Oil & gas exploration services

(G-13661)
GUERILLA TECHNOLOGIES INC
4203 Sw High Meadows Ave (34990-3726)
PHONE..................................772 283-0500
Camille M Parrott, *CEO*
Robert A Parrott IV, *President*
Bill Bradshaw, *VP Sales*
Sal Terranova, *Sales Staff*
Erin Haithcox, *Sales Executive*
EMP: 10 **EST:** 2004
SQ FT: 2,600
SALES (est): 764.5K **Privately Held**
WEB: www.guerillatechnologies.com
SIC: 3699 Electrical equipment & supplies

(G-13662)
H I T LIGHTING CORP
3399 Sw 42nd Ave (34990-5554)
P.O. Box 1199 (34991-1199)
PHONE..................................772 221-1155
Donald Cantor, *President*
EMP: 8 **EST:** 1992
SALES (est): 1MM **Privately Held**
SIC: 3646 Commercial indusl & institutional electric lighting fixtures

(G-13663)
KAZDIN INDUSTRIES INC
5258 Sw Anhinga Ave (34990-4043)
P.O. Box 2472 (34991-2472)
PHONE..................................772 223-5511
Richard H Kazdin, *President*
Sharon J Kazdin, *Vice Pres*
EMP: 7 **EST:** 2007
SALES (est): 99.5K **Privately Held**
SIC: 3554 Paper industries machinery

(G-13664)
KRUNCHY KRISPS LLC
2740 Sw Martin Downs Blvd (34990-6046)
PHONE..................................561 309-7049
EMP: 5
SALES: 500K **Privately Held**
SIC: 2038 Mfg Frozen Specialties

(G-13665)
L & S DESIGN & CONSTRUCTION
3561 Sw Corporate Pkwy (34990-8152)
PHONE..................................772 220-1745
Jeff Seyler, *President*
EMP: 6 **EST:** 1996
SALES (est): 456.7K **Privately Held**
SIC: 3732 Boat building & repairing

(G-13666)
MATAWAN TOOL & MFG CO INC
2861 Sw Brighton Way (34990-6075)
PHONE..................................772 221-3706
EMP: 5 **EST:** 1946
SQ FT: 5,000
SALES (est): 350K **Privately Held**
SIC: 3599 Jobbing Machine Shop

(G-13667)
NATIVE WELDING
3371 Sw 42nd Ave Ste D (34990-5593)
PHONE..................................561 348-0100
Michael A Davis, *Owner*
EMP: 7 **EST:** 2014
SALES (est): 335.5K **Privately Held**
WEB: www.nativewelding.net
SIC: 7692 Welding repair

(G-13668)
OUTSTANDING EVENTS INC
5380 Sw Landing Creek Dr (34990-4125)
PHONE..................................772 463-5406
Eve M Thompson, *Director*
EMP: 11 **EST:** 2001
SALES (est): 768.5K **Privately Held**
WEB: www.outstandingevents.com
SIC: 3411 Food & beverage containers

(G-13669)
PAC SEATING SYSTEMS INC
3370 Sw 42nd Ave (34990-5541)
PHONE..................................772 286-6670
Charles Tufano, *President*
Hector Marini, *Vice Pres*
Andrew Pearl, *Vice Pres*
Alyssa Eidson, *Purchasing*
Mohammad Sallam, *Design Engr*
EMP: 90
SALES (est): 20.7MM **Privately Held**
WEB: www.pac-fl.com
SIC: 3499 Furniture parts, metal

(G-13670)
PARADISE AIR FRESH LLC
3029 Sw 42nd Ave (34990-5556)
PHONE..................................561 972-0375
Bradley Simons, *Vice Pres*
Ryan Simon, *Mng Member*
EMP: 14 **EST:** 2017
SALES (est): 1.9MM **Privately Held**
WEB: www.paradiseairfresh.com
SIC: 2842 Sanitation preparations, disinfectants & deodorants

(G-13671)
PIONEER SCREEN INC
2740 Sw Martin Downs Blvd (34990-6046)
PHONE..................................772 260-3068
Craig Davis Rice, *Principal*
EMP: 8 **EST:** 2009
SALES (est): 136.1K **Privately Held**
SIC: 3442 Screen & storm doors & windows

(G-13672)
RUSSANOS EXPRESS LLC
2946 Sw Mapp Rd (34990-2724)
PHONE..................................772 220-3329
Frank Romano, *Owner*
EMP: 9 **EST:** 2006
SALES (est): 528.9K **Privately Held**
SIC: 2741 Miscellaneous publishing

(G-13673)
SHURHOLD PRODUCTS COMPANY
3119 Sw 42nd Ave (34990-5558)
PHONE..................................772 287-1313
Barry Burhoff, *President*
Brett Berhoff, *Vice Pres*
Lloyd Berhoff, *Vice Pres*
Nicole Veldhius, *Relations*
▲ **EMP:** 9 **EST:** 1972
SQ FT: 9,660
SALES (est): 1.5MM **Privately Held**
WEB: www.shurhold.com
SIC: 3991 3732 2298 Brushes, household or industrial; boat building & repairing; cordage & twine

(G-13674)
SPECTOR MANUFACTURING INC
22 Sw Riverway Blvd (34990-4238)
PHONE..................................860 559-6068
EMP: 8 **EST:** 2017
SALES (est): 96K **Privately Held**
WEB: www.spectec.biz
SIC: 3999 Manufacturing industries

(G-13675)
TENDONEASE LLC
1738 Sw Foxpoint Trl (34990-5726)
PHONE..................................888 224-0319
EMP: 5 **EST:** 2007
SALES (est): 340K **Privately Held**
SIC: 3842 3949 Mfg Surgical Appliances/Supplies Mfg Sporting/Athletic Goods

(G-13676)
TREASURE CST CURB & THERM PLAS
2580 Sw Hidden Pond Way (34990-2053)
PHONE..................................772 287-0391
Mary Bailey, *President*
EMP: 6 **EST:** 1996
SALES (est): 453.3K **Privately Held**
SIC: 3272 Concrete products, precast

(G-13677)
UCT COATINGS INC (PA)
Also Called: Uct Defense
3300 Sw 42nd Ave (34990-5539)
PHONE..................................772 872-7110
Don Weeks, *CEO*
Tim Donahue, *Chairman*
John S Bourret, *Vice Pres*
Scott Bourret, *Vice Pres*
Lou D'Ambrosio, *Vice Pres*
▲ **EMP:** 18 **EST:** 2000
SQ FT: 24,000
SALES: 13.1MM **Privately Held**
WEB: www.uctcoatings.com
SIC: 3479 Coating of metals & formed products

(G-13678)
W KOST INC
4175 Sw Martin Hwy (34990-5524)
PHONE..................................772 286-3700
Walter G Kost, *CEO*
Chris Kost, *President*
Christopher J Kost, *Principal*
▼ **EMP:** 46 **EST:** 1980
SQ FT: 16,000
SALES (est): 2.7MM **Privately Held**
SIC: 2439 Trusses, wooden roof

Palm Coast
Flagler County

(G-13679)
5THELEMENT INDIAN CUISINE LLC
101 Palm Harbor Pkwy (32137-8004)
PHONE..................................386 302-0202
Jerry Martinho Fernandes,
EMP: 7 **EST:** 2017
SALES (est): 2.7MM **Privately Held**
WEB: www.flaglerrestaurants.com
SIC: 2819 Elements

(G-13680)
ACE TOOLS
17 Lee Dr (32137-9700)
PHONE..................................386 302-5152
Mark Grillo, *Principal*
EMP: 9 **EST:** 2016
SALES (est): 479.7K **Privately Held**
WEB: www.acetools.com
SIC: 3599 Industrial machinery

(G-13681)
AIR SUPPORT TECKS
14 Bird Haven Pl (32137-9318)
PHONE..................................386 986-5301
Jillian S Burns, *Principal*
EMP: 6 **EST:** 2009
SALES (est): 75.3K **Privately Held**
SIC: 3721 Aircraft

(G-13682)
AIRRENU LLC
6 Poinette Pl (32164-6767)
PHONE..................................386 246-8694
Vincent Valles, *Principal*
EMP: 6 **EST:** 2012
SALES (est): 148.3K **Privately Held**
WEB: www.air-renu.com
SIC: 2844 Cosmetic preparations

(G-13683)
ALTIUM PACKAGING LLC
71 Hargrove Grade (32137-5114)
PHONE..................................386 246-4000
Danny Lafferman, *Branch Mgr*
EMP: 19
SALES (corp-wide): 12.5B **Publicly Held**
WEB: www.altiumpkg.com
SIC: 3089 Plastic containers, except foam
HQ: Altium Packaging Llc
2500 Windy Ridge Pkwy Se # 1400
Atlanta GA 30339
678 742-4600

(G-13684)
AVEOENGINEERING LLC
Also Called: Aveotech International
1200 Cinnamon Beach Way # 1122
(32137-5328)
PHONE..................................631 747-6671
Christian Nielsen, *CEO*
Jana Nielsen, *General Mgr*
Michal Gregor, *Supervisor*
EMP: 7 **EST:** 2010
SALES (est): 970.9K **Privately Held**
WEB: www.aveoengineering.com
SIC: 3728 Research & dev by manuf., aircraft parts & auxiliary equip

(G-13685)
AVRORA INC
7 Richfield Pl (32164-6518)
PHONE..................................386 246-9112
Andrei Zborovsky, *President*
EMP: 6 **EST:** 2005
SALES (est): 379.1K **Privately Held**
WEB: www.avrorainc.com
SIC: 2511 Wood household furniture

(G-13686)
BODY MANUFACTUR E INC
4982 Palm Coast Pkwy Nw (32137-3638)
PHONE..................................386 264-6040
EMP: 8 **EST:** 2019
SALES (est): 219.1K **Privately Held**
SIC: 3999 Manufacturing industries

(G-13687)
CLASS A PRINTING LLC
11 Industry Dr (32137-5104)
PHONE..................................386 447-0520
Christina Rice, *President*
EMP: 5 **EST:** 1997
SQ FT: 1,258
SALES (est): 706.3K **Privately Held**
WEB: www.classaprinting.com
SIC: 2752 Commercial printing, offset

(G-13688)
COMISKEY INDUSTRIES INC
18 Eastlake Dr (32137-1520)
PHONE..................................201 925-0998
Jeremy Cox, *Principal*
EMP: 7 **EST:** 2016
SALES (est): 96K **Privately Held**
WEB: www.comiskey.com
SIC: 3999 Manufacturing industries

(G-13689)
CONC-STEEL INC
250 Palm Coast Pkwy Ne (32137-8224)
PHONE..................................516 882-5551
John S Koszalkowski, *Principal*
EMP: 6 **EST:** 2018
SALES (est): 386.2K **Privately Held**
WEB: www.conc-steel.com
SIC: 3312 Blast furnaces & steel mills

(G-13690)
CREATIONS IN CABINETRY INC
2 Market Pl (32137-5107)
PHONE..................................386 237-3082
Robert Baez, *Principal*
EMP: 7 **EST:** 2008
SALES (est): 138.1K **Privately Held**
WEB: www.cabinetrycreationsinc.com
SIC: 2434 Wood kitchen cabinets

(G-13691)
DIMPLE PRODUCTS INC
7 Clear Ct (32137-9047)
PHONE..................................704 320-0700
Richard Jodoin, *President*
EMP: 7 **EST:** 2015
SALES (est): 458K **Privately Held**
WEB: www.drainplugmagnets.com
SIC: 3714 Motor vehicle parts & accessories

(G-13692)
DYNAMIC ENGRG INNOVATIONS INC
32 Hargrove Grade (32137-5101)
P.O. Box 352919 (32135-2919)
PHONE..................................386 445-6000
Robert Stockman, *President*
Richard Stockman, *Vice Pres*
Erica Zevallos, *Marketing Staff*
▲ **EMP:** 211 **EST:** 1939
SQ FT: 48,000
SALES (est): 21.6MM **Privately Held**
WEB: www.amradmanufacturing.com
SIC: 3675 Electronic capacitors

(G-13693)
FINETEST INC (PA)
1 Industry Dr Ste C (32137-5104)
PHONE..................................386 569-6189
Moise N Hamaoui, *President*
Nessim Hamoui, *Vice Pres*
EMP: 6 **EST:** 1989
SQ FT: 5,000
SALES (est): 2MM **Privately Held**
WEB: www.finetest.com
SIC: 3825 Test equipment for electronic & electric measurement

(G-13694)
FLIGHT VELOCITY
279 Old Moody Blvd (32164-2470)
PHONE..................................866 937-9371
EMP: 7 **EST:** 2017
SALES (est): 1MM **Privately Held**
WEB: www.flightvelocity.com
SIC: 3728 Aircraft parts & equipment

(G-13695)
FRANK THE KIT EXPRT PALM COAST
28 Farmbrook Ln (32137-8210)
PHONE..................................386 264-6105
EMP: 6 **EST:** 2016
SALES (est): 87K **Privately Held**
WEB: www.palmcoastobserver.com
SIC: 2711 Newspapers, publishing & printing

(G-13696)
G&G QUALITY SERVICES INC
72 Wynnfield Dr (32164-4227)
PHONE..................................386 566-0309
Gabor Varadi, *President*
EMP: 7 **EST:** 2013
SALES (est): 106.8K **Privately Held**
SIC: 2434 Wood kitchen cabinets

(G-13697)
GALTRONICS TELEMETRY INC
1 Hargrove Grade Ste 5 (32137-5159)
P.O. Box 803338, Chicago IL (60680-3338)
PHONE..................................386 202-2055
Graydon Parsons, *President*
Michael Lafferty, *Vice Pres*
Sean Lafferty, *Vice Pres*
EMP: 10 **EST:** 2009
SQ FT: 4,000
SALES (est): 801.9K **Privately Held**
WEB: www.galtronics.com
SIC: 3822 Auto controls regulating residntl & coml environmt & applncs

(G-13698)
GIOIA SAILS SOUTH LLC
14 Commerce Blvd (32164-3126)
P.O. Box 352918 (32135-2918)
PHONE..................................386 597-2876
Donald T Gioia, *Mng Member*
EMP: 55 **EST:** 2007
SALES (est): 9.1MM
SALES (corp-wide): 24.2MM **Privately Held**
WEB: www.gioiasailssouth.com
SIC: 2394 Canvas & related products
PA: Gioia Sails, Inc.
1951 Rutgers Blvd
Lakewood NJ 08701
732 901-6770

(G-13699)
INTERNATIONAL TOOL MCHS OF FLA
Also Called: ITM
5 Industry Dr (32137-5104)
PHONE..................................386 446-0500
Karl H Giebmanns, *President*
Karl Giebmanns, *Chief Engr*
Jennifr Sager, *Med Doctor*
Brandon Hornick, *Prgrmr*
Peter Chenson, *Director*
▲ **EMP:** 32 **EST:** 1981
SQ FT: 25,000
SALES (est): 4.4MM **Privately Held**
WEB: www.floridagrinding.com
SIC: 3541 Machine tool replacement & repair parts, metal cutting types

(G-13700)
KEITH EICKERT POWER PDTS LLC
11 Industry Dr (32137-5108)
PHONE..................................386 446-0660
Julian Sullivan, *President*
Juliana L Sullivan,
EMP: 10 **EST:** 1990
SQ FT: 10,000
SALES (est): 2MM **Privately Held**
WEB: www.hardin-marine.com
SIC: 3519 5088 Marine engines; marine crafts & supplies

(G-13701)
LIDIAS EMBROIDERY
29 Old Kings Rd N Ste 1a (32137-8232)
PHONE..................................386 447-2293
Lidia Bastos, *President*
EMP: 6 **EST:** 2013
SALES (est): 147.1K **Privately Held**
WEB: www.lidiasembroidery.com
SIC: 2395 Embroidery products, except schiffli machine; embroidery & art needlework

(G-13702)
MANAGED DATA ASSOC INC
Also Called: Custom Cable Crafters
12 Walla Pl (32164-7667)
PHONE..................................386 449-8419
Donna Shadron, *President*
EMP: 6 **EST:** 2017
SALES (est): 362.1K **Privately Held**
WEB: www.mdacables.com
SIC: 3357 5063 Fiber optic cable (insulated); telephone & telegraph wire & cable

(G-13703)
MCKINNA CORPORATION
Also Called: McKinna Yachts
17 S Waterview Dr (32137-1624)
PHONE..................................386 446-8822
Robert Million, *President*
Carolyn Million, *Vice Pres*
◆ **EMP:** 5 **EST:** 1994
SQ FT: 25,000
SALES (est): 391.8K **Privately Held**
SIC: 3732 Yachts, building & repairing

(G-13704)
NEWS-JOURNAL CORPORATION
4984 Palm Coast Pkwy Nw # 5
(32137-3620)
PHONE..................................386 283-5664
EMP: 18
SALES (corp-wide): 68.8MM **Privately Held**
WEB: www.news-journalonline.com
SIC: 2711 Newspapers, publishing & printing
PA: News-Journal Corporation
901 6th St
Daytona Beach FL 32117
386 252-1511

(G-13705)
PALM COAST CRUSH 2
135 London Dr (32137-9760)
PHONE..................................386 447-2768
Joseph Colasanti, *Principal*
EMP: 6 **EST:** 2015
SALES (est): 62.3K **Privately Held**
WEB: www.palmcoastobserver.com
SIC: 2084 Wines, brandy & brandy spirits

(G-13706)
PALM COAST OBSERVER LLC
1 Florida Park Dr N # 104 (32137-3843)
P.O. Box 353850 (32135-3850)
PHONE..................................386 447-9723
Jonathan Simmons, *Editor*
Susan Moore, *Accounts Mgr*
Brian McMillan, *Adv Mgr*
Bonnie Hamilton, *Office Mgr*
Matthew G Walsh,
EMP: 22 **EST:** 2010
SALES (est): 2.9MM **Privately Held**
WEB: www.palmcoastobserver.com
SIC: 2711 Newspapers, publishing & printing

(G-13707)
R & C SALES & MFG INC
18 Hargrove Grade Ste 101 (32137-5161)
PHONE..................................904 824-2223
Robert Atkins, *President*
Carol Atkins, *Corp Secy*
EMP: 14 **EST:** 1978
SALES (est): 1MM **Privately Held**
SIC: 3523 Farm machinery & equipment

(G-13708)
SDM INDUSTRIES INC
13 Hargrove Grade (32137-5114)
PHONE..................................904 814-2814
Shawn D Moksnes, *Principal*
EMP: 9 **EST:** 2012
SALES (est): 401.3K **Privately Held**
SIC: 3999 Manufacturing industries

(G-13709)
SKD SMOOTHIE INC
1 Watermill Pl (32164-7645)
PHONE..................................386 931-4953
Christine Kraus, *Principal*
EMP: 6 **EST:** 2014
SALES (est): 140K **Privately Held**
SIC: 2037 Frozen fruits & vegetables

(G-13710)
SMART GUARD SHUTTERS LLC
79 Pritchard Dr (32164-7184)
PHONE..................................386 227-6295
EMP: 8 **EST:** 2018
SALES (est): 1.3MM **Privately Held**
WEB: www.smartguardshutters.com
SIC: 3442 Shutters, door or window: metal

(G-13711)
SUNRISE
26 N Village Dr (32137-1603)
PHONE..................................386 627-5029
Sonya Romero, *Principal*
EMP: 6 **EST:** 2015
SALES (est): 72.4K **Privately Held**
WEB: www.sunrisesunset.com
SIC: 2591 Window blinds

(G-13712)
SWEETSIES
26 Ullman Pl (32164-5906)
P.O. Box 731764, Ormond Beach (32173-1764)
PHONE..................................386 566-6762
Amber Hadley, *Principal*
EMP: 8
SALES (est): 421.2K **Privately Held**
SIC: 2051 Cakes, bakery: except frozen

(G-13713)
TOTAL PERFORMANCE INC
Also Called: Cool Flex
75 N Lakewalk Dr (32137-1302)
PHONE..................................203 265-5667
Michael V Lauria, *President*
Brian Mc Allister, *Sales Mgr*
EMP: 9 **EST:** 1971
SQ FT: 7,500
SALES (est): 269.3K **Privately Held**
SIC: 3711 3714 3592 5531 Motor vehicles & car bodies; motor vehicle parts & accessories; carburetors; automotive parts; automotive supplies & parts

(G-13714)
VLADMIR LTD
Also Called: Amrad
32 Hargrove Grade (32137-5101)
PHONE..................................386 445-6000
EMP: 25
SALES (corp-wide): 19.8MM **Privately Held**
WEB: www.globalthesource.com
SIC: 3675 Electronic capacitors
PA: Vladmir, Ltd.
1648 N Lake Pass
Universal City TX 78148
800 531-5967

Palm Harbor
Pinellas County

(G-13715)
3LIONS PUBLISHING INC
3958 Talah Dr (34684-2457)
PHONE..................................727 744-8683
Carlos A Leyva, *Principal*
EMP: 6 **EST:** 2018
SALES (est): 59.2K **Privately Held**
WEB: www.digitalbusinesslawgroup.com
SIC: 2741 Miscellaneous publishing

(G-13716)
ACCENT NEON & SIGN COMPANY (PA)
1179 Ridgecrest Ct (34683-2732)
PHONE..................................727 784-8414
Todd Ritchey, *Owner*
EMP: 5 **EST:** 1984
SALES (est): 411K **Privately Held**
WEB: www.accentneon.com
SIC: 3993 1799 5046 Neon signs; sign installation & maintenance; neon signs

(G-13717)
ALH SYSTEMS INC
1862 Eagle Ridge Blvd (34685-3302)
PHONE..................................727 787-6306
EMP: 9
SQ FT: 3,750
SALES: 1.4MM **Privately Held**
SIC: 3549 Assembly Of Machines Specializing In Flight Training Equipment And Flight Simulators

(G-13718)
AMERCN CABINETS GRANITE FLOORS
32140 Us Highway 19 N (34684-3709)
PHONE..................................727 303-0678
EMP: 11 **EST:** 2018
SALES (est): 715.9K **Privately Held**
WEB: www.americancgf.com
SIC: 2541 2434 3996 Counter & sink tops; wood kitchen cabinets; hard surface floor coverings

(G-13719)
ANTIQUE AUTOMOBILE RADIO INC
700 Tampa Rd (34683-5454)
PHONE..................................727 785-8733
Daniel Schulz, *President*
Daisy Schulz, *General Mgr*
Matt Simanteris, *Production*
EMP: 6 **EST:** 1993
SQ FT: 5,604
SALES (est): 477.5K **Privately Held**
WEB: www.radiosforoldcars.com
SIC: 3663 Radio receiver networks

(G-13720)
ASSET GUARDIAN INC
2706 Alt 19 Ste 254 (34683-2655)
PHONE..................................727 942-2246
Wade B Moss, *Principal*
EMP: 7 **EST:** 2010
SALES (est): 440.2K **Privately Held**
WEB: www.polygraphtampabay.com
SIC: 3829 Polygraph devices

(G-13721)
AVERY DENNISON CORPORATION
720 Sandy Hook Rd (34683-3734)
PHONE..................................727 787-1651
EMP: 118
SALES (corp-wide): 6.9B **Publicly Held**
SIC: 2672 Paper; Coated And Laminated, Nec
PA: Avery Dennison Corporation
207 N Goode Ave
Glendale CA 91203
626 304-2000

(G-13722)
AVERY DENNISON CORPORATION
2706 Altmate 19 N Ste 314 (34683)
PHONE..................................727 785-6995
EMP: 115
SALES (corp-wide): 6.3B **Publicly Held**
SIC: 2672 Mfg Coated/Laminated Paper
PA: Avery Dennison Corporation
207 N Goode Ave Fl 6
Glendale CA 91203
626 304-2000

(G-13723)
BAY AREA SECURITY SHRED
Also Called: Secure On-Site Shredding
301 Bear Ridge Cir (34683-5483)
P.O. Box 357, Dunedin (34697-0357)
PHONE..................................877 974-7337
Gloria Schmeider, *President*
John D Schmeider, *Vice Pres*
John Schmeider, *Vice Pres*
EMP: 10 **EST:** 1994
SQ FT: 2,000
SALES (est): 985.7K **Privately Held**
SIC: 3589 7389 Shredders, industrial & commercial; document & office record destruction

(G-13724)
BEAST ROW INC
Also Called: Mixers Bar & Grille
3430 E Lake Rd Ste 1 (34685-2414)
PHONE..................................727 787-2710
Nancy A Dattilo, *Principal*
EMP: 7 **EST:** 2009
SALES (est): 160.1K **Privately Held**
SIC: 2599 Bar, restaurant & cafeteria furniture

(G-13725)
BECK GRAPHICS INC
1114 Florida Ave Ste B (34683-4331)
PHONE..................................727 443-3803
John D Beck, *President*
Paul Beck, *Treasurer*
EMP: 26 **EST:** 1985
SQ FT: 3,000
SALES (est): 636.2K **Privately Held**
SIC: 2752 Commercial printing, offset

(G-13726)
CAVOK CAPITAL LLC
855 Virginia Ave (34683-5227)
PHONE..................................727 789-0951
Todd Dolphin, *Mng Member*
EMP: 16 **EST:** 2019
SALES (est): 1MM **Privately Held**
SIC: 3999 1731 Manufacturing industries; electric power systems contractors

(G-13727)
CELLMIC LLC
34266 Us Highway 19 N (34684-2147)
PHONE..................................310 443-2070
Neven Karlovac, *CEO*
EMP: 6 **EST:** 2011
SALES (est): 407.1K **Privately Held**
SIC: 3826 Analytical instruments

(G-13728)
CHATTAM INDUSTRIES INC
36181 E Lake Rd Ste 144 (34685-3142)
PHONE..................................727 748-2419
Rebecca Russo, *Vice Pres*
EMP: 6 **EST:** 2016
SALES (est): 163.1K **Privately Held**
SIC: 3999 Manufacturing industries

(G-13729)
CIRRUS SOFTWARE LLC
34125 Us Highway 19 N # 310 (34684-2112)
PHONE..................................727 450-7804
Matthew Brosious, *Mng Member*
EMP: 9 **EST:** 2015
SALES (est): 168.8K **Privately Held**
SIC: 7372 Business oriented computer software

(G-13730)
CORINTHIAN CATAMARANS LLC
4338 Auston Way (34685-4017)
PHONE..................................813 334-1029
Robert Muhlhan,
Paula J Muhlhan,
EMP: 11 **EST:** 2002
SQ FT: 2,000
SALES (est): 537.4K **Privately Held**
WEB: www.corinthiancatamarans.com
SIC: 3732 Boat building & repairing

(G-13731)
CRAEMER US CORPORATION
2927 Pinewood Run (34684-4920)
PHONE..................................727 312-8859
Axel Breitkreuz, *President*
EMP: 7 **EST:** 2018
SALES (est): 202.1K **Privately Held**
WEB: www.craemer.com
SIC: 3089 Pallets, plastic

(G-13732)
DANAHER MOTION
2112 Mary Ln (34685-2109)
PHONE..................................727 789-0446
Bruce Stephan, *Manager*
EMP: 9 **EST:** 2014
SALES (est): 233.7K **Privately Held**
SIC: 3823 Water quality monitoring & control systems

(G-13733)
DOMTAR INDUSTRIES INC
2598 Lakeside Ct (34684-1718)
PHONE..................................727 421-6919
▼ **EMP:** 8 **EST:** 2011
SALES (est): 93K **Privately Held**
WEB: www.domtar.com
SIC: 2621 Paper mills

(G-13734)
DOWNES TRADING CO
5730 Stag Thicket Ln (34685-2536)
PHONE..................................813 855-7122
James Downes, *President*
Mary Downes, *Vice Pres*
EMP: 8 **EST:** 2003
SALES (est): 638.2K **Privately Held**
SIC: 1389 5199 Construction, repair & dismantling services; nondurable goods

(G-13735)
DREAM CUIZINE
4952 Ridgemoor Blvd (34685-1744)
PHONE..................................727 943-8289
Gayle Kufro, *President*
Jolene Essex, *Vice Pres*
Frank Essex, *Director*
Joseph Kufro, *Director*
EMP: 6
SALES (est): 340K **Privately Held**
WEB: www.oregonrvdealers.com
SIC: 2099 Ready-to-eat meals, salads & sandwiches

(G-13736)
EMPIRICA
904 Old Mill Pond Rd (34683-1728)
P.O. Box 16112, Clearwater (33766-6112)
PHONE..................................727 403-0399
Judy Goulde, *Principal*
EMP: 11 **EST:** 2004
SALES (est): 141.7K **Privately Held**
SIC: 1389 Oil field services

(G-13737)
GOFORIT INC
Also Called: Sir Speedy
34034 Us Highway 19 N (34684-2645)
PHONE..................................727 785-7616
Eugene M Goldman, *President*
Ronnie Goldman, *Corp Secy*
EMP: 5 **EST:** 1982
SQ FT: 1,600
SALES (est): 784K **Privately Held**
WEB: www.sirspeedy.com
SIC: 2752 7334 Commercial printing, lithographic; photocopying & duplicating services

(G-13738)
GULF COAST PROGRAM
3515 Alt 19 Ste B (34683-1413)
PHONE..................................727 945-1402
Phillip Nathanson, *President*
EMP: 5 **EST:** 1997
SALES (est): 395.3K **Privately Held**
SIC: 7372 Prepackaged software

(G-13739)
HARBOR MACHINE INC
374 Foxcroft Dr E (34683-5613)
PHONE..................................727 772-9515
Garry J Czipri, *President*
EMP: 7 **EST:** 2008
SALES (est): 292.1K **Privately Held**
WEB: www.harbormachine.com
SIC: 3599 Machine shop, jobbing & repair

(G-13740)
INSPECS USA LC
30798 Us Highway 19 N (34684-4411)
PHONE..................................727 771-7710
Vincent Wright, *President*
Brookelyn Sager, *Sales Staff*
▲ **EMP:** 16 **EST:** 1999
SQ FT: 5,679
SALES (est): 3.8MM
SALES (corp-wide): 47.4MM **Privately Held**
WEB: www.inspecs.com
SIC: 3851 Protective eyeware
HQ: Inspecs Limited
7-10 Kelso Place Upper Bristol Road
Bath BA1 3
122 571-7060

(G-13741)
J D B DENSE FLOW INC
1004 Bee Pond Rd (34683-1407)
P.O. Box 38 (34682-0038)
PHONE..................................727 785-8500
Cameron Boothe, *President*
EMP: 10 **EST:** 1985
SQ FT: 1,300
SALES (est): 992.5K **Privately Held**
WEB: www.jdbdenseflow.com
SIC: 3535 5084 Pneumatic tube conveyor systems; industrial machinery & equipment

(G-13742)
KEVINS CUSTOM WOODWORKING
Also Called: Kcw Cnc and Laser Engraving
246 Arbor Dr E (34683-5705)
PHONE.....727 804-8422
Terrie Leadbeater, *Principal*
Kevin Leadbeater, *Mng Member*
EMP: 7 **EST:** 2009
SALES (est): 524.7K **Privately Held**
WEB: www.kevinscustomwoodworking.com
SIC: 2431 Millwork

(G-13743)
L3HARRIS TECHNOLOGIES INC
2330 Grove Valley Ave (34683-3227)
PHONE.....727 415-6592
EMP: 6
SALES (corp-wide): 3.7B **Publicly Held**
WEB: www.l3harris.com
SIC: 3812 Search & navigation equipment
PA: L3harris Technologies, Inc.
1025 W Nasa Blvd
Melbourne FL 32919
321 727-9100

(G-13744)
LANE CARE LLC ✪
3241 Fox Chase Cir N (34683-2359)
PHONE.....727 316-3708
Matthew Lane, *CEO*
Jamie Jackson,
EMP: 10 **EST:** 2020
SALES (est): 573.7K **Privately Held**
SIC: 3841 5047 Surgical & medical instruments; medical equipment & supplies

(G-13745)
LONE STAR BEEF JERKY LLC
724 Glengary Ln (34683-6332)
PHONE.....806 241-4188
Clint D Shobert, *Principal*
EMP: 6 **EST:** 2019
SALES (est): 319.5K **Privately Held**
WEB: www.lonestarbeefjerkyshop.com
SIC: 2013 Snack sticks, including jerky: from purchased meat

(G-13746)
MATRIX MEDIA LLC
989 Georgia Ave (34683-4255)
PHONE.....435 313-2877
Robert Pulsipher,
EMP: 8 **EST:** 2019
SALES (est): 599.7K **Privately Held**
SIC: 3571 Computers, digital, analog or hybrid

(G-13747)
NATIONAL CUSTOM INSIGNIA
1676 Arabian Ln (34685-3342)
PHONE.....813 781-8806
William Witrak, *President*
EMP: 7 **EST:** 2012
SALES (est): 127.3K **Privately Held**
WEB: www.ringsource.com
SIC: 3911 Jewelry, precious metal

(G-13748)
NEW MARKET ENTERPRISES LTD
Also Called: Dynamo Shredder Company
392 Harbor Ridge Dr (34683-1426)
PHONE.....484 341-8004
James Mokhiber, *CEO*
Johanna E Mokhiber, *President*
Christopher J Mokhiber, *Vice Pres*
Elizabeth Ficca, *Treasurer*
▲ **EMP:** 10 **EST:** 1997
SALES (est): 754.7K **Privately Held**
WEB: www.newmarketent.com
SIC: 3579 5044 Forms handling equipment; office equipment

(G-13749)
OSCOR INC (PA)
3816 Desoto Blvd (34683-1618)
PHONE.....727 937-2511
Thomas Osypka, *President*
Miguel Rodriguez, *COO*
Noel Perez, *Vice Pres*
Bethania Tavarez, *Vice Pres*
David Henderson, *Facilities Mgr*
◆ **EMP:** 125 **EST:** 1982
SQ FT: 25,000
SALES (est): 56.8MM **Privately Held**
WEB: www.oscor.com
SIC: 3841 5047 Surgical & medical instruments; medical equipment & supplies

(G-13750)
PITMAN ALLEN BOAT REPR & MAINT
970 Cortland Way (34683-6011)
PHONE.....727 772-9848
Allen Pitman, *President*
EMP: 9 **EST:** 1998
SALES (est): 588K **Privately Held**
SIC: 3732 Boat building & repairing

(G-13751)
PRESSURE SHINE LLC
2665 Walnut Dr (34683-6545)
PHONE.....727 216-8543
Seth L Newton, *Principal*
EMP: 6 **EST:** 2009
SALES (est): 104.7K **Privately Held**
SIC: 3589 High pressure cleaning equipment

(G-13752)
PRINT STORE LLC
4722 Kylemore Ct (34685-2648)
PHONE.....727 656-1376
Joseph Sineno Jr, *President*
EMP: 6 **EST:** 2011
SALES (est): 222.4K **Privately Held**
SIC: 2752 Commercial printing, lithographic

(G-13753)
PURE WATER SULOTINS LLC
35168 Us Highway 19 N (34684-1929)
PHONE.....727 784-7400
EMP: 6 **EST:** 2010
SALES (est): 166.9K **Privately Held**
SIC: 2086 Pasteurized & mineral waters, bottled & canned

(G-13754)
R&K MEHALL INC
211 Whisper Lake Rd (34683-5547)
P.O. Box 342, Crystal Beach (34681-0342)
PHONE.....727 781-8780
Richard J Mehall, *Principal*
EMP: 9 **EST:** 2007
SALES (est): 261.6K **Privately Held**
SIC: 3582 Washing machines, laundry: commercial, incl. coin-operated

(G-13755)
RADIANCE RADIOLOGY INC
37566 Us Highway 19 N (34684-1019)
PHONE.....727 934-5500
Andrey Salamakha, *President*
EMP: 5 **EST:** 2009
SALES (est): 476.8K **Privately Held**
WEB: www.radianceradiology.com
SIC: 3826 Magnetic resonance imaging apparatus

(G-13756)
RAE SERVICES INC
1700 Arabian Ln (34685-3343)
PHONE.....727 480-9940
Ben Kugler, *Principal*
EMP: 8 **EST:** 2016
SALES (est): 101.5K **Privately Held**
SIC: 3829 Measuring & controlling devices

(G-13757)
RAINBOWS END
Also Called: Rainbows End Quilt Shoppe
1450 Wetherington Way (34683-6446)
PHONE.....727 733-8572
Mary Ellen Facsina, *Partner*
Michelle Facsina, *Partner*
Eileen Roski, *Partner*
EMP: 12 **EST:** 1984
SALES (est): 671.3K **Privately Held**
WEB: www.rainbowsendquiltshoppe.blogspot.com
SIC: 2395 5949 Quilting & quilting supplies; sewing, needlework & piece goods

(G-13758)
REAL PRINT & SHIP INC
4047 Carlyle Lakes Blvd (34685-1040)
PHONE.....727 787-1949
Alan Goniwich, *Principal*
EMP: 9 **EST:** 2017
SALES (est): 391.7K **Privately Held**
SIC: 2752 Commercial printing, lithographic

(G-13759)
REGENERATIVE PROC PLANT LLC
34176 Us Highway 19 N (34684-2144)
PHONE.....727 781-0818
C Randall Harrell, *CEO*
Marissa Morris, *Vice Pres*
Pam Perko, *Comptroller*
Gerald Beougher,
EMP: 20 **EST:** 2013
SALES (est): 1.9MM **Privately Held**
WEB: www.regenerativeplant.org
SIC: 2834 Pharmaceutical preparations

(G-13760)
SIVO BRICK PAVERS INC
4279 Tremblay Way (34685-2645)
PHONE.....813 917-3859
Ivan D Vila, *President*
EMP: 8 **EST:** 2005
SALES (est): 143K **Privately Held**
SIC: 3531 Pavers

(G-13761)
SKY-HIGH SIGN & LIGHTING INC
30 Citrus Dr (34684-1207)
PHONE.....813 994-3954
Don Stapleton, *Principal*
EMP: 8 **EST:** 2009
SALES (est): 357.8K **Privately Held**
WEB: www.skyhigh-signs.com
SIC: 3993 Electric signs

(G-13762)
SOUTHERN SWITCH & CONTACTS
855 Virginia Ave (34683-5227)
PHONE.....727 789-0951
Mahendra Doshi, *President*
AMI Shah, *Vice Pres*
EMP: 10 **EST:** 1993
SQ FT: 6,000
SALES (est): 2MM **Privately Held**
WEB: www.southernswitch.com
SIC: 3643 3625 Contacts, electrical; industrial electrical relays & switches

(G-13763)
SUNCOAST LED DISPLAYS LLC
2366 Knoll Ave S (34683-3115)
PHONE.....727 683-2777
John Kinsel, *Sales Mgr*
Jordan Kinsel, *Mng Member*
EMP: 14 **EST:** 2011
SALES (est): 1MM **Privately Held**
WEB: www.suncoastleddisplays.com
SIC: 3674 3577 Light emitting diodes; graphic displays, except graphic terminals

(G-13764)
SWEET SPOT
2609 Alt 19 (34683-2624)
PHONE.....727 784-2277
Kim Verheyleweghen, *Manager*
EMP: 5 **EST:** 2011
SALES (est): 317.6K **Privately Held**
WEB: www.sweetspotworld.com
SIC: 2024 Ice cream, bulk

(G-13765)
TARVIN MOBILE HOME SERVICE
329 Archimedes St (34683)
PHONE.....727 734-3400
Melvin B Tarvin, *Principal*
EMP: 7 **EST:** 2001
SALES (est): 89.5K **Privately Held**
SIC: 3365 Aluminum foundries

(G-13766)
TK - AUTEK INC
Also Called: Autek Spray Booths
270 Foxcroft Dr E (34683-5611)
PHONE.....727 572-7473
Jack Kimball, *President*
Cheri Kimball, *Corp Secy*
Thomas Kimball, *Vice Pres*
EMP: 8 **EST:** 1999
SALES (est): 629.1K **Privately Held**
SIC: 3444 Booths, spray: prefabricated sheet metal

(G-13767)
VODA TECHNOLOGIES LLC
3909 Mimosa Pl (34685-3675)
PHONE.....727 645-6030
Elzina Singh, *Manager*
EMP: 6 **EST:** 2019
SALES (est): 328.5K **Privately Held**
WEB: www.vodatechnologies.com
SIC: 3589 Water filters & softeners, household type

GEOGRAPHIC

(G-13768)
VREELAND WOODWORKING LLC
1407 Tampa Rd (34683-5649)
PHONE.....727 365-0241
Benjamin Vreeland, *Principal*
EMP: 7 **EST:** 2010
SALES (est): 221.1K **Privately Held**
SIC: 2431 Millwork

(G-13769)
WESTLUND ENGINEERING INC
Also Called: W&W Engineering Company
3116 Roxmere Dr (34685-1733)
PHONE.....727 572-4343
Paul O Wright, *President*
Rory L Westlund, *Vice Pres*
Chip Bombard, *Opers Mgr*
Ryan Vernick, *Technician*
EMP: 9 **EST:** 1993
SQ FT: 16,000
SALES (est): 366.1K **Privately Held**
WEB: www.westlundeng.com
SIC: 3549 3565 Assembly machines, including robotic; packaging machinery

(G-13770)
ZOHO STONE LLC
34318 Us Highway 19 N (34684-2149)
PHONE.....727 230-6956
Michel Zohouri, *Mng Member*
▲ **EMP:** 5 **EST:** 2008
SALES (est): 390K **Privately Held**
WEB: www.zohostone.com
SIC: 3272 Concrete products

Palm Springs
Palm Beach County

(G-13771)
ALENAC METALS CORP
Also Called: Alenac & Associates
2180 S Congress Ave A (33406-7630)
PHONE.....561 877-4109
Nathalia Pabon, *President*
Guillermo Pabon, *Vice Pres*
Alejandro Pabon, *CFO*
Carmenza Chahin, *Admin Sec*
EMP: 24 **EST:** 2013
SALES (est): 2.7MM **Privately Held**
WEB: www.alenacmetals.com
SIC: 3446 Architectural metalwork

(G-13772)
ALL AMRCAN TRLR CONNECTION INC
3531 Lake Worth Rd (33461-4030)
PHONE.....561 582-1800
Shawn Lago, *CEO*
Theresa Lago, *President*
John M Lago, *Vice Pres*
Linda Combast, *Office Mgr*
Bridget Lago, *Director*
▼ **EMP:** 8 **EST:** 1980
SALES (est): 4MM **Privately Held**
WEB: www.allamericantrailer.com
SIC: 3715 5511 5599 Truck trailers; trucks, tractors & trailers: new & used; utility trailers

(G-13773)
AMERICAN MBL RESTORATION INC
43 Barbados Dr (33461-2829)
PHONE.....561 502-0764
Roberto Reyes, *President*
EMP: 7 **EST:** 2013

SALES (est): 205.1K **Privately Held**
SIC: 3281 Cut stone & stone products

(G-13774)
DESIGNSTOGO INC
4317 10th Ave N (33461-2312)
PHONE..................................561 432-1313
Cesar Sanchez, *President*
EMP: 7 **EST:** 1988
SALES (est): 940.9K **Privately Held**
WEB: www.designs2go.net
SIC: 3993 Signs & advertising specialties

(G-13775)
M WEGENER INC
24 Springdale Cir (33461-6323)
PHONE..................................561 848-2408
M Wegener, *President*
EMP: 5 **EST:** 1997
SALES (est): 310K **Privately Held**
WEB: www.mwegenercabinets.com
SIC: 2434 Wood kitchen cabinets

(G-13776)
MARKO GARAGE DOORS & GATES INC
248 Davis Rd (33461-1903)
PHONE..................................561 547-4001
Timothy W Coorough, *Principal*
Crystal Marko, *Sales Staff*
EMP: 7 **EST:** 2008
SALES (est): 270.4K **Privately Held**
WEB: www.markogaragedoors.com
SIC: 2431 3429 Garage doors, overhead: wood; door opening & closing devices, except electrical

(G-13777)
MG CABINET INSTALLERS LLC
3860 Miller Rd Apt B (33461-3697)
PHONE..................................561 530-7961
Manuel Garcia Garcia, *Principal*
EMP: 6 **EST:** 2018
SALES (est): 420.1K **Privately Held**
SIC: 2434 Wood kitchen cabinets

(G-13778)
OXYGEN DEVELOPMENT LLC (PA)
1525 S Congress Ave (33406-5916)
PHONE..................................954 480-2675
Alex Venot, *General Mgr*
Mark Feller, *CFO*
Elena Bland, *Financial Analy*
Maria Compres, *Sales Mgr*
Jones Paige, *Sales Mgr*
◆ **EMP:** 104 **EST:** 2002
SQ FT: 200,000
SALES (est): 57.4MM **Privately Held**
WEB: www.oxygendevelopment.com
SIC: 2844 Toilet preparations

(G-13779)
PALM BEACH PRECIOUS METALS
3200 Frost Rd (33406-7928)
PHONE..................................561 662-6025
Joseph H Trebbe, *Principal*
EMP: 6 **EST:** 2008
SALES (est): 105.4K **Privately Held**
SIC: 3339 Precious metals

(G-13780)
SOUTH FLORIDA LABORATORY LLC
3395 Lake Worth Rd (33461-6902)
P.O. Box 904107, Charlotte NC (28290-0001)
PHONE..................................954 889-0335
Flavia Tanner, *Mng Member*
Marc Tanner,
EMP: 9 **EST:** 2011
SALES (est): 642.5K **Privately Held**
SIC: 3821 Clinical laboratory instruments, except medical & dental

Palmetto
Manatee County

(G-13781)
365 SUN LLC
Also Called: Natalia Likhacheva
515 15th Ave W (34221-4437)
PHONE..................................208 357-8062
Lance I Thompson, *Manager*
EMP: 8 **EST:** 2017
SALES (est): 526.2K **Privately Held**
SIC: 2844 Hair preparations, including shampoos

(G-13782)
AAA ARCHITECTURAL ELEMENTS
Also Called: A A A Architectural Materials
1751 12th St E (34221-6461)
P.O. Box 282 (34220-0282)
PHONE..................................941 722-1910
Richard Cary, *President*
Steven Kosoff, *Vice Pres*
Pam Spencer, *Sales Executive*
EMP: 18 **EST:** 1988
SQ FT: 22,940
SALES (est): 1.1MM **Privately Held**
WEB: www.buildingshapes.com
SIC: 3086 2851 Plastics foam products; lacquers, varnishes, enamels & other coatings

(G-13783)
AAA CAST STONE INC
1470 12th St E (34221-4176)
PHONE..................................941 721-8092
Larry Haveman, *President*
Bryan Haveman, *Sales Executive*
Sandra Eichmuller, *Office Mgr*
EMP: 20 **EST:** 2002
SALES (est): 3.7MM **Privately Held**
WEB: www.aaacaststone.com
SIC: 3272 Cast stone, concrete

(G-13784)
ALLEGRO NUTRITION INC
Also Called: Gaspari Nutrition
6111 Horse Mill Pl (34221-7398)
PHONE..................................732 364-3777
Richard Gaspari, *President*
Oscar Iturralde, *Treasurer*
Troy Johnson, *Sales Staff*
Michael Maling, *Manager*
Nick Scragg, *Manager*
▼ **EMP:** 25 **EST:** 2014
SALES (est): 5.1MM **Privately Held**
WEB: www.allegro.ie
SIC: 2023 Dietary supplements, dairy & non-dairy based
HQ: Allegro Limited
Jamestown House
Dublin D11 P
185 806-00

(G-13785)
ALLIED MOLDED PRODUCTS LLC
1145 13th Ave E (34221-4167)
P.O. Box 186 (34220-0186)
PHONE..................................941 723-3072
Bill Harvey, *CEO*
Greg Miller, *President*
Larry Fox, *Chairman*
EMP: 50 **EST:** 1990
SQ FT: 40,000
SALES (est): 5.7MM **Privately Held**
WEB: www.allied-molded.com
SIC: 3229 Glass fiber products

(G-13786)
AMICITIA PHARMA LLC
5919 60th Pl E (34221-7044)
PHONE..................................941 722-0172
Sokha Yim, *Principal*
EMP: 6 **EST:** 2010
SALES (est): 117.6K **Privately Held**
SIC: 2834 Pharmaceutical preparations

(G-13787)
ATI ACCURATE TECHNOLOGY
1180 8th Ave W (34221-3810)
PHONE..................................239 206-1240
EMP: 7 **EST:** 2019
SALES (est): 1.1MM **Privately Held**
WEB: www.igbts.us
SIC: 3312 Stainless steel

(G-13788)
AUTOMOTIVE ARMOR MFG INC
1150 13th Ave E (34221-4166)
PHONE..................................941 721-3335
Stephen A Rodhouse, *President*
Gloria Rodhouse, *Treasurer*
Paul Rodhouse, *Admin Sec*
▲ **EMP:** 11 **EST:** 1998
SQ FT: 6,500
SALES (est): 2.6MM **Privately Held**
WEB: www.auto-armor.com
SIC: 3312 Armor plate

(G-13789)
CASUAL TONE INC
Also Called: Casualcraft
509 9th St W (34221-4713)
PHONE..................................941 722-5643
Craig Libkie, *President*
James Stewart, *General Mgr*
Tony Zulino, *CFO*
EMP: 12 **EST:** 2001
SALES (est): 107.1K **Privately Held**
WEB: www.floridapatio.net
SIC: 2514 Metal lawn & garden furniture

(G-13790)
CEMEX MATERIALS LLC
600 9th St W (34221-4716)
PHONE..................................941 722-4578
Mark McHayle, *Branch Mgr*
EMP: 73
SQ FT: 28,888 **Privately Held**
SIC: 3273 5032 5211 3441 Ready-mixed concrete; concrete mixtures; concrete & cinder block; fabricated structural metal; concrete block & brick; brick & structural clay tile
HQ: Cemex Materials Llc
1501 Belvedere Rd
West Palm Beach FL 33406
561 833-5555

(G-13791)
CHRIS INDUSTRIES CORP
Also Called: CIC Conveyors
1118 8th Ave W (34221-3810)
PHONE..................................941 729-7600
Jeff Van Hoose, *President*
Eric Jackson, *Principal*
EMP: 6 **EST:** 2010
SALES (est): 121.5K **Privately Held**
SIC: 3535 Conveyors & conveying equipment

(G-13792)
COASTAL FUELS MKTG INC
804 N Dock St (34221-6612)
PHONE..................................941 722-7753
Greg Pound, *President*
▲ **EMP:** 8 **EST:** 1989
SALES (est): 573.1K **Privately Held**
SIC: 2869 Fuels

(G-13793)
COMPUTER TECHNICIAN INC
829 8th Ave W (34221-4709)
P.O. Box 21378, Bradenton (34204-1378)
PHONE..................................941 479-0242
Cedrick Lane, *Principal*
Tayon Wynn, *Manager*
EMP: 7 **EST:** 2016
SALES (est): 103.1K **Privately Held**
SIC: 3571 3572 7378 Electronic computers; computer storage devices; computer & data processing equipment repair/maintenance

(G-13794)
CUSTOM MEDICAL SYSTEMS INC
404 10th Ave W (34221-5032)
PHONE..................................941 722-3434
Allan A Lovesky, *President*
EMP: 7 **EST:** 1991
SQ FT: 2,000
SALES (est): 900.6K **Privately Held**
SIC: 3842 Wheelchairs

(G-13795)
DENKE LABORATORIES INC
Also Called: Hascall-Denke
12285 Us Highway 41 N (34221-8607)
P.O. Box 909 (34220-0909)
PHONE..................................941 721-0568
Michael Hascall, *President*
Tim Delille, *Project Mgr*
Roy Schneider, *Research*
Mary B Hascall, *Admin Sec*
Mary Hascall, *Admin Sec*
EMP: 25 **EST:** 1986
SQ FT: 28,000
SALES (est): 3.7MM **Privately Held**
WEB: www.hascall-denke.com
SIC: 3663 Antennas, transmitting & communications

(G-13796)
EN-VISION AMERICA INC
825 4th St W (34221-5013)
PHONE..................................309 452-3088
Phillip C Raistrick, *President*
David Raistrick, *Vice Pres*
Tom Morr, *Opers Staff*
Amanda Tolson, *Sales Staff*
Jenna Reed, *Marketing Staff*
▲ **EMP:** 15 **EST:** 1996
SQ FT: 3,000
SALES (est): 2.2MM **Privately Held**
WEB: www.envisionamerica.com
SIC: 3827 Optical instruments & lenses

(G-13797)
FATHYM INC
2303 14th St W (34221-2957)
P.O. Box 3007, Boulder CO (80307-3007)
PHONE..................................303 905-4402
Matthew Smith, *President*
Gerard Verbeck, *CFO*
Christina Szoke, *Chief Mktg Ofcr*
Christy Szoke, *Chief Mktg Ofcr*
George Greenwood, *Manager*
EMP: 12 **EST:** 2014
SALES (est): 18K **Privately Held**
WEB: www.fathym.com
SIC: 2721 7371 8711 Periodicals; custom computer programming services; engineering services

(G-13798)
FATOR FASTENERS USA LLC
1905 Intermodal Cir (34221-6648)
PHONE..................................941 479-8518
Alex Garcia,
EMP: 6 **EST:** 2017
SALES (est): 89.9K **Privately Held**
WEB: www.fatorgroup.com
SIC: 3965 Fasteners

(G-13799)
FLORIDA FINISHER INC
509 9th St W (34221-4713)
PHONE..................................941 722-5643
James Stewart, *President*
Blair Squire, *Vice Pres*
Greg Stewart, *Vice Pres*
EMP: 6 **EST:** 1996
SALES (est): 448.2K **Privately Held**
SIC: 2514 5712 Metal lawn & garden furniture; furniture stores

(G-13800)
GAEMMERLER (US) CORPORATION
2906 Corporate Way (34221-8488)
PHONE..................................941 465-4400
Gunter Gammerler, *Principal*
▲ **EMP:** 6 **EST:** 2008
SALES (est): 138.3K **Privately Held**
SIC: 3535 Conveyors & conveying equipment

(G-13801)
GREEN FOREST INDUSTRIES INC
1365 12th St E (34221-4169)
PHONE..................................941 721-0504
Brian Vance, *President*
EMP: 20 **EST:** 1994
SQ FT: 10,000
SALES (est): 6MM **Privately Held**
WEB: www.greenforestindustries.com
SIC: 3299 2431 Ornamental & architectural plaster work; millwork

▲ = Import ▼=Export
◆ =Import/Export

(G-13802)
GULF COAST GROWERS FLORIDA LLC ✪
2105 S Dock St (34221-8667)
PHONE....................................941 737-2532
James Grainer, *Mng Member*
EMP: 100 **EST:** 2020
SALES (est): 6.4MM **Privately Held**
SIC: 2033 Tomato purees: packaged in cans, jars, etc.

(G-13803)
GULFSTREAM NATURAL GAS SYS LLC
4610 Buckeye Rd (34221-9502)
PHONE....................................941 723-7000
Al Taylor, *Manager*
EMP: 8 **Privately Held**
WEB: www.gulfstreamgas.com
SIC: 1382 Oil & gas exploration services
PA: Gulfstream Natural Gas System, L.L.C.
2701 N Rocky Point Dr # 1050
Tampa FL 33607

(G-13804)
H Q INC
210 9th Street Dr W (34221-4802)
PHONE....................................941 721-7588
William S Hicks, *President*
Steven Cook, *Engineer*
EMP: 15 **EST:** 1986
SQ FT: 2,000
SALES (est): 681.2K **Privately Held**
WEB: www.hqinc.net
SIC: 3845 3823 Electromedical apparatus; industrial instrmnts msrmnt display/control process variable

(G-13805)
HASCALL ENGINEERING AND MFG CO
Also Called: Denke Labratories
1608 20th Ave E (34221-6504)
P.O. Box 909 (34220-0909)
PHONE....................................941 723-2833
Michael Hascall, *President*
Joe Hughes, *COO*
Daniel Pakosz, *Director*
EMP: 13 **EST:** 1988
SQ FT: 5,000
SALES (est): 381.2K **Privately Held**
WEB: www.hascall-denke.com
SIC: 3679 Antennas, receiving; electronic circuits

(G-13806)
HTI
210 9th Street Dr W (34221-4802)
PHONE....................................941 723-4570
Vaughn Y Haight, *CEO*
Lee Carbonell, *General Mgr*
Lee Carbonelli, *Marketing Staff*
EMP: 9 **EST:** 2008
SALES (est): 119K **Privately Held**
WEB: www.hqinc.net
SIC: 3841 Surgical & medical instruments

(G-13807)
HYDROPLUS INC
615 Riviera Dunes Way # 207
(34221-7146)
PHONE....................................941 479-7473
Hasan Kocahan, *President*
EMP: 10 **EST:** 1995
SALES (est): 2.8MM
SALES (corp-wide): 17.7MM **Privately Held**
WEB: www.hydroplus.com
SIC: 3511 1629 Hydraulic turbine generator set units, complete; dams, waterways, docks & other marine construction
HQ: Hydroplus
5 Cours Ferdinand De Lesseps
Rueil Malmaison 92500

(G-13808)
JSB ENTERPRISES INC
Also Called: Die Verse Tool & Manufacturing
1650 12th St E (34221-6437)
PHONE....................................941 723-2288
Jeffrey S Bauman, *President*
EMP: 20 **EST:** 1985
SQ FT: 20,000
SALES (est): 2MM **Privately Held**
SIC: 3544 Dies & die holders for metal cutting, forming, die casting

(G-13809)
JUPITER MAR INTL HOLDINGS INC (PA)
1103 12th Ave E (34221-4146)
PHONE....................................941 729-5000
Carl M Herndon Sr, *President*
Carisa Albrecht, *Principal*
Lawrence S Tierney, *COO*
Carston Koopman, *QC Mgr*
Brad Meilink, *Engineer*
▼ **EMP:** 59 **EST:** 1989
SQ FT: 4,800
SALES (est): 13.2MM **Privately Held**
WEB: www.jupitermarine.com
SIC: 3732 Boat building & repairing

(G-13810)
MANOR STEEL FABRICATORS
1507 18th Avenue Dr E (34221-6503)
PHONE....................................941 722-8077
Deborah Shuck, *Owner*
EMP: 7 **EST:** 2010
SALES (est): 178.5K **Privately Held**
WEB: www.steel-fabricators-erectors.cmac.ws
SIC: 3312 Blast furnaces & steel mills

(G-13811)
MASTER CABINET MAKER INC
5004 Us Highway 41 N A (34221-2031)
PHONE....................................941 723-0278
Christina Schipper, *Principal*
EMP: 8 **EST:** 2005
SALES (est): 866.9K **Privately Held**
WEB: www.themastercabinetmaker.com
SIC: 2434 Wood kitchen cabinets

(G-13812)
MEDTEL SERVICES LLC (PA)
2511 Corporate Way (34221-8478)
PHONE....................................941 753-5000
Timothy Callahan, *Exec VP*
Duncan Anderson, *Vice Pres*
Robert Ramey, *Vice Pres*
David Rourke, *Vice Pres*
Phalay Touch, *Production*
▲ **EMP:** 33 **EST:** 2012
SQ FT: 5,000
SALES (est): 7.5MM **Privately Held**
WEB: www.medtelservices.com
SIC: 3661 Telephones & telephone apparatus

(G-13813)
MITTEN MANUFACTURING
1614 20th St E Unit 102 (34221-3291)
PHONE....................................941 722-1818
Chad Seyer, *President*
Gene Waggoner, *Manager*
EMP: 7 **EST:** 2011
SALES (est): 171.3K **Privately Held**
WEB: www.mitten-manufacturing.com
SIC: 3999 Manufacturing industries

(G-13814)
PALMETTO CANNING COMPANY
3601 Us Highway 41 N (34221-8801)
P.O. Box 155 (34220-0155)
PHONE....................................941 722-1100
Jonathan Greenlaw, *President*
Heather Baggs, *Corp Secy*
Stephanie G Gardner, *Vice Pres*
◆ **EMP:** 15 **EST:** 1927
SQ FT: 32,000
SALES (est): 3.3MM **Privately Held**
WEB: www.palmettocanning.com
SIC: 2033 Jellies, edible, including imitation: in cans, jars, etc.; preserves, including imitation: in cans, jars, etc.; marmalade: packaged in cans, jars, etc.; fruit juices: packaged in cans, jars, etc.

(G-13815)
PATHWAY HOLDINGS LLC
5002 Us Highway 41 N (34221-2025)
PHONE....................................813 514-7899
Stephen Gans, *Mng Member*
EMP: 8 **EST:** 2008
SALES (est): 246.3K **Privately Held**
SIC: 2873 Fertilizers: natural (organic), except compost

(G-13816)
PICKHARDT PROFESSIONAL SR
4329 14th Street Cir (34221-5702)
P.O. Box 415, Parrish (34219-0415)
PHONE....................................941 737-7262
Vernon Pickhardt, *President*
EMP: 5 **EST:** 2010
SALES (est): 500K **Privately Held**
WEB: www.pickhardtservices.com
SIC: 3524 Lawn & garden equipment

(G-13817)
PORT MANATEE SHIP REPAIR
2114 Piney Point Rd (34221-9551)
P.O. Box 2547, Oldsmar (34677-0048)
PHONE....................................941 417-2613
Carlos Buqueras, *CFO*
Frank Kerney,
EMP: 48 **EST:** 2015
SQ FT: 12,000
SALES (est): 5MM **Privately Held**
WEB: www.manateeshiprepair.com
SIC: 3731 Shipbuilding & repairing

(G-13818)
PROGRESSIVE INDUSTRIAL INC
1412 18th Avenue Dr E (34221-6500)
PHONE....................................941 723-0201
Michael McCormick, *President*
Brian Degulis, *Vice Pres*
EMP: 12 **EST:** 1994
SQ FT: 7,500
SALES: 1.2MM **Privately Held**
WEB: www.pushboats-barges.com
SIC: 3731 3732 Tugboats, building & repairing; boat building & repairing

(G-13819)
PROVEN INDUSTRIES INC
2310 S Dock St Ste 111 (34221-8892)
PHONE....................................813 895-4385
Ronald I Lee, *President*
EMP: 11 **EST:** 2011
SALES (est): 651.3K **Privately Held**
WEB: www.provenlocks.com
SIC: 3429 Keys, locks & related hardware

(G-13820)
QUEST CONTROLS INC (PA)
208 9th Street Dr W (34221-4802)
PHONE....................................941 729-4799
Edward Goggin, *President*
Kenneth Nickel, *Exec VP*
Diane Griebe, *QC Mgr*
Chuck Fulks, *CFO*
Melissa Arrigo, *Controller*
EMP: 11 **EST:** 1989
SQ FT: 10,000
SALES (est): 9MM **Privately Held**
WEB: www.questcontrols.com
SIC: 3829 3625 Measuring & controlling devices; relays & industrial controls

(G-13821)
READY CONTAINMENT LLC
2300 S Dock St Ste 101 (34221-8890)
PHONE....................................941 739-9486
Scott Sagalow,
Lisa Eisenberg,
Rich Eisenberg,
Doreen Salow,
EMP: 16 **EST:** 2003
SQ FT: 21,000
SALES (est): 5.2MM **Privately Held**
WEB: www.readycontainment.com
SIC: 3069 Rubber automotive products

(G-13822)
SEA FORCE CENTER CONSOLE LLC (PA) ✪
12277 Us Highway 41 N (34221-8607)
PHONE....................................941 417-7017
Mark Calzaretta,
EMP: 20 **EST:** 2020
SALES (est): 216.5K **Privately Held**
SIC: 3732 Boat building & repairing

(G-13823)
ST PETE PAPER COMPANY
2324 20th St E (34221-3288)
PHONE....................................727 572-9868
EMP: 7
SALES (est): 1.5MM **Privately Held**
SIC: 2653 Mfg Corrugated/Solid Fiber Boxes

(G-13824)
STEVEN HERRANZ CUSTOM COATINGS
527 37th Street Ct W (34221-9153)
PHONE....................................941 915-4686
Stephen Herranz, *Principal*
EMP: 6 **EST:** 2011
SALES (est): 135.5K **Privately Held**
SIC: 3479 Metal coating & allied service

(G-13825)
STORAGE BUILDING COMPANY LLC
429 10th Ave W Ste B (34221-5048)
P.O. Box 7805, Lakeland (33807-7805)
PHONE....................................863 738-1319
Thomas Massarella, *Mng Member*
EMP: 16 **EST:** 2019
SALES (est): 3.4MM **Privately Held**
WEB: www.storagebuildingcompany.com
SIC: 3441 1791 Building components, structural steel; structural steel erection

(G-13826)
SUNCOAST INVESTMENS OF PA
1511 20th Ave E (34221-6524)
PHONE....................................941 722-5391
Knapp Robert, *Owner*
Lawhun Jed, *Exec VP*
EMP: 6 **EST:** 2014
SALES (est): 310.3K **Privately Held**
SIC: 3993 Signs & advertising specialties

(G-13827)
T C B PRODUCTS INC
1507 17th St E (34221-2854)
PHONE....................................941 723-9820
Lindsay Rolfe, *President*
◆ **EMP:** 20 **EST:** 1998
SQ FT: 22,000
SALES (est): 669.3K **Privately Held**
WEB: www.tcbproducts.com
SIC: 3694 Ignition coils, automotive

(G-13828)
TAYLOR CONCRETE INC
503 10th St E (34221)
P.O. Box 740, Parrish (34219-0740)
PHONE....................................941 737-7225
Nathan Taylor Jr, *President*
Spencer Taylor, *Vice Pres*
Rachael Perez, *Treasurer*
EMP: 5 **EST:** 1954
SQ FT: 3,000
SALES (est): 440.5K **Privately Held**
SIC: 3272 1711 Septic tanks, concrete; septic system construction

(G-13829)
THATCHER CHEMICAL FLORIDA INC
2905 Inland Transport St (34221-7736)
PHONE....................................386 490-1642
Kasey Hanson, *General Mgr*
EMP: 6
SALES (corp-wide): 461.7MM **Privately Held**
SIC: 2819 Industrial inorganic chemicals
HQ: Thatcher Chemical Of Florida, Inc.
245 Hazen Rd
Deland FL 32720
386 734-3966

(G-13830)
TRILECTRON
11001 Us Highway 41 N (34221-7700)
PHONE....................................941 721-1000
Cheryl Morton, *Principal*
Doug Garner, *Project Mgr*
Shelley Liddy, *Controller*
Kathleen Burns, *Sales Staff*
▲ **EMP:** 5 **EST:** 2007
SALES (est): 601.9K **Privately Held**
WEB: www.itwgse.com
SIC: 3812 Aircraft flight instruments

(G-13831)
TROPIC ISLES CO-OP INC
1503 28th Ave W (34221-3519)
PHONE....................................941 721-8888
Clyde Martin, *President*

Mark Kreuger, *Admin Sec*
EMP: 12 **EST:** 2002
SALES (est): 1.1MM **Privately Held**
WEB: www.tropicisles.net
SIC: 2451 Mobile homes

(G-13832)
VERDE GSE INC
12291 Us Highway 41 N (34221-8607)
P.O. Box 601, Ellenton (34222-0601)
PHONE..................................888 837-5221
Richard Hansen, *CEO*
Alex Long, *Principal*
Ben Newell, *Principal*
Ty Newell, *Principal*
Christina Hansen, *COO*
EMP: 23 **EST:** 2013
SALES (est): 4.9MM **Privately Held**
WEB: www.verdegse.com
SIC: 3585 Refrigeration & heating equipment

(G-13833)
VIENNA BEEF LTD
Also Called: Chipico South
2650 Corporate Way (34221-8480)
PHONE..................................941 723-7234
Callie Sullivan, *Human Resources*
Cindy Bogusz, *Manager*
EMP: 273
SQ FT: 24,530
SALES (corp-wide): 101.9MM **Privately Held**
WEB: www.viennabeef.com
SIC: 2013 2035 Prepared beef products from purchased beef; pickles, sauces & salad dressings
PA: Vienna Beef Ltd.
2501 W Fulton St
Chicago IL 60612
773 278-7800

(G-13834)
WALKER ELECTRIC INC
340 42nd Street Ct W (34221-9738)
PHONE..................................941 729-5015
Rose Walker, *Vice Pres*
EMP: 7 **EST:** 2011
SALES (est): 368.9K **Privately Held**
WEB: www.walkerelectricfl.com
SIC: 3699 1731 Electrical equipment & supplies; electrical work

(G-13835)
WALKER PRODUCTS
1507 17th St E (34221-2854)
PHONE..................................941 723-9820
EMP: 69
SALES (corp-wide): 49.1MM **Privately Held**
WEB: www.walkerproducts.com
SIC: 3714 Motor vehicle parts & accessories
PA: Walker Products
525 W Congress St
Pacific MO 63069
636 257-2400

(G-13836)
WESTCOAST METALWORKS INC
Also Called: Stainless Stl Fbrction Svcs Fl
3308 39th St E (34221-6330)
PHONE..................................941 920-3201
Sheldon K Clements, *Principal*
EMP: 7 **EST:** 2005
SALES (est): 327.1K **Privately Held**
WEB: www.westcoastmetalworks.com
SIC: 7692 Welding repair

(G-13837)
WIRETEC IGNITION INC
1901 4th St W (34221-4305)
PHONE..................................407 578-4569
Brian Moore, *President*
David Dirkse, *Principal*
Brenda Obrien, *CFO*
◆ **EMP:** 11 **EST:** 1995
SQ FT: 40,000
SALES (est): 613.1K **Privately Held**
SIC: 3694 3357 Spark plugs for internal combustion engines; automotive wire & cable, except ignition sets: nonferrous

(G-13838)
WOODMAN CABINETS INC
6911 95th Ln E (34221-9243)
PHONE..................................561 558-2550
Kevin Ionta, *Principal*
EMP: 7 **EST:** 2012
SALES (est): 96K **Privately Held**
SIC: 2434 Wood kitchen cabinets

Palmetto Bay
Miami-Dade County

(G-13839)
AMER-CON CORP
18001 Old Cutler Rd # 401 (33157-6434)
P.O. Box 566359, Miami (33256-6359)
PHONE..................................786 293-8004
Carlos Rapaport, *President*
Guillermo Rapaport, *Vice Pres*
Richard Rapaport, *Vice Pres*
Robert Rapaport, *Vice Pres*
Henry Rapaport, *CFO*
◆ **EMP:** 26 **EST:** 1988
SQ FT: 4,500
SALES (est): 3.4MM **Privately Held**
WEB: www.amer-con.com
SIC: 3537 3711 3713 4131 Industrial trucks & tractors; bus & other large specialty vehicle assembly; truck & bus bodies; intercity & rural bus transportation; school buses; construction machinery

(G-13840)
BEAUTY WITH KELLEY INC
9845 E Fern St (33157-5413)
PHONE..................................786 757-6485
Kelley Stanczyk, *President*
EMP: 11 **EST:** 2018
SALES (est): 560.7K **Privately Held**
SIC: 2844 Toilet preparations

(G-13841)
CARIBBEAN TODAY NEWS MAGAZINE
Also Called: Caribbean Publishing Service
9020 Sw 152nd St (33157-1928)
PHONE..................................305 238-2868
Peter Webley, *Publisher*
Gordon Williams, *Editor*
EMP: 10 **EST:** 1989
SALES (est): 1.1MM **Privately Held**
WEB: www.caribbeantoday.com
SIC: 2711 Newspapers, publishing & printing

(G-13842)
CORPORATE PRINT RESOURCES INC
7900 Sw 160th St (33157-3759)
PHONE..................................305 968-2037
EMP: 6 **EST:** 2004
SALES (est): 239.9K **Privately Held**
WEB: www.cprprints.com
SIC: 2752 Commercial printing, lithographic

(G-13843)
FUELMATICS CORP
17641 Sw 87th Ave (33157-6024)
PHONE..................................305 807-4923
Sten Corfitsen, *CEO*
EMP: 12 **EST:** 2010
SALES (est): 503.7K **Privately Held**
WEB: www.fuelmatics.com
SIC: 3714 8742 Motor vehicle parts & accessories; automation & robotics consultant

(G-13844)
GIGVAOI FIFTH AND LENOX
18001 Old Cutler Rd # 307 (33157-6419)
PHONE..................................305 604-0635
EMP: 6 **EST:** 2015
SALES (est): 133.4K **Privately Held**
SIC: 3585 Refrigeration & heating equipment

(G-13845)
GRAPHIC JET SIGNS LLC
17358 S Dixie Hwy (33157-4319)
PHONE..................................786 552-2098
Alexis Rodriguez, *Principal*
EMP: 6 **EST:** 2016
SALES (est): 104.5K **Privately Held**
SIC: 3993 Signs & advertising specialties

(G-13846)
GREAT AMERICA BEVERAGE CO LLC
8515 Sw 139th Ter (33158-1069)
PHONE..................................786 763-2027
Yolanda Zablah, *CEO*
Oscar Larach, *President*
EMP: 6 **EST:** 2013
SALES (est): 122.5K **Privately Held**
SIC: 2086 7389 Iced tea & fruit drinks, bottled & canned; business services

(G-13847)
HOLYLAND TAPESTRIES INC
14565 Sw 75th Ave (33158-1620)
PHONE..................................305 255-7955
Micki Lewis, *President*
EMP: 6 **EST:** 2001
SALES (est): 121.3K **Privately Held**
WEB: www.holylandtapestries.com
SIC: 2211 Tapestry fabrics, cotton

(G-13848)
ICO USA CORP
15815 Sw 89th Ave (33157-1910)
PHONE..................................305 253-0871
Yolanda Padilla, *President*
Andres G Padilla, *Vice Pres*
Manuel De Quintana, *Manager*
EMP: 5 **EST:** 2005
SALES (est): 364K **Privately Held**
SIC: 3699 Security control equipment & systems

(G-13849)
INKPRESSIONS INC
Also Called: Expert Printing and Graphics
13804 Sw 83rd Ct (33158-1028)
PHONE..................................305 261-0872
Alberto Silveira, *President*
Enrique Barrios, *Vice Pres*
EMP: 8 **EST:** 1988
SALES (est): 351.2K **Privately Held**
SIC: 2752 Commercial printing, offset

(G-13850)
METAL 2 METAL INC
Also Called: Manufacturing
17040 Sw 87th Ct (33157-4639)
PHONE..................................954 253-9450
Alejandro Selva, *President*
EMP: 5 **EST:** 2009
SALES (est): 410.5K **Privately Held**
SIC: 3443 3444 7381 3711 Weldments; pipe, sheet metal; sheet metal specialties, not stamped; detective & armored car services; cars, armored, assembly of

(G-13851)
MICROTOOL AND INSTRUMENT INC
15203 Sw 87th Ave (33157-2047)
PHONE..................................786 242-8780
Jennifer Leach, *President*
Neil Leach, *Vice Pres*
Brandy Myers, *Marketing Staff*
EMP: 36 **EST:** 1954
SQ FT: 4,500
SALES (est): 343.2K
SALES (corp-wide): 5.7MM **Privately Held**
SIC: 3545 3532 3425 3291 Diamond cutting tools for turning, boring, burnishing, etc.; mining machinery; saw blades & handsaws; abrasive products
PA: Diamonds Unlimited
1401 Brickell Ave
Miami FL
305 358-7770

(G-13852)
PAGE GOLFS YELLOW DIRECTORY
7251 Sw 152nd St (33157-2513)
PHONE..................................305 378-8038
David M Burnham, *President*
EMP: 10 **EST:** 1994
SALES (est): 543.5K **Privately Held**
WEB: www.golfyellowpages.com
SIC: 2741 Telephone & other directory publishing

(G-13853)
SANDOW SPECIALTY PRINTING INC
8260 Sw 151st St (33158-1958)
PHONE..................................305 255-5697
Leonard Sandow, *Principal*
EMP: 6 **EST:** 2016
SALES (est): 124.8K **Privately Held**
SIC: 2752 Commercial printing, offset

(G-13854)
SERVDATA INC
18001 Old Cutler Rd # 631 (33157-6441)
PHONE..................................305 269-7374
Yadira Chavez, *Financial Analy*
Kenneth L Burkhart, *Director*
EMP: 6 **EST:** 1999
SALES (est): 735.8K **Privately Held**
WEB: www.servdata.com
SIC: 7372 Prepackaged software

(G-13855)
TRAVELING CANVAS CORPORATION
15400 Sw 67th Ct (33157-2612)
PHONE..................................305 259-2001
Claudette B Davis, *Principal*
EMP: 7 **EST:** 2010
SALES (est): 68.9K **Privately Held**
SIC: 2211 Canvas

(G-13856)
VERTICAL REALITY INC
17511 Sw 99th Rd (33157-5313)
PHONE..................................305 238-4522
Anthony Kay, *CEO*
Kenneth Sharkey, *President*
◆ **EMP:** 8 **EST:** 1995
SQ FT: 5,000
SALES (est): 658.9K **Privately Held**
WEB: www.verticalreality.com
SIC: 3599 3949 Amusement park equipment; sporting & athletic goods

(G-13857)
VERTICAL REALITY MFG INC
17511 Sw 99th Rd (33157-5313)
PHONE..................................305 238-4522
Kenneth Sharkey, *CEO*
▲ **EMP:** 3 **EST:** 2008
SALES (est): 6.5MM **Privately Held**
SIC: 3599 Amusement park equipment

(G-13858)
WILLIAM BYRD & SONS INC
14720 Sw 83rd Pl (33158-1975)
P.O. Box 560058, Miami (33256-0058)
PHONE..................................786 573-3251
Robert Byrd, *President*
William Byrd, *Chairman*
James Byrd, *Admin Sec*
EMP: 3 **EST:** 1968
SALES (est): 9MM **Privately Held**
SIC: 3253 8611 Ceramic wall & floor tile; manufacturers' institute

Panacea
Wakulla County

(G-13859)
BROOKS WELDING & CONCRETE SHOP
Also Called: Brooks Concrete Service
1532 Coastal Hwy (32346-2154)
P.O. Box 82 (32346-0082)
PHONE..................................850 984-5279
James Brooks II, *President*
EMP: 10 **EST:** 1974
SQ FT: 2,000
SALES (est): 969.6K **Privately Held**
SIC: 3273 Ready-mixed concrete

(G-13860)
OUTLAW OYSTER COMPANY LLC
16 Chickasaw St (32346-2368)
PHONE..................................850 841-9344
Denita Sassor, *Principal*
Denita R Sassor, *Manager*
EMP: 7 **EST:** 2016

SALES (est): 543.8K Privately Held
WEB: www.outlawoysters.com
SIC: 2091 Oysters, preserved & cured

Panama City
Bay County

(G-13861)
AIR TEMP OF AMERICA INC
423 E 16th St (32405-5456)
PHONE..................................850 340-3017
Ricardo Herrera, *Manager*
EMP: 1 EST: 2018
SQ FT: 10,000
SALES (est): 7MM Privately Held
WEB: www.airtemp.com.mx
SIC: 3714 3629 Motor vehicle parts & accessories; radiators & radiator shells & cores, motor vehicle; condensers, for motors or generators
HQ: Air Temp De Mexico, S.A. De C.V.
Km. 10 Carr. Merida - Uman Tablaje
Rustico No. 419
Uman YUC. 97390

(G-13862)
ALLEN CUSTOM CABINETRY INC
6545 Bayline Dr (32404-4805)
PHONE..................................850 625-4713
EMP: 6 EST: 2018
SALES (est): 234.5K Privately Held
SIC: 2434 Wood kitchen cabinets

(G-13863)
AMERICAN CLASSIFIEDS
Also Called: Thrifty Nickle Want ADS
1522 Chestnut Ave (32405-2576)
P.O. Box 35115 (32412-5115)
PHONE..................................850 747-1155
Frank Kerr, *President*
EMP: 12 EST: 2006
SALES (est): 266.8K Privately Held
SIC: 2711 2741 Job printing & newspaper publishing combined; miscellaneous publishing

(G-13864)
ARGOS USA LLC
1601 Maple Ave (32405-6044)
PHONE..................................850 872-1209
Romelda Porter, *Purch Mgr*
Deveron Hooker, *Purchasing*
Rocky Dillard, *Credit Staff*
Patrick Passmore, *Human Res Mgr*
Tom Slosser, *Sales Staff*
EMP: 28 Privately Held
WEB: www.argos-us.com
SIC: 3273 Ready-mixed concrete
HQ: Argos Usa Llc
3015 Windward Plz Ste 300
Alpharetta GA 30005
678 368-4300

(G-13865)
ART OF IRON INC
311 W 35th Ct (32405-3358)
P.O. Box 32 (32402-0032)
PHONE..................................850 819-1500
Debra S Sanders, *Principal*
EMP: 7 EST: 2006
SALES (est): 306.7K Privately Held
WEB: www.artofironpanamacity.com
SIC: 7692 Welding repair

(G-13866)
ASAP BRICK PAVERS AND MORE
2320 N East Ave (32405-6218)
PHONE..................................850 522-7123
Daniel Brooks, *Principal*
EMP: 7 EST: 2015
SALES (est): 113.3K Privately Held
WEB: www.asapbrickpavers.com
SIC: 2951 Asphalt paving mixtures & blocks

(G-13867)
BAY COUNTY BULLET
1714 W 23rd St (32405-2932)
PHONE..................................850 640-0855
Phil Lucas, *Principal*
EMP: 7 EST: 2009
SALES (est): 134.7K Privately Held
WEB: www.baybullet.com
SIC: 2711 Newspapers, publishing & printing

(G-13868)
BAY QUALITY PROSTHETIC LLC
2195 Jenks Ave Ste C (32405-4683)
PHONE..................................850 522-5343
Glenn Cottrill, *Principal*
EMP: 7 EST: 2014
SALES (est): 225.3K Privately Held
WEB: www.bayprosthetics.com
SIC: 3842 Limbs, artificial; prosthetic appliances

(G-13869)
BERG EUROPIPE HOLDING CORP (HQ)
5315 W 19th St (32401-1090)
P.O. Box 59209 (32412-0209)
PHONE..................................850 769-2273
Michael Graef, *Ch of Bd*
Dave Delie, *President*
Koichi Konuma, *VP Bus Dvlpt*
Angela Cherry, *Human Res Dir*
Anne Robinson, *Sales Staff*
EMP: 210 EST: 1983
SALES (est): 78.7MM
SALES (corp-wide): 859.1MM Privately Held
WEB: www.bergpipe.com
SIC: 3312 Pipes, iron & steel
PA: Europipe Gmbh
Pilgerstr. 2
Mulheim An Der Ruhr 45473
208 976-0

(G-13870)
BERG PIPE PANAMA CITY CORP (DH)
5315 W 19th St (32401-1090)
P.O. Box 59209 (32412-0209)
PHONE..................................850 769-2273
Ingo Riemer, *President*
George Price, *General Mgr*
Michael Berg, *Principal*
Vincent N Berg, *Principal*
John Burton, *COO*
◆ EMP: 210 EST: 1979
SQ FT: 20,000
SALES (est): 78.7MM
SALES (corp-wide): 859.1MM Privately Held
WEB: www.bergpipe.com
SIC: 3317 Pipes, seamless steel

(G-13871)
BESTWAY PORTABLE BUILDING INC
2919 N Highway 231 (32405-6801)
PHONE..................................850 747-1984
Ricky Smith, *Manager*
EMP: 10
SQ FT: 7,600 Privately Held
WEB: www.bestwayportablebuildings.com
SIC: 3448 Prefabricated metal buildings
PA: Bestway Portable Building Inc
2815 E 15th St
Panama City FL 32405

(G-13872)
BIG COUNTRY SMALL ENGINE
5412 E Highway 22 (32404-6324)
PHONE..................................850 348-9022
David Lagrange, *General Mgr*
EMP: 7 EST: 2012
SALES (est): 149.4K Privately Held
SIC: 3599 Machine shop, jobbing & repair

(G-13873)
BISI FASTENERS LLC
2009 Poplar Pl 302 (32405-8213)
PHONE..................................850 913-0101
EMP: 7 EST: 2018
SALES (est): 268K Privately Held
WEB: www.bisifasteners.com
SIC: 3965 Fasteners

(G-13874)
BRUNSWICK CORPORATION
Also Called: Mercury Marine Power Division
11 College Ave (32401-4847)
PHONE..................................850 769-1011
Bill Harris, *Branch Mgr*
EMP: 9
SALES (corp-wide): 4.3B Publicly Held
WEB: www.brunswick.com
SIC: 3519 Outboard motors
PA: Brunswick Corporation
26125 N Riverwoods Blvd # 500
Mettawa IL 60045
847 735-4700

(G-13875)
BUS BULLETIN INC
3822 Patrick Rd (32409-6605)
PHONE..................................850 271-0017
John R Smith, *Owner*
EMP: 6 EST: 2011
SALES (est): 201.8K Privately Held
WEB: www.busbulletin.com
SIC: 2711 Newspapers, publishing & printing

(G-13876)
CCBCC OPERATIONS LLC
Also Called: Coca-Cola
300 W 5th St (32401-2608)
PHONE..................................850 785-6171
Grey Brewington, *Branch Mgr*
EMP: 63
SQ FT: 10,000
SALES (corp-wide): 5B Publicly Held
WEB: www.coca-cola.com
SIC: 2086 Bottled & canned soft drinks
HQ: Ccbcc Operations, Llc
4100 Coca Cola Plz
Charlotte NC 28211
704 364-8728

(G-13877)
CEDAR CREEK LOGGING INC
4138 Harry Wells Rd (32409-2472)
PHONE..................................850 832-0133
Shane Messick, *Principal*
EMP: 15 EST: 2013
SALES (est): 1.4MM Privately Held
SIC: 2411 Logging camps & contractors

(G-13878)
CEMEX MATERIALS LLC
714 Transmitter Rd (32401-5365)
PHONE..................................850 769-2243
Eric Werning, *Principal*
EMP: 73 Privately Held
SIC: 3273 Ready-mixed concrete
HQ: Cemex Materials Llc
1501 Belvedere Rd
West Palm Beach FL 33406
561 833-5555

(G-13879)
CHARLES BRYANT ENTERPRISES
Also Called: Mrs Traylors Plntn Style Foods
2700 Whisperwood Ln (32405-4485)
PHONE..................................850 785-3604
Charles Bryant, *President*
Steve Schnackenberg, *Vice Pres*
Carolyn Bryant, *Admin Sec*
EMP: 7 EST: 1982
SQ FT: 1,600
SALES (est): 350K Privately Held
SIC: 2041 2099 2038 Doughs, frozen or refrigerated; food preparations; frozen specialties

(G-13880)
CHENEGA MANUFACTURING SVCS LLC
1509 Saint Andrews Blvd (32405-2835)
P.O. Box 240988, Anchorage AK (99524-0988)
PHONE..................................850 763-6013
Paul Edwards, *General Mgr*
Robert Kelly, *Buyer*
Ken Ogden,
Lori Schneider, *Administration*
EMP: 35
SALES: 1.2MM Privately Held
WEB: www.chenegaehf.com
SIC: 3629 Electronic generation equipment
PA: Chenega Corporation
3000 C St Ste 301
Anchorage AK 99503

(G-13881)
CLAYTON HOMES INC
Also Called: Love Homes
2310 E 15th St (32405-6346)
PHONE..................................850 785-3302
Jeremy King, *Manager*
EMP: 6
SALES (corp-wide): 245.5B Publicly Held
WEB: www.claytonhomes.com
SIC: 2451 Mobile homes
HQ: Clayton Homes, Inc.
5000 Clayton Rd
Maryville TN 37804
865 380-3000

(G-13882)
COASTAL ACQUISITIONS FLA LLC (PA)
2120 E Business 98 (32401-4383)
PHONE..................................850 769-9423
William Carr,
Jerry Carr,
Phillip Santora,
EMP: 11 EST: 2017
SALES (est): 2.1MM Privately Held
WEB: www.allmetalbuildingsystems.com
SIC: 3441 Fabricated structural metal

(G-13883)
COASTAL ACQUISITIONS FLA LLC
Also Called: All Metal Roofing
2120 E 5th St (32401-4383)
PHONE..................................850 769-9423
Jim Armour, *Branch Mgr*
EMP: 10
SALES (corp-wide): 2.1MM Privately Held
WEB: www.allmetalbuildingsystems.com
SIC: 2952 1761 Roofing materials; roofing contractor
PA: Coastal Acquisitions Of Florida, Llc
2120 E Business 98
Panama City FL 32401
850 769-9423

(G-13884)
COASTAL LOGGING INC
4138 Harry Wells Rd (32409-2472)
PHONE..................................850 832-0133
Russell Scott, *Principal*
EMP: 11 EST: 2009
SALES (est): 717.3K Privately Held
SIC: 2411 Logging

(G-13885)
COASTAL MACHINE LLC
7424 Coastal Dr (32404-4015)
PHONE..................................850 769-6117
Gregory Clubbs,
EMP: 7 EST: 2016
SALES (est): 532.4K Privately Held
SIC: 3451 3728 3443 3541 Screw machine products; aircraft parts & equipment; fabricated plate work (boiler shop); machine tools, metal cutting type; machine tools, metal forming type

(G-13886)
COASTAL MILLWORKS & MORE LLC
1714 Wolfrun Ln (32405-8804)
PHONE..................................850 250-6672
Derik Hall, *Manager*
EMP: 7 EST: 2017
SALES (est): 152.8K Privately Held
WEB: www.coastalmillworks.com
SIC: 2431 Millwork

(G-13887)
COLOR PRESS PRINT INC
3430 Highway 77 Ste D (32405-5011)
PHONE..................................850 763-9884
Lorayne J Evans, *President*
Henry H Evans III, *Vice Pres*
EMP: 5 EST: 1985
SQ FT: 5,000
SALES (est): 559.2K Privately Held
WEB: www.colorpressprinting.com
SIC: 2752 Commercial printing, offset

GEOGRAPHIC

(G-13888)
CREAMER CORP
338 W Highway 388 (32409-1108)
P.O. Box 8566 (32409-8566)
PHONE..................................850 265-2700
EMP: 7
SALES (est): 885K **Privately Held**
SIC: 2411 2421 Logging Sawmill/Planing Mill

(G-13889)
CREATIVE PRINTING BAY CNTY INC
Also Called: Creative Prtg & Screen Designs
1328 Harrison Ave (32401-2435)
PHONE..................................850 784-1645
Stephen J Ruff, *President*
Sheila Ruff, *Vice Pres*
EMP: 10 **EST:** 1982
SQ FT: 5,000
SALES (est): 1.2MM **Privately Held**
WEB: www.getcreativepc.com
SIC: 3993 2752 Signs & advertising specialties; commercial printing, offset

(G-13890)
CUSTOM WOODWORKING
4312 Brewton Ln (32404-5206)
PHONE..................................850 319-4440
Mark G Welch, *President*
EMP: 6 **EST:** 2017
SALES (est): 110.1K **Privately Held**
SIC: 2431 Millwork

(G-13891)
DESTINATION PAVERS LLC
2827 Cynthia Ct (32405-7210)
PHONE..................................850 319-6551
Filho Osvaldino A Santos, *Principal*
EMP: 9 **EST:** 2012
SALES (est): 1.7MM **Privately Held**
SIC: 3531 Pavers

(G-13892)
DETECT INC (PA)
2817 Highway 77 (32405-4409)
PHONE..................................850 763-7200
Gary W Andrews, *Ch of Bd*
Ronald L Merritt, *Chairman*
Larry Hayes, *Prdtn Mgr*
Bob Weber, *Engineer*
Gary Zimmerman, *Engineer*
EMP: 19 **EST:** 2003
SQ FT: 7,000
SALES (est): 11.8MM **Privately Held**
WEB: www.detect-inc.com
SIC: 3812 Radar systems & equipment

(G-13893)
DIGITRAX INC
2443 Transmitter Rd (32404-3157)
PHONE..................................850 872-9890
Zana Ireland, *President*
Anthony Ireland, *Chairman*
Stan Miller, *Purch Mgr*
▲ **EMP:** 45 **EST:** 1993
SQ FT: 12,000
SALES (est): 7.2MM **Privately Held**
WEB: www.digitrax.com
SIC: 3612 Power & distribution transformers; specialty transformers

(G-13894)
DOVER CYLINDER HEAD INC (PA)
2704 W 15th St 98 (32401-1360)
PHONE..................................850 785-6569
James Thomas Dover, *President*
Dianne Jones, *Corp Secy*
Dan Gardner, *Vice Pres*
EMP: 26 **EST:** 1979
SQ FT: 40,000
SALES (est): 2.4MM **Privately Held**
WEB: www.doverpanamacity.com
SIC: 3714 Motor vehicle parts & accessories

(G-13895)
EASTERN SHIPBUILDING GROUP INC (PA)
2200 Nelson Ave (32401-4969)
PHONE..................................850 763-1900
Brian D Isernia, *President*
Benny C Bramblette, *General Mgr*
Donnie Bowen, *Superintendent*
Henry Sapp, *Superintendent*
Jacob Stevens, *Superintendent*
▲ **EMP:** 450
SQ FT: 200,000
SALES: 147.8MM **Privately Held**
WEB: www.easternshipbuilding.com
SIC: 3731 Shipbuilding & repairing

(G-13896)
EASTERN SHIPBUILDING GROUP INC
13300 Allanton Rd (32404-2816)
PHONE..................................850 522-7400
Chris Hill, *Project Mgr*
Kenneth Winpigler, *Project Mgr*
Joe Murphy, *Purch Mgr*
Carol Decker, *Buyer*
Cindy Jorde, *Buyer*
EMP: 525
SALES (corp-wide): 147.8MM **Privately Held**
WEB: www.easternshipbuilding.com
SIC: 3441 Fabricated structural metal for ships; ship sections, prefabricated metal
PA: Eastern Shipbuilding Group, Inc.
2200 Nelson Ave
Panama City FL 32401
850 763-1900

(G-13897)
EASTERN SHIPYARDS INC
2200 Nelson Ave (32401-4969)
P.O. Box 960 (32402-0960)
PHONE..................................850 763-1900
Brian D'Isernia, *President*
Kenneth Monroe, *Vice Pres*
Marvin Serna, *VP Opers*
Joseph Murphy, *Purch Mgr*
Tammara Lashley, *Supervisor*
EMP: 73 **EST:** 1987
SALES (est): 7.4MM **Privately Held**
SIC: 3731 Shipbuilding & repairing

(G-13898)
EL JALICIENSE INC
232 S Tyndall Pkwy (32404-6723)
PHONE..................................850 481-1232
Jesus Carranza, *President*
EMP: 15 **EST:** 2016
SALES (est): 603.3K **Privately Held**
WEB: www.jaliciense.com
SIC: 2099 Seasonings & spices

(G-13899)
EMERALD COAST FABRICATION
53o Gulf View Dr (32413-3001)
PHONE..................................850 235-1174
James Tatanish, *Owner*
EMP: 7 **EST:** 2002
SALES (est): 54.8K **Privately Held**
WEB: www.emeraldcoastfabrication.com
SIC: 2399 Fabricated textile products

(G-13900)
FAT AND WEIRD COOKIE CO LLC
2540 Jenks Ave (32405-4310)
PHONE..................................850 832-9150
EMP: 14 **EST:** 2018
SALES (est): 4MM **Privately Held**
SIC: 2051 Bakery products, partially cooked (except frozen)

(G-13901)
FIBEROPTIC ENGINEERING CORP
6541 Bayline Dr (32404-4805)
PHONE..................................850 763-2289
Francis Pettis, *President*
Ken Pettis, *Vice Pres*
EMP: 16 **EST:** 1979
SQ FT: 8,900
SALES (est): 546.9K **Privately Held**
WEB: www.fiberopticengineeringcorp.com
SIC: 3827 Optical test & inspection equipment

(G-13902)
FINLAYSON ENTERPRISES INC
Also Called: CF Sign and Stamp Company
1802 Beck Ave (32405-2569)
PHONE..................................850 785-7953
Carolyn Finlayson, *President*
EMP: 8 **EST:** 1984
SQ FT: 2,000
SALES (est): 741.2K **Privately Held**
SIC: 3953 3993 3479 Embossing seals & hand stamps; signs, not made in custom sign painting shops; engraving jewelry silverware, or metal

(G-13903)
FLORIDA CUSTOM CABINETS INC
3536 E Orlando Rd (32404-2051)
PHONE..................................850 769-4781
William Lawrence, *President*
EMP: 6 **EST:** 2002
SQ FT: 4,000
SALES (est): 475.2K **Privately Held**
WEB: www.floridacustomcabinetsinc.com
SIC: 2434 Wood kitchen cabinets

(G-13904)
FLOWERS BAKING CO LLC
2133 Transmitter Rd (32404-3154)
PHONE..................................850 763-2541
Buddy Danley, *Manager*
EMP: 7
SALES (corp-wide): 4.3B **Publicly Held**
SIC: 2051 Bread, cake & related products
HQ: Flowers Baking Co. Of Lynchburg, Llc
1905 Hollins Mill Rd
Lynchburg VA 24503
434 528-0441

(G-13905)
FREEMAN ELECTRIC CO INC
534 Oak Ave (32401-2648)
P.O. Box 2267 (32402-2267)
PHONE..................................850 785-7448
John T Duncan III, *President*
Michael A Duncan, *Vice Pres*
Margaret Duncan, *Treasurer*
Mike Conroy, *Manager*
EMP: 12 **EST:** 1936
SQ FT: 10,000
SALES (est): 1.5MM **Privately Held**
WEB: www.signcompanydothan.com
SIC: 3993 1761 1731 Electric signs; sheet metalwork; general electrical contractor

(G-13906)
GADDIE CONSTRUCTION CO
3391 State Ave (32405-3346)
PHONE..................................850 215-8421
William R Gaddie, *Principal*
EMP: 6 **EST:** 2008
SALES (est): 84.6K **Privately Held**
SIC: 2822 Synthetic rubber

(G-13907)
GARMENT GEAR INC
1522 Degama Ave (32405-3717)
PHONE..................................850 215-2121
Daniel Strickland, *President*
Dallas Strickland, *Vice Pres*
EMP: 10 **EST:** 2000
SQ FT: 9,000
SALES (est): 2.7MM **Privately Held**
WEB: www.garmentgear.com
SIC: 2759 Screen printing

(G-13908)
GENERAL SCIENTIFIC CORPORATION
Also Called: General Scientific Mfg
1300 Thomas Dr (32408-5801)
PHONE..................................850 866-9636
Otto Fazekas, *Controller*
Sharon Chang, *VP Sales*
Karl Schwartz, *Comms Dir*
Sharon Watley, *Branch Mgr*
Dustin Torres, *Manager*
EMP: 6
SALES (corp-wide): 7.4MM **Privately Held**
WEB: www.surgitel.com
SIC: 3625 3812 3728 3699 Marine & navy auxiliary controls; search & navigation equipment; aircraft parts & equipment; electrical equipment & supplies
PA: General Scientific Corporation
7925 Jones Branch Dr # 2300
Mc Lean VA 22102
703 561-4169

(G-13909)
GIGLI ENTERPRISES INC (PA)
Also Called: Divers Den
4833 E Business Hwy 98 (32404-7019)
PHONE..................................850 871-4777
Joann Moore, *President*
Stacie R Galbreath, *Vice Pres*
Lana Blood,
EMP: 6 **EST:** 1986
SQ FT: 8,000
SALES (est): 2.3MM **Privately Held**
WEB: www.giglienterprises.com
SIC: 3728 5941 Aircraft parts & equipment; skin diving, scuba equipment & supplies

(G-13910)
GKN AEROSPACE FLORIDA LLC
6051 Ventr Crossings Blvd (32409-1165)
P.O. Box 4009, Hazelwood MO (63042-0609)
PHONE..................................314 412-8311
Clayton Fox, *Director*
Douglas Steinman,
EMP: 99 **EST:** 2016
SALES (est): 22.8MM
SALES (corp-wide): 11.6B **Privately Held**
WEB: www.gkn.com
SIC: 3721 3812 Aircraft; aircraft/aerospace flight instruments & guidance systems
HQ: Gkn Limited
2nd Floor, One Central Boulevard
Solihull W MIDLANDS B90 8
121 210-9800

(G-13911)
GULF COAST HYPERBERIC INC
Also Called: Gulf Coast Hyperbarics
215 Forest Park Cir (32405-4916)
PHONE..................................850 271-1441
James W Mc Carthy, *President*
EMP: 5 **EST:** 1984
SALES (est): 432.7K **Privately Held**
WEB: www.gulfcoasthyperbarics.com
SIC: 3841 Medical instruments & equipment, blood & bone work

(G-13912)
GULF COAST TIMBER COMPANY
8206 S Holland Rd (32409-2060)
PHONE..................................850 271-8818
EMP: 8
SALES (est): 952K **Privately Held**
SIC: 2411 Logging

(G-13913)
GULF GLO BANNERS AND SIGNS LLC
8808 Front Beach Rd (32407-4232)
P.O. Box 9591 (32417-9591)
PHONE..................................850 234-0952
John Anderson, *Mng Member*
Susan Anderson,
EMP: 7 **EST:** 1978
SQ FT: 1,200
SALES (est): 508.9K **Privately Held**
WEB: www.gulfglo.com
SIC: 2399 5961 Banners, made from fabric; mail order house

(G-13914)
HELI-TECH INC
3621 Frankford Ave (32405-1907)
PHONE..................................850 763-9000
Kennen Thrasher, *President*
Anna Thrasher, *Corp Secy*
James Gunner Thrasher, *Vice Pres*
EMP: 15 **EST:** 1988
SQ FT: 21,000
SALES (est): 2.5MM **Privately Held**
WEB: www.helitechinc.com
SIC: 3721 3728 4581 5599 Helicopters; aircraft parts & equipment; aircraft servicing & repairing; aircraft instruments, equipment or parts

(G-13915)
HOME WORKS BAY COUNTY INC
4902 E Highway 98 (32404-6831)
PHONE..................................850 215-7880
Gregory T Guidry, *President*

▲ = Import ▼=Export
◆ =Import/Export

EMP: 5 EST: 2005
SALES (est): 329.4K Privately Held
WEB: www.homeworksofbaycounty.net
SIC: 2434 2499 Wood kitchen cabinets; decorative wood & woodwork

(G-13916)
ICE SHEET METAL LLC
29 E 10th St (32401-2980)
PHONE....850 872-2129
Michael J Hobbs R,
Van Willoughby,
EMP: 8 EST: 2019
SALES (est): 543.9K Privately Held
SIC: 3444 Sheet metalwork

(G-13917)
INK TRAX INC
238 W 5th St (32401-2643)
PHONE....850 235-4849
Jerry Walters, *President*
Stephanie Tulacz, *Graphic Designe*
EMP: 10 EST: 1994
SQ FT: 7,500
SALES (est): 960K Privately Held
WEB: www.inktrax.com
SIC: 2759 Screen printing

(G-13918)
INSTITUTE FOR PROSTHETIC ADVAN
Also Called: IPA Prosthetics & Orthotics
2315 Ruth Hentz Ave (32405-2260)
P.O. Box 960, Lynn Haven (32444-0960)
PHONE....850 784-0320
John Fredrick, *Owner*
EMP: 8 EST: 1995
SQ FT: 3,180
SALES (est): 767.4K Privately Held
SIC: 3842 5999 Limbs, artificial; orthopedic & prosthesis applications

(G-13919)
J & J DOOR MANUFACTURING INC
2325 Transmitter Rd (32404-3156)
PHONE....850 769-2554
Jayson Gay, *President*
Jerry L Weeks Jr, *Vice Pres*
EMP: 20 EST: 1995
SQ FT: 16,000
SALES (est): 1.2MM Privately Held
WEB: www.jandjdoormfg.com
SIC: 2431 Millwork

(G-13920)
JAYCO WOODWORKS INC
9338 Resota Beach Rd (32409-2184)
PHONE....850 814-3041
Michael J Parish, *Principal*
EMP: 7 EST: 2003
SALES (est): 213.9K Privately Held
SIC: 2431 Millwork

(G-13921)
JETBOATPILOT LLC
3825b W Highway 390 (32405-3229)
PHONE....850 960-3236
Will Owen, *CEO*
EMP: 11 EST: 2010
SALES (est): 2.1MM Privately Held
WEB: www.jetboatpilot.com
SIC: 3531 5088 Marine related equipment; marine supplies

(G-13922)
JOHNSON BROTHERS WHL MEATS INC
1640 Martin Luther King J (32405-5430)
P.O. Box 729 (32402-0729)
PHONE....850 763-2828
Paul Johnson, *President*
David Johnson, *General Mgr*
David M Johnson, *Corp Secy*
EMP: 30 EST: 1930
SQ FT: 2,115
SALES (est): 1.3MM Privately Held
SIC: 2011 5141 2015 2013 Meat packing plants; groceries, general line; poultry slaughtering & processing; sausages & other prepared meats

(G-13923)
K & K PRECISION MANUFACTURING
2307 Industrial Dr (32405-6039)
P.O. Box 839, Lynn Haven (32444-0839)
PHONE....850 769-9080
Ronald Kiefer, *President*
Glen Kiefer, *General Mgr*
Mary Kiefer, *Corp Secy*
EMP: 6 EST: 1978
SQ FT: 7,000
SALES (est): 479.5K Privately Held
SIC: 3599 Machine shop, jobbing & repair

(G-13924)
KRATON CHEMICAL LLC
2 S Everitt Ave (32401-4989)
PHONE....850 785-8521
Callie Noble, *Sr Project Mgr*
EMP: 57 EST: 2017
SALES (est): 6.4MM Privately Held
WEB: www.kraton.com
SIC: 2819 2869 2899 5169 Industrial inorganic chemicals; industrial organic chemicals; chemical preparations; industrial chemicals

(G-13925)
LEGACY VULCAN LLC
Also Called: Panama City Yard
2 Edwards Dr (32405-6097)
PHONE....850 914-9661
Eddie Wickfield, *Manager*
EMP: 6 Publicly Held
WEB: www.vulcanmaterials.com
SIC: 3273 Ready-mixed concrete
HQ: Legacy Vulcan, Llc
1200 Urban Center Dr
Vestavia AL 35242
205 298-3000

(G-13926)
LISA MC CALL
1740 Sherman Ave (32405-6283)
PHONE....850 265-4241
Randell McCall, *Owner*
Lisa Mc Call, *Co-Owner*
EMP: 10 EST: 2005
SALES (est): 635.8K Privately Held
SIC: 3599 Machine shop, jobbing & repair

(G-13927)
MARINE TRANSPORTATION SVCS INC
Also Called: Queen Craft
3615 Calhoun Ave (32405-1906)
PHONE....850 215-4557
Victor Hollis, *Manager*
EMP: 30
SQ FT: 41,210
SALES (corp-wide): 3.5MM Privately Held
WEB: www.marinetransportationservices.com
SIC: 3731 3732 Commercial cargo ships, building & repairing; boat building & repairing
PA: Marine Transportation Services, Inc.
3615 Calhoun Ave
Panama City FL 32405
850 769-1459

(G-13928)
MARITECH MACHINE INC
1740 Sherman Ave (32405-6283)
PHONE....850 872-0852
Randell McCall, *President*
Lisa McCall, *Vice Pres*
EMP: 20 EST: 1991
SQ FT: 7,000
SALES (est): 2.5MM Privately Held
WEB: www.maritechmachineinc.com
SIC: 3599 Machine shop, jobbing & repair

(G-13929)
MILLER MARINE YACHT SVC INC
7141 Grassy Point Rd (32409-1401)
P.O. Box 842, Lynn Haven (32444-0842)
PHONE....850 265-6768
William M Miller, *President*
EMP: 20 EST: 1998
SQ FT: 2,000
SALES (est): 886.8K Privately Held
WEB: www.millermarineinc.net
SIC: 3731 3732 Shipbuilding & repairing; boat building & repairing

(G-13930)
MONKEY SHACK
11840 Front Beach Rd A (32407-3684)
P.O. Box 9377 (32417-9377)
PHONE....850 234-0082
Danny Sedah, *Owner*
EMP: 6 EST: 2003
SALES (est): 500K Privately Held
SIC: 2254 Shirts & t-shirts (underwear), knit

(G-13931)
NEWS HERALD
221 E 23rd St Ste B (32405-4557)
PHONE....850 785-6550
EMP: 10 EST: 2017
SALES (est): 98.1K Privately Held
SIC: 2711 Newspapers, publishing & printing

(G-13932)
NORTHSIDE SHEET METAL INC
2836 Transmitter Rd (32404-3031)
P.O. Box 934 (32402-0934)
PHONE....850 769-1461
Chris Crittendon, *President*
Annette Crinttendon, *Admin Sec*
EMP: 6 EST: 1971
SQ FT: 3,000
SALES (est): 925.4K Privately Held
WEB: www.scallionlaw.com
SIC: 3444 Sheet metalwork

(G-13933)
OCEANEERING INTERNATIONAL INC
Oceanering Umbilical Solutions
1700 C Ave (32401-1057)
PHONE....985 329-3282
Shaun Roedel, *Division Mgr*
Calvin Smith, *Project Mgr*
Dennis Clardy, *Engineer*
Rebecca Lam, *Engineer*
David Emery, *Project Engr*
EMP: 150
SALES (corp-wide): 1.8B Publicly Held
WEB: www.oceaneering.com
SIC: 3357 3643 Fiber optic cable (insulated); power line cable
PA: Oceaneering International Inc
11911 Fm 529 Rd
Houston TX 77041
713 329-4500

(G-13934)
PANAMA CITY CONCRETE INC
1119 Lindenwood Dr (32405-3623)
P.O. Box 15911 (32406-5911)
PHONE....850 851-3637
EMP: 6 EST: 2018
SALES (est): 192.9K Privately Held
WEB: www.panamacityconcretecompany.com
SIC: 3273 Ready-mixed concrete

(G-13935)
PANAMA CITY NEWS HERALD (DH)
Also Called: Florida Freedom Newspapers Inc
501 W 11th St (32401-2330)
P.O. Box 1940 (32402-1940)
PHONE....850 747-5000
James Rosse, *Ch of Bd*
Ray Glenn, *Editor*
Will Glover, *Editor*
Dustin Kent, *Editor*
Jonathan Segal, *Vice Pres*
EMP: 110 EST: 1933
SQ FT: 46,000
SALES (est): 21.6MM
SALES (corp-wide): 3.4B Publicly Held
WEB: www.newsherald.com
SIC: 2711 Newspapers, publishing & printing
HQ: Gatehouse Media, Llc
175 Sullys Trl Fl 3
Pittsford NY 14534
585 598-0030

(G-13936)
PANAMA CITY PALLET INC
1706 Maple Ave (32405-6022)
PHONE....850 769-1040
EMP: 28 EST: 2019
SALES (est): 2.4MM Privately Held
WEB: www.connerindustries.com
SIC: 2448 Pallets, wood

(G-13937)
PANAMA CITY PETRO LLC
7409 E Highway 22 (32404-2501)
PHONE....850 215-9146
EMP: 6 EST: 2019
SALES (est): 131.6K Privately Held
SIC: 2999 Petroleum & coal products

(G-13938)
PANAMA CITY TINT CENTER
526 E 6th St (32401-3025)
PHONE....850 640-0167
Isaiah Dewan Gardner, *Owner*
EMP: 9 EST: 2012
SALES (est): 110K Privately Held
WEB: www.panamacitytoyota.com
SIC: 3211 Window glass, clear & colored

(G-13939)
PANAMA PALLETS CO INC
1706 Maple Ave (32405-6022)
PHONE....850 769-1040
Douglas H Lindsey, *President*
Tim Newitt, *Vice Pres*
EMP: 9 EST: 1995
SALES (est): 880K Privately Held
WEB: www.panamapallet.com
SIC: 2448 Pallets, wood

(G-13940)
PARTHENON PRINTS INC
909 W 39th St (32405-4841)
P.O. Box 2505 (32402-2505)
PHONE....850 769-8321
Gus Harris Jr, *CEO*
Theonne Harris, *President*
Gus Ajr Harris, *Vice Pres*
Chris Harris, *Safety Mgr*
Dorothy M Harris, *CFO*
▲ EMP: 35 EST: 1979
SQ FT: 112,000
SALES (est): 6.8MM Privately Held
WEB: www.parthenonprints.com
SIC: 2679 2396 Wallpaper; fabric printing & stamping

(G-13941)
PHILLIP & ROGER INC
Also Called: Weldco Mechanical Services
2201 N East Ave (32405-6215)
PHONE....850 763-6415
Joe Philip Davis, *President*
Roger Davis, *Corp Secy*
EMP: 8 EST: 1984
SQ FT: 5,400
SALES (est): 288.6K Privately Held
SIC: 7692 Welding repair

(G-13942)
PREMIER BRUSH INC
2230 Industrial Dr (32405-6036)
P.O. Box 15695 (32406-5695)
PHONE....850 271-5736
Brian Stopka, *President*
EMP: 8 EST: 1989
SQ FT: 10,000
SALES (est): 500K Privately Held
WEB: www.premierbrush.com
SIC: 3991 Brushes, except paint & varnish

(G-13943)
RAY MACHINE INC
3711 N Highway 231 (32404-9745)
PHONE....850 784-1116
Anthony Ray, *President*
Deborah Ray, *Controller*
EMP: 10
SQ FT: 8,000
SALES (est): 1.6MM Privately Held
WEB: www.raymachine.us
SIC: 3599 Machine shop, jobbing & repair

(G-13944)
REDDY ICE CORPORATION
1225 Moylan Rd (32407-4065)
P.O. Box 9083 (32417-9083)
PHONE....850 233-0128

David Ciatk, *Manager*
EMP: 12 **Privately Held**
WEB: www.reddyice.com
SIC: 2097 Manufactured ice
HQ: Reddy Ice Corporation
5710 Lbj Fwy Ste 300
Dallas TX 75240
214 526-6740

(G-13945)
RICHARDSONS CABINET WORKS
3724 Chandler Fenn Dr (32404-2246)
PHONE..................................850 832-8298
Charles T Richardson, *Principal*
EMP: 6 **EST:** 2008
SALES (est): 130.5K **Privately Held**
WEB: www.richardsoncabinetworks.com
SIC: 2434 Wood kitchen cabinets

(G-13946)
ROBOTIC SECURITY SYSTEMS INC
6530 E Highway 22 (32404-9521)
PHONE..................................850 871-9300
Joey Blair, *CEO*
EMP: 34 **EST:** 2003
SALES (est): 2.6MM **Privately Held**
WEB: www.rssi.com
SIC: 3441 Fabricated structural metal

(G-13947)
ROBOTICS FABRICATION INC
5835 Bay Line Dr (32404)
PHONE..................................850 896-4987
William Lewis, *President*
Larry Eod, *Opers Staff*
Lawrence Johns, *Opers Staff*
Keith Stallter Cfcm, *Contract Mgr*
Keith Stallter, *Contract Mgr*
EMP: 21 **EST:** 2011
SALES (est): 4MM **Privately Held**
WEB: www.roboticsfabrication.com
SIC: 3549 8744 1794 Assembly machines, including robotic; ; excavation & grading, building construction

(G-13948)
RSSI BARRIERS LLC
6530 E Highway 22 (32404-9521)
PHONE..................................850 871-9300
JD Dunn, *Parts Mgr*
Amanda B Blair, *Mng Member*
George Douglas, *Sr Project Mgr*
Joey W Blair,
EMP: 20 **EST:** 2010
SQ FT: 10,000
SALES (est): 5.6MM **Privately Held**
WEB: www.rssi.com
SIC: 3499 Barricades, metal

(G-13949)
SIGNS UNLIMITED OF BAY COUNTY
507 E 7th St (32401-3036)
P.O. Box 1664 (32402-1664)
PHONE..................................850 785-1061
Martin E Bell, *President*
Matin Bell II, *Vice Pres*
EMP: 5 **EST:** 1980
SQ FT: 5,000
SALES (est): 643.1K **Privately Held**
WEB: www.signsunlimitedpc.com
SIC: 3993 1799 Electric signs; neon signs; sign installation & maintenance

(G-13950)
SILVER SHEET FLORIDA INC
17742 Ashley Dr (32413-5119)
PHONE..................................850 230-9711
Tollie Potgieter, *President*
Annaliz Potgieter, *Vice Pres*
Mark Walden, *Manager*
EMP: 25 **EST:** 2003
SALES (est): 861.9K **Privately Held**
WEB: www.silversheetenterprises.com
SIC: 3444 Sheet metalwork

(G-13951)
SISCO MARINE LLC
Also Called: Marine Inland Fabricators
1725 Buchanan St (32409-1482)
PHONE..................................850 265-1383
Rudy Sistrunk, *Mng Member*
▼ **EMP:** 20 **EST:** 1980
SQ FT: 5,472
SALES (est): 2.3MM **Privately Held**
WEB: www.marineinland.com
SIC: 3731 Shipbuilding & repairing

(G-13952)
STEEL CITY INC
749 E 15th St (32405-5416)
P.O. Box 35036 (32412-5036)
PHONE..................................850 785-9596
Randall Coatney Jr, *CEO*
Steve Barnett, *President*
Rhonda C Williams, *Principal*
Rhonda Williams, *Treasurer*
EMP: 12 **EST:** 1983
SQ FT: 45,000
SALES (est): 2.6MM **Privately Held**
WEB: www.steelcitypc.com
SIC: 3441 5051 3444 1791 Fabricated structural metal; steel; sheet metalwork; structural steel erection; cranes & aerial lift equipment, rental or leasing

(G-13953)
SUNSHINE PIPING INC
6513 Bayline Dr (32404-4805)
PHONE..................................850 763-4834
Shirley P Scott, *President*
EMP: 25 **EST:** 1990
SQ FT: 60,000
SALES (est): 3.6MM **Privately Held**
WEB: www.hstrial-sunshinepipingin.homestead.com
SIC: 3498 Fabricated pipe & fittings

(G-13954)
TAUNTON TRUSS CO RED LOBS
910 E 23rd St (32405-5328)
PHONE..................................850 785-5566
Dave Parsons, *Principal*
EMP: 6 **EST:** 2005
SALES (est): 79.8K **Privately Held**
SIC: 2439 Trusses, wooden roof

(G-13955)
TEX-COAT LLC (HQ)
2422 E 15th St (32405-6348)
PHONE..................................800 454-0340
Chase Bean, *President*
Daniel Curry, *Vice Pres*
EMP: 39 **EST:** 2019
SALES (est): 12.3MM
SALES (corp-wide): 129.5MM **Privately Held**
WEB: www.texcote.com
SIC: 2851 Paints & paint additives
PA: Tnemec Company, Inc.
123 W 23rd Ave
Kansas City MO 64116
816 483-3400

(G-13956)
TRANE TECHNOLOGIES COMPANY LLC
Also Called: Ingersoll-Rand
200 Aberdeen Loop (32405-6413)
P.O. Box 1410, Lynn Haven (32444-6210)
PHONE..................................850 873-8200
Julie Smith, *Branch Mgr*
EMP: 700 **Privately Held**
WEB: www.ingersollrand.com
SIC: 3585 Air conditioning units, complete: domestic or industrial
HQ: Trane Technologies Company Llc
800 Beaty St
Davidson NC 28036
704 655-4000

(G-13957)
TRIPLE H CSTM WLDG FBRCTION LL
7420 Kingman St (32408-7617)
PHONE..................................850 851-5097
Jeremy A Farrow, *Principal*
EMP: 6 **EST:** 2017
SALES (est): 338.5K **Privately Held**
SIC: 7692 Welding repair

(G-13958)
U D T INC
2304 Grant Ave (32405-1359)
PHONE..................................850 784-0537
Troy Balsters, *President*
John Balsters, *Vice Pres*
Ken Clammer, *Program Mgr*
Robert Anglen, *IT/INT Sup*
Cassie L Osborn, *Admin Sec*
EMP: 8
SQ FT: 15,000
SALES (est): 1.5MM **Privately Held**
WEB: www.udtmachine.com
SIC: 3599 Machine shop, jobbing & repair

(G-13959)
US IRONWORKS COMPANY
328 Wahoo Rd (32408-7264)
P.O. Box 9220, Panama City Beach (32417-9220)
PHONE..................................850 588-5995
Michael R Owen, *President*
Joseph Fanell, *Vice Pres*
Ji H Bushell, *Admin Sec*
EMP: 15 **EST:** 2010
SALES (est): 1.3MM **Privately Held**
SIC: 3446 Architectural metalwork

(G-13960)
VERTICAL LAND INC (PA)
7950 Front Beach Rd (32407-4817)
PHONE..................................850 819-2535
Cynthia M Carter, *President*
EMP: 13 **EST:** 1977
SQ FT: 6,000
SALES (est): 2MM **Privately Held**
SIC: 2231 5714 5719 Felts, blanketing & upholstery fabrics: wool; draperies; window shades

(G-13961)
VERTICAL LAND INC
621 Mckenzie Ave (32401-3061)
PHONE..................................850 244-5263
Peggy Unknw, *President*
EMP: 12
SALES (corp-wide): 2MM **Privately Held**
SIC: 2591 2391 Blinds vertical; curtains & draperies
PA: Vertical Land, Inc.
7950 Front Beach Rd
Panama City FL 32407
850 819-2535

(G-13962)
WELLSTREAM INC
Also Called: Prime Flexible Products
6521 Bayline Dr (32404-4805)
PHONE..................................281 249-0900
Ashley Clack, *Associate*
EMP: 45
SALES (corp-wide): 1MM **Privately Held**
SIC: 3569 Filters & strainers, pipeline
PA: Wellstream Inc.
11202 Equity Dr Ste 350
Houston TX 77041
281 249-0900

(G-13963)
WELLSTREAM INTERNATIONAL LTD
6521 Bayline Dr (32404-4805)
PHONE..................................850 636-4800
Jeff Jordan, *Manager*
EMP: 250
SALES (corp-wide): 20.7B **Publicly Held**
WEB: www.bhge.com
SIC: 3317 3084 Steel pipe & tubes; plastics pipe
HQ: Wellstream International Limited
Wellstream House
Newcastle-Upon-Tyne NE6 3

(G-13964)
WESTROCK CP LLC
1 S Everitt Ave (32401-6900)
PHONE..................................850 785-4311
Joy Jones, *Branch Mgr*
EMP: 86
SALES (corp-wide): 17.5B **Publicly Held**
WEB: www.westrock.com
SIC: 2653 Boxes, corrugated: made from purchased materials
HQ: Westrock Cp, Llc
1000 Abernathy Rd Ste 125
Atlanta GA 30328

(G-13965)
WORLD STONE AND DESIGN LLC
19709 Panama Cy Bch Pkwy (32413-3924)
PHONE..................................850 235-0399
Rodrigo Mancilla, *Mng Member*
Girley Leiti,
EMP: 9 **EST:** 2004
SALES (est): 763.2K **Privately Held**
WEB: www.worldstonedesign.com
SIC: 3443 Fabricated plate work (boiler shop)

Panama City
Walton County

(G-13966)
ARRIAGA ORIGINALS
10343 E County Highway 30 # 112 (32461-6943)
PHONE..................................850 231-0084
EMP: 12
SALES (est): 1.2MM **Privately Held**
SIC: 3911 Mfg Precious Metal Jewelry

Panama City Beach
Bay County

(G-13967)
5 STAR COATINGS LLC
126 Escanaba Ave (32413-2205)
PHONE..................................850 628-3743
James Paravalos, *Principal*
EMP: 7 **EST:** 2011
SALES (est): 64.4K **Privately Held**
SIC: 3479 Metal coating & allied service

(G-13968)
ABIDE FAMILY WINERY INC
8401 N Lagoon Dr (32408-5110)
PHONE..................................850 258-0743
John Webster, *Principal*
EMP: 6 **EST:** 2018
SALES (est): 89.4K **Privately Held**
SIC: 2084 Wines

(G-13969)
ADVANCED DRAINAGE SYSTEMS INC
12405 Panama Cy Bch Pkwy (32407-2707)
PHONE..................................850 234-0004
EMP: 6
SALES (corp-wide): 1.9B **Publicly Held**
WEB: www.adspipe.com
SIC: 3084 Plastics pipe
PA: Advanced Drainage Systems, Inc.
4640 Trueman Blvd
Hilliard OH 43026
614 658-0050

(G-13970)
ARGOS USA LLC
17800 Ashley Dr (32413-5001)
PHONE..................................850 235-9600
Adam Kirkland, *Opers Mgr*
Ross Adolph, *Regl Sales Mgr*
Andy Workman, *Branch Mgr*
EMP: 28 **Privately Held**
WEB: www.argos-us.com
SIC: 3273 Ready-mixed concrete
HQ: Argos Usa Llc
3015 Windward Plz Ste 300
Alpharetta GA 30005
678 368-4300

(G-13971)
BAE SYSTEMS TECH SOL SRVC INC
600 Grand Panama Blvd (32407-3459)
PHONE..................................850 236-2428
Stephen Appleby, *Director*
EMP: 6
SALES (corp-wide): 25.6B **Privately Held**
SIC: 3812 Navigational systems & instruments
HQ: Bae Systems Technology Solutions & Services Inc.
520 Gaither Rd
Rockville MD 20850
703 847-5820

(G-13972)
BAY CABINETS AND MILLWORKS
20679 Panama Cy Bch Pkwy (32413-3722)
PHONE..................................850 215-1485
EMP: 8 **EST:** 2018
SALES (est): 717.2K **Privately Held**
WEB: www.baycabinetspc.com
SIC: 2434 Wood kitchen cabinets

(G-13973)
BOBCAT OF WIREGRASS INC (PA)
127 Griffin Blvd (32413-5123)
PHONE..................................334 792-5121
Ricky Ball, *President*
Heather Willis, *Office Mgr*
EMP: 10 **EST:** 2003
SALES (est): 1.2MM **Privately Held**
SIC: 3694 Engine electrical equipment

(G-13974)
BRUCE ROLAND ✪
Also Called: Visions Auto Spa
8000 Front Beach Rd (32407-4819)
PHONE..................................850 775-1497
Bruce Roland, *Owner*
EMP: 6 **EST:** 2021
SALES (est): 355.2K **Privately Held**
SIC: 2842 Automobile polish

(G-13975)
C4 GROUP LLC
7510 Holley Cir (32408-4952)
PHONE..................................850 230-4541
Kent Henry, *Buyer*
Scott E Therriault, *Mng Member*
Scott Therriault, *Mng Member*
Karen Therriault,
EMP: 14 **EST:** 2005
SALES (est): 1.3MM **Privately Held**
WEB: www.c4group.biz
SIC: 3599 Machine & other job shop work

(G-13976)
COAST PRODUCTS LLC
169 Griffin Blvd Unit 106 (32413-5239)
PHONE..................................850 235-2090
Robert Easter, *Mng Member*
EMP: 11 **EST:** 2009
SQ FT: 2,000
SALES (est): 1.1MM **Privately Held**
WEB: www.coastoem.com
SIC: 3088 Plastics plumbing fixtures

(G-13977)
GNS EMBROIDERY
1713 Moylan Rd (32407-4016)
PHONE..................................850 775-1147
Steve Owens, *Owner*
EMP: 6 **EST:** 2015
SALES (est): 310.3K **Privately Held**
WEB: www.gnsembroideryshop.com
SIC: 2395 Embroidery products, except schiffli machine; embroidery & art needlework

(G-13978)
GULF COAST CABINETRY INC
22200 Panama Cy Bch Pkwy (32413-3226)
PHONE..................................850 769-3799
Roger Clark, *President*
EMP: 6 **EST:** 2016
SQ FT: 1,800
SALES (est): 1.3MM **Privately Held**
WEB: www.gulfcoastcabinetry.com
SIC: 2434 Wood kitchen cabinets

(G-13979)
JOYNER INC
9740 Steel Field Rd (32413-9462)
PHONE..................................850 832-6326
Jeff B Joyner, *President*
EMP: 7 **EST:** 2007
SALES (est): 1.4MM **Privately Held**
SIC: 2411 5031 Logging; lumber, plywood & millwork

(G-13980)
MINE SURVIVAL INC
9210 Pnama Cy Bch Pkwy St (32407)
PHONE..................................850 774-0025
Robert N Moran, *President*
David Cowgill, *Vice Pres*
▼ **EMP:** 5 **EST:** 2014
SQ FT: 5,000
SALES (est): 5MM **Privately Held**
WEB: www.minesurvival.com
SIC: 3949 Skin diving equipment, scuba type

(G-13981)
PANHANDLE PAINT & DCTG LLC
Also Called: Benjamin Moore Authorized Ret
8103 Panama City Bch Pkwy (32407-4860)
P.O. Box 1810, Lynn Haven (32444-5810)
PHONE..................................850 596-9248
George Bass, *Mng Member*
EMP: 8 **EST:** 2013
SALES (est): 1MM **Privately Held**
WEB: www.panhandlepaints.com
SIC: 2851 5251 5231 Paints & allied products; hardware; paint, glass & wallpaper

(G-13982)
PARADIGM LEADERS LLC
Also Called: Paradigm Plastics
7946 Front Beach Rd (32407-4817)
PHONE..................................850 441-3289
Jamiel Vadell, *CEO*
Michelle Darko, *Office Mgr*
Richard Barnes, *CIO*
EMP: 5 **EST:** 2015
SALES (est): 458.5K **Privately Held**
WEB: www.paradigmleaders.com
SIC: 3089 8331 8249 5999 Injection molding of plastics; job training & vocational rehabilitation services; job training services; manpower training; business training services; educational aids & electronic training materials

(G-13983)
PRESS PRINT GRAPHICS LLC
106 N Gulf Blvd Ste C (32413-2884)
PHONE..................................850 249-3700
Jeff Weeks, *Manager*
Jeffrey Weeks,
Christopher Weeks,
EMP: 12 **EST:** 2008
SALES (est): 928.9K **Privately Held**
WEB: www.pressprintgraphics.com
SIC: 2752 Commercial printing, offset

(G-13984)
SIMPLY CABINETS LLC
630 Malaga Pl (32413-3934)
PHONE..................................850 541-3712
Zebulon T Taft, *Branch Mgr*
EMP: 12
SALES (corp-wide): 77.1K **Privately Held**
WEB: www.simplycabinetspcb.com
SIC: 2434 Wood kitchen cabinets
PA: Simply Cabinets, Llc
9527 Clarence St
Panama City Beach FL

(G-13985)
TEXTURED COATINGS
169 Griffin Blvd (32413-5238)
P.O. Box 35008, Panama City (32412-5008)
PHONE..................................850 360-1451
EMP: 7 **EST:** 2019
SALES (est): 945.8K **Privately Held**
SIC: 2851 Paints & allied products

(G-13986)
WORTHINGTON MILLWORK LLC
17842 Ashley Dr C (32413-5001)
PHONE..................................800 872-1608
Jay Kyle Boatwright, *Principal*
Lindsay Haisten, *Office Mgr*
EMP: 8 **EST:** 2004
SQ FT: 30,000
SALES (est): 1.1MM **Privately Held**
WEB: www.worthingtonmillwork.com
SIC: 2431 Millwork

Parkland
Broward County

(G-13987)
ABSOLUTE TECHNOLOGIES INC
6320 Nw 61st Ave (33067-4400)
PHONE..................................954 868-9045
John E Dagostino, *Principal*
EMP: 7 **EST:** 2012
SALES (est): 78K **Privately Held**
WEB: www.absolutetechnologies.com
SIC: 3599 Machine shop, jobbing & repair

(G-13988)
ATLANTIC MULTI FAMILY I LLC
9045 Vista Way (33076-2865)
PHONE..................................301 233-1261
James W Theobald, *Administration*
EMP: 17 **EST:** 2010
SALES (est): 2.5MM **Privately Held**
SIC: 3571 Personal computers (microcomputers)

(G-13989)
BECKER MICROBIAL PRODUCTS INC
11146 Nw 69th Pl (33076-3846)
PHONE..................................954 345-9321
Terry L Couch, *President*
▼ **EMP:** 8 **EST:** 1980
SALES (est): 670.6K **Privately Held**
WEB: www.beckermicrobialproductsinc.com
SIC: 2836 8733 Bacteriological media; bacteriological research

(G-13990)
CK DOCKSIDE SERVICES INC
6141 Nw 80th Ter (33067-1132)
PHONE..................................954 254-0263
Craig Koblitz, *Principal*
EMP: 6 **EST:** 2008
SALES (est): 158.5K **Privately Held**
SIC: 3732 Boat building & repairing

(G-13991)
INDIAN TONERS USA COMPANY
10625 Nw 69th Pl (33076-2969)
PHONE..................................954 600-5483
EMP: 6 **EST:** 2016
SALES (est): 260.2K **Privately Held**
WEB: www.indiantoners.com
SIC: 2893 Printing ink

(G-13992)
INNOVATIVE MONEY CONCEPTS
12560 Nw 83rd Ct (33076-4931)
PHONE..................................954 748-6197
Paul D Salvati, *Director*
EMP: 6 **EST:** 1995
SALES (est): 341.1K **Privately Held**
WEB: www.moneyconcepts.com
SIC: 3471 Plating of metals or formed products

(G-13993)
JIBE LTG N AMER LTD LBLTY CO
5917 Nw 63rd Way (33067-1525)
PHONE..................................954 899-4040
Todd Darling,
EMP: 6
SALES (est): 251.5K **Privately Held**
SIC: 3648 Lighting fixtures, except electric: residential

(G-13994)
JIMENEZ ENTERPRISES GROUP
5851 Holmberg Rd Apt 3723 (33067-4527)
PHONE..................................561 391-6800
Eduardo Jimenez, *Principal*
EMP: 19
SALES (corp-wide): 86.6K **Privately Held**
SIC: 3841 Surgical & medical instruments
PA: Jimenez Enterprises Group, Corp
10855 Nw 50th St Apt 204
Doral FL 33178
561 542-7709

(G-13995)
LEMON GRASS INDUSTRIES INC
5920 Nw 59th Ave (33067-4427)
PHONE..................................954 418-6110
Suzette Cascio, *President*
Frances Cascio, *Vice Pres*
▼ **EMP:** 5
SALES (est): 759.8K **Privately Held**
WEB: www.lemongrasscandles.com
SIC: 3999 Candles

(G-13996)
LIMB PRESERVATION INST INC
11529 Nw 72nd Pl (33076-3352)
PHONE..................................954 755-5726
Robert Snyder, *Principal*
EMP: 6 **EST:** 2013
SALES (est): 79.7K **Privately Held**
WEB: www.limbpreservationcolorado.com
SIC: 3842 Limbs, artificial

(G-13997)
PACIFIC LINK IMPORTS INC
11497 Nw 81st Pl (33076-4967)
PHONE..................................954 605-6071
James Baron, *President*
Kathy Baron, *CFO*
▲ **EMP:** 2 **EST:** 2015
SALES (est): 10.5MM **Privately Held**
WEB: www.pacificlinkimports.com
SIC: 3089 2676 Kitchenware, plastic; napkins, paper: made from purchased paper

(G-13998)
PEEKE INDUSTRIES INC
6529 Nw 99th Ave (33076-2333)
PHONE..................................954 796-1938
Maryruth Peeke, *Principal*
EMP: 6 **EST:** 2017
SALES (est): 99.3K **Privately Held**
SIC: 3999 Manufacturing industries

(G-13999)
PROMOWEAR
9547 Cinnamon Ct (33076-4419)
PHONE..................................561 372-0505
Andrea Bomwell, *President*
EMP: 6 **EST:** 2006
SALES (est): 663.4K **Privately Held**
WEB: www.promowearusa.com
SIC: 2395 Embroidery products, except schiffli machine; embroidery & art needlework

(G-14000)
SAFETOGETHER LTD LIABILITY CO
5917 Nw 63rd Way (33067-1525)
PHONE..................................954 227-2236
Todd Darling, *CEO*
Scott Racy, *CEO*
Mehron Talebi, *Principal*
Robert King, *Exec VP*
Christopher Mackie, *Director*
EMP: 8
SALES (est): 319.7K **Privately Held**
SIC: 3646 Commercial indusl & institutional electric lighting fixtures

(G-14001)
SKYMASTERS AVIATION LLC
6640 Stratford Dr (33067-1655)
PHONE..................................954 796-7622
Leslie Naveh,
EMP: 6 **EST:** 2007
SALES (est): 90.4K **Privately Held**
WEB: www.skymastersaviation.com
SIC: 3728 Aircraft parts & equipment

(G-14002)
SUPERIOR FABRICS INC
7901 S Woodridge Dr (33067-2392)
PHONE..................................954 975-8122
Alex Fryburg, *Ch of Bd*
Robert Fryburg, *President*
David Fryburg, *Vice Pres*
EMP: 37 **EST:** 1895
SALES (est): 750.2K **Privately Held**
WEB: www.superiorfabrics.com
SIC: 2211 2297 2221 Broadwoven fabric mills, cotton; nonwoven fabrics; broadwoven fabric mills, manmade

Parrish
Manatee County

(G-14003)
ANGLO SILVER LINER CO
7019 Indus Valley Cir (34219-2861)
PHONE....................................508 943-1440
Dilip Mehta, *President*
Paul Fitzpatrick, *Editor*
EMP: 10 **EST:** 1998
SALES (est): 276.3K **Privately Held**
SIC: 2221 Broadwoven fabric mills, manmade

(G-14004)
B2 INTEGRATIONS LLC
5315 105th Ter E (34219-4545)
PHONE....................................727 871-7025
Christopher Bennett, *Principal*
EMP: 6 **EST:** 2016
SALES (est): 94.7K **Privately Held**
SIC: 7372 Prepackaged software

(G-14005)
CARRIERS DIRECT INC
2623 Little Country Rd (34219-9262)
PHONE....................................941 776-2979
Neil Bradley, *CEO*
EMP: 14 **EST:** 2011
SQ FT: 27,000
SALES (est): 1.7MM **Privately Held**
WEB: www.carriersdirect.us
SIC: 3537 Trucks: freight, baggage, etc.: industrial, except mining

(G-14006)
GRAPHIX SOLUTIONS OF AMERICA
12015 Major Turner Run (34219-1263)
PHONE....................................727 898-6744
Lee F Romig, *President*
EMP: 11 **EST:** 1938
SQ FT: 6,000
SALES (est): 301.7K **Privately Held**
SIC: 2752 2759 Commercial printing, offset; commercial printing

(G-14007)
SHORELINE PUBLISHING INC
3629 Wilderness Blvd W (34219-9350)
PHONE....................................914 500-5456
EMP: 6 **EST:** 2014
SALES (est): 99.6K **Privately Held**
WEB: www.shorelinepublishing.com
SIC: 2741 Miscellaneous publishing

Patrick Afb
Brevard County

(G-14008)
RAYTHEON COMPANY
1034 S Patrick Dr (32925-3516)
PHONE....................................321 494-3323
EMP: 6
SALES (corp-wide): 56.5B **Publicly Held**
WEB: www.rtx.com
SIC: 3812 Search & navigation equipment
HQ: Raytheon Company
870 Winter St
Waltham MA 02451
781 522-3000

Pembroke Park
Broward County

(G-14009)
INUSA MANUFACTURING LLC
2500 Sw 32nd Ave (33023-7703)
PHONE....................................786 451-5227
Moises Sterental, *Principal*
EMP: 7 **EST:** 2017
SALES (est): 643.9K **Privately Held**
SIC: 3999 Manufacturing industries

(G-14010)
PSTEIN INC
Also Called: Philip Stein
4350 W Hllandale Bch Blvd (33023-4479)
PHONE....................................305 373-0037
Wilhelm Stein, *President*
Miguel Martinez, *President*
Ruthie Mink, *Vice Pres*
Elisa Orlandi, *Manager*
Gary Seymour, *Manager*
◆ **EMP:** 40 **EST:** 2002
SQ FT: 9,662
SALES (est): 12MM **Privately Held**
WEB: www.philipstein.com
SIC: 3873 Watches, clocks, watchcases & parts

(G-14011)
ROWE INDUSTRIES INC
2525 Sw 32nd Ave (33023-7706)
P.O. Box 189, Annapolis MD (21404-0189)
PHONE....................................302 855-0585
Brooke Kinney, *President*
Doug Kinney, *Principal*
Betty J Adkins, *Vice Pres*
EMP: 16 **EST:** 1985
SALES (est): 2.2MM **Privately Held**
WEB: www.roweindustries.com
SIC: 2822 3496 Silicone rubbers; miscellaneous fabricated wire products
PA: Anr Partners, Inc.
626 Main St
Ceredo WV 25507

(G-14012)
SALT INTERNATIONAL CORP
2798 Sw 32nd Ave (33023-7702)
PHONE....................................305 698-8889
Salvatore Tizzoni, *President*
▲ **EMP:** 7 **EST:** 2008
SALES (est): 2.2MM **Privately Held**
WEB: www.saltintl.com
SIC: 3669 Visual communication systems

Pembroke Pines
Broward County

(G-14013)
A CROWN MOLDING SPECIALIST
9714 Nw 24th Ct (33024-1436)
PHONE....................................954 665-5640
Shawn Kelker, *Principal*
EMP: 11 **EST:** 2010
SALES (est): 509.7K **Privately Held**
WEB: www.crownmaxmolding.com
SIC: 3089 Molding primary plastic

(G-14014)
ADHESIVE MANUFACTURERS INC
1572 Nw 182nd Way (33029-3091)
PHONE....................................305 495-8018
Alan Klein, *President*
EMP: 8 **EST:** 2001
SALES (est): 87.2K **Privately Held**
SIC: 2891 Adhesives

(G-14015)
ADVANCED LIVING QUARTERS INC
Also Called: Alq Business Development
426 Sw 191st Ter (33029-5463)
PHONE....................................954 684-9392
Julio Juarbe, *Principal*
EMP: 6 **EST:** 2016
SALES (est): 71.9K **Privately Held**
SIC: 3131 Quarters

(G-14016)
AERIAL BANNERS INC
601 Sw 77th Way (33023-2591)
PHONE....................................954 893-0099
Bob Benyo, *President*
Dana Benyo, *Vice Pres*
Ryan Hiott, *Accounts Mgr*
Dan Banners, *Maintence Staff*
EMP: 15 **EST:** 1994
SALES (est): 2.4MM **Privately Held**
WEB: www.aerialbanners.com
SIC: 3993 Signs & advertising specialties

(G-14017)
AERONATE INC
20851 Johnson St Ste 109 (33029-1924)
PHONE....................................954 358-7145
Roberto Carcano, *President*
Juan Pablo Carcano, *Vice Pres*
EMP: 7 **EST:** 2010
SALES (est): 1.1MM **Privately Held**
WEB: www.aeronate.com
SIC: 3728 Aircraft parts & equipment

(G-14018)
AEROSPACE AUTOMATION LLC
830 Sw 174th Ter (33029-4213)
PHONE....................................954 260-2844
Shane M Link, *Mng Member*
David Krebs, *Mng Member*
Terence Link, *Mng Member*
EMP: 7 **EST:** 2008
SALES (est): 270.2K **Privately Held**
SIC: 3812 Aircraft/aerospace flight instruments & guidance systems

(G-14019)
ALL GOLF
Also Called: Allgolf
950 N Flamingo Rd (33028-1002)
PHONE....................................954 441-1333
Jeff Osenkowski, *General Mgr*
EMP: 9 **EST:** 2001
SALES (est): 278.7K **Privately Held**
SIC: 3949 Sporting & athletic goods

(G-14020)
AMERICA ENERGY INC
20861 Johnson St Ste 115 (33029-1927)
PHONE....................................954 762-7763
Alberto Aure, *President*
Claudia Pl, *Finance*
▲ **EMP:** 9 **EST:** 2007
SQ FT: 3,000
SALES (est): 1MM **Privately Held**
WEB: www.america-energy.com
SIC: 3563 3613 Air & gas compressors including vacuum pumps; vacuum pumps, except laboratory; control panels, electric

(G-14021)
AVENTURA COOKIES INC
1868 Nw 140th Ter (33028-2845)
PHONE....................................954 447-4525
Mohammed Alamgir, *Principal*
EMP: 6 **EST:** 2005
SALES (est): 81.4K **Privately Held**
SIC: 2052 Cookies

(G-14022)
BECKMAN COULTER INC
1 Sw 129th Ave Ste 201 (33027-1716)
PHONE....................................954 432-4336
Dean Beckman, *Principal*
Ernie Thomas, *Manager*
EMP: 8 **EST:** 2012
SALES (est): 270.9K **Privately Held**
WEB: www.beckmancoulter.com
SIC: 3826 Analytical instruments

(G-14023)
BIGBYTE SOFTWARE SYSTEMS INC
2214 Nw 171st Ter (33028-2050)
PHONE....................................917 370-1733
David Ging, *CFO*
EMP: 10 **EST:** 2016
SALES (est): 30.7K **Privately Held**
WEB: www.bigbytesoftware.com
SIC: 7372 Prepackaged software

(G-14024)
BNB BUSINESS SYSTEMS INC
18623 Sw 7th St (33029-6005)
PHONE....................................954 538-0669
Fitzroy S Benjamin, *Owner*
EMP: 7 **EST:** 2010
SALES (est): 90.6K **Privately Held**
SIC: 2522 Office furniture, except wood

(G-14025)
BROWARD PRINT
1560 N University Dr (33024-5035)
PHONE....................................954 272-2272
Meishan Guarriello, *Owner*
EMP: 6 **EST:** 2007
SALES (est): 92.3K **Privately Held**
SIC: 2752 Commercial printing, lithographic

(G-14026)
CEMEX MATERIALS LLC
Also Called: Pembroke Pines FL Readymix
17301 Pines Blvd (33029-1508)
PHONE....................................954 431-7655
David Packerd, *Branch Mgr*
EMP: 73
SQ FT: 17,263 **Privately Held**
SIC: 3273 5032 5211 Ready-mixed concrete; concrete mixtures; concrete & cinder block
HQ: Cemex Materials Llc
1501 Belvedere Rd
West Palm Beach FL 33406
561 833-5555

(G-14027)
CERP SOFTWARE INC
17411 Nw 8th St (33029-3112)
PHONE....................................954 607-1417
Camilo E Rodriguez, *Principal*
EMP: 6 **EST:** 2008
SALES (est): 106K **Privately Held**
SIC: 7372 Application computer software

(G-14028)
CLIMAX AM LLC
Also Called: South Beach Helicopters
7201 S Arprt Rd Hngar 303 Hangar (33023)
PHONE....................................786 502-5757
Mark Pomeranz, *Principal*
EMP: 6 **EST:** 1999
SALES (est): 104.1K **Privately Held**
WEB: www.southbeachhelicopters.com
SIC: 3721 Helicopters

(G-14029)
COOPPA NEWS REPORTER
13550 Sw 10th St (33027-6445)
PHONE....................................954 437-8864
Maritza Bulnes, *Principal*
EMP: 9 **EST:** 1997
SALES (est): 296.9K **Privately Held**
SIC: 2711 Newspapers, publishing & printing

(G-14030)
DREAMLINE AEROSPACE
7649 Pines Blvd (33024-6912)
PHONE....................................954 544-2365
Rafaela Martinez, *Principal*
EMP: 7 **EST:** 2013
SALES (est): 134.2K **Privately Held**
SIC: 3721 Aircraft

(G-14031)
ELIZABETH ARDEN INC (DH)
880 Sw 145th Ave Ste 200 (33027-6171)
PHONE....................................954 364-6900
E Scott Beattie, *Ch of Bd*
George Cleary, *President*
Jue Wong, *President*
Valerie Riley, *General Mgr*
Randal Chalifour, *Business Mgr*
◆ **EMP:** 684 **EST:** 1960
SQ FT: 19,000
SALES (est): 858MM **Publicly Held**
WEB: www.elizabetharden.com
SIC: 2844 Cosmetic preparations; perfumes, natural or synthetic; colognes; lotions, shaving

(G-14032)
EMPHASYS CMPT SOLUTIONS INC
Also Called: Emphasys Software
1200 Sw 145th Ave Ste 301 (33027-6240)
PHONE....................................305 599-2531
Michael Byrne, *CEO*
Carlos Rivero, *Sales Mgr*
Lindsey Stern, *Client Mgr*
Alejandro Preciado, *Sr Project Mgr*
Crystal Kirby, *Manager*
EMP: 50 **EST:** 1983
SALES (est): 12.3MM
SALES (corp-wide): 3.9B **Privately Held**
WEB: www.emphasys-software.com
SIC: 7372 Prepackaged software
PA: Constellation Software Inc
20 Adelaide St E Suite 1200
Toronto ON M5C 2

▲ = Import ▼=Export
◆ =Import/Export

(G-14033)
ETHNERGY INTERNATIONAL INC
1524 Sw 59 Ln (33027)
PHONE..................................954 499-1582
EMP: 40
SALES (est): 6.8MM **Privately Held**
SIC: 2869 Industrial Organic Chemicals, Nec

(G-14034)
EVOLUTION LIGHTING LLC (PA)
880 Sw 145th Ave Ste 100 (33027-6171)
P.O. Box 398299, Miami Beach (33239-8299)
PHONE..................................305 558-4777
A Corydon Meyer, *CEO*
Richard Giron, *Exec VP*
Wilfredo Figueras, *Vice Pres*
Adam Herman, *Vice Pres*
Marc J Leder, *Vice Pres*
◆ **EMP:** 30 **EST:** 2009
SALES (est): 22.6MM **Privately Held**
WEB: www.luciditylights.com
SIC: 3645 3648 3646 Residential lighting fixtures; lighting equipment; desk lamps, commercial

(G-14035)
GLAMER MEDSPA LLC
2114 N Flamingo Rd (33028-3501)
PHONE..................................305 744-6908
Danique Campbell,
EMP: 10 **EST:** 2018
SALES (est): 409.5K **Privately Held**
SIC: 2844 Cosmetic preparations

(G-14036)
GLOBAL ALUMINUM SOLUTIONS LLC
13558 Nw 9th Ct (33028-3151)
PHONE..................................954 636-4143
Juan C Aragon Diaz,
Francisco J Aragon Diaz,
EMP: 6 **EST:** 2009
SALES (est): 444.7K **Privately Held**
SIC: 3354 Aluminum extruded products

(G-14037)
GOOD CHANCE INC
20851 Johnson St Ste 107 (33029-1924)
PHONE..................................754 263-2792
Thomas Tong, *Principal*
▲ **EMP:** 7 **EST:** 2008
SALES (est): 109.9K **Privately Held**
SIC: 2299 Textile goods

(G-14038)
GOOD CHANCE TEXTILE INC
20851 Johnson St Ste 107 (33029-1924)
PHONE..................................754 263-2792
Chuen F Chan, *President*
◆ **EMP:** 18 **EST:** 2005
SALES (est): 708.8K **Privately Held**
WEB: www.goodchancetextile.com
SIC: 2329 Men's & boys' sportswear & athletic clothing

(G-14039)
GYPSUM BD SPECIALISTS USA CORP
Also Called: GBS
241 Nw 217th Way (33029-1019)
PHONE..................................954 348-8869
Jeannie Juri, *President*
EMP: 5 **EST:** 2016
SALES (est): 416.1K **Privately Held**
SIC: 3275 Gypsum board

(G-14040)
HAWK PROTECTION INCORPORATED
1020 Sw 98th Ave (33025-3698)
PHONE..................................954 980-9631
Eugene Greene, *CEO*
EMP: 6 **EST:** 2003
SALES (est): 454.7K
SALES (corp-wide): 91.7MM **Privately Held**
WEB: www.cooneengroup.com
SIC: 3842 Personal safety equipment
PA: Cooneen By Design Limited
23 Cooneen Road
Fivemiletown BT75
288 952-1401

(G-14041)
HOIPONG CUSTOMS INC
18331 Pines Blvd (33029-1421)
PHONE..................................954 684-9232
Pong Craig Hoi, *President*
EMP: 7 **EST:** 2012
SALES (est): 222.4K **Privately Held**
SIC: 2752 Commercial printing, lithographic

(G-14042)
INPRODELCA INC
702 Nw 170th Ter (33028-2119)
PHONE..................................865 687-7921
Jesus Caballero, *Principal*
EMP: 6 **EST:** 2010
SALES (est): 86.5K **Privately Held**
SIC: 3441 Fabricated structural metal

(G-14043)
JET FUEL CATERING LLC
1920 Nw 137th Way (33028-2608)
PHONE..................................954 804-1146
Robert A Del Castillo Jr, *Manager*
EMP: 9 **EST:** 2017
SALES (est): 814.5K **Privately Held**
WEB: www.jetfuelmeals.com
SIC: 2911 Jet fuels

(G-14044)
JMF DGITAL PRINT SOLUTIONS INC
19150 Sw 16th St (33029-6137)
PHONE..................................954 362-4929
Maria D Ochoa, *Principal*
EMP: 7 **EST:** 2009
SALES: 128.7K **Privately Held**
WEB: www.jmf-digital.com
SIC: 2752 Commercial printing, lithographic

(G-14045)
LW ROZZO INC
17200 Pines Blvd (33029-1505)
PHONE..................................954 435-8501
John C Sessa, *President*
EMP: 29 **EST:** 1955
SALES (est): 12.8MM **Privately Held**
SIC: 1411 Dimension stone

(G-14046)
M X CORPORATION
Also Called: Kitchens By US
1531 Nw 180th Way (33029-3040)
PHONE..................................305 597-9881
Simon Chew, *President*
EMP: 5 **EST:** 1990
SALES (est): 852.9K **Privately Held**
SIC: 2434 Wood kitchen cabinets

(G-14047)
MERCAWORLD AND CIA LLC
20871 Johnson St Ste 115 (33029-1918)
PHONE..................................786 212-5905
Marianne Caesar, *Editor*
Chris Shearer, *Manager*
Karin Gould, *Senior Mgr*
Fabio Lozano, *Director*
Colleen Moore, *Assistant*
EMP: 7 **EST:** 2013
SALES (est): 684.1K **Privately Held**
SIC: 2721 Periodicals
PA: Mercaworld Y Compania Sas
Avenida 19 118 95 Ofc 602
Bogota

(G-14048)
MONUMENTAL ENTERPRISES INC
7958 Pines Blvd Ste 242 (33024-6918)
PHONE..................................305 803-8493
Jessica Serrano, *Principal*
EMP: 5 **EST:** 2016
SALES (est): 341.6K **Privately Held**
SIC: 3272 8742 Monuments & grave markers, except terrazo; marketing consulting services

(G-14049)
MOOG INC
9000 Sheridan St Ste 168 (33024-8808)
PHONE..................................716 652-2000
EMP: 6
SALES (corp-wide): 2.8B **Publicly Held**
WEB: www.moog.com
SIC: 3812 3492 3625 3769 Aircraft control systems, electronic; fluid power valves for aircraft; relays & industrial controls; actuators, industrial; guided missile & space vehicle parts & auxiliary equipment; aircraft parts & equipment; surgical & medical instruments
PA: Moog Inc.
400 Jamison Rd
Elma NY 14059
716 652-2000

(G-14050)
MWR SIGN ENTERPRISES INC
Also Called: Fastsigns
9909 Pines Blvd (33024-6174)
PHONE..................................954 914-2709
Mike Ruckdefchel, *Owner*
EMP: 7 **EST:** 2001
SALES (est): 981.1K **Privately Held**
WEB: www.fastsigns.com
SIC: 3993 Signs & advertising specialties

(G-14051)
NAP IMPEX LLC
622 Sw 158th Ter (33027-1134)
PHONE..................................954 272-8453
Noman A Paracha, *Principal*
EMP: 6 **EST:** 2010
SALES (est): 126.1K **Privately Held**
WEB: www.napimpex.com
SIC: 2911 Petroleum refining

(G-14052)
NOXTAK CORP
21011 Johnson St Ste 110 (33029-1914)
PHONE..................................786 586-7927
Jose Joaquin Machado Luengas, *CEO*
Marianella Romero Fernandez, *Development*
Carlos Emilio Aguilar, *CFO*
Jeremias Martorell, *Accountant*
Carlos Augusto Aguilar Silva, *Director*
EMP: 6 **EST:** 2016
SQ FT: 1,690
SALES (est): 629.5K **Privately Held**
WEB: www.noxtak.com
SIC: 3822 3823 Auto controls regulating residntl & coml environmt & applncs; computer interface equipment for industrial process control

(G-14053)
P & M SHEET METAL CORP
134 Nw 109th Ave Apt 304 (33026-5133)
PHONE..................................954 618-8513
Ro Y Perez, *Principal*
EMP: 7 **EST:** 2018
SALES (est): 529.9K **Privately Held**
SIC: 3444 Sheet metalwork

(G-14054)
PRESS ROOM INC
619 Sw 159th Ter (33027-1140)
PHONE..................................954 792-6729
Joseph Digiaimo, *President*
EMP: 5 **EST:** 1989
SALES (est): 450.1K **Privately Held**
SIC: 2752 Commercial printing, offset

(G-14055)
R & A PERFORMANCE FUEL INC
12951 Nw 1st St (33028-2286)
PHONE..................................954 237-9824
Roberto Dominguez, *Principal*
EMP: 7 **EST:** 2010
SALES (est): 128.1K **Privately Held**
SIC: 2869 Fuels

(G-14056)
RBS WOODWORK CORP (PA)
378 Nw 153rd Ave (33028-1823)
PHONE..................................754 214-7682
Ambrozio P De Sousa, *Principal*
EMP: 18 **EST:** 2012
SALES (est): 264.9K **Privately Held**
SIC: 2431 Millwork

(G-14057)
RICHARDS BRAZILIAN SAUSAGE LLC
18503 Pines Blvd Ste 310 (33029-1406)
PHONE..................................786 609-3554
Richard Santos,
EMP: 8 **EST:** 2013
SALES (est): 560.7K **Privately Held**
WEB: www.richardsbraziliansausage.com
SIC: 2013 Sausages & other prepared meats

(G-14058)
SALSA PEMBROKE PINES INC
601 Sw 145th Ter (33027-1449)
PHONE..................................954 461-0532
David Pettit, *Principal*
EMP: 30 **EST:** 2006
SALES (est): 1.4MM **Privately Held**
SIC: 2099 Dips, except cheese & sour cream based

(G-14059)
SIEMENS INDUSTRY INC
2270 Nw 185th Way (33029-3864)
PHONE..................................954 436-8848
EMP: 71
SALES (corp-wide): 89.6B **Privately Held**
SIC: 3613 Mfg Switchboards
HQ: Siemens Industry, Inc.
1000 Deerfield Pkwy
Buffalo Grove IL 60089
847 215-1000

(G-14060)
SOUTH FLORIDA SHEET METAL (PA)
2038 Nw 141st Ave (33028-2853)
PHONE..................................954 647-6457
Wayne Boser, *President*
Harold Woods, *Vice Pres*
EMP: 11 **EST:** 1998
SALES (est): 1.2MM **Privately Held**
WEB: www.smart32.org
SIC: 3444 Ducts, sheet metal

(G-14061)
SUPPLY EXPEDITERS INTL INC
911 Nw 209th Ave Ste 103 (33029-2112)
PHONE..................................305 805-4255
▼ **EMP:** 12
SQ FT: 2,400
SALES (est): 2.2MM **Privately Held**
SIC: 3443 Mfg Fabricated Plate Work

(G-14062)
SURIPARTS CORP
20861 Johnson St Ste 116 (33029-1927)
PHONE..................................954 639-7700
Rafael J Falcon, *President*
▼ **EMP:** 5 **EST:** 2004
SALES (est): 806.4K **Privately Held**
WEB: www.suriparts.com
SIC: 3812 Aircraft control instruments

(G-14063)
SYNDESIS INC
392 Sw 159th Dr (33027-1141)
PHONE..................................954 483-9548
Kleanthis Goozis, *Principal*
EMP: 6 **EST:** 2008
SALES (est): 220K **Privately Held**
SIC: 2819 Industrial inorganic chemicals

(G-14064)
TAPIOCA FIT
156 N University Dr (33024-6714)
PHONE..................................954 842-3924
Luiz A Da Silva Machado, *Principal*
EMP: 6 **EST:** 2016
SALES (est): 305K **Privately Held**
SIC: 2046 Tapioca

(G-14065)
TECNOMETALES ONIS CNC LLC
21011 Johnson St Ste 110 (33029-1914)
PHONE..................................786 637-8316
Jose L Suarez, *Mng Member*
EMP: 6 **EST:** 2017
SALES (est): 175.3K **Privately Held**
SIC: 3315 Staples, steel: wire or cut

(G-14066)
TRUSS WILLIAM
17800 Nw 14th St (33029-3133)
PHONE..................................954 438-4710
William Truss, *Principal*
EMP: 7 **EST:** 2005
SALES (est): 212.2K **Privately Held**
SIC: 2439 Structural wood members

(G-14067)
TWS FABRICATORS ✪
2001 N Us Highway 27 (33029-2109)
PHONE..................................954 983-9749
EMP: 12 **EST:** 2020
SALES (est): 2.4MM **Privately Held**
WEB: www.twsfab.com
SIC: 3599 Industrial machinery

(G-14068)
ULTIMATE COMPRESSOR LLC
400 S Hollybrook Dr Apt 1 (33025-1290)
PHONE..................................305 720-3079
Steven Orozco, *Principal*
EMP: 5 **EST:** 2017
SALES (est): 499.9K **Privately Held**
WEB: www.ultimatecompressor.com
SIC: 3563 Air & gas compressors

(G-14069)
UNIA INTERNATIONAL CORP
18501 Pines Blvd Ste 202 (33029-1416)
PHONE..................................954 404-6076
Jun MA, *President*
EMP: 8 **EST:** 2017
SALES (est): 88.3K **Privately Held**
SIC: 3694 Armatures, automotive

(G-14070)
VENTILEX INC
Also Called: Motors For Less
20871 Jhnson St Units 103 (33029)
PHONE..................................954 433-1321
Jacques Urrutia, *President*
Ilse Murillo, *Bookkeeper*
Morita Casoetto, *Sales Staff*
Evlyn Amador, *Admin Sec*
EMP: 8 **EST:** 2005
SALES (est): 1MM **Privately Held**
WEB: www.motorsnation.net
SIC: 3564 Ventilating fans: industrial or commercial

(G-14071)
VINLAND MARKETING INC
1152 N University Dr # 304 (33024-5000)
PHONE..................................954 602-2177
Glauber Granero, *President*
EMP: 8 **EST:** 1998
SALES (est): 156.7K **Privately Held**
WEB: www.vinlandpaper.com
SIC: 2621 2679 Paper mills; paper products, converted

(G-14072)
YMG IRON WORK & METAL DESIGN
21650 Nw 3rd Pl (33029-1043)
PHONE..................................305 343-2537
Munoz Garcia Yovannys A, *Principal*
EMP: 6 **EST:** 2014
SALES (est): 561.7K **Privately Held**
WEB: www.ymgironworks.com
SIC: 3446 Architectural metalwork

(G-14073)
YOLO CONSULTING LLC
Also Called: Citypavers
2364 Nw 159th Ave (33028-2439)
PHONE..................................954 993-4517
Roger Jung,
EMP: 7 **EST:** 2012
SALES (est): 20K **Privately Held**
SIC: 2951 Asphalt paving mixtures & blocks

Pensacola
Escambia County

(G-14074)
850 SCREEN PRINTING LLC
698 E Heinberg St Ste 101 (32502-4154)
PHONE..................................850 549-7861
Chris Phillips, *Principal*
EMP: 6 **EST:** 2017
SALES (est): 312.2K **Privately Held**
WEB: www.850screenprinting.com
SIC: 2759 Screen printing

(G-14075)
A A A CABINETS
Also Called: AAA Custom Cabinets
6435 Ard Rd (32526-9406)
P.O. Box 19012 (32523-9012)
PHONE..................................850 438-8337
Donnie Brusso, *Owner*
EMP: 6 **EST:** 1979
SQ FT: 3,200
SALES (est): 372.6K **Privately Held**
SIC: 2434 5712 2511 Wood kitchen cabinets; cabinet work, custom; wood household furniture

(G-14076)
ABEKA PRINT SHOP INC
Also Called: PCC Print Shop, Inc.
118 Saint John St (32503-7644)
PHONE..................................850 478-8496
Bill Rice III, *Ch of Bd*
Arlin Horton, *Vice Ch Bd*
Ben M East, *Treasurer*
Brent Phillips, *Manager*
Beverly M Crawford, *Director*
EMP: 40 **EST:** 1996
SALES (est): 12.4MM
SALES (corp-wide): 124.3MM **Privately Held**
WEB: www.pcci.edu
SIC: 2759 Commercial printing
PA: Pensacola Christian College, Inc.
250 Brent Ln
Pensacola FL 32503
850 478-8496

(G-14077)
ABOVE LLC
Also Called: Big Rhino Screen Printing
140 Industrial Blvd (32505-2202)
PHONE..................................850 469-9028
Carol Mackey, *Sales Executive*
John Velaski, *Sales Executive*
Lifford Van Gestel,
Joseph Kowalski,
EMP: 10 **EST:** 2015
SALES (est): 1.4MM **Privately Held**
WEB: www.bigrhino.com
SIC: 2759 2395 5199 5699 Screen printing; embroidery products, except schiffli machine; advertising specialties; T-shirts, custom printed

(G-14078)
ACCU METAL
3987 N W St Ste 13 (32505-4063)
PHONE..................................850 912-4855
Daniel Widmer, *Owner*
EMP: 5 **EST:** 1985
SQ FT: 6,917
SALES (est): 926.2K **Privately Held**
WEB: www.accumetal.com
SIC: 3544 3089 Special dies & tools; jigs & fixtures; injection molding of plastics

(G-14079)
ACTIGRAPH LLC
102 E Garden St (32502-5624)
PHONE..................................850 332-7900
Doug Cross, *Engineer*
Leslie Broadus, *Manager*
Joshua Macdonald, *Manager*
EMP: 8 **EST:** 2017
SALES (est): 379.6K **Privately Held**
WEB: www.actigraphcorp.com
SIC: 3845 Electromedical equipment

(G-14080)
ACTIGRAPH LLC
49 E Chase St (32502-5619)
PHONE..................................850 332-7900
Keith Biggs, *CEO*
Jeff Arnett, *President*
Jeff Miller, *President*
Cyntech Trust, *Principal*
Shari Butz, *Vice Pres*
EMP: 17 **EST:** 2004
SQ FT: 3,500
SALES (est): 3.6MM **Privately Held**
WEB: www.actigraphcorp.com
SIC: 3845 7371 Patient monitoring apparatus; custom computer programming services

(G-14081)
ADAMS HURRICANE PROTECTION INC
Also Called: Rolltech Hurricanes Shutters
2302 Whaley Ave (32503-4972)
PHONE..................................850 434-2336
John Adams, *President*
EMP: 10 **EST:** 2000
SALES (est): 1.7MM **Privately Held**
WEB: www.rolltechhurricaneshutters.com
SIC: 3442 Shutters, door or window: metal

(G-14082)
ADVANCED BIOSERVICES LLC
5401 Corp Wds Dr Ste 500 (32504-5912)
PHONE..................................850 476-7999
EMP: 115 **Privately Held**
SIC: 2836 Mfg Biological Products
PA: Advanced Bioservices Llc
19255 Vanowen St
Reseda CA 91335

(G-14083)
ADVANCED DSIGN TECH SYSTEMS IN
1300 E Olive Rd (32514-4820)
PHONE..................................850 462-2868
Kevin W Stephens, *President*
Rodger Stephens, *Vice Pres*
EMP: 23 **EST:** 2008
SALES (est): 1.1MM **Privately Held**
SIC: 3699 Security control equipment & systems

(G-14084)
ADVANCED FURNITURE SVCS INC
8631 Match St (32514-3488)
PHONE..................................850 390-3442
Tirell Wilson, *President*
EMP: 10 **EST:** 2004
SALES (est): 401.5K **Privately Held**
SIC: 2522 Office furniture, except wood

(G-14085)
AGRI-SOURCE FUELS LLC
120 E Main St Ste A (32502-6096)
PHONE..................................352 521-3460
EMP: 42
SQ FT: 60,000
SALES (est): 4.7MM **Privately Held**
SIC: 2869 Mfg Industrial Organic Chemicals

(G-14086)
AGS ELECTRONICS INC
4400 Bayou Blvd Ste 53b (32503-1909)
PHONE..................................850 471-1551
Giulio Simonelli, *President*
Patricia Simonelli, *Vice Pres*
◆ **EMP:** 5
SQ FT: 3,400
SALES (est): 3.5MM **Privately Held**
WEB: www.agselectronics.com
SIC: 3674 Semiconductors & related devices

(G-14087)
AIR-TECH OF PENSACOLA INC
2317 Town St (32505-5121)
P.O. Box 18180 (32523-8180)
PHONE..................................850 433-6443
Samuel T Brubaker, *President*
Todd Brubaker, *Vice Pres*
Joe Hoggle, *Engineer*
Paul Atkins, *Sales Staff*
Kolton Hanke, *Sales Staff*
EMP: 15 **EST:** 2005
SALES (est): 5.1MM **Privately Held**
WEB: www.airtechfl.com
SIC: 3634 Fans, exhaust & ventilating, electric: household

(G-14088)
APW
911 N 63rd Ave (32506-4523)
PHONE..................................850 332-7023
Carl Crenshaw, *Principal*
EMP: 8 **EST:** 2011
SALES (est): 203.9K **Privately Held**
WEB: www.apwks.com
SIC: 3644 Raceways

(G-14089)
ARCHITECTURAL SPC TRDG CO
310 Hickory St (32505-4406)
PHONE..................................850 435-2507
Jeffrey S Taggart, *CEO*
Jeff Taggart, *CEO*
Thomas J Stevens, *President*
Edna Howard, *Corp Secy*
Mathew S Stevens, *Vice Pres*
EMP: 59 **EST:** 1990
SQ FT: 55,000
SALES (est): 6.8MM **Privately Held**
WEB: www.astcinc.com
SIC: 2431 Millwork

(G-14090)
ARCO MARINE INC
Also Called: Arco Automotive Products
3921 W Navy Blvd (32507-1221)
P.O. Box 16547 (32507-6547)
PHONE..................................850 455-5476
Jason Crawford, *President*
Jenni Auxier, *Accountant*
▲ **EMP:** 30 **EST:** 1960
SQ FT: 10,000
SALES (est): 4.5MM **Privately Held**
WEB: www.arcomarine.com
SIC: 3694 5063 Engine electrical equipment; electrical apparatus & equipment

(G-14091)
ARMORED FROG INC
6404 Rambler Dr (32505-1806)
PHONE..................................850 418-2048
Joe Sinkovich, *President*
Janet Wayman, *Manager*
EMP: 7 **EST:** 2012
SALES (est): 366K **Privately Held**
WEB: www.thearmoredfrog.com
SIC: 2519 Lawn & garden furniture, except wood & metal

(G-14092)
ARNOLD MANUFACTURING INC
Also Called: Arnold Mnfacturing-A M C Trlrs
2300 Town St (32505-5122)
PHONE..................................850 470-9200
Fax: 850 470-1040
EMP: 8
SQ FT: 15,000
SALES: 1MM **Privately Held**
SIC: 3715 Builds Truck Trailers

(G-14093)
AT WORK UNIFORMS
2211 N Pace Blvd (32505-5837)
PHONE..................................850 435-3133
Charles Campbell, *General Mgr*
EMP: 7 **EST:** 2019
SALES (est): 113.7K **Privately Held**
WEB: www.atworkuniforms.com
SIC: 2326 Work uniforms

(G-14094)
AUTOMATED ACCOUNTING ASSOC INC
1665 Governors Dr (32514-8497)
PHONE..................................512 669-1000
G Talburt, *President*
Talburt Greg, *Principal*
EMP: 5 **EST:** 1996
SALES (est): 362.6K **Privately Held**
SIC: 7372 8721 8621 Prepackaged software; accounting, auditing & bookkeeping; accounting association

(G-14095)
AUTOMATION CONSULTING INC
Also Called: Porche Systems
7100 Plantation Rd Ste 17 (32504-6234)
PHONE..................................850 477-6477
Charles M Sanders, *President*
Lorna Gay Sanders, *Corp Secy*
John Abrams, *Vice Pres*
Kary Louden, *Analyst*
EMP: 11 **EST:** 1983
SQ FT: 4,050

▲ = Import ▼=Export
◆ =Import/Export

SALES (est): 229.8K **Privately Held**
WEB: www.autocon.net
SIC: 3669 7371 3429 Intercommunication systems, electric; custom computer programming services; manufactured hardware (general)

(G-14096)
BAM ENTERPRISES INC
Also Called: Eye-Dye
2906 N Davis Hwy (32503-3532)
P.O. Box 2280 (32513-2280)
PHONE....850 469-8872
Robert Bizzell, *President*
Sara Jiron, *COO*
Scott Martin, *Vice Pres*
Michael Hays, *Accountant*
EMP: 26 **EST:** 1987
SQ FT: 10,000
SALES (est): 2.9MM **Privately Held**
WEB: www.eye-dye.com
SIC: 2261 2759 Dyeing cotton broadwoven fabrics; screen printing

(G-14097)
BELL STEEL COMPANY (PA)
530 S C St (32502-5426)
P.O. Box 12109 (32591-2109)
PHONE....850 432-1545
Randall R Bell III, *President*
Britney B Thompson, *Project Mgr*
James Herbert, *Warehouse Mgr*
Carl Trahan, *Purch Mgr*
Curtis Smith, *QC Mgr*
EMP: 72 **EST:** 1957
SQ FT: 361,000
SALES (est): 18MM **Privately Held**
WEB: www.bellsteel.com
SIC: 3441 5051 Building components, structural steel; steel

(G-14098)
BELL STEEL COMPANY
Also Called: Steel Systems
8788 Paul Starr Dr (32514-7047)
P.O. Box 9579 (32513-9579)
PHONE....850 479-2980
Hugh Bostick, *Sales Mgr*
Randall R Bell III, *Branch Mgr*
EMP: 14
SALES (corp-wide): 18MM **Privately Held**
WEB: www.bellsteel.com
SIC: 3441 Building components, structural steel
PA: Bell Steel Company
530 S C St
Pensacola FL 32502
850 432-1545

(G-14099)
BEST PRICE DIGITAL LENSES INC
2013 W Yonge St (32501-1560)
PHONE....850 361-4401
EMP: 8 **EST:** 2014
SALES (est): 924.5K **Privately Held**
WEB: www.bpdigitallab.com
SIC: 3851 Ophthalmic goods

(G-14100)
BLACKLIDGE EMULSIONS INC
4375 Mccoy Dr (32503-2224)
PHONE....850 432-3496
EMP: 7
SALES (corp-wide): 44.4MM **Privately Held**
SIC: 2951 Mfg Asphalt Mixtures/Blocks
PA: Blacklidge Emulsions, Inc.
12251 Bernard Pkwy # 200
Gulfport MS 39503
228 863-3878

(G-14101)
BLUE TARPON CONSTRUCTION LLC
119 W Garden St (32502-5617)
PHONE....251 223-3630
Sydney Cody, *CEO*
EMP: 6 **EST:** 2019
SALES (est): 78.8K **Privately Held**
SIC: 1389 Construction, repair & dismantling services

(G-14102)
BODREE PRINTING COMPANY INC
3310 N W St (32505-3953)
P.O. Box 3005 (32516-3005)
PHONE....850 455-8511
Gay Bodree, *President*
EMP: 14 **EST:** 1963
SALES (est): 574.8K **Privately Held**
WEB: www.bodree.com
SIC: 2752 2789 Commercial printing, offset; bookbinding & related work

(G-14103)
BONSAL AMERICAN INC
Also Called: Bonsai American
150 E Olive Rd (32514-4529)
PHONE....850 476-4223
Chris Cox, *President*
EMP: 9
SQ FT: 14,824
SALES (corp-wide): 27.5B **Privately Held**
SIC: 3272 Dry mixture concrete
HQ: Bonsal American, Inc.
625 Griffith Rd Ste 100
Charlotte NC 28217
704 525-1621

(G-14104)
BRASWELL CUSTOM CABINETS
9 Clarinda Ln (32505-4309)
PHONE....850 436-2645
Jerry Braswell, *Owner*
EMP: 7 **EST:** 1999
SQ FT: 17,000
SALES (est): 718.1K **Privately Held**
WEB: www.braswellcabinets.com
SIC: 2434 Wood kitchen cabinets

(G-14105)
BREATHING SYSTEMS INC
8800 Grow Dr (32514-7050)
PHONE....850 477-2324
Peter Thew, *President*
David Marrie, *General Mgr*
Gordon Bradley Alidor, *Treasurer*
EMP: 6 **EST:** 1986
SQ FT: 3,600
SALES (est): 1.1MM
SALES (corp-wide): 91.2MM **Privately Held**
WEB: www.breathingsystems.us
SIC: 3841 Surgical & medical instruments
HQ: Hydroprocessing Associates, Llc
6016 Highway 63
Moss Point MS 39563

(G-14106)
BROWN COMPANY
Also Called: Brown Fabrication
Aileron Ave Ste N.10102 (32506)
PHONE....850 455-0971
Patrick Brown, *President*
Andrew Majewski, *Corp Secy*
Amy Fithen, *Sales Staff*
EMP: 5 **EST:** 1983
SQ FT: 14,000
SALES (est): 584.5K **Privately Held**
WEB: www.brown-co.com
SIC: 3089 Thermoformed finished plastic products

(G-14107)
BROWNSVILLE ORNA IR WORKS INC
Also Called: Brownsville Welding
3520 Mobile Hwy (32505-6540)
PHONE....850 433-0521
Paul Stinson, *President*
Kay Stinson, *Corp Secy*
Anthony Alex Stinson, *Vice Pres*
EMP: 7 **EST:** 1989
SQ FT: 5,000
SALES (est): 1.9MM **Privately Held**
WEB: www.brownsvillewelding.com
SIC: 7692 Welding repair

(G-14108)
BRUNKEN MANUFACTURING CO INC
4205 W Jackson St (32505-7233)
PHONE....850 438-2478
Curtis Boone, *President*
Cornelia Boone, *Corp Secy*
Lavona Boone, *Vice Pres*
EMP: 6 **EST:** 1968
SQ FT: 4,500
SALES (est): 403.3K **Privately Held**
WEB: www.brunkenmfg.com
SIC: 2399 Fishing nets

(G-14109)
BUMPER DOCTOR
95 Airport Blvd (32503-7623)
PHONE....850 341-1771
Dave Lee, *Principal*
EMP: 8 **EST:** 2007
SALES (est): 107.2K **Privately Held**
SIC: 3479 Painting of metal products

(G-14110)
BURRIS INVESTMENT GROUP INC
10648 Mac Gregor Dr (32514-8309)
PHONE....850 623-3845
Howard Burris, *Ch of Bd*
Greg Lowery, *President*
William Burris, *Vice Pres*
EMP: 35 **EST:** 1983
SALES (est): 2.7MM
SALES (corp-wide): 1B **Publicly Held**
WEB: www.jjsnack.com
SIC: 2045 Doughs, frozen or refrigerated: from purchased flour
PA: J & J Snack Foods Corp.
6000 Central Hwy
Pennsauken NJ 08109
856 665-9533

(G-14111)
CABINET DESIGN AND CNSTR LLC
Also Called: Cdc Woodworking
101 S Pace Blvd (32502-5003)
PHONE....850 393-9724
William Hinson, *CFO*
William A Hinson,
Matthew Hinson,
EMP: 8 **EST:** 2004
SALES (est): 820.7K **Privately Held**
WEB: www.cdcwoodworking.com
SIC: 2434 2431 Wood kitchen cabinets; millwork

(G-14112)
CARPET CLINIC LLC
6927 Kelvin Ter (32503-7351)
P.O. Box 11544 (32524-1544)
PHONE....850 232-1170
Brian Ross,
EMP: 8 **EST:** 2009
SALES (est): 225.7K **Privately Held**
WEB: www.thecarpetclinic.com
SIC: 2273 Carpets & rugs

(G-14113)
CHECK ASSIST
9270 University Pkwy # 105 (32514-5533)
P.O. Box 10207 (32524-0207)
PHONE....850 857-7752
Jim Eliason, *Principal*
Russell Thompson, *Info Tech Dir*
EMP: 7 **EST:** 2007
SALES (est): 14.5K **Privately Held**
WEB: www.checkassistflorida.com
SIC: 3944 Banks, toy

(G-14114)
CLASSIC DESIGN AND MFG
Also Called: Classic Sign & Mirror
909 N Tarragona St (32501-3178)
PHONE....850 433-4981
Michael Sheehan, *President*
Suzanne Zukoski, *Vice Pres*
EMP: 6 **EST:** 1981
SQ FT: 6,000
SALES (est): 861.4K **Privately Held**
WEB: www.durabrac.com
SIC: 3993 Signs, not made in custom sign painting shops

(G-14115)
COASTAL FOAM SYSTEMS LLC
3276 W Scott St (32505-5427)
PHONE....850 470-9827
Randy Marshal, *Mng Member*
Eric Alford,
Curtis Bolton,
Danny Marshal,
EMP: 5 **EST:** 2005
SALES (est): 480.4K **Privately Held**
SIC: 3086 Insulation or cushioning material, foamed plastic

(G-14116)
COLLEGEFROG INC
418 W Garden St (32502-4752)
PHONE....850 696-1500
Jeff Phillips, *President*
James Hosman, *Treasurer*
Joshua Sams, *Admin Sec*
EMP: 7 **EST:** 2012
SALES (est): 655K **Privately Held**
WEB: www.accountingfly.com
SIC: 7372 Business oriented computer software

(G-14117)
COMMERCIAL DOOR SYSTEMS FLA LL
612 W Romana St (32502-5549)
PHONE....850 466-5906
Deborah Volentine, *Project Mgr*
Steve Ball, *Sales Staff*
Stephanie Morin, *Office Mgr*
Kent Simmons, *Mng Member*
Travis Miller, *Maintence Staff*
EMP: 16 **EST:** 2017
SALES (est): 2.2MM **Privately Held**
SIC: 2431 Doors & door parts & trim, wood

(G-14118)
COMMSTRUCTURES INC
101 E Roberts Rd (32534-9535)
PHONE....850 968-9293
James B Hobbs, *President*
James Y Harpole, *Vice Pres*
James Harpole, *Vice Pres*
Kevin Wilkes, *Plant Mgr*
Charles Sumlin, *Project Mgr*
◆ **EMP:** 53 **EST:** 1997
SQ FT: 56,300
SALES (est): 16.8MM **Privately Held**
WEB: www.commstructures.com
SIC: 3663 Antennas, transmitting & communications

(G-14119)
COPY CAT PRINTING LLC
3636 N L St Ste D-A (32505-5663)
PHONE....850 438-5566
Janet McDonald, *Mng Member*
EMP: 7 **EST:** 2012
SALES (est): 482.7K **Privately Held**
WEB: www.copycatpensacola.com
SIC: 2752 Commercial printing, offset

(G-14120)
COTTON PICKIN SHIRTS PLUS
2211 N Pace Blvd (32505-5837)
PHONE....850 435-3133
Charles Campbell, *Ch of Bd*
EMP: 7 **EST:** 1991
SQ FT: 1,500
SALES (est): 343.4K **Privately Held**
WEB: www.cottonpickin.com
SIC: 2395 2759 5699 Embroidery products, except schiffli machine; screen printing; customized clothing & apparel

(G-14121)
CURRENT PRODUCTS COMPANY LLC
1995 Hollywood Ave (32505-5369)
PHONE....850 435-4994
Willis J Mullet, *President*
Mike Fox, *Mfg Staff*
Sean Scalf, *Engineer*
Curtis Scott, *Electrical Engi*
Bette Denniston, *CFO*
EMP: 24 **EST:** 2010
SQ FT: 40,000
SALES (est): 2MM **Privately Held**
WEB: www.currentproductscorp.com
SIC: 2591 Shade, curtain & drapery hardware

(G-14122)
CUSTOM WD DESIGNS OF PENSACOLA
3335 Addison Dr (32514-7065)
P.O. Box 537, Bagdad (32530-0537)
PHONE....850 476-9663
EMP: 10
SQ FT: 7,500

SALES: 600K **Privately Held**
SIC: 2434 2431 Mfg Wood Kitchen Cabinets Mfg Millwork

(G-14123)
D & D WELDING INC
2715 N W St (32505-4937)
PHONE..................................850 438-9011
David Siefert, *President*
Sharen Siefert, *Admin Sec*
EMP: 5 **EST:** 1973
SQ FT: 5,000
SALES (est): 745K **Privately Held**
SIC: 7692 Welding repair

(G-14124)
D & M TRUSS CO
2620 W Michigan Ave (32526-2213)
PHONE..................................850 944-4864
F O Dickerson, *President*
John Williams, *Bookkeeper*
Jeromey Smith, *Technician*
Shawn Ward, *Technician*
EMP: 23 **EST:** 1965
SQ FT: 10,000
SALES (est): 3.5MM **Privately Held**
WEB: www.dmtruss.com
SIC: 2439 Trusses, wooden roof

(G-14125)
DAWS MANUFACTURING COMPANY INC (PA)
Also Called: Better Built
8811 Grow Dr (32514-7051)
PHONE..................................850 478-3298
Daws Hc, *President*
Clint Daws, *President*
Brenda Daws, *Corp Secy*
Harold C Daws II, *Vice Pres*
Barry Joyner, *Opers Mgr*
▲ **EMP:** 200 **EST:** 1985
SQ FT: 185,000
SALES (est): 26.9MM **Privately Held**
WEB: www.truckaddons.com
SIC: 3469 5085 Boxes, stamped metal; boxes, crates, etc., other than paper

(G-14126)
DE LUNA COFFEE INTL INC
Also Called: Twisted Coffee Canyon Roasters
1014 Underwood Ave Ste D (32504-8929)
PHONE..................................850 478-6371
Edward F Lemox III, *President*
EMP: 9 **EST:** 2014
SQ FT: 6,500
SALES (est): 900K **Privately Held**
WEB: www.delunacoffee.com
SIC: 2095 5149 Roasted coffee; coffee & tea

(G-14127)
DEFENSE STAMPING & ENGINEERING (PA)
3911 Mobile Hwy (32505-6126)
PHONE..................................850 438-6105
Anita Nordendale, *CEO*
Mark Strader, *President*
Kelly Nordendale, *Vice Pres*
EMP: 34 **EST:** 1989
SQ FT: 33,000
SALES (est): 2.5MM **Privately Held**
WEB: www.defense-stamping-engineering.sbcontract.com
SIC: 3469 3312 3599 Metal stampings; tool & die steel; machine shop, jobbing & repair

(G-14128)
DELUNA TOOLE LLC
Also Called: Brand Bros.
6565 N W St Ste 260 (32505-1725)
PHONE..................................850 435-4063
Dean Toole, *Owner*
EMP: 8 **EST:** 2015
SALES (est): 400.6K **Privately Held**
SIC: 2759 Screen printing

(G-14129)
DEMING DESIGNS INC
1090 Cobblestone Dr (32514-7159)
PHONE..................................850 478-5765
Micheal S Deming, *President*
EMP: 15 **EST:** 1994
SALES (est): 1MM **Privately Held**
WEB: www.beachwheelchair.com
SIC: 3842 7389 Wheelchairs;

(G-14130)
DESIGN SYSTEMS SOUTH INC
4765 Baywind Dr (32514-7827)
PHONE..................................850 293-1905
Robert Dance, *President*
Edie Dance, *Vice Pres*
EMP: 7 **EST:** 1974
SQ FT: 40,000
SALES (est): 166.5K **Privately Held**
WEB: www.design-systems-south-inc.pensacola.fl.amfibi.company
SIC: 2512 2511 Chairs: upholstered on wood frames; wood household furniture

(G-14131)
DIGECON PLASTICS INTERNATIONAL
Also Called: Address-O-Lite
3255 Potter St (32514-3518)
PHONE..................................850 477-5483
Ronald R Smith, *President*
EMP: 10 **EST:** 1990
SQ FT: 41,000
SALES (est): 504.3K **Privately Held**
SIC: 3645 3641 3646 5063 Garden, patio, walkway & yard lighting fixtures: electric; electric lamps; commercial indusl & institutional electric lighting fixtures; lighting fixtures

(G-14132)
DIXON SCREEN PRINTING LLC
Also Called: Jack W Dixon
312 W Detroit Blvd (32534-3771)
PHONE..................................850 476-3924
Jack Dixon, *President*
Jack W Dixon, *Owner*
Jason Dixon, *Sales Mgr*
EMP: 9 **EST:** 1973
SQ FT: 11,800
SALES (est): 606.5K **Privately Held**
WEB: www.dixontshirts.com
SIC: 2396 5941 Screen printing on fabric articles; team sports equipment

(G-14133)
DLUX PRINTING INC
Also Called: Dlux Printing & Publishing
3320 N W St (32505-3953)
PHONE..................................850 457-8494
Gerald Mandel, *President*
Michelle Mandel, *CFO*
Jimmy Robinson, *Sales Staff*
Janet Carter, *Technician*
EMP: 16 **EST:** 1991
SALES (est): 4.8MM **Privately Held**
SIC: 2752 Commercial printing, offset

(G-14134)
DMR WOODWORKS LLC
1161 W Detroit Blvd (32534-1809)
PHONE..................................850 969-9261
Stephen T Rouse, *Principal*
EMP: 6 **EST:** 2005
SALES (est): 200.6K **Privately Held**
WEB: www.dmrwoodworks.com
SIC: 2431 Millwork

(G-14135)
E M CHADBOURNE INDS LLC
192 Hewitt St (32503-2265)
PHONE..................................850 429-1797
Caroline C Demaria, *Manager*
EMP: 8 **EST:** 2006
SALES (est): 159.9K **Privately Held**
SIC: 3999 Manufacturing industries

(G-14136)
EARLY FOODS LLC
1630 E Lee St (32503-6130)
PHONE..................................850 791-3319
Stephen S Early, *Principal*
EMP: 6
SALES (est): 417.7K **Privately Held**
SIC: 2099 Food preparations

(G-14137)
EASTBURN WOODWORKS INC
2620 Hollywood Ave (32505-4845)
PHONE..................................850 456-8090
Kenneth Eastburn, *President*
Iris Eastburn, *Vice Pres*
EMP: 14 **EST:** 1997
SQ FT: 8,000
SALES (est): 1MM **Privately Held**
WEB: www.eastburnwoodworks.com
SIC: 2434 Wood kitchen cabinets

(G-14138)
EDS ALUMINUM BUILDINGS INC (PA)
9555 Pensacola Blvd (32534-1239)
PHONE..................................850 476-2169
Ed Vignolo, *President*
EMP: 7 **EST:** 1972
SQ FT: 3,000
SALES (est): 733K **Privately Held**
WEB: www.edsaluminumbuildings.com
SIC: 3448 5211 5599 Buildings, portable: prefabricated metal; prefabricated buildings; utility trailers

(G-14139)
ELITE PRINTING & MARKETING INC
3636 N L St Ste D-A (32505-5248)
PHONE..................................850 474-0894
Andrew Dennis III, *Owner*
EMP: 5 **EST:** 1982
SQ FT: 10,000
SALES (est): 577.5K **Privately Held**
WEB: www.printingbyelite.espwebsite.com
SIC: 2752 2759 3993 Commercial printing, offset; letterpress & screen printing; letterpress printing; signs & advertising specialties

(G-14140)
ELLIS TRAP AND CAGE MFG INC
9601 N Palafox St Ste 6b (32534-1273)
PHONE..................................850 969-1302
Sean Ellis, *President*
EMP: 5 **EST:** 1995
SQ FT: 3,000
SALES (est): 514.1K **Privately Held**
WEB: www.drpalu.com
SIC: 3429 3496 Animal traps, iron or steel; crab traps, steel; traps, animal & fish

(G-14141)
EMERALD COAST FABRICATORS
2120 W Wright St (32505-7941)
PHONE..................................850 554-6172
David Scallan, *Manager*
EMP: 7 **EST:** 2017
SALES (est): 1MM **Privately Held**
WEB: www.frmpeo.com
SIC: 3441 Fabricated structural metal

(G-14142)
EMERALD COAST MET FABRICATION
9215 Latham St (32514-5824)
PHONE..................................850 465-3517
Paul G Sjordal, *Principal*
EMP: 6 **EST:** 2016
SALES (est): 72.9K **Privately Held**
SIC: 3499 Fabricated metal products

(G-14143)
EMERALD COAST MFG LLC
4121 Warehouse Ln (32505-4061)
PHONE..................................850 469-1133
Sharon C Yarbrough,
Ronnie E Jones,
EMP: 8 **EST:** 2019
SALES (est): 612.8K **Privately Held**
WEB: www.emeraldcoastmfg.com
SIC: 3519 Marine engines

(G-14144)
EPI CABINETS
2632 Hollywood Ave (32505-4845)
P.O. Box 11401 (32524-1401)
PHONE..................................850 665-0659
Marybeth Edwards, *Administration*
EMP: 6 **EST:** 2016
SALES (est): 163.2K **Privately Held**
WEB: www.epicabinets.weebly.com
SIC: 2434 Wood kitchen cabinets

(G-14145)
ESCAMBIA WELDING AND FAB INC
2474 W Nine Mile Rd B (32534-9419)
PHONE..................................850 477-3901
Phyllis Keller, *President*
EMP: 5 **EST:** 2005
SALES (est): 457.6K **Privately Held**
SIC: 7692 Welding repair

(G-14146)
ESTHER INDUSTRIES INC
107 Industrial Blvd (32505-2201)
PHONE..................................850 456-6163
EMP: 6
SALES (est): 217.3K **Privately Held**
SIC: 3999 Mfg Misc Products

(G-14147)
EYE WALL INDUSTRIES INC
3920 W Navy Blvd (32507-1200)
PHONE..................................850 607-2288
Kristian R Fernandez, *Principal*
EMP: 7 **EST:** 2018
SALES (est): 284.6K **Privately Held**
WEB: www.dbemeraldcoast.com
SIC: 3999 Manufacturing industries

(G-14148)
FAIRBANKS AND FAIRBANKS INC
405 S K St (32502-5206)
PHONE..................................850 293-1184
Fairbanks William R, *Principal*
EMP: 6 **EST:** 2013
SALES (est): 112.8K **Privately Held**
SIC: 3489 Ordnance & accessories

(G-14149)
FASTSIGNS
6060 Tippin Ave (32504-8218)
PHONE..................................850 477-9744
Scott Thomas, *President*
Mary Thomas, *Vice Pres*
Jason Lamb, *Graphic Designe*
EMP: 6 **EST:** 1991
SQ FT: 1,500
SALES (est): 708.8K **Privately Held**
WEB: www.fastsigns.com
SIC: 3993 7319 5999 Signs & advertising specialties; display advertising service; banners

(G-14150)
FERTEC INC
141 Terry Dr (32503-7066)
PHONE..................................850 478-6480
Ronald Bray, *President*
John R Bray, *Chairman*
EMP: 11 **EST:** 1976
SALES (est): 144.2K **Privately Held**
SIC: 3448 Prefabricated metal components

(G-14151)
FISHER CABINET COMPANY LLC
3900 N Palafox St (32505-4418)
PHONE..................................850 944-4171
Scott Fisher, *President*
Scott A Fisher, *President*
EMP: 24 **EST:** 1987
SQ FT: 14,000
SALES: 2.8MM **Privately Held**
SIC: 2541 2434 3083 Cabinets, except refrigerated: show, display, etc.: wood; wood kitchen cabinets; plastic finished products, laminated

(G-14152)
FJ CABINETS & WOODWORKING LLC
509 N K St (32501-3625)
PHONE..................................850 433-3925
Frederick James, *Owner*
EMP: 6 **EST:** 2011
SALES (est): 121.8K **Privately Held**
SIC: 2431 Millwork

(G-14153)
FLAT ISLAND BOATWORKS LLC
700 Myrick St (32505-8051)
PHONE..................................850 434-8295
Michael Bredesen, *Owner*
EMP: 7 **EST:** 2009
SALES (est): 631.7K **Privately Held**
WEB: www.flatislandboatworks.com
SIC: 3732 Boat building & repairing

(G-14154)
FLORIDA COCA-COLA BOTTLING CO
7330 N Davis Hwy (32504-6314)
PHONE..................................850 478-4800
Steve Langham, *Manager*
EMP: 403
SALES (corp-wide): 33B **Publicly Held**
WEB: www.coca-cola.com
SIC: 2086 5149 Bottled & canned soft drinks; groceries & related products
HQ: Florida Coca-Cola Bottling Company
521 Lake Kathy Dr
Brandon FL 33510
813 569-2600

(G-14155)
FLUID METALWORKS INC -105
55 S A St (32502-5551)
PHONE..................................850 332-0103
Brandon Godwin, *Principal*
EMP: 9 **EST:** 2012
SALES (est): 858.7K **Privately Held**
WEB: www.fluidmetalworks.com
SIC: 3446 Architectural metalwork

(G-14156)
FOIL INC
201 E Wright St (32501-4917)
PHONE..................................442 233-3645
EMP: 6 **EST:** 1989
SALES (est): 112.7K **Privately Held**
WEB: www.getfoil.com
SIC: 3949 Water sports equipment

(G-14157)
FOOT-IN-YOUR-MOUTH INC
Also Called: Thermodyne Powder Coating
9721 Fowler Ave (32534-1007)
PHONE..................................850 438-0876
Jeffrey Hoskins, *President*
Julie Taylor, *Accountant*
EMP: 10 **EST:** 1989
SQ FT: 60,000
SALES (est): 1MM **Privately Held**
WEB: www.thermodynepowdercoating.com
SIC: 3479 Coating of metals & formed products

(G-14158)
FORTIFIED BUILDING PDTS INC
Also Called: Fortified Shutters
2001 W Government St (32502-5151)
P.O. Box 4905 (32507-0905)
PHONE..................................850 432-2485
John Roche, *President*
EMP: 20 **EST:** 2014
SALES (est): 2.7MM **Privately Held**
WEB: www.fortifiedshutters.com
SIC: 3442 Louvers, shutters, jalousies & similar items

(G-14159)
FRANKLIN BAKING COMPANY LLC
Also Called: Flowers Baking
9201 N Davis Hwy (32514-5846)
PHONE..................................850 478-8360
Tim Watson, *Branch Mgr*
EMP: 9
SALES (corp-wide): 4.3B **Publicly Held**
SIC: 2051 Bread, cake & related products
HQ: Franklin Baking Company, Llc
500 W Grantham St
Goldsboro NC 27530
919 735-0344

(G-14160)
GATLIN GROUP LLC
6979 Raburn Rd (32526-8085)
PHONE..................................850 941-0959
Justin A Gatlin, *Manager*
EMP: 7 **EST:** 2014
SALES (est): 135.8K **Privately Held**
WEB: www.kodaypress.com
SIC: 2759 Commercial printing

(G-14161)
GE RENEWABLES NORTH AMER LLC (HQ)
Also Called: G E Generators
8301 Scenic Hwy (32514-7810)
PHONE..................................850 474-4011
John C Rice, *CEO*
Lawrence Blystone, *Vice Pres*
Blair Simmons, *Mng Member*
John Kreniki, *Mng Member*
William Standera, *Mng Member*
◆ **EMP:** 185 **EST:** 2000
SALES (est): 55.1MM
SALES (corp-wide): 79.6B **Publicly Held**
WEB: www.ge.com
SIC: 3621 Power generators
PA: General Electric Company
5 Necco St
Boston MA 02210
617 443-3000

(G-14162)
GEMS JEWELRY & UNIQUES
Also Called: Silver, Sword, and Stone
306 Bremen Ave (32507-2978)
P.O. Box 4628 (32507-0628)
PHONE..................................850 456-8105
Victor Martine, *Owner*
EMP: 6 **EST:** 1975
SALES (est): 221.5K **Privately Held**
WEB: www.silverswordandstone.com
SIC: 3911 5932 Jewelry, precious metal; used merchandise stores

(G-14163)
GREENSCAPE LABORATORIES INC
1311 E La Rua St (32501-4149)
PHONE..................................850 723-7496
James Scheltema, *Partner*
EMP: 8 **EST:** 2014
SALES (est): 121.6K **Privately Held**
WEB: www.mjnalab.com
SIC: 2899 Food contamination testing or screening kits

(G-14164)
GREGORY MICHAEL GENUNG
11520 Aruba Dr (32506-1210)
PHONE..................................850 572-4407
Gregory Genung, *Principal*
EMP: 7 **EST:** 2018
SALES (est): 178.1K **Privately Held**
SIC: 2752 Commercial printing, lithographic

(G-14165)
GUIDED PARTICLE SYSTEMS INC
1000 College Blvd Bldg 11 (32504-8910)
P.O. Box 12621 (32591-2621)
PHONE..................................727 424-8790
Carolyn Fries, *President*
David Fries, *Vice Pres*
EMP: 6 **EST:** 2016
SQ FT: 448
SALES (est): 494.5K **Privately Held**
SIC: 3559 3555 Semiconductor manufacturing machinery; photoengraving machines

(G-14166)
GULF COAST ELC MTR SVC INC
3810 Hopkins St (32505-5223)
P.O. Box 1322 (32591-1322)
PHONE..................................850 433-5134
Higinio Rodriguez, *President*
Higinio Rodriguez III, *Vice Pres*
Moises Rodriguez, *Vice Pres*
Victor Rodriguez, *Vice Pres*
Susana Rodriguez, *Treasurer*
EMP: 33 **EST:** 1978
SQ FT: 9,675
SALES (est): 4.2MM **Privately Held**
WEB: www.gcemsinc.com
SIC: 7694 7699 Rewinding stators; electric motor repair; pumps & pumping equipment repair

(G-14167)
GULF STATES AUTOMATION INC
245 W Airport Blvd Ste B (32505-2254)
PHONE..................................850 475-0724
Steve Gaidos, *President*
Lisa Cox, *Vice Pres*
Henry Hiebert, *Project Mgr*
Robert Mann, *Sales Engr*
EMP: 21 **EST:** 1992
SQ FT: 2,000
SALES (est): 4.2MM **Privately Held**
WEB: www.gulfstatesautomation.com
SIC: 3822 Air conditioning & refrigeration controls

(G-14168)
GULF TOOL CORPORATION
8470 Gulf Beach Hwy (32507-2636)
PHONE..................................850 456-0840
Paul Robinson, *President*
C Joe Robinson, *Chairman*
Joy Thomas, *CPA*
Barbara Robinson, *Admin Sec*
EMP: 19 **EST:** 1978
SQ FT: 11,000
SALES (est): 1.8MM **Privately Held**
WEB: www.gulftoolcorp.com
SIC: 3544 3545 Special dies & tools; machine tool accessories

(G-14169)
HD SIGNS & LIGHTING
9400 N Davis Hwy (32514-7646)
PHONE..................................850 484-9829
EMP: 6 **EST:** 2018
SALES (est): 175.8K **Privately Held**
WEB: www.hdsigns.co
SIC: 3993 Signs & advertising specialties

(G-14170)
HEAR FOR YOU HEARING AID CTR
1805 Creighton Rd Ste 1 (32504-7265)
PHONE..................................850 316-4414
John Dennis, *Principal*
EMP: 6 **EST:** 2019
SALES (est): 277.4K **Privately Held**
SIC: 3842 Hearing aids

(G-14171)
HEIGHTS TOWER SYSTEMS INC
1529 Gulf Beach Hwy (32507-3065)
PHONE..................................850 455-1210
Drake Dimitry, *President*
EMP: 6 **EST:** 1986
SQ FT: 12,000
SALES (est): 1MM **Privately Held**
WEB: www.heightstowers.com
SIC: 3441 Tower sections, radio & television transmission

(G-14172)
HILL ENTERPRISES LLC
125 Terry Dr (32503-7024)
PHONE..................................850 478-4455
Ned Jones, *Mng Member*
EMP: 8 **EST:** 2017
SALES (est): 501.5K **Privately Held**
WEB: www.hillenterprises.net
SIC: 2431 3442 Door sashes, wood; sash, door or window: metal

(G-14173)
HITACHI CABLE AMERICA INC
Automotive Products Div
9101 Ely St (32514-7019)
PHONE..................................850 476-0907
Barbara Everitte, *CFO*
Takao Otsuka, *Manager*
EMP: 118 **Privately Held**
WEB: www.hca.hitachi-cable.com
SIC: 3052 Automobile hose, rubber
HQ: Hitachi Cable America Inc.
2 Manhattanville Rd # 301
Purchase NY 10577
914 694-9200

(G-14174)
HOM ADE FOODS INC
10648 Mac Gregor Dr (32514-8309)
PHONE..................................850 444-4740
Greg Lowery, *Principal*
EMP: 78 **EST:** 2008
SALES (est): 894.8K
SALES (corp-wide): 1B **Publicly Held**
WEB: www.jjsnack.com
SIC: 2038 Frozen specialties
PA: J & J Snack Foods Corp.
6000 Central Hwy
Pennsauken NJ 08109
856 665-9533

(G-14175)
IAN-CONRAD BERGAN LLC (PA)
Also Called: Bergan Tank Control
1001 E Belmont St (32501-4100)
PHONE..................................850 434-1286
Knut R Bergan, *President*
Rob Chandler, *Production*
Bob Toole, *Engineer*
Knut Bergan, *Sales Staff*
Melina Pheabus, *Admin Mgr*
▲ **EMP:** 41 **EST:** 1980
SQ FT: 40,000
SALES (est): 10.9MM **Privately Held**
WEB: www.bergan-blue.com
SIC: 3823 Industrial instrmnts msrmnt display/control process variable

(G-14176)
INDEPENDENT FLORIDA SUN
226 Palafox Pl (32502-5846)
P.O. Box 12082 (32591-2082)
PHONE..................................850 438-8115
Justin Griffith, *Art Dir*
EMP: 6 **EST:** 2018
SALES (est): 62.9K **Privately Held**
WEB: www.inweekly.net
SIC: 2711 Newspapers, publishing & printing

(G-14177)
INDIGO RIVER PUBLISHING
3 W Garden St Ste 718 (32502-5636)
PHONE..................................256 404-5884
Adam Tillinghast, *Principal*
EMP: 8 **EST:** 2012
SALES (est): 986.4K **Privately Held**
WEB: www.indigoriverpublishing.com
SIC: 2741 Miscellaneous publishing

(G-14178)
INGRAM SIGNALIZATION INC
4522 N Davis Hwy (32503-2769)
PHONE..................................850 433-8267
Traci Ingram-Gay, *President*
William Wilson, *Vice Pres*
EMP: 32 **EST:** 1959
SQ FT: 6,500
SALES (est): 6.6MM **Privately Held**
WEB: www.ingramcorp.com
SIC: 3669 1731 Transportation signaling devices; electrical work

(G-14179)
INSTANT IMPRINTS
570 Pheasant Ct (32514-1488)
PHONE..................................850 474-9184
Anthony Myers, *Principal*
EMP: 6 **EST:** 2007
SALES (est): 116.3K **Privately Held**
WEB: www.instantimprints.com
SIC: 2752 Commercial printing, lithographic

(G-14180)
INTERNATIONAL POLYMER SVCS LLC
3431 Mai Kai Dr (32526-2423)
PHONE..................................401 529-6855
Fred Sivell,
EMP: 6 **EST:** 2009
SALES (est): 118.1K **Privately Held**
SIC: 2822 Ethylene-propylene rubbers, EPDM polymers

(G-14181)
J R C CONCRETE PRODUCTS INC
994 S Fairfield Dr Lot 2 (32506-8926)
PHONE..................................850 456-9665
Jim Nicholson, *President*
Peggy Nicholson, *Vice Pres*
EMP: 7 **EST:** 2004
SQ FT: 2,172
SALES (est): 851.3K **Privately Held**
WEB: www.jrcconcreteproducts.com
SIC: 3272 Concrete products

(G-14182)
JAYCO SCREENS INC
9131 W Highway 98 (32506-6057)
P.O. Box 36214 (32516-6214)
PHONE..................................850 456-0673
Fax: 850 453-6949
EMP: 9
SQ FT: 14,000

SALES (est): 910K **Privately Held**
SIC: 3533 3496 5082 Mfg Oil/Gas Field Machinery Mfg Misc Fabricated Wire Products Whol Construction/Mining Equipment

(G-14183)
JOE HEARN INNOVATIVE TECH LLC
Also Called: Jhi Technology
600 Univ Ofc Blvd 17c (32504-6238)
P.O. Box 10562 (32524-0562)
PHONE..................................850 898-3744
Joseph Hearn Jr, *Principal*
Deena Hearn, *Principal*
EMP: 10 **EST:** 2013
SALES (est): 617.4K **Privately Held**
SIC: 3663 3812 1799 4959 ; search & navigation equipment; office furniture installation; sanitary services; building maintenance services; janitorial service, contract basis

(G-14184)
JOHNNY UNDER PRESSURE LLC
7250 Frank Reeder Rd (32526-9117)
PHONE..................................850 530-8763
Regena Suchy, *Principal*
Johnny Stevison,
EMP: 9 **EST:** 2015
SALES (est): 1.2MM **Privately Held**
WEB: www.pressurewashingboynton-beach.com
SIC: 2491 Wood preserving

(G-14185)
JOHNSON WELL EQUIPMENT INC
8480 Gulf Beach Hwy (32507-2636)
P.O. Box 3364 (32516-3364)
PHONE..................................850 453-3131
Julius W Davis, *President*
EMP: 8 **EST:** 1965
SQ FT: 15,000
SALES (est): 1MM **Privately Held**
WEB: www.johnsonwellequipment.com
SIC: 3589 3496 Water filters & softeners, household type; miscellaneous fabricated wire products

(G-14186)
JONAS SOFTWARE USA INC
9295 Scenic Hwy (32514-8055)
PHONE..................................800 476-0094
EMP: 6 **EST:** 2015
SALES (est): 97.4K **Privately Held**
WEB: www.jonassoftware.com
SIC: 7372 Prepackaged software

(G-14187)
JUPITER BACH NORTH AMERICA INC
3301 Bill Metzger Ln (32514-7078)
PHONE..................................850 476-6304
Jens Kristensen, *CEO*
Winston Guidry, *Vice Pres*
Dan Henry, *Prdtn Mgr*
Henrick Nielsen, *CFO*
Edward Austin, *Human Resources*
▲ **EMP:** 180 **EST:** 2006
SALES (est): 52.2MM
SALES (corp-wide): 68.4K **Privately Held**
WEB: www.jupiterbach.com
SIC: 3511 Turbines & turbine generator set units, complete
HQ: Jupiter Bach A/S
Theilgaards Alle 4
KOge 4600
558 933-33

(G-14188)
KELTON COMPANY LLC
220 W Garden St Ste 605 (32502-5744)
P.O. Box 230 (32591-0230)
PHONE..................................850 434-6830
Thom W Sylte, *Mng Member*
Edwina Burchardt,
Tom Sylte,
Edmund F Kelton Trust,
EMP: 8 **EST:** 1978
SQ FT: 1,600
SALES (est): 1MM **Privately Held**
SIC: 1382 Oil & gas exploration services

(G-14189)
KENNETH S JARRELL INC
Also Called: David's Novelties
9859 N Palafox St (32534-1226)
PHONE..................................334 215-7774
Kenneth S Jarrell, *President*
John Sewell, *General Mgr*
▲ **EMP:** 10 **EST:** 1978
SALES (est): 1.3MM **Privately Held**
SIC: 2899 Incense

(G-14190)
KRATON CHEMICAL LLC
411 S Pace Blvd (32502-5009)
PHONE..................................850 438-9222
Marcello Boldrini, *Vice Pres*
Heba K Botros, *Vice Pres*
EMP: 14 **EST:** 2017
SALES (est): 2.9MM **Privately Held**
WEB: www.kraton.com
SIC: 2821 Plastics materials & resins

(G-14191)
LABEL COMPANY
680 E Heinberg St (32502-4146)
P.O. Box 1753 (32591-1753)
PHONE..................................850 438-7334
Roger Van Surksum, *President*
EMP: 18 **EST:** 1980
SQ FT: 12,000
SALES (est): 1.2MM **Privately Held**
WEB: www.thelabelco.com
SIC: 2752 Commercial printing, offset

(G-14192)
LEONARD-MARTIN CORPORATION
Also Called: A & J Mugs
24 N Palafox St (32502-5626)
PHONE..................................850 434-2203
Daniel Lindemann, *President*
Dan Lindemann, *President*
EMP: 6 **EST:** 1981
SALES (est): 694.1K **Privately Held**
SIC: 2759 3269 5999 Decals: printing; business forms: printing; decalcomania work on china & glass; alcoholic beverage making equipment & supplies

(G-14193)
LIGHTING TECHNOLOGIES
1810 Barrancas Ave (32502-5215)
PHONE..................................850 462-1790
Greg Johnson, *Manager*
▲ **EMP:** 15 **EST:** 2014
SALES (est): 4.2MM **Privately Held**
WEB: www.lightingtechnologies.com
SIC: 3648 Outdoor lighting equipment

(G-14194)
LINENWOOD HOME LLC
24 E Brainerd St (32501-2619)
PHONE..................................850 607-7445
Natasha Williams, *Principal*
EMP: 5 **EST:** 2016
SALES (est): 332.3K **Privately Held**
WEB: www.linenwoodhome.com
SIC: 2499 Wood products

(G-14195)
LOCALTOOLBOX INC
Also Called: 100 Feet Deep
2720 Bayou Grande Blvd (32507-2882)
PHONE..................................415 250-3232
James Robbins, *Principal*
EMP: 9 **EST:** 2017
SALES (est): 341.9K **Privately Held**
WEB: www.localtoolbox.com
SIC: 2711 Newspapers, publishing & printing

(G-14196)
LOSOBE LLC
943 Candlestick Ct (32514-1549)
PHONE..................................850 748-3162
Jeff Bere, *Principal*
EMP: 7 **EST:** 2016
SALES (est): 150.6K **Privately Held**
WEB: www.barehandcollective.com
SIC: 2431 Millwork

(G-14197)
LOST KEY PUBLISHING LLC
7166 Sharp Reef Rd (32507-9421)
PHONE..................................850 380-6680
Fred Garth, *Principal*
EMP: 7 **EST:** 2009
SALES (est): 147.5K **Privately Held**
WEB: www.lostkey.com
SIC: 2741 Miscellaneous publishing

(G-14198)
M & W ELECTRIC MOTORS INC
1250 Barrancas Ave (32502-4513)
PHONE..................................850 433-0400
Thomas A Nichols Jr, *President*
Thomas Nichols Jr, *President*
Aaron Hall, *Vice Pres*
Bill Searcy, *Treasurer*
William F Searcy Jr, *Treasurer*
EMP: 8 **EST:** 1958
SQ FT: 6,160
SALES (est): 536.3K **Privately Held**
SIC: 7694 5063 5999 Electric motor repair; motors, electric; motors, electric

(G-14199)
MACHINE TOOL MASTERS INC
Also Called: Mtm
3947 Stoddard Rd (32526-8765)
P.O. Box 18369 (32523-8369)
PHONE..................................850 432-2829
EMP: 13
SQ FT: 6,000
SALES: 900K **Privately Held**
SIC: 3599 Mfg Industrial Machinery

(G-14200)
MARTIN MARIETTA
271 S Pace Blvd (32502-5005)
PHONE..................................850 432-8112
EMP: 6 **EST:** 2017
SALES (est): 74.2K **Privately Held**
WEB: www.martinmarietta.com
SIC: 1422 Crushed & broken limestone

(G-14201)
MARTINS FMOUS PSTRY SHOPPE INC
195 E Fairfield Dr (32503-2956)
PHONE..................................800 548-1200
EMP: 6
SALES (corp-wide): 123.7MM **Privately Held**
WEB: www.potatorolls.com
SIC: 2015 Poultry slaughtering & processing
PA: Martin's Famous Pastry Shoppe, Inc.
1000 Potato Roll Ln
Chambersburg PA 17202
800 548-1200

(G-14202)
MC SQUARED GROUP INC
Also Called: Marketing Bar, The
260 S Tarragona St # 140 (32502-6061)
PHONE..................................850 435-4600
Michelle Sarra, *CEO*
EMP: 6 **EST:** 2011
SQ FT: 1,400
SALES (est): 500.2K **Privately Held**
WEB: www.mc2printing.com
SIC: 2752 7311 8742 7389 Advertising posters, lithographed; advertising consultant; marketing consulting services; advertising, promotional & trade show services; graphic arts & related design; printed media advertising representatives

(G-14203)
MCDIRT INDUSTRIES INC
5570 Bellview Ave (32526-9415)
PHONE..................................850 944-0112
Phillip V McCoy, *President*
Linda McCoy, *Vice Pres*
EMP: 10 **EST:** 1992
SQ FT: 1,500
SALES (est): 850K **Privately Held**
WEB: www.mcdirt.net
SIC: 1442 Construction sand mining

(G-14204)
MCGRAIL SIGNS & GRAPHICS LLC
1011 N P St (32505-6837)
PHONE..................................850 435-1017
James McGrail, *Mng Member*
EMP: 6 **EST:** 1998
SALES (est): 401.6K **Privately Held**
SIC: 3993 Signs & advertising specialties

(G-14205)
MEDICAL ENERGY INC
8806 Paul Starr Dr (32514-7061)
P.O. Box 777818, Henderson NV (89077-7818)
PHONE..................................850 313-6277
David Lewing, *CEO*
Michelle Scott, *Vice Pres*
Meghan Marchant, *Manager*
Jason Lewing, *Director*
EMP: 6 **EST:** 1987
SALES (est): 1.2MM **Privately Held**
WEB: www.medicalenergy.com
SIC: 3841 Surgical & medical instruments

(G-14206)
MERCURY MACHINING CO INC (PA)
1085 W Gimble St (32502-5455)
PHONE..................................850 433-5017
Dale Macarthy, *President*
EMP: 39 **EST:** 1966
SQ FT: 7,000
SALES (est): 5.7MM **Privately Held**
WEB: www.mercurymachining.com
SIC: 3599 Machine shop, jobbing & repair

(G-14207)
METAL CRAFT OF PENSACOLA INC
Also Called: Metalcraft
4 E Hannah St (32534-3413)
PHONE..................................850 478-8333
Chris Stinson, *President*
EMP: 21 **EST:** 1994
SQ FT: 5,750
SALES (est): 1.5MM **Privately Held**
WEB: www.metalcraftofpensacola.com
SIC: 2514 7692 Lawn furniture: metal; welding repair

(G-14208)
METROTECH MEDIA & LIGHTING INC
38 S Blue Angel Pkwy # 108 (32506-6045)
PHONE..................................844 463-8761
David L Benavent, *COO*
EMP: 7 **EST:** 2015
SALES (est): 659.1K **Privately Held**
WEB: www.metrotechlight.com
SIC: 3646 Commercial indusl & institutional electric lighting fixtures

(G-14209)
MID WEST LETTERING COMPANY
Also Called: Sunbelt Lettering
7800 Sears Blvd (32514-4544)
PHONE..................................850 477-6522
Fax: 850 484-5390
EMP: 25
SQ FT: 8,880
SALES (est): 3.3MM
SALES (corp-wide): 5.6MM **Privately Held**
SIC: 3559 2399 2752 2395 Mfg Misc Industry Mach Mfg Fabrctd Textile Pdts Lithographic Coml Print Pleating/Stitching Svcs
PA: Mid West Lettering Company
645 Bellefontaine Ave
Marion OH
740 382-1905

(G-14210)
NAI PRINT SOLUTIONS LLC
457 Strandview Dr (32534-1372)
PHONE..................................850 637-1260
Taris Wickizer, *Principal*
EMP: 6 **EST:** 2008
SALES (est): 407.4K **Privately Held**
WEB: www.naiprint.com
SIC: 2752 Commercial printing, offset

(G-14211)
NATIONAL STD PARTS ASSOC INC
Also Called: Nspa
1301 E Belmont St (32501-4135)
PHONE..................................850 456-5771
John E Endacott, *CEO*
J Brooks Endacott, *President*
▲ **EMP:** 52 **EST:** 1980
SQ FT: 15,000

SALES (est): 9MM **Privately Held**
WEB: www.nspa.com
SIC: 3643 3613 5085 Connectors & terminals for electrical devices; power connectors, electric; fasteners & fastening equipment

(G-14212)
NORTH AMERICAN SIGNAL LLC
1810 Barrancas Ave (32502-5215)
PHONE..................................850 462-1790
Greg Johnson, *Vice Pres*
Michael R Day, *Mng Member*
EMP: 9 **EST:** 2015
SALES (est): 176.9K **Privately Held**
WEB: www.northamericansignal.com
SIC: 3669 Traffic signals, electric

(G-14213)
OASIS ALIGNMENT SERVICES INC
7501 Sears Blvd (32514-4539)
PHONE..................................850 484-2994
Myron Smith, *Principal*
Dave Cox, *Director*
EMP: 10
SALES (corp-wide): 14.6MM **Privately Held**
WEB: www.oasisalignment.com
SIC: 3827 Aiming circles (fire control equipment)
PA: Oasis Alignment Services, Llc
363 Pickering Rd
Rochester NH 03867
603 332-9641

(G-14214)
OFFSHORE INLAND MAR OLFLD SVCS
640 S Barracks St (32502-6053)
PHONE..................................251 443-5550
Robin D Roberts, *CEO*
Jesse Odom, *Superintendent*
Crystal Yasurek, *Vice Pres*
Anna Smith, *Project Mgr*
Brian Hall, *Foreman/Supr*
▲ **EMP:** 125 **EST:** 2001
SALES (est): 39.1MM **Privately Held**
WEB: www.offshoreinland.com
SIC: 1389 Oil field services; oil consultants; gas field services
PA: Oimo Holdings, Inc
2735 Middle Rd
Mobile AL 36605

(G-14215)
OLD CITY BUILDING
201 E Government St (32502-6018)
PHONE..................................850 432-7723
W H F Wiltshire, *President*
Gordon E Welch,
EMP: 8 **EST:** 1960
SALES (est): 1.1MM **Privately Held**
SIC: 1381 Drilling oil & gas wells

(G-14216)
ON-SITE LIGHTING & SIGN SVCS
5925 Flaxman St (32506-4029)
PHONE..................................256 693-1018
EMP: 8 **EST:** 2012
SALES (est): 98.3K **Privately Held**
WEB: www.onsitelighting.com
SIC: 3993 Signs & advertising specialties

(G-14217)
ORDERCOUNTER INC
Also Called: Order Counter Com Point Svc S
9270 University Pkwy # 102 (32514-9447)
PHONE..................................850 332-5540
Thomas Barrineau IV, *CEO*
Crystal Barrineau, *Marketing Staff*
EMP: 12 **EST:** 2006
SQ FT: 500
SALES (est): 1.3MM **Privately Held**
WEB: www.home.ordercounter.com
SIC: 7372 Business oriented computer software

(G-14218)
P A VIVID PATHOLOGY (PA)
Also Called: Medical Examiners Office Dst 1
5149 N 9th Ave Ste 122 (32504-8779)
P.O. Box 10450 (32524-0450)
PHONE..................................850 416-7780
Thomas J Lawrence MD, *Principal*
John Bray, *Vice Pres*
Emily Arias, *Accountant*
Samantha Stevens, *Human Res Mgr*
Mark Blalock, *Supervisor*
EMP: 3 **EST:** 1969
SALES (est): 3.3MM **Privately Held**
WEB: www.vividpathology.com
SIC: 2711 Newspapers, publishing & printing

(G-14219)
PALAFOX MARINE INC
490 S L St (32502-5209)
PHONE..................................850 438-9354
Hunter Riddle, *Owner*
Suzanne Riddle, *Manager*
EMP: 10 **EST:** 1973
SQ FT: 5,900
SALES (est): 942.7K **Privately Held**
SIC: 2211 Sail cloth

(G-14220)
PARADIGM PARACHUTE AND DEFENSE
4040 Ashland Ave (32534-1050)
PHONE..................................928 580-9013
Aaron Nazaruk, *Principal*
Alexander Alvarado, *Principal*
Doris Cooper, *Principal*
EMP: 12 **EST:** 2019
SALES (est): 1MM **Privately Held**
WEB: www.paradigmparachute.com
SIC: 2399 Fabricated textile products

(G-14221)
PATTI MARINE ENTERPRISES INC
306 S Pinewood Ln (32507-1374)
P.O. Box 271 (32591-0271)
PHONE..................................850 453-1282
Frank M Patti, *President*
Mandy Patti, *General Mgr*
EMP: 12 **EST:** 2008
SALES (est): 4.2MM **Privately Held**
WEB: www.pattimarine.com
SIC: 3731 Shipbuilding & repairing

(G-14222)
PAULS PALLETS
8928 Abbington Dr (32534-5347)
PHONE..................................850 474-1920
Rene Robert Paul, *Principal*
EMP: 6 **EST:** 2010
SALES (est): 119.9K **Privately Held**
SIC: 2448 Pallets, wood & wood with metal

(G-14223)
PBI/GORDON CORP
8809 Ely St (32514-7064)
PHONE..................................850 478-2770
Cally Miller, *Analyst*
EMP: 18 **EST:** 2019
SALES (est): 74.4K **Privately Held**
WEB: www.pbigordon.com
SIC: 2879 Pesticides, agricultural or household

(G-14224)
PEGASUS LABORATORIES INC (HQ)
Also Called: Trophy Animal Health Care
8809 Ely St (32514-7064)
PHONE..................................850 478-2770
Richard E Martin, *President*
Scott Howard, *Vice Pres*
Donna Logan, *Vice Pres*
Keyli Whelan, *Project Mgr*
Georgette Tacheny, *QC Mgr*
EMP: 79 **EST:** 1987
SQ FT: 46,000
SALES (est): 24.7MM
SALES (corp-wide): 154.3MM **Privately Held**
WEB: www.pegasuslabs.com
SIC: 2834 Veterinary pharmaceutical preparations
PA: Pbi-Gordon Corporation
22701 W 68th Ter
Shawnee KS 66226
816 421-4070

(G-14225)
PENSACOLA ORTHTC & PROSTETIC
5855 Creek Station Dr (32504-8626)
PHONE..................................850 478-7676
EMP: 8
SALES (est): 500K **Privately Held**
SIC: 3842 Mfg Surgical Appliances/Supplies

(G-14226)
PENSACOLA SIGN & GRAPHICS INC
Also Called: SIGNGEEK DBA PENSACOLA SIGN & GRAPHICS
3711 N Palafox St (32505-5236)
PHONE..................................850 433-7878
Steve Orlich, *President*
EMP: 7 **EST:** 1994
SQ FT: 3,000
SALES (est): 849.7K **Privately Held**
WEB: www.pensacolasign.com
SIC: 3993 Signs, not made in custom sign painting shops

(G-14227)
PENSACOLA VOICE INC
213 E Yonge St (32503-3766)
PHONE..................................850 434-6963
Jacqueline Miles, *President*
EMP: 5 **EST:** 1970
SQ FT: 3,000
SALES (est): 616.5K **Privately Held**
WEB: www.pensacolavoice.com
SIC: 2711 8999 7338 Newspapers: publishing only, not printed on site; advertising copy writing; secretarial & court reporting

(G-14228)
PENSACOLA WOOD TREATING CO
1813 E Gadsden St (32501-3532)
PHONE..................................850 433-1300
Susan O McMillan, *President*
EMP: 9 **EST:** 2009
SALES (est): 122.6K **Privately Held**
SIC: 2491 Wood preserving

(G-14229)
PERFORMANCE MACHINING SVCS INC
4161 Warehouse Ln (32505-4061)
PHONE..................................850 469-9106
Jake Ziglioli, *President*
Carla Ziglioli, *Vice Pres*
Greg Mowry, *Manager*
EMP: 15 **EST:** 1995
SQ FT: 7,000
SALES (est): 2.2MM **Privately Held**
SIC: 3599 Machine shop, jobbing & repair

(G-14230)
PINNACLE CABINETS CLOSETS LLC
9900b N Palafox St (32534-1227)
PHONE..................................850 477-5402
Sue Long,
EMP: 6 **EST:** 2009
SALES (est): 437.1K **Privately Held**
WEB: www.pinnaclecabinetsandclosets.com
SIC: 2434 Wood kitchen cabinets

(G-14231)
PLASMINE TECHNOLOGY INC (DH)
3298 Summit Blvd Ste 35 (32503-4350)
PHONE..................................850 438-8550
Steven J Violette, *President*
Brian Williquette, *Manager*
Ralph Emerson, *Director*
Raplh W Emerson Jr, *Director*
◆ **EMP:** 12 **EST:** 1990
SQ FT: 4,700
SALES (est): 14.2MM **Privately Held**
WEB: www.plasmine.com
SIC: 2819 Industrial inorganic chemicals
HQ: Harima Usa, Inc.
1965 Evergreen Blvd # 400
Duluth GA 30096
770 813-1720

(G-14232)
PLASTIC ART SIGN COMPANY INC
3931 W Navy Blvd (32507-1256)
PHONE..................................850 455-4114
John Navarro, *President*
Elizabeth Mae Navarro, *Corp Secy*
Scott Navarro, *Vice Pres*
Harold Dodd, *Sales Staff*
EMP: 10 **EST:** 1969
SQ FT: 8,000
SALES (est): 1.2MM **Privately Held**
WEB: www.plasticartssigns.com
SIC: 3993 Signs & advertising specialties

(G-14233)
PLASTIC COATED PAPERS INC
1701 E Kingsfield Rd (32534-9503)
PHONE..................................850 968-6100
David L Mayo, *President*
William O Helms, *Vice Pres*
James E McGahan, *Vice Pres*
David C Pitts, *Vice Pres*
Pinette M Steven, *Vice Pres*
EMP: 52 **EST:** 1952
SQ FT: 52,000
SALES (est): 16.2MM **Privately Held**
WEB: www.polycoated.com
SIC: 2671 Paper coated or laminated for packaging

(G-14234)
POLLAK INDUSTRIES
2313 Truman Ave (32505-4249)
PHONE..................................850 438-4651
Buffy Spurlock, *Director*
EMP: 8 **EST:** 2002
SQ FT: 6,480
SALES (est): 91K **Privately Held**
WEB: www.arc-gateway.org
SIC: 3272 Concrete products

(G-14235)
POTTERS COFFEE COMPANY
1727 Creighton Rd (32504-7145)
PHONE..................................850 525-1793
Kevin Webster, *President*
EMP: 6 **EST:** 2017
SQ FT: 360
SALES (est): 128.2K **Privately Held**
WEB: www.potters-coffee-company.business.site
SIC: 2095 7389 5149 Roasted coffee; coffee service; coffee, green or roasted

(G-14236)
PRECAST TECHNICAL ASSISTANCE
21 S Tarragona St Ste 101 (32502-6062)
PHONE..................................850 432-8446
William A Lovell Jr, *President*
EMP: 12 **EST:** 2015
SALES (est): 442.2K **Privately Held**
WEB: www.ptac.com
SIC: 3272 Precast terrazo or concrete products

(G-14237)
PRECISION LIFT INDUSTRIES LLC
3605 N Davis Hwy (32503-3021)
PHONE..................................877 770-5862
Scott Humbaugh, *Mng Member*
Pete Seidel, *Technical Staff*
EMP: 8 **EST:** 2010
SALES (est): 1.9MM **Privately Held**
WEB: www.precisionliftindustries.com
SIC: 3534 Elevators & equipment

(G-14238)
PRIME MANUFACTURING CANADA
9235 Roe St (32514-7034)
PHONE..................................850 332-7193
Michelle Jones, *Principal*
Brad Fisher, *VP Opers*
▲ **EMP:** 8 **EST:** 2009
SALES (est): 778.1K **Privately Held**
WEB: www.primerailroadproducts.com
SIC: 3999 Barber & beauty shop equipment

(G-14239)
PRIME PEDAL KARTS LLC
Also Called: Prime Karts
9235 Roe St (32514-7034)
PHONE..................................850 475-0450
Jeffrey L Fisher, *Exec VP*
Ronald Fisher, *Mng Member*
Jeff Fisher,
Derek Lother,

▲ **EMP:** 10 **EST:** 2004
SQ FT: 3,000
SALES (est): 750K **Privately Held**
WEB: www.primekarts.com
SIC: 3944 Automobiles, children's, pedal driven

(G-14240)
PRINTERS OF PENSACOLA LLC
1207 W Garden St (32502-4556)
PHONE..................................850 434-2588
Ray Herring, *President*
Raymond Herring, *President*
Debra Herring, *Vice Pres*
EMP: 5 **EST:** 1975
SQ FT: 1,600
SALES (est): 300K **Privately Held**
WEB: www.printersofpensacola.com
SIC: 2752 7334 2791 Commercial printing, offset; photocopying & duplicating services; typesetting

(G-14241)
PRINTNOW INC
Also Called: Print Now-Business Cards Today
5555 N Davis Hwy Ste H (32503-2065)
P.O. Box 892, Gulf Breeze (32562-0892)
PHONE..................................850 435-1149
Kelley Chism, *President*
Robert A Chism, *Admin Sec*
EMP: 6 **EST:** 2000
SALES (est): 460K **Privately Held**
WEB: www.printnowinc.com
SIC: 2752 Commercial printing, offset

(G-14242)
PUBLISHERS CRCLTION FLFLLMENT
Also Called: PCF
3351b Mclemore Dr (32514-7074)
PHONE..................................877 723-6668
Elisabeth Harrison, *Manager*
EMP: 28
SALES (corp-wide): 58MM **Privately Held**
WEB: www.pcfcorp.com
SIC: 2741 Miscellaneous publishing
PA: Publishers Circulation Fulfillment, Inc.
502 Wshington Ave Ste 500
Towson MD 21204
410 821-8614

(G-14243)
PWS INTERNATIONAL
5 Clarinda Ln (32505-4309)
PHONE..................................850 432-4222
EMP: 9 **EST:** 2010
SALES (est): 19.1K **Privately Held**
WEB: www.pwsintl.com
SIC: 3582 Commercial laundry equipment

(G-14244)
QLTY ALUMN BOAT LIFTS INC
2375 W Herman Ave (32505-4245)
PHONE..................................850 434-6446
Jayne Card, *Principal*
EMP: 7 **EST:** 2015
SALES (est): 456.7K **Privately Held**
WEB: www.boatliftinstructions.com
SIC: 3536 Boat lifts

(G-14245)
QUALITY ALUM BOAT LIFTS INC
2375 W Herman Ave (32505-4245)
PHONE..................................850 434-6446
EMP: 9 **EST:** 2013
SALES (est): 672.4K **Privately Held**
SIC: 3536 Boat lifts

(G-14246)
QUALITY ALUMINUM MANUFACTURING
2375 W Herman Ave (32505-4245)
PHONE..................................850 434-6446
Jayne Card, *Principal*
▼ **EMP:** 6 **EST:** 2011
SALES (est): 174.1K **Privately Held**
SIC: 3999 Manufacturing industries

(G-14247)
R & K PORTABLE BUILDINGS
Also Called: R & K Builders
8120 Pensacola Blvd (32534-4352)
PHONE..................................850 857-7899
Glen Russell, *Partner*
EMP: 9 **EST:** 1981
SQ FT: 540
SALES (est): 129.1K **Privately Held**
WEB: www.rnkbuildings.com
SIC: 3448 1521 Prefabricated metal buildings; patio & deck construction & repair

(G-14248)
R K L ENTERPRISES OF PENSACOLA
Also Called: Speed-D-Print
3740 N Pace Blvd (32505-4352)
PHONE..................................850 432-2335
Rita K Loughridge, *President*
Jack Loughridge, *Corp Secy*
EMP: 10 **EST:** 1983
SQ FT: 3,600
SALES (est): 1.2MM **Privately Held**
WEB: www.speeddprint.com
SIC: 2752 Commercial printing, offset

(G-14249)
RACEWAY
3530 Barrancas Ave (32507-2373)
PHONE..................................850 453-9437
EMP: 7 **EST:** 2018
SALES (est): 220.3K **Privately Held**
WEB: www.racewaystores.com
SIC: 3644 Raceways

(G-14250)
READY MACHINE CORP
6155 Drexel Rd (32504-7906)
PHONE..................................850 479-1722
Krzysztof Roszko, *Owner*
EMP: 7 **EST:** 2003
SALES (est): 420.1K **Privately Held**
WEB: www.ready-machine-corp.business.site
SIC: 3599 Machine shop, jobbing & repair

(G-14251)
REDDY ICE CORPORATION
1511 W Government St (32502-5318)
PHONE..................................850 433-2191
Kenneth Wilson, *Plant Engr*
Tim Brown, *Manager*
EMP: 12 **Privately Held**
WEB: www.reddyice.com
SIC: 2097 5999 Block ice; ice cubes; ice
HQ: Reddy Ice Corporation
5710 Lbj Fwy Ste 300
Dallas TX 75240
214 526-6740

(G-14252)
RENAISSANCE MAN INCORPORATED
Also Called: Renaissance Fabrication
2203 N Pace Blvd (32505-5837)
PHONE..................................850 432-1177
Jon Kevin Marchetti, *President*
EMP: 6 **EST:** 1999
SALES (est): 750K **Privately Held**
WEB: www.renaissancefabrication.com
SIC: 3441 Fabricated structural metal

(G-14253)
RING OF FIRE RADIO LLC
316 S Baylen St (32502-5900)
PHONE..................................866 666-6114
J Michael Papantonio, *Manager*
EMP: 7 **EST:** 2005
SALES (est): 188.3K **Privately Held**
WEB: www.trofire.com
SIC: 2711 Newspapers, publishing & printing

(G-14254)
ROYAL CUP INC
Also Called: Royal Cup Coffee
3741 N Davis Hwy 78 (32503-3023)
P.O. Box 170971, Birmingham AL (35217-0971)
PHONE..................................850 436-4435
Don Gann, *Manager*
EMP: 6
SALES (corp-wide): 243.1MM **Privately Held**
WEB: www.royalcupcoffee.com
SIC: 2095 5149 2099 7389 Roasted coffee; groceries & related products; soft drinks; tea blending; coffee service
PA: Royal Cup Inc.
160 Cleage Dr
Birmingham AL 35217
205 849-5836

(G-14255)
RUDD & SON WELDING INC
Also Called: Rudd Welding
81 E Ten Mile Rd (32534-9706)
P.O. Box 1087, Gonzalez (32560-1087)
PHONE..................................850 476-2110
Charles Edward Rudd, *President*
Patricia I Rudd, *Admin Sec*
EMP: 14 **EST:** 1953
SQ FT: 12,000
SALES (est): 1.6MM **Privately Held**
SIC: 7692 Welding repair

(G-14256)
S&J ALUMINUM WORKS INC
5623 Bauer Rd (32507-9077)
PHONE..................................850 492-5700
Scott Schlyer, *President*
EMP: 8
SALES (est): 650K **Privately Held**
SIC: 3411 Aluminum cans

(G-14257)
SANTA ROSA AUTO PARTS INC
Also Called: Car City Engine and Machine
50 Industrial Blvd (32503-7602)
PHONE..................................850 477-7747
Kenneth A Schepper, *President*
Carl E Schepper, *Vice Pres*
David M Schepper, *Treasurer*
EMP: 29 **EST:** 1959
SQ FT: 13,000
SALES (est): 1.8MM **Privately Held**
WEB: www.carcityengine.com
SIC: 3599 3714 Machine & other job shop work; motor vehicle parts & accessories

(G-14258)
SCHURR SAILS INC
490 S L St (32502-5267)
PHONE..................................850 438-9354
Hunter Riddle, *President*
Alfred L Schurr, *Principal*
Steve Bellows, *Corp Secy*
EMP: 10 **EST:** 1971
SQ FT: 5,000
SALES (est): 401K **Privately Held**
WEB: www.schurr-sails.com
SIC: 2394 3732 Sails: made from purchased materials; boat building & repairing

(G-14259)
SCHWARZ BROS MANUFACTURING CO
1455 Little Creek Dr (32506-8259)
PHONE..................................309 342-5814
Steven Gray, *President*
C Gray, *Treasurer*
EMP: 6 **EST:** 1940
SALES (est): 858.2K **Privately Held**
SIC: 3544 Special dies & tools; jigs & fixtures

(G-14260)
SHANNON SPRAY COATINGS INC
7267 Belgium Rd (32526-3816)
PHONE..................................850 602-7163
Patrick Shannon, *Principal*
EMP: 6 **EST:** 2010
SALES (est): 67.7K **Privately Held**
WEB: www.shannonspraycoatings.com
SIC: 3479 Metal coating & allied service

(G-14261)
SILVER HORN JERKY INC
3715 Mobile Hwy (32505-6122)
PHONE..................................850 208-1433
Qua Dinh, *Principal*
EMP: 13 **EST:** 2018
SALES (est): 643.1K **Privately Held**
WEB: www.silverhornjerky.com
SIC: 2013 Snack sticks, including jerky: from purchased meat

(G-14262)
SMARTCOP INC
Also Called: Consolidated Tech Solutions
9165 Roe St (32514-7032)
PHONE..................................850 429-0082
George Kay Stephenson, *CEO*
George Stephenson, *President*
James Benson, *COO*
Shane Lincke, *Vice Pres*
Steve Williams, *Vice Pres*
EMP: 50 **EST:** 1999
SQ FT: 8,700
SALES (est): 10.8MM **Privately Held**
WEB: www.smartcop.com
SIC: 7372 Prepackaged software

(G-14263)
SOUTHERN ENVIRONMENTAL INC
6690 W Nine Mile Rd (32526-3211)
PHONE..................................850 944-4475
Michael W Hatsfelt, *President*
Andrew Lynch, *Regional Mgr*
John L Jernigan, *Vice Pres*
Johnny L Jernigan, *Vice Pres*
Dale Campbell, *Project Mgr*
EMP: 30 **EST:** 1973
SQ FT: 9,600
SALES (est): 6.1MM **Privately Held**
WEB: www.southernenvironmental.com
SIC: 3822 Thermostats & other environmental sensors

(G-14264)
SOUTHERN STATES GLUING SVCS
3865 N Palafox St (32505-5238)
PHONE..................................850 469-9667
EMP: 8
SQ FT: 8,000
SALES (est): 660K **Privately Held**
SIC: 2672 Adhesive Application

(G-14265)
SOUTHERN TENNIS SUPPLIES
92 W Gadsden St Apt 3 (32501-3976)
PHONE..................................850 936-1772
Chae Johnsen, *Principal*
EMP: 6 **EST:** 2008
SALES (est): 161.7K **Privately Held**
WEB: www.southerntennissupplies.com
SIC: 3949 Sporting & athletic goods

(G-14266)
SOUTHERN WOODWORKS FINE WDWKG
Also Called: Fine Wood Work
1170 Mahogany Mill Rd (32507-3902)
PHONE..................................850 456-0550
Rebecca Bennett, *President*
Becky Bennett, *President*
EMP: 10 **EST:** 1992
SQ FT: 5,000
SALES (est): 892.1K **Privately Held**
WEB: www.southernwoodworksinc.com
SIC: 2541 1751 Wood partitions & fixtures; cabinet & finish carpentry

(G-14267)
SPECIALTY PRODUCTS INC
2325 W Cervantes St (32505-7148)
PHONE..................................850 438-4264
Bud Segers, *President*
Scott McCandless, *Sales Staff*
EMP: 8 **EST:** 2002
SALES (est): 200K **Privately Held**
SIC: 2431 3442 1799 1751 Garage doors, overhead: wood; garage doors, overhead: metal; dock equipment installation, industrial; window & door installation & erection; garage door, installation or erection; garage doors, sale & installation

(G-14268)
SPECTRUMIT INC
1101 N Palafox St (32501-2607)
PHONE..................................850 202-5263
Scott Pfeifer, *President*
Deb Stuckey, *Opers Mgr*
Deborah Stuckey, *Opers Mgr*
EMP: 11 **EST:** 2012
SALES (est): 5.7MM **Privately Held**
WEB: www.spectrumit.net
SIC: 3519 Internal combustion engines

(G-14269)
SPIKER USA CORPORATION
38 S Blue Angel Pkwy (32506-6045)
PHONE..................................850 710-3043
Karon P Butler, *President*
EMP: 7 **EST:** 2015
SALES (est): 306.4K **Privately Held**
SIC: 3221 Glass containers

(G-14270)
SPIKES PRESS & PRINTHOUSE LLC
1201 Barrancas Ave (32502-4512)
PHONE..................................850 438-2293
Luke T Keller, *Mng Member*
EMP: 6 **EST:** 2012
SALES (est): 258.7K **Privately Held**
SIC: 2741 Miscellaneous publishing

(G-14271)
SUNPACK OF PENSACOLA INC
8500 Fowler Ave (32534-1801)
PHONE..................................850 476-9838
John M O Neil, *CEO*
John M Oneill, *President*
▲ **EMP:** 16 **EST:** 1998
SQ FT: 60,000
SALES (est): 4.8MM **Privately Held**
WEB: www.sunpackinc.com
SIC: 3452 5085 3462 Bolts, metal; gaskets; flange, valve & pipe fitting forgings, ferrous

(G-14272)
SWAN NECK WINERY
2115 W Nine Mile Rd (32534-9470)
PHONE..................................850 495-3897
EMP: 6 **EST:** 2017
SALES (est): 161.4K **Privately Held**
SIC: 2084 Wines

(G-14273)
TECHNOLOGIES FOR TOMORROW INC
1106 N 9th Ave (32501-3236)
PHONE..................................850 478-5222
Elizabeth Doenlen, *President*
Pamela L Coco, *Vice Pres*
Daniel Coco, *CFO*
Angel Clark, *Manager*
Dale Collins, *Manager*
EMP: 16 **EST:** 1994
SQ FT: 4,100
SALES (est): 6.9MM **Privately Held**
WEB: www.tftcomputers.com
SIC: 3577 Computer peripheral equipment

(G-14274)
TRANSPORT A/C INC
91 S Madison Dr (32505-3615)
PHONE..................................954 254-4822
Jacob Baker, *CEO*
EMP: 6 **EST:** 2010
SALES (est): 421K **Privately Held**
SIC: 3585 Air conditioning, motor vehicle

(G-14275)
TRIMTEK LEATHER INC
1060 E Cross St (32503-3664)
P.O. Box 1556, Ozark AL (36361-1556)
PHONE..................................706 577-3950
Marlo Leblanc, *Principal*
EMP: 8 **EST:** 2017
SALES (est): 503.7K **Privately Held**
WEB: www.trimtekleather.com
SIC: 3172 Personal leather goods

(G-14276)
TRIOPS INC
Also Called: Toyops
3330 Mclemore Dr Ste B (32514-7077)
P.O. Box 11369 (32524-1369)
PHONE..................................850 479-4415
Eugene Hall, *President*
Christina Jones, *Manager*
Shannon Wix, *Manager*
▲ **EMP:** 6 **EST:** 1993
SALES (est): 500K **Privately Held**
WEB: www.triops.com
SIC: 3944 Science kits: microscopes, chemistry sets, etc.

(G-14277)
TURBINE RESOURCES INTL LLC
2595a Dog Track Rd (32506-7833)
PHONE..................................850 377-0449
James Patrick Meharg,
EMP: 8 **EST:** 2014
SALES (est): 195.7K **Privately Held**
WEB: www.turbineresourcesintl.com
SIC: 3511 Gas turbine generator set units, complete

(G-14278)
UNITED RENTALS NORTH AMER INC
3310 Mclemore Dr (32514-7081)
PHONE..................................850 478-2833
Rick Waters, *Sales/Mktg Mgr*
EMP: 6
SALES (corp-wide): 8.5B **Publicly Held**
WEB: www.unitedrentals.com
SIC: 3561 7359 Pumps, domestic: water or sump; equipment rental & leasing
HQ: United Rentals (North America), Inc.
100 Frst Stmford Pl Ste 7
Stamford CT 06902
203 622-3131

(G-14279)
UNITED STATES GREEN ENRGY CORP
1074 Windchime Way (32503-2548)
PHONE..................................540 295-4843
▼ **EMP:** 30 **EST:** 2009
SQ FT: 300
SALES (est): 2.6MM **Privately Held**
SIC: 3433 Mfg Solar Equipment

(G-14280)
VAPOR ENGINEERING INC
147 Mirabelle Cir (32514-5888)
PHONE..................................850 434-3191
Edward L Kalis, *CEO*
EMP: 10 **EST:** 1964
SQ FT: 10,000
SALES (est): 689.1K **Privately Held**
WEB: www.vaporengineering.com
SIC: 3841 3699 Ultrasonic medical cleaning equipment; electrical equipment & supplies

(G-14281)
VERACITY TECH SOLUTIONS LLC
7004 Pine Forest Rd Ste D (32526-3936)
PHONE..................................402 658-4113
Jim Wagner, *CEO*
Kevin McKinley, *President*
Curtis Evans, *COO*
Chris Chadwick, *Vice Pres*
EMP: 18 **EST:** 2006
SALES (est): 1.3MM **Privately Held**
WEB: www.veracityts.com
SIC: 3829 8734 8331 Measuring & controlling devices; testing laboratories; job training services

(G-14282)
VERHI INC
824 Creighton Rd Ste A (32504-7082)
PHONE..................................850 477-4880
Steven L Gavin, *Principal*
Steve Gavin, *Principal*
EMP: 44 **EST:** 2005
SALES (est): 866.5K
SALES (corp-wide): 1B **Publicly Held**
WEB: www.hangerclinic.com
SIC: 3842 Wheelchairs
PA: Hanger, Inc.
10910 Domain Dr Ste 300
Austin TX 78758
512 777-3800

(G-14283)
VERTEC INC
141 Terry Dr (32503-7066)
PHONE..................................850 478-6480
Ronald R Bray, *President*
Quinlyn Bray, *Corp Secy*
John R Bray, *Vice Pres*
Kendall Bray, *Manager*
Valerie Bevis, *Admin Sec*
EMP: 11 **EST:** 1978
SQ FT: 22,000
SALES (est): 1MM **Privately Held**
WEB: www.vertec.net
SIC: 3823 3444 3845 Industrial process measurement equipment; sheet metal specialties, not stamped; electromedical apparatus

(G-14284)
VIEWPOINT SYSTEMS LLC
730 W Garden St Pensacola (32502)
PHONE..................................850 450-0681
David Conkle, *Partner*
EMP: 12 **EST:** 2011
SALES (est): 1.7MM **Privately Held**
WEB: www.viewpointproducts.com
SIC: 3812 Search & navigation equipment

(G-14285)
VOWELLS DOWNTOWN INC
Also Called: Vowells Printing
1233 Barrancas Ave (32502-4512)
P.O. Box 12644 (32591-2644)
PHONE..................................850 432-5175
Mary Vowell, *President*
John Roberts, *Vice Pres*
Mike Vowell, *Vice Pres*
Sheila Hicks, *Office Mgr*
EMP: 9 **EST:** 1981
SQ FT: 5,000
SALES (est): 750.3K **Privately Held**
WEB: www.vowells.com
SIC: 2752 2796 2791 2789 Commercial printing, offset; platemaking services; typesetting; bookbinding & related work

(G-14286)
WATER TECHNOLOGY OF PENSACOLA
Also Called: A T B Systems
3000 W Nine Mile Rd (32534-9473)
PHONE..................................850 477-4789
William Boesch, *President*
Elise Boesch, *Treasurer*
David Taylor, *Sales Mgr*
EMP: 30 **EST:** 1985
SQ FT: 9,200
SALES (est): 3.9MM **Privately Held**
WEB: www.atbsystems.com
SIC: 3599 Boiler tube cleaners

(G-14287)
WATERBOYZ WBZ INC
Also Called: Wbz Boarding House
380 N 9th Ave (32502-4951)
PHONE..................................850 433-2929
Sean Fell, *President*
▲ **EMP:** 14 **EST:** 1989
SQ FT: 2,000
SALES (est): 792.2K **Privately Held**
WEB: www.waterboyz.com
SIC: 2759 5941 3993 5999 Screen printing; surfing equipment & supplies; signs & advertising specialties; sunglasses

(G-14288)
WIND BLUE TECHNOLOGY LLC
7502 Sears Blvd (32514-4538)
PHONE..................................850 218-9398
Henry A Kelley Jr,
EMP: 17 **EST:** 2019
SALES (est): 12.6MM **Privately Held**
WEB: www.bluewindtechnology.com
SIC: 3086 Plastics foam products

(G-14289)
WINGS THINGS MONOGRAMMING INC
3815 W Navy Blvd (32507-1219)
PHONE..................................850 455-3081
Larry Speed, *President*
EMP: 13 **EST:** 1987
SQ FT: 9,000
SALES (est): 554.4K **Privately Held**
WEB: www.wings-and-things.com
SIC: 2395 Emblems, embroidered; embroidery & art needlework

(G-14290)
WISE RECYCLING 1 LLC
Also Called: Reynolds Aluminum Recycl Div
601 W Hope Dr (32534-4215)
P.O. Box 28737, Baltimore MD (21240)
PHONE..................................850 477-5273
Harold Stone, *Manager*
Llori Freeman, *Manager*
EMP: 10
SALES (corp-wide): 75MM **Privately Held**
WEB: www.wiserecycling.com
SIC: 3341 4953 Aluminum smelting & refining (secondary); refuse systems
PA: Wise Recycling 1, Llc
7600 Rolling Mill Rd
Baltimore MD 21224
410 285-6900

Perry
Taylor County

(G-14291)
AGNER TIMBER SERVICES INC
2450 W Fair Rd (32347-4900)
PHONE..................................850 251-6615
Chad Agner, *President*
EMP: 9 **EST:** 2005
SQ FT: 800
SALES (est): 2.5MM **Privately Held**
SIC: 2411 Logging

(G-14292)
AMERICAN ALUMINUM ACC INC
3291 S Us Highway 19 (32348-6402)
PHONE..................................850 277-0869
Tom Swain, *CEO*
Jennifer Arnold, *President*
Robert Swain, *President*
◆ **EMP:** 35 **EST:** 1989
SQ FT: 59,000
SALES (est): 10MM **Privately Held**
WEB: www.ezrideronline.com
SIC: 3443 Fabricated plate work (boiler shop)

(G-14293)
AMTEC LESS LETHAL SYSTEMS INC
Also Called: Pacem Defense
4700 Providence Rd (32347-1140)
PHONE..................................850 223-4066
Andrew Knaggs, *CEO*
Cory Mills, *Ch of Bd*
Michael Quesenberry, *President*
Jennifer Shoplak, *Principal*
June Dice, *Associate*
▼ **EMP:** 75 **EST:** 2010
SALES (est): 11MM
SALES (corp-wide): 227MM **Privately Held**
WEB: www.lesslethal.com
SIC: 3559 Ammunition & explosives, loading machinery
PA: Pacem Solution International Llc
2941 Frview Pk Dr Ste 550
Falls Church VA 22042
703 309-1891

(G-14294)
BIG TOP MANUFACTURING INC
3255 Us Highway 19 N (32347-0894)
PHONE..................................850 584-7786
Jeffrey Merschman, *President*
Harishma Donthineni, *Project Mgr*
Gw Pridgeon, *Sales Mgr*
Baker Jarvis, *Regl Sales Mgr*
Laura Grubbs, *Sales Staff*
◆ **EMP:** 85 **EST:** 2014
SQ FT: 120,000
SALES (est): 20MM **Privately Held**
WEB: www.bigtopshelters.com
SIC: 2394 Canvas awnings & canopies

(G-14295)
BLUE ROCK INC (PA)
4010 Olan Davis Rd (32347-0366)
PHONE..................................850 584-4324
EMP: 4
SALES: 4.8MM **Privately Held**
SIC: 1422 Crushed/Broken Limestone

(G-14296)
BOLAND TIMBER COMPANY INC
3616 S Byron Butler Pkwy (32348-6434)
P.O. Box 337, Wacissa (32361-0337)
PHONE..................................850 997-5270
Jeffery Boland, *President*
James Boland Jr, *Vice Pres*
Bette Boland, *Treasurer*
Connie Boland, *Admin Sec*
EMP: 34 **EST:** 2000
SQ FT: 1,856

SALES (est): 4.3MM **Privately Held**
WEB: www.timberlandford.com
SIC: 2411 Logging camps & contractors

(G-14297)
CANYON BAY BOATS LLC
1290 Houck Rd (32348-7539)
PHONE..................................850 838-1400
Albert Jarrell, *Principal*
EMP: 8 **EST:** 2012
SALES (est): 84.6K **Privately Held**
WEB: www.canyonbayboatworks.com
SIC: 3732 Boat building & repairing

(G-14298)
CONSOLIDATED FOREST PDTS INC
320 Millinor Rd (32347-1254)
P.O. Box 520090, Longwood (32752-0090)
PHONE..................................407 830-7723
Art Gilpin, *Branch Mgr*
EMP: 6
SALES (corp-wide): 2.7MM **Privately Held**
WEB: www.americanmulch.net
SIC: 2499 2869 Fencing, wood; fuels
PA: Consolidated Forest Products, Inc.
375 Commerce Way
Longwood FL 32750
407 830-7723

(G-14299)
ENERGY TECHNICAL SYSTEMS INC
9319 Puckett Rd (32348-8502)
P.O. Box 714 (32348-0714)
PHONE..................................850 223-2393
Elaine Stanton, *President*
EMP: 12 **EST:** 2001
SQ FT: 19,000
SALES (est): 2MM
SALES (corp-wide): 4.7MM **Privately Held**
WEB: www.etsperry.com
SIC: 3489 3559 3483 3482 Ordnance & accessories; refinery, chemical processing & similar machinery; ammunition components; small arms ammunition
PA: Technical Ordnance Solutions, Llc
9495 Puckett Rd
Perry FL 32348
850 223-2393

(G-14300)
FOLEY CELLULOSE LLC
3510 Contractors Rd (32348-7738)
PHONE..................................850 584-1121
James Hannan,
▲ **EMP:** 558 **EST:** 1992
SALES (est): 90.8MM
SALES (corp-wide): 36.9B **Privately Held**
WEB: www.gp.com
SIC: 2611 Pulp mills
HQ: Georgia-Pacific Llc
133 Peachtree St Nw
Atlanta GA 30303
404 652-4000

(G-14301)
GULF COAST FABRICATORS INC
3480 S Byron Butler Pkwy (32348-6456)
P.O. Box 1421 (32348-7302)
PHONE..................................850 584-5979
Fred Morgan Jr, *President*
Yancie Brannen, *General Mgr*
EMP: 6 **EST:** 1993
SALES (est): 861K **Privately Held**
WEB: www.gcfab.com
SIC: 3441 Fabricated structural metal

(G-14302)
H B TUTUN JR LOGGING INC
2930 Old Foley Rd (32348-5862)
PHONE..................................850 584-9324
EMP: 6 **EST:** 2019
SALES (est): 400.1K **Privately Held**
SIC: 2411 Logging camps & contractors

(G-14303)
HB TUTEN JR LOGGING INC
3870 S Byron Butler Pkwy (32348-6448)
PHONE..................................850 584-9324
Harvey B Tuten Jr, *President*
Charlotte M Lanier, *Admin Sec*
EMP: 20 **EST:** 1996
SALES (est): 1.8MM **Privately Held**
SIC: 2411 Logging camps & contractors

(G-14304)
HBT FORESTRY SERVICES INC
2930 Old Foley Rd (32348-5862)
PHONE..................................850 584-9324
Ben Tuten, *Vice Pres*
EMP: 15 **EST:** 2012
SALES (est): 681.7K **Privately Held**
SIC: 2411 Logging

(G-14305)
JOHN A CRUCE JR INC
311 Glenridge Rd (32348-2204)
P.O. Box 86 (32348-0086)
PHONE..................................850 584-9755
John W Cruce, *President*
J Adam Cruce, *Vice Pres*
EMP: 32 **EST:** 1955
SQ FT: 400
SALES (est): 3.2MM **Privately Held**
SIC: 2411 2421 Logging camps & contractors; pulpwood camp not operating a pulp mill at same site; sawmills & planing mills, general

(G-14306)
LYNN INDUSTRIAL WELDING INC
182 E Park St (32348-5604)
PHONE..................................850 584-4494
John Lynn, *President*
Nancy Lynn, *Corp Secy*
EMP: 7 **EST:** 1982
SALES (est): 778.4K **Privately Held**
WEB: www.rakemaster.net
SIC: 7692 Welding repair

(G-14307)
M&E TIMBER INC
2451 E Ellison Rd (32347-0637)
PHONE..................................850 584-6650
Merritt Pruitt, *President*
EMP: 6 **EST:** 2002
SALES (est): 438.9K **Privately Held**
SIC: 2411 Timber, cut at logging camp

(G-14308)
PERRY COMPOSITES LLC
1290 Houck Rd (32348-7539)
PHONE..................................850 584-8400
Albert Jarrell, *Mng Member*
Cynthia M Jarrell, *Mng Member*
EMP: 8 **EST:** 2009
SALES (est): 282.6K **Privately Held**
SIC: 3732 3229 Boat building & repairing; glass fiber products

(G-14309)
PERRY NEWSPAPERS INC
Also Called: Taco Time
123 S Jefferson St (32347-3232)
P.O. Box 888 (32348-0888)
PHONE..................................850 584-5513
Frank Nixon, *Ch of Bd*
Donald Lincoln, *President*
Bruce E Ratliff, *Vice Pres*
EMP: 19 **EST:** 1964
SQ FT: 1,800
SALES (est): 740.7K **Privately Held**
WEB: www.perrynewspapers.com
SIC: 2711 Commercial printing & newspaper publishing combined

(G-14310)
RDS MANUFACTURING INC
300 Industrial Park Dr (32348-6323)
P.O. Box 1908 (32348-7306)
PHONE..................................850 584-6898
Joseph R Roberts III, *President*
Dennis Davis, *Vice Pres*
Martha Sayers Davis, *Vice Pres*
Sandi Sparks, *Production*
Darrell Austin, *Purch Agent*
▲ **EMP:** 115 **EST:** 1968
SQ FT: 3,800
SALES (est): 13MM **Privately Held**
WEB: www.rdsaluminum.com
SIC: 3443 3714 3469 3354 Fuel tanks (oil, gas, etc.): metal plate; motor vehicle parts & accessories; metal stampings; aluminum extruded products

(G-14311)
REAGAN H FOX III INC
Woods Creek Rd (32347)
PHONE..................................850 584-9229
Reagan H Fox III, *President*
Carolyn T Fox, *Corp Secy*
EMP: 8 **EST:** 1984
SALES (est): 390.9K **Privately Held**
SIC: 2411 Logging camps & contractors

(G-14312)
ROBERTS LUMBER COMPANY INC
3655 E Us 27 Hwy (32347-4608)
P.O. Box 1601 (32348-7304)
PHONE..................................850 584-4573
David Roberts, *President*
Jody Roberts, *Treasurer*
Joseph R Roberts, *Treasurer*
EMP: 12 **EST:** 1960
SQ FT: 3,400
SALES (est): 522.3K **Privately Held**
SIC: 2421 2426 Kiln drying of lumber; hardwood dimension & flooring mills

(G-14313)
SHAWS WELDING INC
Also Called: Shaw's Site Preparation
1530 S Dixie Hwy (32348-5702)
P.O. Box 1017 (32348-1017)
PHONE..................................850 584-7197
John O Shaw, *President*
Irene Shaw, *Corp Secy*
Gilbert Shaw, *Vice Pres*
John E Shaw, *Vice Pres*
Martin Shaw, *Vice Pres*
EMP: 18 **EST:** 1961
SQ FT: 4,800
SALES (est): 1MM **Privately Held**
WEB: www.shawsweldinginc.com
SIC: 7692 Welding repair

(G-14314)
SUPER-PUFFT SNACKS USA INC
700 Super Pufft St (32348-4758)
PHONE..................................905 564-1180
Mahmoud Mrouch, *President*
Walid Amrouch, *Vice Pres*
Lu Qin, *CFO*
Yousif Al-Ali, *Treasurer*
Debbie Cato, *Controller*
EMP: 24 **EST:** 2018
SQ FT: 100
SALES (est): 23.6MM
SALES (corp-wide): 37.4MM **Privately Held**
WEB: www.superpufft.com
SIC: 2096 Cheese curls & puffs
PA: Super-Pufft Snacks Corp
880 Gana Crt
Mississauga ON L5S 1
905 564-1180

(G-14315)
T & R MARINE CORP
3309 E Us 27 Hwy (32347-0605)
PHONE..................................850 584-4261
Troy Thompson III, *President*
Betty Ratliff, *Corp Secy*
Billy Thompson, *Vice Pres*
▼ **EMP:** 8 **EST:** 1970
SQ FT: 16,000
SALES (est): 1.3MM **Privately Held**
WEB: www.trmarine.com
SIC: 3429 Marine hardware

(G-14316)
TECHNICAL ORD SOLUTIONS LLC (PA)
9495 Puckett Rd (32348-8502)
PHONE..................................850 223-2393
Clyde Colburn, *Mng Member*
EMP: 3 **EST:** 2015
SALES (est): 4.7MM **Privately Held**
WEB: www.techordnancesolutions.com
SIC: 3541 Drilling machine tools (metal cutting)

(G-14317)
THULE INC
Also Called: Thule North America
606 Industrial Park Dr (32348-6353)
PHONE..................................850 584-3448
Jimmy Giddens, *Branch Mgr*
EMP: 103 **Privately Held**
WEB: www.thule.com
SIC: 3714 3799 Motor vehicle body components & frame; boat trailers
HQ: Thule, Inc.
42 Silvermine Rd
Seymour CT 06483

(G-14318)
TOPLINE CSTM FABRICATIONS LLC
14781 Radcliff Grade (32348-8838)
PHONE..................................850 295-2481
Jody Davis, *Mng Member*
EMP: 6 **EST:** 2017
SALES (est): 335.8K **Privately Held**
SIC: 3444 Sheet metal specialties, not stamped

(G-14319)
WILLIAMS TIMBER INC
215 Sunset Ln (32348-6017)
PHONE..................................850 584-2760
Bradley Williams, *President*
Velinda Williams, *Treasurer*
EMP: 29 **EST:** 2000
SQ FT: 3,737
SALES (est): 3.7MM **Privately Held**
SIC: 2411 Logging camps & contractors

(G-14320)
WOODS N WATER MAGAZINE INC
3427 Puckett Rd (32348-1801)
PHONE..................................850 584-3824
Patricia Pillow, *President*
Billy Pillow, *Editor*
Billy D Pillow, *Vice Pres*
Jennifer Davis, *Advt Staff*
Declan Pillow, *Manager*
EMP: 7 **EST:** 1978
SQ FT: 4,750
SALES (est): 619.4K **Privately Held**
WEB: www.woodsnwater.net
SIC: 2721 Magazines: publishing only, not printed on site

(G-14321)
WW TIMBER LLC
8999 Us Highway 19 S (32348-5845)
P.O. Box 1167 (32348-1167)
PHONE..................................352 584-4550
Kristopher D Ward, *Manager*
EMP: 6 **EST:** 2005
SALES (est): 196.1K **Privately Held**
SIC: 3999 Manufacturing industries

Pinecrest
Miami-Dade County

(G-14322)
ADVANCED ELECTRONICS LABS INC
7375 Sw 114th St (33156-4632)
PHONE..................................305 255-6401
Alexander Aklepi, *CEO*
G Michele Ryslik, *Shareholder*
EMP: 5 **EST:** 2012
SALES (est): 398K **Privately Held**
WEB: www.advancedesys.com
SIC: 3571 7389 Electronic computers;

(G-14323)
ALL METAL FABRICATION
9621 S Dixie Hwy (33156-2804)
PHONE..................................305 666-3312
David Zisman, *Principal*
▼ **EMP:** 8 **EST:** 2008
SALES (est): 135.5K **Privately Held**
WEB: www.allmetalfabinc.com
SIC: 3499 Fabricated metal products

(G-14324)
ART ON PAPER LLC
9550 Sw 73rd Ave (33156-2919)
PHONE..................................305 615-9096
Ana Lapadula, *Principal*
EMP: 7 **EST:** 2016
SALES (est): 69.6K **Privately Held**
SIC: 2621 Art paper

(G-14325)
BRAZILIAN SMOOTHIE INC
13255 Sw 83rd Ave (33156-6605)
PHONE..................................305 233-5543
Marcos Becari, *Principal*
EMP: 8 **EST:** 2012
SALES (est): 163K **Privately Held**
SIC: 2037 Frozen fruits & vegetables

(G-14326)
CASPER ENGINEERING CORP
7695 Sw 133rd St (33156-6839)
PHONE..................................305 666-4046
Carlos Camps, *President*
Elena Camps, *Treasurer*
▼ **EMP:** 6 **EST:** 1976
SQ FT: 4,100
SALES (est): 995K **Privately Held**
WEB: www.casperengineering.com
SIC: 3569 3599 Gas producers, generators & other gas related equipment; machine shop, jobbing & repair

(G-14327)
CLS HOLDINGS USA INC (PA)
11767 S Dixie Hwy Ste 115 (33156-4438)
PHONE..................................888 438-9132
Jeffrey Binder, *Ch of Bd*
Andrew Glashow, *President*
Gregg Carlson, *CFO*
EMP: 73 **EST:** 2011
SALES: 19.2MM **Publicly Held**
WEB: www.clsholdingsinc.com
SIC: 2833 Medicinals & botanicals

(G-14328)
JORO FASHIONS FLORIDA INC
6650 Sw 123rd St (33156-5557)
PHONE..................................305 888-8110
Jonathan Rubenstein, *President*
◆ **EMP:** 11 **EST:** 1990
SQ FT: 12,500
SALES (est): 711.9K **Privately Held**
SIC: 2339 Women's & misses' outerwear

(G-14329)
NRZ INC
Also Called: Beach Access
12885 Sw 82nd Ave (33156-5916)
PHONE..................................305 345-7303
Nir Tzanani, *CEO*
EMP: 7 **EST:** 2001
SALES (est): 198.5K **Privately Held**
SIC: 2253 Beachwear, knit

(G-14330)
POWERFUL FOODS LLC
Also Called: Powerful Yogurt
9171 S Dixie Hwy (33156-2907)
PHONE..................................305 779-2449
Suzanne Nabavi, *Director*
Carlos Ramirez,
EMP: 9 **EST:** 2012
SALES (est): 6MM **Privately Held**
WEB: www.powerfulnutrition.com
SIC: 2026 Yogurt

(G-14331)
PROFIRE INC
9621 S Dixie Hwy (33156-2804)
PHONE..................................305 665-5313
David Zisman, *President*
Laura Zisman, *Corp Secy*
Jonathon Zisman, *Vice Pres*
EMP: 10 **EST:** 1994
SALES (est): 1.5MM **Privately Held**
SIC: 3631 5046 Barbecues, grills & braziers (outdoor cooking); commercial equipment

(G-14332)
SCRAPLIFE INC
12200 Vista Ln (33156-5741)
PHONE..................................305 776-0727
Mark McHugh, *Principal*
EMP: 6 **EST:** 2003
SALES (est): 152K **Privately Held**
SIC: 2782 Scrapbooks

Pinellas Park
Pinellas County

(G-14333)
ADTEC II TAMPA INC
5440 70th Ave N (33781-4228)
PHONE..................................786 588-3688
David Sideri, *President*
Eric Sideri, *Sales Staff*
Aaron Capra, *Manager*
Linda Remillard, *Manager*
Stephen Sideri, *Manager*
EMP: 34 **EST:** 2007
SALES (est): 4MM **Privately Held**
WEB: www.adtec2.com
SIC: 3471 Electroplating of metals or formed products

(G-14334)
ALL METALS CUSTOM INC
7200 59th St N (33781-4247)
PHONE..................................727 709-4297
Waylon Smith, *Principal*
EMP: 7 **EST:** 2010
SALES (est): 191.4K **Privately Held**
SIC: 3499 Fabricated metal products

(G-14335)
ASHWELL LABEL DIES INC
Also Called: Ashwell Die
6545 44th St N Ste 4003 (33781-0900)
PHONE..................................727 527-0098
Wilfried Jeurink, *President*
Ellen Rifkin, *Accounting Mgr*
▲ **EMP:** 14 **EST:** 1987
SALES (est): 208.2K **Privately Held**
SIC: 2865 3544 Dyes & pigments; special dies, tools, jigs & fixtures

(G-14336)
BAJU PROFESSIONAL BRICK PAVERS
5511 110th Ave N (33782-2234)
PHONE..................................727 234-5300
Daniele B Becil, *Director*
EMP: 7 **EST:** 2005
SALES (est): 153K **Privately Held**
SIC: 3531 Pavers

(G-14337)
BIGORRE AEROSPACE CORP
6295 42nd St N (33781-6041)
PHONE..................................727 525-8115
Fred Ladjimi, *President*
Eric Ladjimi, *Treasurer*
EMP: 11 **EST:** 1987
SQ FT: 2,475
SALES (est): 5MM **Privately Held**
WEB: www.bigorreaerospace.com
SIC: 3728 Aircraft parts & equipment

(G-14338)
CIRCUIT WORKS CO
6405 49th St N Ste B (33781-5764)
PHONE..................................727 544-5336
Jay Finehout, *Owner*
EMP: 6 **EST:** 1986
SQ FT: 2,500
SALES (est): 500.5K **Privately Held**
WEB: www.circuitworks1.com
SIC: 3672 Printed circuit boards

(G-14339)
CJ PUBLISHERS INC
4940 72nd Ave N Ste 200 (33781-4400)
PHONE..................................727 521-6277
Chuck Wray, *President*
EMP: 12 **EST:** 1989
SQ FT: 7,392
SALES (est): 1.2MM **Privately Held**
SIC: 2721 2741 Magazines: publishing only, not printed on site; miscellaneous publishing

(G-14340)
COMTEN INDUSTRIES INC
6405 49th St N Ste A (33781-5764)
PHONE..................................727 520-1200
EMP: 6 **EST:** 2019
SALES (est): 494.1K **Privately Held**
WEB: www.com-ten.com
SIC: 3829 Measuring & controlling devices

(G-14341)
CUSTOM METAL SPECIALTIES INC
3921 69th Ave N (33781-6146)
P.O. Box 2772 (33780-2772)
PHONE..................................727 522-3986
Curt Schlager, *President*
▲ **EMP:** 27 **EST:** 1989
SQ FT: 3,500
SALES (est): 1.4MM **Privately Held**
WEB: www.custommetalspecialtiesinc.com
SIC: 3446 3444 3441 Stairs, fire escapes, balconies, railings & ladders; ornamental metalwork; sheet metalwork; fabricated structural metal

(G-14342)
CUSTOM MFG & ENGRG INC
Also Called: C M E
3690 70th Ave N (33781-4603)
PHONE..................................727 548-0522
Nancy P Crews, *President*
Fred Munro, *Vice Pres*
Adam Berezansky, *Engineer*
Silva Rick, *Senior Engr*
EMP: 65 **EST:** 1996
SQ FT: 40,000
SALES (est): 15.3MM **Privately Held**
WEB: www.custom-mfg-eng.com
SIC: 3699 8711 3679 3499 Electrical equipment & supplies; engineering services; electronic circuits; fire- or burglary-resistive products

(G-14343)
DALIMAR CORP
6295 42nd St N (33781-6041)
PHONE..................................727 525-8115
Eric Ladjimi, *President*
EMP: 6 **EST:** 2005
SQ FT: 9,750
SALES (est): 110.7K **Privately Held**
SIC: 3728 Aircraft parts & equipment

(G-14344)
DOMREY CIGAR LTD COMPANY
3001 Gateway Ctr Pkwy N (33782-6124)
PHONE..................................941 360-8200
Michael Chiusno, *President*
◆ **EMP:** 5 **EST:** 2000
SALES (est): 9MM **Privately Held**
SIC: 2121 Cigars

(G-14345)
ELECTRIC MOTORS LIFT STN SVCS
4480 126th Ave N (33782)
PHONE..................................727 538-4778
Don Delaney, *Principal*
EMP: 7 **EST:** 1988
SQ FT: 6,000
SALES (est): 802.5K **Privately Held**
SIC: 7694 Rebuilding motors, except automotive; hermetics repair

(G-14346)
ENERSYS ADVANCED SYSTEMS INC
5430 70th Ave N (33781-4228)
PHONE..................................610 208-1934
Mike Kulesky, *General Mgr*
EMP: 87
SQ FT: 72,500
SALES (corp-wide): 2.9B **Publicly Held**
SIC: 3691 Storage batteries
HQ: Enersys Advanced Systems Inc.
104 Rock Rd
Horsham PA 19044

(G-14347)
ES MANUFACTURING INC
4590 62nd Ave N (33781-5906)
P.O. Box 11692, Saint Petersburg (33733-1692)
PHONE..................................727 323-4040
Thomas D Elder, *CEO*
▲ **EMP:** 16 **EST:** 1973
SQ FT: 10,000
SALES (est): 1.8MM **Privately Held**
WEB: www.esmfg.com
SIC: 3423 3546 Hand & edge tools; power-driven handtools

(G-14348)
FORCELEADER INC
Also Called: Bioseb
6405 49th St N Ste A (33781-5764)
PHONE..................................727 521-1808
Mary Desevre, *President*
Mireille Desevre, *President*
▼ **EMP:** 9 **EST:** 2008
SQ FT: 30,000
SALES (est): 950K **Privately Held**
SIC: 3829 3495 Measuring & controlling devices; clock springs, precision

(G-14349)
FRITZ DUANE L SR TRE FRIT
8701 40th Way N (33782-5815)
PHONE..................................727 576-1584
Duane Fritz, *Principal*
EMP: 6 **EST:** 2010
SALES (est): 71.5K **Privately Held**
SIC: 2899 Frit

(G-14350)
FRONTIER READY MIX INC
8311 63rd Way N (33781-1235)
PHONE..................................727 544-1000
Edwin L Shearer Jr, *Principal*
EMP: 19 **EST:** 2006
SALES (est): 1MM **Privately Held**
WEB: www.frontierreadymix.com
SIC: 3273 Ready-mixed concrete

(G-14351)
GLOBAL DIVERSIFIED PRODUCTS
Also Called: Hook International
5195 102nd Ave N (33782-3502)
P.O. Box 17822, Clearwater (33762-0822)
PHONE..................................727 209-0854
Kamal S Juneja, *President*
Dwight Moody, *Finance*
▲ **EMP:** 36 **EST:** 1993
SQ FT: 30,000
SALES (est): 3.4MM **Privately Held**
WEB: www.hookinternational.com
SIC: 3291 2992 2899 3425 Wheels, grinding: artificial; lubricating oils & greases; antifreeze compounds; saw blades & handsaws; business consulting

(G-14352)
H&S SWANSON FMLY HOLDINGS INC (HQ)
9000 68th St N (33782-4401)
PHONE..................................727 541-3575
James H Swanson, *President*
Ronald Hiley, *Vice Pres*
Dave Weaver, *Plant Mgr*
Joe Minarik, *Mfg Staff*
Richard Rogers, *Engineer*
EMP: 80 **EST:** 1951
SQ FT: 58,000
SALES (est): 14.1MM
SALES (corp-wide): 98.6MM **Privately Held**
WEB: www.hsswansons.com
SIC: 3599 Machine shop, jobbing & repair

(G-14353)
H2R CORP (PA)
3921 76th Ave N (33781-3610)
PHONE..................................727 541-3444
Daniel Hart, *CEO*
Thai Nguyen, *Engineer*
EMP: 13 **EST:** 2016
SQ FT: 9,800
SALES (est): 3.1MM **Privately Held**
WEB: www.h2rcorp.com
SIC: 1481 1781 1794 8711 Mine exploration, nonmetallic minerals; water well drilling; excavation work; engineering services; testing laboratories

(G-14354)
HIS CABINETRY INC
Also Called: His
6200 49th St N (33781-5718)
PHONE..................................727 527-7262
Quynh Tran, *President*
Skip Fritz, *General Mgr*
Kathie Hill, *Bookkeeper*
Lois Larus, *Sales Staff*
Jeffrey Macdonald, *Director*
EMP: 80 **EST:** 1995
SQ FT: 1,700

SALES (est): 18MM **Privately Held**
WEB: www.hiscabinetry.com
SIC: 2434 Wood kitchen cabinets

(G-14355)
JACE FABRICATION INC
9930 62nd St N (33782-3125)
PHONE..................................727 547-6873
John S Wallace Jr, *Principal*
EMP: 6 **EST:** 2008
SALES (est): 122K **Privately Held**
SIC: 3446 Architectural metalwork

(G-14356)
JB EFFECTS
7682 49th St N (33781-3438)
PHONE..................................727 348-1865
Jimmy Bubenheim, *Owner*
EMP: 6 **EST:** 2011
SALES (est): 143.6K **Privately Held**
WEB: www.jb-effects.com
SIC: 3842 Cosmetic restorations

(G-14357)
JDE DISTRIBUTORS LLC ✪
6553 46th St N Ste 905 (33781-0913)
PHONE..................................727 498-7886
James D Eakins,
EMP: 10 **EST:** 2020
SALES (est): 500K **Privately Held**
WEB: www.jdedistributors.com
SIC: 2842 Sanitation preparations, disinfectants & deodorants

(G-14358)
JSP MANUFACTURING HOLDINGS LLC
6203 80th Ave N (33781-2204)
PHONE..................................727 488-5353
Rocco Braccio, *President*
EMP: 7 **EST:** 2018
SALES (est): 519.5K **Privately Held**
WEB: www.jspmanufacturing.com
SIC: 3999 Manufacturing industries

(G-14359)
KLING FABRICATION INC
6563 46th St N Ste 705 (33781-5926)
PHONE..................................727 321-7233
Laura L Klingensmith, *Principal*
EMP: 10 **EST:** 2019
SALES (est): 748.4K **Privately Held**
WEB: www.klingfabrication.com
SIC: 3444 Sheet metalwork

(G-14360)
KORAL MANUFACTURING INC
8720 66th Ct N (33782-4557)
PHONE..................................727 548-5040
Marla Barkoviak, *President*
EMP: 6 **EST:** 1995
SQ FT: 7,200
SALES (est): 778.8K **Privately Held**
WEB: www.koralmfg.com
SIC: 3599 Machine shop, jobbing & repair

(G-14361)
KORAL PRECISION LLC ✪
8720 66th Ct N (33782-4557)
PHONE..................................727 548-5040
Kimberly Nagulpelli, *Exec Dir*
EMP: 10 **EST:** 2020
SALES (est): 703.4K **Privately Held**
SIC: 3599 Machine & other job shop work

(G-14362)
KWIKIE DUP CTR OF PINELLAS PK
Also Called: Kwikie Printing
8520 49th St N (33781-1554)
PHONE..................................727 544-7788
Charles Kemp, *President*
Patty Hall, *Vice Pres*
Jackie Kemp, *Treasurer*
EMP: 5 **EST:** 1973
SQ FT: 3,000
SALES (est): 486.2K **Privately Held**
SIC: 2752 7389 Commercial printing, offset; printing broker

(G-14363)
LA ZERO INC
8100 Park Blvd N Ste 41 (33781-3778)
PHONE..................................727 545-1175
Lee Aust, *President*
Ann Aust, *Vice Pres*
EMP: 5 **EST:** 1996
SALES (est): 1.1MM **Privately Held**
WEB: www.lazero.org
SIC: 3599 Custom machinery

(G-14364)
LIBERTY WOODWORKING INC
6563 46th St N Ste 702 (33781-5926)
PHONE..................................727 642-9652
William Francis Dunn, *Principal*
William Dunn, *Sales Staff*
EMP: 8 **EST:** 2008
SALES (est): 523.9K **Privately Held**
WEB: www.libertywoodworking.com
SIC: 2431 Millwork

(G-14365)
LOCKHEED MARTIN CORPORATION
Also Called: Lockheed Martin Aeronautics
9300 28th St N Ste A (33782-6122)
PHONE..................................727 578-6940
Nancy King, *Engineer*
Steve Cobb, *Manager*
Emily Harmon, *Manager*
Lindsay Muth, *Director*
Beth Ferguson, *Director*
EMP: 150 **Publicly Held**
WEB: www.lockheedmartin.com
SIC: 3812 Search & navigation equipment
PA: Lockheed Martin Corporation
6801 Rockledge Dr
Bethesda MD 20817

(G-14366)
MADICO INC (DH)
9251 Belcher Rd N Ste A (33782-4203)
PHONE..................................727 327-2544
Shawn Kitchell, *CEO*
Melanie Kuklis, *Vice Pres*
Michael Vegas, *Engineer*
Loren Rideout, *Project Engr*
Chris Layne, *Finance Dir*
◆ **EMP:** 100
SQ FT: 122,000
SALES (est): 54.6MM **Privately Held**
WEB: www.madico.com
SIC: 3081 2295 Unsupported plastics film & sheet; laminating of fabrics; metallizing of fabrics

(G-14367)
MCKENZIE CABINETRY FINE WDWKG
5695 70th Ave N (33781-4262)
PHONE..................................727 424-3707
Sean S McKenzie, *Principal*
EMP: 6 **EST:** 2008
SALES (est): 188.7K **Privately Held**
SIC: 2431 Millwork

(G-14368)
MILL-RITE WOODWORKING CO INC
6401 47th St N (33781-5917)
PHONE..................................727 527-7808
Jennifer Clark, *President*
Robert Clark, *Vice Pres*
Dale Johannes, *Project Mgr*
EMP: 54 **EST:** 1966
SQ FT: 54,000
SALES (est): 7.5MM **Privately Held**
WEB: www.mill-rite.com
SIC: 2431 Doors, wood

(G-14369)
MODERN SILICONE TECH INC
10601 Us Highway 19 N (33782-3426)
PHONE..................................727 873-1805
Paul Capek, *Warehouse Mgr*
Jerry Robinson, *Purch Mgr*
Michelle Wasielewski, *Controller*
Rachel Grunfeld, *Branch Mgr*
David Singer, *Director*
EMP: 130 **Privately Held**
WEB: www.modernsilicone.com
SIC: 3053 3061 2822 Gaskets, packing & sealing devices; mechanical rubber goods; synthetic rubber
PA: Modern Silicone Technologies, Inc.
101 Schelter Rd Ste 102b
Lincolnshire IL 60069

(G-14370)
MOLEX LLC
Also Called: Molex Tampa Bay Operations
4650 62nd Ave N (33781-5944)
PHONE..................................727 521-2700
John Rochford, *Plt & Fclts Mgr*
Chip Walsh, *Manager*
EMP: 14
SALES (corp-wide): 36.9B **Privately Held**
WEB: www.molex.com
SIC: 3678 3679 3643 3357 Electronic connectors; electronic switches; connectors & terminals for electrical devices; communication wire
HQ: Molex, Llc
2222 Wellington Ct
Lisle IL 60532
630 969-4550

(G-14371)
NAIA BRICK PAVERS INC
8216 43rd Way N (33781-1631)
PHONE..................................727 638-4734
Weslley Dasilva, *Principal*
EMP: 6 **EST:** 2010
SALES (est): 151.4K **Privately Held**
SIC: 3531 Pavers

(G-14372)
NOVAK MACHINING INC
3921 69th Ave N (33781-6146)
PHONE..................................727 527-5473
Mark Novak, *President*
EMP: 5 **EST:** 1990
SQ FT: 3,500
SALES (est): 433.2K **Privately Held**
WEB: www.novakmachininginc.com
SIC: 3535 3599 Conveyors & conveying equipment; machine & other job shop work

(G-14373)
OCTAL VENTURES INC
Also Called: Sunrise Yacht Products
6544 44th St N Ste 1205 (33781-5936)
PHONE..................................727 526-9288
Matthew Brunnig, *President*
◆ **EMP:** 11 **EST:** 2018
SQ FT: 7,500
SALES (est): 950K **Privately Held**
SIC: 3496 3089 Netting, woven wire: made from purchased wire; synthetic resin finished products

(G-14374)
ORANGE STATE STEEL CNSTR INC
6201 80th Ave N (33781-2204)
PHONE..................................727 544-3398
Rex Joyner, *President*
Chris Powell, *Vice Pres*
Joel Powell, *Vice Pres*
Pam McGeorge, *Admin Sec*
EMP: 22 **EST:** 1965
SQ FT: 18,000
SALES (est): 2.4MM **Privately Held**
WEB: www.orangestatesteel.com
SIC: 3441 1791 Fabricated structural metal; precast concrete structural framing or panels, placing of

(G-14375)
PHARMACY AUTOMTN SYSTEMS LLC
8790 66th Ct N (33782-4557)
PHONE..................................727 544-6522
Norm Knoth, *Managing Dir*
EMP: 9 **EST:** 2010
SALES (est): 141.8K **Privately Held**
WEB:
www.pharmacyautomationsystems.com
SIC: 3559 Pharmaceutical machinery

(G-14376)
PLATINUM MFG INTL INC
10166 66th St N (33782-3015)
PHONE..................................727 544-4555
Steve Miller, *Principal*
Alex Lashchou, *Opers Staff*
EMP: 13 **EST:** 2010
SALES (est): 252.3K **Privately Held**
SIC: 3999 Manufacturing industries

(G-14377)
POLYPACK INC (PA)
3301 Gateway Ctr Blvd N (33782-6108)
PHONE..................................727 578-5000
Alain A Cerf, *President*
Jacqueline Cerf, *Corp Secy*
Emmanuel Cerf, *Vice Pres*
Olivier Cerf, *Vice Pres*
Cindy Herbeck, *Opers Mgr*
◆ **EMP:** 90 **EST:** 1973
SQ FT: 43,000
SALES (est): 16.4MM **Privately Held**
WEB: www.polypack.com
SIC: 3565 Wrapping machines

(G-14378)
POLYPACK LIMITED PARTNERSHIP
3301 Gateway Ctr Blvd N (33782-6108)
PHONE..................................727 578-5000
Alain A Cerf, *Managing Prtnr*
Olivier Cerf, *VP Opers*
Arturo Davila, *Prdtn Mgr*
Elizabeth Cerp, *Treasurer*
Sara Erdmann, *Asst Controller*
EMP: 34 **EST:** 1994
SQ FT: 43,000
SALES (est): 4.2MM **Privately Held**
WEB: www.polypack.com
SIC: 3565 Packaging machinery

(G-14379)
PRESTIGE SPAS INC
Also Called: Prestige Spa Covers
2875 Mci Dr N (33782-6105)
PHONE..................................727 576-8600
Wesley J Wiley, *President*
Angela Kim,
◆ **EMP:** 75 **EST:** 1989
SQ FT: 50,000
SALES (est): 15.7MM **Privately Held**
WEB: www.prestigespacovers.com
SIC: 3999 Hot tub & spa covers

(G-14380)
PRISTINE ENVIRONMENT LLC
6575 80th Ave N (33781-2136)
PHONE..................................727 541-5748
Kevin Pawlowski, *Mng Member*
EMP: 15 **EST:** 2006
SALES (est): 1.4MM **Privately Held**
SIC: 3589 Water purification equipment, household type

(G-14381)
PROCESS AUTOMATION CORPORATION
Also Called: Pac Printing
5260 87th Ave N (33782-5138)
PHONE..................................727 541-6280
Robert Trope, *President*
John Trope, *Vice Pres*
EMP: 7 **EST:** 1983
SQ FT: 3,200
SALES (est): 950K **Privately Held**
WEB: www.magpac.com
SIC: 3993 Advertising novelties

(G-14382)
PROMED BIOSCIENCES INC
9375 Us Highway 19 N A (33782-5420)
PHONE..................................888 655-9155
Olga Krynina, *Ch of Bd*
EMP: 10 **EST:** 2019
SALES (est): 1,000K **Privately Held**
SIC: 3999

(G-14383)
R S DESIGN INC
6351 46th St N (33781-5921)
PHONE..................................727 525-8292
Richard Smith, *President*
Amy Mensch, *CIO*
EMP: 10 **EST:** 1992
SQ FT: 3,200
SALES (est): 1.9MM **Privately Held**
WEB: www.rsdesigninc.com
SIC: 3089 Injection molding of plastics

(G-14384)
RENEWABLE ENERGY SYSTEMS INC
6531 43rd St N Ste 1604 (33781-0908)
PHONE..................................727 522-0286
Richard Vandesteeg, *CEO*

▲ = Import ▼=Export
◆ =Import/Export

Jason Kersten, *President*
EMP: 5 **EST:** 2005
SALES (est): 364.3K **Privately Held**
SIC: 2911 Diesel fuels

(G-14385)
ROCK N ROLL CUSTOM SCREENED S
Also Called: Native Sun Sports
4590 62nd Ave N (33781-5906)
P.O. Box 40085, Saint Petersburg (33743-0085)
PHONE..................................727 528-2111
George A Mitcheson, *President*
▲ **EMP:** 5 **EST:** 1973
SQ FT: 25,000
SALES (est): 484.9K **Privately Held**
SIC: 2261 5136 5699 Screen printing of cotton broadwoven fabrics; sportswear, men's & boys'; sports apparel

(G-14386)
S N S AUTO SPORTS LLC
7061 49th St N (33781-4402)
PHONE..................................727 546-2700
Brian Grondin, *Principal*
EMP: 8 **EST:** 2012
SALES (est): 261.1K **Privately Held**
WEB: www.snsautosports.com
SIC: 3011 3493 3651 Tires & inner tubes; automobile springs; household audio & video equipment

(G-14387)
SHEET METAL SYSTEMS INC
6482 Park Blvd N Ste A (33781-3141)
PHONE..................................727 548-1711
Raul Perera, *President*
Christine Perera, *Vice Pres*
EMP: 10 **EST:** 2001
SQ FT: 250
SALES (est): 607.6K **Privately Held**
WEB: www.superiormechanical.net
SIC: 3441 Fabricated structural metal

(G-14388)
SIGNARAMA CLEARWATER
7211 Us Highway 19 N (33781-4613)
PHONE..................................727 784-4500
Joann Bradley, *President*
EMP: 6 **EST:** 2017
SALES (est): 147.5K **Privately Held**
SIC: 3993 Signs & advertising specialties

(G-14389)
SOUTHERN IMAGING
6563 46th St N Ste 705 (33781-5926)
PHONE..................................727 954-0133
EMP: 6 **EST:** 2015
SALES (est): 223.8K **Privately Held**
WEB: www.southernimagingcopiers.com
SIC: 2752 Commercial printing, lithographic

(G-14390)
SUNRISE TRAMPOLINES AND NETS
Also Called: Sunrise Yacht Products
6544 44th St N Ste 1205 (33781-5936)
PHONE..................................727 526-9288
Richard Leng, *President*
Eliose Leng, *Admin Sec*
◆ **EMP:** 8 **EST:** 1987
SQ FT: 5,000
SALES (est): 450K **Privately Held**
WEB: www.multihullnets.com
SIC: 3949 Trampolines & equipment

(G-14391)
TEMPO FULFILLMENT INC
10344 66th St N Unit 100 (33782-2305)
PHONE..................................727 914-0659
Piotr Styczen, *President*
EMP: 6 **EST:** 2017
SALES (est): 265.1K **Privately Held**
WEB: www.tempofulfillment.com
SIC: 2752 Commercial printing, offset

(G-14392)
TRANSITIONS OPTICAL INC
Also Called: Transitions Lenses
9251 Belcher Rd N Ste B (33782-4201)
P.O. Box 700 (33780-0700)
PHONE..................................727 545-0400
Paddy McDermott, *President*
Blesila Telebangco, *Vice Pres*
Susan Sanders, *Transportation*
Barbara Vanevery, *Production*
Frank Asare, *Research*
▲ **EMP:** 500 **EST:** 1990
SQ FT: 150,000
SALES (est): 69.8MM
SALES (corp-wide): 1.7MM **Privately Held**
WEB: www.transitions.com
SIC: 3229 3851 Ophthalmic glass, except flat; lenses, ophthalmic
PA: Essilorluxottica
147 Rue De Paris
Charenton Le Pont 94220
149 774-224

(G-14393)
VIN-DOTCO INC
2875 Mci Dr N Unit B (33782-6105)
PHONE..................................727 217-9200
John Dotolo, *President*
EMP: 10 **EST:** 1975
SQ FT: 30,000
SALES (est): 694.1K **Privately Held**
SIC: 2842 Cleaning or polishing preparations

(G-14394)
WOOD & GLASS WORKS LLC
8540 29th Way N Apt 207 (33782-6211)
PHONE..................................727 317-9599
Marek Szostak, *Manager*
EMP: 6 **EST:** 2015
SALES (est): 128K **Privately Held**
SIC: 2499 Wood products

Placida
Charlotte County

(G-14395)
COLONIAL READY MIX LLC
5250 Linwood Rd (33946-5137)
PHONE..................................941 698-4022
Victor G Mellor, *Mng Member*
▲ **EMP:** 7 **EST:** 2007
SALES (est): 133.6K **Privately Held**
SIC: 3273 Ready-mixed concrete

(G-14396)
FORTUNE CANVAS COMPANY INC
210 Green Dolphin Dr (33946-2235)
PHONE..................................941 740-4296
Richard Fortune, *Principal*
EMP: 6 **EST:** 2015
SALES (est): 56.3K **Privately Held**
WEB: www.fortunecanvasco.com
SIC: 2211 Canvas

(G-14397)
LEMON BAY TRUSS & SUPPLY CO
5300 Linwood Rd (33946-5138)
PHONE..................................941 698-0800
Mike Vermeulen, *President*
Allen Triebe, *Vice Pres*
Jane Keim, *Admin Sec*
EMP: 9 **EST:** 1992
SQ FT: 1,200
SALES (est): 140.1K **Privately Held**
SIC: 2439 Trusses, wooden roof

Plant City
Hillsborough County

(G-14398)
AMAYA SOLUTIONS INC
Also Called: American Water Chemicals
1802 Corporate Center Ln (33563-7162)
PHONE..................................813 246-5448
Mohannad Almalki, *President*
Rudy Canezo, *Treasurer*
EMP: 29 **EST:** 2019
SALES (est): 2.5MM **Privately Held**
SIC: 2899 Chemical preparations

(G-14399)
AMERICAN ENGINEERING SVCS INC (PA)
Also Called: AES
1802 Corporate Center Ln (33563-7162)
PHONE..................................813 621-3932
MO Malki, *President*
Rudy Zaneco, *Controller*
Ana Padgett, *Sales Engr*
▲ **EMP:** 7 **EST:** 1985
SQ FT: 23,800
SALES (est): 6.7MM **Privately Held**
WEB: www.aesh2o.com
SIC: 3589 1629 Sewage treatment equipment; waste water & sewage treatment plant construction

(G-14400)
AMERICAN WATER CHEMICALS INC
Also Called: A W C
1802 Corporate Center Ln (33563-7162)
PHONE..................................813 246-5448
Mohannad Almalki, *President*
Scott Garrett, *Purch Mgr*
Rudy Canezo, *Treasurer*
Canezo Rudy, *Treasurer*
Mike Lee, *Natl Sales Mgr*
◆ **EMP:** 14 **EST:** 1993
SQ FT: 5,000
SALES (est): 6.7MM **Privately Held**
WEB: www.membranechemicals.com
SIC: 2899 Water treating compounds
PA: American Engineering Services, Incorporated
1802 Corporate Center Ln
Plant City FL 33563
813 621-3932

(G-14401)
ANUVIA PLANT CITY LLC
660 E County Line Rd (33565)
PHONE..................................407 719-7798
Amy Yoder, *Mng Member*
EMP: 22 **EST:** 2019
SALES (est): 10MM **Privately Held**
WEB: www.anuviaplantnutrients.com
SIC: 2873 Fertilizers: natural (organic), except compost

(G-14402)
ARMOR PRODUCTS MFG INC
2610 Airport Rd (33563-1143)
PHONE..................................813 764-8844
David Carmichael, *President*
Jackie Carmichael, *Corp Secy*
◆ **EMP:** 10 **EST:** 2007
SQ FT: 10,000
SALES (est): 737.7K **Privately Held**
WEB: www.armorbags.com
SIC: 2392 2393 Laundry, garment & storage bags; canvas bags; duffle bags, canvas: made from purchased materials; bags & containers, except sleeping bags: textile

(G-14403)
ATCO RUBBER PRODUCTS INC
2407 Police Center Dr (33566-7173)
PHONE..................................813 754-6678
William Garrow, *Branch Mgr*
EMP: 44 **Publicly Held**
WEB: www.atcoflex.com
SIC: 3564 Air cleaning systems
HQ: Atco Rubber Products, Inc.
7101 Atco Dr
Fort Worth TX 76118
817 595-2894

(G-14404)
B & M INDUSTRIES INC
Also Called: Bodolay Packaging Machine Div
2401 Airport Rd (33563-1110)
PHONE..................................813 754-9960
Mostafa Farid, *President*
Farid Bijan, *Officer*
EMP: 7 **EST:** 1988
SQ FT: 7,500
SALES (est): 1.2MM **Privately Held**
WEB: www.bodolaypackaging.com
SIC: 3565 Packaging machinery

(G-14405)
B & N WLDG & FABRICATION INC
4200 National Guard Dr (33563-1156)
P.O. Box 4767 (33563-0031)
PHONE..................................813 719-3956
Amanda L Bell, *President*
Jamie Bell, *Vice Pres*
Amanda Bell, *Director*
EMP: 30
SQ FT: 1,600
SALES (est): 5.5MM **Privately Held**
WEB: www.bnwelding.com
SIC: 7692 Welding repair

(G-14406)
BANKS AIRCONDITIONING & RFRGN
5001 Miley Rd (33565-3805)
PHONE..................................813 917-8685
Jeff Banks, *President*
Jeannie Banks, *Vice Pres*
EMP: 5 **EST:** 2001
SALES (est): 361.8K **Privately Held**
SIC: 3585 Refrigeration equipment, complete

(G-14407)
BAY AREA SIGNS INC
3858 E Knights Griffin Rd (33565-2206)
PHONE..................................813 677-0237
Ed M Martin, *President*
Pat Martin, *Vice Pres*
EMP: 10 **EST:** 2003
SQ FT: 5,000
SALES (est): 852.6K **Privately Held**
SIC: 3993 Displays & cutouts, window & lobby; electric signs

(G-14408)
BE WHOLE NUTRITION LLC
5840 Highway 60 E (33567-1759)
PHONE..................................813 420-3057
Sean Gill, *Mng Member*
John Gill,
EMP: 8 **EST:** 2014
SALES (est): 340K **Privately Held**
SIC: 2834 5122 Vitamin preparations; vitamins & minerals

(G-14409)
BERRY BEST STITCHING AND EMB
3913 Sparky Ln (33565-5187)
PHONE..................................813 763-7716
Elaine Delvalle, *Principal*
EMP: 6 **EST:** 2016
SALES (est): 162.8K **Privately Held**
SIC: 2395 Embroidery & art needlework

(G-14410)
BLUE CREEK HOLDINGS INC (PA)
6628 N Dormany Rd (33565-3538)
PHONE..................................814 796-1900
Kimberly A Bienvenu, *President*
L Patrick Bienvenu, *Vice Pres*
▲ **EMP:** 7 **EST:** 2002
SALES (est): 948.8K **Privately Held**
SIC: 3084 Plastics pipe

(G-14411)
BRI TIN INDUSTRIES
3112 Emerson Pl (33566-9532)
PHONE..................................941 580-6345
Brian Grimes, *Principal*
EMP: 6 **EST:** 2005
SALES (est): 71.4K **Privately Held**
WEB: www.bri-tin.com
SIC: 3999 Manufacturing industries

(G-14412)
BULK MANUFACTURING FLORIDA INC
3106 Central Dr (33566-1159)
PHONE..................................813 757-2313
Thomas Wawrzyniakowski, *President*
Michael Warczytowa, *Vice Pres*
Lori Vogeler, *Controller*
▼ **EMP:** 15 **EST:** 2000
SQ FT: 32,000
SALES (est): 3.3MM **Privately Held**
WEB: www.bmfla.com
SIC: 3713 Tank truck bodies

(G-14413)
BULK RESOURCES INC (PA)
1507 S Alexander St # 102 (33563-8413)
P.O. Box 3296 (33563-0005)
PHONE..................................813 764-8420
Terry Taylor, *President*
Sherri Alexander, *Admin Sec*
▼ **EMP:** 6 **EST:** 2002
SALES (est): 4.5MM **Privately Held**
WEB: www.bulkresources.biz
SIC: 3523 6159 Trailers & wagons, farm; finance leasing, vehicles: except automobiles & trucks

(G-14414)
C & C SERVICES OF TAMPA INC
Also Called: Honeywell Authorized Dealer
1007 Robinson Rd (33563-1150)
P.O. Box 47988, Tampa (33646-0117)
PHONE..................................813 477-8559
John F Carlucci, *President*
Alan Carter, *Vice Pres*
EMP: 6 **EST:** 2004
SQ FT: 1,300
SALES (est): 1.7MM **Privately Held**
WEB: www.ccservicesoftampainc.com
SIC: 3822 Air conditioning & refrigeration controls

(G-14415)
CANOPY SPECIALIST LLC
3301 State Road 574 (33563-4522)
P.O. Box 5224 (33563-0040)
PHONE..................................813 703-6844
Jerry A Jaeger, *Mng Member*
EMP: 10 **EST:** 2012
SALES (est): 548.3K **Privately Held**
WEB: www.canopyspecialist.com
SIC: 2394 Canvas awnings & canopies

(G-14416)
CAS INDUSTRIES LLC
2914 Appling Woods Pl (33565-5647)
PHONE..................................813 986-2694
Curtis Devane, *Principal*
EMP: 8 **EST:** 2017
SALES (est): 236.1K **Privately Held**
SIC: 3999 Manufacturing industries

(G-14417)
CATAMOUNT MACHINE WORKS LLC ✪
2804 Sydney Rd (33566-1173)
PHONE..................................813 659-0505
Chris Basgall, *Mng Member*
EMP: 12 **EST:** 2020
SALES (est): 574K **Privately Held**
SIC: 3599 Machine shop, jobbing & repair

(G-14418)
CHEMICAL DYNAMICS INC
4206 Business Ln (33566-1163)
P.O. Box 486 (33564-0486)
PHONE..................................813 752-4950
Webster Carson, *Ch of Bd*
David Carson, *President*
Nathan Carson, *Inv Control Mgr*
Hayley Pena, *Buyer*
Betty Carson, *Treasurer*
◆ **EMP:** 31 **EST:** 1973
SQ FT: 18,000
SALES (est): 7.8MM **Privately Held**
WEB: www.chemicaldynamics.com
SIC: 2875 5191 Fertilizers, mixing only; chemicals, agricultural

(G-14419)
COMMERCIAL CONCRETE PDTS INC
2705 Sammonds Rd (33563-4556)
PHONE..................................813 659-3707
James L Byrd Jr, *President*
Mark Baker, *Vice Pres*
Jimmy Byrd, *CFO*
Terri Linton, *Accountant*
Terry Gillis, *Sales Staff*
EMP: 45 **EST:** 1983
SQ FT: 7,585
SALES (est): 7.2MM **Privately Held**
WEB:
www.commercialconcreteproducts.com
SIC: 3272 5211 Concrete products, precast; concrete & cinder block

(G-14420)
CORONET INDUSTRIES INC
4082 Coronet Rd (33566-4004)
PHONE..................................813 752-1161
David K Denner, *CEO*
Chris T Burgess, *Vice Pres*
Sudo Hideo, *Admin Sec*
EMP: 29 **EST:** 1993
SQ FT: 2,000
SALES (est): 10.1MM **Privately Held**
WEB: www.coronetindustries.com
SIC: 2048 Feed supplements
HQ: Onoda Chemical Industry Co., Ltd.
1-15-1, Kaigan
Minato-Ku TKY 105-0

(G-14421)
CUSTOM FABRICATION INC
2604 E Us Highway 92 (33566-7531)
PHONE..................................813 754-7571
Andrew Bookamer, *Office Mgr*
Jeffrey J Cook, *Director*
Melanie Curtis, *Assistant*
EMP: 30 **EST:** 1994
SQ FT: 33,000
SALES (est): 6.1MM **Privately Held**
WEB: www.customfabsteel.com
SIC: 3441 Fabricated structural metal

(G-14422)
CW21 INC
3404 E Us Highway 92 (33566-7432)
P.O. Box 3748 (33563-0013)
PHONE..................................813 754-1760
EMP: 23
SALES (est): 2.4MM **Privately Held**
SIC: 3089 Plastic And Metal Fabrication

(G-14423)
DART CONTAINER COMPANY FLA LLC
4610 Airport Rd (33563-1114)
PHONE..................................813 752-1990
Robert C Dart, *CEO*
EMP: 200 **EST:** 2005
SALES (est): 19MM **Privately Held**
SIC: 3086 3089 Cups & plates, foamed plastic; plastic containers, except foam

(G-14424)
DART CONTAINER CORP FLORIDA
1605 Turkey Creek Rd (33566-0055)
PHONE..................................813 752-6525
William Oberrender, *Safety Dir*
Traynham Matheson, *Prdtn Mgr*
Boyce Barnette, *Maint Spvr*
Isabella Calderon, *Research*
Kevin Myers, *VP Sales*
EMP: 17
SALES (corp-wide): 68.2MM **Privately Held**
WEB: www.dartcontainer.com
SIC: 3086 Plastics foam products
PA: Dart Container Corporation Of Florida
500 Hogsback Rd
Mason MI 48854
800 248-5960

(G-14425)
DOCS WELDING LLC
4708 Schield Ct (33566-0171)
PHONE..................................813 846-5022
James W Faulk, *President*
James Faulk, *Principal*
EMP: 6 **EST:** 2015
SALES (est): 157.8K **Privately Held**
SIC: 7692 Welding repair

(G-14426)
DOYLES FINE WOOD WORKING INC
1019 Redbud Cir (33563-8860)
PHONE..................................813 763-7800
Joseph D Doyle, *Principal*
EMP: 6 **EST:** 2017
SALES (est): 63K **Privately Held**
SIC: 2431 Millwork

(G-14427)
DUKES BREWHOUSE INC
1808 James L Redman Pkwy
(33563-6914)
PHONE..................................813 758-9309
Louis Mendel, *Principal*
EMP: 13 **EST:** 2015
SALES (est): 379.4K **Privately Held**
WEB: www.dukesbrewhouse.com
SIC: 2082 Malt beverages

(G-14428)
DUNCO ROCK & GRAVEL INC
Also Called: Dunco Materials
3115 Sammonds Rd (33563-7314)
PHONE..................................813 752-5622
Monteen Dunn, *President*
Dan Secor, *Vice Pres*
EMP: 5 **EST:** 1983
SALES (est): 1.1MM **Privately Held**
WEB: www.duncomaterials.com
SIC: 3273 Ready-mixed concrete

(G-14429)
EL MIRA SOL INC (PA)
4008 Airport Rd (33563-1108)
PHONE..................................813 754-5857
Guillermo Gama, *President*
Raoul Garcia, *General Mgr*
Patricia L Gama, *Vice Pres*
Marisa Cano, *Sales Staff*
Veronica Salinas, *Sales Staff*
EMP: 60 **EST:** 1987
SQ FT: 20,000
SALES (est): 11.2MM **Privately Held**
WEB: www.elmirasolinc.com
SIC: 2096 5141 5411 Tortilla chips; groceries, general line; grocery stores, independent

(G-14430)
FLORIDA BRICK AND CLAY CO INC
1708 Turkey Creek Rd (33566-0056)
P.O. Box 3341 (33563-0006)
PHONE..................................813 754-1521
Remy Hermida, *CEO*
Antonio Azorin, *President*
William Dodson, *President*
Tony Azorin, *Safety Dir*
Fay Savage, *Mktg Dir*
◆ **EMP:** 18 **EST:** 1963
SQ FT: 2,000
SALES (est): 1MM **Privately Held**
WEB: www.floridabrickandclay.com
SIC: 3253 3251 Quarry tile, clay; paving brick, clay

(G-14431)
FLOYD PUBLICATIONS INC
702 W Dr Mrtn Lther King (33563-5119)
PHONE..................................813 707-8783
Michael Floyd, *President*
Mike Floyd, *Publisher*
Cierra Craft, *Editor*
Dede Floyd, *Office Mgr*
EMP: 6 **EST:** 2000
SALES (est): 689.1K **Privately Held**
WEB: www.focusplantcity.com
SIC: 2741 Miscellaneous publishing

(G-14432)
FREE WING FLIGHT TECHNOLOGIES
607 S Alexander St Ste (33563-5053)
PHONE..................................813 752-8552
Tom Sash, *President*
EMP: 5 **EST:** 2002
SALES (est): 312.8K **Privately Held**
WEB: www.freewing.net
SIC: 3728 Aircraft parts & equipment

(G-14433)
FRIO DISTRIBUTORS INC
Also Called: Ice Pop Factory
1406 Mercantile Ct (33563-1151)
P.O. Box 3514 (33563-0010)
PHONE..................................813 567-1493
Margarita Sanchez, *President*
Ray Sanchez, *General Mgr*
Saul Sanchez, *Opers Staff*
▲ **EMP:** 12 **EST:** 2005
SQ FT: 8,000
SALES (est): 1MM **Privately Held**
WEB: www.icepopfactory.com
SIC: 2024 Juice pops, frozen

(G-14434)
GERDAU AMERISTEEL US INC
Ameristeel Tmapa Fab Rnfrcing
4006 Paul Buchman Hwy (33565)
P.O. Box 3009 (33563-0001)
PHONE..................................813 752-7550
Paul Morin, *Branch Mgr*
EMP: 283
SQ FT: 53,587 **Privately Held**
WEB: www.gerdau.com
SIC: 3449 3441 Miscellaneous metalwork; fabricated structural metal
HQ: Gerdau Ameristeel Us Inc.
4221 W Boy Scout Blvd # 600
Tampa FL 33607
813 286-8383

(G-14435)
GERDAU AMERISTEEL US INC
2100 Joe Mcintosh Rd (33565-7413)
PHONE..................................813 752-7550
S Nakamura, *Vice Pres*
EMP: 21 **EST:** 2003
SALES (est): 89.4K **Privately Held**
WEB: www.gerdau.com
SIC: 3312 Blast furnaces & steel mills

(G-14436)
GOLDEN ALUMINUM EXTRUSION LLC
1650 Alumax Cir (33566-8461)
PHONE..................................330 372-2300
Tom Ploughe, *President*
EMP: 25 **EST:** 1987
SQ FT: 300,000
SALES (est): 1.2MM **Privately Held**
SIC: 3354 Shapes, extruded aluminum

(G-14437)
GREAT WESTERN MALTING CO
Also Called: Country Malt Group
225 S County Line Rd (33566-7301)
PHONE..................................360 991-0888
Mike O'Toole, *President*
EMP: 99 **Privately Held**
WEB: www.greatwesternmalting.com
SIC: 2083 Malt
HQ: Great Western Malting Co.
1705 Nw Harborside Dr
Vancouver WA 98660
360 693-3661

(G-14438)
GT GRANDSTANDS INC
2810 Sydney Rd (33566-1173)
PHONE..................................813 305-1415
John Oconley, *CEO*
Tom Ennis, *President*
Greg Bucknermgr, *Principal*
Ross Rob, *Project Mgr*
Todd Corder, *Engineer*
EMP: 31
SQ FT: 2,000
SALES (est): 8MM **Privately Held**
WEB: www.gtgrandstands.com
SIC: 2531 Public building & related furniture

(G-14439)
JAMES CALDWELL STUMP GRINDING
1310 Whitehurst Rd (33563-1350)
PHONE..................................813 843-1262
James Caldwell, *Principal*
EMP: 7 **EST:** 2005
SALES (est): 134.1K **Privately Held**
SIC: 3599 Grinding castings for the trade

(G-14440)
JAMES HARDIE BUILDING PDTS INC
Also Called: Hardie Pipe
809 S Woodrow Wilson St (33563-4945)
PHONE..................................813 478-1758
Wendy Kowalski, *Vice Pres*
Hercules Stancil, *Project Engr*
Joe Haslwanter, *Electrical Engi*
Mike Schulte, *Manager*
EMP: 85 **Privately Held**
WEB: www.jameshardie.com
SIC: 3259 Clay sewer & drainage pipe & tile

HQ: James Hardie Building Products Inc.
231 S La Salle St # 2000
Chicago IL 60604
312 291-5072

(G-14441)
JTAC INDUSTRIES LLC
2509 Trkey Creek Rd Ste 1 (33566)
PHONE.................................813 928-0628
Joel Jaeb, *CEO*
Joseph Jaeb, *COO*
Stephen Jaeb, *Manager*
EMP: 6 **EST:** 2014
SALES (est): 234.8K **Privately Held**
WEB: www.jtacindustries.com
SIC: 3999 Barber & beauty shop equipment

(G-14442)
KEEL & CURLEY WINERY LLC
5210 Thonotosassa Rd (33565-5700)
PHONE.................................813 752-9100
C Joseph I Keel,
EMP: 16 **EST:** 2008
SALES (est): 2.5MM **Privately Held**
WEB: www.keelfarms.com
SIC: 2084 Wines

(G-14443)
KERRY INC
1111 W Dr Mlk Jr Blvd (33563)
PHONE.................................813 359-5182
Gerry Behan, *CEO*
EMP: 7 **Privately Held**
WEB: www.kerry.com
SIC: 2099 Food preparations
HQ: Kerry Inc.
3400 Millington Rd
Beloit WI 53511
608 363-1200

(G-14444)
KERRY INC
Also Called: Kerry Ingredients & Flavours
1111 W Dr Mrtn Lther King (33563-5106)
PHONE.................................813 359-5181
Susie Brown, *Branch Mgr*
EMP: 7
SQ FT: 21,270 **Privately Held**
WEB: www.kerry.com
SIC: 2034 2037 Dehydrated fruits, vegetables, soups; frozen fruits & vegetables
HQ: Kerry Inc.
3400 Millington Rd
Beloit WI 53511
608 363-1200

(G-14445)
KONE CRANE MAINTENANCE SVCS
Also Called: K C I Kone Crane
2007 Wood Ct Ste 5 (33563-6343)
PHONE.................................813 707-0086
Dayle Smith, *Vice Pres*
EMP: 15 **EST:** 1980
SALES (est): 304.6K **Privately Held**
WEB: www.konecranes.com
SIC: 3536 Hoists, cranes & monorails

(G-14446)
MASTERTASTE INC
205 E Terrace Dr (33563-9015)
PHONE.................................813 754-7392
EMP: 6 **Privately Held**
SIC: 2034 Dehydrated Fruits, Vegetables, Soups, Nsk
HQ: Mastertaste Inc.
160 Terminal Ave
Clark NJ 07066
732 882-0202

(G-14447)
MCCAIN MILLS INC
5605 Paul Buchman Hwy (33565-7305)
PHONE.................................813 752-6478
Joshua D McCain, *Principal*
Trisha Howard, *Manager*
EMP: 9 **EST:** 2018
SALES (est): 941.6K **Privately Held**
WEB: www.mccainmills.com
SIC: 2421 Sawmills & planing mills, general

(G-14448)
METAL SYSTEMS INC
Also Called: Discount Metal Mart
3301 Paul Buchman Hwy (33565-5051)
PHONE.................................813 752-7088
Ferris Waller, *President*
▼ **EMP:** 6 **EST:** 1993
SQ FT: 1,560
SALES (est): 978.3K **Privately Held**
WEB: www.jam-sessions.meetup.com
SIC: 3441 Building components, structural steel

(G-14449)
MTEC TRAILER SUPPLY
3804 Sydney Rd (33566-1191)
PHONE.................................813 659-1647
Dan Wilson, *Chairman*
EMP: 17 **EST:** 1994
SQ FT: 10,000
SALES (est): 205.7K **Privately Held**
SIC: 3451 Screw machine products

(G-14450)
NUCYCLE ENERGY OF TAMPA LLC
2067 S County Line Rd (33566-4545)
PHONE.................................813 848-0509
Amy Radke, *Opers Staff*
Brandon Hageman, *Engineer*
Rachel Leone, *Finance*
Brad Petchulis, *Accounts Exec*
Zachary Schonberger, *Administration*
EMP: 25 **EST:** 2017
SALES (est): 3.2MM **Privately Held**
WEB: www.nucycleenergy.com
SIC: 2097 Block ice

(G-14451)
PAJ INNOVATIVE CONCEPTS INC
Also Called: Catamont Machine Works
2804 Sydney Rd (33566-1173)
PHONE.................................813 659-0505
Allen Jenkins, *CEO*
Peggy Jenkins, *President*
EMP: 20 **EST:** 2002
SALES (est): 1.6MM **Privately Held**
SIC: 3599 Machine shop, jobbing & repair; gasoline filters, internal combustion engine, except auto

(G-14452)
PALLET EXPRESS INC
1503 Turkey Creek Rd (33566-0054)
PHONE.................................813 752-1600
Michael Oliveira, *President*
EMP: 18 **EST:** 2002
SALES (est): 2MM **Privately Held**
WEB: www.palletexpressinc.com
SIC: 2448 Pallets, wood

(G-14453)
PALLET SERVICES INC (PA)
Also Called: Pallet Services of Plant City
1705 Turkey Creek Rd (33566-0057)
P.O. Box 1804, Valrico (33595-1804)
PHONE.................................813 754-7719
George Bernico, *President*
Sarah Bernico, *General Mgr*
Diane Bernico,
EMP: 8 **EST:** 1985
SQ FT: 1,500
SALES (est): 1MM **Privately Held**
WEB: www.palletservicesofpc.com
SIC: 2448 Pallets, wood

(G-14454)
PALLETS PLUS INC
2606 N Airport Rd (33563-1147)
PHONE.................................813 759-6355
Jeffrey Phillips, *President*
Rhonda Phillips, *Vice Pres*
EMP: 9 **EST:** 1993
SALES (est): 987.8K **Privately Held**
SIC: 2448 Pallets, wood

(G-14455)
PARADISE LABEL INC
4021 S Frontage Rd (33566-7504)
PHONE.................................863 860-8779
Darold Stagner, *President*
▼ **EMP:** 12 **EST:** 2003
SQ FT: 100,000
SALES (est): 164.9K **Privately Held**
SIC: 2679 Labels, paper: made from purchased material

(G-14456)
PENINSULA STEEL INC (PA)
4504 Sydney Rd (33566-1195)
PHONE.................................956 795-1966
David Villarreal Valle, *President*
Pablo Villarreal, *President*
Sylvia C Miranda, *Vice Pres*
Aylen Gonzalez, *Manager*
Joe Kuykendall, *Manager*
EMP: 7
SALES (est): 12MM **Privately Held**
WEB: www.peninsulasteel.com
SIC: 3315 Steel wire & related products

(G-14457)
PENINSULA STEEL INC
4504 Sydney Rd (33566-1195)
PHONE.................................813 473-8133
EMP: 20
SALES (corp-wide): 16.5MM **Privately Held**
SIC: 3315 Mfg Steel Wire/Related Products
PA: Peninsula Steel, Inc.
4119 Free Trade St
Laredo TX 33566
956 795-1966

(G-14458)
PLANT CITY OBSERVER LLC
110 E Reynolds St 100b (33563-3361)
PHONE.................................813 704-6850
Sarah Holt, *Manager*
EMP: 8 **EST:** 2019
SALES (est): 251.2K **Privately Held**
WEB: www.plantcityobserver.com
SIC: 2711 Newspapers, publishing & printing

(G-14459)
PLANT CITY POWDER COATING
4604 Us Highway 92 W (33563-8279)
PHONE.................................813 763-6028
Corey Peacock, *Principal*
EMP: 6 **EST:** 2017
SALES (est): 119.3K **Privately Held**
WEB: www.qmwcom.com
SIC: 3441 Fabricated structural metal

(G-14460)
PRO HORIZONS INC
2610 Airport Rd (33563-1143)
PHONE.................................813 764-8844
David Carmichael, *President*
Jackie Carmichael, *Vice Pres*
▲ **EMP:** 7 **EST:** 1999
SALES (est): 143.6K **Privately Held**
WEB: www.paddleboardinglock.com
SIC: 2299 Batting, wadding, padding & fillings

(G-14461)
RESA PWR SLUTIONS PLANT CY LLC
Also Called: Switchgear Unlimited
1401 Mercantile Ct (33563-1152)
PHONE.................................813 752-6550
Larry Loucks, *President*
Al Vila, *General Mgr*
EMP: 15 **EST:** 1986
SQ FT: 70,000
SALES (est): 6MM
SALES (corp-wide): 136.7MM **Privately Held**
WEB: www.resapower.com
SIC: 3625 5063 Switches, electric power; switchgear
PA: Resa Power, Llc
8300 Cypress Pkwy Ste 225
Houston TX 77070
832 900-8340

(G-14462)
REYES INTERLOCKING PAVERS INC
1317 E Calhoun St (33563-3809)
PHONE.................................863 698-9179
Angel Picon Jacinto, *Principal*
EMP: 6 **EST:** 2008
SALES (est): 544.6K **Privately Held**
WEB: www.reyesinterlockingpavers.com
SIC: 3531 Pavers

(G-14463)
ROLLS AXLE LC
702 Hitchcock St (33563-5608)
PHONE.................................813 764-0242
Daniel M Gallagher Jr, *Partner*
Dniel Glger III, *Mng Member*
EMP: 10 **EST:** 1998
SQ FT: 8,000
SALES (est): 384.6K **Privately Held**
WEB: www.rollsaxle.com
SIC: 3799 3841 3792 Boat trailers; surgical & medical instruments; travel trailers & campers

(G-14464)
SENSENICH TECHNOLOGIES INC
2008 Wood Ct (33563-6305)
PHONE.................................813 703-8446
Steve Boser, *President*
John Hozik, *Principal*
EMP: 7 **EST:** 2013
SALES (est): 499.7K **Privately Held**
WEB: www.sensenichtech.com
SIC: 3728 Aircraft parts & equipment

(G-14465)
SHUTTER DOWN STORM PROTECTION
3940 E Knights Griffin Rd (33565-2208)
PHONE.................................813 957-8936
Richard C Bliss, *President*
EMP: 9 **EST:** 2005
SALES (est): 116.3K **Privately Held**
SIC: 3442 Shutters, door or window: metal

(G-14466)
SOUTHAST CLKING SLANT SVCS LLC
2426 Branchwood Rd (33567-3800)
PHONE.................................813 731-8778
Robert G Woods, *Manager*
Robert Woods, *Manager*
EMP: 7 **EST:** 2015
SALES (est): 309.3K **Privately Held**
WEB: www.southeastcaulking.com
SIC: 2891 Sealants

(G-14467)
SQUIRE INDUSTRIES INC
1118 Sparkman Rd (33566-4714)
PHONE.................................813 523-1505
James Tothill, *Principal*
EMP: 8 **EST:** 2011
SALES (est): 92.9K **Privately Held**
SIC: 3999 Manufacturing industries

(G-14468)
STONE METALS LLC
4021 S Frontage Rd (33566-7504)
PHONE.................................813 605-7363
Brian Wedding,
EMP: 8 **EST:** 2019
SALES (est): 2.8MM **Privately Held**
SIC: 1411 Limestone & marble dimension stone

(G-14469)
TATA TEA EXTRACTIONS INC
1001 W Dr Mlk Jr Blvd Martin Luther (33563)
PHONE.................................813 754-2602
Ravi Sankararaman, *President*
Raji Thankappan, *Principal*
◆ **EMP:** 30 **EST:** 1979
SQ FT: 45,000
SALES (est): 5.9MM **Privately Held**
WEB: www.tataconsumer.com
SIC: 2099 Tea blending
PA: Tata Consumer Products Limited
11/13, Botawala Building, 1st Floor,
Mumbai MH 40000

(G-14470)
TELESE INC
Also Called: Quality Metal Works
1207 Wood Ct (33563-6302)
PHONE.................................813 752-6015
Anthony Telese, *President*
Mark Telese, *Vice Pres*
EMP: 33 **EST:** 1983
SQ FT: 22,000

SALES (est): 9.9MM **Privately Held**
SIC: 3444 2542 Sheet metal specialties, not stamped; partitions & fixtures, except wood

(G-14471)
TELESE PROPERTIES INC
Also Called: Quality Metal Works
1207 Wood Ct (33563-6302)
PHONE..................................813 752-6015
Anthony G Telese, *President*
Mark Telese, *Vice Pres*
Bob Youngblood, *Opers Mgr*
Lynn Telese, *Purch Agent*
Amiee Spivey, *Human Res Mgr*
EMP: 60 **EST:** 2001
SALES (est): 8.3MM **Privately Held**
SIC: 3499 Fire- or burglary-resistive products

(G-14472)
TEMPLE TERRACE INDUSTRIES INC
4208 Business Ln (33566-1163)
PHONE..................................813 752-7546
W C Hammontree, *President*
Joseph P Hammontree, *Vice Pres*
David Hammontree, *Treasurer*
Doris J Hammontree, *Admin Sec*
EMP: 19 **EST:** 1952
SQ FT: 50,000
SALES (est): 1.1MM **Privately Held**
WEB: www.reelco.us
SIC: 2499 Reels, plywood

(G-14473)
THOMAS WHITE LLC
1302 N Orange St (33563-2348)
PHONE..................................813 704-4406
Thomas White, *Principal*
EMP: 7 **EST:** 2007
SALES (est): 77.6K **Privately Held**
SIC: 2952 Roofing materials

(G-14474)
TITANIUM GYMNASTICS AND CHEERL
402 W Ball St (33563-5302)
PHONE..................................813 659-2204
EMP: 6 **EST:** 2016
SALES (est): 90.8K **Privately Held**
WEB: www.titaniumgymandcheer.com
SIC: 3356 Titanium

(G-14475)
USMI PALLETS INC
3301 Sam Allen Oaks Cir (33565-5597)
PHONE..................................813 765-4309
Grover D Garrett, *President*
EMP: 8 **EST:** 2009
SALES (est): 278.4K **Privately Held**
WEB: www.usmipallets.com
SIC: 2448 Pallets, wood

(G-14476)
VANAVAC INC
1309 Joe Mcintosh Rd (33565-7454)
PHONE..................................813 752-1391
EMP: 7
SQ FT: 1,500
SALES (est): 1.2MM **Privately Held**
SIC: 2819 Mfg Industrial Inorganic Chemicals

(G-14477)
WARREN EQUIPMENT INC
2299 Us Highway 92 E (33563-2145)
PHONE..................................813 752-5126
Russell Warren, *President*
Duane Chambers, *Vice Pres*
William Gordon, *Plant Mgr*
Barrientes Renee, *Human Resources*
Gregory Pugliese, *Regl Sales Mgr*
EMP: 45 **EST:** 2001
SQ FT: 80,000
SALES (est): 11.6MM **Privately Held**
WEB: www.warrentrailers.com
SIC: 3715 5013 3713 Truck trailers; truck parts & accessories; dump truck bodies

(G-14478)
WEDGWORTH FARMS INC
2607 Sammonds Rd (33563-4554)
PHONE..................................561 996-2076
EMP: 8
SALES (corp-wide): 67.8MM **Privately Held**
WEB: www.wedgworth.com
SIC: 2875 Fertilizers, mixing only
PA: Wedgworth Farms Inc
32260 State Rd 80
Belle Glade FL 33430
561 996-2076

Plantation
Broward County

(G-14479)
2LEAF PRESS INC
1200 S Pine Island Rd (33324-4413)
PHONE..................................646 801-4227
Gabrielle David, *Principal*
EMP: 7 **EST:** 2019
SALES (est): 338.1K **Privately Held**
WEB: www.2leafpress.org
SIC: 2731 Book publishing

(G-14480)
A J M O INDUSTRIES INC
1741 Sw 54th Ter (33317-6025)
PHONE..................................954 587-0206
Louis Ajmo, *Principal*
EMP: 6 **EST:** 2010
SALES (est): 96.2K **Privately Held**
SIC: 3999 Manufacturing industries

(G-14481)
A-PLUS PRTG & GRAPHIC CTR INC
6561 Nw 18th Ct (33313-4520)
PHONE..................................954 327-7315
Richard Erens, *President*
Andrew Moreau, *Manager*
EMP: 40 **EST:** 1991
SALES (est): 7.2MM **Privately Held**
WEB: www.a-plusprinting.com
SIC: 2752 2754 7336 Commercial printing, offset; commercial printing, gravure; graphic arts & related design

(G-14482)
AB ENZYMES INC
150 S Pine Island Rd # 270 (33324-2677)
PHONE..................................954 278-3975
Martin Nielsen, *President*
Karen Lewis, *CFO*
Kelly Lamanna, *Treasurer*
Carmen Sciackitano, *Admin Sec*
Joice Jackson, *Analyst*
▼ **EMP:** 8 **EST:** 2017
SQ FT: 3,000
SALES (est): 10.1MM
SALES (corp-wide): 18.2B **Privately Held**
WEB: www.abenzymes.com
SIC: 2869 Enzymes
HQ: Ab Enzymes Gmbh
Feldbergstr. 78
Darmstadt 64293
615 136-8010

(G-14483)
AB VISTA INC (HQ)
150 S Pine Island Rd (33324-2669)
PHONE..................................954 278-3965
Richard Cooper, *President*
Kelly Lamanna, *Vice Pres*
Dieter Suida, *Vice Pres*
Ian Vincent, *CFO*
Rebecca Marsland, *Marketing Staff*
▲ **EMP:** 9 **EST:** 2002
SALES (est): 10MM
SALES (corp-wide): 18.2B **Privately Held**
WEB: www.abvista.com
SIC: 2048 Prepared feeds
PA: Associated British Foods Plc
10 Grosvenor Street
London W1K 4
207 399-6500

(G-14484)
AB VISTA INC
8151 Peters Rd (33324-4009)
PHONE..................................954 278-3965
Nick Robinson, *Controller*
Matt Reed, *Manager*
Laura Merriman, *Technical Staff*
EMP: 6
SALES (corp-wide): 18.2B **Privately Held**
WEB: www.abvista.com
SIC: 2869 Enzymes
HQ: Ab Vista, Inc.
150 S Pine Island Rd
Plantation FL 33324
954 278-3965

(G-14485)
ABDIVERSIFIED LLC
6825 W Sunrise Blvd (33313-4512)
PHONE..................................954 791-6050
EMP: 31 **EST:** 2016
SALES (est): 2.1MM
SALES (corp-wide): 19.4MM **Privately Held**
WEB: www.fekkai.com
SIC: 2844 Hair preparations, including shampoos
PA: Fekkai Retail, Llc
6825 W Sunrise Blvd
Plantation FL 33313
866 514-8048

(G-14486)
ADMASK INC
Also Called: Superior Printers
6531 Nw 13th Ct (33313-4550)
PHONE..................................954 962-2040
Adib K Skaf, *President*
Maria I Skaf, *Treasurer*
EMP: 6 **EST:** 1994
SALES (est): 743.5K **Privately Held**
SIC: 2752 Commercial printing, offset

(G-14487)
ALLIED TELECOMMUNICATIONS LTD
1500 Nw 65th Ave (33313-4507)
PHONE..................................954 370-9900
Frank D Reynolds, *CEO*
EMP: 10 **EST:** 1989
SQ FT: 3,700
SALES (est): 175.5K **Privately Held**
SIC: 3661 5065 Carrier equipment, telephone or telegraph; telephone equipment

(G-14488)
ALNOOR IMPORT INC
6851 W Sunrise Blvd (33313-4572)
PHONE..................................954 683-9897
Maher Almasri, *President*
◆ **EMP:** 5 **EST:** 2007
SALES (est): 1MM **Privately Held**
WEB: www.alnourimports.com
SIC: 2099 Food preparations

(G-14489)
AMERICAS ATM LLC
8751 W Broward Blvd # 30 (33324-2668)
PHONE..................................954 414-0341
Brad Daniel, *Mng Member*
EMP: 19 **EST:** 2014
SALES (est): 841.7K **Privately Held**
WEB: www.americanatm.com
SIC: 3578 Automatic teller machines (ATM)

(G-14490)
ARMEN CO INC
12140 Nw 12th St (33323-2436)
PHONE..................................305 206-1601
George Davitian, *President*
▼ **EMP:** 70 **EST:** 1984
SQ FT: 20,000
SALES (est): 4.5MM **Privately Held**
SIC: 2339 2329 2369 2269 Sportswear, women's; men's & boys' sportswear & athletic clothing; girls' & children's outerwear; finishing plants; finishing plants, manmade fiber & silk fabrics; finishing plants, cotton

(G-14491)
AROUND AND ABOUT INC
450 N State Road 7 (33317-2834)
PHONE..................................954 584-1954
Richard Conrey, *President*
Carmelo Guerrero, *Research*
Adam Friedman, *CFO*
Carolina Cardenas, *Supervisor*
Shani Villalba, *Graphic Designe*
EMP: 10 **EST:** 2004
SQ FT: 4,696
SALES (est): 1.6MM **Privately Held**
WEB: www.upnwalk.com
SIC: 3842 Limbs, artificial; prosthetic appliances

(G-14492)
ATACAMA RESOURCES INTL INC (PA)
1200 S Pine Island Rd (33324-4413)
PHONE..................................613 421-9733
Glenn B Grant, *CEO*
David Berry, *Ch of Bd*
Daniel Finch, *COO*
William Webb, *CFO*
EMP: 7 **EST:** 2013
SALES (est): 222.8K **Publicly Held**
WEB: www.acrlintl.com
SIC: 3532 Mining machinery

(G-14493)
ATI SALES INC
351 Sw 63rd Ter (33317-3436)
PHONE..................................954 909-4639
Anthony Iannazzone, *Principal*
EMP: 7 **EST:** 2014
SALES (est): 124.6K **Privately Held**
SIC: 3312 Stainless steel

(G-14494)
AUTOMATIC MFG SYSTEMS INC
Also Called: Accuplace
1800 Nw 69th Ave Ste 102 (33313-4583)
PHONE..................................954 791-1500
Jamie P Schlinkmann, *President*
Tony Haubrich, *Engineer*
Alex Schlinkmann, *Info Tech Dir*
Alex W Schlinkmann, *Director*
▲ **EMP:** 30 **EST:** 1997
SQ FT: 75,000
SALES (est): 8.9MM **Privately Held**
WEB: www.accuplace.com
SIC: 3549 3569 Metalworking machinery; assembly machines, non-metalworking

(G-14495)
AVIATION PARTS & TRADE CORP
12331 Nw 7th St (33325-1729)
P.O. Box 15431 (33318-5431)
PHONE..................................954 944-2828
Carlos E Ulloa, *President*
EMP: 6 **EST:** 2012
SALES (est): 681.4K **Privately Held**
WEB: www.aptc.aero
SIC: 3429 3721 Aircraft hardware; aircraft

(G-14496)
BIO THERAPEUTICS INC
Also Called: Phylomed
1850 Nw 69th Ave Ste 1 (33313-4569)
PHONE..................................954 321-5553
Suzanne Mundschenk, *President*
EMP: 8 **EST:** 1984
SALES (est): 824.7K **Privately Held**
SIC: 2834 8733 Pharmaceutical preparations; medical research

(G-14497)
BIOIVT LLC
7500 Nw 5th St (33317-1612)
PHONE..................................516 876-7902
Jorge Bichara, *Site Mgr*
EMP: 7 **EST:** 2013
SALES (est): 107.3K **Privately Held**
WEB: www.bioivt.com
SIC: 2836 Veterinary biological products

(G-14498)
BLACK TIE PUBLISHING INC
10131 Nw 14th St (33322-6531)
PHONE..................................954 472-6003
Ron Feller, *Publisher*
Ronald Feller, *Principal*
EMP: 8 **EST:** 2001
SALES (est): 282.8K **Privately Held**
WEB: www.blacktiepublishing.com
SIC: 2741 Miscellaneous publishing

(G-14499)
CIT AEROSPACE INC
1000 S Pine Island Rd # 500 (33324-3906)
PHONE..................................954 359-2561
Justo Estrada, *Vice Pres*
Ariel Rodriguez, *Vice Pres*
Michelle Stewart, *Vice Pres*

Kelvin Gokool, *Analyst*
EMP: 18 **EST:** 1989
SALES (est): 3.4MM **Privately Held**
WEB: www.cit.com
SIC: 3724 Aircraft engines & engine parts

(G-14500)
CLINICAL DAGNSTC SOLUTIONS INC
1800 Nw 65th Ave (33313-4544)
PHONE..................................954 791-1773
Andrew C Swanson, *President*
Dr Harold R Crews, *Senior VP*
Donald Grantham, *Senior VP*
Karen Bornstein, *Vice Pres*
James Carter, *Vice Pres*
◆ **EMP:** 38 **EST:** 1997
SQ FT: 47,000
SALES (est): 20.4MM **Privately Held**
WEB: www.cdsolinc.com
SIC: 2835 2899 2834 Hemotology diagnostic agents; chemical preparations; pharmaceutical preparations
PA: Boule Diagnostics Ab
Domnarvsgatan 4
Spanga 163 5

(G-14501)
CLOUDFACTORS LLC
1200 S Pine Island Rd (33324-4413)
PHONE..................................866 779-9974
James Keefner, *President*
EMP: 5 **EST:** 2011
SALES (est): 468.5K **Privately Held**
SIC: 7372 7373 7371 5734 Application computer software; value-added resellers, computer systems; computer software development & applications; personal computers

(G-14502)
COOL OCEAN LLC
9810 Sw 4th St (33324-2826)
PHONE..................................954 848-4060
Avraham Zeitoune,
EMP: 7 **EST:** 2013
SALES (est): 509.7K **Privately Held**
WEB: www.coolocean123.com
SIC: 2231 Weaving mill, broadwoven fabrics: wool or similar fabric

(G-14503)
COUNTRY PRIME MEATS USA INC
9695 W Broward Blvd (33324-2321)
PHONE..................................250 396-4111
Peter Springmann, *President*
Markus Springmann, *Director*
EMP: 5 **EST:** 2016
SALES (est): 412K **Privately Held**
WEB: www.countryprime.com
SIC: 2013 Snack sticks, including jerky: from purchased meat

(G-14504)
CROMPCO INC
Also Called: Park Row Printing
6531 Nw 13th Ct (33313-4550)
PHONE..................................954 584-8488
George V Crompton, *President*
Howard Crompton, *Vice Pres*
Judith Crompton, *Admin Sec*
EMP: 10 **EST:** 1976
SQ FT: 3,500
SALES (est): 2MM **Privately Held**
WEB: www.crompco.com
SIC: 2752 Commercial printing, offset

(G-14505)
CUG LLC
950 S Pine Island Rd (33324-3918)
PHONE..................................786 858-0499
Sahily Sanchez,
Edgar Banks,
Isabel Cardoza,
Luis La Verde,
EMP: 12 **EST:** 2018
SALES (est): 1.6MM **Privately Held**
WEB: www.chinausagranites.com
SIC: 3281 3272 5032 Granite, cut & shaped; floor slabs & tiles, precast concrete; ceramic construction materials, excluding refractory

(G-14506)
DAILY ROOM
1000 S Pine Island Rd # 160 (33324-3904)
PHONE..................................754 200-5153
Sebastien Tribout, *Principal*
EMP: 11 **EST:** 2012
SALES (est): 472.5K **Privately Held**
WEB: www.thedailyroom.com
SIC: 2711 Newspapers, publishing & printing

(G-14507)
DAILYCHEW LLC
9355 Nw 18th Pl (33322-5655)
PHONE..................................954 849-0553
Kenneth Jeffus, *Principal*
EMP: 7 **EST:** 2009
SALES (est): 79.9K **Privately Held**
WEB: www.dailychew.com
SIC: 2711 Newspapers, publishing & printing

(G-14508)
DANDY MEDIA CORPORATION
Also Called: Dandyprint.com
1380 Nw 65th Ave Ste A (33313-4555)
PHONE..................................954 616-6800
William T Clegg, *President*
Juan E Soriano, *Vice Pres*
John Melendez, *Treasurer*
EMP: 12 **EST:** 2012
SQ FT: 4,500
SALES (est): 404.6K **Privately Held**
SIC: 2759 Commercial printing

(G-14509)
DAX COPYING AND PRINTING INC
1868 N University Dr # 106 (33322-4129)
PHONE..................................954 236-3000
Bruce Batchelder, *President*
EMP: 6 **EST:** 2009
SQ FT: 3,000
SALES (est): 647.3K **Privately Held**
WEB: www.nationalcolorcopy.com
SIC: 2752 Commercial printing, offset

(G-14510)
ELECTROSOURCE INC
11785 Nw 5th St (33325-1909)
PHONE..................................954 723-0840
Carmen Di Mase, *Principal*
EMP: 8 **EST:** 2010
SALES (est): 150.6K **Privately Held**
SIC: 3679 Microwave components

(G-14511)
ELEMENT-M LLC
9835 Nw 5th Pl (33324-7041)
PHONE..................................954 288-8683
David Kustin, *Principal*
EMP: 7 **EST:** 2010
SALES (est): 558.1K **Privately Held**
WEB: www.contentbacon.com
SIC: 2819 Industrial inorganic chemicals

(G-14512)
EURAMERICA GAS AND OIL CORP
1333 S University Dr # 202 (33324-4087)
PHONE..................................954 858-5714
EMP: 5 **EST:** 2018
SALES (est): 482.9K **Privately Held**
WEB: www.euramericagasoil.com
SIC: 1389 Oil & gas field services

(G-14513)
EVERFRESH JUICE CO INC
8100 Sw 10th St Ste 4000 (33324-3224)
PHONE..................................954 581-0922
Marty Rose, *General Mgr*
Albert Allen, *Principal*
Joe Jarrett, *Manager*
EMP: 24 **EST:** 2010
SALES (est): 2.6MM
SALES (corp-wide): 1B **Publicly Held**
WEB: www.everfreshjuice.com
SIC: 2086 Carbonated beverages, nonalcoholic: bottled & canned; water, pasteurized: packaged in cans, bottles, etc.; fruit drinks (less than 100% juice): packaged in cans, etc.
PA: National Beverage Corp.
8100 Sw 10th St Ste 4000
Plantation FL 33324
954 581-0922

(G-14514)
FEKKAI BRANDS LLC
6825 W Sunrise Blvd (33313-4512)
PHONE..................................954 791-6050
Joel B Ronkin, *Mng Member*
EMP: 11 **EST:** 2015
SALES (est): 389.9K **Privately Held**
SIC: 2844 Shampoos, rinses, conditioners: hair

(G-14515)
FEKKAI RETAIL LLC (PA)
6825 W Sunrise Blvd (33313-4512)
PHONE..................................866 514-8048
Joel Ronkin, *Principal*
EMP: 78 **EST:** 2015
SQ FT: 65,000
SALES (est): 19.4MM **Privately Held**
WEB: www.fekkai.com
SIC: 2844 7231 Hair preparations, including shampoos; unisex hair salons

(G-14516)
FIREFLY AIRCRAFT PARTS INC ✪
150 S Pine Island Rd (33324-2669)
PHONE..................................954 505-1470
Anna Luz, *CEO*
Anna Karina Da Luz, *CEO*
EMP: 6 **EST:** 2021
SALES (est): 282.2K **Privately Held**
SIC: 3728 8742 7389 Aircraft body assemblies & parts; retail trade consultant; brokers' services

(G-14517)
FIRST MATE INC
11950 Nw 27th St (33323-1760)
PHONE..................................954 475-2750
Ron Adams, *President*
Cheryl Adams, *Vice Pres*
EMP: 7 **EST:** 1996
SALES (est): 500K **Privately Held**
SIC: 3699 Door opening & closing devices, electrical

(G-14518)
FREE LIFE INC
320 Nw 69th Ave Apt 150 (33317-2329)
P.O. Box 17281, Fort Lauderdale (33318-7281)
PHONE..................................954 584-8485
Gary L Case, *Principal*
EMP: 7 **EST:** 2010
SALES (est): 144.2K **Privately Held**
SIC: 3523 Farm machinery & equipment

(G-14519)
FRIEDMAN & GREENBERG PA
9675 W Broward Blvd (33324-2321)
PHONE..................................954 370-4774
Robert Friedman, *President*
EMP: 8 **EST:** 1990
SALES (est): 749.6K **Privately Held**
WEB: www.friedmangreenberg.com
SIC: 3312 Fence posts, iron & steel

(G-14520)
GLC 3 & RENTAL CORP
Also Called: GLC 3 Concrete
11490 Nw 20th Ct (33323-2006)
PHONE..................................954 916-1551
George J Lacker, *President*
▼ **EMP:** 5 **EST:** 2001
SALES (est): 654.2K **Privately Held**
SIC: 3271 Concrete block & brick

(G-14521)
GLOBAL INDUSTRIES AND MFG INC
10781 Cleary Blvd Apt 112 (33324-6040)
PHONE..................................954 766-4656
Barry S Grieper, *President*
EMP: 6 **EST:** 2009
SALES (est): 119.9K **Privately Held**
SIC: 3999 Manufacturing industries

(G-14522)
GREENIE TOTS INC
772 Nw 132nd Ave (33325-6173)
PHONE..................................888 316-6126
Jilea Hemmings, *CEO*
EMP: 6 **EST:** 2004
SALES (est): 379.4K **Privately Held**
WEB: www.greenietots.com
SIC: 2038 Frozen specialties

(G-14523)
IBS PARTNERS LTD (PA)
1 N University Dr Ut400a (33324-2038)
PHONE..................................954 581-0922
Nick A Caporella, *General Ptnr*
Nick Caporella, *General Ptnr*
Dean McCoy, *Controller*
◆ **EMP:** 40 **EST:** 1985
SALES (est): 64.3MM **Privately Held**
SIC: 2086 Soft drinks: packaged in cans, bottles, etc.

(G-14524)
ID PRINT INC
6561 Nw 18th Ct (33313-4520)
P.O. Box 16486, Fort Lauderdale (33318-6486)
PHONE..................................954 923-8374
Steve Machusko, *President*
▼ **EMP:** 5 **EST:** 2008
SALES (est): 426.9K **Privately Held**
SIC: 3861 Printing equipment, photographic

(G-14525)
J ROSS PUBLISHING INC
300 S Pine Island Rd # 305 (33324-2621)
PHONE..................................954 727-9333
Dennis Buda, *President*
Stephen Buda, *Vice Pres*
Steve Buda, *Vice Pres*
▲ **EMP:** 7 **EST:** 2002
SQ FT: 1,500
SALES (est): 829K **Privately Held**
WEB: www.jrosspub.com
SIC: 2741 Miscellaneous publishing

(G-14526)
J S TRADING INC
6524 Nw 13th Ct (33313-4549)
PHONE..................................954 791-9035
Surjit Singh, *CEO*
Raj Singh, *Vice Pres*
◆ **EMP:** 6 **EST:** 1984
SQ FT: 15,000
SALES (est): 980.3K **Privately Held**
WEB: www.jstradingincorporated.com
SIC: 2673 2674 Plastic bags: made from purchased materials; paper bags: made from purchased materials

(G-14527)
J SCHOR R INC
Also Called: Sign Solutions
1776 N Pine Island Rd (33322-5233)
PHONE..................................954 621-5279
Robert J Schor, *President*
EMP: 11 **EST:** 2002
SALES (est): 526.7K **Privately Held**
SIC: 3083 Laminated plastics plate & sheet

(G-14528)
KING KANINE LLC (PA)
150 S Pine Island Rd # 115 (33324-2669)
PHONE..................................833 546-4738
Jeffrey M Riman, *Principal*
Lynnette San Miguel,
EMP: 24 **EST:** 2016
SQ FT: 1,500
SALES (est): 1.2MM **Privately Held**
WEB: www.kingkanine.com
SIC: 3999 5999 Pet supplies; pet supplies

(G-14529)
LUXE BRANDS INC (PA)
6825 W Sunrise Blvd (33313-4512)
PHONE..................................954 791-6050
Arvinder S Bajaj, *President*
Jogindar S Bajaj, *Vice Pres*
James Allen Fantau, *Human Res Mgr*
Lolly Gamma, *Human Res Mgr*
Patricia Buttacavoli, *Accounts Exec*
▲ **EMP:** 30
SALES (est): 11.8MM **Privately Held**
WEB: www.luxebrands.com
SIC: 2844 Toilet preparations

(G-14530)
LUXEBRANDS LLC
6825 W Sunrise Blvd (33313-4512)
PHONE..................................866 514-8048
Arvinder S Bajaj, *President*
EMP: 19 **EST:** 2016
SALES (est): 301K
SALES (corp-wide): 19.4MM **Privately Held**
WEB: www.fekkai.com
SIC: 2844 Hair preparations, including shampoos
PA: Fekkai Retail, Llc
6825 W Sunrise Blvd
Plantation FL 33313
866 514-8048

(G-14531)
MARITIME EXECUTIVE LLC
Also Called: Marex
7473 Nw 4th St (33317-2216)
PHONE..................................954 848-9955
Brett Keil, *Vice Pres*
Ben Lennon, *Marketing Mgr*
Zamaslie Corraliza, *Mktg Coord*
John Giorgianni, *Advt Staff*
Anthony Munoz, *Mng Member*
EMP: 8 **EST:** 2006
SALES (est): 1.1MM **Privately Held**
WEB: www.maritime-executive.com
SIC: 2721 Magazines: publishing only, not printed on site

(G-14532)
MAXANT BUTTON & SUPPLY INC
5901 Plantation Rd (33317-1345)
PHONE..................................770 460-2227
Lorna Marden, *President*
Jim Marden, *Admin Sec*
EMP: 5 **EST:** 2002
SQ FT: 5,000
SALES (est): 325K **Privately Held**
SIC: 3965 Buttons & parts

(G-14533)
METHOD MERCHANT INC
Also Called: Godatafeed
150 S Pine Island Rd # 530 (33324-2676)
PHONE..................................954 745-7998
Rotem Grosman, *President*
Karen Meany, *Vice Pres*
Lorraine Carcamo, *Accounts Mgr*
Andres Sepulveda, *Accounts Mgr*
Sean Dailey, *Sales Staff*
EMP: 22 **EST:** 2008
SALES (est): 1.4MM **Privately Held**
SIC: 7372 Business oriented computer software

(G-14534)
MILLCREEK FINE CABINETRY INC
1700 Nw 65th Ave Ste 9 (33313-4581)
PHONE..................................954 801-8595
Ron Carns, *President*
EMP: 6 **EST:** 2002
SALES (est): 85.4K **Privately Held**
SIC: 2434 1751 Wood kitchen cabinets; cabinet & finish carpentry

(G-14535)
MOTOROLA SOLUTIONS INC
8000 W Sunrise Blvd (33322-4170)
PHONE..................................954 723-5000
Kent Martin, *Regional Mgr*
Andrew Crawford, *Business Mgr*
George Nassif, *Business Mgr*
John Kedzierski, *Senior VP*
John Zidar, *Vice Pres*
EMP: 2000
SALES (corp-wide): 7.4B **Publicly Held**
WEB: www.motorolasolutions.com
SIC: 3663 Radio broadcasting & communications equipment
PA: Motorola Solutions, Inc.
500 W Monroe St Ste 4400
Chicago IL 60661
847 576-5000

(G-14536)
MULTIMEDIA EFFECTS INC
Also Called: Storage Heaven
9715 W Broward Blvd Ste 3 (33324-2351)
PHONE..................................800 367-3054
Oral Gordon, *Director*
EMP: 10 **EST:** 2010
SQ FT: 5,000
SALES (est): 2MM **Privately Held**
SIC: 3577 Data conversion equipment, media-to-media: computer

(G-14537)
NATIONAL BEVERAGE CORP (PA)
8100 Sw 10th St Ste 4000 (33324-3224)
P.O. Box 16720, Fort Lauderdale (33318-6720)
PHONE..................................954 581-0922
Nick A Caporella, *Ch of Bd*
Joseph G Caporella, *President*
Michael M King, *Counsel*
James Bolton, *Exec VP*
George Bracken, *Exec VP*
EMP: 370 **EST:** 1985
SALES: 1B **Publicly Held**
WEB: www.nationalbeverage.com
SIC: 2086 Soft drinks: packaged in cans, bottles, etc.; carbonated beverages, nonalcoholic: bottled & canned; water, pasteurized: packaged in cans, bottles, etc.; fruit drinks (less than 100% juice): packaged in cans, etc.

(G-14538)
NATIONAL CHEMICAL SUPPLY INC
6930 Sw 16th St (33317-5084)
P.O. Box 16785, Fort Lauderdale (33318-6785)
PHONE..................................954 683-1645
Phillip Shaffer, *President*
EMP: 8 **EST:** 1991
SQ FT: 4,700
SALES (est): 1MM **Privately Held**
WEB: www.nationalchemicalsupply.com
SIC: 2819 Industrial inorganic chemicals

(G-14539)
NEWBEVCO INC (HQ)
8100 Sw 10th St (33324-3279)
PHONE..................................954 581-0922
Nick A Caporella, *President*
Joseph G Caporella, *President*
EMP: 40 **EST:** 1991
SALES (est): 437.3MM
SALES (corp-wide): 1B **Publicly Held**
WEB: www.nationalbeverage.com
SIC: 2086 Soft drinks: packaged in cans, bottles, etc.
PA: National Beverage Corp.
8100 Sw 10th St Ste 4000
Plantation FL 33324
954 581-0922

(G-14540)
NXGEN BRANDS LLC
Also Called: LEAFYWELL
8032 Lakepointe Dr (33322-5789)
PHONE..................................888 315-6339
Angel Burgos, *CEO*
Tom Reeves, *President*
Nick Brana, *Managing Dir*
Nicholas Brana,
EMP: 30 **EST:** 2017
SALES: 230K
SALES (corp-wide): 1.7MM **Privately Held**
WEB: www.leafywell.com
SIC: 2834 3999 5159 3663 Pharmaceutical preparations; ; ;
PA: Nxgen Brands, Inc.
2322 Se 8th St
Cape Coral FL 33990
954 329-2205

(G-14541)
PANAMTECH INC (PA)
700 Nw 70th Ter (33317-1100)
PHONE..................................954 587-3769
Gloria Carreras, *President*
Rick Carreras, *President*
EMP: 16 **EST:** 1981
SALES (est): 585.3K **Privately Held**
WEB: www.panamtech.com
SIC: 3643 Current-carrying wiring devices

(G-14542)
PLANTATION JOURNAL CORPORATION
7860 Peters Rd Ste F110 (33324-4027)
PHONE..................................954 226-6170
Kevin D Bingham, *President*
EMP: 7 **EST:** 2009
SALES (est): 92K **Privately Held**
SIC: 2711 Newspapers, publishing & printing

(G-14543)
QUICK PRINTS LLC
8201 Peters Rd Ste 1000 (33324-3266)
PHONE..................................954 594-9415
EMP: 7 **EST:** 2016
SALES (est): 533.1K **Privately Held**
SIC: 2752 Commercial printing, offset

(G-14544)
ROBS BAGELAND INC
8201 W Sunrise Blvd (33322-5403)
PHONE..................................954 640-5470
Robert Elbaum, *Principal*
EMP: 8 **EST:** 2012
SALES (est): 951.6K **Privately Held**
WEB: www.robsbageland.net
SIC: 3421 Table & food cutlery, including butchers'

(G-14545)
RONS SAFE & VAULT COMPANY
5541 W Broward Blvd (33317-2619)
PHONE..................................305 527-2901
Ronald E Lasseter, *Principal*
▼ **EMP:** 9 **EST:** 2007
SALES (est): 283.7K **Privately Held**
SIC: 3272 Burial vaults, concrete or precast terrazzo

(G-14546)
RUSH FLYERS
6561 Nw 18th Ct (33313-4520)
PHONE..................................954 332-0509
Richard B Erens, *Principal*
EMP: 10 **EST:** 2009
SALES (est): 426.2K **Privately Held**
WEB: www.rushflyers.com
SIC: 2752 Commercial printing, offset

(G-14547)
S & K PRFMCE MACHINING & FAB
11911 Nw 27th Ct (33323-1713)
PHONE..................................954 306-2214
David Krivak, *Owner*
EMP: 8 **EST:** 2015
SALES (est): 125.8K **Privately Held**
WEB: www.performancemfnc.com
SIC: 3599 Machine shop, jobbing & repair

(G-14548)
SALSA THREE INC
10167 W Sunrise Blvd (33322-7619)
PHONE..................................954 990-2223
Boros Jay N, *Principal*
EMP: 6 **EST:** 2014
SALES (est): 380.7K **Privately Held**
SIC: 2099 Dips, except cheese & sour cream based

(G-14549)
SHASTA BEVERAGES INTL INC
Also Called: Add Some Pop
8100 Sw 10th St Ste 4000 (33324-3224)
PHONE..................................954 581-0922
Nick A Caporella, *President*
Caporella Joseph G, *Vice Pres*
Nin Elsie, *Admin Sec*
EMP: 50 **EST:** 1990
SALES (est): 37.5MM
SALES (corp-wide): 1B **Publicly Held**
SIC: 2086 5149 Carbonated beverages, nonalcoholic: bottled & canned; beverages, except coffee & tea
HQ: Newbevco, Inc.
8100 Sw 10th St
Plantation FL 33324

(G-14550)
SHORE TRENDZ LLC
560 Nw 118th Ave (33325-1828)
PHONE..................................954 608-7375
Mark Deift, *Principal*
Erica Deift, *Principal*
EMP: 6 **EST:** 2013
SALES (est): 558.4K **Privately Held**
WEB: www.shoretrendz.com
SIC: 2389 2369 Disposable garments & accessories; bathing suits & swimwear: girls', children's & infants'

(G-14551)
SIGNATURE METAL FAB LLC
400 Farmington Dr (33317-2633)
PHONE..................................954 214-1161
Spencer A Toot, *Principal*
EMP: 6 **EST:** 2017
SALES (est): 172.8K **Privately Held**
WEB: www.signaturemetalfab.com
SIC: 7692 Welding repair

(G-14552)
SKYHIGH ACCESSORIES INC
4344 Peters Rd (33317-4543)
PHONE..................................954 316-3936
Kirk Drellich, *President*
Scott Ferris, *Sales Staff*
EMP: 5 **EST:** 2001
SQ FT: 4,000
SALES (est): 941K **Privately Held**
WEB: www.skyhighaccessories.com
SIC: 3728 Aircraft parts & equipment

(G-14553)
SMART GLASS SYSTEMS INC
8201 Peters Rd (33324-3265)
PHONE..................................954 801-5349
Alex Martinez, *President*
◆ **EMP:** 5 **EST:** 2009
SALES (est): 500K **Privately Held**
WEB: www.smartglass-systems.com
SIC: 3231 Products of purchased glass

(G-14554)
SOLAR SHADES DRAPERIES & MORE
1081 Nw 101st Way (33322-6505)
PHONE..................................954 600-3419
Marisol Hernandez, *Principal*
EMP: 8 **EST:** 2005
SALES (est): 82.5K **Privately Held**
SIC: 2391 Curtains & draperies

(G-14555)
SOREN TECHNOLOGIES INC
817 S University Dr # 106 (33324-3309)
PHONE..................................954 236-9998
Faiz Satteh, *President*
Shahnaz Satteh, *Vice Pres*
EMP: 10 **EST:** 1997
SALES (est): 589.5K **Privately Held**
WEB: www.beta.sorentech.com
SIC: 7372 7374 Prepackaged software; computer graphics service

(G-14556)
SOURCERERS INC (PA)
10097 Cleary Blvd Ste 289 (33324-1065)
PHONE..................................954 530-2333
David Blum, *President*
▲ **EMP:** 2 **EST:** 2005
SQ FT: 1,000
SALES (est): 6MM **Privately Held**
SIC: 2231 3444 3089 5199 Apparel & outerwear broadwoven fabrics; sheet metalwork; bottle caps, molded plastic; general merchandise, non-durable

(G-14557)
THALES E-SECURITY INC ✪
900 S Pine Island Rd # 710 (33324-3923)
PHONE..................................954 888-6200
EMP: 18 **EST:** 2021
SALES (est): 334.5K **Privately Held**
SIC: 7372 Prepackaged software

(G-14558)
THALES ESECURITY INC
900 S Pine Island Rd (33324-3920)
PHONE..................................954 888-6200
EMP: 22 **EST:** 2001
SALES (est): 645.6K **Privately Held**
SIC: 7372 Prepackaged software

(G-14559)
TIP TOP CANVAS AND UPHL INC
Also Called: Will Garrett Towers
6501 E Tropical Way (33317-3310)
PHONE..................................954 524-6214

David Crosby, *President*
Jeroen Candel, *General Mgr*
Laurence Simone, *Manager*
▼ **EMP:** 7 **EST:** 1989
SALES (est): 417.3K **Privately Held**
SIC: 2394 Canvas & related products

(G-14560)
TRADESTATION TECHNOLOGIES INC (DH)
8050 Sw 10th St Ste 2000 (33324-3205)
PHONE..................................954 652-7000
William R Cruz, *Ch of Bd*
Ralph Cruz, *Ch of Bd*
Salomon Sredni, *President*
Peng Wu, *Engineer*
John Adams, *Software Engr*
EMP: 145 **EST:** 1982
SQ FT: 70,000
SALES (est): 49.2MM **Privately Held**
WEB: www.tradestation.com
SIC: 7372 Prepackaged software
HQ: Tradestation Group, Inc.
8050 Sw 10th St Ste 4000
Plantation FL 33324
954 652-7000

(G-14561)
US DIAGNOSTICS INC
Also Called: Vertaloc
6600 Nw 16th St Ste 1 (33313-4554)
PHONE..................................866 216-5308
Edward Letko, *President*
▲ **EMP:** 20 **EST:** 2005
SALES (est): 1.8MM **Privately Held**
WEB: www.usdiagnostics.net
SIC: 2835 In vitro & in vivo diagnostic substances

(G-14562)
VEEDIS CLINICAL SYSTEMS
1380 N University Dr # 102 (33322-4700)
P.O. Box 8461, Coral Springs (33075-8461)
PHONE..................................954 344-0498
Thomas L Grossjung,
EMP: 5 **EST:** 2012
SALES (est): 309.2K **Privately Held**
WEB: www.veedis.com
SIC: 7372 Business oriented computer software

(G-14563)
VERTICAL SYSTEMS INSPCTONS INC
899 E Country Club Cir (33317-4505)
PHONE..................................954 775-6023
Hector Jiminez, *Principal*
EMP: 8 **EST:** 2008
SALES (est): 203.9K **Privately Held**
SIC: 2591 Blinds vertical

(G-14564)
VICE ALLIANCE CORP
1611 Sw 55th Ave (33317-5925)
PHONE..................................954 792-4240
Christopher C Mobley, *Principal*
EMP: 6 **EST:** 2010
SALES (est): 86.7K **Privately Held**
SIC: 7372 Prepackaged software

(G-14565)
VINLAND CORPORATION
11600 Nw 20th St (33323-2060)
PHONE..................................954 475-9093
Bertho Boman, *President*
Tina Espejo, *Buyer*
▲ **EMP:** 30 **EST:** 1977
SQ FT: 3,000
SALES (est): 1MM **Privately Held**
WEB: www.vinland.com
SIC: 3699 8748 Electrical equipment & supplies; systems analysis or design

(G-14566)
VINLAND INTERNATIONAL INC
1700 Nw 65th Ave Ste 12 (33313-4558)
PHONE..................................954 316-2007
Bertho Boman, *President*
Teresita Boman, *Vice Pres*
Eric Olaes, *Executive*
▲ **EMP:** 32 **EST:** 1994
SQ FT: 3,000
SALES (est): 1.1MM **Privately Held**
WEB: www.vinland.com
SIC: 3571 Electronic computers

(G-14567)
WEPLENISH LLC
150 S Pine Island Rd (33324-2669)
PHONE..................................954 909-4183
Rotem Grosman, *Principal*
Bill Deme, *Opers Staff*
Michael Medwin, *Opers Staff*
EMP: 6 **EST:** 2015
SALES (est): 2.4MM **Privately Held**
WEB: www.weplenish.com
SIC: 3411 Food & beverage containers

Polk City
Polk County

(G-14568)
T BOWER ENTERPRISES INC
1824 Pearce Rd (33868-9751)
PHONE..................................863 984-3050
Todd Bower, *President*
Cathie Bower, *Vice Pres*
EMP: 8 **EST:** 1993
SALES (est): 702.1K **Privately Held**
SIC: 3273 Ready-mixed concrete

Pompano Beach
Broward County

(G-14569)
2KLIFE LLC
2755 W Atl Blvd Ste 104 (33069)
PHONE..................................954 316-9866
Robert F Moise, *Mng Member*
EMP: 7 **EST:** 2013
SALES (est): 189.3K **Privately Held**
SIC: 2741 Miscellaneous publishing

(G-14570)
5 01 FRIDAYS
2605 E Atl Blvd Ste 210b (33062-4948)
PHONE..................................754 444-3561
EMP: 6 **EST:** 2012
SALES (est): 77.6K **Privately Held**
WEB: www.501fridays.com
SIC: 2771 Greeting cards

(G-14571)
A&D PAVERS LLC
341 Avondale Dr Apt 3 (33060-6834)
PHONE..................................954 449-0716
Diaz Dario Cornejo, *Manager*
EMP: 6 **EST:** 2012
SALES (est): 188.4K **Privately Held**
SIC: 2951 Asphalt paving mixtures & blocks

(G-14572)
AB FIRE SPRINKLERS LLC
2759 Nw 19th St (33069-5232)
PHONE..................................954 973-8054
Linda Kanter,
EMP: 8 **EST:** 2018
SALES (est): 582.7K **Privately Held**
WEB: www.abfire.com
SIC: 3432 5063 Lawn hose nozzles & sprinklers; fire alarm systems

(G-14573)
ABRASIVE DYNAMICS INC
1531 Se 24th Ter (33062-7511)
PHONE..................................860 291-0664
Joseph Jakab, *President*
Carol Jakab, *Shareholder*
EMP: 10 **EST:** 1986
SQ FT: 6,000
SALES (est): 496.6K **Privately Held**
SIC: 3291 Abrasive products

(G-14574)
ABSOLUTE POWDER COATING INC
1254 Nw 21st St (33069-1400)
PHONE..................................954 917-2715
Robert Marks, *President*
Daniel H Harcavi, *Technical Staff*
EMP: 16 **EST:** 2003
SALES (est): 2.2MM **Privately Held**
WEB: www.absolutepowdercoat.com
SIC: 3479 Coating of metals & formed products

(G-14575)
ACI HOIST & CRANE INC
2721 Ne 4th Ave (33064-5407)
PHONE..................................954 367-6116
Ronald Fontes, *President*
◆ **EMP:** 5 **EST:** 2003
SALES (est): 987.9K **Privately Held**
WEB: www.acihoist.com
SIC: 3536 Hoists, cranes & monorails

(G-14576)
ACROCRETE INC (DH)
1259 Nw 21st St (33069-1428)
PHONE..................................954 917-4114
Gary Hasbach, *President*
Howard L Ehler Jr, *Vice Pres*
▼ **EMP:** 40 **EST:** 1988
SALES (est): 5MM
SALES (corp-wide): 216.4MM **Privately Held**
SIC: 2821 Acrylic resins
HQ: Imperial Industries, Inc.
1259 Nw 21st St
Pompano Beach FL 33069
954 917-4114

(G-14577)
ADF INTERNATIONAL INC
Also Called: Adf Group
1925 Nw 15th St Ste A (33069-1641)
PHONE..................................954 931-5150
EMP: 12
SALES (corp-wide): 135.8MM **Privately Held**
SIC: 3448 Mfg Prefabricated Metal Buildings
HQ: Adf International, Inc.
1900 Great Bear Ave
Great Falls MT 59404
800 895-4425

(G-14578)
ADHESIVES TECHNOLOGY CORP
Also Called: A T C
450 E Copans Rd (33064-5509)
PHONE..................................754 399-1684
Daniel Pelton, *CEO*
R Hart McIntyre, *President*
Charles Eggert, *Vice Pres*
Tom Richardson, *Vice Pres*
Roy Seroussi, *Vice Pres*
◆ **EMP:** 55
SALES (est): 21.6MM **Privately Held**
WEB: www.atcepoxy.com
SIC: 2891 Adhesives

(G-14579)
ADVANCED CABINETS LLC
1500 Nw 15th Ave Ste 12 (33069-1714)
PHONE..................................954 515-2675
Jason Elkin, *Principal*
EMP: 7 **EST:** 2010
SALES (est): 84.6K **Privately Held**
WEB: www.advancedcabinetscorp.com
SIC: 2434 Wood kitchen cabinets

(G-14580)
ADVANCED MDULAR STRUCTURES INC
Also Called: Advanced Modular Systems
1911 Nw 15th St (33069-1601)
PHONE..................................954 960-1550
Gary Willis, *CEO*
Patti Willis, *Vice Pres*
Marty Madura, *Project Mgr*
▼ **EMP:** 7 **EST:** 1988
SQ FT: 2,500
SALES (est): 955.9K **Privately Held**
WEB: www.advancedmodular.com
SIC: 2452 1541 Prefabricated wood buildings; steel building construction

(G-14581)
AIR SHELTERS USA LLC (PA)
650 Sw 16th Ter (33069-4533)
P.O. Box 667227 (33066-7227)
PHONE..................................215 957-6128
Christine Gagliardi, *Office Mgr*
Newton B Park, *Mng Member*
EMP: 21 **EST:** 2016
SALES (est): 3MM **Privately Held**
WEB: www.zumro.com
SIC: 2394 8322 Canvas awnings & canopies; emergency shelters

(G-14582)
AIR SUPPLY OF FUTURE INC
1950 Nw 15th St Ste A (33069-1614)
PHONE..................................954 977-0877
Paul Bedard, *President*
Liza Muschett, *Principal*
▲ **EMP:** 19 **EST:** 1983
SALES (est): 4.1MM **Privately Held**
WEB: www.airsupplyflorida.com
SIC: 3561 Pumps & pumping equipment

(G-14583)
ALARIS AEROSPACE SYSTEMS LLC
1721 Blount Rd Ste 1 (33069-5104)
PHONE..................................954 596-8736
Bikramjit Jaswal, *President*
Ramnik Soni, *COO*
Joseph Kazes, *Exec VP*
Ian Coke, *QC Mgr*
Joseph Wiegand, *Sales Mgr*
▼ **EMP:** 19 **EST:** 2009
SQ FT: 13,033
SALES (est): 7.8MM **Privately Held**
WEB: www.alarisaero.com
SIC: 3728 Aircraft parts & equipment

(G-14584)
ALL PRO PAVERS HARDSCAPES INC
430 S Dixie Hwy E (33060-6910)
PHONE..................................954 300-6281
Batista Bianca, *Principal*
EMP: 7 **EST:** 2015
SALES (est): 195.4K **Privately Held**
SIC: 2951 Asphalt paving mixtures & blocks

(G-14585)
ALL TANK SERVICES LLC
1903 W Mcnab Rd B (33069-4301)
PHONE..................................954 260-9443
Andrew Driessen, *General Mgr*
EMP: 8 **EST:** 2017
SALES (est): 764.5K **Privately Held**
WEB: www.alltankservicesfl.com
SIC: 2851 3732 Marine paints; boat building & repairing

(G-14586)
ALL VENUE GRAPHICS AND SIGNS
1700 Nw 15th Ave Ste 360 (33069-1717)
PHONE..................................954 399-7446
Randy Risley, *Principal*
EMP: 6 **EST:** 2017
SALES (est): 628.6K **Privately Held**
WEB: www.pompanosigncompany.com
SIC: 3993 Signs & advertising specialties

(G-14587)
ALLIANCE COMMERCIAL EQP INC
2460 Nw 17th Ln Ste 1 (33064-1537)
PHONE..................................772 232-8149
John Bartell, *CEO*
EMP: 7 **EST:** 2012
SQ FT: 9,000
SALES (est): 204.2K **Privately Held**
SIC: 3537 Industrial trucks & tractors

(G-14588)
ALPHA WOODWORK INC
2840 Ne 9th Ter (33064-5326)
PHONE..................................954 347-6251
Daniella Gomes, *Principal*
EMP: 10 **EST:** 2010
SALES (est): 182.2K **Privately Held**
WEB: www.alphawoodwork.com
SIC: 2431 Millwork

(G-14589)
ALPINE ENGINEREED PRODUCTS
1200 Park Central Blvd S (33064-2215)
PHONE..................................954 781-3333
Chris Cronje, *President*
EMP: 21 **EST:** 2000
SALES (est): 1.3MM **Privately Held**
SIC: 3429 Manufactured hardware (general)

(G-14590)
AMERICAN AUTO MARINE WIRING
1414 Sw 13th Ct (33069-4709)
PHONE..................................954 782-0193
Phil Schultz, *President*
EMP: 5 **EST:** 1978
SQ FT: 2,500
SALES (est): 706.5K **Privately Held**
WEB: www.customwiring.com
SIC: 3672 7539 3694 Wiring boards; automotive repair shops; engine electrical equipment

(G-14591)
AMERICAN LW & PROMO PRODS LLC
100 Sw 5th St (33060-7904)
PHONE..................................954 946-5252
Keith Treiber,
Annette Catania,
Salvatore Catania,
EMP: 6 **EST:** 2012
SALES (est): 339.2K **Privately Held**
WEB: www.americanlogowear.com
SIC: 2353 3993 5136 Uniform hats & caps; signs & advertising specialties; advertising novelties; men's & boys' outerwear; men's & boys' sportswear & work clothing

(G-14592)
AMERICAN PAVERS CONSULTANTS
Also Called: American Pavers Manufacturing
1251 Ne 48th St (33064-4910)
PHONE..................................954 418-0000
Joseph S Brito, *President*
EMP: 36 **EST:** 1988
SQ FT: 80,000
SALES (est): 680.4K **Privately Held**
WEB: www.tremron.com
SIC: 3251 Brick & structural clay tile

(G-14593)
AMERICAN PAVERS MANUFACTURING (PA)
1251 Ne 48th St (33064-4910)
PHONE..................................954 418-0000
Joseph Brito, *President*
◆ **EMP:** 5 **EST:** 1985
SALES (est): 1.4MM **Privately Held**
SIC: 3271 Paving blocks, concrete

(G-14594)
AMERICAN TROPHY CO
Also Called: American Name Plate
831 W Mcnab Rd (33060-8937)
PHONE..................................954 782-2250
Steve Trodick, *President*
Harvey Flomenhoft, *Principal*
EMP: 7 **EST:** 1972
SQ FT: 2,500
SALES (est): 658K **Privately Held**
WEB: www.americantrophy.net
SIC: 3914 3999 Trophies; plaques, picture, laminated

(G-14595)
APOLLO ENERGY SYSTEMS INC (PA)
4100 N Powerline Rd D3 (33073-3038)
PHONE..................................954 969-7755
Robert Aronsson, *CEO*
Raymond Douglas, *President*
Barry Iseard, *Vice Pres*
Nejat Veziroglu, *Vice Pres*
Sonny Spoden, *CFO*
▲ **EMP:** 7 **EST:** 1994
SQ FT: 7,000
SALES (est): 1.6MM **Privately Held**
WEB: www.apolloenergysystems.com
SIC: 3629 Electronic generation equipment

(G-14596)
AQUATHIN CORP
950 S Andrews Ave (33069-4604)
PHONE..................................800 462-7634
Alfred J Lipshultz, *President*
Debra L Lipshultz, *Corp Secy*
Jamie Hyman, *VP Sales*
▼ **EMP:** 20 **EST:** 1980
SQ FT: 60,000
SALES (est): 3.9MM **Privately Held**
WEB: www.aquathin.com
SIC: 3589 Water purification equipment, household type; water treatment equipment, industrial

(G-14597)
ARCHITCTRAL DESIGNS METALWORKS
1773 Blount Rd Ste 307 (33069-5124)
PHONE..................................954 532-1331
Richard Gray, *President*
EMP: 6 **EST:** 2000
SALES (est): 98.9K **Privately Held**
SIC: 3446 Stairs, staircases, stair treads: prefabricated metal

(G-14598)
ARCHITECTURAL FOAM SUPPLY INC
100 Sw 12th Ave (33069-3222)
PHONE..................................954 943-6949
John Belcher, *President*
EMP: 24 **EST:** 2001
SQ FT: 65,000
SALES (est): 1.4MM **Privately Held**
WEB: www.newfoamdesign.com
SIC: 3086 Packaging & shipping materials, foamed plastic

(G-14599)
ARMALASER INC
4699 N Federal Hwy # 110 (33064-6510)
PHONE..................................954 937-6054
Richard Hovsepian, *President*
Pat Thompson, *Principal*
EMP: 7
SALES (est): 1.2MM **Privately Held**
WEB: www.armalaser.com
SIC: 3699 Laser systems & equipment

(G-14600)
ART CONNECTION USA LLC
2860 Center Port Cir (33064-2136)
PHONE..................................954 781-0125
David Harari, *President*
Ofer Sadik, *Vice Pres*
Felicia Craig-Silva, *Sales Mgr*
◆ **EMP:** 20 **EST:** 1985
SQ FT: 15,000
SALES (est): 3.9MM **Privately Held**
WEB: www.artconnectionusa.com
SIC: 2499 5023 Picture & mirror frames, wood; mirrors & pictures, framed & unframed

(G-14601)
ART CRAFT METALS INC
1630 Sw 13th Ct (33069-4713)
PHONE..................................954 946-4620
Russell L Davis, *President*
Mark C Davis, *Vice Pres*
Shirley R Davis, *Vice Pres*
Bret R Davis, *Treasurer*
EMP: 29 **EST:** 1958
SALES (est): 8.2MM **Privately Held**
SIC: 3446 Railings, bannisters, guards, etc.: made from metal pipe

(G-14602)
ARTISTIC STATUARY INC
1490 N Powerline Rd (33069-1917)
PHONE..................................954 975-9533
Steve Harrold, *President*
Joanne B Harrold, *Corp Secy*
Arthur C Harrold Sr, *Vice Pres*
Lisa Harrold, *Vice Pres*
◆ **EMP:** 17 **EST:** 1960
SQ FT: 8,400
SALES (est): 356K **Privately Held**
WEB: www.artisticstatuary.com
SIC: 3272 Fountains, concrete; concrete products, precast

(G-14603)
ASSOCIATED STEEL & ALUM CO INC
3017 Nw 25th Ave (33069-1028)
PHONE..................................954 974-7890
Tim Mather, *President*
Nick Anton, *President*
▼ **EMP:** 18 **EST:** 2004
SALES (est): 4.5MM **Privately Held**
WEB: www.asaltdinc.com
SIC: 3312 3354 Blast furnaces & steel mills; aluminum extruded products

(G-14604)
ASSOCIATED STEEL & ALUM LTD
3017 Nw 25th Ave (33069-1028)
PHONE..................................954 974-7890
EMP: 13 **EST:** 2017
SALES (est): 337.4K **Privately Held**
WEB: www.asaltdinc.com
SIC: 3312 Blast furnaces & steel mills

(G-14605)
ASSURA WINDOWS AND DOORS LLC (PA)
1543 N Powerline Rd (33069-1620)
PHONE..................................954 781-4430
Edward Pooley, *President*
EMP: 2 **EST:** 2016
SALES (est): 26.9MM **Privately Held**
WEB: www.assurawindows.com
SIC: 3211 Window glass, clear & colored

(G-14606)
ATLANTIC MOLDING INC (PA)
2750 Ne 4th Ave (33064-5408)
PHONE..................................954 781-9340
Glen K Jones, *President*
Robert E Gunn, *Vice Pres*
▼ **EMP:** 12
SQ FT: 8,000
SALES (est): 1MM **Privately Held**
SIC: 3089 Injection molding of plastics; plastic processing

(G-14607)
ATLAS OPERATIONS INC
325 Sw 15th Ave (33069-3246)
PHONE..................................954 788-1200
Gustavo Barni, *President*
◆ **EMP:** 83 **EST:** 1994
SQ FT: 10,000
SALES (est): 1.8MM **Privately Held**
WEB: www.atlas-operations.com
SIC: 2834 Vitamin, nutrient & hematinic preparations for human use

(G-14608)
AXIS GROUP
4701 N Federal Hwy # 440 (33064-6562)
PHONE..................................954 580-6000
Tom Pughe, *President*
Tom Edwards, *Vice Pres*
EMP: 10 **EST:** 2006
SALES (est): 509.5K **Privately Held**
WEB: www.axisgroup.com
SIC: 3629 Electronic generation equipment

(G-14609)
B R Q GROSSMANS INC
Also Called: Copans Quick Print
2087 N Powerline Rd Ste 1 (33069-1279)
PHONE..................................954 971-1077
Gary Grossman, *President*
Sheila Grossman, *Corp Secy*
Bob Meadows, *Accounts Exec*
EMP: 11 **EST:** 1982
SQ FT: 3,000
SALES (est): 1.6MM **Privately Held**
WEB: www.copansprinting.com
SIC: 2752 2791 2789 2759 Commercial printing, offset; typesetting; bookbinding & related work; commercial printing

(G-14610)
B R SIGNS INC
1301 W Copans Rd Ste B6 (33064-2227)
PHONE..................................954 973-7700
Bill Reicherter, *Manager*
EMP: 7 **EST:** 2018
SALES (est): 374.4K **Privately Held**
SIC: 3993 Signs & advertising specialties

(G-14611)
BADGER CORPORATION
3450 Ne 6th Ter (33064-5218)
PHONE..................................954 942-5277
William B Buerosse Jr, *President*
Diana S Buerosse, *Vice Pres*
EMP: 9 **EST:** 1993
SQ FT: 4,000
SALES (est): 1.5MM **Privately Held**
WEB: www.badgermetalcorp.com
SIC: 3444 Ducts, sheet metal

(G-14612)
BALLISTIC RECOVERY SYSTEMS INC
1543 N Powerline Rd # 3 (33069-1620)
PHONE..................................651 457-7491
Gary Moore, *Vice Pres*
David Blanchard, *Branch Mgr*
EMP: 100
SALES (corp-wide): 28.3MM **Publicly Held**
WEB: www.brsaerospace.com
SIC: 3728 Aircraft parts & equipment
PA: Ballistic Recovery Systems, Inc.
41383 Us 1 Hwy
Pinebluff NC 28373
651 457-7491

(G-14613)
BANKS SIGN SYSTEMS INC
Also Called: Banks, Roy Sign Systems
1791 Blount Rd Ste 1001 (33069-5137)
PHONE..................................954 979-0055
Roy Banks, *President*
Catherine Trinboli, *Vice Pres*
Maria Banks, *Treasurer*
EMP: 7 **EST:** 1983
SQ FT: 2,000
SALES (est): 474.6K **Privately Held**
WEB: www.roybanks.com
SIC: 3993 2752 Signs, not made in custom sign painting shops; commercial printing, lithographic

(G-14614)
BAR MAID CORPORATION (PA)
2950 Nw 22nd Ter (33069-1045)
PHONE..................................954 960-1468
George E Shepherd, *President*
Diane Michaud, *Vice Pres*
Tammie Rice, *Marketing Staff*
Karen Sisco,
▲ **EMP:** 10 **EST:** 1946
SQ FT: 8,000
SALES (est): 2.5MM **Privately Held**
WEB: www.bestinthebar.com
SIC: 3589 2841 Dishwashing machines, commercial; soap & other detergents

(G-14615)
BARI MILLWORK & SUPPLY LLC
Also Called: Rome Supply
1975 Nw 18th St Ste C (33069-1650)
PHONE..................................954 969-9440
Darlene Baldino, *Vice Pres*
Wayne Baldino,
EMP: 27 **EST:** 2007
SALES (est): 5.1MM **Privately Held**
WEB: www.barimillworksupply.com
SIC: 2431 Millwork

(G-14616)
BASANITE INDUSTRIES LLC
2041 Nw 15th Ave (33069-1405)
PHONE..................................954 532-1726
John Rivera, *Principal*
EMP: 14 **EST:** 2019
SALES (est): 5.2MM **Privately Held**
WEB: www.basaltamerica.com
SIC: 3999 Manufacturing industries

(G-14617)
BIOSTEM TECHNOLOGIES INC
2836 Center Port Cir (33064-2136)
PHONE..................................954 380-8342
Jason Matuszewski, *Ch of Bd*
Alex Bolanos, *Opers Mgr*
Larry Jones, *Officer*
EMP: 8 **EST:** 2014
SALES (est): 2MM **Privately Held**
WEB: www.biostemtechnologies.com
SIC: 2834 Pharmaceutical preparations

(G-14618)
BISHOP PHARMA LLC
1000 W Mcnab Rd Ste 234 (33069-4719)
PHONE..................................954 292-7325
Tracy Roloff,
EMP: 6 **EST:** 2016
SALES (est): 150.1K **Privately Held**
SIC: 2834 Pharmaceutical preparations

(G-14619)
BLACKLIDGE EMULSIONS INC
2501 Wiles Rd (33073-3017)
PHONE..................................954 275-7225
James Russo, *Manager*
EMP: 18 **Privately Held**
WEB: www.blacklidge.com
SIC: 2951 Asphalt & asphaltic paving mixtures (not from refineries)
PA: Blacklidge Emulsions, Inc.
12251 Bernard Pkwy # 200
Gulfport MS 39503

(G-14620)
BRAND LABS USA
325 Sw 15th Ave (33069-3246)
PHONE..................................954 532-5390
David Pollock, *CEO*
EMP: 31 **EST:** 2015
SALES (est): 2.3MM **Privately Held**
WEB: www.brandlabsusa.com
SIC: 2844 5999 Cosmetic preparations; hair care products

(G-14621)
BRAND YOU WATERS LLC
2402 Bay Dr (33062-2917)
PHONE..................................786 312-0840
Robert V Plath, *Managing Prtnr*
R V Plath, *Partner*
Michael McBride, *Partner*
EMP: 6 **EST:** 2008
SALES (est): 356.7K **Privately Held**
SIC: 3221 Water bottles, glass

(G-14622)
BRICKLAND PAVERS INC
1259 Sw 46th Ave Apt 1910 (33069-6442)
PHONE..................................561 305-0325
Roosevelt Chaves, *Principal*
EMP: 6 **EST:** 2014
SALES (est): 80.2K **Privately Held**
WEB: www.brickpaversflorida.com
SIC: 2951 Asphalt paving mixtures & blocks

(G-14623)
BROSKI CIDERWORKS LLC
1465 Sw 6th Ct (33069-4532)
PHONE..................................954 657-8947
Cesar D Verdugo,
Daniel Verdugo,
EMP: 8 **EST:** 2015
SALES (est): 368.1K **Privately Held**
WEB: www.broskiciderworks.com
SIC: 2099 Cider, nonalcoholic

(G-14624)
BROWNIES MARINE GROUP INC (PA)
3001 Nw 25th Ave Ste 1 (33069-1028)
PHONE..................................954 462-5570
Christopher Constable, *CEO*
Robert M Carmichael, *President*
Sheila Perrier, *General Mgr*
▲ **EMP:** 8 **EST:** 1981
SQ FT: 16,566
SALES (est): 4.5MM **Publicly Held**
WEB: www.browniesmarinegroup.com
SIC: 3949 3563 Sporting & athletic goods; skin diving equipment, scuba type; air & gas compressors

(G-14625)
BUDGET SIGNS INC
1820 Sw 7th Ave (33060-9028)
PHONE..................................954 941-5710
Bill Simmons, *President*
April Simmons, *Vice Pres*
EMP: 10 **EST:** 1989
SQ FT: 3,000
SALES (est): 627.4K **Privately Held**
SIC: 3993 1799 Electric signs; sign installation & maintenance

(G-14626)
BUST OUT PROMOTIONS LLC
1375 Sw 12th Ave (33069-4630)
PHONE..................................561 305-8313
Michael Meier, *Exec Dir*
EMP: 7 **Privately Held**
WEB: www.mugrugs.net
SIC: 2392 Tablecloths & table settings; tablecloths: made from purchased materials; placemats, plastic or textile
PA: Bust Out Promotions Llc
1050 Hillsboro Mile
Hillsboro Beach FL 33062

(G-14627)
BYRD TECHNOLOGIES INC
Also Called: Mar-Quipt
3100 Sw 10th St (33069-4815)
PHONE..................................954 957-8333
Robert L Byrd, *President*
Garnett Byrd, *President*
Ronda Hood, *Manager*
Tim Schrader, *Manager*
◆ **EMP:** 50
SQ FT: 56,776
SALES (est): 9.3MM **Privately Held**
WEB: www.marquipt.com
SIC: 3429 Marine hardware

(G-14628)
C&A BOATWORKS INC
1711 N Powerline Rd (33069-1624)
PHONE..................................754 366-5549
EMP: 9 **EST:** 2019
SALES (est): 138.6K **Privately Held**
WEB: www.jessiboats.com
SIC: 3732 Boat building & repairing

(G-14629)
C-WORTHY CORP
Also Called: C-Worthy Custom Yacht Canvas
241 Sw 5th Ct (33060-7911)
PHONE..................................954 784-7370
Carol Dykes, *President*
Lenore Stribling, *Admin Sec*
EMP: 14 **EST:** 1995
SALES (est): 1.7MM **Privately Held**
WEB: www.cworthycorp.com
SIC: 2394 3732 2392 Canvas covers & drop cloths; boat building & repairing; household furnishings

(G-14630)
CABINETS BY MARYLIN INC
696 Sw 15th St (33060-8637)
PHONE..................................954 729-3995
Lincon Borda, *Director*
EMP: 9 **EST:** 2001
SALES (est): 100.3K **Privately Held**
WEB: www.tribecashoes.com
SIC: 2434 Wood kitchen cabinets

(G-14631)
CATSKILL EXPRESS LLC
1249 Hammondville Rd (33069-2927)
PHONE..................................954 784-5151
Andrew Brooks, *Principal*
▼ **EMP:** 9 **EST:** 2006
SALES (est): 633.2K **Privately Held**
SIC: 2741 Miscellaneous publishing

(G-14632)
CEMEX CNSTR MTLS FLA LLC
Also Called: Mat Div-Ft Lauder Maint Shop
1150 Nw 24th St (33064-2202)
PHONE..................................954 977-9222
Tim Coughlin, *Branch Mgr*
EMP: 7
SQ FT: 39,156 **Privately Held**
SIC: 3273 Ready-mixed concrete
HQ: Cemex Construction Materials Florida, Llc
1501 Belvedere Rd
West Palm Beach FL 33406

(G-14633)
CERTIFIED METAL FINISHING INC
Also Called: CMF
1420 Sw 28th Ave (33069-4817)
PHONE..................................954 979-0707
David W Sexton Jr, *President*
Fred Binda, *General Mgr*
Antonia Sexton, *Vice Pres*
Rob Heil, *Manager*
Fred Lafond, *Manager*
EMP: 30 **EST:** 1982
SQ FT: 5,510
SALES (est): 5.3MM **Privately Held**
WEB: www.certifiedmetalfinishing.com
SIC: 3471 Anodizing (plating) of metals or formed products; electroplating of metals or formed products

(G-14634)
CHEMKO TECHNICAL SERVICES INC
1000 E Atl Blvd Ste 115 (33060-7471)
PHONE..................................954 783-7673
EMP: 30
SQ FT: 5,000
SALES: 1MM **Privately Held**
SIC: 3823 7699 3312 Mfg Process Control Instruments Repair Services Blast Furnace-Steel Works

(G-14635)
CINALTA CORP
1700 Nw 15th Ave Ste 305 (33069-1707)
PHONE..................................954 815-0612
Frederick Jiii Oconnor, *Director*
EMP: 6 **EST:** 2012
SALES (est): 99.6K **Privately Held**
SIC: 3599 Machine shop, jobbing & repair

(G-14636)
CLASSIC PIZZA CRUSTS INC
1741 Nw 33rd St (33064-1327)
PHONE..................................954 570-8383
Rosalind Fimiano, *President*
▼ **EMP:** 8 **EST:** 1998
SALES (est): 966.3K **Privately Held**
WEB: www.classicpizza.com
SIC: 2038 2041 5812 Pizza, frozen; pizza dough, prepared; pizza restaurants

(G-14637)
CMC BAKERY LLC
4100 N Powerline Rd M2 (33073-3042)
PHONE..................................978 682-2382
David Cafua,
EMP: 40 **EST:** 2015
SALES (est): 1.2MM **Privately Held**
SIC: 2051 Bakery: wholesale or wholesale/retail combined

(G-14638)
COASTAL INDUSTRIES USA LLC
560 Sw 6th Ct (33060-8201)
P.O. Box 903 (33061-0903)
PHONE..................................954 946-5223
Carmela Longo, *Principal*
EMP: 6 **EST:** 2017
SALES (est): 154.1K **Privately Held**
SIC: 3999 Manufacturing industries

(G-14639)
COASTAL WOODWORK INC
380 Sw 12th Ave (33069-3502)
PHONE..................................561 218-3353
Lori Nelson, *President*
EMP: 7 **EST:** 2013
SALES (est): 374.1K **Privately Held**
WEB: www.coastalwoodwork.com
SIC: 2431 Millwork

(G-14640)
COCA-COLA ENTERPRISES
2351 Blount Rd (33069-5116)
PHONE..................................954 917-1108
Sara Hays, *Personnel Exec*
EMP: 10 **EST:** 2017
SALES (est): 129.8K **Privately Held**
WEB: www.coca-cola.com
SIC: 2086 Bottled & canned soft drinks

(G-14641)
COLUMBIA FILMS INC
43 S Pompano Pkwy Ste 461
(33069-3001)
PHONE..................................800 531-3238
Sharond Ragin, *President*
EMP: 9 **EST:** 2013
SQ FT: 3,000
SALES (est): 1MM **Privately Held**
SIC: 3861 7335 7384 Motion picture film; color separation, photographic & movie film; home movies, developing & processing

(G-14642)
COMODERM CORP
2175 N Andrews Ave Ste 4 (33069-1431)
P.O. Box 122, Dania (33004-0122)
PHONE..................................561 756-2929
Sandra Mento, *President*
Elizabeth Mento, *Corp Secy*
Frank Mento, *Vice Pres*
EMP: 5 **EST:** 1994
SALES (est): 638K **Privately Held**
SIC: 2911 Petroleum refining

(G-14643)
CONCEPT 2 MARKET INC
3000 Nw 25th Ave Ste 11 (33069-1048)
PHONE..................................954 974-0022
Maria Kirkeeng, *CEO*
Todd Kirkeeng, *President*
Stephen Ballard, *Vice Pres*
Barbara Mahoney, *Materials Mgr*
Jose Patingo, *Supervisor*
EMP: 15 **EST:** 1994
SALES (est): 4.9MM **Privately Held**
WEB: www.c2mfl.com
SIC: 3679 3672 Loads, electronic; printed circuit boards

(G-14644)
CONQUEST MANUFACTURING FLA LLC
1121 Nw 31st Ave (33069-1109)
PHONE..................................954 655-0139
EMP: 11 **EST:** 2015
SALES (est): 493.7K **Privately Held**
SIC: 3999 Manufacturing industries

(G-14645)
CONSTRUCTION AND ELEC PDTS INC
1800 Nw 15th Ave Ste 155 (33069-1410)
PHONE..................................954 972-9787
Michael L Brody, *President*
▲ **EMP:** 12 **EST:** 2007
SALES (est): 1.4MM **Privately Held**
WEB: www.constructionandelectrical.com
SIC: 3545 5085 2673 3053 Machine tool accessories; gaskets; gaskets & seals; plastic & pliofilm bags; gaskets & sealing devices; screw machine products; bolts, nuts, rivets & washers

(G-14646)
CONSUMER INFORMATION BUREAU
2301 W Sample Rd Ste 4-2a (33073-3010)
PHONE..................................954 971-5079
Jason Bowen, *Owner*
EMP: 5 **EST:** 2002
SALES (est): 469.5K **Privately Held**
WEB:
www.consumerinformationbureau.com
SIC: 7372 Business oriented computer software

(G-14647)
CONTACT ENTERPRISES INC
3170 N Federal Hwy # 100 (33064-6881)
PHONE..................................561 900-5134
Francisco Franca, *Principal*
EMP: 9 **EST:** 2015
SALES (est): 164.8K **Privately Held**
WEB: www.labels123.com
SIC: 2679 Converted paper products

(G-14648)
COOLCRAFT INC
1700 Nw 15th Ave Ste 330 (33069-1716)
PHONE..................................954 946-0070
Glen Ayers, *President*
▲ **EMP:** 8 **EST:** 2000
SQ FT: 5,000
SALES (est): 900K **Privately Held**
SIC: 3432 Plumbing fixture fittings & trim

(G-14649)
COUNTY PLASTICS CORP
1801 Nw 22nd St (33069-1317)
PHONE..................................954 971-9205
Alfred Bohnomme, *Manager*
EMP: 9
SALES (corp-wide): 57.8MM **Privately Held**
WEB: www.chemtainer.com
SIC: 3089 Synthetic resin finished products
PA: County Plastics Corp
361 Neptune Ave
West Babylon NY 11704
631 422-8300

(G-14650)
CRETA GRANITE & MARBLE INC
1900 Nw 33rd St Ste 10 (33064-1340)
PHONE..................................954 956-9993

GEOGRAPHIC

Sara O Gloria, *President*
Christiano Gloria, *Vice Pres*
EMP: 6 **EST:** 1999
SALES (est): 643K **Privately Held**
WEB: www.cretagranite.com
SIC: 3281 5032 1743 Granite, cut & shaped; marble, building: cut & shaped; granite building stone; terrazzo, tile, marble, mosaic work

(G-14651)
CRF GROUP INC
Also Called: Sign-A-Rama
4716 N Powerline Rd (33073-3076)
PHONE..................................954 428-7446
Gary Bogen, *CEO*
Randy Bogen, *Vice Pres*
EMP: 17 **EST:** 2002
SALES (est): 2.4MM **Privately Held**
WEB: www.signarama.com
SIC: 3993 Signs & advertising specialties

(G-14652)
CROWN PRODUCTS LLC (PA)
935 Nw 31st Ave Ste 4 (33069-1190)
PHONE..................................954 917-1118
Fredrick Levine, *CFO*
Jane Trunsky,
▲ **EMP:** 5 **EST:** 2002
SALES (est): 8.7MM **Privately Held**
WEB: www.crownproductsonline.com
SIC: 2673 2842 3999 Plastic bags: made from purchased materials; cleaning or polishing preparations; pet supplies

(G-14653)
CUSTOM CRAFTERS
170 Sw 5th St (33060-7904)
PHONE..................................954 792-6119
Nancy Hebert, *President*
Dan Hebert, *Vice Pres*
EMP: 5 **EST:** 1973
SALES (est): 483.1K **Privately Held**
SIC: 2434 Wood kitchen cabinets

(G-14654)
CUSTOM MARINE CONCEPTS INC (PA)
Also Called: Active Thunderboats
2500 Ne 5th Ave (33064-5414)
PHONE..................................954 782-1111
Patrick Haughey, *President*
EMP: 10 **EST:** 1992
SQ FT: 200
SALES (est): 1.1MM **Privately Held**
SIC: 3732 Boat building & repairing

(G-14655)
CYBER GROUP USA LLC
Also Called: Cushybeds
3770 Park Central Blvd N (33064-2225)
PHONE..................................888 574-9555
Gus Novaes, *Mng Member*
EMP: 15 **EST:** 2015
SALES (est): 776.3K **Privately Held**
SIC: 2023 Dietary supplements, dairy & non-dairy based

(G-14656)
CYCLONE POWER TECHNOLOGIES INC (PA)
601 Ne 26th Ct (33064-5429)
P.O. Box 10916 (33061-6916)
PHONE..................................954 943-8721
Harry Schoell, *Ch of Bd*
Christopher Nelson, *President*
Frankie Fruge, *COO*
Bruce Schames, *CFO*
Scott Vines, *Sales Staff*
EMP: 14 **EST:** 2004
SALES: 175K **Publicly Held**
WEB: www.cyclonepower.com
SIC: 3519 Internal combustion engines

(G-14657)
D R C INDUSTRIES INC
4100 N Powerline Rd Z1 (33073-3077)
PHONE..................................954 971-0699
Roy H Cadogan, *President*
Diana R Cadogan, *Vice Pres*
EMP: 5 **EST:** 1989
SQ FT: 3,200
SALES (est): 474.3K **Privately Held**
SIC: 3471 Finishing, metals or formed products

(G-14658)
DAHER INC (PA)
601 Ne 10th St (33060-5749)
PHONE..................................954 893-1400
Nicolas Chabbert, *Senior VP*
EMP: 3 **EST:** 2018
SALES (est): 4.7MM **Privately Held**
WEB: www.tbm.aero
SIC: 3728 Aircraft parts & equipment

(G-14659)
DENIM LILY LLC
2785 Se 11th St (33062-7034)
PHONE..................................754 264-9331
Kim Spatz, *Owner*
EMP: 7 **EST:** 2011
SALES (est): 132.9K **Privately Held**
SIC: 2211 Denims

(G-14660)
DENTATE PORCELAIN INC
2722 Ne 1st St Ste 1 (33062-4934)
PHONE..................................917 359-7696
Jaime Aponte, *Principal*
EMP: 8 **EST:** 2007
SALES (est): 237.5K **Privately Held**
SIC: 3843 Enamels, dentists'

(G-14661)
DEVCON SECURITY SERVICES CORP
Also Called: Gator Telecom
2801 Gateway Dr (33069-4324)
PHONE..................................813 386-3849
EMP: 20
SALES (corp-wide): 98.4MM **Privately Held**
SIC: 3699 Mfg Electrical Equipment/Supplies
HQ: Devcon Security Services Corp.
2801 Gateway Dr
Pompano Beach FL 33069

(G-14662)
DHB ARMOR GROUP INC (PA)
2102 Sw 2nd St (33069-3116)
PHONE..................................800 413-5155
David Brooks, *Ch of Bd*
EMP: 2 **EST:** 1995
SALES (est): 37.1MM **Privately Held**
WEB: www.pointblankenterprises.com
SIC: 3842 Bulletproof vests

(G-14663)
DHS UNLIMITED INC
Also Called: Dhs Equiptment
4100 N Powerline Rd G3 (33073-3040)
P.O. Box 770776, Coral Springs (33077-0776)
PHONE..................................954 532-2142
David Schatz, *President*
Carrie Schatz, *Vice Pres*
EMP: 5 **EST:** 2003
SQ FT: 4,000
SALES (est): 600K **Privately Held**
SIC: 3531 5082 Construction machinery; general construction machinery & equipment

(G-14664)
DIABETIC CARE RX LLC (PA)
Also Called: Patient Care America
3890 Park Central Blvd N (33064-2264)
PHONE..................................866 348-0441
Patrick Smith, *CEO*
Steven Briggs, *General Mgr*
Thomas Buscemi, *Vice Pres*
Carlos Fonseca, *Warehouse Mgr*
Patricia Gunn, *CFO*
EMP: 30
SQ FT: 8,000
SALES (est): 15.3MM **Privately Held**
WEB: www.pcacorp.com
SIC: 2834 Pharmaceutical preparations

(G-14665)
DIADEM SPORTS LLC (PA)
200 Park Central Blvd S (33064-2197)
PHONE..................................844 434-2336
Evan Specht, *Opers Staff*
Joel Evan Specht, *Mng Member*
Alex J Bartlett,
EMP: 8 **EST:** 2012
SALES (est): 922K **Privately Held**
WEB: www.diademsports.com
SIC: 3949 Racket sports equipment

(G-14666)
DISTRICT 95 WOOD WORKING INC
Also Called: Prime Custom Cabinets & Design
1040 Sw 10th Ave Ste 4 (33069-4628)
PHONE..................................888 400-3136
Franklin Herrera, *President*
Mel O'Keeffe, *Vice Pres*
EMP: 7 **EST:** 2017
SALES (est): 1.2MM **Privately Held**
WEB: www.district95woodwork.com
SIC: 2434 2521 Wood kitchen cabinets; cabinets, office: wood

(G-14667)
DOLL MARINE METAL FABRICATION
250 S Dixie Hwy E (33060-6935)
PHONE..................................954 941-5093
James Doll, *President*
Sherry Doll, *Vice Pres*
EMP: 5 **EST:** 1991
SALES (est): 528.7K **Privately Held**
WEB: www.dolfab.com
SIC: 7692 Welding repair

(G-14668)
DOWNEY GROUP LLC
1100 Nw 15th Ave (33069-1943)
PHONE..................................954 972-0026
Dan Downey, *Mng Member*
Laura Battye, *Manager*
Hugh Higgins,
Joshua Shapiro,
Angela D Soto,
◆ **EMP:** 50 **EST:** 1993
SQ FT: 60,000
SALES (est): 8.9MM **Privately Held**
WEB: www.downeyglass.com
SIC: 3231 Products of purchased glass

(G-14669)
DYNAMIC COLOR INC
200 Park Central Blvd S (33064-2197)
PHONE..................................954 462-0261
Darin Jenkins, *President*
EMP: 9 **EST:** 2000
SALES (est): 638.1K **Privately Held**
WEB: www.dynamiccolor.com
SIC: 2759 Commercial printing

(G-14670)
DYNO LLC (PA)
Also Called: Dyno Merchandise
1571 W Copans Rd Ste 105 (33064-1527)
PHONE..................................954 971-2910
David Gold, *CEO*
Steven Hall, *Vice Pres*
Jorge Suarez, *Warehouse Mgr*
Pattie Jackson, *Purchasing*
Marty Weinbaum, *CFO*
◆ **EMP:** 28
SQ FT: 55,000
SALES (est): 28MM **Privately Held**
WEB: www.dynollc.com
SIC: 3999 Sewing kits, novelty

(G-14671)
EARTH GROUP INC
2200 N Andrews Ave (33069-1423)
PHONE..................................954 979-8444
Gerald Bieber, *President*
▲ **EMP:** 10 **EST:** 1991
SQ FT: 15,860
SALES (est): 1.6MM **Privately Held**
SIC: 2841 Detergents, synthetic organic or inorganic alkaline

(G-14672)
EAST COAST DOOR INC
1297 Se 5th Ave (33060-9304)
PHONE..................................954 868-4700
Lisa Clark, *Manager*
EMP: 11 **EST:** 2000
SALES (est): 209.9K **Privately Held**
WEB: www.eastcoastwindows.com
SIC: 2431 1799 Door frames, wood; special trade contractors

(G-14673)
EDAFA INDUSTRIES INC
1460 Sw 3rd St Ste 6 (33069-3216)
PHONE..................................954 946-0830
Dario Perez, *President*
EMP: 7 **EST:** 1983
SALES (est): 500K **Privately Held**
WEB: www.edafaindustries.com
SIC: 3599 Machine shop, jobbing & repair

(G-14674)
EDGE OF HUMANITY LLC
1801 Ne 51st St (33064-5740)
PHONE..................................954 425-0540
EMP: 6 **EST:** 2019
SALES (est): 122.7K **Privately Held**
WEB: www.edgeofhumanity.com
SIC: 2721 Periodicals

(G-14675)
EDWIN B STIMPSON COMPANY INC (PA)
1515 Sw 13th Ct (33069-4710)
PHONE..................................954 946-3500
Howard C Rau, *CEO*
Ralph E Rau Jr, *President*
Charles Tarling, *President*
Scott H Thomas, *President*
James E Cuenin, *Vice Pres*
▲ **EMP:** 365 **EST:** 1852
SALES (est): 54.9MM **Privately Held**
WEB: www.stimpson.com
SIC: 3452 3469 Washers, metal; rivets, metal; electronic enclosures, stamped or pressed metal

(G-14676)
ELECTRIDUCT INC
1650 Nw 18th St Unit 801 (33069-1634)
PHONE..................................954 867-9100
Joseph R Proto, *President*
▲ **EMP:** 30 **EST:** 1955
SQ FT: 10,000
SALES (est): 4.1MM **Privately Held**
WEB: www.electriduct.com
SIC: 3679 5063 5961 Power supplies, all types: static; cable conduit; tools & hardware, mail order

(G-14677)
ELECTRO-OPTIX INC
2181 N Powerline Rd Ste 1 (33069-1261)
PHONE..................................954 973-2800
Chris Schoenjohn, *President*
Jim Stevens, *Vice Pres*
Freda Zalman, *Vice Pres*
▲ **EMP:** 12 **EST:** 1964
SQ FT: 10,000
SALES (est): 1MM **Privately Held**
WEB: www.electro-optix.com
SIC: 3827 3829 3851 Magnifying instruments, optical; thermometers & temperature sensors; ophthalmic goods

(G-14678)
EMERGENCY VEHICLE SUP CO LLC
2251 Hammondville Rd (33069-1505)
P.O. Box 667392 (33066-7392)
PHONE..................................954 428-5201
Robert G Windesheim,
EMP: 30 **EST:** 2005
SQ FT: 10,000
SALES (est): 4.7MM **Privately Held**
SIC: 3711 5531 3647 5063 Patrol wagons (motor vehicles), assembly of; automobile & truck equipment & parts; automotive parts; dome lights, automotive; flasher lights, automotive; flashlights

(G-14679)
EMPOWERED DIAGNOSTICS LLC ✪
3341 W Mcnab Rd (33069-4808)
PHONE..................................206 228-5990
Rick Hennessey,
EMP: 7 **EST:** 2020
SALES (est): 1.1MM **Privately Held**
WEB: www.empdx.net
SIC: 2836 Biological products, except diagnostic

▲ = Import ▼=Export
◆ =Import/Export

(G-14680)
ENGEAD GB DESIGN & PRTG INC
414 E Sample Rd (33064-4424)
PHONE..................................954 783-5161
EMP: 7
SALES (est): 880.6K **Privately Held**
SIC: 2759 Commercial Printing

(G-14681)
ENOLGAS USA INC
2530 N Powerline Rd # 401 (33069-1056)
PHONE..................................754 205-7902
Vittorio Bonomi, *President*
▲ **EMP:** 5 **EST:** 2008
SQ FT: 3,200
SALES (est): 2.5MM
SALES (corp-wide): 37.5MM **Privately Held**
WEB: www.enolgasusa.com
SIC: 3494 1711 3432 Valves & pipe fittings; plumbing, heating, air-conditioning contractors; plumbing fixture fittings & trim
PA: Enolgas Bonomi Spa
Via Europa 227/229
Concesio BS 25062
030 218-4311

(G-14682)
EPS METAL FINISHING
640 Ne 26th Ct (33064-5430)
PHONE..................................954 782-3073
Campbell Errol, *Principal*
EMP: 8 **EST:** 2011
SALES (est): 109.8K **Privately Held**
SIC: 3471 Finishing, metals or formed products

(G-14683)
ESSEX PLASTICS MIDWEST LLC LC
1531 Nw 12th Ave (33069-1796)
PHONE..................................954 956-1100
Brian Stevenson, *CEO*
▲ **EMP:** 600 **EST:** 1967
SQ FT: 117,000
SALES (est): 51.8MM
SALES (corp-wide): 105.1MM **Privately Held**
WEB: www.isoflexpackaging.com
SIC: 3081 Polyethylene film
HQ: Flexsol Packaging Corp. Of Pompano Beach
1531 Nw 12th Ave
Pompano Beach FL 33069
800 325-7740

(G-14684)
EXCALIBER PRINTING INC
45 S Pompano Pkwy (33069-3001)
PHONE..................................877 542-1699
Walid Hallwaji, *Director*
EMP: 6 **EST:** 2011
SALES (est): 127.5K **Privately Held**
WEB: www.excaliberprinting.com
SIC: 2752 Commercial printing, offset

(G-14685)
EXOTIC COUNTERTOP INC
2160 Nw 22nd St (33069-1341)
PHONE..................................954 979-8188
Ellyson Medeiros, *President*
Milton Freitas, *Vice Pres*
EMP: 6 **EST:** 2009
SALES (est): 600.4K **Privately Held**
WEB: www.exoticcountertops.com
SIC: 3281 5032 Granite, cut & shaped; marble building stone

(G-14686)
EXPRESSIONS IN WOOD
4270 Nw 19th Ave Ste A (33064-8717)
PHONE..................................954 956-0005
EMP: 8
SALES (est): 811.7K **Privately Held**
SIC: 2512 Mfg Upholstered Household Furniture

(G-14687)
FANTASY MARBLE & GRANITE INC
400 Sw 12th Ave Ste 4/5 (33069-3514)
PHONE..................................954 788-0433
Dominic Mathiot, *President*
Anthony Ventura, *Vice Pres*
Haakon Hodge, *Treasurer*
▲ **EMP:** 8 **EST:** 2000
SQ FT: 7,000
SALES (est): 593.5K **Privately Held**
WEB: www.fantasymarbleandgranite.com
SIC: 3281 5032 Granite, cut & shaped; marble building stone

(G-14688)
FCBN LLC
2637 E Atl Blvd 22868 (33062-4939)
PHONE..................................408 505-1324
Heather Obrien,
Kent Clothier,
EMP: 6 **EST:** 2009
SALES (est): 309.6K **Privately Held**
SIC: 7372 Prepackaged software

(G-14689)
FGA PRINTING
Also Called: Creative Printing
2550 N Powerline Rd # 105 (33069-5901)
PHONE..................................954 763-1122
Jim Mautner, *President*
EMP: 5 **EST:** 1990
SALES (est): 450.3K **Privately Held**
SIC: 2752 2791 2759 Commercial printing, offset; typesetting; commercial printing

(G-14690)
FIBERBUILT UMBRELLAS INC
2201 W Atlantic Blvd (33069-2792)
P.O. Box 667110 (33066-7110)
PHONE..................................954 484-9139
Paul Knapp, *President*
Jordan Beckner, *Vice Pres*
Diane Repole, *Purch Mgr*
Jessica B Rosenfeld, *Sales Mgr*
◆ **EMP:** 25 **EST:** 2000
SQ FT: 17,500
SALES (est): 6.9MM **Privately Held**
WEB: www.fiberbuiltumbrellas.com
SIC: 2211 Umbrella cloth, cotton

(G-14691)
FIRST MARKETING COMPANY (PA)
3300 Gateway Dr (33069-4883)
PHONE..................................954 979-0700
Ronald Drenning II, *President*
Ronald Grening, *President*
Harold Hale, *CFO*
David Goldstone, *Director*
Sandra Olivieri, *Director*
EMP: 160 **EST:** 1999
SALES (est): 29.2MM **Privately Held**
WEB: www.first-marketing.com
SIC: 2721 8742 Trade journals: publishing only, not printed on site; management consulting services

(G-14692)
FIRST SIGN CORP
2085 N Powerline Rd Ste 1 (33069-1283)
PHONE..................................954 972-7222
Marilyn Young, *President*
Greg Young, *Treasurer*
Jon Calder, *Sales Staff*
▼ **EMP:** 10 **EST:** 1980
SQ FT: 6,000
SALES (est): 1.1MM **Privately Held**
WEB: www.firstsign.com
SIC: 3993 Signs, not made in custom sign painting shops

(G-14693)
FIRSTPATH LABORATORY SVCS LLC
Also Called: Ritetest
3141 W Mcnab Rd (33069-4806)
PHONE..................................954 977-6977
Ronald M Giffler, *Principal*
EMP: 9 **EST:** 2011
SALES (est): 3.9MM **Privately Held**
WEB: www.firstpathlab.com
SIC: 2869 Laboratory chemicals, organic

(G-14694)
FISCHER PANDA GENERATORS INC
351 S Andrews Ave (33069-3501)
PHONE..................................954 462-2800
Anthony Rushton, *President*
James Ashly Rushton, *COO*
James Rushton, *COO*
Tony Rushton, *Vice Pres*
Gail Inman, *Accountant*
◆ **EMP:** 17 **EST:** 1995
SQ FT: 8,344
SALES (est): 3MM **Privately Held**
WEB: www.fischerpanda.com
SIC: 3621 Motors & generators

(G-14695)
FISCHER PANDA GENERATORS LLC
351 S Andrews Ave (33069-3501)
PHONE..................................954 462-2800
Antoine Miller, *Project Mgr*
Chad Godwin, *Sales Staff*
Anthony Rushton, *Mng Member*
Alan Cowen, *Manager*
EMP: 30 **EST:** 2010
SALES (est): 950K **Privately Held**
WEB: www.fischerpanda.com
SIC: 3621 Motors & generators

(G-14696)
FIVE STAR MILLWORK INC
4100 N Powerline Rd Y4 (33073-3077)
PHONE..................................954 956-7665
William Santana, *President*
Susan Santana, *Treasurer*
EMP: 13 **EST:** 2001
SALES (est): 2.4MM **Privately Held**
WEB: www.fivestarmillwork.net
SIC: 2431 Millwork

(G-14697)
FL INDUSTRIES INC
2930 Ne 8th Ave (33064-5330)
PHONE..................................954 422-3766
Ricardo Fernandez, *President*
EMP: 6 **EST:** 2016
SALES (est): 102.8K **Privately Held**
SIC: 3999 Manufacturing industries

(G-14698)
FLAGSTONE PAVERS SOUTH
1251 Ne 48th St (33064-4910)
PHONE..................................239 225-5646
EMP: 7 **EST:** 2016
SALES (est): 195.6K **Privately Held**
WEB: www.flagstonepavers.com
SIC: 3281 Flagstones

(G-14699)
FLAVANA LLC
1480 S Dixie Hwy E (33060-8517)
P.O. Box 669270 (33066-9270)
PHONE..................................561 285-7034
William Riddick, *Mng Member*
Kenneth Christian, *Mng Member*
David Vogel, *Mng Member*
EMP: 5 **EST:** 2013
SQ FT: 5,100
SALES (est): 400.3K **Privately Held**
SIC: 2111 Cigarettes

(G-14700)
FLEXSOL HOLDING CORP (PA)
1531 Nw 12th Ave (33069-1730)
PHONE..................................954 941-6333
Dave Clarke, *President*
Brian Stevenson, *President*
Ed Stranberg, *COO*
Ros Poplak, *CIO*
◆ **EMP:** 68 **EST:** 1999
SALES (est): 105.1MM **Privately Held**
WEB: www.isoflexpackaging.com
SIC: 2673 3082 3081 Plastic & pliofilm bags; tubes, unsupported plastic; plastic film & sheet

(G-14701)
FLORIDA PRINTING GROUP INC
1850 S Ocean Blvd Apt 904 (33062-7914)
PHONE..................................954 956-8570
Philip Lomenzo, *President*
EMP: 8 **EST:** 1993
SQ FT: 5,000
SALES (est): 298.5K **Privately Held**
WEB: www.floridaprinting.qpg.com
SIC: 2752 Commercial printing, offset

(G-14702)
FLORIDA QUALITY TRUSS INC
3635 Park Central Blvd N (33064-2262)
PHONE..................................954 975-3384
Tolga Adak, *Principal*
EMP: 9 **EST:** 2016
SALES (est): 3.2MM **Privately Held**
WEB: www.flqualitytruss.com
SIC: 2439 Trusses, wooden roof

(G-14703)
FLORIDA QUALITY TRUSS INDS INC (PA)
3635 Park Central Blvd N (33064-2262)
PHONE..................................954 971-3167
Rasmin Adak, *President*
Rasim Guney Adak, *President*
Tolga Adak, *Vice Pres*
◆ **EMP:** 10 **EST:** 1987
SQ FT: 3,000
SALES (est): 4MM **Privately Held**
WEB: www.flqualitytruss.com
SIC: 2439 Trusses, wooden roof

(G-14704)
FORT LAUDERDALE WOODWORKING
3001 Sw 10th St (33069-4814)
PHONE..................................954 935-0366
Charles R Watts, *President*
Sandra L Watts, *Corp Secy*
EMP: 40 **EST:** 1979
SQ FT: 40,000
SALES (est): 3.2MM **Privately Held**
WEB: www.fortlauderdalewoodworking.com
SIC: 2431 Millwork

(G-14705)
FRED M BUSH LLC
Also Called: Bush Brothers
1961 Hammondville Rd (33069-1958)
PHONE..................................561 394-7292
Fred M Bush,
EMP: 7
SALES (est): 187.9K **Privately Held**
SIC: 2431 Millwork

(G-14706)
FURNITURE CONCEPTS 2000 INC
454 Ne 28th St (33064-5438)
PHONE..................................954 946-0310
Dan Kelly, *President*
EMP: 6 **EST:** 1982
SQ FT: 6,000
SALES (est): 503.5K **Privately Held**
SIC: 2434 2511 Wood kitchen cabinets; wood household furniture

(G-14707)
FUSION AC & APPL SVC LLC
Also Called: Hvac
2637 E Atlantic Blvd (33062-4939)
PHONE..................................888 670-8435
Vernon Marquis, *President*
EMP: 5 **EST:** 2014
SALES (est): 386.7K **Privately Held**
WEB: www.fusionairco.com
SIC: 3585 1711 7623 1799 Air conditioning equipment, complete; air conditioning units, complete: domestic or industrial; heating & air conditioning contractors; air conditioning repair; appliance installation; appliance parts

(G-14708)
G BAUMAN FABRICATIONS INC
281 Nw 16th St (33060-5252)
PHONE..................................954 914-8037
Gregory T Bauman, *Principal*
EMP: 6 **EST:** 2008
SALES (est): 147.5K **Privately Held**
WEB: www.buck-inc.com
SIC: 3441 Fabricated structural metal

(G-14709)
G K WINDOW TREATMENTS INC
231 Sw 5th St (33060-7905)
PHONE..................................954 786-2927
Garo Kalpakjian, *President*
EMP: 16 **EST:** 1988
SQ FT: 6,375
SALES (est): 1.7MM **Privately Held**
WEB: www.gkwindowtreatments.com
SIC: 2591 2391 Blinds vertical; curtains & draperies

(G-14710)
GARDCO
316 Ne 1st St (33060-6608)
PHONE..................................954 946-9454
Sherri Thompson, *Manager*
Jim Wick, *Technical Staff*
EMP: 8 **EST:** 2019
SALES (est): 344.4K **Privately Held**
WEB: www.gardco.com
SIC: 3841 Surgical & medical instruments

(G-14711)
GB PRINTING
Also Called: Need Printing
414 E Sample Rd (33064-4424)
PHONE..................................954 941-3778
Lewis Rovero, *President*
EMP: 10 **EST:** 2004
SALES (est): 608.9K **Privately Held**
SIC: 2752 Commercial printing, offset

(G-14712)
GCATO 1959 ENTERPRISES LLC ✪
2750 Nw 11th St (33069-1831)
PHONE..................................954 937-6282
Te Andre Gomion, *Mng Member*
EMP: 8 **EST:** 2020
SALES (est): 285.5K **Privately Held**
WEB: www.l-senterprises.com
SIC: 2599 Food wagons, restaurant

(G-14713)
GCN PUBLISHING INC
Also Called: Gcn Media Services
49 N Federal Hwy 338 (33062-4304)
PHONE..................................203 665-6211
Joanne Persico, *President*
Elaine Goncalves, *Accounts Exec*
EMP: 7 **EST:** 2002
SALES (est): 168.6K **Privately Held**
WEB: www.gcnpublishing.com
SIC: 2741

(G-14714)
GLOBAL HOLDINGS AND DEV LLC
3850 Oaks Clubhouse Dr (33069-3668)
PHONE..................................949 500-4997
Barbara Kaufman, *CEO*
Mark Parsons, *COO*
EMP: 7 **EST:** 2010
SALES (est): 24.6MM **Privately Held**
SIC: 2821 4953 Plastics materials & resins; recycling, waste materials

(G-14715)
GLOBAL PERFORMANCE WINDOWS INC
Also Called: Global Windows
1881 Sw 3rd St (33069-3105)
PHONE..................................954 942-3322
Jean Lefrancois, *President*
Gabriel Matteau, *Corp Secy*
Alain Lefrancois, *Vice Pres*
▲ **EMP:** 15 **EST:** 2006
SALES (est): 3.8MM
SALES (corp-wide): 12.4MM **Privately Held**
WEB: www.epsylon.ca
SIC: 3211 1751 3231 Window glass, clear & colored; window & door (prefabricated) installation; insulating units, multiple-glazed: made from purchased glass
PA: Epsylon Concept Inc
1010 Av Nordique
Quebec QC G1C 0
418 661-6262

(G-14716)
GOLD KARATS JEWELRY LLC ✪
1000 E Atl Blvd Ste 217 (33060-4001)
PHONE..................................561 401-5935
Samantha Fields,
EMP: 6 **EST:** 2021
SALES (est): 41K **Privately Held**
SIC: 3911 Jewelry, precious metal

(G-14717)
GRAPHIC IMAGES INC
2301 Nw 33rd Ct Ste 105 (33069-1000)
PHONE..................................954 984-0015
Gerald J Goudreau, *President*
Ryan Goudreau, *Sales Staff*
Pam Goudreau, *Representative*
EMP: 10 **EST:** 1972
SQ FT: 10,000
SALES (est): 2.5MM **Privately Held**
WEB: www.giprint.com
SIC: 3993 Signs & advertising specialties

(G-14718)
GREAT LOCATIONS INC (PA)
2745 E Atl Blvd Ste 305 (33062-4976)
PHONE..................................954 943-1188
Charles Russell, *President*
EMP: 8 **EST:** 1991
SALES (est): 1.5MM **Privately Held**
WEB: www.greatlocations.com
SIC: 2731 Books: publishing only

(G-14719)
GURTAN DESIGNS
Also Called: Wall Scuplture By Grutan
1048 Sw 4th Ter (33060-8604)
P.O. Box 1708 (33061-1708)
PHONE..................................954 972-6100
Vedat Gurtan, *Partner*
Huat Gurtan, *Partner*
EMP: 8 **EST:** 1978
SQ FT: 4,000
SALES (est): 350K **Privately Held**
WEB: www.gurtan.com
SIC: 3446 Ornamental metalwork

(G-14720)
GVI INDUSTRIES INC
620 Ne 24th St (33064-6402)
PHONE..................................954 514-7283
Thomas M Hynes, *President*
EMP: 6 **EST:** 2011
SALES (est): 72.5K **Privately Held**
SIC: 3999 Manufacturing industries

(G-14721)
HAMILTON SUNDSTRAND CORP
2901 Nw 27th Ave (33069-1010)
PHONE..................................860 654-6252
EMP: 6
SALES (corp-wide): 56.5B **Publicly Held**
WEB: www.utcaerospacesystems.com
SIC: 3724 Aircraft engines & engine parts
HQ: Hamilton Sundstrand Corporation
1 Hamilton Rd
Windsor Locks CT 06096
860 654-6000

(G-14722)
HI TECH PRINTING SYSTEMS INC
3411 Ne 6th Ter (33064-5217)
P.O. Box 50556, Lighthouse Point (33074-0556)
PHONE..................................954 933-9155
David L Trudeau Sr, *President*
Priscilla Trudea, *Vice Pres*
David Trudeau, *Vice Pres*
EMP: 24 **EST:** 1988
SQ FT: 6,400
SALES (est): 4.1MM **Privately Held**
WEB: www.hi-techprinting.com
SIC: 2752 Commercial printing, offset

(G-14723)
HISPANIC CERTIFIED FOODS INC
1741 Nw 33rd St (33064-1327)
PHONE..................................305 772-6815
Perry Burke, *President*
◆ **EMP:** 5 **EST:** 2006
SQ FT: 800,000
SALES (est): 442.1K **Privately Held**
SIC: 2099 5141 Food preparations; food brokers

(G-14724)
HOERBIGER COMPRESSION TECH AME (DH)
3350 Gateway Dr (33069-4841)
PHONE..................................954 974-5700
Franz Gruber, *President*
Peter Laube, *Treasurer*
▲ **EMP:** 350 **EST:** 1999
SQ FT: 25,000
SALES (est): 105.9MM
SALES (corp-wide): 40K **Privately Held**
WEB: www.hoerbiger.com
SIC: 3494 7699 Valves & pipe fittings; valve repair, industrial
HQ: Hoerbiger Holding Ag
Baarerstrasse 18
Zug ZG 6302
415 601-000

(G-14725)
HOERBIGER CORP AMERICA INC (DH)
Also Called: Hoerbiger Compression Technolo
3350 Gateway Dr (33069-4841)
PHONE..................................954 974-5700
Don York, *President*
Thomas Rabil, *Corp Secy*
Hannes Hunschosky, *Exec VP*
Bruce Driggett, *Vice Pres*
Christean Kapp, *Vice Pres*
▲ **EMP:** 260 **EST:** 1963
SQ FT: 185,000
SALES (est): 79.6MM
SALES (corp-wide): 40K **Privately Held**
WEB: www.hoerbiger.com
SIC: 3491 Industrial valves
HQ: Hoerbiger Compression Technology America Holding, Inc.
3350 Gateway Dr
Pompano Beach FL 33069
954 974-5700

(G-14726)
HOME HEALTHCARE 2000 INC
1290 Sw 30th Ave (33069-4825)
P.O. Box 668864 (33066-8864)
PHONE..................................954 977-4450
Joseph Chang, *President*
Barry Cleveland, *Sales Mgr*
EMP: 6 **EST:** 2011
SQ FT: 49,000
SALES (est): 3.4MM **Privately Held**
SIC: 3845 Laser systems & equipment, medical

(G-14727)
HOOVER PUMPING SYSTEMS CORP
2801 N Powerline Rd (33069-1009)
PHONE..................................954 971-7350
Brent Hoover, *President*
Kevin Cavaioli, *Vice Pres*
Pete Lyons, *Mfg Staff*
Donna Hoover, *Treasurer*
Jose Gonzalez, *Technician*
▼ **EMP:** 30 **EST:** 1984
SQ FT: 21,000
SALES (est): 8.3MM **Privately Held**
WEB: www.hooverpumping.com
SIC: 3561 1623 Industrial pumps & parts; water main construction

(G-14728)
IMAGE GRAPHICS 2000 INC
2450 W Sample Rd Ste 20 (33073-3074)
P.O. Box 670276 (33067-0005)
PHONE..................................954 332-3380
Wade Davis, *President*
Chris Panza, *Prdtn Mgr*
Chris Burns, *Manager*
Maria Gomez, *Manager*
EMP: 9 **EST:** 2001
SQ FT: 3,500
SALES (est): 656.8K **Privately Held**
WEB: www.igxboatwraps.com
SIC: 2759 Commercial printing

(G-14729)
IMPERIAL INDUSTRIES INC (HQ)
1259 Nw 21st St (33069-1428)
PHONE..................................954 917-4114
Howard L Ehler Jr, *CEO*
Steven M Healy, *CFO*
◆ **EMP:** 10 **EST:** 1968
SQ FT: 19,600
SALES (est): 16.6MM
SALES (corp-wide): 216.4MM **Privately Held**
WEB: www.qepcorporate.com
SIC: 3441 3272 Building components, structural steel; concrete products
PA: Q.E.P. Co., Inc.
1001 Broken Sound Pkwy Nw A
Boca Raton FL 33487
561 994-5550

(G-14730)
IMPERIAL PRIVACY SYSTEMS LLC
1400 Sw 8th St (33069-4512)
P.O. Box 578 (33061-0578)
PHONE..................................954 782-7130
Brandon Bernardo, *CEO*
Patricia Zane, *President*
Gerald F Shea, *Corp Secy*
Robert J Shea, *Vice Pres*
Gerald Shea, *Treasurer*
▼ **EMP:** 57 **EST:** 1967
SQ FT: 18,000
SALES (est): 3.4MM **Privately Held**
WEB: www.imperialprivacy.com
SIC: 2591 Curtain & drapery rods, poles & fixtures

(G-14731)
INOX STAINLESS SPECIALIST LLC
1336 Sw 8th St (33069-4510)
PHONE..................................407 764-2456
Jorge H Rodriguez, *Manager*
EMP: 11 **EST:** 2014
SALES (est): 2.1MM **Privately Held**
WEB: www.inoxllc.com
SIC: 3441 Fabricated structural metal

(G-14732)
INTERNATIONAL MEDICAL INDS INC
Also Called: IMI
2981 Gateway Dr (33069-4326)
PHONE..................................954 917-9570
Jonathan Vitello, *President*
Susan Vitello, *Vice Pres*
Blaise Barone, *Engineer*
Keyur Bhadani, *Engineer*
Peter Lehel, *Engineer*
◆ **EMP:** 30 **EST:** 1969
SQ FT: 16,000
SALES (est): 9.5MM **Privately Held**
WEB: www.imiweb.com
SIC: 3841 Surgical & medical instruments

(G-14733)
IPRINT 3D USA
2550 N Powerline Rd # 103 (33069-5901)
PHONE..................................888 868-7329
Pedro Perez, *Principal*
EMP: 6 **EST:** 2017
SALES (est): 96.9K **Privately Held**
WEB: www.iprint3dusa.com
SIC: 2752 Commercial printing, lithographic

(G-14734)
J & K 8 INC
Also Called: J&K Kitchen, Bath and Stone
1591 N Powerline Rd (33069-1604)
PHONE..................................954 984-8585
Chuen K Cheng, *President*
Ken Yeung, *Vice Pres*
EMP: 19 **EST:** 2005
SALES (est): 1MM **Privately Held**
WEB: www.jandkcabinetry.com
SIC: 2499 Kitchen, bathroom & household ware: wood

(G-14735)
JAS BUSINESS SOLUTIONS INC
Also Called: JAS Interconnect Solutions
200 Park Central Blvd S (33064-2197)
PHONE..................................954 975-0025
Ronald Scoppettone, *President*
John Scerbo, *President*
Gerald Heller, *Director*
EMP: 25 **EST:** 2006
SALES (est): 2.6MM **Privately Held**
SIC: 3674 Solid state electronic devices

(G-14736)
JMH MARINE INC
Also Called: Accudock
1790 Sw 13th Ct (33069-4715)
P.O. Box 1200, Charlestown NH (03603-1200)
PHONE..................................954 785-7557
John Harrison, *President*
Aj Barcz, *Principal*
Christine Catalano, *Principal*
Kim Holt, *Principal*
Trish Nicholson, *Vice Pres*
▼ **EMP:** 10 **EST:** 1992

SALES (est): 3.5MM **Privately Held**
WEB: www.accudock.com
SIC: 3089 3731 5091 Extruded finished plastic products; drydocks, floating; sporting & recreation goods; watersports equipment & supplies; boats, canoes, watercrafts & equipment

(G-14737)
JONES AWNINGS & CANVAS INC
127 Nw 16th St (33060-5250)
PHONE..................................954 784-6966
Brad Jones, *President*
Scott Riolino, *General Mgr*
Barbara Jones, *Vice Pres*
EMP: 37 **EST:** 1999
SALES (est): 4.8MM **Privately Held**
WEB: www.jonesawnings.com
SIC: 2394 Awnings, fabric: made from purchased materials

(G-14738)
JS2 AEROSPACE CORP
1888 Nw 21st St (33069-1334)
PHONE..................................954 840-3620
Jeffrey Smith, *Principal*
EMP: 9 **EST:** 2018
SALES (est): 1.2MM **Privately Held**
WEB: www.js2aero.aero
SIC: 3728 Aircraft parts & equipment

(G-14739)
KIRA LABS INC
3400 Gateway Dr Ste 100 (33069-4866)
PHONE..................................954 978-4549
David H Rosen, *President*
Lindi Rosen, *Vice Pres*
Ruben Martinez, *Maint Spvr*
Jose Zayas, *Mfg Staff*
Marsha Abraham, *Production*
▲ **EMP:** 10 **EST:** 2003
SQ FT: 28,000
SALES (est): 4.9MM **Privately Held**
WEB: www.kiralabs.com
SIC: 2844 Cosmetic preparations

(G-14740)
KOLICH ELECTRIC MOTOR CO INC
3420 Nw 25th Ave (33069-1063)
PHONE..................................954 969-8605
EMP: 7 **EST:** 2019
SALES (est): 239.5K **Privately Held**
WEB: www.kolichelectricmotor.com
SIC: 7694 Electric motor repair

(G-14741)
L&R IMAGING
2450 W Sample Rd Ste 8 (33073-3034)
PHONE..................................678 691-3204
EMP: 5 **EST:** 2010
SALES (est): 596.3K **Privately Held**
SIC: 3845 Mfg Electromedical Equipment

(G-14742)
LAIRD INTERNATIONAL CORP
2300 Nw 30th Pl Bldg 9 (33069-1025)
PHONE..................................954 532-3794
Cliff Harding, *Principal*
▲ **EMP:** 10 **EST:** 2007
SALES (est): 1MM
SALES (corp-wide): 2MM **Privately Held**
WEB: www.lairdinternational.com
SIC: 3949 Golf equipment
PA: Cutler Sports Corp
4140a Sladeview Cres Unit 5
Mississauga ON
905 271-6555

(G-14743)
LEILA K MOAVERO
Also Called: Executive Prtg & Mailing Svcs
1800 Nw 15th Ave Ste 140 (33069-1410)
PHONE..................................954 978-0018
Leila Moavero, *Owner*
EMP: 5 **EST:** 2011
SQ FT: 2,500
SALES (est): 379K **Privately Held**
SIC: 2741 2752 2791 Business service newsletters: publishing & printing; commercial printing, lithographic; typesetting

(G-14744)
LHOIST NORTH AMERICA ALA LLC
Also Called: Matco Transload Us06
1263 Hammondville Rd (33069-2927)
PHONE..................................817 732-8164
EMP: 25
SALES (corp-wide): 99.4MM **Privately Held**
SIC: 3274 Manufacture Of Lime Products
HQ: Lhoist North America Of Alabama, Llc
3700 Hulen St
Fort Worth TX 76109
817 732-8164

(G-14745)
LION PRESS INC
Also Called: Destination Athlete Broward FL
1913 W Copans Rd (33064-1517)
PHONE..................................954 971-6193
Cynthia Martin, *President*
EMP: 5 **EST:** 1975
SQ FT: 2,000
SALES (est): 888K **Privately Held**
WEB: www.thelionpressprinting.com
SIC: 2752 Commercial printing, offset

(G-14746)
LMB CONSULTANTS INC
Also Called: American Speedy Printing
1280 S Powerline Rd # 17 (33069-4339)
PHONE..................................954 537-9590
Leroy M Borofsky, *President*
Sandra Borofsky, *Admin Sec*
EMP: 9 **EST:** 1985
SQ FT: 1,325
SALES (est): 350K **Privately Held**
WEB: www.allegramarketingprint.com
SIC: 2752 Commercial printing, offset

(G-14747)
LOGOXPRESS INC
Also Called: Sew Right
2520 N Powerline Rd # 303 (33069-1055)
P.O. Box 290640, Port Orange (32129-0640)
PHONE..................................954 973-4994
Naresh Manek, *President*
EMP: 7 **EST:** 2015
SALES (est): 530K **Privately Held**
WEB: www.mylogoxpress.com
SIC: 2395 Embroidery products, except schiffli machine

(G-14748)
LUBREXX SPECIALTY PRODUCTS LLC
Also Called: Fluxxer
4100 N Powerline Rd O1 (33073-3083)
PHONE..................................561 988-7500
Michael A Jimenez,
EMP: 7 **EST:** 2016
SQ FT: 7,000
SALES (est): 1.8MM **Privately Held**
SIC: 2992 Lubricating oils

(G-14749)
M MICRO TECHNOLOGIES INC
Also Called: Microtechnologies
2901 Gateway Dr (33069-4326)
PHONE..................................954 973-6166
Michele Hamilton, *Principal*
Mario Zuchovicki, *Vice Pres*
Antonio Bossiello, *Treasurer*
Tony Bossiello, *Administration*
EMP: 500 **EST:** 2003
SALES (est): 34.3MM **Privately Held**
WEB: www.mic-tec.com
SIC: 3629 3699 Electronic generation equipment; electrical equipment & supplies; high-energy particle physics equipment

(G-14750)
MAGNETIC JEWELLRY INC
2900 W Sample Rd (33073-3024)
PHONE..................................954 975-5868
Michael Goldstein, *Principal*
EMP: 5 **EST:** 2010
SALES (est): 361.1K **Privately Held**
SIC: 3961 Costume jewelry

(G-14751)
MAN CAPITAL CORPORATION (DH)
591 Sw 13th Ter (33069-3519)
PHONE..................................732 582-8220
Siejberd Rottach, *President*
Vin Ritraj, *Treasurer*
◆ **EMP:** 35 **EST:** 1980
SQ FT: 1,500
SALES (est): 65.2MM
SALES (corp-wide): 263.5B **Privately Held**
WEB: www.traton.com
SIC: 3519 Diesel, semi-diesel or duel-fuel engines, including marine
HQ: Traton Se
Dachauer Str. 641
Munchen 80995
893 609-870

(G-14752)
MANCINI INC
Also Called: United States Concrete Pipe
1878 Nw 21st St (33069-1334)
PHONE..................................954 583-7220
Albert P Mancini, *President*
Harry Hargrave, *Vice Pres*
Harold Hendrix, *Vice Pres*
Nicholas D Mancini II, *Vice Pres*
David W Mancini, *Treasurer*
EMP: 46 **EST:** 1983
SQ FT: 48,000
SALES (est): 4.8MM **Privately Held**
WEB: www.unitedstatesconcrete.com
SIC: 3272 Pipe, concrete or lined with concrete

(G-14753)
MARKER INDUSTRIES LLC
3980 Oaks Clubhouse Dr (33069-3684)
PHONE..................................954 907-2647
Mark D Kerr, *Principal*
EMP: 7 **EST:** 2018
SALES (est): 255.4K **Privately Held**
WEB: www.milemarker.com
SIC: 3999 Manufacturing industries

(G-14754)
MASA TRADING LLC
1454 Sw 11th Ter (33069-4701)
PHONE..................................561 729-3293
Sun Xian, *Mng Member*
▲ **EMP:** 10 **EST:** 2011
SALES (est): 1.2MM **Privately Held**
SIC: 2092 Fish, frozen: prepared

(G-14755)
MAXIGRAPHICS INC
2201 W Sample Rd Ste 8-2a (33073-3096)
PHONE..................................954 978-0740
Patricia Silverts, *President*
Douglas Rodibaugh, *Manager*
EMP: 10 **EST:** 1988
SQ FT: 2,500
SALES (est): 744.5K **Privately Held**
WEB: www.maxigraphics.com
SIC: 2759 2752 Commercial printing; commercial printing, lithographic

(G-14756)
MCNEILL SIGNS INC (PA)
555 S Dixie Hwy E (33060-6911)
P.O. Box 1093, Bunnell (32110-1093)
PHONE..................................561 737-6304
Jay R McNeill, *President*
Daniel G Scroggins, *Principal*
Tiffany D Scroggins, *Principal*
Martia S McNeill, *Vice Pres*
EMP: 18 **EST:** 1956
SQ FT: 10,000
SALES (est): 3.2MM **Privately Held**
WEB: www.mcneillsigns.com
SIC: 3993 Neon signs; electric signs; advertising artwork

(G-14757)
MEDISCOPE MANUFACTURING INC
401 Briny Ave Apt 405 (33062-5819)
PHONE..................................954 975-9997
Ralph Martinez, *Branch Mgr*
EMP: 12 **Privately Held**
WEB: www.mediscope-mfg.com
SIC: 3599 Machine shop, jobbing & repair
PA: Mediscope Manufacturing Inc
744 Mountain Blvd Fl 2w
Watchung NJ 07069

(G-14758)
MERRY MAILMAN INC
3907 N Federal Hwy (33064-6042)
PHONE..................................954 786-1146
Carla Felini, *Principal*
EMP: 6 **EST:** 2011
SALES (est): 407.9K **Privately Held**
WEB: www.themerrymailman.com
SIC: 3086 Packaging & shipping materials, foamed plastic

(G-14759)
METAL MAGIX INC
3711 Ne 11th Ave Ste 4 (33064-5164)
PHONE..................................754 235-9996
Frank W Jones, *Principal*
EMP: 7 **EST:** 2010
SALES (est): 1MM **Privately Held**
WEB: www.metalmagix.com
SIC: 3441 Fabricated structural metal

(G-14760)
MG WOODWORK INC
5540 Nw 76th Pl Ste A (33073-3824)
PHONE..................................561 459-7552
Marcio Gama, *Principal*
EMP: 8 **EST:** 2010
SALES (est): 317.2K **Privately Held**
SIC: 2431 Millwork

(G-14761)
MICRO CONTACTS INC
2901 Gateway Dr (33069-4326)
PHONE..................................954 973-6166
Gerald F Tucci, *Branch Mgr*
EMP: 15
SALES (corp-wide): 9MM **Privately Held**
WEB: www.microcontacts.com
SIC: 3643 Contacts, electrical
PA: Micro Contacts, Inc.
1 Enterprise Pl Unit E
Hicksville NY 11801
516 433-4830

(G-14762)
MICRO PNEUMATIC LOGIC INC
Also Called: Microtechnologies
2901 Gateway Dr (33069-4326)
PHONE..................................954 935-6821
G F Tucci, *President*
Michael F Tucci, *President*
Dennis Semet, *Engineer*
Antonio Bossiello, *Treasurer*
Dan Bracewell, *Sales Dir*
◆ **EMP:** 145 **EST:** 1973
SQ FT: 40,000
SALES (est): 29.5MM **Privately Held**
WEB: www.mic-tec.com
SIC: 3492 Control valves, aircraft: hydraulic & pneumatic

(G-14763)
MICRO TYPING SYSTEMS INC
1295 Sw 29th Ave (33069-4359)
PHONE..................................954 970-9500
Charles J Sobolewski, *President*
Harry Malyska, *VP Mfg*
▲ **EMP:** 50 **EST:** 1988
SQ FT: 21,000
SALES (est): 14.7MM
SALES (corp-wide): 705.7MM **Privately Held**
WEB: www.orthoclinicaldiagnostics.com
SIC: 3829 Measuring & controlling devices
PA: Ortho-Clinical Diagnostics, Inc.
1001 Route 202
Raritan NJ 08869
908 218-8000

(G-14764)
MIRART INC
Also Called: Innovations By Mirart
2707 Gateway Dr (33069-4323)
PHONE..................................954 974-5230
Jeff Oster, *President*
Dale Oster, *Corp Secy*
◆ **EMP:** 25 **EST:** 1976
SQ FT: 36,000
SALES (est): 4.3MM **Privately Held**
WEB: www.mirart.com
SIC: 2824 Acrylic fibers

(G-14765)
MIRRORS & MORE INC
3390 Ne 6th Ter (33064-5216)
PHONE..................................954 782-7272
Paul Menditto Jr, *President*
John F Heinle, *Vice Pres*
Jacqueline F Menditto, *Admin Sec*
EMP: 5 **EST:** 1985
SQ FT: 3,000
SALES (est): 444K **Privately Held**
WEB: www.mirrorsandmoreinc.com
SIC: 3231 Mirrored glass

(G-14766)
MJK INDUSTRIES INC
201 Se 3rd Ct (33060-7126)
PHONE..................................954 788-7494
Michael J Kuhl, *President*
EMP: 8 **EST:** 2001
SALES (est): 445.1K **Privately Held**
WEB: www.mjk.com
SIC: 3999 Manufacturing industries

(G-14767)
MODULAR THERMAL TECH LLC (PA)
Also Called: Life Wear Technologies
1520 Sw 5th Ct (33069-3523)
PHONE..................................954 785-1055
Bradley Waugh, *CEO*
Zachary Wunsch, *CFO*
EMP: 20 **EST:** 1974
SALES (est): 9.9MM **Privately Held**
WEB: www.lifeweartechnologies.com
SIC: 2833 Vitamins, natural or synthetic: bulk, uncompounded

(G-14768)
MOR PRINTING INC
Also Called: Mor Printing & Envelopes
610 Sw 12th Ave (33069-4526)
PHONE..................................954 377-1197
Owen Luttinger, *President*
Richard Luttinger, *Corp Secy*
Dave Groth, *Purch Mgr*
Jon Leavy, *Sales Mgr*
Rick Bell, *Accounts Mgr*
▼ **EMP:** 13 **EST:** 1988
SQ FT: 55,000
SALES (est): 4.8MM **Privately Held**
WEB: www.morprinting.com
SIC: 2752 Commercial printing, offset

(G-14769)
MORRIS MICA CABINETS INC
1920 Nw 22nd Ct (33069-1340)
PHONE..................................954 979-6838
Wesley Wong, *President*
Tyrone Wong, *Vice Pres*
Carlisle Wong, *Director*
EMP: 7 **EST:** 1978
SQ FT: 5,600
SALES (est): 886K **Privately Held**
SIC: 2434 2599 Wood kitchen cabinets; cabinets, factory

(G-14770)
N & N INVESTMENT CORPORATION
Also Called: Baron Manufacturing
3001 Nw 16th Ter (33064-1407)
PHONE..................................954 590-3800
Hasu Gavan, *President*
Juan Leal, *Prdtn Mgr*
Karina Lozada, *Buyer*
Rakhi Gavan, *Director*
Ramila Gavan, *Admin Sec*
▼ **EMP:** 50 **EST:** 1961
SQ FT: 100,000
SALES (est): 7.9MM **Privately Held**
SIC: 2431 2521 2511 3993 Millwork; wood office furniture; wood household furniture; signs & advertising specialties; wood partitions & fixtures; partitions & fixtures, except wood

(G-14771)
NEBULA GLASS INTERNATIONAL INC
Also Called: Glasslam
1601 Blount Rd (33069-5102)
PHONE..................................954 975-3233
Stephen E Howes, *CEO*
Violet Howes, *Vice Pres*
◆ **EMP:** 34 **EST:** 1984
SQ FT: 17,000
SALES (est): 2MM **Privately Held**
WEB: www.glasslam.com
SIC: 3229 5169 Art, decorative & novelty glassware; adhesives & sealants

(G-14772)
NEO METAL GLASS LLC
Also Called: Luz General Services
2101 Nw 33rd St Ste 1400 (33069-1029)
PHONE..................................954 532-0340
Anderson Luz, *President*
Barbara Soussa, *Vice Pres*
EMP: 6 **EST:** 2017
SALES (est): 309.2K **Privately Held**
WEB: www.neometalglass.com
SIC: 3312 3231 1793 Stainless steel; doors, glass: made from purchased glass; glass & glazing work

(G-14773)
NEW PELICAN LLC
1636 E Atlantic Blvd (33060-6751)
PHONE..................................954 783-8700
John Geer, *Chief*
Tony K Hill, *Manager*
EMP: 6 **EST:** 2019
SALES (est): 347.6K **Privately Held**
WEB: www.newpelican.com
SIC: 2741 Miscellaneous publishing

(G-14774)
NOBLE WOOD WORKS
225 Nw 16th St (33060-5252)
PHONE..................................561 702-2889
Luis Fernando Prudente, *Principal*
EMP: 9 **EST:** 2010
SALES (est): 413.8K **Privately Held**
WEB: www.noblewoodwork.net
SIC: 2431 Millwork

(G-14775)
NOTICE THAT TEE INC
2501 Nw 34th Pl Ste 27 (33069-5929)
P.O. Box 771255, Coral Springs (33077-1255)
PHONE..................................954 971-1018
Kevin B Bolling, *Principal*
EMP: 6 **EST:** 2009
SALES (est): 241.6K **Privately Held**
SIC: 2759 Screen printing

(G-14776)
NUFORM CABINETRY
1745 N Powerline Rd (33069-1624)
PHONE..................................954 532-2746
Shu Cai, *Principal*
EMP: 6 **EST:** 2016
SALES (est): 115.3K **Privately Held**
WEB: www.nuformkitchen.com
SIC: 2434 Wood kitchen cabinets

(G-14777)
NUGGETS RACING LLC
Also Called: Shepherd Micro Racing USA
3441 Ne 13th Ave (33064-6212)
PHONE..................................954 943-3561
Gregory W Esser, *Principal*
EMP: 7 **EST:** 2012
SALES (est): 143.1K **Privately Held**
WEB: www.nuggetsranchraceway.com
SIC: 3644 Raceways

(G-14778)
OLDCASTLE RETAIL INC
Also Called: Bonsal American
1200 Nw 18th St (33069-1722)
PHONE..................................954 971-1200
John Holloway, *Branch Mgr*
EMP: 399
SALES (corp-wide): 27.5B **Privately Held**
WEB: www.oldcastlecoastal.com
SIC: 3272 3255 Concrete products, precast; tile & brick refractories, except plastic
HQ: Oldcastle Retail, Inc.
625 Griffith Rd Ste 100
Charlotte NC 28217
704 525-1621

(G-14779)
ON SCREEN INK
1360 Hammondville Rd (33069-2906)
PHONE..................................724 516-4999
Allan Levine, *Principal*
EMP: 7 **EST:** 2011
SALES (est): 106.4K **Privately Held**
SIC: 3442 Screen & storm doors & windows

(G-14780)
OPELLE ENTERPRISES INC
Also Called: Bageland
1471 Sw 5th Ct (33069-3524)
PHONE..................................954 942-7338
Jorge Fidel, *President*
Iris Fidel, *Vice Pres*
Barry Gray, *Sales Mgr*
Natalia Fidel, *Sales Staff*
EMP: 32 **EST:** 1989
SQ FT: 20,000
SALES (est): 2.6MM **Privately Held**
WEB: www.opelle.com
SIC: 2051 2053 Bread, cake & related products; bagels, fresh or frozen; frozen bakery products, except bread

(G-14781)
OUR TOWN NEWS
3665 Park Central Blvd N (33064-2262)
PHONE..................................954 979-0991
Eugene Ozar, *Manager*
EMP: 6 **EST:** 2015
SALES (est): 118.6K **Privately Held**
SIC: 2711 Newspapers, publishing & printing

(G-14782)
OUR WAREHOUSE INC
Also Called: Stonehenge Gems
2749 E Atlantic Blvd (33062-4941)
PHONE..................................954 786-1234
Frances Wilson, *President*
Suzette Waldron, *Corp Secy*
EMP: 9 **EST:** 1973
SQ FT: 3,000
SALES (est): 517.3K **Privately Held**
WEB: www.jewelryandcoinbuyer.com
SIC: 3915 5094 Jewelers' findings & materials; jewelry

(G-14783)
PALLET CONSULTANTS CORP (PA)
810 Nw 13th Ave (33069-2029)
P.O. Box 1692 (33061-1692)
PHONE..................................954 946-2212
Gustavo Gutierrez, *CEO*
Brian L Groene, *President*
Tony Buroker, *General Mgr*
Carlo Gruener, *CFO*
Caroline Curtiaga, *Controller*
◆ **EMP:** 39 **EST:** 1992
SQ FT: 400,000
SALES (est): 15MM **Privately Held**
WEB: www.palletconsultants.com
SIC: 2448 7699 8742 Pallets, wood; pallet repair; management consulting services

(G-14784)
PARAMOUNT INDUSTRIES INC (PA)
Also Called: Paramount Sales & Consulting
1020 Sw 10th Ave Ste 6 (33069-4632)
P.O. Box 1030, Boca Raton (33429-1030)
PHONE..................................954 781-3755
Mike Degrandchamp, *President*
Michael De Grandchamp, *Human Res Mgr*
EMP: 25 **EST:** 1982
SQ FT: 12,600
SALES (est): 4.9MM **Privately Held**
WEB: www.iwdesigners.com
SIC: 3679 3672 3643 Harness assemblies for electronic use: wire or cable; printed circuit boards; current-carrying wiring devices

(G-14785)
PATRIOT WELDING INC
151 Sw 5th St W (33060-7903)
PHONE..................................954 798-8819
Carrie W Llano, *Principal*
EMP: 6 **EST:** 2015
SALES (est): 256.8K **Privately Held**
SIC: 7692 Welding repair

(G-14786)
PAVER ACTION INC
3741 Ne 18th Ave (33064-6638)
PHONE..................................954 868-1468
Evair Hottz, *President*
EMP: 6 **EST:** 2005
SALES (est): 172.8K **Privately Held**
SIC: 2951 Asphalt paving mixtures & blocks

(G-14787)
PENEK CHEMICAL INDUSTRIES INC
4100 N Powerline Rd Z5 (33073-3083)
PHONE..................................954 978-6501
Kevin Ressler, *Owner*
EMP: 6 **EST:** 2006
SALES (est): 382.2K **Privately Held**
WEB: www.2173856.uscompaniesdata.com
SIC: 2899 Fuel tank or engine cleaning chemicals

(G-14788)
PERFECT OIL INC
2900 W Sample Rd (33073-3024)
PHONE..................................954 984-8944
Jociane L Landolfa, *Branch Mgr*
EMP: 9 **Privately Held**
WEB: www.perfectoil.com
SIC: 1381 Drilling oil & gas wells
PA: Perfect Oil, Inc.
51 Atwell Dr
West Palm Beach FL 33411

(G-14789)
PETES SEAL COATING
2300 Ne 15th Ter (33064-5535)
PHONE..................................857 251-1912
Pete Smith, *Owner*
EMP: 6 **EST:** 2017
SALES (est): 119.8K **Privately Held**
SIC: 3479 Metal coating & allied service

(G-14790)
PETTIT TOOLS & SUPPLIES INC
4391 Ne 11th Ave (33064-5951)
PHONE..................................954 781-2640
Uzi Jacoby, *President*
William T Pettit Jr, *Vice Pres*
▲ **EMP:** 10 **EST:** 1992
SQ FT: 5,000
SALES (est): 500K **Privately Held**
SIC: 3423 Hand & edge tools

(G-14791)
PG EXPRESS INC
1000 W Mcnab Rd Ste 104 (33069-4719)
PHONE..................................954 788-3263
Franz De Luca, *Principal*
EMP: 7 **EST:** 2014
SALES (est): 276.8K **Privately Held**
WEB: www.pgexpressinc.com
SIC: 2752 Commercial printing, lithographic

(G-14792)
PHOENIX PUBLICATIONS
777 S Federal Hwy (33062-5968)
PHONE..................................954 609-7586
Patti Gottesman, *Principal*
Wendy Weber, *Vice Pres*
EMP: 11 **EST:** 2010
SALES (est): 138.4K **Privately Held**
WEB: www.hometowncouponmagazines.com
SIC: 2741 Miscellaneous publishing

(G-14793)
PHOSCRETE CORPORATION (PA)
1800 Nw 15th Ave Ste 130 (33069-1435)
PHONE..................................561 420-0595
Jean Tremblay, *Exec VP*
Brian Mintz, *Vice Pres*
Marlen La Paz, *Project Dir*
Kyle Bartfay, *Sales Mgr*
Erica Gerhart, *Admin Sec*
EMP: 34 **EST:** 2011
SALES (est): 2.5MM **Privately Held**
WEB: www.phoscrete.com
SIC: 3272 3273 Concrete products, precast; ready-mixed concrete

(G-14794)
PILOT STEEL INC
1950 W Copans Rd (33064-1518)
PHONE..................................954 978-3615
Stuart Andrew Disbury, *President*
◆ **EMP:** 38 **EST:** 1987

SQ FT: 10,000
SALES (est): 6.1MM **Privately Held**
WEB: www.pilotsteel.com
SIC: 3441 Fabricated structural metal

(G-14795)
PK GRAPHICZ
1000 W Mcnab Rd (33069-4719)
PHONE..................................305 534-2184
Joyce Paredes, *Principal*
EMP: 5 **EST:** 2010
SALES (est): 348.8K **Privately Held**
WEB: www.pkgraphics.com
SIC: 2752 Commercial printing, offset

(G-14796)
PLASTIC PARTS INC
4100 N Powerline Rd Z5 (33073-3077)
PHONE..................................954 974-3051
Todd Pores, *President*
EMP: 25 **EST:** 2004
SQ FT: 15,000
SALES (est): 696.6K **Privately Held**
WEB: www.plasticpartsinc.com
SIC: 3089 Injection molding of plastics

(G-14797)
PLASTIC SEALING COMPANY INC
1940 Nw 18th St Ste 1 (33069-1724)
PHONE..................................954 956-9797
Mark Macbride, *Principal*
EMP: 5 **EST:** 1998
SALES (est): 800K **Privately Held**
WEB: www.plasticsealing.com
SIC: 2752 7389 Menus, lithographed; laminating service

(G-14798)
PLASTIC SOLUTIONS OF POMPANO
4100 N Powerline Rd Z5 (33073-3083)
PHONE..................................800 331-7081
Gilbert Gomez, *President*
EMP: 6 **EST:** 2004
SALES (est): 582.5K **Privately Held**
SIC: 3089 Injection molding of plastics

(G-14799)
PLYWOOD EXPRESS INC
2601 Gateway Dr Ste B (33069-4321)
PHONE..................................954 956-7576
Giovana Rodrigues, *President*
Angel Ruiz, *President*
Danny Silva, *Sales Staff*
▲ **EMP:** 25 **EST:** 2011
SALES (est): 3.9MM **Privately Held**
WEB: www.plywoodexpress.com
SIC: 2435 Hardwood veneer & plywood

(G-14800)
POINT BLANK ENTERPRISES INC
Also Called: Protective Products Entps
2102 Sw 2nd St (33069-3116)
PHONE..................................954 846-8222
Tom Steffen, *CEO*
Shelby Carpenter, *Senior VP*
Susan Carrasco, *Buyer*
Ann Anna, *Accountant*
Cory Provenzano, *Director*
EMP: 824 **Privately Held**
WEB: www.pointblankenterprises.com
SIC: 2389 2221 Uniforms & vestments; broadwoven fabric mills, manmade
HQ: Point Blank Enterprises, Inc.
2102 Sw 2nd St
Pompano Beach FL 33069
954 630-0900

(G-14801)
POINT BLANK ENTERPRISES INC (HQ)
Also Called: Protective Group A Point Blank
2102 Sw 2nd St (33069-3116)
PHONE..................................954 630-0900
Daniel Gaston, *CEO*
Paulo Motoki, *COO*
Mark Edwards, *Exec VP*
Michael Foreman, *Exec VP*
Clarence Hutton, *Exec VP*
◆ **EMP:** 824 **EST:** 2011
SALES (est): 216.9MM **Privately Held**
WEB: www.pointblankenterprises.com
SIC: 3842 3462 Bulletproof vests; armor plate, forged iron or steel

(G-14802)
POINT BLANK INTRMDATE HLDG LLC
2102 Sw 2nd St (33069-3116)
PHONE..................................954 630-0900
Daniel Gaston, *CEO*
Samuel White, *President*
Michael Anderson, *Vice Pres*
Shelby Carpenter, *Vice Pres*
Michael Foreman, *Vice Pres*
EMP: 38 **EST:** 2011
SALES (est): 3.2MM **Privately Held**
WEB: www.pointblankenterprises.com
SIC: 2399 Hand woven apparel

(G-14803)
POINT BLANK PROTECTIVE APPRL (PA)
2102 Sw 2nd St (33069-3116)
PHONE..................................954 630-0900
Daniel Gaston, *CEO*
EMP: 501 **EST:** 2017
SALES (est): 50.7MM **Privately Held**
WEB: www.pointblank-shop.com
SIC: 2311 Military uniforms, men's & youths': purchased materials

(G-14804)
POMPANO PELICAN INC
1500 E Atl Blvd Ste A (33060-6769)
P.O. Box 1981 (33061-1981)
PHONE..................................954 783-8700
Anne Siren, *President*
EMP: 6 **EST:** 1993
SQ FT: 2,400
SALES (est): 250K **Privately Held**
WEB: www.newpelican.com
SIC: 2711 Newspapers, publishing & printing

(G-14805)
POMPANO PRECISION PRODUCTS INC (PA)
1100 Sw 12th Ave (33069-4615)
PHONE..................................954 946-6059
George J Spirio, *President*
Debra A Spirio, *Corp Secy*
Debbie Spirio,
EMP: 30 **EST:** 1971
SQ FT: 14,000
SALES (est): 4.3MM **Privately Held**
WEB: www.pompanoprecision.com
SIC: 3599 Machine shop, jobbing & repair

(G-14806)
PRE-MIX MARBLE TITE INC
1259 Nw 21st St (33069-1428)
PHONE..................................954 917-7665
Howard Ehler, *President*
Steve Brown, *Vice Pres*
◆ **EMP:** 50 **EST:** 1995
SALES (est): 4.2MM **Privately Held**
WEB: www.pmmproducts.com
SIC: 3299 Stucco

(G-14807)
PRECISION BRAZING INC
471 Ne 28th St (33064-5437)
PHONE..................................954 942-8971
Joan Bonneau, *President*
EMP: 9 **EST:** 1995
SALES (est): 457.8K **Privately Held**
WEB: www.precisionbrazing.com
SIC: 7692 Brazing

(G-14808)
PRECISION METAL INDUSTRIES INC
1408 Sw 8th St (33069-4512)
PHONE..................................954 942-6303
Gregory S Wilson, *President*
Gerald E Flint, *Vice Pres*
Susan Rosen, *Marketing Staff*
Donna Richards, *Manager*
▲ **EMP:** 81 **EST:** 1986
SQ FT: 140,000
SALES (est): 23.9MM **Privately Held**
WEB: www.pmiquality.com
SIC: 3444 Sheet metal specialties, not stamped

(G-14809)
PRECISION SMALL ENGINE COMPANY
2510 Nw 16th Ln (33064-1562)
PHONE..................................954 974-1960
Andrew Masciarella, *President*
▼ **EMP:** 15 **EST:** 1979
SQ FT: 15,000
SALES (est): 2.2MM **Privately Held**
WEB: www.precisionusa.com
SIC: 3524 Lawn & garden equipment

(G-14810)
PREMIX-MARBLETITE MFG CO (DH)
1259 Nw 21st St (33069-1428)
PHONE..................................954 970-6540
Howard L Ehler Jr, *President*
Betty J Murchison, *Principal*
Lisa M Brock, *Director*
◆ **EMP:** 10 **EST:** 1950
SQ FT: 20,000
SALES (est): 5.7MM
SALES (corp-wide): 216.4MM **Privately Held**
WEB: www.pmmproducts.com
SIC: 3299 3531 Stucco; mixers: ore, plaster, slag, sand, mortar, etc.
HQ: Imperial Industries, Inc.
1259 Nw 21st St
Pompano Beach FL 33069
954 917-4114

(G-14811)
PRESTIGE SERVICE GROUP
2520 Nw 16th Ln (33064-1529)
PHONE..................................954 532-9014
Joseph Richelieu, *Principal*
EMP: 6 **EST:** 2012
SALES (est): 144K **Privately Held**
SIC: 3559 Metal finishing equipment for plating, etc.

(G-14812)
PRIMA FOOD CORP
Also Called: Diana Food Group
4020 Ne 10th Way (33064-5169)
PHONE..................................954 788-0411
Richard Wodnicki, *President*
Diana Berenson, *VP Admin*
Susan Wodnicki, *CFO*
Susan Cameron, *VP Sales*
EMP: 40 **EST:** 2002
SQ FT: 15,000
SALES (est): 5.3MM **Privately Held**
WEB: www.dianafoodgroup.com
SIC: 2099 Food preparations

(G-14813)
PRINCETON CUSTOM CABINETRY
12550 Nw 39th St (33065-2419)
PHONE..................................954 755-7614
Maria Ornelas, *Buyer*
Slawomir Radziewicz, *Engineer*
Cara Andrea, *Finance Mgr*
Joanne Paladino, *Accountant*
Lynn Olszewski, *Manager*
EMP: 9 **EST:** 2015
SALES (est): 79.9K **Privately Held**
SIC: 2434 Wood kitchen cabinets

(G-14814)
PRINTERS PRINTER INC
2681 W Mcnab Rd (33069-4801)
PHONE..................................954 917-2773
Lou Yovino, *President*
Joey Pompa, *Opers Mgr*
Robert Zelinka, *Controller*
Pamela Laine, *Assistant*
▼ **EMP:** 13 **EST:** 1994
SQ FT: 5,000
SALES (est): 3.4MM **Privately Held**
WEB: www.theprintersprinter.com
SIC: 2731 2759 Book publishing; commercial printing

(G-14815)
PRINTING CORP OF AMERICAS INC
Also Called: PCA
620 Sw 12th Ave (33069-4526)
PHONE..................................954 943-6087
Jan D Tuchman, *President*
Gus Gonzalez, *Plant Mgr*
Bud Tuchman, *Finance*
Steve Konecky, *Sales Mgr*
▼ **EMP:** 30 **EST:** 1979
SQ FT: 16,000
SALES (est): 4.3MM **Privately Held**
WEB: www.pcaprintingplus.com
SIC: 2752 Color lithography

(G-14816)
PRINTING MART INC
1951 W Copans Rd Ste 2 (33064-1549)
PHONE..................................954 753-0323
Veronica Massimino, *President*
John Massimino, *Vice Pres*
Nick Massimino, *Manager*
EMP: 8 **EST:** 1975
SQ FT: 5,000
SALES (est): 601.6K **Privately Held**
WEB: www.theprintingmart.com
SIC: 2752 Commercial printing, offset

(G-14817)
PRINTING MART INC SOUTH FLA
1951 W Copans Rd Ste 2 (33064-1549)
PHONE..................................954 753-0323
John Massimino, *CEO*
Veronica Massimino, *Vice Pres*
EMP: 10 **EST:** 2000
SALES (est): 533K **Privately Held**
SIC: 2759 Commercial printing

(G-14818)
PROFAB ELECTRONICS INC
2855 W Mcnab Rd (33069-4803)
PHONE..................................954 917-1998
Debra Levy, *President*
Mark Levy, *President*
Ryan Levy, *General Mgr*
Yoram Rozenberg, *General Mgr*
Gregory Page, *Business Mgr*
▲ **EMP:** 42 **EST:** 1993
SQ FT: 13,000
SALES (est): 16MM **Privately Held**
WEB: www.profabelectronics.com
SIC: 3672 Circuit boards, television & radio printed

(G-14819)
PROFESSIONAL PRTG FOR LESS INC
3907 N Federal Hwy # 242 (33064-6042)
PHONE..................................954 977-3737
Iris Bernstein, *Principal*
EMP: 6 **EST:** 2018
SALES (est): 109.5K **Privately Held**
WEB: www.ineedaprintingquote.com
SIC: 2752 Commercial printing, lithographic

(G-14820)
PROTECTIVE PRODUCTS ENTPS INC
2102 Sw 2nd St (33069-3116)
PHONE..................................954 630-0900
Ivan Habibe, *CFO*
Denise Clark, *Sales Staff*
Tom Steffen,
Michael Beaver,
◆ **EMP:** 46 **EST:** 2010
SQ FT: 20,000
SALES (est): 8.3MM **Privately Held**
WEB: www.pointblankenterprises.com
SIC: 3842 Bulletproof vests
HQ: Point Blank Enterprises, Inc.
2102 Sw 2nd St
Pompano Beach FL 33069
954 630-0900

(G-14821)
PSP INDUSTRIAL LAUNDRY EQP LLC
2700 Gateway Dr (33069-4322)
PHONE..................................305 517-1421
Eric Zamora, *Mng Member*
EMP: 13 **EST:** 2008
SALES (est): 532.4K **Privately Held**
WEB: www.pspindustrial.com
SIC: 3582 Commercial laundry equipment

(G-14822)
QUALITY FINISHERS INC
640 Ne 26th Ct (33064-5430)
PHONE..................................954 782-3073
EMP: 8

SQ FT: 8,200
SALES (est): 540K **Privately Held**
SIC: 3471 Plating/Polishing Service

(G-14823)
QUICK PRINT
1231 S Powerline Rd (33069-4311)
PHONE..................................954 974-2820
Tom Baiocco, *Principal*
EMP: 7 **EST:** 2010
SALES (est): 144.4K **Privately Held**
WEB: www.copansprinting.com
SIC: 2752 Commercial printing, offset

(G-14824)
R & Z VENTURES INC
Also Called: Kennesaw Fruit & Juice
1300 Sw 1st Ct (33069-3204)
PHONE..................................954 532-7938
Len Roseberg, *President*
Matthew G Roseberg, *Vice Pres*
William T Zukerman, *Vice Pres*
Ed Zukerman, *CFO*
▲ **EMP:** 72 **EST:** 1960
SQ FT: 38,000
SALES (est): 15.7MM **Privately Held**
WEB: www.kennesawjuice.com
SIC: 2033 Fruits & fruit products in cans, jars, etc.; fruit juices: packaged in cans, jars, etc.

(G-14825)
RAW ENERGY MATERIALS CORP
170 Se 13th St (33060-9226)
PHONE..................................954 270-9000
Don Smith, *President*
Bill Flores, *Sales Dir*
▲ **EMP:** 11 **EST:** 2008
SALES (est): 615.4K **Privately Held**
WEB: www.newrebar.com
SIC: 3449 Bars, concrete reinforcing: fabricated steel

(G-14826)
REDITEK CORPORATION
2826 Center Port Cir (33064-2136)
PHONE..................................954 781-1069
Bernardo P Laverde Sr, *President*
Bernardo Laverde, *Vice Pres*
Felipe Laverde, *Mfg Staff*
Bernardo R Laverde Jr, *Director*
Anna Lucena, *Admin Sec*
◆ **EMP:** 16 **EST:** 2001
SALES (est): 959.2K **Privately Held**
WEB: www.reditek.net
SIC: 3644 Electric conduits & fittings

(G-14827)
REINECKER GRINDERS CORP
1700 Nw 15th Ave Ste 310 (33069-1707)
PHONE..................................954 974-6190
Frank Holubeck, *President*
▲ **EMP:** 7 **EST:** 2005
SALES (est): 86.4K **Privately Held**
SIC: 3541 Jig boring & grinding machines; crankshaft regrinding machines

(G-14828)
RELIANCE SUPPLY CO USA LLC
1880 Nw 18th St (33069-1616)
PHONE..................................954 971-9111
Paul E Daly, *President*
Nancy Daly, *Corp Secy*
John C Daly, *Vice Pres*
▼ **EMP:** 6 **EST:** 1950
SQ FT: 5,000
SALES (est): 1MM **Privately Held**
WEB: www.surfacelogix.net
SIC: 2851 Paints & allied products

(G-14829)
RELIANT MEDICAL SERVICES INC
3081 W Mcnab Rd (33069-4805)
PHONE..................................954 977-4224
Gulshakar Mithavayani, *President*
Jesus Rodriguez, *Electrical Engi*
Gail Mithavayani, *CFO*
▲ **EMP:** 6
SALES (est): 1.4MM **Privately Held**
WEB: www.reliantmed.com
SIC: 3572 Medical equipment & supplies

(G-14830)
RELIANT MEDICAL SYSTEMS LLC
3081 W Mcnab Rd (33069-4805)
PHONE..................................954 977-4224
Anwar Mithavayani, *CEO*
Gulshakar Mithavayani, *President*
EMP: 8 **EST:** 2014
SALES (est): 705.5K **Privately Held**
WEB: www.reliantmed.com
SIC: 3841 Surgical & medical instruments

(G-14831)
REVOLUTION AIR CRAFT SERVICES
2511 Nw 16th Ln Ste 3 (33064-1538)
PHONE..................................954 747-4773
Rich Brown, *Principal*
Michael Mannise, *Sales Staff*
Vincent Prestigiacomo, *CIO*
EMP: 11 **EST:** 2011
SALES (est): 1MM **Privately Held**
WEB: www.revolutionfyi.com
SIC: 3812 Aircraft/aerospace flight instruments & guidance systems

(G-14832)
RINSEWORKS INC
1700 Nw 15th Ave Ste 330 (33069-1716)
PHONE..................................954 946-0070
Glenn Ayers, *President*
▲ **EMP:** 10 **EST:** 2012
SQ FT: 6,000
SALES (est): 721.3K **Privately Held**
WEB: www.rinseworks.com
SIC: 3261 Bidets, vitreous china

(G-14833)
RJ UNIQUE CABINETS
2600 Hammondville Rd (33069-1558)
PHONE..................................954 708-0893
Alexander Mijangos, *President*
EMP: 6 **EST:** 2007
SALES (est): 127.5K **Privately Held**
SIC: 2434 Wood kitchen cabinets

(G-14834)
ROSS INDUSTRIES INC
Also Called: Nu-Pac Industries
11440 W Sample Rd (33065-7053)
P.O. Box 8528 (33075-8528)
PHONE..................................954 752-2800
EMP: 80
SALES (corp-wide): 18.7MM **Privately Held**
SIC: 3993 3951 Mfg Signs/Advertising Specialties Mfg Pens/Mechanical Pencils
PA: Ross Industries, Inc.
11440 W Sample Rd
Coral Springs FL
845 292-7677

(G-14835)
RT22 CREATIONS INC
1305 Ne 3rd Ave (33060-5741)
PHONE..................................954 254-8258
Terci Rubens, *Principal*
EMP: 6 **EST:** 2015
SALES (est): 204.6K **Privately Held**
WEB: www.rt22creations.com
SIC: 2434 Wood kitchen cabinets

(G-14836)
RTP CORP
2832 Center Port Cir (33064-2136)
P.O. Box 106030, Atlanta GA (30348-6030)
PHONE..................................954 597-5333
Salvatore Provanzano, *President*
Salvatore R Provanzano, *President*
Warren Bitter, *Mfg Dir*
Roseanne Makowiak, *Human Res Mgr*
Eric Wagoner, *Sales Staff*
EMP: 8
SQ FT: 25,000
SALES (est): 4.8MM **Privately Held**
WEB: www.rtpcorp.com
SIC: 3672 Printed circuit boards

(G-14837)
RWC GROUP LLC
Also Called: Kalashnikov USA
3901 Ne 12th Ave Ste 400 (33064-5196)
PHONE..................................754 222-1407
Peter Viskovatykh, *President*
Bill Gentry, *Vice Pres*
Everold Henry, *CFO*
Evrold Henry, *CFO*
▲ **EMP:** 35 **EST:** 2011
SQ FT: 21,000
SALES (est): 5.4MM **Privately Held**
WEB: www.kalashnikov-usa.com
SIC: 3484 Guns (firearms) or gun parts, 30 mm. & below; pistols or pistol parts, 30 mm. & below; shotguns or shotgun parts, 30 mm. & below

(G-14838)
S & S PROPELLER CO INC
3040 Sw 10th St (33069-4813)
PHONE..................................718 359-3393
John Georgil, *President*
EMP: 9
SALES (corp-wide): 5.4MM **Privately Held**
WEB: www.sspropeller.com
SIC: 3366 Propellers, ship
PA: S & S Propeller Co Inc
2615 123rd St
Flushing NY 11354
718 359-3393

(G-14839)
S A MICROTECHNOLOGIES LLC
2901 Gateway Dr (33069-4326)
PHONE..................................954 973-6166
Michael Tucci, *CEO*
Mario Zuchovicki, *COO*
Arturo Araya, *Engineer*
Robert Schaeffer, *Sales Dir*
Godfrey Ponteur, *Admin Mgr*
EMP: 15 **EST:** 2015
SQ FT: 8,000
SALES (est): 6MM **Privately Held**
WEB: www.microtechnologiessa.com
SIC: 3643 3491 Electric switches; compressed gas cylinder valves
PA: Micro Technologies, S.A.
Condominios Logisticos Rc,
Alajuela

(G-14840)
SAVVY ASSOCIATE INC
Also Called: Tromtech
1480 Sw 3rd St Ste 5 (33069-3225)
PHONE..................................954 941-6986
Derrick Miller, *President*
EMP: 10 **EST:** 1983
SQ FT: 3,000
SALES (est): 560K **Privately Held**
SIC: 3599 3841 3769 3728 Electrical discharge machining (EDM); surgical & medical instruments; guided missile & space vehicle parts & auxiliary equipment; aircraft parts & equipment; manufactured hardware (general)

(G-14841)
SC CAPITAL VENTURES INC
Also Called: Next Level
3025 Nw 25th Ave (33069-1028)
PHONE..................................954 657-8563
EMP: 24
SALES (corp-wide): 311.7K **Privately Held**
SIC: 2542 Pallet racks: except wood
PA: Sc Capital Ventures, Inc.
401 Ryland St Ste 200a
Reno NV 89502
800 230-8846

(G-14842)
SCREEN GRAPHICS FLORIDA INC (PA)
1801 N Andrews Ave (33069-1422)
PHONE..................................800 346-4420
Nick Glaros, *President*
Natacha Abreu, *Vice Pres*
Lynn Opperman, *VP Opers*
Matthew Sadowski, *Materials Mgr*
Natasha Bumbeck, *Production*
◆ **EMP:** 45 **EST:** 1973
SQ FT: 47,800
SALES: 13.9MM **Privately Held**
WEB: www.screen-graphics.com
SIC: 2759 2754 Screen printing; commercial printing, gravure

(G-14843)
SDS DENTAL INC
Also Called: Summit Dental Systems
1280 Sw 27th Ave (33069-4320)
PHONE..................................954 730-3636
Cesar Coral, *President*
Veronica Coral, *Vice Pres*
Shaun Taylor, *Vice Pres*
Larry Brady, *Sales Staff*
Ivonne Moctezuma, *Sales Staff*
▲ **EMP:** 28 **EST:** 1986
SQ FT: 50,000
SALES (est): 8MM **Privately Held**
WEB: www.summitdental.com
SIC: 3843 Dental equipment

(G-14844)
SE CUSTOM LIFT SYSTEMS INC
1801 Sw 7th Ave (33060-9027)
P.O. Box 1715 (33061-1715)
PHONE..................................954 941-8090
Mitchell Scavone, *President*
Denise Scavone, *Treasurer*
EMP: 8 **EST:** 1996
SQ FT: 5,000
SALES (est): 1MM **Privately Held**
WEB: www.secboatlifts.com
SIC: 3536 Boat lifts

(G-14845)
SEA 21-21 LLC
2211 Nw 30th Pl (33069-1026)
PHONE..................................954 366-4677
Jorge Fernandez,
EMP: 8 **EST:** 2015
SALES (est): 842.9K **Privately Held**
SIC: 2023 Dietary supplements, dairy & non-dairy based

(G-14846)
SEASIDE GRAPHICS INC
100 Sw 5th St (33060-7904)
PHONE..................................954 782-7151
Stephen Blake, *President*
▼ **EMP:** 7 **EST:** 1975
SQ FT: 3,600
SALES (est): 650K **Privately Held**
WEB: www.seasidegraphics.com
SIC: 2759 Screen printing

(G-14847)
SER-MAT INTERNATIONAL LLC
3200 Nw 27th Ave Ste 106 (33069-6001)
PHONE..................................954 525-1417
Mark Kreisel, *President*
Gregory R Hartenhoff, *General Mgr*
Carlos Camacho, *Opers Staff*
▲ **EMP:** 33 **EST:** 1953
SQ FT: 5,700
SALES (est): 3.3MM **Privately Held**
WEB: www.sermat.aero
SIC: 2273 Carpets & rugs

(G-14848)
SEVEN KEYS CO OF FLORIDA
450 Sw 12th Ave (33069-3504)
PHONE..................................954 946-5010
Henry Stevens, *President*
Sophia Sanso, *Admin Sec*
EMP: 8 **EST:** 1956
SQ FT: 15,000
SALES (est): 1.4MM **Privately Held**
SIC: 2033 Jellies, edible, including imitation: in cans, jars, etc.; preserves, including imitation: in cans, jars, etc.

(G-14849)
SEW WHATS NEW EMBROIDERY INC
2520 N Powerline Rd # 301 (33069-1055)
PHONE..................................954 977-3339
Stuart Rosen, *President*
EMP: 6 **EST:** 2008
SALES (est): 296.8K **Privately Held**
SIC: 2395 5699 Embroidery & art needlework; miscellaneous apparel & accessories

(G-14850)
SIGN UP NOW SIGN COMPANY LLC
620 Se 10th St (33060-9405)
PHONE..................................754 224-9091
Kimberly A Purinton, *Principal*
EMP: 8 **EST:** 2011

SALES (est): 221K Privately Held
WEB: www.signsnow.com
SIC: 3993 Signs & advertising specialties

(G-14851)
SIGNS OF REILLY
1121 W Mcnab Rd (33069-4720)
PHONE....954 263-7829
Michael Reilly, President
EMP: 8 EST: 2007
SALES (est): 256.5K Privately Held
WEB: www.signsofreilly.com
SIC: 3993 Signs & advertising specialties

(G-14852)
SINCERUS PHARMACEUTICALS INC
3265 W Mcnab Rd (33069-4807)
PHONE....800 604-5032
Spencer J Malkin, CEO
Jonathan Fenster, COO
Doris Scabo, Vice Pres
EMP: 110 EST: 2015
SALES (est): 11.1MM Privately Held
SIC: 2844 2834 5122 Cosmetic preparations; dermatologicals; cosmetics

(G-14853)
SMITH BOAT DESIGNS INC
Also Called: Smith Power Boats
1200 S Dixie Hwy W (33060-8519)
PHONE....954 782-1000
Don Smith, President
Dawn Dovner, Manager
EMP: 46 EST: 1984
SQ FT: 16,000
SALES (est): 707K Privately Held
SIC: 3732 Motorized boat, building & repairing

(G-14854)
SMITH SURFACE PREP SYSTEMS INC
Also Called: Smith Surface-Prep Solutions
2504 Nw 19th St (33069-5229)
PHONE....954 941-9744
Mark William Sheahan, CEO
EMP: 53 EST: 2019
SALES (est): 4.1MM
SALES (corp-wide): 1.6B Publicly Held
WEB: www.graco.com
SIC: 3561 Industrial pumps & parts
PA: Graco Inc.
88 11th Ave Ne
Minneapolis MN 55413
612 623-6000

(G-14855)
SOLAR MANUFACTURING INC (PA)
1888 Nw 22nd Ct (33069-1312)
PHONE....954 973-8488
David Stiles, President
Phyllis Stiles, Corp Secy
Richard Stiles, Vice Pres
EMP: 35 EST: 1982
SALES (est): 2.8MM Privately Held
SIC: 3272 Concrete products, precast

(G-14856)
SONG-CHUAN USA INC
2841 Center Port Cir (33064-2135)
PHONE....954 788-5889
Roger Biddle, CEO
Robert Foster, Corp Secy
Sean McCarthy, Vice Pres
Scott Mulkey, Opers Mgr
Bill Simon, Warehouse Mgr
◆ EMP: 14 EST: 1996
SQ FT: 10,000
SALES (est): 4.4MM Privately Held
WEB: www.songchuanusa.com
SIC: 3625 Relays & industrial controls
PA: Song Chuan Precision Co., Ltd.
No. 377, Zhonghua Rd.
New Taipei City TAP 23858

(G-14857)
SOUTH FLA PAVEMENT COATINGS
1831 Nw 33rd St (33064-1308)
PHONE....954 979-5997
Gregory Scott Polk, President
EMP: 10 EST: 2015
SALES (est): 1.1MM Privately Held
SIC: 2851 Lacquers, varnishes, enamels & other coatings

(G-14858)
SOUTH FLORIDA SIGN CO
2133 Nw 22nd St (33069-1342)
PHONE....954 973-6649
Rick Stegman, General Mgr
Richard E Stegman, Principal
Patty Stegman-Biron, CIO
EMP: 7 EST: 2015
SALES (est): 334.3K Privately Held
WEB: www.southfloridasigncompany.com
SIC: 3993 Signs & advertising specialties

(G-14859)
SOUTH FLORIDA STRIP TEES INC
1740 Nw 22nd Ct Ste 10 (33069-1327)
PHONE....954 972-4899
Robert Freeman, President
EMP: 13 EST: 1997
SQ FT: 2,000
SALES (est): 969K Privately Held
WEB: www.activewearcatalog.com
SIC: 2261 Screen printing of cotton broadwoven fabrics

(G-14860)
SOUTH FLORIDA TEXTILE INC
1301 W Copans Rd Ste E7 (33064-2228)
PHONE....954 973-5677
Joseph Lanzaro, President
EMP: 12 EST: 1987
SQ FT: 4,500
SALES (est): 446.7K Privately Held
SIC: 2339 Women's & misses' outerwear

(G-14861)
SOUTHEAST SECURITY PRODUCTS
1387 Sw 12th Ave (33069-4630)
PHONE....954 786-5900
Roy Nilsen, President
Margaret Debonis, Opers Mgr
Margaret Labanowitz, Opers Mgr
John Kelley, Sales Mgr
John Sprague, Sales Mgr
EMP: 8 EST: 1993
SALES (est): 1.1MM Privately Held
WEB: www.sesecurityproducts.com
SIC: 3699 Security control equipment & systems

(G-14862)
SOUTHERN BOATING & YACHTING
Also Called: Southern Boating Magazine
1591 E Atl Blvd Ste 200 (33060-6765)
PHONE....954 522-5515
George A Allen Jr, Chairman
Steve Davis, Chief
Jenilee Pharo, Sales Associate
Vincent Scutellaro, Adv Dir
Erin Brennan, Marketing Staff
▼ EMP: 35 EST: 1972
SALES (est): 5MM Privately Held
WEB: www.southernboating.com
SIC: 2721 Magazines: publishing only, not printed on site

(G-14863)
SOUTHERN GROUTS & MORTARS INC (PA)
Also Called: S G M
1502 Sw 2nd Pl (33069-3291)
PHONE....954 943-2288
Ron Picou, President
Elizabeth Picou-Mckee, Exec VP
Scott Maguire, Opers Staff
Jason Eckenrod, Sales Staff
Tonya Grogg,
◆ EMP: 70 EST: 1978
SQ FT: 50,000
SALES (est): 29.1MM Privately Held
WEB: www.sgm.cc
SIC: 2891 Adhesives

(G-14864)
SOUTHERN MICRO ETCH INC
610 Ne 29th St (33064-5447)
P.O. Box 1089 (33061-1089)
PHONE....954 781-5999
Fax: 954 781-8188
EMP: 12
SALES (est): 1.5MM Privately Held
SIC: 3479 Coating/Engraving Service

(G-14865)
SOUTHSTERN ARSPC SVCS LTD LBLT
1816 Sw 7th Ave (33060-9028)
PHONE....305 992-8257
Nicolas S Smith, President
EMP: 7 EST: 2015
SALES (est): 1.1MM Privately Held
WEB: www.southeasternaerospace.com
SIC: 3721 Aircraft

(G-14866)
SPIEGEL PAVERS INC
3400 Blue Lake Dr Apt 102 (33064-2028)
PHONE....954 687-5797
Marcio E Vieira, President
EMP: 6 EST: 2012
SALES (est): 155.2K Privately Held
SIC: 2951 Asphalt paving mixtures & blocks

(G-14867)
SSE AND ASSOCIATES INC
1500 W Copans Rd Ste A9 (33064-1521)
PHONE....954 973-7144
EMP: 33 Privately Held
WEB: www.sseteam.com
SIC: 3949 Sporting & athletic goods
PA: Sse And Associates, Inc.
569 Canal St
New Smyrna Beach FL 32168

(G-14868)
STAT INDUSTRY INC
90 E Mcnab Rd (33060-9238)
PHONE....561 826-7045
Deborah A Raney, President
Michael Manfred, Mfg Staff
Ray Walvis, Sales Mgr
Dave Skare, Director
EMP: 10 EST: 2009
SQ FT: 3,000
SALES (est): 1.6MM Privately Held
WEB: www.beadedhope.com
SIC: 3728 Aircraft parts & equipment

(G-14869)
STE-RO INC
257 S Cypress Rd Apt 427 (33060-7076)
PHONE....754 234-1789
Istvan Soos, Principal
EMP: 6 EST: 2011
SALES (est): 86.8K Privately Held
SIC: 2095 Roasted coffee

(G-14870)
STEEDA ENGINEERING AND MFG LLC
1351 Nw Steeda Way (33069-1521)
PHONE....954 960-0774
Dario Orlando, Manager
EMP: 6 EST: 2004
SALES (est): 39.6K Privately Held
SIC: 3999 Manufacturing industries

(G-14871)
STIMWAVE LLC
1310 Park Central Blvd S (33064-2217)
PHONE....800 965-5134
Patrick Tompkins, Exec VP
Steven Amelio, CFO
Jim Surek, Ch Credit Ofcr
Stormie Crouch, Sales Staff
Greene Elizabeth, Sales Staff
EMP: 10 EST: 2015
SALES (est): 2.6MM Privately Held
WEB: www.stimwavefreedom.com
SIC: 3845 Electromedical equipment

(G-14872)
STIMWAVE TECHNOLOGIES INC (PA)
1310 Park Central Blvd S (33064-2217)
PHONE....800 965-5134
Laura Perryman, President
James M Rallo, CFO
Martin West, Controller
Erin Valin, Mktg Coord
Kimberly Letourneau, Marketing Staff
EMP: 4 EST: 2010
SALES (est): 3.3MM Privately Held
WEB: www.stimwavefreedom.com
SIC: 3845 Laser systems & equipment, medical

(G-14873)
STONE DESIGN BY SANTOS LLC
1440 Nw 14th Ave (33069-1913)
PHONE....954 366-1919
Marcela P Santos, Mng Member
Farley Dos Santos, Mng Member
EMP: 7 EST: 2018
SALES (est): 289K Privately Held
WEB: www.stonedesignbysantos.com
SIC: 3281 Building stone products

(G-14874)
STONY CREEK SAND & GRAVEL LLC (PA)
2103 N Riverside Dr (33062-1225)
PHONE....804 229-0015
Brian C Purcell,
EMP: 16 EST: 2011
SALES (est): 261.5K Privately Held
WEB: www.stonycreeksand.com
SIC: 1442 Construction sand & gravel

(G-14875)
STRATEGIC BRANDS INC
Also Called: Laurey Co
2810 Center Port Cir (33064-2136)
PHONE....516 745-6100
Steven Friedel, Chairman
Sansford Steiger, Vice Pres
◆ EMP: 10 EST: 1994
SQ FT: 1,600
SALES (est): 1.3MM Privately Held
WEB: www.strategicbrandsincorporated.com
SIC: 3429 Cabinet hardware

(G-14876)
SUN 3D CORPORATION
2530 N Powerline Rd # 402 (33069-1056)
PHONE....954 210-6010
Gustavo Lopez, President
Janice Atherton, Admin Sec
EMP: 9 EST: 2014
SALES (est): 605.2K Privately Held
WEB: www.sun3dcorporation.com
SIC: 2752 Commercial printing, offset

(G-14877)
SUN NATION CORP
2861 Nw 22nd Ter (33069-1045)
PHONE....954 822-5460
Cary Chen, CEO
▲ EMP: 10 EST: 2018
SALES (est): 551.5K Privately Held
WEB: www.sunnationcorp.com
SIC: 3559 Automotive maintenance equipment

(G-14878)
SUNBELT TRANSFORMER LTD
2063 Blount Rd (33069-5110)
PHONE....305 517-3657
Eric Johnson, Branch Mgr
EMP: 9
SALES (corp-wide): 39.6MM Privately Held
WEB: www.sunbeltusa.com
SIC: 3612 Power & distribution transformers
PA: Sunbelt Transformer, Ltd.
1922 S Mrtn Lther King Jr
Temple TX 76504
800 433-3128

(G-14879)
SUNCOAST AUTOMOTIVE PDTS INC
3024 Nw 25th Ave (33069-1027)
PHONE....954 973-4822
James Ferrari, President
Jo Anne Ghiling, Office Mgr
▲ EMP: 12 EST: 1982
SQ FT: 38,000
SALES (est): 429.1K Privately Held
SIC: 3694 Alternators, automotive; motors, starting: automotive & aircraft

GEOGRAPHIC

(G-14880)
SUPERIOR SIGNS AND PRINTS
1800 Nw 15th Ave (33069-1403)
PHONE..................................954 780-6351
Kris Lim, *Principal*
EMP: 6 **EST:** 2014
SALES (est): 227.8K **Privately Held**
WEB: www.superiorsignsandprints.com
SIC: 2752 Commercial printing, lithographic

(G-14881)
SYMMETRICAL STAIR INC
2115 Sw 2nd St (33069-3100)
PHONE..................................561 228-4800
Alphonso J Cheponis III, *President*
Mindy Discala, *Vice Pres*
EMP: 15 **EST:** 1995
SQ FT: 55,000
SALES (est): 1MM **Privately Held**
WEB: www.symmetricalstair.com
SIC: 2431 Staircases & stairs, wood

(G-14882)
T M BUILDING PRODUCTS LTD
601 Nw 12th Ave (33069-2003)
PHONE..................................954 781-4430
Thomas J Metzger, *President*
T M Acquisition Corp, *General Ptnr*
EMP: 5 **EST:** 1989
SQ FT: 85,000
SALES (est): 1.5MM
SALES (corp-wide): 8.9MM **Privately Held**
WEB: www.andlinger.com
SIC: 3442 Sash, door or window: metal
PA: Andlinger & Company, Inc.
520 White Plins Rd Ste 50
Tarrytown NY 10591
914 332-4900

(G-14883)
TANNOUS INNOVATIONS LLC
2157 Nw 22nd St (33069-1344)
PHONE..................................754 220-6645
▲ **EMP:** 5
SALES (est): 561.9K **Privately Held**
SIC: 3631 Mfg Household Cooking Equipment

(G-14884)
TEKK SUPPLY INC
290 Sw 14th Ave (33069-3232)
PHONE..................................954 444-5782
Robert Reiner, *President*
EMP: 6 **EST:** 2012
SALES (est): 1.8MM **Privately Held**
WEB: www.tekkpirates.com
SIC: 3965 5251 5085 Fasteners; tools; industrial supplies

(G-14885)
TELENETPRO INC
43 S Powerline Rd Ste 499 (33069-3001)
PHONE..................................954 333-8633
Luis Aguirre, *President*
EMP: 15 **EST:** 2012
SQ FT: 2,500
SALES (est): 756.9K **Privately Held**
SIC: 3842 5699 5999 Bulletproof vests; military goods & regalia; police supply stores

(G-14886)
TESTMAXX SERVICES CORPORATION
1111 W Mcnab Rd (33069-4720)
PHONE..................................954 946-7100
Michael G Ames, *President*
EMP: 10 **EST:** 1987
SQ FT: 7,000
SALES (est): 1.4MM **Privately Held**
SIC: 3825 8748 Test equipment for electronic & electric measurement; testing services

(G-14887)
TKO PRINT SOLUTIONS INC
Also Called: Think Print
140 Park Central Blvd S (33064-2138)
PHONE..................................954 315-0990
John Laudadio, *President*
EMP: 30 **EST:** 2014
SALES (est): 2.8MM **Privately Held**
WEB: www.thinkprint.com
SIC: 2752 Commercial printing, offset

(G-14888)
TOPS KITCHEN CABINET LLC
1900 Nw 18th St (33069-1618)
PHONE..................................954 933-9988
Ping Lin, *President*
◆ **EMP:** 11 **EST:** 2006
SALES (est): 1.1MM **Privately Held**
WEB: www.topscabinet.net
SIC: 2434 Wood kitchen cabinets

(G-14889)
TPL MANUFACTURING INC
461 Ne 27th St (33064-5431)
PHONE..................................954 783-3400
Koule Lyras, *President*
EMP: 9 **EST:** 2001
SQ FT: 8,000
SALES (est): 878.8K **Privately Held**
WEB: www.tplmanufacturing.com
SIC: 2511 Wood household furniture

(G-14890)
TRI-COUNTY WOODWORKING LLC
3001 Sw 10th St (33069-4814)
PHONE..................................954 850-2222
David R Morisette, *Manager*
EMP: 10 **EST:** 2019
SALES (est): 1MM **Privately Held**
SIC: 2431 Millwork

(G-14891)
TRIFECTA PHRMCEUTICALS USA LLC (PA)
4100 N Powerline Rd J4 (33073-3083)
PHONE..................................888 296-9067
Gregory Brondou, *Mng Member*
▲ **EMP:** 5 **EST:** 2013
SALES (est): 1.3MM **Privately Held**
WEB: www.trifecta-pharma.com
SIC: 2834 Pharmaceutical preparations

(G-14892)
TROPICAL SHOWERS INC
1433 Ne 28th St (33064-6817)
PHONE..................................954 260-5196
Barry White, *Owner*
EMP: 6 **EST:** 2004
SALES (est): 84.1K **Privately Held**
SIC: 3444 Metal housings, enclosures, casings & other containers

(G-14893)
TRUGREEN PRODUCTS LLC
1010 S Ocean Blvd Apt 408 (33062-6625)
PHONE..................................954 629-5794
Howard Serkin, *CEO*
EMP: 8 **EST:** 2017
SALES (est): 47.2K **Privately Held**
WEB: www.trugreen.com
SIC: 2841 7389 Soap & other detergents;

(G-14894)
TSFPR LLC
1501 W Copans Rd (33064-1544)
PHONE..................................954 691-9031
EMP: 16 **EST:** 2018
SALES (est): 633.9K **Privately Held**
SIC: 2759 Screen printing

(G-14895)
TUFLEX MANUFACTURING CO
1406 Sw 8th St (33069-4512)
PHONE..................................954 781-0605
Thomas A Sayward, *President*
Barbara Grasso, *Admin Sec*
EMP: 22 **EST:** 1964
SQ FT: 23,400
SALES (est): 3.5MM **Privately Held**
WEB: www.tuflexmfg.com
SIC: 3089 3713 3088 Plastic & fiberglass tanks; truck & bus bodies; plastics plumbing fixtures

(G-14896)
UIP INTERNATIONAL INC (PA)
1350 S Dixie Hwy E (33060-8515)
P.O. Box 5088, Fort Lauderdale (33310-5088)
PHONE..................................954 785-3539
Howard D White, *President*
Jeff Cronemiller, *Division Mgr*
Horace S White, *Vice Pres*
Howie White, *Vice Pres*
Nancy Bordan, *Controller*
◆ **EMP:** 4 **EST:** 1992
SQ FT: 100,000
SALES (est): 3MM **Privately Held**
WEB: www.uipintl.com
SIC: 3052 Plastic hose

(G-14897)
ULTRA PHARMA LLC
3131 W Mcnab Rd (33069)
PHONE..................................954 532-7539
EMP: 5
SALES (est): 394K **Privately Held**
SIC: 2834 Mfg Pharmaceutical Preparations

(G-14898)
UNAFLEX LLC (PA)
1350 S Dixie Hwy E (33060-8515)
P.O. Box 1229, Anderson SC (29622-1229)
PHONE..................................954 943-5002
Jimmy White, *Human Resources*
Tom Allen, *Accounts Mgr*
Howard D White, *Mng Member*
Horace Ted White II,
Valerie Deorio, *Receptionist*
◆ **EMP:** 25 **EST:** 2010
SQ FT: 100,000
SALES (est): 20.7MM **Privately Held**
WEB: www.fluidhandling.kadant.com
SIC: 3052 3599 2822 Hose, pneumatic: rubber or rubberized fabric; hose, flexible metallic; neoprene, chloroprene

(G-14899)
UNIQUE RABBIT STUDIOS INC
1631 S Dixie Hwy Ste B1 (33060-8951)
PHONE..................................954 691-1390
John W Belcher, *President*
Shane Mitchell, *General Mgr*
EMP: 9 **EST:** 2008
SALES (est): 757.6K **Privately Held**
WEB: www.uniquerabbitstudios.com
SIC: 3299 Architectural sculptures: gypsum, clay, papier mache, etc.

(G-14900)
UNITED CIRCUITS INC
1410 Sw 29th Ave Ste 300 (33069-4849)
PHONE..................................954 971-6860
Javier C Ruiz, *President*
Bob Felder, *Vice Pres*
Cindy Ruiz, *Vice Pres*
Jenny Ruiz, *Purchasing*
Jennifer Ruiz, *Director*
EMP: 12 **EST:** 1993
SQ FT: 5,000
SALES (est): 1.2MM **Privately Held**
WEB: www.united-circuits.com
SIC: 3672 Printed circuit boards

(G-14901)
UNITED PRINTING LLC
2323 Ne 26th Ave (33062-1147)
PHONE..................................954 554-7969
John A Vanbrocklin, *Administration*
EMP: 8 **EST:** 2013
SALES (est): 259K **Privately Held**
WEB: www.united-processing.com
SIC: 2752 Commercial printing, lithographic

(G-14902)
UNITED PRINTING SALES INC
Also Called: Minutemen Printing
51 N Federal Hwy (33062-4304)
PHONE..................................954 942-4300
Robert Johnson, *President*
Rosemary R Johnson, *Vice Pres*
EMP: 5 **EST:** 1996
SALES (est): 306.5K **Privately Held**
WEB: www.chanhassen-mn.minutemanpress.com
SIC: 2752 Commercial printing, lithographic

(G-14903)
UNIVERSAL GENERATORS LLC
5231 Pinetree Rd (33067-4110)
PHONE..................................954 383-5394
Barry Klein, *Principal*
EMP: 6 **EST:** 2014
SALES (est): 83.7K **Privately Held**
WEB: www.universalgenerators.com
SIC: 3621 Motors & generators

(G-14904)
US CONCRETE PRODUCTS CORP
1878 Nw 21st St (33069-1334)
PHONE..................................954 973-0368
Albert Mancini, *President*
Nicholas Mancini, *Treasurer*
▲ **EMP:** 70 **EST:** 1993
SQ FT: 3,600
SALES (est): 12.6MM **Privately Held**
WEB: www.unitedstatesconcrete.com
SIC: 3272 Concrete products, precast

(G-14905)
US CUSTOM FABRICATION INC
1858 Nw 21st St (33069-1306)
PHONE..................................954 917-6161
Lynn Campbell, *President*
Lisa Edwards, *Treasurer*
EMP: 5 **EST:** 2002
SQ FT: 2,500
SALES (est): 726K **Privately Held**
WEB: www.uscustomfab.com
SIC: 3441 Fabricated structural metal

(G-14906)
US RECREATIONAL ALLIANCE INC
Also Called: Coastline Marine
820 Sw 14th Ct (33060-8526)
PHONE..................................954 782-7279
James Strauss, *President*
EMP: 13 **EST:** 2016
SALES (est): 1.1MM **Privately Held**
SIC: 3732 Motorboats, inboard or outboard: building & repairing

(G-14907)
VALLEY FORGE TEXTILES LLC
1390 Sw 30th Ave (33069-4823)
PHONE..................................954 971-1776
Fax: 954 968-4111
▲ **EMP:** 8
SALES (est): 875.9K **Privately Held**
SIC: 2231 2299 2221 2241 Wool Brdwv Fabric Mill Mfg Textile Goods Manmad Brdwv Fabric Mill Narrow Fabric Mill Whol Piece Goods/Notions

(G-14908)
VEE ENTERPRISES INC
Also Called: Graves Company
4100 N Powerline Rd I5 (33073-3083)
P.O. Box 11269 (33061-7269)
PHONE..................................954 960-0300
Peter Erdo, *President*
Deborah Vanzo, *Director*
EMP: 6 **EST:** 1946
SQ FT: 12,000
SALES (est): 454.2K **Privately Held**
WEB: www.gravescompany.com
SIC: 3915 Lapidary work, contract or other

(G-14909)
VIVIDUS LLC
3265 W Mcnab Rd (33069-4807)
PHONE..................................954 326-1954
Alex Chervinsky, *CEO*
Barry Reiter, *COO*
Marc Poirier, *CFO*
EMP: 8 **EST:** 2013
SALES (est): 486.3K **Privately Held**
WEB: www.vividus.com
SIC: 2834 Pharmaceutical preparations

(G-14910)
VURB LLC
2450 W Sample Rd Ste 14 (33073-3074)
PHONE..................................561 441-8870
Anthony Mastrangelo, *Principal*
Carmelo Mastrangelo,
EMP: 11 **EST:** 2014
SALES (est): 296.6K **Privately Held**
WEB: www.popyourpup.com
SIC: 2759 Promotional printing

(G-14911)
W & B SCIENTIFIC INC
Also Called: Bioquem USA
1301 W Copans Rd Ste H7 (33064-2231)
PHONE..................................954 607-1500

Carlos A S Barreto, *President*
EMP: 13 **EST:** 2015
SALES (est): 5.9MM **Privately Held**
WEB: www.wbscientific.com
SIC: 2869 3821 Laboratory chemicals, organic; chemical laboratory apparatus; clinical laboratory instruments, except medical & dental

(G-14912)
WESTECH DEVELOPMENT GROUP INC
Also Called: Westech Industries
3010 N Andrews Avenue Ext (33064-2114)
PHONE....................................954 505-5090
Ning Wang, *Treasurer*
Sam Pascucci, *Admin Sec*
EMP: 8 **EST:** 2011
SALES (est): 891.8K **Privately Held**
SIC: 3861 Cameras & related equipment

(G-14913)
WICKS UNLIMITED INC
1515 Sw 13th Ct (33069-4710)
PHONE....................................631 472-2010
Edwin Stimpson, *Principal*
Bruce Campbell, *Director*
EMP: 6 **EST:** 2000
SQ FT: 300,000
SALES (est): 143.9K **Privately Held**
WEB: www.wicksunlimited.com
SIC: 3999 Candles

(G-14914)
WILLIAMS TENDERS USA INC
451 S Federal Hwy (33062-5901)
PHONE....................................954 648-6560
Christopher Rimmer, *Principal*
◆ **EMP:** 11 **EST:** 2014
SALES (est): 861.7K **Privately Held**
WEB: www.williamsjettenders.com
SIC: 3732 Boat building & repairing

(G-14915)
ZEPSA INDUSTRIES
41 Sw 6th St (33060-7915)
PHONE....................................754 307-2173
EMP: 7 **EST:** 2017
SALES (est): 70.5K **Privately Held**
WEB: www.zepsa.com
SIC: 3999 Manufacturing industries

(G-14916)
ZUMRO MANUFACTURING INC
650 Sw 16th Ter (33069-4533)
P.O. Box 667227 (33066-7227)
PHONE....................................954 782-7779
Win Vanbasten, *President*
Noelia Sanchez, *Prdtn Mgr*
Thamer Azule, *Executive*
▲ **EMP:** 29 **EST:** 2002
SQ FT: 10,000
SALES (est): 1.4MM **Privately Held**
WEB: www.zumro.com
SIC: 3669 Emergency alarms

Ponce De Leon
Walton County

(G-14917)
ARBAN & ASSOCIATES INC
1464 Line Rd (32455-6310)
PHONE....................................850 836-4362
Robert Arban, *President*
Sylvia J Arban, *Corp Secy*
Timothy Alford, *Vice Pres*
EMP: 23 **EST:** 1986
SQ FT: 1,400
SALES (est): 3.9MM **Privately Held**
SIC: 2439 Trusses, wooden roof

(G-14918)
S B LIGHTING LLC
2889 N Highway 81 (32455-6725)
PHONE....................................850 687-1166
Steven S Busby, *Manager*
EMP: 7 **EST:** 2010
SALES (est): 119.2K **Privately Held**
SIC: 3648 Lighting equipment

(G-14919)
U-LOAD DUMPSTERS LLC
Also Called: Brandon Brown Newsom
1450 Mitchell Rd (32455-6308)
PHONE....................................352 318-3045
Brandon Newsom, *Principal*
EMP: 6 **EST:** 2015
SALES (est): 262K **Privately Held**
SIC: 3443 Dumpsters, garbage

(G-14920)
UNITED NTONS SPACE CRPS MLTARY (PA) ✪
Also Called: Majestic Unsc Spcial Intllgnce
10310 County Highway 3280 (32455-4305)
PHONE....................................702 373-2351
Aaron Taylor, *Exec Dir*
EMP: 11 **EST:** 2020
SALES (est): 522K **Privately Held**
WEB: www.majesticdiner.com
SIC: 3443 8211 9221 9711 Nuclear reactors, military or industrial; military academy; bureau of criminal investigation, government; Air Force

Ponce Inlet
Volusia County

(G-14921)
8 GIRLS & A GUY PRINTING LLC
31 Sun Dunes Cir (32127-7053)
PHONE....................................386 492-5976
Anthony J Parker, *Principal*
EMP: 6 **EST:** 2012
SALES (est): 150K **Privately Held**
SIC: 2752 Commercial printing, lithographic

Ponte Vedra
St. Johns County

(G-14922)
2JCP LLC
Also Called: Gt Ice LLC
101 Marketside Ave (32081-1541)
PHONE....................................904 834-3818
Trevor Richter, *VP Bus Dvlpt*
Paul Schuster, *Director*
Stephen Rippon,
Jan Paces,
Trevor Richer,
▲ **EMP:** 7 **EST:** 2012
SALES (est): 3MM
SALES (corp-wide): 609.8K **Privately Held**
WEB: www.2jcp.com
SIC: 3511 Gas turbine generator set units, complete
HQ: 2 Jcp A.S.
Racice 126
Racice 411 0
416 857-511

(G-14923)
COUNTER ACTIVE INC
Also Called: Silestone of Tampa
87 Sanchez Dr E (32082-2446)
PHONE....................................813 626-0022
Robert D Hutto, *President*
Pete Valentine, *Vice Pres*
▲ **EMP:** 10 **EST:** 1999
SQ FT: 20,000
SALES (est): 434.8K **Privately Held**
SIC: 2541 Counter & sink tops

(G-14924)
DAILYS 1113 SHELL
40 Settlement Dr (32081-0758)
PHONE....................................904 608-0219
EMP: 12 **EST:** 2015
SALES (est): 166.2K **Privately Held**
WEB: www.dailys.com
SIC: 2711 Newspapers

(G-14925)
FIVE STAR MARBLE AND STONE
117 Taylor Ridge Ave (32081-8453)
PHONE....................................904 887-4736
Bakir Mehmedinovic, *Principal*
EMP: 7 **EST:** 2019
SALES (est): 509.9K **Privately Held**
SIC: 3281 Cut stone & stone products

(G-14926)
LESKO INDUSTRIES INC
104 Twin Cedar Ct (32082-3681)
PHONE....................................904 273-8293
Ryan Lesko, *Principal*
EMP: 6 **EST:** 2018
SALES (est): 128.8K **Privately Held**
SIC: 3999 Manufacturing industries

(G-14927)
OPTIMUM SPRING MFG INC
150 Hilden Rd Ste 316 (32081-8405)
P.O. Box 600070, Jacksonville (32260-0070)
PHONE....................................904 567-5999
Andrea De Palma, *Principal*
EMP: 7 **EST:** 2015
SALES (est): 151.2K **Privately Held**
WEB: www.optimumspring.com
SIC: 3495 Wire springs

(G-14928)
TREACE MEDICAL CONCEPTS INC
203 Fort Wade Rd Unit 150 (32081-5159)
PHONE....................................904 373-5940
John T Treace, *CEO*
James T Treace, *Ch of Bd*
Joe W Ferguson, *Senior VP*
Dipak A Rajhansa, *Senior VP*
Sean F Scanlan, *Senior VP*
EMP: 133 **EST:** 2014
SQ FT: 23,060
SALES: 57.3MM **Privately Held**
WEB: www.treace.com
SIC: 3841 Fixation appliances, internal

Ponte Vedra Beach
St. Johns County

(G-14929)
AI THOMAS LLC
Also Called: Ait Environmental Technology
220 Pnte Vdra Pk Dr Ste 1 (32082)
PHONE....................................904 553-6202
Dennis Holler, *General Mgr*
Angelo Passantino, *Regional Mgr*
Herman Everidge, *Vice Pres*
Michael Castranova, *Opers Staff*
Cameron Clements, *Manager*
EMP: 30 **EST:** 2006
SALES (est): 857.7K **Privately Held**
WEB: www.mailer.fsu.edu
SIC: 2879 Agricultural chemicals

(G-14930)
ALIVE BY NATURE INC
130 Corridor Rd Ste 3333 (32082-3225)
P.O. Box 3333 (32004-3333)
PHONE....................................800 810-1935
Bryan Nettles, *Principal*
Bryan E Nettles, *Vice Pres*
EMP: 7 **EST:** 2010
SALES (est): 610.9K **Privately Held**
WEB: www.alivebyscience.com
SIC: 2833 Vitamins, natural or synthetic: bulk, uncompounded

(G-14931)
ALTA TECHNOLOGIES INC
285 Plantation Cir S (32082-3936)
PHONE....................................609 538-9500
Paul Snook, *President*
Percy F Leaper, *Chairman*
Laura Snook, *Vice Pres*
Mary Alice-Leaper, *Treasurer*
EMP: 9
SQ FT: 12,000
SALES (est): 2.1MM **Privately Held**
WEB: www.altatechnologies.com
SIC: 3644 2221 Noncurrent-carrying wiring services; fiberglass fabrics

(G-14932)
AMERICAN ATLAS CORP
2309 Sawgrass Village Dr (32082-5008)
PHONE....................................904 273-6090
W R Bornmiller, *President*
EMP: 5 **EST:** 1995
SALES (est): 309.6K **Privately Held**
SIC: 2741 Atlases: publishing & printing

(G-14933)
AQUATEKO INTERNATIONAL LLC
140 Deer Haven Dr (32082-2171)
PHONE....................................904 273-7200
Keith A Kessler, *Principal*
▲ **EMP:** 8 **EST:** 2009
SALES (est): 296.7K **Privately Held**
WEB: www.aquateko.com
SIC: 3496 Traps, animal & fish

(G-14934)
ARTIFICIAL TURF SUPPLY LLC (PA)
830-13 A1a N 160 (32082)
PHONE....................................877 525-8873
Jamieson Curry, *Sales Staff*
David Barbera, *Manager*
EMP: 6 **EST:** 2005
SQ FT: 1,700
SALES (est): 4.2MM **Privately Held**
WEB: www.artificialturfsupply.com
SIC: 2824 2273 2823 Textured yarns, non-cellulosic; carpets & rugs; floor coverings, textile fiber; cellulosic manmade fibers

(G-14935)
CATAPULT GROUP INC
183 Landrum Ln Ste 104 (32082-3838)
PHONE....................................904 834-7728
Carey Elam, *Principal*
EMP: 6 **EST:** 2015
SALES (est): 166.6K **Privately Held**
SIC: 3599 Catapults

(G-14936)
CLOGIC LLC (PA)
Also Called: Clogic Defense
135 Deer Estates Ln (32082-1916)
PHONE....................................860 324-2227
Laurie A Mecca,
Leonard J Mecca,
EMP: 7 **EST:** 2002
SALES (est): 2.4MM **Privately Held**
SIC: 3795 Tanks & tank components

(G-14937)
COLLOIDAL DYNAMICS LLC
5150 Palm Valley Rd # 303 (32082-4633)
PHONE....................................904 686-1536
Laurel Cannon, *Opers Mgr*
David W Cannon,
EMP: 5 **EST:** 2009
SQ FT: 3,000
SALES (est): 864.5K **Privately Held**
WEB: www.colloidal-dynamics.com
SIC: 3829 3821 Measuring & controlling devices; particle size reduction apparatus, laboratory

(G-14938)
COUNTRY CLUB CONCIERGE MAG INC
830-13 A1a N Ste 496 (32082)
PHONE....................................904 223-0204
Ava Electris Cannie, *CEO*
Ava Cannie, *President*
Matthew Koob, *Admin Sec*
EMP: 6 **EST:** 2006
SALES (est): 448.1K **Privately Held**
WEB: www.countryclub-conciergemagazine.com
SIC: 2721 Magazines: publishing only, not printed on site

(G-14939)
DIGITAL OUTPUT
5150 Palm Valley Rd # 103 (32082-4629)
PHONE....................................904 285-9944
Toni Newton, *President*
Thomas Tetreault, *Publisher*
EMP: 6 **EST:** 2016
SALES (est): 81.8K **Privately Held**
SIC: 2211 Broadwoven fabric mills, cotton

(G-14940)
EIGHTEEN DEGREES EIGHTEEN
3787 Palm Valley Rd # 101 (32082-4183)
PHONE....................................904 686-1892
David A San Juan, *Principal*
EMP: 6 **EST:** 2010
SALES (est): 93.5K **Privately Held**
SIC: 2024 Ice cream, bulk

(G-14941)
HANAYA LLC
543 Le Master Dr (32082-2313)
PHONE....................................904 285-7575
Jose R Cortes, *Partner*
George Tan, *Partner*
EMP: 16 **EST:** 2005
SQ FT: 3,000
SALES (est): 934K **Privately Held**
WEB: www.hanayainc.com
SIC: 3449 Miscellaneous metalwork

(G-14942)
INSURANCE PLUS
820 A1a N Ste W18 (32082-3326)
PHONE....................................904 567-1553
EMP: 9 **EST:** 2014
SALES (est): 314.6K **Privately Held**
WEB: www.insurefitness.com
SIC: 2721 Magazines: publishing & printing

(G-14943)
JT ENTERPRISES GROUP LLC (PA)
Also Called: J Turner & Co
280 Village Main St (32082-5087)
PHONE....................................904 803-9338
Jennifer A Turner,
EMP: 20 **EST:** 2014
SALES (est): 3.9MM **Privately Held**
WEB: www.jturner.com
SIC: 2519 Furniture, household: glass, fiberglass & plastic

(G-14944)
KJ COLLECTIONS
12350 Arbor Dr (32082-2101)
PHONE....................................904 285-7745
Kimberly Jackson, *Principal*
EMP: 6 **EST:** 2007
SALES (est): 227.7K **Privately Held**
SIC: 3949 Sporting & athletic goods

(G-14945)
MACPAC INC
830-13 A1a N 477 (32082)
PHONE....................................904 315-6457
James E McDermott, *President*
EMP: 11 **EST:** 2008
SALES (est): 366.1K **Privately Held**
WEB: www.macpacpkg.com
SIC: 2653 Boxes, corrugated: made from purchased materials

(G-14946)
MAXIT CORPORATION
1102 A1a N Ste 206 (32082-4098)
PHONE....................................904 998-9520
Philip Baruch, *CFO*
EMP: 8 **EST:** 1995
SQ FT: 1,500
SALES (est): 1MM **Privately Held**
WEB: www.maxit.com
SIC: 7372 7371 Educational computer software; custom computer programming services

(G-14947)
METROPOLITAN MIX
3108 Sawgrass Village Cir (32082-5037)
PHONE....................................904 242-0743
James Byrne, *Principal*
EMP: 7 **EST:** 2009
SALES (est): 143.3K **Privately Held**
SIC: 3273 Ready-mixed concrete

(G-14948)
OPC NEWS
1102 A1a N Ste 108 (32082-4098)
PHONE....................................904 686-3938
EMP: 6 **EST:** 2017
SALES (est): 193.9K **Privately Held**
SIC: 2711 Newspapers, publishing & printing

(G-14949)
PABLO SURGICAL SOLUTIONS LLC
816 A1a N Ste 200 (32082-3219)
PHONE....................................904 237-4864
Robert Lopresti, *Principal*
Kevin Porter, *Opers Staff*
EMP: 6 **EST:** 2015
SALES (est): 96.4K **Privately Held**
SIC: 3841 Surgical instruments & apparatus

(G-14950)
PETERBROOKE CHOCLAT FCTRY LLC
880 State Rd A1a Ste 4 1 A (32082)
PHONE....................................904 273-7878
Jackie Kolb, *Principal*
Beba Ramirez, *Sales Staff*
EMP: 9
SALES (corp-wide): 42.8MM **Privately Held**
WEB: www.peterbrooke.com
SIC: 2066 5145 Chocolate; candy
HQ: Peterbrooke Chocolate Factory, Llc
249 Copeland St
Jacksonville FL 32204
904 660-2300

(G-14951)
PONTE VEDRA WNS CIVIC ALIANCE
359 San Juan Dr (32082-2822)
PHONE....................................904 834-3543
Barbara K Roberts, *Principal*
EMP: 8 **EST:** 2012
SALES (est): 148.4K **Privately Held**
WEB: www.pontevedrarecorder.com
SIC: 2711 Newspapers, publishing & printing

(G-14952)
RECOVER GEAR LLC
Also Called: One Hundred Ten Percent
822 A1a N (32082-3260)
PHONE....................................904 280-9660
Jason Schoepfer, *Vice Pres*
David Green, *Mng Member*
Jim Philip,
EMP: 6 **EST:** 2009
SALES (est): 719.7K **Privately Held**
SIC: 2339 2329 Women's & misses' athletic clothing & sportswear; men's & boys' sportswear & athletic clothing

(G-14953)
REDDRESS USA INC
822 A1a N Ste 310 (32082-8209)
PHONE....................................800 674-9615
Russell S Lalli, *President*
Robert Mueller, *Principal*
Leonard Ross, *CFO*
EMP: 5 **EST:** 2018
SALES (est): 1.5MM **Privately Held**
WEB: www.reddressmedical.com
SIC: 3841 Surgical & medical instruments
PA: Reddress Ltd
11 Shkedim
Pardes Hanna 37011

(G-14954)
SOFTWARE NUGGETS INC
743 Palmera Dr E (32082-2457)
PHONE....................................904 687-9778
Barbara Pratt, *Supervisor*
EMP: 6 **EST:** 2003
SALES (est): 108.9K **Privately Held**
SIC: 7372 Prepackaged software

(G-14955)
TRUSSES UNLIMITED INC (PA)
Also Called: Lumber Unlimited
320 San Juan Dr (32082-1818)
P.O. Box 12267, Jacksonville (32209-0267)
PHONE....................................904 355-6611
David Myers, *President*
Barbara Brown, *CFO*
Ken Kuester, *Director*
EMP: 65 **EST:** 1965
SQ FT: 6,000
SALES (est): 15.5MM **Privately Held**
SIC: 2439 5031 Trusses, wooden roof; millwork

(G-14956)
UNIVERSAL SCHOOL PRODUCTS INC
2309 Sawgrass Village Dr (32082-5008)
PHONE....................................904 273-8590
Bill Bornmller, *CEO*
EMP: 7 **EST:** 2003
SALES (est): 595.9K **Privately Held**
SIC: 2678 Memorandum books, notebooks & looseleaf filler paper

(G-14957)
WINDRUSHER INC
602 Miramar Ct (32082-2423)
PHONE....................................904 614-5196
Victor Digenti, *Principal*
EMP: 6 **EST:** 2010
SALES (est): 109K **Privately Held**
SIC: 2741 Miscellaneous publishing

(G-14958)
ZASSI HOLDINGS INC (PA)
Also Called: Ezassi
822 A1a N Ste 104 (32082-8208)
PHONE....................................904 432-8315
Peter Von Dyck, *President*
Ray Brandstaetter, *CFO*
Victoria Lane, *Controller*
Eric Haulotte, *Manager*
EMP: 7 **EST:** 1997
SQ FT: 5,000
SALES (est): 2.3MM **Privately Held**
WEB: www.ezassi.com
SIC: 3842 3845 Surgical appliances & supplies; electromedical apparatus

Port Charlotte
Charlotte County

(G-14959)
ALL PHASE CUSTOM MILL SHOP INC
7471 Sawyer Cir (33981-2654)
PHONE....................................941 474-0903
William Woods, *President*
▼ **EMP:** 25 **EST:** 1998
SQ FT: 14,000
SALES (est): 3.3MM **Privately Held**
WEB: www.allphasecustommill.com
SIC: 2431 Millwork

(G-14960)
AMERICAN CNSTR ENTPS INC
Also Called: Ace Door Co
1232 Market Cir Unit 2b (33953-3829)
PHONE....................................941 629-2070
Walter E Helm, *President*
Linda L Helm, *Vice Pres*
EMP: 5 **EST:** 1986
SQ FT: 14,000
SALES (est): 828.6K **Privately Held**
SIC: 2431 3442 Doors & door parts & trim, wood; metal doors

(G-14961)
ARES DEFENSE GROUP LLC
861 Jarvis St (33948-3505)
PHONE....................................941 255-0559
Richard A Perry, *Branch Mgr*
EMP: 10
SALES (corp-wide): 94.4K **Privately Held**
SIC: 3812 Defense systems & equipment
PA: Ares Defense Group Llc
1120 E Twiggs St E588
Tampa FL

(G-14962)
ARGOS READY MIX
580 Prineville St (33954-1027)
PHONE....................................941 629-7713
EMP: 7 **EST:** 2016
SALES (est): 110.5K **Privately Held**
WEB: www.argos-us.com
SIC: 3273 Ready-mixed concrete

(G-14963)
ARMOURY PROPERTY & MOLD INSPEC
18682 Fort Smith Cir (33948-9686)
PHONE....................................813 503-9765
Alex Oros, *President*
EMP: 7 **EST:** 2005
SALES (est): 91.8K **Privately Held**
SIC: 3544 Industrial molds

(G-14964)
BENCHMARK ALUMINUM INC
125 Justine St (33954-4101)
PHONE....................................941 585-9977
Michael St Germain, *Principal*
EMP: 7 **EST:** 2008
SALES (est): 198.5K **Privately Held**
WEB: www.benchmarkaluminumandconstruction.com
SIC: 3334 Primary aluminum

(G-14965)
BLADORN INVESTMENTS INC
Also Called: Monarch Printing & Design
1264 Market Cir Unit 6 (33953-3899)
PHONE....................................941 627-0014
Michael D Bladorn, *President*
Beverly Jensen, *Graphic Designe*
EMP: 7 **EST:** 2006
SQ FT: 1,500
SALES (est): 1MM **Privately Held**
SIC: 2752 Commercial printing, offset

(G-14966)
BOYLE PUBLICATIONS INC
1039 Tamiami Trl (33953-3805)
PHONE....................................941 255-0187
EMP: 5 **EST:** 2019
SALES (est): 312.3K **Privately Held**
SIC: 2741 Miscellaneous publishing

(G-14967)
CABINET MECHANICS LLC
468 Cicero St Nw (33948-6349)
PHONE....................................941 626-0735
Jeffrey Hardman, *Principal*
EMP: 6 **EST:** 2011
SALES (est): 109.2K **Privately Held**
SIC: 2434 Wood kitchen cabinets

(G-14968)
CAST SYSTEMS LLC
19400 Peachland Blvd (33948-2146)
PHONE....................................941 625-3474
Gary E Tschetter, *Mng Member*
EMP: 30 **EST:** 2001
SQ FT: 1,620
SALES (est): 6.1MM **Privately Held**
WEB: www.castsystemsllc.com
SIC: 3272 Concrete products, precast

(G-14969)
CHICAGO ELECTRONIC DISTRS INC
17097 Glenview Ave (33954-1564)
PHONE....................................312 985-6175
Craig Lemoyne, *President*
EMP: 12 **EST:** 2013
SALES (est): 1.7MM **Privately Held**
WEB: www.chicagodist.com
SIC: 3491 3691 2493 3823 Automatic regulating & control valves; storage batteries; insulation board, cellular fiber; fluidic devices, circuits & systems for process control

(G-14970)
COASTAL HURRICANE FILM LLC
807 Thornton Ave Nw (33948-7755)
PHONE....................................941 268-9693
Randy Stalnaker, *Principal*
EMP: 8 **EST:** 2008
SALES (est): 177.8K **Privately Held**
SIC: 3211 Window glass, clear & colored

(G-14971)
COMEX SYSTEMS INC
9380 Nastrand Cir (33981-4031)
P.O. Box 142, Placida (33946-0142)
PHONE....................................908 881-6301
Doug Pryblowski, *President*
EMP: 5 **EST:** 1973
SQ FT: 2,400
SALES (est): 464K **Privately Held**
WEB: www.comexsystems.com
SIC: 2731 Books: publishing only

(G-14972)
COMPTECH GLOBAL SOLUTIONS INC
775 Tamiami Trl Unit B (33953-3059)
PHONE....................................941 766-8100
Victor Rebmann, *Owner*
EMP: 6 **EST:** 2004
SALES (est): 257.1K **Privately Held**
WEB: www.comtechglobal.com
SIC: 2759 4812 Commercial printing; cellular telephone services

(G-14973)
DOLLAR & PENNY STRETCHERS LLC
13100 S Mccall Rd (33981-6401)
PHONE....................941 830-5341
Sheri L Brogan, *Principal*
EMP: 7 **EST:** 2013
SALES (est): 123K **Privately Held**
SIC: 3842 Stretchers

(G-14974)
DOMINION PRINTERS INC
5393 Kennel St (33981-1919)
PHONE....................757 340-1300
Stephan Pahno, *President*
Pete Pahno, *Treasurer*
Mike Pahno, *Admin Sec*
EMP: 7 **EST:** 1984
SQ FT: 4,125
SALES (est): 197.4K **Privately Held**
WEB: www.dominionprinters.com
SIC: 2752 Commercial printing, offset

(G-14975)
ED ALLEN INC
1312 Market Cir Unit 9 (33953-3831)
PHONE....................941 743-2646
Edward A Faiola, *Principal*
EMP: 12 **EST:** 2013
SALES (est): 343.5K **Privately Held**
SIC: 2591 Window blinds

(G-14976)
EDMUND C MIGA
Also Called: Rudolph & ME
23040 Bradford Ave (33952-1721)
PHONE....................941 628-5951
Edmund C Miga, *Owner*
EMP: 8
SALES (est): 200K **Privately Held**
SIC: 3229 Christmas tree ornaments, from glass produced on-site

(G-14977)
ELEGANT REFLECTIONS
168 Waterside St (33954-3183)
PHONE....................941 627-9275
Rhonda Wallis, *Principal*
EMP: 6 **EST:** 2010
SALES (est): 71K **Privately Held**
SIC: 3231 Decorated glassware: chipped, engraved, etched, etc.

(G-14978)
ENERGY NOW LLC
757 Clearview Dr (33953-2042)
PHONE....................941 276-0935
Nancy Kevorkian, *Principal*
EMP: 6 **EST:** 2017
SALES (est): 96.6K **Privately Held**
SIC: 3842 Cotton, including cotton balls: sterile & non-sterile

(G-14979)
EPIGRAM PUBLISHING CO
151 Tillman St (33954-4149)
PHONE....................941 391-5296
Leroy Heggin, *Principal*
EMP: 6 **EST:** 2005
SALES (est): 127K **Privately Held**
SIC: 2741 Miscellaneous publishing

(G-14980)
FASTENER SPECIALTY CORP
24100 Tiseo Blvd Unit 14 (33980-5223)
PHONE....................631 903-4453
EMP: 6 **EST:** 2018
SALES (est): 181.6K **Privately Held**
WEB: www.fastenerspecialty.com
SIC: 3965 Fasteners

(G-14981)
FLOWERS BKG CO BRADENTON LLC
23240 Bayshore Rd (33980-3213)
PHONE....................941 627-0752
EMP: 13
SQ FT: 6,480
SALES (corp-wide): 3.7B **Publicly Held**
SIC: 2051 Mfg Bread
HQ: Flowers Baking Co. Of Bradenton, Llc
6490 Parkland Dr
Sarasota FL 34243
941 758-5656

(G-14982)
FSHS INC
Also Called: Puromax
4210 Whidden Blvd (33980-8407)
PHONE....................941 625-5929
Kevin Greene, *President*
Jeremy Greene, *General Mgr*
Tracy Greene, *Treasurer*
Josh Greene, *Manager*
◆ **EMP:** 6 **EST:** 1996
SALES (est): 1.1MM **Privately Held**
WEB: www.puromax.com
SIC: 3589 5074 Water treatment equipment, industrial; water purification equipment, household type; water purification equipment

(G-14983)
GALAXY AMERICA INC
7431 Sawyer Cir (33981-2654)
PHONE....................941 697-0324
Robin Whincup, *President*
Carol Whincup, *Corp Secy*
◆ **EMP:** 16 **EST:** 2009
SALES (est): 4.7MM **Privately Held**
WEB: www.galaxymultirides.com
SIC: 3944 Hobby horses

(G-14984)
GULF COAST CUSTOM WDWKG INC
21301 Washburn Ave (33952-1576)
PHONE....................941 343-7883
Christopher M Phillips, *Principal*
EMP: 6 **EST:** 2013
SALES (est): 119.3K **Privately Held**
SIC: 2431 Millwork

(G-14985)
HARBOR IMAGING
3430 Tamiami Trl Ste B (33952-8148)
PHONE....................941 883-8383
James White, *President*
Laura Gaura, *Accountant*
James Renn, *Administration*
EMP: 23 **EST:** 2004
SALES (est): 1.8MM **Privately Held**
SIC: 3845 Ultrasonic scanning devices, medical

(G-14986)
JUST COUNTERS OTHER STUFF INC
1489 Market Cir Bldg 309 (33953-3807)
PHONE....................941 235-1300
Mark Kemeny, *President*
Kathy Kemeny, *Vice Pres*
EMP: 10 **EST:** 2002
SALES (est): 1MM **Privately Held**
WEB: www.jcaos.com
SIC: 2541 Counter & sink tops

(G-14987)
LARRYS EXTREME AUDIO TINT LLC
19360 Strathcona Ave (33954-2074)
PHONE....................941 766-8468
Larry Sweeris, *Principal*
EMP: 7 **EST:** 2012
SALES (est): 451.3K **Privately Held**
SIC: 3356 Tin

(G-14988)
LERNER ENTERPRISES INC
19367 Abhenry Cir (33948-7725)
PHONE....................440 323-5529
Arthur L Lerner, *Principal*
Janet Kurtz, *QC Mgr*
Paul Klug, *Administration*
▲ **EMP:** 30 **EST:** 1983
SQ FT: 30,000
SALES (est): 3.6MM **Privately Held**
SIC: 3452 Bolts, nuts, rivets & washers

(G-14989)
M D MOLD LLC
20439 Stardust Ave (33952-1320)
PHONE....................941 214-0854
Mold MD, *Principal*
EMP: 8 **EST:** 2018
SALES (est): 306.3K **Privately Held**
SIC: 3544 Industrial molds

(G-14990)
MS WELDING
2222 Tea St (33948-1111)
PHONE....................941 629-2597
Mark Spalding, *Owner*
EMP: 5 **EST:** 1994
SALES (est): 469.4K **Privately Held**
SIC: 7692 Welding repair

(G-14991)
NORTECH ENGINEERING INC
13001 Cedar Creek Dr (33953-7810)
PHONE....................508 823-8520
EMP: 7
SQ FT: 10,125
SALES (est): 2.4MM **Privately Held**
SIC: 3571 Electronic Computers, Nsk

(G-14992)
PACE MACHINE TOOL INC
13564 Ingraham Blvd (33981-2823)
PHONE....................248 960-9903
Linda Hobbel, *President*
Raymond Hobble, *Vice Pres*
EMP: 20 **EST:** 1989
SALES (est): 293.4K **Privately Held**
SIC: 3599 Machine shop, jobbing & repair

(G-14993)
PEACE RIVER DELI PROVS INC
18480 Paulson Dr (33954-1034)
PHONE....................941 426-4846
Michael Kochman, *Principal*
EMP: 21 **EST:** 2008
SALES (est): 1.3MM **Privately Held**
SIC: 2893 Printing ink

(G-14994)
PRO COLOR COATING LLC
244 Macarthur Dr (33954-2413)
PHONE....................941 661-4769
Gordon C Frost, *Principal*
EMP: 6 **EST:** 2010
SALES (est): 101.9K **Privately Held**
SIC: 3479 Metal coating & allied service

(G-14995)
QUALITY MACHINE SERVICE INC
2199 Fernwood St (33948-1100)
PHONE....................610 554-3917
Charles Rhoades, *President*
Debra Rhoades, *Treasurer*
EMP: 5 **EST:** 1988
SQ FT: 8,000
SALES (est): 419.9K **Privately Held**
WEB: www.qualitymachineserviceinc.net
SIC: 3599 Machine shop, jobbing & repair

(G-14996)
SASHKA CO
992 Tamiami Trl Unit J (33953-3886)
PHONE....................941 764-9741
Christopher A Knipp, *President*
EMP: 6 **EST:** 2018
SALES (est): 232.5K **Privately Held**
WEB: www.sashkaco.com
SIC: 3961 Bracelets, except precious metal

(G-14997)
SHUTTER SOUTHERN CROSS
1109 Tamiami Trl Unit 5 (33953-3828)
PHONE....................941 235-2620
Brant Smith, *Principal*
EMP: 5 **EST:** 2017
SALES (est): 349.5K **Privately Held**
WEB: www.southerncrossshutter.com
SIC: 3442 Shutters, door or window: metal

(G-14998)
SOUTHERN CROSS SHUTTER SYSTEMS
21271 Dearborn Ave (33954-3135)
PHONE....................941 585-2152
Brant J Smith, *Owner*
EMP: 7 **EST:** 2015
SALES (est): 482.2K **Privately Held**
WEB: www.southerncrossshutter.com
SIC: 3442 Shutters, door or window: metal

(G-14999)
STEPHENS GROUP
20101 Peachland Blvd # 2 (33954-2180)
PHONE....................941 623-9689
Craig Stephens, *Principal*
EMP: 6 **EST:** 2010
SALES (est): 102.1K **Privately Held**
SIC: 2731 Book publishing

(G-15000)
SUN COAST MEDIA GROUP INC (HQ)
Also Called: Punta Gorda Sun Herald
23170 Harborview Rd (33980-2100)
PHONE....................941 206-1300
David Dunn-Rankin, *CEO*
Robert Vedder, *Vice Pres*
EMP: 80 **EST:** 1977
SALES (est): 49.3MM
SALES (corp-wide): 333.5MM **Privately Held**
WEB: www.yoursun.com
SIC: 2711 2752 Newspapers, publishing & printing; commercial printing, lithographic
PA: Adams Publishing Group, Llc
103 W Summer St
Greeneville TN 37743
218 348-3391

(G-15001)
SUN COAST MEDIA GROUP INC
Also Called: Green Sheet, The
2726 Tamiami Trl Ste B (33952-5164)
PHONE....................941 206-1900
Robert Knight, *General Mgr*
EMP: 10
SALES (corp-wide): 333.5MM **Privately Held**
WEB: www.yoursun.com
SIC: 2711 Newspapers, publishing & printing
HQ: Sun Coast Media Group, Inc.
23170 Harborview Rd
Port Charlotte FL 33980
941 206-1300

(G-15002)
TROPICAL CUSTOM COATINGS
11354 Zola Ave (33981-7338)
PHONE....................941 475-3663
Timothy Costello, *Principal*
EMP: 7 **EST:** 2012
SALES (est): 233.9K **Privately Held**
SIC: 3479 Metal coating & allied service

(G-15003)
UNDERWTER FISH LIGHT LTD LBLTY
20400 Veterans Blvd (33954-2241)
PHONE....................941 391-5846
John Molle, *Mng Member*
Heidi L Molle,
EMP: 7 **EST:** 2008
SQ FT: 5,000
SALES (est): 932.4K **Privately Held**
WEB: www.underwaterfishlight.com
SIC: 3648 Underwater lighting fixtures

(G-15004)
UNITED SEAL & TAG LABEL CORP
19237 Pine Bluff Ct (33948-9672)
PHONE....................941 625-6799
Robert Freda, *President*
EMP: 8 **EST:** 1919
SQ FT: 10,000
SALES (est): 766.8K **Privately Held**
SIC: 2759 2789 2671 Labels & seals: printing; tags: printing; bookbinding & related work; packaging paper & plastics film, coated & laminated

(G-15005)
VALUESAFES INC
24123 Peachland Blvd (33954-3774)
PHONE....................877 629-6214
Jessica Gilmore, *Principal*
EMP: 6 **EST:** 2010
SALES (est): 201.2K **Privately Held**
WEB: www.valuesafesinc.com
SIC: 3499 Safes & vaults, metal

(G-15006)
VOYAGER OFFROAD LLC
1602 Market Cir Unit 8 (33953-3893)
PHONE....................941 235-7225
Andrew J Nix,
EMP: 9 **EST:** 2011

SALES (est): 1.5MM **Privately Held**
WEB: www.voyagerracks.com
SIC: 7692 Welding repair

(G-15007)
WESTCHESTER GOLD FABRICATORS
4200 Tamiami Trl Ste F (33952-9233)
PHONE.................................941 625-0666
Steven Duke, *President*
Jane Duke, *Vice Pres*
EMP: 8 **EST:** 1978
SQ FT: 5,000
SALES (est): 1MM **Privately Held**
WEB: www.westchestergold.com
SIC: 3911 5932 Jewelry, precious metal; pawnshop

(G-15008)
WOODS DISTINCTIVE DESIGNS
Also Called: Advanced Cabinetry Systems
7450 Sawyer Cir (33981-2653)
PHONE.................................941 698-7535
Frank Wood, *President*
Jeannette Woods, *Vice Pres*
EMP: 11 **EST:** 1997
SALES (est): 1.3MM **Privately Held**
WEB: www.advancedcabinetrypc.com
SIC: 2434 Wood kitchen cabinets

Port Orange
Volusia County

(G-15009)
AUTOMATIC BUSINESS PRODUCTS CO
4480 Eastport Park Way (32127-6044)
PHONE.................................888 742-7639
EMP: 10 **EST:** 2011
SALES (est): 193.6K **Privately Held**
SIC: 2672 Adhesive papers, labels or tapes: from purchased material

(G-15010)
BANAGHAN WOOD PRODUCTS INC
741 Tarry Town Trl (32127-4916)
P.O. Box 291922 (32129-1922)
PHONE.................................386 788-6114
EMP: 29 **EST:** 1993
SALES (est): 2.5MM **Privately Held**
SIC: 2499 Manufactures Wood Products Such As Posts And Poles

(G-15011)
BARROWS ALUMINUM INC
630 Oak Pl Ste H (32127-4372)
PHONE.................................386 767-3445
Raleigh Barrows, *President*
EMP: 10 **EST:** 2001
SALES (est): 910.2K **Privately Held**
WEB: www.tjslawnandgarden.com
SIC: 3355 Rails, rolled & drawn, aluminum

(G-15012)
BECKER DESIGNS INC
4188 Dairy Ct Ste C (32127-4473)
PHONE.................................386 760-2280
Susan Becker, *Owner*
EMP: 5 **EST:** 1994
SQ FT: 3,000
SALES (est): 399.7K **Privately Held**
WEB: www.beckerdesigns.com
SIC: 2339 Athletic clothing: women's, misses' & juniors'

(G-15013)
BODY FUEL LLC
1155 Greenbriar Ave (32127-6009)
PHONE.................................386 566-1855
Donna Braniff, *Principal*
EMP: 6 **EST:** 2010
SALES (est): 113.9K **Privately Held**
SIC: 2869 Fuels

(G-15014)
CUSTOMER SUCCESS LLC
1892 Clubhouse Dr (32128-7366)
PHONE.................................386 265-4882
Wanda Tarnoff, *Manager*
EMP: 10 **EST:** 2017
SALES (est): 162.6K **Privately Held**
WEB: www.totango.com
SIC: 7372 Prepackaged software

(G-15015)
DAYTONA SHEET METAL AND AIR
14 Woodlake Dr (32129-4050)
PHONE.................................386 547-2422
John Manning, *Principal*
EMP: 6 **EST:** 2014
SALES (est): 76K **Privately Held**
SIC: 3444 Sheet metalwork

(G-15016)
DON BELL SIGNS LLC
365 Oak Pl (32127-4388)
PHONE.................................800 824-0080
Gary D Bell, *President*
Jim Wetherell, *Vice Pres*
Frank Boanno, *Sales Mgr*
Diana Grunderman, *Sales Staff*
Ron Hatcher, *Sales Staff*
EMP: 52 **EST:** 1947
SQ FT: 50,000
SALES (est): 12.5MM **Privately Held**
WEB: www.donbellsigns.com
SIC: 3993 Electric signs

(G-15017)
DRAPERY CONTROL SYSTEMS INC
Also Called: Brambier's Windows & Walls
3817 S Nova Rd Ste 104 (32127-4253)
PHONE.................................386 756-0101
Dan Chandler, *Opers Mgr*
Jade Alvarez, *Sales Staff*
Jerry Fekete, *Sales Staff*
Lyle Brambier, *Branch Mgr*
EMP: 7
SALES (corp-wide): 4.9MM **Privately Held**
WEB: www.brambiers.com
SIC: 2221 Upholstery, tapestry & wall covering fabrics
PA: Drapery Control Systems, Inc.
5545 Nw 35th Ave D
Fort Lauderdale FL 33309
305 653-1712

(G-15018)
FUTURESCAPE INC
6119 Del Mar Dr (32127-6743)
PHONE.................................386 679-4120
Ira Wendorf, *President*
Alan Weininger, *Vice Pres*
EMP: 8
SALES (est): 100K **Privately Held**
SIC: 2842 Sanitation preparations, disinfectants & deodorants

(G-15019)
GPS EDUCATION LLC
2463 Old Samsula Rd (32128-6538)
PHONE.................................386 756-7575
Gary Sedacca, *Manager*
EMP: 7 **EST:** 2008
SALES (est): 281.3K **Privately Held**
WEB: www.gps-edu.com
SIC: 3663 Radio & TV communications equipment

(G-15020)
JENZANO INCORPORATED
820 Oak St (32127-4332)
PHONE.................................386 761-4474
John Douglas Jenzano, *President*
Joyce Aycock, *Corp Secy*
John J Jenzano, *Shareholder*
EMP: 10 **EST:** 1966
SALES (est): 1.9MM **Privately Held**
WEB: www.jenzano.com
SIC: 3569 3542 3625 Assembly machines, non-metalworking; machine tools, metal forming type; relays & industrial controls

(G-15021)
KWIK KERB LLC
844 Williams Ln (32127-5855)
PHONE.................................386 453-1004
Mark Durkin, *Principal*
EMP: 7 **EST:** 2005
SALES (est): 159.1K **Privately Held**
WEB: www.kwikkerbbyadele.com
SIC: 3281 Curbing, paving & walkway stone

(G-15022)
LITHOCRAFT INC
4460 S Ridgewood Ave (32127-4516)
P.O. Box 10270, Daytona Beach (32120-0270)
PHONE.................................386 761-3584
Ken Chrysler, *President*
Mary Chrysler, *Corp Secy*
EMP: 5 **EST:** 1976
SQ FT: 3,024
SALES (est): 429.3K **Privately Held**
WEB: www.lithocraftprinting.com
SIC: 2752 Commercial printing, offset

(G-15023)
M C MIETH MANUFACTURING INC
665 Herbert St (32129-3837)
P.O. Box 291129 (32129-1129)
PHONE.................................386 767-3494
Greg Feldman, *President*
Elaine Feldman, *Corp Secy*
Angela Norris, *Vice Pres*
EMP: 11 **EST:** 1959
SQ FT: 4,500
SALES (est): 1.1MM **Privately Held**
WEB: www.holepunch.com
SIC: 3579 Ticket counting machines

(G-15024)
MIX MASTERS INC
523 Virginia Ave Unit B (32127-4450)
PHONE.................................386 846-9239
EMP: 6 **EST:** 2001
SALES (est): 19.1K **Privately Held**
SIC: 3273 Ready-mixed concrete

(G-15025)
MPP COATINGS INC
3837 Long Grove Ln (32129-8629)
PHONE.................................386 334-4484
Carrie L Erdelyan, *Principal*
Adam Erdelyan, *Vice Pres*
EMP: 6 **EST:** 2016
SALES (est): 232.6K **Privately Held**
WEB: www.mppcoatings.com
SIC: 3479 Coating of metals & formed products

(G-15026)
MYSKY AIRCRAFT INC
205 Cessna Blvd Ste 1 (32128-7538)
PHONE.................................386 492-6908
Dieter Canje, *President*
▲ **EMP:** 7 **EST:** 2009
SQ FT: 5,000
SALES (est): 400K **Privately Held**
WEB: www.mysky.aero
SIC: 3721 Aircraft

(G-15027)
PDC
4480 Eastport Park Way (32127-6044)
PHONE.................................386 322-2808
EMP: 11 **EST:** 2018
SALES (est): 1.3MM **Privately Held**
WEB: www.pdcorp.com
SIC: 2834 Pharmaceutical preparations

(G-15028)
PIN HSIAO & ASSOCIATES LLC
4470 Eastport Park Way (32127-6044)
PHONE.................................425 637-3357
EMP: 10 **Privately Held**
SIC: 2051 Bakery: wholesale or wholesale/retail combined
PA: Pin Hsiao & Associates L.L.C.
5501 West Valley Hwy E A101
Sumner WA 98390

(G-15029)
PRIVACY WINDOW DESIGN INC
600 Oak St Ste 2b (32127-4364)
PHONE.................................386 761-7306
Christine Hannah, *President*
John Hannah, *Vice Pres*
EMP: 6 **EST:** 1985
SQ FT: 4,000
SALES (est): 489.6K **Privately Held**
SIC: 2591 Venetian blinds

(G-15030)
RALLY LEATHER & MORE LLC
1066 Chelsea Way (32129-4102)
PHONE.................................516 643-8572
Scott Demonico, *Manager*
EMP: 6 **EST:** 2010
SALES (est): 110.4K **Privately Held**
SIC: 3199 Leather goods

(G-15031)
SANTIAGO
2477 Guava Dr (32128-6508)
PHONE.................................386 527-5822
Santiago Gonzalez, *Principal*
EMP: 6 **EST:** 2014
SALES (est): 91.4K **Privately Held**
SIC: 3541 Lathes

(G-15032)
SCREEN MACHINES LLC
2422 Old Samsula Rd (32128-6537)
P.O. Box 238083 (32123-8083)
PHONE.................................386 527-1368
EMP: 9 **EST:** 2017
SALES (est): 242.3K **Privately Held**
WEB: www.screenmachine.com
SIC: 2752 Offset & photolithographic printing

(G-15033)
SHORELINE SHUTTER SYSTEMS INC
494 Nash Ln (32127-9527)
PHONE.................................386 299-2219
David Vrondran, *Director*
EMP: 8 **EST:** 2001
SALES (est): 80.1K **Privately Held**
SIC: 3442 Shutters, door or window: metal

(G-15034)
SHUTTERS ON SALE INC
1307 Crepe Myrtle Ln (32128-7396)
PHONE.................................386 756-0009
William G Burkett, *Principal*
EMP: 8 **EST:** 2005
SALES (est): 214K **Privately Held**
SIC: 3442 Shutters, door or window: metal

(G-15035)
SPRUCE CREEK CABINETRY INC
601 Lemon St Ste C (32127-4340)
P.O. Box 291597 (32129-1597)
PHONE.................................386 756-0041
Ken Rose, *President*
Dean Rose, *CFO*
EMP: 18 **EST:** 1985
SQ FT: 7,000
SALES (est): 1.2MM **Privately Held**
WEB: www.sprucecreekcabinetry.com
SIC: 2541 2517 2434 5031 Cabinets, except refrigerated: show, display, etc.: wood; table or counter tops, plastic laminated; wood television & radio cabinets; wood kitchen cabinets; kitchen cabinets; cabinet & finish carpentry

(G-15036)
SPRUCE CREEK CNTL CNDO ASSOCIA
4184 Dairy Ct Ste D (32127-4382)
PHONE.................................386 212-4035
EMP: 6 **EST:** 2018
SALES (est): 163K **Privately Held**
WEB: www.sprucecreekproperties.com
SIC: 2652 Setup paperboard boxes

(G-15037)
STOVER MANUFACTURING LLC
919 Alexander Ave (32129-3449)
PHONE.................................386 235-7060
Robert Grooms, *Principal*
Jeff Harris, *Sales Mgr*
EMP: 15 **EST:** 2015
SALES (est): 1.6MM **Privately Held**
SIC: 3999 Manufacturing industries

(G-15038)
SUNSHINE LIGHTERS
730 Glades Ct (32127-4324)
PHONE.................................386 322-1300
Sam Chebaro, *Principal*
▼ **EMP:** 6 **EST:** 2009

SALES (est): 454.8K Privately Held
WEB: www.sunshinewholesale.com
SIC: 3911 Cigarette lighters, precious metal

(G-15039)
TIME ADJUSTERS CONFERENCE INC
Also Called: Time Finance Adjusters
5807 Spruce Creek Wods Dr (32127-0904)
PHONE..................................386 274-4210
Harvey Altes, *CEO*
Margaret Merthe, *President*
EMP: 5 EST: 1971
SALES (est): 478.5K Privately Held
WEB: www.timefinanceadjusters.com
SIC: 2721 8111 2741 Magazines: publishing only, not printed on site; legal services; telephone & other directory publishing

(G-15040)
WORLDWIDE EMBROIDERY INC
4471 Eastport Park Way (32127-6041)
PHONE..................................386 761-2688
Manek Naresh, *President*
EMP: 13 EST: 1998
SQ FT: 10,000
SALES (est): 250.1K Privately Held
SIC: 2395 Embroidery products, except schiffli machine

(G-15041)
WORLDWIDE SPORTSWEAR INC
4471 Eastport Park Way (32127-6041)
P.O. Box 290640 (32129-0640)
PHONE..................................386 761-2688
Naresh Manek, *President*
Ameet Sharma, *COO*
Perry Levine, *Vice Pres*
EMP: 25 EST: 1998
SALES (est): 2.8MM Privately Held
WEB: www.wwspwear.shop
SIC: 2759 Screen printing

Port Richey
Pasco County

(G-15042)
ADVANCED DAGNSTC SOLUTIONS INC
6125 Sherwin Dr (34668-6751)
PHONE..................................352 293-2810
Jim Arnold Jr, *CEO*
Brandon M Womack, *President*
EMP: 12 EST: 2011
SALES (est): 521.6K Privately Held
WEB: www.advdiagnostic.com
SIC: 3841 Diagnostic apparatus, medical

(G-15043)
BET-ER MIX HOLDING INC (PA)
9301 Denton Ave (34667-4340)
P.O. Box 5577, Hudson (34674-5577)
PHONE..................................727 868-9226
Priscilla White, *Principal*
EMP: 7 EST: 2008
SALES (est): 22.5MM Privately Held
WEB: www.betermix.com
SIC: 3273 Ready-mixed concrete

(G-15044)
CARMACKS QUALITY ALUMINUM
8052 Leo Kidd Ave Ste 1 (34668-6620)
PHONE..................................727 846-0305
Bob Carmack, *President*
EMP: 7 EST: 1990
SQ FT: 3,654
SALES (est): 875.1K Privately Held
WEB: www.carmacksqualityaluminum.net
SIC: 3355 Aluminum rolling & drawing

(G-15045)
CEMENT PRODUCTS INC
9301 Denton Ave (34667-4340)
P.O. Box 5577 (34674-5577)
PHONE..................................727 868-9226
John Terry White, *President*
Priscila White, *Vice Pres*
Robert D Hatfield, *Admin Sec*
EMP: 23 EST: 1970
SQ FT: 800
SALES (est): 869K Privately Held
SIC: 3272 3273 3271 3241 Concrete products; ready-mixed concrete; concrete block & brick; cement, hydraulic

(G-15046)
COASTAL RE-MANUFACTURING INC
7620 Valencia Ave (34668-2950)
PHONE..................................727 869-4808
EMP: 7
SQ FT: 8,000
SALES (est): 545.7K Privately Held
SIC: 3714 Re-Mfg Brak Calipers Front Wheel Drive Axles Rack & Pinions

(G-15047)
COX DESIGNER WINDOWS INC
6810 Commerce Ave (34668-6816)
PHONE..................................727 847-1046
Steven Roberts, *President*
Steven Jacobson, *Vice Pres*
Richard McDonald, *Vice Pres*
Domenic Prosperi, *Vice Pres*
EMP: 9 EST: 1996
SQ FT: 4,500
SALES (est): 840.1K Privately Held
WEB: www.coxaluminum.com
SIC: 2431 Windows & window parts & trim, wood

(G-15048)
D MAXWELL COMPANY INC
Also Called: Concrete Systems
8323 Arcola Ave (34667-3622)
PHONE..................................727 868-9151
Dennis Maxwell, *President*
EMP: 5 EST: 1970
SQ FT: 9,600
SALES (est): 895.7K Privately Held
SIC: 3272 Concrete products, precast

(G-15049)
FRAMES & THINGS
Also Called: 1st Call For Install
6137 Ridge Rd (34668-6766)
PHONE..................................727 815-0515
Graham J Staples, *Mng Member*
EMP: 6 EST: 2010
SALES (est): 158.4K Privately Held
WEB: www.framesthings.com
SIC: 3993 Signs & advertising specialties

(G-15050)
FROM TREES INC
6030 Springer Dr (34668-5336)
PHONE..................................813 431-8285
EMP: 6 EST: 2018
SALES (est): 250.5K Privately Held
WEB: www.fromthetrees.com
SIC: 2434 Wood kitchen cabinets

(G-15051)
GENERAL CABINETS INC
15801 Archer St (34667-3817)
PHONE..................................727 863-3404
Donald John Josephik, *President*
Dan Myrick, *Mfg Staff*
Ed Ellis, *Research*
Cindy Rainey, *Office Mgr*
EMP: 21 EST: 1978
SQ FT: 15,000
SALES (est): 1MM Privately Held
WEB: www.generalcabinets.com
SIC: 2434 Wood kitchen cabinets

(G-15052)
HUFF CARBIDE TOOL INC
6541 Industrial Ave (34668-6852)
PHONE..................................727 848-4001
Craig Peterson, *President*
Craig W Peterson, *Vice Pres*
EMP: 14 EST: 1961
SQ FT: 6,200
SALES (est): 1.1MM Privately Held
SIC: 3541 3544 Machine tools, metal cutting type; special dies, tools, jigs & fixtures

(G-15053)
II-VI AEROSPACE & DEFENSE INC
6716 Industrial Ave (34668-6886)
PHONE..................................727 375-8562
EMP: 120
SALES (corp-wide): 3.1B Publicly Held
WEB: www.iiviad.com
SIC: 3827 Optical elements & assemblies, except ophthalmic
HQ: Ii-Vi Aerospace & Defense Inc
36570 Briggs Rd
Murrieta CA 92563
951 926-2994

(G-15054)
ISOAID LLC
7824 Clark Moody Blvd (34668-6709)
P.O. Box 205, New Port Richey (34656-0205)
PHONE..................................727 815-3262
Dennis Cappo, *Sales Staff*
John Cusack, *Director*
Max Taghizadeh,
Jean Hakim,
EMP: 20 EST: 2000
SQ FT: 4,000
SALES (est): 5.2MM Privately Held
WEB: www.isoaid.com
SIC: 2819 Iodine, elemental

(G-15055)
J & E CUSTOM CABINETS
9926 Denton Ave (34667-4388)
PHONE..................................727 868-2820
Effie Mae Deskins, *President*
Johnny A Deskins, *Corp Secy*
EMP: 14 EST: 1983
SQ FT: 20,000
SALES (est): 598.1K Privately Held
SIC: 2434 Wood kitchen cabinets

(G-15056)
JAR-DEN LLC
7400 Castanea Dr (34668-3997)
PHONE..................................860 334-7539
EMP: 7 EST: 2015
SALES (est): 180.8K Privately Held
SIC: 3089 Plastics products

(G-15057)
JAVIDCO SCRATCH N DENT
6302 Ridge Rd (34668-6744)
PHONE..................................727 494-7611
Jacqueline S France, *Principal*
EMP: 6 EST: 2009
SALES (est): 220K Privately Held
SIC: 3531 Automobile wrecker hoists

(G-15058)
JMTM ANUFACTURING INC
6651 Industrial Ave (34668-6864)
PHONE..................................727 847-7665
EMP: 6 EST: 2019
SALES (est): 39.6K Privately Held
WEB: www.jmt.com
SIC: 3999 Manufacturing industries

(G-15059)
L A R MANUFACTURING LLC
6828 Commerce Ave (34668-6816)
PHONE..................................727 846-7860
John W Birkel, *Mng Member*
Peter Reynolds, *Mng Member*
EMP: 5 EST: 1999
SQ FT: 2,400
SALES (est): 357K Privately Held
SIC: 3843 Dental metal

(G-15060)
MADEWELL KITCHENS INC
11619 State Road 52 (34669-3087)
PHONE..................................727 856-1014
James Madewell, *President*
Henry D Madewell Jr, *Vice Pres*
EMP: 27 EST: 1980
SQ FT: 9,000
SALES (est): 2.9MM Privately Held
WEB: www.madewellkitchens.com
SIC: 2434 Wood kitchen cabinets

(G-15061)
MARS PRECISION PRODUCTS INC
8526 Leo Kidd Ave (34668-5313)
PHONE..................................727 846-0505
Christopher Tietz, *Manager*
EMP: 7 EST: 2014
SALES (est): 192.7K Privately Held
SIC: 3519 Internal combustion engines

(G-15062)
PERFECT BRICK PAVERS INC
5626 Quist Dr (34668-6336)
PHONE..................................727 534-2506
Christopher A Cherviok, *Principal*
EMP: 6 EST: 2014
SALES (est): 101.3K Privately Held
SIC: 2951 Asphalt paving mixtures & blocks

(G-15063)
POLISHING BY WILSON O
5521 Bay Blvd Apt 102 (34668-6018)
PHONE..................................727 203-0100
Wilson Otero, *Owner*
EMP: 6 EST: 2015
SALES (est): 85.3K Privately Held
SIC: 3471 Polishing, metals or formed products

(G-15064)
PREMIER PRINTING SIGNS
Also Called: PIP Printing
6520 Industrial Ave Ste 1 (34668-6856)
PHONE..................................727 849-2493
Theodore Cadwallader, *President*
EMP: 6 EST: 1981
SQ FT: 3,000
SALES (est): 919.9K Privately Held
WEB: www.digitalprintingportrichey.com
SIC: 2752 3993 Commercial printing, offset; signs & advertising specialties

(G-15065)
PRO TECH CUSTOM CABINET
9100 Bolton Ave (34667-3778)
P.O. Box 5962 (34674-5962)
PHONE..................................727 863-5143
EMP: 10
SQ FT: 7,000
SALES (est): 850K Privately Held
SIC: 2541 Mfg Cabinets

(G-15066)
PROLIFIC RESOURCE INC
Also Called: Siebers Graphic
12045 Cobble Stone Dr (34667-2414)
PHONE..................................727 868-9341
Dale Sieber, *President*
Rosemary Sieber, *Vice Pres*
EMP: 5 EST: 1974
SALES (est): 412.5K Privately Held
SIC: 2752 Commercial printing, offset

(G-15067)
SEADREAMS BOAT YACHT WORKS LLC
5100 Sunset Blvd (34668-6450)
PHONE..................................727 843-0010
James E Priest,
EMP: 6 EST: 2010
SALES (est): 114.5K Privately Held
SIC: 3732 Yachts, building & repairing

(G-15068)
SEAWAY PLASTICS ENGRG LLC
6041 Siesta Ln (34668-6754)
PHONE..................................727 777-6032
Henry Smitty, *Engineer*
Peter Komasinski, *Sales Engr*
Patrick Buttil, *Manager*
EMP: 9 EST: 2016
SALES (est): 529.1K Privately Held
WEB: www.seawayplastics.com
SIC: 3089 Injection molding of plastics

(G-15069)
SEAWAY PLASTICS ENGRG LLC (HQ)
6006 Siesta Ln (34668-6752)
P.O. Box 927 (34673-0927)
PHONE..................................727 845-3235
Tom Orr, *President*
Paul Bernard, *President*
Jeffrey Cox, *Opers Dir*
John Hanke, *Project Mgr*
Patti Rone, *Purch Agent*
▲ EMP: 100 EST: 1995
SQ FT: 67,000
SALES (est): 35MM
SALES (corp-wide): 68.6MM Privately Held
WEB: www.seawayplastics.com
SIC: 3089 Injection molding of plastics

GEOGRAPHIC

PA: Tonka Bay Equity Partners Llc
301 Carlson Pkwy Ste 325
Hopkins MN 55305
952 345-2030

(G-15070)
SUNCOAST NEWS
11321 Us Highway 19 (34668-1416)
PHONE..................................727 815-1023
Tim Wahl, *Sales Mgr*
EMP: 6 **EST:** 2019
SALES (est): 124.7K **Privately Held**
WEB: www.suncoastnews.com
SIC: 2711 Newspapers, publishing & printing

(G-15071)
SUPERIOR SOLID SURFACE INC
8609 Squib Dr (34668-5342)
PHONE..................................727 842-9947
Robert James, *President*
Brian James, *Corp Secy*
Harry James, *Vice Pres*
EMP: 11 **EST:** 1998
SQ FT: 1,500
SALES (est): 531.6K **Privately Held**
WEB: www.superiorsolidsurface.com
SIC: 2541 Counter & sink tops

(G-15072)
TIMES PUBLISHING COMPANY
Also Called: Saint Petersburg Times
11321 Us Highway 19 (34668-1416)
PHONE..................................727 849-6397
Bill Stevens, *Manager*
EMP: 148
SQ FT: 19,113
SALES (corp-wide): 14.9MM **Privately Held**
WEB: www.tampabay.com
SIC: 2711 Newspapers, publishing & printing
HQ: Times Publishing Company
490 1st Ave S
Saint Petersburg FL 33701
727 893-8111

(G-15073)
TWINSTAR OPTICS & COATINGS INC
Also Called: Twinstar Optics Ctngs Cyrstals
6741 Commerce Ave (34668-6815)
PHONE..................................727 847-2300
Mary Beth Toland, *President*
Robert Thomas, *Vice Pres*
Amanda Minier, *Purchasing*
Mary Beth Thomas-Toland, *CFO*
Melissa Samplatsky,
EMP: 18 **EST:** 1997
SQ FT: 16,600
SALES (est): 2MM **Privately Held**
WEB: www.twinstaroptics.com
SIC: 3827 3845 3695 3826 Lenses, optical: all types except ophthalmic; electromedical equipment; optical disks & tape, blank; laser scientific & engineering instruments

(G-15074)
US BARCODES INC
6740 Commerce Ave (34668-6814)
P.O. Box 1191, Elfers (34680-1191)
PHONE..................................727 849-1196
Junior A Matias, *CEO*
Chad Zielesch, *IT/INT Sup*
EMP: 9 **EST:** 2001
SALES (est): 476.6K **Privately Held**
WEB: www.usbarcodes.com
SIC: 3577 Bar code (magnetic ink) printers

(G-15075)
US SIGNS INC
16631 Scheer Blvd (34667-4237)
PHONE..................................727 862-7933
Sidney Cooper, *President*
Sussie Cooper, *Corp Secy*
Josh Cooper, *Vice Pres*
EMP: 22 **EST:** 1992
SQ FT: 4,000
SALES (est): 2.4MM **Privately Held**
WEB: www.ussignsandletters.com
SIC: 3993 Electric signs

(G-15076)
VINYL ETCHINGS INC
6641 Industrial Ave (34668-6864)
PHONE..................................727 845-5300
Thomas Walter, *President*
Stephen Lazorcak, *Vice Pres*
Jackie Gillespie, *Treasurer*
Vei Forbes, *Manager*
Nancy Forbes, *Admin Sec*
EMP: 9 **EST:** 2003
SALES (est): 765.8K **Privately Held**
WEB: www.vinyletchings.com
SIC: 3993 Signs & advertising specialties

(G-15077)
VLOC INCORPORATED
6716 Industrial Ave (34668-6886)
PHONE..................................727 375-8562
Steve Sacone, *President*
Francis Kramer, *Vice Pres*
Craig A Creaturo, *CFO*
EMP: 120 **EST:** 1996
SQ FT: 65,000
SALES (est): 33.4MM
SALES (corp-wide): 3.1B **Publicly Held**
WEB: www.ii-vi.com
SIC: 3827 Optical elements & assemblies, except ophthalmic
PA: Ii-Vi Incorporated
375 Saxonburg Blvd
Saxonburg PA 16056
724 352-4455

(G-15078)
WHITES HOLDINGS INC CENTL FLA
9301 Denton Ave (34667-4340)
P.O. Box 5577 (34674-5577)
PHONE..................................727 863-6072
Priscilla K White, *President*
John Terry White, *President*
EMP: 15 **EST:** 1981
SQ FT: 3,000
SALES (est): 1.6MM **Privately Held**
SIC: 3271 3273 Concrete block & brick; ready-mixed concrete

(G-15079)
WIDELL INDUSTRIES INC (PA)
6622 Industrial Ave (34668-6897)
P.O. Box 580 (34673-0580)
PHONE..................................800 237-5963
Wayne A Widell, *President*
Chuck Lisowe, *Plant Mgr*
Wayne D Widell, *Admin Sec*
EMP: 65 **EST:** 1980
SQ FT: 70,000
SALES (est): 9.8MM **Privately Held**
WEB: www.widell.com
SIC: 3545 Taps, machine tool; thread cutting dies; gauges (machine tool accessories)

Port Saint Joe
Gulf County

(G-15080)
GULF COUNTY SHIP BUILDING INC
1550 Old Dynamite Dock Rd (32456-6367)
PHONE..................................850 229-9300
John Dixon, *President*
Paul Duncan, *Superintendent*
EMP: 8 **EST:** 1998
SQ FT: 2,600
SALES (est): 154.5K **Privately Held**
WEB: www.gcship.com
SIC: 3731 Shipbuilding & repairing

(G-15081)
MONUMENTAL FABRICATION OF AMER
Also Called: MFA
950 W Rutherford St (32456-5332)
PHONE..................................850 227-9500
Delilah Henderson, *Owner*
Alex Henderson, *Vice Pres*
EMP: 7 **EST:** 2005
SALES (est): 956.8K **Privately Held**
WEB: www.monumentalfabrication.com
SIC: 3446 Architectural metalwork

(G-15082)
RAMSEYS PRINTING & OFFICE PDTS
209 Reid Ave (32456-1823)
PHONE..................................850 227-7468
William Ramsey Jr, *President*
Eric Ramsey, *Vice Pres*
Shirley Ramsey, *Director*
EMP: 6 **EST:** 1995
SQ FT: 100,000
SALES (est): 639.5K **Privately Held**
WEB: www.ramseysprinting.com
SIC: 2752 5112 Commercial printing, lithographic; stationery & office supplies

(G-15083)
READY MIX USA LLC
Also Called: Readymix - Port St Joe
1001 Ccil G Cstin Sr Blvd (32456-1655)
PHONE..................................850 227-7677
EMP: 17
SALES (corp-wide): 14.9B **Privately Held**
SIC: 3273 Mfg Ready-Mixed Concrete
HQ: Ready Mix Usa, Llc
2657 Ruffner Rd
Birmingham AL 35210
205 967-5211

(G-15084)
WALTER GREEN INC
252 Marina Dr (32456-1832)
PHONE..................................850 227-7946
George Duren, *Owner*
Karah Bradley, *Manager*
EMP: 7 **EST:** 2011
SALES (est): 541.6K **Privately Held**
WEB: www.waltergreenboutique.com
SIC: 2389 5632 Men's miscellaneous accessories; apparel accessories

Port Saint Lucie
St. Lucie County

(G-15085)
ALCHEMIST HOLDINGS LLC
Rebar Alchemist
8283 S Us Highway 1 (34952-2859)
PHONE..................................772 340-7774
Andrew Cook, *Principal*
EMP: 10
SALES (corp-wide): 19.1MM **Privately Held**
SIC: 3441 Fabricated structural metal
PA: Alchemist Holdings, Llc
10482 Sw Tibre Ct
Port Saint Lucie FL 34987
772 343-1111

(G-15086)
ALCHEMIST HOLDINGS LLC (PA)
Also Called: Rebar Alchemist
10482 Sw Tibre Ct (34987-2347)
PHONE..................................772 343-1111
Magbis Riley, *Principal*
Asbel Viciedo, *Mng Member*
EMP: 40 **EST:** 2006
SQ FT: 5,500
SALES: 19.1MM **Privately Held**
SIC: 3441 Fabricated structural metal

(G-15087)
APPAREL MACHINERY SERVICES INC
1545 Se S Niemeyer Cir (34952-3507)
PHONE..................................772 335-5350
Ronald J Boser, *President*
Rosanna Boser, *Treasurer*
EMP: 5 **EST:** 1990
SQ FT: 9,000
SALES (est): 2MM **Privately Held**
WEB: www.apparelmachineryservices.com
SIC: 2341 2299 Women's & children's underwear; batting, wadding, padding & fillings

(G-15088)
AQUABACK TECHNOLOGIES INC
9300 Scarborough Ct (34986-3360)
PHONE..................................978 863-1000
William H Zebuhr, *CEO*
Scott Newquist, *CEO*
David Dussault, *COO*
EMP: 10 **EST:** 2010
SALES (est): 1.8MM **Privately Held**
WEB: www.aquaback.com
SIC: 3556 Distillery machinery

(G-15089)
ATLANTIC PRECISION INC
1461 Nw Commerce Ctr Pkwy (34986)
PHONE..................................772 466-1011
Tim Ritter, *President*
EMP: 89 **EST:** 1988
SQ FT: 34,000
SALES (est): 17MM
SALES (corp-wide): 245.5B **Publicly Held**
WEB: www.pccstructurals.com
SIC: 3728 Aircraft parts & equipment
HQ: Pcc Structurals, Inc.
4600 Se Harney Dr
Portland OR 97206
503 777-3881

(G-15090)
BEGINMYPRINTING COM
430 Sw Fairway Lndg (34986-2165)
PHONE..................................772 828-2026
Jennifer Kroitor, *Owner*
EMP: 6 **EST:** 2013
SALES (est): 236.4K **Privately Held**
WEB: www.beginmywebsite.com
SIC: 2752 Commercial printing, lithographic

(G-15091)
BENT PINE PUBLISHING CORP
1402 Sw Bent Pine Cv (34986-2103)
PHONE..................................772 708-0490
Richard Crosby, *Principal*
EMP: 6 **EST:** 2012
SALES (est): 9K **Privately Held**
WEB: www.bentpinepublishing.com
SIC: 2741 Miscellaneous publishing

(G-15092)
BLUEWATER FINISHING LLC
1913 Sw South Macedo Blvd (34984-4346)
PHONE..................................772 460-9457
Alan D Blandford, *Manager*
EMP: 5 **EST:** 2005
SALES (est): 397.2K **Privately Held**
SIC: 3299 Stucco

(G-15093)
BONGIOVI AVIATION LLC
649 Sw Whitmore Dr (34984-3567)
PHONE..................................772 879-0578
Brian Servis, *Business Mgr*
Lawrence Hamelink, *Manager*
Anthony Bongiovi, *Manager*
EMP: 10 **EST:** 2017
SALES (est): 917.3K **Privately Held**
WEB: www.bongioviacoustics.com
SIC: 3699 Electric sound equipment

(G-15094)
BUSY BEE PRINTER
1902 Se Manth Ln (34983-4527)
PHONE..................................772 621-3683
Jay Deffenbaugh, *Principal*
EMP: 6 **EST:** 2008
SALES (est): 120K **Privately Held**
SIC: 2752 Commercial printing, lithographic

(G-15095)
CABINET CNNCTION OF TRSURE CAS (PA)
740 Nw Enterprise Dr (34986-2228)
PHONE..................................772 621-4882
Gary Guterl, *President*
Kenneth Bianco, *Vice Pres*
EMP: 27 **EST:** 1994
SQ FT: 12,000
SALES (est): 3.8MM **Privately Held**
WEB: www.cabinetconnection.net
SIC: 2434 2541 Wood kitchen cabinets; table or counter tops, plastic laminated

(G-15096)
CATCH ONE COMM
Also Called: SC Edge
1850 Sw Fountainview Blvd # 103
(34986-3443)
PHONE..................................772 221-0225

Michael Visconte, *President*
Tina Luve, *Partner*
EMP: 7 **EST:** 1991
SALES (est): 445.5K **Privately Held**
SIC: 3993 Signs & advertising specialties

(G-15097)
CHARUVIL OIL INC DBA VALERO
815 E Prima Vista Blvd (34952-2331)
PHONE..................................772 871-9050
EMP: 5
SALES (est): 326.3K **Privately Held**
SIC: 1389 Oil/Gas Field Services

(G-15098)
CLASSIC WOODWORKS LLC (PA)
513 Se Maple Ter (34983-2654)
PHONE..................................772 398-6258
Michael Joachim Heyer, *Principal*
EMP: 31 **EST:** 2008
SALES (est): 64.9K **Privately Held**
SIC: 2431 Millwork

(G-15099)
COASTAL SHUTTERS INC
303 Nw Hibiscus St (34983-1659)
PHONE..................................954 759-1115
Sergiu Costin, *Principal*
EMP: 6 **EST:** 2018
SALES (est): 209.8K **Privately Held**
WEB: www.localshutters.net
SIC: 3442 Shutters, door or window: metal

(G-15100)
COMPLY ARM
1680 Sw St Lucie W Blvd (34986-1927)
PHONE..................................772 249-0345
Adam Parks, *Principal*
EMP: 7 **EST:** 2016
SALES (est): 177.6K **Privately Held**
WEB: www.complyarm.com
SIC: 7372 Prepackaged software

(G-15101)
CORPORACION INTERNACIONAL DE J
Also Called: Vm Jewelry
2868 Sw Port St Lcie Blvd (34953-2835)
PHONE..................................772 343-1721
Fernando Valbuena, *President*
Guerty Valbuena, *Principal*
EMP: 6 **EST:** 2013
SALES (est): 352.5K **Privately Held**
SIC: 3911 7631 Jewelry apparel; watch, clock & jewelry repair

(G-15102)
DISCOUNT DISTRIBUTORS INC
Also Called: Ball Busines Products
725 Se Port St Lucie Blvd # 106 (34984-5232)
PHONE..................................772 336-0092
Donald E Ball, *President*
Dana Ball, *Products*
EMP: 5 **EST:** 1990
SALES (est): 593.9K **Privately Held**
SIC: 3861 5112 Photographic equipment & supplies; photocopying supplies

(G-15103)
DRAGONFLY GRAPHICS
861 Sw Lakehurst Dr Ste B (34983-2462)
PHONE..................................772 879-9800
Richard G Coffey, *President*
Micheal Coffey, *Vice Pres*
Alan Coffey, *Treasurer*
Kevin Murphy, *Sales Staff*
EMP: 5 **EST:** 1999
SALES (est): 448.7K **Privately Held**
WEB: www.dragonflycentral.com
SIC: 2759 Screen printing

(G-15104)
EASTWARD BOATS INC
1520 Se S Nmyer Cir Ste 6 (34952)
PHONE..................................772 828-1358
David East, *Principal*
EMP: 6 **EST:** 2016
SALES (est): 75.9K **Privately Held**
WEB: www.eastwardboats.com
SIC: 3732 Boat building & repairing

(G-15105)
EL HISPANO
102 Nw Airoso Blvd (34983-1652)
PHONE..................................772 878-6488
Adriana Maga, *Owner*
EMP: 7 **EST:** 2010
SALES (est): 219.5K **Privately Held**
WEB: www.elhispanoparatodos.com
SIC: 2711 Newspapers, publishing & printing

(G-15106)
ENVIROSEAL CORPORATION
1019 Se Hlbrook Ct 1021 (34952)
PHONE..................................772 335-8225
Thomas Stevens, *President*
William A Stevens, *Vice Pres*
▼ **EMP:** 5 **EST:** 1994
SQ FT: 10,000
SALES (est): 974.1K **Privately Held**
WEB: www.enviroseal.com
SIC: 2899 Chemical preparations

(G-15107)
EW SCRIPPS COMPANY
Also Called: Port St. Lucie News
1939 Se Federal Hwy (34986)
PHONE..................................772 408-5300
EMP: 200
SALES (corp-wide): 715.6MM **Publicly Held**
SIC: 2711 Newspapers
PA: The E W Scripps Company
312 Walnut St Ste 2800
Cincinnati OH 45202
513 977-3000

(G-15108)
EXPERT SHUTTER SERVICES INC
668 Sw Whitmore Dr (34984-3512)
PHONE..................................772 871-1915
Mike Heissenberg, *President*
Jamie Heissenberg, *Vice Pres*
EMP: 56 **EST:** 1983
SALES (est): 6.7MM **Privately Held**
WEB: www.expertshutters.com
SIC: 2431 3442 3354 Awnings, blinds & shutters, wood; metal doors, sash & trim; aluminum extruded products

(G-15109)
EZ LODER ADJSTBLE BOAT TRLRS S
1462 Commerce Centre Dr (34986-3208)
PHONE..................................800 323-8190
Randy Johnson, *President*
James Vassallo, *Vice Pres*
Christina Johnson, *Admin Sec*
▼ **EMP:** 5 **EST:** 2005
SALES (est): 862.4K
SALES (corp-wide): 131.7MM **Privately Held**
WEB: www.ezloader.com
SIC: 3799 Boat trailers
PA: E Z Loader Boat Trailers, Inc.
717 N Hamilton St
Spokane WA 99202
574 266-0092

(G-15110)
FOUNTAIN YOUTH BATHROOMS INC
2559 Sw Kenilworth St (34953-2575)
PHONE..................................772 626-9626
Shane R Viens, *President*
Robert Viens, *Vice Pres*
EMP: 10 **EST:** 2007
SALES (est): 481.4K **Privately Held**
SIC: 3088 Tubs (bath, shower & laundry), plastic

(G-15111)
GROOVY TOYS LLC
Also Called: Grooyi
585 Nw Merc Pl Ste 108 (34986)
PHONE..................................772 878-0790
◆ **EMP:** 5
SQ FT: 2,400
SALES (est): 664K **Privately Held**
SIC: 3944 Mfg Games/Toys

(G-15112)
HESS EXPRESS
10453 S Us Highway 1 (34952-5645)
PHONE..................................772 335-9975
Johnson Hess, *President*
EMP: 6 **EST:** 1999
SALES (est): 385.8K **Privately Held**
SIC: 1389 Gas field services

(G-15113)
IDPRODUCTSOURCE
645 Nw Entp Driv Ste (34986)
PHONE..................................772 336-4269
Karole Aspinwall, *President*
Ryan Modica, *Sales Mgr*
EMP: 8 **EST:** 2015
SALES (est): 1.6MM **Privately Held**
WEB: www.idproductsource.com
SIC: 3089 Injection molding of plastics

(G-15114)
IDPRODUCTSOURCE LLC
651 Nw Enterprise Dr (34986-2262)
PHONE..................................772 336-4269
Karole A Aspinwall,
John P Aspinwall,
Gabrielle M Client, *Representative*
EMP: 5 **EST:** 2001
SALES (est): 478.9K **Privately Held**
SIC: 3089 Identification cards, plastic

(G-15115)
JBR EXTERIORS INC
1201 Sw Biltmore St (34983-2486)
PHONE..................................772 873-0600
Brown Johnson, *President*
Rhonda Johnson, *Vice Pres*
John Williams, *Sales Mgr*
Gail Buchmeyer, *Office Mgr*
EMP: 5 **EST:** 1999
SQ FT: 5,824
SALES (est): 1MM **Privately Held**
WEB: www.jbrexteriors.com
SIC: 3448 Screen enclosures

(G-15116)
JUST DOOR TOOLZ LLC
1552 Sw Abingdon Ave (34953-2550)
P.O. Box 7999 (34985-7999)
PHONE..................................954 448-6872
Glen McMorris, *Principal*
Sandra McMorris, *Principal*
EMP: 7 **EST:** 2011
SALES (est): 222.1K **Privately Held**
WEB: www.justdoortoolz.com
SIC: 3423 Carpenters' hand tools, except saws: levels, chisels, etc.

(G-15117)
KNIGHT INDUSTRIES
1001 Sw Cornelia Ave (34953-3238)
PHONE..................................772 344-2053
Allen Solomon, *Principal*
EMP: 6 **EST:** 2008
SALES (est): 66.9K **Privately Held**
SIC: 3999 Manufacturing industries

(G-15118)
LACTALOGICS INC
8883 S Us Highway 1 (34952-3401)
PHONE..................................772 202-0407
Glenn Snow, *CEO*
Laura Salter, *Exec Dir*
EMP: 5 **EST:** 2014
SALES (est): 448.5K **Privately Held**
WEB: www.lactalogics.com
SIC: 2836 Biological products, except diagnostic

(G-15119)
LCR SIGNS & SERVICES
2862 Se Buccaneer Cir (34952-6612)
PHONE..................................772 882-5276
Lawrence Riccard, *Principal*
EMP: 6 **EST:** 2014
SALES (est): 164.7K **Privately Held**
WEB: www.lcrsigns.com
SIC: 3993 Signs & advertising specialties

(G-15120)
LIGHT SOURCE BUSINESS SYSTEMS
Also Called: Lightsource Imaging Solutions
582 Nw Mercantile Pl (34986-2252)
PHONE..................................772 562-5046
Michael Stephens, *President*
Pam Stephens, *Vice Pres*
EMP: 16 **EST:** 1991
SALES (est): 839.2K **Privately Held**
WEB: www.lightsourceimaging.com
SIC: 2759 5734 7699 5943 Laser printing; printers & plotters: computers; printing trades machinery & equipment repair; stationery stores; photographic equipment & supplies

(G-15121)
MARTIN MUNIVE INC
19200 Glades Cut Off Rd (34987-2603)
PHONE..................................772 318-8168
Martin Munive, *Principal*
EMP: 6 **EST:** 2010
SALES (est): 219.5K **Privately Held**
SIC: 3541 Lathes

(G-15122)
MINUTEMAN PRESS
6967 Hancock Dr (34952-8207)
PHONE..................................772 301-0222
EMP: 6 **EST:** 2018
SALES (est): 214.7K **Privately Held**
WEB: www.minutemanpress.com
SIC: 2752 Commercial printing, lithographic

(G-15123)
NEW GNRTION ABNDANT MSSION CH
Also Called: New Gnrtion Jews Abndant Mssio
2017 Sw Tropical Ter (34953-1337)
P.O. Box 324, Plattsburgh NY (12901-0324)
PHONE..................................772 497-5871
Rikem Jean Philipp, *Principal*
EMP: 20 **EST:** 2005
SALES (est): 743.5K **Privately Held**
SIC: 2752 Commercial printing, lithographic

(G-15124)
NIDA-CORE CORPORATION (HQ)
541 Nw Interpark Pl (34986-2217)
PHONE..................................772 343-7300
Damien Jacquinet, *President*
◆ **EMP:** 50 **EST:** 1987
SQ FT: 70,000
SALES (est): 13.3MM
SALES (corp-wide): 32.1B **Publicly Held**
WEB: www.3m.com
SIC: 2679 3086 2821 2221 Honeycomb core & board: made from purchased material; plastics foam products; plastics materials & resins; fiberglass fabrics; flat panels, plastic; machine shop, jobbing & repair
PA: 3m Company
3m Center
Saint Paul MN 55144
651 733-1110

(G-15125)
NORTHEAST PRO-TECH INC
7219 Reserve Creek Dr (34986-3220)
PHONE..................................772 489-8762
EMP: 6
SALES (corp-wide): 1MM **Privately Held**
SIC: 2824 Protein fibers
PA: Northeast Pro-Tech Inc
61 Willet St Bldg L
Passaic NJ 07055
973 777-5654

(G-15126)
OCONNELL TEAM LLC
152 Sw Milburn Cir (34953-5506)
PHONE..................................772 201-3848
John M O'Connell, *Principal*
EMP: 6 **EST:** 2016
SALES (est): 297.5K **Privately Held**
SIC: 3577 Computer peripheral equipment

(G-15127)
OLIVEIRA SERVICES CORP
972 Sw Paar Dr (34953-5623)
PHONE..................................772 834-4803
EMP: 5
SALES (est): 391.9K **Privately Held**
SIC: 2434 Mfg Wood Kitchen Cabinets

(G-15128)
ORACLE CORPORATION
1701 Se Hillmoor Dr D16 (34952-7541)
PHONE..................................772 337-4141
EMP: 191
SALES (corp-wide): 40.4B **Publicly Held**
WEB: www.oracle.com
SIC: 7372 Prepackaged software
PA: Oracle Corporation
2300 Oracle Way
Austin TX 78741
737 867-1000

(G-15129)
PLANTATION SHUTTERS INC
Also Called: Simply Shutters
1388 Commerce Ctr Dr (34986-1300)
P.O. Box 882096 (34988-2096)
PHONE..................................772 208-8245
Timothy McBride, *President*
Jeri McBride, *Admin Sec*
EMP: 9 **EST:** 2017
SALES (est): 617.9K **Privately Held**
WEB: www.plantationshuttersflorida.com
SIC: 3442 Shutters, door or window: metal

(G-15130)
PREMIER LAB SUPPLY INC
691 Nw Enterprise Dr (34986-2204)
PHONE..................................772 873-1700
Daniel Pompa, *President*
Joseph Beckman, *Counsel*
Christina Pompa, *Vice Pres*
John Haugh, *Sales Mgr*
Melissa Miller, *Manager*
◆ **EMP:** 9 **EST:** 1998
SQ FT: 8,500
SALES (est): 2.8MM **Privately Held**
WEB: www.premierlabsupply.com
SIC: 3089 3821 5023 Injection molding of plastics; sample preparation apparatus; glassware

(G-15131)
PROTEGE MEDIA LLC
5945 Nw Dowell Ct (34986-3832)
PHONE..................................310 738-9567
Rodney Henry,
EMP: 5 **EST:** 2016
SALES (est): 1MM **Privately Held**
SIC: 3021 7812 Rubber & plastics footwear; educational motion picture production, television

(G-15132)
R & S METALWORKS & CO LLC
5690 Carlton Rd (34987-3201)
PHONE..................................772 466-3303
Scott M Snowden, *Mng Member*
EMP: 17 **EST:** 2007
SQ FT: 500
SALES (est): 2.8MM **Privately Held**
SIC: 3548 3523 5084 Arc welders, transformer-rectifier; farm machinery & equipment; welding machinery & equipment

(G-15133)
R & S SNACKS LLC
1660 Sw Buttercup Ave (34953-4935)
PHONE..................................954 839-5482
Beau Y Stager, *Manager*
EMP: 8 **EST:** 2017
SALES (est): 513K **Privately Held**
SIC: 2096 Potato chips & similar snacks

(G-15134)
R J REYNOLDS TOBACCO COMPANY
2687 Sw Domina Rd (34953-2778)
PHONE..................................772 873-6955
John Wickline, *Manager*
EMP: 89 **Privately Held**
WEB: www.rjrt.com
SIC: 2111 Cigarettes
HQ: R. J. Reynolds Tobacco Company
401 N Main St
Winston Salem NC 27101
336 741-5000

(G-15135)
RACEWAY ELECTRIC LLC
208 Sw Aubudon Ave (34984-5030)
PHONE..................................772 260-6530
Adam L Race, *Manager*
EMP: 7 **EST:** 2015
SALES (est): 322.1K **Privately Held**
WEB: www.racewayelectricfl.com
SIC: 3644 Raceways

(G-15136)
RENAL ADVANTAGE INC A44
8661 S Us Highway 1 (34952-3331)
PHONE..................................772 807-7229
Janice Hyatt, *Principal*
EMP: 6 **EST:** 2008
SALES (est): 191.7K **Privately Held**
SIC: 3845 Ultrasonic scanning devices, medical

(G-15137)
REPROGRAPHIC SOLUTIONS INC (PA)
234 Sw Port St Lucie Blvd (34984-5044)
PHONE..................................772 340-3430
Bridget Demaio, *President*
EMP: 5 **EST:** 2001
SQ FT: 1,500
SALES (est): 957.5K **Privately Held**
WEB: www.repro718.com
SIC: 2759 5044 Maps: printing; blueprinting equipment

(G-15138)
RICHARD VARNEY SIGNS
3031 Sw Lucerne St (34953-4420)
PHONE..................................772 873-0454
Richard Varney, *President*
EMP: 6 **EST:** 1999
SALES (est): 104.3K **Privately Held**
SIC: 3993 Signs & advertising specialties

(G-15139)
ROGERS SEPTIC TANKS INC
10603 Sw Capraia Way (34986-2888)
PHONE..................................203 259-9947
Roger Thoele, *President*
EMP: 7 **EST:** 1947
SALES (est): 196.1K **Privately Held**
SIC: 3272 Septic tanks, concrete

(G-15140)
RPP DEVICES
625 Nw Commodity Cv (34986-2250)
PHONE..................................772 807-7098
Brian Smith, *Principal*
Alecia Ortiz, *Manager*
▲ **EMP:** 5 **EST:** 2008
SALES (est): 301.3K **Privately Held**
WEB: www.rpp-usa.com
SIC: 3678 Electronic connectors

(G-15141)
SAVAGE VENTURES INC
Also Called: C&L Technologies
1702 Se Village Green Dr (34952-3456)
PHONE..................................772 335-5655
Corey Nsavage, *President*
Miguel Campos, *Vice Pres*
Leo Ambrogi, *Vice Pres*
Ann K Savage, *Treasurer*
Sylvia Charton, *Controller*
EMP: 33 **EST:** 1957
SQ FT: 48,000
SALES (est): 4.7MM **Privately Held**
SIC: 3544 Special dies & tools

(G-15142)
SHUTTERTEK INC
566 Se Floresta Dr (34983-2241)
P.O. Box 881706 (34988-1706)
PHONE..................................772 828-6149
Marco T Lopez Sr, *President*
EMP: 7 **EST:** 2012
SALES (est): 215.7K **Privately Held**
WEB: www.shuttertek.com
SIC: 3442 Shutters, door or window: metal

(G-15143)
SIGNS OF TIMES VENTURES LLC
151 Ne Naranja Ave (34983-8448)
PHONE..................................772 336-4525
Natalie A Klaas, *Principal*
EMP: 6 **EST:** 2010
SALES (est): 72.4K **Privately Held**
WEB: www.ohmygoshinteriors.com
SIC: 3993 Signs & advertising specialties

(G-15144)
SIRE CABINETRY INC
10320 Sw Stephanie Way (34987-1965)
PHONE..................................909 225-4121
Andrew S Slattery, *Principal*
EMP: 6 **EST:** 2015
SALES (est): 53.7K **Privately Held**
SIC: 2434 Wood kitchen cabinets

(G-15145)
SKIES LIMIT PRINTING
10504 S Us Highway 1 (34952-5603)
PHONE..................................772 340-1090
Sande Kornblum, *Principal*
EMP: 6 **EST:** 2008
SALES (est): 521.8K **Privately Held**
WEB: www.skiesthelimitgraphics.com
SIC: 2759 Commercial printing

(G-15146)
SLB1989 INC
Also Called: St Lucie Bakery
1066 Sw Bayshore Blvd (34983-2400)
PHONE..................................772 344-3609
Kelley Arciprete, *President*
EMP: 6 **EST:** 2012
SALES (est): 115.4K **Privately Held**
SIC: 2051 Bread, cake & related products

(G-15147)
STANDOUT HOME SERVICING LLC
1202 Sw Empire St (34983-2468)
PHONE..................................772 708-1110
Joshua Bradley, *Principal*
EMP: 5 **EST:** 2010
SALES (est): 397.2K **Privately Held**
SIC: 1389 Roustabout service

(G-15148)
STERLING FACILITY SERVICES LLC
Also Called: Trailer 1
523 Nw Peacock Blvd (34986-2210)
PHONE..................................772 871-2161
Paul Taglieri, *Vice Pres*
EMP: 9 **EST:** 2004
SALES (est): 420K **Privately Held**
SIC: 3949 Team sports equipment

(G-15149)
STUART MAGAZINE
1950 Se Port St Lucie Blv (34952-5580)
P.O. Box 8136 (34985-8136)
PHONE..................................772 207-7895
EMP: 7 **EST:** 2015
SALES (est): 100.7K **Privately Held**
WEB: www.stuartmagazine.com
SIC: 2721 Magazines: publishing only, not printed on site

(G-15150)
SUN PIPE AND VALVES LLC
710 Nw Enterprise Dr (34986-2228)
PHONE..................................772 408-5530
Rand Calender,
Albert Kocher,
EMP: 8 **EST:** 2005
SALES (est): 455.1K **Privately Held**
SIC: 3494 5074 Valves & pipe fittings; pipes & fittings, plastic

(G-15151)
SYNERGY ANCILLARY SERVICES LLC
Also Called: Sas Group
11350 Sw Village Pkwy (34987-2352)
PHONE..................................561 249-7238
Amy Naples, *Human Res Dir*
Russ Warrington, *Director*
Matthew I Parra Sr,
EMP: 16 **EST:** 2014
SALES (est): 6.4MM **Privately Held**
SIC: 2869 Laboratory chemicals, organic

(G-15152)
SYSTEM DATA RESOURCE
Also Called: Software
11422 Sw Hillcrest Cir (34987-2706)
PHONE..................................954 213-8008
Elva Kulinsky, *CEO*
Frederick Kulinsky, *Vice Pres*
EMP: 6 **EST:** 1989
SQ FT: 1,000
SALES (est): 129.5K **Privately Held**
WEB: www.systemdataresource.com
SIC: 7372 Prepackaged software

(G-15153)
TAMLITE LIGHTING - NEW WHSE
660 Nw Peacock Blvd (34986-2211)
PHONE..................................772 879-7440
Steven Hagadorn, *Regl Sales Mgr*
Melissa Leatherman, *Sales Staff*
Andrew Mitchell, *Sales Staff*
Stephanie Norris, *Sales Staff*
EMP: 7 **EST:** 2017
SALES (est): 518.4K **Privately Held**
SIC: 3648 Lighting equipment

(G-15154)
TOTAL PAVERS CORP
2529 Sw Grotto Cir (34953-2927)
PHONE..................................561 902-7665
Wagner Santos, *Principal*
EMP: 11 **EST:** 2013
SALES (est): 493.6K **Privately Held**
SIC: 2951 Asphalt paving mixtures & blocks

(G-15155)
TREASURE CAST PRENTING MAG INC
2162 Nw Reserve Park Trce (34986-3223)
P.O. Box 880894 (34988-0894)
PHONE..................................772 672-8588
Kara Ferraro, *President*
Don Ferraro, *COO*
EMP: 10 **EST:** 2008
SQ FT: 3,400
SALES (est): 715.3K **Privately Held**
WEB: www.indianrivermagazine.com
SIC: 2721 Magazines: publishing only, not printed on site

(G-15156)
TRISTAN S KOOL DREEMZ
1401 Se Delene Ct (34952-7601)
PHONE..................................772 398-8875
Edward Tristan, *Principal*
EMP: 6 **EST:** 2007
SALES (est): 156.1K **Privately Held**
SIC: 2024 Ice cream & frozen desserts

(G-15157)
TRUENORTH IQ INC
1193 Se Port St Lcie Blvd (34952-5332)
PHONE..................................678 849-5000
Scott Manderville, *CEO*
EMP: 9 **EST:** 2018
SALES (est): 380K **Privately Held**
WEB: www.truenorthiq.com
SIC: 3812 Defense systems & equipment

(G-15158)
UM KITCHEN CABINETS INC
965 Sw North Globe Ave (34953-3419)
PHONE..................................772 224-5445
Gonzalez Margaret, *Principal*
EMP: 6 **EST:** 2015
SALES (est): 77.3K **Privately Held**
SIC: 2434 Wood kitchen cabinets

(G-15159)
UNIQUE DESIGNS & FINISHES INC
1443 Se Huffman Rd (34952-3353)
PHONE..................................772 335-4884
Harry Sanka, *President*
EMP: 10 **EST:** 1997
SALES (est): 1.5MM **Privately Held**
WEB: www.uniquedesignsandfinishes.com
SIC: 3639 Major kitchen appliances, except refrigerators & stoves

(G-15160)
VELEZ CUSTOM CABINETRY CORP
5810 Nw Gillespie Ave (34986-3938)
PHONE..................................772 418-9565
Carlos A Velez, *Principal*
EMP: 7 **EST:** 2008
SALES (est): 186.8K **Privately Held**
WEB: www.velezcustomcabinetry.com
SIC: 2434 Wood kitchen cabinets

(G-15161)
VENTURA FOODS LLC
485 Nw Enterprise Dr (34986-2202)
PHONE.....772 878-1400
Ventura Foods, *Branch Mgr*
EMP: 7 **Privately Held**
WEB: www.venturafoods.com
SIC: 2079 Edible fats & oils
PA: Ventura Foods, Llc
40 Pointe Dr
Brea CA 92821

(G-15162)
VERTICAL VILLAGE INC
10658 S Us Highway 1 (34952-6402)
PHONE.....772 340-0400
James Daugaard, *President*
Chris Daugaard, *Owner*
Joseph Daugaard, *Vice Pres*
Christine Daugaard, *Admin Sec*
EMP: 5 **EST:** 1974
SQ FT: 1,800
SALES (est): 731.6K **Privately Held**
WEB: www.verticalvillage.net
SIC: 2591 2221 5714 5719 Drapery hardware & blinds & shades; window blinds; blinds vertical; draperies & drapery fabrics, manmade fiber & silk; draperies; vertical blinds

(G-15163)
WB MEDICAL TRANSPORT LLC
177 Sw Hawthorne Cir (34953-3531)
PHONE.....561 827-8877
EMP: 6 **EST:** 2018
SALES (est): 496.7K **Privately Held**
SIC: 3089 Plastics products

(G-15164)
WE SIGN IT INC
889 E Prima Vista Blvd (34952-2342)
PHONE.....772 800-7373
EMP: 6
SALES (corp-wide): 144.2K **Privately Held**
SIC: 3993 Signs & advertising specialties
PA: We Sign It Inc
15838 Orange Ave
Fort Pierce FL 34945
772 577-4400

Port Salerno
Martin County

(G-15165)
REUSE SALVAGE INC
40668 Se Russell Way (34992)
P.O. Box 1509 (34992-1509)
PHONE.....772 485-3248
Barbara Blodgett, *President*
EMP: 5 **EST:** 2012
SALES (est): 436.9K **Privately Held**
WEB: www.reusesalvage.com
SIC: 2611 Pulp manufactured from waste or recycled paper

Port St Lucie
St. Lucie County

(G-15166)
1982 HAYWORTH AVENUE LLC
1982 Sw Hayworth Ave (34953-2751)
PHONE.....772 873-1700
Donato Pompa, *Principal*
EMP: 6 **EST:** 2011
SALES (est): 146.9K **Privately Held**
SIC: 3826 Analytical instruments

(G-15167)
AIR SOURCE 1 LLC
585 Nw Merc Pl Ste 103 (34986)
PHONE.....772 626-7604
Robert K Dumont, *Manager*
EMP: 8 **EST:** 2010
SALES (est): 1.1MM **Privately Held**
WEB: www.airsource1llc.com
SIC: 3585 Air conditioning equipment, complete

(G-15168)
BROTHERS WHOLESALE INC
534 Nw Mercantile Pl (34986-2276)
PHONE.....631 831-8484
Joseph Carfino, *President*
Jason Dippolito, *Shareholder*
EMP: 20 **EST:** 2014
SALES (est): 2.1MM **Privately Held**
SIC: 2051 Bagels, fresh or frozen

(G-15169)
CARIBBEAN GLOBAL GROUP CORP
5475 Nw Saint James Dr (34983-3444)
PHONE.....786 449-2767
Francisca Bolton, *Principal*
James Bolton, *Principal*
Magen Bolton, *Principal*
EMP: 10 **EST:** 2016
SALES (est): 589.3K **Privately Held**
SIC: 2842 Specialty cleaning, polishes & sanitation goods

(G-15170)
CARVIZION INC
881 Sw Harvard Rd (34953-2310)
PHONE.....772 807-0307
Hugh W Silvera, *President*
EMP: 6 **EST:** 2010
SALES (est): 71.3K **Privately Held**
SIC: 3714 Motor vehicle parts & accessories

(G-15171)
CITY ELECTRIC SUPPLY COMPANY
Also Called: Tamco Group
660 Nw Peacock Blvd (34986-2211)
PHONE.....772 878-4944
Thomas Mackie, *CEO*
EMP: 235
SQ FT: 230,000
SALES (corp-wide): 1.1MM **Privately Held**
WEB: www.cityelectricsupply.com
SIC: 3646 3645 Commercial indusl & institutional electric lighting fixtures; residential lighting fixtures
HQ: City Electric Supply Company
400 S Record St Ste 700
Dallas TX 75202
214 865-6801

(G-15172)
COMPOSITE ESSENTIAL MTLS LLC
Also Called: C E M
315 Nw Peacock Blvd (34986-2206)
PHONE.....772 344-0034
Maritsa Dan,
◆ **EMP:** 5 **EST:** 2013
SALES (est): 642.8K **Privately Held**
WEB: www.compositeessentials.com
SIC: 2821 5162 3469 Polypropylene resins; resins; honeycombed metal

(G-15173)
EMBROIDERED STITCHES
686 Se Keyes St (34983-2130)
PHONE.....702 751-2770
Debra Herb, *President*
EMP: 6 **EST:** 2017
SALES (est): 193.5K **Privately Held**
SIC: 2395 Embroidery & art needlework

(G-15174)
KING OF SOCKS
2085 Se N Blackwell Dr (34952-7000)
PHONE.....772 204-3286
Jermaine Cooper, *Principal*
EMP: 10 **EST:** 2015
SALES (est): 95.2K **Privately Held**
WEB: www.kingofsocksfl.com
SIC: 2252 Socks

(G-15175)
MOORE SOLUTIONS INC
1680 Se Lyngate Dr # 202 (34952-4300)
PHONE.....772 337-4005
Terrance Moore, *CEO*
EMP: 7 **EST:** 1996
SALES (est): 579.1K **Privately Held**
WEB: www.gomsi.net
SIC: 7372 8748 Educational computer software; test development & evaluation service

(G-15176)
NATURES HEATHY GOURMET
1260 Sw Biltmore St (34983-2487)
PHONE.....772 873-0180
Roland Joaquin, *Owner*
EMP: 30 **EST:** 2005
SALES (est): 2MM **Privately Held**
WEB: www.natureshealthygourmet.com
SIC: 2099 Food preparations

(G-15177)
OCULUS SURGICAL INC
562 Nw Merc Pl Ste 104 (34986)
PHONE.....772 236-2622
Rainer Kirchhuebel, *Principal*
Mike Annen, *Engineer*
William Carpenter, *Sales Staff*
John Discenza, *Sales Staff*
Megan Narewski, *Sales Staff*
EMP: 35 **EST:** 2012
SALES (est): 3.3MM **Privately Held**
WEB: www.oculussurgical.us
SIC: 3841 5047 3829 3821 Surgical & medical instruments; medical & hospital equipment; thermometers, including digital: clinical; incubators, laboratory; optical instruments & lenses

(G-15178)
PAVER PARADISE LLC
2468 Sw Cameo Blvd (34953-2928)
PHONE.....561 843-3031
Robert Malone, *Mng Member*
EMP: 7 **EST:** 2016
SALES (est): 579.2K **Privately Held**
SIC: 3531 Pavers

(G-15179)
SOUTHEAST GEN CONTRS GROUP INC
10380 Sw Vlg Ctr Dr 232 (34987-1931)
PHONE.....877 407-3535
Larry Mark McDonald, *Owner*
EMP: 10 **EST:** 2013
SQ FT: 1,500
SALES (est): 743.1K **Privately Held**
WEB: www.southeastcontracting.com
SIC: 3259 3069 1761 5033 Roofing tile, clay; roofing, membrane rubber; roofing contractor; roofing, asphalt & sheet metal

(G-15180)
TABER INCORPORATED
9624 Sw Nuova Way (34986-2831)
P.O. Box 881629, Port Saint Lucie (34988-1629)
PHONE.....401 245-2800
Jeff D Taber, *President*
EMP: 5 **EST:** 2012
SALES (est): 626.5K **Privately Held**
SIC: 2861 Gum & wood chemicals

(G-15181)
TAMLITE
660 Nw Peacock Blvd (34986-2211)
PHONE.....772 878-4944
Mike Fisher, *COO*
Andy Henderson, *Marketing Staff*
Jamie Nestic, *Office Admin*
Katelynn Antonucci, *Assistant*
EMP: 8 **EST:** 2017
SALES (est): 787.6K **Privately Held**
WEB: www.tamliteusa.com
SIC: 3645 Residential lighting fixtures

Princeton
Miami-Dade County

(G-15182)
BARREIRO CONCRETE MTLS INC
25440 Sw 140th Ave (33032-5433)
PHONE.....305 805-0095
Americo Barreiro, *President*
Able Barreiro, *Vice Pres*
EMP: 48 **EST:** 2004
SQ FT: 25,000
SALES (est): 8.7MM **Privately Held**
SIC: 3272 Concrete products

(G-15183)
CLASSIC TRIM WTP INC
25400 Sw 141st Ave Ste B (33032-5431)
PHONE.....305 258-3090
Frank Vasquez, *President*
Maria Vasquez, *Vice Pres*
EMP: 7 **EST:** 1999
SQ FT: 2,200
SALES (est): 180K **Privately Held**
WEB: www.classictrimcustoms.com
SIC: 2396 Automotive & apparel trimmings

(G-15184)
JERRY METALLO
25490 Sw 141st Ave (33032-5431)
PHONE.....305 972-2927
Jerry Metallo, *Principal*
EMP: 7 **EST:** 2018
SALES (est): 53K **Privately Held**
WEB: www.watertransferprinting.com
SIC: 3999 Manufacturing industries

(G-15185)
KZ MANUFACTURING LLC
Also Called: Dolphin Boats
24601 Packinghouse Rd # 1 (33032-3807)
PHONE.....305 257-2628
Karl Zimmermann,
▼ **EMP:** 8 **EST:** 1961
SQ FT: 7,500
SALES (est): 768.2K **Privately Held**
WEB: www.dolphinboats.com
SIC: 3732 5551 Boats, fiberglass: building & repairing; boat dealers

(G-15186)
SEAHUNTER INC
25545 Sw 140th Ave (33032-5402)
PHONE.....305 257-3344
Jose R Montalvo, *President*
Eduardo Montalvo, *Treasurer*
Eddie Leon, *Sales Dir*
Charlie Schiffer, *Marketing Staff*
John Schiffer, *Technical Staff*
EMP: 59 **EST:** 2002
SQ FT: 9,000
SALES (est): 11.1MM **Privately Held**
WEB: www.seahunterboats.com
SIC: 3732 Boat building & repairing

(G-15187)
TWN INDUSTRIES INC (PA)
25490 Sw 141st Ave (33032-5431)
PHONE.....305 246-5717
Jerry R Metallo, *President*
◆ **EMP:** 6 **EST:** 1983
SALES (est): 1.2MM **Privately Held**
WEB: www.watertransferprinting.com
SIC: 3873 5944 5712 Clocks, assembly of; clocks; outdoor & garden furniture

Punta Gorda
Charlotte County

(G-15188)
A EXTEND LIFE INC
29061 Tortoise Trl (33982-8588)
PHONE.....941 505-7766
Richard A Christensen, *President*
Mariann Christensen, *Treasurer*
EMP: 5 **EST:** 1997
SALES (est): 321.4K **Privately Held**
WEB: www.extend-a-life.com
SIC: 3429 Marine hardware

(G-15189)
ACCENT JEWELRY INC
Also Called: Accent Casting
2373 Talbrook Ter (33983-2732)
PHONE.....941 391-6687
Robert Ricci, *President*
EMP: 10 **EST:** 1984
SALES (est): 638.7K **Privately Held**
SIC: 3961 3914 Costume jewelry, ex. precious metal & semiprecious stones; pewter ware

GEOGRAPHIC

(G-15190)
APPLUS LABORATORIES USA INC (DH)
27256 Mooney Ave Bldg 10 (33982-2457)
PHONE....................................941 205-5700
Marcos Briseno, *Treasurer*
Lluis Martinez, *Director*
EMP: 2 **EST:** 2014
SALES (est): 8.4MM
SALES (corp-wide): 65.5MM **Privately Held**
WEB: www.applus.com
SIC: 3829 Ultrasonic testing equipment
HQ: Lgai Technological Center Sa
Ronda De La Font Del Carme, S/N
Cerdanyola Del Valles 08193
935 672-000

(G-15191)
ARCADIA AEROSPACE INDS LLC (DH)
27256 Mooney Ave Bldg 110 (33982-2457)
PHONE....................................941 205-5700
Charles Bushman, *CEO*
Jeff Phillips, *Opers Staff*
Byron Vines, *Opers Staff*
Ryan Herman, *Engineer*
Ben Lombard, *Engineer*
◆ **EMP:** 40 **EST:** 2008
SQ FT: 38,000
SALES: 2.4MM
SALES (corp-wide): 65.5MM **Privately Held**
WEB: www.arcadiaaerospace.com
SIC: 3728 Aircraft parts & equipment
HQ: Applus Laboratories Usa Inc.
27256 Mooney Ave Bldg 10
Punta Gorda FL 33982
941 205-5700

(G-15192)
ATLAS INNOVATIVE SERVICES INC
220 Shreve St (33950-3320)
P.O. Box 510422 (33951-0422)
PHONE....................................617 259-4529
Mark Ludwig, *Principal*
EMP: 11 **EST:** 2015
SALES (est): 1MM **Privately Held**
WEB: www.atlasinnovative.com
SIC: 7692 Welding repair

(G-15193)
BDC SHELL & AGGREGATE LLC
2000 State Road 31 (33982-9725)
P.O. Box 510249 (33951-0249)
PHONE....................................941 875-6615
Jessica E Lehr,
EMP: 13 **EST:** 2013
SALES (est): 2.8MM **Privately Held**
SIC: 1442 5211 Gravel mining; sand & gravel

(G-15194)
BELLA BLSMIC PRESSED OLIVE INC
439 Ridgecrest Dr (33982-8524)
PHONE....................................941 505-1707
Rebecca Berlin, *Branch Mgr*
EMP: 8
SALES (corp-wide): 941K **Privately Held**
WEB: www.bellabalsamic.net
SIC: 2079 Olive oil
PA: Bella Balsamic & The Pressed Olive, Inc.
1200 W Retta Esplanade
Punta Gorda FL 33950
941 249-3571

(G-15195)
BELLA BLSMIC PRESSED OLIVE INC (PA)
1200 W Retta Esplanade (33950-5325)
PHONE....................................941 249-3571
Rebecca Berlin, *CEO*
Jeremy Berlin, *CFO*
EMP: 20 **EST:** 2019
SALES (est): 941K **Privately Held**
WEB: www.bellabalsamic.net
SIC: 2079 Olive oil

(G-15196)
BERMONT EXCAVATING LLC
37390 Bermont Rd (33982-9525)
PHONE....................................866 367-9557
Joseph Boff, *President*
David Boff, *Vice Pres*
Joe Rice, *Opers Staff*
EMP: 15 **EST:** 2013
SALES (est): 1.8MM **Privately Held**
WEB: www.bermontexcavating.com
SIC: 1442 Construction sand & gravel

(G-15197)
BEST BINDERY CORP
3181 Aloe St (33982-1326)
PHONE....................................941 505-1779
Fernandez Victor, *Principal*
EMP: 6 **EST:** 2010
SALES (est): 76.5K **Privately Held**
SIC: 2789 Bookbinding & related work

(G-15198)
BJMJRX INC
540 Islamorada Blvd (33955-1801)
PHONE....................................941 505-9036
William D Jinkens, *Director*
EMP: 9 **EST:** 2001
SALES (est): 223.2K **Privately Held**
SIC: 2834 Pharmaceutical preparations

(G-15199)
BLACKWELL FAMILY CORPORATION
Also Called: Quickprint Business Center
1869 Manzana Ave (33950-6048)
PHONE....................................941 639-0200
Steven Blackwell, *President*
EMP: 5 **EST:** 2001
SALES (est): 422K **Privately Held**
SIC: 2752 2261 2395 Commercial printing, offset; screen printing of cotton broadwoven fabrics; emblems, embroidered

(G-15200)
BUILT RIGHT POOL HEATERS LLC
28110 Challenger Blvd (33982-2423)
PHONE....................................941 505-1600
Bruce Brooks, *CEO*
Chris Wasdin, *Principal*
EMP: 5 **EST:** 2010
SALES (est): 2.5MM **Privately Held**
WEB: www.builtrightpoolheaters.com
SIC: 3585 Heat pumps, electric
HQ: Zodiac Pool Systems Llc
2882 Whiptail Loop # 100
Carlsbad CA 92010
760 599-9600

(G-15201)
CHARLOTTE COUNTY MIN & MTL INC
Also Called: Southwest Aggregates
16070 Tamiami Trl (33955-7101)
PHONE....................................239 567-1800
Richard Neslund, *President*
EMP: 34 **EST:** 1996
SALES (est): 5.4MM **Privately Held**
SIC: 1442 1499 Construction sand mining; shell mining

(G-15202)
COUGHLAN PRODUCTS CORP
3043 Perdue Ter (33983-3314)
PHONE....................................973 904-1500
Randolph Reynolds, *President*
Patricia Campbell, *Vice Pres*
▲ **EMP:** 15 **EST:** 1990
SALES (est): 334.6K **Privately Held**
SIC: 2844 Toilet preparations

(G-15203)
CREATIVE CUSTOM STAIRS
3857 Acline Rd Unit 104 (33950-8403)
P.O. Box 510878 (33951-0878)
PHONE....................................941 505-0336
EMP: 5 **EST:** 2018
SALES (est): 495.5K **Privately Held**
WEB: www.creativecustomstairs.com
SIC: 2431 Millwork

(G-15204)
DISCRETE ELECTRONICS INC
1205 Elizabeth St Ste I (33950-6054)
PHONE....................................941 575-8700
Alan Meis, *Engineer*
EMP: 6 **EST:** 2015
SALES (est): 171K **Privately Held**
WEB: www.discreteelectronics.com
SIC: 3612 Transformers, except electric

(G-15205)
FLORIDA WOOD CREATIONS INC
42881 Lake Babcock Dr # 200
(33982-5042)
PHONE....................................239 561-5411
David Slabosz, *President*
Dorothy Slabosz, *Treasurer*
Jose Slabosz, *Director*
EMP: 5 **EST:** 1994
SALES (est): 465.5K **Privately Held**
WEB: www.floridawoodcreations.com
SIC: 2431 1799 Window shutters, wood; window treatment installation

(G-15206)
FUSION ENERGY SOLUTIONS LLC
5506 Independence Ct B (33982-7102)
PHONE....................................941 366-9936
Jacquelyn Johnson, *Partner*
▲ **EMP:** 5 **EST:** 2010
SALES (est): 488.9K **Privately Held**
WEB: www.fusionenergysolutions.net
SIC: 3648 Lighting equipment

(G-15207)
GULF CONTOURS INC
7500 Golf Course Blvd (33982-2424)
PHONE....................................941 639-3933
Jerry Goin, *President*
Janet Goin, *Vice Pres*
EMP: 7 **EST:** 1998
SQ FT: 3,600
SALES (est): 907.9K **Privately Held**
WEB: www.gulfcontours.com
SIC: 2434 Wood kitchen cabinets

(G-15208)
HARBOR VIEW BOAT TRAILERS
17 Callao St (33983-4258)
PHONE....................................941 916-3777
George Mazzo, *Principal*
EMP: 7 **EST:** 2010
SALES (est): 468.7K **Privately Held**
SIC: 3799 Boat trailers

(G-15209)
HARPERS MANUFACTURING SPC
24730 Sandhill Blvd # 902 (33983-5240)
PHONE....................................941 629-3490
Thomas J Trotter, *President*
Fay Trotter, *Corp Secy*
EMP: 6 **EST:** 1983
SALES (est): 800K **Privately Held**
SIC: 3496 Screening, woven wire: made from purchased wire

(G-15210)
INNERGY
315 E Olympia Ave # 251 (33950-3823)
PHONE....................................941 815-8655
Jonathan Adams, *Principal*
EMP: 8 **EST:** 2016
SALES (est): 111.1K **Privately Held**
WEB: www.innergy.com
SIC: 7372 Prepackaged software

(G-15211)
ISLAND FEVER LLC
1200 W Retta Esplanade # 19
(33950-5376)
PHONE....................................941 639-6400
John J Johnson, *Principal*
EMP: 6 **EST:** 2007
SALES (est): 353.3K **Privately Held**
WEB: www.islandfever.com
SIC: 3949 Water sports equipment

(G-15212)
LIVING WELL SPENDING LESS INC
307 Taylor St (33950-4829)
PHONE....................................941 209-1811
Chuck Soukup, *Principal*
EMP: 7 **EST:** 2018
SALES (est): 323.7K **Privately Held**
WEB: www.livingwellspendingless.com
SIC: 2741 Miscellaneous publishing

(G-15213)
MARDEN INDUSTRIES INC
26855 Airport Rd (33982-2408)
PHONE....................................863 682-7882
Thomas King, *President*
K David Julian, *Treasurer*
EMP: 18 **EST:** 1992
SQ FT: 27,000
SALES (est): 3.1MM **Privately Held**
WEB: www.mardenind.com
SIC: 3523 3714 5084 3599 Farm machinery & equipment; frames, motor vehicle; industrial machinery & equipment; machine & other job shop work; farm equipment & supplies

(G-15214)
MERCERS FRESH ROASTED COFFEES
4678 Tamiami Trl Unit 109 (33980-2900)
PHONE....................................941 286-7054
David W Mercer, *Principal*
▲ **EMP:** 6 **EST:** 2011
SALES (est): 239.8K **Privately Held**
WEB:
www.mercersfreshroastedcoffeesfl.com
SIC: 2095 Roasted coffee

(G-15215)
METAL-TECH CONTROLS CORP
3441 Saint Croix Ct (33950-8142)
P.O. Box 512113 (33951-2113)
PHONE....................................941 575-7677
Glen F Koedding, *President*
Jayne S Koedding, *Vice Pres*
EMP: 7 **EST:** 1989
SQ FT: 3,200
SALES (est): 932.4K **Privately Held**
WEB: www.metaltechcontrols.com
SIC: 3625 Control equipment, electric

(G-15216)
NATIVE NURSERY
4735 Tamiami Trl (33980-2946)
PHONE....................................941 625-2022
EMP: 6 **EST:** 2019
SALES (est): 514.4K **Privately Held**
SIC: 3272 Concrete products

(G-15217)
NAUTILOFT LLC
3192 Matecumbe Key Rd (33955-1907)
PHONE....................................801 712-6692
Tina L Heaston, *Manager*
EMP: 6 **EST:** 2018
SALES (est): 158.7K **Privately Held**
SIC: 2211 Canvas

(G-15218)
NEW WORLD TRADE INC
8249 Skylane Way Ste 111 (33982-2439)
PHONE....................................941 205-5873
Max Rodriguez, *President*
◆ **EMP:** 19 **EST:** 2002
SALES (est): 1MM **Privately Held**
SIC: 3949 Fishing tackle, general

(G-15219)
PETER WELCHS CUSTOM BOATS
8446 Alfred Blvd (33982-2313)
PHONE....................................941 575-8665
Peter Welch, *Principal*
EMP: 6 **EST:** 2010
SALES (est): 165K **Privately Held**
SIC: 3732 Boat building & repairing

(G-15220)
POSEIDON INDUSTRIES INC
5462 Williamsburg Dr (33982-1784)
PHONE....................................305 812-2582
Veronica Alva, *President*
EMP: 9 **EST:** 2010

SALES (est): 1.3MM Privately Held
WEB: www.poseidonmachinery.com
SIC: 3559 Stone working machinery

(G-15221)
PRO POWDER COATING INC
5474 Williamsburg Dr (33982-1716)
PHONE....941 505-8010
J Patrick Reagan, *President*
Jeremiah Reagan, *President*
EMP: 10 EST: 2001
SALES (est): 1.2MM Privately Held
WEB: www.propowdercoat.com
SIC: 3479 Coating of metals & formed products

(G-15222)
PROMOTIONAL MKTG ONLINE LLC
17377 Ophir Ln (33955-4530)
PHONE....941 347-8564
Peter Prins,
EMP: 6 EST: 2019
SALES (est): 301.7K Privately Held
WEB: www.promotionalmarketingonline.com
SIC: 2759 Promotional printing

(G-15223)
PULSAFEEDER INC
27101 Airport Rd (33982-2411)
PHONE....941 575-2900
Paul Beldham, *Vice Pres*
Mandie Silva, *Opers Mgr*
EMP: 60
SQ FT: 13,255
SALES (corp-wide): 2.3B Publicly Held
WEB: www.pulsa.com
SIC: 3589 3561 Sewage & water treatment equipment; pumps & pumping equipment
HQ: Pulsafeeder, Inc.
2883 Brghton Hnrietta Twn
Rochester NY 14623
585 292-8000

(G-15224)
PULSAFEEDER SPO INC
27101 Airport Rd (33982-2411)
PHONE....941 575-3800
Sunil Samtani, *General Mgr*
EMP: 11 EST: 2015
SALES (est): 330.4K Privately Held
WEB: www.pulsatron.com
SIC: 3589 3561 Sewage & water treatment equipment; pumps & pumping equipment

(G-15225)
R AND R MACHINE SHOP
Also Called: R&R Racing Engines
6601 Taylor Rd (33950-8322)
PHONE....941 621-8143
Michael Riechers, *Principal*
EMP: 13 EST: 2015
SALES (est): 535.2K Privately Held
WEB: www.rrconnectingrods.com
SIC: 3599 Machine shop, jobbing & repair

(G-15226)
R TOWNSEND RESCREENS INC
30390 Cedar Rd (33982-3324)
P.O. Box 4150, North Fort Myers (33918-4150)
PHONE....239 244-4759
Rebecca Townsend, *President*
Rex Browning, *Vice Pres*
EMP: 6 EST: 2013
SALES (est): 270K Privately Held
WEB: www.rtownsendrescreens.com
SIC: 3448 3444 Screen enclosures; metal housings, enclosures, casings & other containers

(G-15227)
RAPID GRAPHIX INC
10251 Tamiami Trl (33950-8314)
PHONE....941 639-2043
Renee Bair, *President*
Duane Wright, *Production*
EMP: 5 EST: 2005
SALES (est): 1MM Privately Held
WEB: www.rapidgraphix.net
SIC: 2752 Commercial printing, offset

(G-15228)
READY BUILDING PRODUCTS INC
7000 Progress Dr (33982-2433)
PHONE....941 639-6222
Pete Shoup, *CEO*
Merle E Bright, *Admin Sec*
EMP: 9 EST: 2010
SQ FT: 65,000
SALES (est): 284.6K Privately Held
SIC: 2674 Cement bags: made from purchased materials

(G-15229)
ROBERT GOMES PUBLISHING INC
8512 Alan Blvd (33982-2321)
PHONE....941 637-6080
Robert Gomes, *Principal*
EMP: 9
SALES (est): 441.4K Privately Held
SIC: 2741 Miscellaneous publishing

(G-15230)
ROYAL PALM PRESS INC
25560 Technology Blvd (33950-4731)
PHONE....941 575-4299
Theodore D Dunn, *President*
EMP: 9 EST: 1997
SQ FT: 3,500
SALES (est): 865.1K Privately Held
WEB: www.royalpalmpress.com
SIC: 2732 Book printing

(G-15231)
SHAMROCK MOBILE DETL & PRESSUR
1029 Eastview Ln (33982-1843)
PHONE....941 286-3572
Gary Joe Gilreath, *Principal*
EMP: 6 EST: 2009
SALES (est): 64.3K Privately Held
SIC: 3452 Washers

(G-15232)
SHINELINE BUFFING & DETAIL
11338 1st Ave (33955-1321)
PHONE....941 268-1033
Diane Adams, *Principal*
EMP: 6 EST: 2005
SALES (est): 149.5K Privately Held
SIC: 3471 Buffing for the trade

(G-15233)
SIGN TECH INC
25191 Olympia Ave Ste 1 (33950-4066)
PHONE....941 575-1349
Mark Sturman, *Owner*
EMP: 6 EST: 2008
SALES (est): 310.6K Privately Held
WEB: www.signtechfl.com
SIC: 3993 Signs & advertising specialties

(G-15234)
SIGNAL GRAPHICS PRINTING LLC
615 Aqui Esta Dr (33950-7001)
P.O. Box 854, Denver CO (80201-0854)
PHONE....303 837-1331
Tom Peck, *Mng Member*
Tom Charlson, *Manager*
EMP: 7 EST: 1986
SALES (est): 890K Privately Held
WEB: www.signalgraphics.com
SIC: 2752 2759 7334 Commercial printing, offset; commercial printing; photocopying & duplicating services

(G-15235)
SOTO INDUSTRIES LLC
3420 Bal Harbor Blvd (33950-8251)
PHONE....941 830-6000
Norman A Cardinale, *Principal*
EMP: 7 EST: 2018
SALES (est): 379.7K Privately Held
SIC: 3999 Manufacturing industries

(G-15236)
STANS SEPTIC SVC & CON PDTS
5287 Duncan Rd (33982-1737)
P.O. Box 511049 (33951-1049)
PHONE....941 639-3976
Louie Pancic, *President*
EMP: 5 EST: 1966
SQ FT: 5,000
SALES (est): 669.2K Privately Held
WEB: www.stansseptic.com
SIC: 3272 1711 Septic tanks, concrete; septic system construction

(G-15237)
SUN COAST MEDIA GROUP INC
Also Called: Desoto Sun
23170 Harborview Rd (33980-2100)
PHONE....863 494-7600
Joe Gallimore, *General Mgr*
EMP: 7
SALES (corp-wide): 333.5MM Privately Held
WEB: www.yoursun.com
SIC: 2711 Newspapers, publishing & printing
HQ: Sun Coast Media Group, Inc.
23170 Harborview Rd
Port Charlotte FL 33980
941 206-1300

(G-15238)
SUPERIOR FABRICATION INC
5524 Independence Ct (33982-1700)
PHONE....941 639-2966
Andrew Giustina, *President*
Anna Giustina, *Corp Secy*
Lori Giustina, *Vice Pres*
EMP: 9 EST: 2009
SQ FT: 6,000
SALES: 929.1K Privately Held
WEB: www.superiorfabricationwelding.com
SIC: 7692 Welding repair

(G-15239)
SUPERTRAK INC
26855 Airport Rd (33982-2408)
PHONE....941 505-7800
Tom King, *President*
K David Julian, *Corp Secy*
Dave Sampson, *Vice Pres*
Ken Carter, *Purchasing*
Tyler Soltis, *Engineer*
▲ EMP: 10 EST: 1986
SQ FT: 31,000
SALES (est): 1.9MM Privately Held
WEB: www.supertrak.com
SIC: 3531 Backhoes, tractors, cranes, plows & similar equipment

(G-15240)
SW PREMIER PRODUCTS LLC
28100 Challenger Blvd # 1 (33982-2403)
PHONE....941 275-6677
Shalon Wild,
Paul Wild,
EMP: 8 EST: 2018
SALES (est): 1.1MM Privately Held
WEB: www.swpremierproducts.com
SIC: 2676 Towels, napkins & tissue paper products

(G-15241)
T D R INC
Also Called: Tony Doukas Racing
30436 Holly Rd (33982-3336)
PHONE....941 505-0800
Tony Doukas, *President*
EMP: 5 EST: 1982
SQ FT: 4,500
SALES (est): 450.9K Privately Held
WEB: www.bansheesuperstore.com
SIC: 3751 Motorcycles, bicycles & parts

(G-15242)
TAHOE INTERACTIVE SYSTEMS INC
601 Woodstork Ln (33982-8592)
P.O. Box 820, Westerville OH (43086-0820)
PHONE....614 891-2323
Carl Ross, *President*
Tim Hunt, *Director*
EMP: 7 EST: 1991
SQ FT: 12,000
SALES (est): 143.3K Privately Held
WEB: www.tahoe-inc.com
SIC: 7372 7375 7371 Prepackaged software; information retrieval services; custom computer programming services

(G-15243)
WATERPROOF CHARTERS INC
320 Cross St (33950-4802)
PHONE....941 639-7626
Shawn Bellestri, *President*
▼ EMP: 9 EST: 1993
SQ FT: 2,200
SALES (est): 1.2MM Privately Held
WEB: www.waterproofcharts.com
SIC: 3812 Nautical instruments

(G-15244)
WEBER SOUTH FL LLC
40800 Cook Brown Rd (33982-7728)
PHONE....239 543-7240
Scott Webber,
Geraldine Weber,
Gregg Weber,
EMP: 8 EST: 2005
SALES (est): 1.8MM Privately Held
SIC: 1241 Coal mining services

Quincy
Gadsden County

(G-15245)
ACTIVE MINERALS INTL LLC
1130 Dade St (32351-4233)
PHONE....410 825-2920
Bert Nix, *Plant Mgr*
Tony Smith, *Production*
Adam Humphreys, *QC Mgr*
Diane McSwain, *Branch Mgr*
EMP: 6
SQ FT: 89,042
SALES (corp-wide): 90.7MM Privately Held
WEB: www.activeminerals.com
SIC: 3295 Minerals, ground or treated
PA: Active Minerals International, Llc
34 Loveton Cir Ste 100
Sparks Glencoe MD 21152
410 825-2920

(G-15246)
BIG BEND REBAR INC
1 Corporate Ct (32351-8002)
PHONE....850 875-8000
Patricia Bates Trotta, *President*
Jose Sandoval, *President*
Joe Trotta, *Vice Pres*
EMP: 10 EST: 2002
SQ FT: 14,500
SALES (est): 4MM Privately Held
WEB: www.bigbendrebar.com
SIC: 3441 Fabricated structural metal

(G-15247)
CLASSIC SHIRTS INC
110 Zeta St (32351-2900)
PHONE....850 875-2200
Bill Sinn, *President*
William Steck, *Vice Pres*
◆ EMP: 16 EST: 1998
SALES (est): 1.9MM Privately Held
WEB: www.classicshirts.com
SIC: 2759 3993 Screen printing; signs & advertising specialties

(G-15248)
ENGELHARD CORP
1101 N Madison St (32352-0981)
PHONE....850 627-7688
Richard Goodell, *Principal*
EMP: 7 EST: 2007
SALES (est): 131.9K Privately Held
SIC: 1499 Miscellaneous nonmetallic minerals

(G-15249)
FLOWERS BAKERIES LLC
Also Called: Flowers Baking Company
321 W Jefferson St (32351-2325)
PHONE....850 875-4997
EMP: 47
SALES (corp-wide): 4.3B Publicly Held
SIC: 2051 Mfg Bread/Related Products
HQ: Flowers Bakeries, Llc
1919 Flowers Cir
Thomasville GA 31757

(G-15250)
GADSDEN COUNTY TIMES INC
Also Called: Times Printing
9 W King St (32351-1701)
P.O. Box 790 (32353-0790)
PHONE..................................850 627-7649
Alana Rich, *General Mgr*
Alice Dupont, *Editor*
Erin Hill, *Sheriff*
Leslie Robert, *Manager*
EMP: 10 **EST:** 1901
SALES (est): 250K **Privately Held**
WEB: www.gadsdencountytimes.com
SIC: 2711 2752 2759 Commercial printing & newspaper publishing combined; commercial printing, lithographic; commercial printing

(G-15251)
IMERYS PERLITE USA INC
612 S Shelfer St (32351-3553)
P.O. Box 999 (32353-0999)
PHONE..................................850 875-1282
Kenny Edwards, *Plant Mgr*
Kenneth Edwards, *Opers-Prdtn-Mfg*
EMP: 9
SQ FT: 18,593
SALES (corp-wide): 3.2MM **Privately Held**
SIC: 3295 Minerals, ground or treated
HQ: Imerys Perlite Usa, Inc.
1732 N 1st St Ste 450
San Jose CA 95112

(G-15252)
JIMMY & TOONS ICECREAM SP LLC
104 E Washington St (32351-2458)
PHONE..................................850 752-2291
Ebony Denson, *CEO*
EMP: 8
SALES (est): 563.6K **Privately Held**
SIC: 2024 Ice cream & frozen desserts

(G-15253)
SBM BEAUTY LLC ✪
831 Sikes St (32351-4403)
PHONE..................................850 567-7338
Shonteesia McMillian,
EMP: 10 **EST:** 2021
SALES (est): 480K **Privately Held**
SIC: 3999 7389 Hair & hair-based products;

(G-15254)
SICAMU INC
1066 Strong Rd (32351-5241)
PHONE..................................850 270-6283
Jose I Pons, *President*
Antonio J Pons, *Vice Pres*
Carmen M Siepermann, *Admin Sec*
EMP: 5 **EST:** 2007
SQ FT: 110,000
SALES (est): 677.8K **Privately Held**
WEB: www.sicamu.com
SIC: 2842 2841 Specialty cleaning, polishes & sanitation goods; soap & other detergents

(G-15255)
SOUTHERN BROTHERS RACING LLC ✪
443 Charlie Harris Loop (32352-6652)
PHONE..................................850 509-2223
Larmarcus Haynes, *Mng Member*
EMP: 9 **EST:** 2021
SALES (est): 330.1K **Privately Held**
SIC: 3799 All terrain vehicles (ATV)

(G-15256)
TRULIEVE CANNABIS CORP (DH)
6749 Ben Bostic Rd (32351-9121)
PHONE..................................844 878-5438
EMP: 19 **EST:** 2018
SALES (est): 521.5MM
SALES (corp-wide): 626.6K **Privately Held**
WEB: www.trulieve.com
SIC: 3999
HQ: Trulieve, Inc.
3494 Martin Hurst Rd
Tallahassee FL 32312
844 878-5438

(G-15257)
WILSONS MONUMENT LLC
1343 S Barack Obama Blvd (32351-8662)
PHONE..................................850 743-8605
Shironda Wilson,
EMP: 6 **EST:** 2017
SALES (est): 155.1K **Privately Held**
SIC: 3272 Monuments & grave markers, except terrazo

Reddick
Marion County

(G-15258)
SCI MATERIALS LLC
15251 N Highway 329 (32686-3038)
PHONE..................................352 878-4979
Steven Counts, *Mng Member*
EMP: 32 **EST:** 2016
SALES (est): 5.3MM **Privately Held**
WEB: www.scirockit.com
SIC: 1422 Limestones, ground; agricultural limestone, ground; lime rock, ground

Redington Beach
Pinellas County

(G-15259)
SAI/RF OF FLORIDA
16012 5th St E (33708-1639)
PHONE..................................727 394-1012
Richard W Gonzalez, *Owner*
EMP: 7 **EST:** 1997
SQ FT: 7,300
SALES (est): 104.4K **Privately Held**
WEB: www.sairf.com
SIC: 3825 Radio frequency measuring equipment

Redington Shores
Pinellas County

(G-15260)
ROCK MY WORLD INC
17733 Long Point Dr (33708-1239)
PHONE..................................727 623-4646
Clifford Kaufman, *President*
Jackie Kaufman, *Vice Pres*
EMP: 5 **EST:** 2009
SALES (est): 300K **Privately Held**
WEB: www.rockmyworldinc.com
SIC: 3911 Jewelry, precious metal

Reunion
Osceola County

(G-15261)
VISIBLE RESULTS USA INC
1550 Corolla Ct 1 (34747-6741)
PHONE..................................913 706-8248
Brandy Dixon, *Manager*
EMP: 10 **Privately Held**
WEB: www.globalred.com.au
SIC: 7372 Prepackaged software
HQ: Lifecycle Digital Nz Limited
L 4, 152 Fanshawe Street
Auckland 1010

Riverview
Hillsborough County

(G-15262)
A MOBILE MECHANIC & WLDG SVC
12504 Balm Riverview Rd (33579-6903)
PHONE..................................813 900-8764
Brett Proctor, *Principal*
EMP: 6 **EST:** 2014
SALES (est): 49K **Privately Held**
SIC: 7692 Welding repair

(G-15263)
AFFORDABLE BOAT CUSHIONS INC
6515 Riverview Dr (33578-4845)
PHONE..................................877 350-2628
Angela Castillo, *President*
EMP: 6 **EST:** 2016
SALES (est): 64.4K **Privately Held**
WEB: www.affordableboatcushions.com
SIC: 2392 Boat cushions

(G-15264)
AIN PLASTICS OF FLORIDA INC
6317 Pelican Creek Cir (33578-8822)
PHONE..................................813 242-6400
Richard J Greaves, *Principal*
EMP: 13 **EST:** 2008
SALES (est): 1MM **Privately Held**
WEB: www.engineeredplasticsblog.info
SIC: 3089 Injection molding of plastics

(G-15265)
BENT CHROME LLC
9506 Glenpointe Dr (33569-5642)
PHONE..................................813 363-3398
Barbara Latham, *Manager*
EMP: 6 **EST:** 2018
SALES (est): 153.3K **Privately Held**
SIC: 3471 Plating & polishing

(G-15266)
CECO & ASSOCIATES INC
Also Called: Ceco Coated Fasteners
6508 S 78th St (33578-8801)
PHONE..................................727 528-0075
Gary Howard, *President*
Justin Howard, *Vice Pres*
Kathleen Howard, *Vice Pres*
▲ **EMP:** 8 **EST:** 2002
SQ FT: 30,000
SALES (est): 1MM **Privately Held**
SIC: 2819 5051 3965 Aluminum compounds; aluminum bars, rods, ingots, sheets, pipes, plates, etc.; fasteners

(G-15267)
CLEVER CABINETRY LLC
10513 Anglecrest Dr (33569-8706)
PHONE..................................813 992-0020
William J Faherty, *Manager*
EMP: 6 **EST:** 2016
SALES (est): 194.7K **Privately Held**
SIC: 2434 Wood kitchen cabinets

(G-15268)
COSTA INDUSTRIES LLC
Also Called: Duvo Websites
10312 Bloomngdale Ave # 1 (33578-3663)
PHONE..................................813 453-3171
Jason J Costa, *Manager*
EMP: 7 **EST:** 2015
SALES (est): 250.5K **Privately Held**
WEB: www.costaindustries.com
SIC: 3999 Manufacturing industries

(G-15269)
CVISTA LLC
4333 Garden Vista Dr (33578-4613)
PHONE..................................813 405-3000
Kevin McCole, *Business Mgr*
Zaneta Munsie, *Buyer*
Martin Paleske, *Director*
Martin Von Paleske, *Director*
Hadi B Lashkajani,
▲ **EMP:** 31 **EST:** 2005
SQ FT: 186,000
SALES (est): 7.8MM **Privately Held**
WEB: www.cvista.com
SIC: 2037 2087 Citrus pulp, dried; extracts, flavoring; bitters (flavoring concentrates)

(G-15270)
EAGLE PROF FLRG REMOVAL
11548 Bay Gardens Loop (33569-2032)
PHONE..................................813 520-3027
Jesus Ramos, *Principal*
EMP: 6 **EST:** 2014
SALES (est): 75.6K **Privately Held**
SIC: 2431 5023 1752 Floor baseboards, wood; floor coverings; wood floor installation & refinishing

(G-15271)
GORILLA BATS LLC
11223 Saint Andrews Ct (33579-7045)
PHONE..................................813 285-9409
Mike V Disalle, *Manager*
EMP: 6 **EST:** 2019
SALES (est): 261.7K **Privately Held**
WEB: www.gorillabaseballbats.com
SIC: 3949 Sporting & athletic goods

(G-15272)
HARPER SCREEN ENCLOSURES LLC
11217 Rice Creek Rd (33569-5180)
PHONE..................................813 417-5937
Daniel Harper, *Principal*
EMP: 6 **EST:** 2007
SALES (est): 204.7K **Privately Held**
WEB: www.harpersscreen.com
SIC: 3448 Screen enclosures

(G-15273)
HOMERUN DERBY BATS ONLY LLC
6931 Potomac Cir (33578-8309)
PHONE..................................813 545-3887
Jeffrey J Pendino, *Principal*
EMP: 6 **EST:** 2015
SALES (est): 251K **Privately Held**
WEB: www.homerunderbybatsonly.com
SIC: 3949 Sporting & athletic goods

(G-15274)
J&JH STUCCO INC
12713 Lovers Ln (33579-6840)
PHONE..................................813 482-5282
Juan J Hernandez, *Principal*
EMP: 6 **EST:** 2012
SALES (est): 140.6K **Privately Held**
SIC: 3299 Stucco

(G-15275)
KUHN FAMILY ENTERPRISES INC
Also Called: Careptrol Bradenton Southshore
11920 Timberhill Dr (33569-5687)
PHONE..................................813 671-5353
Shelley K Kuhn, *Vice Pres*
EMP: 6 **EST:** 2017
SALES (est): 131.7K **Privately Held**
SIC: 2752 Commercial printing, lithographic

(G-15276)
LILIAN OILS ON CANVAS INC
13215 Fawn Lily Dr (33579-0009)
PHONE..................................941 320-6263
Lilian Delgado, *Principal*
EMP: 7 **EST:** 2016
SALES (est): 56.3K **Privately Held**
WEB: www.lilianoilsoncanvas.com
SIC: 2211 Canvas

(G-15277)
MARATHON FIBER OPTICS LLC
12303 Edgeknoll Dr (33579-6800)
PHONE..................................305 902-9010
Violet Dipple, *CEO*
EMP: 6 **EST:** 2016
SALES (est): 187.1K **Privately Held**
WEB: www.marathonfiber.com
SIC: 3357 Nonferrous wiredrawing & insulating

(G-15278)
OSTARA USA LLC (PA)
2720 S Falkenburg Rd (33578-2561)
PHONE..................................813 666-8123
Phillip Abrary, *President*
EMP: 5 **EST:** 2008
SALES (est): 2.6MM **Privately Held**
WEB: www.ostara.com
SIC: 1479 Fertilizer mineral mining

(G-15279)
RANDAZZA ENTERPRISES INC
8824 Van Fleet Rd (33578-5042)
PHONE..................................813 677-0041
Nocif Espat, *President*
Kathleen Randazza, *Vice Pres*
▲ **EMP:** 10 **EST:** 1987
SALES (est): 664.6K **Privately Held**
WEB: www.randazzawastewater.com
SIC: 3589 Water treatment equipment, industrial

(G-15280)
REFERRAL & RESIDUAL EXCHANGE L
9376 Balm Riverview Rd (33569-5104)
PHONE....813 655-5000
EMP: 8 **EST:** 2015
SALES (est): 339.8K **Privately Held**
SIC: 2911 Residues

(G-15281)
RIVERVIEW DRONES INC
11326 Lake Lucaya Dr (33579-4103)
PHONE....813 451-4744
Michael Phillips, *Principal*
EMP: 6 **EST:** 2016
SALES (est): 82.9K **Privately Held**
SIC: 3721 Motorized aircraft

(G-15282)
SAVORY LIFE LLC
6766 Waterton Dr (33578-8388)
PHONE....813 981-2022
Lindsey Wherry, *President*
EMP: 6 **EST:** 2018
SALES (est): 190.7K **Privately Held**
SIC: 2099 Food preparations

(G-15283)
TAMPA BAY PRINT SHOP LLC
2904 S Falkenburg Rd (33578-2554)
PHONE....813 321-8790
Ryan Koenig,
EMP: 7 **EST:** 2018
SALES (est): 250K **Privately Held**
WEB: www.tampabayprintshop.co
SIC: 2759 Screen printing

(G-15284)
TAYLOR MADE SCRUB HATS LLC ✪
10044 Creek Bluff Dr (33578-7559)
PHONE....615 348-7802
Chris Jordon,
EMP: 7 **EST:** 2021
SALES (est): 250K **Privately Held**
WEB: www.taylormadescrubhats.com
SIC: 2211 Scrub cloths

(G-15285)
ULTRAFLEX SYSTEMS FLORIDA INC (PA)
6333 Pelican Creek Cir (33578-8822)
PHONE....973 664-6739
John Schleicher, *President*
Clint Green, *Managing Dir*
Ron Schleicher, *COO*
Tim Wilson, *Sales Staff*
EMP: 11 **EST:** 2016
SALES (est): 11.7MM **Privately Held**
WEB: www.ultraflexx.com
SIC: 2821 Polyvinyl chloride resins (PVC)

(G-15286)
VF IMAGEWEAR INC
8221 Eagle Palm Dr (33578-8893)
PHONE....813 671-2986
Laura Bear, *Manager*
EMP: 6
SALES (corp-wide): 1.6B **Privately Held**
WEB: www.vfsolutions.com
SIC: 2395 5137 5136 Embroidery & art needlework; women's & children's clothing; men's & boys' clothing
HQ: Vf Imagewear, Inc.
545 Marriott Dr Ste 200
Nashville TN 37214
615 565-5000

(G-15287)
WEREVER PRODUCTS INC
Also Called: Werever Waterproof Cabinetry
6120 Pelican Creek Cir (33578-8978)
PHONE....813 241-9701
Matt Boettger, *President*
Jill Kliem, *Sales Mgr*
EMP: 17 **EST:** 2001
SALES (est): 2.4MM **Privately Held**
WEB: www.werever.com
SIC: 2599 5719 5712 Cabinets, factory; barbeque grills; furniture stores

(G-15288)
XYLITOL USA INC
11524 Storywood Dr (33578-3134)
PHONE....303 991-1999
Andrew Reid, *President*
Roger Daher, *Chairman*
Kyle Appleby, *CFO*
Justin Urso, *VP Sales*
Sunir Chandaria, *Director*
▲ **EMP:** 9
SALES (est): 1.6MM **Privately Held**
WEB: www.naturalsweetenerstore.com
SIC: 2099 Sugar

Riviera Beach
Palm Beach County

(G-15289)
3D MEDICAL MANUFACTURING INC
Also Called: 3d Machining
2001 N Congress Ave Ste F (33404-5101)
PHONE....561 842-7175
James E Davis Sr, *CEO*
James E Davis Jr, *President*
Joseph H Davis, *Exec VP*
Laura Thomas, *Warehouse Mgr*
Miguel Freire, *Engineer*
EMP: 203 **EST:** 1994
SALES (est): 39.1MM
SALES (corp-wide): 832.8MM **Privately Held**
WEB: www.tecomet.com
SIC: 3841 Surgical & medical instruments
HQ: Tecomet Inc.
115 Eames St
Wilmington MA 01887
978 642-2400

(G-15290)
ABELE SHEETMETAL WORKS INC
1964 W 9th St Ste 3 (33404-6426)
PHONE....561 471-1134
Fred Abele, *President*
EMP: 11 **EST:** 1995
SQ FT: 2,500
SALES (est): 2MM **Privately Held**
WEB: www.abelesheetmetal.com
SIC: 3444 Sheet metalwork

(G-15291)
ADATIF MEDICAL INCORPORATED (HQ)
3660 Interstate Park Way (33404-5911)
PHONE....561 840-0395
Kerrigan Turner, *Ch of Bd*
Mike Richardson, *Vice Pres*
EMP: 1 **EST:** 1992
SQ FT: 24,000
SALES (est): 9.9MM
SALES (corp-wide): 1.5MM **Privately Held**
WEB: www.perrybaromedical.com
SIC: 3841 Surgical & medical instruments
PA: Adatif International Ltd
211-4150 Rue Sainte-Catherine Ouest
Westmount QC H3Z 2
514 934-4966

(G-15292)
ADDCO MANUFACTURING COMPANY
Also Called: Addco Industries
131 Riviera Dr (33404-2422)
PHONE....828 733-1560
Roland De Marcellus, *Ch of Bd*
Edmond G De Marcellus, *President*
Daniel W Osborne, *Vice Pres*
EMP: 41 **EST:** 1960
SQ FT: 60,000
SALES (est): 935.6K **Privately Held**
WEB: www.addco.net
SIC: 3714 5521 Motor vehicle parts & accessories; used car dealers

(G-15293)
ADVANCED AIR INTERNATIONAL INC
6461 Garden Rd Ste 103 (33404-6315)
PHONE....561 845-8212
Dale L Bell, *President*
Luis Borge, *General Mgr*
Steven M Bell, *Vice Pres*
Larry A Bell, *Treasurer*
EMP: 37 **EST:** 1989
SQ FT: 20,000
SALES (est): 5.7MM **Privately Held**
WEB: www.advancedair.net
SIC: 3089 Injection molding of plastics

(G-15294)
ADVANCED AIR WEST PALM BCH INC
6461 Garden Rd Ste 102 (33404-6315)
PHONE....561 845-8289
Larry Bell, *President*
Larry A Bell, *President*
Steven M Bell, *Vice Pres*
EMP: 26 **EST:** 1989
SQ FT: 10,000
SALES (est): 4.5MM **Privately Held**
WEB: www.aabushings.net
SIC: 3599 5088 Machine shop, jobbing & repair; transportation equipment & supplies

(G-15295)
AFL INDUSTRIES INC
1101 W 13th St (33404-6701)
PHONE....561 848-1826
EMP: 8 **EST:** 2019
SALES (est): 177.5K **Privately Held**
WEB: www.rgf.com
SIC: 3589 Water treatment equipment, industrial

(G-15296)
AKIKNAV INC
Also Called: Pompanette Kitchen's
6667 42nd Ter N Ste 3 (33407-1241)
PHONE....561 842-8091
Nash Shah, *President*
Aarsh Shah, *Business Mgr*
Ashok Shah, *Shareholder*
Hetal Shah, *Shareholder*
Kamlesh Shah, *Shareholder*
EMP: 15 **EST:** 1986
SQ FT: 25,000
SALES (est): 2MM **Privately Held**
SIC: 2434 2541 2542 Wood kitchen cabinets; counters or counter display cases, wood; partitions & fixtures, except wood

(G-15297)
ALPHA HYDRAULICS LLC
999 W 17th St Ste 5 (33404-5402)
PHONE....561 355-0318
Sara Rodriguez, *CEO*
EMP: 5 **EST:** 2014
SALES (est): 304.5K **Privately Held**
WEB: www.alphahydraulicsllc.com
SIC: 3599 7699 3714 1799 Machine shop, jobbing & repair; hydraulic equipment repair; hydraulic fluid power pumps for auto steering mechanism; hydraulic equipment, installation & service; pistons & valves

(G-15298)
AMY CABINETRY
6667 42nd Ter N (33407-1241)
PHONE....561 842-8091
Nash Shah, *Owner*
EMP: 25 **EST:** 1986
SALES (est): 1.1MM **Privately Held**
SIC: 2434 Wood kitchen cabinets

(G-15299)
ATLAS SIGN INDUSTRIES FLA LLC
1077 W Blue Heron Blvd (33404-4227)
PHONE....561 863-6659
Jim Adinolfe, *CEO*
Jeffrey Adinolfe, *CEO*
Mark Bragg, *Project Mgr*
Gary Bennett, *CFO*
Kenny Melesky, *Asst Controller*
▼ **EMP:** 215 **EST:** 1992
SQ FT: 250,000
SALES (est): 44.3MM **Privately Held**
WEB: www.atlasbtw.com
SIC: 3993 Signs & advertising specialties
PA: Atlas Signs Holdings, Inc.
1077 Blue Heron Blvd W
Riviera Beach FL 33404

(G-15300)
B & A MANUFACTURING CO
3665 E Industrial Way (33404-3491)
PHONE....561 848-8648
Norman H Schmotzer, *President*
Carole Schmotzer, *Info Tech Mgr*
Carol Schmotzer, *Admin Sec*
◆ **EMP:** 45 **EST:** 1950
SQ FT: 25,000
SALES (est): 4.9MM **Privately Held**
WEB: www.bamanufacturing.com
SIC: 3545 3532 3423 Drill bits, metalworking; mining machinery; hand & edge tools

(G-15301)
BLACK BART INTERNATIONAL LLC
155 E Blue Heron Blvd R2 (33404-4546)
PHONE....561 842-4045
Bart Miller, *Ch of Bd*
John Tullis Jr, *President*
Gary Tillius, *Vice Pres*
Janck Tullius,
EMP: 8 **EST:** 2003
SQ FT: 3,500
SALES (est): 761.4K **Privately Held**
SIC: 3949 Fishing equipment

(G-15302)
BLACK CORAL RUM LLC (PA)
1231 W 13th St Bldg 15 (33404-6640)
PHONE....561 766-2493
Benjamin C Etheridge, *Manager*
EMP: 29 **EST:** 2012
SALES (est): 655.4K **Privately Held**
WEB: www.steeltiespirits.com
SIC: 2085 Distilled & blended liquors

(G-15303)
BN BIOFUELS LLC
1 E 11th St Ste 202 (33404-6921)
PHONE....312 239-2680
Anthony Quinones, *Owner*
EMP: 6 **EST:** 2011
SQ FT: 11,500
SALES (est): 116K **Privately Held**
SIC: 2869 Industrial organic chemicals

(G-15304)
BORGZINNER INC
1160 W 13th St Ste 10 (33404-6715)
PHONE....561 848-2538
Ken Stevens, *President*
EMP: 22 **EST:** 1891
SALES (est): 2.8MM **Privately Held**
WEB: www.borgzinner.com
SIC: 2599 Cabinets, factory; cafeteria furniture

(G-15305)
BUDGET PRINTING CENTER LLC
4152 Blue Heron Blvd W # 109
(33404-4858)
PHONE....561 848-5700
Jay Goldfarb, *Mng Member*
EMP: 5 **EST:** 2000
SQ FT: 3,000
SALES (est): 316.4K **Privately Held**
SIC: 2752 Commercial printing, offset

(G-15306)
BUSCH CANVAS
2428 Broadway (33404-4533)
PHONE....561 881-1605
Andrea Jarvis, *Principal*
EMP: 8 **EST:** 2010
SALES (est): 205.4K **Privately Held**
WEB: www.buschcanvas.com
SIC: 2394 Canvas & related products

(G-15307)
BUSCH CANVAS & INTERIORS
2428 Broadway (33404-4533)
PHONE....561 881-1605
Andrea Jarvis, *President*
Kim Crawford, *Admin Sec*
EMP: 5 **EST:** 1968
SALES (est): 500K **Privately Held**
WEB: www.buschcanvas.com
SIC: 2211 Canvas

(G-15308)
CANVAS DESIGNERS INC
Also Called: Nautical Flair
1500 Australian Ave Ste 1 (33404-5313)
PHONE....561 881-7663
Michael Erickson, *President*
Pamela Erickson, *Vice Pres*
Heidi Garrison, *Prdtn Mgr*

Diana Demarest, *Marketing Mgr*
Bob Renna, *Manager*
◆ **EMP:** 36 **EST:** 1985
SQ FT: 15,000
SALES (est): 5.5MM **Privately Held**
WEB: www.canvasdesigners.com
SIC: 2394 Canvas & related products

(G-15309)
CAREY-DUNN INC
Also Called: Florida Marine
2001 Broadway Ste 301 (33404-5612)
PHONE....................................561 840-1694
EMP: 15 **EST:** 1996
SQ FT: 25,000
SALES (est): 1.1MM **Privately Held**
SIC: 3732 Boatbuilding/Repairing

(G-15310)
CARPENTERS ROOFG & SHTMTL INC
1701 W 10th St (33404-6431)
PHONE....................................561 833-0341
James E Williams Jr, *President*
Joe Hart, *Vice Pres*
Joseph C Hart, *Vice Pres*
EMP: 35 **EST:** 1931
SQ FT: 10,000
SALES (est): 5MM **Privately Held**
WEB: www.carpentersroofing.com
SIC: 3444 2952 Sheet metalwork; asphalt felts & coatings

(G-15311)
CEMEX MATERIALS LLC
Also Called: Riviera Beach FL Warehouse Bm
501 Avenue S (33404-7109)
PHONE....................................561 881-4472
Arlene Larubbia, *Branch Mgr*
EMP: 73 **Privately Held**
SIC: 3273 Ready-mixed concrete
HQ: Cemex Materials Llc
1501 Belvedere Rd
West Palm Beach FL 33406
561 833-5555

(G-15312)
CLOCK SPRING COMPANY INC
3875 Fiscal Ct (33404-1795)
PHONE....................................561 683-6992
Matthew Boucher, *CEO*
Matt Green, *Vice Pres*
Ian Liess, *Vice Pres*
Ryan Schwarz, *Vice Pres*
Dariusz Chabuz, *Opers Staff*
EMP: 15 **Privately Held**
WEB: www.cs-nri.com
SIC: 2869 2295 5039 Silicones; chemically coated & treated fabrics; structural assemblies, prefabricated: non-wood
PA: Clock Spring Company, Inc.
621 Lockhaven Dr
Houston TX 77073

(G-15313)
CONCRETE PDTS OF PALM BCHES IN
460 Avenue S (33404-7108)
PHONE....................................561 842-2743
Bernard Brunet, *Principal*
EMP: 22 **EST:** 2011
SALES (est): 9.4MM **Privately Held**
SIC: 3272 Concrete products, precast

(G-15314)
CONSULIER ENGINEERING INC (PA)
2391 President Barack Oba (33404-5456)
PHONE....................................561 842-2492
Warren B Mosler, *Ch of Bd*
Alan R Simon, *Treasurer*
EMP: 1 **EST:** 1985
SQ FT: 500
SALES (est): 4MM **Privately Held**
WEB: www.moslerauto.com
SIC: 2841 7373 6211 2879 Soap & other detergents; computer integrated systems design; security brokers & dealers; insecticides & pesticides

(G-15315)
CUSTOM CANVAS AND CUSHIONS
176 E 21st St (33404-5608)
PHONE....................................561 800-8541
EMP: 5 **EST:** 2018
SALES (est): 528.4K **Privately Held**
WEB: www.customcanvas561.com
SIC: 2211 Canvas

(G-15316)
D & R DELIVERY SERVICES OF PB
312 Canterbury Dr W (33407-1321)
PHONE....................................561 602-6427
Morgan Rohan, *CEO*
EMP: 12 **EST:** 2013
SALES (est): 970K **Privately Held**
SIC: 3799 Transportation equipment

(G-15317)
D I H CORPORATION
Also Called: Cutoutz.com
1750 Australian Ave Ste 3 (33404-5328)
PHONE....................................561 881-8705
Henry Goldberg, *President*
Scott Goldberg, *Vice Pres*
EMP: 5 **EST:** 1954
SQ FT: 7,500
SALES (est): 608.3K **Privately Held**
WEB: www.cutoutz.com
SIC: 3993 Displays & cutouts, window & lobby

(G-15318)
DANA ANDREWS WOODWORKING
1748 Australian Ave (33404-5302)
PHONE....................................561 882-0444
Dana Andrews, *Principal*
EMP: 7 **EST:** 2006
SALES (est): 98.3K **Privately Held**
SIC: 2431 Millwork

(G-15319)
DAVID S STOYKA
Also Called: Battery Savers
8125 Monetary Dr Ste H6 (33404-1712)
PHONE....................................561 848-2599
David Stoyka, *Principal*
▲ **EMP:** 5 **EST:** 2005
SALES (est): 950K **Privately Held**
SIC: 3674 Computer logic modules

(G-15320)
DNA SURFACE CONCEPTS INC
1980 Avenue L (33404-5442)
PHONE....................................561 328-7302
Sean M Kelly, *President*
EMP: 10 **EST:** 2014
SALES (est): 793.9K **Privately Held**
WEB: www.dnasurfaceconcepts.com
SIC: 3479 Metal coating & allied service

(G-15321)
DOCTORS SCIENTIFIC ORGANICA LLC (HQ)
Also Called: Smart For Life
1210 W 13th St (33404-6639)
PHONE....................................888 455-9031
Sasson Moulavi, *CEO*
EMP: 10 **EST:** 2007
SALES (est): 26.1MM
SALES (corp-wide): 41MM **Privately Held**
WEB: www.smartforlife.com
SIC: 2834 Pharmaceutical preparations
PA: Smart For Life, Inc.
990 Biscayne Blvd # 1203
Miami FL 33132
786 749-1221

(G-15322)
DRENCH KHARI LLC
331 W 19th St (33404-6126)
PHONE....................................561 507-4723
Pebbles J Brown, *CEO*
EMP: 6 **EST:** 2019
SALES (est): 272.7K **Privately Held**
SIC: 2211 5651 5961 Apparel & outerwear fabrics, cotton; unisex clothing stores;

(G-15323)
E-Z WELD INC
1661 Pres Barack Obama Hw (33404)
PHONE....................................561 844-0241
David Zerfoss, *President*
◆ **EMP:** 36 **EST:** 2006
SALES (est): 6.8MM **Privately Held**
WEB: www.e-zweld.com
SIC: 2952 Roof cement: asphalt, fibrous or plastic

(G-15324)
ECLIPSYS CORP
8017 Via Hacienda (33418-7856)
PHONE....................................404 847-5000
Larry Michaels, *Treasurer*
EMP: 6 **EST:** 2015
SALES (est): 68.7K **Privately Held**
SIC: 3841 Surgical & medical instruments

(G-15325)
ELAINE SMITH INC
7740 Byron Dr (33404-3318)
PHONE....................................561 863-3333
Elaine Smith, *President*
EMP: 16 **EST:** 2005
SALES (est): 1.9MM **Privately Held**
WEB: www.elainesmith.com
SIC: 2392 5023 Cushions & pillows; pillowcases

(G-15326)
EXCELLENT PERFORMANCE INC
Also Called: Pettit Racing
4650 Dyer Blvd (33407-1027)
PHONE....................................561 296-0776
Cameron Worth, *President*
◆ **EMP:** 6 **EST:** 1992
SALES (est): 945K **Privately Held**
WEB: www.pettitracing.com
SIC: 3465 Body parts, automobile: stamped metal

(G-15327)
FAB RITE INC
4636 Dyer Blvd (33407-1027)
PHONE....................................561 848-8181
James Johnson, *CEO*
James Peters, *Vice Pres*
▼ **EMP:** 8 **EST:** 1987
SQ FT: 3,200
SALES (est): 1.4MM **Privately Held**
WEB: www.fabritesteel.com
SIC: 3441 3446 Fabricated structural metal; railings, prefabricated metal

(G-15328)
FISHERMANS CENTER INC
56 E Blue Heron Blvd (33404-4541)
PHONE....................................561 844-5150
William Buckland, *President*
EMP: 7 **EST:** 1955
SQ FT: 2,000
SALES (est): 837.3K **Privately Held**
WEB: www.fishermanscenter.com
SIC: 3949 5941 Fishing tackle, general; fishing equipment

(G-15329)
FLORIDA COCA-COLA BOTTLING CO
6553 Garden Rd (33404-6303)
PHONE....................................561 848-0055
Bernie Roy, *Manager*
EMP: 403
SQ FT: 68,625
SALES (corp-wide): 33B **Publicly Held**
WEB: www.coca-cola.com
SIC: 2086 Bottled & canned soft drinks
HQ: Florida Coca-Cola Bottling Company
521 Lake Kathy Dr
Brandon FL 33510
813 569-2600

(G-15330)
FLORIDA MACHINE & CASTING CO
8011 Monetary Dr Ste A6 (33404-1702)
PHONE....................................561 655-3771
J Andrew Darien, *President*
EMP: 7 **EST:** 1946
SALES (est): 5.4MM
SALES (corp-wide): 18.5MM **Privately Held**
WEB: www.tristatecast.com
SIC: 3365 3366 Machinery castings, aluminum; copper foundries; brass foundry; bronze foundry
PA: Tri-State Cast Technologies Co, Inc
926 N Lake St
Boyne City MI 49712
231 582-0452

(G-15331)
HARMSCO INC (PA)
Also Called: Harmsco Filtration Products
7169 49th Ter N (33407-1003)
PHONE....................................561 848-9628
Harold H Harms, *President*
Greg Willis, *Principal*
Carl Vesperman, *Vice Pres*
Pascal Vanlindt, *Purchasing*
Lori Cooper, *Accounting Mgr*
◆ **EMP:** 75
SQ FT: 120,000
SALES (est): 14.3MM **Privately Held**
WEB: www.harmsco.com
SIC: 3589 2674 Swimming pool filter & water conditioning systems; water treatment equipment, industrial; bags: uncoated paper & multiwall

(G-15332)
HARRY J HONAN
1051 Singer Dr (33404-2764)
PHONE....................................405 273-9315
EMP: 7 **EST:** 2018
SALES (est): 449.9K **Privately Held**
SIC: 3714 Motor vehicle parts & accessories

(G-15333)
HARTMAN WINDOWS AND DOORS LLC
2107 Blue Heron Blvd W (33404-5005)
PHONE....................................561 296-9600
Ashley Hartman, *Exec VP*
Eddie Bustamante, *Vice Pres*
Richard Nourjian, *Manager*
Clifford Hartman,
◆ **EMP:** 68 **EST:** 1996
SQ FT: 32,000
SALES (est): 10.7MM **Privately Held**
WEB: www.hartmanwindows.com
SIC: 2431 5031 Doors, wood; doors & windows

(G-15334)
INTERAMERICAS BEVERAGES INC
1726 Avenue L (33404-5438)
P.O. Box 1433, West Palm Beach (33402-1433)
PHONE....................................561 881-1340
Claudio Bruehmueller, *President*
Gina M Cieri, *Treasurer*
Lateef Khan, *Technical Staff*
Camilla Bruehmueller, *Admin Sec*
EMP: 6 **EST:** 2008
SALES (est): 2MM **Privately Held**
WEB: www.interamericasbeverages.com
SIC: 2087 Flavoring extracts & syrups

(G-15335)
IPTS INC
7221 Hvrhill Bus Pkwy # 103 (33407-1007)
PHONE....................................561 844-8216
Richard Diasio, *President*
John Signorino, *Sales Mgr*
Julia Diasio, *Admin Sec*
▲ **EMP:** 13 **EST:** 1980
SQ FT: 20,000
SALES (est): 3.1MM **Privately Held**
WEB: www.iptsinc.com
SIC: 3568 Power transmission equipment

(G-15336)
ITALIAN ROSE GARLIC PDTS LLC (HQ)
1380 W 15th St (33404-5310)
PHONE....................................561 863-5556
Angelo Fraggos, *CEO*
Byard Ebling, *Vice Pres*
John Lemay, *Vice Pres*
Jonathan Pressnell, *Vice Pres*
Chris Bonomo, *Purch Mgr*
EMP: 120 **EST:** 1979
SQ FT: 36,000

▲ = Import ▼=Export
◆ =Import/Export

SALES (est): 45MM
SALES (corp-wide): 665.7MM **Privately Held**
WEB: www.italian-rose.com
SIC: 2099 2035 6282 Seasonings & spices; pickles, sauces & salad dressings; investment advisory service
PA: Blue Point Capital Partners Llc
127 Public Sq Ste 5100
Cleveland OH 44114
216 535-4700

(G-15337)
K&M POWER SYSTEMS LLC
7641 Central Indus Dr (33404-3431)
PHONE..................................866 945-9100
Derrick E Hoskins, *Principal*
EMP: 7 **EST:** 2018
SALES (est): 270.2K **Privately Held**
WEB: www.kmpowersystems.com
SIC: 3621 Motors & generators

(G-15338)
K-RAIN MANUFACTURING CORP (PA)
Also Called: K Rain
1640 Australian Ave (33404-5306)
PHONE..................................561 721-3936
Carl Kah Jr, *CEO*
Carl Kah III, *President*
Kah Chip, *Opers Mgr*
Shirley J Kah, *Treasurer*
Carrie Rogers, *Sales Staff*
◆ **EMP:** 58 **EST:** 1971
SQ FT: 25,000
SALES (est): 10.4MM **Privately Held**
WEB: www.krain.com
SIC: 3494 3432 3523 3829 Sprinkler systems, field; lawn hose nozzles & sprinklers; irrigation equipment, self-propelled; sprayers & spraying machines, agricultural; rain gauges

(G-15339)
KADASSA INC
3541 Dr Martin Luther Kin (33404-6306)
PHONE..................................954 684-8361
Martin H Arias, *President*
Carmen Arias, *Vice Pres*
EMP: 15 **EST:** 2008
SALES (est): 1.1MM **Privately Held**
WEB: www.kadassainc.wixsite.com
SIC: 3281 Curbing, granite or stone

(G-15340)
KENART HOLDINGS LLC
1380 W 15th St (33404-5310)
PHONE..................................561 863-5556
Ken Berger, *President*
Arthur Conlan, *Vice Pres*
Michael Colin, *Opers Mgr*
Beth Gibson, *Sales Staff*
▲ **EMP:** 110 **EST:** 1979
SQ FT: 40,000
SALES (est): 7.9MM **Privately Held**
SIC: 2099 2035 Seasonings & spices; pickles, sauces & salad dressings

(G-15341)
KNIGHT FIRE & SECURITY INC
7513 Central Indus Dr (33404-3429)
PHONE..................................561 471-8221
Jeffrey B Knight, *President*
EMP: 19 **EST:** 2006
SALES (est): 4.2MM **Privately Held**
WEB: www.knightcorporations.com
SIC: 3699 Security devices

(G-15342)
LAVI ENTERPRISES LLC
Also Called: Doctor Scientific Organica
1210 W 13th St (33404-6639)
PHONE..................................561 721-7170
Margot Hunte, *Principal*
EMP: 57 **EST:** 2012
SALES (est): 3.9MM **Privately Held**
SIC: 2052 Cookies

(G-15343)
LOCKHEED MARTIN CORPORATION
100 E 17th St (33404-5664)
PHONE..................................301 897-6000
John Pfeifler, *Mfg Dir*
Nicholas Asseff, *Engineer*
Ray Boettger, *Engineer*
Joseph Hutchison, *Engineer*
Michael Noyes, *Engineer*
EMP: 6 **Publicly Held**
WEB: www.lockheedmartin.com
SIC: 3812 Search & navigation equipment
PA: Lockheed Martin Corporation
6801 Rockledge Dr
Bethesda MD 20817

(G-15344)
LUKES ICE CREAM
1025 W 17th St (33404-5407)
PHONE..................................561 588-5853
Kevin Lukasewicz, *President*
Jody Lukasewicz, *Vice Pres*
◆ **EMP:** 16 **EST:** 1984
SQ FT: 25,000
SALES (est): 2.9MM **Privately Held**
WEB: www.lukesicecream.com
SIC: 2024 Ice cream, bulk

(G-15345)
M W M SERVICES INC
7655 Enterprise Dr Ste 4 (33404-3339)
PHONE..................................561 844-0955
Eva Carbone, *President*
Cliff Koziel, *General Mgr*
Koziel Waldek, *Mfg Staff*
EMP: 10 **EST:** 1983
SQ FT: 5,000
SALES (est): 1MM **Privately Held**
WEB: www.mwmservices.com
SIC: 3599 Machine shop, jobbing & repair

(G-15346)
MARINE EXHAUST SYSTEMS INC (PA)
3640 Fiscal Ct Ste D (33404-1781)
PHONE..................................561 848-1238
Woodrow E Woods, *Ch of Bd*
Angela Woods, *President*
Sheila Prieschl, *Vice Pres*
Darrin Woods, *Vice Pres*
Manuela Velasquez, *Human Res Dir*
◆ **EMP:** 79 **EST:** 1973
SQ FT: 52,000
SALES (est): 12MM **Privately Held**
WEB: www.marine-exhaust.com
SIC: 3732 7699 3498 3621 Tenders (small motor craft), building & repairing; professional instrument repair services; fabricated pipe & fittings; motors & generators; industrial machinery & equipment; transportation equipment & supplies

(G-15347)
MATHESON TRI-GAS INC
1800 Bee Line Hwy (33404-7105)
PHONE..................................561 615-3000
Craig Oreo, *Manager*
EMP: 6
SQ FT: 1,500 **Privately Held**
WEB: www.mathesongas.com
SIC: 2813 5084 Industrial gases; welding machinery & equipment
HQ: Matheson Tri-Gas, Inc.
3 Mountainview Rd Ste 3 # 3
Warren NJ 07059
908 991-9200

(G-15348)
MICRO TOOL ENGINEERING INC
7575 Centl Indus Dr Ste A (33404-3422)
PHONE..................................561 842-7381
Fran Lacasse, *President*
Pierre La Casse, *Vice Pres*
Dinah Lacasse, *Vice Pres*
EMP: 15 **EST:** 1968
SQ FT: 10,000
SALES (est): 1.1MM **Privately Held**
WEB: www.mte-fl.com
SIC: 3599 3841 3769 3728 Machine shop, jobbing & repair; surgical & medical instruments; guided missile & space vehicle parts & auxiliary equipment; aircraft parts & equipment

(G-15349)
MOORES MAR OF PALM BEACHES INC
1410 Avenue E (33404-6199)
PHONE..................................561 841-2235
James P Moores, *President*
EMP: 6 **EST:** 1986
SQ FT: 5,190
SALES (est): 482.7K **Privately Held**
WEB: www.woodenboatrepair.com
SIC: 3732 Yachts, building & repairing

(G-15350)
MOSER AUTOMOTIVE
2391 President Barack Oba (33404-5456)
PHONE..................................561 881-5665
EMP: 40
SALES (est): 1.2MM **Privately Held**
SIC: 2396 3711 Mfg Auto/Apparel Trimming Mfg Motor Vehicle/Car Bodies

(G-15351)
NATIONAL BEDDING COMPANY LLC
3774 Interstate Park Rd N (33404-5908)
PHONE..................................561 840-8491
EMP: 207 **Privately Held**
WEB: www.jobs.serta.com
SIC: 2515 Mattresses, containing felt, foam rubber, urethane, etc.
HQ: National Bedding Company L.L.C.
2600 Forbs Ave
Hoffman Estates IL 60192

(G-15352)
NEPTUNE RESEARCH INC (PA)
Also Called: N R I
3875 Fiscal Ct Ste 100 (33404-1707)
PHONE..................................561 683-6992
Christopher Lazzar, *President*
Jason Lewis, *President*
Andrea Novak, *Human Res Mgr*
Tammy Bomia, *Regl Sales Mgr*
Tiffany Clark, *Technology*
▼ **EMP:** 38 **EST:** 1982
SQ FT: 27,500
SALES (est): 9.5MM **Privately Held**
WEB: www.cs-nri.com
SIC: 3317 Steel pipe & tubes

(G-15353)
NWL INC
Nwl Capacitors
8050 Monetary Dr (33404-1736)
P.O. Box 10416, West Palm Beach (33419-0416)
PHONE..................................561 848-9009
Robert Seitz, *President*
Arturo Fortuna, *Plant Engr Mgr*
EMP: 106
SALES (corp-wide): 101.3MM **Privately Held**
WEB: www.nwl.com
SIC: 3612 3675 Power transformers, electric; electronic capacitors
HQ: Nwl, Inc.
312 Rising Sun Rd
Bordentown NJ 08505
609 298-7300

(G-15354)
OASE NORTH AMERICA INC
7241 Hvrhill Bus Pkwy # 105 (33407-1014)
PHONE..................................800 365-3880
Andreas Szabados, *CEO*
Michael Selk, *Vice Pres*
Mary Szczecina, *Controller*
Maria Novielli, *Sales Mgr*
Shannon Wenzel, *Cust Mgr*
◆ **EMP:** 6 **EST:** 1994
SALES (est): 2MM
SALES (corp-wide): 2.6MM **Privately Held**
WEB: www.biorb.com
SIC: 3594 3524 5251 Fluid power pumps; lawn & garden equipment; pumps & pumping equipment
HQ: Oase International Holding Gmbh
Tecklenburger Str. 161
Horstel
545 480-0

(G-15355)
OCEAN BLUE GRAPHICS INC
1841 W 10th St Ste 1 (33404-6415)
PHONE..................................561 881-2022
Alan Yansochak, *President*
EMP: 9 **EST:** 2015
SALES (est): 361.7K **Privately Held**
WEB: www.oceanbluegraphics.com
SIC: 2759 2395 Screen printing; art goods for embroidering, stamped: purchased materials

(G-15356)
OCEAN BLUE GRAPHICS DESIGN INC
1841 W 10th St Ste 1 (33404-6415)
PHONE..................................561 881-2022
Alan Yanoschak, *Vice Pres*
▼ **EMP:** 6 **EST:** 2005
SALES (est): 428.2K **Privately Held**
WEB: www.oceanbluegraphics.com
SIC: 2759 Screen printing

(G-15357)
OCEAN MASTER MARINE INC
837 W 13th St Unit C (33404-6702)
PHONE..................................561 840-0448
Mark Hauptner, *President*
Bonnie Hauptner, *Treasurer*
EMP: 8 **EST:** 1975
SQ FT: 3,500
SALES (est): 552.3K **Privately Held**
WEB: www.oceanmasterboats.com
SIC: 3732 Fishing boats: lobster, crab, oyster, etc.: small

(G-15358)
OMEGA LIFT CORPORATION
6701 Garden Rd Ste 1 (33404-5900)
PHONE..................................561 840-0088
Howard Roenkranz, *President*
EMP: 10 **EST:** 1993
SQ FT: 15,000
SALES (est): 362.7K **Privately Held**
SIC: 3559 Rubber working machinery, including tires

(G-15359)
PAVER SYSTEMS LLC (HQ)
Also Called: Oldcastle Coastal
7167 Interpace Rd (33407-1023)
PHONE..................................561 844-5202
C Steven Berry, *Mng Member*
▼ **EMP:** 50 **EST:** 1974
SQ FT: 30,000
SALES (est): 11.2MM
SALES (corp-wide): 118.5MM **Privately Held**
WEB: www.paversystems.com
SIC: 3272 Concrete products
PA: Eagle Corporation
1020 Harris St
Charlottesville VA 22903
434 971-2686

(G-15360)
PENDULUM ONE INC
Also Called: New Dimensions
6555 Garden Rd Ste 13 (33404-6318)
PHONE..................................561 844-8169
Ira D Smith Jr, *President*
Eleanor J Smith, *Corp Secy*
EMP: 6 **EST:** 1974
SQ FT: 5,000
SALES (est): 760.1K **Privately Held**
SIC: 2512 Chairs: upholstered on wood frames; couches, sofas & davenports: upholstered on wood frames; living room furniture: upholstered on wood frames

(G-15361)
PEPSI-COLA BTLG FT LDRDL-PALM
7305 Garden Rd (33404-3490)
PHONE..................................561 848-1000
Paul Groth, *Engineer*
Chris Morrissey, *Sales Staff*
Joel Condra, *Manager*
Conner Hale, *Manager*
EMP: 64 **EST:** 2019
SALES (est): 21MM
SALES (corp-wide): 70.3B **Publicly Held**
WEB: www.pepsico.com
SIC: 2086 Carbonated soft drinks, bottled & canned
PA: Pepsico, Inc.
700 Anderson Hill Rd
Purchase NY 10577
914 253-2000

(G-15362)
PERRY BAROMEDICAL CORPORATION (DH)
3750 Prospect Ave (33404-3443)
PHONE..................................561 840-0395
Kerrigan Turner, *Ch of Bd*
Wayne Mc Cullough, *President*

GEOGRAPHIC

Michael Richardson, *Vice Pres*
Tim Labuhn, *Electrical Engi*
Trisha Cook, *CFO*
◆ **EMP:** 34 **EST:** 1979
SQ FT: 24,000
SALES (est): 6.4MM
SALES (corp-wide): 1.5MM **Privately Held**
WEB: www.perrybaromedical.com
SIC: 3841 Surgical & medical instruments

(G-15363)
PILOT CORP OF PALM BEACHES
Also Called: Bradford Septic Tank Company
7117 49th Ter N (33407-1003)
PHONE....................561 848-2928
Gary Pinkas, *President*
Janet Pinkas, *Vice Pres*
EMP: 18 **EST:** 1960
SALES (est): 3.3MM **Privately Held**
WEB: www.bradfordseptic.com
SIC: 3272 1711 Septic tanks, concrete; septic system construction

(G-15364)
PLAZADOOR CORP
1500 Avenue R Ste 200 (33404-5262)
PHONE....................561 578-5450
Michael Fry, *CEO*
EMP: 25 **EST:** 2018
SALES (est): 1.3MM **Privately Held**
WEB: www.plazadoorcompany.com
SIC: 3089 1793 Fiberglass doors; glass & glazing work

(G-15365)
PORT PRINTING CO
3532 Broadway (33404-2332)
P.O. Box 9162, West Palm Beach (33419-9162)
PHONE....................561 848-1402
Ernie Garvey, *President*
Josie Studstille, *Vice Pres*
EMP: 8 **EST:** 1992
SQ FT: 2,100
SALES (est): 837.2K **Privately Held**
WEB: www.portprinting.com
SIC: 2752 Commercial printing, offset

(G-15366)
PRIME MOLDING TECHNOLOGIES INC
3765 Investment Ln Ste A (33404-1756)
PHONE....................561 721-2799
Richard Volpe, *President*
Sergey Shulyak, *Vice Pres*
Dennis Terwilliger, *Vice Pres*
Karin Volpe, *Prdtn Mgr*
Bob Pfretzschner, *Design Engr*
▲ **EMP:** 25 **EST:** 2002
SQ FT: 15,000
SALES (est): 6.2MM **Privately Held**
WEB: www.primemolding.com
SIC: 3089 Injection molding of plastics

(G-15367)
PRINT IDEA CENTER LLC ✪
7788 Centl Indus Dr Ste 3 (33404-3450)
PHONE....................954 682-6369
Joshua D Thomas,
EMP: 6 **EST:** 2020
SALES (est): 73.2K **Privately Held**
SIC: 2759 Publication printing

(G-15368)
RAMSAY MARINE SERVICES LLC
999 W 17th St Ste 1 (33404-5402)
PHONE....................561 881-1234
Mark Ebanks, *Principal*
Patricia Humphries, *Principal*
EMP: 11 **EST:** 2009
SALES (est): 471.9K **Privately Held**
WEB: www.ramsaymarine.net
SIC: 7692 Welding repair

(G-15369)
REILLY FOAM CORP
3896 Westroads Dr (33407-1227)
PHONE....................561 842-8090
Matt Rider, *Branch Mgr*
Robert Westerfer, *Manager*
EMP: 15
SQ FT: 67,184
SALES (corp-wide): 26.4MM **Privately Held**
WEB: www.reillyfoam.com
SIC: 3086 Plastics foam products
PA: Reilly Foam Corp.
751 5th Ave
King Of Prussia PA 19406
610 834-1900

(G-15370)
RELIABLE TOOL AND MACHINE INC
328 W 11th St (33404-7522)
PHONE....................561 844-8848
Charles Goforth, *President*
EMP: 5 **EST:** 1988
SQ FT: 1,900
SALES (est): 509K **Privately Held**
WEB: www.reliablema.com
SIC: 3599 Machine shop, jobbing & repair

(G-15371)
RENICK ENTERPRISES INC
1211 W 13th St (33404-6640)
PHONE....................561 863-4183
Mike Renick, *President*
Mary Ann Renick, *Corp Secy*
Jack Renick, *Vice Pres*
EMP: 8 **EST:** 1990
SQ FT: 6,300
SALES (est): 790.6K **Privately Held**
SIC: 3599 Machine shop, jobbing & repair

(G-15372)
RGF ENVIRONMENTAL GROUP INC
1101 W 13th St (33404-6701)
PHONE....................800 842-7771
Ronald G Fink, *CEO*
William Svec, *Vice Pres*
Brian Klaiber, *Purch Mgr*
Ray Piescik, *Senior Engr*
Tony Julian, *VP Bus Dvlpt*
▲ **EMP:** 177 **EST:** 1992
SQ FT: 30,000
SALES (est): 31MM **Privately Held**
WEB: www.rgf.com
SIC: 3564 3589 Purification & dust collection equipment; water purification equipment, household type

(G-15373)
RGF MARINE ENVMTL TECH INC
Also Called: Rgf Environmental
1101 W 13th St (33404-6701)
PHONE....................561 848-1826
Ronald G Fink, *President*
Bill Svec, *Vice Pres*
Brian Klaiber, *Purch Mgr*
Tony Julian, *VP Business*
Lisa Bailey, *Sales Mgr*
◆ **EMP:** 50 **EST:** 1992
SALES (est): 10.6MM **Privately Held**
WEB: www.rgf.com
SIC: 3589 Water treatment equipment, industrial

(G-15374)
RP HIGH PERFORMANCE INC
2391 President Barack Oba (33404-5456)
PHONE....................561 863-2800
Ian Grunes, *President*
EMP: 13 **EST:** 2013
SALES (est): 605.3K **Privately Held**
SIC: 3711 Automobile assembly, including specialty automobiles

(G-15375)
SC CABINET LLC
7655 Enterprise Dr (33404-3351)
PHONE....................561 429-5369
EMP: 6 **EST:** 2018
SALES (est): 59.1K **Privately Held**
SIC: 2434 Wood kitchen cabinets

(G-15376)
SECURITY IMPACT GL HLDINGS LLC
Also Called: Safe Glass
6555 Garden Rd Ste 1 (33404-6318)
PHONE....................561 844-3100
Arthur Marino, *Principal*
▲ **EMP:** 8 **EST:** 1998
SALES (est): 366K **Privately Held**
WEB: www.securityimpactglass.com
SIC: 2221 3231 Glass broadwoven fabrics; products of purchased glass

(G-15377)
SEMBCO STL ERECTION MET BLDG
3450 Dr Mrtn Lther King J (33404-6314)
PHONE....................561 863-0606
Wallace C Sease, *President*
Christie Green, *Corp Secy*
Gloria C Sease, *Vice Pres*
EMP: 10 **EST:** 1974
SALES (est): 817.2K **Privately Held**
WEB: www.elbengel.de
SIC: 3441 Fabricated structural metal

(G-15378)
SOLARTECH UNIVERSAL LLC
Also Called: Solar Tech Universal
1800 President Barack Oba (33404-5451)
PHONE....................561 440-8000
Francisco Cestero, *CFO*
Louis Koster, *Mng Member*
Scott Hoover, *Manager*
Jon James, *Technology*
Alex Edelman,
EMP: 46
SQ FT: 30,000
SALES (est): 2.2MM **Privately Held**
WEB: www.solartechuniversal.com
SIC: 3674 Solar cells

(G-15379)
STERLING INDUSTRY LLC
834 W 13th Ct (33404-6727)
PHONE....................561 845-2440
Arlene Brown, *General Mgr*
Thomas J Sterling Sr,
Aida Sterling,
EMP: 25
SALES (est): 4MM **Privately Held**
SIC: 3444 Sheet metalwork

(G-15380)
STERLING STL CSTM ALUM FBRCTON
837 W 13th St (33404-6702)
PHONE....................561 386-7166
Bryan S Bennett, *Principal*
EMP: 15 **EST:** 2014
SALES (est): 173.8K **Privately Held**
WEB: www.sscmetalfabrication.com
SIC: 3441 Fabricated structural metal

(G-15381)
STILLDRAGON NORTH AMERICA LLC
7788 Centl Indus Dr Ste 6 (33404-3450)
PHONE....................561 845-8009
Lawrence Taylor, *Manager*
Jeff Rasmussen, *Manager*
▲ **EMP:** 11 **EST:** 2012
SALES (est): 418.8K **Privately Held**
WEB: www.stilldragon.com
SIC: 2085 Distilled & blended liquors

(G-15382)
STRIDES PHARMA INC
3874 Fiscal Ct Ste 200 (33404-1785)
PHONE....................561 741-6500
Mel Earls, *Branch Mgr*
EMP: 70 **Privately Held**
WEB: www.strides.com
SIC: 2834 Pharmaceutical preparations
HQ: Strides Pharma, Inc.
2 Tower Center Blvd # 1102
East Brunswick NJ 08816
609 815-7671

(G-15383)
SUPERIOR WATERWAY SERVICES INC
6701 Garden Rd Ste 1 (33404-5900)
PHONE....................561 799-5852
Chris J York, *President*
Louis Palermo, *President*
EMP: 10 **EST:** 1999
SALES (est): 1.2MM **Privately Held**
WEB: www.superiorwaterway.com
SIC: 3589 Water treatment equipment, industrial

(G-15384)
TERA INDUSTRIES INC
Also Called: Industrial Technology
7634 Central Indus Dr (33404-3432)
PHONE....................561 848-7272
Steven Malone, *President*
Edward Suh, *Vice Pres*
EMP: 30
SQ FT: 25,000
SALES (est): 2.1MM **Privately Held**
SIC: 7692 3599 Welding repair; machine shop, jobbing & repair

(G-15385)
TOPLINE PRTG & GRAPHICS INC
Also Called: Print Pelican
1401 W 13th St Ste 104 (33404-6609)
PHONE....................561 881-2267
Alan G Morris, *President*
Grant Morris, *President*
▼ **EMP:** 39 **EST:** 1998
SALES (est): 2.6MM **Privately Held**
SIC: 2752 Commercial printing, offset

(G-15386)
TOTAL SIGN SOLUTIONS
7655 Enterprise Dr Ste A8 (33404-3339)
PHONE....................561 264-2551
EMP: 6 **EST:** 2018
SALES (est): 367.4K **Privately Held**
WEB: www.3ddynamicsolutions.com
SIC: 3993 Signs & advertising specialties

(G-15387)
UNITED ASSOCIATES GROUP INC
Also Called: Process Solutions
6701 Garden Rd Ste 1 (33404-5900)
PHONE....................561 840-0050
Howard Rosenkranz, *President*
◆ **EMP:** 18 **EST:** 1991
SQ FT: 20,000
SALES (est): 1.3MM **Privately Held**
SIC: 3552 Textile machinery

(G-15388)
US COMPOSITES
6670 White Dr (33407-1232)
PHONE....................561 588-1001
Mark Ananos, *Principal*
▼ **EMP:** 5 **EST:** 2012
SALES (est): 785.8K **Privately Held**
WEB: www.uscomposites.com
SIC: 2821 Plastics materials & resins

(G-15389)
WEST PALM MACHINING & WELDING
4650 Dyer Blvd (33407-1027)
PHONE....................561 841-2725
Magnolia Mendieta, *CEO*
Steven Mendieta, *General Mgr*
Jose H Mendieta, *Vice Pres*
EMP: 7 **EST:** 2004
SALES (est): 750K **Privately Held**
WEB: www.wpmachine.net
SIC: 3599 7692 Machine shop, jobbing & repair; welding repair

Rockledge
Brevard County

(G-15390)
AAR GOVERNMENT SERVICES INC
Also Called: AAR Wass
Aar Way Ste 101 (32955)
PHONE....................321 361-3461
EMP: 21
SALES (corp-wide): 1.6B **Publicly Held**
WEB: www.aarcorp.com
SIC: 3728 Aircraft parts & equipment
HQ: Aar Government Services, Inc.
1100 N Wood Dale Rd
Wood Dale IL 60191
630 227-2000

(G-15391)
ACCURATE METAL FINSHG FLA INC (PA)
Also Called: Accurate Metal Finishing Fla
500 Gus Hipp Blvd (32955-4803)
PHONE..................................321 636-4900
EMP: 11
SALES (est): 2.6MM **Privately Held**
SIC: 3399 3471 Primary Metal Products, Nsk

(G-15392)
ACCURATE METAL FINSHG FLA INC
500 Gus Hipp Blvd (32955-4803)
PHONE..................................321 636-4900
Norm Lindner, *President*
Norman Lindner, *President*
EMP: 10 **EST:** 1988
SALES (est): 1.2MM **Privately Held**
SIC: 3471 Finishing, metals or formed products

(G-15393)
ADVANCE SOLDER TECHNOLOGY INC
Also Called: Astec
315 Gus Hipp Blvd (32955-4806)
PHONE..................................321 633-4777
Mike Carey, *Principal*
EMP: 11 **EST:** 2015
SALES (est): 1.2MM **Privately Held**
SIC: 3699 Electrical equipment & supplies

(G-15394)
BERRY SIGNS INC
1740 Huntington Ln (32955-3140)
PHONE..................................321 631-6150
Dennis Berry, *President*
Kyle Berry, *Opers Mgr*
EMP: 5 **EST:** 1978
SQ FT: 10,000
SALES (est): 523.7K **Privately Held**
WEB: www.berrysigns.com
SIC: 3993 Electric signs; neon signs

(G-15395)
BREVARD ACHIEVEMENT CENTER INC
1845 Cogswell St (32955-3210)
PHONE..................................321 632-8610
Angie Hoffman, *COO*
Josephine Jo Hughes, *Vice Pres*
Susan McGrath, *Vice Pres*
Andy Vega, *Vice Pres*
Sean Miller, *Project Mgr*
EMP: 470 **EST:** 1969
SQ FT: 35,000
SALES: 31.9MM **Privately Held**
WEB: www.bacbrevard.com
SIC: 3999 8331 8211 Advertising display products; vocational rehabilitation agency; public elementary & secondary schools

(G-15396)
BRYSON OF BREVARD INC
Also Called: Kendal Signs
580 Gus Hipp Blvd (32955-4803)
PHONE..................................321 636-5116
Kendal Mullen, *President*
Sylvia Mulllen, *Vice Pres*
Paul Bender, *Production*
Denise Berg, *Sales Staff*
David Clanton, *Manager*
EMP: 26 **EST:** 1996
SQ FT: 15,000
SALES (est): 4MM **Privately Held**
SIC: 3993 Electric signs

(G-15397)
CABINET DESIGNS OF CENTRAL FLA
596 International Pl (32955-4200)
PHONE..................................321 636-1101
Dan Scott, *President*
Derek Whitten, *Vice Pres*
Sherry Scott, *Treasurer*
EMP: 7 **EST:** 1982
SQ FT: 5,500
SALES (est): 783.9K **Privately Held**
WEB: www.cabinetdesignscfl.com
SIC: 2434 Wood kitchen cabinets

(G-15398)
CARLEY NIGEL HOLDINGS LLC ✪
1041 Cascade Cir Apt 103 (32955-8079)
PHONE..................................407 212-9341
Nigel Carley, *President*
EMP: 10 **EST:** 2021
SALES (est): 950K **Privately Held**
SIC: 2599 Food wagons, restaurant

(G-15399)
CRANCO INDUSTRIES INC
Also Called: Bella Slata Spclty Drssngs Sce
1710 Baldwin St (32955-3205)
PHONE..................................321 690-2695
Ed Cranisky, *President*
Maryalice Kammerer, *Admin Asst*
EMP: 5 **EST:** 1992
SQ FT: 4,000
SALES (est): 498.1K **Privately Held**
WEB: www.crancofoods.com
SIC: 2099 Dressings, salad: dry mixes

(G-15400)
DELTA GROUP ELECTRONICS INC
Also Called: Delta Group Elec Inc Fla
395 Gus Hipp Blvd (32955-4806)
PHONE..................................321 631-0799
Ron Reef, *General Mgr*
George Perez, *Marketing Staff*
Robert Nation, *Supervisor*
EMP: 75
SQ FT: 34,778
SALES (corp-wide): 103.6MM **Privately Held**
WEB: www.deltagroupinc.com
SIC: 3679 3672 Electronic circuits; printed circuit boards
PA: Delta Group Electronics, Inc.
4521a Osuna Rd Ne
Albuquerque NM 87109
505 883-7674

(G-15401)
DESAPRO INC
435 Gus Hipp Blvd (32955-4804)
PHONE..................................321 674-6804
Dominique E Schinabeck, *President*
Connie Kahler, *Controller*
Veronica Long, *Assistant*
EMP: 39 **EST:** 2015
SALES (est): 4.4MM **Privately Held**
WEB: www.desapro.com
SIC: 3499 Boxes for packing & shipping, metal

(G-15402)
DESIGNERS CHOICE CABINETRY
285 Barnes Blvd (32955-5325)
PHONE..................................321 632-0772
Celeste Zotto, *CFO*
Chris Bancroft, *Analyst*
EMP: 16 **EST:** 2018
SALES (est): 3.7MM **Privately Held**
WEB: www.dccabinetry.com
SIC: 2434 Wood kitchen cabinets

(G-15403)
DESIGNERS CHOICE CABINETRY INC (DH)
Also Called: Designer's Choice Cabinetry
100 Tgk Cir (32955-3605)
PHONE..................................321 632-0772
James T Murfin, *CEO*
Celeste Zotto, *CFO*
Tammie Kovach, *Manager*
William Batten, *Technology*
◆ **EMP:** 2 **EST:** 1988
SQ FT: 91,000
SALES (est): 18.3MM
SALES (corp-wide): 591.9MM **Privately Held**
WEB: www.dccabinetry.com
SIC: 2434 Wood kitchen cabinets
HQ: Essential Cabinetry Holdings, Inc.
2838 Grandview Dr
Simpsonville SC 29680
321 632-0772

(G-15404)
DG DESIGN AND PRINT CO LLC
4290 Us Highway 1 Ste A (32955-5317)
PHONE..................................321 446-6435
Daniel Rensing, *Principal*
EMP: 9 **EST:** 2013
SALES (est): 201.4K **Privately Held**
WEB: www.dgdesignandprint.com
SIC: 2752 Commercial printing, lithographic

(G-15405)
DRB PACKAGING LLC
386 Commerce Pkwy (32955-4208)
PHONE..................................321 877-2802
Aryeh Roberts, *CEO*
Craig Day, *President*
Glenn Merithew, *Sales Staff*
Melissa Driggers, *Office Mgr*
EMP: 7 **EST:** 2015
SQ FT: 18,000
SALES (est): 1.2MM **Privately Held**
WEB: www.drbpkg.com
SIC: 3086 Packaging & shipping materials, foamed plastic

(G-15406)
DRB PACKAGING LLC
386 Commerce Pkwy (32955-4208)
PHONE..................................321 877-2802
EMP: 7 **EST:** 2015
SQ FT: 18,490
SALES (est): 417.2K **Privately Held**
SIC: 3086 Mfg Plastic Foam Products

(G-15407)
EAST COAST CABINET CO
100 Eyster Blvd (32955-3606)
PHONE..................................321 392-4686
Billy Pentz, *Owner*
EMP: 8 **EST:** 2005
SALES (est): 1.1MM **Privately Held**
WEB: www.pullmanwest.com
SIC: 2434 Wood kitchen cabinets

(G-15408)
EAST COAST FOAM SUPPLY INC
392 Richard Rd (32955-3183)
PHONE..................................321 433-8231
Joe Lento, *President*
Wendy Zapata-Lento, *Vice Pres*
Wendy Lento, *Executive*
EMP: 9 **EST:** 2006
SALES (est): 1MM **Privately Held**
WEB: www.eastcoastfoamsupply.com
SIC: 3086 Plastics foam products

(G-15409)
ENTECH ONSITE SERVICES LLC
280 Gus Hipp Blvd (32955-4801)
PHONE..................................407 956-8980
John P Marhoefer, *Mng Member*
Anne Herzog,
EMP: 5 **EST:** 2001
SQ FT: 50,000
SALES (est): 478.2K **Privately Held**
WEB: www.entechinnovative.com
SIC: 3599 8711 Carnival machines & equipment, amusement park; engineering services

(G-15410)
EXQUISITE WOOD WORKS BY AL
5565 Schenck Ave Ste 5 (32955-5812)
PHONE..................................321 634-5398
Alvaro Orozco, *Owner*
EMP: 6 **EST:** 2004
SALES (est): 173.6K **Privately Held**
WEB: www.exquisitewoodworks.blogspot.com
SIC: 2431 Millwork

(G-15411)
FAAC INTERNATIONAL INC (DH)
3160 Murrell Rd (32955-4432)
PHONE..................................904 448-8952
Andrea Marcellan, *CEO*
Dan Ollar, *Corp Secy*
Dawn Joanne Kaiser, *Controller*
Kris Tate,
Susan Withrow,
◆ **EMP:** 6 **EST:** 1986
SQ FT: 7,000
SALES (est): 10MM
SALES (corp-wide): 7.3MM **Privately Held**
WEB: www.faacusa.com
SIC: 3625 Motor controls, electric
HQ: Faac Partecipazioni Industriali Srl
Via Monaldo Calari 10
Zola Predosa BO 40069
051 758-518

(G-15412)
FOS LED LIGHTING SOLUTION
5595 Schenck Ave Ste 2ro (32955-5815)
PHONE..................................321 208-8174
EMP: 6 **EST:** 2018
SALES (est): 310.1K **Privately Held**
WEB: www.fos-led.com
SIC: 3648 Lighting equipment

(G-15413)
GAR BUSINESS GROUP LLC
Also Called: Jr Boarts Packaging
386 Commerce Pkwy (32955-4208)
PHONE..................................321 632-5133
Yehuda Roberts,
EMP: 5 **EST:** 2009
SQ FT: 5,000
SALES (est): 468.3K **Privately Held**
SIC: 2653 Corrugated & solid fiber boxes

(G-15414)
GLASSER BOAT WORKS INC
1670 Barrett Dr (32955-3116)
PHONE..................................321 626-0061
Jonathan Glasser, *Principal*
EMP: 6 **EST:** 2016
SALES (est): 296.3K **Privately Held**
WEB: www.glasserboats.net
SIC: 3732 Boat building & repairing

(G-15415)
GOOD 4 TKLC INC
Also Called: Wwgso
5020 Nova Ave (32955-5515)
PHONE..................................321 632-4340
Christopher Brunais, *Vice Pres*
EMP: 7 **EST:** 2005
SQ FT: 1,829
SALES (est): 630.6K **Privately Held**
SIC: 2851 Paints, asphalt or bituminous

(G-15416)
HELICAL COMMUNICATION TECH INC
634 Barnes Blvd Ste 206 (32955-5217)
PHONE..................................561 762-2823
Salvatore Bologna, *CEO*
EMP: 6 **EST:** 2013
SQ FT: 1,400
SALES (est): 686.5K **Privately Held**
WEB: www.helicomtech.com
SIC: 3663 Antennas, transmitting & communications

(G-15417)
HITMAN INDUSTRIES LLC
185 Gus Hipp Blvd (32955-4702)
PHONE..................................321 735-8562
Walter M Falscroft, *Mng Member*
EMP: 14 **EST:** 2016
SALES (est): 3.3MM **Privately Held**
WEB: www.hitmanindustries.net
SIC: 3484 Guns (firearms) or gun parts, 30 mm. & below

(G-15418)
HMB STEEL CORPORATION
4080 Pines Industrial Ave (32955-5323)
PHONE..................................321 636-6511
Forrest F Brewton, *CEO*
Denise McCammon, *President*
Grant McCammon, *COO*
Dina Brewton, *Vice Pres*
Richard Davenport, *Manager*
EMP: 17 **EST:** 1998
SQ FT: 29,150
SALES (est): 4.7MM **Privately Held**
WEB: www.hmbsteel.com
SIC: 3441 Building components, structural steel

(G-15419)
HURRICANE SHTTERS CNTL FLA INC
3460 Us Highway 1 (32955-4928)
PHONE..................................321 639-2622
Frank M Herrera, *Principal*
EMP: 7 **EST:** 2011
SALES (est): 265.3K **Privately Held**
WEB: www.allguardstormshutters.com
SIC: 2431 Door shutters, wood

(G-15420)
HYDRO PRECISION TUBING USA LLC (DH)
Also Called: Sapa Prcsion Tbing Rckldge LLC
100 Gus Hipp Blvd (32955-4701)
PHONE..................................321 636-8147
Sergio Luiz Vendrasco, *President*
Chalonda Gilmore, *Production*
Lisa Douberly, *Treasurer*
Caroline Henrich, *Admin Sec*
◆ **EMP:** 184 **EST:** 1979
SQ FT: 165,000
SALES (est): 84.3MM
SALES (corp-wide): 16.1B **Privately Held**
SIC: 3354 3316 Shapes, extruded aluminum; cold finishing of steel shapes

(G-15421)
HYPERFORM INC (HQ)
Also Called: Seadek
5440 Schenck Ave (32955-5803)
PHONE..................................321 632-6503
Kurt D Wilson, *President*
Tiffany Chancey, *General Mgr*
Serenity Gardner, *COO*
Jason Gardner, *Vice Pres*
James C Wilson, *Vice Pres*
◆ **EMP:** 23 **EST:** 1982
SQ FT: 4,800
SALES (est): 10.9MM
SALES (corp-wide): 2.4B **Publicly Held**
WEB: www.hyperforminc.com
SIC: 3949 Surfboards; windsurfing boards (sailboards) & equipment
PA: Patrick Industries, Inc.
107 W Franklin St
Elkhart IN 46516
574 294-7511

(G-15422)
INTERFACE TECHNOLOGY GROUP INC
2107 Us Highway 1 (32955-3726)
PHONE..................................321 433-1165
Cathy Weber, *President*
Mark Weber, *Treasurer*
Mark J Weber, *Treasurer*
EMP: 6 **EST:** 1987
SQ FT: 5,000
SALES (est): 996.5K **Privately Held**
WEB: www.interfacetechnologygroup.com
SIC: 3663 8711 Radio & TV communications equipment; engineering services

(G-15423)
IRMS INC
2191 Rockledge Dr (32955-5401)
PHONE..................................321 631-1161
Clairece M Knuutila, *President*
Alisa Smith, *Accountant*
Jeananne Estrella, *Finance*
Melissa Milito, *Client Mgr*
Yosdany Perez, *Sales Staff*
EMP: 10 **EST:** 1997
SALES (est): 850K **Privately Held**
WEB: www.irmsinc.com
SIC: 3523 3563 Spreaders, fertilizer; spraying & dusting equipment

(G-15424)
JP DONVAN PRCSION MCHINING LLC
201 Paint St (32955-5802)
PHONE..................................321 383-1171
John Donovan, *President*
EMP: 8 **EST:** 2017
SALES (est): 481.1K **Privately Held**
WEB: www.jpdonovan.com
SIC: 3499 Machine bases, metal

(G-15425)
JW PERFORMANCE TRANSM INC
1826 Baldwin St (32955-3207)
PHONE..................................321 632-6205
John Winters Sr, *President*
Helen Winters, *Vice Pres*
John Winters Jr, *Treasurer*
Tracy Winters, *Admin Sec*
▲ **EMP:** 28 **EST:** 1976
SQ FT: 40,000
SALES (est): 4.5MM **Privately Held**
WEB: www.racewithjw.com
SIC: 3714 3568 3566 Transmissions, motor vehicle; power transmission equipment; speed changers, drives & gears

(G-15426)
K-KRAFT CABINETS INC
1751 Cogswell St (32955-3208)
PHONE..................................321 632-8800
Robert Poloski, *President*
Susan Poloski, *Corp Secy*
EMP: 9 **EST:** 1990
SQ FT: 15,000
SALES (est): 1.2MM **Privately Held**
WEB: www.kkraftcabinets.com
SIC: 2434 Wood kitchen cabinets

(G-15427)
K-KRAFT INDUSTRIES INC
1751 Cogswell St (32955-3208)
PHONE..................................321 632-8800
Robert Poloski Jr, *President*
Susan Poloski, *Corp Secy*
EMP: 10 **EST:** 1972
SQ FT: 3,500
SALES (est): 370.6K **Privately Held**
WEB: www.kkraftcabinets.com
SIC: 2434 Wood kitchen cabinets

(G-15428)
KENDAL SIGNS INC
580 Gus Hipp Blvd (32955-4803)
PHONE..................................321 636-5116
Kendal Mullen, *Principal*
EMP: 45 **EST:** 2016
SALES (est): 3.4MM **Privately Held**
WEB: www.kendalsigns.com
SIC: 3993 Signs & advertising specialties

(G-15429)
LRG SOLUTIONS INC
1950 Murrell Rd Ste 3 (32955-3607)
PHONE..................................321 978-1050
Andrew M Lash, *Principal*
EMP: 10 **EST:** 2017
SALES (est): 516.6K **Privately Held**
WEB: www.lrgsolutions.com
SIC: 3272 Concrete products

(G-15430)
LRM INDUSTRIES INTL INC
Also Called: L R M
135 Gus Hipp Blvd (32955-4702)
PHONE..................................321 635-9797
E Gary Cook, *Ch of Bd*
Jim Callough, *President*
Christine Nowak, *CFO*
EMP: 20 **EST:** 2009
SALES (est): 4MM **Privately Held**
WEB: www.lrmind.com
SIC: 2821 8711 Polyesters; engineering services

(G-15431)
MAGNETIC AUTOMATION CORP
3160 Murrell Rd (32955-4432)
PHONE..................................321 635-8585
Dieter Schwald, *CEO*
Thomas Braunwalder, *President*
Bruce Pate, *Vice Pres*
Hubert Giesbertz, *Treasurer*
Jean K Wortham, *Admin Sec*
◆ **EMP:** 37 **EST:** 1990
SQ FT: 31,004
SALES (est): 5.7MM **Privately Held**
WEB: www.macgolfcharity.com
SIC: 3829 7521 Measuring & controlling devices; parking structure

(G-15432)
MAINSTREAM ENGINEERING CORP
200 Yellow Pl (32955-5327)
PHONE..................................321 631-3550
Robert Scaringe, *President*
Melissa Horstmann, *Production*
Rick Dashnaw, *Purch Mgr*
Anthony Nistico, *Purch Mgr*
Ebere Onuoha, *Purch Mgr*
EMP: 24 **EST:** 1986
SQ FT: 41,900
SALES (est): 13.6MM **Privately Held**
WEB: www.mainstream-engr.com
SIC: 3585 Refrigeration equipment, complete

(G-15433)
MANCHESTER COPPER TUBE LLC
435 Gus Hipp Blvd (32955-4804)
PHONE..................................321 636-1477
James A Lash,
EMP: 18 **EST:** 2005
SQ FT: 37,500
SALES (est): 575.6K **Privately Held**
SIC: 3351 Copper & copper alloy pipe & tube

(G-15434)
MARCONI LINE INC
1870 Huntington Ln (32955-3156)
PHONE..................................321 639-1130
Francis Eades, *President*
Ernest Marconi, *Vice Pres*
Mark Marconi, *Vice Pres*
James Eades, *Treasurer*
Peter Raffaele, *Admin Sec*
EMP: 16 **EST:** 1988
SALES (est): 1MM **Privately Held**
WEB: www.marconiline.com
SIC: 3089 3949 Closures, plastic; bowl covers, plastic; sporting & athletic goods

(G-15435)
MATRIX COMPOSITES INC
275 Barnes Blvd (32955-5325)
PHONE..................................321 633-4480
Farrokh Batliwala, *President*
Michael J Savinelli, *Vice Pres*
Tim Murphy, *QC Mgr*
Richard Hineline, *CFO*
Ken Swarner, *Marketing Staff*
EMP: 106 **EST:** 1993
SQ FT: 30,000
SALES (est): 24.5MM
SALES (corp-wide): 2.4B **Publicly Held**
WEB: www.matrixcomp.com
SIC: 2821 Plastics materials & resins
PA: Itt Inc.
1133 Westchester Ave N-100
White Plains NY 10604
914 641-2000

(G-15436)
METAL ROOF FACTORY INC
599 Gus Hipp Blvd (32955-4810)
PHONE..................................321 632-8300
Thomas E Bruckner, *President*
EMP: 9 **EST:** 1983
SQ FT: 10,000
SALES (est): 1.7MM **Privately Held**
WEB: www.metalrooffactory.com
SIC: 3444 Metal roofing & roof drainage equipment; roof deck, sheet metal

(G-15437)
NAROH MANUFACTURING LLC
185 Gus Hipp Blvd (32955-4702)
PHONE..................................321 806-4875
Robert Horan, *President*
EMP: 10 **EST:** 2012
SALES (est): 727.8K **Privately Held**
SIC: 3484 Guns (firearms) or gun parts, 30 mm. & below

(G-15438)
NETWORKED SOLUTIONS INC
Also Called: Essentialnet Solutions
7145 Turner Rd Ste 102 (32955-5723)
PHONE..................................321 259-3242
John Redrup, *President*
EMP: 6 **EST:** 1997
SQ FT: 2,500
SALES (est): 1MM **Privately Held**
SIC: 7372 7374 Prepackaged software; computer graphics service

(G-15439)
PERRY FIBERGLAS PRODUCTS INC
5415 Village Dr (32955-6570)
PHONE..................................321 609-9036
Thomas E Pulliam, *President*
Richard G Chesrown, *Principal*
Drew H Severs, *Principal*
Michelle Hardway, *HR Admin*
Tom Pulliam, *Sales Executive*
▲ **EMP:** 20 **EST:** 1984
SQ FT: 34,000
SALES (est): 5.6MM **Privately Held**
WEB: www.perryfiberglass.com
SIC: 3089 Plastic containers, except foam

(G-15440)
PHANTOM PRODUCTS INC
474 Barnes Blvd (32955-5321)
PHONE..................................321 690-6729
Damien McDermott, *President*
Christy Morgan, *Office Mgr*
EMP: 15 **EST:** 2004
SQ FT: 45,000
SALES (est): 5.9MM **Privately Held**
WEB: www.phantomlights.com
SIC: 3647 Vehicular lighting equipment

(G-15441)
PRECISION CIRCUITS INC
Also Called: PCI
550 Gus Hipp Blvd (32955-4821)
PHONE..................................321 632-8629
EMP: 20
SQ FT: 5,000
SALES (est): 3.4MM **Privately Held**
SIC: 3672 Mfg Printed Circuit Boards

(G-15442)
R & D SURF
488 Gus Hipp Blvd (32955-4800)
P.O. Box 372811, Satellite Beach (32937-0811)
PHONE..................................321 636-4456
Richard P Carroll, *President*
Marc Baker, *Manager*
▼ **EMP:** 10 **EST:** 1992
SQ FT: 4,800
SALES (est): 609.5K **Privately Held**
WEB: www.randdsurf.com
SIC: 3949 Surfboards

(G-15443)
RICHARDS PAINT MFG CO INC (PA)
200 Paint St (32955-5899)
PHONE..................................321 636-6200
Edward J Richard Sr, *President*
Eric S Richard, *President*
Ruth Richard, *Corp Secy*
Tom Griffey, *Vice Pres*
Pati Lambert, *Vice Pres*
▼ **EMP:** 60
SQ FT: 40,000
SALES (est): 18.8MM **Privately Held**
WEB: www.richardspaint.com
SIC: 2851 5231 Paints & paint additives; paint

(G-15444)
ROCKLEDGE PHRM MFG LLC
Also Called: RPM
417 Richard Rd (32955-3154)
PHONE..................................321 636-0717
Kl Spear, *Mng Member*
Lorri Renaud,
EMP: 17 **EST:** 1984
SQ FT: 30,000
SALES (est): 700K **Privately Held**
WEB: www.rpmrx.com
SIC: 2834 Proprietary drug products
PA: Spear Pharmaceuticals, Inc.
1250 Sussex Tpke Ste G
Naples FL 34110

(G-15445)
SAFE INDUSTRIES INC
396 Gus Hipp Blvd Ste B (32955-4814)
PHONE..................................321 639-8646
Joanne Abernathy, *Principal*
Tonya McCullough, *Manager*
Todd Hecker, *Director*

▲ = Import ▼=Export
◆ =Import/Export

Meredith Martin, *Director*
Chase Cummins, *Admin Sec*
EMP: 10 **EST:** 2009
SALES (est): 2.1MM **Privately Held**
SIC: 2869 Fuels

(G-15446)
SAPA PRCSION TUBING ADRIAN INC
100 Gus Hipp Blvd (32955-4701)
PHONE..................................321 636-8147
Greg Hall, *President*
Jim Vaughan, *Production*
Mike Henderson, *Purchasing*
Kristina Chin, *Engineer*
Bonnie Hughes, *Human Res Mgr*
▲ **EMP:** 39 **EST:** 1924
SQ FT: 180,000
SALES (est): 3.8MM **Privately Held**
SIC: 3354 3463 Aluminum extruded products; aluminum forgings

(G-15447)
SOLTEC ELECTRONICS LLC
1001 Pelican Ln (32955-6409)
PHONE..................................321 288-5689
Dawn Gluskin,
EMP: 5 **EST:** 2008
SALES (est): 2.6MM **Privately Held**
WEB: www.soltecelectronics.com
SIC: 3679 Electronic circuits

(G-15448)
SOLUTIONS MANUFACTURING INC
570 Haverty Ct (32955-3600)
PHONE..................................321 848-0848
Patrick McDonough, *CEO*
Roger A Dixson, *President*
Luis Govantes, *General Mgr*
Tina Nash, *General Mgr*
Faldu Neel, *General Mgr*
▲ **EMP:** 65
SALES (est): 13.2MM **Privately Held**
WEB: www.solutionsmfg.com
SIC: 3672 Printed circuit boards

(G-15449)
SPACE COAST HYDRAULICS INC
1265 Us Highway 1 (32955-2711)
PHONE..................................321 504-6006
Daniel Ferretti, *President*
Karin Ferretti, *Vice Pres*
EMP: 13 **EST:** 2016
SALES (est): 1.1MM **Privately Held**
WEB: www.pirtekusa.com
SIC: 3531 3492 3599 3052 Construction machinery; hose & tube fittings & assemblies, hydraulic/pneumatic; hose, flexible metallic; hose, pneumatic: rubber or rubberized fabric; pistons & valves

(G-15450)
T AND C SALES INC
1950 Murrell Rd Ste 10 (32955-3607)
PHONE..................................321 632-0920
Robert C Cook, *President*
Sara Cook, *Treasurer*
EMP: 6 **EST:** 1978
SQ FT: 7,500
SALES (est): 3MM **Privately Held**
WEB: www.tcsalesinc.com
SIC: 3354 Aluminum extruded products

(G-15451)
TECHNICO OF CENTRAL FLORIDA
1950 Murrell Rd (32955-3618)
PHONE..................................321 631-4414
James Pennington, *Principal*
EMP: 6 **EST:** 2008
SALES (est): 158K **Privately Held**
SIC: 3625 Control equipment, electric

(G-15452)
TECVALCO USA INC
270 Barnes Blvd (32955-5319)
PHONE..................................866 427-3444
Michael Menger, *President*
EMP: 48 **EST:** 2015
SQ FT: 70,000
SALES (est): 6.4MM **Privately Held**
WEB: www.tecvalco.com
SIC: 3533 Oil & gas field machinery

(G-15453)
TEP MANUFACTURING CO
1950 Murrell Rd Ste 5 (32955-3607)
PHONE..................................321 632-1417
Ted Chrostowski, *Owner*
EMP: 5 **EST:** 1988
SALES (est): 372.7K **Privately Held**
SIC: 3599 Machine & other job shop work

(G-15454)
TRESE INC
Also Called: Trese Printing
2040 Murrell Rd (32955-3603)
PHONE..................................321 632-7272
Michael J F Trese, *President*
Rick Francis, *General Mgr*
EMP: 16 **EST:** 1978
SQ FT: 25,000
SALES (est): 1MM **Privately Held**
WEB: www.allegramarketingprint.com
SIC: 2752 Commercial printing, offset

(G-15455)
V AND N ADVANCED AUTO SYS LLC
415 Gus Hipp Blvd (32955-4804)
PHONE..................................321 504-6440
Tito C Visi, *President*
Philip A Napolitano, *Vice Pres*
Jason Gass, *Engineer*
◆ **EMP:** 8 **EST:** 2004
SQ FT: 20,000
SALES (est): 3MM **Privately Held**
WEB: www.vnaas.com
SIC: 3479 5065 8742 3724 Coating of metals & formed products; semiconductor devices; automation & robotics consultant; research & development on aircraft engines & parts

(G-15456)
WAGNER PAVERS CONTRACTOR
403 Hawk St Ste A (32955-3251)
PHONE..................................321 633-5131
Wagner Dutra, *President*
EMP: 6 **EST:** 2001
SQ FT: 3,424
SALES (est): 988.7K **Privately Held**
WEB: www.wagnerpavers.com
SIC: 3531 Pavers

(G-15457)
WHOLESALE SIGN SUPERSTORE INC
580 Gus Hipp Blvd (32955-4803)
PHONE..................................321 212-8458
EMP: 11 **EST:** 2019
SALES (est): 630.1K **Privately Held**
WEB: www.wholesalesignsuperstore.com
SIC: 3993 Signs & advertising specialties

Rocky Point
Hillsborough County

(G-15458)
ALL FLORIDA MARKETING
3001 N Rocky Point Dr E (33607-5810)
PHONE..................................813 281-4641
Jim Lee, *President*
EMP: 5 **EST:** 1998
SALES (est): 403.8K **Privately Held**
SIC: 2851 Paints & allied products

Roseland
Indian River County

(G-15459)
GYPSY MINING INC
Also Called: Cmk
12855 79th Ave (32957)
P.O. Box 144 (32957-0144)
PHONE..................................772 589-5547
Christopher M Kirrie, *President*
Robert C Kirrie, *Vice Pres*
EMP: 8 **EST:** 1982
SQ FT: 4,700
SALES (est): 750K **Privately Held**
SIC: 3369 3949 Lead castings, except die-castings; fishing tackle, general; skin diving equipment, scuba type

Rotonda West
Charlotte County

(G-15460)
US FUELS INC
928 Rotonda Cir (33947-1838)
PHONE..................................254 559-1212
David Jakobot, *Principal*
EMP: 11 **EST:** 2009
SALES (est): 618.3K **Privately Held**
SIC: 2869 Fuels

Royal Palm Beach
Palm Beach County

(G-15461)
ATELIER WOODWORKING
587 105th Ave N Unit 28 (33411-4333)
PHONE..................................561 386-0811
Alex Cosiuck, *President*
Simona Costiuc, *Officer*
EMP: 10 **EST:** 1992
SALES (est): 292.8K **Privately Held**
SIC: 2431 Millwork

(G-15462)
BON BRANDS INC ✪
10299 Sthrn Blvd Unit 21 (33411-4337)
PHONE..................................800 590-7911
Jason Russo, *Owner*
EMP: 15 **EST:** 2020
SALES (est): 666.2K **Privately Held**
SIC: 2841 5122 5169 Soap & other detergents; drugs, proprietaries & sundries; chemicals & allied products

(G-15463)
CORRELL SERVICES INC
260 Crestwood Cir Apt 106 (33411-4965)
PHONE..................................561 358-6952
Robert L Correll Jr, *President*
EMP: 6 **EST:** 2001
SALES (est): 105.4K **Privately Held**
WEB: www.correllservices.com
SIC: 3944 Games, toys & children's vehicles

(G-15464)
CXR STRATEGIES LLC
Also Called: Keratin Salon Direct
1128 Ryal Palm Bch Blvd (33411-1607)
PHONE..................................516 998-0400
Terri M Wescott,
EMP: 7 **EST:** 2018
SALES (est): 79.3K **Privately Held**
SIC: 2844 Hair preparations, including shampoos

(G-15465)
DAKIM INC
Also Called: Print It Plus
11420 Okeechobee Blvd D (33411-8703)
PHONE..................................561 790-0884
Kimberly Leland, *CEO*
David T Leland, *President*
Kimberly H Leland, *Vice Pres*
Sarah Cole, *Prdtn Mgr*
Mary Miller, *Manager*
EMP: 11 **EST:** 1988
SQ FT: 2,480
SALES (est): 1.8MM **Privately Held**
SIC: 3571 2752 1799 3993 Computers, digital, analog or hybrid; commercial printing, offset; sign installation & maintenance; signs & advertising specialties; art copy: publishing & printing; posters: publishing & printing; banners, flags, decals & posters

(G-15466)
ESCUE ENERGY LLC
11903 Southern Blvd (33411-7644)
PHONE..................................561 762-1486
Sohail Quraeshi, *President*
EMP: 7 **EST:** 2015
SALES (est): 157.9K **Privately Held**
SIC: 3511 Turbines & turbine generator sets

(G-15467)
FROYOLICIOUS INC
11081 Sthrn Blvd Ste 110 (33411-4252)
PHONE..................................561 753-4890
CU Hoang, *Principal*
EMP: 5 **EST:** 2010
SALES (est): 369.2K **Privately Held**
WEB: www.myfroyolicious.com
SIC: 2026 Yogurt

(G-15468)
FUELTEC SYSTEMS LLC
11388 Okeechobee Blvd (33411-8705)
PHONE..................................828 212-1141
EMP: 8 **EST:** 2019
SALES (est): 1.1MM **Privately Held**
WEB: www.fueltecsystems.com
SIC: 3559 Special industry machinery

(G-15469)
HEAL AND SHINE INC
11648 Orange Grove Blvd (33411-9133)
PHONE..................................561 801-3423
Lisa Bongers, *Principal*
EMP: 8 **EST:** 2017
SALES (est): 274.9K **Privately Held**
WEB: www.healandshine.com
SIC: 2048 Mineral feed supplements

(G-15470)
HORIZON INDUSTRIES INC
180 Business Park Way B1 (33411-1726)
P.O. Box 212951 (33421-2951)
PHONE..................................561 315-5439
Julianna L Tristano, *President*
Josie Perez, *Manager*
Jason Rosenberg, *IT/INT Sup*
EMP: 10 **EST:** 2011
SALES (est): 853.3K **Privately Held**
WEB: www.horizonindustriesinc.com
SIC: 3999 Atomizers, toiletry

(G-15471)
IMPRINTS INTERNATIONAL INC
150 Businefl Pk Way Ste 2 (33411)
PHONE..................................561 202-0105
Amit Jain, *President*
EMP: 5 **EST:** 2004
SALES (est): 630K **Privately Held**
SIC: 3552 Silk screens for textile industry

(G-15472)
J-KO COMPANY
200 Business Park Way D (33411-1742)
PHONE..................................561 795-7377
Jon Kolquist, *Owner*
EMP: 7 **EST:** 2012
SALES (est): 657.4K **Privately Held**
WEB: www.j-kocompany.com
SIC: 3589 Car washing machinery

(G-15473)
KIKINAZ SCREEN PRINTING INC
336 Sandpiper Ave (33411-2942)
PHONE..................................561 512-3134
Roberto Crucet, *President*
EMP: 6
SALES (est): 95K **Privately Held**
WEB: www.kikinaz.com
SIC: 2752 7389 7336 Commercial printing, lithographic; embroidering of advertising on shirts, etc.; graphic arts & related design

(G-15474)
LANDTECH DATA CORPORATION
Also Called: Landtech Software Co.
1460 Royal Palm Bch Blvd (33411-1608)
PHONE..................................561 790-1265
Edward W Bell, *President*
Wya Bell, *Human Res Mgr*
EMP: 15 **EST:** 1979
SQ FT: 3,500
SALES (est): 2MM **Privately Held**
WEB: www.landtechdata.com
SIC: 7372 7371 Prepackaged software; custom computer programming services

GEOGRAPHIC

(G-15475)
MOLDED MOMENTS ART
1477 Running Oak Ln (33411-6153)
PHONE......................................954 913-0793
Molded Moments, *Principal*
EMP: 6 **EST:** 2012
SALES (est): 107.7K **Privately Held**
SIC: 3089 Molding primary plastic

(G-15476)
NILSSON NILS
Also Called: Advanced Elctronic Diagnostics
1128 Royal Palm Bch (33411-1607)
PHONE......................................561 790-2400
Nils Nilsson, *President*
EMP: 5 **EST:** 1989
SALES (est): 730.5K **Privately Held**
WEB: www.aedhealth.com
SIC: 2835 In vitro & in vivo diagnostic substances

(G-15477)
ROBERT OJEDA METALSMITH INC
10151 Yeoman Ln (33411-3142)
PHONE......................................561 507-5511
Robert J Ojeda, *Principal*
EMP: 6 **EST:** 2017
SALES (est): 638.6K **Privately Held**
WEB: www.rometalsmith.com
SIC: 3441 Fabricated structural metal

(G-15478)
TIMBERWOLF CABINETRY
530 Business Park Way # 7 (33411-1746)
PHONE......................................561 389-5782
Craig Hull, *Principal*
EMP: 6 **EST:** 2010
SALES (est): 101.1K **Privately Held**
SIC: 2434 Wood kitchen cabinets

(G-15479)
WELLINGTON LEATHER LLC
Also Called: Arborossa Leather
320 Business Park Way (33411-1744)
PHONE......................................561 790-0034
Leonardo Mandelbaum, *Mng Member*
Alejandro Mandelbaum,
▲ **EMP:** 6 **EST:** 2013
SALES (est): 518.4K **Privately Held**
SIC: 3199 Boxes, leather

Ruskin
Hillsborough County

(G-15480)
ALL OUT ON A LIMB LLC
1109 15th St Se (33570-4826)
PHONE......................................813 407-6497
Stephen Quillen,
EMP: 7 **EST:** 2014
SALES (est): 241.3K **Privately Held**
WEB: www.alloutonalimb.com
SIC: 3842 0783 Limbs, artificial; removal services, bush & tree

(G-15481)
B & M PRECISION INC
1225 4th St Sw (33570-5348)
PHONE......................................813 645-1188
Miroslav Mitusina, *President*
Fred Hopf, *General Mgr*
Wilfredo Malave, *COO*
Charlene Smith, *Vice Pres*
Steve Raith, *Mfg Dir*
▲ **EMP:** 275 **EST:** 1980
SQ FT: 50,000
SALES (est): 33.5MM **Privately Held**
WEB: www.bmprecision.com
SIC: 3841 Surgical & medical instruments; surgical instruments & apparatus

(G-15482)
BICENTRICS INC
Also Called: Slabs Plus
319 1st St Ne (33570-3629)
P.O. Box 729 (33575-0729)
PHONE......................................813 649-0225
John Haskins, *President*
EMP: 11 **EST:** 1998
SQ FT: 3,000
SALES (est): 1.5MM **Privately Held**
SIC: 3851 Ophthalmic goods

(G-15483)
ELITE CAST STONE INC
1023 Windton Oak Dr (33570-5330)
PHONE......................................305 904-3032
Hesley Sampaio, *Principal*
EMP: 7 **EST:** 2015
SALES (est): 235.6K **Privately Held**
WEB: www.elitecaststone.com
SIC: 3272 Concrete products

(G-15484)
FARMCO MANUFACTURERS INC
1110 4th St Sw (33570-4534)
P.O. Box 1375 (33575-1375)
PHONE......................................813 645-0611
Harold Millis, *President*
Tina Millis, *Vice Pres*
▲ **EMP:** 19 **EST:** 1978
SQ FT: 16,600
SALES (est): 3.2MM **Privately Held**
SIC: 3523 Farm machinery & equipment

(G-15485)
JAN AND JEAN INC
Also Called: Mid State Plastics
1010 E Shell Point Rd (33570-5000)
P.O. Box 188 (33575-0188)
PHONE......................................813 645-0680
Richard L Donati, *President*
Jan Donati, *Treasurer*
◆ **EMP:** 6 **EST:** 1983
SQ FT: 5,000
SALES (est): 832.5K **Privately Held**
WEB: www.midstateplastics.com
SIC: 3089 2673 Plastic containers, except foam; bags: plastic, laminated & coated

(G-15486)
KNOX ALUMINUM INC
720 4th St Sw Ste B (33570-4512)
PHONE......................................813 645-3529
Kenneth Knox, *President*
EMP: 19 **EST:** 1982
SALES (est): 4.8MM **Privately Held**
WEB: www.knoxaluminum.com
SIC: 3448 Screen enclosures

(G-15487)
WEIMER MECHANICAL SERVICES INC
Also Called: Weimer Services
1701 E Shell Point Rd (33570-5029)
PHONE......................................813 645-2258
Robert M Weimer, *CEO*
Susan Weimer, *Vice Pres*
Robert Ray Weimer, *Treasurer*
▼ **EMP:** 6 **EST:** 1981
SQ FT: 5,000
SALES (est): 744.9K **Privately Held**
WEB: www.weimerservices.com
SIC: 7692 7699 Welding repair; mechanical instrument repair

Safety Harbor
Pinellas County

(G-15488)
ADVANCE TOOL COMPANY INC
940 Harbor Lake Ct (34695-2307)
PHONE......................................727 726-8907
James R Hill, *President*
Wesley Hill, *Corp Secy*
EMP: 10 **EST:** 1980
SQ FT: 7,200
SALES (est): 1.2MM **Privately Held**
WEB: www.advancetoolcompany.com
SIC: 3599 Machine shop, jobbing & repair

(G-15489)
BLITZ MICRO TURNING INC
945 Harbor Lake Ct (34695-2303)
P.O. Box 667 (34695-0667)
PHONE......................................727 725-5005
Mark Blitz, *President*
Herman Blitz, *Vice Pres*
Belinda Banister, *Admin Sec*
EMP: 9 **EST:** 1976
SQ FT: 5,000
SALES (est): 600K **Privately Held**
SIC: 3451 3843 Screw machine products; dental equipment

(G-15490)
CLEAR VUE INC (PA)
905 Delaware St (34695-3840)
P.O. Box 86 (34695-0086)
PHONE......................................727 726-5386
David Desaulniers, *President*
Carol A Desaulniers, *Corp Secy*
EMP: 20 **EST:** 1970
SQ FT: 1,200
SALES (est): 3.2MM **Privately Held**
WEB: www.clearvuewindows.net
SIC: 3083 1751 3496 3444 Window sheeting, plastic; window & door (prefabricated) installation; miscellaneous fabricated wire products; sheet metalwork

(G-15491)
DECO POWER LIFT INC
Also Called: Deco Boat Lifts
1041 Harbor Lake Dr (34695-2311)
PHONE......................................727 736-4529
Richard Massell, *President*
Betty Massell, *Safety Mgr*
David Gilbo, *Foreman/Supr*
▼ **EMP:** 10 **EST:** 1994
SALES (est): 1.7MM **Privately Held**
WEB: www.decoboatlift.com
SIC: 3536 Boat lifts

(G-15492)
EMMETI USA LLC
202 10th Ave N Ste A (34695-3480)
PHONE......................................813 490-6252
Luis F Garcia, *Manager*
Fausto Savazzi,
EMP: 17 **EST:** 2005
SALES (est): 755.5K **Privately Held**
SIC: 3535 Robotic conveyors

(G-15493)
FELLOWSHIP ENTERPRISES INC
995 Harbor Lake Dr Ste 10 (34695-2309)
P.O. Box 276 (34695-0276)
PHONE......................................727 726-5997
Peter A Bragdon, *President*
Shirley A Bragdon, *Vice Pres*
EMP: 7 **EST:** 1988
SQ FT: 4,000
SALES (est): 627K **Privately Held**
WEB: www.countertopsflorida.com
SIC: 3089 1799 Synthetic resin finished products; counter top installation

(G-15494)
GENERAL FINE MACHINE CO INC
1010 Park Ct Ste F (34695-3869)
PHONE......................................727 726-5956
Frank Leko, *President*
EMP: 5 **EST:** 1979
SQ FT: 6,000
SALES (est): 476.5K **Privately Held**
WEB: www.generalfinemachine.com
SIC: 3069 3599 Hard rubber & molded rubber products; custom machinery

(G-15495)
HARBOR WOODWORKS
1010 Park Ct Bldg A (34695-3869)
PHONE......................................727 669-0808
Mike Lohmeyer, *Owner*
EMP: 7 **EST:** 1996
SALES (est): 490.1K **Privately Held**
WEB: www.harborwoodworks.com
SIC: 2431 Millwork

(G-15496)
JACOBSEN MANUFACTURING INC (PA)
Also Called: Jacobsen Homes
600 Packard Ct (34695-3001)
P.O. Box 368 (34695-0368)
PHONE......................................727 726-1138
William Robert Jacobsen, *CEO*
Dennis Schrader, *President*
Sidney Boughton, *Vice Pres*
Dusty Rhodes, *VP Human Res*
Tyler Elder, *Sales Staff*
EMP: 205
SQ FT: 2,000
SALES (est): 41.6MM **Privately Held**
WEB: www.jachomes.com
SIC: 2451 3448 2452 Mobile homes, except recreational; prefabricated metal buildings; prefabricated wood buildings

(G-15497)
K & M CUSTOM CABINETRY INC
977 Withlacoochee St A (34695-3466)
PHONE......................................727 791-3993
Michael Carr, *President*
Ronnie Wheelock, *Managing Dir*
Donna Carr, *Vice Pres*
Haleigh Wheelock, *Office Mgr*
EMP: 5 **EST:** 1990
SALES (est): 450K **Privately Held**
WEB: www.kmcabs.business.site
SIC: 2434 Wood kitchen cabinets

(G-15498)
MASTER ALUM & SEC SHUTTER CO
950 Harbor Lake Ct (34695-2307)
PHONE......................................727 725-1744
Mario E Calleja, *President*
Melinda Calleja, *Vice Pres*
EMP: 8 **EST:** 1987
SALES (est): 735.9K **Privately Held**
WEB: www.masteralum.com
SIC: 3442 1751 Shutters, door or window: metal; window & door (prefabricated) installation

(G-15499)
MASTERCUT TOOL CORP
Also Called: McT
965 Harbor Lake Dr (34695-2309)
P.O. Box 902 (34695-0902)
PHONE......................................727 726-5336
Michael A Shaluly, *President*
Vito Ippolito, *Production*
Ylli Hysenlika, *Engineer*
Phet Maharatboutdy, *Manager*
Donald Babinsky, *Technical Staff*
▲ **EMP:** 50 **EST:** 1985
SQ FT: 37,000
SALES (est): 12.4MM **Privately Held**
WEB: www.mastercuttool.com
SIC: 3545 Files, machine tool

(G-15500)
PALEO SIMPLIFIED LLC
605 S Bayshore Blvd (34695-4003)
PHONE......................................813 446-5969
Tamie D Lange, *Vice Pres*
EMP: 7 **EST:** 2011
SALES (est): 104K **Privately Held**
WEB: www.paleosimplified.com
SIC: 2052 Cookies & crackers

(G-15501)
PARADIGM PLASTICS INC
912 3rd St N Ste D (34695-2222)
PHONE......................................727 797-3555
Tommy Edwards, *President*
William Luke Edwards, *Vice Pres*
EMP: 5 **EST:** 1986
SQ FT: 8,000
SALES (est): 960K **Privately Held**
SIC: 2821 Plastics materials & resins

(G-15502)
SAWYER PRODUCTS INC
605 7th Ave N (34695-3027)
P.O. Box 188 (34695-0188)
PHONE......................................727 725-1177
Kurt Avery, *President*
Mary Bausum, *General Mgr*
John Smith, *General Mgr*
Howard C Goode, *Admin Sec*
▲ **EMP:** 20 **EST:** 1984
SQ FT: 16,000
SALES (est): 8MM **Privately Held**
WEB: www.sawyer.com
SIC: 3842 2879 3589 First aid, snake bite & burn kits; agricultural chemicals; water filters & softeners, household type

(G-15503)
SIGNATURE SIGNS INC
Also Called: Creative Wood Graphics
1450 10th St S Unit C (34695-4100)
PHONE......................................727 725-1044
Mark J Dinkel, *President*
Tom Bowers, *Vice Pres*
EMP: 12 **EST:** 1974

▲ = Import ▼=Export
◆ =Import/Export

SQ FT: 7,500
SALES (est): 567.4K **Privately Held**
WEB: www.signaturesignsusa.com
SIC: 3993 Signs, not made in custom sign painting shops

(G-15504)
SMARTCART EV LLC
245 10th Ave N (34695-3415)
PHONE..................................727 906-7001
Joshua Hooks, *CEO*
Jarrett Thorne, *Vice Pres*
EMP: 11
SALES (est): 670.2K **Privately Held**
SIC: 3694 Ignition apparatus & distributors

(G-15505)
SPAULDING CRAFT INC
Also Called: Florida Columns
1053 Harbor Lake Dr (34695-2311)
P.O. Box 357 (34695-0357)
PHONE..................................727 726-2316
Wayne C Spaulding, *President*
Wayne R Spaulding, *President*
Joan Spaulding, *Corp Secy*
▲ **EMP:** 18 **EST:** 1976
SQ FT: 18,900
SALES (est): 1.7MM **Privately Held**
WEB: www.spauldingcraft.com
SIC: 3544 3299 Industrial molds; columns, papier mache or plaster of paris

(G-15506)
STREAMLINE EXTRUSION INC
3105 Ashwood Ln (34695-5002)
P.O. Box 1173 (34695-1173)
PHONE..................................727 796-4277
Paul Hendess, *President*
Susan Hendess, *Vice Pres*
EMP: 10 **EST:** 2006
SALES (est): 500K **Privately Held**
WEB: www.streamlineextrusion.com
SIC: 3083 Plastic finished products, laminated

(G-15507)
VANLYMPIA INC
Also Called: Starmark
605 7th Ave N (34695-3027)
P.O. Box 908 (34695-0908)
PHONE..................................727 725-5055
Richard Lyke, *President*
EMP: 6 **EST:** 1985
SQ FT: 5,500
SALES (est): 547.5K **Privately Held**
SIC: 3842 First aid, snake bite & burn kits

(G-15508)
WATERFORD PRESS INC
1040 Harbor Lake Dr (34695-2310)
P.O. Box 1195, Dunedin (34697-1195)
PHONE..................................727 812-0140
James Kavanagh, *President*
Jill Kavanagh, *Vice Pres*
Mary Carstensen, *Production*
Jenna Risano, *Accounts Mgr*
▲ **EMP:** 31 **EST:** 1994
SQ FT: 1,000
SALES (est): 2.1MM **Privately Held**
WEB: www.waterfordpress.com
SIC: 2741 Guides: publishing only, not printed on site

(G-15509)
WATERFORD PUBLISHING GROUP LLC
Also Called: Waterford Press
1040 Harbor Lake Dr (34695-2310)
PHONE..................................727 812-0140
Brad Hite, *Controller*
Jill Kavanagh Smith,
James Kavanagh,
EMP: 15 **EST:** 2011
SALES (est): 1.1MM **Privately Held**
WEB: www.waterfordpress.com
SIC: 2741 Guides: publishing only, not printed on site

Saint Augustine
St. Johns County

(G-15510)
1565 WOODWORKS LLC
17 Linda Mar Dr (32080-6961)
PHONE..................................904 347-7664
Amber Halcrow, *Principal*
EMP: 6 **EST:** 2017
SALES (est): 493.3K **Privately Held**
WEB: www.1565woodworks.com
SIC: 2431 Millwork

(G-15511)
2G CENRGY PWR SYSTEMS TECH INC (HQ)
Also Called: 2g - Cenergy
205 Commercial Dr (32092-0587)
PHONE..................................904 342-5988
Paul Glenister, *CEO*
Christian Grotholt, *Director*
Phillip Turwitt, *Director*
◆ **EMP:** 35 **EST:** 2009
SQ FT: 60,000
SALES (est): 12.1MM **Privately Held**
WEB: www.2g-energy.com
SIC: 3519 Internal combustion engines

(G-15512)
ABHAI LLC
194 Inlet Dr (32080-3813)
PHONE..................................215 579-1842
Frank Nekoranik, *CPA*
EMP: 6 **EST:** 2014
SALES (est): 303.1K **Privately Held**
SIC: 2834 Solutions, pharmaceutical

(G-15513)
ADVANTAGE EARTH PRODUCTS INC
Also Called: AEP Group
317 Vicki Towers Dr (32092-1757)
PHONE..................................904 329-1430
Robert Randle, *President*
Georges Boyazis, *COO*
Marcela Randle, *CFO*
▲ **EMP:** 13 **EST:** 2009
SALES (est): 3MM **Privately Held**
SIC: 3084 Plastics pipe

(G-15514)
ALUMINUM PRODUCTS
1701 Lakeside Ave Unit 12 (32084-4116)
PHONE..................................904 829-9995
Laura Beckham, *Principal*
EMP: 6 **EST:** 2010
SALES (est): 134.6K **Privately Held**
SIC: 2952 Siding materials

(G-15515)
ALY FABRICATION INC
31 N Saint Augustine Blvd (32080-3780)
PHONE..................................724 898-2990
EMP: 6
SQ FT: 20,000
SALES (est): 996.7K **Privately Held**
SIC: 3443 Mfg Fabricated Plate Work

(G-15516)
AML EXTREME POWDERCOATING
7750 Us Highway 1 S (32086-7919)
PHONE..................................904 794-4313
Maurice Brown, *Principal*
EMP: 7 **EST:** 2007
SALES (est): 358.8K **Privately Held**
SIC: 3479 Coating of metals & formed products

(G-15517)
ANYWHERE GPS LLC
43 Sierras Loop (32086-9041)
PHONE..................................949 468-6842
Michael Shriner, *Manager*
EMP: 6 **EST:** 2017
SALES (est): 229.2K **Privately Held**
SIC: 3663

(G-15518)
ATLANTIC CANDY COMPANY
115 Whetstone Pl (32086-5772)
PHONE..................................904 429-7250
Henry M Whetstone Jr, *President*
Janice F Whetstone, *Vice Pres*
EMP: 35 **EST:** 2015
SALES (est): 3.5MM **Privately Held**
WEB: www.atlanticcandy.com
SIC: 2066 Chocolate

(G-15519)
B & B OF SAINT AUGUSTINE INC
Also Called: B & B Trailers and Accessories
2875 Us Highway 1 S (32086-6303)
PHONE..................................904 829-6855
Thomas E Bennett Jr, *President*
T E Bennett Jr, *Vice Pres*
Debbie Bennett, *Admin Sec*
EMP: 7 **EST:** 1979
SQ FT: 3,375
SALES (est): 500K **Privately Held**
SIC: 7692 Welding repair

(G-15520)
B & B TRAILERS AND ACCESSORIES
2875 Us Highway 1 S (32086-6303)
PHONE..................................904 829-6855
Thomas Bennett Jr, *President*
Deborah Bennett, *Admin Sec*
EMP: 15 **EST:** 2004
SALES (est): 1.1MM **Privately Held**
WEB: www.bbtrailersinc.com
SIC: 3714 5013 Trailer hitches, motor vehicle; motor vehicle supplies & new parts; truck parts & accessories; trailer parts & accessories

(G-15521)
BACKYARD FEED LLC ✪
6400 County Road 214 (32092-9301)
PHONE..................................813 846-5995
Sean J Hellein, *President*
EMP: 7 **EST:** 2020
SALES (est): 383.8K **Privately Held**
WEB: www.backyardfeedco.com
SIC: 2048 Chicken feeds, prepared

(G-15522)
BLUEWATERPRESS LLC (PA)
52 Tuscan Way Ste 202-309 (32092-1850)
PHONE..................................888 247-0793
Joseph F Clark III, *Principal*
EMP: 7 **EST:** 2011
SALES (est): 139.7K **Privately Held**
WEB: www.bluewaterpress.com
SIC: 2711 Newspapers, publishing & printing

(G-15523)
BODHI TREE WOODWORK INC
60 N Saint Augustine Blvd (32080-3753)
PHONE..................................904 540-2655
Thomas Boyle, *Principal*
EMP: 6 **EST:** 2016
SALES (est): 110K **Privately Held**
SIC: 2431 Millwork

(G-15524)
BROOKING INDUSTRIES INC
104 Liberty Center Pl (32092-0919)
PHONE..................................954 533-0765
Richard K Brooking, *President*
Spencer Brooking, *COO*
Edward Spencer Brooking, *Vice Pres*
Melissa Ratliff, *Sales Staff*
▲ **EMP:** 6 **EST:** 1997
SALES (est): 851.2K **Privately Held**
WEB: www.brookingindustries.com
SIC: 3647 Motor vehicle lighting equipment

(G-15525)
BUSHHOG N BLADE WORK
2846 Usina Road Ext (32084-0557)
PHONE..................................904 669-2764
George Smith, *Principal*
EMP: 8 **EST:** 2009
SALES (est): 763.1K **Privately Held**
SIC: 3523 Farm machinery & equipment

(G-15526)
CARLISLE INTERCONNECT TECH INC (HQ)
100 Tensolite Dr (32092-0590)
PHONE..................................904 829-5600
John E Berlin, *President*
David Grice, *Business Mgr*
Amy Ning, *Project Mgr*
Gregg Patz, *Project Mgr*
Juanita Killary, *Export Mgr*
▲ **EMP:** 4563 **EST:** 1993
SALES (est): 1.5B
SALES (corp-wide): 4.2B **Publicly Held**
WEB: www.carlisleit.com
SIC: 3679 3399 3678 3357 Harness assemblies for electronic use: wire or cable; metal fasteners; electronic connectors; communication wire; fiber optic cable (insulated); aircraft wire & cable, nonferrous; current-carrying wiring devices; electrical apparatus & equipment
PA: Carlisle Companies Incorporated
16430 N Scottsdale Rd
Scottsdale AZ 85254
480 781-5000

(G-15527)
CASTLE PUBLISHING LLC
4255 Us Highway 1 S (32086-7046)
PHONE..................................904 794-0112
EMP: 6 **EST:** 2013
SALES (est): 75K **Privately Held**
WEB: www.reiprofessor.com
SIC: 2741 Miscellaneous publishing

(G-15528)
CEMEX CNSTR MTLS FLA LLC
Also Called: Readymix
233 Industry Pl (32095-8601)
PHONE..................................904 827-0369
Brian Bussel, *Branch Mgr*
EMP: 7
SQ FT: 13,180 **Privately Held**
SIC: 3273 Ready-mixed concrete
HQ: Cemex Construction Materials Florida, Llc
1501 Belvedere Rd
West Palm Beach FL 33406

(G-15529)
CENTERLINE STEEL LLC
Also Called: Centerline Brackets
208 W Davis Industrial Dr (32084-8413)
PHONE..................................904 217-4186
Tracy Smith, *CEO*
Chris Smith,
EMP: 25 **EST:** 2013
SQ FT: 9,000
SALES (est): 1.7MM **Privately Held**
WEB: www.countertopbracket.com
SIC: 3499 Fire- or burglary-resistive products

(G-15530)
CLASSIC POKER CHIPS
121 Lancaster Pl (32080-7533)
PHONE..................................207 332-9999
EMP: 6 **EST:** 2019
SALES (est): 109K **Privately Held**
WEB: www.classicpokerchips.com
SIC: 3944 Poker chips

(G-15531)
COCA-COLA COMPANY
90 S Dixie Hwy (32084-6219)
PHONE..................................904 342-5609
Gloria Jean Oneal, *Branch Mgr*
EMP: 6
SALES (corp-wide): 33B **Publicly Held**
WEB: www.coca-colacompany.com
SIC: 2086 Bottled & canned soft drinks
PA: The Coca-Cola Company
1 Coca Cola Plz Nw
Atlanta GA 30313
404 676-2121

(G-15532)
CORE OUTDOORS INC
134 Poole Blvd (32095-8402)
PHONE..................................904 215-6866
EMP: 9 **EST:** 2018
SALES (est): 597.6K **Privately Held**
SIC: 2499 Fencing, docks & other outdoor wood structural products

(G-15533)
DAVID DOBBS ENTERPRISES INC (PA)
Also Called: Menu Design
4600 Us 1 N (32095-5701)
PHONE..................................904 824-6171
David F Dobbs, *President*
Peggy A Dobbs, *Senior VP*
John V Maguire, *Vice Pres*
Evelyn Torres, *Opers Staff*

GEOGRAPHIC

Lindsay Lavercombe, *Sales Staff*
◆ **EMP:** 100 **EST:** 1980
SQ FT: 39,500
SALES (est): 20.3MM **Privately Held**
WEB: www.menudesigns.com
SIC: 2789 2679 2759 2389 Binding only: books, pamphlets, magazines, etc.; book covers, paper; menus: printing; apparel for handicapped; signs & advertising specialties

(G-15534)
DAVID E ASHE SAWMILL
5440 State Road 13 N (32092-1531)
PHONE..................................904 377-4800
David Ashe, *Principal*
EMP: 9 **EST:** 2006
SALES (est): 385.2K **Privately Held**
WEB: www.ashesawmill.com
SIC: 2421 Sawmills & planing mills, general

(G-15535)
DEFENSHIELD INC
7000 Us Highway 1 N # 401 (32095-8359)
PHONE..................................904 679-3942
William White, *President*
Jordan Settle, *Opers Staff*
Troy Harding, *Program Mgr*
EMP: 7 **EST:** 2002
SALES (est): 5MM **Privately Held**
WEB: www.defenshield.com
SIC: 3231 3442 3448 7382 Products of purchased glass; metal doors, sash & trim; prefabricated metal buildings; security systems services; engineering services

(G-15536)
DENTZ DESIGN SCREEN PRTG LLC
56 S Dixie Hwy Ste 3 (32084-0306)
PHONE..................................609 303-0827
Carolyn Dentz, *Principal*
EMP: 7 **EST:** 2011
SALES (est): 156.2K **Privately Held**
SIC: 2752 Commercial printing, lithographic

(G-15537)
DESIGNATED SPORTS INC
Also Called: Designated Diver
3545 Us 1 S Ste A9 (32086-6330)
PHONE..................................904 797-9469
Lori Webb, *President*
Gary Webb, *Vice Pres*
▼ **EMP:** 10 **EST:** 1988
SQ FT: 25,000
SALES (est): 931.3K **Privately Held**
WEB: www.designatedsports.com
SIC: 2759 Screen printing

(G-15538)
DOERRS CSTM CABINETS TRIM LLC
1300 Wildwood Dr (32086-9113)
PHONE..................................904 540-7024
Carl Doerr, *Owner*
EMP: 10 **EST:** 2014
SALES (est): 272.2K **Privately Held**
WEB: www.schoolfurn.org
SIC: 2434 Wood kitchen cabinets

(G-15539)
DOERRS CUSTOM CABINETS & TRIM
1761 Dobbs Rd (32084-6217)
PHONE..................................904 540-7024
EMP: 8 **EST:** 2018
SALES (est): 432.1K **Privately Held**
SIC: 2434 Wood kitchen cabinets

(G-15540)
DYNAMIC WELDING & FAB LLC
2190 Tocoi Ter (32092-9227)
PHONE..................................904 669-4682
Martin Miles, *Principal*
EMP: 8 **EST:** 2016
SALES (est): 288.6K **Privately Held**
SIC: 7692 Welding repair

(G-15541)
ENDORPHIN FARMS INC
3255 Parker Dr (32084-0892)
PHONE..................................904 824-2006
Scott Martin, *President*
EMP: 12 **EST:** 1998
SALES (est): 1.6MM **Privately Held**
WEB: www.bottle-my-sauce.com
SIC: 3221 Bottles for packing, bottling & canning: glass

(G-15542)
EVANS CUSTOM CABINETRY LLC
3595 Fortner Rd (32084-0847)
PHONE..................................904 829-1973
Robert Evans, *Mng Member*
Candice Evans,
EMP: 8 **EST:** 1991
SALES (est): 650K **Privately Held**
WEB: www.evanscustomcabinetry.com
SIC: 2434 Wood kitchen cabinets

(G-15543)
FDA SIGNS LLC
Also Called: Fastsigns 176501
2303 N Ponce De Leon Blvd (32084-2604)
PHONE..................................904 800-1776
EMP: 9 **EST:** 2018
SALES (est): 1.4MM **Privately Held**
WEB: www.fastsigns.com
SIC: 3993 Signs & advertising specialties

(G-15544)
FUEL PRODUCTIONS LLC
1960 Us Highway 1 S 199 (32086-4233)
PHONE..................................904 342-7826
Jay S Ruditis, *Principal*
EMP: 7 **EST:** 2009
SALES (est): 521.7K **Privately Held**
WEB: www.fuelproductions.net
SIC: 2869 Fuels

(G-15545)
GATOR DOOR EAST INC
2150 Dobbs Rd (32086-5249)
PHONE..................................904 824-2827
Ron Platts, *President*
Barbara Platts, *Corp Secy*
Tim Callum, *Vice Pres*
Mike Ausili, *Sales Staff*
Chris Dupont, *Sales Staff*
EMP: 50 **EST:** 1990
SQ FT: 25,000
SALES (est): 9.8MM **Privately Held**
WEB: www.gatordooreast.com
SIC: 2431 3429 Doors & door parts & trim, wood; moldings, wood: unfinished & prefinished; locks or lock sets

(G-15546)
GOLF AMERICA SOUTHWEST FLA INC
Also Called: World Golf Collection
2049 Crown Dr (32092-3606)
PHONE..................................904 688-0280
Timothy J Constatine, *President*
▲ **EMP:** 5 **EST:** 1995
SALES (est): 411.3K **Privately Held**
SIC: 2329 Men's & boys' sportswear & athletic clothing

(G-15547)
H20LOGY INC
3233 County Road 208 (32092-0517)
PHONE..................................904 829-6098
Steve Brandvold, *President*
EMP: 5 **EST:** 1988
SQ FT: 3,500
SALES (est): 500K **Privately Held**
SIC: 2819 5074 Brine; water purification equipment

(G-15548)
H2C BRANDS LLC (PA)
Also Called: Volt Resistance
110 Cumberland Park Dr # 205 (32095-8901)
PHONE..................................904 342-7485
Chris Haffly, *President*
▲ **EMP:** 34 **EST:** 2012
SALES (est): 321.6K **Privately Held**
WEB: www.voltheat.com
SIC: 2253 Warm weather knit outerwear, including beachwear

(G-15549)
HYDRAULICNET LLC
Also Called: Hydraulic Net
6980 Us Highway 1 N # 107 (32095-8374)
PHONE..................................630 543-7630
Stephen L Smith,
▲ **EMP:** 14 **EST:** 1997
SQ FT: 10,000
SALES (est): 1.7MM **Privately Held**
WEB: www.hydraulic.net
SIC: 3566 Reduction gears & gear units for turbines, except automotive

(G-15550)
HYDRO EXTRUSION USA LLC
200 Riviera Blvd (32086-7801)
PHONE..................................904 794-1500
Trond Gjellesvik, *Managing Dir*
Olaf Wigstol, *Managing Dir*
Erika Ahlqvist, *Exec VP*
Chase Reeves, *Plant Mgr*
Ralph Westphal, *Opers Staff*
EMP: 300
SQ FT: 250,000
SALES (corp-wide): 16.1B **Privately Held**
SIC: 3354 3444 3316 Tube, extruded or drawn, aluminum; pipe, extruded, aluminum; shapes, extruded aluminum; sheet metalwork; cold finishing of steel shapes
HQ: Hydro Extrusion Usa, Llc
6250 N River Rd Ste 5000
Rosemont IL 60018

(G-15551)
HYPERBARIC TREATMENT ASSN
129 Sea Grove Main St # 202 (32080-6376)
PHONE..................................804 296-4094
Michelle Riello, *President*
EMP: 6 **EST:** 2012
SALES (est): 272K **Privately Held**
SIC: 3641 Health lamps, infrared or ultraviolet

(G-15552)
ICEMULE COMPANY INC
601 S Ponce De Leon Blvd (32084-4227)
PHONE..................................904 325-9012
James Collie, *President*
▲ **EMP:** 16 **EST:** 2012
SALES (est): 2.6MM **Privately Held**
WEB: www.icemulecoolers.com
SIC: 3086 Ice chests or coolers (portable), foamed plastic

(G-15553)
IDEAL DEALS LLC
Also Called: Ideal Aluminum
3200 Parker Dr (32084-0891)
PHONE..................................386 736-1700
Douglas J Brady, *Co-CEO*
Michael Siegel, *Co-CEO*
Lori Greaves, *COO*
Douglas Brady, *Marketing Mgr*
Chris Pavlik, *Manager*
◆ **EMP:** 107 **EST:** 2010
SQ FT: 170,000
SALES (est): 36.4MM **Privately Held**
WEB: www.ideal-ap.com
SIC: 3334 3479 Primary aluminum; aluminum coating of metal products

(G-15554)
IDEAL GAS LLC
3200 Parker Dr (32084-0891)
PHONE..................................904 417-6470
Bob Bell, *Area Mgr*
Leo Kirby, *COO*
Buddy Dingman, *Sales Staff*
Richard Poremba, *Sales Staff*
Jacqueline Shane, *Office Mgr*
EMP: 5 **EST:** 2015
SALES (est): 2.3MM **Privately Held**
WEB: www.ideal-gas.com
SIC: 1321 Propane (natural) production

(G-15555)
INDUSTRIAL CNSTR SVCS DSIGN IN (PA)
Also Called: Icon
4405 Sartillo Rd Ste A (32095-5240)
PHONE..................................904 827-9795
James Dewitt, *President*
Ronald Avery, *Chairman*
Jason Hoff, *Plant Mgr*
John Lamela, *Project Mgr*
Steve Jenkins, *Admin Sec*
EMP: 99 **EST:** 1981
SALES (est): 21.8MM **Privately Held**
WEB: www.icon-industrial.com
SIC: 3554 Paper mill machinery: plating, slitting, waxing, etc.

(G-15556)
INSPIRED SURF BOARDS
2310 Dobbs Rd (32086-5218)
PHONE..................................904 347-8879
Philip A Baggett, *Owner*
EMP: 8 **EST:** 2000
SALES (est): 264.2K **Privately Held**
SIC: 3949 Surfboards

(G-15557)
INTELBASE SECURITY CORPORATION
400 Night Hawk Ln (32080-7983)
PHONE..................................703 371-9181
Jose Rodriguez, *Principal*
EMP: 8 **EST:** 2016
SALES (est): 327.5K **Privately Held**
SIC: 3674 Microprocessors

(G-15558)
ISLE OF LUXE INC
701 Market St Ste 111 (32095-8803)
PHONE..................................352 745-0515
Robert M Shepard, *President*
EMP: 6 **EST:** 2009
SALES (est): 253.6K **Privately Held**
WEB: www.isleofluxe.com
SIC: 2844 Toilet preparations

(G-15559)
ITALY TILE AND MARBLE INC (PA)
2085 A1a S Ste 304 (32080-6519)
PHONE..................................941 488-5646
Gilberto Vitniski, *President*
Frank Kish III, *Vice Pres*
EMP: 6 **EST:** 2003
SQ FT: 5,000
SALES (est): 570.3K **Privately Held**
WEB: www.italytilesandmarble.com
SIC: 3281 Table tops, marble

(G-15560)
JLS OF ST AUGUSTINE INC
Also Called: Flamingo Travel
3161 Mac Rd (32086-5488)
PHONE..................................904 797-6098
Lynne S Stephenson, *Principal*
EMP: 6 **EST:** 2010
SALES (est): 94.3K **Privately Held**
WEB: www.staugustine.com
SIC: 2711 Newspapers, publishing & printing

(G-15561)
JOHNSONS WOODWORK INCORPORATED
175 Cumberland Park Dr (32095-8954)
PHONE..................................904 826-4100
EMP: 7
SQ FT: 800
SALES: 500K **Privately Held**
SIC: 2431 Mfg Millwork

(G-15562)
JORDAN BROWN INC (PA)
Also Called: Winston Furniture Company Ala
475 W Town Pl Ste 200 (32092-3653)
PHONE..................................904 495-0717
Gene J Moriarty, *President*
Dave Biancofiore, *President*
Chris Carmicle, *President*
Bill Echols, *President*
David Kennedy, *President*
◆ **EMP:** 1 **EST:** 1945
SALES (est): 265.6MM **Privately Held**
WEB: www.brownjordaninc.com
SIC: 2512 2514 Chairs: upholstered on wood frames; metal household furniture

(G-15563)
JRH SPORT INDUSTRIES INC
6550 State Road 16 (32092-2109)
PHONE..................................904 940-3381
EMP: 6

SQ FT: 1,600
SALES (est): 420K **Privately Held**
SIC: 3949 Mfg Sporting/Athletic Goods

(G-15564)
KJ REYNOLDS INC
Also Called: Standard Printing & Copy Ctr
3520 Ag Ctr Dr Ste 306 (32092)
PHONE..................................904 829-6488
Sandi Reynolds, *President*
EMP: 7 **EST:** 2003
SQ FT: 3,000
SALES (est): 902.2K **Privately Held**
WEB: www.kjreynoldsandassociates.com
SIC: 2759 Commercial printing

(G-15565)
LAKEVIEW DIRT CO INC
Also Called: Ldc
497 S Holmes Blvd (32084-8339)
PHONE..................................904 824-2586
Greg A Wilson, *President*
Gary Wilson, *Vice Pres*
EMP: 20 **EST:** 1985
SQ FT: 1,600
SALES (est): 2.7MM **Privately Held**
WEB: www.lakeviewdirt.com
SIC: 1422 1794 Crushed & broken limestone; excavation & grading, building construction

(G-15566)
LYONS MACHINE TOOL CO INC
5115 Cres Technical Ct (32086-5625)
PHONE..................................904 797-1550
Kevin Lyons, *President*
Christine Lyons, *Vice Pres*
Mike Haller, *Manager*
Kyle Lyons, *Manager*
EMP: 29 **EST:** 1965
SQ FT: 2,500
SALES (est): 2.3MM **Privately Held**
WEB: www.lyonsmachinetool.com
SIC: 3599 Machine shop, jobbing & repair

(G-15567)
MATSCHEL OF FLAGLER INC
239 Marshside Dr (32080-5836)
PHONE..................................386 446-4595
EMP: 7 **EST:** 2010
SALES (est): 71.5K **Privately Held**
SIC: 3312 Chemicals & other products derived from coking

(G-15568)
MERIDIAN CABLE LLC
345 Vale Dr (32095-4836)
PHONE..................................847 847-1128
Karin Kinzalow, *Vice Pres*
Leslie Roland, *Warehouse Mgr*
Kelly Avignone, *Sales Staff*
Richard M Kinzalow,
▲ **EMP:** 14 **EST:** 2003
SALES (est): 2.2MM **Privately Held**
WEB: www.meridiancableassemblies.com
SIC: 2298 5051 7389 Cable, fiber; cable, wire;

(G-15569)
METAL TECHNOLOGIES GROUP INC
1105 Registry Blvd (32092-3802)
PHONE..................................904 429-7727
Kimberly Sand, *Principal*
EMP: 6 **EST:** 2017
SALES (est): 65.4K **Privately Held**
WEB: www.metal-technologies.com
SIC: 3599 Machine shop, jobbing & repair

(G-15570)
MICROBIAL DEFENSE SYSTEMS LLC
404 Bostwick Cir (32092-0429)
PHONE..................................989 964-9863
Matthew F Myntti PH D, *Principal*
Matthew F Myntti, *Principal*
EMP: 6 **EST:** 2008
SALES (est): 113.1K **Privately Held**
SIC: 3812 Defense systems & equipment

(G-15571)
MOTLEY ENTERPRISES INC
701 Market St Ste 111 (32095-8803)
PHONE..................................703 966-3997
EMP: 6 **EST:** 2019
SALES (est): 294.3K **Privately Held**
SIC: 3732 Boat building & repairing

(G-15572)
NEW BS WHEEL LLC
321 Ocean Forest Dr (32080-8738)
PHONE..................................309 657-4899
Susan Wentz, *Principal*
EMP: 6 **EST:** 2012
SALES (est): 83.7K **Privately Held**
SIC: 3312 Wheels

(G-15573)
NEWCASTLE SHIPYARDS LLC
106 Dory Rd (32086-5714)
PHONE..................................386 312-0000
Nicholas Keith, *Opers Staff*
Nick Keith, *Opers Staff*
Kevin H Keith, *CFO*
Whinter Leonesio, *Office Mgr*
Whinter R Leonesio, *Office Mgr*
▲ **EMP:** 105 **EST:** 2002
SALES (est): 11.6MM **Privately Held**
WEB: www.newcastleshipyards.com
SIC: 3731 Shipbuilding & repairing

(G-15574)
NORTHROP GRMMAN FELD SPPORT SV (DH)
5000 Us Highway 1 N B02-60 (32095-6200)
PHONE..................................904 810-4665
Ed Faye, *CEO*
▲ **EMP:** 60 **EST:** 1996
SALES (est): 93.7MM **Publicly Held**
WEB: www.northropgrumman.com
SIC: 3721 3761 Aircraft; guided missiles & space vehicles
HQ: Northrop Grumman Systems Corporation
2980 Fairview Park Dr
Falls Church VA 22042
703 280-2900

(G-15575)
NORTHROP GRMMAN TCHNCAL SVCS I
5000 Us Highway 1 N (32095-6200)
PHONE..................................904 825-3300
Steve Timmerman, *Manager*
EMP: 12 **Publicly Held**
SIC: 3812 Search & navigation equipment
HQ: Northrop Grumman Technical Services, Inc.
7575 Colshire Dr
Mc Lean VA 22102
703 556-1144

(G-15576)
NORTHROP GRUMMAN SYSTEMS CORP
5000 Us Highway 1 N (32095-6200)
PHONE..................................904 825-3300
Brian Mahoney, *Vice Pres*
Cecil Privett, *Materials Mgr*
Scott Burton, *Engineer*
Alexander Deloach, *Engineer*
Dan Edwards, *Engineer*
EMP: 206 **Publicly Held**
WEB: www.northropgrumman.com
SIC: 3721 Airplanes, fixed or rotary wing; research & development on aircraft by the manufacturer
HQ: Northrop Grumman Systems Corporation
2980 Fairview Park Dr
Falls Church VA 22042
703 280-2900

(G-15577)
NORTHROP GRUMMAN SYSTEMS CORP
125 International Golf (32095-8461)
PHONE..................................904 810-5957
Steve Congro, *General Mgr*
Sharlyn Anderson, *Purchasing*
EMP: 7 **Publicly Held**
WEB: www.northropgrumman.com
SIC: 3812 Search & navigation equipment
HQ: Northrop Grumman Systems Corporation
2980 Fairview Park Dr
Falls Church VA 22042
703 280-2900

(G-15578)
NORTHROP GRUMMAN SYSTEMS CORP
5000 Us Highway 1 N (32095-6200)
PHONE..................................904 825-3300
Robert Thomas, *Branch Mgr*
Alice Reed, *Analyst*
EMP: 206 **Publicly Held**
WEB: www.northropgrumman.com
SIC: 3721 3761 Airplanes, fixed or rotary wing; guided missiles, complete
HQ: Northrop Grumman Systems Corporation
2980 Fairview Park Dr
Falls Church VA 22042
703 280-2900

(G-15579)
NWH PUBLISHING LLC
659 Los Caminos St (32095-7418)
PHONE..................................904 217-3911
Kevin B Carpenter, *Branch Mgr*
EMP: 10
SALES (corp-wide): 73.7K **Privately Held**
SIC: 2741 Miscellaneous publishing
PA: Nwh Publishing, Llc.
130 Corridor Rd Unit 577
Ponte Vedra Beach FL

(G-15580)
OLD CITY MARINE LLC
Also Called: Nbk Maintenance
76 Dockside Dr Ste 112 (32084-4229)
PHONE..................................904 252-6887
Sean Riley, *Mng Member*
Amy Riley,
EMP: 7 **EST:** 2019
SALES (est): 450.6K **Privately Held**
WEB: www.oldcitymarine.com
SIC: 3731 Patrol boats, building & repairing

(G-15581)
OLD CITY SWEEPSTAKES
2303 N Ponce De Leon Blvd (32084-2604)
PHONE..................................904 808-0456
EMP: 7 **EST:** 2012
SALES (est): 54K **Privately Held**
SIC: 3421 Table & food cutlery, including butchers'

(G-15582)
OLD PORT GROUP LLC
Also Called: Home Mag, The
1301 Plntn Is Dr S 206b (32080-3112)
PHONE..................................904 819-5812
Mark Matrazzo,
EMP: 10 **EST:** 2006
SQ FT: 2,500
SALES (est): 2.1MM **Privately Held**
SIC: 2721 Magazines: publishing & printing

(G-15583)
OLD TOWN TIMBER LLC
205 C St (32080-6823)
PHONE..................................904 217-7046
William A Weeks, *Manager*
EMP: 7 **EST:** 2016
SALES (est): 117.3K **Privately Held**
WEB: www.oldtowntimber.com
SIC: 2431 Millwork

(G-15584)
PARTS CAGE INC ✪
280 Business Park Cir # 412 (32095-8835)
PHONE..................................904 373-7800
Thomas Corrao,
EMP: 10 **EST:** 2021
SALES (est): 360.4K **Privately Held**
SIC: 3728 Aircraft parts & equipment

(G-15585)
PATRIOT PUBLISHING USA LLC
2286 W Clovelly Ln (32092-5003)
PHONE..................................904 217-7632
David West, *Principal*
EMP: 6 **EST:** 2016
SALES (est): 43K **Privately Held**
SIC: 2741 Miscellaneous publishing

(G-15586)
PEARSONS REFACING AND REFACING
67 Carrera St (32084-3545)
PHONE..................................904 591-3850
Byron Pearson, *Principal*
EMP: 6 **EST:** 2014
SALES (est): 275.1K **Privately Held**
WEB: www.pearsonscabinets.com
SIC: 2434 Wood kitchen cabinets

(G-15587)
PIGMENTS BLACK DIAMOND
1316 Barrington Cir (32092-3612)
PHONE..................................904 241-2533
Christopher Downer, *CEO*
EMP: 6 **EST:** 2017
SALES (est): 211.6K **Privately Held**
WEB: www.blackdiamondpigments.com
SIC: 2816 Black pigments

(G-15588)
PIP MARKETING SIGNS PRINT ✪
248 State Road 312 (32086-4241)
PHONE..................................904 825-2372
EMP: 9 **EST:** 2020
SALES (est): 359.9K **Privately Held**
WEB: www.pip.com
SIC: 2752 Commercial printing, offset

(G-15589)
PLAYCORE WISCONSIN INC
405 Golfway West Dr # 302 (32095-8841)
PHONE..................................800 853-5316
EMP: 6 **EST:** 2017
SALES (est): 99K **Privately Held**
WEB: www.playcore.com
SIC: 3949 Playground equipment

(G-15590)
POWER TEK LLC
154 Cornell Rd (32086-6053)
PHONE..................................904 814-7007
Todd E Kelly, *CEO*
EMP: 9 **EST:** 2010
SALES (est): 139.2K **Privately Held**
WEB: www.power-tek.com
SIC: 3479 Metal coating & allied service

(G-15591)
PRODUCTIVE PRODUCTS INC
321 Valverde Ln (32086-8885)
PHONE..................................904 570-5553
John Lawrence, *Manager*
EMP: 9
SALES (corp-wide): 600K **Privately Held**
WEB: www.productiveproducts.com
SIC: 2759 3993 7389 Screen printing; signs, not made in custom sign painting shops; lettering & sign painting services
PA: Productive Products Inc
1003 S Main St
Benton IL
618 439-6915

(G-15592)
QUICK SIGNS
4425 Us Highway 1 S # 101 (32086-3127)
PHONE..................................904 310-1010
EMP: 6 **EST:** 2014
SALES (est): 125.1K **Privately Held**
WEB: www.staugustinequicksigns.com
SIC: 3993 Signs & advertising specialties

(G-15593)
RAIL SCALE INC
111 Nature Walk Pkwy # 105 (32092-3065)
PHONE..................................904 302-5154
James Myers, *CEO*
Jack Payne, *President*
Dennis Myers, *President*
Larry Croucher Sr, *Sales Mgr*
Linda Orlandi, *Office Mgr*
EMP: 20 **EST:** 1999
SQ FT: 1,200
SALES (est): 4MM **Privately Held**
WEB: www.railscale.com
SIC: 3825 Standards & calibration equipment for electrical measuring

(G-15594)
RANKINE-HINMAN MFG CO
6980 Us Highway 1 N # 108 (32095-8374)
PHONE..................................904 808-0404
Robert Rankine, *CEO*
Brian Hinman, *President*
Ann Cummings, *General Mgr*
Fred Siemer, *General Mgr*
Dana Gould, *Admin Sec*
EMP: 10 **EST:** 1992
SQ FT: 4,000

SALES (est): 802.1K **Privately Held**
SIC: 3541 7692 3444 Machine tools, metal cutting type; welding repair; sheet metalwork

(G-15595)
REHADAPT NORTH AMERICA
7619 A1a S (32080-8206)
PHONE..................................904 687-0130
EMP: 6 **EST:** 2012
SALES (est): 122.1K **Privately Held**
WEB: www.rehadapt.com
SIC: 3714 Motor vehicle parts & accessories

(G-15596)
RILEY GEAR CORPORATION (PA)
1 Precision Dr (32092-0593)
PHONE..................................904 829-5652
Donald Esarove, *CEO*
William Osborne III, *Ch of Bd*
Thomas Lowry, *President*
Brent Nicholson, *Plant Mgr*
Steve Palmer, *Mfg Spvr*
▲ **EMP:** 70
SQ FT: 48,400
SALES (est): 12.8MM **Privately Held**
WEB: www.rileygear.com
SIC: 3566 3462 Gears, forged steel; speed changers, drives & gears; gears, power transmission, except automotive

(G-15597)
RILEY RISK INC
1301 Plntn Is Dr S (32080-3108)
PHONE..................................202 601-0500
Jacob Allen, *CEO*
Philip Dwyer, *Treasurer*
EMP: 7 **EST:** 2011
SALES (est): 718.6K **Privately Held**
WEB: www.rileyrisk.com
SIC: 7372 8742 Application computer software; management consulting services

(G-15598)
ROBOT-COSTUMES TECHNOLOGIES
120 Cumberland Park Dr # 305 (32095-8922)
PHONE..................................904 535-0074
Jefferson Leininger, *Principal*
EMP: 6 **EST:** 2010
SALES (est): 202.8K
SALES (corp-wide): 1.2MM **Privately Held**
WEB: www.robotcostumesusa.com
SIC: 2389 Costumes
PA: Creations Jean-Claude Tremblay Inc
3250 Rue Marconi Bureau 1
Mascouche QC J7K 3
450 474-0701

(G-15599)
ROX VOLLEYBALL
3520 Ag Ctr Dr Ste 310 (32092)
PHONE..................................877 769-2121
Danielle Olson, *President*
Troy Olson, *Vice Pres*
April Stapp, *Natl Sales Mgr*
Alexa Downie, *Manager*
EMP: 17 **EST:** 2009
SALES (est): 515.3K **Privately Held**
WEB: www.roxvolleyball.com
SIC: 2339 Uniforms, athletic: women's, misses' & juniors'

(G-15600)
RULON COMPANY OF GEORGIA
2000 Ring Way (32092-4745)
PHONE..................................904 584-1400
Wayne Robison, *President*
Eleanor Robison, *Corp Secy*
Jared Atherton, *Project Mgr*
Wesley Snyder, *Design Engr*
Brian J Tuttle, *CFO*
▼ **EMP:** 130 **EST:** 1973
SQ FT: 85,000
SALES (est): 36.9MM **Privately Held**
WEB: www.rulonco.com
SIC: 2421 Sawmills & planing mills, general

(G-15601)
RUSSELLS BINDERY INC
Also Called: Russell Bindery
90 Palmer St (32084-3454)
P.O. Box 860129 (32086-0129)
PHONE..................................904 829-3100
Tim McMandon, *President*
EMP: 6 **EST:** 1962
SQ FT: 5,000
SALES (est): 241.1K **Privately Held**
SIC: 2789 2782 Bookbinding & related work; blankbooks & looseleaf binders

(G-15602)
SAFETARP CORP
1950 State Road 16 (32084-0810)
PHONE..................................904 824-7277
Fred Payne, *President*
Barry Lawhorne, *Vice Pres*
Robert Moore, *Opers Staff*
Louis Krantz, *Admin Sec*
EMP: 60 **EST:** 1999
SQ FT: 5,000
SALES (est): 4.2MM **Privately Held**
WEB: www.tarpingsollc.com
SIC: 3559 Foundry machinery & equipment

(G-15603)
SAINT AUGUSTINE CAST STONE
4960 Cres Technical Ct (32086-5615)
PHONE..................................904 794-2626
Steve Carcaba, *President*
Leslie Carcaba, *Mfg Staff*
EMP: 8 **EST:** 2003
SALES (est): 665.8K **Privately Held**
SIC: 3272 Stone, cast concrete

(G-15604)
SAPA EXTRSONS ST AUGUSTINE LLC
200 Riviera Blvd (32086-7801)
PHONE..................................904 794-1500
William Russell, *President*
EMP: 894 **EST:** 2014
SALES (est): 4.7MM
SALES (corp-wide): 16.1B **Privately Held**
WEB: www.americanconduit.com
SIC: 3365 3354 Aluminum foundries; tube, extruded or drawn, aluminum
HQ: Hydro Extrusion North America, Llc
6250 N River Rd
Rosemont IL 60018
877 710-7272

(G-15605)
SCHOENHUT LLC
Also Called: Schoenhut Piano Company
6480b Us Highway 1 N (32095-8263)
PHONE..................................904 810-1945
Renee Trinca, *Mng Member*
Leonard Trinca,
▲ **EMP:** 6 **EST:** 1996
SQ FT: 12,000
SALES (est): 1MM **Privately Held**
WEB: www.schoenhut-wholesale-store.myshopify.com
SIC: 3944 Toy musical instruments

(G-15606)
SEARAVEN GLAUBEN LLC
6429 Brevard St (32080-7649)
PHONE..................................727 230-8840
David Ting,
EMP: 10 **EST:** 2019
SALES (est): 445.8K **Privately Held**
SIC: 2911 Petroleum refining

(G-15607)
SEAVIN INC
Also Called: San Sebastian Winery
157 King St (32084-4379)
PHONE..................................904 826-1594
Charles Cox, *Manager*
Ron Guzzetta, *Manager*
Charles G Cox, *Executive*
Mickey Shorter, *Representative*
EMP: 25 **Privately Held**
WEB: www.lakeridgewinery.com
SIC: 2084 Wines
PA: Seavin Inc
19239 Us Highway 27
Clermont FL 34715

(G-15608)
SECURITY AND FIRE ELEC INC (PA)
Also Called: Safe
2590 Dobbs Rd (32086-5244)
PHONE..................................904 844-0964
Donald S Grundy, *President*
Donald Grundy, *President*
Joseph Graham, *Vice Pres*
David H Grundy Jr, *Vice Pres*
Keith Randall, *Vice Pres*
EMP: 29 **EST:** 1983
SQ FT: 7,500
SALES: 3.2MM **Privately Held**
WEB: www.safeinc.com
SIC: 3699 1731 8711 Security devices; fire detection & burglar alarm systems specialization; designing: ship, boat, machine & product

(G-15609)
SHRI GURU KRUPA SMOOTHIES INC
112 Sea Grove Main St (32080-3310)
PHONE..................................904 461-9090
Amitbhai I Patel, *Principal*
EMP: 8 **EST:** 2009
SALES (est): 287.9K **Privately Held**
SIC: 2037 Frozen fruits & vegetables

(G-15610)
SIDING INDUSTRIES OF NTHRN FL
225 Ventura Rd (32080-7372)
PHONE..................................904 814-7923
John J Kelleher III, *Principal*
EMP: 6 **EST:** 2017
SALES (est): 99.9K **Privately Held**
WEB: www.sidingindustries.com
SIC: 3999 Manufacturing industries

(G-15611)
SIGNS NOW ST AUGUSTINE INC
1711 Lakeside Ave Ste 1 (32084-4102)
PHONE..................................904 810-5838
Alein Brown, *President*
Brad Brown, *Vice Pres*
EMP: 5 **EST:** 2000
SQ FT: 3,000
SALES (est): 618.7K **Privately Held**
WEB: www.signsnow.com
SIC: 3993 Signs & advertising specialties

(G-15612)
SIGNS UNLIMITED INC
331 A1a Beach Blvd (32080-5901)
PHONE..................................727 845-0330
Michael Rupp, *President*
Sandy Rupp, *Vice Pres*
EMP: 7 **EST:** 1996
SALES (est): 199.5K **Privately Held**
WEB: www.signsunlimitedinc.com
SIC: 3993 7349 Signs & advertising specialties; lighting maintenance service

(G-15613)
SOHACKI INDUSTRIES INC
185 Cumberland Park Dr (32095-8910)
PHONE..................................904 826-0130
Thomas Sohacki, *CEO*
Thomas J Sohacki, *President*
Joshua Sohacki, *Vice Pres*
David Kananen, *Engineer*
Jennifer Uhrie, *Office Mgr*
EMP: 35 **EST:** 1991
SQ FT: 20,000
SALES (est): 6MM **Privately Held**
WEB: www.sohackiindustries.com
SIC: 3545 3544 3599 3724 Gauges (machine tool accessories); die sets for metal stamping (presses); machine shop, jobbing & repair; aircraft engines & engine parts; machine parts, stamped or pressed metal; aircraft parts & equipment

(G-15614)
SOLAR STIK INC (PA)
226 W King St (32084-4144)
PHONE..................................800 793-4364
Brian Bosley, *CEO*
Albert Zaccor, *Principal*
Stephanie D Hollis, *COO*
Brian Alano, *Engineer*
Gene Hollis, *CFO*
▼ **EMP:** 24 **EST:** 2006
SQ FT: 5,000
SALES (est): 5MM **Privately Held**
WEB: www.solarstik.com
SIC: 3621 Generators for storage battery chargers

(G-15615)
SOUTHERN DRYDOCK INC
8153 Six Mile Way (32092-2237)
PHONE..................................904 355-9945
EMP: 28
SQ FT: 4,000
SALES (est): 4.7MM **Privately Held**
SIC: 3731 Shipbuilding/Repairing

(G-15616)
ST AGSTINE BCHES NEWS JRNL LL
415 Talbot Bay Dr (32086-1813)
PHONE..................................904 501-4556
Todd M Logsdon, *Principal*
EMP: 6 **EST:** 2015
SALES (est): 172.9K **Privately Held**
WEB: www.staugustine.com
SIC: 2711 Newspapers, publishing & printing

(G-15617)
ST AGUSTINE ELC MTR WORKS INC
Also Called: Burnett Industrial Sales
14 Center St (32084-2758)
PHONE..................................904 829-8211
Paul W Burnett Jr, *President*
EMP: 10 **EST:** 1961
SQ FT: 7,800
SALES (est): 1.4MM **Privately Held**
WEB: www.staugustineelectricmotorworks.com
SIC: 7694 Electric motor repair

(G-15618)
ST AUGUSTINE DIST CO LLC
112 Riberia St (32084-4351)
P.O. Box 69 (32085-0069)
PHONE..................................904 825-4962
Matt Stevens, *General Mgr*
Lucas Smith, *Production*
Lucy Montecalvo, *Office Mgr*
Suzanne Flammi, *Manager*
Brendan Wheatley, *Director*
EMP: 20 **EST:** 2011
SALES (est): 5.7MM **Privately Held**
WEB: www.staugustinedistillery.com
SIC: 2085 Distilled & blended liquors

(G-15619)
ST AUGUSTINE MARINA INC
404 Riberia St (32084-5108)
PHONE..................................904 824-4394
John H Luhrs, *President*
Shawn Griffin, *Manager*
Dave Bennett, *CIO*
Roger Yarborough, *Executive*
▼ **EMP:** 35 **EST:** 1993
SALES (est): 2.8MM **Privately Held**
WEB: www.mywindward.com
SIC: 3731 Shipbuilding & repairing

(G-15620)
ST AUGUSTINE RECORD
1 News Pl (32086-6520)
PHONE..................................904 829-6562
Fax: 904 819-3558
EMP: 48
SALES (est): 2.7MM **Privately Held**
SIC: 2711 Newspapers-Publishing/Printing

(G-15621)
ST AUGUSTINE TRAWLERS INC
Also Called: St Augustine Shipbuilding
404 Riberia St (32084-5108)
PHONE..................................904 824-4394
V J O'Neal, *President*
Virginia Weatherly, *Corp Secy*
Donald B Capo, *Vice Pres*
EMP: 15 **EST:** 1971
SALES (est): 212.4K **Privately Held**
WEB: www.mywindward.com
SIC: 3731 Shipbuilding & repairing

(G-15622)
STA CABINET DEPOT
320 State Road 16 (32084-1943)
P.O. Box 840014 (32080-0014)
PHONE..................................719 502-5454
Dylan Jabs, *Principal*
EMP: 7 **EST:** 2018
SALES (est): 525.9K **Privately Held**
WEB: www.stacabinetdepot.com
SIC: 2434 Wood kitchen cabinets

(G-15623)
STATURE SOFTWARE LLC
620 Palencia Club Dr # 104 (32095-8840)
PHONE..................................888 782-8881
Joseph Patalano, *Manager*
EMP: 8 **EST:** 2012
SALES (est): 301.2K **Privately Held**
WEB: www.staturesoftware.com
SIC: 7372 Business oriented computer software

(G-15624)
SUNSTATE UAV LLC
1093 A1a Beach Blvd # 170 (32080-6733)
PHONE..................................904 580-4828
Christopher Stumpf,
EMP: 11 **EST:** 2017
SALES (est): 520.5K **Privately Held**
WEB: www.sunstateuav.com
SIC: 3728 Target drones

(G-15625)
SYBO COMPOSITES LLC
404 Riberia St (32084-5108)
PHONE..................................904 599-7093
Dana Greenwood, *Mng Member*
EMP: 8 **EST:** 2009
SALES (est): 221.1K **Privately Held**
WEB: www.sybocomposites.com
SIC: 2655 Cans, composite: foil-fiber & other: from purchased fiber

(G-15626)
TENSOLITE LLC
Also Called: Carlisle Interconnect Tech
100 Tensolite Dr (32092-0590)
PHONE..................................904 829-5600
Ray Tezack, *Plant Mgr*
Sara Cook, *Senior Buyer*
Greg Condrey, *Engineer*
Shawn Jutte, *Engineer*
Peter Kulaga, *Sales Staff*
▲ **EMP:** 1000 **EST:** 1941
SQ FT: 215,000
SALES (est): 192MM
SALES (corp-wide): 4.2B **Publicly Held**
WEB: www.carlisleit.com
SIC: 3357 3679 3643 Nonferrous wiredrawing & insulating; harness assemblies for electronic use: wire or cable; electric connectors
HQ: Carlisle Corporation
11605 N Community Hse Rd
Charlotte NC 28277

(G-15627)
TREETOP INDUSTRIES LLC
219 Marshside Dr (32080-5836)
PHONE..................................904 471-4412
EMP: 7 **EST:** 2018
SALES (est): 39.6K **Privately Held**
WEB: www.treetop.com
SIC: 3999 Manufacturing industries

(G-15628)
TUISKOMBUIS
3790 Winterhawk Ct (32086-5571)
PHONE..................................904 484-4509
Luzaan Olivier, *Principal*
EMP: 6 **EST:** 2010
SALES (est): 80K **Privately Held**
WEB: www.tuiskombuis.com
SIC: 2038 Ethnic foods, frozen

(G-15629)
UPSTREAM INSTALLATION INC
1835 Us Highway 1 S # 119 (32084-4294)
PHONE..................................904 829-3507
Andrew Voss, *President*
EMP: 5
SALES (est): 450K **Privately Held**
SIC: 2426 Flooring, hardwood

(G-15630)
US MARINE CANVAS
2475 Deer Run Rd (32084-1118)
PHONE..................................904 687-5058
Tabatha Noyes, *Principal*
EMP: 6 **EST:** 2015
SALES (est): 56.3K **Privately Held**
WEB: www.usmarinecanvas.com
SIC: 2394 Canvas & related products

(G-15631)
VESTED METALS INTL LLC
7000 Us Highway 1 N # 503 (32095-8373)
PHONE..................................904 495-7278
Vivian Helwig, *CEO*
EMP: 8 **EST:** 2014
SALES: 4.3MM **Privately Held**
WEB: www.vestedmetals.net
SIC: 3499 5051 Machine bases, metal; metals service centers & offices

(G-15632)
VESTEN WOODWORKS LLC
200 Colorado Springs Way (32092-1926)
PHONE..................................407 780-9295
Steven D Williamson Jr, *Principal*
EMP: 6 **EST:** 2016
SALES (est): 198.8K **Privately Held**
WEB: www.vestenwoodworks.com
SIC: 2431 Millwork

(G-15633)
VILANO INTERIORS INC
112 Oak Ave (32084-2346)
PHONE..................................904 824-3439
Anthony Comeau, *President*
Rhoda Comeau, *Owner*
EMP: 8 **EST:** 1968
SALES (est): 400K **Privately Held**
WEB: www.vilanobeachfl.com
SIC: 3732 Boat building & repairing

(G-15634)
WEBIDCARD INC
Also Called: Swipe K12 School Solutions
89 Mitad Cir (32095-7445)
PHONE..................................443 280-1577
John Amatruda, *CEO*
EMP: 6 **EST:** 2005
SQ FT: 3,000
SALES (est): 471K **Privately Held**
WEB: www.swipesolutionsinc.com
SIC: 7372 Prepackaged software

(G-15635)
WHETSTONE INDUS HOLDINGS INC (PA)
100 Whetstone Pl Ste 100 # 100 (32086-5775)
PHONE..................................904 824-0888
Henry M Whetstone Jr, *President*
EMP: 6 **EST:** 2004
SALES (est): 1.6MM **Privately Held**
SIC: 3569 Liquid automation machinery & equipment

(G-15636)
WHETSTONE INDUSTRIES INC
Also Called: Whetstone Chocolate Factory
100 Whetstone Pl Ste 100 # 100 (32086-5775)
PHONE..................................904 824-0888
Henry M Whetstone Jr, *President*
Greg Morris, *Prdtn Mgr*
EMP: 10 **EST:** 2009
SALES (est): 1.6MM **Privately Held**
WEB: www.firstcoastpulmonary.com
SIC: 2026 Milk, chocolate
PA: Whetstone Industrial Holdings, Inc.
100 Whetstone Pl Ste 100 # 100
Saint Augustine FL 32086

(G-15637)
WILSON MACHINE & WELDING WORKS
5760 Us Highway 1 N (32095-8005)
PHONE..................................904 829-3737
Marvin Wilson, *President*
Janice Wilson, *Corp Secy*
EMP: 8 **EST:** 1957
SQ FT: 3,200
SALES (est): 856.4K **Privately Held**
WEB: www.wilson-machine-welding-works-wilson.business.site
SIC: 3599 7692 Machine shop, jobbing & repair; welding repair

(G-15638)
WINDOWWARE PRO
2085 A1a S Ste 201 (32080-6506)
PHONE..................................904 584-9191
EMP: 8 **EST:** 2016
SALES (est): 208.3K **Privately Held**
WEB: www.windowwarepro.com
SIC: 7372 Prepackaged software

(G-15639)
WOODSHED WOODWORKS LLC
55 Florida Ave (32084-3163)
PHONE..................................904 540-0354
David S Hightower, *Principal*
EMP: 8 **EST:** 2015
SALES (est): 502.6K **Privately Held**
SIC: 2431 Woodwork, interior & ornamental

(G-15640)
YIELD DESIGN
Also Called: Yield - St. Augustine
25 Palmer St (32084-3445)
PHONE..................................402 321-2196
Rachel Grant, *COO*
▲ **EMP:** 5 **EST:** 2014
SALES (est): 368.1K **Privately Held**
WEB: www.yielddesign.co
SIC: 2511 Novelty furniture: wood

Saint Cloud
Osceola County

(G-15641)
50 50 PARMLEY ENVMTL SVCS LLC
913 Robinson Ave (34769-2063)
PHONE..................................407 593-1165
Scott Brown, *Mng Member*
Rick Parmley, *Mng Member*
Rory Parmley, *Mng Member*
EMP: 7 **EST:** 2018
SALES (est): 300K **Privately Held**
SIC: 3523 7342 Spreaders, fertilizer; pest control in structures

(G-15642)
AADI INC
Also Called: St Cloud Door Company
190 E 12th St (34769-3937)
PHONE..................................407 957-4557
Kamlesh Shah, *President*
Ashok Shah, *Vice Pres*
Naresh Shah, *Vice Pres*
Vasant Shah, *Treasurer*
Kenny Shah, *Mktg Coord*
◆ **EMP:** 38 **EST:** 1992
SQ FT: 18,000
SALES (est): 4.8MM **Privately Held**
WEB: www.stclouddoors.com
SIC: 2434 Wood kitchen cabinets

(G-15643)
AMERA TRAIL INC
4840 E I Bronson Memrl (34771)
PHONE..................................407 892-1100
Scott Locke, *President*
Mark Ackerman, *General Mgr*
Diane Bradshaw, *Persnl Dir*
Andy Dormois, *Natl Sales Mgr*
John Bonis, *Sales Mgr*
▼ **EMP:** 40 **EST:** 1985
SQ FT: 24,000
SALES (est): 9.8MM **Privately Held**
WEB: www.ameratrail.com
SIC: 3799 3537 7539 5599 Boat trailers; trailers & trailer equipment; industrial trucks & tractors; trailer repair; utility trailers

(G-15644)
BELGIUM CO INC
1100 Grape Ave Ste 1 (34769-3914)
PHONE..................................407 957-1886
Ivan Mazzaro, *President*
Nino Mazzaro, *Vice Pres*
Gino Mazzaro, *Treasurer*
Lorraine Haussmann, *Sales Mgr*
EMP: 14 **EST:** 1977
SALES (est): 1MM **Privately Held**
WEB: www.thebelgiumco.com
SIC: 2099 Butter, renovated & processed

(G-15645)
BEYERS WELDING INC
4950 Canoe Creek Rd (34772-9183)
PHONE..................................407 892-2834
Earl F Beyer, *Principal*
EMP: 6 **EST:** 1995
SALES (est): 25K **Privately Held**
SIC: 7692 Welding repair

(G-15646)
BIOTOXINS INC
Also Called: Reptile World
5705 E I Bronson Memrl (34771)
PHONE..................................407 892-6905
George Van Horne, *President*
Bonnie Watkins, *Treasurer*
EMP: 6 **EST:** 1972
SQ FT: 2,500
SALES (est): 763.1K **Privately Held**
WEB: www.reptileworldserpentarium.com
SIC: 2836 7999 Venoms; tourist attraction, commercial

(G-15647)
COMPLETE ACCESS CTRL CENTL FLA
2013 Jaffa Dr (34771-5835)
PHONE..................................407 498-0067
Karen P Mauro, *President*
Kandice Apy, *Vice Pres*
EMP: 7 **EST:** 2014
SALES (est): 1.5MM **Privately Held**
WEB: www.cacocf.com
SIC: 3315 3699 Fence gates posts & fittings: steel; welding machines & equipment, ultrasonic

(G-15648)
CORY AUN
3275 Burberry Pl (34772-8759)
PHONE..................................407 957-1133
Cory Aun, *Principal*
EMP: 6 **EST:** 2010
SALES (est): 85.3K **Privately Held**
SIC: 3523 Farm machinery & equipment

(G-15649)
DP INDUSTRIES INC
6375 Carroll Cir (34771-9772)
PHONE..................................321 356-3352
Anthony W Moore, *Principal*
EMP: 8 **EST:** 2017
SALES (est): 220.7K **Privately Held**
WEB: www.dpindustries.com
SIC: 3999 Manufacturing industries

(G-15650)
FLORIDA CUSTOM FABRICATORS
2315 Tyson Rd (34771-7769)
P.O. Box 700668 (34770-0668)
PHONE..................................407 892-8538
Wesley Lassiter, *President*
Ronald Lasitter, *Principal*
Carol Lassiter, *Vice Pres*
EMP: 17 **EST:** 1967
SQ FT: 10,000
SALES (est): 1.5MM **Privately Held**
SIC: 2514 3431 3441 Metal kitchen & dining room furniture; sinks: enameled iron, cast iron or pressed metal; fabricated structural metal

(G-15651)
FOCUS COMMUNITY PUBLICATIONS
980 Orange Ave (34769-3923)
PHONE..................................407 892-0019
Betty Hawes, *President*
Dennis Hawes, *Vice Pres*
EMP: 6 **EST:** 1994
SALES (est): 1.5MM **Privately Held**
WEB:
www.focuscommunitypublications.com
SIC: 2741 Miscellaneous publishing

GEOGRAPHIC

(G-15652)
FREIGHT TRAIN TRUCKING CORP
2503 Bross Dr (34771-7809)
PHONE....................................407 509-0611
Elgin Jefferson, *President*
EMP: 7
SALES (est): 611.5K **Privately Held**
SIC: 3715 Truck trailers

(G-15653)
HESS STATION 09307
Also Called: Amerada Stores
4500 13th St (34769-6706)
PHONE....................................407 891-7156
John Hess, *President*
EMP: 10
SALES (est): 571.9K **Privately Held**
SIC: 1382 Oil & gas exploration services

(G-15654)
HOSELINE INC
1619 Park Commerce Ct (34769-4707)
PHONE....................................407 892-2599
Linda Grafton, *President*
William W Grafton, *Vice Pres*
Matt Grafton, *Sales Staff*
EMP: 13 **EST:** 1985
SQ FT: 15,000
SALES (est): 1.5MM **Privately Held**
WEB: www.hoseline.com
SIC: 3585 Air conditioning, motor vehicle

(G-15655)
IBR LLC
1580 Lake Parkway Dr (34771-8893)
PHONE....................................407 694-6748
Dusan Kuzmanovic, *Principal*
EMP: 6 **EST:** 2006
SALES (est): 163.3K **Privately Held**
SIC: 3652 Pre-recorded records & tapes

(G-15656)
KEMPFER SAWMILL INC
6254 Kempfer Rd (34773-9363)
PHONE....................................407 892-2955
William C Kempfer, *President*
EMP: 16 **EST:** 1984
SALES (est): 1MM **Privately Held**
WEB: www.kempfercattleco.com
SIC: 2421 Sawmills & planing mills, general

(G-15657)
LUCKY DOG PRINTING INC
1404 Hamlin Ave (34771-8585)
PHONE....................................407 346-1663
Don Rogers, *Principal*
▲ **EMP:** 12 **EST:** 2012
SALES (est): 706.1K **Privately Held**
WEB: www.luckydogprinting.com
SIC: 2752 Commercial printing, offset

(G-15658)
MASTERS BLOCK - NORTH LLC
1037 New York Ave (34769-3781)
PHONE....................................407 212-7704
Martha Hauser, *Manager*
EMP: 5 **EST:** 2016
SQ FT: 1,300
SALES (est): 308.7K **Privately Held**
SIC: 2951 3271 3251 5032 Paving blocks; paving blocks, concrete; structural brick & blocks; building blocks; industrial buildings, new construction

(G-15659)
MEGAMALLS INC
Also Called: St Cloud Prtg Signs & Cstm AP
2432 13th St (34769-4127)
P.O. Box 701215 (34770-1215)
PHONE....................................407 891-2111
Robert Caruso, *President*
Lynn Carptender, *CFO*
EMP: 11 **EST:** 1992
SQ FT: 3,750
SALES (est): 946.2K **Privately Held**
WEB: www.stcloudprinting.net
SIC: 2752 Commercial printing, offset

(G-15660)
MIKES ALUMINUM PRODUCTS LLC
4445 Story Rd (34772-8918)
PHONE....................................407 855-1989
Michael Lebruno, *Mng Member*
EMP: 7 **EST:** 1984
SALES (est): 925.1K **Privately Held**
WEB: www.maxantusa.com
SIC: 3469 Metal stampings

(G-15661)
MIRAGE & CO INC
3826 Cedar Hammock Trl (34772-8732)
PHONE....................................407 301-5850
Luis Carlos Freites, *Vice Pres*
EMP: 22 **EST:** 2010
SALES (est): 144.1K **Privately Held**
WEB: www.mirage-mfg.com
SIC: 3732 Boats, fiberglass: building & repairing

(G-15662)
MONUMENTAL RESOLUTIONS INC
1253 Hancock Cir (34769-6768)
PHONE....................................407 973-3577
Aaron Reid, *Principal*
EMP: 6 **EST:** 2017
SALES (est): 91.3K **Privately Held**
SIC: 3272 Monuments & grave markers, except terrazo

(G-15663)
ORANGE PEEL GAZETTE INC
145 E 13th St (34769-4749)
P.O. Box 700792 (34770-0792)
PHONE....................................407 892-5556
Gregory Ke Tester, *Principal*
EMP: 7 **EST:** 2000
SALES (est): 255.3K **Privately Held**
WEB: www.orangepeelgazette.com
SIC: 2711 7313 Newspapers: publishing only, not printed on site; newspaper advertising representative

(G-15664)
ORANGE PEEL GZTTE OF OSCOLA CN (PA)
145 E 13th St (34769-4749)
PHONE....................................407 892-5556
Melissa A Taliento, *Principal*
EMP: 18 **EST:** 2011
SALES (est): 156.2K **Privately Held**
WEB: www.opgosceola.com
SIC: 2711 Newspapers, publishing & printing

(G-15665)
SCHOEN INDUSTRIES INC
4831 Calasans Ave (34771-8269)
PHONE....................................305 491-5993
Marc A Schoen, *Principal*
EMP: 6 **EST:** 2017
SALES (est): 148.3K **Privately Held**
SIC: 3999 Manufacturing industries

(G-15666)
SHANE LALIBERTE LIFT LLC
6449 Adam St (34771-9495)
PHONE....................................407 873-0703
Shane Laliberte, *President*
EMP: 7 **EST:** 2006
SALES (est): 249.1K **Privately Held**
SIC: 3537 Forklift trucks

(G-15667)
ST CLOUD WLDG FABRICATION INC
Also Called: St. Cloud Wldg & Fabrication
3724 Hickory Tree Rd (34772-7548)
P.O. Box 701475 (34770-1475)
PHONE....................................407 957-2344
Bobbie Jean Lollis, *President*
Quient O'Dell Lollis, *Vice Pres*
Dan Leblond, *Project Mgr*
Gene Lollis, *Director*
Jane Lollis, *Admin Sec*
EMP: 23 **EST:** 1976
SQ FT: 5,200
SALES (est): 5MM **Privately Held**
WEB: www.stcloudwelding.com
SIC: 7692 7699 5074 1799 Welding repair; boiler repair shop; heating equipment (hydronic); welding on site

(G-15668)
STEPHEN ODONNELL
5221 Hammock Cir (34771-8766)
PHONE....................................631 664-3594
Stephen O'Donnell, *Principal*
EMP: 7 **EST:** 2017
SALES (est): 111.9K **Privately Held**
SIC: 3089 Plastics products

(G-15669)
SYNERGY REHAB TECHNOLOGIES INC
1404 Hamlin Ave Unit B (34771-8585)
PHONE....................................407 943-7500
Paul A Barattiero, *President*
Laura Shantz, *Vice Pres*
Jacqueline M Barattiero, *Admin Sec*
EMP: 9 **EST:** 2005
SALES (est): 974.5K **Privately Held**
WEB: www.synergyrehab.net
SIC: 3842 Wheelchairs; canes, orthopedic; crutches & walkers

(G-15670)
WOODYS ENTERPRISES LLC
1110b Quotation Ct (34772-5432)
PHONE....................................407 892-1900
Kent S Bowers, *Principal*
Yvonne Glentz, *Asst Mgr*
EMP: 13 **EST:** 2007
SALES (est): 2.6MM **Privately Held**
WEB: www.woodysenterprises.com
SIC: 3088 Shower stalls, fiberglass & plastic

(G-15671)
ZEEEES CORPORATION
Also Called: Fine D-Zign Signs
2008 Jaffa Dr Ste D (34771-5831)
PHONE....................................407 624-3796
Curt Zielinski, *President*
EMP: 8 **EST:** 2016
SALES (est): 541.2K **Privately Held**
SIC: 3993 7336 Signs, not made in custom sign painting shops; graphic arts & related design

Saint James City
Lee County

(G-15672)
1ST ENVIRO-SAFETY INC
10200 Betsy Pkwy (33956-3223)
PHONE....................................239 283-1222
Julius Tidwell, *CEO*
Ted Tidwell, *CEO*
Leon Hesser, *President*
Ann P Tidwell, *President*
EMP: 7 **EST:** 1997
SQ FT: 4,000
SALES (est): 972.2K **Privately Held**
WEB: www.1stenvirosafety.com
SIC: 2842 Specialty cleaning preparations

Saint Johns
St. Johns County

(G-15673)
AR2 PRODUCTS LLC
Also Called: Gopole
1820 State Road 13 Ste 11 (32259-8855)
PHONE....................................800 667-1263
Russell Van Zile, *CEO*
Ryan Vosburg, *Vice Pres*
Anthony Anari, *Opers Staff*
▲ **EMP:** 6 **EST:** 2011
SALES (est): 4.3MM **Privately Held**
WEB: www.gopole.com
SIC: 3861 Cameras & related equipment; lens shades, camera; light meters, camera; shutters, camera

(G-15674)
CABINET OPTIONS INC
1170 Executive Cove Dr (32259-2801)
PHONE....................................904 434-1564
Thomas Legg, *Principal*
EMP: 7 **EST:** 2007
SALES (est): 190.4K **Privately Held**
SIC: 2434 Wood kitchen cabinets

(G-15675)
CUSTOM CUT RUBBER
617 Acorn Ct (32259-5405)
PHONE....................................979 422-2511
Shawn Lundy Spear, *Owner*
EMP: 6 **EST:** 2016
SALES (est): 168.8K **Privately Held**
SIC: 3993 Signs & advertising specialties

(G-15676)
DEPENDABLE WATER INC
320 W Blackjack Br Way (32259-1904)
PHONE....................................904 599-0560
Shandilay Dave, *Branch Mgr*
EMP: 6
SALES (corp-wide): 362.1K **Privately Held**
WEB: www.dependablewaterinc.com
SIC: 2834 Chlorination tablets & kits (water purification)
PA: Dependable Water Inc
7956 102nd Ct
Vero Beach FL 32967
772 563-7473

(G-15677)
DM STRATTON LLC
564 Magnolia Ave (32259-9022)
PHONE....................................904 342-7063
EMP: 6 **EST:** 2017
SALES (est): 261.7K **Privately Held**
SIC: 2411 Logging

(G-15678)
HUMIC GROWTH SOLUTIONS INC
112 Badger Park Dr (32259-2179)
PHONE....................................904 329-1012
Kevin Merritt, *President*
EMP: 9
SALES (corp-wide): 10MM **Privately Held**
SIC: 2879 Soil conditioners
PA: Humic Growth Solutions, Inc.
709 Eastport Rd
Jacksonville FL 32218
904 392-7201

(G-15679)
MCKINNEY WOODWORKING INC
105 Greenbriar Estates Dr (32259-1117)
PHONE....................................904 591-1233
William L McKinney Jr, *Director*
EMP: 6 **EST:** 2001
SALES (est): 71.7K **Privately Held**
SIC: 2431 Millwork

(G-15680)
POPPIN BOX LLC
116 Bartram Oaks Walk (32259-3265)
PHONE....................................904 484-7030
Christine Espinosa, *Mng Member*
James S Aller III, *Mng Member*
EMP: 6 **EST:** 2016
SALES (est): 258.2K **Privately Held**
WEB: www.thepoppinbox.com
SIC: 2064 5411 Popcorn balls or other treated popcorn products; co-operative food stores

(G-15681)
TAVTEK LLC (PA)
450 State Road 13 Ste 106 (32259-3863)
PHONE....................................904 907-7749
Eric Veale, *Manager*
EMP: 7 **EST:** 2018
SALES (est): 204.5K **Privately Held**
WEB: www.tavtekmachine.com
SIC: 3599 Machine shop, jobbing & repair

(G-15682)
TAVTEK LLC
2557 Pheasant Ct W (32259-8353)
PHONE....................................904 907-7749
Eric Veale, *Branch Mgr*
EMP: 7
SALES (corp-wide): 204.5K **Privately Held**
WEB: www.tavtekmachine.com
SIC: 3599 Machine shop, jobbing & repair
PA: Tavtek Llc
450 State Road 13 Ste 106
Saint Johns FL 32259
904 907-7749

(G-15683)
US WOOD WORK & SERVICE
372 W Tropical Trce (32259-1934)
PHONE....................................954 675-7153
Leandro S Silva, *President*

EMP: 6 **EST:** 2016
SALES (est): 128K **Privately Held**
SIC: 2431 Millwork

(G-15684)
VIDACANN LLC
4844 Race Track Rd (32259-2090)
PHONE..................................772 672-1178
David Loop,
EMP: 11 **EST:** 2017
SALES (est): 766K **Privately Held**
WEB: www.vidacann.com
SIC: 3999

(G-15685)
VISION BENEFITS 4 ALL INC
652 Hummingbird Ct (32259-4316)
PHONE..................................888 317-0606
Deborah Stokes, *President*
Karen Stokes, *Vice Pres*
EMP: 6 **EST:** 2012
SALES (est): 307.2K **Privately Held**
WEB: www.visionbenefits4all.com
SIC: 3851 5995 Ophthalmic goods; eyeglasses, prescription

Saint Lucie West
St. Lucie County

(G-15686)
JQ GREEN AMERICA INC
651 Nw Entp Dr Ste 109 (34986)
PHONE..................................786 397-0999
Hao Jin, *President*
EMP: 8 **EST:** 2017
SALES (est): 269.6K **Privately Held**
WEB: www.jqamerica.com
SIC: 3641 5063 Electric light bulbs, complete; light bulbs & related supplies

Saint Petersburg
Pinellas County

(G-15687)
A CHEAPER SHOT LLC ✪
4604 49th St N (33709-3842)
PHONE..................................727 221-3237
Anthony Thompson,
EMP: 10 **EST:** 2021
SALES (est): 150K **Privately Held**
SIC: 3799 Transportation equipment

(G-15688)
A TO Z CONCRETE PRODUCTS INC
Also Called: Stable Concrete Product
4451 8th Ave S (33711-1903)
PHONE..................................727 321-6000
Graeme Malloch, *CEO*
William Majewski, *President*
Shaun Beesley, *Manager*
EMP: 13 **EST:** 1990
SQ FT: 20,000
SALES (est): 647.2K **Privately Held**
SIC: 3272 1542 Concrete stuctural support & building material; building materials, except block or brick: concrete; wall & ceiling squares, concrete; custom builders, non-residential

(G-15689)
AARON MEDICAL INDUSTRIES INC
7100 30th Ave N (33710-2902)
PHONE..................................727 384-2323
Janis Dezso, *Director*
EMP: 7 **EST:** 1970
SALES (est): 123.9K **Privately Held**
SIC: 3841 Surgical & medical instruments

(G-15690)
ACE HIGH PRINTING LLC
3801 16th St N Ste B (33703-5601)
PHONE..................................727 542-3897
Richard A Herbert, *Manager*
EMP: 7 **EST:** 2010
SALES (est): 174.5K **Privately Held**
WEB: www.acehighprint.com
SIC: 2752 Commercial printing, offset

(G-15691)
ADVANCED MANUFACTURING INC
12205 28th St N (33716-1823)
PHONE..................................727 573-3300
Gary Kinley, *President*
Peter Dorflinger, *Corp Secy*
Amy Goodman, *Purchasing*
Leo Suchor, *Controller*
◆ **EMP:** 30 **EST:** 1998
SQ FT: 15,000
SALES (est): 4.7MM
SALES (corp-wide): 17.9MM **Privately Held**
WEB: www.amifla.com
SIC: 3679 3829 3823 3672 Electronic circuits; measuring & controlling devices; industrial instrmnts msrmnt display/control process variable; printed circuit boards; electron tubes; motors & generators
PA: Advanced Medical Instruments, Inc.
3061 W Albany St
Broken Arrow OK 74012
918 250-0566

(G-15692)
AEROSMART ENTERPRISE LLC ✪
7901 4th St N Ste 300 (33702-4399)
PHONE..................................310 499-8878
Eric Valdes, *Principal*
EMP: 31 **EST:** 2021
SALES (est): 1MM **Privately Held**
SIC: 3721 Aircraft

(G-15693)
AEROSPACE COMPONENTS INC
2625 75th St N (33710-2932)
PHONE..................................727 347-9915
Alan Kussy, *President*
Kimberly Kussy, *Vice Pres*
EMP: 16 **EST:** 1986
SALES (est): 2.5MM **Privately Held**
WEB: www.aerospacecomponents.com
SIC: 3599 Machine shop, jobbing & repair
HQ: Hartzell Engine Technologies Llc
2900 Selma Hwy
Montgomery AL 36108

(G-15694)
AFFORDABLE WHEELCHAIR TRANSPRT
6192 39th Ave N (33709-5208)
PHONE..................................727 432-4089
Sharon M Frost, *President*
Jay Roberts, *Pub Rel Staff*
Shannon Villar, *Admin Asst*
EMP: 7 **EST:** 2011
SALES (est): 61.4K **Privately Held**
WEB: www.wheelchairtransport.com
SIC: 3842 Wheelchairs

(G-15695)
AGORA SALES INC (PA)
Also Called: Agora Leather Products
2101 28th St N (33713-4246)
PHONE..................................727 321-0707
Subhash Dave, *President*
Ragu Molleti, *Business Mgr*
Jagat Trivedi, *Vice Pres*
Marco Ramaciere, *Mfg Mgr*
John Hobko, *Purch Mgr*
▲ **EMP:** 267 **EST:** 1985
SQ FT: 36,000
SALES (est): 30.6MM **Privately Held**
WEB: www.agoraedge.com
SIC: 3161 Cases, carrying

(G-15696)
AIR TECHNICAL LLC ✪
7901 4th St N Ste 4612 (33702-4305)
PHONE..................................305 837-3274
Ibrahim Sisic,
EMP: 10 **EST:** 2020
SALES (est): 283.1K **Privately Held**
SIC: 3999 Manufacturing industries

(G-15697)
ALPS SOUTH LLC
Also Called: Alps Orthotics
2895 42nd Ave N (33714-4547)
PHONE..................................727 528-8566
Aldo Laghi, *President*
Kevin McLoone, *Vice Pres*
Jessica Plomatos, *Opers Mgr*
Tommy Hakvongsa, *Mfg Staff*
Jakob McClelland, *Engineer*
▲ **EMP:** 85 **EST:** 1993
SQ FT: 20,000
SALES (est): 18.3MM **Privately Held**
WEB: www.easyliner.com
SIC: 3842 Prosthetic appliances

(G-15698)
ALUMFLO INC
2445 51st Ave N (33714-2601)
PHONE..................................727 527-8494
Wanetta Rodriguez, *President*
Mark Daniel, *Vice Pres*
Steve Rodriguez, *Vice Pres*
EMP: 8 **EST:** 1987
SQ FT: 10,000
SALES (est): 1.5MM **Privately Held**
WEB: www.alumflo.com
SIC: 3444 Awnings, sheet metal

(G-15699)
AMERICAN FIBERTEK INC
Also Called: Afi
745 43rd St S (33711-1920)
PHONE..................................732 302-0660
Jack Fernandes, *President*
Edward Davis, *Vice Pres*
EMP: 50
SALES (est): 10.3MM **Privately Held**
WEB: www.americanfibertek.com
SIC: 3679 3577 Electronic circuits; input/output equipment, computer

(G-15700)
ANAIAH PRESS LLC
6921 39th Ave N (33709-4603)
PHONE..................................727 692-0025
Rose Plantz, *Principal*
EMP: 7 **EST:** 2013
SALES (est): 101.8K **Privately Held**
WEB: www.anaiahpress.wordpress.com
SIC: 2741 Miscellaneous publishing

(G-15701)
ANIMAL BUSINESS CONCEPTS LLC
Also Called: Cool Pet Holistics
3235 Fairfield Ave S (33712-1800)
P.O. Box 76405 (33734-6405)
PHONE..................................727 641-6176
Jennifer G Lewis, *Partner*
Jonathan Lewis,
EMP: 11 **EST:** 2004
SALES (est): 1.7MM **Privately Held**
WEB: www.liquidvet.com
SIC: 2048 Feed supplements

(G-15702)
AOC TECHNOLOGIES INC
10560 Dr Martin L Kng Jr (33716-3718)
PHONE..................................727 577-9749
EMP: 12 **EST:** 2016
SALES (est): 544.5K
SALES (corp-wide): 27.2B **Publicly Held**
WEB: www.jabil.com
SIC: 3672 Printed circuit boards
PA: Jabil Inc.
10560 Dr Mrtn Lther King
Saint Petersburg FL 33716
727 577-9749

(G-15703)
AOG DETAILING SERVICES INC
6798 Crosswinds Dr N B203 (33710-5481)
PHONE..................................727 742-7321
Permeseur Rampersaud, *President*
EMP: 7 **EST:** 2004
SALES (est): 522.9K **Privately Held**
SIC: 3441 8711 1791 Fabricated structural metal; engineering services; structural steel erection

(G-15704)
AQUACAL (PA)
2730 24th St N (33713-4046)
PHONE..................................727 898-2412
William Kent, *CEO*
Lynn Dean, *Manager*
Don Tuch, *Manager*
▼ **EMP:** 22 **EST:** 2010
SALES (est): 12.5MM **Privately Held**
WEB: www.aquacal.com
SIC: 3999 Hot tubs

(G-15705)
AQUACAL AUTOPILOT INC
2737 24th St N (33713-4037)
PHONE..................................727 823-5642
William Kent, *President*
Kent William A, *Principal*
Gary Chisling, *Vice Pres*
Jeff Tawney, *Vice Pres*
Gerson Martinez, *Engineer*
◆ **EMP:** 150 **EST:** 1992
SQ FT: 35,000
SALES (est): 47.6MM **Privately Held**
WEB: www.aquacal.com
SIC: 3585 3569 Air conditioning units, complete: domestic or industrial; heaters, swimming pool: electric

(G-15706)
AQUAFLEX PRINTING LLC
3349 118th Ave N (33716-1852)
PHONE..................................727 914-4922
Tony D Mittelstaedt, *Administration*
EMP: 6 **EST:** 2014
SALES (est): 115.8K **Privately Held**
SIC: 2752 Commercial printing, offset

(G-15707)
ARCHITCTRAL WD WKG MLDING DIV
3291 40th Ave N (33714-4512)
PHONE..................................727 527-7400
Alan Regel, *President*
Richard Regal, *Vice Pres*
EMP: 10 **EST:** 1994
SQ FT: 15,625
SALES (est): 1MM **Privately Held**
WEB: www.architecturalwoodworking.com
SIC: 2431 Millwork

(G-15708)
ARCHITECTURAL FOUNTAINS INC
2010 28th St N (33713-4223)
PHONE..................................727 323-6068
John Stack, *President*
Cathleen Stack, *Vice Pres*
EMP: 5 **EST:** 1983
SQ FT: 3,000
SALES (est): 400K **Privately Held**
WEB: www.architecturalfountaininc.com
SIC: 3272 3299 3499 Fountains, concrete; fountains, plaster of paris; fountains (except drinking), metal

(G-15709)
ARGOS READY MIX LLC
1020 31st St S (33712-1925)
PHONE..................................727 321-4667
EMP: 6 **EST:** 2017
SALES (est): 185.9K **Privately Held**
SIC: 3273 Ready-mixed concrete

(G-15710)
ARJ ART INC
Also Called: Manatee Shirts and Graphics
517 35th Ave N (33704-1233)
PHONE..................................727 535-8633
Richard Groth, *Managing Prtnr*
Mary Kitchin, *Partner*
EMP: 8 **EST:** 2004
SALES (est): 552.7K **Privately Held**
WEB: www.livjaxdan.com
SIC: 2759 Screen printing

(G-15711)
ART & FRAME SOURCE INC (PA)
4251 34th St N (33714-3707)
PHONE..................................727 329-6502
Steven Press, *President*
Mona Press, *Vice Pres*
◆ **EMP:** 35 **EST:** 1978
SQ FT: 17,000
SALES (est): 3.5MM **Privately Held**
WEB: www.artandframesourceinc.com
SIC: 3952 5023 Frames for artists' canvases; home furnishings

(G-15712)
ARTFUL ARNAUTIC ASSEMBLIES LLC
2877 47th Ave N (33714-3129)
PHONE..................................727 522-0055
Todd Freund,
EMP: 6 **EST:** 2015

SALES (est): 403.3K **Privately Held**
WEB: www.artfulaeronautic.com
SIC: 3625 Marine & navy auxiliary controls

(G-15713)
ARTFUL CANVAS DESIGN INC
2877 47th Ave N (33714-3129)
PHONE..................................727 521-0212
Todd Freund, *President*
EMP: 20 **EST:** 1996
SALES (est): 2.9MM **Privately Held**
WEB: www.artfulcanvas.com
SIC: 2394 3441 Canvas boat seats; fabricated structural metal for ships

(G-15714)
ATMCENTRAL
6468 5th Ave S (33707-2333)
PHONE..................................727 345-8460
Barbara Scian, *Principal*
John C Little, *VP Opers*
Jon Taylor, *Technician*
EMP: 5 **EST:** 2007
SALES (est): 407.2K **Privately Held**
WEB: www.atmcentral.com
SIC: 3578 6099 Automatic teller machines (ATM); automated teller machine (ATM) network

(G-15715)
ATTRACTION CENTER PUBG LLC
970 Lake Carillon Dr # 3 (33716-1129)
PHONE..................................814 422-5683
EMP: 6 **EST:** 2017
SALES (est): 112.2K **Privately Held**
WEB: www.attractioncenterpublishing.com
SIC: 2741 Miscellaneous publishing

(G-15716)
AURORA SEMICONDUCTOR LLC
9900 16th St N (33716-4230)
PHONE..................................727 235-6500
EMP: 30
SALES (est): 477.9K **Privately Held**
SIC: 3674 Semiconductors And Related Devices, Nsk

(G-15717)
BARNETT & PUGLIANO INC
200 2nd Ave S (33701-4313)
PHONE..................................727 826-6075
Joseph M Pugliano, *CEO*
George D Sheets, *Vice Pres*
EMP: 9 **EST:** 1998
SALES (est): 197.7K **Privately Held**
SIC: 2752 Commercial printing, lithographic

(G-15718)
BAY CITY WINDOW COMPANY
Also Called: Windows Doors Etc
3220 Bennett St N Ste A (33713-2645)
PHONE..................................727 323-5443
Devin Zimring, *President*
Gina Discianno, *General Mgr*
EMP: 18 **EST:** 1993
SALES (est): 3.6MM **Privately Held**
WEB: www.windowsdoorsetcflorida.com
SIC: 3089 2824 Window frames & sash, plastic; vinyl fibers

(G-15719)
BAYFRONT PRINTING COMPANY
Also Called: Image360 St Petersburg Central
2235 16th Ave N (33713-5623)
PHONE..................................727 823-1965
Algimantas Karnavicius, *President*
Nancy Karnavicius, *Vice Pres*
Laura Guetzloe, *Prdtn Mgr*
EMP: 5 **EST:** 1981
SQ FT: 5,000
SALES (est): 667.1K **Privately Held**
WEB: www.bayprintonline.com
SIC: 3993 2752 Signs & advertising specialties; commercial printing, lithographic

(G-15720)
BIDDISCOMBE INTERNATIONAL LLC
Also Called: Biddiscombe Labs Stylz Pdts
11961 31st Ct N (33716-1808)
PHONE..................................727 299-9287
John H Melville, *President*
Karen Swartz, *Office Mgr*
William Van Valzah, *Manager*
EMP: 10 **EST:** 1980
SQ FT: 8,500
SALES (est): 1.3MM **Privately Held**
WEB: www.biddiscombe.com
SIC: 2844 Cosmetic preparations

(G-15721)
BIG FISH CO CUSTOM CREATIONS
3128 Dr M L K Jr St N Mlk (33704)
PHONE..................................727 525-5010
Carrie Amos Renner, *Principal*
EMP: 8 **EST:** 2008
SALES (est): 993.7K **Privately Held**
WEB: www.bigfishco.com
SIC: 2339 Women's & misses' outerwear

(G-15722)
BLIND MOUTH BREWING CO LLC
3701 50th Ave S (33711-4829)
PHONE..................................727 318-7664
Brenden Markopoulos, *Principal*
EMP: 6 **EST:** 2016
SALES (est): 62.3K **Privately Held**
SIC: 2082 Malt beverages

(G-15723)
BLUE GARDENIA LLC
661 Central Ave (33701-3633)
PHONE..................................727 560-0040
Richard T Alday, *Principal*
EMP: 7 **EST:** 2016
SALES (est): 301.6K **Privately Held**
SIC: 3949 Sporting & athletic goods

(G-15724)
BLUEWATER MARINE SYSTEMS INC ✪
360 Central Ave Ste 800 (33701-3984)
P.O. Box 14217 (33733-4217)
PHONE..................................619 499-7507
James C Booth, *President*
EMP: 6 **EST:** 2020
SALES (est): 797.5K **Privately Held**
SIC: 3448 Docks: prefabricated metal

(G-15725)
BODY LLC
Also Called: Body Nutrition
2950 47th Ave N (33714-3132)
PHONE..................................850 888-2639
Gregory W Simek,
▲ **EMP:** 18
SQ FT: 63,000
SALES (est): 980.2K **Privately Held**
WEB: www.bodynutrition.com
SIC: 2099 Dessert mixes & fillings

(G-15726)
BOOKLOCKER COM INC
200 2nd Ave S (33701-4313)
PHONE..................................727 483-4540
EMP: 10 **EST:** 2019
SALES (est): 648.8K **Privately Held**
WEB: www.booklocker.com
SIC: 2731 Book publishing

(G-15727)
BOYCE ENGINEERING INC
11861 31st Ct N (33716-1806)
PHONE..................................727 572-6318
Boyce D Crowe Sr, *President*
Jackie Crowe, *Marketing Staff*
EMP: 10 **EST:** 1972
SQ FT: 8,500
SALES (est): 936.9K **Privately Held**
SIC: 3089 Molding primary plastic

(G-15728)
BRAND BUILDERS RX LLC
9843 18th St N Ste 150 (33716-4208)
PHONE..................................727 576-4013
EMP: 9
SQ FT: 9,000
SALES (est): 730K **Privately Held**
SIC: 2844 5122 Cosmetic Mfg & Dist

(G-15729)
BREWFAB LLC
2300 31st St N (33713-3703)
PHONE..................................727 823-8333
EMP: 7
SALES (est): 515.3K **Privately Held**
SIC: 3312 3443 5084 Blast Furnace-Steel Work Mfg Fabricated Plate Wrk Whol Industrial Equip

(G-15730)
BTU REPS LLC (PA)
185 23rd Ave N (33704-3431)
PHONE..................................727 235-3591
Joseph P Shukys, *Principal*
EMP: 13 **EST:** 2012
SALES (est): 289.7K **Privately Held**
WEB: www.btureps.com
SIC: 2097 Manufactured ice

(G-15731)
BUFFALO MACHINE MANUFACTURING
3140 39th Ave N (33714-4530)
PHONE..................................727 321-1905
Matt Bryant, *President*
EMP: 6 **EST:** 1999
SQ FT: 2,580
SALES (est): 493.2K **Privately Held**
SIC: 3569 Assembly machines, non-metalworking

(G-15732)
BURKHART ROENTGEN INTL INC
Also Called: Usaxray
3232 Bennett St N (33713-2642)
PHONE..................................727 327-6950
George Burkhart, *President*
Ellen Burkhart, *Vice Pres*
EMP: 10 **EST:** 1996
SQ FT: 6,600
SALES (est): 911.2K **Privately Held**
WEB: www.usaxray.com
SIC: 3842 Radiation shielding aprons, gloves, sheeting, etc.

(G-15733)
C & D PRINTING COMPANY
12150 28th St N (33716-1820)
PHONE..................................727 572-9999
William Serata, *President*
Denise Vilez, *Controller*
Jim Parker, *Accounts Exec*
Suzanne Alvarez, *Sales Staff*
Stephanie Valles, *Marketing Staff*
EMP: 67 **EST:** 1974
SQ FT: 13,000
SALES (est): 9MM **Privately Held**
WEB: www.cndprinting.com
SIC: 2752 Commercial printing, offset

(G-15734)
CAMP AIRCRAFT INC
5300 95th St N (33708-3795)
PHONE..................................727 397-6076
Don Camp, *President*
EMP: 10 **EST:** 1944
SQ FT: 40,000
SALES (est): 1.5MM **Privately Held**
SIC: 3644 3364 Electric conduits & fittings; nonferrous die-castings except aluminum

(G-15735)
CAMP COMPANY ST PETERSBURG
5300 95th St N (33708-3795)
PHONE..................................727 397-6076
Dominick Ciampolillo, *President*
EMP: 23 **EST:** 1977
SQ FT: 40,000
SALES (est): 5.4MM **Privately Held**
WEB: www.campcompany.com
SIC: 3369 Zinc & zinc-base alloy castings, except die-castings

(G-15736)
CAMPOS CHEMICALS
3244 44th Ave N (33714-3810)
PHONE..................................727 412-2774
Roberto B Campos,
Michelle Lorenzo,
EMP: 11 **EST:** 2013
SALES (est): 407.2K **Privately Held**
WEB: www.camposchemicals.com
SIC: 2842 5999 5169 2841 Specialty cleaning, polishes & sanitation goods; rug, upholstery, or dry cleaning detergents or spotters; cleaning equipment & supplies; detergents; soap: granulated, liquid, cake, flaked or chip

(G-15737)
CANNIDA CO LLC
2411 Union St S (33712-3554)
PHONE..................................727 642-3709
Jonah Perkins,
EMP: 6 **EST:** 2016
SALES (est): 131K **Privately Held**
WEB: www.cannida-co.com
SIC: 1389 1522 1542 1541 Construction, repair & dismantling services; residential construction; commercial & office building contractors; industrial buildings, new construction; carpet & upholstery cleaning

(G-15738)
CANVAS
1535 4th St N (33704-4411)
PHONE..................................727 317-5572
EMP: 7 **EST:** 2015
SALES (est): 56.3K **Privately Held**
WEB: www.shopcfg.com
SIC: 2211 Canvas

(G-15739)
CATALENT INC
Also Called: Catalent St Petersburg
2725 Scherer Dr N (33716-1016)
PHONE..................................727 803-2832
Rob Naegely, *Project Engr*
Jorge Santiago, *Project Engr*
Katherine Bush, *Manager*
Deborah Gonzalez, *Manager*
Isha Tiwari, *Manager*
EMP: 15 **Publicly Held**
WEB: www.catalent.com
SIC: 2834 Pharmaceutical preparations
PA: Catalent, Inc.
14 Schoolhouse Rd
Somerset NJ 08873

(G-15740)
CAVAFORM INC (PA)
2700 72nd St N (33710-2916)
PHONE..................................727 384-3676
Dave S Massie, *President*
Mark Schreiter, *Purch Mgr*
David Gunthrop, *QC Mgr*
Chris Outlaw, *Engineer*
Chuck Doerner, *Project Engr*
▲ **EMP:** 1 **EST:** 1978
SQ FT: 30,000
SALES (est): 33.7MM **Privately Held**
WEB: www.cavaform.com
SIC: 3089 Injection molding of plastics

(G-15741)
CAVAFORM INTERNATIONAL LLC
2700 72nd St N (33710-2916)
PHONE..................................727 384-3676
Nick Scalamogna, *Partner*
Ralph Acito, *Production*
Dave S Massie, *Mng Member*
EMP: 75 **EST:** 1999
SQ FT: 30,000
SALES (est): 33.7MM **Privately Held**
WEB: www.cavaform.com
SIC: 3544 Industrial molds
PA: Cavaform, Inc.
2700 72nd St N
Saint Petersburg FL 33710
727 384-3676

(G-15742)
CEMEX CEMENT INC
601 24th St S (33712-1723)
PHONE..................................727 327-5730
Bill Poole, *Branch Mgr*
EMP: 214 **Privately Held**
WEB: www.cemexusa.com
SIC: 3273 Ready-mixed concrete
HQ: Cemex Cement, Inc.
10100 Katy Fwy Ste 300
Houston TX 77043
713 650-6200

(G-15743)
CENTRAL PRINTERS INC
4101 35th St N (33714-3798)
PHONE....727 527-5879
Steve Sanchez, *President*
Philip Sanchez, *Vice Pres*
EMP: 6 **EST:** 1935
SQ FT: 3,000
SALES (est): 950K **Privately Held**
WEB: www.centralprinters.com
SIC: 2752 Commercial printing, offset

(G-15744)
CHEAP BANNERS & SIGNS CENTRAL
5502 Haines Rd N (33714-1999)
PHONE....727 522-7414
Kenneth Anderson, *President*
Mary Lou Anderson, *Vice Pres*
EMP: 5
SALES (est): 300K **Privately Held**
WEB: www.compassbanners.com
SIC: 3993 Signs & advertising specialties

(G-15745)
CHROMATECH DIGITAL INC
Also Called: Chromatech Printing
4301 31st St N (33714-4567)
PHONE....727 528-4711
George Emmanuel Sr, *President*
George Emmanuel Jr, *Vice Pres*
EMP: 22 **EST:** 1996
SQ FT: 20,000
SALES (est): 663K **Privately Held**
WEB: www.chromatechprinting.com
SIC: 2752 Commercial printing, offset

(G-15746)
CIEGA INC
4410 35th St N (33714-3720)
PHONE....727 526-9048
EMP: 8
SALES (est): 1.2MM **Privately Held**
SIC: 2842 5169 Whol & Mfg Environmental Supplies & Services

(G-15747)
COLORGRAPHX INC
Also Called: Beck Graphics
1551 102nd Ave N Ste A (33716-5050)
PHONE....727 572-6364
George R Stulpin, *President*
George Stulpin, *President*
Lee Cox, *Controller*
EMP: 30
SALES (est): 375MM **Privately Held**
WEB: www.colorgraphx.com
SIC: 2752 Commercial printing, offset

(G-15748)
COMMERCIAL INSTLLATION SYSTEMS
6175 Wdrow Wilson Blvd Ne (33703)
PHONE....727 525-2372
Fax: 727 526-7903
EMP: 8
SALES (est): 882.4K **Privately Held**
SIC: 2431 Mfg Millwork

(G-15749)
COMMERCIAL STONE CAB FBRCTORS
3120 46th Ave N (33714-3802)
PHONE....727 209-1141
Lisa Maddux, *President*
Danny Donegan, *Principal*
Steve Stutko, *Sales Executive*
Scott Baller, *Manager*
EMP: 10 **EST:** 2012
SALES (est): 1.1MM **Privately Held**
WEB: www.cscfusa.com
SIC: 1411 1799 2541 1751 Granite dimension stone; kitchen cabinet installation; counter & sink tops; cabinet building & installation; composition stone, plastic

(G-15750)
COMMERCIAL STONE FBRCATORS INC
Also Called: Global Stone Project Entp
3120 46th Ave N (33714-3802)
PHONE....727 209-1141
Lisa Maddux, *President*
EMP: 10 **EST:** 2004
SALES (est): 1.7MM **Privately Held**
WEB: www.gspei.com
SIC: 1411 1799 2541 1751 Granite dimension stone; kitchen cabinet installation; counter top installation; counter & sink tops; cabinet building & installation; composition stone, plastic

(G-15751)
COMPASS BANNERS & PRINTING LLC
5502 Haines Rd N (33714-1999)
PHONE....727 522-7414
Alan Stanton, *Administration*
EMP: 6 **EST:** 2019
SALES (est): 215.1K **Privately Held**
WEB: www.compassbannersandsigns.com
SIC: 2752 Commercial printing, lithographic

(G-15752)
COMPULINK CORPORATION (HQ)
1205 Gandy Blvd N (33702-2428)
PHONE....727 579-1500
Stephen Shevlin, *President*
Robert T Wilkin, *Vice Pres*
Nick Kochey, *Opers Staff*
Debbie Wastney, *Buyer*
Brenda Hodges, *QC Mgr*
EMP: 500
SQ FT: 30,000
SALES (est): 118.7MM **Privately Held**
WEB: www.compulink.com
SIC: 3643 5065 Current-carrying wiring devices; electronic parts

(G-15753)
CONTOURS RX LLC
200 2nd Ave S Ste 701 (33701-4313)
PHONE....727 827-7321
Britain Todd, *Mng Member*
Cassandra Elrod, *Manager*
EMP: 5 **EST:** 2014
SQ FT: 1,800
SALES (est): 342.7K **Privately Held**
WEB: www.contoursrx.com
SIC: 2844 Cosmetic preparations

(G-15754)
CRABIL MANUFACTURING INC
9600 18th St N (33716-4202)
PHONE....727 209-8368
EMP: 27
SQ FT: 23,000
SALES (est): 4.5MM **Privately Held**
SIC: 3599 Mfg Industrial Machinery

(G-15755)
DATA PRO ACCOUNTING SFTWR INC
111 2nd Ave Ne Ste 1200 (33701-3443)
PHONE....727 803-1500
Scott Fenimore, *President*
EMP: 18 **EST:** 1985
SQ FT: 6,400
SALES (est): 749.7K **Privately Held**
WEB: www.dpro.com
SIC: 7372 Prepackaged software

(G-15756)
DAVID CHITTUM
Also Called: High Power Services
1800 Bonita Way S (33712-4212)
PHONE....386 754-6127
David Chittum, *Owner*
EMP: 6 **EST:** 2000
SALES (est): 503.8K **Privately Held**
SIC: 3699 Household electrical equipment

(G-15757)
DELPHI OF FLORIDA INC
12425 28th S N Ste 100 (33716)
PHONE....727 561-9553
Ed Dillabough, *President*
Karen Jones, *Research*
Colleen Hekkanen, *Director*
Catherine Hall, *Nurse*
EMP: 14 **EST:** 2001
SALES (est): 215.7K **Privately Held**
WEB: www.map-health.com
SIC: 3714 Motor vehicle parts & accessories

(G-15758)
DERMAZONE SOLUTIONS INC
2440 30th Ave N (33713-2920)
PHONE....727 446-6882
Deborah Duffey, *President*
Karalyn Schuchert, *Chairman*
Zack Nalic, *Plant Mgr*
Jean Letellier, *QC Mgr*
Shelby Rollins, *Office Mgr*
EMP: 30
SQ FT: 2,000
SALES (est): 5.3MM **Privately Held**
WEB: www.dermazone.com
SIC: 2844 5999 5122 8732 Cosmetic preparations; toiletries, cosmetics & perfumes; cosmetics; research services, except laboratory; commercial research laboratory

(G-15759)
DESIGNS TO SHINE
1033 34th St N (33713-6543)
PHONE....727 525-4297
Maria McGill, *Owner*
Summer Gray, *Owner*
Kerri Sadock, *Purchasing*
Michelle Butler, *Office Mgr*
EMP: 38 **EST:** 1999
SALES (est): 2.5MM **Privately Held**
WEB: www.designstoshine.com
SIC: 2335 5699 Bridal & formal gowns; formal wear

(G-15760)
DGS RETAIL LLC
4400 34th St N Ste L (33714-3741)
PHONE....727 388-4975
EMP: 226
SALES (corp-wide): 200.5MM **Privately Held**
WEB: www.dgsretail.com
SIC: 3993 Signs, not made in custom sign painting shops
PA: Dgs Retail, Llc
8604 W Catalpa Ave # 915
Chicago IL 60656
800 211-9646

(G-15761)
DGS RETAIL LLC
307044th Avenuene N (33714)
PHONE....727 388-4975
Tom Ripley, *Branch Mgr*
EMP: 10
SALES (corp-wide): 200.5MM **Privately Held**
WEB: www.dgsretail.com
SIC: 3993 Signs & advertising specialties
PA: Dgs Retail, Llc
8604 W Catalpa Ave # 915
Chicago IL 60656
800 211-9646

(G-15762)
DONOVAN HOME SERVICES LLC
Also Called: Kyaeto Systems
3390 Gandy Blvd N (33702-2058)
PHONE....813 644-9488
Michael Donovan, *CEO*
EMP: 14 **EST:** 2016
SALES (est): 810.5K **Privately Held**
SIC: 3577 8742 Computer peripheral equipment; management information systems consultant

(G-15763)
DONTECH INDUSTRIES INC
9 Jefferson Ct S (33711-5144)
PHONE....847 682-1776
D L Catton, *Principal*
EMP: 9 **EST:** 2010
SALES (est): 203.2K **Privately Held**
WEB: www.dontechindustriesinc.com
SIC: 3999 Manufacturing industries

(G-15764)
DOORS MOLDING AND MORE
2894 22nd Ave N (33713-4206)
PHONE....727 498-8552
Ngoc Huynh, *Principal*
EMP: 12 **EST:** 2012
SALES (est): 2.2MM **Privately Held**
WEB: www.dmmore.com
SIC: 3089 Molding primary plastic

(G-15765)
DORWARD ENERGY CORPORATION
447 3rd Ave N Ste 400 (33701-3255)
PHONE....727 490-1778
Dave Dorward Jr, *President*
EMP: 7 **EST:** 1955
SQ FT: 750
SALES (est): 1MM **Privately Held**
WEB: www.dorwardenergy.onlinerpts.com
SIC: 1311 Crude petroleum production

(G-15766)
E2G PARTNERS LLC
Also Called: Tampa Microwave
11200 Dr Mrtn Lther King (33716-2330)
PHONE....813 855-2251
Eric Guerrazzi, *President*
EMP: 24 **EST:** 1988
SALES (est): 1.3MM **Privately Held**
SIC: 3663 Microwave communication equipment

(G-15767)
EAGLE LABS INCORPORATED
5000 Park St N Ste 1202 (33709-2236)
PHONE....727 548-1816
Gary Dambach, *CEO*
Todd Dambach, *Vice Pres*
Janet Brambs, *Controller*
EMP: 90 **EST:** 2004
SALES (est): 5.7MM **Privately Held**
WEB: www.eaglelabsinc.com
SIC: 2834 2844 Vitamin, nutrient & hematinic preparations for human use; cosmetic preparations

(G-15768)
ELITE AERO LLC
4828 Queen Palm Ter Ne (33703-6300)
PHONE....727 244-3382
Mark Hansson,
EMP: 9 **EST:** 2009
SALES (est): 324.6K **Privately Held**
WEB: www.eliteaeroco.com
SIC: 3545 Precision tools, machinists'

(G-15769)
EMHART GLASS MANUFACTURING INC
Also Called: Emhart Inex
9875 18th St N (33716-4209)
PHONE....727 535-5502
Glen Long, *Director*
▲ **EMP:** 37 **EST:** 1993
SQ FT: 30,000
SALES (est): 21.8MM
SALES (corp-wide): 3B **Privately Held**
WEB: www.emhartglass.com
SIC: 3565 Bottling & canning machinery
HQ: Emhart Glass Sa
Hinterbergstrasse 22
Steinhausen ZG 6312
417 494-200

(G-15770)
ENSTAR HOLDINGS (US) LLC (HQ)
150 2nd Ave N Fl 3 (33701-3327)
PHONE....727 217-2900
Cheryl D Davis, *Director*
EMP: 100 **EST:** 2014
SALES (est): 152MM **Privately Held**
WEB: www.enstargroup.com
SIC: 3714 3462 3568 Motor vehicle parts & accessories; iron & steel forgings; power transmission equipment

(G-15771)
ENVIRONMENTAL RECOVERY SYSTEMS
7001 Mango Ave S (33707-2023)
PHONE....727 344-3301
Karen Core, *Director*
EMP: 6 **EST:** 1990
SALES (est): 499.5K **Privately Held**
SIC: 3569 8731 3519 Separators for steam, gas, vapor or air (machinery); commercial physical research; internal combustion engines

(G-15772)
EVOLVEGENE LLC
12105 28th St N Ste A (33716-1817)
PHONE....727 623-4052

Mirela Pino, *President*
EMP: 7 **EST:** 2017
SALES (est): 192.8K **Privately Held**
SIC: 2835 Radioactive diagnostic substances

(G-15773)
EVOLVING COAL CORP
Also Called: Ecc
200 2nd Ave S Ste 733 (33701-4313)
PHONE..................................813 944-3100
Alan Petzold, *President*
Jose Bosch, *Vice Pres*
Terry Lin, *Vice Pres*
Roger Wertel, *Admin Sec*
▼ **EMP:** 5 **EST:** 2017
SQ FT: 750
SALES (est): 30MM **Privately Held**
SIC: 1221 1422 Coal preparation plant, bituminous or lignite; crushed & broken limestone

(G-15774)
EXCEL FUEL INC
6201 54th Ave N (33709-1701)
PHONE..................................727 547-5511
Mah'd Msawel, *Principal*
EMP: 7 **EST:** 2012
SALES (est): 365.9K **Privately Held**
SIC: 2869 Fuels

(G-15775)
EXTREME COATINGS
2895 46th Ave N (33714-3811)
PHONE..................................727 528-7998
Curt Kadau, *Principal*
Scott Caplan, *Vice Pres*
Steve Kelsay, *Sales Staff*
Kim Perez, *Sales Staff*
Kaitlyn Roy, *Sales Staff*
EMP: 6 **EST:** 2012
SALES (est): 279.3K **Privately Held**
WEB: www.extremecoatings.net
SIC: 3479 3089 3412 Chasing on metals; injection molding of plastics; barrels, shipping: metal

(G-15776)
FARMER MOLD AND MCH WORKS INC
2904 44th Ave N (33714-3804)
PHONE..................................727 522-0515
James O Gilmour, *President*
◆ **EMP:** 30 **EST:** 1938
SQ FT: 40,000
SALES (est): 4MM **Privately Held**
WEB: www.farmermold.com
SIC: 3599 Machine shop, jobbing & repair

(G-15777)
FASTSIGNS
4058 Park St N (33709-4034)
PHONE..................................727 341-0084
Michael Norris, *Principal*
EMP: 8 **EST:** 2012
SALES (est): 241.4K **Privately Held**
WEB: www.fastsigns.com
SIC: 3993 Signs & advertising specialties

(G-15778)
FIDELITY PRINTING CORPORATION
3662 Morris St N (33713-1697)
PHONE..................................727 522-9557
Robert Julian Hasson, *President*
Robert J Hasson Jr, *President*
James Allen Hasson, *Vice Pres*
William B Hasson, *Vice Pres*
Andy Belanger, *Sales Staff*
EMP: 60 **EST:** 1970
SQ FT: 9,000
SALES (est): 8.5MM **Privately Held**
WEB: www.fidelityprinting.com
SIC: 2752 2791 2789 2759 Commercial printing, offset; typesetting; bookbinding & related work; commercial printing

(G-15779)
FIELD FORENSICS INC
1601 3rd St S (33701-5542)
PHONE..................................727 490-3609
Craig Johnson, *President*
Christine Lekich, *Principal*
Jim Oneil, *Vice Pres*
Sean Meehan, *Research*
Randy Kravarik, *Technical Staff*
▼ **EMP:** 10 **EST:** 1999
SALES (est): 1.5MM **Privately Held**
WEB: www.fieldforensics.com
SIC: 3826 Analytical instruments

(G-15780)
FISHER ELECTRIC TECHNOLOGY INC
2801 72nd St N (33710-2903)
PHONE..................................727 345-9122
Richard Horbal MD, *Ch of Bd*
Nancy J Preis, *President*
Ned Schiff, *General Mgr*
EMP: 12 **EST:** 1987
SQ FT: 10,000
SALES (est): 1MM **Privately Held**
WEB: www.fisherelectric.com
SIC: 3621 Motors & generators

(G-15781)
FIVE SPORTS INC
11880 28th St N Ste 100 (33716-1824)
PHONE..................................727 209-1750
Craig Baroncelli, *President*
EMP: 8 **EST:** 2007
SQ FT: 2,200
SALES (est): 717.7K **Privately Held**
WEB: www.ae-engine.com
SIC: 2721 Magazines: publishing & printing

(G-15782)
FLANDERS CORP
2399 26th Ave N (33713-4039)
PHONE..................................727 822-4411
Robert Amerson, *Chairman*
EMP: 15 **EST:** 2019
SALES (est): 467.9K **Privately Held**
SIC: 3564 Blowers & fans

(G-15783)
FLORIDA ELREHA CORPORATION
2510 Terminal Dr S (33712-1669)
PHONE..................................727 327-6236
Abdul Hamadeh, *President*
Rob Digiovanni, *Vice Pres*
Ahmad Hamadeh, *Vice Pres*
Junis Hamadeh, *Vice Pres*
▲ **EMP:** 42 **EST:** 1990
SQ FT: 100,000
SALES (est): 2.9MM **Privately Held**
WEB: www.elreha.de
SIC: 3672 Printed circuit boards

(G-15784)
FLORIDA PRINT SOLUTIONS INC (PA)
Also Called: Florida Laminating & Uv Svcs
432 31st St N (33713-7600)
PHONE..................................727 327-5500
Danielle Findley, *President*
Jessie Serrano, *President*
Jonathan Tallon, *Marketing Mgr*
Carol Thomas, *Manager*
EMP: 9 **EST:** 2012
SQ FT: 1,500
SALES (est): 2.2MM **Privately Held**
WEB: www.floridaprintsolutions.com
SIC: 2752 Commercial printing, offset

(G-15785)
FLORIDA SHED COMPANY INC (PA)
3865 Tyrone Blvd N (33709-4121)
PHONE..................................727 524-9191
Joseph H Campenella, *President*
Joseph Campenella, *President*
Robert Yankanich, *Admin Sec*
EMP: 28 **EST:** 1997
SALES (est): 4.4MM **Privately Held**
WEB: www.floridashed.com
SIC: 2452 Prefabricated buildings, wood

(G-15786)
FLORIDA STATE GRAPHICS INC
2828 20th Ave N (33713-4202)
PHONE..................................727 328-0733
John Ruzecki, *President*
Richard Ruzecki, *Vice Pres*
EMP: 7 **EST:** 1989
SQ FT: 6,600
SALES (est): 800K **Privately Held**
WEB: www.vinylbinders.com
SIC: 2752 Commercial printing, lithographic

(G-15787)
FLORIDA VAULT SERVICE INC
3007 47th Ave N (33714-3133)
P.O. Box 3977, Bay Pines (33744-3977)
PHONE..................................727 527-4992
Harry Sneadker, *Owner*
EMP: 6 **EST:** 2011
SALES (est): 218.9K **Privately Held**
SIC: 3272 Concrete products

(G-15788)
FORMULATED SOLUTIONS LLC
1776 11th Ave N (33713-5747)
PHONE..................................727 456-0302
EMP: 10 **EST:** 2019
SALES (est): 408.6K **Privately Held**
WEB: www.formulatedsolutions.com
SIC: 2844 Cosmetic preparations

(G-15789)
GA FD SVCS PINELLAS CNTY LLC (PA)
Also Called: G.A. Foods
12200 32nd Ct N (33716-1803)
PHONE..................................727 388-0075
Glenn Davenport, *President*
Neil King, *General Mgr*
John D Hale, *COO*
Beth Valavanis, *COO*
Ritch Brandon, *Vice Pres*
▲ **EMP:** 300 **EST:** 1973
SQ FT: 180,000
SALES (est): 151.6MM **Privately Held**
WEB: www.sunmeadow.com
SIC: 2038 5812 Frozen specialties; contract food services

(G-15790)
GENERAL DYNAMICS-OTS INC (HQ)
11399 16th Ct N Ste 200 (33716-2322)
PHONE..................................727 578-8100
Firat Gezen, *CEO*
Dan Chien, *President*
Charles Hall, *Exec VP*
Tim McAuliffe, *Vice Pres*
Mike Obrien, *Vice Pres*
◆ **EMP:** 100 **EST:** 1948
SALES (est): 814.4MM
SALES (corp-wide): 37.9B **Publicly Held**
WEB: www.gd-ots.com
SIC: 3728 3812 Military aircraft equipment & armament; search & navigation equipment
PA: General Dynamics Corporation
11011 Sunset Hills Rd
Reston VA 20190
703 876-3000

(G-15791)
GENERAL DYNMICS ORD TCTCAL SYS (HQ)
11399 16th Ct N Ste 200 (33716-2322)
PHONE..................................727 578-8100
Michael S Wilson, *President*
Del S Dameron, *Vice Pres*
Gregory Gallopoules, *Vice Pres*
Chris Feather, *Opers Staff*
Chris Jackson, *Mfg Staff*
◆ **EMP:** 230 **EST:** 1996
SQ FT: 150,000
SALES (est): 525.2MM
SALES (corp-wide): 37.9B **Publicly Held**
WEB: www.gd-ots.com
SIC: 3483 3482 2892 3489 Ammunition, except for small arms; small arms ammunition; explosives; ordnance & accessories
PA: General Dynamics Corporation
11011 Sunset Hills Rd
Reston VA 20190
703 876-3000

(G-15792)
GIEBNER ENTERPRISES INC
Also Called: Com-Ten Industries
4760 Brittany Dr S Apt 20 (33715-1673)
PHONE..................................727 520-1200
Betty Giebner, *President*
Tom Giebner, *Corp Secy*
▲ **EMP:** 14 **EST:** 1960
SQ FT: 12,000
SALES (est): 498.9K **Privately Held**
WEB: www.com-ten.com
SIC: 3829 Physical property testing equipment; tensile strength testing equipment

(G-15793)
GLOBAL PRINTING SOLUTIONS INC
2569 25th Ave N (33713-3918)
PHONE..................................727 458-3483
EMP: 6 **EST:** 2018
SALES (est): 389.5K **Privately Held**
WEB: www.seegps.com
SIC: 2752 Commercial printing, offset

(G-15794)
GO 2 PRINT NOW INC
Also Called: G2pn.com
2390 26th Ave N (33713-4040)
P.O. Box 8429, Seminole (33775-8429)
PHONE..................................800 500-4276
Kymberly Wostbrock, *President*
Chris Dunn, *Production*
EMP: 21 **EST:** 2000
SALES (est): 3.5MM **Privately Held**
WEB: www.g2pn.com
SIC: 2759 Commercial printing

(G-15795)
GODWIN AND SINGER INC
1415 Burlington Ave N (33705-1579)
PHONE..................................727 896-8631
Steven Trimm, *President*
Linda Trimm, *Vice Pres*
Linda Trimms, *Vice Pres*
EMP: 9 **EST:** 1945
SQ FT: 3,570
SALES (est): 931.3K **Privately Held**
WEB: www.godwinsinger.com
SIC: 3599 7538 Machine shop, jobbing & repair; engine repair, except diesel: automotive

(G-15796)
GREAT AMERCN NATURAL PDTS INC
Also Called: Bulk Food Grocers
4121 16th St N (33703-5607)
PHONE..................................727 521-4372
Ron Hamilton, *President*
Karan Martinotti, *Controller*
EMP: 21 **EST:** 1970
SQ FT: 2,640
SALES (est): 3.7MM **Privately Held**
WEB: www.greatamerican.biz
SIC: 2833 5499 Vitamins, natural or synthetic: bulk, uncompounded; health & dietetic food stores

(G-15797)
GREEN BENCH MONTHLY
3018 Jackson St N (33704-1951)
P.O. Box 76095 (33734-6095)
PHONE..................................813 417-3944
Anthony Sica, *Principal*
EMP: 9 **EST:** 2016
SALES (est): 572.7K **Privately Held**
WEB: www.greenbenchmonthly.com
SIC: 2721 Periodicals

(G-15798)
GREENCORE LLC
970 Tyrone Blvd N (33710-6333)
PHONE..................................727 251-9837
Arnie Cummings, *Vice Pres*
Holle R Chiappo, *Mng Member*
EMP: 5 **EST:** 2008
SQ FT: 1,000
SALES (est): 418.5K **Privately Held**
WEB: www.greencore.com
SIC: 2891 Cement, except linoleum & tile

(G-15799)
GULFCOAST SAILING INC
1354 20th St N (33713-5743)
PHONE..................................727 823-1968
Tom M Barry, *President*
EMP: 7 **EST:** 1998
SALES (est): 656K **Privately Held**
SIC: 2394 Sails: made from purchased materials

▲ = Import ▼=Export
◆ =Import/Export

(G-15800)
GULL TOOL & MACHINE INC
3033 47th Ave N Frnt (33714-3191)
PHONE.................................727 527-0808
John J Gill, *President*
EMP: 5 **EST:** 1973
SQ FT: 3,500
SALES (est): 390.3K **Privately Held**
SIC: 3599 3519 Machine shop, jobbing & repair; marine engines

(G-15801)
GUNNS WELDING & FABRICATING
4729 96th St N (33708-3738)
PHONE.................................727 393-5238
Joanne Gunn, *President*
Robert Gunn Jr, *Vice Pres*
Judy Larson, *Treasurer*
EMP: 5 **EST:** 1988
SQ FT: 5,000
SALES (est): 562.5K **Privately Held**
SIC: 3599 7692 1799 3441 Custom machinery; machine shop, jobbing & repair; welding repair; welding on site; fabricated structural metal; tube fabricating (contract bending & shaping)

(G-15802)
H & T GLOBAL CIRCUIT FCTRY LLC
Also Called: H&T Global Circuits
2510 Terminal Dr S (33712-1669)
P.O. Box 17744, Clearwater (33762-0744)
PHONE.................................727 327-6236
Dan Schutte, *Business Mgr*
Lisa Davis, *Vice Pres*
Ben Hobbs, *Materials Mgr*
Tamara Jordan, *Purchasing*
Helen Bender, *Engineer*
◆ **EMP:** 80 **EST:** 2001
SQ FT: 35,000
SALES (est): 15.2MM **Privately Held**
WEB: www.htglobalcircuits.com
SIC: 3672 Printed circuit boards

(G-15803)
HALKEY-ROBERTS CORPORATION (HQ)
2700 Halkey Roberts Pl N (33716-4103)
PHONE.................................727 471-4200
David Battat, *President*
Alan King, *Vice Pres*
Lewis P Lecceardone, *Vice Pres*
John H Lucius, *Vice Pres*
Karen Prescott, *Purch Mgr*
▲ **EMP:** 200 **EST:** 1945
SQ FT: 142,000
SALES (est): 72.2MM
SALES (corp-wide): 147.5MM **Publicly Held**
WEB: www.halkeyroberts.com
SIC: 3842 Surgical appliances & supplies
PA: Atrion Corporation
1 Allentown Pkwy
Allen TX 75002
972 390-9800

(G-15804)
HARVEST DAY PRESS
585 Dolphin Ave Se (33705-4141)
PHONE.................................727 822-4961
Dennis Esposito, *Principal*
EMP: 6 **EST:** 2018
SALES (est): 37.5K **Privately Held**
WEB: www.itsabouttimetheanswer.com
SIC: 2741 Miscellaneous publishing

(G-15805)
HERFF JONES LLC
Murphy Cap and Gown Company
4200 31st St N (33714-4584)
PHONE.................................727 527-0696
Tom Carew, *President*
EMP: 7
SALES (corp-wide): 1.1B **Privately Held**
WEB: www.yearbookdiscoveries.com
SIC: 2389 Academic vestments (caps & gowns)
HQ: Herff Jones, Llc
4501 W 62nd St
Indianapolis IN 46268
800 419-5462

(G-15806)
HERITAGE MANUFACTURING SVCS
4365 22nd St N (33714-4144)
PHONE.................................727 906-5599
Jason Bedell, *Principal*
EMP: 7 **EST:** 2011
SALES (est): 118.6K **Privately Held**
SIC: 3443 Metal parts

(G-15807)
HINE AUTOMATION LLC
12495 34th St N Ste B (33716-1833)
PHONE.................................813 749-7519
Karl Pearson, *Opers Staff*
Brendon Cordon, *Engineer*
Raj Subramanya, *Engineer*
Grace Smoker, *Human Resources*
Cheri Maile, *Office Mgr*
EMP: 7 **EST:** 2009
SALES (est): 1.7MM **Privately Held**
WEB: www.hineautomation.com
SIC: 3674 Wafers (semiconductor devices)

(G-15808)
HOT TUB PARTS LLC
6190 45th St N Ste A (33714-1011)
PHONE.................................727 573-9611
Brian K Wiley,
▼ **EMP:** 6 **EST:** 2008
SALES (est): 632.5K **Privately Held**
WEB: www.hottubparts.com
SIC: 3088 Hot tubs, plastic or fiberglass

(G-15809)
HYDRON TECHNOLOGIES INC
9843 18th St N Ste 150 (33716-4208)
PHONE.................................727 342-5050
Helen Canetano, *CEO*
Richard Banakus, *Ch of Bd*
▲ **EMP:** 9 **EST:** 1948
SQ FT: 7,000
SALES (est): 323.1K **Privately Held**
SIC: 2844 Toilet preparations

(G-15810)
I3 MICROSYSTEMS INC
9900 16th St N (33716-4230)
PHONE.................................727 235-6532
James Matthews, *President*
Michelle Eldred, *Vice Pres*
EMP: 42 **EST:** 2017
SALES (est): 5.4MM
SALES (corp-wide): 120.8MM **Privately Held**
WEB: www.i3electronics.com
SIC: 3672 Printed circuit boards
PA: I3 Electronics, Inc.
100 Eldredge St
Binghamton NY 13901
607 238-7077

(G-15811)
ICARE INDUSTRIES INC (PA)
4399 35th St N Ste 100 (33714-3700)
PHONE.................................727 512-3000
James S Payne, *President*
Robert Stevens, *Vice Pres*
Cy Stankiewicz, *CFO*
Greg Gehrig, *Financial Exec*
Kelly Brady, *Human Res Dir*
EMP: 150 **EST:** 1968
SQ FT: 72,000
SALES (est): 49.1MM **Privately Held**
WEB: www.icare.com
SIC: 3851 5995 Ophthalmic goods; contact lenses, prescription; eyeglasses, prescription

(G-15812)
IDEAL PUBLISHING CO INC
Also Called: Lightening Print
3063 Lown St N (33713-2930)
PHONE.................................727 321-0785
John Kavanagh, *President*
EMP: 12 **EST:** 1971
SQ FT: 6,750
SALES (est): 641.3K **Privately Held**
WEB: www.lightningprint.net
SIC: 2752 Commercial printing, offset

(G-15813)
IMAGE EXPERTS INC
4556 36th Ave N (33713-1154)
PHONE.................................727 488-7556
James E Warren Jr, *President*
EMP: 7 **EST:** 2005
SALES (est): 163.6K **Privately Held**
WEB: www.uvimageexperts.com
SIC: 2711 Commercial printing & newspaper publishing combined

(G-15814)
INFOTEK GROUPS INC
11150 4th St N Apt 3013 (33716-2903)
PHONE.................................612 666-0535
EMP: 7 **EST:** 2018
SALES (est): 62.5K **Privately Held**
WEB: www.infotekgroups.com
SIC: 2323 Men's & boys' neckwear

(G-15815)
INFRASTRUCTURE REPAIR SYSTEMS
3113 Lown St N (33713-2932)
PHONE.................................727 327-4216
William Higman, *Principal*
Rosetta Higman, *Principal*
EMP: 5 **EST:** 1997
SQ FT: 3,000
SALES (est): 348.9K **Privately Held**
SIC: 3259 Liner brick or plates for sewer/tank lining, vitrified clay

(G-15816)
INNOVATIVE BASE TECH LLC
Also Called: Ultra Base Systems
5030 Seminole Blvd (33708-3300)
PHONE.................................727 391-9009
Cassandra Felt, *Controller*
David R Barlow, *Mng Member*
EMP: 7 **EST:** 2008
SQ FT: 1,500
SALES (est): 1.5MM **Privately Held**
WEB: www.ultrabasesystems.com
SIC: 3089 Flat panels, plastic

(G-15817)
INTELLITECH INC
11801 28th St N Ste 5 (33716-1813)
PHONE.................................727 914-7000
Barbara H Biller, *President*
Andy Biller, *Vice Pres*
EMP: 24 **EST:** 1995
SQ FT: 12,000
SALES (est): 4.1MM **Privately Held**
WEB: www.intellitech-inc.com
SIC: 3565 Packaging machinery

(G-15818)
ISLAND THE REPORTER INC
1331 Sea Gull Dr S (33707-3833)
PHONE.................................727 631-4730
Arthur Zelenak, *President*
EMP: 6 **EST:** 2006
SALES (est): 77.2K **Privately Held**
SIC: 2759 Newspapers: printing

(G-15819)
J & D OLDJA LLC
4424 34th St N (33714-3712)
PHONE.................................727 526-3240
Tonia Warner, *Office Mgr*
John D Oldja, *Mng Member*
EMP: 10 **EST:** 2010
SALES (est): 831.6K **Privately Held**
WEB: www.oldjaenterprises.com
SIC: 2434 Wood kitchen cabinets

(G-15820)
J & J MARINE SERVICE INC
Also Called: Quickload Custom Built Trlrs
2922 46th Ave N (33714-3814)
PHONE.................................813 741-2190
John D Nowling, *President*
EMP: 6 **EST:** 1981
SALES (est): 602.6K **Privately Held**
SIC: 3799 7539 Boat trailers; trailer repair

(G-15821)
JABIL ADVNCED MECH SLTIONS INC
10560 Dr M Lth Kng Jr St Martin (33716)
PHONE.................................727 577-9749
Timothy L Main, *CEO*
EMP: 49 **EST:** 2010
SALES (est): 7.4MM
SALES (corp-wide): 27.2B **Publicly Held**
WEB: www.jabil.com
SIC: 3672 Printed circuit boards
PA: Jabil Inc.
10560 Dr Mrtn Lther King
Saint Petersburg FL 33716
727 577-9749

(G-15822)
JABIL CIRCUIT
9700 18th St N (33716-4201)
PHONE.................................727 577-9749
EMP: 5
SALES (est): 672.1K **Privately Held**
SIC: 3672 Printed Circuit Boards

(G-15823)
JABIL CIRCUIT LLC (HQ)
10560 Dr Mrtn Lther King (33716-3718)
PHONE.................................727 577-9749
Mark T Mondello, *CEO*
Tim L Main, *Ch of Bd*
William E Peters, *President*
Amy Crawford, *Partner*
Forbes I Alexander, *Principal*
▲ **EMP:** 4 **EST:** 1992
SALES (est): 281MM
SALES (corp-wide): 27.2B **Publicly Held**
WEB: www.jabil.com
SIC: 3672 Circuit boards, television & radio printed
PA: Jabil Inc.
10560 Dr Mrtn Lther King
Saint Petersburg FL 33716
727 577-9749

(G-15824)
JABIL CIRCUIT LLC
3201 34th St S (33711-3828)
PHONE.................................727 577-9749
Daniel Woerner, *Project Mgr*
Samantha McIntyre, *Buyer*
Lewis Carpenter, *Engineer*
Mauricio Zaragoza, *Engineer*
Peter Grei, *Branch Mgr*
EMP: 64
SALES (corp-wide): 27.2B **Publicly Held**
WEB: www.jabil.com
SIC: 3672 Printed circuit boards
HQ: Jabil Circuit, Llc
10560 Dr Mrtn Lther King
Saint Petersburg FL 33716
727 577-9749

(G-15825)
JABIL DEF & AROSPC SVCS LLC (HQ)
10500 Dr Mrtn Lther King (33716-3718)
PHONE.................................727 577-9749
Mark T Mondello, *CEO*
William D Muir J, *COO*
Joseph A McGee, *Exec VP*
Sergio A Cadavid, *Senior VP*
Michael Dastoor, *Senior VP*
EMP: 41 **EST:** 2004
SALES (est): 57.7MM
SALES (corp-wide): 27.2B **Publicly Held**
WEB: www.jabil.com
SIC: 3672 Printed circuit boards
PA: Jabil Inc.
10560 Dr Mrtn Lther King
Saint Petersburg FL 33716
727 577-9749

(G-15826)
JABIL DEF & AROSPC SVCS LLC (HQ)
10560 Dr Mlk Jr St N (33716)
PHONE.................................727 577-9749
EMP: 18
SALES (est): 14.9MM
SALES (corp-wide): 22.1B **Publicly Held**
SIC: 3672 Mfg Printed Circuit Boards
PA: Jabil Inc.
10560 Dr Martin Luther
Saint Petersburg FL 33716
727 577-9749

(G-15827)
JABIL INC (PA)
10560 Dr Mrtn Lther King (33716-3718)
PHONE.................................727 577-9749
Mark T Mondello, *CEO*
Michael J Loparco, *CEO*
Kenneth S Wilson, *CEO*
Timothy L Main, *Ch of Bd*
Thomas A Sansone, *Vice Ch Bd*
EMP: 1344 **EST:** 1966

SALES (est): 27.2B **Publicly Held**
WEB: www.jabil.com
SIC: 3672 Printed circuit boards

(G-15828)
JABIL INC
10500 Dr Mlk Jr St N Dock (33716)
PHONE..................................727 577-9749
EMP: 41
SALES (corp-wide): 27.2B **Publicly Held**
SIC: 3672 Printed Circuit Boards
PA: Jabil Inc.
10560 Dr Mrtn Lther King
Saint Petersburg FL 33716
727 577-9749

(G-15829)
JABIL INC
Also Called: Jabil Luxembourg Manufacturing
1300 Dr Marti Luthe King (33705-1002)
PHONE..................................727 803-3110
Courtney Ryan, *Exec VP*
Ron Anderson, *Human Resources*
Arthur Rawers, *Manager*
EMP: 200
SALES (corp-wide): 27.2B **Publicly Held**
WEB: www.jabil.com
SIC: 3672 Printed circuit boards
PA: Jabil Inc.
10560 Dr Mrtn Lther King
Saint Petersburg FL 33716
727 577-9749

(G-15830)
JABIL INC
10500 Dr Mrtn Lther King (33716-3718)
PHONE..................................727 577-9749
Greg Facchini, *Manager*
EMP: 75
SALES (corp-wide): 27.2B **Publicly Held**
WEB: www.jabil.com
SIC: 3672 Printed circuit boards
PA: Jabil Inc.
10560 Dr Mrtn Lther King
Saint Petersburg FL 33716
727 577-9749

(G-15831)
JACKIE Z STYLE CO ST PETE LLC
Also Called: Jackiezstyleco
113 2nd Ave N (33701-3315)
PHONE..................................727 258-4849
Jackie Zumba, *Owner*
EMP: 8 **EST:** 2012
SALES (est): 758.3K **Privately Held**
WEB: www.jackiezstyle.com
SIC: 2326 5621 Men's & boys' work clothing; women's clothing stores

(G-15832)
JANE AND GEORGE INDUSTRIES
4197 49th Ave S (33711-4619)
PHONE..................................727 698-4903
Nathan E Dameron, *Principal*
EMP: 13 **EST:** 2016
SALES (est): 120.1K **Privately Held**
WEB: www.georgeindustries.com
SIC: 3999 Manufacturing industries

(G-15833)
KING PHARMACEUTICALS LLC
2540 26th Ave N (33713-3929)
PHONE..................................423 989-8000
Elaine Strauss, *Vice Pres*
Jopie Merriweather, *Sales Staff*
Deborah Tiffany, *Manager*
Jill Collins, *Officer*
Mike Mao, *Maintence Staff*
EMP: 38
SALES (corp-wide): 41.9B **Publicly Held**
SIC: 2834 Pharmaceutical preparations
HQ: King Pharmaceuticals Llc
501 5th St
Bristol TN 37620

(G-15834)
KOZUBA & SONS DISTILLERY INC
1960 5th Ave S (33712-1324)
PHONE..................................813 857-8197
Kozuba Maciej, *Principal*
▲ **EMP:** 14 **EST:** 2015
SALES (est): 1.9MM **Privately Held**
WEB: www.kozubadistillery.com
SIC: 2085 Distilled & blended liquors

(G-15835)
L3 AVIATION PRODUCTS INC
Also Called: L3 Technologies
490 1st Ave S Ste 600 (33701-4287)
PHONE..................................941 371-0811
Frank Doran, *President*
Bruce Coffee, *Branch Mgr*
Michelle Crawford, *Software Engr*
EMP: 140
SALES (corp-wide): 3.7B **Publicly Held**
WEB: www.avionics.cas.l3harris.com
SIC: 3769 Guided missile & space vehicle parts & aux eqpt, rsch & dev
HQ: L3 Aviation Products, Inc.
5353 52nd St Se
Grand Rapids MI 49512
616 949-6600

(G-15836)
L3 TECHNOLOGIES INC
490 1st Ave S (33701-4204)
PHONE..................................941 371-0811
Jennifer Ford, *Manager*
EMP: 6
SALES (corp-wide): 3.7B **Publicly Held**
WEB: www.l3harris.com
SIC: 3812 Search & navigation equipment
HQ: L3 Technologies, Inc.
600 3rd Ave Fl 34
New York NY 10016
321 727-9100

(G-15837)
LEGACY VULCAN LLC
1020 31st St S (33712-1925)
PHONE..................................727 321-4667
Paul Beavin, *Branch Mgr*
EMP: 8 **Publicly Held**
WEB: www.vulcanmaterials.com
SIC: 3273 Ready-mixed concrete
HQ: Legacy Vulcan, Llc
1200 Urban Center Dr
Vestavia AL 35242
205 298-3000

(G-15838)
LEISURE ACTIVITIES USA LLC
2399 26th Ave N (33713-4039)
PHONE..................................727 417-7128
Yi Cao, *President*
EMP: 8 **EST:** 2017
SALES (est): 356.5K **Privately Held**
WEB: www.leisureactivitiesusa.com
SIC: 3944 Games, toys & children's vehicles

(G-15839)
LENSTEC INC (PA)
1765 Commerce Ave N (33716-4207)
PHONE..................................727 571-2272
John Clough, *President*
Hayden Beatty, *COO*
Margaret N Clough, *Vice Pres*
Bill Hanley, *Vice Pres*
Rick Harrison, *QC Mgr*
EMP: 29 **EST:** 1993
SQ FT: 23,000
SALES (est): 5.4MM **Privately Held**
WEB: www.lenstec.com
SIC: 3827 Optical instruments & apparatus

(G-15840)
LILLIAN BAY MEDICAL INC
300 10th St S Apt 346 (33705-1704)
PHONE..................................941 815-7373
Brad M Beatty, *President*
EMP: 12
SALES (est): 553.1K **Privately Held**
WEB: www.lillianbaymedical.com
SIC: 2836 Biological products, except diagnostic

(G-15841)
LIMELIGHT PUBLISHING LLC
6677 13th Ave N Ste 3a (33710-8612)
PHONE..................................727 384-5999
Brian P Deeb, *Principal*
EMP: 6 **EST:** 2011
SALES (est): 203K **Privately Held**
WEB: www.deeblawgroup.com
SIC: 2741 Miscellaneous publishing

(G-15842)
LPI INC
6101 45th St N (33714-1038)
PHONE..................................702 403-8555
David Bonior, *Principal*
Frey Louis Jr, *Principal*
EMP: 15 **EST:** 2018
SALES (est): 514.7K **Privately Held**
WEB: www.lpiinc.com
SIC: 3088 Plastics plumbing fixtures

(G-15843)
LUCKE GROUP INC
Also Called: Fastsigns
408 33rd Ave N Ste A (33704-1384)
PHONE..................................727 525-4949
Gary Lucke, *President*
EMP: 6 **EST:** 1997
SQ FT: 4,600
SALES (est): 727.4K **Privately Held**
WEB: www.fastsigns.com
SIC: 3993 Signs & advertising specialties

(G-15844)
LUMASTREAM INC (PA)
2201 1st Ave S (33712-1219)
PHONE..................................727 827-2805
Eric Higgs, *Ch of Bd*
George Gordon, *President*
Rob Kapusta, *Chairman*
Chris Booth, *Vice Pres*
Mike Gaydos, *Vice Pres*
▲ **EMP:** 32 **EST:** 2009
SALES (est): 7.1MM **Privately Held**
WEB: www.lumastream.com
SIC: 3646 Commercial indusl & institutional electric lighting fixtures

(G-15845)
M VICTORIA ENTERPRISES INC
Also Called: 4th St Print Shack
9109 4th St N (33702-3129)
PHONE..................................727 576-8090
Michelle L Grant, *President*
EMP: 7 **EST:** 2008
SALES (est): 268.4K **Privately Held**
SIC: 2752 Commercial printing, offset

(G-15846)
MARCO POLO PUBLICATIONS INC
360 Central Ave Ste 1260 (33701-3865)
PHONE..................................866 610-9441
James Plouf, *President*
David Plouf, *Vice Pres*
Wendy Lahr-Bees, *Marketing Staff*
Jake Braun, *CIO*
EMP: 6 **EST:** 1996
SALES (est): 801.2K **Privately Held**
WEB: www.marcopolopublications.com
SIC: 2759 Publication printing

(G-15847)
MARINE ELECTRONICS ENGINE
4801 96th St N (33708-3740)
PHONE..................................727 459-5593
EMP: 6 **EST:** 2010
SALES (est): 108.8K **Privately Held**
SIC: 3519 Marine engines

(G-15848)
MARINE INDUSTRIAL PAINT CO
4590 60th Ave N (33714-1035)
PHONE..................................727 527-3382
Gregory T Deininger, *President*
Patricia Deininger, *Corp Secy*
Jerome Deininger, *Vice Pres*
Steven Deininger, *Vice Pres*
Carson Deininger, *Technical Staff*
EMP: 16 **EST:** 1962
SQ FT: 10,000
SALES (est): 4.7MM **Privately Held**
WEB: www.tuf-top.com
SIC: 2851 Paints & paint additives

(G-15849)
MARINETEK NORTH AMERICA INC
111 2nd Ave Ne Ste 360 (33701-3580)
PHONE..................................727 498-8741
Richard Murray, *President*
Harri Weckstrom, *Vice Pres*
Jukka Saarikko, *CFO*
Deborah Brook, *Treasurer*
Ilkka Seppala, *Director*
◆ **EMP:** 12 **EST:** 2012
SALES (est): 8.5MM **Privately Held**
WEB: www.marinetek.net
SIC: 3448 Prefabricated metal buildings
PA: Marinetek Group Oy
Mittalinja 2
Vantaa 00210

(G-15850)
MARK WALTERS LLC
1126 15th Ave N (33704-4120)
PHONE..................................727 742-3091
Mark J Walters, *Principal*
EMP: 6 **EST:** 2007
SALES (est): 122.1K **Privately Held**
WEB: www.waltersco.com
SIC: 2741 Miscellaneous publishing

(G-15851)
MAXI-BLAST OF FLORIDA INC
Also Called: Econo-Blast
11000 Gandy Blvd N (33702-1423)
P.O. Box 13027 (33733-3027)
PHONE..................................727 572-0909
Robert A Donaldson, *President*
Dale Fisher, *Vice Pres*
EMP: 8 **EST:** 1980
SQ FT: 10,000
SALES (est): 1.3MM **Privately Held**
WEB: www.maxiblast.com
SIC: 3291 3089 Abrasive products; plastic processing

(G-15852)
MB WELDING INC
7360 46th Ave N (33709-2504)
PHONE..................................727 548-0923
Michele L Barga, *Principal*
EMP: 9 **EST:** 2010
SALES (est): 399.9K **Privately Held**
SIC: 7692 Welding repair

(G-15853)
MCKENNY PRINTING ENTERPRISE
Also Called: Speedpro Imaging St Petersburg
2748 25th St N (33713-3942)
PHONE..................................727 420-4944
Michael McKenny, *CEO*
EMP: 5 **EST:** 2015
SALES (est): 871.3K **Privately Held**
SIC: 3993 5999 7336 3577 Signs & advertising specialties; displays & cutouts, window & lobby; banners, flags, decals & posters; graphic arts & related design; graphic displays, except graphic terminals

(G-15854)
MILLIMETER WAVE PRODUCTS INC
Also Called: Center Technologies
2007 Gandy Blvd N # 1310 (33702-2169)
PHONE..................................727 563-0034
Mark Smith, *President*
Lokesh Saggam, *Project Engr*
Kim Madden, *Technician*
▲ **EMP:** 25 **EST:** 1996
SQ FT: 8,000
SALES (est): 3.2MM **Privately Held**
WEB: www.miwv.com
SIC: 3663 Microwave communication equipment; space satellite communications equipment; satellites, communications

(G-15855)
MILLS & MURPHY SFTWR SYSTEMS
618 94th Ave N (33702-2408)
P.O. Box 56689 (33732-6689)
PHONE..................................727 577-1236
F Edward Murphy, *President*
Scott J Mills, *Vice Pres*
EMP: 22 **EST:** 1991
SQ FT: 5,500
SALES (est): 566.7K **Privately Held**
WEB: www.millsmur.com
SIC: 7372 Prepackaged software

(G-15856)
MITCHELL WOOD WORKS INC
4726 15th Ave S (33711-2328)
PHONE..................................727 321-7586
Kelvin Mitchell, *Director*
EMP: 6 **EST:** 2001

▲ = Import ▼=Export
◆ =Import/Export

SALES (est): 59.1K **Privately Held**
SIC: 2431 Millwork

(G-15857)
MODERN TCHNCAL MOLDING DEV LLC
Also Called: MTM&d
2600 72nd St N (33710-2929)
PHONE....................................727 343-2942
Dave S Massie, *President*
John Basley, *General Mgr*
Dave Gunthrop, *QC Mgr*
EMP: 17 **EST:** 2008
SQ FT: 22,000
SALES (est): 2MM **Privately Held**
WEB: www.mtmd.com
SIC: 3089 Injection molding of plastics; injection molded finished plastic products

(G-15858)
MOLLYS SUDS LLC
7490 30th Ave N A (33710-2304)
PHONE....................................678 361-5456
Monica M Leonard, *President*
Rick Leonard, *Vice Pres*
EMP: 6 **EST:** 2011
SALES (est): 900K **Privately Held**
WEB: www.mollysuds.com
SIC: 2841 2842 Soap & other detergents; laundry cleaning preparations

(G-15859)
MORROW TECHNOLOGIES CORP
Also Called: Janus Displays
12000 28th St N Fl 1 (33716-1853)
PHONE....................................727 531-4000
Sharon Morrow, *President*
Wendy Pohlmann, *Controller*
Sheila Campbell, *Manager*
EMP: 48 **EST:** 1984
SQ FT: 34,000
SALES (est): 8.3MM **Privately Held**
WEB: www.janusdisplays.com
SIC: 3993 Signs & advertising specialties

(G-15860)
MOTHER KOMBUCHA LLC
Also Called: Agua Bucha
4360 28th St N (33714-3924)
PHONE....................................727 767-0408
Vic Donati, *Partner*
Josh Rumschlag, *Partner*
Elizabeth Vanneste, *Partner*
Stephanie Davenport, *Sales Mgr*
Tonya Donati, *Mng Member*
EMP: 10 **EST:** 2014
SQ FT: 13,000
SALES (est): 1.5MM **Privately Held**
WEB: www.motherkombucha.com
SIC: 2099 Tea blending

(G-15861)
MOTOR MAGNETICS INC
2801 72nd St N (33710-2903)
PHONE....................................727 873-3180
Nancy Preis, *President*
Edward Schiff, *Vice Pres*
Victor Marino, *Purchasing*
Richard Horbal MD, *Treasurer*
Denise Layman, *Manager*
▲ **EMP:** 24 **EST:** 1974
SQ FT: 10,000
SALES (est): 4.7MM **Privately Held**
WEB: www.motormagnetics.com
SIC: 3621 Motors, electric

(G-15862)
MTS MEDICATION TECH INC (HQ)
2003 Gandy Blvd N Ste 800 (33702-2167)
PHONE....................................727 576-6311
Todd E Siegel, *CEO*
William G Shields, *President*
Matthew C Hicks, *Corp Secy*
Michael D Stevenson, *COO*
Robert A Martin, *Vice Pres*
▲ **EMP:** 230 **EST:** 1986
SQ FT: 132,500
SALES (est): 49.2MM **Publicly Held**
WEB: www.omnicell.com
SIC: 3565 3089 Packaging machinery; blister or bubble formed packaging, plastic

(G-15863)
MTS PACKAGING SYSTEMS INC (PA)
2003 Gandy Blvd N Ste 800 (33702-2167)
PHONE....................................727 576-6311
Todd E Siegel, *President*
Selm Robin E, *Principal*
Michael Stevenson, *COO*
Michael P Conroy, *CFO*
Stephanie Mueller, *Human Res Dir*
▼ **EMP:** 125 **EST:** 1992
SALES (est): 9.9MM **Privately Held**
SIC: 3089 Blister or bubble formed packaging, plastic

(G-15864)
NDH MEDICAL INC
11001 Roosevelt Blvd N # 150 (33716-2348)
PHONE....................................727 570-2293
Geary A Havran, *President*
Scott W Nicora, *Vice Pres*
EMP: 5 **EST:** 1986
SQ FT: 6,000
SALES (est): 1MM **Privately Held**
WEB: www.ndhmedical.com
SIC: 3841 Surgical instruments & apparatus

(G-15865)
NEW DAWN COFFEE COMPANY
2336 5th Ave S (33712-1631)
PHONE....................................727 321-5155
Terese Delangis, *President*
EMP: 6 **EST:** 1985
SQ FT: 14,000
SALES (est): 464K **Privately Held**
WEB: www.newdawncoffee.com
SIC: 2095 2099 Coffee roasting (except by wholesale grocers); tea blending

(G-15866)
NI-CHRO PLATING CORP
Also Called: M and P Plating
700 37th St S (33711-2119)
PHONE....................................727 327-5118
Peter Valantiejus, *President*
John Kutch, *Vice Pres*
EMP: 5 **EST:** 1972
SQ FT: 3,000
SALES (est): 660.2K **Privately Held**
SIC: 3471 Chromium plating of metals or formed products; plating of metals or formed products

(G-15867)
NORTHEAST WATER RECLAMATION
Also Called: Northast Wtr Rclmtion Fclities
1160 62nd Ave Ne (33702-7626)
PHONE....................................727 893-7779
Steve Leavitt, *Director*
EMP: 6 **EST:** 1918
SALES (est): 89.8K **Privately Held**
SIC: 2899 Water treating compounds

(G-15868)
NYPRO HEALTHCARE LLC
10560 Dr Martin Luther (33716-3718)
PHONE....................................727 577-9749
EMP: 49 **EST:** 2019
SALES (est): 1.2MM
SALES (corp-wide): 27.2B **Publicly Held**
WEB: www.jabil.com
SIC: 3672 Printed circuit boards
PA: Jabil Inc.
10560 Dr Mrtn Lther King
Saint Petersburg FL 33716
727 577-9749

(G-15869)
OAKHURST MARKETING INC
Also Called: Oakhurst Signs
2392 31st St S (33712-3348)
PHONE....................................727 532-8255
Josh Buttitta, *President*
Adam Prescott, *Business Mgr*
Joe Centrone, *COO*
Liana Rollins, *Project Mgr*
Marie Waters, *Opers Staff*
EMP: 7 **EST:** 2005
SALES (est): 1.3MM **Privately Held**
WEB: www.oakhurstsigns.com
SIC: 3993 7336 1799 Signs, not made in custom sign painting shops; commercial art & graphic design; sign installation & maintenance

(G-15870)
OERLIKON USA INC
10050 16th St N (33716-4219)
PHONE....................................727 577-4999
EMP: 23 **EST:** 1975
SALES (est): 586.3K **Privately Held**
WEB: www.oerlikonoc.com
SIC: 3674 Semiconductors & related devices

(G-15871)
OLDJA ENTERPRISES INC
4424 34th St N (33714-3712)
PHONE....................................727 526-3240
EMP: 10 **EST:** 2019
SALES (est): 507.5K **Privately Held**
WEB: www.oldjaenterprises.com
SIC: 2434 Wood kitchen cabinets

(G-15872)
OMALLEY MANUFACTURING INC
Also Called: O'Malley Valve Co.
4228 8th Ave S (33711-2029)
P.O. Box 12766 (33733-2766)
PHONE....................................727 327-6817
Richard Wheeler, *President*
EMP: 8 **EST:** 1910
SQ FT: 8,000
SALES (est): 902.4K **Privately Held**
WEB: www.omalley.com
SIC: 3451 3432 Screw machine products; faucets & spigots, metal & plastic

(G-15873)
OWENS & SONS MARINE INC
Also Called: Aluminum Slide-On Trailers
3601 8th Ave S (33711-2203)
PHONE....................................727 323-1088
William M Owens, *President*
Elizabeth Ann Owens, *Vice Pres*
William Douglas Owens, *Treasurer*
Jeffery Owens, *Admin Sec*
▼ **EMP:** 10 **EST:** 1983
SQ FT: 15,000
SALES (est): 1.4MM **Privately Held**
WEB: www.slideon.com
SIC: 3799 Boat trailers; automobile trailer chassis

(G-15874)
PAINASSIST INC
6199 54th St S (33715-2408)
PHONE....................................248 875-4222
Pramod Kerkar, *Principal*
EMP: 8 **EST:** 2012
SALES (est): 623.3K **Privately Held**
WEB: www.epainassist.com
SIC: 7372 Application computer software

(G-15875)
PEPSI ST PETE
Also Called: Pepsico
4451 34th St N (33714-3711)
PHONE....................................727 527-8113
EMP: 16 **EST:** 2016
SALES (est): 2.7MM **Privately Held**
WEB: www.pepsico.com
SIC: 2086 Carbonated soft drinks, bottled & canned

(G-15876)
PINELLAS PRECISION LASER LLC
4185 35th St N (33714-3705)
PHONE....................................727 420-0388
EMP: 5 **EST:** 2019
SALES (est): 328.1K **Privately Held**
WEB: www.pinellasprecision.com
SIC: 3499 Fabricated metal products

(G-15877)
PINELLAS PROVISION CORPORATION
Also Called: Centerpoint Meats and Prov
201 16th St S (33705-1635)
PHONE....................................727 822-2701
Todd J Reese, *President*
Daniel P Reese, *Vice Pres*
EMP: 23 **EST:** 1972
SQ FT: 15,000
SALES (est): 14MM **Privately Held**
SIC: 2013 5147 Sausages & other prepared meats; meats, fresh

(G-15878)
PIONEER CASEWORK LLC
Also Called: Pioneer Woodworking
7901 4th St N Ste 4616 (33702-4305)
PHONE....................................305 404-3490
Paul E Hughes,
Andrew Elmore,
Martha Elmore,
EMP: 13 **EST:** 1960
SQ FT: 8,700
SALES (est): 561.3K **Privately Held**
WEB: www.pioneerwoodworking.net
SIC: 2434 Wood kitchen cabinets

(G-15879)
PJ DESIGNS INC (PA)
Also Called: Peggy Jennings Design
1515 Park St N (33710-4345)
PHONE....................................727 525-0599
Herb Kosterlitz, *CEO*
James Jennings, *President*
Peggy Jennings, *President*
EMP: 30 **EST:** 1980
SALES (est): 4.2MM **Privately Held**
SIC: 2335 2331 2339 2341 Dresses, paper: cut & sewn; blouses, women's & juniors': made from purchased material; slacks: women's, misses' & juniors'; nightgowns & negligees: women's & children's; robes & dressing gowns

(G-15880)
PLASMA-THERM INC
1150 16th St N (33705-1149)
PHONE....................................856 753-8111
Ronald Deferrari, *President*
David Hawkins, *Technical Staff*
Jason Dearth, *Analyst*
EMP: 34 **EST:** 1991
SALES (est): 494.7K **Privately Held**
WEB: www.plasmatherm.com
SIC: 2836 Plasmas
PA: Plasma-Therm, Llc
10050 16th St N
Saint Petersburg FL 33716

(G-15881)
PLASMA-THERM LLC (PA)
10050 16th St N (33716-4219)
PHONE....................................727 577-4999
Abdul Lateef, *CEO*
Abdul C Latee, *CEO*
Edward Ostan, *President*
James Pollock, *COO*
Jim Garstka, *Vice Pres*
▲ **EMP:** 138 **EST:** 2008
SQ FT: 60,639
SALES (est): 55.3MM **Privately Held**
WEB: www.plasmatherm.com
SIC: 3674 Semiconductors & related devices

(G-15882)
PLAY TAMPA BAY INC
7925 4th St N Ste B (33702-4319)
PHONE....................................727 803-6838
Todd M Boulanger, *Principal*
EMP: 7 **EST:** 2012
SALES (est): 158.5K **Privately Held**
WEB: www.playtampabay.com
SIC: 3949 Playground equipment

(G-15883)
POND INDUSTRIES INC
1942 Iowa Ave Ne (33703-3426)
PHONE....................................727 526-5483
Susan D Poniatowski, *Principal*
EMP: 7 **EST:** 2010
SALES (est): 232.4K **Privately Held**
SIC: 3999 Manufacturing industries

(G-15884)
POPSTOPS MARKETING INC
111 2nd Ave Ne Ste 1201 (33701-3443)
PHONE....................................800 209-4571
J Scott Fenimore, *President*
EMP: 8 **EST:** 2017
SQ FT: 3,000

GEOGRAPHIC

SALES (est): 867.6K **Privately Held**
WEB: www.popstops.com
SIC: 3559 Frame straighteners, automobile (garage equipment)

(G-15885)
POWER PRINTING OF FLORIDA
Also Called: Sir Speedy
956 1st Ave N (33705-1502)
PHONE..................................727 823-1162
Jerry Powers, *President*
James Calvert, *General Mgr*
Zachary Miller, *Graphic Designe*
EMP: 12 **EST:** 1987
SQ FT: 5,300
SALES (est): 2.5MM **Privately Held**
WEB: www.sirspeedystpete.com
SIC: 2752 Commercial printing, lithographic

(G-15886)
POWERCHORD INC
360 Central Ave Fl 5 (33701-3832)
PHONE..................................727 823-1530
William Volmuth, *CEO*
Patrick J Schunk, *President*
Garbis Bedoian, *General Mgr*
Michelle Tipton, *Vice Pres*
Michael Vandiest, *Vice Pres*
EMP: 76 **EST:** 1999
SALES (est): 11.6MM **Privately Held**
WEB: www.powerchord.com
SIC: 7372 Business oriented computer software

(G-15887)
PRECISION CERAMICS USA INC
9843 18th St N Ste 120 (33716-4208)
PHONE..................................727 388-5060
Steve Swallow, *President*
David Ostrow, *Vice Pres*
Kizzan Amer, *VP Bus Dvlpt*
Sally Dumas, *Administration*
EMP: 16 **EST:** 2009
SALES (est): 5.8MM
SALES (corp-wide): 21.8MM **Privately Held**
WEB: www.precision-ceramics.com
SIC: 3253 Wall tile, ceramic
PA: Mcgeoch Technology Limited
86 Lower Tower Street
Birmingham W MIDLANDS B19 3
121 687-5850

(G-15888)
PRECISION METAL PARTS INC
4725 28th St N (33714-3115)
PHONE..................................727 526-9165
John P Garrity, *President*
Cheryl Gallagher, *Marketing Staff*
Dan Murphy, *Technical Staff*
EMP: 20 **EST:** 1947
SQ FT: 16,000
SALES (est): 1.2MM **Privately Held**
WEB: www.precisionperformanceinc.com
SIC: 3451 3541 Screw machine products; machine tools, metal cutting type

(G-15889)
PRINTING FOR A CAUSE LLC
360 Central Ave Ste 800 (33701-3984)
PHONE..................................786 496-0637
EMP: 25
SQ FT: 1,200
SALES: 5.1MM **Privately Held**
SIC: 2752 2741 2731 Internet Publishing And Broadcasting Lithographic Commercial Printing Books-Publishing/Printing

(G-15890)
PRIVATE LABEL SKIN NA LLC
Also Called: World Product Solutions
2260 118th Ave N (33716-1929)
PHONE..................................877 516-2200
Brian Crowdis, *General Mgr*
Vahid Kasliwala, *COO*
Theresa Gay, *Project Mgr*
Fahreta Arnautovic, *Production*
Tony Kreinbrink, *Purchasing*
EMP: 165 **EST:** 2012
SALES (est): 22.5MM **Privately Held**
WEB: www.worldproductsolutions.com
SIC: 2844 7336 Toilet preparations; package design

(G-15891)
PROFILE RACING INC
Also Called: Profile Tool & Gear
4803 95th St N (33708-3725)
PHONE..................................727 392-8307
James Alley, *President*
Nancy Alley, *Vice Pres*
Shane Wanek, *Sales Staff*
▲ **EMP:** 45 **EST:** 1968
SQ FT: 18,000
SALES (est): 6.6MM **Privately Held**
WEB: www.profileracing.com
SIC: 3714 3751 3462 Gears, motor vehicle; bicycles & related parts; iron & steel forgings

(G-15892)
PROGRESS FUELS CORPORATION (DH)
1 Progress Plz Fl 11 (33701-4322)
PHONE..................................727 824-6600
Fax: 727 824-6605
▲ **EMP:** 70 **EST:** 1976
SQ FT: 24,500
SALES (est): 654.5MM
SALES (corp-wide): 23.5B **Publicly Held**
SIC: 1221 Bituminous Coal/Lignite Surface Mining
HQ: Progress Energy, Inc.
410 S Wilmington St
Raleigh NC 27601
704 382-3853

(G-15893)
PROSUN INTERNATIONAL LLC
2442 23rd St N (33713-4018)
PHONE..................................727 825-0400
Tom Henkemans, *President*
Mireille Doffegnies, *Vice Pres*
Laurie Wall, *Accounts Mgr*
Kaitlyn Grady, *Sales Staff*
Scott Lafortune, *Marketing Mgr*
◆ **EMP:** 51 **EST:** 2002
SQ FT: 75,000
SALES (est): 16.6MM **Privately Held**
WEB: www.prosun.com
SIC: 3648 Sun tanning equipment, incl. tanning beds

(G-15894)
PROTECT ALL COATING INC
2458 36th Ave N (33713-1823)
PHONE..................................727 278-7454
Clifton Davis, *CEO*
Jennifer Davis, *Vice Pres*
EMP: 6 **EST:** 2004
SALES (est): 452.9K **Privately Held**
WEB: www.protectall.com
SIC: 3479 Metal coating & allied service

(G-15895)
QUALITY CARPET
4420 44th St N (33714-3518)
PHONE..................................727 527-1359
Timothy Szymczak, *President*
EMP: 6 **EST:** 2007
SALES (est): 143.4K **Privately Held**
SIC: 3423 5087 5713 Carpet layers' hand tools; carpet & rug cleaning equipment & supplies, commercial; carpet installation equipment; carpets

(G-15896)
QUALITY INDUSTRIAL CHEM INC
Also Called: St Pete Auto Aids
3161 118th Ave N (33716-1865)
PHONE..................................727 573-5760
Russell C Profitt, *President*
EMP: 10 **EST:** 1974
SQ FT: 8,000
SALES (est): 728.1K **Privately Held**
SIC: 2842 5087 2891 Cleaning or polishing preparations; service establishment equipment; carwash equipment & supplies; adhesives & sealants

(G-15897)
QUANTUM SPATIAL INC (HQ)
Also Called: Nv5geospatial
10033 Dr Mrtn Lther King (33716-3830)
PHONE..................................920 457-3631
Peter Lamontagne, *President*
Alexa Ramirez, *Manager*
David Grigg, *Director*
Tetiana Gordon, *Analyst*
Emily Sandrowicz, *Analyst*
EMP: 100 **EST:** 1969
SQ FT: 15,000
SALES (est): 65MM
SALES (corp-wide): 659.3MM **Publicly Held**
WEB: www.nv5.com
SIC: 2741 8713 Maps: publishing & printing; surveying services
PA: Nv5 Global, Inc.
200 S Park Rd Ste 350
Hollywood FL 33021
954 495-2112

(G-15898)
RAYTHEON COMPANY
7401 22nd Ave N Bldg D (33710-3804)
PHONE..................................310 647-9438
Thomas Kennedy, *CEO*
Joe Tuckness, *Engineer*
Jan Yang, *Engineer*
W Greg Henson, *Branch Mgr*
Donna Mc Cullough, *Manager*
EMP: 6
SALES (corp-wide): 56.5B **Publicly Held**
WEB: www.rtx.com
SIC: 3812 Radar systems & equipment; sonar systems & equipment
HQ: Raytheon Company
870 Winter St
Waltham MA 02451
781 522-3000

(G-15899)
REAL KETONES LLC ✪
111 2nd Ave Ne Ste 1401 (33701-3480)
PHONE..................................801 244-8610
Paul Peach, *Vice Pres*
Gary Millet, *Mng Member*
EMP: 10 **EST:** 2021
SALES (est): 2.8MM
SALES (corp-wide): 20MM **Privately Held**
WEB: www.realketones.com
SIC: 2833 5499 Inorganic medicinal chemicals: bulk, uncompounded; dietetic foods
PA: Axcess Global , Llc
2157 S Lincoln St
Salt Lake City UT 84106
801 244-8610

(G-15900)
RESTORATIVE CARE AMERICA INC (PA)
Also Called: Rcai
12221 33rd St N (33716-1841)
PHONE..................................727 573-1595
C E Hess, *President*
Nancy Tiller, *Manager*
Nigel Horsley, *Commissioner*
EMP: 91 **EST:** 1975
SQ FT: 35,000
SALES (est): 14MM **Privately Held**
WEB: www.rcai.com
SIC: 3842 Braces, orthopedic; orthopedic appliances

(G-15901)
REV-TECH MFG SOLUTIONS LLC
9900 18th St N Ste 105 (33716-4224)
PHONE..................................727 577-4999
Hector Pujols, *Principal*
EMP: 15 **EST:** 2011
SALES (est): 788.7K **Privately Held**
WEB: www.revtechms.com
SIC: 3999 3441 Beekeepers' supplies; fabricated structural metal

(G-15902)
REVTECH
10050 16th St N (33716-4219)
PHONE..................................727 369-1750
Louis Gomez, *Manager*
EMP: 11 **EST:** 2017
SALES (est): 563.7K **Privately Held**
WEB: www.revtechms.com
SIC: 3599 Machine shop, jobbing & repair

(G-15903)
RS&M CONSULTANTS
2350 34th St N Ste 140 (33713-3614)
PHONE..................................727 323-6983
Lynn Terry, *Principal*
EMP: 6 **EST:** 2016
SALES (est): 86.6K **Privately Held**
WEB: www.rsm-consultants.com
SIC: 3842 Surgical appliances & supplies

(G-15904)
SAINT PETERSBURG CABINETS INC
2547 24th Ave N (33713-4320)
PHONE..................................727 327-4800
Zoran Milic, *President*
Dobrinka Milic, *Treasurer*
EMP: 5 **EST:** 1978
SQ FT: 4,000
SALES (est): 469.2K **Privately Held**
WEB: www.thestpetersburgcabinetco.com
SIC: 2514 2511 Kitchen cabinets: metal; bed frames, except water bed frames: wood

(G-15905)
SANDY-ALEXANDER INC
Also Called: Modern Graphic Arts
1527 102nd Ave N (33716-5049)
PHONE..................................727 579-1527
Eric Reinitz, *General Mgr*
Paul Vogelsang, *General Mgr*
Victor Klein, *Vice Pres*
Leslie Tolbert, *Vice Pres*
Dave Matheu, *Production*
EMP: 100
SALES (corp-wide): 121.9MM **Privately Held**
WEB: www.sandyinc.com
SIC: 2752 Commercial printing, lithographic
PA: Sandy Alexander, Inc.
200 Entin Rd
Clifton NJ 07014
973 470-8100

(G-15906)
SCI UNDERCAR INC (PA)
2447 5th Ave S (33712-1632)
PHONE..................................727 327-2278
Scott McKalvey, *President*
▲ **EMP:** 10 **EST:** 1990
SQ FT: 9,000
SALES (est): 1.8MM **Privately Held**
SIC: 3714 Motor vehicle brake systems & parts

(G-15907)
SCRIBE MANUFACTURING INC
3001 Tech Dr N (33716-1001)
PHONE..................................727 536-7895
EMP: 13
SALES (corp-wide): 42.2MM **Privately Held**
SIC: 3951 Pens & mechanical pencils
PA: Scribe Manufacturing, Inc.
14421 Myerlake Cir
Clearwater FL 33760
727 524-7482

(G-15908)
SEATING INSTALLATION GROUP LLC
Also Called: Sig
12100 31st Ct N (33716-1827)
PHONE..................................727 289-7652
Leah O'Dor,
Eugene O'Dor,
EMP: 13 **EST:** 2013
SQ FT: 1,500
SALES (est): 1.7MM **Privately Held**
WEB: www.si-gp.com
SIC: 2531 Stadium seating

(G-15909)
SENSIDYNE LP
1000 112th Cir N Ste 100 (33716-2358)
PHONE..................................727 530-3602
Howard Mills, *Partner*
Wes Davis, *Partner*
Glenn Warr, *Partner*
Anibal Mulero, *Buyer*
Michael Adams, *Engineer*
◆ **EMP:** 95 **EST:** 1983
SQ FT: 40,000

SALES (est): 22MM
SALES (corp-wide): 240.4MM **Privately Held**
WEB: www.sensidyne.com
SIC: 3823 5084 Industrial instrmnts msrmnt display/control process variable; industrial machinery & equipment
HQ: Schauenburg Management, Inc.
1000 112th Cir N Ste 100
Saint Petersburg FL 33716

(G-15910)
SENSOR SYSTEMS LLC
2800 Anvil St N (33710-2943)
PHONE..................................727 347-2181
Charles Nunziata, *Vice Pres*
Ned Schiff, *Vice Pres*
Abel Elmazouri, *Chief Engr*
James White, *Chief Engr*
Ryan Peterson, *Engineer*
▼ **EMP:** 120 **EST:** 1998
SALES (est): 23.1MM **Privately Held**
WEB: www.sensorsllc.com
SIC: 3829 Measuring & controlling devices

(G-15911)
SERVICE BINDERY ENTERPRISES
Also Called: Service Bindery of Pinellas
3228 Morris St N (33713-2734)
PHONE..................................727 823-9866
Richard L Love, *President*
Sandrell Apatira, *Manager*
Gerly Dennis, *Manager*
EMP: 16 **EST:** 1985
SQ FT: 7,200
SALES (est): 573.1K **Privately Held**
WEB: www.servicebindery.com
SIC: 2789 2675 Binding only: books, pamphlets, magazines, etc.; die-cut paper & board

(G-15912)
SHUKLA MEDICAL INC
8300 Sheen Dr (33709-2222)
PHONE..................................732 474-1769
Rahul Shukla, *President*
Jamie Gilroy, *Natl Sales Mgr*
Sid Desai, *Corp Comm Staff*
EMP: 21 **EST:** 1999
SALES (est): 2.9MM
SALES (corp-wide): 30.3MM **Privately Held**
WEB: www.shuklamedical.com
SIC: 3842 Surgical appliances & supplies
PA: S.S. White Technologies Inc.
8300 Sheen Dr
Saint Petersburg FL 33709
727 626-2800

(G-15913)
SIMPLY RELIABLE INC
10460 Roosevelt Blvd N (33716-3821)
PHONE..................................800 209-9332
John Coffin, *President*
Chris Jaffe, *Vice Pres*
Jonathan Knapp, *CTO*
EMP: 5 **EST:** 2012
SALES (est): 614.1K **Privately Held**
WEB: www.simplyreliable.com
SIC: 7372 Business oriented computer software

(G-15914)
SNUG HARBOR DINGHIES INC
Also Called: Biking Boat Works Company, The
10121 Snug Harbor Rd Ne (33702-1917)
PHONE..................................727 578-0618
Gerald Dalrymple, *President*
Kara Kessler, *Vice Pres*
Eric Rikansrud, *Vice Pres*
EMP: 10 **EST:** 1986
SQ FT: 10,932
SALES (est): 156.2K **Privately Held**
SIC: 3732 Boat building & repairing

(G-15915)
SOLSEEN LLC
Also Called: Big T Printing
2801 16th St N (33704-2516)
PHONE..................................727 322-3131
Todd Moore, *Principal*
David Sistrunk, *Production*
EMP: 7 **EST:** 2012
SQ FT: 4,500
SALES (est): 915.6K **Privately Held**
WEB: www.bigtprinting.com
SIC: 2759 Screen printing

(G-15916)
SOUTHEASTERN MARINE POWER LLC
7398 46th Ave N (33709-2504)
PHONE..................................727 545-2700
Joanne Johannesson, *Treasurer*
Dan Johannesson,
Shane Wallace, *Technician*
Eric K Nelson,
▼ **EMP:** 19 **EST:** 1984
SALES (est): 2.2MM **Privately Held**
WEB: www.semarinepower.com
SIC: 3625 5551 Marine & navy auxiliary controls; boat dealers; outboard motors

(G-15917)
SOUTHERN INTEREST CO INC
Also Called: Doyle Ploch Sailmakers
2233 3rd Ave S (33712-1217)
PHONE..................................727 471-2040
EMP: 18
SQ FT: 5,000
SALES (est): 1.4MM **Privately Held**
SIC: 2394 Mfg Canvas/Related Products

(G-15918)
SOUTHERN STRL STL FLA INC
1000 31st St S (33712-1925)
PHONE..................................727 327-7123
Timothy A Richman, *President*
Brian McGovern, *Vice Pres*
Matthew P Richman, *Vice Pres*
Ken Techton, *Plant Mgr*
Cindy Hughlett, *Project Mgr*
EMP: 26 **EST:** 2015
SALES (est): 2.7MM **Privately Held**
WEB: www.southernstpete.com
SIC: 3441 Fabricated structural metal

(G-15919)
SOUTHERN SUPPLY AND MFG CO
Also Called: Gold Seal Cutlery
1501 22nd St N (33713-5615)
P.O. Box 10066 (33733-0066)
PHONE..................................727 323-7099
▲ **EMP:** 25
SQ FT: 10,000
SALES (est): 4MM **Privately Held**
SIC: 3421 Mfg Cutlery

(G-15920)
SPACE MACHINE & ENGRG CORP
2327 16th Ave N (33713-5625)
PHONE..................................727 323-2221
Allen Loyd, *President*
Edward Marston, *Vice Pres*
Gary Lamachia, *Opers Mgr*
Joe Holub, *QC Mgr*
Barrett Mattingly, *QC Mgr*
▲ **EMP:** 46 **EST:** 1962
SQ FT: 12,000
SALES (est): 7.6MM **Privately Held**
WEB: www.space-machine.com
SIC: 3761 Guided missiles & space vehicles

(G-15921)
SPECTRECOLOGY LLC
8719 Orient Way Ne (33702-3811)
PHONE..................................727 230-1697
EMP: 6 **EST:** 2014
SALES (est): 138.9K **Privately Held**
WEB: www.spectrecology.com
SIC: 3826 Analytical instruments

(G-15922)
SPEEDPRO IMAGING ST PETERSBURG
5111 Queen Palm Ter Ne (33703-6306)
PHONE..................................727 266-0956
Vernard McKenny, *President*
EMP: 5 **EST:** 2016
SALES (est): 322.3K **Privately Held**
WEB: www.speedpro.com
SIC: 3993 7389 3577 7336 Signs & advertising specialties; displays & cutouts, window & lobby; advertising, promotional & trade show services; graphic displays, except graphic terminals; graphic arts & related design; banners, flags, decals & posters

(G-15923)
SS WHITE TECHNOLOGIES INC (PA)
8300 Sheen Dr (33709-2222)
PHONE..................................727 626-2800
Rahul B Shukla, *President*
Steve Grimes, *Managing Dir*
Bernard Marx, *Vice Pres*
Thomas Sarnoski, *Vice Pres*
▲ **EMP:** 170
SQ FT: 90,000
SALES (est): 30.3MM **Privately Held**
WEB: www.sswhite.net
SIC: 3568 Shafts, flexible

(G-15924)
ST PETERSBURG DIST CO LLC
Also Called: Brookhaven Beverage Company
800 31st St S (33712-1923)
PHONE..................................727 581-1544
Eugene Davis, *Production*
Dominic C Iafrate,
EMP: 14 **EST:** 2013
SALES (est): 5MM **Privately Held**
WEB: www.stpetersburgdistillery.com
SIC: 2085 Distilled & blended liquors

(G-15925)
STABIL CONCRETE PRODUCTS LLC
4451 8th Ave S (33711-1903)
PHONE..................................727 321-6000
Gerry Flach, *Exec VP*
Ruth Hardy, *Vice Pres*
Jeff Nolan, *Vice Pres*
Brett Flint, *Plant Mgr*
Tyler Thomas, *Project Mgr*
EMP: 56 **EST:** 2006
SALES (est): 9.2MM **Privately Held**
WEB: www.stabilconcrete.com
SIC: 3272 Concrete products

(G-15926)
STALLION KING LLC
7901 4th St N Ste 4691 (33702-4305)
PHONE..................................321 503-7368
Kyrie Danger, *President*
EMP: 8 **EST:** 2018
SALES (est): 426.9K **Privately Held**
SIC: 7372 Educational computer software

(G-15927)
STEMLER CORPORATION
Also Called: Viking Cases
1873 64th Ave N (33702-7130)
PHONE..................................727 577-1216
Arthur Stemler, *CEO*
Bruce Stemler, *President*
Shirley Stemler, *Admin Sec*
Carol K Strickland, *Asst Sec*
EMP: 28 **EST:** 1975
SQ FT: 12,000
SALES (est): 609K **Privately Held**
WEB: www.thestemlercorporation.com
SIC: 2449 3161 3412 Shipping cases & drums, wood: wirebound & plywood; cases, carrying; metal barrels, drums & pails

(G-15928)
SUNCOAST RESEARCH LABS INC
2901 Anvil St N (33710-2911)
P.O. Box 47254 (33743-7254)
PHONE..................................727 344-7627
Robert Beaman, *President*
Kyle Beaman, *Vice Pres*
Cherie Beaman, *Treasurer*
EMP: 10 **EST:** 1983
SQ FT: 16,000
SALES (est): 2.2MM **Privately Held**
WEB: www.citrusdepot.net
SIC: 2842 Specialty cleaning preparations

(G-15929)
SUNCOAST TRENDS INC
2860 21st Ave N (33713-4204)
PHONE..................................727 321-4948
Rosanna Carl, *President*
Todd Carl, *Vice Pres*
EMP: 6 **EST:** 1975
SQ FT: 6,600
SALES (est): 747.7K **Privately Held**
SIC: 2331 2393 2329 2339 Blouses, women's & juniors': made from purchased material; shirts, women's & juniors': made from purchased materials; bags & containers, except sleeping bags: textile; men's & boys' sportswear & athletic clothing; sportswear, women's; girls' & children's outerwear

(G-15930)
SURFACE ENGRG & ALLOY CO INC (PA)
Also Called: Extreme Coatings
2895 46th Ave N (33714-3811)
PHONE..................................727 528-3734
Curtis Kadau, *President*
Craig Travers, *Prdtn Mgr*
Kim Perez, *Sales Staff*
Travis White, *Manager*
Jon Kogan, *Consultant*
◆ **EMP:** 72 **EST:** 1996
SQ FT: 16,000
SALES (est): 26.8MM **Privately Held**
WEB: www.surfaceengineering.com
SIC: 3699 Welding machines & equipment, ultrasonic

(G-15931)
SWAH-REY 2 LLC
625 Central Ave (33701-3625)
PHONE..................................727 767-0527
Leslie Ann Ciccone,
EMP: 6 **EST:** 2017
SALES (est): 150K **Privately Held**
WEB: www.swah-rey.com
SIC: 2051 Bakery: wholesale or wholesale/retail combined

(G-15932)
TAKEN FOR GRANITE
4481 Pompano Dr Se (33705-4354)
PHONE..................................727 235-1559
Davy Williams, *President*
EMP: 5 **EST:** 2003
SALES (est): 307.7K **Privately Held**
SIC: 3281 Granite, cut & shaped

(G-15933)
TAMPA BAY COATINGS INC
3228 Morris St N (33713-2734)
PHONE..................................727 823-9866
Richard Love, *President*
EMP: 19 **EST:** 2005
SALES (est): 152.7K **Privately Held**
WEB: www.archcoatings.com
SIC: 2672 Coated & laminated paper

(G-15934)
TAMPA BAY SPORTS ENTRMT LLC (PA)
490 1st Ave S (33701-4204)
PHONE..................................727 893-8111
Jeff Vinik, *Chairman*
Kerry O'Reilly, *Mktg Dir*
Anne Putnam, *Marketing Staff*
Jessica Petroski, *Advt Staff*
Christopher Spata, *Producer*
EMP: 345 **EST:** 2010
SALES (est): 134.8MM **Privately Held**
WEB: www.tampabay.com
SIC: 2711 Newspapers, publishing & printing

(G-15935)
TAMPATECHNIK CORPORATION
2530 22nd St N (33713-4010)
PHONE..................................727 823-8889
Paul R Markun, *President*
EMP: 5 **EST:** 2001
SQ FT: 2,000
SALES (est): 491.5K **Privately Held**
WEB: www.tampatechnik.com
SIC: 3599 Machine shop, jobbing & repair

(G-15936)
TAYLOR MEDIA LLC
Also Called: Penny Hoarder, The
490 1st Ave S Ste 800 (33701-4287)
PHONE..................................727 317-5800
Kyle Taylor, *CEO*
Loren Colson, *Controller*
Darrell Davis, *Manager*
Lisanne Lowitt, *Manager*
Tessa Whitmore, *Manager*
EMP: 121 **EST:** 2012
SQ FT: 23,000
SALES (est): 14.9MM
SALES (corp-wide): 177.9K **Privately Held**
WEB: www.thepennyhoarder.com
SIC: 2741 Miscellaneous publishing
HQ: Link Clear Technologies Llc
4050 S 500 W
Salt Lake City UT 84123
801 424-0018

(G-15937)
TECHNO-SOLIS INC
Also Called: Techno Solis USA
301 20th St S (33712-1315)
PHONE..................................727 823-6766
Sebastian Bourgeois, *President*
Sebastien Bourgeois, *Engineer*
Eddy Sanchez, *Engineer*
Stephen Messerschmidt, *Sales Staff*
Steve Messerschmidt, *Sales Staff*
EMP: 10 **EST:** 1976
SQ FT: 11,821
SALES (est): 2.6MM **Privately Held**
WEB: www.techno-solisusa.com
SIC: 3613 Panel & distribution boards & other related apparatus

(G-15938)
TIMES HOLDING CO (DH)
Also Called: Tampa Bay Times Storefront
490 1st Ave S (33701-4223)
P.O. Box 1121 (33731-1121)
PHONE..................................727 893-8111
Andrew Barnes, *Ch of Bd*
Amanda Dearmon, *Editor*
R Micheal Carroll, *Treasurer*
Jessica Attard, *Sales Staff*
Dave Labell, *Marketing Staff*
EMP: 1 **EST:** 1959
SALES (est): 27.2MM
SALES (corp-wide): 14.9MM **Privately Held**
WEB: www.poynter.org
SIC: 2721 2711 Magazines: publishing & printing; newspapers, publishing & printing
HQ: Times Publishing Company
490 1st Ave S
Saint Petersburg FL 33701
727 893-8111

(G-15939)
TIMES MEDIA SERVICES INC
490 1st Ave S (33701-4223)
PHONE..................................727 893-8111
Paul C Tash, *President*
EMP: 247 **EST:** 2017
SALES (est): 1MM
SALES (corp-wide): 14.9MM **Privately Held**
WEB: www.seniorlivingonline.com
SIC: 2711 Newspapers, publishing & printing
HQ: Times Publishing Company
490 1st Ave S
Saint Petersburg FL 33701
727 893-8111

(G-15940)
TIMES PUBLISHING COMPANY (HQ)
490 1st Ave S (33701-4223)
P.O. Box 1121 (33731-1121)
PHONE..................................727 893-8111
Paul Tash, *Ch of Bd*
Corty Andrew P, *Vice Pres*
Jana Jones, *CFO*
Robert Ahlgren, *VP Human Res*
Deluca Joe, *Director*
◆ **EMP:** 700 **EST:** 1884
SQ FT: 224,000
SALES (est): 42.2MM
SALES (corp-wide): 14.9MM **Privately Held**
WEB: www.tampabay.com
SIC: 2711 2721 Commercial printing & newspaper publishing combined; magazines: publishing & printing; periodicals: publishing & printing
PA: The Poynter Institute For Media Studies Inc
801 3rd St S
Saint Petersburg FL 33701
727 821-9494

(G-15941)
TK DEFENSE SOLUTIONS INC
5819 10th St N (33703-1103)
PHONE..................................727 365-6823
John Ifft, *Principal*
EMP: 6 **EST:** 2008
SALES (est): 122.6K **Privately Held**
WEB: www.tkdefenseusa.com
SIC: 3812 Defense systems & equipment

(G-15942)
TRAILBLAZERAI INC
10460 Rsvelt Blvd N 298 (33716-3821)
PHONE..................................727 859-2732
Gregory Perry, *CEO*
EMP: 5
SALES (est): 500K **Privately Held**
SIC: 3761 Guided missiles & space vehicles, research & development

(G-15943)
TREND MAGAZINES INC (DH)
Also Called: Florida Trend Magazine
490 1st Ave S Ste 800 (33701-4287)
P.O. Box 611 (33731-0611)
PHONE..................................727 821-5800
Andrew Corty, *President*
Mark Howard, *Principal*
David Denor, *Business Mgr*
Kristie Stotts, *Business Mgr*
Lynda Keever, *Vice Pres*
EMP: 30 **EST:** 1958
SQ FT: 8,000
SALES (est): 10.3MM
SALES (corp-wide): 14.9MM **Privately Held**
WEB: www.floridatrend.com
SIC: 2721 Magazines: publishing only, not printed on site
HQ: Times Publishing Company
490 1st Ave S
Saint Petersburg FL 33701
727 893-8111

(G-15944)
TRI-TECH OF FLORIDA INC
5151 Park St N (33709-1094)
P.O. Box 12729 (33733-2729)
PHONE..................................727 544-8836
Glenn Maller, *President*
Thomas Logan, *Vice Pres*
EMP: 16 **EST:** 1962
SQ FT: 16,000
SALES (est): 1.1MM **Privately Held**
SIC: 3444 3728 Sheet metalwork; aircraft parts & equipment

(G-15945)
TUF TOP COATINGS
4590 60th Ave N (33714-1035)
PHONE..................................727 527-3382
EMP: 12
SQ FT: 10,000
SALES (est): 967.6K **Privately Held**
SIC: 2851 Mfg Paints/Allied Products

(G-15946)
UNIVERSAL LABELING SYSTEMS INC (PA)
3501 8th Ave S (33711-2201)
PHONE..................................727 327-2123
Douglas Hall, *President*
Jane Marie Hall, *Vice Pres*
Frank Jones, *Prdtn Mgr*
Phillip Hoffmann, *Engineer*
Eileen Gamble, *CFO*
EMP: 46 **EST:** 1968
SQ FT: 35,000
SALES (est): 11.7MM **Privately Held**
WEB: www.universal1.com
SIC: 3565 Labeling machines, industrial

(G-15947)
UNIVERSAL NETWORKING SVCS CO
200 2nd Ave S Ste 432 (33701-4313)
PHONE..................................281 825-9790
Andrea Berg, *CEO*
Waite Ave, *Vice Pres*
EMP: 5 **EST:** 2013
SALES (est): 314.2K **Privately Held**
WEB: www.universal1.com
SIC: 3629 Electronic generation equipment

(G-15948)
UNIVERSAL STNCLING MKG SYSTEMS
205 15th Ave Se (33701-5607)
P.O. Box 871 (33731-0871)
PHONE..................................727 894-3027
Donald C Wright Jr, *President*
Karen Surdyk, *Vice Pres*
Stephen M Surdyk, *Vice Pres*
Mary Brown, *Manager*
David Daily, *IT Specialist*
EMP: 37 **EST:** 1904
SQ FT: 10,500
SALES (est): 3MM **Privately Held**
WEB: www.marking-systems.com
SIC: 3953 3555 Stencil machines (marking devices); printing trades machinery

(G-15949)
US NATURAL GAS CORP
735 Arlington Ave N # 308 (33701-3606)
PHONE..................................727 482-1505
Wayne Anderson, *Ch of Bd*
Jim Anderson, *Vice Pres*
Chuck Kretchman, *CFO*
EMP: 5
SALES (est): 622.3K **Privately Held**
SIC: 1381 1311 Drilling oil & gas wells; crude petroleum & natural gas

(G-15950)
VANGUARD SYSTEMS CORP
10460 Roosevelt Blvd N (33716-3821)
PHONE..................................727 528-0121
EMP: 7 **EST:** 2012
SALES (est): 352.7K **Privately Held**
WEB: www.vanguardsystemscorp.com
SIC: 3089 Injection molding of plastics

(G-15951)
VERIDIEN CORPORATION (PA)
1100 4th St N Ste 202 (33701-1790)
PHONE..................................727 576-1600
Russell D Van Zandt, *Ch of Bd*
Rene A Gareau, *Vice Ch Bd*
Sheldon C Fenton, *President*
Albina Otte, *Director*
EMP: 10 **EST:** 1991
SQ FT: 6,000
SALES (est): 759.1K **Privately Held**
WEB: www.veridien.com
SIC: 2842 Sanitation preparations, disinfectants & deodorants

(G-15952)
VETTE BRAKES & PRODUCTS INC
7490 30th Ave N (33710-2304)
P.O. Box 47861 (33743-7861)
PHONE..................................727 345-5292
Angelo Gonzalez, *President*
Josephine Gonzalez, *Vice Pres*
Alan Gonzalez, *Director*
Gary Gonzalez, *Director*
EMP: 21 **EST:** 1977
SQ FT: 22,000
SALES (est): 1MM **Privately Held**
WEB: www.vbandp.com
SIC: 3714 3493 Motor vehicle brake systems & parts; steel springs, except wire

(G-15953)
VICTORS TRIM MOLDING CROWN BAS
6142 38th Ave N (33710-1722)
PHONE..................................727 403-6057
Victor Menendez, *President*
EMP: 6 **EST:** 2006
SALES (est): 85.2K **Privately Held**
SIC: 3089 Injection molding of plastics

(G-15954)
VICTUS CAPITAL ENTERPRISES INC (PA)
1780 102nd Ave N Ste 500 (33716-3603)
PHONE..................................727 442-6677
Al Zwan, *President*
Millie Calderon, *Controller*
Ken Stamey, *Accountant*
Thomas Newhart, *VP Sales*
EMP: 41 **EST:** 1990
SALES (est): 3.4MM **Privately Held**
SIC: 3661 3825 Fiber optics communications equipment; digital test equipment, electronic & electrical circuits

(G-15955)
VIVA 5 LLC (DH)
Also Called: Growve
239 2nd Ave S Ste 200 (33701-4333)
PHONE..................................561 239-2239
Brian Baer, *President*
Vic Peroni, *COO*
Mark Jaggi, *CFO*
EMP: 93 **EST:** 2006
SALES (est): 12.1MM
SALES (corp-wide): 14.6MM **Privately Held**
WEB: www.viva5corp.com
SIC: 2833 Vitamins, natural or synthetic: bulk, uncompounded

(G-15956)
WEEKLY CHALLENGER NEWSPAPER
2500 Dr Mrtn Lther King J (33705-3554)
P.O. Box 35130 (33705-0503)
PHONE..................................727 896-2922
Ethel Johnson, *Owner*
Lyn Johnson, *Publisher*
EMP: 8 **EST:** 1967
SQ FT: 500
SALES (est): 165.2K **Privately Held**
WEB: www.theweeklychallenger.com
SIC: 2711 Newspapers, publishing & printing

(G-15957)
WEST COAST SHUTTERS SUNBURST
128 19th St S Ste B (33712-1307)
PHONE..................................727 894-0044
Joseph Fecera, *President*
Lisa Fecera, *Vice Pres*
EMP: 16 **EST:** 1990
SQ FT: 9,000
SALES (est): 2.5MM **Privately Held**
WEB: www.westcoastshutters.com
SIC: 3442 5023 5211 Shutters, door or window: metal; window covering parts & accessories; door & window products

(G-15958)
WEST PHRM SVCS FLA INC
5111 Park St N (33709-1009)
PHONE..................................727 546-2402
Don Morel, *CEO*
Fredrick S McCleery, *President*
Michael A Anderson, *Vice Pres*
Fred McCleery, *Vice Pres*
Rick Valentine, *Site Mgr*
◆ **EMP:** 351 **EST:** 1993
SQ FT: 44,500
SALES (est): 80.2MM
SALES (corp-wide): 2.1B **Publicly Held**
WEB: www.westpharma.com
SIC: 2834 Pharmaceutical preparations
PA: West Pharmaceutical Services, Inc.
530 Herman O West Dr
Exton PA 19341
610 594-2900

(G-15959)
WHITEHOUSE CUSTOM SCRN PR ✪
7183 30th Ave N (33710-2913)
PHONE..................................727 321-7398
Phyllis Race, *Sales Staff*
EMP: 6 **EST:** 2020
SALES (est): 517.7K **Privately Held**
SIC: 2759 Screen printing

(G-15960)
WILLIAM LEUPOLD SR
Also Called: Architectural and Woodworking
3291 40th Ave N (33714-4512)
PHONE..................................727 527-7400
William Leupold, *Principal*
Blanca Bonilla, *Manager*
EMP: 9 **EST:** 2001
SALES (est): 358.6K **Privately Held**
SIC: 2431 Millwork

(G-15961)
WILLIAMS JEWELRY AND MFG CO
3152 Morris St N (33713-2937)
P.O. Box 136178, Clermont (34713-6178)
PHONE..................................727 823-7676
Denise W Ferreira, *President*
EMP: 8 **EST:** 1883
SALES (est): 684.4K **Privately Held**
WEB: www.wjjewelry.com
SIC: 3911 3999 2448 Medals, precious or semiprecious metal; pins (jewelry), precious metal; plaques, picture, laminated; cargo containers, wood

(G-15962)
WILLY WALT INC
2390 26th Ave N (33713-4040)
PHONE..................................727 209-2872
Mark Ingles, *Owner*
EMP: 6 **EST:** 2008
SALES (est): 131.9K **Privately Held**
SIC: 2752 Commercial printing, offset

(G-15963)
WOOD ONE LLC
2416 52nd Ave N (33714-2604)
PHONE..................................727 639-5620
Patrick C Smith, *Principal*
EMP: 7 **EST:** 2015
SALES (est): 412.6K **Privately Held**
WEB: www.woodone.us
SIC: 2431 Millwork

(G-15964)
WOOVFU INC ✪
7901 4th St N Ste 300 (33702-4399)
PHONE..................................719 301-1661
Bill Havre, *CEO*
EMP: 13 **EST:** 2021
SALES (est): 583.4K **Privately Held**
SIC: 2273 Door mats: paper, grass, reed, coir, sisal, jute, rags, etc.

(G-15965)
WORKING COW HOMEMADE INC
4711 34th St N Unit F (33714-3060)
PHONE..................................727 572-7251
Timothy Pappas, *President*
Sonia Pappas, *Vice Pres*
▼ **EMP:** 15 **EST:** 1991
SQ FT: 4,400
SALES (est): 1.4MM **Privately Held**
WEB: www.workingcow.com
SIC: 2024 Ice cream & frozen desserts

(G-15966)
YOGURTOLOGY
3043 4th St N (33704-2104)
PHONE..................................727 895-1393
EMP: 7 **EST:** 2011
SALES (est): 285.7K **Privately Held**
WEB: www.yogurtology.com
SIC: 2024 Ice cream, bulk

(G-15967)
YOURMEMBERSHIPCOM INC (PA)
9620 Exec Ctr Dr N Ste 20 (33702-2429)
PHONE..................................727 827-0046
William Stover Jr, *Ch of Bd*
Sharon Love, *President*
Tamer Ali, *Vice Pres*
Quinn C Brady, *Vice Pres*
Larry Palmer, *Vice Pres*
EMP: 42 **EST:** 2012
SALES (est): 7.6MM **Privately Held**
WEB: www.yourmembership.com
SIC: 7372 Application computer software

(G-15968)
YSI INC (DH)
Also Called: Integrated Systems & Services
9843 18th St N Ste 1200 (33716-4208)
PHONE..................................727 565-2201
Rick Omlor, *President*
Leon Erdman, *CFO*
Thomas Goucher, *Technical Staff*
Susan Miller, *Admin Sec*
EMP: 12 **EST:** 1988
SQ FT: 20,250
SALES (est): 5.1MM **Publicly Held**
WEB: www.ysi.com
SIC: 3826 Analytical instruments
HQ: Ysi Incorporated
1700 Brannum Ln 1725
Yellow Springs OH 45387
937 767-7241

(G-15969)
YUNG PAYPER CHASERS ENTRMT LLC ✪
695 Central Ave (33701-3669)
PHONE..................................727 239-2880
Lorenzo Arscott,
EMP: 10 **EST:** 2020
SALES (est): 261K **Privately Held**
SIC: 2741 Music book & sheet music publishing

(G-15970)
ZD REALTY LLC
2135 13th Ave N (33713-4001)
PHONE..................................866 672-1212
James P Markus, *Mng Member*
▲ **EMP:** 17 **EST:** 2007
SALES (est): 3.9MM **Privately Held**
SIC: 3861 Cameras & related equipment

San Antonio
Pasco County

(G-15971)
C & M MILLWORK INC
30450 Commerce Dr (33576-8002)
PHONE..................................352 588-5050
George Curry, *Vice Pres*
Allen Curry, *Office Mgr*
EMP: 15 **EST:** 1980
SQ FT: 20,000
SALES (est): 1.3MM **Privately Held**
WEB: www.cmmillwork.com
SIC: 2431 Millwork

(G-15972)
FROG PUBLICATIONS INC
11820 Uradco Pl Ste 105 (33576-7140)
PHONE..................................352 588-2082
Mary Jo Hand, *President*
Dennis Hand, *Vice Pres*
▲ **EMP:** 8 **EST:** 1975
SQ FT: 1,000
SALES (est): 1MM **Privately Held**
WEB: www.frog.com
SIC: 2741 Miscellaneous publishing

(G-15973)
HARRISON METALS INC
11640 Corporate Lake Blvd (33576-8084)
PHONE..................................352 588-2436
John W Harris III, *President*
Jan Harris, *Manager*
EMP: 8 **EST:** 2006
SALES (est): 1.7MM **Privately Held**
WEB: www.harrisonmetals.com
SIC: 3441 Fabricated structural metal

(G-15974)
METALFAB INC (PA)
28212 Rice Rd (33576-7855)
P.O. Box 1184 (33576-1184)
PHONE..................................352 588-9901
Walter M Ruda, *President*
Carol Knapp, *Office Mgr*
EMP: 11 **EST:** 1997
SALES (est): 1.4MM **Privately Held**
WEB: www.metalfab-inc.com
SIC: 3444 Sheet metalwork

(G-15975)
PATRIOT FOUNDATION SYSTEMS LLC
30427 Commerce Dr (33576-8003)
PHONE..................................352 668-4842
Warren Neumann, *CEO*
Jason Neumann, *President*
Ed Latour, *Vice Pres*
Jennifer Odom, *CFO*
▲ **EMP:** 5 **EST:** 2011
SQ FT: 12,000
SALES (est): 800K **Privately Held**
WEB: www.patriothelicals.com
SIC: 3531 Construction machinery attachments

(G-15976)
PYROTECNICO OF FLORIDA LLC
30435 Commerce Dr Ste 102 (33576-8031)
P.O. Box 1030 (33576-1030)
PHONE..................................352 588-5086
Douglas Aller, *Principal*
Paul Gaffney, *Facilities Mgr*
Paige Phillips, *Producer*
Beth Stone, *Director*
▲ **EMP:** 18 **EST:** 2001
SALES (est): 209.3K **Privately Held**
SIC: 2899 Chemical preparations

(G-15977)
RACK IT TRUCK RACKS
30904 State Road 52 (33576-8060)
P.O. Box 9, Port Richey (34673-0009)
PHONE..................................800 354-1900
David Graham, *Owner*
EMP: 10 **EST:** 1995
SALES (est): 600.9K **Privately Held**
SIC: 3537 Cabs, for industrial trucks & tractors

(G-15978)
S & R FASTENER CO INC
Also Called: International Epoxies Sealers
30241 Commerce Dr (33576-8056)
P.O. Box 185 (33576-0185)
PHONE..................................352 588-0768
Peter Albert, *Sales Staff*
Alan Wolf, *Sales Staff*
Rick Rogers, *Manager*
EMP: 7
SQ FT: 20,800
SALES (corp-wide): 10MM **Privately Held**
WEB: www.srfast.com
SIC: 2891 Epoxy adhesives
PA: S & R Fastener Co., Inc.
30241 Commerce Dr
San Antonio FL 33576
352 588-0768

(G-15979)
SAFE WORKPLACE INC (PA)
10321 Buncombe Way (33576-4633)
P.O. Box 7705, Wesley Chapel (33545-0113)
PHONE..................................813 657-7233
Kathleen R Bogo, *President*
Lawrence P Bogo, *Vice Pres*
Bretton P Bogo, *Treasurer*
William Bogo, *Sales Associate*
William S Bogo, *Admin Sec*
EMP: 7 **EST:** 2004
SALES (est): 850K **Privately Held**
WEB: www.safeworkplaceinc.com
SIC: 3842 Clothing, fire resistant & protective

Sanderson
Baker County

(G-15980)
FLORIDA WIRE & CABLE
1 Wiremil Rd (32087-9500)
PHONE..................................904 275-2101
Sam Lande, *Principal*
EMP: 7 **EST:** 2005
SALES (est): 110.5K **Privately Held**
WEB: www.floridawire.com
SIC: 3496 Miscellaneous fabricated wire products

(G-15981)
GRIFFIS TIMBER INC
11625 Willie Griffis Rd (32087-2289)
P.O. Box 8 (32087-0008)
PHONE..................................904 275-2372
Penny G Croft, *President*
EMP: 7 **EST:** 1975
SQ FT: 2,400
SALES (est): 237.5K **Privately Held**
SIC: 2411 Timber, cut at logging camp

(G-15982)
INSTEEL WIRE PRODUCTS COMPANY
Also Called: Wiremil Division
1 Wiremill Rd (32087)
PHONE..................................904 275-2100
Joice Davis, *Branch Mgr*
EMP: 30
SALES (corp-wide): 472.6MM **Publicly Held**
WEB: www.insteel.com
SIC: 3272 3496 Concrete products; miscellaneous fabricated wire products
HQ: Insteel Wire Products Company
1373 Boggs Dr
Mount Airy NC 27030
336 719-9000

(G-15983)
SANDERSON PIPE CORPORATION (PA)
1 Enterprise Blvd (32087-9501)
P.O. Box 700 (32087-0700)
PHONE..................................904 275-3289
Barry Ian King, *President*
Frank Traina, *Exec VP*
Bob Eberle, *Vice Pres*
Nick Stroud, *Maintence Staff*
▼ **EMP:** 72 **EST:** 1996
SALES (est): 23.6MM **Privately Held**
WEB: www.sandersonpipe.com
SIC: 3084 Plastics pipe

Sanford
Seminole County

(G-15984)
A & L TOOLINGS LLC
349 Fairfield Dr (32771-6829)
PHONE..................................407 242-7114
Ricardo Lopez Melendez, *President*
Armando Cartagena, *Director*
EMP: 7 **EST:** 2016
SALES (est): 283.5K **Privately Held**
WEB: www.altooling.com
SIC: 3541 Boring mills

(G-15985)
A W R CABINETS INC
4155 Saint Johns Pkwy # 1800 (32771-6398)
PHONE..................................407 323-1415
Stephen Elliot, *President*
EMP: 10 **EST:** 2000
SQ FT: 3,000
SALES (est): 500K **Privately Held**
WEB: www.awrcabinets.com
SIC: 2434 7319 Wood kitchen cabinets; display advertising service

(G-15986)
ACKUE INTERNATIONAL LLC
5305 Pen Ave (32773-9468)
PHONE..................................407 323-8688
George Acha, *Director*
▲ **EMP:** 7 **EST:** 2008
SALES (est): 234.7K **Privately Held**
SIC: 2499 Decorative wood & woodwork

(G-15987)
ACME CAP & CLOTHING INC
Also Called: Acme Cap & Branding
221 Bellagio Cir (32771-5001)
PHONE..................................407 321-5100
Felix G Quintana, *President*
Kara Hamby, *Principal*
Bill Miller, *Principal*
Kara Leggett, *Asst Mgr*
EMP: 6 **EST:** 2003

SALES (est): 570K **Privately Held**
WEB: www.acmecap.com
SIC: 2395 Embroidery products, except schiffli machine

(G-15988)
AEROTEC ALUMINIUM INC
1696 N Beardall Ave (32771-9684)
PHONE..................................407 324-5400
Kimberly Mooers, *President*
EMP: 7 **EST:** 2010
SALES (est): 633.4K **Privately Held**
WEB: www.aerotechaluminum.com
SIC: 3446 Architectural metalwork

(G-15989)
AGRIUM ADVANCED TECH US INC
2451 Old Lake Mary Rd (32771-4103)
PHONE..................................407 302-2024
EMP: 10
SALES (corp-wide): 16B **Privately Held**
SIC: 2873 Mfg Nitrogenous Fertilizers
HQ: Agrium Advanced Technologies (U.S.) Inc.
2915 Rocky Mountain Ave # 400
Loveland CO 80538
970 292-9000

(G-15990)
ALPHA TECHNOLOGY USA CORP
Also Called: Futurecow
5401 Penn Ave (32773)
PHONE..................................407 571-2060
Kevin Dole, *President*
Kevin Cole, *Principal*
Karl Ruf, *Facilities Mgr*
▲ **EMP:** 15 **EST:** 2008
SALES (est): 4.1MM **Privately Held**
SIC: 3523 Farm machinery & equipment

(G-15991)
ALT THUYAN
Also Called: H M D
2025 Wp Ball Blvd (32771-7211)
PHONE..................................407 302-3655
Thuyan Alt, *President*
Justin Alt, *Vice Pres*
EMP: 8 **EST:** 2005
SALES (est): 358.9K **Privately Held**
SIC: 2844 Manicure preparations

(G-15992)
AMERICAN BRONZE FOUNDRY INC (PA)
Also Called: Decorators Resource Centl Fla
1650 E Lake Mary Blvd (32773-7130)
PHONE..................................407 328-8090
Charles L Wambold, *President*
Renee Wambold, *Principal*
◆ **EMP:** 18 **EST:** 1991
SQ FT: 22,000
SALES (est): 2.5MM **Privately Held**
WEB: www.americanbronze.com
SIC: 3366 Bronze foundry

(G-15993)
AMERICAN TECHNOLOGY PDTS INC
211 Northstar Ct (32771-6674)
PHONE..................................407 960-1722
Sajjad Jaffer, *President*
EMP: 11 **EST:** 2012
SALES (est): 1.9MM **Privately Held**
WEB: www.serverdiskdrives.com
SIC: 3674 Semiconductors & related devices

(G-15994)
AMICK CSTM WOODCRAFT & DESIGN
1450 Kastner Pl Ste 112 (32771-8005)
PHONE..................................407 324-8525
Scott L Amick, *President*
EMP: 8 **EST:** 1990
SALES (est): 758K **Privately Held**
WEB: www.amick-custom-woodcraft-design-in-sanford-fl.cityfos.com
SIC: 2499 2541 2517 2434 Decorative wood & woodwork; wood partitions & fixtures; wood television & radio cabinets; wood kitchen cabinets; cabinet & finish carpentry

(G-15995)
ARGONIDE CORPORATION
291 Power Ct (32771-9406)
PHONE..................................407 322-2500
Frederick Tepper, *CEO*
Ray Knispel, *Exec VP*
Stuart Frank, *Marketing Mgr*
Pamela Knorr, *Mktg Coord*
Debra Hull, *Marketing Staff*
▲ **EMP:** 10 **EST:** 1994
SQ FT: 15,000
SALES (est): 1.5MM **Privately Held**
WEB: www.argonide.com
SIC: 3499 Fire- or burglary-resistive products

(G-15996)
ASTRUMSAT COMMUNICATIONS LLC
1919 W 1st St (32771-1648)
PHONE..................................954 368-9980
David Horacek, *President*
Michele Loguidice, *Director*
EMP: 5 **EST:** 2010
SALES (est): 2.4MM **Privately Held**
WEB: www.astrumsat.com
SIC: 3663 Satellites, communications

(G-15997)
ATLAS HELICOPTER INC
1000 S Park Ave Apt 3 (32771-2584)
PHONE..................................321 696-4342
Loren C Friedle, *Principal*
EMP: 6 **EST:** 2013
SALES (est): 67.9K **Privately Held**
WEB: www.atlashelicopterinc.com
SIC: 3728 Aircraft parts & equipment

(G-15998)
ATLAS SOUTHEAST PAPERS INC
3401 Saint Johns Pkwy (32771-6363)
PHONE..................................407 330-9118
Peter Leibman, *President*
Patrick Fodale, *CFO*
Robert Pistilli, *Treasurer*
Anne Higgins, *Manager*
◆ **EMP:** 90 **EST:** 2014
SALES (est): 21.2MM
SALES (corp-wide): 2.9B **Privately Held**
WEB: www.atlaspapermills.com
SIC: 2621 Tissue paper
HQ: Resolute Fp Florida Inc.
3301 Nw 107th St
Miami FL 33167
800 562-2860

(G-15999)
AUTOMATIC COAX AND CABLE INC
4060 Saint Johns Pkwy (32771-6374)
PHONE..................................407 322-7622
Glenda D Martinet, *President*
Glenn Harbor, *General Mgr*
Kim Casper, *Engineer*
Gary S Martinet, *Director*
Cliff Cochran, *Executive*
EMP: 45 **EST:** 1998
SQ FT: 8,000
SALES (est): 7.3MM **Privately Held**
WEB: www.autocoax.com
SIC: 3679 Harness assemblies for electronic use: wire or cable

(G-16000)
B & I GENERATORS LLC
2100 S Park Ave (32771-4350)
PHONE..................................407 474-6216
Gale Bandy,
Selma Inman,
EMP: 6 **EST:** 2019
SALES (est): 88.3K **Privately Held**
SIC: 3621 Motors & generators

(G-16001)
BATTER TO PLATTER LLC
Also Called: Batter Co. Dessert Collection
2660 Jewett Ln (32771-1678)
PHONE..................................203 309-7632
Sarah Whalley, *Mng Member*
EMP: 9 **EST:** 2018
SALES (est): 739.7K **Privately Held**
WEB: www.batter.co
SIC: 2051 Cakes, pies & pastries

(G-16002)
BENADA ALUMINUM PRODUCTS LLC
2540 Jewett Ln (32771-1687)
PHONE..................................407 323-3300
Paul D Melnuk, *CEO*
Paul Melnuk, *CEO*
Monte Friedkin, *President*
John Walseth, *Managing Dir*
Antjuan Altman, *Top Exec*
▼ **EMP:** 180 **EST:** 2011
SALES (est): 45.9MM **Privately Held**
WEB: www.benada.com
SIC: 3354 Aluminum extruded products

(G-16003)
BIZCARD XPRESS SANFORD LLC
1744 Rinehart Rd (32771-6590)
PHONE..................................407 688-8902
Fortunato Morello Jr,
EMP: 6 **EST:** 2010
SALES (est): 429.8K **Privately Held**
SIC: 2752 Commercial printing, offset

(G-16004)
BOMBARDIER TRNSP HLDNGS USA IN
801 Sunrail Dr (32771-0001)
PHONE..................................407 450-4855
Shawn Furniss, *Foreman/Supr*
Caren Steller, *Manager*
EMP: 6 **Privately Held**
SIC: 3721 Aircraft
HQ: Bombardier Transportation (Holdings) Usa Inc.
1251 Waterfront Pl
Pittsburgh PA 15222
412 655-5700

(G-16005)
BOSS LASER LLC
608 Trestle Pt (32771-8200)
PHONE..................................888 652-1555
Daniel L Fox II, *Partner*
Brittany Raspo, *Purchasing*
Cru Matos, *Manager*
Michelle McManus, *Office Admin*
Michael D Pinnock,
▲ **EMP:** 52 **EST:** 2012
SALES (est): 9.8MM **Privately Held**
WEB: www.bosslaser.com
SIC: 3699 Laser systems & equipment; laser welding, drilling & cutting equipment

(G-16006)
CALIGIURI CORPORATION
Also Called: Empress Sissi
518 Central Park Dr (32771-6672)
P.O. Box 471485, Lake Monroe (32747-1485)
PHONE..................................407 324-4441
Miguel Caligiuri, *President*
Karina Caligiuri, *Vice Pres*
EMP: 35 **EST:** 1990
SQ FT: 15,000
SALES (est): 2.5MM **Privately Held**
WEB: www.empresssissi.com
SIC: 2053 Frozen bakery products, except bread

(G-16007)
CAPSMITH INC (PA)
2240 Old Lake Mary Rd (32771-4178)
PHONE..................................407 328-7660
Daniel C Smith, *President*
Danny Smith, *General Mgr*
Marsha Smith, *Treasurer*
Tom Spence, *Comptroller*
Betty Green, *Sales Staff*
◆ **EMP:** 23 **EST:** 1985
SQ FT: 12,000
SALES (est): 4.4MM **Privately Held**
WEB: www.capsmith.com
SIC: 2261 2395 2759 Screen printing of cotton broadwoven fabrics; embroidery & art needlework; screen printing

(G-16008)
CEMEX MATERIALS LLC
2210 W 25th St (32771-4137)
PHONE..................................407 322-8862
Bill Sloniger, *Plant Mgr*
Greg Vanlanot, *Plant Mgr*
Ed Hollback, *Terminal Mgr*
Bryan Meskill, *Branch Mgr*
EMP: 40
SQ FT: 1,778 **Privately Held**
SIC: 3273 3271 Ready-mixed concrete; concrete block & brick
HQ: Cemex Materials Llc
1501 Belvedere Rd
West Palm Beach FL 33406
561 833-5555

(G-16009)
CENTRAL FLORIDA PUBLISHING INC
Also Called: Palm Springs Printing
300 N French Ave (32771-1118)
P.O. Box 1057 (32772-1057)
PHONE..................................407 682-1221
Lawrence Blunk, *COO*
EMP: 6
SALES (corp-wide): 3.3MM **Privately Held**
WEB: www.centralfloridapublishing.com
SIC: 2752 Commercial printing, offset
PA: Central Florida Publishing, Inc.
700 W Fulton St
Sanford FL 32771
407 323-5204

(G-16010)
CENTRAL FLORIDA PUBLISHING INC (PA)
700 W Fulton St (32771-1102)
P.O. Box 1057 (32772-1057)
PHONE..................................407 323-5204
Patrick A Tubbs, *CEO*
Robert Mason, *President*
Lawrence Blunk, *COO*
Tom Thomas, *CFO*
EMP: 18 **EST:** 1996
SQ FT: 21,000
SALES (est): 3.3MM **Privately Held**
WEB: www.centralfloridapublishing.com
SIC: 2791 2711 2741 2721 Typesetting; newspapers, publishing & printing; miscellaneous publishing; periodicals

(G-16011)
CENTRO DE DIAGNOSTICO
Also Called: Centro Ddgnstico Y Tratamiento
253 Bellagio Cir (32771-5001)
PHONE..................................407 865-7020
Robert B Haghgou, *Principal*
Nathan Cook, *Vice Pres*
Lisa Ferguson, *Vice Pres*
Lisa Wilk, *Vice Pres*
Hushang S Haghgou, *Director*
EMP: 5 **EST:** 1997
SQ FT: 7,000
SALES (est): 5MM **Privately Held**
SIC: 2834 Pharmaceutical preparations

(G-16012)
CENTRYS LLC
750 Monroe Rd (32771-8877)
PHONE..................................407 476-4786
EMP: 30
SALES: 5MM **Privately Held**
SIC: 3699 Mfg Electrical Equipment/Supplies

(G-16013)
CHIANTIS
685 Towne Center Blvd (32771-7494)
PHONE..................................407 484-6510
Nick Majaika, *Manager*
EMP: 7 **EST:** 2012
SALES (est): 168K **Privately Held**
WEB: www.chiantispizza.com
SIC: 2033 Pizza sauce: packaged in cans, jars, etc.

(G-16014)
CHOCOLATE COMPASS LLC
5899 Pearl Estates Ln (32771-8520)
PHONE..................................407 600-0145
Harry Jenkins, *Owner*
EMP: 7 **EST:** 2016
SALES (est): 468.9K **Privately Held**
WEB: www.chocolatecompass.com
SIC: 2026 Milk, chocolate

(G-16015)
CIRCUITRONICS LLC
223 Hickman Dr Ste 101 (32771-8212)
PHONE..................................407 322-8300
Bipin Patel, *President*

▲ = Import ▼=Export
◆ =Import/Export

Alok Patel, *Vice Pres*
EMP: 15 **EST:** 1995
SQ FT: 15,000
SALES (est): 2.9MM **Privately Held**
WEB: www.circuitronics.org
SIC: 3672 8711 Printed circuit boards; engineering services

(G-16016)
CLOUDKISS BEVERAGES INC
3031 S Mellonville Ave (32773-8744)
PHONE..................................407 324-8500
Thomas Barfell, *CEO*
Thomas Kirkeminde, *President*
Don Knudsen, *CFO*
Miller Cooper, *Admin Sec*
EMP: 38 **EST:** 1991
SQ FT: 81,000
SALES (est): 3.4MM **Privately Held**
SIC: 2086 Soft drinks: packaged in cans, bottles, etc.

(G-16017)
COBHAM SATCOM
1538 Tropic Park Dr (32773-6323)
PHONE..................................407 650-9054
Brian Anderson, *Sales Mgr*
Scott Lewis, *Supervisor*
George Tong, *Director*
EMP: 18 **EST:** 2013
SALES (est): 4.5MM
SALES (corp-wide): 177.9K **Privately Held**
WEB: www.cobham.com
SIC: 3663 Satellites, communications
HQ: Cobham Limited
Tringham House
Bournemouth
120 288-2020

(G-16018)
COMMERCIAL WOOD DESIGNS INC
257 Power Ct (32771-9406)
PHONE..................................407 302-9063
Jairo Fernandez, *President*
Tanya Fernandez, *Vice Pres*
Chris Lipscomb, *Opers Dir*
EMP: 19 **EST:** 2004
SQ FT: 9,000
SALES (est): 2.9MM **Privately Held**
WEB: www.commercialwooddesigns.com
SIC: 2491 Millwork, treated wood

(G-16019)
COMPAK COMPANIES LLC
Also Called: Celebration Cup
751 Cornwall Rd (32773-5856)
PHONE..................................321 249-9590
Robert L Johnson, *President*
Carl Buford, *VP Opers*
Jaquie Johnson, *Sales Staff*
Joeann McClandon, *Software Engr*
▲ **EMP:** 16 **EST:** 2003
SQ FT: 47,000
SALES (est): 5.1MM **Privately Held**
WEB: www.celebrationcup.com
SIC: 3089 Cups, plastic, except foam

(G-16020)
COMPASS PUBLISHING LLC
671 Progress Way (32771-6989)
P.O. Box 952674, Lake Mary (32795-2674)
PHONE..................................407 328-0970
Andrea Tolbert,
Andy Tolbert,
EMP: 5 **EST:** 2004
SALES (est): 416.2K **Privately Held**
SIC: 2741 Miscellaneous publishing

(G-16021)
COMPRO SOLUTION
1670 Tropic Park Dr (32773-6335)
PHONE..................................407 733-4130
Mehboob N Ali, *President*
Arifa Suleman, *Sales Mgr*
Parpia Arifa, *Sales Staff*
EMP: 5 **EST:** 2004
SALES (est): 413.5K **Privately Held**
WEB: www.comprosolution.com
SIC: 3577 Computer peripheral equipment

(G-16022)
CONSOLIDATED LABEL CO
2001 E Lake Mary Blvd (32773-7140)
PHONE..................................407 339-2626
Joel R Carmany, *President*
Greg Solodko, *COO*
Annette Carmany, *Vice Pres*
Scott Carpenter, *QC Mgr*
Bob Sebald, *QC Mgr*
▼ **EMP:** 200 **EST:** 1980
SQ FT: 80,000
SALES (est): 41.2MM **Privately Held**
WEB: www.consolidatedlabel.com
SIC: 2752 2679 Commercial printing, offset; labels, paper: made from purchased material

(G-16023)
CONTROLOGIX LLC
Also Called: Clx Engineering
361 S White Cedar Rd (32771-6650)
PHONE..................................407 878-2774
Mike Sigler, *Vice Pres*
Stephanie Brown, *Project Mgr*
Cory Charles, *Engineer*
Terry Gallagher, *Marketing Staff*
Lyn Johnson, *Director*
EMP: 32 **EST:** 1998
SQ FT: 10,000
SALES (est): 10MM **Privately Held**
WEB: www.clxengineering.com
SIC: 3823 Computer interface equipment for industrial process control

(G-16024)
COOPER-STANDARD AUTOMOTIVE INC
3551 W 1st St (32771-8852)
PHONE..................................407 330-3323
Josue Ramos, *Manager*
EMP: 25
SALES (corp-wide): 2.3B **Publicly Held**
WEB: www.cooperstandard.com
SIC: 3465 Body parts, automobile: stamped metal
HQ: Cooper-Standard Automotive Inc.
40300 Traditions Dr
Northville MI 48168
248 596-5900

(G-16025)
COOPER-STANDARD AUTOMOTIVE INC
501 Cornwall Rd Ste 2773 (32773-5879)
PHONE..................................407 330-3323
Gerald Dunkleman, *Plant Mgr*
EMP: 75
SALES (corp-wide): 2.3B **Publicly Held**
WEB: www.cooperstandard.com
SIC: 3465 Body parts, automobile: stamped metal
HQ: Cooper-Standard Automotive Inc.
40300 Traditions Dr
Northville MI 48168
248 596-5900

(G-16026)
COVERALL ALUMINUM INC
1980 Dolgner Pl Ste 1068 (32771-9231)
PHONE..................................321 377-7874
Peter Wojtas, *President*
EMP: 10 **EST:** 1999
SALES (est): 1.1MM **Privately Held**
SIC: 3479 Aluminum coating of metal products

(G-16027)
CRANKSHAFT REBUILDERS INC
1200 Albright Rd (32771-1670)
PHONE..................................407 323-4870
Dan Hunt, *President*
Larry J Eriksson, *Principal*
EMP: 56 **EST:** 1963
SQ FT: 56,000
SALES (est): 4.6MM **Privately Held**
WEB: www.crankshaftrebuilders.com
SIC: 3599 3714 Crankshafts & camshafts, machining; motor vehicle parts & accessories

(G-16028)
CRITICAL DISPOSABLES INC
700 Martin L King Jr Blvd (32771-9531)
PHONE..................................407 330-1154
Autry O V Debusk, *President*
◆ **EMP:** 20 **EST:** 1981
SQ FT: 20,000
SALES (est): 2.4MM
SALES (corp-wide): 3.6MM **Privately Held**
WEB: www.deroyal.com
SIC: 3841 3845 Surgical & medical instruments; electromedical equipment
PA: De Royal
200 Debusk Ln
Powell TN 37849
865 938-7828

(G-16029)
CRYSTAL PHOTONICS INC
5525 Benchmark Ln (32773-8115)
PHONE..................................407 328-9111
Bruce Chai, *President*
Yiting Fei, *Research*
Caroline C Chai, *Treasurer*
Phillip Chu, *CIO*
Shen Jen, *Technology*
▲ **EMP:** 30 **EST:** 1995
SQ FT: 76,000
SALES (est): 7.5MM **Privately Held**
WEB: www.jccsoc.com
SIC: 3823 Industrial instrmnts msrmnt display/control process variable

(G-16030)
CULTURE CARTEL MEDIA INC
105 Rockwood Way (32771-6809)
PHONE..................................407 680-8923
Trinita S White, *Principal*
EMP: 6 **EST:** 2019
SALES (est): 74.4K **Privately Held**
WEB: www.culturecartel.com
SIC: 2836 Culture media

(G-16031)
DANIELS WHL SIGN & PLAS INC
5224 W State Road 46 (32771-9230)
PHONE..................................386 736-4918
EMP: 9 **EST:** 2006
SALES (est): 109.3K **Privately Held**
WEB: www.wholesalesignsuperstore.com
SIC: 3993 Signs & advertising specialties

(G-16032)
DAVID RUSSELL ANODIZING
2501 Mccracken Rd (32771-1602)
PHONE..................................407 302-4041
David Russell, *Owner*
▼ **EMP:** 9 **EST:** 1998
SQ FT: 21,000
SALES (est): 892.7K **Privately Held**
WEB: www.davidrussellanodizing.com
SIC: 3471 Anodizing (plating) of metals or formed products

(G-16033)
DECIMAL LLC
121 Central Park Pl (32771-6633)
PHONE..................................407 330-3300
Richard Sweat, *President*
Gus Rathgeber, *COO*
Mary Snyder, *Project Mgr*
Justin Moon, *Prdtn Mgr*
John Roman, *Facilities Mgr*
EMP: 50 **EST:** 1986
SQ FT: 36,000
SALES (est): 11.6MM **Privately Held**
WEB: www.dotdecimal.com
SIC: 3842 5047 Personal safety equipment; hospital equipment & furniture

(G-16034)
DEEP OCEAN WOODWORKS INC
Also Called: Wood Arts of India
6289 Bordeaux Cir (32771-6489)
PHONE..................................407 687-2773
Milan Desai, *Principal*
EMP: 7 **EST:** 2017
SALES (est): 105.2K **Privately Held**
SIC: 2431 Millwork

(G-16035)
DEL AIR ELECTRIC CO
201 Tech Dr (32771-6627)
PHONE..................................407 531-1173
EMP: 9 **EST:** 2015
SALES (est): 244.7K **Privately Held**
WEB: www.delair.com
SIC: 3699 1731 Electrical equipment & supplies; electrical work

(G-16036)
DESIGN CUSTOM MILLWORK INC
130 Tech Dr (32771-6662)
P.O. Box 150419, Altamonte Springs (32715-0419)
PHONE..................................407 878-1267
James Blackburn, *President*
Fred Gemeinhardt, *Vice Pres*
EMP: 25 **EST:** 1999
SQ FT: 8,000
SALES (est): 4MM **Privately Held**
WEB: www.designcustommillworkinc.com
SIC: 2431 Millwork

(G-16037)
DNT SOFTWARE CORP
1710 Beacon Dr (32771-9723)
PHONE..................................407 323-0987
Deering N Treppard, *President*
EMP: 5 **EST:** 2000
SALES (est): 356.3K **Privately Held**
SIC: 7372 Prepackaged software

(G-16038)
EARNEST PRODUCTS INC
Also Called: Earnest Metal Fabrication
2000 E Lake Mary Blvd (32773-7133)
PHONE..................................407 831-1588
Bryan H Earnest, *President*
Ilias Lamrani, *Engineer*
Mark Greenlaw, *CFO*
Ron Compton, *Human Resources*
Duane Greer, *Supervisor*
EMP: 98 **EST:** 1992
SQ FT: 60,000
SALES (est): 29.7MM **Privately Held**
WEB: www.earnestproducts.com
SIC: 3444 Sheet metalwork

(G-16039)
EAST 46TH AUTO SALES INC
Also Called: East 46th Trailor Sales
3710 E State Road 46 (32771-9159)
PHONE..................................407 322-3100
Charles Brannon, *President*
Patricia Brannon, *Admin Sec*
EMP: 10 **EST:** 1984
SQ FT: 7,800
SALES (est): 999.6K **Privately Held**
WEB: www.east46trailers.com
SIC: 3799 5511 3792 Horse trailers, except fifth-wheel type; trucks, tractors & trailers: new & used; travel trailers & campers

(G-16040)
ELECTRONIC COMPONENTS FAS INC
1305 Hstric Gldsboro Blvd (32771-2759)
PHONE..................................407 328-8111
Oscar Redden, *Principal*
Jackie Quinn, *Principal*
Roslyn Redden, *Principal*
Terrell Redden, *Principal*
EMP: 5 **EST:** 2019
SALES (est): 303.4K **Privately Held**
SIC: 3728 Aircraft parts & equipment

(G-16041)
ELLIS & ASSOCIATES OF SANFORD
Also Called: Computer Center of Sanford
915 W 1st St Ste B (32771-1125)
P.O. Box 2746 (32772-2746)
PHONE..................................407 322-1128
EMP: 5
SQ FT: 1,500
SALES (est): 611.3K **Privately Held**
SIC: 7372 Prepackaged Software Services

(G-16042)
EVERGREEN SWEETENERS INC
2200 Country Club Rd (32771-4053)
PHONE..................................407 323-4250
Tom Girdner, *Vice Pres*
Craig Green, *Vice Pres*
Sean Peters, *Warehouse Mgr*
Michele Jones, *Office Mgr*
Tom Robinson, *Branch Mgr*
EMP: 15
SALES (corp-wide): 10.3MM **Privately Held**
WEB: www.esweeteners.com
SIC: 2099 Sugar

PA: Evergreen Sweeteners, Inc.
1936 Hollywood Blvd # 20
Hollywood FL 33020
954 381-7776

(G-16043)
EXCALIBUR COACH
1830 Bobby Lee Pt (32771-8075)
PHONE....................................407 302-9139
Doug Stolfo, *Officer*
EMP: 8 **EST:** 2006
SALES (est): 1.1MM **Privately Held**
WEB: www.excaliburservice.com
SIC: 3792 Trailer coaches, automobile

(G-16044)
FATEZZI INC
5305 Pen Ave (32773-9468)
PHONE....................................407 323-8688
George Acha, *Branch Mgr*
EMP: 9
SALES (corp-wide): 330.6K **Privately Held**
WEB: www.fatezziwood.com
SIC: 2493 Reconstituted wood products
PA: Fatezzi Inc
587 Dunmar Cir
Winter Springs FL 32708
407 695-1209

(G-16045)
FATHERS TABLE LLC (PA)
Also Called: Father's Table, The
2100 Country Club Rd (32771-4051)
P.O. Box 1509 (32772-1509)
PHONE....................................407 324-1200
David Glass, *Vice Pres*
Michael Bishop, *Opers Mgr*
David Nelson, *Prdtn Mgr*
Michael Keenan, *VP Sales*
John Hicks, *Sales Mgr*
EMP: 250 **EST:** 1999
SALES (est): 98.3MM **Privately Held**
WEB: www.thefatherstable.com
SIC: 2099 Food preparations

(G-16046)
FEA INC
Also Called: Freedom Enterprise & Associate
5333 Pen Ave (32773-9468)
PHONE....................................407 330-3535
Ann E King, *President*
Howard King, *General Mgr*
EMP: 12 **EST:** 2001
SQ FT: 5,000
SALES (est): 3MM **Privately Held**
WEB: www.feawaterjet.com
SIC: 3711 Military motor vehicle assembly

(G-16047)
FLORIDA CONTAINER SERVICES
3795 S Sanford Ave (32773-6001)
PHONE....................................407 302-2197
Kurt Till, *Manager*
EMP: 10 **EST:** 2008
SALES (est): 778.3K **Privately Held**
WEB: www.floridashippingcontainers.com
SIC: 3272 Garbage boxes, concrete

(G-16048)
FLORIDA CRAFT DISTRIBUTORS LLC
2650 Jewett Ln (32771-1678)
PHONE....................................813 528-7902
Judith A Forsley, *Mng Member*
EMP: 12 **EST:** 2014
SALES (est): 442.2K **Privately Held**
SIC: 2082 Beer (alcoholic beverage)

(G-16049)
FLORIDA EXTRUDERS INTL INC
2540 Jewett Ln (32771-1687)
P.O. Box 14213, Fort Lauderdale (33302-4213)
PHONE....................................407 323-3300
Joel G Lehman, *President*
Joel Lehman, *President*
Luis Giammattei, *Design Engr*
◆ **EMP:** 72 **EST:** 1989
SQ FT: 400,000
SALES (est): 5.3MM **Privately Held**
WEB: www.floridaextruders.com
SIC: 3354 Aluminum extruded products

(G-16050)
FREEPORT FOUNTAINS LLC
1510 Kastner Pl Ste 3 (32771-9308)
PHONE....................................407 330-1150
Joel Wolcott, *Principal*
Kim Vollet, *Business Mgr*
Joel M Wolcott, *Chief Engr*
Robert Vasquez, *Design Engr*
Diane Vollet, *Sales Staff*
EMP: 20 **EST:** 1981
SALES (est): 3.7MM **Privately Held**
WEB: www.freeportfountains.com
SIC: 3272 Fountains, concrete

(G-16051)
FUELS UNLIMITED INC
509 S French Ave (32771-1875)
P.O. Box 259 (32772-0259)
PHONE....................................407 302-3193
Karen Violet, *Principal*
EMP: 6 **EST:** 2006
SALES (est): 317.3K **Privately Held**
SIC: 1382 Oil & gas exploration services

(G-16052)
FURNITURE DESIGN OF CENTL FLA
Also Called: Furniture Design Gallery
219 Hickman Dr (32771-8201)
PHONE....................................407 330-4430
Ebrahim Hamzeloui, *President*
Mohammad Hamzeloui, *Vice Pres*
EMP: 14 **EST:** 1985
SQ FT: 15,500
SALES (est): 842.7K **Privately Held**
WEB: www.furnituredesigngallery.com
SIC: 2511 2521 Wood household furniture; cabinets, office: wood

(G-16053)
G & R MACHINE INC
701 Cornwall Rd Ste A (32773-7334)
PHONE....................................407 324-1600
Matthew Silvey, *Principal*
EMP: 5 **EST:** 1999
SALES (est): 407.7K **Privately Held**
SIC: 3542 Forging machinery & hammers

(G-16054)
GATOR DOCK & MARINE LLC
Also Called: CMI International
2880 S Mellonville Ave (32773-9686)
PHONE....................................407 323-0190
John E Irvine, *Mng Member*
Michael S Crane,
Jon W Fleischman,
Randolph Fortener,
John Yeocock,
▼ **EMP:** 16 **EST:** 1987
SALES (est): 5.2MM
SALES (corp-wide): 120.9MM **Privately Held**
WEB: www.cmilc.com
SIC: 3999 1629 Dock equipment & supplies, industrial; dock construction
HQ: Cmi Limited Co.
605 Molly Ln Ste 150
Woodstock GA 30189

(G-16055)
GENEVA FOODS LLC (PA)
2664 Jewett Ln (32771-1678)
P.O. Box 720691, Atlanta GA (30358-2691)
PHONE....................................407 302-4751
Tom Bandemer, *Mng Member*
Peter A Corteville,
▲ **EMP:** 14 **EST:** 1983
SQ FT: 12,000
SALES (est): 2.5MM **Privately Held**
SIC: 2034 Dried & dehydrated soup mixes

(G-16056)
GLEMAN SONS CSTM WOODWORKS LLC
110 Tech Dr (32771-6625)
PHONE....................................407 314-9638
Adrian Gleman, *Manager*
EMP: 12 **EST:** 2017
SALES (est): 707.4K **Privately Held**
WEB: www.glemanandsons.com
SIC: 2431 Millwork

(G-16057)
GREEN CREATIVE LLC
519 Codisco Way (32771-6618)
PHONE....................................866 774-5433
Michael P Santoni, *Treasurer*
Cole Zucker, *Mng Member*
Guillaume Vidal,
▲ **EMP:** 50 **EST:** 2011
SALES (est): 9.7MM
SALES (corp-wide): 1.2B **Privately Held**
WEB: www.greencreative.com
SIC: 3646 Commercial indusl & institutional electric lighting fixtures
PA: Harbour Group Ltd.
7733 Forsyth Blvd Fl 23
Saint Louis MO 63105
314 727-5550

(G-16058)
GREYFIELD HOLDINGS INC (PA)
900 Central Park Dr (32771-6634)
PHONE....................................407 830-8861
Bradley Osleger, *President*
Keith Treadwell, *General Mgr*
Kenneth Osleger, *Principal*
Ben Scott, *Opers Staff*
Tracy Roberson, *Purchasing*
▲ **EMP:** 30 **EST:** 1991
SQ FT: 11,000
SALES (est): 6MM **Privately Held**
WEB: www.onsightindustries.com
SIC: 3993 Electric signs

(G-16059)
H & M PRINTING INC
Also Called: Magnolia Press
104 Loren Ct (32771-6321)
PHONE....................................407 831-8030
Mary Hargon, *President*
Michael Patrick Hargon, *Vice Pres*
Michael Daven Port, *Vice Pres*
Kitty Hull, *Sales Staff*
Debby Knorowski, *Sales Staff*
EMP: 17 **EST:** 1973
SQ FT: 8,000
SALES (est): 2.2MM **Privately Held**
WEB: www.magnoliapress.net
SIC: 2796 2752 2789 Platemaking services; commercial printing, offset; bookbinding & related work

(G-16060)
HEAVY HWY INFRASTRUCTURE LLC
2210 W 25th St (32771-4137)
P.O. Box 2161 (32772-2161)
PHONE....................................407 323-8853
Jennifer Flores, *Mng Member*
John Piecguch,
EMP: 75 **EST:** 2014
SQ FT: 1,000
SALES (est): 11MM **Privately Held**
WEB: www.floridahhi.com
SIC: 3272 Floor slabs & tiles, precast concrete

(G-16061)
HERNON MANUFACTURING INC
121 Tech Dr (32771-6663)
PHONE....................................407 322-4000
Harry Arnon, *President*
Karen Arnon, *Exec VP*
Tom Bray, *Plant Mgr*
Gary Butler, *Plant Mgr*
Roberto Flores, *Plant Mgr*
▲ **EMP:** 71 **EST:** 1978
SQ FT: 30,000
SALES (est): 14.4MM **Privately Held**
WEB: www.hernon.com
SIC: 3089 2891 Tissue dispensers, plastic; epoxy adhesives

(G-16062)
HILL DERMACEUTICALS INC
2650 S Mellonville Ave (32773-9311)
PHONE....................................407 323-1887
Jerry S Roth, *President*
Sharon Dudash, *General Mgr*
Susan G Roth, *Corp Secy*
EMP: 35 **EST:** 1979
SQ FT: 27,000
SALES (est): 8.3MM **Privately Held**
WEB: www.hillderm.com
SIC: 2834 Pharmaceutical preparations

(G-16063)
HILL LABS INC
2650 S Mellonville Ave (32773-9311)
PHONE....................................407 323-1887
Jerry Roth, *President*
EMP: 35 **EST:** 1989
SALES (est): 4.1MM **Privately Held**
WEB: www.hillderm.com
SIC: 2834 Pharmaceutical preparations

(G-16064)
ICORP-IFOAM SPECIALTY PRODUCTS
250 Power Ct (32771-9404)
P.O. Box 470036, Lake Monroe (32747-0036)
PHONE....................................407 328-8500
Phillip Landers, *President*
Chet Vansyckel, *Opers Staff*
EMP: 6 **EST:** 1991
SQ FT: 6,800
SALES (est): 933.6K **Privately Held**
WEB: www.sniffnstop.com
SIC: 3086 Plastics foam products

(G-16065)
INDOOR TRAMPOLINE ARENA INC
Also Called: Reboundersz Purchasing Dev
605 Hickman Cir (32771-6904)
P.O. Box 952949, Lake Mary (32795-2949)
PHONE....................................321 222-1300
Marcus E Gurley, *CEO*
Melvin Horn, *COO*
Kiki Rosas, *Director*
EMP: 13 **EST:** 2010
SQ FT: 11,000
SALES (est): 1.5MM **Privately Held**
WEB: www.rebounderzfranchise.com
SIC: 3949 Trampolines & equipment

(G-16066)
INDUSTRIAL SCAN INC
223 Hickman Dr Ste 109 (32771-8212)
PHONE....................................407 322-3664
Ishwar Singh, *President*
Vicki Hart, *Manager*
EMP: 21 **EST:** 1991
SQ FT: 15,000
SALES (est): 2.6MM **Privately Held**
WEB: www.industrialscan.com
SIC: 3577 8711 Optical scanning devices; designing: ship, boat, machine & product

(G-16067)
INNOVATIVE SIGNS INC
957 Penfield Cv (32773-8165)
P.O. Box 951851, Lake Mary (32795-1851)
PHONE....................................407 830-5155
Bart Baker, *President*
Bart H Baker, *President*
Jeffrey Gardner, *Manager*
Lisa Garvin, *CIO*
Wendy J Baker, *Admin Sec*
EMP: 5 **EST:** 1984
SALES (est): 488.7K **Privately Held**
WEB: www.innovativesigns.com
SIC: 3993 Signs, not made in custom sign painting shops

(G-16068)
INTEGRATED DESIGN & DEVELOP
410 W 4th St (32771-1840)
PHONE....................................407 268-4300
Tiffany Kath, *President*
Russel Kath, *Vice Pres*
Russell Kath, *Manager*
EMP: 6 **EST:** 2005
SQ FT: 8,000
SALES (est): 1MM **Privately Held**
WEB: www.iddfl.com
SIC: 3599 3489 3451 7389 Machine shop, jobbing & repair; ordnance & accessories; screw machine products; design, commercial & industrial

(G-16069)
INVACARE FLORIDA CORPORATION
2101 E Lake Mary Blvd (32773-7141)
PHONE....................................407 321-5630
A Malachi Mixon III, *CEO*
Gerald B Blouch, *President*
Jerome E Fox, *Vice Pres*

Anthony C Laplaca, *Admin Sec*
Fernando Baerga, *Administration*
◆ **EMP:** 300 **EST:** 1996
SALES (est): 78.9MM
SALES (corp-wide): 850.6MM **Publicly Held**
WEB: www.invacare.com
SIC: 3842 Surgical appliances & supplies
PA: Invacare Corporation
1 Invacare Way
Elyria OH 44035
440 329-6000

(G-16070)
J & J INTERNATIONAL CORP
Also Called: Action Label
240 Power Ct Ste 132 (32771-9400)
PHONE..................................407 349-7114
Jim Schenk, *President*
EMP: 26 **EST:** 1997
SQ FT: 5,000
SALES (est): 4.6MM **Privately Held**
WEB: www.actionlabel.com
SIC: 2671 2752 Packaging paper & plastics film, coated & laminated; commercial printing, lithographic

(G-16071)
JAMAR CNSTR FABRICATION INC
119 Commerce Way (32771-3085)
PHONE..................................321 400-0333
Mark Pick, *Principal*
EMP: 8 **EST:** 2017
SALES (est): 419.6K **Privately Held**
WEB: www.jamarfab.com
SIC: 3441 Fabricated structural metal

(G-16072)
JAMCO INDUSTRIAL INC
3800 Entp Way Ste 1110 (32771)
PHONE..................................866 848-5400
Abbas Jamal, *President*
Tim Jamal, *Vice Pres*
Imtiaz Jamal, *Director*
EMP: 11 **EST:** 2012
SALES (est): 1MM **Privately Held**
WEB: www.jamco1.com
SIC: 3537 Forklift trucks

(G-16073)
JAMES G DOWLING
1375 Palm Way (32773-6807)
PHONE..................................407 509-9484
James G Dowling, *Owner*
EMP: 7 **EST:** 2003
SALES (est): 209.8K **Privately Held**
SIC: 1442 Construction sand & gravel

(G-16074)
JONES COMMUNICATIONS INC
312 W 1st St Ste 503 (32771-1206)
PHONE..................................407 448-6615
Jim Jones, *President*
Bill Davis, *Vice Pres*
EMP: 7 **EST:** 2009
SALES (est): 950K **Privately Held**
SIC: 3531 Construction machinery

(G-16075)
JRS LIMB & TREE LLC
297 Grant Line Rd (32771-9091)
PHONE..................................407 383-4843
Gerald F Williams Jr, *Manager*
EMP: 7 **EST:** 2016
SALES (est): 292K **Privately Held**
SIC: 3842 Limbs, artificial

(G-16076)
JRT MANUFACTURING LLC
421 Cornwall Rd (32773-5871)
PHONE..................................321 363-4133
Charles Chuck Johnson, *Purch Mgr*
David Thomson,
Maria Thomson,
EMP: 10 **EST:** 2013
SQ FT: 25,000
SALES (est): 1.9MM **Privately Held**
WEB: www.jrtmanufacturingllc.com
SIC: 3672 Printed circuit boards

(G-16077)
KEMCO INDUSTRIES LLC
70 Keyes Ave (32773-6074)
PHONE..................................407 322-1230
Ty S Kracht, *CEO*
Ty Kracht, *General Mgr*
Tye Kraft, *General Mgr*
Ted Swartzlander, *COO*
Pat Hodgkins, *Project Mgr*
▼ **EMP:** 80
SQ FT: 55,000
SALES (est): 10MM **Privately Held**
WEB: www.kemco.com
SIC: 3441 3625 3613 3444 Fabricated structural metal; relays & industrial controls; switchgear & switchboard apparatus; sheet metalwork; engraving service

(G-16078)
KENNY SKYLIGHTS LLC
5294 Tower Way (32773-8201)
PHONE..................................407 330-5150
Lee Walls,
EMP: 8 **EST:** 2005
SALES (est): 405.3K **Privately Held**
SIC: 3211 Skylight glass

(G-16079)
KID-U-NOT INC
1201 Central Park Dr (32771-6638)
PHONE..................................407 324-2112
Linda T Rubel, *President*
Jeni Brizard,
◆ **EMP:** 50 **EST:** 1989
SQ FT: 40,000
SALES (est): 6.8MM **Privately Held**
WEB: www.wekidunot.com
SIC: 2396 Screen printing on fabric articles

(G-16080)
LEGACY VULCAN LLC
4150 Maverick Ct (32771-6902)
PHONE..................................407 321-5323
Lawrence McIntyre, *Manager*
EMP: 7 **Publicly Held**
WEB: www.vulcanmaterials.com
SIC: 3273 Ready-mixed concrete
HQ: Legacy Vulcan, Llc
1200 Urban Center Dr
Vestavia AL 35242
205 298-3000

(G-16081)
LOGGERHEAD DISTILLERY LLC
124 W 2nd St (32771-1212)
PHONE..................................321 800-8566
Colby Theisen, *Mng Member*
EMP: 7 **EST:** 2018
SALES (est): 163.3K **Privately Held**
WEB: www.loggerheaddistillery.com
SIC: 2085 Distilled & blended liquors

(G-16082)
MATHEWS ASSOCIATES INC
Also Called: Battery Assemblers
220 Power Ct (32771-9530)
PHONE..................................407 323-3390
Daniel Perreault, *CEO*
Philip Perreault, *President*
Judy J Perreault, *Treasurer*
▲ **EMP:** 160 **EST:** 1980
SQ FT: 20,000
SALES (est): 24.5MM **Privately Held**
WEB: www.maifl.com
SIC: 3691 3629 3812 3672 Batteries, rechargeable; electronic generation equipment; search & navigation equipment; printed circuit boards

(G-16083)
MATT TALBOT INDUSTRIES LLC
218 S Oak Ave (32771-1238)
PHONE..................................407 718-7636
John T Hagan, *Principal*
EMP: 6 **EST:** 2016
SALES (est): 103.8K **Privately Held**
SIC: 3999 Manufacturing industries

(G-16084)
MBF INDUSTRIES INC
210 Tech Dr (32771-6662)
PHONE..................................407 323-9414
John W Baker III, *President*
Nilsson Natasha, *Managing Dir*
Tom Vanderluitgaren, *Vice Pres*
Dean Feller, *Production*
Franz Iporre, *Engineer*
EMP: 35 **EST:** 1992
SQ FT: 32,000
SALES (est): 7.7MM **Privately Held**
WEB: www.mbfindustries.com
SIC: 3799 Trailers & trailer equipment

(G-16085)
MCCARTHY FABRICATION LLC
201 N Maple Ave Ste 2 (32771-1106)
P.O. Box 1543 (32772-1543)
PHONE..................................407 943-4909
Eli Ramirez, *Project Mgr*
Charles C McCarthy, *Mng Member*
Elliott Ramirez, *Manager*
EMP: 16 **EST:** 2018
SALES (est): 3.5MM **Privately Held**
WEB: www.mccarthyfabricationllc.com
SIC: 3441 Fabricated structural metal

(G-16086)
MCES LLC
2499 Old Lake Mary Rd # 102 (32771-4192)
PHONE..................................321 363-4977
Carlos Gonzalez, *Mng Member*
Shug Brandell, *Director*
EMP: 8 **EST:** 2010
SALES (est): 1.2MM **Privately Held**
WEB: www.mymces.com
SIC: 3571 7699 3577 Electronic computers; agricultural equipment repair services; decoders, computer peripheral equipment

(G-16087)
METAL WORKS BY GAL
5650 S Sanford Ave (32773-9431)
PHONE..................................407 486-7198
Gal Schwartz, *Principal*
EMP: 9 **EST:** 2010
SALES (est): 517.8K **Privately Held**
SIC: 3444 Sheet metalwork

(G-16088)
MOBILE SPECIALTIES INC
Also Called: Mobile Walkways
1683 N Beardall Ave # 117 (32771-9616)
P.O. Box 622363, Oviedo (32762-2363)
PHONE..................................407 878-5469
Dennis Towell, *CEO*
▼ **EMP:** 8 **EST:** 2007
SQ FT: 11,000
SALES (est): 943.5K **Privately Held**
WEB: www.industrialcrewquarters.com
SIC: 3534 Walkways, moving

(G-16089)
MOBILITE CORPORATION
2101 E Lake Mary Blvd (32773-6099)
PHONE..................................407 321-5630
Gerald B Blouch, *President*
EMP: 66 **EST:** 1979
SQ FT: 113,000
SALES (est): 1.5MM
SALES (corp-wide): 850.6MM **Publicly Held**
WEB: www.invacare.com
SIC: 2514 3841 Beds, including folding & cabinet, household: metal; inhalation therapy equipment
PA: Invacare Corporation
1 Invacare Way
Elyria OH 44035
440 329-6000

(G-16090)
MOLDED POLY INNOVATIONS INC
2635 S French Ave (32773-5115)
PHONE..................................407 314-1778
Katie Field, *Principal*
EMP: 11 **EST:** 2009
SALES (est): 137.7K **Privately Held**
WEB: www.imageartistry.com
SIC: 3089 Molding primary plastic

(G-16091)
MOTHER EARTH STONE LLC
4035 Maronda Way (32771-6503)
P.O. Box 470996, Lake Monroe (32747-0996)
PHONE..................................407 878-2854
Clint Coleman, *Mng Member*
EMP: 12 **EST:** 2010
SALES (est): 1.5MM **Privately Held**
WEB: www.mother-earth-stone-llc.business.site
SIC: 3281 3272 1771 Cut stone & stone products; concrete products, precast; concrete work

(G-16092)
NULINE SENSORS LLC
210 Specialty Pt (32771-6641)
PHONE..................................407 473-0765
Jim Monsor, *CEO*
Audrey Mohlenhoff, *Electrical Engi*
William McEllen, *Agent*
Will McEllen, *Info Tech Mgr*
Jeffrey D Stone,
EMP: 8 **EST:** 2013
SQ FT: 15,450
SALES (est): 1MM **Privately Held**
WEB: www.nulinesensors.com
SIC: 3841 5047 3845 Diagnostic apparatus, medical; patient monitoring equipment; diagnostic equipment, medical; arc lamp units, electrotherapeutic (except IR & UV)

(G-16093)
OMEGA MEDICAL IMAGING LLC
3400 Saint Johns Pkwy # 1020 (32771-6769)
PHONE..................................407 323-9400
Brian Fleming, *CEO*
John Newman, *Manager*
Linda Robb, *Admin Asst*
EMP: 24 **EST:** 1990
SQ FT: 17,000
SALES (est): 6.3MM **Privately Held**
WEB: www.omegamedicalimaging.com
SIC: 3844 5047 X-ray apparatus & tubes; hospital equipment & furniture

(G-16094)
ONE RESONANCE SENSORS
101 Gordon St (32771-6323)
PHONE..................................407 323-9933
Greg Holifield, *CEO*
EMP: 8 **EST:** 2013
SALES (est): 511.9K **Privately Held**
SIC: 3826 Magnetic resonance imaging apparatus

(G-16095)
ONE RESONANCE SENSORS LLC
101 Gordon St (32771-6323)
PHONE..................................407 637-0771
Pablo Prado, *CEO*
Gregory Holifield,
Will McEllen,
EMP: 10 **EST:** 2011
SALES (est): 749.9K **Privately Held**
WEB: www.bottledliquidscanner.com
SIC: 3674 Semiconductors & related devices

(G-16096)
ONLINE LABELS LLC (PA)
2001 E Lake Mary Blvd (32773-7140)
PHONE..................................407 936-3900
David Carmany, *President*
Matt Hamilton, *General Mgr*
Brandon Morel, *Project Mgr*
Matthew Stoltz, *Accountant*
David Ramirez, *Manager*
▼ **EMP:** 48 **EST:** 1999
SALES (est): 28.9MM **Privately Held**
WEB: www.onlinelabels.com
SIC: 2672 5999 Adhesive papers, labels or tapes: from purchased material; packaging materials: boxes, padding, etc.

(G-16097)
ORLANDO COMMERCIAL MILLWORK
5054 Hidden Path Way (32771-7478)
PHONE..................................407 549-2679
EMP: 6 **EST:** 2018
SALES (est): 148.7K **Privately Held**
WEB: www.commercialmillworksinc.com
SIC: 2431 Millwork

(G-16098)
OWENS DISTRIBUTORS INC
2850 W Airport Blvd (32771-1610)
P.O. Box 1358 (32772-1358)
PHONE..................................407 302-8602

Peter Owens, *President*
Susan M Owens, *Vice Pres*
Susan Owens, *Vice Pres*
Milton Kingsley, *Warehouse Mgr*
Melanie Aborgast, *Office Mgr*
EMP: 20 **EST:** 1994
SQ FT: 20,000
SALES (est): 4.2MM **Privately Held**
WEB: www.owensdistributors.com
SIC: 2841 Detergents, synthetic organic or inorganic alkaline; dishwashing compounds

(G-16099)
PARAGON PRODUCTS INC
Also Called: Creative Printing & Publishing
2300 Old Lake Mary Rd (32771-4189)
PHONE....................................407 302-9147
Richard Roy, *President*
Barbara Dizon, *Marketing Staff*
EMP: 20 **EST:** 1971
SQ FT: 5,500
SALES (est): 3.3MM **Privately Held**
WEB: www.cpponline.com
SIC: 2752 Commercial printing, offset

(G-16100)
PAULS TWING DSPTCH CNTL FLA I
1919 W 1st St (32771-1648)
PHONE....................................407 323-4446
Paul A Lanza, *President*
EMP: 9 **EST:** 2003
SALES (est): 322.5K **Privately Held**
WEB: www.paulstruckrepair.net
SIC: 3799 Towing bars & systems

(G-16101)
PHOENIX DEWATERING INC
1980 Cameron Ave (32771-9674)
P.O. Box 952742, Lake Mary (32795-2742)
PHONE....................................407 330-7015
Terry Miles, *President*
James Miles, *Corp Secy*
EMP: 16 **EST:** 1994
SALES (est): 3.8MM **Privately Held**
SIC: 3561 3533 Pumps & pumping equipment; water well drilling equipment

(G-16102)
PIKE POLE PRESS
1506 Magnolia Ave (32771-3438)
PHONE....................................407 474-7453
Tim Deppen, *Owner*
EMP: 6 **EST:** 2010
SALES (est): 197.2K **Privately Held**
WEB: www.gen2innovations.com
SIC: 2741 Miscellaneous publishing

(G-16103)
POWELL WOODWORKING LLC
5150 Sage Cedar Pl (32771-9339)
PHONE....................................407 883-9181
Marc R Powell, *Manager*
EMP: 9 **EST:** 2017
SALES (est): 619.9K **Privately Held**
WEB: www.powellwoodworking.net
SIC: 2431 Millwork

(G-16104)
PRE-CAST SPECIALTIES INC
Also Called: Pcsi
3850 E Lake Mary Blvd (32773-6609)
PHONE....................................954 781-4040
Fred A Cianelli, *President*
Gene Leach, *COO*
John Meyer, *Project Mgr*
Alfred A Cianelli Jr, *Treasurer*
Sam Nader, *Controller*
◆ **EMP:** 200 **EST:** 1971
SQ FT: 14,949
SALES (est): 21.8MM **Privately Held**
WEB: www.precastspecialties.com
SIC: 3272 Concrete products, precast

(G-16105)
PRE-CAST SPECIALTIES LLC (PA)
Also Called: Precast Specialties
3850 E Lake Mary Blvd (32773-6609)
PHONE....................................954 781-4040
Margie Metzgar, *Purch Mgr*
Dean Jenness Locke, *Mng Member*
EMP: 17 **EST:** 2015
SALES (est): 8.4MM **Privately Held**
WEB: www.precastspecialties.com
SIC: 3272 Concrete products, precast

(G-16106)
PRESCIENT LOGISTICS LLC
Also Called: Repscrubs
576 Monroe Rd Ste 1304 (32771-8819)
PHONE....................................407 547-2680
Carrie Hardyman, *Partner*
Jennifer Feuer, *Human Res Mgr*
Carlie Sutherland, *Marketing Staff*
Jeffrey Feuer, *Mng Member*
Brian Hanson, *CIO*
EMP: 10 **EST:** 2013
SQ FT: 6,500
SALES (est): 500K **Privately Held**
WEB: www.repscrubs.com
SIC: 2389 Hospital gowns

(G-16107)
PURE ESSENTIAL
6788 Sylvan Woods Dr (32771-6447)
PHONE....................................407 732-7225
Marjorie Michael, *Principal*
EMP: 6 **EST:** 2017
SALES (est): 80.3K **Privately Held**
WEB: www.eoproducts.com
SIC: 2844 Toilet preparations

(G-16108)
QUANTUMFLO INC
Also Called: Manufacturing
2664 Jewett Ln (32771-1678)
PHONE....................................407 807-7050
David Carrier, *CEO*
David P Carrier, *President*
Edward Ross, *Vice Pres*
Mann Robert, *Engineer*
Michael B Carrier, *CFO*
EMP: 31 **EST:** 2007
SQ FT: 10,000
SALES (est): 4.3MM **Privately Held**
WEB: www.quantumflo.com
SIC: 3561 Industrial pumps & parts

(G-16109)
RAINBOW POOL SUPPLY INC
2920 W Airport Blvd (32771-4818)
PHONE....................................407 324-9616
Jean Riese, *Principal*
EMP: 9 **EST:** 2008
SALES (est): 219.6K **Privately Held**
SIC: 3089 Plastic processing

(G-16110)
RILEY & COMPANY INC (PA)
5491 Benchmark Ln (32773-6433)
PHONE....................................407 265-9963
Larry Riley, *President*
Audrey Bowman, *General Mgr*
Keith Hawkins, *Project Mgr*
Trever Riley, *Representative*
EMP: 12 **EST:** 2000
SQ FT: 10,000
SALES (est): 2MM **Privately Held**
WEB: www.rileyandco.com
SIC: 3999 Atomizers, toiletry

(G-16111)
ROWE MANUFACTURING LLC
722 Golden Spike Ln (32771-8213)
PHONE....................................407 324-5757
Gerald L Rowe Jr,
Donna Rowe,
EMP: 13 **EST:** 2002
SQ FT: 4,150
SALES (est): 2MM **Privately Held**
WEB: www.rowemfgllc.com
SIC: 3599 Machine shop, jobbing & repair

(G-16112)
RUGBY ROAD CORP
Also Called: Newer Spreader
3941 Saint Johns Pkwy (32771-6373)
PHONE....................................407 328-5474
Rick Gaughan, *President*
Bonita S Gaughan, *Principal*
EMP: 6 **EST:** 2005
SQ FT: 5,000
SALES (est): 1.5MM **Privately Held**
SIC: 3523 Spreaders, fertilizer

(G-16113)
RUSSELL BROS ALUM ANDZING CTIN
Also Called: Russell Bros Alum Anodizing
1001 Cornwall Rd (32773-5873)
PHONE....................................407 323-5619
Charles Russell, *President*
EMP: 12 **EST:** 1980
SQ FT: 5,000
SALES (est): 137.9K **Privately Held**
SIC: 3471 Anodizing (plating) of metals or formed products

(G-16114)
SEMINOLE COUNTY PUBLIC SCHOOLS
1722 W Airport Blvd (32771-4000)
PHONE....................................407 320-0393
Joel Renda, *Manager*
Kris Sefried, *Teacher*
EMP: 10
SALES (corp-wide): 668.7MM **Privately Held**
WEB: www.scps.us
SIC: 2732 Book printing
HQ: Seminole County Public Schools
400 E Lake Mary Blvd
Sanford FL 32773
407 320-0000

(G-16115)
SIGNS JUST FOR YOU INC
4009 W State Road 46 (32771-9721)
PHONE....................................407 927-0226
EMP: 5 **EST:** 2019
SALES (est): 330.5K **Privately Held**
WEB: www.signsjustforyou.com
SIC: 3993 Signs & advertising specialties

(G-16116)
SIMPLY GROUP II LLC
Also Called: Simplynas
4366 Ronald Reagan Blvd (32773-6315)
PHONE....................................407 960-4690
Fatema Mawji, *CEO*
Tony Salazar,
EMP: 6 **EST:** 2010
SALES (est): 1.9MM **Privately Held**
WEB: www.simplynas.com
SIC: 3572 Computer storage devices

(G-16117)
SNK AMERICA INC
Also Called: Somec
3551 W State Road 46 (32771-8852)
PHONE....................................407 831-7766
Kevin Lousch, *Officer*
EMP: 10 **EST:** 2013
SALES (est): 805K **Privately Held**
WEB: www.someccontainers.com
SIC: 3541 Machine tools, metal cutting type

(G-16118)
SOFIE CO
136 Commerce Way (32771-3091)
PHONE....................................407 321-9076
Timothy Stone, *President*
Chris Williams, *General Mgr*
Kirk McCall, *Manager*
Todd Bejian,
EMP: 16
SQ FT: 8,050 **Privately Held**
WEB: www.sofie.com
SIC: 2834 Pharmaceutical preparations
HQ: Sofie Co.
21000 Atl Blvd Ste 730
Dulles VA 20166

(G-16119)
SOUTHERN MFG & FABRICATION LLC
2000 E Lake Mary Blvd (32773-7133)
PHONE....................................407 894-8851
Bryan H Earnest, *Principal*
EMP: 11 **EST:** 2011
SALES (est): 2MM **Privately Held**
WEB: www.southernmfg.com
SIC: 3443 Tanks, standard or custom fabricated: metal plate

(G-16120)
ST JOHNS OPTICAL SYSTEMS LLC
101 Gordon St (32771-6323)
PHONE....................................407 280-3787
Gregory Holifield,
Ronald Driggers,
EMP: 5 **EST:** 2013
SALES (est): 328.6K **Privately Held**
WEB: www.stjohnsopticalsystems.com
SIC: 3826 Laser scientific & engineering instruments

(G-16121)
STEEL PLUS SERVICE CENTER INC
2525 Magnolia Ave (32773-5135)
PHONE....................................407 328-7169
Frank Brooklyn, *President*
EMP: 6 **EST:** 1992
SQ FT: 2,400
SALES (est): 250K **Privately Held**
SIC: 7692 7539 Welding repair; trailer repair

(G-16122)
SUNSTATE AWNG GRPHIC DSIGN INC
50 Keyes Ave (32773-6074)
PHONE....................................407 260-6118
Mark A Nelen, *Ch of Bd*
Alan M Hanley, *President*
EMP: 26 **EST:** 1989
SQ FT: 8,000
SALES (est): 3.2MM **Privately Held**
WEB: www.sunstateawning.com
SIC: 2394 Awnings, fabric: made from purchased materials

(G-16123)
SUPERCHIPS INC
1790 E Airport Blvd (32773-6805)
PHONE....................................407 585-7000
Ron Turcotte, *President*
Chris Rookey, *Senior Engr*
Guadalupe Soto, *CFO*
Wendy Curry, *Finance*
Karen Server, *Admin Sec*
EMP: 23 **EST:** 1992
SQ FT: 25,000
SALES (est): 1.9MM **Privately Held**
WEB: www.superchips.com
SIC: 3571 Electronic computers

(G-16124)
T J SALES ASSOCIATES INC
4355 Saint Johns Pkwy (32771-6381)
PHONE....................................407 328-0777
Randy Lusigman, *Manager*
EMP: 8
SALES (corp-wide): 2.7MM **Privately Held**
SIC: 3699 Laser systems & equipment
PA: T J Sales Associates Inc
3155 State Route 10 # 204
Denville NJ 07834
407 328-0777

(G-16125)
T N R TECHNICAL INC (PA)
301 Central Park Dr (32771-6692)
PHONE....................................407 321-3011
Wayne Thaw, *CEO*
Mitchell Thaw, *President*
Anne Provost, *CFO*
Jerri Steinbach, *Sales Staff*
◆ **EMP:** 13 **EST:** 1979
SQ FT: 8,000
SALES (est): 5.5MM **Privately Held**
WEB: www.tnrtechnical.com
SIC: 3691 3692 Storage batteries; dry cell batteries, single or multiple cell

(G-16126)
TEAM SOLUTIONS DENTAL LLC
2675 S Design Ct (32773-8120)
PHONE....................................407 542-1552
Jason M Defranco,
EMP: 80 **EST:** 2013
SALES (est): 5.4MM **Privately Held**
WEB: www.tsdlab.com
SIC: 3999 Manufacturing industries

(G-16127)
TESSERACT SENSORS LLC
101 Gordon St (32771-6323)
PHONE..................................407 385-2498
Gil C Barrett Jr,
EMP: 14 **EST:** 2010
SALES (est): 2.5MM **Privately Held**
SIC: 3674 Radiation sensors

(G-16128)
TORTILLERIA LAMEXICANA 7 INC
2715 S Orlando Dr (32773-5311)
PHONE..................................407 324-3100
Meguel Hornho, *President*
EMP: 10 **EST:** 2005
SALES (est): 558.3K **Privately Held**
SIC: 2099 Tortillas, fresh or refrigerated

(G-16129)
TOS MANUFACTURING INC
Also Called: Deskrafters
4280 Saint Johns Pkwy (32771-6378)
PHONE..................................407 330-3880
Roger Morin, *President*
EMP: 10 **EST:** 1992
SQ FT: 10,000
SALES (est): 136.8K **Privately Held**
SIC: 2521 Wood office furniture

(G-16130)
U C CABINET INC
222 Hickman Dr (32771-6917)
PHONE..................................407 322-0968
Joseph Scheuering, *President*
James C Scheuering, *Vice Pres*
Jeffrey T Scheuering, *Vice Pres*
John R Scheuering, *Vice Pres*
Joseph R Scheuering Jr, *Vice Pres*
EMP: 6 **EST:** 1981
SQ FT: 1,500
SALES (est): 531.4K **Privately Held**
SIC: 2434 Wood kitchen cabinets

(G-16131)
VENTURE CIRCLE ENTERPRISES LLC
140 Maritime Dr (32771-6320)
P.O. Box 6068, Winter Park (32793-6068)
PHONE..................................407 678-7489
Tina Coalburn, *Purchasing*
Ivor Singer, *Mng Member*
Ivor A Singer Jr,
▲ **EMP:** 12 **EST:** 1987
SALES (est): 2MM **Privately Held**
WEB: www.creativeimagesvce.com
SIC: 3429 5023 Builders' hardware; home furnishings

(G-16132)
VENTURE CIRCLE INTL LLC
140 Maritime Dr (32771-6320)
PHONE..................................407 677-6004
Marc N Lieberman,
Sheldon Rosenberg,
EMP: 11 **EST:** 2017
SALES (est): 603K **Privately Held**
WEB: www.venturecirclellc.com
SIC: 3231 Framed mirrors

(G-16133)
VERTICAL AVIATION TECHNOLOGIES
1609 Hangar Rd Bldg 332 (32773-6826)
PHONE..................................407 322-9488
Brad Clark, *President*
Bethany Wallace, *Assistant*
▼ **EMP:** 12 **EST:** 1988
SQ FT: 12,000
SALES (est): 1.9MM **Privately Held**
WEB: www.vertical-aviation.com
SIC: 3721 4581 Helicopters; aircraft servicing & repairing

(G-16134)
WATERFALL INDUSTRIES INC
Also Called: Benchmark of Florida
915 Cornwall Rd (32773-7312)
PHONE..................................407 330-2003
Anthony Di Ottavio, *President*
Glen R Moller, *Vice Pres*
Anthony Lupo, *CIO*
◆ **EMP:** 12 **EST:** 1991
SQ FT: 72,000
SALES (est): 2.5MM **Privately Held**
WEB: www.discoveryworldfurniture.com
SIC: 2511 5021 1542 1541 Wood household furniture; waterbeds; beds & bedding; household furniture; nonresidential construction; industrial buildings & warehouses

(G-16135)
WATTS TECHNOLOGIES LLC
Also Called: Queteq
2647 N Design Ct (32773-8119)
PHONE..................................407 512-5750
John Watts, *Mng Member*
EMP: 10 **EST:** 2019
SALES (est): 1.3MM **Privately Held**
WEB: www.watts.com
SIC: 3629 Electronic generation equipment

(G-16136)
WAYNE METAL PRODUCTS INC
5461 Benchmark Ln (32773-6433)
PHONE..................................407 321-7168
Wayne J Holmes, *President*
Glen R Holmes, *Vice Pres*
EMP: 5 **EST:** 1955
SQ FT: 5,000
SALES (est): 375.9K **Privately Held**
WEB: www.waynemetalproductsinc.com
SIC: 3843 3841 Sterilizers, dental; surgical & medical instruments

(G-16137)
WE RE ORGANIZED
1441 Kastner Pl Unit 111 (32771-8514)
PHONE..................................407 323-5133
Rick Goolsby, *Owner*
Dwaine Massey, *Owner*
EMP: 6 **EST:** 2006
SALES (est): 494.6K **Privately Held**
SIC: 2434 Wood kitchen cabinets

(G-16138)
WEST END
202 Sanford Ave (32771-1342)
PHONE..................................407 322-7475
John Lejarzar, *Principal*
EMP: 11 **EST:** 2007
SALES (est): 458.7K **Privately Held**
WEB: www.drinkatwestend.com
SIC: 2599 Bar, restaurant & cafeteria furniture

(G-16139)
WHOLLY HEMP INC
187 Brushcreek Dr (32771-7753)
PHONE..................................813 785-6231
Christopher R Visser, *Principal*
EMP: 9 **EST:** 2017
SALES (est): 564.6K **Privately Held**
WEB: www.cbdoilsandedibles.com
SIC: 3999

(G-16140)
WINDERA POWER SYSTEMS INC
703 Progress Way (32771-6987)
PHONE..................................407 808-1271
Richard W Burt, *CEO*
EMP: 6 **EST:** 2010
SALES (est): 141.5K **Privately Held**
WEB: www.winderapowersystems.com
SIC: 3621 Power generators

(G-16141)
WORTH COMPANY LLC
608 Trestle Pt (32771-8200)
PHONE..................................888 652-1555
Daniel Fox, *Mng Member*
Oliver Pinnock,
EMP: 7 **EST:** 2015
SALES (est): 106.1K **Privately Held**
SIC: 2759 Engraving

(G-16142)
YESCO SIGN AND LIGHTING
1940 Dolgner Pl (32771-9225)
PHONE..................................407 321-3577
James Abbott, *Manager*
EMP: 9 **EST:** 2015
SALES (est): 284.7K **Privately Held**
WEB: www.yesco.com
SIC: 3993 Signs & advertising specialties

Sanibel
Lee County

(G-16143)
CAPTIVA CURRENT INC
Also Called: Santa Bell Capitav Group
2340 Periwinkle Way (33957-3221)
P.O. Box 809 (33957-0809)
PHONE..................................239 574-1110
Valerie Harring, *Editor*
EMP: 15 **EST:** 1973
SALES (est): 260.3K **Privately Held**
WEB: www.captivacurrent.com
SIC: 2711 Newspapers: publishing only, not printed on site

(G-16144)
CHELLE WALTON PUBLISHING
936 Main St (33957-4530)
PHONE..................................239 699-4754
Chelle Walton, *Principal*
EMP: 6 **EST:** 2009
SALES (est): 103.4K **Privately Held**
SIC: 2741 Miscellaneous publishing

(G-16145)
CT HYDRAULICS INC
Also Called: Cooper
1845 Ardsley Way (33957-4110)
PHONE..................................724 342-3089
Kyle Klaric, *Managing Dir*
▲ **EMP:** 12 **EST:** 2008
SALES (est): 967K **Privately Held**
SIC: 3429 Manufactured hardware (general)

(G-16146)
IBTM ENGINEERING INC
1291 Par View Dr (33957-6401)
P.O. Box 1679, Telluride CO (81435-1679)
PHONE..................................239 246-1876
Edward Merralls, *President*
EMP: 6 **EST:** 2003
SALES (est): 365K **Privately Held**
SIC: 3694 Engine electrical equipment

(G-16147)
LORKEN PUBLICATIONS INC (PA)
Also Called: Island Sun Newspaper
1640 Periwinkle Way Ste 2 (33957-4401)
PHONE..................................239 395-1213
Lorin Arundel, *Principal*
EMP: 7 **EST:** 1993
SQ FT: 1,200
SALES (est): 833.8K **Privately Held**
SIC: 2711 Newspapers: publishing only, not printed on site

(G-16148)
MAXWELLS SANIBEL LIME-ELO INC
392 Raintree Pl (33957-5634)
P.O. Box 805 (33957-0805)
PHONE..................................239 472-8618
Catherine T Maxwell, *Vice Pres*
EMP: 6 **EST:** 2016
SALES (est): 165.3K **Privately Held**
WEB: www.captivasanibel.com
SIC: 2711 Newspapers: publishing only, not printed on site

(G-16149)
SANTIVA CHRONICLE LLC
1420 Albatross Rd (33957-3604)
PHONE..................................239 472-0559
Shannen Hayes, *Publisher*
David Staver, *Principal*
EMP: 9 **EST:** 2013
SALES (est): 222.2K **Privately Held**
SIC: 2711 Newspapers, publishing & printing

(G-16150)
TOTI MEDIA INC
2422 Palm Ridge Rd # 103 (33957-3202)
P.O. Box 1227 (33957-1227)
PHONE..................................239 472-0205
Daniela Jaeger, *President*
Gysbertus H Tober, *President*
Roeland Pells, *Corp Secy*
Daniella Jaeger, *Vice Pres*
Brian Stromlund, *Vice Pres*
▼ **EMP:** 5 **EST:** 1996
SQ FT: 983
SALES (est): 1.4MM **Privately Held**
WEB: www.totimedia.com
SIC: 2721 Magazines: publishing only, not printed on site
PA: Sidney Nominees Limited
In Care Of: Bienheim Trust (Bvi) Limited
Road Town

Santa Rosa Beach
Walton County

(G-16151)
A WORLD OF SIGNS
77 Shannon Ln (32459-4270)
P.O. Box 242, Mary Esther (32569-0242)
PHONE..................................850 267-1331
EMP: 6 **EST:** 2009
SALES (est): 79.5K **Privately Held**
WEB: www.aworldofsigns.com
SIC: 3993 Signs & advertising specialties

(G-16152)
BASIC INDUSTRIES GLOBAL LLC
108 Woodward Dr (32459-3650)
P.O. Box 1057 (32459-1057)
PHONE..................................850 622-5924
Scott Morrison,
EMP: 7 **EST:** 2012
SALES (est): 137.3K **Privately Held**
SIC: 3241 Cement, hydraulic

(G-16153)
CAPSTORM LLC
3906 Us Highway 98 W # 1159 (32459-4026)
PHONE..................................314 403-2143
Rebecca Gray, *VP Bus Dvlpt*
Mary Smith, *Mng Member*
Mary D Smith, *Mng Member*
Gregory B Smith,
EMP: 6 **EST:** 2015
SALES (est): 380.3K **Privately Held**
WEB: www.capstorm.com
SIC: 7372 Business oriented computer software

(G-16154)
CNS MILLWORKS INC
164 N Brookwood Dr (32459-5683)
PHONE..................................850 259-9206
EMP: 6 **EST:** 2019
SALES (est): 65.4K **Privately Held**
WEB: www.cnsmillworks.com
SIC: 2431 Millwork

(G-16155)
COASTAL CRANE AND RIGGING INC
54 Pisces Dr (32459-5400)
PHONE..................................850 460-1766
EMP: 8 **EST:** 2016
SALES (est): 264.7K **Privately Held**
WEB: www.coastalcranerigging.com
SIC: 3531 3536 5082 5084 Cranes; cranes, industrial plant; cranes, construction; cranes, industrial

(G-16156)
COPY SYSTEMS BUSINESS CENTER
4821 Us Highway 98 W # 102 (32459-8575)
PHONE..................................850 650-0886
Paul Dupree Woolman, *President*
EMP: 6 **EST:** 1995
SQ FT: 400
SALES (est): 86K **Privately Held**
WEB: www.copysystemsonline.com
SIC: 2759 Screen printing

(G-16157)
DEFENSE LEADERSHIP FORUM
174 Watercolor Way (32459-7350)
PHONE..................................202 375-9587
William S Loiry, *Principal*
Brooke Rosicka, *Vice Pres*
EMP: 6 **EST:** 2016

SALES (est): 258.5K **Privately Held**
WEB: www.defenseleadershipforum.org
SIC: 3812 Defense systems & equipment

(G-16158)
EMERALD COAST CABINETS INC
Also Called: Canac Kitchens Northwest Fla
5597 Us Highway 98 W # 101
(32459-3282)
PHONE..................................850 267-2290
Nick Zargari, *President*
EMP: 11 **EST:** 1991
SQ FT: 1,700
SALES (est): 309.5K **Privately Held**
SIC: 2434 Wood kitchen cabinets

(G-16159)
EMERALD COAST MEDIA & MKTG
Also Called: Walton Son Newspapers
790 N County Highway 393 (32459-7018)
P.O. Box 2363 (32459-2363)
PHONE..................................850 267-4555
Fax: 850 267-0929
EMP: 23 **EST:** 1996
SALES (est): 1.3MM
SALES (corp-wide): 2.3B **Privately Held**
SIC: 2711 Newspapers-Publishing/Printing
HQ: Freedom Communications, Inc.
625 N Grand Ave
Santa Ana CA 92701
714 796-7000

(G-16160)
GRMS SERVICING LLC
249 Mack Byou Loop Ste 30 (32459)
P.O. Box 2548 (32459-2548)
PHONE..................................850 278-1000
Reynolds Henderson, *Manager*
EMP: 5 **EST:** 2010
SALES (est): 351.3K **Privately Held**
SIC: 1389 Roustabout service

(G-16161)
JDK IMPORTS INC (PA)
Also Called: Shoe Jewels
87 Whispering Lake Dr (32459-4289)
P.O. Box 786, Highlands NC (28741-0786)
PHONE..................................850 865-0297
Julie D Kovach, *President*
Frank D Kovach, *Admin Sec*
EMP: 15 **EST:** 2010
SALES (est): 58.7K **Privately Held**
SIC: 3111 Shoe leather

(G-16162)
KIRBY ACQUISITIONS LLC
294 Hunters Rd (32459-8311)
PHONE..................................850 687-8703
Jeff Kirby, *Principal*
Jeff A Kirby,
EMP: 7 **EST:** 2010
SALES (est): 116.1K **Privately Held**
SIC: 3714 Motor vehicle parts & accessories

(G-16163)
LITTLE PICKLE LLC
Also Called: Pickle Factory
38 Clayton Ln Ste 19 (32459-5775)
PHONE..................................850 231-1290
Jeffrey Fehr,
EMP: 8 **EST:** 2009
SALES (est): 258.8K **Privately Held**
WEB: www.picklepizza.com
SIC: 2035 Pickles, sauces & salad dressings

(G-16164)
NORTH FLORIDA BRICK PAVERS LLC
664 E Shipwreck Rd (32459-8003)
PHONE..................................850 255-0336
Roderick J Booker, *Principal*
EMP: 6 **EST:** 2008
SALES (est): 443K **Privately Held**
SIC: 3531 Pavers

(G-16165)
QTRONICS INC
279 Santa Rosa St (32459-3803)
PHONE..................................850 267-0102
Mike Griffin, *President*
EMP: 5 **EST:** 1992
SALES (est): 381.1K **Privately Held**
WEB: www.gricor.com
SIC: 3571 Personal computers (microcomputers)

(G-16166)
S2 PASS HOLDINGS LLC ✪
116 Mc Davis Blvd # 230 (32459-5085)
PHONE..................................706 773-4097
Hudson Shumate, *Mng Member*
Marcellus Smith, *CTO*
EMP: 5 **EST:** 2020
SALES (est): 323.8K **Privately Held**
SIC: 7372 7389 Educational computer software;

(G-16167)
SELECT PUBLISHING LLC
56 Denny Dr (32459-5010)
PHONE..................................850 464-6477
Carnella D Bracciale, *Principal*
EMP: 6 **EST:** 2012
SALES (est): 90.2K **Privately Held**
SIC: 2741 Miscellaneous publishing

(G-16168)
SRB SERVICING LLC
249 Mack Bayou Loop # 302 (32459-7197)
P.O. Box 1350 (32459-1350)
PHONE..................................850 278-1000
Jackie Mauro, *Principal*
Scott Covell, *Nurse*
EMP: 5 **EST:** 2008
SALES (est): 804.4K **Privately Held**
WEB: www.srbservicing.com
SIC: 1389 Roustabout service

(G-16169)
WAY BRIGHT SIGN SYSTEMS
93 Dune Lakes Cir E305 (32459-8393)
P.O. Box 293, Watertown TN (37184-0293)
PHONE..................................615 480-4602
Chris Henderson, *President*
EMP: 9 **EST:** 2014
SALES (est): 78K **Privately Held**
WEB: www.brightsign.biz
SIC: 3993 Signs & advertising specialties

Sarasota
Manatee County

(G-16170)
ABC HAMMERS
7216 21st St E (34243-3903)
PHONE..................................708 343-9900
EMP: 6 **EST:** 2019
SALES (est): 581.1K **Privately Held**
WEB: www.abchammers.com
SIC: 3423 Hand & edge tools

(G-16171)
ACH SOLUTION USA INC
1165 Commerce Blvd N (34243-5056)
PHONE..................................941 355-9488
Steven Broadbent, *General Mgr*
EMP: 7 **EST:** 2018
SALES (est): 763.8K **Privately Held**
WEB: www.ach-solution.at
SIC: 3714 Motor vehicle parts & accessories

(G-16172)
AEROSOURCE INC (DH)
2250 Whitfield Ave (34243-3926)
PHONE..................................941 751-2620
Mitchell W Millett, *President*
Kevin F Macmanus, *Exec VP*
▲ **EMP:** 25 **EST:** 1987
SQ FT: 17,500
SALES (est): 19.2MM
SALES (corp-wide): 639.8MM **Privately Held**
WEB: www.safran-group.com
SIC: 3728 Aircraft parts & equipment
HQ: Safran Electrical & Power
Parc D Activite Andromede
Beauzelle 31700
562 870-500

(G-16173)
ALFA LAVAL INC
2359 Trailmate Dr (34243-4041)
PHONE..................................941 727-1900
Arthur McCutthan, *Branch Mgr*
John Hall, *Manager*
EMP: 9 **Privately Held**
WEB: www.alfalaval.us
SIC: 3491 3433 Industrial valves; heating equipment, except electric
HQ: Alfa Laval Inc.
5400 Intl Trade Dr
Richmond VA 23231
866 253-2528

(G-16174)
ALNITAK CORPORATION
6791 Whitfield Indus Ave (34243-5415)
PHONE..................................941 727-1122
Andrew Sewell, *President*
Anthony Dertouzos, *Vice Pres*
Mark Marshik, *Manager*
EMP: 10 **EST:** 1992
SQ FT: 8,150
SALES (est): 1.2MM **Privately Held**
WEB: www.alnitak.com
SIC: 3599 Machine shop, jobbing & repair

(G-16175)
ARCHER PHARMACEUTICALS INC
2040 Whitfield Ave (34243-3956)
PHONE..................................941 752-2949
Michael Mullan, *President*
Nicole Russ, *General Mgr*
Fiona Crawford, *Vice Pres*
Parka Dodd, *CFO*
Peter N Townshend, *Admin Sec*
EMP: 10 **EST:** 2008
SALES (est): 1.2MM **Privately Held**
WEB: www.archerpharmaceuticals.com
SIC: 2834 Pharmaceutical preparations

(G-16176)
ARMORIT PRECISION LLC
2280 Trailmate Dr Ste 103 (34243-4078)
PHONE..................................941 751-1292
Floyd Asbury,
EMP: 10 **EST:** 2007
SQ FT: 12,000
SALES (est): 255.7K **Privately Held**
WEB: www.armorit.com
SIC: 3545 Precision tools, machinists'

(G-16177)
ARMORIT PRECISON
6423 Parkland Dr (34243-4035)
PHONE..................................941 751-6635
Floyd Asbury, *Sales Executive*
EMP: 6 **EST:** 2018
SALES (est): 98.1K **Privately Held**
WEB: www.armorit.com
SIC: 3599 Machine shop, jobbing & repair

(G-16178)
ARTISAN TOOL & DIE LLC
2305 72nd Ave E (34243-3952)
PHONE..................................765 288-6653
EMP: 6 **EST:** 2019
SALES (est): 185K **Privately Held**
WEB: www.artisantoolanddie.com
SIC: 3089 Injection molding of plastics

(G-16179)
ATHCO INC (PA)
1009 Tallevast Rd (34243-3259)
PHONE..................................941 351-1600
Stuart Goldman, *CEO*
David Berger, *Ch of Bd*
Jerry Beckerman, *President*
◆ **EMP:** 25 **EST:** 1990
SQ FT: 39,000
SALES (est): 5.8MM **Privately Held**
SIC: 2339 2329 2369 Athletic clothing: women's, misses' & juniors'; men's & boys' sportswear & athletic clothing; girls' & children's outerwear

(G-16180)
BARKER BOATWORKS LLC
7910 25th Ct E Unit 115 (34243-2842)
PHONE..................................941 233-8640
Kevin Barker, *Sales Staff*
EMP: 12 **EST:** 2014
SALES (est): 934.7K **Privately Held**
WEB: www.barkerboatworks.com
SIC: 3732 Boat building & repairing

(G-16181)
BENZ RESEARCH AND DEV LLC
6447 Parkland Dr (34243-4035)
P.O. Box 1839 (34230-1839)
PHONE..................................941 758-8256
Steve Brauner, *General Mgr*
Steve Grant, *Engineer*
Neal Mangin, *Engineer*
Rekash Vasant, *Engineer*
Lorrie Pomroy, *Office Mgr*
EMP: 36 **EST:** 1980
SQ FT: 35,000
SALES (est): 8.4MM **Privately Held**
WEB: www.benzrd.com
SIC: 3827 Lenses, optical: all types except ophthalmic

(G-16182)
BEST BRAND BOTTLERS INC
6620 19th St E Unit 109 (34243-4056)
PHONE..................................941 755-1941
Ken A Lewis, *Principal*
EMP: 12 **EST:** 2011
SALES (est): 467.5K **Privately Held**
WEB: www.bestbrandbottlers.com
SIC: 2099 Food preparations

(G-16183)
BHD PRECISION PRODUCTS INC
2120 Whitfield Park Loop (34243-4013)
PHONE..................................941 753-0003
Howard A Hughes, *Principal*
EMP: 8 **EST:** 2018
SALES (est): 610.1K **Privately Held**
SIC: 3499 Fabricated metal products

(G-16184)
BIOLIFE LLC
8163 25th Ct E (34243-2800)
PHONE..................................941 360-1300
Kelly Keene, *Vice Pres*
Claudia Masselink, *Vice Pres*
Kurt Vadelund, *Vice Pres*
Tim Capp, *CFO*
Nick Wright, *Sales Staff*
EMP: 39 **EST:** 1998
SQ FT: 20,000
SALES (est): 12.2MM **Privately Held**
WEB: www.biolife.com
SIC: 2834 Powders, pharmaceutical

(G-16185)
CANTERBURY HOUSE PUBLISHING
6928 W Country Club Dr N (34243-3501)
PHONE..................................941 312-6912
Wendy Dingwall, *Principal*
EMP: 7 **EST:** 2015
SALES (est): 104.3K **Privately Held**
WEB: www.canterburyhousepublishing.com
SIC: 2741 Miscellaneous publishing

(G-16186)
CAPACITY INC
Also Called: Go Puck
2240 72nd Ave E (34243-3985)
P.O. Box 1766, Tallevast (34270-1766)
PHONE..................................855 440-7825
Samuel Fuller, *Principal*
EMP: 20 **EST:** 2012
SALES (est): 1.4MM **Privately Held**
WEB: www.gopuck.com
SIC: 3621 1731 Storage battery chargers, motor & engine generator type; electrical work

(G-16187)
CAPSTONE CG LLC
6348 17th Street Cir E (34243-5426)
PHONE..................................941 371-3321
Robert Lodge, *President*
Wilbur Hopper, *Principal*
Shane Rogers, *Principal*
EMP: 15 **EST:** 2016
SALES (est): 2.2MM **Privately Held**
SIC: 3449 Fabricated bar joists & concrete reinforcing bars; bars, concrete reinforcing: fabricated steel; curtain wall, metal

(G-16188)
CC SPORTSWEAR INC
Also Called: Windy City Apparel
2331 Whtfeld Indus Way Un (34243)
PHONE..................................941 351-4205
Thomas Carollo, *CEO*

Stacey Carollo, *President*
EMP: 7 **EST:** 2014
SALES (est): 520.6K **Privately Held**
WEB: www.windycityapparel.org
SIC: 2759 2395 Screen printing; embroidery & art needlework

(G-16189)
CE HOOTON SALES LLC
1901 Whitfield Park Loop (34243-4150)
P.O. Box 110346, Lakewood Rch (34211-0005)
PHONE..................................305 255-9722
Linda J Long,
A G Mullins,
Bert Mullins,
Nancy Mullins,
Patrick L Mullins,
EMP: 10 **EST:** 1963
SALES (est): 730.3K **Privately Held**
WEB: www.cehootonsales.com
SIC: 3589 Water treatment equipment, industrial

(G-16190)
CHISM MANUFACTURING SVCS LLC
Also Called: CMS
6416 Parkland Dr (34243-4038)
PHONE..................................941 896-9671
David Chism, *Mng Member*
EMP: 10 **EST:** 2012
SQ FT: 12,000
SALES (est): 1.5MM **Privately Held**
SIC: 3621 3441 Exciter assemblies (motor or generator parts); tower sections, radio & television transmission

(G-16191)
CHRIS CRAFT CORPORATION
Also Called: Chris-Craft
8161 15th St E (34243-2709)
PHONE..................................941 351-4900
Stephen F Heese, *President*
Steve Callahan, *Vice Pres*
Jeff Ellis, *Vice Pres*
Gavan Hunt, *Vice Pres*
Aaron Kouba, *Vice Pres*
◆ **EMP:** 250 **EST:** 2001
SQ FT: 128,800
SALES (est): 33.2MM
SALES (corp-wide): 2.3B **Publicly Held**
WEB: www.chriscraft.com
SIC: 3732 Boats, fiberglass: building & repairing
PA: Winnebago Industries, Inc.
605 W Crystal Lake Rd
Forest City IA 50436
641 585-3535

(G-16192)
COAST CONTROLS INC
7500 Commerce Ct (34243-3217)
PHONE..................................941 355-7555
Thomas Marks, *President*
Andrey Kharitonenko, *Engineer*
EMP: 12 **EST:** 1992
SQ FT: 11,000
SALES (est): 1.7MM **Privately Held**
WEB: www.coastcontrols.com
SIC: 3823 3625 Industrial instrmnts msrmnt display/control process variable; relays & industrial controls

(G-16193)
COATING APPLICATION TECH INC
1851 67th Ave E (34243-4149)
PHONE..................................781 850-5080
Joseph W Selbeck, *Principal*
EMP: 14 **EST:** 2016
SALES (est): 2.8MM **Privately Held**
WEB: www.coatingapplication.com
SIC: 2851 Paints & allied products

(G-16194)
CONTAINER HANDLING SOLUTIONS
1349 W University Pkwy (34243-2704)
PHONE..................................941 359-2095
Michael Burkart, *President*
EMP: 8 **EST:** 1997
SALES (est): 1MM **Privately Held**
SIC: 3535 Conveyors & conveying equipment

(G-16195)
CONTEMPORARY CABINETS GULF CST
2245 Whitfield Indus Way (34243-4065)
PHONE..................................941 758-3060
Brian Wade, *Principal*
EMP: 7 **EST:** 2007
SALES (est): 795.9K **Privately Held**
SIC: 2434 Wood kitchen cabinets

(G-16196)
CONVEYOR CONCEPTS CORPORATION
2323 Whitfield Park Ave (34243-4032)
PHONE..................................941 751-1200
Bernard J Moltchan, *President*
Raymond Moltchan, *Vice Pres*
EMP: 7 **EST:** 2002
SQ FT: 13,000
SALES (est): 864.5K **Privately Held**
WEB: www.conveyorconceptsinc.com
SIC: 3535 Conveyors & conveying equipment

(G-16197)
COOPER NOTIFICATION INC
7246 16th St E Unit 105 (34243-6817)
PHONE..................................941 487-2300
Kenneth V Camarco, *President*
Randal S Heara, *President*
James T Burrell, *Vice Pres*
David Lorey, *Vice Pres*
Tyler W Johnson, *Treasurer*
▲ **EMP:** 70 **EST:** 1993
SQ FT: 5,000
SALES (est): 4.7MM **Privately Held**
WEB: www.eaton.com
SIC: 3663 Radio broadcasting & communications equipment
HQ: Cooper Industries Unlimited Company
41a Drury Street
Dublin D02 C

(G-16198)
COPALO INC
Also Called: Yellowfin Yachts, Inc.
6510 19th St E (34243-4187)
PHONE..................................941 753-7828
Wylie Nagler, *President*
▼ **EMP:** 106 **EST:** 1992
SQ FT: 70,000
SALES (est): 18.5MM
SALES (corp-wide): 20.8MM **Privately Held**
WEB: www.yellowfin.com
SIC: 3732 Boats, fiberglass: building & repairing
PA: Warbird Marine Holdings, Llc
4700 Nw 132nd St
Opa Locka FL 33054
844 341-2504

(G-16199)
COVOCUP LLC
6621 19th St E (34243-4181)
PHONE..................................855 204-5106
John Walters, *COO*
EMP: 6 **EST:** 2011
SALES (est): 354.7K **Privately Held**
SIC: 3089 Injection molding of plastics; tumblers, plastic

(G-16200)
CRUISE CAR INC
1227 Hardin Ave (34243-5024)
PHONE..................................941 929-1630
Adam Sulimirski, *President*
Greg Hyde, *COO*
Nathan Kalin, *Exec VP*
Susan Lebourgeois, *Office Mgr*
◆ **EMP:** 12
SQ FT: 8,816
SALES (est): 2.5MM **Privately Held**
WEB: www.cruisecarinc.com
SIC: 3799 Cars, off-highway: electric

(G-16201)
CUTTING EDGE MOLDINGS LLC
Also Called: Cutting Edge Archtctral Mldngs
7116 24th Ct E (34243-3993)
PHONE..................................734 649-1500
Melvyn Keshishian, *Mng Member*
Sandra Brennan, *Officer*
EMP: 9 **EST:** 2010
SALES (est): 916.2K **Privately Held**
WEB: www.cuttingedgemoldings.com
SIC: 3299 Moldings, architectural: plaster of paris

(G-16202)
D & B MACHINE INC
1855 61st St (34243-2232)
PHONE..................................941 355-8002
David L Frostad, *CEO*
Betty D Chromy-Frostad, *CFO*
EMP: 45 **EST:** 1991
SQ FT: 14,800
SALES (est): 7.1MM **Privately Held**
WEB: www.dandbmachine.com
SIC: 3599 Machine shop, jobbing & repair

(G-16203)
DANKER LABORATORIES INC
Also Called: Danker Labs
1144 Tallevast Rd Ste 106 (34243-6213)
PHONE..................................941 758-7711
Jeri Struve, *President*
Connie Rodewald, *Treasurer*
Gwen Norris, *Mktg Dir*
EMP: 12 **EST:** 1958
SQ FT: 5,200
SALES (est): 539.7K **Privately Held**
WEB: www.dankerlabs.com
SIC: 3851 5048 Contact lenses; contact lenses

(G-16204)
DART CONTAINER CORP FLORIDA
Also Called: Flight Management
8010 15th St E (34243-2714)
PHONE..................................941 358-1202
William Faulkner, *Manager*
EMP: 17
SALES (corp-wide): 68.2MM **Privately Held**
WEB: www.dartcontainer.com
SIC: 3086 Plastics foam products
PA: Dart Container Corporation Of Florida
500 Hogsback Rd
Mason MI 48854
800 248-5960

(G-16205)
DENTSPLY SIRONA INC
Also Called: Dentsply Raintree Glenroe
7290 26th Ct E (34243-3963)
PHONE..................................941 527-4450
Patrick Francis, *District Mgr*
Serina Damesworth, *Engineer*
Matthew Graham, *Senior Mgr*
EMP: 72
SALES (corp-wide): 3.3B **Publicly Held**
WEB: www.sirona.com
SIC: 3843 Dental equipment & supplies
PA: Dentsply Sirona Inc.
13320b Balntyn Corp Pl
Charlotte NC 28277
844 848-0137

(G-16206)
DGP ENTERPRISES INC
Also Called: Royal Patio Mfg
1130 Commerce Blvd N (34243-5044)
PHONE..................................941 729-2373
David G Peace, *President*
Greg Hale, *Vice Pres*
Vicky Followell, *Controller*
EMP: 13 **EST:** 1991
SQ FT: 50,000
SALES (est): 608.6K **Privately Held**
SIC: 2514 Metal lawn & garden furniture

(G-16207)
DISCOUNT AWNINGS INC
6620 19th St E Unit 111 (34243-4056)
PHONE..................................941 753-5700
Steven Judd, *President*
Kimberley Judd, *Vice Pres*
EMP: 7 **EST:** 1988
SQ FT: 2,750
SALES (est): 1MM **Privately Held**
WEB: www.discountawningsinc.com
SIC: 2394 Awnings, fabric: made from purchased materials

(G-16208)
DOWE GALLAGHER AEROSPACE
7425 16th St E (34243-6807)
PHONE..................................941 256-2179
EMP: 6 **EST:** 2017
SALES (est): 109.6K **Privately Held**
SIC: 3721 Aircraft

(G-16209)
DUKANE SEACOM INC
7135 16th St E Ste 101 (34243-6818)
PHONE..................................941 739-3200
Anish Patel, *President*
EMP: 208 **EST:** 2009
SQ FT: 4,500
SALES (est): 9.7MM **Publicly Held**
WEB: www.dukaneseacom.com
SIC: 3728 3519 Aircraft power transmission equipment; controls, remote, for boats
HQ: Heico Electronic Technologies Corp.
3000 Taft St
Hollywood FL 33021
954 987-6101

(G-16210)
DULOND TOOL & ENGINEERING INC
2306 Whitfield Park Loop (34243-4045)
P.O. Box 308, Tallevast (34270-0308)
PHONE..................................941 758-4489
Jeffrey Benson, *President*
Gregory J Brunette, *Vice Pres*
EMP: 13 **EST:** 1975
SQ FT: 12,500
SALES (est): 3.2MM **Privately Held**
WEB: www.dulond-tool-engineering-inc.sb-contract.com
SIC: 3599 Machine shop, jobbing & repair

(G-16211)
ENCORE INC
6487 Parkland Dr Ste 111 (34243-4091)
PHONE..................................941 359-3599
Margaret Bennett, *President*
▲ **EMP:** 16 **EST:** 1987
SQ FT: 5,000
SALES (est): 2.6MM **Privately Held**
WEB: www.revivepremium.com
SIC: 3842 Surgical appliances & supplies

(G-16212)
FAMILY OF SMITH INC (PA)
Also Called: Coast Laser Center
5899 Whitfield Ave # 104 (34243-6152)
PHONE..................................941 726-0873
Stephen J Smith, *President*
EMP: 23 **EST:** 2006
SALES (est): 176.2K **Privately Held**
SIC: 3841 Surgical lasers

(G-16213)
FIRST TEE SARASOTA/MANATEE
7741 15th St E (34243-2715)
PHONE..................................941 685-5072
Mary A Andrews, *Principal*
EMP: 6 **EST:** 2008
SALES (est): 86K **Privately Held**
WEB: www.firstteesarasotamanatee.org
SIC: 3949 Shafts, golf club

(G-16214)
FLORIDA SNCAST HELICOPTERS LLC
Also Called: Rotor Works
8191 N Tamiami Trl # 104 (34243-2052)
PHONE..................................941 355-1525
William Cooper, *Owner*
Brian Cooper,
Robin Cooper,
Sarah Cooper,
EMP: 10 **EST:** 2003
SALES (est): 857.1K **Privately Held**
WEB: www.floridasuncoasthelicopters.com
SIC: 3721 5088 4522 7363 Helicopters; helicopter parts; flying charter service; pilot service, aviation

(G-16215)
FLOWERS BKG CO BRADENTON LLC (HQ)
Also Called: Flowers Bakery
6490 Parkland Dr (34243-4036)
P.O. Box 20539, Bradenton (34204-0539)
PHONE....................................941 758-5656
Marta J Turner, *Exec VP*
Bill Steeves, *Controller*
Todd Thompson, *Sales Staff*
Michael Lord, *Mng Member*
George Strickland, *Mng Member*
EMP: 207 **EST:** 1984
SQ FT: 40,000
SALES (est): 37.6MM
SALES (corp-wide): 4.3B **Publicly Held**
WEB: www.flobradconf.com
SIC: 2051 Bread, all types (white, wheat, rye, etc): fresh or frozen; rolls, bread type: fresh or frozen
PA: Flowers Foods, Inc.
1919 Flowers Cir
Thomasville GA 31757
912 226-9110

(G-16216)
G G SCHMITT & SONS INC
7230 15th St E (34243-3276)
PHONE....................................717 394-3701
Ronald Schmitt, *President*
Gervase A Schmitt, *Vice Pres*
Steve Schmitt, *Vice Pres*
Brian Barr, *Plant Mgr*
Kurt Bender, *Engineer*
▲ **EMP:** 135 **EST:** 1951
SALES (est): 26MM
SALES (corp-wide): 2.4B **Publicly Held**
WEB: www.ggschmitt.com
SIC: 3429 3743 Marine hardware; railroad equipment
PA: Patrick Industries, Inc.
107 W Franklin St
Elkhart IN 46516
574 294-7511

(G-16217)
GANNET TECHNOLOGIES LLC
7135 16th St E Ste 115 (34243-6818)
PHONE....................................941 870-3444
Richard Greenwell, *Administration*
EMP: 10 **EST:** 2017
SALES (est): 628.8K **Privately Held**
WEB: www.gannettechnologies.com
SIC: 3812 Search & navigation equipment

(G-16218)
GATOR STAMPINGS INTL INC
6610 33rd St E (34243-4123)
PHONE....................................941 753-9598
Paul Cronen, *President*
John Cronen, *Vice Pres*
Norman Bush, *Engineer*
Broderick Erb, *Senior Engr*
Christie Borda Lescano, *Treasurer*
EMP: 80
SQ FT: 57,000
SALES (est): 22.7MM **Privately Held**
WEB: www.gatorstamping.com
SIC: 3469 Stamping metal for the trade

(G-16219)
GENERAL PNEUMATICS INFLATION
2236 72nd Ave E (34243-3985)
PHONE....................................941 216-3500
Timothy Longano, *General Mgr*
Tim Longino, *General Mgr*
Steven Fournier, *Mng Member*
EMP: 5 **EST:** 2015
SALES (est): 379.2K **Privately Held**
WEB: www.gpinflation.com
SIC: 3324 Aerospace investment castings, ferrous

(G-16220)
GLENROE TECHNOLOGIES INC
7290 26th Ct E (34243-3963)
PHONE....................................941 554-5262
Charles Robbins, *Manager*
EMP: 13 **EST:** 2016
SALES (est): 374.9K **Privately Held**
SIC: 3843 Dental equipment & supplies

(G-16221)
GLOBAL ORDNANCE LLC (PA)
2150 Whitfield Ave (34243-3925)
PHONE....................................941 549-8388
Marc Morales, *CEO*
Carrie Morales, *President*
Lee Jackson, *Vice Pres*
Kelly Hartman, *Senior Engr*
Patrick Martin, *Controller*
EMP: 25 **EST:** 2013
SQ FT: 45,000
SALES: 173.3MM **Privately Held**
WEB: www.globalordnance.com
SIC: 3482 3483 3484 3489 Small arms ammunition; ammunition, except for small arms; small arms; ordnance & accessories; brokers' services

(G-16222)
GOBCZYNSKIS PRINTERY INC
Also Called: Printery, The
6452 Parkland Dr (34243-4036)
P.O. Box 110403, Lakewood Rch (34211-0006)
PHONE....................................941 758-5734
Gene Gobczynski, *President*
Janet Gobczynski, *Corp Secy*
EMP: 8 **EST:** 1986
SQ FT: 5,612
SALES (est): 665.1K **Privately Held**
WEB: www.sirspeedysarasota.com
SIC: 2752 Commercial printing, offset

(G-16223)
GOGPS USA INC
7152 15th St E (34243-3203)
PHONE....................................941 751-2363
Simon Williams, *President*
EMP: 15 **EST:** 2012
SALES (est): 4.7MM
SALES (corp-wide): 428.7K **Privately Held**
WEB: www.gogps.com
SIC: 3663 Radio & TV communications equipment
PA: Go Gps
1100 South Service Rd Suite 422
Stoney Creek ON L8E 0
866 964-6477

(G-16224)
GREG VALLEY
Also Called: Superior Shutters
2010 Whitfield Park Loop (34243-4006)
P.O. Box 110703, Lakewood Rch (34211-0009)
PHONE....................................941 739-6628
Greg Valley, *Owner*
EMP: 10 **EST:** 1996
SQ FT: 8,000
SALES (est): 500K **Privately Held**
SIC: 2431 5023 5211 Window shutters, wood; window furnishings; screens, door & window

(G-16225)
GT MACHINING
1400 Commerce Blvd Ste G (34243-5071)
PHONE....................................941 809-5735
Bob Peterka, *Principal*
EMP: 9 **EST:** 2007
SALES (est): 348.7K **Privately Held**
WEB: www.kenklakdo.com
SIC: 3599 Machine shop, jobbing & repair

(G-16226)
HELI AVIATION FLORIDA LLC
8191 N Tamiami Trl (34243-2052)
PHONE....................................941 355-1525
Niclas Herle, *Mng Member*
EMP: 6 **EST:** 2012
SQ FT: 10,000
SALES: 493.2K **Privately Held**
WEB: www.heliaf.com
SIC: 3721 7363 4512 0783 Helicopters; pilot service, aviation; helicopter carrier, scheduled; tree trimming services for public utility lines; flying charter service

(G-16227)
HELIOS TECHNOLOGIES INC (PA)
1500 W University Pkwy (34243-2217)
PHONE....................................941 362-1200
Tricia L Fulton, *CEO*
Philippe Lemaitre, *Ch of Bd*
Matteo Arduini, *President*
Raj Menon, *President*
Nick Leboutillier, *Engineer*
EMP: 586 **EST:** 1970
SALES: 523MM **Publicly Held**
WEB: www.heliostechnologies.com
SIC: 3492 Control valves, fluid power: hydraulic & pneumatic

(G-16228)
HONEYCOMB ARCFT REPR CTR LLC
1950 Limbus Ave (34243-3900)
PHONE....................................850 610-0334
Ken Arnold, *Mng Member*
Steven Walker, *Manager*
Gerald Werfel,
EMP: 20 **EST:** 2015
SALES (est): 1.2MM **Privately Held**
WEB: www.harcllc.com
SIC: 3728 Ailerons, aircraft

(G-16229)
HONEYCOMB COMPANY AMERICA INC
1950 Limbus Ave (34243-3900)
PHONE....................................941 756-8781
Steven J Walker, *President*
Dan G Judge III, *COO*
Terry Sowers, *Facilities Mgr*
Harold Osban Jr, *CFO*
Victor Graves, *Manager*
EMP: 112 **EST:** 1955
SQ FT: 185,000
SALES (est): 23.9MM
SALES (corp-wide): 48.9MM **Privately Held**
WEB: www.hcoainc.com
SIC: 3728 Panel assembly (hydromatic propeller test stands), aircraft; aircraft body assemblies & parts
HQ: Overall-Honeycomb, Llc
1950 Limbus Ave
Sarasota FL 34243
941 756-8781

(G-16230)
HOVEROUND CORPORATION (PA)
2151 Whitfield Indus Way (34243-4047)
PHONE....................................941 739-6200
Thomas E Kruse, *President*
Scott Davidson, *Editor*
Joyce Boyle, *COO*
Tony N Digiovanni, *Vice Pres*
Jeff Moone, *Vice Pres*
▲ **EMP:** 303
SQ FT: 47,000
SALES (est): 99.2MM **Privately Held**
WEB: www.hoveround.com
SIC: 3842 Wheelchairs

(G-16231)
HYDROGEL VISION CORPORATION
Also Called: Extreme H2o
7575 Commerce Ct (34243-3218)
PHONE....................................941 739-1382
Mikael Totterman, *CEO*
Hue Tang, *Production*
Tung Nguyen, *Research*
Jason Leitzman, *Manager*
▲ **EMP:** 71 **EST:** 2002
SALES (est): 9.4MM
SALES (corp-wide): 13.8MM **Privately Held**
WEB: www.cleriovision.com
SIC: 3841 Surgical & medical instruments
PA: Clerio Vision, Inc.
1892 Winton Rd S Ste 140b
Rochester NY 14618
617 216-7881

(G-16232)
ICON WELDING & FABRICATION
8145 27th St E (34243-2874)
PHONE....................................941 822-8822
Michael J Norrito, *President*
EMP: 26 **EST:** 2013
SALES (est): 3.7MM **Privately Held**
WEB: www.iconmetalcreations.com
SIC: 2431 3446 Staircases, stairs & railings; architectural metalwork

(G-16233)
IDENTITY HOLDING COMPANY LLC
7525 Pennsylvania Ave # 101 (34243-5065)
PHONE....................................941 355-5171
EMP: 249 **Privately Held**
WEB: www.identitygroup.com
SIC: 3953 Marking devices
PA: Identity Holding Company, Llc
1480 Gould Dr
Cookeville TN 38506

(G-16234)
INDUSTRIAL SHREDDERS LLC
1920 Whitfield Ave (34243-3921)
PHONE....................................941 753-2815
EMP: 16 **EST:** 2018
SALES (est): 1.3MM **Privately Held**
WEB: www.cmshredders.com
SIC: 3559 Special industry machinery

(G-16235)
INDUSTRY STANDARD TECHNOLOGY
Also Called: I S T
1868 University Pkwy (34243-2225)
PHONE....................................941 355-2100
Frank Stafford, *President*
EMP: 9 **EST:** 1984
SQ FT: 5,000
SALES (est): 731.3K **Privately Held**
WEB: www.industrystandardtech.com
SIC: 3629 3571 7629 Electronic generation equipment; personal computers (microcomputers); electronic equipment repair

(G-16236)
INLAND SPECIALTIES
7655 Matoaka Rd (34243-3302)
PHONE....................................941 351-6300
Becky Carlin, *Chairman*
EMP: 6 **EST:** 2019
SALES (est): 73.4K **Privately Held**
WEB: www.inlandspecialties.com
SIC: 3452 Bolts, nuts, rivets & washers

(G-16237)
INLAND SPECIALTIES INC
6424 Parkland Dr (34243-4038)
PHONE....................................941 756-1234
Becky Carlin, *Chairman*
EMP: 7 **EST:** 2010
SALES (est): 102.9K **Privately Held**
WEB: www.inlandspecialties.com
SIC: 3429 Manufactured hardware (general)

(G-16238)
INNOVATION MARINE CORPORATION
8011 15th St E (34243-2713)
PHONE....................................941 355-7852
Richard Lamore, *President*
Dennis Mathe, *Vice Pres*
Scott Yow, *Purch Dir*
Harry Bell, *Engineer*
Joyce Lamore, *Shareholder*
◆ **EMP:** 20 **EST:** 1983
SQ FT: 28,000
SALES (est): 3MM **Privately Held**
WEB: www.innovation-marine.com
SIC: 3561 3519 Pumps & pumping equipment; internal combustion engines

(G-16239)
INNOVATIVE POWER SOLUTIONS LLC
Also Called: Ips
2250 Whitfield Ave (34243-3926)
PHONE....................................732 544-1075
Gene Terry, *Vice Pres*
Eli Liebermann,
Johnathan Cseh, *Administration*
Santiago Lagunas,
Bill Schatzow,
▲ **EMP:** 35 **EST:** 1999
SALES (est): 5.1MM **Privately Held**
WEB: www.ips-llc.com
SIC: 3621 Motors & generators

(G-16240)
INSULATOR SEAL INCORPORATED (HQ)
6460 Parkland Dr (34243-4036)
PHONE....................................941 751-2880
Joe Brownell, *CEO*
Michael A Del Castello, *President*
Mark Russo, *Production*
EMP: 40 **EST:** 1988
SQ FT: 25,000
SALES (est): 13.6MM
SALES (corp-wide): 104.1MM **Privately Held**
WEB: www.mdcprecision.com
SIC: 3264 3644 Insulators, electrical: porcelain; insulators & insulation materials, electrical
PA: Mdc Vacuum Products, Llc
30962 Santana St
Hayward CA 94544
510 265-3500

(G-16241)
J&J SHEET MTAL FABERCATION LLC
728 Winter Garden Dr (34243-1021)
PHONE....................................941 752-0569
Joshua M Cripe, *Principal*
EMP: 8 **EST:** 2016
SALES (est): 1.1MM **Privately Held**
SIC: 3499 Fabricated metal products

(G-16242)
JUST STEEL INC
3100 Whitfield Ave Ste B (34243-3380)
PHONE....................................941 755-7811
Francisco Orduno, *President*
EMP: 10 **EST:** 1993
SQ FT: 2,500
SALES (est): 1.6MM **Privately Held**
WEB: www.juststeel.net
SIC: 3441 3312 7692 Fabricated structural metal; fence posts, iron & steel; welding repair

(G-16243)
K H S INC
5501 N Washington Blvd (34243-2249)
PHONE....................................941 359-4000
Jeff Piekarski, *Maintenance Dir*
Bonita Cihasky, *Engineer*
Ian Lytwyn, *Engineer*
Helen Meurer, *Engineer*
Oliver Watmough, *Engineer*
▲ **EMP:** 70 **EST:** 1996
SALES (est): 52.4MM
SALES (corp-wide): 8.3B **Privately Held**
WEB: www.khs.com
SIC: 3565 Packaging machinery
HQ: Khs Gmbh
Juchostr. 20
Dortmund 44143
231 569-0

(G-16244)
K PRO SUPPLY CO INC
2135 Whitfield Park Ave (34243-4086)
PHONE....................................941 758-1226
Chris Kerrigan, *President*
Joyce Kerrigan, *Admin Sec*
EMP: 5 **EST:** 1986
SQ FT: 14,250
SALES (est): 455.8K **Privately Held**
WEB: www.kpropaintballnetting.com
SIC: 2221 Polyethylene broadwoven fabrics

(G-16245)
KEY PACKAGING COMPANY INC
7350 15th St E (34243-3274)
PHONE....................................941 355-2728
E L Smith, *President*
Steve Akel, *Project Mgr*
Anthony Mims, *QC Mgr*
Erick Ames, *Engineer*
Joan Finch, *Controller*
▲ **EMP:** 50 **EST:** 1958
SQ FT: 42,000
SALES (est): 12MM **Privately Held**
WEB: www.keypackaging.com
SIC: 3086 Cups & plates, foamed plastic; packaging & shipping materials, foamed plastic

(G-16246)
KLUGMAN ENTERPRISES LLC
7410 Linden Ln (34243-5129)
PHONE....................................352 318-9623
Max Klugman, *Owner*
Dhalma I Klugman, *Mng Member*
EMP: 5 **EST:** 2005
SALES (est): 394.6K **Privately Held**
WEB: www.klugmanenterprises.com
SIC: 2599 Carts, restaurant equipment

(G-16247)
LAKERIDGE FALLS ART LEAGUE
4200 Lakeridge Blvd (34243-4280)
PHONE....................................941 360-1046
Velma Ware, *Principal*
EMP: 6 **EST:** 2012
SALES (est): 159.8K **Privately Held**
WEB: www.lakeridgefalls.org
SIC: 3999 Framed artwork

(G-16248)
LARRICK GROUP INC
1845 57th St (34243-2228)
P.O. Box 758, Oneco (34264-0758)
PHONE....................................941 351-2700
Lauren Danielson, *President*
Vince Scuilla, *COO*
Diane Doctoroff, *Office Mgr*
Tim Cahoon, *Manager*
Robert Craig, *Director*
EMP: 20 **EST:** 1990
SQ FT: 14,000
SALES (est): 7.3MM **Privately Held**
SIC: 2836 8731 Culture media; commercial physical research

(G-16249)
LASER LENS TEK INC
Also Called: American Photonics
6621 19th St E (34243-4181)
PHONE....................................941 752-5811
Barry Tyler, *President*
Lou D 'alessandro, *Sales Staff*
William Landers, *Manager*
▲ **EMP:** 12 **EST:** 2001
SQ FT: 18,000
SALES (est): 2.3MM **Privately Held**
WEB: www.american-photonics.myshopify.com
SIC: 3827 Optical instruments & lenses

(G-16250)
LATITUDE 235 COFFEE AND TEA (PA)
7245 21st St E (34243-3998)
PHONE....................................941 556-2600
Dimitry Erez, *President*
Holly Erez, *Vice Pres*
Patricia Tibbs, *Manager*
Gene Erez, *Director*
◆ **EMP:** 14 **EST:** 2003
SALES (est): 1.6MM **Privately Held**
WEB: www.latitudecoffee.com
SIC: 2095 5149 Coffee roasting (except by wholesale grocers); coffee & tea

(G-16251)
LUMISHORE USA LLC
7127 24th Ct E (34243-3992)
PHONE....................................941 405-3302
Eifrion Evans, *CEO*
Chris Myers, *Natl Sales Mgr*
Corinne Fresko, *Marketing Staff*
Gareth Evans, *CTO*
EMP: 8 **EST:** 2015
SALES (est): 168.4K **Privately Held**
WEB: www.lumishore.com
SIC: 3647 Boat & ship lighting fixtures

(G-16252)
MANATEE TOOL INC
1400 Commerce Blvd Ste Cd
(34243-5069)
PHONE....................................941 355-9252
EMP: 5
SALES (est): 376.8K **Privately Held**
SIC: 3599 Machine Shop & Assembly Svcs

(G-16253)
MATRIX24 LABORATORIES LLC
Also Called: Eversafe
1453 Tallevast Rd (34243-5036)
P.O. Box 3954 (34230-3954)
PHONE....................................941 879-3048
Blethen Craig, *Vice Pres*
Greg Blethes,
▼ **EMP:** 10 **EST:** 2011
SQ FT: 2,500
SALES (est): 300K **Privately Held**
SIC: 2879 Insecticides & pesticides

(G-16254)
MAXEFF INDUSTRIES INC
1251 Commerce Blvd S (34243-5018)
PHONE....................................941 893-5804
Gerald Goche, *Principal*
▲ **EMP:** 8 **EST:** 2013
SALES (est): 326.6K **Privately Held**
WEB: www.adventechinc.com
SIC: 3999 Manufacturing industries

(G-16255)
MEDONE SURGICAL INC
670 Tallevast Rd (34243-3254)
PHONE....................................941 359-3129
Bruce A Beckstein, *President*
Lisa S Beckstein, *Vice Pres*
Julie Ovens, *Vice Pres*
Steve Whitt, *Prdtn Mgr*
John Martin, *Sales Staff*
▲ **EMP:** 12
SQ FT: 2,000
SALES (est): 2.4MM **Privately Held**
WEB: www.medone.com
SIC: 3841 5047 Surgical & medical instruments; medical equipment & supplies

(G-16256)
METAL CREATIONS SARASOTA LLC
1235 Tallevast Rd (34243-3271)
PHONE....................................941 922-7096
Ramiro Corona,
EMP: 15 **EST:** 2014
SALES (est): 1.1MM **Privately Held**
WEB: www.metalcreationsofsarasota.com
SIC: 3499 3446 1799 7389 Fire- or burglary-resistive products; architectural metalwork; ornamental metal work; design services; sheet metalwork

(G-16257)
MIO PUBLICATION INC
Also Called: Keels & Wheels
1864 University Pkwy (34243-2225)
P.O. Box 567, Tallevast (34270-0567)
PHONE....................................941 351-2411
James Dygert, *President*
Judith Dygert, *Treasurer*
EMP: 8 **EST:** 1978
SQ FT: 16,760
SALES (est): 200.3K **Privately Held**
WEB: www.keelsandwheelsmagazine.com
SIC: 2721 Magazines: publishing only, not printed on site

(G-16258)
MOBILEBITS HOLDINGS CORP (PA)
5901 N Honore Ave Ste 120 (34243-2632)
PHONE....................................941 225-6115
Kent Kirschner, *CEO*
Cristina M Iturrino, *Counsel*
James Burk, *CFO*
EMP: 8 **EST:** 2009
SALES: 417.8K **Publicly Held**
SIC: 7372 Prepackaged software

(G-16259)
MOISTTECH CORP
6408 Parkland Dr Ste 104 (34243-5410)
PHONE....................................941 351-7870
John Fordham, *President*
Harold Ribot, *Sales Staff*
Sarah Hammond, *Mktg Coord*
EMP: 10 **EST:** 2013
SALES (est): 2.1MM **Privately Held**
WEB: www.moisttech.com
SIC: 3822 Temperature controls, automatic

(G-16260)
MULTI-FLEX LLC
8046 36th Street Cir E (34243-6308)
PHONE....................................941 360-6500
Peter Rosenquist, *President*
EMP: 7 **EST:** 1991
SALES (est): 892.7K **Privately Held**
WEB: www.simplimatic.com
SIC: 3535 Conveyors & conveying equipment
PA: Se Holdings Llc
1046 W London Park Dr
Forest VA 24551

(G-16261)
MUSTANG VACUUM SYSTEMS INC
7135 16th St E Ste 115 (34243-6818)
PHONE....................................941 377-1440
Dean Ganzhorn, *CEO*
Richard Greenwell, *President*
Robert Choquette, *Vice Pres*
Christopher Hubkowski, *Buyer*
Brent McGary, *Purchasing*
EMP: 45 **EST:** 2005
SQ FT: 50,000
SALES (est): 9.7MM **Privately Held**
WEB: www.mustangvac.com
SIC: 3569 Industrial shock absorbers

(G-16262)
N A COMANDULLI LLC
6935 15th St E Units105 (34243-7200)
PHONE....................................941 870-2878
Ivano Tirapelle, *Mng Member*
▲ **EMP:** 5 **EST:** 2013
SALES (est): 1MM
SALES (corp-wide): 20MM **Privately Held**
WEB: www.comandulli-na.com
SIC: 2842 Polishing preparations & related products
PA: Comandulli Costruzioni Meccaniche Srl
Via Medaglie D'argento 20
Castelleone CR 26012
037 456-161

(G-16263)
NADCO TAPES & LABELS INC
2240 72nd Ter E (34243-3997)
PHONE....................................941 751-6693
Rena J Doniger, *President*
Neil Doniger, *Vice Pres*
EMP: 35
SALES (est): 6.3MM **Privately Held**
WEB: www.nadco-inc.com
SIC: 2241 2679 Fabric tapes; tags & labels, paper

(G-16264)
NATIONWIDE PRTCTIVE CTING MFRS
7106 24th Ct E (34243-3993)
PHONE....................................941 753-7500
Dorothy E Ungarelli, *President*
Robert Gocinski, *Vice Pres*
Jarred Dluginski, *Sales Associate*
▼ **EMP:** 36 **EST:** 1964
SQ FT: 15,000
SALES (est): 6.8MM **Privately Held**
WEB: www.nationwidecoatings.com
SIC: 2851 Paints & allied products

(G-16265)
NATURAL-IMMUNOGENICS CORP
7504 Pennsylvania Ave (34243-5047)
PHONE....................................888 328-8840
Benjamin Quinto, *Co-President*
Theodore Quinto, *Co-President*
Carol Cotton Riggins, *Controller*
Diana Hinkle, *Manager*
Scott Loach, *Director*
EMP: 65 **EST:** 1998
SQ FT: 7,000
SALES (est): 17.3MM **Privately Held**
WEB: www.naturalimmunogenics.com
SIC: 2834 2833 5499 Pharmaceutical preparations; medicinals & botanicals; health foods

(G-16266)
NEW BREED CLOTHING LLC
1120 Magellan Dr (34243-4423)
PHONE....................................941 773-7406

Nicholas Johnson,
EMP: 9 **EST:** 2006
SQ FT: 1,100
SALES (est): 390K **Privately Held**
SIC: 2211 Apparel & outerwear fabrics, cotton

(G-16267)
NORMANDIN LLC
2206 72nd Dr E (34243-3988)
PHONE..................................941 739-8046
Ronnie Cho, *Sales Mgr*
Mark Matter, *Sales Staff*
Si Dao, *Sales Associate*
Scott Normandin, *Manager*
George Tavares, *Manager*
EMP: 10 **EST:** 2002
SALES (est): 1.4MM **Privately Held**
SIC: 3444 Sheet metalwork

(G-16268)
ONE BIOTECHNOLOGY COMPANY
1833 57th St Ste A (34243-2228)
P.O. Box 758, Oneco (34264-0758)
PHONE..................................941 355-8451
Vince Scuilla, *President*
EMP: 8 **EST:** 1995
SQ FT: 13,000
SALES (est): 471.4K **Privately Held**
WEB: www.1biotechnology.com
SIC: 2836 Culture media

(G-16269)
OVERALL-HONEYCOMB LLC (HQ)
1950 Limbus Ave (34243-3900)
P.O. Box 2375 (34230-2375)
PHONE..................................941 756-8781
EMP: 100 **EST:** 2013
SALES (est): 23.9MM
SALES (corp-wide): 48.9MM **Privately Held**
WEB: www.hcoainc.com
SIC: 3724 Aircraft engines & engine parts
PA: Overall, Llc
29 Commonwealth Ave # 401
Boston MA 02116
857 263-7961

(G-16270)
PALLET RECALL INC
6755 33rd St E (34243-4129)
PHONE..................................941 727-1944
Timothy Bragg, *President*
EMP: 7 **EST:** 1994
SALES (est): 582.1K **Privately Held**
SIC: 2448 Pallets, wood

(G-16271)
PARCUS MEDICAL LLC
6423 Parkland Dr (34243-4035)
PHONE..................................941 755-7965
Bart Bracy, *Founder*
David Davis, *Mfg Staff*
Kevin Burch, *Engineer*
Chris Hotary, *Marketing Staff*
Lauren Blakely, *Manager*
EMP: 18 **EST:** 2007
SALES (est): 8.1MM **Publicly Held**
WEB: www.parcusmedical.com
SIC: 3841 Surgical & medical instruments
PA: Anika Therapeutics, Inc.
32 Wiggins Ave
Bedford MA 01730

(G-16272)
PASSION LABELS & PACKAGING
1223 Tallevast Rd (34243-3271)
PHONE..................................941 312-5003
Shane Barrett, *Principal*
Michael Hadsell, *VP Mktg*
EMP: 27 **EST:** 2011
SQ FT: 5,250
SALES (est): 3.7MM **Privately Held**
WEB: www.passionlabels.com
SIC: 2679 5131 2759 Tags & labels, paper; labels, paper: made from purchased material; labels; flexographic printing

(G-16273)
PATRICK INDUSTRIES INC
Also Called: Design Cncepts/Marine Concepts
6805 15th St E (34243-3210)
PHONE..................................941 556-6311
Robert Long, *Branch Mgr*
EMP: 208
SALES (corp-wide): 2.4B **Publicly Held**
WEB: www.patrickind.com
SIC: 3429 Marine hardware
PA: Patrick Industries, Inc.
107 W Franklin St
Elkhart IN 46516
574 294-7511

(G-16274)
PATRICK INDUSTRIES INC
Also Called: Marine Concepts
6805 15th St E (34243-3210)
PHONE..................................941 556-6311
EMP: 20
SALES (est): 7.4MM **Privately Held**
SIC: 3732 8711 Boatbuilding/Repairing Engineering Services

(G-16275)
PEEK TRAFFIC CORPORATION
6408 Parkland Dr Ste 102 (34243-5410)
PHONE..................................941 366-8770
Alejandro Brunell, *CEO*
Rolando Garcia, *COO*
Rene Almeida, *Technical Staff*
◆ **EMP:** 130 **EST:** 2003
SALES (est): 21.3MM
SALES (corp-wide): 45.7MM **Privately Held**
WEB: www.peektraffic.com
SIC: 3669 Transportation signaling devices
PA: Signal Group, Inc.
5401 N Sam Houston Pkwy W
Houston TX 77086
281 453-0200

(G-16276)
PESTWEST USA LLC
7135 16th St E Ste 124 (34243-6818)
P.O. Box 2234 (34230-2234)
PHONE..................................941 358-1983
◆ **EMP:** 9
SQ FT: 5,000
SALES (est): 3.6MM **Privately Held**
SIC: 3699 Mfg Electrical Equipment/Supplies

(G-16277)
PLANT PARTNERS INC
6691 33rd St E Ste B3 (34243-4604)
PHONE..................................941 752-1039
George Aiello, *Owner*
EMP: 10
SALES (corp-wide): 7.7MM **Privately Held**
WEB: www.tropex.com
SIC: 3579 Mailing, letter handling & addressing machines
PA: Plant Partners, Inc.
3220 Whitfield Ave
Sarasota FL 34243
941 753-5066

(G-16278)
PLATINUM LTG PRODUCTIONS LLC
8051 N Tamiami Trl D10 (34243-2066)
PHONE..................................941 320-1906
Angela Congdon, *Principal*
EMP: 8 **EST:** 2016
SALES (est): 2.2MM **Privately Held**
WEB:
www.platinumlightingproductions.com
SIC: 3648 Stage lighting equipment

(G-16279)
PREMIER PRFMCE INTERIORS INC
Also Called: Ppi
6304 17th Street Cir E (34243-5424)
PHONE..................................941 752-6271
Lee Wingard, *President*
Jim Cowan, *Vice Pres*
Missy Cowan, *Sales Staff*
▲ **EMP:** 30 **EST:** 2000
SALES (est): 5.2MM **Privately Held**
WEB: www.ppi-fl.com
SIC: 3732 Boat building & repairing

(G-16280)
QUALITY CONTRACT MFG SVCS LLC
Also Called: Qcms
1905 72nd Dr E (34243-8901)
PHONE..................................941 355-7787
Kevin Beachler,
EMP: 10 **EST:** 2007
SQ FT: 6,000
SALES (est): 1.1MM **Privately Held**
WEB: www.qcmsfl.com
SIC: 3572 Computer tape drives & components

(G-16281)
RADIANT POWER CORP (DH)
7135 16th St E Ste 101 (34243-6818)
PHONE..................................941 739-3200
Anish Patel, *President*
Chuck Schofield, *Vice Pres*
Carlos L Macau, *Treasurer*
Elizabeth R Letendre, *Asst Sec*
EMP: 138 **EST:** 1999
SQ FT: 10,000
SALES (est): 38.7MM **Publicly Held**
WEB: www.rpcaero.com
SIC: 3812 5088 3728 3647 Search & navigation equipment; transportation equipment & supplies; aircraft parts & equipment; aircraft lighting fixtures
HQ: Heico Electronic Technologies Corp.
3000 Taft St
Hollywood FL 33021
954 987-6101

(G-16282)
RADIANT POWER IDC LLC
7135 16th St E Ste 101 (34243-6818)
PHONE..................................760 945-0230
William J Lang, *President*
Matthew K Thomas, *CFO*
John Moyer, *Marketing Staff*
EMP: 50 **EST:** 1976
SQ FT: 30,000
SALES (est): 18.2MM **Publicly Held**
WEB: www.rpcaero.com
SIC: 3812 Aircraft control systems, electronic
HQ: Radiant Power Corp.
7135 16th St E Ste 101
Sarasota FL 34243
941 739-3200

(G-16283)
RADIANT-SEACOM REPAIRS CORP
7135 16th St E Ste 101 (34243-6818)
PHONE..................................941 739-3200
Anish Patel, *President*
EMP: 9 **EST:** 2017
SALES (est): 2.5MM **Publicly Held**
WEB: www.rpcaero.com
SIC: 3724 Aircraft engines & engine parts
PA: Heico Corporation
3000 Taft St
Hollywood FL 33021

(G-16284)
RAPID COMPOSITES LLC
2216 72nd Dr E (34243-3937)
PHONE..................................941 322-6647
Alan Taylor, *Mng Member*
EMP: 6 **EST:** 2012
SQ FT: 5,000
SALES (est): 1.2MM **Privately Held**
WEB: www.rapidcomposites.com
SIC: 2655 3624 7373 8711 Cans, composite: foil-fiber & other: from purchased fiber; fibers, carbon & graphite; systems engineering, computer related; mechanical engineering; electrical or electronic engineering;
PA: Taylor & Lego Holdings, Llc
34655 State Road 70 E
Myakka City FL 34251
941 322-6647

(G-16285)
ROAD SIGNS INC
2017 Whitfield Park Dr (34243-4094)
P.O. Box 2973 (34230-2973)
PHONE..................................941 321-0695
Keith Bernard, *President*
Carol Bergere, *Principal*
Holly Bergere, *Manager*
EMP: 5 **EST:** 2005
SALES (est): 498.8K **Privately Held**
WEB: www.nowthatsawrap.com
SIC: 3993 Electric signs

(G-16286)
ROBSON CORPORATION
2231 Whitfield Park Loop (34243-4043)
PHONE..................................941 753-6935
Gary F Dinsdale, *President*
Jim Schreiber, *General Mgr*
Mallory J Dinsdale, *Vice Pres*
Craig Abbott, *Sr Project Mgr*
◆ **EMP:** 50 **EST:** 1985
SQ FT: 45,000
SALES (est): 6.9MM **Privately Held**
WEB: www.robsonchurchsigns.com
SIC: 3993 Neon signs

(G-16287)
ROCK BOTTOM BOTTLES LLC
1447 Tallevast Rd (34243-5035)
PHONE..................................901 237-9929
Dustine Keith, *Managing Prtnr*
James Cirillo, *Mng Member*
Michael J Boling Jr,
▲ **EMP:** 6 **EST:** 2014
SQ FT: 5,000
SALES (est): 766.1K **Privately Held**
WEB: www.rockbottombottles.com
SIC: 3221 3085 Glass containers; plastics bottles

(G-16288)
SAFRAN POWER UK LTD
Also Called: Labinal Power Systems
2250 Whitfield Ave (34243-3926)
PHONE..................................941 739-7207
Jorge Ortega, *Exec VP*
EMP: 5 **EST:** 2013
SQ FT: 2,100
SALES (est): 370K **Privately Held**
WEB: www.safran-group.com
SIC: 3728 Aircraft parts & equipment

(G-16289)
SAFRAN POWER USA LLC
2250 Whitfield Ave (34243-3926)
PHONE..................................941 758-7726
David Vollrath, *General Mgr*
Nicolette Midzio, *Buyer*
Casey Hodge, *Manager*
EMP: 140
SALES (corp-wide): 639.8MM **Privately Held**
WEB: www.safran-group.com
SIC: 3728 4581 Aircraft parts & equipment; aircraft maintenance & repair services
HQ: Safran Power Usa, Llc
8380 Darrow Rd
Twinsburg OH 44087
330 487-2000

(G-16290)
SANIT TECHNOLOGIES LLC
Also Called: Durisan
7810 25th Ct E Unit 106 (34243-2841)
PHONE..................................941 351-9114
Arthur Wein, *Principal*
Andrew Cervasio, *Mng Member*
Troy Daland,
EMP: 32 **EST:** 2014
SQ FT: 33,259
SALES (est): 80K **Privately Held**
WEB: www.sanittechnologies.com
SIC: 2841 Soap & other detergents; detergents, synthetic organic or inorganic alkaline

(G-16291)
SARASOTA BOAT WORKS INC
2245 Whtfld Indus Way Un (34243)
PHONE..................................941 366-3357
Brian Helms, *Principal*
EMP: 6 **EST:** 2010
SALES (est): 141.9K **Privately Held**
WEB: www.sarasotaboatworksinc.com
SIC: 3732 Boat building & repairing

(G-16292)
SARASOTA HERALD-TRIBUNE
1800 University Pkwy (34243-2298)
PHONE....941 358-4000
Jim Spear, *Manager*
EMP: 120
SALES (corp-wide): 272.8MM **Privately Held**
WEB: www.heraldtribune.com
SIC: 2711 Newspapers, publishing & printing
HQ: Sarasota Herald-Tribune
801 S Tamiami Trl
Sarasota FL 34236
941 953-7755

(G-16293)
SARASOTA PRECISION ENGRG INC (PA)
2305 72nd Ave E (34243-3952)
PHONE....941 727-3444
Doug Mansfield, *President*
Mike Ontiveros, *Vice Pres*
Pat Clevenger, *Project Mgr*
Michael Leporati, *Prdtn Mgr*
Nikki Mansfield, *Office Mgr*
▲ **EMP:** 18 **EST:** 2003
SQ FT: 20,000
SALES (est): 4.6MM **Privately Held**
WEB: www.spe-inc.com
SIC: 3312 Tool & die steel & alloys

(G-16294)
SCOTT SIGN SYSTEMS INC (HQ)
7525 Pennsylvania Ave C (34243-5065)
P.O. Box 1047, Tallevast (34270-1047)
PHONE....941 355-5171
Brad Wolf, *CEO*
Kathy Hannon, *President*
Brian Mogensen, *CFO*
Stewart Abbott, *Treasurer*
Paul Maggio, *Director*
◆ **EMP:** 24 **EST:** 1957
SQ FT: 102,000
SALES (est): 4.2MM
SALES (corp-wide): 271.1MM **Privately Held**
WEB: www.identitygroup.com
SIC: 3089 3086 Injection molding of plastics; plastics foam products
PA: Identity Group Holdings Corp.
1480 Gould Dr
Cookeville TN 38506
931 432-4000

(G-16295)
SIF TECHNOLOGY COMPANY LLC
7245 16th St E Unit 101 (34243-6813)
PHONE....941 225-8363
Mel Cobbin, *Manager*
Bobb Mabbot, *CTO*
Gina Mascio,
EMP: 8
SALES (est): 536.1K **Privately Held**
SIC: 3571 Computers, digital, analog or hybrid

(G-16296)
SILVER BAY LLC
Also Called: Quasar Light Therapy
1431 Tallevast Rd (34243-5035)
PHONE....941 306-5812
Peter Nesbitt,
EMP: 10 **EST:** 2008
SALES (est): 887.2K **Privately Held**
SIC: 3845 Laser systems & equipment, medical

(G-16297)
SIMPLIMATIC AUTOMATION
7245 16th St E Unit 114 (34243-6813)
PHONE....941 360-6500
EMP: 8 **EST:** 2011
SALES (est): 104K **Privately Held**
WEB: www.simplimatic.com
SIC: 3365 Machinery castings, aluminum

(G-16298)
SRQ SIGN PARTNERS LLC
1621 W University Pkwy (34243-2732)
PHONE....941 357-0319
EMP: 11 **EST:** 2018
SALES (est): 308K **Privately Held**
WEB: www.wholesalechannellettersigns.com
SIC: 3993 Signs & advertising specialties

(G-16299)
SRQ SIGN PARTNERS LLC
8466 Lockwood Ridge Rd (34243-2951)
PHONE....941 417-4000
EMP: 6 **EST:** 2019
SALES (est): 170.5K **Privately Held**
WEB: www.wholesalechannellettersigns.com
SIC: 3993 Signs & advertising specialties

(G-16300)
STABIL CONCRETE PAVERS LLC
7080 28th Street Ct E (34243-3300)
PHONE....941 739-7823
▲ **EMP:** 21
SALES (est): 5MM **Privately Held**
SIC: 3531 Mfg Construction Machinery

(G-16301)
STEELE INDUSTRIES INC
7910 N Tamiami Trl # 104 (34243-1900)
PHONE....800 674-7302
Dominick Steele, *CEO*
EMP: 9 **EST:** 2019
SALES (est): 692.8K **Privately Held**
WEB: www.steeleindustries.com
SIC: 3812 Defense systems & equipment

(G-16302)
STELLA SEALANTS CORP
6915 15th St E Ste 201 (34243-7203)
PHONE....941 357-1566
EMP: 6 **EST:** 2018
SALES (est): 184.1K **Privately Held**
WEB: www.stellasealants.com
SIC: 2891 Sealants

(G-16303)
STUDIO 21 LIGHTING INC
Also Called: Madison Avenue Furniture
1227 Hardin Ave (34243-5024)
PHONE....941 355-2677
Simon T Levell, *President*
▲ **EMP:** 25 **EST:** 1991
SQ FT: 45,000
SALES (est): 4.4MM **Privately Held**
SIC: 3645 Floor lamps

(G-16304)
SUN COAST INDUSTRIES LLC
7350 26th Ct E (34243-3947)
PHONE....941 355-7166
Richard Hofmann, *President*
Kathy Kruse, *President*
EMP: 90 **EST:** 1979
SQ FT: 146,000
SALES (est): 4.2MM **Publicly Held**
WEB: www.mysuncoast.com
SIC: 3089 Caps, plastic
HQ: Berry Global, Inc.
101 Oakley St
Evansville IN 47710

(G-16305)
SUN GRAPHIC TECHNOLOGIES INC
Also Called: Sun Screenprinting Lindycal
2310 Whitfield Park Ave (34243-4084)
P.O. Box 807 (34230-0807)
PHONE....941 753-7541
William F Blechta, *President*
Bill Blechta, *Principal*
George E Blechta, *Corp Secy*
Rob Harris, *COO*
Robert Harris, *COO*
EMP: 23 **EST:** 1978
SQ FT: 16,000
SALES (est): 3.1MM **Privately Held**
WEB: www.sungraphictechnologies.com
SIC: 2759 3993 3953 2752 Screen printing; signs & advertising specialties; marking devices; commercial printing, lithographic

(G-16306)
SUNSHINE TOOL LLC
7245 16th St E Unit 114 (34243-6813)
PHONE....941 351-6330
Steve Reese, *Sales Mgr*
John Barrett, *Mng Member*
Bonnie Perkins, *Executive Asst*
EMP: 5 **EST:** 2007
SALES (est): 1MM **Privately Held**
WEB: www.sunshinemachining.com
SIC: 3559 3535 3599 Robots, molding & forming plastics; robotic conveyors; machine & other job shop work; machine shop, jobbing & repair

(G-16307)
SUPERIOR ELECTRONICS
7519 Pennsylvania Ave # 102
(34243-5015)
PHONE....941 355-9500
Ben Price, *Owner*
EMP: 5 **EST:** 2006
SALES (est): 385.2K **Privately Held**
SIC: 3679 5065 Harness assemblies for electronic use: wire or cable; electronic parts & equipment

(G-16308)
TALON MARINE
1968 Whitfield Park Ave (34243-4048)
PHONE....941 753-7400
Gary Armington, *Managing Prtnr*
William S Armington, *Partner*
Robert Wilkens, *General Mgr*
EMP: 6 **EST:** 1978
SQ FT: 18,000
SALES (est): 415.1K **Privately Held**
SIC: 3732 Boats, fiberglass: building & repairing

(G-16309)
TEAKDECKING SYSTEMS INC
7061 15th St E (34243-3243)
PHONE....941 756-0600
Michael G Havey, *Ch of Bd*
Richard Strauss, *President*
Kenneth A Etchison, *Treasurer*
Jeff Scott, *Supervisor*
EMP: 52 **EST:** 2007
SALES (est): 14.9MM **Privately Held**
WEB: www.teakdecking.com
SIC: 2499 Applicators, wood

(G-16310)
TINTOMETER INC (HQ)
Also Called: Orbeco-Hellige
6456 Parkland Dr (34243-4036)
PHONE....941 756-6410
Bradley K Martell, *President*
Matthew Meyers, *Materials Mgr*
Cindy Workman, *Warehouse Mgr*
Joan Lambert, *Accountant*
Melissa Pickle, *Marketing Mgr*
▲ **EMP:** 10 **EST:** 1985
SQ FT: 20,000
SALES (est): 4.5MM
SALES (corp-wide): 30.9MM **Privately Held**
WEB: www.lovibond.com
SIC: 3821 Laboratory apparatus, except heating & measuring
PA: Tintometer Gesellschaft Mit Beschrankter Haftung
Schleefstr. 8-12
Dortmund 44287
231 945-100

(G-16311)
TITAN OIL TOOLS LLC
8466 Lockwood Ridge Rd (34243-2951)
PHONE....941 356-3010
Roy Pandeo, *Manager*
EMP: 9 **EST:** 2013
SALES (est): 923.1K **Privately Held**
WEB: www.titanoiltools.com
SIC: 1389 Oil field services

(G-16312)
TORQUE TECHNOLOGIES PRODUCTS
Also Called: Goizper USA
1623 W University Pkwy (34243-2732)
PHONE....630 462-1188
Bradley H Binks, *President*
Maynard N Wood, *Treasurer*
Johnhny Jander, *Manager*
Patrick Montgomery, *Manager*
Harry L Binks, *Director*
▲ **EMP:** 5 **EST:** 2005
SALES (est): 886.2K **Privately Held**
WEB: www.goizperusa.com
SIC: 3568 Power transmission equipment

(G-16313)
TOTAL KOATINGS INC
8161 Misty Oaks Blvd (34243-3113)
PHONE....941 870-0369
Charles R Smith, *Principal*
Jodie Smith, *Office Mgr*
EMP: 6 **EST:** 2008
SALES (est): 98.7K **Privately Held**
WEB: www.totalkoatings.com
SIC: 2541 Counter & sink tops

(G-16314)
TRIDENT BUILDING SYSTEMS INC
2812 Tallevast Rd (34243-3914)
PHONE....941 755-7073
Carl Petrat, *President*
Debbie Mavis, *General Mgr*
Cindy L Petrat-Hayden, *Corp Secy*
Willard G Petrat, *Vice Pres*
Emil Straubel, *Project Mgr*
EMP: 170 **EST:** 1986
SQ FT: 52,000
SALES (est): 25.3MM **Privately Held**
WEB: www.tridentbuildingsystems.com
SIC: 3448 Prefabricated metal buildings

(G-16315)
TRINITY GRAPHIC USA INC
885 Tallevast Rd Ste D (34243-3323)
PHONE....941 355-2636
Robert J Smithson, *CEO*
William Ceperich, *CEO*
Gregory Barba, *President*
Mark Barnard, *Vice Pres*
Simon Smithson, *Vice Pres*
EMP: 18 **EST:** 1987
SQ FT: 6,750
SALES (est): 4.8MM **Privately Held**
WEB: www.trinitygraphic.com
SIC: 3555 2796 Printing plates; platemaking services

(G-16316)
TROJAN FLA POWDR COATING INC
1300 Hardin Ave (34243-5067)
PHONE....941 351-0500
EMP: 24 **EST:** 2011
SALES (est): 1.1MM **Privately Held**
WEB: www.trojanpowder.com
SIC: 3479 Coating of metals & formed products

(G-16317)
TSM CHAMP LLC
2359 Trailmate Dr (34243-4041)
PHONE....615 806-7900
Joseph Apuzzo,
EMP: 55 **EST:** 2016
SALES (est): 17.3MM
SALES (corp-wide): 53.1MM **Privately Held**
WEB: www.thermalsolutionsmfg.com
SIC: 3491 3585 Industrial valves; refrigeration & heating equipment
PA: Thermal Solutions Manufacturing, Inc.
15 Century Blvd Ste 102
Nashville TN 37214
800 359-9186

(G-16318)
TUMI HOLDINGS INC
140 University Town Cente (34243-4178)
PHONE....941 866-6304
EMP: 7
SALES (corp-wide): 177.9K **Privately Held**
WEB: www.tumi.com
SIC: 3161 Traveling bags; clothing & apparel carrying cases; satchels
HQ: Tumi Holdings, Inc.
499 Thornall St Ste 10
Edison NJ 08837
908 756-4400

(G-16319)
UFLEX USA INC
6442 Parkland Dr (34243-4038)
PHONE....941 351-2628
Anna G Gai, *President*
Rick Rice, *Purchasing*

Steven Wasserman, *Sales Staff*
◆ **EMP:** 22 **EST:** 1999
SQ FT: 40,000
SALES (est): 5.5MM **Privately Held**
SIC: 3531 5091 Marine related equipment; boat accessories & parts

(G-16320)
UK SAILMAKERS INC (PA)
Also Called: Uk Sailmakers Sarasota
324 Bernard Ave (34243-1904)
PHONE....................................941 365-7245
Greg Knighton, *President*
Alan Capellin, *Principal*
Gregg Knighton, *Principal*
Bob Revou, *Principal*
EMP: 7 **EST:** 2005
SALES (est): 626.5K **Privately Held**
WEB: www.knightonsailmakers.com
SIC: 3732 Sailboats, building & repairing

(G-16321)
UNITED RENTALS NORTH AMER INC
6851 26th Ct E (34243-4159)
PHONE....................................941 755-3177
John Treston, *Manager*
Barry Carney, *Manager*
EMP: 9
SALES (corp-wide): 8.5B **Publicly Held**
WEB: www.unitedrentals.com
SIC: 3561 7353 Pumps, domestic: water or sump; heavy construction equipment rental
HQ: United Rentals (North America), Inc.
100 Frst Stmford Pl Ste 7
Stamford CT 06902
203 622-3131

(G-16322)
VAULT SPIRITS COMPANY
8437 Tuttle Ave Ste 202 (34243-2868)
PHONE....................................941 306-3331
Amanda Witkowski, *Principal*
EMP: 6 **EST:** 2016
SALES (est): 111.6K **Privately Held**
SIC: 2084 Wines, brandy & brandy spirits

(G-16323)
VOLCANO INDUSTRIES INC
1125 Commerce Blvd N (34243-5056)
PHONE....................................770 300-0041
Thomas C Hanson, *Principal*
EMP: 10 **EST:** 2017
SALES (est): 440.2K **Privately Held**
SIC: 3999 Manufacturing industries

(G-16324)
WATERWAY SYSTEMS LLC
7010 28th Street Ct E (34243-3310)
PHONE....................................941 752-3554
EMP: 6
SQ FT: 3,000
SALES (est): 40.6K **Privately Held**
SIC: 3231 3089 Mfg Glass & Plastic Windshields

(G-16325)
WESCO PARTNERS INC
1125 Commerce Blvd N (34243-5056)
PHONE....................................941 484-8224
David O'Halloran, *President*
EMP: 44 **EST:** 1984
SALES (est): 4.8MM
SALES (corp-wide): 5MM **Privately Held**
WEB: www.wescofountains.blogspot.com
SIC: 3272 3499 3446 Concrete products; fountains (except drinking), metal; architectural metalwork
PA: Manufacturing Futures, Inc.
40 Haskell Dr
Cleveland OH 44108
216 903-7993

(G-16326)
WEST COAST SIGNS
2310 Whitfield Indus Way (34243-4062)
PHONE....................................941 755-5686
Robin Morrow, *President*
Linda Dunning, *Office Admin*
EMP: 21 **EST:** 1996
SQ FT: 25,000
SALES (est): 2.2MM **Privately Held**
SIC: 3993 Electric signs

Sarasota
Sarasota County

(G-16327)
6425 HOLLYWOOD BLVD LLC
6430 Hollywood Blvd (34231-3010)
PHONE....................................941 923-2954
Paul Couzelis, *Principal*
EMP: 6 **EST:** 2015
SALES (est): 169.3K **Privately Held**
SIC: 2499 Wood products

(G-16328)
A ALBRTINI CSTM WIN TREATMENTS
Also Called: A Albrtini Cstm Wndows Trtmnts
4023 Sawyer Rd Ofc (34233-1209)
PHONE....................................941 925-2556
Ronald Albertini, *President*
EMP: 7
SQ FT: 2,000
SALES (est): 674.4K **Privately Held**
SIC: 2591 Drapery hardware & blinds & shades

(G-16329)
A CAPPELA PUBLISHING INC (PA)
Also Called: Advocate House
913 Tennessee Ln (34234-5712)
P.O. Box 3691 (34230-3691)
PHONE....................................941 351-2050
Patrika Vaughn, *President*
EMP: 12 **EST:** 1996
SQ FT: 2,500 **Privately Held**
WEB: www.acappela.com
SIC: 2741 Miscellaneous publishing

(G-16330)
A2Z UNIFORMS INC
999 Cattlemen Rd Unit G (34232-2849)
PHONE....................................941 254-3194
Jarek Zaremba, *President*
EMP: 6 **EST:** 1999
SQ FT: 2,400
SALES (est): 811.7K **Privately Held**
WEB: www.a2zuniforms.com
SIC: 2395 5699 Embroidery & art needlework; emblems, embroidered; uniforms & work clothing

(G-16331)
AAP INDUSTRIAL INC
Also Called: Aap Pump and Motor Works
1634 Barber Rd (34240-9393)
PHONE....................................941 377-4373
Todd Carter, *Vice Pres*
EMP: 20 **EST:** 2013
SQ FT: 9,000
SALES (est): 2.1MM **Privately Held**
WEB: www.aappumpandmotor.com
SIC: 7694 7699 Electric motor repair; compressor repair

(G-16332)
ACADEMIC PUBLICATION SVCS INC
3131 Clark Rd Ste 102 (34231-7320)
PHONE....................................941 925-4474
John Wolf, *President*
Rhoda Wolf, *CFO*
EMP: 7 **EST:** 1997
SALES (est): 93.5K **Privately Held**
SIC: 2759 2741 Publication printing; miscellaneous publishing

(G-16333)
ADHESIVE TECHNOLOGIES FLA LLC
411 Pheasant Way (34236-1915)
PHONE....................................941 228-0295
Lawrence Oconnor, *Principal*
EMP: 6 **EST:** 2014
SALES (est): 252.2K **Privately Held**
SIC: 2891 Adhesives

(G-16334)
ADVANCED VACUUM SYSTEMS LLC
2025d Porter Lake Dr (34240-8834)
PHONE....................................941 378-4565
Craig Lubkey, *President*
EMP: 8 **EST:** 2005
SALES (est): 347.2K **Privately Held**
WEB: www.avsvacuumsystems.com
SIC: 3999 Chairs, hydraulic, barber & beauty shop

(G-16335)
AFFORDBLE PRSRVTION RSTORATION
2647 Britannia Rd (34231-4972)
PHONE....................................941 527-1416
Jennifer L Sparks, *President*
EMP: 6 **EST:** 2014
SALES (est): 156.8K **Privately Held**
SIC: 1389 Construction, repair & dismantling services

(G-16336)
AGI SOLUTIONS INC
4023 Sawyer Rd Unit 140 (34233-1273)
PHONE....................................888 987-8425
EMP: 6 **EST:** 2017
SALES (est): 141.9K **Privately Held**
WEB: www.agisolutions.com
SIC: 3993 Signs & advertising specialties

(G-16337)
AKUWA SOLUTIONS GROUP INC (PA)
6431 Porter Rd Ste 1 (34240)
PHONE....................................941 343-9947
Terry Nelson, *CEO*
Karin Nelson, *Vice Pres*
EMP: 10 **EST:** 2000
SQ FT: 2,000
SALES (est): 2MM **Privately Held**
WEB: www.akuwa.com
SIC: 3825 3674 3679 7373 Network analyzers; integrated circuits, semiconductor networks, etc.; pulse forming networks; local area network (LAN) systems integrator

(G-16338)
ALADDIN EQUIPMENT COMPANY
900 Sarasota Center Blvd (34240-8847)
PHONE....................................941 371-3732
Lindy L Smith, *Ch of Bd*
Jack McKissock, *President*
John Miller, *Vice Pres*
David Paoli, *Purch Mgr*
Dave Poali, *Purch Mgr*
◆ **EMP:** 55 **EST:** 1950
SQ FT: 108,000
SALES (est): 7.9MM **Privately Held**
WEB: www.aladdin1950.com
SIC: 3589 Swimming pool filter & water conditioning systems

(G-16339)
ALBRECHT CONSULTING INC
1350 Global Ct (34240-7856)
PHONE....................................941 377-7755
Jeff Albrecht, *President*
Beverly Albrecht, *Vice Pres*
EMP: 15 **EST:** 1994
SALES (est): 2.4MM **Privately Held**
WEB: www.albrechtcabinets.com
SIC: 2434 Wood kitchen cabinets

(G-16340)
ALL GRANITE & MARBLE CORP
1909 N Washington Blvd (34234-7528)
PHONE....................................508 248-9393
Altamiro Abranches, *President*
Ricardo Neves, *Admin Sec*
▲ **EMP:** 6 **EST:** 2004
SALES (est): 628.4K **Privately Held**
WEB: www.allgraniteandmarblesarasota.com
SIC: 3281 1741 Granite, cut & shaped; marble, building: cut & shaped; masonry & other stonework

(G-16341)
ALVIS INDUSTRIES INC
3300 Linden Dr (34232-4938)
PHONE....................................941 377-7800
Troy D Alvis, *Principal*
EMP: 8 **EST:** 2004
SALES (est): 374.3K **Privately Held**
WEB: www.alvisindustriesinc.com
SIC: 3999 Manufacturing industries

(G-16342)
ANDROS BOATWORKS INC
202 Industrial Blvd (34234)
PHONE....................................941 351-9702
Andrew D Eggebrecht, *President*
Danny Eggebrecht, *Vice Pres*
Donald Eggebrecht, *Vice Pres*
EMP: 12 **EST:** 2005
SQ FT: 22,000
SALES (est): 199.9K **Privately Held**
WEB: www.androsboats.com
SIC: 3732 Motorboats, inboard or outboard: building & repairing

(G-16343)
APOLLO SUNGUARD SYSTEMS INC
Also Called: Apollo Shade Systems
4487 Ashton Rd (34233-2284)
PHONE....................................941 925-3000
Kevin Connelly, *President*
Danielle Cibello, *Vice Pres*
Jesse Carr, *Controller*
Cathy Tassie, *Receptionist*
▲ **EMP:** 15 **EST:** 2001
SQ FT: 10,000
SALES (est): 4MM **Privately Held**
WEB: www.apollosunguard.com
SIC: 2394 3714 5063 Canopies, fabric: made from purchased materials; motor vehicle electrical equipment; electrical apparatus & equipment

(G-16344)
APPLE A DAY INC
803 Bell Rd (34240-9507)
PHONE....................................941 377-5404
Bruce Heiman, *President*
EMP: 6 **EST:** 1993
SALES (est): 229.5K **Privately Held**
SIC: 2082 Beer (alcoholic beverage)

(G-16345)
AQUA WHOLESALE INC
1155 Cattlemen Rd Ste B (34232-2836)
PHONE....................................941 341-0847
Larry Eaton, *President*
Sandra K Eaton, *Vice Pres*
John Wilyat, *Purch Mgr*
Sandy Eaton, *Office Mgr*
Susan Harris, *Office Mgr*
▼ **EMP:** 6 **EST:** 2001
SQ FT: 7,500
SALES (est): 891.5K **Privately Held**
WEB: www.aqua-wholesale.com
SIC: 3589 Water treatment equipment, industrial

(G-16346)
AQUARIUS SILK SCREEN INC
5931 Palmer Blvd (34232-2841)
PHONE....................................941 377-3059
Ronald A Ernst, *President*
EMP: 6 **EST:** 1980
SQ FT: 5,400
SALES (est): 722K **Privately Held**
SIC: 2261 Screen printing of cotton broadwoven fabrics

(G-16347)
ARCHITCTURAL MBL IMPORTERS INC
2560 12th St (34237-2943)
PHONE....................................941 365-3552
James Newby, *President*
▲ **EMP:** 21 **EST:** 1981
SALES (est): 1.9MM **Privately Held**
WEB: www.architecturalmarble.com
SIC: 3281 1743 5032 Household articles, except furniture: cut stone; marble installation, interior; marble building stone

(G-16348)
ARGOS USA LLC
6000 Deacon Pl (34238-2719)
PHONE....................................866 322-4547
EMP: 6 **EST:** 2018
SALES (est): 103.1K **Privately Held**
WEB: www.argos-us.com
SIC: 3273 Ready-mixed concrete

(G-16349)
ARTISTIC CUSTOM COATINGS INC
5606 Nutmeg Ave (34231-2531)
PHONE....................................941 822-5608
Larry E Rowe Jr, *Principal*
Larry Rowe, *Principal*
EMP: 6 **EST:** 2013
SALES (est): 69.8K **Privately Held**
SIC: 3479 Metal coating & allied service

(G-16350)
ASHTON MANUFACTURING LLC
Also Called: Suntech Doors
1633 Northgate Blvd (34234-2117)
PHONE....................................941 351-5529
Joe Zuza, *Prdtn Mgr*
Chris Nelson, *Opers Staff*
Carol Garrison, *Sales Staff*
Terry Ashton,
EMP: 10 **EST:** 2006
SQ FT: 9,300
SALES (est): 1MM **Privately Held**
SIC: 3442 Screen & storm doors & windows

(G-16351)
ASO CORPORATION (HQ)
300 Sarasota Center Blvd (34240-9381)
PHONE....................................941 378-6600
Yasuhiro Kuki, *President*
Wes Kolodziejczyk, *President*
Mike Willison, *President*
Shawn O 'brien, *General Mgr*
Erin Jones, *Business Mgr*
EMP: 100 **EST:** 1986
SALES (est): 46.8MM **Privately Held**
WEB: www.asocorp.com
SIC: 3842 Surgical appliances & supplies

(G-16352)
ASO LLC (DH)
Also Called: A S O
300 Sarasota Center Blvd (34240-9381)
PHONE....................................941 379-0300
Mike Willison, *President*
John D Macaskill,
Craig Gesell,
Yasushi Kuki,
Keila Rodriguez, *Contractor*
◆ **EMP:** 238 **EST:** 1986
SQ FT: 150,000
SALES (est): 46.8MM **Privately Held**
WEB: www.asocorp.com
SIC: 3842 5122 Bandages: plastic, muslin, plaster of paris, etc.; bandages
HQ: Aso Corporation
300 Sarasota Center Blvd
Sarasota FL 34240
941 378-6600

(G-16353)
ASPHERICON INC
2601 Cattlemen Rd Ste 301 (34232-6231)
PHONE....................................941 564-0890
Steffen Schneider, *President*
Sabrina Matthias, *President*
Alexander Wolf Zschaebitz, *Principal*
EMP: 11 **EST:** 2013
SALES (est): 1.7MM
SALES (corp-wide): 18.8MM **Privately Held**
WEB: www.asp50hericon.com
SIC: 3827 Optical instruments & lenses
PA: Asphericon Gmbh
Stockholmer Str. 9
Jena 07747
364 131-0050

(G-16354)
ASV STONE LLC
6664 Duck Pond Ln (34240-6603)
PHONE....................................941 268-5321
Aleksandr F Filipskiy, *Principal*
EMP: 6 **EST:** 2011
SALES (est): 136.1K **Privately Held**
SIC: 3281 Building stone products

(G-16355)
ATI PRO AV LLC
3764 Lena Ln (34240-8682)
PHONE....................................941 322-1008
Timothy Tobias Benshoff, *Manager*
EMP: 6 **EST:** 2017
SALES (est): 90.8K **Privately Held**
SIC: 3312 Stainless steel

(G-16356)
ATLANTIC CONCRETE PRODUCTS INC
Also Called: Atlantic Steel Fabricators
1701 Myrtle St (34234-4817)
PHONE....................................941 355-2988
Dan Dallas, *Manager*
EMP: 62
SALES (corp-wide): 28MM **Privately Held**
WEB: www.atlanticconcrete.com
SIC: 3272 Concrete products, precast
PA: Atlantic Concrete Products, Inc.
8900 Old Route 13
Bristol PA 19007
215 945-5600

(G-16357)
ATLANTIC TNG LLC
1701 Myrtle St (34234-4817)
P.O. Box 729 (34230-0729)
PHONE....................................941 355-2988
Kristen Dodd, *Production*
Joe Abraham, *Engineer*
Megan Ditcher, *Mng Member*
EMP: 25 **EST:** 2010
SQ FT: 6,000
SALES (est): 2.5MM **Privately Held**
WEB: www.atlantictng.com
SIC: 3272 Concrete products, precast

(G-16358)
AUTISAN INTERNATIONAL INC
612 Lotus Ln (34242-1210)
PHONE....................................941 349-7029
J J Jackson, *President*
EMP: 5 **EST:** 1996
SQ FT: 4,250
SALES (est): 339.1K **Privately Held**
WEB: www.autisan.com
SIC: 3089 Injection molding of plastics

(G-16359)
AUTOMATED VACUUM SYSTEMS INC
2228b Industrial Blvd (34234-3120)
PHONE....................................941 378-4565
Craig Lubkey, *President*
▲ **EMP:** 8 **EST:** 1997
SQ FT: 12,000
SALES (est): 655K **Privately Held**
WEB: www.avsvacuumsystems.com
SIC: 3559 Optical lens machinery

(G-16360)
B & T PALLETS INC
7952 Fruitville Rd (34240-8829)
PHONE....................................941 360-0562
Tim McGowan, *Vice Pres*
EMP: 6 **EST:** 2013
SALES (est): 71.4K **Privately Held**
SIC: 2448 Pallets, wood & wood with metal

(G-16361)
BALPACK INCORPORATED
5438 Ashton Ct (34233-3403)
PHONE....................................941 371-7323
Pavel Balcar, *President*
Roman Balcar, *Exec VP*
▲ **EMP:** 8 **EST:** 2003
SQ FT: 1,711
SALES (est): 1.8MM **Privately Held**
WEB: www.balpackinc.com
SIC: 3565 Packaging machinery

(G-16362)
BASECRETE TECHNOLOGIES LLC
7969 Moyer Ave (34240-2539)
PHONE....................................941 312-5142
Kenneth L Pearce, *Sales Staff*
Vito Mariano, *Mng Member*
Kenneth Pearce,
EMP: 18 **EST:** 2015
SALES (est): 1.1MM **Privately Held**
WEB: www.basecreteusa.com
SIC: 3241 Cement, hydraulic

(G-16363)
BEAN COUNTERS PRO
5602 Marquesas Cir # 102 (34233-3310)
PHONE....................................941 504-1157
Denise Porter, *Principal*
EMP: 6 **EST:** 2010
SALES (est): 70.2K **Privately Held**
SIC: 3131 Counters

(G-16364)
BELVOIR PUBLICATIONS INC
Also Called: Belvoir Media Group
7820 Holiday Dr (34231-5316)
PHONE....................................941 929-1720
EMP: 50
SALES (corp-wide): 49.9MM **Privately Held**
WEB: www.belvoir.com
SIC: 2731 Book publishing
PA: Belvoir Publications Inc
800 Connecticut Ave 4w02
Norwalk CT 06854
203 857-3100

(G-16365)
BLUTEC GLASS FABRICATION LLC
5342 Clark Rd Unit 125 (34233-3227)
PHONE....................................941 232-1600
Robert J Guzzo,
James Guzzo,
EMP: 9 **EST:** 2016
SALES (est): 501.5K **Privately Held**
WEB: www.blutecglass.com
SIC: 2295 5231 Varnished glass & coated fiberglass fabrics; glass

(G-16366)
BOHEMIAN BOATWORKS LLC
5140 Jungle Plum Rd (34242-1433)
PHONE....................................941 321-1499
David Janes, *Principal*
EMP: 6 **EST:** 2010
SALES (est): 134.4K **Privately Held**
SIC: 3732 Boat building & repairing

(G-16367)
BOWMAN ANALYTICS INC
5824 Bee Ridge Rd (34233-5065)
PHONE....................................847 781-3523
EMP: 8 **EST:** 2019
SALES (est): 1.1MM **Privately Held**
SIC: 3826 Analytical instruments

(G-16368)
BRESEE WOODWORK INC
Also Called: Elite Woodwork
1795 Desoto Rd (34234-3066)
PHONE....................................941 355-2591
Marc Bresee, *President*
Debbie Bresee, *Treasurer*
EMP: 10 **EST:** 1997
SALES (est): 1.3MM **Privately Held**
WEB: www.elitewood.net
SIC: 2434 1751 Wood kitchen cabinets; carpentry work

(G-16369)
BRETON USA CUSTOMERS SVC CORP
1753 Northgate Blvd (34234-2138)
PHONE....................................941 360-2700
Dario Toncelli, *President*
Magdalena Picardi, *General Mgr*
Gianrico Filippetto, *Vice Pres*
Lorenzo Del Mutolo, *Treasurer*
Gerard J Van Der Bas, *Manager*
▲ **EMP:** 15 **EST:** 2004
SALES (est): 950K **Privately Held**
WEB: www.bretonusa.com
SIC: 3441 3281 Fabricated structural metal; dimension stone for buildings

(G-16370)
BRONZART FOUNDRY INC
5415 Ashton Ct Unit H (34233-3454)
PHONE....................................941 922-9106
Richard A Frignoca, *President*
Tamzen M Frignoca, *Corp Secy*
▼ **EMP:** 10 **EST:** 1979
SQ FT: 3,500
SALES (est): 1.5MM **Privately Held**
WEB: www.bronzartfoundry.com
SIC: 3366 Castings (except die): bronze

(G-16371)
BUFFALO WHEELCHAIR INC
4130 S Tamiami Trl (34231-3608)
PHONE....................................941 921-6331
James C Travis, *President*
EMP: 7 **EST:** 2018
SALES (est): 118.9K **Privately Held**
WEB: www.buffalowheelchair.com
SIC: 3842 Wheelchairs

(G-16372)
BUILDERS DOOR AND SUPPLY INC
2022 12th St (34237-2702)
PHONE....................................941 955-2311
David A Johnson, *President*
Coleen Johnson, *Vice Pres*
EMP: 14 **EST:** 1991
SALES (est): 1MM **Privately Held**
WEB: www.buildersdoorandsupply.com
SIC: 2431 5031 3442 Doors, wood; millwork; metal doors, sash & trim

(G-16373)
BULLETIN NET INC
6000 S Tamiami Trl (34231-3950)
PHONE....................................941 468-2569
Bruce Herbert, *President*
EMP: 11 **EST:** 1995
SALES (est): 225.2K **Privately Held**
SIC: 2711 Newspapers, publishing & printing

(G-16374)
BYERLY CUSTOM DESIGN INC
743 Gantt Ave (34232-6703)
PHONE....................................941 371-7498
Carl Byerly, *President*
Christopher Byerly, *Vice Pres*
Pam Byerly, *Admin Sec*
EMP: 5 **EST:** 1984
SQ FT: 5,000
SALES (est): 800K **Privately Held**
SIC: 2434 Wood kitchen cabinets

(G-16375)
CABINETS BY WFC INC
6092 Clark Center Ave (34238-2716)
PHONE....................................941 355-2703
David L Koffman, *President*
Jeffrey Bloch, *Vice Pres*
Christopher Dowling, *Vice Pres*
Jeffrey P Koffman, *Vice Pres*
Michael R O'Connor, *Vice Pres*
EMP: 10 **EST:** 2017
SALES (est): 267.2K **Privately Held**
SIC: 2434 Wood kitchen cabinets

(G-16376)
CABINETSCAPES LLC
8455 Midnight Pass Rd (34242-2705)
PHONE....................................941 539-0013
Karen McKeivier, *Branch Mgr*
EMP: 9
SALES (corp-wide): 94.4K **Privately Held**
SIC: 2434 Wood kitchen cabinets
PA: Cabinetscapes, Llc
120 Venetian Way Ste 15
Merritt Island FL

(G-16377)
CAE HEALTHCARE INC (DH)
6300 Edgelake Dr (34240-8817)
PHONE....................................941 377-5562
Marc Parent, *CEO*
Michael Bernstein, *President*
Jay Anton, *Vice Pres*
Ray Shuford, *Vice Pres*
Thomas E Whytas, *CFO*
EMP: 198 **EST:** 1994
SQ FT: 76,000
SALES (est): 55.4MM
SALES (corp-wide): 2.3B **Privately Held**
WEB: www.caehealthcare.com
SIC: 3841 Surgical instruments & apparatus
HQ: Cae Healthcare Canada Inc
8585 Ch De La Cote-De-Liesse
Saint-Laurent QC H4T 1
514 341-6780

(G-16378)
CAE HEALTHCARE USA INC
6300 Edgelake Dr (34240-8817)
PHONE....................................941 377-5562
Marc Parent, *President*
Guillaume Herve, *Vice Pres*
▲ **EMP:** 36 **EST:** 2010

GEOGRAPHIC

SALES (est): 4.8MM
SALES (corp-wide): 2.3B **Privately Held**
WEB: www.caehealthcare.com
SIC: 3699 Flight simulators (training aids), electronic
PA: Cae Inc
8585 Ch De La Cote-De-Liesse
Saint-Laurent QC H4T 1
514 341-6780

(G-16379)
CAMPUS PUBLICATIONS INC
2975 Bee Ridge Rd Ste D (34239-7100)
PHONE..................................941 780-1326
Carol Moore, *President*
EMP: 8 **EST:** 1999
SQ FT: 800
SALES (est): 300K **Privately Held**
WEB: www.campuspublicationsinc.com
SIC: 2741 Miscellaneous publishing

(G-16380)
CANVAS WEST INC
1470 12th St (34236-3313)
PHONE..................................941 355-0780
Michael W Town, *President*
Micheal Town, *Owner*
EMP: 6 **EST:** 1990
SQ FT: 1,500
SALES (est): 673.1K **Privately Held**
SIC: 2394 5999 Canvas & related products; canvas products

(G-16381)
CEMEX CNSTR MTLS FLA LLC
Also Called: Sarasota Cattlemen Rm
622 Cattlemen Rd (34232-6317)
PHONE..................................800 992-3639
Richard A Buckelew, *Branch Mgr*
EMP: 14 **Privately Held**
SIC: 3272 Concrete products, precast
HQ: Cemex Construction Materials Florida, Llc
1501 Belvedere Rd
West Palm Beach FL 33406

(G-16382)
CHELTEC INC
2215 Industrial Blvd (34234-3119)
PHONE..................................941 355-1045
Denise Delancy, *President*
Tom O'Neill, *Vice Pres*
Jason Marquez, *Sales Staff*
EMP: 7 **EST:** 1996
SQ FT: 9,600
SALES (est): 1.2MM **Privately Held**
WEB: www.cheltec.com
SIC: 2819 Chemicals, high purity: refined from technical grade

(G-16383)
CHOICE TOOL & MOLD LLC
901 Sarasota Center Blvd (34240-7816)
PHONE..................................941 371-6767
James C Westman,
EMP: 19 **EST:** 1996
SALES (est): 2.7MM **Privately Held**
WEB: www.octexgroup.com
SIC: 3089 Injection molding of plastics
PA: Octex Holdings, Llc
901 Sarasota Center Blvd
Sarasota FL 34240

(G-16384)
CJB INDUSTRIES INC
23 N Blvd Of Presidents (34236-1304)
PHONE..................................941 552-8397
Shaun Douglas, *Principal*
EMP: 18 **EST:** 2012
SALES (est): 126.3K **Privately Held**
WEB: www.cjbindustries.com
SIC: 2899 Chemical preparations

(G-16385)
CLOUD INDUSTRIES
8275 Shadow Pine Way (34238-5619)
PHONE..................................816 213-2730
Paul Shoemaker, *Principal*
EMP: 9 **EST:** 2017
SALES (est): 637.4K **Privately Held**
WEB: www.cloudindustries.com
SIC: 3999 Manufacturing industries

(G-16386)
COASTAL PRINTING INC SARASOTA
4391 Independence Ct (34234-2155)
PHONE..................................941 351-1515
Alan Guttridge, *CEO*
Alan R Guttridge Jr, *President*
Terry Rayner, *COO*
Janet T Guttridge, *Vice Pres*
Andrew Keighley, *Vice Pres*
EMP: 49
SALES (est): 11.4MM **Privately Held**
WEB: www.coastalprint.com
SIC: 2752 2796 2791 Lithographing on metal; platemaking services; typesetting

(G-16387)
COCA-COLA BOTTLING CO
1126 N Lime Ave (34237-3514)
PHONE..................................844 863-2653
Todd Graff, *Manager*
EMP: 6 **EST:** 2017
SALES (est): 79.4K **Privately Held**
WEB: www.coca-cola.com
SIC: 2086 Bottled & canned soft drinks

(G-16388)
COCA-COLA COMPANY
2150 47th St (34234-3111)
PHONE..................................941 351-4695
Frank Copla, *General Mgr*
EMP: 6
SALES (corp-wide): 33B **Publicly Held**
WEB: www.coca-colacompany.com
SIC: 2086 Bottled & canned soft drinks
PA: The Coca-Cola Company
1 Coca Cola Plz Nw
Atlanta GA 30313
404 676-2121

(G-16389)
COMMERCIAL INSULATING GLASS CO (PA)
Also Called: C I G
6200 Porter Rd (34240-9696)
PHONE..................................941 378-9100
Jeffery A Winsler, *President*
Rafael Molina, *Plant Mgr*
Mike Estes, *Natl Sales Mgr*
Juan De Jesus, *Sales Staff*
Linda Harrison, *Director*
▲ **EMP:** 78 **EST:** 1990
SALES (est): 11.2MM **Privately Held**
WEB: www.cigglass.com
SIC: 3211 3231 Insulating glass, sealed units; products of purchased glass

(G-16390)
COMMERCIAL RFRG DOOR CO INC
Also Called: Styleline Doors
6200 Porter Rd (34240-9696)
PHONE..................................941 371-8110
Jeffrey Winsler, *President*
Rob Winsler, *Vice Pres*
Linda Gabriel, *Controller*
Brian Gill, *Maintence Staff*
EMP: 8 **EST:** 1975
SQ FT: 68,759
SALES (est): 4.9MM **Privately Held**
WEB: www.styleline.com
SIC: 3442 3231 Metal doors; products of purchased glass

(G-16391)
CONEXUS TECHNOLOGIES INC
1145 Horizon View Dr (34242-3848)
PHONE..................................513 779-5448
▲ **EMP:** 15
SQ FT: 1,200
SALES (est): 3MM **Privately Held**
SIC: 2298 Mfg Cordage/Twine

(G-16392)
CONNECTPRESS LTD
2015 S Tuttle Ave Ste A (34239-4150)
P.O. Box 1418 (34230-1418)
PHONE..................................505 629-0695
Daniel Raker, *President*
EMP: 10 **EST:** 2016
SALES (est): 276.7K **Privately Held**
WEB: www.connectpress.com
SIC: 2741 Miscellaneous publishing

(G-16393)
CONRADO SALAS JR LLC
125 Avenida Veneccia (34242-2033)
PHONE..................................941 587-5919
Conrado Salas, *President*
EMP: 7 **EST:** 2005
SALES (est): 193.4K **Privately Held**
SIC: 3423 Carpenters' hand tools, except saws: levels, chisels, etc.

(G-16394)
COOK SPRING CO
233 Sarasota Center Blvd (34240-9380)
PHONE..................................941 377-5766
Randall A Cook, *President*
◆ **EMP:** 75 **EST:** 1954
SQ FT: 90,000
SALES (est): 12.3MM **Privately Held**
WEB: www.cookspring.com
SIC: 3495 Wire springs

(G-16395)
CREATIVE TECH SARASOTA INC
5959 Palmer Blvd (34232-2841)
PHONE..................................941 371-2743
Thomas W Turner, *President*
Michael A Turner, *Corp Secy*
Kenneth Turner, *Vice Pres*
EMP: 9 **EST:** 1969
SQ FT: 12,500
SALES (est): 729.6K **Privately Held**
WEB: www.creative-technology.com
SIC: 2731 2732 Books: publishing & printing; book printing

(G-16396)
CROP LLC
2320 Gulf Gate Dr (34231-5608)
PHONE..................................941 923-8640
Karen L Odierna, *Principal*
EMP: 13 **EST:** 2014
SALES (est): 1.3MM **Privately Held**
WEB: www.cropjuice.com
SIC: 2037 Frozen fruits & vegetables

(G-16397)
CSO SYSTEMS INC
4139 N Washington Blvd (34234-4840)
PHONE..................................941 355-5653
Larry Cavalluzi, *President*
Alina Duncan, *Bookkeeper*
EMP: 11 **EST:** 2000
SQ FT: 100,000
SALES (est): 825.6K **Privately Held**
SIC: 3993 Signs & advertising specialties

(G-16398)
CUSTOM CABINETS INC
7350 Deer Crossing Ct (34240-7411)
PHONE..................................941 366-0428
Cloyd E Ridenour, *President*
Josh Ridenour, *Vice Pres*
Kathryn Ridenour, *Admin Sec*
EMP: 10 **EST:** 1972
SALES (est): 900K **Privately Held**
SIC: 2434 2511 5712 2541 Wood kitchen cabinets; wood household furniture; furniture stores; wood partitions & fixtures

(G-16399)
CUSTOM COLORS POWDER COATING
1930 21st St (34234-7517)
PHONE..................................941 953-7997
Lynn J King, *President*
Tom Parise, *Vice Pres*
EMP: 5 **EST:** 1992
SQ FT: 5,000
SALES (est): 719.6K **Privately Held**
WEB: www.customcolorspowdercoating.com
SIC: 3479 Coating of metals & formed products

(G-16400)
D B WELDING FABRICATION
6292 Tower Ln Unit 2 (34240-7853)
PHONE..................................941 379-2319
David C Brisson Psd, *Principal*
Dan Brisson, *Principal*
EMP: 5 **EST:** 2011
SALES (est): 600K **Privately Held**
WEB: www.dbweldingandfab.com
SIC: 7692 Welding repair

(G-16401)
D W A INC (PA)
Also Called: Country Store Interiors
5401 Palmer Blvd (34232-2731)
PHONE..................................941 444-1134
Donald W Atha, *President*
Bonnie Atha, *Corp Secy*
EMP: 14 **EST:** 1966
SQ FT: 4,000
SALES (est): 1.8MM **Privately Held**
WEB: www.countrystoreinteriors.com
SIC: 2591 2211 5714 2392 Venetian blinds; draperies & drapery fabrics, cotton; draperies; household furnishings; curtains & draperies

(G-16402)
D& R PRINTING LLC
6569 Tarawa Dr (34241-5645)
PHONE..................................941 378-3311
Lori Benvenuto,
EMP: 8 **EST:** 2013
SALES (est): 271.4K **Privately Held**
SIC: 2752 Commercial printing, offset

(G-16403)
D&R PRINTING LLC
Also Called: Mercury Printing
4281 Clark Rd (34233-2405)
PHONE..................................941 378-3311
Lori Benvenuto, *Mng Member*
Robert Benvenuto, *Mng Member*
EMP: 8 **EST:** 2013
SALES (est): 263.2K **Privately Held**
SIC: 2752 Commercial printing, offset

(G-16404)
DART CONTAINER CORP FLORIDA
Logistical Management
1952 Field Rd Ste B3 (34231-2315)
PHONE..................................941 358-1202
William R Dart, *President*
Kirk Harnish, *Plant Mgr*
Ted Esteves, *Manager*
Andrea Correa, *Assistant*
EMP: 17
SALES (corp-wide): 68.2MM **Privately Held**
WEB: www.dartcontainer.com
SIC: 3086 Plastics foam products
PA: Dart Container Corporation Of Florida
500 Hogsback Rd
Mason MI 48854
800 248-5960

(G-16405)
DAYTON INDUSTRIAL CORPORATION
2237 Industrial Blvd (34234-3119)
PHONE..................................941 351-4454
Fax: 941 351-6081
EMP: 5
SQ FT: 2,500
SALES (est): 450K **Privately Held**
SIC: 3663 5065 Mfg Radio Receivers

(G-16406)
DCWFAB LLC
3374 Howell Pl (34232-2317)
PHONE..................................941 320-6095
Daniel Chilton, *Owner*
EMP: 5 **EST:** 2015
SALES (est): 340.6K **Privately Held**
WEB: www.dcwfab.com
SIC: 7692 Welding repair

(G-16407)
DEFENDER SCREENS INTERNATIONAL
5330 Pinkney Ave Bldg 6 (34233-2420)
PHONE..................................866 802-0400
EMP: 6 **EST:** 2018
SALES (est): 352.8K **Privately Held**
WEB: www.defenderscreens.com
SIC: 2431 Millwork

(G-16408)
DELACOM DETECTION SYSTEMS LLC
7463 Roxye Ln (34240-7815)
P.O. Box 50005 (34232-0300)
PHONE..................................941 544-6636
Dennis Akers, *CEO*
EMP: 8 **EST:** 2008

SALES (est): 627.4K **Privately Held**
SIC: 1389 Detection & analysis service, gas

(G-16409)
DESCO MANUFACTURING INC
4561 Samuel St (34233-3482)
P.O. Box 21448 (34276-4448)
PHONE..................................941 925-7029
Scott McCloud, *President*
Ruth Sistrunk, *Sales Executive*
EMP: 12 **EST:** 1988
SQ FT: 23,000
SALES (est): 1.2MM **Privately Held**
WEB: www.descospray.com
SIC: 3563 Spraying & dusting equipment

(G-16410)
DESIGN WORKS BY TECH PDTS INC (DH)
Also Called: N A Whittenburg
4500 Carmichael Ave (34234-2133)
PHONE..................................941 355-2703
Burton I Koffman, *Ch of Bd*
Charles M Custin, *President*
Milton Koffman, *Vice Pres*
Richard E Koffman, *Vice Pres*
David Melin, *Vice Pres*
◆ **EMP:** 20
SQ FT: 75,000
SALES (est): 37.2MM
SALES (corp-wide): 4MM **Privately Held**
WEB: www.floridadesignworks.com
SIC: 3086 5074 5032 5087 Plastics foam products; plumbing fittings & supplies; tile, clay or other ceramic, excluding refractory; upholsterers' equipment & supplies; pillows, bed: made from purchased materials; windows
HQ: Great American Industries Inc
300 Plaza Dr
Vestal NY 13850
607 729-9331

(G-16411)
DESSERTS2GO INC
3960 Bellwood Dr (34232-3308)
PHONE..................................941 379-0488
Susan J Salzman, *Principal*
EMP: 6 **EST:** 2007
SALES (est): 146.1K **Privately Held**
WEB: www.desserts2go.com
SIC: 2024 Ice cream & frozen desserts

(G-16412)
DOLPHIN PADDLESPORTS INC
6018 S Tamiami Trl (34231-3950)
PHONE..................................941 924-2785
Mark Goodwin, *Principal*
EMP: 10 **EST:** 1989
SALES (est): 611K **Privately Held**
WEB: www.floridakayak.com
SIC: 2499 Oars & paddles, wood

(G-16413)
DONGILI INVESTMENT GROUP INC
Also Called: Label Tape Systems
5563 Marquesas Cir (34233-3332)
P.O. Box 49407 (34230-6407)
PHONE..................................941 927-3003
Paul Santostasi, *President*
Donna Hall, *Vice Pres*
Rosemarie Santostasi, *Vice Pres*
Gina Synder, *Vice Pres*
Lisa Castorina, *Admin Sec*
EMP: 10 **EST:** 1986
SQ FT: 3,300
SALES (est): 1.3MM **Privately Held**
WEB: www.labelandtapesystems.com
SIC: 2754 2759 Labels: gravure printing; labels & seals: printing

(G-16414)
DOUGLAS A FISHER INC
Also Called: Ullman Sails Florida
957 N Lime Ave (34237-3510)
PHONE..................................941 951-0189
Douglas A Fisher, *President*
EMP: 5 **EST:** 1986
SQ FT: 6,000
SALES (est): 532.6K **Privately Held**
SIC: 2394 Sails: made from purchased materials

(G-16415)
DRUM CIRCLE DISTILLING LLC
2212 Industrial Blvd (34234-3120)
PHONE..................................941 358-1900
Troy Roberts, *Principal*
Nanci Roberts, *Senior Mgr*
▲ **EMP:** 15 **EST:** 2009
SALES (est): 1MM **Privately Held**
WEB: www.siestakeyrum.com
SIC: 2085 Distillers' dried grains & solubles & alcohol

(G-16416)
DYCO
6222 Tower Ln Unit A10 (34240-8887)
PHONE..................................941 484-9057
Terri Dyer, *President*
EMP: 8 **EST:** 2012
SALES (est): 131.2K **Privately Held**
WEB: www.dyco-inc.com
SIC: 3589 Water treatment equipment, industrial

(G-16417)
ELECTRO MECHANICAL SOUTH INC
1575 Cattlemen Rd Ste 133 (34232-6278)
PHONE..................................941 342-9111
Richard B Romanoff, *CEO*
Shirley Romanoff, *President*
Patricia Howell, *Office Admin*
EMP: 25 **EST:** 1992
SQ FT: 6,000
SALES (est): 2.5MM **Privately Held**
WEB: www.ems-fl.com
SIC: 7694 7629 Electric motor repair; rewinding stators; electrical repair shops

(G-16418)
ELEMENT MDTERRANEAN STEAKHOUSE
1413 Main St (34236-5714)
PHONE..................................407 873-6829
EMP: 5 **EST:** 2019
SALES (est): 347.2K **Privately Held**
WEB: www.elementsrq.com
SIC: 2819 Elements

(G-16419)
EMBROID ME
5931 Palmer Blvd (34232-2841)
PHONE..................................941 312-5494
Michele A McIntire, *Administration*
EMP: 6 **EST:** 2016
SALES (est): 85.2K **Privately Held**
SIC: 2395 Embroidery & art needlework

(G-16420)
ENGLISH IRONWORKS INC
1960 21st St (34234-7517)
PHONE..................................941 364-9120
Frank Southern, *Owner*
Penelope Southern, *Co-Owner*
EMP: 5 **EST:** 1993
SQ FT: 4,500
SALES (est): 545.9K **Privately Held**
WEB: www.englishironworks.com
SIC: 3446 Architectural metalwork

(G-16421)
EPIC EXTRUSION INC
8141 Blaikie Ct Ste 3 (34240-8328)
PHONE..................................941 378-0835
Charles F Gasek, *President*
Pauline Gasek, *Vice Pres*
EMP: 8 **EST:** 1982
SQ FT: 3,000
SALES (est): 591.6K **Privately Held**
WEB: www.trajanscimed.com
SIC: 3089 Injection molding of plastics

(G-16422)
ESTETIKA SKIN & LASER SPE
1463 Tangier Way (34239-5832)
PHONE..................................262 646-9222
Karl Lickteig, *Principal*
EMP: 10 **EST:** 2007
SALES (est): 134.4K **Privately Held**
WEB: www.estetikaskin.com
SIC: 3845 Laser systems & equipment, medical

(G-16423)
EVIES GOLF CENTER
4735 Bee Ridge Rd (34233-1415)
PHONE..................................941 377-2399
Michael Evanoff, *Owner*
EMP: 8 **EST:** 1999
SQ FT: 3,000
SALES (est): 700.7K **Privately Held**
WEB: www.eviesgolf.com
SIC: 3949 Driving ranges, golf, electronic

(G-16424)
FAES SRT INC
7619 Trillium Blvd (34241-5207)
PHONE..................................941 960-6742
EMP: 9 **EST:** 2017
SALES (est): 268.4K **Privately Held**
WEB: www.faes.com
SIC: 3714 Motor vehicle parts & accessories

(G-16425)
FALFAS CABINET & STONE LLC
1705 Cattlemen Rd (34232-6261)
PHONE..................................941 960-2065
Jeff Falfas, *Principal*
EMP: 8 **EST:** 2015
SALES (est): 976.4K **Privately Held**
WEB: www.falfascabinetsandstone.com
SIC: 2434 Wood kitchen cabinets

(G-16426)
FAN AMERICA INC
2235 6th St (34237-2801)
PHONE..................................941 955-9788
Rainer Blomster, *President*
▲ **EMP:** 5 **EST:** 1989
SQ FT: 10,000
SALES (est): 769.4K **Privately Held**
WEB: www.fanam.com
SIC: 3564 3634 Blowing fans: industrial or commercial; fans, exhaust & ventilating, electric: household

(G-16427)
FANAM INC
2043 Global Ct (34240-7843)
PHONE..................................941 955-9788
Daniel Selberg, *President*
Rainer Blomster, *President*
▲ **EMP:** 6 **EST:** 2003
SALES (est): 587.2K **Privately Held**
WEB: www.fanam.com
SIC: 3564 Blowers & fans

(G-16428)
FARO INDUSTRIALE SPA CO
6208 Clark Center Ave (34238-2752)
PHONE..................................941 925-3004
Marino Bertoli, *President*
EMP: 6 **EST:** 2019
SALES (est): 106.7K **Privately Held**
WEB: www.faro-bearings.com
SIC: 3562 Ball bearings & parts

(G-16429)
FINE WOODWORKING
2243 Valencia Dr (34239-5310)
PHONE..................................941 957-0863
Philip Shaffer, *Principal*
EMP: 6 **EST:** 2009
SALES (est): 87.7K **Privately Held**
SIC: 2431 Millwork

(G-16430)
FINECRAFT CUSTOM CABINETRY
6209 Clarity Ct (34240-9620)
PHONE..................................941 378-1901
Paul Martinelli, *President*
EMP: 5 **EST:** 1991
SQ FT: 5,000
SALES (est): 462K **Privately Held**
WEB: www.finecraftcabinetry.com
SIC: 2434 Wood kitchen cabinets

(G-16431)
FINECRAFT CUSTOM CABINETS
4333 S Tamiami Trl (34231-3461)
PHONE..................................941 312-6598
EMP: 6 **EST:** 2019
SALES (est): 231.8K **Privately Held**
WEB: www.finecraftcabinetry.com
SIC: 2434 Wood kitchen cabinets

(G-16432)
FIRE FLY FUELS INC
1550 Global Ct (34240-7860)
PHONE..................................941 404-6820
George P Tyson, *President*
Tammy Fultz, *Executive*
EMP: 7 **EST:** 2011
SALES (est): 1.2MM **Privately Held**
WEB: www.fireflyfuel.com
SIC: 2869 Fuels

(G-16433)
FIRST EDITION DESIGN INC
Also Called: First Edition Design Pubg
5202 Old Ashwood Dr (34233-3483)
PHONE..................................941 921-2607
Deborah Gordon, *Principal*
EMP: 9 **EST:** 2010
SALES (est): 252.7K **Privately Held**
WEB: www.firsteditiondesignpublishing.com
SIC: 2731 7336 Book publishing; commercial art & graphic design

(G-16434)
FLORIDA FAMILY MAGAZINE
Also Called: Family Magazines
4851 Hoyer Dr (34241-9222)
PHONE..................................941 922-5437
Mary E Winkle, *President*
Mary Winkle, *President*
Beth Winkle, *Publisher*
Paul Winkle, *Vice Pres*
Elizabeth Winkle, *Sales Executive*
EMP: 8 **EST:** 1996
SALES (est): 692.3K **Privately Held**
WEB: www.nuovobride.com
SIC: 2721 Magazines: publishing only, not printed on site

(G-16435)
FLORIDA HERITAGE WDWKG LLC
2237 Industrial Blvd (34234-3119)
PHONE..................................941 705-9980
Brandon Semrinec, *Principal*
EMP: 7 **EST:** 2016
SALES (est): 430.8K **Privately Held**
WEB: www.fhwoodworking.com
SIC: 2431 Millwork

(G-16436)
FLORIDA HOMES MAGAZINE
1900 Main St Ste 312 (34236-5927)
PHONE..................................941 227-7331
Julie R Gibson, *President*
EMP: 7 **EST:** 2013
SALES (est): 345.4K **Privately Held**
WEB: www.floridahomesmag.com
SIC: 2721 Magazines: publishing only, not printed on site

(G-16437)
FLORIDA KNIFE CO
1735 Apex Rd (34240-9386)
PHONE..................................941 371-2104
Thomas P Johanning, *President*
EMP: 25 **EST:** 1978
SQ FT: 26,000
SALES (est): 2.8MM **Privately Held**
WEB: www.florida-knife.com
SIC: 3545 3541 3423 Machine knives, metalworking; machine tools, metal cutting type; hand & edge tools

(G-16438)
FLORIDA TAPE & LABELS INC
5717b Lawton Dr (34233-2492)
PHONE..................................941 921-5788
Peter Hosmer, *President*
Vicki Hosmer, *Corp Secy*
EMP: 10 **EST:** 1968
SQ FT: 7,500
SALES (est): 845.4K **Privately Held**
SIC: 3069 2759 2752 2672 Tape, pressure sensitive: rubber; labels & seals: printing; commercial printing, lithographic; coated & laminated paper; automotive & apparel trimmings

(G-16439)
FOOTE WOODWORKING INC
8347 Midnight Pass Rd (34242-2703)
PHONE..................................941 923-6553
Steven W Foote, *Director*

EMP: 10 **EST:** 2001
SALES (est): 158.7K **Privately Held**
WEB: www.footewoodworking.com
SIC: 2431 Millwork

(G-16440)
FRZ MARINE
3152 Lena Ln (34240-9767)
PHONE..................................941 322-2631
Frederick Hutchinson, *Principal*
EMP: 7 **EST:** 2005
SALES (est): 188.3K **Privately Held**
SIC: 3531 Marine related equipment

(G-16441)
FUENTES CUSTOM WOODWORK LLC
1490 Blvd Of The Arts (34236-2905)
PHONE..................................941 232-0635
Omar Rodriguez, *Manager*
EMP: 5 **EST:** 2015
SALES (est): 389.1K **Privately Held**
WEB: www.fuentescustomwoodwork.com
SIC: 2431 Millwork

(G-16442)
FUJI INTERNATIONAL LLC
6259 Sturbridge Ct (34238-3700)
PHONE..................................941 961-5472
Kenneth W Wade, *Mng Member*
EMP: 18 **EST:** 2006
SALES (est): 787.8K **Privately Held**
WEB: www.fuji-kikai.co.jp
SIC: 3542 Machine tools, metal forming type
PA: Fuji Machine Works Co., Ltd.
1-14-32, Mitejima, Nishiyodogawa-Ku
Osaka OSK 555-0

(G-16443)
FULL CUT TABS LLC
2153 10th St (34237-3430)
PHONE..................................941 316-1510
EMP: 15 **EST:** 2015
SALES (est): 929.5K **Privately Held**
WEB: www.fullcuttabs.com
SIC: 2671 Packaging paper & plastics film, coated & laminated

(G-16444)
G K WOODWORKS
5365 Matthew Ct (34231-6356)
PHONE..................................941 232-3910
George Karabatsos, *Owner*
EMP: 6 **EST:** 2001
SALES (est): 459.2K **Privately Held**
SIC: 2434 Wood kitchen cabinets

(G-16445)
G PHILLIPS AND SONS LLC
8987 Wildlife Loop (34238-4001)
PHONE..................................248 705-5873
Richard Harding,
Michael Harding,
EMP: 10 **EST:** 2011
SALES (est): 10MM **Privately Held**
WEB: www.gpsagrecycle.com
SIC: 2821 Plastics materials & resins

(G-16446)
GAIL P SCHERER DBA/FLAG LADY O
4539 Winners Cir (34238-5354)
PHONE..................................941 926-9460
Gail Scherer, *Principal*
EMP: 6 **EST:** 2005
SALES (est): 62.3K **Privately Held**
SIC: 2399 Fabricated textile products

(G-16447)
GENERAL MACHINE COMPANY INC
5207 Malaga Ave (34235-3422)
PHONE..................................941 756-2815
Richard Wilson, *President*
Betty E Wilson, *Corp Secy*
EMP: 6 **EST:** 1981
SQ FT: 4,200
SALES (est): 200K **Privately Held**
SIC: 3599 Machine shop, jobbing & repair

(G-16448)
GENIE CAP INC
Also Called: Nwi
4410 Independence Ct (34234-4727)
PHONE..................................941 355-5730
Neide S Santos, *CEO*
EMP: 18 **EST:** 2012
SALES (est): 539K **Privately Held**
WEB: www.guardgenie.com
SIC: 3221 Bottles for packing, bottling & canning: glass

(G-16449)
GETFPV LLC
1060 Goodrich Ave (34236-4305)
PHONE..................................941 444-0021
Tim Nilson, *President*
Andy Graber, *Vice Pres*
Adam Burzynski, *Controller*
EMP: 22 **EST:** 2017
SALES (est): 3.2MM
SALES (corp-wide): 8.4MM **Privately Held**
WEB: www.getfpv.com
SIC: 3944 Games, toys & children's vehicles
PA: Lumenier Holdco Llc
1060 Goodrich Ave
Sarasota FL 34236
941 444-0021

(G-16450)
GLOBAL SEVEN INC
1936 Grove St (34239-4510)
PHONE..................................973 664-1900
Jonathan Dean, *Principal*
EMP: 6 **EST:** 2018
SALES (est): 176.9K **Privately Held**
SIC: 2899 Chemical preparations

(G-16451)
GOLF AGRONOMICS SAND & HLG INC
2165 17th St (34234-7653)
PHONE..................................800 626-1359
Richard G Colyer, *President*
Dale L Mitchell, *Vice Pres*
EMP: 7 **EST:** 2000
SALES (est): 1.2MM **Privately Held**
SIC: 3523 Soil preparation machinery, except turf & grounds

(G-16452)
GPS INDUSTRIES LLC
1358 Fruitville Rd # 210 (34236-5023)
PHONE..................................941 894-8030
Kevin Carpenter, *Branch Mgr*
EMP: 6 **Privately Held**
WEB: www.clubcar.com
SIC: 3663
HQ: Gps Industries, Llc
1074 N Orange Ave
Sarasota FL 34236

(G-16453)
GULF COAST BUSINESS REVIEW
650 Central Ave Ste 5 (34236-4090)
PHONE..................................941 906-9386
David Beliles, *Chairman*
EMP: 6 **EST:** 1996
SALES (est): 112.9K **Privately Held**
SIC: 2711 Newspapers, publishing & printing

(G-16454)
GULF COAST SIGNS SARASOTA INC
1713 Northgate Blvd (34234-2195)
PHONE..................................941 355-8841
Hidayet L Kutat, *CEO*
Kathi Johnson, *Supervisor*
Kathi Johnson-Arco, *Admin Asst*
EMP: 30 **EST:** 1975
SQ FT: 15,000
SALES (est): 7MM **Privately Held**
WEB: www.gulfcoastsigns.com
SIC: 3993 Electric signs; displays & cutouts, window & lobby; letters for signs, metal; name plates: except engraved, etched, etc.: metal

(G-16455)
GUTHMAN SIGNS LLC
519 Interstate Ct (34240-9494)
PHONE..................................941 218-0014
EMP: 6 **EST:** 2019
SALES (est): 700.1K **Privately Held**
WEB: www.guthmansigns.com
SIC: 3993 Signs & advertising specialties

(G-16456)
H V PAYNE MFG LLC
164 Cowpen Ln (34240-9704)
PHONE..................................941 773-1112
EMP: 7 **EST:** 2017
SALES (est): 641.5K **Privately Held**
WEB: www.paynemfg.com
SIC: 3999 Manufacturing industries

(G-16457)
HALIFAX MEDIA GROUP LLC
Also Called: Sarasota Herald Tribune
1777 Main St Ste 200 (34236-5836)
PHONE..................................941 361-4800
Patrick Dorsey, *Publisher*
EMP: 168
SALES (corp-wide): 3.4B **Publicly Held**
WEB: www.gannett.com
SIC: 2711 Newspapers, publishing & printing
HQ: Halifax Media Group, Llc
2339 Beville Rd
Daytona Beach FL 32119
386 265-6700

(G-16458)
HARBOR HOMES
2624 Marlette St (34231-2945)
PHONE..................................941 320-2670
J Brian Bardwick, *Principal*
EMP: 7 **EST:** 2006
SALES (est): 193.7K **Privately Held**
SIC: 2451 Mobile homes, personal or private use

(G-16459)
HENSOLDT AVIONICS USA LLC
2480 Fruitville Rd Ste 6 (34237-6204)
PHONE..................................941 306-1328
Joseph Scott, *CEO*
Herbert Lustig, *Manager*
Megan Rich, *Software Dev*
EMP: 7 **EST:** 2008
SQ FT: 4,500
SALES (est): 1MM **Privately Held**
WEB: www.euroavionics.com
SIC: 3812 3728 7371 5065 Search & navigation equipment; aircraft parts & equipment; computer software development & applications; electronic parts & equipment

(G-16460)
HILTON INTERNATIONAL INDS
6055 Porter Way (34232-6222)
PHONE..................................941 371-2600
Antony Quinn, *President*
Russ Coyle, *Manager*
▲ **EMP:** 42 **EST:** 1958
SQ FT: 11,700
SALES (est): 865.6K **Privately Held**
WEB: www.hiltonind.com
SIC: 3559 3549 Electronic component making machinery; metalworking machinery

(G-16461)
HOWMEDICA OSTEONICS CORP
Also Called: Striker Orthopedic
8235 Blaikie Ct (34240-8323)
PHONE..................................941 378-4600
Michael Orr, *Sales Associate*
Gianni Dattolico, *Associate*
EMP: 9
SALES (corp-wide): 14.3B **Publicly Held**
SIC: 3842 Surgical appliances & supplies
HQ: Howmedica Osteonics Corp.
325 Corporate Dr
Mahwah NJ 07430
201 831-5000

(G-16462)
HULAS MARKET PLACE LLC
1508 Stickney Point Rd (34231-3718)
PHONE..................................941 704-3305
Janice Marquard, *Manager*
EMP: 6 **EST:** 2011
SALES (est): 71.7K **Privately Held**
SIC: 2024 Ice cream, bulk

(G-16463)
IB FURNITURE INC
1236 Porter Rd Unit 4 (34240-9619)
PHONE..................................941 371-5764
Brian Himes, *President*
EMP: 5 **EST:** 1992
SQ FT: 2,500
SALES (est): 600K **Privately Held**
WEB: www.corradoknives.com
SIC: 2511 Wood household furniture

(G-16464)
IJKB LLC
502 N Spoonbill Dr (34236-1818)
PHONE..................................941 953-9046
Kenneth B Mooney, *Manager*
EMP: 7 **EST:** 2015
SALES (est): 206.8K **Privately Held**
SIC: 2211 Gauze

(G-16465)
INFORMA USA INC
101 Paramount Dr Ste 100 (34232-6044)
PHONE..................................561 361-6017
Peter Rigby, *Ch of Bd*
Kenneth B Bohlin, *President*
Aharon Shamash, *Managing Dir*
Patricia Giardina, *Principal*
Briana Hudson, *Business Mgr*
▲ **EMP:** 825
SQ FT: 32,000
SALES (est): 155.6MM
SALES (corp-wide): 3.7B **Privately Held**
WEB: www.informa.com
SIC: 2731 8742 Pamphlets: publishing only, not printed on site; business planning & organizing services
HQ: Informa Group Limited
Mortimer House 37-41
London W1T 3
207 017-5000

(G-16466)
INRAD OPTICS INC
2935 51st St (34234-3325)
PHONE..................................941 544-8278
EMP: 6 **EST:** 2018
SALES (est): 123.7K **Privately Held**
WEB: www.inradoptics.com
SIC: 3699 Laser systems & equipment

(G-16467)
INTEGRTED SIGN ENGRG DSIGN LLC
7007 Webber Rd (34240-9348)
PHONE..................................941 379-5918
Gerald A Lee, *Principal*
EMP: 6 **EST:** 2008
SALES (est): 142.9K **Privately Held**
SIC: 3993 Signs & advertising specialties

(G-16468)
INTERNATIONAL COMPOSITE
1468 Northgate Blvd (34234-4746)
PHONE..................................206 349-7468
EMP: 5 **EST:** 2016
SALES (est): 454.9K **Privately Held**
WEB: www.orcacomposites.com
SIC: 2821 Plastics materials & resins

(G-16469)
INTERTAPE POLYMER CORP (DH)
Also Called: I P G
100 Paramount Dr Ste 300 (34232-6051)
PHONE..................................888 898-7834
Gregory Yull, *President*
Randi Botth, *Senior VP*
Jeffrey Crystal, *Senior VP*
Douglas Malette, *Senior VP*
Shawn Nelson, *Senior VP*
▲ **EMP:** 200 **EST:** 1987
SQ FT: 184,000
SALES (est): 509.6MM
SALES (corp-wide): 1.1B **Privately Held**
WEB: www.itape.com
SIC: 2672 Tape, pressure sensitive: made from purchased materials
HQ: Ipg (Us) Inc
100 Paramount Dr Ste 300
Sarasota FL 34232
941 727-5788

(G-16470)
INTERTAPE POLYMR WOVEN USA INC (DH)
Also Called: Maiweave
100 Paramount Dr Ste 300 (34232-6051)
PHONE..................................800 474-8273
Gregory Yull, *President*
Randi Booth, *Senior VP*
Silvano Iaboni, *Vice Pres*
Jeffrey Crystal, *Treasurer*
EMP: 5 **EST:** 2018
SALES (est): 25MM
SALES (corp-wide): 1.1B **Privately Held**
WEB: www.itape.com
SIC: 2231 Overcoatings: wool, mohair or similar fibers
HQ: Ipg (Us) Holdings Inc.
100 Paramount Dr Ste 300
Sarasota FL 34232
941 727-5788

(G-16471)
IPG (US) HOLDINGS INC (HQ)
Also Called: Intertape Polymer Group
100 Paramount Dr Ste 300 (34232-6051)
PHONE..................................941 727-5788
James Pantelidis, *Ch of Bd*
Jim Bob Carpenter, *President*
Burgess Hildreth, *President*
Gregary Yull, *President*
Randi Booth, *Vice Pres*
◆ **EMP:** 75 **EST:** 1997
SQ FT: 20,000
SALES (est): 571.4MM
SALES (corp-wide): 1.1B **Privately Held**
WEB: www.itape.com
SIC: 2672 3953 Tape, pressure sensitive: made from purchased materials; stencils, painting & marking
PA: Le Groupe Intertape Polymer Inc
9999 Boul Cavendish Bureau 200
Saint-Laurent QC H4M 2
514 731-7591

(G-16472)
IPG (US) INC (DH)
100 Paramount Dr Ste 300 (34232-6051)
PHONE..................................941 727-5788
Dale Mc Sween, *President*
Burgess Hildreth, *Vice Pres*
Mary B Thompson, *Vice Pres*
EMP: 1 **EST:** 1997
SALES (est): 546.4MM
SALES (corp-wide): 1.1B **Privately Held**
WEB: www.itape.com
SIC: 2672 3953 Tape, pressure sensitive: made from purchased materials; stencils, painting & marking
HQ: Ipg (Us) Holdings Inc.
100 Paramount Dr Ste 300
Sarasota FL 34232
941 727-5788

(G-16473)
ISLAND LIFESTYLE IMPORTERS LLC
426 Interstate Ct (34240-8765)
PHONE..................................941 378-3200
Kenneth R Frailing, *Principal*
EMP: 5 **EST:** 2016
SALES (est): 374.4K **Privately Held**
WEB: www.islandlifestyleimporters.com
SIC: 3999 Cigarette & cigar products & accessories

(G-16474)
J & N STONE INC
6111 Clark Center Ave (34238-2722)
PHONE..................................941 924-6200
EMP: 34
SALES (corp-wide): 7.8MM **Privately Held**
SIC: 3272 Mfg Concrete Products
PA: J & N Stone, Inc.
135 Bargain Barn Rd
Davenport FL 33837
863 422-7369

(G-16475)
J T E INC
Also Called: Signs By Tomorrow
3959 Sawyer Rd (34233-1218)
PHONE..................................941 925-2605
Tim Eastwood, *President*
Janet Eastwood, *Vice Pres*
EMP: 5 **EST:** 1991
SALES (est): 500K **Privately Held**
WEB: www.signsbytomorrow.com
SIC: 3993 Signs & advertising specialties

(G-16476)
JAMESTOWN KITCHENS INC
4050 N Washington Blvd (34234-4837)
PHONE..................................941 359-1166
James Gerard, *President*
Brian Higgins, *General Mgr*
EMP: 4 **EST:** 2009
SQ FT: 3,000
SALES (est): 3MM **Privately Held**
WEB: www.jamestownkitchenssarasota.com
SIC: 2434 Wood kitchen cabinets

(G-16477)
JJ SCREENPRINT LLC
1850 Porter Lake Dr Ste 1 (34240-7802)
PHONE..................................941 587-1801
Jacob E Jock, *Manager*
EMP: 7 **EST:** 2015
SALES (est): 302.8K **Privately Held**
WEB: www.theorythreads.com
SIC: 2752 Commercial printing, lithographic

(G-16478)
K & A AUDIO INC
4604 Ashton Rd (34233-3488)
P.O. Box 668, Osprey (34229-0668)
PHONE..................................941 925-7648
Kim Martinelli, *President*
Anthony Milat, *Vice Pres*
EMP: 11 **EST:** 1995
SALES (est): 899.5K **Privately Held**
WEB: www.kaaudio.com
SIC: 3651 Household audio & video equipment

(G-16479)
K & D WELDING LLC ✪
848 Gantt Ave (34232-6700)
PHONE..................................941 586-0258
Kenny Mitchell, *Principal*
EMP: 6 **EST:** 2020
SALES (est): 227.8K **Privately Held**
SIC: 7692 Welding repair

(G-16480)
KANALFLAKT INC (PA)
1712 Northgate Blvd (34234-2116)
PHONE..................................941 359-3267
Oliver Green, *President*
▲ **EMP:** 11 **EST:** 1981
SQ FT: 20,000
SALES (est): 9.1MM **Privately Held**
SIC: 3564 5084 Blowing fans: industrial or commercial; fans, industrial

(G-16481)
KANE-MILLER CORP (PA)
1515 Ringling Blvd # 840 (34236-6781)
PHONE..................................941 346-2003
Stanley B Kane, *CEO*
Harold Oelbaum, *President*
Robert Wininger, *CFO*
Kira Lynn, *Executive*
EMP: 5 **EST:** 1920
SALES (est): 38.6MM **Privately Held**
WEB: www.kanemillercorp.com
SIC: 2077 Tallow rendering, inedible

(G-16482)
KITCHENS XTREME LLC
4181 Taggart Cay S # 301 (34233-4831)
PHONE..................................941 387-5181
Randy Baxter, *Principal*
EMP: 6 **EST:** 2010
SALES (est): 188.4K **Privately Held**
WEB: www.kitchenrefacinginsarasotafl.com
SIC: 2273 Carpets & rugs

(G-16483)
KOALA TEE INC (USA)
2160 17th St (34234-7654)
PHONE..................................941 954-7700
Jess Manley, *President*
Carmen Manley, *General Mgr*
Barry D Fox, *Vice Pres*
Bert Davis, *Production*
Sheri Hirschberg, *Accounts Mgr*
EMP: 27 **EST:** 1976
SQ FT: 11,000
SALES (est): 3.1MM **Privately Held**
WEB: www.koalatee.com
SIC: 2759 7336 7389 5199 Screen printing; silk screen design; embroidering of advertising on shirts, etc.; advertising specialties

(G-16484)
KSR PUBLISHING INC
2477 Stickney Point Rd 315b (34231-4022)
PHONE..................................941 388-7050
Kristine S Russell, *President*
Kara Nadeau, *Editor*
Jim Russell, *Sales Mgr*
EMP: 24 **EST:** 2003
SALES (est): 2.3MM **Privately Held**
WEB: www.hpnonline.com
SIC: 2741 Miscellaneous publishing

(G-16485)
L3 TECHNOLOGIES INC
Also Called: Medical Education Technologies
6300 Edgelake Dr (34240-8817)
PHONE..................................941 377-5562
EMP: 6
SALES (corp-wide): 3.7B **Publicly Held**
WEB: www.l3harris.com
SIC: 3663 Telemetering equipment, electronic
HQ: L3 Technologies, Inc.
600 3rd Ave Fl 34
New York NY 10016
321 727-9100

(G-16486)
LA PERLELLE LLC
17 Fillmore Dr (34236-1425)
PHONE..................................941 388-2458
EMP: 6 **EST:** 2008
SALES (est): 150K **Privately Held**
WEB: www.starmandscircle.wordpress.com
SIC: 3423 Jewelers' hand tools

(G-16487)
LEDA PRINTING INC
Also Called: Sir Speedy
3939 S Tamiami Trl (34231-3605)
PHONE..................................941 922-1563
Eileen C Rosenzweig, *President*
Jackie Sanderson, *Vice Pres*
Michael Sanderson, *Admin Sec*
EMP: 25 **EST:** 1979
SQ FT: 7,500
SALES (est): 4.3MM **Privately Held**
WEB: www.sirspeedy.com
SIC: 2752 2791 2789 2759 Commercial printing, lithographic; typesetting; bookbinding & related work; commercial printing

(G-16488)
LIFE IN A TEE SHIRT PRTG LLC
2905 Woodpine Cir (34231-6325)
PHONE..................................941 927-0116
Teresa McNeil, *Principal*
EMP: 6 **EST:** 2016
SALES (est): 139.2K **Privately Held**
SIC: 2752 Commercial printing, lithographic

(G-16489)
LOCATION 3 HOLDINGS LLC
Also Called: Cabinets Extraordinaire
5686 Fruitville Rd (34232-6407)
PHONE..................................941 342-3443
Tracy Cotterill, *Vice Pres*
Dawn Hlasnick, *Human Resources*
Jason L Cotterill, *Mng Member*
Joseph Menna, *Sr Project Mgr*
Dianna Graham, *Manager*
EMP: 13 **EST:** 2013
SQ FT: 2,300
SALES (est): 15.3MM **Privately Held**
WEB: www.cabinetsextra.com
SIC: 2499 5211 5722 Kitchen, bathroom & household ware: wood; bathroom fixtures, equipment & supplies; kitchens, complete (sinks, cabinets, etc.)
PA: Location 3 Pty Ltd
Shop 3 221 Brisbane Road
Biggera Waters QLD 4216

(G-16490)
LOTUS STRESS RELIEF LLC
2965 Bee Ridge Rd (34239-7194)
PHONE..................................941 706-2778
Marcia W Schulte, *Principal*
Marcia Schulte, *Marketing Staff*
Allan A Schulte, *Exec Dir*
EMP: 10 **EST:** 2008
SALES (est): 2.7MM **Privately Held**
WEB: www.lotusstressrelief.com
SIC: 2833 Medicinals & botanicals

(G-16491)
LUMENIER HOLDCO LLC (PA)
1060 Goodrich Ave (34236-4305)
PHONE..................................941 444-0021
Tim Nilson, *President*
Andy Graber, *Vice Pres*
EMP: 1 **EST:** 2017
SALES (est): 8.4MM **Privately Held**
WEB: www.getfpv.com
SIC: 3944 3721 Games, toys & children's vehicles; motorized aircraft

(G-16492)
LUMENIER LLC
1060 Goodrich Ave (34236-4305)
PHONE..................................941 444-0021
Tim Nilson, *President*
Andy Graber, *Vice Pres*
EMP: 14 **EST:** 2017
SALES (est): 4.9MM
SALES (corp-wide): 8.4MM **Privately Held**
WEB: www.getfpv.com
SIC: 3721 Motorized aircraft
PA: Lumenier Holdco Llc
1060 Goodrich Ave
Sarasota FL 34236
941 444-0021

(G-16493)
LUXE PRINTS LLC ✪
329 Central Ave (34236-4915)
PHONE..................................941 484-4500
EMP: 6 **EST:** 2020
SALES (est): 358.9K **Privately Held**
WEB: www.artisticphotocanvas.com
SIC: 2752 Commercial printing, lithographic

(G-16494)
M3 BIOPHARMA INC
5437 Manchini St (34238-2153)
PHONE..................................858 603-8296
Matthew Pino, *Administration*
EMP: 7 **EST:** 2015
SALES (est): 159K **Privately Held**
SIC: 2834 Pharmaceutical preparations

(G-16495)
MAD AT SAD LLC
Also Called: Kombucha 221b.c.
4050 Middle Ave (34234-2111)
PHONE..................................941 203-8854
Eric Lundquist, *Mng Member*
Anthony Rechul, *Director*
EMP: 15 **EST:** 2013
SALES (est): 2.2MM **Privately Held**
WEB: www.kombucha221bc.com
SIC: 2099 Tea blending

(G-16496)
MAGNOLIA CUSTOM CABINETRY
1830 S Osprey Ave Ste 107 (34239-3615)
PHONE..................................941 906-8744
Ryan Abel, *Principal*
EMP: 7 **EST:** 2015
SALES (est): 575K **Privately Held**
WEB: www.magnoliasrq.com
SIC: 2434 Wood kitchen cabinets

(G-16497)
MAINSTREAM FIBER NETWORKS
5124 Redbriar Ct (34238-4322)
PHONE..................................941 807-6100
J Terry Drury, *CEO*
EMP: 6 **EST:** 2005
SALES (est): 1MM **Privately Held**
WEB: www.msfiber.net
SIC: 2655 Fiber cans, drums & similar products

(G-16498)
MAKI PRINTING LLC
1173 Palmer Wood Ct (34236-2635)
PHONE..................................941 809-7574

EMP: 10
SALES (corp-wide): 232.2K **Privately Held**
SIC: 2752 Commercial printing, lithographic
PA: Maki Printing Llc
4130 Boca Pointe Dr
Sarasota FL 34238
941 925-4802

(G-16499)
MAKI PRINTING LLC (PA)
Also Called: Benchmark Blueprinting
4130 Boca Pointe Dr (34238-5572)
PHONE..................................941 925-4802
Raymond Hautamaki, *Principal*
EMP: 11 **EST:** 2018
SALES (est): 232.2K **Privately Held**
SIC: 2752 Commercial printing, lithographic

(G-16500)
MANASOTA OPTICS INC
Also Called: Moi
1743 Northgate Blvd (34234-2138)
PHONE..................................941 359-1748
Jonah Lowery, *President*
David A Lowery, *President*
EMP: 9 **EST:** 1994
SQ FT: 5,000
SALES (est): 1.3MM **Privately Held**
WEB: www.manasotaoptics.com
SIC: 3827 Optical instruments & apparatus; mirrors, optical

(G-16501)
MANASOTA PALLETS
7952 Fruitville Rd (34240-8829)
PHONE..................................941 360-0562
Bryan Sehkay, *Owner*
EMP: 13 **EST:** 2001
SALES (est): 878.7K **Privately Held**
SIC: 2448 Pallets, wood

(G-16502)
MARBELITE INTERNATIONAL CORP
1500 Global Ct (34240-7860)
PHONE..................................941 378-0860
Sam Contrasto, *President*
Marsha Contrasto, *Corp Secy*
Robert Kopfle, *Warehouse Mgr*
Josh Milligan, *Manager*
▼ **EMP:** 7 **EST:** 1992
SQ FT: 16,000
SALES (est): 1.5MM **Privately Held**
WEB: www.marbelite.com
SIC: 2952 5072 Coating compounds, tar; hand tools

(G-16503)
MARCHANT MACHINE CORPORATION
Also Called: Manufcturers Metal Forming Mch
8713 Amaretto Ave (34238-4501)
P.O. Box 138, Beltsville MD (20704-0138)
PHONE..................................301 937-4481
Daryl C Marchant, *President*
Don A Marchant, *Treasurer*
Lois Marchant, *Admin Sec*
EMP: 7 **EST:** 1953
SALES (est): 545.4K **Privately Held**
WEB: www.marchantmachine.com
SIC: 3549 Metalworking machinery

(G-16504)
MARTIN & VLEMINCKX RIDES LLC (HQ)
253 Cosmopolitan Ct (34236-6894)
PHONE..................................407 566-0036
Charles Bingham, *Partner*
Pierre Cloutier, *Vice Pres*
Kevin C Hehn, *Vice Pres*
David Welsh, *Project Mgr*
Gerry Gosine, *VP Sales*
EMP: 5 **EST:** 2003
SALES (est): 3.3MM
SALES (corp-wide): 836.1K **Privately Held**
WEB: www.martin-vleminckx.com
SIC: 3441 Fabricated structural metal
PA: Martin, G. & A. Vleminckx Amusement Ltd
1255 Boul Laird Bureau 215
Mont-Royal QC H3P 2
514 733-0060

(G-16505)
MDC ENGINEERING INC (PA)
Also Called: Packaging Machines
1701 Desoto Rd (34234-3066)
PHONE..................................941 358-0610
Michelle Bergeron, *President*
Jon Ford, *CFO*
▲ **EMP:** 13 **EST:** 2002
SQ FT: 15,000
SALES (est): 3.2MM **Privately Held**
WEB: www.rndautomation.com
SIC: 3565 Vacuum packaging machinery

(G-16506)
MERCANTILE TWO
28 S Blvd Of Presidents (34236-1424)
PHONE..................................941 388-0059
EMP: 9 **EST:** 2016
SALES (est): 226.9K **Privately Held**
SIC: 2721 Magazines: publishing only, not printed on site

(G-16507)
MICTRON INC
8130 Fruitville Rd (34240-5204)
PHONE..................................941 371-6564
Myron Weinstein, *President*
Ron Smith, *Corp Secy*
Rolf Kopp, *Vice Pres*
EMP: 23 **EST:** 1962
SQ FT: 20,140
SALES (est): 1.5MM **Privately Held**
WEB: www.mictron.net
SIC: 3599 Machine shop, jobbing & repair

(G-16508)
MIDNITE SON II OF SARASOTA
Also Called: John Measel Cabinets
1257 Porter Rd (34240-9627)
PHONE..................................941 377-6029
John Measel, *President*
EMP: 9 **EST:** 1983
SQ FT: 6,000
SALES (est): 728.4K **Privately Held**
SIC: 2434 Wood kitchen cabinets

(G-16509)
MILES PARTNERSHIP II LLC (PA)
Also Called: See Magazines
6751 Prof Pkwy W Ste 200 (34240)
PHONE..................................941 342-2300
Roger W Miles, *CEO*
David Burgess, *President*
Lauren Bourgoing, *Vice Pres*
Nate Huff, *Vice Pres*
Ryan Thompson, *Vice Pres*
▲ **EMP:** 120
SQ FT: 15,364
SALES (est): 24.7MM **Privately Held**
WEB: www.milespartnership.com
SIC: 2721 Magazines: publishing only, not printed on site; statistical reports (periodicals): publishing only

(G-16510)
MILLER BROTHERS CONTRACTORS
Also Called: Septic Tank Drain Fld/Nsite Sw
990 Cattlemen Rd (34232-2810)
PHONE..................................941 371-4162
Albert E Miller Jr, *President*
Roger Miller, *Principal*
EMP: 10 **EST:** 1968
SQ FT: 1,500
SALES (est): 2.1MM **Privately Held**
WEB: www.millerbrosinc.com
SIC: 3272 7699 1711 Septic tanks, concrete; septic tank cleaning service; septic system construction

(G-16511)
MKM SARASOTA LLC
2363 Industrial Blvd (34234-3121)
PHONE..................................941 358-0383
Raymond Gibson, *President*
Mark Nightingale, *Director*
Marty Myers, *Executive*
EMP: 30 **EST:** 2015
SQ FT: 18,000
SALES (est): 2MM **Privately Held**
WEB: www.mkmsarasotallc.com
SIC: 3451 3599 Screw machine products; machine shop, jobbing & repair

(G-16512)
MODERN SETTINGS LLC
6331 Porter Rd Unit 8 (34240-9701)
PHONE..................................800 645-5585
Harry Bender, *Mng Member*
Charles Binder,
EMP: 8 **EST:** 1951
SQ FT: 22,000
SALES (est): 678.9K **Privately Held**
WEB: www.modernsettings.com
SIC: 3915 Jewelers' findings & materials

(G-16513)
MORAN WOODWORKING LLC
275 Herons Run Dr Apt 707 (34232-1749)
PHONE..................................941 600-8842
Charles J Moran, *Principal*
EMP: 6 **EST:** 2019
SALES (est): 245.7K **Privately Held**
SIC: 2431 Millwork

(G-16514)
MORNING STAR OF SARASOTA INC
Also Called: Graber Cabinets
1985 Cattlemen Rd Unit A (34232-6258)
PHONE..................................941 371-0392
Todd Schleicher, *President*
Patricia Schleicher, *Corp Secy*
EMP: 9 **EST:** 1969
SQ FT: 7,000
SALES (est): 738.8K **Privately Held**
WEB: www.grabercabinets.com
SIC: 2522 2519 2541 2434 Office chairs, benches & stools, except wood; lawn & garden furniture, except wood & metal; wood partitions & fixtures; wood kitchen cabinets

(G-16515)
MR BONES STUMP GRINDING
5590 Swift Rd (34231-6210)
P.O. Box 19115 (34276-2115)
PHONE..................................941 927-0790
Troy Zengel, *Principal*
EMP: 9 **EST:** 2001
SALES (est): 1.2MM **Privately Held**
SIC: 3599 Grinding castings for the trade

(G-16516)
MR GOODWOOD INC
4643 Meadowview Cir (34233-1971)
PHONE..................................941 961-4478
Mark Sackerlotzky, *Principal*
EMP: 7 **EST:** 2010
SALES (est): 94.8K **Privately Held**
WEB: www.mrgoodwood.net
SIC: 2434 Wood kitchen cabinets

(G-16517)
MUMFORD MICRO MCH WORKS LLC
1882 Porter Lake Dr # 103 (34240-7808)
PHONE..................................814 720-7291
Jeremy Mumford, *General Mgr*
EMP: 9 **EST:** 2017
SALES (est): 497.2K **Privately Held**
WEB: www.precisionmicromachine.com
SIC: 3999 Manufacturing industries

(G-16518)
MURSE PROPERTIES LLC
6650 S Tammy Amy Trl (34231)
PHONE..................................941 966-3380
John Murse, *President*
Lucy Murse, *Vice Pres*
EMP: 7 **EST:** 1987
SQ FT: 20,214
SALES (est): 137.6K **Privately Held**
SIC: 2273 5713 Carpets & rugs; rugs

(G-16519)
NATURAL STONE SLTONS FNEST SRS (PA)
2303 17th St (34234-1902)
PHONE..................................941 954-1100
Doris Fox, *Mng Member*
EMP: 21 **EST:** 2010
SALES (est): 3.4MM **Privately Held**
WEB: www.nssmillworks.com
SIC: 3281 1799 Granite, cut & shaped; counter top installation

(G-16520)
NATURES BIOSCIENCE LLC
5020 Clark Rd (34233-3231)
PHONE..................................800 570-7450
EMP: 6 **EST:** 2017
SALES (est): 1.2MM **Privately Held**
WEB: www.naturesbioscience.com
SIC: 2834 Pharmaceutical preparations

(G-16521)
NATURES OWN PEST CONTROL INC
1899 Porter Lake Dr # 103 (34240-7897)
PHONE..................................941 378-3334
Mark Studtmann, *President*
Travis Wellbrock, *Vice Pres*
Ida D'Eptorre, *Manager*
EMP: 6 **EST:** 1984
SALES (est): 434.1K **Privately Held**
SIC: 2879 7342 Insecticides & pesticides; pest control services

(G-16522)
NC IV INC
Also Called: NC II
1788 Barber Rd (34240-8304)
PHONE..................................941 378-9133
Robert Price, *President*
Mary Price, *Vice Pres*
Michael Hancock, *Accounts Mgr*
◆ **EMP:** 10 **EST:** 1992
SQ FT: 10,000
SALES (est): 2.5MM **Privately Held**
WEB: www.nctwo.com
SIC: 3663 Cable television equipment

(G-16523)
NEAT PRINT INC
Also Called: Divine Coffee Roasters
2147 Porter Lake Dr Ste G (34240-8854)
PHONE..................................941 545-1517
Raca Dejan, *Principal*
EMP: 11 **EST:** 2011
SALES (est): 1.1MM **Privately Held**
WEB: www.neatprint.com
SIC: 2752 Commercial printing, lithographic

(G-16524)
NEVER WRONG TOYS & GAMES LLC ✪
2201 Cantu Ct Ste 100 (34232-6254)
PHONE..................................941 371-0909
Eva Wong, *Mng Member*
EMP: 7 **EST:** 2020
SALES (est): 446.3K **Privately Held**
WEB: www.neverwrongtoys.com
SIC: 3944 Games, toys & children's vehicles

(G-16525)
NKEM INC
Also Called: Cymed
1451 Sarasota Center Blvd (34240-7803)
PHONE..................................800 582-0707
Walter Leise, *President*
EMP: 10 **EST:** 2009
SQ FT: 10,640
SALES (est): 363.5K **Privately Held**
SIC: 3841 Surgical & medical instruments

(G-16526)
NUMERATOR TECHNOLOGIES INC
862 Freeling Dr (34242-1025)
P.O. Box 868 (34230-0868)
PHONE..................................941 807-5333
James Turner, *President*
▼ **EMP:** 8 **EST:** 2008
SALES (est): 454.6K **Privately Held**
WEB: www.numeratortech.com
SIC: 2879 Agricultural chemicals

(G-16527)
NUTRITIOUS YOU LLC
6583 Midnight Pass Rd (34242-2506)
PHONE..................................941 203-5203
Marina Sommers, *Principal*
EMP: 6 **EST:** 2012
SQ FT: 700

SALES (est): 448.9K Privately Held
WEB: www.nutritiousyou.com
SIC: 2099 Food preparations

(G-16528)
OBSERVER GROUP INC
Also Called: Longboat Observer
1970 Main St Fl 3 (34236-5923)
P.O. Box 3169 (34230-3169)
PHONE....................................941 383-5509
Matthew G Walsh, *President*
David Beliles, *Chairman*
EMP: 23 EST: 1978
SALES (est): 4.7MM Privately Held
WEB: www.yourobserver.com
SIC: 2711 Newspapers, publishing & printing

(G-16529)
OBSERVER MEDIA GROUP INC (PA)
Also Called: Observer Group
1970 Main St Fl 3 (34236-5923)
P.O. Box 3169 (34230-3169)
PHONE....................................941 366-3468
Emily Walsh, *President*
Matthew Walsh, *Principal*
Kaelyn Adix, *Editor*
Emma Burke, *Advt Staff*
Jason Camillo, *Software Engr*
EMP: 75 EST: 2004
SALES (est): 13.2MM Privately Held
WEB: www.yourobserver.com
SIC: 2711 Commercial printing & newspaper publishing combined; newspapers, publishing & printing

(G-16530)
OCTEX HOLDINGS LLC (PA)
901 Sarasota Center Blvd (34240-7816)
PHONE....................................941 371-6767
James C Westman, *CEO*
James Westman, *CEO*
John Hoskins, *President*
Jonathan D Goetze, *Partner*
Dan Mallon, *CFO*
EMP: 54 EST: 2009
SQ FT: 60,000
SALES (est): 17.5MM Privately Held
WEB: www.octexgroup.com
SIC: 3089 Injection molding of plastics

(G-16531)
OLLO USA LLC
1223 S Tamiami Trl (34239-2208)
PHONE....................................941 366-0600
Edward H Sarbey, *CEO*
John A McCann, *COO*
◆ EMP: 7 EST: 2011
SQ FT: 12,500
SALES (est): 172.1K Privately Held
WEB: www.ollousa.com
SIC: 2789 7389 Display mounting; design services

(G-16532)
OMNISYS LLC
Also Called: Voicetech
551 N Cattlemen Rd (34232-6448)
PHONE....................................800 325-2017
Jerry Bowen, *Manager*
EMP: 27 Privately Held
WEB: www.omnisys.com
SIC: 3661 Electronic secretary
PA: Omnisys, Llc
15950 Dallas Pkwy Ste 350
Dallas TX 75248

(G-16533)
ORCA COMPOSITES LLC
1468 Northgate Blvd (34234-4746)
PHONE....................................206 349-5300
Scott Macindoe, *Principal*
EMP: 19 EST: 2016
SALES (est): 2.4MM Privately Held
WEB: www.orcacomposites.com
SIC: 2821 Plastics materials & resins

(G-16534)
PACER ELECTRONICS FLORIDA INC (PA)
1555 Apex Rd (34240-9390)
PHONE....................................941 378-5774
Joseph Swiatkowski, *CEO*
John M Swiatkowski, *President*
Mary Swiatkowski, *Corp Secy*
▼ EMP: 22 EST: 1984
SQ FT: 45,000
SALES (est): 9.9MM Privately Held
WEB: www.pacergroup.net
SIC: 3679 5063 Harness assemblies for electronic use: wire or cable; wiring devices

(G-16535)
PALLET DUDE LLC
7952 Fruitville Rd (34240-8829)
PHONE....................................941 720-1667
Brian Sehlke, *Manager*
EMP: 10 EST: 2016
SALES (est): 1.1MM Privately Held
SIC: 2448 Pallets, wood

(G-16536)
PAT CLARK CUSTOM WOODWORKING L
5180 Island Date St (34232-5655)
PHONE....................................941 376-1387
Patrick L Clark, *Principal*
EMP: 7 EST: 2003
SALES (est): 240K Privately Held
SIC: 2431 Millwork

(G-16537)
PATRICE INC
1747 Independence Blvd E (34234-2137)
P.O. Box 291848, Kerrville TX (78029-1848)
PHONE....................................941 359-2577
Patrice Viles, *President*
EMP: 10 EST: 1988
SALES (est): 774.6K Privately Held
WEB: www.patricejewelry.com
SIC: 3961 5944 Costume jewelry; jewelry stores

(G-16538)
PATTYS ON MAIN LLC
1400 Main St (34236-5701)
PHONE....................................941 650-9080
Rafael Perez, *Principal*
EMP: 8 EST: 2011
SALES (est): 269.9K Privately Held
WEB: www.pattysonmain.com
SIC: 3421 Table & food cutlery, including butchers'

(G-16539)
PEARTREE CABINETS AND DESIGN
1635 12th St (34236-2605)
PHONE....................................941 377-7655
Robert Poirier, *Principal*
EMP: 8 EST: 2015
SALES (est): 390.6K Privately Held
WEB: www.peartreecabinetsanddesign.com
SIC: 2434 Wood kitchen cabinets

(G-16540)
PEPPER TREE
1269 1st St Ste 7 (34236-5518)
PHONE....................................941 922-2662
Julie A Howell, *Principal*
EMP: 6 EST: 2005
SALES (est): 233.5K Privately Held
SIC: 7372 Publishers' computer software

(G-16541)
PEPPERTREE PRESS LLC
6341 Yellow Wood Pl (34241-8319)
PHONE....................................941 922-2662
EMP: 6 EST: 2006
SALES (est): 80.5K Privately Held
WEB: www.peppertreepublishing.com
SIC: 2741 Miscellaneous publishing

(G-16542)
PEPSI-COLA BOTTLING CO TAMPA
7881 Fruitville Rd (34240-9280)
PHONE....................................941 378-1058
Joanie Sandoval, *General Mgr*
Ahmed Saber, *Plant Mgr*
Nicholas Vanbenschoten, *Finance*
Ryan Morris, *Sales Staff*
Gerald Patton, *Manager*
EMP: 224
SALES (corp-wide): 70.3B Publicly Held
WEB: www.pepsico.com
SIC: 2086 Carbonated soft drinks, bottled & canned
HQ: Pepsi-Cola Bottling Company Of Tampa
11315 N 30th St
Tampa FL 33612
813 971-2550

(G-16543)
PETERSON MANUFACTURING LLC
155 Cattlemen Rd (34232-6397)
PHONE....................................941 371-4989
Dale Hersey,
EMP: 18 EST: 2019
SALES (est): 1.3MM Privately Held
SIC: 3999 Manufacturing industries

(G-16544)
PETERSON MANUFACTURING CO INC
155 Cattlemen Rd (34232-6397)
PHONE....................................941 371-4989
Bob Longo, *General Mgr*
Charles W Naylor, *Chairman*
Al Anderson, *Vice Pres*
Melissa Bontrager, *Controller*
EMP: 35 EST: 1957
SQ FT: 33,000
SALES (est): 3.6MM Privately Held
WEB: www.petersonmfg.com
SIC: 3469 3965 3498 Stamping metal for the trade; fasteners, buttons, needles & pins; fabricated pipe & fittings

(G-16545)
PLEASURE INTERIORS LLC
2207 Industrial Blvd (34234-3119)
PHONE....................................941 756-9969
EMP: 25
SALES (est): 2.5MM Privately Held
SIC: 2431 2499 3553 Mfg Millwork Mfg Wood Products Mfg Woodworking Machinery

(G-16546)
POLY COATINGS OF SOUTH INC
5944 Sandphil Rd (34232-6326)
PHONE....................................941 371-8555
Bernard Zapatha, *President*
Glenn Zapatha, *Vice Pres*
Elaine Zapatha, *Admin Sec*
EMP: 10 EST: 1980
SQ FT: 9,000
SALES (est): 2MM Privately Held
WEB: www.polycoatings.com
SIC: 3471 2851 3399 Finishing, metals or formed products; paints & allied products; laminating steel

(G-16547)
PRIME PAVERS INC
7235 Mauna Loa Blvd (34241-5975)
PHONE....................................941 320-7878
Mauricio Delima, *Branch Mgr*
EMP: 20 Privately Held
WEB: www.primepavers.net
SIC: 2951 Asphalt paving mixtures & blocks
PA: Prime Pavers Inc
1851 57th St
Sarasota FL 34243

(G-16548)
PROTEK ELECTRONICS INC
1781 Independence Blvd (34234-2106)
PHONE....................................941 351-4399
Douglas Santoro, *CEO*
Mike Messer, *Production*
Todd Barham, *Marketing Staff*
EMP: 46 EST: 1987
SQ FT: 15,000
SALES (est): 5.4MM
SALES (corp-wide): 6.8MM Privately Held
SIC: 3679 3672 Electronic circuits; printed circuit boards
PA: Ibis L.L.C.
20416 Harper Ave
Harper Woods MI 48225
313 642-1740

(G-16549)
PROTOTYPE PLASTICS LLC
1523 Edgar Pl (34240-9054)
PHONE....................................941 371-3380
EMP: 6 EST: 2015
SALES (est): 116K Privately Held
SIC: 3089 Plastic containers, except foam

(G-16550)
QUALITY CABINET RECOVERING
3316 Bay Oaks Dr (34234-6546)
PHONE....................................941 378-1715
Al Forestandi, *Principal*
EMP: 6 EST: 2008
SALES (est): 213.2K Privately Held
SIC: 2434 Wood kitchen cabinets

(G-16551)
QUALITY CARTON INC
Also Called: Quality Carton of Florida
4686 Ashton Rd (34233-3408)
P.O. Box 20492 (34276-3492)
PHONE....................................941 921-1770
Frank Kowack, *Manager*
Kowack Frank, *Manager*
EMP: 6 Privately Held
WEB: www.qualitycartonofflorida.com
SIC: 3565 Carton packing machines
PA: Quality Carton, Inc.
1 International Blvd # 610
Mahwah NJ 07495

(G-16552)
QUALITY DRIVEN
4023 Sawyer Rd Unit 216 (34233-1276)
PHONE....................................941 923-3322
Jeremy A Howe, *Owner*
EMP: 7 EST: 2013
SALES (est): 331.6K Privately Held
WEB: www.qualitydrivensrq.com
SIC: 7694 Motor repair services

(G-16553)
QUALITY POWDER COATING INC
2025 Porter Lake Dr F (34240-8834)
PHONE....................................941 378-0051
Steve Schwart, *Principal*
Troy Newport, *Natl Sales Mgr*
EMP: 16 EST: 1998
SALES (est): 1.1MM Privately Held
SIC: 3471 Finishing, metals or formed products

(G-16554)
RB KANALFLAKT INC
1712 Northgate Blvd (34234-2116)
PHONE....................................941 359-3267
Ola Wettergren, *President*
Rainer Blomster, *Principal*
Gerald Engstrom, *Principal*
▲ EMP: 36 EST: 1981
SALES (est): 1.3MM
SALES (corp-wide): 9.1MM Privately Held
SIC: 3564 Blowers & fans
PA: Kanalflakt, Inc
1712 Northgate Blvd
Sarasota FL 34234
941 359-3267

(G-16555)
RECYCLED VINYL
848 Myrtle St (34234-5233)
PHONE....................................727 434-1857
Kim Bass, *Principal*
EMP: 7 EST: 2010
SALES (est): 89K Privately Held
SIC: 3081 7389 Vinyl film & sheet; business services

(G-16556)
REDMONT SIGN LLC (PA)
Also Called: Stewart Signs
2201 Cantu Ct Ste 215 (34232-6255)
PHONE....................................941 378-4242
John A Yax, *Vice Pres*
Candi AIN, *Accounting Mgr*
Tim Crowe, *Sales Staff*
Josh Brasher, *Mng Member*
Ashley Hall, *Manager*
▼ EMP: 72 EST: 1968
SQ FT: 12,500

GEOGRAPHIC

SALES (est): 13.5MM **Privately Held**
WEB: www.stewartsigns.com
SIC: 3993 5099 Signs & advertising specialties; signs, except electric

(G-16557)
REEF RUNNER CHARTERS LLC
2561 Marblehead Dr (34231-5181)
PHONE..................................941 921-0560
Hunter Roberts, *Principal*
EMP: 6 **EST:** 2009
SALES (est): 120.4K **Privately Held**
SIC: 3949 Water sports equipment

(G-16558)
REGIONAL CNSTR RESOURCES INC
66 N Washington Dr (34236-1416)
P.O. Box 1233, Montgomery TX (77356-1233)
PHONE..................................713 789-5131
EMP: 20
SQ FT: 4,500
SALES (est): 2.6MM **Privately Held**
SIC: 3446 Mfg Architectural Metalwork

(G-16559)
RFG PETRO SYSTEMS LLC (PA)
32 S Osprey Ave Ste 1 (34236-5843)
PHONE..................................941 487-7524
EMP: 12 **EST:** 2012
SALES (est): 1.4MM **Privately Held**
WEB: www.rfgpetrosystems.com
SIC: 3533 Bits, oil & gas field tools: rock

(G-16560)
ROBERTSON TRANSFORMER CO
Also Called: Robertson Worldwide
4152 Independence Ct C2 (34234-2147)
PHONE..................................708 388-2315
William Bryant, *CEO*
Dale Marcus, *CFO*
Augusta Nanney, *Controller*
▲ **EMP:** 40 **EST:** 1979
SALES (est): 5.7MM
SALES (corp-wide): 6MM **Privately Held**
WEB: www.robertsonlighting.com
SIC: 3612 3621 5063 3641 Fluorescent lighting transformers; motors & generators; electrical apparatus & equipment; ultraviolet lamps
PA: North Point Investments, Inc
70 W Madison St Ste 3500
Chicago IL 60602
312 977-4386

(G-16561)
ROOF-A-CIDE WEST LLC
1640 Field Rd (34231-2306)
PHONE..................................877 258-8998
Irene M Graziosi, *Principal*
EMP: 7 **EST:** 2011
SALES (est): 96.8K **Privately Held**
WEB: www.roof-a-cide-west.com
SIC: 3199 Leather goods

(G-16562)
ROPER INDUSTRIAL PDTS INV CO
6901 Prof Pkwy E Ste 200 (34240)
PHONE..................................941 556-2601
Thomas R McNeill Esq, *Principal*
EMP: 14 **EST:** 2014
SALES (est): 2.7MM
SALES (corp-wide): 5.5B **Publicly Held**
WEB: www.ropertech.com
SIC: 3823 Industrial instrmnts msrmnt display/control process variable
PA: Roper Technologies, Inc.
6901 Prof Pkwy E Ste 200
Sarasota FL 34240
941 556-2601

(G-16563)
ROPER TECHNOLOGIES INC (PA)
6901 Prof Pkwy E Ste 200 (34240)
PHONE..................................941 556-2601
Wilbur Prezzano, *Ch of Bd*
L Neil Hunn, *President*
Munther Juma, *Managing Dir*
Michael Rossi, *Div Sub Head*
Andrew Barger, *Counsel*
EMP: 21 **EST:** 1981
SQ FT: 29,000
SALES (est): 5.5B **Publicly Held**
WEB: www.ropertech.com
SIC: 3563 3491 3826 3829 Air & gas compressors; valves, automatic control; process control regulator valves; solenoid valves; petroleum product analyzing apparatus; vibration meters, analyzers & calibrators; temperature instruments: industrial process type; computer software systems analysis & design, custom; computer software development

(G-16564)
ROYAL TEES INC
5556 Palmer Blvd (34232-2734)
PHONE..................................941 366-0056
Mario Comparetto Jr, *President*
Ann Marie Barrena, *Systems Mgr*
EMP: 12 **EST:** 1980
SQ FT: 4,550
SALES (est): 631.2K **Privately Held**
WEB: www.royal-tees.com
SIC: 2261 7389 2396 Screen printing of cotton broadwoven fabrics; textile & apparel services; automotive & apparel trimmings

(G-16565)
ROYCE INTERNATIONAL LLC (DH)
3400 S Tamiami Trl # 300 (34239-6093)
PHONE..................................941 894-1228
Harvinder Anand, *CEO*
▲ **EMP:** 8 **EST:** 2010
SQ FT: 1,400
SALES (est): 12.4MM
SALES (corp-wide): 6B **Publicly Held**
WEB: www.gabrielchem.com
SIC: 2819 Industrial inorganic chemicals
HQ: Gabriel Performance Products, Llc
388 S Main St Ste 320
Akron OH 44311
866 800-2436

(G-16566)
RP INTERNATIONAL LLC (PA)
Also Called: Royce
3400 S Tamiami Trl # 300 (34239-6023)
PHONE..................................941 894-1228
Harry Anand, *President*
Kevin Palmer, *Vice Pres*
Albert Royce III, *Treasurer*
Mert Nurhan, *Manager*
Roberta Body, *Admin Sec*
▲ **EMP:** 37 **EST:** 2009
SQ FT: 100,000
SALES (est): 3.4MM **Privately Held**
SIC: 2869 Industrial organic chemicals

(G-16567)
S AND S MORRIS LLC
Also Called: Finest Global Products. Com
1630 Assisi Dr (34231-1765)
PHONE..................................404 431-7803
Steve Morris, *Principal*
Sarah Hazel, *Vice Pres*
EMP: 10 **EST:** 2016
SQ FT: 3,500
SALES (est): 1.3MM **Privately Held**
SIC: 3599 Flexible metal hose, tubing & bellows

(G-16568)
S R Q STORM PROTECTION LLC
1899 Porter Lake Dr # 105 (34240-7897)
PHONE..................................941 341-0334
Jon Reymond, *Mng Member*
EMP: 7 **EST:** 2017
SALES (est): 524.6K **Privately Held**
WEB: www.srqstormprotection.com
SIC: 2431 Blinds (shutters), wood

(G-16569)
SAB FUELS INC
2616 Stickney Point Rd (34231-6020)
PHONE..................................786 213-3399
Sabbuba Hasan, *Principal*
EMP: 8 **EST:** 2014
SALES (est): 583.5K **Privately Held**
SIC: 2869 Fuels

(G-16570)
SALCO INDUSTRIES INC
263 Field End St (34240-9703)
PHONE..................................941 377-7717
Salvatore Caputo, *President*
Theodora Caputo, *Vice Pres*
EMP: 13 **EST:** 1971
SQ FT: 6,000
SALES (est): 1.1MM **Privately Held**
WEB: www.salco.com
SIC: 3699 5065 3825 Security control equipment & systems; security control equipment & systems; instruments to measure electricity

(G-16571)
SAMARK TECHNOLOGY CORPORATION
15 Paradise Plz Ste 300 (34239-6905)
PHONE..................................941 955-4325
Mark Walter, *President*
EMP: 7 **EST:** 2017
SALES (est): 199K **Privately Held**
WEB: www.nanosurgerytech.com
SIC: 3841 Surgical & medical instruments

(G-16572)
SANBUR INC
Also Called: Signs In One Day
4118 Bee Ridge Rd (34233-2553)
PHONE..................................941 371-7446
Ken Frank, *President*
Niolet Travis, *Electrical Engi*
EMP: 13 **EST:** 1991
SALES (est): 1.6MM **Privately Held**
WEB: www.sarasotasign.com
SIC: 3993 7629 Signs, not made in custom sign painting shops; electrical equipment repair services

(G-16573)
SARAH LOUISE INC
8263 Blaikie Ct (34240-8323)
PHONE..................................941 377-9656
Leonard Given, *President*
Jan Gallock, *Exec VP*
Paul Gallock, *Senior VP*
Janice Gallock, *Vice Pres*
Diane Given, *Vice Pres*
▲ **EMP:** 10 **EST:** 1986
SALES (est): 959.8K **Privately Held**
WEB: www.sarah-louise.com
SIC: 2369 5137 5136 Girls' & children's outerwear; women's & children's clothing; men's & boys' clothing

(G-16574)
SARASOTA ARCHITECTURAL WDWKG
6110 Clark Center Ave (34238-2743)
PHONE..................................941 684-1614
Richard A Perrone, *Principal*
EMP: 10 **EST:** 2016
SALES (est): 502.5K **Privately Held**
WEB: www.saww.us
SIC: 2431 Millwork

(G-16575)
SARASOTA BYFRONT PLG ORGNZTION
655 N Tamiami Trl (34236-4045)
PHONE..................................941 203-5316
EMP: 9 **EST:** 2017
SALES (est): 114.9K **Privately Held**
WEB: www.thebaysarasota.org
SIC: 2741

(G-16576)
SARASOTA CABINETRY INC
3080 N Washington Blvd # 25 (34234-6245)
PHONE..................................941 351-5588
Don Miller, *President*
Gary Miller, *Vice Pres*
EMP: 11 **EST:** 1986
SQ FT: 15,000
SALES (est): 501.4K **Privately Held**
WEB: www.sarasotacabinetryinc.com
SIC: 2434 Wood kitchen cabinets

(G-16577)
SARASOTA COTTAGES LLC
1628 7th St (34236-4121)
P.O. Box 3004 (34230-3004)
PHONE..................................941 724-2245
Andrea Seager, *Manager*
EMP: 7 **EST:** 2018
SALES (est): 275.5K **Privately Held**
WEB: www.sarasotamagazine.com
SIC: 2721 Magazines: publishing only, not printed on site

(G-16578)
SARASOTA HERALD-TRIBUNE (HQ)
801 S Tamiami Trl (34236-7824)
P.O. Box 1719 (34230-1719)
PHONE..................................941 953-7755
James Weeks, *President*
Steve Ainsley, *President*
Micheal E Ryan, *Vice Pres*
David Gorham, *Treasurer*
Margaret Garner, *Consultant*
EMP: 300 **EST:** 1925
SQ FT: 20,000
SALES (est): 89.6MM
SALES (corp-wide): 272.8MM **Privately Held**
WEB: www.heraldtribune.com
SIC: 2711 Newspapers, publishing & printing
PA: Halifax Media Holdings, Llc
901 6th St
Daytona Beach FL 32117
386 681-2404

(G-16579)
SARASOTA HERALD-TRIBUNE
1777 Main St Ste 400 (34236-5868)
PHONE..................................941 953-7755
Krisztina Gogolyak, *Business Mgr*
Kim Christie, *Accounts Mgr*
Alan Monroe, *Director*
Roxanna Shepherd, *Executive*
EMP: 30
SALES (corp-wide): 272.8MM **Privately Held**
WEB: www.heraldtribune.com
SIC: 2711 7313 7319 Newspapers, publishing & printing; newspaper advertising representative; display advertising service
HQ: Sarasota Herald-Tribune
801 S Tamiami Trl
Sarasota FL 34236
941 953-7755

(G-16580)
SARASOTA SHOWER DOOR COMPANY
Also Called: Quality Enclosures
2025e Porter Lake Dr (34240-8834)
PHONE..................................941 378-0051
Manny Schwart, *President*
Steve Schwart, *Vice Pres*
Oliver Concepcion, *Engineer*
◆ **EMP:** 8 **EST:** 1991
SQ FT: 6,000
SALES (est): 1.8MM **Privately Held**
WEB: www.qualityenclosures.com
SIC: 3231 Doors, glass: made from purchased glass

(G-16581)
SARASOTA SIGNS AND VISUALS
Also Called: Fastsigns
4070 N Washington Blvd (34234-4837)
PHONE..................................941 355-5746
Peter Tunberg, *Owner*
Kristen Cruz, *Corp Comm Staff*
EMP: 6 **EST:** 2006
SALES (est): 889.8K **Privately Held**
WEB: www.fastsigns.com
SIC: 3993 5999 7319 Signs & advertising specialties; banners, flags, decals & posters; display advertising service

(G-16582)
SARASOTA-MANATEE ORIGINALS INC
1215 S Tamiami Trl (34239-2208)
PHONE..................................941 365-2800
Michael Klauber, *President*
Sarah Firstenberger, *Exec Dir*
EMP: 6 **EST:** 2011
SALES (est): 359.8K **Privately Held**
WEB: www.eatlikealocal.com
SIC: 3421 Table & food cutlery, including butchers'

(G-16583)
SARASOTAS FINEST MBL GRAN INC
550 Mango Ave (34237-6130)
PHONE..................................941 365-9697
EMP: 7
SALES (est): 40K **Privately Held**
SIC: 2493 3281 Mfg Reconstituted Wood Products Mfg Cut Stone/Products

(G-16584)
SAVORY STREET
411 N Orange Ave (34236-5003)
PHONE..................................941 312-4027
EMP: 8 **EST:** 2010
SALES (est): 575.1K **Privately Held**
SIC: 2051 Mfg Bread/Related Products

(G-16585)
SCIENCE DAILY LLC
4034 Roberts Point Rd (34242-1162)
PHONE..................................239 596-2624
Daniel Hogan, *Principal*
EMP: 7 **EST:** 2012
SALES (est): 148.6K **Privately Held**
SIC: 2711 Newspapers, publishing & printing

(G-16586)
SCOTT PAINT COMPANY LLC (HQ)
7839 Fruitville Rd (34240-9280)
PHONE..................................941 371-0015
Bill Tayler, *Area Mgr*
George Lorch, *VP Mfg*
Donald K Strube Jr,
Richard K Strube,
▼ **EMP:** 1 **EST:** 1965
SQ FT: 85,000
SALES (est): 3MM
SALES (corp-wide): 18.5MM **Privately Held**
WEB: www.floridapaints.com
SIC: 2851 5231 5198 Paints & paint additives; paint; paints, varnishes & supplies
PA: Florida Paints & Coatings, Llc
78 3rd St
Winter Garden FL 34787
407 986-1000

(G-16587)
SCRUBS 941
5641 Clark Rd (34233-3216)
PHONE..................................941 373-0029
EMP: 6 **EST:** 2019
SALES (est): 67K **Privately Held**
WEB: www.scrubs941.com
SIC: 2326 Men's & boys' work clothing

(G-16588)
SCULLY INDUSTRIES
314 Island Cir (34242-1938)
PHONE..................................941 349-5561
Neil Scully, *Principal*
EMP: 6 **EST:** 2008
SALES (est): 140.8K **Privately Held**
WEB: www.scully.com
SIC: 3999 Manufacturing industries

(G-16589)
SEAPRESS INC
Also Called: Mercury Printing
4281 Clark Rd (34233-2405)
PHONE..................................941 366-8494
Harry R Pore, *President*
Susan Pore, *Admin Sec*
EMP: 7 **EST:** 1973
SALES (est): 894.2K **Privately Held**
WEB: www.sarasotaprinter.com
SIC: 2752 Commercial printing, offset

(G-16590)
SEBRING SOFTWARE LLC (PA)
1400 Cattlemen Rd Ste 101 (34232-6246)
PHONE..................................941 377-0715
Allan J Barberio, *CFO*
Julie Durkee, *Director*
EMP: 49 **EST:** 2007
SALES: 20MM **Privately Held**
SIC: 7372 Application computer software

(G-16591)
SELECT MACHINERY INC
4590 Ashton Rd (34233-3487)
PHONE..................................941 960-1970
Henry P Koelmel, *Director*
EMP: 8 **EST:** 2015
SALES (est): 124.2K **Privately Held**
WEB: www.selectmachineryinc.com
SIC: 3599 Industrial machinery

(G-16592)
SENTRY PROTECTION TECHNOLOGY
6202 Clarity Ct (34240-9601)
PHONE..................................941 306-4949
Arthur James, *President*
EMP: 6 **EST:** 2010
SALES (est): 94.8K **Privately Held**
SIC: 3442 Metal doors, sash & trim

(G-16593)
SERBIN PRINTING INC
1500 N Washington Blvd (34236-2723)
PHONE..................................941 366-0755
Mark J Serbin, *President*
Robin Clark, *Vice Pres*
Jim Keen, *Vice Pres*
EMP: 35 **EST:** 1971
SQ FT: 26,500
SALES (est): 5.1MM **Privately Held**
WEB: www.serbinprinting.com
SIC: 2752 Commercial printing, offset

(G-16594)
SIGN WORKS INC
2491 15th St (34237-2902)
P.O. Box 18274 (34276-1274)
PHONE..................................941 894-7927
James Hampton, *Principal*
EMP: 6 **EST:** 2016
SALES (est): 50.6K **Privately Held**
WEB: www.signworks.com
SIC: 3993 Signs & advertising specialties

(G-16595)
SIGNARAMA-SARASOTA
4435 S Tamiami Trl (34231-3428)
PHONE..................................941 554-8798
Kathy Elliott, *Principal*
EMP: 9 **EST:** 2011
SALES (est): 308.9K **Privately Held**
SIC: 3993 Signs & advertising specialties

(G-16596)
SIGNS PLUS NEW IDS-NEW TECH IN
4242 Mcintosh Ln (34232-5027)
PHONE..................................941 378-4262
Robert W Klinger, *President*
Robert H Klinger, *President*
Don Voglund, *Vice Pres*
Sally Klinger, *Treasurer*
Bob Blanken, *Manager*
EMP: 15 **EST:** 1988
SQ FT: 4,000
SALES (est): 3.1MM **Privately Held**
WEB: www.signsplussigns.com
SIC: 3993 Signs & advertising specialties

(G-16597)
SILVER STAR ON LIME LLC
2739 Aspinwall St (34237-5208)
PHONE..................................941 312-4566
Victoria J Krone, *Owner*
EMP: 8 **EST:** 2011
SALES (est): 308.5K **Privately Held**
SIC: 3274 Lime

(G-16598)
SIMPLEX MANUFACTURING INC
Also Called: Simplex Tool and Mold
6300 Tower Ln Unit 4 (34240-7837)
PHONE..................................941 378-8700
Runar Sigurdsson, *President*
Steve Fennema, *Vice Pres*
Timothy T Gauthier, *Vice Pres*
EMP: 23 **EST:** 1997
SQ FT: 6,700
SALES (est): 1.1MM **Privately Held**
SIC: 3599 3544 Machine shop, jobbing & repair; special dies, tools, jigs & fixtures

(G-16599)
SLEEPMED INCORPORATED
5432 Bee Ridge Rd Ste 170 (34233-1515)
PHONE..................................941 361-3035
EMP: 13
SALES (corp-wide): 7.7MM **Privately Held**
WEB: www.sleepmedinc.com
SIC: 3841 Surgical & medical instruments
HQ: Sleepmed Incorporated
3330 Cumberland Blvd Se # 800
Atlanta GA 30339

(G-16600)
SMART MATERIAL CORP (PA)
2170 Main St Ste 302 (34237-6040)
P.O. Box 1115, Osprey (34229-1115)
PHONE..................................941 870-3337
Thomas Daue, *President*
Madeleine Daue, *Sales Staff*
EMP: 15 **EST:** 2000
SQ FT: 800
SALES (est): 2MM **Privately Held**
WEB: www.smart-material.com
SIC: 3264 3728 3829 Magnets, permanent: ceramic or ferrite; refueling equipment for use in flight, airplane; measuring & controlling devices

(G-16601)
SPOTLIGHT GRAPHICS INC
6054 Clark Center Ave (34238-2716)
PHONE..................................941 929-1500
John H Souza, *President*
Ron Morris, *Electrical Engi*
Arlene Morris, *Treasurer*
Renee Phinney, *Accounts Exec*
Dennis Pavao, *Sales Staff*
EMP: 32 **EST:** 1987
SQ FT: 16,000
SALES (est): 7.8MM **Privately Held**
WEB: www.spotlightgraphics.com
SIC: 2752 Commercial printing, offset

(G-16602)
SSVM PARTNERS INC
Also Called: Sterling Manufacturing
8293 Consumer Ct (34240-7862)
PHONE..................................239 825-6282
Tom Shapiro, *President*
Steve Shapiro, *Corp Secy*
Michael Vansyckle, *Engineer*
EMP: 75 **EST:** 1990
SQ FT: 25,000
SALES (est): 13.4MM **Privately Held**
WEB: www.interiorlogicgroup.com
SIC: 2541 Counter & sink tops
HQ: Interior Logic Group, Inc.
10 Bunsen
Irvine CA 92618
800 959-8333

(G-16603)
ST ACQUISITIONS LLC
Also Called: Sure Torque
1701 Desoto Rd (34234-3066)
PHONE..................................941 753-1095
Francis Caudron, *Purchasing*
Joe Witkauskis, *Regl Sales Mgr*
Jim Lyons, *Sales Staff*
Bob Burke, *Manager*
Michelle Bergeron,
EMP: 8 **EST:** 1991
SQ FT: 1,000
SALES (est): 1MM
SALES (corp-wide): 3.2MM **Privately Held**
WEB: www.torque.mesalabs.com
SIC: 3829 Physical property testing equipment
PA: M.D.C. Engineering, Inc.
1701 Desoto Rd
Sarasota FL 34234
941 358-0610

(G-16604)
STEEL PRODUCTS INC
1821 Myrtle St (34234-4820)
PHONE..................................941 351-8128
Tom Losee, *President*
Karen Losee, *Vice Pres*
EMP: 8 **EST:** 1967
SQ FT: 9,000
SALES (est): 841.1K **Privately Held**
WEB: www.steelproductsinc.com
SIC: 7692 3441 Welding repair; fabricated structural metal

(G-16605)
STONE TREND INTERNATIONAL INC
6244 Clark Center Ave # 3 (34238-1722)
P.O. Box 3018 (34230-3018)
PHONE..................................941 927-9113
Jaren Levitt, *President*
Julio Gonzales, *Exec VP*
Sue Kim, *Exec VP*
Theresa Levitt, *Exec VP*
Anthony Ritchie, *Vice Pres*
▲ **EMP:** 25 **EST:** 1995
SQ FT: 10,000
SALES (est): 3.7MM **Privately Held**
SIC: 3281 5032 1411 Cut stone & stone products; marble building stone; dimension stone

(G-16606)
STREETWISE MAPS INC (DH)
4376 Independence Ct A (34234-4711)
P.O. Box 10612, Prescott AZ (86304-0612)
PHONE..................................941 358-1956
Michael Brown, *President*
EMP: 11 **EST:** 1983
SALES (est): 992.5K
SALES (corp-wide): 943.6MM **Privately Held**
WEB: www.streetwisemaps.com
SIC: 2741 Maps: publishing only, not printed on site
HQ: Michelin North America, Inc.
1 Parkway S
Greenville SC 29615
864 458-5000

(G-16607)
STUDIO LUXE CSTM CABINETRY LLC
2035 Constitution Blvd (34231-4108)
PHONE..................................941 371-4010
David E Wentzel, *Mng Member*
EMP: 7 **EST:** 2016
SALES (est): 392.4K **Privately Held**
WEB: www.studioluxedesigns.com
SIC: 2434 2514 Wood kitchen cabinets; kitchen cabinets: metal

(G-16608)
SUNCOAST SIGN SHOP INC
8466 Cookwood Rdg (34231)
PHONE..................................941 448-5835
Brian R Gregg, *President*
Gregory R Hornagold, *Corp Secy*
EMP: 11 **EST:** 2008
SALES (est): 180.9K **Privately Held**
WEB:
www.wholesalechannelletter signs.com
SIC: 3993 Signs & advertising specialties

(G-16609)
SUNNIBUNNI
1916 Bay Rd (34239-6903)
PHONE..................................941 554-8744
Alexandra Van Wie, *President*
EMP: 10 **EST:** 2017
SALES (est): 632.6K **Privately Held**
WEB: www.sunnibunni.com
SIC: 2024 Ice cream & frozen desserts

(G-16610)
SUNSET CADILLAC OF SARASOTA
2200 Bee Ridge Rd (34239-6201)
PHONE..................................941 922-1571
Steve Montanaro, *General Mgr*
Greg Doan, *Technician*
EMP: 11 **EST:** 2019
SALES (est): 938.4K **Privately Held**
WEB: www.sunsetcadillacsarasota.com
SIC: 3089 Automotive parts, plastic

(G-16611)
SUNSET METAL FABRICATION INC
1211 Porter Rd Unit 7 (34240-9621)
PHONE..................................386 215-4520
Steve Larimer, *Principal*
EMP: 8 **EST:** 2016
SALES (est): 279.1K **Privately Held**
WEB: www.sunsetmetalfabfl.com
SIC: 3499 Fabricated metal products

(G-16612)
SUPER SENSITIVE STRING SLS CO
1805 Apex Rd (34240-2304)
PHONE..................................941 371-0016
John V Cavanaugh, *President*
Ellen Cavanaugh, *Vice Pres*
▲ **EMP:** 20 **EST:** 1930
SQ FT: 16,000
SALES (est): 779K **Privately Held**
WEB: www.supersensitive.com
SIC: **3931** 3812 3296 Strings, musical instrument; search & navigation equipment; mineral wool

(G-16613)
SWOOGO LLC (PA)
4646 Ashton Rd (34233-3408)
PHONE..................................212 655-9810
Leonora Valvo, *President*
Tim Cummins,
Neil Keefe,
EMP: 6 **EST:** 2015
SALES (est): 609K **Privately Held**
WEB: www.get.swoogo.com
SIC: **7372** 7389 Business oriented computer software; business services

(G-16614)
T V HI LITES PENNY SAVER INC
Also Called: Pet Pages
6950 Webber Rd (34240-8665)
P.O. Box 22083 (34276-5083)
PHONE..................................941 378-5353
David Deacy, *President*
EMP: 9 **EST:** 1995
SQ FT: 2,000
SALES (est): 156.3K **Privately Held**
WEB: www.petpages.com
SIC: **2721** Magazines: publishing & printing

(G-16615)
TARGET GRAPHICS INC
2053 13th St (34237-2705)
PHONE..................................941 365-8809
John P Masio, *President*
EMP: 16 **EST:** 1988
SQ FT: 8,800
SALES (est): 2.1MM **Privately Held**
WEB: www.targetgraphics.net
SIC: **2752** 2759 Commercial printing, offset; laser printing

(G-16616)
TATTOO FACTORY INC (PA)
Also Called: Tattoo Promotion Factory
2828 Proctor Rd Ste 2 (34231-6423)
PHONE..................................941 923-4110
Stephen Bloom, *President*
EMP: 21 **EST:** 1995
SQ FT: 15,000
SALES (est): 2.7MM **Privately Held**
WEB: www.tattoopromotionfactory.com
SIC: **2759** 3993 Promotional printing; signs & advertising specialties

(G-16617)
TAYLOR & FRANCIS GROUP LLC
Accounts Payable Division
1990 Main St Ste 750 (34236-8000)
PHONE..................................800 516-0186
Paul Dukes, *Publisher*
Maya Davis, *Marketing Staff*
Myles Stavis, *Marketing Staff*
EMP: 53
SALES (corp-wide): 2.2B **Privately Held**
WEB: www.taylorandfrancis.com
SIC: **2741** Miscellaneous publishing
HQ: Taylor & Francis Group, Llc
6000 Broken Sound Pkwy Nw # 300
Boca Raton FL 33487
561 994-0555

(G-16618)
TAYLOR ELECTRONICS INC
7061b S Tamiami Trl (34231-5559)
P.O. Box 20669 (34276-3669)
PHONE..................................941 925-3605
Wilbur Taylor, *President*
Russell M Bailey Jr, *Vice Pres*
Cheryl Taylor, *Treasurer*
Buzz Taylor, *Manager*
Patricia A Bailey, *Admin Sec*
EMP: 10 **EST:** 1936
SALES (est): 1MM **Privately Held**
WEB: www.taylorphaseguard.com
SIC: **3625** Motor controls & accessories

(G-16619)
TAYLOR MADE PLASTICS INC
1561 Global Ct Ste A (34240-7827)
PHONE..................................941 926-0200
Kevin Larkin, *President*
Luke Larkin, *Vice Pres*
Joe Barnett, *Admin Sec*
EMP: 8 **EST:** 1995
SQ FT: 8,500
SALES (est): 889.3K **Privately Held**
WEB: www.thepipeplug.com
SIC: **3084** Plastics pipe

(G-16620)
TECHPUBS LTD
Also Called: Eduself
65 Strathmore Blvd (34233-1323)
PHONE..................................201 541-1192
Mario Hallphone, *President*
Miriam Halfon, *Vice Pres*
EMP: 17 **EST:** 2009
SALES (est): 760.7K **Privately Held**
SIC: **2741** 7389 Technical manual & paper publishing; business services

(G-16621)
TOP SHELF CUSTOM CABINETRY (PA)
3365 Spring Mill Cir (34239-6719)
PHONE..................................941 726-2393
Michael D Yates, *Principal*
EMP: 8 **EST:** 2008
SALES (est): 159.6K **Privately Held**
WEB: www.topshelfcustomcabinetry.com
SIC: **2434** Wood kitchen cabinets

(G-16622)
TORRINGTON BRUSH WORKS INC (PA)
4377 Independence Ct (34234-4722)
PHONE..................................941 355-1499
Michael Grimaldi, *President*
Sidney W Fitzgerald, *President*
John Fitzgerald, *Vice Pres*
Robert Petrovits, *Admin Sec*
◆ **EMP:** 17 **EST:** 1907
SQ FT: 12,500
SALES (est): 3.1MM **Privately Held**
WEB: www.torringtonbrushes.com
SIC: **3991** 5085 5719 Brooms & brushes; brushes, industrial; brushes

(G-16623)
TORTILLERIA DONA CHELA
1155 N Washington Blvd (34236-3407)
PHONE..................................941 953-4045
EMP: 6
SALES (est): 436.5K **Privately Held**
SIC: **2099** Mfg Food Preparations

(G-16624)
TRAFALGER COMMUNICATIONS INC
Also Called: Srq Media Group
331 S Pineapple Ave (34236-7019)
PHONE..................................941 365-7702
Lisl Liang, *President*
Wes Roberts, *Vice Pres*
Ashley Grant, *Director*
Scott Armitage, *Admin Sec*
EMP: 41 **EST:** 1997
SQ FT: 6,000
SALES (est): 5.2MM **Privately Held**
WEB: www.srqmagazine.com
SIC: **2721** Magazines: publishing only, not printed on site

(G-16625)
TREASURE COVE II INC
8927 S Tamiami Trl (34238-3145)
PHONE..................................941 966-2004
Dan Hering, *Vice Pres*
EMP: 15 **EST:** 1956
SQ FT: 2,400
SALES (est): 1.1MM **Privately Held**
WEB: www.treasurecove2.com
SIC: **3299** 5947 Non-metallic mineral statuary & other decorative products; gift shop

(G-16626)
ULTRAFAST SYSTEMS LLC
8330 Consumer Ct (34240-7868)
PHONE..................................941 360-2161
Alex Gusev, *Principal*
EMP: 10 **EST:** 2006
SALES (est): 1.8MM **Privately Held**
WEB: www.ultrafastsystems.com
SIC: **3826** Analytical instruments

(G-16627)
UNIQUE TECHNOLOGY INC
1523 Edgar Pl (34240-9054)
PHONE..................................941 358-5410
Arthur James, *President*
Nancy James, *Principal*
◆ **EMP:** 28 **EST:** 1981
SQ FT: 8,000
SALES (est): 3.2MM **Privately Held**
WEB: www.utindustries.com
SIC: **3442** Metal doors

(G-16628)
UNIQUE TECHNOLOGY INDS LLC
1523 Edgar Pl (34240-9054)
PHONE..................................941 358-5410
Michael Tildale,
EMP: 12 **EST:** 2012
SQ FT: 35,000
SALES (est): 1.7MM **Privately Held**
WEB: www.utindustries.com
SIC: **2431** Door screens, wood frame

(G-16629)
UNIROYAL ENGINEERED PDTS LLC (HQ)
1800 2nd St Ste 970 (34236-5992)
PHONE..................................941 906-8580
Howard R Curd, *CEO*
Howard F Curd, *President*
George L Sanchez, *Exec VP*
Dave Urbin, *Vice Pres*
Bernard A Wagner, *CFO*
▲ **EMP:** 15 **EST:** 2003
SQ FT: 230,000
SALES (est): 60.1MM
SALES (corp-wide): 60.2MM **Publicly Held**
WEB: www.uniroyalglobal.com
SIC: **2824** 2295 Vinyl fibers; textured yarns, non-cellulosic; leather, artificial or imitation
PA: Uniroyal Global Engineered Products, Inc.
1800 2nd St Ste 970
Sarasota FL 34236
941 906-8580

(G-16630)
UNIROYAL GLOBL ENGNRED PDTS IN (PA)
1800 2nd St Ste 970 (34236-5992)
PHONE..................................941 906-8580
Howard R Curd, *Ch of Bd*
Edmund C King, *Ch of Bd*
Karl Kroening, *Manager*
Joe Mercadante, *Director*
EMP: 12 **EST:** 1992
SQ FT: 9,010
SALES: 60.2MM **Publicly Held**
WEB: www.uniroyalglobal.com
SIC: **2824** 2396 Vinyl fibers; automotive trimmings, fabric

(G-16631)
UNITED STATES AWNING COMPANY
Also Called: U S Awning
1935 18th St (34234-7508)
PHONE..................................941 955-7010
Raymond Hautamaki, *President*
Ann Hautamaki, *Corp Secy*
Mark Schamp, *Vice Pres*
EMP: 33 **EST:** 1965
SQ FT: 6,000
SALES (est): 3.1MM **Privately Held**
WEB: www.unitedstatesawningco.com
SIC: **2394** 3444 Awnings, fabric: made from purchased materials; awnings, sheet metal

(G-16632)
US PET IMAGING LLC (PA)
Also Called: Imaging For Life
3830 Bee Ridge Rd Ste 100 (34233-1105)
P.O. Box 25487 (34277-2487)
PHONE..................................941 921-0383
Neil Bedi,
Inita Bedi,
EMP: 7 **EST:** 2002
SALES (est): 1.1MM **Privately Held**
WEB: www.imagingforlife.net
SIC: **2835** In vitro & in vivo diagnostic substances

(G-16633)
VILLAR STONE & PAVER WORKS LLC
1140 Seaside Dr (34242-2525)
PHONE..................................860 209-2907
Joseph Villar, *Principal*
EMP: 6
SALES (est): 488.3K **Privately Held**
SIC: **3531** Pavers

(G-16634)
VISTA SYSTEM LLC
1800 N East Ave Ste 102 (34234-7600)
PHONE..................................941 365-4646
Sam Schneider, *General Mgr*
Pnina Kedar, *Business Mgr*
Terry Greer, *Marketing Staff*
Barak Silber, *Manager*
Erez Halivni,
◆ **EMP:** 36 **EST:** 2000
SQ FT: 11,000
SALES (est): 5.4MM **Privately Held**
WEB: www.vistasystem.com
SIC: **3993** Signs & advertising specialties

(G-16635)
WATERFALL LLC
4438 Ardale St (34232-4016)
PHONE..................................941 342-7417
Michael Herrygers, *Principal*
EMP: 6 **EST:** 2010
SALES (est): 145.1K **Privately Held**
SIC: **7372** Business oriented computer software

(G-16636)
WES HOLDINGS CORP
Also Called: De Loach Industries
818 Cattlemen Rd (34232-2811)
PHONE..................................941 371-4995
Anthony De Loach, *President*
Mark Gorrell, *Vice Pres*
EMP: 15 **EST:** 1959
SQ FT: 8,000
SALES (est): 2.4MM
SALES (corp-wide): 9.8MM **Privately Held**
WEB: www.deloachindustries.com
SIC: **3564** 3823 Air purification equipment; water quality monitoring & control systems
PA: Water Equipment Services, Inc.
6389 Tower Ln
Sarasota FL 34240
941 371-7617

(G-16637)
WES INDUSTRIES INC (PA)
6389 Tower Ln (34240-8810)
PHONE..................................941 371-7617
Anthony Deloach, *President*
Travis Deloach, *Vice Pres*
EMP: 19 **EST:** 2013
SALES (est): 3.2MM **Privately Held**
WEB: www.wesinc.com
SIC: **3443** 1711 Water tanks, metal plate; solar energy contractor

(G-16638)
WF FUEL
300 N Washington Blvd (34236-4236)
PHONE..................................941 706-4953
Konstantin Razionov, *Manager*
EMP: 7 **EST:** 2013
SALES (est): 363.8K **Privately Held**
SIC: **2869** Fuels

(G-16639)
WHOLE TOMATO SOFTWARE INC
1990 Main St Ste 750 (34236-8000)
PHONE..................................408 323-1590
EMP: 5 **EST:** 2019
SALES (est): 373.4K **Privately Held**
WEB: www.wholetomato.com
SIC: 7372 Prepackaged software

(G-16640)
WILLIAM B RUDOW INC
1122 Goodrich Ave (34236-2617)
P.O. Box 2300 (34230-2300)
PHONE..................................941 957-4200
David Wertheimer, *President*
Steven Wertheimer, *Vice Pres*
▼ **EMP:** 8 **EST:** 1946
SQ FT: 5,000
SALES (est): 836.9K **Privately Held**
WEB: www.suckers.com
SIC: 3089 3555 Injection molded finished plastic products; printing trade parts & attachments

(G-16641)
WINDOW CRAFTSMEN INC
6031 Clark Center Ave (34238-2718)
PHONE..................................941 922-1844
Robert Detweiler, *President*
Steve Gerety, *Director*
EMP: 20 **EST:** 1965
SQ FT: 18,000
SALES (est): 2.3MM **Privately Held**
WEB: www.windowcraftsmen.com
SIC: 3442 3444 3429 Screen & storm doors & windows; sheet metalwork; manufactured hardware (general)

(G-16642)
WINSULATOR CORPORATION
3350 S Osprey Ave (34239-5900)
PHONE..................................941 365-7901
Edward Vervane, *CEO*
EMP: 5 **EST:** 2005
SALES (est): 900K **Privately Held**
WEB: www.winsulator.com
SIC: 2431 5211 Windows & window parts & trim, wood; windows, storm: wood or metal

(G-16643)
WIRED RITE SYSTEMS INC
1748 Independence Blvd C5 (34234-2150)
PHONE..................................707 838-1122
Mark Owades, *President*
Monika Tomorowicz, *General Mgr*
Roger Abby, *Engineer*
▲ **EMP:** 15
SQ FT: 10,000
SALES (est): 2.1MM **Privately Held**
WEB: www.wiredrite.com
SIC: 3612 Control transformers

(G-16644)
WITTS WOODWORKING INC
1963 Racimo Dr (34240-9426)
PHONE..................................941 544-8812
Merlin J Wittmer, *President*
EMP: 7 **EST:** 2016
SALES (est): 171.1K **Privately Held**
WEB: www.wittswoodworking.com
SIC: 2431 Millwork

(G-16645)
WORLD PRECISION INSTRS LLC (PA)
175 Sarasota Center Blvd (34240-8750)
PHONE..................................941 371-1003
Karol Macdonald, *Vice Pres*
Cheryl Halter, *CFO*
Mathias Belz, *Director*
EMP: 62 **EST:** 2016
SALES (est): 5.1MM **Privately Held**
WEB: www.wpiinc.com
SIC: 3826 3829 Analytical instruments; measuring & controlling devices

(G-16646)
ZIPTEK LLC
1250 S Tamiami Trl # 303 (34239-2221)
PHONE..................................941 953-5509
William Bennett, *CEO*
EMP: 14 **EST:** 2012
SALES (est): 1.6MM **Privately Held**
WEB: www.ziptekglobal.com
SIC: 3841 Surgical & medical instruments

(G-16647)
ZOO HOLDINGS LLC
Also Called: Sign Zoo
4139 N Wa Blvd (34234-4840)
PHONE..................................941 355-5653
Jen Aaron, *Prdtn Mgr*
Melissa Pickelsimer, *Accounts Mgr*
Jaclyn Rebel, *Mktg Dir*
Larry Cavalluzzi,
Jason Getman, *Representative*
EMP: 5 **EST:** 2004
SALES (est): 1MM **Privately Held**
WEB: www.signzoo.com
SIC: 3993 Signs & advertising specialties

Satellite Beach
Brevard County

(G-16648)
BANANA BAG SOLUTIONS LLC
450 Sherwood Ave (32937-3052)
PHONE..................................321 917-4334
Brian Dery,
EMP: 8 **EST:** 2015
SALES (est): 338.6K **Privately Held**
SIC: 2087 Concentrates, drink

(G-16649)
BROWN DOG PROPELLER LLC
405 Dove Ln (32937-3735)
PHONE..................................321 254-7767
Ronald Dubinsky, *Principal*
EMP: 6 **EST:** 2009
SALES (est): 295.2K **Privately Held**
SIC: 3366 Propellers

(G-16650)
CAMBRA SOAP COMPANY
209 Ellwood Ave (32937-3130)
PHONE..................................321 525-7575
David W Cupp, *Principal*
EMP: 6 **EST:** 2010
SALES (est): 92.1K **Privately Held**
WEB: www.cambrasoap.blogspot.com
SIC: 2841 Soap & other detergents

(G-16651)
COASTAL ANGLER MAGAZINE
1296 Highway A1a (32937-2480)
PHONE..................................850 586-3474
Kevin Ogle, *Publisher*
EMP: 6 **EST:** 2017
SALES (est): 73.1K **Privately Held**
WEB: www.coastalanglermag.com
SIC: 2721 Periodicals

(G-16652)
J I S ASSOCIATES
445 Cardinal Dr (32937-3707)
PHONE..................................321 777-6829
Vickie Dupont, *Engineer*
EMP: 6 **EST:** 1988
SALES (est): 90K **Privately Held**
SIC: 3661 Telephone & telegraph apparatus

(G-16653)
NEWSNOTES LLC ✪
610 Ocean St (32937-5443)
PHONE..................................407 949-8185
Gary H Weiner, *Principal*
Kristen Dringenberg, *Manager*
EMP: 6 **EST:** 2021
SALES (est): 362.9K **Privately Held**
SIC: 2752 Commercial printing, lithographic

Sebastian
Brevard County

(G-16654)
AMERICAN SIGN LETTERS
8140 Evernia St Unit 1 (32976-2584)
PHONE..................................772 643-4012
EMP: 6 **EST:** 2018
SALES (est): 219.3K **Privately Held**
WEB: www.americansignletters.com
SIC: 3993 Signs & advertising specialties

(G-16655)
JODE CORPORATION
9565 Riverview Dr (32976-3142)
PHONE..................................321 684-1769
Debra L Marshall, *President*
EMP: 6 **EST:** 2002
SALES (est): 434.8K **Privately Held**
SIC: 2211 Apparel & outerwear fabrics, cotton

Sebastian
Indian River County

(G-16656)
BRUNO DANGER CUSTOM CABINETS
761 S Easy St (32958-5022)
PHONE..................................754 366-1302
Bruno P Danger, *Principal*
EMP: 7 **EST:** 2016
SALES (est): 467.9K **Privately Held**
SIC: 2434 Wood kitchen cabinets

(G-16657)
CASTLE SOFTWARE INC
626 Layport Dr (32958-4412)
PHONE..................................800 345-7606
Steve Hersh, *Vice Pres*
EMP: 5 **EST:** 2001
SALES (est): 402.3K **Privately Held**
WEB: www.castlelearning.com
SIC: 7372 8748 Prepackaged software; business consulting

(G-16658)
EXPERT PROMOTIONS LLC
Also Called: American Sign
434 Georgia Blvd (32958-4528)
PHONE..................................772 643-4012
Benjamin Furino, *President*
EMP: 17 **EST:** 2017
SALES (est): 1.2MM **Privately Held**
WEB: www.expertpromotionsllc.com
SIC: 3993 Neon signs

(G-16659)
FLORIDA PALLET LLC
14325 78th Ave (32958-3276)
PHONE..................................772 562-4900
James E Blandino,
Robert P Mellin,
EMP: 6 **EST:** 2005
SQ FT: 10,000
SALES (est): 479.6K **Privately Held**
WEB: www.floridapallet.com
SIC: 2448 5999 Pallets, wood; packaging materials: boxes, padding, etc.

(G-16660)
FORD WIRE AND CABLE CORP
7756 130th St (32958-3613)
PHONE..................................772 388-3660
William S Ford, *CEO*
Laurie Ford Russelburg, *President*
Charlotte Ford, *Corp Secy*
Dale Ford, *Vice Pres*
Steven Ford, *VP Mktg*
▲ **EMP:** 30 **EST:** 1986
SQ FT: 40,000
SALES (est): 602.3K **Privately Held**
SIC: 3357 Building wire & cable, nonferrous

(G-16661)
GATE CFV SOLUTIONS INC
Also Called: Global Agriculture Tech Engrg
100 Sebastian Indus Pl (32958-4627)
PHONE..................................772 388-3387
John R Newton, *CEO*
Gillian N Callaghan, *President*
Peter Brooke, *Research*
Michael Newton, *Director*
EMP: 7 **EST:** 1998
SQ FT: 7,000
SALES (est): 1MM **Privately Held**
WEB: www.gatecfv.com
SIC: 3491 3494 3585 Water works valves; valves & pipe fittings; soda fountain & beverage dispensing equipment & parts

(G-16662)
GRAPH-PLEX CORP
5240 95th St (32958-6372)
PHONE..................................772 766-3866
Denise Rita Webster, *Principal*
EMP: 11 **EST:** 2018
SALES (est): 244.8K **Privately Held**
WEB: www.graphplex.com
SIC: 3993 Signs & advertising specialties

(G-16663)
IONEMOTO INC
Also Called: Tightails
300 Industrial Cir (32958-3685)
PHONE..................................617 784-1401
Frederic P Baly, *Principal*
EMP: 7 **EST:** 2017
SALES (est): 1MM **Privately Held**
WEB: www.ionemoto.com
SIC: 3714 Motor vehicle parts & accessories

(G-16664)
JENCOR PUBLISHING INC
104 Miller Dr (32958-6984)
PHONE..................................772 589-5578
Jennifer Hansen, *Principal*
EMP: 6 **EST:** 2009
SALES (est): 67.1K **Privately Held**
SIC: 2741 Miscellaneous publishing

(G-16665)
KNIGHT BACON ASSOCIATES
9577 Gator Dr Unit 1 (32958-8562)
PHONE..................................772 388-5115
Jonathan Bacon, *Principal*
Jonathan K Bacon, *Principal*
EMP: 5 **EST:** 2010
SALES (est): 488.4K **Privately Held**
WEB: www.kbacon.sorensenrealestate.com
SIC: 3577 Printers & plotters

(G-16666)
LOPRESTI SPEED MERCHANTS INC
Also Called: Lopresti Aviation
210 Airport Dr E (32958-3957)
PHONE..................................772 562-4757
Tyler Wheeler, *CEO*
Curt Lopresti, *President*
David Lopresti, *Vice Pres*
Bryan Bochinski, *Products*
▼ **EMP:** 24 **EST:** 1991
SQ FT: 19,000
SALES (est): 3MM **Privately Held**
WEB: www.flywat.com
SIC: 3728 Aircraft parts & equipment

(G-16667)
MACHO PRODUCTS INC
10045 102nd Ter (32958-7831)
PHONE..................................800 327-6812
Amir K Shadab, *CEO*
Clive R Parker, *CFO*
Ashley Brown, *Marketing Staff*
◆ **EMP:** 50 **EST:** 1980
SQ FT: 75,000
SALES (est): 11.9MM **Privately Held**
WEB: www.macho.com
SIC: 3949 Protective sporting equipment

(G-16668)
MC MILLER CO INC
11640 Us Highway 1 (32958-8426)
PHONE..................................772 794-9448
Melvin C Miller II, *Ch of Bd*
Joseph Mekus, *President*
Albert J Hilberts, *Vice Pres*
Paula Wiley, *Sales Mgr*
Kathy Allen, *Sales Staff*
EMP: 30 **EST:** 1945
SQ FT: 15,000
SALES (est): 7.1MM **Privately Held**
WEB: www.mcmiller.com
SIC: 3825 3829 Instruments to measure electricity; measuring & controlling devices

(G-16669)
MDI PRODUCTS LLC
10055 102nd Ter (32958-7831)
PHONE..................................772 228-7371
Clive Parker,
Nancy Grossbart,

Amir Shadab,
▲ **EMP:** 11 **EST:** 2000
SALES (est): 836.5K **Privately Held**
WEB: www.macho.com
SIC: 3089 Injection molded finished plastic products

(G-16670)
MECHANICAL DESIGN CORP
100 Industrial Park Blvd (32958-5764)
PHONE..................................772 388-8782
Rick Pino, *President*
EMP: 5 **EST:** 2001
SQ FT: 23,632
SALES (est): 1.8MM **Privately Held**
WEB: www.mechanicaldesigncorp.net
SIC: 1389 Pipe testing, oil field service

(G-16671)
PROFOLD INC
10300 99th Way (32958-7827)
P.O. Box 780929 (32978-0929)
PHONE..................................772 589-0063
Leo A Haydt III, *President*
John Pinchin, *Principal*
Richard A Edmisten, *Director*
John R Pinchin, *Director*
EMP: 48 **EST:** 1982
SQ FT: 45,000
SALES (est): 4.3MM **Privately Held**
WEB: www.profold.com
SIC: 3554 Folding machines, paper

(G-16672)
SHARK SKINZ
Also Called: Schark Skinz
300 Industrial Park Blvd # 5 (32958-5772)
P.O. Box 22, Grant (32949-0022)
PHONE..................................772 388-9621
David Lee, *Owner*
▲ **EMP:** 6 **EST:** 1992
SQ FT: 5,000
SALES (est): 353.4K **Privately Held**
WEB: www.ionemoto.com
SIC: 3714 3728 5085 5088 Motor vehicle parts & accessories; aircraft body assemblies & parts; bearings; aircraft & parts; motorcycle parts & accessories; aircraft instruments, equipment or parts

(G-16673)
TOTAL PRINT INC
1132 Us Highway 1 (32958-4147)
PHONE..................................772 589-9658
Jeffrey E Fabick, *President*
EMP: 5 **EST:** 1988
SQ FT: 1,400
SALES (est): 549K **Privately Held**
SIC: 2752 Commercial printing, offset; business form & card printing, lithographic

(G-16674)
TRITON SUBMARINES LLC
10055 102nd Ter (32958-7831)
PHONE..................................772 770-1995
Patrick Lahey, *President*
L Bruce Jones, *Partner*
Troy Engen, *General Mgr*
Ronald Stamm, *Project Mgr*
Borja Hidalgo, *Prdtn Mgr*
◆ **EMP:** 25 **EST:** 1999
SQ FT: 20,000
SALES (est): 5.8MM **Privately Held**
WEB: www.tritonsubs.com
SIC: 3731 Submarines, building & repairing

(G-16675)
US GENERATOR INC
725 Commerce Center Dr J (32958-3135)
PHONE..................................772 778-0131
William N Broocke, *President*
EMP: 8 **EST:** 2005
SALES (est): 1MM **Privately Held**
WEB: www.usgenerator.org
SIC: 3621 5063 5064 Motors & generators; electrical apparatus & equipment; electrical appliances, major

(G-16676)
V-RAPTOR AIRCRAFT LLC (PA)
7756 130th St (32958-3613)
PHONE..................................772 388-3334
Jeff Kerlo, *Mng Member*
Taras Rud,
EMP: 3 **EST:** 2010
SALES (est): 4MM **Privately Held**
SIC: 3728 Aircraft parts & equipment

(G-16677)
VELOCITY AIRCRAFT INC
200 Airport Dr W (32958-3918)
PHONE..................................772 589-1860
Charles Xia, *Principal*
EMP: 8 **EST:** 2017
SALES (est): 102.7K **Privately Held**
WEB: www.velocityaircraft.com
SIC: 3728 Aircraft parts & equipment

(G-16678)
VELOCITY INC
200 Airport Dr W (32958-3918)
PHONE..................................772 589-1860
Duane Swing, *CEO*
B Scott Swing, *President*
Chris Parr, *Director*
▲ **EMP:** 19 **EST:** 1986
SQ FT: 15,000
SALES (est): 3MM **Privately Held**
WEB: www.velocityaircraft.com
SIC: 3721 Airplanes, fixed or rotary wing

Sebring
Highlands County

(G-16679)
ABBOTT DIABETES CARE
6928 Matanzas Dr (33872-7912)
PHONE..................................863 385-7910
EMP: 6 **EST:** 2019
SALES (est): 171.5K **Privately Held**
WEB: www.abbott.com
SIC: 2834 Pharmaceutical preparations

(G-16680)
ALPHA GENERAL SERVICES INC
1578 Alpha Rd E (33870-4598)
P.O. Box 3331 (33871-3331)
PHONE..................................863 382-1544
Richard Lapudula, *President*
Paul Suppa, *Vice Pres*
Priscilla Jones, *Office Mgr*
▼ **EMP:** 20 **EST:** 1978
SQ FT: 45,000
SALES (est): 3.9MM **Privately Held**
WEB: www.alphageneral.com
SIC: 3089 4952 Septic tanks, plastic; sewerage systems

(G-16681)
AMERIKAN LLC
2006 Fortune Blvd (33870-5502)
PHONE..................................863 314-9417
Chris Koscho, *President*
Gregg Branning, *Vice Pres*
John C Orr, *Vice Pres*
Salvatore Incanno, *Treasurer*
EMP: 24 **EST:** 2004
SALES (est): 6.7MM **Privately Held**
SIC: 3089 Plastic containers, except foam

(G-16682)
BAPTIST MID-MISSIONS INC
Also Called: Editorial Bautista Independent
3417 Kenilworth Blvd (33870-4469)
PHONE..................................863 382-6350
Darrel Jingst, *Prdtn Mgr*
Tim Fry, *Manager*
Bruce Burkholder, *Director*
Mark Seymour, *Director*
Rachel Hancock, *Admin Asst*
EMP: 10
SQ FT: 3,500
SALES (corp-wide): 16.2MM **Privately Held**
WEB: www.bmm.org
SIC: 2759 Publication printing
PA: Baptist Mid-Missions, Inc.
7749 Webster Rd
Cleveland OH 44130
440 826-3930

(G-16683)
BIG O BOATS LLC
1350 Industrial Way E (33870-4596)
PHONE..................................863 697-6319
James McKay,
EMP: 6 **EST:** 2011
SALES (est): 180.6K **Privately Held**
WEB: www.bigoboats.com
SIC: 3732 Boat building & repairing

(G-16684)
CREATIVE SERVICES OF CENTL FLA
Also Called: Creative Printing
2023 Us Highway 27 N (33870-1860)
PHONE..................................863 385-8383
Stephen Kirouac, *President*
Michael Kirouac, *Vice Pres*
Pam Kirouac, *Vice Pres*
EMP: 5 **EST:** 1985
SALES (est): 452.9K **Privately Held**
WEB: www.creativeprinting.net
SIC: 2752 Commercial printing, offset

(G-16685)
D & N CABINETRY INC
2920 Kenilworth Blvd (33870-4307)
PHONE..................................863 471-1500
Nicholas Hucke, *President*
EMP: 11 **EST:** 1986
SQ FT: 2,960
SALES (est): 1.7MM **Privately Held**
WEB: www.dncabinetry.com
SIC: 2434 Wood kitchen cabinets

(G-16686)
DARREN THOMAS GLASS CO INC
251 Commercial Ct (33876-6524)
P.O. Box 7822 (33872-0114)
PHONE..................................863 655-9500
Darren Thomas, *President*
Mary Thomas, *Admin Sec*
EMP: 5 **EST:** 2007
SALES (est): 536K **Privately Held**
WEB: www.neverfogrvwindow.com
SIC: 3231 7536 Products of purchased glass; automotive glass replacement shops

(G-16687)
E-STONE USA CORP
8041 Haywood Taylor Blvd (33870-7505)
PHONE..................................863 655-1273
Andrea Di Giuseppe, *CEO*
Livio Magni, *COO*
◆ **EMP:** 70 **EST:** 2014
SALES (est): 2MM **Privately Held**
WEB: www.trend-group.com
SIC: 3272 5031 Tile, precast terrazzo or concrete; building materials, interior
PA: Trend Group Spa
Piazzale Torquato Fraccon 8
Vicenza VI 36100

(G-16688)
E-STONE USA CORPORATION
472 Webster Turn Dr (33870-7507)
PHONE..................................954 266-6793
EMP: 54
SALES (corp-wide): 29MM **Privately Held**
WEB: www.trend-group.com
SIC: 3272 Floor slabs & tiles, precast concrete
HQ: E-Stone Usa Corporation
1565 Nw 36th St
Miami FL 33142

(G-16689)
EVERGLADES FOODS INC
6120 State Road 66 (33875-5942)
PHONE..................................863 655-2214
G Seth Howard, *President*
Mark Gose, *Vice Pres*
Chris Sebring, *Vice Pres*
EMP: 6 **EST:** 1976
SQ FT: 6,000
SALES (est): 780.5K **Privately Held**
WEB: www.evergladesseasoning.com
SIC: 2099 5141 5499 Seasonings: dry mixes; food brokers; spices & herbs

(G-16690)
EXCALIBUR AIRCRAFT
6439 Tractor Rd (33876-5741)
PHONE..................................863 385-9486
Ray Bratton, *Owner*
EMP: 5 **EST:** 1997
SALES (est): 568.2K **Privately Held**
WEB: www.excaliburaircraft.com
SIC: 3721 Aircraft

(G-16691)
FUNDER AMERICA INC
12 Crosley Ln (33870-7501)
PHONE..................................863 655-0208
Jonathan Albert, *Plant Mgr*
Peter Funder, *Branch Mgr*
EMP: 6
SALES (corp-wide): 26.5MM **Privately Held**
WEB: www.funderamerica.com
SIC: 3089 Laminating of plastic
PA: Funder America, Inc.
200 Funder Dr
Mocksville NC 27028
336 751-3501

(G-16692)
GATOR SHACK
4651 Us Highway 98 (33876-9561)
PHONE..................................863 381-2222
Steve C Stokes, *President*
EMP: 9 **EST:** 2012
SALES (est): 344.5K **Privately Held**
WEB: www.gatorshack1.com
SIC: 3421 Table & food cutlery, including butchers'

(G-16693)
GB CABINETS INCORPORATED
3907 Palazzo St (33872-2260)
PHONE..................................863 446-0676
Gary R Barnes, *Owner*
EMP: 6 **EST:** 2011
SALES (est): 148.4K **Privately Held**
SIC: 2434 Wood kitchen cabinets

(G-16694)
HIGHLAND CABINET INC
Also Called: Highland Cabinet Shop
739 Glenwood Ave (33870-3040)
PHONE..................................863 385-4396
Tom Braswell, *President*
Larry Mercure, *Mfg Staff*
EMP: 5 **EST:** 1978
SALES (est): 500K **Privately Held**
WEB: www.highlandscabinet.com
SIC: 2434 Wood kitchen cabinets

(G-16695)
HUCKE MANUFACTURING INC
Also Called: Advanced Door Concepts
222 Commercial Pl (33876-6526)
PHONE..................................863 655-3667
Margaret Hucke, *President*
Nicholas Hucke, *Vice Pres*
EMP: 6 **EST:** 2014
SQ FT: 7,500
SALES (est): 800K **Privately Held**
WEB: www.advdoor.com
SIC: 2541 Cabinets, lockers & shelving

(G-16696)
KEAVYS CORNER LLC
12413 Us Highway 98 (33876-9489)
PHONE..................................863 658-0235
Stephen Pardee, *CEO*
EMP: 7 **EST:** 2010
SALES (est): 350K **Privately Held**
WEB: www.kvlab.com
SIC: 3821 Laboratory equipment: fume hoods, distillation racks, etc.

(G-16697)
LESCO INC
425 Haywood Taylor Blvd (33870-7535)
PHONE..................................863 655-2424
Hal Berry, *Dir Ops-Prd-Mfg*
EMP: 18
SALES (corp-wide): 35.5B **Publicly Held**
SIC: 2875 Fertilizers, mixing only
HQ: Lesco, Inc.
1385 E 36th St
Cleveland OH 44114
216 706-9250

(G-16698)
LIGHT-TECH INC
8880 W Josephine Rd (33875-7213)
PHONE..................................863 385-6000
Lance A Giller, *President*
Sharon A Giller, *Corp Secy*
Roger Giller, *Vice Pres*
EMP: 7 **EST:** 1949
SALES (est): 600.1K **Privately Held**
WEB: www.light-tech.com
SIC: 3827 Optical instruments & apparatus

▲ = Import ▼=Export
◆ =Import/Export

(G-16699)
MACHINE TECHNOLOGY INC
108 Investment Ct (33876-6617)
PHONE....................................863 298-8001
Chris Nelson, *President*
EMP: 5 **EST:** 2017
SALES (est): 320.7K **Privately Held**
WEB: www.machine-technology.net
SIC: 3599 Machine shop, jobbing & repair

(G-16700)
ON SITE AG SERVICES
359 S Commerce Ave (33870-3607)
PHONE....................................863 382-7502
Curtis Donovan, *President*
EMP: 14 **EST:** 2017
SALES (est): 1MM **Privately Held**
SIC: 3523 Combines (harvester-threshers)

(G-16701)
PARK PLACE MANUFACTURING INC
454 Park St (33870-3225)
PHONE....................................863 382-0126
Ken Wacaster, *President*
EMP: 12 **EST:** 1997
SALES (est): 524.8K **Privately Held**
WEB: www.parkplacetruss.com
SIC: 3448 2439 Trusses & framing: prefabricated metal; structural wood members

(G-16702)
PARK PLACE TRUSS INC
500 Park St (33870-3227)
PHONE....................................863 382-0126
Keith Wacaster, *President*
EMP: 17 **EST:** 2003
SALES (est): 1.2MM **Privately Held**
SIC: 2439 Trusses, wooden roof

(G-16703)
PARK PLACE TRUSS & DESIGN INC ✪
206 W Center Ave (33870-3106)
PHONE....................................863 382-0126
Keith Wacaster, *CEO*
EMP: 28 **EST:** 2021
SALES (est): 1.6MM **Privately Held**
SIC: 2439 Trusses, wooden roof

(G-16704)
PRO ART AMERICA INC
620 Red Oak Ave (33870-3209)
PHONE....................................863 385-4242
William Dailey, *Principal*
EMP: 6 **EST:** 2011
SALES (est): 124.3K **Privately Held**
SIC: 2759 Commercial printing

(G-16705)
SCOSTA CORP (PA)
3670 Commerce Center Dr (33870-5538)
PHONE....................................863 385-8242
Scott Stanley II, *President*
Joe Falis, *General Mgr*
Madeline F Stanley, *Treasurer*
Tanya Davis, *Sales Staff*
EMP: 107 **EST:** 1979
SALES (est): 10.7MM **Privately Held**
WEB: www.scostacorp.com
SIC: 2439 Trusses, wooden roof

(G-16706)
SEA HAWK INDUSTRIES INC
Also Called: Sea Hawk Boats
523 Pear St (33870-3058)
PHONE....................................863 385-1995
Ginger Wyatt, *President*
Mike Wyatt, *Vice Pres*
▼ **EMP:** 9 **EST:** 1998
SQ FT: 3,000
SALES (est): 778.6K **Privately Held**
WEB: www.seahawkboats.com
SIC: 3732 Boat building & repairing

(G-16707)
SEBRING CUSTOM TANNING INC
429 Webster Turn Dr (33870-7543)
PHONE....................................863 655-1600
David Travers, *President*
EMP: 7 **EST:** 1986
SQ FT: 180,000
SALES (est): 972.2K **Privately Held**
WEB: www.sebringcustomtanning.com
SIC: 3111 Tanneries, leather

(G-16708)
SEBRING SEPTIC TANK PRECAST CO
Also Called: Sebring's Precast Products
8037 Associate Blvd (33876-6616)
PHONE....................................863 655-2030
Warren Copeland, *President*
Warren D Copeland, *President*
Sandra B Copeland, *Corp Secy*
EMP: 26 **EST:** 1978
SQ FT: 5,400
SALES (est): 3.7MM **Privately Held**
WEB: www.sebringprecast.com
SIC: 3272 3523 Septic tanks, concrete; farm machinery & equipment

(G-16709)
SMITHS WOODWORKS INC
4216 Shad Dr (33870-8424)
PHONE....................................863 381-6564
Timothy Smith, *Principal*
EMP: 6 **EST:** 1995
SALES (est): 228.1K **Privately Held**
WEB: www.niceknobs.com
SIC: 2431 Millwork

(G-16710)
SPANCRETE OF FLORIDA LLC
400 Deer Trl E (33876-6500)
PHONE....................................863 655-1515
Toll Free:....................................888 -
Mike Whalen, *President*
EMP: 30 **EST:** 1999
SALES (est): 3.7MM **Privately Held**
SIC: 3272 Concrete products, precast

(G-16711)
SPANCRETE SOUTHEAST INC
400 Deer Trl E (33876-6500)
P.O. Box 828, Waukesha WI (53187-0828)
PHONE....................................863 655-1515
John R Nagy, *President*
Todd Backus, *Vice Pres*
Julie Machia, *Human Res Mgr*
EMP: 1 **EST:** 2007
SALES (est): 4.9MM
SALES (corp-wide): 61.9MM **Privately Held**
WEB: www.spancrete.com
SIC: 3272 Concrete products, precast
PA: The Spancrete Group Inc
N16w23415 Stone Ridge Dr
Waukesha WI 53188
414 290-9000

(G-16712)
STRATONET INC (PA)
935 Mall Ring Rd (33870-8515)
PHONE....................................863 382-8503
Delton E Delaney, *President*
Arthur Wolfe, *Corp Secy*
EMP: 9 **EST:** 1992
SQ FT: 2,000
SALES (est): 1.5MM **Privately Held**
WEB: www.stratonet.net
SIC: 7372 Prepackaged software

(G-16713)
SUPERSWEET FROG LLC
2932 Us Highway 27 N (33870-1627)
PHONE....................................863 386-4917
Judith Bryan, *Principal*
EMP: 7 **EST:** 2014
SALES (est): 365.5K **Privately Held**
SIC: 2024 Yogurt desserts, frozen

(G-16714)
TECNAM US INC
29536 Flying Fortress Ln (33870-7514)
PHONE....................................863 655-2400
Paolo Pascale, *CEO*
Giovanni Pascale, *Managing Dir*
▲ **EMP:** 15 **EST:** 2014
SALES (est): 1.6MM **Privately Held**
WEB: www.tecnam.com
SIC: 3721 Aircraft

(G-16715)
THE HC COMPANIES INC
Also Called: Amerikan
2006 Fortune Blvd (33870-5502)
PHONE....................................863 314-9417
EMP: 96
SALES (corp-wide): 486.7MM **Privately Held**
WEB: www.hc-companies.com
SIC: 2821 Plastics materials & resins
HQ: The Hc Companies Inc
15150 Madison Rd
Middlefield OH 44062
440 632-3333

(G-16716)
TRADEWINDS POWER CORP
Also Called: John Deere Authorized Dealer
2717 Alt Us Hwy 27 S (33870-4970)
PHONE....................................863 382-2166
Thomas J Tracey, *President*
Jorge Rodriguez, *Engineer*
Caitlin Chason, *Sales Staff*
Spencer Dickerson, *Sales Staff*
Gabriel Berkebile, *Manager*
EMP: 10 **Privately Held**
WEB: www.deere.com
SIC: 3694 3561 5082 Engine electrical equipment; pumps & pumping equipment; construction & mining machinery
HQ: Tradewinds Power Corp.
5820 Nw 84th Ave
Doral FL 33166

(G-16717)
TURF CARE SUPPLY CORP
422 Webster Turn Dr (33870-7507)
PHONE....................................863 655-2424
Nick Martinelli, *General Mgr*
EMP: 37 **Privately Held**
WEB: www.turfcaresupply.com
SIC: 2873 Nitrogenous fertilizers
HQ: Turf Care Supply Corp.
50 Pearl Rd Ste 200
Brunswick OH 44212

(G-16718)
WINNTEL USA
Also Called: Winner Group
4014 Vilabella Dr (33872-1554)
PHONE....................................863 451-1789
Ejaj Chowdhury, *Owner*
EMP: 9 **EST:** 2010
SALES (est): 91.6K **Privately Held**
SIC: 2329 Men's & boys' clothing

(G-16719)
YARBROUGH TIRE SVC INC
1532 Sebring Pkwy (33870-5100)
PHONE....................................863 385-1574
Danny Yarbrough, *Manager*
EMP: 7 **EST:** 2018
SALES (est): 512K **Privately Held**
SIC: 3714 Motor vehicle parts & accessories

Seffner

Hillsborough County

(G-16720)
ARMOR INDUSTRIES CORP
6703 Pemberton View Dr (33584-2423)
PHONE....................................813 240-5903
Albert J Morhard, *Principal*
EMP: 7 **EST:** 2010
SALES (est): 152.5K **Privately Held**
SIC: 3999 Manufacturing industries

(G-16721)
BAEZ ENTERPRISES CORP
6315 Morning Star Dr (33584-2901)
PHONE....................................813 317-7277
Frank Felix Baez, *President*
Erbis Baez, *Treasurer*
EMP: 11 **EST:** 2004
SALES (est): 877.3K **Privately Held**
SIC: 3585 Air conditioning equipment, complete

(G-16722)
CAPTAIN CABINETS LLC
6705 Pemberton View Dr (33584-2423)
PHONE....................................813 685-7179
Leo Hans, *Principal*
EMP: 6 **EST:** 2017
SALES (est): 109.3K **Privately Held**
WEB: www.captcabinets.com
SIC: 2434 Wood kitchen cabinets

(G-16723)
CAST-CRETE USA LLC
6324 County Road 579 (33584-3006)
P.O. Box 24567, Tampa (33623-4567)
PHONE....................................813 621-4641
James Connelly, *CEO*
Craig Parrino, *President*
Daniel Cheney, *CFO*
Sal Deriggi, *Natl Sales Mgr*
Anthony Livelsberger, *Sales Staff*
▼ **EMP:** 99 **EST:** 1997
SALES (est): 21.2MM **Privately Held**
WEB: www.castcrete.com
SIC: 3272 5211 Lintels, concrete; lumber & other building materials

(G-16724)
DE VINCO COMPANY
435 Canning Plant Rd (33584-4645)
P.O. Box 155, Palmetto (34220-0155)
PHONE....................................941 722-1100
Devin Greenlaw, *President*
Jonathan C Greenlaw, *Vice Pres*
EMP: 7 **EST:** 2017
SQ FT: 120,000
SALES (est): 518.3K **Privately Held**
WEB: www.bulkcookingwines.com
SIC: 2084 Wines

(G-16725)
EVO MOTORS LLC
11809 E Us Highway 92 (33584-3413)
PHONE....................................813 621-7799
Mike Atir, *Manager*
EMP: 11 **EST:** 2012
SALES (est): 2.6MM **Privately Held**
WEB: www.evomotorsusa.com
SIC: 3594 5521 5511 Motors, pneumatic; used car dealers; new & used car dealers

(G-16726)
FLORIDA ENGINEERED CONSTRU (PA)
Also Called: Cast Crete Tampa
6324 County Road 579 (33584-3006)
PHONE....................................813 621-4641
Shea Hughes, *CEO*
Ralph W Hughes, *Ch of Bd*
William J Kardash, *President*
John Stanton, *President*
Carolyn Potter, *Human Resources*
◆ **EMP:** 225 **EST:** 1955
SQ FT: 10,000
SALES (est): 28.5MM **Privately Held**
WEB: www.castcrete.com
SIC: 3272 5031 2439 Concrete products, precast; concrete stuctural support & building material; building materials, exterior; trusses, wooden roof

(G-16727)
GABLE ENTERPRISES
1008 Lenna Ave (33584-5136)
PHONE....................................727 455-5576
Michael Gable, *Owner*
EMP: 10 **EST:** 1982
SALES (est): 100K **Privately Held**
WEB: www.gableenterprises.com
SIC: 3732 3731 Boat building & repairing; shipbuilding & repairing

(G-16728)
GARDNERS SCREEN ENCLOSURES
1113 Lake Shore Ranch Dr (33584-5564)
PHONE....................................813 843-8527
Timothy Gardner, *Principal*
EMP: 10 **EST:** 2005
SALES (est): 132.7K **Privately Held**
WEB: www.screenenclosurepros.com
SIC: 3448 Screen enclosures

(G-16729)
GPM FAB & SUPPLY LLC
1504 Lenna Ave (33584-5122)
P.O. Box 1303 (33583-1303)
PHONE....................................813 689-7107
Henry Lloyd, *Mng Member*
Lindy Lloyd,
EMP: 5 **EST:** 1989
SQ FT: 8,000
SALES (est): 896.8K **Privately Held**
WEB: www.gpmfab.com
SIC: 3317 3498 Steel pipe & tubes; fabricated pipe & fittings

(G-16730)
GUNTER SEPTIC TANK MFG
1434 E Dr Mrtn Lther King (33584-4841)
PHONE..................................813 654-1214
Danny Gunter, *Owner*
Aubery Coleman, *Manager*
EMP: 5 **EST:** 1987
SALES (est): 500K **Privately Held**
WEB: www.gunterseptictanks.com
SIC: 3272 5039 Septic tanks, concrete; septic tanks

(G-16731)
OLD OAK TRUSS COMPANY
1460 State Rd 574 (33584)
PHONE..................................813 689-6597
David Ledbetter, *President*
EMP: 8 **EST:** 1993
SALES (est): 886.4K **Privately Held**
WEB: www.oldoaktrusscompany.com
SIC: 2439 Trusses, wooden roof

(G-16732)
TAMPABAY CUSTOM DOOR LLC
447 Arch Ridge Loop (33584-3703)
PHONE..................................813 842-3667
An Tu, *Principal*
EMP: 7 **EST:** 2013
SALES (est): 191.1K **Privately Held**
SIC: 2431 Doors & door parts & trim, wood

(G-16733)
TAYLOR COMMUNICATIONS INC
12003 Embarcadero Dr (33584-3455)
PHONE..................................813 689-5099
EMP: 17
SALES (corp-wide): 3.6B **Privately Held**
WEB: www.taylor.com
SIC: 2761 Manifold business forms
HQ: Taylor Communications, Inc.
1725 Roe Crest Dr
North Mankato MN 56003
866 541-0937

(G-16734)
TSN MANUFACTURING INC
807 Hickory Fork Dr (33584-4755)
PHONE..................................727 709-9802
Tim Ngo, *Principal*
EMP: 11 **EST:** 2011
SALES (est): 326.2K **Privately Held**
WEB: www.tsnmanufacturing.com
SIC: 3999 Manufacturing industries

Seminole
Pinellas County

(G-16735)
ADVA-LITE INC
8285 Bryan Dairy Rd (33777-1350)
PHONE..................................727 369-5319
William A Dolan II, *President*
Don Pollo, *CFO*
▲ **EMP:** 39 **EST:** 1963
SQ FT: 80,000
SALES (est): 1.1MM
SALES (corp-wide): 23MM **Privately Held**
WEB: www.camsingglobal.com
SIC: 3648 3692 2396 Flashlights; primary batteries, dry & wet; automotive & apparel trimmings
PA: Camsing Global, Llc
8285 Bryan Dairy Rd
Seminole FL 33777
727 369-5319

(G-16736)
ADVANCED PRINTING
7245 Bryan Dairy Rd (33777-1540)
PHONE..................................727 545-9000
Jeff Anderson, *Owner*
EMP: 6 **EST:** 2015
SALES (est): 253.3K **Privately Held**
WEB: www.advancedprintingfl.com
SIC: 2752 Commercial printing, offset

(G-16737)
ALLEN SHUFFLEBOARD LLC
6595 Seminole Blvd (33772-6314)
PHONE..................................727 399-8877
Jim Allen, *President*
Sam Allen, *Principal*
◆ **EMP:** 7 **EST:** 1948
SQ FT: 8,200
SALES (est): 736.6K **Privately Held**
WEB: www.shuffleboard-1.com
SIC: 3949 7011 2842 Shuffleboards & shuffleboard equipment; hotels & motels; specialty cleaning, polishes & sanitation goods

(G-16738)
ANDERSON PRINTING SERVICES INC
Also Called: Sir Speedy
7245 Bryan Dairy Rd (33777-1540)
PHONE..................................727 545-9000
Jeffrey Anderson, *President*
Matt Anderson, *Vice Pres*
EMP: 22 **EST:** 1973
SQ FT: 5,300
SALES (est): 2.9MM **Privately Held**
WEB: www.sirspeedy.com
SIC: 2752 Commercial printing, lithographic

(G-16739)
APPLIED NEUROSCIENCE INC
8200 Bryan Dairy Rd # 315 (33777-1355)
PHONE..................................727 324-8922
EMP: 7 **EST:** 2014
SALES (est): 270.2K **Privately Held**
SIC: 7372 Prepackaged software

(G-16740)
AVALON SIGN SOLUTIONS INC
11125 Park Blvd (33772-4757)
PHONE..................................727 398-6126
Matthew Cicco, *Principal*
EMP: 8 **EST:** 2012
SALES (est): 254.1K **Privately Held**
WEB: www.avalonsignsolutions.com
SIC: 3993 Signs & advertising specialties

(G-16741)
BEACH BEACON
9911 Seminole Blvd (33772-2536)
PHONE..................................727 397-5563
Gerard Boutin, *Principal*
EMP: 11 **EST:** 2001
SALES (est): 372.6K **Privately Held**
WEB: www.tbnweekly.com
SIC: 2711 Newspapers, publishing & printing

(G-16742)
BEYETTE WOODWORKING LLC
8584 Mockingbird Ln (33777-3529)
PHONE..................................727 254-8705
Joseph R Beyette, *Principal*
EMP: 6 **EST:** 2011
SALES (est): 110K **Privately Held**
SIC: 2431 Millwork

(G-16743)
BLACK MOUNTAIN APPAREL INC
10490 75th St Ste A (33777-1413)
PHONE..................................727 216-6419
Melissa Newman, *President*
Harlan Newman, *Vice Pres*
▲ **EMP:** 22 **EST:** 1995
SQ FT: 10,000
SALES (est): 1.6MM **Privately Held**
WEB: www.blackmountainapparel.com
SIC: 2311 Men's & boys' suits & coats

(G-16744)
COMCEPT SOLUTIONS LLC
13799 Park Blvd Ste 307 (33776-3402)
PHONE..................................727 535-1900
Glenn D Atwell,
Joe D Mattos,
EMP: 20 **EST:** 1993
SALES (est): 3.1MM **Privately Held**
WEB: www.comcept.net
SIC: 3575 7311 7372 Computer terminals, monitors & components; advertising agencies; prepackaged software

(G-16745)
CUSTOM CABINETS
11060 70th Ave (33772-6308)
PHONE..................................727 392-1676
James Warren, *President*
Sandra Davis, *Office Mgr*
EMP: 5 **EST:** 2015
SALES (est): 600K **Privately Held**
WEB: www.advancedcustomcabinets.net
SIC: 2434 Wood kitchen cabinets

(G-16746)
ELECTRODES INC
10350 62nd Ter (33772-6937)
PHONE..................................727 698-7498
Brian Abbott, *Principal*
EMP: 9 **EST:** 2011
SALES (est): 113.3K **Privately Held**
WEB: www.electrodesinc.com
SIC: 3599 Industrial machinery

(G-16747)
FRITO-LAY NORTH AMERICA INC
10255 Kay Dr (33772)
PHONE..................................972 334-7000
EMP: 6
SALES (corp-wide): 70.3B **Publicly Held**
WEB: www.fritolay.com
SIC: 2086 5812 Carbonated soft drinks, bottled & canned; fast-food restaurant, chain
HQ: Frito-Lay North America, Inc.
7701 Legacy Dr
Plano TX 75024

(G-16748)
INTERNTONAL LINEAR MATRIX CORP
10831 Canal St (33777-1636)
PHONE..................................727 549-1808
Jennifer Foster, *General Mgr*
Jennifer Griffin, *Vice Pres*
EMP: 10 **EST:** 2007
SALES (est): 1MM **Privately Held**
WEB: www.ilmusa.com
SIC: 3699 Linear accelerators

(G-16749)
LIGHTNING PHASE II INC
10700 76th Ct (33777-1440)
PHONE..................................727 539-1800
Andrew Cecere, *Ch of Bd*
Jeff C Sproat, *Vice Pres*
Claire Knafla, *Opers Mgr*
Jon Benjamin, *Engineer*
Matt McNulty, *VP Finance*
EMP: 1 **EST:** 1985
SQ FT: 25,000
SALES (est): 6.5MM
SALES (corp-wide): 25.2B **Publicly Held**
WEB: www.elavon.com
SIC: 7372 7373 7378 Application computer software; computer integrated systems design; computer maintenance & repair
HQ: Elavon, Inc.
2 Concourse Pkwy Ste 800
Atlanta GA 30328

(G-16750)
LIGHTSTONE WOODWORKING LLC
8842 Commodore Dr (33776-1907)
PHONE..................................727 424-2660
Lichtenstein Alan, *Principal*
EMP: 6 **EST:** 2019
SALES (est): 251.5K **Privately Held**
SIC: 2431 Millwork

(G-16751)
LONDOS FINE CABINETRY LLC
6901 Bryan Dairy Rd # 130 (33777-1600)
PHONE..................................727 544-2929
Jerimiah Londos, *Mng Member*
Christoffer Londos,
EMP: 6 **EST:** 2012
SQ FT: 5,000
SALES (est): 479.1K **Privately Held**
WEB: www.londosfinecabinetry.com
SIC: 2434 Wood kitchen cabinets

(G-16752)
METAL FRONTS INC
10930 75th St (33777-1432)
PHONE..................................727 547-6700
George Misenhelder, *CEO*
Steven Elsenheimer, *Opers Staff*
EMP: 5 **EST:** 1995
SALES (est): 868.7K **Privately Held**
WEB: www.metalfronts.com
SIC: 3442 Store fronts, prefabricated, metal

(G-16753)
MILES OF SMILES RIDES INC
Also Called: Air-Flo/Erwood Heating and A/C
10530 72nd St Ste 705 (33777-1522)
PHONE..................................727 528-1227
Stuart J Long, *President*
EMP: 10 **EST:** 2007
SALES (est): 1.5MM **Privately Held**
SIC: 3585 1711 Heating & air conditioning combination units; heating & air conditioning contractors

(G-16754)
MODULAR MOLDING INTL INC
Also Called: M & M Industries
10521 75th St Ste B (33777-1434)
P.O. Box 10412, Largo (33773-0412)
PHONE..................................727 541-1333
Frank Meola, *President*
Mary Ann Meola, *CFO*
EMP: 31 **EST:** 1991
SQ FT: 17,000
SALES (est): 4.7MM **Privately Held**
WEB: www.mm-international.com
SIC: 3089 Injection molding of plastics

(G-16755)
MODULAR SIGN
8287 138th St (33776-2942)
PHONE..................................727 391-2423
Robert Gullick, *Owner*
EMP: 6 **EST:** 2008
SALES (est): 78.9K **Privately Held**
SIC: 3993 Signs & advertising specialties

(G-16756)
PRECISION RESISTOR CO INC
9442 Laura Anne Dr (33776-1600)
PHONE..................................727 541-5771
Fred A Dusenberry Jr, *President*
Robert L Wright, *Corp Secy*
EMP: 28 **EST:** 1932
SALES (est): 2.4MM **Privately Held**
WEB: www.precisionresistor.com
SIC: 3676 Electronic resistors

(G-16757)
PREFERRED CUSTOM PRINTING LLC
Also Called: Coconut Tree Btq & Gallery
7000 Bryan Dairy Rd B2 (33777-1612)
PHONE..................................727 443-1900
David L Braun,
Kim Braun,
EMP: 11 **EST:** 2007
SALES (est): 621.7K **Privately Held**
WEB: www.pcpprinting.com
SIC: 2741 2396 Art copy: publishing & printing; fabric printing & stamping

(G-16758)
PROTECH NUTRACEUTICALS INC
10321 72nd St (33777-1542)
PHONE..................................727 466-0770
Joseph Moretti, *President*
Chris Thornal, *Opers Mgr*
Angie Brett, *Purchasing*
Donna Moretti, *CFO*
EMP: 12
SQ FT: 10,000
SALES (est): 3.2MM **Privately Held**
WEB: www.protechnutra.com
SIC: 2834 Pharmaceuticals

(G-16759)
READERS DRECT PUBLICATIONS INC
9404 94th St (33777-2109)
PHONE..................................727 643-8616
Brenda Battalio, *Principal*
EMP: 6 **EST:** 2010
SALES (est): 116.7K **Privately Held**
SIC: 2741 Miscellaneous publishing

(G-16760)
RUSCH ELECTRIC MOTOR REPAIR CO
13000 Lois Ave (33776-1809)
PHONE..................................727 319-3388

Robert Leocata, *President*
Maria Leocata, *Treasurer*
EMP: 6 **EST:** 1943
SQ FT: 3,000
SALES (est): 176.2K **Privately Held**
SIC: 7694 5063 Electric motor repair; motors, electric

(G-16761)
SSH HOLDING INC
10055 Seminole Blvd (33772-2539)
PHONE..................................678 942-1800
Kirby Sims, *CEO*
Fred Hill III, *COO*
Connie Copelan, *Vice Pres*
Randy Figur, *Vice Pres*
Bruce Kirschner, *Vice Pres*
◆ **EMP:** 73 **EST:** 1993
SALES (est): 12.2MM
SALES (corp-wide): 526.7MM **Publicly Held**
WEB: www.hpi.net
SIC: 2395 Emblems, embroidered
PA: Superior Group Of Companies, Inc.
10055 Seminole Blvd
Seminole FL 33772
727 397-9611

(G-16762)
STARLITE INC
10861 91st Ter (33772-3045)
P.O. Box 20004, Saint Petersburg (33742-0004)
PHONE..................................727 392-2929
George Darwin, *President*
Tony Darwin, *President*
Barbara Fluharty, *Vice Pres*
Barbara Jowers, *Vice Pres*
George Scheffler Sr, *Vice Pres*
EMP: 17 **EST:** 1983
SALES (est): 404K **Privately Held**
WEB: www.starlite-inc.com
SIC: 2731 Books: publishing & printing

(G-16763)
STONECRFTERS ARCHTCTRAL PRCAST (PA)
10820 75th St Ste A (33777-1424)
PHONE..................................727 544-1210
Bill Morris, *Partner*
Dennis Nelucci, *Principal*
EMP: 10 **EST:** 1998
SALES (est): 3.2MM **Privately Held**
WEB: www.stonecraftersfl.com
SIC: 3272 3281 Siding, precast stone; cut stone & stone products

(G-16764)
SUPERIOR GROUP COMPANIES INC (PA)
10055 Seminole Blvd (33772-2539)
P.O. Box 4002 (33775-4002)
PHONE..................................727 397-9611
Michael Benstock, *CEO*
Sidney Kirschner, *Ch of Bd*
Andrew D Demott Jr, *COO*
Peter Benstock, *Exec VP*
Charles Sheppard, *Senior VP*
◆ **EMP:** 826 **EST:** 1920
SQ FT: 60,000
SALES: 526.7MM **Publicly Held**
WEB: www.superiorgroupofcompanies.com
SIC: 2389 3999 7389 Uniforms & vestments; identification badges & insignia; telemarketing services

(G-16765)
SUPERIOR GROUP COMPANIES INC
Universal Cotton Division
10055 Seminole Blvd (33772-2539)
P.O. Box 4002 (33775-4002)
PHONE..................................727 397-9611
Lorraine Becker, *Principal*
Dick Snyder, *Principal*
Michael Benstock, *Branch Mgr*
EMP: 7
SALES (corp-wide): 526.7MM **Publicly Held**
WEB: www.superiorgroupofcompanies.com
SIC: 2211 Laundry nets
PA: Superior Group Of Companies, Inc.
10055 Seminole Blvd
Seminole FL 33772
727 397-9611

(G-16766)
SUPERIOR SURGICAL MFG CO
10055 Seminole Blvd (33772-2539)
P.O. Box 4002 (33775-4002)
PHONE..................................800 727-8643
Michael Benstock, *Principal*
EMP: 10 **EST:** 2007
SALES (est): 242.6K **Privately Held**
WEB: www.superiorgroupofcompanies.com
SIC: 3842 Surgical appliances & supplies

(G-16767)
TACO METALS INC
Also Called: Taco Marine
6950 Bryan Dairy Rd Ste A (33777-1606)
PHONE..................................727 224-4282
Cliston Warren, *Branch Mgr*
EMP: 10
SALES (corp-wide): 2.4B **Publicly Held**
WEB: www.tacometals.com
SIC: 3089 Plastic boats & other marine equipment
HQ: Taco Metals, Llc
50 Ne 179th St
Miami FL 33162
305 652-8566

(G-16768)
TAMPA BAY NEWSPAPERS INC
9911 Seminole Blvd (33772-2536)
PHONE..................................727 397-5563
Dan Autry, *Principal*
EMP: 740 **EST:** 1997
SALES (est): 3.6MM
SALES (corp-wide): 14.9MM **Privately Held**
WEB: www.tbnweekly.com
SIC: 2711 Newspapers, publishing & printing
HQ: Times Publishing Company
490 1st Ave S
Saint Petersburg FL 33701
727 893-8111

(G-16769)
UNIMED SURGICAL PRODUCTS INC
10401 Belcher Rd S (33777-1415)
PHONE..................................727 546-1900
EMP: 34
SQ FT: 18,000
SALES (est): 4.9MM **Privately Held**
SIC: 3841 Mfg Surgical/Medical Instruments

(G-16770)
VMS USA INC
8060 Cypress Garden Ct (33777-3001)
P.O. Box 10252, Largo (33773-0252)
PHONE..................................727 434-1577
Hans Konle, *President*
Konle Hans, *Principal*
EMP: 10 **EST:** 2012
SQ FT: 7,000
SALES (est): 2.5MM **Privately Held**
WEB: www.vms-usa-inc.com
SIC: 3565 Packaging machinery

(G-16771)
WIDE OPEN ARMORY LLC
8200 113th St Ste 104 (33772-4111)
PHONE..................................727 202-5980
Brian Thomas,
EMP: 5 **EST:** 2012
SALES (est): 426.5K **Privately Held**
WEB: www.wideopenarmory.com
SIC: 3484 3482 Small arms; small arms ammunition

(G-16772)
XPONDR CORPORATION
10751 75th St (33777-1423)
P.O. Box 3430, Pinellas Park (33780-3430)
PHONE..................................727 541-4149
Lincoln Charlot, *President*
Michael Bryan, *Vice Pres*
◆ **EMP:** 22 **EST:** 1994
SQ FT: 11,000
SALES (est): 2.9MM **Privately Held**
WEB: www.xpondr.com
SIC: 3699 Security control equipment & systems

(G-16773)
ZHONE TECHNOLOGIES INC
7340 Bryan Dairy Rd # 150 (33777-1551)
PHONE..................................510 777-7151
EMP: 8 **EST:** 2016
SALES (est): 1MM **Privately Held**
WEB: www.dzsi.com
SIC: 3661 Fiber optics communications equipment

Shalimar
Okaloosa County

(G-16774)
EMERALD SAILS
100 Old Ferry Rd (32579-1215)
P.O. Box 800 (32579-0800)
PHONE..................................850 240-4777
Brian Harrison, *Principal*
▲ **EMP:** 10 **EST:** 2010
SALES (est): 161.7K **Privately Held**
WEB: www.canvasrepairsshalimarfl.com
SIC: 3444 Awnings & canopies

(G-16775)
GLOBAL TELEMETRY SYSTEMS INC
Also Called: GTS
70 6th Ave (32579-1841)
P.O. Box 800 (32579-0800)
PHONE..................................850 651-3388
Robert Harrison, *President*
Brian Harrison, *Vice Pres*
EMP: 7 **EST:** 1997
SALES (est): 1MM **Privately Held**
SIC: 3829 5065 Measuring & controlling devices; electronic parts & equipment

(G-16776)
MOTOROLA SOLUTIONS INC
60 2nd St (32579-1769)
P.O. Box 874 (32579-0874)
PHONE..................................850 651-1725
EMP: 6
SALES (corp-wide): 7.4B **Publicly Held**
WEB: www.motorolasolutions.com
SIC: 3663 Radio & TV communications equipment
PA: Motorola Solutions, Inc.
500 W Monroe St Ste 4400
Chicago IL 60661
847 576-5000

(G-16777)
SIERRA NEVADA CORPORATION
1150 N Eglin Pkwy (32579-1227)
PHONE..................................850 659-3600
Fatih Ozmen, *CEO*
Philip Barcelon, *Software Engr*
EMP: 32
SALES (corp-wide): 2.3B **Privately Held**
WEB: www.sncorp.com
SIC: 3812 3663 3699 Search & navigation equipment; radio & TV communications equipment; countermeasure simulators, electric
PA: Sierra Nevada Corporation
444 Salomon Cir
Sparks NV 89434
775 331-0222

(G-16778)
TRINITY SIGNS LLC
1111 N Eglin Pkwy (32579-1228)
PHONE..................................850 502-7634
Cheryl J Smith, *Principal*
EMP: 8 **EST:** 2015
SALES (est): 327K **Privately Held**
WEB: www.trinitysignsllc.com
SIC: 3993 Electric signs

(G-16779)
WIZARD PUBLICATIONS ✪
775 Blvard Of The Chmpons (32579)
PHONE..................................808 823-8815
Lisa Pollak, *Vice Pres*
EMP: 7 **EST:** 2020
SALES (est): 274.4K **Privately Held**
WEB: www.revealedtravelguides.com
SIC: 2741 Miscellaneous publishing

Silver Springs
Marion County

(G-16780)
A-1 CITY WIDE SEWER SERVICE
Also Called: Brown's Septics
6342 E Highway 326 (34488-1151)
P.O. Box 1057 (34489-1057)
PHONE..................................352 236-4456
Raymond W Brown, *President*
Barbara M Brown, *Treasurer*
EMP: 16 **EST:** 1975
SALES (est): 649.3K **Privately Held**
SIC: 3272 Concrete products, precast; septic tanks, concrete

(G-16781)
DURAPOLY INDUSTRIES INC
191 N Highway 314a (34488-5138)
PHONE..................................352 622-3455
Calvin Francis, *President*
Gary F Francis, *Vice Pres*
EMP: 9 **EST:** 1997
SQ FT: 6,000
SALES (est): 812.2K **Privately Held**
WEB: www.durapolyboats.com
SIC: 3443 Water tanks, metal plate

(G-16782)
GEORGIA-PACIFIC LLC
5240 Ne 64th Ave (34488-1340)
PHONE..................................404 652-4000
Fred Jackson, *Manager*
EMP: 50 **Privately Held**
SIC: 2439 Mfg Structural Wood Members

(G-16783)
PETE PETERSON SIGNS INC
11094 Ne Highway 314 (34488-2236)
PHONE..................................352 625-2307
Peter Peterson, *CEO*
Mary Peterson, *Corp Secy*
EMP: 5 **EST:** 1951
SQ FT: 2,275
SALES (est): 480K **Privately Held**
WEB: www.petepetersonsigns.com
SIC: 3993 Electric signs

(G-16784)
STANDARD SAND & SILICA COMPANY
15450 Ne 14th Street Rd (34488-4520)
PHONE..................................352 625-2385
John Smith, *Opers-Prdtn-Mfg*
Charles Wren, *Sales Staff*
EMP: 8
SQ FT: 1,344
SALES (corp-wide): 50.3MM **Privately Held**
WEB: www.standardsand.com
SIC: 1481 Mine & quarry services, nonmetallic minerals
PA: Standard Sand & Silica Company
1850 Us Highway 17 92 N
Davenport FL 33837
863 422-7100

Sopchoppy
Wakulla County

(G-16785)
OCOOW LLC
2340 Sopchoppy Hwy (32358-1431)
P.O. Box 554 (32358-0554)
PHONE..................................805 266-7616
Tracie Tinghitella, *Principal*
EMP: 9 **EST:** 2015
SALES (est): 917.6K **Privately Held**
SIC: 2891 Adhesives & sealants

Sorrento
Lake County

(G-16786)
GC TRAFFIC SIGNS AND SUP INC
Also Called: Gc Signs and Supply
31713 Long Acres Dr (32776-9295)
PHONE..................................352 735-8445

Norman Gaines, *President*
David Houghton, *Principal*
Michael Cermak, *Vice Pres*
EMP: 7 **EST:** 2017
SALES (est): 135.4K **Privately Held**
WEB: www.gcsignandsupply.com
SIC: 3993 Signs, not made in custom sign painting shops

(G-16787)
J & S CYPRESS INC
28625 Cypress Mill Rd (32776-9553)
P.O. Box 322 (32776-0322)
PHONE..................................352 383-3864
Ethel Chavis, *President*
EMP: 10 **EST:** 1973
SQ FT: 900
SALES (est): 892.6K **Privately Held**
WEB: www.cypressthings.com
SIC: 2421 2511 2434 Sawmills & planing mills, general; wood household furniture; wood kitchen cabinets

(G-16788)
LAKE COUNTY FORKLIFT SOLUTIONS
25808 Eufaula Way (32776-9678)
PHONE..................................352 735-4024
Danny J Donahue, *Principal*
EMP: 6 **EST:** 2007
SALES (est): 83.9K **Privately Held**
SIC: 3537 Industrial trucks & tractors

(G-16789)
MEACHEM STEEL INC
25546 High Hampton Cir (32776-7739)
PHONE..................................352 735-7333
Lori Dewitt, *CEO*
Carrlynn Dewitt, *Vice Pres*
EMP: 7 **EST:** 1996
SQ FT: 12,000
SALES (est): 660.1K **Privately Held**
SIC: 3441 Fabricated structural metal

(G-16790)
MILSPEC PRODUCTS INC
31537 Long Acres Dr (32776-9295)
PHONE..................................352 735-0065
Jeremy Summers, *President*
Jeff Summers, *Vice Pres*
EMP: 5 **EST:** 1993
SQ FT: 6,000
SALES (est): 747.7K **Privately Held**
WEB: www.milspecproducts.com
SIC: 3728 Aircraft parts & equipment

(G-16791)
PRECISION METAL SERVICES INC
33243 Equestrian Trl (32776-9193)
PHONE..................................407 843-3682
Jack Brush, *President*
Heather Brush, *Corp Secy*
EMP: 10 **EST:** 1965
SALES (est): 819.2K **Privately Held**
WEB: www.precisionmetalservices.com
SIC: 3444 3479 Sheet metal specialties, not stamped; painting of metal products

(G-16792)
R F LABORATORIES INC
31355 Bear Pond Dr # 46 (32776-9012)
PHONE..................................920 564-2700
David J Zima, *President*
EMP: 17 **EST:** 1994
SQ FT: 2,000
SALES (est): 180.6K **Privately Held**
WEB: www.rflab.com
SIC: 3663 Pagers (one-way)

(G-16793)
RADIO OEM INC
31355 State Road 46 (32776)
PHONE..................................920 564-6622
David Zima, *CEO*
Tina Zima, *CFO*
EMP: 8 **EST:** 2004
SALES (est): 170K **Privately Held**
SIC: 3651 Electronic kits for home assembly: radio, TV, phonograph

South Bay
Palm Beach County

(G-16794)
DUBBS FRESH DETAILING LLC ✪
235 Nw 1st Ave (33493-1807)
PHONE..................................813 770-5194
Derrick Bethea,
EMP: 6 **EST:** 2021
SALES (est): 87.2K **Privately Held**
SIC: 3714 Cleaners, air, motor vehicle

(G-16795)
FLORIDA CRYSTALS CORPORATION
Also Called: Florida Crystals Food
8501 S Us Hwy 27 Ave (33493-2302)
P.O. Box 9 (33493-0009)
PHONE..................................561 992-5635
Joseph Sommers, *Engineer*
Ricardo Hernandez, *Controller*
Kevin Dick, *Branch Mgr*
Matthew Gilbert, *Manager*
Yolanda Lee, *Administration*
EMP: 190
SALES (corp-wide): 2.1B **Privately Held**
WEB: www.floridacrystals.com
SIC: 2061 2062 Raw cane sugar; cane sugar refining
HQ: Florida Crystals Corporation
1 N Clematis St Ste 200
West Palm Beach FL 33401
561 655-6303

(G-16796)
OKEELANTA CORPORATION
Also Called: Okeelanta Sugar
6 Mile S Of S Bay Hwy 27 (33493)
P.O. Box 86 (33493-8600)
PHONE..................................561 996-9072
Jose Gonzalez, *General Mgr*
Ricardo Lima, *Manager*
EMP: 200
SALES (corp-wide): 2.1B **Privately Held**
WEB: www.floridacrystals.com
SIC: 2061 Raw cane sugar
HQ: Okeelanta Corporation
1 N Clematis St Ste 200
West Palm Beach FL 33401
561 366-5100

(G-16797)
SANCHEZ BROTHERS CORP
Also Called: Sb Pallets
6500 Us Highway 27 S (33493-2203)
P.O. Box 39 (33493-0039)
PHONE..................................561 992-0062
Jorge Sanchez, *President*
▲ **EMP:** 15 **EST:** 1993
SQ FT: 250,000
SALES (est): 2.4MM **Privately Held**
WEB: www.sbpallets.com
SIC: 2448 Pallets, wood

South Daytona
Volusia County

(G-16798)
BELSNICKEL ENTERPRISES INC
901 Valencia Rd (32119-2548)
PHONE..................................386 256-5367
Sally Moyer, *President*
◆ **EMP:** 10 **EST:** 1994
SALES (est): 900K **Privately Held**
WEB: www.thebellpeople.com
SIC: 3931 Bells (musical instruments)

(G-16799)
CENTRAL SIGNS VOLUSIA CNTY INC
497 Buchanan Way (32119-2955)
PHONE..................................386 341-4842
Paul J Payne, *President*
EMP: 6 **EST:** 1964
SALES (est): 134.6K **Privately Held**
SIC: 3993 Signs & advertising specialties

(G-16800)
COUCHMAN PRINTING COMPANY
Also Called: Printing.com
1634 S Ridgewood Ave (32119-8409)
PHONE..................................386 756-3052
Terry Davis, *Owner*
EMP: 7 **EST:** 1947
SQ FT: 3,075
SALES (est): 663K **Privately Held**
WEB: www.couchmanprinting.com
SIC: 2759 2752 Commercial printing; commercial printing, lithographic

(G-16801)
FLORIDA PLNTN SHUTTERS LLC
Also Called: US Blinds
1725 S Nova Rd Ste A1 (32119-1739)
PHONE..................................386 788-7766
Tom Russel, *President*
EMP: 7 **EST:** 1998
SALES (est): 915.8K **Privately Held**
WEB: www.floridaplantationshutters.com
SIC: 2591 Window blinds

(G-16802)
HOT OFF PRESS
952 Big Tree Rd (32119-2518)
PHONE..................................386 238-8700
Harry Campbell, *Principal*
EMP: 7 **EST:** 2007
SALES (est): 140K **Privately Held**
SIC: 2741 Miscellaneous publishing

(G-16803)
MARIS WORDEN AEROSPACE INC
2001 S Ridgewood Ave (32119-2288)
PHONE..................................514 895-8075
Julia A Maris, *Principal*
EMP: 7 **EST:** 2010
SALES (est): 116.4K **Privately Held**
SIC: 3721 Aircraft

(G-16804)
MERLE HARRIS ENTERPRISES INC
Also Called: Publishers of Seniors Today
724 Big Tree Rd (32119-2754)
PHONE..................................386 677-7060
Merle Harris, *President*
EMP: 5 **EST:** 1976
SQ FT: 1,000
SALES (est): 340K **Privately Held**
WEB: www.seniorstodaynewspaper.com
SIC: 2711 Newspapers, publishing & printing

(G-16805)
ONE HOUR PRINTING
661 Beville Rd Ste 109 (32119-1954)
PHONE..................................386 763-3111
Angela Sabato, *Owner*
EMP: 8 **EST:** 2007
SALES (est): 512.8K **Privately Held**
SIC: 2752 Commercial printing, offset

(G-16806)
PARRILLO INC
Also Called: Permacraft Sign & Trophies Co
1644 S Ridgewood Ave (32119-8410)
PHONE..................................386 767-8011
August Parrillo Sr, *President*
Carmen Parrillo, *Treasurer*
EMP: 6 **EST:** 1972
SQ FT: 10,285
SALES (est): 736.4K **Privately Held**
SIC: 3993 3999 3914 Neon signs; plaques, picture, laminated; trophies

(G-16807)
PATTICAKES CUPCAKERY LLC
964 Reed Canal Rd (32119-3154)
PHONE..................................386 383-1782
Neva Lefebvre, *Principal*
EMP: 6 **EST:** 2013
SALES (est): 105.9K **Privately Held**
SIC: 2051 Bread, cake & related products

(G-16808)
RGU COLOR INC
3133 S Ridgewood Ave # 1 (32119-3579)
PHONE..................................386 252-9979
Dennis Fogell, *President*
EMP: 5 **EST:** 2006
SALES (est): 664K **Privately Held**
WEB: www.rgucolor.com
SIC: 2752 Commercial printing, offset

(G-16809)
SIGN-O-SAURUS OF DAYTONA INC
Also Called: SOS Sign & Lighting Services
2127 S Ridgewood Ave (32119-3015)
PHONE..................................386 322-5222
Angela Kopnicky, *CEO*
Howard G Martin, *President*
EMP: 5 **EST:** 2004
SALES (est): 470.8K **Privately Held**
WEB: www.soscustomsigns.com
SIC: 3993 Signs, not made in custom sign painting shops

(G-16810)
STANDARD RIVET COMPANY INC
1640 S Segrave St (32119-2122)
PHONE..................................386 872-6477
Stephen Wallace, *President*
Stephen W Wallace, *General Mgr*
Paula Wallace, *Treasurer*
EMP: 10 **EST:** 1888
SQ FT: 34,000
SALES (est): 928.6K **Privately Held**
WEB: www.standardrivet.com
SIC: 3452 3542 Rivets, metal; riveting machines

South Miami
Miami-Dade County

(G-16811)
AGRANCO CORP (USA)
5966 S Dixie Hwy Ste 300 (33143-5177)
PHONE..................................877 592-0031
▼ **EMP:** 10
SALES (est): 182.2K **Privately Held**
SIC: 2879 4959 7699 7389 Mfg Agricultural Chemcl Sanitary Services Repair Services Business Services

(G-16812)
ANGLER PRO BOATS LLC
7755 Sw 66th St (33143-2710)
PHONE..................................305 525-4943
Christopher A Grillo,
EMP: 7 **EST:** 2016
SALES (est): 27.9K **Privately Held**
SIC: 3732 Boat building & repairing

(G-16813)
CAROL CITY OPA LOCKA NEWS
6796 Sw 62nd Ave (33143-3306)
PHONE..................................305 669-7355
Micheal Miller, *CEO*
Albie Barnes, *Accounts Exec*
Bill Kress, *Consultant*
EMP: 50
SALES (est): 2.5MM **Privately Held**
SIC: 2711 Newspapers, publishing & printing

(G-16814)
COUNTDOWN TODAY INC
6001 Sw 70th St Apt 532 (33143-3447)
P.O. Box 331537, Miami (33233-1537)
PHONE..................................415 420-2849
Fran Bradley, *Principal*
EMP: 6 **EST:** 2019
SALES (est): 295.1K **Privately Held**
SIC: 3993 Signs & advertising specialties

(G-16815)
DIVERSITYPRO CORP
6632 Sw 64th Ave (33143-3230)
PHONE..................................305 691-2348
Marc Wolff, *President*
Richard Fernandes, *Treasurer*
Jonathan David, *Admin Sec*
EMP: 35 **EST:** 2000
SQ FT: 70,000
SALES (est): 2.3MM **Privately Held**
SIC: 2676 2673 Sanitary paper products; bags: plastic, laminated & coated

▲ = Import ▼=Export
◆ =Import/Export

(G-16816)
EMC SOUTH FLORIDA LLC
Also Called: Forever Yung Altrntive Hlthcar
6075 Sunset Dr Ste 201 (33143-5061)
PHONE..................................786 352-9327
Paul L Guadagno, *President*
EMP: 6 **EST:** 2016
SALES (est): 294.3K **Privately Held**
WEB: www.emcsouthflorida.com
SIC: 3572 Computer storage devices

(G-16817)
GAPV
7800 Sw 57th Ave Ste 219c (33143-5523)
PHONE..................................786 257-1681
Evannan Romero, *Mng Member*
EMP: 7
SALES (est): 80K **Privately Held**
SIC: 1389 Oil consultants

(G-16818)
JAM WELDING SERVICE INC
5818 Sw 68th St (33143-3621)
PHONE..................................305 662-3787
Alvaro Espinoza, *President*
Martin Espinosa, *Vice Pres*
Gladys Espinosa, *Admin Sec*
EMP: 11 **EST:** 1992
SQ FT: 2,400
SALES (est): 1MM **Privately Held**
SIC: 7692 Welding repair

(G-16819)
JL WELDING INC
6510 Sw 64th Ct (33143-3204)
PHONE..................................786 442-4319
Joe Lewis Chandler, *President*
Inez Chandler, *Vice Pres*
EMP: 10 **EST:** 1988
SALES (est): 541.1K **Privately Held**
WEB: www.jlweldinginc.net
SIC: 7692 Welding repair

(G-16820)
LENNTECH USA LLC
5975 Sunset Dr Ste 802 (33143-5174)
PHONE..................................877 453-8095
EMP: 8 **EST:** 2019
SALES (est): 1MM **Privately Held**
WEB: www.lenntech.com
SIC: 3589 Water treatment equipment, industrial

(G-16821)
LPS GROUP LLC (PA)
7900 Sw 57th Ave Ph 23 (33143-5546)
PHONE..................................305 668-8780
Sidney J Harden Jr,
EMP: 7 **EST:** 2000
SALES (est): 816K **Privately Held**
WEB: www.lpsgroup.com
SIC: 7372 Business oriented computer software

(G-16822)
MILLER PUBLISHING CO INC
Also Called: Home Town News
6796 Sw 62nd Ave (33143-3306)
PHONE..................................305 669-7355
Hope Miller, *President*
Georgia Tate, *Admin Sec*
EMP: 14 **EST:** 1974
SQ FT: 6,000
SALES (est): 312.2K **Privately Held**
SIC: 2711 Newspapers, publishing & printing

(G-16823)
MOBILEPOWER LLC
5975 Sunset Dr (33143-5166)
PHONE..................................843 706-6108
Kevin Resnick, *Mng Member*
▲ **EMP:** 12 **EST:** 2010
SQ FT: 1,200
SALES (est): 814.5K **Privately Held**
WEB: www.mobilepower-us.com
SIC: 3714 Motor vehicle parts & accessories

(G-16824)
ORGANABIO LLC
7800 Sw 57th Ave Ste 225 (33143-5523)
PHONE..................................305 676-2586
Justin Irizarry, *CEO*
Laura Malagon, *Vice Pres*
Jordan Greenberg, *Research*
Petra Roulhac, *Manager*
EMP: 15 **EST:** 2018
SALES (est): 1.5MM **Privately Held**
WEB: www.organabio.com
SIC: 2836 Biological products, except diagnostic

(G-16825)
PINECREST TRIBUNE
6796 Sw 62nd Ave (33143-3306)
P.O. Box 431970, Miami (33243-1970)
PHONE..................................305 662-2277
Grant Miller, *Partner*
Michael Miller, *Partner*
EMP: 12 **EST:** 2001
SQ FT: 1,447
SALES (est): 373.9K **Privately Held**
WEB: www.communitynewspapers.com
SIC: 2711 Newspapers, publishing & printing

(G-16826)
S A GLORIA CORP
6705 S Red Rd Ste 405 (33143-3638)
PHONE..................................305 575-2900
EMP: 20 **Privately Held**
WEB: www.gloria.com.pe
SIC: 2023 Dried & powdered milk & milk products
HQ: Leche Gloria S.A.
Av. Republica De Panama 2461
Lima LM 13

(G-16827)
SEAL OUTDOORS INC
5900 Sw 56th Ter (33143-2270)
PHONE..................................877 323-7325
Daniela King, *CEO*
Herbert King, *COO*
EMP: 10 **EST:** 2015
SALES (est): 200K **Privately Held**
WEB: www.sealshoecovers.com
SIC: 2385 7389 Waterproof outerwear;

(G-16828)
SOLAR TINT INC
5887 Sw 70th St (33143-3624)
PHONE..................................305 663-4663
Robert Flores, *President*
EMP: 5 **EST:** 1990
SALES (est): 482.6K **Privately Held**
WEB: www.solartintinc.com
SIC: 3479 1799 Painting, coating & hot dipping; glass tinting, architectural or automotive

(G-16829)
SOUTH FLORIDA FINGER PRINTING
5900 Sw 73rd St Ste 304 (33143-5162)
PHONE..................................305 661-1636
Marilyn Caplin, *Principal*
EMP: 6 **EST:** 2008
SALES (est): 153.2K **Privately Held**
WEB: www.southfloridafingerprinting.com
SIC: 2759 Commercial printing

(G-16830)
SOUTH FLORIDA INSTITUT
7600 Sw 57th Ave Ste 201 (33143-5408)
PHONE..................................305 668-2853
Rafael Antun MD, *Principal*
EMP: 7 **EST:** 2007
SALES (est): 678K **Privately Held**
WEB: www.lvrsouthflorida.com
SIC: 3826 Laser scientific & engineering instruments

(G-16831)
TRADELAND AMERICAS INC
7900 Sw 57th Ave Ste 24 (33143-5546)
PHONE..................................786 718-1490
Ricardo Camacho, *President*
EMP: 7 **EST:** 2019
SALES (est): 169.4K **Privately Held**
SIC: 3273 3295 Ready-mixed concrete; blast furnace slag

(G-16832)
YOUR HOMETOWN NEWSPAPER INC
Also Called: Kendall News
6796 Sw 62nd Ave (33143-3306)
P.O. Box 431970, Miami (33243-1970)
PHONE..................................305 669-7355
Michael Miller, *President*
Albie Barnes, *Accounts Exec*
Aaron Guerrero, *Accounts Exec*
EMP: 30 **EST:** 1982
SQ FT: 6,400
SALES (est): 4.5MM **Privately Held**
SIC: 2711 Commercial printing & newspaper publishing combined

South Pasadena
Pinellas County

(G-16833)
386 NANOTECH INC
6860 Gulfport Blvd S (33707-2108)
PHONE..................................727 252-9580
Lisa Frick, *President*
Bradley Mescavage, *Vice Pres*
EMP: 14 **EST:** 2007
SALES (est): 671.2K **Privately Held**
WEB: www.386nanotechnology.com
SIC: 2891 Sealants

(G-16834)
FLORIDA ORANGE GROVES INC
1500 Pasadena Ave S (33707-3718)
PHONE..................................727 347-4025
Vincent R Shook, *President*
Lance Shook, *Exec VP*
Lance M Shook, *Vice Pres*
Gladys L Shook, *Treasurer*
Raymond E Shook, *Director*
EMP: 17 **EST:** 1977
SQ FT: 6,700
SALES: 2MM **Privately Held**
WEB: www.floridawine.com
SIC: 2084 Wines

Southwest Ranches
Broward County

(G-16835)
A PLUS TRAILERS
5801 Sw 210th Ter (33332-1532)
PHONE..................................786 395-0799
Eddie Flores, *President*
EMP: 8 **EST:** 2016
SALES (est): 592.4K **Privately Held**
WEB: www.954trailers.com
SIC: 7692 7539 5599 3799 Welding repair; trailer repair; utility trailers; trailers & trailer equipment

(G-16836)
AIRIND INCORPORATED
6511 Melaleuca Rd (33330-3830)
PHONE..................................954 252-0900
Robert Charles, *President*
Nancy Charles, *Vice Pres*
EMP: 6
SQ FT: 7,724
SALES (est): 1MM **Privately Held**
SIC: 3728 Aircraft parts & equipment

(G-16837)
DYER INDUSTRIES INC
5501 Sw 163rd Ave (33331-1443)
PHONE..................................954 434-9065
Timothy James Dyer, *Principal*
EMP: 6 **EST:** 2008
SALES (est): 183.9K **Privately Held**
SIC: 3999 Manufacturing industries

(G-16838)
JBLAZE INC
4910 Sw 172nd Ave (33331-1222)
PHONE..................................954 680-3962
EMP: 5
SALES (est): 466.5K **Privately Held**
SIC: 2323 Mfg Men's/Boy's Neckwear

(G-16839)
OSTEEN PLASTIC INC
17539 Sw 59th Ct (33331-2345)
PHONE..................................954 434-4921
Richard Osteen, *President*
EMP: 5 **EST:** 1971
SALES (est): 419.4K **Privately Held**
SIC: 3544 3523 Special dies, tools, jigs & fixtures; farm machinery & equipment

(G-16840)
PRO PUBLISHING INC
18020 Sw 66th St (33331-1860)
PHONE..................................954 888-7726
Aida Corrada-Bertsch, *President*
◆ **EMP:** 7 **EST:** 1986
SALES (est): 751.8K **Privately Held**
WEB: www.iconixink.com
SIC: 2731 5961 5192 Books: publishing only; book club, mail order; books

(G-16841)
SKIN PRO INTERNATIONAL INC
14345 Sunset Ln (33330-3407)
PHONE..................................305 528-9095
Timothy Schmidt, *Principal*
EMP: 11 **EST:** 2013
SALES (est): 536.1K **Privately Held**
WEB: www.skinpro.com
SIC: 2844 Toilet preparations

(G-16842)
SOUTH FLORIDA RODENTS
17200 Sw 65th Ct (33331-1741)
PHONE..................................954 410-5635
Jack Saunders, *Principal*
EMP: 7 **EST:** 2008
SALES (est): 268.2K **Privately Held**
WEB: www.southfloridarodents.com
SIC: 3999 Pet supplies

Sparr
Marion County

(G-16843)
D M C INDUSTRIES INC
13530 N Jacksonville Rd (32192)
P.O. Box 473 (32192-0473)
PHONE..................................352 620-9322
Dennis M Cauthen, *President*
Diane M Cauthen, *Vice Pres*
EMP: 6 **EST:** 1993
SALES (est): 687.6K **Privately Held**
WEB: www.dmcindustriesinc.com
SIC: 1389 Construction, repair & dismantling services

Spring Hill
Hernando County

(G-16844)
ACCUFORM SIGNS
11119 Holbrook St (34609-3840)
PHONE..................................800 237-1001
Bryan S Glidden, *Principal*
EMP: 12 **EST:** 2011
SALES (est): 670.8K **Privately Held**
WEB: www.accuform.com
SIC: 3993 Signs & advertising specialties

(G-16845)
AJS ALUMINUM INC
5441 Spring Hill Dr (34606-4563)
PHONE..................................352 688-7631
Andrew Jata, *President*
EMP: 5 **EST:** 1987
SQ FT: 2,500
SALES (est): 1.7MM **Privately Held**
WEB: www.ajsaluminum.com
SIC: 3334 Primary aluminum

(G-16846)
AMASCOTT LLC
4142 Mariner Blvd (34609-2468)
PHONE..................................352 683-4895
Tetyana Dickson, *Principal*
EMP: 5 **EST:** 2011
SALES (est): 426.7K **Privately Held**
WEB: www.amascott.com
SIC: 3825 Instruments to measure electricity

(G-16847)
ATLAS INDUSTRIAL SCALES INC
3715 Commercial Way (34606-2303)
PHONE..................................352 610-9989
Douglas Salerno, *Principal*
EMP: 8 **EST:** 2012

SALES (est): 88.7K **Privately Held**
WEB: www.atlasscales.com
SIC: 3596 Industrial scales

(G-16848)
BEAUTIFUL HOMES INC
471 Mariner Blvd (34609-5680)
P.O. Box 11251 (34610-0251)
PHONE....................................800 403-1480
Richard Burkhart, *President*
Mark Lepper, *Corp Secy*
EMP: 5 **EST**: 2005
SALES (est): 668.2K **Privately Held**
WEB: www.stairpartsusa.com
SIC: 3534 Stair elevators, motor powered

(G-16849)
CAPITAL PUBLISHING INC
7341 Spring Hill Dr (34606-4300)
PHONE....................................813 286-8444
EMP: 9 **EST**: 1998
SALES (est): 134.1K **Privately Held**
WEB: www.capitalpublishing.com
SIC: 2741 Miscellaneous publishing

(G-16850)
CUPCAKE HEAVEN
2721 Forest Rd (34606-3377)
PHONE....................................352 610-4433
Denise E Cornelius, *Principal*
EMP: 6 **EST**: 2009
SALES (est): 243K **Privately Held**
WEB: www.cupcakeheavenspringhill.com
SIC: 2051 Cakes, bakery: except frozen

(G-16851)
CUSTOM CULTERED MARBLE INC
3052 Commerce Ave (34609-4530)
PHONE....................................239 823-8241
Nelson Medina, *Principal*
EMP: 7 **EST**: 2018
SALES (est): 345.6K **Privately Held**
SIC: 3281 Cut stone & stone products

(G-16852)
FLORIDA SCREEN ENCLOSURES LLC
1451 Alameda Dr (34609-5712)
PHONE....................................352 398-5679
William E Chandler, *Principal*
EMP: 6 **EST**: 2019
SALES (est): 88.9K **Privately Held**
WEB: www.naturecoastaluminum.com
SIC: 3448 Screen enclosures

(G-16853)
FLORIDA STAINLESS STEEL ACC
5601 Cactus Cir (34606-5516)
PHONE....................................727 207-2575
Gary Peterson, *Principal*
EMP: 6 **EST**: 2010
SALES (est): 96K **Privately Held**
SIC: 3312 Stainless steel

(G-16854)
GRAY INFORMATION SOLUTIONS INC
12812 Coronado Dr (34609-5843)
PHONE....................................352 684-6655
Gary G Gray, *President*
Gary Gray, *President*
Vickie Gray, *Vice Pres*
EMP: 5 **EST**: 2003
SQ FT: 2,000
SALES (est): 382K **Privately Held**
WEB: www.grainformationsolutions.com
SIC: 3825 Network analyzers

(G-16855)
J-KUP CORP
Also Called: Sir Speedy
1260 Lori Dr (34606-4561)
PHONE....................................352 683-5629
Tom Kupcik, *President*
EMP: 12 **EST**: 2008
SALES (est): 1.3MM **Privately Held**
WEB: www.sirspeedy.com
SIC: 2752 Commercial printing, lithographic

(G-16856)
LASER INTERCEPTOR USA LLC
5769 Greystone Dr (34609-0477)
PHONE....................................352 688-0708
Clifford M Crane, *Principal*
EMP: 8 **EST**: 2009
SALES (est): 297.1K **Privately Held**
WEB: www.laser-interceptorusa.com
SIC: 3699 Electrical equipment & supplies

(G-16857)
NATURE CAST ANT-VNOM INDEX LLC
9204 Chase St (34606-1608)
PHONE....................................352 683-0647
Joseph W Keefer, *Manager*
EMP: 6 **EST**: 2014
SALES (est): 230K **Privately Held**
SIC: 2836 Venoms

(G-16858)
PHONE WAVE INC
178 Mariner Blvd (34609-5689)
PHONE....................................352 683-8101
Charles Dale Lemons, *COO*
EMP: 7 **EST**: 2009
SALES (est): 352.4K **Privately Held**
SIC: 3571 Electronic computers

(G-16859)
PROFESSONAL PAVER RESTORATIONS
3259 Dothan Ave (34609-3123)
PHONE....................................352 797-8411
Eric J Carrasco, *Principal*
EMP: 6 **EST**: 2010
SALES (est): 162.1K **Privately Held**
SIC: 3531 Pavers

(G-16860)
REAL NEWS REAL FAST
9365 Northcliffe Blvd (34606-1551)
PHONE....................................727 485-6055
Floyd Lemons, *Principal*
EMP: 6 **EST**: 2017
SALES (est): 220.8K **Privately Held**
SIC: 2711 Newspapers, publishing & printing

(G-16861)
ROMEO OHANA LLC
Also Called: 808 Island Treats
138 Mariner Blvd (34609-5687)
PHONE....................................808 500-3420
Michael C Romeo, *Mng Member*
EMP: 10 **EST**: 2018
SALES (est): 814.2K **Privately Held**
WEB: www.romeoohana.com
SIC: 2024 Ice cream & frozen desserts

(G-16862)
S&H ARCYLIC COATINGS INC
4673 Chamber Ct (34609-1605)
PHONE....................................352 232-1249
Harold G Toms IV, *President*
EMP: 8 **EST**: 2004
SALES (est): 67.5K **Privately Held**
SIC: 3479 Metal coating & allied service

(G-16863)
SIR SPEEDY PRINTING CENTER
1260 Lori Dr (34606-4561)
PHONE....................................352 683-8758
Fax: 352 683-8793
EMP: 12 **EST**: 2010
SALES (est): 610K **Privately Held**
SIC: 2752 Lithographic Commercial Printing

(G-16864)
SOLLUNAR ENERGY INC
4142 Mariner Blvd Ste 510 (34609-2468)
PHONE....................................352 293-2347
Dale Hobbie, *President*
EMP: 8 **EST**: 2008
SQ FT: 50,000
SALES (est): 116.9K **Privately Held**
SIC: 3674 Photovoltaic devices, solid state

(G-16865)
SPRING HILL BAKERY LLC
374 Winthrop Dr (34609-2090)
PHONE....................................954 825-3419
Elecia Madaffari,
EMP: 25 **EST**: 2018
SALES (est): 1MM **Privately Held**
WEB: www.springhillbakery.com
SIC: 2051 Bread, cake & related products

(G-16866)
STALL MASTER COMPANY (PA)
4377 Commercial Way (34606-1963)
PHONE....................................352 279-0089
Michael McHugh, *President*
Lynne McHugh, *Vice Pres*
EMP: 8 **EST**: 2004
SALES (est): 1.6MM **Privately Held**
WEB: www.stallmaster.com
SIC: 2421 Sawdust, shavings & wood chips

(G-16867)
T & S MOBILE WELDING LLC
6152 Tipton Ln (34606-4736)
PHONE....................................727 505-9407
Sandra Gast, *Principal*
EMP: 6 **EST**: 2010
SALES (est): 152.3K **Privately Held**
SIC: 7692 Welding repair

(G-16868)
TOP TORCH WLDG & FABRICATION
4326 Hedgewood Ave (34608-3306)
PHONE....................................352 835-1174
Daniel Lee Youngblood, *Owner*
EMP: 6 **EST**: 2016
SALES (est): 93K **Privately Held**
SIC: 7692 Welding repair

(G-16869)
TUTELA MONITORING SYSTEMS LLC
485 Mariner Blvd (34609-5680)
PHONE....................................941 462-1067
Steve Peck, *President*
Bruce Anderson, *COO*
EMP: 8 **EST**: 2005
SALES (est): 2.6MM
SALES (corp-wide): 17.7MM **Privately Held**
WEB: www.checkit.net
SIC: 3823 Industrial instrmnts msrmnt display/control process variable
PA: Checkit Plc
Broers Building
Cambridge CAMBS CB3 0
180 340-7757

Spring Hill
Pasco County

(G-16870)
BELOCAL PRO INC
12717 Flamingo Pkwy (34610-8020)
PHONE....................................727 379-9576
Russell M Taylor Jr, *President*
Edwin H Klaameyer Jr, *Principal*
Erik P Cocks, *Vice Pres*
EMP: 6 **EST**: 2017
SALES (est): 190.3K **Privately Held**
WEB: www.belocalpro.com
SIC: 2741 Miscellaneous publishing

(G-16871)
CSW CABINET SERVICES INC
17711 Overstreet Ln (34610-7331)
PHONE....................................727 267-1767
Craig S Wilborn, *President*
EMP: 6 **EST**: 2005
SALES (est): 73.4K **Privately Held**
SIC: 2434 Wood kitchen cabinets

(G-16872)
DAVID R CASE
18519 Floralton Dr (34610-1307)
PHONE....................................727 808-9330
David Case, *Principal*
EMP: 6 **EST**: 2011
SALES (est): 112.1K **Privately Held**
SIC: 3523 Farm machinery & equipment

(G-16873)
ISPY EQUITIES
12309 Field Point Way (34610-3366)
PHONE....................................813 731-0676
Lisa Marsala, *Principal*
EMP: 6 **EST**: 2016
SALES (est): 100.9K **Privately Held**
SIC: 2024 Ice cream & frozen desserts

(G-16874)
KELLEYS KRAFTS AND KREATIONS
12224 Hamlin Rd (34610-8815)
PHONE....................................813 508-1051
Kelley Ann Huff, *Owner*
EMP: 6 **EST**: 2013
SALES (est): 123.9K **Privately Held**
SIC: 2022 Natural cheese

(G-16875)
KEVIN MURRAY WELDING PROJ DBA
18151 Bosley Dr (34610-8109)
PHONE....................................813 323-3543
Kevin M Murray, *Principal*
EMP: 6 **EST**: 2009
SALES (est): 107.7K **Privately Held**
SIC: 7692 Welding repair

(G-16876)
NO LIMIT TS AND PRINTS LLC
11811 Pasco Trails Blvd (34610-4800)
PHONE....................................813 933-3424
Traci McCracken, *Manager*
EMP: 6 **EST**: 2014
SALES (est): 171.2K **Privately Held**
SIC: 2752 Commercial printing, offset

(G-16877)
STAINLESS STEEL GUIDE RODS
17205 Monteverde Dr (34610-7366)
PHONE....................................727 207-0583
Marty Wanyo, *Principal*
EMP: 6 **EST**: 2018
SALES (est): 90.8K **Privately Held**
WEB: www.ssguiderods.com
SIC: 3312 Stainless steel

(G-16878)
STRONG TOWER VINEYARD
17810 Forge Dr (34610-3080)
PHONE....................................352 799-7612
Janis McKnight, *Executive Asst*
EMP: 5 **EST**: 2005
SQ FT: 2,648
SALES (est): 334.7K **Privately Held**
WEB: www.strongtowervineyard.com
SIC: 2084 Wines

St Pete Beach
Pinellas County

(G-16879)
ECOTECH WATER LLC
7121 Gulf Blvd (33706-1943)
PHONE....................................877 341-9500
T E Janssen,
EMP: 8 **EST**: 2006
SALES (est): 257.5K **Privately Held**
WEB: www.ecotechwater.com
SIC: 3261 Vitreous plumbing fixtures

(G-16880)
ELLIS WOOD COLLECTION LTD
420 64th Ave Apt 302 (33706-2186)
PHONE....................................610 372-2880
Craig Weatherholtz, *President*
EMP: 14 **EST**: 1985
SQ FT: 54,000
SALES (est): 652.5K **Privately Held**
SIC: 2541 Store fixtures, wood

(G-16881)
EMERALD TECHNOLOGIES CORP
3807 Belle Vista Dr E (33706-2628)
PHONE....................................773 244-0092
James E Quinn, *Owner*
EMP: 5 **EST**: 1991
SALES (est): 372K **Privately Held**
SIC: 7372 Prepackaged software

(G-16882)
JB THOME & CO INC
1110 Boca Ciega Isle Dr (33706-2544)
PHONE....................................727 642-0588
Heather E Polansky, *Principal*
EMP: 6 **EST**: 2018

SALES (est): 243.7K **Privately Held**
WEB: www.bulkspirits.com
SIC: 2085 Distilled & blended liquors

(G-16883)
PUBLIC IMAGE PRINTING INC
5050 Gulf Blvd Ste C (33706-2417)
PHONE..................................727 363-1800
Mark Nathans, *President*
EMP: 8 **EST:** 1987
SALES (est): 486.1K **Privately Held**
WEB: www.publicimageprinting.com
SIC: 2752 Commercial printing, offset

(G-16884)
TROPICAL MBC LLC
246 75th Ave (33706-1828)
PHONE..................................727 498-6511
Reichbach Abraham, *Principal*
EMP: 7 **EST:** 2010
SALES (est): 549.2K **Privately Held**
SIC: 7372 Application computer software

(G-16885)
WASHINGTON PENN PLASTICS CO
4600 Mirabella Ct (33706-2576)
PHONE..................................724 228-1260
EMP: 11 **EST:** 2012
SALES (est): 85K **Privately Held**
SIC: 2821 Plastics materials & resins

Starke
Bradford County

(G-16886)
ACORE SHELVING & PRODUCTS INC
1460 Ne State Road 16 (32091-6598)
P.O. Box 67 (32091-0067)
PHONE..................................904 964-4320
Don Thompson Sr, *President*
Hayden Thompson, *Prdtn Mgr*
Joyce C Thompson, *Controller*
EMP: 8 **EST:** 2004
SALES (est): 650K **Privately Held**
WEB: www.acoreshelving.com
SIC: 2541 Cabinets, lockers & shelving

(G-16887)
BRADFORD COUNTY TELEGRAPH INC (PA)
Also Called: Union County Times
135 W Call St (32091-3210)
PHONE..................................904 964-6305
John M Miller, *President*
Anne M Miller, *Vice Pres*
Jewel O'Neal, *Treasurer*
EMP: 12 **EST:** 1877
SQ FT: 4,000
SALES (est): 3.4MM **Privately Held**
WEB: www.bctelegraph.com
SIC: 2711 2752 5943 Newspapers, publishing & printing; commercial printing, offset; office forms & supplies

(G-16888)
CARPORTS ANYWHERE INC
10858 Se County Road 221 (32091-7853)
P.O. Box 776 (32091-0776)
PHONE..................................352 468-1116
Christina Curles, *President*
EMP: 19 **EST:** 2015
SALES (est): 1.6MM **Privately Held**
WEB: www.carportsanywhere.com
SIC: 3448 Prefabricated metal buildings

(G-16889)
CHEMOURS COMPANY FC LLC
Florida Plant (32091)
PHONE..................................904 964-1230
David Podmeyer, *Manager*
EMP: 77
SALES (corp-wide): 4.9B **Publicly Held**
WEB: www.chemours.com
SIC: 3532 Mining machinery
HQ: The Chemours Company Fc Llc
1007 Market St
Wilmington DE 19898
302 773-1000

(G-16890)
CHEMOURS COMPANY FC LLC
5222 Treat Rd (32091)
P.O. Box 753 (32091-0753)
PHONE..................................904 964-1200
David J Podmeyer, *Manager*
EMP: 128
SALES (corp-wide): 4.9B **Publicly Held**
WEB: www.chemours.com
SIC: 1446 3295 1041 1031 Industrial sand; minerals, ground or treated; gold ores; lead & zinc ores; copper ores; iron ores
HQ: The Chemours Company Fc Llc
1007 Market St
Wilmington DE 19898
302 773-1000

(G-16891)
CORRUGATED HELP LLC
1219 W Madison St (32091-3020)
PHONE..................................904 874-7285
Paul Horner, *Principal*
EMP: 6 **EST:** 2012
SALES (est): 73.3K **Privately Held**
WEB: www.corrugatedbundler.com
SIC: 2653 Corrugated & solid fiber boxes

(G-16892)
DARLING INGREDIENTS INC
Also Called: Hampton Hexane Transfer Stn
11313 Se 52nd Ave (32091-6801)
PHONE..................................904 964-8083
Brad Huffman, *Branch Mgr*
EMP: 7
SALES (corp-wide): 3.3B **Publicly Held**
WEB: www.darlingii.com
SIC: 2077 Animal & marine fats & oils
PA: Darling Ingredients Inc.
5601 N Macarthur Blvd
Irving TX 75038
972 717-0300

(G-16893)
DIVISION 5 FLORIDA INC
Also Called: Division 5 Steel
417 E Weldon St (32091-2365)
P.O. Box 6058 (32091-6058)
PHONE..................................904 964-4513
Kenneth Frisbee, *President*
Mark A Spaur, *Vice Pres*
Justin Pace, *Project Mgr*
Charline Shaw, *Manager*
EMP: 20
SQ FT: 9,000
SALES (est): 5.5MM **Privately Held**
WEB: www.division5steel.com
SIC: 3441 1542 Building components, structural steel; design & erection, combined: non-residential

(G-16894)
GRIFFIN INDUSTRIES LLC
Bakery Feeds
11313 Se 52nd Ave (32091-6801)
PHONE..................................904 964-8083
Pete Weider, *Branch Mgr*
EMP: 49
SALES (corp-wide): 3.3B **Publicly Held**
WEB: www.griffinind.com
SIC: 2077 2048 Grease rendering, inedible; tallow rendering, inedible; prepared feeds
HQ: Griffin Industries Llc
4221 Alexandria Pike
Cold Spring KY 41076
859 781-2010

(G-16895)
JONES FIELD SERVICES PAMELA
9904 Nw County Road 229 (32091-5093)
PHONE..................................904 368-9777
Pamela L Thompson, *Principal*
EMP: 5 **EST:** 2014
SALES (est): 303.6K **Privately Held**
SIC: 1311 Crude petroleum & natural gas

(G-16896)
PRESTIGE ALUMINUM RAILING INC
4778 Se 142nd Way (32091-6878)
P.O. Box 366 (32091-0366)
PHONE..................................904 966-2163
James Frisbee, *President*
Mike Cribby, *Vice Pres*
Terry Sorensen, *Vice Pres*
Steve White, *Shareholder*
EMP: 9 **EST:** 1997
SALES (est): 977.9K **Privately Held**
SIC: 3355 Aluminum rail & structural shapes

(G-16897)
STARKE WASTE WTR TRTMNT PLANT
602 Edwards Rd (32091-3802)
PHONE..................................904 964-7999
Fred Magyari, *Principal*
Ricky Thompson, *Director*
EMP: 5 **EST:** 2002
SALES (est): 344.2K **Privately Held**
SIC: 3589 Water treatment equipment, industrial

Steinhatchee
Taylor County

(G-16898)
OUTDOOR PRODUCTS LLC
125 Sw 284th Ave (32359-3107)
PHONE..................................352 473-0886
Jennifer Poppell, *Principal*
EMP: 6 **EST:** 2015
SALES (est): 95.5K **Privately Held**
WEB: www.outdoorproducts.com
SIC: 2329 5699 2339 Men's & boys' sportswear & athletic clothing; athletic (warmup, sweat & jogging) suits: men's & boys'; customized clothing & apparel; athletic clothing: women's, misses' & juniors'

Stuart
Martin County

(G-16899)
A1 CLEANING CONCEPTS INC
173 Se Norfolk Blvd (34997-5572)
PHONE..................................772 288-7214
Galan Joynes, *CEO*
Heather Joynes, *Manager*
EMP: 5 **EST:** 2002
SALES (est): 450K **Privately Held**
WEB: www.pressurecleaningfl.com
SIC: 3589 High pressure cleaning equipment

(G-16900)
AAA MONTEREY DISCOUNT VACUUM
514 Se Monterey Rd (34994-4408)
PHONE..................................772 288-5233
Cliff Peranio, *President*
Leo Peranio, *President*
EMP: 5 **EST:** 1987
SALES (est): 393.6K **Privately Held**
WEB: www.montereyvacuum.net
SIC: 3635 7629 7623 Household vacuum cleaners; vacuum cleaner repair; refrigeration service & repair

(G-16901)
ABLE CLOSETS INC
218 Sw Federal Hwy Ste B (34994-2004)
PHONE..................................772 781-8250
James Sisto, *President*
EMP: 9 **EST:** 2004
SALES (est): 1MM **Privately Held**
WEB: www.ableclosets.com
SIC: 3089 Organizers for closets, drawers, etc.: plastic

(G-16902)
ACRYFIN COATINGS LLC
901 Nw New Providence Rd (34994-8918)
PHONE..................................772 631-3899
John D Kicklighter, *Manager*
EMP: 8 **EST:** 2016
SALES (est): 737.6K **Privately Held**
WEB: www.acryfin.com
SIC: 2952 Asphalt felts & coatings

(G-16903)
ADVANCED HURRICANE PROTECTION
4517 Se Commerce Ave (34997-8860)
PHONE..................................772 220-1200
John Zervopoulos, *President*
EMP: 5 **EST:** 1996
SALES (est): 800K **Privately Held**
WEB: www.advancedhurricane.net
SIC: 3442 Shutters, door or window: metal

(G-16904)
ADVANTAGE SOFTWARE INC
925 Se Central Pkwy (34994-3904)
PHONE..................................772 288-3266
Greg Seely, *President*
Portia Seely, *Corp Secy*
Megan Seely, *Prdtn Mgr*
Jeremy Thorne, *Research*
Cathy Barbre, *Sales Staff*
EMP: 32 **EST:** 1987
SQ FT: 5,000
SALES (est): 6.4MM **Privately Held**
WEB: www.eclipsecat.com
SIC: 7372 Business oriented computer software

(G-16905)
AMERICAN ENRGY INNOVATIONS LLC
6800 Sw Jack James Dr (34997-6200)
PHONE..................................772 221-9100
Philip Catsman, *Mng Member*
Dominick Lacombe,
EMP: 10 **EST:** 2011
SQ FT: 40,000
SALES (est): 920K **Privately Held**
WEB: www.williscustomyachts.com
SIC: 3728 Aircraft body & wing assemblies & parts

(G-16906)
AMPERSAND GRAPHICS INC
553 Se Monterey Rd (34994-4407)
PHONE..................................772 283-1359
Dennis Clark, *President*
Elaine Clark, *Vice Pres*
Jeremy Savard, *Art Dir*
◆ **EMP:** 22 **EST:** 1977
SQ FT: 6,000
SALES (est): 1.8MM **Privately Held**
WEB: www.ampersand-graphics.com
SIC: 2759 5199 2396 Screen printing; advertising specialties; automotive & apparel trimmings

(G-16907)
AMPERSAND SHIRT SHACK
553 Se Monterey Rd (34994-4407)
PHONE..................................772 600-8743
Brad Love, *CEO*
Victoria Love, *President*
Jeremy Savard, *Art Dir*
▼ **EMP:** 10 **EST:** 2011
SALES (est): 800K **Privately Held**
WEB: www.ampersand-graphics.com
SIC: 2759 Screen printing

(G-16908)
ARCHITECTURAL SIGNCRAFTERS
3195 Se Gran Park Way (34997-6701)
PHONE..................................772 600-5032
EMP: 5
SALES: 480K **Privately Held**
SIC: 3993 Mfg Signs/Advertising Specialties

(G-16909)
ARMAGEDDON MANUFACTURING
3170 Se Dominica Ter (34997-5718)
PHONE..................................772 208-5288
Ariel Paxson, *Principal*
EMP: 6 **EST:** 2017
SALES (est): 269.4K **Privately Held**
WEB: www.armageddonmfg.com
SIC: 3999 Manufacturing industries

(G-16910)
ARTHUR COX
Also Called: A & J Boatworks
4800 Se Anchor Ave (34997-1904)
PHONE..................................772 286-5339
Arthur Cox, *Owner*

GEOGRAPHIC

EMP: 6 **EST:** 2003
SALES (est): 345.7K **Privately Held**
SIC: 3732 Boat building & repairing

(G-16911)
BAUSCH AMERICAN TOWERS LLC
6800 Sw Jack James Dr # 3 (34997-6200)
PHONE..................................772 283-2771
C Timothy Bausch,
▲ **EMP:** 15 **EST:** 1977
SQ FT: 10,000
SALES (est): 1.2MM **Privately Held**
SIC: 3441 3732 3446 3444 Fabricated structural metal for ships; boat building & repairing; architectural metalwork; sheet metalwork

(G-16912)
BAUSCH ENTERPRISES INC
3171 Se Waaler St (34997-5923)
P.O. Box 326, Port Salerno (34992-0326)
PHONE..................................772 220-6652
Dana Bausch, *President*
EMP: 10 **EST:** 1996
SQ FT: 7,000
SALES (est): 1.4MM **Privately Held**
WEB: www.bauschenterprises.com
SIC: 3444 3732 Sheet metalwork; boat building & repairing

(G-16913)
BE MERRY
320 Se Denver Ave (34994-2138)
PHONE..................................772 324-8289
Anne Falco, *Principal*
EMP: 8 **EST:** 2012
SALES (est): 452.3K **Privately Held**
SIC: 3421 Table & food cutlery, including butchers'

(G-16914)
BEACHCOMBER FIBRGLS TECH INC
3355 Se Lionel Ter (34997-8870)
PHONE..................................772 283-0200
Michael Cohen, *President*
▼ **EMP:** 5 **EST:** 1978
SQ FT: 4,000
SALES (est): 600K **Privately Held**
WEB: www.beachfiber.com
SIC: 3089 5551 3429 Molding primary plastic; marine supplies & equipment; manufactured hardware (general)

(G-16915)
BEATA BORDAS
6172 Se Riverboat Dr (34997-1527)
PHONE..................................772 349-2568
Beata Bordas, *Owner*
EMP: 6 **EST:** 2000
SALES (est): 167.2K **Privately Held**
SIC: 3999 Massage machines, electric: barber & beauty shops

(G-16916)
BILL SHUDA
6088 Se Woodfield Ct (34997-6361)
PHONE..................................772 220-6620
William Shuda, *Principal*
EMP: 6 **EST:** 2010
SALES (est): 102.7K **Privately Held**
WEB: www.homeportcharts.com
SIC: 3732 Boat building & repairing

(G-16917)
BLAIR PROPELLER MA
3009 Se Monroe St (34997-5981)
PHONE..................................772 283-1453
Todd Blair, *Owner*
EMP: 6 **EST:** 2018
SALES (est): 1MM **Privately Held**
WEB: www.blairpropeller.com
SIC: 3366 Propellers

(G-16918)
BONADEO BOAT WORKS LLC
4431 Se Commerce Ave (34997-5742)
P.O. Box 328 (34995-0328)
PHONE..................................772 341-9820
Larry Bonadeo,
Tony Bonadeo,
Denise Sovel-Bonadeo,
▼ **EMP:** 8 **EST:** 2004
SQ FT: 600
SALES (est): 679.7K **Privately Held**
WEB: www.bonadeoboatworks.com
SIC: 3732 Boat building & repairing

(G-16919)
C&C DIVERSIFIED SERVICES LLC
7954 Sw Jack James Dr (34997-7241)
P.O. Box 517, Indiantown (34956-0517)
PHONE..................................772 597-1022
Brian Critoph, *Manager*
Daniel Cox,
EMP: 9 **EST:** 2005
SALES (est): 2.6MM **Privately Held**
WEB: www.ccdiversifiedgas.com
SIC: 1311 Crude petroleum & natural gas production

(G-16920)
CEDRUS INC
Also Called: American Stairs
9011 Sw Old Kansas Ave (34997-7218)
PHONE..................................772 286-2082
Mahmoud Mikati, *Ch of Bd*
Jamil Mikati, *President*
Jihad Mikati, *Vice Pres*
Rhonda Roarke, *Admin Sec*
EMP: 20 **EST:** 1984
SALES (est): 4MM **Privately Held**
WEB: www.americanstairparts.com
SIC: 2431 3446 3442 Staircases & stairs, wood; doors, wood; stairs, staircases, stair treads: prefabricated metal; molding, trim & stripping

(G-16921)
CEMEX MATERIALS LLC
1232 Se Dixie Cutoff Rd (34994-3436)
PHONE..................................772 287-0502
Lester Fultz, *Branch Mgr*
EMP: 73
SQ FT: 2,947 **Privately Held**
SIC: 3273 5032 5211 Ready-mixed concrete; concrete mixtures; concrete & cinder block
HQ: Cemex Materials Llc
1501 Belvedere Rd
West Palm Beach FL 33406
561 833-5555

(G-16922)
CFM&D LLC
2550 Se Willoughby Blvd (34994-4701)
PHONE..................................772 220-8938
James E Allen, *Principal*
EMP: 6 **EST:** 2012
SALES (est): 678.1K **Privately Held**
SIC: 2099 Food preparations

(G-16923)
CHITTUM YACHTS LLC
4953 Se Pine Knoll Way (34997-6995)
PHONE..................................386 589-7224
Hal Chittum, *Manager*
EMP: 24
SALES (corp-wide): 2.6MM **Privately Held**
SIC: 3732 Boat building & repairing
PA: Chittum Yachts, Llc
4577 Sw Cargo Way
Palm City FL 34990
386 589-7224

(G-16924)
CHLORINATORS INC
1044 Se Dixie Cutoff Rd (34994-3436)
P.O. Box 1518 (34995-1518)
PHONE..................................772 288-4854
Diane Haskett, *Ch of Bd*
Aimee Foley, *Purchasing*
Royce Johnson, *Regl Sales Mgr*
Jill Majka, *Marketing Mgr*
EMP: 37 **EST:** 1975
SQ FT: 10,600
SALES (est): 7.3MM **Privately Held**
WEB: www.regalchlorinators.com
SIC: 3589 Water treatment equipment, industrial

(G-16925)
CONEHEADS FROZEN CUSTARDS
43 Sw Flagler Ave (34994-2140)
PHONE..................................772 600-7730
Timothy F Stoklosa, *Mng Member*
EMP: 6 **EST:** 2010
SALES (est): 117.4K **Privately Held**
SIC: 2024 Ice cream, bulk

(G-16926)
CONNECTYX TECHNOLOGIES CORP
850 Nw Federal Hwy # 411 (34994-1019)
P.O. Box 2478, Palm City (34991-2478)
PHONE..................................772 221-8240
Ronn Schuman, *President*
EMP: 8 **EST:** 2003
SQ FT: 3,000
SALES (est): 1MM
SALES (corp-wide): 1.8MM **Privately Held**
WEB: www.tap4emergency.info
SIC: 7372 Business oriented computer software
PA: Connectyx Technologies Holdings Group, Inc.
850 Nw Federal Hwy
Stuart FL 34994
772 221-8240

(G-16927)
CONSTRUCTION JOURNAL LTD (PA)
400 Sw 7th St (34994-2908)
PHONE..................................772 781-2144
Richard J Goldman, *President*
Stephen Burgmeyer, *Editor*
Jay Bumgardner, *Business Mgr*
Alanna Collins, *Business Mgr*
Deneen Grove, *Business Mgr*
EMP: 79 **EST:** 1996
SQ FT: 9,000
SALES (est): 19.4MM **Privately Held**
WEB: www.constructionjournal.com
SIC: 2721 Trade journals: publishing only, not printed on site

(G-16928)
CROWDER CUSTOM RODS INC
Also Called: Crowder Rods
3040 Se Dominica Ter (34997-5716)
P.O. Box 276, Jensen Beach (34958-0276)
PHONE..................................772 220-8108
Robert Crowder, *President*
Matt Potsko, *Vice Pres*
EMP: 9 **EST:** 1998
SQ FT: 2,500
SALES (est): 678.7K **Privately Held**
WEB: www.crowderrods.com
SIC: 3949 5941 Fishing equipment; sporting goods & bicycle shops

(G-16929)
CRUNCHI LLC
7671 Sw Ellipse Way (34997-7251)
PHONE..................................772 600-8082
Dante A Weston, *Mng Member*
EMP: 6 **EST:** 2019
SALES (est): 221.7K **Privately Held**
WEB: www.crunchi.com
SIC: 2844 Toilet preparations

(G-16930)
DANFOSS LLC
7560 Sw Jack James Dr (34997-7258)
PHONE..................................772 219-0745
Daniel Foss, *Branch Mgr*
Lisa Walker, *Manager*
EMP: 7
SALES (corp-wide): 83.5K **Privately Held**
WEB: www.danfoss.com
SIC: 3585 Refrigeration & heating equipment
HQ: Danfoss, Llc
11655 Crossroads Cir
Baltimore MD 21220
410 931-8250

(G-16931)
DELAWARE CHASSIS WORKS
3513 Se Gran Park Way (34997-8808)
PHONE..................................302 378-3013
Joe Timney, *Owner*
Tonya Turk, *Vice Pres*
EMP: 7 **EST:** 1979
SALES (est): 300K **Privately Held**
WEB: www.delawarechassisworks.com
SIC: 3711 Automobile assembly, including specialty automobiles

(G-16932)
DESIGNER SERVICES OF
3241 Se Slater St (34997-5704)
PHONE..................................772 286-0855
Michael Schmidt, *President*
EMP: 5 **EST:** 1969
SQ FT: 6,500
SALES (est): 403.1K **Privately Held**
WEB: www.designerservices.com
SIC: 3999 Models, general, except toy

(G-16933)
DRONES SHOP LLC
4406 Se Graham Dr (34997-1544)
PHONE..................................772 224-8118
Matthew Tatem, *Principal*
EMP: 7 **EST:** 2015
SALES (est): 553.2K **Privately Held**
WEB: www.tatemseo.com
SIC: 3728 Target drones

(G-16934)
DYNAMIC PRECISION GROUP INC (PA)
3651 Se Commerce Ave (34997-4967)
PHONE..................................772 287-7770
Greg Bennett, *President*
EMP: 48 **EST:** 2011
SALES (est): 402.2MM **Privately Held**
WEB: www.paradigmprecision.com
SIC: 3724 3444 Engine mount parts, aircraft; sheet metalwork

(G-16935)
E M P INC
Also Called: Stuart Propeller & Marine
4340 Se Commerce Ave (34997-5726)
PHONE..................................772 286-7343
Edward A Morgan III, *President*
◆ **EMP:** 7 **EST:** 1983
SQ FT: 12,750
SALES (est): 843K **Privately Held**
WEB: www.stuartpropeller.net
SIC: 3599 5088 7692 Propellers, ship & boat: machined; marine propulsion machinery & equipment; welding repair

(G-16936)
ECOSPHERE TECHNOLOGIES INC (PA)
3491 Se Gran Park Way (34997-8804)
PHONE..................................772 287-4846
Dennis McGuire, *Ch of Bd*
Michael Donn Sr, *COO*
Jacqueline McGuire, *Senior VP*
Jamar Blackmon, *Opers Mgr*
David Brooks, *CFO*
EMP: 17 **EST:** 1998
SQ FT: 14,700
SALES: 91.1K **Publicly Held**
WEB: www.ecospheretech.com
SIC: 3589 Water treatment equipment, industrial

(G-16937)
ELC SALES LLC
4699 Se Bywood Ter (34997-2116)
PHONE..................................772 285-5230
Eugene Caiazzo, *Mng Member*
EMP: 1
SALES (est): 3MM **Privately Held**
SIC: 3646 Commercial indusl & institutional electric lighting fixtures

(G-16938)
ENERGYBIONICS LLC
519 Sw Glen Crest Way (34997-7253)
PHONE..................................561 229-4985
Sean Ebersold, *CEO*
EMP: 8 **EST:** 2012
SALES (est): 2.1MM **Privately Held**
SIC: 3571 Minicomputers

(G-16939)
EVAN LLOYD DESIGNS
3576 Se Dixie Hwy (34997-5245)
P.O. Box 369, Sweet Home OR (97386-0369)
PHONE..................................772 286-7723
EMP: 8
SALES (est): 640K **Privately Held**
SIC: 3911 Mfg Precious Metal Jewelry

(G-16940)
FLAGSHIP MARINE INC
3211 Se Gran Park Way (34997-6702)
PHONE..................................772 781-4242
Thomas C Martland, *President*
▼ **EMP:** 7 **EST:** 1989
SALES (est): 1MM **Privately Held**
WEB: www.flagshipmarine.com
SIC: 3585 3531 3663 Air conditioning equipment, complete; marine related equipment; television closed circuit equipment

(G-16941)
FLORIDA COLOR PRINTING INC
1501 Se Decker Ave # 110 (34994-3964)
PHONE..................................772 286-7264
Allan Everett, *Principal*
EMP: 6 **EST:** 1985
SALES (est): 210.4K **Privately Held**
WEB: www.floridacolor.com
SIC: 2752 Commercial printing, offset

(G-16942)
FRESHCO LTD
Also Called: Indian River Select
7929 Sw Jack James Dr (34997-7243)
PHONE..................................772 287-2111
Clifford F Burg, *Partner*
James Burg, *Partner*
Sharon Burg, *Partner*
Wendy Grieve, *Partner*
J Patrick Schirard, *Partner*
EMP: 40 **EST:** 1995
SQ FT: 33,000
SALES (est): 7MM **Privately Held**
WEB: www.freshcopackaging.com
SIC: 2033 Fruits & fruit products in cans, jars, etc.

(G-16943)
G & K ALUMINUM INC
3110 Se Slater St (34997-5703)
PHONE..................................772 283-1297
Gene Rastrelli, *President*
John Rastrelli, *Vice Pres*
▼ **EMP:** 10 **EST:** 1978
SQ FT: 10,000
SALES (est): 879K **Privately Held**
WEB: www.gkaluminum.com
SIC: 3365 3949 3444 Aluminum foundries; sporting & athletic goods; sheet metalwork

(G-16944)
GAME FISHERMAN INC
1384 Nw Coconut Point Ln (34994-9484)
PHONE..................................772 220-4850
Michael T Matlack, *President*
Jeanne Matlack, *Admin Sec*
▲ **EMP:** 10 **EST:** 1984
SALES (est): 899.7K **Privately Held**
WEB: www.gamefisherman.com
SIC: 3732 8748 Fishing boats: lobster, crab, oyster, etc.: small; business consulting

(G-16945)
GARLINGTON LANDEWEER MARINE
3370 Se Slater St (34997-5705)
PHONE..................................772 283-7124
Peter Landeweer, *President*
Evert Landeweer, *Vice Pres*
Mary Jordon, *Sales Dir*
Robb Maas, *Asst Sec*
EMP: 30 **EST:** 1984
SQ FT: 19,000
SALES (est): 10MM **Privately Held**
WEB: www.garlingtonyachts.com
SIC: 3732 Yachts, building & repairing

(G-16946)
GB AIRLINK INC
Also Called: Savi Air
2524 Se Wtham Feld Dr Uni (34996)
PHONE..................................561 593-7284
Michael Donoghue, *CEO*
Gabe Houston, *COO*
EMP: 8 **EST:** 1996
SALES (est): 717.6K **Privately Held**
WEB: www.savi-air.com
SIC: 3721 Aircraft

(G-16947)
GOULD SIGNS INC
3035 Se Waaler St (34997-5948)
P.O. Box 1090, Port Salerno (34992-1090)
PHONE..................................772 221-1218
Donald E Gould, *President*
Joseph Gould, *Vice Pres*
EMP: 9 **EST:** 1982
SQ FT: 6,500
SALES (est): 660K **Privately Held**
SIC: 3993 1799 Electric signs; sign installation & maintenance

(G-16948)
GRAPHIC DESIGNS INTL INC
3161 Se Slater St (34997-5756)
P.O. Box 2431 (34995-2431)
PHONE..................................772 287-0000
Alison Gallagher, *President*
Kimberly Amsalem, *General Mgr*
Margaret Holt, *Corp Secy*
Kevin Gallagher, *Vice Pres*
EMP: 14 **EST:** 1994
SQ FT: 3,600
SALES (est): 1.8MM **Privately Held**
WEB: www.graphicdesignsinternational.com
SIC: 3993 Signs & advertising specialties

(G-16949)
GRINDHARD COATINGS INC
7850 Sw Ellipse Way (34997-7246)
PHONE..................................772 221-9986
Austin Weiss, *Principal*
EMP: 9 **EST:** 2017
SALES (est): 135.2K **Privately Held**
SIC: 3479 Metal coating & allied service

(G-16950)
GULFSTREAM ALUM & SHUTTER CORP
1673 Se Pomeroy St (34997-3901)
PHONE..................................772 287-6476
John L O'Brien, *President*
Barbara O'Brien, *Corp Secy*
▼ **EMP:** 23 **EST:** 1979
SQ FT: 20,000
SALES (est): 4.7MM **Privately Held**
WEB: www.gulfshutters.com
SIC: 3442 3448 1751 Louvers, shutters, jalousies & similar items; prefabricated metal buildings; carports: prefabricated metal; screen enclosures; window & door installation & erection

(G-16951)
GULFSTREAM LAND COMPANY LLC
Also Called: Riverwatch Marina & Boatyard
200 Sw Monterey Rd (34994-4612)
PHONE..................................772 286-3456
Erik Bishop, *General Mgr*
Marion Walker, *Office Mgr*
William E Biggs, *Mng Member*
Brett Cherry, *Director*
Arthur E Biggs,
EMP: 18 **EST:** 2001
SALES (est): 675.5K **Privately Held**
SIC: 3731 4493 Shipbuilding & repairing; marinas

(G-16952)
GYRO-GALE INC
2981 Se Dominica Ter # 4 (34997-5753)
P.O. Box 2650 (34995-2650)
PHONE..................................772 283-1711
Maged Metwally, *President*
Nagwa Metwally, *Corp Secy*
Asmaa Metwally, *Opers Mgr*
Zeyad Metwally, *VP Engrg*
▼ **EMP:** 6 **EST:** 1976
SQ FT: 3,000
SALES (est): 834.3K **Privately Held**
WEB: www.gyrogalestabilizers.com
SIC: 3499 3537 Stabilizing bars (cargo), metal; cradles, boat

(G-16953)
H2OCEAN LLC (PA)
7938 Sw Jack James Dr (34997-7241)
PHONE..................................866 420-2326
Marty Stern, *Vice Pres*
Scott Stier, *VP Opers*
Geri A Kolos, *CFO*
Brandon Ron, *Sales Staff*
Ocean Aid, *Marketing Staff*
◆ **EMP:** 15 **EST:** 2001
SQ FT: 30,000
SALES (est): 10.2MM **Privately Held**
WEB: www.h2ocean.com
SIC: 2844 Mouthwashes

(G-16954)
HAKE YACHTS INC
4550 Se Hampton Ct (34997-5707)
PHONE..................................772 287-3200
Jon Scot, *Agent*
EMP: 7 **EST:** 2019
SALES (est): 366.4K **Privately Held**
WEB: www.hakeyachts.com
SIC: 3732 Boat building & repairing

(G-16955)
HURRICANE MARINE MANUFACTURING
3301 Se Slater St (34997-5706)
PHONE..................................772 260-3950
EMP: 11 **EST:** 2018
SALES (est): 1.4MM **Privately Held**
WEB: www.hurricaneboatlifts.com
SIC: 3999 Manufacturing industries

(G-16956)
I P TEAM INC
701 Nw Federal Hwy # 301 (34994-1061)
PHONE..................................772 398-4664
Randall L Sparks, *CEO*
Brigett Matthews, *Prdtn Mgr*
Sparks Andy, *Human Res Mgr*
James Sparks, *Accounts Exec*
Michelle Pedro, *Marketing Staff*
EMP: 26 **EST:** 2009
SALES (est): 3.4MM **Privately Held**
WEB: www.teamip.com
SIC: 2759 Screen printing

(G-16957)
IMPERIAL PHOTOENGRAVING
11013 Sw Redwing Dr (34997-2719)
PHONE..................................772 924-1731
Jim D Rueth, *Principal*
EMP: 8 **EST:** 2010
SALES (est): 426.1K **Privately Held**
SIC: 3423 Engravers' tools, hand

(G-16958)
INFRARED ASSOCIATES INC
2851 Se Monroe St (34997-5913)
PHONE..................................772 223-6670
Frederick W Rothe, *President*
EMP: 12 **EST:** 1997
SQ FT: 5,200
SALES (est): 2.1MM **Privately Held**
WEB: www.irassociates.com
SIC: 3823 Infrared instruments, industrial process type

(G-16959)
INTERNATIONAL PRTG AD SPC INC
Also Called: Team Ip
701 Nw Federal Hwy # 301 (34994-1005)
P.O. Box 7609, Port Saint Lucie (34985-7609)
PHONE..................................772 398-4664
Randall L Sparks, *President*
Blaine Isbell, *Vice Pres*
Jill Harrison, *Director*
Jackie Walker, *Director*
▲ **EMP:** 40 **EST:** 1992
SALES (est): 9MM **Privately Held**
SIC: 2759 Screen printing

(G-16960)
JETSTREAM FABRICATION LLC
1880 Se Federal Hwy (34994-3914)
PHONE..................................772 287-3338
Karl Lust, *Manager*
EMP: 5
SALES (est): 725K **Privately Held**
SIC: 3499 Fabricated metal products

(G-16961)
JGLC ENTERPRISES LLC
Also Called: Sheet Metal Unlimited
3920 Se Commerce Ave (34997-4958)
PHONE..................................772 223-7393
Lynette Crocker, *Mng Member*
Jose Guth, *Mng Member*
EMP: 24 **EST:** 2006
SALES (est): 3MM **Privately Held**
WEB: www.sheetmetalunlimited.com
SIC: 3441 Fabricated structural metal

(G-16962)
JIM SMITH BOATS INC
4396 Se Commerce Ave (34997-5723)
PHONE..................................772 286-9049
John A Vance, *President*
B R Boniface, *Vice Pres*
EMP: 16 **EST:** 1980
SQ FT: 10,000
SALES (est): 811.3K **Privately Held**
WEB: www.jimsmithboats.com
SIC: 3732 Boat building & repairing

(G-16963)
K BAUSCH MFG CORP
2813 Se Monroe St (34997-5904)
PHONE..................................772 485-2426
EMP: 6 **EST:** 2019
SALES (est): 392.1K **Privately Held**
SIC: 3999 Manufacturing industries

(G-16964)
KAREPAT GROUP INC
4800 Se Anchor Ave (34997-1904)
PHONE..................................772 286-5339
Arthur Cox, *Treasurer*
EMP: 9 **EST:** 2001
SALES (est): 921K **Privately Held**
SIC: 3731 Shipbuilding & repairing

(G-16965)
KINANE CORP
Also Called: Minuteman Press
310 Se Denver Ave (34994-2138)
PHONE..................................772 288-6580
Timothy Kinane, *President*
Erica Kinane-Kelley, *Info Tech Mgr*
EMP: 13 **EST:** 1987
SQ FT: 4,500
SALES (est): 1.5MM **Privately Held**
WEB: www.kinaneprinting.com
SIC: 2752 Commercial printing, lithographic

(G-16966)
KLP INVESTMENTS LLC
1424 Se Macarthur Blvd (34996-4929)
PHONE..................................401 762-4357
EMP: 5 **EST:** 2018
SALES (est): 359.2K **Privately Held**
SIC: 2899 Chemical preparations

(G-16967)
KNIGHT WELDING SUPPLY LLC
3131 Se Waaler St (34997-5923)
PHONE..................................561 889-5342
EMP: 6 **EST:** 2019
SALES (est): 580.5K **Privately Held**
WEB: www.knightweldingsupply.com
SIC: 7692 Welding repair

(G-16968)
L & H BOATS INC
3350 Se Slater St (34997-5705)
PHONE..................................772 288-2291
Glenn Muller, *President*
Eric Meyer, *President*
John Meyer, *Vice Pres*
Linda Straub, *Treasurer*
Ella Smith, *Admin Sec*
EMP: 7 **EST:** 1992
SALES (est): 775.3K **Privately Held**
WEB: www.lhboats.com
SIC: 3732 Fishing boats: lobster, crab, oyster, etc.: small

(G-16969)
LARSEN
3 Melody Ln (34996-6708)
PHONE..................................305 989-4043
Louis Larsen, *Principal*
EMP: 6 **EST:** 2017
SALES (est): 259.3K **Privately Held**
SIC: 3732 Boat building & repairing

(G-16970)
LENCO MARINE SOLUTIONS LLC
4700 Se Municipal Ct (34997-8871)
PHONE..................................772 288-2662
Sam Mullinax, *CEO*
Richard Devito, *President*

GEOGRAPHIC

Brian Henneman, *Project Mgr*
Kevin Kortum, *Foreman/Supr*
Katie Sterling, *Human Resources*
▲ **EMP:** 33 **EST:** 1998
SQ FT: 22,000
SALES (est): 14.4MM
SALES (corp-wide): 4.3B **Publicly Held**
WEB: www.lencomarine.com
SIC: 3429 Marine hardware
HQ: Power Products, Llc
N85w12545 Westbrook Xing
Menomonee Falls WI 53051
262 293-0600

(G-16971)
MACK SALES INC
3129 Se Dominica Ter (34997-5754)
PHONE..................................772 283-2306
Travis Blain, *President*
Collin Mac, *CFO*
▼ **EMP:** 9 **EST:** 1988
SALES (est): 2.3MM **Privately Held**
WEB: www.macksails.com
SIC: 3732 Boat building & repairing

(G-16972)
MAILBOX PUBLISHING INC
Also Called: Ocean Media
3727 Se Ocean Blvd Ste 20 (34996-6740)
PHONE..................................772 334-2121
Glen Fetzner, *CEO*
EMP: 25 **EST:** 1997
SALES (est): 2.1MM **Privately Held**
SIC: 2721 Magazines: publishing only, not printed on site

(G-16973)
MARINE CUSTOMS UNLIMITED ✪
3355 Se Dixie Hwy (34997-5240)
PHONE..................................772 223-8005
Brian Odonnell, *Owner*
EMP: 10 **EST:** 2020
SALES (est): 291K **Privately Held**
WEB: www.marinecustoms.com
SIC: 2394 Canvas boat seats

(G-16974)
MARINE DIGITAL INTEGRATORS LLC
7667 Sw Ellipse Way (34997-7251)
PHONE..................................772 210-2403
Yvan Cote, *President*
EMP: 27 **EST:** 2014
SALES (est): 7.6MM
SALES (corp-wide): 1.8B **Privately Held**
WEB: www.seastarsolutions.com
SIC: 3699 Electrical equipment & supplies
HQ: Sierra International Llc
1 Sierra Pl
Litchfield IL 62056
217 324-9400

(G-16975)
MARKCAM INC
4361 Se Commerce Ave (34997-5728)
PHONE..................................772 283-7189
Mark Willis, *Principal*
EMP: 6 **EST:** 2006
SALES (est): 97.5K **Privately Held**
WEB: www.willismarineinc.com
SIC: 3732 Boat building & repairing

(G-16976)
MICRO HYBRIDS INC (PA)
2600 Se Ocean Blvd Apt D5 (34996-3415)
PHONE..................................772 225-4206
Martha Richardson, *President*
EMP: 6 **EST:** 1985
SALES (est): 570.3K **Privately Held**
WEB: www.microhybrids.com
SIC: 3679 Electronic circuits

(G-16977)
MINDER RESEARCH INC
3000 Se Waaler St (34997-5937)
P.O. Box 47 (34995-0047)
PHONE..................................772 463-6522
Debbie Druiem, *President*
Janice Melendez, *Controller*
Jennifer Zwicky, *Manager*
▲ **EMP:** 10 **EST:** 2013
SALES (est): 1.2MM **Privately Held**
WEB: www.minderresearch.com
SIC: 3714 Motor vehicle parts & accessories

(G-16978)
MR GUTTER CUTTER INC
3102 Se Dixie Hwy (34997-5044)
PHONE..................................772 286-7780
Craig Rice, *President*
EMP: 16 **EST:** 1985
SQ FT: 5,600
SALES (est): 758.9K **Privately Held**
SIC: 3444 Gutters, sheet metal

(G-16979)
MULTICOLOR PRINTING INC
1249 Se Dixie Cutoff Rd (34994-3490)
PHONE..................................772 287-1676
Stephen Schmoyer, *President*
EMP: 8 **EST:** 1968
SALES (est): 712.2K **Privately Held**
WEB: www.gomulticolor.com
SIC: 2752 2791 2789 Commercial printing, offset; typesetting; bookbinding & related work

(G-16980)
NEW ENGLAND GRANITE & MARBLE
890 Sw Enterprise Way (34997-7210)
PHONE..................................772 283-8667
Carlos R Salvatierra, *President*
Francisco Coelho Jr, *Admin Sec*
▲ **EMP:** 9 **EST:** 2009
SALES (est): 1.7MM **Privately Held**
WEB: www.newenglandgranite.net
SIC: 3281 1743 Curbing, granite or stone; marble installation, interior

(G-16981)
NITRO LEISURE PRODUCTS INC
Also Called: Nitro Gulf
4490 Se Cheri Ct (34997-5709)
PHONE..................................414 272-5084
J Hanover, *Manager*
EMP: 30
SALES (corp-wide): 26MM **Privately Held**
WEB: www.nitrogolf.com
SIC: 3949 Balls: baseball, football, basketball, etc.
HQ: Nitro Leisure Products Inc
1943 Se Airport Rd
Stuart FL

(G-16982)
OMEGA POWER SYSTEMS INC
4443 Se Commerce Ave (34997-5742)
P.O. Box 406, Port Salerno (34992-0406)
PHONE..................................772 219-0045
Frank Dlouhy, *President*
Michelle Mathis, *Admin Sec*
EMP: 5 **EST:** 1994
SALES (est): 799.6K **Privately Held**
WEB: www.omegaps.com
SIC: 3643 3825 Lightning protection equipment; electrical energy measuring equipment

(G-16983)
OMT INC
Also Called: Stylecraft Fine Cabinetry
648 Se Monterey Rd (34994-4410)
PHONE..................................772 287-3762
John Waugh, *President*
Cathie Armstrong-Moore, *Vice Pres*
EMP: 8 **EST:** 1973
SALES (est): 712.8K **Privately Held**
WEB: www.stylecraftfinecabinetry.com
SIC: 2434 Wood kitchen cabinets

(G-16984)
ORGANIC CANE COMPANY INC
923 Se Lincoln Ave (34994-3810)
PHONE..................................561 385-4081
Daniel Consonni, *President*
EMP: 6 **EST:** 2018
SALES (est): 62.3K **Privately Held**
SIC: 2061 Raw cane sugar

(G-16985)
PACE MACHINE & TOOL INC
7986 Sw Jack James Dr (34997-7241)
PHONE..................................561 747-5444
Monica Dirr, *President*
Ken Desch, *Principal*
Richard Dirr Jr, *Vice Pres*
Mark Van Sleete, *Buyer*
EMP: 17 **EST:** 1978
SQ FT: 5,000
SALES (est): 3.5MM **Privately Held**
WEB: www.pacemachine.com
SIC: 3544 Special dies & tools

(G-16986)
PALMER MANUFACTURING CO LLC
3651 Se Commerce Ave (34997-4967)
PHONE..................................772 287-7770
EMP: 11
SALES (corp-wide): 402.2MM **Privately Held**
SIC: 3724 Aircraft engines & engine parts
HQ: Palmer Manufacturing Co., Llc.
243 Medford St
Malden MA 02148
781 321-0480

(G-16987)
PERFORMANCE TECHNOLOGY 2000
1501 Se Decker Ave # 129 (34994-3989)
PHONE..................................772 463-1056
Arthur Scornavacca, *Principal*
EMP: 8 **EST:** 2004
SALES (est): 494.1K **Privately Held**
SIC: 3825 Internal combustion engine analyzers, to test electronics

(G-16988)
PHOTO GRAPHICS
1601 Nw Federal Hwy (34994-9629)
PHONE..................................772 220-1430
EMP: 7 **EST:** 2019
SALES (est): 253K **Privately Held**
WEB: www.photographicsusa.com
SIC: 2752 Commercial printing, offset

(G-16989)
PLATING TECHNOLOGIES INC
2971 Se Dominica Ter # 12 (34997-5713)
PHONE..................................772 220-4201
Lois R Hartzog, *President*
Dee Hartzog, *Vice Pres*
EMP: 8 **EST:** 1991
SQ FT: 6,000
SALES (est): 749.5K **Privately Held**
WEB: www.platingtechnologies.net
SIC: 2819 Industrial inorganic chemicals

(G-16990)
POCKETEC INC
50 Ne Dixie Hwy Ste E7 (34994-1874)
PHONE..................................772 692-8020
Kenneth Featherstone, *Principal*
▲ **EMP:** 7 **EST:** 2006
SALES (est): 342.1K **Privately Held**
WEB: www.ladyclassic.com
SIC: 3949 Sporting & athletic goods

(G-16991)
PORT ST LUCIE NEWS
Also Called: Stuart News
1939 Se Federal Hwy (34994-3915)
PHONE..................................772 287-1550
Barrett Sanders, *Editor*
Candace Anderson, *Vice Pres*
David Giles, *Vice Pres*
Carolyn Micheli, *Vice Pres*
Alison Morris, *Vice Pres*
EMP: 42 **EST:** 2010
SALES (est): 940.1K **Privately Held**
SIC: 2711 Newspapers, publishing & printing

(G-16992)
POWER SPORTS TREASURE COAST
Also Called: Treasure Coast Seadoo Yamaha
2212 Se Indian St (34997-4923)
PHONE..................................772 463-6428
Brandon Radcliff, *Owner*
EMP: 7 **EST:** 2004
SALES (est): 382.5K **Privately Held**
SIC: 3799 All terrain vehicles (ATV)

(G-16993)
QUICK PROTECTIVE SYSTEMS INC
421 Sw California Ave # 101 (34994-2905)
P.O. Box 1559 (34995-1559)
PHONE..................................772 220-3315
EMP: 5 **EST:** 2001
SQ FT: 3,000
SALES: 3MM **Privately Held**
SIC: 3842 Mfg Surgical Appliances/Supplies

(G-16994)
QUORUM MARINE & ELEC INC
Also Called: Ocean Breeze
2951 Se Dominica Ter (34997-5712)
PHONE..................................772 220-0038
Carolyn Baruch, *President*
Jennifer Heinemann, *Vice Pres*
Joseph Baruch, *Director*
◆ **EMP:** 21 **EST:** 1994
SQ FT: 14,000
SALES (est): 2.5MM **Privately Held**
WEB: www.oceanbreezeac.com
SIC: 3585 Refrigeration & heating equipment

(G-16995)
R J MARINE GROUP INC
619 Nw Baker Rd (34994-1032)
PHONE..................................772 232-6590
Cheryl L Bragg, *President*
EMP: 5 **EST:** 2010
SALES (est): 446.8K **Privately Held**
WEB: www.marineelectronicstc.com
SIC: 3429 Marine hardware

(G-16996)
RADIOTRONICS INC
Also Called: Acek9.com
1315 Sw Commerce Way (34997-7231)
PHONE..................................772 600-7574
John J Johnston, *President*
John Johnston, *President*
▲ **EMP:** 10 **EST:** 1973
SQ FT: 3,000
SALES (est): 1.1MM **Privately Held**
WEB: www.acek9.com
SIC: 3663 Radio & TV communications equipment

(G-16997)
RAPID INDUSTRIES INC
3100 Se Waaler St (34997-5924)
PHONE..................................772 287-0651
Donald E Rice, *Principal*
Frank Caprio, *Maintence Staff*
EMP: 18 **EST:** 2013
SALES (est): 574K **Privately Held**
WEB: www.rapidindustries.com
SIC: 3999 Manufacturing industries

(G-16998)
RDC MANUFACTURING INC
3353 Se Gran Park Way (34997-8837)
PHONE..................................772 286-6921
Renee D Ciferri, *Principal*
EMP: 6 **EST:** 2009
SALES (est): 95.4K **Privately Held**
SIC: 3999 Manufacturing industries

(G-16999)
REACHTV
1976 Nw Fork Rd (34994-9416)
PHONE..................................772 934-6349
Janet Jaye Edwards, *Owner*
Michael Edwards, *Manager*
Janet Edwards, *Director*
EMP: 7 **EST:** 2011
SALES (est): 221.1K **Privately Held**
WEB: www.reachtvonline.com
SIC: 3999 5999 Education aids, devices & supplies; education aids, devices & supplies

(G-17000)
REDKEYS DIES
1680 Sw Wildcat Trl (34997-4806)
PHONE..................................772 463-5824
Keith S Weisgerber, *Owner*
EMP: 6 **EST:** 2008
SALES (est): 84.4K **Privately Held**
SIC: 3544 Special dies & tools

(G-17001)
REDSLED DBA BULLDOG EQUIPMENT
2691 Sw Windship Way (34997-9126)
PHONE..................................954 448-5221
Jason Simione, *President*
Dana Heinsen, *Vice Pres*
EMP: 11 **EST:** 2001
SQ FT: 8,000

SALES (est): 1.4MM **Privately Held**
WEB: www.bulldogequipment.us
SIC: 2824 Nylon fibers

(G-17002)
ROBERT MCKEE ENTERPRISES INC
7481 Sw Jack James Dr (34997-7228)
PHONE.....772 291-2159
Robert McKee, *President*
EMP: 8 **EST:** 2016
SALES (est): 642.9K **Privately Held**
WEB: www.mckees37.com
SIC: 2842 Waxes for wood, leather & other materials

(G-17003)
RONALD M HART INC
Also Called: Earthtnes In Hrmony With Nture
43 Sw Osceola St (34994-2117)
PHONE.....772 600-8497
Ron M Hart, *President*
EMP: 5 **EST:** 2003
SALES (est): 652.9K **Privately Held**
WEB: www.terrafermata.com
SIC: 3269 5261 0781 Art & ornamental ware, pottery; nurseries; landscape planning services

(G-17004)
RUPP MARINE INC
4761 Se Anchor Ave (34997-1902)
P.O. Box F, Port Salerno (34992-0167)
PHONE.....772 286-5300
Herbert E Rupp II, *Ch of Bd*
Ron Karpanty, *Vice Pres*
Scott A Rupp, *Vice Pres*
▼ **EMP:** 13 **EST:** 1977
SQ FT: 7,600
SALES (est): 2.4MM **Privately Held**
WEB: www.ruppmarine.com
SIC: 3429 3732 Marine hardware; boat building & repairing

(G-17005)
RWLA ENTERPRISES LLC
2810 Se Dune Dr Apt 1104 (34996-1931)
PHONE.....772 334-1248
EMP: 15 **EST:** 2007
SALES (est): 1.4MM **Privately Held**
SIC: 2721 Magazine

(G-17006)
SEAROBOTICS CORPORATION
7765 Sw Ellipse Way (34997-7245)
P.O. Box 30909, West Palm Beach (33420-0909)
PHONE.....772 742-3700
Donald T Darling, *CEO*
Roger Horn, *Project Mgr*
Geoff Douglass, *Engineer*
Sandy Young, *Office Mgr*
Janet Horn, *Planning*
EMP: 28 **EST:** 1999
SQ FT: 12,000
SALES (est): 5.2MM **Privately Held**
WEB: www.searobotics.com
SIC: 3731 Shipbuilding & repairing

(G-17007)
SEATORQUE CONTROL SYSTEMS LLC
2779 Se Monroe St (34997-5958)
PHONE.....772 220-3020
Peter Stolper, *Mng Member*
James Burke, *Manager*
Janet Stolper, *Manager*
▲ **EMP:** 25 **EST:** 2005
SALES (est): 3.3MM **Privately Held**
WEB: www.seatorque.com
SIC: 3625 Marine & navy auxiliary controls

(G-17008)
SEMICONDUCTOR TECHNOLOGY INC
3131 Se Jay St (34997-5964)
P.O. Box 474 (34995-0474)
PHONE.....772 341-0800
EMP: 7 **EST:** 2019
SALES (est): 672.3K **Privately Held**
SIC: 3674 Semiconductors & related devices

(G-17009)
SESOLINC GRP INC (PA)
50 Se Ocean Blvd Ste 202 (34994-2222)
PHONE.....772 287-9090
Harry Ford III, *President*
Matthew Bush, *Counsel*
Kaycee Harris, *Sales Mgr*
Michael Joiner, *Director*
Stephen Nelson, *Director*
▲ **EMP:** 14 **EST:** 1993
SQ FT: 1,300
SALES (est): 9MM **Privately Held**
WEB: www.sesolinc.com
SIC: 3448 2819 Prefabricated metal components; industrial inorganic chemicals

(G-17010)
SHEARWATER MARINE FL INC ✪
4519 Se Commerce Ave (34997-8860)
PHONE.....772 781-5553
James Dragseth, *President*
EMP: 26 **EST:** 2020
SALES (est): 1.8MM **Privately Held**
SIC: 3732 3714 3731 Boat building & repairing; motor vehicle parts & accessories; shipbuilding & repairing

(G-17011)
SHEET METAL UNLIMITED
3920 Se Commerce Ave (34997-4958)
PHONE.....772 872-7440
EMP: 7 **EST:** 2018
SALES (est): 841.7K **Privately Held**
WEB: www.sheetmetalunlimited.com
SIC: 3444 Sheet metalwork

(G-17012)
SHOCKSOCKS LLC
727 Nw Federal Hwy (34994-1016)
PHONE.....352 258-0496
Ricardo A Romagosa, *Principal*
EMP: 8 **EST:** 2016
SALES (est): 257K **Privately Held**
WEB: www.shocksocks.com
SIC: 2759 Screen printing

(G-17013)
SIGNS OF TIME INC
1700 Sw Belgrave Ter (34997-7044)
P.O. Box 1786 (34995-1786)
PHONE.....772 240-9590
Stephen Fenton, *President*
EMP: 7 **EST:** 2010
SALES (est): 289.2K **Privately Held**
SIC: 3993 Signs & advertising specialties

(G-17014)
SIKORSKY AIRCRAFT CORP
2324 Se Liberator Ln (34996-4037)
PHONE.....772 210-0849
EMP: 7 **EST:** 2018
SALES (est): 331.7K **Privately Held**
SIC: 3812 Search & navigation equipment

(G-17015)
SIN PIN INC
600 Nw Dixie Hwy (34994-1118)
PHONE.....877 805-5665
Majd Ibrahim, *Principal*
EMP: 8 **EST:** 2011
SALES (est): 125.2K **Privately Held**
WEB: www.sinpin.com
SIC: 3452 Pins

(G-17016)
SMITHS INTERCONNECT GROUP LTD
8851 Sw Old Kansas Ave (34997-7204)
PHONE.....805 370-5580
EMP: 7
SALES (corp-wide): 4.1B **Privately Held**
SIC: 3679 Mfg Electronic Components
HQ: Smiths Interconnect Group Limited
130 Centennial Park
Borehamwood HERTS WD6 3
208 450-8033

(G-17017)
SMITHS INTRCNNECT AMERICAS INC
8851 Sw Old Kansas Ave (34997-7204)
PHONE.....772 286-9300
Rob Torsiello, *Vice Pres*
Joe Hite, *Safety Mgr*
Tim Meehan, *Director*
Anthea Collier, *Officer*
EMP: 308
SALES (corp-wide): 3.1B **Privately Held**
WEB: www.smithsinterconnect.com
SIC: 3679 Microwave components; attenuators
HQ: Smiths Interconnect Americas, Inc.
5101 Richland Ave
Kansas City KS 66106
913 342-5544

(G-17018)
SOLAR ELECTRIC POWER COMPANY
Also Called: Sepco
1521 Se Palm Ct (34994-4914)
PHONE.....772 220-6615
Steven R Robbins, *President*
Steven Burns, *Vice Pres*
Susan Robbins, *Vice Pres*
Buddy Straszewski, *Engineer*
Shawn Tefft, *Sales Staff*
◆ **EMP:** 14
SQ FT: 10,000
SALES (est): 3.4MM **Privately Held**
WEB: www.sepco-solarlighting.com
SIC: 3674 5063 Photovoltaic devices, solid state; lighting fixtures, commercial & industrial

(G-17019)
SOUTH BCH ORTHTICS PRSTHTICS I
7305 Sw Gaines Ave (34997-7332)
PHONE.....352 512-0262
Mark Selleck, *CEO*
EMP: 10 **EST:** 2013
SALES (est): 505.3K **Privately Held**
WEB: www.southbeachop.com
SIC: 3842 Orthopedic appliances

(G-17020)
SP SIGN LLC
Also Called: Sign-A-Rama
2201 Se Indian St Unit E4 (34997-4984)
PHONE.....772 562-0955
Kim Williamson, *Mng Member*
EMP: 10 **EST:** 2015
SALES (est): 455.2K **Privately Held**
WEB: www.signarama.com
SIC: 3993 Signs & advertising specialties

(G-17021)
SPEEDPRO IMAGING
7765 Sw Ellipse Way (34997-7245)
PHONE.....772 320-9385
EMP: 6 **EST:** 2017
SALES (est): 189K **Privately Held**
WEB: www.speedpro.com
SIC: 3993 Signs & advertising specialties

(G-17022)
STEVE FRENCH ENTPS LTD LLC
2871 Se Monroe St C (34997-5913)
PHONE.....772 692-0222
Steven French, *Principal*
Stephen M French, *Manager*
EMP: 6 **EST:** 2010
SALES (est): 76.1K **Privately Held**
SIC: 3624 Fibers, carbon & graphite

(G-17023)
STUART BOAT WORKS INC
3515 Se Lionel Ter (34997-8800)
PHONE.....772 600-7121
Jeffrey E Futch, *President*
Terri L Futch, *Vice Pres*
EMP: 10 **EST:** 2008
SALES (est): 1.1MM **Privately Held**
WEB: www.stuartboatworks.com
SIC: 3732 7389 Boat building & repairing;

(G-17024)
STUART NEWS (DH)
1939 Se Federal Hwy (34994-3915)
P.O. Box 9009 (34995-9009)
PHONE.....772 287-1550
Bob Brunjes, *President*
EMP: 225 **EST:** 1976
SALES (est): 47.2MM
SALES (corp-wide): 3.4B **Publicly Held**
WEB: www.cityofstuart.us
SIC: 2711 Newspapers, publishing & printing
HQ: Journal Media Group, Inc.
333 W State St
Milwaukee WI 53203
414 224-2000

(G-17025)
STUART NEWS
Also Called: Jupiter Courier
1939 Se Federal Hwy (34994-3915)
PHONE.....772 287-1550
John Maletzke, *Branch Mgr*
EMP: 115
SALES (corp-wide): 3.4B **Publicly Held**
WEB: www.cityofstuart.us
SIC: 2711 Newspapers, publishing & printing
HQ: The Stuart News
1939 Se Federal Hwy
Stuart FL 34994
772 287-1550

(G-17026)
STUART STAIR & FURNITURE MFG
3220 Se Dominica Ter (34997-5758)
PHONE.....772 287-4097
Carl Stewart, *President*
Elsie Stewart, *Treasurer*
EMP: 8 **EST:** 1987
SQ FT: 5,500
SALES (est): 855.2K **Privately Held**
WEB: www.stuartstair.com
SIC: 2426 2431 Furniture stock & parts, hardwood; staircases, stairs & railings

(G-17027)
STUART WEB INC
5675 Se Grouper Ave (34997-3103)
PHONE.....772 287-8022
Thomas Hawken, *President*
Diane K Hawken, *Corp Secy*
Kevin Hawken, *Vice Pres*
◆ **EMP:** 45
SQ FT: 14,999
SALES (est): 8.6MM **Privately Held**
WEB: www.stuartweb.com
SIC: 2752 Commercial printing, offset

(G-17028)
STUART WEB INC
1521 Se Palm Ct (34994-4914)
PHONE.....772 287-8022
EMP: 7 **EST:** 2019
SALES (est): 220.6K **Privately Held**
WEB: www.stuartweb.com
SIC: 2752 Commercial printing, offset

(G-17029)
STUART YACHT BUILDERS
450 Sw Salerno Rd (34997-6250)
PHONE.....561 747-1947
Greg N Burdick, *President*
Nancy G Burdick, *Corp Secy*
Douglas T Newbigin, *Vice Pres*
EMP: 11 **EST:** 1982
SQ FT: 10,000
SALES (est): 1.4MM **Privately Held**
WEB: www.stuartyachtsales.com
SIC: 3732 5091 3949 3441 Yachts, building & repairing; sporting & recreation goods; sporting & athletic goods; fabricated structural metal
HQ: Stuart Yacht Corporation
602 Sw Anchorage Way
Stuart FL 34994
772 286-9800

(G-17030)
SUPERIOR KITCHENS INC (PA)
2680 Se Federal Hwy (34994-4535)
PHONE.....772 286-6801
Marcel Rappold, *President*
Jerry Erbe, *Sales Staff*
Barbara Johnston, *Admin Sec*
EMP: 14 **EST:** 1955
SQ FT: 24,000
SALES (est): 2.6MM **Privately Held**
WEB: www.superiorkitchensinc.com
SIC: 2434 Wood kitchen cabinets

(G-17031)
SWEET INDUSTRIES LLC
3561 Se Micanopy Ter (34997-5458)
PHONE.....904 228-9655
Eric Sweet, *Principal*
EMP: 6 **EST:** 2016

GEOGRAPHIC

SALES (est): 209.1K **Privately Held**
SIC: 3999 Manufacturing industries

(G-17032)
TALARIA COMPANY LLC
4550 Se Boatyard Ave (34997-1921)
PHONE..................................772 403-5387
Darryl Schmiermund, *Manager*
EMP: 90
SALES (corp-wide): 209.7MM **Privately Held**
WEB: www.hinckleyyachts.com
SIC: 3732 Boat building & repairing
PA: The Talaria Company Llc
1 Lil Hrbr Landing Prt
Portsmouth RI 02871
401 683-7100

(G-17033)
TARA BIEK CREATIVE
4745 Se Desoto Ave (34997-6809)
PHONE..................................772 486-3684
EMP: 6 **EST:** 2018
SALES (est): 340.2K **Privately Held**
WEB: www.tarabiekcreative.com
SIC: 2752 Commercial printing, lithographic

(G-17034)
TEAM IP SPORTS LLC
850 Nw Federal Hwy 229 (34994-1019)
PHONE..................................772 398-4664
Randall L Sparks,
Andrew J Sparks,
Bradall E Sparks,
Mary Lou Sparks,
EMP: 13 **EST:** 2004
SALES (est): 698.1K **Privately Held**
WEB: www.teamip.com
SIC: 2211 Print cloths, cotton

(G-17035)
TORTILLERIA GALLO DE ORO LLC
3511 Se Dixie Hwy (34997-5244)
PHONE..................................561 818-7829
Manuel E Perez, *Branch Mgr*
EMP: 7
SALES (corp-wide): 359K **Privately Held**
SIC: 2099 Tortillas, fresh or refrigerated
PA: Tortilleria Gallo De Oro Llc
2100 Longwood Rd
West Palm Beach FL

(G-17036)
TREASURE COAST CANVAS
6538 Se Federal Hwy (34997-8315)
PHONE..................................772 210-2588
Cullen Lowery, *Administration*
EMP: 8 **EST:** 2014
SALES (est): 275.8K **Privately Held**
WEB: www.candccanvas.com
SIC: 2394 Awnings, fabric: made from purchased materials

(G-17037)
TREASURE COAST MACHINES INC
3081 Se Slater St (34997-5702)
PHONE..................................772 283-2024
Fax: 772 283-1624
EMP: 18
SALES: 1.5MM **Privately Held**
SIC: 3599 3724 Mfg Industrial Machinery Mfg Aircraft Engines/Parts

(G-17038)
TREASURE COAST PUBLISHING INC
Also Called: Georgia Coast Publications
1939 S Federal Hwy (34994)
PHONE..................................772 221-4289
Tom Webber, *President*
EMP: 10 **EST:** 1996
SALES (est): 527.3K **Privately Held**
SIC: 2711 2741 Newspapers; miscellaneous publishing

(G-17039)
TRIUMPH AEROSTRUCTURES LLC
Also Called: Triumph Arstrctres - Vght Coml
1845 Se Airport Rd (34996-4012)
PHONE..................................772 463-8700
Greg Rust, *Vice Chairman*
Jolis Rodriguez, *COO*
Tracy Belton, *Vice Pres*
Kevin Carney, *Opers Mgr*
Mike Monroy, *Facilities Mgr*
EMP: 34 **Publicly Held**
WEB: www.qarbonaerospace.com
SIC: 3728 Aircraft parts & equipment
HQ: Triumph Aerostructures, Llc
1550 Liberty Ridge Dr
Chesterbrook PA 19087

(G-17040)
TRU-ART SIGNS &GRAPHIX INC
5596 Sw Evans Dr (34997-6349)
PHONE..................................561 371-2388
Albert S Hatfield, *Principal*
EMP: 6 **EST:** 2018
SALES (est): 331.6K **Privately Held**
SIC: 3993 Signs & advertising specialties

(G-17041)
TURBOCOMBUSTOR TECHNOLOGY INC (HQ)
Also Called: Paradigm Precision
3651 Se Commerce Ave (34997-4981)
PHONE..................................772 287-7770
Greg Bennett, *President*
John Furnare, *Opers Staff*
Jerardo Aguilar, *Engineer*
Louis Gill, *Engineer*
Terry Peek, *Engineer*
▲ **EMP:** 350 **EST:** 1972
SQ FT: 120,000
SALES (est): 141.4MM
SALES (corp-wide): 402.2MM **Privately Held**
WEB: www.palmermfgco.com
SIC: 3724 3728 3444 Engine mount parts, aircraft; aircraft parts & equipment; sheet metalwork
PA: Dynamic Precision Group, Inc.
3651 Se Commerce Ave
Stuart FL 34997
772 287-7770

(G-17042)
ULTRA LITE TENDERS LLC
4399 Se Whiticar Way (34997-6143)
PHONE..................................214 215-2725
Kendall Koelling,
EMP: 6 **EST:** 2019
SALES (est): 86K **Privately Held**
WEB: www.ultenders.com
SIC: 3731 Lighthouse tenders, building & repairing

(G-17043)
UNISOURCE STONE INC
2575 Se Federal Hwy # 101 (34994-4918)
PHONE..................................561 493-0660
Russ Carbone, *President*
Elizabeth Hamill, *Treasurer*
▲ **EMP:** 7 **EST:** 1998
SQ FT: 7,500
SALES (est): 209.7K **Privately Held**
WEB: www.unisourcestone.com
SIC: 3281 Marble, building: cut & shaped

(G-17044)
US PAVERSCAPE LLC
1735 Se Federal Hwy (34994-3952)
PHONE..................................772 223-7287
Ray Paulding, *Mng Member*
◆ **EMP:** 80 **EST:** 2000
SQ FT: 5,832
SALES (est): 13.5MM **Privately Held**
WEB: www.uspaverscape.com
SIC: 3272 Concrete products

(G-17045)
VIESEL FUEL LLC
1000 Se Monterey Cmns # 206 (34996-3342)
PHONE..................................772 781-4300
Michelle Nyberg, *Vice Pres*
Stuart M Lamb, *Mng Member*
Stuart Lamb, *Mng Member*
◆ **EMP:** 30 **EST:** 2009
SALES (est): 8MM **Privately Held**
WEB: www.gstarbio.com
SIC: 2869 Fuels

(G-17046)
VIRCO MFG CORPORATION
6882 Se Raintree Ave (34997-2241)
PHONE..................................772 834-8261
EMP: 6 **EST:** 2018
SALES (est): 76.7K **Privately Held**
WEB: www.virco.com
SIC: 3999 Manufacturing industries

(G-17047)
WATERBLASTING TECHNOLOGIES INC (PA)
Also Called: Hog Technologies
3920 Se Commerce Ave (34997-4958)
PHONE..................................772 223-7393
James P Crocker, *President*
Mike Nardone, *COO*
Adam Baldwin, *Vice Pres*
Dave Friday, *Vice Pres*
Vince Giordano, *Vice Pres*
◆ **EMP:** 146 **EST:** 2005
SALES (est): 32.3MM **Privately Held**
WEB: www.waterblastingtechnologies.com
SIC: 3531 Construction machinery

(G-17048)
WHITE ALUMINUM FABRICATION INC
3195 Se Lionel Ter (34997-8816)
PHONE..................................772 219-3245
Ronald E White, *President*
Victoria White, *Vice Pres*
◆ **EMP:** 50 **EST:** 2000
SQ FT: 15,000
SALES (est): 9.3MM **Privately Held**
WEB: www.whitealuminum.net
SIC: 3355 Aluminum rail & structural shapes

(G-17049)
WHITICAR BOAT WORKS INC (PA)
3636 Se Old St Lucie Blvd (34996-5155)
P.O. Box 1109 (34995-1109)
PHONE..................................772 287-2883
Jim Dragseth, *President*
John Whiticar, *Treasurer*
Tom Berryhill, *Manager*
Brian Magnant, *Manager*
Calvin Powell, *Supervisor*
EMP: 38 **EST:** 1947
SQ FT: 24,000
SALES (est): 5MM **Privately Held**
WEB: www.whiticar.com
SIC: 3732 5551 Motorized boat, building & repairing; marine supplies

(G-17050)
WILLIS CUSTOM YACHTS LLC ✪
6800 Sw Jack James Dr # 1 (34997-6200)
PHONE..................................772 221-9100
Doug West, *President*
Mark Willis,
Ron Kirschner,
EMP: 130 **EST:** 2021
SALES (est): 5.4MM **Privately Held**
SIC: 3732 Yachts, building & repairing

(G-17051)
WILLIS MARINE INC
4361 Se Commerce Ave (34997-5728)
PHONE..................................772 283-7189
Mark Willis, *President*
EMP: 5 **EST:** 1990
SQ FT: 5,000
SALES (est): 835.4K **Privately Held**
WEB: www.willismarineinc.com
SIC: 3732 Boat building & repairing

(G-17052)
WMR CYCLE PERFORMANCE INC
Also Called: Cyclelogic Products
7749 Sw Ellipse Way (34997-7245)
PHONE..................................772 426-3000
David Kimmey, *President*
EMP: 5 **EST:** 1998
SQ FT: 2,500
SALES (est): 660K **Privately Held**
WEB: www.wmr1.com
SIC: 3751 Motorcycles & related parts; motorcycle accessories

(G-17053)
WWW TCPALM COMPANY
1939 S Federal Hwy (34994)
PHONE..................................772 287-1550
Thomas Webber Jr, *Director*
Sommer Brugal, *Education*
EMP: 13 **EST:** 2001
SALES (est): 436.9K **Privately Held**
WEB: www.tcpalm.com
SIC: 2711 Newspapers

(G-17054)
ZAZZ ENGINEERING INC
7833 Sw Ellipse Way (34997-7247)
PHONE..................................561 594-0123
Gregory N Newton, *President*
Richard Clemence, *Principal*
George O Macdonald, *Vice Pres*
George Macdonald, *Vice Pres*
EMP: 6 **EST:** 2008
SALES (est): 750K **Privately Held**
WEB: www.zazzengineering.com
SIC: 3564 Ventilating fans: industrial or commercial

Summerfield
Marion County

(G-17055)
A & J COMMERCIAL SEATING INC
10485 Se 158th Pl (34491-7648)
PHONE..................................352 288-2022
John Plourde, *President*
Norma Plourde, *Corp Secy*
Tammy Benoit, *Vice Pres*
EMP: 12 **EST:** 1963
SQ FT: 13,000
SALES (est): 522.6K **Privately Held**
WEB: www.ajseating.com
SIC: 2599 2531 Restaurant furniture, wood or metal; public building & related furniture

(G-17056)
ADVANCED WLDG FBRCTION DSIGN L
13540 Se 31st Ave (34491-2102)
PHONE..................................352 237-9800
Aaron O'Brien,
Heather O'Brien,
Reynold D Wolter,
Warnieta L Wolter,
EMP: 7 **EST:** 2011
SALES (est): 762.5K **Privately Held**
SIC: 7692 Welding repair

(G-17057)
BEA SUE VINEYARDS INC
Also Called: Dragon Flower Winery
11025 Se Highway 42 (34491-6627)
PHONE..................................352 446-5204
Shannon M Peacock, *President*
EMP: 7 **EST:** 2014
SALES (est): 246.6K **Privately Held**
SIC: 2084 Wines

(G-17058)
CREATIVE CURBING
15340 Se 73rd Ave (34491-4223)
P.O. Box 1259 (34492-1259)
PHONE..................................352 347-3329
Kevin Reedy, *Principal*
EMP: 9 **EST:** 2001
SALES (est): 345.6K **Privately Held**
WEB: www.creativecurbing.net
SIC: 3281 Curbing, paving & walkway stone

(G-17059)
KURTS CUSTOM WOODWORKS
13636 Se 33rd Ct (34491-2104)
PHONE..................................352 693-5407
Kurt F Hoffman, *Principal*
EMP: 6 **EST:** 2018
SALES (est): 205.9K **Privately Held**
SIC: 2431 Millwork

(G-17060)
LUCKY BLINDS SHUTTERS LLC
9390 Se 163rd Ln (34491-8802)
PHONE..................................352 239-8475
EMP: 6 **EST:** 2018
SALES (est): 277.2K **Privately Held**
WEB: www.luckyshutters.com
SIC: 2591 Drapery hardware & blinds & shades

(G-17061)
RIDE AND TUBE INC
16625 Se 19th Ct (34491-6019)
PHONE....................................352 454-8194
Eddie Rosier, *President*
EMP: 10 **EST:** 2018
SALES (est): 148.8K **Privately Held**
WEB: www.rideandtube.com
SIC: **3317** Steel pipe & tubes

(G-17062)
SOUTH MARION MEATS
13770 S Highway 475 (34491-2020)
PHONE....................................352 245-2096
EMP: 6
SALES (est): 350K **Privately Held**
SIC: **2011** 5421 2013 Meat Packing Plant Ret Meat/Fish Mfg Prepared Meats

(G-17063)
STEPHEN SHIVES
Also Called: S & S Enterprises
14628 Se 95th Ct (34491-3611)
PHONE....................................352 454-6522
Stephen Shives, *Owner*
EMP: 5 **EST:** 2014
SALES (est): 322.6K **Privately Held**
WEB: www.runawaycampers.com
SIC: **3792** Travel trailers & campers

(G-17064)
WORLD MANUFACTURING LLC
17103 Se 110th Court Rd (34491-1878)
PHONE....................................843 751-9375
Kenneth Ejr Damon, *Administration*
EMP: 6 **EST:** 2016
SALES (est): 199.2K **Privately Held**
SIC: **3999** Manufacturing industries

Summerland Key
Monroe County

(G-17065)
CERTIFIED MOLD TREATMENT LLC
17277 Allamanda Dr (33042-3709)
P.O. Box 420311 (33042-0311)
PHONE....................................305 879-1839
Gary V Marsden, *Principal*
EMP: 6 **EST:** 2008
SALES (est): 351.2K **Privately Held**
SIC: **3544** Industrial molds

(G-17066)
WANTZLOEBEN RES SOLUTIONS LLC
17277 Allamanda Dr (33042-3709)
PHONE....................................972 273-0190
Heather Wantzloeben, *Principal*
EMP: 6 **EST:** 2013
SALES (est): 86K **Privately Held**
SIC: **3761** Guided missiles & space vehicles

Sumterville
Sumter County

(G-17067)
ARCOSA TRFFIC LTG STRCTRES LLC
1749 Cr 525e (33585-5346)
PHONE....................................352 748-4258
EMP: 50
SALES (corp-wide): 1.9B **Publicly Held**
WEB: www.arcosa.com
SIC: **3441** Fabricated structural metal
HQ: Arcosa Traffic And Lighting Structures, Llc
500 N Akard St
Dallas TX 75201
972 942-6500

(G-17068)
FLORIDA DESIGNER CABINETS INC
1034 S Us 301 (33585-5132)
P.O. Box 98 (33585-0098)
PHONE....................................352 793-8555
Barry Mann, *President*
Barbara Mann, *Corp Secy*
▼ **EMP:** 16 **EST:** 1990
SQ FT: 7,000
SALES (est): 1.2MM **Privately Held**
WEB: www.fladc.com
SIC: **2599** 2541 2517 2434 Cabinets, factory; wood partitions & fixtures; wood television & radio cabinets; wood kitchen cabinets

(G-17069)
SUWANNEE AMERICAN CEM CO LLC (HQ)
Also Called: Ash Grove
4750 E C 470 (33585-5342)
P.O. Box 445 (33585-0445)
PHONE....................................352 569-5393
Cary O Cohrs, *President*
Rhiana Roncone, *President*
Dana B Moran, *Vice Pres*
Darryl Needels, *Purchasing*
Ginger Fredricksen, *Credit Mgr*
EMP: 57 **EST:** 2006
SALES (est): 37.6MM
SALES (corp-wide): 27.5B **Privately Held**
WEB: www.sacement.com
SIC: **3272** Concrete products
PA: Crh Public Limited Company
Stonemasons Way
Dublin D16 K
140 410-00

Sun City Center
Hillsborough County

(G-17070)
BUTTERFIELD PRESS
1504 N Lake Dr (33573-5015)
PHONE....................................813 634-3940
Keith Connes, *Owner*
EMP: 6 **EST:** 2014
SALES (est): 209.3K **Privately Held**
SIC: **2741** Miscellaneous publishing

(G-17071)
PSS COMMUNICATIONS INC
Also Called: Data Line
309 Bryce Ct (33573-6260)
PHONE....................................408 496-3330
Paul R Fales, *CEO*
Marlene C Fales, *President*
Marlene Fales, *CFO*
EMP: 12 **EST:** 2004
SALES (est): 2.4MM **Privately Held**
SIC: **3661** Telephones & telephone apparatus

(G-17072)
SOUTH BAY HOSPITAL
4016 Sun City Center Blvd (33573-5298)
PHONE....................................813 634-3301
Sheldon Barr, *CEO*
Jennifer Wells China, *Chairman*
Cheryl Quimby, *Opers Staff*
Angie Searls, *QA Dir*
Warren Pate, *CFO*
EMP: 392 **EST:** 1992
SALES (est): 23.2MM **Privately Held**
WEB: www.southbayhospital.com
SIC: **3821** Chemical laboratory apparatus

Sunny Isles Beach
Miami-Dade County

(G-17073)
COLA GROUP RIVERSIDE LLC
16047 Collins Ave # 2103 (33160-5557)
PHONE....................................305 940-0277
Louis Cola, *Principal*
EMP: 6 **EST:** 2011
SALES (est): 129.3K **Privately Held**
SIC: **2086** Soft drinks: packaged in cans, bottles, etc.

(G-17074)
E-LIBRO CORPORATION
16699 Collins Ave # 1002 (33160-5408)
PHONE....................................305 466-0155
Eduardo Varela-Cid, *CEO*
Felipe Varela Lucas, *President*
Marlen Lucas, *Administration*
EMP: 16 **EST:** 2002
SALES (est): 1.6MM **Privately Held**
WEB: www.e-libro.us
SIC: **2731** Book publishing

(G-17075)
ECOMBUSTIBLE PRODUCTS LLC
15901 Collins Ave Apt 901 (33160-4765)
PHONE....................................305 792-1952
Jorge D Arevalo, *Mng Member*
EMP: 7 **EST:** 2015
SALES (est): 184.2K **Privately Held**
WEB: www.ecombustible.com
SIC: **3823** Combustion control instruments

(G-17076)
ESTRADAS FIBERGLASS MFG CORP
16900 N Bay Rd Apt 803 (33160-4266)
PHONE....................................954 924-8778
EMP: 6
SQ FT: 2,500
SALES: 675K **Privately Held**
SIC: **3089** Mfg Plastic Products

(G-17077)
GENUINE AD INC
17600 N Bay Rd Apt 406 (33160-2832)
PHONE....................................786 399-6484
Pablo Brochado, *Principal*
EMP: 8 **EST:** 2008
SALES (est): 285.5K **Privately Held**
SIC: **2759** Commercial printing

(G-17078)
GESCO ICE CREAM VENDING CORP (PA)
17555 Collins Ave # 2903 (33160-2882)
PHONE....................................718 782-3232
Jeffrey Gesser, *President*
EMP: 10 **EST:** 1977
SQ FT: 2,000
SALES (est): 985.9K **Privately Held**
SIC: **2656** Ice cream containers: made from purchased material

(G-17079)
INOX LLC
Also Called: American Pipes and Tubes Co
19201 Collins Ave Ste 131 (33160-2202)
PHONE....................................305 409-2764
Maksim Tabunou, *CEO*
Siarhei Karankevich,
Victor Savthouk,
EMP: 5 **EST:** 2010
SQ FT: 250
SALES (est): 375.9K **Privately Held**
WEB: www.inoxllc.com
SIC: **2421** Furniture dimension stock, softwood

(G-17080)
SKAMPAS PERFORMANCE GROUP
19201 Collins Ave Cu-137 (33160-2202)
PHONE....................................305 974-0047
Morris Laloshi, *Owner*
EMP: 7 **EST:** 2014
SALES (est): 247.7K **Privately Held**
SIC: **2841** Soap & other detergents

(G-17081)
TERFA LITTER USA INC
17720 N Bay Rd Apt 5a (33160-2806)
PHONE....................................416 358-4495
Jukka Karjalainen, *Principal*
Andrei Sobolevsky, *Vice Pres*
EMP: 10
SALES (est): 342.2K **Privately Held**
SIC: **3295** 8742 7389 Cat box litter; sales (including sales management) consultant; business services

(G-17082)
TRANS-RESOURCES LLC
17780 Collins Ave (33160-2827)
PHONE....................................305 933-8301
Rick Chitwood, *Vice Pres*
Oren Shmueli, *Controller*
Mark Hirsh, *Executive*
EMP: 736 **EST:** 1985
SQ FT: 3,000
SALES (est): 48MM **Privately Held**
WEB: www.valueyourpension.com
SIC: **2873** 2819 2879 Nitrogen solutions (fertilizer); industrial inorganic chemicals; potasssium nitrate & sulfate; fungicides, herbicides

Sunrise
Broward County

(G-17083)
AEROSPACE ROTABLES INC
5151 Nw 109th Ave (33351-8003)
PHONE....................................954 452-0056
Marco Villavicencio, *President*
Edmundo Aguilar, *Pastor*
Marlene Villavicencio, *Vice Pres*
Hai Nguyen, *Project Mgr*
Maribel Castro, *Purchasing*
▲ **EMP:** 14 **EST:** 1998
SQ FT: 8,000
SALES (est): 2.6MM **Privately Held**
WEB: www.aerospacerotables.com
SIC: **3728** Aircraft body assemblies & parts

(G-17084)
AIM SHUTTERS
5054 N Hiatus Rd (33351-8017)
PHONE....................................954 861-6666
Hector Budejen, *Principal*
EMP: 7 **EST:** 2010
SALES (est): 113.4K **Privately Held**
SIC: **3442** Metal doors, sash & trim

(G-17085)
AIRSTOX INC
13680 Nw 5th St Ste 140 (33325-6234)
P.O. Box 267520, Fort Lauderdale (33326-7520)
PHONE....................................954 618-6573
Jeffrey G Thomas, *President*
EMP: 7 **EST:** 2006
SALES (est): 524.9K **Privately Held**
SIC: **3724** Aircraft engines & engine parts

(G-17086)
ALBER CORP
Also Called: Vertiv
7775 W Oakland Park Blvd (33351-6703)
PHONE....................................954 377-7101
Derek Alber, *President*
S Hassell, *President*
Jeffrey T Blind, *Corp Secy*
Alina Crombie, *Sales Staff*
EMP: 100 **EST:** 1992
SQ FT: 35,000
SALES (est): 18.6MM
SALES (corp-wide): 4.3B **Publicly Held**
WEB: www.vertiv.com
SIC: **3825** Battery testers, electrical
HQ: Vertiv Corporation
1050 Dearborn Dr
Columbus OH 43085
614 888-0246

(G-17087)
ALIGN OPTICS INC
4700 N Hiatus Rd Ste 144a (33351-7904)
PHONE....................................954 748-1715
Derek Verma, *President*
▲ **EMP:** 5 **EST:** 1997
SQ FT: 2,200
SALES (est): 483.4K **Privately Held**
WEB: www.alignoptics.com
SIC: **3827** Optical instruments & lenses

(G-17088)
ALLERGAN SALES LLC
13800 Nw 2nd St Ste 190 (33325-6243)
PHONE....................................787 406-1203
Luis Marrero, *Principal*
Talley Wright, *Business Mgr*
Lori Franke, *Director*
Christina Vituli, *Director*
EMP: 34 **EST:** 2019
SALES (est): 8.7MM **Privately Held**
WEB: www.allergan.com
SIC: **2834** Pharmaceutical preparations

(G-17089)
ALTUM AEROSPACE
13680 Nw 5th St Ste 140 (33325-6234)
PHONE....................................954 618-6573
EMP: 15 **EST:** 2011

SALES (est): 3.2MM **Privately Held**
SIC: 3721 3429 Mfg Aircraft Mfg Hardware

(G-17090)
AMERICAN BIDET COMPANY
10821 Nw 50th St (33351-8091)
P.O. Box 266333, Fort Lauderdale (33326-6333)
PHONE..................................954 981-1111
Arnold Cohen, *President*
EMP: 12 **EST:** 1963
SQ FT: 20,000
SALES (est): 973K **Privately Held**
SIC: 3261 Bidets, vitreous china

(G-17091)
ANDRX CORPORATION
13900 Nw 2nd St Ste 100 (33325-6215)
PHONE..................................954 585-1770
David Fernandez, *Manager*
EMP: 161 **Privately Held**
WEB: www.andrx.com
SIC: 2834 Pharmaceutical preparations
HQ: Andrx Corporation
4955 Orange Dr
Davie FL 33314

(G-17092)
AUSOIL INTERNATIONAL CORP (PA)
4612 N Hiatus Rd (33351-7909)
PHONE..................................954 249-8060
Jose Ruiz, *CEO*
Tony Pestano, *Accountant*
Danilo Egred, *Director*
▲ **EMP:** 69 **EST:** 2011
SALES (est): 172.7K **Privately Held**
SIC: 2875 Fertilizers, mixing only

(G-17093)
BACKBONE INTERCONNECT LLC
10501 Nw 50th St 104-3 (33351-8012)
PHONE..................................954 800-4749
EMP: 23
SQ FT: 2,000
SALES (est): 1MM **Privately Held**
SIC: 3678 3612 3644 3679 Mfg Elec Connectors Mfg Transformers Mfg Non-conductv Wire Dvc Mfg Elec Components

(G-17094)
BAUER COMPRESSORS INC
10052 Nw 53rd St (33351-8068)
PHONE..................................757 855-6006
EMP: 6
SALES (corp-wide): 65MM **Privately Held**
SIC: 2813 5091 Industrial Gases
PA: Bauer Compressors, Inc.
1328 Azalea Garden Rd
Norfolk VA 23502
757 855-6006

(G-17095)
BCB INTERNATIONAL INC
12010 Nw 29th Pl (33323-1540)
PHONE..................................727 754-4911
Paul Ames, *Sales Staff*
EMP: 6 **EST:** 2019
SALES (est): 84.4K **Privately Held**
WEB: www.bcbinusa.com
SIC: 2397 Schiffli machine embroideries

(G-17096)
BENCHMARK CONNECTOR CORP
4501 Nw 103rd Ave (33351-7936)
PHONE..................................954 746-9929
David Brand, *President*
Vincent Zarella, *Vice Pres*
Bob Larocca, *Accounts Exec*
Alex Zarrella, *Accounts Exec*
Jose Merced, *Manager*
▲ **EMP:** 41 **EST:** 1997
SQ FT: 16,500
SALES (est): 8MM **Privately Held**
WEB: www.benchmarkconnector.com
SIC: 3678 Electronic connectors

(G-17097)
BJ BURNS INCORPORATED
Also Called: Outlook International Electric
1411 Sawgrs Corp Pkwy (33323-2888)
PHONE..................................305 572-9500
Antonio Hyppolite, *President*
Hodari Burns, *Vice Pres*
Frank Telfort, *Vice Pres*
Frantz Telfort, *Vice Pres*
EMP: 37 **EST:** 2000
SALES (est): 3MM **Privately Held**
SIC: 3699 1731 5063 Electrical equipment & supplies; general electrical contractor; boxes & fittings, electrical

(G-17098)
BKBL HOLDINGS LTD
Also Called: Quest Drape
5031 N Hiatus Rd (33351-8018)
PHONE..................................954 920-6772
Alex Soto, *General Mgr*
Orlando Camacho, *Opers Mgr*
EMP: 8
SALES (corp-wide): 19.8MM **Privately Held**
SIC: 2391 Curtains & draperies
PA: Bkbl Holdings, Ltd.
2591 Dallas Pkwy Ste 201
Frisco TX 75034
214 436-4161

(G-17099)
BLUE LIGHT USA CORP
4625 Nw 103rd Ave (33351-7914)
PHONE..................................954 766-4308
F F Chade Yammine, *Principal*
Fabiana Yammine, *Vice Pres*
EMP: 7 **EST:** 2016
SALES (est): 532.7K **Privately Held**
WEB: www.ydconfeccoes.com
SIC: 2211 5651 Jean fabrics; denims; jeans stores
PA: Y.D. Confeccoes Ltda
Av. Queiroz Filho 1560
Sao Paulo SP 05319

(G-17100)
BOLTON MEDICAL INC
Also Called: Terumo Aortic
799 International Pkwy (33325-6220)
PHONE..................................954 838-9699
Oscar Rostigliosi, *CEO*
Jose Maria Rubiralta, *President*
Donna Bean, *Vice Pres*
Allan Buti, *Vice Pres*
Jeffrey Mifek, *Vice Pres*
EMP: 390
SQ FT: 24,000
SALES (est): 79.2MM **Privately Held**
WEB: www.terumoaortic.com
SIC: 3841 Surgical & medical instruments
PA: Terumo Corporation
2-44-1, Hatagaya
Shibuya-Ku TKY 151-0

(G-17101)
BUNDY SIGNS LLC
4556 N Hiatus Rd (33351-7987)
PHONE..................................954 296-0784
EMP: 7 **EST:** 2018
SALES (est): 911.8K **Privately Held**
WEB: www.bundysigns.com
SIC: 3993 Signs & advertising specialties

(G-17102)
BYOSCIENCE
Also Called: Gut Armor
1305 Shotgun Rd (33326-1935)
PHONE..................................754 240-4052
Richard P O'Shea, *Principal*
EMP: 8 **EST:** 2019
SQ FT: 4,282
SALES (est): 72.6K **Privately Held**
SIC: 2023 Dietary supplements, dairy & non-dairy based

(G-17103)
CALIBER SALES ENGINEERING INC (PA)
5373 N Hiatus Rd (33351-8718)
PHONE..................................954 430-6234
Sharon Erickson, *President*
David R Mazoff, *President*
Vivian M Alvarez, *Treasurer*
Yonnatan Coronell, *Sales Staff*
Jesselyn Soto, *Sales Staff*
◆ **EMP:** 22 **EST:** 1987
SALES: 13.5MM **Privately Held**
WEB: www.calibersales.com
SIC: 3691 Storage batteries

(G-17104)
CAPACITOR AND COMPONENTS LLC
11841 Nw 38th Pl (33323-2691)
PHONE..................................954 798-8943
Robert Jasiewicz, *Mng Member*
EMP: 26 **EST:** 2003
SQ FT: 144
SALES (est): 500K
SALES (corp-wide): 93.7B **Publicly Held**
WEB: www.capacitorsupplier.com
SIC: 3679 Electronic circuits
PA: Bank Of America Corporation
100 N Tryon St Ste 170
Charlotte NC 28202
704 386-5681

(G-17105)
CHAMPION NUTRITION INC
Also Called: Champion Performance Products
1301 Sawgrs Corp Pkwy (33323-2813)
PHONE..................................954 233-3300
Jose Minski, *CEO*
Reshma Patel, *Vice Pres*
▼ **EMP:** 1 **EST:** 2008
SALES (est): 6.9MM
SALES (corp-wide): 7.3B **Publicly Held**
WEB: www.champion-nutrition.com
SIC: 2099 Food preparations
HQ: Nature's Products, Inc.
1221 Broadway
Oakland CA 94612
954 233-3300

(G-17106)
COASTAL AIRCRAFT PARTS LLC
2999 Nw 115th Ter (33323-1607)
PHONE..................................954 980-6929
Arthur Downey, *Principal*
EMP: 6 **EST:** 2006
SALES (est): 239.7K **Privately Held**
WEB: www.coastalaircraftparts.com
SIC: 3999 Airplane models, except toy

(G-17107)
COMPONEXX CORP
789 Shotgun Rd (33326-1940)
P.O. Box 268293, Fort Lauderdale (33326-8293)
PHONE..................................954 236-6569
Edwin Diaz, *President*
Max Diaz, *Vice Pres*
Maria Sanchez,
▲ **EMP:** 9 **EST:** 2005
SQ FT: 5,200
SALES (est): 1.3MM **Privately Held**
WEB: www.componexx.com
SIC: 3663 Cable television equipment

(G-17108)
COMPUTATIONAL SYSTEMS INC
Also Called: Emerson Latin America
1300 Concord Ter Ste 400 (33323-2899)
PHONE..................................954 846-5030
Dario Kanevsky, *Vice Pres*
Scott Lewis, *Opers Mgr*
Orlando Adriana, *Finance*
Rebecca Earhart, *Sr Project Mgr*
Joe Viers, *Supervisor*
EMP: 123
SALES (corp-wide): 16.7B **Publicly Held**
SIC: 3823 Industrial instrmnts msrmnt display/control process variable
HQ: Computational Systems, Incorporated
8000 West Florissant Ave
Saint Louis MO 63136
314 553-2000

(G-17109)
COUNTWISE LLC (PA)
1149 Sawgrs Corp Pkwy (33323-2847)
PHONE..................................954 846-7011
Jacques Stephane, *Sales Executive*
Philip Tomlin, *Sales Executive*
Joseph Taylor, *Manager*
Bill Altmann, *Software Dev*
Ilan Lev Ran,
EMP: 19 **EST:** 2003
SALES (est): 3MM **Privately Held**
WEB: www.countwise.com
SIC: 3824 Tally counters

(G-17110)
CRYSTAL COMMUNICATIONS INC
5600 Nw 102nd Ave Ste M (33351-8709)
PHONE..................................954 474-3072
Adam Jacobs, *President*
Michael Vidal, *Vice Pres*
▲ **EMP:** 8 **EST:** 1998
SALES (est): 1.9MM **Privately Held**
WEB: www.crystalcommunications.net
SIC: 3663 Satellites, communications; television closed circuit equipment

(G-17111)
CRYSTAL POOL SERVICE INC
10718 Nw 53rd St (33351-8025)
PHONE..................................954 444-8282
Jeffrey Kohler, *President*
EMP: 13 **EST:** 1989
SALES (est): 1.2MM **Privately Held**
WEB: www.crystalpoolsvc.com
SIC: 3589 5091 Commercial cooking & foodwarming equipment; watersports equipment & supplies

(G-17112)
CSI HOME DECOR INC
5365 N Hiatus Rd (33351-8718)
PHONE..................................754 301-2147
Paul Dunkley, *Principal*
EMP: 7 **EST:** 2016
SALES (est): 125K **Privately Held**
WEB: www.csihomedecor.com
SIC: 2434 Wood kitchen cabinets

(G-17113)
CUSTOM MOSAICS INC
11110 W Oakland Park Blvd (33351-6808)
PHONE..................................954 610-9436
Joe Stephens, *President*
▲ **EMP:** 8 **EST:** 1998
SQ FT: 2,500
SALES (est): 741.6K **Privately Held**
WEB: www.custommosaicsinc.com
SIC: 3253 Mosaic tile, glazed & unglazed: ceramic

(G-17114)
DAILY GRIND STUMPGRINDING
10330 Nw 31st Ct (33351-6839)
PHONE..................................954 588-4640
David Melkonian, *Principal*
EMP: 6 **EST:** 2008
SALES (est): 119.9K **Privately Held**
SIC: 3599 Grinding castings for the trade

(G-17115)
DIGITAL ANTENNA INC
5325 Nw 108th Ave (33351-8755)
PHONE..................................954 747-7022
Anthony D Gallagher, *President*
Joanne Gallagher, *Vice Pres*
Joanne Johnson, *Vice Pres*
Brian Fluharty, *Materials Mgr*
John Jones, *VP Engrg*
▲ **EMP:** 12 **EST:** 1993
SQ FT: 22,000
SALES (est): 1.7MM **Privately Held**
WEB: www.digitalantenna.com
SIC: 3679 1629 Antennas, receiving; marine construction

(G-17116)
DP EMB & SCREEN PRINTS INC
3485 N Hiatus Rd (33351-7501)
PHONE..................................954 245-5902
Carmen Rivera, *Principal*
EMP: 9 **EST:** 2012
SALES (est): 280.7K **Privately Held**
SIC: 2395 Embroidery & art needlework

(G-17117)
E-LIQUIDS INVESTMENT GROUP LLC
Also Called: Humo E-Liquids
591 Swgrss Corp Pkwy (33325-6211)
PHONE..................................954 507-6060
Steven Sosa,
EMP: 20 **EST:** 2016
SALES (est): 2.5MM **Privately Held**
WEB: www.eliquidsgroup.com
SIC: 2899 Chemical preparations

▲ = Import ▼=Export
◆ =Import/Export

(G-17118)
EGM MANUFACTURING CORP
10032 Nw 53rd St (33351-8068)
PHONE..................................954 440-0445
J Antonio Morales Salinas, *CEO*
Jose Antonio Morales Salinas, *CEO*
Rosalia Morales, *Manager*
▲ **EMP:** 18 **EST:** 2013
SALES (est): 794.7K **Privately Held**
WEB: www.egm-mfg.com
SIC: 3999 Barber & beauty shop equipment

(G-17119)
ENTIRE SELECT INC
Also Called: Mon Reve
10857 Nw 50th St (33351-8091)
PHONE..................................954 674-2368
Benjamin Perelmuter, *President*
Jun Sheng, *Vice Pres*
EMP: 3 **EST:** 2012
SALES (est): 3.5MM **Privately Held**
SIC: 2331 2321 Women's & misses' blouses & shirts; men's & boys' furnishings

(G-17120)
EQUS LOGISTICS LLC
Also Called: Altum Aerospace
13680 Nw 5th St Ste 140 (33325-6234)
P.O. Box 267520, Fort Lauderdale (33326-7520)
PHONE..................................954 618-6573
Viviana Varela, *General Mgr*
Mayra Tapias, *Purchasing*
Camilo Saltos, *Research*
Eda Clevenger, *Sales Staff*
Alejandro Valencia, *Mng Member*
EMP: 10 **EST:** 2009
SQ FT: 1,600
SALES (est): 2MM **Privately Held**
SIC: 3728 Aircraft parts & equipment

(G-17121)
EZVERIFY & VALIDATE LLC
1401 Nw 136th Ave Ste 400 (33323-2861)
PHONE..................................855 398-3981
Tim Ford, *Vice Pres*
EMP: 9 **EST:** 2016
SALES (est): 260.6K **Privately Held**
WEB: www.ezverify.me
SIC: 7372 Prepackaged software

(G-17122)
FARATECH LLC
5373 N Nob Hill Rd (33351-4751)
PHONE..................................954 651-7287
EMP: 6 **EST:** 2016
SALES (est): 357.8K **Privately Held**
WEB: www.faratech.us
SIC: 3571 Electronic computers

(G-17123)
FAST SERVICE SIGNS INC
10257 Nw 53rd St (33351-8076)
PHONE..................................954 380-0451
Karina Romero, *President*
EMP: 6 **EST:** 2011
SALES (est): 104.6K **Privately Held**
WEB: www.fastservicesigns.com
SIC: 3993 Signs & advertising specialties

(G-17124)
FOREST RESEARCH INSTITUTE INC
13800 Nw 2nd St Ste 190 (33325-6243)
PHONE..................................954 622-5600
Marco Taglietti MD, *President*
EMP: 24 **EST:** 2008
SALES (est): 3.5MM **Privately Held**
WEB: www.allergan.com
SIC: 2834 Pharmaceutical preparations
HQ: Allergan Sales, Llc
2525 Dupont Dr
Irvine CA 92612

(G-17125)
GAYNOR GROUP INC
Also Called: Gem Industries
5030 N Hiatus Rd (33351-8017)
P.O. Box 450061, Fort Lauderdale (33345-0061)
PHONE..................................954 749-1228
Steve Gaynor, *President*
◆ **EMP:** 6 **EST:** 1954
SQ FT: 4,100
SALES (est): 829.3K **Privately Held**
SIC: 3541 2999 Buffing & polishing machines; waxes, petroleum: not produced in petroleum refineries

(G-17126)
GLOW BENCH SYSTEMS INTL (PA)
1580 Sawgrs Corp Pkwy # 13 (33323-2859)
PHONE..................................954 315-4615
Danny W Beauchamp, *President*
Rein Luning, *Treasurer*
Elba Hinckley, *Admin Sec*
EMP: 7 **EST:** 2002
SALES (est): 412.3K **Privately Held**
SIC: 3993 7389 Signs & advertising specialties; advertising, promotional & trade show services

(G-17127)
GRAVITY INK & STITCH INC
2910 Nw 130th Ave Apt 112 (33323-3057)
PHONE..................................954 558-0119
Jayne Schiffres,
EMP: 7 **EST:** 2016
SALES (est): 66.6K **Privately Held**
WEB: www.gravityinkandstitch.com
SIC: 2395 Embroidery & art needlework

(G-17128)
INNEUROCO INC (PA)
4635 Nw 103rd Ave (33351-7914)
PHONE..................................954 742-5988
Marc Litzenberg, *President*
Monique Weller, *Engineer*
Maria Largaespada, *Manager*
EMP: 19 **EST:** 2016
SALES (est): 3.9MM **Privately Held**
WEB: www.inneuroco.com
SIC: 3841 Catheters

(G-17129)
INTER GARD R&D LLC
15491 Sw 12th St (33326-1991)
PHONE..................................954 476-5574
Alberto Alarcon, *Principal*
EMP: 11 **EST:** 2008
SALES (est): 505.1K **Privately Held**
SIC: 3429 Manufactured hardware (general)

(G-17130)
INTERNTNAL NTRCTCALS GROUP INC
Also Called: Ing Phrmctcal Pdts Prvate Lbel
771 Shotgun Rd (33326-1940)
PHONE..................................786 518-2903
Douglas Guardo, *President*
Mario A Villalobos, *Director*
▲ **EMP:** 8 **EST:** 2009
SALES (est): 1.3MM **Privately Held**
WEB: www.ingpharmaceutical.net
SIC: 2834 Vitamin preparations

(G-17131)
ITALIAN HAIR EXTENSION INC
Also Called: Blue Butterfly Hair Extensions
10770 Nw 53rd St (33351-8031)
PHONE..................................954 839-5366
Raphael I Arvili, *President*
EMP: 6 **EST:** 2009
SALES (est): 39.6K **Privately Held**
WEB: www.bbhairextensions.com
SIC: 3999 Hair & hair-based products

(G-17132)
J & J INC
Also Called: Eagle Painting
10062 Nw 50th St (33351-8019)
PHONE..................................954 746-7300
John Field, *President*
Janet Field, *Corp Secy*
▲ **EMP:** 6 **EST:** 1992
SQ FT: 1,400
SALES (est): 737.9K **Privately Held**
SIC: 2851 Paints & allied products

(G-17133)
J AND A MAINTENANCE
6220 Nw 15th St (33313-4625)
PHONE..................................754 234-0708
Jean Augustin, *Owner*
EMP: 13 **EST:** 2003
SALES (est): 164.1K **Privately Held**
WEB: www.res-tek.com
SIC: 3679 Electronic components

(G-17134)
JAMALI INDUSTRIES LLC
1455 Nw 126th Ln (33323-5105)
PHONE..................................954 908-5075
Arash Jamali, *Principal*
EMP: 7 **EST:** 2016
SALES (est): 358.9K **Privately Held**
SIC: 3999 Manufacturing industries

(G-17135)
JAZWARES LLC (DH)
1067 Shotgun Rd (33326-1906)
PHONE..................................954 845-0800
Judd Zebersky, *President*
Laura Zebersky, *COO*
Matthew Siesel, *CFO*
▲ **EMP:** 55 **EST:** 1997
SQ FT: 4,700
SALES (est): 107.5MM
SALES (corp-wide): 8.9B **Publicly Held**
WEB: www.jazwares.com
SIC: 3944 5092 Games, toys & children's vehicles; toys & games
HQ: Alleghany Capital Corporation
1411 Broadway Fl 34
New York NY 10018
212 752-1356

(G-17136)
JEM ART INC
Also Called: Stratton Home Decor
801 Shotgun Rd (33326-1946)
PHONE..................................954 966-7078
Evan Merkur, *President*
Michael Siegel, *Vice Pres*
Gabriela Parsons, *Project Mgr*
Jorge Castillo, *Controller*
Anais Cowley, *Manager*
◆ **EMP:** 29 **EST:** 1984
SQ FT: 30,000
SALES (est): 5.5MM **Privately Held**
WEB: www.strattonhomedecor.com
SIC: 2499 Picture frame molding, finished

(G-17137)
JLD MANUFACTURING CORP
Also Called: Jewelry Tray Factory, The
4747 N Nob Hill Rd Ste 8 (33351-4742)
PHONE..................................877 358-5462
Diana Burgos, *President*
EMP: 7 **EST:** 2010
SALES (est): 591.9K **Privately Held**
SIC: 3911 Jewelry, precious metal

(G-17138)
JMS DESIGNS OF FLORIDA INC
4550 N Hiatus Rd (33351-7944)
PHONE..................................954 572-6100
Bruce Sharkey, *President*
EMP: 7 **EST:** 1993
SALES (est): 899.3K **Privately Held**
WEB: www.jmsdesigns.com
SIC: 2759 Commercial printing

(G-17139)
KLOTH INC
Also Called: Planet
10111 Nw 46th St (33351-7934)
PHONE..................................954 578-5687
Lauren Grossman, *President*
▲ **EMP:** 7 **EST:** 2002
SALES (est): 781.3K **Privately Held**
SIC: 3144 Women's footwear, except athletic

(G-17140)
L A RUST INC
10231 Nw 53rd St (33351-8062)
PHONE..................................954 749-5009
Juan O'Campo, *President*
Loriene O'Campo, *Treasurer*
EMP: 10 **EST:** 1986
SQ FT: 1,400
SALES (est): 1.3MM **Privately Held**
WEB: www.larust.com
SIC: 3479 Coating, rust preventive

(G-17141)
LAWTON LLC
Also Called: Hydra Hair Care
10001 W Oklnd Pk Blvd (33351-6925)
PHONE..................................833 493-7226
Linda Hamilton,
Melinda Daniels,
Askia Gordon,
Rhonda Lawing,
Reginald Pope,
EMP: 6 **EST:** 2014
SALES (est): 150K **Privately Held**
SIC: 2844 Toilet preparations

(G-17142)
LEGGETT & PLATT INCORPORATED
Also Called: Gribetz International
13800 Nw 4th St (33325-6207)
PHONE..................................954 846-0300
Steve Bertucci, *Controller*
Teresa Krajick, *Marketing Staff*
EMP: 57
SALES (corp-wide): 4.2B **Publicly Held**
WEB: www.leggett.com
SIC: 2515 Mattresses & bedsprings
PA: Leggett & Platt, Incorporated
1 Leggett Rd
Carthage MO 64836
417 358-8131

(G-17143)
LIGHTN UP INC
10401 Nw 53rd St (33351-8014)
PHONE..................................954 797-7778
Stuart Yadgaroff, *President*
Melody Berger, *Office Mgr*
EMP: 10 **EST:** 1992
SQ FT: 28,000
SALES (est): 11.5MM **Privately Held**
WEB: www.lightnupfl.com
SIC: 3646 Commercial indusl & institutional electric lighting fixtures

(G-17144)
LUI TECHNICAL SERVICES INC
11821 Nw 34th Pl (33323-1233)
PHONE..................................954 803-7610
Luis H Ruiz, *President*
EMP: 6 **EST:** 2006
SALES (est): 590.7K **Privately Held**
WEB: www.luitechnical.amawebs.com
SIC: 3699 Electrical equipment & supplies

(G-17145)
LUXURY WORLD LLC
4667 Nw 103rd Ave (33351-7916)
PHONE..................................954 746-8776
Isaac Cohen,
Gina Cohen,
EMP: 9 **EST:** 2009
SALES (est): 310.5K **Privately Held**
SIC: 2844 Toilet preparations

(G-17146)
MDR LLC
14101 Nw 4th St (33325-6209)
PHONE..................................954 845-9500
Denise Elliott, *Marketing Staff*
James B Riley, *Mng Member*
Lily Wang, *Manager*
Carlo Abel, *Producer*
Patricia Riley,
◆ **EMP:** 150 **EST:** 1984
SQ FT: 50,000
SALES (est): 15.3MM **Privately Held**
WEB: www.mdr.com
SIC: 2834 Vitamin preparations

(G-17147)
MODERNO PORCELAIN WORKS LLC
13807 Nw 4th St (33325-6214)
PHONE..................................954 607-3535
Douglas Dillard,
EMP: 10
SALES (corp-wide): 12.8MM **Privately Held**
WEB: www.modernoworks.com
SIC: 3281 Cut stone & stone products
PA: Moderno Porcelain Works, Llc
11760 Clay Rd
Houston TX 77043
713 360-6837

(G-17148)
MONTRES CORUM USA LLC
14050 Nw 14th St Ste 110 (33323-2851)
PHONE..................................954 279-1220
Severin Wunderman,
EMP: 26 **EST:** 1999

GEOGRAPHIC

SALES (est): 1.6MM **Privately Held**
WEB: www.corum-watches.com
SIC: 3873 Watches, clocks, watchcases & parts
HQ: Montres Corum Sarl
Rue Du Petit-Chateau 1
La Chaux-De-Fonds NE 2300
329 670-670

(G-17149)
MOTOR CITY CLASSICS INC
12717 W Sunrise Blvd (33323-0902)
PHONE..................................954 473-2201
Maurice Oujevolk, *President*
Gladys Oujevolk, *Vice Pres*
▲ **EMP:** 5 **EST:** 1998
SALES (est): 919.9K **Privately Held**
WEB: www.motorcityclassicsinc.com
SIC: 3364 Nonferrous die-castings except aluminum

(G-17150)
NANO DIMENSION USA INC
Also Called: Nano Dimension 3d
13798 Nw 4th St Ste 315 (33325-6227)
P.O. Box 1227, Santa Clara CA (95052-1227)
PHONE..................................650 209-2866
Simon Fried, *President*
Ziki Peled, *COO*
Jaim Nulman, *Exec VP*
Tal Fridkin, *Marketing Mgr*
EMP: 21 **EST:** 2017
SALES (est): 3.8MM **Privately Held**
WEB: www.nano-di.com
SIC: 3672 Printed circuit boards
PA: Nano Dimension Ltd
2 Ilan Ramon
Ness Ziona 74036

(G-17151)
NEOPOD SYSTEMS LLC (PA)
Also Called: Juan Bermudez
1329 Shotgun Rd (33326-1935)
PHONE..................................954 603-3100
Daniel Rourke, *Vice Pres*
Michael Miller, *Opers Staff*
Juan Bermudez,
Charles Ermer,
▼ **EMP:** 10 **EST:** 2009
SALES (est): 4.9MM **Privately Held**
WEB: www.neopodsystems.com
SIC: 2452 3448 Prefabricated wood buildings; prefabricated metal buildings

(G-17152)
NIPPON MACIWUMEI CO
Also Called: McW Parts
4500 N Hiatus Rd Ste 214 (33351-7984)
PHONE..................................954 533-7747
Camila G Orsi, *President*
EMP: 17 **EST:** 2019
SALES (est): 1.3MM **Privately Held**
SIC: 3531 Construction machinery

(G-17153)
OCEAN PHARMACEUTICALS INC
5373 N Hiatus Rd (33351-8718)
PHONE..................................954 473-4717
Jeffrey Friedman, *CEO*
Jasara Mohammed, *Director*
EMP: 10
SALES (est): 673.8K **Privately Held**
SIC: 2834 Pharmaceutical preparations

(G-17154)
OUR CITY MEDIA OF FLORIDA LLC
400 Swgrss Corp Pkwy 200c (33325-6249)
PHONE..................................954 306-1007
Sven Budzisch, *President*
Terrance Jaillet, *Principal*
Gabriela Moscoso, *Office Mgr*
EMP: 10 **EST:** 2008
SALES (est): 927.7K **Privately Held**
WEB: www.ourcitymedia.com
SIC: 2721 Magazines: publishing & printing

(G-17155)
OUR FLORIDA PUBLISHING
9581 Sunrise Lakes Blvd # 312 (33322-6145)
PHONE..................................904 859-2805
Michael Finegold, *Principal*
EMP: 6 **EST:** 2010
SALES (est): 119.4K **Privately Held**
SIC: 2741 Miscellaneous publishing

(G-17156)
PAAL TECHNOLOGIES INC
5387 N Nob Hill Rd (33351-4761)
PHONE..................................954 368-5000
Prem Chandran, *CEO*
Latha Chandran, *Ch of Bd*
EMP: 5 **EST:** 2001
SALES (est): 705.6K **Privately Held**
WEB: www.paaltech.com
SIC: 3679 3677 Harness assemblies for electronic use: wire or cable; electronic coils, transformers & other inductors

(G-17157)
PERALTA GROUP INC
Also Called: Waterheaterdepot.com
4566 N Hiatus Rd (33351-7987)
PHONE..................................954 502-8100
Victor Peralta, *President*
EMP: 6 **EST:** 2000
SALES (est): 609.5K **Privately Held**
WEB: www.peraltagroup.com
SIC: 3639 5731 Hot water heaters, household; radio, television & electronic stores

(G-17158)
PLATTSCO INC
1343 Shotgun Rd (33326-1935)
PHONE..................................954 744-4099
Platts John II, *Principal*
EMP: 7 **EST:** 2012
SALES (est): 180.2K **Privately Held**
WEB: www.varsityblue.net
SIC: 2741 Miscellaneous publishing

(G-17159)
PPI INTERNATIONAL CORP
1649 Nw 136th Ave (33323-2802)
PHONE..................................954 838-1008
Caroline J Pandorf, *President*
Warren Pandorf, *CFO*
EMP: 63 **EST:** 1993
SQ FT: 15,000
SALES (est): 904.8K **Privately Held**
SIC: 3842 Bulletproof vests

(G-17160)
PREFERRED PCKS PBLICATIONS INC
1335 Shotgun Rd (33326-1935)
P.O. Box 267700, Fort Lauderdale (33326-7700)
PHONE..................................954 377-8000
Lawrence Moorman, *President*
Colleen Moorman, *Treasurer*
Marc Moorman, *Admin Sec*
EMP: 11 **EST:** 2004
SALES (est): 257.6K **Privately Held**
WEB: www.playbook.com
SIC: 2741 Miscellaneous publishing

(G-17161)
PRIME MERIDIAN TRADING CORP
4624 N Hiatus Rd (33351-7909)
P.O. Box 450358, Fort Lauderdale (33345-0358)
PHONE..................................954 727-2152
Luz A Arbelaez, *President*
Patrick Williams, *Vice Pres*
◆ **EMP:** 9 **EST:** 1998
SQ FT: 2,000
SALES (est): 1.6MM **Privately Held**
WEB: www.primemeridian.net
SIC: 3669 5065 3661 Emergency alarms; telephone & telegraphic equipment; telephone equipment; fiber optics communications equipment

(G-17162)
PRINT HOPPER
4634 N Hiatus Rd (33351-7977)
PHONE..................................954 770-3007
EMP: 5 **EST:** 2019
SALES (est): 367.8K **Privately Held**
SIC: 2752 Commercial printing, lithographic

(G-17163)
PRINTING AND LABELS INC
5405 Nw 102nd Ave Ste 218 (33351-8743)
PHONE..................................954 578-4411
Kake Andris, *President*
EMP: 7 **EST:** 2011
SALES (est): 83.9K **Privately Held**
SIC: 2752 Commercial printing, lithographic

(G-17164)
PRINTRUST INC
Also Called: Minuteman Press
4617 Nw 103rd Ave (33351-7914)
PHONE..................................954 572-0790
Felix Abraham, *President*
EMP: 9 **EST:** 2015
SALES (est): 252.3K **Privately Held**
WEB: www.chanhassen-mn.minutemanpress.com
SIC: 2752 Commercial printing, lithographic

(G-17165)
PROWIN INDUSTRIES INC
6120 Nw 11th St (33313-6116)
PHONE..................................954 584-5686
Sandra Rowland, *President*
EMP: 7 **EST:** 2004
SALES (est): 104.4K **Privately Held**
SIC: 3999 Manufacturing industries

(G-17166)
PULLING INC
12797 Nw 13th St (33323-3135)
PHONE..................................305 224-2469
Julio E Ibanez, *Principal*
EMP: 6 **EST:** 2010
SALES (est): 87.4K **Privately Held**
SIC: 1389 Construction, repair & dismantling services

(G-17167)
RAINBOW LGHT NTRTNAL SYSTEMS I (DH)
1301 Sawgrs Corp Pkwy (33323-2813)
PHONE..................................954 233-3300
Jose Minski, *CEO*
Linda Kahler, *President*
Sharon Minski, *Vice Pres*
EMP: 5 **EST:** 1981
SALES (est): 13.5MM
SALES (corp-wide): 7.3B **Publicly Held**
SIC: 2833 2834 5961 Vitamins, natural or synthetic: bulk, uncompounded; pharmaceutical preparations; catalog & mail-order houses
HQ: Nature's Products, Inc.
1221 Broadway
Oakland CA 94612
954 233-3300

(G-17168)
RDE CONNECTORS & CABLES INC
5277 Nw 108th Ave (33351-8070)
PHONE..................................954 746-6400
Reinhard Derksen, *President*
Angelika Derksen, *Vice Pres*
EMP: 10 **EST:** 1992
SQ FT: 3,000
SALES (est): 2.8MM
SALES (corp-wide): 2.7B **Privately Held**
WEB: www.rde-usa.com
SIC: 3678 Electronic connectors
PA: Phoenix Contact Gmbh & Co. Kg
Flachsmarktstr. 8
Blomberg 32825
523 530-0

(G-17169)
RESTORATION GAMES LLC
12717 W Sunrise Blvd (33323-0902)
PHONE..................................954 937-1970
Justin Jacobson,
EMP: 7 **EST:** 2016
SALES (est): 869.1K **Privately Held**
WEB: www.restorationgames.com
SIC: 7372 Prepackaged software

(G-17170)
ROTBURG INSTRUMENTS AMER INC
1560 Sawgrass Corporate (33323-2858)
PHONE..................................954 331-8046
Genaro Cardenas, *President*
EMP: 11 **EST:** 1998
SALES (est): 237.5K **Privately Held**
WEB: www.rotburg.com
SIC: 3841 Surgical instruments & apparatus

(G-17171)
SCHNEIDER ELECTRIC IT CORP
490 Swgrss Corp Pkwy (33325-6253)
PHONE..................................305 266-5005
Tim Figueredo, *District Mgr*
Eileen Caballero, *Marketing Staff*
Fernando Garcia, *Branch Mgr*
Joshua Rivers, *Manager*
Rafael Santos, *Manager*
EMP: 8
SALES (corp-wide): 177.9K **Privately Held**
WEB: www.se.com
SIC: 3629 Power conversion units, a.c. to d.c.: static-electric
HQ: Schneider Electric It Corporation
132 Fairgrounds Rd
West Kingston RI 02892
401 789-5735

(G-17172)
SKY MEDICAL INC
5229 Nw 108th Ave (33351-8044)
PHONE..................................954 747-3188
Todd Tyrrell, *President*
Tony Tyrrell, *Vice Pres*
Matt Jansen, *Prdtn Mgr*
Christopher Appet, *Sales Staff*
Chris Appet, *Mktg Dir*
EMP: 17 **EST:** 1996
SQ FT: 8,000
SALES (est): 2.4MM **Privately Held**
WEB: www.taos1.com
SIC: 3841 3842 Surgical & medical instruments; surgical appliances & supplies

(G-17173)
SLASHER PRINTING CENTER INC
Also Called: Slasher Printing Services
6701 Nw 22nd St (33313-3953)
PHONE..................................305 835-7366
Ainswith Smith, *President*
EMP: 6 **EST:** 1976
SALES (est): 524.9K **Privately Held**
SIC: 2759 Commercial printing

(G-17174)
SMOOTHIES RECHARGE
2101 N University Dr (33322-3935)
PHONE..................................954 999-0332
EMP: 8 **EST:** 2014
SALES (est): 382.3K **Privately Held**
WEB: www.rechargesmoothies.com
SIC: 2037 Frozen fruits & vegetables

(G-17175)
SMURFIT KAPPA PACKAGING LLC (DH)
Also Called: Smurfit Kappa The America's
1301 Intl Pkwy Ste 550 (33323)
PHONE..................................954 838-9738
Maria Cabre, *Purch Mgr*
Latisha Boles, *Purch Agent*
Carlos Arango, *Buyer*
Ian Curley, *CFO*
Eduardo Garces Holguin, *Controller*
◆ **EMP:** 14 **EST:** 1989
SQ FT: 6,174
SALES (est): 41.3MM **Privately Held**
WEB: www.smurfitkappa.com
SIC: 2653 Boxes, corrugated: made from purchased materials

(G-17176)
SPEC-TEC MANUFACTURING INC
10794 Nw 53rd St (33351-8031)
PHONE..................................954 749-4204
Scott Barrett, *President*
Tracy Barrett, *Corp Secy*
EMP: 5 **EST:** 1996
SQ FT: 3,000
SALES (est): 744.1K **Privately Held**
SIC: 3669 Emergency alarms

(G-17177)
SRT WIRELESS LLC
1613 Nw 136th Ave Bldg C (33323-2896)
PHONE..................................954 797-7850

Jorge Rodriguez, *Engineer*
Richard Lund, *Mng Member*
EMP: 5 **EST:** 2011
SALES (est): 3MM **Privately Held**
WEB: www.srtwireless.net
SIC: 3663 Satellites, communications

(G-17178)
SSE PUBLICATIONS LLC
1 Panther Pkwy (33323-5315)
PHONE..................................954 835-7616
Carol Duncanson, *Principal*
EMP: 10 **EST:** 2008
SALES (est): 379.5K **Privately Held**
SIC: 2741 Miscellaneous publishing

(G-17179)
STRATA ANALYTICS HOLDG US LLC
1560 Sawgrs Corp Pkwy (33323-2858)
PHONE..................................954 349-4630
Julio Ardiles, *CEO*
Martin Ozores,
Martin Roos, *Advisor*
EMP: 59 **EST:** 2015
SALES: 1.4MM **Privately Held**
WEB: www.strataanalytics.us
SIC: 7372 Business oriented computer software

(G-17180)
STUSH AP USA/STUSH STYLE LLC
2500 N University Dr (33322-3003)
PHONE..................................404 940-3445
Janette Derby-Green, *CEO*
Janette Derby, *Mng Member*
EMP: 11 **EST:** 2012
SQ FT: 1,500
SALES (est): 1.3MM **Privately Held**
SIC: 3144 2331 2335 5136 Women's footwear, except athletic; blouses, women's & juniors': made from purchased material; women's, juniors' & misses' dresses; men's & boys' clothing; women's & children's dresses, suits, skirts & blouses; men's & boys' trousers & slacks

(G-17181)
SUMIFLEX LLC
773 Shotgun Rd (33326-1940)
PHONE..................................954 578-6998
Javier Galarraga, *Mng Member*
EMP: 5 **EST:** 2012
SALES (est): 716.5K **Privately Held**
WEB: www.sumiflex.com
SIC: 3089 Billfold inserts, plastic

(G-17182)
SURVIVAL PRODUCTS INC
1655 Nw 136th Ave M (33323-2802)
PHONE..................................954 966-7329
German Alvarez, *CEO*
Peter Loeb, *President*
Donna Rogers, *Vice Pres*
◆ **EMP:** 9 **EST:** 1970
SALES (est): 25MM **Privately Held**
WEB: www.avi-aviation.com
SIC: 3728 7929 8711 Aircraft parts & equipment; actors; consulting engineer

(G-17183)
SYI INC
Also Called: Secretbandz
10152 Nw 50th St (33351-8026)
PHONE..................................954 323-2483
Shuaib A Khan, *Treasurer*
EMP: 7 **EST:** 2015
SALES (est): 177.6K **Privately Held**
WEB: www.secretbandz.com
SIC: 2869 2821 Silicones; silicone resins

(G-17184)
TAG HEUER
1800 Sawgrass Mills Cir (33323-3921)
PHONE..................................954 846-2103
Tag Heuer, *Principal*
EMP: 6 **EST:** 2009
SALES (est): 167K **Privately Held**
WEB: www.tagheuer.com
SIC: 3643 Outlets, electric: convenience

(G-17185)
TAYLOR COMMUNICATIONS INC
1551 Sawgrs Corp Pkwy 1 (33323-2828)
PHONE..................................954 632-6501
Thomas Dougherty, *General Mgr*
EMP: 17
SALES (corp-wide): 3.6B **Privately Held**
WEB: www.taylor.com
SIC: 2761 Manifold business forms
HQ: Taylor Communications, Inc.
1725 Roe Crest Dr
North Mankato MN 56003
866 541-0937

(G-17186)
TEVA PHARMACEUTICALS
13900 Nw 2nd St (33325-6215)
PHONE..................................954 382-7729
EMP: 16 **EST:** 2019
SALES (est): 2.4MM **Privately Held**
WEB: www.tevapharm.com
SIC: 2834 Pharmaceutical preparations

(G-17187)
THOMAS J COLA
12759 Nw 15th St (33323-3103)
PHONE..................................954 846-0868
Thomas J Cola, *Principal*
EMP: 6 **EST:** 2009
SALES (est): 211.3K **Privately Held**
SIC: 2086 Soft drinks: packaged in cans, bottles, etc.

(G-17188)
THOR GUARD INC (PA)
Also Called: Thor Guard Weather
1193 Sawgrs Corp Pkwy (33323-2847)
P.O. Box 451987, Fort Lauderdale (33345-1987)
PHONE..................................954 835-0900
Peter L Townsend Sr, *CEO*
Robert Dugan, *President*
EMP: 16 **EST:** 1988
SQ FT: 8,300
SALES (est): 2.2MM **Privately Held**
WEB: www.thorguard.com
SIC: 3643 Lightning protection equipment

(G-17189)
TNI MANUFACTURING INC (PA)
4635 Nw 103rd Ave (33351-7914)
PHONE..................................954 742-5988
Daniel Sablyak, *CEO*
EMP: 7 **EST:** 2006
SALES (est): 679.7K **Privately Held**
SIC: 3841 Catheters

(G-17190)
TONBO IMAGING INC
1351 Sawgrs Corp Pkwy # 104 (33323-2831)
PHONE..................................814 441-0475
Jagret Patel, *CEO*
Sudeep George, *Vice Pres*
Cecilia D'Souza, *CFO*
Ankit Kumar, *CTO*
EMP: 8 **EST:** 2012
SALES (est): 474K **Privately Held**
WEB: www.tonboimaging.com
SIC: 3826 Magnetic resonance imaging apparatus

(G-17191)
TSD GROUP CORP
306 International Pkwy B (33325-6273)
PHONE..................................954 940-2111
Maria M Paredes, *President*
Danna Olivo, *Director*
EMP: 14 **EST:** 2012
SQ FT: 3,000
SALES (est): 1.2MM **Privately Held**
SIC: 2911 Aromatic chemical products

(G-17192)
ULTIMATE MACHINING CORPORATION
4741 Nw 103rd Ave (33351-7922)
PHONE..................................954 749-9810
Tommy Foresman Sr, *President*
EMP: 6
SALES (est): 320K **Privately Held**
SIC: 3599 Machine shop, jobbing & repair

(G-17193)
US PACK GROUP LLC
5011 N Hiatus Rd (33351-8018)
PHONE..................................954 556-1840
Marco Flores, *Mng Member*
Aarron Hirshbein, *Mng Member*
Cesar Flores, *Director*
Salvador Alcalde, *Shareholder*
Cesar A Flores,
EMP: 8 **EST:** 2010
SQ FT: 15,000
SALES (est): 2MM **Privately Held**
WEB: www.uspackgroup.com
SIC: 3085 Plastics bottles

(G-17194)
US STEM CELL INC (PA)
1560 Sawgrs Corp Pkwy # 4 (33323-2855)
PHONE..................................954 835-1500
William P Murphy Jr, *Ch of Bd*
Mike Tomas, *President*
Kristin C Comella, *Officer*
EMP: 10 **EST:** 1999
SQ FT: 4,860
SALES: 277K **Publicly Held**
WEB: www.us-stemcell.com
SIC: 2834 8731 Pharmaceutical preparations; commercial physical research; biological research

(G-17195)
VEROCH LLC
10573 Nw 53rd St (33351-8030)
PHONE..................................954 990-7544
Edel Pontes, *Mng Member*
▲ **EMP:** 7 **EST:** 2012
SALES (est): 695K **Privately Held**
WEB: www.veroch.com
SIC: 3829 Testing equipment: abrasion, shearing strength, etc.

(G-17196)
VERTIV CORPORATION
7775 W Oakland Park Blvd (33351)
PHONE..................................954 377-7101
EMP: 100
SALES (corp-wide): 4.3B **Publicly Held**
WEB: www.vertiv.com
SIC: 3825 Electrical energy measuring equipment
HQ: Vertiv Corporation
1050 Dearborn Dr
Columbus OH 43085
614 888-0246

(G-17197)
VOLAERO UAV DRNES HLDINGS CORP
Also Called: Volaero Drones
5375 N Hiatus Rd (33351-8718)
PHONE..................................954 261-3105
Charles Zwebner, *President*
Kevin Sanders, *Development*
Jeff Fidelin, *Senior Mgr*
EMP: 10 **EST:** 2016
SQ FT: 2,000
SALES (est): 2.3MM **Privately Held**
WEB: www.volaerodrones.com
SIC: 3721 Motorized aircraft

(G-17198)
WIALAN TECHNOLOGIES LLC (PA)
10271 Nw 46th St (33351-7963)
PHONE..................................954 749-3481
Eduardo Garcia, *CEO*
Victor M Tapia, *President*
Reggie Bergeron, *COO*
James Andrew Connolly III, *Admin Sec*
Timothy Peabody,
EMP: 31 **EST:** 2011
SALES (est): 602.4K **Publicly Held**
WEB: www.wialan.com
SIC: 3663 4813 5045 Airborne radio communications equipment; ; computer software

(G-17199)
WORLD ELECTRONICS INC
10794 Nw 53rd St (33351-8031)
PHONE..................................954 318-1044
Scott Barrett, *President*
Beate Barrett, *President*
Edward Seltzer, *Principal*
Roy Schwarts, *CFO*
EMP: 9 **EST:** 1979
SALES (est): 798.3K **Privately Held**
WEB: www.triodeel.com
SIC: 3699 Security control equipment & systems

(G-17200)
YSL GRAPHICS LLC
4642 N Hiatus Rd (33351-7977)
PHONE..................................954 916-7255
Jose Y Ramirez,
Maria Cortes,
John Lara,
Stephanie Ramirez,
EMP: 8 **EST:** 2011
SALES (est): 417.9K **Privately Held**
WEB: www.yslsigns.com
SIC: 3993 Signs & advertising specialties

Surfside
Miami-Dade County

(G-17201)
CANVAS STUDIO INC
8877 Collins Ave Apt 502 (33154-3500)
PHONE..................................305 987-5895
Dianie Birbragher, *Principal*
EMP: 6 **EST:** 2017
SALES (est): 46.5K **Privately Held**
SIC: 2211 Canvas

(G-17202)
DAIRY FAIRY LLC
9457 Harding Ave (33154-2803)
PHONE..................................305 865-1506
Jessica L Weiss Levison, *Administration*
EMP: 7 **EST:** 2012
SALES (est): 287.1K **Privately Held**
SIC: 2026 Yogurt

(G-17203)
JIVA CUBES INC
9264 Dickens Ave (33154-3032)
PHONE..................................305 788-1200
Allen Gomberg, *Manager*
EMP: 8 **EST:** 2013
SALES (est): 552K **Privately Held**
SIC: 3589 Coffee brewing equipment

(G-17204)
NUCOR LLC
8835 Harding Ave (33154-3418)
PHONE..................................786 290-9328
Javier Nunez, *Manager*
EMP: 7 **EST:** 2015
SALES (est): 173.8K **Privately Held**
WEB: www.nucor.com
SIC: 3312 Blast furnaces & steel mills

(G-17205)
PEEKABOO ORGANICS LLC
8918 Abbott Ave (33154-3431)
PHONE..................................305 527-7162
Jessica Levison, *CEO*
EMP: 1 **EST:** 2019
SALES (est): 3MM **Privately Held**
WEB: www.eatpeekaboo.com
SIC: 2024 Ice cream & ice milk

(G-17206)
SK WORLDWIDE LLC (PA)
9553 Harding Ave Ste 310 (33154-2510)
PHONE..................................786 360-4842
Jacky Koenig, *President*
Eddy E Silvera, *Principal*
EMP: 5 **EST:** 2011
SALES (est): 426.8K **Privately Held**
SIC: 3661 Telephones & telephone apparatus

(G-17207)
SKATEBOARD SUPERCROSS LLC
725 92nd St (33154-3019)
PHONE..................................786 529-8187
Jonathan Strauss, *Principal*
EMP: 9 **EST:** 2014
SALES (est): 778.7K **Privately Held**
WEB: www.skateboardsupercross.com
SIC: 3949 Skateboards

Sweetwater
Miami-Dade County

(G-17208)
DIGIPRINT & DESIGN CORP
1460 Nw 107th Ave Ste R (33172-2734)
P.O. Box 228824, Miami (33222-8824)
PHONE..................................786 464-1770
Guillermo Torres, *Director*
EMP: 7 **EST:** 2005
SALES (est): 145.8K **Privately Held**
SIC: 3993 Signs & advertising specialties

(G-17209)
FLORIDA INTERNATIONAL FIRM INC
1750 Nw 107th Ave P408 (33172-2895)
PHONE..................................305 450-5920
Silvio R Burneo, *President*
Rosa A Macedo, *Treasurer*
Marco A Burneo, *Director*
Karla A Soule, *Director*
Luis E Barriga, *Admin Sec*
EMP: 6 **EST:** 2005
SALES (est): 72.7K **Privately Held**
SIC: 2032 2035 Canned specialties; vegetables, pickled

Tallahassee
Leon County

(G-17210)
A J TROPHIES & AWARDS INC (PA)
Also Called: Awards 4u
1387 E Lafayette St (32301-4724)
PHONE..................................850 878-7187
Samuel G Varn, *President*
Joni Wilson, *General Mgr*
Nancy C Varn, *Corp Secy*
Nancy Varn, *Store Mgr*
Cassidy Parsons, *Sales Mgr*
▲ **EMP:** 32 **EST:** 1987
SQ FT: 12,000
SALES (est): 4.1MM **Privately Held**
SIC: 3914 3993 Trophies; signs & advertising specialties

(G-17211)
ABRAHAM GEORGE INC
1410 Market St (32312-1758)
PHONE..................................850 523-0757
May A Todd, *President*
May Todd, *President*
George David May, *Vice Pres*
Todd Abraham May, *Vice Pres*
Richard Barnes, *CIO*
EMP: 10 **EST:** 1988
SQ FT: 2,000
SALES (est): 1.1MM **Privately Held**
WEB: www.agpatio.com
SIC: 3499 Furniture parts, metal

(G-17212)
ACME BRICK COMPANY
660 Capital Cir Ne (32301-3514)
PHONE..................................850 531-0725
Buster Warmack, *Branch Mgr*
EMP: 12
SALES (corp-wide): 245.5B **Publicly Held**
WEB: www.brick.com
SIC: 3251 Brick & structural clay tile
HQ: Acme Brick Company
3024 Acme Brick Plz
Fort Worth TX 76109

(G-17213)
AERO AMERICAN DETAILING LLC
3254 Capital Cir Sw (32310-8723)
P.O. Box 15856 (32317-5856)
PHONE..................................850 459-7425
Richard Brown,
EMP: 6 **EST:** 2013
SALES (est): 102.4K **Privately Held**
WEB: www.aeroamericandetailing.com
SIC: 3823 Water quality monitoring & control systems

(G-17214)
AGP HOLDING CORP (PA)
2935 Kerry Forest Pkwy (32309-6825)
P.O. Box 12728 (32317-2728)
PHONE..................................850 668-0006
Herman R Arnold, *CEO*
Kenneth Ellis, *President*
James E Chalmers, *Vice Pres*
Robert W Espy, *Vice Pres*
Deborah K Ellis, *CFO*
EMP: 5 **EST:** 1989
SQ FT: 2,000
SALES (est): 11.5MM **Privately Held**
WEB: www.suncoastbedding.com
SIC: 2499 Beekeeping supplies, wood

(G-17215)
AGRI-PRODUCTS INC (HQ)
3015 N Shnnon Lkes Dr Ste (32309)
P.O. Box 12728 (32317-2728)
PHONE..................................850 668-0006
Arnold Herman R III, *CEO*
James E Chalmers, *President*
H Ross Arnold III, *Corp Secy*
Robert W Espy, *Vice Pres*
Deborah K Ellis, *CFO*
◆ **EMP:** 5 **EST:** 1988
SQ FT: 2,000
SALES (est): 10MM **Privately Held**
WEB: www.suncoastbedding.com
SIC: 2499 Beekeeping supplies, wood

(G-17216)
ALI KAMAKHI ✪
Also Called: Jareed Online Publishing LLC
5663 Tecumseh Dr (32312-4848)
PHONE..................................850 405-8591
Ali Kamakhi, *Owner*
EMP: 14 **EST:** 2020
SALES (est): 100K **Privately Held**
SIC: 2711 Newspapers: publishing only, not printed on site

(G-17217)
ALL-PRO EQUIPMENT & RENTAL INC
2800 Mahan Dr (32308-5410)
P.O. Box 38355 (32315-8355)
PHONE..................................850 656-0208
Robin Barber, *President*
EMP: 10 **EST:** 2004
SALES (est): 2.3MM **Privately Held**
WEB: www.tallahasseeallpro.com
SIC: 3524 Lawn & garden tractors & equipment

(G-17218)
AMRAMP NORTH FL
3025 Southshore Cir (32312-1822)
PHONE..................................904 424-3331
EMP: 6 **EST:** 2018
SALES (est): 88.9K **Privately Held**
WEB: www.amramp.com
SIC: 3448 Ramps: prefabricated metal

(G-17219)
ANCHOR INDUSTRIES LLC
2305 Braeburn Cir (32309-3003)
PHONE..................................850 509-8344
Erika C Harnett,
EMP: 6 **EST:** 2007
SALES (est): 79.7K **Privately Held**
WEB: www.pcmi.vpweb.com
SIC: 3999 Manufacturing industries

(G-17220)
ANTHONY WRIGHT WELDING
311 Ross Rd (32305-7484)
PHONE..................................850 544-1831
Anthony Wright, *Principal*
EMP: 6 **EST:** 2008
SALES (est): 434.9K **Privately Held**
WEB: www.awrightweldingllc.com
SIC: 7692 Welding repair

(G-17221)
APEXEON BIOMEDICAL LLC
3075 Hawks Landing Dr (32309-7224)
PHONE..................................850 878-2150
Thompson Donald, *Principal*
EMP: 5 **EST:** 2016
SALES (est): 365.5K **Privately Held**
SIC: 2836 Biological products, except diagnostic

(G-17222)
ARCPOINT OF TALLAHASSEE INC (PA)
3520 N Monroe St (32303-2745)
PHONE..................................850 201-2500
Carrie Norris, *Principal*
EMP: 82 **EST:** 2010
SALES (est): 424.7K **Privately Held**
SIC: 2899

(G-17223)
ARGOS USA LLC
1005 Kissimmee St (32310-5324)
PHONE..................................850 576-4141
EMP: 8 **EST:** 2014
SALES (est): 177.8K **Privately Held**
WEB: www.argos-us.com
SIC: 3273 Ready-mixed concrete

(G-17224)
ASYSCO INC
1424 Piedmont Dr E # 100 (32308-7956)
PHONE..................................850 383-2522
Katrina Goldman, *Finance Mgr*
EMP: 9 **EST:** 2017
SALES (est): 366K **Privately Held**
SIC: 7372 Prepackaged software

(G-17225)
BACKWOODS CROSSING LLC
6725 Mahan Dr (32308-1413)
PHONE..................................850 765-3753
Jesse Rice, *Principal*
EMP: 11 **EST:** 2016
SALES (est): 381.4K **Privately Held**
WEB: www.backwoodscrossing.com
SIC: 2499 Wood products

(G-17226)
BAVA INC
Also Called: Commercial Printing
1403 Maclay Commerce Dr (32312-3963)
PHONE..................................850 893-4799
Keith R Balon, *President*
Ken Van Gordon, *Vice Pres*
EMP: 10 **EST:** 1974
SQ FT: 4,000
SALES (est): 707.8K **Privately Held**
WEB: www.cpctallahassee.com
SIC: 2752 2791 2789 Commercial printing, offset; typesetting; bookbinding & related work

(G-17227)
BE THE SOLUTION INC
1400 Village Square Blvd (32312-1250)
PHONE..................................850 545-2043
Geraldine Phipps, *Principal*
EMP: 5 **EST:** 2009
SALES: 370.3K **Privately Held**
WEB: www.bethesolution.us
SIC: 3999 Pet supplies

(G-17228)
BLACK NEWS CHANNEL LLC
2320 Killearn Center Blvd (32309-3524)
PHONE..................................844 262-3968
Robert J Brillante, *CEO*
Julius C Watts Jr, *Ch of Bd*
Jim Zerwekh, *COO*
Bryan Couch, *Opers Staff*
EMP: 86 **EST:** 2004
SALES (est): 9.8MM **Privately Held**
WEB: www.blacknewschannel.com
SIC: 3663 Television broadcasting & communications equipment

(G-17229)
BUCKS CORPORATION INC
Also Called: Fastsigns
1920 N Monroe St (32303-4726)
PHONE..................................850 894-2400
John M Buck, *President*
Marilyn M Buck, *Vice Pres*
Thanh Tran, *Sales Staff*
Jared Brock, *Manager*
EMP: 10 **EST:** 2000
SQ FT: 1,700
SALES (est): 1.9MM **Privately Held**
WEB: www.fastsigns.com
SIC: 3993 Signs & advertising specialties

(G-17230)
CAPITAL TECHNOLOGY SOLUTIONS
3920 Monterey Pines Trl (32309-6337)
PHONE..................................850 562-3321
Christopher A Lewis, *Principal*
EMP: 7 **EST:** 2002
SALES (est): 179.8K **Privately Held**
WEB: www.technology.jmco.com
SIC: 3652 Pre-recorded records & tapes

(G-17231)
CEMEX CEMENT INC
3440 Weems Rd (32317-7506)
P.O. Box 14596 (32317-4596)
PHONE..................................850 942-4582
Tim Shenuski, *Branch Mgr*
EMP: 214 **Privately Held**
WEB: www.cemexusa.com
SIC: 3271 3273 Blocks, concrete: acoustical; ready-mixed concrete
HQ: Cemex Cement, Inc.
10100 Katy Fwy Ste 300
Houston TX 77043
713 650-6200

(G-17232)
CFS INC
2151 Delta Blvd Ste 101 (32303-4243)
PHONE..................................850 386-2902
Mike Conlan, *CEO*
Marsha Conlan, *President*
William Rodas, *Accounts Mgr*
Stalvey Jerrod, *Marketing Staff*
Michael Dwinell, *Manager*
▼ **EMP:** 10 **EST:** 2000
SQ FT: 4,738
SALES (est): 1.3MM **Privately Held**
WEB: www.cfssolutions.com
SIC: 7372 Business oriented computer software

(G-17233)
CHIEF CABINETS LLC
4329 W Pensacola St Ste 3 (32304-3722)
PHONE..................................850 545-5055
Ryan Boyle, *Principal*
EMP: 7 **EST:** 2016
SALES (est): 252.7K **Privately Held**
WEB: www.chiefcabinets.com
SIC: 2434 Wood kitchen cabinets

(G-17234)
CLEAR VIEW COATINGS LLC
4514 Deslin Ct (32305-6400)
PHONE..................................850 210-0155
Claudine Vieux, *Principal*
EMP: 13 **EST:** 2013
SALES (est): 1.3MM **Privately Held**
WEB: www.clearviewcoating.com
SIC: 3479 1721 Etching & engraving; residential painting; exterior residential painting contractor; commercial painting; exterior commercial painting contractor

(G-17235)
CLOTHESLINE INC
1369 E Lafayette St Ste A (32301-4781)
PHONE..................................850 877-9171
David Lachter, *President*
Debra Lachter, *Vice Pres*
Dana Lachter, *Treasurer*
Dawn Lachter, *Admin Sec*
EMP: 14 **EST:** 1981
SQ FT: 9,000
SALES (est): 898.6K **Privately Held**
SIC: 2396 5651 2395 Screen printing on fabric articles; family clothing stores; emblems, embroidered

(G-17236)
CONSOLIDATED METAL PRODUCTS
3416 Garber Dr (32303-1114)
PHONE..................................850 576-2167
William C Gadd, *President*
Amy Roberts, *Administration*
EMP: 8 **EST:** 1985
SQ FT: 15,000
SALES (est): 1.2MM **Privately Held**
WEB: www.cmpbuildingproducts.com
SIC: 3444 5031 5039 Canopies, sheet metal; lumber, plywood & millwork; building materials, exterior; prefabricated structures

(G-17237)
COOL COW
2819 Mahan Dr Ste 110 (32308-5492)
PHONE.................................229 272-5495
Brian Jackson, *Owner*
EMP: 6 **EST:** 2009
SALES (est): 138.5K **Privately Held**
SIC: 2024 Ice cream, bulk

(G-17238)
COPY WELL INC
Also Called: Express Printing
927 N Monroe St (32303-6142)
P.O. Box 16063 (32317-6063)
PHONE.................................850 222-9777
Taroon Shah, *President*
Sameera Shah, *Vice Pres*
Salil T Shah, *Admin Sec*
EMP: 16 **EST:** 1986
SQ FT: 4,500
SALES (est): 1MM **Privately Held**
SIC: 2752 Commercial printing, offset

(G-17239)
COR INTERNATIONAL (NOT INC)
3204 Hastie Rd (32305-6764)
PHONE.................................850 766-2866
Orazo Whited, *Branch Mgr*
EMP: 7
SALES (corp-wide): 491.7K **Privately Held**
SIC: 2834 Pharmaceutical preparations
PA: Cor International, Inc (Not Inc)
444 Appleyard Dr
Tallahassee FL 32304

(G-17240)
DANFOSS LLC
Also Called: Danfoss Turbocor Compressors
1769 E Paul Dirac Dr (32310-3707)
PHONE.................................850 504-4800
Ricardo Schneider, *Branch Mgr*
Thomas Hultgren, *Manager*
Micah Stephens, *Technical Staff*
EMP: 145
SALES (corp-wide): 83.5K **Privately Held**
WEB: www.danfoss.com
SIC: 3563 3585 Air & gas compressors; refrigeration & heating equipment
HQ: Danfoss, Llc
11655 Crossroads Cir
Baltimore MD 21220
410 931-8250

(G-17241)
DDD HAMS INC
1519 Capital Cir Ne (32308-6279)
PHONE.................................850 205-1426
EMP: 6 **EST:** 2016
SALES (est): 189.9K **Privately Held**
SIC: 2013 Prepared pork products from purchased pork

(G-17242)
DEBRUYNE ENTERPRISE INC
Also Called: Wood Dimensions
5186 Woodlane Cir (32303-6812)
PHONE.................................850 562-0491
Thomas Debruyne, *President*
Mike Brown, *Principal*
EMP: 10 **EST:** 1978
SQ FT: 8,000
SALES (est): 1.4MM **Privately Held**
SIC: 2434 Wood kitchen cabinets

(G-17243)
DREAMSPINNER PRESS LLC
10800 Kilcrease Way (32305-1824)
PHONE.................................800 970-3759
Holly Gerrell, *CEO*
Jocelin Potash, *Editor*
April Arrington, *CFO*
Poppy Dennison, *Marketing Staff*
Katie Obbink, *Librarian*
EMP: 12 **EST:** 2007
SALES (est): 1.8MM **Privately Held**
WEB: www.dreamspinnerpress.com
SIC: 2741 Miscellaneous publishing

(G-17244)
DURRA PRINT INC
3044 W Tharpe St (32303-1186)
PHONE.................................850 222-4768
Tim Durrance, *President*
EMP: 25 **EST:** 1972
SQ FT: 14,000
SALES (est): 1.9MM **Privately Held**
WEB: www.durraprint.com
SIC: 2752 2796 2791 2789 Commercial printing, offset; platemaking services; typesetting; bookbinding & related work; commercial printing

(G-17245)
DURRA QUICK PRINT INC
1334 N Monroe St (32303-5527)
PHONE.................................850 681-2900
Sarah F Allen, *President*
EMP: 5 **EST:** 1983
SQ FT: 3,000
SALES (est): 439.5K **Privately Held**
WEB: www.durraprint.com
SIC: 2752 2759 Commercial printing, offset; commercial printing

(G-17246)
DVH MACLEOD CORP
Also Called: Sir Speedy
1100 N Monroe St Ste A (32303-6172)
PHONE.................................850 224-6760
David Macleod, *President*
Valerie Macleod, *Corp Secy*
Bernie Jimenez, *Manager*
EMP: 14 **EST:** 1974
SQ FT: 3,000
SALES (est): 511.5K **Privately Held**
WEB: www.sirspeedy.com
SIC: 2752 2791 Commercial printing, lithographic; typesetting

(G-17247)
EMINENT TECHNOLOGY INC
225 E Palmer Ave (32301-5533)
PHONE.................................850 575-5655
Bruce Thigpen, *President*
Will L Stewart, *Vice Pres*
Rob Stewart, *Manager*
EMP: 5 **EST:** 1982
SQ FT: 9,000
SALES (est): 634.8K **Privately Held**
WEB: www.eminent-tech.com
SIC: 3651 Loudspeakers, electrodynamic or magnetic; phonograph turntables

(G-17248)
ENDEVOURS TOGETHER LLC
2211 Orleans Dr (32308-5926)
PHONE.................................850 274-2641
Christine R Small, *Principal*
EMP: 6 **EST:** 2010
SALES (est): 76.4K **Privately Held**
WEB: www.endeavourstogether.com
SIC: 2833 Botanical products, medicinal: ground, graded or milled

(G-17249)
EVERYDAY FEMINISM LLC
75 N Woodward Ave (32313-7500)
PHONE.................................202 643-1001
Jamie Utt, *Credit Staff*
Sandra Kim, *Mng Member*
Derek Ellerman, *Mng Member*
EMP: 6 **EST:** 2012
SALES (est): 120K **Privately Held**
WEB: www.everydayfeminism.com
SIC: 2741 7389 Miscellaneous publishing;

(G-17250)
F S VIEW FLA FLAMBEAU NEWSPPR
277 N Magnolia Dr (32301-2664)
P.O. Box 20208 (32316-0208)
PHONE.................................850 561-6653
Robert Parker, *President*
EMP: 22 **EST:** 1992
SQ FT: 1,400
SALES (est): 613K **Privately Held**
WEB: www.fsunews.com
SIC: 2711 Newspapers, publishing & printing

(G-17251)
FIRST COMMUNICATIONS INC
2910 Krry Frest Pkwy Ste (32309)
PHONE.................................850 668-7990
Charles C Livingston Jr, *President*
Michelle Sweeney, *Corp Secy*
Betty Boyett, *Shareholder*
Jeffrey C Livingston, *Shareholder*
EMP: 70 **EST:** 1993
SALES (est): 3.7MM **Privately Held**
SIC: 3669 3663 4812 Visual communication systems; radio broadcasting & communications equipment; radio telephone communication

(G-17252)
FLORIDA BID REPORTING SERVICE
313 Williams St Ste 11 (32303-6231)
P.O. Box 37189 (32315-7189)
PHONE.................................850 539-7522
Wayland D Burgess Jr, *President*
EMP: 10 **EST:** 1987
SQ FT: 800
SALES (est): 873.1K **Privately Held**
WEB: www.floridabid.com
SIC: 2721 Magazines: publishing only, not printed on site

(G-17253)
FLORIDA COCA-COLA BOTTLING CO
2050 Maryland Cir (32303-3197)
PHONE.................................850 575-6122
Deank Hank, *Branch Mgr*
EMP: 403
SQ FT: 47,250
SALES (corp-wide): 33B **Publicly Held**
WEB: www.coca-cola.com
SIC: 2086 Bottled & canned soft drinks
HQ: Florida Coca-Cola Bottling Company
521 Lake Kathy Dr
Brandon FL 33510
813 569-2600

(G-17254)
FLORIDA PHOSPHATE COUNCIL INC
215 S Monroe St Ste 730 (32301-1804)
PHONE.................................863 904-0641
David L Townsend, *Principal*
EMP: 6 **EST:** 2011
SALES (est): 87.9K **Privately Held**
WEB: www.floridaphosphatepcinc.com
SIC: 2874 Phosphates

(G-17255)
FLORIDA PRINT FINISHERS INC
Also Called: Florida Tees
1621 Capital Cir Ne Ste F (32308-5501)
PHONE.................................850 877-8503
James A Walker, *President*
James Walker Jr, *Vice Pres*
EMP: 5 **EST:** 1967
SALES (est): 349.3K **Privately Held**
SIC: 2789 2675 Trade binding services; die-cut paper & board

(G-17256)
FLOWERS BKG CO THOMASVILLE LLC
3385 S Monroe St (32301-6979)
PHONE.................................229 226-5331
Chris Mulford, *Manager*
EMP: 14
SALES (corp-wide): 4.3B **Publicly Held**
WEB: www.ilovegoats.com
SIC: 2051 Bread, all types (white, wheat, rye, etc): fresh or frozen
HQ: Flowers Baking Co Of Thomasville Llc
300 S Madison St
Thomasville GA 31792
229 226-5331

(G-17257)
FOAMSEAL HURRICANE ADHESIVE
2017 Chatsworth Way (32309-2993)
PHONE.................................850 766-2000
Scott H Friedman, *Principal*
EMP: 6 **EST:** 2005
SALES (est): 78.9K **Privately Held**
WEB: www.foamseal1.com
SIC: 2891 Adhesives

(G-17258)
FREDDIE GLENNS WOODWORK LLC
819 Brighton Rd (32301)
PHONE.................................850 556-7163
Freddie Glenn, *Principal*
EMP: 6 **EST:** 2010
SALES (est): 126.1K **Privately Held**
SIC: 2431 Millwork

(G-17259)
FULL PRESS APPAREL INC
3445 Garber Dr (32303-1115)
PHONE.................................850 222-1003
Daniel Shrine, *President*
Danny Shrine, *President*
Chris Norris, *Prdtn Mgr*
Kelley Brewer, *Mktg Coord*
Vince Labolito, *Art Dir*
EMP: 12 **EST:** 1997
SQ FT: 8,500
SALES (est): 1.5MM **Privately Held**
WEB: www.fullpressapparel.com
SIC: 2759 2396 2395 Screen printing; automotive & apparel trimmings; pleating & stitching

(G-17260)
GANDY PRINTERS INC
1800 S Monroe St (32301-5528)
PHONE.................................850 222-5847
Bernard L Gandy III, *President*
EMP: 17 **EST:** 1970
SQ FT: 10,000
SALES (est): 2.2MM **Privately Held**
WEB: www.gandyprinters.com
SIC: 2752 2789 2759 Commercial printing, offset; bookbinding & related work; commercial printing

(G-17261)
GARVIN MANAGEMENT COMPANY INC (PA)
Also Called: Insty-Prints
4042 Sawgrass Cir (32309-2890)
PHONE.................................850 893-4719
William Garvin Sr, *President*
EMP: 5 **EST:** 1979
SQ FT: 2,600
SALES (est): 482K **Privately Held**
WEB: www.instyprints.com
SIC: 2752 7334 Commercial printing, offset; photocopying & duplicating services

(G-17262)
GENERAL CAPACITOR LLC
132-1 Hamilton Park Dr (32304)
PHONE.................................510 371-2700
Linda Zhong, *CEO*
Hao Chen, *Mng Member*
Jianping Zheng,
▲ **EMP:** 7 **EST:** 2011
SALES (est): 603.9K **Privately Held**
SIC: 3629 3675 Capacitors & condensers; electronic capacitors

(G-17263)
GENERAL DYNMICS LAND SYSTEMS I
2930 Commonwealth Blvd (32303-3155)
PHONE.................................850 574-4700
Wynn Koehler, *General Mgr*
Steve Rolph, *General Mgr*
Edward Harris, *Chief*
Dana Pastor, *Regional Mgr*
Michael Bolon, *Vice Pres*
EMP: 6
SALES (corp-wide): 37.9B **Publicly Held**
WEB: www.gdls.com
SIC: 3812 Radio magnetic instrumentation
HQ: General Dynamics Land Systems Inc.
38500 Mound Rd
Sterling Heights MI 48310
586 825-4000

(G-17264)
GEORGESOFT INC
207 W Park Ave Ste B (32301-7715)
PHONE.................................850 329-5517
Kostiantyn Romanchenko, *President*
EMP: 7 **EST:** 2015
SALES (est): 420.6K **Privately Held**
SIC: 7372 Application computer software

(G-17265)
GET HAMS INC
3396 Lakeshore Dr (32312-1305)
PHONE.................................850 386-7123
Leonard M Taylor, *President*
EMP: 9 **EST:** 2002
SALES (est): 533.8K **Privately Held**
SIC: 2013 Prepared pork products from purchased pork

(G-17266)
GRAPHIC PRESS CORPORATION
5123a Woodlane Cir Ste A (32303-6862)
PHONE..................................850 562-2262
Dawn Azar Madsen, *President*
Norm Madse, *Vice Pres*
EMP: 5 **EST:** 1992
SQ FT: 7,500
SALES (est): 687.1K **Privately Held**
WEB: www.gp-print.com
SIC: 2752 Commercial printing, offset

(G-17267)
GT TECHNOLOGIES INC
2919 Commonwealth Blvd (32303-3156)
PHONE..................................850 575-8181
Jon Baucher, *Vice Pres*
Ron Krause, *Plant Mgr*
Harold Brown, *QC Mgr*
George Brearley, *Engineer*
David Gosbee, *Engineer*
EMP: 200
SALES (corp-wide): 1B **Privately Held**
WEB: www.gttechnologies.com
SIC: 3714 Motor vehicle engines & parts
HQ: Gt Technologies, Inc.
5859 E Executive Dr
Westland MI 48185
734 467-8371

(G-17268)
GT TECHNOLOGIES I INC
2919 Commonwealth Blvd (32303-3156)
PHONE..................................850 575-8181
William E Redmond Jr, *CEO*
Mark Mueller, *General Mgr*
Robert Novo, *Vice Pres*
Douglas J Grierson, *CFO*
Mike Spadarotto, *CFO*
▲ **EMP:** 1 **EST:** 2006
SALES (est): 37.8MM
SALES (corp-wide): 1B **Privately Held**
WEB: www.gttechnologies.com
SIC: 3714 Motor vehicle engines & parts
HQ: Gentek, Inc.
90 E Halsey Rd Ste 301
Parsippany NJ 07054
973 515-0900

(G-17269)
GTO ACCESS SYSTEMS LLC
3121 Hartsfield Rd (32303-3149)
PHONE..................................850 575-0176
Shaun Burke, *President*
Joseph A Kelley, *President*
Douglas Waldal, *President*
John Bentley, *Human Res Dir*
Joe Schenke, *Sales Dir*
◆ **EMP:** 90 **EST:** 1987
SQ FT: 75,000
SALES (est): 25.1MM
SALES (corp-wide): 11.6B **Privately Held**
WEB: www.nortekcontrol.com
SIC: 3699 Security devices
HQ: Nortek Security & Control Llc
5919 Sea Otter Pl Ste 100
Carlsbad CA 92010
760 438-7000

(G-17270)
GULF ATLANTIC CULVERT COMPANY
5344 Gateway Dr (32303-6842)
P.O. Box 4002 (32315-4002)
PHONE..................................850 562-2384
Francis Wallace, *President*
James W McCook III, *Corp Secy*
W Howell Jarrard, *Vice Pres*
EMP: 15 **EST:** 1984
SQ FT: 1,800
SALES (est): 1.2MM **Privately Held**
WEB: www.gaculvert.com
SIC: 3444 3498 3312 Pipe, sheet metal; fabricated pipe & fittings; blast furnaces & steel mills

(G-17271)
GUN VAULT
3305 Capital Cir Ne # 103 (32308-1589)
PHONE..................................850 391-7651
EMP: 5
SALES (est): 400K **Privately Held**
SIC: 3272 Mfg Concrete Products

(G-17272)
H B SHERMAN TRAPS INC
3731 Peddie Dr (32303-1103)
P.O. Box 20267 (32316-0267)
PHONE..................................850 575-8727
Gerald E Phillips, *President*
Rebecca Anne Colon, *Vice Pres*
Rebecca Sciabica, *IT Executive*
Sandra Screws, *Admin Sec*
EMP: 9 **EST:** 1961
SQ FT: 5,000
SALES (est): 987K **Privately Held**
WEB: www.shermantraps.com
SIC: 3429 Animal traps, iron or steel

(G-17273)
HANGER PRSTHETCS & ORTHO INC
Also Called: Hanger Clinic
2717 Mahan Dr Ste 2 (32308-5499)
PHONE..................................850 216-2392
Sam Liang, *President*
Eric Rancharran, *Manager*
EMP: 8
SALES (corp-wide): 1B **Publicly Held**
WEB: www.hangerclinic.com
SIC: 3842 Limbs, artificial; braces, orthopedic
HQ: Hanger Prosthetics & Orthotics, Inc.
10910 Domain Dr Ste 300
Austin TX 78758
512 777-3800

(G-17274)
HARBOR ENTPS LTD LBLTY CO
2417 Fleischmann Rd Ste 4 (32308-4505)
PHONE..................................229 403-0756
Todd Vanderbeek, *CFO*
Jackson Rackley, *Branch Mgr*
EMP: 10 **Privately Held**
WEB: www.harborsc.com
SIC: 3312 Structural shapes & pilings, steel
PA: Harbor Fed Con Llc
125 N Broad St Ste 404
Thomasville GA 31792
229 226-0911

(G-17275)
HARVEST PRINT & BUS SVCS INC ✪
1613 Capital Cir Ne (32308-5501)
PHONE..................................850 681-2488
Anisur M Rahman, *President*
EMP: 10 **EST:** 2021
SALES (est): 750.5K **Privately Held**
SIC: 2759 Commercial printing

(G-17276)
HARVEST PRINT MKTG SLTIONS LLC
Also Called: Harvest Printing
1613 Capital Cir Ne (32308-5501)
PHONE..................................850 681-2488
Tim Kleman,
Christy Kleman,
EMP: 6 **EST:** 2017
SALES (est): 395.6K **Privately Held**
WEB: www.harvest-press.com
SIC: 2752 Commercial printing, offset

(G-17277)
HARVEST PRTG & COPY CTR INC
1613 Capital Cir Ne (32308-5501)
PHONE..................................850 681-2488
Miguel Jimenez, *President*
Theresa Jimenez, *Treasurer*
Ken Bowden, *Technology*
Don Drewek, *Graphic Designe*
EMP: 17 **EST:** 1985
SQ FT: 9,000
SALES (est): 1.9MM **Privately Held**
WEB: www.harvest-press.com
SIC: 2752 Commercial printing, offset

(G-17278)
HOMES MEDIA SOLUTIONS LLC (DH)
Also Called: Agent Advantage
325 John Knox Rd Bldg 200 (32303-4114)
PHONE..................................850 350-7800
EMP: 16 **EST:** 2015
SALES (est): 8.8MM **Privately Held**
WEB: www.agentadvantage.com
SIC: 2721 Periodicals

(G-17279)
HONEYWELL INTERNATIONAL INC
1531 Commonwealth Bus Dr (32303-1193)
PHONE..................................281 546-0993
EMP: 6
SALES (corp-wide): 32.6B **Publicly Held**
WEB: www.honeywell.com
SIC: 3724 Aircraft engines & engine parts
PA: Honeywell International Inc.
300 S Tryon St
Charlotte NC 28202
704 627-6200

(G-17280)
HORSESHOE KNOLL LC
2982 Giverny Cir (32309-8202)
PHONE..................................850 894-0824
Walter Scott Newbern III,
EMP: 8 **EST:** 2001
SALES (est): 105K **Privately Held**
SIC: 3462 Horseshoes

(G-17281)
INTELLIGENT ROBOTICS INC
3697 Longfellow Rd (32311-3724)
PHONE..................................850 728-7353
Piyush Kumar, *Principal*
Tathagata Mukherjee, *Principal*
Amit Chourasia, *Bd of Directors*
Sachin Jambawalikar, *Bd of Directors*
Veena Kumari, *Bd of Directors*
EMP: 6 **EST:** 2016
SALES: 194.5K **Privately Held**
WEB: www.intelligentrobotics.org
SIC: 3549 9661 7389 Assembly machines, including robotic; space research & technology;

(G-17282)
JAY WALKER ENTERPRISES INC
1934 Iron Bridge Rd (32318)
P.O. Box 180335 (32318-0003)
PHONE..................................850 539-7668
Jay Walker, *Owner*
EMP: 7 **EST:** 2010
SALES (est): 124.8K **Privately Held**
WEB: www.jaywalkerenterprises.com
SIC: 3272 Fireplace & chimney material: concrete

(G-17283)
JITA PRESS INC
3283 Sugar Berry Way (32303-7371)
PHONE..................................850 329-0884
Carla N Lowe-Tucker, *Principal*
EMP: 6 **EST:** 2018
SALES (est): 87.9K **Privately Held**
SIC: 2741 Miscellaneous publishing

(G-17284)
JOHN HURST OUTDOOR SVCS LLC
3694 Corinth Dr (32308-4035)
PHONE..................................850 556-7459
Johnny H Hurst Jr,
EMP: 5 **EST:** 2007
SALES (est): 415.7K **Privately Held**
WEB:
www.johnhurstlawncaretallahassee.com
SIC: 2499 Fencing, docks & other outdoor wood structural products

(G-17285)
JUDICIAL & ADM RES ASSOC
Also Called: Florida Law Weekly
1327 N Adams St (32303-5522)
P.O. Box 4284 (32315-4284)
PHONE..................................850 222-3171
Neil Young, *President*
Sharon Young, *Vice Pres*
Ernest Page,
EMP: 15 **EST:** 1975
SQ FT: 5,000
SALES (est): 1.3MM **Privately Held**
WEB: www.floridalawweekly.com
SIC: 2721 Magazines: publishing only, not printed on site

(G-17286)
KAMELEON PRESS INC
1925 Benjamin Chaires Rd (32317-7476)
PHONE..................................850 566-2522
Kelly K Rysavy, *President*
EMP: 8 **EST:** 2001
SALES (est): 113K **Privately Held**
WEB: www.kameleonpress.com
SIC: 2741 Miscellaneous publishing

(G-17287)
KCW ELECTRIC COMPANY INC
4765 Shelfer Rd (32305-7411)
PHONE..................................850 878-2051
Robert E Scribner, *President*
Donald T Scribner, *Vice Pres*
EMP: 5 **EST:** 1946
SQ FT: 9,000
SALES (est): 660.4K **Privately Held**
WEB: www.kcwwaterwell.com
SIC: 7694 7699 5531 7549 Electric motor repair; pumps & pumping equipment repair; automobile air conditioning equipment, sale, installation; automotive maintenance services

(G-17288)
KENNY-TS INC
1471 Capital Cir Nw # 10 (32303-1311)
P.O. Box 962 (32302-0962)
PHONE..................................850 575-6644
Kenneth Thompson, *President*
Anthony Donaldson, *Corp Secy*
Robert W Thompson, *Shareholder*
EMP: 13 **EST:** 1998
SQ FT: 2,000
SALES (est): 1MM **Privately Held**
WEB: www.kennytees.com
SIC: 2759 Screen printing

(G-17289)
LAWRENCE COMMERCIAL SYSTEMS
451 Geddie Rd (32304-8690)
PHONE..................................850 574-8723
Richard Lawrence, *Owner*
EMP: 11 **EST:** 1977
SALES (est): 1.3MM **Privately Held**
SIC: 3463 Aluminum forgings

(G-17290)
LESLIE INDUSTRIES INC
2454 Centerville Rd (32308-4418)
P.O. Box 13405 (32317-3405)
PHONE..................................850 422-0099
Harold C Leslie, *President*
David McGeachy, *Prdtn Mgr*
Sue Morgan, *Accounts Mgr*
EMP: 11 **EST:** 1981
SQ FT: 3,000
SALES (est): 322.8K **Privately Held**
WEB: www.leslieindustries.com
SIC: 3448 Buildings, portable: prefabricated metal

(G-17291)
LITHO HAUS PRINTERS INC (PA)
Also Called: Lithohaus Printers
2843 Industrial Plaza Dr A1 (32301-3507)
PHONE..................................850 671-6600
Dianne Nagle, *President*
Bill Pickron, *Vice Pres*
Ritchie Pickron, *Manager*
EMP: 9 **EST:** 1983
SQ FT: 9,500
SALES (est): 2.2MM **Privately Held**
WEB: www.lithohaus.com
SIC: 2752 Commercial printing, offset

(G-17292)
LOBBY DOCS LLC
3472 Weems Rd (32317-7513)
PHONE..................................850 294-0013
James Parsons, *Ch of Bd*
EMP: 7 **EST:** 2014
SALES (est): 246.2K **Privately Held**
SIC: 7372 Business oriented computer software

(G-17293)
MAG-TAGS INC
Also Called: Signprinters
4446 Sierra Ct (32309-2293)
PHONE..................................850 294-1809

▲ = Import ▼=Export
◆ =Import/Export

Carolyn Pippenger, *President*
Alan Pippenger, *Admin Sec*
EMP: 6 **EST:** 1982
SQ FT: 6,000
SALES (est): 523.5K **Privately Held**
SIC: 3993 Signs, not made in custom sign painting shops

(G-17294)
MAN-TRANS LLC
4920 Woodlane Cir (32303-6810)
PHONE..................................850 222-6993
Darryl Moore, *Mng Member*
◆ **EMP:** 17 **EST:** 1997
SQ FT: 33,000
SALES (est): 1.1MM **Privately Held**
WEB: www.manualtransmission.net
SIC: 3568 5063 5085 3714 Power transmission equipment; transformers & transmission equipment; power transmission equipment & apparatus; motor vehicle parts & accessories

(G-17295)
MARLIN COATINGS LLC
3666 Peddie Dr (32303-1126)
PHONE..................................850 224-1370
Kyle Rockwell, *Principal*
EMP: 13 **EST:** 2006
SALES (est): 382.5K **Privately Held**
SIC: 3479 Metal coating & allied service

(G-17296)
MARQUIS SOFTWARE DEV INC
1625 Summit Lake Dr # 105 (32317-7940)
PHONE..................................850 877-8864
Edward Fishback, *President*
Glenn Fishback, *Vice Pres*
Olu Fayemi, *Project Mgr*
Stephen Payne, *Research*
Meredith Fishback, *Bookkeeper*
EMP: 100
SALES: 11.8MM **Privately Held**
WEB: www.marquisware.com
SIC: 7372 Prepackaged software

(G-17297)
MARTINS FMOUS PSTRY SHOPPE INC
4525 Capital Cir Nw (32303-7252)
PHONE..................................800 548-1200
EMP: 6
SALES (corp-wide): 123.7MM **Privately Held**
WEB: www.potatorolls.com
SIC: 2051 Rolls, bread type: fresh or frozen
PA: Martin's Famous Pastry Shoppe, Inc.
1000 Potato Roll Ln
Chambersburg PA 17202
800 548-1200

(G-17298)
MATHERSON ORGANICS LLC
75 N Woodward Ave 85899 (32313-7500)
PHONE..................................850 792-4007
Michael C Chan,
EMP: 4 **EST:** 2016
SALES (est): 3MM **Privately Held**
SIC: 2844 Cosmetic preparations

(G-17299)
MEDAFFINITY CORPORATION
2350 Phillips Rd Apt 1110 (32308-5346)
PHONE..................................850 254-9690
Dustin A Holt, *Principal*
Neil Skene, *Vice Chairman*
EMP: 11 **EST:** 2010
SALES (est): 253.8K **Privately Held**
WEB: www.medaffinity.com
SIC: 7372 Prepackaged software

(G-17300)
METAL FABRICATION AND
3600 Weems Rd Ste D (32317-7500)
PHONE..................................850 205-2300
Stephanie P Turner, *Mng Member*
Len Turner,
Matt Turner,
EMP: 9 **EST:** 2005
SALES (est): 767K **Privately Held**
WEB: www.metalfabtallahassee.com
SIC: 7692 Welding repair

(G-17301)
MII OIL HOLDING INC
1201 Hays St (32301-2699)
PHONE..................................321 200-0039
Armando Mormina, *CEO*
EMP: 242 **EST:** 2011
SALES (est): 2.7MM **Privately Held**
WEB: www.mii-holding.org
SIC: 1389 Oil field services

(G-17302)
MITCHAM MEDIA GROUP LLC
Also Called: Tallahassee Woman Magazine
4032 Mclaughlin Dr (32309-2759)
P.O. Box 16616 (32317-6616)
PHONE..................................850 893-9624
Michelle A Mitcham,
EMP: 5 **EST:** 2018
SALES (est): 477.1K **Privately Held**
SIC: 2721 Magazines: publishing & printing

(G-17303)
MODERN DIGITAL IMAGING INC
Also Called: Printing.com
519 N Monroe St (32301-1259)
PHONE..................................850 222-7514
Denise S Perrin, *President*
Tom Perrin, *Owner*
Thomas B Perrin, *Vice Pres*
EMP: 10 **EST:** 2003
SQ FT: 4,700
SALES (est): 1MM **Privately Held**
WEB: www.gomdi.net
SIC: 2752 Commercial printing, offset

(G-17304)
MUNICIPAL CODE CORPORATION (HQ)
1700 Capital Cir Sw (32310-9250)
P.O. Box 2235 (32316-2235)
PHONE..................................850 576-3171
George R Langford, *Ch of Bd*
A Lawton Langford, *President*
Ramona Connors, *Editor*
Michal Ford, *Editor*
Jennifer Shirah, *Editor*
EMP: 100 **EST:** 1951
SQ FT: 40,000
SALES (est): 28.2MM **Privately Held**
WEB: www.municode.com
SIC: 2741 2721 2731 Directories: publishing & printing; periodicals; book publishing

(G-17305)
NOPETRO LLC
1152 Capital Cir Nw (32304-9234)
PHONE..................................305 441-9059
Jonathan Locke, *President*
Jorge Herrera, *Mng Member*
Jose David Santizo, *Manager*
EMP: 8 **EST:** 2008
SALES (est): 2.3MM **Privately Held**
SIC: 1321 Natural gas liquids

(G-17306)
NORTHLAND MANUFACTURING INC
3485 S Monroe St (32301-7200)
P.O. Box 6247 (32314-6247)
PHONE..................................850 878-5149
Anita Sandel, *President*
Paul Birdwell, *Vice Pres*
EMP: 6 **EST:** 1974
SQ FT: 9,000
SALES (est): 719.3K **Privately Held**
WEB: www.northlandmanufacturing.com
SIC: 2842 Industrial plant disinfectants or deodorants

(G-17307)
NRG INDUSTRIES INC
10631 Lake Iamonia Dr (32312-5101)
PHONE..................................850 510-7174
William Harvey Bond Jr, *Principal*
EMP: 6 **EST:** 2008
SALES (est): 75.8K **Privately Held**
WEB: www.nrgindustries.com
SIC: 3999 Manufacturing industries

(G-17308)
OOMPHA INC
Also Called: Karmanos Printing & Graphics
1754 Thomasville Rd (32303-5708)
PHONE..................................850 222-7210
Beverley Karmanos, *President*
George Karmanos, *Vice Pres*
Amanda Armanos, *Admin Sec*
EMP: 5 **EST:** 1984
SQ FT: 4,800
SALES (est): 483.2K **Privately Held**
WEB: www.karmanosprinting.com
SIC: 2752 2791 2789 Commercial printing, offset; typesetting; bookbinding & related work

(G-17309)
PIXE INTERNATIONAL CORP
2306 Domingo Dr (32304-1311)
P.O. Box 2744 (32316-2744)
PHONE..................................850 574-6469
J William Nelson, *President*
Becky Selden Hoffman, *Treasurer*
EMP: 8 **EST:** 1977
SQ FT: 600
SALES (est): 667.6K **Privately Held**
WEB: www.pixeintl.com
SIC: 3829 5084 Measuring & controlling devices; industrial machinery & equipment

(G-17310)
PREMIERE SERVICES INC
2305 Garland Ct 1 (32303-8341)
PHONE..................................678 815-6078
Ladonna Jackson, *Principal*
EMP: 12 **EST:** 2015
SALES (est): 868.9K **Privately Held**
SIC: 3714 Motor vehicle engines & parts

(G-17311)
PRINTWORKS
4753 Blountstown Hwy (32304-2773)
PHONE..................................850 681-6909
Michael Bartoszewicz, *Principal*
EMP: 6 **EST:** 2009
SALES (est): 233.3K **Privately Held**
WEB: www.printworks.info
SIC: 2752 Commercial printing, offset

(G-17312)
PROTEK CUSTOM COATINGS LLC
1320 Gateshead Cir (32317-9548)
PHONE..................................850 656-7923
Lynn L Penny, *Principal*
EMP: 6 **EST:** 2007
SALES (est): 347.3K **Privately Held**
WEB: www.protekcoatings.com
SIC: 3479 Metal coating & allied service

(G-17313)
RAGZ
2827 Industrial Plaza Dr (32301-3542)
PHONE..................................850 656-1223
EMP: 6 **EST:** 2019
SALES (est): 142.2K **Privately Held**
WEB: www.ragz.biz
SIC: 2759 Screen printing

(G-17314)
RAPID RATER COMPANY
Also Called: Rapid Press
3626 Cagney Dr (32309-3341)
P.O. Box 13055 (32317-3055)
PHONE..................................850 893-7346
Lourdes Madsen, *President*
Natalie Castillo, *Vice Pres*
Henry Madsen, *Vice Pres*
EMP: 24
SQ FT: 10,000
SALES (est): 2.2MM **Privately Held**
WEB: www.rapidpress.com
SIC: 2741 2752 2759 2789 Technical manuals: publishing & printing; technical papers: publishing & printing; commercial printing, offset; announcements: engraved; envelopes: printing; invitations: printing; stationery: printing; magazines, binding; pamphlets, binding; trade binding services

(G-17315)
REFRESHMENT SERVICES INC
Also Called: Pepsico
3919 W Pensacola St (32304-2837)
PHONE..................................850 574-0281
Jason Murphy, *General Mgr*
Al Hudgins, *Branch Mgr*
EMP: 70
SQ FT: 36,021
SALES (corp-wide): 45.2MM **Privately Held**
WEB: www.refreshmentservicespepsi.com
SIC: 2086 4226 Soft drinks: packaged in cans, bottles, etc.; special warehousing & storage
PA: Refreshment Services, Inc.
1121 Locust St
Quincy IL 62301
217 223-8600

(G-17316)
RIPPEE CONSTRUCTION INC
2107 Delta Way (32303-4224)
PHONE..................................850 668-6805
Carol Rippee, *President*
EMP: 6 **EST:** 1995
SALES (est): 1.7MM **Privately Held**
WEB: www.rippeeconstruction.com
SIC: 1389 Construction, repair & dismantling services; haulage, oil field

(G-17317)
ROSE PRINTING CO INC ✪
2504 Harriman Cir (32308-0920)
PHONE..................................850 339-8093
Charles Rosenberg, *President*
EMP: 8 **EST:** 2020
SALES (est): 101.5K **Privately Held**
SIC: 2752 Commercial printing, offset

(G-17318)
ROUND TABLE TOOLS INC
Also Called: King Arthur's Tools
3645 Hartsfield Rd (32303-1142)
PHONE..................................850 877-7650
Arthur Aveling, *President*
Pamela Aveling, *Exec VP*
Celeste Tucker, *Administration*
▲ **EMP:** 7 **EST:** 1987
SQ FT: 7,500
SALES (est): 1MM **Privately Held**
WEB: www.katools.com
SIC: 3423 3425 5072 2499 Edge tools for woodworking: augers, bits, gimlets, etc.; saw blades for hand or power saws; hardware; decorative wood & woodwork

(G-17319)
ROWLAND PUBLISHING INC
Also Called: Tallahassee Magazine
1932 Miccosukee Rd (32308-5328)
P.O. Box 1837 (32302-1837)
PHONE..................................850 878-0554
Brian Rowland, *President*
Janecia Britt, *Editor*
Jeff Price, *Editor*
McKenzie Burleigh, *Vice Pres*
Daniel Vitter, *Prdtn Mgr*
EMP: 25 **EST:** 1990
SQ FT: 1,500
SALES (est): 3.8MM **Privately Held**
WEB: www.rowlandpublishing.com
SIC: 2721 7313 Magazines: publishing only, not printed on site; trade journals: publishing only, not printed on site; magazine advertising representative

(G-17320)
RUVOS LLC (PA)
2252 Klarn Ctr Blvd (32309-3577)
PHONE..................................850 254-7270
Francis De Wet,
Jeffrey A Couch,
Eduardo Gonzalez Loumiet,
EMP: 11 **EST:** 2004
SQ FT: 6,600
SALES (est): 2.8MM **Privately Held**
WEB: www.ruvos.com
SIC: 7372 Business oriented computer software

(G-17321)
SCREENING LEON & REPAIR INC
1223 Airport Dr (32304-4704)
PHONE..................................850 575-2840
Thomas Herring, *President*
Judy Miester, *Admin Sec*
EMP: 7 **EST:** 1976
SQ FT: 9,000
SALES (est): 850.8K **Privately Held**
WEB: www.leonscreening.com
SIC: 3442 5211 Screens, window, metal; windows, storm: wood or metal

(G-17322)
SEVEN HLLS SLUTION SPECIALISTS
1254 Ocala Rd (32304-1548)
PHONE..................................850 575-0566
EMP: 6
SQ FT: 1,000
SALES (est): 172K **Privately Held**
SIC: 7372 Software Publishing

(G-17323)
SIGNARAMA
897 N Monroe St (32303-6176)
PHONE..................................850 656-3200
EMP: 7 **EST:** 2016
SALES (est): 185.1K **Privately Held**
WEB: www.signarama.com
SIC: 3993 Signs & advertising specialties

(G-17324)
SIGNS NOW (PA)
1551 Capital Cir Se Ste 6 (32301-5141)
PHONE..................................850 383-6500
Wesley Morgan, *President*
EMP: 5 **EST:** 1990
SALES (est): 799.3K **Privately Held**
WEB: www.signsnow.com
SIC: 3993 Signs & advertising specialties

(G-17325)
SKAGFIELD CORPORATION (PA)
Also Called: Skandia Window Fashions
270 Crossway Rd (32305-3460)
P.O. Box 6566 (32314-6566)
PHONE..................................850 878-1144
Hilmar O Skagfield, *President*
Larry Sack, *Vice Pres*
Daniel Sullivan, *Vice Pres*
Sarah Sharp-Gilbert, *Plant Mgr*
William Hughes, *Treasurer*
▲ **EMP:** 87 **EST:** 1966
SQ FT: 85,000
SALES (est): 21MM **Privately Held**
WEB: www.skandiawf.com
SIC: 2591 Window blinds; window shades

(G-17326)
SLOAN CUSTOM WOODWORKING LLC
5559 Hampton Woods Way (32311-8106)
PHONE..................................850 766-5620
Jason Sloan, *Principal*
EMP: 6 **EST:** 2014
SALES (est): 88.6K **Privately Held**
SIC: 2431 Millwork

(G-17327)
SOUTHEAST REVIEW INC
405 Williams Building (32306-1000)
PHONE..................................850 644-4230
Jesse Goolsby, *Manager*
Erin Hoover, *Director*
EMP: 8 **EST:** 1979
SALES (est): 88.8K **Privately Held**
WEB: www.southeastreview.org
SIC: 2721 Periodicals

(G-17328)
SPA CONCEPTS INC
Also Called: Sanitation Products of America
3191 W Tharpe St (32303-1133)
PHONE..................................850 575-0921
Ajay Chadha, *Vice Pres*
Carl Owenby, *Teacher*
EMP: 16 **EST:** 2005
SALES (est): 2.1MM **Privately Held**
WEB:
www.sanitationproductsofamerica.com
SIC: 2842 Specialty cleaning preparations

(G-17329)
SPIRIT SALES CORPORATION
2818 Industrial Plaza Dr D (32301-3557)
PHONE..................................850 878-0366
EMP: 6
SQ FT: 750
SALES (est): 325K **Privately Held**
SIC: 2329 5699 5136 Mfg Men's/Boy's Clothing Ret Misc Apparel/Accessories Whol Men's/Boy's Clothing

(G-17330)
SPRAY BOX LLC
768 Lupine Ln (32308-6256)
PHONE..................................850 567-2724
Justin J Wheeless, *Principal*
EMP: 6 **EST:** 2012
SALES (est): 90.7K **Privately Held**
WEB: www.thespraybox.com
SIC: 3523 Sprayers & spraying machines, agricultural

(G-17331)
STATE OF FLORIDA
250 Marriott Dr (32301-2983)
PHONE..................................850 488-1234
Rick Totka, *Sales Mgr*
Lisa Kumpf, *Sales Staff*
Ken Davis, *Marketing Staff*
Jack May, *Manager*
Justin Rock, *Manager*
EMP: 20 **EST:** 2019
SALES (est): 5MM **Privately Held**
WEB: www.flalottery.com
SIC: 3999 Manufacturing industries

(G-17332)
SYN-TECH SYSTEMS INC (PA)
Also Called: Syntech
100 Four Points Way (32305-7091)
P.O. Box 5258 (32314-5258)
PHONE..................................850 878-2558
Douglas R Dunlap, *President*
Gene Meadows, *Business Mgr*
Frank McGoogan, *COO*
Dave Oglesby, *Vice Pres*
David B Oglesby, *Vice Pres*
EMP: 180 **EST:** 1987
SQ FT: 52,000
SALES: 31.8MM **Privately Held**
WEB: www.myfuelmaster.com
SIC: 3571 3569 Electronic computers; liquid automation machinery & equipment

(G-17333)
SYNDICATED PROGRAMMING INC
Also Called: Capital Outlook Newspaper
1363 Mahan Dr (32308-5107)
PHONE..................................850 877-0105
Roosevelt Wilson, *President*
EMP: 7 **EST:** 1987
SALES (est): 587.5K **Privately Held**
WEB: www.capitaloutlook.com
SIC: 2711 Newspapers, publishing & printing

(G-17334)
SYNERGY BIOLOGICS LLC
2849 Pablo Ave (32308-4288)
PHONE..................................850 656-4277
David Hill, *Principal*
EMP: 6 **EST:** 2015
SALES (est): 450.3K **Privately Held**
WEB: www.synergybiologics.net
SIC: 2836 Biological products, except diagnostic

(G-17335)
TALLAHASSEE DEMOCRAT
277 N Magnolia Dr (32301-2664)
P.O. Box 990 (32302-0990)
PHONE..................................850 599-2100
John Miller, *Founder*
EMP: 21 **EST:** 2018
SALES (est): 3.1MM **Privately Held**
WEB: www.tallahassee.com
SIC: 2711 Newspapers, publishing & printing

(G-17336)
TALLAHASSEE ENGRAVING & AWARD
1387 E Lafayette St (32301-4724)
PHONE..................................850 878-7187
Sam Varn, *Owner*
Jeff Wilson, *Purch Mgr*
Amy Starkey, *Controller*
Cassidy Parsons, *Sales Staff*
Justin Varn, *Sales Associate*
EMP: 7 **EST:** 2011
SALES (est): 154.9K **Privately Held**
SIC: 3231 Products of purchased glass

(G-17337)
TALLAHASSEE WELDING & MCH SP
Also Called: Tallahassee Powder Coating
1220 Lake Bradford Rd (32304-4733)
P.O. Box 2472 (32316-2472)
PHONE..................................850 576-9596
George A Small, *President*
Allison Small, *Principal*
Kenneth G Small, *Vice Pres*
EMP: 23 **EST:** 1942
SQ FT: 10,000
SALES (est): 3.5MM **Privately Held**
WEB: www.tallahasseewelding.com
SIC: 3599 7692 Machine shop, jobbing & repair; welding repair

(G-17338)
TARGET PRINT & MAIL
2843 Industrial Plaza Dr A1 (32301-3537)
PHONE..................................850 671-6600
Courtney Carter, *Graphic Designe*
EMP: 9 **EST:** 2019
SALES (est): 746.1K **Privately Held**
WEB: www.targetprintmail.com
SIC: 2752 Commercial printing, offset

(G-17339)
TERMINAL SERVICE COMPANY
2778 W Tharpe St (32303-8614)
P.O. Box 1200 (32302-1200)
PHONE..................................850 739-5702
Thomas Panebianco, *President*
Bob Landrum, *Corp Secy*
Donnie Alford, *Vice Pres*
Joe Audie, *Vice Pres*
Donald Gainey, *Purch Agent*
EMP: 178 **EST:** 1953
SQ FT: 30,000
SALES (est): 2.6MM
SALES (corp-wide): 263.4MM **Privately Held**
WEB: www.mckenzietanklines.com
SIC: 3713 7539 3715 Tank truck bodies; trailer repair; truck trailers
HQ: Mckenzie Property Management, Inc.
1966 Commonwealth Ln
Tallahassee FL 32303
850 576-1221

(G-17340)
TIMES PUBLISHING COMPANY
Also Called: St Petersburg Times
336 E College Ave Ste 303 (32301-1560)
PHONE..................................850 224-7263
Steve Busquet, *Principal*
EMP: 6
SALES (corp-wide): 14.9MM **Privately Held**
WEB: www.tampabay.com
SIC: 2711 Newspapers, publishing & printing
HQ: Times Publishing Company
490 1st Ave S
Saint Petersburg FL 33701
727 893-8111

(G-17341)
TRAK ENGINEERING INCORPORATED
2901 Crescent Dr (32301-3535)
PHONE..................................850 878-4585
John R Blyth, *President*
Rob Weaver, *Business Mgr*
Katherine M Blyth, *Vice Pres*
James Marlow, *Vice Pres*
Bolong Lui, *Engineer*
EMP: 36
SQ FT: 9,000
SALES (est): 2.7MM **Privately Held**
WEB: www.trakeng.com
SIC: 3824 Fluid meters & counting devices

(G-17342)
TRI-STATE DEMOLITION LLC
5272 Crawfordville Rd (32305-8914)
P.O. Box 5581 (32314-5581)
PHONE..................................850 597-8722
Ryan M Carroll,
Roy L Avery III,
EMP: 8 **EST:** 2019
SALES (est): 595.3K **Privately Held**
WEB: www.tristatedemo.com
SIC: 1081 Metal mining exploration & development services

(G-17343)
VELOCITY MACHINE WORKS LLC
364 Marpan Ln (32305-0904)
PHONE..................................850 727-5066
Hillar Kalda, *Partner*
Jacob Money, *Info Tech Mgr*
EMP: 10 **EST:** 2013
SALES (est): 834.8K **Privately Held**
WEB: www.velocitymachineworks.com
SIC: 3599 Machine shop, jobbing & repair

(G-17344)
VY SPINE LLC ✪
2236 Capital Cir Ne # 103 (32308-8305)
PHONE..................................866 489-7746
Jordan Hendrickson,
EMP: 9 **EST:** 2021
SALES (est): 353.6K **Privately Held**
SIC: 3842 Surgical appliances & supplies

(G-17345)
WILLIAMS ORTHTC-PROSTHETIC INC
2360 Centerville Rd (32308-4318)
P.O. Box 15035 (32317-5035)
PHONE..................................850 385-6655
Richard C Williams Jr, *President*
Cathy Williams, *Vice Pres*
Chris Wells,
EMP: 9 **EST:** 1952
SQ FT: 3,200
SALES (est): 1.4MM **Privately Held**
WEB: www.williamsoandp.com
SIC: 3842 Orthopedic appliances; limbs, artificial

(G-17346)
WILLIES WILD
4556 Capital Cir Nw (32303-7215)
PHONE..................................850 597-8116
EMP: 6 **EST:** 2011
SALES (est): 130.6K **Privately Held**
SIC: 3421 Table & food cutlery, including butchers'

(G-17347)
WOODWORKS BY MIKE INC
1527 Coombs Dr (32308-4710)
P.O. Box 634, Saint Marks (32355-0634)
PHONE..................................850 567-2086
Michael J Butler, *President*
EMP: 6 **EST:** 2004
SALES (est): 60.1K **Privately Held**
SIC: 2431 Millwork

(G-17348)
WWWSURESHOTSIDSCOM LLC
3516 Clifden Dr (32309-2424)
PHONE..................................850 906-0745
Richard Horne, *Principal*
EMP: 7 **EST:** 2012
SALES (est): 236.3K **Privately Held**
WEB: www.sureshotsids.com
SIC: 2099 Food preparations

Tamarac
Broward County

(G-17349)
ALEGRO INDUSTRIES INC
7880 N University Dr # 200 (33321-2124)
PHONE..................................702 943-0978
Mario Gaete, *President*
EMP: 57 **EST:** 2010
SQ FT: 5,000
SALES (est): 12MM **Privately Held**
SIC: 3672 Printed circuit boards

(G-17350)
AMERICAN METAL FABRICATION LLC
5476 Nw 59th Pl (33319-2432)
PHONE..................................954 736-9819
Cassandra J Lyle, *Manager*
EMP: 11 **EST:** 2016
SALES (est): 65.7K **Privately Held**
WEB: www.americanmetalfab.com
SIC: 3499 Fabricated metal products

(G-17351)
AUTHORITY SOFTWARE LLC
7154 N University Dr # 211 (33321-2916)
PHONE..................................877 603-9653
Louis A Mandic, *Mng Member*
Natalie Perez-Mandic, *Mng Member*
Michael Yuen, *Director*
EMP: 6 **EST:** 2006
SALES (est): 579.2K **Privately Held**
WEB: www.authoritysoftware.com
SIC: 7372 Prepackaged software

(G-17352)
AZCUE PUMPS USA INC
10308 W Mcnab Rd (33321-1813)
PHONE..................................954 597-7602
Themis Giachos Sr, *President*
Ana Maria Giachos, *Vice Pres*
Lynn Teti, *Sales Staff*
◆ **EMP:** 5 **EST:** 1997
SALES (est): 424.7K **Privately Held**
WEB: www.azcuepumps.com
SIC: 3561 Industrial pumps & parts

(G-17353)
D & G CUSTOM CABINETRY INC
5712 Coco Palm Dr (33319-6115)
PHONE..................................954 561-8822
▲ **EMP:** 15
SALES (est): 2.1MM **Privately Held**
SIC: 2434 Mfg Wood Kitchen Cabinets

(G-17354)
DESH-VIDESH MEDIA GROUP INC
10088 W Mcnab Rd (33321-1895)
PHONE..................................954 784-8100
Aruna R Shah, *President*
Sheetal Shah, *Vice Pres*
Raj Shah, *Manager*
Rajni Shah, *Admin Sec*
EMP: 12 **EST:** 1993
SALES (est): 541.6K **Privately Held**
WEB: www.deshvidesh.com
SIC: 2721 Magazines: publishing only, not printed on site

(G-17355)
ELECTRICAL CONTROLS INC
Also Called: E C I
9510 Bradshaw Ln (33321-6357)
PHONE..................................954 801-6846
Gregory Anderson, *President*
Elaine Anderson, *Corp Secy*
EMP: 15 **EST:** 1973
SQ FT: 15,000
SALES (est): 504.4K **Privately Held**
SIC: 3613 3625 1731 Panelboards & distribution boards, electric; relays & industrial controls; electronic controls installation

(G-17356)
FLORIDA A&G CO INC
Also Called: Arch Mirror North
10200 Nw 67th St (33321-6404)
P.O. Box 25127, Fort Lauderdale (33320-5127)
PHONE..................................800 432-8132
Leon Silverstein, *President*
Robert Silverstein, *Director*
▲ **EMP:** 1570 **EST:** 1989
SQ FT: 135,000
SALES (est): 45.9MM **Privately Held**
SIC: 3442 5039 Metal doors; glass construction materials

(G-17357)
GRAPHIC AND PRINTING SVCS CORP
Also Called: Image Impressions
5035 Nw 37th Ave (33309-3301)
PHONE..................................954 486-8868
Ray Cheng, *President*
Julianne Cheng, *Manager*
▲ **EMP:** 7 **EST:** 1995
SALES (est): 826.9K **Privately Held**
SIC: 2752 2759 Commercial printing, offset; commercial printing

(G-17358)
INTERPLEX LABS LTD
6690 N Hiatus Rd (33321-6403)
PHONE..................................954 718-9953
Jack Siedler, *CEO*
Bernie Koppel, *President*
Solange Eckert, *Engineer*
Irvin Klein, *Treasurer*
Carlos Leite, *Manager*
EMP: 65 **EST:** 1992
SALES (est): 6.2MM **Privately Held**
SIC: 3559 Electroplating machinery & equipment
HQ: Nas Cp Corp.
1434 110th St Apt 4a
College Point NY 11356
718 961-6757

(G-17359)
IQ FORMULATIONS LLC
Also Called: Metabolic Nutrition
10151 Nw 67th St (33321-6400)
PHONE..................................954 533-9256
Jay Cohen, *Mng Member*
Ron Kainec, *Officer*
▲ **EMP:** 51 **EST:** 2010
SALES (est): 16MM **Privately Held**
WEB: www.iqformulations.com
SIC: 2023 7372 Dietary supplements, dairy & non-dairy based; application computer software

(G-17360)
JCS LIMITED CORPORATION
7611 Nw 70th Ave (33321-5224)
PHONE..................................954 822-2887
Jose E Morales, *President*
EMP: 7 **EST:** 2015
SALES (est): 300K **Privately Held**
SIC: 2434 1799 Wood kitchen cabinets; kitchen & bathroom remodeling

(G-17361)
KSM ELECTRONICS INC (PA)
5607 N Hiatus Rd Ste 600 (33321-6409)
PHONE..................................954 642-7050
Stephen Benjamin, *President*
Josh Salcedo, *COO*
Ana Oliveira, *Production*
Nicky Billington, *Purchasing*
Oscar Lopez, *CFO*
◆ **EMP:** 80 **EST:** 1975
SQ FT: 30,000
SALES (est): 57.7MM **Privately Held**
WEB: www.ksmelectronics.com
SIC: 3679 3629 Harness assemblies for electronic use: wire or cable; static elimination equipment, industrial

(G-17362)
MAGRUDERS WOODWORKING INC
5861 Woodland Point Dr (33319-6266)
P.O. Box 260223, Pembroke Pines (33026-7223)
PHONE..................................954 649-0861
Don Magruder, *Principal*
EMP: 6 **EST:** 2017
SALES (est): 91.4K **Privately Held**
SIC: 2431 Millwork

(G-17363)
METAL BUILDING KINGS
8050 N University Dr (33321-2115)
PHONE..................................412 522-4797
Aaron Troy, *President*
EMP: 9 **EST:** 2016
SQ FT: 1,500
SALES (est): 575.1K **Privately Held**
WEB: www.metalgaragekits.com
SIC: 3448 Prefabricated metal buildings

(G-17364)
PARASOL FILMS INC
9503 Nw 73rd St (33321-3024)
PHONE..................................954 478-8661
Erik Baquero, *Director*
EMP: 6 **EST:** 2001
SALES (est): 237.5K **Privately Held**
SIC: 2851 Paints & allied products

(G-17365)
PRISM MUSIC INC
9905 Nw 71st St (33321-1802)
PHONE..................................954 718-6850
EMP: 6 **EST:** 2001
SALES (est): 67.6K **Privately Held**
WEB: www.prismmusic.com
SIC: 2741 Miscellaneous publishing

(G-17366)
RICHLINE GROUP INC
Also Called: Aurafin-Oroamerica
6701 Nob Hill Rd (33321-6402)
PHONE..................................954 718-3200
Michael Milgrom, *President*
Dave Meleski, *Branch Mgr*
EMP: 300
SALES (corp-wide): 245.5B **Publicly Held**
WEB: www.richlinegroup.com
SIC: 3911 Necklaces, precious metal
HQ: Richline Group, Inc.
1385 Broadway Fl 14
New York NY 10018

(G-17367)
RONAELE MUSTANG INC
5965 Manchester Way (33321-4192)
PHONE..................................954 319-7433
Edward R Monfort, *President*
Suzane Monfort, *Principal*
EMP: 7 **EST:** 2005
SALES (est): 112.9K **Privately Held**
SIC: 3824 Gas meters, domestic & large capacity: industrial

(G-17368)
SHILOH IMPORT/EXPORT LLC
7049 Woodmont Way (33321-2655)
PHONE..................................404 514-4109
Conrad Rowe, *CEO*
EMP: 6 **EST:** 2014
SALES (est): 337.6K **Privately Held**
SIC: 2099 Chili pepper or powder

(G-17369)
SOUTH FLORIDA PARENTING
6501 Nob Hill Rd (33321-6422)
PHONE..................................954 747-3050
Justo Rey, *President*
EMP: 83 **EST:** 1990
SALES (est): 1.1MM
SALES (corp-wide): 746.2MM **Privately Held**
WEB: www.sun-sentinel.com
SIC: 2721 Magazines: publishing only, not printed on site
HQ: Sun-Sentinel Company, Llc
500 E Broward Blvd # 800
Fort Lauderdale FL 33394
954 356-4000

(G-17370)
WINSTON & SONS INC
9735 Nw 76th St (33321-1954)
PHONE..................................954 562-1984
Frank Winston Jr, *President*
Donna Johnson, *Vice Pres*
Richard Winston, *Treasurer*
Anna Winston, *Admin Sec*
EMP: 9 **EST:** 1974
SQ FT: 15,000
SALES (est): 379.4K **Privately Held**
SIC: 2511 2522 Wood household furniture; office furniture, except wood

Tampa
Hillsborough County

(G-17371)
10 ROOF COTTAGE LLC
Also Called: Odhams Press
5809 St 1st St (33611)
PHONE..................................888 667-6961
Nancy Lackman, *Manager*
EMP: 5 **EST:** 2010
SALES (est): 437.9K **Privately Held**
WEB: www.stickpretty.com
SIC: 2891 Adhesives

(G-17372)
1506 N FLORIDA LLC
1505 N Florida Ave (33602-2613)
P.O. Box 800 (33601-0800)
PHONE..................................813 229-0900
Michael Kass, *Manager*
EMP: 6 **EST:** 2010
SALES (est): 363.6K **Privately Held**
WEB: www.garagistemeadery.com
SIC: 2084 Wines

(G-17373)
3B GLOBAL LLC (PA)
Also Called: Oral Stericlean
1202 Race Track Rd (33626)
PHONE..................................813 350-7872
Teresa Birney,
▲ **EMP:** 8 **EST:** 2011
SALES (est): 2.8MM **Privately Held**
WEB: www.go3bglobal.com
SIC: 3843 Sterilizers, dental

(G-17374)
4714 FOODS INC
4714 Causeway Blvd (33619-5240)
PHONE..................................813 787-8911
Naser Khawaja, *Principal*
EMP: 6 **EST:** 2010
SALES (est): 287.8K **Privately Held**
SIC: 2099 Food preparations

(G-17375)
A JS PRO PERCUSSION CENTER
4340 W Hillsborough Ave # 208 (33614-5560)
PHONE..................................813 361-4939
Aj Altieri, *President*
Grace Altieri, *Treasurer*
EMP: 8 **EST:** 1999
SQ FT: 8,000
SALES (est): 463.9K **Privately Held**
WEB: www.propercussion.com
SIC: 3931 Drums, parts & accessories (musical instruments)

(G-17376)
A RE DOOR CABINETS INC
2502 W Carmen St Apt 1 (33609-1748)
PHONE..................................813 419-0007
David G Toneff, *President*
EMP: 7 **EST:** 2012
SALES (est): 172.3K **Privately Held**
WEB: www.re-a-door-cabinets.com
SIC: 2434 Wood kitchen cabinets

(G-17377)
A&J MANUFACTURING INC
Also Called: Chargriller
5001 W Cypress St (33607-3803)
PHONE..................................912 638-4724
John Simms II, *President*
▲ **EMP:** 45 **EST:** 2007
SALES (est): 4MM **Privately Held**
WEB: www.chargriller.com
SIC: 3631 Barbecues, grills & braziers (outdoor cooking)

(G-17378)
AA CASEY COMPANY
5124 N Nebraska Ave (33603-2364)
PHONE..................................813 234-8831
John A Casey, *President*
Deeann Curci, *Corp Secy*
Richard Casey, *Vice Pres*
Rick Salm, *Buyer*
Manuel Whitworth, *Sales Staff*
EMP: 15 **EST:** 2008
SALES (est): 3.5MM **Privately Held**
WEB: www.aacasey.com
SIC: 3531 Construction machinery

(G-17379)
AAA-AFFORDABLE PALLETS & REELS
2811 N 76th St (33619-2523)
PHONE..................................813 740-8009
EMP: 8
SALES (est): 490K **Privately Held**
SIC: 2448 Mfg Wood Pallets/Skids

(G-17380)
AARONS PALLETS
5006 S 50th St (33619-9515)
PHONE..................................813 627-3225
Aaron Gavrian, *Principal*
EMP: 6 **EST:** 2012
SALES (est): 205.5K **Privately Held**
WEB: www.aaronspallets.com
SIC: 2448 Pallets, wood

(G-17381)
ABAWI FIT LLC
1327 E 7th Ave Ste 204 (33605-3607)
PHONE..................................813 215-1833
Wade Abawi, *CEO*

Jonathan Nimphie, *COO*
EMP: 8 **EST:** 2018
SALES (est): 100K **Privately Held**
SIC: 7372 Application computer software

(G-17382)
ABBEY ROGERS
10150 Highland Manor Dr (33610-9713)
PHONE.................................813 645-1400
William B Simons IV, *President*
John Felter, *Engineer*
Will Thurman, *Teacher*
EMP: 5 **EST:** 2009
SALES (est): 377.5K **Privately Held**
WEB: www.abbeyrogers.com
SIC: 3491 Process control regulator valves

(G-17383)
ABCO INDUSTRIES LLC
5604 W Linebaugh Ave (33624-5071)
PHONE.................................813 605-5900
Adilen Lio,
EMP: 6 **EST:** 2015
SALES (est): 458K **Privately Held**
WEB: www.abcogear.com
SIC: 2393 3172 Duffle bags, canvas: made from purchased materials; personal leather goods

(G-17384)
ACACIA INC
904 N Rome Ave (33606-1040)
P.O. Box 4527 (33677-4527)
PHONE.................................813 253-2789
Mike Griggs, *President*
◆ **EMP:** 10 **EST:** 1997
SALES (est): 736.2K **Privately Held**
WEB: www.acacia-inc.com
SIC: 3089 Plastics products

(G-17385)
ACCENTIA BIOPHARMACEUTICALS (PA)
324 S Hyde Park Ave # 350 (33606-4127)
PHONE.................................813 864-2554
Francis E O Donnell Jr, *Ch of Bd*
Samuel S Duffey, *President*
Douglas W Calder, *Vice Pres*
Garrison J Hasara, *CFO*
Carlos F Santos PHD, *Officer*
EMP: 15 **EST:** 2002
SQ FT: 7,400
SALES (est): 8.5MM **Privately Held**
WEB: www.accentia.net
SIC: 2834 Pharmaceutical preparations

(G-17386)
ACCURATE WLDG FABRICATION LLC
11029 Clay Pit Rd (33610-9741)
PHONE.................................727 483-3125
Gordon Smith,
EMP: 5 **EST:** 2017
SALES (est): 357.5K **Privately Held**
SIC: 7692 Welding repair

(G-17387)
ADM II EXHIBITS & DISPLAYS INC
5690 W Crenshaw St (33634-3013)
PHONE.................................813 887-1960
Susan Tanonico, *President*
Shannon Bennett, *VP Sls/Mktg*
Mike Handley, *Manager*
EMP: 15 **EST:** 1987
SQ FT: 3,000
SALES (est): 2.5MM **Privately Held**
WEB: www.admtwo.com
SIC: 3993 Signs & advertising specialties

(G-17388)
ADVANCED TECH & TSTG LABS
3802 Spectrum Blvd # 143 (33612-9212)
PHONE.................................352 871-3802
Lovely Goswami, *President*
Dilip Goswami, *Director*
EMP: 6 **EST:** 1994
SQ FT: 2,000
SALES (est): 801.5K **Privately Held**
WEB: www.molekule.com
SIC: 3564 Air purification equipment; filters, air: furnaces, air conditioning equipment, etc.

(G-17389)
AERO SIMULATION INC
8720 E Sligh Ave (33610-9206)
PHONE.................................813 628-4447
Michael Conti, *CEO*
Daniel Deschnow, *Vice Pres*
Kevin Cahill, *Opers Staff*
Luke Archer, *Engineer*
Jeffrey Lawson, *Engineer*
EMP: 125 **EST:** 1983
SALES (est): 50.7MM **Privately Held**
WEB: www.aerosimulation.com
SIC: 3699 Flight simulators (training aids), electronic

(G-17390)
AFLG INVSTMNTS-INDUSTRIALS LLC (PA)
701 Suth Hward Ave 106 (33606)
PHONE.................................813 443-8203
Freddy Russian, *Principal*
Anthony Russian, *Assistant VP*
Doug Joseph,
◆ **EMP:** 9 **EST:** 2016
SALES (est): 6MM **Privately Held**
SIC: 3542 3569 Mechanical (pneumatic or hydraulic) metal forming machines; liquid automation machinery & equipment

(G-17391)
AGGRESSIVE BOX INC
5444 Pioneer Park Blvd A (33634-4309)
PHONE.................................813 901-9600
Keith Oller, *President*
Aleshia Oller, *Vice Pres*
Derek Alfonso, *Accounts Mgr*
Lisa Oller, *Manager*
EMP: 12 **EST:** 1995
SQ FT: 4,000
SALES (est): 3.4MM **Privately Held**
WEB: www.aggressivebox.com
SIC: 2653 Boxes, corrugated: made from purchased materials

(G-17392)
AGILE RISK MANAGEMENT LLC
Also Called: F-Response
3333 W Kennedy Blvd # 201 (33609-2959)
PHONE.................................800 317-5497
Matthew M Shannon, *Principal*
Matthew J Decker,
Sean Lynch, *Analyst*
EMP: 5 **EST:** 2003
SQ FT: 1,300
SALES: 3.1MM **Privately Held**
WEB: www.f-switch.com
SIC: 7372 Business oriented computer software

(G-17393)
AGUA CONTROL LLC
5609 E Adamo Dr Ste D (33619-3253)
PHONE.................................813 663-0701
Alejandro Bolivar, *Sales Staff*
Luis Salcedo, *Mng Member*
EMP: 6 **EST:** 2009
SALES (est): 63K **Privately Held**
WEB: www.aguacontrolusa.com
SIC: 3589 Water treatment equipment, industrial

(G-17394)
AIMS PRINTING LLC
1302 Cherrywood Ave (33613-1547)
PHONE.................................813 313-9574
Ibrahim Jivanjee, *Principal*
EMP: 7 **EST:** 2009
SALES (est): 28.3K **Privately Held**
WEB: www.aimsprinting.com
SIC: 2752 Commercial printing, offset

(G-17395)
AIRITE AIR CONDITIONING INC
Also Called: Honeywell Authorized Dealer
5321 W Crenshaw St (33634-2406)
PHONE.................................813 886-0235
Bruce M Silverman, *President*
Victoria Silverman, *President*
Michael Venoy, *Exec VP*
Jeff Steiner, *Vice Pres*
Dee Venoy, *Vice Pres*
EMP: 45 **EST:** 1970
SQ FT: 24,000
SALES (est): 6.9MM **Privately Held**
WEB: www.airiteair.com
SIC: 3444 1711 Sheet metalwork; warm air heating & air conditioning contractor

(G-17396)
AL-FA CABINETS INC
4803 N Grady Ave (33614-6301)
PHONE.................................813 876-4205
Hector Gonzalez Jr, *President*
Caridad Gonzalez, *Corp Secy*
Hector Gonzales Sr, *Sales Staff*
EMP: 11 **EST:** 1973
SQ FT: 20,000
SALES (est): 309.3K **Privately Held**
WEB: www.alfacabinets.com
SIC: 2434 2431 Wood kitchen cabinets; millwork

(G-17397)
ALDALI INC
4821 N Hale Ave (33614-6517)
PHONE.................................877 384-9494
Melissa Morgado, *President*
Melissa Astorquiza, *Exec Dir*
◆ **EMP:** 10 **EST:** 2009
SQ FT: 2,500
SALES (est): 925.6K **Privately Held**
WEB: www.asteeza.com
SIC: 2833 Drugs & herbs: grading, grinding & milling

(G-17398)
ALL COAST MANUFACTURING INC
2433 S 86th St Ste F (33619-4909)
PHONE.................................813 626-2264
Jeff George, *President*
Roy George, *Vice Pres*
EMP: 6 **EST:** 1993
SALES (est): 821.3K **Privately Held**
SIC: 3334 Primary aluminum

(G-17399)
ALL NATURALS DIRECT
12191 W Linebaugh Ave (33626-1732)
PHONE.................................813 792-3777
Melony D Rivera, *Owner*
EMP: 9 **EST:** 2013
SALES (est): 339.3K **Privately Held**
SIC: 2032 5963 5149 Ethnic foods: canned, jarred, etc.; Mexican foods: packaged in cans, jars, etc.; food services, direct sales; specialty food items

(G-17400)
ALLEGRA MARKETING
2705 N Falkenburg Rd (33619-0920)
PHONE.................................813 664-1129
Sam Mancie, *Owner*
Matt Shelley, *Accounts Mgr*
EMP: 9 **EST:** 2017
SALES (est): 590.3K **Privately Held**
WEB: www.allegramarketingprint.com
SIC: 2752 Commercial printing, offset

(G-17401)
ALLIED FOAM FABRICATORS LLC (PA) ✪
216 Kelsey Ln (33619-4300)
PHONE.................................813 626-0090
Alan Rash, *Mng Member*
EMP: 72 **EST:** 2020
SALES (est): 5MM **Privately Held**
WEB: www.alliedfoamfab.com
SIC: 3086 Packaging & shipping materials, foamed plastic

(G-17402)
ALLIED MANUFACTURING INC (PA)
Also Called: Dalpro Commercial Rfrgn
203 Kelsey Ln Ste G (33619-4334)
PHONE.................................813 502-0300
Jeffrey Montelione, *President*
Lili Montelione, *COO*
EMP: 8 **EST:** 2016
SALES (est): 1.3MM **Privately Held**
WEB: www.valprorefrigeration.com
SIC: 3585 Refrigeration & heating equipment

(G-17403)
ALLOY FABRICATORS INC
13925 Monroes Business Pa (33635-6309)
PHONE.................................813 925-0222
Thomas J Szikszay, *President*
David Sharon, *Mfg Staff*
EMP: 8 **EST:** 2013
SALES (est): 169.7K **Privately Held**
WEB: www.alloyfabinc.com
SIC: 2834 Tranquilizers or mental drug preparations

(G-17404)
ALLSTATE LGHTNING PRTCTION LLC
7201 Sheldon Rd (33615-2328)
PHONE.................................813 240-2736
Jill Epperson, *Managing Prtnr*
EMP: 6 **EST:** 2014
SALES (est): 828.3K **Privately Held**
WEB: www.allstatelp.com
SIC: 3643 Lightning protection equipment

(G-17405)
ALPHAGRAPHICS US658
105 N Falkenburg Rd Ste D (33619-0902)
PHONE.................................813 689-7788
Art Coley, *President*
EMP: 12 **EST:** 2012
SALES (est): 269.7K **Privately Held**
WEB: www.alphagraphics.com
SIC: 2752 Commercial printing, lithographic

(G-17406)
ALTA EQUIPMENT HOLDINGS INC
8418 Palm River Rd (33619-4314)
PHONE.................................813 519-4097
EMP: 8
SALES (corp-wide): 873.6MM **Publicly Held**
WEB: www.materialhandling.altaequipment.com
SIC: 3537 Industrial trucks & tractors
HQ: Alta Equipment Holdings, Inc.
13211 Merriman Rd
Livonia MI 48150

(G-17407)
ALTEC INC
Also Called: Altec Service Center
1041 S 86th St (33619-4916)
PHONE.................................813 372-0058
EMP: 8
SALES (corp-wide): 1.2B **Privately Held**
WEB: www.altec.com
SIC: 3531 Derricks, except oil & gas field
PA: Altec, Inc.
210 Inverness Center Dr
Birmingham AL 35242
205 991-7733

(G-17408)
ALTERED MEDIA INC
100 S Ashley Dr Ste 600 (33602-5300)
PHONE.................................813 397-3892
Rashad Freeman, *CEO*
EMP: 10 **EST:** 2019
SALES (est): 592.7K **Privately Held**
SIC: 2741

(G-17409)
ALTIUM PACKAGING LLC
4961 Distribution Dr (33605-5925)
PHONE.................................813 248-4300
Paul Reed, *Plant Mgr*
Tony Kalodimos, *Manager*
Jose Hernandez, *Maintence Staff*
EMP: 19
SQ FT: 22,500
SALES (corp-wide): 12.5B **Publicly Held**
WEB: www.altiumpkg.com
SIC: 3089 3085 Plastic containers, except foam; plastics bottles
HQ: Altium Packaging Llc
2500 Windy Ridge Pkwy Se # 1400
Atlanta GA 30339
678 742-4600

(G-17410)
ALTO RECYCLING LLC
5701 W Linebaugh Ave (33624-5074)
PHONE.................................813 962-0140
Stewart Smith, *President*

EMP: 9
SALES (est): 2MM Privately Held
WEB: www.altorecycling.net
SIC: 3559 Recycling machinery

(G-17411)
ALZAMEND NEURO INC
3802 Spectrum Blvd # 112 (33612-9212)
PHONE....................................844 722-6333
Stephan Jackman, *CEO*
Milton C Ault III, *Ch of Bd*
David Katzoff, *COO*
Henry C W Nisser, *Exec VP*
Kenneth S Cragun, *CFO*
EMP: 5 EST: 2016
SALES (est): 582.7K Privately Held
WEB: www.thealzamendstory.com
SIC: 2834 Pharmaceutical preparations

(G-17412)
AMALIE OIL COMPANY (PA)
1601 Mcclosky Blvd (33605-6710)
PHONE....................................813 248-1988
Harry J Barket, *Ch of Bd*
Richard Barkett, *COO*
Manny Bonet, *Exec VP*
Anthony Barkett, *Vice Pres*
Lori Auen, *Human Res Mgr*
◆ EMP: 167 EST: 1957
SQ FT: 135,000
SALES (est): 110.4MM Privately Held
WEB: www.amalie.com
SIC: 2992 3085 Lubricating oils; plastics bottles

(G-17413)
AMERI PRODU PRODU COMPA OF PIN
12157 W Linebaugh Ave # 335 (33626-1732)
PHONE....................................813 925-0144
Joseph Muraco, *President*
Kevin Mullen, *Vice Pres*
EMP: 5 EST: 1995
SALES (est): 1.1MM Privately Held
WEB: www.americanproducts.com
SIC: 3443 Metal parts

(G-17414)
AMERICAN ARCHTCTRAL FOAM WRKS
Also Called: Aafw-Kimco
7810 Professional Pl (33637-6744)
PHONE....................................813 443-0791
John P Mistal, *President*
Kenneth Drummond, *Vice Pres*
Bobby White, *CFO*
EMP: 10 EST: 2008
SQ FT: 12,000
SALES (est): 1.5MM Privately Held
WEB: www.americanarchitecturalfoam.com
SIC: 3086 Plastics foam products

(G-17415)
AMERICAN BOTTLING COMPANY
Also Called: Seven-Up Snapple Southeast
5266 Eagle Trail Dr (33634-1295)
PHONE....................................813 806-2931
John Perry, *Manager*
EMP: 17
SQ FT: 53,997 Publicly Held
WEB: www.keurigdrpepper.com
SIC: 2086 Soft drinks: packaged in cans, bottles, etc.
HQ: The American Bottling Company
6425 Hall Of Fame Ln
Frisco TX 75034

(G-17416)
AMERICAN CITY BUS JOURNALS INC
Also Called: Tampa Bay Business Journal
4890 W Kennedy Blvd # 85 (33609-1851)
P.O. Box 24185 (33623-4185)
PHONE....................................813 873-8225
EMP: 9
SALES (corp-wide): 5B Privately Held
SIC: 2711 Newspapers-Publishing/Printing
HQ: American City Business Journals, Inc.
120 W Morehead St Ste 400
Charlotte NC 28202
704 973-1000

(G-17417)
AMERICAN LOUVERED PRODUCTS CO
4910 W Knollwood St (33634-8073)
PHONE....................................813 884-1441
John Saunders, *President*
▲ EMP: 24 EST: 1959
SALES (est): 1.2MM Privately Held
SIC: 2431 Door shutters, wood; doors, wood

(G-17418)
AMERICAN PRODUCTS INC
Also Called: API
13909 Lynmar Blvd (33626-3124)
PHONE....................................813 925-0144
Joseph Muraco, *President*
Kerri Beals, *General Mgr*
Kerri Muraco, *General Mgr*
Kevin Mullan, *Vice Pres*
Christopher Revoldt, *Prdtn Dir*
EMP: 5 EST: 2010
SALES (est): 4.7MM Privately Held
WEB: www.americanproducts.com
SIC: 3443 3354 3089 Metal parts; aluminum extruded products; extruded finished plastic products

(G-17419)
AMERICAN REPROGRAPHICS CO LLC
Also Called: ARC
5005 W Laurel St Ste 102 (33607-3896)
PHONE....................................813 286-8300
Greg York, *Principal*
Michael Sardina, *Production*
EMP: 6
SQ FT: 5,000
SALES (corp-wide): 289.4MM Publicly Held
WEB: www.ryansallans.com
SIC: 2759 Business forms: printing
HQ: American Reprographics Company, L.L.C.
1981 N Broadway Ste 385
Walnut Creek CA 94596
925 949-5100

(G-17420)
AMERICAN SURGICAL MASK LLC ✪
Also Called: American Surgical Mask Co
5508 N 50th St Ste 1000 (33610-4804)
PHONE....................................813 606-4510
Matthew Brandman, *CEO*
Eileen Legler, *Marketing Staff*
Kahora Watanabe,
Charles Young Jr,
EMP: 20 EST: 2020
SALES (est): 1.1MM Privately Held
WEB: www.americansurgicalmask.com
SIC: 3841 Surgical instruments & apparatus

(G-17421)
AMERICAN VINYL COMPANY
6715 N 53rd St (33610-1905)
PHONE....................................813 663-0157
Eric J Wiborg II, *President*
EMP: 18
SALES (corp-wide): 7.9MM Privately Held
WEB: www.avcplastics.com
SIC: 3312 Pipes & tubes
PA: American Vinyl Company
600 W 83rd St
Hialeah FL 33014
305 687-1863

(G-17422)
AMGEN USA INC
2202 N West Shore Blvd # 2 (33607-5747)
P.O. Box 23926 (33623-3926)
PHONE....................................805 447-1000
Angel Perez Nunez, *Director*
Kyle Vallar, *Admin Sec*
EMP: 13
SALES (corp-wide): 25.4B Publicly Held
WEB: www.amgen.com
SIC: 2836 Biological products, except diagnostic
HQ: Amgen Usa Inc.
1 Amgen Center Dr
Thousand Oaks CA 91320

(G-17423)
AMPHENOL CUSTOM CABLE INC (HQ)
Also Called: Custom Cable Industries
3221 Cherry Palm Dr (33619-8334)
PHONE....................................813 623-2232
Stewart Saad, *President*
Joe Macon, *General Mgr*
Jaile Lima, *Vice Pres*
Steve Vickers, *Vice Pres*
Luis Parrado, *Project Mgr*
EMP: 140 EST: 1999
SQ FT: 10,000
SALES (est): 71.9MM
SALES (corp-wide): 8.6B Publicly Held
WEB: www.customcable.com
SIC: 3827 3357 Optical instruments & lenses; fiber optic cable (insulated)
PA: Amphenol Corporation
358 Hall Ave
Wallingford CT 06492
203 265-8900

(G-17424)
AMROB INC
Also Called: Atlantic Printing Ink Company
4719 N Thatcher Ave (33614-6935)
PHONE....................................813 238-6041
Robert C Pettit, *President*
Patrick Laden, *Vice Pres*
Patty Bortstrom, *Manager*
EMP: 6 EST: 1985
SQ FT: 10,000
SALES (est): 532.8K Privately Held
WEB: www.atlanticprintingink.com
SIC: 2893 Printing ink

(G-17425)
ANCHOR GLASS CONTAINER CORP (PA)
3001 N Rocky Point Dr E # 300 (33607-5875)
PHONE....................................813 884-0000
Nipesh Shah, *President*
Jason Achterberg, *General Mgr*
John Sode, *General Mgr*
Jonathan McCarthy, *Business Mgr*
Ken Sigman, *Exec VP*
◆ EMP: 110 EST: 1997
SALES (est): 581.3MM Privately Held
WEB: www.anchorglass.com
SIC: 3221 Glass containers

(G-17426)
ANCHOR MACHINE & FABRICATING
3905 E 7th Ave (33605-4555)
PHONE....................................813 247-3099
Jerome Majetich, *President*
Cheryl Majetich, *Vice Pres*
EMP: 12 EST: 1979
SQ FT: 10,000
SALES (est): 1MM Privately Held
WEB: www.anchormachineshop.com
SIC: 3599 3535 Machine shop, jobbing & repair; conveyors & conveying equipment

(G-17427)
AOCLSC INC (PA)
Also Called: Aocusa
1601 Mcclosky Blvd (33605-6731)
PHONE....................................813 248-1988
Harry Barkett, *President*
Ken Barkett, *CFO*
EMP: 75 EST: 2019
SALES (est): 51MM Privately Held
SIC: 2911 Greases, lubricating

(G-17428)
APOLLO RETAIL SPECIALISTS LLC (DH)
4450 E Adamo Dr Ste 501 (33605-5941)
PHONE....................................813 712-2525
Mike Sunderland, *CEO*
Mark Glenn, *Division Mgr*
Mike Torres, *General Mgr*
Bill Blakley, *District Mgr*
Dustin Hall, *District Mgr*
EMP: 260 EST: 2005
SALES (est): 55.4MM
SALES (corp-wide): 255.7MM Privately Held
WEB: www.apolloretail.com
SIC: 3432 7389 2531 7349 Plumbing fixture fittings & trim; bicycle assembly service; assembly hall furniture; building maintenance services

(G-17429)
APPLIED TECHNOLOGIES GROUP INC
Also Called: Automated Integration
333 N Falkenburg Rd B227 (33619-7893)
P.O. Box 777, Brandon (33509-0777)
PHONE....................................813 413-7025
Steve Van Kley, *President*
Steve Kley, *Principal*
EMP: 7 EST: 2013
SQ FT: 5,000
SALES (est): 1.5MM Privately Held
WEB: www.ai-fl.com
SIC: 3823 7373 8742 Industrial instrmnts msrmnt display/control process variable; computer integrated systems design; management consulting services

(G-17430)
AQUATECH MANUFACTURING LLC
7455 E Adamo Dr (33619-3433)
PHONE....................................813 664-0300
Reg Macquarrie, *Mng Member*
Joe Finella,
▲ EMP: 10 EST: 2011
SALES (est): 1.8MM Privately Held
SIC: 3589 Water treatment equipment, industrial

(G-17431)
ARGOS CEMENT LLC
2001 Maritime Blvd (33605-6760)
PHONE....................................813 247-4831
◆ EMP: 20 EST: 2014
SALES (est): 2.7MM Privately Held
SIC: 3241 Cement, hydraulic

(G-17432)
ARGOS USA LLC
5609 N 50th St (33610-4805)
PHONE....................................813 962-3213
EMP: 28 Privately Held
WEB: www.argos-us.com
SIC: 3273 Ready-mixed concrete
HQ: Argos Usa Llc
3015 Windward Plz Ste 300
Alpharetta GA 30005
678 368-4300

(G-17433)
ARM ALMNUM RLING MNFCTURES LLC
2433 S 86th St Ste F (33619-4909)
PHONE....................................813 626-2264
Jeff George, *Principal*
EMP: 9 EST: 2016
SALES (est): 250.4K Privately Held
SIC: 3999 Manufacturing industries

(G-17434)
ARMA HOLDINGS INC
3030 N Rocky Point Dr W # 800 (33607-5859)
PHONE....................................813 402-0667
Todd Schweitzer, *CEO*
Brian Overstreet, *COO*
Charles Broms, *Vice Pres*
Rick Gillies, *CTO*
James Fugit, *Director*
EMP: 45 EST: 2013
SALES (est): 291.9K Privately Held
SIC: 3728 7376 3484 3483 Aircraft parts & equipment; computer facilities management; small arms; ammunition, except for small arms; computer integrated systems design

(G-17435)
ARMOR OIL PRODUCTS LLC
Also Called: Engine Armour Products
1601 Mcclosky Blvd (33605-6731)
PHONE....................................813 248-1988
David A Barkett,
▲ EMP: 6 EST: 2001

SALES (est): 165K **Privately Held**
WEB: www.enginearmour.com
SIC: 2992 5172 Lubricating oils & greases; petroleum products

(G-17436)
ARROW SHEET METAL WORKS INC
2710 N 36th St (33605-3194)
PHONE..................................813 247-2179
Kathy Philippus, *President*
Robert L Philippus, *Vice Pres*
EMP: 27 **EST**: 1950
SQ FT: 15,000
SALES (est): 4.9MM **Privately Held**
SIC: 3444 Sheet metal specialties, not stamped

(G-17437)
ASAP MAGAZINE & NEWSPAPER
106 W Haya St (33603-2033)
P.O. Box 7635 (33673-7635)
PHONE..................................813 238-0184
Leo Hooper, *Owner*
EMP: 8 **EST**: 1996
SALES (est): 392.3K **Privately Held**
SIC: 2711 Newspapers

(G-17438)
ASHBERRY ACQUISITION COMPANY (PA)
Also Called: Ashberry Water Conditioning
2405 E 4th Ave (33605-5431)
PHONE..................................813 248-0055
James T McMurray, *President*
William Welch, *Vice Pres*
EMP: 10 **EST**: 1947
SQ FT: 3,600
SALES (est): 4.1MM **Privately Held**
WEB: www.ashberrywater.com
SIC: 3589 7359 5999 Water filters & softeners, household type; equipment rental & leasing; water purification equipment

(G-17439)
ASSOCIATED MATERIALS LLC
933 Chad Ln (33619-4331)
PHONE..................................813 621-7058
EMP: 7
SALES (corp-wide): 1.1B **Privately Held**
WEB: www.associatedmaterials.com
SIC: 3089 Plastic containers, except foam
PA: Associated Materials, Llc
3773 State Rd
Cuyahoga Falls OH 44223
330 929-1811

(G-17440)
ASURE SOFTWARE INC
Also Called: Mangrove Navada
5100 W Kennedy Blvd # 300 (33609-5511)
PHONE..................................702 733-9007
Tim Nissen, *Marketing Mgr*
Jennifer Anderson, *Relations*
EMP: 6
SALES (corp-wide): 65.5MM **Publicly Held**
WEB: www.asuresoftware.com
SIC: 7372 Prepackaged software
PA: Asure Software, Inc.
3700 N Capital Of Texas H
Austin TX 78746
512 437-2700

(G-17441)
ATALY INC
Also Called: Ataly Graphics
5828 Johns Rd (33634-4420)
PHONE..................................813 880-9142
Alan Jones, *President*
Wade Carlson, *QC Mgr*
Nick Jones, *Sales Staff*
Christine H Jones, *Director*
Larrie McCleary, *Business Dir*
EMP: 40 **EST**: 1979
SQ FT: 12,000
SALES (est): 5MM **Privately Held**
WEB: www.ataly.com
SIC: 2396 3993 Screen printing on fabric articles; advertising novelties

(G-17442)
ATITLAN ENTERPRISES LLC
Also Called: Hathaspace
16116 Lake Magdalene Blvd (33613-1249)
PHONE..................................813 362-1909
Marcus Lara, *Mng Member*
Dean Chandra, *Mng Member*
EMP: 14 **EST**: 2017
SALES (est): 5.1MM **Privately Held**
SIC: 3564 Air purification equipment

(G-17443)
ATKORE PLASTIC PIPE CORP
Also Called: Heritage Plastics
5128 W Hanna Ave (33634-8020)
PHONE..................................813 884-2525
Jordan Hamilton, *QC Mgr*
Tyler Morrison, *Plant Engr*
Charlie Thebeau, *Sales Staff*
Steve Ferreri, *Supervisor*
Shannon Johnson, *Maintence Staff*
EMP: 32 **Publicly Held**
WEB: www.heritageplastics.com
SIC: 3084 Plastics pipe
HQ: Atkore Plastic Pipe Corporation
1202 N Bowie Dr
Weatherford TX 76086
817 594-8791

(G-17444)
AVATAR PACKAGING INC
5110 W Idlewild Ave (33634-8024)
PHONE..................................813 888-9141
Vance D Fairbanks Jr, *CEO*
Denise M Fairbanks, *President*
Robert J Upcavage, *Vice Pres*
Cody Fairbanks, *Sales Associate*
Cynthia Fairbanks, *Admin Sec*
EMP: 30 **EST**: 1991
SQ FT: 24,700
SALES (est): 5.6MM **Privately Held**
WEB: www.avatarpackaging.com
SIC: 2653 5113 Boxes, corrugated: made from purchased materials; corrugated & solid fiber boxes

(G-17445)
AVI-SPL EMPLYEE EMRGNCY RLIEF (HQ)
Also Called: AVI-Spl Tampa Service
6301 Benjamin Rd Ste 101 (33634-5115)
PHONE..................................813 884-7168
John Zettel, *CEO*
Jeff Davis, *COO*
Steve Benjamin, *Exec VP*
Tim Riek, *Exec VP*
Daniel Smith, *Project Mgr*
▼ **EMP**: 512 **EST**: 2008
SALES (est): 370.1MM **Privately Held**
WEB: www.avispl.com
SIC: 3669 3861 3663 5999 Intercommunication systems, electric; photographic equipment & supplies; radio & TV communications equipment; audio-visual equipment & supplies; video & audio equipment

(G-17446)
AVI-SPL HOLDINGS INC (PA)
6301 Benjamin Rd Ste 101 (33634-5115)
PHONE..................................866 708-5034
John Zettel, *CEO*
Phil Marlowe, *Managing Dir*
Mike Peterson, *Regional Mgr*
John Murphy, *COO*
Tim Riek, *Exec VP*
▼ **EMP**: 2000 **EST**: 2008
SALES (est): 1B **Privately Held**
WEB: www.avispl.com
SIC: 3669 3861 3663 3651 Intercommunication systems, electric; photographic equipment & supplies; radio & TV communications equipment; household audio & video equipment; voice, data & video wiring contractor; electrical appliances, television & radio

(G-17447)
AVI-SPL LLC (HQ)
6301 Benjamin Rd Ste 101 (33634-5115)
PHONE..................................813 884-7168
John Zettel, *CEO*
Tim Riek, *President*
Steve Benjamin, *Exec VP*
Don Mastro, *Exec VP*
Jennifer Haskins, *Vice Pres*
▼ **EMP**: 1958 **EST**: 1980
SQ FT: 38,000
SALES (est): 642.5MM
SALES (corp-wide): 1.1B **Privately Held**
WEB: www.avispl.com
SIC: 3669 5064 3861 3663 Intercommunication systems, electric; electrical appliances, television & radio; photographic equipment & supplies; radio & TV communications equipment; household audio & video equipment; projection apparatus, motion picture & slide
PA: Avi-Spl Global Llc
6301 Benjamin Rd Ste 101
Tampa FL 33634
813 884-7168

(G-17448)
AWNINGS BY COVERSOL
5211 W Hillsborough Ave (33634-5308)
PHONE..................................813 251-4774
EMP: 21
SQ FT: 30,000
SALES: 2MM
SALES (corp-wide): 2.3MM **Privately Held**
SIC: 2394 Mfg Canvas/Related Products
PA: Lad Diversified Holdings Llc
15619 Premiere Dr Ste 201
Tampa FL

(G-17449)
AXIOM DIAGNOSTICS INC
4309 W Tyson Ave (33611-3435)
P.O. Box 13275 (33681-3275)
PHONE..................................813 902-9888
Jesse M Carter, *President*
EMP: 6 **EST**: 1999
SALES (est): 1MM **Privately Held**
WEB: www.axiomdiagnostics.com
SIC: 3821 Clinical laboratory instruments, except medical & dental

(G-17450)
AXON CIRCUIT INC (PA)
424 S Ware Blvd Ste A (33619-4402)
PHONE..................................407 265-7980
Chandra Patel, *President*
Amrish G Patel, *Vice Pres*
Jayan Sanghani, *Vice Pres*
Lee Camacho, *CFO*
Suresh Patel, *Treasurer*
▲ **EMP**: 45 **EST**: 1990
SQ FT: 25,000
SALES (est): 6.2MM **Privately Held**
WEB: www.axoncircuit.com
SIC: 3672 Printed circuit boards

(G-17451)
AZZ POWDER COATING - TAMPA LLC (HQ)
4901 Distribution Dr (33605-5925)
PHONE..................................813 390-2802
David L Bridgforth, *CEO*
EMP: 5 **EST**: 2011
SALES (est): 14.4MM
SALES (corp-wide): 838.9MM **Publicly Held**
WEB: www.azz.com
SIC: 3479 3399 Coating of metals & formed products; powder, metal
PA: Azz Inc.
3100 W 7th St Ste 500
Fort Worth TX 76107
817 810-0095

(G-17452)
B2B SIGN RESOURCE
13359 W Hillsborough Ave (33635-9676)
PHONE..................................813 855-7446
Dori Hazama, *COO*
EMP: 10 **EST**: 2018
SALES (est): 549.9K **Privately Held**
WEB: www.b2bsr.com
SIC: 3993 Signs & advertising specialties

(G-17453)
BADER PROSTHETICS & ORTHOTICS
Also Called: Kinetic Research
5513 W Sligh Ave (33634-4431)
PHONE..................................813 962-6100
Wade Bader, *President*
Reid Bader, *Vice Pres*
Valarie Brien,
EMP: 22 **EST**: 1992
SQ FT: 3,000
SALES (est): 1.2MM **Privately Held**
WEB: www.kineticresearch.com
SIC: 3842 Prosthetic appliances

(G-17454)
BAILEY INDUSTRIES
2414 S Gelman Pl (33619-5332)
PHONE..................................352 326-2898
EMP: 7 **EST**: 2019
SALES (est): 196.3K **Privately Held**
WEB: www.baileyind.com
SIC: 2434 Wood kitchen cabinets

(G-17455)
BARE ARII LLC ✪
10610 N 30th St Apt 13g (33612-6341)
PHONE..................................352 701-6625
Arianna Wade, *Mng Member*
EMP: 7 **EST**: 2021
SALES (est): 274K **Privately Held**
SIC: 3999 Eyelashes, artificial

(G-17456)
BAY AREA GRAPHICS
4040 E Adamo Dr (33605-5904)
PHONE..................................813 247-2400
Wayne Ricketts, *Partner*
Nanci Ricketts, *Partner*
Jeff Soto, *VP Opers*
EMP: 6 **EST**: 1985
SQ FT: 5,000
SALES (est): 440.1K **Privately Held**
WEB: www.bayareagraphics.com
SIC: 2752 Commercial printing, offset

(G-17457)
BAY HARBOR SHEET METAL INC
7909 Professional Pl (33637-6747)
P.O. Box 216, Mango (33550-0216)
PHONE..................................813 740-8662
Darrel Peterson, *President*
EMP: 10 **EST**: 2002
SALES (est): 1.6MM **Privately Held**
WEB: www.bayharborservices.com
SIC: 3444 Sheet metalwork

(G-17458)
BAY NETWORKS INC
6601 Memorial Hwy 200 (33615-4501)
PHONE..................................813 249-8103
EMP: 12 **EST**: 2008
SQ FT: 5,000
SALES (est): 1.3MM **Privately Held**
SIC: 2211 Cotton Broadwoven Fabric Mill

(G-17459)
BAYSHORE BRAND GROUP INC
Also Called: Bayshore Brands
10315 Newport Cir (33612-6527)
PHONE..................................813 384-8275
Jonathan M Holland, *President*
Karen Holland, *Sales Staff*
Mark Holland, *Manager*
EMP: 6 **EST**: 2012
SALES (est): 166.2K **Privately Held**
WEB: www.bayshorebrands.com
SIC: 2759 Screen printing

(G-17460)
BAYTRONICS MANUFACTURING INC
620 E Twiggs St Ste 110 (33602-3938)
PHONE..................................813 434-0401
Timothy Johnson, *President*
EMP: 9 **EST**: 2011
SALES (est): 128.4K **Privately Held**
SIC: 3559 3825 3674 Semiconductor manufacturing machinery; internal combustion engine analyzers, to test electronics; semiconductors & related devices

(G-17461)
BBJ ENVIRONMENTAL LLC
Also Called: B B J Environmental Solutions
9416 E Broadway Ave (33619-7723)
P.O. Box 110301, Stamford CT (06911-0301)
PHONE..................................813 622-8550
Robert Baker, *CEO*
EMP: 7 **EST**: 2009
SALES (est): 560.1K **Privately Held**
WEB: www.bbjenviro.com
SIC: 2899 Chemical preparations

(G-17462)
BEACH PRODUCTS INC
Also Called: Beach Pharmaceuticals
3010 W De Leon St Ste 100 (33609-4008)
P.O. Box 13447 (33681-3447)
PHONE..................................813 839-6565
Richard S Jenkins, *President*
Carole C Jenkins, *Treasurer*
Kelly Harrison, *Senior Mgr*
EMP: 7 **EST:** 1958
SQ FT: 10,000
SALES (est): 1.9MM **Privately Held**
WEB: www.beachlabs.com
SIC: 2834 Pharmaceutical preparations

(G-17463)
BEAUTIFUL CABINETS CORP
1903 W Skagway Ave (33604-1035)
PHONE..................................813 486-9034
Claudia Ardon, *President*
EMP: 7 **EST:** 2008
SALES (est): 87.6K **Privately Held**
SIC: 2434 Wood kitchen cabinets

(G-17464)
BELLINI SYSTEMS INC
4925 Indpdnc Pkwy Ste 400 (33634-7551)
PHONE..................................813 264-9252
Lauren Bellini, *Admin Sec*
EMP: 9 **EST:** 2001
SALES (est): 280.6K **Privately Held**
SIC: 7372 Prepackaged software

(G-17465)
BERTRAM YACHTS LLC (DH)
5250 W Tyson Ave (33611-3224)
PHONE..................................813 527-9899
Peter C Truslow,
EMP: 112 **EST:** 2015
SALES (est): 15.2MM
SALES (corp-wide): 628.2K **Privately Held**
WEB: www.bertram.com
SIC: 3732 Boat building & repairing
HQ: Baglietto Spa
Viale San Bartolomeo 414
La Spezia SP 19126
018 759-831

(G-17466)
BEVEL EXPRESS & TOPS LAC
6026 Benjamin Rd (33634-5104)
PHONE..................................813 887-3174
Yamileth Sanchez, *Principal*
EMP: 9 **EST:** 2006
SALES (est): 480.2K **Privately Held**
WEB: www.bevelexpress.com
SIC: 2741 Miscellaneous publishing

(G-17467)
BEVERAGE BLOCKS INC
218 E Bearss Ave Ste 332 (33613-1625)
PHONE..................................813 309-8711
Michael Patierno, *Chairman*
EMP: 12 **EST:** 2017
SALES (est): 612.4K **Privately Held**
SIC: 2086 2657 Water, pasteurized: packaged in cans, bottles, etc.; food containers, folding: made from purchased material

(G-17468)
BF HURLEY MAT CO INC
6824 S Manhattan Ave # 105 (33616-2549)
P.O. Box 13217 (33681-3217)
PHONE..................................813 837-0616
Richard B Hurley, *President*
Valerie M Eckerson, *Corp Secy*
John Hurley, *Vice Pres*
Michael E Hurley, *Vice Pres*
EMP: 31 **EST:** 1946
SQ FT: 10,355
SALES (est): 9.7MM
SALES (corp-wide): 47.6MM **Privately Held**
WEB: www.hurleymat.com
SIC: 3089 3069 2273 Floor coverings, plastic; mats or matting, rubber; carpets & rugs
PA: Kleen-Tex Industries, Inc.
2312 Peachford Rd Ste C
Atlanta GA 30338
404 991-5500

(G-17469)
BIG BIZ DIRECT
13922 Monroes Business Pa (33635-6370)
PHONE..................................813 978-0584
EMP: 8 **EST:** 2010
SALES (est): 286.1K **Privately Held**
WEB: www.rnrrc.com
SIC: 2752 Commercial printing, lithographic

(G-17470)
BIOMEDTECH LABORATORIES INC (PA)
3802 Spectrum Blvd # 154 (33612-9212)
PHONE..................................813 558-2000
Joachim Sasse, *President*
Jutta Sasse, *Vice Pres*
▲ **EMP:** 11 **EST:** 1998
SQ FT: 3,500
SALES (est): 1.4MM **Privately Held**
WEB: www.biomedtech.com
SIC: 3471 Electroplating & plating

(G-17471)
BISK EDUCATION INC (PA)
Also Called: Bisk Publishing Company
9417 Princess Palm Ave # 400
(33619-8348)
P.O. Box 31028 (33631-3028)
PHONE..................................813 621-6200
Michael Bisk, *CEO*
Clynton Hunt, *Managing Dir*
Nathan M Bisk, *Chairman*
Matt Sargent, *Business Mgr*
Alison Bisk, *Vice Pres*
EMP: 429 **EST:** 1971
SQ FT: 70,000
SALES (est): 100K **Privately Held**
WEB: www.bisk.com
SIC: 2731 Book publishing

(G-17472)
BKR PRINTING INC
3837 Northdale Blvd 179 (33624-1841)
PHONE..................................813 951-8609
Brian L Goodrich, *Principal*
EMP: 7 **EST:** 2008
SALES (est): 231K **Privately Held**
SIC: 2752 Commercial printing, lithographic

(G-17473)
BLACKLIDGE EMULSIONS INC
2701 E 2nd Ave (33605-5502)
PHONE..................................813 247-5699
Ronald Blacklidge, *Owner*
EMP: 18
SQ FT: 1,712 **Privately Held**
WEB: www.blacklidge.com
SIC: 2951 Road materials, bituminous (not from refineries)
PA: Blacklidge Emulsions, Inc.
12251 Bernard Pkwy # 200
Gulfport MS 39503

(G-17474)
BLASTERS READY JET INC
7815 Professional Pl (33637-6745)
PHONE..................................813 985-4500
Scott F Boos, *President*
Natalie B Elliott, *Vice Pres*
Kris Boos, *Controller*
Frederick Boos, *Admin Sec*
▲ **EMP:** 20 **EST:** 2006
SALES (est): 2.8MM **Privately Held**
WEB: www.blasters.net
SIC: 3531 Construction machinery

(G-17475)
BLINGKA INC
3911 Americana Dr (33634-7405)
PHONE..................................800 485-6793
Chandler Rapson, *Chairman*
EMP: 8
SALES (est): 2.3MM **Privately Held**
SIC: 3944 Video game machines, except coin-operated

(G-17476)
BMP USA INC
8105 Anderson Rd (33634-2319)
P.O. Box 15762 (33684-5762)
PHONE..................................813 443-0757
Xianbin Meng, *President*
Linna Shi, *Vice Pres*
Angela Zhang, *IT/INT Sup*
EMP: 59 **EST:** 2013
SALES (est): 6.9MM **Privately Held**
WEB: www.bmp-usa.com
SIC: 3585 Refrigeration & heating equipment

(G-17477)
BMS INTERNATIONAL INC
Also Called: Bob's Machine Shop
8802 E Broadway Ave (33619-7702)
PHONE..................................813 247-7040
Greg Pelini, *President*
▲ **EMP:** 37 **EST:** 1981
SALES (est): 5.3MM **Privately Held**
WEB: www.bobsmachine.com
SIC: 3429 3732 3537 Manufactured hardware (general); boat building & repairing; industrial trucks & tractors

(G-17478)
BOBS BARRICADES INC
5018 24th Ave S (33619-5340)
PHONE..................................813 886-0518
Terry Chapman, *Manager*
EMP: 20
SALES (corp-wide): 34.7MM **Privately Held**
WEB: www.bobsbarricades.com
SIC: 3499 7353 3291 Barricades, metal; heavy construction equipment rental; abrasive products
PA: Bob's Barricades, Inc.
921 Shotgun Rd
Sunrise FL 33326
954 423-2627

(G-17479)
BOND MEDICAL GROUP INC
3837 Northdale Blvd # 36 (33624-1841)
PHONE..................................813 264-5951
Travis Bond, *President*
Lisa Bond, *Exec VP*
EMP: 27 **EST:** 2001
SQ FT: 3,000
SALES (est): 3MM **Privately Held**
WEB: www.bondmedical.com
SIC: 7372 Prepackaged software

(G-17480)
BOND-PRO INC
1501 E 2nd Ave (33605-5005)
PHONE..................................888 789-4985
Joesph Williams, *Principal*
Frederick Duguay, *Principal*
Roger Hurwitz, *Principal*
Jacques Levy, *Chief*
Jeffrey York, *Exec VP*
EMP: 114 **EST:** 2011
SALES (est): 20MM **Privately Held**
WEB: www.bond-pro.com
SIC: 7372 Application computer software

(G-17481)
BOND-PRO LLC
302 Knights Run Ave # 11 (33602-5962)
PHONE..................................813 413-7576
Jeffrey York, *Vice Pres*
Brandon Halprin, *CFO*
EMP: 14 **EST:** 2019
SALES (est): 552.6K **Privately Held**
WEB: www.bond-pro.com
SIC: 7372 Application computer software

(G-17482)
BONSAL AMERICAN INC
Also Called: W R Bonsal Plant 44
5455 N 59th St (33610-2011)
PHONE..................................813 621-2427
William A Ashton, *Branch Mgr*
EMP: 6
SQ FT: 20,000
SALES (corp-wide): 27.5B **Privately Held**
WEB: www.sakrete.com
SIC: 3272 3241 2899 Dry mixture concrete; cement, hydraulic; chemical preparations
HQ: Bonsal American, Inc.
625 Griffith Rd Ste 100
Charlotte NC 28217
704 525-1621

(G-17483)
BORNT ENTERPRISES INC
Also Called: Superior Design Products
9824 Currie Davis Dr (33619-2651)
PHONE..................................813 623-1492
David Bornt, *President*
Bonnie Bornt, *Vice Pres*
Steve Sdp, *Supervisor*
EMP: 35 **EST:** 1980
SQ FT: 15,600
SALES (est): 3.5MM **Privately Held**
WEB: www.superiordesignproducts.com
SIC: 2591 1799 5023 Blinds vertical; window shades; window treatment installation; vertical blinds; window shades

(G-17484)
BRACE INTEGRATED SERVICES INC
8205 E Adamo Dr (33619-3537)
PHONE..................................813 248-6248
Hans Peter Hansen, *Branch Mgr*
EMP: 35
SALES (corp-wide): 2.1B **Privately Held**
SIC: 1389 Construction, repair & dismantling services
HQ: Brace Integrated Services, Inc.
2112 S Custer Ave
Wichita KS 67213
316 832-0292

(G-17485)
BRANDON LOCK & SAFE INC
4630 Eagle Falls Pl (33619-9613)
PHONE..................................813 655-4200
Vickie Musall, *President*
Kyle Keffer, *General Mgr*
Garrett Norris, *Project Mgr*
Larry Musall, *Treasurer*
EMP: 6 **EST:** 1997
SALES (est): 742.8K **Privately Held**
WEB: www.brandonlock.com
SIC: 3429 3499 Locks or lock sets; safes & vaults, metal

(G-17486)
BREEZEMAKER FAN COMPANY INC
1608 N 24th St (33605-5452)
PHONE..................................813 248-5552
Ron Myers, *President*
EMP: 24 **EST:** 1938
SQ FT: 20,000
SALES (est): 868.4K **Privately Held**
WEB: www.breezemaker-fan.com
SIC: 3564 5084 Blowers & fans; industrial machinery & equipment

(G-17487)
BRU FL LLC
8709 Imperial Ct (33635-1513)
PHONE..................................813 431-6815
Christian M Brugal, *Manager*
EMP: 6 **EST:** 2016
SALES (est): 245K **Privately Held**
WEB: www.brufl.com
SIC: 2082 Malt beverages

(G-17488)
BUCKEYE INTERNATIONAL INC
Also Called: Buckeye Cleaning Center
4644 Eagle Falls Pl (33619-9613)
PHONE..................................813 621-6260
Travis McLeod, *Sales Mgr*
Travis McLoud, *Manager*
EMP: 6
SALES (corp-wide): 158.4MM **Privately Held**
WEB: www.buckeyeinternational.com
SIC: 2842 2841 2899 2812 Specialty cleaning preparations; detergents, synthetic organic or inorganic alkaline; chemical preparations; alkalies & chlorine
PA: Buckeye International, Inc.
2700 Wagner Pl
Maryland Heights MO 63043
314 291-1900

(G-17489)
BUILT LLC
602 N Newport Ave (33606-1328)
PHONE..................................813 512-6250
Matthew Cacioppo, *COO*
Andrew Watson, *Mng Member*
EMP: 7 **EST:** 2013

SALES (est): 1.2MM **Privately Held**
WEB: www.builtthings.com
SIC: 2514 Household furniture: upholstered on metal frames

(G-17490)
BURKE PRINTING
10203 Thicket Point Way (33647-3124)
PHONE..................................813 549-9886
Frank Burke, *Principal*
EMP: 6 **EST:** 2010
SALES (est): 136.5K **Privately Held**
SIC: 2752 Commercial printing, lithographic

(G-17491)
BUSCAR INC
3403 W Morrison Ave (33629-5233)
PHONE..................................813 877-7272
Michael Bustillo, *President*
EMP: 6 **EST:** 2015
SALES (est): 329.8K **Privately Held**
SIC: 3571 7378 Electronic computers; computer maintenance & repair

(G-17492)
BUSINESS JRNL PUBLICATIONS INC (DH)
4350 W Cypress St Ste 800 (33607-4180)
PHONE..................................813 342-2472
Arthur Porter, *Principal*
Alexis Muellner, *Editor*
EMP: 38 **EST:** 1984
SQ FT: 70,000
SALES (est): 127.8MM
SALES (corp-wide): 2.8B **Privately Held**
SIC: 2711 Newspapers: publishing only, not printed on site
HQ: American City Business Journals, Inc.
120 W Morehead St Ste 400
Charlotte NC 28202
704 973-1000

(G-17493)
C & S GRAPHICS INC
Also Called: C & S GRAPHICS, INC. DBA ELECTRIC SIGN COMPANY
1335 W North B St (33606-1615)
PHONE..................................813 251-4411
Edward Croney III, *President*
Betsy Croney, *Office Mgr*
EMP: 5 **EST:** 1987
SQ FT: 10,000
SALES (est): 500K **Privately Held**
WEB: www.candsgraphics.com
SIC: 3993 Signs, not made in custom sign painting shops

(G-17494)
C K C INDUSTRIES INC (PA)
4908 Savarese Cir (33634-2403)
P.O. Box 151012 (33684-1012)
PHONE..................................813 888-9468
Charles K Cheng, *President*
Anna Cheng, *Admin Sec*
▲ **EMP:** 9 **EST:** 1983
SQ FT: 15,000
SALES (est): 733K **Privately Held**
WEB: www.ckcindustries.com
SIC: 3829 3672 Temperature sensors, except industrial process & aircraft; printed circuit boards

(G-17495)
C S FASTENERS
4739 Transport Dr (33605-5940)
PHONE..................................813 242-8000
EMP: 7 **EST:** 2019
SALES (est): 184K **Privately Held**
WEB: www.candsfasteners.com
SIC: 3965 Fasteners

(G-17496)
C&C BRICK PAVERS INC
8513 N Otis Ave (33604-1249)
PHONE..................................813 716-8291
Natali Cruz, *Principal*
EMP: 7 **EST:** 2010
SALES (est): 583.8K **Privately Held**
WEB: www.ccbrickpavers.com
SIC: 3531 Pavers

(G-17497)
CABINETS MOREUNLIMITED INC
11802 Spanish Lake Dr (33635-6311)
PHONE..................................813 789-4203
Thomas V Magers, *Principal*
EMP: 6 **EST:** 2011
SALES (est): 180.1K **Privately Held**
WEB: www.cabinetsandmoreunlimited.com
SIC: 2434 Wood kitchen cabinets

(G-17498)
CABINETS PLUS OF AMERICA INC
3853 S Lake Dr Unit 164 (33614-2080)
PHONE..................................813 408-0433
John Crescente P, *Principal*
EMP: 6 **EST:** 2018
SALES (est): 169.1K **Privately Held**
WEB: www.cabinetsplusofamerica.com
SIC: 2434 Wood kitchen cabinets

(G-17499)
CADDIE COMPANY INC
Also Called: First Look Display Group
4104 Causeway Vista Dr (33615-5416)
PHONE..................................267 332-0976
John Disantis, *President*
▲ **EMP:** 18 **EST:** 1998
SALES (est): 3MM **Privately Held**
SIC: 2542 Office & store showcases & display fixtures

(G-17500)
CAE USA INC (DH)
Also Called: Cae USA Products
4908 Tampa West Blvd (33634-2411)
P.O. Box 15000 (33684-5000)
PHONE..................................813 885-7481
Raymond Duquette, *President*
Stawski Carrie, *Business Mgr*
Pascal Grenier, *Vice Pres*
Dan Sharkey, *Vice Pres*
Davin Brannon, *Project Mgr*
◆ **EMP:** 600 **EST:** 1939
SQ FT: 210,000
SALES (est): 427.7MM
SALES (corp-wide): 2.3B **Privately Held**
WEB: www.cae.com
SIC: 3699 7373 8299 8249 Electronic training devices; flight simulators (training aids), electronic; computer integrated systems design; flying instruction; aviation school; engineering services
HQ: Cae(Us) Inc.
1011 Ct Rd Ste 322
Wilmington DE 19805
813 885-7481

(G-17501)
CALMAC CORPORATION
Also Called: Fastsigns
1801 E Fowler Ave (33612-5556)
PHONE..................................813 493-8700
EMP: 14
SALES (corp-wide): 1.4MM **Privately Held**
SIC: 3993 Signsadv Specs
PA: Calmac Corporation
1506 W Kennedy Blvd Ste A
Tampa FL 33606
813 654-7476

(G-17502)
CAMELOT CABINETS INC
6903 Conaty Dr (33634-4417)
PHONE..................................813 876-9150
John Williams, *President*
EMP: 15 **EST:** 1972
SQ FT: 4,000
SALES (est): 997.8K **Privately Held**
WEB: www.camelotcabinetsinc.com
SIC: 2434 Wood kitchen cabinets

(G-17503)
CANARCHY CRAFT
Also Called: Cigar City Brewing
3924 W Spruce St (33607-2441)
PHONE..................................813 348-6363
Neil Callaghan, *General Mgr*
Nick Farhood, *Sales Staff*
Eric Loy, *Manager*
Jeromy Dana, *Supervisor*
Geoff Larose, *Supervisor*
EMP: 41
SALES (corp-wide): 129.1MM **Privately Held**
WEB: www.oskarblues.com
SIC: 2082 5084 Beer (alcoholic beverage); brewery products manufacturing machinery, commercial
PA: Canarchy Craft Brewery Collective Llc
1800 Pike Rd Unit B
Longmont CO 80501
303 776-1914

(G-17504)
CAPRI KITCHENS INC
9507 E Us Highway 92 (33610-5990)
PHONE..................................813 623-1424
Billy Isom, *President*
Wanda Switzer, *Vice Pres*
EMP: 10 **EST:** 1970
SQ FT: 1,000
SALES (est): 721.9K **Privately Held**
SIC: 2434 Wood kitchen cabinets

(G-17505)
CAPTIVE-AIRE SYSTEMS INC
4519 George Rd Ste 150 (33634-7354)
PHONE..................................813 448-7884
Alex Gicale, *Branch Mgr*
Woody Brink, *Technical Staff*
EMP: 22
SALES (corp-wide): 401.1MM **Privately Held**
WEB: www.captiveaire.com
SIC: 3444 Sheet metalwork
PA: Captive-Aire Systems, Inc.
4641 Paragon Park Rd # 104
Raleigh NC 27616
919 882-2410

(G-17506)
CARD QUEST INC
7902 W Waters Ave Ste C (33615-1816)
P.O. Box 1915, Elfers (34680-1915)
PHONE..................................813 288-0004
Shannon L Schofield, *President*
Jeffery L Capshaw, *Vice Pres*
▼ **EMP:** 5 **EST:** 2003
SQ FT: 2,000
SALES (est): 736.9K **Privately Held**
WEB: www.cardquest.com
SIC: 3089 Identification cards, plastic

(G-17507)
CARDINAL HEALTH 414 LLC
3016 Usf Hawthorn Dr (33612)
PHONE..................................813 972-1351
Adam Folesner, *Branch Mgr*
EMP: 7
SALES (corp-wide): 152.9B **Publicly Held**
SIC: 2835 2834 Radioactive diagnostic substances; pharmaceutical preparations
HQ: Cardinal Health 414, Llc
7000 Cardinal Pl
Dublin OH 43017
614 757-5000

(G-17508)
CARE AND LOVE PUBLISHING LLC
1110 E 139th Ave (33613-3419)
PHONE..................................254 462-9134
Stephen J Love, *Principal*
EMP: 6 **EST:** 2016
SALES (est): 94.8K **Privately Held**
SIC: 2741 Miscellaneous publishing

(G-17509)
CARE-METIX PRODUCTS INC
121 Kelsey Ln Ste F (33619-4348)
PHONE..................................813 628-8801
Steve Gibbons, *President*
EMP: 15 **EST:** 1998
SALES (est): 2.3MM **Privately Held**
WEB: www.caremetix.com
SIC: 2841 Soap & other detergents

(G-17510)
CARROLLWOOD CREAMERY
13168 N Dale Mabry Hwy (33618-2406)
PHONE..................................813 926-2023
Jason A Ricci, *Principal*
EMP: 9 **EST:** 2012
SALES (est): 113.8K **Privately Held**
WEB: www.carrollwoodvillage.com
SIC: 2021 Creamery butter

(G-17511)
CARVALHO NATURALS LLC
5806 Cay Cove Ct (33615-4269)
PHONE..................................813 833-8229
Kathalin Carvalho, *Principal*
EMP: 7 **EST:** 2017
SALES (est): 220.2K **Privately Held**
WEB: www.carvalhonaturals.com
SIC: 2099 Food preparations

(G-17512)
CASALE DESIGN SOURCE INC
4002 W State St Ste 100 (33609-1223)
PHONE..................................813 873-3653
Denise Casale, *President*
EMP: 6 **EST:** 2012
SALES (est): 391.4K **Privately Held**
WEB: www.casaledesignsource.com
SIC: 3253 Ceramic wall & floor tile

(G-17513)
CASINO BAKERY INC
2726 N 36th St (33605-3126)
P.O. Box 5828 (33675-5828)
PHONE..................................813 242-0311
Louis Sanchez Jr, *President*
EMP: 10 **EST:** 1946
SQ FT: 2,700
SALES (est): 836K **Privately Held**
SIC: 2051 Bread, all types (white, wheat, rye, etc): fresh or frozen

(G-17514)
CASTOR INC
1701 W Green St (33607-4316)
PHONE..................................813 254-1171
Brian Scott Castor, *President*
Stephen K Castor, *Vice Pres*
Carolyn Newby, *Treasurer*
Alex Castor, *Manager*
▼ **EMP:** 8
SQ FT: 7,000
SALES (est): 1.1MM **Privately Held**
WEB: www.castorcabinets.com
SIC: 2434 5712 Wood kitchen cabinets; cabinet work, custom

(G-17515)
CATALINA FINER FOOD CORP
4709 N Lauber Way (33614-7735)
P.O. Box 15815 (33684-5815)
PHONE..................................813 872-6359
Alejandro Cepero, *President*
Francisco Cepero, *Treasurer*
Justo Luis Cepero, *Admin Sec*
▲ **EMP:** 47 **EST:** 1973
SQ FT: 20,000
SALES (est): 13.9MM **Privately Held**
WEB: www.catalinafoods.com
SIC: 2032 2099 2035 Tamales: packaged in cans, jars, etc.; food preparations; pickles, sauces & salad dressings

(G-17516)
CATALINA FINER MEAT CORP
Also Called: Catalina Finer Foods
4710 W Cayuga St (33614-6949)
P.O. Box 15815 (33684-5815)
PHONE..................................813 876-3910
Alejandro Cepero, *President*
Marta Cepero, *Vice Pres*
Justo Luis Cepero, *Treasurer*
Francisco Cepero, *Admin Sec*
EMP: 18 **EST:** 1982
SQ FT: 7,000
SALES (est): 766.7K **Privately Held**
SIC: 2013 5147 Sausages & other prepared meats; meats & meat products

(G-17517)
CBC BIOTECHNOLOGIES INC
12005 Whitmarsh Ln (33626-1737)
PHONE..................................813 803-6300
EMP: 6 **EST:** 2015
SALES (est): 171.4K **Privately Held**
SIC: 2834 Pharmaceutical preparations

(G-17518)
CBDPHARM LLC
13529 Westshire Dr (33618-2500)
PHONE..................................813 442-5464
Ralph R Smith, *Manager*
EMP: 6 **EST:** 2018
SALES (est): 130.3K **Privately Held**
WEB: www.cbdpharm.com
SIC: 3999

(G-17519)
CEDRICK MCDONALD
Also Called: Exotics By Cedrick
4205 N Florida Ave (33603-3870)
PHONE..................................813 279-1442

Cedrick McDonald, *Owner*
EMP: 7 **EST:** 2016
SALES (est): 65.1K **Privately Held**
WEB: www.exoticsbycedrick.com
SIC: 3144 Dress shoes, women's

(G-17520)
CELIOS CORPORATION
1228 E 7th Ave Ste 313 (33605-3505)
PHONE..................................833 235-4671
Neil Campbell, *CEO*
EMP: 9
SALES (est): 259.3K **Privately Held**
WEB: www.celios.com
SIC: 3999 Manufacturing industries

(G-17521)
CEMEX INC
5503 E Diana St (33610-1903)
PHONE..................................813 663-9712
Gilberto Perez, *President*
Jesus Benavides, *Treasurer*
Joel Hray, *Accounts Mgr*
Ramiro Morales, *Admin Sec*
Camille Murwin, *Admin Asst*
EMP: 35 **EST:** 1991
SALES (est): 3.2MM **Privately Held**
WEB: www.cemexusa.com
SIC: 3273 Ready-mixed concrete

(G-17522)
CEMEX CNSTR MTLS FLA LLC
Also Called: Gypsum Supply - Tampa
9609 Palm River Rd (33619-4433)
PHONE..................................813 621-5575
EMP: 14 **Privately Held**
SIC: 3273 Mfg Ready-Mixed Concrete
HQ: Cemex Construction Materials Florida, Llc
1501 Belvedere Rd
West Palm Beach FL 33406

(G-17523)
CEMEX MATERIALS LLC
6302 N 56th St (33610-4021)
PHONE..................................813 620-3760
Angie Hinkle, *Manager*
EMP: 73 **Privately Held**
SIC: 3273 Ready-mixed concrete
HQ: Cemex Materials Llc
1501 Belvedere Rd
West Palm Beach FL 33406
561 833-5555

(G-17524)
CENTREX POWDERCOATING INC
4901 Distribution Dr (33605-5925)
PHONE..................................813 390-2802
Michael K Trout, *President*
EMP: 9 **EST:** 2003
SALES (est): 500K **Privately Held**
SIC: 3479 Coating of metals & formed products

(G-17525)
CENTURION ARMORING INTL INC
3911 W Eden Roc Cir (33634-7419)
PHONE..................................813 426-3385
Maroun Azzi, *President*
Lena Jammal, *Vice Pres*
▼ **EMP:** 11 **EST:** 2010
SALES (est): 177.6K **Privately Held**
WEB: www.centurion-armoring.com
SIC: 3549 Assembly machines, including robotic

(G-17526)
CENTURION HOLDINGS I LLC
Also Called: Centurion Technologies
324 N Dale Mabry Hwy (33609-1269)
P.O. Box 528, Arnold MO (63010-0528)
PHONE..................................636 349-5425
EMP: 20
SQ FT: 8,000
SALES (est): 2.8MM **Privately Held**
SIC: 3577 Mfg Computer Peripheral Equipment

(G-17527)
CERBERUS CRAFT DISTILLERY LLC
6608 Anderson Rd (33634-4402)
PHONE..................................813 789-1556
Matthew Allen, *Manager*
EMP: 7 **EST:** 2016
SALES (est): 429.4K **Privately Held**
SIC: 2082 Malt beverages

(G-17528)
CERTANTEED GYPS CILING MFG INC (HQ)
4300 W Cypress St Ste 500 (33607-4157)
PHONE..................................813 286-3900
▼ **EMP:** 29
SALES (est): 87.2MM
SALES (corp-wide): 332.4MM **Privately Held**
SIC: 3275 Mfg Gypsum Products

(G-17529)
CERTIFIED WLDG FBRCTION SVCS L
5116 Springwood Dr (33624-4837)
PHONE..................................813 323-4090
George E Gordon, *Principal*
EMP: 6 **EST:** 2012
SALES (est): 152.2K **Privately Held**
SIC: 7692 Welding repair

(G-17530)
CHAD
817 S Macdill Ave (33609-4615)
PHONE..................................727 433-0404
Stephen Myers, *Vice Pres*
Wasson Epps, *Manager*
Daniel Padley, *Manager*
Nathaniel Epps, *Admin Sec*
EMP: 13 **EST:** 2016
SALES (est): 86K **Privately Held**
SIC: 3761 Guided missiles & space vehicles

(G-17531)
CHANNEL INVESTMENTS LLC
Also Called: Tria Beauty
4221 W Boy Scout Blvd # 300 (33607-5765)
PHONE..................................727 599-1360
Sandip Patel,
EMP: 7 **EST:** 2017
SALES (est): 697K **Privately Held**
SIC: 3845 Laser systems & equipment, medical

(G-17532)
CHARGEX LLC ✪
4020 W Kennedy Blvd # 10 (33609-2761)
PHONE..................................855 242-7439
Chase Hebeler, *Mng Member*
EMP: 6 **EST:** 2020
SALES (est): 307.3K **Privately Held**
SIC: 3691 Storage batteries

(G-17533)
CHOLADOS Y MAS
6729 N Armenia Ave (33604-5715)
PHONE..................................813 935-9262
Maria Shirley Cintron, *Principal*
EMP: 8 **EST:** 2010
SALES (est): 127.8K **Privately Held**
SIC: 2024 Ice cream, bulk

(G-17534)
CIGAR CITY BREWPUB LLC (PA)
3924 W Spruce St (33607-2441)
PHONE..................................813 348-6363
Michael Haas, *General Mgr*
Justin Clark, *COO*
Madison Roane, *Prdtn Mgr*
Al Alvarez, *CFO*
Joe Burns, *Natl Sales Mgr*
▲ **EMP:** 136 **EST:** 2007
SALES (est): 7.8MM **Privately Held**
WEB: www.cigarcitybrewing.com
SIC: 2082 5084 Beer (alcoholic beverage); brewery products manufacturing machinery, commercial

(G-17535)
CIGAR CITY SMOKED SALSA LLC
5106 N 30th St (33610-5102)
PHONE..................................813 421-3340
Roy Kane, *Mng Member*
EMP: 5 **EST:** 2018
SQ FT: 2,000
SALES (est): 372.9K **Privately Held**
WEB: www.cigarcitysmokedsalsa.com
SIC: 2035 Pickles, sauces & salad dressings

(G-17536)
CINTAS CORPORATION
3601 W Swann Ave Ste 107 (33609-4517)
PHONE..................................813 874-1401
Kenneth Bahng, *Manager*
EMP: 10
SALES (corp-wide): 7.1B **Publicly Held**
WEB: www.cintas.com
SIC: 2326 Work uniforms
PA: Cintas Corporation
6800 Cintas Blvd
Cincinnati OH 45262
513 459-1200

(G-17537)
CLADDING SYSTEMS INC
3218 E 4th Ave (33605-5716)
PHONE..................................813 250-0786
Elizabeth Lisa Alexander, *President*
Elizabeth G Alexander, *President*
Bill Alexander, *Vice Pres*
William M Alexander, *Vice Pres*
Lee Reese, *Sales Mgr*
◆ **EMP:** 21 **EST:** 2000
SQ FT: 1,300
SALES (est): 4.1MM **Privately Held**
WEB: www.cladsys.com
SIC: 3444 Sheet metalwork

(G-17538)
CLARE INSTRUMENTS (US) INC
Also Called: Seaward Group USA
6304 Benjamin Rd Ste 506 (33634-5128)
PHONE..................................813 886-2775
Rod Taylor, *President*
Frank Belluccia, *General Mgr*
Mark Barron, *Business Mgr*
EMP: 5 **EST:** 2001
SQ FT: 1,500
SALES (est): 1.2MM
SALES (corp-wide): 127MM **Privately Held**
WEB: www.seaward-groupusa.com
SIC: 3699 Electrical equipment & supplies
HQ: Seaward Electronic Limited
18 Bracken Hill
Peterlee CO DURHAM SR8 2
191 586-3511

(G-17539)
CLARK CRAIG ENTERPRISES (PA)
Also Called: Fastsigns
3901 W Kennedy Blvd (33609-2721)
PHONE..................................813 287-0110
Clark Craig, *President*
EMP: 12 **EST:** 1996
SQ FT: 3,600
SALES (est): 3.3MM **Privately Held**
WEB: www.fastsigns.com
SIC: 3993 Signs & advertising specialties

(G-17540)
CLASSIC AUTO A MNFACTORING INC
4901 W Rio Vista Ave A (33634-5356)
PHONE..................................813 251-2356
Alfonso L Sedita, *President*
▲ **EMP:** 18 **EST:** 1982
SALES (est): 497.5K **Privately Held**
WEB: www.classicautoair.com
SIC: 3585 Air conditioning, motor vehicle

(G-17541)
CLEANPAK PRODUCTS LLC
Also Called: Clean Pack Products
221 Hobbs St Ste 108 (33619-8068)
PHONE..................................813 740-8611
George Brydon, *Human Resources*
John Bartolotti, *Sales Associate*
◆ **EMP:** 5 **EST:** 2006
SQ FT: 10,000
SALES (est): 839.8K **Privately Held**
WEB: www.cleanpakproducts.com
SIC: 2899 Chemical preparations

(G-17542)
CLIFTON STUDIO INC
4710 Eisenhower Blvd D (33634-6335)
P.O. Box 273848 (33688-3848)
PHONE..................................813 240-0286
Gilbert Bailie, *President*
EMP: 7 **EST:** 1974
SALES (est): 109.6K **Privately Held**
SIC: 3999 Plaques, picture, laminated

(G-17543)
COASTAL WIPERS INC (PA)
Also Called: Landis Service Company
5705 E Hanna Ave (33610-4036)
PHONE..................................813 628-4464
Gary H Smiles, *President*
Michelle Smiles, *Vice Pres*
Dennis Bahro, *Manager*
◆ **EMP:** 38 **EST:** 1982
SQ FT: 17,000
SALES (est): 8.6MM **Privately Held**
WEB: www.coastalwipers.com
SIC: 2392 Polishing cloths, plain

(G-17544)
COCA-COLA BEVERAGES FLA LLC
9102 Sabal Indus Blvd (33619-8303)
PHONE..................................813 623-5411
Randy Arty, *Branch Mgr*
Jeffrey Cormier, *Supervisor*
Ryan Carter, *CIO*
EMP: 230
SALES (corp-wide): 366.5MM **Privately Held**
WEB: www.cocacolaflorida.com
SIC: 2086 Bottled & canned soft drinks
PA: Coca-Cola Beverages Florida, Llc
10117 Princess Palm Ave # 100
Tampa FL 33610
800 438-2653

(G-17545)
COCA-COLA BEVERAGES FLA LLC (PA)
10117 Princess Palm Ave # 100 (33610-8303)
PHONE..................................800 438-2653
Troy Taylor, *CEO*
Thomas N Benford, *President*
Bernie Roy, *General Mgr*
Joshua Sherwood, *Business Mgr*
Sara Solis, *Business Mgr*
EMP: 356 **EST:** 2015
SALES (est): 366.5MM **Privately Held**
WEB: www.cocacolaflorida.com
SIC: 2086 Bottled & canned soft drinks

(G-17546)
COLOR CONCEPTS PRTG DESIGN CO
2602 Tampa East Blvd (33619-3038)
PHONE..................................813 623-2921
Robin D Wahler, *President*
Dave Collyer, *Vice Pres*
Donald Barnes, *Shareholder*
Gasper Ciaccio, *Shareholder*
EMP: 21 **EST:** 1986
SQ FT: 15,500
SALES (est): 1.7MM **Privately Held**
WEB: www.colorconcepts.com
SIC: 2752 2791 2789 Commercial printing, offset; typesetting; bookbinding & related work

(G-17547)
COMERINT INC
5125 W Rio Vista Ave (33634-5342)
PHONE..................................813 443-2466
Jorge E Ramirez, *President*
EMP: 6 **EST:** 2013
SALES (est): 94.4K **Privately Held**
SIC: 3263 Cookware, fine earthenware

(G-17548)
COMMSKI LLC
7853 Gunn Hwy 252 (33626-1611)
PHONE..................................813 501-0111
Mandy Noegel, *Project Mgr*
Karla Lapinski, *Manager*
Fran Reiter, *Manager*
EMP: 8 **EST:** 2012
SALES (est): 1.5MM **Privately Held**
WEB: www.commski.com
SIC: 3357 5063 7373 Fiber optic cable (insulated); wire & cable; value-added resellers, computer systems

(G-17549)
COMPETITOR GROUP INC
3407 W Dr Ml King Jr 10 (33607)
PHONE..................................858 450-6510
Justin Sands, *Executive Asst*
EMP: 6 **EST:** 2018
SALES (est): 438.5K **Privately Held**
SIC: 2741 Miscellaneous publishing

(G-17550)
COMRES MANUFACTURING INC
7211 Anderson Rd (33634-3001)
PHONE..................................813 249-0391
Steven Cook, *President*
Chuck Imel, *Human Res Dir*
EMP: 17 **EST:** 1989
SQ FT: 20,000
SALES (est): 660.9K **Privately Held**
WEB: www.metpar.com
SIC: 3446 Partitions & supports/studs, including accoustical systems

(G-17551)
CONCEPT DESIGN AND PRINTING
7402 N 56th St Ste 810 (33617-7731)
PHONE..................................813 516-9798
Syed Haider, *Owner*
EMP: 7 **EST:** 2014
SALES (est): 328.1K **Privately Held**
WEB: www.store.conceptdp.com
SIC: 2759 Commercial printing

(G-17552)
CONSOLDTED RSURCE RECOVERY INC
1502 N 50th St (33619-3220)
PHONE..................................813 262-8404
Cindy Cummings, *Manager*
Toni Lubbers, *Director*
EMP: 27 **Privately Held**
WEB: www.resourcerecovery.com
SIC: 2875 1629 Compost; land clearing contractor
PA: Consolidated Resource Recovery, Inc.
3025 Whitfield Ave
Sarasota FL 34243

(G-17553)
CONTROL SOLUTIONS INC
1406 N 16th St (33605-5126)
PHONE..................................813 247-2136
Michael E Vandergriff, *President*
Diana L Vandergriff, *Vice Pres*
EMP: 10 **EST:** 2007
SQ FT: 6,500
SALES (est): 1.2MM **Privately Held**
WEB: www.controlsolutionsinc.com
SIC: 3612 3613 3823 Transformers, except electric; switchgear & switchboard apparatus; industrial instrmnts msrmnt display/control process variable

(G-17554)
COOL COMPONENTS INC
904 E Chelsea St (33603-4137)
PHONE..................................813 322-3814
David T Lee, *President*
▲ **EMP:** 8 **EST:** 2004
SALES (est): 831K **Privately Held**
WEB: www.coolcomponents.com
SIC: 3564 Blowers & fans

(G-17555)
CORESENTIAL ENERGY & LIGHTING
1201 N 50th St (33619-3206)
PHONE..................................919 602-0849
Robin Conway, *President*
Joe Tumlin, *President*
Jamey Yore, *President*
Jeff Conway, *Vice Pres*
Greg Engelbert, *Vice Pres*
EMP: 40 **EST:** 2011
SALES (est): 3MM **Privately Held**
WEB: www.coresential.com
SIC: 3646 Commercial indusl & institutional electric lighting fixtures

(G-17556)
CORESLAB STRUCTURES TAMPA INC
6301 N 56th St (33610-4020)
PHONE..................................602 237-3875
Luigi Franciosa, *President*
Frank Franciosa, *Principal*
Michael Quinlan, *Principal*
Sidney Spiegel, *Principal*
Mario Franciosa, *Corp Secy*
EMP: 160 **EST:** 1993
SQ FT: 5,000
SALES (est): 46MM
SALES (corp-wide): 27.3MM **Privately Held**
WEB: www.coreslab.com
SIC: 3272 Concrete products, precast
HQ: Coreslab Holdings U S Inc
332 Jones Rd Suite 1
Stoney Creek ON
905 643-0220

(G-17557)
CORIN USA LIMITED INC (DH)
12750 Citrus Park Ln # 120 (33625-3784)
PHONE..................................813 977-4469
Stefano Alfonsi, *CEO*
Russ Mabley, *COO*
Chuck Jaggers, *Vice Pres*
Al Nanni, *Vice Pres*
Kathy Trier, *Vice Pres*
▲ **EMP:** 12 **EST:** 1992
SQ FT: 9,911
SALES (est): 6.8MM
SALES (corp-wide): 177.9K **Privately Held**
WEB: www.coringroup.com
SIC: 3841 Surgical & medical instruments
HQ: Corin Limited
Unit 1-4
Cirencester GLOS GL7 1
128 565-9866

(G-17558)
CORONA BRUSHES INC
5065 Savarese Cir (33634-2490)
PHONE..................................813 885-2525
Gregory Waksman, *President*
Benjamin Waksman, *Vice Pres*
Albert Waksman, *Treasurer*
Neil Trenk, *Sales Mgr*
Joyce McCarthy, *Executive*
◆ **EMP:** 60 **EST:** 1961
SQ FT: 65,000
SALES (est): 9.3MM **Privately Held**
WEB: www.coronabrushes.com
SIC: 3991 Paint brushes; paint rollers

(G-17559)
CORRUGATED INDUSTRIES FLA INC
Also Called: Custom Metal Building Products
1920 N Us Highway 301 (33619-2640)
PHONE..................................813 623-6606
Gene Le Bouef Sr, *President*
Gene Lebouef, *President*
▼ **EMP:** 23 **EST:** 1999
SQ FT: 16,000
SALES (est): 2.9MM **Privately Held**
WEB: www.metalroofandwalls.com
SIC: 3444 Sheet metalwork

(G-17560)
COVERALL INTERIORS
5102 W Linebaugh Ave (33624-5032)
PHONE..................................813 961-8261
Dave Friedel, *Manager*
EMP: 8 **EST:** 2017
SALES (est): 57.3K **Privately Held**
SIC: 2591 Drapery hardware & blinds & shades

(G-17561)
CP ROYALTIES LLC
301 W Platt St (33606-2292)
PHONE..................................888 694-9265
Douglas Anacreonte, *Principal*
EMP: 6 **EST:** 2011
SALES (est): 312.9K **Privately Held**
WEB: www.cproyalties.com
SIC: 1382 Oil & gas exploration services

(G-17562)
CREATE AND COMPANY INC
Also Called: Createco
1023 E Columbus Dr (33605-3332)
PHONE..................................813 393-8778
Kristina M York, *President*
Angela T Davis, *Vice Pres*
David A Valladarez, *Vice Pres*
EMP: 10 **EST:** 2015
SALES (est): 1MM **Privately Held**
WEB: www.createandcompany.com
SIC: 3694 Generators, automotive & aircraft

(G-17563)
CREATIVE BUILDER SERVICES INC
Also Called: Creative Mailbox Designs
6422 Harney Rd Ste F (33610-9162)
PHONE..................................813 818-7100
Scott M Tappan, *President*
Nicole Arquiett, *Accountant*
EMP: 35 **EST:** 2016
SALES (est): 3.8MM **Privately Held**
WEB: www.creativemailboxdesigns.com
SIC: 2542 Mail racks & lock boxes, postal service: except wood

(G-17564)
CREATIVE CAR COATS ✪
5553 W Waters Ave (33634-1210)
PHONE..................................813 886-2589
EMP: 6 **EST:** 2020
SALES (est): 221.8K **Privately Held**
WEB: www.c3jersey.com
SIC: 2396 Automotive & apparel trimmings

(G-17565)
CREATIVE LOAFING INC (HQ)
Also Called: Weekly Planet
1911 N 13th St Ste W200 (33605-3652)
PHONE..................................813 739-4800
Marty Petty, *CEO*
Colin Wolf, *Editor*
Scott Harrell, *Chief*
Tammy Bailey, *CFO*
Anthony Carbone, *Executive*
EMP: 50 **EST:** 1988
SQ FT: 8,000
SALES (est): 27.9MM **Privately Held**
WEB: www.atalayacap.com
SIC: 2711 Newspapers: publishing only, not printed on site

(G-17566)
CREATIVE LOAFING INC
Also Called: Eclipse Magazine
1911 N 13th St Fl 1 (33605-3652)
PHONE..................................941 365-6776
Anthony Carbone, *Executive*
EMP: 9 **Privately Held**
SIC: 2711 Newspapers, publishing & printing
HQ: Creative Loafing, Inc.
1911 N 13th St Ste W200
Tampa FL 33605

(G-17567)
CREATIVE SIGN DESIGNS LLC (PA)
Also Called: Creative Mailbox Sign Designs
12801 Commodity Pl (33626-3104)
PHONE..................................813 818-7100
Jamie Harden, *President*
Kelly Crandall, *Co-Owner*
Sam Feldstein, *COO*
Bryan Vaughn, *Vice Pres*
Johanna Lainez, *Project Mgr*
▲ **EMP:** 65
SQ FT: 44,000
SALES (est): 17.7MM **Privately Held**
WEB: www.creativesigndesigns.com
SIC: 3993 Signs & advertising specialties

(G-17568)
CRITICAL COATINGS INC
1307 E Clifton St (33604-6867)
PHONE..................................813 515-7119
Christopher M Trevino, *Vice Pres*
EMP: 6 **EST:** 2017
SALES (est): 91.5K **Privately Held**
SIC: 3479 Metal coating & allied service

(G-17569)
CROWE MANUFACTURING
5203 S Lois Ave (33611-3446)
PHONE..................................813 334-1921
EMP: 9 **EST:** 2018
SALES (est): 49.1K **Privately Held**
WEB: www.crowemanufacturing.com
SIC: 3999 Manufacturing industries

(G-17570)
CROWELL MARINE INC
Also Called: Crowell Companies
7305 N Florida Ave (33604-4837)
PHONE..................................813 236-3625
Terri Crowell, *President*
Robert Crowell, *Director*
EMP: 7 **EST:** 2008
SALES (est): 476.8K **Privately Held**
SIC: 2499 Floating docks, wood

(G-17571)
CSBA DIGITAL PRINTING
3601 Bay Heights Way (33611-1548)
PHONE..................................813 482-1608
Ricardo Ruiz, *Principal*
EMP: 10 **EST:** 2013
SALES (est): 271.1K **Privately Held**
WEB: www.csbaonline.org
SIC: 2752 Commercial printing, offset

(G-17572)
CT NATURAL
2908 W Arch St (33607-5202)
PHONE..................................813 996-6443
Florence McCue-Morris, *Principal*
EMP: 7 **EST:** 2012
SALES (est): 267.4K **Privately Held**
WEB: www.ctnatural.com
SIC: 3599 Boiler tube cleaners

(G-17573)
CUMMINS-WAGNER-FLORIDA LLC (HQ)
9834 Currie Davis Dr (33619-2651)
PHONE..................................813 630-2220
Michael Bilello, *Engineer*
Daniel Orr, *Sales Staff*
Douglas Ardinger, *Mng Member*
EMP: 34 **EST:** 2010
SALES (est): 13.3MM
SALES (corp-wide): 75.7MM **Privately Held**
WEB: www.cummins-wagner.com
SIC: 3556 3519 Dehydrating equipment, food processing; internal combustion engines
PA: Cummins-Wagner Company, Inc.
10901 Pump House Rd
Annapolis Junction MD 20701
800 966-1277

(G-17574)
CURRY CABINETRY INC
4831 E Broadway Ave (33605-4703)
PHONE..................................813 321-3650
Ann Curry, *President*
Bryan Curry, *Vice Pres*
Matt Alexander, *Opers Staff*
Bryan Kelnhofer, *Engineer*
EMP: 22 **EST:** 2008
SQ FT: 8,000
SALES (est): 3.2MM **Privately Held**
WEB: www.currycabinetry.com
SIC: 2434 Wood kitchen cabinets

(G-17575)
CUSHION SOLUTIONS INCORPORATED
802 N Rome Ave (33606-1038)
PHONE..................................813 253-2131
Denis Flagler, *President*
▲ **EMP:** 6 **EST:** 2005
SQ FT: 1,000
SALES (est): 628.9K **Privately Held**
WEB: www.cushionsolutions.net
SIC: 2392 Cushions & pillows

(G-17576)
CUSTOM CABINETS BY JENSEN LLC
1704 W Fig St (33606-1626)
PHONE..................................813 250-0286
Glenn Jensen, *Manager*
EMP: 9 **EST:** 2015
SALES (est): 276K **Privately Held**
SIC: 2434 Wood kitchen cabinets

(G-17577)
CUSTOM CRAFT LAMINATES INC
4705 N Manhattan Ave (33614-6921)
PHONE..................................813 877-7100
James E Blanton, *President*
Sally J Blanton, *Corp Secy*

EMP: 26 **EST:** 1968
SQ FT: 20,000
SALES (est): 1.4MM **Privately Held**
WEB: www.mycabinetcompany.com
SIC: 2434 2521 Wood kitchen cabinets; wood office furniture

(G-17578)
CUSTOM DOOR DIRECT LLC
1100 N 50th St Bldg 2 (33619-3233)
PHONE..................................813 248-5757
EMP: 10 **EST:** 2011
SALES (est): 780K **Privately Held**
SIC: 2431 Mfg Millwork

(G-17579)
CUSTOM KLOSETS & CABINETS INC
6403 N 50th St (33610-4004)
PHONE..................................813 246-4806
Robin Knapp, *President*
Bradford C Frank, *Principal*
Tom Petrou, *Vice Pres*
Manuel Sanchis, *Sales Mgr*
Mike Reidy, *Sales Staff*
EMP: 23 **EST:** 2002
SQ FT: 12,000
SALES (est): 5MM **Privately Held**
WEB: www.customclosetsandcabinets.com
SIC: 2434 Vanities, bathroom: wood

(G-17580)
CUSTOM MARBLE WORKS INC
1905 N 43rd St (33605-4644)
PHONE..................................813 620-0475
Rick Fincher, *President*
Coy E Fincher, *Corp Secy*
◆ **EMP:** 41 **EST:** 1985
SQ FT: 5,000
SALES (est): 2.7MM **Privately Held**
SIC: 3281 3429 3261 2541 Marble, building: cut & shaped; granite, cut & shaped; manufactured hardware (general); vitreous plumbing fixtures; wood partitions & fixtures; dimension stone

(G-17581)
CUSTOM PLASTIC FABRICATORS
6201 Johns Rd Ste 8 (33634-4434)
PHONE..................................813 884-5200
Joseph Gregory Bersano, *Owner*
EMP: 8 **EST:** 2008
SALES (est): 296.6K **Privately Held**
WEB: www.customplasticfab.com
SIC: 3089 Molding primary plastic; netting, plastic; panels, building: plastic; organizers for closets, drawers, etc.: plastic

(G-17582)
CUSTOM QUALITY MFG INC
Also Called: C Q M
5015 Tampa West Blvd (33634-2414)
PHONE..................................813 290-0805
Leon Montanbault, *President*
Dolores Alonso, *Corp Secy*
Michelle Mason, *CFO*
Michele Mason, *Finance*
Al Alvarez, *Sales Engr*
▲ **EMP:** 25 **EST:** 1996
SQ FT: 10,500
SALES (est): 5.7MM **Privately Held**
WEB: www.cqm-inc.com
SIC: 3714 Motor vehicle parts & accessories

(G-17583)
CYPRESS FOLDING CARTONS INC
6025 Jet Port Indus Blvd (33634-5161)
PHONE..................................813 884-5418
Jon Hartzler, *President*
Lisa Hartzler, *Corp Secy*
Austin Hartzler, *Vice Pres*
EMP: 35 **EST:** 1981
SQ FT: 19,000
SALES (est): 4.9MM **Privately Held**
WEB: www.cypressfoldingcartons.com
SIC: 2653 2657 Boxes, corrugated: made from purchased materials; folding paperboard boxes

(G-17584)
D G YUENGLING AND SON INC
11111 N 30th St (33612-6439)
PHONE..................................813 972-8500
Richard L Yuengling Jr, *President*
Donald Cook, *Manager*
Kyle Samuels, *Manager*
EMP: 95
SALES (corp-wide): 52MM **Privately Held**
WEB: www.yuengling.com
SIC: 2082 5182 5181 Beer (alcoholic beverage); ale (alcoholic beverage); porter (alcoholic beverage); wine & distilled beverages; beer & ale
PA: D. G. Yuengling And Son, Incorporated
5th & Mahantongo Sts
Pottsville PA 17901
570 622-4141

(G-17585)
DAILY TRNSFRMTION MNSTRIES INC
12563 Leatherleaf Dr (33626-3051)
PHONE..................................727 847-5152
Alfred Santos, *Principal*
EMP: 6 **EST:** 2010
SALES (est): 110.6K **Privately Held**
SIC: 2711 Newspapers, publishing & printing

(G-17586)
DAIRY-MIX INC
Gulf Coast Plastics
9314 Princess Palm Ave (33619-1364)
PHONE..................................813 621-8098
Thomas Coryn, *Manager*
EMP: 18
SALES (corp-wide): 27.4MM **Privately Held**
WEB: www.dairymix.com
SIC: 2673 5113 3081 2671 Plastic bags: made from purchased materials; bags, paper & disposable plastic; unsupported plastics film & sheet; packaging paper & plastics film, coated & laminated
PA: Dairy-Mix, Inc.
3020 46th Ave N
Saint Petersburg FL 33714
813 621-8098

(G-17587)
DALANE MACHINING INC
13530 Wright Cir (33626-3028)
PHONE..................................813 854-5905
Dale Baird, *President*
Sisk Steve, *General Mgr*
Kyle Tirrell, *Research*
EMP: 26 **EST:** 1992
SQ FT: 8,500
SALES (est): 3.1MM **Privately Held**
WEB: www.dalanemachining.com
SIC: 3599 Machine shop, jobbing & repair

(G-17588)
DALE MABRY HEATING & METAL CO
4313 W South Ave (33614-6465)
PHONE..................................813 877-1574
Fred Besch III, *President*
Becky Cacciatore, *Corp Secy*
Fred Besch Sr, *Vice Pres*
EMP: 6 **EST:** 1947
SQ FT: 2,200
SALES (est): 798.6K **Privately Held**
WEB: www.dalemabryheating-metal.com
SIC: 2434 Wood kitchen cabinets

(G-17589)
DARLING INGREDIENTS INC
1001 Orient Rd (33619-3321)
PHONE..................................863 425-0065
Don Manning, *Manager*
EMP: 7
SQ FT: 4,152
SALES (corp-wide): 3.3B **Publicly Held**
WEB: www.darlingii.com
SIC: 2077 Animal & marine fats & oils
PA: Darling Ingredients Inc.
5601 N Macarthur Blvd
Irving TX 75038
972 717-0300

(G-17590)
DATA COOLING TECH CANADA LLC
Thermotech Enterprises
5110 W Clifton St (33634-8012)
P.O. Box 15698 (33684-5698)
PHONE..................................813 865-4701
Daniel Marshall, *Facilities Mgr*
Amy Clark, *Production*
Jeff McKee, *VP Sales*
Krister Eriksson, *Branch Mgr*
Christopher Kinney, *Technician*
EMP: 25
SALES (corp-wide): 4.7MM **Privately Held**
WEB: www.thermotech-usa.com
SIC: 3585 Heating & air conditioning combination units
PA: Data Cooling Technologies Canada Llc
3092 Euclid Heights Blvd
Cleveland Heights OH 44118
330 954-3800

(G-17591)
DAVID JACOBS PUBG GROUP LLC
14497 N D Mabry Hwy 135 (33618)
PHONE..................................813 321-4119
Bob Ford, *Vice Pres*
Jacob T Wattam, *Manager*
EMP: 15 **EST:** 2012
SALES (est): 4.4MM **Privately Held**
WEB: www.davidjacobspg.com
SIC: 2741 Miscellaneous publishing

(G-17592)
DAVIS FRANKLIN PRINTING CO
520 N Willow Ave (33606-1348)
P.O. Box 22362 (33622-2362)
PHONE..................................813 259-2500
Mace Davis, *Owner*
Vicki Gonzales, *Manager*
EMP: 7 **EST:** 1908
SALES (est): 500K **Privately Held**
SIC: 2759 Commercial printing

(G-17593)
DAYSTAR INTERNATIONAL INC
917 Terra Mar Dr (33613-2003)
PHONE..................................813 281-0200
Glen Freeman, *President*
Charlotte Murray, *Corp Secy*
Tim Backus, *Vice Pres*
EMP: 6 **EST:** 1994
SALES (est): 201.4K **Privately Held**
SIC: 2434 1751 2541 Wood kitchen cabinets; finish & trim carpentry; wood partitions & fixtures

(G-17594)
DCG ENTERPRISES LLC
Also Called: Quality Beverage Services
2702 N 35th St (33605-3122)
P.O. Box 15472 (33684-5472)
PHONE..................................813 931-4303
Paul Vadnais,
EMP: 5 **EST:** 1994
SALES (est): 749.3K **Privately Held**
SIC: 3585 Soda fountain & beverage dispensing equipment & parts

(G-17595)
DDP HOLDINGS LLC (HQ)
4450 E Adamo Dr Ste 501 (33605-5941)
PHONE..................................813 712-2515
Mike Sunderland, *CEO*
Lauren Bishop, *Vice Pres*
EMP: 183 **EST:** 1992
SQ FT: 5,000
SALES (est): 178MM
SALES (corp-wide): 255.7MM **Privately Held**
WEB: www.pbcap.com
SIC: 3432 6512 Plumbing fixture fittings & trim; property operation, retail establishment
PA: Palm Beach Capital Fund I, L.P.
525 S Flagler Dr Ste 208
West Palm Beach FL 33401
561 659-9022

(G-17596)
DDS LAB USA HOLDING
6015 Benjamin Rd Ste 310 (33634-5179)
PHONE..................................813 249-8888
EMP: 100 **EST:** 2005
SALES (est): 6.1MM **Privately Held**
WEB: www.ddslab.com
SIC: 3843 Dental equipment

(G-17597)
DECOWALL
6001 Johns Rd Ste 342 (33634-4459)
P.O. Box 8281 (33674-8281)
PHONE..................................813 886-5226
Phillip Breakey, *Owner*
EMP: 6 **EST:** 1979
SQ FT: 1,500
SALES (est): 489.9K **Privately Held**
WEB: www.decowalltampa.com
SIC: 2431 5046 Millwork; commercial equipment

(G-17598)
DEFENDER SD MANUFACTURING LLC (PA) ✪
324 S Hyde Park Ave # 350 (33606-4127)
PHONE..................................813 864-2570
Barry Feinberg, *Mng Member*
David Helton,
EMP: 15 **EST:** 2020
SALES (est): 5.4MM **Privately Held**
SIC: 2834 Pharmaceutical preparations

(G-17599)
DENNIS HERNANDEZ & ASSOC PA
410 S Cedar Ave (33606-2221)
PHONE..................................813 470-4545
Thomas Keller, *CEO*
EMP: 6 **EST:** 2018
SALES (est): 436.9K **Privately Held**
WEB: www.dennishernandez.com
SIC: 2041 Flour & other grain mill products

(G-17600)
DESIGN LITHO INC
5205 N Florida Ave (33603-2139)
PHONE..................................813 238-7494
Reg Ide, *President*
EMP: 6 **EST:** 1979
SQ FT: 6,000
SALES (est): 650K **Privately Held**
WEB: www.designlitho.com
SIC: 2752 Commercial printing, offset

(G-17601)
DESTINY & LIGHT INC
Also Called: Salon By Destiny & Light, The
5911 Sheldon Rd (33615-3109)
PHONE..................................813 476-8386
Priscilla M Cruz-Charite, *Vice Pres*
EMP: 14 **EST:** 2011
SALES (est): 1.4MM **Privately Held**
WEB: www.destinyandlight.com
SIC: 3999 Hair, dressing of, for the trade

(G-17602)
DEVON-AIRE INC
8505 Sunstate St (33634-1311)
P.O. Box 25112 (33622-5112)
PHONE..................................813 884-9544
Harris Giannella, *President*
Darin Dealvarez, *President*
Andres Lendoiro, *Vice Pres*
Robert Della Penna, *Vice Pres*
◆ **EMP:** 20 **EST:** 1976
SQ FT: 20,000
SALES (est): 603.1K **Privately Held**
WEB: www.devonaire.com
SIC: 2329 2339 3144 Riding clothes:, men's, youths' & boys'; riding habits: women's, misses' & juniors'; boots, canvas or leather: women's

(G-17603)
DFA DAIRY BRANDS FLUID LLC
4219 E 19th Ave (33605-3241)
PHONE..................................813 621-7805
George Abel, *Branch Mgr*
EMP: 30
SALES (corp-wide): 17.8B **Privately Held**
SIC: 2026 Fluid milk
HQ: Dfa Dairy Brands Fluid, Llc
1405 N 98th St
Kansas City KS 66111
816 801-6455

(G-17604)
DIANE DAL LAGO LIMITED COMPANY
5915 Memorial Hwy Ste 115 (33615-5008)
PHONE....................813 374-2473
EMP: 12
SALES (est): 1.2MM **Privately Held**
SIC: 2339 Mfg Women's Sportswear

(G-17605)
DIETZGEN CORPORATION (PA)
121 Kelsey Ln Ste G (33619-4348)
PHONE....................813 286-4767
Darren Letang, *President*
Darren A Letang, *President*
John Vantrease, *CFO*
Robert DOE, *Regl Sales Mgr*
John Sobczak, *Manager*
▼ **EMP:** 45 **EST:** 2009
SALES (est): 42.4MM **Privately Held**
WEB: www.dietzgen.com
SIC: 2679 Paper products, converted

(G-17606)
DIGITAL COLOR PUBLICATIONS LLC
6103 Johns Rd Ste 5 (33634-4428)
PHONE....................813 886-0065
William Ashby, *Principal*
EMP: 7 **EST:** 2008
SALES (est): 183.9K **Privately Held**
SIC: 2741 Miscellaneous publishing

(G-17607)
DIMENSION PHOTO ENGRV CO INC
1507 W Cass St (33606-1207)
PHONE....................813 251-0244
Douglas Drenberg, *President*
Donald W Drenberg, *Chairman*
Debra Gilmore, *Corp Secy*
Donna Gardner, *Vice Pres*
Jim McMahan, *Sales Staff*
EMP: 20 **EST:** 1963
SQ FT: 10,000
SALES (est): 3.9MM **Privately Held**
WEB: www.4dimensionprint.com
SIC: 2752 Commercial printing, offset

(G-17608)
DISBROW CORPORATION (PA)
Also Called: Ad-Co Printing
8412 Sabal Indus Blvd (33619-1327)
PHONE....................813 621-9444
John Disbrow, *President*
Angela Disbrow, *Admin Sec*
▲ **EMP:** 11 **EST:** 1996
SQ FT: 30,000
SALES (est): 3MM **Privately Held**
WEB: www.printfast.com
SIC: 2752 Commercial printing, lithographic

(G-17609)
DIVERSFIED LIFTING SYSTEMS INC
4702 Distribution Dr (33605-5922)
PHONE....................813 248-2299
Billy Crowe, *President*
David Banks, *Research*
◆ **EMP:** 22 **EST:** 1988
SQ FT: 15,000
SALES (est): 3.5MM **Privately Held**
WEB: www.diversifiedlifting.com
SIC: 3537 3536 Platforms, stands, tables, pallets & similar equipment; hoists, cranes & monorails

(G-17610)
DKA DISTRIBUTING LLC
5010 Tampa West Blvd (33634-2412)
PHONE....................800 275-4352
Jim Tackenberg,
EMP: 8 **EST:** 2002
SALES (est): 152K **Privately Held**
WEB: www.dkadistributing.com
SIC: 3639 Major kitchen appliances, except refrigerators & stoves

(G-17611)
DLA DOCUMENT SERVICES
2617 Florida Keys Ave # 25 (33621-5402)
PHONE....................813 828-4646
William Barrett, *Manager*
EMP: 10 **Publicly Held**
WEB: www.documentservices.dla.mil
SIC: 2752 9711 Commercial printing, lithographic; national security
HQ: Dla Document Services
5450 Carlisle Pike Bldg 9
Mechanicsburg PA 17050
717 605-2362

(G-17612)
DOCH LLC ✪
14630 Grenadine Dr Apt 7 (33613-2911)
PHONE....................571 491-7578
Suryanarayana Burri,
EMP: 9 **EST:** 2021
SALES (est): 350.7K **Privately Held**
SIC: 3491 Valves, automatic control

(G-17613)
DOE & INGALLS FLORIDA OPER LLC
9940 Currie Davis Dr # 13 (33619-2669)
PHONE....................813 347-4741
Spencer Todd, *President*
EMP: 5 **EST:** 2005
SQ FT: 10,000
SALES (est): 2.2MM
SALES (corp-wide): 32.2B **Publicly Held**
WEB: www.thermofisher.com
SIC: 3826 Analytical instruments
HQ: Doe & Ingalls Management, Llc
4813 Emperor Blvd Ste 300
Durham NC 27703

(G-17614)
DPI INFORMATION INC
8402 Laurel Fair Cir # 209 (33610-7328)
PHONE....................813 258-8004
Anthony Aguilar, *Principal*
Chris Sharp, *Sales Staff*
Sean Emerson, *Software Dev*
EMP: 16 **EST:** 2008
SALES (est): 1.3MM **Privately Held**
WEB: www.dpiserve.com
SIC: 7372 Operating systems computer software

(G-17615)
DR WORTHINGTON ORTHODONTI
3640 Madaca Ln (33618-2057)
PHONE....................813 968-4040
Julie Worthington, *Principal*
EMP: 6 **EST:** 2010
SALES (est): 95.4K **Privately Held**
WEB: www.worthingtonortho.com
SIC: 3843 Enamels, dentists'

(G-17616)
DREXEL METALS INC
8641 Elm Fair Blvd (33610-7363)
PHONE....................727 572-7900
Bryan Partyka, *Branch Mgr*
EMP: 20
SALES (corp-wide): 4.2B **Publicly Held**
WEB: www.drexmet.com
SIC: 2952 5033 Roofing materials; roofing & siding materials
HQ: Drexel Metals, Inc.
1234 Gardiner Ln
Louisville KY 40213
215 396-4470

(G-17617)
DSE INC (PA)
5201 S West Shore Blvd (33611-5651)
PHONE....................813 443-4809
Dae Y Shin, *President*
Joe D Bedore, *CFO*
Steve Alm, *Manager*
Velton Thomas, *Manager*
Sue Shin, *Business Dir*
EMP: 44 **EST:** 1979
SQ FT: 60,000
SALES (est): 12.2MM **Privately Held**
WEB: www.dse.net
SIC: 3489 3429 3545 3483 Artillery or artillery parts, over 30 mm.; motor vehicle hardware; machine tool accessories; ammunition, except for small arms

(G-17618)
DTSYSTEMS INC
4834 W Gandy Blvd (33611-3003)
P.O. Box 46907 (33646-0108)
PHONE....................813 994-0030
Frank Nicotera, *CEO*
EMP: 5 **EST:** 2000
SQ FT: 1,200
SALES (est): 878K **Privately Held**
WEB: www.keepontracking.com
SIC: 3577 Optical scanning devices

(G-17619)
DUNCANMATTHEWS LLC
7019 Silvermill Dr (33635-9696)
PHONE....................813 466-8290
David Matthews,
EMP: 6
SALES (est): 311.1K **Privately Held**
SIC: 2499 Picture frame molding, finished

(G-17620)
DURAMASTER CYLINDERS
5688 W Crenshaw St (33634-3044)
PHONE....................813 882-0040
Joseph H Greene, *President*
EMP: 13 **EST:** 1989
SALES (est): 1.1MM **Privately Held**
WEB: www.greencocylinders.com
SIC: 3593 5084 3443 Fluid power cylinders, hydraulic or pneumatic; industrial machinery & equipment; fabricated plate work (boiler shop)

(G-17621)
DVC MARKETING
1313 N Howard Ave (33607-5323)
PHONE....................727 442-7125
EMP: 7 **EST:** 2018
SALES (est): 246.3K **Privately Held**
WEB: www.dvc360.com
SIC: 2752 Commercial printing, lithographic

(G-17622)
DYNOTEC PLASTIC INC
2211 N 38th St Ste A (33605-4550)
PHONE....................813 248-5335
Antionio Dodaro, *President*
▼ **EMP:** 7 **EST:** 1993
SALES (est): 601.5K **Privately Held**
SIC: 3089 Injection molding of plastics

(G-17623)
E&M PCKGING LLCDBA CRTIVE SIGN
3001 W Granada St (33629-7203)
PHONE....................813 839-6356
Paula A Fredrick, *Principal*
EMP: 7 **EST:** 2011
SALES (est): 107K **Privately Held**
SIC: 3993 Signs & advertising specialties

(G-17624)
E2 WALLS INC
5692 W Crenshaw St (33634-3013)
P.O. Box 270909 (33688-0909)
PHONE....................813 374-2010
Kenneth P Devars, *President*
Colin C Bowles-Jenner, *Vice Pres*
Donald R Cox, *Vice Pres*
John T Coyle Jr, *Vice Pres*
Kerry P Devars, *Vice Pres*
EMP: 20 **EST:** 2008
SQ FT: 12,000
SALES (est): 4.2MM **Privately Held**
WEB: www.e2walls.com
SIC: 3275 Gypsum products

(G-17625)
EAG-LED LLC (PA)
Also Called: Eagled Global Lights
12918 Commodity Pl (33626-3119)
PHONE....................813 463-2420
John Grant, *Exec VP*
Amy Grant,
Suzanne Smith,
EMP: 179 **EST:** 2001
SALES (est): 10.9MM **Privately Held**
WEB: www.eag-led.com
SIC: 3648 3641 Floodlights; street lighting fixtures; electric lamps & parts for specialized applications

(G-17626)
EAGLE PRINTING
12223 N Florida Ave (33612-4213)
PHONE....................727 469-8622
Kartal Adiguzel, *President*
EMP: 6 **EST:** 2015
SALES (est): 142.8K **Privately Held**
WEB: www.eagleprintingclearwater.com
SIC: 2752 Commercial printing, offset

(G-17627)
EASTMAN KODAK COMPANY
5364 Ehrlich Rd (33624-6979)
PHONE....................813 908-7910
EMP: 72
SALES (corp-wide): 4.1B **Publicly Held**
SIC: 3861 Nonclassified Establishmentmfg Photo Equip/Supplies & Computer Peripheral Equipment
PA: Eastman Kodak Company
343 State St
Rochester NY 14650
585 724-4000

(G-17628)
EATON CORPORATION
Also Called: Cutler Hammer
1511 N West Shore Blvd # 1111 (33607-4523)
PHONE....................813 281-8069
EMP: 8 **Privately Held**
SIC: 3634 3699 5063 Mfg Electric Housewares/Fans Mfg Electrical Equipment/Supplies Whol Electrical Equipment
HQ: Eaton Corporation
1000 Eaton Blvd
Cleveland OH 44122
216 523-5000

(G-17629)
EATON LAW
14812 N Florida Ave (33613-1844)
PHONE....................813 264-4800
EMP: 5 **EST:** 2019
SALES (est): 399.8K **Privately Held**
WEB: www.eaton-law.com
SIC: 3625 Motor controls & accessories

(G-17630)
ED VANCE PRINTING COMPANY INC
Also Called: Dealer Printing Service
6107 Memorial Hwy Ste E7 (33615-4576)
PHONE....................813 882-8888
Edgar V York, *President*
Edward V York, *President*
Jill S York, *Admin Sec*
EMP: 11 **EST:** 1985
SQ FT: 3,300
SALES (est): 412.2K **Privately Held**
SIC: 2752 2791 2789 Commercial printing, offset; typesetting; bookbinding & related work

(G-17631)
ELECTRCAL SYSTEMS CMMNICATIONS
Also Called: Bay Armature and Supply
1601 N 43rd St (33605-5937)
PHONE....................813 248-4275
Donald Kenney, *President*
Jeannie Hamlet, *Manager*
EMP: 7 **EST:** 1970
SQ FT: 25,000
SALES (est): 210.1K **Privately Held**
WEB: www.bayarmature.com
SIC: 7694 5063 5999 Electric motor repair; motors, electric; motors, electric

(G-17632)
ELEMENTS RESTORATION LLC
401 N Ashley Dr (33602-4301)
P.O. Box 10516 (33679-0516)
PHONE....................813 330-2035
John R Mauk, *Manager*
Vanessa Willett, *Director*
EMP: 21 **EST:** 2013
SALES (est): 9.5MM **Privately Held**
WEB: www.erelements.com
SIC: 1389 1522 1542 1799 Construction, repair & dismantling services; residential construction; nonresidential construction; post-disaster renovations

(G-17633)
ELITE WHEEL DISTRIBUTORS INC (PA)
Also Called: Amani
3901 Riga Blvd (33619-1345)
PHONE....................813 673-8393

▲ = Import ▼=Export
◆ =Import/Export

Hamed Milani, *President*
Kamran Milani, *Vice Pres*
Karla Dominguez, *Bookkeeper*
Justin Mahanes, *Sales Mgr*
◆ **EMP:** 13 **EST:** 2008
SALES (est): 7.4MM **Privately Held**
WEB: www.elitewheelwarehouse.com
SIC: 3312 3011 Wheels; tire & inner tube materials & related products

(G-17634)
ELOGIC LEARNING LLC
14934 N Florida Ave (33613-1632)
PHONE..................................813 901-8600
Mark Anderson, *CEO*
Bill Crandall, *Accounts Exec*
Katie Leahy, *Marketing Staff*
EMP: 35 **EST:** 2001
SALES (est): 9.2MM
SALES (corp-wide): 947.8K **Privately Held**
WEB: www.absorblms.com
SIC: 7372 Educational computer software
PA: Absorb Software Inc
685 Centre St S Suite 2500
Calgary AB T2G 1
403 717-1971

(G-17635)
EMC ROOFING LLC
8822 Thomas Oaks Dr # 40 (33626-1666)
PHONE..................................786 597-6604
Ever M Cantillano, *Manager*
EMP: 7 **EST:** 2019
SALES (est): 443.6K **Privately Held**
SIC: 3572 Computer storage devices

(G-17636)
EMI INDUSTRIES LLC (PA)
Also Called: Edwards Manufacturing
1316 Tech Blvd (33619-7865)
PHONE..................................813 626-3166
Mirko Matic, *General Mgr*
Chad Witt, *General Mgr*
Dave Mueller, *COO*
Gerry McDonald, *Exec VP*
Joseph Mery, *Prdtn Mgr*
◆ **EMP:** 130 **EST:** 1978
SQ FT: 10,000
SALES (est): 53.3MM **Privately Held**
WEB: www.emiindustries.com
SIC: 2541 Wood partitions & fixtures; display fixtures, wood; store fixtures, wood

(G-17637)
EMPIRE SCIENTIFIC
Also Called: Empire Central
4504 E Hillsborough Ave (33610-5249)
PHONE..................................630 510-8636
Jeff English, *Owner*
Bob Slipko, *Purch Mgr*
Robert Slipko, *Manager*
▲ **EMP:** 5
SALES (est): 358.4K **Privately Held**
WEB: www.empirescientific.com
SIC: 3692 Primary batteries, dry & wet

(G-17638)
EMPYRE MUSIC PUBLISHING LLC
1101 N Himes Ave Ste B (33607-5020)
PHONE..................................813 873-7700
Darren Howard, *Manager*
EMP: 7 **EST:** 2011
SALES (est): 102.5K **Privately Held**
SIC: 2741 Miscellaneous publishing

(G-17639)
ENCORE BRANDZ COMPANY
8815 N 15th St (33604-1913)
PHONE..................................813 282-7073
Richard Moore, *President*
EMP: 7 **EST:** 2015
SALES (est): 274.7K **Privately Held**
WEB: www.encoreselect.com
SIC: 2361 Dresses: girls', children's & infants'

(G-17640)
ENGINE LAB OF TAMPA INC
201 S 78th St (33619-4225)
PHONE..................................813 630-2422
Susan Deegan, *President*
David Deegan, *Vice Pres*
EMP: 12 **EST:** 1994
SQ FT: 15,600
SALES (est): 534.2K **Privately Held**
WEB: www.enginelaboftampa.com
SIC: 3519 7538 Gas engine rebuilding; engine rebuilding: automotive

(G-17641)
ENGINEERED AIR SYSTEMS INC
Also Called: E A S I
6605 Walton Way (33610-5516)
PHONE..................................813 881-9555
Bruce Loubet, *Vice Pres*
Bruce Loubet Jr, *Vice Pres*
EMP: 12 **EST:** 1987
SALES (est): 2.4MM **Privately Held**
WEB: www.eashvacr.com
SIC: 3585 5065 5039 Refrigeration & heating equipment; telegraph equipment; air ducts, sheet metal; architectural metalwork

(G-17642)
ENGINEERING ANALYSIS GROUP LLC
13902 N Dale Mabry Hwy # 230 (33618-2433)
P.O. Box 340462 (33694-0462)
PHONE..................................813 523-7377
Erin Lykins, *Manager*
EMP: 5 **EST:** 2015
SALES (est): 308K **Privately Held**
SIC: 1389 Testing, measuring, surveying & analysis services

(G-17643)
ENTERRA INC
2801 W Busch Blvd (33618-4500)
PHONE..................................813 514-0531
Jeremy Groves, *Principal*
Alexander Tamplon, *CTO*
EMP: 9 **EST:** 2008
SALES (est): 330.4K **Privately Held**
WEB: www.enterra-inc.com
SIC: 2741 Guides: publishing & printing

(G-17644)
ENVIRO FOCUS TECHNOLOGY
6505 Jewel Ave (33619-2903)
PHONE..................................813 744-5000
Larry Eagan, *Principal*
▲ **EMP:** 7 **EST:** 2011
SALES (est): 304.7K **Privately Held**
SIC: 3341 Secondary nonferrous metals

(G-17645)
ENVIROFOCUS TECHNOLOGIES LLC
1901 N 66th St (33619-2901)
PHONE..................................813 620-3260
Mark Kutoff, *Mng Member*
Maier Kutoff,
Kevin Murphy,
▲ **EMP:** 70 **EST:** 2006
SALES (est): 16.1MM
SALES (corp-wide): 117.3MM **Privately Held**
WEB: www.gopherresource.com
SIC: 3339 Lead & zinc
PA: Gopher Resource, Llc
2900 Lone Oak Pkwy 140a
Eagan MN 55121
651 454-3310

(G-17646)
EPC INC
3629 Queen Palm Dr (33619-1309)
PHONE..................................636 443-1999
Paula Noblitt, *General Mgr*
Parriss Shanno, *Executive*
EMP: 16 **EST:** 2015
SALES (est): 975.1K **Privately Held**
WEB: www.epchc.org
SIC: 3571 Electronic computers

(G-17647)
EPPERSON & COMPANY
5202 Shadowlawn Ave (33610-5310)
PHONE..................................813 626-6125
James M Abbitt Jr, *President*
Rob Harris, *Vice Pres*
Jeffrey F Rowe, *Vice Pres*
Terry Montefusco, *Controller*
Alice A Abbitt, *Shareholder*
▼ **EMP:** 53 **EST:** 1956
SQ FT: 25,000
SALES (est): 9.7MM **Privately Held**
SIC: 3535 Conveyors & conveying equipment

(G-17648)
ERSION INTERNTNAL CTRL SYSTEMS
3030 N Rocky Point Dr W # 1 (33607-5803)
PHONE..................................800 821-7462
Charlie Chase, *President*
Derek Dice, *General Mgr*
Louis Arvai, *Vice Pres*
EMP: 1 **EST:** 2005
SALES (est): 3MM **Privately Held**
WEB: www.iecs.com
SIC: 3272 Concrete products

(G-17649)
ERWIN INC
201 N Franklin St # 2200 (33602-5182)
PHONE..................................813 933-3323
James R Hale, *President*
Andy Harkness, *Sales Staff*
Martyna Kucneryte, *Sales Staff*
Zak Cole, *Manager*
Christopher Spring, *Manager*
EMP: 13 **EST:** 2016
SALES (est): 1.1MM **Privately Held**
WEB: www.erwin.com
SIC: 7372 Prepackaged software

(G-17650)
ETAS TIMEADMIN CORPORATION
307 S Boulevard Ste A (33606-2177)
PHONE..................................813 464-4175
Ventzislav Issaev, *President*
EMP: 6 **EST:** 2010
SALES (est): 136.8K **Privately Held**
WEB: www.timeadmin.com
SIC: 7372 Business oriented computer software

(G-17651)
EVOQUA WATER TECHNOLOGIES LLC
4711 Oak Fair Blvd (33610-7386)
PHONE..................................813 620-0900
Kimberly Callahan, *Sales Staff*
Dave Braykovith, *Manager*
Patrick Francois, *Director*
EMP: 6
SALES (corp-wide): 1.4B **Publicly Held**
WEB: www.evoqua.com
SIC: 3589 Water treatment equipment, industrial
HQ: Evoqua Water Technologies Llc
210 6th Ave Ste 3300
Pittsburgh PA 15222
724 772-0044

(G-17652)
EXACTUS PHARMACY SOLUTIONS INC
8715 Henderson Rd (33634-1143)
P.O. Box 31422 (33631-3422)
PHONE..................................888 314-3874
Dave Gallitano, *CEO*
Thomas L Tran, *Director*
EMP: 71 **EST:** 2007
SALES (est): 10.1MM **Publicly Held**
WEB: www.acariahealth.envolvehealth.com
SIC: 2834 Druggists' preparations (pharmaceuticals)
HQ: Wellcare Health Plans, Inc.
8735 Henderson Rd
Tampa FL 33634
813 290-6200

(G-17653)
EXPRESS ORNAMENTAL LLC
9211 Maybury Ct (33615-1964)
PHONE..................................813 486-0344
Melissa Rodrigues, *Principal*
EMP: 6 **EST:** 2010
SALES (est): 66.5K **Privately Held**
SIC: 3446 Architectural metalwork

(G-17654)
EXPRESS PAVERS LLC
7716 Winging Way Dr (33615-1347)
PHONE..................................813 408-9938
Bruno E Paula, *Principal*
EMP: 7 **EST:** 2014
SALES (est): 140.3K **Privately Held**
SIC: 2951 Asphalt paving mixtures & blocks

(G-17655)
EXPRESS PRESS INC
107 N Jefferson St (33602-5001)
PHONE..................................813 884-3310
Greg Winchell, *President*
Steve Backhaus, *Vice Pres*
Thomas Harrison, *Vice Pres*
Laura Regan, *Executive*
Marvin Hill, *Graphic Designe*
EMP: 16 **EST:** 1980
SALES (est): 2.6MM **Privately Held**
WEB: www.eptampa.com
SIC: 2752 Commercial printing, offset

(G-17656)
FABA CABINETS & SUCH LLC
7029 W Hillsborough Ave (33634-4947)
PHONE..................................813 871-1529
Maribel Martinez, *Principal*
EMP: 6 **EST:** 2015
SALES (est): 142.8K **Privately Held**
SIC: 2434 Wood kitchen cabinets

(G-17657)
FABRICATED PRODUCTS TAMPA INC
1100 S 56th St (33619-3763)
PHONE..................................813 247-4001
Michael H Hunt, *President*
M Lynn Hunt, *Corp Secy*
Steven Hunt, *Vice Pres*
EMP: 40 **EST:** 1974
SALES (est): 7.3MM **Privately Held**
WEB: www.fabricatedprod.com
SIC: 3441 Building components, structural steel

(G-17658)
FAOURS MIRROR CORP
Also Called: Faour Glass Technologies
5119 W Knox St Ste A (33634-8093)
PHONE..................................813 884-3297
John Faour, *President*
Angelo Rivera, *Vice Pres*
Gavin Reisinger, *Project Mgr*
Steve Babbitt, *Opers Mgr*
Tommy Creacy, *Foreman/Supr*
◆ **EMP:** 25 **EST:** 1975
SQ FT: 10,000
SALES (est): 5.5MM **Privately Held**
WEB: www.faourglass.com
SIC: 3211 5039 5231 Flat glass; glass construction materials; glass

(G-17659)
FARADAY INC
802 E Whiting St (33602-4136)
PHONE..................................813 536-6104
Clyde Snodgrass, *CEO*
EMP: 10 **EST:** 2014
SQ FT: 1,200
SALES (est): 705.5K **Privately Held**
WEB: www.myvinonovo.com
SIC: 2084 Wines

(G-17660)
FAST SIGNS
Also Called: Fastsigns
14618 N Dale Mabry Hwy (33618-2024)
PHONE..................................813 999-4981
Stacey Alexander, *CEO*
EMP: 9 **EST:** 2015
SALES (est): 1.3MM **Privately Held**
WEB: www.fastsigns.com
SIC: 3993 Signs & advertising specialties

(G-17661)
FASTENER SOLUTIONS LLC
333 N Falkenburg Rd (33619-7888)
PHONE..................................813 324-8372
Jeremiah Windle, *President*
EMP: 6 **EST:** 2017
SALES (est): 137.9K **Privately Held**
WEB: www.fastenersolutions.com
SIC: 3965 Fasteners

(G-17662)
FASTENER SOLUTIONS LLC
2420 W Stroud Ave (33629-6218)
PHONE..................................813 867-4714
Jeremiah Windle, *Manager*
EMP: 6 **EST:** 2017

SALES (est): 80K Privately Held
WEB: www.fastenersolutions.com
SIC: 3965 Fasteners

(G-17663)
FEATHERLITE EXHIBITS
1715 E Sewaha St (33612-8677)
PHONE....................800 229-5533
Mark Lee, *Principal*
EMP: 9 EST: 2016
SALES (est): 99.4K Privately Held
WEB: www.featherlite.com
SIC: 2541 Wood partitions & fixtures

(G-17664)
FENWALL LLC (PA)
12850 Commodity Pl (33626-3101)
PHONE....................813 343-5979
Joseph Muraco, *Mng Member*
EMP: 64 EST: 2014
SALES (est): 2.6MM Privately Held
WEB: www.fenwalls.com
SIC: 3449 Curtain walls for buildings, steel

(G-17665)
FILTERS PLUS INC
6708 Benjamin Rd Ste 200 (33634-4406)
PHONE....................813 232-2000
Tom Waites, *President*
Jerry Kautz, *Sales Staff*
Steven P Myers, *Director*
Gary Bergeron, *Technician*
EMP: 5 EST: 2004
SALES (est): 1.1MM Privately Held
WEB: www.filtersplus.com
SIC: 3564 Filters, air: furnaces, air conditioning equipment, etc.

(G-17666)
FIRST GRADE FOOD CORPORATION
Also Called: Lucky Fortune Cookie
5134 W Hanna Ave (33634-8020)
PHONE....................813 886-6118
Jimmy Luong, *President*
Tim Luong, *Vice Pres*
◆ EMP: 33 EST: 1986
SQ FT: 11,000
SALES (est): 2MM Privately Held
SIC: 2052 2098 Cookies; macaroni & spaghetti

(G-17667)
FIX N FLY DRONES LLC
2105 N Jamaica St (33607-3128)
PHONE....................321 474-2291
Timothy R Hileman, *Principal*
EMP: 6 EST: 2016
SALES (est): 531.9K Privately Held
WEB: www.fixnflydrones.com
SIC: 3721 Motorized aircraft

(G-17668)
FLAYCO PRODUCTS INC
4821 N Hale Ave (33614-6517)
P.O. Box 15967 (33684-5967)
PHONE....................813 879-1356
Jorge Astorquiza, *President*
Teresa Astorquiza, *Corp Secy*
◆ EMP: 37 EST: 1975
SQ FT: 10,000
SALES (est): 1.5MM Privately Held
WEB: www.flayco.com
SIC: 2087 2099 2033 2034 Extracts, flavoring; food colorings; seasonings & spices; barbecue sauce: packaged in cans, jars, etc.; dried & dehydrated soup mixes; pickles, sauces & salad dressings; dry, condensed, evaporated dairy products

(G-17669)
FLEETMATICS
4211 W Boy Scout Blvd # 4 (33607-5724)
PHONE....................727 483-9016
EMP: 11 EST: 2017
SALES (est): 258.1K Privately Held
WEB: www.verizonconnect.com
SIC: 7372 Prepackaged software

(G-17670)
FLINT LLC
1212 Maydell Dr (33619-4547)
PHONE....................813 622-8899
Eric Chang,
EMP: 5 EST: 2006
SALES (est): 468K Privately Held
WEB: www.flintllc.com
SIC: 3679 Electronic circuits

(G-17671)
FLOORS INC
6205 Johns Rd Ste 1 (33634-4492)
P.O. Box 15573 (33684-5573)
PHONE....................813 879-5720
Michael B Crowley, *President*
Karen Crowley, *Corp Secy*
EMP: 30 EST: 1960
SQ FT: 12,000
SALES (est): 3MM Privately Held
WEB: www.floorsinc.org
SIC: 2273 1771 Floor coverings, textile fiber; flooring contractor

(G-17672)
FLORIDA BLOCK & READY MIX LLC
5208 36th Ave S (33619-6801)
PHONE....................813 623-3700
Hprb Romancky, *Branch Mgr*
EMP: 28
SQ FT: 30,504 Privately Held
SIC: 3273 Ready-mixed concrete
PA: Florida Block & Ready Mix Llc
12795 49th St N
Clearwater FL 33762

(G-17673)
FLORIDA BOAT LIFT
4821 N Manhattan Ave (33614-6413)
PHONE....................813 873-1614
Tom Kraemer, *Owner*
EMP: 7 EST: 2013
SALES (est): 885.1K Privately Held
WEB: www.floridaboatlifts.com
SIC: 3536 Boat lifts

(G-17674)
FLORIDA DACCO/DETROIT INC
3611 W Chestnut St (33607-2556)
PHONE....................813 879-4131
Rick Wicky, *Manager*
▲ EMP: 23 EST: 2000
SALES (est): 1.1MM Privately Held
SIC: 3714 5013 Motor vehicle parts & accessories; motor vehicle supplies & new parts

(G-17675)
FLORIDA DISTILLERY LLC
Also Called: Florida Cane Distillery, The
501 S Falkenburg Rd C5 (33619-8034)
PHONE....................813 347-6565
Lee P Nelson,
Patrick O'Brien,
▼ EMP: 9
SQ FT: 2,200
SALES (est): 470K Privately Held
SIC: 2085 Vodka (alcoholic beverage)

(G-17676)
FLORIDA FISHING PRODUCTS
205 W Ohio Ave (33603-5619)
PHONE....................239 938-4612
William Nelson, *Principal*
EMP: 9 EST: 2017
SALES (est): 480.5K Privately Held
WEB: www.floridafishingproducts.com
SIC: 3949 Sporting & athletic goods

(G-17677)
FLORIDA GLASS OF TAMPA BAY
13929 Lynmar Blvd (33626-3124)
PHONE....................813 925-1330
Joe Muraco, *Principal*
Mary Shields, *CFO*
Marilyn Baker, *Accountant*
▲ EMP: 53 EST: 1993
SALES (est): 2.9MM Privately Held
SIC: 3231 1542 3441 Doors, glass: made from purchased glass; store front construction; fabricated structural metal

(G-17678)
FLORIDA INDUS SOLUTIONS LLC
13773 N Nebraska Ave (33613-3320)
PHONE....................833 746-7347
Rick Sasser,
Julie Sasser,
EMP: 9 EST: 2017
SALES (est): 519.2K Privately Held
WEB: www.floridaindustrialsolutions.com
SIC: 3452 Bolts, nuts, rivets & washers

(G-17679)
FLORIDA INK MFG CO INC
Also Called: F I M C O
1715 Temple St (33619-3161)
PHONE....................813 247-2911
George B Nessmith, *President*
Tiny J Nessmith, *Corp Secy*
John S Nessmith, *Vice Pres*
Scott L Nessmith, *VP Mfg*
EMP: 8 EST: 1983
SQ FT: 16,000
SALES (est): 1.7MM Privately Held
WEB: www.flaink.com
SIC: 2893 Printing ink

(G-17680)
FLORIDA LEVEL & TRANSIT CO INC
Also Called: Flt Geosystems
5468 56th Cmmrce Pk Blvd (33610-6857)
PHONE....................813 623-3307
Paul Browning, *Manager*
EMP: 7
SALES (corp-wide): 8.7MM Privately Held
WEB: www.secure.fltgeosystems.com
SIC: 3829 Measuring & controlling devices
PA: Florida Level & Transit Co., Inc.
809 Progresso Dr
Fort Lauderdale FL 33304
954 763-5300

(G-17681)
FLORIDA MADE DOOR CO (PA)
Also Called: West Bay Door
1 N Dale Mabry Hwy # 950 (33609-2764)
P.O. Box 128, Astatula (34705-0128)
PHONE....................352 742-1000
Frank L Eger Jr, *President*
Joseph P Eger, *Vice Pres*
Bob Brown, *Controller*
◆ EMP: 140 EST: 1954
SQ FT: 130,000
SALES (est): 15.9MM Privately Held
WEB: www.floridamadedoor.com
SIC: 2431 Doors, wood

(G-17682)
FLORIDA MARINE JOINER SVC INC
4917 Hartford St (33619-6715)
P.O. Box 89729 (33689-0412)
PHONE....................813 514-1125
William Doyle, *President*
Marsha Doyle,
▲ EMP: 15 EST: 2012
SALES (est): 1.7MM Privately Held
WEB: www.fmjsi.com
SIC: 2431 1751 7699 1742 Millwork; carpentry work; cabinet & finish carpentry; finish & trim carpentry; boat repair; acoustical & insulation work

(G-17683)
FLORIDA MARINE PRODUCTS INC
2001 E 5th Ave (33605-5221)
PHONE....................813 248-2283
Randolph Urban Pattillo, *President*
Randolph A Pattillo, *Corp Secy*
EMP: 10 EST: 1986
SQ FT: 13,000
SALES (est): 3.4MM Privately Held
WEB: www.fmpusa.com
SIC: 3592 Valves

(G-17684)
FLORIDA PLAYGROUND & STEEL CO
4701 S 50th St (33619-9510)
PHONE....................813 247-2812
Rick Barrs, *President*
▼ EMP: 6 EST: 1942
SQ FT: 8,000
SALES (est): 615K Privately Held
WEB: www.fla-playground.com
SIC: 3949 Playground equipment

(G-17685)
FLORIDA PRE-FAB INC
2907 Sagasta St (33619-6000)
PHONE....................813 247-3934
George Levy, *President*
Alexander Levy, *VP Finance*
Alejandro Pose, *CIO*
▼ EMP: 19 EST: 1972
SQ FT: 95,000
SALES (est): 2.4MM Privately Held
WEB: www.floridaprefab.com
SIC: 3448 Buildings, portable: prefabricated metal

(G-17686)
FLORIDA PRECISION MCH MET WORK
5904 Lynn Rd (33624-4800)
PHONE....................813 486-5050
Guillermo Valdes, *Principal*
EMP: 9 EST: 2008
SALES (est): 111.7K Privately Held
SIC: 3599 Machine shop, jobbing & repair

(G-17687)
FLORIDA PWRTRAIN HYDRULICS INC
Also Called: Tampa Powertrain & Hydraulics
6501 E Adamo Dr (33619-3413)
PHONE....................813 623-6713
Gerald Guinn, *Manager*
EMP: 6
SALES (corp-wide): 6.2MM Privately Held
WEB: www.floridapowertrain.com
SIC: 3714 Motor vehicle parts & accessories
PA: Florida Powertrain & Hydraulics, Inc.
2265 W Beaver St
Jacksonville FL 32209
904 354-5691

(G-17688)
FLORIDA SENTINEL PUBLISHING CO
Also Called: Florida Sentinel Bulletin
2207 E 21st Ave (33605-2043)
P.O. Box 3363 (33601-3363)
PHONE....................813 248-1921
Blythe Andrews III, *President*
EMP: 48 EST: 1945
SQ FT: 4,900
SALES (est): 4.7MM Privately Held
WEB: www.flsentinel.com
SIC: 2711 2752 Newspapers: publishing only, not printed on site; commercial printing, lithographic

(G-17689)
FMC/RHYNO LLC
Also Called: Rhyno Glass
5115 W Knox St (33634-8000)
PHONE....................813 838-2264
Wyatt Castellvi, *Mng Member*
EMP: 38 EST: 2018
SALES (est): 5.9MM Privately Held
SIC: 3211 Flat glass

(G-17690)
FOAM MOLDING LLC
3211 W Beach St (33607-2168)
PHONE....................813 434-7044
Alexis Hernandez, *Principal*
EMP: 6 EST: 2015
SALES (est): 159.7K Privately Held
SIC: 3089 Molding primary plastic

(G-17691)
FOLDERS TABS ET CETERA
4906 Savarese Cir (33634-2403)
PHONE....................813 884-3651
Joe Torrence, *President*
Debbie Torrence, *Vice Pres*
EMP: 11 EST: 1989
SQ FT: 14,000
SALES (est): 495.5K Privately Held
WEB: www.ftec.ws
SIC: 2893 2675 2672 Letterpress or offset ink; die-cut paper & board; coated & laminated paper

(G-17692)
FOUR SEAS TRADING CORP
Also Called: Oceanic Resturant Equipment
1542 N Franklin St (33602-2620)
PHONE....................................813 221-0895
S Cheong Choi, *Principal*
EMP: 6 **EST:** 2008
SALES (est): 67.7K **Privately Held**
WEB: www.gutterhelmetsv.com
SIC: 2599 Restaurant furniture, wood or metal

(G-17693)
FPC PRINTING INC
201 Kelsey Ln (33619-4310)
PHONE....................................813 626-9430
James L Kendall, *President*
Donice Payne, *President*
A J M Mandt, *Director*
EMP: 98 **EST:** 1988
SQ FT: 70,000
SALES (est): 3MM
SALES (corp-wide): 176.9MM **Publicly Held**
WEB: www.hartehanks.com
SIC: 2741 Shopping news: publishing & printing
PA: Harte Hanks, Inc.
2800 Wells Branch Pkwy
Austin TX 78728
512 343-1100

(G-17694)
FREE PRESS PUBLISHING COMPANY
1010 W Cass St (33606-1307)
PHONE....................................813 254-5888
John N Harrison III, *Ch of Bd*
John Harrison IV, *President*
Joann Klay, *Vice Pres*
EMP: 29 **EST:** 1911
SQ FT: 17,000
SALES (est): 2.8MM **Privately Held**
WEB: www.4freepress.com
SIC: 2752 2711 Commercial printing, offset; color lithography; newspapers, publishing & printing

(G-17695)
FREEPORT AMMONIA LLC
100 N Tampa St Ste 3200 (33602-5830)
PHONE....................................813 222-3813
Rosemary Malarkey, *Director*
Frank Mandarino,
Alvin Rosvoll,
Frederik Schultz,
EMP: 6 **EST:** 2014
SALES (est): 107.6K **Privately Held**
SIC: 2873 Ammonia & ammonium salts

(G-17696)
FRESH BRANDZ LLC
6201 Johns Rd Ste 11 (33634-4434)
PHONE....................................813 880-7110
Robert Johnson, *CEO*
EMP: 9 **EST:** 2018
SQ FT: 8,000
SALES (est): 1.7MM **Privately Held**
SIC: 2844 5122 Toilet preparations; toiletries

(G-17697)
FUEL SOLUTIONS LLC
14213 Banbury Way (33624-2620)
PHONE....................................813 969-2506
Bernard Arenas,
Kevin B Banish,
EMP: 8 **EST:** 2008
SALES (est): 803.2K **Privately Held**
SIC: 2869 Fuels

(G-17698)
FUTURE PLUS OF FLORIDA
138 S Dale Mabry Hwy (33609-2837)
PHONE....................................612 240-7275
Daniel R Snyder, *Principal*
EMP: 9 **EST:** 2012
SALES (est): 1.1MM **Privately Held**
SIC: 3692 Primary batteries, dry & wet

(G-17699)
FUZION DIGITAL SIGNS
4409 N Clark Ave (33614-7017)
PHONE....................................844 529-0505
EMP: 7 **EST:** 2015
SALES (est): 309.6K **Privately Held**
WEB: www.fuzioninternational.com
SIC: 3999 Manufacturing industries

(G-17700)
FW SHORING COMPANY
Also Called: Professional Shoring & Supply
7532 Malta Ln (33637-6725)
PHONE....................................813 248-2495
Kevin Chandler, *Branch Mgr*
EMP: 7
SALES (corp-wide): 23.4MM **Privately Held**
WEB: www.efficiencyproduction.com
SIC: 3531 Construction machinery
PA: Fw Shoring Company
685 Hull Rd
Mason MI 48854
517 676-8800

(G-17701)
G G MARKERS INC
4815 N Coolidge Ave (33614-6456)
P.O. Box 47625 (33646-0114)
PHONE....................................813 873-8181
Ben Irimescu, *President*
EMP: 5 **EST:** 2000
SALES (est): 750K **Privately Held**
WEB: www.ggmarkers.com
SIC: 3993 Signs, not made in custom sign painting shops

(G-17702)
GALLOP GROUP INC
2402 S Ardson Pl (33629-7308)
PHONE....................................813 251-6242
Nancy M Peterson, *Principal*
EMP: 7 **EST:** 2010
SALES (est): 127.7K **Privately Held**
WEB: www.jamesmanninglaw.com
SIC: 3241 Cement, hydraulic

(G-17703)
GARDNER ASPHALT CORPORATION (DH)
4161 E 7th Ave (33605-4601)
P.O. Box 5449 (33675-5449)
PHONE....................................813 248-2101
Raymond T Hyer, *Ch of Bd*
Amir Khan, *Vice Pres*
Mike Lazuk, *Vice Pres*
Gustavo Velez, *Plant Mgr*
Jennifer Martinez, *Traffic Mgr*
◆ **EMP:** 64 **EST:** 1945
SQ FT: 40,000
SALES (est): 216.7MM
SALES (corp-wide): 870.7MM **Privately Held**
WEB: www.gardner-gibson.com
SIC: 2951 Asphalt paving mixtures & blocks
HQ: Gardner-Gibson, Incorporated
4161 E 7th Ave
Tampa FL 33605
813 248-2101

(G-17704)
GARDNER ASPHALT CORPORATION
Also Called: Gardber-Gibson
4001 E 7th Ave (33605-4506)
PHONE....................................813 248-2101
Mike Hyer, *Sales Staff*
Mike Sullivan, *Sales Staff*
Menlo Scquera, *Manager*
Neil Loftie, *Info Tech Dir*
EMP: 131
SALES (corp-wide): 870.7MM **Privately Held**
WEB: www.gardner-gibson.com
SIC: 3531 Roofing equipment
HQ: Gardner Asphalt Corporation
4161 E 7th Ave
Tampa FL 33605
813 248-2101

(G-17705)
GARDNER-GIBSON MFG INC (DH)
4161 E 7th Ave (33605-4601)
P.O. Box 5449 (33675-5449)
PHONE....................................813 248-2101
Raymond T Hyer Jr, *President*
Sean W Poole, *Treasurer*
Darminda Ranatunga, *Controller*
Mike Hyer, *Sales Staff*
Thomas Flood, *Manager*
◆ **EMP:** 25 **EST:** 2000
SALES (est): 75.3MM
SALES (corp-wide): 870.7MM **Privately Held**
WEB: www.gardner-gibson.com
SIC: 2951 2891 2952 Asphalt paving mixtures & blocks; adhesives & sealants; roof cement: asphalt, fibrous or plastic
HQ: Gardner-Gibson, Incorporated
4161 E 7th Ave
Tampa FL 33605
813 248-2101

(G-17706)
GEM ASSET ACQUISITION LLC
Also Called: Gemseal Pavements Pdts - Tampa
5050 Denver St (33619-6812)
PHONE....................................813 630-1695
EMP: 17
SALES (corp-wide): 31.7MM **Privately Held**
SIC: 2951 Asphalt paving mixtures & blocks
PA: Gem Asset Acquisition Llc
1855 Lindbergh St Ste 500
Charlotte NC 28208
704 225-3321

(G-17707)
GEMSEAL PAVEMENT PRODUCTS
5050 Denver St (33619-6812)
PHONE....................................305 328-9159
Robert Knarr, *Sales Staff*
Carolyn Bradeen, *Office Mgr*
Chris Mariani, *CIO*
EMP: 10 **EST:** 2017
SALES (est): 1.2MM **Privately Held**
WEB: www.gemsealproducts.com
SIC: 2951 Asphalt paving mixtures & blocks

(G-17708)
GENERAL SAW COMPANY
2902 E Sligh Ave (33610-1412)
PHONE....................................813 231-3167
Timothy Murphy, *President*
EMP: 15 **EST:** 1990
SQ FT: 14,000
SALES (est): 3.2MM **Privately Held**
WEB: www.gensaw.com
SIC: 3441 Fabricated structural metal

(G-17709)
GENESIS SYSTEMS LLC
3108 N Boundary Blvd # 9 (33621-5050)
PHONE....................................417 499-3301
David J Stuckenberg, *CEO*
Shannon Stuckenberg, *CEO*
EMP: 9 **EST:** 2008
SALES (est): 1MM **Privately Held**
WEB: www.genesissystems.global
SIC: 3589 Water treatment equipment, industrial

(G-17710)
GERDAU AMERISTEEL CORP (HQ)
4221 W Boy Scout Blvd # 600 (33607-5760)
P.O. Box 31328 (33631-3328)
PHONE....................................813 286-8383
Mario Longhi, *President*
Guilherme C Gerdau Johannpeter, *President*
Rick Szink, *General Mgr*
Tony Klippel, *Superintendent*
Dean Wner, *Superintendent*
◆ **EMP:** 560 **EST:** 1956
SALES (est): 1.4B **Privately Held**
WEB: www.jobs.gerdau.com
SIC: 3312 Blast furnaces & steel mills

(G-17711)
GERDAU AMERISTEEL US INC (DH)
Also Called: Gerdau Long Steel North Amer
4221 W Boy Scout Blvd # 600 (33607-5760)
P.O. Box 31328 (33631-3328)
PHONE....................................813 286-8383
Peter J Campo, *CEO*
Guilherme G Johannpeter, *President*
Andre Johannpeter, *Principal*
Franz Olbrich, *Principal*
Darlene Quintilliani, *Principal*
◆ **EMP:** 300 **EST:** 1956
SQ FT: 68,310
SALES (est): 1.5B **Privately Held**
WEB: www.gerdau.com
SIC: 3312 3449 3315 Hot-rolled iron & steel products; bars & bar shapes, steel, hot-rolled; structural shapes & pilings, steel; bars, concrete reinforcing: fabricated steel; spikes, steel: wire or cut; welded steel wire fabric; nails, steel: wire or cut
HQ: Gerdau Usa Inc.
4221 W Boy Scout Blvd
Tampa FL 33607
813 286-8383

(G-17712)
GERDAU USA INC (DH)
Also Called: Gerdau Long Steel America
4221 W Boy Scout Blvd (33607-5743)
PHONE....................................813 286-8383
Guilherme Johannpeter, *President*
Peter J Campo, *Vice Pres*
Carl W Czarnik, *Vice Pres*
Rodrigo Ferreira De Souza, *Vice Pres*
Chia Wang, *Vice Pres*
◆ **EMP:** 350
SQ FT: 35,000
SALES (est): 5.8B **Privately Held**
WEB: www.gerdau.com
SIC: 3449 3315 3312 Bars, concrete reinforcing: fabricated steel; spikes, steel: wire or cut; welded steel wire fabric; nails, steel: wire or cut; hot-rolled iron & steel products
HQ: Gerdau Ameristeel Corporation
1801 Hopkins St
Whitby ON L1N 5
905 668-8811

(G-17713)
GLIDER PRINTING LLC
13377 W Hillsborough Ave Uni (33635-9717)
PHONE....................................813 601-8907
Mark Hammonds, *Principal*
EMP: 5 **EST:** 2016
SALES (est): 323.6K **Privately Held**
SIC: 2752 Commercial printing, lithographic

(G-17714)
GLOBAL COMPOSITE USA INC
6608 S West Shore Blvd (33616-1458)
PHONE....................................813 898-7987
Matt Major, *President*
EMP: 50
SALES (est): 1MM **Privately Held**
SIC: 3999 Manufacturing industries

(G-17715)
GLOBAL FRICTION PRODUCTS INC
2003 S 50th St (33619-5225)
PHONE....................................813 241-2700
Billy Peek, *President*
Stacy Peek, *Vice Pres*
EMP: 10 **EST:** 1996
SQ FT: 2,000
SALES (est): 2.8MM **Privately Held**
WEB: www.globalfrictionproducts.com
SIC: 3469 Metal stampings

(G-17716)
GLOBAL MEDIA PRESS CORP
6723 N Armenia Ave (33604-5715)
P.O. Box 15657 (33684-5657)
PHONE....................................813 857-5898
Mario F Vallejo, *President*
EMP: 6 **EST:** 2011
SALES (est): 86.7K **Privately Held**
SIC: 2741 Miscellaneous publishing

(G-17717)
GLOBAL PRODUCTS GROUP LLC (PA)
13760 Reptron Blvd (33626-3040)
PHONE....................................866 320-4367
Gene Weitz, *Mng Member*
EMP: 27 **EST:** 2018
SALES (est): 94.4K **Privately Held**
SIC: 3999

GEOGRAPHIC

(G-17718)
GLOBAL SEASHELL INDUSTRIES LLC
4930 Distribution Dr (33605-5926)
P.O. Box 129, Los Fresnos TX (78566-0129)
PHONE....................................813 677-6674
Elizabeth Harris, *Manager*
◆ **EMP:** 8 **EST:** 2010
SALES (est): 814K **Privately Held**
WEB: www.globalseashell.com
SIC: 3999 Manufacturing industries

(G-17719)
GLOBAL VILLAGE VENTURES
5415 W Sligh Ave Ste 102 (33634-4488)
PHONE....................................813 453-6199
Sven Boermeester, *Principal*
EMP: 6 **EST:** 2017
SALES (est): 102.9K **Privately Held**
SIC: 2731 Books: publishing & printing

(G-17720)
GOLD COAST PRINTING INC
401 E Jackson St Ste 2340 (33602-5226)
PHONE....................................813 853-2219
Steven Bicking, *President*
EMP: 6 **EST:** 2016
SQ FT: 4,000
SALES (est): 142.5K **Privately Held**
SIC: 2752 Commercial printing, lithographic

(G-17721)
GOLD REFINERY
18019 Palm Breeze Dr (33647-2839)
PHONE....................................813 220-5067
Joanne Wagner, *Principal*
EMP: 6 **EST:** 2010
SALES (est): 229.2K **Privately Held**
SIC: 3559 Refinery, chemical processing & similar machinery

(G-17722)
GOTOBILLING INC
Also Called: Omnifund
218 E Bearss Ave Ste 368 (33613-1625)
PHONE....................................800 305-1534
Steve Roderick, *CEO*
EMP: 13 **EST:** 2007
SALES (est): 1.1MM **Privately Held**
WEB: www.omnifund.com
SIC: 7372 Business oriented computer software

(G-17723)
GRABBER CONSTRUCTION PDTS INC
5835 Barry Rd Ste 107 (33634-3020)
PHONE....................................813 249-2281
Jim Briggers, *Manager*
EMP: 7
SALES (corp-wide): 1B **Privately Held**
WEB: www.grabberman.com
SIC: 3452 5032 5085 Screws, metal; drywall materials; fasteners, industrial: nuts, bolts, screws, etc.
HQ: Grabber Construction Products, Inc.
5255 W 11000 N Ste 100
Highland UT 84003
801 492-3880

(G-17724)
GRANITE SERVICES INTL INC
Also Called: Pen Power
201 N Franklin St # 1000 (33602-5182)
PHONE....................................813 242-7400
Randy Willis, *President*
Mort Smith, *Vice Pres*
Morgan Williams, *CFO*
Mica Segui, *VP Human Res*
EMP: 11 **EST:** 2002
SALES (est): 10.4MM
SALES (corp-wide): 79.6B **Publicly Held**
SIC: 3519 7363 8711 Gasoline engines; help supply services; engineering services
HQ: Fieldcore Service Solutions International Llc
201 N Franklin St # 1000
Tampa FL 33602
813 242-7400

(G-17725)
GRANITE WORLD INC
7024 Benjamin Rd (33634-3034)
PHONE....................................813 243-6556
Rudolfo Vidal, *President*
Julie Vidal, *Vice Pres*
EMP: 26 **EST:** 2000
SQ FT: 10,000
SALES (est): 1.3MM **Privately Held**
WEB: www.graniteworldinc.com
SIC: 3281 1423 Cut stone & stone products; crushed & broken granite

(G-17726)
GRASS PRO SHOPS INC
303 S Falkenburg Rd (33619-8027)
PHONE....................................813 381-3890
Raymond Ham, *President*
James Dombrosky, *Manager*
EMP: 17 **EST:** 2009
SALES (est): 2.8MM **Privately Held**
WEB: www.grassproshops.com
SIC: 3537 Industrial trucks & tractors

(G-17727)
GREAT AMERICAN ROLLING PPR CO
5015 W Nassau St (33607-3814)
PHONE....................................813 928-9166
Joel Prackler, *President*
EMP: 6 **EST:** 2016
SALES (est): 84.3K **Privately Held**
WEB: www.garpusa.com
SIC: 2621 Wrapping paper

(G-17728)
GREENCO MANUFACTURING CORP
Also Called: Duramaster
5688 W Crenshaw St Frnt (33634-3043)
PHONE....................................813 882-4400
Joseph T Green, *President*
Jaime Howe, *Controller*
EMP: 24 **EST:** 1970
SQ FT: 20,000
SALES (est): 3MM **Privately Held**
WEB: www.greencocylinders.com
SIC: 3593 3443 Fluid power cylinders, hydraulic or pneumatic; fabricated plate work (boiler shop)

(G-17729)
GRIFFIN INDUSTRIES LLC
1001 Orient Rd (33619-3321)
PHONE....................................813 626-1135
Garry Byrd, *General Mgr*
Patrick Collins, *General Mgr*
Robert Huffman, *General Mgr*
Jerome Levy, *General Mgr*
Tom Molini, *General Mgr*
EMP: 49
SQ FT: 33,078
SALES (corp-wide): 3.3B **Publicly Held**
WEB: www.griffinind.com
SIC: 2077 5199 Tallow rendering, inedible; oils, animal or vegetable
HQ: Griffin Industries Llc
4221 Alexandria Pike
Cold Spring KY 41076
859 781-2010

(G-17730)
GRIZZLY PRODUCTS CORP
4406 W Virginia Ave (33614-7742)
P.O. Box 422 (33601-0422)
PHONE....................................813 545-3828
Russell P Mathews, *President*
EMP: 10 **EST:** 2012
SALES (est): 1.4MM **Privately Held**
WEB: www.grizzlytargets.com
SIC: 3441 Fabricated structural metal

(G-17731)
GSM SOFTWARE TECHNOLOGIES INC
20020 Tamiami Ave (33647-3367)
PHONE....................................813 907-2124
G Shaker Munirathnam, *President*
Gnana Shaker Munirathnam, *President*
Gnana Munirathnam, *Human Res Mgr*
EMP: 5 **EST:** 2011
SALES (est): 300K **Privately Held**
WEB: www.gsmsoftech.com
SIC: 7372 Prepackaged software

(G-17732)
GUARDIAN AG PLAS CORP
5401 W Kennedy Blvd # 75 (33609-2428)
PHONE....................................813 286-8680
Clayton W McNeel, *President*
Ian E McNeel, *Vice Pres*
Rene M Wood, *CFO*
▲ **EMP:** 8 **EST:** 2007
SQ FT: 3,500
SALES (est): 80.6K **Privately Held**
SIC: 3081 Unsupported plastics film & sheet

(G-17733)
GULF COAST PAINT & SUPPLIES
Also Called: Abe Paints
1910 N Us Highway 301 (33619-2640)
PHONE....................................813 932-3093
EMP: 14 **EST:** 2018
SALES (est): 1.7MM **Privately Held**
WEB: www.gulfcoastpaint.com
SIC: 2851 Paints & allied products

(G-17734)
GULF COAST REBAR INC
1301 E 4th Ave (33605-5013)
P.O. Box 75588 (33675-0588)
PHONE....................................813 247-1200
Chad E Jones, *President*
EMP: 50
SALES (corp-wide): 9.2MM **Privately Held**
WEB: www.gulfcoastrebar.com
SIC: 3449 1541 Bars, concrete reinforcing: fabricated steel; steel building construction
PA: Gulf Coast Rebar, Inc.
4560 Shiloh Mill Blvd
Jacksonville FL 32246
904 982-0521

(G-17735)
GULF MARINE REPAIR CORPORATION (PA)
Also Called: G M R
1800 Grant St (33605-6042)
PHONE....................................813 247-3153
Aaron Hendry, *President*
Claude R Watts, *Vice Pres*
Alex Santiago, *Foreman/Supr*
Viorel Racovita, *Engineer*
Dennis E Manelli, *Treasurer*
▲ **EMP:** 189 **EST:** 1988
SQ FT: 12,500
SALES (est): 27.2MM **Privately Held**
WEB: www.gulfmarinerepair.com
SIC: 3731 Shipbuilding & repairing

(G-17736)
GULFPORT INDUSTRIES INC
6308 Benjamin Rd Ste 714 (33634-5174)
PHONE....................................813 885-1000
Bob Nedic, *Manager*
EMP: 12 **EST:** 2007
SALES (est): 273.9K **Privately Held**
WEB: www.gulfport-corp.com
SIC: 2431 3442 5031 Doors, wood; metal doors; doors & windows

(G-17737)
GULFSTREAM UNSNKABLE BOATS LLC
Also Called: Gulfstream Yachts
5251 W Tyson Ave (33611-3223)
PHONE....................................813 820-6100
Perry Kyra, *Business Mgr*
Molly Edwards, *Purch Mgr*
Huntington James, *Mng Member*
EMP: 12 **EST:** 2008
SALES (est): 1.5MM **Privately Held**
WEB: www.gulfstreamyachts.com
SIC: 3732 Boat building & repairing

(G-17738)
GUNN PRTG & LITHOGRAPHY INC
4415 W Dr Martin L King Martin Luther (33614)
PHONE....................................813 870-6010
Clark Gunn, *CEO*
Pat Gunn, *President*
Edna Gunn, *Corp Secy*
EMP: 15 **EST:** 1985
SQ FT: 10,000
SALES (est): 2.1MM **Privately Held**
WEB: www.gunnprinting.com
SIC: 2752 Commercial printing, offset

(G-17739)
H-CYTE INC (PA)
Also Called: MEDOVEX
201 E Kennedy Blvd # 700 (33602-5181)
PHONE....................................844 633-6839
Richard Greif, *CEO*
Steve Gorlin, *Ch of Bd*
William Horne, *Ch of Bd*
Larry Papasan, *Ch of Bd*
Ann Miller, *COO*
EMP: 23 **EST:** 2013
SALES (est): 2.1MM **Publicly Held**
WEB: www.hcyte.com
SIC: 3841 Surgical & medical instruments

(G-17740)
HALLMARK EMBLEMS INC
2401 N Tampa St (33602-2136)
P.O. Box 172838 (33672-0838)
PHONE....................................813 223-5427
Thomas C Burgeson, *President*
Karen Burgeson, *Vice Pres*
Scott Delarco, *Vice Pres*
Scott E Delarco, *Vice Pres*
Hugh Perrette, *Sales Staff*
▲ **EMP:** 68 **EST:** 1981
SQ FT: 44,000
SALES (est): 8.2MM **Privately Held**
WEB: www.hallmarkemblems.com
SIC: 2399 Aprons, breast (harness)

(G-17741)
HAMAN INDUSTRIES INC
Also Called: Tampa Pallet Co
2402 S 54th St (33619-5364)
P.O. Box 310386 (33680-0386)
PHONE....................................813 626-5700
Frederic E Haman, *President*
Carol Haman, *Vice Pres*
EMP: 12 **EST:** 1954
SQ FT: 6,200
SALES (est): 2.3MM **Privately Held**
WEB: www.tampapallet.com
SIC: 2441 2448 Nailed wood boxes & shook; pallets, wood

(G-17742)
HANES-HARRIS DESIGN CONS
Also Called: Sign Art Group, The
6106 N Nebraska Ave Ste A (33604-6877)
PHONE....................................813 237-0202
EMP: 5
SALES (est): 558.6K **Privately Held**
SIC: 3993 Mfg Signs

(G-17743)
HARCROS CHEMICALS INC
5132 Trenton St (33619-6834)
PHONE....................................813 247-4531
Sharon Armstrong, *Purchasing*
Skye Athey, *Purchasing*
Tom Hillyer, *Branch Mgr*
Sue Ernest, *Manager*
EMP: 23
SALES (corp-wide): 408.4MM **Privately Held**
WEB: www.harcros.com
SIC: 2869 2819 Industrial organic chemicals; industrial inorganic chemicals
PA: Harcros Chemicals Inc.
5200 Speaker Rd
Kansas City KS 66106
913 321-3131

(G-17744)
HARPER LIMBACH LLC
9051 Fla Min Blvd Ste 103 (33634)
PHONE....................................813 207-0057
Erich Muensterman, *Vice Pres*
Joshua Booth, *Project Mgr*
Luis Aguiar, *Opers Mgr*
Brian Krot, *Purch Mgr*
Christopher Lanza, *Project Engr*
EMP: 9 **Privately Held**
WEB: www.harperlimbach.com
SIC: 3495 Mechanical springs, precision
HQ: Harper Limbach Llc
5102 W Laurel St Ste 800
Tampa FL 33607
407 321-8100

(G-17745)
HARSCO CORPORATION
Also Called: Reed Minerals Division
5950 Old 41a Hwy (33619-8758)
P.O. Box 2308, Gibsonton (33534-2308)
PHONE....................................717 506-2071
Doug Norris, *Manager*
EMP: 10
SALES (corp-wide): 1.8B **Publicly Held**
WEB: www.harsco.com
SIC: 3295 3291 2952 Slag, crushed or ground; abrasive products; asphalt felts & coatings
PA: Harsco Corporation
350 Poplar Church Rd
Camp Hill PA 17011
717 763-7064

(G-17746)
HATCH TRANSFORMERS INC
Also Called: HATCH LIGHTING
7821 Woodland Center Blvd (33614-2410)
PHONE....................................813 288-8006
Michael Hatch, *CEO*
Kevin Chisholm, *Sales Staff*
Robin Shepherd, *Office Mgr*
▲ **EMP:** 22 **EST:** 1980
SQ FT: 10,000
SALES (est): 5.9MM **Privately Held**
WEB: www.hatchlighting.com
SIC: 3612 Lighting transformers, fluorescent; lighting transformers, street & airport

(G-17747)
HAWKS NUTS INC
Also Called: Hawks Orgnal Jmbo Bled Peanuts
4713 N Hale Ave (33614-6515)
PHONE....................................813 872-0900
Mildred M Hawks, *President*
Paul Hawks, *Vice Pres*
EMP: 11 **EST:** 1995
SQ FT: 50,000
SALES (est): 1.8MM **Privately Held**
WEB: www.hawksboiledpeanuts.com
SIC: 2076 Peanut oil, cake or meal

(G-17748)
HAWVER ALUMINUM FOUNDRY INC
9526 N Trask St (33624-5137)
P.O. Box 270481 (33688-0481)
PHONE....................................813 961-1497
James A Hawver, *President*
Judith Hawver, *Vice Pres*
EMP: 9 **EST:** 1969
SQ FT: 8,000
SALES (est): 992.2K **Privately Held**
WEB: www.hawvercastings.com
SIC: 3366 Copper foundries

(G-17749)
HEAT-PIPE TECHNOLOGY INC
6904 Parke East Blvd (33610-4115)
PHONE....................................813 470-4250
Tom Manenti, *CEO*
Eugene M Toombs, *President*
Gene Toombs IV, *President*
Mazan Awad, *Vice Pres*
Bonnie Daniels, *Vice Pres*
◆ **EMP:** 30 **EST:** 1983
SALES (est): 19.6MM
SALES (corp-wide): 245.5B **Publicly Held**
WEB: www.heatpipe.com
SIC: 3585 Air conditioning condensers & condensing units; dehumidifiers electric, except portable
HQ: Mitek Industries, Inc.
16023 Swinly Rdg
Chesterfield MO 63017
314 434-1200

(G-17750)
HENDRY CORPORATION
1800 Grant St (33605-6042)
PHONE....................................813 241-9206
Aaron Hendry, *President*
Hal Hendry, *General Mgr*
Dennis E Manelli, *Vice Pres*
Dale West, *CFO*
EMP: 89 **EST:** 1926
SQ FT: 3,000
SALES (est): 10.5MM **Privately Held**
WEB: www.hendrymarineindustries.com
SIC: 3731 1629 Shipbuilding & repairing; marine construction

(G-17751)
HENDRY MARINE INDUSTRIES INC
1800 Grant St (33605-6042)
PHONE....................................813 241-9206
Aaron W Hendry, *Principal*
Eric F Smith, *COO*
Stephanie Koch, *Human Res Dir*
Angela Baylis, *Manager*
Harry Hendry, *Manager*
EMP: 22 **EST:** 2011
SALES (est): 1MM **Privately Held**
WEB: www.hendrymarineindustries.com
SIC: 3731 Shipbuilding & repairing

(G-17752)
HENDRY SHIPYARD JOINT VENTR 1
1800 Grant St (33605-6042)
PHONE....................................813 241-9206
Aaron Hendry, *Manager*
EMP: 20 **EST:** 2012
SALES (est): 500.5K **Privately Held**
WEB: www.hendrymarineindustries.com
SIC: 3731 Barges, building & repairing

(G-17753)
HERITAGE MEDCALL LLC
202 E Virginia Ave (33603-4821)
PHONE....................................813 221-1000
Donald R Musselman, *CEO*
Justin Franke, *President*
EMP: 13 **EST:** 2012
SQ FT: 2,500
SALES (est): 2.4MM **Privately Held**
WEB: www.heritagemedcall.com
SIC: 3669 Emergency alarms

(G-17754)
HIGHLANDS ETHANOL LLC
Also Called: Vercipia Biofuels
2202 N West Shore Blvd (33607-5747)
PHONE....................................813 421-1090
John Doyle, *Vice Pres*
EMP: 7 **EST:** 2010
SALES (est): 2.3MM
SALES (corp-wide): 180.3B **Privately Held**
WEB: www.vercipia.com
SIC: 2869 Ethyl alcohol, ethanol
PA: Bp P.L.C.
1 St. James's Square
London SW1Y
207 496-4000

(G-17755)
HILL DONNELLY CORPORATION (PA)
Also Called: Onesource Information Services
10126 Windhorst Rd (33619-7826)
PHONE....................................800 525-1242
Lee H Hill III, *President*
EMP: 54 **EST:** 1917
SQ FT: 10,000
SALES (est): 3.9MM **Privately Held**
SIC: 2741 7331 3572 Telephone & other directory publishing; direct mail advertising services; computer storage devices

(G-17756)
HIPPO TAMPA LLC
605 Bosphorous Ave (33606-3915)
PHONE....................................813 391-9152
Gerald Fraser, *Owner*
EMP: 8 **EST:** 2007
SALES (est): 239.4K **Privately Held**
SIC: 3089 Garbage containers, plastic

(G-17757)
HITMASTER GRAPHICS LLC
1706 W Fig St (33606-1626)
PHONE....................................813 250-0555
Lynette McKown, *Vice Pres*
Allen D Cenal,
William Garvin,
Stuart A McKown,
EMP: 15 **EST:** 2008
SALES (est): 1.8MM **Privately Held**
WEB: www.hitmastergraphics.com
SIC: 2759 2395 Screen printing; embroidery & art needlework

(G-17758)
HOB CORPORATION
Also Called: Palladium Graphics
5604 E 122nd Ave (33617)
PHONE....................................813 988-2272
Jack T O'Brien, *President*
Keith O'Brien, *Vice Pres*
Mary E O'Brien, *Admin Sec*
EMP: 6 **EST:** 1985
SQ FT: 5,000
SALES (est): 356.1K **Privately Held**
WEB: www.palladiumgraphics.com
SIC: 2396 3993 2752 2395 Screen printing on fabric articles; signs & advertising specialties; commercial printing, lithographic; pleating & stitching

(G-17759)
HOLLAND PUMP COMPANY
6426 Causeway Blvd (33619-6350)
PHONE....................................813 626-0599
Sharlene Hedrick, *Mktg Coord*
John Blanchette, *Branch Mgr*
EMP: 6
SQ FT: 5,560
SALES (corp-wide): 20.1MM **Privately Held**
WEB: www.hollandpump.com
SIC: 3561 7359 Pumps & pumping equipment; equipment rental & leasing
PA: Holland Pump Company
7312 Westport Pl
West Palm Beach FL 33413
561 697-3333

(G-17760)
HOME PRIDE CABINETS INC
8503 Sunstate St (33634-1311)
PHONE....................................813 887-3782
Bernie Gaydos, *President*
EMP: 19 **EST:** 1990
SALES (est): 3.8MM **Privately Held**
WEB: www.homepridecabinets.com
SIC: 2517 2541 2521 2434 Wood television & radio cabinets; wood partitions & fixtures; wood office furniture; wood kitchen cabinets

(G-17761)
HORNBLASTERS INC
Also Called: Mini Truckin
6511 N 54th St (33610-1907)
PHONE....................................813 783-8058
Mathew L Heller, *President*
Manny Rizzo, *Sls & Mktg Exec*
EMP: 20 **EST:** 2002
SALES (est): 3.6MM **Privately Held**
WEB: www.hornblasters.com
SIC: 3714 5013 5015 5531 Horns, motor vehicle; springs, shock absorbers & struts; automotive accessories, used; automotive accessories

(G-17762)
HOWARD IMPRINTING MACHINE CO
5013 Tampa West Blvd (33634-2414)
P.O. Box 15027 (33684-5027)
PHONE....................................813 884-2398
James Wrobbel, *President*
Bill Wrobbel, *Vice Pres*
Ray J Wrobbel, *Vice Pres*
▲ **EMP:** 8 **EST:** 1931
SQ FT: 10,000
SALES (est): 1MM **Privately Held**
WEB: www.howardimprinting.com
SIC: 3555 5084 Printing trades machinery; printing trades machinery, equipment & supplies

(G-17763)
HOWMEDICA OSTEONICS CORP
Also Called: Stryker Orthopaedics
8731 Florida Mining Blvd (33634-1259)
PHONE....................................813 886-3450
Tommy Edwards, *President*
Kevin Dufford, *Sales Staff*
EMP: 9
SALES (corp-wide): 14.3B **Publicly Held**
SIC: 3842 Surgical appliances & supplies
HQ: Howmedica Osteonics Corp.
325 Corporate Dr
Mahwah NJ 07430
201 831-5000

(G-17764)
HOWMEDICA OSTEONICS CORP
Also Called: Stryker Spines
405 N Reo St Ste 310 (33609-1064)
PHONE....................................813 288-0760
Jay Baker, *Manager*
EMP: 49
SALES (corp-wide): 14.3B **Publicly Held**
SIC: 3841 Surgical & medical instruments
HQ: Howmedica Osteonics Corp.
325 Corporate Dr
Mahwah NJ 07430
201 831-5000

(G-17765)
HR EASE INC
2002 N Lois Ave Ste 220 (33607-2395)
PHONE....................................813 414-0040
Susanne Kinsella Gill, *CEO*
Hank Gill, *Principal*
John Tedesco, *Business Mgr*
Michelle Mauro, *Prgrmr*
EMP: 8 **EST:** 2000
SQ FT: 800
SALES (est): 730K **Privately Held**
WEB: www.hrease.com
SIC: 7372 Business oriented computer software

(G-17766)
HTS CONTROLS INC
4918 W Grace St (33607-3806)
P.O. Box 24169 (33623-4169)
PHONE....................................813 287-5512
EMP: 10
SALES (est): 1.2MM
SALES (corp-wide): 34.1MM **Privately Held**
SIC: 3625 3621 Mfg Relays/Industrial Controls Mfg Motors/Generators
PA: Carter & Verplanck, Inc.
4910 W Cypress St
Tampa FL 33607
813 287-0709

(G-17767)
ICECOLD2 LLC
Also Called: Icecool World
10004 N Dale Mabry Hwy (33618-4494)
PHONE....................................855 326-2665
Bhavash Patel, *Mng Member*
Sarah Kimber, *Executive Asst*
EMP: 8 **EST:** 2014
SALES (est): 231K **Privately Held**
WEB: www.ecocoolworld.com
SIC: 3585 Air conditioning condensers & condensing units

(G-17768)
ICI CUSTOM PARTS INC
13911 Bittersweet Way (33625-6426)
PHONE....................................813 888-7979
Russell O McKee Sr, *President*
Tammy Lyman, *Corp Secy*
Joanne McKee, *Senior VP*
Balinda K Cardinale, *Treasurer*
Michael L Vaughn, *Admin Sec*
EMP: 23 **EST:** 2001
SALES (est): 1.5MM **Privately Held**
WEB: www.icicustomparts.com
SIC: 3589 3625 Dishwashing machines, commercial; control equipment, electric

(G-17769)
ICON AIRCRAFT INC
825 Severn Ave (33606-4015)
PHONE....................................813 387-6603
Warren Curry, *Branch Mgr*
EMP: 16 **Privately Held**
WEB: www.iconaircraft.com
SIC: 3728 Aircraft parts & equipment
PA: Icon Aircraft, Inc.
2141 Icon Way
Vacaville CA 95688

(G-17770)
IFCO SYSTEMS US LLC (PA)
3030 N Rocky Point Dr W # 300 (33607-5903)
PHONE....................................813 463-4103
Candice Herndon, *President*

Daniel Walsh, *President*
Russ Bunker, *General Mgr*
Wade Caplinger, *General Mgr*
Tony Flores, *General Mgr*
▼ **EMP:** 20 **EST:** 1994
SQ FT: 5,000
SALES (est): 56.8MM **Privately Held**
WEB: www.ifco.com
SIC: 3081 Packing materials, plastic sheet

(G-17771)
ILLUMINATIONS HOLIDAY LTG LLC
8708 Elmdale Pl (33637-4327)
PHONE..................................813 334-4827
Timothy A Gay, *President*
EMP: 6 **EST:** 2011
SALES (est): 87.6K **Privately Held**
SIC: 3648 Lighting equipment

(G-17772)
IMAGE DEPOT
Also Called: D & J Logos
2017 E Fowler Ave (33612-5503)
PHONE..................................813 685-7116
John Kamenar, *President*
EMP: 9 **EST:** 1992
SALES (est): 1MM **Privately Held**
SIC: 2759 5099 2396 2395 Advertising literature: printing; souvenirs; automotive & apparel trimmings; pleating & stitching

(G-17773)
IMAGE ONE CORPORATION
6202 Benjamin Rd Ste 103 (33634-5184)
PHONE..................................813 888-8288
Michael Lutz, *General Mgr*
Ada Martinez, *HR Admin*
James Alvarez, *Manager*
Marissa Powell, *Manager*
William Lennon,
EMP: 67 **EST:** 1994
SQ FT: 13,000
SALES (est): 9.4MM **Privately Held**
WEB: www.image-1.com
SIC: 7372 Prepackaged software

(G-17774)
IMPACT SAFE GLASS CORPORATION
2705 N 35th St (33605-3121)
PHONE..................................813 247-5528
Carrie Condon, *President*
EMP: 9 **EST:** 1999
SALES (est): 228.9K **Privately Held**
WEB: www.impactsafeglass.com
SIC: 3211 Insulating glass, sealed units

(G-17775)
IN THE NEWS INC
3706 N Ridge Ave (33603-4527)
P.O. Box 30176 (33630-3176)
PHONE..................................813 882-8886
Barry J Murante, *President*
Heather Duncan, *General Mgr*
June Lacava, *General Mgr*
Martha Ostria, *Human Res Mgr*
Michelle Ferguson, *Train & Dev Mgr*
EMP: 90 **EST:** 1987
SALES (est): 10MM **Privately Held**
WEB: www.inthenewsonline.com
SIC: 3999 5999 2399 Plaques, picture, laminated; trophies & plaques; banners, made from fabric

(G-17776)
IN TOUCH ELECTRONICS LLC
13944 Lynmar Blvd Bldg 2 (33626-3123)
PHONE..................................813 818-9990
Progeny International,
EMP: 6 **EST:** 2011
SALES (est): 487.7K **Privately Held**
WEB: www.intouchdisplays.com
SIC: 3577 Graphic displays, except graphic terminals

(G-17777)
INDEPENDENT RESOURCES INC (PA)
5010 N Nebraska Ave (33603-2339)
P.O. Box 23489 (33623-3489)
PHONE..................................813 237-0945
David J Curbelo, *President*
Daniel R Curbelo Sr, *Chairman*
Jeremy K Starling, *Vice Pres*
Debbie Curbelo, *CFO*
Deborah D Curbelo, *CFO*
EMP: 23 **EST:** 1977
SQ FT: 6,125
SALES (est): 3.4MM **Privately Held**
SIC: 2752 5943 5199 2761 Commercial printing, offset; office forms & supplies; advertising specialties; manifold business forms

(G-17778)
INDICALI INC
15310 Amberly Dr Ste 250 (33647-1642)
PHONE..................................831 905-4780
Nitin Patel MD, *CEO*
EMP: 5 **EST:** 1996
SQ FT: 300
SALES (est): 655.7K **Privately Held**
SIC: 2834 Vitamin, nutrient & hematinic preparations for human use

(G-17779)
INDUSTRIAL & MARINE MAINT
5511 24th Ave S (33619-5372)
P.O. Box 2781, Brandon (33509-2781)
PHONE..................................813 622-8338
Larry Chatham, *President*
Chad Duncan, *Vice Pres*
EMP: 9 **EST:** 1985
SQ FT: 5,000
SALES (est): 895.4K **Privately Held**
SIC: 7692 3599 Welding repair; machine shop, jobbing & repair

(G-17780)
INDUSTRIAL COATING SOLUTIONS
7307 Yardley Way (33647-1216)
P.O. Box 48703 (33646-0123)
PHONE..................................813 333-8988
George B Bashline Jr, *Principal*
EMP: 7 **EST:** 2010
SALES (est): 239.6K **Privately Held**
WEB: www.industrialpaintingsolutions.com
SIC: 3479 Metal coating & allied service

(G-17781)
INDUSTRIAL GLVANIZERS AMER INC
Also Called: Industrial Galvanizers Tampa
9520 E Broadway Ave (33619-7721)
PHONE..................................813 621-8990
Mark Mellon, *Branch Mgr*
EMP: 43 **Privately Held**
WEB: www.valmontcoatings.com
SIC: 3479 Galvanizing of iron, steel or end-formed products
HQ: Industrial Galvanizers America, Inc.
3535 Halifax Rd Ste A
Petersburg VA 23805

(G-17782)
INDUSTRIAL PROJECTS SERVICES
4102 W Linebaugh Ave # 103
(33624-5296)
P.O. Box 274231 (33688-4231)
PHONE..................................813 265-2957
John D Miller, *President*
Louis Galazzo, *Partner*
Blake Miller, *Principal*
Devan Taylor,
EMP: 7 **EST:** 1993
SQ FT: 8,000
SALES (est): 945.9K **Privately Held**
WEB: www.industrialprojectsreport.com
SIC: 2721 Trade journals: publishing only, not printed on site

(G-17783)
INFOR PUBLIC SECTOR INC
Also Called: Fka Enroute Emergency Systems
3501 E Frontage Rd # 350 (33607-1704)
PHONE..................................813 207-6911
Molly Crews, *Vice Pres*
Margaret Moran, *Vice Pres*
EMP: 34
SALES (corp-wide): 36.9B **Privately Held**
WEB: www.enroute911.com
SIC: 7372 Prepackaged software
HQ: Infor Public Sector, Inc.
11092 Sun Center Dr
Rancho Cordova CA 95670
916 921-0883

(G-17784)
INNOVATIA MEDICAL SYSTEMS LLC
450 Knights Run Ave # 1003 (33602-6300)
PHONE..................................908 385-2802
Richard D Gitlin, *Managing Prtnr*
EMP: 6 **EST:** 2010
SALES (est): 208.5K **Privately Held**
SIC: 3845 Electromedical equipment

(G-17785)
INNOVATIVE SPINE CARE
8333 Gunn Hwy (33626-1608)
PHONE..................................813 920-3022
Stephen Watson, *Principal*
EMP: 8 **EST:** 2012
SALES (est): 639.7K **Privately Held**
WEB: www.gotspinepain.com
SIC: 3842 Prosthetic appliances

(G-17786)
INNQUEST CORPORATION
Also Called: Innquest Software
500 N West Shore Blvd # 950
(33609-5002)
PHONE..................................813 288-4900
Chuck Dunaj, *President*
Lorraine Quigley, *Office Mgr*
Ashlyn Staples, *Manager*
EMP: 16 **EST:** 1997
SALES (est): 4.2MM
SALES (corp-wide): 172.5K **Privately Held**
WEB: www.innquest.com
SIC: 7372 Prepackaged software
PA: Valsoft Corporation Inc
7405 Rte Transcanadienne Ste 100
Montreal QC H4T 1
514 316-7647

(G-17787)
INTEGRATED CABLE SOLUTIONS
5905 Johns Rd Ste 101 (33634-4513)
PHONE..................................813 769-5740
Karen Saoirse, *Mng Member*
Paul Bergfield, *Manager*
Paul Berkfield,
Robert Dill,
EMP: 30 **EST:** 2003
SQ FT: 8,500
SALES (est): 2MM **Privately Held**
WEB: www.icscable.com
SIC: 3357 Nonferrous wiredrawing & insulating

(G-17788)
INTEGRITY PRSTHETICS ORTHOTICS
12206 Bruce B Downs Blvd (33612-9224)
PHONE..................................813 416-5905
Clarence E Crowe, *Principal*
EMP: 7 **EST:** 2012
SALES (est): 149.4K **Privately Held**
WEB: www.integritypando.com
SIC: 3842 Orthopedic appliances

(G-17789)
INTERBAY AIR COMPRESSORS INC
Also Called: Honda Generators of Tampa
5110 S West Shore Blvd (33611-5650)
P.O. Box 13442 (33681-3442)
PHONE..................................813 831-8213
Manuel Guzman, *President*
▼ **EMP:** 7 **EST:** 1982
SQ FT: 6,000
SALES (est): 1.7MM **Privately Held**
WEB: www.hondageneratorsoftampa.powerdealer.honda.com
SIC: 3563 Air & gas compressors including vacuum pumps

(G-17790)
INTERNATIONAL SHIP REPAIR & MA
1601 Sahlman Dr (33605-6077)
PHONE..................................813 247-1118
Paul Duffy, *President*
George H Lorton, *Principal*
EMP: 15
SALES (corp-wide): 26.8MM **Privately Held**
WEB: www.internationalship.com
SIC: 3731 Shipbuilding & repairing
PA: International Ship Repair & Marine Services, Inc.
1616 Penny St
Tampa FL 33605
813 247-1118

(G-17791)
INTERTAPE POLYMER CORP
Intertape Polymer Group
9940 Currie Davis Dr (33619-2669)
PHONE..................................813 621-8410
Mike McQuire, *Manager*
Sean Struble, *Manager*
EMP: 12
SALES (corp-wide): 1.1B **Privately Held**
WEB: www.itape.com
SIC: 2672 Tape, pressure sensitive: made from purchased materials
HQ: Intertape Polymer Corp.
100 Paramount Dr Ste 300
Sarasota FL 34232
888 898-7834

(G-17792)
INTREPID MACHINE INC
12020 Race Track Rd (33626-3109)
PHONE..................................813 854-3825
Clinton Ken, *Principal*
EMP: 7 **EST:** 2016
SALES (est): 145.8K **Privately Held**
WEB: www.intrepidmachine.com
SIC: 3599 Machine shop, jobbing & repair

(G-17793)
IPVISION SOFTWARE LLC
5905 Johns Rd (33634-4521)
PHONE..................................813 728-3175
Mark Felberg, *Mng Member*
EMP: 10 **EST:** 2006
SALES (est): 649.7K **Privately Held**
WEB: www.ipvisionsoftware.com
SIC: 7372 Prepackaged software

(G-17794)
ISLAND DESIGNS OUTLET INC
Also Called: Idex International
14501 Mccormick Dr (33626-3023)
PHONE..................................813 855-0020
Robert Emerson, *President*
▼ **EMP:** 41 **EST:** 1989
SQ FT: 11,613
SALES (est): 6MM **Privately Held**
WEB: www.idexint.net
SIC: 2395 2396 Embroidery products, except schiffli machine; automotive & apparel trimmings

(G-17795)
IT HAD TO BE TOLD PUBG LLC
330 Inner Harbour Cir (33602-5967)
PHONE..................................813 810-5961
Wayne Curtiss, *Principal*
EMP: 6 **EST:** 2017
SALES (est): 45.4K **Privately Held**
WEB: www.ithadtobetold.com
SIC: 2741 Miscellaneous publishing

(G-17796)
ITALIAN CAST STONES INC
5418 W Ingraham St (33616-1916)
PHONE..................................813 902-8900
Rosy Conto, *President*
Donte Conto, *Vice Pres*
Conto Kevin, *Engineer*
Dante Conto, *Manager*
EMP: 25 **EST:** 2000
SALES (est): 1.9MM **Privately Held**
WEB: www.italiancaststone.com
SIC: 3281 3086 Household articles, except furniture: cut stone; plastics foam products

(G-17797)
J C NEWMAN CIGAR CO (PA)
2701 N 16th St (33605-2616)
P.O. Box 2030 (33601-2030)
PHONE..................................813 248-2124
Stanford J Newman, *Ch of Bd*
Eric M Newman, *President*
Heather Hill, *COO*
Robert C Newman, *Exec VP*
Rich Dolak, *Vice Pres*

◆ **EMP:** 100 **EST:** 1895
SQ FT: 100,000
SALES (est): 34.1MM **Privately Held**
WEB: www.jcnewman.com
SIC: 2121 5194 Cigars; cigars

(G-17798)
J K & M INK CORPORATION
Also Called: JK&m Ink
4714 N Thatcher Ave (33614-6936)
PHONE..................................813 875-3106
Martin J Lenhart, *President*
Mary Lenhart, *Treasurer*
EMP: 6 **EST:** 1995
SQ FT: 5,700
SALES (est): 827.5K **Privately Held**
SIC: 2752 Commercial printing, offset

(G-17799)
J SQUARED MANAGEMENT II LLC
Also Called: Apple Spice Box Lnch Dlvry Ctr
5909 Breckenridge Pkwy F (33610-4237)
PHONE..................................813 373-5359
William R Whitmer, *Mng Member*
William R Witmer, *Mng Member*
EMP: 11
SALES (est): 408.1K **Privately Held**
SIC: 2099 5812 Box lunches, for sale off premises; eating places

(G-17800)
J W L TRADING COMPANY INC
Also Called: Ameriseam
13801 W Hillsborough Ave (33635-9677)
PHONE..................................813 854-1128
James W Larsen, *President*
EMP: 10 **EST:** 1996
SQ FT: 2,500
SALES (est): 432.4K **Privately Held**
WEB: www.ameriseam.net
SIC: 2394 Convertible tops, canvas or boat: from purchased materials

(G-17801)
JADE TACTICAL DISASTER RELIEF
Also Called: Security Hmntrian Rlief Envmtl
3816 W Sligh Ave (33614-3961)
PHONE..................................850 270-4077
Steven Rahl, *President*
Yaritza Rahl, *Vice Pres*
EMP: 138 **EST:** 2017
SALES (est): 7.7MM **Privately Held**
SIC: 3812 3721 3711 7381 Search & navigation equipment; aircraft; motor vehicles & car bodies; detective & armored car services; security systems services; charitable organization

(G-17802)
JAK CORPORATE HOLDINGS INC
Also Called: Diji Integrated Press
4920 W Cypress St Ste 100 (33607-3837)
P.O. Box 262573 (33685-2573)
PHONE..................................813 289-1660
Kathleen Muraski, *President*
Jeff Murawski, *Vice Pres*
EMP: 10 **EST:** 1985
SQ FT: 4,000
SALES (est): 1.5MM **Privately Held**
WEB: www.dijipress.com
SIC: 2752 Commercial printing, offset

(G-17803)
JAMISON INDUSTRIES INC
Also Called: Jamison Paints
7710 N Ola Ave (33604-4067)
PHONE..................................813 886-4888
Jamison Derek, *President*
EMP: 10 **EST:** 2013
SALES (est): 550.3K **Privately Held**
WEB: www.jamisonind.com
SIC: 3599 Machine shop, jobbing & repair

(G-17804)
JAY STRONG LIGHTING INC
2007 W Dekle Ave (33606-3213)
PHONE..................................813 253-0490
Jay Strong, *Principal*
EMP: 6 **EST:** 2010
SALES (est): 136.8K **Privately Held**
SIC: 3648 Lighting equipment

(G-17805)
JKS INDUSTRIES INC (PA)
4644 W Gandy Blvd (33611-3300)
PHONE..................................727 573-1305
Ken Shin, *President*
Jennifer Shin, *Vice Pres*
EMP: 10
SQ FT: 12,500
SALES (est): 8.1MM **Privately Held**
WEB: www.jksindustries.net
SIC: 3499 8742 Strapping, metal; management consulting services

(G-17806)
JLB ENTERPRISES TAMPA INC
Also Called: Tampa Pool Company
4508 Grainary Ave (33624-2127)
PHONE..................................813 545-3830
EMP: 7 **EST:** 2018
SALES (est): 366.7K **Privately Held**
SIC: 3732 Boat building & repairing

(G-17807)
JMN ALUMINUM
8503 Westridge Dr (33615-1725)
PHONE..................................813 325-7807
Delio Navarro, *Owner*
EMP: 6 **EST:** 2010
SALES (est): 270.4K **Privately Held**
WEB: www.jmnaluminum.com
SIC: 3334 7389 Primary aluminum;

(G-17808)
JOHNSON & JACKSON GLASS PDTS
Also Called: Glass Pros of Tampa
4912 N Manhattan Ave (33614-6420)
PHONE..................................813 630-9774
Eric D Johnson, *President*
Eric Johnson, *President*
EMP: 12 **EST:** 2001
SQ FT: 5,200
SALES (est): 2.2MM **Privately Held**
SIC: 3449 3442 Curtain wall, metal; metal doors, sash & trim

(G-17809)
JOHNSON & JOHNSON
8800 Grand Oak Cir # 500 (33637-2006)
PHONE..................................813 972-0204
John Jennings, *Engineer*
Jad Fakhreddine, *Credit Staff*
Cory Nedd, *Credit Staff*
Marshella Pounds, *Human Resources*
Anderson Santo, *Branch Mgr*
EMP: 9
SALES (corp-wide): 82.5B **Publicly Held**
WEB: www.jnj.com
SIC: 3842 Surgical appliances & supplies
PA: Johnson & Johnson
1 Johnson And Johnson Plz
New Brunswick NJ 08933
732 524-0400

(G-17810)
JR BRICKS PAVERS INC
207 Jason Dr (33615-3135)
PHONE..................................813 516-3554
EMP: 6 **EST:** 2014
SALES (est): 83.6K **Privately Held**
SIC: 2951 Asphalt paving mixtures & blocks

(G-17811)
JRF TECHNOLOGY LLC
9830 Currie Davis Dr (33619-2651)
PHONE..................................813 443-5273
James Rossman, *President*
Richard C Fielder, *Managing Dir*
EMP: 13 **EST:** 2007
SALES (est): 3.6MM **Privately Held**
WEB: www.jrftechnology.com
SIC: 2821 Plastics materials & resins

(G-17812)
JUST FOR NETS
4817 N Lois Ave Ste 104 (33614-6570)
P.O. Box 15695 (33684-5695)
PHONE..................................813 871-1133
San F Lee, *President*
▼ **EMP:** 12 **EST:** 1982
SALES (est): 416.4K **Privately Held**
WEB: www.justfornets.com
SIC: 3949 Sporting & athletic goods

(G-17813)
KABINETS BY KINSEY INC
3815 N Florida Ave (33603-4909)
PHONE..................................813 222-0460
Charles Kinsey, *President*
EMP: 23 **EST:** 1984
SALES (est): 1.2MM **Privately Held**
WEB: www.kabinetsbykinsey.com
SIC: 2521 Wood office filing cabinets & bookcases

(G-17814)
KALTEC ELECTRONICS INC
Also Called: Digital Watchdog
5436 W Crenshaw St (33634-3009)
PHONE..................................813 888-9555
George Bloch, *Regional Mgr*
Jay Kelly, *Engineer*
Louis Riccomini, *Sales Staff*
Karen Horvath, *Branch Mgr*
Peter Shin, *Manager*
EMP: 14
SALES (corp-wide): 52MM **Privately Held**
WEB: www.digital-watchdog.com
SIC: 3669 Visual communication systems
PA: Kaltec Electronics, Inc.
16220 Bloomfield Ave
Cerritos CA 90703
813 888-9555

(G-17815)
KAMAJ BUSINESS GROUP INC
601 N Ashley Dr Ste 1 (33602-4334)
PHONE..................................813 863-9967
Julius Brown, *CEO*
EMP: 10 **EST:** 2017
SALES (est): 1MM **Privately Held**
WEB: www.kamaj-business-group.business.site
SIC: 2329 2339 Athletic (warmup, sweat & jogging) suits: men's & boys'; men's & boys' athletic uniforms; women's & misses' athletic clothing & sportswear

(G-17816)
KAWASUMI LABORATORIES AMER INC
10002 Princess Palm Ave # 324 (33619-1395)
P.O. Box 24355 (33623-4355)
PHONE..................................813 630-5554
T Ishikawa, *Principal*
Y Umeki, *Principal*
Tracie Lowe, *Treasurer*
Sarah Korman, *Sales Mgr*
Charles Dolan, *Sales Staff*
▲ **EMP:** 17 **EST:** 1991
SALES (est): 3.3MM **Privately Held**
WEB: www.kawasumiamerica.com
SIC: 3841 Surgical & medical instruments
HQ: Sb-Kawasumi Laboratories, Inc.
2-15-2, Konan
Minato-Ku TKY 108-0

(G-17817)
KEENE METAL FABRICATORS INC
5912 E Broadway Ave (33619-2816)
PHONE..................................813 621-2455
Fred Keene Sr, *Ch of Bd*
Fred P Keene Jr, *President*
Gary Keene, *Corp Secy*
William Keene, *Vice Pres*
EMP: 30 **EST:** 1948
SQ FT: 6,500
SALES (est): 2.9MM **Privately Held**
SIC: 3441 3444 Fabricated structural metal; sheet metalwork

(G-17818)
KENFAR CORPORATION
5926 Jet Port Industrial (33634-5158)
PHONE..................................813 443-5222
Licio Zanzi, *CEO*
EMP: 5 **EST:** 1997
SALES (est): 359K **Privately Held**
SIC: 3556 Ice cream manufacturing machinery

(G-17819)
KEURIG DR PEPPER INC
5266 Eagle Trail Dr (33634-1295)
PHONE..................................561 227-1424
EMP: 6 **Publicly Held**
WEB: www.keurigdrpepper.com
SIC: 2086 Soft drinks: packaged in cans, bottles, etc.
PA: Keurig Dr Pepper Inc.
53 South Ave
Burlington MA 01803

(G-17820)
KEYSTONE COLOR WORKS INC
2411 S Hesperides St (33629-5540)
PHONE..................................813 250-1313
Baxter Smith, *President*
Susan Smith, *Principal*
Constance Spencer, *Principal*
EMP: 6 **EST:** 1919
SQ FT: 20,000
SALES (est): 728.4K **Privately Held**
SIC: 2865 2816 Color pigments, organic; inorganic pigments

(G-17821)
KEYSTONE RV COMPANY
1201 Old Hopewell Rd # 9 (33619-2608)
PHONE..................................813 228-0625
Deth Watson, *Manager*
EMP: 120
SALES (corp-wide): 12.3B **Publicly Held**
WEB: www.keystonerv.com
SIC: 3999 Barber & beauty shop equipment
HQ: Keystone Rv Company
2642 Hackberry Dr
Goshen IN 46526

(G-17822)
KEYSTONE STEEL PRODUCTS CO
3101 E 2nd Ave (33605-5705)
P.O. Box 76133 (33675-1133)
PHONE..................................813 248-9828
Michael S Barowski, *President*
▲ **EMP:** 6 **EST:** 1968
SQ FT: 15,000
SALES (est): 946.3K **Privately Held**
SIC: 3315 Steel wire & related products

(G-17823)
KEYTROLLER LLC
3907 W Martin Luther King (33614)
PHONE..................................813 877-4500
Ned Mavrommatis, *CFO*
Mike Wilson, *Regl Sales Mgr*
Chris Wolfe, *Mng Member*
Prasad Vaizurs, *Software Dev*
EMP: 15 **EST:** 2017
SQ FT: 1,300
SALES (est): 7MM
SALES (corp-wide): 113.5MM **Publicly Held**
WEB: www.powerfleet.com
SIC: 3629 3596 3663 3674 Electronic generation equipment; weighing machines & apparatus; television closed circuit equipment; ; light emitting diodes; burglar alarm apparatus, electric; industrial machinery & equipment
HQ: I.D. Systems, Inc.
123 Tice Blvd Ste 101
Woodcliff Lake NJ 07677

(G-17824)
KEYTROLLER LLC
3907 W Dr Mart Luth Kng B Martin Luther King (33614)
PHONE..................................813 877-4500
▲ **EMP:** 9
SQ FT: 1,300
SALES (est): 1.6MM **Privately Held**
SIC: 3629 Mfg Electrical Industrial Apparatus

(G-17825)
KIMBALL ELECTRONICS TAMPA INC
13750 Reptron Blvd (33626-3040)
PHONE..................................813 814-5229
Mahmod Zand, *Opers Mgr*
Toby Ice, *Engineer*
Dinesh Patel, *Engineer*
Tim Morris, *Manager*
EMP: 194
SALES (corp-wide): 1.2B **Publicly Held**
WEB: www.kimballelectronics.com
SIC: 3679 3672 Electronic circuits; printed circuit boards

HQ: Kimball Electronics Tampa Inc
1205 Kimball Blvd
Jasper IN 47546
812 634-4000

(G-17826)
KINETIC RESEARCH INC
5513 W Sligh Ave (33634-4431)
PHONE....................................813 962-6300
Wade Bader, *President*
Reid Bader, *General Mgr*
EMP: 19 **EST:** 2001
SALES (est): 1.1MM **Privately Held**
WEB: www.kineticresearch.com
SIC: 3842 Prosthetic appliances

(G-17827)
KISS POLYMERS LLC
12515 Sugar Pine Way (33624-5712)
P.O. Box 274087 (33688-4087)
PHONE....................................813 962-2703
Cynthia Renee Kent, *Principal*
Jarrod R Kent, *Principal*
Keith Kent, *Principal*
EMP: 10 **EST:** 2005
SALES (est): 762.1K **Privately Held**
WEB: www.kisspolymers.com
SIC: 2851 3721 Shellac (protective coating); research & development on aircraft by the manufacturer

(G-17828)
KITCHEN AND BATH UNIVERSE INC
Also Called: Cabinet and Stone
6606 N 56th St (33610-1918)
PHONE....................................813 887-5658
Rong Sheng You, *President*
Qing Chan, *Vice Pres*
Kam Ting Wong, *Admin Sec*
◆ **EMP:** 11 **EST:** 2010
SQ FT: 3,500
SALES (est): 1.5MM **Privately Held**
WEB: www.cabinetnstoneintl.com
SIC: 2434 Wood kitchen cabinets

(G-17829)
KOHO SOFTWARE INC
Also Called: Quest Desk Solutions
6030 Printery St Unit 103 (33616-1414)
PHONE....................................813 390-1309
William Doucette, *President*
Rohany Karya, *Consultant*
EMP: 6 **EST:** 2014
SALES (est): 538.2K **Privately Held**
WEB: www.kohosoftware.com
SIC: 7372 Prepackaged software

(G-17830)
KUSSER GRANITEWORKS USA INC
Also Called: Kusser Fountainworks
3109 E 4th Ave (33605-5713)
PHONE....................................813 248-3428
Josef Kusser, *President*
Alan Castle, *Vice Pres*
Jeff Castle, *Vice Pres*
Adrian Donnelly, *Project Mgr*
Judy Castle, *Opers Staff*
▲ **EMP:** 9
SQ FT: 10,100
SALES (est): 3MM **Privately Held**
WEB: www.kusserusa.com
SIC: 3281 Granite, cut & shaped

(G-17831)
L3HARRIS TECHNOLOGIES INC
5690 W Cypress St Ste B (33607-1724)
PHONE....................................260 451-6814
EMP: 195
SALES (corp-wide): 11.3B **Publicly Held**
SIC: 3823 3812 Engineering Services
PA: L3harris Technologies, Inc.
1025 W Nasa Blvd
Melbourne FL 32919
321 727-9100

(G-17832)
LA GACETA PUBLISHING INC
Also Called: La Gaceta Tri-Lingual Weekly
3210 E 7th Ave (33605-4302)
PHONE....................................813 248-3921
Roland Manteiga, *President*
Angela Manteiga, *Corp Secy*
EMP: 13 **EST:** 1922
SQ FT: 20,000
SALES (est): 874.1K **Privately Held**
WEB: www.lagacetanewspaper.com
SIC: 2711 Newspapers: publishing only, not printed on site

(G-17833)
LABLOGIC SYSTEMS INC
1911 N Us Highway 301 # 140
(33619-2650)
PHONE....................................813 626-6848
Richard Brown, *President*
Mark Appel, *Regional Mgr*
John Rogus, *Regional Mgr*
Victor Tchiprout, *Exec VP*
Woodcock Robert, *Human Res Mgr*
EMP: 12 **EST:** 1990
SQ FT: 5,000
SALES (est): 2MM **Privately Held**
WEB: www.lablogic.com
SIC: 3826 Analytical instruments

(G-17834)
LAKESHORE CUSTOM WOOD PRODUCTS
5210 Shadowlawn Ave (33610-5310)
PHONE....................................813 623-2790
Kenneth Sparks, *President*
Chad Oleson, *Vice Pres*
Erika Oleson, *Admin Sec*
EMP: 9 **EST:** 1980
SQ FT: 4,500
SALES (est): 970K **Privately Held**
SIC: 2434 Wood kitchen cabinets

(G-17835)
LANFRANCHI NORTH AMERICA INC
8401 Benjamin Rd Ste A (33634-1203)
PHONE....................................813 901-5333
Davide Danna, *President*
Mario Lanfranchi, *Chairman*
Gisele D Rios, *Manager*
Salvatore Staino, *Manager*
▲ **EMP:** 15 **EST:** 2002
SQ FT: 2,800
SALES (est): 3.1MM
SALES (corp-wide): 16.5MM **Privately Held**
WEB: www.lanfranchigroup.com
SIC: 3565 Packaging machinery
PA: Lanfranchi Srl
Via Scodoncello 41
Collecchio PR 43044
052 154-1011

(G-17836)
LATTERI & SONS INC
Also Called: Latteri & Sons Vault and Monu
305 N Glen Ave (33609-1416)
PHONE....................................813 876-1800
Evelia Latteri, *President*
Anthony Latteri Jr, *Vice Pres*
EMP: 5
SQ FT: 2,784
SALES (est): 370K **Privately Held**
SIC: 3272 5999 Burial vaults, concrete or precast terrazzo; monuments, finished to custom order

(G-17837)
LAYCOCK SYSTEMS INC
1601 N 43rd St (33605-5937)
PHONE....................................813 248-3555
Charles Snead, *Owner*
▲ **EMP:** 10 **EST:** 1982
SQ FT: 23,000
SALES (est): 912.9K **Privately Held**
WEB: www.laycocksystems.com
SIC: 3546 Power-driven handtools

(G-17838)
LEADER TECH INC
Also Called: Heico Company
12420 Race Track Rd (33626-3117)
PHONE....................................813 855-6921
Tracy Kuhns, *President*
Gary Mandile, *Safety Mgr*
Andrew Pelaez, *Production*
Rhonda Dietrich, *Buyer*
Lee Branham, *Engineer*
EMP: 100 **EST:** 1984
SQ FT: 42,500
SALES (est): 25.9MM **Publicly Held**
WEB: www.leadertechinc.com
SIC: 3469 Metal stampings
HQ: Heico Electronic Technologies Corp.
3000 Taft St
Hollywood FL 33021
954 987-6101

(G-17839)
LEE FISHER INTERNATIONAL INC
Also Called: Just For Nets
3922 W Osborne Ave (33614-6551)
P.O. Box 15695 (33684-5695)
PHONE....................................813 875-6296
San Fu Lee, *President*
Hsueh Hsiang Lee, *Treasurer*
◆ **EMP:** 25 **EST:** 1982
SQ FT: 20,000
SALES (est): 5.1MM **Privately Held**
WEB: www.leefisherintl.com
SIC: 2298 2399 Fishing lines, nets, seines: made in cordage or twine mills; fishing nets

(G-17840)
LEGACY COMPONENTS LLC
4613 N Clark Ave (33614-7038)
PHONE....................................813 964-6805
John Donovan, *Accounts Exec*
Sheldon Manning, *Accounts Exec*
Steve Stuart, *Sales Staff*
Kenneth Alvarez, *Mng Member*
Jason Grajales, *Manager*
EMP: 11 **EST:** 2011
SALES (est): 3.5MM **Privately Held**
WEB: www.legacycomponentsnow.com
SIC: 3674 Semiconductors & related devices

(G-17841)
LEHIGH CEMENT COMPANY LLC
3920 Pendola Point Rd (33619-9500)
PHONE....................................813 248-4000
Ed Bringman, *Branch Mgr*
EMP: 44
SALES (corp-wide): 20.8B **Privately Held**
WEB: www.lehighwhitecement.com
SIC: 3273 Ready-mixed concrete
HQ: Lehigh Cement Company Llc
300 E John Carpenter Fwy
Irving TX 75062
877 534-4442

(G-17842)
LEHIGH WHITE CEMENT CO LLC
3920 Pendola Point Rd (33619-9500)
PHONE....................................561 812-7441
Gerrhard Milla, *Branch Mgr*
EMP: 140 **Privately Held**
WEB: www.lehighwhitecement.com
SIC: 2891 Adhesives & sealants
HQ: Lehigh White Cement Company, Llc
1601 Forum Pl Ste 1110
West Palm Beach FL 33401
561 812-7439

(G-17843)
LG ENTERPRISES PAVERS INC
8711 Lindenhurst Pl (33634-1088)
PHONE....................................813 412-9235
Bruno Galindo, *Principal*
EMP: 6 **EST:** 2011
SALES (est): 83K **Privately Held**
SIC: 3531 Pavers

(G-17844)
LG HAUSYS AMERICA INC
1820 Massaro Blvd Ste 300 (33619-3014)
PHONE....................................813 249-7658
EMP: 37 **Privately Held**
WEB: www.lxhausys.com
SIC: 2541 Counter & sink tops
HQ: Lx Hausys America, Inc.
900 Cir 75 Pkwy Se # 1500
Atlanta GA 30339
678 486-8210

(G-17845)
LIFE PROTEOMICS INC
8875 Hidden River Pkwy (33637-1035)
PHONE....................................813 864-7646
Robert Brabenec, *President*
EMP: 10
SALES (est): 950K **Privately Held**
SIC: 3829 8731 Measuring & controlling devices; medical research, commercial

(G-17846)
LIFEGARD PRFCATION SYSTEMS LLC
7028 W Waters Ave Ste 228 (33634-2292)
PHONE....................................813 875-7777
Kenneth E Conley, *Mng Member*
Mancely Conley, *Mng Member*
EMP: 5 **EST:** 1988
SQ FT: 2,500
SALES (est): 688.7K **Privately Held**
WEB: www.stores.lifeguardsystems.com
SIC: 3589 Water purification equipment, household type

(G-17847)
LINPHARMA INC
601 S Fremont Ave (33606-2401)
PHONE....................................888 989-3237
Mario Hofer, *Principal*
EMP: 7 **EST:** 2013
SALES (est): 541.6K **Privately Held**
WEB: www.petadolex.com
SIC: 2834 Pharmaceutical preparations

(G-17848)
LIONS INTL MGT GROUP INC
8875 Hidden River Pkwy # 304
(33637-1035)
PHONE....................................813 367-2517
Johnny Adkins, *CEO*
Brittney Nemeth, *Opers Staff*
EMP: 10 **EST:** 2015
SALES (est): 503K **Privately Held**
SIC: 3088 0781 3711 7342 Plastics plumbing fixtures; landscape architects; motor vehicles & car bodies; rest room cleaning service; protective devices, security

(G-17849)
LIQUIDCAPSULE MFG LLC
9216 Palm River Rd # 203 (33619-4479)
PHONE....................................813 431-0532
Frederick H Miller,
Adolfo Graubard,
EMP: 10 **EST:** 2006
SALES (est): 1.2MM **Privately Held**
WEB: www.liquidcapsule.com
SIC: 2834 Pills, pharmaceutical

(G-17850)
LITHIUM BATTERY COMPANY LLC
4912 W Knox St Ste 100 (33634-8006)
PHONE....................................813 504-0074
Ronald Staron, *General Mgr*
Nathan Staron, *Co-Venturer*
EMP: 10 **EST:** 2012
SALES (est): 1.5MM **Privately Held**
WEB: www.lithiumbatterycompany.com
SIC: 3625 3629 3621 3691 Truck controls, industrial battery; battery chargers, rectifying or nonrotating; generators for storage battery chargers; storage batteries

(G-17851)
LIVELY COMPANY LLC ✪
501 E Jackson St Ste 301 (33602-4929)
PHONE....................................617 737-1199
Damon Brown, *Mng Member*
EMP: 10 **EST:** 2021
SALES (est): 413.1K **Privately Held**
SIC: 2844 Toothpastes or powders, dentifrices

(G-17852)
LIVING FUEL INC
1409 W Swann Ave (33606-2532)
P.O. Box 1038 (33601-1038)
PHONE....................................813 254-0777
Kc Craichy, *Principal*
James Casale, *Director*
EMP: 9 **EST:** 2012
SALES (est): 7.5MM **Privately Held**
WEB: www.livingfuel.com
SIC: 2869 Fuels

(G-17853)
LIZHENG STINLESS STL TUBE COIL
3902 Henderson Blvd # 207 (33629-5038)
PHONE....................................888 582-8820
Kechen Tang, *President*
EMP: 6 **EST:** 2016

SALES (est): 94.3K Privately Held
WEB: www.lizhengcoils.com
SIC: 3443 Fabricated plate work (boiler shop)

(G-17854)
LJK & TS PARTNERS INC
Also Called: Bay City X-Press Signs & Prtg
7031 Benjamin Rd Ste E (33634-3015)
PHONE....................941 661-5675
Libor J Kuzel, *Vice Pres*
EMP: 6 EST: 2017
SALES (est): 114.3K Privately Held
SIC: 2752 Commercial printing, lithographic

(G-17855)
LLC BEST BLOCK
5609 N 50th St (33610-4805)
PHONE....................239 789-3531
EMP: 21
SALES (corp-wide): 4.1MM Privately Held
SIC: 3251 Paving brick, clay
PA: Llc Best Block
2858 Sidney Ave
Orlando FL 32810
239 789-3531

(G-17856)
LOADMASTER ALUM BOAT TRLRS INC
10105 Cedar Run (33619-8003)
PHONE....................813 689-3096
Pamela L Paulsen, *President*
EMP: 30 EST: 1994
SQ FT: 24,000
SALES (est): 3.5MM Privately Held
WEB: www.loadmastertrailer.com
SIC: 3715 5599 Trailer bodies; utility trailers

(G-17857)
LOCAL VALUE MAGAZINE
301 W Platt St (33606-2292)
PHONE....................813 421-6781
EMP: 6 EST: 2008
SALES (est): 120K Privately Held
WEB: www.localvaluemagazine.com
SIC: 2721 Periodicals

(G-17858)
LOGAN LABORATORIES LLC
4919 Memorial Hwy Ste 200 (33634-7500)
PHONE....................813 316-4824
Michael Doyle, *CEO*
William Milo, *Vice Pres*
EMP: 5 EST: 2011
SALES (est): 469.1K
SALES (corp-wide): 1.9B Publicly Held
WEB: www.surgerypartners.com
SIC: 3821 8071 Clinical laboratory instruments, except medical & dental; medical laboratories
HQ: Surgery Partners, Inc.
310 Sven Sprng Way Ste 50
Brentwood TN 37027
615 234-5900

(G-17859)
LONZA
5709 Johns Rd Ste 1209 (33634-4315)
PHONE....................727 608-6802
EMP: 7 EST: 2017
SALES (est): 689.5K Privately Held
WEB: www.capsugel.com
SIC: 2834 Pharmaceutical preparations

(G-17860)
LORI ROBERTS PRINT SHOP I
6101 Johns Rd Ste 9 (33634-4425)
PHONE....................813 882-8456
Lorelei Roberts, *Principal*
EMP: 10 EST: 2005
SALES (est): 135K Privately Held
SIC: 2752 Commercial printing, offset

(G-17861)
LOW LIFE INDUSTRIES INC
5004 W Linebaugh Ave A (33624-5030)
PHONE....................813 609-5599
Dicks Mark W, *Principal*
EMP: 5 EST: 2015
SALES (est): 367.6K Privately Held
WEB: www.lowlifeindustries.com
SIC: 3999 Manufacturing industries

(G-17862)
LUBOV MANUFACTURING INC
Also Called: Belcher Gear Manufacturing
4747 N West Shore Blvd (33614-6957)
PHONE....................813 873-2640
Michael Lubov, *President*
EMP: 5 EST: 1990
SALES (est): 510.1K Privately Held
SIC: 3566 3462 Gears, power transmission, except automotive; iron & steel forgings

(G-17863)
LUIS MARTINEZ CIGAR CO
2701 N 16th St (33605-2616)
P.O. Box 76061 (33675-1061)
PHONE....................800 822-4427
Eric Newman, *President*
EMP: 8 EST: 1985
SQ FT: 100,000
SALES (est): 1.5MM
SALES (corp-wide): 34.1MM Privately Held
WEB: www.lmcigars.com
SIC: 2121 Cigars
PA: J. C. Newman Cigar Co.
2701 N 16th St
Tampa FL 33605
813 248-2124

(G-17864)
LUTHER INDUSTRIES LLC
3101 River Grove Dr (33610-1135)
PHONE....................813 833-5652
Paul Kelly, *General Mgr*
EMP: 9 EST: 2018
SALES (est): 507.8K Privately Held
WEB: www.luther-industries.com
SIC: 3999 Manufacturing industries

(G-17865)
LUXURY STONE
10020 Us Highway 301 N (33637-5305)
PHONE....................813 985-0850
Alek Eynxzar, *Principal*
▲ EMP: 6 EST: 2007
SALES (est): 203K Privately Held
WEB: www.luxury-stone.com
SIC: 3281 Table tops, marble

(G-17866)
LV THOMPSON INC
Also Called: Tamco
5015 E Hillsborough Ave (33610-4814)
PHONE....................813 248-3456
Leslie V Thompson, *President*
▲ EMP: 125 EST: 1979
SQ FT: 31,000
SALES (est): 20MM Privately Held
WEB: www.tamcometalroof.com
SIC: 3444 5051 5032 Metal roofing & roof drainage equipment; metals service centers & offices; aggregate

(G-17867)
LYNDAN INC
5402 E Hanna Ave (33610-4033)
PHONE....................813 977-6683
Dana L Guy, *President*
Lynda Carlton, *Corp Secy*
Kim Roberts, *Manager*
Phyllis M Thornberg, *Director*
EMP: 40 EST: 1981
SQ FT: 20,000
SALES (est): 3.7MM Privately Held
WEB: www.lyndan.com
SIC: 2541 2434 2431 Cabinets, except refrigerated: show, display, etc.: wood; wood kitchen cabinets; millwork

(G-17868)
M & N CAPITAL ENTERPRISES LLC
Also Called: Tent Renters Supply
5160 W Clifton St (33634-8012)
PHONE....................800 865-5064
Matthew Perra, *President*
EMP: 15 EST: 2016
SALES (est): 1.2MM Privately Held
WEB: www.tentsupply.com
SIC: 2394 Tents: made from purchased materials

(G-17869)
M P TENNIS INC (PA)
14843 N Dale Mabry Hwy (33618-2027)
PHONE....................813 961-8844
Mike Pratt, *President*
Amy Bovard, *Vice Pres*
EMP: 5 EST: 1998
SALES (est): 897K Privately Held
WEB: www.mptennis-sports.com
SIC: 3949 Tennis equipment & supplies

(G-17870)
MAC PALLETS
2805 Sabina Ct (33610-1447)
PHONE....................813 340-3246
Luis A Macias, *Principal*
EMP: 6 EST: 2008
SALES (est): 78.3K Privately Held
SIC: 2448 Pallets, wood & wood with metal

(G-17871)
MAD INC
Also Called: Gutcher's Quickprint
3805 W San Nicholas St (33629-6307)
PHONE....................813 251-9334
David Gutcher, *President*
Mark Gutcher, *Treasurer*
EMP: 5 EST: 1976
SQ FT: 2,000
SALES (est): 750K Privately Held
WEB: www.store.gotospark.com
SIC: 2752 Commercial printing, offset

(G-17872)
MAD CHILLER EXTRACTS LLC
118 S Howard Ave (33606-1725)
PHONE....................813 304-1664
Adon Williams, *Principal*
EMP: 6 EST: 2019
SALES (est): 285.4K Privately Held
WEB: www.madchillerworld.com
SIC: 2836 Extracts

(G-17873)
MAGELLAN PHARMACEUTICALS INC
1202 Tech Blvd Ste 106 (33619-7863)
PHONE....................813 623-6800
John Cronan, *President*
EMP: 5 EST: 2013
SALES (est): 603.9K Privately Held
WEB: www.magellanbioscience.com
SIC: 2834 Pharmaceutical preparations

(G-17874)
MAGNUM AUDIO GROUP INC
4504 W Spruce St Apt 112 (33607-5790)
PHONE....................813 870-2857
Randi Crooks, *President*
Randy Crooks, *President*
David Biggers, *Vice Pres*
Robert Floyd, *Vice Pres*
EMP: 9 EST: 2000
SALES (est): 750K Privately Held
WEB: www.magnumaudiogroup.com
SIC: 3651 Audio electronic systems

(G-17875)
MAJOR PARTITIONS LTD CORP
405 S Dale Mabry Hwy # 260 (33609-2820)
PHONE....................813 286-8634
EMP: 30
SQ FT: 300
SALES (est): 2.9MM Privately Held
SIC: 2541 Mfg Wood Partitions/Fixtures

(G-17876)
MANAGEMENT HLTH SOLUTIONS INC (PA)
Also Called: Syft
5701 E Hillsborough Ave (33610-5423)
P.O. Box 320548, Fairfield CT (06825-0548)
PHONE....................888 647-4621
Todd J Plesko, *CEO*
Kevin Kiley, *COO*
Miriam Achour, *Vice Pres*
Rebecca Addison, *Vice Pres*
Steven Herz, *Vice Pres*
EMP: 323 EST: 1999
SQ FT: 1,200
SALES (est): 51.1MM Privately Held
WEB: www.syftco.com
SIC: 7372 8742 Business oriented computer software; materials mgmt. (purchasing, handling, inventory) consultant

(G-17877)
MANCI GRAPHICS CORP
Also Called: Allegra Print & Imaging Center
2705 N Falkenburg Rd (33619-0920)
PHONE....................813 664-1129
Linda Manci, *President*
Sam Manci, *Vice Pres*
EMP: 8 EST: 1996
SQ FT: 3,000
SALES (est): 1.4MM Privately Held
WEB: www.allegramarketingprint.com
SIC: 2752 Commercial printing, offset

(G-17878)
MANTUA MANUFACTURING CO
8108 Krauss Blvd B (33619-3009)
PHONE....................813 621-3714
Michael Bosler, *Manager*
EMP: 9
SQ FT: 38,720
SALES (corp-wide): 77.9MM Privately Held
WEB: www.bedframes.com
SIC: 2514 3446 2511 3443 Frames for box springs or bedsprings: metal; architectural metalwork; wood household furniture; fabricated plate work (boiler shop)
PA: Mantua Manufacturing Co.
31050 Diamond Pkwy
Solon OH 44139
800 333-8333

(G-17879)
MARCELA CREATIONS INC
1802 W Kennedy Blvd (33606-1645)
PHONE....................813 253-0556
Dora Boggio, *President*
Raul Boggio MD, *Vice Pres*
Richard Barnes, *CIO*
EMP: 9 EST: 1987
SQ FT: 3,000
SALES (est): 993.7K Privately Held
WEB: www.marcelagifts.com
SIC: 3999 Novelties, bric-a-brac & hobby kits

(G-17880)
MARITIME SEC STRTEGIES FLA LLC
5251 W Tyson Ave (33611-3223)
PHONE....................912 704-0300
John K Ross,
EMP: 5 EST: 2007
SALES (est): 360.6K Privately Held
SIC: 3731 Shipbuilding & repairing

(G-17881)
MARK MASTER INC
11111 N 46th St (33617-2009)
PHONE....................813 988-6000
Kevin A Govin, *CEO*
R Mark Govin, *President*
Luis A Romero, *COO*
Luis Romero, *COO*
Steve Simms, *Opers Staff*
▲ EMP: 85 EST: 1933
SQ FT: 40,000
SALES: 9.5MM Privately Held
WEB: www.markmasterinc.com
SIC: 3953 5943 Marking devices; stationery stores

(G-17882)
MARLON INC
Also Called: Pvc Spiral Supply
8513 Sunstate St (33634-1322)
PHONE....................813 901-8488
Jack Jackson, *General Mgr*
Larry Jackson, *Manager*
EMP: 10
SALES (corp-wide): 4.4MM Privately Held
WEB: www.pvcspiralsupply.com
SIC: 3089 Plastic processing
PA: Marlon, Inc.
123 E 45th St
Boise ID 83714
208 377-9301

GEOGRAPHIC

(G-17883)
MARLYN STEEL DECKS INC
6808 Harney Rd (33610-9699)
PHONE..................................813 621-1375
Richard R James, *President*
Jeannie James, *COO*
Chris R James, *Vice Pres*
Jeannie S James, *Vice Pres*
▼ **EMP:** 10 **EST:** 1994
SQ FT: 5,000
SALES (est): 2.5MM **Privately Held**
WEB: www.marlynsteel.com
SIC: 3444 Sheet metalwork

(G-17884)
MARLYN STEEL PRODUCTS INC
6808 Harney Rd (33610-9699)
PHONE..................................813 621-1375
Richard R James, *President*
Evelyn K James, *Vice Pres*
Jeannie S James, *Vice Pres*
R Chris James, *Vice Pres*
EMP: 33 **EST:** 1960
SQ FT: 62,800
SALES (est): 4.2MM **Privately Held**
WEB: www.marlynsteel.com
SIC: 3441 3444 1752 Fabricated structural metal; sheet metalwork; floor laying & floor work

(G-17885)
MARQUEZ CUSTOM CABINETS INC
9222 Lazy Ln (33614-1514)
PHONE..................................813 352-8027
Yunieski Hernandez, *President*
EMP: 7 **EST:** 2017
SALES (est): 111.3K **Privately Held**
WEB: www.marquezcustomcabinets.com
SIC: 2434 Wood kitchen cabinets

(G-17886)
MARTIN LITHOGRAPH INC
Also Called: Mli Intgrted Graphic Solutions
505 N Rome Ave (33606-1250)
P.O. Box 4240 (33677-4240)
PHONE..................................813 254-1553
Martin Saavedra Jr, *President*
Jennifer Saavedra, *Corp Secy*
Janice Saavedra, *Vice Pres*
EMP: 43
SQ FT: 27,500
SALES (est): 5MM **Privately Held**
WEB: www.mlicorp.com
SIC: 2752 Commercial printing, offset

(G-17887)
MASONITE CORPORATION (HQ)
Also Called: Masonite Architectural
1242 E 5th Ave (33605-4904)
PHONE..................................813 877-2726
Frederick J Lynch, *President*
Mike Hildebrandt, *General Mgr*
Alex Legall, *Senior VP*
Clare Doyle, *Vice Pres*
Jim Kingry, *Vice Pres*
▲ **EMP:** 100 **EST:** 1925
SALES (est): 1.5B
SALES (corp-wide): 2.2B **Publicly Held**
WEB: www.masonite.com
SIC: 2431 3469 Doors, wood; doors & door parts & trim, wood; stamping metal for the trade
PA: Masonite International Corporation
1242 E 5th Ave
Tampa FL 33605
800 895-2723

(G-17888)
MASONITE HOLDINGS INC
201 N Franklin St Ste 300 (33602-5105)
PHONE..................................813 877-2726
Fred Lynch, *President*
◆ **EMP:** 11 **EST:** 1991
SQ FT: 4,000
SALES (est): 4.3MM
SALES (corp-wide): 2.2B **Publicly Held**
WEB: www.masonite.com
SIC: 2431 3442 Doors, wood; metal doors
PA: Masonite International Corporation
1242 E 5th Ave
Tampa FL 33605
800 895-2723

(G-17889)
MASONITE INTERNATIONAL CORP (PA)
1242 E 5th Ave (33605-4904)
PHONE..................................800 895-2723
Howard C Heckes, *President*
Chris Ball, *President*
Clare Doyle, *Senior VP*
Alex Legall, *Senior VP*
Robert E Lewis, *Senior VP*
◆ **EMP:** 100 **EST:** 1925
SQ FT: 80,000
SALES: 2.2B **Publicly Held**
WEB: www.masonite.com
SIC: 2431 3442 Doors, wood; metal doors

(G-17890)
MASONITE US CORPORATION
Also Called: Masonite International
1242 E 5th Ave (33605-4904)
PHONE..................................813 877-2726
Ken Sreeman, *President*
Steve Swartzmiller, *Senior VP*
David Perkins, *Vice Pres*
Quentin Rosandich, *Accounts Mgr*
Joe Berg, *Sales Staff*
EMP: 82 **EST:** 2004
SALES (est): 8MM **Privately Held**
WEB: www.masonite.com
SIC: 2431 Doors, wood

(G-17891)
MASSACHUSETTS BAY CLAM CO INC
13605 W Hillsborough Ave (33635-9653)
P.O. Box 208, Oldsmar (34677-0208)
PHONE..................................813 855-4599
Fax: 813 855-3944
EMP: 10
SQ FT: 6,000
SALES (est): 980K **Privately Held**
SIC: 2092 2022 Mfg Fresh/Frozen Packaged Fish Mfg Cheese

(G-17892)
MASSEYS METALS
2251 Massaro Blvd (33619-3021)
P.O. Box 89297 (33689-0404)
PHONE..................................813 626-8275
James R Massey, *President*
Juanita Massey, *Corp Secy*
Alan Massey, *Vice Pres*
Cris Massey, *Vice Pres*
EMP: 42 **EST:** 1971
SQ FT: 25,600
SALES (est): 4.9MM **Privately Held**
WEB: www.masseymetalscompany.com
SIC: 3444 Sheet metal specialties, not stamped

(G-17893)
MATCHWARE INC (PA)
511 W Bay St Ste 460 (33606-2770)
PHONE..................................800 880-2810
Ulrik Merrild, *President*
Christina Daniels, *COO*
Nick Aliantro, *Accountant*
◆ **EMP:** 5 **EST:** 2001
SALES (est): 1.1MM **Privately Held**
WEB: www.matchware.com
SIC: 7372 Prepackaged software

(G-17894)
MATERIAL CONVEYING MAINT INC (PA)
4901 30th Ave S (33619-6061)
PHONE..................................813 740-1111
Nelson G Castellano, *President*
Venera Campanelli, *Exec Dir*
EMP: 42 **EST:** 2014
SALES (est): 2.6MM **Privately Held**
WEB: www.gomcmi.com
SIC: 3535 Conveyors & conveying equipment

(G-17895)
MAY & WELL INC
8907 Regents Park Dr # 390 (33647-3401)
PHONE..................................813 333-5806
Zhiqing Han, *Principal*
EMP: 7 **EST:** 2010
SALES (est): 135.4K **Privately Held**
SIC: 2655 Fiber shipping & mailing containers

(G-17896)
MAYWORTH SHOWCASE WORKS INC
1711 W State St (33606-1043)
PHONE..................................813 251-1558
John W Mayworth Jr, *President*
Don Scranton, *Vice Pres*
EMP: 6 **EST:** 1920
SQ FT: 10,000
SALES (est): 878.3K **Privately Held**
SIC: 2431 2541 Millwork; wood partitions & fixtures

(G-17897)
MC CONNIE ENTERPRISES INC
Also Called: Mc Connie Fence
4707 30th Ave S (33619-6033)
PHONE..................................813 247-3827
Andreas Mc Connie, *President*
Helga E Mc Connie, *Corp Secy*
Paul Hughes, *Commercial*
EMP: 5 **EST:** 1973
SQ FT: 3,700
SALES (est): 968.7K **Privately Held**
WEB: www.mcconniefence.com
SIC: 2499 2298 Fencing, wood; fishing lines, nets, seines: made in cordage or twine mills

(G-17898)
MDCO INC
Also Called: Electronic Manufacturing Co
13440 Wright Cir (33626-3026)
PHONE..................................813 855-4068
Norman Blais, *President*
EMP: 11 **EST:** 1980
SQ FT: 10,000
SALES (est): 1MM **Privately Held**
SIC: 3679 Electronic circuits

(G-17899)
MEC CRYO LLC ✪
4430 E Adamo Dr Ste 305 (33605-5933)
PHONE..................................813 644-3764
Patrick Donovan, *Mng Member*
Benjamin Lacrosse,
EMP: 30 **EST:** 2021
SALES (est): 1.1MM **Privately Held**
SIC: 3559 Cryogenic machinery, industrial

(G-17900)
MEMPHIS METAL MANUFACTURING CO
10811 Barbados Isle Dr (33647-2792)
P.O. Box 11271, Memphis TN (38111-0271)
PHONE..................................901 276-6363
William B Mason III, *President*
Jake Taylor, *Manager*
EMP: 10 **EST:** 1945
SALES (est): 1MM **Privately Held**
WEB: www.memphis-metal.com
SIC: 3444 Sheet metalwork

(G-17901)
MERCHANTS METALS INC
Meadow Burke Products
2835 Overpass Rd Ste 100 (33619-1323)
PHONE..................................813 333-5515
Jose Martinez, *General Mgr*
Dave Kelly, *Vice Pres*
David Lampi, *Vice Pres*
Garrett Kendle, *Opers Mgr*
David Underwood, *Opers Mgr*
EMP: 100
SQ FT: 67,684 **Privately Held**
WEB: www.merchantsmetals.com
SIC: 3315 Wire & fabricated wire products
HQ: Merchants Metals Llc
211 Perimeter Center Pkwy
Atlanta GA 30346
770 741-0300

(G-17902)
MERCHANTS METALS LLC
4921 Joanne Kearney Blvd (33619-8603)
PHONE..................................813 980-0938
Billy Howell, *Manager*
EMP: 10 **Privately Held**
WEB: www.merchantsmetals.com
SIC: 3496 Fencing, made from purchased wire
HQ: Merchants Metals Llc
211 Perimeter Center Pkwy
Atlanta GA 30346
770 741-0300

(G-17903)
MERIT FASTENER CORPORATION
5416 56th Cmmerce Pk Blvd (33610-6857)
PHONE..................................813 626-3748
Bob Groom, *Opers Mgr*
Donna Young, *Technical Staff*
EMP: 8
SALES (corp-wide): 5.6MM **Privately Held**
WEB: www.meritfasteners.com
SIC: 3599 3491 Machine & other job shop work; industrial valves
PA: Merit Fastener Corporation
2510 N Ronald Reagan Blvd
Longwood FL 32750
407 331-4815

(G-17904)
METAL PROCESSORS INC
200 S Falkenburg Rd (33619-8041)
P.O. Box 3087, Brandon (33509-3087)
PHONE..................................813 654-0050
Lance C Cowieson, *President*
Leslie A Godwin, *Corp Secy*
Bill Winnette, *Purchasing*
EMP: 40 **EST:** 1982
SQ FT: 93,000
SALES (est): 4.3MM **Privately Held**
WEB: www.metalprocessors.com
SIC: 3312 Blast furnaces & steel mills

(G-17905)
METALCRAFT SERVICES TAMPA INC
10706 Nh 46th St (33617)
PHONE..................................813 558-8700
Gene E Pleus, *President*
Gene Pleus, *President*
Scott Yeo, *General Mgr*
Shane Pratt, *QC Mgr*
Matthew Pleus, *Sales Staff*
EMP: 4 **EST:** 1987
SQ FT: 4,000
SALES (est): 3MM **Privately Held**
WEB: www.metalcraftservices.com
SIC: 3441 Fabricated structural metal

(G-17906)
METRO LIFE MEDIA INC
Also Called: Orlando Metro Magazine
3404 S Omar Ave (33629-8214)
PHONE..................................813 745-3658
Stephen P Parag II, *President*
Ronda M Parag, *Manager*
EMP: 7 **EST:** 2005
SALES (est): 272.2K **Privately Held**
WEB: www.tampabaywed.com
SIC: 2721 Magazines: publishing & printing

(G-17907)
MILBANK MANUFACTURING CO
3214 Queen Palm Dr (33619-1304)
PHONE..................................813 623-2681
EMP: 10 **EST:** 2017
SALES (est): 140.8K **Privately Held**
WEB: www.milbankworks.com
SIC: 3999 Manufacturing industries

(G-17908)
MILLWORK 360 LLC
12941 Memorial Hwy (33635-9529)
P.O. Box 1916, Oldsmar (34677-6916)
PHONE..................................813 854-3100
Mike Williams, *President*
Jamie Burge, *CFO*
Paul McKendry, *Sales Staff*
EMP: 25 **EST:** 2010
SQ FT: 80,000
SALES (est): 4.3MM
SALES (corp-wide): 31.1MM **Privately Held**
WEB: www.millwork360.net
SIC: 2431 Millwork
PA: The Marwin Company Inc
107 Mcqueen St
West Columbia SC 29172
803 776-2396

(G-17909)
MINUTEMAN INDUSTRIES INC
Also Called: Minuteman Systems & Alarms
1407 E 5th Ave (33605-5021)
P.O. Box 3474, Apollo Beach (33572-1004)
PHONE..................................813 248-1776

▲ = Import ▼=Export
◆ =Import/Export

Terry Grewer, *President*
EMP: 6 **EST:** 1975
SQ FT: 3,600
SALES (est): 719.7K **Privately Held**
WEB: www.minutemanst.com
SIC: 3669 5065 Burglar alarm apparatus, electric; electronic parts & equipment

(G-17910)
MINUTEMAN PRESS
5519 Hanley Rd (33634-4900)
PHONE....................................813 884-2476
Manny Fernandez, *Principal*
EMP: 20 **EST:** 1992
SALES (est): 524.8K **Privately Held**
WEB: www.minutemanpress.com
SIC: 2752 Commercial printing, lithographic

(G-17911)
MITEK USA INC
6904 Parke East Blvd (33610-4115)
PHONE....................................813 906-3122
EMP: 7 **EST:** 2017
SALES (est): 295.9K **Privately Held**
WEB: www.mitek-us.com
SIC: 3443 Truss plates, metal

(G-17912)
MMO INDUSTRIES INC
4710 Eisenhower Blvd A1 (33634-6308)
PHONE....................................727 452-8665
Kenley Matheny, *Principal*
EMP: 7 **EST:** 2016
SALES (est): 288.6K **Privately Held**
SIC: 3999 Manufacturing industries

(G-17913)
MOBILE MEALS
8909 Magnolia Chase Cir (33647-2220)
PHONE....................................813 907-6325
Elizabeth Mekdeci, *Executive*
EMP: 7 **EST:** 2009
SALES (est): 169K **Privately Held**
SIC: 2099 Food preparations

(G-17914)
MODERN CABINETRY AND AMP MLLWK (PA)
5330 Ehrlich Rd Ste 102 (33624-6977)
PHONE....................................813 426-6941
Dave Veal, *President*
EMP: 19 **EST:** 2010
SALES (est): 352.4K **Privately Held**
WEB: www.moderncabinetry.com
SIC: 2434 Wood kitchen cabinets

(G-17915)
MOLDING DEPOT INC
3707 W Carmen St (33609-1303)
P.O. Box 10067 (33679-0067)
PHONE....................................813 348-4837
John L Rosende, *President*
Chris Rosende, *Vice Pres*
EMP: 36 **EST:** 2000
SALES (est): 1.8MM **Privately Held**
WEB: www.mouldingdepot.com
SIC: 3089 Molding primary plastic

(G-17916)
MOLEKULE INC
3802 Spectrum Blvd # 143 (33612-9212)
PHONE....................................352 871-3803
Lovely Goswami, *President*
EMP: 6
SALES (corp-wide): 2.9MM **Privately Held**
WEB: www.molekule.com
SIC: 3822 3829 Air flow controllers, air conditioning & refrigeration; measuring & controlling devices
PA: Molekule, Inc.
1301 Folsom St
San Francisco CA 94103
352 871-3803

(G-17917)
MOMENRY INC
100 S Ashley Dr Ste 600 (33602-5300)
PHONE....................................318 668-0888
EMP: 11
SALES (est): 239.1K **Privately Held**
SIC: 7372 Prepackaged Software Services

(G-17918)
MOROCCAN KHLII INC
808 N Macdill Ave (33609-1532)
PHONE....................................813 699-0096
Hicham H Tadlaoui, *CEO*
EMP: 7 **EST:** 2011
SALES (est): 108.9K **Privately Held**
WEB: www.moroccanjerky.com
SIC: 2013 Beef, dried: from purchased meat; snack sticks, including jerky: from purchased meat

(G-17919)
MOSAIC COMPANY (PA)
101 E Kennedy Blvd # 2500 (33602-3650)
PHONE....................................813 775-4200
Gregory L Ebel, *Ch of Bd*
James C O'Rourke, *President*
Mark J Isaacson, *Senior VP*
Carl Burks, *Production*
Cheryl Arnold, *Engineer*
◆ **EMP:** 502 **EST:** 2004
SALES: 8.6B **Publicly Held**
WEB: www.mosaicco.com
SIC: 2874 2819 Phosphatic fertilizers; phosphates; muriate of potash, not from mines

(G-17920)
MS SOFTWARE INC
5101 Vinson Dr (33610-5508)
PHONE....................................813 258-1735
Simmons Michael, *Principal*
EMP: 6 **EST:** 2016
SALES (est): 123.9K **Privately Held**
SIC: 7372 Prepackaged software

(G-17921)
MXN INC
Also Called: Sir Speedy
10120 Woodberry Rd (33619-8006)
PHONE....................................813 654-3173
James Mixon, *President*
EMP: 5 **EST:** 1992
SQ FT: 1,500
SALES (est): 635.5K **Privately Held**
WEB: www.sirspeedy.com
SIC: 2752 Commercial printing, lithographic

(G-17922)
MY CLONE SOLUTION
4532 W Kennedy Blvd 183 (33609-2042)
PHONE....................................813 442-9925
Brook Borup, *Principal*
Sarah Farnan, *Manager*
EMP: 11 **EST:** 2014
SALES (est): 1.1MM **Privately Held**
WEB: www.myclonesolution.com
SIC: 7372 Prepackaged software

(G-17923)
MY REVIEWERS LLC
Also Called: Myreviewers
3802 Spectrum Blvd 8 (33612-9212)
PHONE....................................813 404-9734
Joseph Moxley, *Mng Member*
EMP: 5 **EST:** 2013
SALES (est): 369K **Privately Held**
SIC: 7372 Educational computer software

(G-17924)
MYERS PRINTING INC
5601 N Florida Ave (33604-6911)
PHONE....................................813 237-0288
Phillip Myers, *President*
EMP: 5 **EST:** 1985
SALES (est): 507.5K **Privately Held**
SIC: 2752 Commercial printing, offset

(G-17925)
MYMD PHARMACEUTICALS INC
324 S Hyde Park Ave # 350 (33606-4127)
PHONE....................................813 864-2566
James A McNulty, *Principal*
Sonny Jones, *VP Opers*
EMP: 11 **EST:** 2016
SALES (est): 1.1MM **Privately Held**
WEB: www.mymd.com
SIC: 2834 Pharmaceutical preparations

(G-17926)
N-EAR PRO INC
Also Called: N Ear Pro
4821 N Grady Ave (33614-6513)
PHONE....................................877 290-4599
EMP: 40
SQ FT: 2,000
SALES (est): 1.2MM **Privately Held**
SIC: 3842 Mfg Surgical Appliances/Supplies

(G-17927)
N3XT L3VEL 2 POINT 0 LLC ✪
1248 E Hillsborough Ave (33604-7201)
PHONE....................................863 777-3778
Julius Jones, *Mng Member*
Davon Jackson Jr, *Mng Member*
John Rowland Jr, *Mng Member*
EMP: 11 **EST:** 2021
SALES (est): 378.3K **Privately Held**
SIC: 2211 Lawns, cotton

(G-17928)
N3XT UP EXOTIC LLC ✪
1248 E Hillsborough Ave (33604-7201)
PHONE....................................863 777-3778
Stanley Dillard,
EMP: 7 **EST:** 2021
SALES (est): 269K **Privately Held**
SIC: 3199 Dog furnishings: collars, leashes, muzzles, etc.: leather

(G-17929)
NATIONAL CUSTOM INSIGNIA INC
8875 Hdden Rver Pkwy Ste (33637)
P.O. Box 1190, Oldsmar (34677-1190)
PHONE....................................813 313-2561
William Witrak, *President*
Bill Michaels, *Vice Pres*
EMP: 14 **EST:** 1996
SALES (est): 516.6K **Privately Held**
WEB: www.lapelpins.com
SIC: 3915 Jewelers' materials & lapidary work

(G-17930)
NATIONAL CYLINDER HEAD EXCHANG
4408 N Thatcher Ave (33614-7631)
PHONE....................................813 870-6340
Charles Lantry, *President*
EMP: 7 **EST:** 1983
SQ FT: 2,500
SALES (est): 600K **Privately Held**
WEB: www.national-cylinder-head-exchange.usautos.repair
SIC: 3593 3599 Fluid power cylinders, hydraulic or pneumatic; machine shop, jobbing & repair

(G-17931)
NATIONAL DIESEL ENGINE INC
253 S 78th St (33619-4225)
PHONE....................................810 516-6855
Steve Spencer, *President*
EMP: 10
SALES (est): 1MM **Privately Held**
WEB: www.nationaldieselengineinc.com
SIC: 3519 Diesel engine rebuilding

(G-17932)
NATIONAL HEALTH ALLIANCE LLC
500 N West Shore Blvd # 640 (33609-1910)
PHONE....................................727 504-3915
Manindra K Garg,
EMP: 8 **EST:** 2013
SALES (est): 842.9K **Privately Held**
SIC: 2833 Vitamins, natural or synthetic: bulk, uncompounded

(G-17933)
NATIONWIDE INDUSTRIES INC (PA)
3505 Cragmont Dr (33619-8340)
PHONE....................................813 988-2628
Christopher Kliefoth, *President*
Marc Poirier, *CFO*
Rachel Tiller, *Controller*
Dave Hutchins, *Manager*
◆ **EMP:** 27 **EST:** 1990
SALES (est): 13.8MM **Privately Held**
WEB: www.nationwideindustries.com
SIC: 3442 1799 3315 Metal doors, sash & trim; fence construction; fence gates posts & fittings: steel

(G-17934)
NAVIERA COFFEE MILLS INC
Also Called: El Molino Coffee
2012 E 7th Ave (33605-3902)
P.O. Box 5036 (33675-5036)
PHONE....................................813 248-2521
Danilo V Fernandez, *President*
Carmelina Fernandez, *Vice Pres*
Marge Raymond, *Comptroller*
EMP: 20 **EST:** 1921
SQ FT: 10,000
SALES (est): 1.9MM **Privately Held**
WEB: www.elmolinocoffee.com
SIC: 2095 Coffee roasting (except by wholesale grocers)

(G-17935)
NCI
11327 Countryway Blvd (33626-2610)
PHONE....................................813 749-1799
EMP: 6 **EST:** 2018
SALES (est): 204.6K **Privately Held**
SIC: 3825 Instruments to measure electricity

(G-17936)
NEBRASKA PRINTING INC
3849 W Azeele St (33609-3921)
PHONE....................................813 870-6871
Charles Cuervo Jr, *CEO*
Greg Nelson, *Principal*
Mark Mercer, *CFO*
Ralph Chille, *Director*
EMP: 20 **EST:** 1932
SALES (est): 1.2MM **Privately Held**
WEB: www.nebcofl.com
SIC: 2752 Commercial printing, offset

(G-17937)
NEWSPAPER PRINTING COMPANY
5210 S Lois Ave (33611-3445)
PHONE....................................813 839-0035
John L Tevlin, *President*
Herb Facas, *President*
Bryan Waterhouse, *President*
Jeff Thomson, *Plant Supt*
Janice Brooks, *Controller*
▼ **EMP:** 200 **EST:** 1984
SQ FT: 12,000
SALES (est): 31.5MM **Privately Held**
WEB: www.npcprinting.com
SIC: 2752 Commercial printing, offset

(G-17938)
NEXT GENERATION HOME PDTS INC
Also Called: Nextgen
701 S Howard Ave (33606-2473)
PHONE....................................727 834-9400
Bob Dolatowski, *President*
David M Schifino, *Admin Sec*
▲ **EMP:** 6 **EST:** 2001
SQ FT: 6,000
SALES (est): 578.4K **Privately Held**
WEB: www.nextgen.us
SIC: 3825 5065 Frequency meters: electrical, mechanical & electronic; electronic parts

(G-17939)
NIC4 INC
111 Kelsey Ln Ste D (33619-4357)
PHONE....................................877 455-2131
Chad Gatlin, *CEO*
EMP: 19 **EST:** 2011
SALES (est): 7.5MM
SALES (corp-wide): 1.1MM **Privately Held**
WEB: www.nic4.com
SIC: 3663 4899 Space satellite communications equipment; satellite earth stations
PA: Network Innovations Inc
4424 Manilla Rd Se
Calgary AB T2G 4
403 287-5000

(G-17940)
NIGHTSCENES INC
Also Called: Qssi
12802 Commodity Pl (33626-3101)
P.O. Box 1169, Oldsmar (34677-1169)
PHONE....................................813 855-9416
Johnie R Edens, *President*
Rick Edens, *President*

Mary D Edens, *Vice Pres*
Dan Kennedy, *Director*
◆ **EMP:** 10 **EST:** 1992
SALES (est): 1.6MM **Privately Held**
SIC: 3648 Outdoor lighting equipment

(G-17941)
NIVEL PARTS AND MFG CO LLC
3608 Queen Palm Dr Ste A (33619-1317)
PHONE..................................904 421-3004
EMP: 7 **EST:** 2017
SALES (est): 82.3K **Privately Held**
WEB: www.nivelparts.com
SIC: 3999 Manufacturing industries

(G-17942)
NPC OF TAMPA INC
5210 S Lois Ave (33611-3445)
PHONE..................................813 839-0035
John L Tevlin Jr, *President*
Jennifer L Dal Sasso, *Treasurer*
Cheryl L Tevlin, *Admin Sec*
EMP: 14 **EST:** 1992
SQ FT: 66,984
SALES (est): 150.8K **Privately Held**
WEB: www.npcprinting.com
SIC: 2721 2789 2711 Magazines: publishing & printing; bookbinding & related work; magazines, binding; commercial printing & newspaper publishing combined

(G-17943)
NUTRACEUTICAL CORPORATION
Also Called: Aubrey Organics
5046 W Linebaugh Ave (33624-5030)
PHONE..................................813 877-4186
Curt Valva, *President*
John Dalessandro, *Chief Mktg Ofcr*
EMP: 7
SALES (corp-wide): 319.3MM **Privately Held**
WEB: www.nutraceutical.com
SIC: 2844 Cosmetic preparations
HQ: Nutraceutical Corporation
580 W 300 N
Ogden UT 84404

(G-17944)
OCEANA SOFTWARE CORP
5202 Quarrystone Ln (33624-2506)
PHONE..................................813 335-6966
Jeffrey L Odell, *Principal*
EMP: 7 **EST:** 2002
SALES (est): 416.2K **Privately Held**
SIC: 7372 Prepackaged software

(G-17945)
ODYSSEY MANUFACTURING CO (PA)
1484 Massaro Blvd (33619-3006)
PHONE..................................813 635-0339
Marvin T Rakes, *President*
Stephen W Sidelko, *Vice Pres*
Butch Dempsey, *Plant Mgr*
Michael Azzarella, *Project Mgr*
Pavol Plecenik, *Manager*
EMP: 45 **EST:** 1998
SQ FT: 17,722
SALES (est): 15MM **Privately Held**
WEB: www.odysseymanufacturing.com
SIC: 2842 Bleaches, household: dry or liquid

(G-17946)
ODYSSEY MANUFACTURING CO
5361 Hartford St (33619)
PHONE..................................813 635-0339
Pat Allmand, *General Mgr*
EMP: 10
SALES (corp-wide): 15MM **Privately Held**
WEB: www.odysseymanufacturing.com
SIC: 2812 Chlorine, compressed or liquefied
PA: Odyssey Manufacturing Co
1484 Massaro Blvd
Tampa FL 33619
813 635-0339

(G-17947)
OLD 97 COMPANY (HQ)
4829 E 7th Ave (33605-4703)
PHONE..................................813 246-4180
Frank Ferola, *President*
EMP: 11 **EST:** 1955
SALES (est): 13.9MM
SALES (corp-wide): 29.8MM **Privately Held**
WEB: www.thestephanco.com
SIC: 2844 Toilet preparations
PA: The Stephan Co
2211 Reach Rd Ste B4
Williamsport PA 17701
800 634-1996

(G-17948)
OLD HERITAGE MEDCALL INC
202 E Virginia Ave (33603-4821)
PHONE..................................813 221-1000
Donald R Musselman, *President*
Jerry Patterson, *Vice Pres*
EMP: 13
SQ FT: 2,500
SALES (est): 1.5MM **Privately Held**
WEB: www.heritagemedcall.com
SIC: 3669 Emergency alarms

(G-17949)
OLD MEETING HOUSE HOME MADE IC
901 S Howard Ave (33606-2418)
PHONE..................................813 254-0977
Mathew Hoffman,
EMP: 10 **EST:** 2003
SALES (est): 720.7K **Privately Held**
SIC: 2024 Ice cream & frozen desserts

(G-17950)
OLDCASTLE ARCHITECTURAL INC
5603 Anderson Rd (33614-5313)
PHONE..................................813 886-7761
James R Bird, *President*
Rose Huges, *Admin Sec*
EMP: 44 **EST:** 1966
SQ FT: 2,600
SALES (est): 2.1MM **Privately Held**
WEB: www.oldcastlecoastal.com
SIC: 3272 Concrete products; dry mixture concrete

(G-17951)
OLDCASTLE BUILDINGENVELOPE INC
Also Called: HGP Industries
5115 Hartford St (33619-6815)
PHONE..................................813 247-3184
Mike Boretski, *General Mgr*
Scott Reynolds, *Manager*
EMP: 100
SQ FT: 68,195
SALES (corp-wide): 27.5B **Privately Held**
WEB: www.obe.com
SIC: 3231 5231 Tempered glass: made from purchased glass; insulating glass: made from purchased glass; glass
HQ: Oldcastle Buildingenvelope, Inc.
5005 Lyndon B Johnson Fwy # 1050
Dallas TX 75244
214 273-3400

(G-17952)
OLDCASTLE COASTAL
5455 N 59th St (33610-2011)
PHONE..................................813 621-2427
Frank Ketchum, *Owner*
Jason Barr, *Vice Pres*
Spencer Korb, *Plant Mgr*
Amgad Beshara, *Engineer*
Patrick Knapik, *Regl Sales Mgr*
EMP: 14 **EST:** 2018
SALES (est): 5.4MM **Privately Held**
SIC: 3273 Ready-mixed concrete

(G-17953)
OLDCASTLE COASTAL INC
Coloroc Materials
5603 Anderson Rd (33614-5313)
PHONE..................................813 886-7761
Craig Akers, *Sales Staff*
Doug McCall, *Manager*
EMP: 8
SALES (corp-wide): 27.5B **Privately Held**
WEB: www.oldcastlecoastal.com
SIC: 3272 Concrete products
HQ: Oldcastle Coastal, Inc.
4630 Woodland Corporate B
Tampa FL 33614

(G-17954)
OLDCASTLE COASTAL INC
8910 N 12th St (33604-1811)
PHONE..................................813 932-1007
Kevin Cintle, *Manager*
EMP: 7
SALES (corp-wide): 27.5B **Privately Held**
WEB: www.oldcastlecoastal.com
SIC: 3272 Covers, catch basin: concrete
HQ: Oldcastle Coastal, Inc.
4630 Woodland Corporate B
Tampa FL 33614

(G-17955)
OLDCASTLE COASTAL INC (DH)
4630 Woodland Corporate B (33614-2415)
PHONE..................................813 367-9780
Tim Ortman, *President*
Bill Braswell, *Vice Pres*
Judy Paredes, *Human Res Dir*
EMP: 219 **EST:** 2003
SQ FT: 45,000
SALES (est): 102.8MM
SALES (corp-wide): 27.5B **Privately Held**
WEB: www.oldcastlecoastal.com
SIC: 3272 Covers, catch basin: concrete
HQ: Crh Americas, Inc.
900 Ashwood Pkwy Ste 600
Atlanta GA 30338
770 804-3363

(G-17956)
OMNIRELIANT CORPORATION
4218 W Linebaugh Ave (33624-5241)
PHONE..................................813 909-9191
Paul Morrison, *President*
Chris Phillips, *CFO*
EMP: 2 **EST:** 2006
SQ FT: 1,000
SALES (est): 50MM **Privately Held**
WEB: www.omnireliant.com
SIC: 2844 Perfumes & colognes

(G-17957)
ONSIGHT INDUSTRIES
221 Hobbs St (33619-8068)
PHONE..................................407 830-8861
EMP: 6 **EST:** 1991
SALES (est): 79.8K **Privately Held**
WEB: www.onsightindustries.com
SIC: 3993 2759 Signs & advertising specialties; commercial printing

(G-17958)
OPEN PALM PRESS INC
3839 W Kennedy Blvd (33609-2719)
PHONE..................................813 870-3839
EMP: 8 **EST:** 2019
SALES (est): 37.5K **Privately Held**
WEB: www.openpalmlaw.com
SIC: 2741 Miscellaneous publishing

(G-17959)
ORAGENICS INC (PA)
4902 Eisenhower Blvd # 125 (33634-6342)
PHONE..................................813 286-7900
Frederick W Telling, *Ch of Bd*
Alan F Joslyn, *President*
Martin Handfield, *Senior VP*
Steven Mulcahy, *Opers Staff*
Michael Sullivan, *CFO*
EMP: 4 **EST:** 1999
SQ FT: 2,207
SALES (est): 8.3MM **Publicly Held**
WEB: www.oragenics.com
SIC: 2834 Pharmaceutical preparations

(G-17960)
ORNAMENTAL DESIGN IRONWORKS
4706 N Falkenburg Rd (33610-5918)
PHONE..................................813 626-8449
Michael Ward, *President*
Darlene Yerby, *Admin Sec*
EMP: 20 **EST:** 1950
SQ FT: 5,000
SALES (est): 2.2MM **Privately Held**
WEB: www.odi-tampa.com
SIC: 3446 3444 Architectural metalwork; sheet metalwork

(G-17961)
ORTEGA CUSTOM CABINETS INC
7006 Hazelhurst Ct (33615-2945)
PHONE..................................813 403-7101
Uziel Ortega Martinez, *President*
EMP: 5 **EST:** 2010
SALES (est): 326.7K **Privately Held**
WEB: www.tampacabinetmaker.com
SIC: 2434 Wood kitchen cabinets

(G-17962)
ORTHOPEDIC DESIGNS N AMER INC
5912 Breckenridge Pkwy F (33610-4200)
PHONE..................................813 443-4905
Chuck Masek, *President*
Nathan Masek, *Manager*
Steven Lozier, *Representative*
EMP: 5 **EST:** 2009
SALES (est): 810.7K **Privately Held**
WEB: www.odi-na.com
SIC: 3841 Bone plates & screws; bone rongeurs; bone drills

(G-17963)
OSG AMERICA LLC
302 Knights Run Ave # 1200 (33602-5962)
PHONE..................................813 209-0600
Myles R Itkin, *President*
Henry P Flinter, *CFO*
EMP: 76 **EST:** 2007
SALES (est): 6.3MM
SALES (corp-wide): 418.6MM **Publicly Held**
WEB: www.osg.com
SIC: 3731 Shipbuilding & repairing
HQ: Osg America L.P.
302 Knights Run Ave
Tampa FL 33602

(G-17964)
OUTDOOR AMERICA IMAGES INC (PA)
Also Called: Oai
4545 W Hillsborough Ave (33614-5441)
PHONE..................................813 888-8796
Michael A Garcia, *President*
Michael Garcia, *Principal*
Brunilda L Vazquez, *Treasurer*
Ray Perry, *Sales Staff*
Kelly Breslin, *Manager*
▲ **EMP:** 21 **EST:** 1989
SQ FT: 35,000
SALES (est): 8MM **Privately Held**
SIC: 2399 7336 Banners, made from fabric; graphic arts & related design

(G-17965)
OUTPUT PRINTING CORP
Also Called: Allegra Print Imging Dwntwn Tm
107 N Jefferson St (33602-5001)
PHONE..................................813 228-8800
Joel Routman, *President*
Jeff Routman, *Opers Staff*
Nancy Routman, *Treasurer*
Jason Routman, *Marketing Staff*
EMP: 10 **EST:** 1989
SQ FT: 4,000
SALES (est): 1.9MM **Privately Held**
WEB: www.allegramarketingprint.com
SIC: 2752 2791 2789 Commercial printing, offset; typesetting; bookbinding & related work

(G-17966)
OUTREACH CORPORATION
Also Called: Sales
1208 E Kennedy Blvd (33602-3504)
PHONE..................................888 938-7356
EMP: 12
SALES (corp-wide): 50.9MM **Privately Held**
WEB: www.outreach.io
SIC: 7372 Business oriented computer software
PA: Outreach Corporation
333 Elliott Ave W Ste 500
Seattle WA 98119
206 235-3672

(G-17967)
PACA FOODS LLC
5212 Cone Rd (33610-5302)
PHONE..................................813 628-8228

Michael Shepardson, *CEO*
Steve De Luca, *Controller*
EMP: 30 **EST:** 1991
SQ FT: 50,000
SALES (est): 10MM **Privately Held**
WEB: www.pacafoods.com
SIC: 2099 Food preparations

(G-17968)
PACIFIC DIE CAST INC (PA)
Also Called: Duraguard Products
12802 Commodity Pl (33626-3101)
P.O. Box 369, Oldsmar (34677-0369)
PHONE.................................813 316-2221
Johnie R Edens, *President*
Shannon Edens, *Vice Pres*
Mary D Edens, *Admin Sec*
▲ **EMP:** 10 **EST:** 2000
SQ FT: 97,000
SALES (est): 12.7MM **Privately Held**
SIC: 3544 Special dies & tools

(G-17969)
PADGETT COMMUNICATIONS INC
5005 W Laurel St Ste 103 (33607-3896)
PHONE.................................727 323-5800
Todd Padgett, *President*
Jenna Clous, *Project Mgr*
Trina Landers, *Project Mgr*
Shannon Maestre, *Project Mgr*
Jessica Sullens, *Office Mgr*
EMP: 27 **EST:** 1994
SALES (est): 4.1MM **Privately Held**
WEB: www.pcipro.com
SIC: 3669 5045 3651 Intercommunication systems, electric; computers, peripherals & software; household audio & video equipment

(G-17970)
PANE RUSTICA BAKERY & CAFE
3225 S Macdill Ave (33629-8171)
PHONE.................................813 902-8828
Karen Kruszewski, *Owner*
EMP: 10 **EST:** 1999
SALES (est): 1.2MM **Privately Held**
WEB: www.panerusticabakery.com
SIC: 2051 5461 Bakery: wholesale or wholesale/retail combined; bakeries

(G-17971)
PANGENEX CORPORATION (PA)
9950 Princess Palm Ave (33619-8302)
PHONE.................................352 346-4045
Jeffrey M Roman, *President*
EMP: 5 **EST:** 2008
SALES (est): 833.1K **Privately Held**
SIC: 2023 Dietary supplements, dairy & non-dairy based

(G-17972)
PANTOGRAMS INC
4537 S Dale Mabry Hwy (33611-1425)
PHONE.................................813 839-5697
Scott Colman, *President*
Jen Lasky, *Manager*
◆ **EMP:** 8 **EST:** 2015
SQ FT: 13,000
SALES (est): 234.1K **Privately Held**
WEB: www.pantograms.com
SIC: 3552 Embroidery machines

(G-17973)
PANTOGRAMS MFG CO INC
Also Called: EMB Supplies
4537 S Dale Mabry Hwy (33611-1425)
PHONE.................................813 839-5697
John Colman, *CEO*
Larry Sheppard, *Principal*
Linda Colman, *Corp Secy*
Aaron McMahon, *Warehouse Mgr*
Brandon Epperson, *Manager*
▲ **EMP:** 32 **EST:** 1979
SQ FT: 12,000
SALES (est): 2.3MM **Privately Held**
WEB: www.pantograms.com
SIC: 3552 2397 7371 Embroidery machines; schiffli machine embroideries; computer software development

(G-17974)
PARADISE INC (PA)
5110 W Poe Ave (33629-7527)
PHONE.................................813 752-1155
Melvin S Gordon, *Ch of Bd*
Randy S Gordon, *President*
Mark H Gordon, *Exec VP*
Tracy W Schulis, *Senior VP*
Paul M Long, *Vice Pres*
▲ **EMP:** 120 **EST:** 1961
SQ FT: 350,000
SALES: 20.1MM **Privately Held**
WEB: www.paradisefruitco.com
SIC: 2064 3089 Fruits: candied, crystallized, or glazed; molding primary plastic

(G-17975)
PARAGON GLOBL SUP SLUTIONS LLC
301 W Platt St Ste 98 (33606-2292)
PHONE.................................813 745-9902
Charles Fletcher, *President*
EMP: 4
SQ FT: 200
SALES (est): 3MM **Privately Held**
WEB: www.paragonglobalsupply.com
SIC: 3069 3089 Rubber automotive products; injection molding of plastics

(G-17976)
PARAGON WATER SYSTEMS INC
13805 Monroe Park (33635-6369)
PHONE.................................727 538-4704
George Lutich, *President*
John H Douglas, *President*
Peter Cicchetto, *COO*
Syed Shah, *Vice Pres*
Matthew Simmons, *Plant Supt*
▲ **EMP:** 39 **EST:** 1988
SQ FT: 20,000
SALES (est): 14.2MM
SALES (corp-wide): 652.7MM **Privately Held**
WEB: www.paragonwater.com
SIC: 3589 Water filters & softeners, household type
PA: Culligan International Company
9399 W Higgins Rd # 1100
Rosemont IL 60018
847 430-2800

(G-17977)
PARALLEL FLORIDA LLC
2203 N Lois Ave Ste M275 (33607-2698)
PHONE.................................404 920-4890
William Wrigley, *CEO*
James Whitcomb, *CFO*
EMP: 1000 **EST:** 2015
SALES (est): 168.8MM **Privately Held**
WEB: www.surterra.com
SIC: 2834 Vitamin, nutrient & hematinic preparations for human use
HQ: Surterra Holdings Inc.
116 E 4th St
Ocilla GA 31774
229 457-9498

(G-17978)
PATIO PRODUCTS MFG LLC
9706 E Us Highway 92 (33610-5930)
PHONE.................................813 664-0158
Larry Stephens, *President*
EMP: 17 **EST:** 2010
SQ FT: 17,500
SALES (est): 1.9MM **Privately Held**
WEB: www.patioproductsmfg.com
SIC: 3442 Metal doors

(G-17979)
PDMA CORPORATION
5909 Hampton Oaks Pkwy C (33610-9581)
PHONE.................................813 621-6463
Timothy R Owen, *President*
Fred Baker, *Vice Pres*
Todd Gunderson, *Vice Pres*
Pak Wong, *Vice Pres*
David McKinnon, *Project Mgr*
EMP: 45
SQ FT: 13,000
SALES: 13.7MM **Privately Held**
WEB: www.pdma.com
SIC: 3825 7389 Test equipment for electronic & electric measurement; industrial & commercial equipment inspection service

(G-17980)
PEAK NUTRITIONAL PRODUCTS LLC
5525 Johns Rd Ste 905 (33634-4514)
PHONE.................................813 884-4989
Robert J Lebeau, *President*
Mike Connors, *Sales Staff*
Vesselina Iltcheva, *Manager*
Ted Jackson, *Director*
▲ **EMP:** 40
SALES (est): 8.3MM **Privately Held**
WEB: www.peaknutritionalproducts.com
SIC: 2023 2834 Dietary supplements, dairy & non-dairy based; proprietary drug products

(G-17981)
PEARCEY ENTERPRISE
7806 N 52nd St (33617-8108)
PHONE.................................904 235-3096
Randall Pearcey, *Principal*
Michael Chapman, *Project Leader*
EMP: 7 **EST:** 2010
SALES (est): 128K **Privately Held**
WEB: www.pearceyreport.com
SIC: 2711 Newspapers

(G-17982)
PEPSI-COLA BOTTLING CO TAMPA (DH)
11315 N 30th St (33612-6495)
PHONE.................................813 971-2550
Brenda C Barnes, *President*
Jackie Chapman, *Maint Spvr*
Tony Allen, *Opers Staff*
Peter Bridgman, *Treasurer*
Gerrett Hall, *Manager*
◆ **EMP:** 200 **EST:** 1936
SALES (est): 265.2MM
SALES (corp-wide): 70.3B **Publicly Held**
WEB: www.pepsico.com
SIC: 2086 Carbonated soft drinks, bottled & canned
HQ: Pepsi-Cola Metropolitan Bottling Company, Inc.
1111 Westchester Ave
White Plains NY 10604
914 767-6000

(G-17983)
PERCH SECURITY INC
4110 George Rd Ste 200 (33634-7411)
PHONE.................................844 500-1810
Aharon Chenin, *CEO*
David Powell, *Vice Pres*
Gary Dobkin, *Opers Staff*
Mark Shamshoian, *Controller*
Channing Applegarth, *Manager*
EMP: 50 **EST:** 2017
SALES (est): 14.1MM
SALES (corp-wide): 95.9MM **Privately Held**
WEB: www.perchsecurity.com
SIC: 7372 Application computer software
PA: Connectwise, Llc
4110 George Rd Ste 200
Tampa FL 33634
813 463-4700

(G-17984)
PET DECLARATION INC
13915 River Willow Pl (33637-1010)
PHONE.................................772 215-1607
Gena Norris, *President*
EMP: 6 **EST:** 2017
SALES (est): 138.1K **Privately Held**
SIC: 3999 Pet supplies

(G-17985)
PETNET SOLUTIONS INC
9204 Florida Palm Dr (33619-4352)
PHONE.................................813 627-0022
Chris Connely, *Branch Mgr*
EMP: 7
SALES (corp-wide): 67.4B **Privately Held**
WEB: www.siemens.com
SIC: 2835 Radioactive diagnostic substances
HQ: Petnet Solutions, Inc.
810 Innovation Dr
Knoxville TN 37932
865 218-2000

(G-17986)
PETROTECH SERVICES INC
1807 E 2nd Ave (33605-5201)
PHONE.................................813 248-0743
EMP: 16 **Privately Held**
SIC: 3498 Fabricated pipe & fittings
PA: Petrotech Services Inc
4041 Maritime Blvd
Tampa FL 33605

(G-17987)
PETROTECH SERVICES INC (PA)
4041 Maritime Blvd (33605-6849)
P.O. Box 76235 (33675-1235)
PHONE.................................813 248-0743
Gloria Kane, *President*
Lawrence Kane, *Treasurer*
EMP: 77 **EST:** 1991
SQ FT: 2,000
SALES (est): 3.3MM **Privately Held**
SIC: 3498 3441 Fabricated pipe & fittings; fabricated structural metal

(G-17988)
PHIL & BRENDA JOHNSON INC
Also Called: Sir Speedy
5609 E Hillsborough Ave (33610-5414)
PHONE.................................813 623-5478
Phil Johnson, *President*
Brenda Johnson, *Vice Pres*
EMP: 13 **EST:** 1983
SQ FT: 4,000
SALES (est): 1.8MM **Privately Held**
WEB: www.tampafl390.sirspeedy.com
SIC: 2752 Commercial printing, lithographic

(G-17989)
PHIL LAU
Also Called: International Specialist
16309 Millan De Avila (33613-1090)
P.O. Box 271430 (33688-1430)
PHONE.................................813 631-8643
Phil Lau, *Owner*
Christopher Lau, *Vice Pres*
Kayla Lau, *CFO*
▲ **EMP:** 10 **EST:** 1971
SALES (est): 699.9K **Privately Held**
SIC: 3679 Electronic components

(G-17990)
PHILLYS FAMOUS WATER ICE INC
Also Called: Philly Swirl
1102 N 28th St (33605-6246)
PHONE.................................813 248-8644
Craig Millican, *General Mgr*
James Askin, *Transportation*
Pete Caspari, *Chief Engr*
Kathy Knox, *CFO*
Rick Marquez, *Controller*
EMP: 110 **EST:** 2006
SALES (est): 23MM
SALES (corp-wide): 1B **Publicly Held**
WEB: www.phillyswirl.com
SIC: 2024 Ices, flavored (frozen dessert)
PA: J & J Snack Foods Corp.
6000 Central Hwy
Pennsauken NJ 08109
856 665-9533

(G-17991)
PHILS CAKE BOX BAKERIES INC
Also Called: Alessi Bakery
4705 W Cayuga St (33614-6948)
PHONE.................................813 348-0128
Gary Horstmann, *COO*
Tarek Ibrahim, *COO*
Jacquie Pissanos, *Vice Pres*
Tony Moon, *Controller*
Sandra Hiddeman, *Marketing Staff*
EMP: 94
SALES (corp-wide): 34.4MM **Privately Held**
WEB: www.alessibakery.com
SIC: 2051 Bakery: wholesale or wholesale/retail combined
PA: Phil's Cake Box Bakeries, Inc.
5202 Eagle Trail Dr
Tampa FL 33634
813 348-0128

(G-17992)
PHOTOENGRAVING INC (PA)
Also Called: Truplate
502 N Willow Ave (33606-1338)
PHONE..................................813 253-3427
Edward L Dalton Jr, *President*
Joe Velazquez, *Vice Pres*
Rachel Dalton, *Treasurer*
▲ **EMP:** 30 **EST:** 1953
SQ FT: 20,000
SALES (est): 2.9MM **Privately Held**
WEB: www.photoengravinginc.com
SIC: 3861 2752 2796 Plates, photographic (sensitized); commercial printing, lithographic; platemaking services

(G-17993)
PIP PRINTING 622 INC
10428 N Florida Ave (33612-6709)
PHONE..................................813 935-8113
John J Driscoll, *Director*
EMP: 5 **EST:** 2001
SALES (est): 476K **Privately Held**
WEB: www.pip.com
SIC: 2752 Commercial printing, offset

(G-17994)
PITNEY BOWES INC
5310 Cypress Center Dr # 110
(33609-1041)
P.O. Box 867, Hartford CT (06143-0867)
PHONE..................................813 639-1110
Joyce Taylor, *Manager*
Mark Margait, *Technician*
EMP: 100
SALES (corp-wide): 3.5B **Publicly Held**
WEB: www.pitneybowes.com
SIC: 3579 Postage meters
PA: Pitney Bowes Inc.
3001 Summer St
Stamford CT 06905
203 356-5000

(G-17995)
PLASTICS AMERICA INCORPORATED
8501 E Adamo Dr (33619-3510)
PHONE..................................813 620-3711
Bob Belzer, *President*
Chris Wiggins, *COO*
Dave Modisette, *Vice Pres*
EMP: 6 **EST:** 1991
SQ FT: 5,000
SALES (est): 808.7K **Privately Held**
WEB: www.plasticsamerica.com
SIC: 2821 5162 5085 Plastics materials & resins; plastics sheets & rods; industrial supplies

(G-17996)
POLYMER LOGISTICS INC (HQ)
4630 Woodlnd Corp Blvd # 209
(33614-2429)
PHONE..................................877 462-6195
Robert Engle, *CEO*
Salim Baltagi, *Vice Pres*
Tom Clark, *Site Mgr*
Nancy Walsh, *CFO*
Pauline Pearce, *Accountant*
◆ **EMP:** 30 **EST:** 2006
SALES (est): 49.9MM
SALES (corp-wide): 217.9MM **Privately Held**
WEB: www.toscaltd.com
SIC: 3089 5085 5162 Pallets, plastic; boxes, crates, etc., other than paper; plastics materials & basic shapes
PA: Tosca Services, Llc
1175 Peachtree St Ne # 1900
Atlanta GA 30361
920 569-5335

(G-17997)
POMPANETTE LLC
Pompanette Gray
7712 Cheri Ct (33634-2419)
PHONE..................................813 885-2182
Richard Truell, *President*
Mark Carpenter, *General Mgr*
Craig Erb, *Materials Mgr*
Paul Adams, *Purch Agent*
Michael Haber, *Branch Mgr*
EMP: 40
SQ FT: 132,230
SALES (corp-wide): 34.2MM **Privately Held**
WEB: www.pompanettellc.com
SIC: 3732 3089 3949 3429 Boats, rigid: plastics; boats, nonrigid: plastic; sporting & athletic goods; manufactured hardware (general); products of purchased glass
PA: Pompanette, Llc
73 Southwest St
Charlestown NH 03603
717 569-2300

(G-17998)
POWERSPORTS 911 INC
5911 Benjamin Center Dr (33634-5239)
PHONE..................................813 769-2468
Ryan Heath, *President*
EMP: 6 **EST:** 2016
SALES (est): 1.6MM
SALES (corp-wide): 5.3MM **Privately Held**
WEB: www.webrivergroup.com
SIC: 3751 Motorcycles & related parts
PA: Web River Group, Inc.
5911 Benjamin Center Dr
Tampa FL 33634
813 769-2451

(G-17999)
PPG ARCHITECTURAL FINISHES INC
Also Called: Glidden Professional Paint Ctr
3102 W Kennedy Blvd (33609-3005)
PHONE..................................813 877-5841
EMP: 7
SALES (corp-wide): 15.3B **Publicly Held**
SIC: 2891 Mfg Adhesives/Sealants
HQ: Ppg Architectural Finishes, Inc.
1 Ppg Pl
Pittsburgh PA 15272
412 434-3131

(G-18000)
PPG INC
Also Called: Promo Printing Group
5133 W Cypress St (33607-1701)
PHONE..................................813 831-9902
William Gillespie, *President*
Steven W Richter, *Vice Pres*
◆ **EMP:** 10 **EST:** 1998
SQ FT: 2,000
SALES (est): 1.9MM **Privately Held**
WEB: www.promoprintinggroup.com
SIC: 2752 Commercial printing, offset

(G-18001)
PRECIOUS METALS BUYERS LLC (PA)
6201 Johns Rd Ste 5 (33634-4434)
PHONE..................................813 880-9544
Jorge Rodriguez, *Principal*
EMP: 8 **EST:** 2010
SALES (est): 180.6K **Privately Held**
SIC: 3339 Precious metals

(G-18002)
PRECIOUS METALS BUYERS LLC
7028 W Waters Ave (33634-2292)
PHONE..................................813 417-7857
Jorge Rodriguez, *Branch Mgr*
EMP: 17
SALES (corp-wide): 180.6K **Privately Held**
SIC: 3339 Precious metals
PA: Precious Metals Buyers, Llc
6201 Johns Rd Ste 5
Tampa FL 33634
813 880-9544

(G-18003)
PRECISION AMMUNITION LLC
5402 E Diana St (33610-1926)
PHONE..................................813 626-0077
Daniel L Powers Jr, *Mng Member*
▲ **EMP:** 8 **EST:** 2000
SQ FT: 16,000
SALES (est): 851.6K **Privately Held**
SIC: 3482 Small arms ammunition

(G-18004)
PRECISION COAT OF FLORIDA
10410 Canary Isle Dr (33647-2712)
PHONE..................................813 986-1611
Phillip Manzi, *President*
Phillip Manzi Sr, *Vice Pres*
EMP: 6
SQ FT: 4,000
SALES (est): 700K **Privately Held**
SIC: 3479 Aluminum coating of metal products

(G-18005)
PRECISION COMM SVCS INC (DH)
7710 N 30th St (33610-1118)
PHONE..................................813 238-1000
Forbes Alexander, *CEO*
James Simmons, *Vice Pres*
Ed Traupman, *Vice Pres*
Michael Kenny, *VP Mfg*
Harold Greathouse, *CFO*
◆ **EMP:** 200 **EST:** 1971
SQ FT: 90,000
SALES (est): 79.5MM **Privately Held**
SIC: 3661 Telephones & telephone apparatus
HQ: Telmar Network Technology, Inc.
901 Jupiter Rd
Plano TX 75074
972 836-0400

(G-18006)
PRECISION ERS
7710 N 30th St (33610-1118)
PHONE..................................813 257-0900
Rick Flanagan, *Vice Pres*
Wayne Chafin, *Buyer*
Michael Plumb, *Director*
EMP: 20 **EST:** 2017
SALES (est): 5.4MM **Privately Held**
SIC: 3599 Machine shop, jobbing & repair

(G-18007)
PREMDOR FINANCE LLC
1 N Dale Mabry Hwy # 950 (33609-2764)
PHONE..................................813 877-2726
EMP: 9 **EST:** 2009
SALES (est): 104.1K **Privately Held**
SIC: 2431 Doors, wood

(G-18008)
PREMIER PALLETS INC
5805 Breckenridge Pkwy A (33610-4250)
PHONE..................................813 986-4889
Scott Shaw, *President*
Michele Shaw, *Vice Pres*
Timothy Arnold, *Sales Staff*
EMP: 5 **EST:** 1993
SALES (est): 1.1MM **Privately Held**
WEB: www.premier-pallets.com
SIC: 2448 Pallets, wood

(G-18009)
PRIDE FLORIDA
1913 N Us Highway 301 # 100
(33619-2644)
PHONE..................................813 621-9262
Doug Rickel, *Exec Dir*
EMP: 6 **EST:** 2007
SALES (est): 266.1K **Privately Held**
WEB: www.stpetepride.org
SIC: 3842 5047 Wheelchairs; medical & hospital equipment

(G-18010)
PRIMAL INNOVATION TECH LLC
10150 Highland Manor Dr # 200
(33610-9712)
PHONE..................................407 558-9366
Gregory Holified,
Gregory Holifield,
EMP: 10 **EST:** 2012
SALES (est): 710.8K **Privately Held**
WEB: www.primalinnotech.com
SIC: 3661 8748 7372 Telephone & telegraph apparatus; communications consulting; prepackaged software

(G-18011)
PRIMO WATER CORPORATION
4221 W Boy Scout Blvd (33607-5743)
PHONE..................................844 237-7466
Thomas Harrington, *CEO*
Jerry Fowden, *Ch of Bd*
Jon Kathol, *Vice Pres*
William Jamieson, *CIO*
Jay Wells, *Officer*
EMP: 8880 **EST:** 1955
SALES (est): 2.3B
SALES (corp-wide): 41.7MM **Publicly Held**
WEB: www.primowater.com
SIC: 2086 Bottled & canned soft drinks
PA: Primo Water Corporation
1200 Britannia Rd E
Mississauga ON L4W 4
877 830-0653

(G-18012)
PRINCETON TOOL SOUTH LLC
9009 King Palm Dr (33619-8364)
PHONE..................................813 600-8143
Pamela K Bevington, *Principal*
Stephen Tedrick, *Supervisor*
EMP: 17 **EST:** 2018
SALES (est): 1MM **Privately Held**
WEB: www.princetontool.com
SIC: 3599 Machine shop, jobbing & repair

(G-18013)
PRINT ETC INC
13121 Canopy Creek Dr (33625-5902)
PHONE..................................813 972-2800
Dennis Kinard, *Owner*
EMP: 12 **EST:** 2006
SALES (est): 504.6K **Privately Held**
WEB: www.brandprintmarket.com
SIC: 2752 Commercial printing, offset

(G-18014)
PRINT SHACK
5011 W Hillsborough Ave C (33634-5309)
PHONE..................................813 885-4152
Michael W Hoover, *Principal*
EMP: 6 **EST:** 2019
SALES (est): 169.4K **Privately Held**
SIC: 2752 Commercial printing, offset

(G-18015)
PRINTER S PRIDE INC
Also Called: Bob S Busy Bee Printing
7211 N Dale Mabry Hwy # 10
(33614-2669)
PHONE..................................813 932-8683
Beth Seiler Waxler, *President*
Liz Chevalier, *Manager*
EMP: 8 **EST:** 1976
SALES (est): 838.7K **Privately Held**
SIC: 2752 Commercial printing, offset

(G-18016)
PRINTING SERVICES PLUS LLC ✪
Also Called: Tampa Printing Solutions
100 S Ashley Dr (33602-5304)
P.O. Box 21722 (33622-1722)
PHONE..................................813 279-1903
Jason Lange, *Mng Member*
EMP: 19 **EST:** 2020
SALES (est): 783K **Privately Held**
SIC: 2752 2759 3999 2711 Commercial printing, lithographic; commercial printing, offset; commercial printing; newspapers: printing; manufacturing industries; commercial printing & newspaper publishing combined

(G-18017)
PRO FAB
11910 Dietz Dr (33626-3612)
PHONE..................................813 545-2861
Chris Fleischer, *Principal*
EMP: 6 **EST:** 2010
SALES (est): 124.1K **Privately Held**
SIC: 3441 Fabricated structural metal

(G-18018)
PRO-TECH COATINGS INC
3201 E 3rd Ave (33605-5711)
PHONE..................................813 248-1477
Arthur Quade, *Ch of Bd*
Dale Quade, *President*
John Jones, *Office Mgr*
EMP: 8 **EST:** 1980
SQ FT: 7,500
SALES (est): 1.2MM **Privately Held**
SIC: 2851 2992 Epoxy coatings; lubricating oils & greases

(G-18019)
PROBIORA HEALTH LLC
6302 Benjamin Rd Ste 409 (33634-5116)
PHONE..................................214 559-2994
Christine Koski,

Belinda O'Halloran,
EMP: 5 **EST:** 2016
SALES (est): 833.9K **Privately Held**
WEB: www.probiorahealth.com
SIC: **2844** Oral preparations

(G-18020)
PRODUCT DEV PARTNERS LLC
Also Called: Pd Partners
6291 W Linebaugh Ave (33625-5639)
P.O. Box 13449 (33681-3449)
PHONE....................................813 908-6775
Alan Kimber, *Finance*
Steve Jenkins,
EMP: 12 **EST:** 2000
SALES (est): 3.5MM **Privately Held**
SIC: **2834** Pharmaceutical preparations

(G-18021)
PROFESSIONAL PRODUCTS
4949 Marbrisa Dr Apt 102 (33624-6300)
PHONE....................................323 754-1287
Brian Wald, *Principal*
Michelle Wyman, *Manager*
EMP: 9 **EST:** 2005
SALES (est): 487K **Privately Held**
WEB: www.professional-products.com
SIC: **3714** Manifolds, motor vehicle

(G-18022)
PROXIMITY MILLS LLC
Also Called: Top 10 Floors
4020 W Kennedy Blvd # 10 (33609-2761)
PHONE....................................813 251-3060
Zach Kennedy, *Managing Prtnr*
Charlie Kennedy, *Mng Member*
John V Weller,
▲ **EMP:** 12 **EST:** 2008
SALES (est): 638.9K **Privately Held**
SIC: **2273** Carpets & rugs

(G-18023)
PURAGLOBE FLORIDA LLC
4420 Pendola Point Rd (33619-9689)
PHONE....................................813 247-1754
Matt Bulley,
EMP: 39
SALES (corp-wide): 18.1MM **Privately Held**
WEB: www.puraglobe.com
SIC: **1389** Servicing oil & gas wells
PA: Puraglobe Florida, Llc
435 Devon Park Dr
Wayne PA 19087
813 247-1754

(G-18024)
PURE SOLUTIONS INC
14100 Mccormick Dr (33626-3018)
PHONE....................................813 925-1098
James Powers, *CEO*
Jennifer Cook, *COO*
Charles Powers, *COO*
▲ **EMP:** 20 **EST:** 2001
SQ FT: 15,500
SALES (est): 5.5MM **Privately Held**
WEB: www.epuresolutions.com
SIC: **2869** 5499 Perfumes, flavorings & food additives; health & dietetic food stores

(G-18025)
PURE-CHLOR SYSTEMS FLORIDA INC
Also Called: Alfaparf Milano
8200 Nw 33rd St Ste 109 (33614)
PHONE....................................305 437-9937
Davide Cortinovis, *CEO*
Jaskulski Mark, *President*
Barry Billingsley, *Business Mgr*
Mark Jaskulski, *COO*
Betsy Hamlett, *Senior VP*
▼ **EMP:** 15 **EST:** 1998
SALES (est): 2.5MM **Privately Held**
WEB: www.alfaparfgroup.com
SIC: **2844** Hair coloring preparations
HQ: Alfa Parf Group Spa
Via Ciserano Snc
Osio Sotto BG 24046

(G-18026)
PUT YOUR NAME ON IT LLC
Also Called: Minisportsballs.com
16057 Tampa Palms Blvd W # 4
(33647-2001)
PHONE....................................813 972-1460
Mike Howard, *Controller*
Nancy Kahn,
EMP: 5 **EST:** 2001
SALES (est): 714.6K **Privately Held**
WEB: www.minisportsballs.com
SIC: **2759** 3069 3993 7389 Imprinting; balloons, advertising & toy: rubber; advertising novelties; advertising, promotional & trade show services; advertising specialties

(G-18027)
PUZZLE PIECES SUPPORT SERVIC
4809 E Busch Blvd Ste 205 (33617-6099)
PHONE....................................813 985-3232
EMP: 5 **EST:** 2015
SALES (est): 307.2K **Privately Held**
WEB: www.puzzlepiecesfl.org
SIC: **3944** Puzzles

(G-18028)
PYRAMID IMAGING INC
945 E 11th Ave (33605-3531)
PHONE....................................813 984-0125
Rex Lee, *President*
Christine Lee, *COO*
Chris Lee, *Opers Mgr*
Heather Conyers, *Manager*
EMP: 9 **EST:** 2001
SQ FT: 1,800
SALES (est): 5MM **Privately Held**
WEB: www.pyramidimaging.com
SIC: **3827** 8711 3823 Optical instruments & lenses; engineering services; industrial instrmnts msrmnt display/control process variable

(G-18029)
QPS COMPANIES INC (PA)
Also Called: Olympic Case Co
9110 King Palm Dr Ste 101 (33619-8312)
PHONE....................................813 246-5525
John S Jackoboice II, *CEO*
John Jackoboice II, *President*
Michelle Karakash, *Treasurer*
Otis Jackoboice, *VP Sales*
Bob Farina, *Regl Sales Mgr*
EMP: 40 **EST:** 1996
SQ FT: 18,000
SALES (est): 10.3MM **Privately Held**
SIC: **2449** 3161 Shipping cases & drums, wood: wirebound & plywood; luggage

(G-18030)
QUALITY BUILDING CONTROLS INC
Also Called: Albireo Energy
10011 Williams Rd (33624-5047)
PHONE....................................813 885-5005
Jerry Dohse, *President*
Dan Whittemore, *Project Mgr*
Scott Bacon, *Opers Mgr*
Melissa Allen, *Manager*
Lorenis Rios, *Admin Asst*
EMP: 20 **EST:** 1997
SQ FT: 3,000
SALES (est): 3MM **Privately Held**
WEB: www.qualitybuildingcontrols.com
SIC: **3613** Control panels, electric

(G-18031)
QUALITY ENGINEERED PRODUCTS CO
4506 Quality Ln (33634-6324)
P.O. Box 22213 (33622-2213)
PHONE....................................813 885-1693
Burton Bernstein, *President*
Andrew Bernstein, *Vice Pres*
Nina Bernstein, *Treasurer*
▼ **EMP:** 23 **EST:** 1961
SQ FT: 18,000
SALES (est): 4.4MM **Privately Held**
WEB: www.qepco.biz
SIC: **2431** 3442 5031 Doors, wood; window & door frames; doors & windows

(G-18032)
QUALITY METAL FABRICATORS INC
2610 E 5th Ave (33605-5504)
PHONE....................................813 831-7320
Earl Roberts Jr, *President*
Jason Burgess, *Vice Pres*
Earl Roberts III, *Vice Pres*
Steven Roberts, *Vice Pres*
Brian Fields, *Manager*
EMP: 38 **EST:** 1983
SQ FT: 7,500
SALES (est): 5.8MM **Privately Held**
WEB: www.qmfgroup.com
SIC: **3441** Fabricated structural metal

(G-18033)
QUALITY STEEL FABRICATORS INC
4544 Hartford St (33619-6708)
PHONE....................................813 247-7110
Dale Auten, *President*
John Auten, *Vice Pres*
Shane Culberson, *Prdtn Mgr*
EMP: 10
SQ FT: 15,000
SALES: 1.7MM **Privately Held**
WEB: www.qualitysteelfab.com
SIC: **3441** Fabricated structural metal

(G-18034)
QUARTZO LLC
5115 Shadowlawn Ave (33610-5399)
PHONE....................................888 813-3442
Ernesto Sanchez,
EMP: 12 **EST:** 2018
SALES (est): 1.2MM **Privately Held**
WEB: www.quartzousa.com
SIC: **3281** Building stone products

(G-18035)
QUICKSILVER PRTG & COPYING INC
3816a W Sligh Ave (33614-3961)
PHONE....................................813 888-6811
Andy Wardrop, *President*
Victoria Wardrop, *Vice Pres*
EMP: 6 **EST:** 1978
SALES (est): 710.5K **Privately Held**
WEB: www.quicksilverprinting.com
SIC: **2752** Commercial printing, offset

(G-18036)
R & J CUSTOM CABINETS INC
3907 W Cayuga St (33614-7048)
PHONE....................................813 871-5779
Richard Smith, *President*
Jeff Gamble, *Treasurer*
Brian Robertson, *Admin Sec*
EMP: 7 **EST:** 2002
SQ FT: 5,000
SALES (est): 708.9K **Privately Held**
WEB: www.rjcustomcabinets.com
SIC: **2434** Wood kitchen cabinets

(G-18037)
RACE PERFORMANCE MACHINE SHOP
4707 N Lois Ave (33614-7046)
PHONE....................................813 443-8225
Reinaldo Suarez, *Owner*
EMP: 7 **EST:** 2010
SALES (est): 554.3K **Privately Held**
WEB: www.raysperformance.business.site
SIC: **3599** Machine shop, jobbing & repair

(G-18038)
RAMAC INC
16503 Cayman Dr (33624-1065)
PHONE....................................813 962-2793
Robert Mackenzie, *Owner*
EMP: 6 **EST:** 2015
SALES (est): 93.6K **Privately Held**
SIC: **3599** Industrial machinery

(G-18039)
RAVEN FOREST OPERATING LLC ✪
13014 N Dale Mbry Hwy # 736
(33618-2808)
PHONE....................................727 497-2727
Tony Ferguson,
EMP: 10 **EST:** 2020
SALES (est): 504.2K **Privately Held**
SIC: **1381** Drilling oil & gas wells

(G-18040)
RB CUSTOM WELDING LLC
5210 E 10th Ave (33619-2710)
PHONE....................................813 280-9860
EMP: 8
SALES (est): 40.4K **Privately Held**
SIC: **7692** 1799 Welding Repair Trade Contractor

(G-18041)
RCR COFFEE COMPANY INC (PA)
402 N 22nd St (33605-6086)
PHONE....................................813 248-6264
Richard Perez, *CEO*
Denise Reddick, *President*
Mary Jean Perez, *Vice Pres*
Ron Perez, *Treasurer*
Julie Beck, *Cust Svc Dir*
EMP: 30 **EST:** 1966
SQ FT: 60,000
SALES (est): 3.9MM **Privately Held**
SIC: **2095** 5149 Coffee roasting (except by wholesale grocers); groceries & related products; tea; coffee, green or roasted; cocoa

(G-18042)
REAH GROUP LLC
2721 W Gray St (33609-1732)
PHONE....................................727 423-0668
Annemarie Hare, *Principal*
Robert Emmerson, *Mng Member*
EMP: 5 **EST:** 2016
SALES (est): 600K **Privately Held**
SIC: **2591** Drapery hardware & blinds & shades

(G-18043)
REDQUIN PUBLISHING LLC
201 E Kennedy Blvd # 600 (33602-5181)
PHONE....................................813 314-4500
Paul M Quin, *Principal*
EMP: 6 **EST:** 2010
SALES (est): 122K **Privately Held**
SIC: **2741** Miscellaneous publishing

(G-18044)
REFLEX PUBG ERIC REFLEX CO
777 S Harbour Island Blvd (33602-5729)
PHONE....................................813 314-8810
Todd Brandon, *Principal*
EMP: 7 **EST:** 2008
SALES (est): 311.4K **Privately Held**
WEB: www.reflex.com
SIC: **2741** Miscellaneous publishing

(G-18045)
REFRESCO BEVERAGES US INC
8112 Woodland Center Blvd (33614-2403)
PHONE....................................813 313-1711
Jerry Fowden, *Manager*
EMP: 49
SALES (corp-wide): 1.3B **Privately Held**
WEB: www.refresco-na.com
SIC: **2086** Bottled & canned soft drinks
HQ: Refresco Beverages Us Inc.
8112 Woodland Center Blvd
Tampa FL 33614

(G-18046)
REFRESCO BEVERAGES US INC
4506 Acline Dr E (33605-5909)
PHONE....................................813 241-0147
Martin Cooke, *President*
Kevin Lucas, *Mfg Dir*
Darin Clark, *Plant Mgr*
Tham Le, *Finance Mgr*
Brian Vanley, *Human Resources*
EMP: 120
SALES (corp-wide): 1.3B **Privately Held**
WEB: www.primowatercorp.com
SIC: **2086** 5149 Carbonated beverages, nonalcoholic: bottled & canned; groceries & related products
HQ: Refresco Beverages Us Inc.
8112 Woodland Center Blvd
Tampa FL 33614

(G-18047)
REFRESCO BEVERAGES US INC (HQ)
8112 Woodland Center Blvd (33614-2403)
P.O. Box 201810, San Antonio TX (78220-8810)
PHONE....................................813 313-1800
Brad Goist, *CEO*
Stephen Corby, *Managing Dir*
Monica Consonery, *Exec VP*
Shayron Barnes-Selby, *Vice Pres*
Ridha Boussetta, *Vice Pres*

◆ **EMP:** 140 **EST:** 1991
SQ FT: 10,600
SALES (est): 1B
SALES (corp-wide): 1.3B **Privately Held**
WEB: www.refresco-na.com
SIC: 2086 Soft drinks: packaged in cans, bottles, etc.
PA: Refresco Us Holding Inc.
8118 Woodland Center Blvd
Tampa FL 33614
813 313-1863

(G-18048)
REFRESCO BEVERAGES US INC
Also Called: Cott Beverage
8112 Woodland Center Blvd (33614-2403)
PHONE..................................314 994-7545
Jintana Toth, *Finance*
Ted Szpargala, *Manager*
Anthony Correa, *Software Dev*
Kyla Gribbins, *Director*
EMP: 49
SALES (corp-wide): 1.3B **Privately Held**
WEB: www.primowatercorp.com
SIC: 2086 Carbonated beverages, nonalcoholic: bottled & canned
HQ: Refresco Beverages Us Inc.
8112 Woodland Center Blvd
Tampa FL 33614

(G-18049)
REFRESCO US HOLDING INC (PA)
8118 Woodland Center Blvd (33614-2403)
PHONE..................................813 313-1863
Brad Goist, *President*
Ridha Boussetta, *Vice Pres*
William Wise, *Manager*
EMP: 22 **EST:** 2016
SQ FT: 5,000
SALES (est): 1.3B **Privately Held**
WEB: www.keurigdrpepper.com
SIC: 2086 Carbonated beverages, nonalcoholic: bottled & canned

(G-18050)
REIMINK PRINTING INC
Also Called: AlphaGraphics
4209 W Kennedy Blvd (33609-2230)
PHONE..................................813 289-4663
Marsha Reimink, *President*
James Reimink, *President*
EMP: 6 **EST:** 1984
SQ FT: 3,000
SALES (est): 996.7K **Privately Held**
WEB: www.alphagraphics.com
SIC: 2752 7334 7331 2791 Commercial printing, lithographic; photocopying & duplicating services; mailing service; typesetting; bookbinding & related work; posters: publishing & printing

(G-18051)
RELIATEX INC
6004 Bonacker Dr (33610-4879)
PHONE..................................813 621-6021
Cuquy Fairbanks, *Sales Staff*
Judy Lister, *Sales Staff*
Donald J Miller, *Systems Mgr*
EMP: 29
SALES (corp-wide): 23.7MM **Privately Held**
WEB: www.reliatex.com
SIC: 3069 2221 Foam rubber; broadwoven fabric mills, manmade
PA: Reliatex, Inc.
2201 Nw 72nd Ave
Miami FL 33122
305 592-3220

(G-18052)
RES TEXTILES INC
4511 N Himes Ave Ste 200 (33614-7085)
PHONE..................................813 476-5524
EMP: 6 **EST:** 2013
SALES (est): 276.6K **Privately Held**
SIC: 2389 Apparel & accessories

(G-18053)
RESIDENTIAL ACOUSTICS LLC
Also Called: Commercial Acoustics
6122 Benjamin Rd (33634-5106)
PHONE..................................813 922-2390
Walker Peek, *CEO*
Dylan C McCandless,
EMP: 15 **EST:** 2013
SALES (est): 1.3MM **Privately Held**
WEB: www.residential-acoustics.com
SIC: 2391 Curtains & draperies

(G-18054)
RESTORATIVE PRODUCTS INC
13560 Wright Cir (33626-3028)
PHONE..................................813 342-4432
Craig Turtzo, *President*
EMP: 17 **EST:** 1992
SQ FT: 6,000
SALES (est): 387.4K **Privately Held**
SIC: 3842 Braces, orthopedic

(G-18055)
RETREAT
123 S Hyde Park Ave (33606-1929)
P.O. Box 13109 (33681-3109)
PHONE..................................813 254-2014
Richard Calderoni, *Principal*
EMP: 7 **EST:** 2007
SALES (est): 647.5K **Privately Held**
WEB: www.retreattampa.com
SIC: 2064 Candy bars, including chocolate covered bars

(G-18056)
RICHLAND TOWERS INC
400 N Ashley Dr Ste 2500 (33602-4348)
PHONE..................................813 286-4140
Neil S Atkinson, *President*
Jack H Bray, *Chairman*
Anthony Flores, *Vice Pres*
Dale A West, *Vice Pres*
EMP: 31 **EST:** 1996
SQ FT: 10,000
SALES (est): 4.5MM **Privately Held**
SIC: 3441 6552 Tower sections, radio & television transmission; subdividers & developers

(G-18057)
RIGAL RAMON & MARITZA
Also Called: Signs By Ramon
4917 Rockledge Cir (33624-1058)
PHONE..................................813 968-2380
Ramon Rigal, *Owner*
EMP: 6 **EST:** 1997
SALES (est): 156.1K **Privately Held**
SIC: 3993 Signs, not made in custom sign painting shops

(G-18058)
RINALDI PRINTING COMPANY
Also Called: Rinaldi Printing & Packaging
4514 E Adamo Dr (33605-5967)
PHONE..................................813 569-0033
William S Rinaldi Sr, *Ch of Bd*
William S Rinaldi Jr, *President*
Steve Rinaldi Sr, *Chairman*
Steve Kimbler, *Vice Pres*
Greg Bennett, *Production*
EMP: 46 **EST:** 1905
SQ FT: 36,000
SALES (est): 7.6MM **Privately Held**
WEB: www.rinaldiprinting.com
SIC: 2752 2759 Commercial printing, offset; letterpress printing

(G-18059)
RIPA & ASSOCIATES INC
1409 Tech Blvd Ste 1 (33619-7830)
PHONE..................................813 623-6777
Frank P Ripa, *CEO*
Chris Laface, *President*
Chuck Sylvester, *Superintendent*
John Wiggins, *Superintendent*
Don Campbell, *Project Mgr*
EMP: 135 **EST:** 1998
SALES (est): 25.6MM **Privately Held**
WEB: www.ripaconstruction.com
SIC: 2261 Roller printing of cotton broadwoven fabrics

(G-18060)
RIVERHAWK FAST SEA FRAMES LLC
5251 W Tyson Ave (33611-3223)
PHONE..................................912 484-3112
Mark Hornsby, *CEO*
EMP: 6 **EST:** 2008
SALES (est): 515.8K **Privately Held**
WEB: www.rhfsf.urnge.net
SIC: 3731 Shipbuilding & repairing

(G-18061)
RLS (USA) INC
7802 Woodland Center Blvd (33614-2409)
PHONE..................................561 596-0556
Gruner Werner, *CEO*
Mark Elliott, *Principal*
Gerhardus Van Niererk, *Director*
John Chapman, *Admin Sec*
EMP: 503 **EST:** 2019
SALES (est): 54.6MM **Privately Held**
SIC: 2834 Pharmaceutical preparations

(G-18062)
RMR DISTRIBUTORS INC
9610 Norwood Dr (33624-5115)
PHONE..................................813 908-1141
Robert M Russo, *President*
Tim Parham, *Administration*
EMP: 25 **EST:** 1993
SQ FT: 10,000
SALES (est): 2.8MM **Privately Held**
WEB: www.designsbyrmr.com
SIC: 2759 Screen printing

(G-18063)
ROBBINS MANUFACTURING COMPANY (PA)
Also Called: Robbins Lumber
1003 E 131st Ave (33612-4436)
P.O. Box 17939 (33682-7939)
PHONE..................................813 971-3030
Dionel E Cotanda, *President*
Laurence W Hall Jr, *Chairman*
Peter Shuman, *Exec VP*
William E Brown, *Vice Pres*
Jerome Robbins II, *Vice Pres*
◆ **EMP:** 120
SQ FT: 6,000
SALES (est): 77MM **Privately Held**
WEB: www.robbinslumber.com
SIC: 2491 5031 Wood preserving; lumber, plywood & millwork

(G-18064)
ROBBINS MANUFACTURING COMPANY
1003 E 131st Ave (33612-4436)
PHONE..................................888 558-8199
Bruce Lee, *Branch Mgr*
EMP: 260
SALES (corp-wide): 77MM **Privately Held**
WEB: www.robbinslumber.com
SIC: 2491 Poles, posts & pilings: treated wood
PA: Robbins Manufacturing Company Inc
1003 E 131st Ave
Tampa FL 33612
813 971-3030

(G-18065)
ROBERTSON BILLIARD SUPS INC
Also Called: Billiards & Barstools
1721 N Franklin St (33602-2623)
PHONE..................................813 229-2778
Tom Rodgers, *President*
Debra Robertson Rodgers, *Corp Secy*
Stephen Rodgers, *Manager*
Charles Robertson Sr, *Shareholder*
◆ **EMP:** 7 **EST:** 1930
SQ FT: 15,000
SALES (est): 864.1K **Privately Held**
WEB: www.robertsonbilliards.com
SIC: 3949 5091 5941 Billiard & pool equipment & supplies, general; billiard equipment & supplies; pool & billiard tables

(G-18066)
ROCK BROTHERS BREWING LLC
1901 N 15th St (33605-3659)
PHONE..................................917 324-8175
Kevin Lilly, *Branch Mgr*
EMP: 7
SALES (corp-wide): 55.2K **Privately Held**
WEB: www.rockbrothersbrewing.com
SIC: 2082 Malt beverages
PA: Rock Brothers Brewing, Llc
410 S Cedar Ave
Tampa FL

(G-18067)
ROLLERCOAT INDUSTRIES INC
Also Called: Roller Coat Industries
10135 E Us Highway 92 (33610-5965)
PHONE..................................813 621-4668
Joseph L Lancaster, *CEO*
Robert S Lancaster, *Corp Secy*
Danny Wright, *Sales Staff*
Mike Lancaster, *Director*
▼ **EMP:** 30
SQ FT: 16,000
SALES (est): 5.2MM **Privately Held**
WEB: www.rollercoat.com
SIC: 3991 Paint rollers

(G-18068)
ROMARK LABORATORIES LC
3000 Bayport Dr Ste 200 (33607-8416)
PHONE..................................813 282-8544
Jean Francois Rossignol, *Ch of Bd*
Marc S Ayers, *President*
Marc D Lebovitz, *Principal*
Celine Rossignol, *COO*
Stefan Comhaire, *Opers Staff*
▲ **EMP:** 45 **EST:** 1993
SQ FT: 11,000
SALES (est): 25.9MM **Privately Held**
WEB: www.romark.com
SIC: 2834 Pharmaceutical preparations

(G-18069)
ROSS SLADE INC
205 N Armenia Ave Ste 101 (33609-2322)
PHONE..................................813 250-0488
William Slade, *President*
Jeff D Ross, *Vice Pres*
Joesph Cox, *Sales Engr*
Tim Hart, *Sales Engr*
Matthew Reeves, *Sales Engr*
EMP: 5 **EST:** 2002
SQ FT: 1,100
SALES (est): 2.5MM **Privately Held**
WEB: www.sladerossinc.com
SIC: 3585 Heating & air conditioning combination units

(G-18070)
ROYAL CUP INC
3502 Queen Palm Dr Ste A (33619-1391)
PHONE..................................813 664-8902
Scott Scotty, *Vice Pres*
Bill Hann, *Manager*
EMP: 7
SALES (corp-wide): 243.1MM **Privately Held**
WEB: www.royalcupcoffee.com
SIC: 2095 5149 2099 2087 Roasted coffee; coffee & tea; food preparations; flavoring extracts & syrups
PA: Royal Cup Inc.
160 Cleage Dr
Birmingham AL 35217
205 849-5836

(G-18071)
RSC INDUSTRIES INC
Also Called: Robert's Saw Company
5451 W Waters Ave (33634-1214)
PHONE..................................813 886-4711
Robert L Scamardo, *President*
▲ **EMP:** 15 **EST:** 1970
SQ FT: 8,000
SALES (est): 551.7K **Privately Held**
SIC: 3425 7699 Saw blades & handsaws; knife, saw & tool sharpening & repair

(G-18072)
RUBENS CUSTOM CABINETS INC
1310 W Termino St (33612-7760)
PHONE..................................813 510-8397
Betsy A Urrea, *President*
EMP: 6 **EST:** 2017
SALES (est): 407.9K **Privately Held**
SIC: 2434 Wood kitchen cabinets

(G-18073)
RUSTIC STEEL CREATIONS INC
3919 N Highland Ave (33603-4723)
PHONE..................................813 222-0016
Dominique C Martinez, *President*
Dominique Martinez, *President*
EMP: 8 **EST:** 2004
SQ FT: 4,450

SALES (est): 1.3MM **Privately Held**
WEB: www.rusticsteel.com
SIC: 3446 Stairs, staircases, stair treads: prefabricated metal

(G-18074)
S C R PRECISION TUBE BENDING
5407 24th Ave S (33619-5370)
PHONE.....813 622-7091
Patricia M Shafer, *President*
▲ **EMP:** 12 **EST:** 1986
SQ FT: 10,000
SALES (est): 2.2MM **Privately Held**
WEB: www.scrprecision.com
SIC: 3498 Tube fabricating (contract bending & shaping)

(G-18075)
S I P CORPORATION
Also Called: Universal Gear
7210 Anderson Rd Ste A (33634-3010)
PHONE.....813 884-8300
Mark Pilger, *President*
Michele Pilger, *CFO*
EMP: 10 **EST:** 1902
SQ FT: 8,000
SALES (est): 1.2MM **Privately Held**
WEB: www.sipgrinder.com
SIC: 3546 3566 Grinders, portable: electric or pneumatic; gears, power transmission, except automotive

(G-18076)
S TAM CABINETS INC
5555 W Linebaugh Ave N (33624-5089)
PHONE.....813 310-2263
Tam G Ha, *Principal*
EMP: 6 **EST:** 2009
SALES (est): 70.2K **Privately Held**
SIC: 2434 Wood kitchen cabinets

(G-18077)
S&J 34102 INC
Also Called: Ark Natural Product For Pets
609 E Jackson St Ste 100 (33602-4933)
PHONE.....239 592-9388
Susan D Weiss, *President*
Joni Bott, *Vice Pres*
Ark Naturals, *Marketing Staff*
Cheryl Kuzman, *Office Mgr*
Eric Delgado, *Manager*
▲ **EMP:** 8 **EST:** 1996
SALES (est): 1.5MM **Privately Held**
SIC: 2834 Vitamin, nutrient & hematinic preparations for human use

(G-18078)
S&S CRAFTSMEN INC
6404 E Columbus Dr (33619-1659)
P.O. Box 76123 (33675-1123)
PHONE.....813 247-4429
Thomas M Stenglein, *President*
Leonard J Rosende Jr, *Vice Pres*
Billy Jarboe II, *Sales Staff*
◆ **EMP:** 15
SQ FT: 40,000
SALES (est): 3.3MM **Privately Held**
WEB: www.ssiwoodproducts.com
SIC: 2431 Moldings, wood: unfinished & prefinished

(G-18079)
SACHI TECH INC
Also Called: Pikmykid, Kidio
5005 W Laurel St Ste 204 (33607-3836)
PHONE.....813 649-8028
Saravana Bhava, *CEO*
Rey Bermudez, *Engineer*
Chase Belisle, *Consultant*
Tonya Morningstar, *Consultant*
Sandra Pena, *Agent*
EMP: 12 **EST:** 2014
SALES (est): 1.6MM **Privately Held**
WEB: www.pikmykid.com
SIC: 7372 7371 Prepackaged software; software programming applications

(G-18080)
SAF AEROSPACE LLC
8006 N Highland Ave (33604-4006)
PHONE.....813 376-0883
Patrick Marsh,
EMP: 6 **EST:** 2013
SALES (est): 309.3K **Privately Held**
SIC: 3724 3728 7389 Aircraft engines & engine parts; aircraft parts & equipment; business services

(G-18081)
SANTOS FROZEN FOODS INC
2746 W Main St (33607-3317)
P.O. Box 4431 (33677-4431)
PHONE.....813 875-4901
Geraldine Rosner, *President*
Kenneth Rosner, *Vice Pres*
Delores Zambito, *Treasurer*
EMP: 10 **EST:** 1962
SQ FT: 3,000
SALES (est): 798.2K **Privately Held**
SIC: 2092 2099 Crabcakes, frozen; crabmeat, frozen; potatoes, peeled for the trade

(G-18082)
SECURE BIOMETRIC CORPORATION
Also Called: Global Biometric
2909 W Bay Court Ave (33611-1601)
P.O. Box 10188 (33679-0188)
PHONE.....813 832-1164
Michael Shapiro, *CEO*
EMP: 8 **EST:** 2002
SALES (est): 1,000K **Privately Held**
SIC: 3699 Security devices

(G-18083)
SENIOR VOICE AMERICA INC
3820 Northdale Blvd 205a (33624-1855)
PHONE.....813 444-1011
Timm Harmon, *Principal*
Deb Goldman, *Manager*
EMP: 12 **EST:** 2012
SALES (est): 292K **Privately Held**
WEB: www.seniorvoiceamerica.com
SIC: 2711 Newspapers, publishing & printing

(G-18084)
SEPTIMIUS LLC
4910 Savarese Cir (33634-2403)
PHONE.....813 484-4168
Derek Hennecke, *Principal*
EMP: 8 **EST:** 2015
SALES (est): 394.6K **Privately Held**
SIC: 2834 Pharmaceutical preparations

(G-18085)
SERIGRAPHIC ARTS INC
6806 Parke East Blvd (33610-4144)
PHONE.....813 626-1070
David W Johnson, *President*
David D Bennett, *Vice Pres*
EMP: 16 **EST:** 1971
SQ FT: 20,000
SALES (est): 2.3MM **Privately Held**
WEB: www.serigraphicarts.com
SIC: 2759 7389 5199 Screen printing; laminating service; advertising specialties

(G-18086)
SERVICE D N D DUMPSTER
7909 Professional Pl (33637-6747)
PHONE.....813 989-3867
Darrel Peterson, *President*
EMP: 7 **EST:** 2016
SALES (est): 155.9K **Privately Held**
SIC: 3443 Dumpsters, garbage

(G-18087)
SEXTANT MARKETING LLC
1860 N Avnida Rpblica De (33605)
PHONE.....800 691-9980
Dean Gething, *Vice Pres*
Trudi Kessler, *Assoc VP*
Shannon Young, *Marketing Staff*
Jose Clark-Hilery, *Director*
Matthew Speer, *Officer*
EMP: 13 **EST:** 2015
SALES (est): 2.8MM **Privately Held**
WEB: www.sextantmktg.com
SIC: 3812 Sextants

(G-18088)
SGS DESIGNS INC
1515 W Cypress St (33606-1013)
PHONE.....813 258-2691
James Avery, *President*
Ryan Avery, *Vice Pres*
EMP: 7 **EST:** 1996
SQ FT: 4,000
SALES (est): 752.5K **Privately Held**
WEB: www.sgsdesignsinc.com
SIC: 2759 Screen printing

(G-18089)
SHAFERS CLASSIC REPRODUCTIONS
Also Called: SCR
5407 24th Ave S (33619-5370)
PHONE.....813 622-7091
Warren Shafer, *President*
Patricia Shafer, *Vice Pres*
Keri Siderio, *Marketing Mgr*
Shane Majetich, *Manager*
Juan Concepcion, *Info Tech Dir*
▲ **EMP:** 9 **EST:** 1984
SQ FT: 3,000
SALES (est): 1.1MM **Privately Held**
WEB: www.shafersclassic.com
SIC: 3714 5531 3498 Motor vehicle parts & accessories; automotive & home supply stores; fabricated pipe & fittings

(G-18090)
SHAIN INC
4801 George Rd Ste 180 (33634-6200)
PHONE.....813 889-9614
Judy Tomlinson, *Principal*
EMP: 7 **EST:** 2010
SALES (est): 179.6K **Privately Held**
SIC: 3829 Measuring & controlling devices

(G-18091)
SHARPER EDGE
4821 N Clark Ave (33614-6503)
PHONE.....813 871-3343
Micheal Heiberger, *Owner*
Gordon Parker, *Sales Staff*
EMP: 10 **EST:** 1990
SQ FT: 4,340
SALES (est): 432.9K **Privately Held**
WEB: www.sharperedgenet.com
SIC: 2759 Screen printing

(G-18092)
SHAWN WILLIAM SHUMAKE LLC
Also Called: Sws Contracting
9307 N 14th St (33612-8101)
PHONE.....813 374-2469
Shawn W Shumake, *Mng Member*
Kelli Curry, *Manager*
EMP: 8 **EST:** 2014
SALES (est): 2MM **Privately Held**
SIC: 7692 Welding repair

(G-18093)
SHEAFFER BOATS INC
3916 W South Ave (33614-6552)
PHONE.....813 872-7644
Ben Sheaffer, *President*
EMP: 5 **EST:** 2000
SALES (est): 345.7K **Privately Held**
WEB: www.sheaffermarine.com
SIC: 3732 Boat building & repairing

(G-18094)
SHEAFFER MARINE INC
Also Called: Boat Doctor, The
3916 W South Ave (33614-6552)
PHONE.....813 872-7311
Benjamin R Sheaffer, *President*
EMP: 10 **EST:** 1967
SQ FT: 3,000
SALES (est): 1.1MM **Privately Held**
WEB: www.sheaffermarine.com
SIC: 3732 Yachts, building & repairing

(G-18095)
SHEFFIELD STEEL CORPORATION
Also Called: Gerdau Ameristeel
4221 W Boy Scout Blvd # 600 (33607-5760)
PHONE.....918 245-1335
Mario Longhi, *CEO*
Philip Casey, *Ch of Bd*
Neil McCullouhs, *Vice Pres*
▲ **EMP:** 5101 **EST:** 1929
SQ FT: 616,548
SALES (est): 3.7MM **Privately Held**
WEB: www.gerdau.com
SIC: 3312 Bars & bar shapes, steel, cold-finished: own hot-rolled
HQ: Gerdau Ameristeel Us Inc.
4221 W Boy Scout Blvd # 600
Tampa FL 33607
813 286-8383

(G-18096)
SHIPPING DEPOT INC
4835 W Cypress St (33607-4716)
PHONE.....813 347-2494
Cecilia M Reid, *Principal*
EMP: 17 **EST:** 2005
SALES (est): 1.3MM **Privately Held**
WEB: www.ashippingdepot.com
SIC: 3714 PVC valves

(G-18097)
SHIRLEY SIMON & ASSOCIATES LLC
Also Called: TNT
4951b E Adamo Dr Ste 216 (33605-5913)
PHONE.....813 247-2100
Matthew Simon, *Mng Member*
EMP: 5 **EST:** 2011
SQ FT: 1,500
SALES (est): 500K **Privately Held**
SIC: 3711 Truck tractors for highway use, assembly of

(G-18098)
SHIRTS & CAPS INC
Also Called: Classb.com
9437 Corporate Lake Dr (33634-2359)
PHONE.....813 788-7026
Eric H Hilferding, *President*
Eric Hilferding, *President*
Terry L Hilferding, *Production*
Robert H Hilferding, *Treasurer*
Robert Hilferding, *Treasurer*
▲ **EMP:** 13 **EST:** 1982
SQ FT: 2,400
SALES (est): 576.5K **Privately Held**
WEB: www.classb.com
SIC: 2396 5651 7389 3993 Screen printing on fabric articles; unisex clothing stores; engraving service; signs & advertising specialties; pleating & stitching

(G-18099)
SIGN A RAMA
Also Called: Sign-A-Rama
3118 Belmore Rd (33618-3629)
PHONE.....813 264-0022
Michael Pearson, *Principal*
▼ **EMP:** 7 **EST:** 2008
SALES (est): 116.7K **Privately Held**
WEB: www.signarama.com
SIC: 3993 Signs & advertising specialties

(G-18100)
SIGN N DRIVE
1015 E Hillsborough Ave (33604-7203)
P.O. Box 17312 (33682-7312)
PHONE.....813 999-4837
EMP: 5 **EST:** 2019
SALES (est): 339.3K **Privately Held**
SIC: 3993 Signs & advertising specialties

(G-18101)
SIGN SOLUTIONS OF TAMPA BAY
3921 W Dr M Lthr Kng Jr Martin Luther (33614)
PHONE.....813 269-5990
Ron Neave, *President*
Gregory A Bullock, *Principal*
EMP: 5 **EST:** 2001
SALES (est): 450K **Privately Held**
WEB: www.signsolutionstb.com
SIC: 3993 Signs, not made in custom sign painting shops

(G-18102)
SIGN SYSTEMS GRPHIC DSIGNS INC
5031 W Grace St (33607-3807)
PHONE.....813 281-2400
Thomas F Weber, *President*
Karen Kunkle, *Vice Pres*
Kelly Kline, *Manager*
EMP: 7 **EST:** 1987
SQ FT: 6,901
SALES (est): 80K **Privately Held**
WEB: www.signsystemstampa.com
SIC: 3993 Signs, not made in custom sign painting shops; electric signs

GEOGRAPHIC

(G-18103)
SIGNATURE GRANITE INC
3904 S 51st St (33619-6802)
PHONE....................................813 443-5597
Eddie Beltran, *President*
EMP: 11 **EST:** 2011
SALES (est): 588.4K **Privately Held**
WEB: www.signaturexp.com
SIC: 3281 Granite, cut & shaped

(G-18104)
SIGNS OF AMERICA TAMPA CORP
4025 W Waters Ave (33614-1976)
PHONE....................................813 243-9243
EMP: 6 **EST:** 2019
SALES (est): 295K **Privately Held**
WEB: www.signs-of-america-tampa-corp.business.site
SIC: 3993 Signs & advertising specialties

(G-18105)
SIGNS USA INC
4123 W Hillsborough Ave (33614-5609)
PHONE....................................813 901-9333
Thomas R Miano, *President*
Janet Miano, *Vice Pres*
EMP: 10 **EST:** 1994
SQ FT: 3,700
SALES (est): 1.5MM **Privately Held**
WEB: www.signsusainc.com
SIC: 3993 Signs & advertising specialties

(G-18106)
SITECRAFTERS OF FLORIDA INC
3242 Henderson Blvd # 200 (33609-3094)
PHONE....................................813 258-4696
Jeffrey Hardeman, *President*
Wayne Futch, *Principal*
Steve Howell, *Manager*
EMP: 38 **EST:** 2003
SALES (est): 3.7MM **Privately Held**
WEB: www.sitecraftersfl.com
SIC: 3993 Signs & advertising specialties

(G-18107)
SKINUTRA INC
5136 W Clifton St (33634-8012)
PHONE....................................813 992-1742
John S Patneaude, *Principal*
EMP: 9 **EST:** 2014
SALES (est): 206.7K **Privately Held**
WEB: www.skinutra.com
SIC: 2834 Vitamin, nutrient & hematinic preparations for human use

(G-18108)
SLEEP INTERNATIONAL LLC (PA)
5223 16th Ave S (33619-5386)
PHONE....................................813 247-5337
Adam Weinman, *President*
Patrick Murphy, *CFO*
◆ **EMP:** 49 **EST:** 2011
SALES (est): 9.1MM **Privately Held**
SIC: 2515 Mattresses & bedsprings

(G-18109)
SMART GUIDES
20013 Outpost Point Dr (33647-3560)
PHONE....................................813 534-0940
Frank Curtin, *Principal*
EMP: 8 **EST:** 2007
SALES (est): 315.7K **Privately Held**
SIC: 7372 8742 Business oriented computer software; management consulting services

(G-18110)
SMARTSCIENCE LABORATORIES INC
13760 Reptron Blvd (33626-3040)
PHONE....................................813 925-8454
Gene C Weitz, *President*
Dave Johnson, *Vice Pres*
▲ **EMP:** 15
SQ FT: 30,000
SALES (est): 5.5MM **Privately Held**
WEB: www.smartsciencelabs.com
SIC: 2834 8742 Pharmaceutical preparations; manufacturing management consultant

(G-18111)
SMITHS INTERCONNECT INC (HQ)
4726 Eisenhower Blvd (33634-6309)
PHONE....................................813 901-7200
Richard Pea, *President*
Cheri Evangelist, *General Mgr*
Vince Novo, *Prdtn Mgr*
Jose Gil, *Mfg Staff*
Eric Behm, *Production*
▼ **EMP:** 176 **EST:** 1960
SQ FT: 120,000
SALES: 35.8MM
SALES (corp-wide): 3.1B **Privately Held**
WEB: www.smithsinterconnect.com
SIC: 3812 3661 3663 3669 Search & navigation equipment; telephone station equipment & parts, wire; airborne radio communications equipment; intercommunication systems, electric; printed circuit boards; modules, solid state
PA: Smiths Group Plc
4th Floor
London SW1Y
207 004-1600

(G-18112)
SMITHS INTERCONNECT INC
Also Called: Channel Microwave
4726 Eisenhower Blvd (33634-6309)
PHONE....................................813 901-7200
Mike Kujawa, *General Mgr*
EMP: 153
SALES (corp-wide): 3.1B **Privately Held**
WEB: www.smithsinterconnect.com
SIC: 3679 Microwave components
HQ: Smiths Interconnect, Inc.
4726 Eisenhower Blvd
Tampa FL 33634
813 901-7200

(G-18113)
SOE SOFTWARE CORPORATION
Also Called: Scytl
1111 N West Shore Blvd # 300
(33607-4711)
PHONE....................................813 490-7150
Marc Fartello, *CEO*
Jordi Puiggali, *Senior VP*
Johnathan Brill, *Vice Pres*
Jonathan Brill, *Vice Pres*
Muriel Moscardini, *Vice Pres*
EMP: 26 **EST:** 2002
SALES (est): 9MM **Privately Held**
WEB: www.scytl.us
SIC: 7372 Business oriented computer software

(G-18114)
SOL DAVIS PRINTING INC
5205 N Lois Ave (33614-6550)
PHONE....................................813 353-3609
Sol Davis, *President*
Amey Kendall, *Mktg Dir*
Jenny Matos, *Manager*
EMP: 21 **EST:** 1999
SQ FT: 8,500
SALES (est): 1.1MM **Privately Held**
WEB: www.soldavisprinting.com
SIC: 2752 Commercial printing, offset

(G-18115)
SOPHIX SOLUTIONS INC
1228 E 7th Ave Ste 225 (33605-3505)
PHONE....................................813 837-9555
Mark Eckerty,
Robert S Fleming Jr,
Gregory T Moore,
EMP: 6 **EST:** 2004
SALES (est): 722.8K **Privately Held**
WEB: www.sophix.net
SIC: 7372 Business oriented computer software

(G-18116)
SOUTHEAST COMPOUNDING PHRM LLC
3906 Cragmont Dr (33619-8305)
PHONE....................................813 644-7700
Jeff Steele,
Geoff Becker,
Warren Cal Gray Jr,
Milton Larrea,
Frank Ruddy,
EMP: 9 **EST:** 2012
SALES (est): 1MM **Privately Held**
WEB: www.southeastcompounding.com
SIC: 2834 Pharmaceutical preparations

(G-18117)
SOUTHEAST DAIRY PROCESSORS INC
Also Called: Flavor Right Foods SE
3811 E Columbus Dr (33605-3220)
P.O. Box 5088 (33675-5088)
PHONE....................................813 620-1516
William B Tiller, *President*
Donald Tiller Jr, *Vice Pres*
Vickie Osborne, *Treasurer*
EMP: 29 **EST:** 1988
SQ FT: 25,000
SALES (est): 19.4MM
SALES (corp-wide): 29.1MM **Privately Held**
WEB: www.flavorright.com
SIC: 2026 Milk processing (pasteurizing, homogenizing, bottling); half & half
PA: Flavor Right Foods Group, Inc.
2517 E Chambers St
Phoenix AZ 85040
602 232-2570

(G-18118)
SOUTHEAST PRINT PROGRAMS INC
5023 W Rio Vista Ave (33634-5316)
PHONE....................................813 885-3203
EMP: 46
SQ FT: 5,000
SALES (est): 2.2MM **Privately Held**
SIC: 2752 7331 Commercial Printing, Lithographic

(G-18119)
SOUTHEASTERN SEATING INC
903 E 17th Ave (33605-2532)
PHONE....................................813 273-9858
Eugene J Freeman, *President*
Jerry Freidman, *President*
Nick Freeman, *Sales Staff*
Richard Barnes, *CIO*
Jerry Angel, *Technician*
EMP: 15 **EST:** 1999
SQ FT: 15,000
SALES (est): 4.2MM **Privately Held**
WEB: www.seseating.com
SIC: 2531 2452 7359 Stadium furniture; prefabricated wood buildings; equipment rental & leasing

(G-18120)
SOUTHERN MFG TECH INC
5910 Johns Rd (33634-4422)
PHONE....................................954 953-9537
Roy Sweatman, *CEO*
Joe Paciella, *Mfg Spvr*
Gordon Dunn, *Engineer*
Sithea Ean, *Plant Engr*
Shannon Sweatman, *Human Res Dir*
EMP: 100
SQ FT: 20,000
SALES (est): 20.7MM **Privately Held**
WEB: www.smt-tampa.com
SIC: 3599 Machine shop, jobbing & repair

(G-18121)
SOUTHERN WINDING SERVICE INC
5302 Saint Paul St (33619-6100)
PHONE....................................813 621-6555
Francis O Jobe, *Ch of Bd*
Leo M Letourneau, *President*
Laura Chirichigno, *CFO*
▲ **EMP:** 33 **EST:** 1948
SQ FT: 15,000
SALES (est): 2.8MM **Privately Held**
WEB: www.southernwinding.com
SIC: 7694 Electric motor repair

(G-18122)
SOUTHPRINT CORP
6816 N River Blvd (33604-5444)
PHONE....................................813 237-8000
Jack Barnes, *CEO*
Patricia Brannon, *President*
Shirley Worsham, *Vice Pres*
EMP: 8 **EST:** 1968
SQ FT: 20,000
SALES (est): 358.2K **Privately Held**
WEB: www.southprintcorp.com
SIC: 2752 Commercial printing, offset

(G-18123)
SPECTRUM RUGS & MORE LLC
1009 W Indiana Ave (33603-4505)
PHONE....................................813 453-4242
Ayman Alhomsi, *Manager*
EMP: 6 **EST:** 2017
SALES (est): 158.8K **Privately Held**
SIC: 2752 Commercial printing, lithographic

(G-18124)
SPEEDLINE ATHLETIC WEAR INC
1804 N Habana Ave (33607-3345)
P.O. Box 4150 (33677-4150)
PHONE....................................813 876-1375
Steven Malzone, *President*
Denis Malzone, *Vice Pres*
Buddy Carter, *Sales Executive*
▲ **EMP:** 41 **EST:** 1936
SQ FT: 60,000
SALES (est): 6.6MM **Privately Held**
WEB: www.speedlineathletic.com
SIC: 2329 2339 Men's & boys' athletic uniforms; uniforms, athletic: women's, misses' & juniors'

(G-18125)
SPEEDLINE TEAM SPORTS INC
1804 N Habana Ave (33607-3345)
PHONE....................................813 876-1375
Steven Malzone, *President*
Steve Malzone, *Principal*
Shane Davis, *Manager*
John Oliva, *Director*
EMP: 12 **EST:** 2013
SALES (est): 732.8K **Privately Held**
WEB: www.speedlineathletic.com
SIC: 2329 2339 Men's & boys' sportswear & athletic clothing; women's & misses' outerwear

(G-18126)
SPHERE ACCESS INC (PA)
400 N Ashley Dr Ste 1775 (33602-4338)
PHONE....................................336 501-6159
Osama Sabbah, *CEO*
EMP: 15 **EST:** 2018
SALES (est): 2.6MM **Privately Held**
WEB: www.sphereaccess.com
SIC: 7372 6799 Business oriented computer software; venture capital companies

(G-18127)
SPORT PRODUCTS OF TAMPA INC
8721 Ashworth Dr (33647-2269)
PHONE....................................813 630-5552
Willis J Collier, *President*
EMP: 8 **EST:** 1986
SALES (est): 251.3K **Privately Held**
WEB: www.sportproductsoftampainc.com
SIC: 2221 3069 3949 2339 Nylon broadwoven fabrics; wet suits, rubber; sporting & athletic goods; women's & misses' outerwear

(G-18128)
SRS SOFTWARE LLC
Also Called: SRS Health Software
4221 W Boy Scout Blvd # 200
(33607-5745)
PHONE....................................201 802-1300
Khal Rai, *President*
Robert Harmonay, *COO*
Daniel McGraw, *Senior VP*
Keegan Dowling, *Vice Pres*
Lester Parada, *Vice Pres*
EMP: 13 **EST:** 2013
SALES (est): 6.8MM **Privately Held**
WEB: www.srs-health.com
SIC: 7372 Prepackaged software
PA: Nextech Systems, Llc
4221 W Boy Scout Blvd
Tampa FL 33607

(G-18129)
STANDARD INDUSTRIES INC
Also Called: GAF Materials
5138 Madison Ave (33619-9641)
PHONE....................................813 248-7000
Stewart McCallum, *Finance Other*

▲ = Import ▼=Export
◆ =Import/Export

Charles AMS, *Regl Sales Mgr*
Darrell S Norrington, *Branch Mgr*
Mike Finster, *Manager*
EMP: 95
SALES (corp-wide): 4.4B **Privately Held**
WEB: www.gaf.com
SIC: 2493 2952 2951 Insulation & roofing material, reconstituted wood; asphalt felts & coatings; asphalt paving mixtures & blocks
HQ: Standard Industries Inc.
1 Campus Dr
Parsippany NJ 07054

(G-18130)
STANLEY CHAIR COMPANY INC
5110 W Hanna Ave (33634-8088)
PHONE..................................813 884-1436
Burton Osiason, *President*
Carol A Osiason, *Vice Pres*
Neal Osiason, *Vice Pres*
Randy Osiason, *Vice Pres*
◆ **EMP:** 37 **EST:** 1946
SQ FT: 45,000
SALES (est): 2.5MM **Privately Held**
WEB: www.stanleychair.com
SIC: 2512 Upholstered household furniture

(G-18131)
STAR QUALITY INC
4006 W Crest Ave (33614-6540)
PHONE..................................813 875-9955
Maximo Sanchez, *President*
Denise Sanchez, *Treasurer*
EMP: 16
SQ FT: 31,000
SALES (est): 3MM **Privately Held**
WEB: www.starqualityinc.com
SIC: 2521 2434 Cabinets, office: wood; bookcases, office: wood; vanities, bathroom: wood

(G-18132)
STELLARNET INC
14390 Carlson Cir (33626-3003)
PHONE..................................813 855-8687
Will Pierce, *President*
Ava Grubman, *Vice Pres*
EMP: 10 **EST:** 1991
SALES (est): 2.3MM **Privately Held**
WEB: www.shopstellarnet.com
SIC: 3826 3829 Spectrometers; measuring & controlling devices

(G-18133)
STICKER KARMER
5405 W Crenshaw St (33634-3008)
PHONE..................................813 802-1826
EMP: 6 **EST:** 2016
SALES (est): 140K **Privately Held**
SIC: 2759 Commercial printing

(G-18134)
STM INDUSTRIES LLC
9524 N Trask St (33624-5137)
PHONE..................................813 854-3544
Leland Holland,
Katharine Holland,
EMP: 10 **EST:** 2017
SALES (est): 1.1MM **Privately Held**
WEB: www.stmindustries.com
SIC: 2221 Glass & fiberglass broadwoven fabrics

(G-18135)
STREET ELEMENTS MAGAZINE INC
3902 E Powhatan Ave (33610-3753)
PHONE..................................813 935-5894
Kevin Campbell, *Principal*
EMP: 10 **EST:** 2007
SALES (est): 255.1K **Privately Held**
WEB: www.streetelementsmagazine.com
SIC: 2721 Magazines: publishing only, not printed on site

(G-18136)
STRONG PUBLICATIONS LLC (PA)
13046 Race Track Rd (33626-1302)
PHONE..................................813 852-9933
Rickey W George, *Principal*
EMP: 29 **EST:** 2007
SALES (est): 264.8K **Privately Held**
WEB: www.myhardwear.com
SIC: 2741 Miscellaneous publishing

(G-18137)
SULA TOO LLC
1405 Tampa Park Plaza St (33605-4821)
PHONE..................................813 368-1628
EMP: 5 **EST:** 2018
SALES (est): 324.9K **Privately Held**
WEB: www.sulatoo.com
SIC: 2741 Miscellaneous publishing

(G-18138)
SUN COAST SURGICAL & MED SUP
2711 N 58th St (33619-1628)
PHONE..................................813 881-0065
Ron E Dial, *Owner*
Steve Dial, *Co-Owner*
EMP: 5 **EST:** 2007
SALES (est): 480.5K **Privately Held**
WEB: www.suncoastsurgical.com
SIC: 3841 Surgical & medical instruments

(G-18139)
SUN COATINGS INC
Also Called: Sun Paints & Coatings
4701 E 7th Ave (33605-4701)
PHONE..................................727 531-4100
Doug Mattscheck, *CEO*
Ken Lewis, *Plant Mgr*
▲ **EMP:** 30 **EST:** 1971
SALES (est): 12.9MM
SALES (corp-wide): 870.7MM **Privately Held**
WEB: www.suncoatings.com
SIC: 2851 Paints & paint additives
PA: Innovative Chemical Products Group, Llc
150 Dascomb Rd
Andover MA 01810
978 623-9980

(G-18140)
SUN METALS SYSTEMS INC
5008 Tampa West Blvd (33634-2412)
PHONE..................................813 889-0718
James G Hatton, *CEO*
Shalle Van Horn, *President*
James G Hatton III, *Vice Pres*
Jim Woolsey, *QC Mgr*
◆ **EMP:** 20 **EST:** 1999
SQ FT: 75,000
SALES (est): 4.1MM **Privately Held**
WEB: www.sunmetalssystems.com
SIC: 3442 Metal doors, sash & trim

(G-18141)
SUN-PAC MANUFACTURING INC
14201 Mccormick Dr (33626-3063)
PHONE..................................813 925-8787
Gary Henderson, *CEO*
Theresa Henderson, *Managing Dir*
Mike Heintz, *Manager*
Riggs Heather, *Admin Asst*
EMP: 40
SALES (est): 3.1MM **Privately Held**
WEB: www.sunpacmanufacturing.com
SIC: 2023 Dietary supplements, dairy & non-dairy based

(G-18142)
SUNCOAST CARTONS & CRATING LLC
5601 Airport Blvd (33634-5305)
P.O. Box 56017, Saint Petersburg (33732-6017)
PHONE..................................813 242-8477
Maria Brooks, *President*
William Brooks, *Vice Pres*
EMP: 8 **EST:** 2001
SQ FT: 7,500
SALES (est): 800K **Privately Held**
SIC: 2653 Boxes, corrugated: made from purchased materials

(G-18143)
SUNCOAST ELECTRIC MOTOR SVC
2502 E 5th Ave (33605-5518)
PHONE..................................813 247-4104
William P Bannar, *President*
Caryl Giordano, *Admin Sec*
▼ **EMP:** 12 **EST:** 1990
SQ FT: 5,000
SALES (est): 2.5MM **Privately Held**
WEB: www.suncoastelectricmotor.com
SIC: 7694 5999 Electric motor repair; motors, electric

(G-18144)
SUNCOAST REBUILD CENTER INC
2717 N 58th St (33619-1628)
PHONE..................................813 238-3433
Glenn McCabe, *President*
Peter McCabe, *Vice Pres*
Ricky Mullins, *Sales Staff*
EMP: 10 **EST:** 1988
SALES (est): 1.1MM **Privately Held**
WEB: www.suncoastrebuilding.com
SIC: 3568 3714 Power transmission equipment; transmissions, motor vehicle

(G-18145)
SUNCOAST SIGNS INC
9601 E Us Highway 92 (33610-5927)
PHONE..................................813 664-0699
Scott Robinson, *President*
Karen Robinson, *Admin Sec*
EMP: 8 **EST:** 1985
SALES (est): 987.5K **Privately Held**
WEB: www.suncoastsigns.com
SIC: 3993 7532 5099 Signs, not made in custom sign painting shops; truck painting & lettering; signs, except electric

(G-18146)
SUNCOAST SPECIALTY PRTG INC
Also Called: Printing.com
6401 N River Blvd (33604-6021)
PHONE..................................813 951-0899
Brice A Wolford, *Principal*
EMP: 6 **EST:** 2010
SALES (est): 134.3K **Privately Held**
WEB: www.suncoastspecialtyprinting.com
SIC: 2759 Commercial printing

(G-18147)
SURF OUTFITTER
1413 S Howard Ave Ste 104 (33606-3176)
PHONE..................................813 489-4587
Daniel Hater, *Administration*
EMP: 8 **EST:** 2013
SALES (est): 118.4K **Privately Held**
WEB: www.surfoutfitter.com
SIC: 2369 2329 Bathing suits & swimwear: girls', children's & infants'; men's & boys' sportswear & athletic clothing

(G-18148)
SYNDAVER LABS INC (PA)
8506 Benjamin Rd Ste C (33634-1242)
PHONE..................................813 600-5530
Christopher Sakezles, *President*
Sam Olsen, *Opers Staff*
James Sicardi, *Buyer*
Terence Terenzi, *CFO*
Marjorie Bulone, *Marketing Mgr*
EMP: 58 **EST:** 2009
SALES (est): 10MM **Privately Held**
WEB: www.syndaver.com
SIC: 3842 Surgical appliances & supplies

(G-18149)
SYPRIS ELECTRONICS LLC (HQ)
10421 University Ctr Dr (33612-6422)
PHONE..................................813 972-6000
Shasta White, *Info Tech Mgr*
Darin Garner, *Director*
Jeffrey T Gill,
Robert E Gill,
James M Long,
▲ **EMP:** 413 **EST:** 1965
SQ FT: 50,000
SALES (est): 52.7MM
SALES (corp-wide): 82.3MM **Publicly Held**
WEB: www.sypriselectronics.com
SIC: 3672 3679 Printed circuit boards; electronic circuits
PA: Sypris Solutions, Inc.
101 Bullitt Ln Ste 450
Louisville KY 40222
502 329-2000

(G-18150)
T C DELIVERIES
7002 Parke East Blvd (33610-4132)
PHONE..................................813 881-1830
Stan Pascarelli, *Opers Staff*
Kevin McMahon, *Manager*
EMP: 6 **EST:** 2016
SALES (est): 167.4K **Privately Held**
SIC: 2893 Printing ink

(G-18151)
T DISNEY TRUCKING & GRADING
9250 Bay Plaza Blvd # 311 (33619-4465)
PHONE..................................813 443-6258
EMP: 27
SQ FT: 1,500
SALES: 15MM **Privately Held**
SIC: 3713 Mfg Truck/Bus Bodies

(G-18152)
T L SHEET METAL INC
4203 N Lauber Way Ste 8 (33614)
P.O. Box 8838 (33674-8838)
PHONE..................................813 871-3780
Tom Williams, *President*
Mary Williams, *Vice Pres*
EMP: 6 **EST:** 1988
SQ FT: 6,500
SALES (est): 871.3K **Privately Held**
SIC: 3441 Fabricated structural metal

(G-18153)
TAE TRANS ATLANTIC ELEC INC (PA)
Also Called: Empire Scientific
4504 E Hillsborough Ave (33610-5249)
P.O. Box 817, Deer Park NY (11729-0981)
PHONE..................................631 595-9206
Janet English, *President*
Jeffrey English, *Vice Pres*
Spencer Slipko, *Vice Pres*
Susan Feeny-Wenz, *Natl Sales Mgr*
Moe Michael, *Executive*
▲ **EMP:** 23 **EST:** 1965
SQ FT: 1,500
SALES (est): 3.4MM **Privately Held**
SIC: 3692 5063 Primary batteries, dry & wet; batteries

(G-18154)
TALON INNOVATIONS FL CORP
1217 Tech Blvd (33619-7833)
PHONE..................................320 251-0390
James Williams, *President*
Mike Rowley, *Mfg Spvr*
Jeremy Johnson, *Engineer*
Tamara Cote, *Cust Mgr*
EMP: 45 **EST:** 1978
SQ FT: 20,000
SALES (est): 12.8MM
SALES (corp-wide): 124.8MM **Publicly Held**
WEB: www.ichorsystems.com
SIC: 3599 Machine shop, jobbing & repair
HQ: Talon Innovations Corporation
1003 Industrial Dr S
Sauk Rapids MN 56379
320 251-0390

(G-18155)
TAMPA AMALGAMATED STEEL CORP
5215 Saint Paul St (33619-6117)
P.O. Box 2031 (33601-2031)
PHONE..................................813 621-0550
Tommy E Craddock, *President*
John E Craddock, *Corp Secy*
Robert E Craddock, *Vice Pres*
Robert Craddock, *Vice Pres*
Dale Damgaard, *Engineer*
EMP: 18 **EST:** 1964
SQ FT: 40,000
SALES (est): 6MM **Privately Held**
WEB: www.tascoonline.com
SIC: 3441 7692 Building components, structural steel; welding repair

(G-18156)
TAMPA AMALGAMATED STEEL CORP
Also Called: Tasco
5215 Saint Paul St (33619-6117)
PHONE..................................813 621-0550
Tommy E Craddock, *President*

EMP: 8 **EST:** 2016
SALES (est): 454.2K **Privately Held**
WEB: www.tascoonline.com
SIC: 3441 Fabricated structural metal

(G-18157)
TAMPA ARMATURE WORKS INC
Also Called: Taw Tampa Service Center
440 S 78th St (33619-4223)
P.O. Box 3381 (33601-3381)
PHONE.................................813 612-2600
Mike Wherley, *Controller*
Al Jackson, *Accounts Mgr*
Robin Morton, *Office Mgr*
Doug Ragsdale, *Branch Mgr*
Jim Peplow, *Manager*
EMP: 104
SALES (corp-wide): 169.6MM **Privately Held**
WEB: www.tawinc.com
SIC: 7694 3621 5063 Electric motor repair; motors & generators; motors, electric; generators; electrical supplies
PA: Tampa Armature Works, Inc.
6312 S 78th St
Riverview FL 33578
813 621-5661

(G-18158)
TAMPA BAY MACHINING INC
13601 Mccormick Dr (33626-3049)
PHONE.................................813 855-8456
Jeff Kefauver, *President*
Tammy Coe, *Vice Pres*
EMP: 49 **EST:** 1981
SQ FT: 25,000
SALES: 4.5MM **Privately Held**
WEB: www.tampabaymachining.com
SIC: 3599 Machine shop, jobbing & repair

(G-18159)
TAMPA BAY POWDER COATING INC
9601 Norwood Dr Ste B (33624-5300)
PHONE.................................813 964-5667
David Nelson, *Principal*
EMP: 8 **EST:** 2018
SALES (est): 593.9K **Privately Held**
WEB:
www.buffaloavenuepowdercoating.com
SIC: 3479 Coating of metals & formed products

(G-18160)
TAMPA BAY POWERSPORTS LLC
13521 N Florida Ave (33613-3214)
PHONE.................................813 968-7888
Drew Hall, *Parts Mgr*
Mansor Thomas, *Sales Mgr*
John Scott, *Sales Staff*
Laurie Stanford, *Office Mgr*
Rodin Younessi,
EMP: 35 **EST:** 2005
SALES (est): 4.8MM **Privately Held**
WEB: www.tampabaypowersports.com
SIC: 3751 5571 Motorcycles, bicycles & parts; motorcycle dealers

(G-18161)
TAMPA BAY PRESS INC
4710 Eisenhower Blvd B12 (33634-6308)
PHONE.................................813 886-1415
John Hedler, *President*
EMP: 17 **EST:** 1987
SQ FT: 18,000
SALES (est): 1MM **Privately Held**
WEB: www.tampabaypressinc.com
SIC: 2752 Commercial printing, offset

(G-18162)
TAMPA BRASS AND ALUMINUM CORP
Also Called: T B A
8511 Florida Mining Blvd (33634-1200)
PHONE.................................813 885-6064
Sam Leto Jr, *Ch of Bd*
Christopher S Leto, *President*
Jason Leto, *COO*
Ken Sowers, *Project Mgr*
Andrew Mc Gregor, *QC Mgr*
▲ **EMP:** 105 **EST:** 1957
SQ FT: 64,500
SALES (est): 39.2MM **Privately Held**
WEB: www.tampabrass.com
SIC: 3369 3599 Nonferrous foundries; machine shop, jobbing & repair

(G-18163)
TAMPA CONTRACTORS SUPPLY INC
Also Called: Alliance Contractors Supply
5017 N Coolidge Ave (33614-6421)
PHONE.................................813 418-7284
Jerry Monts De Oca, *President*
EMP: 21 **EST:** 2011
SQ FT: 26,000
SALES (est): 2.4MM **Privately Held**
SIC: 2431 Millwork

(G-18164)
TAMPA FIBERGLASS INC
4209 Raleigh St (33619-6059)
PHONE.................................813 248-6828
Stephen Cook, *President*
Brian Cook, *Vice Pres*
Patricia Cook, *Vice Pres*
Edie Restall, *Office Mgr*
Colton McCleave, *Maintence Staff*
EMP: 18 **EST:** 1972
SQ FT: 1,000
SALES (est): 474.7K **Privately Held**
WEB: www.tampafiberglass.com
SIC: 3589 1799 Water treatment equipment, industrial; fiberglass work

(G-18165)
TAMPA MARINE FABRICATORS LLC
8702 E Broadway Ave (33619-7710)
PHONE.................................813 664-1700
Charles Cailliau,
EMP: 5 **EST:** 2010
SALES (est): 424.1K **Privately Held**
WEB: www.tampametalfab.com
SIC: 3441 Fabricated structural metal

(G-18166)
TAMPA MEDIA GROUP INC
Also Called: Tampa Tribune Company, The
202 S Parker St (33606-2379)
P.O. Box 31101, Saint Petersburg (33731-1107)
PHONE.................................813 259-7711
EMP: 200
SALES (corp-wide): 83.3MM **Privately Held**
SIC: 2711 Newspapers-Publishing/Printing
PA: Tampa Media Group, Inc.
202 S Parker St
Tampa FL 33606
813 259-7711

(G-18167)
TAMPA MEDIA GROUP INC (PA)
Also Called: Tampa Tribune, The
202 S Parker St (33606-2379)
PHONE.................................813 259-7711
Robert Loring, *Principal*
Gary Alcock, *Principal*
EMP: 400 **EST:** 2012
SALES (est): 88.4MM **Privately Held**
WEB: www.tampabay.com
SIC: 2711 Newspapers, publishing & printing

(G-18168)
TAMPA MEDIA GROUP LLC
Also Called: Tbo
202 S Parker St (33606-2379)
PHONE.................................813 259-7100
Cyrus Nikou,
Robert Loring,
EMP: 7 **EST:** 2013
SALES (est): 208.8K **Privately Held**
WEB: www.tampabay.com
SIC: 2711 2721 Newspapers, publishing & printing; periodicals

(G-18169)
TAMPA METAL WORKS INC
6601 N 50th St (33610-1843)
PHONE.................................813 628-9223
Charles S Allen, *President*
Tim Jenkins, *Vice Pres*
EMP: 11 **EST:** 1987
SALES (est): 1MM **Privately Held**
WEB: www.tampametalworksinc.com
SIC: 3444 Sheet metalwork

(G-18170)
TAMPA MULTI ROLL SHEET METAL
4438 Bass St (33617-8202)
PHONE.................................813 340-3554
EMP: 7 **EST:** 2015
SALES (est): 83.7K **Privately Held**
WEB: www.multiroll.net
SIC: 3444 Sheet metalwork

(G-18171)
TAMPA PRINTING COMPANY
4907 N Florida Ave (33603-2119)
PHONE.................................813 612-7746
F Michael Bittman, *President*
Barbara Tomlinson, *Admin Sec*
EMP: 27 **EST:** 1911
SALES (est): 1.9MM **Privately Held**
SIC: 2752 2791 2759 Commercial printing, offset; typesetting; commercial printing

(G-18172)
TAMPA SHEET METAL COMPANY
1402 W Kennedy Blvd (33606-1847)
PHONE.................................813 251-1845
John L Jiretz, *President*
Carolyn Murphy, *Mktg Dir*
EMP: 53 **EST:** 1920
SQ FT: 24,000
SALES (est): 5.1MM **Privately Held**
WEB: www.tampasheetmetal.com
SIC: 3444 Sheet metalwork

(G-18173)
TAMPA SHIP LLC
1130 Mcclosky Blvd (33605-6722)
P.O. Box 310, Galliano LA (70354-0310)
PHONE.................................813 248-9310
Patrick O'Donnell, *Purch Mgr*
Costel Anton, *Purchasing*
Mark Layman, *Purchasing*
Tony Pellegrino, *Accounting Mgr*
Gary J Chouest, *Mng Member*
▲ **EMP:** 327 **EST:** 2008
SQ FT: 15,000
SALES (est): 47.1MM **Privately Held**
WEB: www.tampabayship.com
SIC: 3731 Shipbuilding & repairing

(G-18174)
TAMPA STEEL ERECTING COMPANY
5127 Bloomingdale Ave (33619-9662)
PHONE.................................813 677-7184
Robert J Clark Jr, *President*
Donna Carter, *Corp Secy*
John M Clark, *Vice Pres*
Ronald Teope, *Controller*
EMP: 74 **EST:** 1945
SQ FT: 180,000
SALES (est): 20MM **Privately Held**
WEB: www.tampasteelerecting.com
SIC: 3441 Fabricated structural metal

(G-18175)
TARIN SERVICES LLC
5404 24th Ave S (33619-5369)
PHONE.................................803 526-9643
Armando Tarin, *Principal*
EMP: 6 **EST:** 2010
SALES (est): 475.8K **Privately Held**
SIC: 7692 Automotive welding

(G-18176)
TAW PAYROLL INC
440 S 78th St (33619-4223)
PHONE.................................813 621-5661
J A Turner Sr, *Principal*
EMP: 19 **EST:** 2010
SALES (est): 254.3K **Privately Held**
WEB: www.tawinc.com
SIC: 7694 Electric motor repair

(G-18177)
TAYLOR COMMUNICATIONS INC
5131 Tampa West Blvd (33634-2408)
PHONE.................................813 886-5511
Brian Freund, *Production*
Sonja Charrier, *Buyer*
Gary Reeves, *Manager*
Brenda Lynch, *Manager*
Sara Mason, *Manager*
EMP: 17
SALES (corp-wide): 3.6B **Privately Held**
WEB: www.taylor.com
SIC: 2761 2672 Manifold business forms; coated & laminated paper
HQ: Taylor Communications, Inc.
1725 Roe Crest Dr
North Mankato MN 56003
866 541-0937

(G-18178)
TECHNOCABLE WIRING SPECIALIST
3110 Cherry Palm Dr # 380 (33619-8321)
PHONE.................................813 664-0697
Richard Zach, *Manager*
EMP: 13
SALES (est): 522K **Privately Held**
WEB: www.technocable.com
SIC: 2655 Fiber cans, drums & similar products

(G-18179)
TECHNOLGY TRAINING ASSOCIATES
Also Called: Club Information Systems
326 S Plant Ave (33606-2347)
PHONE.................................813 249-0303
Mike Higgins, *President*
Thomas Howard, *Exec VP*
Janet Taylor, *Technology*
Jodda Perry, *IT/INT Sup*
Jan Taylor, *Training Dir*
EMP: 24 **EST:** 1997
SQ FT: 4,000
SALES (est): 2.8MM **Privately Held**
WEB: www.tta.club
SIC: 7372 Business oriented computer software

(G-18180)
TECO DIVERSIFIED INC (DH)
702 N Franklin St (33602-4429)
P.O. Box 111 (33601-0111)
PHONE.................................813 228-4111
Steve Winistorfer, *President*
Gordan L Gillette, *CFO*
Melody Goedert, *Human Res Mgr*
Victoria Bernal, *Manager*
▼ **EMP:** 4 **EST:** 1987
SALES (est): 344.3MM
SALES (corp-wide): 4.5B **Privately Held**
WEB: www.photographyongold.com
SIC: 1221 Bituminous coal & lignite-surface mining
HQ: Teco Energy, Inc.
702 N Franklin St
Tampa FL 33602
813 228-1111

(G-18181)
TELEPHONY PARTNERS LLC
Also Called: Acuity Technologies
5215 W Laurel St Ste 210 (33607-1728)
PHONE.................................813 769-4690
Josh Anderson, *CEO*
Ronna Terzado, *Partner*
Kris Mathey, *Vice Pres*
Natalie Wilcox, *Marketing Staff*
Shannon Cleveland, *Director*
EMP: 31 **EST:** 2002
SALES (est): 3.5MM **Privately Held**
WEB: www.acuitytech.com
SIC: 7372 7389 Business oriented computer software; telephone services

(G-18182)
TELEXPRESS LA MUSICA INC
6310 N Armenia Ave Ste A (33604-5777)
PHONE.................................813 879-1914
Lillian Hernandez, *Principal*
EMP: 9 **EST:** 2007
SALES (est): 499.5K **Privately Held**
WEB: www.telexpresscargo.com
SIC: 2741 Miscellaneous publishing

(G-18183)
TEN STAR SUPPLY CO INC
Also Called: Ten Star Promotions
7902 Hopi Pl (33634-2418)
PHONE.................................813 254-6921
Donna Killoren, *CEO*
Jack Killoren, *President*
EMP: 8 **EST:** 1956
SQ FT: 3,500

▲ = Import ▼=Export
◆ =Import/Export

SALES (est): 970.2K **Privately Held**
WEB: www.tenstarsupply.com
SIC: 2759 Screen printing

(G-18184)
TETRA PROCESS TECHNOLOGY
5415 W Sligh Ave Ste 102 (33634-4488)
PHONE..................................813 886-9331
▼ **EMP:** 8
SALES (est): 523.7K **Privately Held**
SIC: 3589 Mfg Service Industry Machinery

(G-18185)
THERMAL MATRIX INTL LLC
101 E Kennedy Blvd # 322 (33602-5179)
PHONE..................................813 222-3274
Richard Salem, *CEO*
Robert McDaniel, *General Mgr*
Chris Jadick, *Vice Pres*
EMP: 9 **EST:** 2008
SALES (est): 246.4K **Privately Held**
WEB: www.thermalmatrixusa.net
SIC: 3827 Optical instruments & lenses

(G-18186)
TIM GARDNERS VITAMART INC (PA)
3001 N Rocky Point Dr E (33607-5810)
PHONE..................................813 908-7843
Brandie S Gardner, *Principal*
EMP: 48 **EST:** 2010
SALES (est): 191.9K **Privately Held**
SIC: 2834 5499 Vitamin, nutrient & hematinic preparations for human use; vitamin food stores

(G-18187)
TIMELESS TREASURES DOLL CLUB
12020 Steppingstone Blvd (33635-6252)
PHONE..................................813 854-6208
Judy Smith, *President*
Kathleen Short, *Treasurer*
EMP: 30 **EST:** 2014
SALES (est): 835.6K **Privately Held**
SIC: 3942 Miniature dolls, collectors'

(G-18188)
TITAN PETROLEUM CORPORATION
Also Called: Poc Archer's Arrow Joint
4830 W Kennedy Blvd # 60 (33609-2564)
PHONE..................................813 280-4833
Stephen Plunkett, *Ch of Bd*
EMP: 6 **EST:** 2013
SQ FT: 150
SALES (est): 147.3K **Privately Held**
SIC: 1389 1311 1381 Servicing oil & gas wells; crude petroleum & natural gas production; redrilling oil & gas wells

(G-18189)
TITANIUM DANCE CHALLENGE LLC
4045 Shoreside Cir (33624-2371)
PHONE..................................813 340-0903
Ashley Massicotte, *Principal*
EMP: 6 **EST:** 2016
SALES (est): 107.5K **Privately Held**
SIC: 3356 Titanium

(G-18190)
TL FAHRINGER CO INC
Also Called: T L Fahringer
10103 Cedar Run (33619-8003)
P.O. Box 1412, Brandon (33509-1412)
PHONE..................................813 681-2373
Elizabeth Fahringer, *CEO*
Jennifer Fahringer, *Vice Pres*
John Zaso, *Opers Mgr*
EMP: 8 **EST:** 1977
SQ FT: 8,400
SALES (est): 1.2MM **Privately Held**
WEB: www.fahringer.com
SIC: 3728 3549 3548 3496 Aircraft parts & equipment; metalworking machinery; welding apparatus; miscellaneous fabricated wire products

(G-18191)
TLD LLC
14512 N Nebraska Ave (33613-1429)
PHONE..................................813 927-7554
Terri M Casteel, *Principal*
EMP: 6 **EST:** 2015
SALES (est): 328.4K **Privately Held**
SIC: 3321 Gray & ductile iron foundries

(G-18192)
TMG MANUFACTURING CORP
5517 W Sligh Ave Ste 100 (33634-4507)
PHONE..................................813 464-2299
Joseph Bloomfield, *President*
Patricia Mansour, *CFO*
EMP: 14 **EST:** 2003
SALES (est): 3.3MM **Privately Held**
WEB: www.tmgmfg.com
SIC: 3532 Concentration machinery (metallurgical or mining)

(G-18193)
TOM JAMES COMPANY
2005 Pan Am Cir Ste 110 (33607-2380)
PHONE..................................813 204-9699
Jim Nolan, *Branch Mgr*
EMP: 6
SALES (corp-wide): 421.8MM **Privately Held**
WEB: www.tomjames.com
SIC: 2311 2339 Suits, men's & boys': made from purchased materials; women's & misses' athletic clothing & sportswear
PA: Tom James Company
263 Seaboard Ln
Franklin TN 37067
615 771-1122

(G-18194)
TONERTYPE INC
5100 W Cypress St (33607-1702)
PHONE..................................813 915-1300
David T Shaver, *President*
Clyde C Shaver, *Vice Pres*
Carolyn Shaver, *Manager*
▼ **EMP:** 25 **EST:** 1995
SQ FT: 11,500
SALES (est): 3.4MM **Privately Held**
WEB: www.tonertypeprint.com
SIC: 3861 2759 Printing equipment, photographic; commercial printing

(G-18195)
TOTAL SPCALTY PUBLICATIONS LLC (PA)
Also Called: Corporate Sports & Entrtmt
1715 N West Shore Blvd # 266 (33607-3931)
PHONE..................................813 405-2610
Shawn Ferris, *Sales Staff*
Derrick Phillips, *Sales Staff*
Rick Castillo, *Advt Staff*
Eric Kenny, *Advt Staff*
Isabella Rodriguez, *Advt Staff*
EMP: 80 **EST:** 2009
SALES (est): 528.1K **Privately Held**
WEB: www.tspnational.com
SIC: 2741 Miscellaneous publishing

(G-18196)
TOTALPRINT USA
5100 W Cypress St (33607-1702)
PHONE..................................855 915-1300
EMP: 7 **EST:** 2017
SALES (est): 184.7K **Privately Held**
WEB: www.totalprintusa.com
SIC: 2752 5044 5112 3577 Commercial printing, lithographic; office equipment; laserjet supplies; printers, computer

(G-18197)
TRANSPRTATION CTRL SYSTEMS INC
1030 S 86th St (33619-4946)
PHONE..................................813 630-2800
Steve Gillis, *President*
John T Gillis, *President*
Scott Gillis, *Vice Pres*
Steven Gillis, *Vice Pres*
Alex Grooms, *Engineer*
▼ **EMP:** 32 **EST:** 1976
SALES (est): 10.1MM **Privately Held**
WEB: www.tcstraffic.com
SIC: 3669 Traffic signals, electric

(G-18198)
TREPKO INC
4893 W Waters Ave Ste C-F (33634-1314)
PHONE..................................813 443-0794
Jesper Hanson, *President*
Jesus Perez, *Sales Staff*
EMP: 19 **EST:** 2014
SALES (est): 2.5MM
SALES (corp-wide): 52.7MM **Privately Held**
WEB: www.trepko.com
SIC: 3565 Packaging machinery
HQ: Trepko A/S
Energivej 30
Ballerup 2750
439 922-44

(G-18199)
TRI INC
107 S Willow Ave (33606-1945)
PHONE..................................813 267-1201
Brian Marshall, *President*
EMP: 10
SALES (est): 350K **Privately Held**
SIC: 3299 Moldings, architectural: plaster of paris

(G-18200)
TRIAL EXHIBITS INC (PA)
1177 W Cass St (33606-1308)
PHONE..................................813 258-6153
Jack Stein, *President*
Benjamin B Broome, *Regional Mgr*
Benjamin Broome, *Regional Mgr*
Kathleen Stein, *Vice Pres*
Jeremiah Hodges, *CFO*
EMP: 12 **EST:** 1989
SALES (est): 2.7MM **Privately Held**
WEB: www.trialexhibitsinc.com
SIC: 3999 7336 Preparation of slides & exhibits; commercial art & graphic design

(G-18201)
TRIPLE J MARKETING LLC
301 W Platt St (33606-2292)
PHONE..................................813 247-6999
EMP: 21
SQ FT: 10,000
SALES: 1.2MM **Privately Held**
SIC: 3695 Mfg Magnetic/Optical Recording Media

(G-18202)
TROPICAL ENTERPRISES INTL (PA)
Also Called: Tmarketing Products
8625 Florida Mining Blvd (33634-1261)
PHONE..................................813 837-9800
Kimberly Canavian, *President*
Sarah Cross, *Principal*
Melissa Dweyer, *Principal*
Maycee Mullarkey, *Principal*
Aldo Ortiz, *Principal*
EMP: 18 **EST:** 2000
SALES (est): 5.1MM **Privately Held**
WEB: www.tmarketingproducts.com
SIC: 2844 Face creams or lotions

(G-18203)
TRUE GRIT ABRASIVES INC
7015 E 14th Ave (33619-2921)
PHONE..................................813 247-5219
Arthur Thorn, *President*
Richard Toe, *President*
Geraldine Mann, *Vice Pres*
Omid Zee, *Executive*
▼ **EMP:** 20 **EST:** 1979
SQ FT: 10,000
SALES (est): 1.5MM **Privately Held**
WEB: www.truegritabrasives.com
SIC: 3291 5085 Abrasive products; abrasives

(G-18204)
TRUESOUTH MARINE CORP
4810 Culbreath Isles Rd (33629-4827)
PHONE..................................813 286-0716
William McCoy, *President*
EMP: 5 **EST:** 2014
SALES (est): 305.6K **Privately Held**
SIC: 3732 Yachts, building & repairing

(G-18205)
TRUVOICE TELECOM INC
3102 Cherry Palm Dr # 145 (33619-8316)
PHONE..................................888 448-5556
Stephen Jones, *CEO*
Alan Hickey, *Director*
EMP: 5 **EST:** 2016
SALES (est): 2.2MM **Privately Held**
WEB: www.truvoicetelecom.com
SIC: 3661 Headsets, telephone

(G-18206)
TRYANA LLC
Also Called: Metals Supermarket
4901 W Rio Vista Ave A (33634-5356)
PHONE..................................813 467-9916
Brian Thompson, *Mng Member*
EMP: 5 **EST:** 2014
SALES (est): 612K **Privately Held**
WEB: www.metalsupermarkets.com
SIC: 3441 Fabricated structural metal

(G-18207)
TSN MANUFACTURING
4011 E 21st Ave (33605-2307)
PHONE..................................813 740-1876
Tim Ngo, *President*
EMP: 11 **EST:** 2010
SALES (est): 171.4K **Privately Held**
WEB: www.tsnmanufacturing.com
SIC: 3999 Manufacturing industries

(G-18208)
TTI HOLDINGS INC (PA)
2710 E 5th Ave (33605-5522)
PHONE..................................813 623-2675
David D Hale, *CEO*
Brian S Albert, *CEO*
Calvin H Reed, *President*
David E Newlin, *Vice Pres*
Federico Rivas, *Engineer*
◆ **EMP:** 2 **EST:** 1994
SQ FT: 100,000
SALES (est): 57.5MM **Privately Held**
WEB: www.tti-fss.com
SIC: 3443 3446 3441 Tanks, standard or custom fabricated: metal plate; stairs, staircases, stair treads: prefabricated metal; fabricated structural metal

(G-18209)
TWO PAPER CHASERS LLC
3214 W San Miguel St (33629-5949)
PHONE..................................813 251-5090
Paul A Carlisle, *Principal*
EMP: 7 **EST:** 2007
SALES (est): 125.4K **Privately Held**
SIC: 2653 Corrugated & solid fiber boxes

(G-18210)
U B CORP
9829 Wilsky Blvd (33615-1399)
PHONE..................................813 884-1463
Cynthia Fairbanks, *President*
Robert J Upcavage, *President*
Lawrence J Bauer Jr, *CFO*
David Gluck, *Treasurer*
Cynthia M Fairbanks, *Sales Executive*
EMP: 9 **EST:** 1968
SQ FT: 20,000
SALES (est): 2MM **Privately Held**
WEB: www.ubcorp.com
SIC: 3663 Microwave communication equipment

(G-18211)
UDC USA INC (PA)
Also Called: Ultra Defense
501 E Kennedy Blvd # 801 (33602-5201)
PHONE..................................813 281-0200
Matthew Herring, *CEO*
Meghan Fonte, *Program Mgr*
◆ **EMP:** 24 **EST:** 2008
SQ FT: 1,900
SALES (est): 4.8MM **Privately Held**
WEB: www.udcusa.com
SIC: 3728 8711 7373 Aircraft parts & equipment; aircraft assemblies, subassemblies & parts; engineering services; systems integration services

(G-18212)
UFP TAMPA LLC
Also Called: Universal Forest Products
1003 E 131st Ave (33612-4436)
PHONE..................................813 971-3030
Justin Elwell, *Vice Pres*
EMP: 36 **EST:** 2017
SALES (est): 10MM
SALES (corp-wide): 5.1B **Publicly Held**
WEB: www.ufpi.com
SIC: 2491 Millwork, treated wood
PA: Ufp Industries, Inc.
2801 E Beltline Ave Ne
Grand Rapids MI 49525
616 364-6161

GEOGRAPHIC

(G-18213)
ULTIMATE SIGN SERVICE LLC
8328 Civic Rd (33615-4548)
PHONE.................................813 210-3166
Sumi Park, *Principal*
EMP: 6 **EST:** 2010
SALES (est): 127.8K **Privately Held**
WEB: www.ultimatesignco.com
SIC: 3993 Signs & advertising specialties

(G-18214)
ULTRASONICS AND MAGNETICS
Also Called: Q Sea
5275 Causeway Blvd Ste 2 (33619-6134)
PHONE.................................813 740-1800
Frank Aguilar, *Manager*
EMP: 21 **Privately Held**
SIC: 1389 Testing, measuring, surveying & analysis services
PA: Ultrasonics And Magnetics Corp
405 Lake Village Blvd
Slidell LA 70461

(G-18215)
ULTROID TECHNOLOGIES INC
3140 W Kennedy Blvd (33609-3075)
PHONE.................................877 858-0555
Michael Knox, *CEO*
Wycliffe McIntosh, *CEO*
EMP: 7 **EST:** 2005
SALES (est): 824.2K **Privately Held**
WEB: www.ultroid.com
SIC: 3841 Surgical & medical instruments

(G-18216)
UNCLE JOHNS PRIDE LLC
Also Called: Crofton & Sons
10250 Woodberry Rd (33619-8008)
PHONE.................................813 685-7745
Lonnie Brantley, *Transportation*
Denny Simmers, *CFO*
Angela Lewis, *Manager*
Mark Beswick,
Julie McBride,
EMP: 72 **EST:** 2015
SQ FT: 45,000
SALES (est): 14.4MM **Privately Held**
WEB: www.unclejohnspride.com
SIC: 2013 Smoked meats from purchased meat
PA: Blue Planet Holdings Llc
1738 Clarendon Pl
Lakeland FL 33803
863 559-1236

(G-18217)
UNIFORM NAMETAPE COMPANY INC
5701 S Dale Mabry Hwy (33611-4229)
PHONE.................................813 839-6737
John P Colman, *President*
Travis Bell, *General Mgr*
Linda L Colman, *Corp Secy*
EMP: 13 **EST:** 1973
SQ FT: 3,000
SALES (est): 1.3MM **Privately Held**
WEB: www.uniformnametape.com
SIC: 2395 Embroidery products, except schiffli machine

(G-18218)
UNIPRESS CORPORATION
3501 Queen Palm Dr (33619-1392)
PHONE.................................813 623-3731
Peter Hamlin, *President*
Ronnie Lechowicz, *Production*
Gary C Johnson, *Treasurer*
Robb Johnson, *Manager*
Jerry Blakey, *Technology*
▼ **EMP:** 80 **EST:** 1982
SQ FT: 75,000
SALES (est): 22.2MM **Privately Held**
WEB: www.unipresscorp.com
SIC: 3582 Pressing machines, commercial laundry & drycleaning; drycleaning equipment & machinery, commercial

(G-18219)
UNITED ARMOUR PRODUCTS LLC
1601 N 39th St (33605-5852)
PHONE.................................813 767-9624
David Barkett, *Mng Member*
George Chaconas,
EMP: 7 **EST:** 2012
SQ FT: 50,000
SALES (est): 550K **Privately Held**
WEB: www.unitedarmour.com
SIC: 2992 Lubricating oils; brake fluid (hydraulic): made from purchased materials

(G-18220)
UNITED ELECTRIC MOTOR INC
Also Called: ARC United Electric Motor
905 E Ida St (33603-4317)
P.O. Box 669, Seffner (33583-0669)
PHONE.................................813 238-7872
Robert Burk, *CEO*
EMP: 8 **EST:** 1974
SQ FT: 3,000
SALES (est): 837.5K **Privately Held**
WEB: www.unitedelectricmotortampafl.com
SIC: 7694 5063 5999 Electric motor repair; motors, electric; motors, electric

(G-18221)
UNITED GRANITE INC
3906 S 51st St (33619-6802)
PHONE.................................813 391-4323
Johana Perez Marquez, *President*
Jesus Perez Marquez, *Vice Pres*
EMP: 16 **EST:** 2013
SALES (est): 2.4MM **Privately Held**
WEB: www.unitedgraniteus.com
SIC: 3441 Fabricated structural metal

(G-18222)
UNIVERSAL HM HLTH INDUS SUPS I
7320 E Fletcher Ave (33637-0916)
P.O. Box 290314 (33687-0314)
PHONE.................................813 493-7904
Anthony R Smith, *President*
EMP: 5 **EST:** 1988
SQ FT: 30,000
SALES: 1.3MM **Privately Held**
WEB: www.universalhomehealth.com
SIC: 3842 2389 3841 5047 Personal safety equipment; hospital gowns; surgical & medical instruments; medical equipment & supplies

(G-18223)
UNIVERSAL SCREEN GRAPHICS INC
4897 W Waters Ave Ste H (33634-1318)
PHONE.................................813 623-5335
Tim Packrall, *President*
Kim Johnson, *Vice Pres*
Dianne Packrall, *Office Mgr*
EMP: 28 **EST:** 1991
SQ FT: 8,500
SALES (est): 5.4MM **Privately Held**
WEB: www.usgfla.com
SIC: 2759 2791 2396 Screen printing; typesetting; automotive & apparel trimmings

(G-18224)
UR CABINETS
4042 W Kennedy Blvd (33609-2750)
PHONE.................................813 434-6454
EMP: 7 **EST:** 2018
SALES (est): 349.3K **Privately Held**
WEB: www.urcabinets.com
SIC: 2434 Wood kitchen cabinets

(G-18225)
URBAN METALS LLC
Also Called: TAMPA STEEL & SUPPLY
1301 N 26th St (33605-5534)
PHONE.................................813 241-2801
Troy A Underwood, *Mng Member*
EMP: 19 **EST:** 2018
SALES (est): 2.8MM **Privately Held**
WEB: www.tampasteel.com
SIC: 3312 5051 Bars & bar shapes, steel, hot-rolled; metals service centers & offices

(G-18226)
US CHINA MINING GROUP INC
15310 Amberly Dr Ste 250 (33647-1642)
PHONE.................................813 514-2873
Guoqing Yue, *Ch of Bd*
Hongwen LI, *President*
Xinyu Peng, *CFO*
EMP: 92 **EST:** 2004
SALES (est): 1.1MM **Privately Held**
WEB: www.uschinamining.com
SIC: 1241 Coal mining exploration & test boring

(G-18227)
US ORTHOTICS INC
8605 Palm River Rd (33619-4317)
PHONE.................................813 621-7797
Anthony E Velazquez, *President*
EMP: 15 **EST:** 1979
SQ FT: 10,000
SALES (est): 2MM **Privately Held**
WEB: www.usorthotics.com
SIC: 3842 Orthopedic appliances

(G-18228)
US PATRIOT LLC
3108 N Boundary Blvd (33621-5050)
PHONE.................................803 787-9398
Phillips N Dee, *Branch Mgr*
EMP: 10
SALES (corp-wide): 83.1MM **Privately Held**
WEB: www.uspatriottactical.com
SIC: 2311 Military uniforms, men's & youths': purchased materials
PA: Us Patriot Llc
131 Berkshire Dr
Columbia SC 29223
800 805-5294

(G-18229)
USA EXTERIOR LLC
301 W Platt St Ste 144 (33606-2292)
PHONE.................................813 515-5181
Obi V Green,
EMP: 6 **EST:** 2011
SALES (est): 154.5K **Privately Held**
WEB: www.usaexterior.com
SIC: 2431 Window shutters, wood

(G-18230)
UVISORS
4919 W Bartlett Dr (33603-1606)
PHONE.................................813 716-1113
Todd Jackson, *Principal*
EMP: 7 **EST:** 2012
SALES (est): 112.3K **Privately Held**
SIC: 2657 Paperboard backs for blister or skin packages

(G-18231)
VADE MECUM PUBG GROUP LLC
4327 Honey Vista Cir (33624-6714)
PHONE.................................813 969-1623
Karl Klicker, *Principal*
EMP: 6 **EST:** 2010
SALES (est): 122K **Privately Held**
WEB: www.vademecumpublishing.com
SIC: 2741 Miscellaneous publishing

(G-18232)
VALCO GROUP INC
Also Called: Roll A Way
2203 N Lois Ave Ste 937 (33607-2318)
PHONE.................................813 870-0482
John Coffill, *President*
John Coffioll, *Chairman*
Lynn Conlen, *Admin Sec*
EMP: 150
SQ FT: 68,000
SALES (est): 13.8MM **Privately Held**
SIC: 3442 Shutters, door or window: metal

(G-18233)
VAN GOGH SIGNS & DISPLAYS
5020 N Florida Ave (33603-2122)
PHONE.................................813 849-7446
John Miller, *Owner*
EMP: 6 **EST:** 2005
SALES (est): 91.3K **Privately Held**
SIC: 3993 Signs & advertising specialties

(G-18234)
VASQUEZ CUSTOM METALS INC
3723 N 15th St (33610-8105)
PHONE.................................813 248-3348
EMP: 6 **EST:** 2019
SALES (est): 281.2K **Privately Held**
WEB: www.vasquezcustommetals.com
SIC: 3446 Architectural metalwork

(G-18235)
VECOM USA LLC
4803 George Rd Ste 300 (33634-6234)
PHONE.................................813 901-5300
J Vanstarrenburg,
Robert H Baaij,
Stephen Eifert,
EMP: 6 **EST:** 2004
SQ FT: 2,250
SALES (est): 973.9K **Privately Held**
WEB: www.irwincar.com
SIC: 3669 Intercommunication systems, electric

(G-18236)
VECTOR-SOLUTIONSCOM INC (PA)
Also Called: Vector Solutions
4890 W Kennedy Blvd # 30 (33609-1851)
PHONE.................................813 207-0012
Marc Scheipe, *CEO*
Denise Segalla, *CEO*
Kelly Cook, *Partner*
Kris Russell, *Editor*
John-Michael Larry, *Regional Mgr*
EMP: 25 **EST:** 2016
SALES (est): 90.1MM **Privately Held**
WEB: www.vectorsolutions.com
SIC: 7372 Educational computer software

(G-18237)
VERIFIED LABEL & PRINT INC
7905 Hopi Pl (33634-2418)
PHONE.................................813 290-7721
Raymond H Sikorski, *President*
Pamela Haley, *Project Mgr*
EMP: 12 **EST:** 1995
SQ FT: 4,500
SALES (est): 3.9MM **Privately Held**
WEB: www.verifiedlabel.com
SIC: 2752 Commercial printing, offset

(G-18238)
VERSATILE PACKAGERS LLC
933 Chad Ln Ste C (33619-4331)
PHONE.................................813 664-1171
Mike Gullinese, *Opers Mgr*
Scott Krajcir, *QC Mgr*
Julian Bossong,
EMP: 13 **EST:** 2009
SALES (est): 4.2MM **Privately Held**
WEB: www.versatilepackagers.com
SIC: 2679 Wrappers, paper (unprinted): made from purchased material

(G-18239)
VERSEA HOLDINGS INC
1000 N Florida Ave (33602-3808)
PHONE.................................800 397-0670
Sean Fetcho, *CEO*
Stephen Porada, *COO*
Joe Magnemi, *CFO*
Chris Duncan, *Ch Credit Ofcr*
Gary Lewandowsk, *Chief Mktg Ofcr*
EMP: 22 **EST:** 2019
SALES (est): 2.5MM **Privately Held**
WEB: www.versea.com
SIC: 2834 Pharmaceutical preparations

(G-18240)
VERTIMAX LLC
8108 Benjamin Rd Ste 201 (33634-2302)
PHONE.................................800 699-5867
Maureen Orourke, *CFO*
Michael Wehrell, *Mng Member*
Jason Hyber, *Manager*
Maureen O'Rourke,
◆ **EMP:** 9 **EST:** 1988
SQ FT: 2,500
SALES (est): 5.3MM **Privately Held**
WEB: www.vertimax.com
SIC: 3949 8331 Exercise equipment; skill training center

(G-18241)
VGCM LLC
Also Called: Tampa Yard
3510 Pendola Point Rd (33619-9525)
PHONE.................................813 247-7625
Myron Cantin, *Branch Mgr*
Burton Hershel, *Manager*
EMP: 10 **Publicly Held**
SIC: 1411 Dimension stone
HQ: Vgcm, Llc
1200 Urban Center Dr
Vestavia AL 35242

(G-18242)
VGCM LLC
Also Called: Port Canaveral Yard
2001 Maritime Blvd (33605-6760)
PHONE....................................813 620-4889
James Pease, *Manager*
EMP: 62 **Publicly Held**
SIC: 1411 Dimension stone
HQ: Vgcm, Llc
1200 Urban Center Dr
Vestavia AL 35242

(G-18243)
VIASAT INC
Also Called: Field Office
4211 W Boy Scout Blvd # 550
(33607-5928)
PHONE....................................813 880-5000
Fred Rhyne, *Principal*
John Ross, *Engineer*
Robert Jimenez, *Natl Sales Mgr*
Thomas Garner, *Software Engr*
Courtney Tilque, *Administration*
EMP: 6
SALES (corp-wide): 2.2B **Publicly Held**
WEB: www.viasat.com
SIC: 3663 Radio & TV communications equipment
PA: Viasat, Inc.
6155 El Camino Real
Carlsbad CA 92009
760 476-2200

(G-18244)
VICKERY AND COMPANY
7911 Professional Pl (33637-6747)
PHONE....................................813 987-2100
Dennis W Barber, *President*
Lindsay Barber, *Vice Pres*
Holly Barber, *Sales Staff*
Nathan Barber, *Manager*
EMP: 10 **EST:** 1944
SQ FT: 3,000
SALES (est): 1.6MM **Privately Held**
WEB: www.vickerycompany.com
SIC: 3561 5074 Pumps, domestic: water or sump; heating equipment (hydronic)

(G-18245)
VIDAL SHUTTERS AND BLINDS LLC
275 Byshore Blvd Unit 401 (33606)
PHONE....................................813 601-1068
Larry Vidal, *Manager*
EMP: 6 **EST:** 2019
SALES (est): 69.4K **Privately Held**
SIC: 2591 Window blinds

(G-18246)
VIDEO DISPLAY CORPORATION
13948 Lynmar Blvd (33626-3123)
PHONE....................................813 854-2259
Ronald D Ordway, *Branch Mgr*
EMP: 21
SALES (corp-wide): 12.5MM **Publicly Held**
WEB: www.videodisplay.com
SIC: 3679 Liquid crystal displays (LCD)
PA: Video Display Corporation
1868 Tucker Industrial Rd
Tucker GA 30084
770 938-2080

(G-18247)
VIGO IMPORTING COMPANY
Also Called: Can-America
4701 Tony Alessi Sr Ave (33614-5499)
P.O. Box 15584 (33684-5584)
PHONE....................................813 884-3491
Anthony Alessi, *President*
Alfred Alessi, *Vice Pres*
Fred Alessi, *Vice Pres*
Emilio Settecasi, *Prdtn Dir*
Dave Regaldo, *Plant Mgr*
◆ **EMP:** 187 **EST:** 1947
SQ FT: 165,000
SALES (est): 43.1MM **Privately Held**
WEB: www.vigo-alessi.com
SIC: 2099 2079 5149 5141 Rice, uncooked: packaged with other ingredients; bread crumbs, not made in bakeries; olive oil; specialty food items; groceries, general line

(G-18248)
VULCAN MATERIALS COMPANY
2001 Maritime Blvd (33605-6760)
PHONE....................................205 298-3000
Phil Dieulio, *Branch Mgr*
EMP: 17 **Publicly Held**
WEB: www.vulcanmaterials.com
SIC: 3273 Ready-mixed concrete
PA: Vulcan Materials Company
1200 Urban Center Dr
Vestavia AL 35242

(G-18249)
W & W MANUFACTURING CO
4504 E Hillsborough Ave (33610-5249)
PHONE....................................516 942-0011
Jeffrey Weitzman, *President*
Saundrice Lucas, *Administration*
▲ **EMP:** 26 **EST:** 1975
SALES (est): 1.9MM **Privately Held**
WEB: www.ww-manufacturing.com
SIC: 3691 3825 3663 Storage batteries; instruments to measure electricity; radio & TV communications equipment

(G-18250)
W D WILSON INC (PA)
Also Called: Wilson Msclineous Fabrications
3005 S 54th St (33619-6105)
PHONE....................................813 626-6989
William D Wilson, *President*
Jackie Wilson, *Treasurer*
EMP: 44 **EST:** 1985
SQ FT: 4,800
SALES (est): 2.8MM **Privately Held**
SIC: 3429 3441 3446 3444 Marine hardware; fabricated structural metal; architectural metalwork; sheet metalwork; fabricated plate work (boiler shop)

(G-18251)
WASHINGTON CL INC
Also Called: Washington Free Weekly
810 N Howard Ave (33606-1027)
PHONE....................................813 739-4800
Richard Gilbert, *CEO*
▲ **EMP:** 18 **EST:** 2007
SALES (est): 726.3K **Privately Held**
SIC: 2711 Newspapers: publishing only, not printed on site
HQ: Creative Loafing, Inc.
1911 N 13th St Ste W200
Tampa FL 33605

(G-18252)
WEEKLY PLANET OF SARASOTA INC
Also Called: Creative Loafing Sarasota
810 N Howard Ave (33606-1027)
PHONE....................................813 739-4800
Angela Lafon, *Principal*
EMP: 17 **EST:** 2008
SALES (est): 1MM **Privately Held**
SIC: 2711 Newspapers, publishing & printing
HQ: Creative Loafing, Inc.
1911 N 13th St Ste W200
Tampa FL 33605

(G-18253)
WEEKLY SCHULTE VALDES
1635 N Tampa St Ste 100 (33602-2629)
PHONE....................................813 221-1154
Christopher Schulte, *Principal*
Chris Schulte, *Mng Member*
Lauren Agnone, *Admin Asst*
Nellie Pawlowski, *Legal Staff*
Tyler Antar, *Associate*
EMP: 22 **EST:** 2009
SALES (est): 5.2MM **Privately Held**
WEB: www.wsvlegal.com
SIC: 2711 Newspapers

(G-18254)
WERE IN STITCHES
14807 N Florida Ave (33613-1825)
P.O. Box 2137, Lutz (33548-2137)
PHONE....................................813 264-4804
Molly Berberich, *President*
Peter Berberich, *Vice Pres*
▼ **EMP:** 6 **EST:** 1993
SQ FT: 1,500
SALES (est): 500K **Privately Held**
WEB: www.wereinstitches.com
SIC: 2395 Embroidery products, except schiffli machine

(G-18255)
WEST CENTRAL SIGNS INC
Also Called: Sign Star
3502 Queen Palm Dr Ste C (33619-1391)
PHONE....................................813 980-6763
Daniel V Powell, *President*
Theresa Powell, *Corp Secy*
Andrew Powell, *Vice Pres*
Robert D Powell, *Vice Pres*
Terri Mitchell, *Manager*
▼ **EMP:** 45
SALES (est): 5.9MM **Privately Held**
WEB: www.signstar.net
SIC: 3993 Neon signs

(G-18256)
WHITE MOP WRINGER COMPANY
10702 N 46th St (33617-3480)
PHONE....................................813 971-2223
Jeff Baker, *VP Mfg*
Thomas R Halluska, *CFO*
R Halluska, *CFO*
Bob Eukovich, *VP Sales*
Bob Schneider, *VP Sales*
EMP: 248 **EST:** 1986
SQ FT: 130,000
SALES (est): 10.2MM **Privately Held**
SIC: 3589 Commercial cleaning equipment; vacuum cleaners & sweepers, electric: industrial; floor washing & polishing machines, commercial; mop wringers

(G-18257)
WHITECAP PROMOTIONS LLC
2523 Cozumel Dr (33618-1901)
PHONE....................................813 960-4918
Brandon Jones,
Jim Denison,
EMP: 6 **EST:** 2010
SALES (est): 394.2K **Privately Held**
WEB: www.whitecap.com
SIC: 2759 Promotional printing

(G-18258)
WILBERT E BERAN
7025 Oakview Cir (33634-2248)
PHONE....................................813 882-0178
Wilbert Beran, *Principal*
EMP: 6 **EST:** 2010
SALES (est): 195.9K **Privately Held**
SIC: 3272 Burial vaults, concrete or precast terrazzo

(G-18259)
WILLSONET INC
Also Called: Cyber Security Solutions
2502 N Rocky Point Dr # 820
(33607-1421)
PHONE....................................813 336-8175
Horacio Maysonet, *CEO*
Thomas Williams, *CTO*
EMP: 30 **EST:** 2015
SALES (est): 2.5MM **Privately Held**
SIC: 7372 7373 7371 7379 Prepackaged software; computer integrated systems design; custom computer programming services; computer related consulting services

(G-18260)
WOOD PRODUCT SERVICES INC
2417 N 70th St (33619-2931)
P.O. Box 18063 (33679-8063)
PHONE....................................813 248-2221
Pedro Jimenez, *President*
Maria Jeminz, *Vice Pres*
EMP: 39 **EST:** 1998
SQ FT: 10,675
SALES (est): 3.7MM **Privately Held**
SIC: 2439 Trusses, wooden roof

(G-18261)
WOODWORKS OF TAMPA BAY LLC
333 N Falkenburg Rd B209 (33619-7892)
PHONE....................................813 330-5836
Karen Hall,
EMP: 6 **EST:** 2016
SALES (est): 81.3K **Privately Held**
WEB: www.woodworksoftampabayllc.com
SIC: 2431 Millwork

(G-18262)
WORKFORCE AUDIO INC
4821 N Grady Ave (33614-6513)
PHONE....................................866 360-6416
Mark Engel, *CEO*
EMP: 20 **EST:** 2018
SQ FT: 4,500
SALES (est): 1.2MM **Privately Held**
SIC: 3679 Electronic components

(G-18263)
WORLD POLITICS REVIEW LLC
825 S Orleans Ave (33606-2938)
P.O. Box 10398 (33679-0398)
PHONE....................................202 903-8398
Hampton Stephens, *Principal*
Judah Grunstein, *Manager*
EMP: 8 **EST:** 2016
SALES (est): 345.2K **Privately Held**
WEB: www.worldpoliticsreview.com
SIC: 2721 Periodicals

(G-18264)
WORLDGLASS CORPORATION
5600 Airport Blvd Ste C (33634-5315)
PHONE....................................813 609-2453
Dan Daniels, *President*
David Daniels, *Opers Staff*
EMP: 8 **EST:** 2007
SALES (est): 1.6MM **Privately Held**
WEB: www.danielscorporation.com
SIC: 3231 3751 Products of purchased glass; bicycles & related parts

(G-18265)
WORLDWIDE DOOR COMPONENTS INC (PA)
Also Called: World Wide Hardware
5017 N Coolidge Ave (33614-6421)
P.O. Box 262049 (33685-2049)
PHONE....................................813 870-0003
Jerry Monts De Oca, *President*
Mark Wheeler, *Sales Staff*
◆ **EMP:** 45 **EST:** 1985
SQ FT: 26,000
SALES (est): 9.5MM **Privately Held**
WEB: www.4everframe.com
SIC: 3442 Metal doors, sash & trim

(G-18266)
WORTHINGTON INDUSTRIES LLC
17501 Preserve Walk Ln (33647-3465)
PHONE....................................813 979-1000
Deborah H Need, *Principal*
EMP: 7 **EST:** 2015
SALES (est): 149.7K **Privately Held**
WEB: www.worthingtonindustries.com
SIC: 3999 Manufacturing industries

(G-18267)
WOW BUSINESS
400 N Tampa St Ste 1000 (33602-4714)
PHONE....................................813 301-2620
EMP: 12 **EST:** 2017
SALES (est): 2.1MM **Privately Held**
WEB: www.wowforbusiness.com
SIC: 2431 Doors, wood

(G-18268)
WURTH WOOD GROUP INC
5102 W Hanna Ave (33634-8020)
PHONE....................................800 432-1149
EMP: 14 **EST:** 2018
SALES (est): 326.2K **Privately Held**
WEB: www.wurthwoodgroup.com
SIC: 2499 Extension planks, wood

(G-18269)
WWS CONTRACTING LLC
142 W Platt St (33606-2315)
PHONE....................................813 868-3100
Tim Miller,
EMP: 30
SALES (est): 1.1MM **Privately Held**
SIC: 3589 Car washing machinery

(G-18270)
XCELIENCE LLC
5415 W Laurel St (33607-1729)
PHONE....................................813 286-0404
Derek G Hennecke, *President*
Sharon L Burgess, *Senior VP*
Theodore S Koontz, *Vice Pres*
Douglas J O'Dowd, *CFO*

GEOGRAPHIC

EMP: 50
SALES (corp-wide): 4.9B **Privately Held**
WEB: www.pharma.lonza.com
SIC: 2834 Powders, pharmaceutical; solutions, pharmaceutical
HQ: Xcelience, Llc
4910 Savarese Cir
Tampa FL 33634

(G-18271)
XCELIENCE LLC
4901 W Grace St (33607-3805)
PHONE..................................813 286-0404
Derek G Hennecke, *President*
Sharon L Burgess, *Senior VP*
Theodore S Koontz, *Vice Pres*
Douglas J O'Dowd, *CFO*
EMP: 50
SALES (corp-wide): 4.9B **Privately Held**
WEB: www.pharma.lonza.com
SIC: 2834 Powders, pharmaceutical; solutions, pharmaceutical
HQ: Xcelience, Llc
4910 Savarese Cir
Tampa FL 33634

(G-18272)
XCELIENCE LLC (DH)
4910 Savarese Cir (33634-2403)
PHONE..................................813 286-0404
Derek G Hennecke, *CEO*
Lindon Fellows, *COO*
Sharon L Burgess, *Senior VP*
Joseph Iacobucci, *Vice Pres*
Paul F Skultety-Phd, *Vice Pres*
EMP: 55 **EST:** 2006
SQ FT: 50,000
SALES (est): 26.3MM
SALES (corp-wide): 4.9B **Privately Held**
WEB: www.pharma.lonza.com
SIC: 2834 Chlorination tablets & kits (water purification)
HQ: Xcelience Holdings, Llc
4910 Savarese Cir
Tampa FL 33634
813 286-0404

(G-18273)
XCELIENCE HOLDINGS LLC (DH)
4910 Savarese Cir (33634-2403)
PHONE..................................813 286-0404
Derek G Hennecke, *President*
Lindon Fellows, *COO*
Douglas J O'Dowd, *CFO*
▲ **EMP:** 100 **EST:** 2006
SALES (est): 26.3MM
SALES (corp-wide): 4.9B **Privately Held**
WEB: www.pharma.lonza.com
SIC: 2834 Chlorination tablets & kits (water purification)

(G-18274)
YOGURTOLOGY
3017 W Gandy Blvd (33611-2825)
PHONE..................................813 839-4200
Nikki Manecke, *General Mgr*
EMP: 8 **EST:** 2013
SALES (est): 314.2K **Privately Held**
WEB: www.yogurtology.com
SIC: 2026 Yogurt

(G-18275)
YOGURTOLOGY
12400 N Dale Mabry Hwy B (33618-3493)
PHONE..................................813 969-2500
EMP: 7 **EST:** 2012
SALES (est): 254.1K **Privately Held**
WEB: www.yogurtology.com
SIC: 2026 Yogurt

(G-18276)
YOGURTOLOGY
7889 Gunn Hwy (33626-1611)
PHONE..................................813 926-9090
Dianne Heady, *Branch Mgr*
EMP: 7 **EST:** 2011
SALES (est): 226.6K **Privately Held**
SIC: 2026 Yogurt

(G-18277)
YOUR NAME PRINTING
6502 N 54th St (33610-1908)
PHONE..................................813 621-2400
Christine M Fitzgibbon, *Owner*
Scott E Poindexter, *Owner*
EMP: 7 **EST:** 2018
SALES (est): 727.6K **Privately Held**
WEB: www.yournameprinting.com
SIC: 2752 Commercial printing, offset

(G-18278)
YOUR NAME PRTG ENVLOPE MFG INC (PA)
508 Hobbs St (33619-8000)
PHONE..................................813 643-1443
Christine Fitzgibbon, *President*
Scott Poindexter, *Vice Pres*
EMP: 5 **EST:** 1997
SQ FT: 8,200
SALES (est): 1.5MM **Privately Held**
WEB: www.yournameprinting.com
SIC: 2621 Stationery, envelope & tablet papers

(G-18279)
Z & L PARTNERS INC
Also Called: Image360 South Tampa
4920 W Cypress St Ste 100 (33607-3837)
PHONE..................................813 639-0066
Zachary R Davis, *President*
Leslie M Davis, *Vice Pres*
Octavia Williams, *Manager*
Zach Davis, *Info Tech Mgr*
EMP: 5 **EST:** 2002
SQ FT: 2,000
SALES (est): 360K **Privately Held**
SIC: 3993 Signs & advertising specialties

(G-18280)
ZENNERGY LLC
3918 N Highland Ave (33603-4724)
PHONE..................................813 382-3460
John Venzon, *CEO*
Stephen Tarte, *Chairman*
Jeff Tarte, *Exec VP*
Sheila Tarte, *CFO*
Mike Brock, *Controller*
EMP: 10 **EST:** 2015
SALES (est): 611.5K **Privately Held**
WEB: www.zennergyllc.com
SIC: 3492 3531 Control valves, fluid power: hydraulic & pneumatic; backhoe mounted, hydraulically powered attachments

Tarpon Springs
Pinellas County

(G-18281)
A & B OF TARPON CORPORATION
40200 Us Highway 19 N (34689-4836)
PHONE..................................727 940-5333
Ibrahim Abde, *Principal*
Don Neher, *COO*
EMP: 21 **EST:** 2012
SALES (est): 126.9K **Privately Held**
SIC: 3565 Packaging machinery

(G-18282)
ALTA PHARMA LLC
1245 N Florida Ave (34689-2003)
PHONE..................................727 942-7645
George Bobotas, *Manager*
EMP: 6 **EST:** 2010
SALES (est): 232K **Privately Held**
SIC: 2834 Pharmaceutical preparations

(G-18283)
B&B CUSTOM SHEET METAL INC
770 N Grosse Ave Ste B (34689-4001)
PHONE..................................727 938-8083
James A Housh, *President*
Matthew B Housh, *Vice Pres*
Rebecca M Housh, *CFO*
EMP: 6 **EST:** 2004
SALES (est): 524.6K **Privately Held**
WEB: www.bbcustomsheetmetal.com
SIC: 3444 Sheet metalwork

(G-18284)
BOB LAFERRIERE AIRCRAFT INC
2769 Saint Andrews Blvd (34688-6312)
PHONE..................................727 709-2704
Robert J Laferriere, *Principal*
EMP: 6 **EST:** 2010
SALES (est): 70.2K **Privately Held**
SIC: 3721 Aircraft

(G-18285)
C DYER DEVELOPMENT GROUP LLC
1125 Lake St (34689-5512)
PHONE..................................727 423-6169
Chasen Dyer, *Principal*
EMP: 7 **EST:** 2015
SALES (est): 230.9K **Privately Held**
WEB: www.cdyerdevelopmentgroup.com
SIC: 3842 Traction apparatus

(G-18286)
CARIBONGO
735 Ddecanese Blvd Ste 35 (34689)
PHONE..................................727 944-5200
Ann Fried, *Principal*
EMP: 6 **EST:** 2007
SALES (est): 92.3K **Privately Held**
WEB: www.caribongo.com
SIC: 2759 Screen printing

(G-18287)
CAROL PRINTING CORPORATION
373 Wood Dove Ave (34689-7530)
PHONE..................................631 315-5061
Martin Egeland, *Principal*
EMP: 7 **EST:** 2010
SALES (est): 122.1K **Privately Held**
SIC: 2752 Commercial printing, offset

(G-18288)
CASCO SERVICES INC
Also Called: Architectural Metal Works
153 E Oakwood St (34689-3645)
PHONE..................................727 942-1888
Conrad Shrader, *President*
Heather Seiter, *Admin Sec*
EMP: 16 **EST:** 1988
SQ FT: 9,000
SALES (est): 800K **Privately Held**
SIC: 3446 Architectural metalwork

(G-18289)
CHEANY INC
Also Called: Sonic Print
119 E Tarpon Ave (34689-3451)
PHONE..................................813 443-5271
Zac Sitzberger, *CEO*
Brian Cheaney, *President*
Ray Banacki, *Site Mgr*
Alisa Bowles, *Sales Staff*
Steven Lacks, *Marketing Mgr*
EMP: 9 **EST:** 2000
SALES (est): 5.8MM **Privately Held**
WEB: www.sonicprint.com
SIC: 2752 Commercial printing, offset
PA: Keys And Lanier, Llc
425 E Spruce St
Tarpon Springs FL 34689
866 357-1333

(G-18290)
CREATIVE WOODWORKING CONCEPTS
905 Rivo Pl (34689-4141)
PHONE..................................727 937-4165
William M Shadrick, *President*
Daniel Beltram, *Corp Secy*
Harry Roenick, *Vice Pres*
Mark Pikulski, *Opers Staff*
Nancy Anderson, *Office Mgr*
EMP: 25 **EST:** 1984
SQ FT: 20,000
SALES (est): 4.1MM **Privately Held**
WEB: www.cwcwood.com
SIC: 2431 2521 Millwork; cabinets, office: wood

(G-18291)
CRUSTYS BREAD BAKERY
438 Athens St (34689-3161)
PHONE..................................727 937-9041
Monica L Canales, *Principal*
EMP: 6 **EST:** 2002
SQ FT: 3,550
SALES (est): 167.6K **Privately Held**
WEB:
www.crustybreadbakery.myfreesites.net
SIC: 2051 Bread, cake & related products

(G-18292)
DECON USA
15 Central Ct (34689-3209)
PHONE..................................440 610-5009
EMP: 7 **EST:** 2014
SALES (est): 159.8K **Privately Held**
WEB: www.jordahlusa.com
SIC: 3444 Sheet metalwork

(G-18293)
DELICAE GOURMET LLC
1310 E Lake Dr (34688-8110)
PHONE..................................727 942-2502
Barbara Macaluso, *Owner*
Meg Scott, *Sales Staff*
EMP: 7 **EST:** 1997
SQ FT: 4,000
SALES (est): 750K **Privately Held**
WEB: www.delicaegourmet.com
SIC: 2099 Food preparations

(G-18294)
DEMELLE BIOPHARMA LLC
1245 N Florida Ave (34689-2003)
PHONE..................................908 240-8939
George Bobotas,
Maria Bobotas,
Demetra Dukas,
Abdel A Fawzy,
Eleni Lelekis,
EMP: 5 **EST:** 2008
SALES (est): 335K **Privately Held**
WEB: www.demellebiopharma.com
SIC: 2834 7389 Pharmaceutical preparations;

(G-18295)
DORADO CUSTOM BOATS LLC
1400 L And R Indus Blvd (34689-6807)
PHONE..................................727 786-3800
Andrea Garcia, *Controller*
EMP: 10 **EST:** 2011
SALES (est): 720.6K **Privately Held**
WEB: www.doradocustomboats.com
SIC: 3732 Boat building & repairing

(G-18296)
DUCKWORTH STEEL BOATS INC
1051 Island Ave (34689-6917)
PHONE..................................727 934-2550
Ernest Duckworth, *President*
Paul J Raymond, *Admin Sec*
EMP: 5 **EST:** 1979
SQ FT: 10,000
SALES (est): 651K **Privately Held**
WEB: www.duckboats.tripod.com
SIC: 3732 Boat building & repairing

(G-18297)
EAGLE ATHLETIC WEAR INC (PA)
Also Called: Graphics Screen Printing & EMB
720 E Tarpon Ave (34689-4250)
PHONE..................................727 937-6147
Imar Tzekas, *Ch of Bd*
Jim Ismaili, *President*
John Ismaili, *Vice Pres*
EMP: 10 **EST:** 1982
SQ FT: 13,000
SALES (est): 803.3K **Privately Held**
SIC: 2396 2395 5199 Screen printing on fabric articles; embroidery products, except schiffli machine; advertising specialties

(G-18298)
EAGLE EYE GLOBAL TRACKING LLC
39620 Us Highway 19 N (34689-7912)
PHONE..................................727 399-6888
William Stathopolous, *Principal*
EMP: 6 **EST:** 2012
SALES (est): 126.3K **Privately Held**
WEB: www.birdseyeglobaltracking.com
SIC: 3651 Electronic kits for home assembly: radio, TV, phonograph

(G-18299)
ENG MANUFACTURING INC
773 Wesley Ave (34689-6711)
PHONE..................................727 942-3868
Emanuel Ginnis, *President*
Jeannette Ginnis, *CFO*
Janelle McCarthy, *Natl Sales Mgr*
EMP: 6 **EST:** 2002

SALES (est): 687.8K **Privately Held**
WEB: www.engwelding.com
SIC: 7692 1622 Welding repair; bridge, tunnel & elevated highway

(G-18300)
F O F PLASTICS INC
1614 Tallahassee Dr (34689-2242)
PHONE..................................727 937-2144
EMP: 6
SALES (est): 480K **Privately Held**
SIC: 2821 Mfg Plastic Products

(G-18301)
FLORIDA DREDGE AND DOCK LLC
1040 Island Ave (34689-6916)
PHONE..................................727 942-7888
Messinger Bruce, *Vice Pres*
Travis Fletcher, *Manager*
William D Fletcher,
Chester E Fletcher,
EMP: 28 **EST:** 2006
SQ FT: 2,000
SALES (est): 2.6MM **Privately Held**
WEB: www.floridadredge.com
SIC: 3731 Dredges, building & repairing

(G-18302)
GAUSE BUILT MARINE INC
728 Wesley Ave Ste 10 (34689-6749)
PHONE..................................727 937-9113
David Gause, *Principal*
EMP: 24 **EST:** 2002
SALES (est): 1.1MM **Privately Held**
WEB: www.gausebuiltboats.com
SIC: 3732 Sailboats, building & repairing

(G-18303)
GRAPHIX SCREEN PRINTING
720 E Tarpon Ave (34689-4250)
PHONE..................................727 937-6147
John Ismili, *Vice Pres*
EMP: 6 **EST:** 1997
SALES (est): 162.1K **Privately Held**
WEB: www.graphixscreenprinting.com
SIC: 2759 Screen printing

(G-18304)
GUARDIAN SOLAR LLC
764 Anclote Rd Ste A (34689-6764)
PHONE..................................727 504-2790
Glen D Upchurch, *President*
▲ **EMP:** 12 **EST:** 2007
SALES (est): 1.9MM **Privately Held**
WEB: www.guardiansolar.com
SIC: 3674 Solar cells

(G-18305)
HART GRAPHICS
1307 E Lemon St (34689-5422)
PHONE..................................727 938-7018
Joyce A Hartman, *Principal*
EMP: 7 **EST:** 2003
SALES (est): 130K **Privately Held**
SIC: 2752 Commercial printing, lithographic

(G-18306)
HENDERSON PRESTRESS CON INC
822 Anclote Rd (34689-6699)
PHONE..................................727 938-2828
Dirk V Henderson, *President*
EMP: 10 **EST:** 1987
SQ FT: 2,000
SALES (est): 1.5MM **Privately Held**
WEB: www.hendersonprestressedconcrete.com
SIC: 3272 Piling, prefabricated concrete

(G-18307)
HOPKINS MANUFACTURING CO
855 Pine St (34689-5902)
PHONE..................................620 591-8229
EMP: 6 **EST:** 2018
SALES (est): 94.6K **Privately Held**
WEB: www.hopkinsmfg.com
SIC: 3999 Manufacturing industries

(G-18308)
HTH ENGINEERING INC
Also Called: Start Stop.com
825 Cypress Trails Dr (34688-9044)
P.O. Box 855, Elfers (34680-0855)
PHONE..................................727 939-8853
Joe Winner, *President*
EMP: 20 **EST:** 1987
SALES (est): 1.8MM **Privately Held**
WEB: www.startstop.com
SIC: 3579 5044 Dictating machines; dictating machines

(G-18309)
IMAGINE THAT INC
Also Called: Architectural Metal Works
155 E Oakwood St (34689-3645)
PHONE..................................813 728-8324
Kristy Seiter, *President*
EMP: 15 **EST:** 2015
SALES (est): 1MM **Privately Held**
WEB: www.imaginethatinmetal.com
SIC: 3441 Fabricated structural metal

(G-18310)
JABM ADVISORS INC
2839 Grey Oaks Blvd (34688-8159)
PHONE..................................727 458-3755
Kevin Jajuga, *Principal*
EMP: 8 **EST:** 2019
SALES (est): 248.4K **Privately Held**
SIC: 3732 Boat building & repairing

(G-18311)
JRL SERVICE CO
332 Anclote Rd (34689-6909)
PHONE..................................727 243-4734
John Lendell, *Principal*
EMP: 6 **EST:** 2012
SALES (est): 108.3K **Privately Held**
SIC: 3519 Outboard motors

(G-18312)
KNIGHTS POWDER COATING LLC
712 Wesley Ave (34689-6729)
PHONE..................................727 906-5130
Michael Knight, *Principal*
EMP: 6 **EST:** 2016
SALES (est): 90.1K **Privately Held**
SIC: 2952 Asphalt felts & coatings

(G-18313)
LIQUID ED INC
740 Wesley Ave (34689-6710)
PHONE..................................727 943-8616
Russell G Armitage, *President*
Russell G Armitade, *President*
EMP: 5 **EST:** 1984
SQ FT: 8,000
SALES (est): 553.5K **Privately Held**
SIC: 3949 5091 Golf equipment; golf equipment

(G-18314)
M & C ASSEMBLIES INC
904 Live Oak St (34689-4140)
P.O. Box 1738, Oldsmar (34677-1738)
PHONE..................................800 462-7779
Dixie Eklund, *CEO*
A Clifton Cannon Jr, *President*
EMP: 600 **EST:** 1991
SQ FT: 11,000
SALES (est): 24.9MM **Privately Held**
WEB: www.mcassemblies.com
SIC: 3432 Plastic plumbing fixture fittings, assembly

(G-18315)
MARRAKECH INC
Also Called: Express
720 Wesley Ave Ste 10 (34689-6746)
PHONE..................................727 942-2218
Shirley Cooperman, *President*
Steen Sigmund, *Vice Pres*
◆ **EMP:** 8 **EST:** 1979
SQ FT: 8,000
SALES (est): 643.1K **Privately Held**
WEB: www.marrak.com
SIC: 2752 Commercial printing, offset

(G-18316)
NEIGHBORHOOD NEWS & LIFESTYLES
220 S Safford Ave (34689-3648)
PHONE..................................727 943-0551
Tim Selby, *President*
EMP: 10 **EST:** 2006
SALES (est): 310.6K **Privately Held**
WEB: www.tbnewsandlifestyles.com
SIC: 2711 Newspapers, publishing & printing

(G-18317)
NP INDUSTRIAL COATING INC
631 Baynard Dr (34689-2259)
PHONE..................................727 485-6113
Nikolaos Papadimitriou, *Principal*
EMP: 6 **EST:** 2016
SALES (est): 66.8K **Privately Held**
SIC: 2952 Asphalt felts & coatings

(G-18318)
OXZGEN INC
40180 Us Highway 19 N (34689-8334)
PHONE..................................844 569-9436
EMP: 9 **EST:** 2002
SALES (est): 145K **Privately Held**
WEB: www.oxzgen.com
SIC: 3999

(G-18319)
PAPOUS CRAFT DISTILLERY LLC
Also Called: Tarpon Springs Distillery
605 N Pinellas Ave (34689-3343)
PHONE..................................813 766-9539
Barry Butler, *President*
EMP: 7 **EST:** 2018
SALES (est): 439.6K **Privately Held**
WEB: www.tarponspringsdistillery.net
SIC: 2085 Distilled & blended liquors

(G-18320)
PLASTIC CONCEPTS LTD INC
1456 L And R Indus Blvd (34689-6808)
P.O. Box 400 (34688-0400)
PHONE..................................727 942-6684
Peter Karantonis, *President*
EMP: 16 **EST:** 1990
SQ FT: 18,000
SALES (est): 656.4K **Privately Held**
SIC: 3089 Injection molding of plastics

(G-18321)
PRECISION AUTO TINT DSIGN CORP
Also Called: Precision Window Films
746 Haven Pl (34689-4809)
PHONE..................................727 385-8788
Christopher Paine, *President*
EMP: 5 **EST:** 2008
SALES (est): 600K **Privately Held**
SIC: 3993 1799 3211 Signs & advertising specialties; fiberglass work; flat glass

(G-18322)
READING TRUCK BODY LLC
1476 L And R Indus Blvd (34689-6809)
PHONE..................................727 943-8911
Alan Farash, *President*
Stephanie Lane, *Human Resources*
EMP: 20
SALES (corp-wide): 1.3B **Privately Held**
WEB: www.readingtruck.com
SIC: 3713 7532 5531 Truck bodies (motor vehicles); body shop, trucks; automotive accessories; automotive parts
HQ: Reading Truck Body, Llc
201 Hancock Blvd
Reading PA 19611
610 775-3301

(G-18323)
READING TRUCK BODY LLC
1476 L&R Industrial Blvd (34689)
PHONE..................................727 943-8911
Alan Farash, *President*
EMP: 25
SALES (corp-wide): 1.3B **Privately Held**
WEB: www.readingtruck.com
SIC: 3713 3444 Truck beds; truck bodies (motor vehicles); sheet metalwork
HQ: Reading Truck Body, Llc
201 Hancock Blvd
Reading PA 19611
610 775-3301

(G-18324)
SEITER ENTERPRISES INC
155 E Oakwood St (34689-3645)
P.O. Box 3116, Holiday (34692-0116)
PHONE..................................813 728-8324
Kristy Seiter, *President*
EMP: 11 **EST:** 2009
SALES (est): 291.8K **Privately Held**
WEB: www.imaginethatinmetal.com
SIC: 3499 Fabricated metal products

(G-18325)
SPONGE MERCHANT INTERNATIONAL
1028 Peninsula Ave (34689-2126)
PHONE..................................727 919-3523
George Billiris, *Principal*
EMP: 7 **EST:** 2001
SALES (est): 94.1K **Privately Held**
SIC: 3842 Sponges, surgical

(G-18326)
STAMAS YACHT INC
300 Pampas Ave (34689-3299)
PHONE..................................727 937-4118
John P Stamas, *President*
George P Stamas, *Treasurer*
EMP: 70 **EST:** 1952
SQ FT: 100,000
SALES (est): 8.9MM **Privately Held**
WEB: www.stamas.com
SIC: 3732 Boats, fiberglass: building & repairing

(G-18327)
SUN-ROCK INC
904 Anclote Rd (34689-6627)
PHONE..................................727 938-0013
Edmund Windstrup, *President*
Dan Windstrup, *Vice Pres*
Barbara Windstrup, *Treasurer*
EMP: 16 **EST:** 1969
SQ FT: 6,400
SALES (est): 1MM **Privately Held**
WEB: www.sun-rock.com
SIC: 3299 Moldings, architectural: plaster of paris

(G-18328)
TARPON STNLESS FABRICATORS INC
Also Called: T S F
911 Rivo Pl Ste B (34689-4141)
PHONE..................................727 942-1821
Daniel Beltram, *President*
EMP: 28 **EST:** 1987
SQ FT: 17,000
SALES (est): 5.2MM **Privately Held**
SIC: 3444 Restaurant sheet metalwork

(G-18329)
VAC CUBES INC
536 E Tarpon Ave Ste 5 (34689-4344)
PHONE..................................727 944-3337
Susan Kroupa, *President*
Larry Kroupa, *President*
Nicholas Kroupa, *Treasurer*
EMP: 6 **EST:** 1985
SALES (est): 519.5K **Privately Held**
WEB: www.vac-cube.com
SIC: 3563 Air & gas compressors including vacuum pumps

(G-18330)
WEEHOO INC
803 Whitcomb Blvd (34689-2649)
PHONE..................................720 477-3700
Stephen M Rodgers, *Principal*
▲ **EMP:** 5 **EST:** 2008
SALES (est): 891.3K **Privately Held**
WEB: www.rideweehoo.com
SIC: 3429 Bicycle racks, automotive

(G-18331)
WEST FLORIDA PRECISION MCH LLC
728 Anclote Rd (34689-6703)
PHONE..................................727 939-0030
Chip Mortensen, *President*
Charles E Mortensen Jr, *President*

GEOGRAPHIC

Dan Mortensen, *Engineer*
Barbara Mortensen, *Office Mgr*
Carlton R Swick, *Mng Member*
EMP: 11 **EST:** 2009
SQ FT: 11,000
SALES (est): 1MM **Privately Held**
WEB: www.wfpmachine.com
SIC: 3599 Machine shop, jobbing & repair

Tavares
Lake County

(G-18332)
1ST VERTICAL BLIND COMPANY
Also Called: 1st Vertical Blind Factory
207 E Burleigh Blvd (32778-2403)
PHONE..................................352 343-3363
Joseph Pesce, *President*
William Larry Edwards, *Vice Pres*
Gwen Pesce, *Treasurer*
EMP: 6 **EST:** 1983
SALES (est): 423.1K **Privately Held**
SIC: 2591 Blinds vertical

(G-18333)
ACROTURN INDUSTRIES USA LLC
4640 Lake Industrial Blvd (32778-9510)
PHONE..................................754 205-7178
Slavko Grguric, *CEO*
EMP: 13 **EST:** 2014
SALES (est): 308.8K **Privately Held**
WEB: www.acroturn.com
SIC: 3999 Manufacturing industries

(G-18334)
ANGLE TRUSS CO INC
29652 State Road 19 (32778-4248)
P.O. Box 1091 (32778-1091)
PHONE..................................352 343-7477
Mario Caropreso, *President*
Paul Caropreso, *Treasurer*
EMP: 11 **EST:** 1975
SQ FT: 1,100
SALES (est): 2.3MM **Privately Held**
WEB: www.angletruss.com
SIC: 2439 Trusses, wooden roof

(G-18335)
EAGLE QUALITY COMPONENTS LLC
280 Hummer Way (32778-9761)
P.O. Box 1618 (32778-1618)
PHONE..................................352 516-4838
Anthony Soos, *Mng Member*
EMP: 12 **EST:** 2011
SQ FT: 7,000
SALES (est): 1MM **Privately Held**
WEB: www.eaglequality.net
SIC: 3599 Machine shop, jobbing & repair

(G-18336)
EXPERT MOLD REMOVAL INC
14929 Lenze Dr (32778-9786)
PHONE..................................407 925-6443
Roger Lewis, *Principal*
EMP: 8 **EST:** 2010
SALES (est): 143K **Privately Held**
WEB: www.expertmoldtestingfl.com
SIC: 3544 Industrial molds

(G-18337)
FLORIDA TRIDENT TRADING LLC
Also Called: Florida Trading Company
3801 State Road 19 (32778-4234)
PHONE..................................352 253-1400
Fax: 352 253-1402
EMP: 14
SQ FT: 14,000
SALES (est): 2.1MM **Privately Held**
SIC: 3732 Boatbuilding/Repairing

(G-18338)
GELANDER INDUSTRIES INC
611 Southridge Indl Dr (32778)
PHONE..................................352 343-3100
Kim Sechler, *President*
Robert J Sechler, *Vice Pres*
▼ **EMP:** 16 **EST:** 1986
SQ FT: 3,200
SALES (est): 4.1MM **Privately Held**
WEB: www.gelanderindustries.com
SIC: 3446 Railings, prefabricated metal

(G-18339)
GREASE TEC HOLDING LLC
28615 Lake Indus Blvd (32778-9741)
PHONE..................................352 742-2440
Hank Fisher, *President*
EMP: 6 **EST:** 1994
SQ FT: 1,500
SALES (est): 750K **Privately Held**
SIC: 2079 Cooking oils, except corn: vegetable refined

(G-18340)
GWS TOOL LLC
Also Called: Gw Schultz Tool
595 County Road 448 (32778-6109)
PHONE..................................352 343-8778
Greg Schultz, *President*
Chris Schulte, *General Mgr*
Adam Lafferty, *Exec VP*
Drew Strauchen, *Vice Pres*
Ryan Morin, *Mfg Staff*
▲ **EMP:** 14 **EST:** 1990
SQ FT: 16,000
SALES (est): 5.3MM
SALES (corp-wide): 40.3MM **Privately Held**
WEB: www.gwstoolgroup.com
SIC: 3545 3479 Diamond cutting tools for turning, boring, burnishing, etc.; etching & engraving
PA: Gws Tool Holdings, Llc
595 County Road 448
Tavares FL 32778
352 343-8778

(G-18341)
GWS TOOL HOLDINGS LLC (PA)
Also Called: Gws Tool Group
595 County Road 448 (32778-6109)
PHONE..................................352 343-8778
Rick McIntyre, *CEO*
Kevin Zimmerman, *Exec VP*
EMP: 32 **EST:** 2014
SALES (est): 40.3MM **Privately Held**
WEB: www.gwstoolgroup.com
SIC: 3545 Precision measuring tools

(G-18342)
HDH AGRI PRODUCTS LLC
27536 County Road 561 (32778-9460)
PHONE..................................352 343-3484
Helen A Sanders,
Paul R Leonard,
▼ **EMP:** 6 **EST:** 2006
SALES (est): 711.4K **Privately Held**
WEB: www.hdhagriproducts.com
SIC: 3565 Packaging machinery

(G-18343)
J F V DESIGNS INC
Also Called: Veneer Source
220 Southridge Indus Dr (32778-9126)
PHONE..................................321 228-7469
Jeffrey Vaida, *President*
EMP: 10 **EST:** 1992
SQ FT: 6,000
SALES (est): 915.2K **Privately Held**
WEB: www.jfvdesigns.com
SIC: 2521 Wood office furniture

(G-18344)
KIRTECH ENTERPRISES INC
Also Called: Blue Sky Die Company
28210 Lake Indus Blvd (32778-9742)
PHONE..................................352 742-7222
Rudolph Kirst, *President*
Marilyn Kirst, *Corp Secy*
EMP: 12 **EST:** 1984
SQ FT: 12,000
SALES (est): 1.8MM **Privately Held**
WEB: www.blueskydie.com
SIC: 3544 Special dies & tools

(G-18345)
LEGACY VULCAN CORP
Also Called: Vulcan Materials
27222 County Road 561 (32778-9459)
P.O. Box 176, Astatula (34705-0176)
PHONE..................................352 742-2122
EMP: 9
SALES (corp-wide): 2.9B **Publicly Held**
SIC: 1442 Construction Sand/Gravel
HQ: Legacy Vulcan, Llc
1200 Urban Center Dr
Vestavia AL 35242
205 298-3000

(G-18346)
M A K MANUFACTURING INC
13742 County Road 448 (32778-9422)
PHONE..................................352 343-5881
Leonard Barrett, *Owner*
EMP: 8 **EST:** 1995
SALES (est): 105.1K **Privately Held**
WEB: www.makmanufacturing.com
SIC: 3535 Conveyors & conveying equipment

(G-18347)
MAKM ANUFACTURING INC
13742 County Road 448 (32778-9422)
PHONE..................................352 343-5881
EMP: 6 **EST:** 2019
SALES (est): 331.7K **Privately Held**
SIC: 3999 Manufacturing industries

(G-18348)
MILLWORK PLUS INC
262 Hummer Way (32778-9761)
P.O. Box 14 (32778-0014)
PHONE..................................352 343-2121
Roy A Comer Jr, *President*
EMP: 6 **EST:** 2000
SALES (est): 505.7K **Privately Held**
WEB: www.millworkplus.us
SIC: 2431 Millwork

(G-18349)
MITTS AND MERRILL LP
28623 Lake Indus Blvd (32778-9741)
PHONE..................................352 343-7001
Maschinfabrik Fromag, *Partner*
Jim Barrett, *General Mgr*
▲ **EMP:** 7 **EST:** 1992
SQ FT: 10,000
SALES (est): 2.4MM
SALES (corp-wide): 1.8MM **Privately Held**
WEB: www.mitts-merrill.com
SIC: 3541 3545 3544 Machine tools, metal cutting: exotic (explosive, etc.); machine tool accessories; special dies, tools, jigs & fixtures
HQ: Maschinenfabrik Fromag Gmbh & Co. Kg
Am Klingelbach 2
Frondenberg/Ruhr 58730
237 375-60

(G-18350)
PALMATE LLC
Also Called: Florida Extracts
200 County Road 448 (32778-6123)
PHONE..................................352 508-7800
Jeff Field, *President*
EMP: 24 **EST:** 2019
SALES (est): 2.5MM **Privately Held**
SIC: 2833 2834 Medicinals & botanicals; extracts of botanicals: powdered, pilular, solid or fluid

(G-18351)
PROGRESSIVE AERODYNE INC
3801 State Road 19 (32778-4234)
PHONE..................................352 253-0108
Kerry Richter, *President*
Paige Lynette, *Vice Pres*
Chuck Matthews, *Human Res Mgr*
Kevin Oaks, *Marketing Staff*
Wayne Richter, *Admin Sec*
EMP: 9 **EST:** 1993
SQ FT: 10,000
SALES (est): 1MM **Privately Held**
WEB: www.searey.com
SIC: 3721 Aircraft

(G-18352)
SENTINEL CMMNCTONS NEWS VNTRES
Also Called: Lake Sentinel
2012 Classique Ln (32778-5787)
PHONE..................................352 742-5900
Denise Lewis, *Manager*
EMP: 9
SALES (corp-wide): 4.5B **Publicly Held**
WEB: www.orlandosentinel.com
SIC: 2711 2741 Commercial printing & newspaper publishing combined; miscellaneous publishing
HQ: Sentinel Communications News Ventures Inc.
633 N Orange Ave
Orlando FL 32801
407 420-5000

(G-18353)
SOUTHRIDGE OUTDOOR STORAGE
595 County Road 448 (32778-6109)
PHONE..................................352 516-5598
Lauren Schultz, *Principal*
EMP: 7 **EST:** 2005
SALES (est): 233.2K **Privately Held**
SIC: 3599 Industrial machinery

(G-18354)
SPENCER FABRICATIONS INC
29511 County Road 561 (32778-9492)
PHONE..................................352 343-0014
Greg S Leonard, *President*
Mark E Fogarty, *Principal*
Jay Persaud, *COO*
Kawal G Persaud, *COO*
Paula M Andrews, *Vice Pres*
EMP: 20 **EST:** 1994
SALES (est): 2.5MM **Privately Held**
WEB: www.spenfab.com
SIC: 3443 3444 3441 Fabricated plate work (boiler shop); sheet metalwork; fabricated structural metal

(G-18355)
TRIDENT PONTOONS INC
28240 Lake Indus Blvd (32778-9742)
PHONE..................................352 253-1400
Robert H Cunningham III, *Principal*
EMP: 8 **EST:** 2012
SALES (est): 782.3K **Privately Held**
WEB: www.tridentpontoons.com
SIC: 3731 Ferryboats, building & repairing

(G-18356)
US CONVEYOR SOLUTIONS INC
3714 County Road 561 (32778-9497)
PHONE..................................352 343-0085
Larry Schumacher, *President*
EMP: 15 **EST:** 2001
SQ FT: 7,500
SALES (est): 3.2MM **Privately Held**
WEB: www.southernconveyor.net
SIC: 3535 Conveyors & conveying equipment

(G-18357)
US SECURITY DEFENSE CORP
1181 E Alfred St (32778-3474)
P.O. Box 590122, Orlando (32859-0122)
PHONE..................................407 979-1478
Angel Rodriguez, *CEO*
EMP: 50 **EST:** 2019
SALES (est): 2.7MM **Privately Held**
SIC: 3484 Guns (firearms) or gun parts, 30 mm. & below

(G-18358)
V-BRO PRODUCTS LLC
28114 County Road 561 (32778-9463)
PHONE..................................352 267-6235
Scott Brockie, *Managing Prtnr*
Joshua Stein, *Opers Staff*
Jason Wilson, *Engineer*
David Mills, *Sales Staff*
Cris Dimitriou, *Manager*
▲ **EMP:** 10 **EST:** 2004
SALES (est): 1.7MM **Privately Held**
SIC: 3536 Davits

(G-18359)
VISION CONVEYOR INC
32834 Lakeshore Dr (32778-5036)
PHONE..................................352 343-3300
Audie M Newman, *Vice Pres*
EMP: 13 **EST:** 2015
SALES (est): 1.8MM **Privately Held**
WEB: www.visionconveyor.com
SIC: 3441 Fabricated structural metal

(G-18360)
WALKER STAINLESS EQP CO LLC
27620 County Road 561 (32778-9410)
PHONE..................................352 343-2606
Jerry Stokes, *Manager*
EMP: 7
SALES (corp-wide): 1.4B **Publicly Held**
WEB: www.wabashnational.com
SIC: 3443 Fabricated plate work (boiler shop)
HQ: Walker Stainless Equipment Company Llc
625 W State St
New Lisbon WI 53950
608 562-7500

Tavernier
Monroe County

(G-18361)
BOAT LIFTS OF SOUTH FLORIDA
89170 Overseas Hwy (33070-2025)
PHONE..................................305 522-1320
Cynthia Hughes, *Principal*
EMP: 6 **EST:** 2017
SALES (est): 95.5K **Privately Held**
WEB: www.boatliftsofsouthflorida.com
SIC: 3536 Boat lifts

(G-18362)
PRANA ORGANIC PLANT OILS INC
174 Dove Creek Dr (33070-2922)
PHONE..................................216 288-2054
Jessica G Stone, *Director*
EMP: 7 **EST:** 2017
SALES (est): 163.2K **Privately Held**
WEB: www.plantpranaoils.com
SIC: 2099 Food preparations

(G-18363)
THECLIPCOM INC
91766 Overseas Hwy (33070-2642)
PHONE..................................305 599-3871
Beau Bennett, *President*
EMP: 5 **EST:** 1995
SALES (est): 611.4K **Privately Held**
WEB: www.theclip.com
SIC: 3317 Steel pipe & tubes

(G-18364)
WHITE SQUARE CHEMICAL INC
91760 Overseas Hwy (33070-2642)
P.O. Box 1907, Islamorada (33036-1907)
PHONE..................................302 212-4555
Nicholas Hawkins, *Principal*
Adama Blanco, *COO*
Adam Blanco, *Exec Dir*
EMP: 10 **EST:** 2013
SALES (est): 669K **Privately Held**
WEB: www.wsqchem.com
SIC: 3843 Dental equipment & supplies

Temple Terrace
Hillsborough County

(G-18365)
360 O AND P INC
5311 E Fletcher Ave (33617-1147)
PHONE..................................813 985-5000
Greg S Bauer, *Principal*
EMP: 8 **EST:** 2007
SALES (est): 176.8K **Privately Held**
WEB: www.360oandp.com
SIC: 3842 Surgical appliances & supplies

(G-18366)
BAE SYSTEMS INFO & ELEC SYS
12906 Tampa Oaks Blvd # 101 (33637-1153)
PHONE..................................813 979-4392
Michael Hanna, *Senior Engr*
Drew Fisher, *Sales Dir*
Bernardo Egusquiza, *Manager*
EMP: 124
SALES (corp-wide): 25.6B **Privately Held**
WEB: www.baesystems.com
SIC: 3812 Navigational systems & instruments
HQ: Bae Systems Information And Electronic Systems Integration Inc.
65 Spit Brook Rd
Nashua NH 03060
603 885-4321

(G-18367)
CIRCOR INTERNATIONAL INC
Also Called: Cpc-Cryolab
12501 Telecom Dr (33637-0906)
PHONE..................................813 978-1000
Sandy Petersen, *Senior Buyer*
Lynne Price-Regan, *Senior Buyer*
Gus Camacho, *Manager*
Jason Carpenter, *Manager*
Douglas Hunter, *Manager*
EMP: 7
SALES (corp-wide): 773.2MM **Publicly Held**
WEB: www.circor.com
SIC: 3491 Industrial valves
PA: Circor International, Inc.
30 Corporate Dr Ste 200
Burlington MA 01803
781 270-1200

(G-18368)
FLORIDA HEALTH CARE NEWS INC
215 Bullard Pkwy (33617-5511)
PHONE..................................813 989-1330
Barry Levine, *President*
Michelle Brooks, *Creative Dir*
Nerissa Johnson MBA, *Graphic Designe*
EMP: 27 **EST:** 1987
SALES (est): 5.3MM **Privately Held**
WEB: www.ifoundmydoctor.com
SIC: 2711 Newspapers, publishing & printing

(G-18369)
FLORIDA SPRAYERS INC (PA)
8808 Venture Cv Ste 101 (33637-6703)
PHONE..................................813 989-0500
Joseph C Fowler, *President*
Betty A Fowler, *Corp Secy*
EMP: 5 **EST:** 1985
SQ FT: 7,000
SALES (est): 807K **Privately Held**
WEB: www.flsprayers.com
SIC: 3523 5083 Sprayers & spraying machines, agricultural; agricultural machinery

(G-18370)
INNOVATIVE INSTRUMENTS INC
8533 Queen Brooks Ct (33637-4914)
PHONE..................................813 727-0676
Ghadah R Taha, *Principal*
EMP: 6 **EST:** 2016
SALES (est): 336.7K **Privately Held**
WEB: www.2in.com
SIC: 3829 Measuring & controlling devices

(G-18371)
LESLIE CONTROLS INC (HQ)
Also Called: Circor
12501 Telecom Dr (33637-0903)
PHONE..................................813 978-1000
David A Bloss Sr, *President*
Alan R Carlsen, *Vice Pres*
Jason Carpenter, *Buyer*
Antonio Roberson, *Engineer*
Ronald Schlau, *Engineer*
◆ **EMP:** 180 **EST:** 1900
SQ FT: 150,000
SALES (est): 65.5MM
SALES (corp-wide): 773.2MM **Publicly Held**
WEB: www.lesliecontrols.com
SIC: 3491 3433 3822 3593 Automatic regulating & control valves; valves, automatic control; pressure valves & regulators, industrial; solenoid valves; steam heating apparatus; auto controls regulating residntl & coml environmt & applncs; fluid power cylinders & actuators; valves & pipe fittings; fluid power valves & hose fittings
PA: Circor International, Inc.
30 Corporate Dr Ste 200
Burlington MA 01803
781 270-1200

(G-18372)
M & B PRODUCTS INC (PA)
8601 Harney Rd (33637-6605)
PHONE..................................813 988-2211
Dale Mc Clellan, *President*
Mary Mc Clellan, *Corp Secy*
Mary McClellani, *Corp Secy*
Thomas Hammerschmidt, *Vice Pres*
Howard Hutchinson, *Vice Pres*
◆ **EMP:** 167 **EST:** 1987
SQ FT: 9,600
SALES (est): 29.4MM **Privately Held**
WEB: www.mbproducts.com
SIC: 2033 Fruit juices: packaged in cans, jars, etc.

(G-18373)
P & J GRAPHICS INC
11407 Cerca Del Rio Pl (33617-2618)
PHONE..................................813 626-3243
Peter K Goltermann, *President*
Jean Ann Goltermann, *Principal*
Fritz Goltermann, *Vice Pres*
EMP: 11 **EST:** 1987
SALES (est): 330.5K **Privately Held**
WEB: www.pandjgraphics.com
SIC: 2752 Commercial printing, offset

(G-18374)
PHOENIX ENTERPRISES FLA LLC
Also Called: Pro-Tools
7616 Industrial Ln (33637-6715)
PHONE..................................813 986-9000
Cynthia Mullen, *President*
EMP: 10 **EST:** 2015
SQ FT: 20,000
SALES (est): 670.6K **Privately Held**
SIC: 3542 Bending machines

(G-18375)
PRO-COPY INC
5219 E Fowler Ave (33617-2190)
P.O. Box 16489, Tampa (33687-6489)
PHONE..................................813 988-5900
Jon E Statham, *President*
Summer Gambrell, *General Mgr*
Summer Shibley, *General Mgr*
Joan Statham, *Treasurer*
EMP: 18 **EST:** 1987
SALES (est): 2.5MM **Privately Held**
WEB: www.pro-copy.com
SIC: 2752 Commercial printing, offset

(G-18376)
RENAISSANCE STEEL LLC
6508 E Fowler Ave (33617-2406)
PHONE..................................941 773-7290
Don Ball,
Bill Bishop,
Don Wallace,
EMP: 15 **EST:** 2004
SQ FT: 65,000
SALES (est): 1.1MM **Privately Held**
SIC: 3312 Plate, steel

(G-18377)
SCOOTER LINK
10910 Gillette Ave (33617-3102)
PHONE..................................813 985-3075
Joseph Lopinto, *President*
EMP: 6 **EST:** 2009
SALES (est): 87.4K **Privately Held**
WEB: www.link.city
SIC: 3842 Wheelchairs

(G-18378)
SEMILAB USA LLC (PA)
Also Called: Semilab Sdi
12415 Telecom Dr (33637-0912)
PHONE..................................813 977-2244
Andrew Findley, *CEO*
Amy Mueller, *Admin Sec*
EMP: 34
SALES (est): 10.9MM **Privately Held**
WEB: www.semilab.com
SIC: 3699 3825 3674 Electrical equipment & supplies; instruments to measure electricity; semiconductors & related devices

(G-18379)
SUNCOAST PALLETS INC
11506 Cerca Del Rio Pl (33617-2621)
PHONE..................................813 988-1623
EMP: 8
SALES (est): 947.5K **Privately Held**
SIC: 2448 Mfg Wood Pallets/Skids

(G-18380)
SUNSHINE PEANUT COMPANY (PA)
7405 Temple Terrace Hwy A (33637-5786)
P.O. Box 290153, Tampa (33687-0153)
PHONE..................................813 988-6987
Jeff Turbeville, *President*
Jeff J Turbeville, *President*
Allison Turbeville, *Vice Pres*
Ernest S Turbeville Jr, *Vice Pres*
Sonny Turbeville, *CFO*
EMP: 13 **EST:** 2005
SALES (est): 4.4MM **Privately Held**
WEB: www.sunshinepeanut.com
SIC: 2099 Food preparations

(G-18381)
TAMPA BAYS COATINGS SCREENING
528 Lantern Cir (33617-3724)
PHONE..................................813 230-1610
Robert Bays, *Principal*
EMP: 6 **EST:** 2010
SALES (est): 118.7K **Privately Held**
SIC: 3479 Metal coating & allied service

(G-18382)
VURAM INC ✪
12802 Tampa Oaks Blvd # 241 (33637-1915)
PHONE..................................813 421-8000
Akhila Natarajan, *President*
EMP: 16 **EST:** 2021
SALES (est): 1.2MM **Privately Held**
WEB: www.vuram.com
SIC: 7372 Business oriented computer software

(G-18383)
WESTCOAST BRACE & LIMB INC (PA)
Also Called: West Coast Brace & Limb
5311 E Fletcher Ave (33617-1147)
PHONE..................................813 985-5000
Greg S Bauer, *President*
Christopher Pardo, *COO*
Chris Wilson, *Project Mgr*
Greg Bender, *Mktg Dir*
Albert Ford, *Manager*
EMP: 15 **EST:** 1981
SQ FT: 5,000
SALES (est): 4.7MM **Privately Held**
WEB: www.wcbl.com
SIC: 3842 Limbs, artificial; braces, orthopedic

Tequesta
Palm Beach County

(G-18384)
GILBANE BOATWORKS LLC
19137 Se Federal Hwy # 1 (33469-1755)
PHONE..................................561 744-2223
John Kennedy, *Manager*
Matthew R Gilbane,
EMP: 7 **EST:** 2008
SALES (est): 452.1K **Privately Held**
WEB: www.gilbaneboatworks.com
SIC: 3732 Boat building & repairing

(G-18385)
HAYES LESS LETHAL LLC
18955 Se Homewood Ave (33469-1636)
PHONE..................................561 201-2186
John Hayes, *CEO*
EMP: 5 **EST:** 2018
SQ FT: 4,000
SALES (est): 306.7K **Privately Held**
WEB: www.hayeslesslethal.com
SIC: 3699 8748 Security devices; business consulting

(G-18386)
PALM BEACH SMOOTHIES COM INC
150 N Us Highway 1 Ste 5 (33469-2726)
P.O. Box 4313, Jupiter (33469-1020)
PHONE..................................561 379-8647
Brian Van Brock, *Principal*
EMP: 8 **EST:** 2009
SALES (est): 108.8K **Privately Held**
SIC: 2037 Frozen fruits & vegetables

(G-18387)
PREMIER GLOBAL ENTERPRISES
Also Called: Sir Speedy
133 N Us Highway 1 (33469-2737)
PHONE..................................561 747-7303
Richard Goldberg, *Owner*
Rick Goldberg, *Finance*
EMP: 8 **EST:** 1983
SALES (est): 1.2MM **Privately Held**
WEB: www.sirspeedy.com
SIC: 2752 2791 Commercial printing, lithographic; typesetting

The Villages
Lake County

(G-18388)
A BAR CODE BUSINESS INC
505 Sunbelt Rd Ste 8 (32159-5607)
PHONE..................................352 750-0077
Steven Belford, *President*
Elizabeth Shaw, *Corp Secy*
Steve Belford, *Sales Mgr*
Erik Russell, *Info Tech Mgr*
▼ **EMP:** 6 **EST:** 1993
SQ FT: 400
SALES (est): 660K **Privately Held**
WEB: www.abarcodebusiness.com
SIC: 2759 Labels & seals: printing

The Villages
Sumter County

(G-18389)
C F PRINT LTD INC
3174 Dressendorfer Dr (32163-4215)
PHONE..................................631 567-2110
EMP: 10
SALES (est): 963.8K **Privately Held**
SIC: 2752 Lithographic Commercial Printing

(G-18390)
GARVINOS LLC (PA)
1081 Canal St (32162-1687)
PHONE..................................352 430-1435
Gary Bonnie, *Owner*
EMP: 9 **EST:** 2005
SALES (est): 538.3K **Privately Held**
WEB: www.garvinos.com
SIC: 3911 5813 Cigar & cigarette accessories; wine bar

(G-18391)
GOLDYS BOX CO
3267 Trussler Ter (32163-0020)
PHONE..................................954 648-1623
Howard Goldberg, *President*
EMP: 8 **EST:** 2005
SALES (est): 142.8K **Privately Held**
SIC: 2652 Setup paperboard boxes

(G-18392)
MAJIC STAIRS INC
744 Abaco Path (32163-6001)
PHONE..................................352 255-1390
EMP: 7
SALES (corp-wide): 803.9K **Privately Held**
WEB: www.majicstairsinc.com
SIC: 3446 Stairs, staircases, stair treads: prefabricated metal
PA: Majic Stairs Inc.
120 Cypress Rd
Ocala FL 34472
352 446-6295

(G-18393)
STREETROD PRODUCTIONS INC
Also Called: Streetrod Productions Florida
11962 County Road 101 (32162-9335)
PHONE..................................352 751-3953
Heidi Ressler, *General Mgr*
EMP: 9 **Privately Held**
WEB: www.streetrodgolfcars.com
SIC: 3799 Golf carts, powered
PA: Streetrod Productions, Inc.
809 S Front St
Montezuma IA 50171

(G-18394)
SUNGLOW INDUSTRIES
700 Iva Pl (32162-8750)
PHONE..................................304 554-2552
EMP: 7 **EST:** 2017
SALES (est): 125K **Privately Held**
WEB: www.sunglowind.com
SIC: 3999 Manufacturing industries

(G-18395)
TWO MERMAIDS VILLAGES LLC (PA)
Also Called: Two Mermaids Swim & Resort Wr
1039 Canal St (32162-1686)
PHONE..................................352 259-4722
David Ring,
Tina Ring,
EMP: 5 **EST:** 2009
SALES (est): 456.5K **Privately Held**
WEB: www.twomermaidsvillages.com
SIC: 2253 Knit outerwear mills

(G-18396)
VENDOR GUIDE PUBLICATIONS INC
3574 Gentle Ter (32163-2794)
PHONE..................................407 399-0745
Julie B Pope-Mills, *Principal*
EMP: 6 **EST:** 2015
SALES (est): 70.1K **Privately Held**
SIC: 2741 Miscellaneous publishing

(G-18397)
WEBELECTRIC PRODUCTS INC
333 Colony Blvd (32162-6084)
PHONE..................................440 389-5647
Lawrence T Mazza, *Principal*
EMP: 8 **EST:** 2012
SALES (est): 129.4K **Privately Held**
WEB: www.webelectricproducts.com
SIC: 3714 Motor vehicle parts & accessories

Thonotosassa
Hillsborough County

(G-18398)
A1 PALLETS LLC
11802 N Us Highway 301 (33592-2950)
P.O. Box 82864, Tampa (33682-2864)
PHONE..................................813 598-9165
EMP: 6 **EST:** 2017
SALES (est): 227.1K **Privately Held**
WEB: www.a1palletstampa.com
SIC: 2448 Pallets, wood

(G-18399)
COMMERCIAL DUCT SYSTEMS LLC
9707 Williams Rd (33592-3554)
PHONE..................................877 237-3828
Marcia Thompson, *CFO*
Gary Gibson, *Sales Staff*
Marsha Thompson, *Mng Member*
Rodney Parrish, *CIO*
Brenda Levy,
▼ **EMP:** 100 **EST:** 2005
SQ FT: 90,000
SALES (est): 10MM **Privately Held**
WEB: www.commercialduct.com
SIC: 3714 Air conditioner parts, motor vehicle

(G-18400)
DAVID THIESSENS PAVERS INC
12203 Floral Ln (33592-2750)
PHONE..................................813 516-1389
David Thiessen, *Director*
▼ **EMP:** 7 **EST:** 2010
SALES (est): 77.9K **Privately Held**
SIC: 3531 Pavers

(G-18401)
HORSE & PONY
11819 Hazen Ave (33592-2818)
P.O. Box 2145, Seffner (33583-2145)
PHONE..................................813 986-1003
Miriam Lauer, *Principal*
EMP: 7 **EST:** 2007
SALES (est): 217.4K **Privately Held**
WEB: www.horseandponynews.com
SIC: 2711 Commercial printing & newspaper publishing combined

(G-18402)
NESTLE USA INC
Also Called: Nestle Professional
11471 N Us Highway 301 # 10
(33592-3532)
PHONE..................................813 273-5355
Jonathan Jackman, *Branch Mgr*
Rachel Goldberg, *Manager*
EMP: 208
SALES (corp-wide): 92.3B **Privately Held**
WEB: www.nestleusa.com
SIC: 2023 Dry, condensed, evaporated dairy products
HQ: Nestle Usa, Inc.
1812 N Moore St Ste 118
Rosslyn VA 22209
440 264-7249

(G-18403)
NESTLE USA INC
Also Called: Nestle Professional Vitality
11441 N Us Highway 301 (33592-3533)
PHONE..................................813 301-4638
EMP: 73
SALES (corp-wide): 92.3B **Privately Held**
WEB: www.nestleusa.com
SIC: 2064 Candy & other confectionery products
HQ: Nestle Usa, Inc.
1812 N Moore St Ste 118
Rosslyn VA 22209
440 264-7249

(G-18404)
STAY-SEALED INC
3454 Airfield Dr W (33592)
P.O. Box 5844, Plant City (33563-0050)
PHONE..................................866 978-2973
EMP: 7 **EST:** 2010
SALES (est): 187.9K **Privately Held**
WEB: www.staysealed.com
SIC: 3829 Fuel system instruments, aircraft

Tierra Verde
Pinellas County

(G-18405)
ADJ INC
Also Called: Adj Marketing
860 Pinellas Bayway S (33715-2151)
PHONE..................................727 289-6173
Andrew D Jackson, *President*
Christopher Hillman, *VP Sales*
◆ **EMP:** 19 **EST:** 2003
SQ FT: 200,000
SALES (est): 15MM **Privately Held**
SIC: 3674 Light emitting diodes

Titusville
Brevard County

(G-18406)
A SIGN
3670 S Hopkins Ave (32780-5707)
PHONE..................................321 264-0077
Mark Frank, *Principal*
EMP: 9 **EST:** 2007
SALES (est): 471.5K **Privately Held**
WEB: www.asigncompany.com
SIC: 3993 Signs & advertising specialties

(G-18407)
A1A SPORTBIKE LLC
Also Called: Core Moto
1500 Shepard Dr (32780-7953)
PHONE..................................321 806-3995
Luke McCracken,
EMP: 9 **EST:** 2006
SALES (est): 278.6K **Privately Held**
SIC: 3751 Motorcycle accessories

(G-18408)
ABA-CON INC
11 S Brown Ave (32796-3329)
P.O. Box 308 (32781-0308)
PHONE..................................321 567-4967
Stephen Reaves, *Vice Pres*
Arden Ballard, *Project Mgr*
Mary Ballard, *Treasurer*
Danielle Ballard, *Manager*
EMP: 10 **EST:** 2008
SQ FT: 3,500
SALES (est): 1.6MM **Privately Held**
WEB: www.aba-con.com
SIC: 3795 Tanks & tank components

(G-18409)
ACCURATE METAL DOOR INC
1355 White Dr Ste 103 (32780-9602)
PHONE..................................321 305-5951
Jacqueline Hoolsema, *Manager*
EMP: 5 **EST:** 2004
SALES (est): 453.2K **Privately Held**
WEB: www.accuratemetaldoor.com
SIC: 3442 1796 Metal doors, sash & trim; installing building equipment

(G-18410)
ACCURATE POWDER COATING INC
1417 Chaffee Dr Ste 10 (32780-7931)
PHONE..................................321 269-6972
Tony Banks, *Owner*
EMP: 6 **EST:** 2005
SALES (est): 496.9K **Privately Held**
WEB: www.accuratepowdercoating.net
SIC: 3479 Coating of metals & formed products

(G-18411)
AERO ELECTRONICS SYSTEMS INC
411 S Park Ave (32796-7621)
P.O. Box 547 (32781-0547)
PHONE..................................321 269-0478
Joanne Murell Griffin, *President*
Michael Moody, *Opers Mgr*
Mike Zeiger, *Opers Mgr*
Sheri Wilson, *Controller*
Ronald Thompson, *Marketing Staff*
EMP: 7 **EST:** 2003
SQ FT: 20,000
SALES (est): 4.1MM **Privately Held**
WEB: www.aeroelectronics.net
SIC: 3679 Harness assemblies for electronic use: wire or cable

(G-18412)
AERO SEATING TECHNOLOGIES LLC
Also Called: Embraer Aero Seating Tech
1600 Armstrong Dr (32780-7964)
PHONE..................................321 264-5600
EMP: 6 **EST:** 2019
SALES (est): 402.2K **Privately Held**
SIC: 3714 Motor vehicle parts & accessories

(G-18413)
ANDERSON MFG & UPHOLSTERY INC
1427 Chaffee Dr Ste 4 (32780-7951)
PHONE..................................321 267-7028
Tena Anderson, *President*
EMP: 8 **EST:** 1997
SQ FT: 500
SALES (est): 920.1K **Privately Held**
WEB: www.amfg.us
SIC: 2211 Upholstery fabrics, cotton

(G-18414)
BIG TIME TAILGATE LLC
805 Marina Rd (32796-2837)
PHONE..................................407 509-5163
Jay M Parsons,
EMP: 6 **EST:** 2015

▲ = Import ▼=Export
◆ =Import/Export

SALES (est): 131.3K Privately Held
WEB: www.bigtimetailgate.com
SIC: 3792 Travel trailers & campers

(G-18415)
BLUEPOINT FABRICATION INC
Also Called: Blue Point Fabrication
3340 Lillian Blvd (32780-9636)
PHONE.................................321 269-0073
Thomas G Benyon, *President*
Mark Gabbot, *Vice Pres*
EMP: 14 EST: 1997
SALES (est): 1.1MM Privately Held
WEB: www.bluepointfabrication.com
SIC: 7692 Welding repair

(G-18416)
BOEING COMPANY
100 Boeing Way (32780-8046)
PHONE.................................312 544-2000
Bruce Melmick, *Vice Pres*
Diane Thomas, *Office Admin*
EMP: 6
SQ FT: 85,774
SALES (corp-wide): 58.1B Publicly Held
WEB: www.boeing.com
SIC: 3721 Airplanes, fixed or rotary wing
PA: The Boeing Company
100 N Riverside Plz
Chicago IL 60606
312 544-2000

(G-18417)
BREVARD ALUMINUM CNSTR CO
4655 Calle Corto (32780-6723)
PHONE.................................321 383-9255
Larry Rhoades, *Owner*
EMP: 5 EST: 1986
SQ FT: 800
SALES (est): 632.5K Privately Held
WEB: www.brevardaluminuminc.com
SIC: 3442 Screens, window, metal

(G-18418)
BRINSEA PRODUCTS INC
704 N Dixie Ave (32796-2017)
PHONE.................................321 267-7009
Frank Pearce, *President*
Pascale Deffieux-Pearce, *Vice Pres*
Diana Marquis, *Treasurer*
▲ EMP: 5 EST: 1996
SQ FT: 4,883
SALES (est): 668.4K Privately Held
WEB: www.brinsea.com
SIC: 3523 5191 Incubators & brooders, farm; farm supplies

(G-18419)
C & R DESIGNS INC
Also Called: Print123.com
1227 Garden St (32796-3310)
PHONE.................................321 383-2255
Christine Bean, *Owner*
Ryen Bean, *Co-Owner*
EMP: 5 EST: 1989
SQ FT: 10,000
SALES (est): 461.5K Privately Held
WEB: www.print123.com
SIC: 2789 7336 3571 2752 Bookbinding & related work; commercial art & graphic design; electronic computers; commercial printing, lithographic; die-cut paper & board

(G-18420)
C & R DESIGNS PRINTING LLC
Also Called: Print123.com
415 Main St (32796-3531)
PHONE.................................321 383-2255
Ryen A Bean, *Mng Member*
Christine C Bean,
EMP: 8 EST: 2012
SALES (est): 377K Privately Held
SIC: 2789 7336 3571 Bookbinding & related work; commercial art & graphic design; electronic computers

(G-18421)
C SPEED LLC
6855 Tico Rd Ste 103 (32780-8000)
PHONE.................................321 336-7939
EMP: 9
SALES (corp-wide): 4.9MM Privately Held
SIC: 3812 Mfg Search/Navigation Equipment
PA: C Speed, Llc
316 Commerce Blvd
Liverpool NY 13088
315 453-1043

(G-18422)
CEMEX MATERIALS LLC
511 Garden St (32796-3404)
PHONE.................................321 636-5121
Dwayne Marabolo, *Branch Mgr*
EMP: 27 Privately Held
SIC: 3271 Blocks, concrete or cinder: standard
HQ: Cemex Materials Llc
1501 Belvedere Rd
West Palm Beach FL 33406
561 833-5555

(G-18423)
CENTRAL SAND INC
6855 Tico Rd Unit 8 (32780-8000)
PHONE.................................321 632-0308
Dale L Morris, *President*
Lori L Morris, *Corp Secy*
EMP: 8 EST: 1982
SALES (est): 1.7MM Privately Held
WEB: www.centralsanddredging.com
SIC: 1442 Construction sand mining

(G-18424)
COMPOSITE HOLDINGS INC (PA)
805 Marina Rd (32796-2837)
PHONE.................................321 268-9625
Jeffrey W Gray, *CEO*
Harley Mc Donald, *Ch of Bd*
Matt Mc Donald, *President*
Gerard Beutler, *Partner*
Dana Greenwood, *Plant Mgr*
▲ EMP: 46 EST: 1993
SQ FT: 100,000
SALES (est): 7.8MM Privately Held
SIC: 3732 3711 3089 2823 Boat building & repairing; motor vehicles & car bodies; plastic boats & other marine equipment; cellulosic manmade fibers

(G-18425)
CORETEK INDUSTRIES INC
1300 White Dr Ste A (32780-9600)
PHONE.................................321 385-2860
Bertram M Oliff, *President*
EMP: 5 EST: 1999
SALES (est): 450K Privately Held
WEB: www.coretek.com
SIC: 3661 Telephone & telegraph apparatus

(G-18426)
CUPCAKES ON MAIN
3065 Westwood Dr (32796-1606)
PHONE.................................321 693-7236
Cynthia M Tomes, *Principal*
EMP: 6 EST: 2013
SALES (est): 89.5K Privately Held
SIC: 2024 Ice cream & frozen desserts

(G-18427)
D & D MANUFACTURING LLC
2655 Cherrywood Ln (32780-5909)
P.O. Box 560962, Rockledge (32956-0962)
PHONE.................................321 890-0069
Dale Polk, *Mng Member*
Debra Akridge,
EMP: 10 EST: 2008
SALES (est): 1.1MM Privately Held
SIC: 3496 Mats & matting

(G-18428)
EAGLE SIGNS
1250 Cheney Hwy Unit B (32780-8917)
PHONE.................................321 863-9844
Andrew E Wiedmann, *Principal*
EMP: 7 EST: 2008
SALES (est): 78.5K Privately Held
WEB: www.eaglesigns.com
SIC: 3993 Signs & advertising specialties

(G-18429)
FIRST SHOT MOLD AND TOOL
1125 White Dr (32780-9603)
PHONE.................................321 269-0031
John Vogt, *Owner*
▲ EMP: 5 EST: 1994
SQ FT: 6,000
SALES (est): 523.1K Privately Held
SIC: 3089 Injection molding of plastics

(G-18430)
GALAXY MEDALS INC
1125 White Dr (32780-9603)
PHONE.................................321 269-0840
Phyllis Jankowski, *President*
David Summers, *Vice Pres*
Duane Summers, *Vice Pres*
Denise E Summers, *Admin Sec*
EMP: 7 EST: 1970
SQ FT: 22,000
SALES (est): 916.4K Privately Held
WEB: www.galaxymedals.com
SIC: 3961 Costume jewelry

(G-18431)
GRAPHIC REPRODUCTIONS INC
Also Called: Graphic Press
2214 Garden St Ste B (32796-2581)
PHONE.................................321 267-1111
Leonard Piotrowski, *President*
EMP: 7 EST: 1976
SQ FT: 2,200
SALES (est): 975.7K Privately Held
WEB: www.graphicpressfla.com
SIC: 2752 Commercial printing, offset

(G-18432)
HELLS BAY BOATWORKS LLC
1520 Chaffee Dr (32780-7922)
PHONE.................................321 383-8223
J Bryan Broderick, *CEO*
Curtis Suggs, *Plant Mgr*
Mona Brown, *CFO*
Randy McBride, *Sales Mgr*
Bryan Broderick, *Sales Staff*
◆ EMP: 26 EST: 2002
SALES (est): 5MM Privately Held
WEB: www.hellsbayboatworks.com
SIC: 3732 Boats, fiberglass: building & repairing

(G-18433)
HELLS BAY MARINE INC
Also Called: Hell's Bay Boatworks
1520 Chaffee Dr (32780-7922)
PHONE.................................321 383-8223
Chris Peterson, *President*
▼ EMP: 33 EST: 2006
SQ FT: 25,000
SALES (est): 2.4MM Privately Held
WEB: www.hellsbayboatworks.com
SIC: 3732 Boats, fiberglass: building & repairing

(G-18434)
INTEGRITY BUSINESS SVCS INC (PA)
Also Called: Fine Line Printing & Graphics
3700 S Hopkins Ave Ste E (32780-5786)
PHONE.................................321 267-9294
Lee Descalzo, *President*
EMP: 5 EST: 1989
SQ FT: 1,400
SALES (est): 908.7K Privately Held
WEB: www.finelineprint.com
SIC: 2752 Commercial printing, offset

(G-18435)
JSSA INC
Also Called: Synergy Metal Finishing
895 Buffalo Rd (32796-2601)
PHONE.................................321 383-7798
John K Smith, *President*
Sandra F Smith, *Vice Pres*
Toni Miller, *QC Mgr*
Tammy Benson, *Office Mgr*
EMP: 45 EST: 2006
SQ FT: 16,000
SALES (est): 3.7MM Privately Held
WEB: www.synergymetalfinishing.com
SIC: 3471 Electroplating of metals or formed products

(G-18436)
K J C O INC (PA)
481 Ambleside Dr (32780-2329)
PHONE.................................954 401-4299
Ken Jackson, *President*
EMP: 6 EST: 1983
SQ FT: 4,000
SALES (est): 815.8K Privately Held
SIC: 3599 Machine shop, jobbing & repair

(G-18437)
K-O CONCEPTS INC
1200 White Dr Ste D (32780-9611)
PHONE.................................407 296-7788
Mindy L Ritz-Owen, *CEO*
EMP: 7 EST: 1995
SQ FT: 9,000
SALES (est): 1MM Privately Held
WEB: www.k-oconcepts.com
SIC: 3845 Laser systems & equipment, medical

(G-18438)
KAVI SKIN SOLUTIONS INC
3520 South St (32780-2918)
PHONE.................................415 839-5156
Ben Cohn, *Manager*
EMP: 20
SALES (corp-wide): 2.6MM Privately Held
WEB: www.kaviskin.com
SIC: 2834 Pharmaceutical preparations
PA: Kavi Skin Solutions, Inc.
700 Larkspur Landing Cir
Larkspur CA 94939
415 839-5156

(G-18439)
KITE BUM INC
2575 Shady Oaks Dr (32796-1985)
PHONE.................................321 267-6393
Roy S Ratcliff Jr, *President*
EMP: 6 EST: 2014
SALES (est): 75.5K Privately Held
WEB: www.kitebum.shop
SIC: 3944 Kites

(G-18440)
KNIGHT VISION LLLP
701 Columbia Blvd (32780-7902)
PHONE.................................321 607-9900
C Reed Knight Jr, *General Ptnr*
Michael Adkins, *Info Tech Mgr*
EMP: 11 EST: 2007
SALES (est): 540.3K Privately Held
SIC: 3827 Gun sights, optical

(G-18441)
KNIGHTS MANUFACTURING COMPANY
701 Columbia Blvd (32780-7902)
PHONE.................................321 607-9900
C Reed Knight Jr, *President*
Gary Perry, *COO*
Ken Greenslade, *Vice Pres*
Paul Pikel, *Export Mgr*
Wendy Miller, *Purch Mgr*
EMP: 52 EST: 1992
SQ FT: 60,000
SALES (est): 9.7MM Privately Held
WEB: www.knightarmco.com
SIC: 3484 8734 8731 Guns (firearms) or gun parts, 30 mm. & below; testing laboratories; commercial physical research

(G-18442)
LIFESTYLE PRINTWORKS INC
1300 Armstrong Dr Ste 10 (32780-7930)
PHONE.................................321 604-1531
Thomas Meadows, *President*
EMP: 6 EST: 2017
SALES (est): 233.3K Privately Held
WEB: www.lifestyleprintworks.com
SIC: 2759 Screen printing

(G-18443)
LOCKHEED MARTIN CORPORATION
1100 Lockheed Way (32780-7910)
PHONE.................................321 264-7924
Bryan McGilvray, *Engineer*
Sybil Hamilton, *Branch Mgr*
EMP: 6 Publicly Held
WEB: www.lockheedmartin.com
SIC: 3812 Search & navigation equipment
PA: Lockheed Martin Corporation
6801 Rockledge Dr
Bethesda MD 20817

(G-18444)
MADART
3635 S Ridge Cir (32796-1866)
PHONE.................................321 961-9264
Megan Duncanson, *Principal*
EMP: 6 **EST:** 2011
SALES (est): 70.9K **Privately Held**
WEB: www.madartdesigns.com
SIC: 3229 Art, decorative & novelty glassware

(G-18445)
MARBLE DESIGNS OF FL INC
1975 Silver Star Rd (32796-5118)
PHONE.................................321 269-6920
Jeff Hackney, *President*
EMP: 6 **EST:** 1984
SQ FT: 10,000
SALES (est): 689.3K **Privately Held**
WEB: www.marbledesignsofflorida.com
SIC: 3281 5211 Marble, building: cut & shaped; masonry materials & supplies

(G-18446)
MARIMBA COCINA MEXICANA II INC
3758 S Washington Ave (32780-5739)
PHONE.................................321 268-6960
Martinez Ana L, *Principal*
EMP: 8 **EST:** 2013
SALES (est): 271.3K **Privately Held**
WEB: www.lasmarimbas.com
SIC: 3931 Marimbas

(G-18447)
OLYMPIAN LED INC
3620 S Hopkins Ave (32780-5733)
PHONE.................................321 747-3220
Braden P O'Keefe, *President*
EMP: 5 **EST:** 2014
SQ FT: 3,620
SALES (est): 10MM **Privately Held**
WEB: www.olympianled.com
SIC: 3993 Electric signs

(G-18448)
PARAGON PLASTICS INC
1401 Armstrong Dr (32780-7950)
PHONE.................................321 631-6212
David Trout, *President*
Dan Tucker, *Sales Engr*
▼ **EMP:** 23 **EST:** 1995
SQ FT: 25,000
SALES (est): 6.7MM **Privately Held**
WEB: www.paragonplastics.net
SIC: 3089 Plastic hardware & building products; plastic processing

(G-18449)
PC OF TITUSVILLE INC
701 Columbia Blvd (32780-7902)
PHONE.................................321 267-1161
Reed Knight, *Director*
EMP: 19 **EST:** 2004
SALES (est): 1.4MM **Privately Held**
SIC: 3471 Plating of metals or formed products

(G-18450)
PCM PRODUCTS INC
1225 White Dr (32780-9630)
PHONE.................................321 267-7500
Paul Richards, *President*
Liv E Richards, *Treasurer*
Lisa Randolph, *Office Mgr*
EMP: 24
SQ FT: 20,000
SALES (est): 3.5MM **Privately Held**
WEB: www.pcmproducts.com
SIC: 3479 Etching, photochemical

(G-18451)
PHARMCO LABORATORIES INC
3520 South St (32780-2918)
PHONE.................................321 268-1313
Robert L Cohn, *President*
Ben Cohn, *VP Opers*
▲ **EMP:** 6 **EST:** 1979
SQ FT: 22,000
SALES (est): 1.1MM **Privately Held**
WEB: www.pharmcolabs.com
SIC: 2899 2833 Chemical preparations; medicinals & botanicals

(G-18452)
PRATT CNC
1325 White Dr (32780-9605)
PHONE.................................321 482-9494
Richard Pratt, *President*
EMP: 7 **EST:** 2016
SALES (est): 273.8K **Privately Held**
WEB: www.prattcnc.com
SIC: 3599 Machine shop, jobbing & repair

(G-18453)
PRECISION SHAPES INC (PA)
8835 Grissom Pkwy (32780-7904)
P.O. Box 5099 (32783-5099)
PHONE.................................321 269-2555
Susan Palma, *President*
Jesse Palma, *Business Mgr*
Cheryl Cleveland, *Vice Pres*
Colleen Watson, *QC Mgr*
Omar Carambot, *Manager*
EMP: 44 **EST:** 1941
SQ FT: 30,000
SALES (est): 9.1MM **Privately Held**
WEB: www.precisionshapes.net
SIC: 3452 3451 3724 3599 Bolts, nuts, rivets & washers; screw machine products; aircraft engines & engine parts; machine shop, jobbing & repair; aircraft hardware; aircraft body & wing assemblies & parts

(G-18454)
R&R ASSEMBLY SERVICES
448 N Dixie Ave (32796-2610)
PHONE.................................407 797-8325
Robert Somppi, *Principal*
EMP: 6 **EST:** 2016
SALES (est): 52.8K **Privately Held**
WEB: www.rrassemblysvcs.com
SIC: 3999 Manufacturing industries

(G-18455)
REK MANUFACTURING INC
1419 Chaffee Dr Ste 4 (32780-7933)
PHONE.................................321 269-3533
Richard W Koch, *President*
Walter E Koch, *Vice Pres*
EMP: 5
SQ FT: 7,100
SALES (est): 300K **Privately Held**
SIC: 3089 3469 Injection molding of plastics; machine parts, stamped or pressed metal

(G-18456)
RENZETTI INC
8800 Grissom Pkwy (32780-7999)
PHONE.................................321 267-7705
Andrew Renzetti, *President*
Lily Renzetti, *Vice Pres*
▲ **EMP:** 10 **EST:** 1974
SQ FT: 16,119
SALES (est): 1.3MM **Privately Held**
WEB: www.renzetti.com
SIC: 3949 3599 Fishing equipment; flies, fishing: artificial; machine shop, jobbing & repair

(G-18457)
RESPONSIVE MACHINING INC
1650 Chaffee Dr (32780-7922)
PHONE.................................321 225-4011
Helen McCourt, *President*
Suzanne M Hall, *President*
David K Hall, *Vice Pres*
Tanya Severson, *Controller*
EMP: 10 **EST:** 1996
SQ FT: 5,600
SALES (est): 700K **Privately Held**
SIC: 7692 3444 3599 Welding repair; sheet metalwork; machine & other job shop work

(G-18458)
RICHARD C GOOD
Also Called: Specialty Packaging & Display
1125 White Dr (32780-9603)
P.O. Box 234, Sharpes (32959-0234)
PHONE.................................321 639-6383
Richard C Good, *Owner*
EMP: 5 **EST:** 1985
SALES (est): 300K **Privately Held**
SIC: 2657 Folding paperboard boxes

(G-18459)
RICHARD K PRATT LLC
Also Called: Pratt Plastics
1325 White Dr (32780-9605)
PHONE.................................321 482-9494
Danielle D Pratt, *Principal*
Richard Pratt,
EMP: 7 **EST:** 2015
SALES (est): 512.7K **Privately Held**
WEB: www.prattcnc.com
SIC: 3999 Manufacturing industries

(G-18460)
ROCK RIDGE MATERIALS INC
Also Called: Statewide Materials
1525 White Dr (32780-9629)
PHONE.................................321 268-8455
Christine Ruth, *Principal*
EMP: 19 **EST:** 2014
SALES (est): 6.3MM **Privately Held**
WEB: www.swmagg.com
SIC: 1422 5211 1423 1429 Crushed & broken limestone; sand & gravel; crushed & broken granite; riprap quarrying; dump truck haulage; stone, crushed or broken

(G-18461)
SOUTHERN INNOVATIVE ENERGY INC
4373 Fletcher Ln Ste 2 (32780-2857)
PHONE.................................321 747-9205
Kim Mercanti, *Senior Partner*
Raymond Giamporcaro, *Admin Sec*
EMP: 9 **EST:** 2011
SALES (est): 461.7K **Privately Held**
SIC: 3561 3494 3511 Pumps & pumping equipment; valves & pipe fittings; plumbing & heating valves; steam turbine generator set units, complete

(G-18462)
SPACECOAST CABLE & HARNESS INC
3400 Lillian Blvd (32780-9601)
PHONE.................................321 269-0377
Brian Hulsberg, *President*
EMP: 25 **EST:** 1999
SALES (est): 4.1MM **Privately Held**
WEB: www.spacecoastcableandharness.com
SIC: 3679 Electronic circuits

(G-18463)
SRM BLINDS INC
4381 Derbyshire Dr (32780-5964)
PHONE.................................321 269-5332
Steven Michell, *Principal*
EMP: 6 **EST:** 2007
SALES (est): 171.8K **Privately Held**
SIC: 2591 Window blinds

(G-18464)
STARLINE EDUCATION INC
1375 War Eagle Blvd (32796-1531)
PHONE.................................808 631-1818
Sandra Combs, *Principal*
EMP: 8 **EST:** 2017
SALES (est): 279K **Privately Held**
WEB: www.starlinepress.com
SIC: 2731 Book publishing

(G-18465)
STINGER FIBERGLASS DESIGNS INC
1525 Armstrong Dr (32780-7950)
PHONE.................................321 268-1118
Arthur J Schricker, *President*
EMP: 12 **EST:** 2001
SALES (est): 1.2MM **Privately Held**
SIC: 3732 Boats, fiberglass: building & repairing

(G-18466)
SUN ELECTRONIC SYSTEMS INC
1845 Shepard Dr (32780-7920)
PHONE.................................321 383-9400
Gary Clifford, *President*
Veronica Pasqua, *Corp Secy*
Maria Fisher, *Purch Mgr*
Deanna Jeffery, *Sales Staff*
EMP: 14 **EST:** 1980
SQ FT: 13,000
SALES (est): 1.1MM **Privately Held**
WEB: www.sunelectronics.com
SIC: 3625 3826 Electric controls & control accessories, industrial; environmental testing equipment

(G-18467)
TECHCODES LLC
2701 Sherwood Dr (32796-3735)
PHONE.................................321 529-4122
Phillip Vega,
Kim Vega,
Brandon White,
Jodye White,
EMP: 6 **EST:** 2012
SALES (est): 243.4K **Privately Held**
SIC: 3663 4813 3812 8748 Airborne radio communications equipment; space satellite communications equipment; data telephone communications; antennas, radar or communications; telecommunications consultant; local area network (LAN) systems integrator

(G-18468)
THUNDERBIRD PRESS INC
205 N Mantor Ave (32796-4606)
PHONE.................................321 269-7616
Shearer Kennedy, *President*
Scott Kennedy, *Vice Pres*
Dave Forrest, *Sales Mgr*
EMP: 10 **EST:** 1975
SQ FT: 4,280
SALES (est): 2MM **Privately Held**
WEB: www.thunderbird-press.com
SIC: 2752 Commercial printing, offset

(G-18469)
TOWNSEND CERAMICS & GLASS INC
Also Called: Townsend's
3535 South St (32780-2906)
PHONE.................................321 269-5671
John Townsend, *President*
Ann Townsend, *Corp Secy*
Kelvin Townsend, *Vice Pres*
EMP: 10 **EST:** 1969
SQ FT: 13,000
SALES (est): 485.3K **Privately Held**
SIC: 3269 5947 Figures: pottery, china, earthenware & stoneware; gift, novelty & souvenir shop

(G-18470)
TRUSSWOOD INC
3620 Bobbi Ln (32780-2917)
PHONE.................................321 383-0366
Jean Francois Langelier, *President*
Dominic Thibault, *Vice Pres*
Tracey Zelman, *Sales Staff*
Charles Thibault, *Executive*
Chad Voorhees, *Associate*
EMP: 60 **EST:** 1999
SQ FT: 6,000
SALES (est): 13.5MM **Privately Held**
WEB: www.trusswood.net
SIC: 2439 Trusses, wooden roof

(G-18471)
US APPLIED PHYS ICS GROUP
1650 Chaffee Dr (32780-7922)
PHONE.................................321 567-7270
EMP: 7 **EST:** 2019
SALES (est): 848.6K **Privately Held**
SIC: 3674 Semiconductors & related devices

(G-18472)
US APPLIED PHYSICS GROUP LLC
7065 Challenger Ave (32780-8201)
PHONE.................................321 607-9023
Richard McCourt, *President*
James Hoffman, *Mng Member*
EMP: 6 **EST:** 2014
SALES (est): 354.3K **Privately Held**
SIC: 3674 Diodes, solid state (germanium, silicon, etc.)

(G-18473)
WINDSOR WINDOW COMPANY
Woodgrain Distribution
1450 Shepard Dr (32780-7921)
PHONE.................................321 385-3880
Robert Mickle, *Division Mgr*
EMP: 15 **Privately Held**

WEB: www.woodgrain.com
SIC: 2431 3442 Moldings, wood: unfinished & prefinished; moldings & trim, except automobile: metal
HQ: Windsor Window Company
300 Nw 16th St
Fruitland ID 83619
800 452-3801

Treasure Island
Pinellas County

(G-18474)
BURN BRITE METALS CO INC
425 Capri Blvd (33706-2941)
PHONE..................................727 360-4408
Joseph Roberts, *Principal*
EMP: 6 EST: 2008
SALES (est): 187.9K Privately Held
SIC: 3471 Coloring & finishing of aluminum or formed products

(G-18475)
HITKING SPORTS LLC
10100 Paradise Blvd (33706-3117)
PHONE..................................941 661-2753
Danny K Palmer, *Principal*
EMP: 6 EST: 2016
SALES (est): 213.1K Privately Held
SIC: 2759 Screen printing

(G-18476)
NIGELLA INDUSTRIES INC
11975 3rd St E Apt 1 (33706-4547)
PHONE..................................813 404-7923
Aaron Fournie, *President*
EMP: 9 EST: 2011
SALES (est): 545.8K Privately Held
SIC: 3999 Barber & beauty shop equipment

(G-18477)
RAND & LONDON LLC
279 104th Ave (33706-4805)
PHONE..................................727 363-0800
Jeffrey M Solomon, *Principal*
EMP: 6 EST: 2010
SALES (est): 184.4K Privately Held
WEB: www.whispersresort.com
SIC: 3131 Rands

(G-18478)
SUNCOAST KINGFISH CLASSIC LLC
12781 Kingfish Dr (33706-5021)
P.O. Box 531801, Saint Petersburg (33747-1801)
PHONE..................................970 708-7997
Jack H Byington, *Manager*
EMP: 6 EST: 2013
SALES (est): 97.1K Privately Held
WEB: www.suncoastkingfishclassic.com
SIC: 3731 Shipbuilding & repairing

(G-18479)
VINE AND GRIND LLC
Also Called: Vine & Grind
111 107th Ave Ste 1 (33706-4722)
PHONE..................................727 420-3122
Jared Leal, *Principal*
EMP: 6 EST: 2016
SALES (est): 553K Privately Held
WEB: www.vineandgrind.com
SIC: 3599 Grinding castings for the trade

Trenton
Gilchrist County

(G-18480)
AYERS PUBLISHING INC
Also Called: Ayers Office Supply
207 N Main St (32693-3439)
P.O. Box 127 (32693-0127)
PHONE..................................352 463-7135
John M Ayers II, *President*
Carrie A Mizell, *Principal*
EMP: 5 EST: 1934
SALES (est): 573.7K Privately Held
WEB: www.gilchristcountyjournal.net
SIC: 2711 5943 Newspapers: publishing only, not printed on site; commercial printing & newspaper publishing combined; office forms & supplies

(G-18481)
COMPOSITE-FX SALES LLC
9069 Se County Road 319 (32693-2660)
PHONE..................................352 538-1624
Dwight Junkin, *Principal*
EMP: 9 EST: 2006
SALES (est): 646.2K Privately Held
WEB: www.composite-fx.com
SIC: 3728 Aircraft parts & equipment

(G-18482)
COUNTRY MAN S
7100 Se State Road 26 (32693-2882)
PHONE..................................352 472-8699
Arnold Hughes, *Principal*
EMP: 6 EST: 2010
SALES (est): 149.2K Privately Held
SIC: 3531 Automobile wrecker hoists

Trinity
Pasco County

(G-18483)
CAPITOL CONVEYORS INC
1429 Warrington Way (34655-7219)
PHONE..................................727 314-7474
Robert Dersham, *CEO*
EMP: 9 EST: 2007
SQ FT: 900
SALES (est): 4MM Privately Held
WEB: www.capitolconveyorsinc.com
SIC: 3535 Conveyors & conveying equipment

(G-18484)
ENODIS HOLDINGS INC (HQ)
2227 Welbilt Blvd (34655-5130)
PHONE..................................727 375-7010
David McCulloch, *CEO*
EMP: 174 EST: 2009
SALES (est): 37.1MM
SALES (corp-wide): 1.1B Publicly Held
WEB: www.welbilt.com
SIC: 3589 Commercial cooking & foodwarming equipment
PA: Welbilt, Inc.
2227 Welbilt Blvd
Trinity FL 34655
727 375-7010

(G-18485)
FACTS ENGINEERING LLC
8049 Photonics Dr (34655-5128)
PHONE..................................727 375-8888
Rick Walker, *Vice Pres*
Kimberly Meek, *Purch Mgr*
Jose Estrada, *Engineer*
Michael Cooke, *Design Engr*
Bruce Louzon, *Design Engr*
▲ EMP: 50 EST: 1986
SQ FT: 20,000
SALES (est): 10.3MM Privately Held
WEB: www.facts-eng.com
SIC: 3823 3625 Industrial process control instruments; relays & industrial controls

(G-18486)
GARRETT TIN & BROTHER INC
2536 Palesta Dr (34655-5156)
PHONE..................................727 236-5434
Garrett S Tin, *Principal*
EMP: 6 EST: 2008
SALES (est): 128.6K Privately Held
SIC: 3356 Tin

(G-18487)
KYSOR INDUSTRIAL CORPORATION (HQ)
Also Called: Kysor Warren
2227 Welbilt Blvd (34655-5130)
PHONE..................................727 376-8600
Richard Osborne, *President*
Kirk Goss, *Vice Pres*
Donald Holmes, *Treasurer*
◆ EMP: 12 EST: 1925
SQ FT: 8,000
SALES (est): 281.4MM
SALES (corp-wide): 1.1B Publicly Held
WEB: www.welbilt.com
SIC: 3714 3585 Motor vehicle engines & parts; refrigeration equipment, complete
PA: Welbilt, Inc.
2227 Welbilt Blvd
Trinity FL 34655
727 375-7010

(G-18488)
MEOPTA USA INC
Also Called: Tyrolit Company
7826 Photonics Dr (34655-5127)
PHONE..................................631 436-5900
Gerald J Rausnitz, *President*
Reinhard Seipp, *General Mgr*
David Rausnitz, *COO*
Martin Ruml, *Buyer*
Egon Rausnitz, *Treasurer*
▲ EMP: 140 EST: 1957
SQ FT: 41,500
SALES (est): 27.5MM
SALES (corp-wide): 221.7K Privately Held
WEB: www.meopta.com
SIC: 3827 Lenses, optical: all types except ophthalmic
PA: Cong Dao Nguyen
U Rezne 374
Zelezna Ruda

(G-18489)
SOUTHEASTERN ASSEMBLIES INC
2112 Larchwood Ct (34655-4952)
PHONE..................................727 376-1411
Douglas Misener, *Principal*
EMP: 6 EST: 2016
SALES (est): 161.2K Privately Held
SIC: 3999 Manufacturing industries

(G-18490)
TZH INDUSTRIES INC
1731 Swamp Rose Ln (34655-4980)
PHONE..................................727 807-3000
Joseph Eber, *Principal*
EMP: 6 EST: 2016
SALES (est): 92.5K Privately Held
SIC: 3999 Manufacturing industries

(G-18491)
WELBILT INC (PA)
2227 Welbilt Blvd (34655-5130)
PHONE..................................727 375-7010
Cynthia M Egnotovich, *Ch of Bd*
William C Johnson, *President*
Josef Matosevic, *COO*
Richard N Caron, *Exec VP*
Joel H Horn, *Exec VP*
EMP: 641 EST: 1902
SQ FT: 50,000
SALES (est): 1.1B Publicly Held
WEB: www.welbilt.com
SIC: 3589 3585 Commercial cooking & foodwarming equipment; food warming equipment, commercial; ice making machinery; cold drink dispensing equipment (not coin-operated)

(G-18492)
WESTRAN CORPORATION
2227 Welbilt Blvd (34655-5130)
PHONE..................................727 375-7010
David Frase, *Principal*
EMP: 6 EST: 2010
SALES (est): 1.2MM
SALES (corp-wide): 1.1B Publicly Held
WEB: www.welbilt.com
SIC: 3585 Refrigeration & heating equipment
PA: Welbilt, Inc.
2227 Welbilt Blvd
Trinity FL 34655
727 375-7010

Tyndall Afb
Bay County

(G-18493)
AERO TECH SERVICE ASSOC INC
1311 Florida Ave (32403-5207)
PHONE..................................850 286-1378
Mike Garrett, *Manager*
EMP: 17 Privately Held
WEB: www.atsainc.com
SIC: 3721 Autogiros
PA: Aero Tech Service Associates, Inc.
909 S Meridian Ave # 200
Oklahoma City OK 73108

(G-18494)
RAYTHEON COMPANY
1279 Florida Ave (32403-5205)
PHONE..................................850 286-6343
Aldo Egas, *Engineer*
EMP: 6
SALES (corp-wide): 56.5B Publicly Held
WEB: www.rtx.com
SIC: 3812 Defense systems & equipment
HQ: Raytheon Company
870 Winter St
Waltham MA 02451
781 522-3000

Umatilla
Lake County

(G-18495)
ANGERY AMERICAN ENTERPRISES
22741 Will Murphy Rd (32784-7533)
PHONE..................................352 669-2198
Chris Weatherman, *Principal*
EMP: 7 EST: 2015
SALES (est): 90.9K Privately Held
WEB: www.angeryamerican.tv
SIC: 2741 Miscellaneous publishing

(G-18496)
CHASE METALS INC
38051 State Road 19 (32784-8357)
PHONE..................................352 669-1254
Brent C Creasman, *President*
Alan D Twibel, *Vice Pres*
EMP: 30 EST: 2001
SALES (est): 533.2K Privately Held
SIC: 3541 Lathes

(G-18497)
COFFIN CABINETRY & TRIM MICHAE
91 S Pine Ave (32784-9096)
PHONE..................................352 217-3729
Michael Coffin, *Principal*
EMP: 6 EST: 2011
SALES (est): 176.5K Privately Held
WEB: www.michaelscoffin.com
SIC: 2434 Wood kitchen cabinets

(G-18498)
DOERFLER MANUFACTURING INC
235 N Central Ave (32784-7565)
PHONE..................................763 772-3728
George A Doerfler, *President*
EMP: 5 EST: 2008
SQ FT: 7,000
SALES (est): 758.3K Privately Held
WEB: www.doerflermfg.com
SIC: 2844 Face creams or lotions

(G-18499)
MERCER PRODUCTS COMPANY INC
37235 State Road 19 (32784-8070)
PHONE..................................352 357-0057
Gerry Glatz, *Vice Pres*
EMP: 25 EST: 1958
SALES (est): 12.8MM
SALES (corp-wide): 686.3MM Privately Held
WEB: www.burkeindustries.com
SIC: 3089 Plastic hardware & building products

GEOGRAPHIC

HQ: Burke Industries (Delaware), Inc.
2250 S 10th St
San Jose CA 95112
408 297-3500

(G-18500)
OUTPOST NORTH LAKE
131 N Central Ave (32784-7568)
P.O. Box 1099 (32784-1099)
PHONE....................352 669-2430
Matt Newby, *Owner*
EMP: 5 **EST:** 1979
SQ FT: 2,270
SALES (est): 327K **Privately Held**
WEB: www.thenorthlakeoutpost.com
SIC: 2711 Newspapers, publishing & printing

(G-18501)
PLASTIC COMPOSITES INC ✪
630 Goodbar Ave (32784-7628)
PHONE....................352 669-5822
John Purland, *Principal*
EMP: 10 **EST:** 2021
SALES (est): 860K **Privately Held**
SIC: 3089 Plastic processing

(G-18502)
SPECIALTY FABRICATION WLDG INC
680 Goodbar Ave (32784-7628)
P.O. Box 981 (32784-0981)
PHONE....................352 669-9353
Michael Purvis, *President*
Cott Purvis, *Vice Pres*
Karen Purvis, *Admin Sec*
EMP: 5 **EST:** 2004
SALES (est): 517.9K **Privately Held**
SIC: 7692 Welding repair

(G-18503)
STERLING EQP MFG CENTL FLA INC
803 Line St (32784-8671)
PHONE....................352 669-3255
Pete Rogers, *President*
Greg Rogers, *Vice Pres*
Wade Rogers, *Vice Pres*
EMP: 5 **EST:** 1976
SQ FT: 10,000
SALES (est): 669.7K **Privately Held**
WEB: www.sterling-equipment.com
SIC: 3465 Moldings or trim, automobile: stamped metal

University Park
Manatee County

(G-18504)
DUMPSTERMAXX
5265 University Pkwy # 101 (34201-3012)
PHONE....................805 552-6299
Rafael M Calle Jr, *Manager*
EMP: 5 **EST:** 2017
SALES (est): 526K **Privately Held**
WEB: www.dumpstermaxx.com
SIC: 3443 Dumpsters, garbage

Valparaiso
Okaloosa County

(G-18505)
AMERICAN ATHLETIC UNIFORMS INC
90 Eastview Ave (32580-1375)
PHONE....................850 729-1205
Roger Noel, *President*
Geraldine Noel, *Vice Pres*
Gerri Noel, *Manager*
EMP: 10 **EST:** 1987
SQ FT: 4,400
SALES (est): 700K **Privately Held**
WEB: www.aau-inc.mybigcommerce.com
SIC: 2329 2339 Athletic (warmup, sweat & jogging) suits: men's & boys'; sportswear, women's

(G-18506)
BAYOU OUTDOOR EQUIPMENT
Also Called: Schwabs Enterprises
489 Valparaiso Pkwy (32580-1274)
PHONE....................850 729-2711
Jim Allen, *Owner*
EMP: 13 **EST:** 1999
SALES (est): 771.7K **Privately Held**
SIC: 3546 Saws & sawing equipment

(G-18507)
BAYOU PRINTING INC
Also Called: Ccp Bayou Printing
113 S John Sims Pkwy (32580-1211)
PHONE....................850 678-5444
Philip Pink, *President*
EMP: 10 **EST:** 1982
SQ FT: 2,045
SALES (est): 500K **Privately Held**
SIC: 2752 2741 2791 2789 Commercial printing, offset; newsletter publishing; yearbooks: publishing & printing; typesetting; bookbinding & related work

(G-18508)
BRADLEY INDUS TEXTILES INC
101 S John Sims Pkwy (32580-1211)
P.O. Box 254 (32580-0254)
PHONE....................850 678-6111
Anthony S Bradley, *President*
EMP: 10 **EST:** 1977
SALES (est): 1.9MM **Privately Held**
WEB: www.bradleygeosynthetics.com
SIC: 2999 2221 Coke; broadwoven fabric mills, manmade

(G-18509)
CUSTOM FBRICATIONS OF FREEPORT
479 Old Florida Sr 10 Rd (32580-1427)
PHONE....................850 729-0500
William Moulton, *President*
Lenore Moulton, *Corp Secy*
EMP: 10 **EST:** 2000
SQ FT: 3,200
SALES (est): 815.7K **Privately Held**
WEB: www.water91306.com
SIC: 3355 1799 1791 2431 Aluminum rail & structural shapes; ornamental metal work; structural steel erection; staircases, stairs & railings

(G-18510)
FLORIDA COCA-COLA BOTTLING CO
647 Valparaiso Pkwy (32580-1135)
PHONE....................850 678-9370
Ed Hall, *Branch Mgr*
EMP: 403
SQ FT: 28,528
SALES (corp-wide): 33B **Publicly Held**
WEB: www.coca-cola.com
SIC: 2086 Bottled & canned soft drinks
HQ: Florida Coca-Cola Bottling Company
521 Lake Kathy Dr
Brandon FL 33510
813 569-2600

(G-18511)
FULL CIRCLE INTEGRATION LLC
127b N John Sims Pkwy (32580-1005)
PHONE....................504 615-5501
Paul M Topp, *CEO*
Grant Martin, *COO*
Michael Hayes, *Marketing Staff*
EMP: 11 **EST:** 2009
SQ FT: 3,000
SALES (est): 818.4K **Privately Held**
WEB: www.innoventormilitary.com
SIC: 3812 8711 3721 Defense systems & equipment; engineering services; aircraft

(G-18512)
J B WOODWORKING INC
625 Valparaiso Pkwy # 202 (32580-1172)
PHONE....................850 362-6362
Joshua D Baker, *President*
Rachael M Baker, *Vice Pres*
EMP: 7 **EST:** 2015
SALES (est): 176.3K **Privately Held**
SIC: 2431 Millwork

(G-18513)
KENS GAS PIPING INC
419 Adams Ave Ste A (32580-1257)
PHONE....................850 897-4149
Kenneth C Corbitt, *Principal*
EMP: 7 **EST:** 2014
SALES (est): 570.5K **Privately Held**
SIC: 1382 Oil & gas exploration services

Valrico
Hillsborough County

(G-18514)
ALL AMERICAN COATINGS LLC
2512 Gotham Way (33596-6377)
PHONE....................941 730-9397
Ryan T Sullivan, *President*
EMP: 6 **EST:** 2016
SALES (est): 88.7K **Privately Held**
SIC: 3479 Metal coating & allied service

(G-18515)
AXRDHAM CORP
2134 Ridgemore Dr (33594-3200)
PHONE....................813 653-9588
▲ **EMP:** 6
SQ FT: 2,400
SALES (est): 346.5K **Privately Held**
SIC: 2099 Mfg Food Preparations

(G-18516)
BLOOMINGDALE GAZETTE INC
3244 Lithia Pinecrest Rd # 101 (33596-5681)
PHONE....................813 681-2051
EMP: 6
SALES (est): 269.6K **Privately Held**
SIC: 2711 Newspaper Publishing Co

(G-18517)
FABRICATED WIRE PRODUCTS INC
401 Lutie Dr (33594-2926)
P.O. Box 671, Dover (33527-0671)
PHONE....................813 802-8463
Byrd Chad L, *Principal*
EMP: 7 **EST:** 2014
SALES (est): 481.4K **Privately Held**
WEB: www.harborcountrybike.com
SIC: 3496 Miscellaneous fabricated wire products

(G-18518)
FASTSIGNS
1110 Lakemont Dr (33594-6620)
PHONE....................813 625-1800
EMP: 6 **EST:** 2012
SALES (est): 71K **Privately Held**
WEB: www.fastsigns.com
SIC: 3993 Signs & advertising specialties

(G-18519)
HOLLOW METAL INC
2803 Park Meadow Dr (33594-4654)
PHONE....................813 246-4112
Norris Gordon, *President*
EMP: 12 **EST:** 1995
SALES (est): 736.3K **Privately Held**
SIC: 3442 Sash, door or window: metal

(G-18520)
KRAFT HEINZ FOODS COMPANY
5806 Peach Heather Trl (33596-9250)
PHONE....................813 810-5298
Mitch Hersh, *Principal*
EMP: 7
SALES (corp-wide): 26.1B **Publicly Held**
WEB: www.kraftheinzcompany.com
SIC: 2033 Canned fruits & specialties
HQ: Kraft Heinz Foods Company
1 Ppg Pl Ste 3400
Pittsburgh PA 15222
412 456-5700

(G-18521)
LINCOLN TACTICAL LLC
1319 Brahma Dr (33594-4914)
PHONE....................813 419-3110
Ryan Thomas,
Tiffany Thomas,
EMP: 10 **EST:** 2011
SALES (est): 292.3K **Privately Held**
WEB: www.lincolntactical.net
SIC: 3465 Body parts, automobile: stamped metal

(G-18522)
MAJESTIC METALS INC
1807 N Waterman Dr (33594-5434)
PHONE....................813 380-6885
Jason Martin, *Branch Mgr*
EMP: 12
SALES (corp-wide): 5.3MM **Privately Held**
WEB: www.majesticmetalsinc.com
SIC: 3448 Prefabricated metal buildings
PA: Majestic Metals, Inc.
192 American Way
Madison MS 39110
601 856-3600

(G-18523)
MARX BROTHERS CABINETS INC
1935 Erin Brooke Dr (33594-4012)
P.O. Box 451 (33595-0451)
PHONE....................813 695-1473
Duncan Marx, *Principal*
EMP: 6 **EST:** 2009
SALES (est): 69.3K **Privately Held**
WEB: www.marxbrothersinc.com
SIC: 2434 Wood kitchen cabinets

(G-18524)
RAE LAUNO CORPORATION
Also Called: Gourmet Cup
2606 Durant Oaks Dr (33596-5932)
PHONE....................813 242-4281
Benjamin Rayfield, *President*
Eric Rayfield, *Vice Pres*
▲ **EMP:** 8 **EST:** 1997
SALES (est): 250.9K **Privately Held**
SIC: 2095 5149 Roasted coffee; coffee, green or roasted

(G-18525)
TITAN TRAILERS LLC
2406 E State Road 60 (33595-8001)
PHONE....................813 298-8597
Noah Winter,
EMP: 6 **EST:** 2018
SALES (est): 137K **Privately Held**
WEB: www.titantrailers.com
SIC: 3999 Manufacturing industries

Venice
Sarasota County

(G-18526)
ABSOLUTE ALUMINUM INC
Also Called: Absolute Aluminum & Cnstr
1220 Ogden Rd (34285-5530)
PHONE....................941 497-7777
Dale E Desjardins Jr, *President*
Adam Rankin, *General Mgr*
Mark Popp, *Prdtn Mgr*
Valerie Cervantes, *Production*
Paul White, *Engineer*
EMP: 78 **EST:** 1988
SQ FT: 29,000
SALES (est): 24.2MM **Privately Held**
WEB: www.absolutealuminum.com
SIC: 3354 Aluminum extruded products

(G-18527)
ABSOLUTE WINDOW AND DOOR INC
177 Center Rd (34285-5572)
PHONE....................941 485-7774
Shawn Garathy, *President*
EMP: 9 **EST:** 2000
SQ FT: 3,000
SALES (est): 1MM **Privately Held**
WEB: www.absolutewindowanddoor.net
SIC: 2431 1751 5211 Doors, wood; window & door (prefabricated) installation; windows, storm: wood or metal

(G-18528)
ADVANCED MARBLE PRODUCTS INC (PA)
177 James St (34285-5553)
PHONE....................941 485-7775
David Peterson, *President*

EMP: 6 EST: 1985
SQ FT: 4,800
SALES (est): 570.3K Privately Held
WEB: www.ceodavesnetwork.com
SIC: 3281 Marble, building: cut & shaped

(G-18529)
AES SERVICES INC
575 Bluebell Rd (34293-3162)
PHONE.....941 237-1446
Angelina E Sigmon, *Principal*
EMP: 6 EST: 2013
SALES (est): 175K Privately Held
WEB: www.aes.com
SIC: 1381 Drilling oil & gas wells

(G-18530)
AESTHETICS COMPLETE INC
1164 Ponderosa Rd (34293-6359)
PHONE.....610 265-3535
EMP: 7 EST: 2018
SALES (est): 39.6K Privately Held
SIC: 3999 Manufacturing industries

(G-18531)
AMBO FOODS LLC
727 Commerce Dr Unit C (34292-1723)
PHONE.....941 485-4400
Bo Martinsen, *Mng Member*
Anne M Chalmers,
EMP: 8 EST: 2008
SALES (est): 506.3K Privately Held
WEB: www.omega3innovations.com
SIC: 2052 Cookies

(G-18532)
AMBO HEALTH LLC
Also Called: Omega3 Innovations
727 Commerce Dr (34292-1723)
PHONE.....866 414-0188
May-Elise Martinsen, *Director*
Anne-Marie Chalmers,
Bo Martinsen,
EMP: 9 EST: 2008
SALES (est): 938.9K Privately Held
WEB: www.omega3innovations.com
SIC: 2834 Druggists' preparations (pharmaceuticals)

(G-18533)
AMERICAN ARCHTCTURAL MLLWK LLC
248 James St (34285-5529)
PHONE.....844 307-9571
Maria West,
EMP: 19 EST: 2012
SALES (est): 1.2MM Privately Held
WEB: www.millworkusa.com
SIC: 2431 Millwork

(G-18534)
B G CABINETS LLC
177 S Jackson Rd (34292-4101)
PHONE.....941 485-0040
James J Lehan, *Principal*
EMP: 7 EST: 2011
SALES (est): 197.9K Privately Held
SIC: 2434 Wood kitchen cabinets

(G-18535)
BOBS TWIST N SHAKE
420 Us Highway 41 Byp N (34285-6056)
PHONE.....941 485-5152
Bob Johnson, *President*
EMP: 6 EST: 2010
SALES (est): 297.7K Privately Held
SIC: 2024 Ice cream, bulk

(G-18536)
CAMCORP INDUSTRIES INC
170 Rich St (34292-3107)
PHONE.....941 488-5000
David Demarest, *President*
Dorian Demarest, *Vice Pres*
EMP: 6 EST: 1986
SQ FT: 5,000
SALES (est): 903.3K Privately Held
WEB: www.camcorponline.com
SIC: 3599 3444 Machine shop, jobbing & repair; sheet metalwork

(G-18537)
CMR FL SOLUTIONS LLC
2532 Oneida Rd (34293-3230)
PHONE.....586 206-2517
EMP: 7 EST: 2009
SALES (est): 185.2K Privately Held
SIC: 1389 Construction, repair & dismantling services

(G-18538)
CRANE CO
730 Commerce Dr (34292-1726)
PHONE.....941 480-9101
Donald Borden, *Branch Mgr*
EMP: 6
SQ FT: 39,906
SALES (corp-wide): 2.9B Publicly Held
WEB: www.craneco.com
SIC: 3589 Water treatment equipment, industrial; water purification equipment, household type
PA: Crane Co.
100 1st Stamford Pl # 300
Stamford CT 06902
203 363-7300

(G-18539)
CRANE ENVIRONMENTAL INC
Also Called: Crane Environmental Products
730 Commerce Dr (34292-1726)
PHONE.....941 480-9101
Thomas J Perlitz, *President*
▼ EMP: 76 EST: 1991
SALES (est): 6.5MM
SALES (corp-wide): 2.9B Publicly Held
WEB: www.craneco.com
SIC: 3589 Water treatment equipment, industrial; water purification equipment, household type
PA: Crane Co.
100 1st Stamford Pl # 300
Stamford CT 06902
203 363-7300

(G-18540)
D-R MEDIA AND INVESTMENTS LLC
Also Called: Publishing
300 Tamiami Trl S (34285-2422)
PHONE.....941 207-1602
David Dunn-Rankin, *CEO*
Michael Ruppel, *CFO*
EMP: 70 EST: 2018
SALES (est): 5.9MM Privately Held
WEB: www.d-rmedia.com
SIC: 2711 7922 Commercial printing & newspaper publishing combined; entertainment promotion

(G-18541)
DIGITAL SCOREBOARDS LLC
333 Suth Tmami Trail Ste (34285)
PHONE.....888 738-4230
EMP: 22 EST: 2015
SALES (est): 85.9K Privately Held
WEB: www.digitalscoreboards.net
SIC: 3571 Computers, digital, analog or hybrid

(G-18542)
DILLS ENTERPRISES LLC
Also Called: UNI Glide Trailer
301 Seaboard Ave (34285-4623)
PHONE.....941 493-1993
Robert Dills,
EMP: 5 EST: 1986
SQ FT: 32,000
SALES (est): 622.3K Privately Held
SIC: 3715 3444 2451 Truck trailers; sheet metalwork; mobile homes

(G-18543)
DYNAMIC VISIONS INC
355 Center Ct (34285-5506)
PHONE.....941 497-1984
William J Gill, *President*
Sara Gill, *Vice Pres*
EMP: 30 EST: 1988
SQ FT: 75,000
SALES (est): 2.9MM Privately Held
SIC: 3081 3211 Vinyl film & sheet; construction glass

(G-18544)
DYNAMIS EPOXY LLC
415 E Venice Ave (34285-4632)
PHONE.....941 488-3999
John Caramanian, *President*
EMP: 5 EST: 2006
SALES (est): 508.6K Privately Held
WEB: www.dcdynamis.com
SIC: 2891 2851 1771 Epoxy adhesives; marine paints; epoxy coatings; concrete repair

(G-18545)
DYNAMIS INC
415 E Venice Ave (34285-4632)
PHONE.....941 488-3999
John Caramanian, *President*
Cheryl Caramanian, *General Mgr*
EMP: 9 EST: 1947
SQ FT: 10,000
SALES (est): 1.6MM Privately Held
WEB: www.dcdynamis.com
SIC: 2851 Lacquers, varnishes, enamels & other coatings

(G-18546)
EMCEE ELECTRONICS INC (PA)
520 Cypress Ave (34285-4603)
PHONE.....941 485-1515
David Corzilius, *President*
Allan Barberio, *General Mgr*
Donna Neu, *Vice Pres*
EMP: 29 EST: 1958
SQ FT: 10,000
SALES (est): 4MM Privately Held
WEB: www.emcee-electronics.com
SIC: 3823 3829 Industrial instrmnts msrmnt display/control process variable; measuring & controlling devices

(G-18547)
ENZYMEDICA INC
771 Commerce Dr Ste 3 (34292-1731)
PHONE.....941 505-5565
Scott Sensenbrenner, *CEO*
Adrianne Newsome, *Partner*
Lou Destefano, *Principal*
Thomas G Bohager, *Chairman*
Paul Davison, *Exec VP*
EMP: 36 EST: 1998
SQ FT: 14,000
SALES (est): 11MM Privately Held
WEB: www.enzymedica.com
SIC: 2899 Gelatin capsules

(G-18548)
FLEX INNOVATIONS INC
313 Seaboard Ave Unit B (34285-4668)
PHONE.....866 310-3539
Dan B Asher, *Principal*
EMP: 9 EST: 2015
SALES (est): 319.4K Privately Held
WEB: www.flexinnovations.com
SIC: 3999 Manufacturing industries

(G-18549)
GENERAL RUBBER CORPORATION
Also Called: Technical Sales & Engineering
405 Commercial Ct Ste C (34292-1653)
PHONE.....941 412-0001
EMP: 8
SALES (corp-wide): 5.7MM Privately Held
WEB: www.general-rubber.com
SIC: 3069 Mallets, rubber; tubing, rubber; valves, hard rubber
PA: General Rubber Corporation
2201 E Ganley Rd
Tucson AZ 85706
520 889-2979

(G-18550)
GLASPRO
Also Called: Zap Skim'ers
101 Pond Cypress Rd (34292-1736)
PHONE.....941 488-4586
Robert H Smetts, *President*
Dave Scott, *Opers Mgr*
Karen Stewart, *Mktg Dir*
◆ EMP: 28 EST: 1989
SQ FT: 25,000
SALES (est): 4.7MM Privately Held
WEB: www.zapskimboards.com
SIC: 3949 Surfboards

(G-18551)
GULF BREEZE APPAREL LLC
616 Cypress Ave (34285-4605)
PHONE.....941 488-8337
Chad Jacob, *Manager*
EMP: 8 EST: 2009
SALES (est): 381.2K Privately Held
WEB: www.gulfbreezeapparel.com
SIC: 2759 Screen printing

(G-18552)
H & H SIGNS INC
426 E Venice Ave (34285-4631)
PHONE.....941 485-0556
John Hinshaw, *President*
EMP: 5 EST: 1996
SQ FT: 2,200
SALES (est): 474.8K Privately Held
WEB: www.hhsigns.com
SIC: 3993 Signs, not made in custom sign painting shops

(G-18553)
HARN RO SYSTEMS INC
310 Center Ct (34285-5505)
PHONE.....941 488-9671
James A Harn, *President*
Joe Chapman, *General Mgr*
Julia E Nemeth-Harn, *Vice Pres*
Jon Harn, *Project Engr*
Andrey Kharitonenko, *Project Engr*
▲ EMP: 22 EST: 1972
SQ FT: 40,000
SALES (est): 5.7MM Privately Held
WEB: www.harnrosystems.com
SIC: 3589 Water treatment equipment, industrial

(G-18554)
HOPE TECHNICAL SALES & SVCS
692 Sawgrass Bridge Rd (34292-4480)
PHONE.....941 412-1204
Jack Diggs, *Owner*
EMP: 5 EST: 1998
SALES (est): 361.1K Privately Held
SIC: 3714 Bumpers & bumperettes, motor vehicle

(G-18555)
HUNT VENTURES INC
232 Bahama St (34285-2450)
PHONE.....941 375-3699
Darin J Hunt, *Principal*
EMP: 10 EST: 2005
SALES (est): 1.9MM Privately Held
WEB: www.luminarysource.com
SIC: 1382 Oil & gas exploration services

(G-18556)
INLINE FILLING SYSTEMS LLC
216 Seaboard Ave (34285-4618)
PHONE.....941 486-8800
Samuel Lubus, *President*
◆ EMP: 30 EST: 1996
SQ FT: 26,000
SALES (est): 6.9MM
SALES (corp-wide): 2.5B Publicly Held
WEB: www.fillers.com
SIC: 3565 Bag opening, filling & closing machines
PA: The Middleby Corporation
1400 Toastmaster Dr
Elgin IL 60120
847 741-3300

(G-18557)
JOHN FRANKLIN MOWERY
100 W Venice Ave Ste E (34285-1928)
P.O. Box 489 (34284-0489)
PHONE.....202 468-8644
John F Mowery, *Principal*
EMP: 6 EST: 2016
SALES (est): 377.4K Privately Held
WEB: www.restorepaper.com
SIC: 2621 Book paper

(G-18558)
K V WATER EQUIPMENT & KRANE CO
Also Called: Krane Environmental
730 Commerce Dr (34292-1726)
PHONE.....941 723-0707
Don Borden, *President*
EMP: 10 EST: 1993
SQ FT: 10,000
SALES (est): 300.5K Privately Held
SIC: 3589 Water purification equipment, household type

GEOGRAPHIC

(G-18559)
KENT MFG FLA KEYS INC
248 James St (34285-5529)
PHONE..................................941 488-0355
Ronald K Drobisch, *Principal*
Melissa Guthrie, *Office Mgr*
EMP: 11 **EST:** 2016
SALES (est): 119.2K **Privately Held**
WEB: www.kentmfg.com
SIC: 3999 Manufacturing industries

(G-18560)
LOAD BANKS DIRECT LLC
309 Nassau St N (34285-1420)
P.O. Box 631287, Cincinnati OH (45263-1287)
PHONE..................................859 554-2522
Martin Glover, *President*
EMP: 12 **EST:** 2012
SQ FT: 10,000
SALES (est): 2.1MM **Privately Held**
WEB: www.loadbanksdirect.com
SIC: 3699 Electrical equipment & supplies

(G-18561)
LOUVERS WINDOW FASHIONS
1233 Waterside Ln (34285-6447)
PHONE..................................941 275-2655
Joseph Mason, *Principal*
EMP: 6 **EST:** 2012
SALES (est): 151.3K **Privately Held**
SIC: 2591 Venetian blinds

(G-18562)
MARITIME CUSTOM DESIGNS INC
170 Rich St (34292-3107)
PHONE..................................941 716-0255
Timothy McChesney, *President*
EMP: 8 **EST:** 2004
SALES (est): 156.9K **Privately Held**
SIC: 3089 Plastic boats & other marine equipment

(G-18563)
NASTY CHOPPERS INC
5010 Linda St (34293-6741)
PHONE..................................941 234-7743
Thomas Ball, *Principal*
EMP: 6 **EST:** 2008
SALES (est): 64.4K **Privately Held**
SIC: 3751 Motorcycles & related parts

(G-18564)
NICKOLS CBINETRY WOODWORKS INC
765 U S 41 Byp S Bypass S (34285)
PHONE..................................941 485-7894
Gary Nickols, *President*
EMP: 8 **EST:** 2003
SALES (est): 451.5K **Privately Held**
WEB: www.nickolscabinetry.com
SIC: 2434 Wood kitchen cabinets

(G-18565)
PACKARD COMPANY INC
787 Commerce Dr (34292-1747)
PHONE..................................941 451-8201
Gary Packard, *Principal*
EMP: 8 **EST:** 2016
SALES (est): 149.8K **Privately Held**
WEB: www.packardandco.com
SIC: 2434 Wood kitchen cabinets

(G-18566)
PARADISE CABLE INDUSTRIES
723 Commerce Dr Unit H (34292-1742)
PHONE..................................941 488-6092
Jon Bossoli, *President*
Tim Alexander, *Vice Pres*
EMP: 13 **EST:** 2011
SALES (est): 950K **Privately Held**
WEB: www.paradisecableind.com
SIC: 3679 Harness assemblies for electronic use: wire or cable

(G-18567)
PITELKA PLASTERING STUCCO
4951 Summertree Rd (34293-4254)
PHONE..................................630 235-5611
Bob Pitelka, *Owner*
EMP: 6 **EST:** 2009
SALES (est): 125.9K **Privately Held**
WEB: www.pitelkaplastering.com
SIC: 3299 Stucco

(G-18568)
RAYNETCRM LLC
121 Ginger Rd (34293-1521)
PHONE..................................813 489-9565
Ales Seifert,
Jaroslav Bazala,
Dusan Galik,
Lukas Rajsky,
EMP: 18 **EST:** 2014
SALES (est): 676.5K **Privately Held**
WEB: www.raynetcrm.com
SIC: 7372 Business oriented computer software

(G-18569)
RICHARD GRIGGS CUSTOM WOODWORK
1008 Mohawk Rd (34293-5378)
PHONE..................................941 223-9376
Richard Griggs, *Director*
EMP: 6 **EST:** 2004
SALES (est): 132.6K **Privately Held**
SIC: 2431 Millwork

(G-18570)
RICHARD MEER INVESTMENTS INC
Also Called: Buddy's Pizza
822 Pinebrook Rd (34285-7103)
PHONE..................................941 484-6551
Ailene Charlton, *President*
Larry Delor, *Vice Pres*
EMP: 6 **EST:** 1981
SALES (est): 311.7K **Privately Held**
SIC: 2032 5812 Italian foods: packaged in cans, jars, etc.; Italian restaurant; pizza restaurants

(G-18571)
RSSS 1 LLC
224 Pensacola Rd (34285-2326)
PHONE..................................941 483-3293
Stephen F Sherman, *Principal*
EMP: 6 **EST:** 2011
SALES (est): 140.2K **Privately Held**
SIC: 3011 Tires & inner tubes

(G-18572)
SCENTSTIONAL SOAPS CANDLES INC
730 Commerce Dr (34292-1726)
PHONE..................................941 485-1443
Amy R Morrison, *President*
Cathy Pidorenko, *Principal*
Stephen J Morrison, *Vice Pres*
Lori Gant, *Human Res Dir*
Janiece Cranmer, *VP Sales*
▲ **EMP:** 14 **EST:** 2003
SALES (est): 5.6MM **Privately Held**
WEB: www.scentsational-products.com
SIC: 2841 3999 5199 5999 Soap & other detergents; candles; candles; candle shops

(G-18573)
SINOFRESH HEALTHCARE INC (PA)
2357 S Tamiami Trl Unit 3 (34293-5022)
PHONE..................................941 270-2627
Thomas Fitzgerald, *Ch of Bd*
David R Olund, *President*
EMP: 8 **EST:** 1999
SQ FT: 2,500
SALES (est): 1.6MM **Privately Held**
WEB: www.sinofresh.com
SIC: 2834 Drugs affecting parasitic & infective diseases

(G-18574)
SOMATICS LLC
720 Commerce Dr Unit 101 (34292-1750)
PHONE..................................847 234-6761
Richard Abrams,
EMP: 7 **EST:** 1984
SQ FT: 1,400
SALES (est): 888.5K **Privately Held**
WEB: www.thymatron.com
SIC: 3845 Electromedical equipment

(G-18575)
SOUTHERN SPRING & STAMPING INC (PA)
401 Substation Rd (34285-6077)
PHONE..................................941 488-2276
Jeff Deaterly, *President*
Dee Deaterly, *Treasurer*
Lloyd Weed, *Admin Sec*
EMP: 50 **EST:** 1957
SQ FT: 40,000
SALES (est): 10MM **Privately Held**
WEB: www.southernspring.com
SIC: 3495 3496 3469 3493 Precision springs; miscellaneous fabricated wire products; metal stampings; steel springs, except wire

(G-18576)
SPERRY MARKETING GROUP INC
Also Called: Sperry Manufacturing
107 Corporation Way (34285-5524)
PHONE..................................941 483-4667
Steve Perry, *President*
▲ **EMP:** 12 **EST:** 1986
SQ FT: 15,000
SALES (est): 770K **Privately Held**
WEB: www.sperrymfg.com
SIC: 2392 Tablecloths: made from purchased materials; pads & padding, table: except asbestos, felt or rattan; chair covers & pads: made from purchased materials

(G-18577)
STEVE PRINTER INC
601 Cypress Ave (34285-4606)
PHONE..................................941 375-8657
Steve Smallwood, *President*
EMP: 8 **EST:** 2009
SALES (est): 124.2K **Privately Held**
SIC: 2752 Commercial printing, offset

(G-18578)
SUN COAST MEDIA GROUP INC
Venice Gondolier Sun
200 E Venice Ave Fl 1 (34285-1941)
P.O. Box 2390, Port Charlotte (33949)
PHONE..................................941 207-1000
Chris Weber, *President*
Bob Vedder, *Principal*
Robin Marotta, *Prdtn Mgr*
Marty Blubaugh, *Production*
Ken Shelby, *Production*
EMP: 60
SALES (corp-wide): 333.5MM **Privately Held**
WEB: www.yoursun.com
SIC: 2711 Newspapers, publishing & printing
HQ: Sun Coast Media Group, Inc.
23170 Harborview Rd
Port Charlotte FL 33980
941 206-1300

(G-18579)
SUNS UP OF SWF LLC
191 Lee Rd (34292-2523)
PHONE..................................301 470-2678
Mark Graham, *Manager*
EMP: 5 **EST:** 2011
SALES (est): 687.3K **Privately Held**
WEB: www.fixmycasablancafan.com
SIC: 3634 Ceiling fans

(G-18580)
TOMATOES & OLIVE OIL LLC
1055 Us Highway 41 Byp S (34285-4343)
PHONE..................................941 822-9709
Morgan Glickman, *Principal*
EMP: 6 **EST:** 2016
SALES (est): 276.7K **Privately Held**
SIC: 2079 Olive oil

(G-18581)
TOP HAT FOOD SERVICES LLC
11799 Granite Woods Loop (34292-4113)
PHONE..................................630 825-2800
Katherine Rini, *Manager*
EMP: 6 **EST:** 2018
SALES (est): 111.3K **Privately Held**
SIC: 2024 5812 Yogurt desserts, frozen; frozen yogurt stand

(G-18582)
TURBINE WELD INDUSTRIES LLC
402 Substation Rd (34285-6076)
PHONE..................................941 485-5113
David Venarge, *Principal*
Michael Halpin, *Principal*
Beth Laurenson, *Principal*
EMP: 40 **EST:** 2019
SALES (est): 2.6MM **Privately Held**
WEB: www.turbineweld.com
SIC: 3724 Aircraft engines & engine parts

(G-18583)
USSI LLC
752 Commerce Dr Ste 15 (34292-1744)
PHONE..................................941 244-2408
EMP: 15
SALES (est): 571.5K **Privately Held**
SIC: 2891 Mfg Adhesives/Sealants

(G-18584)
VAPRZONE LLC
448 Us Highway 41 Byp N (34285-6056)
PHONE..................................941 882-4841
Michael Brown, *Mng Member*
Penelope A Brown,
Joseph Gonzalez,
EMP: 8 **EST:** 2013
SALES (est): 350K **Privately Held**
WEB: www.vaprzone.com
SIC: 2899 2111 Oils & essential oils; cigarettes

(G-18585)
VENICE GRANIT & MARBLE INC
159 Progress Cir (34285-5537)
PHONE..................................941 483-4363
Charles Custin, *President*
Jeffrey Koffman, *Vice Pres*
▲ **EMP:** 7 **EST:** 1999
SALES (est): 511.2K **Privately Held**
WEB: www.kitchenbathinternational.com
SIC: 3281 2541 Table tops, marble; counter & sink tops

(G-18586)
VENICE PRINT CENTER
200 E Venice Ave (34285-1941)
PHONE..................................941 206-1414
EMP: 6 **EST:** 2018
SALES (est): 107.5K **Privately Held**
WEB: www.veniceprintcenter.com
SIC: 2752 Commercial printing, lithographic

Vernon
Washington County

(G-18587)
TIMBURR EXPRESS LLC
3765 Highway 79 (32462-3726)
PHONE..................................850 535-1488
David Haselow, *Mng Member*
EMP: 7 **EST:** 2015
SALES (est): 528.2K **Privately Held**
SIC: 3531 Logging equipment

Vero Beach
Indian River County

(G-18588)
2204 AVENUE X LLC
1275 Us Highway 1 Unit 2 (32960-4706)
PHONE..................................407 619-1410
Robin Filosa, *President*
Alexander Filosa, *Principal*
Mary Ann Filosa, *Vice Pres*
Lisa Filosa, *Treasurer*
EMP: 7 **EST:** 2015
SALES (est): 785.9K **Privately Held**
SIC: 3679 Electronic components

(G-18589)
AA PERFORMANCE
955 13th Ln (32960-4732)
PHONE..................................772 672-1164
EMP: 6 **EST:** 2013
SALES (est): 169.6K **Privately Held**
SIC: 3714 Motor vehicle parts & accessories

(G-18590)
ACTION PRINTERS INC
2571 Stockbridge Sq Sw (32962-4217)
PHONE..................................772 567-4377
Kim E Barrett, *President*
Sharon K Schroeder, *Vice Pres*

EMP: 8 EST: 1961
SQ FT: 5,500
SALES (est): 795.6K Privately Held
WEB: www.verobeach.minutemanpress.com
SIC: 2752 Commercial printing, offset

(G-18591)
ALL PHASE WELDING LLC
8356 E 98th Ave (32967-2819)
PHONE 772 834-2980
Leslie Fletcher, *Principal*
EMP: 6 EST: 2017
SALES (est): 67.2K Privately Held
SIC: 7692 Welding repair

(G-18592)
ALUMA TOWER COMPANY INC (HQ)
1639 Old Dixie Hwy (32960-3656)
P.O. Box 2806 (32961-2806)
PHONE 772 567-3423
Robert A Main Jr, *President*
John Hall, *Vice Pres*
Shane Mullan, *Purch Mgr*
Susan E Main, *CFO*
William C Main, *Treasurer*
▼ EMP: 20 EST: 1974
SQ FT: 18,000
SALES (est): 15MM
SALES (corp-wide): 34.7MM Privately Held
WEB: www.alumatower.com
SIC: 3441 Tower sections, radio & television transmission
PA: Main, Robert A & Sons Holding Company Inc
20-21 Wagaraw Rd
Fair Lawn NJ 07410
201 447-3700

(G-18593)
ALUMA TOWER COMPANY INC
926 Old Dixie Hwy (32960-4357)
PHONE 772 567-3423
John Hall, *Vice Pres*
Joseph Blume, *Sales Engr*
EMP: 15
SALES (corp-wide): 34.7MM Privately Held
WEB: www.alumatower.com
SIC: 3441 Tower sections, radio & television transmission
HQ: Aluma Tower Company, Inc.
1639 Old Dixie Hwy
Vero Beach FL 32960
772 567-3423

(G-18594)
APPROVED TURBO COMPONENTS INC
663 2nd Ln (32962-2951)
PHONE 559 627-3600
Michael Rogers, *President*
▲ EMP: 10 EST: 1998
SALES (est): 911K Privately Held
WEB: www.approvedturbo.com
SIC: 3724 Turbo-superchargers, aircraft

(G-18595)
ATLAS ORGNICS INDIAN RIVER LLC
925 74th Ave Sw (32968-9755)
PHONE 772 563-9336
Joseph McMillin, *Mng Member*
Gary Nihard,
EMP: 10 EST: 2019
SALES (est): 711.9K Privately Held
WEB: www.atlasorganics.net
SIC: 2875 Compost

(G-18596)
AUTOPAX INC
6602 Liberty Pl (32966-8991)
PHONE 772 563-0131
John Inglis, *Owner*
EMP: 6 EST: 2008
SALES (est): 94.7K Privately Held
SIC: 3086 Packaging & shipping materials, foamed plastic

(G-18597)
B & F WASTE SOLUTIONS LLC
Also Called: Anytime Waste
4901 Bethel Creek Dr F (32963-1276)
P.O. Box 690729 (32969-0729)
PHONE 772 336-1113
Beatrice Sartor, *Mng Member*
EMP: 5 EST: 2011
SQ FT: 1,200
SALES (est): 500K Privately Held
SIC: 3443 Industrial vessels, tanks & containers

(G-18598)
BACK COUNTRY INC
636 34th Ter (32968-1224)
PHONE 772 532-6174
Eric Davis, *President*
Nancy Grebe, *Treasurer*
Danielle Albertson, *Admin Sec*
EMP: 6 EST: 1993
SQ FT: 1,400
SALES (est): 250K Privately Held
WEB: www.backcountry.com
SIC: 3949 5611 5941 5948 Fishing equipment; men's & boys' clothing stores; fishing equipment; luggage, except footlockers & trunks

(G-18599)
BIGG PUBLISHING
5082 4th Ln (32968-1863)
PHONE 772 563-0425
EMP: 6 EST: 2008
SALES (est): 94K Privately Held
SIC: 2741 Miscellaneous publishing

(G-18600)
BITVISORY INC
601 21st St Ste 300 (32960-0860)
PHONE 801 336-6626
Jonathan Wesley,
EMP: 6 EST: 2017
SALES (est): 96.3K Privately Held
SIC: 7372 Application computer software

(G-18601)
BLACK DIAMOND SYSTEMS CORP (PA)
1305 Cape Pointe Cir (32963-3995)
PHONE 917 539-7309
David Brand, *CFO*
EMP: 96 EST: 2019
SALES (est): 4.5MM Privately Held
SIC: 3571 Electronic computers

(G-18602)
BLACKHAWK CONSTRUCTION CO INC (PA)
Also Called: Blackhawk Quarry Co of Fla
3060 Airport West Dr (32960-1993)
PHONE 321 258-4957
Andrew Machata, *President*
Adele Machata, *Vice Pres*
EMP: 29 EST: 1965
SQ FT: 11,000
SALES (est): 2.8MM Privately Held
WEB: www.blackhawkconstructionaz.com
SIC: 1499 Shell mining

(G-18603)
BREWER INTERNATIONAL INC
605 90th Ave (32968-9751)
P.O. Box 690037 (32969-0037)
PHONE 772 562-0555
Jesse Cruz, *President*
Stephen Brewer, *President*
James Brewer, *Vice Pres*
Linda Brewer, *Administration*
EMP: 10 EST: 1970
SQ FT: 14,000
SALES (est): 2.2MM Privately Held
WEB: www.brewerint.com
SIC: 2879 2842 3999 Agricultural chemicals; specialty cleaning preparations; barber & beauty shop equipment

(G-18604)
BRICK PAVERS BY MENDOZA INC (PA)
1235 S Us Highway 1 (32962-6450)
PHONE 772 925-1666
Elias Mendoza-Hernandez, *President*
Pedro Martinez, *Vice Pres*
David Mendoza, *Vice Pres*
EMP: 52 EST: 2014
SALES (est): 401.2K Privately Held
SIC: 2951 Asphalt paving mixtures & blocks

(G-18605)
BRICK PAVERS BY MENDOZA INC
1986 21st St Sw (32962-7915)
PHONE 772 408-2005
J Carmen Mendoza-Hernandez, *Manager*
EMP: 18
SALES (corp-wide): 401.2K Privately Held
SIC: 2951 Asphalt paving mixtures & blocks
PA: Brick Pavers By Mendoza Inc
1235 S Us Highway 1
Vero Beach FL 32962
772 925-1666

(G-18606)
BRYANTS PRECISION M F G CORP
Also Called: Bryant Machine Shop
1803 Wilbur Ave (32960-5567)
P.O. Box 2844 (32961-2844)
PHONE 772 569-2319
Brenda Bryant, *President*
L Dale Bryant Jr, *General Mgr*
EMP: 28 EST: 1984
SQ FT: 8,000
SALES (est): 4.9MM Privately Held
WEB: www.bryantprecision.net
SIC: 3599 Machine shop, jobbing & repair

(G-18607)
BUCK PILE INC
2801 Ocean Dr Ste 101 (32963-2016)
PHONE 772 492-1056
Christopher Smoot, *President*
Sarah Smoot, *Vice Pres*
Alex Smoot, *Manager*
Elizabeth Foster, *Admin Sec*
EMP: 7 EST: 1984
SQ FT: 1,500
SALES (est): 663.5K Privately Held
WEB: www.pilebuck.com
SIC: 2711 2731 Newspapers: publishing only, not printed on site; books: publishing only

(G-18608)
CABINETREE COLLECTION INC
860 35th Ct Sw (32968-5062)
PHONE 772 569-4761
Douglas Hampel, *President*
EMP: 10 EST: 1991
SQ FT: 5,000
SALES (est): 989.5K Privately Held
WEB: www.cabinetreecollection.com
SIC: 2434 Wood kitchen cabinets

(G-18609)
CALENDAR ARTS LLC ✪
1191 Us Highway 1 (32960-5790)
PHONE 407 285-8139
Kanessia Emory,
EMP: 10 EST: 2021
SALES (est): 200K Privately Held
SIC: 3229 Art, decorative & novelty glassware

(G-18610)
CHARLESTON WINERY
465 18th St (32960-6210)
PHONE 843 425-1265
Kevin Simback, *Principal*
EMP: 7 EST: 2014
SALES (est): 221.3K Privately Held
SIC: 2084 Wines

(G-18611)
CONNECT SLUTIONS WORLDWIDE LLC
Also Called: Symbee/Symbee Connect
1602 Indian Bay Dr (32963-2210)
PHONE 407 492-9370
Jerry E Perkins, *CEO*
Lance Guthrie, *Principal*
Jerry Perkins, *Principal*
EMP: 5 EST: 2019
SALES (est): 385.3K Privately Held
WEB: www.connectbestsolutionsllc.com
SIC: 7372 Prepackaged software

(G-18612)
CONRAD PICKEL STUDIO INC
7777 20th St (32966-1314)
PHONE 772 567-1710
R Paul Pickel, *President*
Kristi Pickel, *Corp Secy*
Lisa Pickel, *Vice Pres*
▲ EMP: 9 EST: 1946
SQ FT: 4,000
SALES (est): 1MM Privately Held
WEB: www.pickelstudio.com
SIC: 3231 Stained glass: made from purchased glass; mosaics, glass: made from purchased glass

(G-18613)
CONSTRUCTCONNECT INC
2001 9th Ave Ste 204 (32960-6415)
PHONE 772 770-6003
Dave Conway, *Branch Mgr*
EMP: 200
SALES (corp-wide): 5.5B Publicly Held
WEB: www.isqft.com
SIC: 2721 Magazines: publishing only, not printed on site
HQ: Constructconnect, Inc.
3825 Edwards Rd Ste 800
Cincinnati OH 45209
800 364-2059

(G-18614)
CUSTOM WALL SYSTEMS INC
9495 22nd St (32966-3056)
PHONE 772 408-3006
Mark Unterreiner, *Principal*
EMP: 8 EST: 2016
SALES (est): 389.2K Privately Held
SIC: 3299 Stucco

(G-18615)
DEPENDABLE WATER INC (PA)
7956 102nd Ct (32967-2893)
PHONE 772 563-7473
Jason Decker, *Principal*
EMP: 35 EST: 2019
SALES (est): 362.1K Privately Held
WEB: www.dependablewaterinc.com
SIC: 2834 1781 3589 Chlorination tablets & kits (water purification); water well servicing; water filters & softeners, household type; water purification equipment, household type; water treatment equipment, industrial

(G-18616)
EMERGE INTERACTIVE INC (PA)
5375 Sol Rue Cir (32967-7025)
PHONE 772 563-0570
John C Belknap, *Ch of Bd*
David C Warren, *President*
Robert E Drury, *Exec VP*
Mark S Fox, *Exec VP*
Marvin L Slosman, *Exec VP*
EMP: 23 EST: 1994
SQ FT: 10,798 Privately Held
SIC: 3556 Food products machinery; meat processing machinery

(G-18617)
FLOAT-ON CORPORATION
1925 98th Ave (32966-3034)
PHONE 772 569-4440
L Ralph Poppell, *Chairman*
Timothy R Poppell, *Vice Pres*
▼ EMP: 22 EST: 1967
SQ FT: 30,208
SALES (est): 4.9MM Privately Held
WEB: www.floaton.com
SIC: 3799 3444 Boat trailers; sheet metalwork

(G-18618)
FLORIDA MOLD MITIGATORS LLC
7025 29th Ct (32967-5754)
PHONE 772 633-3415
Bryant D William, *Principal*
EMP: 6 EST: 2015
SALES (est): 109.4K Privately Held
SIC: 3544 Industrial molds

(G-18619)
FLORIDA SHUTTERS INC
1055 Commerce Ave (32960-5772)
PHONE 772 569-2200

Thomas L Pease, *President*
John Matranga, *Mfg Staff*
Dale Brown, *Purchasing*
Jill Pease, *Admin Sec*
▼ **EMP:** 45 **EST:** 1979
SQ FT: 18,000
SALES (est): 8.6MM **Privately Held**
WEB: www.floridashuttersinc.com
SIC: 3444 3442 2394 1799 Awnings, sheet metal; shutters, door or window: metal; awnings, fabric: made from purchased materials; awning installation

(G-18620)
FLOWERS BAKING CO MIAMI LLC
3215 Aviation Blvd (32960-7905)
PHONE..................................772 778-3990
David Gandy, *Office Mgr*
EMP: 10
SALES (corp-wide): 4.3B **Publicly Held**
SIC: 2051 Bakery: wholesale or whole-sale/retail combined
HQ: Flowers Baking Co. Of Miami, Llc
17800 Nw Miami Ct
Miami FL 33169
305 652-3416

(G-18621)
FOLEY PUBLISHING LLC
7530 15th Ln (32966-1229)
P.O. Box 691302 (32969-1302)
PHONE..................................908 766-6006
Jaclyn Foley,
EMP: 7 **EST:** 2018
SALES (est): 222.1K **Privately Held**
WEB: www.bartender.com
SIC: 2741 Miscellaneous publishing

(G-18622)
FROSTING
2915 Cardinal Dr (32963-1916)
PHONE..................................772 234-2915
Barbaralee C Monday, *Principal*
EMP: 8 **EST:** 2009
SALES (est): 546.9K **Privately Held**
WEB: www.frostingverobeach.com
SIC: 2051 Bakery: wholesale or whole-sale/retail combined

(G-18623)
GRANITE ENVIRONMENTAL LLC ✪
Also Called: Gei Works
5400 85th St (32967-5544)
PHONE..................................772 646-0597
Karen Allan, *General Mgr*
Keith Eismann,
John Schlueter,
EMP: 12 **EST:** 2020
SALES (est): 1MM **Privately Held**
SIC: 3272 Incinerators, concrete

(G-18624)
H317 LOGISTICS LLC
9019 Somerset Bay Ln # 402
(32963-5603)
PHONE..................................404 307-1621
Douglas H Lynn Jr, *Mng Member*
Mark Bragg,
Charles Pethel,
EMP: 6 **EST:** 2014
SQ FT: 16,000
SALES (est): 561.5K **Privately Held**
SIC: 2512 Upholstered household furniture

(G-18625)
HDL THERAPEUTICS INC
601 21st St Ste 300 (32960-0860)
PHONE..................................772 453-2770
Michael M Matin, *CEO*
EMP: 7 **EST:** 2016
SALES (est): 600.1K **Privately Held**
WEB: www.hdltherapeutics.com
SIC: 3841 Medical instruments & equipment, blood & bone work

(G-18626)
HYBRID SOURCES INC
2950 43rd Ave (32960-1914)
PHONE..................................772 563-9100
Richard A Vogel, *CEO*
Arleen N Vogel, *President*
Patricia Amoroso, *Principal*
Richard Barnes, *Engineer*
Richard Vogel, *Info Tech Mgr*
▼ **EMP:** 15 **EST:** 1985
SQ FT: 5,000
SALES (est): 2.3MM **Privately Held**
WEB: www.hybridsources.com
SIC: 3674 Integrated circuits, semiconductor networks, etc.

(G-18627)
I WENTWORTH INC
645 Beachland Blvd (32963-1725)
PHONE..................................561 231-7544
A D Teaze, *Principal*
EMP: 6 **EST:** 2009
SALES (est): 112.4K **Privately Held**
SIC: 2782 Blankbooks & looseleaf binders

(G-18628)
IMPERIAL IMPRINTING LLC
8815 92nd Ct (32967-3543)
PHONE..................................772 633-8256
Tera Adams, *Principal*
EMP: 7 **EST:** 2016
SALES (est): 402.7K **Privately Held**
WEB: www.imperialimprinting.com
SIC: 2752 Commercial printing, offset

(G-18629)
INDIAN RIVER ALL-FAB INC
1119 18th Pl (32960-3649)
PHONE..................................772 778-0032
John R Cooper, *President*
EMP: 7 **EST:** 1987
SQ FT: 4,500
SALES (est): 998.5K **Privately Held**
WEB: www.indianriverchamber.com
SIC: 3599 Machine shop, jobbing & repair

(G-18630)
INEOS NEW PLANET BIOENERGY LLC
925 74th Ave Sw (32968-9755)
PHONE..................................772 794-7900
Peter Williams, *CEO*
David King, *President*
Mark Niederschulte, *COO*
Martin Olavesen, *CFO*
John McNally, *Info Tech Dir*
▲ **EMP:** 25 **EST:** 2009
SALES (est): 2MM
SALES (corp-wide): 1.1MM **Privately Held**
WEB: www.jupengbio.com
SIC: 2821 Plastics materials & resins
HQ: Jupeng Bio Sa
C/O Fabien Gillioz, Avocat, etude
Ochsner & Associes
GenCve GE 1204
216 241-721

(G-18631)
INQUIRER NEWSPAPERS INC
2046 Treasure Coast Plz (32960-0927)
PHONE..................................772 257-6230
John Patrick, *Director*
EMP: 8 **EST:** 2011
SALES (est): 127.9K **Privately Held**
WEB: www.inquirer.com
SIC: 2711 Newspapers, publishing & printing

(G-18632)
IOMARTCLOUD INC
601 21st St (32960-0801)
PHONE..................................954 880-1680
Angus Macsween, *CEO*
Richard Logan, *CFO*
William Strain, *CTO*
EMP: 7 **EST:** 2013
SQ FT: 3,000
SALES (est): 1.6MM
SALES (corp-wide): 157.6MM **Privately Held**
WEB: www.easyspace.com
SIC: 7372 Business oriented computer software
PA: Iomart Group Plc
Lister Pavilion
Glasgow G20 0
141 931-6400

(G-18633)
JIM BAIRD CABINETS
1020 11th Pl Ste 1 (32960-2139)
PHONE..................................772 569-0936
Jim Baird, *President*
EMP: 5 **EST:** 1984
SALES (est): 467.9K **Privately Held**
WEB: www.jimbairdcabinets.com
SIC: 2434 Vanities, bathroom: wood

(G-18634)
JOHANNSEN BOAT WORKS INC
690 4th Pl Ste D (32962-1671)
P.O. Box 2311 (32961-2311)
PHONE..................................772 567-4612
Mark Johannsen, *President*
Suzanne Johannsen, *Vice Pres*
▼ **EMP:** 5 **EST:** 1978
SALES (est): 431.6K **Privately Held**
WEB: www.trinka.com
SIC: 3732 Boats, fiberglass: building & repairing

(G-18635)
KAMCO INDUSTRIES LLC
5720 Us Highway 1 (32967-7531)
PHONE..................................772 299-1401
Keith A Moskowitz, *Manager*
EMP: 10 **EST:** 2016
SALES (est): 130K **Privately Held**
WEB: www.kumi-na.com
SIC: 3999 Manufacturing industries

(G-18636)
KITE VN CORPORATION
1045 Winding River Rd (32963-2550)
PHONE..................................772 234-3484
Keith Kite, *Principal*
EMP: 7 **EST:** 2017
SALES (est): 45.1K **Privately Held**
SIC: 3944 Kites

(G-18637)
KREATECK INTERNATIONAL CORP
1707 20th St (32960-3567)
PHONE..................................772 925-1216
Rocio Coronado, *President*
Brenda Coronado, *Vice Pres*
Luis Coronado, *Vice Pres*
Sergio Coronado, *Vice Pres*
EMP: 12 **EST:** 2004
SALES (est): 578.8K **Privately Held**
WEB: www.kreateck.com
SIC: 7372 7373 8731 Prepackaged software; computer integrated systems design; computer (hardware) development

(G-18638)
LATITUDE 27 CANVAS
2306 7th Ave (32960-5166)
PHONE..................................772 321-6361
Tony W Sitko, *Principal*
EMP: 7 **EST:** 2007
SALES (est): 129.2K **Privately Held**
WEB: www.latitude-27-canvas.business.site
SIC: 2211 Canvas

(G-18639)
LINENMASTER LLC
601 21st St Ste 300 (32960-0860)
PHONE..................................772 212-2710
James Adler,
EMP: 20 **EST:** 2019
SALES (est): 1.1MM **Privately Held**
WEB: www.linenmaster.com
SIC: 7372 Prepackaged software

(G-18640)
LITTERBIN LLC
669 2nd Ln (32962-2951)
PHONE..................................772 633-7184
Michael W Rogers, *Administration*
EMP: 7 **EST:** 2016
SALES (est): 313.9K **Privately Held**
WEB: www.litterbin.net
SIC: 2673 Trash bags (plastic film): made from purchased materials

(G-18641)
MARY ANGEL
6700 37th St (32966-1412)
PHONE..................................772 299-1392
Paul Thornton, *Principal*
EMP: 6 **EST:** 2004
SALES (est): 329.6K **Privately Held**
WEB: www.starwear.us
SIC: 2323 Men's & boys' neckwear

(G-18642)
MAXRODON MARBLE INC
2250 Old Dixie Hwy Se (32962-7407)
P.O. Box 881 (32961-0881)
PHONE..................................772 562-7543
Ralph P Hamilton, *President*
Kathy Hamilton, *Treasurer*
EMP: 6 **EST:** 1974
SALES (est): 300K **Privately Held**
SIC: 3272 Art marble, concrete; window sills, cast stone

(G-18643)
MELANIE R BUSH PAVERS
8316 106th Ave (32967-3639)
PHONE..................................772 501-7295
Melanie Bush, *Principal*
EMP: 7 **EST:** 2013
SALES (est): 122.3K **Privately Held**
WEB: www.mrbpavers.com
SIC: 2951 Asphalt paving mixtures & blocks

(G-18644)
MORNING STAR PERSONALIZED AP
Also Called: New Wave Designs
621 2nd Ln (32962-2939)
PHONE..................................772 569-8412
Natall Barsalou, *President*
Joseph Brown, *President*
EMP: 8 **EST:** 1983
SQ FT: 6,000
SALES (est): 500K **Privately Held**
WEB: www.morningstartshirts.com
SIC: 2759 Screen printing

(G-18645)
MOULTON PUBLICATIONS INC
Also Called: Vero Beach Magazine
956 20th St Ste 101 (32960-6423)
PHONE..................................772 234-8871
Beth Moulton, *President*
Susan Haller, *Accounts Exec*
Jennifer Croom, *Manager*
Lisa Diggins, *CIO*
Renee Brady, *Art Dir*
EMP: 9 **EST:** 1996
SALES (est): 1.3MM **Privately Held**
SIC: 2721 Magazines: publishing only, not printed on site

(G-18646)
NATIONAL AEROSPACE GROUP INC
928 36th Ct Sw (32968-4963)
P.O. Box 690575 (32969-0575)
PHONE..................................817 226-0315
Sujan Ghimire, *President*
EMP: 7 **EST:** 2017
SALES (est): 533K **Privately Held**
WEB: www.nationalaerogroup.com
SIC: 3728 Aircraft parts & equipment

(G-18647)
NOVURANIA OF AMERICA INC
2105 S Us Highway 1 (32962-7402)
PHONE..................................772 567-9200
Robert Collada, *President*
Carlo Cozzio, *COO*
Flavia Pellegrini, *Exec VP*
Sylvia Collada, *Treasurer*
Barbara Mixson, *Manager*
◆ **EMP:** 73 **EST:** 1990
SALES (est): 13.8MM
SALES (corp-wide): 15.6MM **Privately Held**
WEB: www.novurania.com
SIC: 3732 Boat building & repairing
PA: Novurania Spa
Via Circonvallazione 3
Tione Di Trento TN 38079
046 533-9311

(G-18648)
NURSERYMENS SURE-GRO CORP
4390 Us Highway 1 (32967-1507)
PHONE..................................772 770-0462
Lawrence R Walker, *President*
EMP: 7 **EST:** 1974
SQ FT: 6,000

▲ = Import ▼=Export
◆ =Import/Export

SALES (est): 908K Privately Held
WEB: www.suregro.net
SIC: 2873 2874 Nitrogenous fertilizers; phosphatic fertilizers

(G-18649)
NYLACARB CORP
1725 98th Ave (32966-3032)
PHONE....772 569-5999
Scott Cooley, *President*
Daug Cooley, *Vice Pres*
Frank Cooley Jr, *Vice Pres*
EMP: 25 EST: 1987
SQ FT: 27,000
SALES (est): 6.6MM Privately Held
WEB: www.nylacarb.com
SIC: 3089 Injection molding of plastics

(G-18650)
PARABEL USA INC
1991 74th Ave Ste B (32966-5110)
PHONE....978 905-0958
Anthony Tiarks, *CEO*
Anne-Marie Parker, *Business Mgr*
Lucille Forbes, *Purchasing*
Molly Sproston, *Research*
Kathleen McFadden, *CFO*
EMP: 10 EST: 2013
SALES (est): 6.1MM Privately Held
WEB: www.parabel.com
SIC: 2869 6794 Industrial organic chemicals; patent buying, licensing, leasing
PA: Parabel Ltd
Sheikh Zayed Road Near Royal Orchid
Abu Dhabi

(G-18651)
PAVER TECHNOLOGIES LLC
2110 Captains Walk (32963-2821)
PHONE....772 213-8905
Tim Berry, *Principal*
Timothy Berry,
Paulo Alberto,
Rick Berry,
Brian Dahl,
EMP: 9 EST: 2016
SALES (est): 785.9K Privately Held
WEB: www.pavertech.com
SIC: 2951 5032 Paving blocks; paving mixtures; paving materials; paving mixtures

(G-18652)
PCP TACTICAL LLC
3895 39th Sq (32960-1812)
P.O. Box 643401 (32964-3401)
PHONE....772 473-3472
Thomas L Corr, *Manager*
Charles A Padgett,
EMP: 6 EST: 2010
SALES (est): 1.1MM Privately Held
SIC: 3482 Small arms ammunition

(G-18653)
PIPER AIRCRAFT INC (PA)
2926 Piper Dr (32960-1964)
PHONE....772 567-4361
Simon Caldecott, *CEO*
Jalal Jamil, *General Mgr*
Drew McEwen, *Principal*
John Calcagno, *Vice Pres*
James Punk, *Vice Pres*
EMP: 825 EST: 1937
SQ FT: 1,000,000
SALES (est): 228.8MM Privately Held
WEB: www.piper.com
SIC: 3721 3728 Airplanes, fixed or rotary wing; aircraft parts & equipment

(G-18654)
PLANT FOODS INC
5051 41st St (32967-1901)
P.O. Box 1089 (32961-1089)
PHONE....772 567-5741
Robert Geary III, *President*
Edward J Geary, *Exec VP*
Mj Connelly, *Treasurer*
David Geary, *Admin Sec*
▼ EMP: 35 EST: 1985
SQ FT: 7,500
SALES (est): 10.8MM Privately Held
WEB: www.plantfoodsinc.com
SIC: 2875 2653 Fertilizers, mixing only; boxes, corrugated: made from purchased materials

(G-18655)
QCAB LLC
281 53rd Cir Vero Bch Fl (32968)
PHONE....305 510-2566
Lydia Todman, *Mng Member*
James Maton,
EMP: 5 EST: 2015
SALES (est): 700K Privately Held
WEB: www.myqcab.com
SIC: 3534 Elevators & equipment

(G-18656)
QOL MEDICAL LLC (PA)
3405 Ocean Dr (32963-1620)
PHONE....772 584-3640
Frederick Cooper, *CEO*
William Dupere, *COO*
Jackson Tubbs, *Production*
William Bryant, *CFO*
Paul Capozello, *Regl Sales Mgr*
EMP: 2 EST: 2005
SALES (est): 4.7MM Privately Held
WEB: www.qolmed.com
SIC: 2834 Pills, pharmaceutical

(G-18657)
QUIK TEK INC
2046 Treasure Coast Plz (32960-0927)
PHONE....772 501-3471
Don Biscoe, *Principal*
EMP: 7 EST: 2016
SALES (est): 92.3K Privately Held
WEB: www.quiktekmachining.com
SIC: 3599 Machine shop, jobbing & repair

(G-18658)
R & L MANUFACTURING INC
5021 41st St Unit 2 (32967-1965)
PHONE....772 770-9300
EMP: 10
SQ FT: 8,000
SALES (est): 1.5MM Privately Held
SIC: 3565 Mfg Packaging Machinery

(G-18659)
ROBOMOW USA INC
9050 16th Pl Ste 1 (32966-7583)
P.O. Box 1329, Roseland (32957-1329)
PHONE....844 762-6669
Udi Peless, *CEO*
Karsten Beck, *COO*
EMP: 5 EST: 2013
SQ FT: 1,000
SALES (est): 2.2MM Privately Held
WEB: www.usa.robomow.com
SIC: 3524 Grass catchers, lawn mower

(G-18660)
ROURKE EDUCATIONAL MEDIA LLC
2066 14th Ave Ste 101 (32960-4419)
P.O. Box 820 (32961-0820)
PHONE....772 234-6001
James Colandrea, *President*
Ira Hernowitz, *President*
Keli Sipperley, *Editor*
Craig Lopetz, *VP Mktg*
Janine Fisher, *Graphic Designe*
▲ EMP: 26 EST: 2000
SQ FT: 2,500
SALES (est): 3.1MM Privately Held
WEB: www.rourkeeducationalmedia.com
SIC: 2731 Books: publishing only

(G-18661)
ROURKE RAY PUBLISHING CO INC
Also Called: Rourke Publishing Group
1701 Highway A1a Ste 300 (32963-2263)
PHONE....772 234-6001
James Colandrea, *President*
Steve Oehler, *Administration*
EMP: 9 EST: 1980
SQ FT: 1,500
SALES (est): 670K Privately Held
SIC: 2731 Book clubs: publishing only, not printed on site

(G-18662)
SEBASTIAN SEA PRODUCTS IN
1800 Us Highway 1 (32960-0903)
PHONE....772 321-3997
Joseph Fenyak, *Principal*
EMP: 6 EST: 2006
SALES (est): 86.1K Privately Held
SIC: 3999 Manufacturing industries

(G-18663)
SEE-RAY PLUMBING INC
2020 Old Dixie Hwy Se (32962-7256)
PHONE....772 489-2474
Raymond F Causley, *President*
Raymond Causley, *President*
AMI-Jo Causley, *Vice Pres*
EMP: 23 EST: 2006
SALES (est): 3.3MM Privately Held
WEB: www.seerayplumbing.com
SIC: 3088 2842 Bathroom fixtures, plastic; drain pipe solvents or cleaners

(G-18664)
SHAVER PROPERTIES INC
Also Called: Shaver Millwork
6010 Old Dixie Hwy Ste K (32967-7539)
PHONE....772 569-3466
Robert A Shaver, *President*
Jason A Shaver, *Corp Secy*
Mark A Shaver, *Vice Pres*
▼ EMP: 37 EST: 1980
SQ FT: 26,000
SALES (est): 1.4MM Privately Held
WEB: www.shavermillwork.com
SIC: 2431 Doors, wood

(G-18665)
SNOWS CUSTOM FURNITURE INC
4009 Us Highway 1 (32960-1552)
PHONE....772 794-4430
Steven C Long, *President*
EMP: 6 EST: 2005
SALES (est): 300K Privately Held
WEB: www.snowcabinetry.com
SIC: 2434 Wood kitchen cabinets

(G-18666)
SPEECH BIN
1965 25th Ave (32960-3062)
PHONE....772 770-0006
Joseph M Binney, *CEO*
Jan Binney, *President*
EMP: 10 EST: 1984
SQ FT: 5,000
SALES (est): 989.8K Privately Held
SIC: 2731 Books: publishing & printing

(G-18667)
SPINNAKER VERO INC
Also Called: Minuteman Press
983 12th St Ste A (32960-6726)
PHONE....772 567-4645
Steven Brunk, *President*
Carlene M Brunk, *Corp Secy*
Christina Cassell, *Cust Mgr*
Geoff Krysl, *Manager*
EMP: 10 EST: 2007
SQ FT: 15,000
SALES (est): 2MM Privately Held
WEB: www.chanhassen-mn.minutemanpress.com
SIC: 2752 Commercial printing, lithographic

(G-18668)
STEPHS WOODWORKING LLC
6065 21st St Sw (32968-9427)
PHONE....772 571-2661
Elena Bouyssou, *Principal*
EMP: 7 EST: 2014
SALES (est): 140.4K Privately Held
SIC: 2431 Millwork

(G-18669)
SWEET CREATIONS BY L S YOUNG
953 Old Dixie Hwy Ste B11 (32960-4373)
PHONE....772 584-7206
Lori Young, *Principal*
EMP: 8 EST: 2011
SALES (est): 425.7K Privately Held
WEB: www.sweetcreationsverobeach.com
SIC: 2051 Bakery: wholesale or wholesale/retail combined

(G-18670)
THEFT PROTECTION COM CORP
Also Called: Compuclamp
656 Broadway St (32960-5116)
PHONE....772 231-6677
Lawrence P Westfield, *President*
EMP: 10 EST: 1994
SALES (est): 740.4K Privately Held
SIC: 3699 Security devices

(G-18671)
TIE COLLECTION LLC
8071 Westfield Cir (32966-5146)
PHONE....305 323-1420
Dainelys Torres, *Mng Member*
EMP: 8 EST: 2014
SALES (est): 455.2K Privately Held
SIC: 2241 5611 Tie tapes, woven or braided; tie shops

(G-18672)
UNIQUE MARBLE INC
780 8th Ct (32962-1647)
PHONE....772 766-4432
Fred Chavis, *President*
Manuel Dimech, *Vice Pres*
EMP: 10 EST: 1981
SQ FT: 13,750
SALES (est): 637.7K Privately Held
WEB: www.bridgesbyclassen.com
SIC: 3281 5211 Cut stone & stone products; bathroom fixtures, equipment & supplies

(G-18673)
UNITED JICE COMPANIES AMER INC
Also Called: Juiceco
505 66th Ave Sw (32968-9371)
PHONE....772 562-5442
Steve Bogen, *CEO*
Marc Craen, *COO*
Colton Greg, *Plant Mgr*
Brenda Motley, *Controller*
David McGill, *Sales Staff*
◆ EMP: 60 EST: 2002
SQ FT: 2,000
SALES (est): 14.9MM Privately Held
WEB: www.unitedjuice.com
SIC: 2033 Fruit juices: packaged in cans, jars, etc.

(G-18674)
UNIVERSAL WOOD DESIGN
1708 Old Dixie Hwy # 102 (32960-0440)
PHONE....772 569-5389
Arthur Noriega, *President*
EMP: 13 EST: 1981
SQ FT: 8,000
SALES (est): 450.6K Privately Held
WEB: www.universalwooddesign.com
SIC: 2434 2431 Wood kitchen cabinets; millwork

(G-18675)
US SUBMARINES INC (PA)
9015 17th Pl (32966-6601)
PHONE....208 687-9057
L Bruce Jones, *President*
Ellis C Adams, *Vice Pres*
EMP: 15 EST: 1993
SQ FT: 15,000
SALES (est): 1.6MM Privately Held
WEB: www.tritonsubs.com
SIC: 3731 Submarines, building & repairing

(G-18676)
VB CUSTOM SIGNS INC
2555 27th Ave Ste G4 (32960-1988)
PHONE....772 713-5678
Justin McClure, *Principal*
EMP: 6 EST: 2017
SALES (est): 96.6K Privately Held
SIC: 3993 Signs & advertising specialties

(G-18677)
VERO BEACH 32963 MEDIA
4855 Highway A1a (32963-1279)
PHONE....772 226-7924
EMP: 7 EST: 2019
SALES (est): 121.2K Privately Held
WEB: www.vb32963online.com
SIC: 2711 Newspapers, publishing & printing

(G-18678)
VERO BEACH PRINTING INC
3280 Quay Dock Rd (32967-5955)
P.O. Box 1059 (32961-1059)
PHONE....772 562-4267

GEOGRAPHIC

Alvin Walker, *President*
EMP: 6 **EST:** 1952
SQ FT: 3,200
SALES (est): 446.3K **Privately Held**
WEB: www.verobeach.com
SIC: 2752 Commercial printing, offset

(G-18679)
VERO NEWS
1240 Olde Doubloon Dr (32963-2453)
PHONE..................................772 234-5727
Milton Benjamin, *Principal*
EMP: 10 **EST:** 2001
SALES (est): 93.8K **Privately Held**
WEB: www.veronews.com
SIC: 2711 Newspapers, publishing & printing

(G-18680)
VIRGINIA KELLY
1825 Bridgepointe Cir # 14 (32967-6834)
PHONE..................................954 415-8056
Virginia Kelly, *Principal*
EMP: 6 **EST:** 2010
SALES (est): 93.1K **Privately Held**
SIC: 2741 Miscellaneous publishing

(G-18681)
WESTROM SOFTWARE
903 7th Ave (32960-5991)
PHONE..................................866 480-1879
Bill Westrom, *CEO*
EMP: 9 **EST:** 2011
SALES (est): 306.3K **Privately Held**
WEB: www.westromsoftware.com
SIC: 7372 Application computer software

(G-18682)
WHIGHAM CITRUS PACKING HOUSE
Also Called: Whigham Citrus Pkg Hse McHy
10525 State Road 60 (32966-3210)
P.O. Box 690185 (32969-0185)
PHONE..................................772 569-7190
Daniel Whigham, *President*
EMP: 5 **EST:** 1960
SQ FT: 20,000
SALES (est): 667.4K **Privately Held**
SIC: 3556 Packing house machinery

(G-18683)
WHITE ROSE INSTALLATION
1266 14th Ave Sw (32962-5323)
PHONE..................................772 562-6698
Laurie Rose, *President*
EMP: 10
SALES (est): 700K **Privately Held**
SIC: 3444 Sheet metalwork

Virginia Gardens
Miami-Dade County

(G-18684)
BOEING COMPANY
6601 Nw 36th St (33166-6922)
PHONE..................................786 265-9965
Johnathan Pham, *Engineer*
Michael Shim, *Branch Mgr*
EMP: 6
SALES (corp-wide): 58.1B **Publicly Held**
WEB: www.boeing.com
SIC: 3721 Airplanes, fixed or rotary wing
PA: The Boeing Company
100 N Riverside Plz
Chicago IL 60606
312 544-2000

(G-18685)
CITY PUBLICATIONS SOUTH FL
6501 Nw 36th St Ste 300 (33166-6963)
PHONE..................................305 495-3311
Rob Doughty, *Principal*
EMP: 6 **EST:** 2016
SALES (est): 37.5K **Privately Held**
WEB: www.citypubsouthflorida.com
SIC: 2741 Miscellaneous publishing

(G-18686)
DARMIVEN INC
6355 Nw 36th St Ste 506 (33166-7058)
PHONE..................................305 871-1157
Mariangel Caicoya, *President*
Carlos E Obregon, *President*
Felipe J Gonzalez, *Treasurer*
▼ **EMP:** 7 **EST:** 1994
SALES (est): 1.4MM **Privately Held**
WEB: www.degouveia-web.sharepoint.com
SIC: 2731 8742 Book publishing; management consulting services
PA: Continental Publishing Company Inc
C/O Arias Fabrega & Fabrega
Panama City

(G-18687)
DISTRIBUIDORA CONTINENTAL SA
Also Called: Overseas Publishing Management
6355 Nw 36th St Ste 506 (33166-7058)
PHONE..................................305 374-4474
EMP: 10 **Privately Held**
SIC: 2711 2721 Newspapers; magazines: publishing only, not printed on site
PA: Distribuidora Continental S.A.
Final Av. San Martin,
Caracas D.F.

(G-18688)
E T PLASTERING INC
3831 Nw 58th Ct (33166-5728)
PHONE..................................305 874-7082
Emilio Trenzado, *President*
Anna C Trenzado, *Admin Sec*
▼ **EMP:** 10 **EST:** 1983
SALES (est): 924.4K **Privately Held**
SIC: 3541 3299 1742 Lathes; stucco; plastering, drywall & insulation

(G-18689)
ET PUBLISHING INTERNATIONAL (PA)
Also Called: Editorial Televisa Publishing
6355 Nw 36th St (33166-7009)
PHONE..................................305 871-6400
Rodrigo Edwards, *President*
Rodrigo S Sepulveda Edwards Mc, *President*
Elmis Reyes, *Publisher*
Marcia Morgado, *Editor*
Jorge Lutteroth Echegoyen Mv, *Vice Pres*
◆ **EMP:** 80
SQ FT: 150,000
SALES (est): 19.7MM **Privately Held**
WEB: www.televisainternacional.com
SIC: 2721 Magazines: publishing only, not printed on site

Wauchula
Hardee County

(G-18690)
DEBUT DEVELOPMENT LLC
897 S 6th Ave Ste 1 (33873-3309)
PHONE..................................863 448-9081
Vanessa Thomas, *Mng Member*
Kristin A Giuliani,
EMP: 8 **EST:** 2015
SQ FT: 4,000
SALES (est): 150K **Privately Held**
WEB: www.debutdevelopmentllc.com
SIC: 3842 3999 Cosmetic restorations; atomizers, toiletry

(G-18691)
EZPRODUCTS INTERNATIONAL INC
612 N Florida Ave (33873-3041)
P.O. Box 1289 (33873-1289)
PHONE..................................863 735-0813
David H Brown, *Principal*
Diane Rue, *Vice Pres*
EMP: 7 **EST:** 2004
SQ FT: 2,800
SALES (est): 994.2K **Privately Held**
WEB: www.ezpi.us
SIC: 3471 Cleaning, polishing & finishing

(G-18692)
FRANZ A ULLRICH JR
Also Called: Ullrich's
514 N Florida Ave (33873-2110)
PHONE..................................863 773-4653
Franz A Ullrich Jr, *Owner*
EMP: 6 **EST:** 1938
SALES (est): 319.2K **Privately Held**
WEB: www.hiflowpumpandmachine.com
SIC: 7692 3523 Welding repair; farm machinery & equipment

(G-18693)
HERALD-ADVOCATE PUBLISHING CO
115 S 7th Ave (33873-2801)
P.O. Box 338 (33873-0338)
PHONE..................................863 773-3255
James R Kelly, *President*
Jean Kelly, *Vice Pres*
Mildred Kelly, *Director*
EMP: 11 **EST:** 1941
SQ FT: 4,500
SALES (est): 598.4K **Privately Held**
WEB: www.theheraldadvocate.com
SIC: 2711 2752 2761 2759 Commercial printing & newspaper publishing combined; commercial printing, offset; manifold business forms; commercial printing

(G-18694)
JLT CUSTOM WORKS INC
2239 Greenleaf Rd (33873-8200)
PHONE..................................863 245-3371
Jose Torres, *President*
Darlene Torres, *Admin Sec*
EMP: 40 **EST:** 2012
SALES (est): 1.5MM **Privately Held**
WEB: www.jltcustomworks.com
SIC: 1459 0781 Brucite mining; landscape services

(G-18695)
UTILITECH INC
130 W Main St (33873-2820)
P.O. Box 536 (33873-0536)
PHONE..................................863 767-0600
Brent Stephens, *President*
Matthew Thompson, *Vice Pres*
EMP: 11 **EST:** 2014
SALES (est): 1MM **Privately Held**
WEB: www.utili-tech.net
SIC: 7372 7371 8243 Application computer software; business oriented computer software; utility computer software; computer software systems analysis & design, custom; software training, computer

Wausau
Washington County

(G-18696)
BERNICE I FINCH
Also Called: B Finch Logging
1867 6th Ave (32463)
P.O. Box 123 (32463-0123)
PHONE..................................850 638-0082
Bernice I Finch, *Owner*
Geraldine Finch, *Co-Owner*
EMP: 6
SALES (est): 450K **Privately Held**
SIC: 2411 Logging

Webster
Sumter County

(G-18697)
BOYETT TIMBER INC
45260 Lcchee Clay Sink Rd (33597)
PHONE..................................352 583-2138
Tim Boyett, *President*
EMP: 8 **EST:** 1990
SQ FT: 600
SALES (est): 1.3MM **Privately Held**
WEB: www.boyetttimbermulch.com
SIC: 2421 2426 2499 Lumber: rough, sawed or planed; lumber, hardwood dimension; mauls, wood

(G-18698)
ROBBINS MANUFACTUING CO
12904 Sr 471 (33597-5114)
P.O. Box 295 (33597-0295)
PHONE..................................352 793-2443
EMP: 70
SALES (est): 437.7K **Privately Held**
SIC: 2421 Sawmill/Planing Mill

Weeki Wachee
Hernando County

(G-18699)
A 1 FABRICATIONS INC
12440 Charlton Dr (34614-1914)
PHONE..................................352 410-0752
Beverly Earle, *Principal*
EMP: 7 **EST:** 2011
SALES (est): 87.5K **Privately Held**
SIC: 3089 Injection molding of plastics

(G-18700)
ANU INDUSTRIES INC (PA)
8123 River Country Dr (34607-2132)
PHONE..................................813 927-7254
Ken Husuliak, *President*
EMP: 33 **EST:** 2001
SALES (est): 374.5K **Privately Held**
SIC: 3999 Manufacturing industries

(G-18701)
CARDBOARD ONLY INC
11080 Wdlnd Waters Blvd (34613)
PHONE..................................352 345-5060
William P Drinkwater, *Principal*
EMP: 6 **EST:** 2008
SALES (est): 69.1K **Privately Held**
SIC: 2631 Cardboard

(G-18702)
ECLIPSE EHR SOLUTIONS LLC
11242 Commercial Way (34614-3063)
PHONE..................................352 488-0081
Michael Norworth, *Manager*
EMP: 14 **EST:** 2018
SQ FT: 2,520
SALES (est): 828.7K **Privately Held**
SIC: 7372 Business oriented computer software

(G-18703)
FLORIDA NORTH INC
10294 Maybird Ave (34613-3610)
PHONE..................................352 606-2408
Sara Nelson, *Principal*
EMP: 7
SALES (corp-wide): 650K **Privately Held**
WEB: www.floridanorth.com
SIC: 3949 Swimming pools, plastic
PA: Florida North, Inc.
134 Vanderwerken Rd
Sloansville NY 12160
518 868-2888

(G-18704)
MICROTEX ELECTRONICS INC
13191 Kingfisher Rd (34614-2106)
P.O. Box 950372, Lake Mary (32795-0372)
PHONE..................................386 426-1922
John E Knight, *President*
John Knight, *President*
Elaine Knight, *Vice Pres*
EMP: 5 **EST:** 1994
SALES (est): 316K **Privately Held**
WEB: www.microtex.net
SIC: 3545 Micrometers

Weirsdale
Marion County

(G-18705)
FINE WOODWORKS
15145 Se 175th St (32195-3120)
PHONE..................................954 448-9206
Robert Ives, *Principal*
EMP: 6 **EST:** 2010
SALES (est): 85.3K **Privately Held**
SIC: 2431 Millwork

Wellborn
Suwannee County

(G-18706)
BUTLER LOGGING INC
5570 Bulb Farm Rd (32094-2560)
PHONE..................................386 963-2720
Larry G Butler, *President*
EMP: 7 **EST:** 2016

SALES (est): 108.7K **Privately Held**
SIC: 2411 Logging camps & contractors

Wellington
Palm Beach County

(G-18707)
5 STAR BUILDERS INC
Also Called: Five Star Builders W Palm Bch
3180 Frlane Frms Rd Ste 2 (33414)
PHONE..................................561 795-1282
Art Beyer, *President*
James T Williamson, *Vice Pres*
EMP: 5 **EST:** 1996
SALES (est): 737.8K **Privately Held**
WEB: www.support.website-creator.org
SIC: 3523 Barn stanchions & standards

(G-18708)
ADVANCED THERMAL TECH INC (DH)
Also Called: Be Aerospace
1400 Corporate Center Way (33414-2105)
PHONE..................................561 791-5000
Amin J Khoury, *Ch of Bd*
Bruce Thayer, *President*
Cameron H Adamson, *Vice Pres*
Alan Goldstein, *Buyer*
Lisa Parker, *Buyer*
▲ **EMP:** 29 **EST:** 1997
SQ FT: 20,000
SALES (est): 6.9MM
SALES (corp-wide): 56.5B **Publicly Held**
WEB: www.beaerospace.com
SIC: 3728 Aircraft parts & equipment
HQ: B/E Aerospace, Inc.
1400 Corporate Center Way
Wellington FL 33414
410 266-2048

(G-18709)
ARYA GROUP LLC
11858 Forest Hill Blvd (33414-6291)
PHONE..................................561 792-9992
EMP: 9 **EST:** 2017
SALES (est): 890.1K **Privately Held**
SIC: 3431 Metal sanitary ware

(G-18710)
B/E AEROSPACE INC (DH)
Also Called: Rockwell Collins
1400 Corporate Center Way (33414-2105)
PHONE..................................410 266-2048
Kelly Ortberg, *CEO*
Edward Gager, *President*
William Godecker, *President*
Jon Buff, *Business Mgr*
Mike Beroth, *Vice Pres*
▲ **EMP:** 30 **EST:** 1987
SQ FT: 31,300
SALES (est): 1.6B
SALES (corp-wide): 56.5B **Publicly Held**
WEB: www.beaerospace.com
SIC: 2531 3728 3647 Seats, aircraft; aircraft parts & equipment; aircraft lighting fixtures

(G-18711)
BODY CHEMISTRY INDUSTRIES IN C
2247 Stotesbury Way (33414-6443)
PHONE..................................561 253-4438
Errol Henry, *Principal*
EMP: 6 **EST:** 2014
SALES (est): 95.5K **Privately Held**
SIC: 3999 Manufacturing industries

(G-18712)
BRUNO PUBLISHING
873 Lake Wellington Dr (33414-7971)
PHONE..................................561 333-7682
Jack Joseph Rosen, *Principal*
EMP: 6 **EST:** 2010
SALES (est): 4.6K **Privately Held**
WEB: www.brunoartgroup.com
SIC: 2741 Miscellaneous publishing

(G-18713)
CHILI PRODUKT KFT ✪
9850 Scribner Ln (33414-6486)
PHONE..................................954 655-4111
Zsolt Bucko, *CEO*
EMP: 40 **EST:** 2020
SALES (est): 1.2MM **Privately Held**
WEB: www.spice-paprika.com
SIC: 2099 Spices, including grinding

(G-18714)
CLASSIC INDUSTRIES INC
3111 Fortune Way (33414-8712)
PHONE..................................561 855-4609
Jessica Brown, *President*
EMP: 12 **EST:** 2015
SALES (est): 107.4K **Privately Held**
WEB: www.classicindustries.com
SIC: 3999 Manufacturing industries

(G-18715)
DS SHUTTERS GROUP INC
13278 Moonstone Ter (33414-7960)
PHONE..................................772 260-6393
Daniel A Saavedra, *Principal*
EMP: 6 **EST:** 2018
SALES (est): 88.9K **Privately Held**
SIC: 3442 Shutters, door or window: metal

(G-18716)
EXCES INTERNATIONAL LLC
3460 Frlane Frms Rd Ste 1 (33414)
PHONE..................................561 880-8920
EMP: 6 **EST:** 2019
SALES (est): 312.7K **Privately Held**
WEB: www.equilineamerica.com
SIC: 2323 Men's & boys' neckwear

(G-18717)
FIRST CLASS LIAISONS LLC
2470 Wellington Green Dr (33414-9321)
PHONE..................................954 882-8634
Amieke Reid, *CEO*
EMP: 7 **EST:** 2017
SALES (est): 360K **Privately Held**
SIC: 3441 Railroad car racks, for transporting vehicles: steel

(G-18718)
FORCE ENTERPRISES COATINGS LLC
12302 Sannenwood Ln (33414-4981)
PHONE..................................561 480-7298
Richard Alloe, *Principal*
EMP: 13 **EST:** 2016
SALES (est): 4MM **Privately Held**
SIC: 3559 Fiber optics strand coating machinery

(G-18719)
GONZALEZ AEROSPACE SERVICES
1035 S State Road 7 # 313 (33414-6134)
PHONE..................................561 227-1575
Jose Gonzalez, *Principal*
EMP: 6 **EST:** 2016
SALES (est): 110.9K **Privately Held**
SIC: 3721 Aircraft

(G-18720)
INNOVATE AUDIO VISUAL INC
3460 Frlane Frms Rd Ste 1 (33414)
PHONE..................................561 249-1117
Juan Laucirica, *President*
Amy Fiorillo, *CFO*
EMP: 7
SALES (est): 566.9K **Privately Held**
WEB: www.innovate-av.com
SIC: 3861 Photographic equipment & supplies

(G-18721)
JOHN SCREEN SERVICE LLC
1210 Mystic Way (33414-5614)
PHONE..................................561 798-3132
John G Reid, *Principal*
EMP: 6 **EST:** 2012
SALES (est): 203.9K **Privately Held**
WEB: www.poolscreenrepair.com
SIC: 3442 Screen & storm doors & windows

(G-18722)
LAKE POINT RESTORATION LLC
12012 South Shore Blvd # 10
(33414-6507)
PHONE..................................561 924-9100
Bonnie Owen, *Controller*
Richard Hegarty, *Office Mgr*
Harold D Rusbridge, *Mng Member*
Danny Pridgen, *Administration*
Francis J Laird IV,
EMP: 26 **EST:** 2007
SALES (est): 1,000K **Privately Held**
WEB: www.lakepointrestoration.com
SIC: 1422 Crushed & broken limestone

(G-18723)
LEONIDAS CUSTOMS INC
1054 Larch Way (33414-5102)
PHONE..................................561 542-4151
Nicholas Laverg, *President*
EMP: 6 **EST:** 2012
SALES (est): 135.7K **Privately Held**
WEB: www.leonidascustoms.com
SIC: 3489 Ordnance & accessories

(G-18724)
MARBLE DOCTORS LLC (PA)
Also Called: Artistic Services Kit & Bath
1198 Mulberry Pl (33414-8566)
PHONE..................................203 794-1000
Sergio Gomes Da Silva,
Kelly Dasilca,
EMP: 53 **EST:** 2008
SQ FT: 1,200
SALES (est): 286.7K **Privately Held**
SIC: 3281 1743 Marble, building: cut & shaped; marble installation, interior

(G-18725)
NEWSPAPER PUBLISHERS INC
Also Called: Town Crier Newspaper
12794 Frest Hl Blvd Ste 3 (33414)
PHONE..................................561 793-7606
Phyllis Manning, *President*
Joshua Manning, *Admin Sec*
EMP: 23 **EST:** 1998
SALES (est): 1.8MM **Privately Held**
WEB: www.gotowncrier.com
SIC: 2711 Newspapers: publishing only, not printed on site

(G-18726)
ONTYTE LLC
3460 Fairlane Farms Rd # 15
(33414-8755)
PHONE..................................561 880-8920
Paul Yanke,
Ashley Yanke,
▲ **EMP:** 8 **EST:** 2009
SALES (est): 250.6K **Privately Held**
WEB: www.ontyte.com
SIC: 3199 Stirrups, wood or metal

(G-18727)
PICCIONIS FROZEN DESSERTS
489 Goldenwood Way (33414-4971)
PHONE..................................561 633-5759
Sandro A Piccioni, *Principal*
EMP: 6 **EST:** 2012
SALES (est): 88.3K **Privately Held**
SIC: 2024 Ice cream & frozen desserts

(G-18728)
REAL EXTRACT VENTURES INC
2200 Merriweather Way (33414-6428)
PHONE..................................561 371-3532
Sajid Ahmed, *President*
EMP: 6 **EST:** 2017
SALES (est): 81.2K **Privately Held**
SIC: 2836 Extracts

(G-18729)
REV PERSONAL CARE LLC
2905 Payson Way (33414-3409)
PHONE..................................832 217-8585
Fabian Maclaren,
David Giuliano,
EMP: 6 **EST:** 2017
SQ FT: 6,000
SALES (est): 319.6K **Privately Held**
SIC: 2844 Cosmetic preparations

(G-18730)
SHADE EXPERTS USA LLC
11117 Alameda Bay Ct (33414-8811)
PHONE..................................561 422-3200
Jeff Costa, *Managing Prtnr*
Mariza Costa, *Principal*
EMP: 10 **EST:** 2015
SALES (est): 115.6K **Privately Held**
WEB: www.theshadeexpertsusa.com
SIC: 3999 Manufacturing industries

(G-18731)
SHEAS SALSA LLC
11328 Regatta Ln (33449-7420)
PHONE..................................954 371-7781
Shea C Osteen, *Manager*
EMP: 6 **EST:** 2017
SALES (est): 378.9K **Privately Held**
SIC: 2099 Dips, except cheese & sour cream based

(G-18732)
SHINING TREE INC
2952 Payson Way (33414-3409)
PHONE..................................855 688-7987
EMP: 10 **EST:** 2014
SALES (est): 370K **Privately Held**
SIC: 2041 5149 Flour And Other Grain Mill Products, Nsk

(G-18733)
SIGNCRAFT LLC
3694 Old Lighthouse Cir (33414-8843)
PHONE..................................561 543-0034
Robin Intoppa, *Vice Pres*
Linda Prusiecki, *Mng Member*
Brian K Waxman,
EMP: 7 **EST:** 2007
SQ FT: 20,000
SALES (est): 212.1K **Privately Held**
SIC: 3993 Signs & advertising specialties

(G-18734)
SIGNS SUPREME INC
17224 Gulf Pine Cir (33414-6360)
PHONE..................................561 795-0111
Valerie Walton, *President*
Douglas Walton, *Vice Pres*
▲ **EMP:** 7 **EST:** 1999
SQ FT: 8,000
SALES (est): 176K **Privately Held**
SIC: 3993 Signs & advertising specialties

(G-18735)
SJS WOODWORKING LLC
207 Pleasant Wood Dr (33414-4716)
PHONE..................................561 704-5990
Sean J Shappee, *Principal*
EMP: 6 **EST:** 2010
SALES (est): 122K **Privately Held**
SIC: 2431 Millwork

(G-18736)
SOUTHEAST CARBON WORKS INC
1243 Canyon Way (33414-3143)
PHONE..................................561 422-1798
Jorge Ferrin, *Principal*
EMP: 9 **EST:** 2010
SALES (est): 95.6K **Privately Held**
SIC: 3714 Motor vehicle parts & accessories

(G-18737)
STONE SET TECHNOLOGIES LLC
Also Called: Sun-Ray Setting
12161 Ken Adams Way # 210
(33414-3192)
PHONE..................................954 565-4979
Allen Jecnavorian, *Managing Prtnr*
EMP: 6 **EST:** 1999
SALES (est): 212.1K **Privately Held**
WEB: www.presetstone.com
SIC: 3911 Jewelry, precious metal

(G-18738)
TROIKA GROUP INC
12300 South Shore Blvd # 20
(33414-6509)
PHONE..................................561 313-1119
EMP: 5 **EST:** 2019
SALES (est): 351.9K **Privately Held**
SIC: 3341 Secondary nonferrous metals

(G-18739)
WHITE HORSE FASHION CUISINE
14440 Pierson Rd (33414-7673)
PHONE..................................561 847-4549
EMP: 9 **EST:** 2014
SALES (est): 114.6K **Privately Held**
WEB: www.olisfashioncuisine.com
SIC: 2299 Textile goods

Wesley Chapel
Pasco County

(G-18740)
BELT MAINTENANCE GROUP INC (PA)
27658 Cashford Cir # 102 (33544-6959)
PHONE..................................813 907-9316
Alba Benitez, *President*
Carl Debord, *Vice Pres*
EMP: 6
SQ FT: 17,000
SALES (est): 1.2MM **Privately Held**
WEB: www.beltmaintenance.com
SIC: 3496 Conveyor belts

(G-18741)
BOOST LAB INC
31050 Chatterly Dr (33543-6811)
PHONE..................................813 443-0531
Kirk Riollano, *Principal*
Ryan Hostetler, *Production*
EMP: 10 **EST:** 2010
SALES (est): 427.1K **Privately Held**
WEB: www.theboostlab.com
SIC: 3714 Motor vehicle parts & accessories

(G-18742)
COREYCO LLC
6253 Candlewood Dr (33544-5834)
PHONE..................................813 469-1203
Tracey Munroe, *Mng Member*
Corey Munroe,
John E Munroe,
EMP: 9 **EST:** 2008
SALES (est): 1.6MM **Privately Held**
WEB: www.coreyco.net
SIC: 3273 Ready-mixed concrete

(G-18743)
DATAMENTORS LLC (PA)
Also Called: V12 Data
2319 Oak Myrtle Ln (33544-6329)
PHONE..................................813 960-7800
Andrew Frawley, *CEO*
Anders Ekman, *President*
Sasa Zorovic, *COO*
Peg Kuman, *Exec VP*
Michelle Taves, *Exec VP*
EMP: 35 **EST:** 1999
SQ FT: 5,000
SALES (est): 16MM **Privately Held**
WEB: www.v12data.com
SIC: 7372 Business oriented computer software

(G-18744)
ELEMENTS OF STYLEZ
30040 State Road 54 (33543-4500)
PHONE..................................813 575-8416
Daniel Quintana, *Principal*
EMP: 7 **EST:** 2018
SALES (est): 1.5MM **Privately Held**
WEB: www.elements-of-stylez-barber-shop.business.site
SIC: 2819 Industrial inorganic chemicals

(G-18745)
FIRST WINDOWS INCORPORATED
27524 Cashford Cir (33544-6947)
PHONE..................................813 508-9388
Eric Rodriguez, *Principal*
EMP: 5 **EST:** 2017
SALES (est): 417K **Privately Held**
SIC: 3442 Window & door frames

(G-18746)
FLORIDA STL FRAME TRUSS MFG LL
2312 Cypress Cv Ste 101 (33544-6785)
PHONE..................................813 460-0006
Khamir H Patel, *Mng Member*
Hardevbhai D Patel, *Mng Member*
EMP: 9 **EST:** 2018
SALES (est): 1MM **Privately Held**
WEB: www.fsftm.com
SIC: 3312 Bars & bar shapes, steel, cold-finished: own hot-rolled

(G-18747)
FORCE IMAGING GROUP LLC
Also Called: Thermalroll.com
1936 Bruce B Downs Blvd (33544-9262)
PHONE..................................888 406-2120
Blaise Collura,
EMP: 8 **EST:** 2012
SALES (est): 576.7K **Privately Held**
WEB: www.thermalroll.com
SIC: 2679 Tags & labels, paper

(G-18748)
GRAPHICS PDTS EXCELLENCE INC
Also Called: Clear Vision Signs and Systems
5335 Emory Dr (33543-4640)
PHONE..................................813 884-1578
Joseph Torrence, *Principal*
Deborah Torrence, *CFO*
EMP: 13 **EST:** 2003
SALES (est): 1MM **Privately Held**
WEB: www.gpxtabs.com
SIC: 3993 Signs & advertising specialties

(G-18749)
ILER GROUP INC
Also Called: Fleetistics
2604 Cypress Ridge Blvd # 102 (33544-6311)
PHONE..................................813 600-1738
Eron Iler, *President*
Amy Anderson, *VP Finance*
Amy Anderson Iler, *VP Finance*
Amy Iler, *VP Finance*
Hope Duke, *Bookkeeper*
EMP: 18 **EST:** 2001
SQ FT: 2,500
SALES (est): 3.4MM **Privately Held**
WEB: www.ilergroup.com
SIC: 3531 5012 Trucks, off-highway; trucks, commercial

(G-18750)
KERICURE INC
Also Called: Champion Seal
26620 Easy St (33544-5711)
PHONE..................................855 888-5374
Kerriann Greenhalgh, *CEO*
Kerriann R Greenhalgh, *President*
EMP: 10 **EST:** 2011
SALES (est): 1MM **Privately Held**
WEB: www.kericure.com
SIC: 3842 Surgical appliances & supplies

(G-18751)
LOCAL BIZ SPOT INC (PA)
Also Called: Bizzspot
26747 Saxony Way (33544-6486)
PHONE..................................866 446-1790
Ryan Anderson, *President*
Brad Anderson, *Vice Pres*
EMP: 5 **EST:** 2008
SALES (est): 400K **Privately Held**
WEB: www.bizzspot.com
SIC: 3993 Signs & advertising specialties

(G-18752)
LULULEMON
28211 Paseo Dr Ste 160 (33543-5380)
PHONE..................................813 973-3879
EMP: 7 **EST:** 1998
SALES (est): 42.5K **Privately Held**
SIC: 2389 Apparel & accessories

(G-18753)
NATURES POWER AND ENERGY LLC
30131 Clearview Dr (33545-3010)
PHONE..................................813 907-6279
Walter Rooney,
Dave Beruska,
Paul Cooper,
Dorraine Rooney,
EMP: 10 **EST:** 2012
SALES (est): 523.9K **Privately Held**
WEB: www.naturespowerandenergy.us
SIC: 3699 7389 High-energy particle physics equipment; business services

(G-18754)
NEBULA LED LIGHTING SYSTEMS OF
28832 Falling Leaves Way (33543-5761)
PHONE..................................813 907-0001
Mark J Rosenberg, *Mng Member*
Leslie Franken, *Office Spvr*
EMP: 5 **EST:** 2007
SALES (est): 1MM
SALES (corp-wide): 2.5MM **Privately Held**
WEB: www.nebulalighting.com
SIC: 3674 5063 Light emitting diodes; lighting fixtures
PA: M R Enterprises Llc
28832 Falling Leaves Way
Wesley Chapel FL 33543
813 924-0303

(G-18755)
OLIVE TREE II
2653 Bruce B Downs Blvd (33544-9206)
PHONE..................................813 991-8781
EMP: 7 **EST:** 2016
SALES (est): 945.9K **Privately Held**
SIC: 2079 Olive oil

(G-18756)
PRIMETIME INDUSTRIES LLC
32671 Natural Bridge Rd (33543-7209)
PHONE..................................813 781-0196
Joshua Boddiford, *Partner*
EMP: 2 **EST:** 2018
SALES: 3.1MM **Privately Held**
SIC: 3842 5084 Personal safety equipment; safety equipment

(G-18757)
PULSE DISPLAYS LLC
27334 Bonterra Loop (33544-5139)
PHONE..................................314 971-8700
Larry Sternle, *President*
EMP: 7 **EST:** 2017
SALES (est): 91.1K **Privately Held**
WEB: www.pulsedisplays.com
SIC: 3699 Pulse amplifiers

(G-18758)
ROSELLE PUBLISHING
6415 Gentle Ben Cir (33544-3448)
PHONE..................................813 907-5250
Charles Hull, *Principal*
EMP: 6 **EST:** 2015
SALES (est): 66.5K **Privately Held**
WEB: www.rosellepublishing.com
SIC: 2741 Miscellaneous publishing

(G-18759)
SUN VALLEY TECH SOLUTIONS INC
31437 Heatherstone Dr (33543-6877)
PHONE..................................480 463-4101
Joshua Lee, *President*
Jennifer Lee, *CFO*
EMP: 6 **EST:** 2006
SALES (est): 346.2K **Privately Held**
SIC: 7372 Application computer software

(G-18760)
TRANSPORT PC USA INC
Also Called: Gator Freds
1423 Baythorn Dr (33543-7804)
PHONE..................................813 264-1700
Alfredo Medina, *President*
Sandra Perez Medina, *President*
EMP: 8 **EST:** 2003
SALES (est): 737.7K **Privately Held**
SIC: 3599 Carnival machines & equipment, amusement park

(G-18761)
TROPICAL PAVER SEALING
4834 Windingbrook Trl (33544-7482)
PHONE..................................727 786-4011
Amanda Wyandt, *Mng Member*
EMP: 6 **EST:** 2014
SALES (est): 250K **Privately Held**
WEB: www.tropicalpaversealing.com
SIC: 3531 7389 Pavers;

(G-18762)
ULTRASONIC TECHNOLOGIES INC
27247 Breakers Dr (33544-6612)
PHONE..................................813 973-1702
Sergei Ostapenko, *CEO*
▼ **EMP:** 8 **EST:** 1997
SALES (est): 992.9K **Privately Held**
WEB: www.ultrasonictech.com
SIC: 3629 Electronic generation equipment

(G-18763)
VDH WORLDWIDE LLC
6452 Quail Hollow Blvd (33544-3410)
PHONE..................................866 304-2388
Bryan Pennington, *Principal*
EMP: 6 **EST:** 2013
SALES (est): 137.1K **Privately Held**
WEB: www.vdh.virginia.gov
SIC: 3999 Manufacturing industries

(G-18764)
WESLEY CHAPEL FUEL INC
27616 Wesley Chapel Blvd (33544-4200)
PHONE..................................813 907-9994
Richard Elkhoury, *Principal*
EMP: 9 **EST:** 2010
SALES (est): 762.7K **Privately Held**
WEB: www.wesleychapeltuffy.com
SIC: 2869 Fuels

West Melbourne
Brevard County

(G-18765)
AMERICAN PRESSURE SYSTEMS INC
7608 Emerald Dr (32904-1166)
PHONE..................................321 914-0827
Tad Hoskins, *President*
Ford Hoskins, *Vice Pres*
EMP: 8 **EST:** 2010
SALES (est): 655.6K **Privately Held**
WEB: www.americanpressuresystems.com
SIC: 3589 High pressure cleaning equipment

(G-18766)
AXIOM MANUFACTURING INC
962 Hailey St (32904-8204)
PHONE..................................321 223-3394
Jonah King, *President*
EMP: 8 **EST:** 2016
SALES (est): 115.3K **Privately Held**
WEB: www.axman.com
SIC: 3999 Manufacturing industries

(G-18767)
BK TECHNOLOGIES INC (HQ)
7100 Technology Dr (32904-1525)
PHONE..................................321 984-1414
John M Suzuki, *CEO*
E Gray Payne, *Ch of Bd*
Timothy A Vitou, *President*
Henry R Willis, *COO*
Cindy Kippley MBA, *Vice Pres*
▲ **EMP:** 11 **EST:** 1947
SQ FT: 54,000
SALES: 40.1MM
SALES (corp-wide): 49.3MM **Publicly Held**
WEB: www.bktechnologies.com
SIC: 3663 Radio broadcasting & communications equipment
PA: Bk Technologies Corporation
7100 Technology Dr
West Melbourne FL 32904
321 984-1414

(G-18768)
BK TECHNOLOGIES CORPORATION (PA)
7100 Technology Dr (32904-1525)
PHONE..................................321 984-1414
D Kyle Cerminara, *Ch of Bd*
Lewis M Johnson, *Ch of Bd*
John Suzuki, *President*
Timothy A Vitou, *President*
Henry R Willis, *COO*
EMP: 19 **EST:** 1947
SQ FT: 54,000
SALES: 49.3MM **Publicly Held**
WEB: www.bktechnologies.com
SIC: 3663 Radio broadcasting & communications equipment

(G-18769)
CEDARS FOOD INC
2110 Dairy Rd Ste 101 (32904-5200)
PHONE..................................321 724-2624
Eddin Chams, *Principal*
EMP: 8 **EST:** 2012

SALES (est): 685.5K Privately Held
WEB: www.cedarsfoods.com
SIC: 2015 Poultry slaughtering & processing

(G-18770)
COB INDUSTRIES INC
6909 Vickie Cir (32904-2252)
P.O. Box 361175, Melbourne (32936-1175)
PHONE 321 723-3200
Cletus M O'Brien, *President*
Veronica O'Brien, *Vice Pres*
Kurt Brown, *Sales Staff*
▲ EMP: 7
SQ FT: 11,000
SALES (est): 1.4MM Privately Held
WEB: www.cob-industries.com
SIC: 3544 3423 Special dies & tools; mechanics' hand tools

(G-18771)
DEFENSE ARTS & SCIENCES LLC
2240 Pine Meadow Ave (32904-6551)
PHONE 321 768-0671
Doug Samuels, *Principal*
EMP: 6 EST: 2008
SALES (est): 133.8K Privately Held
SIC: 3812 Defense systems & equipment

(G-18772)
DOCTOR GRANITE AND CABINETS
3532 Chica Cir (32904-6836)
PHONE 321 368-1779
Ronald J Isaza, *Principal*
EMP: 8 EST: 2015
SALES (est): 378.4K Privately Held
SIC: 2434 Wood kitchen cabinets

(G-18773)
ELEMENT MTLS TECH JUPITER LLC
Also Called: Element Melbourne
7780 Technology Dr (32904-1575)
PHONE 321 327-8985
Jo Wetz, *Principal*
Mike Mather, *Principal*
EMP: 12 EST: 2013
SALES (est): 2.4MM
SALES (corp-wide): 782.6MM Privately Held
WEB: www.element.com
SIC: 2819 Elements
PA: Element Materials Technology Group Limited
10 Lower Grosvenor Place
London SW1W
203 540-1820

(G-18774)
GATCHELL VIOLINS COMPANY INC
1377 W New Haven Ave (32904-3901)
PHONE 321 733-1499
Allen Gatchell, *Owner*
▲ EMP: 10 EST: 2003
SALES (est): 903.5K Privately Held
WEB: www.gatchellviolins.com
SIC: 3931 Violins & parts; violas & parts

(G-18775)
IMPRESSIVE PAVERS INC
2883 Glasbern Cir (32904-8080)
PHONE 321 508-9991
Kenneth L Goetz Jr, *Principal*
EMP: 7 EST: 2014
SALES (est): 244K Privately Held
SIC: 2951 Asphalt paving mixtures & blocks

(G-18776)
INFINITY PCB INC
4195 W New Haven Ave Rear (32904-1702)
PHONE 321 804-8045
Eric A Schwartz, *Principal*
EMP: 6 EST: 2014
SALES (est): 158.3K Privately Held
WEB: www.infinitypcb.com
SIC: 3672 Printed circuit boards

(G-18777)
MOOG INC
Also Called: Electro-Optical Imaging
4300 Fortune Pl Ste A (32904-1527)
PHONE 321 435-8722
Chris Fedele, *Principal*
EMP: 10
SALES (corp-wide): 2.8B Publicly Held
WEB: www.moog.com
SIC: 3812 3769 3861 Electronic detection systems (aeronautical); defense systems & equipment; missile guidance systems & equipment; pictorial deviation indicators; guided missile & space vehicle parts & aux eqpt, rsch & dev; photo reconnaissance systems
PA: Moog Inc.
400 Jamison Rd
Elma NY 14059
716 652-2000

(G-18778)
UNITED SPACE COAST CABLES INC
7703 Tech Dr Ste 100 (32904)
PHONE 321 952-1040
Bryan Holm, *President*
Denise Shaw, *President*
David Brownell, *Buyer*
Brian Comstock, *Manager*
Ron Lewis, *Manager*
EMP: 40 EST: 2011
SALES (est): 6.6MM Privately Held
WEB: www.unitedscc.com
SIC: 3699 Electrical equipment & supplies

(G-18779)
WATERSHPES BY GREG GNSTROM INC
2163 Ohio St (32904-6142)
PHONE 321 777-5432
Greg Ginstrom, *Principal*
EMP: 7 EST: 2016
SALES (est): 277.3K Privately Held
WEB: www.watershapesbygreg.com
SIC: 3993 Signs & advertising specialties

(G-18780)
ZPACKS CORP
7703 Technology Dr (32904-1573)
PHONE 321 215-5658
Joseph E Valesko, *President*
Matt Favero, *Manager*
Will Wood, *Director*
EMP: 14 EST: 2014
SALES (est): 3.2MM Privately Held
WEB: www.zpacks.com
SIC: 3172 Personal leather goods

West Miami
Miami-Dade County

(G-18781)
DABY PRODUCTS CARISEN
5757 Sw 8th St (33144-5060)
PHONE 305 559-3018
Daby Sully, *Principal*
EMP: 6 EST: 1997
SALES (est): 125K Privately Held
SIC: 2844 Cosmetic preparations

West Palm Beach
Palm Beach County

(G-18782)
5HP INVESTMENTS LLC
Also Called: Minuteman Press
2822 S Dixie Hwy (33405-1543)
PHONE 561 655-5355
Daniel Hernandez,
Raquel Presas,
EMP: 14 EST: 2014
SALES (est): 2.1MM Privately Held
WEB: www.chanhassen-mn.minutemanpress.com
SIC: 2752 Commercial printing, lithographic

(G-18783)
5NINE SOFTWARE INC
1555 Palm Bch Lkes Blvd S (33401)
PHONE 561 898-1100
Karen Armor, *CEO*
Morgan Holm, *Vice Pres*
Konstantin Malkov, *CTO*
EMP: 25 EST: 2009
SQ FT: 1,500
SALES (est): 4.8MM
SALES (corp-wide): 261.7K Privately Held
WEB: www.acronis.com
SIC: 7372 Prepackaged software
HQ: Acronis International Gmbh
Eurohaus
Schaffhausen SH 8200
526 302-800

(G-18784)
A PALLET CO INC
9750 Galleon Dr (33411-1806)
PHONE 561 798-1564
Rocco Zito, *President*
EMP: 8 EST: 2002
SALES (est): 631.4K Privately Held
WEB: www.apallet.net
SIC: 2448 Pallets, wood

(G-18785)
A&M CLEANING SOLUTIONS LLC ✪
4400 N Terrace Dr (33407-3738)
PHONE 786 559-7093
Margo H Mitchell,
EMP: 10 EST: 2020
SALES (est): 438.6K Privately Held
SIC: 3589 Commercial cleaning equipment

(G-18786)
ACE MARKING DEVICES CORP
Also Called: Ace Rubber Stamp
3308 S Dixie Hwy (33405-1949)
P.O. Box 6425 (33405-6425)
PHONE 561 833-4073
Walter Zajkowski Jr, *President*
Gertrude Zajkowski, *Corp Secy*
David J Zajkowski, *Vice Pres*
EMP: 7 EST: 1940
SQ FT: 1,600
SALES (est): 515.5K Privately Held
WEB: www.usacustom.com
SIC: 3953 5943 Embossing seals & hand stamps; office forms & supplies

(G-18787)
ACS OF WEST PALM BEACH INC
1300 N Florida Mango Rd # 34 (33409-5259)
PHONE 561 844-5790
Matthew McClellan, *President*
Sam Cabrera, *General Mgr*
EMP: 8 EST: 2014
SALES (est): 4MM Privately Held
SIC: 2674 Vacuum cleaner bags: made from purchased materials

(G-18788)
ACTION MFG & SUP WPB LLC
2711 Vista Pkwy Ste B5 (33411-2732)
PHONE 239 574-3443
Lena Pilgrim, *Vice Pres*
Justin Marshall, *Sales Staff*
EMP: 9 EST: 2013
SALES (est): 598.9K Privately Held
WEB: www.actionmfg.com
SIC: 3589 Water treatment equipment, industrial

(G-18789)
ACTION WEEKLY CORP
Also Called: Semenario Accion
3708 Georgia Ave (33405-2125)
PHONE 561 586-8699
Maria Triana, *President*
EMP: 5 EST: 1997
SALES (est): 512.4K Privately Held
WEB: www.semanarioaccion.com
SIC: 2721 8661 Magazines: publishing only, not printed on site; religious organizations

(G-18790)
ADVATECH CORPORATION
250 S Australian Ave # 1504 (33401-5018)
PHONE 732 803-8000
Gerald F Richman, *President*
Michael Spiegel, *Vice Pres*
Richard Margulies, *CFO*
EMP: 7 EST: 1990
SALES (est): 757.1K Privately Held
SIC: 3589 Water treatment equipment, industrial

(G-18791)
AGD SYSTEMS CORPORATION
10130 Northlake Blvd # 2 (33412-1101)
PHONE 561 722-5561
Mark Daniels, *President*
Hunter Daniels, *Principal*
Rob Wentz, *Principal*
EMP: 7 EST: 2015
SALES (est): 218.4K Privately Held
WEB: www.agdsystems.com
SIC: 3728 4512 4789 Aircraft parts & equipment; air transportation, scheduled; air cargo carrier, scheduled; helicopter carrier, scheduled; space flight operations, except government

(G-18792)
ALCHIBA INC
505 S Flagler Dr Ste 900 (33401-5948)
PHONE 561 832-9292
James Clark, *Officer*
EMP: 6 EST: 2011
SALES (est): 96.3K Privately Held
SIC: 7372 Prepackaged software

(G-18793)
ALDEMA SERVICES INC
4895 Royal Ct N (33415-2824)
PHONE 561 860-0693
Patricia Guerra, *President*
EMP: 6 EST: 2018
SALES (est): 104.2K Privately Held
WEB: www.susquehannatranscript.com
SIC: 2711 Newspapers: publishing only, not printed on site

(G-18794)
ALTERNATIVE DAILY
400 Clematis St Ste 203 (33401-5322)
PHONE 561 628-4711
Stephen Steranka, *Principal*
David Sigler, *CFO*
Steve Steranka, *Marketing Staff*
EMP: 9 EST: 2017
SALES (est): 362.7K Privately Held
WEB: www.thealternativedaily.com
SIC: 2711 Newspapers

(G-18795)
ALTERNATIVE SIGN GROUP INC
8955 120th Ave N (33412-2634)
PHONE 561 722-9272
David Lanter, *Administration*
EMP: 8 EST: 2014
SALES (est): 547.3K Privately Held
WEB: www.asgsign.com
SIC: 3993 Signs & advertising specialties

(G-18796)
AMERICAN AWNING COMPANY INC
537 Pine Ter (33405-2697)
PHONE 561 832-7123
Dale Di Persico, *President*
Daniel Di Persico, *Vice Pres*
Stephany Di Persico, *Exec Dir*
Dawn Mattei, *Admin Sec*
EMP: 26 EST: 1955
SALES (est): 1.8MM Privately Held
WEB: www.americanawning.com
SIC: 2394 Awnings, fabric: made from purchased materials

(G-18797)
APPLIED SOFTWARE INC
737 Sandy Point Ln (33410-3427)
P.O. Box 30698 (33420-0698)
PHONE 215 297-9441
Janis Josephson, *President*
EMP: 8 EST: 1973
SQ FT: 4,000

SALES (est): 646.6K **Privately Held**
WEB: www.asisoft.com
SIC: 7372 Application computer software

(G-18798)
ARCHITECTURAL DETAIL & WDWKG
2617 Pinewood Ave (33407-5436)
PHONE..................................561 835-4005
Christian Hentschl, *President*
Mathew Mayfield, *Vice Pres*
EMP: 6 **EST:** 1993
SQ FT: 3,000
SALES (est): 994.8K **Privately Held**
WEB: www.adwwinc.com
SIC: 2431 Millwork

(G-18799)
ARCOAT COATINGS CORPORATION
2351 Vista Pkwy Ste 500 (33411-6728)
PHONE..................................561 422-9900
Richard Jaffin, *Branch Mgr*
EMP: 21
SALES (corp-wide): 5.1MM **Privately Held**
WEB: www.arcoat.com
SIC: 3479 Coating of metals & formed products
PA: Arcoat Coatings Corporation
615 Broadway
Hastings On Hudson NY 10706
914 478-9400

(G-18800)
ARISE PRINTS LLC
12217 Coconut Row Rd (33410-2078)
PHONE..................................561 371-6959
Kenneth F Kahn, *Manager*
EMP: 9 **EST:** 2017
SALES (est): 92.3K **Privately Held**
WEB: www.ariseprints.com
SIC: 2752 Commercial printing, lithographic

(G-18801)
ARMBRUST AVIATION GROUP INC
Also Called: World Jet Fuel Report
8895 N Military Trl # 201 (33410-6220)
PHONE..................................561 355-8488
John H Armbrust, *President*
Pauline H Armbrust, *Vice Pres*
Carol Ward, *Accounting Dir*
Andrea Caballero, *Mktg Coord*
Ramon Lo, *Marketing Staff*
EMP: 26 **EST:** 1986
SQ FT: 3,000
SALES (est): 1MM **Privately Held**
WEB: www.armbrustaviation.com
SIC: 2731 8748 2721 Book publishing; business consulting; periodicals

(G-18802)
AROUND HOUSE PUBLISHING INC
5405 Okchobee Blvd # 305 (33417-4554)
PHONE..................................561 969-7412
EMP: 19 **EST:** 1997
SALES (est): 1.3MM **Privately Held**
WEB: www.athpublishing.com
SIC: 2721 Magazines: publishing only, not printed on site

(G-18803)
ART OF PRINTING INC
1500 N Fl Mango Rd Ste 4 (33409-5208)
PHONE..................................561 640-7344
EMP: 6
SALES (est): 719.9K **Privately Held**
SIC: 2759 Commercial Printing

(G-18804)
ARTWORKS INTERNATIONAL
420 6th St (33401-3908)
PHONE..................................561 833-9165
Sioban Torres, *Owner*
▲ **EMP:** 9 **EST:** 2006
SALES (est): 200.8K **Privately Held**
SIC: 2499 5023 Picture frame molding, finished; frames & framing, picture & mirror

(G-18805)
ASSOCIATED INTERIOR DESGR SVC
4300 Georgia Ave (33405-2522)
PHONE..................................561 655-4926
Sara Petti, *President*
Richard Petti, *Vice Pres*
Scott McNutt, *Manager*
EMP: 18 **EST:** 1974
SQ FT: 6,500
SALES (est): 3MM **Privately Held**
WEB: www.associateddesignerservice.com
SIC: 2211 2512 2392 2391 Draperies & drapery fabrics, cotton; living room furniture: upholstered on wood frames; bedspreads & bed sets: made from purchased materials; curtains & draperies

(G-18806)
AZUL STONE LLC
920 Fern St (33401-5718)
PHONE..................................561 655-9385
Ihab Nasser, *Principal*
Ayman A Nasser, *Mng Member*
EMP: 12 **EST:** 2014
SALES (est): 1.2MM **Privately Held**
WEB: www.azulstone.com
SIC: 1411 5032 Limestone & marble dimension stone; granite dimension stone; marble building stone

(G-18807)
B E PRESSURE SUPPLY INC
Also Called: Be Pressure Supply
5483 Leaper Dr (33407-7000)
PHONE..................................561 688-9246
John Pankow,
Nick Braber,
◆ **EMP:** 10 **EST:** 1992
SALES (est): 1.3MM **Privately Held**
WEB: www.bepowerequipment.com
SIC: 3569 Blast cleaning equipment, dustless

(G-18808)
B G SERVICE COMPANY INC
1400 Alabama Ave Ste 15 (33401-7048)
P.O. Box 2259 (33402-2259)
PHONE..................................561 659-1471
John Frost, *Ch of Bd*
Timothy Frost, *President*
Ashwinee Basani, *QC Mgr*
Mary Frost, *Treasurer*
Jennifer Frost, *Admin Sec*
EMP: 36 **EST:** 1964
SQ FT: 19,000
SALES (est): 7.1MM **Privately Held**
WEB: www.bgservice.com
SIC: 3643 3694 Current-carrying wiring devices; engine electrical equipment; ignition apparatus, internal combustion engines

(G-18809)
B M H CONCRETE INC
6811 Belvedere Rd (33413-1012)
P.O. Box 18453 (33416-8453)
PHONE..................................561 615-0011
Jay Major Callaway Jr, *President*
EMP: 13 **EST:** 1999
SALES (est): 1.9MM **Privately Held**
WEB: www.bmhconcrete.com
SIC: 3273 Ready-mixed concrete

(G-18810)
B&K COUNTRY FEEDS LLC
912 Jamaican Dr (33415-3816)
PHONE..................................561 701-1852
Beverly Rys,
EMP: 5 **EST:** 2018
SALES (est): 335.2K **Privately Held**
SIC: 2048 Prepared feeds

(G-18811)
BABICAKES LLC
1279 Summit Run Cir (33415-4744)
PHONE..................................561 507-0331
Kerry Gordon,
EMP: 6 **EST:** 2013
SALES (est): 102.4K **Privately Held**
WEB: www.nicholslocksmith.com
SIC: 2051 5149 Cakes, bakery: except frozen; crackers, cookies & bakery products

(G-18812)
BACH SIGN GROUP INC
2289 Carambola Rd (33406-5222)
PHONE..................................561 848-3440
Carla Hilterbrick, *President*
Robert Hilterbrick, *Vice Pres*
EMP: 9 **EST:** 1994
SALES (est): 560.7K **Privately Held**
WEB: www.bachsign.com
SIC: 3993 Signs & advertising specialties

(G-18813)
BAMA PRINTING LLC
2257 Vista Pkwy Ste 11 (33411-2726)
PHONE..................................561 855-7641
John Vanginhoven, *Mng Member*
Mark Vanginhoven, *Mng Member*
EMP: 30 **EST:** 2012
SALES (est): 1.9MM **Privately Held**
WEB: www.printbama.com
SIC: 2752 Commercial printing, offset

(G-18814)
BDC FLORIDA LLC
Also Called: Native Outfitters
1300 N Florida Mango Rd # 30 (33409-5258)
PHONE..................................561 249-0900
Gene Caiazzo,
EMP: 14 **EST:** 2017
SALES (est): 1.1MM **Privately Held**
WEB: www.nativeoutfitters.com
SIC: 2361 2329 T-shirts & tops: girls', children's & infants'; men's & boys' sportswear & athletic clothing; men's & boys' athletic uniforms; windbreakers: men's, youths' & boys'

(G-18815)
BECARRO INTERNATIONAL CORP (PA)
Also Called: Sondra Roberts
917 S Military Trl Ste C3 (33415-3928)
PHONE..................................561 737-5585
Robert Camche, *President*
Glenn Camche, *Vice Pres*
Robyn Albaum, *Sales Mgr*
◆ **EMP:** 2 **EST:** 2003
SQ FT: 10,000
SALES (est): 3.9MM **Privately Held**
SIC: 3171 Handbags, women's

(G-18816)
BEE WELDING INC
Also Called: Bee Access Products
2145 Indian Rd (33409-3221)
PHONE..................................561 616-9003
John Belmonte, *President*
Tom Dejong, *Vice Pres*
Patrick Hickey, *Vice Pres*
Brian Andrews, *Engineer*
William S McAllister, *Treasurer*
▲ **EMP:** 18 **EST:** 1986
SALES (est): 8MM **Privately Held**
WEB: www.beeaccess.com
SIC: 7692 Welding repair

(G-18817)
BEESFREE INC
Also Called: Bees Vita Plus
2101 Vista Pkwy Ste 122 (33411-2706)
PHONE..................................561 939-4860
Andrea Festuccia, *Ch of Bd*
David W Todhunter, *President*
Juan Carlos Trabucco, *Director*
EMP: 5
SALES (est): 437.7K **Privately Held**
WEB: www.beesfree.biz
SIC: 2899 Chemical preparations

(G-18818)
BEST METAL WORK
3301 Elec Way Ste A (33407)
PHONE..................................561 842-1960
Glenn Simmons, *Owner*
EMP: 8 **EST:** 2007
SALES (est): 364.5K **Privately Held**
WEB: www.pbironman.com
SIC: 3599 Machine shop, jobbing & repair

(G-18819)
BIO BUBBLE PETS LLC
1400 Centrepark Blvd # 860 (33401-7421)
PHONE..................................561 998-5350
Steven Berlin, *Vice Pres*
Al Venezia,
▲ **EMP:** 11 **EST:** 2010
SALES (est): 15.6MM **Privately Held**
WEB: www.biobubblepets.com
SIC: 3089 Plastic processing
HQ: Vetements Peerless Inc
8888 Boul Pie-Ix
Montreal QC H1Z 4
514 593-9300

(G-18820)
BIONITROGEN HOLDINGS CORP (PA)
Also Called: Hidenet Scrities Architectures
1400 Centrepark Blvd # 860 (33401-7402)
PHONE..................................561 600-9550
Graham Copley, *CEO*
Bryan B Kornegay Jr, *President*
Ernesto Ernie Iznaga, *Vice Pres*
EMP: 5 **EST:** 1990
SALES (est): 1.2MM **Privately Held**
WEB: www.bionitrogen.com
SIC: 2873 Nitrogenous fertilizers

(G-18821)
BIOSCULPTURE TECHNOLOGY INC (PA)
1701 S Flagler Dr Apt 607 (33401-7341)
PHONE..................................561 651-7816
Robert L Cucin MD, *CEO*
Robert L D, *CEO*
Jack Meskunas, *CFO*
Deborah Salerno, *CFO*
Gayer Cucin, *Treasurer*
EMP: 24 **EST:** 2001
SQ FT: 3,500
SALES (est): 2.2MM **Privately Held**
WEB: www.biosculpturetechnology.com
SIC: 3841 Surgical & medical instruments

(G-18822)
BIRDSALL MARINE DESIGN INC
530 Nottingham Blvd (33405-2635)
PHONE..................................561 832-7879
Robert P Birdsall, *President*
▼ **EMP:** 20 **EST:** 1979
SQ FT: 14,000
SALES (est): 3.9MM **Privately Held**
WEB: www.marineproducts.net
SIC: 3429 5961 3732 3444 Marine hardware; mail order house, order taking office only; boat building & repairing; sheet metalwork

(G-18823)
BK NATURALS LLC
2611 Mercer Ave 4 (33401-7415)
PHONE..................................561 870-0592
Kimba Williams, *General Mgr*
Barbara J McLaren,
Kimba M Williams,
EMP: 9 **EST:** 2017
SALES (est): 885.6K **Privately Held**
SIC: 2676 Feminine hygiene paper products

(G-18824)
BLAST OFF EQUIPMENT INC
2350 S Military Trl (33415-7544)
PHONE..................................561 964-6199
Vickie Finnegan, *President*
EMP: 15 **EST:** 1984
SQ FT: 5,000
SALES (est): 1.3MM **Privately Held**
WEB: www.blastoffequipment.com
SIC: 3589 High pressure cleaning equipment

(G-18825)
BLUMER & STANTON ENTERPRISES (PA)
5112 Georgia Ave (33405-3192)
PHONE..................................561 585-2525
Roger Stanton, *President*
Marcille S Irwin, *Vice Pres*
Marcille Irwin, *Vice Pres*
William W Stanton, *Vice Pres*
Kenneth B Potter Jr, *Treasurer*
EMP: 12 **EST:** 1995
SQ FT: 30,000
SALES (est): 9.9MM **Privately Held**
WEB: www.blumerandstanton.com
SIC: 2431 Millwork

(G-18826)
BLUMER & STANTON INC
5112 Georgia Ave (33405-3192)
PHONE..................................561 585-2525
Roger Stanton, *President*
Marcille S Irwin, *Vice Pres*
Marcille Irwin, *Vice Pres*
Charles A Stanton, *Vice Pres*
William W Stanton, *Vice Pres*
▼ **EMP:** 17 **EST:** 1946
SQ FT: 30,000
SALES (est): 9.9MM **Privately Held**
WEB: www.blumerandstanton.com
SIC: 2431 Millwork
PA: Blumer & Stanton Enterprises, Inc
5112 Georgia Ave
West Palm Beach FL 33405
561 585-2525

(G-18827)
BOB KLINE QUALITY METAL INC
2511 Division Ave (33407-5345)
PHONE..................................561 659-4245
Robert M Kline, *President*
Bobby Kline, *Manager*
EMP: 5 **EST:** 1976
SQ FT: 2,200
SALES (est): 805.5K **Privately Held**
WEB: www.bob-kline-quality-metal-inc.hub.biz
SIC: 3444 7692 Sheet metal specialties, not stamped; welding repair

(G-18828)
BROTHERS PAVERS AND PRECAST
1008 Mcintosh St (33405-3014)
PHONE..................................561 662-9075
Mynor Hernandez, *Principal*
EMP: 7 **EST:** 2014
SALES (est): 198.1K **Privately Held**
SIC: 3272 Precast terrazo or concrete products

(G-18829)
BT GLASS & MIRROR INC
3748 Prospect Ave Ste 4 (33404-3488)
PHONE..................................561 841-7676
Scott Taylor, *President*
EMP: 6 **EST:** 1999
SQ FT: 32,000
SALES (est): 671.6K **Privately Held**
SIC: 3231 1793 Mirrored glass; glass & glazing work

(G-18830)
BUDDY PAULS INC
301 Clematis St Ste 300 (33401-4611)
PHONE..................................561 578-9813
Bryan Williams, *CEO*
EMP: 5
SALES (est): 750K **Privately Held**
SIC: 2087 Flavoring extracts & syrups

(G-18831)
BUSH BROTHERS PROVISION CO
1931 N Dixie Hwy (33407-6007)
PHONE..................................561 832-6666
Harry Bush, *President*
Billy Bush, *Vice Pres*
John Bush, *Opers Staff*
Doug Bush, *Finance Mgr*
Curtis Bush, *Finance*
▼ **EMP:** 25 **EST:** 1925
SQ FT: 27,000
SALES (est): 5.6MM **Privately Held**
WEB: www.bush-brothers.com
SIC: 2013 5147 Sausages & other prepared meats; meats, fresh

(G-18832)
CABINETS & COUNTERS
2373 Florida St (33406-4404)
PHONE..................................561 444-3083
Donald Newkirk, *Principal*
EMP: 6 **EST:** 2006
SALES (est): 64.7K **Privately Held**
SIC: 2434 Wood kitchen cabinets

(G-18833)
CADENCE KEEN INNOVATIONS INC
Also Called: Cki Solutions
1655 Palm Bch Lkes Blvd S (33401)
PHONE..................................561 249-2219
Sam Montross, *CEO*
Steven Gordon, *President*
Catalina Lluis, *Admin Asst*
EMP: 6 **EST:** 1996
SQ FT: 2,200
SALES (est): 1MM **Privately Held**
WEB: www.ckisolutions.us
SIC: 2514 Beds, including folding & cabinet, household: metal

(G-18834)
CAPRISTO USA
4188 Westroads Dr # 130 (33407-1249)
PHONE..................................561 882-9885
Andrea Taurino, *President*
EMP: 6 **EST:** 2016
SALES (est): 265.1K **Privately Held**
WEB: www.capristoexhaust.com
SIC: 3714 Motor vehicle parts & accessories

(G-18835)
CAROLINA CLUBS INC
11064 68th St N (33412-1831)
PHONE..................................561 753-6948
Kevin Lane, *President*
George Lane, *Principal*
Thomas Lane, *Vice Pres*
Karen Lane, *Treasurer*
EMP: 5 **EST:** 1990
SALES (est): 483.3K **Privately Held**
WEB: www.carolinaclubs.com
SIC: 3949 Baseball equipment & supplies, general

(G-18836)
CC CONTROL CORP
5760 Corporate Way (33407-2004)
PHONE..................................561 293-3975
James J Hecht, *President*
Luis L Garcia, *Vice Pres*
Matthew Skidmore, *Shareholder*
EMP: 20
SQ FT: 13,200
SALES: 10.2MM **Privately Held**
WEB: www.cccontrolcorp.com
SIC: 3625 Electric controls & control accessories, industrial

(G-18837)
CEMEX CNSTR MTLS ATL LLC (DH)
1501 Belvedere Rd (33406-1501)
PHONE..................................561 833-5555
Fernando A Gonzalez, *CEO*
Maher Al-Haffar, *Exec VP*
Mauricio Doehner, *Exec VP*
Jaime Elizondo, *Vice Pres*
Joaqun Estrada, *Vice Pres*
▲ **EMP:** 100 **EST:** 1988
SALES (est): 62.7MM **Privately Held**
WEB: www.cemex.com
SIC: 3272 Concrete products
HQ: Cemex, Inc.
10100 Katy Fwy Ste 300
Houston TX 77043
713 650-6200

(G-18838)
CEMEX CNSTR MTLS FLA LLC
Also Called: Mat Div-Palm Beach Maint Shop
1021 N Railroad Ave (33401-3305)
PHONE..................................561 832-6646
Chuck Carew, *Branch Mgr*
EMP: 10
SQ FT: 7,896 **Privately Held**
SIC: 3444 5032 3273 5211 Sheet metalwork; concrete mixtures; ready-mixed concrete; concrete & cinder block
HQ: Cemex Construction Materials Florida, Llc
1501 Belvedere Rd
West Palm Beach FL 33406

(G-18839)
CEMEX CNSTR MTLS FLA LLC (DH)
1501 Belvedere Rd (33406-1501)
PHONE..................................561 833-5555
Gonzalo Galindo, *President*
Kelly C Anderson, *Vice Pres*
Greg Hazle, *Vice Pres*
Jim Reed, *Human Res Mgr*
Thomas Edgeller,
▼ **EMP:** 16 **EST:** 2008
SALES (est): 260.4MM **Privately Held**
WEB: www.cemex.com
SIC: 3273 Ready-mixed concrete
HQ: Cemex, Inc.
10100 Katy Fwy Ste 300
Houston TX 77043
713 650-6200

(G-18840)
CEMEX CNSTR MTLS PCF LLC (DH)
1501 Belvedere Rd (33406-1501)
PHONE..................................561 833-5555
Rob Cutter, *President*
▲ **EMP:** 100 **EST:** 2008
SALES (est): 595.1MM **Privately Held**
WEB: www.cemex.com
SIC: 3272 Concrete products
HQ: Cemex, Inc.
10100 Katy Fwy Ste 300
Houston TX 77043
713 650-6200

(G-18841)
CEMEX MATERIALS LLC (DH)
1501 Belvedere Rd (33406-1501)
P.O. Box 24635 (33416-4635)
PHONE..................................561 833-5555
Duncan Gage, *President*
Karl Watson, *President*
Karl H Watson Jr,
Bob Capasso,
Robert J Capasso,
◆ **EMP:** 200
SQ FT: 72,000
SALES (est): 1.9B **Privately Held**
WEB: www.cemex.com
SIC: 3271 3273 3272 1422 Blocks, concrete or cinder: standard; ready-mixed concrete; pipe, concrete or lined with concrete; crushed & broken limestone
HQ: Cemex, Inc.
10100 Katy Fwy Ste 300
Houston TX 77043
713 650-6200

(G-18842)
CEMEX MATERIALS LLC
9111 Southern Blvd (33411-3626)
PHONE..................................561 793-1442
David Clark, *Branch Mgr*
EMP: 73 **Privately Held**
SIC: 3271 3273 3272 1422 Blocks, concrete or cinder: standard; ready-mixed concrete; concrete products; crushed & broken limestone
HQ: Cemex Materials Llc
1501 Belvedere Rd
West Palm Beach FL 33406
561 833-5555

(G-18843)
CENTURION RESIDENTIAL INDS
3819 Heath Cir N (33407-3180)
PHONE..................................561 574-1483
Laverne Ferguson, *Director*
EMP: 22 **EST:** 2001
SALES (est): 133.6K **Privately Held**
WEB: www.centurionind.com
SIC: 3999 Manufacturing industries

(G-18844)
CGI PRINTERS LLC
2820 Tennis Club Dr # 202 (33417-2953)
PHONE..................................561 969-9999
Luis Pastor, *Mng Member*
EMP: 7 **EST:** 2015
SALES (est): 148.6K **Privately Held**
SIC: 2752 Commercial printing, offset

(G-18845)
CHANNEL INDUSTRIES INC
Also Called: Pelican Pumps
511 29th St (33407-5115)
P.O. Box 65, Canal Point (33438-0065)
PHONE..................................561 214-0637
James Goldie, *President*
Christine Goldie, *Vice Pres*
Craig White, *Engineer*
EMP: 13 **EST:** 1941
SQ FT: 10,000
SALES (est): 1.5MM **Privately Held**
SIC: 3561 7699 7692 Pumps & pumping equipment; farm machinery repair; welding repair

(G-18846)
CHIDSEY CUSTOM WOODWORKS
4327 Willow Pond Cir (33417-8248)
PHONE..................................561 632-9728
Donald Chidsey, *Principal*
EMP: 6 **EST:** 2010
SALES (est): 96.5K **Privately Held**
SIC: 2431 Millwork

(G-18847)
CLINICAL CHMSTRY SPCLISTS CORP
Also Called: Ir Clinical
6901 Okeechobee Blvd D5-L3 (33411-2511)
PHONE..................................919 554-1424
Larry Denney, *CEO*
◆ **EMP:** 10
SQ FT: 3,000
SALES (est): 10MM **Privately Held**
SIC: 3841 Diagnostic apparatus, medical

(G-18848)
COASTAL MILLWORKS INC
3810 Consumer St Ste 2 (33404-1710)
PHONE..................................561 881-7755
John B Maffett, *President*
Mary R Maffett, *Corp Secy*
Carl Tourigny, *Project Mgr*
Tony Perez, *Prdtn Mgr*
Matt Carothers, *Supervisor*
EMP: 40 **EST:** 1990
SQ FT: 26,000
SALES (est): 10.8MM **Privately Held**
WEB: www.coastalmillworks.com
SIC: 2431 Millwork

(G-18849)
CONTRACTING CNC MACHINING INC
8360 Currency Dr Ste 7 (33404-1714)
PHONE..................................561 494-0703
Michael Vernsey, *President*
EMP: 7 **EST:** 2006
SALES (est): 942.3K **Privately Held**
SIC: 3965 Fasteners, buttons, needles & pins

(G-18850)
CORAL REEF CAST STONE INC
Also Called: Jhr Management
6100 Georgia Ave (33405-3950)
P.O. Box 540549, Greenacres (33454-0549)
PHONE..................................561 586-1900
Rhoda Meyers, *President*
Cheryl Smart, *Manager*
▼ **EMP:** 14 **EST:** 1995
SQ FT: 14,447
SALES (est): 1.7MM **Privately Held**
WEB: www.coralreefcaststone.com
SIC: 3272 Stone, cast concrete

(G-18851)
COVERT ARMOR LLC
1101 Clare Ave Ste 2 (33401-6967)
PHONE..................................561 459-8077
EMP: 10 **EST:** 2018
SALES (est): 537.2K **Privately Held**
WEB: www.covertarmor.com
SIC: 3949 Sporting & athletic goods

(G-18852)
CROWN SEAMLESS GUTTERS INC
7880 Coconut Blvd (33412-2256)
PHONE..................................561 748-9919
Joshua Muller, *President*
Jason Brackett, *General Mgr*
Richard Muller, *Vice Pres*
Sara Muller, *Admin Sec*
EMP: 15 **EST:** 1976
SALES (est): 1.1MM **Privately Held**
WEB: www.crownseamlessgutters.net
SIC: 3444 1711 Gutters, sheet metal; heating & air conditioning contractors

(G-18853)
DELTA MG
4440 S Tiffany Dr Ste 8 (33407)
PHONE..................................561 840-0577
Danilo Alcantara, *President*
Eliseo Fancane, *Vice Pres*
EMP: 6 **EST:** 2007
SALES (est): 800K **Privately Held**
WEB: www.deltamg.com
SIC: 2499 Tiles, cork

(G-18854)
DIAMOND ADVERTISING & MKTG
Also Called: South Florida Time
1200 S Flagler Dr Apt 106 (33401-6701)
P.O. Box 222 (33402-0222)
PHONE..................................561 833-5129
Audrey Diamonds, *Owner*
Cy Caine, *Director*
Robin Diamand, *Director*
EMP: 10 **EST:** 2003
SALES (est): 685.7K **Privately Held**
SIC: 2721 Magazines: publishing & printing

(G-18855)
DISCOVERY TANK TESTING INC
1209 Gateway Rd Ste 203 (33403-1929)
P.O. Box 14207, North Palm Beach (33408-0207)
PHONE..................................561 840-1666
Jerry Pellegrino, *President*
Javier Cruz, *Opers Staff*
EMP: 5 **EST:** 1987
SQ FT: 1,800
SALES (est): 500K **Privately Held**
WEB: www.discoverytanktesting.com
SIC: 1389 Testing, measuring, surveying & analysis services

(G-18856)
DUNCANSON DYNASTY INC
Also Called: Soft Water Techs
723 39th St (33407-4111)
PHONE..................................561 288-1349
Roddrick E Duncanson Sr, *President*
EMP: 8 **EST:** 2017
SALES (est): 434.3K **Privately Held**
SIC: 2899 Water treating compounds

(G-18857)
DURACELL COMPANY
515 N Flagler Dr Ste 1600 (33401-4346)
PHONE..................................561 494-7550
Carolina Martinize, *Branch Mgr*
EMP: 30
SALES (corp-wide): 245.5B **Publicly Held**
WEB: www.duracell.com
SIC: 3691 Storage batteries
HQ: The Duracell Company
14 Research Dr
Bethel CT 06801
203 796-4000

(G-18858)
DYNAMIC METALS LLC
340 Pike Rd (33411-3837)
PHONE..................................561 629-7304
Jesus Lara,
EMP: 11 **EST:** 2015
SALES (est): 491.3K **Privately Held**
SIC: 3444 Roof deck, sheet metal

(G-18859)
EASTERN METAL SUPPLY NC INC
4268 Westroads Dr (33407-1201)
PHONE..................................800 432-2204
Isabel Linares, *Manager*
EMP: 13 **Privately Held**
WEB: www.easternmetal.com
SIC: 3441 Fabricated structural metal
PA: Eastern Metal Supply Of North Carolina, Inc.
2925 Stewart Creek Blvd
Charlotte NC 28216

(G-18860)
ECOSMART SURFACE & COATING TEC
1313 S Killian Dr (33403-1918)
PHONE..................................402 319-1607
EMP: 8 **EST:** 2014
SALES (est): 110.3K **Privately Held**
SIC: 3479 Metal coating & allied service

(G-18861)
EL LATINO NEWSPAPER
4404 Georgia Ave Ste A (33405-2500)
PHONE..................................561 835-4913
EMP: 6
SALES (est): 188.2K **Privately Held**
SIC: 2711 Newspapers-Publishing/Printing

(G-18862)
ENGINEERED EQUIPMENT CORP
777 S Flagler Dr Ste 800 (33401-6161)
PHONE..................................561 839-4008
Ronald Regan, *Principal*
EMP: 12 **EST:** 2018
SALES (est): 2.3MM **Privately Held**
WEB: www.engineeredequipmentcorp.com
SIC: 2521 Panel systems & partitions (free-standing), office: wood

(G-18863)
ETC PALM BEACH LLC
1800 Okeechobee Rd # 100 (33409-5207)
PHONE..................................561 881-8118
Paul Biava, *Mng Member*
EMP: 70 **EST:** 2017
SALES (est): 9.9MM **Privately Held**
WEB: www.etcsimplify.com
SIC: 3699 Security control equipment & systems

(G-18864)
ETECH SIMULATION CORP (PA)
2721 Vista Pkwy Ste C13 (33411-6723)
PHONE..................................561 922-9792
Jairo Leiva, *Principal*
Esteban Okret, *Regional Mgr*
Rocio Schettino, *Project Mgr*
Jairo Rivera, *VP Sales*
Michael Leininger, *Accounts Mgr*
EMP: 47 **EST:** 2017
SALES (est): 10.9MM **Privately Held**
WEB: www.etechsimulation.com
SIC: 3812 Search & navigation equipment

(G-18865)
EUROPEAN CABINETS & DESIGN LLC
4050 Westgate Ave (33409-4732)
PHONE..................................561 684-1440
EMP: 7 **EST:** 2019
SALES (est): 524.5K **Privately Held**
WEB: www.europeancabinetsanddesign.com
SIC: 2434 Wood kitchen cabinets

(G-18866)
EVOLUTION METALS CORP ✪
Also Called: Metals & Mining
516 S Dixie Hwy (33401-5810)
PHONE..................................561 531-2314
David Wilcox, *CEO*
EMP: 20 **EST:** 2020
SALES (est): 1.3MM **Privately Held**
WEB: www.evolution-metals.com
SIC: 1081 Metal mining services; metal mining exploration & development services

(G-18867)
F D SIGNWORKS LLC
Also Called: Identifire Safety
941 S Military Trl F5 (33415-3980)
PHONE..................................561 248-6323
Matthew Hyman, *Principal*
EMP: 6 **EST:** 2014
SALES (est): 355.2K **Privately Held**
WEB: www.identifiresafety.com
SIC: 3993 Signs & advertising specialties

(G-18868)
FACTORYMART INC
3875 Fiscal Ct Ste 400 (33404-1707)
PHONE..................................561 202-9820
John Didonato, *Principal*
EMP: 12 **EST:** 2011
SALES (est): 378.6K **Privately Held**
WEB: www.factorymart.com
SIC: 2752 Commercial printing, offset

(G-18869)
FALCONS CASTL BLINDS GLOBL FLA
3316 Lake Ave (33405-1814)
PHONE..................................561 727-4332
Yasmany Falcon Rojas, *President*
EMP: 6 **EST:** 2019
SALES (est): 57.3K **Privately Held**
SIC: 2591 Window blinds

(G-18870)
FERRIN SIGNS INC
945 26th St (33407-5314)
PHONE..................................561 802-4242
Ralph Lashells, *President*
Dan May, *Vice Pres*
Danielle Hannon, *Project Mgr*
Tim Lewzader, *Accounts Exec*
EMP: 22 **EST:** 1991
SQ FT: 18,000
SALES (est): 3.4MM **Privately Held**
WEB: www.ferrinsigns.com
SIC: 3993 Electric signs

(G-18871)
FINE LINE PAVERS INC
6480 Bischoff Rd (33413)
PHONE..................................561 389-9819
Edgar W Garcia, *Principal*
EMP: 6 **EST:** 2008
SALES (est): 522.9K **Privately Held**
WEB: www.finelinepaversinc.com
SIC: 3531 Pavers

(G-18872)
FIRST IMPRSSION DORS MLLWK INC
346 Pike Rd Ste 6 (33411-3819)
PHONE..................................561 798-6684
Darren Dobkins, *President*
Greg Dobkins, *Sales Staff*
▼ **EMP:** 11 **EST:** 2003
SALES (est): 2MM **Privately Held**
WEB: www.fidminc.com
SIC: 2431 Millwork

(G-18873)
FLAVORWORKS INC
10130 Northlake Blvd (33412-1101)
PHONE..................................561 588-8246
Jonathan Pierce, *President*
▼ **EMP:** 22 **EST:** 1998
SQ FT: 15,400
SALES (est): 2.4MM **Privately Held**
WEB: www.flavorworksfoodgroup.com
SIC: 2099 Food preparations

(G-18874)
FLORIDA CRYSTAL REFINERY INC (DH)
1 N Clematis St Ste 200 (33401-5551)
P.O. Box 1059, Palm Beach (33480-1059)
PHONE..................................561 366-5200
Alfonso Fanjul Jr, *Ch of Bd*
Jose Fanjul, *President*
Donald W Carson, *Vice Pres*
Rick Blomqvist, *Treasurer*
Ricardo Martinez, *Controller*
▼ **EMP:** 5 **EST:** 1978
SQ FT: 9,000
SALES (est): 21.4MM
SALES (corp-wide): 2.1B **Privately Held**
WEB: www.floridacrystals.com
SIC: 2062 Cane sugar refining
HQ: Okeelanta Corporation
1 N Clematis St Ste 200
West Palm Beach FL 33401
561 366-5100

(G-18875)
FLORIDA CRYSTALS CORPORATION (HQ)
1 N Clematis St Ste 200 (33401-5551)
P.O. Box 4671 (33402-4671)
PHONE..................................561 655-6303
Alfonso Fanjul, *Ch of Bd*
Jose F Fanjul Jr, *Vice Chairman*
Jose Fanjul, *Vice Pres*
Juan Porro, *Vice Pres*
Chris Winterling, *Vice Pres*
▲ **EMP:** 100 **EST:** 1962
SALES (est): 561.8MM
SALES (corp-wide): 2.1B **Privately Held**
WEB: www.floridacrystals.com
SIC: 2061 2062 2044 4911 Raw cane sugar; cane sugar refining; rice milling; electric services
PA: Fanjul Corp.
1 N Clematis St Ste 200
West Palm Beach FL 33401
561 655-6303

(G-18876)
FLORIDA CRYSTALS CORPORATION
626 N Dixie Hwy (33401-3918)
PHONE..................................561 366-5000
Rafael Gregorich, *Superintendent*
Benjamin Sadler, *Counsel*
Connie Matthews, *Vice Pres*
Jose Perez, *Vice Pres*
Erik Schickling, *Project Mgr*
EMP: 190
SALES (corp-wide): 2.1B **Privately Held**
WEB: www.floridacrystals.com
SIC: 2061 2062 0133 Raw cane sugar; cane sugar refining; sugarcane & sugar beets
HQ: Florida Crystals Corporation
1 N Clematis St Ste 200
West Palm Beach FL 33401
561 655-6303

(G-18877)
FLORIDA CRYSTALS CORPORATION
Also Called: Purchasing Department
1 N Clematis St Ste 400 (33401-5552)
PHONE..................................561 515-8080
Robert Darnell, *Regional Mgr*
Jeremy Surpin, *Regional Mgr*
David Tack, *Project Mgr*
James Omealy, *Research*
Michelle Tittl, *Research*
EMP: 190
SALES (corp-wide): 2.1B **Privately Held**
WEB: www.floridacrystals.com
SIC: 2061 2062 2044 4911 Raw cane sugar; cane sugar refining; rice milling; electric services
HQ: Florida Crystals Corporation
1 N Clematis St Ste 200
West Palm Beach FL 33401
561 655-6303

(G-18878)
FLORIDA CRYSTALS FOOD CORP
1 N Clematis St Ste 200 (33401-5551)
PHONE..................................561 366-5100
Armando A Tabernilla, *Principal*
Ed Starr, *Regional Mgr*
Stacey Griffith, *Sales Staff*
▲ **EMP:** 598 **EST:** 2011
SALES (est): 3.1MM
SALES (corp-wide): 2.1B **Privately Held**
WEB: www.floridacrystals.com
SIC: 2061 Raw cane sugar
HQ: Florida Crystals Corporation
1 N Clematis St Ste 200
West Palm Beach FL 33401
561 655-6303

(G-18879)
FLORIDA DESIGN MFG ASSOC INC
7430 Pine Tree Ln (33406-6821)
P.O. Box 10505 (33419-0505)
PHONE..................................561 533-0733
John Shanks, *President*
EMP: 10
SQ FT: 6,000
SALES (est): 951.6K **Privately Held**
SIC: 2542 1799 Counters or counter display cases: except wood; counter top installation

(G-18880)
FLORIDA SUGAR DISTRIBUTORS (DH)
1 N Clematis St Ste 310 (33401-5551)
PHONE..................................561 655-6303
Alfonso Fanjul, *Ch of Bd*
Rick Blomquist, *Vice Pres*
EMP: 20 **EST:** 1994
SQ FT: 5,200

▲ = Import ▼=Export
◆ =Import/Export

SALES (est): 21.7MM
SALES (corp-wide): 2.1B Privately Held
WEB: www.floridacrystals.com
SIC: 2062 Cane sugar refining
HQ: Florida Crystals Corporation
1 N Clematis St Ste 200
West Palm Beach FL 33401
561 655-6303

(G-18881)
FOUR WD CONSULTING & PUBG LLC
5405 Okchobee Blvd # 201 (33417-4543)
PHONE....216 533-2203
Homas J Ryan,
EMP: 6 EST: 2019
SALES (est): 400.5K Privately Held
WEB: www.savingsguidemagazine.com
SIC: 2741 Miscellaneous publishing

(G-18882)
FOVICO INC
Also Called: Aqua Solutions
15908 77th Trl N (33418-1854)
PHONE....561 624-5400
Forrest R Vincent, *President*
EMP: 15 EST: 2008
SALES (est): 1.1MM Privately Held
SIC: 3589 Water treatment equipment, industrial

(G-18883)
FOWLERS SHEET METAL INC
4716 Georgia Ave (33405-2897)
PHONE....561 659-3309
Brenda Fowler, *President*
Brian Fowler, *Vice Pres*
Daniel Fowler, *Admin Sec*
EMP: 13 EST: 1980
SQ FT: 2,500
SALES (est): 2.5MM Privately Held
WEB: www.fowlerssheetmetal.com
SIC: 3444 Sheet metalwork

(G-18884)
FRITZ COMMERCIAL PRINTING INC
5401 S Dixie Hwy (33405-3232)
PHONE....561 585-6869
Fritz Jean-Louis, *President*
EMP: 6 EST: 2006
SALES (est): 359.2K Privately Held
SIC: 2759 Commercial printing

(G-18885)
FULLY PROMOTED
1369 N Military Trl (33409-6016)
PHONE....561 615-8655
EMP: 8 EST: 2018
SALES (est): 345.6K Privately Held
WEB: www.fullypromoted.com
SIC: 2395 Embroidery & art needlework

(G-18886)
GEORGE GILLESPIE CABINETS
15611 78th Dr N (33418-1857)
PHONE....561 744-6191
George C Gillespie Jr, *President*
EMP: 8 EST: 2010
SALES (est): 377.7K Privately Held
SIC: 2434 Wood kitchen cabinets

(G-18887)
GEORGIA MKTG & SIGN CO LLC
Also Called: Signarama - Woodstock
2121 Vista Pkwy (33411-2706)
PHONE....800 286-8671
Steve Dabbs,
EMP: 7 EST: 2011
SQ FT: 1,500
SALES (est): 457.5K Privately Held
WEB: www.signarama.com
SIC: 3993 Signs & advertising specialties

(G-18888)
GIZMOS LION SHEET METAL INC
1648 Donna Rd (33409-5202)
PHONE....561 684-8480
EMP: 12 EST: 2019
SALES (est): 772.5K Privately Held
SIC: 3444 Sheet metalwork

(G-18889)
GRAPHICS DESIGNER INC
Also Called: Sign-A-Rama
1367 N Military Trl (33409-6016)
PHONE....561 687-7993
Lino Defeo, *President*
EMP: 11 EST: 1990
SQ FT: 2,400
SALES (est): 1,000K Privately Held
WEB: www.signarama.com
SIC: 3993 2752 2671 Signs & advertising specialties; commercial printing, lithographic; packaging paper & plastics film, coated & laminated

(G-18890)
GREEN TOUCH INDUSTRIES INC
100 Us Highway 1 (33403-3550)
P.O. Box 30614, Palm Beach Gardens (33420-0614)
PHONE....561 659-5525
Dan Keegan, *Owner*
▲ EMP: 8 EST: 2011
SALES (est): 847.9K Privately Held
WEB: www.trailerracks.com
SIC: 3999 Manufacturing industries

(G-18891)
GROWHEALTHY HOLDINGS LLC
324 Datura St (33401-5414)
P.O. Box 708, Lake Wales (33859-0708)
PHONE....863 223-8882
Don Clifford, *CEO*
EMP: 10 EST: 2014
SALES (est): 5MM
SALES (corp-wide): 78.3MM Privately Held
WEB: www.growhealthy.com
SIC: 2834 Pharmaceutical preparations
PA: Ianthus Capital Holdings, Inc
22 Adelaide St W Suite 2740
Toronto ON M5H 4
416 591-1525

(G-18892)
GULFSTREAM WOODWORK LLC
4901 Georgia Ave (33405-3113)
PHONE....561 231-1810
Michael A Sandholzer, *Principal*
EMP: 6 EST: 2018
SALES (est): 189.1K Privately Held
WEB: www.gulfstream.com
SIC: 2431 Millwork

(G-18893)
HDD LLC
412 Clematis St (33401-5312)
PHONE....561 346-9054
Hessan Musallet, *Manager*
EMP: 7 EST: 2013
SALES (est): 286.7K Privately Held
SIC: 2084 Wines, brandy & brandy spirits

(G-18894)
HERPEL INC (PA)
6400 Georgia Ave (33405-4220)
PHONE....561 585-5573
Frederick Herpel, *President*
Joan McDonald, *Admin Sec*
▼ EMP: 14 EST: 1948
SQ FT: 20,000
SALES (est): 2.1MM Privately Held
WEB: www.herpelcaststone.com
SIC: 3272 Tile, precast terrazzo or concrete

(G-18895)
HIGH END CABINETS LLC
4715 Georgia Ave (33405-2813)
PHONE....561 469-8237
Jesus Alcala, *Principal*
EMP: 7 EST: 2017
SALES (est): 95.6K Privately Held
WEB: www.highendcabinetsllc.com
SIC: 2434 Wood kitchen cabinets

(G-18896)
HOLLAND PUMP COMPANY (PA)
7312 Westport Pl (33413-1661)
PHONE....561 697-3333
Thomas Vossman, *CEO*
Bill Blodgett, *Chairman*
Eugene Lant, *Vice Pres*
Mike Cressman, *Opers Mgr*
Dennis Olsen, *Opers Mgr*
◆ EMP: 7 EST: 1978
SQ FT: 21,000
SALES (est): 20.1MM Privately Held
WEB: www.hollandpump.com
SIC: 3561 7359 Pumps & pumping equipment; equipment rental & leasing

(G-18897)
HONEYCOMMCORE LLC (PA)
15771 80th Dr N (33418-1837)
PHONE....561 747-2678
William M Marvel,
Bill Marvel,
▲ EMP: 5 EST: 2004
SQ FT: 10,000
SALES (est): 1.3MM Privately Held
WEB: www.aluminum-honeycomb.com
SIC: 3999 Honeycomb foundations (beekeepers' supplies)

(G-18898)
HOWIES INSTANT PRINTING INC
1572 Palm Bch Lakes Blvd (33401-2338)
PHONE....561 686-8699
EMP: 10
SQ FT: 2,500
SALES (est): 1.1MM Privately Held
SIC: 2752 2759 Offset Printing & Commercial Printing

(G-18899)
I FOUND IT
9339 Highway A1a Alt (33403-1440)
PHONE....561 557-2881
EMP: 6 EST: 2013
SALES (est): 148.8K Privately Held
SIC: 2521 Wood office furniture

(G-18900)
I-POP INC
475 N Cleary Rd Unit 4 (33413-1626)
PHONE....561 567-9000
Devorah Leo, *CEO*
Steven Leo, *President*
EMP: 32 EST: 2013
SALES (est): 850K Privately Held
WEB: www.rsc-ny.com
SIC: 2531 Assembly hall furniture

(G-18901)
IMAGE INTERNATIONAL INC
8040 Belvedere Rd Ste 1 (33411-3202)
PHONE....561 793-9560
Janna Levendofsky, *President*
EMP: 7 EST: 2002
SALES (est): 492K Privately Held
SIC: 2844 Cosmetic preparations

(G-18902)
INCITY SECURITY INC
Also Called: Incity Property Management
3560 Inv Ln Ste 102 (33404)
PHONE....561 306-9228
John Sizer, *President*
EMP: 17 EST: 2012
SALES (est): 5.1MM Privately Held
SIC: 3861 2085 5063 1731 Cameras & related equipment; gin (alcoholic beverage); rum (alcoholic beverage); alarm systems; burglar alarm systems; computer installation; computer software; modems, monitors, terminals & disk drives: computers
PA: Intercity Alarms And Security Systems (Pty) Ltd
4 Sandberg Stdenver
GP 1401

(G-18903)
INDIAN RIVER BIODIESEL LLC
1810 Okeechobee Rd Ste A (33409-5237)
PHONE....321 586-7670
Christopher C Burdett,
EMP: 6 EST: 2016
SALES (est): 133.9K Privately Held
WEB: www.indianriverbiodiesel.com
SIC: 2911 Diesel fuels

(G-18904)
INNOVA HOME LLC
6200 S Dixie Hwy (33405-4329)
PHONE....561 855-2450
Michel McNabb, *Mng Member*
EMP: 7 EST: 2015
SALES (est): 259.8K Privately Held
SIC: 2084 Wines, brandy & brandy spirits

(G-18905)
INNOVATIVE FLARE LLC
7750 Okeechobee Blvd 4-7 (33411-2104)
PHONE....561 247-2776
Collin P Lynch, *President*
EMP: 5 EST: 2016
SALES (est): 349K Privately Held
WEB: www.innovativeflare.com
SIC: 2899 Flares

(G-18906)
INSANEJOURNALCOM
2372 Pinewood Ln (33415-7330)
PHONE....561 315-9311
Jason Vervlied, *Owner*
EMP: 6 EST: 2011
SALES (est): 87.8K Privately Held
WEB: www.insanejournal.com
SIC: 2741 Miscellaneous publishing

(G-18907)
INTEGRA CONNECT LLC (PA)
501 S Flagler Dr Ste 600 (33401-5914)
PHONE....800 742-3069
Charles Saunders, *CEO*
Christian Herrick, *Vice Pres*
Nikko Khazana, *Vice Pres*
David Artim, *Opers Staff*
Nathan Kodak, *Engineer*
EMP: 12 EST: 2013
SQ FT: 1,000
SALES (est): 98MM Privately Held
WEB: www.integraconnect.com
SIC: 7372 Business oriented computer software

(G-18908)
ISLA INSTRUMENTS LLC
13884 71st Pl N (33412-2127)
PHONE....561 603-4685
Bradley Holland,
EMP: 11 EST: 2016
SALES (est): 260K Privately Held
WEB: www.islainstruments.com
SIC: 3931 Musical instruments

(G-18909)
J & I VENTURES INC
Also Called: Ocean Tech
4390 Westroads Dr Ste 2 (33407-1226)
PHONE....561 845-0030
Jack P Bates, *President*
Jesse Underhill, *Production*
▲ EMP: 29 EST: 2004
SALES (est): 1.9MM Privately Held
SIC: 3069 Wet suits, rubber

(G-18910)
J A CUSTOM
3042 Ike Rd Ste 17 (33411)
PHONE....561 615-4680
Jorge A Angel Jr, *Owner*
EMP: 9 EST: 2010
SALES (est): 77.3K Privately Held
WEB: www.jacustomfab.com
SIC: 3441 3446 Fabricated structural metal; ornamental metalwork

(G-18911)
JDJSIS INC
8645 N Military Trl # 501 (33410-6296)
PHONE....561 732-2388
Anthony Accaputo, *Principal*
EMP: 6 EST: 2010
SALES (est): 95.5K Privately Held
SIC: 2759 Commercial printing

(G-18912)
JKA PUMP SPECIALISTS
5407 N Haverhill Rd 344-345 (33407-7008)
PHONE....561 686-4455
▲ EMP: 9 EST: 2012
SALES (est): 1.9MM Privately Held
WEB: www.jkapump.com
SIC: 3561 Industrial pumps & parts

(G-18913)
JOCKEY INTERNATIONAL INC
Also Called: Jockey Outl - Palm Bch Outlets
1781 Palmbeachlakes (33401)
PHONE....561 689-7646
EMP: 6

GEOGRAPHIC

SALES (corp-wide): 395.9MM **Privately Held**
WEB: www.jockey.com
SIC: 2254 2341 2322 Knit underwear mills; women's & children's underwear; men's & boys' underwear & nightwear
PA: Jockey International, Inc.
2300 60th St
Kenosha WI 53140
262 658-8111

(G-18914)
JOHN E ANDERSON ✪
Also Called: Nauttyboiz Extreme Printing
505 16th St 1 (33407-6409)
PHONE..................................305 741-8400
John E Anderson, *Owner*
EMP: 6 **EST:** 2020
SALES (est): 206.8K **Privately Held**
SIC: 2211 Print cloths, cotton

(G-18915)
JSR WELLNESS INC
5500 Village Blvd Ste 202 (33407-1961)
PHONE..................................561 748-2477
Jordan Rubin, *CEO*
Rich Petti, *COO*
Jeff Brams, *Vice Pres*
Teresa Miller, *Vice Pres*
Erik Schmitt, *Vice Pres*
▲ **EMP:** 79 **EST:** 2000
SQ FT: 20,000
SALES (est): 16.9MM **Privately Held**
SIC: 2834 Vitamin, nutrient & hematinic preparations for human use

(G-18916)
JUSTICE GOVERNMENT SUPPLY INC
555 Pacific Grove Dr # 2 (33401-8312)
PHONE..................................954 559-3038
Grady Renville, *CEO*
Steven Pietro, *President*
EMP: 5 **EST:** 2016
SALES (est): 494K **Privately Held**
WEB: www.jgsfoods.com
SIC: 2011 Meat packing plants

(G-18917)
K AND G FOOD SERVICES LLC
Also Called: Pbg Golf Restaurant
9500 Sandhill Crane Dr (33412-6301)
PHONE..................................954 857-9283
Gustavo Seminario, *Principal*
Eddie Guillen, *Opers Staff*
Matt Marken, *Corp Comm Staff*
Tim Ford, *Manager*
Dorian Hawkins, *Officer*
EMP: 6 **EST:** 2015
SALES (est): 112.4K **Privately Held**
SIC: 2099 5141 Food preparations; food brokers

(G-18918)
K&T STONEWORKS INC
101 N Benoist Farms Rd (33411-3743)
PHONE..................................561 798-8486
Karen Kendall, *President*
◆ **EMP:** 11 **EST:** 1997
SALES (est): 1.3MM **Privately Held**
WEB: www.ktstoneworks.com
SIC: 3272 Stone, cast concrete

(G-18919)
K12 PRINT INC
3875 Fiscal Ct Ste 400 (33404-1707)
PHONE..................................800 764-7600
John Didonato, *President*
John Kilburg, *Vice Pres*
EMP: 10 **EST:** 2017
SALES (est): 345.9K **Privately Held**
WEB: www.k12print.com
SIC: 2752 Commercial printing, offset

(G-18920)
KINETIC FUSION CORP
12781 56th Pl N (33411-8538)
PHONE..................................561 352-1670
Duane A Lawrence, *Branch Mgr*
EMP: 6
SALES (corp-wide): 123.3K **Privately Held**
SIC: 7692 Welding repair
PA: Kinetic Fusion Corp
15211 67th Ct N
Loxahatchee FL
561 383-7490

(G-18921)
KINGMAN CUSTOM STAIRS & TRIM L
436 Lytle St (33405-4622)
PHONE..................................561 547-9888
Frederick D Kingman, *Principal*
EMP: 8 **EST:** 2006
SALES (est): 879.8K **Privately Held**
WEB: www.kingmanstairsandfloors.com
SIC: 3272 Floor slabs & tiles, precast concrete

(G-18922)
L & L ORNAMENTAL IRON WORKS
5601 Georgia Ave (33405-3709)
PHONE..................................561 547-5605
Gina Perez, *President*
Leo Perez, *Owner*
▼ **EMP:** 12 **EST:** 1992
SALES (est): 1.8MM **Privately Held**
WEB: www.llironworks.com
SIC: 3446 Architectural metalwork

(G-18923)
LA PERRADA DEL GORDO BOCA LLC
2650 S Military Trl (33415-7514)
PHONE..................................561 968-6978
Miguel A Martinez, *Mng Member*
Elizabeth Novoa, *Mng Member*
Nelson G Villalba, *Mng Member*
EMP: 10 **EST:** 2007
SALES (est): 2.5MM **Privately Held**
WEB: www.laperradadelgordo.com
SIC: 3411 Food & beverage containers

(G-18924)
LAKE PARK AUTO MACHINE INC
404 Foresta Ter (33415-2614)
PHONE..................................561 848-6197
Fax: 561 848-9514
EMP: 6
SQ FT: 1,800
SALES (est): 709K **Privately Held**
SIC: 3599 Machine Shop Jobbing And Repair

(G-18925)
LAKEWOOD MANUFACTURING CO INC ✪
Also Called: Lakewood Manufacutring
10696 Grande Blvd (33412-1309)
P.O. Box 2185, Westminster MD (21158-7185)
PHONE..................................443 398-5015
Doug Widlake, *President*
▲ **EMP:** 150 **EST:** 2021
SALES (est): 9.7MM **Privately Held**
WEB: www.lakewood-manufacturing.com
SIC: 2511 5712 Wood household furniture; furniture stores; unfinished furniture

(G-18926)
LAND MARINE SERVICE INC
2590 W Edgewater Dr (33410-2436)
PHONE..................................561 626-2947
Jim Jesteadt, *Owner*
EMP: 6 **EST:** 1996
SALES (est): 441.1K **Privately Held**
SIC: 3732 Boats, fiberglass: building & repairing

(G-18927)
LARRYS RIGS
2460 Sunset Dr (33415-7428)
PHONE..................................561 967-7791
EMP: 7
SALES (est): 130K **Privately Held**
SIC: 3949 Manufactures Fishing Rigs

(G-18928)
LEHIGH WHITE CEMENT CO LLC (DH)
1601 Forum Pl Ste 1110 (33401-8104)
PHONE..................................561 812-7439
Daniel Harrington, *CEO*
Kirk Nielsen, *VP Sls/Mktg*
EMP: 100 **EST:** 1897
SALES (est): 50.6MM **Privately Held**
WEB: www.lehighwhitecement.com
SIC: 2891 Cement, except linoleum & tile

(G-18929)
LEVINSON BUILT LLC
1638 Donna Rd (33409-5202)
PHONE..................................561 712-9882
Matthew Levinson, *Branch Mgr*
EMP: 12
SALES (corp-wide): 1.4MM **Privately Held**
WEB: www.levinsonbuilt.com
SIC: 3442 Screen & storm doors & windows
PA: Levinson Built, Llc
1638 Donna Rd
West Palm Beach FL 33409
561 712-9882

(G-18930)
LION INK PRINT INC
8091 N Military Trl Ste 7 (33410-6351)
Rural Route 404 Winter (33410)
PHONE..................................561 358-8925
Edward Maldonado, *CEO*
Amalfia C Maldonado, *Principal*
EMP: 9 **EST:** 2010
SALES (est): 276.4K **Privately Held**
WEB: www.lioninkprint.com
SIC: 2752 Commercial printing, lithographic

(G-18931)
LION SHEET METAL INC
1648 Donna Rd (33409-5202)
PHONE..................................561 840-0540
Paul Ditocco, *Owner*
▼ **EMP:** 14 **EST:** 2007
SALES (est): 1.4MM **Privately Held**
WEB: www.lionsm.com
SIC: 3444 Sheet metalwork

(G-18932)
LIONESS PUBLICATION HOUSE
5612 56th Way (33409-7106)
PHONE..................................561 670-4645
Ingrid Jennings, *Principal*
EMP: 6 **EST:** 2013
SALES (est): 109.5K **Privately Held**
SIC: 2741 Miscellaneous publishing

(G-18933)
LOCKHEED MARTIN CORPORATION
1400 Nrthpint Pkwy Ste 10 (33407)
PHONE..................................561 494-2501
David Layton, *Chief Engr*
Stephen Goldberg, *Engineer*
Matthew Gordon, *Engineer*
Michael Schoenewolff, *Engineer*
Edmund Shea, *Branch Mgr*
EMP: 6 **Publicly Held**
WEB: www.lockheedmartin.com
SIC: 3812 Search & navigation equipment
PA: Lockheed Martin Corporation
6801 Rockledge Dr
Bethesda MD 20817

(G-18934)
LOGUS MANUFACTURING CORP
Also Called: Logus Microwave
1711 Longwood Rd Ste A (33409-6491)
PHONE..................................561 842-3550
Tom Hack, *President*
John Leonard, *Opers Dir*
Barry O 'connell, *Engineer*
Barry Oconnell, *Engineer*
Don Tarca, *Engineer*
EMP: 46 **EST:** 1961
SQ FT: 34,000
SALES (est): 11.5MM **Privately Held**
WEB: www.logus.com
SIC: 3679 5065 3825 3678 Microwave components; electronic parts & equipment; instruments to measure electricity; electronic connectors; current-carrying wiring devices; nonferrous wiredrawing & insulating

(G-18935)
LORDS PLACE THRIFT STORE
750 S Military Trl (33415-3963)
PHONE..................................561 660-7942
EMP: 6 **EST:** 2019
SALES (est): 46K **Privately Held**
WEB: www.thelordsplace.org
SIC: 3993 Signs & advertising specialties

(G-18936)
M D H GRAPHIC SERVICES INC
5001 Georgia Ave (33405-3101)
PHONE..................................561 533-9000
George W Davison, *President*
EMP: 10 **EST:** 1978
SQ FT: 3,800
SALES (est): 822.1K **Privately Held**
WEB: www.mdhprinting.com
SIC: 2752 Commercial printing, offset

(G-18937)
M&D SIGNS
2898 Forest Hill Blvd (33406-5959)
PHONE..................................561 296-3636
Mike Gonzalez, *Manager*
EMP: 6 **EST:** 2006
SALES (est): 135.7K **Privately Held**
SIC: 3993 Signs & advertising specialties

(G-18938)
MAIN TAPE CO INC
521 27th St (33407-5458)
PHONE..................................561 248-8867
David Venanzi, *Plant Engr*
Bethann Belardo, *Accountant*
Troy Marshall, *Sales Mgr*
EMP: 8 **EST:** 2012
SALES (est): 214K **Privately Held**
WEB: www.maintape.com
SIC: 3842 Surgical appliances & supplies

(G-18939)
MAKO HOSE & RUBBER CO
8331 Mc Allister Way 100a (33411-3713)
PHONE..................................561 795-6200
John Cobb, *President*
Kim Cobb, *Corp Secy*
Manuel R Perez, *Vice Pres*
▼ **EMP:** 5 **EST:** 1990
SQ FT: 5,500
SALES (est): 930.2K **Privately Held**
WEB: www.makohose.com
SIC: 3069 3492 Sheeting, rubber or rubberized fabric; hose & tube fittings & assemblies, hydraulic/pneumatic

(G-18940)
MAN ENTERPRISES 3 LLC
Also Called: Better Copy Center
3845 Investment Ln Ste 1 (33404-1766)
P.O. Box 14031, North Palm Beach (33408-0031)
PHONE..................................561 655-4944
Christopher T Wilson, *Mng Member*
EMP: 6 **EST:** 2009
SALES (est): 500K **Privately Held**
SIC: 3652 7374 7334 2752 Phonograph records, prerecorded; data processing & preparation; photocopying & duplicating services; commercial printing, lithographic; motion picture & video production; printing trades machinery

(G-18941)
MARBON INC
10723 Ibis Reserve Cir (33412-1341)
PHONE..................................561 822-9999
Edward Bonieski, *President*
Paul Vassalotti, *Vice Pres*
Vera Bonieski, *Treasurer*
EMP: 14 **EST:** 1994
SQ FT: 37,000
SALES (est): 559.3K **Privately Held**
WEB: www.marbon.com
SIC: 3272 Cast stone, concrete

(G-18942)
MARK PLATING CO
441 25th St (33407-5407)
PHONE..................................561 655-4370
Kevin Hendrickson, *President*
Kristi Hendrickson, *Partner*
Shirley Hendrickson, *Partner*
EMP: 6 **EST:** 1977
SQ FT: 1,800
SALES (est): 695.8K **Privately Held**
WEB: www.markplating.com
SIC: 3471 Plating of metals or formed products

▲ = Import ▼=Export
◆ =Import/Export

(G-18943)
MARKET INK USA INC
1000 S Military Trl Ste D (33415-4774)
PHONE....................................561 502-3438
Jonatan Guzman, *President*
Jose Dominguez, *Vice Pres*
EMP: 7 **EST:** 2011
SALES (est): 175.7K **Privately Held**
WEB: www.marketink.net
SIC: 2752 Commercial printing, offset

(G-18944)
MASONWAYS INDSTRCTBLE PLAS LLC
580 Village Blvd Ste 330 (33409-1953)
PHONE....................................561 478-8838
Debbie Shrake, *Vice Pres*
Susan Chander, *Consultant*
Judd Ettinger,
Shelly Ettinger,
Anna Swartz,
EMP: 20 **EST:** 1978
SQ FT: 2,000
SALES (est): 4.6MM **Privately Held**
WEB: www.masonways.com
SIC: 3089 Pallets, plastic

(G-18945)
MATRIX COATINGS CORP
3575 Investment Ln (33404-1728)
PHONE....................................561 848-1288
Larry Sloan, *President*
Dave Barbato, *Principal*
Terry Sloan, *Principal*
EMP: 12 **EST:** 2019
SALES (est): 1.1MM **Privately Held**
WEB: www.matrixcoat.com
SIC: 3479 Coating of metals & formed products

(G-18946)
MATRIX COATINGS INC
3575 Investment Ln (33404-1728)
PHONE....................................561 848-1288
Jack Thygesen, *President*
EMP: 9 **EST:** 2002
SQ FT: 20,000
SALES (est): 1.4MM **Privately Held**
WEB: www.musselbuster.com
SIC: 3479 Coating of metals & formed products

(G-18947)
MC SOFTWARE LLC
12300 South Shore Blvd (33414-6509)
PHONE....................................801 621-3900
EMP: 7 **EST:** 2016
SALES (est): 137.6K **Privately Held**
SIC: 7372 Prepackaged software

(G-18948)
MEMO LABS INC
8390 Currency Dr Ste 4 (33404-1745)
PHONE....................................561 842-0586
Barbara Daniels, *Ch of Bd*
Jack Daniels, *President*
Bob Carter, *Vice Pres*
Bernice Czapkewicz, *Admin Sec*
▲ **EMP:** 10 **EST:** 1981
SQ FT: 4,000
SALES (est): 754K **Privately Held**
SIC: 3672 Printed circuit boards

(G-18949)
MERCHANTS METALS LLC
1601 Hill Ave Ste B (33407-2233)
PHONE....................................561 478-0059
David Hickaersos, *Manager*
EMP: 8 **Privately Held**
WEB: www.merchantsmetals.com
SIC: 3496 Fencing, made from purchased wire; mesh, made from purchased wire; concrete reinforcing mesh & wire
HQ: Merchants Metals Llc
211 Perimeter Center Pkwy
Atlanta GA 30346
770 741-0300

(G-18950)
MICA CRAFT & DESIGN INC
3905 Investment Ln Ste 15 (33404-1700)
PHONE....................................561 863-5354
Paul Sharone, *President*
Diane Sharone, *Corp Secy*
EMP: 16 **EST:** 1984
SQ FT: 7,000
SALES (est): 1MM **Privately Held**
WEB: www.micacraftanddesign.com
SIC: 3429 2434 Furniture builders' & other household hardware; wood kitchen cabinets

(G-18951)
MICROGERM DEFENSE LLC
2257 Vista Pk Way Ste 22 (33411)
PHONE....................................561 309-0842
Amin Rahi, *Branch Mgr*
EMP: 20
SALES (corp-wide): 119.9K **Privately Held**
SIC: 3812 Defense systems & equipment
PA: Microgerm Defense, Llc
8577 Estate Dr
West Palm Beach FL

(G-18952)
MICROSALT INC ✪
515 N Flagler Dr Ste P300 (33401-4326)
PHONE....................................877 825-0655
Victor Hugo Manzanilla, *CEO*
EMP: 6 **EST:** 2020
SALES (est): 94.4K **Privately Held**
SIC: 2899 Salt

(G-18953)
MIMZY FROYO DELIGHTS LLC
600 S Rosemary Ave # 162 (33401-6314)
PHONE....................................917 862-9520
Cang M Truong, *Manager*
EMP: 6 **EST:** 2012
SALES (est): 218.3K **Privately Held**
SIC: 2024 Yogurt desserts, frozen

(G-18954)
MOBILE AUTO SOLUTIONS LLC ✪
1578 Quail Dr Apt 10 (33409-4757)
PHONE....................................561 903-5328
Marquisha Wright,
EMP: 8 **EST:** 2021
SALES (est): 120K **Privately Held**
SIC: 2273 7389 Automobile floor coverings, except rubber or plastic;

(G-18955)
N2W SOFTWARE INC
1555 Palm Beach Lakes Blv (33401-2342)
PHONE....................................561 225-2483
Jason Judge, *CEO*
Andrew Langsam, *COO*
Brigette McDonald, *Sales Staff*
Ezra Charm, *VP Mktg*
Arlene De La Torre, *Office Mgr*
EMP: 14 **EST:** 2012
SQ FT: 3,000
SALES (est): 4.7MM
SALES (corp-wide): 778.5K **Privately Held**
WEB: www.n2ws.com
SIC: 7372 Utility computer software
HQ: Veeam Software Group Gmbh
Lindenstrasse 16
Baar ZG
417 667-131

(G-18956)
NAILBOUTIQUE OF WPB LLC
1225 N Military Trl 4d (33409-6059)
PHONE....................................954 756-2699
EMP: 6 **EST:** 2018
SALES (est): 114.6K **Privately Held**
WEB: www.wpb.org
SIC: 3999 Fingernails, artificial

(G-18957)
NATIONAL DIRECT SIGNS
777 S Flagler Dr (33401-6161)
PHONE....................................561 320-2102
Daniela Skeen, *Mng Member*
EMP: 50 **EST:** 2017
SALES (est): 1.7MM **Privately Held**
WEB: www.nationaldirectsigns.com
SIC: 3993 Signs & advertising specialties

(G-18958)
NATURES EARTH PRODUCTS INC
2200 N Fl Mango Rd # 403 (33409-6468)
PHONE....................................561 688-8101
Kenyon Allen Simard, *CEO*
Bill Magner, *Opers Mgr*
▼ **EMP:** 20 **EST:** 1993
SQ FT: 6,000
SALES (est): 3.6MM **Privately Held**
WEB: www.naturesearth.com
SIC: 3297 Cement refractories, nonclay

(G-18959)
NAZTEC INTERNATIONAL GROUP LLC
263 N Jog Rd (33413-1712)
PHONE....................................561 802-4110
Pazhoor Mohamed, *Branch Mgr*
EMP: 10
SALES (corp-wide): 3MM **Privately Held**
WEB: www.naztecgroup.com
SIC: 3579 Voting machines
PA: Naztec International Group, Llc
8983 Okeechobee Blvd # 202
West Palm Beach FL 33411
561 802-4110

(G-18960)
NAZTEC INTERNATIONAL GROUP LLC (PA)
Also Called: Smartpoll Election Solutions
8983 Okeechobee Blvd # 202
(33411-5115)
PHONE....................................561 802-4110
Saeeda Mohamed, *Vice Pres*
Abdur Rahman, *Marketing Staff*
Sal Pazhoor, *Mng Member*
Alma Valdez, *Manager*
▲ **EMP:** 13 **EST:** 2003
SQ FT: 3,500
SALES (est): 3MM **Privately Held**
WEB: www.naztecgroup.com
SIC: 3579 7379 5049 5013 Voting machines; computer related consulting services; engineers' equipment & supplies; automotive supplies & parts

(G-18961)
NENEM INC
1287 Waterway Cove Dr (33414-5723)
PHONE....................................561 389-2010
Noileen Richardson, *Principal*
EMP: 6 **EST:** 2008
SALES (est): 76.4K **Privately Held**
SIC: 2741 Miscellaneous publishing

(G-18962)
NEPTUNE PETROLEUM LLC
3974 Okeechobee Blvd # 2 (33409-4043)
PHONE....................................561 684-2844
EMP: 8 **EST:** 2007
SALES (est): 740K **Privately Held**
SIC: 1311 Crude Petroleum/Natural Gas Production

(G-18963)
NEW HOPE SUGAR COMPANY
1 N Clematis St (33401-5550)
PHONE....................................561 366-5120
Oscar R Hernandez, *Principal*
EMP: 9 **EST:** 2007
SALES (est): 265.6K **Privately Held**
SIC: 2099 Food preparations

(G-18964)
NEWSMAX MEDIA INC
1501 Nrthpint Pkwy Ste 10 (33407)
PHONE....................................561 686-1165
Andy Brown, *Senior VP*
EMP: 10
SALES (corp-wide): 127.9MM **Privately Held**
WEB: www.newsmax.com
SIC: 2721 2741 Periodicals; miscellaneous publishing
PA: Newsmax Media, Inc.
750 Park Of Commerce Dr # 100
Boca Raton FL 33487
561 686-1165

(G-18965)
NIKIANI INC
Also Called: Buggy Guard
717 Maritime Way (33410-3425)
PHONE....................................305 606-1104
Annette M Atteridge, *President*
Christopher B Atteridge, *Vice Pres*
▲ **EMP:** 5 **EST:** 2005
SQ FT: 1,000
SALES (est): 457.8K **Privately Held**
WEB: www.nikiani.com
SIC: 3944 Strollers, baby (vehicle)

(G-18966)
NITV FEDERAL SERVICES LLC
11400 Fortune Cir (33414-8741)
PHONE....................................561 798-6280
Jim Kane, *Marketing Staff*
David Hughes, *Exec Dir*
EMP: 6 **EST:** 2003
SALES (est): 792.7K **Privately Held**
WEB: www.cvsa1.com
SIC: 3669 Communications equipment

(G-18967)
NOA INTERNATIONAL INC
Also Called: Rock & Roll
2361 Vista Pkwy Ste 1 (33411-2780)
PHONE....................................954 835-5258
Paul J Johansson, *President*
Paul D Johansson, *Vice Pres*
EMP: 5 **EST:** 2010
SALES (est): 700K **Privately Held**
WEB: www.noaintl.com
SIC: 3842 Wheelchairs

(G-18968)
NOVO AERO SERVICES LLC
6965 Vista Pkwy N Ste 16 (33411-6757)
PHONE....................................786 319-8637
Leonardo Novo, *Principal*
EMP: 9 **EST:** 2014
SALES (est): 585.9K **Privately Held**
WEB: www.novoaeroservices.com
SIC: 3728 Aircraft parts & equipment

(G-18969)
OCEANVISTA PUBLISHING LLC
6605 S Dixie Hwy (33405-4446)
PHONE....................................561 547-5730
Maurice Sotillo, *Principal*
EMP: 6 **EST:** 2011
SALES (est): 75.3K **Privately Held**
SIC: 2741 Miscellaneous publishing

(G-18970)
OKEECHOBEE PETROLEUM LLC
6970 Okeechobee Blvd (33411-2508)
PHONE....................................561 478-1083
Paula Lean, *Principal*
EMP: 9 **EST:** 2008
SALES (est): 615.6K **Privately Held**
SIC: 2911 Petroleum refining

(G-18971)
OKEELANTA CORPORATION (HQ)
Also Called: Florida Crystals
1 N Clematis St Ste 200 (33401-5551)
P.O. Box 1059, Palm Beach (33480-1059)
PHONE....................................561 366-5100
Alfonso Fanjul Jr, *Ch of Bd*
Jose Fanjul, *President*
Evelyn Hopkins, *Counsel*
Nicole Rocco, *Counsel*
Donald W Carson, *Exec VP*
◆ **EMP:** 35 **EST:** 1984
SQ FT: 9,000
SALES (est): 131.2MM
SALES (corp-wide): 2.1B **Privately Held**
WEB: www.floridacrystals.com
SIC: 2061 2062 Raw cane sugar; cane sugar refining
PA: Fanjul Corp.
1 N Clematis St Ste 200
West Palm Beach FL 33401
561 655-6303

(G-18972)
OLIVERI WOODWORKING INC
3001 Tuxedo Ave (33405-1031)
PHONE....................................561 478-7233
Vincent Oliveri, *President*
Angelina Oliveri, *Opers Staff*
EMP: 19 **EST:** 1988
SALES (est): 661K **Privately Held**
WEB: www.oliverimillworks.com
SIC: 2431 5211 3442 Woodwork, interior & ornamental; cabinets, kitchen; moldings & trim, except automobile: metal

(G-18973)
ONE STOP GENERATOR SHOP INC
3600 Inv Ln Ste 104 (33404)
PHONE....................561 840-0009
Jon Andio, *President*
EMP: 8 **EST:** 2007
SALES (est): 1.7MM **Privately Held**
WEB: www.1stopgeneratorshop.com
SIC: 3621 Motors & generators

(G-18974)
OTIS ELEVATOR COMPANY
5500 Village Blvd Ste 101 (33407-1961)
PHONE....................561 618-4831
Jorge Castillo, *Counsel*
EMP: 500
SALES (corp-wide): 12.7B **Publicly Held**
WEB: www.otis.com
SIC: 3534 1796 7699 Elevators & equipment; installing building equipment; miscellaneous building item repair services
HQ: Otis Elevator Company
1 Carrier Pl
Farmington CT 06032
860 676-6000

(G-18975)
OXBOW CALCINING LLC
1601 Forum Pl Ph 2 (33401-8104)
PHONE....................580 874-2201
Jonathan Bartley, *Project Engr*
Rick Thurlow, *Regl Sales Mgr*
Paul Koenig, *Manager*
EMP: 108 **EST:** 2015
SALES (est): 19.3MM **Privately Held**
WEB: www.oxbow.com
SIC: 2911 Petroleum refining

(G-18976)
OXBOW CALCINING USA INC (DH)
1601 Forum Pl Ste 1400 (33401-8104)
PHONE....................580 874-2201
Steve Fried, *Exec VP*
Zachary Shipley, *CFO*
EMP: 100 **EST:** 1998
SALES (est): 81.1MM
SALES (corp-wide): 633.2MM **Privately Held**
WEB: www.oxbow.com
SIC: 2999 Coke (not from refineries), petroleum

(G-18977)
OXBOW CARBON LLC (DH)
1601 Forum Pl Ste 1400 (33401-8104)
PHONE....................561 907-5400
William I Koch, *CEO*
Jim Freney, *Exec VP*
Gord McIntosh, *Exec VP*
Roy J Schorsch, *Exec VP*
William D Parmelee, *CFO*
EMP: 101 **EST:** 2006
SALES (est): 581.1MM
SALES (corp-wide): 633.2MM **Privately Held**
WEB: www.oxbow.com
SIC: 1241 2999 5052 Coal mining services; coke, calcined petroleum: made from purchased materials; coal
HQ: Oxbow Corporation
1601 Forum Pl Ste 1400
West Palm Beach FL 33401
561 907-5400

(G-18978)
OXBOW ENTERPRISES INTL LLC
1601 Forum Pl Ste 1400 (33401-8104)
PHONE....................561 907-5400
EMP: 5
SALES (est): 564.5K **Privately Held**
SIC: 1241 2999 5052 Coal mining services; coke, calcined petroleum: made from purchased materials; coal

(G-18979)
OZ NATURALS LLC
319 Clematis St Ste 700 (33401-4622)
PHONE....................561 602-2932
Samer Marwani, *Sales Staff*
Richard C Romero,
▲ **EMP:** 5 **EST:** 2015
SALES (est): 1MM **Privately Held**
WEB: www.oznaturals.com
SIC: 2844 Toilet preparations

(G-18980)
P B C CULTURAL COUNSEL
1555 Palm Bch Lakes Blvd (33401-2323)
PHONE....................561 471-2903
Rena Blades, *CEO*
Rina Blades, *President*
Sonya Davis, *Vice Pres*
EMP: 10 **EST:** 2005
SALES (est): 909.7K **Privately Held**
SIC: 2836 Culture media

(G-18981)
PALM BEACH CAST STONE INC
Also Called: Palm Beach Limestone
809 N Railroad Ave (33401-3301)
PHONE....................561 835-4085
Steve Ford, *President*
Jeannie Foss, *Regional Mgr*
William Thayer, *Manager*
▼ **EMP:** 45 **EST:** 1984
SALES (est): 5.1MM **Privately Held**
WEB: www.pbcaststone.com
SIC: 3272 Cast stone, concrete

(G-18982)
PALM BEACH EMBROIDERY USA INC
8645 N Military Trl (33410-6294)
PHONE....................561 506-6307
Robert L Marzullo, *Principal*
EMP: 6 **EST:** 2014
SALES (est): 508.8K **Privately Held**
WEB: www.palmbeachembroidery.com
SIC: 2395 Embroidery products, except schiffli machine

(G-18983)
PALM BEACH IRON WORKS INC
7768 Belvedere Rd (33411-3896)
PHONE....................561 683-1816
Jim Roy Higgins Jr, *President*
Elsie S Higgins, *Corp Secy*
Jim Roy Higgins Sr, *Vice Pres*
David Phillips, *Sales Staff*
Jorge Pires, *Sales Staff*
▼ **EMP:** 22 **EST:** 1973
SQ FT: 25,000
SALES (est): 2.7MM **Privately Held**
WEB: www.pbiron.com
SIC: 3441 Fabricated structural metal

(G-18984)
PALM BEACH LIQUIDATION COMPANY (PA)
Also Called: Naples Illustrated
1000 N Dixie Hwy Ste C (33401-3349)
P.O. Box 3344, Palm Beach (33480-1544)
PHONE....................561 659-0210
Randie Dalia, *Publisher*
Ronald Woods, *Chairman*
Karen Powell, *COO*
Dina Turner, *Sls & Mktg Exec*
Melissa Schwartz, *Accounts Mgr*
EMP: 26 **EST:** 1952
SQ FT: 4,500
SALES (est): 5MM **Privately Held**
WEB: www.palmbeachillustrated.com
SIC: 2721 Magazines: publishing only, not printed on site

(G-18985)
PALM BEACH NEWSPAPERS INC
Also Called: Palm Beach Daily News
2751 S Dixie Hwy (33405-1298)
P.O. Box 1151, Palm Beach (33480-1151)
PHONE....................561 820-3800
Michael Brockman, *Partner*
V B Breckenridge, *Treasurer*
Joyce Harr, *Branch Mgr*
EMP: 79
SALES (corp-wide): 1.6MM **Privately Held**
WEB: www.palmbeachpost.com
SIC: 2721 2711 2741 Magazines: publishing & printing; newspapers, publishing & printing; miscellaneous publishing
HQ: Palm Beach Newspapers, Inc.
6205-A Pchtree Dnwody Rd
Atlanta GA 30328
678 645-0000

(G-18986)
PALM PRINT INC
Also Called: Sir Speedy
919 N Dixie Hwy (33401-3329)
PHONE....................561 833-9661
Yuda Raz, *President*
Shauna Makrealeas, *General Mgr*
EMP: 12 **EST:** 1981
SQ FT: 3,600
SALES (est): 1.9MM **Privately Held**
WEB: www.sirspeedypb.com
SIC: 2752 Commercial printing, lithographic

(G-18987)
PARALLAX HEALTH SCIENCES INC (PA)
2054 Vsta Pkwy Emrald Vw (33411)
PHONE....................888 263-9799
Paul R Arena, *Ch of Bd*
David L Stark, *President*
Calli R Bucci, *CFO*
Nathaniel T Bradley, *CTO*
EMP: 6 **EST:** 2005
SALES: 128.6K **Publicly Held**
WEB: www.parallaxhealthsciences.com
SIC: 3841 8731 5047 Diagnostic apparatus, medical; biological research; medical equipment & supplies

(G-18988)
PASSPORT PBLCATIONS MEDIA CORP
Also Called: Palm Bch Pssport Pblctons Mdia
1555 Palm Beach Lakes Blv (33401-2335)
PHONE....................561 615-3900
Robert Kirschner, *President*
Peter Greenberg, *Publisher*
Patrick Gamble, *Editor*
John Thomason, *Editor*
Michelle R Kirschner, *Treasurer*
EMP: 21 **EST:** 1989
SQ FT: 4,000
SALES (est): 3.4MM **Privately Held**
WEB: www.passportpublications.com
SIC: 2721 7311 Magazines: publishing only, not printed on site; advertising agencies

(G-18989)
PATHFNDERS PALM BCH-MRTIN CNTY
Also Called: Palm Beach Post
2751 S Dixie Hwy (33405-1233)
PHONE....................561 820-4262
Janie Fogt, *President*
Jim Hayward, *Editor*
Annette Jones, *Editor*
Dominic Pugliese, *Editor*
Carol Rose, *Editor*
EMP: 95 **EST:** 2010
SALES: 111.4K **Privately Held**
WEB: www.palmbeachpost.com
SIC: 2711 Newspapers, publishing & printing

(G-18990)
PAUL HIMBER INC
5324 Georgia Ave (33405-3520)
P.O. Box 6007 (33405-6007)
PHONE....................561 586-3741
Paul Himber, *President*
Elizabeth A Himber, *Vice Pres*
EMP: 10 **EST:** 1979
SQ FT: 5,000
SALES (est): 682K **Privately Held**
WEB: www.paulhimberinc.com
SIC: 2391 5023 Draperies, plastic & textile: from purchased materials; draperies

(G-18991)
PAW PRINT CO
1593 Trotter Ct (33414-1063)
PHONE....................561 753-5588
Peter Wiesner, *Vice Pres*
EMP: 6 **EST:** 2006
SALES (est): 446.3K **Privately Held**
WEB: www.pawprintsco.com
SIC: 2752 Commercial printing, offset

(G-18992)
PEAKTOP TECHNOLOGIES INC
1727 Okeechobee Rd (33409-5225)
PHONE....................561 598-6005
Jeff Robins, *President*
Greg Shutte, *Vice Pres*
Mark Wilson, *Vice Pres*
▲ **EMP:** 8 **EST:** 2003
SQ FT: 1,000
SALES (est): 122.8K **Privately Held**
SIC: 3089 Watering pots, plastic

(G-18993)
PEMSUM INDUSTRIES INC
120 S Olive Ave Ste 311 (33401-5549)
PHONE....................561 623-3151
Ra G Bernal-Mora, *President*
EMP: 6 **EST:** 2017
SALES (est): 94.3K **Privately Held**
SIC: 3999 Manufacturing industries

(G-18994)
PETER FLAGG WOODWORK
103 E Chandler Rd (33406-3201)
PHONE....................561 307-4200
Peter Flagg, *Principal*
EMP: 7 **EST:** 2005
SALES (est): 67.7K **Privately Held**
SIC: 2431 Millwork

(G-18995)
PETER T AMANN
Also Called: Poly Systems Co
8111 Garden Rd Ste G (33404-1751)
PHONE....................561 848-2770
Peter T Amann, *Owner*
EMP: 6 **EST:** 1972
SQ FT: 6,600
SALES (est): 486.6K **Privately Held**
SIC: 2732 5162 2678 5199 Pamphlets: printing only, not published on site; plastics materials & basic shapes; tablets & pads, book & writing: from purchased materials; packaging materials

(G-18996)
PETROLEUM MARINE LLC
15985 Meadow Wood Dr (33414-9027)
PHONE....................561 422-9018
Karen A Doyle,
EMP: 6 **EST:** 2003
SALES (est): 621.8K **Privately Held**
WEB: www.petroleummarineconstruction.com
SIC: 2911 Petroleum refining

(G-18997)
PHIL ROWE SIGNS INC
805 N Dixie Hwy (33401-3327)
PHONE....................561 832-8688
Stephen Rowe, *President*
Allayne Rowe, *Admin Sec*
EMP: 5 **EST:** 1949
SQ FT: 3,500
SALES (est): 378.5K **Privately Held**
SIC: 3993 Signs & advertising specialties

(G-18998)
PINEAPPLE GROVE WOODWORKS
3740 Prospect Ave (33404-3445)
PHONE....................561 676-1287
EMP: 8 **EST:** 2017
SALES (est): 483.7K **Privately Held**
SIC: 2431 Millwork

(G-18999)
PLATINUM SIGNS INC
2898 Forest Hill Blvd (33406-5959)
PHONE....................561 296-3636
Diana Almeida, *Principal*
EMP: 6 **EST:** 2016
SALES (est): 49.4K **Privately Held**
WEB: www.platinum-signs.com
SIC: 3993 Signs & advertising specialties

(G-19000)
POM PERFORMANCE COATINGS LLC
2264 S Wallen Dr (33410-2550)
PHONE....................561 441-7611
Timothy R Morrison, *Manager*
EMP: 6 **EST:** 2017
SALES (est): 69.9K **Privately Held**
WEB: www.livelikejake.com
SIC: 3479 Metal coating & allied service

(G-19001)
POMA CORPORATION
9040 Belvedere Rd (33411-3636)
PHONE..................................561 790-5799
Patrick Whelan, *Ch of Bd*
David Zajac, *President*
Roger Seitz, *Purch Dir*
EMP: 62 **EST:** 1983
SQ FT: 52,000
SALES (est): 1.5MM **Privately Held**
WEB: www.pomametals.com
SIC: 3355 3442 Rails, rolled & drawn, aluminum; storm doors or windows, metal

(G-19002)
PORATH FINE CABINETRY INC
3101 Tuxedo Ave (33405-1033)
PHONE..................................561 616-9400
Shaul Porath, *President*
EMP: 22 **EST:** 1991
SQ FT: 78,000
SALES (est): 4.4MM **Privately Held**
WEB: www.porathcabinets.com
SIC: 2434 Wood kitchen cabinets

(G-19003)
PRECISION EQUIPMENT CO INC
197 65th Ter N (33413-1715)
PHONE..................................561 689-4400
Henry J Goyette, *President*
Annette Goyette, *Vice Pres*
EMP: 9 **EST:** 1996
SQ FT: 7,000
SALES (est): 758.1K **Privately Held**
SIC: 3799 Trailers & trailer equipment

(G-19004)
PREMIER PALLET RECYCLER LLC
1230 Gateway Rd Ste 1 (33403-1956)
PHONE..................................561 722-0457
James A Wilson, *Principal*
EMP: 9 **EST:** 2016
SALES (est): 87.5K **Privately Held**
WEB: www.premier-pallets.com
SIC: 2448 Pallets, wood

(G-19005)
PRESSURE SYSTEMS INNVTIONS LLC
3750 Investment Ln Ste 4 (33404-1765)
PHONE..................................561 249-2708
John Pankow, *Mng Member*
EMP: 11 **EST:** 2012
SALES (est): 1.5MM **Privately Held**
WEB: www.pressuresystemsinnovations.com
SIC: 3699 5063 Cleaning equipment, ultrasonic, except medical & dental; electrical supplies

(G-19006)
PRESTIGE/AB READY MIX LLC (PA)
7228 Westport Pl Ste C (33413-1683)
PHONE..................................561 478-9980
Brian Mahoney,
Patti-Lee D'Ausilio, *Admin Sec*
Beat Kahail,
EMP: 20 **EST:** 2002
SALES (est): 11.2MM **Privately Held**
SIC: 3273 Ready-mixed concrete

(G-19007)
PRIMETIME SPORTS AGENTS INC
500 Pacific Grove Dr (33401-8340)
PHONE..................................561 371-4421
Steve Riniker, *Managing Prtnr*
Jeffrey Villanueva, *Administration*
EMP: 6 **EST:** 2016
SALES (est): 125.7K **Privately Held**
WEB: www.primetimesportsagents.com
SIC: 3949 Sporting & athletic goods

(G-19008)
PROTO PLUS INC
350 Tall Pines Rd Ste B (33413-1700)
PHONE..................................561 471-5325
Steve L Price, *President*
Doug Ball, *Vice Pres*
Zozislaw Kozirl, *Vice Pres*
EMP: 5 **EST:** 2003
SALES (est): 430.9K **Privately Held**
WEB: www.protoplusinc.com
SIC: 3599 Machine shop, jobbing & repair

(G-19009)
PSPC ESCROW II CORP
1450 Centrepark Blvd # 21 (33401-7429)
PHONE..................................561 207-9600
EMP: 8 **EST:** 2017
SALES (est): 81.8K **Privately Held**
SIC: 2869 Industrial organic chemicals

(G-19010)
PURAGEN LLC (DH)
Also Called: Oxbow Activated Carbon LLC
1601 Forum Pl Ste 1400 (33401-8104)
P.O. Box 4444, Oceanside CA (92052-4444)
PHONE..................................561 907-5400
Kenneth Schaeffer, *President*
Kimberly Walsh, *Vice Pres*
◆ **EMP:** 25 **EST:** 1998
SQ FT: 10,000
SALES (est): 24.7MM
SALES (corp-wide): 633.2MM **Privately Held**
WEB: www.puragen.com
SIC: 2819 5052 Charcoal (carbon), activated; coal

(G-19011)
PURE GLOBAL BRANDS INC (PA)
Also Called: Global Quality Brands
500 S Australian Ave (33401-6223)
PHONE..................................866 498-5269
Patricia Gail Frank, *President*
Susan Carlin, *Vice Pres*
Mitch Carlin, *Director*
Kinsey Harris, *Officer*
◆ **EMP:** 7 **EST:** 2006
SQ FT: 5,000
SALES (est): 1.6MM **Privately Held**
WEB: www.globalqualitybrands.com
SIC: 3949 5091 Gymnasium equipment; gymnasium equipment

(G-19012)
PURE LABS LLC
240 10th St 1 (33401-3502)
PHONE..................................561 659-2229
Robin Case, *Principal*
EMP: 8 **EST:** 2008
SALES (est): 246.2K **Privately Held**
WEB: www.gopurelabs.com
SIC: 2844 Toilet preparations

(G-19013)
PURECOAT INTERNATIONAL LLC (PA)
3301 Elec Way Ste B (33407)
P.O. Box 4406 (33402-4406)
PHONE..................................561 844-0100
George Bognar, *President*
Ron Keohan, *Prdtn Mgr*
Rob Sagehorn, *Purchasing*
Brenda Gleason, *Manager*
Rachel Trabada, *Manager*
EMP: 42 **EST:** 1987
SQ FT: 39,500
SALES (est): 6.3MM **Privately Held**
WEB: www.purecoat.com
SIC: 3471 Electroplating of metals or formed products

(G-19014)
QUALITY READY MIX INC (PA)
1501 Belvedere Rd (33406-1501)
PHONE..................................561 833-5555
Cemex Constmaterialssouth, *Principal*
EMP: 421 **EST:** 2012
SALES (est): 22.5MM **Privately Held**
SIC: 3273 Ready-mixed concrete

(G-19015)
R & R DOOR AND TRIM INC
8111 Garden Rd Ste J (33404-1751)
P.O. Box 9491 (33419-9491)
PHONE..................................561 844-5496
Robert M Danculovich, *President*
EMP: 5 **EST:** 1988
SQ FT: 5,000
SALES (est): 453.3K **Privately Held**
WEB: www.rrdoorandtrim.com
SIC: 2431 5031 Doors, wood; doors & windows; millwork

(G-19016)
R DORIAN MILLWORKS LLC
2361 Vista Pkwy Ste 7 (33411-2780)
PHONE..................................561 863-9125
Paul Reilly, *Manager*
EMP: 12 **EST:** 2015
SALES (est): 1MM **Privately Held**
SIC: 2431 Millwork

(G-19017)
REDDY ICE CORPORATION
7719 Garden Rd (33404-3415)
PHONE..................................561 881-9501
Wayne Macmullen, *General Mgr*
EMP: 12
SQ FT: 21,200 **Privately Held**
WEB: www.reddyice.com
SIC: 2097 Manufactured ice
HQ: Reddy Ice Corporation
5710 Lbj Fwy Ste 300
Dallas TX 75240
214 526-6740

(G-19018)
REICH METAL FABRICATORS INC
5405 Webster Ave (33405-3203)
P.O. Box 6036 (33405-6036)
PHONE..................................561 585-3173
James Bailey, *President*
John Childs, *Vice Pres*
Marion Bailey, *Admin Sec*
▼ **EMP:** 30 **EST:** 1918
SQ FT: 12,000
SALES (est): 3.1MM **Privately Held**
SIC: 3442 3446 Metal doors, sash & trim; architectural metalwork

(G-19019)
REWARD LIGHTING NET LLC
6000 Georgia Ave Ste 10 (33405-3946)
PHONE..................................561 832-1819
John J J Shea, *Principal*
EMP: 5 **EST:** 2015
SALES (est): 512.9K **Privately Held**
WEB: www.rewardlight.com
SIC: 3648 Lighting equipment

(G-19020)
RICH ICE CREAM CO
2915 S Dixie Hwy (33405-1585)
PHONE..................................561 833-7585
Randall Rich, *President*
John P Rich, *Chairman*
Renee Farias, *Business Mgr*
Martha R Rich, *Corp Secy*
Donald A Rich, *Vice Pres*
▼ **EMP:** 134 **EST:** 1946
SQ FT: 10,000
SALES (est): 23.7MM **Privately Held**
WEB: www.richicecream.com
SIC: 2024 Ice cream, bulk

(G-19021)
ROBERT ST CROIX SCULPTURE STU
1400 Alabama Ave Ste 6 (33401-7048)
PHONE..................................561 835-1753
Robert St Croix, *Owner*
EMP: 6 **EST:** 1996
SALES (est): 734K **Privately Held**
WEB: www.robertstcroix.com
SIC: 3366 Copper foundries

(G-19022)
ROCKET TOWNE INC
412 Tall Pines Rd (33413-1717)
PHONE..................................561 478-1274
Jack Lucas, *President*
EMP: 9 **EST:** 2001
SALES (est): 624.9K **Privately Held**
SIC: 2899 Pyrotechnic ammunition: flares, signals, rockets, etc.

(G-19023)
RONMAR INDUSTRIES INC
8990 Lakes Blvd (33412-1550)
PHONE..................................561 630-8035
Marvin Starger, *President*
Ronny Starger, *Vice Pres*
EMP: 10 **EST:** 1965
SQ FT: 7,000
SALES (est): 279.8K **Privately Held**
WEB: www.ronmarindustries.com
SIC: 2399 2353 3143 3144 Horse & pet accessories, textile; saddle cloth; hats & caps; boots, dress or casual: men's; boots, canvas or leather: women's; men's & boys' furnishings

(G-19024)
RORO INC
300 S Australian Ave # 16 (33401-5083)
PHONE..................................561 909-6220
EMP: 19 **EST:** 2003
SALES (est): 3.7MM **Privately Held**
SIC: 3496 Conveyor belts

(G-19025)
SANBORN RESOURCES LTD
777 S Flagler Dr (33401-6161)
PHONE..................................561 551-6161
Ryan Sanborn, *Principal*
EMP: 6 **EST:** 2014
SALES (est): 113.6K **Privately Held**
SIC: 3295 Minerals, ground or treated

(G-19026)
SB SIGNS INC
Also Called: Signs By Tomorrow
1300 N Florida Mango Rd # 20 (33409-5259)
PHONE..................................561 688-9100
Scott Bedford, *President*
Dave Tripp, *Sales Staff*
Mary Lou Bedford, *Admin Sec*
EMP: 5 **EST:** 1997
SQ FT: 2,300
SALES (est): 605K **Privately Held**
WEB: www.sbsigns.net
SIC: 3993 Signs & advertising specialties

(G-19027)
SECURE CNSTR SYSTEMS LLC
Also Called: Secure Wall
801b Pike Rd (33411-3846)
PHONE..................................561 687-9512
Pat McLaughlin, *Principal*
Jim Chamberlin,
EMP: 7 **EST:** 1998
SALES (est): 90K **Privately Held**
SIC: 3271 Blocks, concrete: insulating

(G-19028)
SETTY ENTERPRISES INC
Also Called: B T I
4128 Westroads Dr # 225 (33407-1253)
PHONE..................................561 844-3711
Swamy N Setty, *President*
Kiran Setty, *Vice Pres*
Shashi Setty, *Vice Pres*
EMP: 17 **EST:** 1994
SQ FT: 12,000
SALES (est): 2.5MM **Privately Held**
WEB: www.e-bti.com
SIC: 3728 3599 Aircraft body assemblies & parts; machine shop, jobbing & repair

(G-19029)
SHANKER INDUSTRIES REALTY INC (PA)
3900 Fiscal Ct Ste 100 (33404-1726)
PHONE..................................631 940-9889
John Shanker, *President*
Francine Shanker, *Exec VP*
Frances Shanker, *Vice Pres*
▲ **EMP:** 5 **EST:** 1896
SALES (est): 1MM **Privately Held**
WEB: www.shanko.com
SIC: 3446 Ornamental metalwork

(G-19030)
SHELMET CORP
400 Columbia Dr (33409-1958)
PHONE..................................561 688-9700
Sheldon Derer, *Principal*
EMP: 6 **EST:** 2010
SALES (est): 105.1K **Privately Held**
WEB: www.shelmet.com
SIC: 3334 Primary aluminum

(G-19031)
SHOPWORKS LLC
1101 N Olive Ave (33401-3513)
PHONE..................................561 491-6000
Denise Brooks, *Marketing Staff*
Greg Stevens, *Manager*
Omar Castillo, *Technical Staff*

Jay Malanga,
EMP: 9 **EST:** 1996
SALES (est): 1.1MM **Privately Held**
WEB: www.shopworx.com
SIC: 7372 Prepackaged software

(G-19032)
SIGN A RAMA INC (HQ)
Also Called: Sign-A-Rama
2121 Vista Pkwy (33411-2706)
PHONE.................................561 640-5570
Ray Titus, *CEO*
Brian Kinney, *President*
Gary Lengel, *Exec VP*
David Ross, *Exec VP*
Craig Hyman, *Vice Pres*
▼ **EMP:** 45 **EST:** 1986
SQ FT: 20,500
SALES (est): 53.4MM **Privately Held**
WEB: www.signaramaworthington.com
SIC: 3993 Signs & advertising specialties

(G-19033)
SILENT STANDBY POWER SUP LLC
3866 Prospect Ave Ste 5 (33404-3343)
PHONE.................................954 253-9557
Frank Freedman, *Mng Member*
EMP: 8 **EST:** 2009
SALES (est): 880.4K **Privately Held**
WEB: www.indoorgenerator.com
SIC: 3621 Power generators

(G-19034)
SILK SAFARI INC
613 Madeline Dr (33413-3421)
PHONE.................................561 689-3882
Jodie Quackenbush, *Treasurer*
EMP: 6 **EST:** 2016
SALES (est): 96.8K **Privately Held**
SIC: 3272 Concrete products

(G-19035)
SIMPLIFIED FABRICATORS INC
9040 Belvedere Rd (33411-3636)
PHONE.................................561 335-3488
Jean Chardon, *President*
EMP: 35 **EST:** 2017
SALES (est): 4.2MM **Privately Held**
WEB: www.simplifiedfabricators.com
SIC: 3713 Truck bodies & parts

(G-19036)
SOCKETS & SPECIALS INC
Also Called: Fastener Specialties Mfg Co
7110 Georgia Ave (33405-4556)
PHONE.................................561 582-7022
Richard Perkaus Jr, *President*
Donna Perkaus, *Vice Pres*
EMP: 18 **EST:** 1975
SQ FT: 4,500
SALES (est): 1MM **Privately Held**
WEB: www.fastenerspecialties.com
SIC: 3452 Screws, metal

(G-19037)
SOFTWARE PRODUCT SOLUTIONS LLC
12713 Westport Cir (33414-5537)
PHONE.................................561 798-6727
Joseph Carrigan, *Principal*
EMP: 5 **EST:** 2007
SALES (est): 322.7K **Privately Held**
SIC: 7372 Prepackaged software

(G-19038)
SOLITRON DEVICES INC
3301 Electronics Way C (33407-4697)
PHONE.................................561 848-4311
Tim Eriksen, *CEO*
David W Pointer, *Ch of Bd*
Mark W Matson, *President*
Jack Worthen, *General Mgr*
Victor Alberico, *Engineer*
EMP: 74 **EST:** 1959
SQ FT: 47,000
SALES: 10.5MM **Privately Held**
WEB: www.solitrondevices.com
SIC: 3674 3676 Integrated circuits, semiconductor networks, etc.; electronic resistors

(G-19039)
SOUTH FLORIDA FIELD TECHS INC
1598 Newhaven Point Ln (33411-6624)
PHONE.................................954 325-6548
John Randolph, *Director*
EMP: 8 **EST:** 2010
SALES (est): 513.2K **Privately Held**
SIC: 3732 Boat building & repairing

(G-19040)
SOUTHEASTERN PRESTRESSED CON
860 N Benoist Farms Rd (33411-3749)
P.O. Box 3768 (33402-3768)
PHONE.................................561 793-1177
Martin E Murphy Sr, *President*
EMP: 12 **EST:** 1966
SQ FT: 1,000
SALES (est): 3.4MM **Privately Held**
WEB: www.seprestressed.com
SIC: 3272 Prestressed concrete products
PA: Jamco, Inc.
1615 Clare Ave
West Palm Beach FL 33401
561 655-3634

(G-19041)
STATE LIGHTING CO INC
405 4th Way (33407-6670)
PHONE.................................561 371-9529
Perry S Weisberg, *President*
EMP: 7 **EST:** 2009
SALES (est): 482.8K **Privately Held**
WEB: www.litetouchsupply.com
SIC: 3648 Lighting equipment

(G-19042)
STATEMENTS 2000 LLC
1374 N Killian Dr Ste A (33403-1901)
PHONE.................................561 249-1587
Jon Cohen, *Principal*
EMP: 7 **EST:** 2010
SALES (est): 962.9K **Privately Held**
WEB: www.statements2000.com
SIC: 3446 Architectural metalwork

(G-19043)
STELLAR SIGNS GRAP
5401 N Haverhill Rd (33407-7005)
PHONE.................................561 721-6060
EMP: 6 **EST:** 2019
SALES (est): 487.3K **Privately Held**
WEB: www.stellar-signs.com
SIC: 3993 Signs & advertising specialties

(G-19044)
STEVEN K BAKUM INC
Also Called: Sir Speedy
4634 S Dixie Hwy (33405-2932)
PHONE.................................561 804-9110
Steven K Bakum, *President*
Theresa Bakum, *Vice Pres*
EMP: 6 **EST:** 1982
SQ FT: 3,000
SALES (est): 889.1K **Privately Held**
WEB: www.sirspeedy.com
SIC: 2752 2791 2789 Commercial printing, lithographic; typesetting; bookbinding & related work

(G-19045)
STILL WATER INDUSTRIES INC
8400 Garden Rd Ste A (33404-1773)
PHONE.................................561 845-6033
John S Rey, *President*
Jeff Rey, *Vice Pres*
EMP: 7 **EST:** 1995
SQ FT: 12,800
SALES (est): 689.8K **Privately Held**
SIC: 2541 2517 Cabinets, except refrigerated: show, display, etc.: wood; home entertainment unit cabinets, wood

(G-19046)
STORM DEPOT OF PALM BEACH
1202 S Congress Ave Ste A (33406-5402)
PHONE.................................561 721-9800
Frank Roca, *Partner*
EMP: 10 **EST:** 2005
SALES (est): 646.8K **Privately Held**
WEB: www.hurricaneshutterswestpalmbeach.com
SIC: 2431 Awnings, blinds & shutters, wood

(G-19047)
SUGAR DEVELOPMENT CORP
1940 S Club Dr (33414-9088)
PHONE.................................561 784-0604
Sudhir Patel, *President*
Ajay Pater, *Vice Pres*
Bob Connor, *Director*
▲ **EMP:** 6 **EST:** 1999
SALES (est): 1.8MM **Privately Held**
WEB: www.sudeco.com
SIC: 3556 Sugar plant machinery

(G-19048)
SUNDAR PUBLISHING
234 Cortez Rd (33405-4106)
PHONE.................................305 335-1930
Lindsay Scherr, *Principal*
EMP: 6 **EST:** 2017
SALES (est): 157.8K **Privately Held**
SIC: 2741 Miscellaneous publishing

(G-19049)
SUNSHINE LTD TAPE & LABEL SPC
Also Called: Sunshine Tape & Label
516 24th St (33407-5404)
PHONE.................................561 832-9656
Larry Susauter, *President*
Joe Lindall, *Vice Pres*
Joseph Shalle, *Vice Pres*
EMP: 12 **EST:** 1985
SQ FT: 7,000
SALES (est): 640K **Privately Held**
SIC: 2672 Tape, pressure sensitive: made from purchased materials

(G-19050)
SUNSHINE PRINTING INC (PA)
Also Called: Preferred Printing & Graphics
2605 Old Okeechobee Rd (33409-4146)
PHONE.................................561 478-2602
Dennis Watrous, *President*
Tim Gonyer, *Vice Pres*
Kevin Watrous, *Vice Pres*
▲ **EMP:** 16 **EST:** 1983
SQ FT: 7,500
SALES (est): 2.2MM **Privately Held**
WEB: www.preferredprinting.net
SIC: 2752 2791 2789 Commercial printing, offset; typesetting; bookbinding & related work

(G-19051)
SUPERIOR LEAF INC
Also Called: Superleaf
523 Ogston St Ste A (33405-2610)
P.O. Box 540403, Greenacres (33454-0403)
PHONE.................................561 480-2464
EMP: 7 **EST:** 2014
SQ FT: 3,500
SALES (est): 75K **Privately Held**
WEB: www.superiorleaf.com
SIC: 2621 Specialty papers

(G-19052)
SV MICROWAVE INC
2400 Cntre Pk W Dr Ste 10 (33409)
PHONE.................................561 840-1800
Subi Katragadda, *CEO*
Andrew Dinsdale, *Business Mgr*
Heri Aponte, *Vice Pres*
Laura Lopez, *Vice Pres*
Jeannette Roldan, *Vice Pres*
EMP: 150 **EST:** 1992
SQ FT: 20,000
SALES (est): 55.2MM
SALES (corp-wide): 8.6B **Publicly Held**
WEB: www.svmicro.com
SIC: 3679 5065 3678 Microwave components; electronic parts & equipment; electronic connectors
PA: Amphenol Corporation
358 Hall Ave
Wallingford CT 06492
203 265-8900

(G-19053)
SWAROVSKI NORTH AMERICA LTD
10300 W Frest Hl Blvd Ste (33414)
PHONE.................................561 791-7757
Pat Boroom, *Branch Mgr*
EMP: 6
SALES (corp-wide): 4.5B **Privately Held**
WEB: www.swarovski.com
SIC: 3961 Costume jewelry
HQ: Swarovski North America Limited
1 Kenney Dr
Cranston RI 02920
401 463-6400

(G-19054)
SWEET MIX LLC
2644 Starwood Cir (33406-5196)
PHONE.................................561 227-8332
Fabian Maly, *Principal*
EMP: 6 **EST:** 2019
SALES (est): 350.1K **Privately Held**
SIC: 3273 Ready-mixed concrete

(G-19055)
SYSTEM 48 PLUS INC
3866 Prospect Ave Ste 1 (33404-3343)
PHONE.................................561 844-5305
Max Houss, *Director*
EMP: 9 **EST:** 1998
SALES (est): 252.4K **Privately Held**
WEB: www.spiritual-connections.com
SIC: 3599 Industrial machinery

(G-19056)
T M TOOLING INC
7341 Westport Pl Ste B (33413-1604)
PHONE.................................561 712-0903
Lindi Meier, *President*
Terry Meier, *Vice Pres*
EMP: 27 **EST:** 1985
SQ FT: 9,500
SALES (est): 561.8K **Privately Held**
WEB: www.tmtooling.com
SIC: 3599 Machine shop, jobbing & repair

(G-19057)
TALENT WEAR LLC
14812 64th Way N (33418-1964)
PHONE.................................561 624-3030
Joey Moynihan, *Executive Asst*
EMP: 6 **EST:** 2008
SALES (est): 246.4K **Privately Held**
SIC: 2253 T-shirts & tops, knit

(G-19058)
TEE LINE CORP
11883 62nd Ln N (33412-2052)
PHONE.................................786 350-9526
Upton Coke, *Principal*
EMP: 20 **EST:** 2012
SALES (est): 1.2MM **Privately Held**
SIC: 2759 Screen printing

(G-19059)
TEF-GEL INC
1601 Hill Ave (33407-2233)
PHONE.................................561 845-1086
Robert P Mergenthaler, *Principal*
EMP: 10 **EST:** 2009
SALES (est): 165.8K **Privately Held**
WEB: www.tefgel45.com
SIC: 3812 Aircraft/aerospace flight instruments & guidance systems

(G-19060)
THERMO ARL US INC (PA)
Also Called: Baird
1400 Northpoint Pkwy # 50 (33407-1976)
PHONE.................................800 532-4752
Marc Casper, *CEO*
Robert Boyd,
Dan Shine,
EMP: 30 **EST:** 2001
SALES (est): 7.2MM **Privately Held**
SIC: 3826 3829 3827 Spectrometers; measuring & controlling devices; optical instruments & lenses

(G-19061)
THERMO ELECTRON NORTH AMER LLC (DH)
1400 Nrthpint Pkwy Ste 10 (33407)
PHONE.................................561 688-8700
Seth H Hoogasian, *Senior VP*
Kenneth J Apicerno, *Vice Pres*
Christy Green, *Sales Staff*
EMP: 396 **EST:** 2002
SQ FT: 22,750
SALES (est): 127MM
SALES (corp-wide): 32.2B **Publicly Held**
WEB: www.fishersci.com
SIC: 3826 Analytical instruments

HQ: Thermo Fisher Scientific West Palm Holdings Llc
168 3rd Ave
Waltham MA 02451
781 622-1000

(G-19062)
THERMO FISHER SCIENTIFIC INC
1400 Nrthpint Pkwy Ste 10 (33407)
P.O. Box 11448 (33419-1448)
PHONE....................561 688-8700
Kenneth Gray, *Vice Pres*
Bob Brister, *Sales Staff*
Karl Kastner, *Sales Staff*
Ronald George, *Business Anlyst*
Timothy Fahrenholz, *Technical Staff*
EMP: 307
SALES (corp-wide): 32.2B **Publicly Held**
WEB: www.thermofisher.com
SIC: 3826 5049 Analytical instruments; scientific instruments
PA: Thermo Fisher Scientific Inc.
168 3rd Ave
Waltham MA 02451
781 622-1000

(G-19063)
TIELVE CABINETSINC
2122 Tarragon Rd (33415-7010)
PHONE....................561 267-3740
Ramon F Tielve, *Principal*
EMP: 6 **EST:** 2012
SALES (est): 167.1K **Privately Held**
SIC: 2434 Wood kitchen cabinets

(G-19064)
TIMES MICROWAVE SYSTEMS INC
2400 Cntre Pk W Dr Ste 10 (33409)
PHONE....................203 949-8400
Marc Degan, *Opers Mgr*
EMP: 10
SALES (corp-wide): 8.6B **Publicly Held**
WEB: www.timesmicrowave.com
SIC: 3357 Nonferrous wiredrawing & insulating
HQ: Times Microwave Systems, Inc.
358 Hall Ave
Wallingford CT 06492
203 949-8400

(G-19065)
TITAN NATURAL FOCUS CORP
2701 Vista Pkwy (33411-5614)
PHONE....................305 778-7005
Marcel Brunner, *CEO*
Golnesa Brunner, *Marketing Staff*
EMP: 9 **EST:** 2015
SALES (est): 117.7K **Privately Held**
WEB: www.titannaturalfocus.com
SIC: 2086 Bottled & canned soft drinks

(G-19066)
TNT CUSTOM CABINETRY INC
11093 49th St N (33411-8014)
PHONE....................561 662-0964
Thomas Harper Brannigan, *Principal*
EMP: 8 **EST:** 2004
SALES (est): 473.3K **Privately Held**
WEB: www.tntcustombuilders.com
SIC: 2434 Wood kitchen cabinets

(G-19067)
TOLLIVER ALUMINUM SERVICE INC
Also Called: Tolliver Powder Coating
6810 Georgia Ave (33405-4520)
PHONE....................561 582-8939
Brandon Greer, *President*
Eric Lebano, *General Mgr*
Wayne Frinkle, *Personnel*
▼ **EMP:** 18 **EST:** 1999
SQ FT: 15,000
SALES (est): 2.7MM **Privately Held**
WEB: www.tolliverpc.com
SIC: 3479 Coating of metals & formed products

(G-19068)
TOP CTERS YCHT RESTORATION LLC
11852 61st St N (33412-2062)
PHONE....................561 818-9259
David Walter,
EMP: 6 **EST:** 2018
SALES (est): 140K **Privately Held**
WEB: www.topcoatersyachtrestoration.com
SIC: 3732 Boat building & repairing

(G-19069)
TOTALLY GLASS & BLINDS LLC
1027 Egremont Dr (33406-5032)
PHONE....................561 929-6125
Marcel Llerena Alvarez, *Manager*
EMP: 7 **EST:** 2010
SALES (est): 57.3K **Privately Held**
SIC: 2591 Window blinds

(G-19070)
TRU CANE SUGAR CORP
1 N Clematis St Ste 200 (33401-5551)
PHONE....................561 833-1731
EMP: 7 **EST:** 2019
SALES (est): 473.7K **Privately Held**
SIC: 2061 Raw cane sugar

(G-19071)
TULIPAN BAKERY INC (PA)
740 Belvedere Rd (33405-1108)
PHONE....................561 832-6107
Jose Allione, *President*
Stella Allione, *Vice Pres*
EMP: 11 **EST:** 1971
SQ FT: 2,400
SALES (est): 1MM **Privately Held**
WEB: www.tulipanbakery.com
SIC: 2051 5812 Bakery: wholesale or wholesale/retail combined; cafeteria

(G-19072)
TV PUBLISHING
417 Lake Dora Dr (33411-2370)
PHONE....................954 773-6967
Robert E Platshorn, *Principal*
EMP: 6 **EST:** 2009
SALES (est): 115K **Privately Held**
SIC: 2741 Miscellaneous publishing

(G-19073)
U S COMPOSITES INC
5101 Georgia Ave (33405-3103)
PHONE....................561 588-1001
Mark Ananos, *President*
▼ **EMP:** 5 **EST:** 2000
SALES (est): 999.1K **Privately Held**
WEB: www.uscomposites.com
SIC: 2821 Plastics materials & resins

(G-19074)
UFG GROUP INC (PA)
Also Called: United Franchise Group
2121 Vista Pkwy (33411-2706)
PHONE....................561 425-6829
Raymond Titus, *President*
Kyle Bostwick, *Regional Mgr*
Michael Glick, *Regional Mgr*
Charles Kowanetz, *Regional Mgr*
Eric Redden, *Regional Mgr*
EMP: 8 **EST:** 2005
SALES (est): 104.4MM **Privately Held**
WEB: www.unitedfranchisegroup.com
SIC: 3993 Signs & advertising specialties

(G-19075)
UNITED STRINGS INTL LLC
352 Tall Pines Rd Ste G (33413-1737)
PHONE....................561 790-4191
Jorge F Monteiro, *Principal*
▲ **EMP:** 6 **EST:** 2012
SALES (est): 483K **Privately Held**
WEB: www.larchetbrasil.com
SIC: 3949 Arrows, archery

(G-19076)
US TRUSS INC
3400 45th St (33407-1844)
PHONE....................561 686-4000
Erol Tuzcu, *President*
Kemal Aldemir, *Engineer*
EMP: 41 **EST:** 1990
SQ FT: 35,000
SALES (est): 6.4MM **Privately Held**
WEB: www.ustruss.com
SIC: 2439 Trusses, wooden roof

(G-19077)
VECELLIO MANAGEMENT SVCS INC
101 Sansburys Way (33411-3670)
P.O. Box 15065 (33416-5065)
PHONE....................561 793-2102
Leo A Vecellio Jr, *President*
Robert D Smith, *Corp Secy*
Christopher Vecellio, *Vice Pres*
Kathryn C Vecellio, *Vice Pres*
Michael A Vecellio, *Vice Pres*
EMP: 27 **EST:** 2004
SALES (est): 13.5MM **Privately Held**
WEB: www.vecelliogroup.com
SIC: 1241 Mining services: lignite

(G-19078)
VERTARIB INC (PA)
Also Called: Thermacon
9005 Southern Blvd (33411-3625)
PHONE....................877 815-8610
Alan Dinow, *CEO*
▼ **EMP:** 25 **EST:** 2009
SQ FT: 10,000
SALES (est): 4MM **Privately Held**
WEB: www.vertarib.com
SIC: 3443 Tank towers, metal plate

(G-19079)
VESTAS
5411 S Olive Ave (33405-3344)
PHONE....................561 588-9933
Vesta T Hetherington, *Owner*
EMP: 8 **EST:** 2014
SALES (est): 156.7K **Privately Held**
SIC: 3511 Turbines & turbine generator sets

(G-19080)
VIRAG DISTRIBUTION LLC
Also Called: Virag Biosciences
700 S Rosemary Ave # 204 (33401-6313)
PHONE....................844 448-4724
Koutsogiannis Vas, *Mng Member*
EMP: 6 **EST:** 2019
SALES (est): 712.7K **Privately Held**
WEB: www.virag.bio
SIC: 3999

(G-19081)
VITAL SOLUTIONS LLC
3755 Fiscal Ct Ste 2 (33404-1704)
PHONE....................561 848-1717
Michelle Haas,
EMP: 5 **EST:** 2011
SQ FT: 6,000
SALES (est): 470.6K **Privately Held**
WEB: www.vitaloxide.com
SIC: 2836 Antitoxins

(G-19082)
VITAL USA INC
525 S Flagler Dr Ste 301 (33401-5932)
PHONE....................561 282-6074
Irwin Gross, *CEO*
Robert Faber, *CFO*
Mark Haig Khachaturi, *CTO*
EMP: 12 **EST:** 2017
SQ FT: 3,100
SALES (est): 1.6MM **Privately Held**
SIC: 3841 Surgical & medical instruments
PA: Arc Devices Limited
C/O Ion Equity Limited 15 Pembroke Street Lower
Dublin

(G-19083)
WAFER WORLD INC
1100 Tech Pl Ste 104 (33407)
PHONE....................561 842-4441
Sean Quinn, *President*
▼ **EMP:** 14 **EST:** 1985
SQ FT: 2,800
SALES (est): 2.2MM **Privately Held**
WEB: www.waferworld.com
SIC: 3674 Integrated circuits, semiconductor networks, etc.

(G-19084)
WALLACE INDUSTRIES INC
316 Valencia Rd (33401-7932)
PHONE....................561 833-8554
Paul R Kludt, *President*
EMP: 8 **EST:** 2011
SALES (est): 260.7K **Privately Held**
SIC: 3999 Manufacturing industries

(G-19085)
WE MIX YOU MATCH INC
6524 Patricia Dr (33413-3402)
PHONE....................561 615-0253
Dr Connie L Ingram, *President*
EMP: 9 **EST:** 2005
SALES (est): 108.7K **Privately Held**
SIC: 3273 Ready-mixed concrete

(G-19086)
WHITE COUNTY STONE LLC
135 Churchill Rd (33405-4143)
PHONE....................415 516-0849
Peter Lombardi, *Mng Member*
EMP: 31 **EST:** 2017
SALES (est): 900K **Privately Held**
SIC: 1429 Boulder, crushed & broken-quarrying

(G-19087)
WILD PRINTS LLC
12415 76th Rd N (33412-2277)
PHONE....................561 800-6536
Michelle Brennan, *Mng Member*
EMP: 6 **EST:** 2013
SALES (est): 436.1K **Privately Held**
WEB: www.wildprints561.com
SIC: 2752 Commercial printing, lithographic

(G-19088)
WINDSOR & YORK INC
7233 Southern Blvd (33413-1648)
P.O. Box 2617, Palm Beach (33480-2617)
PHONE....................561 687-8424
Peter B Newton, *President*
Linda Flower, *President*
EMP: 5 **EST:** 1996
SALES (est): 312.4K **Privately Held**
SIC: 2295 Leather, artificial or imitation

(G-19089)
WOOD U ENVISION
4252 Westroads Dr (33407-1219)
PHONE....................561 601-1973
Thomas Fasig, *Owner*
EMP: 6 **EST:** 2012
SALES (est): 700K **Privately Held**
SIC: 2434 Wood kitchen cabinets

(G-19090)
YONDER WOODWORKS INC
4901 Georgia Ave (33405-3113)
PHONE....................561 547-5777
Prior Powers, *President*
Judy Powers, *Owner*
EMP: 5 **EST:** 1985
SQ FT: 8,000
SALES (est): 558.9K **Privately Held**
WEB: www.yonderwoodworks.net
SIC: 2511 Wood household furniture

West Park
Broward County

(G-19091)
AK INDUSTRIES LLC
3530 Sw 47th Ave (33023-5553)
PHONE....................954 662-7038
Donald Sarmento, *Principal*
EMP: 10 **EST:** 2012
SALES (est): 146.3K **Privately Held**
WEB: www.akindustries.com
SIC: 3999 Manufacturing industries

(G-19092)
EBCO ENVMTL BINS & CNTRS INC
2101 Sw 56th Ter (33023-3011)
PHONE....................954 967-9999
Eduardo Brandao, *President*
Sonia Toro, *Admin Sec*
▼ **EMP:** 16 **EST:** 1994
SALES (est): 501.6K **Privately Held**
SIC: 3589 Garbage disposers & compactors, commercial

(G-19093)
GNJ MANUFACTURING INC
5811 Hallandale Bch Blvd (33023-5243)
PHONE....................................305 651-8644
Eric Gavara, *President*
▲ **EMP:** 35 **EST:** 1998
SQ FT: 30,000
SALES (est): 4MM **Privately Held**
WEB: www.supremebodyjewelry.com
SIC: 3911 5999 Jewelry apparel; mobile telephones & equipment

(G-19094)
HOLLYWOOD IRON WORKS INC
2313 Sw 57th Ter (33023-4026)
PHONE....................................954 962-0556
Joseph Caparelli, *President*
Ernest Caparelli, *President*
Irma Caparelli, *Director*
▼ **EMP:** 10
SQ FT: 12,000
SALES (est): 3.2MM **Privately Held**
WEB: www.hollywoodiron.com
SIC: 3312 3441 Structural shapes & pilings, steel; fabricated structural metal

(G-19095)
I T PACS PRO SOFTWARE INC
5612 Pembroke Rd Ste A (33023-2304)
PHONE....................................954 678-1270
Robert Daniel, *Principal*
EMP: 8 **EST:** 2015
SALES (est): 534.6K **Privately Held**
WEB: www.itpacspro.com
SIC: 7372 Educational computer software

(G-19096)
MIAMI TRUCOLOR OFFSET SVC CO
2211 Sw 57th Ter (33023-3024)
PHONE....................................954 962-5230
Donald Melton, *President*
EMP: 9 **EST:** 1962
SQ FT: 20,000
SALES (est): 890.8K **Privately Held**
SIC: 2752 2796 Commercial printing, offset; color separations for printing

(G-19097)
Q & O CUSTOM WOODWORK INC
5939 Sw 23rd St (33023-4006)
PHONE....................................954 391-8281
Oral Mitchell, *Principal*
EMP: 6 **EST:** 2011
SALES (est): 66.9K **Privately Held**
SIC: 2431 Millwork

(G-19098)
SHORELINE FOUNDATION INC
Also Called: Sfi
2781 Sw 56th Ave (33023-4166)
PHONE....................................954 985-0981
James A Royo, *President*
Fred Maxwell, *General Mgr*
Barry Reed, *Corp Secy*
John McGee, *Vice Pres*
Efrain D 'aleccio, *Safety Dir*
◆ **EMP:** 110 **EST:** 1986
SQ FT: 3,960
SALES (est): 17.9MM **Privately Held**
WEB: www.shorelinefoundation.com
SIC: 3448 1629 Prefabricated metal buildings; pile driving contractor; marine construction; dock construction

Weston
Broward County

(G-19099)
4BIDDENKNOWLEDGE INC
2645 Executive Park Dr (33331-3624)
PHONE....................................954 245-0086
Billy Carson, *CEO*
EMP: 5 **EST:** 2016
SALES (est): 599.9K **Privately Held**
WEB: www.4biddenknowledge.com
SIC: 2741 Miscellaneous publishing

(G-19100)
911 EQUIPMENT INC (PA)
2645 Executive Park Dr (33331-3624)
PHONE....................................954 217-1745
Franco L Tortolani, *President*
Francisco Ramos, *Vice Pres*
▼ **EMP:** 14 **EST:** 2003
SALES (est): 2MM **Privately Held**
WEB: www.equipment911.com
SIC: 3569 Firefighting apparatus & related equipment

(G-19101)
954 SAVINGS MAGAZINE
405 Sailboat Cir (33326-1505)
PHONE....................................954 900-4649
EMP: 5
SALES (est): 334.3K **Privately Held**
SIC: 2721 Periodicals-Publishing/Printing

(G-19102)
ABC INTERCARGO LLC
2800 Glades Cir Ste 137 (33327-9100)
PHONE....................................954 908-5200
Leyde Janeth Pardo, *Exec Dir*
Freddy Godoy Leon, *Director*
Maria I Gonzalez,
EMP: 8 **EST:** 2011
SALES (est): 1.2MM **Privately Held**
WEB: www.abcintercargo.com
SIC: 3728 Aircraft parts & equipment

(G-19103)
AFFINEON LIGHTING
16709 Amber Lk (33331-3165)
PHONE....................................407 448-3434
Teddy Van Bemmel, *Partner*
EMP: 10 **EST:** 2008
SALES (est): 236K **Privately Held**
SIC: 3646 Commercial indusl & institutional electric lighting fixtures

(G-19104)
AMINSA CORP
612 Bald Cypress Rd (33327-2456)
PHONE....................................954 865-1289
EMP: 7 **EST:** 2018
SALES (est): 672.3K **Privately Held**
WEB: www.aminsausa.com
SIC: 3441 Fabricated structural metal

(G-19105)
ANDRX CORPORATION
2915 Weston Rd (33331-3654)
PHONE....................................954 217-4500
Danys Martinez, *Production*
Debi Abelow, *Technology*
Donna Thompson, *Representative*
EMP: 161 **Privately Held**
WEB: www.andrx.com
SIC: 2834 Pharmaceutical preparations
HQ: Andrx Corporation
4955 Orange Dr
Davie FL 33314

(G-19106)
APACHE SHEET METAL
631 Stanton Ln (33326-4501)
PHONE....................................954 214-4468
Thomas Corette, *Owner*
EMP: 8 **EST:** 1984
SALES (est): 350K **Privately Held**
SIC: 3444 Sheet metalwork

(G-19107)
APOTEX CORP (DH)
2400 N Commerce Pkwy # 400
(33326-3253)
PHONE....................................954 384-8007
Peter Hardwick, *President*
Bernard C Sherman, *Chairman*
Jim Young, *Exec VP*
Jack Kay, *Vice Pres*
Emmanuel Obanu, *Vice Pres*
▲ **EMP:** 43 **EST:** 1992
SALES (est): 81.1MM
SALES (corp-wide): 1.1B **Privately Held**
WEB: www.apotex.com
SIC: 2834 Pharmaceutical preparations
HQ: Apotex Holdings Inc
150 Signet Dr
North York ON M9L 1
416 749-9300

(G-19108)
ARGUS INTERNATIONAL INC
318 Indian Trce (33326-2996)
PHONE....................................305 888-4881
Alfonso Hernandez, *President*
Roberto B Bequillard, *President*
Frederick Bustamante, *Admin Sec*
◆ **EMP:** 28 **EST:** 1989
SALES (est): 923.1K **Privately Held**
WEB: www.theargusgroup.us
SIC: 2331 Blouses, women's & juniors': made from purchased material
PA: Central American Cutting Center S.A. De C.V.
Zona Franca Miramar
Comalapa

(G-19109)
AUTOMOTIVE ADVERTISING ASSOC
1045 Woodfall Ct (33326-2833)
PHONE....................................954 389-6500
Fred Stangle, *Principal*
EMP: 8 **EST:** 2016
SALES (est): 278.5K **Privately Held**
WEB: www.automotiveadvertisingassociates.com
SIC: 3993 Signs & advertising specialties

(G-19110)
BEANO PUBLISHING LLC
1575 N Park Dr Ste 100 (33326-3230)
PHONE....................................954 689-8339
Rafael Wynn, *CFO*
Bryan Taylor,
Dina Taylor,
EMP: 10 **EST:** 2000
SALES (est): 1.1MM **Privately Held**
WEB: www.beanopublishing.com
SIC: 2741 Miscellaneous publishing

(G-19111)
BF WESTON LLC
2810 Weston Rd (33331-3636)
PHONE....................................561 844-5528
EMP: 51
SALES (corp-wide): 1.6MM **Privately Held**
SIC: 3011 Tires & inner tubes
PA: Bf Weston, Llc
105 Us Highway 1
North Palm Beach FL 33408
561 844-5528

(G-19112)
BIGG D ENTERTAINMENT LLC
904 Stillwater Ct (33327-2130)
PHONE....................................917 204-0292
Derrick Baker,
EMP: 5 **EST:** 2005
SALES (est): 500K **Privately Held**
SIC: 2741 Music book & sheet music publishing

(G-19113)
BIORESOURCE TECHNOLOGY
1800 N Commerce Pkwy # 1 (33326-3221)
PHONE....................................954 792-5222
David Reichenbach, *President*
Ron Dilling, *COO*
Thomas Hunter, *Director*
EMP: 20 **EST:** 2003
SQ FT: 23,000
SALES (est): 5.4MM **Privately Held**
WEB: www.brt-us.com
SIC: 2836 Biological products, except diagnostic

(G-19114)
CACAO FRUIT COMPANY
1500 Weston Rd Ste 200 (33326-3264)
PHONE....................................954 449-8704
Joseph W Montgomery III, *President*
EMP: 8 **EST:** 2017
SALES (est): 309.8K **Privately Held**
WEB: www.cacaofruitco.com
SIC: 2099 Food preparations

(G-19115)
CANVAS FOODS CORP
19266 Seneca Ave (33332-2437)
PHONE....................................786 529-8041
Ignacio Aguerrevere, *Principal*
EMP: 7 **EST:** 2016
SALES (est): 46.5K **Privately Held**
SIC: 2211 Canvas

(G-19116)
CNH INDUSTRIAL AMERICA LLC
3265 Meridian Pkwy # 124 (33331-3523)
PHONE....................................954 389-9779
EMP: 15
SALES (corp-wide): 28B **Privately Held**
SIC: 3523 Mfg Farm Equipments
HQ: Cnh Industrial America Llc
700 State St
Racine WI 60527
262 636-6011

(G-19117)
CONTRACT MFG SOLUTIONS INC
Also Called: Cmsi
1880 N Commerce Pkwy # 1 (33326-3223)
PHONE....................................954 424-9813
Edwin Aguilera, *President*
Don Lisiewski, *Principal*
Zana Maldonado, *Principal*
Kristin Aguilera, *Corp Secy*
EMP: 18 **EST:** 2001
SALES (est): 369.5K **Privately Held**
WEB: www.nikaousa.com
SIC: 3841 Surgical & medical instruments

(G-19118)
CROSS ATLANTIC COMMODITIES INC (PA)
Also Called: Cxac
4581 Weston Rd Ste 273 (33331-3141)
PHONE....................................954 678-0698
Jorge Bravo, *President*
EMP: 5 **EST:** 1998
SALES (est): 957.3K **Publicly Held**
WEB: www.crossac.com
SIC: 2024 5143 Ice cream & frozen desserts; ice cream & ices

(G-19119)
D V M PHARMACEUTICALS INC
3040 Universal Blvd (33331-3573)
PHONE....................................305 575-6950
Jane H Hsiao, *CEO*
EMP: 76 **EST:** 1975
SALES (est): 12.3MM **Privately Held**
WEB: www.tevapharm.com
SIC: 2834 Veterinary pharmaceutical preparations
HQ: Ivax Corporation
4400 Biscayne Blvd
Miami FL 33137
305 329-3795

(G-19120)
DIAMOND MOBA AMERICAS INC
2731 Executive Park Dr # 4 (33331-3619)
PHONE....................................954 384-5828
Dennis Glanert, *Production*
Troy Sigriest, *CFO*
▼ **EMP:** 100 **EST:** 2010
SQ FT: 1,500
SALES (est): 40MM
SALES (corp-wide): 1.7MM **Privately Held**
WEB: www.moba.net
SIC: 3565 Packaging machinery
HQ: Moba Group B.V.
Stationsweg 117
Barneveld 3771
342 455-655

(G-19121)
DOUBLE J OF BROWARD INC (PA)
Also Called: Ritchie Swimwear
1800 N Commerce Pkwy # 2 (33326-3221)
PHONE....................................954 659-8880
Richard Berger, *CEO*
Michael Berger, *President*
Nina Berger, *Corp Secy*
◆ **EMP:** 23 **EST:** 1979
SQ FT: 13,000
SALES (est): 5.5MM **Privately Held**
SIC: 2339 5699 Bathing suits: women's, misses' & juniors'; athletic clothing: women's, misses' & juniors'; bathing suits; sports apparel

(G-19122)
ESTIMATOR SOFTWARE LLC
16102 Emerald Estates Dr (33331-6118)
PHONE....................................203 682-6436
Mark L Myers, *Manager*
EMP: 7 **EST:** 2012

SALES (est): 164.5K **Privately Held**
WEB: www.estimatorcloud.com
SIC: 7372 Business oriented computer software

(G-19123)
FASSI EQUIPMENT INC
Also Called: Fassiequipment.com
2800 Glades Cir Ste 127 (33327-2278)
PHONE..................................954 385-6555
Ricardo Fassi, *President*
◆ **EMP:** 6 **EST:** 2000
SQ FT: 2,000
SALES (est): 902.4K **Privately Held**
WEB: www.fassidigital.com
SIC: 2759 Screen printing

(G-19124)
FASSIDIGITALCOM INC
2800 Gldes Crcles Ste 127 (33327)
PHONE..................................954 385-6555
Riccardo Fassi, *President*
Maria Eugenia Fassi, *Vice Pres*
EMP: 11 **EST:** 2015
SALES (est): 179.8K **Privately Held**
WEB: www.fassidigital.com
SIC: 2759 7336 Screen printing; commercial art & graphic design

(G-19125)
FLORIDA FRESHNER CORP
1138 Sunflower Cir (33327-2105)
PHONE..................................954 349-0348
Jack Benmaor, *Principal*
EMP: 7 **EST:** 2010
SALES (est): 136.6K **Privately Held**
WEB: www.floridafreshner.com
SIC: 3999 Manufacturing industries

(G-19126)
FOREST RESEARCH INSTITUTE INC
2915 Weston Rd (33331-3627)
PHONE..................................631 436-4600
William J Candee, *Ch of Bd*
Marco Taglietti, *Vice Pres*
EMP: 18 **EST:** 2008
SALES (est): 802.1K **Privately Held**
SIC: 2834 Pharmaceutical preparations

(G-19127)
FRANJA CORP
1515 Veracruz Ln (33327-1735)
PHONE..................................954 659-1950
Javier Oviedo, *President*
Diana Rueas, *Principal*
Diana Rojas, *Marketing Staff*
EMP: 5 **EST:** 2001
SALES (est): 347.3K **Privately Held**
WEB: www.tusanteojos.com
SIC: 2721 Magazines: publishing & printing

(G-19128)
FUEL LIFE 1 LLC
869 Falling Water Rd (33326-3556)
PHONE..................................954 652-1735
Heberto Hernandez, *Owner*
EMP: 7 **EST:** 2018
SALES (est): 1.1MM **Privately Held**
SIC: 2869 Fuels

(G-19129)
G & G LATIN BUSINESS INC
16668 Saddle Club Rd (33326-1816)
PHONE..................................954 385-8085
Glenys Garcia, *President*
EMP: 7 **EST:** 2008
SALES (est): 463.8K **Privately Held**
SIC: 2099 Food preparations

(G-19130)
GASEOUS FUEL SYSTEMS CORP
Also Called: GFS
3360 Entp Ave Ste 180 (33331)
PHONE..................................954 693-9475
Kenneth Green, *CEO*
Jason Green, *President*
George Aguilera, *Vice Pres*
Warren J Roy, *CFO*
Arpesh Mehta, *Director*
EMP: 6 **EST:** 1998
SALES (est): 1.4MM **Privately Held**
WEB: www.gfs-corp.com
SIC: 2869 Fuels

(G-19131)
GENESIS 50 20 LLC ✪
16682 Royal Poinciana Dr (33326-1572)
PHONE..................................954 860-8175
Ivy Higgins Pimentel, *Mng Member*
EMP: 6 **EST:** 2021
SALES (est): 289.4K **Privately Held**
SIC: 2211 Print cloths, cotton

(G-19132)
GFS CORP
3360 Entp Ave Ste 180 (33331)
PHONE..................................954 693-9657
Scott A Greenwald, *Mng Member*
Jen Hupf, *Manager*
EMP: 46 **EST:** 1992
SALES (est): 3.2MM **Privately Held**
WEB: www.gfs-corp.com
SIC: 3519 Diesel engine rebuilding; governors, pump, for diesel engines

(G-19133)
GIFT WRAP MY FACE LLC
16791 Royal Poinciana Dr (33326-1542)
PHONE..................................305 788-1473
Aryel Rivero,
Vanessa Clavijo,
EMP: 15 **EST:** 2014
SALES (est): 1.8MM **Privately Held**
WEB: www.giftwrapmyface.com
SIC: 2679 Gift wrap & novelties, paper

(G-19134)
GOLD-REP CORPORATION
Also Called: Sigillu
750 Heritage Dr (33326-4539)
PHONE..................................954 892-5868
Felipe Yungman, *CEO*
Douglas Haskins, *Manager*
EMP: 5 **EST:** 2010
SALES (est): 300K **Privately Held**
SIC: 7372 Prepackaged software

(G-19135)
GRAMPUS ENTERPRISES INC
Also Called: Grampus Tech
2800 Glades Cir Ste 109 (33327-2270)
PHONE..................................305 491-9827
Jim Fang, *President*
Jack Cai, *Exec Dir*
MEI Fang, *Director*
▲ **EMP:** 5 **EST:** 1999
SALES (est): 429.5K **Privately Held**
SIC: 3827 Optical instruments & lenses

(G-19136)
GYROSOLAR CORP
2655 Edgewater Dr (33332-3400)
PHONE..................................954 554-9990
Eukeni Urrechaga, *President*
EMP: 9 **EST:** 2015
SALES (est): 1MM **Privately Held**
SIC: 3334 Aluminum ingots & slabs

(G-19137)
HABIBCO WOODWORKS LLC
1049 Nautica Dr (33327-2133)
PHONE..................................954 659-8501
Habib J Fadel, *Principal*
EMP: 6 **EST:** 2018
SALES (est): 59.5K **Privately Held**
SIC: 2431 Millwork

(G-19138)
IANOROD JB LLC
Also Called: Juiceblendz
4579 Weston Rd (33331-3141)
PHONE..................................954 217-3014
Iliana Ianotto, *Mng Member*
Michael Lawand, *Director*
EMP: 8 **EST:** 2011
SALES (est): 859K **Privately Held**
SIC: 2023 Dietary supplements, dairy & non-dairy based
PA: Grafiplast Ca
Av Principal Con Calle E
Charallave

(G-19139)
ILIAD BIOTECHNOLOGIES LLC
4581 Weston Rd Ste 260 (33331-3141)
PHONE..................................954 336-0777
Keith Rubin MD, *CEO*
Ken Solovay, *COO*
EMP: 7 **EST:** 2012
SALES (est): 377.7K **Privately Held**
WEB: www.iliadbio.com
SIC: 2836 Vaccines

(G-19140)
IN PRESS MARKETING
2487 Quail Roost Dr (33327-1434)
PHONE..................................954 659-9332
Rosaline Fernandez, *Owner*
EMP: 6 **EST:** 2002
SALES (est): 83.3K **Privately Held**
SIC: 2741 Miscellaneous publishing

(G-19141)
INCEPTRA LLC (PA)
1900 N Commerce Pkwy (33326-3236)
PHONE..................................954 442-5400
Timothy Peterson, *CEO*
James Ryan, *Ch of Bd*
Daniel J Smith, *President*
Aamer Khan, *Engineer*
Horace Pardais, *CFO*
EMP: 21
SALES (est): 13.8MM **Privately Held**
WEB: www.inceptra.com
SIC: 7372 7373 8243 Prepackaged software; computer integrated systems design; operator training, computer

(G-19142)
INSIGHT SOFTWARE LLC (HQ)
Also Called: My Vision Express
3265 Meridian Pkwy # 112 (33331-3505)
PHONE..................................305 495-0022
Chris Cummings, *COO*
Luis Necuze, *Manager*
Jennifer Childress, *Director*
EMP: 100 **EST:** 2004
SQ FT: 1,500
SALES (est): 26.9MM
SALES (corp-wide): 394.4MM **Privately Held**
WEB: www.eyecareleaders.com
SIC: 7372 Prepackaged software
PA: Eli Global, Llc
2222 Sedwick Rd
Durham NC 27713
972 448-9084

(G-19143)
ITELECOM USA INC
Also Called: Go Lighting Service
1422 Canary Island Dr (33327-2348)
PHONE..................................305 557-4660
Marcelo Lefort, *President*
Juan Bauza, *Business Mgr*
Christopher Zanyk, *Vice Pres*
Leonardo Bustos, *Treasurer*
Jesse Revilla, *Manager*
EMP: 7 **EST:** 2010
SALES (est): 23.2MM **Privately Held**
WEB: www.itelecomusa.com
SIC: 3663 3674 7349 8748 Satellites, communications; light emitting diodes; lighting maintenance service; telecommunications consultant; systems software development services

(G-19144)
IVAX TEVA
2945 W Corp Lks Blvd A (33331-3626)
PHONE..................................954 384-5316
Zulma Morris, *Vice Pres*
EMP: 8 **EST:** 2008
SALES (est): 528.6K **Privately Held**
SIC: 2834 Pharmaceutical preparations

(G-19145)
JURITIS USA LLC
2500 Weston Rd Ste 105 (33331-3616)
PHONE..................................954 529-2168
Marcelo De Azeredo Souccar,
EMP: 9 **EST:** 2017
SALES (est): 461.4K **Privately Held**
WEB: www.juritis.com
SIC: 7372 Business oriented computer software

(G-19146)
KIKISTEESCOM LLC
762 Verona Lake Dr (33326-3537)
P.O. Box 266376, Fort Lauderdale (33326-6376)
PHONE..................................954 314-7147
Enrique Sznapstajler, *Principal*
EMP: 7 **EST:** 2018
SALES (est): 373.8K **Privately Held**
WEB: www.kikistees.com
SIC: 2759 Screen printing

(G-19147)
LIFESTYLE PUBLICATIONS LLC
1675 Market St Ste 203 (33326-3681)
PHONE..................................954 217-1165
Gary Israel, *Publisher*
David Sherman, *Principal*
Jill Horowitz, *Vice Pres*
EMP: 9 **EST:** 2017
SALES (est): 37.5K **Privately Held**
WEB: www.lifestylepubs.com
SIC: 2741 Miscellaneous publishing

(G-19148)
LOUIS POULSEN USA INC
Also Called: Poulsen Lighting
3260 Meridian Pkwy (33331-3502)
PHONE..................................954 349-2525
Kent S Pedersen, *President*
Claus Brix, *Vice Pres*
Liane Barr, *Regl Sales Mgr*
◆ **EMP:** 60 **EST:** 1985
SQ FT: 14,400
SALES (est): 12.7MM
SALES (corp-wide): 177.9K **Privately Held**
WEB: www.louispoulsen.com
SIC: 3645 3646 5063 Residential lighting fixtures; commercial indusl & institutional electric lighting fixtures; lighting fixtures
HQ: Louis Poulsen A/S
Kuglegardsvej 19
KObenhavn 1434
703 314-14

(G-19149)
MAKO SURGICAL CORP (HQ)
Also Called: Stryker Mako
3365 Enterprise Ave (33331-3524)
PHONE..................................866 647-6256
Kevin A Lobo, *Ch of Bd*
Menashe R Frank, *Senior VP*
Duncan Moffat, *Vice Pres*
Sean Farrell, *Engineer*
Thomas Martinez, *Engineer*
▲ **EMP:** 315 **EST:** 2004
SQ FT: 68,000
SALES (est): 137MM
SALES (corp-wide): 14.3B **Publicly Held**
WEB: www.stryker.com
SIC: 3842 Orthopedic appliances; trusses, orthopedic & surgical
PA: Stryker Corporation
2825 Airview Blvd
Portage MI 49002
269 385-2600

(G-19150)
MUNDI INTL TRADING CORP
1971 Landing Way (33326-2381)
PHONE..................................305 205-0062
Ivan Moran, *President*
Tracie Moran, *Vice Pres*
EMP: 5
SALES (est): 436.7K **Privately Held**
SIC: 2295 Coated fabrics, not rubberized

(G-19151)
MVS INTERNATIONAL INC
702 Willow Bend Rd (33327-1826)
PHONE..................................954 727-3383
Maricel De Michele, *President*
Juan Iliopulos, *Vice Pres*
EMP: 6 **EST:** 2006
SQ FT: 2,000
SALES (est): 450K **Privately Held**
WEB: www.mvsinternational.net
SIC: 2086 5963 2066 Water, pasteurized: packaged in cans, bottles, etc.; fruit drinks (less than 100% juice): packaged in cans, etc.; snacks, direct sales; chocolate & cocoa products

(G-19152)
NATIONAL STONEWORKS LLC
Also Called: US Granite and Quartz
3360 Entp Ave Ste 100 (33331)
PHONE..................................954 349-1609
Everett Parris, *Controller*
Mitchel Hires, *Mng Member*
Fred Hires,
▲ **EMP:** 50 **EST:** 2009

GEOGRAPHIC

SALES (est): 25MM **Privately Held**
WEB: www.constructionresourcesusa.com
SIC: 3281 2434 Table tops, marble; wood kitchen cabinets
PA: Cr Home, Llc
196 Rio Cir
Decatur GA 30030

(G-19153)
NETWORKS ASSETS LLC
Also Called: Starbridge Networks
3265 Meridian Pkwy # 134 (33331-3523)
PHONE..................................954 334-1390
Enrique Diaz, *Mng Member*
Cristina Kellert,
▲ **EMP:** 19 **EST:** 2003
SQ FT: 5,000
SALES (est): 676K **Privately Held**
WEB: www.networksassets.com
SIC: 3661 Telephones & telephone apparatus

(G-19154)
NORTHRICH FLORIDA LLC
Also Called: Nationwide Coils & Coatings
2111 N Commerce Pkwy (33326-3236)
PHONE..................................954 678-6602
Robert Evans,
Walter Dickinson,
EMP: 10 **EST:** 2017
SALES (est): 1.5MM **Privately Held**
WEB: www.northrich.com
SIC: 3585 Air conditioning equipment, complete

(G-19155)
ORACLE ESSENCE INC
1341 St Tropez Cir (33326-3015)
P.O. Box 267910 (33326-7910)
PHONE..................................786 258-8153
Greg Toth, *Branch Mgr*
EMP: 11
SALES (corp-wide): 94.4K **Privately Held**
WEB: www.oracleessence.com
SIC: 7372 Prepackaged software
PA: Oracle Essence, Inc.
4700 N Hiatus Rd
Sunrise FL

(G-19156)
ORIGINAL IMPRESSIONS LLC
Also Called: Oi Distribution
2965 W Corp Lks Blvd (33331-3626)
PHONE..................................305 233-1322
Ismael Diaz, *President*
Wayne Mergenthal, *President*
Ivan Alvarez, *Prdtn Mgr*
Ivan Melcon, *Human Res Dir*
Mayda Guerra, *Human Res Mgr*
▼ **EMP:** 190 **EST:** 1982
SALES (est): 35.6MM
SALES (corp-wide): 43.1MM **Privately Held**
WEB: www.originalimpressions.com
SIC: 2752 7331 7371 8732 Commercial printing, offset; direct mail advertising services; computer software development & applications; market analysis or research
PA: Postal Center International, Inc.
2965 W Corp Lks Blvd
Weston FL 33331
954 321-5644

(G-19157)
ORIZON 360
1840 N Commerce Pkwy # 3 (33326-3222)
PHONE..................................888 979-0360
EMP: 10 **EST:** 2016
SALES (est): 489.5K **Privately Held**
SIC: 7372 Prepackaged software

(G-19158)
OXIGENO NITROGENO INC
Also Called: Tex Medical
16200 Golf Club Rd (33326-1696)
PHONE..................................954 659-3881
Rosa A Sanchez, *President*
Estebaldo J Martinez, *Vice Pres*
EMP: 10 **EST:** 2013
SALES (est): 325.3K **Privately Held**
SIC: 3443 Industrial vessels, tanks & containers

(G-19159)
PACKAGING & RESOURCES INC
19245 S Gardenia Ave (33332-4401)
P.O. Box 266271, Fort Lauderdale (33326-6271)
PHONE..................................954 288-9678
Juan Arenas, *President*
◆ **EMP:** 5 **EST:** 1999
SALES (est): 659.2K **Privately Held**
WEB: www.packres.com
SIC: 3221 Bottles for packing, bottling & canning: glass

(G-19160)
POWER GRID PROS INC
618 Heritage Dr (33326-4538)
PHONE..................................716 378-1419
Jonathan Woodworth, *President*
Jean Paul Combeau, *Vice Pres*
Guy Combeau, *Treasurer*
Deborah Limburg, *Admin Sec*
EMP: 5 **EST:** 2018
SALES (est): 750K **Privately Held**
SIC: 3613 Fuses, electric

(G-19161)
PROFESSIONAL LABORATORIES INC
Also Called: Pro-Lab
1675 N Commerce Pkwy (33326-3205)
P.O. Box 267730, Fort Lauderdale (33326-7730)
PHONE..................................954 384-4446
James McDonnell, *CEO*
Bob Irvine, *Vice Pres*
Todd Marine, *Vice Pres*
Matt Adams, *CFO*
Ranee McDonnell, *Human Res Dir*
EMP: 42 **EST:** 1998
SQ FT: 30,000
SALES (est): 78MM **Privately Held**
WEB: www.prolabinc.com
SIC: 3826 Environmental testing equipment

(G-19162)
R-DA TRADING LLC
2893 Executive Park Dr (33331-3664)
PHONE..................................954 278-6983
Carlos A Gutierrez, *Mng Member*
Josue D Rivas, *Mng Member*
EMP: 9 **EST:** 2012
SALES (est): 870.4K **Privately Held**
SIC: 2834 2869 Pharmaceutical preparations; perfumes, flavorings & food additives

(G-19163)
RAFI PUBLICATIONS LLC
885 Crestview Cir (33327-1847)
PHONE..................................954 384-4166
Randi G Fine, *Manager*
EMP: 6 **EST:** 2017
SALES (est): 41.3K **Privately Held**
SIC: 2741 Miscellaneous publishing

(G-19164)
REDUCTION INTERNATIONAL LLC
2700 Glades Cir Ste 116 (33327-2263)
PHONE..................................954 905-5999
Carlos Garcia, *Mng Member*
EMP: 6 **EST:** 2007
SALES (est): 198.7K **Privately Held**
WEB: www.reductioninternational.com
SIC: 3559 Plastics working machinery

(G-19165)
S J TURBINE LLC
1109 Waterbrook Ln (33326-2831)
PHONE..................................954 804-4779
Stephen A Johnson, *Owner*
EMP: 6 **EST:** 2010
SALES (est): 200.2K **Privately Held**
WEB: www.sjturbine.com
SIC: 3599 Industrial machinery

(G-19166)
S V BAGS AMERICA INC
1563 Sandpiper Cir (33327-1646)
PHONE..................................954 577-9091
Claude Levy, *President*
Elliot Levy, *Vice Pres*
▼ **EMP:** 5 **EST:** 2000
SALES (est): 421.6K **Privately Held**
WEB: www.grupoelliot.com
SIC: 2674 5162 Paper bags: made from purchased materials; plastics materials

(G-19167)
SCUTTI AMERICA INC
2700 Glades Cir Ste 160 (33327-2296)
PHONE..................................954 384-2377
Heriberto Sprecace, *President*
Alejandro Carrizales, *Vice Pres*
Rosa A Barquero, *Treasurer*
Maria Isabel Carrizales, *Admin Sec*
EMP: 11 **EST:** 2000
SALES (est): 921.2K **Privately Held**
WEB: www.scuttiamerica.com
SIC: 3531 Cement silos (batch plant)

(G-19168)
SUPERSONIC IMAGINE INC
2625 Weston Rd (33331-3614)
PHONE..................................954 660-3528
Bernard Dorenboos, *President*
Elisabeth Winter, *Treasurer*
Claire Phalippou, *Controller*
EMP: 8 **EST:** 2007
SQ FT: 300
SALES (est): 2.8MM
SALES (corp-wide): 22MM **Privately Held**
WEB: www.supersonicimagine.com
SIC: 3845 Ultrasonic scanning devices, medical
PA: Supersonic Imagine
Les Jardins De La Duranne Bt E Et Bt F
Aix En Provence 13080
960 418-623

(G-19169)
THALO ASSIST LLC
2893 Executive Park Dr # 203 (33331-3664)
PHONE..................................786 340-6892
Henry Cristo, *Mng Member*
EMP: 7 **EST:** 2018
SALES (est): 250K **Privately Held**
WEB: www.thaloassist.com
SIC: 7372 4724 Application computer software; travel agencies

(G-19170)
THERET BICOM INC
725 Tanglewood Cir (33327-1839)
PHONE..................................917 796-1443
Maurice White, *Principal*
EMP: 7 **EST:** 2016
SALES (est): 91.5K **Privately Held**
SIC: 2834 Pharmaceutical preparations

(G-19171)
THETRADEBAYCOM LLC
451 Conservation Dr (33327-2474)
PHONE..................................954 607-2405
Alfredo E Valenzuela,
Gabriela G Ugarte,
EMP: 9 **EST:** 2015
SALES (est): 555K **Privately Held**
SIC: 2092 Shrimp, frozen: prepared

(G-19172)
TRAINCAT MODEL SALES INC
3709 Heron Ridge Ln (33331-3709)
PHONE..................................954 385-8999
Robert L Knight Jr, *Principal*
EMP: 6 **EST:** 2010
SALES (est): 124.1K **Privately Held**
WEB: www.traincat2.com
SIC: 3999 Manufacturing industries

(G-19173)
UKG INC
1485 N Park Dr (33326-3215)
PHONE..................................954 331-7000
Aron AIN, *CEO*
Cezar Camara, *Engineer*
Adriana Quintero, *Accounting Mgr*
Janice Gessa, *Accountant*
Thomas Lohmeyer, *Accountant*
EMP: 80
SALES (corp-wide): 1.1B **Privately Held**
WEB: www.ultimatesoftware.com
SIC: 7372 Business oriented computer software
HQ: Ukg Inc.
900 Chelmsford St Ste 212
Lowell MA 01851

(G-19174)
UNITE PARENT CORP (PA)
2000 Ultimate Way (33326-3643)
PHONE..................................800 432-1729
Scott Scherr, *Ch of Bd*
Ryan Chai, *Counsel*
Bethanie Haynes, *Counsel*
John Machado, *Vice Pres*
Mike De Miranda, *Opers Staff*
EMP: 70 **EST:** 2019
SALES (est): 1.1B **Privately Held**
SIC: 7372 Business oriented computer software

(G-19175)
URBAPRINT LLC
649 Conservation Dr (33327-2468)
PHONE..................................786 502-3223
Adriana Perrotta, *President*
EMP: 7 **EST:** 2016
SALES (est): 173.1K **Privately Held**
WEB: www.urbaprint.com
SIC: 2752 Commercial printing, lithographic

(G-19176)
USA SIGN COMPANY
1503 Island Way (33326-3623)
PHONE..................................954 497-3293
Charlie Centanni, *Principal*
EMP: 7 **EST:** 2007
SALES (est): 150K **Privately Held**
WEB: www.usasigns.us
SIC: 3993 Signs & advertising specialties

(G-19177)
VLEX 1450 LLC
1199 Hidden Valley Way (33327-1819)
PHONE..................................954 218-5443
Andreina Manzo, *Principal*
EMP: 8 **EST:** 2014
SALES (est): 356K **Privately Held**
SIC: 2741 Miscellaneous publishing

(G-19178)
WISE GAS FUEL CARD LLC
1058 Bluewood Ter (33327-2056)
PHONE..................................954 636-4291
Christine A Slager, *Principal*
EMP: 6 **EST:** 2010
SALES (est): 176.5K **Privately Held**
SIC: 2869 Fuels

(G-19179)
XIKAR INC
3350 Entp Ave Ste 120 (33331)
PHONE..................................816 474-7555
Michael J Giordano, *CEO*
Michael Cellucci, *President*
Anthony D'Eri, *Business Mgr*
Tim Webster, *COO*
Scott Almsberger, *Exec VP*
◆ **EMP:** 30 **EST:** 1996
SALES (est): 50MM
SALES (corp-wide): 50.7MM **Privately Held**
WEB: www.xikar.com
SIC: 3999 Cigarette & cigar products & accessories
PA: Quality Importers Trading Company, Llc
3350 Entp Ave Ste 120
Weston FL 33331
888 795-4839

(G-19180)
ZEROLL CO (HQ)
3355 Entp Ave Ste 160 (33331)
P.O. Box 999, Fort Pierce (34954-0999)
PHONE..................................772 461-3811
O Neal Asbury, *CEO*
▲ **EMP:** 15 **EST:** 1935
SQ FT: 25,000
SALES (est): 1MM
SALES (corp-wide): 208MM **Privately Held**
WEB: www.zeroll.com
SIC: 3469 Utensils, household: metal, except cast
PA: Greenfield World Trade, Inc.
3355 Entp Ave Ste 160
Fort Lauderdale FL 33331
954 202-7419

▲ = Import ▼=Export
◆ =Import/Export

Westville
Holmes County

(G-19181)
L AND D LOGGING
701 Sandspur Rd (32464-2632)
PHONE..........850 859-1013
Woodie L Dupree Jr, *Principal*
EMP: 6 **EST:** 2008
SALES (est): 427.3K **Privately Held**
SIC: 2411 Logging camps & contractors

(G-19182)
WOODIE L DUPREE
Also Called: Dupree Logging
409 Sandspur Rd (32464-2631)
PHONE..........850 859-2496
Woodie L Dupree, *Owner*
Woodie Dupree, *Owner*
EMP: 6 **EST:** 1967
SALES (est): 273.1K **Privately Held**
SIC: 2411 Logging camps & contractors

Wewahitchka
Gulf County

(G-19183)
TUCKER TRCKG LOG JHNNY E TCKER
2371 County Road 381 (32465-5502)
PHONE..........850 258-1982
Eddie Belle White, *Principal*
EMP: 6 **EST:** 2009
SALES (est): 485.9K **Privately Held**
SIC: 2411 Logging

(G-19184)
WHITFIELD TIMBER CO INC (PA)
101 N Highway 71 (32465-9507)
P.O. Box 674 (32465-0674)
PHONE..........850 639-5556
Theodore L Whitfield, *President*
Doris Kay Whitfield, *Treasurer*
EMP: 30 **EST:** 1975
SQ FT: 4,000
SALES (est): 4.5MM **Privately Held**
SIC: 2411 2421 Pulpwood contractors engaged in cutting; sawmills & planing mills, general

White Springs
Hamilton County

(G-19185)
B&M LOGGING INC
10616 Se County Road 135 (32096-1604)
PHONE..........386 397-1145
Tammy Ogburn, *President*
EMP: 8 **EST:** 1993
SALES (est): 928.6K **Privately Held**
SIC: 2411 Logging camps & contractors

(G-19186)
BTR LOGGING INC
10249 Se 161st Ave (32096-2210)
P.O. Box 180 (32096-0180)
PHONE..........386 397-0730
Byron Ogburn, *President*
EMP: 8 **EST:** 2016
SALES (est): 256K **Privately Held**
SIC: 2411 Logging camps & contractors

(G-19187)
HIZER MACHINE MFG INC
12137 Se Us Highway 41 (32096-2501)
P.O. Box E (32096-0279)
PHONE..........386 755-3155
James Hizer, *President*
Katheryn Hizer, *Treasurer*
EMP: 6 **EST:** 1998
SQ FT: 1,600
SALES (est): 671.8K **Privately Held**
SIC: 3561 Pumps & pumping equipment

(G-19188)
RESCAR COMPANIES INC
16950 Se County Road 137 (32096-2533)
PHONE..........386 397-2656
Brent Seoph, *General Mgr*
EMP: 6
SALES (corp-wide): 48.3MM **Privately Held**
WEB: www.rescar.com
SIC: 3743 Railroad car rebuilding
PA: Rescar Companies, Inc.
1101 31st St Ste 250
Downers Grove IL 60515
630 963-1114

(G-19189)
WHITE SPRINGS AG CHEM INC
Also Called: Pcs Phosphate/White Springs
15843 Se 78th St (32096-2703)
P.O. Box 300 (32096-0300)
PHONE..........386 397-8101
William J Doyle, *CEO*
Prentiss Adams, *Manager*
Al Murphy, *Officer*
◆ **EMP:** 900 **EST:** 1994
SQ FT: 1,200
SALES (est): 320.7MM
SALES (corp-wide): 20.9B **Privately Held**
WEB: www.nutrien.com
SIC: 1475 2874 Phosphate rock; phosphates; plant foods, mixed: from plants making phosphatic fertilizer
HQ: Potash Corporation Of Saskatchewan Inc
122 1st Ave S Suite 500
Saskatoon SK S7K 7
306 933-8500

Wildwood
Sumter County

(G-19190)
ALUMNE MANUFACTURING INC
801 Industrial Dr (34785-4710)
PHONE..........352 748-3229
Lester D Yancey, *President*
Anita Yancey, *Vice Pres*
Barbara Rusin, *Bookkeeper*
EMP: 6 **EST:** 1989
SQ FT: 30,000
SALES (est): 680.8K **Privately Held**
WEB: www.alumne.com
SIC: 3715 Truck trailers

(G-19191)
BOB & LEES CABINETS
4386 Warm Springs Ave (34785-8058)
PHONE..........352 748-3553
John S Smith, *Partner*
Robert L Wagner, *Partner*
EMP: 15 **EST:** 1971
SALES (est): 1.7MM **Privately Held**
SIC: 2542 2434 Cabinets: show, display or storage: except wood; wood kitchen cabinets

(G-19192)
CEMEX CNSTR MTLS FLA LLC
Also Called: Gypsum Supply - Wildwood
4270 County Road 124a (34785-7617)
PHONE..........352 330-1115
Jennifer Lee, *Branch Mgr*
EMP: 10 **Privately Held**
WEB: www.rosenmaterials.com
SIC: 3273 Ready-mixed concrete
HQ: Cemex Construction Materials Florida, Llc
1501 Belvedere Rd
West Palm Beach FL 33406

(G-19193)
CHARLOTTE PIPE AND FOUNDRY CO
4149 County Road 124a (34785-7651)
P.O. Box 220 (34785-0220)
PHONE..........352 748-8100
Brandon Skolnik, *Sales Mgr*
James Young, *Manager*
EMP: 29
SALES (corp-wide): 346.8MM **Privately Held**
WEB: www.charlottepipe.com
SIC: 3084 Plastics pipe
PA: Charlotte Pipe And Foundry Company
2109 Randolph Rd
Charlotte NC 28207
704 372-5030

(G-19194)
GLOBAL TIRE RCYCL OF SMTER CNT
1201 Industrial Dr (34785-5202)
PHONE..........352 330-2213
Robert Bjork, *Vice Pres*
EMP: 30 **EST:** 1996
SQ FT: 48,000
SALES (est): 1.8MM **Privately Held**
WEB: www.gtrcrumbrubber.com
SIC: 3069 Reclaimed rubber & specialty rubber compounds
PA: Global Tire Recycling Inc
1201 Industrial Dr
Wildwood FL 34785

(G-19195)
GLOBAL TIRE RECYCLING INC (PA)
1201 Industrial Dr (34785-5202)
PHONE..........352 330-2213
Mark Bailey, *President*
Patricia Johns, *Accounting Mgr*
Susan Lovejoy, *Sr Consultant*
D Watson, *Sr Consultant*
▼ **EMP:** 15 **EST:** 1996
SQ FT: 38,520
SALES (est): 5.1MM **Privately Held**
SIC: 3069 Reclaimed rubber & specialty rubber compounds

(G-19196)
JENNIFER YODER SUNG
Also Called: T & D Screen Enclosures
9235 County Road 128d (34785-9177)
PHONE..........352 748-6655
Lorraine Ferri, *Principal*
EMP: 8 **EST:** 2010
SALES (est): 960.8K **Privately Held**
SIC: 3448 Screen enclosures

(G-19197)
LITTORAL MARINE LLC
Also Called: Crevalle Boats
1520 Industrial Dr (34785-9418)
PHONE..........352 400-4222
Roger B Taylor Jr, *COO*
Mike Hankins, *Vice Pres*
Engels Nick, *Vice Pres*
Steve Truitt, *Vice Pres*
Michael Hankins, *Opers Mgr*
EMP: 35
SQ FT: 40,000
SALES (est): 9MM **Privately Held**
WEB: www.crevalleboats.com
SIC: 3732 Boat building & repairing

(G-19198)
OLDCASTLE INFRASTRUCTURE INC
Also Called: Utility Vault
1410 Industrial Dr (34785-5204)
P.O. Box 238 (34785-0238)
PHONE..........800 642-1540
James Wimington, *General Mgr*
EMP: 10
SALES (corp-wide): 27.5B **Privately Held**
WEB: www.oldcastleinfrastructure.com
SIC: 3272 Concrete products
HQ: Oldcastle Infrastructure, Inc.
7000 Central Pkwy Ste 800
Atlanta GA 30328
770 270-5000

(G-19199)
PRINT ALL PROMOTIONS LLC
18202 Sandalwood Dr 18 (34785-9706)
PHONE..........800 971-3209
Sheryl Ryan, *Principal*
EMP: 6 **EST:** 2008
SALES (est): 303.4K **Privately Held**
WEB: www.printallpromotions.com
SIC: 2752 Commercial printing, lithographic

(G-19200)
PROGRESS RAIL SERVICES CORP
4198 E County Road 462 (34785-8760)
PHONE..........352 748-8008
Steve Hunt, *Manager*
EMP: 6
SALES (corp-wide): 41.7B **Publicly Held**
WEB: www.progressrail.com
SIC: 3559 Recycling machinery; cryogenic machinery, industrial
HQ: Progress Rail Services Corporation
1600 Progress Dr
Albertville AL 35950
256 505-6421

(G-19201)
STONE CENTRAL OF CENTRAL FLA
3200 Ne 37th Pl (34785-7832)
PHONE..........352 689-0075
Philip Shibler, *President*
Jennifer G Shibler, *Vice Pres*
EMP: 12 **EST:** 2005
SQ FT: 7,000
SALES (est): 1MM **Privately Held**
WEB: www.stonecentralinc.com
SIC: 3272 Cast stone, concrete

(G-19202)
SYMRNA READY MIX
8302 Ne 44th Dr (34785-9183)
PHONE..........352 330-1001
EMP: 13 **EST:** 2017
SALES (est): 154.2K **Privately Held**
WEB: www.smyrnareadymix.com
SIC: 3273 Ready-mixed concrete

(G-19203)
T AND M WOODWORKING INC
3321 Ne 37th Pl (34785-7851)
PHONE..........352 748-6655
Nathan Yoder, *President*
EMP: 8 **EST:** 2016
SALES (est): 93.8K **Privately Held**
SIC: 2431 Millwork

(G-19204)
TDSE INC
3187 Ne 37th Pl (34785-7800)
PHONE..........352 399-6413
Matthew L Yoder, *President*
EMP: 50 **EST:** 2018
SALES (est): 4.1MM **Privately Held**
WEB: www.tdseinc.com
SIC: 3448 Screen enclosures

(G-19205)
TEREX CORPORATION
Also Called: Telelect East
3400 Ne 37th Pl (34785-7848)
PHONE..........352 330-4044
EMP: 8
SALES (corp-wide): 7B **Publicly Held**
SIC: 3537 Mfg Industrial Trucks/Tractors
PA: Terex Corporation
200 Nyala Farms Rd Ste 2
Westport CT 06850
203 222-7170

(G-19206)
XPRESS MATERIALS LLC
8302 Ne 44th Dr (34785-9183)
PHONE..........352 748-2200
Claude Graham,
Dan Graham,
Jeff Graham,
Jim Graham,
EMP: 15 **EST:** 2003
SALES (est): 1.3MM **Privately Held**
SIC: 3273 Ready-mixed concrete

Williston
Levy County

(G-19207)
A & N CORPORATION
Also Called: Ancorp
707 Sw 19th Ave (32696-2427)
PHONE..........352 528-4100
Daniel N Vaudreuil, *President*
Glenn W Vaudreuil, *Vice Pres*
Jon Rohrer, *Project Mgr*
Rick Shroyer, *QC Mgr*
Kim Folken, *Engineer*
◆ **EMP:** 90 **EST:** 1965
SQ FT: 42,000
SALES (est): 29.5MM **Privately Held**
WEB: www.ancorp.com
SIC: 3494 Valves & pipe fittings

GEOGRAPHIC

(G-19208)
A AND H LOGGING INC
333 Se 4th Ave (32696-2647)
P.O. Box 986 (32696-0986)
PHONE..................................352 528-3868
Art Nussel, *President*
EMP: 5 **EST:** 1988
SALES (est): 1MM **Privately Held**
SIC: 2411 0811 Logging camps & contractors; timber tracts

(G-19209)
AMERICAN COMPOSITES ENGRG
20751 Ne Highway 27 (32696-3109)
PHONE..................................352 528-5007
Ronny Walker, *Principal*
EMP: 12
SALES (corp-wide): 5.3MM **Privately Held**
WEB: www.qualityfrp.com
SIC: 3089 Plastic containers, except foam
HQ: American Composites Engineering Inc
1090 W Saint James St
Tarboro NC 27886

(G-19210)
BREEDEN PULPWOOD INC
Off Hwy 41 (32696)
P.O. Box 421 (32696-0421)
PHONE..................................352 528-5243
James E Breeden, *President*
Lisa Breeden, *Treasurer*
EMP: 13 **EST:** 1969
SALES (est): 1.1MM **Privately Held**
SIC: 2411 Pulpwood contractors engaged in cutting

(G-19211)
HARRISON LOGGING
17701 Nw 133rd Court Rd (32696-4417)
PHONE..................................352 591-2779
William C Harrison Jr, *President*
EMP: 14 **EST:** 1971
SALES (est): 586.3K **Privately Held**
WEB: www.harrisonloggingco.com
SIC: 2411 Logging camps & contractors

(G-19212)
HOWELL LOGGING & LAND CLEARING
20253 Ne 20th St (32696-7333)
PHONE..................................352 528-2698
Tarrel Howell, *Owner*
▼ **EMP:** 6 **EST:** 2002
SQ FT: 2,301
SALES (est): 510K **Privately Held**
WEB: www.alpinecarpetcleaning.us
SIC: 2411 Logging camps & contractors

(G-19213)
RJ STAAB STONE CO
824 N Main St (32696-1706)
PHONE..................................352 377-3313
Ronald J Staab, *Vice Pres*
EMP: 6 **EST:** 2012
SALES (est): 277.7K **Privately Held**
WEB: www.rjstaabstonecompany.com
SIC: 3272 Concrete products, precast

(G-19214)
RJ STAAB STONE COMPANY FLA LLC
824 N Main St (32696-1706)
PHONE..................................352 222-5989
James D Henderson, *Principal*
EMP: 5 **EST:** 2014
SALES (est): 304.6K **Privately Held**
WEB: www.rjstaabstonecompany.com
SIC: 3272 Concrete products

(G-19215)
SHADOW TRAILERS INC
951 Sw 21st Pl (32696-2453)
PHONE..................................352 529-2190
Larry R Pruitt, *CEO*
EMP: 45 **EST:** 2003
SALES (est): 9.7MM **Privately Held**
WEB: www.shadowtrailer.com
SIC: 3715 Trailers or vans for transporting horses

(G-19216)
WILLISTON TIMBER CO INC
4351 Ne 176th Ave (32696-4807)
PHONE..................................352 528-2699
Eddie Hodge, *President*
John Hodge, *Vice Pres*
Julie Hodge, *Treasurer*
Christine Hodge, *Admin Sec*
EMP: 26 **EST:** 1977
SQ FT: 6,000
SALES (est): 7.5MM **Privately Held**
SIC: 2421 Sawmills & planing mills, general

Wilton Manors
Broward County

(G-19217)
CUSTOM DOORS & SPECIALTIES
2637 N Andrews Ave (33311-2509)
PHONE..................................954 763-4214
John Ouelette, *Director*
EMP: 9 **EST:** 2001
SALES (est): 106.6K **Privately Held**
SIC: 2431 Doors & door parts & trim, wood

(G-19218)
GENESIS HEALTH INSTITUTE INC
1001 Ne 26th St (33305-1243)
PHONE..................................954 561-3175
Ferdinand Cabrera, *President*
EMP: 9 **EST:** 2007
SALES (est): 1.3MM **Privately Held**
WEB: www.ghinstitute.com
SIC: 2834 Dermatologicals

(G-19219)
POWERS INDUSTRIES LLC (PA)
2715 Ne 6th Ln (33334-2507)
PHONE..................................786 444-3616
Pamela Powers, *Principal*
▲ **EMP:** 14 **EST:** 2009
SALES (est): 99.8K **Privately Held**
SIC: 3999 Manufacturing industries

(G-19220)
SOUTHFLORIDAGAYNEWSCOM
2520 N Dixie Hwy (33305-1247)
PHONE..................................954 530-4970
Norm Kent, *Manager*
EMP: 13 **EST:** 2013
SALES (est): 328.6K **Privately Held**
WEB: www.southfloridagaynews.com
SIC: 2711 Newspapers, publishing & printing

(G-19221)
VENICE QUARTERS INC
Also Called: Hotspot Magazine of Florida
2435 N Dixie Hwy (33305-2239)
PHONE..................................954 318-3483
Cleto J Beuren, *President*
Brian Burda, *Business Mgr*
Peter J Clark, *Vice Pres*
EMP: 22 **EST:** 1998
SALES (est): 1.4MM **Privately Held**
SIC: 2721 8742 Magazines: publishing only, not printed on site; marketing consulting services

Wimauma
Hillsborough County

(G-19222)
RED DIAMOND SALSA LLC
18632 S Us Highway 301 (33598-7543)
PHONE..................................813 672-7707
German J Torres, *Principal*
EMP: 9 **EST:** 2009
SALES (est): 164.1K **Privately Held**
SIC: 2099 Dips, except cheese & sour cream based

(G-19223)
SEA FORCE IX INC
1403 Pinetree Cir (33598-7612)
PHONE..................................941 721-9009
Ronald Rookstool, *Owner*
Chris Mackenzie, *Purch Mgr*
Gail Rookstool, *Office Mgr*
Sydney Kline, *Consultant*
Ronald R Rookstool, *CIO*
EMP: 20 **EST:** 2004
SALES (est): 2.4MM **Privately Held**
WEB: www.seaforceboats.com
SIC: 3732 Yachts, building & repairing

(G-19224)
SKYWAY SIGNS AND WRAPS LLC
2911 Arrowsmith Rd (33598-7601)
PHONE..................................727 692-2786
Anthony S Cormier Jr, *Principal*
EMP: 7 **EST:** 2016
SALES (est): 134.6K **Privately Held**
WEB: www.skywaysignsandwraps.com
SIC: 3993 Signs & advertising specialties

Windermere
Orange County

(G-19225)
ALPHA OMEGA COMMERCIAL LIMITED (PA)
5820 Nature View Dr (34786-5130)
PHONE..................................407 925-7913
Sandro Motta, *President*
Sonia Motta, *Vice Pres*
◆ **EMP:** 1 **EST:** 2018
SQ FT: 750
SALES (est): 8MM **Privately Held**
WEB: www.omegaalpha.us
SIC: 2032 Ethnic foods: canned, jarred, etc.

(G-19226)
BIRDS EYE DRONES LLC
6174 Louise Cove Dr (34786-8935)
PHONE..................................321 355-3415
Vikash Mahadeo, *Principal*
EMP: 6 **EST:** 2016
SALES (est): 143.1K **Privately Held**
WEB: www.dronephotographyorlando.com
SIC: 3721 Motorized aircraft

(G-19227)
FUELMYSCHOOL
4344 Indian Deer Rd (34786-3181)
PHONE..................................407 952-1030
Krista Monteleone, *Principal*
EMP: 6 **EST:** 2011
SALES (est): 238.7K **Privately Held**
WEB: www.fuelmyschool.com
SIC: 2869 Fuels

(G-19228)
ICON EMBROIDERY INC
2833 Butler Bay Dr N (34786-6113)
PHONE..................................407 858-0886
Charles Wilson, *President*
EMP: 5 **EST:** 1991
SQ FT: 20,000
SALES (est): 694.4K **Privately Held**
WEB: www.iecshirt.com
SIC: 2339 2329 2396 2395 Sportswear, women's; men's & boys' sportswear & athletic clothing; automotive & apparel trimmings; pleating & stitching

(G-19229)
IPRO FORCE LLC
6929 Corley Ave (34786-9483)
PHONE..................................603 766-8716
Molly Schwartz, *Owner*
EMP: 6 **EST:** 2015
SALES (est): 97.9K **Privately Held**
WEB: www.neomarkets.com
SIC: 2911 Petroleum refining

(G-19230)
JAMUNA1 LLC
4654 River Gem Ave (34786-3180)
PHONE..................................407 313-5927
Manish Parikh, *President*
Amish Parikh, *Manager*
EMP: 6 **EST:** 2014
SALES (est): 286.9K **Privately Held**
SIC: 3589 Service industry machinery

(G-19231)
JETSPARES INTERNATIONAL INC
10650 Chase Rd Bldg 5 (34786-8972)
P.O. Box 889 (34786-0889)
PHONE..................................407 876-3978
Toby Silverton, *President*
Jonathan Jomes, *President*
▲ **EMP:** 8 **EST:** 1985
SQ FT: 6,000
SALES (est): 699.9K **Privately Held**
WEB: www.jetspares.com
SIC: 3728 Aircraft parts & equipment

(G-19232)
KABRIT REPAIR SERVICES LLC ✪
9118 Panzani Pl (34786-8136)
PHONE..................................407 714-1470
Tralonnie Tisdale,
EMP: 15 **EST:** 2021
SALES (est): 266.3K **Privately Held**
SIC: 1389 Construction, repair & dismantling services

(G-19233)
KEY LIME CUSTOMS LLC
1040 W 2nd Ave (34786-8517)
PHONE..................................407 353-9942
Steven Voorhees, *Manager*
EMP: 7 **EST:** 2011
SALES (est): 115.8K **Privately Held**
WEB: www.keylimemarine.com
SIC: 3274 Lime

(G-19234)
LA GENOMICS LLC
5939 Blakeford Dr (34786-5601)
PHONE..................................407 909-1120
Jose Clavier, *Principal*
EMP: 7 **EST:** 2016
SALES (est): 92.9K **Privately Held**
SIC: 2835 Microbiology & virology diagnostic products

(G-19235)
LIYANARCHI DESIGN LLC
13433 Sunkiss Loop (34786-3161)
PHONE..................................954 330-5034
Aston Liyanarchi, *Principal*
EMP: 6 **EST:** 2016
SALES (est): 105.1K **Privately Held**
SIC: 3711 Automobile assembly, including specialty automobiles

(G-19236)
LOGSDON AND ASSOCIATES INC
13049 Lake Roper Ct (34786-5822)
PHONE..................................407 292-0084
Curtis A Logsdon, *President*
Cynthia M Logsdon, *Vice Pres*
Ryan Logsdon, *Opers Staff*
EMP: 5 **EST:** 1990
SALES (est): 464.3K **Privately Held**
WEB: www.logsdonandassociates.com
SIC: 2394 5031 Canopies, fabric: made from purchased materials; skylights, all materials

(G-19237)
MATRIX MARKETING SOLUTIONS
13629 Lake Cawood Dr (34786-7002)
PHONE..................................407 654-5736
Sean Irvine, *Principal*
EMP: 9 **EST:** 2002
SALES (est): 242.4K **Privately Held**
WEB: www.matrixmarketinggroup.com
SIC: 2752 Commercial printing, lithographic

(G-19238)
MCCOLL DISPLAY SOLUTIONS
8416 Iron Mountain Trl (34786-9478)
PHONE..................................813 333-6613
Kimberly Bellis, *Principal*
EMP: 12 **EST:** 2014
SALES (est): 536.3K **Privately Held**
WEB: www.mccolldisplay.com
SIC: 3993 Signs & advertising specialties

▲ = Import ▼=Export
◆ =Import/Export

(G-19239)
MILLENIA FROYO LLC
9066 Harbor Isle Dr (34786-8350)
PHONE..................................407 694-9938
Ariff Khimani, *Principal*
EMP: 8 **EST:** 2010
SALES (est): 432.2K **Privately Held**
SIC: 2024 Yogurt desserts, frozen

(G-19240)
PROFESSIONAL SFTWR CONSORTIUM
5040 Down Point Ln (34786-8401)
PHONE..................................407 909-9168
Richard Gorstak, *President*
Jon Nash, *Manager*
Linda Gorstak, *Admin Sec*
EMP: 10 **EST:** 2002
SALES (est): 820K **Privately Held**
WEB: www.profsft.com
SIC: 7372 Prepackaged software

(G-19241)
PURE WATER CHANGES INC
7775 Maslin St (34786-6346)
PHONE..................................407 699-2837
Bobby G Pinson Jr, *President*
EMP: 10 **EST:** 2017
SALES (est): 1MM **Privately Held**
WEB: www.purewaterchanges.com
SIC: 3589 Water treatment equipment, industrial

(G-19242)
RUKE INC
1226 Main St (34786-8702)
PHONE..................................239 292-2553
Victoria Ruke, *Principal*
EMP: 6 **EST:** 2017
SALES (est): 115K **Privately Held**
SIC: 3714 Motor vehicle parts & accessories

(G-19243)
SERENDIPITY PUBLISHING
5432 Tildens Grove Blvd (34786-5709)
PHONE..................................407 905-5076
Algernon Callier, *Principal*
EMP: 6 **EST:** 2004
SALES (est): 128.7K **Privately Held**
SIC: 2741 Miscellaneous publishing

(G-19244)
STITCHYOURPHOTOCOM
7652 Billingham St (34786-6343)
PHONE..................................321 297-6103
David Bottisti, *Principal*
EMP: 9 **EST:** 2010
SALES (est): 48K **Privately Held**
WEB: www.stitchyourphoto.com
SIC: 2395 Embroidery & art needlework

(G-19245)
TAKEDA PHRMCEUTICALS N AMER IN
336 E 5th Ave (34786-3504)
PHONE..................................561 818-0925
George Dubois, *Principal*
Milton Sanchez, *Sales Staff*
EMP: 7 **EST:** 2016
SALES (est): 145.7K **Privately Held**
WEB: www.takeda.com
SIC: 2834 Pharmaceutical preparations

(G-19246)
TIMBERWOLF ORGANICS LTD LBLTY
13506 Summerport Vlg Pkwy (34786-7366)
PHONE..................................407 877-8779
Mark Heyward, *CEO*
Heather Winkler, *Marketing Staff*
EMP: 10 **EST:** 2007
SALES (est): 959.3K **Privately Held**
WEB: www.timberwolforganics.com
SIC: 3999 Pet supplies

(G-19247)
TREMONTI PROJECT PUBG LLC
6137 Cartmel Ln (34786-5420)
PHONE..................................407 217-7140
Mark Tremonti, *Branch Mgr*
EMP: 12
SALES (corp-wide): 100.3K **Privately Held**
SIC: 2741 Miscellaneous publishing
PA: The Tremonti Project Publishing Llc
6108 Kirkstone Ln
Windermere FL

(G-19248)
VINTNERS COLLECTIONS
13918 Caywood Pond Dr (34786-3109)
PHONE..................................407 654-9019
Marilyn Vogel, *Principal*
EMP: 6 **EST:** 2016
SALES (est): 114K **Privately Held**
SIC: 2084 Wines, brandy & brandy spirits

(G-19249)
VIPER 4X4
11924 Perspective Dr (34786-6511)
PHONE..................................305 468-9818
Nelson Suarez, *Principal*
Trautman Fred, *Director*
▼ **EMP:** 16 **EST:** 2010
SALES (est): 453.1K **Privately Held**
WEB: www.vpr4x4.com
SIC: 3799 All terrain vehicles (ATV)

(G-19250)
WATERBRICK INTERNATIONAL INC
13506 Smmrport Vlg Pkwy S (34786-7366)
P.O. Box 770969, Winter Garden (34777-0969)
PHONE..................................877 420-9283
Kevin Adams, *President*
▼ **EMP:** 5 **EST:** 2008
SALES (est): 510.6K **Privately Held**
WEB: www.waterbrick.org
SIC: 3089 5091 8322 5085 Plastic & fiberglass tanks; boats, canoes, watercrafts & equipment; temporary relief service; packing, industrial

(G-19251)
WINDERMERE NANNIES LLC ✪
6526 Old Brick Rd Ste 120 (34786-5839)
PHONE..................................407 782-2057
Katelyn Arias, *CEO*
EMP: 12 **EST:** 2020
SALES (est): 120K **Privately Held**
SIC: 7372 7361 Application computer software; employment agencies

Winter Garden
Orange County

(G-19252)
ARCANA TILEWORKS
1226 Wntr Gdn Vnlnd Rd (34787-4451)
PHONE..................................407 492-0668
Nancy T Krug, *Owner*
EMP: 5 **EST:** 2006
SALES (est): 419.3K **Privately Held**
WEB: www.arcanatileworks.com
SIC: 3253 Floor tile, ceramic

(G-19253)
BALSYS TECHNOLOGY GROUP INC
930 Carter Rd Ste 228 (34787-4105)
PHONE..................................407 656-3719
Larry Lamoray, *President*
EMP: 5 **EST:** 2000
SQ FT: 6,000
SALES (est): 647.8K **Privately Held**
SIC: 3663 Television broadcasting & communications equipment

(G-19254)
CANDELA CONTROLS INC
751 Business Park Blvd # 101 (34787-5704)
PHONE..................................407 654-2420
Bill Ellis, *President*
Dale Ward, *General Mgr*
Carol Cimino, *Project Mgr*
Mark Colvin, *Project Mgr*
Kacey Conn, *Project Mgr*
EMP: 38 **EST:** 1999
SQ FT: 10,000
SALES (est): 7.3MM **Privately Held**
WEB: www.candelacontrols.com
SIC: 3646 3648 Commercial indusl & institutional electric lighting fixtures; lighting equipment

(G-19255)
CEMEX CEMENT INC
201 Hennis Rd (34787-2410)
PHONE..................................407 877-9623
Frank Craddock, *Vice Pres*
EMP: 214 **Privately Held**
WEB: www.cemexusa.com
SIC: 3273 Ready-mixed concrete
HQ: Cemex Cement, Inc.
10100 Katy Fwy Ste 300
Houston TX 77043
713 650-6200

(G-19256)
CERTIFIED WHL EXTERIOR PDTS
902 Carter Rd Ste 300 (34787-4144)
PHONE..................................407 654-7170
Karen E Smith, *President*
Michael P Smith, *Vice Pres*
EMP: 5 **EST:** 2001
SQ FT: 4,400
SALES (est): 488.1K **Privately Held**
WEB: www.cwproductsinc.com
SIC: 2821 5072 Vinyl resins; builders' hardware

(G-19257)
CHOCTAW TRADING CO INC
Also Called: Choctaw Willy
99 W Plant St (34787-3139)
PHONE..................................407 905-9917
Ken Kelly, *President*
Wayne Bird, *President*
EMP: 7 **EST:** 1989
SALES (est): 237.9K **Privately Held**
SIC: 2033 5812 Barbecue sauce: packaged in cans, jars, etc.; eating places

(G-19258)
CONCEPT SOFTWARE INC
Also Called: Softwarekey.com
1319 Green Frest Ct Ste 4 (34787)
P.O. Box 770459 (34777-0459)
PHONE..................................321 250-6670
Michael Wozniak, *President*
EMP: 6 **EST:** 1991
SALES (est): 350K **Privately Held**
WEB: www.softwarekey.com
SIC: 7372 8748 Prepackaged software; systems analysis & engineering consulting services

(G-19259)
DACKOR INC
Also Called: Dackor 3d Laminates
310 E Crown Point Rd (34787-2998)
PHONE..................................407 654-5013
Mark V Viers, *President*
Yumi Viers, *Treasurer*
Reina Zelaya, *Natl Sales Mgr*
Jennifer Atkins, *Manager*
Scott Edwards, *Representative*
▲ **EMP:** 12 **EST:** 2003
SALES (est): 2.4MM **Privately Held**
WEB: www.dackor.com
SIC: 2435 Hardwood veneer & plywood

(G-19260)
DECOSTA WOODWORKING LLC
763 Home Grove Dr (34787-6502)
PHONE..................................508 802-7765
Bryan M Decosta, *Principal*
EMP: 6 **EST:** 2010
SALES (est): 104.6K **Privately Held**
SIC: 2431 Millwork

(G-19261)
EASY PAVERS CORP
334 Windford Ct (34787-6061)
PHONE..................................407 967-0511
Aldemir Arpini, *Principal*
EMP: 7 **EST:** 2013
SALES (est): 119.4K **Privately Held**
SIC: 2951 Asphalt paving mixtures & blocks

(G-19262)
EDASHOP INC
Also Called: Anacom Electronica
15388 Arcadia Bluff Loop (34787-8158)
PHONE..................................786 565-9197
Carlos Eugenio Lion, *President*
Gus Salinas, *General Mgr*
EMP: 9 **EST:** 1995
SALES (est): 1.1MM **Privately Held**
WEB: www.edashop.com
SIC: 7372 5063 Prepackaged software; electrical apparatus & equipment

(G-19263)
EXPRESS SIGNS & GRAPHICS INC
547 Garden Heights Dr (34787-2218)
PHONE..................................407 889-4433
Phillip Zabukovec, *President*
David Zabukovec, *Treasurer*
Tabitha Zabukovec, *Admin Sec*
EMP: 15 **EST:** 1993
SQ FT: 4,500
SALES (est): 787.2K **Privately Held**
SIC: 3993 5199 2752 Electric signs; advertising specialties; commercial printing, lithographic

(G-19264)
FLORIDA METAL-CRAFT INC
47 S Dillard St (34787-3116)
P.O. Box 771179 (34777-1179)
PHONE..................................407 656-1100
Thomas Burnett, *President*
Robert Burnett, *Vice Pres*
EMP: 13 **EST:** 1931
SQ FT: 10,000
SALES (est): 1.2MM **Privately Held**
WEB: www.floridametalcraft.com
SIC: 3444 3599 Sheet metalwork; machine shop, jobbing & repair

(G-19265)
GALLANT INC
1267 Wntr Gdn Vnlnd Rd # 230 (34787-6701)
PHONE..................................800 330-1343
▲ **EMP:** 8
SQ FT: 1,800
SALES (est): 1.4MM **Privately Held**
SIC: 3069 7389 8742 5094 Mfg Fabrcatd Rubber Prdt Business Services Mgmt Consulting Svcs Whol Jewelry/Precs Stone Mfg Men/Boy Work Clothng

(G-19266)
HANCOR INC
115 N West Crown Point Rd (34787-2948)
PHONE..................................863 655-5499
Ron Buckley, *Principal*
EMP: 33
SALES (corp-wide): 1.9B **Publicly Held**
WEB: www.adspipe.com
SIC: 2821 3084 Polyurethane resins; plastics pipe
HQ: Hancor, Inc.
4640 Trueman Blvd
Hilliard OH 43026
614 658-0050

(G-19267)
HEALTHLINE MEDICAL PDTS INC
1065 E Story Rd (34787-3732)
PHONE..................................407 656-0704
Jim Magnuson, *President*
▲ **EMP:** 20 **EST:** 1994
SQ FT: 100,000
SALES (est): 1.3MM **Privately Held**
WEB: www.healthlinemedical.com
SIC: 3842 5047 Surgical appliances & supplies; medical equipment & supplies

(G-19268)
HILL PRINTING INC
1220 Wntr Gdn Vnlnd Rd # 104 (34787-6373)
PHONE..................................407 654-4282
Kenneth L Hill, *President*
EMP: 9 **EST:** 1996
SQ FT: 2,000
SALES (est): 1MM **Privately Held**
WEB: www.hillprinting.com
SIC: 2752 Post cards, picture: lithographed

(G-19269)
HOLLYWOOD HOUNDZ LLC
4101 Briar Gate Ln (34787-5521)
PHONE..................................407 614-2108
Alexandre Lima, *Principal*
EMP: 8 **EST:** 2016
SALES (est): 365.5K **Privately Held**
SIC: 2499 Wood products

(G-19270)
INGELUB CORP
12935 W Colonial Dr (34787-4101)
PHONE..................................407 656-8800
Helmer Alarcon, *Principal*
EMP: 15
SALES (corp-wide): 507.2K **Privately Held**
SIC: 3569 Filters
PA: Ingelub Corp
7519 Tattant Blvd
Windermere FL

(G-19271)
IRON SHARPENS IR TRAINING LLC
2038 Black Lake Blvd (34787-4658)
PHONE..................................407 614-4500
Philip Burton, *Administration*
EMP: 6 **EST:** 2019
SALES (est): 119.8K **Privately Held**
WEB: www.ironsharpensirontraining.com
SIC: 3312 Blast furnaces & steel mills

(G-19272)
KONADOCKS LLC
230 Deer Island Rd (34787-9457)
P.O. Box 784267 (34778-4267)
PHONE..................................407 909-0606
Brian Hall,
EMP: 6 **EST:** 2017
SALES (est): 527.1K **Privately Held**
WEB: www.konadocks.com
SIC: 2499 Applicators, wood

(G-19273)
LEK TECHNOLOGY CONSULTANTS
12788 Gillard Rd (34787-5224)
P.O. Box 783635 (34778-3635)
PHONE..................................407 877-6505
Wade Lowe, *President*
Firpo Guerrero, *Engineer*
EMP: 5 **EST:** 2002
SALES (est): 1.1MM **Privately Held**
WEB: www.lekcomp.com
SIC: 3571 Computers, digital, analog or hybrid

(G-19274)
LIFECO FOODS NORTH AMERICA
855 E Plant St Ste 1700 (34787-3167)
PHONE..................................321 348-5896
Nabil Belizario, *CEO*
EMP: 6 **EST:** 2018
SALES (est): 528.3K **Privately Held**
SIC: 2099 Food preparations
PA: Life Company Industria Alimenticia Eireli
Av. Sao Francisco De Assis 1490
Hortolandia SP 13183

(G-19275)
LOTTS CONCRETE PRODUCTS INC
429 Hennis Rd (34787-2407)
P.O. Box 771255 (34777-1255)
PHONE..................................407 656-2112
Johnnie P Lott Jr, *President*
Willer D Lott, *Corp Secy*
Belinda Fleming, *Vice Pres*
Chelsea Sengel, *Bookkeeper*
April Dunigan, *Human Resources*
▼ **EMP:** 50 **EST:** 1963
SQ FT: 15,000
SALES (est): 14.9MM **Privately Held**
WEB: www.lottsconcrete.com
SIC: 3272 Concrete products

(G-19276)
MAYN FOCUS LLC
2057 Harbor Cove Way (34787-5478)
PHONE..................................603 801-8406
John A Maynard, *Manager*
EMP: 6 **EST:** 2016
SALES (est): 162.7K **Privately Held**
SIC: 3826 8748 Analytical instruments; business consulting; systems analysis & engineering consulting services

(G-19277)
MOTOR COACH INDS INTL INC
1155 Elboc Way (34787-4487)
PHONE..................................407 246-1414
EMP: 19
SALES (corp-wide): 2.3B **Privately Held**
SIC: 3714 Mfg Motor Vehicle Parts & Accessories
HQ: Motor Coach Industries International, Inc.
200 E Oakton St
Des Plaines IL 60018
847 285-2000

(G-19278)
OBSERVER GROUP
446 N Dillard St (34787-2861)
PHONE..................................407 654-5500
EMP: 8 **EST:** 2013
SALES (est): 174.9K **Privately Held**
SIC: 2711 Newspapers, publishing & printing

(G-19279)
PAUL TINSLEY ENGRAVING
236 Virginia Dr (34787-2837)
PHONE..................................407 656-4344
Paul Tinsley, *Owner*
EMP: 6 **EST:** 2002
SALES (est): 97.1K **Privately Held**
SIC: 2499 Trophy bases, wood

(G-19280)
PRINT ADMINISTRATE
1273 Winter Gdn (34787-6702)
PHONE..................................407 877-5923
Buddy Carpenito, *Partner*
EMP: 8 **EST:** 2017
SALES (est): 70.5K **Privately Held**
WEB: www.printadministrate.com
SIC: 2752 Commercial printing, lithographic

(G-19281)
PRODALIM USA INC
355 9th St (34787-3651)
PHONE..................................407 656-1000
Tsahi I Berezovsky, *President*
Ran Harpaz, *Counsel*
Eusebio Navarro, *Prdtn Mgr*
Makwan Ahmad, *Production*
Heraldo Haynes, *Production*
EMP: 1 **EST:** 2017
SALES (est): 3.4MM
SALES (corp-wide): 63.6MM **Privately Held**
WEB: www.prodalim.com
SIC: 2086 Carbonated beverages, nonalcoholic: bottled & canned
PA: Prodalim B.V.
Vierhavensstraat 30
Rotterdam 3029

(G-19282)
QUALITY PRECAST & COMPANY
Also Called: R and R Rebar
416 E Bay St (34787-3112)
P.O. Box 625, Fruitland Park (34731-0625)
PHONE..................................407 877-1000
Mike Phelps, *President*
John Waldron, *Sales Staff*
EMP: 17 **EST:** 1969
SALES (est): 178.1K **Privately Held**
WEB: www.qualityprecast.com
SIC: 3272 Concrete products, precast

(G-19283)
RIEGL USA INC
14707 W Colonial Dr (34787-4220)
PHONE..................................407 248-9927
James Van Rens, *President*
Kelly Martin, *Finance*
Miranda Welky, *Mktg Coord*
Jillian Kreider, *Marketing Staff*
Christopher Percell, *Manager*
EMP: 21 **EST:** 1993
SQ FT: 8,000
SALES (est): 7.9MM **Privately Held**
WEB: www.rieglusa.com
SIC: 3812 3823 3599 3829 Search & navigation equipment; controllers for process variables, all types; custom machinery; measuring & controlling devices

(G-19284)
RTC SOFTWARE LLC
14602 Black Cherry Trl (34787-6271)
PHONE..................................407 765-7462
Ronald Caylor, *Prgrmr*
EMP: 6 **EST:** 2012
SALES (est): 72.5K **Privately Held**
WEB: www.rtcsoftware.azurewebsites.net
SIC: 7372 7371 Prepackaged software; computer software development & applications

(G-19285)
SLR RIFLEWORKS LLC
1232 Wntr Gdn Vnlnd Rd (34787-4453)
PHONE..................................855 757-7435
EMP: 7 **EST:** 2018
SALES (est): 892.6K **Privately Held**
WEB: www.slrrifleworks.com
SIC: 3489 Ordnance & accessories

(G-19286)
SUNCITI INDUSTRIES INC
3402 Rex Dr (34787-9799)
PHONE..................................407 877-8081
Philip Bruno, *Director*
EMP: 9 **EST:** 2001
SALES (est): 47.6K **Privately Held**
WEB: www.fathervapor.com
SIC: 3999 Manufacturing industries

(G-19287)
VENOM ALLSTARS LLC
1205 Crown Park Cir (34787-2417)
PHONE..................................407 575-3484
Nguyen Khang, *Principal*
EMP: 7 **EST:** 2015
SALES (est): 81.8K **Privately Held**
WEB: www.venomallstars.com
SIC: 2836 Venoms

(G-19288)
VICX LLC
Also Called: Majic Nails
1273 Wntr Gdn Vnlnd Rd (34787-6702)
PHONE..................................407 674-2073
Rodrigo Cabral, *Principal*
EMP: 13 **EST:** 2010
SALES (est): 926.5K **Privately Held**
WEB: www.magicnails.com.br
SIC: 3999 Fingernails, artificial
PA: Magic Nails Comercio De Cosmeticos Importacao E Exportacao Ltda
Av. Salvador Allende 6700
Rio De Janeiro RJ 22790

(G-19289)
WASTE MANAGEMENT INC FLORIDA
5400 Rex Dr (34787-9164)
PHONE..................................954 984-2000
David Myhan, *President*
EMP: 25
SALES (est): 7MM
SALES (corp-wide): 15.2B **Publicly Held**
WEB: www.wm.com
SIC: 1499 1422 4953 Gemstone & industrial diamond mining; crushed & broken limestone; sanitary landfill operation
PA: Waste Management, Inc.
800 Capitol St Ste 3000
Houston TX 77002
713 512-6200

(G-19290)
WINDERMERE CABINETRY LLC
13675 Sunset Lakes Cir (34787-5448)
PHONE..................................321 263-5181
Greg Meece, *Principal*
EMP: 6 **EST:** 2009
SALES (est): 185.2K **Privately Held**
SIC: 2434 Wood kitchen cabinets

(G-19291)
WINTER GARDEN TIMES INC
Also Called: West Orange Times
661 Garden Commerce Pkwy (34787-5714)
P.O. Box 770309 (34777-0309)
PHONE..................................407 656-2121
Dawn Willis, *President*
Troy Herring, *Editor*
Hannah Swayze, *Editor*
Allison Brunelle, *Opers Staff*
Ann Carpenter, *Executive*
EMP: 22 **EST:** 1913
SALES (est): 1MM **Privately Held**
WEB: www.orangeobserver.com
SIC: 2711 Newspapers, publishing & printing

Winter Haven
Polk County

(G-19292)
90-MINUTE BOOKS LLC
302 Martinique Dr (33884-1707)
PHONE..................................863 318-0464
Stuart Bell,
EMP: 6 **EST:** 2015
SALES (est): 300K **Privately Held**
WEB: www.90minutebooks.com
SIC: 2731 Books: publishing only

(G-19293)
A L MATERIALS
1380 42nd St Nw (33881-1944)
PHONE..................................863 551-0980
Danny McKerahan, *President*
EMP: 6 **EST:** 2017
SALES (est): 101.2K **Privately Held**
WEB: www.a-lmaterials.com
SIC: 3273 Ready-mixed concrete

(G-19294)
ACME DYNAMICS INC (PA)
545 Avenue K Se (33880-4215)
PHONE..................................813 752-3137
Joseph A Murphy, *President*
Christopher Irwin, *Exec VP*
◆ **EMP:** 10
SQ FT: 19,197
SALES (est): 1.7MM **Privately Held**
WEB: www.acmedynamics.com
SIC: 3561 Pumps, oil well & field

(G-19295)
ADVANTAGE PLASTICS NY INC
654 Post Ave Sw (33880-4353)
P.O. Box 2590 (33883-2590)
PHONE..................................863 291-4407
John Salva, *President*
EMP: 13 **EST:** 1995
SQ FT: 5,000
SALES (est): 2.3MM **Privately Held**
WEB: www.advplasticsny.com
SIC: 3089 Injection molding of plastics; plastic processing

(G-19296)
AJS FABRICATION LLC
5754 State Road 542 W # 2 (33880-5151)
PHONE..................................863 514-9630
Anthony Jay Detrick, *Owner*
EMP: 6 **EST:** 2017
SALES (est): 268.2K **Privately Held**
WEB: www.ajsfabrication.com
SIC: 7692 Welding repair

(G-19297)
ALFREDO WELDING SERVICE LLC
5599 Commercial Blvd (33880-1009)
PHONE..................................954 770-8744
EMP: 5 **EST:** 2019
SALES (est): 480.2K **Privately Held**
SIC: 7692 Welding repair

(G-19298)
ALUMINUM TANK INDUSTRIES INC
36 Spirit Lake Rd (33880-1245)
PHONE..................................863 401-9474
Daniel Lamonica, *President*
EMP: 7 **EST:** 2004

▲ = Import ▼=Export
◆ =Import/Export

SALES (est): 950K Privately Held
WEB: www.atitank.com
SIC: 3443 Fabricated plate work (boiler shop)

(G-19299)
AMERICAN VULKAN CORPORATION (DH)
Also Called: Shrieve Chemical Co Chemi
2525 Dundee Rd (33884-1169)
P.O. Box 673 (33882-0673)
PHONE....863 324-2424
Thomas Falz, *President*
Wayne Dowers, *Vice Pres*
Thomas Lehner, *Vice Pres*
Eric Mower, *Vice Pres*
Rudy Horak, *Opers Staff*
◆ EMP: 37 EST: 1971
SQ FT: 40,000
SALES (est): 24.6MM
SALES (corp-wide): 1.9MM Privately Held
WEB: www.vulkan.com
SIC: 3568 Shafts, flexible; couplings, shaft: rigid, flexible, universal joint, etc.
HQ: Vulkan Kupplungs- Und Getriebebau Bernhard Hackforth Gmbh & Co. Kg
Heerstr. 66
Herne 44653
232 592-20

(G-19300)
ARDS AWNING & UPHOLSTERY INC
503 5th St Sw (33880-3306)
PHONE....863 293-2442
David Ard, *President*
Randall Ard, *Vice Pres*
EMP: 27 EST: 1961
SQ FT: 49,000
SALES (est): 1.3MM Privately Held
WEB: www.ardsawnings.com
SIC: 2394 7641 2211 Awnings, fabric: made from purchased materials; furniture upholstery repair; draperies & drapery fabrics, cotton

(G-19301)
B&M RC RACING
4336 Shadow Wood Way (33880-1531)
PHONE....313 518-3999
Michael L King, *Owner*
EMP: 8 EST: 2019
SALES (est): 225K Privately Held
WEB: www.bandmrcracing.com
SIC: 3542 Gear rolling machines

(G-19302)
BAXTER CUSTOM FABRICATION INC
133 Browning Cir (33884-2334)
PHONE....863 289-9819
Baxter Kevin, *Principal*
EMP: 9 EST: 2014
SALES (est): 264.2K Privately Held
SIC: 3499 Novelties & giftware, including trophies

(G-19303)
BLACK OAK INDUSTRIES INC
9518 Waterford Oaks Blvd (33884-3297)
PHONE....863 307-1566
Lisa A Bates, *Principal*
EMP: 6 EST: 2017
SALES (est): 299.7K Privately Held
SIC: 3999 Manufacturing industries

(G-19304)
BOLAND PRODUCTION SUPPLY INC
507 Burns Ln (33884-1148)
PHONE....863 324-7784
John M Boland, *President*
David S Hays, *General Mgr*
John S Boland, *Vice Pres*
Ardis L Boland, *Admin Sec*
Ardis Boland, *Admin Sec*
EMP: 7 EST: 1993
SQ FT: 3,000
SALES (est): 446.1K Privately Held
WEB: www.bolandfx-com.3dcartstores.com
SIC: 2892 2899 7819 5099 Secondary high explosives; flares, fireworks & similar preparations; equipment & prop rental, motion picture production; firearms & ammunition, except sporting; paper shells: empty, blank or loaded: 30 mm. & below

(G-19305)
BORDEN DAIRY COMPANY FLA LLC
1000 6th St Sw (33880-3334)
PHONE....863 298-9742
Jeff Monroe, *Division Mgr*
George Milam, *Manager*
EMP: 64
SALES (corp-wide): 513.8MM Privately Held
SIC: 2026 5143 5142 2037 Fermented & cultured milk products; dairy products, except dried or canned; packaged frozen goods; frozen fruits & vegetables
HQ: Borden Dairy Company Of Florida, Llc
308 Avenue G Sw
Winter Haven FL 33880

(G-19306)
BROWN INTERNATIONAL CORP LLC
333 Avenue M Nw (33881-2405)
P.O. Box 713 (33882-0713)
PHONE....863 299-2111
J P Devito, *Vice Pres*
Victor Onchi, *Vice Pres*
Clarissa Albarran, *Engineer*
Thomas Landgraf, *Engineer*
Jordan Wrigley, *Engineer*
▲ EMP: 5 EST: 2005
SALES (est): 4.6MM
SALES (corp-wide): 82.6MM Privately Held
WEB: www.brown-intl.com
SIC: 2033 Fruit juices: fresh
HQ: Atlas Pacific Engineering Company
1 Atlas Ave
Pueblo CO 81001
719 948-3040

(G-19307)
BRUNS MFG HOMES
10 Spirit Lake Rd (33880-1245)
PHONE....863 294-4949
Jim Burn, *Owner*
EMP: 6 EST: 2006
SALES (est): 118.4K Privately Held
SIC: 3999 Manufacturing industries

(G-19308)
BURR PRINTING CO INC
Also Called: Larry Burr Printing Co
4212 Hammond Dr (33881-9701)
P.O. Box 980 (33882-0980)
PHONE....863 294-3166
George Burr IV, *President*
EMP: 5 EST: 1930
SQ FT: 2,600
SALES (est): 719.3K Privately Held
SIC: 2752 3953 2791 Lithographing on metal; commercial printing, offset; marking devices; typesetting

(G-19309)
C & S PLASTICS
1550 5th St Sw (33880-3729)
PHONE....863 294-5628
Chris Cooper, *President*
Jeremy Ledford, *Prdtn Mgr*
Eric Yarbrough, *Maintence Staff*
EMP: 27 EST: 1987
SQ FT: 5,600
SALES (est): 3.7MM Privately Held
WEB: www.candsplastics.com
SIC: 3084 3429 3089 Plastics pipe; furniture hardware; extruded finished plastic products

(G-19310)
C C CALHOUN INC
3750 W Lake Hamilton Dr (33881-9261)
P.O. Box 1877, Dundee (33838-1877)
PHONE....863 292-9511
Charles M Carnes, *President*
Lawrence Cahoon, *Corp Secy*
Gary Carnes, *Vice Pres*
EMP: 25 EST: 1996
SALES (est): 8MM Privately Held
WEB: www.cccalhoun.com
SIC: 1442 1459 Sand mining; clays, except kaolin & ball

(G-19311)
CARIBBEAN DISTILLERS LLC
2200 3rd St Nw (33881-1402)
P.O. Box 1447, Lake Alfred (33850-1447)
PHONE....863 508-1175
Alberto Rivera, *Senior VP*
◆ EMP: 16 EST: 2011
SALES (est): 950K Privately Held
SIC: 2085 Distilled & blended liquors

(G-19312)
CENTRAL FLA BUS SOLUTIONS INC
Also Called: Propak Software
150 3rd St Sw (33880-2979)
P.O. Box 1056 (33882-1056)
PHONE....863 297-9293
John R Sauer, *President*
Richard H Montney Jr, *Vice Pres*
EMP: 9 EST: 1992
SQ FT: 4,000
SALES (est): 1MM Privately Held
SIC: 7372 Business oriented computer software

(G-19313)
CERTAINTEED CORPORATION (DH)
Also Called: Certainteed Machine Works
101 Hatfield Rd (33880-1325)
PHONE....863 294-3206
Blair Gaida, *General Mgr*
EMP: 14 EST: 1936
SQ FT: 60,000
SALES (est): 6MM
SALES (corp-wide): 332.4MM Privately Held
WEB: www.certainteed.com
SIC: 3564 Blowing fans: industrial or commercial
HQ: Certainteed Llc
20 Moores Rd
Malvern PA 19355
610 893-5000

(G-19314)
CHILTON SIGNS & DESIGNS LLC
549 Pope Ave Nw (33881-4678)
PHONE....863 438-0880
Christopher Chilton, *Administration*
EMP: 7 EST: 2019
SALES (est): 1.7MM Privately Held
WEB: www.chiltonsigns.com
SIC: 3993 Signs & advertising specialties

(G-19315)
CITY OF WINTER HAVEN
125 N Lake Silver Dr Nw (33881-2450)
PHONE....863 291-5858
Janet Hollaway, *Principal*
EMP: 25 EST: 2013
SALES (est): 361.9K Privately Held
WEB: www.mywinterhaven.com
SIC: 2741

(G-19316)
CUSTOM FLANGE PIPE LLC
3700 W Lake Hamilton Dr (33881-9261)
PHONE....863 353-6602
Tom Klingensmith,
EMP: 10 EST: 2017
SALES (est): 1.3MM Privately Held
SIC: 3321 Cast iron pipe & fittings

(G-19317)
DC APPAREL INC
3260 Dundee Rd (33884-1102)
PHONE....863 325-9273
Francis D McCrystal, *President*
Chris Broyles, *Vice Pres*
EMP: 5 EST: 2007
SALES (est): 659.8K Privately Held
WEB: www.dcapparelinc.com
SIC: 2759 Screen printing

(G-19318)
DUMONT WELDER SERVICES INC
143 Argentina Dr (33880-1662)
PHONE....863 969-7498
Angel M Dumont, *Vice Pres*
EMP: 6 EST: 2015
SALES (est): 44.4K Privately Held
SIC: 7692 Welding repair

(G-19319)
EXPRESS PRTG WINTER HAVEN INC
757 Cypress Gardens Blvd (33880-4712)
PHONE....863 294-3286
Mark Alford, *Principal*
EMP: 6 EST: 2006
SALES (est): 83.9K Privately Held
SIC: 2752 Commercial printing, lithographic

(G-19320)
FLORIDA AIRBOAT PROPELLER
404 Burns Ln (33884-1147)
PHONE....863 324-1653
Tim Wagman, *President*
Billy Wagman, *Vice Pres*
Roberta Wagman, *Treasurer*
Louise Wagman, *Admin Sec*
EMP: 7
SQ FT: 4,500
SALES (est): 858.2K Privately Held
WEB: www.floridaairboatpropellers.com
SIC: 3366 Copper foundries

(G-19321)
FLORIDA CENTRAL EXTRUSION INC
3700 Dundee Rd Unit 9 (33884-1190)
P.O. Box 1852, Dundee (33838-1852)
PHONE....863 324-2541
Pat Sabin, *Owner*
John P Sabin, *Owner*
EMP: 6 EST: 1985
SQ FT: 6,800
SALES (est): 511K Privately Held
SIC: 3089 Injection molding of plastics

(G-19322)
FOOD PARTNERS INC
340 W Central Ave Ste 200 (33880-2967)
P.O. Box 1478 (33882-1478)
PHONE....863 298-8771
Webb Tanner, *President*
Shelly Prickett, *Finance*
Angie Peebles, *Sales Mgr*
Rhonda Freeman, *Accounts Mgr*
Jose Velazquez, *Accounts Mgr*
◆ EMP: 10
SQ FT: 2,000
SALES (est): 50MM Privately Held
WEB: www.foodpartners.com
SIC: 2037 Fruit juices, frozen

(G-19323)
FORTERRA PIPE & PRECAST LLC
1285 Lucerne Loop Rd Ne (33881-9607)
PHONE....863 401-6800
Antonio Kalinish, *Branch Mgr*
EMP: 37
SALES (corp-wide): 1.5B Publicly Held
WEB: www.forterrabp.com
SIC: 3272 Concrete products, precast
HQ: Forterra Pipe & Precast, Llc
511 E John Carpenter Fwy
Irving TX 75062
469 458-7973

(G-19324)
FOUR PURLS
1226 7th St Nw (33881-2303)
PHONE....863 293-6261
Laura Lee Dobratz, *Principal*
EMP: 5 EST: 2010
SALES (est): 406.9K Privately Held
WEB: www.fourpurls.com
SIC: 2281 Crochet yarn, spun

(G-19325)
GATEHOUSE MEDIA LLC
Also Called: News Chief
455 6th St Nw (33881-4061)
P.O. Box 1440 (33882-1440)
PHONE....863 401-6900

Robin Quillon, *Principal*
EMP: 14
SQ FT: 24,000
SALES (corp-wide): 3.4B **Publicly Held**
WEB: www.gannett.com
SIC: 2721 2741 2711 Periodicals; miscellaneous publishing; newspapers
HQ: Gatehouse Media, Llc
175 Sullys Trl Fl 3
Pittsford NY 14534
585 598-0030

(G-19326)
GLOBAL GL LC
Also Called: Greased Lightning
343 Hamilton Shores Dr Ne (33881-5711)
PHONE..................................863 551-1079
EMP: 5
SQ FT: 6,000
SALES (est): 907.5K **Privately Held**
SIC: 2911 2843 Petroleum Refiner Mfg Surface Active Agents

(G-19327)
HAVEN COFFEE ROASTERS LLC ✪
140 3rd St Sw (33880-2907)
PHONE..................................863 251-9619
Jonathan Lane, *Mng Member*
EMP: 6 **EST:** 2020
SALES (est): 279.4K **Privately Held**
SIC: 2095 Coffee roasting (except by wholesale grocers)

(G-19328)
HI TECH CONSTRUCTION SVC INC
5540 Commercial Blvd (33880-1008)
P.O. Box 878 (33882-0878)
PHONE..................................863 968-0731
Carl Allen Bryan, *President*
Sara Bryan, *Vice Pres*
EMP: 21 **EST:** 1996
SQ FT: 6,000
SALES (est): 1.5MM **Privately Held**
SIC: 2452 Modular homes, prefabricated, wood

(G-19329)
HIGH PERFORMANCE SYSTEMS INC
1201 Amercn Superior Blvd (33880-5553)
PHONE..................................863 294-5566
Richard Muto, *President*
Tony Piedra, *Vice Pres*
John Taylor, *Vice Pres*
Jackie Trautwein, *Purchasing*
◆ **EMP:** 23 **EST:** 1991
SQ FT: 120,000
SALES (est): 612.3K **Privately Held**
WEB: www.hpscoatings.com
SIC: 3479 Coating of metals & formed products

(G-19330)
INTEGRITY PROSTHETICS
135 1st St S (33880-3005)
PHONE..................................863 875-7063
EMP: 6 **EST:** 2017
SALES (est): 138.6K **Privately Held**
WEB: www.integritypando.com
SIC: 3842 Prosthetic appliances

(G-19331)
JC PUBLISHERS LLC
4844 Osprey Way (33881-9106)
PHONE..................................863 875-6071
Judy L Bowman, *Principal*
Ted Bowman, *Consultant*
EMP: 6 **EST:** 2010
SALES (est): 92.9K **Privately Held**
WEB: www.jcpublishers.net
SIC: 2741 Miscellaneous publishing

(G-19332)
KOMMERCIAL REFRIGERATION INC
810 Hillside Ct N (33881-9773)
PHONE..................................863 299-3000
John Waldman, *President*
Cheryl Waldman, *Admin Sec*
EMP: 5 **EST:** 1987
SQ FT: 400
SALES (est): 660K **Privately Held**
SIC: 3585 1711 Air conditioning equipment, complete; refrigeration contractor

(G-19333)
KOS INDUSTRIES INC
3056 Cypress Gardens Rd (33884-2257)
PHONE..................................863 318-1511
Daniel Kosinski, *President*
EMP: 6 **EST:** 2005
SALES (est): 131.4K **Privately Held**
SIC: 3999 5045 5734 3571 Barber & beauty shop equipment; computers, peripherals & software; computers & accessories, personal & home entertainment; modems, monitors, terminals & disk drives: computers; electronic computers; personal computers (microcomputers)

(G-19334)
KR WARD INC
Also Called: A Ward Design
1000 Hoover Rd (33884-2801)
PHONE..................................863 325-9070
Kevin R Ward, *President*
EMP: 7 **EST:** 2003
SQ FT: 1,000
SALES (est): 665.5K **Privately Held**
SIC: 2434 Wood kitchen cabinets

(G-19335)
LAPORTE INV HOLDINGS INC
Also Called: Sign Effex
512 6th St Nw (33881-4009)
PHONE..................................863 294-4498
Wayne M Laporte, *President*
Kimberly K Laporte, *Vice Pres*
Wayne Laporte, *Officer*
EMP: 9 **EST:** 2013
SQ FT: 1,000
SALES (est): 827.3K **Privately Held**
SIC: 3993 6719 Signs & advertising specialties; investment holding companies, except banks

(G-19336)
MECHANICAL DYNAMICS INC
1116 5th St Sw (33880-3725)
PHONE..................................863 292-0709
Jeff Hughes, *President*
EMP: 26 **EST:** 1995
SQ FT: 5,000
SALES (est): 5MM **Privately Held**
WEB: www.mechanicaldynamics.com
SIC: 3441 Fabricated structural metal

(G-19337)
MESSNER PUBLICATIONS INC
Also Called: Messner Printing
3250 Dundee Rd (33884-1113)
PHONE..................................863 318-1595
Jeff Messner, *President*
Jerry Messner Jr, *VP Opers*
Ann Messner, *Production*
Scott Messner, *VP Sales*
Chuck Aiken, *Sales Mgr*
EMP: 24 **EST:** 2001
SALES (est): 3.4MM **Privately Held**
WEB: www.4lpi.com
SIC: 2741 Miscellaneous publishing

(G-19338)
OWENS CORNING SALES LLC
3327 Queens Cove Loop (33880-5012)
PHONE..................................863 291-3046
Kelly Beerman, *Chairman*
EMP: 40 **Publicly Held**
WEB: www.owenscorning.com
SIC: 3296 3229 Fiberglass insulation; insulation: rock wool, slag & silica minerals; acoustical board & tile, mineral wool; roofing mats, mineral wool; glass fibers, textile; yarn, fiberglass
HQ: Owens Corning Sales, Llc
1 Owens Corning Pkwy
Toledo OH 43659
419 248-8000

(G-19339)
PALMETTO GROUP LLC
1530 Drexel Ave Ne (33881-4439)
PHONE..................................863 294-8070
Sheila Leavey, *Branch Mgr*
Thomas Leavey, *Mng Member*
EMP: 8
SALES (corp-wide): 94.4K **Privately Held**
SIC: 3567 Incinerators, metal: domestic or commercial
PA: Palmetto Group Llc
1625 Olmsted Ln
Fernandina Beach FL

(G-19340)
PEPSI-COLA METRO BTLG CO INC
5023 Recker Hwy (33880-1234)
PHONE..................................863 551-4500
Michael Sales, *Manager*
Steve Leslie, *Manager*
EMP: 6
SALES (corp-wide): 70.3B **Publicly Held**
WEB: www.pepsico.com
SIC: 2086 Soft drinks: packaged in cans, bottles, etc.
HQ: Pepsi-Cola Metropolitan Bottling Company, Inc.
1111 Westchester Ave
White Plains NY 10604
914 767-6000

(G-19341)
PETERS STRUCTURAL PRODUCTS
1320 Hidden Creek Ct (33880-5029)
PHONE..................................863 229-5275
Robert Peters, *Principal*
EMP: 7 **EST:** 2016
SALES (est): 77.8K **Privately Held**
WEB: www.petersstructuralproducts.com
SIC: 3441 Fabricated structural metal

(G-19342)
POLK COUNTY DEMOCRAT (PA)
99 3rd St Nw (33881-4609)
PHONE..................................863 533-4183
Loyal Frisbie, *President*
S L Frisbie IV, *Vice Pres*
Alan Walrond, *CFO*
Mary G Frisbie, *Treasurer*
Gary Peach, *Accounts Exec*
EMP: 17 **EST:** 1946
SQ FT: 12,600
SALES (est): 1.1MM **Privately Held**
WEB: www.midfloridanewspapers.com
SIC: 2711 Commercial printing & newspaper publishing combined

(G-19343)
PRECISION PLASTICS GROUP INC
Also Called: C & S Plastics
1635 7th St Sw (33880-3818)
PHONE..................................863 299-6639
Christopher Cooper, *CEO*
Don Millman, *Vice Pres*
Eric Yarbrough, *Maintence Staff*
EMP: 30 **EST:** 2017
SALES (est): 2.9MM **Privately Held**
WEB: www.candsplastics.com
SIC: 3089 Injection molding of plastics

(G-19344)
PREFERRED PALLETS LLC
4353 Fussell Ln (33880-4848)
PHONE..................................863 401-9517
EMP: 8
SALES (est): 732.5K **Privately Held**
SIC: 2448 Mfg Wood Pallets/Skids

(G-19345)
PRIVI LLC
141 E Central Ave Ste 300 (33880-6339)
PHONE..................................863 294-0373
Philip Castleberg, *Principal*
EMP: 6 **EST:** 2015
SALES (est): 120.5K **Privately Held**
WEB: www.goprivi.com
SIC: 7372 Prepackaged software

(G-19346)
PRO TRIM OF CENTRAL FLORIDA
2456 Hartridge Point Dr W (33881-1288)
PHONE..................................863 294-4646
Tommy Matthews, *Owner*
EMP: 5 **EST:** 2004
SALES (est): 432.6K **Privately Held**
SIC: 3465 Body parts, automobile: stamped metal

(G-19347)
PRODUCTION SYSTEM ENGINEERING
3204 E Lake Hamilton Dr (33881)
PHONE..................................863 299-7330
Gary Niemann, *President*
Randy Grulke, *General Mgr*
Meredith Niemann, *Vice Pres*
Meridth Niemann, *Shareholder*
EMP: 10 **EST:** 1978
SQ FT: 12,000
SALES (est): 802.2K **Privately Held**
SIC: 3565 Packaging machinery

(G-19348)
PROFESSIONAL OFFICE SVCS INC
64 Industrial Blvd (33880-1030)
P.O. Box 245, Auburndale (33823-0245)
PHONE..................................863 967-6634
Ken P Spurling, *General Mgr*
Kathleen Price, *Plant Mgr*
EMP: 7
SQ FT: 33,120
SALES (corp-wide): 75.4MM **Privately Held**
WEB: www.poscorp.com
SIC: 3578 2761 2752 5943 Calculating & accounting equipment; manifold business forms; commercial printing, lithographic; office forms & supplies
PA: Professional Office Services, Inc.
2757 Burton Ave
Waterloo IA 50703
319 235-6777

(G-19349)
PROGRAPHIX INC
2614 Avenue G Nw (33880-2139)
PHONE..................................863 298-8081
Deanna Morris, *President*
EMP: 5 **EST:** 2001
SQ FT: 5,000
SALES (est): 450K **Privately Held**
WEB: www.pgaustin.com
SIC: 2759 Screen printing

(G-19350)
PSI CUSTOMS
132 Argentina Dr (33880-1601)
PHONE..................................863 661-4211
Derek A Spires, *Principal*
EMP: 6 **EST:** 2007
SALES (est): 102K **Privately Held**
SIC: 3465 Body parts, automobile: stamped metal

(G-19351)
RALLY POINT PUBLICATIONS LLC (PA)
234 Ruby Lake Ln (33884-3266)
PHONE..................................863 221-6304
Daniel Martin Jarvis, *Owner*
EMP: 19 **EST:** 2017
SALES (est): 108.2K **Privately Held**
WEB: www.rallypointpublications.com
SIC: 2741 Miscellaneous publishing

(G-19352)
RAY GRAPHICS INC
Also Called: Raygraphics
1895 Executive Rd (33884-1123)
PHONE..................................863 325-0911
Carol Morrow, *President*
EMP: 23 **EST:** 1988
SQ FT: 2,500
SALES (est): 1MM **Privately Held**
WEB: www.raygraphicsapparel.com
SIC: 2759 2396 2395 Screen printing; automotive & apparel trimmings; embroidery products, except schiffli machine

(G-19353)
S S DESIGNS INC
5558 Commercial Blvd (33880-1008)
P.O. Box 834 (33882-0834)
PHONE..................................863 965-2576
Bob Carter, *President*
Benjamin Carter, *Vice Pres*
Kevin Ray, *Vice Pres*
Cynthia Zimmerman, *Vice Pres*
Doug Heminger, *Adv Mgr*
EMP: 85 **EST:** 1976
SQ FT: 100,000

▲ = Import ▼=Export
◆ =Import/Export

SALES (est): 12MM Privately Held
WEB: www.ssdesigns.net
SIC: 2396 2395 Screen printing on fabric articles; embroidery products, except schiffli machine

(G-19354)
SABCON UNDERGROUND LLC
1730 Dundee Rd (33884-1018)
PHONE.................................863 268-8225
Kellie Burns, *Mng Member*
EMP: 23 EST: 2016
SALES (est): 2.8MM Privately Held
SIC: 1381 Directional drilling oil & gas wells

(G-19355)
SIGNCORP INC
512 6th St Nw (33881-4009)
PHONE.................................863 224-1331
Kathleen Jax, *Sr Project Mgr*
EMP: 6 EST: 2016
SALES (est): 163.4K Privately Held
WEB: www.signcorpinc.com
SIC: 3993 Signs & advertising specialties

(G-19356)
SOLAR ENERGY SPECIALIST CORP
1130 1st St S (33880-3903)
PHONE.................................863 514-9532
Tanesha L Bouthner, *President*
EMP: 7 EST: 2016
SALES (est): 134.2K Privately Held
WEB: www.solarenergyspecialistcorp.com
SIC: 3433 Solar heaters & collectors

(G-19357)
SOUTHAST PROTEIN PURVEYORS LLC
604 Lake Elizabeth Dr (33884-1434)
P.O. Box 1024, Auburndale (33823-1024)
PHONE.................................912 354-2770
Jay Javetz, *Mng Member*
Stephen Saterbo,
EMP: 4 EST: 2005
SQ FT: 2,000
SALES (est): 15MM Privately Held
SIC: 2013 Frozen meats from purchased meat

(G-19358)
STACY LEE MONTGOMERY
Also Called: Stacy's Printing
6320 Cypress Gardens Blvd (33884-3176)
PHONE.................................863 662-3163
Stacy Lee Montgomery, *Owner*
EMP: 8 EST: 2016
SALES (est): 277.8K Privately Held
SIC: 2752 Commercial printing, offset

(G-19359)
SUPERIOR PALLETS LLC
4353 Fussell Ln (33880-4848)
PHONE.................................863 875-4041
EMP: 7
SALES (est): 418.7K Privately Held
SIC: 2448 Mfg Wood Pallets/Skids

(G-19360)
SUPERIOR UNLIMITED ENTERPRISES
Also Called: Cypress Signs
160 Spirit Lake Rd (33880-1242)
PHONE.................................863 294-1683
Donie Bowman, *President*
Bruce Mc Whirter, *Plant Mgr*
Mark Bowman, *Treasurer*
EMP: 9 EST: 1977
SQ FT: 4,000
SALES (est): 1.2MM Privately Held
WEB: www.cypresssigns.com
SIC: 3993 7699 Signs, not made in custom sign painting shops; professional instrument repair services

(G-19361)
TARGET MARINE INC
Also Called: Target Marine Manufacturers
125 Bomber Rd (33880-5666)
PHONE.................................863 293-3592
Charles Monts De Oca, *President*
EMP: 9 EST: 1980
SALES (est): 67.1K Privately Held
SIC: 3732 Boats, fiberglass: building & repairing

(G-19362)
TAYCO INDUSTRIES INC
245 Ruby Lake Ln (33884-3267)
PHONE.................................863 318-9264
Gregory O Taylor, *Director*
EMP: 6 EST: 2018
SALES (est): 43.6K Privately Held
WEB: www.tayco.com
SIC: 3999 Manufacturing industries

(G-19363)
TENSIK INC
3955 W Lake Hamilton Dr (33881-9272)
PHONE.................................954 937-9505
Eduardo Fuenmayor, *CEO*
EMP: 5 EST: 2019
SALES (est): 410.5K Privately Held
WEB: www.tensikusa.com
SIC: 3531 Concrete plants

(G-19364)
TRAVIS LH LLC ✪
Also Called: Lh Travis
1800 42nd St Nw (33881-1948)
PHONE.................................863 967-0628
Erica Hamilton,
EMP: 10 EST: 2020
SALES (est): 861.9K Privately Held
WEB: www.lhtravis.com
SIC: 3569 Lubrication equipment, industrial

(G-19365)
UNITED ADHESIVE PRODUCTS INC
4202 Hammond Dr (33881-9701)
PHONE.................................863 698-9484
Jennifer Schaal, *Principal*
EMP: 7 EST: 2016
SALES (est): 135.6K Privately Held
SIC: 2891 Adhesives

(G-19366)
VASS HOLDINGS INC (PA)
146 Avenue B Nw (33881-4506)
P.O. Box 1707 (33882-1707)
PHONE.................................863 295-5664
Howard Levasseur Jr, *President*
Marylin Riggs, *CFO*
EMP: 4 EST: 1993
SQ FT: 1,800
SALES (est): 18.1MM Privately Held
SIC: 2899 Chemical preparations

(G-19367)
WM G ROE & SONS INC
Also Called: Noble Worldwide Fla Citrus Sls
500 Avenue R Sw (33880-3871)
P.O. Box 900 (33882-0900)
PHONE.................................863 294-3577
Quentin J Roe, *President*
Allison Lee, *Principal*
William G Roe II, *Vice Pres*
April Porter, *CFO*
Amber Glass, *Sales Staff*
▲ EMP: 500 EST: 1927
SQ FT: 40,000
SALES (est): 48MM Privately Held
WEB: www.noblecitrus.com
SIC: 2033 Fruit juices: fresh

(G-19368)
WOLFF CONTROLS CORPORATION
2929 Dundee Rd (33884-1170)
P.O. Box 9407 (33883-9407)
PHONE.................................863 324-0423
Peter Wolff, *President*
Inga Wolff Stettler, *Corp Secy*
Marshall Smith, *Research*
Brigitte Wolff, *Asst Treas*
EMP: 13 EST: 1978
SQ FT: 1,766
SALES (est): 1.2MM Privately Held
WEB: www.wolffcontrols.com
SIC: 3625 Electric controls & control accessories, industrial

(G-19369)
YAUCHLER PROPERTIES LLC
119 Avenue D Se (33880-3525)
PHONE.................................863 662-5570
Eugene P Yauchler, *Principal*
EMP: 15 EST: 2008
SALES (est): 1MM Privately Held
SIC: 3589 Swimming pool filter & water conditioning systems

Winter Park
Orange County

(G-19370)
ACCORD INDUSTRIES LLC (HQ)
Also Called: Concrete Products-Division
4001 Forsyth Rd (32792-6833)
P.O. Box 35430, Charlotte NC (28235-5430)
PHONE.................................407 671-6989
Mr Michael Kline, *Vice Pres*
Debbie Deford, *CFO*
Diane Wiggins,
◆ EMP: 95 EST: 1990
SQ FT: 2,500
SALES (est): 16.5MM
SALES (corp-wide): 101.9MM Privately Held
WEB: www.universal100.com
SIC: 3084 3444 3317 3272 Plastics pipe; sheet metalwork; steel pipe & tubes; prestressed concrete products
PA: Alliance Holdings, Inc.
100 Witmer Rd Ste 170
Horsham PA 19044
215 706-0873

(G-19371)
ACE CUSTOM SIGNS OF WINTER PK
922 Orange Ave (32789-4707)
PHONE.................................407 257-6475
EMP: 7 EST: 2019
SALES (est): 398.5K Privately Held
WEB: www.acecustomsignsofwinterpark.com
SIC: 3993 Signs & advertising specialties

(G-19372)
ADVANCED CYLINDER HEADS
2830 Forsyth Rd Ste 450 (32792-8218)
PHONE.................................407 671-2886
James Spinelli, *Principal*
EMP: 8 EST: 2007
SALES (est): 94.5K Privately Held
WEB: www.advancedcylinderheads.com
SIC: 3599 Machine shop, jobbing & repair

(G-19373)
ADVANTAGE DRILLS INC
7039 Pecan Ct (32792-7541)
PHONE.................................407 478-2487
Randy Lobeck, *President*
EMP: 5 EST: 2002
SQ FT: 2,000
SALES (est): 750K Privately Held
WEB: www.advantagedrills.com
SIC: 3545 5084 Drill bits, metalworking; metalworking tools (such as drills, taps, dies, files)

(G-19374)
AI2 INC
1400 Bonnie Burn Cir (32789-5703)
PHONE.................................407 645-3234
Roger D Ray, *Director*
Jennifer R Clark, *Admin Sec*
EMP: 6 EST: 2001
SALES (est): 112.9K Privately Held
WEB: www.ai2inc.com
SIC: 7372 Educational computer software

(G-19375)
ALPHA CARD COMPACT MEDIA LLC
941 W Morse Blvd Ste 100 (32789-3781)
PHONE.................................407 698-3592
Ian Whitfield,
EMP: 8 EST: 2018
SALES (est): 256.1K Privately Held
WEB: www.alpha-cards.com
SIC: 2759 Card printing & engraving, except greeting

(G-19376)
AM2F ENERGY INC
501 N Orlando Ave 313-256 (32789-7313)
PHONE.................................407 505-1127
Juyoung Kim, *President*
Yoonjung Kim, *Vice Pres*
EMP: 7 EST: 2011
SALES (est): 170.9K Privately Held
WEB: www.am2fenergy.com
SIC: 2992 Lubricating oils & greases

(G-19377)
API TECH NORTH AMERICA INC
941 W Morse Blvd Ste 100 (32789-3781)
PHONE.................................929 255-1231
EMP: 6 EST: 2019
SALES (est): 166.2K Privately Held
SIC: 3679 Microwave components

(G-19378)
AQUA ENGINEERING & EQUIPMENT
7206 Aloma Ave (32792-7102)
PHONE.................................407 599-2123
Marianne Brizio, *President*
▲ EMP: 11 EST: 2000
SQ FT: 1,800
SALES (est): 1.4MM Privately Held
WEB: www.aquariumwaterfilters.com
SIC: 3589 5074 Water treatment equipment, industrial; water purification equipment

(G-19379)
ARCHITCTRAL SHTMTL FABRICATORS
Also Called: Asmf
2720 Forsyth Rd Ste 200 (32792-8212)
PHONE.................................407 672-9086
Jeremiah Dice, *President*
Matthew David Dice, *Manager*
EMP: 5 EST: 2005
SQ FT: 5,000
SALES (est): 374.6K Privately Held
SIC: 3444 Sheet metalwork

(G-19380)
ARSENAL INDUSTRIES LLC
750 S Orlando Ave Ste 200 (32789-4872)
PHONE.................................407 506-2698
Jennifer Dunham, *Principal*
EMP: 11 EST: 2017
SALES (est): 783.2K Privately Held
WEB: www.arsenalgrowth.com
SIC: 3999 Manufacturing industries

(G-19381)
ARSENAL VENTURE PARTNERS FLA
750 S Orlando Ave Ste 200 (32789-4872)
PHONE.................................407 838-1400
Jason Rottenberg, *General Ptnr*
Amy Brooks, *Finance Dir*
Christopher Fountas, *Director*
John Nolan, *Advisor*
EMP: 9 EST: 2012
SALES (est): 236K Privately Held
WEB: www.arsenalgrowth.com
SIC: 3999 Manufacturing industries

(G-19382)
BINDERY LLC
611 N Wymore Rd Ste 100 (32789-2848)
PHONE.................................407 647-7777
Larry J Herring, *Principal*
EMP: 8 EST: 2001
SALES (est): 156.3K Privately Held
SIC: 2789 Bookbinding & related work

(G-19383)
BONNIER CORPORATION (DH)
480 N Orlando Ave Ste 236 (32789-2918)
PHONE.................................407 628-4802
David Ritchie, *CEO*
David Benz, *Publisher*
Megan Jordan, *Publisher*
David Morel, *Publisher*
Parker Stair, *Publisher*
EMP: 200 EST: 2007
SALES (est): 269.7MM
SALES (corp-wide): 2.4B Privately Held
WEB: www.bonniercorp.com
SIC: 2721 Magazines: publishing only, not printed on site

GEOGRAPHIC

HQ: Bonnier Ab
Kungsgatan 49
Stockholm 111 2
873 640-00

(G-19384)
BOONE BAIT CO INC
1501 Minnesota Ave (32789-4622)
P.O. Box 2966 (32790-2966)
PHONE..................................407 975-8775
Peter F Foley, *President*
▲ **EMP**: 13 **EST**: 1953
SQ FT: 14,000
SALES (est): 671.9K **Privately Held**
WEB: www.boonebait.com
SIC: **3949** 5941 Lures, fishing: artificial; sporting goods & bicycle shops

(G-19385)
BYTHENET PUBLISHING
2500 Lee Rd (32789-1752)
PHONE..................................407 691-2806
Donald Cuniff, *Principal*
EMP: 6 **EST**: 2015
SALES (est): 105.3K **Privately Held**
SIC: **2741** Miscellaneous publishing

(G-19386)
C & M MANUFACTURING LLC
4212 Metric Dr (32792-6819)
PHONE..................................407 673-9601
Chad J Berecz, *Manager*
EMP: 8 **EST**: 2017
SALES (est): 458.5K **Privately Held**
WEB: www.cm-manufacturing.com
SIC: **3999** Barber & beauty shop equipment

(G-19387)
C E S WIRELESS TECH CORP
931 S Semoran Blvd # 200 (32792-5396)
PHONE..................................407 681-0869
Pat Lohan, *President*
William Mercurio, *Chairman*
Ada Gaston, *Corp Secy*
Pam McFarland, *Manager*
EMP: 28 **EST**: 1974
SQ FT: 15,000
SALES (est): 1MM **Privately Held**
WEB: www.ceswireless.com
SIC: **3663** Mobile communication equipment

(G-19388)
C&A LOZARO INC
3000 N Goldenrod Rd (32792-8708)
PHONE..................................407 671-8809
Diego Lozano, *President*
EMP: 12
SALES (est): 600K **Privately Held**
SIC: **2024** Ice cream & frozen desserts

(G-19389)
CABINET MARKET LLC
3413 Forsyth Rd Ste B (32792-7443)
PHONE..................................321 203-2598
Guillermo Rente, *President*
EMP: 6 **EST**: 2012
SALES (est): 238.7K **Privately Held**
WEB: www.orlandocabinetmarket.com
SIC: **2434** Wood kitchen cabinets

(G-19390)
CABINET SYSTEMS OF CENTRAL FLA
2716 Forsyth Rd Ste 114 (32792-8204)
PHONE..................................407 678-0994
Jeff Hebert, *President*
Dennis Jones, *Vice Pres*
EMP: 6 **EST**: 1983
SQ FT: 5,200
SALES (est): 508.6K **Privately Held**
SIC: **2434** Wood kitchen cabinets

(G-19391)
CATO STEEL CO
3928 Forsyth Rd (32792-6813)
PHONE..................................407 671-3333
Allen McCormick, *President*
Amy Pruitt, *Office Mgr*
Tracy Gironda, *Admin Asst*
EMP: 17 **EST**: 1963
SQ FT: 2,500
SALES (est): 2MM **Privately Held**
WEB: www.catosteel.com
SIC: **3444** 3441 Sheet metalwork; fabricated structural metal

(G-19392)
CHAMPION SHTMTL FABRICATION
6450 University Blvd B2 (32792-7434)
PHONE..................................407 509-7439
Patrick Madden, *President*
▲ **EMP**: 7 **EST**: 2011
SALES (est): 110K **Privately Held**
WEB: www.championcontractingservices.com
SIC: **3499** Fire- or burglary-resistive products

(G-19393)
CHARGERS AND CASES LLC
Also Called: Distinct.ink
2281 Lee Rd Ste 105 (32789-7208)
PHONE..................................352 587-2539
Daren Ellington, *Principal*
Daren M Ellington, *Manager*
EMP: 9 **EST**: 2011
SALES (est): 680.6K **Privately Held**
SIC: **3523** Farm machinery & equipment

(G-19394)
CHIN & CHIN ENTERPRISES INC
3580 Aloma Ave Ste 5 (32792-4011)
PHONE..................................407 478-8726
Luong Moc Tran, *President*
James Chin, *Vice Pres*
Thomas Chin, *Vice Pres*
David Hansen, *Vice Pres*
EMP: 11 **EST**: 2003
SQ FT: 750
SALES (est): 198.9K **Privately Held**
SIC: **2599** Food wagons, restaurant

(G-19395)
CITY PRINTS SIGNS & FLYERS
2131 W Fairbanks Ave (32789-4507)
PHONE..................................407 532-6078
EMP: 6 **EST**: 2010
SALES (est): 111.6K **Privately Held**
SIC: **2752** Commercial printing, offset

(G-19396)
CONTROL MICRO SYSTEMS INC
4420 Metric Dr Ste A (32792-6961)
PHONE..................................407 679-9716
Timothy Miller, *President*
Victor Rivera, *Buyer*
Kevin Chang, *Engineer*
Jason Dembkoski, *Engineer*
Danish Riaz, *Engineer*
▲ **EMP**: 49
SQ FT: 25,000
SALES (est): 15MM **Privately Held**
WEB: www.cmslaser.com
SIC: **3699** Laser systems & equipment

(G-19397)
CUP PLUS USA
4440 Metric Dr (32792-6933)
PHONE..................................321 972-1968
Lawrence Griller, *Principal*
▲ **EMP**: 6 **EST**: 2010
SALES (est): 109.8K **Privately Held**
SIC: **2821** Plastics materials & resins

(G-19398)
CUSTOM COMFORT MEDTEK LLC
3939 Forsyth Rd Ste A (32792-6835)
P.O. Box 4779 (32793-4779)
PHONE..................................407 332-0062
Doug D Patton, *Vice Pres*
Peter Gaughn,
◆ **EMP**: 20 **EST**: 1987
SQ FT: 50,000
SALES (est): 3.6MM **Privately Held**
WEB: www.customcomfort.com
SIC: **2599** Hospital furniture, except beds

(G-19399)
DAILY BUZZ
3260 University Blvd (32792-7431)
PHONE..................................407 673-5400
Steve Bailey, *Principal*
EMP: 6 **EST**: 2007
SALES (est): 109.1K **Privately Held**
WEB: www.dailybuzznow.com
SIC: **2711** Newspapers, publishing & printing

(G-19400)
DAIN M BAYER
2333 Chantilly Ave (32789-1341)
PHONE..................................407 647-0679
Timothy Bayer, *Principal*
EMP: 7 **EST**: 2001
SALES (est): 253.1K **Privately Held**
SIC: **2834** Pharmaceutical preparations

(G-19401)
DARK LAKE SOFTWARE INC
Also Called: Dark Lake Systems
1229 Wading Waters Cir (32792-3162)
PHONE..................................407 602-8046
Bradley Foley, *Principal*
EMP: 15 **EST**: 2010
SALES (est): 1.6MM **Privately Held**
WEB: www.darklakesoftware.com
SIC: **7372** Application computer software

(G-19402)
DIGITAL PRINTING SOLUTIONS INC
6438 University Blvd # 12 (32792-7417)
PHONE..................................407 671-8715
Kevin Johnson, *President*
Terry Sutton, *Vice Pres*
Ellen Burch, *Sales Staff*
EMP: 47 **EST**: 2001
SQ FT: 23,000
SALES (est): 5MM **Privately Held**
WEB: www.dpscan.com
SIC: **2752** Commercial printing, offset

(G-19403)
DIVERSIFIED MINING INC
2178 Crandon Ave (32789-3382)
PHONE..................................407 923-3194
Jefferson A Bootes, *President*
EMP: 7 **EST**: 2011
SALES (est): 155.6K **Privately Held**
SIC: **1241** Coal mining services

(G-19404)
DMC COMPONENTS INTL LLC
Also Called: Data Image
4202 Metric Dr (32792-6819)
PHONE..................................407 478-4064
Michael P Dathe, *CEO*
Bill Reichert, *Sales Executive*
▲ **EMP**: 7 **EST**: 1999
SALES (est): 1.2MM **Privately Held**
WEB: www.dataimagelcd.com
SIC: **3679** 3699 Liquid crystal displays (LCD); electrical equipment & supplies

(G-19405)
DREWLU ENTERPRISES INC
Also Called: Printing USA
3412 Aloma Ave Ste 1 (32792-3900)
PHONE..................................407 478-7872
Jean Horning, *President*
Dean A Horning, *Vice Pres*
EMP: 7 **EST**: 1986
SQ FT: 4,000
SALES (est): 1.1MM **Privately Held**
WEB: www.onesourceonestop.com
SIC: **2759** Screen printing

(G-19406)
F C MACHINE CORPORATION
4212 Metric Dr (32792-6819)
PHONE..................................407 673-9601
Frank Cordi, *President*
Michele Cordi, *Admin Sec*
EMP: 8 **EST**: 1990
SQ FT: 3,000
SALES (est): 736.2K **Privately Held**
WEB: www.fcmachineshop.com
SIC: **3599** Machine shop, jobbing & repair

(G-19407)
FAITHFUL HEART FROYO LLC
2405 Whitehall Cir (32792-4752)
PHONE..................................407 325-3052
Laura S Williams, *Principal*
EMP: 7 **EST**: 2014
SALES (est): 225.5K **Privately Held**
SIC: **2024** Yogurt desserts, frozen

(G-19408)
GREAT MAGNET LLC
1701 Winter Green Blvd (32792-2277)
PHONE..................................407 260-0591
Brien Wilson,
Robert Caldarazzo,
Troy Radike,
EMP: 10 **EST**: 2004
SALES (est): 136.9K **Privately Held**
SIC: **3086** Packaging & shipping materials, foamed plastic

(G-19409)
H D QUICKPRINT & DISC OFF SUPS
Also Called: H D Quikprint & Disc Off Sups
2721 Forsyth Rd Ste 101 (32792-8207)
PHONE..................................407 678-1355
J K Berthold, *CEO*
Mark Berthold, *President*
Cristine Schilling, *Vice Pres*
EMP: 5 **EST**: 1977
SALES (est): 450K **Privately Held**
WEB: www.hdquikprint.com
SIC: **2752** 5943 Commercial printing, offset; office forms & supplies

(G-19410)
HERFF JONES INC
Also Called: Herff Jones
112 N Wymore Rd (32789-3453)
PHONE..................................407 647-4373
Joe K Slaughter, *President*
Matthew R Barth, *Vice Pres*
Mark D Dillman, *Vice Pres*
Larry T Hill, *Vice Pres*
Kenneth G Langlois, *Vice Pres*
EMP: 6 **EST**: 1994
SQ FT: 2,299
SALES (est): 769.9K **Privately Held**
WEB: www.herfforlando.com
SIC: **2752** Commercial printing, lithographic

(G-19411)
HORIZON DUPLICATION INC
Also Called: Horizon Media Express
841 Nicolet Ave Ste 5 (32789-4618)
PHONE..................................407 767-5000
Peter Schimpf, *President*
Ann Stuart, *CFO*
Kevin Tucker, *Manager*
EMP: 7 **EST**: 1991
SQ FT: 10,000
SALES: 774.6K **Privately Held**
WEB: www.horizonmediaexpress.com
SIC: **3695** 5735 Computer software tape & disks: blank, rigid & floppy; compact discs

(G-19412)
IMMUNE THERAPEUTICS INC
2431 Aloma Ave 124 (32792-2541)
PHONE..................................888 613-8802
Michael K Handley, *CEO*
Roscoe Moore Jr, *Ch of Bd*
Christopher Pearce, *COO*
Peter Aronstam, *CFO*
Clifford D Selsky R, *Director*
EMP: 20 **EST**: 1993
SALES (est): 3.3MM **Privately Held**
WEB: www.immunetherapeutics.com
SIC: **2834** Pharmaceutical preparations

(G-19413)
INFRARED SYSTEMS DEV CORP
7319 Sandscove Ct Ste 4 (32792-6979)
PHONE..................................407 679-5101
Andrew Duran, *President*
Jeffrey Bueltmann, *Vice Pres*
Carlene Duran, *Vice Pres*
EMP: 14 **EST**: 1997
SQ FT: 6,500
SALES (est): 2MM **Privately Held**
WEB: www.infraredsystems.com
SIC: **3826** Laser scientific & engineering instruments

(G-19414)
ITNORLANDO INC
1201 S Orlando Ave # 205 (32789-7109)
PHONE..................................407 900-7572
Harold Barley, *Vice Pres*
Zain Durrani, *Opers Mgr*
Kimber Threet, *Exec Dir*
EMP: 6 **EST**: 2006

SALES (est): 45.6K Privately Held
WEB: www.itnorlando.org
SIC: 3799 Automobile trailer chassis

(G-19415)
J BRISTOL LLC
2715 Norris Ave (32789-6667)
PHONE.................................407 488-6744
Jason P Bristol, *Manager*
EMP: 7 EST: 2016
SALES (est): 190.9K Privately Held
SIC: 2621 Paper mills

(G-19416)
JEREMIAHS ORIGINAL WATER ICE (PA)
Also Called: Jeremiahs Original Italian Ice
6864 Aloma Ave (32792-6824)
P.O. Box 947824, Maitland (32794-7824)
PHONE.................................407 679-2665
Jeremy Litwack, *President*
Jacklyn Dennery, *Store Mgr*
Jeremiah Dessert, *Technology*
EMP: 6 EST: 1994
SQ FT: 1,500
SALES (est): 1.6MM Privately Held
WEB: www.jeremiahsice.com
SIC: 2024 5812 5451 Ice cream & frozen desserts; fast food restaurants & stands; ice cream (packaged)

(G-19417)
LAC INC
3580 Aloma Ave Ste 1 (32792-4011)
PHONE.................................407 671-6610
Lacey Sharp, *Principal*
EMP: 9 EST: 2005
SALES (est): 126.8K Privately Held
SIC: 3552 Embroidery machines

(G-19418)
LEGACY PUBLISHING SERVICES
1883 Lee Rd (32789-2102)
PHONE.................................407 647-3787
▲ EMP: 8
SALES: 350K Privately Held
SIC: 2731 Books-Publishing/Printing

(G-19419)
LR DUMPSTERS LLC
1950 Aster Dr (32792-6238)
PHONE.................................321 279-0169
Leonardo Lopez, *Principal*
EMP: 6 EST: 2018
SALES (est): 156.7K Privately Held
SIC: 3443 Dumpsters, garbage

(G-19420)
LUCKY DOG SCREEN PRINTING MG
2716 Forsyth Rd Ste 105 (32792-8204)
PHONE.................................407 629-8838
Susan Marcus, *President*
EMP: 8 EST: 1995
SALES (est): 183.3K Privately Held
WEB: www.luckydogfl.com
SIC: 2759 7389 Screen printing; embroidering of advertising on shirts, etc.

(G-19421)
LUONG MOC III INC
3580 Aloma Ave Ste 5 (32792-4011)
PHONE.................................407 478-8726
Luong Moc Tran, *President*
EMP: 50
SALES (est): 1.6MM Privately Held
SIC: 2599 Food wagons, restaurant

(G-19422)
MEISTER MEDIA WORLDWIDE INC
2431 Aloma Ave 124 (32792-2541)
P.O. Box 940640, Maitland (32794-0640)
PHONE.................................407 539-6552
Beck Barnes, *Editor*
Judy Gill-Totten, *Editor*
Richard Jones, *Editor*
Robin Siktberg, *Editor*
Brian Sparks, *Editor*
EMP: 6
SALES (corp-wide): 27.5MM Privately Held
WEB: www.meistermedia.com
SIC: 2721 Magazines: publishing only, not printed on site
PA: Meister Media Worldwide Inc.
37733 Euclid Ave
Willoughby OH 44094
440 942-2000

(G-19423)
METRO DEFENSE SERVICES INC
3001 Aloma Ave 227 (32792-3752)
PHONE.................................407 285-2304
Bruce Chatterton, *President*
EMP: 7 EST: 2007
SALES (est): 80.3K Privately Held
SIC: 3812 Defense systems & equipment

(G-19424)
METROPOLIS GRAPHICS INC
805 S Orlando Ave Ste D (32789-4869)
PHONE.................................407 740-5455
Darrell Robinson, *President*
EMP: 8 EST: 1989
SQ FT: 1,000
SALES (est): 1.2MM Privately Held
WEB: www.metropolisgraphics.com
SIC: 2759 5199 Screen printing; advertising specialties

(G-19425)
MICRO JIG INC
7212 Sandscove Ct (32792-6908)
PHONE.................................855 747-7233
Henry Wang, *President*
Steve Thomas, *Finance*
David Garcia, *Art Dir*
EMP: 7 EST: 2001
SALES (est): 1.1MM Privately Held
WEB: www.microjig.com
SIC: 3423 Hand & edge tools

(G-19426)
MIKES PRINT SHOP INC
2118 Poinciana Rd (32792-1827)
PHONE.................................407 718-4964
Michael P Schuermann, *President*
EMP: 9 EST: 1970
SALES (est): 502.4K Privately Held
WEB: www.flprinting.net
SIC: 2752 2791 2789 2672 Commercial printing, offset; typesetting; bookbinding & related work; coated & laminated paper

(G-19427)
MOBILE RUGGED TECH CORP
931 S Semoran Blvd # 204 (32792-5317)
PHONE.................................781 771-6743
Robinson B Nunez, *President*
EMP: 5 EST: 2008
SQ FT: 7,500
SALES (est): 453.1K Privately Held
SIC: 3429 Manufactured hardware (general)

(G-19428)
NIVCOE INTERNATIONAL DEV
2020 W Fairbanks Ave # 102 (32789-4522)
PHONE.................................321 282-3666
Reginal Ovince, *President*
EMP: 15 EST: 2007
SALES (est): 857.7K Privately Held
SIC: 1389 Construction, repair & dismantling services

(G-19429)
PETER MARCUS PARADIGM LLC
Also Called: Guygiene Group, The
1331 Lakeview Dr (32789-5039)
PHONE.................................877 887-8696
Siciak Charlie, *Principal*
Sam Nebel,
Charlie C Siciak,
▲ EMP: 14 EST: 2013
SALES (est): 589.1K Privately Held
WEB: www.goodwipes.com
SIC: 2676 Cleansing tissues: made from purchased paper

(G-19430)
PIN MAKERS
803 S Orlando Ave (32789-4868)
PHONE.................................877 825-6120
EMP: 7 EST: 2017
SALES (est): 280.9K Privately Held
WEB: www.pinmakers.com
SIC: 3911 Jewelry, precious metal

(G-19431)
PLAYOFF TECHNOLOGIES LLC
Also Called: Sponsor Locker
1430 Elizabeth Dr (32789-2733)
PHONE.................................407 497-2202
Charles E Harris, *CEO*
EMP: 7 EST: 2013
SALES (est): 408.7K Privately Held
WEB: www.playofftech.com
SIC: 7372 Prepackaged software

(G-19432)
POBLOCKI SIGN CO SOUTHEAST LLC
7005 Stapoint Ct (32792-6696)
PHONE.................................407 660-3174
EMP: 7
SALES (est): 427.4K Privately Held
SIC: 3993 Signs & advertising specialties

(G-19433)
PRINTS THE PPR OF WNTER PK LLC
1597 Hillcrest Ave (32789-5754)
PHONE.................................407 740-0989
Julie Wordell, *Manager*
EMP: 6 EST: 2011
SALES (est): 106.1K Privately Held
SIC: 2752 Commercial printing, lithographic

(G-19434)
QUALITY FORMS & PRINTING CO
3071 Autumn Ct (32792-1738)
PHONE.................................407 671-8026
Toni G Quaglia, *Principal*
EMP: 6 EST: 2008
SALES (est): 117.9K Privately Held
SIC: 2752 Commercial printing, offset

(G-19435)
QUICK CANS INC
7034 Arbor Ct (32792-7529)
PHONE.................................407 415-1361
James M Urichko, *Principal*
EMP: 7 EST: 2010
SALES (est): 93.5K Privately Held
SIC: 3089 Garbage containers, plastic

(G-19436)
RAND TITLE CORPORATION
400 N New York Ave (32789-3159)
PHONE.................................407 622-7263
Robert Sirianni Jr, *Principal*
EMP: 7 EST: 2009
SALES (est): 229K Privately Held
WEB: www.leadingedgetitleorlando.com
SIC: 3131 Rands

(G-19437)
RE-THINK IT INC
6869 Stapoint Ct Ste 107 (32792-6603)
PHONE.................................407 671-6000
Amy M Shumway, *President*
Craig Shumway, *Vice Pres*
▲ EMP: 15 EST: 1987
SQ FT: 2,500
SALES (est): 3.1MM Privately Held
WEB: www.re-play.com
SIC: 3069 Sponge rubber & sponge rubber products

(G-19438)
REDBERD PRINTING
803 S Orlando Ave (32789-4868)
PHONE.................................407 622-2292
Peter R Cleeveley, *Principal*
EMP: 9 EST: 2009
SALES (est): 75.1K Privately Held
WEB: www.redbirdprinting.com
SIC: 2752 Commercial printing, offset

(G-19439)
REDBIRD PRINTING
803 S Orlando Ave Ste J (32789-4868)
PHONE.................................904 654-8371
Cleeveley R John, *CFO*
EMP: 9 EST: 2017
SALES (est): 250.7K Privately Held
WEB: www.redbirdprinting.com
SIC: 2752 Commercial printing, offset

(G-19440)
REGAL CABINETS INC
3903 Forsyth Rd (32792-6834)
PHONE.................................407 678-1003
Faramarz Sadri, *President*
EMP: 10 EST: 1995
SQ FT: 10,519
SALES (est): 1MM Privately Held
WEB: www.regalcabinetsfl.com
SIC: 2434 Wood kitchen cabinets

(G-19441)
REV AMBLANCE GROUP ORLANDO INC (DH)
Also Called: Wheeled Coach Industries
2737 Forsyth Rd (32792-6673)
P.O. Box 677339, Orlando (32867-7339)
PHONE.................................407 677-7777
Robert L Collins, *President*
Joe Leggett, *President*
Donald Lynn Collins, *Corp Secy*
Grisell Carballido, *Vice Pres*
Dino Cusamano, *Vice Pres*
◆ EMP: 360 EST: 1975
SQ FT: 200,000
SALES (est): 95.8MM Publicly Held
WEB: www.wheeledcoach.com
SIC: 3711 Ambulances (motor vehicles), assembly of
HQ: Collins Industries, Inc.
15 Compound Dr
Hutchinson KS 67502
620 663-5551

(G-19442)
SIGHTHOUND INC
101 S New York Ave # 211 (32789-4298)
PHONE.................................650 564-4364
Jonathan Taylor, *CEO*
Stephen Neish, *President*
Ananda Lawson, *Marketing Staff*
Brent Richardson, *Software Dev*
EMP: 14 EST: 2012
SQ FT: 900
SALES (est): 1.1MM Privately Held
WEB: www.sighthound.com
SIC: 7372 Application computer software

(G-19443)
SIGNS NOW INC
1003 S Orlando Ave (32789-4850)
PHONE.................................407 628-2410
Michelle Gonzalez, *President*
Juan Gonzalez, *Vice Pres*
EMP: 5 EST: 1990
SALES (est): 388.3K Privately Held
WEB: www.signsnow.com
SIC: 3993 Signs & advertising specialties

(G-19444)
SIGNWAY INC
2964 Forsyth Rd (32792-6690)
P.O. Box 195486, Winter Springs (32719-5486)
PHONE.................................407 696-7446
Steve Bryan, *President*
Jeff Bryan, *Vice Pres*
EMP: 5 EST: 2001
SALES (est): 528.3K Privately Held
WEB: www.signwayinc.com
SIC: 3993 Signs, not made in custom sign painting shops

(G-19445)
SIMETRI INC
Also Called: Trauma Tattoos
7005 University Blvd (32792-6719)
PHONE.................................321 972-9980
Angela Alban Naranjo, *President*
Tom Seland, *Director*
Mitchell Hatton, *Analyst*
EMP: 24 EST: 2011
SQ FT: 5,500
SALES (est): 3.5MM Privately Held
WEB: www.simetri.us
SIC: 3999 Mannequins

(G-19446)
SONNYS STRINGS INC
311 E Morse Blvd Apt 1-3 (32789-3833)
PHONE..................................407 862-4905
Sonia Glatting, *President*
▲ **EMP:** 8 **EST:** 1972
SQ FT: 600
SALES (est): 224.8K **Privately Held**
SIC: 3961 Costume jewelry, ex. precious metal & semiprecious stones

(G-19447)
SPINENET LLC
1300 Minnesota Ave # 200 (32789-4800)
PHONE..................................321 439-1806
King Floyd, *President*
EMP: 12 **EST:** 2006
SALES (est): 718.2K **Privately Held**
WEB: www.spinenetllc.com
SIC: 3842 Implants, surgical

(G-19448)
STAY SMART CARE LLC
941 W Morse Blvd (32789-3734)
PHONE..................................321 682-7113
Alan Young, *Officer*
Mark Feinberg,
EMP: 5 **EST:** 2018
SALES (est): 992.4K **Privately Held**
WEB: www.staysmartcare.com
SIC: 7372 Application computer software
PA: Feinberg Health Partners, Llc
941 W Morse Blvd
Winter Park FL 32789
321 682-7113

(G-19449)
STELLAR SIGN AND DESIGN LLC
7005 Stapoint Ct (32792-6696)
PHONE..................................407 660-3174
Kenneth Soday, *President*
Steven Hauck, *Managing Prtnr*
Wanda Erickson, *General Mgr*
Steve Hauck, *Vice Pres*
Tom Hughes, *Manager*
EMP: 18 **EST:** 2014
SALES (est): 2.6MM **Privately Held**
WEB: www.poblocki.com
SIC: 3993 Electric signs

(G-19450)
T BEATTIE ENTERPRISES
Also Called: American Heritage Press
7208 Aloma Ave Ste 300 (32792-7134)
PHONE..................................407 679-2000
Richard Beattie, *President*
EMP: 15 **EST:** 1969
SQ FT: 3,600
SALES (est): 616.3K **Privately Held**
SIC: 2752 Commercial printing, offset

(G-19451)
TAPINFLUENCE INC
480 N Orlando Ave Ste 200 (32789-2918)
PHONE..................................720 726-4071
Promise Phelon, *CEO*
Brian Brady, *Director*
EMP: 21 **EST:** 2009
SALES (est): 3MM **Publicly Held**
WEB: www.tapinfluence.com
SIC: 7372 Business oriented computer software
PA: Izea Worldwide, Inc.
1317 Edgewater Dr 1880
Orlando FL 32804

(G-19452)
TENNESSEE TOOL AND FIXTURE LLC
1750 Barcelona Way (32789-5672)
PHONE..................................931 954-5316
Scott Neidig, *Business Mgr*
Rob Brooks, *Mng Member*
EMP: 13 **EST:** 2017
SALES (est): 2MM **Privately Held**
WEB: www.tntool.com
SIC: 3544 Special dies & tools

(G-19453)
TITANIUM PERFORMANCE LLC
1233 Valley Creek Run (32792-8156)
PHONE..................................407 712-5770
Ty Sochacki, *Principal*
EMP: 5 **EST:** 2015
SALES (est): 329.2K **Privately Held**
SIC: 3356 Titanium

(G-19454)
U S HARDWARE SUPPLY INC
4675 Metric Dr (32792-6980)
PHONE..................................407 657-1551
Nissim Astrouck, *President*
Becky C Clark, *Manager*
EMP: 22 **EST:** 1981
SQ FT: 30,000
SALES (est): 4.8MM **Privately Held**
WEB: www.ushardwaresupply.com
SIC: 3714 3429 3469 3542 Motor vehicle parts & accessories; clamps, couplings, nozzles & other metal hose fittings; metal stampings; machine tools, metal forming type; bolts, nuts, rivets & washers

(G-19455)
URECON SYSTEMS INC
4046 N Goldenrod Rd 162 (32792-8911)
PHONE..................................321 638-2364
EMP: 150
SALES (est): 1.3MM **Privately Held**
SIC: 2295 Mfg Coated Fabrics

(G-19456)
URECON SYSTEMS INC
7136 Smallow Run (32792)
PHONE..................................904 695-3332
Gregg Gaylard, *President*
Maurice Tousignant, *President*
Christian Phenix, *Vice Pres*
Nicole Stojc, *Controller*
EMP: 41 **EST:** 1994
SALES (est): 1MM
SALES (corp-wide): 10MM **Privately Held**
WEB: www.urecon.com
SIC: 3321 Cast iron pipe & fittings
HQ: Gf Urecon Ltd
75 Boul Dupont
Coteau-Du-Lac QC J0P 1
450 455-0961

(G-19457)
WATERBOY SPORTS LLC
1717 Minnesota Ave Ste A (32789-4614)
PHONE..................................407 869-9881
Robert Mercer,
EMP: 6 **EST:** 2013
SQ FT: 4,500
SALES (est): 222.1K **Privately Held**
WEB: www.waterboysports.com
SIC: 3949 Team sports equipment

(G-19458)
WILSONS MACHINE PRODUCTS INC
1844 Kentucky Ave (32789-4529)
PHONE..................................407 644-2020
Douglas T Stevenson, *President*
Douglas Stevenson, *Mfg Staff*
Sherry Gaidry, *CFO*
EMP: 38 **EST:** 1947
SQ FT: 10,400
SALES (est): 4.5MM **Privately Held**
WEB: www.wilsons-machine.com
SIC: 3599 Machine shop, jobbing & repair

(G-19459)
WINTER PARK DISTILLING CO LLC
1288 Orange Ave (32789-4940)
P.O. Box 2878 (32790-2878)
PHONE..................................407 801-2714
EMP: 10 **EST:** 2017
SALES (est): 358.5K **Privately Held**
WEB: www.wpdistilling.com
SIC: 2085 Distilled & blended liquors

(G-19460)
WINTER PARK PUBLISHING CO LLC
201 W Canton Ave Ste 125b (32789-3172)
PHONE..................................941 320-6627
EMP: 9 **EST:** 2018
SALES (est): 1.1MM **Privately Held**
WEB: www.winterparkmag.com
SIC: 2741 Miscellaneous publishing

(G-19461)
WORKING MOTHER MEDIA INC
Also Called: Diversity Best Practices
480 N Orlando Ave Ste 236 (32789-2918)
PHONE..................................212 351-6400
Carol Evans, *President*
Joan Labarge, *Publisher*
Michele Siegel, *Research*
Michele Zito, *Research*
Nancy Colter, *CFO*
EMP: 51 **EST:** 2001
SALES (est): 11.9MM
SALES (corp-wide): 2.4B **Privately Held**
WEB: www.workingmother.com
SIC: 2721 4813 Magazines: publishing only, not printed on site;
HQ: Bonnier Corporation
480 N Orlando Ave Ste 236
Winter Park FL 32789

(G-19462)
WORLD PUBLICATIONS INC
460 N Orlando Ave Ste 200 (32789-2920)
PHONE..................................407 628-4802
Terry L Snow, *Principal*
EMP: 5 **EST:** 2011
SALES (est): 554.3K **Privately Held**
WEB: www.cruisingworld.com
SIC: 2721 Magazines: publishing only, not printed on site

(G-19463)
YEAGER MANUFACTURING TECH LLC
6869 Stapoint Ct Ste 101 (32792-6603)
PHONE..................................407 573-7033
Zachary Yeager, *President*
EMP: 12 **EST:** 2018
SALES (est): 1.1MM **Privately Held**
WEB: www.yeagermanufacturing.com
SIC: 3999 3499 Manufacturing industries; fabricated metal products

(G-19464)
ZEL TECH TRINING SOLUTIONS LLC
7123 University Blvd (32792-6722)
PHONE..................................757 722-5565
Jack L Ezzell Jr, *CEO*
Jim Grant, *President*
William Barfield, *General Mgr*
Lynn Taylor, *CFO*
Mike Chesser, *Analyst*
EMP: 27 **EST:** 2012
SALES (est): 2.8MM **Privately Held**
WEB: www.zeltech.com
SIC: 3541 Machine tools, metal cutting type

Winter Springs
Seminole County

(G-19465)
ACCESS ABLE TECHNOLOGIES INC
360 Old Sanford Oviedo Rd (32708-2664)
PHONE..................................407 834-2999
Kenneth B Mc Garvey, *President*
Christie Mc Garvey, *Vice Pres*
Carolyn Mc Garvey, *Treasurer*
Ken McGarvey, *Human Res Mgr*
EMP: 5 **EST:** 1993
SQ FT: 3,600
SALES (est): 732K **Privately Held**
WEB: www.accessabletech.com
SIC: 2295 Sealing or insulating tape for pipe: coated fiberglass

(G-19466)
ADAPTIVE INSIGHTS INC
1401 Town Plaza Ct (32708-6222)
PHONE..................................800 303-6346
EMP: 7 **Publicly Held**
WEB: www.adaptiveplanning.com
SIC: 7372 Business oriented computer software
HQ: Adaptive Insights Llc
2300 Geng Rd Ste 100
Palo Alto CA 94303
650 528-7500

(G-19467)
AIREHEALTH INC (PA)
1511 E State Road 434 # 2 (32708-5644)
PHONE..................................407 280-4107
Stacie Ruth, *CEO*
Frank O 'neill, *Engineer*
Matt Weed, *Development*
Kayla Mangan, *Finance*
Ralph Asencio, *Senior Mgr*
EMP: 12 **EST:** 2018
SALES (est): 1.3MM **Privately Held**
SIC: 3845 Respiratory analysis equipment, electromedical

(G-19468)
BARCODE AUTOMATION INC
207 N Moss Rd Ste 105 (32708-2591)
PHONE..................................407 327-2177
Doug Jarrett, *President*
Elizabeth Seibert, *Vice Pres*
Elizabeth B Seibert, *Opers Mgr*
Jim Pope, *Opers Staff*
Ryan Waxberg, *Marketing Staff*
EMP: 10 **EST:** 1996
SALES (est): 1.2MM **Privately Held**
WEB: www.barcode-automation.com
SIC: 3625 Control equipment, electric

(G-19469)
BOB VIOLETT MODELS INC
Also Called: B V M
3481 State Road 419 (32708-2667)
PHONE..................................407 327-6333
Robert Violet, *President*
▲ **EMP:** 20 **EST:** 1982
SQ FT: 8,500
SALES (est): 2.3MM **Privately Held**
WEB: www.bvmjets.com
SIC: 3944 Craft & hobby kits & sets

(G-19470)
CUSTOM CFT WINDOWS & DOORS INC
1436 Northern Way (32708-3848)
PHONE..................................407 834-5400
George Lawlor, *President*
EMP: 11 **EST:** 1984
SQ FT: 20,640
SALES (est): 405.8K **Privately Held**
SIC: 3442 3444 3231 2431 Window & door frames; sheet metalwork; products of purchased glass; millwork; door & window products; doors & windows

(G-19471)
DANIEL LAMPERT COMMUNICATIONS
Also Called: Dlc
101 Brookshire Ct (32708-6303)
P.O. Box 151719, Altamonte Springs (32715-1719)
PHONE..................................407 327-7000
Daniel Lampert, *President*
EMP: 10 **EST:** 1998
SALES (est): 2.2MM **Privately Held**
WEB: www.daniellampert.com
SIC: 7372 Prepackaged software

(G-19472)
EQUITY GROUP USA INC
1129 Citrus Oaks Run (32708-4800)
PHONE..................................407 421-6464
Carlos Lafont, *President*
EMP: 5 **EST:** 2006
SALES (est): 733.9K **Privately Held**
WEB: www.egroupu.com
SIC: 3357 2411 3496 Nonferrous wiredrawing & insulating; rails, fence: round or split; mesh, made from purchased wire

(G-19473)
HBYS ENTERPRISES LLC
Also Called: Pin Creator, The
1170 Tree Swallow Dr # 347 (32708-2826)
PHONE..................................855 290-9900
Jeff Steiner,
EMP: 10 **EST:** 2009
SALES (est): 544.9K **Privately Held**
SIC: 3999 Identification badges & insignia

(G-19474)
IPAC INC
Also Called: Interntnal Pckg Athntic Cisine
1270 Belle Ave Unit 115 (32708-1905)
PHONE..................................407 699-7507

Steve Adamission, *President*
Paul Adamission, *Vice Pres*
Seth Van Der Stelt, *Manager*
EMP: 5 **EST:** 1995
SQ FT: 3,000
SALES (est): 1MM **Privately Held**
WEB: www.copack.com
SIC: 2099 Tortillas, fresh or refrigerated

(G-19475)
IRADIMED CORPORATION
1025 Willa Springs Dr (32708-5235)
PHONE..................................407 677-8022
Roger Susi, *Ch of Bd*
Steven Kachelmeyer, *Vice Pres*
Lynn Neuhardt, *Vice Pres*
Tom Foshee, *Prdtn Mgr*
Raymond Ascue, *Mfg Mgr*
▲ **EMP:** 110 **EST:** 1992
SQ FT: 23,100
SALES: 31.7MM **Privately Held**
WEB: www.iradimed.com
SIC: 3841 Diagnostic apparatus, medical

(G-19476)
IRVIN TECHNOLOGIES INC
1081 Willa Springs Dr (32708-5235)
PHONE..................................866 245-9356
Anthony Irvin, *President*
Anthony W Irvin, *Principal*
Kevin Lebeau, *Vice Pres*
Brian Hooker, *Engineer*
Kevin Speed, *Admin Sec*
EMP: 38 **EST:** 2003
SQ FT: 24,000
SALES (est): 6.4MM **Privately Held**
WEB: www.itiengineering.com
SIC: 3728 5045 7371 7373 Aircraft parts & equipment; computers, peripherals & software; custom computer programming services; computer integrated systems design; data processing & preparation; engineering services

(G-19477)
LATIN GODDESS PRESS INC
872 Leopard Trl (32708-4147)
PHONE..................................917 703-1356
Bermudez Anibal, *Principal*
EMP: 7 **EST:** 2015
SALES (est): 66.5K **Privately Held**
SIC: 2741 Miscellaneous publishing

(G-19478)
LINQS INC
1511 E State Road 434 # 2 (32708-5644)
PHONE..................................321 244-2626
Ozkan Erdem, *President*
Ozkan M Erdem, *President*
Ken Arkin, *Business Mgr*
EMP: 10 **EST:** 2010
SALES (est): 667.5K **Privately Held**
WEB: www.linqsdata.com
SIC: 7372 Business oriented computer software

(G-19479)
MICROSIMULATORS INC
1612 White Dove Dr (32708-3864)
PHONE..................................407 696-8722
David J Smith Sr, *CEO*
R Spencer Hughes, *Vice Pres*
EMP: 9 **EST:** 1999
SALES (est): 769.6K **Privately Held**
SIC: 3699 Flight simulators (training aids), electronic

(G-19480)
PREMIX-MARBLETITE MFG CO
325 Old Sanford Oviedo Rd (32708-2627)
PHONE..................................407 327-0830
Henry Dye, *Manager*
EMP: 13
SQ FT: 1,905
SALES (corp-wide): 216.4MM **Privately Held**
WEB: www.pmmproducts.com
SIC: 3299 3275 Stucco; gypsum products
HQ: Premix-Marbletite Manufacturing Co Inc
1259 Nw 21st St
Pompano Beach FL 33069
954 970-6540

(G-19481)
PRO CO INC
910 Belle Ave Ste 1000 (32708-2968)
PHONE..................................321 422-0900
Brian Mullins, *President*
William Grabe, *Vice Pres*
Cheryl Helmly, *Sales Staff*
EMP: 5 **EST:** 1989
SQ FT: 2,000
SALES (est): 1.1MM **Privately Held**
WEB: www.pro-co.com
SIC: 3625 Control equipment, electric

(G-19482)
PROGRAM WORKS INC
1511 E State Road 434 # 2001 (32708-5646)
P.O. Box 4225, Sanford (32772-4225)
PHONE..................................407 489-4140
Carol Beyner, *Principal*
EMP: 12 **EST:** 2011
SALES (est): 602.5K **Privately Held**
WEB: www.workschedule.net
SIC: 7372 Prepackaged software

(G-19483)
REK DESIGN & PRINT LLC
1306 Winter Springs Blvd (32708-3801)
PHONE..................................407 331-5100
Ghassan Rahal, *Mng Member*
EMP: 8 **EST:** 2016
SALES (est): 176.6K **Privately Held**
SIC: 2752 Commercial printing, lithographic

(G-19484)
STRAIGHTLINE METALS
1150 Belle Ave (32708-2962)
PHONE..................................407 988-2353
EMP: 6 **EST:** 2018
SALES (est): 101.2K **Privately Held**
WEB: www.straightlinemetals.com
SIC: 3444 Sheet metalwork

(G-19485)
STREAMLINE TECHNOLOGIES INC
1900 Town Plaza Ct (32708-6208)
PHONE..................................407 679-1696
Peter Singhofen, *President*
Annamarie Singhofen, *Treasurer*
EMP: 6 **EST:** 1987
SALES (est): 883.2K **Privately Held**
WEB: www.streamnologies.com
SIC: 7372 7371 Application computer software; computer software development & applications

(G-19486)
T T PUBLICATIONS INC
Also Called: Tow Times
203 W State Road 434 A (32708-2598)
P.O. Box 522020, Longwood (32752-2020)
PHONE..................................407 327-4817
Dave Jones, *President*
Tim Jackson, *Editor*
Peter Aspesi, *Treasurer*
Dennis Brewer, *Treasurer*
William Giorgis, *Admin Sec*
EMP: 29 **EST:** 1983
SQ FT: 3,000
SALES (est): 3.1MM **Privately Held**
WEB: www.towtimes.com
SIC: 2721 Magazines: publishing only, not printed on site

(G-19487)
UNLIMITED WELDING INC
235 Old Sanford Oviedo Rd (32708-2651)
PHONE..................................407 327-3333
Bonnie Smith, *President*
Brian Smith, *Vice Pres*
Robert Rutherford, *Project Mgr*
Nicky Marjama, *Credit Mgr*
EMP: 30
SQ FT: 22,000
SALES (est): 9MM **Privately Held**
WEB: www.unlimitedwelding.com
SIC: 3441 7692 Fabricated structural metal; welding repair

(G-19488)
WALT DITTMER AND SONS INC
Also Called: Dittmer Architectural Aluminum
1006 Shepard Rd (32708-2018)
PHONE..................................407 699-1755
Dana S Callan, *President*
Walter J Dittmer, *Vice Pres*
Dennis Laskowski, *Safety Mgr*
Jeff Chisholm, *Production*
Rick Carroll, *Technology*
EMP: 36 **EST:** 1962
SQ FT: 26,000
SALES (est): 4.7MM **Privately Held**
WEB: www.dittdeck.com
SIC: 3354 3089 Shapes, extruded aluminum; plastic hardware & building products

(G-19489)
WILLIAMS MINERALS CO INC
168 Seville Chase Dr (32708-3920)
PHONE..................................304 897-6003
Brenda J Williams, *President*
Keith A Williams, *Vice Pres*
EMP: 6 **EST:** 1975
SALES (est): 377.1K **Privately Held**
SIC: 2517 5099 Wood television & radio cabinets; novelties, durable

Yalaha
Lake County

(G-19490)
HOLLYWOOD DESIGN & CONCEPTS
26534 Bloomfield Ave (34797-3426)
PHONE..................................954 458-4634
David L Wade, *President*
Julie Elsbury, *Vice Pres*
EMP: 11 **EST:** 1994
SQ FT: 8,000
SALES (est): 491.6K **Privately Held**
SIC: 3446 3444 Stairs, staircases, stair treads: prefabricated metal; railings, banisters, guards, etc.: made from metal pipe; sheet metalwork

Yankeetown
Levy County

(G-19491)
SNOOK INDUSTRIES
5217 Riverside Dr (34498-2238)
P.O. Box 250 (34498-0250)
PHONE..................................352 447-0735
Robert Snook, *President*
EMP: 6 **EST:** 1994
SALES (est): 157.7K **Privately Held**
SIC: 3999 Manufacturing industries

Yulee
Nassau County

(G-19492)
50 HWY 17 S INC
850822 Us Highway 17 (32097-6826)
P.O. Box 1033 (32041-1033)
PHONE..................................904 225-1077
Matt Clarkston, *President*
EMP: 7 **EST:** 2005
SALES (est): 295.3K **Privately Held**
SIC: 3949 Bowling alleys & accessories

(G-19493)
A M RAYONIER PRODUCTS INC
1 Rayonier Way (32097-0002)
PHONE..................................904 261-3611
CA McDonald, *Manager*
EMP: 300
SALES (corp-wide): 1.7B **Publicly Held**
WEB: www.rayonieram.com
SIC: 2679 Pressed fiber products from wood pulp: from purchased goods
HQ: Rayonier A.M. Products Inc.
1301 Riverplace Blvd
Jacksonville FL 32207
904 357-9100

(G-19494)
AB AMPERE INDUSTRIAL PANELS
96266 Dowling Dr (32097-6319)
PHONE..................................904 379-4168
Sharon M Caserta, *Principal*
EMP: 7 **EST:** 2012
SALES (est): 255.7K **Privately Held**
SIC: 3825 Electrical power measuring equipment

(G-19495)
ALM TECHNOLOGIES INC
Also Called: Definitive Design
850816 Us Highway 17 (32097-6826)
P.O. Box 707 (32041-0707)
PHONE..................................904 849-7212
Michael J Piscatella, *President*
Steve Crow, *VP Opers*
Jake Costello, *Engineer*
Angela Gross, *Director*
Robin Mosley, *Administration*
EMP: 25 **EST:** 2011
SQ FT: 14,000
SALES (est): 4.6MM **Privately Held**
WEB: www.almtechnologiesinc.com
SIC: 3324 3728 Aerospace investment castings, ferrous; aircraft parts & equipment

(G-19496)
FIRST COAST FABRICATION INC
96144 Nassau Pl (32097-8626)
P.O. Box 1800 (32041-1800)
PHONE..................................904 849-7426
Christopher D Wolfe, *President*
Christopher Wolfe, *President*
Douglas H Wolfe, *President*
K Patsy Wolfe, *Treasurer*
EMP: 8 **EST:** 1979
SQ FT: 9,000
SALES (est): 1.6MM **Privately Held**
WEB: www.carolinafosterkidsfoundation.org
SIC: 7692 3599 Welding repair; machine shop, jobbing & repair

(G-19497)
FLORIDA MCH WORKS LTD PARTNR
86412 Gene Lassere Blvd (32097-3379)
P.O. Box 2710 (32041-2710)
PHONE..................................904 225-2090
Rebecca Armstrong, *Managing Prtnr*
Mike Price, *Mfg Mgr*
Mike Gall, *Engineer*
Bill Skipper, *Sales Staff*
Frank Showers, *Manager*
EMP: 10 **EST:** 2002
SQ FT: 38,000
SALES (est): 2.2MM **Privately Held**
WEB: www.floridamachineworks.com
SIC: 3599 Machine shop, jobbing & repair

(G-19498)
GILMAN BUILDING PRODUCTS LLC
581705 White Oak Rd (32097-2169)
PHONE..................................904 548-1000
EMP: 10 **EST:** 2019
SALES (est): 1MM **Privately Held**
SIC: 2421 Sawmills & planing mills, general

(G-19499)
RAYONIER INC
Fernandina Mill Division
1 Rayonier Way (32097-0002)
PHONE..................................904 277-1343
Robin Mock, *Safety Mgr*
Steve Olsen, *Manager*
Seth Walker, *Manager*
EMP: 41
SALES (corp-wide): 859.1MM **Publicly Held**
WEB: www.rayonier.com
SIC: 2611 2823 Pulp mills; cellulosic manmade fibers
PA: Rayonier Inc.
1 Rayonier Way
Yulee FL 32097
904 357-9100

(G-19500)
SCIENCE FIRST LLC
86475 Gene Lassere Blvd (32097-3378)
PHONE..................................904 225-5558
Aaron Bell, *President*
Mark Eidemueller, *Vice Pres*
Robert Exon, *Foreman/Supr*
Lori Chorbak, *Purch Mgr*
Derick Douglas, *Engineer*
◆ **EMP:** 35
SALES (est): 8MM **Privately Held**
WEB: www.sciencefirst.com
SIC: 3999 Education aids, devices & supplies

(G-19501)
SOYTHANE TECHNOLOGIES INC
Also Called: Expandothane
850709 Us Highway 17 (32097-3984)
P.O. Box 879 (32041-0879)
PHONE..................................904 225-1047
Fred A Akel, *President*
▲ **EMP:** 10 **EST:** 2009
SALES (est): 331.1K **Privately Held**
WEB: www.soythane.com
SIC: 2851 Polyurethane coatings

Zellwood
Orange County

(G-19502)
ANUVIA PLANT NTRNTS HLDNGS LLC
6751 W Jones Ave (32798)
P.O. Box 220 (32798-0220)
PHONE..................................352 720-7070
EMP: 6
SALES (est): 567K **Privately Held**
SIC: 2873 Nitrogenous Fertilizers, Nsk

(G-19503)
GOHO ENTERPRISES INC
Also Called: Auto Kare
3351 Laughlan Rd (32798)
P.O. Box 610 (32798-0610)
PHONE..................................407 884-0770
Douglas Gondera, *President*
Timothy Hoatson, *Treasurer*
EMP: 10 **EST:** 1979
SALES (est): 699.6K **Privately Held**
SIC: 2842 5169 Specialty cleaning, polishes & sanitation goods; chemicals & allied products

(G-19504)
K & M TRUSS INC
2844 N Ornge Blssom Trl (32798)
P.O. Box 1138 (32798-1138)
PHONE..................................407 880-4551
Micheal Farvis, *President*
EMP: 8 **EST:** 2006
SQ FT: 900
SALES (est): 837.1K **Privately Held**
WEB: www.kmtruss.com
SIC: 2439 Trusses, wooden roof

(G-19505)
ZELLWIN FARMS COMPANY (PA)
6052 Jones Ave (32798)
P.O. Box 188 (32798-0188)
PHONE..................................407 886-9241
Glen Rogers, *President*
Suzanne P Roberts, *Corp Secy*
M C Jorgenson, *Vice Pres*
Kennedy Charles W, *Vice Pres*
Thomas L Youngs, *Vice Pres*
▲ **EMP:** 50 **EST:** 1947
SALES (est): 22.6MM **Privately Held**
WEB: www.zellwin.com
SIC: 2671 Packaging paper & plastics film, coated & laminated

Zephyrhills
Pasco County

(G-19506)
ALL CRAFT MARINE LLC
Also Called: Century Boats
40047 County Road 54 (33540-7951)
PHONE..................................813 236-8879
Bryan Lucius, *Senior VP*
Thomas A Alsup, *Vice Pres*
Frederick H Brown Jr, *CFO*
Skip Sorenson, *Mng Member*
Jessica English, *Admin Asst*
EMP: 44 **EST:** 2004
SALES (est): 8.9MM **Privately Held**
WEB: www.centuryboats.com
SIC: 3732 Motorized boat, building & repairing

(G-19507)
ALTIUM PACKAGING LLC
4330 20th St (33542-6703)
PHONE..................................813 782-2695
Dan Sarris, *Plant Mgr*
EMP: 19
SALES (corp-wide): 12.5B **Publicly Held**
WEB: www.altiumpkg.com
SIC: 3089 Plastic containers, except foam
HQ: Altium Packaging Llc
2500 Windy Ridge Pkwy Se # 1400
Atlanta GA 30339
678 742-4600

(G-19508)
AVIATION INSTRUMENT TECH INC (PA)
39520 Aviation Ave (33542-5293)
PHONE..................................813 783-3361
Dave Teichman, *President*
Jeffrey Rosenberg, *CFO*
▲ **EMP:** 13 **EST:** 1997
SALES (est): 4MM **Privately Held**
WEB: www.aircraftinstruments.com
SIC: 3699 3812 4581 Flight simulators (training aids), electronic; aircraft control instruments; aircraft maintenance & repair services

(G-19509)
CALIBER COATING INC
39615 Dawson Chase Dr (33540-7342)
PHONE..................................813 928-1461
Christopher Stubbs, *Principal*
EMP: 7 **EST:** 2016
SALES (est): 129.9K **Privately Held**
SIC: 3479 Metal coating & allied service

(G-19510)
CENTRAL STATE AGGREGATES LLC
41150 Yonkers Blvd (33541)
P.O. Box 100, Crystal Springs (33524-0100)
PHONE..................................813 788-0454
Dan Coy, *Sales Staff*
Brandell Kemble, *Mng Member*
EMP: 16 **EST:** 2007
SALES (est): 5.5MM **Privately Held**
WEB: www.csagg.com
SIC: 1411 Dimension stone

(G-19511)
CISAM LLC
32789 Eiland Blvd (33545-5268)
PHONE..................................813 404-4180
EMP: 6 **EST:** 2018
SALES (est): 632.6K **Privately Held**
WEB: www.cisamservice.com
SIC: 3559 Special industry machinery

(G-19512)
CRAZY 4 SIGNS LLC
4819 Allen Rd (33541-3553)
PHONE..................................813 239-3085
Deborah Patel, *Principal*
EMP: 6 **EST:** 2015
SALES (est): 532.1K **Privately Held**
WEB: www.crazy4signs.com
SIC: 3993 Signs & advertising specialties

(G-19513)
DADS POWDER COATING
40420 Free Fall Ave (33542-5801)
PHONE..................................813 715-6561
Cameron Shaun Evans, *Principal*
EMP: 9 **EST:** 2014
SALES (est): 1.5MM **Privately Held**
WEB: www.dadspowdercoating.com
SIC: 3479 Coating of metals & formed products

(G-19514)
DIXIE RESTORATIONS LLC
2212 Hilda Ann Rd (33540-7206)
PHONE..................................813 785-2159
EMP: 7 **EST:** 2018
SALES (est): 801.7K **Privately Held**
SIC: 3089 Automotive parts, plastic

(G-19515)
ELEVATED DUMPSTERS LLC
37550 Phelps Rd (33541-7434)
PHONE..................................813 732-6338
Frank J Brassart, *President*
EMP: 9 **EST:** 2017
SALES (est): 738.8K **Privately Held**
SIC: 3443 Dumpsters, garbage

(G-19516)
ENDLESS COATINGS INC
8607 Gall Blvd (33541-7469)
PHONE..................................813 714-5395
EMP: 6 **EST:** 2009
SALES (est): 86.3K **Privately Held**
SIC: 3479 Metal coating & allied service

(G-19517)
FAST FORWARD RACE ENGINES INC
2610 Paul S Buchman Hwy (33540-3104)
PHONE..................................813 788-1794
Amanda S Long, *President*
EMP: 6 **EST:** 2009
SALES (est): 82.5K **Privately Held**
WEB: www.fastforwardracecars.com
SIC: 3519 Internal combustion engines

(G-19518)
FIREDRAKE INC
39309 Air Park Rd (33542-5240)
PHONE..................................813 713-8902
John Cooley, *President*
EMP: 9 **EST:** 1985
SQ FT: 3,500
SALES (est): 500K **Privately Held**
WEB: www.firedrakeinc.com
SIC: 3082 7389 3993 3544 Unsupported plastics profile shapes; lettering service; signs & advertising specialties; special dies, tools, jigs & fixtures

(G-19519)
FLEX TEC COATING SERVICES LLC
3348 Anata Dr (33541-5040)
PHONE..................................813 481-8354
Alexander B Robles, *President*
EMP: 6 **EST:** 2016
SALES (est): 123.2K **Privately Held**
WEB: www.flex-tec.com
SIC: 3599 Machine shop, jobbing & repair

(G-19520)
FLUSHING AMUSEMENT INC
40423 Air Time Ave (33542-5837)
PHONE..................................813 780-7900
Lenin Budloo, *President*
Annette Budloo, *Treasurer*
EMP: 5 **EST:** 1987
SQ FT: 7,500
SALES (est): 367K **Privately Held**
WEB: www.flushingmfg.com
SIC: 3999 Coin-operated amusement machines

(G-19521)
GILLETTE SIGN & LIGHTING INC
1609 Warbler St (33540-3383)
P.O. Box 924, Dade City (33526-0924)
PHONE..................................352 256-2225
Wyatt Gillette, *Principal*
EMP: 7 **EST:** 2015
SALES (est): 355.3K **Privately Held**
SIC: 3993 Signs & advertising specialties

(G-19522)
HOYLES LOGGING
40430 Jerry Rd (33540-7104)
PHONE..................................813 782-1164
C Hoyle, *Principal*
EMP: 5 **EST:** 2002
SALES (est): 302.6K **Privately Held**
SIC: 2411 Logging camps & contractors

(G-19523)
INSTACRETE MOBILE CONCRETE
6253 Candlewood Dr (33544-5834)
PHONE..................................813 956-3741
John E Munroe, *President*
EMP: 11 **EST:** 2004
SALES (est): 272.9K **Privately Held**
SIC: 3273 Ready-mixed concrete

(G-19524)
JOHN ERIC MADDEN
Also Called: Team One Furniture Resources
34811 Arbor Green Pl (33541-2776)
PHONE..................................813 395-3314
John Madden, *Owner*
EMP: 6 **EST:** 2017
SALES (est): 336.1K **Privately Held**
SIC: 2522 7641 1799 7217 Office furniture, except wood; office furniture repair & maintenance; office furniture installation; carpet & furniture cleaning on location; interior commercial painting contractor;

(G-19525)
JOYCE TELECTRONICS CORP
40421 Chancey Rd Ste 101 (33542-1507)
PHONE..................................727 461-3525
Peter Joyce, *President*
Christopher Joyce, *Vice Pres*
Michael J Joyce, *Vice Pres*
Penny Joyce, *Treasurer*
EMP: 15 **EST:** 1950
SALES (est): 2.2MM **Privately Held**
WEB: www.joycetelectronicscorp.com
SIC: 3679 Headphones, radio

(G-19526)
LATHAM PLASTICS INC
40119 County Road 54 (33540-7953)
PHONE..................................813 783-7212
EMP: 7 **EST:** 2017
SALES (est): 128.6K **Privately Held**
SIC: 3089 Plastics products

(G-19527)
LINVILLE ENTERPRISES LLC
38333 5th Ave (33542-4978)
PHONE..................................813 782-1558
Jane Linville, *Principal*
Danny Linville,
EMP: 5 **EST:** 2010
SALES (est): 310.4K **Privately Held**
SIC: 2711 Newspapers, publishing & printing

(G-19528)
OLDCASTLE COASTAL INC
3749 Copeland Dr (33542-8404)
PHONE..................................813 783-1970
Tim Ortman, *President*
EMP: 1 **EST:** 2007
SALES (est): 12.3MM
SALES (corp-wide): 27.5B **Privately Held**
WEB: www.oldcastlecoastal.com
SIC: 3272 Concrete products
HQ: Oldcastle Coastal, Inc.
4630 Woodland Corporate B
Tampa FL 33614

(G-19529)
ORBITAL CORPORATION OF TAMPA
40421 Chancey Rd Ste 101 (33542-1507)
PHONE..................................813 782-7300
Josh Thakrar, *President*
Shirley Sylvester, *Exec Sec*
EMP: 5 **EST:** 1994
SQ FT: 4,000
SALES (est): 1.8MM **Privately Held**
WEB: www.orbitalcorp.net
SIC: 3315 Cable, steel: insulated or armored

(G-19530)
PASCO VISION CENTER
Also Called: Pusateri, Thomas J MD
38038 North Ave (33542-7468)
PHONE..................................813 788-7656
Stephanie Papello, *Principal*
EMP: 9
SALES (est): 590K **Privately Held**
SIC: 3851 Eyeglasses, lenses & frames

▲ = Import ▼=Export
◆ =Import/Export

(G-19531)
PERFECT REFLECTIONS INC
7708 Avocet Dr (33544-2638)
PHONE..................................813 991-4361
Greg Saunders, *Principal*
EMP: 7 **EST:** 2005
SALES (est): 151.6K **Privately Held**
SIC: 3229 Pressed & blown glass

(G-19532)
PICKET FENCE CHILDRENS
4931 Allen Rd (33541-3527)
PHONE..................................813 713-8589
Robin Beldin, *Principal*
EMP: 6 **EST:** 2016
SALES (est): 86.9K **Privately Held**
SIC: 2273 Carpets & rugs

(G-19533)
PLAZA MATERIALS CORP
41150 Yonkers Blvd (33541)
P.O. Box 100, Crystal Springs (33524-0100)
PHONE..................................813 788-0454
Marcus Jobes, *President*
EMP: 66 **EST:** 1990
SQ FT: 7,000
SALES (est): 4.1MM
SALES (corp-wide): 357.6MM **Privately Held**
WEB: www.yonkerscontractingco.com
SIC: 1411 Dimension stone
PA: Yonkers Contracting Co Inc
969 Midland Ave
Yonkers NY 10704
914 965-1500

(G-19534)
REPUBLIC NEWSPAPERS INC
Zephyrhills News
38333 5th Ave (33542-4978)
P.O. Box 638 (33539-0638)
PHONE..................................813 782-1558
Linda Wood, *Controller*
Janet Gillis, *Loan Officer*
David Walters, *Advt Staff*
EMP: 8
SQ FT: 3,451 **Privately Held**
WEB: www.republicnewspapers.com
SIC: 2711 Newspapers, publishing & printing
PA: Republic Newspapers, Inc.
11863 Kingston Pike
Knoxville TN 37934

(G-19535)
RESORT WINDOW TREATMENTS INC
5157 Gall Blvd (33542-4964)
PHONE..................................813 355-4877
Nancy Bradford, *President*
Steve Bradford, *Vice Pres*
EMP: 5 **EST:** 1998
SQ FT: 10,000
SALES (est): 1MM **Privately Held**
SIC: 2591 Drapery hardware & blinds & shades

(G-19536)
SPECIALTY POWDER COATING LLC
7640 Chenkin Rd (33540-1937)
PHONE..................................813 782-2720
Bonnie L Brock, *President*
Bonnie Brock, *Principal*
EMP: 5 **EST:** 2014
SALES (est): 379.9K **Privately Held**
WEB: www.specialtypowdercoating.com
SIC: 3479 Coating of metals & formed products

(G-19537)
STATEWIDE CSTM CBINETS FLA INC
38535 Palm Grove Dr (33542-7360)
PHONE..................................813 788-3856
Jerry H Moates III, *President*
Rhonda Moates, *Corp Secy*
EMP: 8 **EST:** 1969
SQ FT: 1,000
SALES (est): 1.5MM **Privately Held**
WEB: www.statewidecabinets.com
SIC: 2434 Wood kitchen cabinets

(G-19538)
SUNRISE MANUFACTURING INTL INC
4035 Correia Dr (33542-7116)
PHONE..................................813 780-7369
Henri Pohjolainen, *President*
EMP: 15 **EST:** 2004
SALES (est): 1.3MM **Privately Held**
WEB: www.skydivewings.com
SIC: 3542 Metal container making machines: cans, etc.

(G-19539)
SWANS FEED MILL
8916 Fort King Rd (33541-7421)
PHONE..................................813 782-6969
James Swan, *Partner*
Steven E Swan, *Partner*
Wolfred Swan, *Partner*
EMP: 5 **EST:** 1972
SQ FT: 3,600
SALES (est): 575K **Privately Held**
SIC: 2048 Prepared feeds

(G-19540)
TACTICAL PRCHUTE DLVRY SYSTEMS
4035 Correia Dr (33542-7116)
PHONE..................................813 782-7482
Henri Pohjolainen, *President*
Nina Luoto, *General Mgr*
EMP: 10 **EST:** 2007
SALES (est): 527.6K **Privately Held**
WEB: www.tpdsairborne.com
SIC: 3999 2399 Barber & beauty shop equipment; parachutes

(G-19541)
TEKNA MANUFACTURING LLC
39248 South Ave (33542-5254)
P.O. Box 3263 (33539-3263)
PHONE..................................813 782-6700
Phillip P Janca, *President*
Janet Lessnau, *Managing Dir*
Carol R Janca, *Vice Pres*
◆ **EMP:** 8 **EST:** 2012
SALES (est): 6MM **Privately Held**
WEB: www.hyperbaric-chamber.com
SIC: 3999 Atomizers, toiletry

(G-19542)
WHEELBLAST INC
3951 Copeland Dr (33542-8403)
PHONE..................................813 715-7117
Micheal B Lynch, *President*
Larry Levin, *Finance*
▲ **EMP:** 25 **EST:** 1973
SQ FT: 20,000
SALES (est): 4.5MM **Privately Held**
WEB: www.wheelblastinc.com
SIC: 3479 Coating of metals & formed products

(G-19543)
ZEPHYR FEED COMPANY INC
40140 Lynbrook Dr (33540-7902)
P.O. Box 2679 (33539-2679)
PHONE..................................813 782-1578
Lois Linville, *President*
Danny Linville, *President*
Terry Linville, *Corp Secy*
EMP: 7 **EST:** 1968
SQ FT: 12,000
SALES (est): 748.1K **Privately Held**
SIC: 2048 Chicken feeds, prepared

Zolfo Springs
Hardee County

(G-19544)
CIRCLE C TIMBER INC
2086 Fish Branch Rd (33890-2701)
PHONE..................................863 735-0383
Garit W Cooper, *President*
Krystle A Cooper, *Corp Secy*
EMP: 6 **EST:** 2006
SALES (est): 500K **Privately Held**
SIC: 2411 Logging camps & contractors

(G-19545)
FLORIDA BEEF INC
441 State Road 64 E (33890-9641)
P.O. Box 1004, Alma GA (31510-0140)
PHONE..................................912 632-1183
D Clay Lee, *President*
Phil Wysong, *CFO*
EMP: 50 **EST:** 2001
SQ FT: 8,000
SALES (est): 8.2MM **Privately Held**
SIC: 2011 Beef products from beef slaughtered on site

(G-19546)
MANCINI PACKING COMPANY
Also Called: Manicini Foods
3500 Mancini Pl (33890-4710)
P.O. Box 157 (33890-0157)
PHONE..................................863 735-2000
Richard A Mancini, *President*
Maria Prieto, *Production*
J D Mancini MD, *Director*
Margaret Mancini, *Director*
Mary Mancini, *Director*
▲ **EMP:** 100 **EST:** 1922
SQ FT: 64,000
SALES (est): 13.4MM **Privately Held**
WEB: www.mancinifoods.com
SIC: 2033 Canned fruits & specialties

(G-19547)
NEWVIDA PRODUCTS LLC
4757 Sweetwater Rd (33890-2736)
PHONE..................................863 781-9232
Marlon Pendergrass, *Principal*
EMP: 9 **EST:** 2014
SALES (est): 119.5K **Privately Held**
SIC: 3999 Manufacturing industries

SIC INDEX

Standard Industrial Classification Alphabetical Index

SIC

SIC INDEX

Standard Industrial Classification Numerical Index

SIC NO	PRODUCT

10 metal mining

1011 Iron Ores
1021 Copper Ores
1031 Lead & Zinc Ores
1041 Gold Ores
1044 Silver Ores
1061 Ferroalloy Ores, Except Vanadium
1081 Metal Mining Svcs

12 coal mining

1221 Bituminous Coal & Lignite: Surface Mining
1241 Coal Mining Svcs

13 oil and gas extraction

1311 Crude Petroleum & Natural Gas
1321 Natural Gas Liquids
1381 Drilling Oil & Gas Wells
1382 Oil & Gas Field Exploration Svcs
1389 Oil & Gas Field Svcs, NEC

14 mining and quarrying of nonmetallic minerals, except fuels

1411 Dimension Stone
1422 Crushed & Broken Limestone
1423 Crushed & Broken Granite
1429 Crushed & Broken Stone, NEC
1442 Construction Sand & Gravel
1446 Industrial Sand
1459 Clay, Ceramic & Refractory Minerals, NEC
1475 Phosphate Rock
1479 Chemical & Fertilizer Mining
1481 Nonmetallic Minerals Svcs, Except Fuels
1499 Miscellaneous Nonmetallic Mining

20 food and kindred products

2011 Meat Packing Plants
2013 Sausages & Meat Prdts
2015 Poultry Slaughtering, Dressing & Processing
2021 Butter
2022 Cheese
2023 Milk, Condensed & Evaporated
2024 Ice Cream
2026 Milk
2032 Canned Specialties
2033 Canned Fruits, Vegetables & Preserves
2034 Dried Fruits, Vegetables & Soup
2035 Pickled Fruits, Vegetables, Sauces & Dressings
2037 Frozen Fruits, Juices & Vegetables
2038 Frozen Specialties
2041 Flour, Grain Milling
2043 Cereal Breakfast Foods
2044 Rice Milling
2045 Flour, Blended & Prepared
2046 Wet Corn Milling
2047 Dog & Cat Food
2048 Prepared Feeds For Animals & Fowls
2051 Bread, Bakery Prdts Exc Cookies & Crackers
2052 Cookies & Crackers
2053 Frozen Bakery Prdts
2061 Sugar, Cane
2062 Sugar, Cane Refining
2064 Candy & Confectionery Prdts
2066 Chocolate & Cocoa Prdts
2068 Salted & Roasted Nuts & Seeds
2075 Soybean Oil Mills
2076 Vegetable Oil Mills
2077 Animal, Marine Fats & Oils
2079 Shortening, Oils & Margarine
2082 Malt Beverages
2083 Malt
2084 Wine & Brandy
2085 Liquors, Distilled, Rectified & Blended
2086 Soft Drinks
2087 Flavoring Extracts & Syrups
2091 Fish & Seafoods, Canned & Cured
2092 Fish & Seafoods, Fresh & Frozen
2095 Coffee
2096 Potato Chips & Similar Prdts
2097 Ice
2098 Macaroni, Spaghetti & Noodles
2099 Food Preparations, NEC

21 tobacco products

2111 Cigarettes
2121 Cigars
2131 Tobacco, Chewing & Snuff

22 textile mill products

2211 Cotton, Woven Fabric
2221 Silk & Man-Made Fiber
2231 Wool, Woven Fabric
2241 Fabric Mills, Cotton, Wool, Silk & Man-Made
2251 Hosiery, Women's Full & Knee Length
2252 Hosiery, Except Women's
2253 Knit Outerwear Mills
2254 Knit Underwear Mills
2258 Lace & Warp Knit Fabric Mills
2259 Knitting Mills, NEC
2261 Cotton Fabric Finishers
2262 Silk & Man-Made Fabric Finishers
2269 Textile Finishers, NEC
2273 Carpets & Rugs
2281 Yarn Spinning Mills
2282 Yarn Texturizing, Throwing, Twisting & Winding Mills
2284 Thread Mills
2295 Fabrics Coated Not Rubberized
2297 Fabrics, Nonwoven
2298 Cordage & Twine
2299 Textile Goods, NEC

23 apparel and other finished products made from fabrics and similar material

2311 Men's & Boys' Suits, Coats & Overcoats
2321 Men's & Boys' Shirts
2322 Men's & Boys' Underwear & Nightwear
2323 Men's & Boys' Neckwear
2325 Men's & Boys' Separate Trousers & Casual Slacks
2326 Men's & Boys' Work Clothing
2329 Men's & Boys' Clothing, NEC
2331 Women's & Misses' Blouses
2335 Women's & Misses' Dresses
2337 Women's & Misses' Suits, Coats & Skirts
2339 Women's & Misses' Outerwear, NEC
2341 Women's, Misses' & Children's Underwear & Nightwear
2342 Brassieres, Girdles & Garments
2353 Hats, Caps & Millinery
2361 Children's & Infants' Dresses & Blouses
2369 Girls' & Infants' Outerwear, NEC
2371 Fur Goods
2381 Dress & Work Gloves
2384 Robes & Dressing Gowns
2385 Waterproof Outerwear
2386 Leather & Sheep Lined Clothing
2387 Apparel Belts
2389 Apparel & Accessories, NEC
2391 Curtains & Draperies
2392 House furnishings: Textile
2393 Textile Bags
2394 Canvas Prdts
2395 Pleating & Stitching For The Trade
2396 Automotive Trimmings, Apparel Findings, Related Prdts
2397 Schiffli Machine Embroideries
2399 Fabricated Textile Prdts, NEC

24 lumber and wood products, except furniture

2411 Logging
2421 Saw & Planing Mills
2426 Hardwood Dimension & Flooring Mills
2429 Special Prdt Sawmills, NEC
2431 Millwork
2434 Wood Kitchen Cabinets
2435 Hardwood Veneer & Plywood
2436 Softwood Veneer & Plywood
2439 Structural Wood Members, NEC
2441 Wood Boxes
2448 Wood Pallets & Skids
2449 Wood Containers, NEC
2451 Mobile Homes
2452 Prefabricated Wood Buildings & Cmpnts
2491 Wood Preserving
2493 Reconstituted Wood Prdts
2499 Wood Prdts, NEC

25 furniture and fixtures

2511 Wood Household Furniture
2512 Wood Household Furniture, Upholstered
2514 Metal Household Furniture
2515 Mattresses & Bedsprings
2517 Wood T V, Radio, Phono & Sewing Cabinets
2519 Household Furniture, NEC
2521 Wood Office Furniture
2522 Office Furniture, Except Wood
2531 Public Building & Related Furniture
2541 Wood, Office & Store Fixtures
2542 Partitions & Fixtures, Except Wood
2591 Drapery Hardware, Window Blinds & Shades
2599 Furniture & Fixtures, NEC

26 paper and allied products

2611 Pulp Mills
2621 Paper Mills
2631 Paperboard Mills
2652 Set-Up Paperboard Boxes
2653 Corrugated & Solid Fiber Boxes
2655 Fiber Cans, Tubes & Drums
2656 Sanitary Food Containers
2657 Folding Paperboard Boxes
2671 Paper Coating & Laminating for Packaging
2672 Paper Coating & Laminating, Exc for Packaging
2673 Bags: Plastics, Laminated & Coated
2674 Bags: Uncoated Paper & Multiwall
2675 Die-Cut Paper & Board
2676 Sanitary Paper Prdts
2677 Envelopes
2678 Stationery Prdts
2679 Converted Paper Prdts, NEC

27 printing, publishing, and allied industries

2711 Newspapers: Publishing & Printing
2721 Periodicals: Publishing & Printing
2731 Books: Publishing & Printing
2732 Book Printing, Not Publishing
2741 Misc Publishing
2752 Commercial Printing: Lithographic
2754 Commercial Printing: Gravure
2759 Commercial Printing
2761 Manifold Business Forms
2771 Greeting Card Publishing
2782 Blankbooks & Looseleaf Binders
2789 Bookbinding
2791 Typesetting
2796 Platemaking & Related Svcs

28 chemicals and allied products

2812 Alkalies & Chlorine
2813 Industrial Gases
2816 Inorganic Pigments
2819 Indl Inorganic Chemicals, NEC
2821 Plastics, Mtrls & Nonvulcanizable Elastomers
2822 Synthetic Rubber (Vulcanizable Elastomers)
2823 Cellulosic Man-Made Fibers
2824 Synthetic Organic Fibers, Exc Cellulosic
2833 Medicinal Chemicals & Botanical Prdts
2834 Pharmaceuticals
2835 Diagnostic Substances
2836 Biological Prdts, Exc Diagnostic Substances
2841 Soap & Detergents
2842 Spec Cleaning, Polishing & Sanitation Preparations
2843 Surface Active & Finishing Agents, Sulfonated Oils
2844 Perfumes, Cosmetics & Toilet Preparations
2851 Paints, Varnishes, Lacquers, Enamels
2861 Gum & Wood Chemicals
2865 Cyclic-Crudes, Intermediates, Dyes & Org Pigments
2869 Industrial Organic Chemicals, NEC
2873 Nitrogenous Fertilizers
2874 Phosphatic Fertilizers
2875 Fertilizers, Mixing Only
2879 Pesticides & Agricultural Chemicals, NEC
2891 Adhesives & Sealants
2892 Explosives
2893 Printing Ink
2899 Chemical Preparations, NEC

29 petroleum refining and related industries

2911 Petroleum Refining
2951 Paving Mixtures & Blocks
2952 Asphalt Felts & Coatings
2992 Lubricating Oils & Greases
2999 Products Of Petroleum & Coal, NEC

SIC INDEX

SIC NO PRODUCT

30 rubber and miscellaneous plastics products

3011 Tires & Inner Tubes
3021 Rubber & Plastic Footwear
3052 Rubber & Plastic Hose & Belting
3053 Gaskets, Packing & Sealing Devices
3061 Molded, Extruded & Lathe-Cut Rubber Mechanical Goods
3069 Fabricated Rubber Prdts, NEC
3081 Plastic Unsupported Sheet & Film
3082 Plastic Unsupported Profile Shapes
3083 Plastic Laminated Plate & Sheet
3084 Plastic Pipe
3085 Plastic Bottles
3086 Plastic Foam Prdts
3087 Custom Compounding Of Purchased Plastic Resins
3088 Plastic Plumbing Fixtures
3089 Plastic Prdts

31 leather and leather products

3111 Leather Tanning & Finishing
3131 Boot & Shoe Cut Stock & Findings
3142 House Slippers
3143 Men's Footwear, Exc Athletic
3144 Women's Footwear, Exc Athletic
3151 Leather Gloves & Mittens
3161 Luggage
3171 Handbags & Purses
3172 Personal Leather Goods
3199 Leather Goods, NEC

32 stone, clay, glass, and concrete products

3211 Flat Glass
3221 Glass Containers
3229 Pressed & Blown Glassware, NEC
3231 Glass Prdts Made Of Purchased Glass
3241 Cement, Hydraulic
3251 Brick & Structural Clay Tile
3253 Ceramic Tile
3255 Clay Refractories
3259 Structural Clay Prdts, NEC
3261 China Plumbing Fixtures & Fittings
3263 Earthenware, Whiteware, Table & Kitchen Articles
3264 Porcelain Electrical Splys
3269 Pottery Prdts, NEC
3271 Concrete Block & Brick
3272 Concrete Prdts
3273 Ready-Mixed Concrete
3274 Lime
3275 Gypsum Prdts
3281 Cut Stone Prdts
3291 Abrasive Prdts
3292 Asbestos products
3295 Minerals & Earths: Ground Or Treated
3296 Mineral Wool
3297 Nonclay Refractories
3299 Nonmetallic Mineral Prdts, NEC

33 primary metal industries

3312 Blast Furnaces, Coke Ovens, Steel & Rolling Mills
3313 Electrometallurgical Prdts
3315 Steel Wire Drawing & Nails & Spikes
3316 Cold Rolled Steel Sheet, Strip & Bars
3317 Steel Pipe & Tubes
3321 Gray Iron Foundries
3322 Malleable Iron Foundries
3324 Steel Investment Foundries
3325 Steel Foundries, NEC
3331 Primary Smelting & Refining Of Copper
3334 Primary Production Of Aluminum
3339 Primary Nonferrous Metals, NEC
3341 Secondary Smelting & Refining Of Nonferrous Metals
3351 Rolling, Drawing & Extruding Of Copper
3353 Aluminum Sheet, Plate & Foil
3354 Aluminum Extruded Prdts
3355 Aluminum Rolling & Drawing, NEC
3356 Rolling, Drawing-Extruding Of Nonferrous Metals
3357 Nonferrous Wire Drawing
3363 Aluminum Die Castings
3364 Nonferrous Die Castings, Exc Aluminum
3365 Aluminum Foundries
3366 Copper Foundries
3369 Nonferrous Foundries: Castings, NEC
3398 Metal Heat Treating
3399 Primary Metal Prdts, NEC

34 fabricated metal products, except machinery and transportation equipment

3411 Metal Cans
3412 Metal Barrels, Drums, Kegs & Pails
3421 Cutlery
3423 Hand & Edge Tools
3425 Hand Saws & Saw Blades
3429 Hardware, NEC
3431 Enameled Iron & Metal Sanitary Ware
3432 Plumbing Fixture Fittings & Trim, Brass
3433 Heating Eqpt
3441 Fabricated Structural Steel
3442 Metal Doors, Sash, Frames, Molding & Trim
3443 Fabricated Plate Work
3444 Sheet Metal Work
3446 Architectural & Ornamental Metal Work
3448 Prefabricated Metal Buildings & Cmpnts
3449 Misc Structural Metal Work
3451 Screw Machine Prdts
3452 Bolts, Nuts, Screws, Rivets & Washers
3462 Iron & Steel Forgings
3463 Nonferrous Forgings
3465 Automotive Stampings
3469 Metal Stampings, NEC
3471 Electroplating, Plating, Polishing, Anodizing & Coloring
3479 Coating & Engraving, NEC
3482 Small Arms Ammunition
3483 Ammunition, Large
3484 Small Arms
3489 Ordnance & Access, NEC
3491 Industrial Valves
3492 Fluid Power Valves & Hose Fittings
3493 Steel Springs, Except Wire
3494 Valves & Pipe Fittings, NEC
3495 Wire Springs
3496 Misc Fabricated Wire Prdts
3497 Metal Foil & Leaf
3498 Fabricated Pipe & Pipe Fittings
3499 Fabricated Metal Prdts, NEC

35 industrial and commercial machinery and computer equipment

3511 Steam, Gas & Hydraulic Turbines & Engines
3519 Internal Combustion Engines, NEC
3523 Farm Machinery & Eqpt
3524 Garden, Lawn Tractors & Eqpt
3531 Construction Machinery & Eqpt
3532 Mining Machinery & Eqpt
3533 Oil Field Machinery & Eqpt
3534 Elevators & Moving Stairways
3535 Conveyors & Eqpt
3536 Hoists, Cranes & Monorails
3537 Indl Trucks, Tractors, Trailers & Stackers
3541 Machine Tools: Cutting
3542 Machine Tools: Forming
3543 Industrial Patterns
3544 Dies, Tools, Jigs, Fixtures & Indl Molds
3545 Machine Tool Access
3546 Power Hand Tools
3547 Rolling Mill Machinery & Eqpt
3548 Welding Apparatus
3549 Metalworking Machinery, NEC
3552 Textile Machinery
3553 Woodworking Machinery
3554 Paper Inds Machinery
3555 Printing Trades Machinery & Eqpt
3556 Food Prdts Machinery
3559 Special Ind Machinery, NEC
3561 Pumps & Pumping Eqpt
3562 Ball & Roller Bearings
3563 Air & Gas Compressors
3564 Blowers & Fans
3565 Packaging Machinery
3566 Speed Changers, Drives & Gears
3567 Indl Process Furnaces & Ovens
3568 Mechanical Power Transmission Eqpt, NEC
3569 Indl Machinery & Eqpt, NEC
3571 Electronic Computers
3572 Computer Storage Devices
3575 Computer Terminals
3577 Computer Peripheral Eqpt, NEC
3578 Calculating & Accounting Eqpt
3579 Office Machines, NEC
3581 Automatic Vending Machines
3582 Commercial Laundry, Dry Clean & Pressing Mchs
3585 Air Conditioning & Heating Eqpt
3586 Measuring & Dispensing Pumps
3589 Service Ind Machines, NEC
3592 Carburetors, Pistons, Rings & Valves
3593 Fluid Power Cylinders & Actuators
3594 Fluid Power Pumps & Motors
3596 Scales & Balances, Exc Laboratory
3599 Machinery & Eqpt, Indl & Commercial, NEC

36 electronic and other electrical equipment and components, except computer

3612 Power, Distribution & Specialty Transformers
3613 Switchgear & Switchboard Apparatus
3621 Motors & Generators
3624 Carbon & Graphite Prdts
3625 Relays & Indl Controls
3629 Electrical Indl Apparatus, NEC
3631 Household Cooking Eqpt
3632 Household Refrigerators & Freezers
3633 Household Laundry Eqpt
3634 Electric Household Appliances
3635 Household Vacuum Cleaners
3639 Household Appliances, NEC
3641 Electric Lamps
3643 Current-Carrying Wiring Devices
3644 Noncurrent-Carrying Wiring Devices
3645 Residential Lighting Fixtures
3646 Commercial, Indl & Institutional Lighting Fixtures
3647 Vehicular Lighting Eqpt
3648 Lighting Eqpt, NEC
3651 Household Audio & Video Eqpt
3652 Phonograph Records & Magnetic Tape
3661 Telephone & Telegraph Apparatus
3663 Radio & T V Communications, Systs & Eqpt, Broadcast/Studio
3669 Communications Eqpt, NEC
3671 Radio & T V Receiving Electron Tubes
3672 Printed Circuit Boards
3674 Semiconductors
3675 Electronic Capacitors
3676 Electronic Resistors
3677 Electronic Coils & Transformers
3678 Electronic Connectors
3679 Electronic Components, NEC
3691 Storage Batteries
3692 Primary Batteries: Dry & Wet
3694 Electrical Eqpt For Internal Combustion Engines
3695 Recording Media
3699 Electrical Machinery, Eqpt & Splys, NEC

37 transportation equipment

3711 Motor Vehicles & Car Bodies
3713 Truck & Bus Bodies
3714 Motor Vehicle Parts & Access
3715 Truck Trailers
3716 Motor Homes
3721 Aircraft
3724 Aircraft Engines & Engine Parts
3728 Aircraft Parts & Eqpt, NEC
3731 Shipbuilding & Repairing
3732 Boat Building & Repairing
3743 Railroad Eqpt
3751 Motorcycles, Bicycles & Parts
3761 Guided Missiles & Space Vehicles
3764 Guided Missile/Space Vehicle Propulsion Units & parts
3769 Guided Missile/Space Vehicle Parts & Eqpt, NEC
3792 Travel Trailers & Campers
3795 Tanks & Tank Components
3799 Transportation Eqpt, NEC

38 measuring, analyzing and controlling instruments; photographic, medical an

3812 Search, Detection, Navigation & Guidance Systs & Instrs
3821 Laboratory Apparatus & Furniture
3822 Automatic Temperature Controls
3823 Indl Instruments For Meas, Display & Control
3824 Fluid Meters & Counters
3825 Instrs For Measuring & Testing Electricity
3826 Analytical Instruments
3827 Optical Instruments
3829 Measuring & Controlling Devices, NEC
3841 Surgical & Medical Instrs & Apparatus
3842 Orthopedic, Prosthetic & Surgical Appliances/Splys
3843 Dental Eqpt & Splys
3844 X-ray Apparatus & Tubes
3845 Electromedical & Electrotherapeutic Apparatus
3851 Ophthalmic Goods
3861 Photographic Eqpt & Splys
3873 Watch & Clock Devices & Parts

39 miscellaneous manufacturing industries

3911 Jewelry: Precious Metal
3914 Silverware, Plated & Stainless Steel Ware
3915 Jewelers Findings & Lapidary Work
3931 Musical Instruments
3942 Dolls & Stuffed Toys
3944 Games, Toys & Children's Vehicles
3949 Sporting & Athletic Goods, NEC
3951 Pens & Mechanical Pencils

S I C

SIC SECTION

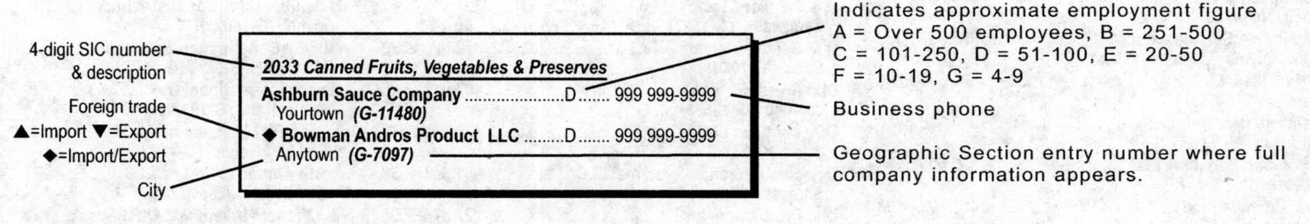

See footnotes for symbols and codes identification.

- The SIC codes in this section are from the latest Standard Industrial Classification manual published by the U.S. Government's Office of Management and Budget. For more information regarding SICs, see the Explanatory Notes.
- Companies may be listed under multiple classifications.

10 METAL MINING

1011 Iron Ores

Chemours Company Fc LLC ....C....... 904 964-1200
Starke ***(G-16890)***
Meelko Co ....G....... 845 600-3379
Opa Locka ***(G-12337)***
Tyrex Ore & Minerals Company ....G....... 305 333-5288
Miami ***(G-10520)***
US Iron LLC ....F....... 765 210-4111
Miramar Beach ***(G-11070)***

1021 Copper Ores

Chemours Company Fc LLC ....C....... 904 964-1200
Starke ***(G-16890)***
Goldfield Cnsld Mines Co ....D....... 321 724-1700
Melbourne ***(G-8837)***
▲ Pd Wire & Cable Sales Corp ....F....... 305 648-7790
Doral ***(G-3456)***
▲ Smart Group Traders Inc ....G....... 850 460-5130
Destin ***(G-3207)***
US Precious Metals Inc ....G....... 786 814-5804
Coral Gables ***(G-2202)***

1031 Lead & Zinc Ores

Chemours Company Fc LLC ....C....... 904 964-1200
Starke ***(G-16890)***

1041 Gold Ores

Bromide Mining LLC ....F....... 786 477-6229
Doral ***(G-3287)***
Chemours Company Fc LLC ....C....... 904 964-1200
Starke ***(G-16890)***
Goldfield Cnsld Mines Co ....D....... 321 724-1700
Melbourne ***(G-8837)***
◆ Iamgold Purchasing Svcs Inc ....G....... 713 671-5973
Doral ***(G-3386)***
International Weatherization ....G....... 954 818-3288
Fort Lauderdale ***(G-4065)***
New World Gold Corporation ....D....... 561 962-4139
Boca Raton ***(G-641)***
▲ Smart Group Traders Inc ....G....... 850 460-5130
Destin ***(G-3207)***
Thierry Brouzet Inc ....G....... 727 449-0158
Clearwater ***(G-1918)***
US Precious Metals Inc ....G....... 786 814-5804
Coral Gables ***(G-2202)***

1044 Silver Ores

Goldfield Cnsld Mines Co ....D....... 321 724-1700
Melbourne ***(G-8837)***
▲ Smart Group Traders Inc ....G....... 850 460-5130
Destin ***(G-3207)***
US Precious Metals Inc ....G....... 786 814-5804
Coral Gables ***(G-2202)***

1061 Ferroalloy Ores, Except Vanadium

▲ Georgian American Alloys Inc ....E....... 305 375-7560
Miami ***(G-9629)***

1081 Metal Mining Svcs

Allied Metals LLC ....F....... 305 635-3360
Miami ***(G-9117)***
American Aggregates LLC ....F....... 813 352-2124
Boca Raton ***(G-420)***
Benchmark Metals Inc ....G....... 239 699-0802
Cape Coral ***(G-1388)***
Evolution Metals Corp ....E....... 561 531-2314
West Palm Beach ***(G-18866)***
Nyrstar Us Inc ....C....... 954 400-6464
Fort Lauderdale ***(G-4145)***
Osler Incorporated ....E....... 954 767-6339
Fort Lauderdale ***(G-4152)***
Tri-State Demolition LLC ....G....... 850 597-8722
Tallahassee ***(G-17342)***
US Precious Metals Inc ....G....... 786 814-5804
Coral Gables ***(G-2202)***

12 COAL MINING

1221 Bituminous Coal & Lignite: Surface Mining

▼ Evolving Coal Corp ....G....... 813 944-3100
Saint Petersburg ***(G-15773)***
North American Coal Corp ....G....... 305 824-9018
Miami ***(G-10077)***
▲ Progress Fuels Corporation ....D....... 727 824-6600
Saint Petersburg ***(G-15892)***
▼ Teco Diversified Inc ....G....... 813 228-4111
Tampa ***(G-18180)***

1241 Coal Mining Svcs

Carbon Resources Inc ....G....... 941 746-8089
Bradenton ***(G-1014)***
Carbon Resources of Florida ....G....... 941 746-8089
Bradenton ***(G-1015)***
Cline Resource and Dev Co ....D....... 561 626-4999
Palm Beach Gardens ***(G-13580)***
Diversified Mining Inc ....G....... 407 923-3194
Winter Park ***(G-19403)***
◆ Keystone Industries LLC ....F....... 239 337-7474
Jacksonville ***(G-6535)***
Mosaic ....E....... 863 860-1328
Lakeland ***(G-7754)***
North American Mining ....G....... 305 824-3181
Medley ***(G-8698)***
Oxbow Carbon LLC ....C....... 561 907-5400
West Palm Beach ***(G-18977)***
Oxbow Enterprises Intl LLC ....G....... 561 907-5400
West Palm Beach ***(G-18978)***
US China Mining Group Inc ....D....... 813 514-2873
Tampa ***(G-18226)***
Vecellio Management Svcs Inc ....E....... 561 793-2102
West Palm Beach ***(G-19077)***
Weber South Fl LLC ....G....... 239 543-7240
Punta Gorda ***(G-15244)***

13 OIL AND GAS EXTRACTION

1311 Crude Petroleum & Natural Gas

Breitburn Operating LP ....D....... 713 452-2266
Jay ***(G-6963)***
C&C Diversified Services LLC ....G....... 772 597-1022
Stuart ***(G-16919)***
Delta Oil ....G....... 813 323-3113
Brandon ***(G-1156)***
Dorward Energy Corporation ....G....... 727 490-1778
Saint Petersburg ***(G-15765)***
E-Direct Oil Inc ....G....... 518 366-2208
Naples ***(G-11232)***
Fromkin Energy LLC ....G....... 954 683-2509
Coral Springs ***(G-2249)***
Jones Field Services Pamela ....G....... 904 368-9777
Starke ***(G-16895)***
K20 Oil LLC ....G....... 954 421-1735
Deerfield Beach ***(G-2852)***
Maverick Natural Resources LLC ....E....... 239 657-2171
Immokalee ***(G-6053)***
Neptune Petroleum LLC ....G....... 561 684-2844
West Palm Beach ***(G-18962)***
Noumenon Corporation ....G....... 302 296-5460
Cape Coral ***(G-1451)***
▼ South Florida Petro Svcs LLC ....G....... 561 793-2102
Fort Lauderdale ***(G-4246)***
Sustainable Projects Group Inc ....G....... 239 316-4593
Naples ***(G-11429)***
Tg Oil Services ....G....... 407 576-9571
Davie ***(G-2604)***
Titan Petroleum Corporation ....G....... 813 280-4833
Tampa ***(G-18188)***
United Energy Corporation ....G....... 904 296-1168
Jacksonville ***(G-6880)***
US Natural Gas Corp ....G....... 727 482-1505
Saint Petersburg ***(G-15949)***
Venkata SAI Corporation ....G....... 352 746-7076
Beverly Hills ***(G-380)***

1321 Natural Gas Liquids

Ideal Gas LLC ....G....... 904 417-6470
Saint Augustine ***(G-15554)***
Mar-Co Gas Services Inc ....G....... 561 745-0085
Jupiter ***(G-7072)***
Nopetro LLC ....G....... 305 441-9059
Tallahassee ***(G-17305)***
◆ Pyrolyzer LLC ....G....... 561 400-1608
Boca Raton ***(G-677)***

1381 Drilling Oil & Gas Wells

Accountble Drctional Drillillc ....G....... 239 226-1606
Fort Myers ***(G-4343)***
AES Services Inc ....G....... 941 237-1446
Venice ***(G-18529)***
Betwell Oil & Gas Company ....G....... 305 821-8300
Hialeah ***(G-5325)***
Bore Tech Inc ....G....... 904 262-0752
Jacksonville ***(G-6226)***
Centerline Drctnal Drlg Svc In ....E....... 863 674-0913
Labelle ***(G-7317)***
Danny Brawley ....G....... 239 597-0084
Naples ***(G-11220)***
Full Bore Directional Inc ....G....... 727 327-7784
Gulfport ***(G-5133)***
Full Circle Directional Inc ....G....... 352 568-0639
Bushnell ***(G-1317)***
Jaffer Wll Drllng A Div of AC ....F....... 954 523-6669
Hialeah ***(G-5460)***
Old City Building ....G....... 850 432-7723
Pensacola ***(G-14215)***
Perfect Oil Inc ....G....... 954 984-8944
Pompano Beach ***(G-14788)***
Precision Directional Drlg LLC ....F....... 941 320-8308
Bradenton ***(G-1101)***
Pretec Directional Drlg LLC ....F....... 786 220-7667
Coral Gables ***(G-2186)***
Raven Forest Operating LLC ....F....... 727 497-2727
Tampa ***(G-18039)***
Sabcon Underground LLC ....E....... 863 268-8225
Winter Haven ***(G-19354)***
Titan Petroleum Corporation ....G....... 813 280-4833
Tampa ***(G-18188)***
US Natural Gas Corp ....G....... 727 482-1505
Saint Petersburg ***(G-15949)***
Warensford Well Drilling Inc ....G....... 386 738-3257
Deland ***(G-3031)***

1382 Oil & Gas Field Exploration Svcs

Albasol LLC......G....830 334-3280
Miami *(G-9100)*
Atlantic Gas Services LLC......G....386 957-3668
New Smyrna Beach *(G-11525)*
CP Royalties LLC......G....888 694-9265
Tampa *(G-17561)*
Dauntless Usa Inc......F....904 996-8800
Jacksonville *(G-6312)*
Exploration Services LLC......G....352 505-3578
Gainesville *(G-4917)*
Fuels Unlimited Inc......G....407 302-3193
Sanford *(G-16051)*
Green Gas America Inc......D....772 220-0717
Palm City *(G-13660)*
Gulfstream Natural Gas Sys LLC......G....941 723-7000
Palmetto *(G-13803)*
Hess Station 09307......F....407 891-7156
Saint Cloud *(G-15653)*
HRF Exploration & Prod LLC......F....561 847-4743
Palm Beach *(G-13556)*
Hunt Ventures Inc......F....941 375-3699
Venice *(G-18555)*
Interntnal Tech Sltons Sup LLC......G....305 364-5229
Doral *(G-3393)*
Kelton Company LLC......G....850 434-6830
Pensacola *(G-14188)*
Kens Gas Piping Inc......G....850 897-4149
Valparaiso *(G-18513)*
Nakasawa Mining and Energy LLC......G....305 302-4980
Miami *(G-10060)*
O Neill Industries Intl Inc......G....850 754-0312
Cantonment *(G-1344)*
Pegasus Resources Corp......G....561 575-2393
Jupiter *(G-7091)*
Platinum Group Usa Inc......F....561 274-7553
Delray Beach *(G-3119)*
Reliance Petro Holdings LLC......F....352 390-8039
Ocala *(G-12036)*
Seacor Marine LLC......D....954 523-2200
Fort Lauderdale *(G-4228)*
Superior Oil 2016 Inc......G....305 851-5140
Miami *(G-10437)*
Tri C Petroleum Inc......G....941 756-3370
Bradenton *(G-1129)*
Whittington Energy Co......G....321 984-2128
Melbourne *(G-8974)*

1389 Oil & Gas Field Svcs, NEC

A Plus Construction Svcs Inc......E....904 612-0597
Jacksonville *(G-6111)*
Advance Green Energy Inc......G....352 765-3850
Inverness *(G-6081)*
Affordble Prsrvtion Rstoration......G....941 527-1416
Sarasota *(G-16335)*
Alfresco Air......F....786 275-5111
Miami *(G-9103)*
All-Jer Construction Usa Inc......G....305 257-0225
Miami *(G-9114)*
American Silica Holdings LLC......G....352 796-8855
Brooksville *(G-1211)*
Blue Tarpon Construction LLC......G....251 223-3630
Pensacola *(G-14101)*
Bodman Oil & Gas LLC......G....239 430-8545
Naples *(G-11190)*
Brace Integrated Services Inc......E....813 248-6248
Tampa *(G-17484)*
Broit Builders Inc......E....239 300-6900
Naples *(G-11195)*
Buena Vista Construction Co......E....407 828-2104
Lake Buena Vista *(G-7335)*
◆ **Bukkehave Inc**......G....954 525-9788
Fort Lauderdale *(G-3876)*
CA Pipeline Inc......G....305 969-4655
Miami *(G-9297)*
Canna Construction LLC......G....239 450-2141
Fort Myers *(G-4386)*
Cannida Co LLC......G....727 642-3709
Saint Petersburg *(G-15737)*
CB Designing Inc......G....407 927-1808
Orlando *(G-12557)*
Certified Mold Free Corp......G....954 614-7100
Davie *(G-2508)*
Charuvil Oil Inc DBA Valero......G....772 871-9050
Port Saint Lucie *(G-15097)*
CMR FL Solutions LLC......G....586 206-2517
Venice *(G-18537)*
Cohen Capital LLC......G....954 661-8270
Fort Lauderdale *(G-3908)*
Compact Contract Inc......G....352 817-8058
Ocala *(G-11906)*
D & S Pallets Inc......D....727 540-0061
Clearwater *(G-1647)*
D M C Industries Inc......G....352 620-9322
Sparr *(G-16843)*
Dbn Investment LLC......F....407 917-2525
Orlando *(G-12658)*
DDy Martinez LLC......F....786 263-2672
Doral *(G-3325)*
Delacom Detection Systems LLC......G....941 544-6636
Sarasota *(G-16408)*
Dilo Production Inc......G....727 376-5593
Odessa *(G-12116)*
Discovery Tank Testing Inc......G....561 840-1666
West Palm Beach *(G-18855)*
Downes Trading Co......G....813 855-7122
Palm Harbor *(G-13734)*
Ducksteins Services......G....352 449-5678
Leesburg *(G-8151)*
E 3 Maintenance......E....904 708-7208
Jacksonville *(G-6343)*
Ed-Gar Leasing Company Inc......F....904 284-1900
Green Cove Springs *(G-5060)*
Elements Restoration LLC......E....813 330-2035
Tampa *(G-17632)*
Elyse Installations LLC......E....904 322-4754
Jacksonville *(G-6360)*
Empirica......F....727 403-0399
Palm Harbor *(G-13736)*
Engineering Analysis Group LLC......G....813 523-7377
Tampa *(G-17642)*
Epoc CNG LLC......G....561 706-4140
Fort Lauderdale *(G-3973)*
Euramerica Gas and Oil Corp......G....954 858-5714
Plantation *(G-14512)*
Expressway Oil Corp......G....786 302-9534
Medley *(G-8650)*
Five Star Field Services......G....347 446-6816
Boynton Beach *(G-905)*
Foster & Foster Worldwide LLC......F....352 362-9102
Apopka *(G-145)*
Gapv......G....786 257-1681
South Miami *(G-16817)*
Gas One Inc......G....561 483-0504
Boca Raton *(G-542)*
Genos Construction Inc......D....234 303-3427
Dade City *(G-2428)*
Grms Servicing LLC......G....850 278-1000
Santa Rosa Beach *(G-16160)*
Hess Express......G....772 335-9975
Port Saint Lucie *(G-15112)*
Hoerbiger America Holding Inc......B....954 422-9850
Deerfield Beach *(G-2840)*
Hoerbiger America Holding Inc......A....954 422-9850
Deerfield Beach *(G-2841)*
House Doctair Inc......F....239 349-7497
Ave Maria *(G-257)*
I C T S America Inc......G....786 307-2993
Doral *(G-3385)*
J&D Oil Field Intl Inc......G....305 436-0024
Doral *(G-3399)*
Jab-B-Inc......G....813 803-3995
Lutz *(G-8393)*
Jdt Servicing LLC......G....813 909-8640
Lutz *(G-8394)*
John A Pulling Jr......G....239 593-5247
Naples *(G-11298)*
Kabrit Repair Services LLC......F....407 714-1470
Windermere *(G-19232)*
Kr Solutions Group US LLC......G....305 307-8353
Doral *(G-3412)*
Legacy Cnstr Rmdlg Clg Svcs LL......E....800 638-9646
Hallandale Beach *(G-5197)*
Los Primos Express Service......G....786 701-3297
Miami *(G-9912)*
Lucas Construction Inc......G....386 623-0088
Ormond Beach *(G-13383)*
Mc Assembly International LLC......F....321 253-0541
Melbourne *(G-8885)*
MCR Compression Services LLC......F....432 552-8720
North Port *(G-11743)*
Mechanical Design Corp......G....772 388-8782
Sebastian *(G-16670)*
Mecol Oil Tools Corp......F....305 638-7686
Miami *(G-9962)*
MEI Companies Inc......G....352 361-6895
Citra *(G-1557)*
Michael L Larviere Inc......F....239 267-2738
Fort Myers *(G-4530)*
Mll Oil Holding Inc......C....321 200-0039
Tallahassee *(G-17301)*
Millenium Oil & Gas Distrs Inc......F....305 220-3669
Miami *(G-10022)*
Muelby Construction Services......E....561 376-7614
North Palm Beach *(G-11723)*
Nivcoe International Dev......F....321 282-3666
Winter Park *(G-19428)*
Norjac Oil & Gas Inc or J......G....954 779-3192
Fort Lauderdale *(G-4142)*
North America Wireline LLC......G....870 365-5401
Gulf Breeze *(G-5122)*
▲ **Offshore Inland Mar Olfld Svcs**......C....251 443-5550
Pensacola *(G-14214)*
Oils R US 1 800......G....305 681-0909
Miami *(G-10093)*
Pulling Inc......G....305 224-2469
Sunrise *(G-17166)*
Puraglobe Florida LLC......E....813 247-1754
Tampa *(G-18023)*
Rachel Ally......F....727 804-9596
Hudson *(G-6036)*
Randolph Cnstr Group Inc......G....954 276-2889
Delray Beach *(G-3133)*
Rapid Response......G....407 774-9877
Altamonte Springs *(G-69)*
Rippee Construction Inc......G....850 668-6805
Tallahassee *(G-17316)*
Ryan Tire & Petroleum Inc......G....239 334-1351
Fort Myers *(G-4588)*
Servicing Solutions Group......G....727 216-4477
Clearwater *(G-1874)*
Sherry J Bertucelli Inc......G....407 760-7585
Orlando *(G-13180)*
Solution Asset Management LLC......G....786 288-9408
Hollywood *(G-5911)*
Southern Underground Inds......F....954 226-3865
Miami Lakes *(G-10862)*
Srb Servicing LLC......G....850 278-1000
Santa Rosa Beach *(G-16168)*
Standout Home Servicing LLC......G....772 708-1110
Port Saint Lucie *(G-15147)*
Sunshine Oil and Gas Inc......G....305 367-3100
Miami *(G-10435)*
Sunshine Spray Foam Insulation......G....239 221-8704
Bonita Springs *(G-859)*
Suvillaga Construction MGT LLC......F....305 323-8380
Miami *(G-10444)*
Ten4 Solutions LLC......G....302 544-1120
Nokomis *(G-11589)*
Titan Oil Tools LLC......G....941 356-3010
Sarasota *(G-16311)*
Titan Petroleum Corporation......G....813 280-4833
Tampa *(G-18188)*
▲ **Tricen Technologies Fla LLC**......F....866 620-9407
Fort Pierce *(G-4758)*
Ultrasonics and Magnetics......E....813 740-1800
Tampa *(G-18214)*
W2e International Corp......G....561 362-9595
Boca Raton *(G-786)*
Walters Tools LLC......G....321 537-4788
Palm Bay *(G-13546)*
Warensford Well Drilling Inc......G....386 738-3257
Deland *(G-3031)*
Weldcorp Industries......E....561 339-7713
Jupiter *(G-7147)*
Will Watson Construction LLC......G....850 586-5349
Fort Walton Beach *(G-4840)*
Williams Industrial Svcs LLC......E....904 696-9994
Jacksonville *(G-6922)*
Worrell Water Technologies LLC......G....434 973-6365
Delray Beach *(G-3161)*
Yatfl Inc......G....786 643-8660
Miami *(G-10625)*

14 MINING AND QUARRYING OF NONMETALLIC MINERALS, EXCEPT FUELS

1411 Dimension Stone

▲ **ARC Stone III LLC**......F....561 478-8805
Lake Worth Beach *(G-7603)*
Azul Stone LLC......F....561 655-9385
West Palm Beach *(G-18806)*
▲ **Cavastone LLC**......G....561 994-9100
Boca Raton *(G-472)*
Central State Aggregates LLC......F....813 788-0454
Zephyrhills *(G-19510)*

Commercial Stone Cab Fbrctors..........F........ 727 209-1141
Saint Petersburg *(G-15749)*
Commercial Stone Fbrcators Inc..........F........ 727 209-1141
Saint Petersburg *(G-15750)*
◆ **Custom Marble Works Inc**..........E........ 813 620-0475
Tampa *(G-17580)*
Denali Investments Inc..........G........ 386 364-2979
Live Oak *(G-8230)*
Five Stones Mine LLC..........F........ 813 967-2123
Canal Point *(G-1331)*
▲ **Granite Imports Inc**..........G........ 732 500-2549
Boynton Beach *(G-915)*
Hatch Enterprises Inc..........G........ 386 935-1419
Branford *(G-1186)*
◆ **Keystone Products Inc**..........F........ 305 245-4716
Homestead *(G-5976)*
LW Rozzo Inc..........E........ 954 435-8501
Pembroke Pines *(G-14045)*
OCC My Stone LLC..........G........ 786 352-1567
Miami Lakes *(G-10832)*
▲ **Old World Marble and Gran Inc**..........G........ 239 596-4777
Naples *(G-11350)*
◆ **Paramount Depot LLC**..........F........ 786 275-0107
Doral *(G-3453)*
Plaza Materials Corp..........D........ 813 788-0454
Zephyrhills *(G-19533)*
Quality Stones R US LLC..........G........ 904 551-5619
Jacksonville *(G-6700)*
Reyes Granite & Marble Corp..........F........ 305 599-7330
Miami *(G-10259)*
Rockers Stone Inc..........G........ 305 447-1231
Miami *(G-10273)*
Southern Contracting N FL Inc..........G........ 850 674-3570
Blountstown *(G-387)*
Southern Rock & Lime Inc..........F........ 850 674-5089
Blountstown *(G-388)*
Stone Center Inc..........F........ 863 669-0292
Lakeland *(G-7808)*
Stone Metals LLC..........G........ 813 605-7363
Plant City *(G-14468)*
Stone Mosaics..........G........ 321 773-3635
Palm Bay *(G-13541)*
▼ **Stone Systems South Fla LLC**..........F........ 954 584-4058
Lauderhill *(G-8121)*
▲ **Stone Trend International Inc**..........E........ 941 927-9113
Sarasota *(G-16605)*
Vgcm LLC..........F........ 813 247-7625
Tampa *(G-18241)*
Vgcm LLC..........D........ 813 620-4889
Tampa *(G-18242)*
Youngquist Brothers Rock Inc..........D........ 239 267-6000
Fort Myers *(G-4657)*

1422 Crushed & Broken Limestone

A Mining Group LLC..........E........ 386 752-7585
Lake City *(G-7345)*
Anderson Mining Corporation..........G........ 352 542-7942
Old Town *(G-12195)*
Argos..........G........ 305 592-3501
Miami *(G-9168)*
Bedrock Resources LLC..........E........ 352 369-8600
Ocala *(G-11885)*
Blue Rock Inc..........G........ 850 584-4324
Perry *(G-14295)*
Cemex Cnstr Mtls Fla LLC..........F........ 855 292-8453
Naples *(G-11203)*
◆ **Cemex Materials LLC**..........C........ 561 833-5555
West Palm Beach *(G-18841)*
Cemex Materials LLC..........D........ 352 435-0783
Okahumpka *(G-12169)*
Cemex Materials LLC..........D........ 305 558-0315
Miami *(G-9337)*
Cemex Materials LLC..........D........ 561 793-1442
West Palm Beach *(G-18842)*
Cemex Materials LLC..........D........ 561 743-4039
Jupiter *(G-7019)*
Colitz Mining Co Inc..........F........ 352 795-2409
Crystal River *(G-2374)*
Crystal River Quarries Inc..........E........ 352 795-2828
Crystal River *(G-2375)*
Dixie Lime Andstone Co..........F........ 352 512-0180
Ocala *(G-11920)*
Dolomite Inc..........E........ 850 482-4962
Marianna *(G-8576)*
Eagle Engrg & Land Dev Inc..........F........ 913 948-4320
Boynton Beach *(G-900)*
▼ **Evolving Coal Corp**..........G........ 813 944-3100
Saint Petersburg *(G-15773)*
◆ **Florida Rock Industries**..........C........ 904 355-1781
Jacksonville *(G-6402)*
Helms Hauling & Materials Llc..........F........ 850 218-6895
Niceville *(G-11569)*
Lake Point Restoration LLC..........E........ 561 924-9100
Wellington *(G-18722)*
Lakeview Dirt Co Inc..........E........ 904 824-2586
Saint Augustine *(G-15565)*
Legacy Vulcan LLC..........F........ 352 796-5690
Brooksville *(G-1245)*
Lhoist North America Tenn Inc..........F........ 352 629-7990
Ocala *(G-11983)*
Limestone Products Company..........G........ 352 472-2116
Newberry *(G-11558)*
Marianna Lime Products Inc..........G........ 850 526-3580
Marianna *(G-8581)*
Marianna Limestone LLC..........F........ 954 581-1220
Marianna *(G-8582)*
Martin Marietta..........G........ 850 432-8112
Pensacola *(G-14200)*
Rinker Materials Corp Con..........G........ 305 818-4952
Doral *(G-3486)*
Rock Ridge Materials Inc..........F........ 321 268-8455
Titusville *(G-18460)*
SCI Materials LLC..........E........ 352 878-4979
Reddick *(G-15258)*
Vecellio & Grogan Inc..........D........ 305 822-5322
Hialeah *(G-5674)*
Waste Management Inc Florida..........E........ 954 984-2000
Winter Garden *(G-19289)*

1423 Crushed & Broken Granite

Granite World Inc..........E........ 813 243-6556
Tampa *(G-17725)*
Rock Ridge Materials Inc..........F........ 321 268-8455
Titusville *(G-18460)*

1429 Crushed & Broken Stone, NEC

Rock Ridge Materials Inc..........F........ 321 268-8455
Titusville *(G-18460)*
South Carolina Minerals Inc..........D........ 352 365-6522
Leesburg *(G-8174)*
White County Stone LLC..........E........ 415 516-0849
West Palm Beach *(G-19086)*

1442 Construction Sand & Gravel

Atlantic Earth Materials..........F........ 321 631-0600
Cocoa *(G-1996)*
Aurora Stone & Gravel LLC..........G........ 321 253-4808
Melbourne *(G-8772)*
Bdc Shell & Aggregate LLC..........F........ 941 875-6615
Punta Gorda *(G-15193)*
Bergeron Sand & Rock Min Inc..........E........ 954 680-6100
Fort Lauderdale *(G-3847)*
Bermont Excavating LLC..........F........ 866 367-9557
Punta Gorda *(G-15196)*
Bonita Grande Mining LLC..........F........ 239 947-6402
Bonita Springs *(G-817)*
C C Calhoun Inc..........E........ 863 292-9511
Winter Haven *(G-19310)*
Cemex Cnstr Mtls Fla LLC..........F........ 800 992-3639
Moore Haven *(G-11086)*
Central Sand Inc..........G........ 321 632-0308
Titusville *(G-18423)*
Charlotte County Min & Mtl Inc..........E........ 239 567-1800
Punta Gorda *(G-15201)*
Corbin Sand and Clay Inc..........G........ 850 638-8462
Chipley *(G-1542)*
Dan Frame & Trim Inc..........G........ 352 726-4567
Inverness *(G-6085)*
ER Jahna Industries Inc..........F........ 863 675-3942
La Belle *(G-7316)*
ER Jahna Industries Inc..........G........ 863 422-7617
Haines City *(G-5142)*
G2c Enterprises Inc..........F........ 850 398-5368
Crestview *(G-2348)*
G2c Enterprises Inc..........F........ 850 585-4166
Crestview *(G-2349)*
Garcia Mining Company LLC..........F........ 863 902-9777
Clewiston *(G-1981)*
Hector Corporation..........G........ 786 308-5853
Miami *(G-9697)*
Helms Hauling & Materials Llc..........F........ 850 218-6895
Niceville *(G-11569)*
James G Dowling..........G........ 407 509-9484
Sanford *(G-16073)*
Legacy Vulcan LLC..........F........ 352 394-6196
Clermont *(G-1967)*
Legacy Vulcan Corp..........G........ 352 742-2122
Tavares *(G-18345)*
McDirt Industries Inc..........F........ 850 944-0112
Pensacola *(G-14203)*
Professional Site & Trnspt Inc..........F........ 386 239-6800
Daytona Beach *(G-2700)*
Rockpack Inc..........E........ 407 757-0798
Apopka *(G-182)*
Sand Power Volleyball..........G........ 813 786-8055
Brandon *(G-1177)*
SMR Aggregates Inc..........E........ 941 907-0041
Lakewood Ranch *(G-7841)*
Sod Depot & Gravel Inc..........G........ 321 728-2766
Palm Bay *(G-13535)*
Stewart Materials Inc..........G........ 561 972-4517
Jupiter *(G-7123)*
Stony Creek Sand & Gravel LLC..........F........ 804 229-0015
Pompano Beach *(G-14874)*
Vecellio & Grogan Inc..........D........ 305 822-5322
Hialeah *(G-5674)*
Vetcon Construction Inc..........G........ 352 234-6668
Ocala *(G-12070)*

1446 Industrial Sand

Chemours Company Fc LLC..........C........ 904 964-1200
Starke *(G-16890)*
Don Schick LLC..........G........ 954 491-9042
Oakland Park *(G-11800)*
In Diversified Plant Services..........F........ 813 453-7025
Lutz *(G-8390)*
Marine Concepts..........F........ 239 283-0800
Cape Coral *(G-1445)*
Sand Hill Rock LLC..........G........ 772 216-4852
Okeechobee *(G-12191)*
◆ **Standard Sand & Silica Company**..........E........ 863 422-7100
Davenport *(G-2483)*
Standard Sand & Silica Company..........G........ 863 419-9673
Haines City *(G-5148)*

1459 Clay, Ceramic & Refractory Minerals, NEC

C C Calhoun Inc..........E........ 863 292-9511
Winter Haven *(G-19310)*
Jlt Custom Works Inc..........E........ 863 245-3371
Wauchula *(G-18694)*

1475 Phosphate Rock

◆ **White Springs AG Chem Inc**..........A........ 386 397-8101
White Springs *(G-19189)*

1479 Chemical & Fertilizer Mining

Ostara Usa LLC..........G........ 813 666-8123
Riverview *(G-15278)*

1481 Nonmetallic Minerals Svcs, Except Fuels

Diatomite Corp of America..........G........ 305 466-0075
Miami *(G-9465)*
Environmental Contractors Inc..........F........ 305 556-6942
Hialeah *(G-5399)*
Express Removal Service LLC..........G........ 305 303-8249
Miami Gardens *(G-10739)*
Fcs Holdings Inc..........E........ 352 793-5151
Center Hill *(G-1526)*
H2r Corp..........F........ 727 541-3444
Pinellas Park *(G-14353)*
Kiskeya Minerals Usa LLC..........G........ 305 328-5082
Miami *(G-9823)*
◆ **Qci Britannic Inc**..........G........ 305 860-0102
Coral Gables *(G-2188)*
Standard Sand & Silica Company..........G........ 352 625-2385
Silver Springs *(G-16784)*

1499 Miscellaneous Nonmetallic Mining

4 Power International Stones..........G........ 407 286-4677
Orlando *(G-12418)*
Acg Materials..........G........ 405 366-9500
Marianna *(G-8574)*
Blackhawk Construction Co Inc..........E........ 321 258-4957
Vero Beach *(G-18602)*
Charlotte County Min & Mtl Inc..........E........ 239 567-1800
Punta Gorda *(G-15201)*
Copaco Inc..........F........ 407 333-3041
Orange City *(G-12374)*
◆ **Coraldom Usa LLC**..........G........ 305 716-0200
Miami *(G-9402)*
Engelhard Corp..........G........ 850 627-7688
Quincy *(G-15248)*
ER Jahna Industries Inc..........E........ 863 424-0730
Davenport *(G-2478)*
Harrison Gypsum LLC..........E........ 850 762-4315
Marianna *(G-8578)*

Marion Rock Inc ....E 352 687-2023
Ocala (G-11994)
SMR Aggregates Inc ....E 941 907-0041
Lakewood Ranch (G-7841)
Sun Gro Horticulture Dist Inc ....G 407 291-1676
Orlando (G-13222)
Sunshine ....G 305 382-6677
Miami (G-10433)
Ultimate Stnwrks Centl Fla LLC ....G 407 412-5981
Orlando (G-13288)
Waste Management Inc Florida ....E 954 984-2000
Winter Garden (G-19289)
Western Graphite Inc ....F 850 270-2808
Monticello (G-11083)

20 FOOD AND KINDRED PRODUCTS

2011 Meat Packing Plants

Adirondack Meat Company Inc ....F 518 585-2333
Cape Coral (G-1374)
Apakus Inc ....F 305 403-2603
Coral Gables (G-2123)
Azar Industries Inc ....E 904 358-2354
Jacksonville (G-6184)
Bruss Company ....E 904 693-0688
Jacksonville (G-6240)
Bubba Foods LLC ....C 904 482-1900
Jacksonville (G-6242)
Cargill Meat Solutions Corp ....B 305 826-3699
Hialeah (G-5340)
Cedena Carmenn ....G 305 681-1222
Opa Locka (G-12298)
Central Beef Ind LLC ....C 352 793-3671
Center Hill (G-1525)
Dutch Packing Co Inc ....G 305 871-3640
Miami (G-9488)
Egea Food LLC ....F 833 353-6637
Miami (G-9504)
▲ El Toro Meat Packing Corp ....D 305 836-4461
Miami (G-9509)
Florida Beef Inc ....E 912 632-1183
Zolfo Springs (G-19545)
FM Meat Products Ltd Partnr ....E 352 546-3000
Fort Mc Coy (G-4337)
Gourmet 3005 Inc ....G 786 334-6250
Hialeah (G-5434)
Henrys Hickory House Inc ....D 904 493-4420
Jacksonville (G-6469)
High Top Products Corp ....D 305 633-3287
Miami (G-9710)
Johnson Brothers Whl Meats Inc ....E 850 763-2828
Panama City (G-13922)
Justice Government Supply Inc ....G 954 559-3038
West Palm Beach (G-18916)
Kelly Foods ....G 904 354-7600
Jacksonville (G-6534)
La Montina Inc ....E 305 324-0083
Miami (G-9844)
Madson Inc ....F 305 863-7390
Medley (G-8681)
Martinez Distributors Corp ....E 305 882-8282
Miami (G-9952)
Polks Meat Products Inc ....G 813 961-2881
Lutz (G-8410)
Prg Packing Corp ....E 201 242-5500
Madison (G-8453)
South Marion Meats ....G 352 245-2096
Summerfield (G-17062)
Special Americas Bbq Inc ....E 305 637-7377
Miami (G-10399)
Tyson Foods Inc ....G 904 693-0688
Jacksonville (G-6873)

2013 Sausages & Meat Prdts

Adirondack Meat Company Inc ....F 518 585-2333
Cape Coral (G-1374)
Amba Ham Company Inc ....G 305 754-0001
Miami (G-9134)
Ben Jammin Island Jerky Llc ....G 904 220-2067
Jacksonville (G-6203)
Blue Planet Holdings LLC ....F 863 559-1236
Lakeland (G-7647)
▼ Bush Brothers Provision Co ....E 561 832-6666
West Palm Beach (G-18831)
▲ Cabreras Spanish Sausages LLC ....G 305 882-1040
Hialeah (G-5339)
Catalina Finer Meat Corp ....F 813 876-3910
Tampa (G-17516)
Cheney Ofs Inc ....A 407 292-3223
Orlando (G-12579)
Country Prime Meats USA Inc ....G 250 396-4111
Plantation (G-14503)
Ddd Hams Inc ....G 850 205-1426
Tallahassee (G-17241)
▼ Discos Y Empanadas Argentina ....F 305 326-9300
Miami (G-9469)
Dutch Packing Co Inc ....G 305 871-3640
Miami (G-9488)
E&M Innovative Forager LLC ....E 954 923-0056
Hallandale Beach (G-5182)
◆ Elore Enterprises LLC ....E 305 477-1650
Miami (G-9519)
▲ Elore Holdings Inc ....G 305 477-1650
Miami (G-9520)
Florida Jerky Enterprises Inc ....G 256 682-2959
Orlando (G-12750)
Future Foods LLC ....G 786 390-5226
Lake Worth (G-7551)
Get Hams Inc ....G 850 386-7123
Tallahassee (G-17265)
Golden Boar Product Corp ....G 305 500-9392
Miami (G-9646)
Grub Company ....F 347 464-9770
Ormond Beach (G-13375)
Henrys Hickory House Inc ....D 904 493-4420
Jacksonville (G-6469)
High Top Products Corp ....D 305 633-3287
Miami (G-9710)
Hillshire Brands Company ....G 321 637-9765
Cocoa (G-2029)
Hot Dog Shoppe LLC ....G 850 682-3649
Crestview (G-2351)
Immokalee Ranch ....G 239 657-2000
Immokalee (G-6052)
Johnson Brothers Whl Meats Inc ....E 850 763-2828
Panama City (G-13922)
◆ Kuando Trading Corp ....F 786 603-3772
Miami (G-9833)
La Coronella Meat Processing ....F 305 691-2630
Miami (G-9838)
La Esquina Del Le Billto ....E 305 477-4225
Doral (G-3415)
La Montina Inc ....E 305 324-0083
Miami (G-9844)
La Villarena Meat & Pork Inc ....F 305 759-0555
Miami (G-9849)
Latin Amercn Meats & Foods USA ....G 305 477-2700
Miami (G-9867)
Lone Star Beef Jerky LLC ....G 806 241-4188
Palm Harbor (G-13745)
Majestics Business USA LLC ....G 305 713-9773
North Miami (G-11645)
Moroccan Khlii Inc ....G 813 699-0096
Tampa (G-17918)
New Best Packers Inc ....E 386 328-5127
Palatka (G-13487)
On Base Foods Group LLC ....F 248 672-7659
Avon Park (G-291)
Pamplona Foods Inc ....G 305 970-4120
Miami (G-10135)
Pinellas Provision Corporation ....E 727 822-2701
Saint Petersburg (G-15877)
Port of Palm Cold Storage Inc ....E 386 328-5127
Palatka (G-13489)
Red Smith Foods Inc ....E 954 581-1996
Davie (G-2583)
Richards Brazilian Sausage LLC ....G 786 609-3554
Pembroke Pines (G-14057)
Silver Horn Jerky Inc ....F 850 208-1433
Pensacola (G-14261)
South Marion Meats ....G 352 245-2096
Summerfield (G-17062)
Southast Protein Purveyors LLC ....G 912 354-2770
Winter Haven (G-19357)
Special Americas Bbq Inc ....E 305 637-7377
Miami (G-10399)
Stanfords Jerky ....G 813 817-5953
Brandon (G-1181)
Uncle Johns Pride LLC ....D 813 685-7745
Tampa (G-18216)
Vienna Beef Ltd ....B 941 723-7234
Palmetto (G-13833)

2015 Poultry Slaughtering, Dressing & Processing

Asian Food Solutions Inc ....E 888 499-6888
Oviedo (G-13414)
Cedars Food Inc ....G 321 724-2624
West Melbourne (G-18769)
E&M Innovative Forager LLC ....E 954 923-0056
Hallandale Beach (G-5182)
International Fd Solutions Inc ....E 888 499-6888
Oviedo (G-13440)
Johnson Brothers Whl Meats Inc ....E 850 763-2828
Panama City (G-13922)
Martins Fmous Pstry Shoppe Inc ....G 800 548-1200
Lake City (G-7367)
Martins Fmous Pstry Shoppe Inc ....G 800 548-1200
Lynn Haven (G-8434)
Martins Fmous Pstry Shoppe Inc ....G 800 548-1200
Pensacola (G-14201)
Pilgrims Pride Corporation ....G 386 362-4171
Live Oak (G-8236)
Premium Quality Meats Inc ....G 239 309-4418
Miramar (G-11029)

2021 Butter

Canal Creamery ....G 386 410-4703
New Smyrna Beach (G-11529)
Carrollwood Creamery ....G 813 926-2023
Tampa (G-17510)
Magical Creamery LLC ....G 407 719-6866
Lake Mary (G-7430)
Trinity Creamery Inc ....G 813 926-2023
Odessa (G-12160)

2022 Cheese

Bufalinda USA LLC ....G 305 979-9258
Miami Beach (G-10650)
▼ Goloso Food Llc ....G 321 277-2055
Orlando (G-12786)
Kelleys Krafts and Kreations ....G 813 508-1051
Spring Hill (G-16874)
▲ Lanzas Distributor Inc ....G 305 885-5966
Miami (G-9858)
▲ Mambi Cheese Company Inc ....F 305 324-5282
Miami (G-9940)
Massachusetts Bay Clam Co Inc ....F 813 855-4599
Tampa (G-17891)
Mondelez Global LLC ....E 305 774-6273
Coral Gables (G-2179)

2023 Milk, Condensed & Evaporated

▼ Allegro Nutrition Inc ....E 732 364-3777
Palmetto (G-13784)
Amino Cell Inc ....F 352 291-0200
Ocala (G-11874)
▲ Beauty & Health Corporation ....G 305 259-8181
Cutler Bay (G-2388)
Betancourt Sports Ntrtn LLC ....G 305 593-9296
Miami Lakes (G-10768)
Bkn International Inc ....G 301 518-7153
Miami (G-9254)
Bl Bio Lab LLC ....F 727 900-2707
Clearwater (G-1609)
Blue Sky Labs LLC ....G 901 268-6988
Jacksonville (G-6214)
Byoscience ....G 754 240-4052
Sunrise (G-17102)
Cerno Pharmaceuticals LLC ....G 786 763-2766
Miami (G-9343)
▲ Climb Your Mountain Inc ....E 571 571-8623
Medley (G-8632)
Cyber Group USA LLC ....F 888 574-9555
Pompano Beach (G-14655)
Essona Organics Inc ....G 716 481-0183
Delray Beach (G-3076)
◆ Flayco Products Inc ....E 813 879-1356
Tampa (G-17668)
Fleda Pharmaceuticals Corp ....G 813 920-9882
Odessa (G-12120)
Fresh Start Beverage Company ....G 561 757-6541
Boca Raton (G-540)
Full Lf Natural Hlth Pdts LLC ....G 954 889-4019
Hollywood (G-5825)
Function Please LLC ....G 305 792-7900
Hollywood (G-5827)
Green Essentials LLC ....E 786 584-4377
Miami (G-9666)
Health & Muscles ....G 305 225-2929
Miami (G-9691)
Ianorod JB LLC ....G 954 217-3014
Weston (G-19138)
▲ Iq Formulations Llc ....D 954 533-9256
Tamarac (G-17359)
Maxam Group LLC ....F 305 952-3227
Miami (G-9958)
Naked Whey Inc ....G 352 246-7294
Miami (G-10061)

- **Naturecity LLC** G 800 593-2563 Boca Raton *(G-636)*
- **Nestle Usa Inc** C 813 273-5355 Thonotosassa *(G-18402)*
- **New Dairy Opco LLC** B 305 652-3720 North Miami Beach *(G-11694)*
- **Nutrition Laboratories Inc** E 915 496-7531 Clearwater *(G-1814)*
- **Ohana Liquids LLC** G 888 642-6244 New Smyrna Beach *(G-11540)*
- **Omnimark Enterprises LLC** G 516 351-9075 Orlando *(G-13022)*
- **Pangenex Corporation** G 352 346-4045 Tampa *(G-17971)*
- ▲ **Peak Nutritional Products LLC** E 813 884-4989 Tampa *(G-17980)*
- **Prime Life Ntrtn Companyllc** G 754 307-7137 Deerfield Beach *(G-2890)*
- **S A Gloria Corp** E 305 575-2900 South Miami *(G-16826)*
- **Saputo Dairy Foods Usa LLC** G 904 354-0406 Jacksonville *(G-6751)*
- **Sawgrass Nutra Labs LLC** E 844 688-7244 Jacksonville *(G-6753)*
- **Sea 21-21 LLC** G 954 366-4677 Pompano Beach *(G-14845)*
- **Sun-Pac Manufacturing Inc** E 813 925-8787 Tampa *(G-18141)*
- **Sunshine Supplements Inc** F 407 751-4299 Orlando *(G-13227)*
- **Twinlab Cnsld Holdings Inc** E 561 443-4301 Boca Raton *(G-759)*
- **Vital Health Corp** G 407 522-1125 Orlando *(G-13307)*
- **Vital Health Corporation** G 407 522-1125 Orlando *(G-13308)*
- **Vitapak LLC** G 954 661-0390 Fort Lauderdale *(G-4309)*

2024 Ice Cream

- **A Means To A Vend Inc** F 954 533-8330 Oakland Park *(G-11772)*
- **Alcas USA Corp** G 305 591-3325 Fort Lauderdale *(G-3795)*
- **Big Bend Ice Cream Co** G 850 539-7778 Havana *(G-5233)*
- **Bobs Twist N Shake** G 941 485-5152 Venice *(G-18535)*
- **Brain Freeze Nitrogen** G 786 235-8505 Doral *(G-3284)*
- **Buzz Pop Cocktails Corporation** F 727 275-9848 Holiday *(G-5736)*
- **C&A Lozaro Inc** F 407 671-8809 Winter Park *(G-19388)*
- **Carpe Diem Ice Cream LLC** G 305 504-4469 Key West *(G-7180)*
- **Cesibon** G 239 682-5028 Naples *(G-11206)*
- **Cholados Y Mas** G 813 935-9262 Tampa *(G-17533)*
- ◆ **Clondalkin LLC** E 866 545-8703 Largo *(G-7925)*
- **Coco Gelato Corp** E 786 621-2444 Miami *(G-9372)*
- **Cold Stone Creamery-Parkland** G 954 341-8033 Coral Springs *(G-2232)*
- **Coneheads Frozen Custards** G 772 600-7730 Stuart *(G-16925)*
- **Conopco Inc** E 727 573-1591 Clearwater *(G-1635)*
- **Cool Cow** G 229 272-5495 Tallahassee *(G-17237)*
- **Cool Treat** G 407 248-0743 Orlando *(G-12619)*
- **Cross Atlantic Commodities Inc** G 954 678-0698 Weston *(G-19118)*
- **Cupcakes On Main** G 321 693-7236 Titusville *(G-18426)*
- **D I Y Yogert** G 239 471-2177 Cape Coral *(G-1409)*
- **Daisy V Castillo Vendor** G 305 254-1427 Cutler Bay *(G-2391)*
- **Darifair Foods Inc** E 904 268-8999 Jacksonville *(G-6311)*
- **Dean Dairy Holdings LLC** D 239 334-1114 Fort Myers *(G-4428)*
- **Deliciosa Food Group Inc** F 954 492-6131 Miami *(G-9448)*
- **Desserts2go Inc** G 941 379-0488 Sarasota *(G-16411)*
- **Dolci Peccati LLC** G 954 632-8551 Miami *(G-9475)*
- **Eden Fast Frozen Dessert LLC** F 787 375-0826 Kissimmee *(G-7242)*
- **Eds Delight LLC** G 305 632-3051 North Miami Beach *(G-11672)*
- **Eighteen Degrees Eighteen** G 904 686-1892 Ponte Vedra Beach *(G-14940)*
- **Faithful Heart Froyo LLC** G 407 325-3052 Winter Park *(G-19407)*
- **Florida Froyo Inc** G 407 977-4911 Lake Mary *(G-7417)*
- ▼ **Food Marketing Consultants Inc** G 954 322-2668 Miramar *(G-10992)*
- ▲ **Frio Distributors Inc** F 813 567-1493 Plant City *(G-14433)*
- **Gelateria Milani LLC** F 305 532-8562 Miami Beach *(G-10672)*
- **Gelato Petrini LLC** F 561 600-4088 Delray Beach *(G-3084)*
- ▲ **Gourmet Parisien Inc** G 305 778-0756 Hollywood *(G-5828)*
- ▲ **GS Gelato and Desserts Inc** E 850 243-5455 Fort Walton Beach *(G-4805)*
- **Guanabana & Co LLC** F 904 891-5256 Jacksonville *(G-6456)*
- **Happy Mix LLC** G 954 880-0160 Cooper City *(G-2112)*
- **HM Factory LLC** G 305 897-0004 Miami *(G-9714)*
- **HM Froyos LLC** G 561 339-0603 Orlando *(G-12804)*
- **Hulas Market Place LLC** G 941 704-3305 Sarasota *(G-16462)*
- **Ice Cream & Gifts LLC** G 352 237-2660 Ocala *(G-11969)*
- ▼ **Ice Cream Club Inc** E 561 731-3331 Boynton Beach *(G-917)*
- **Icecapade Frozen Treats Inc** G 904 314-4190 Jacksonville *(G-6487)*
- **Island Dream Itln Ice Dssrts L** F 904 778-6839 Jacksonville *(G-6503)*
- **Ispy Equities** G 813 731-0676 Spring Hill *(G-16873)*
- **Jeremiahs Original Water Ice** G 407 679-2665 Winter Park *(G-19416)*
- **Jimmy & Toons Icecream Sp LLC** G 850 752-2291 Quincy *(G-15252)*
- **Just Now Jennings LLC** G 239 331-0315 Naples *(G-11301)*
- **Kissimmee Smoke Shop** G 407 952-6181 Kissimmee *(G-7265)*
- **Latin Dairy Foods LLC** F 305 888-1788 Miami *(G-9869)*
- **Lefab Commercial LLC** F 305 456-1306 Coral Gables *(G-2172)*
- **Lilas Desserts Inc** F 305 252-1441 Miami *(G-9893)*
- **Los Coquitos** G 407 289-9315 Kissimmee *(G-7271)*
- ◆ **Lukes Ice Cream** F 561 588-5853 Riviera Beach *(G-15344)*
- **Maria E Acosta** G 305 231-5543 Hialeah *(G-5501)*
- **Mattheessons** G 305 296-1616 Key West *(G-7195)*
- **McConnell Corp** G 305 296-6124 Key West *(G-7196)*
- ▲ **Miami Foods Distrs USA Inc** F 305 512-3246 Hialeah *(G-5510)*
- **Millenia Froyo LLC** G 407 694-9938 Windermere *(G-19239)*
- **Mimzy Froyo Delights LLC** G 917 862-9520 West Palm Beach *(G-18953)*
- **Mix It At Loop** G 407 201-8948 Kissimmee *(G-7276)*
- **Muse Gelato Inc** F 407 363-1443 Orlando *(G-12988)*
- **Old Meeting House Home Made Ic** F 813 254-0977 Tampa *(G-17949)*
- **Peekaboo Organics LLC** G 305 527-7162 Surfside *(G-17205)*
- **Phillys Famous Water Ice Inc** C 813 248-8644 Tampa *(G-17990)*
- **Piccionis Frozen Desserts** G 561 633-5759 Wellington *(G-18727)*
- **Renacer Bros LLC** G 305 935-6777 Miami *(G-10251)*
- **Rhonda Clanton** G 305 502-7050 Hialeah *(G-5599)*
- ▼ **Rich Ice Cream Co** C 561 833-7585 West Palm Beach *(G-19020)*
- **Romeo Ohana LLC** F 808 500-3420 Spring Hill *(G-16861)*
- **Ronnie & Moes Italian Ice LLC** G 786 970-1805 Miami *(G-10280)*
- **Simply Sweet Company Inc** G 386 873-6516 Deland *(G-3013)*
- **Smart Stream Inc** F 904 223-1511 Jacksonville *(G-6780)*
- **Sunnibunni** F 941 554-8744 Sarasota *(G-16609)*
- **Supersweet Frog LLC** G 863 386-4917 Sebring *(G-16713)*
- **Sweet Spot** G 727 784-2277 Palm Harbor *(G-13764)*
- **Sweet Treats** G 239 598-3311 Naples *(G-11430)*
- **Sweetreats of Naples Inc** G 239 598-3311 Naples *(G-11431)*
- ▼ **Todays Frozen Desserts Inc** F 305 994-9940 Miami *(G-10485)*
- **Top Hat Food Services LLC** G 630 825-2800 Venice *(G-18581)*
- **Tristan S Kool Dreemz** G 772 398-8875 Port Saint Lucie *(G-15156)*
- **Tropical Skoops Llc** G 954 440-8736 Miramar *(G-11053)*
- **Uncle Carlos Gelatos** G 810 523-8506 Fort Pierce *(G-4765)*
- **Valentini Italian Spc Co** G 305 638-0822 Miami *(G-10563)*
- **Vegan Suckers LLc** F 904 265-5263 Jacksonville *(G-6894)*
- **Verdu-Us LLC** F 407 776-3017 Davenport *(G-2485)*
- ▼ **Working Cow Homemade Inc** F 727 572-7251 Saint Petersburg *(G-15965)*
- **Worlds Greatest Ice Cream Inc** F 305 538-0207 Miami Beach *(G-10730)*
- **Y3k LLC** G 561 835-0404 Palm Beach *(G-13563)*
- **Yogurt Breeze LLC** G 407 412-5939 Orlando *(G-13338)*
- **Yogurtology** G 727 895-1393 Saint Petersburg *(G-15966)*

2026 Milk

- **Attitude Drinks Incorporated** G 561 227-2727 North Palm Beach *(G-11717)*
- **Borden Dairy Company Fla LLC** D 863 298-9742 Winter Haven *(G-19305)*
- **Brain Freeze Nitrogen** G 786 235-8505 Doral *(G-3284)*
- **Chocolate Compass LLC** G 407 600-0145 Sanford *(G-16014)*
- **Colormet Foods LLC** F 888 775-3966 Miami *(G-9382)*
- **Dairy Fairy LLC** G 305 865-1506 Surfside *(G-17202)*
- **Darifair Foods Inc** E 904 268-8999 Jacksonville *(G-6311)*
- **Dfa Dairy Brands Fluid LLC** G 352 754-1750 Brooksville *(G-1226)*
- **Dfa Dairy Brands Fluid LLC** F 386 775-6700 Jacksonville *(G-6318)*
- **Dfa Dairy Brands Fluid LLC** G 386 775-6700 Melbourne *(G-8803)*
- **Dfa Dairy Brands Fluid LLC** E 813 621-7805 Tampa *(G-17603)*
- ▼ **Fluid Handling Support Corp** F 786 623-2105 Doral *(G-3354)*
- **Froyolicious Inc** G 561 753-4890 Royal Palm Beach *(G-15467)*
- **Louis Sherry Company LLC** G 904 482-1900 Jacksonville *(G-6565)*
- **Powerful Foods LLC** G 305 779-2449 Pinecrest *(G-14330)*
- ▲ **Pura Vida Dairy Inc** F 305 817-1762 Hialeah *(G-5584)*
- **Sneakz LLC** G 201 693-5695 Jupiter *(G-7116)*
- **Southeast Dairy Processors Inc** E 813 620-1516 Tampa *(G-18117)*
- **Spoons Chilly** G 321 610-8966 Melbourne *(G-8943)*
- **Tias Milkshakes and More** G 954 391-8753 Hollywood *(G-5924)*
- **Whetstone Industries Inc** F 904 824-0888 Saint Augustine *(G-15636)*

SIC

Wwf Operating Company LLC ....E....... 904 354-0406
Jacksonville *(G-6930)*
Yogurt Breeze LLC ....G....... 407 412-5939
Orlando *(G-13338)*
Yogurtology ....G....... 813 839-4200
Tampa *(G-18274)*
Yogurtology ....G....... 813 969-2500
Tampa *(G-18275)*
Yogurtology ....G....... 813 926-9090
Tampa *(G-18276)*

2032 Canned Specialties

Ait USA Corp ....G....... 786 953-5918
Miami *(G-9098)*
All Naturals Direct ....G....... 813 792-3777
Tampa *(G-17399)*
◆ **Alpha Omega Commercial Limited** ....G....... 407 925-7913
Windermere *(G-19225)*
▲ **Catalina Finer Food Corp** ....E....... 813 872-6359
Tampa *(G-17515)*
▲ **Comep Usa Inc** ....E....... 786 554-2211
Miami *(G-9386)*
◆ **Conchita Foods Inc** ....D....... 305 888-9703
Medley *(G-8633)*
Delarosa Real Foods LLC ....D....... 718 333-0333
Lauderdale Lakes *(G-8085)*
Florida International Firm Inc ....G....... 305 450-5920
Sweetwater *(G-17209)*
Kraft Heinz Foods Company ....G....... 407 786-8157
Longwood *(G-8301)*
MA Fine Foods LLC ....G....... 305 878-6277
Miami *(G-9929)*
▼ **Magnificat Holdings LLC** ....G....... 727 798-0512
Clearwater *(G-1771)*
Nanas Original Stromboli Inc ....G....... 954 771-6262
Fort Lauderdale *(G-4129)*
Olas Foods Specialty Mkt Inc ....E....... 813 447-5127
Kenneth City *(G-7153)*
Rancheritos ....G....... 561 479-0046
Boca Raton *(G-680)*
Richard Meer Investments Inc ....G....... 941 484-6551
Venice *(G-18570)*
◆ **RL Schreiber Inc** ....D....... 954 972-7102
Fort Lauderdale *(G-4208)*
Suzanne Chalet Foods Inc ....G....... 863 676-6011
Lake Wales *(G-7524)*
Whole Enchlada Fresh Mxcan Gri ....F....... 954 561-4040
Fort Lauderdale *(G-4322)*

2033 Canned Fruits, Vegetables & Preserves

◆ **Allapattah Industries Inc** ....E....... 305 324-5900
Miami *(G-9116)*
▲ **Ardmore Farms LLC** ....D....... 386 734-4634
Deland *(G-2960)*
Barbecue Superstore ....G....... 305 635-4427
Miami *(G-9217)*
▲ **Ben Hill Griffin Inc** ....E....... 863 635-2281
Frostproof *(G-4855)*
▲ **Brown International Corp LLC** ....G....... 863 299-2111
Winter Haven *(G-19306)*
Chiantis ....G....... 407 484-6510
Sanford *(G-16013)*
Choctaw Trading Co Inc ....G....... 407 905-9917
Winter Garden *(G-19257)*
Coca-Cola Company ....G....... 727 736-7101
Dunedin *(G-3574)*
Coca-Cola Company ....G....... 407 565-2465
Apopka *(G-123)*
◆ **Coco Lopez Inc** ....G....... 954 450-3100
Miramar *(G-10980)*
◆ **Conchita Foods Inc** ....D....... 305 888-9703
Medley *(G-8633)*
Cordoba Foods LLC ....E....... 305 733-4768
Hialeah *(G-5355)*
Cutrale Citrus Juices USA Inc ....B....... 352 728-7800
Leesburg *(G-8149)*
▲ **Cutrale Farms Inc** ....D....... 863 965-5000
Auburndale *(G-238)*
◆ **Del Monte Fresh Produce NA Inc** .....E....... 305 520-8400
Coral Gables *(G-2138)*
◆ **Flayco Products Inc** ....E....... 813 879-1356
Tampa *(G-17668)*
◆ **Florida Food Products LLC** ....D....... 352 357-4141
Eustis *(G-3707)*
◆ **Florida Refresco Inc** ....C....... 863 665-5515
Lakeland *(G-7693)*
Freshco Ltd ....E....... 772 287-2111
Stuart *(G-16942)*
Fruit Dynamics LLC ....C....... 239 643-7373
Naples *(G-11251)*
◆ **Fruselva Usa LLC** ....F....... 949 798-0061
Miami *(G-9602)*
Gem Freshco LLC ....D....... 772 595-0070
Fort Pierce *(G-4699)*
Gma-Food LLC ....G....... 646 469-8599
Lutz *(G-8385)*
Good Jams LLC ....G....... 702 379-5551
Boca Raton *(G-548)*
Gulf Coast Growers Florida LLC ....D....... 941 737-2532
Palmetto *(G-13802)*
Hot Sauce Harrys Inc ....G....... 941 423-7092
North Port *(G-11741)*
Idsolution Inc ....G....... 305 603-9835
Medley *(G-8667)*
Jammin Jams USA LLC ....G....... 305 494-5617
Miami *(G-9786)*
Juice Tyme Inc ....G....... 631 424-2850
Frostproof *(G-4860)*
Kraft Heinz Foods Company ....G....... 813 810-5298
Valrico *(G-18520)*
Kraft Heinz Foods Company ....G....... 305 428-7152
Coral Gables *(G-2167)*
Kraft Heinz Foods Company ....G....... 305 476-7000
Coral Gables *(G-2168)*
Kraft Heinz Foods Company ....G....... 239 694-3663
Fort Myers *(G-4513)*
Kraft Heinz Foods Company ....G....... 904 695-1300
Jacksonville *(G-6545)*
Lakewood Organics LLC ....D....... 305 324-5900
Miami *(G-9852)*
◆ **M & B Products Inc** ....C....... 813 988-2211
Temple Terrace *(G-18372)*
▲ **Mancini Packing Company** ....D....... 863 735-2000
Zolfo Springs *(G-19546)*
▲ **Ouhlala Gourmet Corp** ....F....... 305 774-7332
Coral Gables *(G-2182)*
◆ **Palmetto Canning Company** ....F....... 941 722-1100
Palmetto *(G-13814)*
Pepsico Inc ....G....... 407 933-5542
Kissimmee *(G-7286)*
▲ **R & Z Ventures Inc** ....D....... 954 532-7938
Pompano Beach *(G-14824)*
Raw Foods International Llc ....F....... 305 856-1991
Coral Gables *(G-2190)*
Sam S Accrsio Sons Pkg Prod In ....F....... 305 246-3455
Homestead *(G-5990)*
Seven Keys Co of Florida ....G....... 954 946-5010
Pompano Beach *(G-14848)*
Sun Orchard LLC ....D....... 863 422-5062
Haines City *(G-5150)*
▲ **Sun Orchard LLC** ....E....... 786 646-9200
Miami *(G-10428)*
▲ **Tropicana Manufacturing Co Inc** ......G....... 312 821-1000
Bradenton *(G-1132)*
▲ **Tropicana Products Inc** ....A....... 941 747-4461
Bradenton *(G-1133)*
Tropicana Products Inc ....G....... 772 465-2030
Fort Pierce *(G-4759)*
Tropicana Products Inc ....G....... 850 610-8849
Defuniak Springs *(G-2950)*
◆ **United Jice Companies Amer Inc** ......D....... 772 562-5442
Vero Beach *(G-18673)*
Watts Juicery ....F....... 904 372-0693
Atlantic Beach *(G-228)*
Wharton Pepper Co ....G....... 850 997-4359
Monticello *(G-11084)*
▲ **Wm G Roe & Sons Inc** ....B....... 863 294-3577
Winter Haven *(G-19367)*

2034 Dried Fruits, Vegetables & Soup

◆ **Conchita Foods Inc** ....D....... 305 888-9703
Medley *(G-8633)*
Culinary Concepts Inc ....E....... 407 228-0069
Orlando *(G-12635)*
Ferris Groves ....G....... 352 860-0366
Floral City *(G-3766)*
◆ **Flayco Products Inc** ....E....... 813 879-1356
Tampa *(G-17668)*
▲ **Geneva Foods LLC** ....F....... 407 302-4751
Sanford *(G-16055)*
Green Leaf Foods LLC ....G....... 305 308-9167
Miramar *(G-11001)*
Kerry Inc ....G....... 813 359-5181
Plant City *(G-14444)*
Major Products Company ....E....... 386 673-8381
Ormond Beach *(G-13384)*
Mastertaste Inc ....G....... 813 754-7392
Plant City *(G-14446)*
Presage Analytics Inc ....G....... 800 309-1704
Bonita Springs *(G-849)*
◆ **RL Schreiber Inc** ....D....... 954 972-7102
Fort Lauderdale *(G-4208)*
Story Citrus Inc ....E....... 863 638-1619
Lake Wales *(G-7522)*
Wedgworths Inc ....F....... 561 996-2076
Lake Placid *(G-7495)*

2035 Pickled Fruits, Vegetables, Sauces & Dressings

Alfa Products LLC ....G....... 901 218-0802
Deland *(G-2956)*
▲ **Catalina Finer Food Corp** ....E....... 813 872-6359
Tampa *(G-17515)*
Cigar City Smoked Salsa LLC ....G....... 813 421-3340
Tampa *(G-17535)*
Culinary Concepts Inc ....E....... 407 228-0069
Orlando *(G-12635)*
Destination Bvi II Inc ....G....... 850 699-9551
Destin *(G-3188)*
Doctor Pickle LLC ....F....... 772 985-5919
Boca Raton *(G-505)*
Filthy Food LLC ....D....... 786 916-5556
Miami *(G-9567)*
◆ **Flayco Products Inc** ....E....... 813 879-1356
Tampa *(G-17668)*
Florida International Firm Inc ....G....... 305 450-5920
Sweetwater *(G-17209)*
Hoerndler Inc ....G....... 239 643-2008
Naples *(G-11279)*
Italian Rose Garlic Pdts LLC ....C....... 561 863-5556
Riviera Beach *(G-15336)*
Joys International Foods Inc ....G....... 321 242-6520
Melbourne *(G-8855)*
▲ **Kenart Holdings Llc** ....C....... 561 863-5556
Riviera Beach *(G-15340)*
Kraft Heinz Foods Company ....G....... 904 695-1300
Jacksonville *(G-6545)*
La Lechonera Products Inc ....F....... 305 635-2303
Miami *(G-9841)*
Little Pickle LLC ....G....... 850 231-1290
Santa Rosa Beach *(G-16163)*
Los Atntcos Sndwich Cuban Cafe ....G....... 407 282-2322
Orlando *(G-12936)*
Mizkan America Inc ....F....... 863 956-0391
Lake Alfred *(G-7333)*
Pickled Art Inc ....G....... 954 635-7370
Fort Lauderdale *(G-4167)*
Pickles Plus ....G....... 941 661-6139
North Port *(G-11747)*
Premier Distributor of Miami ....G....... 305 821-9671
Hialeah *(G-5565)*
◆ **Rickeys World Famous Sauce Inc** ....F....... 954 829-9464
Hollywood *(G-5901)*
◆ **RL Schreiber Inc** ....D....... 954 972-7102
Fort Lauderdale *(G-4208)*
Suzanne Chalet Foods Inc ....G....... 863 676-6011
Lake Wales *(G-7524)*
Vienna Beef Ltd ....B....... 941 723-7234
Palmetto *(G-13833)*
Wharton Pepper Co ....G....... 850 997-4359
Monticello *(G-11084)*

2037 Frozen Fruits, Juices & Vegetables

◆ **Allapattah Industries Inc** ....E....... 305 324-5900
Miami *(G-9116)*
▲ **Ardmore Farms LLC** ....D....... 386 734-4634
Deland *(G-2960)*
Ata Group of Companies Inc ....G....... 352 735-1588
Mount Dora *(G-11097)*
Boca Smoothies LLC ....G....... 772 323-2117
Jupiter *(G-7013)*
Borden Dairy Company Fla LLC ....D....... 863 298-9742
Winter Haven *(G-19305)*
Brazilian Smoothie Inc ....G....... 305 233-5543
Pinecrest *(G-14325)*
Bru Bottling Inc ....G....... 561 324-5053
Juno Beach *(G-6977)*
Cebev LLC ....G....... 918 830-4417
Boca Raton *(G-475)*
Chunky Plates LLC ....G....... 321 746-3346
Orlando *(G-12583)*
◆ **Citrus World Inc** ....A....... 863 676-1411
Lake Wales *(G-7503)*
Citrus World ADM Svcs Inc ....G....... 863 676-1411
Lake Wales *(G-7504)*
Citrus World Services Inc ....F....... 863 676-1411
Lake Wales *(G-7505)*
Clonts Groves Inc ....F....... 407 359-4103
Oviedo *(G-13420)*

Coca-Cola Company ....G 407 565-2465
Apopka (G-123)
Corines Frsh Fruits/Vegetbles ....G 352 708-6247
Clermont (G-1955)
Country Frits Juices Nurs Corp ....G 786 302-8487
Miami (G-9408)
Country Pure Foods Inc ....B 904 734-4634
Deland (G-2965)
Crop LLC ....F 941 923-8640
Sarasota (G-16396)
Cutrale Citrus Juices USA Inc ....B 352 728-7800
Leesburg (G-8149)
▲ Cvista LLC ....E 813 405-3000
Riverview (G-15269)
Daves Super Smoothies LLC ....G 407 293-7334
Orlando (G-12653)
◆ Florida Food Products LLC ....D 352 357-4141
Eustis (G-3707)
Floridas Natural Food Svc Inc ....E 888 657-6600
Lake Wales (G-7510)
◆ Food Partners Inc ....F 863 298-8771
Winter Haven (G-19322)
Fresh Blends North America Inc ....F 531 665-8200
Delray Beach (G-3081)
◆ Grand Products International ....G 386 736-3528
Deland (G-2981)
Green Plant LLC ....E 305 397-9394
Miami (G-9669)
Healtheintentions Inc ....G 954 394-8867
Miami (G-9693)
▲ Interfries Inc ....G 786 427-1427
Miami (G-9755)
Juice Tyme Inc ....G 631 424-2850
Frostproof (G-4860)
Kerry Inc ....G 813 359-5181
Plant City (G-14444)
Key Biscayne Smoothie Company ....G 305 441-7882
Coral Gables (G-2163)
▲ King Brands LLC ....E 239 313-2057
Fort Myers (G-4511)
Manatee Smoothies LLC ....G 985 640-3088
Lakewood Ranch (G-7840)
◆ Natural Fruit Corp ....E 305 887-7525
Hialeah (G-5533)
Oakland Park Smoothie Inc ....G 954 567-0871
Fort Lauderdale (G-4146)
▼ Orchid Island Juice Co Inc ....D 772 465-1122
Fort Pierce (G-4727)
Palm Beach Smoothies Com Inc ....G 561 379-8647
Tequesta (G-18386)
Pl Smoothie LLC ....G 954 554-0450
Davie (G-2574)
Raw Foods International Llc ....F 305 856-1991
Coral Gables (G-2190)
Refreshing Smoothie ....G 904 549-5366
Jacksonville (G-6712)
Shri Guru Krupa Smoothies Inc ....G 904 461-9090
Saint Augustine (G-15609)
◆ Silver Springs Citrus Inc ....C 352 324-2101
Howey In The Hills (G-6012)
Skd Smoothie Inc ....G 386 931-4953
Palm Coast (G-13709)
Smoothie Corp ....E 305 588-0867
Miami (G-10365)
Smoothie Operator By JC Inc ....G 786 367-4245
Miami (G-10366)
Smoothies Recharge ....G 954 999-0332
Sunrise (G-17174)
◆ Southern Grdns Ctrus Hldg Corp ....G 863 983-8121
Clewiston (G-1986)
▲ Sun Orchard LLC ....E 786 646-9200
Miami (G-10428)
Sunluver Smoothies Inc ....G 239 331-5431
Naples (G-11425)
◆ Sunnyland Usa Inc ....G 772 293-0293
Fort Pierce (G-4752)
Totally Bananas LLC ....F 954 674-9421
Davie (G-2607)
▲ Tropicana Products Inc ....A 941 747-4461
Bradenton (G-1133)
Tropicana Products Inc ....G 772 465-2030
Fort Pierce (G-4759)
▲ World Wide Frozen Foods LLC ....G 954 266-8500
Fort Lauderdale (G-4328)

2038 Frozen Specialties

Asian Food Solutions Inc ....E 888 499-6888
Oviedo (G-13414)
Charles Bryant Enterprises ....G 850 785-3604
Panama City (G-13879)
Chefs Commissary LLC ....D 321 303-2947
Orlando (G-12578)
▼ Classic Pizza Crusts Inc ....G 954 570-8383
Pompano Beach (G-14636)
Comida Vida Inc ....G 855 720-7663
Oviedo (G-13421)
▼ Discos Y Empanadas Argentina ....F 305 326-9300
Miami (G-9469)
▲ GA Fd Svcs Pinellas Cnty LLC ....B 727 388-0075
Saint Petersburg (G-15789)
GA Fd Svcs Pinellas Cnty LLC ....E 954 972-8884
Fort Lauderdale (G-4017)
GA Fd Svcs Pinellas Cnty LLC ....E 239 693-5090
Fort Myers (G-4465)
Greenie Tots Inc ....G 888 316-6126
Plantation (G-14522)
Hom Ade Foods Inc ....D 850 444-4740
Pensacola (G-14174)
International Fd Solutions Inc ....E 888 499-6888
Oviedo (G-13440)
Jo MO Enterprises Inc ....G 708 599-8098
Boca Raton (G-582)
Kibby Foods LLC ....F 305 456-3635
Hialeah (G-5472)
Krunchy Krisps LLC ....G 561 309-7049
Palm City (G-13664)
Lillys Gstrnmia Itlana Fla Inc ....G 305 655-2111
Hallandale Beach (G-5198)
Madan Corporation ....G 954 925-0077
Dania Beach (G-2467)
◆ Patty King Inc ....E 305 817-1888
Hialeah (G-5555)
Pizza Spice Packet LLC ....G 718 831-7036
Boca Raton (G-666)
Sukalde Inc ....E 786 399-0087
Coral Gables (G-2197)
Thrive Frozen Nutrition Inc ....F 407 960-4883
Orlando (G-13256)
Tuiskombuis ....G 904 484-4509
Saint Augustine (G-15628)
Uren North America LLC ....G 410 924-3478
Coral Gables (G-2201)
Very Tasty LLC ....F 305 636-4140
Miami (G-10575)
Zesty Brands LLC ....F 954 348-2827
Orlando (G-13339)

2041 Flour, Grain Milling

Bay State Milling Company ....E 772 597-2056
Indiantown (G-6071)
Change This World ....G 407 900-8840
Orlando (G-12575)
Charles Bryant Enterprises ....G 850 785-3604
Panama City (G-13879)
▼ Classic Pizza Crusts Inc ....G 954 570-8383
Pompano Beach (G-14636)
Dennis Hernandez & Assoc PA ....G 813 470-4545
Tampa (G-17599)
Majesty Foods LLC ....E 305 817-1888
Hialeah (G-5497)
Shining Tree Inc ....F 855 688-7987
Wellington (G-18732)
Southland Milling Co ....G 850 674-8448
Blountstown (G-389)

2043 Cereal Breakfast Foods

Ilex Organics LLC ....F 386 566-3826
Edgewater (G-3625)
▼ Productos Las Delicias Inc ....G 305 760-4223
Hialeah (G-5577)

2044 Rice Milling

◆ Conchita Foods Inc ....D 305 888-9703
Medley (G-8633)
◆ Deeja Foods Inc ....G 321 402-8300
Kissimmee (G-7237)
▲ Florida Crystals Corporation ....D 561 655-6303
West Palm Beach (G-18875)
Florida Crystals Corporation ....C 561 515-8080
West Palm Beach (G-18877)
Florida Gold Foods LLC ....F 347 595-1983
Kissimmee (G-7245)
Hyperion Managing LLC ....G 904 612-3987
Jacksonville (G-6485)

2045 Flour, Blended & Prepared

Big L Brands Inc ....F 888 552-9768
Boca Raton (G-447)
Burris Investment Group Inc ....E 850 623-3845
Pensacola (G-14110)
Hom/Ade Food Sales Inc ....G 850 623-3845
Bagdad (G-298)

2046 Wet Corn Milling

▲ Element Eliquid LLC ....F 754 260-5500
Miramar (G-10988)
Plant Theory LLC ....G 305 672-5785
Miami Beach (G-10702)
Tapioca Fit ....G 954 842-3924
Pembroke Pines (G-14064)

2047 Dog & Cat Food

All American Pet Company Inc ....F 561 337-5340
Palm Beach Gardens (G-13565)
▼ Natural Crvings Pet Treats LLC ....G 786 404-8099
Homestead (G-5985)
Snif-Snax Ltd ....F 786 613-7007
Miami (G-10368)
▼ Synergy Labs Inc ....E 954 525-1133
Fort Lauderdale (G-4271)
Zesty Paws LLC ....E 407 358-6601
Orlando (G-13340)

2048 Prepared Feeds For Animals & Fowls

▲ AB Vista Inc ....G 954 278-3965
Plantation (G-14483)
▼ Agranco Corp (usa) ....F 877 592-0031
South Miami (G-16811)
Animal Business Concepts LLC ....F 727 641-6176
Saint Petersburg (G-15701)
B&K Country Feeds LLC ....G 561 701-1852
West Palm Beach (G-18810)
Backyard Feed LLC ....G 813 846-5995
Saint Augustine (G-15521)
Branch Properties Inc ....D 352 732-4143
Ocala (G-11890)
BRT Oakleaf Pet Inc ....G 904 563-1212
Jacksonville (G-6239)
Buddy Custard Inc ....G 561 715-3785
Fort Lauderdale (G-3874)
Coronet Industries Inc ....E 813 752-1161
Plant City (G-14420)
Dairy Feeds Inc ....G 863 763-0258
Okeechobee (G-12175)
Dalian Platinum Chem Ltd Corp ....G 954 501-0564
Fort Lauderdale (G-3931)
Furst-Mcness Company ....G 386 755-5605
Lake City (G-7355)
Gator Feed Co Inc ....F 863 763-3337
Okeechobee (G-12179)
Griffin Industries LLC ....E 904 964-8083
Starke (G-16894)
Hay Tech ....G 850 592-2424
Bascom (G-336)
Heal and Shine Inc ....G 561 801-3423
Royal Palm Beach (G-15469)
◆ Higgins Group Corp ....E 305 681-4444
Miami (G-9709)
Karnak Corporation ....G 352 481-4145
East Palatka (G-3604)
Knights Farm Fresh Feeds Inc ....G 352 793-2242
Bushnell (G-1318)
Monticello Milling Co Inc ....G 850 997-5521
Monticello (G-11079)
Mr Gummy Vitamins LLC ....G 855 674-8669
Opa Locka (G-12341)
Nulab Inc ....D 727 446-1126
Clearwater (G-1813)
Ocala Breeders Sales Co Inc ....E 352 237-4667
Ocala (G-12007)
Paws Off Prime K9 Cuisine LLC ....G 305 546-7475
Miami (G-10145)
Perfectus Pet Food LLC ....G 800 774-3296
Hollywood (G-5890)
Plantation Botanicals Inc ....E 863 675-2984
Felda (G-3722)
Purina Animal Nutrition LLC ....F 863 262-4332
Lakeland (G-7772)
◆ Seminole Stores Inc ....F 352 732-4143
Ocala (G-12044)
Special Nutrients LLC ....F 305 857-9830
Coconut Grove (G-2105)
Stratford Care Usa Inc ....G 877 498-2002
Odessa (G-12157)
Swans Feed Mill ....G 813 782-6969
Zephyrhills (G-19539)
▲ Tropicana Products Inc ....A 941 747-4461
Bradenton (G-1133)

SIC

Zephyr Feed Company Inc G 813 782-1578
Zephyrhills *(G-19543)*

2051 Bread, Bakery Prdts Exc Cookies & Crackers

904 Sweet Treatz Street LLC G 800 889-3298
Jacksonville *(G-6105)*
Achsahs Delight Bakery LLC G 954 533-1843
Fort Lauderdale *(G-3778)*
Babicakes LLC G 561 507-0331
West Palm Beach *(G-18811)*
Bakerly LLC E 305 608-4479
Coral Gables *(G-2125)*
Batter To Platter LLC G 203 309-7632
Sanford *(G-16001)*
Bauducco Manufacturing Inc F 305 477-9270
Miami *(G-9225)*
Bauducco USA Holding Company G 305 477-9270
Miami *(G-9226)*
Bella Vista Bakery Inc E 954 759-1920
Doral *(G-3266)*
Bimbo Bakeries USA G 941 875-5945
North Port *(G-11732)*
Bimbo Bakeries USA F 954 968-7684
Fort Lauderdale *(G-3853)*
Bkn International Inc G 301 518-7153
Miami *(G-9254)*
Bks Bakery Inc G 386 216-0540
Deltona *(G-3164)*
Brooklyn Water Enterprises Inc E 877 224-3580
Delray Beach *(G-3053)*
Brothers Wholesale Inc E 631 831-8484
Port St Lucie *(G-15168)*
Brownsugarbae LLC G 954 554-0318
Fort Lauderdale *(G-3872)*
Buttercream Cpcakes Cof Sp Inc F 305 669-8181
Coral Gables *(G-2128)*
Caamacosta Inc G 954 987-5895
Hollywood *(G-5793)*
Carlees Creations Inc G 786 232-0050
Miami *(G-9319)*
Casino Bakery Inc F 813 242-0311
Tampa *(G-17513)*
Cedars Bakery Group Inc F 407 476-6593
Orlando *(G-12559)*
Churrico Factory LLC G 239 989-7616
Fort Myers *(G-4394)*
Claddah Corp F 407 834-8881
Casselberry *(G-1501)*
Clear Distribution Inc G 904 330-5624
Jacksonville *(G-6267)*
CMC Bakery LLC E 978 682-2382
Pompano Beach *(G-14637)*
Coleo LLC F 215 436-0902
Daytona Beach *(G-2645)*
Corvatsch Corp F 305 775-2831
Miami Beach *(G-10658)*
Crustys Bread Bakery G 727 937-9041
Tarpon Springs *(G-18291)*
Cupcake Inc G 407 644-7800
Maitland *(G-8464)*
Cupcake Girls Dessert Company G 904 372-4579
Jacksonville Beach *(G-6941)*
Cupcake Heaven G 352 610-4433
Spring Hill *(G-16850)*
Cupcakes Frsting Sprinkles LLC G 305 769-3393
Opa Locka *(G-12304)*
Cusanos Italian Bakery Inc E 786 506-4281
Orlando *(G-12637)*
Darland Bakery Inc F 407 894-1061
Orlando *(G-12648)*
Delicio Baking Company Inc G 305 865-5664
Miami Beach *(G-10662)*
Dip-A-Dee Donuts E 352 460-4266
Leesburg *(G-8150)*
Duval Bakery Products Inc G 904 354-7878
Jacksonville *(G-6339)*
Ebs Quality Service Inc F 305 595-4048
Miami *(G-9497)*
Edca Bakery Corporation F 305 448-7843
Coral Gables *(G-2141)*
Egg Roll Skins Inc F 305 836-0571
Hialeah *(G-5391)*
El Trigal International G 305 594-6610
Medley *(G-8646)*
Empanada Lady Co F 786 271-6460
Miami *(G-9525)*
Enchanting Creations G 305 978-2828
Miami Shores *(G-10884)*
Farartis LLC G 305 594-5704
Miami *(G-9559)*
Fat and Weird Cookie Co LLC F 850 832-9150
Panama City *(G-13900)*
Five Star Bakery G 954 983-6133
Miramar *(G-10991)*
Flowers Bakeries LLC E 850 875-4997
Quincy *(G-15249)*
Flowers Baking Co LLC G 850 763-2541
Panama City *(G-13904)*
Flowers Baking Co Lakeland Inc E 863 682-1155
Lakeland *(G-7694)*
Flowers Baking Co Miami LLC F 772 778-3990
Vero Beach *(G-18620)*
Flowers Baking Co Miami LLC E 305 599-8457
Doral *(G-3353)*
◆ **Flowers Baking Co Miami LLC** D 305 652-3416
Miami *(G-9589)*
Flowers Bkg Co Bradenton LLC F 941 627-0752
Port Charlotte *(G-14981)*
Flowers Bkg Co Bradenton LLC E 941 758-5656
Lakeland *(G-7695)*
Flowers Bkg Co Bradenton LLC F 941 758-5656
Avon Park *(G-287)*
Flowers Bkg Co Bradenton LLC E 941 758-5656
Orlando *(G-12760)*
Flowers Bkg Co Bradenton LLC E 941 758-5656
Hudson *(G-6025)*
Flowers Bkg Co Bradenton LLC E 941 758-5656
Kissimmee *(G-7246)*
Flowers Bkg Co Bradenton LLC E 941 758-5656
Bonita Springs *(G-832)*
Flowers Bkg Co Bradenton LLC E 941 758-5656
Bradenton *(G-1043)*
Flowers Bkg Co Bradenton LLC C 941 758-5656
Sarasota *(G-16215)*
Flowers Bkg Co Thomasville LLC F 229 226-5331
Tallahassee *(G-17256)*
▼ **Flowers Bkg Jacksonville LLC** D 904 354-3771
Jacksonville *(G-6407)*
Forno De Minas Usa Inc F 954 840-6533
Deerfield Beach *(G-2826)*
Franklin Baking Company LLC G 850 478-8360
Pensacola *(G-14159)*
Fresh On Fifth G 305 234-5678
Miami Beach *(G-10669)*
Frosting G 772 234-2915
Vero Beach *(G-18622)*
Gfoodz LLC G 561 703-4505
Boynton Beach *(G-912)*
Gigliola Inc G 954 564-7871
Fort Lauderdale *(G-4021)*
Giovannis Bakery Inc F 727 536-2253
Largo *(G-7958)*
Gregomarc LLC G 305 559-9777
Miami *(G-9670)*
H&K Home Supplies Distrs LLC F 786 308-6024
Homestead *(G-5966)*
Heara Inc G 305 651-5200
Miami *(G-9694)*
◆ **Hometown Foods Usa LLC** C 305 887-5200
Medley *(G-8665)*
Ipq Trade Corp F 786 522-2310
Miami *(G-9768)*
Juan F Montano G 305 274-0512
Miami *(G-9811)*
Kellys Bakery Corp F 305 685-4622
Opa Locka *(G-12330)*
La Mansion Latina LLC G 305 406-1606
Miami *(G-9843)*
La Province Inc F 305 538-2406
Miami *(G-9847)*
Lisa Bakery Inc G 305 888-8431
Hialeah *(G-5487)*
Magnolias Gurmet Bky Itln Deli G 352 207-2667
Ocala *(G-11990)*
Marnis Dolce G 407 915-7607
Apopka *(G-157)*
Martins Fmous Pstry Shoppe Inc G 800 548-1200
Tallahassee *(G-17297)*
Merenguitoscom LLC G 305 685-2709
Hialeah *(G-5505)*
Mishas Cupcakes Inc E 786 200-6153
Miami *(G-10028)*
Mr GS Foods F 352 799-1806
Brooksville *(G-1255)*
Nani Sweets LLC G 305 793-1077
Hialeah *(G-5532)*
New Marco Foods Inc F 305 836-0571
Hialeah *(G-5538)*
▲ **New Vbb LLC** E 904 631-5978
Jacksonville *(G-6629)*
New York Intl Bread Co D 407 843-9744
Orlando *(G-13000)*
Nostalgic Specialty Foods Inc G 561 391-8600
Boca Raton *(G-650)*
Obem Foods Inc G 305 887-0258
Miami Springs *(G-10896)*
On A Roll Distributors Inc G 352 726-3420
Inverness *(G-6093)*
OPelle Enterprises Inc E 954 942-7338
Pompano Beach *(G-14780)*
Orlando Donut Mfg LLC F 407 933-7111
Kissimmee *(G-7281)*
Palanjian Enterprises Inc F 850 244-2848
Fort Walton Beach *(G-4820)*
◆ **Panamerican Food LLC** E 305 594-5704
Miramar *(G-11026)*
Panapastry LLC G 305 883-1557
Medley *(G-8702)*
Pane Rustica Bakery & Cafe F 813 902-8828
Tampa *(G-17970)*
Parinto Global Enterprises LLC G 305 606-3107
Doral *(G-3454)*
Patticakes Cupcakery LLC G 386 383-1782
South Daytona *(G-16807)*
▲ **Payo LLC** G 786 368-8655
Davie *(G-2567)*
Phils Cake Box Bakeries Inc D 813 348-0128
Tampa *(G-17991)*
Pin Hsiao & Associates LLC F 425 637-3357
Port Orange *(G-15028)*
▲ **Popcorn Cellar LLC** G 239 272-8494
Naples *(G-11372)*
Richardson Family Products LLC G 239 896-3595
Lehigh Acres *(G-8205)*
Rouzbeh Inc E 727 587-7077
Largo *(G-8042)*
Savory Street G 941 312-4027
Sarasota *(G-16584)*
Simply Cupcakes G 239 262-5184
Naples *(G-11404)*
Slb1989 Inc G 772 344-3609
Port Saint Lucie *(G-15146)*
▲ **Slim and Soft Bread LLC** F 305 759-2126
North Miami *(G-11656)*
Southern Bakeries Inc C 863 682-1155
Lakeland *(G-7800)*
Spring Hill Bakery LLC E 954 825-3419
Spring Hill *(G-16865)*
St Johns Bky & Gourmet Fd Co F 813 727-3528
Jacksonville *(G-6806)*
▲ **Star Bakery Inc** F 305 633-4284
Miami *(G-10409)*
Swah-Rey 2 LLC G 727 767-0527
Saint Petersburg *(G-15931)*
Swami Foods LLC F 888 697-9264
Lake Mary *(G-7453)*
Sweet Creations By L S Young G 772 584-7206
Vero Beach *(G-18669)*
Sweetsies G 386 566-6762
Palm Coast *(G-13712)*
T & W Inc G 305 887-0258
Miami Springs *(G-10898)*
Todo En Uno G 305 263-6934
Miami *(G-10486)*
▲ **Tts Food LLC** G 305 622-2726
Hialeah *(G-5652)*
Tulipan Bakery Inc F 561 832-6107
West Palm Beach *(G-19071)*
Tuly Corporation F 305 633-0710
Miami *(G-10512)*
Unicornio Bakery LLC F 786 665-1602
Doral *(G-3535)*
Universal Bakery LLC G 786 566-3303
Opa Locka *(G-12367)*
Way Beyond Bagels Inc F 561 638-1320
Delray Beach *(G-3159)*
Willie Maes Pies LLC G 407 655-9360
Kissimmee *(G-7315)*

2052 Cookies & Crackers

Ambo Foods LLC G 941 485-4400
Venice *(G-18531)*
Aventura Cookies Inc G 954 447-4525
Pembroke Pines *(G-14021)*
Barjor Baking Group LLC G 239 325-8591
Naples *(G-11183)*
▲ **Bingo Bakery Inc** F 305 545-9993
Miami *(G-9246)*

Brownie Lady LLC ....G.... 954 989-0630
Hollywood (G-5791)
Carpe Diem Ice Cream LLC ....G.... 305 504-4469
Key West (G-7180)
◆ First Grade Food Corporation ....E.... 813 886-6118
Tampa (G-17666)
◆ Gilda Industries Inc ....D.... 305 887-8286
Hialeah (G-5431)
Jada Foods LLC ....F.... 305 319-0263
Hallandale Beach (G-5193)
Lavi Enterprises LLC ....D.... 561 721-7170
Riviera Beach (G-15342)
Lindley Foods LLC ....G.... 407 884-9433
Apopka (G-156)
Magnolias Gurmet Bky Itln Deli ....G.... 352 207-2667
Ocala (G-11990)
Megatron Equity Partners Inc ....F.... 305 789-6688
Miami (G-9972)
Paleo Simplified LLC ....G.... 813 446-5969
Safety Harbor (G-15500)
Ricos Tostaditos Inc ....F.... 305 885-7392
Hialeah (G-5601)
Rika Bakeries Inc ....F.... 305 691-5673
Hialeah (G-5602)
Selmas Cookies Inc ....E.... 407 884-9433
Apopka (G-185)
Smart Snacks LLC ....G.... 954 860-8833
Hollywood (G-5909)
▲ Star Bakery Inc ....F.... 305 633-4284
Miami (G-10409)
Tuly Corporation ....F.... 305 633-0710
Miami (G-10512)

2053 Frozen Bakery Prdts

▲ Blue Coast Bakers LLC ....E.... 386 944-0800
Ormond Beach (G-13355)
Caligiuri Corporation ....E.... 407 324-4441
Sanford (G-16006)
Dawn Foods Inc ....G.... 866 218-3801
Medley (G-8641)
Epic Harvests LLC ....E.... 904 503-5143
Jacksonville (G-6369)
◆ Hometown Foods Usa LLC ....C.... 305 887-5200
Medley (G-8665)
La Autentica ....G.... 786 409-3779
Hialeah (G-5480)
OPelle Enterprises Inc ....E.... 954 942-7338
Pompano Beach (G-14780)
Sugar Fancies LLC ....G.... 786 558-9087
Miami (G-10427)
▲ Sunsof Inc ....E.... 305 691-1875
Hialeah (G-5641)

2061 Sugar, Cane

Add-V LLC ....G.... 305 496-2445
Lauderhill (G-8099)
Alvean Americas Inc ....F.... 305 606-0770
Coral Gables (G-2121)
Atlantic Sugar Association ....F.... 561 996-6541
Belle Glade (G-344)
▲ Florida Crystals Corporation ....D.... 561 655-6303
West Palm Beach (G-18875)
Florida Crystals Corporation ....C.... 561 366-5000
West Palm Beach (G-18876)
Florida Crystals Corporation ....C.... 561 992-5635
South Bay (G-16795)
Florida Crystals Corporation ....C.... 561 515-8080
West Palm Beach (G-18877)
▲ Florida Crystals Food Corp ....A.... 561 366-5100
West Palm Beach (G-18878)
Okeelanta Corporation ....C.... 561 996-9072
South Bay (G-16796)
◆ Okeelanta Corporation ....E.... 561 366-5100
West Palm Beach (G-18971)
Organic Cane Company Inc ....G.... 561 385-4081
Stuart (G-16984)
▲ Sugar Cane Growers Coop Fla ....B.... 561 996-5556
Belle Glade (G-351)
Tru Cane Sugar Corp ....G.... 561 833-1731
West Palm Beach (G-19070)

2062 Sugar, Cane Refining

American Sugar Refining Inc ....G.... 561 962-8106
Boca Raton (G-423)
Atlantic Sugar Association ....F.... 561 996-6541
Belle Glade (G-344)
▲ B and M Sugar Products LLC ....G.... 305 897-8427
Miami (G-9208)
▼ Florida Crystal Refinery Inc ....G.... 561 366-5200
West Palm Beach (G-18874)
▲ Florida Crystals Corporation ....D.... 561 655-6303
West Palm Beach (G-18875)
Florida Crystals Corporation ....C.... 561 366-5000
West Palm Beach (G-18876)
Florida Crystals Corporation ....C.... 561 992-5635
South Bay (G-16795)
Florida Crystals Corporation ....C.... 561 515-8080
West Palm Beach (G-18877)
Florida Sugar Distributors ....E.... 561 655-6303
West Palm Beach (G-18880)
Florida Sugar Farmers ....F.... 863 983-7276
Clewiston (G-1980)
Merkavah International Inc ....G.... 305 909-6798
Miami (G-9981)
◆ Okeelanta Corporation ....E.... 561 366-5100
West Palm Beach (G-18971)
Osceola Farms Co ....A.... 561 924-7156
Pahokee (G-13470)

2064 Candy & Confectionery Prdts

▲ Amazon Origins Inc ....G.... 239 404-1818
Naples (G-11159)
B & B Bons LLC ....G.... 954 940-4900
Fort Lauderdale (G-3836)
▼ Barnard Nut Company Inc ....D.... 305 836-9999
Miami (G-9221)
Bbx Sweet Holdings LLC ....F.... 954 940-4000
Fort Lauderdale (G-3843)
▲ Behrs Chocolates By Design ....G.... 407 648-2020
Orlando (G-12510)
Brownbag Popcorn Company LLC ....G.... 561 212-5664
Boca Raton (G-467)
Candies and Beyond Inc ....G.... 954 828-2255
Miami Lakes (G-10774)
Cozy Bar ....F.... 305 532-2699
Miami Beach (G-10659)
Florida Candy Factory Inc ....F.... 727 446-0024
Clearwater (G-1687)
▲ Hoffman Commercial Group Inc ....E.... 561 967-2213
Greenacres (G-5082)
Jne Candy Co LLC ....F.... 407 622-6292
Orlando (G-12857)
Kizable LLC ....G.... 727 600-3469
Fort Lauderdale (G-4090)
Lollipop Children Center Inc ....G.... 386 755-3953
Lake City (G-7366)
Louis Sherry Company LLC ....G.... 904 482-1900
Jacksonville (G-6565)
Mauer Sports Nutrition Inc ....G.... 888 609-2489
Fort Myers (G-4524)
Nestle Usa Inc ....D.... 813 301-4638
Thonotosassa (G-18403)
P B C Central ....G.... 407 648-2020
Orlando (G-13041)
▲ Paradise Inc ....C.... 813 752-1155
Tampa (G-17974)
Poppin Box LLC ....G.... 904 484-7030
Saint Johns (G-15680)
Retreat ....G.... 813 254-2014
Tampa (G-18055)
Ricos Tostaditos Inc ....F.... 305 885-7392
Hialeah (G-5601)
Send It Sweetly LLC ....G.... 239 850-5500
Cape Coral (G-1468)
◆ Signature Brands LLC ....B.... 352 622-3134
Ocala (G-12050)
Signature Brands LLC ....D.... 352 622-3134
Ocala (G-12051)
▼ Sweet Tooth Inc ....G.... 305 682-1400
North Miami Beach (G-11706)
Tropical Taffy Naples Inc ....G.... 239 571-3761
Naples (G-11445)

2066 Chocolate & Cocoa Prdts

Araya Inc ....G.... 305 229-6868
Miami (G-9161)
Art Edibles Inc ....G.... 407 603-4043
Oviedo (G-13413)
Atlantic Candy Company ....E.... 904 429-7250
Saint Augustine (G-15518)
▲ Behrs Chocolates By Design ....G.... 407 648-2020
Orlando (G-12510)
Chocolate Guys LLC ....G.... 561 278-5889
Delray Beach (G-3060)
David Delights LLC ....G.... 407 648-2020
Orlando (G-12654)
Fantasy Chocolates Inc ....E.... 561 276-9007
Orlando (G-12732)
▲ Hoffman Commercial Group Inc ....E.... 561 967-2213
Greenacres (G-5082)
Kay Peak Group Inc ....G.... 754 307-5400
Margate (G-8554)
Mvs International Inc ....G.... 954 727-3383
Weston (G-19151)
P B C Central ....G.... 407 648-2020
Orlando (G-13041)
Peterbrooke Choclat Fctry LLC ....G.... 904 273-7878
Ponte Vedra Beach (G-14950)
Pinnacle Foods Inc ....G.... 321 952-7926
Melbourne Beach (G-8981)
▼ Sweet Tooth Inc ....G.... 305 682-1400
North Miami Beach (G-11706)
Venchi US Inc ....G.... 646 448-8663
Miami (G-10572)
▲ Whole Coffee Company LLC ....D.... 786 364-4444
Miami (G-10604)

2068 Salted & Roasted Nuts & Seeds

IL Nuts Inc ....G.... 786 366-4536
Miami (G-9732)
Papa Johns Peanuts Inc ....E.... 904 389-2511
Jacksonville (G-6656)
Royal Ancient Superfoods ....G.... 305 600-1747
Doral (G-3492)
Veronicas Health Crunch LLC ....G.... 352 409-1124
Freeport (G-4853)

2075 Soybean Oil Mills

Amerifood Corp ....G.... 305 305-5951
Miami (G-9149)

2076 Vegetable Oil Mills

C P Vegetable Oil Inc ....F.... 954 584-0420
Fort Lauderdale (G-3879)
Hawks Nuts Inc ....F.... 813 872-0900
Tampa (G-17747)
◆ Trujillo Oil Plant Inc ....F.... 305 696-8701
Miami (G-10510)

2077 Animal, Marine Fats & Oils

◆ Conchita Foods Inc ....D.... 305 888-9703
Medley (G-8633)
Darling Ingredients Inc ....G.... 904 964-8083
Starke (G-16892)
Darling Ingredients Inc ....G.... 407 856-7667
Orlando (G-12649)
Darling Ingredients Inc ....G.... 863 425-0065
Tampa (G-17589)
Darling Ingredients Inc ....G.... 239 693-2300
Fort Myers (G-4425)
Griffin Industries LLC ....E.... 904 964-8083
Starke (G-16894)
Griffin Industries LLC ....E.... 407 857-5474
Orlando (G-12789)
Griffin Industries LLC ....E.... 813 626-1135
Tampa (G-17729)
Kane-Miller Corp ....G.... 941 346-2003
Sarasota (G-16481)
Openwater Seafood LLC ....G.... 407 440-0656
Orlando (G-13026)
Valley Proteins (de) Inc ....D.... 704 718-6568
Jacksonville (G-6891)
Valley Proteins (de) Inc ....D.... 910 282-7900
Mulberry (G-11140)

2079 Shortening, Oils & Margarine

Bella Blsmic Pressed Olive Inc ....G.... 941 505-1707
Punta Gorda (G-15194)
Bella Blsmic Pressed Olive Inc ....E.... 941 249-3571
Punta Gorda (G-15195)
Estero FL ....G.... 239 289-9511
Estero (G-3688)
Grease TEC Holding LLC ....G.... 352 742-2440
Tavares (G-18339)
Miami Oliveoil & Beyond Llc ....G.... 954 632-2762
Doral (G-3436)
Olive 30a Oil Inc ....G.... 850 909-0099
Inlet Beach (G-6077)
Olive Amelia LLC ....G.... 904 310-3603
Fernandina Beach (G-3746)
Olive Naples Oil Company ....E.... 239 596-3000
Naples (G-11351)
Olive Oil Co of Fort Myers ....G.... 239 821-4630
Naples (G-11352)
Olive Tree II ....G.... 813 991-8781
Wesley Chapel (G-18755)
Ormond Beach Olive Oil ....G.... 386 333-9236
Ormond Beach (G-13390)

Tomatoes & Olive Oil LLC G 941 822-9709
Venice *(G-18580)*

◆ **United Oil Packers Inc** E 305 687-6457
Miami *(G-10537)*

Ventura Foods LLC G 772 878-1400
Port Saint Lucie *(G-15161)*

◆ **Vigo Importing Company** C 813 884-3491
Tampa *(G-18247)*

2082 Malt Beverages

Anheuser-Busch Incorporated G 863 646-7357
Lakeland *(G-7636)*

Anheuser-Busch Companies LLC D 407 251-4049
Orlando *(G-12480)*

Apple A Day Inc G 941 377-5404
Sarasota *(G-16344)*

Blind Mouth Brewing Co LLC G 727 318-7664
Saint Petersburg *(G-15722)*

Bold City Braves LLC F 904 545-3480
Jacksonville *(G-6223)*

Brew Central LLC F 936 714-3402
Jacksonville *(G-6236)*

▲ **Brew Hub LLC** D 863 698-7600
Lakeland *(G-7650)*

Bru Fl LLC G 813 431-6815
Tampa *(G-17487)*

Canarchy Craft E 813 348-6363
Tampa *(G-17503)*

Center For Vital Living DBA F 239 213-2222
Naples *(G-11205)*

Cerberus Craft Distillery LLC G 813 789-1556
Tampa *(G-17527)*

▲ **Cigar City Brewpub LLC** C 813 348-6363
Tampa *(G-17534)*

D G Yuengling and Son Inc D 813 972-8500
Tampa *(G-17584)*

Dukes Brewhouse Inc F 813 758-9309
Plant City *(G-14427)*

Ellipsis Brewing G 407 556-3241
Orlando *(G-12707)*

Fantasy Brewmasters LLC G 239 206-3247
Naples *(G-11244)*

Florida Brewery Inc G 305 621-0099
Miami *(G-9580)*

◆ **Florida Brewery Inc** E 863 965-1825
Auburndale *(G-242)*

Florida Craft Distributors LLC F 813 528-7902
Sanford *(G-16048)*

Great Bay Distributors Inc C 727 584-8626
Holiday *(G-5741)*

In The Loop Brewing Inc G 813 857-0111
Land O Lakes *(G-7856)*

Indian River Brewery Corp E 321 728-4114
Cape Canaveral *(G-1361)*

International Keg Rental LLC F 407 900-9992
Orlando *(G-12836)*

JJ Taylor Distrg Fla Inc G 239 267-1006
Fort Myers *(G-4504)*

Krome Brewing Company LLC G 786 601-9337
Miami *(G-9832)*

▲ **Le Mundo Vino LLC** F 786 369-5232
Miami *(G-9875)*

Main & Six Brewing Company LLC G 904 673-0144
Jacksonville *(G-6575)*

Molson Coors Brewing Company G 305 792-6620
Miami *(G-10037)*

Orlando Brewing Partners G 407 843-6783
Orlando *(G-13032)*

Pair ODice Brewing Co LLC G 727 755-3423
Clearwater *(G-1825)*

Rock Brothers Brewing LLC G 917 324-8175
Tampa *(G-18066)*

▲ **Rpd Management LLC** G 904 710-8911
Jacksonville *(G-6738)*

Sourglass Brewing G 407 262-0056
Longwood *(G-8337)*

Titanic Brewing Company Inc F 305 668-1742
Coral Gables *(G-2199)*

2083 Malt

◆ **Florida Brewery Inc** E 863 965-1825
Auburndale *(G-242)*

Great Western Malting Co D 360 991-0888
Plant City *(G-14437)*

2084 Wine & Brandy

1506 N Florida LLC G 813 229-0900
Tampa *(G-17372)*

Abide Family Winery Inc G 850 258-0743
Panama City Beach *(G-13968)*

Amizetta Vineyards G 707 963-1460
Marco Island *(G-8523)*

▲ **Barton & Guestier Usa Inc** G 305 895-9757
Miami *(G-9224)*

Bea Sue Vineyards Inc G 352 446-5204
Summerfield *(G-17057)*

Brumate LLC G 317 474-7352
Fort Lauderdale *(G-3873)*

▲ **Buena Cepa Wines LLC** G 310 621-2566
Key Biscayne *(G-7154)*

Buenavida Imports LLC G 305 988-5992
Doral *(G-3288)*

Catanias Winery LLC G 941 321-9650
Englewood *(G-3672)*

Cavallo Estate Winery LLC G 352 500-9463
Lecanto *(G-8130)*

Charleston Winery G 843 425-1265
Vero Beach *(G-18610)*

Chautuqua Vineyards Winery Inc F 850 892-5887
Defuniak Springs *(G-2940)*

Coopers Hawk Intrmdate Hldg LL G 904 996-2466
Jacksonville *(G-6288)*

Corkscrew Winery G 352 751-1787
Ocala *(G-11909)*

De Vinco Company G 941 722-1100
Seffner *(G-16724)*

Elk Creek Wine G 561 529-2822
Jupiter *(G-7033)*

Faraday Inc F 813 536-6104
Tampa *(G-17659)*

Florida Orange Groves Inc F 727 347-4025
South Pasadena *(G-16834)*

Florida Rum Company LLC E 305 791-1221
Hollywood *(G-5823)*

Florida Winery Inc G 727 362-0008
Madeira Beach *(G-8446)*

Fws Distributors LLC G 561 312-3318
Miami *(G-9606)*

Fws Distributors LLC G 305 677-9663
Orlando *(G-12768)*

Gravity Produce LLC G 269 471-9463
Fort Myers Beach *(G-4663)*

▲ **Harvest Moon Distributors LLC** G 321 297-7942
Orlando *(G-12795)*

Hdd LLC G 561 346-9054
West Palm Beach *(G-18893)*

Headwaters Management LLC G 608 209-3111
Fort Lauderdale *(G-4046)*

Henscratch Farms Inc G 863 699-2060
Lake Placid *(G-7489)*

Hilliard Bruce Vineyards LLC G 305 979-2601
Miami Beach *(G-10678)*

Innova Home LLC G 561 855-2450
West Palm Beach *(G-18904)*

Italian Moonshiners Inc G 954 687-4500
Doral *(G-3395)*

▲ **JD Wine Concepts LLC** G 407 730-3082
Orlando *(G-12854)*

Johns Pass Winery G 727 362-0008
Madeira Beach *(G-8447)*

Keel & Curley Winery LLC F 813 752-9100
Plant City *(G-14442)*

Land O Lakes Winery LLC G 813 995-9463
Land O Lakes *(G-7859)*

▲ **Luxe Vintages LLC** G 561 558-7399
Delray Beach *(G-3103)*

Maestro Winery G 308 627-6436
Jacksonville *(G-6574)*

Masso Estate Winery LLC F 305 707-7749
Coral Gables *(G-2174)*

Monarq Americas LLC F 305 632-7448
Coral Gables *(G-2178)*

▲ **Orvino Imports & Distrg Inc** F 954 785-3100
Coral Springs *(G-2300)*

Palm Coast Crush 2 G 386 447-2768
Palm Coast *(G-13705)*

Pierced Ciderworks G 772 302-3863
Fort Pierce *(G-4733)*

Royal Manor Vineyard & Winery G 386 684-6270
Interlachen *(G-6079)*

Sapore Di Vino Inc F 561 818-8411
Miami *(G-10305)*

▲ **Schnebly Redlands Winery Inc** E 786 247-2060
Homestead *(G-5992)*

▲ **Seavin Inc** E 352 394-8627
Clermont *(G-1973)*

Seavin Inc E 904 826-1594
Saint Augustine *(G-15607)*

Slainte Wines Inc G 954 474-4547
Davie *(G-2592)*

So NAPA G 407 782-0459
New Smyrna Beach *(G-11544)*

Sokol Vineyards LLC G 352 368-4069
Ocala *(G-12055)*

Stirling Winery G 727 734-4025
Dunedin *(G-3589)*

Strong Tower Vineyard G 352 799-7612
Spring Hill *(G-16878)*

Swan Neck Winery G 850 495-3897
Pensacola *(G-14272)*

Tampa Wines LLC G 727 799-9463
Clearwater *(G-1905)*

◆ **Tita Itln Import & Export LLC** G 305 608-4258
Miami *(G-10480)*

Vault Spirits Company G 941 306-3331
Sarasota *(G-16322)*

▲ **Vicente Gandia Pla** C 310 699-8559
Miami *(G-10580)*

Vicente Gandia Usa Inc G 310 699-8559
Miami *(G-10581)*

Vines Worldwide LLC G 786 353-2102
North Miami *(G-11662)*

Vineyard 101 LLC G 727 819-5300
Hudson *(G-6043)*

Vinita USA Co G 650 260-5161
Miami *(G-10585)*

Vino Del Grotto G 321 508-1478
Elkton *(G-3652)*

Vintners Collections G 407 654-9019
Windermere *(G-19248)*

Whispering Oaks Winery G 352 748-0449
Oxford *(G-13465)*

Wild Diamond Vineyards LLC G 305 892-8699
North Miami *(G-11664)*

Wine Tasters of Naples Inc G 239 961-1522
Naples *(G-11457)*

Wine World Inc G 786 348-8780
Miami *(G-10610)*

2085 Liquors, Distilled, Rectified & Blended

Arco Globas Trading LLC E 305 707-7702
De Leon Springs *(G-2737)*

◆ **Bacardi Bottling Corporation** C 904 757-1290
Jacksonville *(G-6187)*

▼ **Big Cypress Distillery LLC** G 786 228-9740
Miami *(G-9244)*

Black Coral Rum LLC E 561 766-2493
Riviera Beach *(G-15302)*

Buzz Pop Cocktails Corporation F 727 275-9848
Holiday *(G-5736)*

◆ **Caribbean Distillers LLC** F 863 508-1175
Winter Haven *(G-19311)*

Chef Distilled LLC G 305 747-8236
Key West *(G-7182)*

Diageo North America Inc D 305 476-7761
Coral Gables *(G-2139)*

Dr Spirits Company LLC G 561 349-5005
Lake Worth *(G-7546)*

▲ **Drum Circle Distilling LLC** F 941 358-1900
Sarasota *(G-16415)*

Florida Distillers Co F 863 967-4481
Auburndale *(G-243)*

▼ **Florida Distillery LLC** G 813 347-6565
Tampa *(G-17675)*

Florida Rum Company LLC E 305 791-1221
Hollywood *(G-5823)*

Four Seas Distilling Co LLC G 813 645-0057
Apollo Beach *(G-104)*

Hemingway Rum Company LLC F 305 414-8754
Key West *(G-7189)*

Incity Security Inc F 561 306-9228
West Palm Beach *(G-18902)*

Island Joys G 561 201-6005
Fort Lauderdale *(G-4067)*

Italian Moonshiners Inc G 954 687-4500
Doral *(G-3395)*

JB Thome & Co Inc G 727 642-0588
St Pete Beach *(G-16882)*

Key West Smuggler Co G 916 995-1873
Key West *(G-7191)*

▲ **Kozuba & Sons Distillery Inc** F 813 857-8197
Saint Petersburg *(G-15834)*

La Tropical Brewing Co LLC G 786 362-5429
Coral Gables *(G-2170)*

▲ **Leblon LLC** G 954 649-0148
Miami *(G-9878)*

List Distillery LLC F 239 208-7214
Fort Myers *(G-4519)*

Loggerhead Distillery LLC G 321 800-8566
Sanford *(G-16081)*

Manifest Distilling LLC....F.... 904 619-1479
Jacksonville *(G-6577)*
Marlin & Barrel Distillery LLC....G.... 321 230-4755
Fernandina Beach *(G-3743)*
Mezcal Hub LLC....G.... 561 373-7972
Lake Worth *(G-7569)*
Miami Cocktail Company Inc....F.... 305 482-1974
Miami *(G-9994)*
Papous Craft Distillery LLC....G.... 813 766-9539
Tarpon Springs *(G-18319)*
Ron Matusalem & Matusa Fla Inc....F.... 305 448-8255
Miami *(G-10279)*
Scottish Spirits Imports Inc....F.... 954 332-1116
Fort Lauderdale *(G-4225)*
St Augustine Dist Co LLC....E.... 904 825-4962
Saint Augustine *(G-15618)*
St Petersburg Dist Co LLC....F.... 727 581-1544
Saint Petersburg *(G-15924)*
▲ **Stilldragon North America LLC**....F.... 561 845-8009
Riviera Beach *(G-15381)*
Sugar Works Distillery LLC....G.... 386 463-0120
New Smyrna Beach *(G-11546)*
Timber Creek Distilling Llc....G.... 408 439-0973
Destin *(G-3208)*
Wicked Dolphin Distillery....G.... 239 565-7947
Cape Coral *(G-1495)*
Winter Park Distilling Co LLC....F.... 407 801-2714
Winter Park *(G-19459)*
◆ **World Frost Inc**....G.... 786 439-4445
Miami *(G-10620)*

2086 Soft Drinks

7 Up Snapple Southeast....G.... 407 839-1706
Orlando *(G-12421)*
7up Snapple....G.... 561 732-7395
Boynton Beach *(G-871)*
▲ **Al-Rite Fruits and Syrups Inc**....G.... 305 652-2540
Miami *(G-9099)*
▲ **AMA Waters LLC**....G.... 786 400-1630
Miami *(G-9129)*
American Bottling Company....F.... 813 806-2931
Tampa *(G-17415)*
American Bottling Company....F.... 561 732-7395
Boynton Beach *(G-875)*
American Bottling Company....F.... 772 461-3383
Fort Pierce *(G-4673)*
American Bottling Company....F.... 941 758-7010
Bradenton *(G-987)*
American Bottling Company....F.... 863 665-6128
Lakeland *(G-7633)*
American Bottling Company....F.... 239 489-0838
Fort Myers *(G-4357)*
American Bottling Company....F.... 904 739-1000
Jacksonville *(G-6146)*
Anupack LLC....G.... 407 850-1960
Orlando *(G-12481)*
APRU LLC....G.... 888 741-3777
Orlando *(G-12483)*
Aqua Pure LLC....G.... 407 521-3055
Orlando *(G-12484)*
Aqua Pure Water Co Inc....G.... 954 744-4210
Hollywood *(G-5773)*
Arkay Distributing Inc....G.... 954 536-8413
Fort Lauderdale *(G-3822)*
Asterion Beverages Inc....G.... 866 335-2672
Doral *(G-3256)*
◆ **Bacardi Bottling Corporation**....C.... 904 757-1290
Jacksonville *(G-6187)*
Beverage Blocks Inc....F.... 813 309-8711
Tampa *(G-17467)*
Beverage Canners Inc....G.... 305 714-7000
Miami *(G-9239)*
▼ **Beverage Canners International**....E.... 305 714-7000
Miami *(G-9240)*
◆ **Beverage Corp Intl Inc**....D.... 305 714-7000
Miami *(G-9241)*
Bighill Corporation....G.... 786 497-1875
Miami Beach *(G-10647)*
Camel Enterprises Corp....F.... 954 234-2559
Miami *(G-9304)*
Canada Dry of Florida....G.... 941 758-7010
Bradenton *(G-1012)*
Car Care Haven LLC....G.... 855 464-2836
Englewood *(G-3671)*
▼ **Cawy Bottling Co Inc**....E.... 305 634-8669
Miami *(G-9328)*
Ccbcc Operations LLC....D.... 850 785-6171
Panama City *(G-13876)*
Celsius Holdings Inc....D.... 561 276-2239
Boca Raton *(G-477)*

Cg Roxane LLC....E.... 407 241-1640
Orlando *(G-12573)*
▼ **Chem-Free System Inc**....G.... 954 258-5415
Delray Beach *(G-3059)*
Clewiston Water Btlg Co LLC....G.... 863 902-1317
Clewiston *(G-1977)*
Cloudkiss Beverages Inc....E.... 407 324-8500
Sanford *(G-16016)*
Coca Cola Bottling Co....E.... 813 569-3030
Brandon *(G-1153)*
Coca Cola Enterprises Inc....G.... 305 256-3628
Miami *(G-9369)*
Coca-Cola Beverages Fla LLC....C.... 813 623-5411
Tampa *(G-17544)*
Coca-Cola Beverages Fla LLC....B.... 800 438-2653
Tampa *(G-17545)*
Coca-Cola Beverages Fla LLC....C.... 407 295-9290
Orlando *(G-12595)*
Coca-Cola Beverages Fla LLC....B.... 904 786-2720
Jacksonville *(G-6278)*
Coca-Cola Bottling Co....F.... 305 378-1073
Miami *(G-9370)*
Coca-Cola Bottling Co....G.... 844 863-2653
Sarasota *(G-16387)*
Coca-Cola Btlg Centl Fla LLC....F.... 832 260-0462
Brandon *(G-1154)*
Coca-Cola Co....G.... 407 287-4527
Clermont *(G-1954)*
Coca-Cola Company....G.... 407 886-1568
Apopka *(G-121)*
Coca-Cola Company....G.... 941 351-4695
Sarasota *(G-16388)*
Coca-Cola Company....G.... 954 985-5000
Hollywood *(G-5802)*
◆ **Coca-Cola Company**....E.... 404 676-2121
Apopka *(G-122)*
Coca-Cola Company....G.... 904 342-5609
Saint Augustine *(G-15531)*
Coca-Cola Company....G.... 407 560-0107
Orlando *(G-12596)*
Coca-Cola Company....G.... 727 736-7101
Dunedin *(G-3574)*
Coca-Cola Company....C.... 407 295-9290
Orlando *(G-12597)*
Coca-Cola Company....G.... 954 961-8564
Hollywood *(G-5803)*
Coca-Cola Company....G.... 407 565-2465
Apopka *(G-123)*
Coca-Cola Company Distribution....F.... 407 814-1327
Apopka *(G-125)*
Coca-Cola Enterprises....F.... 954 917-1108
Pompano Beach *(G-14640)*
Coca-Cola Refreshments USA Inc....G.... 863 551-3700
Auburndale *(G-235)*
◆ **Cola Construction Inc**....G.... 305 218-3985
Miami Beach *(G-10657)*
Cola Group Riverside LLC....G.... 305 940-0277
Sunny Isles Beach *(G-17073)*
Crystal River Water Pollution....F.... 352 795-3199
Crystal River *(G-2376)*
Cutrale Citrus Juices USA Inc....B.... 352 728-7800
Leesburg *(G-8149)*
▼ **D D B Corporation**....G.... 305 721-9506
Miami *(G-9426)*
Dna Brands Inc....G.... 561 654-5722
Lauderdale By The SE *(G-8084)*
Dr Pepper Bottling Co....G.... 407 354-5800
Orlando *(G-12682)*
Dr Pepper/Seven Up Inc....F.... 321 433-3622
Cocoa *(G-2015)*
Dr Pepper/Seven Up Inc....F.... 352 732-9777
Ocala *(G-11925)*
Dr Pepper/Seven Up Inc....F.... 561 995-6260
Boca Raton *(G-508)*
Everfresh Juice Co Inc....E.... 954 581-0922
Plantation *(G-14513)*
Florida Coca-Cola Bottling Co....B.... 561 848-0055
Riviera Beach *(G-15329)*
◆ **Florida Coca-Cola Bottling Co**....B.... 813 569-2600
Brandon *(G-1159)*
Florida Coca-Cola Bottling Co....B.... 772 461-3636
Fort Pierce *(G-4698)*
Florida Coca-Cola Bottling Co....B.... 850 678-9370
Valparaiso *(G-18510)*
Florida Coca-Cola Bottling Co....B.... 850 478-4800
Pensacola *(G-14154)*
Florida Coca-Cola Bottling Co....B.... 850 575-6122
Tallahassee *(G-17253)*
◆ **Florida Refresco Inc**....C.... 863 665-5515
Lakeland *(G-7693)*

Fresh Start Beverage Company....G.... 561 757-6541
Boca Raton *(G-540)*
Frito-Lay North America Inc....G.... 972 334-7000
Seminole *(G-16747)*
Great America Beverage Co LLC....G.... 786 763-2027
Palmetto Bay *(G-13846)*
H & H Products Company....E.... 407 299-5410
Orlando *(G-12793)*
Home Bistro Inc....G.... 561 227-2727
Miami Beach *(G-10679)*
◆ **Ibs Partners Ltd**....E.... 954 581-0922
Plantation *(G-14523)*
ICEE Company....F.... 954 966-7502
Dania *(G-2447)*
▲ **Interbeverage LLC**....G.... 305 961-1110
Miami *(G-9754)*
Keurig Dr Pepper Inc....G.... 561 227-1424
Tampa *(G-17819)*
▼ **Keystone Water Company LLC**....F.... 863 465-1932
Lake Placid *(G-7490)*
Kona Gold LLC....F.... 844 714-2224
Melbourne *(G-8861)*
Lee McCullough Inc....G.... 352 796-7100
Brooksville *(G-1244)*
▲ **Lorina Inc**....F.... 305 779-3085
Doral *(G-3419)*
Mega 4s Bottling Company LLC....G.... 305 815-3775
Miami *(G-9971)*
Milca Bottling Company....F.... 305 365-0044
Key Biscayne *(G-7160)*
Mipe Corp....G.... 305 825-1195
Hialeah *(G-5521)*
Mvs International Inc....G.... 954 727-3383
Weston *(G-19151)*
National Beverage Corp....B.... 954 581-0922
Plantation *(G-14537)*
National Beverage Corp....G.... 352 357-7130
Eustis *(G-3715)*
Newbevco Inc....E.... 954 581-0922
Plantation *(G-14539)*
Niagara Bottling LLC....G.... 352 429-3611
Groveland *(G-5102)*
Nubo Bottle Company LLC....G.... 954 283-9057
Boynton Beach *(G-938)*
Opreme Beverage Corp....G.... 954 699-0669
Jupiter *(G-7088)*
Panamco LLC....F.... 305 856-7100
Miami *(G-10137)*
Pepsi Beverages Company....E.... 407 241-4110
Orlando *(G-13060)*
Pepsi Bottling Group....G.... 863 452-9920
Avon Park *(G-292)*
Pepsi Bottling Group Inc....G.... 863 687-7605
Lakeland *(G-7765)*
Pepsi St Pete....F.... 727 527-8113
Saint Petersburg *(G-15875)*
Pepsi-Cola Bottling Co Tampa....C.... 239 643-4642
Naples *(G-11360)*
◆ **Pepsi-Cola Bottling Co Tampa**....C.... 813 971-2550
Tampa *(G-17982)*
Pepsi-Cola Bottling Co Tampa....C.... 941 378-1058
Sarasota *(G-16542)*
Pepsi-Cola Bottling Co Tampa....F.... 407 857-3301
Orlando *(G-13061)*
Pepsi-Cola Bottling Co Tampa....C.... 239 337-2011
Fort Myers *(G-4567)*
Pepsi-Cola Bottling Co Tampa....C.... 727 942-3664
Holiday *(G-5748)*
Pepsi-Cola Bottling Co Tampa....C.... 407 826-5929
Orlando *(G-13062)*
Pepsi-Cola Btlg Ft Ldrdl-Palm....D.... 561 848-1000
Riviera Beach *(G-15361)*
Pepsi-Cola Metro Btlg Co Inc....C.... 904 733-1627
Jacksonville *(G-6668)*
Pepsi-Cola Metro Btlg Co Inc....G.... 407 354-5800
Orlando *(G-13063)*
Pepsi-Cola Metro Btlg Co Inc....G.... 386 752-8956
Lake City *(G-7375)*
Pepsi-Cola Metro Btlg Co Inc....G.... 352 376-8276
Gainesville *(G-4980)*
Pepsi-Cola Metro Btlg Co Inc....G.... 863 551-4500
Winter Haven *(G-19340)*
Pepsi-Cola Metro Btlg Co Inc....G.... 352 629-8911
Ocala *(G-12024)*
Pepsi-Cola Metro Btlg Co Inc....G.... 321 242-2984
Melbourne *(G-8906)*
Pepsi-Cola Metro Btlg Co Inc....G.... 352 797-1160
Brooksville *(G-1260)*
Pepsi-Cola Metro Btlg Co Inc....C.... 772 464-6150
Fort Pierce *(G-4731)*

SIC

Pepsico Inc ... G ... 305 593-7500
Medley (G-8703)
Pepsico Inc ... G ... 800 433-2652
Deerfield Beach (G-2885)
Pepsico Inc ... G ... 407 933-5542
Kissimmee (G-7286)
Pepsico Beverage Distributors ... G ... 305 537-4477
Miami (G-10152)
Pepsico Latin America Beverage ... F ... 305 537-4477
Miami (G-10153)
Polenghi Usa Inc ... F ... 954 637-4900
Deerfield Beach (G-2887)
Primo Water Corporation ... A ... 844 237-7466
Tampa (G-18011)
Prodalim USA Inc ... G ... 407 656-1000
Winter Garden (G-19281)
Pure Water Sulotins LLC ... G ... 727 784-7400
Palm Harbor (G-13753)
Quaker Oats Company ... C ... 407 846-5926
Kissimmee (G-7292)
◆ R-Lines LLC ... G ... 954 457-7777
Hallandale Beach (G-5207)
Refresco Beverages US Inc ... E ... 813 313-1711
Tampa (G-18045)
Refresco Beverages US Inc ... C ... 813 241-0147
Tampa (G-18046)
◆ Refresco Beverages US Inc ... C ... 813 313-1800
Tampa (G-18047)
Refresco Beverages US Inc ... E ... 314 994-7545
Tampa (G-18048)
Refresco US Holding Inc ... E ... 813 313-1863
Tampa (G-18049)
Refreshment Services Inc ... D ... 850 574-0281
Tallahassee (G-17315)
Royal Crown Developers LLC ... G ... 561 305-4588
Boca Raton (G-694)
Sergeant Bretts Coffee LLC ... G ... 561 451-0048
Coconut Creek (G-2094)
Shasta Beverages Intl Inc ... E ... 954 581-0922
Plantation (G-14549)
◆ Silver Springs Citrus Inc ... C ... 352 324-2101
Howey In The Hills (G-6012)
Silver Springs Citrus LLC ... E ... 352 324-2101
Howey In The Hills (G-6013)
Snapple Beverages ... F ... 941 758-7010
Bradenton (G-1115)
▲ SOS Food Lab LLC ... E ... 305 594-9933
Hialeah Gardens (G-5699)
▲ South Pacific Trading Company ... E ... 352 567-2200
Dade City (G-2435)
◆ Southeast Atlantic Bev Corp ... B ... 904 731-3644
Jacksonville (G-6785)
▼ Southeast Atlantic Bevera ... G ... 904 739-1000
Miami (G-10384)
▲ Southeast Bottling & Bev Co ... D ... 352 567-2200
Dade City (G-2436)
◆ Sunshine Bottling Co ... E ... 305 592-4366
Doral (G-3517)
Swire Pacific Holdings Inc ... F ... 305 371-3877
Miami (G-10448)
Thomas J Cola ... G ... 954 846-0868
Sunrise (G-17187)
Titan Natural Focus Corp ... G ... 305 778-7005
West Palm Beach (G-19065)
Tropical Bottling Corporation ... G ... 786 636-6169
Medley (G-8743)
▲ Tropicana Products Inc ... A ... 941 747-4461
Bradenton (G-1133)
◆ Ultra-Pure Bottled Water Inc ... F ... 281 731-0258
North Miami (G-11660)
Venga LLC ... G ... 561 665-8200
Delray Beach (G-3156)
▲ VIP Drinks Bottling LLC ... G ... 239 214-8190
Cape Coral (G-1491)
◆ Vital Pharmaceuticals Inc ... C ... 954 641-0570
Fort Lauderdale (G-4308)
Water Boy Inc ... F ... 239 461-0860
Fort Myers (G-4650)

2087 Flavoring Extracts & Syrups

▲ Al-Rite Fruits and Syrups Inc ... G ... 305 652-2540
Miami (G-9099)
▲ Aromatech Flavorings Inc ... G ... 407 277-5727
Orlando (G-12489)
Atlantic Bev Group USA Inc ... G ... 239 334-3016
Fort Myers (G-4368)
Banana Bag Solutions LLC ... G ... 321 917-4334
Satellite Beach (G-16648)
Bev-Co Enterprises Inc ... E ... 786 362-6368
Miami (G-9238)
Bev-Co Enterprises Inc ... E ... 786 953-7109
Doral (G-3270)
Buddy Pauls Inc ... G ... 561 578-9813
West Palm Beach (G-18830)
▼ Celsius Inc ... F ... 561 276-2239
Boca Raton (G-476)
Coastal Promotions Inc ... G ... 850 460-2270
Destin (G-3186)
Coca-Cola Company ... G ... 407 565-2465
Apopka (G-123)
Coca-Cola Company ... G ... 407 886-1568
Apopka (G-121)
Coca-Cola Company ... G ... 407 358-6758
Apopka (G-124)
Coca-Cola Company ... G ... 954 961-8564
Hollywood (G-5803)
▲ Cvista LLC ... E ... 813 405-3000
Riverview (G-15269)
◆ Flayco Products Inc ... E ... 813 879-1356
Tampa (G-17668)
Florida Flvors Cncentrates Inc ... G ... 561 775-5714
Palm Beach Gardens (G-13591)
▼ Florida Natural Flavors Inc ... E ... 407 834-5979
Casselberry (G-1503)
Fresh Start Beverage Company ... G ... 561 757-6541
Boca Raton (G-540)
Givaudan Fragrances Corp ... E ... 863 667-0821
Lakeland (G-7698)
H & H Products Company ... E ... 407 299-5410
Orlando (G-12793)
Interamericas Beverages Inc ... G ... 561 881-1340
Riviera Beach (G-15334)
◆ Lemon-X Corporation ... G ... 863 635-8400
Frostproof (G-4861)
◆ Monin Inc ... C ... 727 461-3033
Clearwater (G-1791)
▲ Nutrition Laboratories Inc ... E ... 727 442-2747
Clearwater (G-1815)
▲ Pinzon Caramel Syrup ... G ... 305 591-2472
Miami (G-10165)
Pouchfill Packaging LLC ... F ... 386 274-1600
Daytona Beach (G-2695)
Prima Foods International Inc ... G ... 352 732-9148
Ocala (G-12031)
Rehydrade LLC ... G ... 561 419-5656
Boca Raton (G-687)
Royal Cup Inc ... G ... 813 664-8902
Tampa (G-18070)
Skinny Mixes LLC ... G ... 727 826-0306
Clearwater (G-1879)
Splash Beverage Group Inc ... G ... 954 745-5815
Fort Lauderdale (G-4254)
Squeeze It Corp ... G ... 954 851-2443
Aventura (G-281)
▼ Sunny Hill International Inc ... G ... 386 736-5757
Deland (G-3016)
Taste Advantage LLC ... G ... 863 619-8101
Lakeland (G-7816)
Top Drinks USA Corp ... G ... 305 407-3514
Miami (G-10490)
Yos Bottling LLC ... F ... 863 258-6820
Dade City (G-2437)

2091 Fish & Seafoods, Canned & Cured

Captain Rustys ... G ... 813 244-2799
Lorida (G-8354)
Ceh Llc ... G ... 941 518-6747
Bradenton (G-1017)
M & R Seafood Inc ... F ... 352 498-5150
Cross City (G-2365)
Miracle Seafood Manufacturers ... G ... 850 653-2114
Apalachicola (G-98)
Outlaw Oyster Company LLC ... G ... 850 841-9344
Panacea (G-13860)
◆ Select Europe Inc ... G ... 407 931-1820
Deerfield Beach (G-2908)

2092 Fish & Seafoods, Fresh & Frozen

681 Seafood & Southern Bites ... G ... 954 573-7320
Deerfield Beach (G-2759)
Buddy Ward & Sons Seafood ... G ... 850 653-8522
Apalachicola (G-97)
Ceh Llc ... G ... 941 518-6747
Bradenton (G-1017)
Chiefland Crab Company Inc ... E ... 352 493-4887
Chiefland (G-1535)
Del Rosario Enterprises Inc ... F ... 786 547-6812
Medley (G-8642)
◆ Florida Fresh Seafood Corp ... F ... 305 694-1733
Miami (G-9583)
Global Aliment Inc ... G ... 786 536-5261
Doral (G-3368)
Juniors Bait and Seafood Inc ... E ... 321 480-5492
Melbourne (G-8856)
M & R Seafood Inc ... F ... 352 498-5150
Cross City (G-2365)
▲ Masa Trading LLC ... F ... 561 729-3293
Pompano Beach (G-14754)
Massachusetts Bay Clam Co Inc ... F ... 813 855-4599
Tampa (G-17891)
Miracle Seafood Manufacturers ... G ... 850 653-2114
Apalachicola (G-98)
Santos Frozen Foods Inc ... F ... 813 875-4901
Tampa (G-18081)
▲ Shaws Sthern Blle Frz Fods In ... D ... 904 768-1591
Jacksonville (G-6763)
Skip One Seafood Inc ... G ... 239 463-8788
Fort Myers Beach (G-4666)
Thetradebaycom LLC ... G ... 954 607-2405
Weston (G-19171)

2095 Coffee

Allcoffee LLC ... G ... 305 685-6856
Opa Locka (G-12285)
Aroma Coffee Service Inc ... G ... 239 481-7262
Fort Myers (G-4367)
Babys Coffee LLC ... G ... 305 744-9866
Key West (G-7178)
▲ Burke Brands LLC ... F ... 305 249-5628
Miami (G-9285)
C&D Purveyors Inc ... G ... 305 562-8541
Miami (G-9294)
▲ Clr Roasters LLC ... E ... 305 591-0040
Miami (G-9365)
Coca-Cola Company ... G ... 407 358-6758
Apopka (G-124)
Coffee Unlimited LLC ... F ... 305 685-6366
Opa Locka (G-12302)
Conali Express Corp ... G ... 954 531-9573
Fort Lauderdale (G-3914)
De Luna Coffee Intl Inc ... G ... 850 478-6371
Pensacola (G-14126)
◆ Distribuidora Giorgio Usa LLC ... F ... 305 685-6366
Opa Locka (G-12307)
Dna Brands Inc ... G ... 561 654-5722
Lauderdale By The SE (G-8084)
Dupuy Silo Facility LLC ... C ... 904 899-7200
Jacksonville (G-6337)
◆ Espresso Disposition Corp 1 ... D ... 305 594-9062
Miami (G-9536)
Gold Coffee Roasters Inc ... F ... 561 746-8110
Jupiter (G-7050)
Grand Havana Inc ... G ... 305 297-2207
Miami Beach (G-10674)
Haven Coffee Roasters LLC ... G ... 863 251-9619
Winter Haven (G-19327)
J M Smucker Company ... G ... 305 594-2886
Medley (G-8674)
Javalution Coffee Company ... F ... 954 568-1747
Fort Lauderdale (G-4077)
Kraft Heinz Foods Company ... G ... 904 632-3400
Jacksonville (G-6544)
Kraken Koffee LLC ... G ... 833 546-3725
Coral Gables (G-2169)
◆ Latitude 235 Coffee and Tea ... F ... 941 556-2600
Sarasota (G-16250)
List + Beisler Corp ... E ... 646 866-6960
Miami (G-9898)
◆ Melitta North America Inc ... D ... 727 535-2111
Clearwater (G-1779)
◆ Melitta Usa Inc ... D ... 727 535-2111
Clearwater (G-1780)
▲ Mercers Fresh Roasted Coffees ... G ... 941 286-7054
Punta Gorda (G-15214)
Naviera Coffee Mills Inc ... E ... 813 248-2521
Tampa (G-17934)
New Dawn Coffee Company ... G ... 727 321-5155
Saint Petersburg (G-15865)
Potters Coffee Company ... G ... 850 525-1793
Pensacola (G-14235)
▼ Productos Las Delicias Inc ... G ... 305 760-4223
Hialeah (G-5577)
▲ Rae Launo Corporation ... G ... 813 242-4281
Valrico (G-18524)
Rcr Coffee Company Inc ... E ... 813 248-6264
Tampa (G-18041)
Royal Cup Inc ... G ... 813 664-8902
Tampa (G-18070)
Royal Cup Inc ... G ... 850 436-4435
Pensacola (G-14254)

Sergeant Bretts Coffee LLC..................G....... 561 451-0048
Coconut Creek *(G-2094)*
Ste-Ro Inc..................G....... 754 234-1789
Pompano Beach *(G-14869)*
▲ Whole Coffee Company LLC..................D....... 786 364-4444
Miami *(G-10604)*

2096 Potato Chips & Similar Prdts

El Mira Sol Inc..................D....... 813 754-5857
Plant City *(G-14429)*
Frito-Lay North America Inc..................G....... 407 295-1810
Orlando *(G-12766)*
Kerry Consulting Corp..................F....... 561 364-9969
Boynton Beach *(G-926)*
Mio Gourment Products LLC..................F....... 305 219-0253
Hialeah *(G-5520)*
Pepsico Inc..................G....... 800 433-2652
Deerfield Beach *(G-2885)*
Pretz Snacks Corp..................G....... 718 869-2762
Doral *(G-3470)*
R & S Snacks LLC..................G....... 954 839-5482
Port Saint Lucie *(G-15133)*
Rap Snacks Inc..................G....... 305 926-9594
Miami *(G-10239)*
▲ Specialty Food Group LLC..................G....... 305 392-5000
Doral *(G-3509)*
Super-Pufft Snacks Usa Inc..................E....... 905 564-1180
Perry *(G-14314)*

2097 Ice

▼ Atlantic Dry Ice Corportion..................F....... 305 592-7000
Miami *(G-9182)*
Btu Reps LLC..................F....... 727 235-3591
Saint Petersburg *(G-15730)*
Central Florida Ice Services..................G....... 407 779-0161
Orlando *(G-12568)*
Fanning Springs Ice Company..................G....... 352 463-1999
Old Town *(G-12196)*
Florida Ice Corporation..................F....... 305 685-9377
Opa Locka *(G-12316)*
Gainesville Ice Company..................F....... 352 378-2604
Gainesville *(G-4926)*
Hialeah Distribution Corp..................E....... 786 200-2498
Hialeah *(G-5444)*
◆ Ice Magic-Orlando Inc..................D....... 407 816-1905
Orlando *(G-12819)*
Nucycle Energy of Tampa LLC..................E....... 813 848-0509
Plant City *(G-14450)*
Orlando Ice Servive Corp..................G....... 407 999-4940
Orlando *(G-13033)*
Reddy Ice Corporation..................G....... 772 461-5046
Fort Pierce *(G-4740)*
Reddy Ice Corporation..................F....... 850 433-2191
Pensacola *(G-14251)*
Reddy Ice Corporation..................F....... 904 388-2653
Jacksonville *(G-6710)*
Reddy Ice Corporation..................F....... 850 233-0128
Panama City *(G-13944)*
Reddy Ice Corporation..................F....... 561 881-9501
West Palm Beach *(G-19017)*
Reddy Ice Inc..................G....... 407 296-8300
Orlando *(G-13123)*

2098 Macaroni, Spaghetti & Noodles

◆ First Grade Food Corporation..................E....... 813 886-6118
Tampa *(G-17666)*
Jo MO Enterprises Inc..................G....... 708 599-8098
Boca Raton *(G-582)*
Lillys Gstrnmia Itlana Fla Inc..................G....... 305 655-2111
Hallandale Beach *(G-5198)*
Mama Asian Noodle Bar..................F....... 954 973-1670
Coconut Creek *(G-2089)*
Noodle Time Inc..................D....... 305 593-0770
Miami *(G-10075)*
Termine Ravioli Manufacturing..................F....... 954 983-3711
Hollywood *(G-5923)*

2099 Food Preparations, NEC

4714 Foods Inc..................G....... 813 787-8911
Tampa *(G-17374)*
Abraaham Rosa Seasonings Inc..................G....... 386 453-4827
Deland *(G-2952)*
Adelheidis Commercial Inc..................G....... 239 384-8642
Naples *(G-11149)*
▲ Al-Rite Fruits and Syrups Inc..................G....... 305 652-2540
Miami *(G-9099)*
◆ Alnoor Import Inc..................G....... 954 683-9897
Plantation *(G-14488)*
Amaranth Lf Sciences Phrm Inc..................F....... 561 756-8291
Boca Raton *(G-419)*
◆ ARA Food Corporation..................D....... 305 592-5558
Miami *(G-9160)*
Argen Foods..................G....... 305 884-0037
Medley *(G-8612)*
▲ Axrdham Corp..................G....... 813 653-9588
Valrico *(G-18515)*
Aztlan Foods Corp..................E....... 786 202-8301
Medley *(G-8618)*
Baby Food Chef LLC..................G....... 305 335-5990
Hollywood *(G-5781)*
▼ Barnard Nut Company Inc..................D....... 305 836-9999
Miami *(G-9221)*
◆ Bavaria Corporation..................F....... 407 880-0322
Apopka *(G-115)*
▲ Bees Brothers LLC..................G....... 305 529-5789
Coral Gables *(G-2126)*
Belgium Co Inc..................F....... 407 957-1886
Saint Cloud *(G-15644)*
Best Brand Bottlers Inc..................F....... 941 755-1941
Sarasota *(G-16182)*
▲ Bijol and Spices Inc..................G....... 305 634-9030
Miami *(G-9245)*
Bio-Revival LLC..................F....... 561 667-3990
Jupiter *(G-7009)*
Blue Stone Usa LLC..................F....... 305 494-1141
Coral Gables *(G-2127)*
▲ Body LLC..................F....... 850 888-2639
Saint Petersburg *(G-15725)*
◆ Brefaros Nobile Food LLC..................E....... 305 621-0074
Miami Lakes *(G-10771)*
Brianas Salad LLC..................G....... 954 608-0953
Boca Raton *(G-465)*
Broski Ciderworks LLC..................G....... 954 657-8947
Pompano Beach *(G-14623)*
Burma Spice Inc..................G....... 863 254-0960
Moore Haven *(G-11085)*
C & E Innovative MGT LLC..................G....... 727 408-5146
Clearwater *(G-1619)*
Cacao Fruit Company..................G....... 954 449-8704
Weston *(G-19114)*
▼ Captain Foods Inc..................G....... 386 428-5833
New Smyrna Beach *(G-11530)*
Carne Asada Tortilleria Nicas..................G....... 305 221-7001
Miami *(G-9321)*
Carvalho Naturals LLC..................G....... 813 833-8229
Tampa *(G-17511)*
▲ Catalina Finer Food Corp..................E....... 813 872-6359
Tampa *(G-17515)*
CFM&d LLC..................G....... 772 220-8938
Stuart *(G-16922)*
▼ Champion Nutrition Inc..................G....... 954 233-3300
Sunrise *(G-17105)*
Charles Bryant Enterprises..................G....... 850 785-3604
Panama City *(G-13879)*
Chili Produkt Kft..................E....... 954 655-4111
Wellington *(G-18713)*
◆ Coco Lopez Inc..................G....... 954 450-3100
Miramar *(G-10980)*
Conagra Brands Inc..................G....... 904 417-0964
Elkton *(G-3648)*
Cranco Industries Inc..................G....... 321 690-2695
Rockledge *(G-15399)*
Culinary Concepts Inc..................E....... 407 228-0069
Orlando *(G-12635)*
De Todos Tortillas Inc..................G....... 305 248-4402
Homestead *(G-5961)*
Delarosa Real Foods LLC..................D....... 718 333-0333
Lauderdale Lakes *(G-8085)*
Deli Fresh Foods Inc..................F....... 305 652-2848
Miami *(G-9446)*
Delicae Gourmet LLC..................G....... 727 942-2502
Tarpon Springs *(G-18293)*
Dinner Belle Inc..................G....... 747 210-6284
Lauderhill *(G-8108)*
Dole..................G....... 305 925-7900
Doral *(G-3331)*
Dolmar Foods Inc..................F....... 262 303-6026
Belleview *(G-368)*
Dream Cuizine..................G....... 727 943-8289
Palm Harbor *(G-13735)*
Early Foods LLC..................G....... 850 791-3319
Pensacola *(G-14136)*
Easy Foods Inc..................C....... 321 300-1104
Kissimmee *(G-7241)*
◆ Easy Foods Inc..................E....... 305 599-0357
Doral *(G-3339)*
Egg Roll Skins Inc..................F....... 305 836-0571
Hialeah *(G-5391)*
El Jaliciense Inc..................F....... 850 481-1232
Panama City *(G-13898)*
El Sabor Spices Inc..................F....... 305 691-2300
Miami *(G-9507)*
Encompass Mktg & Dev Group Inc..................G....... 407 420-7777
Orlando *(G-12711)*
Everglades Foods Inc..................G....... 863 655-2214
Sebring *(G-16689)*
Evergreen Sweeteners Inc..................F....... 305 835-6907
Miami *(G-9541)*
◆ Evergreen Sweeteners Inc..................F....... 954 381-7776
Hollywood *(G-5818)*
Evergreen Sweeteners Inc..................F....... 407 323-4250
Sanford *(G-16042)*
Fathers Table LLC..................C....... 407 324-1200
Sanford *(G-16045)*
Five Star Gurmet Foods Fla Inc..................C....... 239 280-0336
Naples *(G-11246)*
▼ Flavorworks Inc..................E....... 561 588-8246
West Palm Beach *(G-18873)*
◆ Flayco Products Inc..................E....... 813 879-1356
Tampa *(G-17668)*
◆ Flo Sun Land Corporation..................E....... 561 655-6303
Palm Beach *(G-13554)*
Floribbean Inc..................G....... 844 282-8459
Miami *(G-9579)*
Florida Algae LLC..................G....... 954 213-2693
Fort Lauderdale *(G-3999)*
Fritanga Y Tortilla Modra..................G....... 305 649-9377
Miami *(G-9598)*
Frito-Lay North America Inc..................G....... 407 295-1810
Orlando *(G-12766)*
G & G Latin Business Inc..................G....... 954 385-8085
Weston *(G-19129)*
GA Fd Svcs Pinellas Cnty LLC..................E....... 239 693-5090
Fort Myers *(G-4465)*
Galloway Foods Inc..................G....... 305 670-7600
Coral Gables *(G-2148)*
Gourmet Food Solutions LLC..................E....... 413 687-3285
Aventura *(G-272)*
Grand Havana Inc..................G....... 305 297-2207
Miami Beach *(G-10674)*
▼ Greek Island Spice Inc..................G....... 954 761-7161
Fort Lauderdale *(G-4029)*
Greenes Reserve Inc..................F....... 954 304-0791
Ocala *(G-11962)*
Handal Foods LLC..................G....... 954 753-0649
Coral Springs *(G-2251)*
◆ Hispanic Certified Foods Inc..................G....... 305 772-6815
Pompano Beach *(G-14723)*
Ipac Inc..................G....... 407 699-7507
Winter Springs *(G-19474)*
Italian Rose Garlic Pdts LLC..................C....... 561 863-5556
Riviera Beach *(G-15336)*
J Squared Management II LLC..................F....... 813 373-5359
Tampa *(G-17799)*
Jayshree Holdings Inc..................E....... 352 429-1000
Groveland *(G-5098)*
▲ Jenard Fresh Incorporated..................E....... 407 851-9432
Orlando *(G-12855)*
Jo MO Enterprises Inc..................G....... 708 599-8098
Boca Raton *(G-582)*
K and G Food Services LLC..................G....... 954 857-9283
West Palm Beach *(G-18917)*
▲ Kenart Holdings Llc..................C....... 561 863-5556
Riviera Beach *(G-15340)*
Kerry Inc..................G....... 813 359-5182
Plant City *(G-14443)*
Kulfi LLC..................E....... 855 488-4273
Boca Raton *(G-593)*
L & A Quality Products Inc..................G....... 305 326-9300
Miami *(G-9834)*
▲ La Autentica Foods Inc..................E....... 305 888-6727
Hialeah *(G-5481)*
La Chiquita Tortilla Mfr..................E....... 407 251-8290
Orlando *(G-12884)*
▼ La Real Foods Inc..................E....... 305 232-6449
Miami *(G-9848)*
Life Spice and Ingredients LLC..................E....... 708 301-0447
Palm Beach *(G-13557)*
Lifeco Foods North America..................G....... 321 348-5896
Winter Garden *(G-19274)*
Lillys Gstrnmia Itlana Fla Inc..................G....... 305 655-2111
Hallandale Beach *(G-5198)*
Los Atntcos Sndwich Cuban Cafe..................G....... 407 282-2322
Orlando *(G-12936)*
Mad At SAD LLC..................F....... 941 203-8854
Sarasota *(G-16495)*
Massimo & Umberto Inc..................G....... 954 993-0842
Dania Beach *(G-2469)*

S I C

McCormick & Company Inc G 904 247-7773
Jacksonville Beach *(G-6950)*
McCormick Restaurant Services F 561 706-5554
Boca Raton *(G-613)*
McM Food Corp G 305 885-9254
Medley *(G-8685)*
ME Thompson Inc G 904 356-6258
Jacksonville *(G-6587)*
ME Thompson Inc D 863 667-3732
Lakeland *(G-7749)*
Mestizo Foods LLC C 352 414-4900
Ocala *(G-11998)*
Miami Oliveoil & Beyond Llc G 954 632-2762
Doral *(G-3436)*
Mizkan America Inc F 863 956-0391
Lake Alfred *(G-7333)*
Mobile Meals G 813 907-6325
Tampa *(G-17913)*
Mother Kombucha LLC F 727 767-0408
Saint Petersburg *(G-15860)*
Mr Americas 2 LLC G 407 217-2282
Orlando *(G-12983)*
Mr Bills Fine Foods G 727 581-9850
Clearwater *(G-1794)*
My Familys Seasonings LLC F 863 698-7968
Clearwater *(G-1798)*
Nana Foods Inc G 407 363-7183
Orlando *(G-12989)*
Natures Heathy Gourmet E 772 873-0180
Port St Lucie *(G-15176)*
New Dawn Coffee Company G 727 321-5155
Saint Petersburg *(G-15865)*
New Hope Sugar Company G 561 366-5120
West Palm Beach *(G-18963)*
Nex-Xos Worldwide LLC F 305 433-8376
Hollywood *(G-5882)*
Nutrifusion LLC F 404 240-0030
Naples *(G-11347)*
Nutritious You LLC G 941 203-5203
Sarasota *(G-16527)*
Oakbrook Sales Inc F 800 773-0979
Boca Raton *(G-652)*
OH Catering Inc G 305 903-9271
Miami *(G-10092)*
Organic Amazon Corp G 305 365-7811
Key Biscayne *(G-7161)*
▼ **Oriental Packing Company Inc** F 305 235-1829
Miami *(G-10117)*
▲ **Osceola Farms Co** E 561 655-6303
Palm Beach *(G-13560)*
Osceola Farms Co A 561 924-7156
Pahokee *(G-13470)*
Paca Foods LLC E 813 628-8228
Tampa *(G-17967)*
Pantaleon Commodities Corp F 786 542-6333
Miami *(G-10139)*
◆ **Plantain Products Company** E 800 477-2447
Miami *(G-10168)*
Prana Organic Plant Oils Inc G 216 288-2054
Tavernier *(G-18362)*
Prege G 954 908-1535
Fort Lauderdale *(G-4174)*
Prima Food Corp E 954 788-0411
Pompano Beach *(G-14812)*
Qsrr Corporation G 305 322-9867
Hallandale Beach *(G-5205)*
Quality Bakery Products LLC G 954 779-3663
Fort Lauderdale *(G-4189)*
Radchen USA Inc G 786 270-7628
Doral *(G-3479)*
Red Diamond Salsa LLC G 813 672-7707
Wimauma *(G-19222)*
Respect Foods G 561 557-2832
Palm Beach Gardens *(G-13622)*
Rj Foods G 863 425-3282
Mulberry *(G-11134)*
◆ **RL Schreiber Inc** D 954 972-7102
Fort Lauderdale *(G-4208)*
Royal Cup Inc G 813 664-8902
Tampa *(G-18070)*
Royal Cup Inc G 850 436-4435
Pensacola *(G-14254)*
Sage Imports Corp G 305 962-0631
Coral Gables *(G-2192)*
Salsa Cuba Inc G 305 993-9757
Hialeah *(G-5610)*
Salsa Pembroke Pines Inc E 954 461-0532
Pembroke Pines *(G-14058)*
Salsa Three Inc G 954 990-2223
Plantation *(G-14548)*
Santos Frozen Foods Inc F 813 875-4901
Tampa *(G-18081)*
Savory Life LLC G 813 981-2022
Riverview *(G-15282)*
▼ **Sazon Inc** E 305 591-9785
Doral *(G-3496)*
Sentry Food Solutions LLC G 904 482-1900
Jacksonville *(G-6761)*
Sheas Salsa LLC G 954 371-7781
Wellington *(G-18731)*
Shiloh Import/Export LLC G 404 514-4109
Tamarac *(G-17368)*
▲ **SOS Food Lab LLC** E 305 594-9933
Hialeah Gardens *(G-5699)*
◆ **Spice World LLC** C 407 851-9432
Orlando *(G-13207)*
Stripping Alpaca LLC F 207 208-9687
Miami Beach *(G-10717)*
◆ **Strumba Media LLC** G 800 948-4205
Miami *(G-10423)*
Sunrise Foods LLC G 904 613-4756
Jacksonville *(G-6823)*
Sunshine Packing & Noodle Co G 904 355-7561
Jacksonville *(G-6826)*
Sunshine Peanut Company F 813 988-6987
Temple Terrace *(G-18380)*
Supper On Wheels Inc G 305 205-8999
Miami *(G-10440)*
▲ **Survivor Industries Inc** E 805 385-5560
Doral *(G-3520)*
Sweet Additions LLC F 561 472-0178
Palm Beach Gardens *(G-13630)*
T&S Kitchen and Bbq LLC G 863 608-6223
Lakeland *(G-7815)*
Tasteful Delight LLC F 305 879-6487
Lakeland *(G-7817)*
◆ **Tata Tea Extractions Inc** E 813 754-2602
Plant City *(G-14469)*
▲ **Taylor Farms Florida Inc** B 407 859-3373
Orlando *(G-13242)*
Tdr Food Distribution LLC G 561 860-7617
Orlando *(G-13243)*
Thunder Bay Foods Corporation F 727 943-0606
Oldsmar *(G-12271)*
Torro Foods LLC G 305 558-3212
Miami Lakes *(G-10871)*
Tortilla Bay G 941 778-3663
Holmes Beach *(G-5947)*
Tortilleria America Inc G 239 462-2175
Fort Myers *(G-4633)*
Tortilleria Dona Chela G 941 953-4045
Sarasota *(G-16623)*
Tortilleria El Triunfo LLC G 954 270-7832
Fort Lauderdale *(G-4287)*
Tortilleria Gallo De Oro G 561 503-3751
Lake Worth *(G-7592)*
Tortilleria Gallo De Oro LLC G 561 818-7829
Stuart *(G-17035)*
Tortilleria La Rancherita G 941 747-7949
Bradenton *(G-1127)*
Tortilleria Lamexicana 7 Inc F 407 324-3100
Sanford *(G-16128)*
▲ **Total Nutrition Technology LLC** E 352 435-0050
Leesburg *(G-8178)*
Triton Seafood Co F 305 888-8999
Medley *(G-8742)*
Twinlab Corporation B 800 645-5626
Boca Raton *(G-761)*
Tys Hometown Cafe Bistro LLC G 786 208-1163
Miami *(G-10521)*
◆ **Vigo Importing Company** C 813 884-3491
Tampa *(G-18247)*
West Development Group LLC G 407 308-5020
Orlando *(G-13322)*
Wwwsureshotsidscom LLC G 850 906-0745
Tallahassee *(G-17348)*
▲ **Xylitol USA Inc** G 303 991-1999
Riverview *(G-15288)*
Yfan LLC G 786 453-3724
Miami Lakes *(G-10883)*

21 TOBACCO PRODUCTS

2111 Cigarettes

◆ **Commonwealth Brands Inc** C 800 481-5814
Fort Lauderdale *(G-3912)*
▲ **Dosal Tobacco Corporation** E 305 685-2949
Opa Locka *(G-12309)*
Flavana LLC G 561 285-7034
Pompano Beach *(G-14699)*
◆ **Healthier Choices MGT Corp** C 305 600-5004
Hollywood *(G-5836)*
R J Reynolds Tobacco Company D 772 873-6955
Port Saint Lucie *(G-15134)*
Soleil Capital LP D 954 715-7001
Fort Lauderdale *(G-4242)*
V2 Cigs F 305 517-1149
Miami Beach *(G-10725)*
V2 Cigs E 305 240-6387
Miami *(G-10561)*
Vapor Group Inc F 954 792-8450
Miami *(G-10567)*
Vaprzone LLC G 941 882-4841
Venice *(G-18584)*
Vector Group Ltd C 305 579-8000
Miami *(G-10571)*
Vgr Holding LLC D 305 579-8000
Miami *(G-10576)*

2121 Cigars

◆ **Consolidated Cigr Holdings Inc** A 954 772-9000
Fort Lauderdale *(G-3915)*
◆ **Domrey Cigar Ltd Company** G 941 360-8200
Pinellas Park *(G-14344)*
▲ **Dosal Tobacco Corporation** E 305 685-2949
Opa Locka *(G-12309)*
Havana Dreams LLC G 305 322-7599
Miami *(G-9690)*
◆ **Itg Cigars Inc** D 954 772-9000
Fort Lauderdale *(G-4071)*
◆ **J C Newman Cigar Co** D 813 248-2124
Tampa *(G-17797)*
La Luna Ltd G 305 644-0444
Miami *(G-9842)*
Luis Martinez Cigar Co G 800 822-4427
Tampa *(G-17863)*
Moore & Bode Group LLC G 786 615-9389
Homestead *(G-5984)*
New Century G 305 670-3510
Miami *(G-10066)*
South Beach Cigar Factory LLC G 786 216-7475
Miami Beach *(G-10714)*
◆ **Swisher International Inc** G 904 353-4311
Jacksonville *(G-6830)*

2131 Tobacco, Chewing & Snuff

Accendo Tobacco LLC G 305 407-2222
Miami *(G-9060)*
◆ **Commonwealth Brands Inc** C 800 481-5814
Fort Lauderdale *(G-3912)*
◆ **Drew Estate LLC** E 786 581-1800
Miami *(G-9485)*
Eternal Smoke Inc G 407 984-5090
Orlando *(G-12718)*
Jti Duty-Free USA Inc G 305 377-3922
Miami *(G-9810)*
Lakay Vita LLC G 786 985-7552
Hallandale Beach *(G-5196)*
Swisher Intl Group Inc A 904 353-4311
Jacksonville *(G-6831)*

22 TEXTILE MILL PRODUCTS

2211 Cotton, Woven Fabric

▲ **Alcee Industries Inc** F 407 468-4573
Orlando *(G-12448)*
Anderson Mfg & Upholstery Inc G 321 267-7028
Titusville *(G-18413)*
Ards Awning & Upholstery Inc E 863 293-2442
Winter Haven *(G-19300)*
Associated Interior Desgr Svc F 561 655-4926
West Palm Beach *(G-18805)*
Ata Group of Companies Inc G 352 735-1588
Mount Dora *(G-11097)*
Bahamas Uphl & Mar Canvas Inc F 305 992-4346
Miami *(G-9214)*
Bay Networks Inc F 813 249-8103
Tampa *(G-17458)*
▲ **Bestcanvas Inc** F 305 759-7800
Miami *(G-9236)*
Blue Light USA Corp G 954 766-4308
Sunrise *(G-17099)*
BMW & Associates Inc G 352 694-2300
Ocala *(G-11888)*
Busch Canvas & Interiors G 561 881-1605
Riviera Beach *(G-15307)*
Business World Trading Inc F 305 238-0724
Miami *(G-9288)*

Camera2canvas LLC F 850 276-6990
Lynn Haven *(G-8431)*
Canvas G 727 317-5572
Saint Petersburg *(G-15738)*
Canvas Clinical Research F 561 229-0002
Lake Worth *(G-7538)*
Canvas Foods Corp G 786 529-8041
Weston *(G-19115)*
Canvas Freaks LLC G 407 978-6224
Orlando *(G-12547)*
Canvas Land Surveying LLC G 321 689-5330
Longwood *(G-8263)*
Canvas Studio Inc G 305 987-5895
Surfside *(G-17201)*
Canvas Tattoo LLC G 561 870-7929
Boynton Beach *(G-886)*
Captain Canvas & More G 561 881-2278
Lake Park *(G-7467)*
Caribbean Canvas and Mari G 786 972-6377
Miami *(G-9314)*
▲ Chrome Connection Corp G 305 947-9191
North Miami Beach *(G-11669)*
Classic Canvas & Upholstery G 954 850-4994
Hollywood *(G-5801)*
Creative Canvas Centl Fla Inc F 407 661-1211
Altamonte Springs *(G-39)*
Custom Canvas and Cushions G 561 800-8541
Riviera Beach *(G-15315)*
D W A Inc F 941 444-1134
Sarasota *(G-16401)*
Denim Lily LLC G 754 264-9331
Pompano Beach *(G-14659)*
Designers Wholesale Workroom F 239 434-7633
Naples *(G-11226)*
Dhf Marketing Inc F 305 884-8077
Hialeah *(G-5371)*
Diction Wear LLC G 954 696-5490
Fort Lauderdale *(G-3940)*
Digital Output G 904 285-9944
Ponte Vedra Beach *(G-14939)*
Discovery Canvas East Coast Co G 786 487-8897
Miami *(G-9471)*
Distinctive Creat Intr Wkshp I F 954 921-1861
Hollywood *(G-5812)*
Dreamboat Canvas LLC G 954 536-2415
Hollywood *(G-5813)*
Drench Khari LLC G 561 507-4723
Riviera Beach *(G-15322)*
Energy Services Providers Inc F 305 947-7880
Miramar *(G-10989)*
◆ Fiberbuilt Umbrellas Inc E 954 484-9139
Pompano Beach *(G-14690)*
Firebird Scrubs and More LLC G 904 258-7514
Orange Park *(G-12392)*
Fit Canvas Inc F 954 258-9352
Margate *(G-8544)*
Fortune Canvas Company Inc G 941 740-4296
Placida *(G-14396)*
Fury Surf Shack G 305 747-0799
Key West *(G-7187)*
Genesis 50 20 LLC G 954 860-8175
Weston *(G-19131)*
Genuine Denim G 305 491-1326
North Miami Beach *(G-11680)*
Gingham Gator LLC G 352 475-1985
Melrose *(G-8985)*
Great American Woodworks Inc F 727 375-1212
Odessa *(G-12124)*
Guyton Industries LLC E 772 208-3019
Indiantown *(G-6073)*
Holyland Tapestries Inc G 305 255-7955
Palmetto Bay *(G-13847)*
Ijkb LLC G 941 953-9046
Sarasota *(G-16464)*
◆ Indigo Mountain Inc G 239 947-0023
Naples *(G-11285)*
International Draperies Inc G 954 590-3897
Margate *(G-8550)*
Intertex Miami LLC G 305 627-3536
Miami *(G-9763)*
JM Ocean Mar Canvas & Uphl Inc G 786 473-7143
Hallandale *(G-5158)*
Jode Corporation G 321 684-1769
Sebastian *(G-16655)*
John E Anderson G 305 741-8400
West Palm Beach *(G-18914)*
Jones Awnings & Canvas Inc G 407 845-9400
Orlando *(G-12860)*
◆ Jose Leal Enterprises Inc D 305 887-9611
Hialeah *(G-5467)*
K L Distributing Inc G 415 800-2158
Hudson *(G-6030)*
L7 Apparel & Denim Company LLC G 954 867-8124
Hollywood *(G-5857)*
Latitude 27 Canvas G 772 321-6361
Vero Beach *(G-18638)*
Lead 2 Design G 954 757-6116
Coral Springs *(G-2272)*
Lilian Oils On Canvas Inc G 941 320-6263
Riverview *(G-15276)*
Marine Canvas Inc G 305 325-1830
Miami *(G-9948)*
Mollys Marine Service LLC G 239 262-2628
Naples *(G-11329)*
My Blank Canvas G 386 747-5254
Deland *(G-3003)*
N3xt L3vel 2 Point 0 LLC F 863 777-3778
Tampa *(G-17927)*
Nautiloft LLC G 801 712-6692
Punta Gorda *(G-15217)*
New Breed Clothing llc G 941 773-7406
Sarasota *(G-16266)*
Official Gear Company Inc G 407 721-9110
Ormond Beach *(G-13387)*
Palafox Marine Inc F 850 438-9354
Pensacola *(G-14219)*
Phoenix Custom Gear LLC G 561 808-7181
Delray Beach *(G-3116)*
Pure Canvas Inc G 561 818-2655
Greenacres *(G-5085)*
RAD Wear Inc G 352 727-4498
Gainesville *(G-4988)*
Sea and Shore Custom Canvas Up G 954 983-3060
Hollywood *(G-5905)*
Sea Canvas Inc G 954 462-7525
Fort Lauderdale *(G-4227)*
Southern Balloon Works Inc G 727 388-8360
Jacksonville *(G-6793)*
Sunshine Canvas Inc G 352 787-4436
Leesburg *(G-8175)*
Superior Fabrics Inc E 954 975-8122
Parkland *(G-14002)*
Superior Group Companies Inc G 727 397-9611
Seminole *(G-16765)*
Taylor Made Scrub Hats LLC G 615 348-7802
Riverview *(G-15284)*
Team Hammer Screen Printing G 863 666-1108
Lakeland *(G-7818)*
Team Ip Sports LLC F 772 398-4664
Stuart *(G-17034)*
▲ Tex Z-E Corp G 305 769-0202
Opa Locka *(G-12364)*
Traveling Canvas Corporation G 305 259-2001
Palmetto Bay *(G-13855)*
Unimd Scrubs LLC G 954 245-1509
Hallandale Beach *(G-5220)*
▼ Unique Originals Inc F 305 634-2274
Fort Lauderdale *(G-4293)*
West Point Stevens G 850 638-9421
Chipley *(G-1547)*
Westpoint Home Inc B 850 415-4100
Chipley *(G-1548)*
Westpoint Home Inc B 850 415-4100
Chipley *(G-1549)*
▲ Windbrella Products Corp E 561 734-5222
Boynton Beach *(G-974)*
Zellermayer Supply Corp F 561 848-0057
Mangonia Park *(G-8515)*

2221 Silk & Man-Made Fiber

AA Fiberglass Inc G 904 355-5511
Jacksonville *(G-6114)*
Accurate Reproductions Inc F 407 814-1622
Apopka *(G-108)*
Alta Technologies Inc G 609 538-9500
Ponte Vedra Beach *(G-14931)*
Anglo Silver Liner Co F 508 943-1440
Parrish *(G-14003)*
Bedding Acquisition LLC G 561 997-6900
Boca Raton *(G-443)*
Bradley Indus Textiles Inc F 850 678-6111
Valparaiso *(G-18508)*
Car Care Haven LLC G 855 464-2836
Englewood *(G-3671)*
▲ CBI Industries Inc G 305 796-9346
Miami *(G-9329)*
◆ Dillon Yarn Corporation C 973 684-1600
Fort Lauderdale *(G-3941)*
Drapery Control Systems Inc G 386 756-0101
Port Orange *(G-15017)*
▼ Drapery Control Systems Inc F 305 653-1712
Fort Lauderdale *(G-3949)*
Dti Design Trend Inc F 954 680-8370
Hialeah *(G-5379)*
Fastglas G 904 765-2222
Jacksonville *(G-6380)*
◆ Glasrite Inc F 863 967-8151
Auburndale *(G-244)*
J & H Supply Co Inc G 561 582-3346
Lake Worth *(G-7558)*
Jaynor Furnishings Inc G 954 973-8446
Coconut Creek *(G-2085)*
K Pro Supply Co Inc G 941 758-1226
Sarasota *(G-16244)*
Legend Moto LLC G 863 946-2002
Moore Haven *(G-11087)*
Merritt Precision Tech Inc G 321 453-2334
Merritt Island *(G-9003)*
Metritek Group LLC G 561 995-2414
Boca Raton *(G-621)*
◆ Miami Prestige Interiors Inc E 305 685-3343
Miami *(G-10005)*
Mutual Industries North Inc D 239 332-2400
Fort Myers *(G-4541)*
◆ Nida-Core Corporation E 772 343-7300
Port Saint Lucie *(G-15124)*
Point Blank Enterprises Inc A 954 846-8222
Pompano Beach *(G-14800)*
◆ R S Apparel Inc F 305 599-4939
Doral *(G-3478)*
Reliatex Inc E 813 621-6021
Tampa *(G-18051)*
Remas Draperies Etc Inc G 904 845-9300
Hilliard *(G-5716)*
Rfl & Figlio LLC F 904 765-2222
Jacksonville *(G-6723)*
Saten Leaf Nursery Inc F 305 216-5340
Homestead *(G-5991)*
Satin Sensation Co G 786 290-4114
Miami *(G-10306)*
◆ Schooner Prints Inc D 727 397-8572
Largo *(G-8045)*
▲ Security Impact GL Hldings LLC G 561 844-3100
Riviera Beach *(G-15376)*
▼ Smittys Boat Tops and Mar Eqp G 305 245-0229
Homestead *(G-5993)*
Sport Products of Tampa Inc G 813 630-5552
Tampa *(G-18127)*
Stm Industries LLC F 813 854-3544
Tampa *(G-18134)*
Stylors Inc F 904 765-4453
Jacksonville *(G-6820)*
Sunshine Nylon Products Inc G 352 754-9932
Brooksville *(G-1277)*
Superior Fabrics Inc E 954 975-8122
Parkland *(G-14002)*
▲ Valley Forge Textiles LLC G 954 971-1776
Pompano Beach *(G-14907)*
Vertical Village Inc G 772 340-0400
Port Saint Lucie *(G-15162)*

2231 Wool, Woven Fabric

Cool Ocean LLC G 954 848-4060
Plantation *(G-14502)*
Intertape Polymr Woven USA Inc G 800 474-8273
Sarasota *(G-16470)*
▲ Sourcerers Inc G 954 530-2333
Plantation *(G-14556)*
▲ Valley Forge Textiles LLC G 954 971-1776
Pompano Beach *(G-14907)*
Vertical Land Inc F 850 819-2535
Panama City *(G-13960)*

2241 Fabric Mills, Cotton, Wool, Silk & Man-Made

▲ American Elastic & Tape Inc G 305 888-0303
Hialeah *(G-5289)*
◆ Eastern Shores Printing E 305 685-8976
Opa Locka *(G-12312)*
Express Label Co Inc E 407 332-4774
Longwood *(G-8278)*
◆ Garflex Inc D 305 436-8915
Doral *(G-3358)*
◆ Lg-TEC Corporation G 305 770-4005
Hollywood *(G-5859)*
M & H Enterprises Inc G 305 885-5945
Hialeah *(G-5494)*
▼ Mansfield International Inc G 954 632-3280
Fort Lauderdale *(G-4112)*

S I C

Nadco Tapes & Labels Inc E 941 751-6693
Sarasota *(G-16263)*
Nissi Elastic Corp G 305 968-3812
Hialeah *(G-5542)*
Tie Collection LLC G 305 323-1420
Vero Beach *(G-18671)*
▲ **Valley Forge Textiles LLC** G 954 971-1776
Pompano Beach *(G-14907)*

2251 Hosiery, Women's Full & Knee Length

New Concepts Distrs Intl LLC F 305 463-8735
Doral *(G-3444)*
▲ **Triumph Hosiery Corp** G 954 929-6021
Hollywood *(G-5928)*

2252 Hosiery, Except Women's

American Stock LLC G 904 641-2055
Jacksonville *(G-6151)*
King of Socks F 772 204-3286
Port St Lucie *(G-15174)*
▲ **Leopard Brands Inc** G 954 794-0007
Boca Raton *(G-599)*
Pop Em Sock Ems G 850 287-3778
Gulf Breeze *(G-5124)*
Royalty Enterprises LLC G 786 380-7774
Miami Beach *(G-10706)*
Shashi LLC G 561 447-8800
Delray Beach *(G-3140)*
Skater Socks F 850 424-6764
Destin *(G-3206)*
▲ **Triumph Hosiery Corp** G 954 929-6021
Hollywood *(G-5928)*

2253 Knit Outerwear Mills

▼ **A & S Entertainment LLC** F 305 627-3456
Miami *(G-9032)*
Absolutely Suitable G 561 653-6380
Palm Beach *(G-13548)*
Balzarano John F 239 455-1231
Naples *(G-11181)*
Bnj Noble Inc F 954 987-1040
Davie *(G-2503)*
Color Touch Inc F 954 444-1999
Lauderhill *(G-8104)*
▼ **Coral Club Tee Shirts Inc** G 305 828-6939
Hialeah *(G-5354)*
▲ **Daisy Crazy Inc** G 305 300-5144
Doral *(G-3321)*
▲ **H2c Brands LLC** E 904 342-7485
Saint Augustine *(G-15548)*
House of Llull Atlier G 305 964-7921
Miami *(G-9720)*
Jonel Knitting Mills Inc E 305 887-7333
Hialeah *(G-5466)*
Mk Brothers Inc G 407 847-9547
Kissimmee *(G-7277)*
Nrz Inc G 305 345-7303
Pinecrest *(G-14329)*
Reflections Beach & Resortwear G 954 776-1230
Laud By Sea *(G-8083)*
Swf Bonita Beach Inc D 239 466-6600
Bonita Springs *(G-860)*
◆ **Swim By Chuck Handy Inc** G 305 519-4946
North Miami Beach *(G-11707)*
Talent Wear LLC G 561 624-3030
West Palm Beach *(G-19057)*
Two Mermaids Villages LLC G 352 259-4722
The Villages *(G-18395)*
▼ **Veronica Knits Inc** F 305 887-7333
Hialeah *(G-5676)*

2254 Knit Underwear Mills

Eyedose Inc G 786 853-6194
Miami *(G-9550)*
◆ **Intradeco Apparel Inc** C 305 264-8888
Medley *(G-8671)*
Jockey International Inc G 561 689-7646
West Palm Beach *(G-18913)*
Mark Benton E 754 203-9377
Boca Raton *(G-608)*
Monkey Shack G 850 234-0082
Panama City *(G-13930)*
▲ **Sweet and Vicious LLC** F 772 907-3030
Lake Worth *(G-7589)*

2258 Lace & Warp Knit Fabric Mills

Burbank Trawl Makers Inc E 904 321-0976
Jacksonville *(G-6244)*
C&S Ostomy Pouch Covers Inc G 941 423-8542
North Port *(G-11736)*
Intermas Nets USA Inc G 305 442-1416
Coral Gables *(G-2160)*
Jayco International LLC D 407 855-8880
Orlando *(G-12852)*
◆ **Metritek Corporation** C 561 995-2414
Coral Springs *(G-2283)*
▲ **Wyla Inc** E 904 886-4338
Jacksonville *(G-6931)*

2259 Knitting Mills, NEC

Fajas Colombianas USA LLC G 786 326-0002
Hialeah *(G-5403)*

2261 Cotton Fabric Finishers

▲ **American Mentality Inc** G 407 599-7255
Longwood *(G-8254)*
Aquarius Silk Screen Inc G 941 377-3059
Sarasota *(G-16346)*
Arca Knitting Inc D 305 836-0155
Hialeah *(G-5303)*
▼ **Armen Co Inc** D 305 206-1601
Plantation *(G-14490)*
Bam Enterprises Inc E 850 469-8872
Pensacola *(G-14096)*
Blackwell Family Corporation G 941 639-0200
Punta Gorda *(G-15199)*
◆ **Capsmith Inc** E 407 328-7660
Sanford *(G-16007)*
▲ **Colortone Inc** E 954 455-0200
Hallandale Beach *(G-5178)*
Cubco Inc F 386 254-2706
Daytona Beach *(G-2650)*
Daytona Trophy Inc F 386 253-2806
Daytona Beach *(G-2656)*
▼ **Happy Endings of Miami Inc** G 305 759-4467
Miami *(G-9686)*
Michelle Lynn Solutions Inc G 786 413-0455
Miami *(G-10016)*
Mid-Florida Sportswear LLC E 386 258-5632
Daytona Beach *(G-2686)*
Ripa & Associates Inc C 813 623-6777
Tampa *(G-18059)*
▲ **Rock N Roll Custom Screened S** G 727 528-2111
Pinellas Park *(G-14385)*
Royal Tees Inc F 941 366-0056
Sarasota *(G-16564)*
Screenprint Plus Inc E 239 549-7284
Cape Coral *(G-1467)*
◆ **Screenworks Usa Inc** C 407 426-9999
Orlando *(G-13170)*
◆ **Sherry Manufacturing Co Inc** C 305 693-7000
Miami *(G-10338)*
South Florida Strip Tees Inc F 954 972-4899
Pompano Beach *(G-14859)*

2262 Silk & Man-Made Fabric Finishers

Apparel Printers G 352 463-8850
Alachua *(G-4)*
▼ **Armen Co Inc** D 305 206-1601
Plantation *(G-14490)*
Bagindd Prints F 954 971-9000
Coral Springs *(G-2223)*
▲ **Blue Ocean Press Inc** E 954 973-1819
Fort Lauderdale *(G-3859)*
▲ **Cottonimagescom Inc** E 305 251-2560
Doral *(G-3311)*
Creative Shirts Intl Inc F 954 351-0909
Oakland Park *(G-11792)*
Dowling Graphics Inc E 727 573-5997
Clearwater *(G-1657)*
Lance Lashelle G 425 820-8888
Boca Raton *(G-594)*
Metal Spray Painting Powder G 954 227-2744
Coral Springs *(G-2281)*
▼ **Orange Sunshine Graphics Inc** G 954 797-7425
Davie *(G-2562)*

2269 Textile Finishers, NEC

▼ **Armen Co Inc** D 305 206-1601
Plantation *(G-14490)*
▲ **Colortone Inc** E 954 455-0200
Hallandale Beach *(G-5178)*
◆ **Finotex USA Corp** E 305 593-1102
Miami *(G-9570)*
Florida Marking Products LLC E 407 834-3000
Longwood *(G-8283)*
Lance Lashelle G 425 820-8888
Boca Raton *(G-594)*
PHI CHI Foundation Inc G 561 526-3401
Margate *(G-8560)*
Technifinish Inc F 727 576-5955
Clearwater *(G-1911)*

2273 Carpets & Rugs

Area Rugs Mfg Inc G 904 398-5481
Jacksonville *(G-6166)*
Artificial Turf Supply LLC G 877 525-8873
Ponte Vedra Beach *(G-14934)*
Bearded Mohawk LLC G 913 680-9829
Deltona *(G-3163)*
BF Hurley Mat Co Inc E 813 837-0616
Tampa *(G-17468)*
Carpet Clinic LLC G 850 232-1170
Pensacola *(G-14112)*
Design-A-Rug Inc F 954 943-7487
Deerfield Beach *(G-2812)*
Drab To Fab G 941 475-7700
Englewood *(G-3675)*
Dyn-O-Mat Inc G 561 747-2301
Jupiter *(G-7029)*
Dynomat Inc E 561 747-2301
Jupiter *(G-7030)*
▼ **Englert Arts Inc** G 561 241-9924
Boca Raton *(G-518)*
Floors Inc E 813 879-5720
Tampa *(G-17671)*
▲ **Glassflake International Inc** G 904 268-4000
Jacksonville *(G-6436)*
Hanteri Enterprises Corp F 813 949-8729
Lutz *(G-8388)*
▲ **International Mdse Sources Inc** C 239 430-9993
Naples *(G-11289)*
Kitchens Xtreme LLC G 941 387-5181
Sarasota *(G-16482)*
Milliken & Company G 352 244-2267
Gainesville *(G-4963)*
Mobile Auto Solutions LLC G 561 903-5328
West Palm Beach *(G-18954)*
Mohawk Industries Inc G 918 272-0184
Hollywood *(G-5878)*
Murse Properties LLC G 941 966-3380
Sarasota *(G-16518)*
Niba Designs Inc F 305 456-6230
Hollywood *(G-5883)*
Picket Fence Childrens G 813 713-8589
Zephyrhills *(G-19532)*
▲ **Proximity Mills LLC** F 813 251-3060
Tampa *(G-18022)*
Rampell Software F 561 628-5102
Palm Beach *(G-13561)*
▲ **Ser-Mat International LLC** E 954 525-1417
Pompano Beach *(G-14847)*
Woovfu Inc F 719 301-1661
Saint Petersburg *(G-15964)*

2281 Yarn Spinning Mills

Four Purls G 863 293-6261
Winter Haven *(G-19324)*
Southern Fiber Inc F 786 916-3052
Miami Lakes *(G-10861)*

2282 Yarn Texturizing, Throwing, Twisting & Winding Mills

◆ **Dillon Yarn Corporation** C 973 684-1600
Fort Lauderdale *(G-3941)*

2284 Thread Mills

▼ **Florida Thread & Trimming** G 954 240-2474
Hialeah *(G-5415)*
John & Betsy Hovland G 727 449-2032
Clearwater *(G-1744)*

2295 Fabrics Coated Not Rubberized

Access Able Technologies Inc G 407 834-2999
Winter Springs *(G-19465)*
Blutec Glass Fabrication LLC G 941 232-1600
Sarasota *(G-16365)*
◆ **C M I Enterprises Inc** E 305 622-6410
Opa Locka *(G-12297)*
Clock Spring Company Inc F 561 683-6992
Riviera Beach *(G-15312)*
Enviroworks Inc F 407 889-5533
Apopka *(G-137)*
Fiskars Brands Inc G 407 889-5533
Apopka *(G-142)*

◆ **Madico Inc**.....D..... 727 327-2544
Pinellas Park *(G-14366)*
Metalex LLC.....D..... 941 918-4431
Nokomis *(G-11585)*
Mundi Intl Trading Corp.....G..... 305 205-0062
Weston *(G-19150)*
Patrick Industries Inc.....G..... 352 732-8841
Ocala *(G-12023)*
RSR Industrial Coatings Inc.....F..... 863 537-1110
Bartow *(G-332)*
Sabic Innovative Plastics.....G..... 386 409-5540
New Smyrna Beach *(G-11541)*
Trann Technologies Inc.....G..... 888 668-6700
Mossy Head *(G-11094)*
▲ **Uniroyal Engineered Pdts LLC**.....F..... 941 906-8580
Sarasota *(G-16629)*
Urecon Systems Inc.....C..... 321 638-2364
Winter Park *(G-19455)*
Windsor & York Inc.....G..... 561 687-8424
West Palm Beach *(G-19088)*

2297 Fabrics, Nonwoven

▼ **Cerex Advanced Fabrics Inc**.....D..... 850 968-0100
Cantonment *(G-1336)*
Mutual Industries North Inc.....D..... 239 332-2400
Fort Myers *(G-4541)*
Superior Fabrics Inc.....E..... 954 975-8122
Parkland *(G-14002)*

2298 Cordage & Twine

◆ **American Wire Group Inc**.....F..... 954 455-3050
Aventura *(G-260)*
Applied Fiber Holdings LLC.....E..... 850 539-7720
Havana *(G-5230)*
▲ **Applied Fiber Mfg LLC**.....E..... 850 539-7720
Havana *(G-5231)*
▼ **Atlantic Wire and Rigging Inc**.....G..... 321 633-1552
Cocoa *(G-1997)*
Bubba Rope LLC.....G..... 877 499-8494
Altamonte Springs *(G-35)*
◆ **Chiptech Inc**.....F..... 954 454-3554
Hallandale *(G-5154)*
▲ **Conexus Technologies Inc**.....F..... 513 779-5448
Sarasota *(G-16391)*
▲ **Consolidated Cordage Corp**.....F..... 561 347-7247
Boca Raton *(G-488)*
Csl of America Inc.....F..... 407 849-7070
Orlando *(G-12629)*
E Quality Cables Inc.....F..... 321 242-4820
Melbourne *(G-8817)*
▲ **Frank Murray & Sons Inc**.....F..... 561 845-1366
Fort Lauderdale *(G-4012)*
Gulf Cable LLC.....C..... 201 720-2417
Milton *(G-10932)*
◆ **Hofmann & Leavy Inc**.....D..... 954 698-0000
Deerfield Beach *(G-2842)*
◆ **Lee Fisher International Inc**.....E..... 813 875-6296
Tampa *(G-17839)*
Mc Connie Enterprises Inc.....G..... 813 247-3827
Tampa *(G-17897)*
▲ **Meridian Cable LLC**.....F..... 847 847-1128
Saint Augustine *(G-15568)*
◆ **Miami Cordage LLC**.....E..... 305 636-3000
Miami *(G-9996)*
Nets Depot Inc.....F..... 305 215-5579
Medley *(G-8694)*
◆ **Newlink Cabling Systems Inc**.....F..... 305 477-8063
Medley *(G-8697)*
Rat Trap Bait Company Inc.....F..... 863 967-2148
Auburndale *(G-251)*
▼ **Rope Works Inc**.....F..... 954 525-6575
Fort Lauderdale *(G-4213)*
▲ **Shurhold Products Company**.....G..... 772 287-1313
Palm City *(G-13673)*
◆ **Sunshine Cordage Corporation**.....G..... 305 592-3750
Miami *(G-10434)*

2299 Textile Goods, NEC

Apparel Industries.....G..... 786 362-5958
Doral *(G-3252)*
Apparel Machinery Services Inc.....G..... 772 335-5350
Port Saint Lucie *(G-15087)*
Divas Fashion.....G..... 786 717-7039
Miami *(G-9472)*
Garco Manufacturing Co Inc.....G..... 321 868-3778
Cocoa Beach *(G-2064)*
▲ **Good Chance Inc**.....G..... 754 263-2792
Pembroke Pines *(G-14037)*
Gvj Corp.....G..... 786 224-2808
Miami *(G-9683)*
H2 Home Collection Inc.....F..... 714 916-9513
Jacksonville *(G-6459)*
▲ **Hamburg House Inc**.....E..... 305 557-9913
Hialeah *(G-5442)*
◆ **Harbor Linen LLC**.....D..... 305 805-8085
Medley *(G-8661)*
▲ **Imported Yarns LLC**.....G..... 239 405-2974
Estero *(G-3691)*
▲ **Lahia America Corp**.....F..... 305 254-6212
Miami *(G-9851)*
Mario Kenny.....G..... 786 274-0527
Miami *(G-9949)*
Niba Designs Inc.....F..... 305 456-6230
Hollywood *(G-5883)*
▲ **Pro Horizons Inc**.....G..... 813 764-8844
Plant City *(G-14460)*
South Florida Cutting.....F..... 305 693-6711
Hialeah *(G-5625)*
Terracassa LLC.....G..... 786 581-7741
Miami *(G-10468)*
▲ **Valley Forge Textiles LLC**.....G..... 954 971-1776
Pompano Beach *(G-14907)*
◆ **Vintage Fashion**.....G..... 786 631-4048
Hialeah *(G-5680)*
White Horse Fashion Cuisine.....G..... 561 847-4549
Wellington *(G-18739)*
Yesil Inc.....F..... 516 858-0244
Boca Raton *(G-796)*

23 APPAREL AND OTHER FINISHED PRODUCTS MADE FROM FABRICS AND SIMILAR MATERIAL

2311 Men's & Boys' Suits, Coats & Overcoats

◆ **A G A Electronics Corp**.....F..... 305 592-1860
Miami *(G-9038)*
◆ **Apparel Imports Inc**.....E..... 800 428-6849
Miami *(G-9157)*
Bid Excellence Co LLC.....G..... 609 929-9019
Miami *(G-9243)*
▲ **Black Mountain Apparel Inc**.....E..... 727 216-6419
Seminole *(G-16743)*
Burn Proof Gear LLC.....G..... 786 634-7406
Miami *(G-9286)*
Cadre Holdings Inc.....C..... 904 741-5400
Jacksonville *(G-6249)*
▲ **Cameron Textiles Inc**.....G..... 954 454-6482
Palm City *(G-13644)*
Eglin Air Force Base.....D..... 850 882-5422
Eglin Afb *(G-3642)*
Eglin Air Force Base.....C..... 850 882-3315
Eglin Afb *(G-3643)*
◆ **Global Trading Inc**.....F..... 305 471-4455
Miami *(G-9642)*
L C Industries Inc.....E..... 850 581-0117
Hurlburt Field *(G-6044)*
Mario Kenny.....G..... 786 274-0527
Miami *(G-9949)*
Maui Holdings LLC.....A..... 904 741-5400
Palm Beach *(G-13558)*
▼ **Onyx Protective Group Inc**.....F..... 305 282-4455
Miami *(G-10108)*
Point Blank Protective Apprl.....A..... 954 630-0900
Pompano Beach *(G-14803)*
Tennier Industries Inc.....G..... 561 999-9710
Boca Raton *(G-746)*
Tom James Company.....G..... 813 204-9699
Tampa *(G-18193)*
▼ **Tycoon Tutti Inc**.....E..... 305 624-7811
Miami *(G-10519)*
◆ **Uniform Authority Inc**.....D..... 305 625-8050
Miami *(G-10529)*
US Patriot LLC.....F..... 803 787-9398
Tampa *(G-18228)*

2321 Men's & Boys' Shirts

◆ **A G A Electronics Corp**.....F..... 305 592-1860
Miami *(G-9038)*
◆ **Dynasty Apparel Corp**.....D..... 305 685-3490
Opa Locka *(G-12310)*
Entire Select Inc.....G..... 954 674-2368
Sunrise *(G-17119)*
Feds Apparel.....E..... 954 932-0685
Davie *(G-2524)*
Feldenkreis Holdings LLC.....E..... 305 592-2830
Doral *(G-3350)*
La Providencia Express Co.....G..... 305 409-9894
Miami *(G-9846)*
Leo Fashions Inc.....F..... 305 887-1032
Hialeah *(G-5484)*
Perry Ellis International Inc.....B..... 305 592-2830
Doral *(G-3458)*
Pvh Corp.....F..... 850 269-0482
Miramar Beach *(G-11068)*
▲ **Regina Behar Enterprises Inc**.....E..... 305 557-5212
Miramar *(G-11035)*
Ronmar Industries Inc.....F..... 561 630-8035
West Palm Beach *(G-19023)*
Sashay Sourcing LLC.....G..... 239 454-4940
Fort Myers *(G-4597)*
◆ **Stanley Industries of S Fla**.....G..... 954 929-8770
Hollywood *(G-5915)*
▼ **Tycoon Tutti Inc**.....E..... 305 624-7811
Miami *(G-10519)*

2322 Men's & Boys' Underwear & Nightwear

Jockey International Inc.....G..... 561 689-7646
West Palm Beach *(G-18913)*
◆ **Val DOr Apparel LLC**.....G..... 954 363-7340
Coconut Creek *(G-2100)*

2323 Men's & Boys' Neckwear

Bonito & Company LLC.....G..... 561 451-7494
Boca Raton *(G-460)*
Breezy Swimwear.....G..... 305 763-9570
Miami *(G-9275)*
Caveat.....G..... 305 501-4646
Miami *(G-9326)*
Chervo USA Inc.....G..... 561 510-2458
North Palm Beach *(G-11721)*
Element Outdoors LLC.....G..... 888 589-9589
Pace *(G-13468)*
Exces International LLC.....G..... 561 880-8920
Wellington *(G-18716)*
Infotek Groups Inc.....G..... 612 666-0535
Saint Petersburg *(G-15814)*
Jblaze Inc.....G..... 954 680-3962
Southwest Ranches *(G-16838)*
Mary Angel.....G..... 772 299-1392
Vero Beach *(G-18641)*
Prive Porter LLC.....G..... 561 479-9200
Boca Raton *(G-675)*
Pure 32 LLC.....G..... 813 792-9219
Odessa *(G-12144)*
Siyufy International Inc.....G..... 352 512-0658
Ocala *(G-12054)*
Tailored LLC.....G..... 239 249-9636
Naples *(G-11434)*

2325 Men's & Boys' Separate Trousers & Casual Slacks

Arno Belo Inc.....G..... 800 734-2356
Hallandale Beach *(G-5170)*
◆ **Dynasty Apparel Corp**.....D..... 305 685-3490
Opa Locka *(G-12310)*
Goen3 Corporation.....G..... 407 601-6000
Orlando *(G-12785)*
La Providencia Express Co.....G..... 305 409-9894
Miami *(G-9846)*
◆ **Lagaci Inc**.....F..... 954 929-1395
Fort Lauderdale *(G-4093)*
Lee Lowsky.....G..... 904 470-4110
Jacksonville *(G-6551)*
Original Pnguin Drect Oprtions.....F..... 305 592-2830
Doral *(G-3452)*
Perry Ellis International Inc.....B..... 305 592-2830
Doral *(G-3458)*
◆ **Stanley Industries of S Fla**.....G..... 954 929-8770
Hollywood *(G-5915)*
Stush AP USA/Stush Style LLC.....F..... 404 940-3445
Sunrise *(G-17180)*
◆ **Supreme International LLC**.....A..... 305 592-2830
Doral *(G-3519)*

2326 Men's & Boys' Work Clothing

▲ **Affordable Med Scrubs LLC**.....F..... 419 222-1088
Miami *(G-9086)*
Anmapec Corporation.....F..... 786 897-5389
Miami *(G-9154)*
At Work Uniforms.....G..... 850 435-3133
Pensacola *(G-14093)*
Bid Excellence Co LLC.....G..... 609 929-9019
Miami *(G-9243)*
▲ **Box Seat Clothing Company**.....G..... 800 787-7792
Jacksonville *(G-6227)*
Boxseat Inc.....F..... 850 656-1223
Jacksonville *(G-6228)*

SIC

▲ Cameron Textiles Inc ....G.... 954 454-6482
Palm City (G-13644)
Cintas Corporation ....F.... 813 874-1401
Tampa (G-17536)
Cintas Corporation ....G.... 239 693-8722
Fort Myers (G-4396)
▲ CSC Racing Corporation ....F.... 248 548-5727
Jupiter (G-7021)
▲ CTI Group Worldwide Svcs Inc ....G.... 954 568-5900
Fort Lauderdale (G-3922)
◆ Dmr Creative Marketing LLC ....G.... 954 725-3750
Deerfield Beach (G-2816)
Fabrox LLC ....E.... 904 342-4048
Ormond Beach (G-13371)
▲ Gallant Inc ....G.... 800 330-1343
Winter Garden (G-19265)
◆ Global Trading Inc ....F.... 305 471-4455
Miami (G-9642)
Gulfshore Clothier LLC ....G.... 239 450-8437
Naples (G-11273)
▲ International Clothiers Inc ....F.... 914 715-5600
Miami (G-9756)
◆ Ivory International Inc ....C.... 305 687-2244
Medley (G-8672)
▲ JA Uniforms Inc ....F.... 305 234-1231
Miami (G-9784)
Jackie Z Style Co St Pete LLC ....G.... 727 258-4849
Saint Petersburg (G-15831)
▼ M R M S Inc ....G.... 305 576-3000
Miami (G-9927)
Mario Kenny ....G.... 786 274-0527
Miami (G-9949)
R&S Intrnational Inv Group LLC ....F.... 305 576-3000
Miami (G-10234)
Saint George Industries LLC ....E.... 786 212-1176
Miami (G-10298)
Samarian Products LLC ....E.... 212 781-2121
Naples (G-11390)
Scrubs 941 ....G.... 941 373-0029
Sarasota (G-16587)
Skwholesalenet ....F.... 305 372-3751
Miami (G-10358)
Tees By Bo Inc ....G.... 305 382-8551
Miami (G-10465)
◆ Uniform Authority Inc ....D.... 305 625-8050
Miami (G-10529)
Uzzi Amphibious Gear LLC ....F.... 954 777-9595
Hallandale Beach (G-5223)
▲ Wayloo Inc ....G.... 954 914-3192
Fort Lauderdale (G-4317)
Zayas Fashions Inc ....E.... 305 823-1438
Hialeah (G-5695)

2329 Men's & Boys' Clothing, NEC

Adidas North America Inc ....G.... 321 677-0078
Orlando (G-12431)
American Athletic Uniforms Inc ....F.... 850 729-1205
Valparaiso (G-18505)
Anmapec Corporation ....F.... 786 897-5389
Miami (G-9154)
▼ Armen Co Inc ....D.... 305 206-1601
Plantation (G-14490)
Arno Belo Inc ....G.... 800 734-2356
Hallandale Beach (G-5170)
◆ Athco Inc ....E.... 941 351-1600
Sarasota (G-16179)
B & B Industries of Orlando ....G.... 407 366-1800
Oviedo (G-13417)
▲ Bakers Sports Inc ....E.... 904 388-8126
Jacksonville (G-6192)
Bdc Florida LLC ....F.... 561 249-0900
West Palm Beach (G-18814)
◆ Devon-Aire Inc ....E.... 813 884-9544
Tampa (G-17602)
Excess Liquidator LLC ....G.... 407 247-9105
Oviedo (G-13429)
◆ Exist Inc ....D.... 954 739-7030
Fort Lauderdale (G-3982)
Fabrox LLC ....E.... 904 342-4048
Ormond Beach (G-13371)
Fashion Pool USA Inc ....G.... 970 367-4797
Jupiter (G-7040)
Fitletic Sports LLC ....G.... 305 907-6663
Hallandale Beach (G-5186)
▲ Golf America Southwest Fla Inc ....G.... 904 688-0280
Saint Augustine (G-15546)
◆ Good Chance Textile Inc ....F.... 754 263-2792
Pembroke Pines (G-14038)
Hexskin LLC ....G.... 305 901-1573
Miami (G-9706)
Icon Embroidery Inc ....G.... 407 858-0886
Windermere (G-19228)
◆ In Gear Fashions Inc ....D.... 305 830-2900
Miami Gardens (G-10747)
Jamerica Inc ....G.... 561 488-6247
Boca Raton (G-575)
◆ JMP Fashion Inc ....F.... 305 633-9920
Miami (G-9799)
John M Caldwell Distrg Co Inc ....G.... 305 685-9822
Opa Locka (G-12329)
Kamaj Business Group Inc ....F.... 813 863-9967
Tampa (G-17815)
Onca Gear LLC ....G.... 857 253-8207
Hialeah (G-5549)
Outdoor Products LLC ....G.... 352 473-0886
Steinhatchee (G-16898)
Recover Gear LLC ....G.... 904 280-9660
Ponte Vedra Beach (G-14952)
Richard Appelbaum & Associates ....G.... 813 920-0300
Odessa (G-12145)
▲ Speedline Athletic Wear Inc ....E.... 813 876-1375
Tampa (G-18124)
Speedline Team Sports Inc ....F.... 813 876-1375
Tampa (G-18125)
Spirit Sales Corporation ....G.... 850 878-0366
Tallahassee (G-17329)
◆ Sportailor Inc ....D.... 305 754-3255
Miami (G-10406)
Sports Structure Intl LLC ....G.... 305 777-2225
Miami Beach (G-10715)
Suncoast Trends Inc ....G.... 727 321-4948
Saint Petersburg (G-15929)
Surf Outfitter ....G.... 813 489-4587
Tampa (G-18147)
Surf Style Inc ....E.... 954 926-6666
Hollywood (G-5919)
▲ T Shirt Center Inc ....G.... 305 655-1955
Miami (G-10455)
▲ Tactical Products Group LLC ....E.... 561 265-4066
Boynton Beach (G-967)
◆ Team Edition Apparel Inc ....C.... 941 744-2041
Bradenton (G-1125)
Ultimate Overstock LLC ....E.... 407 851-1017
Orlando (G-13287)
Ultimate Swimwear Inc ....G.... 386 668-8900
Altamonte Springs (G-80)
◆ Val DOr Apparel LLC ....G.... 954 363-7340
Coconut Creek (G-2100)
Winntel USA ....G.... 863 451-1789
Sebring (G-16718)

2331 Women's & Misses' Blouses

Apyelen Curves LLC ....F.... 904 434-8768
Jacksonville (G-6162)
◆ Argus International Inc ....E.... 305 888-4881
Weston (G-19108)
Co-Edikit ....G.... 863 802-1000
Lakeland (G-7658)
▲ Daisy Crazy Inc ....G.... 305 300-5144
Doral (G-3321)
▲ Decoy Inc ....F.... 305 633-6384
Miami (G-9443)
Entire Select Inc ....G.... 954 674-2368
Sunrise (G-17119)
Goen3 Corporation ....G.... 407 601-6000
Orlando (G-12785)
H M J Corporation ....F.... 954 229-1873
Fort Lauderdale (G-4037)
Johnny Devil Inc ....G.... 305 634-0700
Miami (G-9800)
▲ Kamtex USA Incorporated ....G.... 954 733-1044
Lauderdale Lakes (G-8089)
Kleids Enterprises Inc ....G.... 727 796-7900
Clearwater (G-1751)
Leo Fashions Inc ....F.... 305 887-1032
Hialeah (G-5484)
Matteo Graphics Inc ....F.... 239 652-1002
Cape Coral (G-1446)
PJ Designs Inc ....E.... 727 525-0599
Saint Petersburg (G-15879)
R&S Intrnational Inv Group LLC ....F.... 305 576-3000
Miami (G-10234)
◆ Stanley Industries of S Fla ....G.... 954 929-8770
Hollywood (G-5915)
Stush AP USA/Stush Style LLC ....F.... 404 940-3445
Sunrise (G-17180)
Suncoast Trends Inc ....G.... 727 321-4948
Saint Petersburg (G-15929)
◆ Supreme International LLC ....A.... 305 592-2830
Doral (G-3519)
◆ Val DOr Apparel LLC ....G.... 954 363-7340
Coconut Creek (G-2100)
Vargas Enterprises Inc ....G.... 561 989-0908
Boca Raton (G-775)
Wbt Apparel Inc ....G.... 305 891-1107
North Miami (G-11663)

2335 Women's & Misses' Dresses

A Fine Affair Dj ....G.... 319 899-2071
Kissimmee (G-7215)
▲ AA Oldco Inc ....D.... 215 659-5300
Delray Beach (G-3038)
▲ Amj DOT LLC ....G.... 646 249-0273
Boca Raton (G-426)
Ancient Language Inc ....G.... 413 344-4042
Orlando (G-12477)
Arde Apparel Inc ....E.... 305 326-0861
Miami (G-9166)
CD Greeting LLC ....G.... 954 530-1301
Fort Lauderdale (G-3887)
Classic Stars Inc ....G.... 305 871-6767
Miami (G-9362)
Designs To Shine ....E.... 727 525-4297
Saint Petersburg (G-15759)
▲ Janine of London Inc ....G.... 954 772-3593
Fort Lauderdale (G-4075)
▲ Laura Knit Collection Inc ....C.... 305 945-8222
North Miami Beach (G-11690)
Meek Chic Queen Inc ....G.... 407 920-8135
Coral Springs (G-2278)
Miller Creative Works Inc ....G.... 904 504-3212
Jacksonville (G-6608)
▼ Mori Lee LLC ....E.... 954 418-6165
Deerfield Beach (G-2876)
PJ Designs Inc ....E.... 727 525-0599
Saint Petersburg (G-15879)
◆ Stanley Industries of S Fla ....G.... 954 929-8770
Hollywood (G-5915)
Stush AP USA/Stush Style LLC ....F.... 404 940-3445
Sunrise (G-17180)
Weddings By Tina ....G.... 904 235-3740
Jacksonville (G-6908)
Yoly Munoz Corp ....G.... 305 860-3839
Miami (G-10627)

2337 Women's & Misses' Suits, Coats & Skirts

Cintas Corporation ....G.... 239 693-8722
Fort Myers (G-4396)
▲ International Clothiers Inc ....F.... 914 715-5600
Miami (G-9756)
◆ Interntnal Export Uniforms Inc ....E.... 305 869-9900
Miami (G-9761)
Kleids Enterprises Inc ....G.... 727 796-7900
Clearwater (G-1751)
▲ Laura Knit Collection Inc ....C.... 305 945-8222
North Miami Beach (G-11690)
Perry Ellis International Inc ....B.... 305 592-2830
Doral (G-3458)
◆ Uniform Authority Inc ....D.... 305 625-8050
Miami (G-10529)

2339 Women's & Misses' Outerwear, NEC

A Living Testimony LLC ....G.... 352 406-0249
Eustis (G-3699)
A-1 Sportswear Inc ....G.... 305 773-7028
Hialeah (G-5260)
Algy Trimmings Co Inc ....D.... 954 457-8100
Miami (G-9104)
American Athletic Uniforms Inc ....F.... 850 729-1205
Valparaiso (G-18505)
Anmapec Corporation ....F.... 786 897-5389
Miami (G-9154)
ANue Ligne Inc ....G.... 305 638-7979
Miami (G-9155)
▼ Armen Co Inc ....D.... 305 206-1601
Plantation (G-14490)
Arno Belo Inc ....G.... 800 734-2356
Hallandale Beach (G-5170)
◆ Athco Inc ....E.... 941 351-1600
Sarasota (G-16179)
B & B Industries of Orlando ....G.... 407 366-1800
Oviedo (G-13417)
Becker Designs Inc ....G.... 386 760-2280
Port Orange (G-15012)
Big Fish Co Custom Creations ....G.... 727 525-5010
Saint Petersburg (G-15721)
Can Can Concealment LLC ....G.... 727 841-6930
Odessa (G-12109)

Cima Activewear LLC ....G.... 239 273-6055
Estero *(G-3687)*
Coastal Paddle Co LLC ....F.... 850 916-1600
Gulf Breeze *(G-5114)*
▲ **Daisy Crazy Inc** ....G.... 305 300-5144
Doral *(G-3321)*
◆ **Devon-Aire Inc** ....E.... 813 884-9544
Tampa *(G-17602)*
◆ **Di Di Designs Inc** ....F.... 305 836-0266
Opa Locka *(G-12306)*
Diane Dal Lago Limited Company ....F.... 813 374-2473
Tampa *(G-17604)*
▼ **Dilan Enterprises Inc** ....E.... 305 887-3051
Hialeah *(G-5373)*
◆ **Double J of Broward Inc** ....E.... 954 659-8880
Weston *(G-19121)*
Earth & Sea Wear LLC ....E.... 786 332-2236
Doral *(G-3338)*
Excess Liquidator LLC ....G.... 407 247-9105
Oviedo *(G-13429)*
Fashion Pool USA Inc ....G.... 970 367-4797
Jupiter *(G-7040)*
▲ **Finesta Inc** ....G.... 786 439-1647
Miami *(G-9569)*
Fitletic Sports LLC ....G.... 305 907-6663
Hallandale Beach *(G-5186)*
◆ **Great Cir Vntures Holdings LLC** ....D.... 305 638-2650
Doral *(G-3372)*
◆ **Happy Kids For Kids Inc** ....F.... 954 730-7922
Lauderhill *(G-8111)*
Icon Embroidery Inc ....G.... 407 858-0886
Windermere *(G-19228)*
◆ **In Gear Fashions Inc** ....D.... 305 830-2900
Miami Gardens *(G-10747)*
◆ **Ivory International Inc** ....C.... 305 687-2244
Medley *(G-8672)*
Jazanique Wickson ....G.... 815 221-7155
Miami Beach *(G-10684)*
◆ **JMP Fashion Inc** ....F.... 305 633-9920
Miami *(G-9799)*
John M Caldwell Distrg Co Inc ....G.... 305 685-9822
Opa Locka *(G-12329)*
Johnny Devil Inc ....G.... 305 634-0700
Miami *(G-9800)*
◆ **Joro Fashions Florida Inc** ....F.... 305 888-8110
Pinecrest *(G-14328)*
Kamaj Business Group Inc ....F.... 813 863-9967
Tampa *(G-17815)*
Karigam Enterprises Inc ....G.... 305 358-7755
Miami *(G-9815)*
◆ **Lagaci Inc** ....F.... 954 929-1395
Fort Lauderdale *(G-4093)*
Lan Designs Inc ....G.... 305 661-7878
Miami *(G-9853)*
▲ **Lear Investors Inc** ....G.... 305 681-8582
Opa Locka *(G-12333)*
Lisa Todd International LLC ....G.... 305 445-2632
Miami *(G-9897)*
Manatee Bay Enterprises Inc ....F.... 407 245-3600
Orlando *(G-12947)*
Maria Fuentes LLC ....G.... 305 717-3404
Miami *(G-9947)*
Matteo Graphics Inc ....F.... 239 652-1002
Cape Coral *(G-1446)*
Momentum Comfort Gear Inc ....G.... 305 653-5050
Miami *(G-10038)*
New Concepts Distrs Intl LLC ....F.... 305 463-8735
Doral *(G-3444)*
Nordic Group LLC ....E.... 561 789-8676
Boca Raton *(G-647)*
Ocean Waves Inc ....F.... 904 372-4743
Jacksonville Beach *(G-6953)*
◆ **Olian Inc** ....E.... 305 233-9116
Miami *(G-10094)*
Outdoor Products LLC ....G.... 352 473-0886
Steinhatchee *(G-16898)*
Perry Ellis International Inc ....B.... 305 592-2830
Doral *(G-3458)*
PJ Designs Inc ....E.... 727 525-0599
Saint Petersburg *(G-15879)*
Recover Gear LLC ....G.... 904 280-9660
Ponte Vedra Beach *(G-14952)*
Regency Cap & Gown Company ....E.... 904 724-3500
Jacksonville *(G-6713)*
Rox Volleyball ....F.... 877 769-2121
Saint Augustine *(G-15599)*
Saint George Industries LLC ....E.... 786 212-1176
Miami *(G-10298)*
Salt Life LLC ....G.... 904 595-5370
Jacksonville Beach *(G-6957)*
Shangri-La Enterprises ....G.... 305 672-6683
Miami Beach *(G-10709)*
Shgar Kane Couture Inc ....G.... 407 205-8038
Orlando *(G-13181)*
Sir Winston Garments Inc ....F.... 305 499-3144
Miami *(G-10355)*
South Florida Textile Inc ....F.... 954 973-5677
Pompano Beach *(G-14860)*
◆ **Southpoint Sportswear LLC** ....G.... 305 885-3045
Medley *(G-8727)*
Sovita Retail Inc ....E.... 888 871-2408
Orlando *(G-13204)*
▲ **Speedline Athletic Wear Inc** ....E.... 813 876-1375
Tampa *(G-18124)*
Speedline Team Sports Inc ....F.... 813 876-1375
Tampa *(G-18125)*
Sport Products of Tampa Inc ....G.... 813 630-5552
Tampa *(G-18127)*
Suncoast Trends Inc ....G.... 727 321-4948
Saint Petersburg *(G-15929)*
▲ **T Shirt Center Inc** ....G.... 305 655-1955
Miami *(G-10455)*
Tom James Company ....G.... 813 204-9699
Tampa *(G-18193)*
Ultimate Swimwear Inc ....G.... 386 668-8900
Altamonte Springs *(G-80)*
Uzzi Amphibious Gear LLC ....F.... 954 777-9595
Hallandale Beach *(G-5223)*
◆ **Val DOr Apparel LLC** ....G.... 954 363-7340
Coconut Creek *(G-2100)*
Valentina Signa Inc ....G.... 305 264-0673
Miami *(G-10562)*
Veggiespetit Pois Inc ....E.... 305 826-7867
Hialeah *(G-5675)*
Venus Manufacturing Co Inc ....D.... 904 645-3187
Jacksonville *(G-6895)*
Winds ....F.... 239 948-0777
Bonita Springs *(G-863)*

2341 Women's, Misses' & Children's Underwear & Nightwear

Apparel Machinery Services Inc ....G.... 772 335-5350
Port Saint Lucie *(G-15087)*
▲ **Decoy Inc** ....F.... 305 633-6384
Miami *(G-9443)*
Fenix Wester Corp ....G.... 305 324-9105
Miami *(G-9562)*
JC Voyage LLC ....G.... 603 686-0065
Boca Raton *(G-579)*
Jockey International Inc ....G.... 561 689-7646
West Palm Beach *(G-18913)*
▲ **Kamtex USA Incorporated** ....G.... 954 733-1044
Lauderdale Lakes *(G-8089)*
PJ Designs Inc ....E.... 727 525-0599
Saint Petersburg *(G-15879)*
Sweet and Vicious LLC ....G.... 305 576-0012
Miami *(G-10446)*
◆ **Val DOr Apparel LLC** ....G.... 954 363-7340
Coconut Creek *(G-2100)*
Vanity Fair Brands LP ....G.... 904 538-0288
Jacksonville *(G-6892)*

2342 Brassieres, Girdles & Garments

▲ **Kamtex USA Incorporated** ....G.... 954 733-1044
Lauderdale Lakes *(G-8089)*
New Concepts Distrs Intl LLC ....F.... 305 463-8735
Doral *(G-3444)*
Universal Brass Fabrication ....F.... 561 691-5445
Palm Beach Gardens *(G-13633)*

2353 Hats, Caps & Millinery

American Lw & Promo Prods LLC ....G.... 954 946-5252
Pompano Beach *(G-14591)*
◆ **Bernard Cap LLC** ....C.... 305 822-4800
Hialeah *(G-5322)*
Coolhead Helmet LLC ....G.... 786 292-4829
Miami *(G-9399)*
▲ **D Turin & Company Inc** ....E.... 305 825-2004
Hialeah *(G-5361)*
Feds Apparel ....E.... 954 932-0685
Davie *(G-2524)*
Imagination Creations Inc ....E.... 561 744-7802
Jupiter *(G-7055)*
John Lacquey Enterprises Inc ....F.... 386 935-1705
Branford *(G-1187)*
Natural Hats and More LLC ....E.... 954 549-0819
Hollywood *(G-5880)*
Ronmar Industries Inc ....F.... 561 630-8035
West Palm Beach *(G-19023)*
◆ **Royal Headwear & EMB Inc** ....G.... 305 889-8480
Medley *(G-8720)*
Salt Life LLC ....G.... 904 595-5370
Jacksonville Beach *(G-6957)*
Sunshine Cap Company ....F.... 863 688-8147
Lakeland *(G-7812)*
Tinfoil Hats LLC ....G.... 407 844-0578
Miami *(G-10479)*

2361 Children's & Infants' Dresses & Blouses

◆ **A G A Electronics Corp** ....F.... 305 592-1860
Miami *(G-9038)*
Bdc Florida LLC ....F.... 561 249-0900
West Palm Beach *(G-18814)*
Bossy Princess LLC ....G.... 786 285-4435
Aventura *(G-265)*
Encore Brandz Company ....G.... 813 282-7073
Tampa *(G-17639)*
La Providencia Express Co ....G.... 305 409-9894
Miami *(G-9846)*

2369 Girls' & Infants' Outerwear, NEC

Agua Viva LLC ....G.... 954 802-3255
Miami Beach *(G-10637)*
▼ **Armen Co Inc** ....D.... 305 206-1601
Plantation *(G-14490)*
◆ **Athco Inc** ....E.... 941 351-1600
Sarasota *(G-16179)*
▼ **Dilan Enterprises Inc** ....E.... 305 887-3051
Hialeah *(G-5373)*
▲ **DSC Sales of SC Inc** ....F.... 813 854-3131
Oldsmar *(G-12222)*
Florida Christn Conference Inc ....G.... 407 460-8259
Kissimmee *(G-7244)*
◆ **Ivory International Inc** ....C.... 305 687-2244
Medley *(G-8672)*
Kona Gold LLC ....F.... 844 714-2224
Melbourne *(G-8861)*
Manatee Bay Enterprises Inc ....F.... 407 245-3600
Orlando *(G-12947)*
◆ **Puppet Workshop Inc** ....C.... 305 666-2655
Hialeah *(G-5583)*
▲ **Resort Poolside Shops Inc** ....G.... 407 256-5853
Belle Isle *(G-358)*
Rme Studio Inc ....G.... 305 409-0856
Miami *(G-10268)*
▲ **Sarah Louise Inc** ....F.... 941 377-9656
Sarasota *(G-16573)*
Shore Trendz LLC ....G.... 954 608-7375
Plantation *(G-14550)*
Suncoast Trends Inc ....G.... 727 321-4948
Saint Petersburg *(G-15929)*
Surf Outfitter ....G.... 813 489-4587
Tampa *(G-18147)*
Tca Pool Inc ....G.... 954 600-2448
Deerfield Beach *(G-2924)*

2371 Fur Goods

Wannagofast LLC ....G.... 850 585-5168
Destin *(G-3209)*

2381 Dress & Work Gloves

I ABC Corp ....G.... 904 645-6000
Jacksonville *(G-6486)*
Niefeld Group LLC ....G.... 786 587-7423
Hialeah *(G-5541)*
Parker Protective Products LLC ....F.... 800 879-0329
North Miami *(G-11650)*
Warren Heim Corp ....E.... 772 466-8265
Fort Pierce *(G-4768)*

2384 Robes & Dressing Gowns

▲ **Boca Terry LLC** ....F.... 954 312-4400
Deerfield Beach *(G-2787)*
Lyric Choir Gown Company ....G.... 904 725-7977
Jacksonville *(G-6567)*
PJ Designs Inc ....E.... 727 525-0599
Saint Petersburg *(G-15879)*
◆ **Terry Boca Inc** ....G.... 561 893-0333
Deerfield Beach *(G-2925)*

2385 Waterproof Outerwear

Loksak Inc ....G.... 239 331-5550
Naples *(G-11315)*
Monarch Safety Products Inc ....G.... 407 442-0269
Orlando *(G-12977)*
Sara Glove Company Inc ....G.... 866 664-7272
Naples *(G-11392)*

Seal Outdoors Inc F 877 323-7325
South Miami *(G-16827)*

2386 Leather & Sheep Lined Clothing

Oceanstyle LLC G 305 672-9400
Miami Beach *(G-10699)*
Shaikh Rizwan G 202 740-9796
Lakeland *(G-7789)*
Tagua Leather Corporation G 305 637-3014
Miami *(G-10458)*

2387 Apparel Belts

Belts Inc G 714 572-3636
Hialeah *(G-5320)*
Tagua Leather Corporation G 305 637-3014
Miami *(G-10458)*
◆ **Zeppelin Products Inc** F 954 989-8808
Hallandale Beach *(G-5226)*

2389 Apparel & Accessories, NEC

Algy Trimmings Co Inc D 954 457-8100
Miami *(G-9104)*
Antonyo Denard Llc F 904 290-1579
Jacksonville *(G-6159)*
▲ **Bold Look Inc** E 305 687-8725
Miami *(G-9265)*
C&D Sign and Lighting Svcs LLC G 863 937-9323
Lakeland *(G-7652)*
Can Can Concealment LLC G 727 841-6930
Odessa *(G-12109)*
▲ **Carter-Health Disposables LLC** G 407 296-6689
Orlando *(G-12553)*
◆ **David Dobbs Enterprises Inc** D 904 824-6171
Saint Augustine *(G-15533)*
Davis-Wick Talent MGT LLC E 407 369-1614
Margate *(G-8541)*
Exclusive Apparel LLC F 800 859-6260
Fort Lauderdale *(G-3981)*
Fashion Connection Miami Inc G 305 882-0782
Hialeah *(G-5405)*
◆ **Garflex Inc** D 305 436-8915
Doral *(G-3358)*
Geekshive Inc F 888 797-4335
Miami *(G-9620)*
▲ **Goruck LLC** E 904 708-2081
Jacksonville Beach *(G-6944)*
Goruck Holdings LLC F 904 708-2081
Jacksonville Beach *(G-6945)*
Greater Miami Elks Lodge Inc F 305 754-5899
Miami *(G-9663)*
Herff Jones LLC G 727 527-0696
Saint Petersburg *(G-15805)*
Jewels Handmade LLC F 407 283-9951
Orlando *(G-12856)*
Keepmefresh G 502 407-7902
Clermont *(G-1965)*
Lululemon G 813 973-3879
Wesley Chapel *(G-18752)*
Mhms Corp E 813 948-0504
Lutz *(G-8401)*
Michael Kors G 813 413-3310
Brandon *(G-1167)*
Miss BS Inc G 305 981-9900
North Miami Beach *(G-11692)*
My Glam Choice Inc G 786 586-7927
Miami *(G-10056)*
Point Blank Enterprises Inc A 954 846-8222
Pompano Beach *(G-14800)*
Prescient Logistics LLC F 407 547-2680
Sanford *(G-16106)*
◆ **Price Chopper Inc** E 407 679-1600
Orlando *(G-13085)*
Purpleglassboutique LLC G 407 601-2641
Orlando *(G-13101)*
Regency Cap & Gown Company E 904 724-3500
Jacksonville *(G-6713)*
RES Textiles Inc G 813 476-5524
Tampa *(G-18052)*
Robot-Costumes Technologies G 904 535-0074
Saint Augustine *(G-15598)*
Sashay Sourcing LLC G 239 454-4940
Fort Myers *(G-4597)*
Shore Trendz LLC G 954 608-7375
Plantation *(G-14550)*
Slate Solutions LLC E 754 200-6752
Davie *(G-2593)*
Sparkles and Suspenders FL G 754 701-4528
Lauderhill *(G-8120)*
Stuntwear LLC G 305 842-2115
Miami Beach *(G-10718)*
◆ **Superior Group Companies Inc** A 727 397-9611
Seminole *(G-16764)*
The Alluring Group Inc F 800 731-2280
Miramar *(G-11051)*
Universal HM Hlth Indus Sups I G 813 493-7904
Tampa *(G-18222)*
Walter Green Inc G 850 227-7946
Port Saint Joe *(G-15084)*
▲ **Wayloo Inc** G 954 914-3192
Fort Lauderdale *(G-4317)*
Wesol Distribution LLC G 407 921-9248
Casselberry *(G-1521)*
Wristband Supply LLC F 954 571-3993
Deerfield Beach *(G-2937)*
◆ **Zeppelin Products Inc** F 954 989-8808
Hallandale Beach *(G-5226)*

2391 Curtains & Draperies

Associated Interior Desgr Svc F 561 655-4926
West Palm Beach *(G-18805)*
Bkbl Holdings Ltd G 954 920-6772
Sunrise *(G-17098)*
D W A Inc F 941 444-1134
Sarasota *(G-16401)*
Drapery Masters LLC G 407 448-6898
Kissimmee *(G-7239)*
▲ **Fabric Innovations Inc** E 305 860-5757
Miami *(G-9555)*
G K Window Treatments Inc F 954 786-2927
Pompano Beach *(G-14709)*
◆ **Kenco Hospitality Inc** D 954 921-5434
Fort Lauderdale *(G-4087)*
Mws Drapery Inc E 305 794-3811
Hialeah *(G-5530)*
Paul Himber Inc F 561 586-3741
West Palm Beach *(G-18990)*
▼ **Powless Drapery Service Inc** E 954 566-7863
Oakland Park *(G-11831)*
Quest Drape G 407 888-8164
Orlando *(G-13105)*
Remas Draperies Etc Inc G 904 845-9300
Hilliard *(G-5716)*
Residential Acoustics LLC F 813 922-2390
Tampa *(G-18053)*
Shades By Ana Inc G 305 238-4858
Miami *(G-10333)*
Solar Shades Draperies & More G 954 600-3419
Plantation *(G-14554)*
Suncoast Fabrics Inc G 239 566-3313
Naples *(G-11422)*
Sutton Draperies Inc F 305 653-7738
Miami *(G-10443)*
Tiffany Quilting & Drapery F 407 834-6386
Longwood *(G-8343)*
Top Trtment Cstomes Accesories G 239 936-4600
Fort Myers *(G-4632)*
Vertical Land Inc F 850 244-5263
Panama City *(G-13961)*
Westpoint Home Inc B 850 415-4100
Chipley *(G-1549)*

2392 House furnishings: Textile

Affordable Boat Cushions Inc G 877 350-2628
Riverview *(G-15263)*
◆ **Armor Products Mfg Inc** F 813 764-8844
Plant City *(G-14402)*
Associated Interior Desgr Svc F 561 655-4926
West Palm Beach *(G-18805)*
Bedding Acquisition LLC G 561 997-6900
Boca Raton *(G-443)*
◆ **Beyond White Spa LLC** G 866 399-8867
Miami *(G-9242)*
Brenda Naused G 352 344-4729
Daytona Beach *(G-2636)*
Bust Out Promotions LLC G 561 305-8313
Pompano Beach *(G-14626)*
C-Worthy Corp F 954 784-7370
Pompano Beach *(G-14629)*
▲ **Cameron Textiles Inc** G 954 454-6482
Palm City *(G-13644)*
◆ **Coastal Wipers Inc** E 813 628-4464
Tampa *(G-17543)*
▲ **Cushion Solutions Incorporated** G 813 253-2131
Tampa *(G-17575)*
D W A Inc F 941 444-1134
Sarasota *(G-16401)*
◆ **Design Works By Tech Pdts Inc** E 941 355-2703
Sarasota *(G-16410)*
Distinctive Creat Intr Wkshp I F 954 921-1861
Hollywood *(G-5812)*
Elaine Smith Inc F 561 863-3333
Riviera Beach *(G-15325)*
▲ **Elegant House Intl LLC** G 954 457-8836
Hallandale *(G-5157)*
▼ **Florida Pillow Company** G 407 648-9121
Orlando *(G-12752)*
General Pillows & Fiber Inc G 305 884-8300
Hialeah *(G-5427)*
Hollander HM Fshons Hldngs LLC F 212 302-6571
Boca Raton *(G-557)*
Home Source Manufacturing Inc E 404 663-0647
Marianna *(G-8579)*
Hygenator Pillow Service Inc G 305 325-0250
Miami *(G-9723)*
◆ **Kenco Hospitality Inc** D 954 921-5434
Fort Lauderdale *(G-4087)*
Kenco Quilting & Textiles Inc F 954 921-5434
Fort Lauderdale *(G-4088)*
Mac D&D Inc G 305 821-9452
Hialeah *(G-5495)*
Mecox Gardens & Pottery Inc G 561 805-8611
Palm Beach *(G-13559)*
◆ **Miami Prestige Interiors Inc** E 305 685-3343
Miami *(G-10005)*
National Custom Table Pads G 239 596-6805
Naples *(G-11341)*
◆ **Pacific Coast Feather LLC** C 206 624-1057
Boca Raton *(G-659)*
Pillow Plus Manufacturing Inc G 305 652-2218
Miami *(G-10163)*
▲ **Premier Plastics LLC** E 305 805-3333
Boynton Beach *(G-943)*
Remas Draperies Etc Inc G 904 845-9300
Hilliard *(G-5716)*
Sands At St Lucie G 772 489-9499
Fort Pierce *(G-4742)*
◆ **Shower Doors & More Inc** G 954 358-2014
Fort Lauderdale *(G-4231)*
▲ **Sperry Marketing Group Inc** F 941 483-4667
Venice *(G-18576)*
Superior Sleep Technology Inc F 305 888-0953
Hialeah *(G-5642)*
Tiffany Quilting & Drapery F 407 834-6386
Longwood *(G-8343)*
Top Trtment Cstomes Accesories G 239 936-4600
Fort Myers *(G-4632)*
◆ **Troy Industries Inc** E 305 324-1742
Doral *(G-3534)*
▲ **Tuka Imports LLC** G 305 640-8336
Miami *(G-10511)*
▼ **United Pillow Mfg Inc** F 305 636-9747
Miami *(G-10538)*
V M Visual Mdsg Dctr Group Inc F 305 759-9910
Miami *(G-10560)*
▼ **Victors Cstm Qilting Bedspread** G 305 362-1990
Hialeah *(G-5678)*
Westpoint Home Inc B 850 415-4100
Chipley *(G-1549)*
Youmop LLC G 248 343-2013
Lake Worth *(G-7600)*

2393 Textile Bags

Abco Industries LLC G 813 605-5900
Tampa *(G-17383)*
Advanced Sewing G 954 484-2100
Fort Lauderdale *(G-3784)*
◆ **Armor Products Mfg Inc** F 813 764-8844
Plant City *(G-14402)*
◆ **Black Ops LLC** G 305 450-0127
Hialeah *(G-5329)*
▲ **Cameron Textiles Inc** G 954 454-6482
Palm City *(G-13644)*
Matteo Graphics Inc F 239 652-1002
Cape Coral *(G-1446)*
▲ **Paper Bag Manufacturers Inc** F 305 685-1100
Opa Locka *(G-12349)*
◆ **Safety Intl Bags & Straps** F 407 830-0888
Casselberry *(G-1517)*
Shelleys Cushions Mfg Inc E 305 633-1790
Miami *(G-10337)*
Suncoast Trends Inc G 727 321-4948
Saint Petersburg *(G-15929)*
Warren Heim Corp E 772 466-8265
Fort Pierce *(G-4768)*
▲ **Wayloo Inc** G 954 914-3192
Fort Lauderdale *(G-4317)*
Youthful Innovations LLC G 239 596-2200
Naples *(G-11463)*

2394 Canvas Prdts

A & A Central Florida ....F 407 648-5666
Altamonte Springs *(G-24)*
A B C Canvas Inc ....G....... 239 542-0909
Cape Coral *(G-1370)*
ABc Awning & Canvas Co Inc ....F 321 253-1960
Delray Beach *(G-3039)*
Advanced Awning & Design LLC ....G....... 904 724-5567
Jacksonville *(G-6121)*
Ae Tent LLC ....E 305 691-0191
Miami *(G-9079)*
◆ **Aer-Flo Canvas Products Inc** ....D....... 941 747-4151
Bradenton *(G-984)*
Air Shelters USA LLC ....E 215 957-6128
Pompano Beach *(G-14581)*
American Awning Company Inc ....E 561 832-7123
West Palm Beach *(G-18796)*
▼ **American Marine Coverings Inc** ....F 305 889-5355
Hialeah *(G-5292)*
▲ **Apollo Sunguard Systems Inc** ....F 941 925-3000
Sarasota *(G-16343)*
Ards Awning & Upholstery Inc ....E 863 293-2442
Winter Haven *(G-19300)*
Artful Canvas Design Inc ....E 727 521-0212
Saint Petersburg *(G-15713)*
Atlantic Sails Makers ....G....... 305 567-1773
Miami *(G-9183)*
Awnings By Coversol ....E 813 251-4774
Tampa *(G-17448)*
▼ **Awnings of Hollywood Inc** ....E 954 963-7717
Hollywood *(G-5780)*
▼ **Bayside Canvas Yacht Interiors** ....G....... 954 792-8535
Fort Lauderdale *(G-3842)*
◆ **Big Top Manufacturing Inc** ....D....... 850 584-7786
Perry *(G-14294)*
▼ **Biscayne Awning & Shade Co** ....E 305 638-7933
Miami *(G-9250)*
▼ **Boatswains Locker Inc** ....E 904 388-0231
Jacksonville *(G-6218)*
Busch Canvas ....G....... 561 881-1605
Riviera Beach *(G-15306)*
C&D Canvas Inc ....G....... 954 924-3433
Davie *(G-2504)*
C-Worthy Corp ....F 954 784-7370
Pompano Beach *(G-14629)*
Canopy Specialist LLC ....F 813 703-6844
Plant City *(G-14415)*
◆ **Canvas Designers Inc** ....E 561 881-7663
Riviera Beach *(G-15308)*
Canvas Shop Inc ....G....... 407 898-6001
Orlando *(G-12548)*
Canvas West Inc ....G....... 941 355-0780
Sarasota *(G-16380)*
Coastal Awngs Hrrcane Prtction ....G....... 407 923-9482
Orlando *(G-12592)*
Coastal Canvas and Awning Co ....F 239 433-1114
Fort Myers *(G-4400)*
Cosner Manufacturing LLC ....F 863 676-2579
Lake Wales *(G-7506)*
Creative Energies Inc ....G....... 352 351-9448
Ocala *(G-11911)*
Cross Key Marine Canvas Inc ....G....... 305 451-1302
Key Largo *(G-7167)*
Delisser Enterprises Inc ....G....... 305 649-6001
Miami *(G-9449)*
Delray Awning Inc ....F 561 276-5381
Delray Beach *(G-3069)*
Discount Awnings Inc ....G....... 941 753-5700
Sarasota *(G-16207)*
Discount Boat Tops Inc ....G....... 727 536-4412
Largo *(G-7933)*
Douglas A Fisher Inc ....G....... 941 951-0189
Sarasota *(G-16414)*
◆ **Economy Tent International Inc** ....D....... 305 691-0191
Miami *(G-9500)*
▲ **Evora Enterprises Inc** ....F 305 261-4522
Ocala *(G-11934)*
▲ **Fabis Group Corporation** ....G....... 305 718-3638
Miami *(G-9553)*
Fabis Group Corporation ....G....... 305 718-3638
Miami *(G-9554)*
▼ **Florida Shutters Inc** ....E 772 569-2200
Vero Beach *(G-18619)*
◆ **Gar Industries Corp** ....F 954 456-8088
Hallandale Beach *(G-5188)*
Germain Canvas & Awning Co ....G....... 305 751-4963
Miami *(G-9631)*
Gioia Sails South LLC ....D....... 386 597-2876
Palm Coast *(G-13698)*
Got It Inc ....G....... 954 899-0001
Boca Raton *(G-550)*
Gulfcoast Sailing Inc ....G....... 727 823-1968
Saint Petersburg *(G-15799)*
▼ **Hoover Canvas Products Co** ....E 954 764-1711
Oakland Park *(G-11811)*
Hoover Canvas Products Co ....F 954 541-9745
Mangonia Park *(G-8502)*
Hoover Canvas Products Co ....F 561 844-4444
Mangonia Park *(G-8503)*
Iis Incorporated ....G....... 561 547-4297
Boynton Beach *(G-918)*
Industrial Shadeports Inc ....G....... 954 755-0661
Fort Lauderdale *(G-4058)*
▼ **Innovative Indus Solutions Inc** ....G....... 561 733-1548
Boynton Beach *(G-920)*
J W L Trading Company Inc ....F....... 813 854-1128
Tampa *(G-17800)*
Jones Awnings & Canvas Inc ....E 954 784-6966
Pompano Beach *(G-14737)*
Logsdon and Associates Inc ....G....... 407 292-0084
Windermere *(G-19236)*
M & N Capital Enterprises LLC ....F 800 865-5064
Tampa *(G-17868)*
Major Canvas Products Inc ....F....... 954 764-1711
Oakland Park *(G-11821)*
Marine Customs Unlimited ....F 772 223-8005
Stuart *(G-16973)*
Mason-Florida LLC ....F 352 638-9003
Leesburg *(G-8165)*
◆ **Miami Beach Awning Co** ....E 305 576-2029
Miami *(G-9993)*
▲ **Milliken & Milliken Inc** ....E 941 474-0223
Englewood *(G-3680)*
Mpc Group LLC ....G....... 773 927-4120
Deland *(G-3001)*
▼ **Paradise Awnings Corporation** ....E 305 597-5714
Miami *(G-10141)*
Pipe Welders Inc ....D....... 954 587-8400
Fort Lauderdale *(G-4168)*
Portable-Shade USA LLC ....G....... 321 704-8100
Cocoa *(G-2041)*
◆ **Schnupp Manufacturing Co Inc** ....G....... 305 325-0520
Miami *(G-10312)*
Schurr Sails Inc ....F 850 438-9354
Pensacola *(G-14258)*
Scotties Canvas & Mar Sup LLC ....G....... 239 995-7479
North Fort Myers *(G-11604)*
Sea King Kanvas & Shade Inc ....G....... 239 481-3535
Fort Myers *(G-4602)*
Ship Shape Canvas and Awng LLC ....G....... 954 480-8889
Delray Beach *(G-3141)*
▼ **Smittys Boat Tops and Mar Eqp** ....G....... 305 245-0229
Homestead *(G-5993)*
Southern Awning Inc ....E 561 586-0464
Lake Worth *(G-7587)*
Southern Interest Co Inc ....F 727 471-2040
Saint Petersburg *(G-15917)*
Sunstate Awng Grphic Dsign Inc ....E 407 260-6118
Sanford *(G-16122)*
▲ **Taylor Made Systems Brdnton In** ....C....... 941 747-1900
Oviedo *(G-13461)*
▼ **Texene LLC** ....F 305 200-5001
Miami Lakes *(G-10867)*
▲ **Thomas Sign and Awning Co Inc** ....C....... 727 573-7757
Clearwater *(G-1919)*
Thompson Awning & Shutter Co ....E 904 355-1616
Jacksonville *(G-6849)*
▼ **Tip Top Canvas and Uphl Inc** ....G....... 954 524-6214
Plantation *(G-14559)*
Treasure Coast Canvas ....G....... 772 210-2588
Stuart *(G-17036)*
Tropical Awning of Florida ....F....... 561 276-1144
Delray Beach *(G-3151)*
United States Awning Company ....E 941 955-7010
Sarasota *(G-16631)*
US Marine Canvas ....G....... 904 687-5058
Saint Augustine *(G-15630)*
◆ **US Spars Inc** ....G....... 386 462-3760
Gainesville *(G-5014)*
Utilis Usa LLC ....G....... 850 226-7043
Fort Walton Beach *(G-4836)*
Uts Systems LLC ....G....... 850 226-4301
Fort Walton Beach *(G-4837)*
◆ **World of Awnings Inc** ....F 305 884-6699
Hialeah *(G-5689)*
Yacht Furnishing By Eclip ....G....... 954 792-7339
Davie *(G-2617)*

2395 Pleating & Stitching For The Trade

A2z Uniforms Inc ....G....... 941 254-3194
Sarasota *(G-16330)*
Above LLC ....F 850 469-9028
Pensacola *(G-14077)*
Acme Cap & Clothing Inc ....G....... 407 321-5100
Sanford *(G-15987)*
◆ **Active Line Corp** ....F 786 766-1944
Hialeah *(G-5268)*
Aero Stitch Inc ....G....... 305 978-3446
Miami *(G-9081)*
All Stitched Up LLC ....G....... 352 316-4859
Newberry *(G-11550)*
American S-Shore Plting Sttchi ....G....... 305 978-9934
Hialeah *(G-5295)*
Apparel Expressions LLC ....G....... 850 314-0100
Fort Walton Beach *(G-4777)*
Apparel Printers ....G....... 352 463-8850
Alachua *(G-4)*
▼ **Atlas Embroidery LLC** ....D....... 954 625-2411
Fort Lauderdale *(G-3829)*
Atticus Screen Printing T ....G....... 407 365-9911
Oviedo *(G-13415)*
▲ **Bakers Sports Inc** ....E 904 388-8126
Jacksonville *(G-6192)*
Bartman Enterprises Inc ....G....... 321 259-4898
Melbourne *(G-8777)*
Bc Sales ....G....... 941 708-2727
Bradenton *(G-994)*
Ben Kaufman Sales Co Inc ....E 305 688-2144
Medley *(G-8621)*
Berry Best Stitching and EMB ....G....... 813 763-7716
Plant City *(G-14409)*
Blackwell Family Corporation ....G....... 941 639-0200
Punta Gorda *(G-15199)*
▲ **Blue Ocean Press Inc** ....E 954 973-1819
Fort Lauderdale *(G-3859)*
Brooklyn Stitch Inc ....G....... 786 280-1730
Miami *(G-9279)*
◆ **Capsmith Inc** ....E 407 328-7660
Sanford *(G-16007)*
Caribbean Emblems ....G....... 305 593-8183
Doral *(G-3291)*
CC Sportswear Inc ....G....... 941 351-4205
Sarasota *(G-16188)*
Clothesline Inc ....F 850 877-9171
Tallahassee *(G-17235)*
Cotton Pickin Shirts Plus ....G....... 850 435-3133
Pensacola *(G-14120)*
Creative Images Embrodiery ....G....... 904 730-5660
Jacksonville *(G-6298)*
Creative Shirts Intl Inc ....F 954 351-0909
Oakland Park *(G-11792)*
Cubco Inc ....F 386 254-2706
Daytona Beach *(G-2650)*
Dapp Embroidery Inc ....G....... 407 260-1600
Longwood *(G-8272)*
Designers Top Shop Inc ....G....... 863 453-3855
Avon Park *(G-285)*
DP EMB & Screen Prints Inc ....G....... 954 245-5902
Sunrise *(G-17116)*
Eagle Athletic Wear Inc ....F 727 937-6147
Tarpon Springs *(G-18297)*
Embroid ME ....G....... 941 312-5494
Sarasota *(G-16419)*
Embroidered Stitches ....G....... 702 751-2770
Port St Lucie *(G-15173)*
Embroidertoo LLC ....G....... 813 909-0239
Lutz *(G-8382)*
Embroidery Chimp LLC ....G....... 561 775-9195
Palm Beach Gardens *(G-13586)*
Embroidery Plus ....G....... 561 439-8943
Lantana *(G-7872)*
Embroidery USA Inc ....G....... 305 477-9973
Miami *(G-9521)*
Embroidme - North Miami Beach ....G....... 954 434-2191
Cooper City *(G-2111)*
Embroidme Clearwater Co ....G....... 813 803-0763
Clearwater *(G-1670)*
Embroservice LLC ....F 305 267-2323
Miami *(G-9522)*
▲ **Florida Embroidered Patch &** ....F 561 748-9356
Jupiter *(G-7044)*
Florida Embroidme Jacksonville ....G....... 904 309-9535
Jacksonville *(G-6397)*
Full Press Apparel Inc ....F 850 222-1003
Tallahassee *(G-17259)*
Fully Promoted ....G....... 239 593-2193
Naples *(G-11253)*

S I C

Fully Promoted......G...... 561 615-8655
West Palm Beach *(G-18885)*
G J Embroidery Inc......G...... 407 284-8036
Orlando *(G-12769)*
G6 Embroidery LLC......G...... 904 729-1191
Jacksonville *(G-6419)*
Gns Embroidery......G...... 850 775-1147
Panama City Beach *(G-13977)*
Goal Line Embroidery......G...... 305 295-7585
Key West *(G-7188)*
Good Catch Inc......G...... 305 757-7700
Miami *(G-9648)*
Gravity Ink & Stitch Inc......G...... 954 558-0119
Sunrise *(G-17127)*
▲ Hamburg House Inc......E...... 305 557-9913
Hialeah *(G-5442)*
Hes Products Inc......G...... 407 834-0741
Ormond Beach *(G-13376)*
Hitmaster Graphics LLC......F...... 813 250-0555
Tampa *(G-17757)*
HOB Corporation......G...... 813 988-2272
Tampa *(G-17758)*
Icon Embroidery Inc......G...... 407 858-0886
Windermere *(G-19228)*
Image Depot......G...... 813 685-7116
Tampa *(G-17772)*
▼ Island Designs Outlet Inc......E...... 813 855-0020
Tampa *(G-17794)*
Jax Embroidery......G...... 904 367-4335
Jacksonville *(G-6517)*
JC Santos Embroidery......G...... 407 201-8617
Kissimmee *(G-7257)*
Joni Industries Inc......F...... 352 799-5456
Brooksville *(G-1240)*
Jr Embroidery Inc......G...... 305 253-6968
Miami *(G-9807)*
Legacy Sports Inc......E...... 352 732-6759
Ocala *(G-11981)*
Lidias Embroidery......G...... 386 447-2293
Palm Coast *(G-13701)*
Lifes A Stitch......G...... 386 385-3079
Palatka *(G-13484)*
Logoxpress Inc......G...... 954 973-4994
Pompano Beach *(G-14747)*
Mid West Lettering Company......E...... 850 477-6522
Pensacola *(G-14209)*
Mid-Florida Sportswear LLC......E...... 386 258-5632
Daytona Beach *(G-2686)*
New Tampa Embroidme of......G...... 813 994-0118
Lutz *(G-8405)*
Ocean Blue Graphics Inc......G...... 561 881-2022
Riviera Beach *(G-15355)*
Palm Beach Embroidery USA Inc......G...... 561 506-6307
West Palm Beach *(G-18982)*
Paradise Cstm Screening & EMB......E...... 954 566-9096
Davie *(G-2566)*
Paradise EMB & Silkscreen Inc......G...... 305 595-6441
Miami *(G-10142)*
Pei Shores Inc......G...... 407 523-2899
Orlando *(G-13057)*
Pixie Dusted Stitches......G...... 207 776-3277
Gotha *(G-5041)*
Preferred Stitching Inc......G...... 813 737-3996
Lithia *(G-8222)*
Print Art Screen Printing Inc......F...... 386 258-5186
Daytona Beach *(G-2698)*
Prodigy Customs......G...... 407 832-1752
Altamonte Springs *(G-67)*
Prologo Branding LLC......G...... 407 730-9831
Orlando *(G-13097)*
Promowear......G...... 561 372-0505
Parkland *(G-13999)*
◆ R Y D Enterprises Inc......E...... 305 655-1045
Miami *(G-10233)*
Rainbows End......F...... 727 733-8572
Palm Harbor *(G-13757)*
Ray Graphics Inc......E...... 863 325-0911
Winter Haven *(G-19352)*
Reliable Custom Imprints Corp......G...... 407 834-0571
Longwood *(G-8331)*
Rhinestntransfersdirectcom Inc......G...... 484 254-6410
Orlando *(G-13134)*
◆ Royal Headwear & EMB Inc......G...... 305 889-8480
Medley *(G-8720)*
S S Designs Inc......D...... 863 965-2576
Winter Haven *(G-19353)*
▼ Say What Screen Prtg & EMB Inc......G...... 941 745-5822
Bradenton *(G-1112)*
Seaside Stitching......G...... 321 455-6427
Merritt Island *(G-9013)*
Sew Whats New Embroidery Inc......G...... 954 977-3339
Pompano Beach *(G-14849)*
◆ Sharp Marketing LLC......G...... 954 565-2711
Oakland Park *(G-11838)*
▲ Shirts & Caps Inc......F...... 813 788-7026
Tampa *(G-18098)*
◆ Southern International Svcs......F...... 954 349-7321
Miami *(G-10387)*
Squeegee Stitch Graphix LLC......G...... 850 256-4926
Century *(G-1528)*
◆ Ssh Holding Inc......D...... 678 942-1800
Seminole *(G-16761)*
Stitch Ink Inc......G...... 954 203-0868
Lauderdale Lakes *(G-8094)*
Stitch Logo Inc......G...... 727 446-0228
Clearwater *(G-1889)*
Stitchez LLC......G...... 904 221-9148
Jacksonville *(G-6815)*
Stitching Heart LLC......G...... 904 379-7990
Jacksonville *(G-6816)*
Stitchnship......G...... 216 409-6700
Bay Harbor Islands *(G-340)*
Stitchyourphotocom......G...... 321 297-6103
Windermere *(G-19244)*
STS Apparel Corp......F...... 305 628-4000
Hialeah *(G-5636)*
T-Wiz Prtg & EMB Designs LLC......E...... 954 280-8949
Fort Lauderdale *(G-4273)*
Thread Graphics Embroidery......G...... 407 688-7026
Deland *(G-3021)*
Tiffany Quilting & Drapery......F...... 407 834-6386
Longwood *(G-8343)*
Turin Em Inc......F...... 305 825-2004
Hialeah *(G-5653)*
Uniform Nametape Company Inc......F...... 813 839-6737
Tampa *(G-18217)*
Vf Imagewear Inc......G...... 813 671-2986
Riverview *(G-15286)*
Vivid Images USA Inc......F...... 904 620-0303
Jacksonville *(G-6902)*
▲ VSF Corp......E...... 305 769-2202
Miami *(G-10593)*
Vyp Services LLC......G...... 305 593-8183
Doral *(G-3546)*
Wearable Nalia LLC......G...... 561 629-5804
Haverhill *(G-5241)*
▼ Were In Stitches......G...... 813 264-4804
Tampa *(G-18254)*
Western Ivy......G...... 352 622-5767
Ocala *(G-12075)*
▲ Wheeler Trading Inc......F...... 305 430-7100
Miami Lakes *(G-10880)*
William Fster Entp Embrdme Jck......G...... 904 329-1549
Jacksonville *(G-6921)*
Wings Things Monogramming Inc......F...... 850 455-3081
Pensacola *(G-14289)*
World Emblem International Inc......C...... 305 899-9006
Hollywood *(G-5941)*
Worldwide Embroidery Inc......F...... 386 761-2688
Port Orange *(G-15040)*

2396 Automotive Trimmings, Apparel Findings, Related Prdts

▲ Adva-Lite Inc......E...... 727 369-5319
Seminole *(G-16735)*
Aloha Screen Printing Inc......G...... 850 934-4716
Gulf Breeze *(G-5111)*
◆ Ampersand Graphics Inc......E...... 772 283-1359
Stuart *(G-16906)*
Ataly Inc......E...... 813 880-9142
Tampa *(G-17441)*
Automated Services Inc......F...... 772 461-3388
Fort Pierce *(G-4679)*
▲ Bakers Sports Inc......E...... 904 388-8126
Jacksonville *(G-6192)*
Baru Agency Incorporated......G...... 305 259-8800
Doral *(G-3264)*
Buchanan Signs Screen Process......E...... 904 725-5500
Jacksonville *(G-6243)*
Catalyst Fabric Solutions LLC......E...... 850 396-4325
Marianna *(G-8575)*
Classic Trim Wtp Inc......G...... 305 258-3090
Princeton *(G-15183)*
Clothesline Inc......F...... 850 877-9171
Tallahassee *(G-17235)*
Countrywide Screen Printing......G...... 239 333-4020
Fort Myers *(G-4411)*
Creative Car Coats......G...... 813 886-2589
Tampa *(G-17564)*
Custom Grafix Industries Inc......G...... 727 530-7300
Largo *(G-7929)*
Dixon Screen Printing LLC......G...... 850 476-3924
Pensacola *(G-14132)*
Eagle Athletic Wear Inc......F...... 727 937-6147
Tarpon Springs *(G-18297)*
◆ Eastern Shores Printing......E...... 305 685-8976
Opa Locka *(G-12312)*
Elite Graphics......G...... 305 331-2678
Hialeah *(G-5392)*
EMB Wholesale......G...... 904 452-4362
Jacksonville *(G-6361)*
Expert TS of Jacksonville......F...... 904 387-2500
Jacksonville *(G-6374)*
Florida Screen Services Inc......F...... 407 316-0466
Orlando *(G-12755)*
Florida Tape & Labels Inc......F...... 941 921-5788
Sarasota *(G-16438)*
Full Press Apparel Inc......F...... 850 222-1003
Tallahassee *(G-17259)*
◆ H Sixto Distributors Inc......F...... 305 688-5242
Opa Locka *(G-12322)*
Hes Products Inc......G...... 407 834-0741
Ormond Beach *(G-13376)*
HOB Corporation......G...... 813 988-2272
Tampa *(G-17758)*
◆ Hofmann & Leavy Inc......D...... 954 698-0000
Deerfield Beach *(G-2842)*
Icon Embroidery Inc......G...... 407 858-0886
Windermere *(G-19228)*
Image Depot......G...... 813 685-7116
Tampa *(G-17772)*
▼ Island Designs Outlet Inc......E...... 813 855-0020
Tampa *(G-17794)*
Joni Industries Inc......F...... 352 799-5456
Brooksville *(G-1240)*
◆ Kid-U-Not Inc......E...... 407 324-2112
Sanford *(G-16079)*
Manatee Bay Enterprises Inc......F...... 407 245-3600
Orlando *(G-12947)*
McGee Enterprises Inc......G...... 904 328-3226
Jacksonville *(G-6585)*
Moser Automotive......E...... 561 881-5665
Riviera Beach *(G-15350)*
National Traffic Signs Inc......G...... 727 446-7983
Clearwater *(G-1802)*
Open Market Enterprises LLC......G...... 407 322-5434
Orlando *(G-13024)*
Paradise Cstm Screening & EMB......E...... 954 566-9096
Davie *(G-2566)*
▲ Parthenon Prints Inc......E...... 850 769-8321
Panama City *(G-13940)*
PHI CHI Foundation Inc......G...... 561 526-3401
Margate *(G-8560)*
Preferred Custom Printing LLC......F...... 727 443-1900
Seminole *(G-16757)*
Premier Manufacturing Pdts LLC......F...... 239 542-0260
Cape Coral *(G-1456)*
Print Shack......G...... 352 799-2972
Brooksville *(G-1262)*
Promo Daddy LLC......F...... 877 557-2336
Melbourne *(G-8913)*
Ray Graphics Inc......E...... 863 325-0911
Winter Haven *(G-19352)*
Reliable Custom Imprints Corp......G...... 407 834-0571
Longwood *(G-8331)*
Royal Tees Inc......F...... 941 366-0056
Sarasota *(G-16564)*
S S Designs Inc......D...... 863 965-2576
Winter Haven *(G-19353)*
Saint George Industries LLC......E...... 786 212-1176
Miami *(G-10298)*
Screen Art Posters Inc......E...... 305 681-4641
Hialeah *(G-5612)*
Serigraphia Inc......E...... 850 243-9743
Fort Walton Beach *(G-4832)*
▲ Shirts & Caps Inc......F...... 813 788-7026
Tampa *(G-18098)*
◆ Southern International Svcs......F...... 954 349-7321
Miami *(G-10387)*
Steven Chancas......F...... 352 629-5016
Ocala *(G-12059)*
Synergy Sports LLC......G...... 239 593-9374
Naples *(G-11432)*
T&T Detailing Inc......G...... 407 414-6710
Orlando *(G-13239)*
◆ Team Edition Apparel Inc......C...... 941 744-2041
Bradenton *(G-1125)*
Tiptops Inc......G...... 352 357-9559
Eustis *(G-3719)*

Uniroyal Globl Engnred Pdts In.....F.....941 906-8580
Sarasota *(G-16630)*
Universal Screen Graphics Inc.....E.....813 623-5335
Tampa *(G-18223)*
Vanlex Clothing Inc.....E.....305 431-4669
Miami Lakes *(G-10878)*
Vivid Images USA Inc.....F.....904 620-0303
Jacksonville *(G-6902)*
▼ Walter Haas Graphics Inc.....E.....305 883-2257
Hialeah *(G-5685)*
Williams Specialties Inc.....G.....305 769-9925
Hialeah *(G-5687)*
World Event Promotions LLC.....E.....800 214-3408
Miami *(G-10619)*

2397 Schiffli Machine Embroideries

Bcb International Inc.....G.....727 754-4911
Sunrise *(G-17095)*
Bnj Noble Inc.....F.....954 987-1040
Davie *(G-2503)*
Gattas Corp.....G.....727 733-5886
Dunedin *(G-3578)*
Liquid Edge LLC.....G.....904 637-1494
Orange Park *(G-12398)*
▲ Pantograms Mfg Co Inc.....E.....813 839-5697
Tampa *(G-17973)*
◆ Royal Headwear & EMB Inc.....G.....305 889-8480
Medley *(G-8720)*
Screenprint Plus Inc.....E.....239 549-7284
Cape Coral *(G-1467)*

2399 Fabricated Textile Prdts, NEC

Aerodyne Research LLC.....F.....813 891-6300
Deland *(G-2954)*
AMI Graphics Inc.....E.....352 629-4455
Ocala *(G-11873)*
◆ Boulder Blimp Company Inc.....F.....303 664-1122
Miami *(G-9271)*
Brunken Manufacturing Co Inc.....G.....850 438-2478
Pensacola *(G-14108)*
Buchanan Signs Screen Process.....E.....904 725-5500
Jacksonville *(G-6243)*
Burbank Trawl Makers Inc.....E.....904 321-0976
Jacksonville *(G-6244)*
▲ CSC Racing Corporation.....F.....248 548-5727
Jupiter *(G-7021)*
Delray Awning Inc.....F.....561 276-5381
Delray Beach *(G-3069)*
Dti Design Trend Inc.....F.....954 680-8370
Hialeah *(G-5379)*
Eiff Aerodynamics Inc.....F.....386 734-3958
Deland *(G-2974)*
Emerald Coast Fabrication.....G.....850 235-1174
Panama City *(G-13899)*
Express Badging Services Inc.....F.....321 784-5925
Cocoa Beach *(G-2062)*
Find A Friend LLC.....G.....813 293-1584
Land O Lakes *(G-7855)*
Fluid Wings LLC.....F.....888 245-5843
Deland *(G-2978)*
Flyrite Banner Makers Inc.....F.....352 873-7501
Ocala *(G-11949)*
Gail P Scherer DBA/Flag Lady O.....G.....941 926-9460
Sarasota *(G-16446)*
Gulf Glo Banners and Signs LLC.....G.....850 234-0952
Panama City *(G-13913)*
▲ Hallmark Emblems Inc.....D.....813 223-5427
Tampa *(G-17740)*
I-Partner Group Inc.....G.....239 449-4749
Bonita Springs *(G-838)*
▲ Imprint Promotions LLC.....G.....321 622-8946
Melbourne *(G-8850)*
In The News Inc.....D.....813 882-8886
Tampa *(G-17775)*
Key Safety Systems Inc.....G.....863 668-6000
Lakeland *(G-7726)*
Keystone 75 Inc.....G.....954 430-1880
Hollywood *(G-5856)*
Kiteman Productions Inc.....G.....407 943-8480
Orlando *(G-12874)*
◆ Lee Fisher International Inc.....E.....813 875-6296
Tampa *(G-17839)*
Mid West Lettering Company.....E.....850 477-6522
Pensacola *(G-14209)*
Olympus Group Inc.....G.....407 851-6229
Orlando *(G-13021)*
▲ Outdoor America Images Inc.....E.....813 888-8796
Tampa *(G-17964)*
Paradigm Parachute and Defense.....F.....928 580-9013
Pensacola *(G-14220)*
▲ Performance Designs Inc.....C.....386 738-2224
Deland *(G-3009)*
Pets2go International Inc.....E.....404 625-9606
Homestead *(G-5987)*
Point Blank Intrmdate Hldg LLC.....E.....954 630-0900
Pompano Beach *(G-14802)*
Promo Daddy LLC.....F.....877 557-2336
Melbourne *(G-8913)*
Quality Shavings South Florida.....E.....561 433-9955
Lake Worth *(G-7584)*
Rolin Industries Inc.....G.....850 654-1704
Fort Walton Beach *(G-4831)*
Ronmar Industries Inc.....F.....561 630-8035
West Palm Beach *(G-19023)*
◆ S E Inc.....E.....407 859-9317
Orlando *(G-13151)*
Sandi Johnson.....G.....561 389-1035
Dunnellon *(G-3599)*
▲ Sargent Seat Cover Co Inc.....E.....904 355-2529
Jacksonville *(G-6752)*
Seat Savers Plus Inc.....G.....305 256-7863
Miami *(G-10318)*
▲ Seatbelt Solutions Llc.....E.....855 642-3964
Jupiter *(G-7111)*
Signature AVI US Holdings Inc.....F.....407 648-7230
Orlando *(G-13193)*
South Florida Cutting.....F.....305 693-6711
Hialeah *(G-5625)*
T-Formation Inc Tallahassee.....D.....850 574-0122
Midway *(G-10919)*
Tactical Prchute Dlvry Systems.....F.....813 782-7482
Zephyrhills *(G-19540)*
▼ Universal Seat Covers Auto ACC.....G.....305 262-3955
Miami *(G-10543)*
USA Vigil.....G.....386 736-8464
Deland *(G-3029)*

24 LUMBER AND WOOD PRODUCTS, EXCEPT FURNITURE

2411 Logging

4 C Timber Inc.....G.....386 937-0806
Palatka *(G-13471)*
A and H Logging Inc.....G.....352 528-3868
Williston *(G-19208)*
A L Baxley & Sons Inc.....E.....352 629-5137
Citra *(G-1555)*
A&H Logging Inc.....G.....352 528-3868
Morriston *(G-11091)*
Agner Timber Services Inc.....G.....850 251-6615
Perry *(G-14291)*
Apalachee Pole Company Inc.....E.....850 643-2121
Bristol *(G-1191)*
Ata Group of Companies Inc.....G.....352 735-1588
Mount Dora *(G-11097)*
B & B Timber Company.....G.....904 284-5541
Green Cove Springs *(G-5055)*
B&M Logging Inc.....G.....386 397-1145
White Springs *(G-19185)*
Bailey Timber Co Inc.....F.....850 674-2080
Blountstown *(G-384)*
Barnes & Sons Wood Producers.....G.....386 935-2229
Branford *(G-1185)*
Bbts Logging LLC.....G.....850 997-2436
Monticello *(G-11075)*
Bernice I Finch.....G.....850 638-0082
Wausau *(G-18696)*
Black Creek Logging.....G.....904 591-9681
Middleburg *(G-10904)*
Boland Timber Company Inc.....E.....850 997-5270
Perry *(G-14296)*
Breeden Pulpwood Inc.....F.....352 528-5243
Williston *(G-19210)*
BTR Logging Inc.....G.....386 397-0730
White Springs *(G-19186)*
Bushnell Saw Mill Inc.....G.....352 793-2740
Bushnell *(G-1313)*
Butler Logging Inc.....G.....386 963-2720
Wellborn *(G-18706)*
C & G Timber Harvesters Inc.....G.....850 643-1340
Bristol *(G-1192)*
C F Webb and Sons Logging LLC.....G.....850 971-5565
Lee *(G-8137)*
Cedar Creek Logging Inc.....F.....850 832-0133
Panama City *(G-13877)*
Charlie S Logging Inc.....G.....850 643-1145
Bristol *(G-1193)*
Circle C Timber Inc.....G.....863 735-0383
Zolfo Springs *(G-19544)*
Coastal Logging Inc.....F.....850 832-0133
Panama City *(G-13884)*
Cooper Timber Harvesting Inc.....F.....863 494-0240
Arcadia *(G-202)*
CP Logging Inc.....F.....850 379-8698
Hosford *(G-6008)*
Creamer Corp.....G.....850 265-2700
Panama City *(G-13888)*
D & S Logging Inc.....G.....850 638-5500
Chipley *(G-1543)*
Davanti Doors Llc.....G.....239 842-8341
Fort Myers *(G-4426)*
Dm Stratton LLC.....G.....904 342-7063
Saint Johns *(G-15677)*
Donald Smith Logging Inc.....G.....850 697-3975
Carrabelle *(G-1497)*
Equity Group Usa Inc.....G.....407 421-6464
Winter Springs *(G-19472)*
Feagle Logging LLC.....G.....386 365-2689
Lake City *(G-7354)*
Flatwoods Forest Products Inc.....F.....352 787-1161
Leesburg *(G-8156)*
Florida Cental Logging Inc.....F.....863 272-5364
Lakeland *(G-7690)*
▼ Florida Fence Post Co Inc.....G.....863 735-1361
Ona *(G-12280)*
Florida Pole Settlers & Crane.....G.....772 283-6820
Palm City *(G-13657)*
Flowers Logging Co Inc.....G.....850 639-2856
Kinard *(G-7213)*
G Black Logging LLC.....G.....850 379-8747
Hosford *(G-6009)*
G Haddock Rowland Inc.....G.....904 845-2725
Hilliard *(G-5706)*
Geiger Logging Inc.....E.....904 845-7534
Hilliard *(G-5707)*
Gray Logging LLC.....G.....850 973-3863
Madison *(G-8449)*
Gray Logging LLC.....G.....850 973-3863
Madison *(G-8450)*
Griffis Timber Inc.....G.....904 275-2372
Sanderson *(G-15981)*
Gulf Coast Timber Company.....G.....850 271-8818
Panama City *(G-13912)*
H B Tutun Jr Logging Inc.....G.....850 584-9324
Perry *(G-14302)*
H Jones Timber LLC.....G.....386 312-0603
Palatka *(G-13482)*
Hardy Logging Company Inc.....G.....850 994-1955
Pace *(G-13469)*
Harrison Logging.....F.....352 591-2779
Williston *(G-19211)*
Harry Pickett.....G.....904 845-4643
Hilliard *(G-5709)*
HB Tuten Jr Logging Inc.....E.....850 584-9324
Perry *(G-14303)*
Hbt Forestry Services Inc.....F.....850 584-9324
Perry *(G-14304)*
Henry W Long.....G.....352 542-7068
Old Town *(G-12197)*
Hobbs Trucking LLC.....G.....904 463-5681
Hilliard *(G-5710)*
▼ Howell Logging & Land Clearing.....G.....352 528-2698
Williston *(G-19212)*
Hoyles Logging.....G.....813 782-1164
Zephyrhills *(G-19522)*
Huntley Stemwood Inc.....G.....904 237-4005
Middleburg *(G-10906)*
J Q Bell & Sons.....G.....904 879-1597
Callahan *(G-1325)*
John A Cruce Jr Inc.....E.....850 584-9755
Perry *(G-14305)*
John L Shadd Enterprises.....F.....386 496-3989
Lake Butler *(G-7338)*
Johnny Sellers Logging Inc.....G.....850 643-5214
Bristol *(G-1196)*
Johns & Conner Inc.....G.....904 845-4430
Hilliard *(G-5711)*
Johns & Conner Logging Inc.....G.....904 845-4430
Hilliard *(G-5712)*
Johns & Connor Inc.....G.....904 845-4541
Hilliard *(G-5713)*
Joiner Land Clearing LLC.....G.....850 997-5729
Monticello *(G-11078)*
Joiners Enterprises Inc.....F.....850 623-5593
Milton *(G-10933)*
Joyner Inc.....G.....850 832-6326
Panama City Beach *(G-13979)*
Kenneth P Green.....G.....850 643-5851
Bristol *(G-1197)*

SIC

Key Logging ....G.... 386 328-6984
Hollister (G-5754)
▼ L A Ornamental & Rack Corp ....G.... 305 696-0419
Miami (G-9835)
L and D Logging ....G.... 850 859-1013
Westville (G-19181)
L W Timber Co Inc ....G.... 850 592-2597
Greenwood (G-5089)
M & L Timber Inc ....G.... 386 437-0895
Bunnell (G-1302)
M&E Timber Inc ....G.... 850 584-6650
Perry (G-14307)
Marvin J Dericho ....G.... 407 290-0109
Orlando (G-12951)
McClellan Logging Inc ....G.... 352 468-1856
Hampton (G-5227)
McMillan Logging Inc ....F.... 850 643-4819
Bristol (G-1199)
P & S Logging Inc ....F.... 904 845-4256
Hilliard (G-5715)
Padgetts Pulpwood Inc ....G.... 904 282-5112
Middleburg (G-10911)
Paul White Logging Inc ....G.... 850 379-8651
Hosford (G-6010)
Pearce Logging LLC ....G.... 386 365-1880
Lake Butler (G-7340)
Pine Top Logging LLC ....G.... 386 365-0857
Branford (G-1188)
Randall Birge ....G.... 850 373-6131
Bonifay (G-807)
Randy Morris Logging Inc ....F.... 850 773-9010
Chipley (G-1545)
Rbj Timber Inc ....G.... 904 879-1597
Callahan (G-1328)
Reagan H Fox III Inc ....G.... 850 584-9229
Perry (G-14311)
Richard Brown Logging Inc ....F.... 850 379-8674
Hosford (G-6011)
Ridgeway Timber Inc ....G.... 352 463-6013
Bell (G-342)
Riverland Logging Inc ....G.... 904 845-4326
Hilliard (G-5717)
Rozar Logging Inc ....G.... 352 267-0829
Groveland (G-5107)
S&J Logging Inc ....G.... 904 237-7774
Glen Saint Mary (G-5038)
Santo Domingo Timber Co LLC ....G.... 561 627-4000
Palm Beach Gardens (G-13623)
South Amercn Lbr & Timber LLC ....G.... 786 280-8326
Miami (G-10381)
Southern Wood Services LLC ....G.... 352 279-3208
Brooksville (G-1272)
Stratton Inc Dm ....G.... 904 268-6052
Jacksonville (G-6818)
Tucker Trckg Log Jhnny E Tcker ....G.... 850 258-1982
Wewahitchka (G-19183)
Tumbling Pines Inc ....F.... 386 437-2668
Bunnell (G-1310)
TW Byrds Sons Inc ....E.... 386 935-1544
Branford (G-1190)
Underwood Butcher Block Co Inc ....F.... 904 338-2348
Jacksonville (G-6877)
Usher Land & Timber Inc ....E.... 352 493-4221
Chiefland (G-1539)
Van Aernam Logging & Trucking ....F.... 352 498-5809
Cross City (G-2369)
Van Zant Timber Incorporated ....G.... 904 845-4661
Hilliard (G-5720)
Walden Timber Harvesting Inc ....F.... 850 674-4884
Altha (G-86)
Warwick Logging ....G.... 386 328-9358
East Palatka (G-3609)
West Fraser Inc ....D.... 904 786-4155
Jacksonville (G-6910)
Whitfield Timber Co Inc ....E.... 850 639-5556
Wewahitchka (G-19184)
Williams Timber Inc ....E.... 850 584-2760
Perry (G-14319)
Woodie L Dupree ....G.... 850 859-2496
Westville (G-19182)

2421 Saw & Planing Mills

A L Baxley & Sons Inc ....E.... 352 629-5137
Citra (G-1555)
Apalachee Pole Company Inc ....G.... 850 263-4457
Graceville (G-5042)
Aw Gates Inc ....G.... 954 341-2180
Coral Springs (G-2221)
Bailey Timber Co Inc ....F.... 850 674-2080
Blountstown (G-384)
Big River Cypress & Hardwood ....F.... 850 674-5991
Blountstown (G-385)
Boyett Timber Inc ....G.... 352 583-2138
Webster (G-18697)
Bushnell Saw Mill Inc ....G.... 352 793-2740
Bushnell (G-1313)
Creamer Corp ....G.... 850 265-2700
Panama City (G-13888)
Cross City Lumber LLC ....F.... 352 578-8078
Cross City (G-2363)
David E Ashe Sawmill ....G.... 904 377-4800
Saint Augustine (G-15534)
▲ Ecosan LLC ....G.... 954 446-5929
Coral Gables (G-2140)
Florida North Lumber Co Inc ....D.... 850 643-2238
Bristol (G-1194)
Florida North Lumber Inc ....E.... 850 263-4457
Bristol (G-1195)
Fraser West Inc ....D.... 901 620-4200
Jacksonville (G-6414)
Fuqua Sawmill Inc ....G.... 352 236-3456
Ocala (G-11952)
Gilman Building Products LLC ....F.... 904 548-1000
Yulee (G-19498)
▲ Global Prime Wood LLC ....G.... 770 292-9200
Aventura (G-271)
Great South Timber & Lbr Inc ....E.... 386 752-3774
Lake City (G-7357)
Great South Timber & Lbr Inc ....F.... 386 755-3046
Lake City (G-7358)
Griffin Sawmill & Woodworking ....G.... 863 241-5180
Lake Wales (G-7512)
Griffis Lumber LLC ....G.... 352 372-9965
Gainesville (G-4933)
Hartsock Sawmill Inc ....G.... 352 753-3581
Lady Lake (G-7326)
Idaho Timber LLC ....C.... 386 758-8111
Lake City (G-7361)
Innovative Cnstr Group LLC ....C.... 904 398-5690
Jacksonville (G-6496)
Inox LLC ....G.... 305 409-2764
Sunny Isles Beach (G-17079)
▼ International Closet Center ....G.... 305 883-6551
Medley (G-8670)
J & S Cypress Inc ....F.... 352 383-3864
Sorrento (G-16787)
J W Dawson Co Inc ....E.... 305 634-8618
Miami (G-9783)
John A Cruce Jr Inc ....E.... 850 584-9755
Perry (G-14305)
Kempfer Sawmill Inc ....F.... 407 892-2955
Saint Cloud (G-15656)
Maxville LLC ....C.... 904 289-7261
Jacksonville (G-6582)
McCain Mills Inc ....G.... 813 752-6478
Plant City (G-14447)
Meridian Centre ....G.... 253 620-4542
Boca Raton (G-619)
North Florida Woodlands Inc ....F.... 850 643-2238
Bristol (G-1201)
Rex Lumber Graceville LLC ....C.... 850 263-2056
Graceville (G-5044)
Rex Lumber LLC ....F.... 850 643-2172
Bristol (G-1202)
Rex Lumber LLC ....F.... 850 263-4457
Graceville (G-5045)
Robbins Manufactuing Co ....D.... 352 793-2443
Webster (G-18698)
Roberts Lumber Company Inc ....F.... 850 584-4573
Perry (G-14312)
▼ Rulon Company of Georgia ....C.... 904 584-1400
Saint Augustine (G-15600)
▲ Shade Systems Inc ....E.... 352 237-0135
Ocala (G-12046)
Southern Fuelwood Inc ....E.... 352 472-4324
Newberry (G-11561)
Southern Wood Services LLC ....G.... 352 279-3208
Brooksville (G-1272)
Spanish Trail Lumber Co LLC ....C.... 850 592-8512
Marianna (G-8586)
Stall Master Company ....G.... 352 279-0089
Spring Hill (G-16866)
Tatum Brothers Lumber Co Inc ....E.... 904 782-3690
Lawtey (G-8126)
Ufp Palm Bch LLC DBA Ufp Mami ....D.... 786 837-0552
Miami (G-10523)
West Fraser Inc ....D.... 904 786-4155
Jacksonville (G-6910)
West Fraser Inc ....D.... 850 587-1000
Mc David (G-8602)
Whitfield Timber Co Inc ....E.... 850 639-5556
Wewahitchka (G-19184)
Williston Timber Co Inc ....E.... 352 528-2699
Williston (G-19216)

2426 Hardwood Dimension & Flooring Mills

A L Baxley & Sons Inc ....E.... 352 629-5137
Citra (G-1555)
Aj Originals Inc ....G.... 954 563-9911
Fort Lauderdale (G-3793)
Big River Cypress & Hardwood ....F.... 850 674-5991
Blountstown (G-385)
Bona Enterprises Inc ....G.... 954 927-4889
Dania (G-2439)
Boyett Timber Inc ....G.... 352 583-2138
Webster (G-18697)
Bushnell Saw Mill Inc ....G.... 352 793-2740
Bushnell (G-1313)
▲ Cryntel Enterprises Ltd Inc ....G.... 954 577-7844
Davie (G-2511)
Cut Services LLC ....G.... 305 560-0905
Doral (G-3317)
David R Nassivera Inc ....E.... 352 351-1176
Ocala (G-11917)
Designer Lifestyles LLC ....F.... 904 631-8954
Jacksonville (G-6317)
Fraser West Inc ....D.... 901 620-4200
Jacksonville (G-6414)
Giovanni Art In Custom Furn ....G.... 954 698-1008
Deerfield Beach (G-2831)
Goodwin Lumber Company Inc ....F.... 352 466-0339
Micanopy (G-10901)
Heisler Hardwood Inc ....G.... 727 410-0401
Clearwater (G-1713)
It Is Finished Inc ....G.... 813 598-9585
Land O Lakes (G-7857)
Iverica Industrial Inc ....F.... 305 691-1659
Hialeah (G-5458)
Juan Pampanas Designs Inc ....G.... 305 573-7550
Miami (G-9812)
Maggac Corporation ....G.... 561 439-2707
Lake Worth (G-7567)
New T Management Inc ....G.... 954 927-4889
Dania (G-2454)
◆ Resolute Cross City LLC ....G.... 352 498-3363
Cross City (G-2367)
Resolute Cross Cy RE Hldngs LL ....F.... 352 498-3363
Cross City (G-2368)
Roberts Lumber Company Inc ....F.... 850 584-4573
Perry (G-14312)
Roorda Buiders Inc ....G.... 727 410-7776
Odessa (G-12147)
Smart Floors LLC ....G.... 239 500-1234
Naples (G-11405)
▼ Smittys Boat Tops and Mar Eqp ....G.... 305 245-0229
Homestead (G-5993)
Stuart Stair & Furniture Mfg ....G.... 772 287-4097
Stuart (G-17026)
Upstream Installation Inc ....G.... 904 829-3507
Saint Augustine (G-15629)
West Fraser Inc ....D.... 850 587-1000
Mc David (G-8602)
West Fraser Inc ....D.... 904 786-4155
Jacksonville (G-6910)

2429 Special Prdt Sawmills, NEC

Diamondback Barrels LLC ....F.... 321 305-5995
Cocoa (G-2009)
Twisted Fusion Nutrition ....F.... 646 719-3041
Brandon (G-1183)

2431 Millwork

1565 Woodworks LLC ....G.... 904 347-7664
Saint Augustine (G-15510)
1st Chice Hrrcane Prtction LLC ....F.... 239 325-3400
Bonita Springs (G-809)
A Izquierdo Enterprises LLC ....G.... 786 558-6657
Miami (G-9040)
A L Custom Wood Corp ....G.... 305 557-2434
Hialeah (G-5257)
A-1 Door Systems Inc ....F.... 904 327-7206
Jacksonville (G-6112)
AB Wood Work Inc ....G.... 786 701-3611
Miami (G-9051)
Absolute Window and Door Inc ....G.... 941 485-7774
Venice (G-18527)
Accent Woodworking Inc ....G.... 727 522-2700
Largo (G-7883)
Ace Shutter & Shelves LLC ....G.... 239 314-9136
Cape Coral (G-1372)

Actual Woodworking Inc ....G.... 305 606-7849
Naples (G-11148)
Adams Bros Cabinetry Inc ....D.... 941 639-7188
North Port (G-11731)
▲ Advanced Millwork Inc ....E.... 407 294-1927
Orlando (G-12433)
AJ AZ Woodwork Inc ....G.... 561 859-4963
Margate (G-8534)
Akira Wood Inc ....E.... 352 375-0691
Gainesville (G-4871)
Al & Sons Millwork Inc ....E.... 352 245-9191
Belleview (G-366)
Al-FA Cabinets Inc ....F.... 813 876-4205
Tampa (G-17396)
Alda Stevens Woodworking ....G.... 850 897-4967
Niceville (G-11562)
Algoma Hardwoods Inc ....E.... 865 471-6300
Orlando (G-12453)
All American Woodwork ....G.... 727 210-5214
Clearwater Beach (G-1948)
▼ All Phase Custom Mill Shop Inc ....E.... 941 474-0903
Port Charlotte (G-14959)
All Pro Chelo Corp ....G.... 786 317-3914
Hialeah (G-5280)
Alliance Cabinets & Millwork ....G.... 407 802-9921
Deerfield Beach (G-2774)
Alpha Woodwork Inc ....F.... 954 347-6251
Pompano Beach (G-14588)
American Archtctural Mllwk LLC ....F.... 844 307-9571
Venice (G-18533)
American Cnstr Entps Inc ....G.... 941 629-2070
Port Charlotte (G-14960)
American Fine Woodwork LLC ....G.... 954 261-9793
Davie (G-2495)
▲ American Louvered Products Co ....E.... 813 884-1441
Tampa (G-17417)
▼ Architctral Mlding Mllwrks Inc ....E.... 305 638-8900
Miami (G-9163)
Architctral Mllwk Slutions Inc ....G.... 727 441-1409
Largo (G-7899)
Architctral WD Wkg Mlding Div ....F.... 727 527-7400
Saint Petersburg (G-15707)
▼ Architctral Wdwrks Cbnetry Inc ....F.... 561 848-8595
Palm Beach Gardens (G-13568)
Architctural WD Pdts of Naples ....G.... 239 260-7156
Naples (G-11167)
Architectural Detail & Wdwkg ....G.... 561 835-4005
West Palm Beach (G-18798)
Architectural Spc Trdg Co ....D.... 850 435-2507
Pensacola (G-14089)
Ark Woodwork Inc ....G.... 561 809-7957
Boca Raton (G-429)
Art Staircase & Woodwork LLC ....G.... 239 440-6591
Cape Coral (G-1384)
Artemisa Luxury Mill Work ....G.... 305 439-3246
Medley (G-8615)
Artisan Wood Works Inc ....E.... 239 321-9122
Naples (G-11172)
Artisanis Guild ....F.... 239 591-3203
Naples (G-11173)
Artistic Doors Inc ....G.... 561 582-0348
Lake Worth Beach (G-7604)
Atelier Woodworking ....F.... 561 386-0811
Royal Palm Beach (G-15461)
Atlantic Custom Woodcraft Corp ....E.... 727 645-6905
Odessa (G-12103)
Atlantic West Molding & Mllwk ....F.... 239 261-2874
Naples (G-11175)
Aventura Custom Woodwork ....G.... 305 891-9093
North Miami (G-11626)
Bach Woodworking LLC ....G.... 651 329-1220
Boynton Beach (G-882)
Baer Family Woodworking ....G.... 954 297-2991
Hollywood (G-5783)
Bari Millwork & Supply LLC ....E.... 954 969-9440
Pompano Beach (G-14615)
▼ Bay Meadow Architectural Mllwk ....E.... 407 332-7992
Longwood (G-8261)
Belets Millwork Inc ....F.... 904 353-8600
Jacksonville (G-6202)
Beyette Woodworking LLC ....G.... 727 254-8705
Seminole (G-16742)
Big Wood Millwork Sales Inc ....G.... 305 471-1155
Doral (G-3273)
Bindels Custom Woodwork Inc ....G.... 727 776-5233
North Port (G-11733)
Black Pearl Woodworks LLC ....G.... 954 214-0899
Loxahatchee (G-8358)
Blumer & Stanton Enterprises ....F.... 561 585-2525
West Palm Beach (G-18825)
▼ Blumer & Stanton Inc ....F.... 561 585-2525
West Palm Beach (G-18826)
Bodhi Tree Woodwork Inc ....G.... 904 540-2655
Saint Augustine (G-15523)
Bosshardt Realty ....G.... 352 494-1400
Gainesville (G-4889)
Bosworth Millwork LLC ....G.... 305 942-9017
Key Largo (G-7166)
Brazilian Wood Works Inc ....G.... 786 468-5712
Miami (G-9274)
Builders Door and Supply Inc ....F.... 941 955-2311
Sarasota (G-16372)
C & M Millwork Inc ....F.... 352 588-5050
San Antonio (G-15971)
Cabinet Design and Cnstr LLC ....G.... 850 393-9724
Pensacola (G-14111)
Carolina Woodworks Inc ....G.... 954 692-4662
Deerfield Beach (G-2796)
Casework of America Inc ....G.... 904 695-0996
Jacksonville (G-6256)
Casons Quality Care Svcs LLC ....G.... 386 365-1016
Lulu (G-8368)
Catharine E Armstrong ....G.... 321 704-5042
Indialantic (G-6057)
Cedrus Inc ....E.... 772 286-2082
Stuart (G-16920)
Century Millworks ....F.... 850 256-2565
Century (G-1527)
CG Quality Woodworks Inc ....G.... 305 231-3480
Hialeah (G-5341)
Chidsey Custom Woodworks ....G.... 561 632-9728
West Palm Beach (G-18846)
Classic Woodworks LLC ....E.... 772 398-6258
Port Saint Lucie (G-15098)
Cns Millworks Inc ....G.... 850 259-9206
Santa Rosa Beach (G-16154)
Coastal Awngs Hrrcane Prtction ....G.... 407 923-9482
Orlando (G-12592)
Coastal Door & Mllwk Svcs LLC ....F.... 561 266-3716
Delray Beach (G-3061)
Coastal Mfg & Fabrication Inc ....G.... 352 799-8706
Brooksville (G-1221)
Coastal Millworks Inc ....E.... 561 881-7755
West Palm Beach (G-18848)
Coastal Millworks & More LLC ....G.... 850 250-6672
Panama City (G-13886)
Coastal Woodwork Inc ....G.... 561 218-3353
Pompano Beach (G-14639)
Commercial Door Systems Fla LL ....F.... 850 466-5906
Pensacola (G-14117)
Commercial Instllation Systems ....G.... 727 525-2372
Saint Petersburg (G-15748)
Commercial Millworks Inc ....F.... 407 648-2787
Orlando (G-12606)
Conrad Markle Bldr & Cbnt ....G.... 904 744-4569
Jacksonville (G-6283)
Conway Bldg Cstm Woodworks LLC ....G.... 407 738-9266
Kissimmee (G-7232)
▲ Cornerstone Kitchens Inc ....C.... 239 332-3020
Fort Myers (G-4410)
Cox Designer Windows Inc ....G.... 727 847-1046
Port Richey (G-15047)
Crawfords Custom Woodwork ....G.... 904 782-1375
Lawtey (G-8124)
Creative Concepts Orlando Inc ....E.... 407 260-1435
Longwood (G-8268)
Creative Custom Stairs ....G.... 941 505-0336
Punta Gorda (G-15203)
Creative Millwork Inc ....G.... 305 885-5474
Hialeah (G-5357)
Creative Woodworking Concepts ....E.... 727 937-4165
Tarpon Springs (G-18290)
▲ Crystal Panepinto Inc ....G.... 941 475-9235
Englewood (G-3674)
Cubos LLC ....G.... 786 299-2671
Miami (G-9418)
Custom Cft Windows & Doors Inc ....F.... 407 834-5400
Winter Springs (G-19470)
Custom Door Direct Llc ....F.... 813 248-5757
Tampa (G-17578)
Custom Doors & Specialties ....G.... 954 763-4214
Wilton Manors (G-19217)
Custom Fbrications of Freeport ....F.... 850 729-0500
Valparaiso (G-18509)
Custom Install Solutions Inc ....F.... 916 601-1190
Boca Raton (G-494)
Custom Marine Joinery Inc ....G.... 954 822-6057
Oakland Park (G-11793)
Custom WD Architectural Mllwk ....G.... 786 290-5412
Miami (G-9420)
Custom WD Designs of Pensacola ....F.... 850 476-9663
Pensacola (G-14122)
Custom Woodworking ....G.... 850 319-4440
Panama City (G-13890)
Cwac Custom Woodworking & Cabi ....G.... 407 343-7774
Kissimmee (G-7236)
Cws Holding Company LLC ....D.... 352 368-6922
Ocala (G-11915)
D & D Building Contractors ....G.... 954 791-2075
Davie (G-2513)
D R Nickelson & Company Inc ....F.... 386 755-6565
Lake City (G-7353)
D&D Wood Working Inc ....G.... 407 427-0106
Orlando (G-12643)
▼ Dade Truss Company Inc ....C.... 305 592-8245
Miami (G-9431)
Dana Andrews Woodworking ....G.... 561 882-0444
Riviera Beach (G-15318)
Dayoris Doors ....G.... 954 374-8538
Miramar (G-10982)
Decor Custom Woodwork LLC ....G.... 561 631-3240
Greenacres (G-5079)
Decosta Woodworking LLC ....G.... 508 802-7765
Winter Garden (G-19260)
Decowall ....G.... 813 886-5226
Tampa (G-17597)
Deep Ocean Woodworks Inc ....G.... 407 687-2773
Sanford (G-16034)
Defender Screens International ....G.... 866 802-0400
Sarasota (G-16407)
▼ Delet Doors Inc ....F.... 786 250-4506
Miami (G-9445)
▼ Dependable Shutter Service Inc ....E.... 954 583-1411
Davie (G-2516)
Design Custom Millwork Inc ....E.... 407 878-1267
Sanford (G-16036)
Designer Door Products Inc ....G.... 786 800-3855
Miami (G-9459)
Designers Specialty Cab Co Inc ....E.... 954 776-4500
Miami (G-9460)
Designers Specialty Cab Co Inc ....E.... 954 868-3440
Fort Lauderdale (G-3938)
Diversified Woodworks LLC ....G.... 321 591-9935
Indialantic (G-6058)
Dmr Woodworks LLC ....G.... 850 969-9261
Pensacola (G-14134)
▼ Door Styles Inc ....E.... 305 653-4447
Miami (G-9480)
Doors 4 U Inc ....G.... 786 400-2298
Medley (G-8643)
Doyles Fine Wood Working Inc ....G.... 813 763-7800
Plant City (G-14426)
DTF Woodworks ....G.... 954 317-6443
Fort Lauderdale (G-3950)
E & E Woodcraft Corp ....F.... 305 556-1443
Hialeah (G-5384)
Eagle Prof Flrg Removal ....G.... 813 520-3027
Riverview (G-15270)
Eagle View Windows Inc ....F.... 904 647-8221
Jacksonville (G-6346)
East Coast Door Inc ....F.... 954 868-4700
Pompano Beach (G-14672)
▼ Eco Window Systems LLC ....B.... 305 885-5299
Medley (G-8645)
▲ Effearredi Usa Inc ....F.... 786 725-4948
Miami (G-9503)
El Custom Wood Creations Inc ....G.... 786 337-0014
Dania (G-2444)
Errico Custom Woodworks Inc ....G.... 561 306-0046
Jupiter (G-7036)
Evm Woodwork Corp ....G.... 954 970-4352
North Lauderdale (G-11614)
Evm Woodworks Corp ....G.... 954 655-6414
North Lauderdale (G-11615)
Evolution Woodworking ....G.... 407 221-5031
Geneva (G-5020)
Excel Millwork & Moulding Inc ....E.... 850 576-7228
Midway (G-10917)
Excell Woodwork Corp ....G.... 954 461-0465
Margate (G-8542)
Expert Shutter Services Inc ....D.... 772 871-1915
Port Saint Lucie (G-15108)
Exquisite Wood Works By Al ....G.... 321 634-5398
Rockledge (G-15410)
Extreme Iron & Wood Work Inc ....G.... 407 925-2448
Lake Alfred (G-7331)
F & J Woodworking Inc ....G.... 239 455-8823
Naples (G-11242)
F W I Inc ....F.... 407 509-9739
Longwood (G-8280)

SIC

◆ **Federal Millwork Corp** .... E 954 522-0653
Fort Lauderdale *(G-3990)*
Fine Archtctral Mllwk Shutters .... F 954 491-2055
Fort Lauderdale *(G-3993)*
Fine Woodworking .... G 941 957-0863
Sarasota *(G-16429)*
Fine Woodworks .... G 954 448-9206
Weirsdale *(G-18705)*
▼ **First Imprssion Dors Mllwk Inc** .... F 561 798-6684
West Palm Beach *(G-18872)*
Five Star Millwork Inc .... F 954 956-7665
Pompano Beach *(G-14696)*
Fj Cabinets & Woodworking LLC .... G 850 433-3925
Pensacola *(G-14152)*
Florida Frames Inc .... F 727 572-4064
Clearwater *(G-1688)*
Florida Heritage Wdwkg LLC .... G 941 705-9980
Sarasota *(G-16435)*
◆ **Florida Made Door Co** .... C 352 742-1000
Tampa *(G-17681)*
▲ **Florida Marine Joiner Svc Inc** .... F 813 514-1125
Tampa *(G-17682)*
Florida Wood Creations Inc .... G 239 561-5411
Punta Gorda *(G-15205)*
Foote Woodworking Inc .... F 941 923-6553
Sarasota *(G-16439)*
Fort Lauderdale Woodworking .... E 954 935-0366
Pompano Beach *(G-14704)*
Fraser Millworks Inc .... G 904 768-7710
Jacksonville *(G-6413)*
Fred M Bush LLC .... G 561 394-7292
Pompano Beach *(G-14705)*
Freddie Glenns Woodwork LLC .... G 850 556-7163
Tallahassee *(G-17258)*
Fry Trim Works Inc .... G 772 260-8486
Jensen Beach *(G-6969)*
Fuentes Custom Woodwork LLC .... G 941 232-0635
Sarasota *(G-16441)*
▼ **Future Modes Inc** .... G 305 654-9995
Miami *(G-9605)*
G & H Reclaim LLC .... G 904 879-2091
Callahan *(G-1324)*
Garcia Woodwork Entps Inc .... G 954 226-3906
Oakland Park *(G-11807)*
Gator Door East Inc .... E 904 824-2827
Saint Augustine *(G-15545)*
Gecko Woodworks .... G 239 738-8283
Fort Myers *(G-4467)*
General Stair Corporation .... E 305 769-9900
Hialeah *(G-5428)*
GF Woodworks .... G 407 716-3712
Altamonte Springs *(G-48)*
Gleman Sons Cstm Woodworks LLC .... F 407 314-9638
Sanford *(G-16056)*
Gloval Displays Inc .... E 800 972-0353
Miami Gardens *(G-10742)*
Golden Wood Works LLC .... G 239 677-8540
Cape Coral *(G-1430)*
Goodwin Lumber Company Inc .... F 352 466-0339
Micanopy *(G-10901)*
Grand Woodworking Llc .... F 239 594-9663
Naples *(G-11266)*
Gravitystorm Inc .... F 772 519-3009
Fort Pierce *(G-4703)*
Greatwoodworks .... G 239 200-4848
Fort Myers *(G-4472)*
Green Forest Industries Inc .... E 941 721-0504
Palmetto *(G-13801)*
Greg Valley .... F 941 739-6628
Sarasota *(G-16224)*
▼ **Guardian Hurricane Protection** .... F 305 805-7050
Miami Lakes *(G-10796)*
Gulf Coast Custom Wdwkg Inc .... G 941 343-7883
Port Charlotte *(G-14984)*
Gulfport Industries Inc .... F 813 885-1000
Tampa *(G-17736)*
Gulfshore Custom Woodworks LLC .... F 239 205-0777
Cape Coral *(G-1432)*
Gulfstream Woodwork LLC .... G 561 231-1810
West Palm Beach *(G-18892)*
Habibco Woodworks LLC .... G 954 659-8501
Weston *(G-19137)*
Handcraft Woodworking Inc .... E 954 418-6356
Deerfield Beach *(G-2835)*
Harbor Woodworks .... G 727 669-0808
Safety Harbor *(G-15495)*
Harlen S Woodworking .... G 850 774-2224
Lynn Haven *(G-8433)*
Harris Woodworks LLC .... G 561 543-3265
Palm Beach Gardens *(G-13594)*

◆ **Hartman Windows and Doors LLC** .... D 561 296-9600
Riviera Beach *(G-15333)*
Hill Enterprises LLC .... G 850 478-4455
Pensacola *(G-14172)*
Hire Authority .... F 561 477-6663
Miami *(G-9712)*
◆ **Hollywood Woodwork Inc** .... D 954 920-5009
Hollywood *(G-5845)*
Hollywood Woodwork LLC .... F 954 920-5009
Hollywood *(G-5846)*
Hughes Trim Llc .... D 863 206-6048
Orlando *(G-12814)*
Hurricane Shtters Cntl Fla Inc .... G 321 639-2622
Rockledge *(G-15419)*
Icon Welding & Fabrication .... E 941 822-8822
Sarasota *(G-16232)*
Ilan Custom Woodwork LLC .... F 727 272-5364
Dunedin *(G-3580)*
▼ **Infinite Ret Design & Mfg Corp** .... F 305 967-8339
Miami *(G-9741)*
Innovtive Win Cncpts Doors Inc .... F 561 493-2303
Boynton Beach *(G-921)*
Ironclad Impact Wndows Dors LL .... G 954 743-4321
Davie *(G-2538)*
Island Millwork Inc .... F 352 694-5565
Ocala *(G-11971)*
Island Park Custom Woodworking .... G 239 437-9670
Fort Myers *(G-4496)*
Island Shutter Co Inc .... E 386 738-9455
Deland *(G-2985)*
Islandoor Company .... G 954 524-3667
Fort Lauderdale *(G-4069)*
Ita Inc .... F 386 301-5172
Ormond Beach *(G-13381)*
J & J Door Manufacturing Inc .... E 850 769-2554
Panama City *(G-13919)*
J B Woodworking Inc .... G 850 362-6362
Valparaiso *(G-18512)*
J L Finish Woodwork Inc .... G 954 609-4387
North Lauderdale *(G-11616)*
J-Coast Woodworks LLC .... G 561 262-6144
Jupiter *(G-7059)*
Jambco Millwork Inc .... F 954 977-4998
Margate *(G-8551)*
Jayco Woodworks Inc .... G 850 814-3041
Panama City *(G-13920)*
JB Wood Werks LLC .... G 239 314-4462
Cape Coral *(G-1440)*
Jeb Thermofoil of South Fla .... G 305 887-6214
Hialeah *(G-5464)*
Jehova Jireh Wood Work Prof .... G 850 862-7131
Fort Walton Beach *(G-4810)*
Jireh Woodwork Inc .... G 954 515-8041
Deerfield Beach *(G-2851)*
Jjc Woodworks Inc .... G 954 461-0088
Lauderhill *(G-8112)*
Jk2 Scenic LLC .... E 407 703-2977
Apopka *(G-150)*
JM Custom Millworks Inc .... F 561 582-5600
Mangonia Park *(G-8505)*
JM Custom Woodworking .... F 561 582-5600
Mangonia Park *(G-8506)*
John S Wilson Inc .... F 410 442-2400
Naples *(G-11299)*
Johnson Woodworking .... G 772 473-1404
Malabar *(G-8490)*
Johnsons Woodwork Incorporated .... G 904 826-4100
Saint Augustine *(G-15561)*
Jorges Finest Woodworks Inc .... G 305 491-4380
Miami *(G-9802)*
Jr Wood Works Inc .... G 305 401-6056
Miami *(G-9808)*
Juan Alemany Woodwork .... G 407 350-4072
Kissimmee *(G-7259)*
Kdavid Woodwork & Design Inc .... F 754 205-2433
North Lauderdale *(G-11617)*
Kenneth E Keller .... G 239 649-7579
Naples *(G-11305)*
Kevco Builders Inc .... F 352 308-8025
Eustis *(G-3711)*
Kevins Custom Woodworking .... G 727 804-8422
Palm Harbor *(G-13742)*
◆ **Kmi International Inc** .... E 561 588-5514
Lake Worth *(G-7562)*
Kurts Custom Woodworks .... G 352 693-5407
Summerfield *(G-17059)*
L and TW Oodwork LLC .... G 305 742-4362
Homestead *(G-5978)*
Lake Door and Trim Inc .... F 352 589-5566
Eustis *(G-3712)*

Legend Design and Production .... G 305 270-1156
Miami *(G-9881)*
Liberty Woodworking Inc .... G 727 642-9652
Pinellas Park *(G-14364)*
Lightstone Woodworking LLC .... G 727 424-2660
Seminole *(G-16750)*
Local Wood Inc .... G 561 410-2113
North Palm Beach *(G-11722)*
Local Woodwork LLC .... G 954 551-1515
Margate *(G-8556)*
Lombardis Woodworking .... G 305 439-7208
Miami Springs *(G-10894)*
Losobe LLC .... G 850 748-3162
Pensacola *(G-14196)*
Luxury Woodworking Soluti .... G 786 398-1785
Hialeah *(G-5492)*
Lyndan Inc .... E 813 977-6683
Tampa *(G-17867)*
▲ **M & M Enterprises Daytona LLC** .... G 386 672-1554
Daytona Beach *(G-2681)*
Magnolia Millwork Intl Inc .... G 407 585-3470
Casselberry *(G-1510)*
Magruders Woodworking Inc .... G 954 649-0861
Tamarac *(G-17362)*
Marko Garage Doors & Gates Inc .... G 561 547-4001
Palm Springs *(G-13776)*
▲ **Masonite Corporation** .... D 813 877-2726
Tampa *(G-17887)*
◆ **Masonite Holdings Inc** .... F 813 877-2726
Tampa *(G-17888)*
◆ **Masonite International Corp** .... D 800 895-2723
Tampa *(G-17889)*
Masonite US Corporation .... D 813 877-2726
Tampa *(G-17890)*
Mayworth Showcase Works Inc .... G 813 251-1558
Tampa *(G-17896)*
McKenzie Cabinetry Fine Wdwkg .... G 727 424-3707
Pinellas Park *(G-14367)*
McKinney Woodworking Inc .... G 904 591-1233
Saint Johns *(G-15679)*
Medeiros Custom Wood Work .... G 305 970-0472
Miami *(G-9965)*
Melbourne Architectural Mllwk .... F 321 308-3297
Melbourne *(G-8887)*
Mg Woodwork Inc .... G 561 459-7552
Pompano Beach *(G-14760)*
Miles of Wood Inc .... G 305 300-6370
Miami *(G-10021)*
Mill-Rite Woodworking Co Inc .... D 727 527-7808
Pinellas Park *(G-14368)*
Millennium Glass Inc .... G 305 638-1785
Miami *(G-10024)*
Mills & Nebraska Door & Trim .... F 407 472-2742
Orlando *(G-12971)*
Millwork 360 LLC .... E 813 854-3100
Tampa *(G-17908)*
Millwork and Design Inc .... G 352 544-0444
Brooksville *(G-1253)*
Millwork Masters LLC .... F 727 807-6221
New Port Richey *(G-11501)*
Millwork Plus Inc .... G 352 343-2121
Tavares *(G-18348)*
Mirage Woodworking Inc .... G 305 606-7043
Hialeah *(G-5522)*
Mitchell Wood Works Inc .... G 727 321-7586
Saint Petersburg *(G-15856)*
Mjr Woodworks LLC .... F 407 403-5430
Apopka *(G-162)*
Mm Wood Designs Inc .... G 561 602-2775
Delray Beach *(G-3108)*
Mohamed Lamrana Jalloh .... G 347 305-5556
Miami Beach *(G-10695)*
Moran Woodworking LLC .... G 941 600-8842
Sarasota *(G-16513)*
Mr Foamy Southwest Fl LLC .... F 239 461-3110
Fort Myers *(G-4540)*
▼ **N & N Investment Corporation** .... E 954 590-3800
Pompano Beach *(G-14770)*
Naples Woodworks Inc .... G 239 287-1632
Naples *(G-11340)*
National Woodworks Inc .... G 407 489-3572
Orlando *(G-12992)*
Natural Beauty Wood Products .... F 561 732-0224
Boynton Beach *(G-937)*
Natural Wood Works LLC .... G 954 445-1493
Hialeah *(G-5534)*
Navarre Beach Woodworks .... G 850 781-7884
Navarre *(G-11470)*
◆ **New Age Windows & Doors Corp** .... F 305 889-0703
Medley *(G-8695)*

New Style Wood Work Corp..........G....... 305 989-9665
Hialeah *(G-5539)*
New Woodworks Inc..........G....... 954 520-4812
Oakland Park *(G-11824)*
Newmil Inc..........F....... 954 444-4471
Fort Lauderdale *(G-4140)*
Noble Wood Works..........G....... 561 702-2889
Pompano Beach *(G-14774)*
Noble Woodworks Inc..........G....... 561 702-2889
Boca Raton *(G-645)*
Ocean Woodworks Inc..........G....... 904 246-7178
Atlantic Beach *(G-225)*
Old Town Timber LLC..........G....... 904 217-7046
Saint Augustine *(G-15583)*
Oliveri Woodworking Inc..........F....... 561 478-7233
West Palm Beach *(G-18972)*
Omega Garage Doors Inc..........F....... 352 620-8830
Melbourne *(G-8901)*
Orlando Commercial Millwork..........G....... 407 549-2679
Sanford *(G-16097)*
Orlando Shutters LLC..........E....... 407 495-5250
Lake Mary *(G-7440)*
Oscars Woodworks Inc..........G....... 786 543-9200
Hialeah *(G-5553)*
Ouro Custom Woodwork Inc..........F....... 954 428-0735
Deerfield Beach *(G-2881)*
Palm Beach Cstm Woodworks LLC..........F....... 561 575-5335
Mangonia Park *(G-8508)*
Palm Beach Woodwork Co Inc..........G....... 561 844-8818
Mangonia Park *(G-8509)*
Pat Clark Custom Woodworking L..........G....... 941 376-1387
Sarasota *(G-16536)*
Peace Millwork Co Inc..........E....... 305 573-6222
Miami *(G-10147)*
Pecky Cypress & More LLC..........G....... 772 215-0430
Jupiter *(G-7090)*
Performnce Glzing Slutions LLC..........G....... 305 975-3717
Miami *(G-10154)*
Pestanos Woodworking LLC..........G....... 954 448-3932
Miami *(G-10155)*
Peter Flagg Woodwork..........G....... 561 307-4200
West Palm Beach *(G-18994)*
◆ PGT Industries Inc..........A....... 941 480-1600
North Venice *(G-11761)*
▼ PGT Innovations Inc..........A....... 941 480-1600
North Venice *(G-11762)*
Phil Buckner Woodworks Inc..........G....... 904 339-4475
Jacksonville *(G-6671)*
Pineapple Grove Woodworks..........G....... 561 676-1287
West Palm Beach *(G-18998)*
Pleasure Interiors LLC..........E....... 941 756-9969
Sarasota *(G-16545)*
Powell Woodworking LLC..........G....... 407 883-9181
Sanford *(G-16103)*
▼ Pradere Manufacturing Corp..........F....... 305 823-0190
Hialeah *(G-5563)*
Premdor Finance LLC..........G....... 813 877-2726
Tampa *(G-18007)*
Prime Woodwork Inc..........G....... 786 226-5646
Hialeah *(G-5571)*
Pro Millwork Installations..........G....... 561 302-5869
Boynton Beach *(G-945)*
Pro Trim Millwork Inc..........G....... 239 592-5454
Naples *(G-11375)*
Q & O Custom Woodwork Inc..........G....... 954 391-8281
West Park *(G-19097)*
Quality 1 Appraisal Inc..........G....... 786 859-4085
Hialeah *(G-5587)*
▼ Quality Engineered Products Co..........E....... 813 885-1693
Tampa *(G-18031)*
Quality Railings Miami Corp..........G....... 786 400-0462
Hialeah *(G-5590)*
R & R Door and Trim Inc..........G....... 561 844-5496
West Palm Beach *(G-19015)*
R Dorian Millworks LLC..........F....... 561 863-9125
West Palm Beach *(G-19016)*
R K Constructors of Centl Fla..........G....... 407 222-5376
Orlando *(G-13110)*
Radica LLC..........G....... 954 383-0089
Doral *(G-3480)*
Ramos Woodwork LLC..........G....... 954 861-7679
Deerfield Beach *(G-2899)*
Rbs Woodwork Corp..........F....... 754 214-7682
Pembroke Pines *(G-14056)*
Redwood Custom Woodworking..........F....... 407 529-9877
Orlando *(G-13124)*
Remior Industries Inc..........E....... 305 883-8722
Miami *(G-10250)*
Renaissance Custom Woodworking..........G....... 561 212-9885
Delray Beach *(G-3135)*
Renovatec Enterprise Inc..........G....... 954 444-8694
Fort Lauderdale *(G-4202)*
▼ Rich Woodturning Inc..........F....... 305 573-9142
Miami Lakes *(G-10851)*
Richard Griggs Custom Woodwork..........G....... 941 223-9376
Venice *(G-18569)*
River Craft LLC..........F....... 407 867-0584
Orlando *(G-13141)*
Riverview Millworks Inc..........G....... 904 764-9571
Jacksonville *(G-6729)*
Rolu Woodcraft Inc..........F....... 305 685-0914
Hialeah *(G-5605)*
Roy Smith S Screen..........F....... 561 792-3381
Loxahatchee *(G-8363)*
Rubinelli Woodwork Inc..........G....... 954 445-0537
Boca Raton *(G-695)*
S + L Millworks Inc..........G....... 813 413-6260
Lutz *(G-8415)*
S M I Cabinetry Inc..........E....... 407 841-0292
Orlando *(G-13152)*
S R Q Storm Protection LLC..........G....... 941 341-0334
Sarasota *(G-16568)*
◆ S&S Craftsmen Inc..........F....... 813 247-4429
Tampa *(G-18078)*
Sailfish Woodworks LLC..........G....... 772 708-2791
Jensen Beach *(G-6973)*
Sailor Made Cstm Woodworks LLC..........G....... 805 587-1197
Palm Bay *(G-13533)*
Sailor Made Custom Woodworks L..........G....... 805 587-1197
Melbourne *(G-8924)*
Sarasota Architectural Wdwkg..........F....... 941 684-1614
Sarasota *(G-16574)*
SCi Architectural Wdwrk Inc..........F....... 954 247-9601
Fort Lauderdale *(G-4224)*
Scott-Douglas Design Inc..........G....... 727 535-7900
Largo *(G-8046)*
▼ Seco South II Inc..........F....... 727 536-1924
Largo *(G-8050)*
Second 2 None Wood Work Inc..........G....... 786 299-3580
Miami *(G-10319)*
Security World Electronics..........G....... 786 285-5303
Miami Gardens *(G-10754)*
▲ Shades To You LLC..........G....... 407 889-0049
Apopka *(G-186)*
▼ Shaver Properties Inc..........E....... 772 569-3466
Vero Beach *(G-18664)*
Shutterman Storm & Security..........F....... 239 455-9166
Naples *(G-11400)*
Shutters Wholesale..........G....... 770 410-9525
Jacksonville *(G-6768)*
Simpson..........F....... 954 804-0829
Coconut Creek *(G-2095)*
Siw Solutions LLC..........D....... 561 274-9392
Delray Beach *(G-3142)*
SJS Woodworking LLC..........G....... 561 704-5990
Wellington *(G-18735)*
Sloan Custom Woodworking LLC..........G....... 850 766-5620
Tallahassee *(G-17326)*
Smiths Woodworks Inc..........G....... 863 381-6564
Sebring *(G-16709)*
Sol-A-Trol Aluminum Pdts Inc..........E....... 305 681-2020
Opa Locka *(G-12359)*
South Florida Stairs Inc..........F....... 561 822-3110
Boynton Beach *(G-962)*
South Florida Woodworkers Inc..........G....... 954 868-5043
Fort Lauderdale *(G-4249)*
Southern Door Technologies..........G....... 386 496-3844
Lake Butler *(G-7342)*
Southwest Woodwork Inc..........F....... 239 213-0126
Naples *(G-11411)*
Spacewerks Inc..........F....... 727 540-9714
Clearwater *(G-1885)*
Specialty Products Inc..........G....... 850 438-4264
Pensacola *(G-14267)*
Splinter Woodworking Inc..........G....... 305 731-9334
Delray Beach *(G-3145)*
Stairways By Angel LLC..........G....... 407 790-7181
Orlando *(G-13210)*
Stephs Woodworking LLC..........G....... 772 571-2661
Vero Beach *(G-18668)*
Storm Depot of Palm Beach..........F....... 561 721-9800
West Palm Beach *(G-19046)*
Stuart Stair & Furniture Mfg..........G....... 772 287-4097
Stuart *(G-17026)*
Superior Door Works & More LLC..........G....... 850 880-6579
Freeport *(G-4852)*
Superior Millwork Company Inc..........F....... 904 355-5676
Jacksonville *(G-6828)*
▲ Superior Trim & Door Inc..........E....... 407 408-7624
Apopka *(G-190)*
Symmetrical Stair Inc..........F....... 561 228-4800
Pompano Beach *(G-14881)*
▼ Synergy Thermal Foils Inc..........F....... 954 420-9553
Coral Springs *(G-2319)*
T and M Woodworking Inc..........G....... 352 748-6655
Wildwood *(G-19203)*
T-M Fabrications LLC..........G....... 386 295-5302
Ormond Beach *(G-13404)*
Tag Media Group LLC..........G....... 239 288-0499
Fort Myers *(G-4622)*
Tampa Contractors Supply Inc..........E....... 813 418-7284
Tampa *(G-18163)*
Tampabay Custom Door LLC..........G....... 813 842-3667
Seffner *(G-16732)*
Tarpon Woodworks LLC..........G....... 407 446-9450
Orlando *(G-13241)*
Taylor-Cotton-Ridley Inc..........D....... 904 733-8373
Jacksonville *(G-6840)*
Tcr Woodworks Inc..........G....... 561 827-6676
Boynton Beach *(G-968)*
◆ Teak Isle Inc..........C....... 407 656-8885
Ocoee *(G-12091)*
Terrades Custom Woodworks Inc..........G....... 305 316-2908
Hialeah *(G-5648)*
Terry D Triplett Inc..........G....... 561 251-3641
Mangonia Park *(G-8513)*
Thomas Rley Artisans Guild Inc..........E....... 239 591-3203
Naples *(G-11440)*
Timbercraft of Naples Inc..........G....... 239 566-2559
Naples *(G-11442)*
Timberland Door LLC..........E....... 727 539-8600
Largo *(G-8067)*
Top Notch Wood Works Inc..........G....... 954 445-7861
Miami *(G-10491)*
Tri-County Woodworking LLC..........F....... 954 850-2222
Pompano Beach *(G-14890)*
Tru Craft Woodworks LLC..........G....... 561 441-2742
Delray Beach *(G-3152)*
Trucraft Specialties Inc..........G....... 561 441-2742
Delray Beach *(G-3153)*
▲ Ultimate Door of Palm Beach..........F....... 561 642-2828
Lake Worth *(G-7595)*
Ultimate Wdwkg & Design Inc..........G....... 754 223-4004
Oakland Park *(G-11854)*
▼ Unique Originals Inc..........F....... 305 634-2274
Fort Lauderdale *(G-4293)*
Unique Technology Inds LLC..........F....... 941 358-5410
Sarasota *(G-16628)*
Universal Wood Design..........F....... 772 569-5389
Vero Beach *(G-18674)*
US Wood Work & Service..........G....... 954 675-7153
Saint Johns *(G-15683)*
USA Exterior LLC..........G....... 813 515-5181
Tampa *(G-18229)*
Vesten Woodworks LLC..........G....... 407 780-9295
Saint Augustine *(G-15632)*
▼ Viking Kabinets Inc..........E....... 305 238-9025
Cutler Bay *(G-2420)*
Vision Woodworking Inc..........G....... 407 493-9665
Groveland *(G-5109)*
Visions Millwork Inc..........F....... 239 390-0811
Fort Myers *(G-4648)*
Vreeland Woodworking LLC..........G....... 727 365-0241
Palm Harbor *(G-13768)*
W C H Enterprises Inc..........G....... 239 267-7549
Fort Myers *(G-4649)*
Waterhuse Archtctral Wdwrk LLC..........F....... 786 534-4943
Miami *(G-10596)*
West Harbour Woodworking LLC..........G....... 954 822-7543
Lauderdale Lakes *(G-8096)*
William Leupold Sr..........G....... 727 527-7400
Saint Petersburg *(G-15960)*
Willie D Wood Works Inc..........G....... 305 969-6522
Miami *(G-10608)*
Windsor Window Company..........F....... 321 385-3880
Titusville *(G-18473)*
Winsulator Corporation..........G....... 941 365-7901
Sarasota *(G-16642)*
Wishbone Woodworking Inc..........G....... 239 262-7230
Naples *(G-11459)*
Witts Woodworking Inc..........G....... 941 544-8812
Sarasota *(G-16644)*
Wonder Emporium Millwork Fab..........G....... 407 850-3131
Orlando *(G-13328)*
Wood One LLC..........G....... 727 639-5620
Saint Petersburg *(G-15963)*
Woodshed Woodworks LLC..........G....... 904 540-0354
Saint Augustine *(G-15639)*
Woodwork In Nova Architectural..........G....... 954 448-2962
Margate *(G-8573)*

Woodwork Unlimited Inc........F....... 352 267-4051
Oxford *(G-13466)*
Woodworkers Cabinet Inc........F....... 239 593-1718
Naples *(G-11460)*
Woodworking Inc........G....... 727 442-6876
Clearwater *(G-1943)*
Woodworks By Mike Inc........G....... 850 567-2086
Tallahassee *(G-17347)*
Woodworks For You........G....... 386 717-4169
Deland *(G-3036)*
Woodworks of Tampa Bay LLC........G....... 813 330-5836
Tampa *(G-18261)*
◆ **World of Awnings Inc**........F....... 305 884-6699
Hialeah *(G-5689)*
Worthington Millwork LLC........G....... 800 872-1608
Panama City Beach *(G-13986)*
Wow Business........F....... 813 301-2620
Tampa *(G-18267)*
Y F Leung Inc........G....... 305 651-6851
North Miami Beach *(G-11714)*

2434 Wood Kitchen Cabinets

▲ **3 Stars Kitchen Cabinets Corp**........G....... 786 285-7147
Hialeah *(G-5252)*
4k Cabinets........G....... 727 507-0444
Largo *(G-7880)*
A A A Cabinets........G....... 850 438-8337
Pensacola *(G-14075)*
A Better Kitchen Cabinets Inc........G....... 786 234-1897
Homestead *(G-5951)*
A RE Door Cabinets Inc........G....... 813 419-0007
Tampa *(G-17376)*
A W R Cabinets Inc........F....... 407 323-1415
Sanford *(G-15985)*
A1 Custom Mica Inc........G....... 954 893-0063
Hollywood *(G-5763)*
◆ **Aadi Inc**........E....... 407 957-4557
Saint Cloud *(G-15642)*
About Face Cabinetry & Refacin........F....... 813 777-4088
Lutz *(G-8371)*
Absolute Wood Creations LLC........G....... 954 251-2202
Hallandale Beach *(G-5167)*
Adams Bros Cabinetry Inc........G....... 863 993-0501
Arcadia *(G-198)*
Advanced Cabinetry Inventions........G....... 305 866-1160
North Bay Village *(G-11592)*
Advanced Cabinets LLC........G....... 954 515-2675
Pompano Beach *(G-14579)*
Advanced Kitchen & Cabinet........G....... 305 251-9344
Cutler Bay *(G-2383)*
Aj Originals Inc........G....... 954 563-9911
Fort Lauderdale *(G-3793)*
Akiknav Inc........F....... 561 842-8091
Riviera Beach *(G-15296)*
Al-FA Cabinets Inc........F....... 813 876-4205
Tampa *(G-17396)*
Albrecht Consulting Inc........F....... 941 377-7755
Sarasota *(G-16339)*
All American Kit & Bath LLC........G....... 305 599-9000
Doral *(G-3238)*
◆ **All Wood Cabinetry LLC**........E....... 866 367-2516
Bartow *(G-305)*
Allen Custom Cabinetry Inc........G....... 850 625-4713
Panama City *(G-13862)*
Altamonte Woodworking Co Inc........G....... 407 331-0020
Altamonte Springs *(G-29)*
AM Cabinets LLC........G....... 321 663-4319
Altamonte Springs *(G-30)*
Amazing Cabinet Store LLC........F....... 407 270-7865
Orlando *(G-12466)*
Amercn Cabinets Granite Floors........F....... 727 303-0678
Palm Harbor *(G-13718)*
American Cabinet Works Inc........G....... 904 672-6649
Jacksonville *(G-6147)*
Amick Cstm Woodcraft & Design........G....... 407 324-8525
Sanford *(G-15994)*
Amy Cabinetry........E....... 561 842-8091
Riviera Beach *(G-15298)*
Andrews Cabinet........F....... 850 994-0836
Milton *(G-10921)*
Antique & Modern Cabinets Inc........E....... 904 393-9055
Jacksonville *(G-6158)*
▼ **Architctral Wdwrks Cbnetry Inc**........F....... 561 848-8595
Palm Beach Gardens *(G-13568)*
Argenal Cabinets Inc........G....... 863 670-7973
Lakeland *(G-7638)*
Art Wood Cabinets Corp........G....... 754 367-0742
Deerfield Beach *(G-2779)*
Assocate Cbinetmakers Palm Bch........G....... 561 743-9566
Jupiter *(G-7001)*
◆ **Avon Cabinet Corporation**........C....... 941 755-2866
Bradenton *(G-993)*
B & K Discount Cabinets LLC........F....... 321 254-2322
Melbourne *(G-8775)*
B G Cabinets Llc........G....... 941 485-0040
Venice *(G-18534)*
Bailey Industries........G....... 352 326-2898
Tampa *(G-17454)*
▲ **Bailey Industries Inc**........E....... 352 326-2898
Leesburg *(G-8144)*
Batista Cabinets Inc........G....... 407 922-3459
Kissimmee *(G-7222)*
Bauformat South-East LLC........G....... 201 693-6635
Fort Lauderdale *(G-3841)*
Bay Cabinets and Millworks........G....... 850 215-1485
Panama City Beach *(G-13972)*
Beaches Woodcraft Inc........F....... 904 249-0785
Atlantic Beach *(G-217)*
Beautiful Cabinets Corp........G....... 813 486-9034
Tampa *(G-17463)*
Bennetts Custom Cabinets Inc........E....... 904 751-1455
Jacksonville *(G-6206)*
Beverly Acquisitions Inc........F....... 561 746-3827
Jupiter *(G-7007)*
BK Stainless Inc........G....... 786 474-0203
Miami *(G-9253)*
Bob & Lees Cabinets........F....... 352 748-3553
Wildwood *(G-19191)*
Braden Kitchens Inc........E....... 321 636-4700
Cocoa *(G-1999)*
Braswell Custom Cabinets........G....... 850 436-2645
Pensacola *(G-14104)*
Bresee Woodwork Inc........F....... 941 355-2591
Sarasota *(G-16368)*
Broward Custom Woodwork LLC........G....... 352 376-4732
Deerfield Beach *(G-2791)*
Bruno Danger Custom Cabinets........G....... 754 366-1302
Sebastian *(G-16656)*
Built Rght Ktchens of Palm Cas........G....... 386 437-7077
Bunnell *(G-1299)*
Built Rite Cabinets Inc........G....... 352 447-2238
Inglis *(G-6075)*
Busy Bee Cabinets Inc........D....... 941 628-2025
North Port *(G-11734)*
Byerly Custom Design Inc........G....... 941 371-7498
Sarasota *(G-16374)*
Cabinet Cnnction of Trsure Cas........E....... 772 621-4882
Port Saint Lucie *(G-15095)*
Cabinet Collection Inc........G....... 239 478-0359
Bonita Springs *(G-822)*
Cabinet Design and Cnstr LLC........G....... 850 393-9724
Pensacola *(G-14111)*
Cabinet Designs of Central Fla........G....... 321 636-1101
Rockledge *(G-15397)*
Cabinet Designs of Sarasota........F....... 941 739-1607
Bradenton *(G-1010)*
Cabinet Dreams & Things Inc........G....... 727 514-0847
Hudson *(G-6017)*
Cabinet Factory Outlet........G....... 386 323-0778
Daytona Beach *(G-2637)*
Cabinet Genies........G....... 239 458-8563
Cape Coral *(G-1399)*
Cabinet Guy 2012 Inc........G....... 305 796-5242
Davie *(G-2505)*
Cabinet Guy of Englewood Inc........G....... 941 475-9454
Englewood *(G-3670)*
Cabinet Kings LLC........G....... 239 288-6740
Fort Myers *(G-4383)*
Cabinet Market LLC........G....... 321 203-2598
Winter Park *(G-19389)*
Cabinet Masters Inc........G....... 727 535-0020
Largo *(G-7918)*
Cabinet Mechanics LLC........G....... 941 626-0735
Port Charlotte *(G-14967)*
Cabinet Options Inc........G....... 904 434-1564
Saint Johns *(G-15674)*
Cabinet Specialist Inc........G....... 239 641-6931
Naples *(G-11198)*
Cabinet Systems of Central Fla........G....... 407 678-0994
Winter Park *(G-19390)*
Cabinetree Collection Inc........F....... 772 569-4761
Vero Beach *(G-18608)*
Cabinetry Masters LLC........G....... 954 549-8646
Jacksonville *(G-6248)*
Cabinets & Counters........G....... 561 444-3083
West Palm Beach *(G-18832)*
Cabinets -N- More Inc........G....... 321 355-9548
Cocoa *(G-2003)*
Cabinets By Design........G....... 954 829-2923
Oakland Park *(G-11788)*
Cabinets By Marylin Inc........G....... 954 729-3995
Pompano Beach *(G-14630)*
Cabinets By Wfc Inc........F....... 941 355-2703
Sarasota *(G-16375)*
Cabinets Direct USA........F....... 862 704-6138
Delray Beach *(G-3055)*
Cabinets Extraordinaire Inc........F....... 618 925-0515
Bradenton *(G-1011)*
Cabinets Moreunlimited Inc........G....... 813 789-4203
Tampa *(G-17497)*
Cabinets One LLC........G....... 407 227-1147
Orlando *(G-12542)*
Cabinets Plus Inc........F....... 239 574-7020
Cape Coral *(G-1400)*
Cabinets Plus of America Inc........G....... 813 408-0433
Tampa *(G-17498)*
Cabinetscapes LLC........G....... 941 539-0013
Sarasota *(G-16376)*
Cabinetsync Inc........G....... 239 690-6122
Fort Myers *(G-4384)*
Camelot Cabinets Inc........F....... 813 876-9150
Tampa *(G-17502)*
Candi-Lyn Cabinetry........G....... 863 860-2505
Bartow *(G-311)*
Capri Kitchens Inc........F....... 813 623-1424
Tampa *(G-17504)*
Captain Cabinets LLC........G....... 813 685-7179
Seffner *(G-16722)*
Caravaggio Cabinetry Inc........F....... 561 609-3355
Lake Worth *(G-7539)*
Caribbean Cbinets Counters Inc........G....... 239 292-8073
Fort Myers *(G-4389)*
Carlos Velez Cabinets & Instal........G....... 407 929-3402
Orlando *(G-12551)*
Carloss Cabinets Inc........G....... 863 853-4255
Lakeland *(G-7653)*
Carters Cabinetry Inc........E....... 386 677-4192
Ormond Beach *(G-13357)*
▼ **Castor Inc**........G....... 813 254-1171
Tampa *(G-17514)*
Cayo Hueso Enterprises Inc........E....... 305 747-0020
Key West *(G-7181)*
CC Kitchen Cabinets Corp........G....... 786 457-1494
Miami *(G-9330)*
Century Millworks........F....... 850 256-2565
Century *(G-1527)*
Cepero Remodeling Inc........G....... 305 265-1888
Miami *(G-9341)*
Chief Cabinets LLC........G....... 850 545-5055
Tallahassee *(G-17233)*
Choice Cabinets LLC........G....... 352 629-1556
Ocala *(G-11902)*
Cianos Tile & Marble Inc........E....... 239 267-8453
Fort Myers *(G-4395)*
Classic Cabinets and More LLC........G....... 727 239-8869
Largo *(G-7923)*
Classic Kitchens Brevard Inc........G....... 321 327-5972
Melbourne *(G-8790)*
Clever Cabinetry LLC........G....... 813 992-0020
Riverview *(G-15267)*
Cljp Inc........E....... 850 678-8819
Niceville *(G-11564)*
Closet Pros........G....... 305 240-7775
Key West *(G-7183)*
Clover Interior Systems Inc........F....... 941 484-1300
Nokomis *(G-11580)*
▲ **Cnc Cabinet Components Inc**........F....... 321 956-3470
Melbourne *(G-8791)*
Coastal Cabinets & Countertops........G....... 850 424-3940
Miramar Beach *(G-11065)*
Coastal Closet Co of Fla LLC........G....... 239 826-3807
Fort Myers *(G-4401)*
Coastal Custom Woodwork LLC........G....... 904 945-2299
Jacksonville *(G-6275)*
Coastline Cbntry Cstm Mllwk LL........F....... 239 208-2876
Fort Myers *(G-4405)*
Coffin Cabinetry & Trim Michae........G....... 352 217-3729
Umatilla *(G-18497)*
Concept One Custom Cabine........G....... 954 829-3505
Hollywood *(G-5804)*
Contemporary Cabinets Gulf CST........G....... 941 758-3060
Sarasota *(G-16195)*
Contractors Cabinet Company........G....... 786 492-7118
Margate *(G-8540)*
Coral Cabinet Inc........G....... 305 484-8702
Miami *(G-9400)*
Corn-E-Lee Woodcrafts........G....... 239 574-2414
Cape Coral *(G-1406)*
Counter Productions Inc........G....... 386 673-6500
Daytona Beach *(G-2647)*

Country Cabinets ....G.... 850 547-5477
Bonifay *(G-802)*
Creations In Cabinetry Inc ....G.... 386 237-3082
Palm Coast *(G-13690)*
Creative Cabinet Concepts Inc ....F.... 239 939-1313
Fort Myers *(G-4413)*
Creative Concepts Orlando Inc ....E.... 407 260-1435
Longwood *(G-8268)*
Creative Teaching Cabinets ....G.... 754 205-0886
Deerfield Beach *(G-2806)*
Csi Home Decor Inc ....G.... 754 301-2147
Sunrise *(G-17112)*
Csw Cabinet Services Inc ....G.... 727 267-1767
Spring Hill *(G-16871)*
Curry Cabinetry Inc ....E.... 813 321-3650
Tampa *(G-17574)*
Curtis K Foulks ....G.... 239 454-9663
Fort Myers *(G-4419)*
Custom Cabinet Doors & More In ....G.... 954 318-1881
Fort Lauderdale *(G-3923)*
Custom Cabinet Factory Inc ....G.... 352 429-7722
Groveland *(G-5094)*
Custom Cabinets ....G.... 727 392-1676
Seminole *(G-16745)*
Custom Cabinets By Jensen LLC ....G.... 813 250-0286
Tampa *(G-17576)*
Custom Cabinets Design Inc ....G.... 561 210-3423
Deerfield Beach *(G-2807)*
Custom Cabinets Inc ....F.... 941 366-0428
Sarasota *(G-16398)*
Custom Cabinets SW Florida LLC ....G.... 239 415-3350
Fort Myers *(G-4420)*
Custom Carpentry Plus LLC ....F.... 305 972-3735
Cutler Bay *(G-2390)*
Custom Craft Laminates Inc ....E.... 813 877-7100
Tampa *(G-17577)*
Custom Crafters ....G.... 954 792-6119
Pompano Beach *(G-14653)*
Custom Drawers of Swfl LLC ....G.... 239 226-1699
Fort Myers *(G-4421)*
Custom Klosets & Cabinets Inc ....E.... 813 246-4806
Tampa *(G-17579)*
Custom WD Designs of Pensacola ....F.... 850 476-9663
Pensacola *(G-14122)*
Custom Wood Products Inc ....G.... 904 737-6906
Jacksonville *(G-6304)*
▲ D & G Custom Cabinetry Inc ....F.... 954 561-8822
Tamarac *(G-17353)*
D & G Millwork & Cabinetry LLC ....G.... 305 830-3000
Miami *(G-9424)*
D & N Cabinetry Inc ....F.... 863 471-1500
Sebring *(G-16685)*
D R Nickelson & Company Inc ....F.... 386 755-6565
Lake City *(G-7353)*
D T Woodcrafters Corp ....E.... 305 556-3771
Hialeah *(G-5360)*
Da Vinci Cabinetry LLC ....F.... 239 633-7957
Bonita Springs *(G-828)*
▼ Dade Doors Inc ....F.... 305 556-8980
Hialeah *(G-5362)*
Dale Mabry Heating & Metal Co ....G.... 813 877-1574
Tampa *(G-17588)*
Dale Smith Cabinetry LLC ....G.... 407 625-2274
Orlando *(G-12645)*
Darmar Cabinets Inc ....G.... 786 556-5784
Miami Lakes *(G-10778)*
Daystar International Inc ....G.... 813 281-0200
Tampa *(G-17593)*
Debruyne Enterprise Inc ....F.... 850 562-0491
Tallahassee *(G-17242)*
Deluxe Clsets Cabinets Stn LLC ....G.... 786 879-3371
Miami *(G-9452)*
Demoss Cabinetry LLC ....F.... 863 738-0080
Lakeland *(G-7673)*
Design Your Kit Clset More Inc ....G.... 786 227-6412
Miami *(G-9458)*
Designers Choice Cabinetry ....F.... 321 632-0772
Rockledge *(G-15402)*
◆ Designers Choice Cabinetry Inc ....G.... 321 632-0772
Rockledge *(G-15403)*
Devine Cabinetry LLC ....G.... 941 716-0339
North Port *(G-11737)*
Distinctive Cabinet Designs ....G.... 239 641-5165
Naples *(G-11228)*
District 95 Wood Working Inc ....G.... 888 400-3136
Pompano Beach *(G-14666)*
Dixie Workshop Inc ....G.... 352 629-4699
Ocala *(G-11922)*
Dj Cabinet Factory Inc ....G.... 786 483-8868
Hialeah *(G-5375)*
Dl Cabinetry Orlando LLC ....G.... 504 669-7847
Orlando *(G-12679)*
Dma Cabinets Inc ....F.... 352 249-8147
Lecanto *(G-8133)*
Doctor Granite and Cabinets ....G.... 321 368-1779
West Melbourne *(G-18772)*
Doerrs Cstm Cabinets Trim LLC ....F.... 904 540-7024
Saint Augustine *(G-15538)*
Doerrs Custom Cabinets & Trim ....G.... 904 540-7024
Saint Augustine *(G-15539)*
Dons Cabinets and Woodworking ....F.... 727 863-3404
Hudson *(G-6022)*
◆ Doormark Inc ....E.... 954 418-4700
Deerfield Beach *(G-2817)*
Dukemans Custom Woodworking ....G.... 904 355-5188
Jacksonville *(G-6333)*
E & D Kitchen Cabinet Inc ....G.... 786 343-8558
Hialeah *(G-5383)*
East Coast Cabinet Co ....G.... 321 392-4686
Rockledge *(G-15407)*
East Coast Fixtures & Mllwk Co ....G.... 904 733-9711
Jacksonville *(G-6349)*
Eastburn Woodworks Inc ....F.... 850 456-8090
Pensacola *(G-14137)*
EC Cabinets Inc ....G.... 305 887-2091
Hialeah *(G-5387)*
Eco Woodwork and Design Inc ....G.... 954 326-8806
Oakland Park *(G-11802)*
Elite Cabinet Coatings ....G.... 352 795-2655
Crystal River *(G-2377)*
Elite Cabinetry Inc ....G.... 239 262-1144
Naples *(G-11235)*
Emerald Coast Cabinets Inc ....F.... 850 267-2290
Santa Rosa Beach *(G-16158)*
Empire Stone and Cabinets ....E.... 305 885-7092
Hialeah *(G-5397)*
Epi Cabinets ....G.... 850 665-0659
Pensacola *(G-14144)*
Esquadro Inc ....G.... 754 367-3098
Deerfield Beach *(G-2823)*
Eternity Cabinets ....G.... 239 482-7172
Fort Myers *(G-4445)*
▼ Eurocraft Cabinets Inc ....G.... 561 948-3034
Boca Raton *(G-523)*
European Cabinets & Design LLC ....G.... 561 684-1440
West Palm Beach *(G-18865)*
Evans Custom Cabinetry LLC ....G.... 904 829-1973
Saint Augustine *(G-15542)*
Everest Cabinets Inc ....G.... 407 790-7819
Orlando *(G-12721)*
F & S Mill Works ....G.... 407 349-9948
Geneva *(G-5021)*
Faba Cabinets & Such LLC ....G.... 813 871-1529
Tampa *(G-17656)*
Factory Direct Cab Refacing ....G.... 954 445-6635
Hollywood *(G-5819)*
Falfas Cabinet & Stone LLC ....G.... 941 960-2065
Sarasota *(G-16425)*
Fgt Cabinetry LLC ....G.... 321 800-2036
Orlando *(G-12737)*
▲ Final Touch Molding Cabinetry ....F.... 239 948-7856
Bonita Springs *(G-831)*
Fine Archtctral Mllwk Shutters ....F.... 954 491-2055
Fort Lauderdale *(G-3993)*
Fine Wood Design Inc ....G.... 727 531-8000
Largo *(G-7947)*
Finecraft Custom Cabinetry ....G.... 941 378-1901
Sarasota *(G-16430)*
Finecraft Custom Cabinets ....G.... 941 312-6598
Sarasota *(G-16431)*
Fisher Cabinet Company LLC ....E.... 850 944-4171
Pensacola *(G-14151)*
FL Central Cnstr & Rmdlg ....G.... 863 701-3548
Lakeland *(G-7687)*
Florida Custom Cabinets Inc ....G.... 850 769-4781
Panama City *(G-13903)*
▼ Florida Designer Cabinets Inc ....F.... 352 793-8555
Sumterville *(G-17068)*
Florida Kit Cbnets Amercn Corp ....G.... 305 828-2830
Hialeah *(G-5414)*
Florida Plywoods Inc ....D.... 850 948-2211
Greenville *(G-5088)*
Florida West Poggenpohl ....G.... 239 948-9005
Estero *(G-3689)*
From Trees Inc ....G.... 813 431-8285
Port Richey *(G-15050)*
Furniture Concepts 2000 Inc ....G.... 954 946-0310
Pompano Beach *(G-14706)*
Furnival Cabinetry LLC ....G.... 321 638-1223
Cocoa *(G-2025)*
Furnival Construction LLC ....F.... 321 638-1223
Cocoa *(G-2026)*
Future Kitchen Corp ....G.... 786 356-3746
Hialeah *(G-5418)*
G K Woodworks ....G.... 941 232-3910
Sarasota *(G-16444)*
G&G Quality Services Inc ....G.... 386 566-0309
Palm Coast *(G-13696)*
Gannon Charles Berchman III ....G.... 239 514-0243
Naples *(G-11258)*
Garcia Armando Custom Cabinets ....G.... 305 775-5674
Miami *(G-9613)*
Garys Cabinets and More LLC ....G.... 941 585-8001
Fort Myers *(G-4466)*
Gater Custom Cabinet & Doors ....G.... 904 778-2300
Jacksonville *(G-6425)*
Gb Cabinets Incorporated ....G.... 863 446-0676
Sebring *(G-16693)*
Gc Cabinet Express LLC ....G.... 561 662-0369
Lake Park *(G-7473)*
Gemstone Cabinetry LLC ....G.... 941 426-5656
North Port *(G-11740)*
General Cabinets Inc ....E.... 727 863-3404
Port Richey *(G-15051)*
George Gillespie Cabinets ....G.... 561 744-6191
West Palm Beach *(G-18886)*
Gilmans Custom Furn & Cabinets ....F.... 352 746-3532
Lecanto *(G-8134)*
Glenny Stone Works Inc ....G.... 786 502-3918
Doral *(G-3367)*
▲ Global Cabinet Distributors ....G.... 305 625-9814
Miami Lakes *(G-10795)*
Global Custom Cabinets LLC ....G.... 407 738-0146
Kissimmee *(G-7250)*
Gontech Custom Wood Corp ....G.... 305 323-0765
Miami *(G-9647)*
Great American Imports Llc ....G.... 786 524-4120
Miami *(G-9661)*
Gregorys Cabinets Inc ....G.... 239 450-8840
Naples *(G-11268)*
Gs Cabinets Inc ....G.... 305 986-4768
Miami *(G-9681)*
Guerra Universal Cabinet I ....G.... 561 317-4079
Lake Worth *(G-7554)*
Gulf Coast Cabinetry Inc ....G.... 850 769-3799
Panama City Beach *(G-13978)*
Gulf Contours Inc ....G.... 941 639-3933
Punta Gorda *(G-15207)*
Hammond Kitchens & Bath LLC ....F.... 321 768-9549
Melbourne *(G-8840)*
Hand Carved Creations ....G.... 561 893-0292
Boca Raton *(G-555)*
▼ Hector & Hector Inc ....F.... 305 629-8864
Miami *(G-9696)*
Heller Cabinetry Inc ....F.... 321 729-9690
Melbourne *(G-8842)*
Herman Cabinets Inc ....G.... 727 459-6730
Largo *(G-7970)*
High End Cabinets LLC ....G.... 561 469-8237
West Palm Beach *(G-18895)*
Highland Cabinet Inc ....G.... 863 385-4396
Sebring *(G-16694)*
HIS Cabinetry Inc ....D.... 727 527-7262
Pinellas Park *(G-14354)*
Home Art Corporation ....F.... 352 326-3337
Fruitland Park *(G-4865)*
Home Design Group Corp ....G.... 305 888-5836
Hialeah *(G-5449)*
Home Pride Cabinets Inc ....F.... 813 887-3782
Tampa *(G-17760)*
Home Works Bay County Inc ....G.... 850 215-7880
Panama City *(G-13915)*
House of Cabinets Ltd Inc ....G.... 352 795-5300
Crystal River *(G-2379)*
Hudson Cabinets & Millwork LLC ....F.... 239 218-0451
Fort Myers *(G-4486)*
Imperial Kitchens Inc ....G.... 239 208-9359
Fort Myers *(G-4492)*
▼ Infinite Ret Design & Mfg Corp ....F.... 305 967-8339
Miami *(G-9741)*
Innovations Cabinets Corp ....G.... 305 458-9395
Miami *(G-9748)*
Innovtive Cabinets Closets Inc ....F.... 904 475-2336
Jacksonville *(G-6498)*
Insight Cabinetry LLC ....G.... 352 818-9708
Eustis *(G-3709)*
Integral WD Cstm Cabinetry LLC ....F.... 561 361-5111
Boca Raton *(G-566)*
Interlachen Cabinets Inc ....G.... 352 481-6078
Hawthorne *(G-5244)*

SIC

Italian Cabinetry Inc......F...... 786 534-2742
Miami *(G-9774)*
J & A Custom Cabinetry Inc......G...... 786 255-4181
Homestead *(G-5974)*
J & D Oldja LLC......F...... 727 526-3240
Saint Petersburg *(G-15819)*
J & E Custom Cabinets......F...... 727 868-2820
Port Richey *(G-15055)*
J & J Custom Mica Inc......F...... 239 433-2828
Fort Myers *(G-4498)*
J & S Cypress Inc......F...... 352 383-3864
Sorrento *(G-16787)*
J J Cabinets Appliances......G...... 786 573-0300
Miami *(G-9782)*
J M Interiors Inc......G...... 305 891-6121
North Miami *(G-11642)*
J V Installations Corp......E...... 407 849-0262
Orlando *(G-12848)*
Jaiba Cabinets Inc......G...... 305 364-3646
Hialeah *(G-5461)*
Jam Cabinets & Investments LLC......F...... 305 823-9020
Hialeah *(G-5462)*
James Simmons Cabinets Inc......G...... 407 468-1802
Orlando *(G-12850)*
Jamestown Kitchens Inc......G...... 941 359-1166
Sarasota *(G-16476)*
Jay Robinson Cabinet Sales Inc......G...... 954 298-3009
Oakland Park *(G-11816)*
JC Best Finish Cabinet Inc......G...... 786 216-5571
Miami *(G-9788)*
Jcs Limited Corporation......G...... 954 822-2887
Tamarac *(G-17360)*
Jean Richard Kitchen Cabinets......G...... 786 285-5506
Miami *(G-9793)*
Jeffrey Bowden Cabinets LLC......G...... 727 992-9187
New Port Richey *(G-11495)*
Jesus Cabinets Corp......G...... 786 285-1088
Hialeah *(G-5465)*
Jesus Cabinets Corp......G...... 786 237-6299
Miami *(G-9795)*
Jfaure LLC......G...... 239 631-5324
Naples *(G-11296)*
Jim Baird Cabinets......G...... 772 569-0936
Vero Beach *(G-18633)*
Jim Rinaldos Cabinetry Inc......F...... 813 788-2715
Dade City *(G-2430)*
Juan Rodriguez Cabinetry Corp......G...... 305 467-3878
Hialeah *(G-5470)*
K & M Custom Cabinetry Inc......G...... 727 791-3993
Safety Harbor *(G-15497)*
K P Kitchens Corp......G...... 954 322-9087
Miramar *(G-11008)*
K-Kraft Cabinets Inc......G...... 321 632-8800
Rockledge *(G-15426)*
K-Kraft Industries Inc......F...... 321 632-8800
Rockledge *(G-15427)*
Kasse Cabinets Inc......G...... 407 285-2738
Orlando *(G-12866)*
Kbf Design Gallery Inc......G...... 407 830-7703
Maitland *(G-8469)*
Kc & B Custom Inc......G...... 561 276-1887
Delray Beach *(G-3099)*
Kings & Queens Cabinets......G...... 863 646-6972
Lakeland *(G-7728)*
◆ Kitchen and Bath Universe Inc......F...... 813 887-5658
Tampa *(G-17828)*
▲ Kitchen USA Inc......G...... 904 714-1970
Jacksonville *(G-6539)*
Kitchens By US......F...... 407 745-4923
Orlando *(G-12872)*
Kitchens Crafters Inc......G...... 407 788-0560
Longwood *(G-8300)*
Kitchens Rta LLC......G...... 407 969-0902
Orlando *(G-12873)*
Knothole Creations Inc......G...... 727 561-9107
Clearwater *(G-1753)*
KR Ward Inc......G...... 863 325-9070
Winter Haven *(G-19334)*
Lakeshore Custom Wood Products......G...... 813 623-2790
Tampa *(G-17834)*
Larsen Cabinetmaker Co......G...... 305 252-1212
Miami *(G-9860)*
Latino Cabinet Center Plus LLC......G...... 786 663-0909
North Miami Beach *(G-11689)*
Lee Cabinets Corp......G...... 786 291-5871
Miami *(G-9879)*
Legacy Building Supply Company......G...... 850 729-5901
Niceville *(G-11570)*
Leiton Decor & Design......G...... 786 286-4776
Miami *(G-9882)*

Lfh Southernstone LLC......G...... 727 538-0123
Clearwater *(G-1759)*
Lily Ann Cabinets - Tampa Bay......G...... 727 877-8180
Largo *(G-8000)*
Londos Fine Cabinetry LLC......G...... 727 544-2929
Seminole *(G-16751)*
Luxurable Kitchen & Bath Llc......G...... 727 286-8927
Largo *(G-8004)*
Lyndan Inc......E...... 813 977-6683
Tampa *(G-17867)*
M & E Kitchen Cabinets Inc......G...... 786 346-9987
Hialeah *(G-5493)*
M Cabinets......G...... 305 968-8188
Miami *(G-9924)*
M Wegener Inc......G...... 561 848-2408
Palm Springs *(G-13775)*
M X Corporation......G...... 305 597-9881
Pembroke Pines *(G-14046)*
M&L Cabinets Inc......G...... 941 761-8100
Bradenton *(G-1074)*
MAc Entps Tampa Bay Inc......G...... 813 363-2601
New Port Richey *(G-11499)*
Madewell Kitchens Inc......E...... 727 856-1014
Port Richey *(G-15060)*
Maggac Corporation......G...... 561 439-2707
Lake Worth *(G-7567)*
Magnolia Custom Cabinetry......G...... 941 906-8744
Sarasota *(G-16496)*
Mahan Cabinets......G...... 305 255-3325
Cutler Bay *(G-2403)*
Majestic Woodworks......G...... 352 429-2520
Groveland *(G-5100)*
Manatee Cabinets Inc......G...... 941 792-8656
Bradenton *(G-1075)*
Marquez Custom Cabinets Inc......G...... 813 352-8027
Tampa *(G-17885)*
Marx Brothers Cabinets Inc......G...... 813 695-1473
Valrico *(G-18523)*
Master Cabinet Maker Inc......G...... 941 723-0278
Palmetto *(G-13811)*
Master Cabinets LLC......G...... 239 324-9701
Ave Maria *(G-258)*
Master Kitchen Cabinets......G...... 239 225-9668
Fort Myers *(G-4523)*
▼ Master-Kraft Cabinetry......G...... 863 661-2083
Auburndale *(G-249)*
McCallum Cabinets Inc......F...... 352 372-2344
Gainesville *(G-4957)*
Metro Door Brickell LLC......G...... 786 326-4748
Miami *(G-9986)*
Mg Cabinet Installers LLC......G...... 561 530-7961
Palm Springs *(G-13777)*
◆ Miacucina LLC......G...... 305 792-9494
Miami *(G-9990)*
◆ Miacucina LLC......F...... 305 444-7383
Coral Gables *(G-2176)*
Mica Craft & Design Inc......F...... 561 863-5354
West Palm Beach *(G-18950)*
Mica Pdts & WD of Boca Raton......E...... 561 395-4686
Boca Raton *(G-622)*
Micaworks Cabinetry Inc......G...... 352 336-1707
Gainesville *(G-4962)*
Michigan Avenue Bridge Inc......F...... 352 236-4044
Ocala *(G-12000)*
Midnite Son II of Sarasota......G...... 941 377-6029
Sarasota *(G-16508)*
Mike Pulver LLC......G...... 386 747-8951
Deland *(G-2996)*
Millcreek Fine Cabinetry Inc......G...... 954 801-8595
Plantation *(G-14534)*
Mister Cabinet Deluxe Inc......G...... 305 205-3601
Hialeah *(G-5523)*
MJM Cabinet Inc......G...... 786 953-5000
Hialeah *(G-5524)*
Mobius Business Group Inc......F...... 239 274-8900
Fort Myers *(G-4535)*
Modern Cabinetry and AMP Mllwk......F...... 813 426-6941
Tampa *(G-17914)*
Moose Tracts Inc......G...... 407 491-1412
Orlando *(G-12979)*
Moralmar Kitchen Cabinets......E...... 305 819-8402
Hialeah *(G-5527)*
Morgan Cabinet Restylers LLC......G...... 813 931-4663
Lutz *(G-8403)*
Morning Star of Sarasota Inc......G...... 941 371-0392
Sarasota *(G-16514)*
Morris Mica Cabinets Inc......G...... 954 979-6838
Pompano Beach *(G-14769)*
Mr Goodwood Inc......G...... 941 961-4478
Sarasota *(G-16516)*

Mundy Kitchen Cabinet Inc......G...... 786 298-0131
Miami Lakes *(G-10825)*
▲ National Stoneworks LLC......E...... 954 349-1609
Weston *(G-19152)*
Neocabinet Inc......G...... 310 927-1008
Hollywood *(G-5881)*
◆ Nfjb Inc......E...... 954 771-1100
Fort Lauderdale *(G-4141)*
Nickols Cbinetry Woodworks Inc......G...... 941 485-7894
Venice *(G-18564)*
▼ Nosta Inc......G...... 305 634-1435
Miami *(G-10079)*
Nuform Cabinetry......G...... 954 532-2746
Pompano Beach *(G-14776)*
Ocean Kitchen Cabinets......G...... 352 745-7110
Gainesville *(G-4974)*
Oldja Enterprises Inc......F...... 727 526-3240
Saint Petersburg *(G-15871)*
Oliveira Services Corp......G...... 772 834-4803
Port Saint Lucie *(G-15127)*
Oly Custom Cabinets Miami Inc......G...... 305 216-3947
Miami *(G-10096)*
Omax Home Inc......F...... 239 980-2755
Fort Myers *(G-4558)*
Omt Inc......G...... 772 287-3762
Stuart *(G-16983)*
Orka Cabinets Inc......G...... 954 907-2456
Coral Springs *(G-2299)*
Ortega & Velazco Cabinet Inc......G...... 305 726-9097
Miami *(G-10121)*
Ortega Custom Cabinets Inc......G...... 813 403-7101
Tampa *(G-17961)*
Packard Company Inc......G...... 941 451-8201
Venice *(G-18565)*
Palm Beach Cstm Cabinetry Inc......G...... 561 859-9071
Lake Worth *(G-7577)*
Palm Beach Trim Inc......E...... 561 588-8746
Davie *(G-2565)*
Peace Millwork Co Inc......E...... 305 573-6222
Miami *(G-10147)*
Pearsons Refacing and Refacing......G...... 904 591-3850
Saint Augustine *(G-15586)*
Peartree Cabinets and Design......G...... 941 377-7655
Sarasota *(G-16539)*
Pedano Custom Furniture Inc......G...... 904 704-9329
Jacksonville *(G-6664)*
Pinellas Custom Cabinets Inc......G...... 727 864-4263
Largo *(G-8027)*
Pinnacle Cabinets Closets LLC......G...... 850 477-5402
Pensacola *(G-14230)*
Pioneer Casework LLC......F...... 305 404-3490
Saint Petersburg *(G-15878)*
Plastic and Products Mktg LLC......F...... 352 867-8078
Ocala *(G-12028)*
PLC Cabinets Installed Ltd......G...... 239 641-7565
Naples *(G-11370)*
Porath Fine Cabinetry Inc......E...... 561 616-9400
West Palm Beach *(G-19002)*
Posh Cabinets......G...... 954 444-5441
Boca Raton *(G-669)*
Precision Cabinetry LLC......G...... 386 218-3340
Deltona *(G-3177)*
Premier Cabinets LLC......G...... 407 760-9060
Oviedo *(G-13454)*
Princeton Custom Cabinetry......G...... 954 755-7614
Pompano Beach *(G-14813)*
Princeton Industries Inc......E...... 954 344-9155
Margate *(G-8563)*
Pro Kitchen Cabinets Corp......G...... 786 768-4291
Cutler Bay *(G-2409)*
Procraft Cabinetry Florida LLC......G...... 754 212-2277
Deerfield Beach *(G-2895)*
Professional Kitchen Cabinets......G...... 305 888-5660
Hialeah *(G-5578)*
Project Pros Woodworking Inc......G...... 239 454-6800
Fort Myers *(G-4573)*
Prolific Cabinetry & More Inc......G...... 904 448-6575
Jacksonville *(G-6695)*
PS Cabinet Works Inc......G...... 239 850-2162
Lehigh Acres *(G-8204)*
Quality Cabinet Recovering......G...... 941 378-1715
Sarasota *(G-16550)*
Quality Cabinets & Counters......F...... 239 948-5364
Fort Myers *(G-4577)*
Quality Cbinets By Stewart LLC......G...... 954 624-6877
Hallandale Beach *(G-5206)*
Quality Creations Inc......G...... 727 571-4332
Clearwater *(G-1855)*
Quality Custom Cabinet Design......G...... 352 728-4292
Leesburg *(G-8169)*

R & J Custom Cabinets Inc....G....813 871-5779
Tampa (G-18036)
R & R Designer Cabinets Inc....G....954 735-6435
Oakland Park (G-11834)
R & R Doors Corp....G....305 982-8106
Hialeah (G-5592)
R and D Kitchen Cabinets Corp....G....305 305-2390
Miami (G-10230)
Rainbow Cabinets Inc....G....352 236-4044
Ocala (G-12035)
RARe Cabinets Inc....G....407 415-3730
Altamonte Springs (G-70)
RB Cabinetry LLC....F....850 685-5316
Destin (G-3203)
RCS Wood Crafters LLC....G....305 836-0120
Hialeah (G-5595)
Regal Cabinets Inc....F....407 678-1003
Winter Park (G-19440)
Regency Custom Cabinets Inc....F....239 332-7977
Fort Myers (G-4580)
Regent Cabinetry and More Inc....G....239 693-2207
Fort Myers (G-4581)
Reliable Cabinet Designs....F....941 473-3403
Englewood (G-3666)
Rich Maid Cabinets Inc....F....727 572-4857
Clearwater (G-1860)
Richard Bryan Ingram LLC....G....407 677-7779
Orlando (G-13137)
Richardsons Cabinet Works....G....850 832-8298
Panama City (G-13945)
Riks Cabinetry Inc....G....561 929-5260
Lauderdale Lakes (G-8092)
Ritter Kit Bath & Closet LLC....G....239 272-4551
Naples (G-11385)
River City Cstm Cabinetry Inc....F....904 247-0807
Jacksonville (G-6727)
Rj Unique Cabinets....G....954 708-0893
Pompano Beach (G-14833)
RMM Cabinets LLC....G....954 588-6353
Boca Raton (G-691)
Robert Duffy Cabinets Inc....G....239 777-0372
Marco Island (G-8526)
Rolu Woodcraft Inc....F....305 685-0914
Hialeah (G-5605)
Rt22 Creations Inc....G....954 254-8258
Pompano Beach (G-14835)
Rta Cabinets & More LLC....G....321 288-3068
Indian Harbour Beach (G-6066)
Rubens Custom Cabinets Inc....G....813 510-8397
Tampa (G-18072)
S Aj Cabinets Inc....G....321 264-2872
Mims (G-10952)
S M I Cabinetry Inc....E....407 841-0292
Orlando (G-13152)
S Tam Cabinets Inc....G....813 310-2263
Tampa (G-18076)
Sahara Cabinets Inc....F....239 334-1151
Fort Myers (G-4593)
Sarasota Cabinetry Inc....F....941 351-5588
Sarasota (G-16576)
Sarasota Kitchens and Closets....G....941 722-7505
Bradenton (G-1111)
Sasquatch Cabinet Company....G....941 365-4950
Lakewood Ranch (G-7846)
Sbr Custom Cabinets Inc....G....407 765-8134
Orlando (G-13165)
SC Cabinet LLC....G....561 429-5369
Riviera Beach (G-15375)
Seaside Premium Cabinets....G....850 533-6801
Destin (G-3205)
Serenity Slid Srfaces Amer LLC....G....352 459-1561
Mount Dora (G-11112)
Sevilla Cabinets Inc....F....305 888-2174
Hialeah (G-5616)
Showcase Marble Inc....F....386 253-6646
Daytona Beach (G-2714)
Signature Cabinets....G....954 563-8584
Oakland Park (G-11840)
Simply Cabinets LLC....F....850 541-3712
Panama City Beach (G-13984)
Simply Closets & Cabinets....G....239 994-4264
Alva (G-91)
SIRE Cabinetry Inc....G....909 225-4121
Port Saint Lucie (G-15144)
Smith Products Co Inc....F....386 325-4534
Palatka (G-13492)
Smokey Mountain Cabinets Inc....F....386 325-1677
Palatka (G-13493)
Snows Custom Furniture Inc....G....772 794-4430
Vero Beach (G-18665)
Sobrino Custom Cabinets Inc....G....786 564-2699
Hialeah (G-5623)
▼ Southeast Woodcrafters Inc....F....561 392-2929
Boca Raton (G-724)
Southernstone Cabinets Inc....E....727 538-0123
Clearwater (G-1883)
Souvay Cabinetry Inc....G....239 273-5947
Naples (G-11412)
Spacemakers Closets SW Fla Inc....G....239 598-0222
Naples (G-11413)
Sparks Cabinetry....G....954 367-2750
Hollywood (G-5914)
Spaulding Custom Cabinets....G....904 768-4640
Jacksonville (G-6802)
Speed Custom Cabinet Corp....G....407 953-1479
Orlando (G-13205)
Spruce Creek Cabinetry Inc....F....386 756-0041
Port Orange (G-15035)
STA Cabinet Depot....G....719 502-5454
Saint Augustine (G-15622)
Star Quality Inc....F....813 875-9955
Tampa (G-18131)
Statewide Cstm Cbinets Fla Inc....G....813 788-3856
Zephyrhills (G-19537)
Stephen B Fine Cabinetry Inc....G....561 512-2850
Boynton Beach (G-963)
Steve Unser Cabinetry Inc....F....239 631-2951
Naples (G-11417)
Studio Luxe Cstm Cabinetry LLC....G....941 371-4010
Sarasota (G-16607)
Stylecraft Cabinets Mfg Inc....G....941 474-4824
Englewood (G-3668)
Sungraf Inc....F....954 456-8500
Hallandale Beach (G-5216)
Sunshine Alance Cabinets Mllwk....F....954 621-7444
Deerfield Beach (G-2919)
Superior Kitchens Inc....F....772 286-6801
Stuart (G-17030)
T&Y Cabinets Inc....G....305 512-0802
Hialeah (G-5646)
▲ Tarzen International LLC....G....239 243-0711
Fort Myers (G-4624)
Techno Cabinets Inc....G....305 910-9929
Doral (G-3525)
Thomas C Gibbs Custom Cabinets....G....239 872-6279
Fort Myers (G-4626)
Thomas Rley Artisans Guild Inc....E....239 591-3203
Naples (G-11440)
Tielve Cabinetsinc....G....561 267-3740
West Palm Beach (G-19063)
Timberwolf Cabinetry....G....561 389-5782
Royal Palm Beach (G-15478)
TJ Cabinetry Inc....F....407 886-8294
Orlando (G-13260)
Tj Cabinetry Inc....G....407 801-5124
Apopka (G-191)
Tk Cabinets....G....386 325-6906
Palatka (G-13496)
TNT Custom Cabinetry Inc....G....561 662-0964
West Palm Beach (G-19066)
Top Drawer Cabinetry & Carpent....G....772 370-4624
Fort Pierce (G-4756)
▼ Top Kitchen Cabinets....G....305 392-9938
Medley (G-8740)
Top Shelf Custom Cabinetry....G....941 726-2393
Sarasota (G-16621)
Tops Cabinet....G....954 544-2006
Hallandale (G-5163)
◆ Tops Kitchen Cabinet LLC....F....954 933-9988
Pompano Beach (G-14888)
Tradewind Custom Cabinetry LLC....G....239 257-3295
Cape Coral (G-1487)
Trim-Pak Corporation....E....407 851-8900
Orlando (G-13273)
Tws Cabinets LLC....F....863 614-4693
Lakeland (G-7827)
U C Cabinet Inc....G....407 322-0968
Sanford (G-16130)
Ultimate Outdoor Cabinetry Inc....G....941 713-5295
Bradenton (G-1135)
Um Kitchen Cabinets Inc....G....772 224-5445
Port Saint Lucie (G-15158)
Underwood Butcher Block Co Inc....F....904 338-2348
Jacksonville (G-6877)
United Cabinets Corp....G....305 887-5050
Hialeah (G-5660)
Universal Kit Cabinets Closets....G....305 406-9096
Kissimmee (G-7307)
Universal Kitchen Center Inc....G....305 218-5108
Hialeah (G-5664)
Universal Wood Design....F....772 569-5389
Vero Beach (G-18674)
Uptown Cstm Cabinets of Naples....G....239 825-8432
Naples (G-11448)
Ur Cabinets....G....813 434-6454
Tampa (G-18224)
V G Carpentry LLC....G....786 531-7824
Hialeah (G-5672)
▲ Vanbert Corporation....G....561 945-5856
Delray Beach (G-3154)
Velez Custom Cabinetry Corp....G....772 418-9565
Port Saint Lucie (G-15160)
Veneta Cucine Inc....G....305 949-5223
North Miami Beach (G-11709)
Venice Custom Cabinets Inc....G....941 488-5000
Nokomis (G-11591)
Victory Custom Cabinetry....G....727 937-2284
Holiday (G-5751)
Viking Woodworking....G....352 237-5050
Ocala (G-12071)
W E W Enterprises Inc....F....941 751-6610
Bradenton (G-1144)
Walker Wood Products Inc....G....904 448-5202
Jacksonville (G-6905)
We RE Organized....G....407 323-5133
Sanford (G-16137)
▼ Welshman Investment Corp....G....407 933-4444
Kissimmee (G-7310)
West Cast Cbnets Clsets Flrg I....F....239 481-8109
Fort Myers (G-4652)
West Coast Custom Cabinetry....F....239 481-8109
Fort Myers (G-4653)
Windermere Cabinetry LLC....G....321 263-5181
Winter Garden (G-19290)
▼ Windward Associates Corp....F....954 336-8085
Dania (G-2461)
Wogans Cstm Cbnets Rfacing LLC....G....904 343-8917
Jacksonville (G-6926)
Wood Aspects....G....321 800-8875
Deland (G-3035)
Wood Scapes Interiors....G....386 454-1540
High Springs (G-5703)
Wood U Envision....G....561 601-1973
West Palm Beach (G-19089)
▲ Wood Zone Inc....G....305 971-5550
Miami (G-10617)
Woodman Cabinets Inc....G....561 558-2550
Palmetto (G-13838)
Woods Distinctive Designs....F....941 698-7535
Port Charlotte (G-15008)
Woodtech Global Inc....F....941 371-0392
Bradenton (G-1148)
Woodwards Cabinets Inc....G....850 835-0071
Freeport (G-4854)
Woodworkers Cabinet Naples Inc....G....239 593-1718
Naples (G-11461)
Woodworks Cabinetry Inc....G....904 924-5300
Jacksonville (G-6928)
Woodworks Kit & Bath Designs....F....813 926-0570
Odessa (G-12166)
Woodworkx Unlimited Inc....G....772 882-4197
Fort Pierce (G-4771)
X-Treme Wood Cabinets Corp....G....305 537-8378
Cutler Bay (G-2422)
Y F Leung Inc....G....305 651-6851
North Miami Beach (G-11714)
Your Cabinet Source Inc....G....352 728-3806
Leesburg (G-8182)
Your Dreams Cabinets Corp....G....305 305-3729
Hialeah (G-5693)
Yp General Work & Cabinets....G....786 317-0973
Miami (G-10628)
Zbc Cabinetry....G....239 332-2940
Fort Myers (G-4659)
Zk Cabinets Inc....G....407 421-7307
Orlando (G-13343)

2435 Hardwood Veneer & Plywood

▼ Coastal Plywood Company....B....800 359-6432
Havana (G-5236)
▲ Dackor Inc....F....407 654-5013
Winter Garden (G-19259)
Esco Industries Inc....F....863 666-3696
Lakeland (G-7681)
Goodwin Lumber Company Inc....F....352 466-0339
Micanopy (G-10901)
▲ Plywood Express Inc....E....954 956-7576
Pompano Beach (G-14799)
Thomas Rley Artisans Guild Inc....E....239 591-3203
Naples (G-11440)

SIC

2436 Softwood Veneer & Plywood

◆ **Coastal Forest Resources Co** ....B 850 539-6432
Havana *(G-5235)*
▲ **Corelite Inc** ....F 305 921-4292
Hialeah *(G-5356)*
Cross City Veneer Company Inc ....D 352 498-3226
Cross City *(G-2364)*
Thomas Rley Artisans Guild Inc ....E 239 591-3203
Naples *(G-11440)*

2439 Structural Wood Members, NEC

▼ **A-1 Roof Trusses Ltd Company** ....F 270 316-9409
Coral Springs *(G-2210)*
A-1 Roof Trusses Ltd Company ....C 772 409-1010
Fort Pierce *(G-4668)*
Accu-Span Truss Co ....E 407 321-1440
Longwood *(G-8250)*
American Truss ....G 352 493-9700
Chiefland *(G-1529)*
American Truss Chiefland LL ....G 352 493-9700
Chiefland *(G-1530)*
Anderson Truss LLC ....E 386 752-3103
Lake City *(G-7348)*
Angle Truss Co Inc ....F 352 343-7477
Tavares *(G-18334)*
Arban & Associates Inc ....E 850 836-4362
Ponce De Leon *(G-14917)*
▼ **Architctral Mlding Mllwrks Inc** ....E 305 638-8900
Miami *(G-9163)*
B and B Roof and Floor Trusses ....G 850 265-4119
Lynn Haven *(G-8429)*
▼ **Best Truss Company** ....D 305 667-6797
Miami *(G-9235)*
Big Bend Truss Components Inc ....F 850 539-5351
Havana *(G-5234)*
Bruce Component Systems Inc ....F 352 628-0522
Lecanto *(G-8129)*
Bushnell Truss Enterprises LLC ....F 352 793-6090
Bushnell *(G-1314)*
Casmin Inc ....G 352 253-5000
Mount Dora *(G-11099)*
▼ **Central Florida Truss Inc** ....E 863 533-0821
Bartow *(G-312)*
▼ **Chambers Truss Inc** ....D 772 465-2012
Fort Pierce *(G-4687)*
CMF Truss Inc ....E 352 796-5805
Brooksville *(G-1220)*
Custom Truss LLC ....F 561 266-3451
Boynton Beach *(G-895)*
D & M Truss Co ....E 850 944-4864
Pensacola *(G-14124)*
D J Trusses Unlimited Inc ....F 863 687-4796
Lakeland *(G-7670)*
▼ **Dade Truss Company Inc** ....C 305 592-8245
Miami *(G-9431)*
Dan Boudreau Inc ....G 407 491-7611
Oviedo *(G-13425)*
◆ **Deco Truss Company Inc** ....E 305 257-1910
Homestead *(G-5962)*
Duley Truss Inc ....E 352 465-0964
Dunnellon *(G-3593)*
Emerald Coast Truss LLC ....E 850 623-1967
Milton *(G-10927)*
Fine Archtctral Mllwk Shutters ....F 954 491-2055
Fort Lauderdale *(G-3993)*
◆ **Florida Engineered Constru** ....C 813 621-4641
Seffner *(G-16726)*
Florida Forest Products LLC ....E 727 585-2067
Largo *(G-7949)*
Florida Quality Truss Inc ....G 954 975-3384
Pompano Beach *(G-14702)*
◆ **Florida Quality Truss Inds Inc** ....F 954 971-3167
Pompano Beach *(G-14703)*
Florida Truss Corporation ....G 407 438-2553
Orlando *(G-12758)*
Freeport Truss Company Inc ....F 850 835-4541
Freeport *(G-4846)*
Georgia-Pacific LLC ....E 404 652-4000
Silver Springs *(G-16782)*
Gulf Coast Truss Co Inc ....F 239 278-1819
Fort Myers *(G-4478)*
Hitech Truss Inc ....G 352 797-0877
Brooksville *(G-1234)*
Hitek Property LLC ....F 352 797-0877
Brooksville *(G-1235)*
Joseph J Taylor Truss ....G 321 482-4039
Melbourne *(G-8854)*
K & M Truss Inc ....G 407 880-4551
Zellwood *(G-19504)*
Kennedy Craft Cabinets Inc ....G 239 598-1566
Naples *(G-11304)*
Lemon Bay Truss & Supply Co ....G 941 698-0800
Placida *(G-14397)*
Marianna Truss Inc ....E 850 594-5420
Marianna *(G-8583)*
Martinez Builders Supply LLC ....D 772 466-2480
Fort Pierce *(G-4714)*
▼ **Martinez Truss Company Inc** ....F 305 883-6261
Medley *(G-8684)*
Mayo Truss Co Inc ....F 386 294-3988
Mayo *(G-8596)*
Mid-Florida Lbr Acqisitions Inc ....E 863 533-0155
Bartow *(G-325)*
Nexgen Framing System LLC ....F 321 508-6763
Palm Bay *(G-13525)*
Old Oak Truss Company ....G 813 689-6597
Seffner *(G-16731)*
Pacific Arches Corporation ....F 352 236-7787
Ocala *(G-12020)*
Park Place Manufacturing Inc ....F 863 382-0126
Sebring *(G-16701)*
Park Place Truss Inc ....F 863 382-0126
Sebring *(G-16702)*
Park Place Truss & Design Inc ....E 863 382-0126
Sebring *(G-16703)*
Pelliccione Builders Sup Inc ....F 941 334-3014
North Fort Myers *(G-11602)*
Ridgway Roof Truss Company ....D 352 376-4436
Gainesville *(G-4991)*
Royal Truss Corp ....F 786 222-1100
Medley *(G-8721)*
Santa Fe Truss Company Inc ....F 386 454-7711
Bell *(G-343)*
Scosta Corp ....C 863 385-8242
Sebring *(G-16705)*
Southern Truss Companies Inc ....D 772 464-4160
Fort Pierce *(G-4748)*
Southwest Strl Systems Inc ....E 239 693-6000
Fort Myers *(G-4609)*
Standard Truss & Roof Sup Inc ....E 863 422-8293
Haines City *(G-5149)*
Superior Truss Systems Inc ....D 305 591-9918
Doral *(G-3518)*
Taunton Truss Co Red Lobs ....G 850 785-5566
Panama City *(G-13954)*
True House Inc ....C 386 325-9085
East Palatka *(G-3608)*
True House Inc ....F 904 757-7500
Jacksonville *(G-6870)*
Truss Spans Unlimited LLC ....G 352 274-0306
Ocala *(G-12063)*
Truss Systems LLC ....G 386 255-3009
Bunnell *(G-1308)*
Truss Systems of Vlsia Flgler ....F 386 255-3009
Bunnell *(G-1309)*
Truss William ....G 954 438-4710
Pembroke Pines *(G-14066)*
Trusscorp International Inc ....E 305 882-8826
Medley *(G-8744)*
Trusses Unlimited Inc ....D 904 355-6611
Ponte Vedra Beach *(G-14955)*
Trussway Manufacturing Inc ....F 407 857-2777
Orlando *(G-13279)*
Trusswood Inc ....D 321 383-0366
Titusville *(G-18470)*
US Truss Inc ....E 561 686-4000
West Palm Beach *(G-19076)*
▼ **W Kost Inc** ....E 772 286-3700
Palm City *(G-13678)*
Wood Product Services Inc ....E 813 248-2221
Tampa *(G-18260)*
Yandles Quality Roof Trusses ....G 352 732-3000
Ocala *(G-12078)*

2441 Wood Boxes

▼ **Air-Flite Containers Inc** ....G 407 679-1200
Orlando *(G-12444)*
▼ **Allcases Reekstin & Assoc Inc** ....F 813 891-1313
Oldsmar *(G-12200)*
Animal Air Service Inc ....E 305 218-1759
Doral *(G-3250)*
Cross City Veneer Company Inc ....D 352 498-3226
Cross City *(G-2364)*
◆ **Custom Crate & Logistics Co** ....G 954 527-5742
Fort Lauderdale *(G-3924)*
Haman Industries Inc ....F 813 626-5700
Tampa *(G-17741)*
L & M Pallet Services Inc ....F 863 519-3502
Bartow *(G-322)*
Palm Beach Trim Inc ....E 561 588-8746
Davie *(G-2565)*

2448 Wood Pallets & Skids

A Pallet Co Inc ....G 561 798-1564
West Palm Beach *(G-18784)*
A Quallity Pallet Company ....G 239 245-0900
Fort Myers *(G-4341)*
A1 Pallets LLC ....G 813 598-9165
Thonotosassa *(G-18398)*
◆ **AA Florida Pallets** ....G 305 805-1522
Medley *(G-8603)*
Aaa-Affordable Pallets & Reels ....G 813 740-8009
Tampa *(G-17379)*
Aarons Pallets ....G 813 627-3225
Tampa *(G-17380)*
AB Used Pallets Inc ....F 305 594-2776
Miami *(G-9050)*
Advanced Pallets Inc ....E 954 785-1215
Margate *(G-8531)*
All State Pallets Company LLC ....F 407 855-8087
Orlando *(G-12454)*
Amigo Pallets Inc ....G 305 631-2452
Medley *(G-8609)*
Amigo Pallets Inc ....F 305 302-9751
Miami *(G-9150)*
B & T Pallets Inc ....G 941 360-0562
Sarasota *(G-16360)*
Best Pallets of FL LLC ....G 386 624-5575
Deland *(G-2962)*
Brothers Pallets ....G 863 944-5278
Lakeland *(G-7651)*
Buckley Pallets ....G 727 415-4497
Clearwater *(G-1616)*
Buckley Pallets LLC ....F 727 415-4497
Clearwater *(G-1617)*
Cal Air Forwarding ....G 305 871-4552
Miami *(G-9302)*
Camara Industries LLC ....F 407 879-2549
Orlando *(G-12544)*
Cienfuegos Pallets Corp ....G 786 703-3686
Medley *(G-8631)*
Compact Container Systems LLC ....F 561 392-6910
Boca Raton *(G-487)*
Container Mfg Solutions ....E 888 805-8785
Cutler Bay *(G-2389)*
D & S Pallet Recycle Center ....G 352 351-0070
Ocala *(G-11916)*
D & S Pallets Inc ....D 727 540-0061
Clearwater *(G-1647)*
Diversified Pallets Inc ....F 904 491-6800
Fernandina Beach *(G-3735)*
Floor Tech LLC ....F 407 855-8087
Orlando *(G-12745)*
Florida AA Pallets Inc ....G 305 805-1522
Medley *(G-8651)*
▼ **Florida Funeral Shipping Cntrs** ....G 954 957-9259
Fort Lauderdale *(G-4000)*
Florida Pallet LLC ....G 772 562-4900
Sebastian *(G-16659)*
Freeman Pallets Inc ....G 352 328-9326
Gainesville *(G-4924)*
Global Bamboo Technologies Inc ....E 707 730-0288
Ocala *(G-11956)*
▼ **Global Galan Logistics Inc** ....G 754 263-2708
Miramar *(G-10999)*
Gt Pallets LLC ....G 786 541-6532
Miami *(G-9682)*
Haman Industries Inc ....F 813 626-5700
Tampa *(G-17741)*
◆ **Jacksonville Box & Woodwork Co** ....F 904 354-1441
Jacksonville *(G-6510)*
L & M Pallet Services Inc ....F 863 519-3502
Bartow *(G-322)*
Lifdek Corporation ....G 321 759-3422
Melbourne *(G-8872)*
Mac Pallets ....G 813 340-3246
Tampa *(G-17870)*
Manasota Pallets ....F 941 360-0562
Sarasota *(G-16501)*
Marianna Truss Inc ....E 850 594-5420
Marianna *(G-8583)*
Monison Pallets Inc ....F 904 359-0235
Jacksonville *(G-6614)*
Monison Pallets Inc ....F 305 637-1600
Miami *(G-10040)*
Muchochos Saw Mill & Pallets ....G 786 899-0535
Miami Springs *(G-10895)*
National Pallets ....E 305 324-1021
Miami *(G-10062)*

▲ **Opa-Locka Pallets Inc**......F....... 305 681-8212
Opa Locka ***(G-12347)***
Pal-King Inc......E....... 904 334-8797
Jacksonville ***(G-6652)***
◆ **Pallet Consultants Corp**......E....... 954 946-2212
Pompano Beach ***(G-14783)***
Pallet Depot LLC......E....... 863 686-6245
Lakeland ***(G-7761)***
Pallet Direct Inc......G....... 888 433-1727
Naples ***(G-11354)***
Pallet Doctor Inc......G....... 904 444-2514
Jacksonville ***(G-6653)***
Pallet Dude LLC......F....... 941 720-1667
Sarasota ***(G-16535)***
▲ **Pallet Enterprises of Florida**......G....... 305 836-3204
Miami ***(G-10131)***
Pallet Enterprises Orlando Inc......G....... 407 888-3200
Orlando ***(G-13044)***
Pallet Ex Jacksonville Inc......E....... 904 781-2500
Jacksonville ***(G-6654)***
Pallet Exchange Inc......F....... 386 734-0133
Orange City ***(G-12377)***
Pallet Express Inc......F....... 813 752-1600
Plant City ***(G-14452)***
Pallet Express of Jkvl Inc......F....... 904 781-2500
Jacksonville ***(G-6655)***
Pallet Holdings LLC......D....... 561 367-0009
Boca Raton ***(G-660)***
Pallet Industries Inc......F....... 954 935-5804
Deerfield Beach ***(G-2882)***
Pallet One of Mobile LLC......F....... 251 960-1107
Bartow ***(G-326)***
Pallet Racks Plus LLC......G....... 321 203-6634
Orlando ***(G-13045)***
Pallet Recall Inc......G....... 941 727-1944
Sarasota ***(G-16270)***
Pallet Services Inc......G....... 813 754-7719
Plant City ***(G-14453)***
Pallet Solutions Inc......G....... 305 801-8314
Miami ***(G-10132)***
◆ **Palletone Inc**......E....... 800 771-1147
Bartow ***(G-327)***
▲ **Palletone of Texas LP**......D....... 903 628-5695
Bartow ***(G-328)***
Palletone of Texas LP......D....... 863 533-1147
Bartow ***(G-329)***
Pallets Inc......G....... 407 492-0857
Apopka ***(G-169)***
Pallets Plus Inc......G....... 813 759-6355
Plant City ***(G-14454)***
Pallets To Go Inc......F....... 305 654-0303
Miami ***(G-10133)***
Panama City Pallet Inc......E....... 850 769-1040
Panama City ***(G-13936)***
Panama Pallets Co Inc......G....... 850 769-1040
Panama City ***(G-13939)***
Pauls Pallets......G....... 850 474-1920
Pensacola ***(G-14222)***
Phoenix Wood Products Inc......E....... 888 304-1131
Ocala ***(G-12026)***
Placetas Pallet Corp......G....... 305 633-4262
Hialeah ***(G-5559)***
Preferred Pallets Llc......G....... 863 401-9517
Winter Haven ***(G-19344)***
Premier Pallet Recycler LLC......G....... 561 722-0457
West Palm Beach ***(G-19004)***
Premier Pallets Inc......G....... 813 986-4889
Tampa ***(G-18008)***
Ralph & Llerena Pallets Inc......G....... 305 446-2651
Hialeah ***(G-5593)***
Rass Fast Pallet Inc......G....... 786 877-2854
Miami ***(G-10241)***
Raymond Newkirk......G....... 772 359-0237
Fort Pierce ***(G-4737)***
Regional Trailer Repair Inc......F....... 912 484-7729
Jacksonville ***(G-6714)***
▲ **Ricks Pallet Co Inc**......G....... 305 884-4896
Hialeah ***(G-5600)***
▼ **Rima Cargo LLC**......G....... 305 477-8002
Miami ***(G-10264)***
Romeros Pallets of Jax......G....... 904 329-2962
Jacksonville ***(G-6734)***
S&B Pallet Corp......G....... 305 525-0872
Miami ***(G-10293)***
▲ **Sanchez Brothers Corp**......F....... 561 992-0062
South Bay ***(G-16797)***
Sophistcted Pllet Woodworx LLC......G....... 561 795-0739
Loxahatchee ***(G-8364)***
South Florida Pallet Inc......G....... 305 330-7663
Miami ***(G-10383)***
South Florida Pallets Dist......F....... 305 330-7663
Doral ***(G-3506)***
Southeastern Pallets Inc......G....... 904 783-8363
Jacksonville ***(G-6791)***
Suncoast Pallets Inc......G....... 813 988-1623
Temple Terrace ***(G-18379)***
Superior Pallets Llc......G....... 863 875-4041
Winter Haven ***(G-19359)***
Tropical Pallets Inc......G....... 305 634-0346
Miami ***(G-10508)***
USA Express Pallets Corp......G....... 786 251-9543
Miami ***(G-10554)***
Usmi Pallets Inc......G....... 813 765-4309
Plant City ***(G-14475)***
Walling Crate Company......F....... 352 787-5211
Leesburg ***(G-8180)***
Williams Jewelry and Mfg Co......G....... 727 823-7676
Saint Petersburg ***(G-15961)***
Xtreme Pallets Inc......G....... 954 302-8915
Coconut Creek ***(G-2104)***

2449 Wood Containers, NEC

▼ **Allcases Reekstin & Assoc Inc**......F....... 813 891-1313
Oldsmar ***(G-12200)***
Millenium Wood Boxes Inc......G....... 305 969-5510
Miami ***(G-10023)***
Qps Companies Inc......E....... 813 246-5525
Tampa ***(G-18029)***
Quantum Development LLC......G....... 954 587-4205
Fort Lauderdale ***(G-4192)***
Southern Closet Systems Inc......G....... 813 926-9348
Odessa ***(G-12153)***
Stemler Corporation......E....... 727 577-1216
Saint Petersburg ***(G-15927)***
Walling Crate Company......F....... 352 787-5211
Leesburg ***(G-8180)***

2451 Mobile Homes

◆ **America Trading Inc**......F....... 305 256-0101
Miami ***(G-9139)***
Brightman......G....... 386 752-4883
Lake City ***(G-7349)***
Center Seal Inc......G....... 863 965-7124
Auburndale ***(G-232)***
▼ **Chariot Eagle Inc**......C....... 623 936-7545
Ocala ***(G-11901)***
Clayton Homes Inc......G....... 850 785-3302
Panama City ***(G-13881)***
Dills Enterprises LLC......G....... 941 493-1993
Venice ***(G-18542)***
Eiq Mobility Inc......G....... 561 691-7171
Juno Beach ***(G-6979)***
Florida Harbor Homes Inc......F....... 941 284-8363
Englewood ***(G-3677)***
Good Rep Inc......G....... 407 869-6531
Longwood ***(G-8285)***
Harbor Homes......G....... 941 320-2670
Sarasota ***(G-16458)***
Jacobsen Factory Outlet......G....... 386 438-8458
Lake City ***(G-7362)***
Jacobsen Manufacturing Inc......C....... 727 726-1138
Safety Harbor ***(G-15496)***
Linman Inc......B....... 904 755-6800
Lake City ***(G-7365)***
Marlin Darlin Air LLC......G....... 727 726-1136
Belleair Bluffs ***(G-363)***
Nobility Homes Inc......D....... 352 732-5157
Ocala ***(G-12006)***
Nobility Homes Inc......E....... 352 245-5126
Belleview ***(G-373)***
Realty Systems Inc......F....... 386 439-0460
Flagler Beach ***(G-3756)***
Rolling Greens Mobile Home Pk......G....... 352 624-0022
Ocala ***(G-12039)***
Southern Pines Inc......G....... 239 947-1515
Bonita Springs ***(G-855)***
Step Zone LLC......G....... 850 983-3758
Milton ***(G-10940)***
Stone Harbor Homes LLC......G....... 239 672-7687
Cape Coral ***(G-1479)***
Tridor Group Inc......F....... 786 707-2241
Miami ***(G-10506)***
Tropic Isles Co-Op Inc......F....... 941 721-8888
Palmetto ***(G-13831)***
Wayne Dixon LLC......G....... 352 279-6886
Brooksville ***(G-1291)***

2452 Prefabricated Wood Buildings & Cmp-nts

▼ **Advanced Mdular Structures Inc**......G....... 954 960-1550
Pompano Beach ***(G-14580)***
All Modular Service Inc......F....... 352 429-0868
Mascotte ***(G-8593)***
Amazon Sheds and Gazebos Inc......F....... 239 498-5558
Fort Myers ***(G-4355)***
▼ **Chariot Eagle Inc**......C....... 623 936-7545
Ocala ***(G-11901)***
East Coast Floats LLC......G....... 407 203-5628
Orlando ***(G-12694)***
Florida Shed Company Inc......E....... 727 524-9191
Saint Petersburg ***(G-15785)***
HI Tech Construction Svc Inc......E....... 863 968-0731
Winter Haven ***(G-19328)***
◆ **Innova Eco Bldg Systems LLC**......E....... 305 455-7707
Miami ***(G-9746)***
▼ **Island Style Homes Inc**......G....... 772 464-6259
Fort Pierce ***(G-4709)***
Jacobsen Manufacturing Inc......C....... 727 726-1138
Safety Harbor ***(G-15496)***
Jennings Mobile HM Set Up LLC......F....... 863 965-0883
Auburndale ***(G-247)***
▼ **Neopod Systems LLC**......F....... 954 603-3100
Sunrise ***(G-17151)***
◆ **Quality Cmpnents Tampa Bay LLC**......G....... 727 623-4909
Largo ***(G-8034)***
Riverhead Housing Inc......G....... 630 688-6791
Fort Lauderdale ***(G-4206)***
South Country Sheds LLC......F....... 863 491-8700
Arcadia ***(G-205)***
Southeastern Seating Inc......F....... 813 273-9858
Tampa ***(G-18119)***
Stalo Modulars LLC......F....... 786 713-2410
Miami ***(G-10408)***
▼ **Suncrest Sheds Inc**......F....... 863 675-8600
Labelle ***(G-7324)***
▲ **Surepods LLC**......D....... 407 859-7034
Orlando ***(G-13232)***
Truss Systems LLC......G....... 386 255-3009
Bunnell ***(G-1308)***
Truss Systems of Vlsia Flgler......F....... 386 255-3009
Bunnell ***(G-1309)***

2491 Wood Preserving

All Moldings Inc......G....... 305 556-6171
Hialeah ***(G-5279)***
Apalachee Pole Company Inc......E....... 850 643-2121
Bristol ***(G-1191)***
Arnold Lumber Company Inc......F....... 850 547-5733
Bonifay ***(G-798)***
◆ **Coastal Forest Resources Co**......B....... 850 539-6432
Havana ***(G-5235)***
Commercial Casework Inc......D....... 904 264-4222
Jacksonville ***(G-6280)***
Commercial Wood Designs Inc......F....... 407 302-9063
Sanford ***(G-16018)***
▼ **F & R General Interiors Corp**......F....... 305 635-4747
Hialeah ***(G-5402)***
Great Southern Wood Prsv Inc......E....... 352 793-9410
Lake Panasoffkee ***(G-7463)***
▼ **Infinite Ret Design & Mfg Corp**......F....... 305 967-8339
Miami ***(G-9741)***
International Weatherization......G....... 954 818-3288
Fort Lauderdale ***(G-4065)***
John Andersen......G....... 407 702-4891
Apopka ***(G-151)***
Johnny Under Pressure LLC......G....... 850 530-8763
Pensacola ***(G-14184)***
Larry C Cribb......G....... 904 845-2804
Hilliard ***(G-5714)***
Mirandas Woodcraft LLC......G....... 954 306-3568
Lauderhill ***(G-8115)***
Pensacola Wood Treating Co......G....... 850 433-1300
Pensacola ***(G-14228)***
◆ **Robbins Manufacturing Company**......C....... 813 971-3030
Tampa ***(G-18063)***
Robbins Manufacturing Company......B....... 888 558-8199
Tampa ***(G-18064)***
Southern Lbr & Treating Co Inc......F....... 904 695-0784
Jacksonville ***(G-6795)***
Ufp Orlando LLC......F....... 407 982-3312
Orlando ***(G-13285)***
Ufp Tampa LLC......E....... 813 971-3030
Tampa ***(G-18212)***
York Bridge Concepts Inc......E....... 813 482-0613
Lutz ***(G-8426)***

SIC

2493 Reconstituted Wood Prdts

◆ **Allied Plastics Co Inc** .... E 904 359-0386
Jacksonville *(G-6138)*
Chicago Electronic Distrs Inc .... F 312 985-6175
Port Charlotte *(G-14969)*
Continental Palatka LLC .... D 703 480-3800
Palatka *(G-13475)*
Custom Cornhole Boards Inc .... E 407 203-6886
Orlando *(G-12638)*
Enviva Pellets Cottondale LLC .... E 850 557-7357
Cottondale *(G-2331)*
Fatezzi Inc .... G 407 323-8688
Sanford *(G-16044)*
Florida Plywoods Inc .... D 850 948-2211
Greenville *(G-5088)*
GL Shavings LLC .... G 352 360-0063
Groveland *(G-5096)*
Jabs Investors Corp .... F 561 540-2693
Lake Worth Beach *(G-7614)*
◆ **Polyglass USA Inc** .... D 954 246-8888
Deerfield Beach *(G-2888)*
Sarasotas Finest MBL Gran Inc .... G 941 365-9697
Sarasota *(G-16583)*
Standard Industries Inc .... D 813 248-7000
Tampa *(G-18129)*

2499 Wood Prdts, NEC

4303 Silverwood LLC .... G 904 900-1702
Jacksonville *(G-6102)*
6425 Hollywood Blvd LLC .... G 941 923-2954
Sarasota *(G-16327)*
A B Survey Supply Entps Inc .... G 772 464-9500
Fort Pierce *(G-4667)*
A Plus Kitchen & Bath .... G 754 200-4207
Lauderhill *(G-8098)*
Abbott Citrus Ladders Inc .... G 863 773-6322
Bowling Green *(G-864)*
ABC Fence Systems Inc .... F 850 638-8876
Chipley *(G-1540)*
▲ **Ackue International LLC** .... G 407 323-8688
Sanford *(G-15986)*
Agp Holding Corp .... G 850 668-0006
Tallahassee *(G-17214)*
◆ **Agri-Products Inc** .... G 850 668-0006
Tallahassee *(G-17215)*
Agri-Source Inc .... E 352 351-2700
Ocala *(G-11866)*
Amick Cstm Woodcraft & Design .... G 407 324-8525
Sanford *(G-15994)*
◆ **Art & Frame Direct Inc** .... C 407 857-6000
Orlando *(G-12491)*
▲ **Art & Frame Drct/Timeless Inds** .... G 407 857-6000
Orlando *(G-12492)*
◆ **Art Connection Usa LLC** .... E 954 781-0125
Pompano Beach *(G-14600)*
▲ **Artworks International** .... G 561 833-9165
West Palm Beach *(G-18804)*
Backwoods Crossing Llc .... F 850 765-3753
Tallahassee *(G-17225)*
Banaghan Wood Products Inc .... E 386 788-6114
Port Orange *(G-15010)*
Blackwater Folk Art Inc .... G 850 623-3470
Milton *(G-10922)*
Boyett Timber Inc .... G 352 583-2138
Webster *(G-18697)*
Burnham Woods Untd Civic Group .... G 954 532-2675
North Lauderdale *(G-11612)*
C & S Foliage .... G 352 357-4847
Eustis *(G-3704)*
Carpentree Creation .... G 904 300-4008
Jacksonville *(G-6255)*
Cinega Custom Framing & Design .... E 904 495-1846
Orange Park *(G-12386)*
Coastal Paddle Co LLC .... F 850 916-1600
Gulf Breeze *(G-5114)*
Consolidated Forest Pdts Inc .... G 407 830-7723
Perry *(G-14298)*
Consolidated Forest Pdts Inc .... F 407 830-7723
Longwood *(G-8267)*
Coral Gables Custom Design Inc .... F 305 591-7575
Miami *(G-9401)*
Core Outdoors Inc .... G 904 215-6866
Saint Augustine *(G-15532)*
Crowell Marine Inc .... G 813 236-3625
Tampa *(G-17570)*
Cubos LLC .... G 786 299-2671
Miami *(G-9418)*
▼ **Danielle Fence Mfg Co Inc** .... D 863 425-3182
Mulberry *(G-11121)*
Davanti Doors Llc .... G 239 842-8341
Fort Myers *(G-4426)*
Del Mar Hollywood LLC .... G 786 325-8335
Miami Beach *(G-10661)*
▼ **Delet Doors Inc** .... F 786 250-4506
Miami *(G-9445)*
Delta Mg .... G 561 840-0577
West Palm Beach *(G-18853)*
Designer Lifestyles LLC .... F 904 631-8954
Jacksonville *(G-6317)*
Dixie Workshop Inc .... G 352 629-4699
Ocala *(G-11922)*
Dolphin Kitchen & Bath .... G 305 482-9486
Miami *(G-9476)*
Dolphin Paddlesports Inc .... F 941 924-2785
Sarasota *(G-16412)*
Duncanmatthews LLC .... G 813 466-8290
Tampa *(G-17619)*
E & M Recycling Inc .... G 561 718-1092
Lake Worth *(G-7548)*
East Coast Cooling Tower Inc .... F 904 551-5527
Jacksonville *(G-6348)*
Excel Millwork & Moulding Inc .... E 850 576-7228
Midway *(G-10917)*
Fanatics Mounted Memories Inc .... E 866 578-9115
Jacksonville *(G-6378)*
Fine Line Custom Millwork LLC .... E 941 628-9611
Arcadia *(G-203)*
▼ **Florida Cypress & Fence Co** .... G 561 392-3011
Palm City *(G-13656)*
Florida Frames Inc .... F 727 572-4064
Clearwater *(G-1688)*
Forestry Resources Inc .... E 239 332-3966
Fort Myers *(G-4457)*
▲ **Frametastic Inc** .... F 954 567-2800
Fort Lauderdale *(G-4011)*
G and W Craftsman LLC .... G 440 453-2770
Naples *(G-11256)*
Generations Metier Inc .... E 239 283-9209
Cape Coral *(G-1428)*
Hohol Marine Products .... G 386 734-0630
Deland *(G-2983)*
Hollywood Houndz LLC .... G 407 614-2108
Winter Garden *(G-19269)*
Hollywood Lodging Inc .... G 305 803-7455
Hollywood *(G-5843)*
Home Works Bay County Inc .... G 850 215-7880
Panama City *(G-13915)*
J & K 8 Inc .... F 954 984-8585
Pompano Beach *(G-14734)*
J T S Woodworking Inc .... G 561 272-7996
Delray Beach *(G-3094)*
◆ **Jem Art Inc** .... E 954 966-7078
Sunrise *(G-17136)*
John Hurst Outdoor Svcs LLC .... G 850 556-7459
Tallahassee *(G-17284)*
JRP Screen Printing Inc .... E 305 333-4244
Hialeah *(G-5469)*
K & B Landscape Supplies Inc .... G 800 330-8816
Deland *(G-2990)*
K K Woodworking .... G 321 724-1298
Malabar *(G-8491)*
Konadocks LLC .... G 407 909-0606
Winter Garden *(G-19272)*
Laundromart .... G 561 487-4343
Boca Raton *(G-598)*
Linenwood Home LLC .... G 850 607-7445
Pensacola *(G-14194)*
Location 3 Holdings LLC .... F 941 342-3443
Sarasota *(G-16489)*
Madden Millworks .... G 310 514-2640
Jacksonville *(G-6573)*
Mamalu Wood LLC .... G 305 261-6332
Miami *(G-9939)*
Mc Connie Enterprises Inc .... G 813 247-3827
Tampa *(G-17897)*
▼ **Miami Decor Inc** .... F 800 235-2197
Miami *(G-9998)*
Mm Wildwood LLC .... G 917 609-7128
Oxford *(G-13464)*
Mounted Memories Inc .... F 866 236-2541
Miramar *(G-11018)*
◆ **Noveltex Miami Inc** .... E 305 887-8191
Hialeah *(G-5544)*
Paul Tinsley Engraving .... G 407 656-4344
Winter Garden *(G-19279)*
Petit Custom Wood Works .... G 954 200-3111
Davie *(G-2570)*
Pixotine Products Inc .... G 305 479-1335
Jupiter *(G-7093)*
Pleasure Interiors LLC .... E 941 756-9969
Sarasota *(G-16545)*
▲ **R P M Industries Inc** .... E 315 255-1105
Hobe Sound *(G-5726)*
Randy Wheeler .... G 850 997-1248
Monticello *(G-11081)*
▼ **Rich Woodturning Inc** .... F 305 573-9142
Miami Lakes *(G-10851)*
▲ **Round Table Tools Inc** .... G 850 877-7650
Tallahassee *(G-17318)*
▲ **Russell Hobbs Inc** .... D 954 883-1000
Miramar *(G-11037)*
Sandy Finished Wood Inc .... E 954 615-7271
Fort Lauderdale *(G-4223)*
Silverman Fence Mfg Inc .... G 904 730-0882
Jacksonville *(G-6774)*
Sira .... G 352 377-4947
Gainesville *(G-4999)*
▼ **Southern Softwoods Inc** .... E 863 666-1404
Lakeland *(G-7801)*
Spray-Tech Staining Inc .... F 407 443-4239
Longwood *(G-8339)*
Strasser Enterprises .... G 386 677-5163
Daytona Beach *(G-2720)*
Summit ATL Productions LLC .... F 407 930-5488
Orlando *(G-13221)*
Teakdecking Systems Inc .... D 941 756-0600
Sarasota *(G-16309)*
Temple Terrace Industries Inc .... F 813 752-7546
Plant City *(G-14472)*
▼ **Three Brothers Boards** .... G 386 310-4927
Daytona Beach *(G-2726)*
Total Vision Design Group .... G 407 438-6933
Orlando *(G-13263)*
Tree Stake Solutions LLC .... G 407 920-0507
Orlando *(G-13269)*
◆ **W R Williams Enterprises Inc** .... G 813 677-2000
Gibsonton *(G-5035)*
▼ **Welshman Investment Corp** .... G 407 933-4444
Kissimmee *(G-7310)*
West Development Group LLC .... G 407 308-5020
Orlando *(G-13322)*
Weston Park At Longwood STA .... G 321 422-3546
Longwood *(G-8350)*
Wood & Glass Works LLC .... G 727 317-9599
Pinellas Park *(G-14394)*
Wood Splinter Corp .... G 305 721-7215
Miami *(G-10616)*
Wood U LLC .... G 954 560-2000
Oakland Park *(G-11862)*
Woodcrafts By Angel Inc .... G 352 754-9335
Brooksville *(G-1293)*
Wooden It Be Nice .... G 352 797-0427
Brooksville *(G-1294)*
Wurth Wood Group Inc .... F 800 432-1149
Tampa *(G-18268)*
Yahl Mulching & Recycling Inc .... F 239 352-7888
Naples *(G-11462)*
Zeta Kitchen & Bath Inc .... G 786 552-2322
Miami *(G-10630)*

25 FURNITURE AND FIXTURES

2511 Wood Household Furniture

A A A Cabinets .... G 850 438-8337
Pensacola *(G-14075)*
▲ **Ahus Inc** .... E 305 572-9052
Miami Gardens *(G-10732)*
Aj Originals Inc .... G 954 563-9911
Fort Lauderdale *(G-3793)*
◆ **Allied Plastics Co Inc** .... E 904 359-0386
Jacksonville *(G-6138)*
American Frame Furniture Inc .... G 305 548-3018
Miami *(G-9142)*
Annette M Wellington Hall Inc .... G 954 437-9880
Hollywood *(G-5772)*
Avrora Inc .... G 386 246-9112
Palm Coast *(G-13685)*
B C Cabinetry .... G 561 393-8937
Boca Raton *(G-436)*
Beaches Woodcraft Inc .... F 904 249-0785
Atlantic Beach *(G-217)*
Belle Isle Furniture LLC .... G 407 408-1266
Belle Isle *(G-356)*
▲ **Blue Water Chairs Inc** .... E 954 318-0840
Fort Lauderdale *(G-3860)*
Bon Vivant Interiors Inc .... E 305 576-8066
Opa Locka *(G-12296)*
Bpc LLC .... F 305 987-9517
Miami *(G-9272)*

Capitol Furniture Mfg LLC....G....954 485-5000
Boca Raton *(G-469)*
Carsons Cabinetry and Design....G....352 373-8292
Archer *(G-207)*
▲ Cedar Fresh Home Products LLC....G....305 975-8524
Miami *(G-9332)*
◆ Closetmaid LLC....B....352 401-6000
Orlando *(G-12591)*
Contemporary Interiors Inc....E....352 620-8686
Ocala *(G-11907)*
Cramco Inc....G....305 634-7500
Miami *(G-9409)*
Creative Woodwork Miami Inc....F....305 634-3100
Miami *(G-9411)*
Custom Beach Huts LLC....G....305 439-3991
Coral Gables *(G-2135)*
Custom Cabinets Inc....F....941 366-0428
Sarasota *(G-16398)*
Custom Mica Furniture Inc....G....305 888-8480
Hialeah *(G-5359)*
Davila Woodworking Inc....G....954 458-0460
Hallandale Beach *(G-5180)*
Design Systems South Inc....G....850 293-1905
Pensacola *(G-14130)*
Dixie Workshop Inc....G....352 629-4699
Ocala *(G-11922)*
Ecco Doors LLC....G....561 392-3533
Boynton Beach *(G-901)*
▲ Elegant House Intl LLC....G....954 457-8836
Hallandale *(G-5157)*
Fine Archtctral Mllwk Shutters....F....954 491-2055
Fort Lauderdale *(G-3993)*
Furniture Concepts 2000 Inc....G....954 946-0310
Pompano Beach *(G-14706)*
Furniture Design of Centl Fla....F....407 330-4430
Sanford *(G-16052)*
Genie Shelf....G....305 213-4382
Miami *(G-9627)*
Gilmans Custom Furn & Cabinets....F....352 746-3532
Lecanto *(G-8134)*
▲ Glodea Store Corp....G....888 400-4937
Jacksonville *(G-6439)*
Grand Buffet....G....941 752-3388
Bradenton *(G-1052)*
Gulf South Distributors Inc....F....850 244-1522
Fort Walton Beach *(G-4807)*
IB Furniture Inc....G....941 371-5764
Sarasota *(G-16463)*
▼ Infinite Ret Design & Mfg Corp....F....305 967-8339
Miami *(G-9741)*
Italkraft LLC....E....305 406-1301
Doral *(G-3396)*
J & S Cypress Inc....F....352 383-3864
Sorrento *(G-16787)*
J M Interiors Inc....G....305 891-6121
North Miami *(G-11642)*
J T S Woodworking Inc....G....561 272-7996
Delray Beach *(G-3094)*
Ken Clearys Two LLC....F....727 573-0700
Clearwater *(G-1749)*
▲ Lakewood Manufacturing Co Inc....C....443 398-5015
West Palm Beach *(G-18925)*
Lawko Inc....G....904 389-2850
Jacksonville *(G-6550)*
Lifetime Environmental Designs....G....352 237-7177
Ocala *(G-11984)*
Madison Millwork & Cabinet Co....E....954 966-7551
Hollywood *(G-5868)*
Maggac Corporation....G....561 439-2707
Lake Worth *(G-7567)*
Mantua Manufacturing Co....G....813 621-3714
Tampa *(G-17878)*
◆ Manufacturing By Skema Inc....G....954 797-7325
Davie *(G-2548)*
McCallum Cabinets Inc....F....352 372-2344
Gainesville *(G-4957)*
Mica Visions Inc....G....727 712-3213
Clearwater *(G-1784)*
Mobius Business Group Inc....F....239 274-8900
Fort Myers *(G-4535)*
Mr Mica Wood Inc....F....561 278-5821
Delray Beach *(G-3109)*
▼ N & N Investment Corporation....E....954 590-3800
Pompano Beach *(G-14770)*
◆ Nfjb Inc....E....954 771-1100
Fort Lauderdale *(G-4141)*
Noell Design Group Inc....G....561 391-9942
Boca Raton *(G-646)*
▼ Nosta Inc....G....305 634-1435
Miami *(G-10079)*
Omni Dsgns Ldscp Mngements LLC....G....561 339-4800
Jupiter *(G-7087)*
Pastrana Prime LLC....F....407 470-9339
Orlando *(G-13052)*
Perri Brothers and Associates....G....305 887-8686
Medley *(G-8704)*
Pinellas Custom Cabinets Inc....G....727 864-4263
Largo *(G-8027)*
▲ PKolino LLC....G....888 403-8992
Miami *(G-10167)*
Princeton Industries Inc....E....954 344-9155
Margate *(G-8563)*
R & R Mica Works Inc....G....305 231-1887
Miami Lakes *(G-10847)*
◆ Raytash Inc....G....561 347-8863
Boca Raton *(G-681)*
Riverstone Snctary - Cbd - Inc....G....954 473-1254
Fort Lauderdale *(G-4207)*
Rm Custom Woodcraft Inc....G....786 355-7387
Miami *(G-10267)*
Rolu Woodcraft Inc....F....305 685-0914
Hialeah *(G-5605)*
Saint Petersburg Cabinets Inc....G....727 327-4800
Saint Petersburg *(G-15904)*
Shelfgenie....G....877 814-3643
Naples *(G-11398)*
▲ Silverline Furniture Corp....G....305 663-9560
Miami *(G-10349)*
Simply45 LLC....G....954 982-2017
Fort Lauderdale *(G-4235)*
Smith Products Co Inc....F....386 325-4534
Palatka *(G-13492)*
Spacios Design Group Inc....F....305 696-1766
Miami *(G-10393)*
Thomas Rley Artisans Guild Inc....E....239 591-3203
Naples *(G-11440)*
TPL Manufacturing Inc....G....954 783-3400
Pompano Beach *(G-14889)*
Unlimited Cabinet Designs Inc....F....954 923-3269
Hallandale *(G-5165)*
Utopia Grilling LLC....G....727 488-1355
New Port Richey *(G-11518)*
Via Cabinets Corp....G....407 633-1915
Orlando *(G-13301)*
▼ Viking Kabinets Inc....E....305 238-9025
Cutler Bay *(G-2420)*
◆ Waterfall Industries Inc....F....407 330-2003
Sanford *(G-16134)*
Willson & Son Industry Inc....G....954 972-5073
Margate *(G-8572)*
Winston & Sons Inc....G....954 562-1984
Tamarac *(G-17370)*
Wood Drams Inc of Palm Beaches....G....561 842-9814
Lake Park *(G-7482)*
Woodcraft LLC....G....850 217-7757
Navarre *(G-11476)*
Woodcrafts By Angel Inc....G....352 754-9335
Brooksville *(G-1293)*
Y F Leung Inc....G....305 651-6851
North Miami Beach *(G-11714)*
▲ Yield Design....G....402 321-2196
Saint Augustine *(G-15640)*
Yonder Woodworks Inc....G....561 547-5777
West Palm Beach *(G-19090)*

2512 Wood Household Furniture, Upholstered

▼ American Marine Coverings Inc....F....305 889-5355
Hialeah *(G-5292)*
Andrews Warehouse Partnership....G....954 524-3330
Fort Lauderdale *(G-3817)*
Architctral Wdwkg Concepts Inc....G....239 434-0549
Naples *(G-11166)*
Associated Interior Desgr Svc....F....561 655-4926
West Palm Beach *(G-18805)*
Bon Vivant Interiors Inc....E....305 576-8066
Opa Locka *(G-12296)*
Capitol Furniture Mfg LLC....G....954 485-5000
Boca Raton *(G-469)*
◆ Capris Furniture Inds Inc....C....352 629-8889
Ocala *(G-11893)*
▲ Carlton Mfg Inc....G....352 465-2153
Dunnellon *(G-3594)*
Contemporary Interiors Inc....E....352 620-8686
Ocala *(G-11907)*
Design Furnishings Inc....E....407 294-0507
Orlando *(G-12663)*
Design Systems South Inc....G....850 293-1905
Pensacola *(G-14130)*
Devon Chase & Company....G....407 438-6466
Orlando *(G-12667)*
▲ Elegant House Intl LLC....G....954 457-8836
Hallandale *(G-5157)*
Expressions In Wood....G....954 956-0005
Pompano Beach *(G-14686)*
Grafton Furniture Company....E....305 696-3811
Miami *(G-9653)*
H317 Logistics LLC....G....404 307-1621
Vero Beach *(G-18624)*
Home Art Corporation....F....352 326-3337
Fruitland Park *(G-4865)*
◆ Jordan Brown Inc....G....904 495-0717
Saint Augustine *(G-15562)*
◆ Koki Interiors Furn Mfg Inc....F....305 558-6573
Hialeah *(G-5475)*
Martinson Mica Wood Pdts Inc....G....305 688-4445
Opa Locka *(G-12335)*
Modern Happy Home Llc....G....954 436-0055
Fort Lauderdale *(G-4123)*
▲ Nordic Line Inc....E....561 338-5545
Boca Raton *(G-648)*
Pendulum One Inc....G....561 844-8169
Riviera Beach *(G-15360)*
Ruby Vanrum....G....850 643-5155
Bristol *(G-1203)*
S&S Global Supply LLC....G....786 529-4799
Hialeah *(G-5608)*
Shores Global LLC....G....305 716-0848
Miami *(G-10340)*
Spring Oaks LLC....F....352 592-1150
Brooksville *(G-1276)*
◆ Stanley Chair Company Inc....E....813 884-1436
Tampa *(G-18130)*
◆ Unimat Industries LLC....G....305 716-0358
Miami *(G-10530)*
▼ Unique Originals Inc....F....305 634-2274
Fort Lauderdale *(G-4293)*

2514 Metal Household Furniture

▲ American Household Inc....D....561 912-4100
Boca Raton *(G-422)*
Built LLC....G....813 512-6250
Tampa *(G-17489)*
Cadence Keen Innovations Inc....G....561 249-2219
West Palm Beach *(G-18833)*
Casual Tone Inc....F....941 722-5643
Palmetto *(G-13789)*
Cramco Inc....G....305 634-7500
Miami *(G-9409)*
Dgp Enterprises Inc....F....941 729-2373
Sarasota *(G-16206)*
FL Central Cnstr & Rmdlg....G....863 701-3548
Lakeland *(G-7687)*
Florida Custom Fabricators....F....407 892-8538
Saint Cloud *(G-15650)*
Florida Finisher Inc....G....941 722-5643
Palmetto *(G-13799)*
Gk Inc....E....215 223-7207
Fort Lauderdale *(G-4022)*
Got It Inc....G....954 899-0001
Boca Raton *(G-550)*
J M Interiors Inc....G....305 891-6121
North Miami *(G-11642)*
◆ Jordan Brown Inc....G....904 495-0717
Saint Augustine *(G-15562)*
Kit Residential Designs Inc....G....305 796-5940
Hialeah *(G-5473)*
▼ Mag Works Inc....E....305 823-4440
Hialeah *(G-5496)*
Mantua Manufacturing Co....G....813 621-3714
Tampa *(G-17878)*
▼ Medallion Leisure Furniture....E....305 626-0000
Miami *(G-9964)*
Metal Craft of Pensacola Inc....E....850 478-8333
Pensacola *(G-14207)*
Mobilite Corporation....D....407 321-5630
Sanford *(G-16089)*
▼ Murphy Bed USA Inc....E....954 493-9001
Fort Lauderdale *(G-4127)*
Saint Petersburg Cabinets Inc....G....727 327-4800
Saint Petersburg *(G-15904)*
▲ Schwarzmann LLC....G....561 654-3653
Delray Beach *(G-3138)*
Studio Luxe Cstm Cabinetry LLC....G....941 371-4010
Sarasota *(G-16607)*
Sunbeam Americas Holdings LLC....C....561 912-4100
Boca Raton *(G-736)*
◆ Suncoast Aluminum Furn Inc....E....239 267-8300
Fort Myers *(G-4615)*

SIC

Sungraf Inc......F...... 954 456-8500
Hallandale Beach *(G-5216)*
Trainor Metal Products Inc......G...... 561 395-5520
Boca Raton *(G-754)*
◆ **Tuuci LLC**......C...... 305 634-5116
Hialeah *(G-5654)*
Tuuci Worldwide......G...... 305 634-5116
Hialeah *(G-5655)*
◆ **Tuuci Worldwide LLC**......C...... 305 634-5116
Miami *(G-10514)*
Wall Bed Systems Inc......G...... 419 738-5207
Clearwater *(G-1936)*

2515 Mattresses & Bedsprings

▼ **Biscayne Bedding Intl LLC**......E...... 305 633-4634
Hialeah *(G-5327)*
Blu Sleep Products LLC......G...... 866 973-7614
Deerfield Beach *(G-2785)*
Corsicana Bedding LLC......E...... 863 519-5905
Bartow *(G-313)*
Devon Chase & Company......G...... 407 438-6466
Orlando *(G-12667)*
Diaz Brothers Corp......G...... 305 364-4911
Hialeah *(G-5372)*
Leggett & Platt Incorporated......D...... 954 846-0300
Sunrise *(G-17142)*
▼ **Murphy Bed USA Inc**......E...... 954 493-9001
Fort Lauderdale *(G-4127)*
National Bedding Company LLC......C...... 561 840-8491
Riviera Beach *(G-15351)*
Plushbeds Inc......G...... 888 449-5738
Boca Raton *(G-667)*
Rex Fox Enterprises Inc......F...... 386 677-3752
Daytona Beach *(G-2704)*
S&S Global Supply LLC......G...... 786 529-4799
Hialeah *(G-5608)*
Savor Sleep LLC......G...... 860 577-2867
Naples *(G-11393)*
◆ **Sleep International LLC**......E...... 813 247-5337
Tampa *(G-18108)*
▼ **Sleeprite Industries Inc**......E...... 650 344-1980
Boca Raton *(G-720)*
▼ **Star Bedding Mfg Corp**......E...... 305 887-5209
Hialeah *(G-5632)*
▼ **Symbol Mattress Florida Inc**......G...... 407 343-4626
Kissimmee *(G-7302)*
Teralife LLC......G...... 407 434-0408
Orlando *(G-13248)*
United Beddings Corp......F...... 786 333-4795
Hialeah *(G-5659)*
Zeno Furniture & Mat Mfg Co......G...... 954 764-1212
Fort Lauderdale *(G-4335)*

2517 Wood T V, Radio, Phono & Sewing Cabinets

Amick Cstm Woodcraft & Design......G...... 407 324-8525
Sanford *(G-15994)*
Bon Vivant Interiors Inc......E...... 305 576-8066
Opa Locka *(G-12296)*
Dons Cabinets and Woodworking......F...... 727 863-3404
Hudson *(G-6022)*
▲ **Elegant House Intl LLC**......G...... 954 457-8836
Hallandale *(G-5157)*
▼ **Florida Designer Cabinets Inc**......F...... 352 793-8555
Sumterville *(G-17068)*
Home Pride Cabinets Inc......F...... 813 887-3782
Tampa *(G-17760)*
J & J Custom Mica Inc......F...... 239 433-2828
Fort Myers *(G-4498)*
McCallum Cabinets Inc......F...... 352 372-2344
Gainesville *(G-4957)*
Spruce Creek Cabinetry Inc......F...... 386 756-0041
Port Orange *(G-15035)*
Still Water Industries Inc......G...... 561 845-6033
West Palm Beach *(G-19045)*
Williams Minerals Co Inc......G...... 304 897-6003
Winter Springs *(G-19489)*
Y F Leung Inc......G...... 305 651-6851
North Miami Beach *(G-11714)*

2519 Household Furniture, NEC

Alluring Design LLC......G...... 305 582-3481
Hialeah *(G-5283)*
Alumatech Manufacturing Inc......E...... 941 748-8880
Bradenton *(G-986)*
Arcadia Thrift LLC......G...... 863 993-2004
Arcadia *(G-199)*
Armored Frog Inc......G...... 850 418-2048
Pensacola *(G-14091)*
◆ **Ashley Bryan International Inc**......E...... 954 351-1199
Deerfield Beach *(G-2780)*
◆ **Bass Industries Inc**......E...... 305 751-2716
Hialeah *(G-5316)*
Bossa Hospitality......G...... 305 394-3994
Orlando *(G-12533)*
◆ **Capris Furniture Inds Inc**......C...... 352 629-8889
Ocala *(G-11893)*
▼ **Caribbean Fiberglass Products**......F...... 305 888-0774
Miami *(G-9315)*
◆ **Conquest Financial Management**......D...... 305 630-8950
Miami *(G-9393)*
▲ **Cordaroys Wholesale Inc**......G...... 352 332-1837
Gainesville *(G-4897)*
▼ **E-Sea Rider LLC**......G...... 727 863-3333
Holiday *(G-5739)*
Flexshopper LLC......E...... 561 922-6609
Boca Raton *(G-530)*
GLS Assoc Inc......G...... 561 451-1999
Boca Raton *(G-546)*
Jt Enterprises Group LLC......E...... 904 803-9338
Ponte Vedra Beach *(G-14943)*
Jt Enterprises Group LLC......F...... 904 551-2680
Jacksonville *(G-6528)*
Morning Star of Sarasota Inc......G...... 941 371-0392
Sarasota *(G-16514)*
Outpost 30a LLC......F...... 850 909-0138
Inlet Beach *(G-6078)*
▲ **Sole Inc**......G...... 305 513-2603
Doral *(G-3505)*
Source Contract LLC......F...... 305 630-8950
Miami *(G-10380)*

2521 Wood Office Furniture

◆ **Allied Plastics Co Inc**......E...... 904 359-0386
Jacksonville *(G-6138)*
Antique & Modern Cabinets Inc......E...... 904 393-9055
Jacksonville *(G-6158)*
Barstool Comforts LLC......G...... 610 737-5856
Kissimmee *(G-7220)*
Braden Kitchens Inc......E...... 321 636-4700
Cocoa *(G-1999)*
Cabinet Masters Inc......G...... 727 535-0020
Largo *(G-7918)*
▲ **Camilo Office Furniture Inc**......D...... 305 261-5366
Miami *(G-9305)*
Camilo Office Furniture Inc......G...... 305 261-5366
Miami *(G-9306)*
Contemporary Interiors Inc......E...... 352 620-8686
Ocala *(G-11907)*
Corpdesign......F...... 866 323-6055
Miami *(G-9404)*
Creative Concepts Orlando Inc......E...... 407 260-1435
Longwood *(G-8268)*
Creative Woodworking Concepts......E...... 727 937-4165
Tarpon Springs *(G-18290)*
Custom Craft Laminates Inc......E...... 813 877-7100
Tampa *(G-17577)*
District 95 Wood Working Inc......G...... 888 400-3136
Pompano Beach *(G-14666)*
Dons Cabinets and Woodworking......F...... 727 863-3404
Hudson *(G-6022)*
◆ **Edgeline Industries LLC**......F...... 954 727-5272
Deerfield Beach *(G-2821)*
Engineered Equipment Corp......F...... 561 839-4008
West Palm Beach *(G-18862)*
F & S Cabinets Inc......E...... 386 822-9525
Deland *(G-2976)*
Furniture Design of Centl Fla......F...... 407 330-4430
Sanford *(G-16052)*
Gilmans Custom Furn & Cabinets......F...... 352 746-3532
Lecanto *(G-8134)*
Home Pride Cabinets Inc......F...... 813 887-3782
Tampa *(G-17760)*
I Found It......G...... 561 557-2881
West Palm Beach *(G-18899)*
J F V Designs Inc......F...... 321 228-7469
Tavares *(G-18343)*
J T S Woodworking Inc......G...... 561 272-7996
Delray Beach *(G-3094)*
Kabinets By Kinsey Inc......E...... 813 222-0460
Tampa *(G-17813)*
Ken Clearys Two LLC......F...... 727 573-0700
Clearwater *(G-1749)*
Kings & Queens Cabinets......G...... 863 646-6972
Lakeland *(G-7728)*
McCabinet Inc......F...... 727 608-5929
Largo *(G-8007)*
McCallum Cabinets Inc......F...... 352 372-2344
Gainesville *(G-4957)*
▼ **N & N Investment Corporation**......E...... 954 590-3800
Pompano Beach *(G-14770)*
Office Furniture By Tempo Inc......F...... 305 685-3077
Hialeah *(G-5548)*
Pinellas Custom Cabinets Inc......G...... 727 864-4263
Largo *(G-8027)*
▼ **Pradere Manufacturing Corp**......F...... 305 823-0190
Hialeah *(G-5563)*
Rolu Woodcraft Inc......F...... 305 685-0914
Hialeah *(G-5605)*
Roque Brothers Corp......F...... 305 885-6995
Miami *(G-10281)*
S M I Cabinetry Inc......E...... 407 841-0292
Orlando *(G-13152)*
Star Quality Inc......F...... 813 875-9955
Tampa *(G-18131)*
TOS Manufacturing Inc......F...... 407 330-3880
Sanford *(G-16129)*
Viccarbe Inc......E...... 305 670-0979
Miami *(G-10579)*
Wonder Emporium Millwork Fab......G...... 407 850-3131
Orlando *(G-13328)*

2522 Office Furniture, Except Wood

Advanced Furniture Svcs Inc......F...... 850 390-3442
Pensacola *(G-14084)*
◆ **Allied Plastics Co Inc**......E...... 904 359-0386
Jacksonville *(G-6138)*
▼ **Avl Systems Inc**......E...... 352 854-1170
Ocala *(G-11882)*
Bnb Business Systems Inc......G...... 954 538-0669
Pembroke Pines *(G-14024)*
Buckeye Used Office Furn Inc......G...... 727 457-5287
Largo *(G-7916)*
Cayman Manufacturing Inc......E...... 954 421-1170
Deerfield Beach *(G-2797)*
▼ **Cayman Nat Mfg & Installation**......D...... 954 421-1170
Deerfield Beach *(G-2798)*
Dons Cabinets and Woodworking......F...... 727 863-3404
Hudson *(G-6022)*
Euroker LLC......G...... 305 477-0096
Doral *(G-3345)*
Gk Inc......E...... 215 223-7207
Fort Lauderdale *(G-4022)*
John Eric Madden......G...... 813 395-3314
Zephyrhills *(G-19524)*
Manning Company......G...... 954 523-9355
Fort Lauderdale *(G-4111)*
Morning Star of Sarasota Inc......G...... 941 371-0392
Sarasota *(G-16514)*
New Vision Furniture Inc......G...... 305 562-9428
Opa Locka *(G-12346)*
Nightingale Corp......G...... 800 363-8954
Palm Beach Gardens *(G-13611)*
◆ **Office Express Corp**......F...... 786 503-6800
Miami *(G-10090)*
Sungraf Inc......F...... 954 456-8500
Hallandale Beach *(G-5216)*
Systematix Inc......E...... 850 983-2213
Milton *(G-10942)*
United Chair Industries LLC......G...... 386 333-0800
Odessa *(G-12162)*
Viccarbe Inc......E...... 305 670-0979
Miami *(G-10579)*
Winston & Sons Inc......G...... 954 562-1984
Tamarac *(G-17370)*

2531 Public Building & Related Furniture

A & J Commercial Seating Inc......F...... 352 288-2022
Summerfield *(G-17055)*
◆ **Allied Plastics Co Inc**......E...... 904 359-0386
Jacksonville *(G-6138)*
Antique & Modern Cabinets Inc......E...... 904 393-9055
Jacksonville *(G-6158)*
Apollo Retail Specialists LLC......B...... 813 712-2525
Tampa *(G-17428)*
◆ **Ashley Bryan International Inc**......E...... 954 351-1199
Deerfield Beach *(G-2780)*
Aviation Intl Solutions LLC......G...... 305 267-7117
Hialeah *(G-5313)*
▲ **B/E Aerospace Inc**......E...... 410 266-2048
Wellington *(G-18710)*
▲ **Benchmark Design Group Inc**......F...... 904 246-5060
Jacksonville Beach *(G-6939)*
Cayman Manufacturing Inc......E...... 954 421-1170
Deerfield Beach *(G-2797)*
Cinema Crafters Inc......G...... 305 891-6121
North Miami *(G-11632)*
Contemporary Interiors Inc......E...... 352 620-8686
Ocala *(G-11907)*

Divatti & Co LLC....G.... 786 354-1888
Miramar *(G-10985)*
▼ **F & R General Interiors Corp**....F.... 305 635-4747
Hialeah *(G-5402)*
Griffin & Holman Inc....G.... 904 781-4531
Jacksonville *(G-6452)*
Gt Grandstands Inc....E.... 813 305-1415
Plant City *(G-14438)*
I-Pop Inc....E.... 561 567-9000
West Palm Beach *(G-18900)*
◆ **Kron Designs LLC**....G.... 954 941-0800
Fort Lauderdale *(G-4091)*
▲ **Miami Grandstand Entertainment**....G.... 305 636-9665
Hialeah *(G-5511)*
Seating Constructors Usa Inc....F.... 813 505-7560
Brooksville *(G-1267)*
Seating Installation Group LLC....F.... 727 289-7652
Saint Petersburg *(G-15908)*
Series Usa LLC....G.... 305 932-4626
Miami *(G-10327)*
Southeastern Seating Inc....F.... 813 273-9858
Tampa *(G-18119)*
Vehicle Maint Program Inc....F.... 561 362-6080
Boca Raton *(G-776)*

2541 Wood, Office & Store Fixtures

Ace Shutter & Shelves LLC....G.... 239 314-9136
Cape Coral *(G-1372)*
Acore Shelving & Products Inc....G.... 904 964-4320
Starke *(G-16886)*
▲ **AGR Fabricators Inc**....F.... 904 733-9393
Jacksonville *(G-6129)*
◆ **AGR of Florida Inc**....E.... 904 733-9393
Jacksonville *(G-6130)*
Ajb Enterprises of Florida....G.... 352 331-9569
Gainesville *(G-4870)*
Akiknav Inc....F.... 561 842-8091
Riviera Beach *(G-15296)*
Amercn Cabinets Granite Floors....F.... 727 303-0678
Palm Harbor *(G-13718)*
Amick Cstm Woodcraft & Design....G.... 407 324-8525
Sanford *(G-15994)*
Antique & Modern Cabinets Inc....E.... 904 393-9055
Jacksonville *(G-6158)*
◆ **Artco Group Inc**....D.... 305 638-1785
Miami *(G-9172)*
Belets Millwork Inc....F.... 904 353-8600
Jacksonville *(G-6202)*
▲ **Blues Design Group LLC**....F.... 305 586-3630
Miami *(G-9262)*
Braden Kitchens Inc....E.... 321 636-4700
Cocoa *(G-1999)*
Brazil America Srones Inc....G.... 305 915-0123
Hallandale Beach *(G-5174)*
▲ **Byblos Group Inc**....G.... 305 662-6666
Miami *(G-9291)*
Cabinet Cnnction of Trsure Cas....E.... 772 621-4882
Port Saint Lucie *(G-15095)*
Cabinets Plus Inc....F.... 239 574-7020
Cape Coral *(G-1400)*
Capital Contracting & Design....E.... 908 561-8411
Fort Lauderdale *(G-3881)*
▲ **Caseworks International Inc**....F.... 954 933-9102
Fort Lauderdale *(G-3884)*
Central Fla Kit Bath Srfces In....F.... 352 307-2333
Ocala *(G-11898)*
Cianos Tile & Marble Inc....E.... 239 267-8453
Fort Myers *(G-4395)*
Commercial Stone Cab Fbrctors....F.... 727 209-1141
Saint Petersburg *(G-15749)*
Commercial Stone Fbrcators Inc....F.... 727 209-1141
Saint Petersburg *(G-15750)*
Corn-E-Lee Woodcrafts....G.... 239 574-2414
Cape Coral *(G-1406)*
Corry Cabinet Company Inc....E.... 850 539-6455
Havana *(G-5237)*
▲ **Counter Active Inc**....F.... 813 626-0022
Ponte Vedra *(G-14923)*
Countertop Solutions Inc....G.... 239 961-0663
Naples *(G-11217)*
Creaction Industry Llc....F.... 305 779-4851
Medley *(G-8637)*
Creative Cabinet Concepts Inc....F.... 239 939-1313
Fort Myers *(G-4413)*
Creative Countertops Inc....F.... 904 387-2800
Jacksonville *(G-6296)*
Custom Cabinets Inc....F.... 941 366-0428
Sarasota *(G-16398)*
◆ **Custom Marble Works Inc**....E.... 813 620-0475
Tampa *(G-17580)*

D T Woodcrafters Corp....E.... 305 556-3771
Hialeah *(G-5360)*
Daystar International Inc....G.... 813 281-0200
Tampa *(G-17593)*
◆ **Designers Tops Inc**....F.... 305 599-9973
Miami *(G-9461)*
Duval Fixtures Inc....E.... 904 757-3964
Jacksonville *(G-6340)*
East Coast Fixtures & Mllwk Co....G.... 904 733-9711
Jacksonville *(G-6349)*
Ellis Wood Collection Ltd....F.... 610 372-2880
St Pete Beach *(G-16880)*
◆ **EMI Industries LLC**....C.... 813 626-3166
Tampa *(G-17636)*
Extreme Wood Works S Fla Inc....F.... 305 463-8614
Doral *(G-3346)*
Featherlite Exhibits....G.... 800 229-5533
Tampa *(G-17663)*
Fisher Cabinet Company LLC....E.... 850 944-4171
Pensacola *(G-14151)*
▼ **Florida Designer Cabinets Inc**....F.... 352 793-8555
Sumterville *(G-17068)*
◆ **Front of House Inc**....E.... 305 757-7940
Miami *(G-9599)*
Furniture Concepts Inc....G.... 727 535-0093
Largo *(G-7954)*
Gds....G.... 305 764-0920
North Miami *(G-11640)*
Global Stone Collection LLC....E.... 772 467-1924
Fort Pierce *(G-4700)*
Gloval Displays Inc....E.... 800 972-0353
Miami Gardens *(G-10742)*
Gulf Coast Installers LLC....F.... 239 273-4663
Bonita Springs *(G-836)*
Guyton Industries LLC....E.... 772 208-3019
Indiantown *(G-6073)*
Harwil Fixtures Inc....F.... 904 692-1051
Hastings *(G-5228)*
Home Pride Cabinets Inc....F.... 813 887-3782
Tampa *(G-17760)*
Hucke Manufacturing Inc....G.... 863 655-3667
Sebring *(G-16695)*
Hugh Robinson Inc....G.... 954 484-0660
Lauderdale Lakes *(G-8088)*
J & J Custom Mica Inc....F.... 239 433-2828
Fort Myers *(G-4498)*
J M Interiors Inc....G.... 305 891-6121
North Miami *(G-11642)*
Jnc Habitat Investments Inc....F.... 954 249-7469
Coral Springs *(G-2264)*
Just Counters Other Stuff Inc....F.... 941 235-1300
Port Charlotte *(G-14986)*
Kitchen Counter Connections....E.... 386 677-9471
Ormond Beach *(G-13382)*
Kitchen Dsgns By Joan E Rbbins....G.... 321 727-0012
Melbourne *(G-8860)*
Larsen Cabinetmaker Co....G.... 305 252-1212
Miami *(G-9860)*
Lg Hausys America Inc....E.... 813 249-7658
Tampa *(G-17844)*
▲ **List Industries Inc**....B.... 954 429-9155
Deerfield Beach *(G-2859)*
Load King Manufacturing Co....C.... 904 354-8882
Jacksonville *(G-6560)*
Lyndan Inc....E.... 813 977-6683
Tampa *(G-17867)*
Mahan Cabinets....G.... 305 255-3325
Cutler Bay *(G-2403)*
Major Partitions Ltd Corp....E.... 813 286-8634
Tampa *(G-17875)*
Mayworth Showcase Works Inc....G.... 813 251-1558
Tampa *(G-17896)*
McCallum Cabinets Inc....F.... 352 372-2344
Gainesville *(G-4957)*
Mobius Business Group Inc....F.... 239 274-8900
Fort Myers *(G-4535)*
Morning Star of Sarasota Inc....G.... 941 371-0392
Sarasota *(G-16514)*
Mr Mica Wood Inc....F.... 561 278-5821
Delray Beach *(G-3109)*
▼ **N & N Investment Corporation**....E.... 954 590-3800
Pompano Beach *(G-14770)*
Nauset Enterprises Inc....G.... 727 443-3469
Clearwater *(G-1804)*
▲ **New River Cabinet & Fix Inc**....E.... 954 938-9200
Fort Lauderdale *(G-4137)*
Premier Coatings LLC....E.... 954 797-9275
Fort Lauderdale *(G-4175)*
Princeton Industries Inc....E.... 954 344-9155
Margate *(G-8563)*

Pro Tech Custom Cabinet....F.... 727 863-5143
Port Richey *(G-15065)*
S M I Cabinetry Inc....E.... 407 841-0292
Orlando *(G-13152)*
◆ **Salvia Tile & Stone Inc**....F.... 239 643-7770
Naples *(G-11389)*
Sam Weiss Woodworking Inc....G.... 954 975-8158
Margate *(G-8566)*
Sand Dollar Charters LLC....G.... 903 734-5376
New Smyrna Beach *(G-11542)*
Schrappers Fine Cabinetry Inc....F.... 561 746-3827
Jupiter *(G-7109)*
Southern Woodworks Fine Wdwkg....F.... 850 456-0550
Pensacola *(G-14266)*
Spruce Creek Cabinetry Inc....F.... 386 756-0041
Port Orange *(G-15035)*
Ssvm Partners Inc....D.... 239 825-6282
Sarasota *(G-16602)*
Still Water Industries Inc....G.... 561 845-6033
West Palm Beach *(G-19045)*
Superior Solid Surface Inc....F.... 727 842-9947
Port Richey *(G-15071)*
Synergy Custom Fixtures Corp....C.... 305 693-0055
Hialeah *(G-5645)*
▼ **T & R Store Fixtures Inc**....E.... 305 751-0377
Miami *(G-10453)*
Total Koatings Inc....G.... 941 870-0369
Sarasota *(G-16313)*
Trasport John....G.... 321 452-6789
Merritt Island *(G-9016)*
Unlimited Cabinet Designs Inc....F.... 954 923-3269
Hallandale *(G-5165)*
▲ **Venice Granit & Marble Inc**....G.... 941 483-4363
Venice *(G-18585)*
Wonder Emporium Millwork Fab....G.... 407 850-3131
Orlando *(G-13328)*
Y F Leung Inc....G.... 305 651-6851
North Miami Beach *(G-11714)*

2542 Partitions & Fixtures, Except Wood

Acryplex Inc....G.... 305 633-7636
Miami *(G-9066)*
▼ **Adapto Storage Products**....E.... 305 887-9563
Hialeah *(G-5269)*
Akiknav Inc....F.... 561 842-8091
Riviera Beach *(G-15296)*
◆ **American Sani Partition Corp**....E.... 407 656-0611
Ocoee *(G-12082)*
Asottu Inc....F.... 626 627-6021
Orlando *(G-12494)*
◆ **Bass Industries Inc**....E.... 305 751-2716
Hialeah *(G-5316)*
Bob & Lees Cabinets....F.... 352 748-3553
Wildwood *(G-19191)*
Bruce R Ely Enterprise Inc....F.... 727 573-1643
Clearwater *(G-1614)*
▲ **Caddie Company Inc**....F.... 267 332-0976
Tampa *(G-17499)*
Capital Contracting & Design....E.... 908 561-8411
Fort Lauderdale *(G-3881)*
Ccp of Miami Inc....G.... 305 233-6534
Miami *(G-9331)*
Creative Builder Services Inc....E.... 813 818-7100
Tampa *(G-17563)*
Davis Mail Services Inc....C.... 904 477-7970
Jacksonville *(G-6314)*
Dons Cabinets and Woodworking....F.... 727 863-3404
Hudson *(G-6022)*
East Coast Fixtures & Mllwk Co....G.... 904 733-9711
Jacksonville *(G-6349)*
▼ **Emjac Industries Inc**....D.... 305 883-2194
Hialeah *(G-5395)*
Florida Design Mfg Assoc Inc....F.... 561 533-0733
West Palm Beach *(G-18879)*
Gulf Coast Installers LLC....F.... 239 273-4663
Bonita Springs *(G-836)*
Gulf South Distributors Inc....F.... 850 244-1522
Fort Walton Beach *(G-4807)*
Iverica Industrial Inc....F.... 305 691-1659
Hialeah *(G-5458)*
James Spear Design Inc....G.... 727 592-9600
Largo *(G-7986)*
Kitchen Counter Connections....E.... 386 677-9471
Ormond Beach *(G-13382)*
Km Industrial Racking Inc....G.... 813 900-7457
Largo *(G-7993)*
La Fabrika Retail Services LLC....G.... 786 525-4491
Miami *(G-9840)*
▲ **List Industries Inc**....B.... 954 429-9155
Deerfield Beach *(G-2859)*

S
I
C

List Plymouth LLC.....E..... 954 429-9155
Deerfield Beach *(G-2861)*
Load King Manufacturing Co.....C..... 904 354-8882
Jacksonville *(G-6560)*
▼ N & N Investment Corporation.....E..... 954 590-3800
Pompano Beach *(G-14770)*
Nauset Enterprises Inc.....G..... 727 443-3469
Clearwater *(G-1804)*
▲ New River Cabinet & Fix Inc.....E..... 954 938-9200
Fort Lauderdale *(G-4137)*
Sam Weiss Woodworking Inc.....G..... 954 975-8158
Margate *(G-8566)*
SC Capital Ventures Inc.....E..... 954 657-8563
Pompano Beach *(G-14841)*
Synergy Custom Fixtures Corp.....C..... 305 693-0055
Hialeah *(G-5645)*
Szabo Pos Displays Inc.....G..... 941 778-0192
Bradenton *(G-1124)*
▼ T & R Store Fixtures Inc.....E..... 305 751-0377
Miami *(G-10453)*
Tcm Imagineering Inc.....F..... 407 323-6494
Deland *(G-3017)*
◆ Teak Isle Inc.....C..... 407 656-8885
Ocoee *(G-12091)*
Telese Inc.....E..... 813 752-6015
Plant City *(G-14470)*
◆ United State Postal Service.....F..... 904 783-7145
Jacksonville *(G-6882)*
Valiant Products Inc.....E..... 863 688-7998
Lakeland *(G-7829)*
World Indus Resources Corp.....E..... 727 572-9991
Clearwater *(G-1944)*

2591 Drapery Hardware, Window Blinds & Shades

1st Vertical Blind Company.....G..... 352 343-3363
Tavares *(G-18332)*
A Albrtini Cstm Win Treatments.....G..... 941 925-2556
Sarasota *(G-16328)*
A&I Aluminum Shutters.....G..... 561 223-5877
Lake Worth *(G-7527)*
A1cm.....G..... 954 716-3216
Miami *(G-9047)*
▲ Aero Shade Technologies Inc.....G..... 772 562-2243
Fort Pierce *(G-4670)*
▲ Aerospace Tech Group Inc.....D..... 561 244-7400
Boca Raton *(G-406)*
Affordable Quality Blinds Inc.....G..... 786 412-4840
Miami *(G-9087)*
▼ American Blind Corporation.....F..... 305 262-2009
Miami *(G-9140)*
▼ B & D Precision Tools Inc.....E..... 305 885-1583
Hialeah *(G-5314)*
▼ Biscayne Awning & Shade Co.....E..... 305 638-7933
Miami *(G-9250)*
Blind and Drapery Gallery Inc.....G..... 239 948-7611
Bonita Springs *(G-816)*
Blind Monkey.....G..... 954 533-3090
Fort Lauderdale *(G-3857)*
Blind Wizard Too Inc.....G..... 954 755-3828
Coral Springs *(G-2228)*
Blinds 321 Inc.....G..... 305 336-9221
Miami *(G-9257)*
Blinds By Randy LLC.....G..... 305 300-1147
Miami Gardens *(G-10735)*
Blinds Dr LLC.....G..... 305 394-4808
Miami *(G-9258)*
Blinds Express.....G..... 954 826-6185
Oakland Park *(G-11786)*
Blinds Plus Shutters & Shades.....G..... 352 430-7200
Leesburg *(G-8145)*
Blinds R Us Corp.....G..... 305 303-2072
Miami *(G-9259)*
Blinds Shades Industries Corp.....G..... 786 445-2144
Miami *(G-9260)*
Blinds Side.....G..... 888 610-8366
Cape Canaveral *(G-1352)*
BMW & Associates Inc.....G..... 352 694-2300
Ocala *(G-11888)*
Bornt Enterprises Inc.....E..... 813 623-1492
Tampa *(G-17483)*
Cardenas Roberto Blinds of Fla.....G..... 315 807-6878
Miami *(G-9312)*
Casa Blinds Interior Corp.....G..... 786 219-7157
Doral *(G-3293)*
Ceco Inc.....F..... 561 265-1111
Boynton Beach *(G-889)*
Coverall Interiors.....G..... 813 961-8261
Tampa *(G-17560)*
Current Products Company LLC.....E..... 850 435-4994
Pensacola *(G-14121)*
D W A Inc.....F..... 941 444-1134
Sarasota *(G-16401)*
Deco Abrusci International LLC.....F..... 305 406-3401
Doral *(G-3326)*
▼ Deco Shades Solutions Inc.....G..... 305 558-9800
Hialeah *(G-5367)*
Designers Wholesale Workroom.....F..... 239 434-7633
Naples *(G-11226)*
Diy Blinds Inc.....G..... 305 692-8877
North Miami Beach *(G-11671)*
Dizenzo Manufacturing Intl.....G..... 954 978-4624
Deerfield Beach *(G-2815)*
Ed Allen Inc.....F..... 941 743-2646
Port Charlotte *(G-14975)*
Eddy Storm Protection.....G..... 386 248-1631
Daytona Beach *(G-2661)*
Etchart LLC.....G..... 321 504-4060
Cocoa *(G-2021)*
Falcons Castl Blinds Globl Fla.....G..... 561 727-4332
West Palm Beach *(G-18869)*
Florida Plntn Shutters LLC.....G..... 386 788-7766
South Daytona *(G-16801)*
Florida Prnts Blind Chldren In.....G..... 407 257-7637
Orlando *(G-12753)*
Floridian Blinds Llc.....G..... 786 250-4697
Miami *(G-9587)*
G K Window Treatments Inc.....F..... 954 786-2927
Pompano Beach *(G-14709)*
Gator Blinds & Shutters.....G..... 352 375-1995
Ocala *(G-11954)*
Gator Custom Blinds.....G..... 352 867-0448
Ocala *(G-11955)*
Grannys Cheesecake & More Inc.....G..... 561 847-6599
Okeechobee *(G-12180)*
Gulf Coast Shades & Blinds LLC.....F..... 850 332-2100
Gulf Breeze *(G-5118)*
▼ Imperial Privacy Systems LLC.....D..... 954 782-7130
Pompano Beach *(G-14730)*
Island Shutter Co Inc.....E..... 386 738-9455
Deland *(G-2985)*
▼ Kelsies Blinds.....G..... 407 977-0827
Oviedo *(G-13445)*
Kristine Window Treatments LLC.....F..... 305 623-8302
Hialeah *(G-5476)*
Lavish Blinds Corp.....G..... 786 229-8134
Cutler Bay *(G-2400)*
Louvers Window Fashions.....G..... 941 275-2655
Venice *(G-18561)*
Lucky Blinds Shutters LLC.....G..... 352 239-8475
Summerfield *(G-17060)*
Mastercraft Shtters Blinds LLC.....G..... 904 379-7544
Jacksonville *(G-6581)*
Mpalacios Blinds Inc.....G..... 239 601-4864
Lehigh Acres *(G-8200)*
◆ Myriam Interiors Inc.....G..... 305 626-9898
Hialeah *(G-5531)*
North W Fla Cncil of Blind Cor.....G..... 850 982-7867
Gulf Breeze *(G-5123)*
Orlando Blinds Factory.....F..... 407 697-0521
Orlando *(G-13031)*
Orlando Shutters LLC.....E..... 407 495-5250
Lake Mary *(G-7440)*
◆ Ortega Industries and Mfg.....D..... 305 688-0090
Opa Locka *(G-12348)*
Poseidon Window Treatments LLC.....G..... 954 920-1112
Dania Beach *(G-2472)*
Privacy Window Design Inc.....G..... 386 761-7306
Port Orange *(G-15029)*
Reah Group LLC.....G..... 727 423-0668
Tampa *(G-18042)*
Resort Window Treatments Inc.....G..... 813 355-4877
Zephyrhills *(G-19535)*
Royal Blinds LLC.....F..... 786 253-8126
Miami *(G-10283)*
▲ Shades To You LLC.....G..... 407 889-0049
Apopka *(G-186)*
▲ Skagfield Corporation.....D..... 850 878-1144
Tallahassee *(G-17325)*
▼ Solar Venetian Blinds Inc.....G..... 305 634-4553
Miami *(G-10371)*
Southeast Window Coverings.....G..... 904 372-0326
Jacksonville *(G-6788)*
Srm Blinds Inc.....G..... 321 269-5332
Titusville *(G-18463)*
Stand Vertical Inc.....G..... 407 474-0456
Orlando *(G-13212)*
Statewide Blnds Shtters More I.....G..... 813 480-8638
New Port Richey *(G-11511)*
Sun City Blinds LLC.....F..... 727 522-6695
Ellenton *(G-3655)*
Sunrise.....G..... 386 627-5029
Palm Coast *(G-13711)*
▼ Superior Shade & Blind Co Inc.....E..... 954 975-8122
Coral Springs *(G-2317)*
Sutton Draperies Inc.....F..... 305 653-7738
Miami *(G-10443)*
Thompson Awning & Shutter Co.....E..... 904 355-1616
Jacksonville *(G-6849)*
TMMR Holdings LLC.....E..... 407 295-5200
Ocoee *(G-12092)*
Top Trtment Cstomes Accesories.....G..... 239 936-4600
Fort Myers *(G-4632)*
▼ Total Window Inc.....G..... 954 921-0109
Dania *(G-2459)*
Totally Glass & Blinds Llc.....G..... 561 929-6125
West Palm Beach *(G-19069)*
Tropic Shield Inc.....F..... 954 731-5553
Lauderdale Lakes *(G-8095)*
United Vertical Blinds LLC.....F..... 786 348-8000
Miami *(G-10539)*
USA Recmar Corp.....G..... 786 554-3505
Miami *(G-10555)*
Vertical Assesment Assoc LLC.....E..... 850 210-0401
Blountstown *(G-390)*
Vertical Flight Technology Inc.....F..... 407 687-3126
Melbourne *(G-8970)*
Vertical Land Inc.....F..... 850 244-5263
Panama City *(G-13961)*
Vertical Systems Inspctons Inc.....G..... 954 775-6023
Plantation *(G-14563)*
Vertical Village Inc.....G..... 772 340-0400
Port Saint Lucie *(G-15162)*
Vidal Shutters and Blinds LLC.....G..... 813 601-1068
Tampa *(G-18245)*
▲ Vista Products Inc.....D..... 904 725-2242
Jacksonville *(G-6900)*
Worldwide Draperies West LLC.....F..... 305 887-9611
Hialeah *(G-5690)*

2599 Furniture & Fixtures, NEC

A & J Commercial Seating Inc.....F..... 352 288-2022
Summerfield *(G-17055)*
A1a Raw LLC.....G..... 321 777-2526
Indialantic *(G-6055)*
Aj Originals Inc.....G..... 954 563-9911
Fort Lauderdale *(G-3793)*
American Metal Products Inc.....G..... 407 293-0090
Orlando *(G-12471)*
American Technical Furn LLC.....G..... 866 239-4204
Holly Hill *(G-5755)*
Asemblu Inc.....F..... 800 827-4419
Hialeah *(G-5308)*
Beast Row Inc.....G..... 727 787-2710
Palm Harbor *(G-13724)*
▲ Blue Leaf Hospitality Inc.....F..... 305 668-3000
Miami *(G-9261)*
BMC Services Inc.....F..... 954 587-6337
Fort Lauderdale *(G-3862)*
BMW Entertainment LLC.....F..... 850 502-4590
Destin *(G-3213)*
Borgzinner Inc.....E..... 561 848-2538
Riviera Beach *(G-15304)*
Bryan Ashley Inc.....E..... 954 351-1199
Deerfield Beach *(G-2793)*
▲ Byblos Group Inc.....G..... 305 662-6666
Miami *(G-9291)*
Captain Max.....G..... 954 987-8552
Miramar *(G-10976)*
Carley Nigel Holdings LLC.....F..... 407 212-9341
Rockledge *(G-15398)*
Cg Burgers.....F..... 954 618-6450
Fort Lauderdale *(G-3893)*
Chin & Chin Enterprises Inc.....F..... 407 478-8726
Winter Park *(G-19394)*
Commercial Casework Inc.....D..... 904 264-4222
Jacksonville *(G-6280)*
◆ Custom Comfort Medtek LLC.....E..... 407 332-0062
Winter Park *(G-19398)*
▲ D G Morrison Inc.....F..... 813 865-0208
Odessa *(G-12114)*
Deepstream Designs Inc.....G..... 305 857-0466
Miami *(G-9444)*
Design Furnishings Inc.....E..... 407 294-0507
Orlando *(G-12663)*
Distinct Dsgns Cstm Coml Case.....G..... 727 530-0119
Largo *(G-7934)*
Drinks On ME 305 LLC.....F..... 786 488-2356
Miami *(G-9486)*

▲ **E&T Horizons Ltd Liability Co** ....F 321 704-1244
Melbourne *(G-8818)*
▲ **England Trading Company LLC** ......E 888 969-4190
Jacksonville *(G-6365)*
▼ **Florida Designer Cabinets Inc** ....F 352 793-8555
Sumterville *(G-17068)*
Four Seas Trading Corp ....G....... 813 221-0895
Tampa *(G-17692)*
Gcato 1959 Enterprises LLC ....G....... 954 937-6282
Pompano Beach *(G-14712)*
Good Times Sports Bar and Gril ....G....... 239 369-7000
Lehigh Acres *(G-8191)*
Gulf South Distributors Inc ....F 850 244-1522
Fort Walton Beach *(G-4807)*
Guyton Industries LLC ....E 772 208-3019
Indiantown *(G-6073)*
Honduras Food Services Inc ....E 310 940-2071
Gainesville *(G-4937)*
Italian Cabinetry Inc ....F 786 534-2742
Miami *(G-9774)*
James Spear Design Inc ....G....... 727 592-9600
Largo *(G-7986)*
Kci ....G....... 352 572-2873
Lecanto *(G-8136)*
Klugman Enterprises LLC ....G....... 352 318-9623
Sarasota *(G-16246)*
◆ **Kron Designs LLC** ....G....... 954 941-0800
Fort Lauderdale *(G-4091)*
Larsen Cabinetmaker Co ....G....... 305 252-1212
Miami *(G-9860)*
Load King Manufacturing Co ....C....... 904 354-8882
Jacksonville *(G-6560)*
Luong Moc III Inc ....E 407 478-8726
Winter Park *(G-19421)*
Medtek Medical Solutions LLC ....F 786 458-8080
Miami *(G-9968)*
Mhkap LLC ....G....... 239 919-0786
Naples *(G-11327)*
▼ **Miranda Eldorado Mfg Co** ....G....... 727 586-0707
Largo *(G-8012)*
Morris Mica Cabinets Inc ....G....... 954 979-6838
Pompano Beach *(G-14769)*
Mr Real Deal barbque LLC ....G....... 561 271-8749
Delray Beach *(G-3110)*
My Passion On A Plate LLC ....F 954 857-6382
North Lauderdale *(G-11618)*
Nanni Usa LLC ....G....... 305 450-4853
Coral Gables *(G-2180)*
▲ **Octametro LLC** ....G....... 305 715-9713
Doral *(G-3448)*
One Group ....D....... 305 604-6999
Miami Beach *(G-10700)*
▲ **One World Resource LLC** ....E 305 445-9199
Miami *(G-10105)*
Regency Custom Cabinets Inc ....F 239 332-7977
Fort Myers *(G-4580)*
Safeguard of South Florid ....G....... 561 499-7600
Delray Beach *(G-3137)*
SC Gastronomic Crew Inc ....E 786 864-1212
Coral Gables *(G-2194)*
◆ **Seaking Inc** ....E 954 961-6629
Davie *(G-2589)*
Smarte Carte Inc ....G....... 407 857-5841
Orlando *(G-13198)*
TLC Food Truck LLC ....F 305 879-2488
Miami *(G-10481)*
◆ **Ultima Design South Fla Inc** ....F 305 477-9300
Medley *(G-8746)*
Werever Products Inc ....F 813 241-9701
Riverview *(G-15287)*
West End ....F 407 322-7475
Sanford *(G-16138)*
▲ **Winco Mfg LLC** ....D....... 352 854-2929
Ocala *(G-12076)*
Wj Bergin Cabinetry LLC ....E 407 271-8982
Orlando *(G-13326)*
Wood Stile Inc ....G....... 561 329-4671
North Palm Beach *(G-11730)*
Yard House Hallandale Bch LLC ....G....... 561 691-6901
Palm Beach Gardens *(G-13636)*

26 PAPER AND ALLIED PRODUCTS

2611 Pulp Mills

ABC Recyclers Collier Cnty Inc ....G....... 239 643-2302
Naples *(G-11145)*
All Green Recycling Inc ....F 754 204-3707
Hollywood *(G-5769)*
▲ **Foley Cellulose LLC** ....A 850 584-1121
Perry *(G-14300)*
▲ **Hogenkamp Research Inc** ....F 850 677-1072
Gulf Breeze *(G-5119)*
Ies Sales and Service LLC ....G....... 305 525-6079
Miami *(G-9731)*
Platinium Rosis Inc ....G....... 786 617-9973
Miami Beach *(G-10703)*
Rayonier Inc ....E 904 277-1343
Yulee *(G-19499)*
Reuse Salvage Inc ....G....... 772 485-3248
Port Salerno *(G-15165)*
Southern Wood Services LLC ....G....... 352 279-3208
Brooksville *(G-1272)*
Stellar On-Site LLC ....F 904 945-1908
Hilliard *(G-5719)*
▲ **Suzano Pulp & Paper** ....G....... 954 772-7716
Fort Lauderdale *(G-4270)*
Universal PC Organization Inc ....G....... 321 285-9206
Orlando *(G-13296)*

2621 Paper Mills

▲ **3tissue LLC** ....G....... 904 540-4335
Jacksonville *(G-6101)*
▲ **Advanced Cmmncations Holdg Inc** ..D....... 954 753-0100
Coral Springs *(G-2213)*
Art On Paper LLC ....G....... 305 615-9096
Pinecrest *(G-14324)*
◆ **Atlas Paper Mills LLC** ....F 800 562-2860
Miami *(G-9187)*
Atlas Paper Mills LLC ....C....... 305 835-8046
Hialeah *(G-5311)*
◆ **Atlas Southeast Papers Inc** ....D....... 407 330-9118
Sanford *(G-15998)*
Bristol Venture Service LLC ....G....... 407 844-8629
Orlando *(G-12536)*
Bristols Elite ....G....... 954 651-3574
Hollywood *(G-5790)*
◆ **Commonwealth Brands Inc** ....C....... 800 481-5814
Fort Lauderdale *(G-3912)*
▼ **Domtar Industries Inc** ....G....... 727 421-6919
Palm Harbor *(G-13733)*
Ep6 Group Inc ....G....... 772 332-9100
Fort Pierce *(G-4695)*
▼ **Excel Converting Inc** ....F 786 318-2222
Miami *(G-9542)*
F3 Analytics LLC ....G....... 404 551-2600
Boca Grande *(G-392)*
Fraser West Inc ....D....... 901 620-4200
Jacksonville *(G-6414)*
Georgia-Pacific LLC ....E 386 328-8826
Palatka *(G-13481)*
Global Tissue Group Jax ....F 904 861-3290
Jacksonville *(G-6438)*
Gold Bond Building Pdts LLC ....E 813 672-8269
Gibsonton *(G-5028)*
Great American Rolling Ppr Co ....G....... 813 928-9166
Tampa *(G-17727)*
▲ **Green Forest Products LLC** ....G....... 352 341-5500
Inverness *(G-6089)*
Gtg-Jax LLC ....E 904 861-3290
Jacksonville *(G-6454)*
▲ **Hammer Head Group Inc** ....E 305 436-5691
Doral *(G-3377)*
Iteg LLC ....F 305 399-2510
Fort Lauderdale *(G-4070)*
J Bristol LLC ....G....... 407 488-6744
Winter Park *(G-19415)*
John Franklin Mowery ....G....... 202 468-8644
Venice *(G-18557)*
Key West Printing LLC ....G....... 305 517-6711
Key West *(G-7190)*
▼ **Main Packaging Supply** ....E 305 863-7176
Miami *(G-9936)*
Monadnock Paper Mills Inc ....G....... 603 588-8672
Lutz *(G-8402)*
N V Texpack Group ....F 305 358-9696
Miami *(G-10057)*
Niche Digital Media Corp ....G....... 561 768-9793
Jupiter *(G-7081)*
Paper Chase ....G....... 561 641-5319
Lake Worth *(G-7579)*
Papers Unlimited Plus Inc ....G....... 215 947-1155
Palm Beach Gardens *(G-13616)*
◆ **Peninsula Tissue Corporation** ....G....... 305 863-0704
Miami *(G-10151)*
▲ **Pro Edge Cutlery LLC** ....G....... 239 304-8000
Naples *(G-11374)*
Probag Inc ....F 305 883-3266
Medley *(G-8712)*
Resolute FP Florida Inc ....D....... 800 562-2860
Miami *(G-10257)*
Resolute Tissue LLC ....F 305 636-5741
Miami *(G-10258)*
Resolute Tissue Sales ....C....... 800 562-2860
Hialeah *(G-5597)*
Scratch Off Store ....G....... 800 584-9937
Oviedo *(G-13456)*
Sinergie Printing Inc ....G....... 786 493-6167
Miami *(G-10353)*
▼ **Sun Paper Company** ....E 305 887-0040
Doral *(G-3516)*
Superior Leaf Inc ....G....... 561 480-2464
West Palm Beach *(G-19051)*
▲ **Suzano Pulp & Paper** ....G....... 954 772-7716
Fort Lauderdale *(G-4270)*
Vertpac LLC ....E 407 886-9010
Apopka *(G-195)*
Vinland Marketing Inc ....G....... 954 602-2177
Pembroke Pines *(G-14071)*
West Fraser Inc ....D....... 850 587-1000
Mc David *(G-8602)*
Wise Business Forms Inc ....E 770 442-1060
Opa Locka *(G-12369)*
Your Name Prtg Envlope Mfg Inc ....G....... 813 643-1443
Tampa *(G-18278)*

2631 Paperboard Mills

Biodegradable Packaging Corp ....E 305 824-1164
Miami Lakes *(G-10769)*
Caquin Group Llc ....F 786 303-2700
Aventura *(G-266)*
Cardboard Only Inc ....G....... 352 345-5060
Weeki Wachee *(G-18701)*
◆ **Design Containers Inc** ....D....... 904 764-6541
Jacksonville *(G-6316)*
Flex Pack USA LLC ....G....... 407 704-0800
Orlando *(G-12744)*
Great Northern Corporation ....E 920 739-3671
Jacksonville *(G-6446)*
▼ **Ies Sales and Service LLC** ....G....... 305 687-9400
Opa Locka *(G-12324)*
Keepit Neat ....G....... 352 867-0541
Anthony *(G-96)*
◆ **Matrix Packaging of Florida** ....G....... 305 358-9696
Miami *(G-9956)*
▼ **Porter Pizza Box Florida Inc** ....E 800 626-0828
Lakeland *(G-7770)*
Sfada Tag Agency Inc ....F 305 981-1077
North Miami *(G-11654)*
Sonoco Products Company ....E 386 424-0970
New Smyrna Beach *(G-11545)*
Tommy & Giordy Buy/Sell ....G....... 786 797-6973
Opa Locka *(G-12365)*
Westrock Cp LLC ....C....... 904 714-7151
Jacksonville *(G-6914)*
Westrock Cp LLC ....G....... 954 522-3684
Fort Lauderdale *(G-4320)*
Westrock Cp LLC ....E 407 843-1300
Orlando *(G-13323)*
▲ **White Cardboard Corp** ....G....... 786 260-4692
Miami *(G-10600)*

2652 Set-Up Paperboard Boxes

Goldys Box Co ....G....... 954 648-1623
The Villages *(G-18391)*
Gulf Packaging Co ....F 727 441-1117
Clearwater *(G-1708)*
McMill LLC ....G....... 561 279-3232
Boca Raton *(G-615)*
Paper Box ....G....... 407 415-7262
Lake Mary *(G-7441)*
▲ **Simkins Industries Inc** ....F 305 899-8184
Miami *(G-10350)*
Spruce Creek Cntl Cndo Associa ....G....... 386 212-4035
Port Orange *(G-15036)*
Tropical Paper Box ....G....... 305 592-5520
Doral *(G-3533)*

2653 Corrugated & Solid Fiber Boxes

Advanced Design & Packg Inc ....F 904 356-6063
Jacksonville *(G-6123)*
Aggressive Box Inc ....F 813 901-9600
Tampa *(G-17391)*
▼ **Air-Flite Containers Inc** ....G....... 407 679-1200
Orlando *(G-12444)*
Argo Crates & Containers ....G....... 786 487-4607
Doral *(G-3254)*
Avatar Packaging Inc ....E 813 888-9141
Tampa *(G-17444)*
▼ **Avon Corrugated/Florida Corp** ....F 305 770-3439
Miami *(G-9200)*

Barco Sales & Mfg Inc ...F ... 954 563-3922
Oakland Park (G-11784)
Biodegradable Packaging Corp ...E ... 305 824-1164
Miami Lakes (G-10769)
Birdiebox LLC ...E ... 786 762-2975
Miami (G-9249)
▲ Central Florida Box Corp ...E ... 407 936-1277
Lake Mary (G-7404)
Corrugated Help LLC ...G ... 904 874-7285
Starke (G-16891)
Cypress Folding Cartons Inc ...E ... 813 884-5418
Tampa (G-17583)
▼ Dusobox Corporation ...D ... 407 855-5120
Orlando (G-12692)
Flamm Industries Inc ...G ... 904 356-2876
Jacksonville (G-6393)
Florida Packg & Graphics Inc ...F ... 954 781-1440
Fort Lauderdale (G-4002)
Gar Business Group LLC ...G ... 321 632-5133
Rockledge (G-15413)
◆ Hitex Marketing Group Inc ...G ... 305 406-1150
Miami (G-9713)
◆ Ic Industries Inc ...D ... 305 696-8330
Hialeah (G-5451)
K & G Box Inc ...D ... 904 356-6063
Jacksonville (G-6529)
Macpac Inc ...F ... 904 315-6457
Ponte Vedra Beach (G-14945)
▼ Mas Entrprses of Ft Lauderdale ...E ... 904 356-9606
Fort Lauderdale (G-4113)
◆ Max-Pak Inc ...C ... 863 682-0123
Lakeland (G-7747)
▲ Micon Packaging Inc ...C ... 813 855-4651
Oldsmar (G-12249)
Omni Displays LLC ...E ... 352 799-9997
Brooksville (G-1257)
Packaging Alternatives Corp ...F ... 352 867-5050
Ocala (G-12021)
Packaging Corporation America ...G ... 386 792-0810
Jasper (G-6960)
▼ Plant Foods Inc ...E ... 772 567-5741
Vero Beach (G-18654)
Pratt Industries Inc ...G ... 863 439-4184
Dundee (G-3568)
Republic Packaging Florida Inc ...E ... 305 685-5175
Opa Locka (G-12355)
Schwarz Partners Packaging LLC ...C ... 863 682-0123
Lakeland (G-7788)
Sfbc LLC ...E ... 978 342-8921
Boca Raton (G-707)
◆ Smurfit Kappa Packaging LLC ...F ... 954 838-9738
Sunrise (G-17175)
Specialty Fin Consulting Corp ...B ... 717 246-1661
Longboat Key (G-8247)
St Pete Paper Company ...G ... 727 572-9868
Palmetto (G-13823)
Suncoast Cartons & Crating LLC ...G ... 813 242-8477
Tampa (G-18142)
▼ Sunshine Packaging Inc ...F ... 305 887-8141
Hialeah (G-5639)
Two Paper Chasers LLC ...G ... 813 251-5090
Tampa (G-18209)
Ultrabox Inc ...F ... 941 371-0000
Bradenton (G-1136)
▲ UNI-Box Inc ...E ... 954 733-3550
Oakland Park (G-11855)
Westrock Cp LLC ...C ... 904 261-5551
Fernandina Beach (G-3749)
Westrock Cp LLC ...C ... 904 356-5611
Jacksonville (G-6913)
Westrock Cp LLC ...D ... 850 785-4311
Panama City (G-13964)
Westrock Cp LLC ...G ... 239 658-8221
Immokalee (G-6054)
Westrock CP LLC ...E ... 407 859-9701
Orlando (G-13324)
Westrock Rkt LLC ...C ... 904 714-1643
Jacksonville (G-6915)

2655 Fiber Cans, Tubes & Drums

Caraustar Indus Cnsmr Pdts Gro ...E ... 386 328-8335
Palatka (G-13474)
CMI Microclimates Inc ...G ... 607 569-2738
Inverness (G-6082)
▲ Custom Manufacturing Inc ...G ... 607 569-2738
Inverness (G-6084)
◆ Design Containers Inc ...D ... 904 764-6541
Jacksonville (G-6316)
Mainstream Fiber Networks ...G ... 941 807-6100
Sarasota (G-16497)
◆ Matrix Packaging of Florida ...G ... 305 358-9696
Miami (G-9956)
May & Well Inc ...G ... 813 333-5806
Tampa (G-17895)
Petroleum Containment Inc ...E ... 904 358-1700
Jacksonville (G-6669)
Rapid Composites LLC ...G ... 941 322-6647
Sarasota (G-16284)
Sybo Composites LLC ...G ... 904 599-7093
Saint Augustine (G-15625)
Technocable Wiring Specialist ...F ... 813 664-0697
Tampa (G-18178)
Trio Envmtl Solutions LLC ...F ... 850 543-9125
Mary Esther (G-8592)

2656 Sanitary Food Containers

◆ Converpack Inc ...G ... 786 304-1680
Medley (G-8634)
▲ CU Holdings LLC ...D ... 904 483-5700
Jacksonville (G-6302)
Eco Cups International Corp ...F ... 407 308-1764
Orlando (G-12696)
Estal Usa Inc ...G ... 305 728-3272
Miami (G-9537)
Gesco Ice Cream Vending Corp ...F ... 718 782-3232
Sunny Isles Beach (G-17078)
Hg Brokerage Services Inc ...G ... 407 294-3507
Orlando (G-12800)
Mike and Val Tupper Ind ...G ... 904 757-7566
Jacksonville (G-6604)
Pride Straws LLC ...G ... 407 754-5833
Miami (G-10192)
Sic Products LLC ...G ... 904 374-2639
Naples (G-11401)
Tellus Products LLC ...E ... 561 996-5556
Belle Glade (G-352)

2657 Folding Paperboard Boxes

Beverage Blocks Inc ...F ... 813 309-8711
Tampa (G-17467)
Caribbean Box Company ...F ... 305 667-4900
Miami (G-9313)
Cypress Folding Cartons Inc ...E ... 813 884-5418
Tampa (G-17583)
Gulf Packaging Co ...F ... 727 441-1117
Clearwater (G-1708)
Latham Marine Inc ...E ... 954 462-3055
Fort Lauderdale (G-4096)
R G Management Inc ...E ... 407 889-3100
Orlando (G-13109)
Richard C Good ...G ... 321 639-6383
Titusville (G-18458)
Southeast Finishing Group Inc ...E ... 407 299-4620
Orlando (G-13202)
▼ Sunshine Packaging Inc ...F ... 305 887-8141
Hialeah (G-5639)
Uvisors ...G ... 813 716-1113
Tampa (G-18230)

2671 Paper Coating & Laminating for Packaging

A Plus Lamination & Finshg Inc ...F ... 305 636-9888
Miami (G-9041)
▼ Almi Intl Plastic Inds Inc ...G ... 954 920-6836
Hollywood (G-5771)
Apakus Inc ...F ... 305 403-2603
Coral Gables (G-2123)
◆ Attesa Holdings Group LLC ...G ... 305 777-3567
Miami (G-9190)
Dairy-Mix Inc ...F ... 813 621-8098
Tampa (G-17586)
Estal Usa Inc ...G ... 305 728-3272
Miami (G-9537)
Four G Enterprises Inc ...E ... 407 834-4143
Longwood (G-8284)
Full Cut Tabs LLC ...F ... 941 316-1510
Sarasota (G-16443)
Graphics Designer Inc ...F ... 561 687-7993
West Palm Beach (G-18889)
Great Northern Corporation ...E ... 920 739-3671
Jacksonville (G-6446)
Gulf Packaging Co ...F ... 727 441-1117
Clearwater (G-1708)
Holmes Stamp Company ...E ... 904 396-2291
Jacksonville (G-6476)
J & J International Corp ...E ... 407 349-7114
Sanford (G-16070)
◆ Jr Plastics Corporation ...D ... 352 401-0880
Ocala (G-11972)
Label Graphics Inc ...G ... 561 798-8180
Lake Worth (G-7563)
Labelpro Inc ...F ... 727 538-2149
Clearwater (G-1757)
Legar Inc ...F ... 561 635-5882
Boynton Beach (G-928)
Mr Cool Waters Inc ...F ... 305 234-6311
Miami (G-10048)
Plastic Coated Papers Inc ...D ... 850 968-6100
Pensacola (G-14233)
Storopack Inc ...G ... 305 805-9696
Medley (G-8731)
Trend At LLC ...F ... 786 300-2550
Miami (G-10505)
Tutti Hogar International LLC ...G ... 305 705-4735
Miami (G-10513)
United Seal & Tag Label Corp ...G ... 941 625-6799
Port Charlotte (G-15004)
World Indus Resources Corp ...E ... 727 572-9991
Clearwater (G-1944)
▲ Zellwin Farms Company ...E ... 407 886-9241
Zellwood (G-19505)

2672 Paper Coating & Laminating, Exc for Packaging

Automatic Business Products Co ...F ... 888 742-7639
Port Orange (G-15009)
Avery Dennison Corporation ...C ... 305 228-8740
Miami (G-9197)
Avery Dennison Corporation ...C ... 727 787-1651
Palm Harbor (G-13721)
Avery Dennison Corporation ...C ... 727 785-6995
Palm Harbor (G-13722)
▼ Blue Ribbon Tag & Label Corp ...E ... 954 922-9292
Hollywood (G-5788)
Brand Label Inc ...E ... 904 737-6433
Jacksonville (G-6231)
Express Label Co Inc ...E ... 407 332-4774
Longwood (G-8278)
Florida Tape & Labels Inc ...F ... 941 921-5788
Sarasota (G-16438)
Folders Tabs Et Cetera ...F ... 813 884-3651
Tampa (G-17691)
▲ Intertape Polymer Corp ...C ... 888 898-7834
Sarasota (G-16469)
Intertape Polymer Corp ...F ... 813 621-8410
Tampa (G-17791)
◆ Ipg (us) Holdings Inc ...D ... 941 727-5788
Sarasota (G-16471)
Ipg (us) Inc ...G ... 941 727-5788
Sarasota (G-16472)
▲ J & P Deerfield Inc ...F ... 954 571-6665
Deerfield Beach (G-2849)
Keithco Inc ...G ... 352 351-4741
Ocala (G-11976)
Labelpro Inc ...F ... 727 538-2149
Clearwater (G-1757)
Midds Inc ...E ... 561 586-6220
Lake Worth Beach (G-7615)
Mikes Print Shop Inc ...G ... 407 718-4964
Winter Park (G-19426)
◆ One Step Papers LLC ...G ... 305 238-2296
Miami (G-10103)
▼ Online Labels LLC ...E ... 407 936-3900
Sanford (G-16096)
Southeast Id LLC ...F ... 954 571-6665
Miami Lakes (G-10859)
Southern States Gluing Svcs ...G ... 850 469-9667
Pensacola (G-14264)
Suncoast Identification Tech ...G ... 239 277-9922
Fort Myers (G-4616)
Sunshine Ltd Tape & Label Spc ...F ... 561 832-9656
West Palm Beach (G-19049)
Tampa Bay Coatings Inc ...F ... 727 823-9866
Saint Petersburg (G-15933)
▲ Tapesouth Inc ...G ... 904 642-1800
Gainesville (G-5007)
Taylor Communications Inc ...F ... 813 886-5511
Tampa (G-18177)
◆ Terry Boca Inc ...G ... 561 893-0333
Deerfield Beach (G-2925)

2673 Bags: Plastics, Laminated & Coated

Bags Express Inc ...G ... 305 500-9849
Doral (G-3263)
▲ Biobag Americas Inc ...F ... 727 789-1646
Dunedin (G-3570)
Cavadas Ruben & Trisha Wagner ...G ... 407 248-2659
Orlando (G-12556)

Coastal Films of Florida D 904 786-2031
Jacksonville *(G-6276)*
▲ **Construction and Elec Pdts Inc** F 954 972-9787
Pompano Beach *(G-14645)*
Cosner Manufacturing LLC F 863 676-2579
Lake Wales *(G-7506)*
▲ **Crown Products LLC** G 954 917-1118
Pompano Beach *(G-14652)*
CSR Enterprise Ltd G 954 624-2284
North Miami *(G-11635)*
Dairy-Mix Inc F 813 621-8098
Tampa *(G-17586)*
Daisies Closets G 863 838-5056
Lakeland *(G-7671)*
Diversitypro Corp E 305 691-2348
South Miami *(G-16815)*
▲ **Dynasel Incorporated** G 972 733-4447
Deerfield Beach *(G-2819)*
◆ **Flexsol Holding Corp** D 954 941-6333
Pompano Beach *(G-14700)*
▲ **H Goicoechea Inc** F 305 805-3333
Hialeah *(G-5441)*
◆ **H Sixto Distributors Inc** F 305 688-5242
Opa Locka *(G-12322)*
Inteplast Engineered Films Inc D 407 851-6620
Orlando *(G-12834)*
◆ **J S Trading Inc** G 954 791-9035
Plantation *(G-14526)*
◆ **Jan and Jean Inc** G 813 645-0680
Ruskin *(G-15485)*
◆ **Jr Plastics Corporation** D 352 401-0880
Ocala *(G-11972)*
▲ **Koszegi Industries Inc** E 954 419-9544
Deerfield Beach *(G-2855)*
Litterbin LLC G 772 633-7184
Vero Beach *(G-18640)*
Mhms Corp E 813 948-0504
Lutz *(G-8401)*
▲ **Plastix Usa LLC** D 305 891-0091
Hollywood *(G-5892)*
Poly Plastic Packaging Co Inc E 561 498-9040
Boca Raton *(G-668)*
Premium Absrbent Dspsables LLC E 561 737-6377
Boynton Beach *(G-944)*
Pro Pak Enterprises Inc F 888 375-2275
Deerfield Beach *(G-2894)*
R & D Sleeves Llc E 407 886-9010
Apopka *(G-178)*
▼ **Seal-Tite Plastic Packg Co Inc** D 305 264-9015
Miami *(G-10316)*
Sigma Extruding Corp G 904 786-2031
Jacksonville *(G-6769)*
▲ **Starlock Inc** G 305 477-2303
Doral *(G-3511)*
Sterling Mdr Inc F 954 725-2777
Deerfield Beach *(G-2917)*
US American Plastic Corp F 305 200-3683
Miami *(G-10551)*

2674 Bags: Uncoated Paper & Multiwall

ACS of West Palm Beach Inc G 561 844-5790
West Palm Beach *(G-18787)*
Aspen Products Inc E 904 579-4366
Fleming Island *(G-3759)*
▼ **Atlantic Ship Supply Inc** G 954 961-8885
Hallandale *(G-5153)*
▲ **Bryce Foster Inc** G 800 371-0395
Altamonte Springs *(G-34)*
◆ **Harmsco Inc** D 561 848-9628
Riviera Beach *(G-15331)*
◆ **J S Trading Inc** G 954 791-9035
Plantation *(G-14526)*
▲ **Paper Bag Manufacturers Inc** F 305 685-1100
Opa Locka *(G-12349)*
Ready Building Products Inc G 941 639-6222
Punta Gorda *(G-15228)*
▼ **S V Bags America Inc** G 954 577-9091
Weston *(G-19166)*
Tak Paper Corp G 786 287-8900
Doral *(G-3522)*
Trend At LLC F 786 300-2550
Miami *(G-10505)*

2675 Die-Cut Paper & Board

Advanced Printing Finshg Inc F 305 836-8581
Hialeah *(G-5272)*
Bros Williams Printing Inc G 305 769-9925
Hialeah *(G-5332)*
C & R Designs Inc G 321 383-2255
Titusville *(G-18419)*
Florida Print Finishers Inc G 850 877-8503
Tallahassee *(G-17255)*
Folders Tabs Et Cetera F 813 884-3651
Tampa *(G-17691)*
Knopf & Sons Bindery Inc F 904 355-4411
Jacksonville *(G-6543)*
▲ **Maq Investments Group Inc** E 305 691-1468
Miami Lakes *(G-10811)*
Packaging Alternatives Corp F 352 867-5050
Ocala *(G-12021)*
Service Bindery Enterprises F 727 823-9866
Saint Petersburg *(G-15911)*
Southeast Finishing Group Inc E 407 299-4620
Orlando *(G-13202)*
Specialty Fin Consulting Corp B 717 246-1661
Longboat Key *(G-8247)*
Super Grafix Inc F 561 585-1519
Boca Raton *(G-739)*
Top Notch Diecutting Foil STA G 904 346-3511
Jacksonville *(G-6863)*

2676 Sanitary Paper Prdts

All About Her F 954 559-5175
Davie *(G-2491)*
◆ **Anthem South LLC** E 973 779-1982
Medley *(G-8610)*
Bk Naturals LLC G 561 870-0592
West Palm Beach *(G-18823)*
Diversitypro Corp E 305 691-2348
South Miami *(G-16815)*
◆ **Esteemed Brands Inc** F 954 442-3923
Miramar *(G-10990)*
Green Leaf Foods LLC G 305 308-9167
Miramar *(G-11001)*
◆ **Impex of Doral Inc** E 305 470-0041
Medley *(G-8669)*
Johnson & Johnson D 954 534-1141
Dania Beach *(G-2466)*
Lifelink Foundation Inc E 407 218-8783
Orlando *(G-12909)*
▲ **Pacific Link Imports Inc** G 954 605-6071
Parkland *(G-13997)*
Papers Unlimited Plus Inc G 215 947-1155
Palm Beach Gardens *(G-13616)*
▲ **Peter Marcus Paradigm LLC** F 877 887-8696
Winter Park *(G-19429)*
Playtex Manufacturing Inc E 386 677-9559
Ormond Beach *(G-13391)*
◆ **Softex Paper Inc** D 386 328-8488
Palatka *(G-13494)*
SW Premier Products LLC G 941 275-6677
Punta Gorda *(G-15240)*
▼ **Threez Company LLC** G 904 422-9224
Jacksonville *(G-6853)*
Threez Company LLC G 904 651-1444
Jacksonville *(G-6854)*
Wonderworld 100 LLC F 407 618-3207
Orlando *(G-13329)*

2677 Envelopes

Cenveo Worldwide Limited B 321 207-0403
Longwood *(G-8265)*
Double Envelope Corporation B 352 375-0738
Gainesville *(G-4907)*
Everglades Envelope Co Inc G 954 783-7920
Fort Lauderdale *(G-3976)*
Mac Paper Converters LLC C 800 334-7026
Jacksonville *(G-6570)*
▼ **Services On Demand Print Inc** E 305 681-5345
Hallandale Beach *(G-5209)*
▲ **Starlock Inc** G 305 477-2303
Doral *(G-3511)*
◆ **Winsted Thermographers Inc** F 305 944-7862
Hallandale Beach *(G-5225)*

2678 Stationery Prdts

3nstar Inc F 786 233-7011
Doral *(G-3216)*
Peter T Amann G 561 848-2770
West Palm Beach *(G-18995)*
Universal School Products Inc G 904 273-8590
Ponte Vedra Beach *(G-14956)*
Universal Tech Inc G 786 220-8032
Miami *(G-10545)*

2679 Converted Paper Prdts, NEC

A M Rayonier Products Inc B 904 261-3611
Yulee *(G-19493)*
American Label Group Inc F 386 274-5234
Daytona Beach *(G-2623)*
◆ **Amerifax Acquisition Corp** G 305 828-1701
Hialeah *(G-5297)*
▲ **Amtec Sales Inc** F 800 994-3318
Miami *(G-9153)*
Auto Tag of America Inc D 941 739-8841
Bradenton *(G-992)*
Automated Paper Converters G 954 925-0721
Hollywood *(G-5779)*
▼ **Consolidated Label Co** C 407 339-2626
Sanford *(G-16022)*
Contact Enterprises Inc G 561 900-5134
Pompano Beach *(G-14647)*
◆ **David Dobbs Enterprises Inc** D 904 824-6171
Saint Augustine *(G-15533)*
▼ **Dietzgen Corporation** E 813 286-4767
Tampa *(G-17605)*
Express Label Co Inc E 407 332-4774
Longwood *(G-8278)*
◆ **Express Paper Company Inc** F 305 685-4929
Miami Lakes *(G-10787)*
Force Imaging Group LLC G 888 406-2120
Wesley Chapel *(G-18747)*
Gainesville Sun F 352 374-5000
Gainesville *(G-4928)*
Gift Wrap My Face LLC F 305 788-1473
Weston *(G-19133)*
▲ **Inovart Inc** G 941 751-2324
Bradenton *(G-1061)*
Nadco Tapes & Labels Inc E 941 751-6693
Sarasota *(G-16263)*
◆ **Nicolette Mayer Collection Inc** G 561 241-6906
Boca Raton *(G-644)*
◆ **Nida-Core Corporation** E 772 343-7300
Port Saint Lucie *(G-15124)*
◆ **Palmas Printing Inc** E 321 984-4451
Melbourne *(G-8904)*
Palmland Paper Co Inc G 954 764-6910
Fort Lauderdale *(G-4154)*
◆ **Panelfold Inc** C 305 688-3501
Miami *(G-10138)*
▼ **Paradise Label Inc** F 863 860-8779
Plant City *(G-14455)*
▲ **Parthenon Prints Inc** E 850 769-8321
Panama City *(G-13940)*
◆ **Parti Line International Inc** F 504 522-0300
Largo *(G-8023)*
Passion Labels & Packaging E 941 312-5003
Sarasota *(G-16272)*
Prosegur Eas Usa LLC F 561 900-2744
Deerfield Beach *(G-2897)*
Putnam Paper & Packaging Inc F 904 328-5101
Palatka *(G-13491)*
R & D Sleeves Llc E 407 886-9010
Apopka *(G-178)*
Richard Wagner LLC G 239 450-1721
Naples *(G-11383)*
Rotary Manufacturing LLC F 941 564-8038
North Port *(G-11748)*
Specialty Fin Consulting Corp B 717 246-1661
Longboat Key *(G-8247)*
Versatile Packagers LLC F 813 664-1171
Tampa *(G-18238)*
Vinland Marketing Inc G 954 602-2177
Pembroke Pines *(G-14071)*
▲ **Wrap-Art Inc** G 954 428-1819
Deerfield Beach *(G-2936)*

27 PRINTING, PUBLISHING, AND ALLIED INDUSTRIES

2711 Newspapers: Publishing & Printing

925 Nuevos Cubanos Inc G 954 806-8375
Fort Lauderdale *(G-3773)*
A M Coplan Associates G 904 737-6996
Jacksonville *(G-6110)*
▲ **Advanced Cmmncations Holdg Inc** D 954 753-0100
Coral Springs *(G-2213)*
Alachua Today Inc G 386 462-3355
Alachua *(G-1)*
Aldema Services Inc G 561 860-0693
West Palm Beach *(G-18793)*
Ali Kamakhi F 850 405-8591
Tallahassee *(G-17216)*
Alm Media LLC G 954 468-2600
Fort Lauderdale *(G-3809)*
Almanac LLC F 415 310-5143
Miami *(G-9119)*

SIC

Alternative Daily......G...... 561 628-4711
West Palm Beach *(G-18794)*
American City Bus Journals Inc......G...... 813 873-8225
Tampa *(G-17416)*
American Classifieds......F...... 850 747-1155
Panama City *(G-13863)*
Anna Andres......G...... 239 335-0233
Fort Myers *(G-4364)*
ASAP Magazine & Newspaper......G...... 813 238-0184
Tampa *(G-17437)*
Aw Publishing......F...... 305 856-7000
Miami *(G-9201)*
Ayers Publishing Inc......G...... 352 463-7135
Trenton *(G-18480)*
B Squared of Chiefland LLC......F...... 352 507-2195
Chiefland *(G-1532)*
Baker County Press Inc......G...... 904 259-2400
Macclenny *(G-8442)*
Bay County Bullet......G...... 850 640-0855
Panama City *(G-13867)*
▼ **Bcc-Bgle Cmmnctons Crp-Clrin L**......F...... 305 270-3333
Miami *(G-9228)*
Beach Beacon......F...... 727 397-5563
Seminole *(G-16741)*
Better Built Group Inc......G...... 850 803-4044
Destin *(G-3212)*
Bi-Ads Inc......F...... 954 525-1489
Fort Lauderdale *(G-3849)*
Bloomingdale Gazette Inc......G...... 813 681-2051
Valrico *(G-18516)*
Bluewaterpress LLC......G...... 888 247-0793
Saint Augustine *(G-15522)*
Boca Raton Observer......G...... 561 702-3086
Boca Raton *(G-453)*
Bonita Daily News......E...... 239 213-6060
Naples *(G-11191)*
Bradford County Telegraph Inc......F...... 904 964-6305
Starke *(G-16887)*
Brasileiras & Brasileiros Inc......G...... 407 855-9541
Orlando *(G-12534)*
Brazilian Clssfied ADS-Chei In......G...... 954 570-7568
Deerfield Beach *(G-2789)*
Breeze Corporation......C...... 239 574-1110
Cape Coral *(G-1395)*
Breeze Corporation......C...... 239 765-0400
Fort Myers Beach *(G-4660)*
Breeze Corporation......G...... 239 425-8860
Fort Myers *(G-4381)*
Breeze Newspapers......F...... 239 574-1116
Fort Myers *(G-4382)*
Breeze Newspapers......G...... 239 574-1110
Cape Coral *(G-1396)*
Brevard Business News......F...... 321 951-7777
Melbourne *(G-8786)*
Buck Pile Inc......G...... 772 492-1056
Vero Beach *(G-18607)*
Bulletin Net Inc......F...... 941 468-2569
Sarasota *(G-16373)*
Bus Bulletin Inc......G...... 850 271-0017
Panama City *(G-13875)*
Business Jrnl Publications Inc......E...... 904 396-3502
Jacksonville *(G-6246)*
Business Jrnl Publications Inc......E...... 813 342-2472
Tampa *(G-17492)*
Business Report of N Cntrl FL......G...... 352 275-9469
Gainesville *(G-4890)*
Captiva Current Inc......F...... 239 574-1110
Sanibel *(G-16143)*
Caribbean Today News Magazine......F...... 305 238-2868
Palmetto Bay *(G-13841)*
Carillon Publishing LLC......G...... 407 363-0375
Orlando *(G-12550)*
Carol City Opa Locka News......E...... 305 669-7355
South Miami *(G-16813)*
Caxton Newspapers Inc......E...... 305 538-9700
Miami Beach *(G-10652)*
Cedar Key Beacon......G...... 352 493-4796
Chiefland *(G-1534)*
Central Florida Publishing Inc......F...... 407 323-5204
Sanford *(G-16010)*
Charisma Media......D...... 407 333-0600
Lake Mary *(G-7405)*
Chipley Newspapers Inc......G...... 850 638-0212
Bonifay *(G-801)*
Citrus Publishing LLC......C...... 352 563-6363
Crystal River *(G-2373)*
Coffee News Clearwater......G...... 727 789-6677
Oldsmar *(G-12217)*
Coinweek LLC......F...... 407 786-5555
Longwood *(G-8266)*

Com Miami Corporation......G...... 305 376-5040
Miami *(G-9384)*
Community News Papers Inc......G...... 386 752-1293
Lake City *(G-7351)*
Community News Publications......F...... 813 909-2800
Lutz *(G-8378)*
Cooke Communications Fla LLC......D...... 305 292-7777
Key West *(G-7184)*
Cooppa News Reporter......G...... 954 437-8864
Pembroke Pines *(G-14029)*
▲ **Cottonimagescom Inc**......E...... 305 251-2560
Doral *(G-3311)*
Creative Loafing Inc......E...... 813 739-4800
Tampa *(G-17565)*
Creative Loafing Inc......G...... 941 365-6776
Tampa *(G-17566)*
Current......G...... 954 262-8455
Davie *(G-2512)*
Cve Reporter Inc......F...... 954 421-5566
Deerfield Beach *(G-2810)*
D-R Media and Investments LLC......D...... 941 207-1602
Venice *(G-18540)*
Daily Buzz......G...... 407 673-5400
Winter Park *(G-19399)*
Daily Green......G...... 352 226-8288
Gainesville *(G-4903)*
Daily Melt......G...... 305 519-2585
Miami *(G-9432)*
Daily Melt......G...... 305 573-9700
Miami *(G-9433)*
Daily Multiservices Inc......G...... 786 286-3817
Hialeah *(G-5364)*
Daily News Inc......G...... 386 312-5200
Palatka *(G-13476)*
Daily Room......F...... 754 200-5153
Plantation *(G-14506)*
Daily Therapy Services Inc......G...... 954 649-3620
Lauderhill *(G-8107)*
Daily Trnsfrmtion Mnstries Inc......G...... 727 847-5152
Tampa *(G-17585)*
Dailychew LLC......G...... 954 849-0553
Plantation *(G-14507)*
Dailys......F...... 904 448-0562
Jacksonville *(G-6308)*
Dailys......F...... 904 880-4784
Jacksonville *(G-6309)*
Dailys 1113 Shell......F...... 904 608-0219
Ponte Vedra *(G-14924)*
Defuniak Springs Herald Breeze......G...... 850 892-3232
Defuniak Springs *(G-2941)*
Destin Log......C...... 850 837-2828
Fort Walton Beach *(G-4790)*
Distribuidora Continental SA......F...... 305 374-4474
Virginia Gardens *(G-18687)*
Doral Family Journal LLC......G...... 305 300-4594
Doral *(G-3334)*
Downtown Projects I LLC......G...... 352 226-8288
Gainesville *(G-4909)*
Eco Informativo......G...... 786 362-6789
Miami *(G-9499)*
Eglin Flyer......G...... 850 678-4581
Niceville *(G-11565)*
El Colusa News......G...... 786 845-6868
Miami *(G-9505)*
El Global News......G...... 305 212-1361
Doral *(G-3341)*
El Hispano......G...... 772 878-6488
Port Saint Lucie *(G-15105)*
El Latino Newspaper......G...... 561 835-4913
West Palm Beach *(G-18861)*
Emerald Coast Media & Mktg......E...... 850 267-4555
Santa Rosa Beach *(G-16159)*
Europrint Inc......F...... 407 869-9955
Altamonte Springs *(G-45)*
EW Scripps Company......C...... 772 408-5300
Port Saint Lucie *(G-15107)*
F S View Fla Flambeau Newsppr......E...... 850 561-6653
Tallahassee *(G-17250)*
Fernandina Observer Inc......G...... 904 261-4372
Fernandina Beach *(G-3738)*
First Class Media Inc......G...... 561 719-3433
Jupiter *(G-7043)*
Five Star Sports Tickets......F...... 440 899-2000
Hallandale Beach *(G-5187)*
Florida Catholic Media Inc......G...... 407 373-0075
Orlando *(G-12747)*
Florida E Coast Supersonics Tc......G...... 386 689-2367
New Smyrna Beach *(G-11533)*
Florida Health Care News Inc......E...... 813 989-1330
Temple Terrace *(G-18368)*

Florida Sentinel Publishing Co......E...... 813 248-1921
Tampa *(G-17688)*
Florida Star Inc......F...... 904 766-8834
Jacksonville *(G-6403)*
Florida Weekly......G...... 239 333-2135
Fort Myers *(G-4454)*
Foliage Enterprises Inc......E...... 407 886-2777
Apopka *(G-144)*
▲ **Forum Publishing Group Inc**......C...... 954 698-6397
Deerfield Beach *(G-2827)*
Forum Publishing Group Inc......D...... 954 596-5650
Deerfield Beach *(G-2828)*
Forward Defuniak Incorporated......G...... 850 830-7663
Defuniak Springs *(G-2943)*
Frank The Kit Exprt Palm Coast......G...... 386 264-6105
Palm Coast *(G-13695)*
Free Press......G...... 305 853-7277
Key Largo *(G-7171)*
Free Press Publishing Company......E...... 813 254-5888
Tampa *(G-17694)*
Gadsden County Times Inc......F...... 850 627-7649
Quincy *(G-15250)*
Gainesville......G...... 352 339-0294
Gainesville *(G-4925)*
Gainesville Sun Publishing Co......B...... 352 378-1411
Gainesville *(G-4929)*
Galactic News Service......G...... 239 431-7470
Naples *(G-11257)*
Gatehouse Media LLC......F...... 863 401-6900
Winter Haven *(G-19325)*
Go Latinos Magazine LLC......G...... 786 601-7693
Homestead *(G-5965)*
Gospel Journal......G...... 904 389-9635
Jacksonville *(G-6443)*
Grass River Publshing......G...... 954 974-7383
Margate *(G-8548)*
Greene Publishing Inc......F...... 850 973-6397
Madison *(G-8451)*
Greentree Marketing Svcs Inc......F...... 800 557-9567
Fort Lauderdale *(G-4031)*
Greenwood Lake News Inc......F...... 845 477-2575
Hudson *(G-6027)*
Griffon Graphics Inc......G...... 954 922-1800
Hollywood *(G-5833)*
Grupo De Diarios America LLC......G...... 305 577-0094
Miami *(G-9679)*
Gulf Breeze News Inc......G...... 850 932-8986
Gulf Breeze *(G-5117)*
Gulf Coast Business Review......G...... 941 906-9386
Sarasota *(G-16453)*
Gulfcoast Gabber Inc......G...... 727 321-6965
Gulfport *(G-5134)*
Halifax Media Group LLC......B...... 386 265-6700
Daytona Beach *(G-2670)*
Halifax Media Group LLC......C...... 941 361-4800
Sarasota *(G-16457)*
Halifax Media Holdings LLC......E...... 386 681-2404
Daytona Beach *(G-2671)*
Hammill Post......G...... 352 304-8675
Ocala *(G-11964)*
Hammond Enterprises......G...... 386 575-2402
Leesburg *(G-8160)*
Harborpoint Media LLC......C...... 352 365-8200
Leesburg *(G-8161)*
Herald-Advocate Publishing Co......F...... 863 773-3255
Wauchula *(G-18693)*
Heritage Centl Fla Jewish News......F...... 407 834-8277
Fern Park *(G-3729)*
Home Examiner Inc......G...... 786 897-8349
Miami *(G-9717)*
Home Town Journal......G...... 904 259-9141
Glen Saint Mary *(G-5036)*
Homestead Newspapers Inc......A...... 305 245-2311
Homestead *(G-5968)*
▲ **Hometown News LC**......E...... 772 465-5656
Fort Pierce *(G-4706)*
Hometown News LC......G...... 321 242-1013
Melbourne *(G-8846)*
Hopkins & Daughter Inc......G...... 941 964-2995
Boca Grande *(G-393)*
Horizon Publications Inc......G...... 386 427-1000
New Smyrna Beach *(G-11535)*
Horse & Pony......G...... 813 986-1003
Thonotosassa *(G-18401)*
Howard Scripts Inc......G...... 561 746-5111
Jupiter *(G-7054)*
Image Experts Inc......G...... 727 488-7556
Saint Petersburg *(G-15813)*
Impremedia LLC......G...... 407 767-0070
Longwood *(G-8289)*

Independent Florida Sun........................G....... 850 438-8115
Pensacola *(G-14176)*
Independent Newsmedia Inc USA.........G....... 863 983-9148
Okeechobee *(G-12182)*
Inquirer Newspapers Inc........................G....... 772 257-6230
Vero Beach *(G-18631)*
Island Sand Paper....................................G....... 239 290-4038
Fort Myers Beach *(G-4664)*
J&J Suwannee Enterprises LLC..........G....... 386 658-1721
Live Oak *(G-8233)*
Jacksonville Free Press........................F....... 904 634-1993
Jacksonville *(G-6511)*
Jewish Press Group of Tmpa Bay.........G....... 727 535-4400
Largo *(G-7988)*
Jls of St Augustine Inc..........................G....... 904 797-6098
Saint Augustine *(G-15560)*
Job News..E....... 904 296-3006
Jacksonville *(G-6524)*
Key West Printing LLC...........................G....... 305 517-6711
Key West *(G-7190)*
Keynoter Publishing Co Inc...................F....... 305 743-5551
Marathon *(G-8519)*
▲ **Knight-Rddr/Miami Herald Cr Un**......F....... 305 376-2181
Miami *(G-9828)*
La Gaceta Publishing Inc........................F....... 813 248-3921
Tampa *(G-17832)*
Lake News LLC..F....... 407 251-1314
Orlando *(G-12888)*
Lake Worth Herald Press........................E....... 561 585-9387
Lake Worth *(G-7564)*
Las Amrcas Mltimedia Group LLC.........E....... 305 633-3341
Miami *(G-9861)*
Leader Group...E....... 904 249-7475
Jacksonville Beach *(G-6947)*
Ledger..B....... 863 802-7000
Lakeland *(G-7733)*
Lf Senior Communications Group........F....... 561 392-4550
Boca Raton *(G-602)*
Liberty Calhoun Journal Inc..................G....... 850 643-3333
Bristol *(G-1198)*
Libre..G....... 305 267-2000
Miami *(G-9889)*
Linville Enterprises LLC........................G....... 813 782-1558
Zephyrhills *(G-19527)*
Local Community News Inc....................G....... 904 886-4919
Callahan *(G-1326)*
Localtoolbox Inc......................................G....... 415 250-3232
Pensacola *(G-14195)*
Longboat Key News Inc..........................F....... 941 387-2200
Longboat Key *(G-8245)*
Lorken Publications Inc..........................G....... 239 395-1213
Sanibel *(G-16147)*
Macbonner Inc..F....... 941 778-7978
Holmes Beach *(G-5946)*
Maxwells Sanibel Lime-Elo Inc.............G....... 239 472-8618
Sanibel *(G-16148)*
McClatchy Shared Services Ctr............D....... 305 740-8800
Doral *(G-3427)*
Medleycom Incorporated........................E....... 408 745-5418
Delray Beach *(G-3105)*
Merle Harris Enterprises Inc..................G....... 386 677-7060
South Daytona *(G-16804)*
Miami Herald...F....... 305 269-7768
Miami *(G-10002)*
Miami Herald...G....... 800 843-4372
Doral *(G-3433)*
Miami News 24 Inc...................................G....... 786 331-8141
Doral *(G-3435)*
Miami Slice LLC.......................................G....... 786 200-2723
Miami *(G-10011)*
Miami Times..E....... 305 694-6210
Miami *(G-10015)*
Mid-Florida Publications Inc..................G....... 352 589-8811
Mount Dora *(G-11107)*
Miller Publishing Co Inc..........................F....... 305 669-7355
South Miami *(G-16822)*
Milton Newspapers Inc............................A....... 850 623-2120
Milton *(G-10935)*
Monticello News.......................................F....... 850 997-3568
Monticello *(G-11080)*
National Newspaper Placem...................G....... 866 404-5913
Lake Mary *(G-7438)*
National Tchncal Cmmunications..........G....... 407 671-7777
Orlando *(G-12991)*
Ne Media Group Inc..................................G....... 954 733-8393
Oakland Park *(G-11823)*
Neighborhood News & Lifestyles...........F....... 727 943-0551
Tarpon Springs *(G-18316)*
News Features USA Inc...........................G....... 305 298-5313
Miami Beach *(G-10698)*
News Herald...F....... 850 785-6550
Panama City *(G-13931)*
News Leader Inc..E....... 352 242-9818
Clermont *(G-1970)*
▲ **News-Journal Corporation**...................A....... 386 252-1511
Daytona Beach *(G-2690)*
News-Journal Corporation......................F....... 386 283-5664
Palm Coast *(G-13704)*
Newspaper Printing Company...............G....... 727 572-7488
Clearwater *(G-1808)*
Newspaper Publishers Inc......................E....... 561 793-7606
Wellington *(G-18725)*
Nexstar Broadcasting Inc.......................F....... 863 683-6531
Lakeland *(G-7757)*
North Central Advertiser Inc...................G....... 386 755-2917
Lake City *(G-7370)*
Northwest Florida Daily News................G....... 850 863-1111
Fort Walton Beach *(G-4819)*
Npc of Tampa Inc......................................F....... 813 839-0035
Tampa *(G-17942)*
Observer Group...G....... 407 654-5500
Winter Garden *(G-19278)*
Observer Group and Gulf Coast.............G....... 239 263-0122
Naples *(G-11349)*
Observer Group Inc...................................E....... 941 383-5509
Sarasota *(G-16528)*
Observer Media Group Inc.......................D....... 941 366-3468
Sarasota *(G-16529)*
Ocala Centre 6...G....... 305 322-7365
Ocala *(G-12008)*
Ocala Star Banner Corporation..............C....... 352 867-4010
Ocala *(G-12016)*
Ocala Swamp LLC.....................................G....... 352 732-4260
Ocala *(G-12017)*
Ocalanow Com...G....... 352 433-2497
Ocala *(G-12018)*
Office of Medical Examiner.....................G....... 772 464-7378
Fort Pierce *(G-4724)*
One World Media LLC...............................G....... 786 762-3030
Miami *(G-10104)*
OPC News...G....... 904 686-3938
Ponte Vedra Beach *(G-14948)*
Orange Peel Gazette.................................G....... 407 312-7335
Altamonte Springs *(G-60)*
Orange Peel Gazette Inc..........................G....... 407 892-5556
Saint Cloud *(G-15663)*
Orange Peel Gazette Treasur..................G....... 772 489-8005
Fort Pierce *(G-4726)*
Orange Peel Gztte of Oscola CN...........F....... 407 892-5556
Saint Cloud *(G-15664)*
Ord of Ahepa Ch 356 Daily & T..............G....... 727 791-1040
Clearwater *(G-1820)*
Orlando Times Inc.....................................G....... 407 841-3052
Orlando *(G-13037)*
Ormond Beach Observer..........................F....... 386 492-2784
Ormond Beach *(G-13389)*
Osceola Star...G....... 407 933-0174
Kissimmee *(G-7282)*
Osceola Woman Newspaper LLC...........G....... 407 891-9771
Kissimmee *(G-7283)*
Our Town News..G....... 954 979-0991
Pompano Beach *(G-14781)*
Our Village Okeechobee Inc....................G....... 863 467-0158
Okeechobee *(G-12188)*
Outpost North Lake....................................G....... 352 669-2430
Umatilla *(G-18500)*
Overseas Radio LLC..................................G....... 305 296-1630
Key West *(G-7200)*
P A Vivid Pathology..................................G....... 850 416-7780
Pensacola *(G-14218)*
Palm Beach Gardens Fla Wkly................G....... 561 904-6443
Palm Beach Gardens *(G-13615)*
Palm Beach Newspapers Inc...................D....... 561 820-3800
West Palm Beach *(G-18985)*
Palm Coast Observer LLC........................E....... 386 447-9723
Palm Coast *(G-13706)*
Panama City News Herald........................C....... 850 747-5000
Panama City *(G-13935)*
Panama City News Herald........................C....... 850 863-1111
Fort Walton Beach *(G-4821)*
Pathfnders Palm Bch-Mrtin Cnty............D....... 561 820-4262
West Palm Beach *(G-18989)*
Pearcey Enterprise....................................G....... 904 235-3096
Tampa *(G-17981)*
Pennysaver...G....... 718 986-6437
Deland *(G-3008)*
Pensacola Voice Inc..................................G....... 850 434-6963
Pensacola *(G-14227)*
Perry Newspapers Inc...............................F....... 850 584-5513
Perry *(G-14309)*
Photo Finishing News Inc........................G....... 239 992-4421
Naples *(G-11363)*
Pinecrest Tribune......................................F....... 305 662-2277
South Miami *(G-16825)*
Plant City Observer LLC...........................G....... 813 704-6850
Plant City *(G-14458)*
Plantation Journal Corporation..............G....... 954 226-6170
Plantation *(G-14542)*
Polk County Democrat..............................F....... 863 533-4183
Winter Haven *(G-19342)*
Pompano Pelican Inc.................................G....... 954 783-8700
Pompano Beach *(G-14804)*
Ponte Vedra Wns Civic Aliance..............G....... 904 834-3543
Ponte Vedra Beach *(G-14951)*
Port St Lucie News....................................E....... 772 287-1550
Stuart *(G-16991)*
Pressnet Corp..G....... 786 728-1369
Miami *(G-10189)*
Prestige Publication Group.....................E....... 305 538-9700
Miami Beach *(G-10705)*
Printing Services Plus LLC......................F....... 813 279-1903
Tampa *(G-18016)*
Prison Legal News.....................................F....... 561 360-2523
Lake Worth *(G-7583)*
Progress House..G....... 321 298-4652
Palm Bay *(G-13529)*
Purple Dove..G....... 904 261-5227
Fernandina Beach *(G-3747)*
Real News Real Fast.................................G....... 727 485-6055
Spring Hill *(G-16860)*
Reed Brennan Media Associates............E....... 407 894-7300
Orlando *(G-13125)*
Republic Newspapers Inc.........................G....... 813 782-1558
Zephyrhills *(G-19534)*
Republic Newspapers Inc.........................F....... 352 394-2183
Clermont *(G-1972)*
Resident Cmnty News Group Inc............F....... 904 962-6876
Jacksonville *(G-6716)*
Resident Community News......................G....... 904 388-8839
Jacksonville *(G-6717)*
Review Newspapers...................................G....... 941 474-4351
Englewood *(G-3682)*
Ring of Fire Radio LLC.............................G....... 866 666-6114
Pensacola *(G-14253)*
Rolling Greens News.................................G....... 352 236-0007
Ocala *(G-12040)*
Ronecker Holdings LLC............................G....... 813 855-5559
Oldsmar *(G-12268)*
◆ **Samara Publishing**..................................G....... 305 361-3333
Key Biscayne *(G-7162)*
Santiago of Key West Inc..........................G....... 305 304-6063
Key West *(G-7202)*
Santiva Chronicle.......................................G....... 239 437-9324
Fort Myers *(G-4596)*
Santiva Chronicle LLC..............................G....... 239 472-0559
Sanibel *(G-16149)*
Sarasota Herald-Tribune...........................C....... 941 358-4000
Sarasota *(G-16292)*
Sarasota Herald-Tribune...........................C....... 941 745-7808
Bradenton *(G-1110)*
Sarasota Herald-Tribune...........................B....... 941 953-7755
Sarasota *(G-16578)*
Sarasota Herald-Tribune...........................E....... 941 953-7755
Sarasota *(G-16579)*
Science Daily LLC......................................G....... 239 596-2624
Sarasota *(G-16585)*
Seabreeze Communications Group........F....... 239 278-4222
Fort Myers *(G-4603)*
Senior Life of Florida.................................F....... 321 242-1235
Melbourne *(G-8930)*
Senior Voice America Inc..........................F....... 813 444-1011
Tampa *(G-18083)*
Sentinel Cmmnctons News Vntres.........G....... 407 420-6229
Longwood *(G-8335)*
Sentinel Cmmnctons News Vntres.........G....... 407 420-5291
Orlando *(G-13173)*
Sentinel Cmmnctons News Vntres.........G....... 352 742-5900
Tavares *(G-18352)*
Sentinel Communicatns News Ven........A....... 407 420-5000
Orlando *(G-13174)*
Sentinel Sq Off Bldg MGT & Lsg............G....... 727 461-7700
Clearwater *(G-1873)*
Sep Communications LLC.........................F....... 561 998-0870
Boca Raton *(G-706)*
South Florida Digest Inc............................F....... 954 458-0635
Hallandale Beach *(G-5214)*
▼ **Southeast Offset Inc**...............................E....... 305 623-7788
Miami Lakes *(G-10860)*
Southeast Publishing Co Inc.....................G....... 239 213-1277
Naples *(G-11408)*

Southfloridagaynewscom F 954 530-4970
Wilton Manors *(G-19220)*
Southwest Fla Newspapers Inc G 239 574-9733
Cape Coral *(G-1476)*
St Agstine Bches News Jrnl LL G 904 501-4556
Saint Augustine *(G-15616)*
St Augustine Record E 904 829-6562
Saint Augustine *(G-15620)*
Star Editorial Inc G 561 997-7733
Boca Raton *(G-730)*
Stuart News C 772 287-1550
Stuart *(G-17024)*
Stuart News C 772 287-1550
Stuart *(G-17025)*
Sun Coast Media Group Inc D 941 206-1300
Port Charlotte *(G-15000)*
Sun Coast Media Group Inc D 941 207-1000
Venice *(G-18578)*
Sun Coast Media Group Inc G 863 494-7600
Punta Gorda *(G-15237)*
Sun Coast Media Group Inc E 941 681-3000
Englewood *(G-3684)*
Sun Coast Media Group Inc F 941 206-1900
Port Charlotte *(G-15001)*
▲ **Sun-Sentinel Company LLC** B 954 356-4000
Fort Lauderdale *(G-4265)*
Sun-Sentinel Company LLC E 954 356-4000
Deerfield Beach *(G-2918)*
Sun-Sentinel Company Inc G 561 736-2208
Boynton Beach *(G-964)*
Sun-Sentinel Company Inc F 954 735-6414
Fort Lauderdale *(G-4266)*
Suncoast News G 727 815-1023
Port Richey *(G-15070)*
Suwannee Fund LLC G 386 963-1149
Live Oak *(G-8242)*
Suwanneearc G 386 362-1796
Live Oak *(G-8243)*
Swapper G 850 973-6653
Madison *(G-8454)*
Sweetwater Today Inc G 305 456-4724
Miami *(G-10447)*
Syndicated Programming Inc G 850 877-0105
Tallahassee *(G-17333)*
Tallahassee Democrat E 850 599-2100
Tallahassee *(G-17335)*
Tampa Bay Newspapers Inc A 727 397-5563
Seminole *(G-16768)*
Tampa Bay Sports Entrmt LLC B 727 893-8111
Saint Petersburg *(G-15934)*
Tampa Bay Times G 352 754-6100
Brooksville *(G-1278)*
Tampa Media Group Inc C 813 259-7711
Tampa *(G-18166)*
Tampa Media Group Inc B 813 259-7711
Tampa *(G-18167)*
Tampa Media Group LLC G 813 259-7100
Tampa *(G-18168)*
◆ **Ter Prints Usa Inc** E 305 953-7789
Hollywood *(G-5922)*
The Scranton Times L P E 407 377-0400
Orlando *(G-13253)*
Times Holding Co G 727 893-8111
Saint Petersburg *(G-15938)*
Times Media Services Inc C 727 893-8111
Saint Petersburg *(G-15939)*
◆ **Times Publishing Company** A 727 893-8111
Saint Petersburg *(G-15940)*
Times Publishing Company C 727 849-6397
Port Richey *(G-15072)*
Times Publishing Company G 850 224-7263
Tallahassee *(G-17340)*
Times Publishing Company C 352 567-6660
Inverness *(G-6097)*
Todays Restaurant News Inc G 561 620-8888
Boca Raton *(G-751)*
Tom Watson Enterprises Inc G 352 683-5097
Hudson *(G-6040)*
Treasure Chest of Sweetwater G 407 788-0020
Longwood *(G-8344)*
Treasure Coast Publishing Inc F 772 221-4289
Stuart *(G-17038)*
Tri-County Bulletin G 352 493-4796
Chiefland *(G-1538)*
Triangle Shopping Guide Inc G 352 589-8811
Mount Dora *(G-11116)*
Trusted Daily Solutions G 954 461-5131
Lighthouse Point *(G-8213)*
Turtlehue LLC G 561 775-6614
North Palm Beach *(G-11728)*

Various Inc C 561 900-3691
Delray Beach *(G-3155)*
Vero Beach 32963 Media G 772 226-7924
Vero Beach *(G-18677)*
Vero News F 772 234-5727
Vero Beach *(G-18679)*
Vista Semanal G 239 263-4785
Naples *(G-11452)*
Voice of South Marion G 352 245-3161
Belleview *(G-376)*
Voice Publishing Co Inc G 305 687-5555
Hialeah *(G-5683)*
Wakulla News F 850 926-7102
Crawfordville *(G-2337)*
▲ **Washington CL Inc** F 813 739-4800
Tampa *(G-18251)*
Washington County News F 850 638-4242
Chipley *(G-1546)*
Weekly Challenger Newspaper G 727 896-2922
Saint Petersburg *(G-15956)*
Weekly Newspaper F 305 743-0844
Marathon *(G-8521)*
Weekly Planet of Sarasota Inc F 813 739-4800
Tampa *(G-18252)*
Weekly Schulte Valdes E 813 221-1154
Tampa *(G-18253)*
West Bolusia Beacon F 386 734-4622
Deland *(G-3033)*
Whatever Lo Que Sea LLC G 786 429-3462
Miami *(G-10599)*
White Miami LLC G 305 579-9115
Miami *(G-10601)*
Will & Mia Corp F 617 943-6914
Miami *(G-10607)*
Winter Garden Times Inc E 407 656-2121
Winter Garden *(G-19291)*
Wood Television LLC G 727 815-1000
New Port Richey *(G-11521)*
Wood Television LLC G 352 544-5200
Brooksville *(G-1292)*
Woody Hatcher G 850 526-1501
Marianna *(G-8588)*
Worldbox Corporation G 305 253-8800
Miami *(G-10621)*
Worldcity Inc G 305 441-2244
Coral Gables *(G-2207)*
Worldwide Media Svcs Group Inc D 561 989-1342
Boca Raton *(G-792)*
Worldwide Media Svcs Group Inc E 561 989-1342
Boca Raton *(G-793)*
Www Tcpalm Company F 772 287-1550
Stuart *(G-17053)*
Your Hometown Newspaper Inc E 305 669-7355
South Miami *(G-16832)*

2721 Periodicals: Publishing & Printing

3522091611 F 352 671-1909
Newberry *(G-11548)*
954 Savings Magazine G 954 900-4649
Weston *(G-19101)*
A & A Publishing Corp E 561 982-8960
Boca Raton *(G-395)*
Aacecorp Inc G 904 353-7878
Jacksonville *(G-6115)*
Academy Publishing Inc E 407 736-0100
Orlando *(G-12427)*
Action Weekly Corp G 561 586-8699
West Palm Beach *(G-18789)*
Akers Media Group Inc F 352 787-4112
Leesburg *(G-8140)*
Always Fun Inc G 954 258-4377
Cooper City *(G-2108)*
▼ **American Accounting Assn** E 941 921-7747
Lakewood Ranch *(G-7836)*
American Chiropractor F 305 434-8865
Miami *(G-9141)*
▼ **American Welding Society Inc** D 305 443-9353
Doral *(G-3247)*
Armbrust Aviation Group Inc E 561 355-8488
West Palm Beach *(G-18801)*
Around House Publishing Inc F 561 969-7412
West Palm Beach *(G-18802)*
Artnexus Online Inc E 305 891-7270
North Miami *(G-11625)*
Automundo Productions Inc G 305 541-4198
Coral Gables *(G-2124)*
▲ **Back To Godhead Inc** F 386 462-0481
Alachua *(G-8)*
Best Community Magazine G 407 571-2980
Altamonte Springs *(G-32)*

▲ **Betrock Information Systems** E 954 981-2821
Cooper City *(G-2110)*
Black College Monthly Inc G 352 335-5771
Gainesville *(G-4887)*
Black College Today Inc G 954 344-4469
Coral Springs *(G-2226)*
Blackfist Magazine LLC F 904 864-8695
Miami *(G-9255)*
▲ **Boat International Media Inc** G 954 522-2628
Fort Lauderdale *(G-3864)*
Bocadelray Life Magazine G 954 421-9797
Coconut Creek *(G-2071)*
Bonita Gente Magazine G 239 331-7952
Naples *(G-11192)*
Bonnier Corporation G 954 830-4460
Fort Lauderdale *(G-3866)*
Bonnier Corporation C 407 628-4802
Winter Park *(G-19383)*
Boswell JM & Associates Inc G 239 949-2311
Bonita Springs *(G-820)*
Brevard Softball Magazine Inc F 321 453-3711
Merritt Island *(G-8995)*
Brooklands New Media LLC G 305 901-9674
Miami Beach *(G-10648)*
Central Florida Publishing Inc F 407 323-5204
Sanford *(G-16010)*
CJ Publishers Inc F 727 521-6277
Pinellas Park *(G-14339)*
Coastal Angler Magazine G 850 586-3474
Satellite Beach *(G-16651)*
Coastal Communications Corp F 561 989-0600
Boca Raton *(G-486)*
Cole Enterprises Inc G 727 441-4101
Clearwater *(G-1632)*
Community News Publications F 813 909-2800
Lutz *(G-8378)*
Conric Holdings LLC F 239 690-9840
Fort Myers *(G-4408)*
Constructconnect Inc C 772 770-6003
Vero Beach *(G-18613)*
Construction Bulletin Inc F 904 388-0336
Jacksonville *(G-6284)*
Construction Journal Ltd D 772 781-2144
Stuart *(G-16927)*
Coral Gables Living G 786 552-6464
Coral Gables *(G-2133)*
Country Club Concierge Mag Inc G 904 223-0204
Ponte Vedra Beach *(G-14938)*
Data Publishers Inc F 954 752-2332
Coral Springs *(G-2237)*
Desh-Videsh Media Group Inc F 954 784-8100
Tamarac *(G-17354)*
Diamond Advertising & Mktg F 561 833-5129
West Palm Beach *(G-18854)*
▲ **Direct Response Publication** F 561 620-3010
Boca Raton *(G-503)*
Distribuidora Continental SA F 305 374-4474
Virginia Gardens *(G-18687)*
Diversityinc Media LLC F 973 494-0539
Palm Beach *(G-13553)*
Dolphin/Curtis Publishing Co G 305 594-0508
Miami Springs *(G-10890)*
Dupont Publishing Inc D 727 573-9339
Clearwater *(G-1661)*
Ebella Magazine G 239 431-7231
Naples *(G-11234)*
Edge of Humanity LLC G 954 425-0540
Pompano Beach *(G-14674)*
Endeavor Publications Inc G 352 369-1104
Ocala *(G-11932)*
◆ **Et Publishing International** D 305 871-6400
Virginia Gardens *(G-18689)*
Fathym Inc F 303 905-4402
Palmetto *(G-13797)*
First Marketing Company C 954 979-0700
Pompano Beach *(G-14691)*
Five Sports Inc G 727 209-1750
Saint Petersburg *(G-15781)*
Florida Bid Reporting Service F 850 539-7522
Tallahassee *(G-17252)*
Florida Design Inc E 561 997-1660
Boca Raton *(G-531)*
Florida Eqine Publications Inc F 352 732-8686
Ocala *(G-11945)*
Florida Family Magazine G 941 922-5437
Sarasota *(G-16434)*
Florida Homes Magazine G 941 227-7331
Sarasota *(G-16436)*
Florida Media Inc F 407 816-9596
Lake Mary *(G-7418)*

Floridas Hotspots Publishing................F 954 928-1862
Oakland Park *(G-11806)*
Franja Corp..................................G....... 954 659-1950
Weston *(G-19127)*
Fundacion Educativa Carlos M..............G....... 305 859-9617
Miami *(G-9604)*
Gatehouse Media LLC.........................F....... 863 401-6900
Winter Haven *(G-19325)*
Goodpress Publishing LLC....................G....... 561 865-8101
Delray Beach *(G-3085)*
Grandstand Publishing LLC..................G....... 847 491-6440
Orlando *(G-12787)*
Green Bench Monthly..........................G....... 813 417-3944
Saint Petersburg *(G-15797)*
Grupo Editorial Expansion.....................G....... 305 374-9003
Coral Gables *(G-2153)*
Gulf Publishing Company Inc................F....... 727 596-2863
Largo *(G-7968)*
Gulfshore Business............................G....... 239 887-1930
Naples *(G-11272)*
Gulfstream Media Group Inc.................E....... 954 462-4488
Fort Lauderdale *(G-4035)*
▼ **Haute Living Inc**.............................E....... 305 798-1373
Miami *(G-9689)*
Home and Design Magazine..................G....... 239 598-4826
Naples *(G-11280)*
Home Improver Inc.............................F....... 239 549-6901
Cape Coral *(G-1435)*
Homemag Inc...................................F....... 239 549-6960
Cape Coral *(G-1436)*
Homes Media Solutions LLC................F....... 850 350-7800
Tallahassee *(G-17278)*
Howard Publications Inc......................G....... 904 355-2601
Jacksonville *(G-6480)*
IMS Publishing Inc............................G....... 954 761-8777
Fort Lauderdale *(G-4056)*
In Focus Interactive Magazine..............G....... 954 966-1233
Miramar *(G-11003)*
In The Bite......................................F....... 561 529-3940
Jupiter *(G-7056)*
Industrial Projects Services..................G....... 813 265-2957
Tampa *(G-17782)*
Insurance Plus..................................G....... 904 567-1553
Ponte Vedra Beach *(G-14942)*
Interior Design..................................F....... 646 805-0200
Boca Raton *(G-568)*
Interior Dsign Media Group LLC............D....... 561 750-0151
Boca Raton *(G-569)*
International Cnstr Pubg.....................G....... 305 668-4999
Miami *(G-9757)*
International Guidelines Ctr..................G....... 407 878-7606
Lake Mary *(G-7425)*
Jazziz Magazine Inc...........................E....... 561 893-6868
Boca Raton *(G-578)*
Jes Publishing Corp...........................E....... 561 997-8683
Boca Raton *(G-580)*
Judicial & ADM RES Assoc..................F....... 850 222-3171
Tallahassee *(G-17285)*
Kenney Communications Inc.................F....... 407 859-3113
Orlando *(G-12869)*
L C Clark Publishing Inc.....................F....... 561 627-3393
Palm Beach Gardens *(G-13601)*
Lakeside Publishing Co LLC..................G....... 847 491-6440
Palm Beach Gardens *(G-13602)*
▲ **Latin Amrcn Fncl Pblctions Inc**..........F....... 305 416-5261
Miami *(G-9868)*
Latin Press Inc..................................F....... 305 285-3133
Miami *(G-9870)*
Lf Senior Communications Group..........F....... 561 392-4550
Boca Raton *(G-602)*
Lifestyle Magazine..............................G....... 386 423-2772
New Smyrna Beach *(G-11537)*
Lifestyle Media Group LLC...................F....... 954 377-9470
Fort Lauderdale *(G-4100)*
Local Value Magazine..........................G....... 813 421-6781
Tampa *(G-17857)*
Los Latinos Magazine Inc.....................F....... 305 882-9074
Hialeah *(G-5488)*
Lrp Publications Inc...........................C....... 215 784-0860
Palm Beach Gardens *(G-13608)*
Magazine Morris................................G....... 561 963-0231
Lake Worth *(G-7566)*
Magic Magazine.................................G....... 407 420-6080
Orlando *(G-12945)*
Mailbox Publishing Inc........................E....... 772 334-2121
Stuart *(G-16972)*
Maritime Executive LLC.......................G....... 954 848-9955
Plantation *(G-14531)*
Mary Lake Life Mag Inc.......................G....... 407 324-2644
Lake Mary *(G-7431)*
Mary Lake Life Magazine Inc................F....... 407 324-2644
Lake Mary *(G-7432)*
Mas Editorial Corp.............................G....... 305 748-0124
Hollywood *(G-5870)*
Meister Media Worldwide Inc................G....... 407 539-6552
Winter Park *(G-19422)*
Mercantile Two.................................G....... 941 388-0059
Sarasota *(G-16506)*
Mercaworld and CIA LLC......................G....... 786 212-5905
Pembroke Pines *(G-14047)*
Metro Life Media Inc...........................G....... 813 745-3658
Tampa *(G-17906)*
▲ **Miles Partnership II LLC**....................C....... 941 342-2300
Sarasota *(G-16509)*
Mio Publication Inc.............................G....... 941 351-2411
Sarasota *(G-16257)*
Mitcham Media Group LLC...................G....... 850 893-9624
Tallahassee *(G-17302)*
More Woodturning Magazine.................G....... 508 838-1933
Bradenton *(G-1081)*
▼ **Motorsport Marketing Inc**..................E....... 386 239-0523
Holly Hill *(G-5760)*
Moulton Publications Inc......................G....... 772 234-8871
Vero Beach *(G-18645)*
Municipal Code Corporation..................D....... 850 576-3171
Tallahassee *(G-17304)*
N Media Group LLC............................E....... 239 594-1322
Naples *(G-11333)*
Naples Illustrated...............................G....... 239 434-6966
Naples *(G-11335)*
Netexpressusa Inc..............................G....... 888 575-1245
Fort Myers *(G-4545)*
Newsmax Media Inc............................F....... 561 686-1165
West Palm Beach *(G-18964)*
Nostalgic America Inc.........................F....... 561 585-1724
Boca Raton *(G-649)*
Npc of Tampa Inc...............................F....... 813 839-0035
Tampa *(G-17942)*
Ocala Magazine.................................E....... 352 622-2995
Ocala *(G-12010)*
Ocala Publication Incorporated..............E....... 352 732-0073
Ocala *(G-12015)*
Old Port Group LLC............................F....... 904 819-5812
Saint Augustine *(G-15582)*
◆ **On-Board Media Inc**........................D....... 305 673-0400
Doral *(G-3450)*
Open House Magazine Inc....................G....... 305 576-6011
Miami *(G-10109)*
Our City Media of Florida LLC...............F....... 954 306-1007
Sunrise *(G-17154)*
Our Seniors Guidecom Inc....................G....... 904 655-2130
Jacksonville *(G-6649)*
Oxendine Publishing Inc......................E....... 352 373-6907
Gainesville *(G-4978)*
Oxpecker Enterprise Inc.......................G....... 305 253-5301
Miami *(G-10124)*
PA C Publishing Inc.............................G....... 813 814-1505
Oldsmar *(G-12255)*
Pageantry Tlent Entrmt Svcs In.............G....... 407 260-2262
Longwood *(G-8319)*
Palm Beach Liquidation Company..........E....... 561 659-0210
West Palm Beach *(G-18984)*
Palm Beach Media Group Inc................G....... 239 434-6966
Naples *(G-11355)*
Palm Beach Newspapers Inc.................D....... 561 820-3800
West Palm Beach *(G-18985)*
Passport Pblcations Media Corp............E....... 561 615-3900
West Palm Beach *(G-18988)*
Patterson Publishing...........................F....... 863 701-2707
Lakeland *(G-7763)*
PCI Communications Inc......................G....... 941 729-5202
Ellenton *(G-3654)*
Phoenix Media Network Inc..................E....... 561 994-1118
Boca Raton *(G-664)*
Pinstripe Magazine LLC.......................G....... 201 310-5398
Naples *(G-11366)*
Playbill Southern Publishing.................F....... 305 595-1984
Miami *(G-10169)*
▲ **Plus Communications Inc**..................D....... 407 333-0600
Lake Mary *(G-7443)*
Polo Players Edition............................G....... 561 968-5208
Lake Worth *(G-7581)*
Quad Intl Incorporated........................D....... 305 662-5959
Doral *(G-3474)*
Quanturo Publishing Inc......................E....... 305 373-3700
Miami *(G-10223)*
R T Publishing Inc...............................G....... 904 886-4919
Jacksonville *(G-6702)*
Recommend Travel Publications.............F....... 305 826-4763
Miami Lakes *(G-10849)*
Ronald A Ferguson..............................G....... 786 488-4019
Fort Lauderdale *(G-4212)*
Rowland Publishing Inc........................E....... 850 878-0554
Tallahassee *(G-17319)*
Rwla Enterprises LLC..........................F....... 772 334-1248
Stuart *(G-17005)*
Sandow Media LLC.............................F....... 646 805-0200
Boca Raton *(G-699)*
▲ **Sandow Media LLC**...........................D....... 561 961-7749
Boca Raton *(G-700)*
Sandy Lender Inc................................F....... 239 272-8613
Cape Coral *(G-1464)*
Sarasota Cottages LLC.........................G....... 941 724-2245
Sarasota *(G-16577)*
Seabreeze Communications Group.........F....... 239 278-4222
Fort Myers *(G-4603)*
See Coastal Media LLC........................G....... 386 562-2213
Daytona Beach *(G-2711)*
Sep Communications LLC.....................F....... 561 998-0870
Boca Raton *(G-706)*
Shelton Group LLC..............................G....... 321 676-8981
Melbourne *(G-8931)*
Showcase Publications Inc....................E....... 863 687-4377
Lakeland *(G-7791)*
Signcraft Publishing Co Inc...................F....... 239 939-4644
Fort Myers *(G-4604)*
South Florida Parenting........................D....... 954 747-3050
Tamarac *(G-17369)*
South Florida Sport Fishing...................F....... 954 942-7261
Fort Lauderdale *(G-4247)*
South Florida Sport Fishing...................F....... 954 942-7261
Fort Lauderdale *(G-4248)*
Southeast Review Inc..........................G....... 850 644-4230
Tallahassee *(G-17327)*
▼ **Southern Boating & Yachting**...............E....... 954 522-5515
Pompano Beach *(G-14862)*
◆ **Spanish House Inc**............................E....... 305 503-1191
Medley *(G-8728)*
▼ **Spanish Peri & Bk Sls Inc**..................D....... 305 592-3919
Doral *(G-3508)*
Special Editionspublishing....................G....... 407 862-7737
Altamonte Springs *(G-76)*
Special Publications Inc........................F....... 352 622-2995
Ocala *(G-12056)*
Sport America Magazine.......................G....... 727 391-3099
Madeira Beach *(G-8448)*
Stern Bloom Media Inc.........................E....... 954 454-8522
Miami *(G-10414)*
Stream Line Publishing Inc....................F....... 561 655-8778
Boca Raton *(G-732)*
Streamline Publishing Inc......................G....... 561 655-8778
Boca Raton *(G-733)*
Street Elements Magazine Inc...............F....... 813 935-5894
Tampa *(G-18135)*
Stuart Magazine.................................F....... 954 332-3214
Fort Lauderdale *(G-4263)*
Stuart Magazine.................................G....... 772 207-7895
Port Saint Lucie *(G-15149)*
Swapper..G....... 850 973-6653
Madison *(G-8454)*
T T Publications Inc............................E....... 407 327-4817
Winter Springs *(G-19486)*
T V HI Lites Penny Saver Inc.................G....... 941 378-5353
Sarasota *(G-16614)*
Tampa Bay Publications Inc..................E....... 727 791-4800
Clearwater *(G-1903)*
Tampa Media Group LLC......................G....... 813 259-7100
Tampa *(G-18168)*
▲ **Taylor & Francis Group LLC**...............C....... 561 994-0555
Boca Raton *(G-742)*
Teeze International Inc........................G....... 727 726-3592
Clearwater *(G-1913)*
Time Adjusters Conference Inc..............G....... 386 274-4210
Port Orange *(G-15039)*
Times Holding Co...............................G....... 727 893-8111
Saint Petersburg *(G-15938)*
◆ **Times Publishing Company**...............A....... 727 893-8111
Saint Petersburg *(G-15940)*
Tm Marketing Group LLC.....................G....... 954 848-9955
Fort Lauderdale *(G-4285)*
▼ **Toti Media Inc**..................................G....... 239 472-0205
Sanibel *(G-16150)*
Trafalger Communications Inc...............E....... 941 365-7702
Sarasota *(G-16624)*
Treasure Cast Prenting Mag Inc.............F....... 772 672-8588
Port Saint Lucie *(G-15155)*
Trend Magazines Inc...........................E....... 727 821-5800
Saint Petersburg *(G-15943)*
Turnstile Publishing Company...............D....... 407 563-7000
Orlando *(G-13284)*

Twinlab Corporation ....B 800 645-5626
Boca Raton (G-761)
Twinlab Holdings Inc ....E 800 645-5626
Boca Raton (G-762)
United Advg Publications Inc ....G 407 297-0832
Altamonte Springs (G-81)
Uproxx Media Inc ....F 917 603-2374
Miami Beach (G-10723)
Ural Associates Inc ....G 305 446-9462
Coral Gables (G-2200)
Valleymedia Inc ....E 510 565-7559
Fort Lauderdale (G-4303)
Venice Quarters Inc ....E 954 318-3483
Wilton Manors (G-19221)
Vista Publishing Corporation ....F 305 416-4644
Miami Beach (G-10728)
Vive Creole LLC ....G 954 607-1925
Hollywood (G-5937)
Waste Advantage Corporation ....G 800 358-2873
Jupiter (G-7143)
Weiss Group LLC ....C 561 627-3300
Jupiter (G-7145)
Weiss Research Inc ....C 561 627-3300
Jupiter (G-7146)
Weston Magazine Inc ....G 203 451-1967
Miami Beach (G-10729)
Wheelhouse Direct LLC ....F 239 246-8788
Fort Myers (G-4655)
White Publishing Co Inc ....F 904 389-3622
Jacksonville (G-6919)
Woods n Water Magazine Inc ....G 850 584-3824
Perry (G-14320)
Working Mother Media Inc ....D 212 351-6400
Winter Park (G-19461)
World Politics Review LLC ....G 202 903-8398
Tampa (G-18263)
World Publications Inc ....G 407 628-4802
Winter Park (G-19462)
Worldwide Challenge Magazine ....E 407 826-2390
Orlando (G-13331)
◆ Worth Intl Media Group ....E 305 826-4763
Miami Lakes (G-10881)
Write Stuff Enterprises LLC ....E 954 462-6657
Fort Lauderdale (G-4329)

2731 Books: Publishing & Printing

2leaf Press Inc ....G 646 801-4227
Plantation (G-14479)
4ever Music LLC ....E 407 490-0977
Orlando (G-12419)
90-Minute Books LLC ....G 863 318-0464
Winter Haven (G-19292)
▼ American Accounting Assn ....E 941 921-7747
Lakewood Ranch (G-7836)
Archer Ellison Inc ....G 800 449-4095
Lake Mary (G-7400)
Armbrust Aviation Group Inc ....E 561 355-8488
West Palm Beach (G-18801)
Artex Publishing Inc ....G 727 944-4117
Holiday (G-5734)
Athletic Guide Publishing ....G 386 439-2250
Flagler Beach (G-3752)
Baptist Communications Mission ....F 954 981-2271
Hollywood (G-5784)
Beacon Publishing Inc ....G 888 618-5253
North Palm Beach (G-11718)
Belvoir Publications Inc ....E 941 929-1720
Sarasota (G-16364)
Bisk Education Inc ....B 813 621-6200
Tampa (G-17471)
Booklocker Com Inc ....F 727 483-4540
Saint Petersburg (G-15726)
Buck Pile Inc ....G 772 492-1056
Vero Beach (G-18607)
Builders Publishing Group LLC ....G 407 539-2938
Maitland (G-8461)
Casebriefs LLC ....F 646 240-4401
Boca Raton (G-471)
Center For Business Ownership ....G 239 455-9393
Naples (G-11204)
Coeur De Lion Inc ....E 727 442-4808
Clearwater (G-1631)
Comex Systems Inc ....G 908 881-6301
Port Charlotte (G-14971)
CRC Press LLC ....E 561 994-0555
Boca Raton (G-491)
CRC Press LLC ....E 561 361-6000
Boca Raton (G-492)
Creative Tech Sarasota Inc ....G 941 371-2743
Sarasota (G-16395)
▼ Darmiven Inc ....G 305 871-1157
Virginia Gardens (G-18686)
Digital Propaganda Inc ....F 407 644-8444
Orlando (G-12675)
▲ Direct Response Publication ....F 561 620-3010
Boca Raton (G-503)
E-Libro Corporation ....F 305 466-0155
Sunny Isles Beach (G-17074)
▲ Esperanto Inc ....F 305 513-8980
Doral (G-3344)
First Edition Design Inc ....G 941 921-2607
Sarasota (G-16433)
Florida Sncast Trism Prmotions ....F 727 544-1212
Largo (G-7951)
Fournies Associates ....G 561 445-5102
Delray Beach (G-3079)
▲ Frederic Thomas USA Inc ....F 239 593-8000
Naples (G-11250)
Getabstract Inc ....E 305 936-2626
Miami (G-9633)
◆ Gleim Publications Inc ....D 352 375-0772
Gainesville (G-4931)
Global Village Ventures ....G 813 453-6199
Tampa (G-17719)
Great Hse Mdia Group of Pbls I ....F 407 779-3846
Orlando (G-12788)
Great Locations Inc ....G 954 943-1188
Pompano Beach (G-14718)
H & H Publishing Co Inc ....G 727 442-7760
Clearwater (G-1709)
Houghton Mifflin Harcourt ....D 407 345-2000
Orlando (G-12811)
▲ Informa Usa Inc ....A 561 361-6017
Sarasota (G-16465)
Jabberwocky LLC ....G 310 717-3343
Miami (G-9785)
▲ Legacy Publishing Services ....G 407 647-3787
Winter Park (G-19418)
Living Parables ....G 407 488-6201
Orlando (G-12917)
Lmn Printing Co Inc ....F 386 428-9928
Edgewater (G-3630)
Logoi Inc ....G 305 232-5880
Miami (G-9907)
Management International Inc ....E 954 763-8811
Fort Lauderdale (G-4110)
▲ Maupin House Publishing Inc ....G 800 524-0634
Gainesville (G-4956)
▲ Meadowbrook Inc ....E 800 338-2232
Naples (G-11325)
Mega Book Inc ....G 352 378-4567
Gainesville (G-4960)
Municipal Code Corporation ....D 850 576-3171
Tallahassee (G-17304)
Netexpressusa Inc ....G 888 575-1245
Fort Myers (G-4545)
New Underground RR Pubg Co ....F 305 825-1444
Miami Lakes (G-10830)
◆ New World Publications Inc ....G 904 737-6558
Jacksonville (G-6630)
◆ On-Board Media Inc ....D 305 673-0400
Doral (G-3450)
Phillip Roy Inc ....G 727 593-2700
Largo (G-8026)
▲ Plus Communications Inc ....D 407 333-0600
Lake Mary (G-7443)
Plus Communications Inc ....F 407 333-0600
Lake Mary (G-7444)
▼ Printers Printer Inc ....F 954 917-2773
Pompano Beach (G-14814)
Printing For A Cause LLC ....E 786 496-0637
Saint Petersburg (G-15889)
◆ Pro Publishing Inc ....G 954 888-7726
Southwest Ranches (G-16840)
Reliance Media Inc ....G 505 243-1821
Apopka (G-179)
▲ Rourke Educational Media LLC ....E 772 234-6001
Vero Beach (G-18660)
Rourke Ray Publishing Co Inc ....G 772 234-6001
Vero Beach (G-18661)
Samjay Media Group Orlando LLC ....G 407 865-7526
Longwood (G-8333)
▲ Santillana USA Pubg Co Inc ....D 305 591-9522
Miami (G-10303)
▼ Senda De Vida Publishers ....E 305 262-2627
Miami (G-10323)
Shellie Blum LLC ....G 863 439-3060
Lake Wales (G-7519)
Signcraft Publishing Co Inc ....F 239 939-4644
Fort Myers (G-4604)
▲ Sirs Publishing Inc ....D 800 521-0600
Boca Raton (G-718)
◆ Spanish House Inc ....E 305 503-1191
Medley (G-8728)
Speech Bin ....F 772 770-0006
Vero Beach (G-18666)
Spirit Connection ....G 321 327-3804
Melbourne (G-8942)
Starline Education Inc ....G 808 631-1818
Titusville (G-18464)
Starlite Inc ....F 727 392-2929
Seminole (G-16762)
Stephens Group ....G 941 623-9689
Port Charlotte (G-14999)
▲ Taylor & Francis Group LLC ....C 561 994-0555
Boca Raton (G-742)
Tra Publishing LLP ....F 305 424-6468
Miami (G-10498)
Twinlab Corporation ....B 800 645-5626
Boca Raton (G-761)
▲ Two Little Fishies Inc ....G 305 623-7695
Miami (G-10517)
Wccm-USA Ltd Corporation ....G 904 346-3816
Jacksonville (G-6906)
Write Stuff Enterprises LLC ....E 954 462-6657
Fort Lauderdale (G-4329)
Zondervan Corporation LLC ....G 616 698-3437
Miami (G-10632)

2732 Book Printing, Not Publishing

Bce of Tampa Bay Inc ....G 727 535-7768
Clearwater (G-1604)
Creative Tech Sarasota Inc ....G 941 371-2743
Sarasota (G-16395)
Dasops Inc ....G 386 258-6230
Daytona Beach (G-2652)
Digital Direct Corporation ....G 813 448-9071
Oldsmar (G-12220)
Eaglelithocom Inc ....G 786 521-7211
Miami (G-9494)
Florida Graphic Printing Inc ....F 386 253-4532
Daytona Beach (G-2666)
▼ Jrg Systems Inc ....F 954 962-1020
Fort Lauderdale (G-4081)
Lincoln-Marti Cmnty Agcy Inc ....A 305 643-4888
Miami (G-9895)
Lincoln-Marti Cmnty Agcy Inc ....F 646 463-6120
Miami (G-9896)
McGee Enterprises Inc ....G 904 328-3226
Jacksonville (G-6585)
On Demand Spclty Envelope Corp ....F 305 681-5345
Hallandale Beach (G-5202)
Peter T Amann ....G 561 848-2770
West Palm Beach (G-18995)
Prisna Latino ....G 305 525-9292
Miami (G-10202)
Reliance Media Inc ....G 505 243-1821
Apopka (G-179)
Royal Palm Press Inc ....G 941 575-4299
Punta Gorda (G-15230)
Seminole County Public Schools ....F 407 320-0393
Sanford (G-16114)
Sosumi Holdings Inc ....E 239 634-3430
Naples (G-11407)
▼ Southeastern Printing Co Inc ....C 772 287-2141
Hialeah (G-5628)
Tone Printing LLC ....G 855 505-8663
Miami (G-10489)

2741 Misc Publishing

2klife LLC ....G 954 316-9866
Pompano Beach (G-14569)
3lions Publishing Inc ....G 727 744-8683
Palm Harbor (G-13715)
4 Horsemen Publications Inc ....G 727 698-0476
Clearwater (G-1559)
4biddenknowledge Inc ....G 954 245-0086
Weston (G-19099)
A Cappela Publishing Inc ....F 941 351-2050
Sarasota (G-16329)
A2f LLC ....G 305 984-9205
Miami (G-9048)
ABC Book Publishers Inc ....G 904 230-0737
Jacksonville (G-6935)
Academic Publication Svcs Inc ....G 941 925-4474
Sarasota (G-16332)
AGM Publishing Inc ....G 727 934-9993
Holiday (G-5733)
Akashic Spirit Publishing LLC ....G 850 974-4944
Defuniak Springs (G-2939)

Akua Rage Entertainment Inc ....G....... 904 627-5312
Jacksonville (G-6132)
Aligned Global ....G....... 305 731-2117
Miami (G-9107)
Altered Media Inc ....F....... 813 397-3892
Tampa (G-17408)
Aluminum Express Inc ....G....... 954 868-2628
Hialeah (G-5284)
Amazin Publishing Inc ....G....... 954 445-6303
Orlando (G-12465)
American Atlas Corp ....G....... 904 273-6090
Ponte Vedra Beach (G-14932)
American Classifieds ....F....... 850 747-1155
Panama City (G-13863)
American Computer & Tech Corp ....G....... 786 738-3220
Miami Beach (G-10640)
AMI Celebrity Publications LLC ....C....... 561 997-7733
Boca Raton (G-424)
AMI Digital Inc ....B....... 561 997-7733
Boca Raton (G-425)
Anaiah Press LLC ....G....... 727 692-0025
Saint Petersburg (G-15700)
Angery American Enterprises ....G....... 352 669-2198
Umatilla (G-18495)
Arsenex Inc ....G....... 407 256-3490
Oviedo (G-13412)
Ascendants Publishing LLC ....G....... 813 391-2745
Gainesville (G-4878)
▲ Atlantic Publishing Group Inc ....D....... 352 622-6220
Ocala (G-11881)
Attraction Center Pubg LLC ....G....... 814 422-5683
Saint Petersburg (G-15715)
B&C Publishing Inc ....G....... 305 385-8216
Miami (G-9210)
Banyan Hill ....G....... 561 455-9045
Delray Beach (G-3049)
Barbes Publishing Inc ....F....... 904 992-9945
Jacksonville (G-6194)
Bayou Printing Inc ....F....... 850 678-5444
Valparaiso (G-18507)
Beano Publishing LLC ....F....... 954 689-8339
Weston (G-19110)
Belleaire Press LLC ....G....... 352 377-1870
Gainesville (G-4885)
Belocal Pro Inc ....G....... 727 379-9576
Spring Hill (G-16870)
Bent Pine Publishing Corp ....G....... 772 708-0490
Port Saint Lucie (G-15091)
Best Publishing Company ....F....... 561 776-6066
North Palm Beach (G-11719)
Bevel Express & Tops Lac ....G....... 813 887-3174
Tampa (G-17466)
Bg Expo Group LLC ....G....... 305 428-3576
Doral (G-3271)
Bigg D Entertainment LLC ....G....... 917 204-0292
Weston (G-19112)
Bigg Publishing ....G....... 772 563-0425
Vero Beach (G-18599)
Bioenergetics Press ....F....... 386 462-5155
Alachua (G-9)
Birdie Publishing LLC ....G....... 561 332-1826
Delray Beach (G-3050)
Black Label Group LLC ....G....... 407 917-1255
Orlando (G-12521)
Black Tie Publishing Inc ....G....... 954 472-6003
Plantation (G-14498)
Bluetoad Inc ....E....... 407 992-8744
Gotha (G-5040)
Bonita Daily News ....E....... 239 213-6060
Naples (G-11191)
Books-A-Million Inc ....G....... 813 571-2062
Brandon (G-1152)
Bot International Inc ....G....... 407 366-6547
Oviedo (G-13419)
Boyle Publications Inc ....G....... 941 255-0187
Port Charlotte (G-14966)
Brazilian Clssfied ADS-Chei In ....G....... 954 570-7568
Deerfield Beach (G-2789)
Breeze Corporation ....C....... 239 765-0400
Fort Myers Beach (G-4660)
Breeze Corporation ....G....... 239 425-8860
Fort Myers (G-4381)
Broadcast Tech Inc ....E....... 786 351-4227
Medley (G-8627)
Brown Dog Publishing Inc ....G....... 904 262-2114
Jacksonville (G-6238)
Bruno Publishing ....G....... 561 333-7682
Wellington (G-18712)
Builders Notice Corporation ....G....... 954 764-1322
Fort Lauderdale (G-3875)
Builders Publishing Group LLC ....G....... 407 539-2938
Maitland (G-8461)
Butterfield Press ....G....... 813 634-3940
Sun City Center (G-17070)
By Invitation Only Pubg Inc ....G....... 954 922-7100
Dania (G-2442)
Bythenet Publishing ....G....... 407 691-2806
Winter Park (G-19385)
Caduceus International Pubg ....F....... 866 280-2900
Gainesville (G-4891)
Calkins Harbor Publishing Inc ....G....... 561 906-4642
North Palm Beach (G-11720)
Campus Publications Inc ....G....... 941 780-1326
Sarasota (G-16379)
Canterbury House Publishing ....G....... 941 312-6912
Sarasota (G-16185)
Capital Publishing Inc ....G....... 813 286-8444
Spring Hill (G-16849)
Carbon Press LLC ....F....... 239 689-4406
Fort Myers (G-4387)
Care and Love Publishing LLC ....G....... 254 462-9134
Tampa (G-17508)
Casey Research LLC ....F....... 561 455-9043
Delray Beach (G-3056)
Casey Weston LLC ....G....... 239 229-8375
Naples (G-11200)
Castle Publishing LLC ....G....... 904 794-0112
Saint Augustine (G-15527)
▼ Catskill Express LLC ....G....... 954 784-5151
Pompano Beach (G-14631)
Cda Ventures Inc ....F....... 305 428-2857
Miami Beach (G-10653)
Central Florida Publishing Inc ....F....... 407 323-5204
Sanford (G-16010)
Chelle Walton Publishing ....G....... 239 699-4754
Sanibel (G-16144)
Christian Publishing Inc ....G....... 813 920-5664
Odessa (G-12110)
Citrus County Life Magazine ....G....... 352 341-4769
Lecanto (G-8132)
City Debate Publishing Company ....G....... 305 868-1161
Miami Beach (G-10656)
City News Publishing LLC ....G....... 305 332-9101
Boca Raton (G-480)
City of Winter Haven ....E....... 863 291-5858
Winter Haven (G-19315)
City Publications South FL ....G....... 305 495-3311
Virginia Gardens (G-18685)
Citygrader LLC ....G....... 305 635-2686
Miami (G-9358)
CJ Publishers Inc ....F....... 727 521-6277
Pinellas Park (G-14339)
Classic Mail Corp ....G....... 386 290-0309
Daytona Beach (G-2642)
Classics Reborn Publishing LLC ....G....... 727 232-6739
New Port Richey (G-11487)
Closeup Inc ....G....... 650 284-8831
Miami (G-9363)
Coastal Directory Company ....F....... 321 777-7076
Melbourne (G-8792)
Collectors International Pubg ....G....... 561 845-7156
Palm Beach (G-13551)
Collidecom LLC ....F....... 407 903-5626
Orlando (G-12602)
Color Press Corp ....G....... 786 621-8491
Miami (G-9380)
Comm Dots LLC Connecting ....F....... 305 505-6009
Miami (G-9388)
Common Sense Publishing LLC ....C....... 561 510-1713
Delray Beach (G-3063)
Compass Publishing LLC ....G....... 407 328-0970
Sanford (G-16020)
Competitor Group Inc ....G....... 858 450-6510
Tampa (G-17549)
Connectpress Ltd ....F....... 505 629-0695
Sarasota (G-16392)
Construction Bulletin Inc ....F....... 904 388-0336
Jacksonville (G-6284)
Consumer Source Inc ....G....... 407 888-0745
Orlando (G-12615)
Convivium Press Inc ....G....... 305 889-0489
Miami (G-9397)
Counter Top Publishing Inc ....G....... 941 321-5811
Bradenton (G-1024)
Countryside Publishing Co Inc ....F....... 813 925-0195
Oldsmar (G-12219)
County of Orange ....G....... 407 649-0076
Orlando (G-12623)
Creative Routes Press ....G....... 561 213-9800
Delray Beach (G-3066)
Croft Publishing Inc ....G....... 352 473-3159
Keystone Heights (G-7206)
◆ Cruising Gide Publications Inc ....G....... 727 733-5322
Dunedin (G-3575)
Cuban Press ....G....... 305 304-9419
Miami (G-9417)
Cutting Edge Sgns Grphics of P ....G....... 727 546-3700
Clearwater (G-1645)
Cycling Quarterly LLC ....E....... 786 367-2497
Fort Lauderdale (G-3926)
D1 Locker LLC ....G....... 305 446-9041
Miami (G-9427)
Dakim Inc ....F....... 561 790-0884
Royal Palm Beach (G-15465)
David Jacobs Pubg Group LLC ....F....... 813 321-4119
Tampa (G-17591)
Davison Publishing Co Inc ....G....... 407 657-3710
Orlando (G-12655)
Davison Publishing Company LLC ....G....... 407 380-8900
Orlando (G-12656)
Digital Color Publications LLC ....G....... 813 886-0065
Tampa (G-17606)
Digital Direct Corporation ....G....... 813 448-9071
Oldsmar (G-12220)
Digital Press ....G....... 407 421-3131
Orlando (G-12674)
Digital Publishing of Florida ....G....... 813 749-8640
Oldsmar (G-12221)
Dion Money Management LLC ....F....... 413 458-4700
Naples (G-11227)
Direct Media Solutions Inc ....G....... 904 419-3675
Jacksonville (G-6319)
Diversified Pubg & Design ....G....... 239 598-4826
Naples (G-11229)
Do You Remember Inc ....G....... 305 987-9111
Miami Beach (G-10663)
Dolph Map Company Inc ....F....... 954 763-4732
Oakland Park (G-11799)
Double R Publishing ....G....... 305 525-3573
Boynton Beach (G-898)
Down Shift LLC ....G....... 813 431-2389
Lutz (G-8381)
Dreamspinner Press LLC ....F....... 800 970-3759
Tallahassee (G-17243)
E1w Games Llc ....F....... 561 255-7370
Delray Beach (G-3071)
Eastgate Publishing Inc ....G....... 772 286-0101
Hobe Sound (G-5724)
ED Publications Inc ....F....... 727 726-3592
Clearwater (G-1663)
Educational Pubg Centl Fla LLC ....G....... 407 234-4401
Mount Dora (G-11101)
Empyre Music Publishing LLC ....G....... 813 873-7700
Tampa (G-17638)
Enterra Inc ....G....... 813 514-0531
Tampa (G-17643)
Epigram Publishing Co ....G....... 941 391-5296
Port Charlotte (G-14979)
Essential Publishing Group LLC ....G....... 410 440-5777
Boca Raton (G-522)
Essential Publishing Group LLC ....E....... 561 570-7165
Greenacres (G-5080)
Everett Pubg - Tampa Bay LLC ....G....... 727 534-3425
New Port Richey (G-11490)
Everyday Feminism LLC ....G....... 202 643-1001
Tallahassee (G-17249)
Ew Publishing LLC ....G....... 305 358-1100
Fort Lauderdale (G-3978)
Ewh Press ....G....... 386 405-5069
Ormond Beach (G-13369)
Expert Subjects LLC ....G....... 786 877-8531
Miami (G-9546)
Express Care of Tampa Bay ....G....... 813 641-0068
Apollo Beach (G-103)
Express Ironing Inc ....G....... 305 261-1072
Miami (G-9548)
F L F Corp ....G....... 561 747-7077
Jupiter (G-7039)
Fabio Napoleoni Artworks ....G....... 207 952-1561
Orlando (G-12731)
Fbr 1804 Inc ....F....... 305 340-3114
North Miami Beach (G-11676)
Ferrari Express Inc ....E....... 305 374-5003
Miami (G-9563)
Fjh Music Company Inc ....E....... 954 382-6061
Davie (G-2525)
Florida Health Publishing LLC ....G....... 847 506-2925
Cape Coral (G-1424)
Florida Living LLC ....G....... 352 556-9691
Brooksville (G-1229)

Flowhance Inc F 305 690-0784
Miami *(G-9590)*
Floyd Publications Inc G 813 707-8783
Plant City *(G-14431)*
Focal Point Publishing LLC G 877 469-9530
Gainesville *(G-4923)*
Focus Community Publications G 407 892-0019
Saint Cloud *(G-15651)*
Foley Publishing LLC G 908 766-6006
Vero Beach *(G-18621)*
Forever Current Music LLC G 213 458-2880
Boca Raton *(G-537)*
Forum Publishing Group Inc D 954 596-5650
Deerfield Beach *(G-2828)*
Four WD Consulting & Pubg LLC G 216 533-2203
West Palm Beach *(G-18881)*
Fpc Printing Inc D 813 626-9430
Tampa *(G-17693)*
Fresh Press F 305 942-8571
North Miami Beach *(G-11678)*
▲ **Frog Publications Inc** G 352 588-2082
San Antonio *(G-15972)*
Front Line Publishing Inc G 813 480-8033
Brandon *(G-1160)*
G S Printers Inc G 305 931-2755
Fort Lauderdale *(G-4016)*
Galan Express Inc G 305 438-8738
Miami *(G-9610)*
Gatehouse Media LLC F 863 401-6900
Winter Haven *(G-19325)*
Gcn Publishing Inc G 203 665-6211
Pompano Beach *(G-14713)*
General Catagraphy Inc G 561 455-4398
Boynton Beach *(G-910)*
Genie Publishing G 863 937-7769
Lakeland *(G-7697)*
GLM Publishing LLC G 561 409-7696
Boca Raton *(G-545)*
Global Directories Inc F 954 571-8283
Deerfield Beach *(G-2832)*
Global Media Press Corp G 813 857-5898
Tampa *(G-17716)*
Global Publishing Inc E 904 262-0491
Jacksonville *(G-6437)*
Globe Boyz International LLC F 305 308-8160
Miami *(G-9643)*
Gmv Holdings LLC G 561 747-7864
Palm Beach Gardens *(G-13592)*
Gnd Publishing LLC G 561 625-1242
Palm Beach Gardens *(G-13593)*
Good Life Publishing Inc G 352 317-6903
Archer *(G-209)*
Grapevine Usa Inc G 786 510-9122
Fort Lauderdale *(G-4025)*
Great Escape Publishing G 561 860-8266
Delray Beach *(G-3087)*
Great Hse Mdia Group of Pbls I F 407 779-3846
Orlando *(G-12788)*
Great Virtualworks LLC F 800 606-6518
Fort Lauderdale *(G-4028)*
Guerrilla Press G 352 281-7420
Gainesville *(G-4934)*
Guest Service Publications Inc F 516 333-3474
Bonita Springs *(G-835)*
Gulf Publishing Company Inc F 727 596-2863
Largo *(G-7968)*
Gulf Shore Press LLC G 727 641-2920
Naples *(G-11271)*
Halldale Media Inc E 407 322-5605
Lake Mary *(G-7420)*
Harvest Day Press G 727 822-4961
Saint Petersburg *(G-15804)*
◆ **Health Communications Inc** D 954 360-0909
Deerfield Beach *(G-2836)*
Helou Regino Publisher LLC G 407 370-7300
Orlando *(G-12797)*
Henjaty Publishing Co G 305 633-9993
Miami *(G-9701)*
Heritage Publishing Inc E 904 296-1304
Jacksonville *(G-6471)*
Hill Donnelly Corporation D 800 525-1242
Tampa *(G-17755)*
Hmh Publishing Co Inc D 617 351-5000
Orlando *(G-12805)*
Hogan Assessment Systems Inc G 904 992-0302
Jacksonville *(G-6473)*
Homes Devoted Inc G 321 473-8567
Melbourne *(G-8845)*
Homes Magazine Inc F 239 334-7168
Fort Myers *(G-4484)*
Hoot/Wisdom Music Pubg LLC G 561 297-3205
Boca Raton *(G-559)*
Hot Off Press G 386 238-8700
South Daytona *(G-16802)*
Howard Scripts Inc G 561 746-5111
Jupiter *(G-7054)*
I M I Publishing Inc G 615 957-9288
Naples *(G-11283)*
Icome2fix LLC F 954 789-4102
Miami *(G-9728)*
Igbo Network LLC F 352 727-4113
Gainesville *(G-4941)*
Igs LLC G 800 419-3014
Homestead *(G-5970)*
IMI Publishing Inc G 239 529-5081
Naples *(G-11284)*
Impact Promotional Pubg LLC F 727 736-6228
Dunedin *(G-3581)*
In Press Marketing G 954 659-9332
Weston *(G-19140)*
Indigo River Publishing G 256 404-5884
Pensacola *(G-14177)*
Ink Publishing Corporation F 786 206-9867
Coral Gables *(G-2158)*
Ink Publishing Corporation E 786 482-2065
Coral Gables *(G-2159)*
Insanejournalcom G 561 315-9311
West Palm Beach *(G-18906)*
Instrument Publication G 352 542-7716
Old Town *(G-12198)*
Irving Publications LLC F 352 219-4688
Gainesville *(G-4947)*
▲ **Island Media Publishing LLC** G 904 556-3002
Fernandina Beach *(G-3739)*
Isocialmedia Digital Marketing G 561 510-1124
Boca Raton *(G-574)*
It Had To Be Told Pubg LLC G 813 810-5961
Tampa *(G-17795)*
▲ **J Ross Publishing Inc** G 954 727-9333
Plantation *(G-14525)*
Jazzy Dogs Publishing G 941 726-0343
Nokomis *(G-11583)*
JC 323 Media Pubg Group Inc G 772 940-3510
Lake Worth *(G-7560)*
JC Publishers LLC G 863 875-6071
Winter Haven *(G-19331)*
Jeanius Publishing LLC G 239 560-5229
Lehigh Acres *(G-8193)*
Jencor Publishing Inc G 772 589-5578
Sebastian *(G-16664)*
Jita Press Inc G 850 329-0884
Tallahassee *(G-17283)*
Jjj & H Inc E 904 389-1130
Jacksonville *(G-6522)*
Kameleon Press Inc G 850 566-2522
Tallahassee *(G-17286)*
Kenney Communications Inc F 407 859-3113
Orlando *(G-12869)*
Kobalt Music Pubg Amer Inc D 305 200-5682
Coral Gables *(G-2166)*
Korangy Publishing Inc D 786 334-5052
Miami *(G-9829)*
▲ **Krieger Publishing Co Inc** F 321 724-9542
Malabar *(G-8493)*
Ksr Publishing Inc E 941 388-7050
Sarasota *(G-16484)*
La Ciudad En Sus Manos LLC G 813 770-4973
Altamonte Springs *(G-52)*
Landslide Publishing Inc G 561 392-4717
Boca Raton *(G-595)*
Latin Goddess Press Inc G 917 703-1356
Winter Springs *(G-19477)*
Lawrenceville Press Inc F 609 737-1148
Lantana *(G-7875)*
Le Publications Inc F 954 766-8433
Fort Lauderdale *(G-4098)*
Legacy Publishing Group G 407 290-8414
Orlando *(G-12902)*
Leila K Moavero G 954 978-0018
Pompano Beach *(G-14743)*
Less Frtnate Mus Pubg Ltd Lblt G 786 663-0385
Miami *(G-9886)*
Levatas D 561 622-4511
Palm Beach Gardens *(G-13604)*
Lifes A Bch Publications LLC G 850 650-2780
Destin *(G-3196)*
Lifestyle Publications LLC G 954 217-1165
Weston *(G-19147)*
Light Age Press Inc G 352 242-4530
Clermont *(G-1968)*
Lighthouse Express World Inc G 754 210-6196
Hollywood *(G-5860)*
Limelight Publishing LLC G 727 384-5999
Saint Petersburg *(G-15841)*
Lioness Publication House G 561 670-4645
West Palm Beach *(G-18932)*
Live Ultimate Inc G 305 532-6882
Miami Beach *(G-10688)*
Living Well Spending Less Inc G 941 209-1811
Punta Gorda *(G-15212)*
Lost Key Publishing LLC G 850 380-6680
Pensacola *(G-14197)*
LTSC LLC G 863 678-0011
Lake Wales *(G-7515)*
Luna Negra Productions Inc G 786 247-1215
Miami *(G-9920)*
M30 Freedom Inc G 813 433-1776
Land O Lakes *(G-7860)*
Mama Bear Lawn Care Press G 863 517-5322
Clewiston *(G-1983)*
Management International Inc E 954 763-8811
Fort Lauderdale *(G-4110)*
Manatee Media Inc F 813 909-2800
Land O Lakes *(G-7861)*
Map & Globe LLC F 407 898-0757
Maitland *(G-8473)*
Mark Walters LLC G 727 742-3091
Saint Petersburg *(G-15850)*
Mark Wayne Adams Inc G 407 756-5862
Longwood *(G-8309)*
Maverick Press Inc G 239 331-8379
Naples *(G-11323)*
Mdz Publishing G 954 680-9956
Cooper City *(G-2114)*
Media Creations Inc G 954 726-0902
Fort Lauderdale *(G-4115)*
Media Digittal LLC G 305 506-0470
Doral *(G-3428)*
Media Edge Communications LLC G 352 313-6700
Gainesville *(G-4959)*
Messner Publications Inc E 863 318-1595
Winter Haven *(G-19337)*
Miami Publicity LLC G 561 215-5189
Miami *(G-10006)*
Milenium Publishing LLC G 786 573-9974
Miami *(G-10020)*
Military One Click LLC G 904 390-7100
Jacksonville *(G-6605)*
Millionaire Publishing LLC G 305 763-8184
Miami Beach *(G-10693)*
Milpro Publications LLC G 321 613-2250
Melbourne *(G-8890)*
Miramar Publishing Inc G 305 695-0639
Miami Beach *(G-10694)*
Mobile Rving G 954 870-7095
Deerfield Beach *(G-2875)*
Msquared Publishing G 786 399-0607
Miami *(G-10050)*
Municipal Code Corporation D 850 576-3171
Tallahassee *(G-17304)*
My Wild Life Press LLC G 515 203-9728
Delray Beach *(G-3111)*
National Subscription Bureau E 800 508-1311
Naples *(G-11343)*
Nationwide Publishing Company E 352 253-0017
Deltona *(G-3176)*
Nenem Inc G 561 389-2010
West Palm Beach *(G-18961)*
Netexpressusa Inc G 888 575-1245
Fort Myers *(G-4545)*
New Pelican LLC G 954 783-8700
Pompano Beach *(G-14773)*
New York Deli Express G 954 572-1442
Lauderhill *(G-8117)*
New You Media LLC F 800 606-6518
Fort Lauderdale *(G-4139)*
Newsmax Media Inc F 561 686-1165
West Palm Beach *(G-18964)*
Nielsen Publishing G 941 539-7579
Nokomis *(G-11586)*
North Metro Media F 850 650-1014
Destin *(G-3199)*
Nwh Publishing Llc F 904 217-3911
Saint Augustine *(G-15579)*
Oceanvista Publishing LLC G 561 547-5730
West Palm Beach *(G-18969)*
Olmstead Publishing LLC G 954 559-0192
Apopka *(G-167)*
Omega Publishing G 727 815-0402
New Port Richey *(G-11504)*

Online German Publisher LLC .... G 239 344-8953
Cape Coral *(G-1453)*
Open Palm Press Inc .... G 813 870-3839
Tampa *(G-17958)*
Orlando Branding Agency LLC .... F 407 692-8868
Oviedo *(G-13451)*
Osborn Publications .... G 305 899-0501
North Miami *(G-11649)*
Our Florida Publishing .... G 904 859-2805
Sunrise *(G-17155)*
Page Golfs Yellow Directory .... F 305 378-8038
Palmetto Bay *(G-13852)*
Page One LLC .... F 833 467-2431
Dania *(G-2455)*
Palm Beach Newspapers Inc .... D 561 820-3800
West Palm Beach *(G-18985)*
Palm Pheon Music Publishing .... G 305 705-2405
North Miami Beach *(G-11696)*
Palm Prnting/Printers Ink Corp .... E 239 332-8600
Fort Myers *(G-4562)*
Pandia Press Inc .... F 352 789-8156
Mount Dora *(G-11109)*
▲ **Panoff Publishing Inc** .... D 954 377-7777
Fort Lauderdale *(G-4155)*
Paradise Publishing Group Inc .... G 941 306-2166
Bradenton *(G-1094)*
Paramount Digital Pubg LLC .... F 813 489-5029
Brandon *(G-1169)*
Paramount Marketing Inc .... F 352 608-8801
Ocala *(G-12022)*
Parkside Publishing LLC .... G 888 386-1115
Delray Beach *(G-3113)*
Patriot Publishing USA LLC .... G 904 217-7632
Saint Augustine *(G-15585)*
Patterson Publishing LLC .... G 863 701-2707
Lakeland *(G-7764)*
Paxen Publishing LLC .... F 321 425-3030
Indian Harbour Beach *(G-6065)*
Pelican Bay Publishing .... G 954 610-7787
Coral Springs *(G-2302)*
Peniel Inc .... G 305 594-2739
Miramar *(G-11028)*
Peppertree Press LLC .... G 941 922-2662
Sarasota *(G-16541)*
Pfa Publishing .... F 727 512-5814
Gulfport *(G-5136)*
Phoenix Publications .... F 954 609-7586
Pompano Beach *(G-14792)*
Pike Pole Press .... G 407 474-7453
Sanford *(G-16102)*
Piloto Music Publisher Corp .... G 321 348-0638
Miami *(G-10164)*
Pink Inc Publishing .... G 904 834-3118
Jacksonville Beach *(G-6954)*
Plattsco Inc .... G 954 744-4099
Sunrise *(G-17158)*
Positive Note Network .... G 712 259-1381
Fort Walton Beach *(G-4823)*
Post Mortem Publications Inc .... G 352 429-1133
Groveland *(G-5105)*
Precision Press LLC .... G 386 872-1639
Daytona Beach *(G-2697)*
Preferred Custom Printing LLC .... F 727 443-1900
Seminole *(G-16757)*
Preferred Pcks Pblications Inc .... F 954 377-8000
Sunrise *(G-17160)*
Premier Publishing Inc .... G 561 394-9066
Boca Raton *(G-673)*
Premium Latin Music Inc .... F 212 873-1472
Miami *(G-10185)*
Press Beauty Facial Bar .... G 561 281-0631
Lake Worth *(G-7582)*
Press Gourmet Sandwiches .... G 954 440-0422
Fort Lauderdale *(G-4179)*
Printing For A Cause LLC .... E 786 496-0637
Saint Petersburg *(G-15889)*
Prism Music Inc .... G 954 718-6850
Tamarac *(G-17365)*
Prs Taco Place .... G 407 440-2803
Orlando *(G-13098)*
Psychlgcal Asssment Rsrces In .... D 813 968-3003
Lutz *(G-8413)*
Publishers Crcltion Flfilment .... E 877 723-6668
Pensacola *(G-14242)*
Publishers Direct Choice LLC .... G 305 264-5998
Miami *(G-10213)*
Publishers Prmotional Svcs Inc .... G 303 431-4080
Clearwater *(G-1853)*
Publishers Whse Sanibel Island .... G 239 267-6151
Fort Myers *(G-4575)*
Publishing Research Inc .... G 954 921-4026
North Miami *(G-11651)*
Quad Intl Incorporated .... D 305 662-5959
Doral *(G-3474)*
Quality Life Publishing Co .... G 239 513-9907
Naples *(G-11379)*
Quantum Spatial Inc .... D 920 457-3631
Saint Petersburg *(G-15897)*
Quick Press .... G 305 418-8744
Doral *(G-3476)*
Quickseries Publishing Inc .... D 954 584-1606
Fort Lauderdale *(G-4197)*
Rafi Publications LLC .... G 954 384-4166
Weston *(G-19163)*
Rally Point Publications LLC .... F 863 221-6304
Winter Haven *(G-19351)*
Rapid Rater Company .... E 850 893-7346
Tallahassee *(G-17314)*
Readers Drect Publications Inc .... G 727 643-8616
Seminole *(G-16759)*
Red Brick Publishing LLC .... G 718 208-3600
Boynton Beach *(G-954)*
Redquin Publishing LLC .... G 813 314-4500
Tampa *(G-18043)*
Reflex Pubg Eric Reflex Co .... G 813 314-8810
Tampa *(G-18044)*
Reimink Printing Inc .... G 813 289-4663
Tampa *(G-18050)*
Rnn Productions LLC .... F 437 238-9501
Miami *(G-10270)*
Robert Gomes Publishing Inc .... G 941 637-6080
Punta Gorda *(G-15229)*
Romeo Roseau Ecommerce .... F 561 633-1352
Boynton Beach *(G-956)*
Rosebandits LLC .... G 305 778-6370
Coral Gables *(G-2191)*
Roselle Publishing .... G 813 907-5250
Wesley Chapel *(G-18758)*
Russanos Express LLC .... G 772 220-3329
Palm City *(G-13672)*
Safety Compliance Publ Inc .... G 844 556-3149
Miramar *(G-11038)*
Sandpaper Publishing Inc .... G 850 939-8040
Gulf Breeze *(G-5125)*
Sarasota Byfront Plg Orgnztion .... G 941 203-5316
Sarasota *(G-16575)*
Saving For College LLC .... F 954 770-5136
Miami *(G-10307)*
Scheduall Scheduall Scheduall .... F 954 334-5400
Hollywood *(G-5904)*
SE Smith Llc .... G 772 461-0482
Fort Pierce *(G-4744)*
Seahill Press Inc .... G 805 845-8636
Leesburg *(G-8170)*
Seal Publishing LLC .... G 813 792-5852
Odessa *(G-12149)*
Select Publishing LLC .... G 850 464-6477
Santa Rosa Beach *(G-16167)*
Sentinel Cmmnctons News Vntres .... G 407 420-5291
Orlando *(G-13173)*
Sentinel Cmmnctons News Vntres .... G 352 742-5900
Tavares *(G-18352)*
Serendipity Publishing .... G 407 905-5076
Windermere *(G-19243)*
Shoreline Publishing Inc .... G 914 500-5456
Parrish *(G-14007)*
Show Publishing LLC .... G 239 272-8477
Naples *(G-11399)*
Sigma Press Inc .... F 904 264-6006
Orange Park *(G-12405)*
Silly Dandelions Inc .... G 727 400-6590
Largo *(G-8053)*
Simon and Baker Inc .... G 561 892-0494
Boca Raton *(G-714)*
Simonsclub LLC .... E 352 246-3636
Gainesville *(G-4997)*
Simpleshow USA Corp .... E 844 468-5447
Miami *(G-10352)*
Sinergie Printing Inc .... G 786 493-6167
Miami *(G-10353)*
Sipradius LLC .... G 954 290-2434
Coral Springs *(G-2313)*
▲ **Sirs Publishing Inc** .... D 800 521-0600
Boca Raton *(G-718)*
Slate Group LLC .... G 786 484-9408
Miami *(G-10361)*
Smilefy Inc .... F 302 465-6606
Hallandale Beach *(G-5211)*
Sony Discos .... G 305 420-4540
Miami *(G-10377)*
Sony/Atv Music Publishing LLC .... G 305 532-9064
Miami Beach *(G-10713)*
Southeast Publications USA Inc .... E 954 368-4686
Deerfield Beach *(G-2915)*
SP Publications LLC .... G 239 595-9040
Miramar Beach *(G-11069)*
Spanish Pubg Ventures Inc .... G 305 220-8044
Miami *(G-10396)*
▲ **Spanish Publishers LLC** .... G 305 233-3365
Miami *(G-10397)*
Spikes Press & Printhouse LLC .... G 850 438-2293
Pensacola *(G-14270)*
SSE Publications LLC .... F 954 835-7616
Sunrise *(G-17178)*
Starewell Publishing LLC .... G 561 694-0365
Palm Beach Gardens *(G-13629)*
Steven Press .... G 954 434-3694
Cooper City *(G-2117)*
Street Talk America .... G 850 547-6186
Bonifay *(G-808)*
Streetwise Maps Inc .... F 941 358-1956
Sarasota *(G-16606)*
Strong Publications LLC .... E 813 852-9933
Tampa *(G-18136)*
Sula Too LLC .... G 813 368-1628
Tampa *(G-18137)*
Sun Publications Florida Inc .... D 321 402-0257
Kissimmee *(G-7299)*
Sun Publications Florida Inc .... E 863 583-1202
Lakeland *(G-7810)*
Sun-Sentinel Company LLC .... E 954 356-4000
Deerfield Beach *(G-2918)*
Sundar Publishing .... G 305 335-1930
West Palm Beach *(G-19048)*
Swi Publishing Inc .... F 352 538-1438
Gainesville *(G-5006)*
Taylor & Francis Group LLC .... D 800 516-0186
Sarasota *(G-16617)*
Taylor Media LLC .... C 727 317-5800
Saint Petersburg *(G-15936)*
Techpubs Ltd .... F 201 541-1192
Sarasota *(G-16620)*
Telexpress La Musica Inc .... G 813 879-1914
Tampa *(G-18182)*
Tightline Publications Inc .... G 954 570-7174
Deerfield Beach *(G-2927)*
Time Adjusters Conference Inc .... G 386 274-4210
Port Orange *(G-15039)*
▲ **Tomsons Inc** .... G 248 646-0677
Englewood *(G-3685)*
Total Spcalty Publications LLC .... D 813 405-2610
Tampa *(G-18195)*
Tower Publications Inc .... F 352 372-5468
Gainesville *(G-5011)*
Toys For Boys Miami LLC .... G 786 464-0160
Miami *(G-10497)*
Tracy Publishing LLC .... G 561 799-4690
Jupiter *(G-7130)*
Trading Post of Central Fla .... G 954 675-2149
Margate *(G-8570)*
Treasure Coast Publishing Inc .... F 772 221-4289
Stuart *(G-17038)*
Tremonti Project Pubg LLC .... F 407 217-7140
Windermere *(G-19247)*
Turtle Publishing Co .... G 904 568-1484
Jacksonville *(G-6872)*
TV Publishing .... G 954 773-6967
West Palm Beach *(G-19072)*
Unique Hits Music Pubg Inc .... G 786 525-9525
Doral *(G-3536)*
United Advg Publications .... G 954 730-9700
Fort Lauderdale *(G-4294)*
◆ **Urano Publishing Inc** .... G 305 233-3365
Miami *(G-10548)*
Vade Mecum Pubg Group LLC .... G 813 969-1623
Tampa *(G-18231)*
Vandeplas Publishing .... G 407 562-1947
Lake Mary *(G-7458)*
Vendor Guide Publications Inc .... G 407 399-0745
The Villages *(G-18396)*
Vida 18com LLC .... G 305 935-6657
Miami *(G-10583)*
Videolinq Streaming Svcs LLC .... G 904 330-1026
Jacksonville *(G-6898)*
Virginia Kelly .... G 954 415-8056
Vero Beach *(G-18680)*
Viscomm Publishing LLC .... G 888 511-0900
Hernando *(G-5249)*
Vj Publications Inc .... G 407 461-0707
Longwood *(G-8347)*

SIC

Employee Codes: A=Over 500 employees, B=251-500
C=101-250, D=51-100, E=20-50, F=10-19, G=4-9

Vlex 1450 LLC .... G 954 218-5443
Weston *(G-19177)*
Walking Bird Publications LLC .... G 954 474-7261
Davie *(G-2611)*
War Chest River LLC .... G 954 736-7704
Miami *(G-10595)*
▲ **Waterford Press Inc** .... E 727 812-0140
Safety Harbor *(G-15508)*
Waterford Publishing Group LLC .... F 727 812-0140
Safety Harbor *(G-15509)*
Waterhouse Press LLC .... G 781 975-6191
Destin *(G-3210)*
Weider Publications LLC .... G 561 998-7424
Boca Raton *(G-788)*
Wemerge Inc .... G 561 305-2070
Coconut Creek *(G-2102)*
Whats Wrong Publishing Co .... G 904 388-3494
Jacksonville *(G-6916)*
White Starr Publishing .... G 305 322-5788
Miami *(G-10602)*
Whiz Bang LLC .... G 305 296-0160
Key West *(G-7204)*
Wilcox and Ray Music Pubg Inc .... G 786 220-1362
Miami *(G-10606)*
Williams and King Publishers .... G 407 914-8134
Orlando *(G-13325)*
Wincor Technology Inc .... G 407 702-0787
Apopka *(G-197)*
Windrusher Inc .... G 904 614-5196
Ponte Vedra Beach *(G-14957)*
Windward Communications Inc .... G 727 584-7191
Largo *(G-8080)*
Winter Park Publishing Co LLC .... G 941 320-6627
Winter Park *(G-19460)*
Wizard Publications .... G 808 823-8815
Shalimar *(G-16779)*
Wohlers Publishing Inc .... G 305 289-1644
Marathon *(G-8522)*
Worldwide Media Svcs Group Inc .... E 561 989-1342
Boca Raton *(G-793)*
Wrongs Without Wremedies LLC .... G 850 423-0828
Crestview *(G-2362)*
Xpress Finance Inc .... F 407 629-0095
Deltona *(G-3182)*
Yp Advrtising Pubg LLC Not LLC .... D 321 956-5400
Melbourne *(G-8978)*
Yung Payper Chasers Entrmt LLC .... F 727 239-2880
Saint Petersburg *(G-15969)*
Zetma LLC .... G 407 237-0233
Orlando *(G-13341)*
Zmh Publishers Inc .... G 239 404-9259
Naples *(G-11464)*

2752 Commercial Printing: Lithographic

24hour Printing Inc .... G 954 247-9575
Lauderhill *(G-8097)*
▼ **3-Dimension Graphics Inc** .... E 305 599-3277
Doral *(G-3215)*
321webprint .... G 321 285-6771
Melbourne *(G-8755)*
352ink Corp .... G 352 373-7547
Gainesville *(G-4866)*
3g Enterprises Inc .... G 754 366-7643
Boynton Beach *(G-870)*
525 Prnting Prmtional Pdts Inc .... G 904 580-5943
Jacksonville *(G-6103)*
▼ **5301 Realty LLC** .... C 305 633-9779
Hialeah *(G-5254)*
5hp Investments LLC .... F 561 655-5355
West Palm Beach *(G-18782)*
8 Girls & A Guy Printing LLC .... G 386 492-5976
Ponce Inlet *(G-14921)*
A & A Printing Services LLC .... G 786 597-6022
Doral *(G-3218)*
A and D Printing & Mailing LLC .... G 850 244-2400
Fort Walton Beach *(G-4773)*
A Fine Print of Miami LLC .... G 305 441-5263
Miami *(G-9037)*
A-Plus Prtg & Graphic Ctr Inc .... E 954 327-7315
Plantation *(G-14481)*
Aawareness Mktg Prtg & Pubg .... G 352 422-3953
Inverness *(G-6080)*
Abbott Printing Co .... D 407 831-2999
Maitland *(G-8456)*
Abby Press Inc .... E 407 847-5565
Kissimmee *(G-7216)*
▼ **Absolute Graphics Inc** .... F 954 792-3488
Davie *(G-2486)*
◆ **AC Graphics Inc** .... E 305 691-3778
Hialeah *(G-5264)*
Accuprint Corporation .... F 954 973-9369
Deerfield Beach *(G-2762)*
Accuprint My Print Shop .... G 954 973-9369
Deerfield Beach *(G-2763)*
Ace Blueprinting Inc .... F 954 771-0104
Fort Lauderdale *(G-3777)*
Ace High Printing LLC .... G 727 542-3897
Saint Petersburg *(G-15690)*
Ace Press Inc .... G 239 334-1118
Fort Myers *(G-4344)*
▼ **Ace Printing Inc** .... F 305 358-2572
Miami *(G-9061)*
Action Printers Inc .... G 772 567-4377
Vero Beach *(G-18590)*
Action Printing Inc .... G 305 592-4646
Miami *(G-9067)*
Admask Inc .... G 954 962-2040
Plantation *(G-14486)*
Adorgraf Corp .... G 786 752-1680
Miami *(G-9072)*
▲ **Advanced Cmmncations Holdg Inc** .. D 954 753-0100
Coral Springs *(G-2213)*
Advanced Graphics & Prtg Inc .... G 954 966-1209
Cooper City *(G-2107)*
Advanced Printing .... G 727 545-9000
Seminole *(G-16736)*
Advermarket Corp .... G 239 541-1144
Cape Coral *(G-1375)*
Advermarket Corp .... G 239 542-1020
Cape Coral *(G-1376)*
Aesthetic Print & Design Inc .... G 352 278-3714
Gainesville *(G-4868)*
Aether Media USA Inc .... G 863 647-5500
Lakeland *(G-7629)*
Agape Graphics & Printing Inc .... G 305 252-9147
Miami *(G-9088)*
Agpb LLC .... F 561 935-4147
Jupiter *(G-6997)*
Aims Printing LLC .... G 813 313-9574
Tampa *(G-17394)*
ALC Group Corp .... G 786 409-7167
Doral *(G-3233)*
◆ **Aleph Graphics Inc** .... G 305 994-9933
Doral *(G-3237)*
Align Kpital Usa LLC .... G 305 423-7100
Miami *(G-9106)*
All Because LLC .... G 407 884-6700
Apopka *(G-111)*
▲ **All In One Mail Shop Inc** .... F 305 233-6100
Miami *(G-9110)*
All Service Graphics Inc .... F 321 259-8957
Melbourne *(G-8763)*
All Star Printing Intl .... G 954 974-0333
Deerfield Beach *(G-2773)*
All-Star Sales Inc .... E 904 396-1653
Jacksonville *(G-6137)*
Allegra Direct - South Inc .... F 586 226-1400
Orlando *(G-12457)*
Allegra Marketing .... G 813 664-1129
Tampa *(G-17400)*
Allegra Marketing Print Design .... G 407 848-1721
Altamonte Springs *(G-28)*
Allegra Print and Imaging .... G 407 246-1567
Orlando *(G-12458)*
Allegra Print Signs Mail .... G 954 963-3886
Hollywood *(G-5770)*
Allied Printing Inc .... D 800 749-7683
Jacksonville *(G-6139)*
Alpha Commercial Printing .... G 561 841-1415
North Palm Beach *(G-11716)*
◆ **Alpha Press Inc** .... F 407 299-2121
Orlando *(G-12461)*
AlphaGraphics Us658 .... F 813 689-7788
Tampa *(G-17405)*
▼ **Alta Systems Inc** .... E 352 372-2534
Gainesville *(G-4873)*
▼ **Amazon Services Inc** .... F 305 663-0585
Miami *(G-9133)*
Ambassador Printing Company .... G 561 330-3668
Delray Beach *(G-3046)*
Amendar Printing Inc .... F 786 287-5189
Miami *(G-9137)*
American Business Cards Inc .... E 314 739-0800
Naples *(G-11161)*
American Specialty Sales Corp .... G 305 947-9700
North Miami *(G-11624)*
▲ **Amtec Sales Inc** .... F 800 994-3318
Miami *(G-9153)*
Anderson Printing Services Inc .... E 727 545-9000
Seminole *(G-16738)*
Apple Printing & Advg Spc Inc .... E 954 524-0493
Fort Lauderdale *(G-3818)*
Aquaflex Printing LLC .... G 727 914-4922
Saint Petersburg *(G-15706)*
▼ **Aquarius Press Inc** .... F 305 688-0066
Opa Locka *(G-12289)*
▼ **Aquinas Inc** .... G 727 842-2254
New Port Richey *(G-11480)*
Ard Printing Solutions LL .... G 305 785-7200
Miami *(G-9165)*
Area Litho Inc .... G 863 687-4656
Lakeland *(G-7637)*
Arfona Printing LLC .... G 312 339-0215
Highland Beach *(G-5705)*
Arise Prints LLC .... G 561 371-6959
West Palm Beach *(G-18800)*
Arjay Printing Company Inc .... G 904 764-6070
Oldsmar *(G-12204)*
Armstrongs Printing & Graphics .... G 850 243-6923
Fort Walton Beach *(G-4778)*
Art In Print Inc .... F 561 877-0995
Delray Beach *(G-3047)*
Artcraft Engraving & Prtg Inc .... E 305 557-9449
Hialeah *(G-5304)*
Artistic Label Company Inc .... G 401 737-0666
Estero *(G-3686)*
Artworks Printing Enterprises .... G 954 893-7984
Hollywood *(G-5775)*
Automated Printing Services .... G 904 731-3244
Jacksonville *(G-6180)*
B D D International Corp .... G 305 573-2416
Miami *(G-9209)*
B J and ME Inc .... G 561 368-5470
Boca Raton *(G-438)*
B R Q Grossmans Inc .... F 954 971-1077
Pompano Beach *(G-14609)*
B2b Printing Corp .... G 312 953-7446
Cocoa Beach *(G-2058)*
Baker County Press Inc .... G 904 259-2400
Macclenny *(G-8442)*
Ballard Printing Inc .... G 904 783-4430
Jacksonville *(G-6193)*
Bama Printing LLC .... E 561 855-7641
West Palm Beach *(G-18813)*
Bandart Enterprises Inc .... E 954 564-1224
Fort Lauderdale *(G-3839)*
Banks Sign Systems Inc .... G 954 979-0055
Pompano Beach *(G-14613)*
Barnett & Pugliano Inc .... G 727 826-6075
Saint Petersburg *(G-15717)*
Bava Inc .... F 850 893-4799
Tallahassee *(G-17226)*
Bay Area Graphics .... G 813 247-2400
Tampa *(G-17456)*
Bayfront Printing Company .... G 727 823-1965
Saint Petersburg *(G-15719)*
Bayou Printing Inc .... F 850 678-5444
Valparaiso *(G-18507)*
▲ **BCT International Inc** .... E 305 563-1224
Fort Lauderdale *(G-3844)*
Beck Graphics Inc .... E 727 443-3803
Palm Harbor *(G-13725)*
Beginmyprinting Com .... G 772 828-2026
Port Saint Lucie *(G-15090)*
▼ **Bellak Color Corporation** .... E 305 854-8525
Doral *(G-3267)*
Bema Inc .... G 954 761-1919
Fort Lauderdale *(G-3846)*
Bestprintingonlinecom LLC .... E 239 263-2106
Naples *(G-11186)*
Bi-Ads Inc .... F 954 525-1489
Fort Lauderdale *(G-3849)*
Big Biz Direct .... G 813 978-0584
Tampa *(G-17469)*
Big Red Q Printing Services .... G 305 477-7848
Doral *(G-3272)*
Bill & Renee Enterprises .... G 321 452-2800
Merritt Island *(G-8993)*
Bills Prestige Printing Inc .... G 352 589-5833
Eustis *(G-3703)*
Bizcard Xpress Sanford LLC .... G 407 688-8902
Sanford *(G-16003)*
Bjm Enterprises Inc .... F 941 746-4171
Bradenton *(G-1000)*
Bkr Printing Inc .... G 813 951-8609
Tampa *(G-17472)*
Blackstone Legal Supplies Inc .... F 305 945-3450
Lauderhill *(G-8103)*
Blackwell Family Corporation .... G 941 639-0200
Punta Gorda *(G-15199)*

Bladorn Investments Inc..........G....... 941 627-0014
Port Charlotte *(G-14965)*
▼ **Blix Corporate Image LLC**..........F....... 305 572-9001
Doral *(G-3278)*
▲ **Blue Ocean Press Inc**..........E....... 954 973-1819
Fort Lauderdale *(G-3859)*
▼ **Blue Ribbon Tag & Label Corp**..........E....... 954 922-9292
Hollywood *(G-5788)*
Bobs Quick Prtg & Copy Ctr..........G....... 561 278-0203
Boynton Beach *(G-883)*
Boca Color Graphics Inc..........F....... 561 391-2229
Boca Raton *(G-450)*
Boca Raton Commercial Printing..........G....... 561 549-0126
Boca Raton *(G-452)*
Boca Raton Printing Co..........G....... 561 395-8404
Boca Raton *(G-454)*
Bodree Printing Company Inc..........F....... 850 455-8511
Pensacola *(G-14102)*
Bonita Printshop Inc..........G....... 239 992-8522
Bonita Springs *(G-818)*
Boostan Inc..........G....... 305 223-5981
Miami *(G-9267)*
Bradford County Telegraph Inc..........F....... 904 964-6305
Starke *(G-16887)*
Brooksville Printing Inc..........G....... 352 848-0016
Brooksville *(G-1217)*
Bros Williams Printing Inc..........G....... 305 769-9925
Hialeah *(G-5332)*
Broward Print..........G....... 954 272-2272
Pembroke Pines *(G-14025)*
Brut Printing Co Inc..........E....... 904 354-5055
Jacksonville *(G-6241)*
Budget Printing Center LLC..........G....... 561 848-5700
Riviera Beach *(G-15305)*
Burke Printing..........G....... 813 549-9886
Tampa *(G-17490)*
Burr Printing Co Inc..........G....... 863 294-3166
Winter Haven *(G-19308)*
Business Cards Tomorrow Inc..........D....... 954 563-1224
Fort Lauderdale *(G-3877)*
Business Center & Printshop..........G....... 786 547-6681
Miami *(G-9287)*
Business Clinic Inc..........G....... 786 473-4573
Hialeah *(G-5336)*
Busy Bee Printer..........G....... 772 621-3683
Port Saint Lucie *(G-15094)*
▼ **Butler Graphics Inc**..........G....... 305 477-1344
Miami *(G-9289)*
C & D Printing Company..........D....... 727 572-9999
Saint Petersburg *(G-15733)*
C & H Printing Inc..........G....... 904 620-8444
Jacksonville *(G-6247)*
C & R Designs Inc..........G....... 321 383-2255
Titusville *(G-18419)*
C & S Press Inc..........D....... 407 841-3000
Orlando *(G-12539)*
C F Print Ltd Inc..........F....... 631 567-2110
The Villages *(G-18389)*
C&D Sign and Lighting Svcs LLC..........G....... 863 937-9323
Lakeland *(G-7652)*
C2 Image & Printing Inc..........G....... 310 892-8316
Hialeah *(G-5338)*
◆ **Calev Systems Inc**..........E....... 786 837-2343
Miami Springs *(G-10888)*
Capra Graphics Inc..........G....... 305 418-4582
Doral *(G-3289)*
Caribbean Discount Ptg Inc..........G....... 954 961-5015
Miramar *(G-10977)*
Carol Printing Corporation..........G....... 631 315-5061
Tarpon Springs *(G-18287)*
Catapult Print and Packg LLC..........F....... 407 717-4323
Orlando *(G-12554)*
Caxton Newspapers Inc..........E....... 305 538-9700
Miami Beach *(G-10652)*
Central Fla Prtg Graphics LLC..........G....... 321 752-8753
Melbourne *(G-8787)*
Central Florida Publishing Inc..........G....... 407 682-1221
Sanford *(G-16009)*
Central Printers Inc..........G....... 727 527-5879
Saint Petersburg *(G-15743)*
Cgi Printers LLC..........G....... 561 969-9999
West Palm Beach *(G-18844)*
Cheany Inc..........G....... 813 443-5271
Tarpon Springs *(G-18289)*
Chromatech Digital Inc..........E....... 727 528-4711
Saint Petersburg *(G-15745)*
Cincinnati Printing Service..........G....... 239 455-0960
Naples *(G-11208)*
City Clors Dgital Prtg Ctr Inc..........E....... 305 471-0816
Doral *(G-3300)*
City Prints LLC..........G....... 407 409-0509
Orlando *(G-12585)*
City Prints Signs & Flyers..........G....... 407 532-6078
Winter Park *(G-19395)*
Class A Printing LLC..........G....... 386 447-0520
Palm Coast *(G-13687)*
Classic Printing & Finish LLC..........G....... 305 817-4242
Hialeah *(G-5347)*
Clear Copy Inc..........E....... 561 369-3900
Boynton Beach *(G-890)*
Coastal Printing Inc Sarasota..........E....... 941 351-1515
Sarasota *(G-16386)*
Coastal Reign Inc..........G....... 863 940-4082
Lakeland *(G-7659)*
Cobalt Laser..........G....... 407 855-2833
Orlando *(G-12594)*
◆ **Colonial Press Intl Inc**..........C....... 305 633-1581
Miami *(G-9379)*
Color Concepts Prtg Design Co..........E....... 813 623-2921
Tampa *(G-17546)*
Color Express Inc..........G....... 305 558-2061
Hialeah *(G-5350)*
Color Press Print Inc..........G....... 850 763-9884
Panama City *(G-13887)*
Coloramax Printing Inc..........F....... 305 541-0322
Miami *(G-9381)*
Colorfast Printing & Graphics..........G....... 727 531-9506
Clearwater *(G-1633)*
Colorgraphx Inc..........E....... 727 572-6364
Saint Petersburg *(G-15747)*
Colorprint Design..........G....... 305 229-8880
Miami *(G-9383)*
Command Print LLC..........G....... 716 583-5175
Bonita Springs *(G-826)*
▼ **Commercial Printers Inc**..........D....... 954 781-3737
Fort Lauderdale *(G-3911)*
Compass Banners & Printing LLC..........G....... 727 522-7414
Saint Petersburg *(G-15751)*
Compass Printing and Marketing..........G....... 954 856-8331
Margate *(G-8539)*
▼ **Consolidated Label Co**..........C....... 407 339-2626
Sanford *(G-16022)*
▼ **Continental Printing Svcs Inc**..........G....... 904 743-6718
Jacksonville *(G-6286)*
Convicted Printing LLC..........G....... 813 304-5568
Brandon *(G-1155)*
Copy Cat Printing LLC..........G....... 850 438-5566
Pensacola *(G-14119)*
Copy Right Bgmd Inc..........F....... 904 680-0343
Jacksonville *(G-6291)*
Copy Van of Florida Inc..........G....... 407 366-7126
Oviedo *(G-13423)*
Copy Well Inc..........F....... 850 222-9777
Tallahassee *(G-17238)*
Copy-Flow Inc..........E....... 305 592-0930
Davie *(G-2509)*
Corona Printing Company Inc..........G....... 754 263-2914
Hallandale *(G-5155)*
Corporate Print Resources Inc..........G....... 305 968-2037
Palmetto Bay *(G-13842)*
Corporate Printing Svcs Inc..........G....... 305 273-6000
Miami *(G-9406)*
Couchman Printing Company..........G....... 386 756-3052
South Daytona *(G-16800)*
Crain Ventures Inc..........G....... 407 933-1820
Kissimmee *(G-7233)*
Creative Biz Center Inc..........G....... 954 918-7322
Lauderhill *(G-8106)*
Creative Color Printing Inc..........G....... 954 701-6763
Davie *(G-2510)*
Creative Design and Print..........G....... 239 325-9163
Naples *(G-11218)*
Creative Printing Bay Cnty Inc..........F....... 850 784-1645
Panama City *(G-13889)*
Creative Prtg Grphic Dsign Inc..........E....... 407 855-0202
Orlando *(G-12627)*
Creative Services of Centl Fla..........G....... 863 385-8383
Sebring *(G-16684)*
Cromer Printing Inc..........F....... 863 422-8651
Haines City *(G-5141)*
Crompco Inc..........F....... 954 584-8488
Plantation *(G-14504)*
Cronus Litho LLC..........F....... 239 325-4846
Naples *(G-11219)*
Crown Printing Inc..........F....... 863 682-4881
Lakeland *(G-7667)*
Csba Digital Printing..........F....... 813 482-1608
Tampa *(G-17571)*
Csmc Inc..........E....... 407 246-1567
Orlando *(G-12630)*
Curry & Sons Inc..........G....... 305 296-8781
Key West *(G-7185)*
Custom Graphics and Plates Inc..........E....... 407 696-5448
Longwood *(G-8269)*
Customer First Inc Naples..........E....... 239 949-8518
Bonita Springs *(G-827)*
D E B Printing & Graphics Inc..........G....... 954 968-0060
Fort Lauderdale *(G-3929)*
▲ **D Turin & Company Inc**..........E....... 305 825-2004
Hialeah *(G-5361)*
D& R Printing LLC..........G....... 941 378-3311
Sarasota *(G-16402)*
D&R Printing LLC..........G....... 941 378-3311
Sarasota *(G-16403)*
Dagher & Sons Inc..........F....... 904 998-0911
Jacksonville *(G-6307)*
Dahlquist Enterprises Inc..........G....... 407 896-2294
Orlando *(G-12644)*
Dakim Inc..........F....... 561 790-0884
Royal Palm Beach *(G-15465)*
Daniels Offset Printing Inc..........G....... 305 261-3263
Cutler Bay *(G-2392)*
Danifer Printing Inc..........G....... 727 849-5883
New Port Richey *(G-11488)*
Dannys Prtg Svc Sups & Eqp Inc..........G....... 305 757-2282
Miami *(G-9435)*
Dark Horse Signs and Prtg LLC..........G....... 850 684-3833
Gulf Breeze *(G-5115)*
Dax Copying and Printing Inc..........G....... 954 236-3000
Plantation *(G-14509)*
DC Style Corp..........G....... 786 391-3780
Miami *(G-9440)*
Delicate Designs Event Plg Inc..........G....... 305 833-8725
Miami *(G-9447)*
Dentz Design Screen Prtg LLC..........G....... 609 303-0827
Saint Augustine *(G-15536)*
Design & Print..........G....... 561 361-8299
Boca Raton *(G-498)*
Design & Print Solutions Inc..........G....... 407 703-7861
Apopka *(G-130)*
Design Litho Inc..........G....... 813 238-7494
Tampa *(G-17600)*
Designers Press Inc..........D....... 407 843-3141
Orlando *(G-12664)*
Detailed Services Inc..........F....... 239 542-2452
Cape Coral *(G-1412)*
Dg Design and Print Co LLC..........G....... 321 446-6435
Rockledge *(G-15404)*
Di Jam Holdings Inc..........F....... 863 967-6949
Auburndale *(G-239)*
Digital Printing Solutions Inc..........E....... 407 671-8715
Winter Park *(G-19402)*
Dimension Photo Engrv Co Inc..........E....... 813 251-0244
Tampa *(G-17607)*
Direct Impressions Inc..........E....... 239 549-4484
Cape Coral *(G-1415)*
▲ **Disbrow Corporation**..........F....... 813 621-9444
Tampa *(G-17608)*
Diversified Graphics Inc..........F....... 407 425-9443
Orlando *(G-12677)*
Dla Document Services..........F....... 813 828-4646
Tampa *(G-17611)*
Dlux Printing Inc..........F....... 850 457-8494
Pensacola *(G-14133)*
Docuprint Corporation..........F....... 305 639-8618
Miami *(G-9474)*
Docuvision Incorporated..........E....... 954 791-0091
Davie *(G-2517)*
Dominion Printers Inc..........G....... 757 340-1300
Port Charlotte *(G-14974)*
Donald Art Company Inc..........G....... 407 831-2525
Longwood *(G-8274)*
Donna Lynn Enterprises Inc..........G....... 772 286-2812
Palm Beach Gardens *(G-13584)*
Donnelley Financial LLC..........F....... 305 371-3900
Miami *(G-9479)*
Donoso Printing Corp..........G....... 786 508-9426
Miami Lakes *(G-10782)*
Doral Dgtal Reprographics Corp..........G....... 305 704-3194
Doral *(G-3333)*
Dowling Graphics Inc..........E....... 727 573-5997
Clearwater *(G-1657)*
Dpdm Inc..........G....... 561 327-4150
Lake Worth *(G-7545)*
Dpf Solutions Group LLC..........G....... 904 580-5343
Jacksonville *(G-6327)*
▲ **Drummond Press Inc**..........D....... 904 354-2818
Jacksonville *(G-6330)*
Dugout Sportswear..........G....... 386 615-0024
Ormond Beach *(G-13365)*

Durra Print Inc ..... E 850 222-4768
Tallahassee *(G-17244)*
Durra Quick Print Inc ..... G 850 681-2900
Tallahassee *(G-17245)*
DVC Marketing ..... G 727 442-7125
Tampa *(G-17621)*
Dvh Macleod Corp ..... F 850 224-6760
Tallahassee *(G-17246)*
▼ Dynacolor Graphics Inc ..... E 305 625-5388
Hialeah *(G-5382)*
Dynamic Printing of Brandon ..... G 813 664-6880
Lithia *(G-8218)*
▼ E & P Printing Corp ..... G 305 715-9545
Miami *(G-9489)*
E3 Graphics Inc ..... G 954 510-1302
Coral Springs *(G-2243)*
Eagle Artistic Printing Inc ..... G 973 476-6301
Boca Raton *(G-511)*
Eagle Printing ..... G 727 469-8622
Tampa *(G-17626)*
East Side Printing & Pubg ..... G 239 369-1244
Lehigh Acres *(G-8189)*
◆ Eastern Shores Printing ..... E 305 685-8976
Opa Locka *(G-12312)*
Economy Printing Co ..... F 904 786-4070
Jacksonville *(G-6354)*
Ed Vance Printing Company Inc ..... F 813 882-8888
Tampa *(G-17630)*
Edigitalprintingcom Inc ..... G 305 378-2325
Miami *(G-9502)*
Edward Thomas Company ..... G 561 746-1441
Jupiter *(G-7032)*
Ejco Inc ..... G 352 375-0797
Gainesville *(G-4913)*
Elite Power Prtg Solutions Inc ..... G 786 387-7164
Miami *(G-9518)*
Elite Printing & Marketing Inc ..... G 850 474-0894
Pensacola *(G-14139)*
Ellison Graphics Corp ..... F 561 746-9256
Jupiter *(G-7034)*
Emerald Prints LLC ..... G 850 460-5532
Niceville *(G-11566)*
Empire Corp Kit of ..... G 800 432-3028
Doral *(G-3343)*
Envision Graphics Inc ..... E 305 470-0083
Miami *(G-9530)*
EO Painter Printing Company ..... F 386 985-4877
De Leon Springs *(G-2738)*
Eprint Inc ..... G 407 930-5870
Orlando *(G-12715)*
Everglades Pro Painters Corp ..... G 786 444-5024
Miami *(G-9540)*
Everything Printing Inc ..... G 239 541-2679
Cape Coral *(G-1420)*
Evolution Signs and Print Inc ..... G 904 634-5666
Jacksonville *(G-6371)*
Excaliber Printing Inc ..... G 877 542-1699
Pompano Beach *(G-14684)*
Express Press Inc ..... F 813 884-3310
Tampa *(G-17655)*
Express Printing & Office Sups ..... G 904 765-9696
Jacksonville *(G-6376)*
Express Printing Center Inc ..... F 813 909-1085
Land O Lakes *(G-7854)*
Express Printing Corporation ..... G 305 546-6369
Miami *(G-9549)*
Express Prtg Winter Haven Inc ..... G 863 294-3286
Winter Haven *(G-19319)*
Express Signs & Graphics Inc ..... F 407 889-4433
Winter Garden *(G-19263)*
Factorymart Inc ..... F 561 202-9820
West Palm Beach *(G-18868)*
Fast Frontier Printing ..... F 407 538-5621
Largo *(G-7943)*
Fermatex Enterprises Inc ..... G 407 332-8320
Orlando *(G-12736)*
Ferrera Embroidery & Prtg Ser ..... G 786 667-2680
Miami *(G-9564)*
FGA Printing ..... G 954 763-1122
Pompano Beach *(G-14689)*
Fidelity Printing Corporation ..... D 727 522-9557
Saint Petersburg *(G-15778)*
Firehouse Promotions Inc ..... G 407 990-1600
Maitland *(G-8465)*
First Impressions Printing ..... F 352 237-6141
Ocala *(G-11943)*
First Imprseesion South Flo ..... G 954 525-0342
Fort Lauderdale *(G-3994)*
First Imprssons Prtg Cmmnctons ..... G 407 831-6100
Longwood *(G-8282)*

Five Star Sports Tickets ..... F 440 899-2000
Hallandale Beach *(G-5187)*
Flamingo Printing of Brevard ..... G 321 723-2771
Melbourne *(G-8833)*
Flash Prints LLC ..... G 786 422-3195
Miami Gardens *(G-10740)*
Flexible Prtg Solutions LLC ..... G 727 446-3014
Clearwater *(G-1684)*
Florida Color Printing Inc ..... G 772 286-7264
Stuart *(G-16941)*
Florida Graphic Printing Inc ..... F 386 253-4532
Daytona Beach *(G-2666)*
Florida Hospital Assn MGT Corp ..... G 407 841-6230
Orlando *(G-12749)*
Florida Print Solutions Inc ..... G 727 327-5500
Saint Petersburg *(G-15784)*
Florida Printing Group Inc ..... G 954 956-8570
Pompano Beach *(G-14701)*
Florida Sentinel Publishing Co ..... E 813 248-1921
Tampa *(G-17688)*
Florida State Graphics Inc ..... G 727 328-0733
Saint Petersburg *(G-15786)*
Florida Tape & Labels Inc ..... F 941 921-5788
Sarasota *(G-16438)*
Flyer Studios Inc ..... F 786 402-9596
Davie *(G-2527)*
Ford Press Inc ..... F 352 787-4650
Leesburg *(G-8159)*
Form Script - Form Print LLC ..... G 954 345-3727
Coral Springs *(G-2247)*
Fort Myers Digital LLC ..... G 239 482-3086
Fort Myers *(G-4458)*
Four G Enterprises Inc ..... E 407 834-4143
Longwood *(G-8284)*
Free Press Publishing Company ..... E 813 254-5888
Tampa *(G-17694)*
Fresh Prints ..... G 813 992-1655
Lutz *(G-8383)*
Fresh Thread Llc ..... F 904 677-9505
Jacksonville *(G-6416)*
Fretto Prints Inc ..... G 904 687-1985
Crystal River *(G-2378)*
G J V Inc ..... G 727 584-7136
Largo *(G-7955)*
G L E M Inc ..... G 727 461-5300
Clearwater *(G-1697)*
G Print Inc ..... G 305 316-2266
Hialeah *(G-5419)*
G S Printers Inc ..... G 305 931-2755
Fort Lauderdale *(G-4016)*
Gabol Screen Printing Co ..... G 305 681-3882
Opa Locka *(G-12319)*
Gadsden County Times Inc ..... F 850 627-7649
Quincy *(G-15250)*
Gandy Printers Inc ..... F 850 222-5847
Tallahassee *(G-17260)*
Garvin Management Company Inc ..... G 850 893-4719
Tallahassee *(G-17261)*
Gator Printing & Design LLC ..... G 352 593-4168
Brooksville *(G-1231)*
Gb Printing ..... F 954 941-3778
Pompano Beach *(G-14711)*
▼ General & Duplicating Services ..... G 305 541-2116
Miami *(G-9623)*
Gentry Printing Company LLC ..... E 727 441-1914
Clearwater *(G-1703)*
Glider Printing LLC ..... G 813 601-8907
Tampa *(G-17713)*
Global Impressions Inc ..... F 727 531-1290
Largo *(G-7962)*
Global Printing Services Inc ..... G 305 446-7628
Coral Gables *(G-2150)*
Global Printing Solutions Inc ..... G 727 458-3483
Saint Petersburg *(G-15793)*
Gobczynskis Printery Inc ..... G 941 758-5734
Sarasota *(G-16222)*
Goforit Inc ..... G 727 785-7616
Palm Harbor *(G-13737)*
Gold Coast Printing Inc ..... G 813 853-2219
Tampa *(G-17720)*
Golden Print Inc ..... G 561 833-9661
Boynton Beach *(G-913)*
Good Impressions ..... G 305 336-0318
Miami *(G-9649)*
Good Time Printing Inc ..... G 352 629-8838
Ocala *(G-11959)*
▲ Graphic and Printing Svcs Corp ..... G 954 486-8868
Tamarac *(G-17357)*
Graphic Dynamics Inc ..... G 954 728-8452
Fort Lauderdale *(G-4026)*

Graphic Masters Inc ..... D 800 230-3873
Miami *(G-9656)*
Graphic Press Corporation ..... G 850 562-2262
Tallahassee *(G-17266)*
Graphic Reproductions Inc ..... G 321 267-1111
Titusville *(G-18431)*
Graphica Services Inc ..... G 305 232-5333
Miami *(G-9657)*
Graphics Designer Inc ..... F 561 687-7993
West Palm Beach *(G-18889)*
▼ Graphics Type Color Entps Inc ..... E 305 591-7600
Miami *(G-9658)*
Graphink Incorporated ..... G 305 468-9463
Doral *(G-3371)*
Graphix Solutions of America ..... F 727 898-6744
Parrish *(G-14006)*
Green Light Printing Inc ..... G 305 576-5858
Miami *(G-9667)*
Green Papers Inc ..... G 305 956-3535
North Miami Beach *(G-11681)*
Gregory Michael Genung ..... G 850 572-4407
Pensacola *(G-14164)*
Grizzly Printing Parlour LLC ..... G 786 416-2494
Miami *(G-9673)*
Grupo Erik USA LLC ..... G 305 447-2611
Hialeah *(G-5438)*
Guerrilla Prtg Solutions LLC ..... G 352 394-7770
Minneola *(G-10954)*
Guest Service Publications Inc ..... F 516 333-3474
Bonita Springs *(G-835)*
Guimar Inc ..... F 305 888-1547
Hialeah *(G-5439)*
Gulf Coast Business World Inc ..... F 850 864-1511
Fort Walton Beach *(G-4806)*
Gunn Prtg & Lithography Inc ..... F 813 870-6010
Tampa *(G-17738)*
H & H Printing Inc ..... F 407 422-2932
Orlando *(G-12792)*
H & M Printing Inc ..... F 407 831-8030
Sanford *(G-16059)*
H D Quickprint & Disc Off Sups ..... G 407 678-1355
Winter Park *(G-19409)*
H&M Phillips Inc ..... G 727 797-4600
Odessa *(G-12125)*
Hamilton Printing Inc ..... G 772 334-0151
Jensen Beach *(G-6970)*
Hart Graphics ..... G 727 938-7018
Tarpon Springs *(G-18305)*
Hartco Inc ..... G 904 353-5259
Jacksonville *(G-6462)*
▲ Hartley Press Inc ..... D 904 398-5141
Jacksonville *(G-6463)*
Hartmans Print Center Inc ..... G 941 475-2220
Englewood *(G-3661)*
Harvest Print Mktg Sltions LLC ..... G 850 681-2488
Tallahassee *(G-17276)*
Harvest Prtg & Copy Ctr Inc ..... F 850 681-2488
Tallahassee *(G-17277)*
Herald-Advocate Publishing Co ..... F 863 773-3255
Wauchula *(G-18693)*
Herff Jones Inc ..... G 407 647-4373
Winter Park *(G-19410)*
Herff Jones LLC ..... G 904 641-4060
Jacksonville *(G-6470)*
Heritage Centl Fla Jewish News ..... F 407 834-8277
Fern Park *(G-3729)*
Hernandez Printing Service ..... F 305 642-0483
Miami *(G-9705)*
Hernando Lithoprinting Inc ..... G 352 796-4136
Brooksville *(G-1233)*
HI Tech Printing Systems Inc ..... E 954 933-9155
Pompano Beach *(G-14722)*
Hilcraft Engraving Inc ..... G 305 871-6100
Miami *(G-9711)*
Hill Printing Inc ..... G 407 654-4282
Winter Garden *(G-19268)*
HOB Corporation ..... G 813 988-2272
Tampa *(G-17758)*
▼ Hobby Press Inc ..... E 305 887-4333
Medley *(G-8664)*
Hoffman Brothers Inc ..... E 407 563-5004
Debary *(G-2750)*
Hoipong Customs Inc ..... G 954 684-9232
Pembroke Pines *(G-14041)*
Howies Instant Printing Inc ..... F 561 686-8699
West Palm Beach *(G-18898)*
Hughes Consolidated Services ..... G 904 438-5710
Jacksonville *(G-6482)*
▼ Hunt Enterprises Inc ..... G 863 682-6187
Lakeland *(G-7707)*

Hurricane Graphics Inc ....E 305 760-9154
Miami Gardens *(G-10746)*
▼ **Hybrid Impressions Inc** ....E 305 392-5029
Hialeah *(G-5450)*
ICM Printing Co Inc ....F 352 377-7468
Gainesville *(G-4940)*
Ideal Publishing Co Inc ....F 727 321-0785
Saint Petersburg *(G-15812)*
Iguana Graphics Inc ....G 813 657-7800
Brandon *(G-1163)*
Image Printing & Graphics LLC ....G 321 783-5555
Cape Canaveral *(G-1360)*
Image Prtg & Digital Svcs Inc ....G 850 244-3380
Mary Esther *(G-8589)*
Imperial Imprinting LLC ....G 772 633-8256
Vero Beach *(G-18628)*
Impressing Design Print ....G 786 615-3695
Hialeah *(G-5453)*
Imprint ....G 941 484-5151
Nokomis *(G-11581)*
In Stock Printers Inc ....G 727 447-2515
Oldsmar *(G-12234)*
Independent Resources Inc ....E 813 237-0945
Tampa *(G-17777)*
Infinite Print LLC ....G 727 942-2121
Holiday *(G-5745)*
Ink Bros Printing LLC ....G 407 494-9585
Longwood *(G-8290)*
Inkpressions Inc ....G 305 261-0872
Palmetto Bay *(G-13849)*
Inky Fingers Printing Inc ....G 904 384-1900
Jacksonville *(G-6495)*
Instant Call Center LLC ....G 321 356-1587
Longwood *(G-8291)*
Instant Imprints ....G 224 764-2198
Orlando *(G-12833)*
Instant Imprints ....G 850 474-9184
Pensacola *(G-14179)*
Instant Locate Inc ....G 800 431-0812
Casselberry *(G-1506)*
Instant Printing & Copy Center ....G 727 849-1199
Holiday *(G-5746)*
Instant Printing Services Inc ....F 727 546-8036
Floral City *(G-3768)*
Instant Ps LLC ....G 786 278-5007
Miami *(G-9751)*
Insty-Prints ....G 352 373-7547
Gainesville *(G-4944)*
▲ **Intec Printing Solutions Corp** ....G 813 949-7799
Lutz *(G-8391)*
Integrity Business Svcs Inc ....G 321 267-9294
Titusville *(G-18434)*
International Printing & Copyi ....G 954 295-5239
Coconut Creek *(G-2084)*
▼ **Interprint Incorporated** ....D 727 531-8957
Clearwater *(G-1734)*
Iprint 3d USA ....G 888 868-7329
Pompano Beach *(G-14733)*
Ironhorse Pressworks Inc ....G 727 462-9988
Clearwater *(G-1737)*
Island Print Shop ....G 239 642-0077
Naples *(G-11293)*
It Busness Solutions Group Inc ....F 407 260-0116
Longwood *(G-8294)*
J & J International Corp ....E 407 349-7114
Sanford *(G-16070)*
J & J Litho Enterprises Inc ....F 239 433-2311
Fort Myers *(G-4499)*
J J M Services Inc ....G 954 437-1880
Miramar *(G-11007)*
J K & M Ink Corporation ....G 813 875-3106
Tampa *(G-17798)*
J M Econo-Print Inc ....G 305 591-3620
Coral Gables *(G-2162)*
J-Kup Corp ....F 352 683-5629
Spring Hill *(G-16855)*
Jak Corporate Holdings Inc ....F 813 289-1660
Tampa *(G-17802)*
Jet Graphics Inc ....F 305 264-4333
Miami *(G-9796)*
Jet Set Printing Inc ....G 407 339-1900
Casselberry *(G-1508)*
Jimbob Printing Inc ....F 850 973-2633
Madison *(G-8452)*
Jj Screenprint LLC ....G 941 587-1801
Sarasota *(G-16477)*
Jjaz Enterprises Inc ....G 407 330-0245
Lake Mary *(G-7427)*
Jkg Group ....G 561 866-2850
Boca Raton *(G-581)*

Jmf Dgital Print Solutions Inc ....G 954 362-4929
Pembroke Pines *(G-14044)*
John Stewart Enterprises Inc ....F 904 356-9392
Jacksonville *(G-6525)*
Jordan Norris Inc ....G 407 846-1400
Orlando *(G-12861)*
JPS Digital LLC ....F 813 501-6040
Inverness *(G-6091)*
▼ **Jrg Systems Inc** ....F 954 962-1020
Fort Lauderdale *(G-4081)*
Just Say Print Inc ....G 954 254-7793
Coral Springs *(G-2267)*
▼ **K Color Corp** ....F 305 579-2290
Miami *(G-9813)*
K R O Enterprises Ltd ....G 309 797-2213
Naples *(G-11302)*
K12 Print Inc ....F 800 764-7600
West Palm Beach *(G-18919)*
Kee Kreative LLC ....G 954 931-2579
Lauderhill *(G-8113)*
Keithco Inc ....G 352 351-4741
Ocala *(G-11976)*
Key West Printing LLC ....G 305 517-6711
Key West *(G-7190)*
Keytag1 LLC ....G 203 982-8448
Deerfield Beach *(G-2853)*
Kights Printing & Office Pdts ....G 904 731-7990
Jacksonville *(G-6537)*
Kikinaz Screen Printing Inc ....G 561 512-3134
Royal Palm Beach *(G-15473)*
Kinane Corp ....F 772 288-6580
Stuart *(G-16965)*
King & Grube Advg & Prtg LLC ....G 727 327-6033
Largo *(G-7990)*
King & Grube Inc ....F 727 327-6033
Largo *(G-7991)*
King Printing & Graphics Inc ....G 813 681-5060
Brandon *(G-1164)*
King Tech Print LLC ....G 786 362-6249
Miami *(G-9822)*
Kissimmee Printing ....G 407 518-2514
Kissimmee *(G-7264)*
Kmg Marketing LLC ....G 727 376-7200
Odessa *(G-12130)*
Kuhn Family Enterprises Inc ....G 813 671-5353
Riverview *(G-15275)*
Kwikie Dup Ctr of Pinellas Pk ....G 727 544-7788
Pinellas Park *(G-14362)*
L & N Label Company Inc ....E 727 442-5400
Clearwater *(G-1755)*
La Mar Orlando LLC ....E 407 423-2051
Orlando *(G-12885)*
Label Company ....F 850 438-7334
Pensacola *(G-14191)*
Label Printing Service ....G 727 820-1226
Clearwater *(G-1756)*
Labelpro Inc ....F 727 538-2149
Clearwater *(G-1757)*
Lake Worth Herald Press ....E 561 585-9387
Lake Worth *(G-7564)*
Lakeland Digital Printing Co ....G 863 509-8049
Lakeland *(G-7730)*
Lance Printers Service Inc ....G 305 256-7982
Miami *(G-9856)*
Laser Light Litho Corp ....F 305 899-0713
North Miami *(G-11643)*
▲ **Lauderdale Graphics Corp** ....E 954 450-0800
Davie *(G-2544)*
▼ **Lawton Printers Inc** ....E 407 260-0400
Orlando *(G-12898)*
Leaderinprint Inc ....G 561 200-9412
Lake Worth *(G-7565)*
Leda Printing Inc ....E 941 922-1563
Sarasota *(G-16487)*
Lee Printing Inc ....F 904 396-5715
Jacksonville Beach *(G-6948)*
Legend Printing Company LLC ....G 904 268-7079
Jacksonville *(G-6553)*
Leila K Moavero ....G 954 978-0018
Pompano Beach *(G-14743)*
Lexprint LLC ....G 305 661-2424
Miami *(G-9888)*
Liberty Crtive - Coml Prtg Prm ....G 407 960-4270
Longwood *(G-8306)*
Life In A Tee Shirt Prtg LLC ....G 941 927-0116
Sarasota *(G-16488)*
Lightning Prtg & Graphics Inc ....G 321 242-7766
Melbourne *(G-8875)*
Lincoln Smith Ventures LLC ....G 863 337-6670
Lakeland *(G-7735)*

Lindsey Macke Bindery Printing ....G 727 514-3570
Odessa *(G-12132)*
Linographics Inc ....F 407 422-8700
Orlando *(G-12913)*
Lion Ink Print Inc ....G 561 358-8925
West Palm Beach *(G-18930)*
Lion Press Inc ....G 954 971-6193
Pompano Beach *(G-14745)*
Lionheart Printers LLC ....G 561 781-8300
Jupiter *(G-7068)*
Lit Prints Inc ....G 305 456-0150
Miami *(G-9900)*
Lit Prints Inc ....G 305 951-5122
Coral Gables *(G-2173)*
Litho Art Inc ....G 305 232-7098
Miami *(G-9902)*
Litho Haus Printers Inc ....G 850 671-6600
Tallahassee *(G-17291)*
Lithocraft Inc ....G 386 761-3584
Port Orange *(G-15022)*
Lithotec Commercial Printing ....F 727 541-4614
Clearwater *(G-1763)*
Ljk & TS Partners Inc ....G 941 661-5675
Tampa *(G-17854)*
Lmb Consultants Inc ....G 954 537-9590
Pompano Beach *(G-14746)*
Lmn Printing Co Inc ....F 386 428-9928
Edgewater *(G-3630)*
Lori Roberts Print Shop I ....F 813 882-8456
Tampa *(G-17860)*
▲ **Lucky Dog Printing Inc** ....F 407 346-1663
Saint Cloud *(G-15657)*
Ludaca Printing Corp ....G 305 300-4355
Miami *(G-9915)*
▼ **Lufemor Inc** ....G 305 557-2162
Hialeah *(G-5490)*
Lumo Print Inc ....G 305 246-0003
Homestead *(G-5981)*
Lutimi Nr Corp ....G 954 245-7986
Miramar *(G-11012)*
Luxe Prints LLC ....G 941 484-4500
Sarasota *(G-16493)*
Lytron Print ....G 954 683-1291
Fort Lauderdale *(G-4106)*
M D H Graphic Services Inc ....F 561 533-9000
West Palm Beach *(G-18936)*
M J Embroidery Screen Prtg LLC ....G 407 239-0246
Orlando *(G-12941)*
M L Solutions Inc ....G 305 506-5113
Miami *(G-9926)*
M Victoria Enterprises Inc ....G 727 576-8090
Saint Petersburg *(G-15845)*
Mad Inc ....G 813 251-9334
Tampa *(G-17871)*
Maddys Print Shop LLC ....G 954 749-0440
Fort Lauderdale *(G-4108)*
Magic Print Copy Center ....G 239 332-4456
Fort Myers *(G-4520)*
Magnaprint Corp ....G 954 376-8416
Oakland Park *(G-11819)*
Maki Printing LLC ....F 941 809-7574
Sarasota *(G-16498)*
Maki Printing LLC ....F 941 925-4802
Sarasota *(G-16499)*
Man Enterprises 3 LLC ....G 561 655-4944
West Palm Beach *(G-18940)*
Manatee Printers Inc ....E 941 746-9100
Bradenton *(G-1076)*
Manci Graphics Corp ....G 813 664-1129
Tampa *(G-17877)*
Marion Nature Park ....G 352 817-3077
Belleview *(G-372)*
Mark V Printing LLC ....G 954 563-2505
Oakland Park *(G-11822)*
Market Ink Usa Inc ....G 561 502-3438
West Palm Beach *(G-18943)*
Marketshare LLC ....G 631 273-0598
Boca Raton *(G-609)*
◆ **Marrakech Inc** ....G 727 942-2218
Tarpon Springs *(G-18315)*
Martin Lithograph Inc ....E 813 254-1553
Tampa *(G-17886)*
Masc Aspen Partners LLC ....G 212 545-1076
Boca Raton *(G-611)*
Matrix Marketing Solutions ....G 407 654-5736
Windermere *(G-19237)*
Maxigraphics Inc ....F 954 978-0740
Pompano Beach *(G-14755)*
Mc Squared Group Inc ....G 850 435-4600
Pensacola *(G-14202)*

S I C

McGee Enterprises Inc .... G 904 328-3226
Jacksonville *(G-6585)*
Medfare LLC .... F 561 998-9444
Boca Raton *(G-617)*
Media Systems Inc .... G 954 427-4411
Coral Springs *(G-2277)*
Megacolor Print LLC .... F 305 499-9395
Miami Beach *(G-10692)*
Megamalls Inc .... F 407 891-2111
Saint Cloud *(G-15659)*
▼ **Menu Men Inc** .... E 305 633-7925
Miami *(G-9976)*
Miami Quality Graphics Inc .... E 305 634-9506
Miami *(G-10007)*
Miami Stitch and Print Center .... G 305 770-4285
Miami *(G-10012)*
Miami Trucolor Offset Svc Co .... G 954 962-5230
West Park *(G-19096)*
▼ **Micro Printing Inc** .... F 954 676-5757
Fort Lauderdale *(G-4121)*
Mid West Lettering Company .... E 850 477-6522
Pensacola *(G-14209)*
Midds Inc .... F 561 586-6220
Lake Worth *(G-7571)*
Midds Inc .... E 561 586-6220
Lake Worth Beach *(G-7615)*
Mikes Print Shop Inc .... G 407 718-4964
Winter Park *(G-19426)*
Milton Newspapers Inc .... A 850 623-2120
Milton *(G-10935)*
Mint Prints .... G 561 900-5432
Deerfield Beach *(G-2873)*
Minute Man Press .... G 727 791-1115
Dunedin *(G-3584)*
Minuteman Press .... F 727 535-3800
Largo *(G-8011)*
Minuteman Press .... E 813 884-2476
Tampa *(G-17910)*
Minuteman Press .... G 904 733-5578
Jacksonville *(G-6609)*
Minuteman Press .... F 305 242-6800
Cutler Bay *(G-2404)*
Minuteman Press .... G 863 337-6670
Lakeland *(G-7752)*
Minuteman Press .... G 503 789-5741
Kissimmee *(G-7275)*
Minuteman Press .... F 386 255-2767
Daytona Beach *(G-2688)*
Minuteman Press .... G 352 728-6333
Leesburg *(G-8166)*
Minuteman Press .... G 772 301-0222
Port Saint Lucie *(G-15122)*
Minuteman Press .... G 954 804-8304
Lake Worth *(G-7573)*
Mmp-Boca Raton LLC .... F 561 392-8626
Boca Raton *(G-627)*
Modern Digital Imaging Inc .... F 850 222-7514
Tallahassee *(G-17303)*
Modern Mail Print Slutions Inc .... E 727 572-6245
Clearwater *(G-1789)*
▼ **MOR Printing Inc** .... F 954 377-1197
Pompano Beach *(G-14768)*
Morten Enterprises Inc .... F 727 531-8957
Clearwater *(G-1792)*
Mp 93 Screen Print and EMB LLC .... F 407 592-3657
Orlando *(G-12982)*
MRM Creative LLC .... G 386 218-5940
Orange City *(G-12376)*
Multicolor Printing Inc .... G 772 287-1676
Stuart *(G-16979)*
Mxn Inc .... G 813 654-3173
Tampa *(G-17921)*
My Print Shop Inc .... F 954 973-9369
Deerfield Beach *(G-2878)*
Myers Printing Inc .... G 813 237-0288
Tampa *(G-17924)*
Nai Print Solutions LLC .... G 850 637-1260
Pensacola *(G-14210)*
Naples Printing Inc .... F 239 643-2442
Naples *(G-11338)*
Nassau Printing & Off Sup Inc .... G 904 879-2305
Callahan *(G-1327)*
▲ **National Multiple Listing Inc** .... E 954 772-8880
Fort Lauderdale *(G-4132)*
National Traffic Signs Inc .... G 727 446-7983
Clearwater *(G-1802)*
NC Printing & Accounting Co .... G 904 327-7701
Jacksonville *(G-6622)*
Ncp Solutions LLC .... D 205 849-5200
Jacksonville *(G-6623)*
Neat Print Inc .... F 941 545-1517
Sarasota *(G-16523)*
Nebraska Printing Inc .... E 813 870-6871
Tampa *(G-17936)*
New Gnrtion Abndant Mssion Ch .... E 772 497-5871
Port Saint Lucie *(G-15123)*
Newsnotes LLC .... G 407 949-8185
Satellite Beach *(G-16653)*
▼ **Newspaper Printing Company** .... C 813 839-0035
Tampa *(G-17937)*
Nexpub Inc .... F 954 392-5889
Miramar *(G-11021)*
Ngp Corporate Square Inc .... E 239 643-3430
Naples *(G-11345)*
No Limit TS and Prints LLC .... G 813 933-3424
Spring Hill *(G-16876)*
North Florida Printing Inc .... G 386 362-1080
Live Oak *(G-8235)*
North Palm Printing Center .... G 561 622-2839
Palm Beach Gardens *(G-13612)*
Northern Litho Inc .... G 239 653-9645
Naples *(G-11346)*
▼ **Nupress of Miami Inc** .... E 305 594-2100
Doral *(G-3446)*
Ocala Print Quick Inc .... G 352 629-0736
Ocala *(G-12014)*
Olmedo Printing Corp .... G 305 262-4666
Miami *(G-10095)*
On The Run Printing .... G 305 733-2619
Miramar *(G-11024)*
One Hour Printing .... G 386 763-3111
South Daytona *(G-16805)*
One Nugget LLc .... G 904 527-3218
Jacksonville *(G-6644)*
Onesource of Florida Inc .... G 904 620-0003
Jacksonville *(G-6645)*
Oompha Inc .... G 850 222-7210
Tallahassee *(G-17308)*
Open Market Enterprises LLC .... G 407 322-5434
Orlando *(G-13024)*
Orchid Printing Inc .... G 786 523-3324
Cutler Bay *(G-2406)*
▼ **Orellana Investments Inc** .... G 305 477-2817
Miami *(G-10115)*
▼ **Original Impressions LLC** .... C 305 233-1322
Weston *(G-19156)*
Outdoor Media Inc .... G 305 529-1400
Coral Gables *(G-2183)*
Output Printing Corp .... F 813 228-8800
Tampa *(G-17965)*
P & G Printing Group Inc .... F 954 971-2511
Margate *(G-8559)*
P & J Graphics Inc .... F 813 626-3243
Temple Terrace *(G-18373)*
Pad Printing Technology Corp .... G 941 739-8667
Bradenton *(G-1091)*
Pad Printing Technology Group .... F 941 739-8667
Bradenton *(G-1092)*
▼ **Palm Beach Junior Clg Prnt Shp** .... F 561 969-0122
Lake Worth *(G-7578)*
Palm Print Inc .... F 561 833-9661
West Palm Beach *(G-18986)*
Palm Prnting/Printers Ink Corp .... E 239 332-8600
Fort Myers *(G-4562)*
Palm Prtg Strgc Solutions LLC .... G 239 332-8600
Fort Myers *(G-4563)*
▼ **Palmetto Printing Inc** .... F 305 253-2444
Miami *(G-10134)*
Pamatian Group Inc .... G 407 291-8387
Orlando *(G-13046)*
◆ **Pan American Graphic Inc** .... E 305 885-1962
Miami Lakes *(G-10834)*
Panther Printing Inc .... E 239 936-5050
Fort Myers *(G-4564)*
Paper Fish Printing Inc .... G 239 481-3555
Fort Myers *(G-4565)*
Paper Palm LLC .... G 407 647-3328
Orlando *(G-13049)*
Paper Pushers of America Inc .... G 386 872-7025
Daytona Beach *(G-2692)*
Paragon Products Inc .... E 407 302-9147
Sanford *(G-16099)*
Parkinson Enterprises Inc .... F 863 688-7900
Lakeland *(G-7762)*
Parkway Printing Inc .... G 239 936-6970
Fort Myers *(G-4566)*
Pasa Services Inc .... E 305 594-8662
Opa Locka *(G-12350)*
Pat Cobb Printing .... G 772 465-5484
Fort Pierce *(G-4729)*
Patriot Press Inc .... F 407 625-7516
Orlando *(G-13053)*
Paw Print Co .... G 561 753-5588
West Palm Beach *(G-18991)*
PCI Communications Inc .... G 941 729-5202
Ellenton *(G-3654)*
Pencil Printing .... G 407 346-4952
Kissimmee *(G-7285)*
Penstripe Graphics .... G 904 726-0200
Jacksonville *(G-6667)*
Peter Printer Inc .... G 305 558-0147
Hialeah *(G-5556)*
◆ **Pfaffco Inc** .... F 305 635-0986
Miami Lakes *(G-10837)*
Pg Express Inc .... G 954 788-3263
Pompano Beach *(G-14791)*
Phantom USA LLC .... G 863 353-5972
Dundee *(G-3567)*
Phil & Brenda Johnson Inc .... F 813 623-5478
Tampa *(G-17988)*
Phillips Graphics Inc .... G 352 622-1776
Ocala *(G-12025)*
Phillips Printing Services LLC .... G 941 526-6570
Bradenton *(G-1095)*
◆ **Phoenix Group Florida Inc** .... G 954 563-1224
Fort Lauderdale *(G-4166)*
Photo Graphics .... G 772 220-1430
Stuart *(G-16988)*
Photo Offset Inc .... F 305 666-1067
Miami *(G-10159)*
▲ **Photoengraving Inc** .... E 813 253-3427
Tampa *(G-17992)*
Pioneer Announcements Inc .... F 305 573-7000
Miami *(G-10166)*
PIP Marketing Signs Print .... G 904 825-2372
Saint Augustine *(G-15588)*
PIP Printing .... G 352 622-3224
Ocala *(G-12027)*
PIP Printing .... G 386 258-3326
Daytona Beach *(G-2694)*
PIP Printing 622 Inc .... G 813 935-8113
Tampa *(G-17993)*
Pk Graphicz .... G 305 534-2184
Pompano Beach *(G-14795)*
Pk Group Inc .... F 239 643-2442
Naples *(G-11368)*
▲ **Plasti-Card Corporation** .... F 305 944-2726
Delray Beach *(G-3117)*
Plastic Sealing Company Inc .... G 954 956-9797
Pompano Beach *(G-14797)*
Playlist Live Inc .... E 877 306-3651
Orlando *(G-13072)*
Podgo Printing LLC .... G 954 874-9100
Hollywood *(G-5893)*
Port Printing Co .... G 561 848-1402
Riviera Beach *(G-15365)*
Power Printing of Florida .... F 727 823-1162
Saint Petersburg *(G-15885)*
◆ **PPG Inc** .... F 813 831-9902
Tampa *(G-18000)*
Precious Prints Inc .... G 786 346-7740
Miami *(G-10183)*
Precise Print Florida .... G 813 960-4958
Lutz *(G-8411)*
Precision Litho Service Inc .... D 727 573-1763
Clearwater *(G-1840)*
Precision Printing of Columbus .... G 561 509-7269
Boynton Beach *(G-942)*
Premier Corporate Printing .... G 305 378-8480
Jacksonville *(G-6683)*
Premier Corporate Printing LLC .... F 305 378-8480
Jacksonville *(G-6684)*
Premier Global Enterprises .... G 561 747-7303
Tequesta *(G-18387)*
Premier Printing Signs .... G 727 849-2493
Port Richey *(G-15064)*
Premier Printing Solutions Inc .... G 305 490-0244
Fort Lauderdale *(G-4177)*
Press Print Graphics LLC .... F 850 249-3700
Panama City Beach *(G-13983)*
Press Printing Enterprises Inc .... E 239 598-1500
Fort Myers *(G-4572)*
Press Room Inc .... G 954 792-6729
Pembroke Pines *(G-14054)*
Pressex Inc .... F 727 299-8500
Clearwater *(G-1845)*
Presto Print II Inc .... G 203 627-2528
Delray Beach *(G-3124)*
Print Administrate .... G 407 877-5923
Winter Garden *(G-19280)*

Print All Promotions LLC ....G.... 800 971-3209
Wildwood *(G-19199)*
Print Basics Inc ....E.... 954 354-0700
Deerfield Beach *(G-2891)*
Print Big Inc ....G.... 305 398-8898
Hialeah *(G-5572)*
Print Bold Corp ....F.... 305 517-1281
Miami *(G-10193)*
Print Direct Inc ....G.... 772 545-9191
Hobe Sound *(G-5725)*
Print Dynamics ....F.... 954 524-9294
Fort Lauderdale *(G-4180)*
Print E-Solution Inc ....G.... 954 588-5454
Deerfield Beach *(G-2892)*
Print Etc Inc ....F.... 813 972-2800
Tampa *(G-18013)*
Print Express ....G.... 904 737-6641
Jacksonville *(G-6686)*
Print Factory LLC ....G.... 954 392-5889
Miramar *(G-11031)*
Print Farm Inc ....E.... 305 592-2895
Miami *(G-10194)*
Print Headquarters ....F.... 772 286-2812
Palm Beach Gardens *(G-13618)*
Print Hopper ....G.... 954 770-3007
Sunrise *(G-17162)*
Print It 4 Less ....G.... 800 370-5591
Delray Beach *(G-3125)*
Print It Usacom Inc ....G.... 954 370-2200
Davie *(G-2575)*
Print Motion Inc ....F.... 305 851-7206
Miami *(G-10195)*
Print My Atm LLC ....G.... 866 292-6179
Orlando *(G-13088)*
Print One Inc ....G.... 813 273-0240
Oldsmar *(G-12262)*
Print Pro Shop Inc ....F.... 305 859-8282
Miami *(G-10196)*
Print Rite Co ....G.... 305 757-0611
Miami *(G-10197)*
Print Shack ....G.... 813 885-4152
Tampa *(G-18014)*
Print Shop of Chiefland Inc ....G.... 352 493-0322
Chiefland *(G-1537)*
Print Solution Digital LLC ....G.... 305 819-7420
Hialeah *(G-5573)*
Print Store LLC ....G.... 727 656-1376
Palm Harbor *(G-13752)*
Print This and That LLC ....F.... 386 752-5905
Lake City *(G-7376)*
Print This and That LLC ....F.... 386 344-4420
Lake City *(G-7377)*
Printed Systems Inc ....G.... 904 281-0909
Jacksonville *(G-6687)*
Printer S Pride Inc ....G.... 813 932-8683
Tampa *(G-18015)*
Printerbazaar Usa Inc ....G.... 954 730-3473
Miami *(G-10199)*
Printers Edge LLC ....F.... 407 294-8542
Orlando *(G-13089)*
Printers For Less LLC ....G.... 954 647-0051
Fort Lauderdale *(G-4181)*
Printers of Pensacola LLC ....G.... 850 434-2588
Pensacola *(G-14240)*
Printing and Labels Inc ....G.... 954 578-4411
Sunrise *(G-17163)*
Printing and Promotion Svcs ....G.... 201 612-0800
Delray Beach *(G-3126)*
Printing Center LLC ....G.... 305 513-9114
Miami *(G-10200)*
Printing Connection Too Inc ....G.... 954 584-4197
Davie *(G-2576)*
▼ Printing Corp of Americas Inc ....E.... 954 943-6087
Pompano Beach *(G-14815)*
Printing Department LLC ....G.... 386 253-7990
Daytona Beach *(G-2699)*
Printing Depot Inc ....G.... 813 855-6758
Oldsmar *(G-12264)*
Printing Edge Inc ....G.... 904 399-3343
Jacksonville *(G-6688)*
Printing Express ....G.... 305 512-0900
Hialeah *(G-5575)*
Printing For A Cause LLC ....E.... 786 496-0637
Saint Petersburg *(G-15889)*
Printing Grphics Cnnection Inc ....G.... 305 222-6144
Miami *(G-10201)*
Printing Impressions Prom ....G.... 904 465-2223
Jacksonville *(G-6689)*
Printing Mart Inc ....G.... 954 753-0323
Pompano Beach *(G-14816)*

Printing Services Plus LLC ....F.... 813 279-1903
Tampa *(G-18016)*
Printing Usa Inc ....F.... 407 857-7468
Orlando *(G-13090)*
Printmaster Inc ....G.... 954 771-6104
Oakland Park *(G-11832)*
Printmor ....F.... 954 247-9405
Coral Springs *(G-2304)*
Printnow Inc ....G.... 850 435-1149
Pensacola *(G-14241)*
Printrust Inc ....G.... 954 572-0790
Sunrise *(G-17164)*
Prints 2 Go Inc ....F.... 727 725-1700
Clearwater *(G-1847)*
Prints Hope International Inc ....G.... 305 528-1593
Miramar *(G-11032)*
Prints The Ppr of Wnter Pk LLC ....G.... 407 740-0989
Winter Park *(G-19433)*
Printshaqcom Inc ....G.... 954 678-7286
Hollywood *(G-5895)*
Printworks ....G.... 850 681-6909
Tallahassee *(G-17311)*
Printworld ....G.... 754 312-5908
Fort Lauderdale *(G-4182)*
Priority Printing Inc ....G.... 727 446-6605
Clearwater *(G-1848)*
Pro-Copy Inc ....F.... 813 988-5900
Temple Terrace *(G-18375)*
Professional Office Svcs Inc ....G.... 863 967-6634
Winter Haven *(G-19348)*
Professional Printing ....G.... 561 845-0514
North Palm Beach *(G-11725)*
Professional Prtg For Less Inc ....G.... 954 977-3737
Pompano Beach *(G-14819)*
Professnal Reproduction of Jax ....G.... 904 389-4141
Jacksonville *(G-6691)*
Progressive Printing Co Inc ....F.... 904 388-0746
Jacksonville *(G-6694)*
Progressive Printing Solutions ....G.... 800 370-5591
Delray Beach *(G-3128)*
Prolific Resource Inc ....G.... 727 868-9341
Port Richey *(G-15066)*
Proprint of Naples Inc ....F.... 239 775-3553
Fort Myers *(G-4574)*
PS & QS Custom Prints LLC ....F.... 352 231-3961
Gainesville *(G-4984)*
Public Image Printing Inc ....G.... 727 363-1800
St Pete Beach *(G-16883)*
Pure Postcards Inc ....F.... 877 446-2434
Clearwater *(G-1854)*
Pyramideye Print Corp ....G.... 786 663-1157
Hialeah *(G-5586)*
Q P Consulting Inc ....G.... 321 727-2442
Melbourne *(G-8916)*
Quality Arts Lcp LLC ....G.... 305 735-2310
Hialeah *(G-5588)*
Quality Forms & Printing Co ....G.... 407 671-8026
Winter Park *(G-19434)*
Quality Printing Inc ....G.... 386 255-1565
Daytona Beach *(G-2701)*
Quick Print ....G.... 954 974-2820
Pompano Beach *(G-14823)*
Quick Prints LLC ....G.... 954 526-9013
Fort Lauderdale *(G-4196)*
Quick Prints LLC ....G.... 954 594-9415
Plantation *(G-14543)*
Quickprint Line ....G.... 561 740-9930
Boynton Beach *(G-950)*
Quicksilver Prtg & Copying Inc ....G.... 813 888-6811
Tampa *(G-18035)*
R K L Enterprises of Pensacola ....F.... 850 432-2335
Pensacola *(G-14248)*
R R H Inc ....F.... 954 966-1209
Hollywood *(G-5900)*
R Smith Printing Inc ....G.... 518 827-7700
Hastings *(G-5229)*
Ra Printing Inc ....G.... 904 733-5578
Jacksonville *(G-6703)*
Rainbow Printing Inc ....G.... 561 364-9000
Boynton Beach *(G-952)*
Ramseys Printing & Office Pdts ....G.... 850 227-7468
Port Saint Joe *(G-15082)*
Ranger Associates Inc ....G.... 407 869-0024
Longwood *(G-8329)*
Rapid Graphix Inc ....G.... 941 639-2043
Punta Gorda *(G-15227)*
Rapid Print Southwest Fla Inc ....G.... 239 590-9797
Fort Myers *(G-4579)*
Rapid Printer Solutions ....G.... 954 769-9553
Fort Lauderdale *(G-4198)*

Rapid Rater Company ....E.... 850 893-7346
Tallahassee *(G-17314)*
Rapid Reproductions LLC ....G.... 607 843-2221
Melbourne Beach *(G-8983)*
Real Print & Ship Inc ....G.... 727 787-1949
Palm Harbor *(G-13758)*
Redberd Printing ....G.... 407 622-2292
Winter Park *(G-19438)*
Redbird Printing ....G.... 904 654-8371
Winter Park *(G-19439)*
Reimink Printing Inc ....G.... 813 289-4663
Tampa *(G-18050)*
Rek Design & Print LLC ....G.... 407 331-5100
Winter Springs *(G-19483)*
Relion Enterprises LLC ....G.... 321 287-4225
Orlando *(G-13130)*
▼ Rennak Inc ....G.... 305 558-0144
Miami Lakes *(G-10850)*
Repro Plus Inc ....F.... 407 843-1492
Orlando *(G-13131)*
Rgu Color Inc ....G.... 386 252-9979
South Daytona *(G-16808)*
Ribbon Printers Unlimited ....G.... 888 546-3310
Boynton Beach *(G-955)*
Rinaldi Printing Company ....E.... 813 569-0033
Tampa *(G-18058)*
Rmf Printing Technologies Inc ....G.... 716 683-7500
Miami *(G-10269)*
Roberts Quality Printing Inc ....E.... 727 442-4011
Clearwater *(G-1862)*
◆ Rodes Printing Corp ....G.... 305 559-5263
Miami *(G-10274)*
Rose Printing Co Inc ....G.... 850 339-8093
Tallahassee *(G-17317)*
Rrhill Printing Solutions Inc ....G.... 786 897-2432
Miami *(G-10285)*
Rush Flyers ....F.... 954 332-0509
Plantation *(G-14546)*
Rush To Excellence Prtg Inc ....G.... 904 367-0100
Jacksonville *(G-6740)*
Rxprinting and Graphics LLC ....G.... 407 965-3039
Orlando *(G-13150)*
▼ S Printing Inc ....G.... 305 633-3343
Miami *(G-10292)*
Salt 1 To 1 ....G.... 407 538-2134
Orlando *(G-13159)*
▼ Sameday Printing Inc ....G.... 800 411-3106
Miami *(G-10301)*
San Marco Place Condo Assn ....G.... 504 812-0352
Jacksonville *(G-6750)*
Sandow Specialty Printing Inc ....G.... 305 255-5697
Palmetto Bay *(G-13853)*
Sandy-Alexander Inc ....D.... 727 579-1527
Saint Petersburg *(G-15905)*
Sanibel Print & Graphics ....G.... 239 454-1001
Fort Myers *(G-4595)*
Saugus Valley Corp ....G.... 954 772-4077
Coral Springs *(G-2310)*
SBT River PIP Project ....E.... 919 469-5095
Orlando *(G-13166)*
Scott Brevard Inc ....G.... 386 698-1121
Crescent City *(G-2342)*
Screen Machines LLC ....G.... 386 527-1368
Port Orange *(G-15032)*
Seapress Inc ....G.... 941 366-8494
Sarasota *(G-16589)*
Securus Brot LLC ....G.... 954 532-8065
Miramar *(G-11041)*
Seminole Paper & Printing Co ....G.... 305 379-8481
Miami *(G-10322)*
Seminole Printing Inc ....G.... 305 823-7204
Hialeah *(G-5614)*
▼ Semprun & Morales Corporation ....F.... 305 698-2554
Hialeah *(G-5615)*
Serbin Printing Inc ....E.... 941 366-0755
Sarasota *(G-16593)*
Sergios Printing Inc ....F.... 305 971-4112
Miami *(G-10326)*
▼ Services On Demand Print Inc ....E.... 305 681-5345
Hallandale Beach *(G-5209)*
Shelbie Press Inc ....G.... 407 896-4600
Orlando *(G-13179)*
Shima Group Corp ....G.... 305 463-0288
Doral *(G-3502)*
Shiny Prints ....F.... 561 200-2872
Jupiter *(G-7112)*
Shoreline Print Group ....G.... 727 481-9358
Cape Coral *(G-1470)*
Shoreline Printing Company ....G.... 954 491-0311
Oakland Park *(G-11839)*

S I C

Short Stop Print Inc ....G.... 941 474-4313
Englewood (G-3683)
Signal Graphics Printing LLC ....G.... 303 837-1331
Punta Gorda (G-15234)
Signature Printing Inc ....F.... 305 828-9992
Miami Lakes (G-10857)
Signature Printing Technology ....G.... 407 963-6291
Altamonte Springs (G-74)
Sir Speedy Printing Center ....F.... 352 683-8758
Spring Hill (G-16863)
▲ Sirs Publishing Inc ....D.... 800 521-0600
Boca Raton (G-718)
SMC Diversified Services Inc ....G.... 863 698-9696
Lakeland (G-7793)
Sobe Express ....G.... 305 674-4454
Miami Beach (G-10712)
Sol Davis Printing Inc ....E.... 813 353-3609
Tampa (G-18114)
Solid Print Solutions Inc ....G.... 561 670-4391
Lake Worth Beach (G-7619)
◆ Solo Printing LLC ....C.... 305 594-8699
Miami (G-10372)
Sonshine Digital Graphics Inc ....F.... 904 858-1000
Jacksonville (G-6784)
SOs Services On Prtg Corp ....G.... 305 225-6000
Hialeah (G-5624)
Sosumi Holdings Inc ....E.... 239 634-3430
Naples (G-11407)
▼ South Broward Printing Inc ....G.... 954 962-1309
Hollywood (G-5912)
▼ South Florida Graphics Corp ....G.... 954 917-0606
Fort Lauderdale (G-4245)
South Florida Print ....G.... 561 807-8584
Deerfield Beach (G-2914)
Southeast Print Programs Inc ....E.... 813 885-3203
Tampa (G-18118)
▼ Southeastern Printing Co Inc ....C.... 772 287-2141
Hialeah (G-5628)
Southern Company Entp Inc ....E.... 904 879-2101
Callahan (G-1329)
Southern Imaging ....G.... 727 954-0133
Pinellas Park (G-14389)
Southern Litho II LLC ....E.... 724 394-3693
Naples (G-11409)
Southprint Corp ....G.... 813 237-8000
Tampa (G-18122)
Spanglish Advertising Cor ....G.... 305 244-0918
Miami (G-10395)
Specialty Screen Printing Inc ....G.... 561 758-4944
Jupiter (G-7120)
Spectrum Rugs & More LLC ....G.... 813 453-4242
Tampa (G-18123)
Speed Print One Inc ....G.... 305 374-5936
Miami (G-10403)
Spett Printing Co Inc ....G.... 561 241-9758
Boca Raton (G-727)
Spinnaker Holding Company ....E.... 561 392-8626
Boca Raton (G-728)
Spinnaker Vero Inc ....F.... 772 567-4645
Vero Beach (G-18667)
Spiritwear Today ....G.... 239 676-7384
Bonita Springs (G-856)
Spotlight Graphics Inc ....E.... 941 929-1500
Sarasota (G-16601)
Sprint Printing Company LLC ....G.... 239 947-2221
Bonita Springs (G-857)
Spyder Graphics Inc ....G.... 954 561-9725
Oakland Park (G-11842)
Stacy Lee Montgomery ....G.... 863 662-3163
Winter Haven (G-19358)
Steve Printer Inc ....G.... 941 375-8657
Venice (G-18577)
Steve Prints ....G.... 561 571-2903
Delray Beach (G-3146)
Steven Chancas ....F.... 352 629-5016
Ocala (G-12059)
Steven K Bakum Inc ....G.... 561 804-9110
West Palm Beach (G-19044)
Steven M Roessler LLC ....G.... 321 773-2300
Indian Harbour Beach (G-6068)
▲ Stewart-Hedrick Inc ....E.... 941 907-0090
Lakewood Ranch (G-7847)
Storterchilds Printing Co Inc ....E.... 352 376-2658
Gainesville (G-5001)
◆ Stuart Web Inc ....E.... 772 287-8022
Stuart (G-17027)
Stuart Web Inc ....G.... 772 287-8022
Stuart (G-17028)
Sun 3d Corporation ....G.... 954 210-6010
Pompano Beach (G-14876)
Sun Belt Graphics Inc ....F.... 954 424-3139
Davie (G-2597)
Sun Coast Media Group Inc ....D.... 941 206-1300
Port Charlotte (G-15000)
Sun Graphic Technologies Inc ....E.... 941 753-7541
Sarasota (G-16305)
Sun Print Management LLC ....E.... 727 945-0255
Holiday (G-5749)
Sun Screen Print Inc ....G.... 904 674-0520
Jacksonville (G-6821)
Sunbelt Dimensional Inc ....G.... 954 424-3139
Davie (G-2598)
Sunbelt Usa Inc ....G.... 239 353-5519
Naples (G-11421)
▲ Suniland Press Inc ....E.... 305 235-8811
Miami (G-10431)
Sunrise Printing & Signs ....G.... 321 284-3803
Kissimmee (G-7300)
▲ Sunshine Printing Inc ....F.... 561 478-2602
West Palm Beach (G-19050)
▼ Super Color Inc ....F.... 954 964-4656
Davie (G-2599)
Superior Signs and Prints ....G.... 954 780-6351
Pompano Beach (G-14880)
Supreme Printing Corp ....G.... 305 591-2916
Hialeah (G-5643)
Swift Print Service Inc ....G.... 239 458-2212
Cape Coral (G-1482)
T Beattie Enterprises ....F.... 407 679-2000
Winter Park (G-19450)
Tag & Label of Florida Inc ....G.... 305 255-1050
Miami (G-10457)
Tags & Labels Printing Inc ....E.... 954 455-2867
Hallandale Beach (G-5218)
Taie Inc ....F.... 954 966-0233
Hollywood (G-5920)
Tampa Bay Press Inc ....F.... 813 886-1415
Tampa (G-18161)
Tampa Printing Company ....E.... 813 612-7746
Tampa (G-18171)
▼ Tan Printing Inc ....G.... 954 986-9869
Hallandale Beach (G-5219)
Tara Biek Creative ....G.... 772 486-3684
Stuart (G-17033)
Target Graphics Inc ....F.... 941 365-8809
Sarasota (G-16615)
Target Print & Mail ....G.... 850 671-6600
Tallahassee (G-17338)
Tempo Fulfillment Inc ....G.... 727 914-0659
Pinellas Park (G-14391)
Th Custom Promo Tions ....G.... 407 704-7921
Orlando (G-13252)
Thalers Printing Center Inc ....G.... 954 741-6522
Lauderhill (G-8122)
Thomas Printworks ....G.... 305 667-4149
Fort Lauderdale (G-4281)
Thunderbird Press Inc ....F.... 321 269-7616
Titusville (G-18468)
Tiba Enterprises Inc ....G.... 561 575-3037
Jupiter (G-7128)
▼ Tiffany and Associates Inc ....E.... 386 252-7351
Daytona Beach (G-2727)
▼ Tiger Business Forms Inc ....E.... 305 888-3528
Hialeah (G-5649)
Time Printing Co Inc ....G.... 904 396-9967
Jacksonville (G-6856)
Tip Top Prtg of Volusia Cnty ....G.... 386 760-7701
Daytona Beach (G-2728)
Tko Print Solutions Inc ....E.... 954 315-0990
Pompano Beach (G-14887)
Tks Printing & Promo Products ....D.... 904 469-0968
Jacksonville (G-6860)
Toms Instant Printing Inc ....G.... 904 396-0686
Jacksonville (G-6861)
Tone Printing LLC ....G.... 855 505-8663
Miami (G-10489)
Top Drawer Inc ....F.... 305 620-1102
Miami Lakes (G-10869)
Top Drawer Printers Inc ....E.... 305 620-1102
Miami Lakes (G-10870)
▼ Topline Prtg & Graphics Inc ....E.... 561 881-2267
Riviera Beach (G-15385)
Total Print Inc ....G.... 772 589-9658
Sebastian (G-16673)
Totalprint USA ....G.... 855 915-1300
Tampa (G-18196)
Town Street Print Shop Inc ....G.... 850 432-8300
Gulf Breeze (G-5130)
Trend Offset Printing Svcs Inc ....D.... 562 598-2446
Jacksonville (G-6869)
Trese Inc ....F.... 321 632-7272
Rockledge (G-15454)
Tri County Printing Co In ....G.... 561 477-8487
Boca Raton (G-755)
Trial Spectrum Inc ....G.... 954 906-5743
Coral Springs (G-2324)
Tropical Prints Inc A Corp ....G.... 305 261-9926
Miami (G-10509)
TST Impreso Inc ....G.... 305 381-5153
Medley (G-8745)
Tucker Lithographic Co ....G.... 904 276-0568
Orange Park (G-12410)
Two B Printing Inc ....G.... 954 566-4886
Oakland Park (G-11851)
◆ Ultra Graphics Corp ....G.... 305 593-0202
Miami (G-10526)
Unik Design & Print Inc ....G.... 786 355-6877
Miami Lakes (G-10872)
Unique Designs Prof Svcs Inc ....F.... 407 296-6204
Orlando (G-13290)
Unique Ink Printing Corp ....G.... 954 829-2801
Boca Raton (G-767)
United Printing LLC ....G.... 954 554-7969
Pompano Beach (G-14901)
United Printing Sales Inc ....G.... 954 942-4300
Pompano Beach (G-14902)
United World Printing Inc ....G.... 407 738-0888
Orlando (G-13295)
Universal Graphics & Prtg Inc ....G.... 561 845-6404
North Palm Beach (G-11729)
▼ Universal Printing Company ....F.... 305 592-5387
Miami (G-10541)
Up2speed Printing Inc ....F.... 850 508-2620
Hialeah (G-5666)
Urbaprint LLC ....G.... 786 502-3223
Weston (G-19175)
V I P Printing ....G.... 386 258-3326
Daytona Beach (G-2730)
V P Press Inc ....F.... 954 581-7531
Fort Lauderdale (G-4301)
Van Charles Inc ....G.... 954 394-3242
Oakland Park (G-11857)
Venice Print Center ....G.... 941 206-1414
Venice (G-18586)
Verified Label & Print Inc ....F.... 813 290-7721
Tampa (G-18237)
Vero Beach Printing Inc ....G.... 772 562-4267
Vero Beach (G-18678)
Village Scribe Printing Co ....F.... 727 585-7388
Largo (G-8074)
Vinylot of Florida Inc ....G.... 954 978-8424
Margate (G-8571)
Vlp Prtg Night CLB Sups LLC ....G.... 561 603-2846
Boca Raton (G-780)
Vision Concepts Ink Inc ....F.... 305 463-8003
Doral (G-3542)
▼ Vista Color Corporation ....D.... 305 635-2000
Doral (G-3544)
Vital Graphics and Signs Inc ....G.... 305 557-8181
Hialeah (G-5681)
Vital Printing Corporation ....F.... 561 659-2367
Lake Worth Beach (G-7623)
Vmak Corp ....F.... 407 260-1199
Longwood (G-8348)
Volusia Printing LLC ....G.... 386 873-7442
Deland (G-3030)
Vowells Downtown Inc ....G.... 850 432-5175
Pensacola (G-14285)
W D H Enterprises Inc ....G.... 941 758-6500
Bradenton (G-1143)
W H L Business Communications ....G.... 561 361-9202
Boca Raton (G-784)
▼ Walter Haas Graphics Inc ....E.... 305 883-2257
Hialeah (G-5685)
▲ Wayloo Inc ....G.... 954 914-3192
Fort Lauderdale (G-4317)
We Print Flyers and Shirts ....G.... 407 902-7128
Orlando (G-13320)
Web Offset Printing Co Inc ....D.... 727 572-7488
Clearwater (G-1937)
Webb-Mason Inc ....G.... 727 531-1112
Largo (G-8079)
Wecando Print LLC ....F.... 754 222-9144
Deerfield Beach (G-2935)
Weidenhamer Corporation ....G.... 850 837-3190
Destin (G-3211)
Wells Legal Supply Inc ....E.... 904 399-1510
Jacksonville (G-6909)
Wild Prints LLC ....G.... 561 800-6536
West Palm Beach (G-19087)

Will-Rite Industries Inc G 305 253-1985
Cutler Bay *(G-2421)*

William Burns G 877 462-5872
Lakeland *(G-7835)*

Willy Walt Inc G 727 209-2872
Saint Petersburg *(G-15962)*

Wilson Printing USA LLC G 727 536-4173
Clearwater *(G-1941)*

Winwood Print G 786 615-3188
Miami *(G-10613)*

WJS Printing Partners Inc G 904 731-0357
Jacksonville *(G-6925)*

Woods Printing of Ocala Inc G 352 629-1665
Ocala *(G-12077)*

Wright Printery Inc G 386 252-6571
Daytona Beach *(G-2733)*

Write Stuff Enterprises LLC E 954 462-6657
Fort Lauderdale *(G-4329)*

▼ Xperient LLC G 407 265-8000
Longwood *(G-8353)*

Xymoprint LLC F 407 504-2170
Orlando *(G-13336)*

Your Name Printing G 813 621-2400
Tampa *(G-18277)*

2754 Commercial Printing: Gravure

A-Plus Prtg & Graphic Ctr Inc E 954 327-7315
Plantation *(G-14481)*

▲ Amtec Sales Inc F 800 994-3318
Miami *(G-9153)*

Brut Printing Co Inc E 904 354-5055
Jacksonville *(G-6241)*

Business Card Ex Tampa Bay Inc D 727 535-7768
Clearwater *(G-1618)*

Collier Business Systems G 239 649-5554
Naples *(G-11215)*

Collins Media & Advg LLC F 954 688-9758
Margate *(G-8538)*

▲ Datamax International Corp B 407 578-8007
Orlando *(G-12651)*

◆ Datamax-Oneil Corporation C 800 816-9649
Orlando *(G-12652)*

DK Events LLC G 305 760-2963
Miami *(G-9473)*

Dongili Investment Group Inc F 941 927-3003
Sarasota *(G-16413)*

Ef Enterprises of North Fla G 904 739-5995
Jacksonville *(G-6356)*

Eti-Label Inc G 305 716-0094
Miami *(G-9538)*

Kreative Drive Inc G 786 845-8605
Doral *(G-3413)*

Miami Engrv Co-Oxford Prtg Co G 305 371-9595
Miami *(G-9999)*

Reprographic Services Inc F 305 859-8282
Miami *(G-10255)*

Restifo Investments LLC F 305 468-0013
Doral *(G-3484)*

◆ Screen Graphics Florida Inc E 800 346-4420
Pompano Beach *(G-14842)*

▲ Starlock Inc G 305 477-2303
Doral *(G-3511)*

Sun Coast Paper & Envelope Inc E 727 545-9566
Largo *(G-8062)*

Tone Printing LLC G 855 505-8663
Miami *(G-10489)*

Unlimited Inpressions Inc G 305 606-2699
Miami *(G-10546)*

Wells Legal Supply Inc E 904 399-1510
Jacksonville *(G-6909)*

2759 Commercial Printing

4 Over LLC F 818 246-1170
Miami *(G-9027)*

850 Screen Printing LLC G 850 549-7861
Pensacola *(G-14074)*

▼ A Bar Code Business Inc G 352 750-0077
The Villages *(G-18388)*

A D Coaches Corner Inc G 786 242-2229
Miami *(G-9036)*

▲ A New World Production E 321 636-6886
Cocoa *(G-1989)*

A Z Printing Delray F 561 330-4154
Delray Beach *(G-3037)*

Aacecorp Inc G 904 353-7878
Jacksonville *(G-6115)*

Abby Press Inc E 407 847-5565
Kissimmee *(G-7216)*

ABC Imaging of Washington F 954 759-2037
Fort Lauderdale *(G-3775)*

Abeka Print Shop Inc E 850 478-8496
Pensacola *(G-14076)*

Above LLC F 850 469-9028
Pensacola *(G-14077)*

▼ Absolute Graphics Inc F 954 792-3488
Davie *(G-2486)*

Academic Publication Svcs Inc G 941 925-4474
Sarasota *(G-16332)*

Academy Publishing Inc E 407 736-0100
Orlando *(G-12427)*

Accuprint My Print Shop G 954 973-9369
Deerfield Beach *(G-2763)*

▼ Acm Screen Printing Inc G 305 547-1552
Miami *(G-9064)*

Admiral Printing Inc G 727 938-9589
Holiday *(G-5732)*

▲ Advanced Cmmncations Holdg Inc D 954 753-0100
Coral Springs *(G-2213)*

Advanced Screen Printing & EMB G 863 648-1268
Lakeland *(G-7628)*

Advanced Xrgrphics Imging Syst E 407 351-0232
Orlando *(G-12434)*

Advantage Prtg Lmnting Fla Inc G 904 737-1613
Jacksonville *(G-6124)*

Adver-T Screen Printing Inc F 727 443-5525
Clearwater *(G-1567)*

Agility Press Inc F 904 731-8989
Jacksonville *(G-6128)*

All Florida Engraving G 352 213-4572
Hawthorne *(G-5243)*

All Pro Ink G 305 252-7644
Cutler Bay *(G-2385)*

All Purpose Prtg Graphics Inc F 904 346-0999
Jacksonville *(G-6135)*

All Star Graphix Inc G 954 772-1972
Oakland Park *(G-11775)*

All-Star Sales Inc E 904 396-1653
Jacksonville *(G-6137)*

▲ Allgeo & Yerkes Entps Inc F 321 255-9030
Melbourne *(G-8764)*

Allied Decals Fla Inc G 800 940-2233
Fort Lauderdale *(G-3800)*

▼ Allied Decals-Fla Inc F 800 940-2233
Fort Lauderdale *(G-3801)*

▲ Allied General Engrv & Plas F 305 626-6585
Opa Locka *(G-12286)*

Aloha Screen Printing Inc G 850 934-4716
Gulf Breeze *(G-5111)*

Alpha Card Compact Media LLC G 407 698-3592
Winter Park *(G-19375)*

▲ Altira Inc D 305 687-8074
Miami *(G-9124)*

Amelia Island Graphics G 904 261-0740
Fernandina Beach *(G-3731)*

American Business Cards Inc E 314 739-0800
Naples *(G-11161)*

▲ American Mentality Inc G 407 599-7255
Longwood *(G-8254)*

American Reprographics Co LLC G 813 286-8300
Tampa *(G-17419)*

American Screen Print Inc G 904 443-0071
Jacksonville *(G-6149)*

◆ Ampersand Graphics Inc E 772 283-1359
Stuart *(G-16906)*

▼ Ampersand Shirt Shack F 772 600-8743
Stuart *(G-16907)*

▲ Amtec Sales Inc F 800 994-3318
Miami *(G-9153)*

Anchor Screen Printing LLC G 850 243-4200
Fort Walton Beach *(G-4775)*

and Tees LLC G 904 745-0773
Jacksonville *(G-6154)*

Apis Cor Inc F 347 404-1481
Melbourne *(G-8769)*

Apparel Printers G 352 463-8850
Alachua *(G-4)*

APS Promotional Solutions Inc F 904 721-4977
Jacksonville *(G-6161)*

Arj Art Inc G 727 535-8633
Saint Petersburg *(G-15710)*

Art of Printing Inc G 561 640-7344
West Palm Beach *(G-18803)*

Art Printing Miami G 786 581-9889
Miami *(G-9171)*

Artworks Printing Enterprises G 954 893-7984
Hollywood *(G-5775)*

ASAP Screen Printing Inc G 352 505-7574
Gainesville *(G-4877)*

Atticus Screen Printing T G 407 365-9911
Oviedo *(G-13415)*

Automated Services Inc F 772 461-3388
Fort Pierce *(G-4679)*

Aw Publishing F 305 856-7000
Miami *(G-9201)*

B R Q Grossmans Inc F 954 971-1077
Pompano Beach *(G-14609)*

Bam Enterprises Inc E 850 469-8872
Pensacola *(G-14096)*

Baptist Mid-Missions Inc F 863 382-6350
Sebring *(G-16682)*

Barjo Printing and Sign G 786 332-2661
Medley *(G-8620)*

Bayshore Brand Group Inc G 813 384-8275
Tampa *(G-17459)*

Beach Embroidery & Screen Ptg G 386 478-3931
New Smyrna Beach *(G-11528)*

▲ Benner China and Glwr of Fla E 904 733-4620
Jacksonville *(G-6205)*

Bills Prestige Printing Inc G 352 589-5833
Eustis *(G-3703)*

Bl Brandhouse LLC G 305 600-7181
Doral *(G-3277)*

Blue Ribbon Tag & Label of PR F 787 858-5300
Hollywood *(G-5789)*

Boostan Inc G 305 223-5981
Miami *(G-9267)*

Breast Thermgrphy of BRWrd&plm G 561 852-5789
Boca Raton *(G-463)*

Bros Williams Printing G 305 769-9925
Hialeah *(G-5331)*

Bros Williams Printing Inc G 305 769-9925
Hialeah *(G-5332)*

Buddy Bridge Inc E 941 488-0799
Nokomis *(G-11578)*

Business Card Ex Tampa Bay Inc D 727 535-7768
Clearwater *(G-1618)*

CAM Broc Sports Inc G 407 933-6524
Kissimmee *(G-7229)*

◆ Capsmith Inc E 407 328-7660
Sanford *(G-16007)*

Captains Custom Tees Inc G 239 424-8206
Lakewood Ranch *(G-7842)*

Caribongo G 727 944-5200
Tarpon Springs *(G-18286)*

◆ Carpe Diem Sales & Mktg Inc E 407 682-1400
Orlando *(G-12552)*

CC Sportswear Inc G 941 351-4205
Sarasota *(G-16188)*

Charitees LLC G 561 542-4616
Hollywood *(G-5798)*

Classic Screen Prtg Design Inc G 407 850-0112
Orlando *(G-12588)*

◆ Classic Shirts Inc F 850 875-2200
Quincy *(G-15247)*

Clear Choice Inc G 407 830-6968
Altamonte Springs *(G-37)*

Clothing Warehouse G 904 354-9002
Jacksonville *(G-6271)*

Coastal Imprinting G 321 543-4169
Melbourne *(G-8793)*

▼ Commercial Printers Inc D 954 781-3737
Fort Lauderdale *(G-3911)*

Comptech Global Solutions Inc G 941 766-8100
Port Charlotte *(G-14972)*

Concept Design and Printing G 813 516-9798
Tampa *(G-17551)*

Copy Systems Business Center G 850 650-0886
Santa Rosa Beach *(G-16156)*

Cor Label LLC G 407 402-6633
Debary *(G-2746)*

▼ Coral Club Tee Shirts Inc G 305 828-6939
Hialeah *(G-5354)*

Core Label LLC E 772 287-2141
Palm City *(G-13649)*

Corporate Printing & Advg Inc F 305 273-6000
Miami *(G-9405)*

Cotton Pickin Shirts Plus G 850 435-3133
Pensacola *(G-14120)*

Couchman Printing Company G 386 756-3052
South Daytona *(G-16800)*

Country Side T-Shirt G 352 372-1015
Gainesville *(G-4899)*

County of Broward G 954 357-7120
Fort Lauderdale *(G-3919)*

▲ Cover Publishing G 239 482-4814
Fort Myers *(G-4412)*

Crain Ventures Inc G 407 933-1820
Kissimmee *(G-7233)*

Creaprint Usa Corp G 786 369-7398
Miami *(G-9410)*

Creative Promotional Products ....G 407 383-7114
Orlando *(G-12626)*
Creative Prtg Grphic Dsign Inc ....E 407 855-0202
Orlando *(G-12627)*
Csmc Inc ....E 407 246-1567
Orlando *(G-12630)*
Cubco Inc ....F 386 254-2706
Daytona Beach *(G-2650)*
Custom Graphics Inc ....G 954 563-6756
Deerfield Beach *(G-2808)*
▲ D G Morrison Inc ....F 813 865-0208
Odessa *(G-12114)*
DAccord Shirts & Guayaberas ....G 305 576-0926
Miami *(G-9428)*
Dahlquist Enterprises Inc ....G 407 896-2294
Orlando *(G-12644)*
Dandy Media Corporation ....F 954 616-6800
Plantation *(G-14508)*
Dannys Prtg Svc Sups & Eqp Inc ....G 305 757-2282
Miami *(G-9435)*
◆ David Dobbs Enterprises Inc ....D 904 824-6171
Saint Augustine *(G-15533)*
Davie Embroidme ....F 954 452-0600
Davie *(G-2515)*
Davis Franklin Printing Co ....G 813 259-2500
Tampa *(G-17592)*
DC Apparel Inc ....G 863 325-9273
Winter Haven *(G-19317)*
Deluna Toole LLC ....G 850 435-4063
Pensacola *(G-14128)*
▼ Designated Sports Inc ....F 904 797-9469
Saint Augustine *(G-15537)*
Designers Press Inc ....D 407 843-3141
Orlando *(G-12664)*
Designers Top Shop Inc ....G 863 453-3855
Avon Park *(G-285)*
Dillco Inc ....F 386 734-7510
Deland *(G-2971)*
DNE Pot Sbob Inc ....F 239 936-8880
Fort Myers *(G-4434)*
Dobbs & Brodeur Bookbinders ....G 305 885-5215
Hialeah *(G-5376)*
Don and Kathy Kesler ....G 305 793-9216
Miami *(G-9477)*
Dongili Investment Group Inc ....F 941 927-3003
Sarasota *(G-16413)*
Dorado Graphix LLC ....G 904 751-4500
Jacksonville *(G-6325)*
Doral Dgtal Reprographics Corp ....G 305 704-3194
Doral *(G-3333)*
Double H Enterprises Inc ....G 972 562-8588
Ormond Beach *(G-13364)*
Douglass Screen Printers Inc ....E 863 687-8545
Lakeland *(G-7677)*
Dragonfly Graphics ....G 772 879-9800
Port Saint Lucie *(G-15103)*
Dragonfly Graphics Inc ....G 352 375-2144
Gainesville *(G-4910)*
Drewlu Enterprises Inc ....G 407 478-7872
Winter Park *(G-19405)*
Drip Communication LLC ....F 407 730-5519
Orlando *(G-12685)*
Durra Print Inc ....E 850 222-4768
Tallahassee *(G-17244)*
Durra Quick Print Inc ....G 850 681-2900
Tallahassee *(G-17245)*
Dxm Marketing Group LLC ....F 904 332-6490
Jacksonville *(G-6342)*
Dynamic Color Inc ....G 954 462-0261
Pompano Beach *(G-14669)*
E&P Solutions and Services Inc ....G 305 715-9545
Miami *(G-9491)*
Easy Rent Inc ....G 904 443-7446
Jacksonville *(G-6351)*
Ef Enterprises of North Fla ....G 904 739-5995
Jacksonville *(G-6356)*
Elite Printing & Marketing Inc ....G 850 474-0894
Pensacola *(G-14139)*
Elton Foil Embossing Inc ....G 904 399-1510
Jacksonville *(G-6359)*
Embroidery Solutions Inc ....G 407 438-8188
Orlando *(G-12708)*
Engead Gb Design & Prtg Inc ....G 954 783-5161
Pompano Beach *(G-14680)*
Envision Graphics Inc ....E 305 470-0083
Miami *(G-9530)*
Epic Promos LLC ....F 561 479-8055
Boca Raton *(G-519)*
ESP Printing ....G 386 263-2949
Bunnell *(G-1300)*
Evolutionary Screen Printing L ....G 863 248-2692
Lakeland *(G-7682)*
◆ Executive Label Inc ....F 954 978-6983
Margate *(G-8543)*
Express Printing Center Inc ....F 813 909-1085
Land O Lakes *(G-7854)*
◆ Fassi Equipment Inc ....G 954 385-6555
Weston *(G-19123)*
Fassidigitalcom Inc ....F 954 385-6555
Weston *(G-19124)*
Fast Labels ....G 904 626-0508
Jacksonville *(G-6379)*
▼ Fdc Print LLC ....D 305 885-8707
Hialeah *(G-5409)*
FGA Printing ....G 954 763-1122
Pompano Beach *(G-14689)*
Fidelity Printing Corporation ....D 727 522-9557
Saint Petersburg *(G-15778)*
First Coast Tee Shirt Co Inc ....G 904 737-1985
Jacksonville *(G-6387)*
Five Star Sports Tickets ....F 440 899-2000
Hallandale Beach *(G-5187)*
Fla Property Holdings Inc ....E 813 888-8796
Miami Lakes *(G-10790)*
Florida Flexible ....G 305 512-2222
Hialeah *(G-5413)*
Florida Graphic Printing Inc ....F 386 253-4532
Daytona Beach *(G-2666)*
Florida Screen Services Inc ....F 407 316-0466
Orlando *(G-12755)*
Florida Sncast Trism Prmotions ....F 727 544-1212
Largo *(G-7951)*
Florida Tape & Labels Inc ....F 941 921-5788
Sarasota *(G-16438)*
Fluid Designs Inc ....G 904 737-1557
Jacksonville *(G-6408)*
Four G Enterprises Inc ....E 407 834-4143
Longwood *(G-8284)*
Friends Professional Sty ....G 561 734-4660
Boynton Beach *(G-908)*
Fritz Commercial Printing Inc ....G 561 585-6869
West Palm Beach *(G-18884)*
Full Press Apparel Inc ....F 850 222-1003
Tallahassee *(G-17259)*
Futch Printing & Mailing Inc ....F 904 388-3995
Jacksonville *(G-6418)*
G S Printers Inc ....G 305 931-2755
Fort Lauderdale *(G-4016)*
Gabrielas Memoirs Inc ....G 305 666-9991
Miami *(G-9608)*
Gadsden County Times Inc ....F 850 627-7649
Quincy *(G-15250)*
Gandy Printers Inc ....F 850 222-5847
Tallahassee *(G-17260)*
Garment Gear Inc ....F 850 215-2121
Panama City *(G-13907)*
Gatlin Group LLC ....G 850 941-0959
Pensacola *(G-14160)*
Genuine Ad Inc ....G 786 399-6484
Sunny Isles Beach *(G-17077)*
Gift Giving Creations Corp ....G 786 239-0229
Hialeah *(G-5430)*
Go 2 Print Now Inc ....E 800 500-4276
Saint Petersburg *(G-15794)*
Good Catch Inc ....G 305 757-7700
Miami *(G-9648)*
Grace Bible Church ....G 850 623-4671
Milton *(G-10930)*
Grafx By Caz (fort Pierce) ....G 772 284-9258
Fort Pierce *(G-4702)*
Granada Prtg & Graphics Corp ....F 305 593-5266
Miami *(G-9655)*
Grand Cypress Group Inc ....G 407 622-1993
Maitland *(G-8467)*
▲ Graphic and Printing Svcs Corp ....G 954 486-8868
Tamarac *(G-17357)*
Graphic Printing Corp ....E 561 994-3586
Boca Raton *(G-551)*
▼ Graphics Type Color Entps Inc ....E 305 591-7600
Miami *(G-9658)*
Graphix Screen Printing ....G 727 937-6147
Tarpon Springs *(G-18303)*
Graphix Solutions of America ....F 727 898-6744
Parrish *(G-14006)*
Great Atlantic Outfitters ....G 904 722-0196
Jacksonville *(G-6445)*
Greater 7th Digital Press Inc ....G 305 681-2412
Miami *(G-9662)*
Greentex America LLC ....F 305 908-8580
Hallandale Beach *(G-5189)*
Greg Allens Inc ....E 904 262-8912
Jacksonville *(G-6450)*
Gulf Breeze Apparel LLC ....G 941 488-8337
Venice *(G-18551)*
Gulf Coast Printing ....E 239 482-5555
Fort Myers *(G-4477)*
H & H Printing Inc ....F 407 422-2932
Orlando *(G-12792)*
◆ Halifax Plastic Inc ....F 386 252-2442
Daytona Beach *(G-2672)*
▼ Happy Endings of Miami Inc ....G 305 759-4467
Miami *(G-9686)*
Harvest Print & Bus Svcs Inc ....F 850 681-2488
Tallahassee *(G-17275)*
Harvey Branker and Assoc PA ....F 954 966-4445
Hollywood *(G-5835)*
Herald-Advocate Publishing Co ....F 863 773-3255
Wauchula *(G-18693)*
Hernandez Printing Service ....F 305 642-0483
Miami *(G-9705)*
Hes Products Inc ....G 407 834-0741
Ormond Beach *(G-13376)*
Hey Day ....G 305 763-8660
Miami Beach *(G-10677)*
Hilcraft Engraving Inc ....G 305 871-6100
Miami *(G-9711)*
◆ Hit Promotional Products Inc ....B 727 541-5561
Largo *(G-7971)*
Hitking Sports LLC ....G 941 661-2753
Treasure Island *(G-18475)*
Hitmaster Graphics LLC ....F 813 250-0555
Tampa *(G-17757)*
Holmes Stamp Company ....E 904 396-2291
Jacksonville *(G-6476)*
Hot Action Sportswear Inc ....E 386 677-5680
Ormond Beach *(G-13377)*
Howies Instant Printing Inc ....F 561 686-8699
West Palm Beach *(G-18898)*
Hunted Tees LLC ....G 407 260-2138
Altamonte Springs *(G-50)*
Hunter Green Group Inc ....G 954 753-9914
Coral Springs *(G-2257)*
I P Team Inc ....E 772 398-4664
Stuart *(G-16956)*
ICM Printing Co Inc ....F 352 377-7468
Gainesville *(G-4940)*
Image Depot ....G 813 685-7116
Tampa *(G-17772)*
Image Graphics 2000 Inc ....G 954 332-3380
Pompano Beach *(G-14728)*
Impact Design Group Inc ....F 904 636-8989
Jacksonville *(G-6490)*
Impress Ink LLC ....F 407 982-5646
Orlando *(G-12825)*
Impressions of Miami Inc ....G 305 666-0277
Miami *(G-9735)*
▲ Imprint Promotions LLC ....G 321 622-8946
Melbourne *(G-8850)*
Industrial Marking Svcs Inc ....G 727 541-7622
Largo *(G-7979)*
▼ Inflatable Design Works Corp ....F 786 242-1049
Miami *(G-9742)*
Ink Trax Inc ....F 850 235-4849
Panama City *(G-13917)*
Instant Printing Services Inc ....F 727 546-8036
Floral City *(G-3768)*
▲ International Prtg Ad Spc Inc ....E 772 398-4664
Stuart *(G-16959)*
Island The Reporter Inc ....G 727 631-4730
Saint Petersburg *(G-15818)*
J J M Services Inc ....G 954 437-1880
Miramar *(G-11007)*
James Hines Printing ....G 904 398-5110
Jacksonville *(G-6515)*
Jdjsis Inc ....G 561 732-2388
West Palm Beach *(G-18911)*
Jet Set Printing Inc ....G 407 339-1900
Casselberry *(G-1508)*
JMS Designs of Florida Inc ....G 954 572-6100
Sunrise *(G-17138)*
Joni Industries Inc ....F 352 799-5456
Brooksville *(G-1240)*
Jose Polanco ....G 305 631-1784
Miami *(G-9804)*
▼ Jrg Systems Inc ....F 954 962-1020
Fort Lauderdale *(G-4081)*
Keithco Inc ....G 352 351-4741
Ocala *(G-11976)*
Kenny-Ts Inc ....F 850 575-6644
Tallahassee *(G-17288)*

Kights Printing & Office Pdts ... G ... 904 731-7990
Jacksonville *(G-6537)*
Kikisteescom LLC ... G ... 954 314-7147
Weston *(G-19146)*
King Printing & Graphics Inc ... G ... 813 681-5060
Brandon *(G-1164)*
Kj Reynolds Inc ... G ... 904 829-6488
Saint Augustine *(G-15564)*
Knopf & Sons Bindery Inc ... F ... 904 355-4411
Jacksonville *(G-6543)*
Koala Tee Inc (usa) ... E ... 941 954-7700
Sarasota *(G-16483)*
Kover Corp ... G ... 305 888-0146
Doral *(G-3411)*
L & N Label Company Inc ... E ... 727 442-5400
Clearwater *(G-1755)*
Label Graphics Inc ... G ... 561 798-8180
Lake Worth *(G-7563)*
▲ Lauderdale Graphics Corp ... E ... 954 450-0800
Davie *(G-2544)*
Leda Printing Inc ... E ... 941 922-1563
Sarasota *(G-16487)*
Ledger ... B ... 863 802-7000
Lakeland *(G-7733)*
Legacy Sports Inc ... E ... 352 732-6759
Ocala *(G-11981)*
Leonard-Martin Corporation ... G ... 850 434-2203
Pensacola *(G-14192)*
Lifestyle Printworks Inc ... G ... 321 604-1531
Titusville *(G-18442)*
Light Source Business Systems ... F ... 772 562-5046
Port Saint Lucie *(G-15120)*
Limited Designs LLC ... G ... 305 547-9909
Miami *(G-9894)*
Logos Promote Inc ... G ... 407 447-5646
Orlando *(G-12935)*
Looper Sports Connection Inc ... G ... 352 796-7974
Brooksville *(G-1247)*
▲ Lowe Gear Printing ... G ... 866 714-9965
Lutz *(G-8396)*
Lrp Conferences LLC ... E ... 215 784-0860
Palm Beach Gardens *(G-13607)*
Lucky Dog Screen Printing Mg ... G ... 407 629-8838
Winter Park *(G-19420)*
Lujotex LLC ... G ... 954 322-1001
Miramar *(G-11011)*
M&M Studios Inc ... G ... 561 744-2754
Jupiter *(G-7070)*
Mango Publications ... G ... 863 583-4773
Lakeland *(G-7743)*
Marco Polo Publications Inc ... G ... 866 610-9441
Saint Petersburg *(G-15846)*
Mark Wsser Graphic Productions ... G ... 305 888-7445
Boynton Beach *(G-932)*
Marlin Graphics Inc ... G ... 561 743-5220
Jupiter *(G-7074)*
Maxigraphics Inc ... F ... 954 978-0740
Pompano Beach *(G-14755)*
Media Works Inc ... F ... 904 398-5518
Jacksonville *(G-6588)*
Meektees LLC ... G ... 786 424-8491
Miami *(G-9970)*
Mendez Brothers LLC ... F ... 305 685-3490
Opa Locka *(G-12338)*
▼ Merchspin Inc ... E ... 877 306-3651
Orlando *(G-12960)*
Metropolis Graphics Inc ... G ... 407 740-5455
Winter Park *(G-19424)*
Miami Engrv Co-Oxford Prtg Co ... G ... 305 371-9595
Miami *(G-9999)*
Miami Epic Tees Corp ... G ... 305 224-3465
Hialeah *(G-5509)*
Miami Quality Graphics Inc ... E ... 305 634-9506
Miami *(G-10007)*
▼ Miami Screenprint Supply ... G ... 305 622-7532
Miami Lakes *(G-10819)*
▲ Miami Tees Inc ... D ... 305 623-3908
Miami Lakes *(G-10820)*
Microcomputer Services ... G ... 561 988-7000
Boca Raton *(G-623)*
Mid State Screen Graphics LLC ... E ... 727 573-2299
Clearwater *(G-1786)*
Mightees LLC ... G ... 201 450-7470
Fort Myers *(G-4534)*
Miller Creative Graphics ... G ... 904 771-5855
Jacksonville *(G-6607)*
Minuteman Press ... F ... 386 255-2767
Daytona Beach *(G-2688)*
▲ Mlxl Productions Inx ... G ... 904 350-0048
Jacksonville *(G-6610)*

Mojowax Media Inc ... G ... 805 550-6013
Bradenton *(G-1080)*
Morning Star Personalized AP ... G ... 772 569-8412
Vero Beach *(G-18644)*
Morris Visitor Publications ... F ... 407 423-0618
Orlando *(G-12981)*
Naylor LLC ... C ... 800 369-6220
Gainesville *(G-4969)*
New Image Printing Promotion ... G ... 904 240-1516
Jacksonville *(G-6627)*
Newbeauty Media Group LLC ... E ... 561 961-7600
Boca Raton *(G-643)*
Newspaper Printing Company ... G ... 727 572-7488
Clearwater *(G-1808)*
Nis Print Inc ... E ... 407 423-7575
Orlando *(G-13004)*
Note It ... G ... 954 593-8616
Hollywood *(G-5884)*
Notice That Tee Inc ... G ... 954 971-1018
Pompano Beach *(G-14775)*
Ocean Blue Graphics Inc ... G ... 561 881-2022
Riviera Beach *(G-15355)*
▼ Ocean Blue Graphics Design Inc ... G ... 561 881-2022
Riviera Beach *(G-15356)*
Onsight Industries ... G ... 407 830-8861
Tampa *(G-17957)*
Outdoor America Images Inc ... E ... 813 888-8796
Miami Lakes *(G-10833)*
Pad Printing Technology Corp ... G ... 941 739-8667
Bradenton *(G-1091)*
◆ Palmas Printing Inc ... E ... 321 984-4451
Melbourne *(G-8904)*
Paris Ink Inc ... G ... 561 990-1194
Boca Raton *(G-663)*
Pasa Services Inc ... E ... 305 594-8662
Opa Locka *(G-12350)*
Passion Labels & Packaging ... E ... 941 312-5003
Sarasota *(G-16272)*
Pathfinder Shirts ... G ... 407 865-6530
Altamonte Springs *(G-62)*
Paul Wales Inc ... F ... 352 371-2120
Gainesville *(G-4979)*
◆ Pfaffco Inc ... F ... 305 635-0986
Miami Lakes *(G-10837)*
PHI CHI Foundation Inc ... G ... 561 526-3401
Margate *(G-8560)*
Picasso Embroidery Systems ... F ... 305 827-9666
Hialeah *(G-5558)*
Pioneer Announcements Inc ... F ... 305 573-7000
Miami *(G-10166)*
Platecrafters Corporation ... F ... 215 997-1990
Longwood *(G-8326)*
Pod Crane Services and Rentals ... G ... 805 291-2675
Miami *(G-10172)*
Poms Enterprises Inc ... G ... 954 358-1359
Margate *(G-8562)*
Positive Screenprint ... G ... 904 381-0963
Jacksonville *(G-6679)*
Power Point Graphics Inc ... G ... 561 351-5599
Boca Raton *(G-670)*
▲ Premier Parties Entertainment ... E ... 352 375-6122
Gainesville *(G-4983)*
Premier Tees ... G ... 941 681-2688
Englewood *(G-3664)*
Print Art Screen Printing Inc ... F ... 386 258-5186
Daytona Beach *(G-2698)*
Print Idea Center LLC ... G ... 954 682-6369
Riviera Beach *(G-15367)*
Print Mart Inc ... G ... 727 796-0064
Dunedin *(G-3587)*
Print Shack ... G ... 352 799-2972
Brooksville *(G-1262)*
Print Shop of Chiefland Inc ... G ... 352 493-0322
Chiefland *(G-1537)*
Printec Inc ... G ... 813 854-1075
Oldsmar *(G-12263)*
▼ Printers Printer Inc ... F ... 954 917-2773
Pompano Beach *(G-14814)*
Printex Worldwide Inc ... G ... 954 518-0722
Hallandale *(G-5161)*
Printhouseusacom Inc ... G ... 305 231-0202
Hialeah *(G-5574)*
Printing Mart Inc South Fla ... F ... 954 753-0323
Pompano Beach *(G-14817)*
Printing Services Plus LLC ... F ... 813 279-1903
Tampa *(G-18016)*
Printnovations Inc ... G ... 305 322-4041
Hallandale Beach *(G-5204)*
Pro Art America Inc ... G ... 863 385-4242
Sebring *(G-16704)*

Procorp LLC ... G ... 904 477-6762
Jacksonville *(G-6690)*
Productive Products Inc ... G ... 904 570-5553
Saint Augustine *(G-15591)*
Prographix Inc ... G ... 863 298-8081
Winter Haven *(G-19349)*
▼ Prolabel Inc ... F ... 305 620-2202
Hialeah *(G-5579)*
Promotional Mktg Online LLC ... G ... 941 347-8564
Punta Gorda *(G-15222)*
Proud Tshirts Corp ... G ... 305 769-3300
Miami *(G-10212)*
Put Your Name On It LLC ... G ... 813 972-1460
Tampa *(G-18026)*
Ragz ... G ... 850 656-1223
Tallahassee *(G-17313)*
Ranger Associates Inc ... G ... 407 869-0024
Longwood *(G-8329)*
Rapid Rater Company ... E ... 850 893-7346
Tallahassee *(G-17314)*
Ray Graphics Inc ... E ... 863 325-0911
Winter Haven *(G-19352)*
Real Thread Inc ... E ... 407 679-3895
Orlando *(G-13119)*
Recreational Screen Printing ... G ... 561 757-5479
Boca Raton *(G-685)*
Red 7 Tees LLC ... G ... 305 793-1440
Crestview *(G-2356)*
▼ Red Hot Trends Inc ... G ... 305 888-6951
Medley *(G-8716)*
Reporgraphics Unlimited Inc ... G ... 386 253-7990
Daytona Beach *(G-2703)*
Reprographic Solutions Inc ... G ... 772 340-3430
Port Saint Lucie *(G-15137)*
▼ Rex Three Inc ... C ... 954 452-8301
Davie *(G-2585)*
Rinaldi Printing Company ... E ... 813 569-0033
Tampa *(G-18058)*
Rinehart Corp ... G ... 850 271-5600
Lynn Haven *(G-8437)*
RMR Distributors Inc ... E ... 813 908-1141
Tampa *(G-18062)*
Roberts Quality Printing Inc ... E ... 727 442-4011
Clearwater *(G-1862)*
Royal Identity Incorporated ... G ... 813 405-4940
Brandon *(G-1176)*
Safari Sun LLC ... E ... 407 339-7291
Altamonte Springs *(G-71)*
Safeprints LLC ... G ... 305 960-7391
Miami *(G-10296)*
Schimmbros Inc ... G ... 407 796-8361
Kissimmee *(G-7296)*
◆ Schooner Prints Inc ... D ... 727 397-8572
Largo *(G-8045)*
Scp Commercial Printing ... G ... 561 998-0870
Boca Raton *(G-703)*
Screen Art Posters Inc ... E ... 305 681-4641
Hialeah *(G-5612)*
◆ Screen Graphics Florida Inc ... E ... 800 346-4420
Pompano Beach *(G-14842)*
Screen Monkey Corp ... G ... 352 746-7091
Homosassa *(G-6005)*
Screen Process Printers Inc ... G ... 904 354-8708
Jacksonville *(G-6757)*
Screen Tech ... G ... 321 536-6091
Merritt Island *(G-9008)*
Seabreeze Publication Centl FL ... G ... 561 741-7770
Jupiter *(G-7110)*
▼ Seaside Graphics Inc ... G ... 954 782-7151
Pompano Beach *(G-14846)*
Seattle Engraving Center LLC ... G ... 206 420-4604
Brandon *(G-1178)*
Sef Americas LLC ... G ... 904 423-0211
Jacksonville *(G-6760)*
Serigraphic Arts Inc ... F ... 813 626-1070
Tampa *(G-18085)*
◆ Serv-Pak Corp ... F ... 954 962-4262
Hollywood *(G-5907)*
▼ Services On Demand Print Inc ... E ... 305 681-5345
Hallandale Beach *(G-5209)*
SGS Designs Inc ... G ... 813 258-2691
Tampa *(G-18088)*
Sharper Edge ... F ... 813 871-3343
Tampa *(G-18091)*
Shirts n Things Inc ... G ... 954 434-7480
Davie *(G-2591)*
Shocksocks LLC ... G ... 352 258-0496
Stuart *(G-17012)*
◆ Sign Depot Co ... F ... 407 894-0090
Orlando *(G-13190)*

SIC

Signal Graphics Printing LLC ...G... 303 837-1331
Punta Gorda *(G-15234)*
Signarama ...G... 239 997-1644
North Fort Myers *(G-11606)*
Silkmasters Inc ...G... 904 372-8958
Gainesville *(G-4996)*
Skies Limit Printing ...G... 772 340-1090
Port Saint Lucie *(G-15145)*
Slasher Printing Center Inc ...G... 305 835-7366
Sunrise *(G-17173)*
◆ Slick Designs & AP Miami Inc ...F... 305 836-7950
Hialeah *(G-5622)*
Solseen LLC ...G... 727 322-3131
Saint Petersburg *(G-15915)*
South Florida Finger Printing ...G... 305 661-1636
South Miami *(G-16829)*
Southeast Finishing Group Inc ...E... 407 299-4620
Orlando *(G-13202)*
Southeast Marketing Concepts ...G... 561 747-7010
Jupiter *(G-7118)*
▼ Southeastern Printing Co Inc ...C... 772 287-2141
Hialeah *(G-5628)*
Southern Tape & Label Inc ...F... 321 632-5275
Cocoa *(G-2052)*
Spett Printing Co Inc ...G... 561 241-9758
Boca Raton *(G-727)*
Splash of Color LLC ...F... 732 735-3090
Jacksonville *(G-6805)*
Sports N Stuff Screen Printing ...G... 407 859-0437
Orlando *(G-13208)*
Sportsanity ...G... 386 873-4688
Deland *(G-3015)*
St Ives Burrups ...G... 305 685-7381
Opa Locka *(G-12360)*
Standard Register Inc ...F... 954 492-9986
Fort Lauderdale *(G-4256)*
Starmakers Rising Inc ...E... 561 989-8999
Boca Raton *(G-731)*
Steven Chancas ...F... 352 629-5016
Ocala *(G-12059)*
Sticker Karmer ...G... 813 802-1826
Tampa *(G-18133)*
Sublimation Station Inc ...G... 407 605-5300
Orlando *(G-13219)*
Sun Business Systems Inc ...G... 727 547-6540
Clearwater *(G-1891)*
Sun Graphic Technologies Inc ...E... 941 753-7541
Sarasota *(G-16305)*
Suncoast Specialty Prtg Inc ...G... 813 951-0899
Tampa *(G-18146)*
Sunshine Printing and Business ...G... 407 846-0126
Kissimmee *(G-7301)*
Sunybell LLC ...F... 727 301-2832
New Port Richey *(G-11512)*
Super Color Digital LLC ...F... 407 240-1660
Orlando *(G-13228)*
T Sals Shirt Co ...F... 850 916-9229
Gulf Breeze *(G-5128)*
▼ T-Shirts Plus Color Inc ...G... 305 267-7664
Miami *(G-10456)*
T-Wiz Prtg & EMB Designs LLC ...E... 954 280-8949
Fort Lauderdale *(G-4273)*
Taie Inc ...F... 954 966-0233
Hollywood *(G-5920)*
Tampa Bay Print Shop LLC ...G... 813 321-8790
Riverview *(G-15283)*
Tampa Printing Company ...E... 813 612-7746
Tampa *(G-18171)*
Tandjteesandcustomizations ...G... 904 901-9227
Jacksonville *(G-6838)*
Target Copy Gainesville Inc ...F... 352 372-1171
Gainesville *(G-5008)*
Target Graphics Inc ...F... 941 365-8809
Sarasota *(G-16615)*
Tattoo Factory Inc ...E... 941 923-4110
Sarasota *(G-16616)*
Tee Line Corp ...E... 786 350-9526
West Palm Beach *(G-19058)*
Tee-N-Jay Services LLC ...G... 407 760-7925
Orlando *(G-13245)*
Teeko Graphics Inc ...G... 386 754-5600
Lake City *(G-7389)*
Tees Please Inc ...G... 857 472-3391
Hobe Sound *(G-5728)*
Tektrol Inc ...G... 305 305-0937
Doral *(G-3527)*
Ten Star Supply Co Inc ...G... 813 254-6921
Tampa *(G-18183)*
Think Outloud Printing ...G... 239 800-3219
Cape Coral *(G-1485)*
Thread and Ink ...G... 904 568-9688
Jacksonville *(G-6851)*
Thread Pit Inc ...G... 352 505-0065
Gainesville *(G-5010)*
Threadbird LLC ...G... 407 545-6506
Orlando *(G-13255)*
Tip Tops of America Inc ...F... 352 357-9559
Eustis *(G-3718)*
Tone Printing LLC ...G... 855 505-8663
Miami *(G-10489)*
▼ Tonertype Inc ...E... 813 915-1300
Tampa *(G-18194)*
Tradingflex Inc ...F... 877 522-3535
Miami *(G-10501)*
▲ Treasured Photo Gifts LLC ...E... 407 324-4816
Lake Mary *(G-7456)*
Trend At LLC ...F... 786 300-2550
Miami *(G-10505)*
◆ Trim-Line of Miami Inc ...F... 305 556-6210
Hialeah *(G-5650)*
Triple Crown Printing ...E... 561 939-6440
Boca Raton *(G-758)*
Tropicolor Photo Service Inc ...G... 305 672-3720
Miami Beach *(G-10721)*
Tru Dimensions Printing Inc ...G... 407 339-3410
Longwood *(G-8345)*
Tsfpr LLC ...F... 954 691-9031
Pompano Beach *(G-14894)*
United Seal & Tag Label Corp ...G... 941 625-6799
Port Charlotte *(G-15004)*
Universal Screen Graphics Inc ...E... 813 623-5335
Tampa *(G-18223)*
Vanlex Clothing Inc ...E... 305 431-4669
Miami Lakes *(G-10878)*
Venue Advertising Inc ...E... 561 844-1778
Jupiter *(G-7140)*
◆ Vicbag LLC ...G... 305 423-7042
Miami *(G-10578)*
Vision Web Offset LLC ...F... 305 433-6188
Miami Lakes *(G-10879)*
Vivid Images USA Inc ...F... 904 620-0303
Jacksonville *(G-6902)*
Vurb LLC ...F... 561 441-8870
Pompano Beach *(G-14910)*
W D H Enterprises Inc ...G... 941 758-6500
Bradenton *(G-1143)*
Walruss Enterprises Inc ...G... 954 525-0342
Fort Lauderdale *(G-4311)*
▼ Walter Haas Graphics Inc ...E... 305 883-2257
Hialeah *(G-5685)*
▲ Waterboyz Wbz Inc ...F... 850 433-2929
Pensacola *(G-14287)*
Wear Fund LLC ...F... 239 313-3907
Fort Myers *(G-4651)*
Westview Corp Inc ...G... 239 643-5699
Naples *(G-11454)*
Whitecap Promotions LLC ...G... 813 960-4918
Tampa *(G-18257)*
Whitehouse Custom Scrn PR ...G... 727 321-7398
Saint Petersburg *(G-15959)*
Wholesale Screen Prtg of Nples ...G... 239 263-7061
Naples *(G-11455)*
Wingard LLC ...F... 904 387-2570
Jacksonville *(G-6923)*
◆ Winsted Thermographers Inc ...F... 305 944-7862
Hallandale Beach *(G-5225)*
Woods Printing of Ocala Inc ...G... 352 629-1665
Ocala *(G-12077)*
World Event Promotions LLC ...E... 800 214-3408
Miami *(G-10619)*
Worldwide Sportswear Inc ...E... 386 761-2688
Port Orange *(G-15041)*
◆ Worldwide Tickets & Labels Inc ...D... 877 426-5754
Boynton Beach *(G-977)*
Worth Company LLC ...G... 888 652-1555
Sanford *(G-16141)*

2761 Manifold Business Forms

America Solutions For Business ...G... 305 971-5400
Miami *(G-9138)*
Arlington Prtg Stationers Inc ...C... 904 358-2928
Jacksonville *(G-6168)*
Blackstone Legal Supplies Inc ...F... 305 945-3450
Lauderhill *(G-8103)*
Business Card Ex Tampa Bay Inc ...D... 727 535-7768
Clearwater *(G-1618)*
Economy Printing Co ...F... 904 786-4070
Jacksonville *(G-6354)*
Herald-Advocate Publishing Co ...F... 863 773-3255
Wauchula *(G-18693)*
Independent Resources Inc ...E... 813 237-0945
Tampa *(G-17777)*
John Stewart Enterprises Inc ...F... 904 356-9392
Jacksonville *(G-6525)*
K R O Enterprises Ltd ...G... 309 797-2213
Naples *(G-11302)*
Professional Office Svcs Inc ...G... 305 756-8632
Miami *(G-10206)*
Professional Office Svcs Inc ...G... 863 967-6634
Winter Haven *(G-19348)*
Southeastern Pegboard Printers ...G... 904 731-0357
Jacksonville *(G-6792)*
Taylor Communications Inc ...F... 813 689-5099
Seffner *(G-16733)*
Taylor Communications Inc ...F... 813 886-5511
Tampa *(G-18177)*
Taylor Communications Inc ...F... 954 632-6501
Sunrise *(G-17185)*
▼ Tiger Business Forms Inc ...E... 305 888-3528
Hialeah *(G-5649)*
Zilla Inc ...F... 904 610-1436
Orange Park *(G-12414)*

2771 Greeting Card Publishing

5 01 Fridays ...G... 754 444-3561
Pompano Beach *(G-14570)*
Montevista Greetings LLC ...G... 305 888-9797
Hialeah *(G-5526)*
Sincere Sentiments Inc ...G... 352 287-1232
Inverness *(G-6096)*
Specialty Productions Inc ...G... 786 399-1393
Miami *(G-10401)*
Starmakers Rising Inc ...E... 561 989-8999
Boca Raton *(G-731)*
Zetma LLC ...G... 407 237-0233
Orlando *(G-13341)*

2782 Blankbooks & Looseleaf Binders

All-Pro Accnting Bkkeeping LLC ...G... 561 212-8418
Lake Worth Beach *(G-7602)*
▼ Allied Decals-Fla Inc ...F... 800 940-2233
Fort Lauderdale *(G-3801)*
Beautiful Deluxe Inc ...G... 305 498-4995
Cutler Bay *(G-2387)*
Cjks Deluxe Inc ...G... 786 657-8726
Hialeah *(G-5346)*
County of Hernando ...F... 352 754-4042
Brooksville *(G-1222)*
Deluxe Stone Inc ...G... 561 236-2322
Boynton Beach *(G-896)*
Dobbs & Brodeur Bookbinders ...G... 305 885-5215
Hialeah *(G-5376)*
▲ Fastkit Corp ...E... 305 599-0839
Doral *(G-3347)*
Fastkit Corp ...G... 754 227-8234
Doral *(G-3348)*
Garcia Deluxe Services Corp ...G... 786 291-4329
Hialeah *(G-5424)*
◆ Hofmann & Leavy Inc ...D... 954 698-0000
Deerfield Beach *(G-2842)*
I Wentworth Inc ...G... 561 231-7544
Vero Beach *(G-18627)*
Invoinet Inc ...D... 305 432-5366
Miami *(G-9765)*
Meishboy Productions Inc ...G... 407 949-1464
Apopka *(G-159)*
Onpoint Global ...E... 651 788-1274
Miami *(G-10107)*
Russells Bindery Inc ...G... 904 829-3100
Saint Augustine *(G-15601)*
Scraplife Inc ...G... 305 776-0727
Pinecrest *(G-14332)*
Umg Recordings Inc ...C... 305 532-4754
Miami Beach *(G-10722)*
▲ US Sample Corp ...E... 954 495-4525
Boca Raton *(G-773)*

2789 Bookbinding

Abby Press Inc ...E... 407 847-5565
Kissimmee *(G-7216)*
All Binders & Indexes Inc ...E... 305 889-9983
Hialeah *(G-5278)*
All-Star Sales Inc ...E... 904 396-1653
Jacksonville *(G-6137)*
▲ Allied General Engrv & Plas ...F... 305 626-6585
Opa Locka *(G-12286)*
American Business Cards Inc ...E... 314 739-0800
Naples *(G-11161)*
Apple Printing & Advg Spc Inc ...E... 954 524-0493
Fort Lauderdale *(G-3818)*

Armstrongs Printing & Graphics ....G.... 850 243-6923
Fort Walton Beach (G-4778)
Arribas Bindery Services Inc ....G.... 954 978-8886
Fort Lauderdale (G-3824)
▼ Assocated Prtg Productions Inc....E.... 305 623-7600
Miami Lakes (G-10763)
B J and ME Inc ....G.... 561 368-5470
Boca Raton (G-438)
B R Q Grossmans Inc ....F.... 954 971-1077
Pompano Beach (G-14609)
Bava Inc ....F.... 850 893-4799
Tallahassee (G-17226)
Bayou Printing Inc ....F.... 850 678-5444
Valparaiso (G-18507)
Best Bindery Corp ....G.... 941 505-1779
Punta Gorda (G-15197)
Bill & Renee Enterprises ....G.... 321 452-2800
Merritt Island (G-8993)
Bindery LLC ....G.... 407 647-7777
Winter Park (G-19382)
Bjm Enterprises Inc ....F.... 941 746-4171
Bradenton (G-1000)
Boca Color Graphics Inc ....F.... 561 391-2229
Boca Raton (G-450)
Bodree Printing Company Inc ....F.... 850 455-8511
Pensacola (G-14102)
Bros Williams Printing Inc ....G.... 305 769-9925
Hialeah (G-5332)
C & R Designs Inc ....G.... 321 383-2255
Titusville (G-18419)
C & R Designs Printing LLC ....G.... 321 383-2255
Titusville (G-18420)
◆ Colonial Press Intl Inc ....C.... 305 633-1581
Miami (G-9379)
Color Concepts Prtg Design Co ....E.... 813 623-2921
Tampa (G-17546)
Color Express Inc ....G.... 305 558-2061
Hialeah (G-5350)
Coloramax Printing Inc ....F.... 305 541-0322
Miami (G-9381)
▼ Commercial Printers Inc ....D.... 954 781-3737
Fort Lauderdale (G-3911)
Copy-Flow Inc ....E.... 305 592-0930
Davie (G-2509)
▲ Creative Concepts Intl LLC ....F.... 888 530-7904
Fort Myers (G-4415)
Creative Prtg Grphic Dsign Inc ....E.... 407 855-0202
Orlando (G-12627)
Csmc Inc ....E.... 407 246-1567
Orlando (G-12630)
Dahlquist Enterprises Inc ....G.... 407 896-2294
Orlando (G-12644)
Dannys Prtg Svc Sups & Eqp Inc ....G.... 305 757-2282
Miami (G-9435)
◆ David Dobbs Enterprises Inc ....D.... 904 824-6171
Saint Augustine (G-15533)
Dobbs & Brodeur Bookbinders ....G.... 305 885-5215
Hialeah (G-5376)
Donna Lynn Enterprises Inc ....G.... 772 286-2812
Palm Beach Gardens (G-13584)
Durra Print Inc ....E.... 850 222-4768
Tallahassee (G-17244)
Ed Vance Printing Company Inc ....F.... 813 882-8888
Tampa (G-17630)
Fidelity Printing Corporation ....D.... 727 522-9557
Saint Petersburg (G-15778)
First Imprssons Prtg Cmmnctons ....G.... 407 831-6100
Longwood (G-8282)
Florida Graphic Printing Inc ....F.... 386 253-4532
Daytona Beach (G-2666)
Florida Print Finishers Inc ....G.... 850 877-8503
Tallahassee (G-17255)
G J V Inc ....G.... 727 584-7136
Largo (G-7955)
G L E M Inc ....G.... 727 461-5300
Clearwater (G-1697)
G S Printers Inc ....G.... 305 931-2755
Fort Lauderdale (G-4016)
Gandy Printers Inc ....F.... 850 222-5847
Tallahassee (G-17260)
Gloval Displays Inc ....E.... 800 972-0353
Miami Gardens (G-10742)
Graphics Arts Bindery Inc ....G.... 352 394-4077
Clermont (G-1962)
Gulf Coast Business World Inc ....F.... 850 864-1511
Fort Walton Beach (G-4806)
H & H Printing Inc ....F.... 407 422-2932
Orlando (G-12792)
H & M Printing Inc ....F.... 407 831-8030
Sanford (G-16059)
Hernandez Printing Service ....F.... 305 642-0483
Miami (G-9705)
ICM Printing Co Inc ....F.... 352 377-7468
Gainesville (G-4940)
Instant Printing Services Inc ....F.... 727 546-8036
Floral City (G-3768)
▼ Interprint Incorporated ....D.... 727 531-8957
Clearwater (G-1734)
J J M Services Inc ....G.... 954 437-1880
Miramar (G-11007)
Jet Graphics Inc ....F.... 305 264-4333
Miami (G-9796)
Jet Set Printing Inc ....G.... 407 339-1900
Casselberry (G-1508)
K R O Enterprises Ltd ....G.... 309 797-2213
Naples (G-11302)
Keithco Inc ....G.... 352 351-4741
Ocala (G-11976)
Kights Printing & Office Pdts ....G.... 904 731-7990
Jacksonville (G-6537)
Knopf & Sons Bindery Inc ....E.... 904 353-5115
Jacksonville (G-6542)
Knopf & Sons Bindery Inc ....F.... 904 355-4411
Jacksonville (G-6543)
Lake Worth Herald Press ....E.... 561 585-9387
Lake Worth (G-7564)
Leda Printing Inc ....E.... 941 922-1563
Sarasota (G-16487)
Mailing & Bindery Systems Inc ....G.... 813 416-8965
Lutz (G-8397)
Midds Inc ....E.... 561 586-6220
Lake Worth Beach (G-7615)
Mikes Print Shop Inc ....G.... 407 718-4964
Winter Park (G-19426)
Multicolor Printing Inc ....G.... 772 287-1676
Stuart (G-16979)
My Print Shop Inc ....F.... 954 973-9369
Deerfield Beach (G-2878)
Ngp Corporate Square Inc ....E.... 239 643-3430
Naples (G-11345)
Npc of Tampa Inc ....F.... 813 839-0035
Tampa (G-17942)
Ocala Print Quick Inc ....G.... 352 629-0736
Ocala (G-12014)
◆ Ollo Usa LLC ....G.... 941 366-0600
Sarasota (G-16531)
Oompha Inc ....G.... 850 222-7210
Tallahassee (G-17308)
Output Printing Corp ....F.... 813 228-8800
Tampa (G-17965)
Parkinson Enterprises Inc ....F.... 863 688-7900
Lakeland (G-7762)
PIP Printing ....G.... 352 622-3224
Ocala (G-12027)
Professional Bindery Inc ....F.... 305 633-3761
Miami (G-10205)
Rapid Rater Company ....E.... 850 893-7346
Tallahassee (G-17314)
Reimink Printing Inc ....G.... 813 289-4663
Tampa (G-18050)
Roberts Quality Printing Inc ....E.... 727 442-4011
Clearwater (G-1862)
Russells Bindery Inc ....G.... 904 829-3100
Saint Augustine (G-15601)
Saugus Valley Corp ....G.... 954 772-4077
Coral Springs (G-2310)
◆ Schooner Prints Inc ....D.... 727 397-8572
Largo (G-8045)
Service Bindery Enterprises ....F.... 727 823-9866
Saint Petersburg (G-15911)
▼ South Broward Printing Inc ....G.... 954 962-1309
Hollywood (G-5912)
Southeast Finishing Group Inc ....E.... 407 299-4620
Orlando (G-13202)
▼ Southeastern Printing Co Inc ....C.... 772 287-2141
Hialeah (G-5628)
Spinnaker Holding Company ....E.... 561 392-8626
Boca Raton (G-728)
Steven K Bakum Inc ....G.... 561 804-9110
West Palm Beach (G-19044)
▲ Sunshine Printing Inc ....F.... 561 478-2602
West Palm Beach (G-19050)
Taie Inc ....F.... 954 966-0233
Hollywood (G-5920)
Target Copy Gainesville Inc ....F.... 352 372-1171
Gainesville (G-5008)
Thalers Printing Center Inc ....G.... 954 741-6522
Lauderhill (G-8122)
Town Street Print Shop Inc ....G.... 850 432-8300
Gulf Breeze (G-5130)
United Seal & Tag Label Corp ....G.... 941 625-6799
Port Charlotte (G-15004)
Universal Graphics & Prtg Inc ....G.... 561 845-6404
North Palm Beach (G-11729)
US Bindery Inc ....E.... 305 622-7070
Miami Lakes (G-10876)
V I P Printing ....G.... 386 258-3326
Daytona Beach (G-2730)
V P Press Inc ....F.... 954 581-7531
Fort Lauderdale (G-4301)
Vmak Corp ....F.... 407 260-1199
Longwood (G-8348)
Voss Bindery Inc ....G.... 904 396-3330
Jacksonville (G-6904)
Vowells Downtown Inc ....G.... 850 432-5175
Pensacola (G-14285)
W D H Enterprises Inc ....G.... 941 758-6500
Bradenton (G-1143)
Zetma LLC ....G.... 407 237-0233
Orlando (G-13341)

2791 Typesetting

Abby Press Inc ....E.... 407 847-5565
Kissimmee (G-7216)
Advanced Typesetting ....G.... 407 834-1741
Fern Park (G-3727)
Aether Media USA Inc ....G.... 863 647-5500
Lakeland (G-7629)
▼ Alta Systems Inc ....E.... 352 372-2534
Gainesville (G-4873)
American Business Cards Inc ....E.... 314 739-0800
Naples (G-11161)
Apple Printing & Advg Spc Inc ....E.... 954 524-0493
Fort Lauderdale (G-3818)
Armstrongs Printing & Graphics ....G.... 850 243-6923
Fort Walton Beach (G-4778)
▼ Assocated Prtg Productions Inc....E.... 305 623-7600
Miami Lakes (G-10763)
B J and ME Inc ....G.... 561 368-5470
Boca Raton (G-438)
B R Q Grossmans Inc ....F.... 954 971-1077
Pompano Beach (G-14609)
Bava Inc ....F.... 850 893-4799
Tallahassee (G-17226)
Bayou Printing Inc ....F.... 850 678-5444
Valparaiso (G-18507)
Bjm Enterprises Inc ....F.... 941 746-4171
Bradenton (G-1000)
Boca Color Graphics Inc ....F.... 561 391-2229
Boca Raton (G-450)
Boca Raton Printing Co ....G.... 561 395-8404
Boca Raton (G-454)
Bros Williams Printing Inc ....G.... 305 769-9925
Hialeah (G-5332)
Burr Printing Co Inc ....G.... 863 294-3166
Winter Haven (G-19308)
Caxton Newspapers Inc ....E.... 305 538-9700
Miami Beach (G-10652)
Central Florida Publishing Inc ....F.... 407 323-5204
Sanford (G-16010)
Coastal Printing Inc Sarasota ....E.... 941 351-1515
Sarasota (G-16386)
Color Concepts Prtg Design Co ....E.... 813 623-2921
Tampa (G-17546)
Color Express Inc ....G.... 305 558-2061
Hialeah (G-5350)
Coloramax Printing Inc ....F.... 305 541-0322
Miami (G-9381)
▼ Commercial Printers Inc ....D.... 954 781-3737
Fort Lauderdale (G-3911)
Creative Prtg Grphic Dsign Inc ....E.... 407 855-0202
Orlando (G-12627)
Csmc Inc ....E.... 407 246-1567
Orlando (G-12630)
Dahlquist Enterprises Inc ....G.... 407 896-2294
Orlando (G-12644)
Dannys Prtg Svc Sups & Eqp Inc ....G.... 305 757-2282
Miami (G-9435)
Durra Print Inc ....E.... 850 222-4768
Tallahassee (G-17244)
Dvh Macleod Corp ....F.... 850 224-6760
Tallahassee (G-17246)
Ed Vance Printing Company Inc ....F.... 813 882-8888
Tampa (G-17630)
Edward Thomas Company ....G.... 561 746-1441
Jupiter (G-7032)
Express Printing & Office Sups ....G.... 904 765-9696
Jacksonville (G-6376)
FGA Printing ....G.... 954 763-1122
Pompano Beach (G-14689)

Fidelity Printing Corporation ....D....... 727 522-9557
Saint Petersburg *(G-15778)*
First Imprssons Prtg Cmmnctons ....G....... 407 831-6100
Longwood *(G-8282)*
Florida Graphic Printing Inc..................F....... 386 253-4532
Daytona Beach *(G-2666)*
Ford Press Inc..F....... 352 787-4650
Leesburg *(G-8159)*
Four G Enterprises Inc ....E....... 407 834-4143
Longwood *(G-8284)*
G J V Inc..G....... 727 584-7136
Largo *(G-7955)*
G S Printers Inc.......................................G....... 305 931-2755
Fort Lauderdale *(G-4016)*
▼ Graphics Type Color Entps Inc.........E....... 305 591-7600
Miami *(G-9658)*
Gulf Coast Business World Inc ....F....... 850 864-1511
Fort Walton Beach *(G-4806)*
Halifax Media Holdings LLC..................E....... 386 681-2404
Daytona Beach *(G-2671)*
Hartco Inc ....G....... 904 353-5259
Jacksonville *(G-6462)*
Hilcraft Engraving Inc.............................G....... 305 871-6100
Miami *(G-9711)*
ICM Printing Co Inc.................................F....... 352 377-7468
Gainesville *(G-4940)*
Image Prtg & Digital Svcs Inc ....G....... 850 244-3380
Mary Esther *(G-8589)*
Impact Design Group Inc ....F....... 904 636-8989
Jacksonville *(G-6490)*
Instant Printing Services Inc..................F....... 727 546-8036
Floral City *(G-3768)*
J J M Services Inc....................................G....... 954 437-1880
Miramar *(G-11007)*
Jet Graphics Inc ....F....... 305 264-4333
Miami *(G-9796)*
Jet Set Printing Inc ....G....... 407 339-1900
Casselberry *(G-1508)*
K R O Enterprises Ltd.............................G....... 309 797-2213
Naples *(G-11302)*
Keithco Inc..G....... 352 351-4741
Ocala *(G-11976)*
Kights Printing & Office Pdts.................G....... 904 731-7990
Jacksonville *(G-6537)*
Lake Worth Herald Press ....E....... 561 585-9387
Lake Worth *(G-7564)*
▲ Lauderdale Graphics Corp ....E....... 954 450-0800
Davie *(G-2544)*
Leda Printing Inc.....................................E....... 941 922-1563
Sarasota *(G-16487)*
Leila K Moavero ....G....... 954 978-0018
Pompano Beach *(G-14743)*
Liberty Calhoun Journal Inc ....G....... 850 643-3333
Bristol *(G-1198)*
Linographics Inc ....F....... 407 422-8700
Orlando *(G-12913)*
▼ Menu Men Inc ....E....... 305 633-7925
Miami *(G-9976)*
Mikes Print Shop Inc...............................G....... 407 718-4964
Winter Park *(G-19426)*
Multicolor Printing Inc ....G....... 772 287-1676
Stuart *(G-16979)*
My Print Shop Inc.....................................F....... 954 973-9369
Deerfield Beach *(G-2878)*
Ngp Corporate Square Inc ....E....... 239 643-3430
Naples *(G-11345)*
Ocala Print Quick Inc...............................G....... 352 629-0736
Ocala *(G-12014)*
Oompha Inc ....G....... 850 222-7210
Tallahassee *(G-17308)*
Output Printing Corp ....F....... 813 228-8800
Tampa *(G-17965)*
Paper Fish Printing Inc............................G....... 239 481-3555
Fort Myers *(G-4565)*
Parkinson Enterprises Inc.......................F....... 863 688-7900
Lakeland *(G-7762)*
PIP Printing...G....... 352 622-3224
Ocala *(G-12027)*
Precision Printing of Columbus ....G....... 561 509-7269
Boynton Beach *(G-942)*
Premier Global Enterprises....................G....... 561 747-7303
Tequesta *(G-18387)*
Print One Inc...G....... 813 273-0240
Oldsmar *(G-12262)*
Printers of Pensacola LLC ....G....... 850 434-2588
Pensacola *(G-14240)*
Reimink Printing Inc ....G....... 813 289-4663
Tampa *(G-18050)*
Roberts Quality Printing Inc ....E....... 727 442-4011
Clearwater *(G-1862)*
▼ S Printing Inc ....G....... 305 633-3343
Miami *(G-10292)*
Saugus Valley Corp ....G....... 954 772-4077
Coral Springs *(G-2310)*
Sergios Printing Inc.................................F....... 305 971-4112
Miami *(G-10326)*
Set Up Inc ....G....... 239 542-4142
Cape Coral *(G-1469)*
▼ South Broward Printing Inc ....G....... 954 962-1309
Hollywood *(G-5912)*
Spinnaker Holding Company.................E....... 561 392-8626
Boca Raton *(G-728)*
Steven K Bakum Inc ....G....... 561 804-9110
West Palm Beach *(G-19044)*
▲ Sunshine Printing Inc ....F....... 561 478-2602
West Palm Beach *(G-19050)*
Supreme Printing Corp...........................G....... 305 591-2916
Hialeah *(G-5643)*
Tampa Printing Company.......................E....... 813 612-7746
Tampa *(G-18171)*
Thalers Printing Center Inc....................G....... 954 741-6522
Lauderhill *(G-8122)*
Toms Instant Printing Inc.......................G....... 904 396-0686
Jacksonville *(G-6861)*
Town Street Print Shop Inc ....G....... 850 432-8300
Gulf Breeze *(G-5130)*
Universal Graphics & Prtg Inc ....G....... 561 845-6404
North Palm Beach *(G-11729)*
Universal Screen Graphics Inc ....E....... 813 623-5335
Tampa *(G-18223)*
V I P Printing...G....... 386 258-3326
Daytona Beach *(G-2730)*
V P Press Inc ....F....... 954 581-7531
Fort Lauderdale *(G-4301)*
Vmak Corp...F....... 407 260-1199
Longwood *(G-8348)*
Vowells Downtown Inc ....G....... 850 432-5175
Pensacola *(G-14285)*
W D H Enterprises Inc ....G....... 941 758-6500
Bradenton *(G-1143)*
Walker Graphics Inc ....G....... 954 964-1688
Hollywood *(G-5939)*

2796 Platemaking & Related Svcs

▼ Ace Printing Inc....................................F....... 305 358-2572
Miami *(G-9061)*
All-Star Sales Inc......................................E....... 904 396-1653
Jacksonville *(G-6137)*
American Business Cards Inc...............E....... 314 739-0800
Naples *(G-11161)*
▼ Associated Prtg Productions Inc.......E....... 305 623-7600
Miami Lakes *(G-10763)*
▼ Bellak Color Corporation ....E....... 305 854-8525
Doral *(G-3267)*
Bjm Enterprises Inc ....F....... 941 746-4171
Bradenton *(G-1000)*
Boca Color Graphics Inc ....F....... 561 391-2229
Boca Raton *(G-450)*
Boca Raton Printing Co...........................G....... 561 395-8404
Boca Raton *(G-454)*
Coastal Printing Inc Sarasota ....E....... 941 351-1515
Sarasota *(G-16386)*
Creative Prtg Grphic Dsign Inc..............E....... 407 855-0202
Orlando *(G-12627)*
Diversified Graphics Inc..........................F....... 407 425-9443
Orlando *(G-12677)*
Dobbs & Brodeur Bookbinders ....G....... 305 885-5215
Hialeah *(G-5376)*
Durra Print Inc..E....... 850 222-4768
Tallahassee *(G-17244)*
Elicar Printing..G....... 305 324-5252
Miami *(G-9514)*
H & M Printing Inc ....F....... 407 831-8030
Sanford *(G-16059)*
Hilcraft Engraving Inc..............................G....... 305 871-6100
Miami *(G-9711)*
Impact Design Group Inc ....F....... 904 636-8989
Jacksonville *(G-6490)*
▼ Interprint Incorporated ....D....... 727 531-8957
Clearwater *(G-1734)*
Keithco Inc...G....... 352 351-4741
Ocala *(G-11976)*
Linographics Inc ....F....... 407 422-8700
Orlando *(G-12913)*
Miami Trucolor Offset Svc Co.................G....... 954 962-5230
West Park *(G-19096)*
◆ Pfaffco Inc..F....... 305 635-0986
Miami Lakes *(G-10837)*
▲ Photoengraving Inc ....E....... 813 253-3427
Tampa *(G-17992)*
Press Printing Enterprises Inc...............E....... 239 598-1500
Fort Myers *(G-4572)*
▼ Rex Three Inc ....C....... 954 452-8301
Davie *(G-2585)*
Roberts Quality Printing Inc ....E....... 727 442-4011
Clearwater *(G-1862)*
Southeast Finishing Group Inc...............E....... 407 299-4620
Orlando *(G-13202)*
Trinity Graphic Usa Inc...........................F....... 941 355-2636
Sarasota *(G-16315)*
Venue Advertising Inc ....E....... 561 844-1778
Jupiter *(G-7140)*
Vowells Downtown Inc ....G....... 850 432-5175
Pensacola *(G-14285)*
Walker Graphics Inc ....G....... 954 964-1688
Hollywood *(G-5939)*

28 CHEMICALS AND ALLIED PRODUCTS

2812 Alkalies & Chlorine

Bio-Lab Inc...F....... 863 709-1411
Lakeland *(G-7646)*
Buckeye International Inc ....G....... 813 621-6260
Tampa *(G-17488)*
Jci Jones Chemicals Inc ....F....... 904 355-0779
Jacksonville *(G-6520)*
Odyssey Manufacturing Co ....F....... 813 635-0339
Tampa *(G-17946)*
◆ Universal Transactions Inc.................E....... 305 887-4677
Medley *(G-8750)*

2813 Industrial Gases

Add Helium ....G....... 239 300-0913
Fort Lauderdale *(G-3782)*
Air Liquide Large Inds US LP ....G....... 321 452-2214
Merritt Island *(G-8987)*
Airgas Usa LLC ....G....... 407 293-6630
Orlando *(G-12446)*
▼ Atlantic Dry Ice Corportion ....F....... 305 592-7000
Miami *(G-9182)*
▼ AVw Inc ....E....... 954 972-3338
Margate *(G-8536)*
Bauer Compressors Inc ....G....... 757 855-6006
Sunrise *(G-17094)*
Equipment Sales & Service Inc ....G....... 727 572-9197
Clearwater *(G-1675)*
EZ Neon Inc ....G....... 561 262-7813
Jupiter *(G-7038)*
Frostbite Nitrogen Ice Cream..................G....... 305 933-5482
Miami *(G-9600)*
Hydrogen Inc...G....... 239 436-6668
Naples *(G-11282)*
Hydrogen One Inc......................................G....... 352 361-6974
Belleview *(G-371)*
Liquid Technolgy Corp..............................F....... 832 804-8650
Oldsmar *(G-12244)*
Matheson Treigas.......................................G....... 850 679-3024
Cantonment *(G-1342)*
Matheson Tri-Gas Inc................................G....... 561 615-3000
Riviera Beach *(G-15347)*
Matheson Tri-Gas Inc................................G....... 727 572-8737
Clearwater *(G-1776)*
Messer LLC..F....... 407 851-3311
Orlando *(G-12961)*
Messer LLC..F....... 925 606-2000
Delray Beach *(G-3106)*
Neon Cowboys LLC ....G....... 949 514-5557
Apopka *(G-165)*
Neon Sleevz LLC..G....... 239 348-0520
Naples *(G-11344)*
Neon Workforce Technologies ....G....... 305 458-8244
Hialeah *(G-5537)*
Nitrogen Jupiter LLC ....G....... 561 662-2150
Jupiter *(G-7083)*
Prodair Corporation....................................G....... 850 994-5511
Milton *(G-10937)*
Rz Service Group LLC...............................G....... 904 402-2313
Jacksonville *(G-6741)*
Vs Carbonics Inc...F....... 305 903-6501
Miami *(G-10591)*

2816 Inorganic Pigments

▲ Dry Color USA LLC ....G....... 407 856-7788
Orlando *(G-12689)*
Keystone Color Works Inc ....G....... 813 250-1313
Tampa *(G-17820)*
Paver Systems LLC ....E....... 407 859-9117
Orlando *(G-13055)*

Pigments Black Diamond G 904 241-2533
Saint Augustine (G-15587)

2819 Indl Inorganic Chemicals, NEC

5th Element Inc G 321 331-7028
Kissimmee (G-7214)
5thelement Indian Cuisine LLC G 386 302-0202
Palm Coast (G-13679)
All Elements Mechanical Corp E 866 306-0359
Longwood (G-8251)
American Carbons Inc G 850 265-4214
Lynn Haven (G-8428)
Arj Medical Inc G 813 855-1557
Oldsmar (G-12203)
Artistic Elements Inc G 561 750-1554
Boca Raton (G-430)
Auto Gard Qmi Inc F 727 847-5441
New Port Richey (G-11481)
Basic Elements LLC G 386 673-3100
Ormond Beach (G-13351)
Bio-Lab Inc F 863 709-1411
Lakeland (G-7646)
Caliber Elements LLC F 352 697-1415
Homosassa (G-6000)
Carbonxt Inc E 352 378-4950
Gainesville (G-4892)
Caribe Express Associates Inc F 305 222-9057
Miami (G-9318)
▲ Ceco & Associates Inc G 727 528-0075
Riverview (G-15266)
Cheltec Inc G 941 355-1045
Sarasota (G-16382)
Creative Carbide Inc F 239 567-0041
Fort Myers (G-4414)
Donau Carbon US Lcc E 352 465-5959
Dunnellon (G-3596)
Drywall Elements F 407 454-7293
Orlando (G-12690)
Element 26 LLC G 413 519-1146
Fort Pierce (G-4693)
Element Aircraft Sales LLC G 954 494-2242
Boca Raton (G-516)
Element Inc Co G 786 208-5693
Miami (G-9512)
Element Mdterranean Steakhouse G 407 873-6829
Sarasota (G-16418)
Element Mtls Tech Jupiter LLC F 321 327-8985
West Melbourne (G-18773)
Element-M LLC G 954 288-8683
Plantation (G-14511)
Elemental Energy Inc G 352 589-5703
Mount Dora (G-11102)
Elemental Mobile Services LLC G 904 768-9840
Jacksonville (G-6358)
Elements Accounting Inc G 305 662-4448
Miami (G-9513)
Elements of Stylez G 813 575-8416
Wesley Chapel (G-18744)
Enchanting Elements G 321 663-9521
Naples (G-11237)
Eternal Elements LLC G 407 830-6968
Altamonte Springs (G-44)
Gns Technologies LLC G 561 367-3774
Boca Raton (G-547)
H20logy Inc G 904 829-6098
Saint Augustine (G-15547)
▲ Hac International Inc E 954 584-4530
Davie (G-2534)
Harcros Chemicals Inc E 813 247-4531
Tampa (G-17743)
Hi-TEC Laboratories Inc E 850 835-6822
Freeport (G-4850)
◆ Holtec International D 561 745-7772
Jupiter (G-7053)
Isoaid LLC E 727 815-3262
Port Richey (G-15054)
Jci Jones Chemicals Inc F 904 355-0779
Jacksonville (G-6520)
JVI Minerals Inc G 561 894-1022
Delray Beach (G-3098)
◆ K C Industries LLC G 863 425-1195
Mulberry (G-11127)
K-Technologies Inc G 863 940-4815
Lakeland (G-7723)
Kraton Chemical LLC D 850 785-8521
Panama City (G-13924)
◆ Lambert Corporation Florida E 407 841-2940
Orlando (G-12889)
◆ Mosaic Company A 813 775-4200
Tampa (G-17919)
Nano Liquitec LLC F 813 447-1742
Lutz (G-8404)
National Chemical Sply F 800 515-9938
Davie (G-2556)
National Chemical Supply Inc G 954 683-1645
Plantation (G-14538)
Nu-Element Inc G 561 322-8904
Deerfield Beach (G-2880)
P S Research Corp G 954 558-8727
Lauderhill (G-8119)
Periodic Elements LLC G 561 972-7791
Jupiter (G-7092)
◆ Plasmine Technology Inc F 850 438-8550
Pensacola (G-14231)
Plating Technologies Inc G 772 220-4201
Stuart (G-16989)
Prince Minerals Inc G 832 241-2169
Mount Dora (G-11111)
◆ Puragen LLC E 561 907-5400
West Palm Beach (G-19010)
Puragen LLC E 760 630-5724
North Palm Beach (G-11726)
Quest Environmental Products G 321 984-4423
Melbourne (G-8917)
▲ Royce International LLC G 941 894-1228
Sarasota (G-16565)
▲ Sesolinc Grp Inc F 772 287-9090
Stuart (G-17009)
Sinmat Commercial LLC F 352 334-7270
Gainesville (G-4998)
◆ Sivance LLC C 352 376-8246
Gainesville (G-5000)
▲ Standard Carbon LLC E 352 465-5959
Dunnellon (G-3600)
Syndesis Inc G 954 483-9548
Pembroke Pines (G-14063)
Taylor Building Elements LLC G 863 287-2228
Auburndale (G-254)
◆ Thatcher Chemical Florida Inc F 386 734-3966
Deland (G-3020)
Thatcher Chemical Florida Inc G 386 490-1642
Palmetto (G-13829)
▲ Trac Ecological America Inc G 954 583-4922
Dania (G-2460)
Trans-Resources LLC A 305 933-8301
Sunny Isles Beach (G-17082)
Vanavac Inc G 813 752-1391
Plant City (G-14476)
◆ Vestagen Tchnical Textiles Inc G 407 781-2570
Orlando (G-13300)
W R Grace & Co - Conn F 561 982-7776
Boca Raton (G-785)
Washington Shores Element G 407 250-6260
Orlando (G-13319)

2821 Plastics, Mtrls & Nonvulcanizable Elastomers

3 Miracles Corporation G 407 796-9292
Orlando (G-12417)
▼ Acrocrete Inc E 954 917-4114
Pompano Beach (G-14576)
Advanced Composite Systems F 904 765-6502
Jacksonville (G-6122)
American Epoxy Coatings LLC F 954 850-1169
Dania Beach (G-2462)
▲ American Sperior Compounds Inc G 716 873-1209
Lithia (G-8215)
▲ American Vinyl Company E 305 687-1863
Hialeah (G-5296)
Anchor Coatings Leesburg Inc E 352 728-0777
Leesburg (G-8142)
Ascend Prfmce Mtls Oprtons LLC B 734 819-0656
Gulf Breeze (G-5112)
Ascend Prfmce Mtls Oprtons LLC A 850 968-7000
Cantonment (G-1335)
Atlantic Marble Company Inc E 904 262-6262
Jacksonville (G-6176)
Atlas Polymers Corp F 786 312-2131
Miami (G-9188)
Automated Services Inc F 772 461-3388
Fort Pierce (G-4679)
Avon Assoc G 561 391-7188
Boca Raton (G-435)
Blue Water Dynamics LLC D 386 957-5464
Edgewater (G-3614)
Braden Kitchens Inc E 321 636-4700
Cocoa (G-1999)
Car Care Haven LLC G 855 464-2836
Englewood (G-3671)
Cellofoam North America Inc E 407 888-4667
Orlando (G-12560)
Certified Whl Exterior Pdts G 407 654-7170
Winter Garden (G-19256)
Charles K Sewell G 407 423-1870
Orlando (G-12576)
◆ Composite Essential Mtls LLC G 772 344-0034
Port St Lucie (G-15172)
Coosa LLC G 904 268-1187
Jacksonville (G-6289)
Creative Countertops Inc F 904 387-2800
Jacksonville (G-6296)
▲ Cup Plus USA G 321 972-1968
Winter Park (G-19397)
◆ Designers Tops Inc F 305 599-9973
Miami (G-9461)
Dioxide Materials Inc F 217 239-1400
Boca Raton (G-502)
Dj Plastics Inc G 407 656-6677
Apopka (G-131)
Dynamic Material Systems LLC G 407 353-6885
Oviedo (G-13427)
F O F Plastics Inc G 727 937-2144
Tarpon Springs (G-18300)
Fairing Xchange LLC G 904 589-5253
Orange Park (G-12391)
Fiberflon Usa Inc G 786 953-7329
Miami (G-9566)
Flying W Plastics Fl Inc F 904 800-2451
Jacksonville (G-6410)
G Phillips and Sons LLC F 248 705-5873
Sarasota (G-16445)
Global Holdings and Dev LLC G 949 500-4997
Pompano Beach (G-14714)
Hancor Inc E 863 655-5499
Winter Garden (G-19266)
Huntsman Properties LLC E 954 282-1797
Fort Lauderdale (G-4053)
Idea Design Studio Inc F 305 823-6008
Doral (G-3387)
▲ Industrial Plastic Pdts Inc E 305 822-3223
Miami Lakes (G-10797)
▲ Ineos New Planet Bioenergy LLC E 772 794-7900
Vero Beach (G-18630)
International Composite G 206 349-7468
Sarasota (G-16468)
Jrf Technology LLC F 813 443-5273
Tampa (G-17811)
Kraton Chemical LLC F 850 438-9222
Pensacola (G-14190)
▼ Linkpoint LLC F 305 903-9191
Key Biscayne (G-7159)
◆ Linvatec Corporation A 727 392-6464
Largo (G-8001)
Lrm Industries Intl Inc E 321 635-9797
Rockledge (G-15430)
Made In America Plastic Inc G 786 310-7816
Medley (G-8680)
Matrix Composites Inc C 321 633-4480
Rockledge (G-15435)
Midgard Inc D 863 696-1224
Lake Wales (G-7516)
◆ Nida-Core Corporation E 772 343-7300
Port Saint Lucie (G-15124)
Olevin Compounds LLC G 954 993-5148
Miramar (G-11023)
Orca Composites LLC F 206 349-5300
Sarasota (G-16533)
Pacific Limited Intl Corp G 305 358-1900
Miami (G-10128)
▼ Pacific Ltd Corp G 305 358-1900
Miami (G-10129)
Paradigm Plastics Inc G 727 797-3555
Safety Harbor (G-15501)
Plastic and Products Mktg LLC F 352 867-8078
Ocala (G-12028)
Plastic Masters International F 386 312-9775
East Palatka (G-3605)
Plastic Specialties Inc F 239 643-0933
Naples (G-11369)
Plastic Trading Intl Inc E 863 688-1983
Lakeland (G-7767)
Plastics America Incorporated G 813 620-3711
Tampa (G-17995)
Plastirex LLC F 305 471-1111
Avon Park (G-293)
Poly-Chem Corp G 305 593-1928
Miami (G-10176)
Polymersan LLC G 305 887-3824
Hialeah (G-5560)

SIC

Preform LLC ...F ... 888 826-5161
Elkton *(G-3650)*
Pro Poly of America Inc ...G ... 352 629-1414
Ocala *(G-12032)*
Pro Poly of America Inc ...E ... 352 629-1414
Ocala *(G-12033)*
Profab Corporation ...E ... 352 369-5515
Ocala *(G-12034)*
Purecycle Technologies Inc ...E ... 877 648-3565
Orlando *(G-13100)*
◆ Ravago Americas LLC ...A ... 407 773-7777
Orlando *(G-13114)*
▲ Ravago Holdings America Inc ...D ... 407 875-9595
Orlando *(G-13115)*
Rayonier A M Products Inc ...D ... 904 357-9100
Jacksonville *(G-6706)*
Rayonier Advanced Mtls Inc ...A ... 904 357-4600
Jacksonville *(G-6707)*
◆ Rayonier AM Sales and Tech Inc ...G ... 904 357-4600
Jacksonville *(G-6708)*
Rehrig Pacific Company ...F ... 407 857-3888
Orlando *(G-13128)*
Southern Plastics & Rubber Co ...E ... 386 672-1167
Ormond Beach *(G-13401)*
Syi Inc ...G ... 954 323-2483
Sunrise *(G-17183)*
Syntex America Corporation ...F ... 954 457-1468
Hallandale Beach *(G-5217)*
T S E Industries Inc ...E ... 727 540-1368
Clearwater *(G-1901)*
◆ Teak Isle Inc ...C ... 407 656-8885
Ocoee *(G-12091)*
TEC Composites Inc ...F ... 904 765-6502
Jacksonville *(G-6841)*
The Hc Companies Inc ...D ... 863 314-9417
Sebring *(G-16715)*
Thermo Compaction Systems Inc ...G ... 863 370-3799
Lakeland *(G-7820)*
◆ Tradepak Inc ...G ... 305 871-2247
Miami *(G-10500)*
Tupperware Products Inc ...E ... 407 826-5050
Orlando *(G-13281)*
▼ U S Composites Inc ...G ... 561 588-1001
West Palm Beach *(G-19073)*
Ultraflex Systems Florida Inc ...F ... 973 664-6739
Riverview *(G-15285)*
US Blanks LLC ...E ... 321 253-3626
Melbourne *(G-8969)*
▼ US Composites ...G ... 561 588-1001
Riviera Beach *(G-15388)*
Washington Penn Plastics Co ...F ... 724 228-1260
St Pete Beach *(G-16885)*
Wheeler Consolidated Inc ...F ... 772 464-4400
Fort Pierce *(G-4770)*

2822 Synthetic Rubber (Vulcanizable Elastomers)

◆ Daytona Rubber Company Inc ...F ... 305 513-4105
Doral *(G-3324)*
Fatovich Technologies LLC ...G ... 772 597-1326
Palm City *(G-13654)*
Gaddie Construction Co ...G ... 850 215-8421
Panama City *(G-13906)*
Goodrich Corporation ...C ... 904 757-3660
Jacksonville *(G-6441)*
International Polymer Svcs LLC ...G ... 401 529-6855
Pensacola *(G-14180)*
Latam Group Corp ...G ... 305 793-8961
Miami *(G-9864)*
Maclan Corporation Inc ...E ... 863 665-4814
Lakeland *(G-7742)*
Modern Silicone Tech Inc ...C ... 727 873-1805
Pinellas Park *(G-14369)*
◆ Rayonier AM Sales and Tech Inc ...G ... 904 357-4600
Jacksonville *(G-6708)*
Rowe Industries Inc ...F ... 302 855-0585
Pembroke Park *(G-14011)*
◆ T S E Industries Inc ...C ... 727 573-7676
Clearwater *(G-1900)*
◆ Unaflex LLC ...E ... 954 943-5002
Pompano Beach *(G-14898)*
◆ Venair Inc ...G ... 305 362-8920
Miami Gardens *(G-10758)*
▲ Vinavil Americas Corporation ...D ... 954 246-8888
Deerfield Beach *(G-2933)*

2823 Cellulosic Man-Made Fibers

Artificial Turf Supply LLC ...G ... 877 525-8873
Ponte Vedra Beach *(G-14934)*
▲ Composite Holdings Inc ...E ... 321 268-9625
Titusville *(G-18424)*
Rayonier Advanced Mtls Inc ...A ... 904 357-4600
Jacksonville *(G-6707)*
Rayonier Inc ...E ... 904 277-1343
Yulee *(G-19499)*

2824 Synthetic Organic Fibers, Exc Cellulosic

American Traffic Safety Mtls ...E ... 904 284-0284
Green Cove Springs *(G-5051)*
Artificial Turf Supply LLC ...G ... 877 525-8873
Ponte Vedra Beach *(G-14934)*
Ascend Prfmce Mtls Oprtons LLC ...A ... 850 968-7000
Cantonment *(G-1335)*
Bay City Window Company ...F ... 727 323-5443
Saint Petersburg *(G-15718)*
◆ Mirart Inc ...E ... 954 974-5230
Pompano Beach *(G-14764)*
Northeast Pro-Tech Inc ...G ... 772 489-8762
Port Saint Lucie *(G-15125)*
Redsled DBA Bulldog Equipment ...F ... 954 448-5221
Stuart *(G-17001)*
◆ Sterling Fibers Inc ...D ... 850 994-5311
Milton *(G-10941)*
Tagalong Inc ...G ... 561 585-7400
Lantana *(G-7877)*
Two Brothers Cultivation LLC ...E ... 954 478-2402
Fort Lauderdale *(G-4291)*
▲ Uniroyal Engineered Pdts LLC ...F ... 941 906-8580
Sarasota *(G-16629)*
Uniroyal Globl Engnred Pdts In ...F ... 941 906-8580
Sarasota *(G-16630)*

2833 Medicinal Chemicals & Botanical Prdts

◆ Aldali Inc ...F ... 877 384-9494
Tampa *(G-17397)*
▲ Alfa Manufacturing LLC ...F ... 305 436-8150
Miami *(G-9102)*
Alive By Nature Inc ...G ... 800 810-1935
Ponte Vedra Beach *(G-14930)*
▲ American Natural Pdts Lab Inc ...G ... 305 261-5152
Miami *(G-9146)*
Atlantic Medical Products LLC ...F ... 727 535-0022
Largo *(G-7901)*
Biobotanical LLC ...F ... 239 458-4534
Cape Coral *(G-1392)*
Boston Ntrceutical Science LLC ...F ... 617 848-4560
Miami *(G-9270)*
Botanica Odomiwale Corp ...G ... 305 381-5834
Hialeah *(G-5330)*
Cansortium Charities Inc ...G ... 305 902-2720
Miami *(G-9308)*
Ccf Holdco LLC ...F ... 800 714-9215
Arcadia *(G-201)*
Ceva Animal Health LLC ...F ... 727 548-8345
Oldsmar *(G-12214)*
CJ Labs Inc ...F ... 305 234-9644
Miami *(G-9359)*
Cls Holdings Usa Inc ...D ... 888 438-9132
Pinecrest *(G-14327)*
Concentrated Aloe Corp ...G ... 386 673-7566
Ormond Beach *(G-13360)*
Coterie Care Inc ...F ... 850 325-0422
Fort Walton Beach *(G-4788)*
De Lima Consultants Group Inc ...F ... 954 933-7030
Coral Springs *(G-2238)*
Dragons Miracle LLC ...G ... 561 670-5546
Boca Raton *(G-509)*
Endevours Together LLC ...G ... 850 274-2641
Tallahassee *(G-17248)*
◆ Fdc Vitamins LLC ...B ... 305 468-1600
Miami Lakes *(G-10789)*
Generex Laboratories LLC ...G ... 239 592-7255
Naples *(G-11260)*
Germkleen LLC ...G ... 954 947-5602
Fort Lauderdale *(G-4020)*
Great Amercn Natural Pdts Inc ...E ... 727 521-4372
Saint Petersburg *(G-15796)*
Guardian Essentials LLC ...G ... 817 401-0200
Delray Beach *(G-3089)*
Immudyne Nutritional LLC ...G ... 914 714-8901
Jacksonville *(G-6489)*
Lab Kingz LLC ...G ... 561 808-4216
Delray Beach *(G-3100)*
Lan Industries LLC ...F ... 305 889-2087
Miami *(G-9854)*
Liv LLC ...E ... 321 276-5302
Miami Lakes *(G-10808)*
Live Wise Naturals LLC ...G ... 866 866-0075
Bradenton *(G-1072)*
Lotus Stress Relief LLC ...F ... 941 706-2778
Sarasota *(G-16490)*
Macrocap Labs Inc ...E ... 321 234-6282
Longwood *(G-8308)*
▼ Midway Labs Usa LLC ...F ... 561 571-6252
Boca Raton *(G-624)*
Modular Thermal Tech LLC ...E ... 954 785-1055
Pompano Beach *(G-14767)*
Morgannas Alchemy LLC ...G ... 727 505-8376
New Port Richey *(G-11502)*
Mydor Industries Inc ...G ... 954 927-1140
Dania *(G-2453)*
National Health Alliance LLC ...G ... 727 504-3915
Tampa *(G-17932)*
Natural-Immunogenics Corp ...D ... 888 328-8840
Sarasota *(G-16265)*
Natures Botanicals Inc ...G ... 727 443-4524
Clearwater *(G-1803)*
Natures Clear LLC ...G ... 561 503-1751
Lake Worth *(G-7575)*
Nulab Inc ...D ... 727 446-1126
Clearwater *(G-1813)*
Nutop International LLC ...G ... 954 909-0010
Fort Lauderdale *(G-4144)*
Ocean Global Inc ...G ... 727 842-7544
New Port Richey *(G-11503)*
One Bio Corp ...B ... 305 328-8662
Aventura *(G-277)*
Pain Away LLC ...G ... 800 215-8739
Deland *(G-3005)*
Palmate LLC ...E ... 352 508-7800
Tavares *(G-18350)*
▲ Pharmco Laboratories Inc ...G ... 321 268-1313
Titusville *(G-18451)*
Plantation Botanicals Inc ...E ... 863 675-2984
Felda *(G-3722)*
Plantation Medicinals Inc ...F ... 863 675-2984
Felda *(G-3723)*
Potnetwork Holdings Inc ...G ... 800 433-0127
Fort Lauderdale *(G-4171)*
Purovite Inc ...G ... 305 364-5727
Miami *(G-10217)*
Rainbow Lght Ntrtnal Systems I ...G ... 954 233-3300
Sunrise *(G-17167)*
Ravenswood Import Export Ltd L ...G ... 863 800-0210
Lake Placid *(G-7494)*
Real Ketones LLC ...F ... 801 244-8610
Saint Petersburg *(G-15899)*
Socratic Solutions Inc ...G ... 813 324-7018
Brandon *(G-1180)*
◆ Terry Laboratories LLC ...F ... 321 259-1630
Melbourne *(G-8960)*
Totally Products LLC ...G ... 786 942-9218
Boca Raton *(G-753)*
Twinlab Cnsld Holdings Inc ...E ... 561 443-4301
Boca Raton *(G-759)*
Twinlab Consolidation Corp ...F ... 800 645-5626
Boca Raton *(G-760)*
Twinlab Corporation ...B ... 800 645-5626
Boca Raton *(G-761)*
Twinlab Holdings Inc ...E ... 800 645-5626
Boca Raton *(G-762)*
Twinlab Holdings Inc ...F ... 800 645-5626
Boca Raton *(G-763)*
Ultimaxx Inc ...F ... 877 300-3424
Boca Raton *(G-764)*
▲ US Nutraceuticals Inc ...E ... 352 357-2004
Eustis *(G-3720)*
Vedic Origins Inc ...G ... 407 712-5614
Altamonte Springs *(G-82)*
Veritas Farms Inc ...F ... 561 288-6603
Fort Lauderdale *(G-4307)*
Vistapharm Inc ...E ... 727 530-1633
Largo *(G-8078)*
Vitalleo LLC ...G ... 904 474-5330
Neptune Beach *(G-11479)*
Vitaminmed LLC ...G ... 727 443-7008
Clearwater *(G-1934)*
Viva 5 LLC ...D ... 561 239-2239
Saint Petersburg *(G-15955)*
We Make Vitamins LLC ...G ... 863 607-6708
Lakeland *(G-7833)*
Wibe Natural ...G ... 305 594-0158
Doral *(G-3549)*
▲ World Perfumes Inc ...F ... 305 822-0004
Opa Locka *(G-12370)*
▲ Xymogen Inc ...B ... 407 445-0203
Orlando *(G-13335)*

2834 Pharmaceuticals

1source Biotechnology LLC ....G....... 305 668-5888
Miami *(G-9022)*
5d Bio Gold LLC ....G....... 561 756-8291
Boca Raton *(G-394)*
Abbott Diabetes Care ....G....... 863 385-7910
Sebring *(G-16679)*
Abhai LLC ....G....... 215 579-1842
Saint Augustine *(G-15512)*
AC Pharma Corp ....G....... 954 773-9735
Margate *(G-8529)*
Accentia Biopharmaceuticals ....F....... 813 864-2554
Tampa *(G-17385)*
Acic Pharmaceuticals Inc ....G....... 954 341-0795
Coral Springs *(G-2212)*
Actavis Laboratories Fl Inc ....C....... 954 305-4414
Davie *(G-2487)*
Advanced Pharma Research Inc ....F....... 786 234-3709
Cutler Bay *(G-2384)*
Advanced Pharmaceutical Inc ....G....... 866 259-7122
North Miami *(G-11622)*
Aegle Therapeutics Corporation ....G....... 305 608-9705
Miami *(G-9080)*
Aenova Doral Manufacturing Inc ....C....... 305 463-2270
Doral *(G-3228)*
Aenova Doral Manufacturing Inc ....F....... 305 463-2263
Doral *(G-3229)*
Aerobotics Technologies Inc ....G....... 407 658-9864
Orlando *(G-12440)*
Aim Immunotech Inc ....F....... 352 448-7797
Ocala *(G-11867)*
Allay Pharmaceutical LLC ....G....... 954 336-1136
Hialeah *(G-5281)*
Allergan Sales LLC ....E....... 787 406-1203
Sunrise *(G-17088)*
Alloy Fabricators Inc ....G....... 813 925-0222
Tampa *(G-17403)*
Alta Pharma LLC ....G....... 727 942-7645
Tarpon Springs *(G-18282)*
▲ **Alternative Laboratories LLC** ....E....... 239 692-9160
Fort Myers *(G-4354)*
Alternative Medical Entps LLC ....F....... 941 702-9955
Apollo Beach *(G-100)*
Alvita Pharma Usa Inc ....G....... 305 961-1623
Doral *(G-3243)*
Alzamend Neuro Inc ....G....... 844 722-6333
Tampa *(G-17411)*
Ambo Health LLC ....G....... 866 414-0188
Venice *(G-18532)*
American Bhvioral RES Inst LLC ....D....... 888 353-1205
Boca Raton *(G-421)*
American Injectables Inc ....F....... 813 435-6014
Brooksville *(G-1210)*
American Pharmaceutical Svcs ....G....... 407 704-5937
Orlando *(G-12473)*
American Vet Sciences LLC ....G....... 727 471-0850
Largo *(G-7895)*
Amerx Health Care Corp ....F....... 727 443-0530
Oldsmar *(G-12201)*
Amicitia Pharma Llc ....G....... 941 722-0172
Palmetto *(G-13786)*
Amino Cell Inc ....F....... 352 291-0200
Ocala *(G-11874)*
Andrx Corporation ....C....... 954 217-4500
Weston *(G-19105)*
Andrx Corporation ....C....... 954 585-1770
Sunrise *(G-17091)*
▲ **Andrx Corporation** ....C....... 954 585-1400
Davie *(G-2497)*
Annona Biosciences Inc ....G....... 888 204-4980
Palm Beach Gardens *(G-13566)*
Apical Pharmaceutical Corp ....G....... 786 331-7200
Doral *(G-3251)*
▲ **Apotex Corp** ....E....... 954 384-8007
Weston *(G-19107)*
Archer Pharmaceuticals Inc ....F....... 941 752-2949
Sarasota *(G-16175)*
◆ **Arnet Pharmaceutical Corp** ....B....... 954 236-9053
Davie *(G-2499)*
Assistrx Inc ....C....... 855 421-4607
Orlando *(G-12495)*
◆ **Atlas Operations Inc** ....D....... 954 788-1200
Pompano Beach *(G-14607)*
Avanti Nutritional Labs LLC ....C....... 305 822-3880
Miami Lakes *(G-10764)*
▲ **Aveva Drug Dlvry Systems Inc** ....D....... 954 430-3340
Miramar *(G-10970)*
Axis Phrm Partners LLC ....G....... 407 936-2949
Lake Mary *(G-7402)*
Azopharma Inc ....G....... 954 536-4738
Miramar *(G-10971)*
Baker Norton US Inc ....D....... 305 575-6000
Miami *(G-9215)*
Barcelona Dr Phillips LLC ....G....... 407 352-9733
Orlando *(G-12506)*
Be Whole Nutrition LLC ....G....... 813 420-3057
Plant City *(G-14408)*
Beach Products Inc ....G....... 813 839-6565
Tampa *(G-17462)*
Beacon Phrm Jupiter LLC ....E....... 212 991-8988
Jupiter *(G-7005)*
▲ **Belcher Holdings Inc** ....C....... 727 530-1585
Largo *(G-7906)*
Belcher Holdings Inc ....F....... 727 471-0850
Largo *(G-7907)*
Belcher Pharmaceuticals LLC ....E....... 727 471-0850
Largo *(G-7908)*
Berman Products LLC ....F....... 561 743-5197
Jupiter *(G-7006)*
Beutlich Pharmaceuticals LLC ....F....... 386 263-8860
Bunnell *(G-1297)*
Bio Therapeutics Inc ....G....... 954 321-5553
Plantation *(G-14496)*
Bio-Nucleonics Pharma Inc ....F....... 305 576-0996
Miami *(G-9247)*
Bio-Pharm LLC ....G....... 973 223-7163
Hallandale Beach *(G-5171)*
Biogaia Biologics Inc ....G....... 786 762-4000
Doral *(G-3275)*
Biolife LLC ....E....... 941 360-1300
Sarasota *(G-16184)*
Biomar Products LLC ....G....... 800 216-2080
Doral *(G-3276)*
Biostem Technologies Inc ....G....... 954 380-8342
Pompano Beach *(G-14617)*
Bishop Pharma LLC ....G....... 954 292-7325
Pompano Beach *(G-14618)*
Bjmjrx Inc ....G....... 941 505-9036
Punta Gorda *(G-15198)*
▼ **Bonne Sante Natural Mfg Inc** ....E....... 305 594-4990
Doral *(G-3281)*
Bpc Plasma Inc ....G....... 561 989-5800
Boca Raton *(G-461)*
Bpc Plasma Inc ....E....... 561 569-3100
Boca Raton *(G-462)*
Bpi Labs LLC ....C....... 727 471-0850
Largo *(G-7912)*
Briemad Inc ....F....... 561 626-4377
Palm Beach Gardens *(G-13572)*
Britvic North America LLC ....F....... 786 641-5041
Miami *(G-9278)*
Capzerpharma Manufacturing LLC ....G....... 561 493-4000
Lake Worth Beach *(G-7609)*
Caq International LLC ....G....... 305 744-1472
Miami *(G-9311)*
Cardinal Health 414 LLC ....G....... 954 202-1883
Fort Lauderdale *(G-3883)*
Cardinal Health 414 LLC ....G....... 813 972-1351
Tampa *(G-17507)*
Catalent Inc ....F....... 727 803-2832
Saint Petersburg *(G-15739)*
Catalyst Pharmaceuticals Inc ....E....... 305 420-3200
Coral Gables *(G-2129)*
Cbc Biotechnologies Inc ....G....... 813 803-6300
Tampa *(G-17517)*
▲ **Ceautamed Worldwide LLC** ....G....... 866 409-6262
Boca Raton *(G-474)*
Celigenex Inc ....G....... 954 957-1058
Fort Lauderdale *(G-3888)*
Centro De Diagnostico ....G....... 407 865-7020
Sanford *(G-16011)*
Cerno Pharmaceuticals LLC ....G....... 786 763-2766
Miami *(G-9343)*
Clearly Derm LLC ....E....... 561 353-3376
Boca Raton *(G-484)*
Cleveland Diabetes Care Inc ....G....... 904 394-2620
Jacksonville *(G-6268)*
◆ **Clinical Dagnstc Solutions Inc** ....E....... 954 791-1773
Plantation *(G-14500)*
Cocrystal Pharma Inc ....G....... 877 262-7123
Miami *(G-9373)*
Community Pharmacy Svcs LLC ....G....... 727 431-8261
Clearwater *(G-1634)*
Concordia Pharmaceuticals Inc ....G....... 786 304-2083
Miami *(G-9391)*
Coqui Rdo Pharmaceuticals Corp ....G....... 787 685-5046
Doral *(G-3307)*
Cor International (not Inc) ....G....... 850 766-2866
Tallahassee *(G-17239)*
Corerx Inc ....F....... 727 259-6950
Clearwater *(G-1637)*
▲ **Corerx Inc** ....C....... 727 259-6950
Clearwater *(G-1638)*
Corerx Pharmaceuticals Inc ....E....... 727 259-6950
Clearwater *(G-1639)*
◆ **Cryothrapy Pain Rlief Pdts Inc** ....G....... 954 364-8192
Hollywood *(G-5806)*
Cyclo Therapeutics Inc ....G....... 386 418-8060
Gainesville *(G-4902)*
D V M Pharmaceuticals Inc ....D....... 305 575-6950
Weston *(G-19119)*
Dain M Bayer ....G....... 407 647-0679
Winter Park *(G-19400)*
Darmerica LLC ....F....... 321 219-9111
Casselberry *(G-1502)*
Dazmed Inc ....G....... 561 571-2020
Boca Raton *(G-495)*
DCS Pharma USA LLC ....G....... 248 979-8866
Miami *(G-9441)*
Defender SD Manufacturing LLC ....F....... 813 864-2570
Tampa *(G-17598)*
Demelle Biopharma LLC ....G....... 908 240-8939
Tarpon Springs *(G-18294)*
Dependable Water Inc ....G....... 904 599-0560
Saint Johns *(G-15676)*
Dependable Water Inc ....E....... 772 563-7473
Vero Beach *(G-18615)*
Dermatonus ....G....... 305 229-3923
Miramar *(G-10983)*
Devatis Inc ....G....... 954 316-4844
Fort Lauderdale *(G-3939)*
▲ **Dextrum Laboratories Inc** ....G....... 305 594-4020
Miami *(G-9462)*
Diabetic Care Rx LLC ....E....... 866 348-0441
Pompano Beach *(G-14664)*
Diva Stuff ....G....... 386 256-2521
Ormond Beach *(G-13363)*
Doctors Scientific Organica LLC ....F....... 888 455-9031
Riviera Beach *(G-15321)*
▲ **Duy Drugs Inc** ....F....... 305 594-3667
Doral *(G-3337)*
Eagle Labs Incorporated ....D....... 727 548-1816
Saint Petersburg *(G-15767)*
Eci Pharmaceuticals LLC ....E....... 954 486-8181
Fort Lauderdale *(G-3959)*
Elite Fitforever LLC ....G....... 305 902-2358
Miami Beach *(G-10664)*
EMJ Pharma Inc ....G....... 973 600-9087
Palm Beach Gardens *(G-13587)*
Enveric Biosciences Inc ....F....... 239 302-1707
Naples *(G-11240)*
Envoy Therapeutics Inc ....G....... 561 210-7705
Jupiter *(G-7035)*
Ephs Holdings Inc ....G....... 212 321-0091
Boynton Beach *(G-903)*
Epigenetix Inc ....F....... 561 543-7569
Delray Beach *(G-3075)*
▼ **ERA Organics Inc** ....G....... 800 579-9817
Clearwater *(G-1676)*
▲ **Erba Diagnostics Inc** ....D....... 305 324-2300
Miami Lakes *(G-10786)*
Exactus Pharmacy Solutions Inc ....D....... 888 314-3874
Tampa *(G-17652)*
Exelan Pharmaceuticals Inc ....G....... 561 287-6631
Boca Raton *(G-525)*
◆ **Farma International Inc** ....F....... 305 670-4416
Miami *(G-9560)*
First Wave Biopharma Inc ....F....... 561 589-7020
Boca Raton *(G-529)*
Fitteam Global LLC ....G....... 586 260-1487
Palm Beach Gardens *(G-13590)*
Florida Nutri Labs LLC ....F....... 863 607-6708
Lakeland *(G-7692)*
Floridas Best Inc ....G....... 407 682-9570
Altamonte Springs *(G-46)*
Forest Research Institute Inc ....F....... 631 436-4600
Weston *(G-19126)*
Forest Research Institute Inc ....E....... 954 622-5600
Sunrise *(G-17124)*
Fresenius Kabi Usa LLC ....E....... 847 550-2300
Doral *(G-3356)*
Full Life Direct LLC ....F....... 800 305-3043
Hollywood *(G-5826)*
Gadal Laboratories Inc ....G....... 786 732-2571
Miami *(G-9609)*
Gand Inc ....G....... 240 575-0622
Miami Beach *(G-10670)*
Genesis Health Institute Inc ....G....... 954 561-3175
Wilton Manors *(G-19218)*

S I C

Gensco Laboratories LLC F 754 263-2898
Doral *(G-3365)*
Global Pharma Analytics LLC F 701 491-7770
Jupiter *(G-7049)*
Global Phrm Compliance G 239 949-4958
Bonita Springs *(G-834)*
Global Reach Rx Pbf LLC F 786 703-1988
Doral *(G-3369)*
Glucorell Inc F 407 384-3388
Maitland *(G-8466)*
Green Roads of Florida G 954 626-0574
Davie *(G-2533)*
Growhealthy Holdings LLC F 863 223-8882
West Palm Beach *(G-18891)*
Grunenthal Services Inc F 786 364-6308
Miami *(G-9678)*
Hanna Pharmaceuticals LLC G 813 409-9327
Lutz *(G-8387)*
▲ **Heritage Skin Care Inc** F 305 757-9264
Miami Shores *(G-10885)*
High Five Products Inc G 239 449-9268
Naples *(G-11276)*
Hill Dermaceuticals Inc E 407 323-1887
Sanford *(G-16062)*
Hill Labs Inc E 407 323-1887
Sanford *(G-16063)*
Immune Therapeutics Inc E 888 613-8802
Winter Park *(G-19412)*
Indicali Inc G 831 905-4780
Tampa *(G-17778)*
Infupharma LLC G 305 301-3389
Hollywood *(G-5848)*
▲ **Ingenus Pharmaceuticals LLC** F 407 354-5365
Orlando *(G-12830)*
◆ **Innova Softgel LLC** C 855 536-8872
Miami *(G-9747)*
Inspire Inc G 321 557-3247
Palm Bay *(G-13517)*
Inter Cell Technologies Inc G 561 575-6868
Jupiter *(G-7058)*
▲ **Interntnal Ntrctcals Group Inc** G 786 518-2903
Sunrise *(G-17130)*
Intratab Labs Inc F 305 887-5850
Miami Springs *(G-10892)*
◆ **Ivax Corporation** C 305 329-3795
Miami *(G-9775)*
▲ **Ivax Pharmaceuticals LLC** C 305 575-6000
Miami *(G-9776)*
Ivax Research Inc D 305 668-7688
Miami *(G-9777)*
Ivax Teva G 954 384-5316
Weston *(G-19144)*
▲ **Jsr Wellness Inc** D 561 748-2477
West Palm Beach *(G-18915)*
Kashiben Say LLC G 352 489-4960
Dunnellon *(G-3598)*
Kavi Skin Solutions Inc E 415 839-5156
Titusville *(G-18438)*
Kd-Pharma Usa Inc G 786 345-5500
Miami *(G-9817)*
Kempharm Inc G 321 939-3416
Celebration *(G-1523)*
King Pharmaceuticals LLC G 954 575-7085
Coral Springs *(G-2269)*
King Pharmaceuticals LLC E 423 989-8000
Saint Petersburg *(G-15833)*
KMA Pharma LLC G 754 220-6936
Lighthouse Point *(G-8209)*
Kova Laboratories Inc G 954 978-8730
Margate *(G-8555)*
Kramer Pharmacal Inc F 305 226-0641
Miami *(G-9830)*
▲ **Krs Global Biotechnology Inc** E 888 502-2050
Boca Raton *(G-592)*
Krs MSA LLC G 727 264-7605
New Port Richey *(G-11497)*
Labelclick Inc G 727 548-8345
Oldsmar *(G-12243)*
▲ **Lf of America Corp** G 561 988-0303
Boca Raton *(G-601)*
Linpharma Inc G 888 989-3237
Tampa *(G-17847)*
Liquidcapsule Mfg LLC F 813 431-0532
Tampa *(G-17849)*
Llorens Phrm Intl Div Inc F 305 716-0595
Miami *(G-9904)*
Longeveron Inc F 305 909-0840
Miami *(G-9909)*
Lonza G 727 608-6802
Tampa *(G-17859)*

Lupin Research Inc E 800 466-1450
Coral Springs *(G-2275)*
M3 Biopharma Inc G 858 603-8296
Sarasota *(G-16494)*
Magellan Pharmaceuticals Inc G 813 623-6800
Tampa *(G-17873)*
Marizyme Inc G 561 935-9955
Jupiter *(G-7073)*
▼ **Mason Vitamins Inc** D 800 327-6005
Miami Lakes *(G-10814)*
Master Nutrition Labs Inc G 786 847-2000
Opa Locka *(G-12336)*
Max Avw Professional LLC F 954 972-3338
Margate *(G-8557)*
Maximilian Zenho & Co Inc G 352 875-1190
Ocala *(G-11996)*
Mayo Clinic G 904 953-2000
Jacksonville *(G-6583)*
Mayo Clinic G 904 953-2000
Jacksonville *(G-6584)*
MCR Amrcan Pharmaceuticals Inc E 352 754-8587
Brooksville *(G-1248)*
◆ **Mdr LLC** C 954 845-9500
Sunrise *(G-17146)*
▼ **Medipharma Inc** G 305 858-7332
Miami *(G-9967)*
Merck Sharp & Dohme Corp D 305 512-6062
Miami Lakes *(G-10818)*
Methapharm Inc G 954 341-0795
Coral Springs *(G-2282)*
Mohnark Pharmaceuticals Inc G 954 607-4559
Davie *(G-2554)*
Mpact Sales Solutions G 630 669-5937
Oakland *(G-11770)*
Muscle Fx LLC G 305 514-0061
North Miami Beach *(G-11693)*
Mymd Pharmaceuticals Inc F 813 864-2566
Tampa *(G-17925)*
Nabi F 561 989-5800
Boca Raton *(G-635)*
Nanobiotech Pharma Inc G 866 568-0178
Coral Springs *(G-2294)*
Natural Vitamins Lab Corp C 305 265-1660
Opa Locka *(G-12343)*
◆ **Natural Vitamins Lab Corp** C 305 265-1660
Opa Locka *(G-12344)*
Natural-Immunogenics Corp D 888 328-8840
Sarasota *(G-16265)*
Nature Medrx Inc F 239 215-8557
Fort Myers *(G-4544)*
Natures Bioscience LLC G 800 570-7450
Sarasota *(G-16520)*
Navinta III Inc G 561 997-6959
Boca Raton *(G-637)*
Neglex Inc F 305 551-4177
Miami *(G-10063)*
Nephron Pharmaceuticals E 407 913-3142
Orlando *(G-12997)*
Nephron Pharmaceuticals Corp E 407 999-2225
Orlando *(G-12998)*
Neuro Pharmalogics Inc G 240 476-4491
Boca Raton *(G-639)*
New World Holdings Inc E 561 888-4939
Boca Raton *(G-642)*
Nextsource Biotechnology LLC G 305 753-6360
Miami *(G-10068)*
Nexus Alliance Corp G 321 945-4283
Longwood *(G-8317)*
North Fort Myers Prescr Sp G 239 599-4120
North Fort Myers *(G-11600)*
Northside Pharmacy LLC G 256 398-7500
Destin *(G-3200)*
▲ **Noven Pharmaceuticals Inc** C 305 964-3393
Miami *(G-10081)*
Noven Therapeutics LLC B 212 682-4420
Miami *(G-10082)*
Nutra Pharma Corp G 954 509-0911
Coral Springs *(G-2298)*
Nutrakey LLC D 321 234-6282
Longwood *(G-8318)*
▲ **Nutramedix LLC** F 561 745-2917
Jupiter *(G-7085)*
Nutrasource LLC E 786 427-4305
Miami *(G-10086)*
Nutricorp LLC G 305 680-4896
Hialeah *(G-5547)*
▲ **Nutrition Laboratories Inc** E 727 442-2747
Clearwater *(G-1815)*
Nxgen Brands LLC E 888 315-6339
Plantation *(G-14540)*

Ocala Pharmacy LLC G 352 509-7890
Ocala *(G-12013)*
Ocean Pharmaceuticals Inc F 954 473-4717
Sunrise *(G-17153)*
One Nursing Care LLC G 954 441-6644
Miramar *(G-11025)*
Opko Health Inc A 305 575-4100
Miami *(G-10111)*
Oragenics Inc G 813 286-7900
Tampa *(G-17959)*
Oryza Pharmaceuticals Inc E 954 881-5481
Coral Springs *(G-2301)*
Pack4u LLC E 407 857-2871
Orlando *(G-13043)*
Palmate LLC E 352 508-7800
Tavares *(G-18350)*
Parallel Florida LLC A 404 920-4890
Tampa *(G-17977)*
PDC F 386 322-2808
Port Orange *(G-15027)*
▲ **Peak Nutritional Products LLC** E 813 884-4989
Tampa *(G-17980)*
▲ **Peak Performance Nutrients Inc** F 561 266-1038
Delray Beach *(G-3114)*
Pegasus Laboratories Inc D 850 478-2770
Pensacola *(G-14224)*
Pharma Formulations Labs Inc G 786 985-1254
Medley *(G-8705)*
Pharma Nature LLC G 305 395-4723
Davie *(G-2571)*
Pharma Resources Inc F 973 780-5241
Altamonte Springs *(G-64)*
Pharmalab Enterprises Inc E 305 821-4002
Miami Lakes *(G-10838)*
Pharmalink Inc C 800 257-3527
Largo *(G-8025)*
Pharmamed USA Inc G 954 533-4462
Fort Lauderdale *(G-4163)*
Pharmatech LLC G 954 581-7881
Davie *(G-2572)*
Pharmatech LLC F 954 629-2444
Davie *(G-2573)*
Pharmatech Pharmatech LLC G 954 583-8778
Fort Lauderdale *(G-4164)*
Pivotal Therapeutics US Inc F 905 856-9797
Boca Raton *(G-665)*
Platinum Group Usa Inc F 561 274-7553
Delray Beach *(G-3119)*
PLD Acquisitions LLC D 305 463-2270
Miami *(G-10170)*
Prestige Brands International E 914 524-6800
Bonita Springs *(G-850)*
Procyon Corporation G 727 447-2998
Clearwater *(G-1849)*
Product Dev Partners LLC F 813 908-6775
Tampa *(G-18020)*
Profounda Health & Beauty F 407 270-7792
Orlando *(G-13096)*
Prosolus Inc G 305 514-0270
Miami *(G-10211)*
Protech Nutraceuticals Inc F 727 466-0770
Seminole *(G-16758)*
Protexin G 786 310-7233
Doral *(G-3472)*
Pure Wave Organics Inc G 321 368-7002
Melbourne *(G-8915)*
Qol Medical LLC G 772 584-3640
Vero Beach *(G-18656)*
Quantum Pharmaceuticals LLC G 321 724-0625
Melbourne Beach *(G-8982)*
R-Da Trading LLC G 954 278-6983
Weston *(G-19162)*
Rainbow Lght Ntrtnal Systems I G 954 233-3300
Sunrise *(G-17167)*
Rapha Pharmaceuticals Inc G 727 946-9444
Orlando *(G-13113)*
Realm Labs LLC F 561 549-9099
Boca Raton *(G-684)*
Regenerative Proc Plant LLC E 727 781-0818
Palm Harbor *(G-13759)*
▲ **Reserveage** F 561 443-5301
Boca Raton *(G-688)*
Rls (usa) Inc A 561 596-0556
Tampa *(G-18061)*
Rockledge Phrm Mfg LLC F 321 636-0717
Rockledge *(G-15444)*
▲ **Romark Laboratories LC** E 813 282-8544
Tampa *(G-18068)*
Rowell Laboratories Inc F 407 929-9445
Apopka *(G-183)*

Rx For Fleas Inc ....F 954 351-9244
Fort Lauderdale *(G-4220)*
▲ **S&J 34102 Inc** ....G 239 592-9388
Tampa *(G-18077)*
Salerno Pharmaceuticals LP ....G 352 799-9813
Brooksville *(G-1266)*
Sanofi US Services Inc ....E 407 736-0226
Orlando *(G-13162)*
Saw Palmetto Berries Cooperati ....G 239 775-4286
Naples *(G-11394)*
Saw Palmetto Florida LLC ....F 239 775-4286
Naples *(G-11395)*
Schering-Plough Corp ....G 407 353-2076
Orlando *(G-13167)*
Script Central LLC ....F 954 805-8581
Miami Beach *(G-10708)*
Septimius LLC ....G 813 484-4168
Tampa *(G-18084)*
▲ **Sho ME Nutriceuticals Inc** ....E 352 797-9600
Brooksville *(G-1269)*
Shriji Swami LLC ....F 904 727-3434
Jacksonville *(G-6767)*
Sincerus Pharmaceuticals Inc ....C 800 604-5032
Pompano Beach *(G-14852)*
Sinofresh Healthcare Inc ....G 941 270-2627
Venice *(G-18573)*
Skingen USA Inc ....G 727 586-3751
Largo *(G-8054)*
Skinutra Inc ....G 813 992-1742
Tampa *(G-18107)*
Smart For Life Inc ....G 786 749-1221
Miami *(G-10363)*
▲ **Smartscience Laboratories Inc** ....F 813 925-8454
Tampa *(G-18110)*
Sofie Co ....F 407 321-9076
Sanford *(G-16118)*
▼ **Solara Inc** ....F 305 592-4748
Miami Lakes *(G-10858)*
Southeast Compounding Phrm LLC ....G 813 644-7700
Tampa *(G-18116)*
Specialty Pharmacy Services ....G 321 953-2004
Melbourne *(G-8940)*
Speer Laboratories LLC ....F 954 586-8700
Fort Lauderdale *(G-4252)*
St Mary Pharmacy LLC ....F 727 585-1333
Largo *(G-8060)*
Stagexchange ....G 239 200-9226
Estero *(G-3697)*
Star Pharmaceuticals LLC ....G 800 845-7827
Fort Lauderdale *(G-4258)*
Stemtech Healthsciences Corp ....E 954 715-6000
Miramar *(G-11047)*
Steriline North America I ....G 941 405-2039
Bradenton *(G-1120)*
Stratco Pharmaceuticals LLC ....F 813 403-5060
Odessa *(G-12156)*
Stratus Pharmaceuticals Inc ....E 305 254-6793
Miami *(G-10420)*
Strides Pharma Inc ....D 561 741-6500
Riviera Beach *(G-15382)*
Swiss Caps Usa Inc ....E 786 345-5505
Miami *(G-10449)*
◆ **Synergylabs LLC** ....E 954 525-1133
Fort Lauderdale *(G-4272)*
Takeda Phrmceuticals N Amer In ....G 561 818-0925
Windermere *(G-19245)*
◆ **Taylor L Max L C** ....G 833 346-9963
Fort Myers *(G-4625)*
Teva Pharmaceuticals ....F 954 382-7729
Sunrise *(G-17186)*
Teva Pharmaceuticals Usa Inc ....E 305 575-6000
Miami *(G-10471)*
▼ **Tg United Inc** ....G 352 799-9813
Brooksville *(G-1279)*
Therapeuticsmd Inc ....C 561 961-1900
Boca Raton *(G-748)*
Theret Bicom Inc ....G 917 796-1443
Weston *(G-19170)*
Tim Gardners Vitamart Inc ....E 813 908-7843
Tampa *(G-18186)*
Total Ntrtn & Therapeutics PA ....G 352 259-5190
Lady Lake *(G-7329)*
Transdermal Technologies Inc ....G 561 848-2345
North Palm Beach *(G-11727)*
◆ **Triad Isotopes Inc** ....E 407 455-6700
Orlando *(G-13271)*
▲ **Trifecta Phrmceuticals USA LLC** ....G 888 296-9067
Pompano Beach *(G-14891)*
Trivecta Pharmaceuticals Inc ....F 561 856-0842
Fort Lauderdale *(G-4289)*
Tropichem Research Labs LLC ....D 561 804-7603
Jupiter *(G-7134)*
Truth Nutrition LLC ....G 754 400-0382
Hollywood *(G-5930)*
Trxade Inc ....G 727 230-1915
Land O Lakes *(G-7868)*
Twinlab Corporation ....B 800 645-5626
Boca Raton *(G-761)*
Twinlab Holdings Inc ....E 800 645-5626
Boca Raton *(G-762)*
Ultra Pharma LLC ....G 954 532-7539
Pompano Beach *(G-14897)*
United Biosource LLC (ubc) ....G 877 599-7748
Lake Mary *(G-7457)*
US Stem Cell Inc ....F 954 835-1500
Sunrise *(G-17194)*
Uspharma Ltd ....D 954 817-4418
Miami Lakes *(G-10877)*
Usvi Pharmaceuticals LLC ....G 305 643-8841
Doral *(G-3539)*
Uvlrx Therapeutics Inc ....F 813 309-1976
Oldsmar *(G-12276)*
Versea Holdings Inc ....E 800 397-0670
Tampa *(G-18239)*
Veru Inc ....B 305 509-6897
Miami *(G-10574)*
Vetbiotek Inc ....F 727 308-2030
Largo *(G-8072)*
Viadiem LLC ....G 407 571-6845
Maitland *(G-8484)*
◆ **Victus LLC** ....E 305 663-2129
Miami *(G-10582)*
Vistakon Pharmaceuticals LLC ....G 904 443-1000
Jacksonville *(G-6901)*
Vistapharm Inc ....E 727 530-1633
Largo *(G-8077)*
Vistapharm Inc ....E 727 530-1633
Largo *(G-8078)*
Vital Pharma Research Inc ....G 786 666-0592
Hialeah *(G-5682)*
Vivalize LLC ....G 305 614-3952
Coral Gables *(G-2205)*
Vividus LLC ....G 954 326-1954
Pompano Beach *(G-14909)*
Watson Therapeutics Inc ....E 954 266-1000
Miramar *(G-11059)*
◆ **West Phrm Svcs Fla Inc** ....B 727 546-2402
Saint Petersburg *(G-15958)*
Wonder Holdings Acquisition ....F 305 379-2322
Miami *(G-10615)*
Xcelience LLC ....E 813 286-0404
Tampa *(G-18270)*
Xcelience LLC ....E 813 286-0404
Tampa *(G-18271)*
Xcelience LLC ....D 813 286-0404
Tampa *(G-18272)*
▲ **Xcelience Holdings LLC** ....D 813 286-0404
Tampa *(G-18273)*

2835 Diagnostic Substances

Advanced Bioprocess LLC ....G 305 927-3661
Miami *(G-9075)*
AP Lifesciences LLC ....F 954 300-7469
Alachua *(G-3)*
Banyan Biomarkers Inc ....G 760 710-0460
Gainesville *(G-4882)*
Cambridge Diagnostic Pdts Inc ....F 954 971-4040
Fort Lauderdale *(G-3880)*
Cardinal Health 414 LLC ....G 954 202-1883
Fort Lauderdale *(G-3883)*
Cardinal Health 414 LLC ....G 813 972-1351
Tampa *(G-17507)*
◆ **Clinical Dagnstc Solutions Inc** ....E 954 791-1773
Plantation *(G-14500)*
Cojali Usa Inc ....F 305 960-7651
Doral *(G-3303)*
◆ **Continental Services Group** ....E 305 633-7700
Miami *(G-9396)*
Continental Services Group ....G 954 327-0809
Fort Lauderdale *(G-3917)*
Doctorxs Allergy Formula ....G 904 758-2088
Jacksonville *(G-6324)*
Evolvegene LLC ....G 727 623-4052
Saint Petersburg *(G-15772)*
Genzyme Corporation ....D 800 245-4363
Miami *(G-9628)*
Infinty Genome Sciences Inc ....G 321 327-7365
Melbourne Beach *(G-8979)*
Inter Cell Technologies Inc ....G 561 575-6868
Jupiter *(G-7058)*
La Genomics LLC ....G 407 909-1120
Windermere *(G-19234)*
Lumos Diagnostics Inc ....E 941 556-1850
Lakewood Ranch *(G-7845)*
Meridian Life Science Inc ....F 561 241-0223
Boca Raton *(G-620)*
Nilsson Nils ....G 561 790-2400
Royal Palm Beach *(G-15476)*
Opko Health Inc ....A 305 575-4100
Miami *(G-10111)*
Petnet Solutions Inc ....G 813 627-0022
Tampa *(G-17985)*
Physicians Imaging LLC ....G 352 383-3716
Mount Dora *(G-11110)*
Positiveid Corporation ....F 561 805-8000
Delray Beach *(G-3121)*
Rapid Genomics LLC ....G 352 213-4741
Jacksonville *(G-6705)*
▲ **Sanzay Corporation** ....E 305 826-9886
Miami *(G-10304)*
Suntree Diagnostic Center ....G 321 259-8800
Melbourne *(G-8951)*
▲ **US Diagnostics Inc** ....E 866 216-5308
Plantation *(G-14561)*
US Pet Imaging LLC ....G 941 795-3780
Bradenton *(G-1138)*
US Pet Imaging LLC ....G 941 921-0383
Sarasota *(G-16632)*

2836 Biological Prdts, Exc Diagnostic Substances

Acuderm Inc ....D 954 733-6935
Fort Lauderdale *(G-3781)*
Adma Biologics Inc ....F 561 989-5800
Boca Raton *(G-400)*
Adma Biomanufacturing LLC ....B 201 478-5552
Boca Raton *(G-401)*
Advanced Bioservices LLC ....C 850 476-7999
Pensacola *(G-14082)*
Amgen USA Inc ....F 805 447-1000
Tampa *(G-17422)*
Amino Cell Inc ....F 352 291-0200
Ocala *(G-11874)*
Apexeon Biomedical LLC ....G 850 878-2150
Tallahassee *(G-17221)*
Applied Genetic Tech Corp ....D 386 462-2204
Alachua *(G-5)*
Aqua Pulsar LLC ....G 772 320-9691
Palm City *(G-13641)*
Assoction Hspnic Hritg Fstival ....G 305 885-5613
Hialeah *(G-5310)*
▼ **Becker Microbial Products Inc** ....G 954 345-9321
Parkland *(G-13989)*
Bioivt LLC ....G 516 876-7902
Plantation *(G-14497)*
Biolife Plasma Services ....G 407 388-1052
Casselberry *(G-1498)*
Bioresource Technology ....E 954 792-5222
Weston *(G-19113)*
Biotoxins Inc ....G 407 892-6905
Saint Cloud *(G-15646)*
Caregivercom Inc ....G 954 893-0550
Oakland Park *(G-11790)*
Citrus Extracts LLC ....F 772 464-9800
Fort Pierce *(G-4688)*
◆ **Clearant Inc** ....G 407 876-3134
Orlando *(G-12589)*
Creative Clture Mdia Group LLC ....G 786 237-0206
Coral Gables *(G-2134)*
Culture Cartel Media Inc ....G 407 680-8923
Sanford *(G-16030)*
Demerx Inc ....G 954 607-3670
Miami *(G-9454)*
▲ **Dyadic International Inc** ....G 561 743-8333
Jupiter *(G-7027)*
Ecological Laboratories Inc ....E 239 573-6650
Cape Coral *(G-1416)*
Empowered Diagnostics LLC ....G 206 228-5990
Pompano Beach *(G-14679)*
Extract Downtown Orlando LLC ....G 407 722-7379
Orlando *(G-12728)*
HCW Biologics Inc ....E 954 842-2024
Miramar *(G-11002)*
Healthy Schools LLC ....C 904 887-4540
Jacksonville *(G-6465)*
Hemarus Llc-Jcksnvle Plsma Ctr ....G 904 642-1005
Jupiter *(G-7052)*
Iliad Biotechnologies LLC ....G 954 336-0777
Weston *(G-19139)*

S
I
C

Immunotek Bio Centers LLC ....E 337 500-1175
Bradenton (G-1059)
Immunotek Bio Centers LLC ....E 561 270-6712
Greenacres (G-5083)
Immunotek Bio Centers LLC ....E 772 577-7194
Fort Pierce (G-4707)
Immunotek Bio Centers LLC ....F 404 345-3570
Cocoa (G-2030)
Inter Cell Technologies Inc ....G 561 575-6868
Jupiter (G-7058)
Lactalogics Inc ....G 772 202-0407
Port Saint Lucie (G-15118)
Larrick Group Inc ....E 941 351-2700
Sarasota (G-16248)
Lillian Bay Medical Inc ....F 941 815-7373
Saint Petersburg (G-15840)
Longeveron Inc ....F 305 909-0840
Miami (G-9909)
M-Biolabs Inc ....G 239 571-0435
Naples (G-11317)
Mad Chiller Extracts LLC ....G 813 304-1664
Tampa (G-17872)
Medrx Inc ....E 727 584-9600
Largo (G-8008)
Nature Cast Ant-Vnom Index LLC ....G 352 683-0647
Spring Hill (G-16857)
One Biotechnology Company ....G 941 355-8451
Sarasota (G-16268)
Organabio LLC ....F 305 676-2586
South Miami (G-16824)
P B C Cultural Counsel ....F 561 471-2903
West Palm Beach (G-18980)
Pet Doc FL LLC ....G 407 437-6614
Oviedo (G-13453)
Plasma Cutting LLC ....G 954 558-1371
Hallandale (G-5160)
Plasma Energy Group LLC ....G 813 760-6385
Odessa (G-12139)
Plasma-Therm Inc ....E 856 753-8111
Saint Petersburg (G-15880)
Players Media Group Inc ....F 509 254-4949
Brooksville (G-1261)
▲ Radiation Shield Tech Inc ....F 866 733-6766
Coral Gables (G-2189)
Real Extract Ventures Inc ....G 561 371-3532
Wellington (G-18728)
Stat Biomedical LLC ....G 210 365-1495
Mims (G-10953)
Synergy Biologics LLC ....G 850 656-4277
Tallahassee (G-17334)
Vc Serum LLC ....G 305 778-2190
Miami (G-10570)
Venom Allstars LLC ....G 407 575-3484
Winter Garden (G-19287)
Vital Solutions LLC ....G 561 848-1717
West Palm Beach (G-19081)

2841 Soap & Detergents

▲ Bar Maid Corporation ....F 954 960-1468
Pompano Beach (G-14614)
Bon Brands Inc ....F 800 590-7911
Royal Palm Beach (G-15462)
Buckeye International Inc ....G 813 621-6260
Tampa (G-17488)
Cambra Soap Company ....G 321 525-7575
Satellite Beach (G-16650)
Cambridge Diagnostic Pdts Inc ....F 954 971-4040
Fort Lauderdale (G-3880)
Campos Chemicals ....F 727 412-2774
Saint Petersburg (G-15736)
Care-Metix Products Inc ....F 813 628-8801
Tampa (G-17509)
Consulier Engineering Inc ....G 561 842-2492
Riviera Beach (G-15314)
▲ Earth Group Inc ....F 954 979-8444
Pompano Beach (G-14671)
Easy Foam Inc ....F 970 927-0209
Homosassa (G-6003)
Eco Concepts Inc ....F 954 920-9700
Hollywood (G-5814)
Ecolab Inc ....G 561 207-6278
Palm Beach Gardens (G-13585)
Ecolab Inc ....F 800 931-8911
Jupiter (G-7031)
Florida Rum Company LLC ....E 305 791-1221
Hollywood (G-5823)
Go Green Marine Inc ....G 850 499-5137
Destin (G-3191)
Loris 1 Inc ....G 727 847-4499
New Port Richey (G-11498)
Mollys Suds LLC ....G 678 361-5456
Saint Petersburg (G-15858)
OHanrahan Consultants Inc ....E 727 531-3375
Largo (G-8019)
Owens Distributors Inc ....E 407 302-8602
Sanford (G-16098)
Pro Chem Products Inc ....G 407 425-5533
Orlando (G-13091)
Purox Brands Corp ....F 305 392-0738
Hialeah (G-5585)
Sanit Technologies LLC ....E 941 351-9114
Sarasota (G-16290)
▲ Scentstional Soaps Candles Inc ....F 941 485-1443
Venice (G-18572)
Sicamu Inc ....G 850 270-6283
Quincy (G-15254)
Skampas Performance Group ....G 305 974-0047
Sunny Isles Beach (G-17080)
Skymo LLC ....F 305 676-6739
Cooper City (G-2115)
Trugreen Products LLC ....G 954 629-5794
Pompano Beach (G-14893)
▲ Ultraclenz LLC ....F 800 931-8911
Jupiter (G-7136)
Whip-It Inventions Inc ....E 850 626-6300
Milton (G-10947)

2842 Spec Cleaning, Polishing & Sanitation Preparations

1st Enviro-Safety Inc ....G 239 283-1222
Saint James City (G-15672)
◆ Allen Shuffleboard LLC ....G 727 399-8877
Seminole (G-16737)
Amazon Cleaning & More Inc ....F 239 594-1733
Naples (G-11158)
American Coatings Corporation ....G 954 970-7820
Margate (G-8535)
and Services ....G 850 805-6455
Fort Walton Beach (G-4776)
◆ Asi Chemical Inc ....F 863 678-1814
Lake Wales (G-7499)
Beyondclean LLC ....F 561 799-5710
Jupiter (G-7008)
Brewer International Inc ....F 772 562-0555
Vero Beach (G-18603)
Bruce Roland ....G 850 775-1497
Panama City Beach (G-13974)
Buckeye International Inc ....G 813 621-6260
Tampa (G-17488)
Campos Chemicals ....F 727 412-2774
Saint Petersburg (G-15736)
Car Care Haven LLC ....G 855 464-2836
Englewood (G-3671)
Caribbean Global Group Corp ....F 786 449-2767
Port St Lucie (G-15169)
◆ Chemco Corp ....E 305 623-4445
Miami Lakes (G-10776)
Chhaya Corporation ....G 407 348-9400
Kissimmee (G-7231)
Ciega Inc ....G 727 526-9048
Saint Petersburg (G-15746)
Clean & Shine Auto Marine ....G 239 261-6563
Naples (G-11211)
Clorox Healthcare Holdings LLC ....E 904 996-7758
Jacksonville (G-6270)
Cogswell Innovations Inc ....G 954 245-8877
Fort Lauderdale (G-3907)
▲ Crown Products LLC ....G 954 917-1118
Pompano Beach (G-14652)
Distingshed Gntlman MBL Dtling ....G 321 200-4331
Orlando (G-12676)
Duct Dynasty ....G 407 730-9081
Orlando (G-12691)
Dudley Blake LLC ....G 904 866-2829
Jacksonville (G-6332)
◆ Dyadic International USA Inc ....G 561 743-8333
Jupiter (G-7028)
Eco Concepts Inc ....F 954 920-9700
Hollywood (G-5814)
Enozo Technologies Inc ....G 512 944-7772
Lakewood Ranch (G-7838)
▼ Falconpro Industries Inc ....G 305 556-4456
Hialeah (G-5404)
Florida Rust ....G 386 259-9940
Deltona (G-3170)
▲ For Life Products LLC ....D 954 747-3300
Miramar (G-10994)
Four Star Products Inc ....G 941 727-6161
Bradenton (G-1044)
▼ Freezetone Products LLC ....F 305 640-0414
Doral (G-3355)
Ft Lauderdale Wax ....G 954 256-9291
Fort Lauderdale (G-4014)
Futurescape Inc ....G 386 679-4120
Port Orange (G-15018)
Goho Enterprises Inc ....F 407 884-0770
Zellwood (G-19503)
▲ Green Bull Products Inc ....G 386 402-0409
New Smyrna (G-11522)
Hinsilblon Ltd Inc ....G 239 418-1133
Fort Myers (G-4483)
Holiday Cleaners Inc ....G 727 842-6989
New Port Richey (G-11492)
Illinois Tool Works Inc ....D 863 665-3338
Lakeland (G-7708)
Impressions Dry Cleaners Inc ....F 561 988-3030
Boca Raton (G-564)
Infinity Manufacturing LLC ....G 954 531-6918
Coconut Creek (G-2079)
Jde Distributors LLC ....F 727 498-7886
Pinellas Park (G-14357)
Kmss Products Inc ....G 800 646-3005
Largo (G-7994)
Lee Chemical Corporation ....G 407 843-6950
Orlando (G-12900)
Marinize Products Corp ....G 954 989-7990
Hollywood (G-5869)
Mollys Suds LLC ....G 678 361-5456
Saint Petersburg (G-15858)
▲ N A Comandulli LLC ....G 941 870-2878
Sarasota (G-16262)
NCH FL Funding LLC ....G 321 777-7777
Melbourne (G-8892)
NCH Marine LLC ....G 754 422-4237
Davie (G-2557)
Northland Manufacturing Inc ....G 850 878-5149
Tallahassee (G-17306)
Nvip LLC ....G 972 435-4097
Naples (G-11348)
Ocean Bio-Chem Inc ....E 954 587-6280
Davie (G-2559)
Odyssey Manufacturing Co ....E 813 635-0339
Tampa (G-17945)
OHanrahan Consultants Inc ....E 727 531-3375
Largo (G-8019)
Paradise Air Fresh LLC ....F 561 972-0375
Palm City (G-13670)
◆ Petruj Chemical Corp ....F 305 556-1271
Miami Lakes (G-10836)
▼ Power Kleen Corporation ....E 813 854-2648
Oldsmar (G-12258)
Pro Chem Products Inc ....G 407 425-5533
Orlando (G-13091)
Puritair LLC ....F 954 281-5105
Fort Lauderdale (G-4186)
Quality Industrial Chem Inc ....F 727 573-5760
Saint Petersburg (G-15896)
Quantum Envmtl Slutions St Inc ....G 800 975-8721
Fort Lauderdale (G-4193)
Reliox Corporation ....G 904 729-5097
Jacksonville (G-6715)
Relu Co ....E 786 717-5665
Doral (G-3482)
Robert McKee Enterprises Inc ....G 772 291-2159
Stuart (G-17002)
Roebic Laboratories Inc ....F 561 799-3380
Jupiter (G-7105)
Samarian Products LLC ....E 212 781-2121
Naples (G-11390)
Saphire Services LLC ....G 386 247-1048
Lake Butler (G-7341)
◆ Seal Shield LLC ....E 877 325-7443
Orlando (G-13172)
See-Ray Plumbing Inc ....E 772 489-2474
Vero Beach (G-18663)
Services NS 18 LLC ....G 786 546-3295
Aventura (G-280)
Sewell Products Florida LLC ....D 863 967-4463
Auburndale (G-252)
▼ Sheila Shine Inc ....E 305 557-1729
Miami (G-10335)
Shelia Shine Inc ....G 305 557-1729
Hialeah (G-5618)
Sicamu Inc ....G 850 270-6283
Quincy (G-15254)
Skymo LLC ....F 305 676-6739
Cooper City (G-2115)
Sltons Envirnmntal Group Assoc ....F 305 665-5594
Miami (G-10362)

Spa Concepts Inc F 850 575-0921
Tallahassee *(G-17328)*
Sparklean G 305 599-8479
Miami *(G-10398)*
◆ **Star-Brite Distributing Inc** E 954 587-6280
Davie *(G-2595)*
Stratford Corporation G 727 443-1573
Clearwater *(G-1890)*
Suncoast Research Labs Inc F 727 344-7627
Saint Petersburg *(G-15928)*
▲ **Trident Trading Inc** G 561 488-0458
Boca Raton *(G-756)*
◆ **Troy Industries Inc** E 305 324-1742
Doral *(G-3534)*
United Sierra Group Corp D 305 297-5835
Miami Lakes *(G-10873)*
▲ **Venco Marine Inc** G 954 923-0036
Hollywood *(G-5936)*
Veridien Corporation F 727 576-1600
Saint Petersburg *(G-15951)*
Victory Valet Services LLC F 904 521-6517
Jacksonville *(G-6897)*
Vin-Dotco Inc F 727 217-9200
Pinellas Park *(G-14393)*
Vonos LLC G 888 698-6667
Orlando *(G-13310)*
▼ **Whr Holdings LLC** D 954 342-4342
Fort Lauderdale *(G-4323)*

2843 Surface Active & Finishing Agents, Sulfonated Oils

Global Gl Lc G 863 551-1079
Winter Haven *(G-19326)*
International Finishes Inc F 561 948-1066
Boca Raton *(G-570)*
Paraflow Energy Solutions LLC E 713 239-0336
Boca Raton *(G-661)*
◆ **Vestagen Tchnical Textiles Inc** G 407 781-2570
Orlando *(G-13300)*

2844 Perfumes, Cosmetics & Toilet Preparations

365 Sun LLC G 208 357-8062
Palmetto *(G-13781)*
4elementum LLC G 305 989-1106
Miami *(G-9028)*
Abdiversified LLC E 954 791-6050
Plantation *(G-14485)*
◆ **Agustin Reyes Inc** F 305 558-8870
Hialeah *(G-5275)*
AIG Technologies Inc F 954 433-0618
Deerfield Beach *(G-2769)*
Airrenu LLC G 386 246-8694
Palm Coast *(G-13682)*
Aleavia Brands LLC G 407 289-2632
Orlando *(G-12451)*
Aleavia LLC G 407 898-5800
Orlando *(G-12452)*
Alfa Manufacturing Group LLC G 305 979-7344
Miami Gardens *(G-10733)*
Alt Thuyan G 407 302-3655
Sanford *(G-15991)*
American Hygenic Laboratories F 305 891-9518
Miami *(G-9144)*
Aquarian Bath Inc G 310 919-0220
Holly Hill *(G-5756)*
Aromavalue Inc G 866 223-7561
Oldsmar *(G-12205)*
Avon Company G 386 405-7208
Jacksonville *(G-6182)*
Ayam Beautycare LLC G 305 318-2598
Aventura *(G-262)*
Ayurdevas Natural Products LLC G 786 322-0909
Miami *(G-9205)*
▲ **B & R Products Inc** F 305 238-1592
Cutler Bay *(G-2386)*
B224 USA Co G 786 598-8805
Holiday *(G-5735)*
Beard Booze LLC G 352 424-0687
Lakeland *(G-7645)*
Beauty Awaits Cosmetics LLC G 754 226-5800
Miramar *(G-10973)*
▼ **Beauty Lab Inc** E 305 687-0071
Opa Locka *(G-12294)*
Beauty With Kelley Inc F 786 757-6485
Palmetto Bay *(G-13840)*
Beautyge Brands Usa Inc C 904 693-1200
Jacksonville *(G-6201)*
Berkant Corp F 305 771-5578
Miami *(G-9232)*
Biddiscombe International LLC F 727 299-9287
Saint Petersburg *(G-15720)*
▲ **Bobbie Weiner Enterprises LLC** G 817 615-8610
North Miami *(G-11628)*
Bpj International LLC G 305 507-8971
Doral *(G-3283)*
Brand Builders Rx LLC G 727 576-4013
Saint Petersburg *(G-15728)*
Brand Labs USA E 954 532-5390
Pompano Beach *(G-14620)*
Breeze Products Inc E 727 521-4482
Largo *(G-7914)*
▼ **Carfore Ltd** G 239 415-2275
Fort Myers *(G-4388)*
▼ **Caribbean Breeze Inc** G 904 261-7831
Fernandina Beach *(G-3732)*
Cbd Brands Inc G 561 325-0482
Jupiter *(G-7016)*
Celeb Luxury LLC F 954 763-0333
Davie *(G-2507)*
Cemi International Inc C 407 859-7701
Orlando *(G-12561)*
◆ **Chelly Cosmetics Manufacturing** G 305 471-9608
Miami *(G-9350)*
◆ **Chemco Corp** E 305 623-4445
Miami Lakes *(G-10776)*
▲ **Christian L International Inc** G 305 947-1722
Miami *(G-9351)*
▼ **Coco Cosmetics Inc** F 305 622-3488
Miami *(G-9371)*
▲ **Cofran International Corp** E 305 592-2644
Doral *(G-3302)*
Contours Rx LLC G 727 827-7321
Saint Petersburg *(G-15753)*
Cosmesis Skincare Inc G 954 963-5090
Hollywood *(G-5805)*
Cosmetic Corp of America Inc E 305 883-8434
Medley *(G-8636)*
Cosmetic Creations Inc G 904 261-7831
Fernandina Beach *(G-3733)*
◆ **Cosmetic Solutions LLC** E 561 226-8600
Boca Raton *(G-490)*
▼ **Cosmetics & Cleaners Intl LLC** E 305 592-5504
Doral *(G-3310)*
Cosmo International Corp E 954 798-4500
Deerfield Beach *(G-2804)*
▲ **Coughlan Products Corp** F 973 904-1500
Punta Gorda *(G-15202)*
Crunchi LLC G 772 600-8082
Stuart *(G-16929)*
▲ **Crusellas & Co Inc** F 305 261-9580
Miami *(G-9414)*
Custom Manufacturing Corp F 305 863-1001
Medley *(G-8639)*
CXR Strategies LLC G 516 998-0400
Royal Palm Beach *(G-15464)*
Daby Products Carisen G 305 559-3018
West Miami *(G-18781)*
Dermazone Solutions Inc E 727 446-6882
Saint Petersburg *(G-15758)*
◆ **Diora Professionnel LLC** F 954 628-5163
Hallandale Beach *(G-5181)*
Doerfler Manufacturing Inc G 763 772-3728
Umatilla *(G-18498)*
Ds Healthcare Group Inc C 888 404-7770
Doral *(G-3336)*
Eagle Labs Incorporated D 727 548-1816
Saint Petersburg *(G-15767)*
Edens Garden Natural H G 585 353-8547
Deltona *(G-3168)*
Edgewell Personal Care Company B 386 673-2024
Ormond Beach *(G-13367)*
▲ **Ei Global Group Llc** G 561 999-8989
Boca Raton *(G-515)*
◆ **Elizabeth Arden Inc** A 954 364-6900
Pembroke Pines *(G-14031)*
▼ **Epitomi Inc** E 305 971-5370
Miami *(G-9532)*
◆ **Esteemed Brands Inc** F 954 442-3923
Miramar *(G-10990)*
Eve Corporation E 305 599-3832
Boca Raton *(G-524)*
▲ **Ewhite LLC** G 954 530-3382
Fort Lauderdale *(G-3979)*
Extreme Care Inc G 239 898-3709
Cape Coral *(G-1421)*
F&J USA LLC E 800 406-6190
Miami Beach *(G-10666)*
Facelove Cosmetics Inc G 786 346-7357
Miami *(G-9556)*
Fekkai Brands LLC F 954 791-6050
Plantation *(G-14514)*
Fekkai Retail LLC D 866 514-8048
Plantation *(G-14515)*
Femmescience LLC G 305 361-0994
Key Biscayne *(G-7155)*
Fhs Enterprises LLC G 754 214-9379
Delray Beach *(G-3078)*
Filorga Americas Inc F 786 266-7429
Miami Beach *(G-10667)*
Firmenich Lakeland G 863 646-0165
Lakeland *(G-7686)*
▼ **Florida Glsd Holdings Inc** C 321 633-4644
Cocoa *(G-2023)*
▲ **Florida Keys Keylime Products** G 305 853-0378
Key Largo *(G-7169)*
◆ **Formulated Solutions LLC** D 727 373-3970
Largo *(G-7953)*
Formulated Solutions LLC F 727 456-0302
Saint Petersburg *(G-15788)*
Fragrance Expresscom LLC G 800 372-4726
Miami *(G-9596)*
Fresh Brandz LLC G 813 880-7110
Tampa *(G-17696)*
Fruitful LLC G 954 534-9828
Miami Lakes *(G-10792)*
Gaias Formula G 954 655-8095
Delray Beach *(G-3082)*
Get Salted LLC G 954 826-3947
Boca Raton *(G-544)*
Glamer Medspa LLC F 305 744-6908
Pembroke Pines *(G-14035)*
▲ **Grafton Products Corp** E 561 738-2886
Boynton Beach *(G-914)*
◆ **H2ocean LLC** F 866 420-2326
Stuart *(G-16953)*
▲ **Hydron Technologies Inc** G 727 342-5050
Saint Petersburg *(G-15809)*
Image International Inc G 561 793-9560
West Palm Beach *(G-18901)*
Inspec Solutions LLC E 866 467-7320
Holly Hill *(G-5758)*
Instanatural LLC E 800 290-6932
Orlando *(G-12832)*
Isle of Luxe Inc G 352 745-0515
Saint Augustine *(G-15558)*
It Smells Good G 904 899-2818
Jacksonville *(G-6504)*
James R Kontorchik LLC G 904 962-0597
Jacksonville *(G-6516)*
Jessups Specialty Products G 407 332-7574
Longwood *(G-8296)*
Joya Essentials LLC G 407 865-0880
Orlando *(G-12862)*
▲ **JP Cosmetics Inc** F 305 231-4963
Hialeah *(G-5468)*
Jupiter Wellness Inc G 561 462-2700
Jupiter *(G-7063)*
▲ **Kayva Distribution LLC** G 305 428-2816
Doral *(G-3406)*
Keralis Inter Inc F 305 345-0849
Miami *(G-9821)*
Keratronix Inc F 954 753-5741
Coral Springs *(G-2268)*
▲ **Kira Labs Inc** F 954 978-4549
Pompano Beach *(G-14739)*
Kookie Kllection Kosmetics LLC F 954 218-4302
Lauderdale Lakes *(G-8090)*
Kreyol Essence LLC F 786 453-8287
Miami *(G-9831)*
▲ **Ladove Inc** D 305 823-8051
Miami Lakes *(G-10803)*
Ladove Industries Inc G 305 624-2456
Miami Lakes *(G-10804)*
Lawton LLC G 833 493-7226
Sunrise *(G-17141)*
▲ **Lf of America Corp** G 561 988-0303
Boca Raton *(G-601)*
Lively Company LLC F 617 737-1199
Tampa *(G-17851)*
Lush Fresh Handmade Cosmetics G 850 650-2434
Destin *(G-3198)*
▲ **Luxe Brands Inc** E 954 791-6050
Plantation *(G-14529)*
Luxebrands LLC F 866 514-8048
Plantation *(G-14530)*
Luxury World LLC G 954 746-8776
Sunrise *(G-17145)*

S I C

◆ **M & S Computer Products Inc** G 561 244-5400
Boynton Beach *(G-930)*

Mar Company Distributors LLC E 786 477-4174
Miami *(G-9943)*

Matherson Organics LLC G 850 792-4007
Tallahassee *(G-17298)*

▲ **Mcllpack Inc** F 561 988-8545
Boca Raton *(G-614)*

▲ **Med-Nap LLC** F 352 796-6020
Brooksville *(G-1249)*

Menscience-Mk G 305 361-0994
Miami *(G-9975)*

Nac USA Corporation G 800 396-0149
Miami *(G-10058)*

Natural4naturalz LLC G 561 621-1546
Clewiston *(G-1985)*

New Mix Products G 904 292-1920
Jacksonville *(G-6628)*

Nohbo Labs LLC G 321 345-5319
Palm Bay *(G-13526)*

▲ **Nutra-Luxe MD LLC** F 239 561-9699
Fort Myers *(G-4552)*

Nutraceutical Corporation G 813 877-4186
Tampa *(G-17943)*

Odara Kanvas Cosmetics F 239 785-8013
Lehigh Acres *(G-8201)*

OL Products Inc D 813 854-3575
Oldsmar *(G-12252)*

Old 97 Company F 813 246-4180
Tampa *(G-17947)*

▲ **Ollie Pippa International Inc** G 888 851-6533
Boca Raton *(G-653)*

Omnireliant Corporation G 813 909-9191
Tampa *(G-17956)*

◆ **Oxygen Development LLC** C 954 480-2675
Palm Springs *(G-13778)*

▲ **Oz Naturals LLC** G 561 602-2932
West Palm Beach *(G-18979)*

Palladio Beauty Group LLC F 954 922-4311
Hollywood *(G-5886)*

▼ **Panama Jack Inc** F 407 843-8110
Orlando *(G-13047)*

▲ **Pb Group LLC** E 954 922-4311
Hollywood *(G-5887)*

Perfumeland F 407 354-3342
Orlando *(G-13065)*

Personal Brands LLC E 855 426-7765
Deerfield Beach *(G-2886)*

Pretty Vulgar LLC G 561 465-8831
Boca Raton *(G-674)*

Prevail Solutions LLC G 727 210-6600
Clearwater *(G-1846)*

◆ **Prime Enterprises LLC** D 305 625-4929
Hialeah *(G-5568)*

Prime Packaging Inc E 305 625-6737
Hialeah *(G-5569)*

Prime Topco LLC G 305 625-4929
Hialeah *(G-5570)*

Private Label Skin Na LLC C 877 516-2200
Saint Petersburg *(G-15890)*

Prive International Inc E 888 750-5850
North Miami Beach *(G-11698)*

Probiora Health LLC G 214 559-2994
Tampa *(G-18019)*

Product Max Group Inc G 813 949-5061
Land O Lakes *(G-7863)*

Products By O2 Inc E 561 392-1892
Boynton Beach *(G-946)*

Promex LLC G 305 884-2400
Hialeah *(G-5581)*

Promoitalia LLC G 305 347-5178
Miami *(G-10209)*

Pulsaderm LLC F 877 474-4038
Fort Myers *(G-4576)*

Pure Essential G 407 732-7225
Sanford *(G-16107)*

Pure Labs LLC G 561 659-2229
West Palm Beach *(G-19012)*

Pure Life Products LLC G 321 578-2060
Miami *(G-10216)*

Pure Source LLC E 305 477-8111
Doral *(G-3473)*

▼ **Pure-Chlor Systems Florida Inc** F 305 437-9937
Tampa *(G-18025)*

Rev Personal Care LLC G 832 217-8585
Wellington *(G-18729)*

Revlon Inc G 904 693-1254
Jacksonville *(G-6721)*

Revlon Consumer Products Corp G 904 378-4167
Jacksonville *(G-6722)*

▲ **Romano Group LLC** F 305 255-4242
Miami *(G-10278)*

◆ **Roux Laboratories Inc** B 904 366-2602
Jacksonville *(G-6736)*

Roux Laboratories Inc G 904 378-4167
Jacksonville *(G-6737)*

Rxgenesys LLC G 786 220-8366
Miami *(G-10290)*

Saavy Naturals G 904 372-0002
Neptune Beach *(G-11477)*

Sabrosol Laboratories LLC G 305 290-4038
North Miami *(G-11653)*

Salon Technologies Intl G 407 301-3726
Orlando *(G-13158)*

Sephora Inside Jcpenney G 386 752-2822
Lake City *(G-7383)*

Sesvalia Usa LLC G 305 615-1987
Coral Gables *(G-2195)*

Shiseido Americas Corporation F 305 416-6021
Miami *(G-10339)*

Sincerus Pharmaceuticals Inc C 800 604-5032
Pompano Beach *(G-14852)*

Skin Pro International Inc F 305 528-9095
Southwest Ranches *(G-16841)*

▲ **Skinmetics Inc** F 305 663-5750
Miami *(G-10357)*

▲ **South Beach Skin Care Inc** F 954 606-5057
Hallandale Beach *(G-5212)*

Stream2sea LLC G 866 960-9513
Bowling Green *(G-869)*

Stylors Inc F 904 765-4453
Jacksonville *(G-6820)*

Sweet & Saltsy Scrubs G 863 853-8874
Lakeland *(G-7814)*

▲ **Swisscosmet Corp** G 727 842-9419
New Port Richey *(G-11514)*

Tanning Research Labs LLC B 386 677-9559
Ormond Beach *(G-13405)*

◆ **Tend Skin International Inc** F 954 382-0800
Davie *(G-2602)*

◆ **Terry Laboratories LLC** F 321 259-1630
Melbourne *(G-8960)*

Three Cay G LLC G 904 930-4554
Jacksonville *(G-6852)*

Tropical Enterprises Intl F 813 837-9800
Tampa *(G-18202)*

Tropichem Research Labs LLC D 561 804-7603
Jupiter *(G-7134)*

▲ **Tupperware Brands Corporation** A 407 826-5050
Orlando *(G-13280)*

▲ **Unico International Trdg Corp** G 561 338-3338
Boca Raton *(G-765)*

▼ **Unilever** F 904 378-0298
Jacksonville *(G-6878)*

United World Imports LLC F 904 208-1252
Jacksonville *(G-6884)*

V P R A R T LLC E 786 205-4526
Hialeah *(G-5673)*

▲ **Van Tibolli Beauty Corp** E 305 390-0044
Fort Lauderdale *(G-4304)*

Vianny Corporation F 239 888-4536
Fort Myers *(G-4646)*

Vienna Beauty Products Co F 937 228-7109
Naples *(G-11451)*

Wake Up Beautiful G 941 792-6500
Bradenton *(G-1145)*

▲ **World Perfumes Inc** F 305 822-0004
Opa Locka *(G-12370)*

◆ **Xtreme Tools International Inc** E 305 622-7474
Opa Locka *(G-12371)*

Younger You Inc G 954 924-4462
Fort Lauderdale *(G-4333)*

2851 Paints, Varnishes, Lacquers, Enamels

AAA Architectural Elements F 941 722-1910
Palmetto *(G-13782)*

▼ **Acrylux Paint Mfg Co Inc** F 954 772-0300
Fort Lauderdale *(G-3780)*

Adsil Inc G 386 274-1382
Daytona Beach *(G-2621)*

All Florida Marketing G 813 281-4641
Rocky Point *(G-15458)*

All Tank Services LLC G 954 260-9443
Pompano Beach *(G-14585)*

All-Weather Coatings LLC G 888 405-8904
Orlando *(G-12455)*

American Coatings Corporation G 954 970-7820
Margate *(G-8535)*

Anchor Coatings Leesburg Inc E 352 728-0777
Leesburg *(G-8142)*

▼ **Anvil Paints & Coatings Inc** F 727 535-1411
Largo *(G-7897)*

Aquatic Technologies Inc F 772 225-4389
Jensen Beach *(G-6966)*

◆ **Associated Paint Inc** F 305 885-1964
Medley *(G-8616)*

Autek Spray Booths G 727 709-4373
Largo *(G-7902)*

Black Diamond Coatings Inc E 800 270-4050
Brooksville *(G-1215)*

Car Care Haven LLC G 855 464-2836
Englewood *(G-3671)*

▼ **Caribbean Paint Company Inc** G 305 594-4500
Doral *(G-3292)*

Cathodic Prtection Tech of Fla G 321 799-0046
Cocoa Beach *(G-2060)*

Coating Application Tech Inc F 781 850-5080
Sarasota *(G-16193)*

Complementary Coatings Corp C 386 428-6461
Orlando *(G-12608)*

Cork Industries Inc E 904 695-2400
Jacksonville *(G-6292)*

▼ **Coronado Paint Co Inc** C 386 428-6461
Orlando *(G-12622)*

Cress Chemical & Equipment Co G 407 425-2846
Orlando *(G-12628)*

▼ **Deako Coating & Chemical Inc** G 305 634-5162
Miami *(G-9442)*

Deako Coatings Chemical F 305 323-9914
Cutler Bay *(G-2393)*

Dekscape G 239 278-3325
Fort Myers *(G-4430)*

◆ **Delta Laboratories Inc** E 305 887-4393
Ocala *(G-11918)*

▼ **Dlz Holdings South Inc** F 352 344-8741
Inverness *(G-6086)*

Dynamis Epoxy LLC G 941 488-3999
Venice *(G-18544)*

Dynamis Inc G 941 488-3999
Venice *(G-18545)*

Ecosmart F 561 328-6488
Lake Park *(G-7468)*

Epoxy Floor Coatings LLC G 920 471-6913
Holiday *(G-5740)*

Epoxy2u of Florida Inc G 239 772-0899
Cape Coral *(G-1418)*

◆ **Faux Effects International Inc** E 772 778-9044
Fort Pierce *(G-4697)*

▼ **Fibre Tech Inc** E 727 539-0844
Largo *(G-7945)*

Findexcom Inc G 561 328-6488
Lake Park *(G-7470)*

Finyl Products Inc G 352 351-4033
Ocala *(G-11942)*

Florida Prtctive Coatings Cons G 407 322-1243
Lake Mary *(G-7419)*

Fort Myers Digital LLC G 239 482-3086
Fort Myers *(G-4458)*

Good 4 Tklc Inc G 321 632-4340
Rockledge *(G-15415)*

Gulf Coast Paint & Supplies F 813 932-3093
Tampa *(G-17733)*

Hco Holding I Corporation F 863 533-0522
Bartow *(G-318)*

Hentzen Coatings Inc F 727 572-4474
Clearwater *(G-1714)*

Hotspray Industrial Coatings F 407 658-5700
Orlando *(G-12810)*

Hy-Tech Thermal Solutions LLC G 321 984-9777
Melbourne *(G-8848)*

▲ **Inseco Inc** F 239 939-1072
Fort Myers *(G-4495)*

International Paint LLC G 321 636-9722
Cocoa *(G-2032)*

International Paint LLC G 305 620-9220
Opa Locka *(G-12326)*

▲ **J & J Inc** G 954 746-7300
Sunrise *(G-17132)*

Jodan Technology Inc G 561 515-5556
Lake Worth *(G-7561)*

▼ **Kel Glo Corp** G 305 751-5641
Miami *(G-9818)*

Ken R Avery Painting Inc E 813 855-5037
Oldsmar *(G-12239)*

Kiss Polymers LLC F 813 962-2703
Tampa *(G-17827)*

◆ **Lambert Corporation Florida** E 407 841-2940
Orlando *(G-12889)*

◆ **Lanco & Harris Corp** D 407 240-4000
Orlando *(G-12890)*

Lapolla Industries LLC.........F....... 954 379-0241
Deerfield Beach *(G-2857)*
Marine Industrial Paint Co.........F....... 727 527-3382
Saint Petersburg *(G-15848)*
Microguard.........G....... 386 274-1382
Daytona Beach *(G-2685)*
▼ **Nationwide Prtctive Cting Mfrs**.........E....... 941 753-7500
Sarasota *(G-16264)*
Nemec.........G....... 407 829-2679
Lake Mary *(G-7439)*
◆ **New Nautical Coatings Inc**.........E....... 727 523-8053
Clearwater *(G-1807)*
P S Research Corp.........G....... 954 558-8727
Lauderhill *(G-8119)*
Paints & Coatings Inc.........E....... 239 997-6645
North Fort Myers *(G-11601)*
Panhandle Paint & Dctg LLC.........G....... 850 596-9248
Panama City Beach *(G-13981)*
Parasol Films Inc.........G....... 954 478-8661
Tamarac *(G-17364)*
Poly Coatings of South Inc.........F....... 941 371-8555
Sarasota *(G-16546)*
Povia Paints Inc.........G....... 239 791-0011
Fort Myers *(G-4571)*
PPG Industries Inc.........E....... 305 477-0541
Doral *(G-3465)*
Pro-Tech Coatings Inc.........G....... 813 248-1477
Tampa *(G-18018)*
▼ **Reliance Supply Co USA LLC**.........G....... 954 971-9111
Pompano Beach *(G-14828)*
Rexpro Services.........G....... 561 328-6488
Lake Park *(G-7479)*
Rezolin LLC.........G....... 386 677-8238
Ormond Beach *(G-13396)*
▼ **Richards Paint Mfg Co Inc**.........D....... 321 636-6200
Rockledge *(G-15443)*
Roberlo Usa Inc.........F....... 786 334-6191
Doral *(G-3487)*
▼ **Scott Paint Company LLC**.........G....... 941 371-0015
Sarasota *(G-16586)*
Sfa Systems Inc.........E....... 561 585-5927
Lake Worth *(G-7586)*
Somay Manufacturing Inc.........G....... 305 637-4757
Miami *(G-10374)*
South Fla Pavement Coatings.........F....... 954 979-5997
Pompano Beach *(G-14857)*
▲ **Soythane Technologies Inc**.........F....... 904 225-1047
Yulee *(G-19501)*
▲ **Sun Coatings Inc**.........E....... 727 531-4100
Tampa *(G-18139)*
Techncal Pntg Jacksonville Inc.........E....... 904 652-1129
Jacksonville *(G-6842)*
Tex-Coat LLC.........E....... 800 454-0340
Panama City *(G-13955)*
Tex-Coat LLC.........G....... 954 581-0771
Fort Lauderdale *(G-4279)*
Textured Coatings.........G....... 850 360-1451
Panama City Beach *(G-13985)*
Tuf Top Coatings.........F....... 727 527-3382
Saint Petersburg *(G-15945)*
▼ **Ultra Tuff Manufacturing Inc**.........G....... 970 252-9457
Hobe Sound *(G-5730)*
Union Chemical Industries Corp.........F....... 716 866-4978
Boca Raton *(G-766)*
▲ **Vinavil Americas Corporation**.........D....... 954 246-8888
Deerfield Beach *(G-2933)*
Zurigo Trading Inc.........G....... 305 244-4681
Miami *(G-10633)*

2861 Gum & Wood Chemicals

AZ Chem Holdings LP.........C....... 800 526-5294
Jacksonville *(G-6183)*
◆ **Kraton Chemical LLC**.........C....... 904 928-8700
Jacksonville *(G-6546)*
Lignotech Florida LLC.........E....... 904 577-9077
Fernandina Beach *(G-3742)*
Taber Incorporated.........G....... 401 245-2800
Port St Lucie *(G-15180)*

2865 Cyclic-Crudes, Intermediates, Dyes & Org Pigments

Ad-Tar.........G....... 561 732-2055
Boynton Beach *(G-872)*
◆ **Allied USA Incorporated**.........G....... 305 235-3950
Miami *(G-9118)*
▲ **Ashwell Label Dies Inc**.........F....... 727 527-0098
Pinellas Park *(G-14335)*
Inter Cell Technologies Inc.........G....... 561 575-6868
Jupiter *(G-7058)*
Keystone Color Works Inc.........G....... 813 250-1313
Tampa *(G-17820)*
Tar Building LLC.........G....... 407 896-7252
Orlando *(G-13240)*

2869 Industrial Organic Chemicals, NEC

4 Fuel LLC.........G....... 954 929-5803
Hollywood *(G-5762)*
▼ **AB Enzymes Inc**.........G....... 954 278-3975
Plantation *(G-14482)*
AB Vista Inc.........G....... 954 278-3965
Plantation *(G-14484)*
Advanced Fuel Injection.........G....... 561 248-6793
Jupiter *(G-6993)*
Aerialife Inc.........G....... 561 990-9299
Lake Worth *(G-7530)*
Aero Fuel LLC.........G....... 352 728-2018
Leesburg *(G-8139)*
Aerojet Rocketdyne De Inc.........C....... 561 882-5150
Jupiter *(G-6996)*
Agri-Source Fuels LLC.........E....... 352 521-3460
Pensacola *(G-14085)*
Air Esscentials Inc.........E....... 305 446-1670
Miami *(G-9091)*
Ameri Food & Fuel Inc.........G....... 727 584-0120
Largo *(G-7892)*
America Marine & Fuel Inc.........G....... 239 261-3715
Naples *(G-11160)*
American Carbons Inc.........G....... 850 265-4214
Lynn Haven *(G-8428)*
American Industrial Group Inc.........F....... 703 757-7683
North Miami Beach *(G-11666)*
▲ **Armmaz Products Inc**.........D....... 863 578-1206
Mulberry *(G-11119)*
Awareness Technology Inc.........C....... 772 283-6540
Palm City *(G-13642)*
Baa LLC.........F....... 954 292-9449
Miramar *(G-10972)*
◆ **Bartow Ethanol Florida LC**.........F....... 863 533-2498
Bartow *(G-307)*
▲ **Bastech LLC**.........E....... 904 737-1722
Jacksonville *(G-6196)*
Big Bend Fuel Inc.........E....... 727 946-8727
Gibsonton *(G-5027)*
Bio Fuel Professionals.........G....... 239 591-3835
Naples *(G-11188)*
Bio-Lab Inc.........F....... 863 709-1411
Lakeland *(G-7646)*
Blue Biofuels Inc.........G....... 561 693-1943
Palm Beach Gardens *(G-13571)*
Bn Biofuels LLC.........G....... 312 239-2680
Riviera Beach *(G-15303)*
Body Fuel LLC.........G....... 386 566-1855
Port Orange *(G-15013)*
Bridgeport Chemical.........G....... 941 753-2520
Bradenton *(G-1002)*
Caribbean Fuels Inc.........G....... 305 233-3016
Miami *(G-9316)*
Cfuel Energy Corp.........G....... 561 336-4084
Miami *(G-9346)*
Chadwick S Fuel Co Inc.........G....... 754 224-8773
Fort Lauderdale *(G-3894)*
Clock Spring Company Inc.........F....... 561 683-6992
Riviera Beach *(G-15312)*
▲ **Coastal Fuels Mktg Inc**.........G....... 941 722-7753
Palmetto *(G-13792)*
Collier Parkway Fuel LLC.........G....... 732 492-4791
Land O Lakes *(G-7851)*
Consolidated Forest Pdts Inc.........F....... 407 830-7723
Longwood *(G-8267)*
Consolidated Forest Pdts Inc.........G....... 407 830-7723
Perry *(G-14298)*
◆ **Cosmo International Corp**.........E....... 954 798-4500
Deerfield Beach *(G-2803)*
Costal Fuels Marketing.........G....... 904 358-6725
Jacksonville *(G-6295)*
Daleo Fuels Inc.........G....... 954 931-3331
Oakland Park *(G-11795)*
Divitae Inc.........G....... 786 585-5556
Hialeah *(G-5374)*
Douglas Fuel II Inc.........G....... 305 620-0707
Miami Gardens *(G-10737)*
E T I Incorporated.........E....... 727 546-6472
Largo *(G-7938)*
Element Solutions Inc.........B....... 561 207-9600
Fort Lauderdale *(G-3968)*
Envirnmental Mfg Solutions LLC.........F....... 321 837-0050
Melbourne *(G-8826)*
▲ **Essential Oil University LLC**.........G....... 502 498-8804
Englewood *(G-3676)*
Ethnergy International Inc.........E....... 954 499-1582
Pembroke Pines *(G-14033)*
Excel Fuel Inc.........G....... 727 547-5511
Saint Petersburg *(G-15774)*
Express Fuel Systems Inc.........G....... 904 525-4052
Jacksonville *(G-6375)*
Fast Fuel Corp.........G....... 786 251-0373
Hialeah *(G-5406)*
Fire Fly Fuels Inc.........G....... 941 404-6820
Sarasota *(G-16432)*
Firstpath Laboratory Svcs LLC.........G....... 954 977-6977
Pompano Beach *(G-14693)*
Florida Rum Company LLC.........E....... 305 791-1221
Hollywood *(G-5823)*
Freon & Fabric.........G....... 386 801-5096
Deltona *(G-3171)*
Fuel Connection.........G....... 305 354-8115
North Miami *(G-11639)*
Fuel Life 1 LLC.........G....... 954 652-1735
Weston *(G-19128)*
Fuel N Go LLC.........G....... 239 656-1072
Estero *(G-3690)*
Fuel Productions LLC.........G....... 904 342-7826
Saint Augustine *(G-15544)*
Fuel Solutions LLC.........G....... 813 969-2506
Tampa *(G-17697)*
Fuel U Fast Inc.........G....... 561 654-0212
Boca Raton *(G-541)*
Fuelmyschool.........G....... 407 952-1030
Windermere *(G-19227)*
Gaseous Fuel Systems Corp.........G....... 954 693-9475
Weston *(G-19130)*
Givaudan Fragrances Corp.........E....... 863 667-0821
Lakeland *(G-7698)*
▲ **Green Biofuels LLC**.........F....... 305 639-3030
Miami *(G-9664)*
Green Biofuels Miami LLC.........F....... 305 639-3030
Miami *(G-9665)*
Green Fuel Systems LLC.........G....... 352 483-5005
Eustis *(G-3708)*
Green Marine Fuels Inc.........F....... 305 775-3546
Miami *(G-9668)*
Greenwave Biodiesel LLC.........G....... 239 682-7700
Fort Lauderdale *(G-4032)*
Harcros Chemicals Inc.........E....... 813 247-4531
Tampa *(G-17743)*
◆ **HB Sealing Products Inc**.........C....... 727 796-1300
Clearwater *(G-1712)*
◆ **Hepburn Industries Inc**.........G....... 305 757-6688
Miami *(G-9702)*
Highlands Ethanol LLC.........G....... 813 421-1090
Tampa *(G-17754)*
▲ **Iff Chemical Holdings Inc**.........C....... 904 783-2180
Jacksonville *(G-6488)*
Kendall Fuel Inc.........G....... 305 270-7735
Miami *(G-9819)*
Kraton Chemical LLC.........D....... 850 785-8521
Panama City *(G-13924)*
Largent Fuels USA LLC.........G....... 786 431-5981
Miami *(G-9859)*
Lee County Fuels Inc.........G....... 239 349-5322
Fort Myers *(G-4517)*
Liles Oil Company.........F....... 407 739-2083
Casselberry *(G-1509)*
Living Fuel Inc.........G....... 813 254-0777
Tampa *(G-17852)*
Mendez Fuel.........G....... 305 227-0470
Miami *(G-9973)*
Mmt Technologies Inc.........G....... 863 619-2926
Lakeland *(G-7753)*
Mobil Boat Fuel Inc.........G....... 941 718-3781
Bradenton *(G-1079)*
Montedana Fuels.........G....... 305 887-6754
Hialeah *(G-5525)*
Natural Ethercom.........G....... 954 274-6801
Coral Springs *(G-2295)*
Natural Organic Products Intl.........G....... 352 383-8252
Mount Dora *(G-11108)*
Natures Fuel Inc.........G....... 407 808-4272
Orlando *(G-12993)*
North America Bio Fuel Corp.........G....... 877 877-9279
Bradenton *(G-1087)*
Nu Earth Labs LLC.........E....... 727 648-4787
Dunedin *(G-3585)*
Omega Energy Usa LLC.........G....... 786 245-0642
Miami *(G-10097)*
On The Go Food & Fuel Inc.........F....... 727 815-0823
New Port Richey *(G-11506)*
◆ **Originates Inc**.........F....... 954 233-2500
Aventura *(G-279)*

SIC

Originclear Inc ... G ... 323 939-6645
Clearwater *(G-1822)*
Parabel Inc ... E ... 321 409-7415
Melbourne *(G-8905)*
Parabel USA Inc ... F ... 978 905-0958
Vero Beach *(G-18650)*
Pentacles Energy GP LLC ... G ... 786 552-9931
Coral Gables *(G-2184)*
Phillips Energy Inc ... G ... 850 682-5127
Crestview *(G-2355)*
Phlexapeel LLC ... G ... 407 990-1854
Melbourne *(G-8907)*
Pspc Escrow II Corp ... G ... 561 207-9600
West Palm Beach *(G-19009)*
▲ **Pure Solutions Inc** ... E ... 813 925-1098
Tampa *(G-18024)*
R & A Performance Fuel Inc ... G ... 954 237-9824
Pembroke Pines *(G-14055)*
R-Da Trading LLC ... G ... 954 278-6983
Weston *(G-19162)*
Rat Trap Bait Company Inc ... F ... 863 967-2148
Auburndale *(G-251)*
Renewable Fuels Group LLC ... G ... 305 388-3028
Miami *(G-10253)*
Rhodes Brothers Miami Inc ... G ... 305 456-9682
Miami Springs *(G-10897)*
Romco Fuels Inc ... F ... 954 474-5392
Davie *(G-2586)*
▲ **Rp International LLC** ... E ... 941 894-1228
Sarasota *(G-16566)*
Sab Fuels Inc ... G ... 786 213-3399
Sarasota *(G-16569)*
Safe Industries Inc ... F ... 321 639-8646
Rockledge *(G-15445)*
Shot of Freon ... G ... 305 917-5893
Lehigh Acres *(G-8207)*
Sincere Fuel Inc ... G ... 954 433-3577
Miramar *(G-11044)*
Skymo LLC ... F ... 305 676-6739
Cooper City *(G-2115)*
Soul Fuel Inc ... G ... 407 448-6533
Orlando *(G-13200)*
South East Fuel LLC ... G ... 407 392-4668
Orlando *(G-13201)*
Southern Fuel Inc ... G ... 904 545-5163
Glen Saint Mary *(G-5039)*
◆ **St Marks Powder Inc** ... B ... 850 577-2824
Crawfordville *(G-2336)*
Syi Inc ... G ... 954 323-2483
Sunrise *(G-17183)*
Symrise Inc ... C ... 904 768-5800
Jacksonville *(G-6833)*
Synergy Ancillary Services LLC ... F ... 561 249-7238
Port Saint Lucie *(G-15151)*
▼ **Td Fuel Inc** ... G ... 561 305-2059
Fort Lauderdale *(G-4274)*
◆ **Terry Laboratories LLC** ... F ... 321 259-1630
Melbourne *(G-8960)*
▼ **Texene LLC** ... F ... 305 200-5001
Miami Lakes *(G-10867)*
United Fuel ... G ... 305 992-2923
Miami *(G-10536)*
US Fuels Inc ... F ... 254 559-1212
Rotonda West *(G-15460)*
◆ **Viesel Fuel LLC** ... E ... 772 781-4300
Stuart *(G-17045)*
W & B Scientific Inc ... F ... 954 607-1500
Pompano Beach *(G-14911)*
Wesley Chapel Fuel Inc ... G ... 813 907-9994
Wesley Chapel *(G-18764)*
Wf Fuel ... G ... 941 706-4953
Sarasota *(G-16638)*
Wise Gas Fuel Card LLC ... G ... 954 636-4291
Weston *(G-19178)*
World Fuel Cx LLC ... F ... 305 428-8000
Doral *(G-3551)*
World Hlth Enrgy Holdings Inc ... F ... 561 870-0440
Boca Raton *(G-791)*

2873 Nitrogenous Fertilizers

Agrium Advanced Tech US Inc ... F ... 407 302-2024
Sanford *(G-15989)*
Anuvia Florida LLC ... F ... 352 720-7070
Mount Dora *(G-11096)*
Anuvia Plant City LLC ... E ... 407 719-7798
Plant City *(G-14401)*
Anuvia Plant Ntrnts Hldngs LLC ... G ... 352 720-7070
Zellwood *(G-19502)*
Barber Fertilizer Company ... E ... 850 263-6324
Campbellton *(G-1330)*
Ben Hill Griffin Inc ... D ... 863 635-2281
Frostproof *(G-4856)*
Bionitrogen Holdings Corp ... G ... 561 600-9550
West Palm Beach *(G-18820)*
Earthsoil Inc ... G ... 888 282-1920
Fleming Island *(G-3761)*
Florida Phosphorus ... G ... 561 983-3208
Key Largo *(G-7170)*
Freeport Ammonia LLC ... G ... 813 222-3813
Tampa *(G-17695)*
Go Green Marine Inc ... G ... 850 499-5137
Destin *(G-3191)*
▲ **Greentechnologies LLC** ... G ... 352 379-7780
Gainesville *(G-4932)*
Growers Fertilizer Corporation ... E ... 863 956-1101
Lake Alfred *(G-7332)*
Natural Organic Products Intl ... G ... 352 383-8252
Mount Dora *(G-11108)*
Nurserymens Sure-Gro Corp ... G ... 772 770-0462
Vero Beach *(G-18648)*
Oceangrown ... F ... 941 921-2401
Fort Pierce *(G-4723)*
Pathway Holdings LLC ... G ... 813 514-7899
Palmetto *(G-13815)*
◆ **Pioneer Ag-Chem Inc** ... E ... 772 464-9300
Fort Pierce *(G-4734)*
◆ **Plant Solutions Inc** ... E ... 305 242-3103
Homestead *(G-5988)*
Proplus Products Inc ... F ... 863 375-2487
Bowling Green *(G-867)*
▲ **Stoller Chemical Co of Florida** ... F ... 352 357-3173
Eustis *(G-3717)*
T Brand Fertilizer Inc ... G ... 386 437-2970
Bunnell *(G-1307)*
Trans-Resources LLC ... A ... 305 933-8301
Sunny Isles Beach *(G-17082)*
Turf Care Supply Corp ... E ... 863 655-2424
Sebring *(G-16717)*
▲ **United AG Svcs Amer Inc** ... F ... 352 793-1682
Lake Panasoffkee *(G-7464)*

2874 Phosphatic Fertilizers

Bastech Inc ... F ... 904 737-1722
Jacksonville *(G-6195)*
Florida Phosphate Council Inc ... G ... 863 904-0641
Tallahassee *(G-17254)*
Growers Fertilizer Corporation ... E ... 863 956-1101
Lake Alfred *(G-7332)*
Mos Holdings Inc ... E ... 763 577-2700
Mulberry *(G-11131)*
◆ **Mosaic Company** ... A ... 813 775-4200
Tampa *(G-17919)*
Mosaic Crop Nutrition LLC ... D ... 813 500-6800
Lithia *(G-8220)*
◆ **Mosaic Fertilizer LLC** ... A ... 813 500-6300
Lithia *(G-8221)*
Novaphos Inc ... E ... 863 285-8607
Fort Meade *(G-4338)*
Nurserymens Sure-Gro Corp ... G ... 772 770-0462
Vero Beach *(G-18648)*
◆ **Plant Solutions Inc** ... E ... 305 242-3103
Homestead *(G-5988)*
◆ **White Springs AG Chem Inc** ... A ... 386 397-8101
White Springs *(G-19189)*

2875 Fertilizers, Mixing Only

Atlas Orgnics Indian River LLC ... F ... 772 563-9336
Vero Beach *(G-18595)*
▲ **Ausoil International Corp** ... D ... 954 249-8060
Sunrise *(G-17092)*
Barber Fertilizer Company ... E ... 850 263-6324
Campbellton *(G-1330)*
▲ **Ben Hill Griffin Inc** ... E ... 863 635-2281
Frostproof *(G-4855)*
Ben Hill Griffin Inc ... D ... 863 635-2281
Frostproof *(G-4856)*
◆ **Chemical Dynamics Inc** ... E ... 813 752-4950
Plant City *(G-14418)*
Consoldted Rsurce Recovery Inc ... E ... 813 262-8404
Tampa *(G-17552)*
Diamond R Fertilizer Co Inc ... F ... 863 763-2158
Okeechobee *(G-12176)*
Earthsoil Inc ... G ... 888 282-1920
Fleming Island *(G-3761)*
Farmers Cooperative Inc ... E ... 386 362-1459
Live Oak *(G-8232)*
Forestry Resources Inc ... E ... 239 332-3966
Fort Myers *(G-4457)*
Genesis II Systems Inc ... G ... 954 489-1124
Fort Lauderdale *(G-4019)*
◆ **Harrells LLC** ... C ... 863 687-2774
Lakeland *(G-7703)*
Jfe Compost ... F ... 863 532-9629
Okeechobee *(G-12183)*
▲ **Klasmann-Deilmann Americas Inc** ... G ... 305 397-8498
Miami *(G-9826)*
Lesco Inc ... F ... 863 655-2424
Sebring *(G-16697)*
▼ **Plant Foods Inc** ... E ... 772 567-5741
Vero Beach *(G-18654)*
S A Florikan-E LLC ... D ... 800 322-8666
Bowling Green *(G-868)*
Sun Gro Horticulture Dist Inc ... G ... 407 291-1676
Orlando *(G-13222)*
Sunshine Organics Compost LLC ... G ... 904 900-3072
Jacksonville *(G-6825)*
▲ **United AG Svcs Amer Inc** ... F ... 352 793-1682
Lake Panasoffkee *(G-7464)*
Wedgworth Farms Inc ... G ... 561 996-2076
Plant City *(G-14478)*
▼ **Wedgworths Inc** ... G ... 561 996-2076
Belle Glade *(G-355)*

2879 Pesticides & Agricultural Chemicals, NEC

◆ **Agra Chem Sales Co Inc** ... G ... 863 453-6450
Avon Park *(G-283)*
▼ **Agranco Corp (usa)** ... F ... 877 592-0031
South Miami *(G-16811)*
Agrosource Inc ... F ... 908 251-3500
Jupiter *(G-6998)*
Ai Thomas LLC ... E ... 904 553-6202
Ponte Vedra Beach *(G-14929)*
Ben Hill Griffin Inc ... D ... 863 635-2281
Frostproof *(G-4856)*
▲ **Biochem Manufacturing Inc** ... E ... 561 799-1590
Jupiter *(G-7010)*
Brandfx LLC ... E ... 321 632-2063
Cocoa *(G-2000)*
Brewer International Inc ... F ... 772 562-0555
Vero Beach *(G-18603)*
Collins and Dupont Interiors ... G ... 239 694-3400
Fort Myers *(G-4406)*
Consulier Engineering Inc ... G ... 561 842-2492
Riviera Beach *(G-15314)*
◆ **Custom Agronomics Inc** ... F ... 772 223-0775
Palm City *(G-13650)*
Diamond R Fertilizer Co Inc ... F ... 863 763-2158
Okeechobee *(G-12176)*
Dupont Fine Homes Inc ... G ... 850 934-8545
Gulf Breeze *(G-5116)*
◆ **Excelag Corp** ... G ... 305 670-0145
Miami *(G-9544)*
◆ **Flottec LLC** ... G ... 973 588-4717
Jupiter *(G-7046)*
Fresh Mark Corporation ... F ... 352 394-7746
Clermont *(G-1961)*
▲ **Glades Formulating Corporation** ... F ... 561 996-4200
Belle Glade *(G-348)*
Growers Fertilizer Corporation ... E ... 863 956-1101
Lake Alfred *(G-7332)*
▼ **Humic Growth Solutions Inc** ... F ... 904 392-7201
Jacksonville *(G-6483)*
Humic Growth Solutions Inc ... G ... 904 329-1012
Green Cove Springs *(G-5066)*
Humic Growth Solutions Inc ... G ... 904 329-1012
Saint Johns *(G-15678)*
Lenoc Chemical Solutions Inc ... G ... 229 499-0665
Bowling Green *(G-866)*
▲ **Levita LLC** ... G ... 954 227-7468
Coral Springs *(G-2273)*
▼ **Matrix24 Laboratories LLC** ... F ... 941 879-3048
Sarasota *(G-16253)*
Morse Enterprises Limited Inc ... G ... 407 682-6500
Miami *(G-10042)*
Natures Own Pest Control Inc ... G ... 941 378-3334
Sarasota *(G-16521)*
North Florida AG Services Inc ... G ... 352 494-3978
Lake City *(G-7371)*
▼ **Numerator Technologies Inc** ... G ... 941 807-5333
Sarasota *(G-16526)*
▼ **Organic Laboratories Inc** ... G ... 772 286-5581
Fort Pierce *(G-4728)*
Pbi/Gordon Corp ... F ... 850 478-2770
Pensacola *(G-14223)*
▲ **Redeagle International LLC** ... G ... 863 682-6698
Lakeland *(G-7777)*
Rx For Fleas Inc ... F ... 954 351-9244
Fort Lauderdale *(G-4220)*

▲ Sawyer Products Inc..........E....... 727 725-1177
Safety Harbor *(G-15502)*
Trans-Resources LLC..........A....... 305 933-8301
Sunny Isles Beach *(G-17082)*
Velmaxxx Enterprises Inc..........G....... 239 689-4343
Fort Myers *(G-4645)*

2891 Adhesives & Sealants

10 Roof Cottage LLC..........G....... 888 667-6961
Tampa *(G-17371)*
386 Nanotech Inc..........F....... 727 252-9580
South Pasadena *(G-16833)*
Adhesive Manufacturers Inc..........G....... 305 495-8018
Pembroke Pines *(G-14014)*
Adhesive Technologies Fla LLC..........G....... 941 228-0295
Sarasota *(G-16333)*
◆ Adhesives Technology Corp..........D....... 754 399-1684
Pompano Beach *(G-14578)*
American Acrylic Adhesives LLC..........F....... 877 422-4583
Largo *(G-7893)*
American Adhesives LLC..........G....... 877 422-4583
Largo *(G-7894)*
Anchor Coatings Leesburg Inc..........E....... 352 728-0777
Leesburg *(G-8142)*
Continental Palatka LLC..........D....... 703 480-3800
Palatka *(G-13475)*
Craig Armstrong..........F....... 786 319-6514
Miami Beach *(G-10660)*
Dynamis Epoxy LLC..........G....... 941 488-3999
Venice *(G-18544)*
Fasco Epoxies Inc..........F....... 772 464-0808
Fort Pierce *(G-4696)*
Foamseal Hurricane Adhesive..........G....... 850 766-2000
Tallahassee *(G-17257)*
◆ Gardner-Gibson Mfg Inc..........E....... 813 248-2101
Tampa *(G-17705)*
Greencore LLC..........G....... 727 251-9837
Saint Petersburg *(G-15798)*
HB Fuller Cnstr Pdts Inc..........G....... 352 372-3931
Gainesville *(G-4935)*
▲ Hernon Manufacturing Inc..........D....... 407 322-4000
Sanford *(G-16061)*
ICP Adhesives Sealants..........G....... 954 905-0531
Coral Springs *(G-2259)*
◆ Jamo Inc..........D....... 305 885-3444
Medley *(G-8676)*
◆ Lambert Corporation Florida..........E....... 407 841-2940
Orlando *(G-12889)*
Lapolla Industries LLC..........F....... 954 379-0241
Deerfield Beach *(G-2857)*
Lehigh White Cement Co LLC..........D....... 561 812-7439
West Palm Beach *(G-18928)*
Lehigh White Cement Co LLC..........C....... 561 812-7441
Tampa *(G-17842)*
◆ Mapei Corporation..........C....... 954 246-8888
Deerfield Beach *(G-2868)*
Masking Systems of America..........F....... 813 920-2271
Odessa *(G-12133)*
Master Painting & Sealants LLC..........G....... 305 910-5104
Miami *(G-9955)*
Mg Coating and Sealantsllc..........G....... 305 409-0915
North Miami *(G-11646)*
◆ Nfk Corporation..........F....... 305 791-2044
Miami *(G-10069)*
Ocoow LLC..........G....... 805 266-7616
Sopchoppy *(G-16785)*
P S Research Corp..........G....... 954 558-8727
Lauderhill *(G-8119)*
Palm Labs Adhesives LLC..........F....... 321 710-4850
Debary *(G-2753)*
PPG Architectural Finishes Inc..........G....... 813 877-5841
Tampa *(G-17999)*
Premium Auto Sealant Usa LLC..........G....... 786 637-2573
Medley *(G-8709)*
Quality Industrial Chem Inc..........F....... 727 573-5760
Saint Petersburg *(G-15896)*
▼ Rcd Corporation..........G....... 352 589-0099
Eustis *(G-3716)*
S & R Fastener Co Inc..........G....... 352 588-0768
San Antonio *(G-15978)*
Southast Clking Slant Svcs LLC..........G....... 813 731-8778
Plant City *(G-14466)*
◆ Southern Grouts & Mortars Inc..........D....... 954 943-2288
Pompano Beach *(G-14863)*
Srm Waterproofing Sealants Inc..........G....... 407 963-3619
Orlando *(G-13209)*
Stella Sealants Corp..........G....... 941 357-1566
Sarasota *(G-16302)*
◆ T S E Industries Inc..........C....... 727 573-7676
Clearwater *(G-1900)*
United Adhesive Products Inc..........G....... 863 698-9484
Winter Haven *(G-19365)*
Ussi LLC..........F....... 941 244-2408
Venice *(G-18583)*

2892 Explosives

Austin Powder Company..........G....... 352 690-7060
Anthony *(G-94)*
Austin Powder Company..........G....... 863 674-0504
Fort Denaud *(G-3770)*
Boland Production Supply Inc..........G....... 863 324-7784
Winter Haven *(G-19304)*
Dyno Nobel Inc..........G....... 352 796-9018
Brooksville *(G-1227)*
◆ General Dynmics Ord Tctcal Sys..........C....... 727 578-8100
Saint Petersburg *(G-15791)*
Ireco Inc..........F....... 239 593-3749
Naples *(G-11292)*
J & G Explosives LLC..........F....... 407 883-0734
Fort Lauderdale *(G-4072)*

2893 Printing Ink

Allied Graphics Inc..........G....... 954 327-8559
Fort Lauderdale *(G-3802)*
Amrob Inc..........G....... 813 238-6041
Tampa *(G-17424)*
Amrob Incorporated..........G....... 813 237-5891
Odessa *(G-12101)*
Florida Ink Mfg Co Inc..........G....... 813 247-2911
Tampa *(G-17679)*
Folders Tabs Et Cetera..........F....... 813 884-3651
Tampa *(G-17691)*
Hailey Cian LLC..........G....... 954 895-7143
Fort Lauderdale *(G-4038)*
Indian Toners USA Company..........G....... 954 600-5483
Parkland *(G-13991)*
Instorescreen LLC..........G....... 646 301-4690
Naples *(G-11287)*
J&S Inks LLC..........G....... 305 999-0304
North Miami Beach *(G-11685)*
◆ One Step Papers LLC..........G....... 305 238-2296
Miami *(G-10103)*
Peace River Deli Provs Inc..........E....... 941 426-4846
Port Charlotte *(G-14993)*
Rainbow Ink Products Inc..........G....... 954 252-6030
Davie *(G-2579)*
T C Deliveries..........G....... 813 881-1830
Tampa *(G-18150)*
◆ US Ink A Div Sun Chem Corp..........G....... 904 786-1474
Middleburg *(G-10914)*
Yes Solutions Gallery LLC..........G....... 352 622-7937
Ocala *(G-12079)*

2899 Chemical Preparations, NEC

21st Century Chemical Inc..........G....... 954 689-7111
Fort Lauderdale *(G-3772)*
A 2 Z of Lake City Inc..........F....... 386 755-0235
Lake City *(G-7343)*
ACC Holdco Inc..........C....... 863 578-1206
Mulberry *(G-11118)*
Advantagecare Inc..........G....... 407 345-8877
Orlando *(G-12435)*
Agarose Unlimited Inc..........G....... 800 850-0659
Gainesville *(G-4869)*
◆ Akj Industries Inc..........G....... 239 939-1696
Fort Myers *(G-4348)*
Amaya Solutions Inc..........E....... 813 246-5448
Plant City *(G-14398)*
◆ American Water Chemicals Inc..........F....... 813 246-5448
Plant City *(G-14400)*
Arcpoint of Tallahassee Inc..........D....... 850 201-2500
Tallahassee *(G-17222)*
▲ Arrmaz Products Inc..........D....... 863 578-1206
Mulberry *(G-11119)*
▲ Aurum Chemicals Corp..........G....... 305 412-4141
Miami *(G-9192)*
▲ B & R Products Inc..........F....... 305 238-1592
Cutler Bay *(G-2386)*
Bbj Environmental LLC..........G....... 813 622-8550
Tampa *(G-17461)*
Beesfree Inc..........G....... 561 939-4860
West Palm Beach *(G-18817)*
Bell Performance Inc..........F....... 407 831-5021
Longwood *(G-8262)*
◆ Belzona Inc..........E....... 305 594-4994
Doral *(G-3269)*
Blue Earth Solutions Inc..........E....... 352 729-0150
Clermont *(G-1949)*
Blue Planet Envmtl Systems..........G....... 321 255-1931
Palm Bay *(G-13505)*
▲ Bluworld Innovations LLC..........D....... 888 499-5433
Orlando *(G-12528)*
Boland Production Supply Inc..........G....... 863 324-7784
Winter Haven *(G-19304)*
Bonsal American Inc..........G....... 813 621-2427
Tampa *(G-17482)*
Buckeye International Inc..........G....... 813 621-6260
Tampa *(G-17488)*
Byte Size It LLC..........G....... 386 785-9311
Deltona *(G-3165)*
C & J Cstm Wldg Fbrication LLC..........G....... 407 414-1739
Kissimmee *(G-7228)*
Camco Chemical..........G....... 239 992-4100
Bonita Springs *(G-823)*
Chem Guard Inc..........F....... 407 402-2798
Casselberry *(G-1500)*
Chemline Inc..........G....... 407 847-4181
Kissimmee *(G-7230)*
Cjb Industries Inc..........F....... 941 552-8397
Sarasota *(G-16384)*
◆ Cleanpak Products LLC..........G....... 813 740-8611
Tampa *(G-17541)*
◆ Clinical Dagnstc Solutions Inc..........E....... 954 791-1773
Plantation *(G-14500)*
Color-Chrome Technologies Inc..........G....... 954 335-0127
Fort Lauderdale *(G-3910)*
Compass Service..........G....... 954 900-4462
Lauderhill *(G-8105)*
DSM Lake City LLC..........G....... 352 861-5843
Ocala *(G-11927)*
Duncanson Dynasty Inc..........G....... 561 288-1349
West Palm Beach *(G-18856)*
◆ Dyadic International USA Inc..........G....... 561 743-8333
Jupiter *(G-7028)*
E-Liquids Investment Group LLC..........E....... 954 507-6060
Sunrise *(G-17117)*
Ecological Laboratories Inc..........E....... 239 573-6650
Cape Coral *(G-1416)*
Edible Flair Inc..........G....... 954 321-3608
Fort Lauderdale *(G-3963)*
Element Solutions Inc..........B....... 561 207-9600
Fort Lauderdale *(G-3968)*
Elisa Technologies Inc..........F....... 352 337-3929
Gainesville *(G-4914)*
▼ Enviroseal Corporation..........G....... 772 335-8225
Port Saint Lucie *(G-15106)*
Enzymedica Inc..........E....... 941 505-5565
Venice *(G-18547)*
▼ Euclid Chemical Company..........F....... 813 886-8811
Odessa *(G-12119)*
▲ Far Research Inc..........E....... 321 723-6160
Palm Bay *(G-13511)*
Felix Reynoso..........G....... 954 497-2330
Oakland Park *(G-11805)*
Flare Clothing Inc..........G....... 863 859-1800
Lakeland *(G-7688)*
Florida Kolmiami Corporation..........G....... 305 582-0114
Miami Lakes *(G-10791)*
Fort Myers Bch Soccer Leag Inc..........G....... 239 353-7567
Fort Myers Beach *(G-4662)*
▼ Freezetone Products LLC..........F....... 305 640-0414
Doral *(G-3355)*
Fritz Duane L Sr Tre Frit..........G....... 727 576-1584
Pinellas Park *(G-14349)*
Fuel Reformation Inc..........G....... 954 800-4289
Fort Lauderdale *(G-4015)*
Geltech Solutions Inc..........E....... 561 427-6144
Jupiter *(G-7048)*
▲ Global Diversified Products..........E....... 727 209-0854
Pinellas Park *(G-14351)*
Global Seven Inc..........G....... 973 664-1900
Sarasota *(G-16450)*
Greenscape Laboratories Inc..........G....... 850 723-7496
Pensacola *(G-14163)*
Illinois Tool Works Inc..........D....... 863 665-3338
Lakeland *(G-7708)*
Increte Systems..........G....... 813 886-8811
Odessa *(G-12126)*
Innovative Flare LLC..........G....... 561 247-2776
West Palm Beach *(G-18905)*
◆ Intercit Inc..........D....... 863 646-0165
Lakeland *(G-7715)*
International Imaging Mtls Inc..........F....... 727 834-8200
Odessa *(G-12128)*
Intrinsic Interventions Inc..........G....... 614 205-8465
Bonita Springs *(G-841)*
Island Salt Company LLC..........G....... 954 610-2590
Fort Lauderdale *(G-4068)*
Jacks Magic Products Inc..........F....... 727 536-4500
Largo *(G-7985)*

SIC

◆ Jamo Inc ....D 305 885-3444
Medley *(G-8676)*
John P Cooksey LLC ....G 850 997-8426
Monticello *(G-11077)*
▲ Kenneth S Jarrell Inc ....F 334 215-7774
Pensacola *(G-14189)*
Klp Investments LLC ....G 401 762-4357
Stuart *(G-16966)*
Kraton Chemical LLC ....D 850 785-8521
Panama City *(G-13924)*
Lake City Mediplex LLC ....F 386 752-2209
Lake City *(G-7363)*
◆ Love Is In The Air Corp ....G 305 828-8181
Hialeah *(G-5489)*
Microsalt Inc ....G 877 825-0655
West Palm Beach *(G-18952)*
Mk Monomers LLC ....G 732 928-5800
Miami *(G-10029)*
Mydor Industries Inc ....G 954 927-1140
Dania *(G-2453)*
Natural Organic Products Intl ....G 352 383-8252
Mount Dora *(G-11108)*
Northeast Water Reclamation ....G 727 893-7779
Saint Petersburg *(G-15867)*
OMI of Lake City LLC ....G 386 288-5632
Lake City *(G-7373)*
P S Research Corp ....G 954 558-8727
Lauderhill *(G-8119)*
Penek Chemical Industries Inc ....G 954 978-6501
Pompano Beach *(G-14787)*
▲ Pharmco Laboratories Inc ....G 321 268-1313
Titusville *(G-18451)*
Plating Resources Inc ....F 321 632-2435
Cocoa *(G-2040)*
◆ Premier Water & Enrgy Tech Inc ....E 904 268-1152
Jacksonville *(G-6685)*
Pressure Point Water Proofing ....G 352 337-9905
Hawthorne *(G-5245)*
Proline Chemical & Plastics LL ....G 850 835-6822
Freeport *(G-4851)*
▲ Pyrotecnico of Florida LLC ....F 352 588-5086
San Antonio *(G-15976)*
◆ Ralph Santore & Sons Inc ....E 386 437-2242
Bunnell *(G-1305)*
Rocket Towne Inc ....G 561 478-1274
West Palm Beach *(G-19022)*
▲ S M D Research Inc ....G 561 451-9895
Boca Raton *(G-696)*
Salt 1to1 Inc ....F 407 721-8107
Orlando *(G-13160)*
◆ Scents Nature Enterprises Corp ....F 305 547-2334
Miami Lakes *(G-10854)*
Separation Technologies ....G 352 794-4160
Crystal River *(G-2381)*
Shield Products Inc ....G 904 880-6060
Doral *(G-3501)*
Southeast Energy Inc ....G 561 883-1051
Boca Raton *(G-723)*
◆ Southeast Intl Chem Co Inc ....G 904 992-4007
Jacksonville *(G-6787)*
Startech Lake City Inc ....F 386 466-1969
Lake City *(G-7387)*
Suns Eye Inc ....G 407 519-4904
Geneva *(G-5023)*
Terlyn Industries Inc ....F 727 592-0772
Clearwater *(G-1916)*
▲ Two Little Fishies Inc ....G 305 623-7695
Miami *(G-10517)*
◆ Universal Transactions Inc ....E 305 887-4677
Medley *(G-8750)*
Vaprzone LLC ....G 941 882-4841
Venice *(G-18584)*
Vass Holdings Inc ....G 863 295-5664
Winter Haven *(G-19366)*

29 PETROLEUM REFINING AND RELATED INDUSTRIES

2911 Petroleum Refining

All American Lube ....G 561 432-0476
Lake Worth *(G-7533)*
Aoclsc Inc ....D 813 248-1988
Tampa *(G-17427)*
Ares Distributors Inc ....G 305 858-0163
Miami *(G-9167)*
Atlantic Jet Center Inc ....G 321 255-7111
Melbourne *(G-8771)*
AZ Chem Holdings LP ....C 800 526-5294
Jacksonville *(G-6183)*
Boostane LLC ....F 239 908-1615
Bonita Springs *(G-819)*
▼ Citilube Inc ....F 305 681-6064
Miami *(G-9355)*
Clean Energy ESb Inc ....E 202 905-6726
Coral Gables *(G-2131)*
Comoderm Corp ....G 561 756-2929
Pompano Beach *(G-14642)*
Dion Fuels LLC ....F 305 296-2000
Key West *(G-7186)*
Donald Ross Gas Inc ....G 561 776-1324
Jupiter *(G-7026)*
DOT Green Energy Inc ....G 717 505-8686
Clearwater *(G-1654)*
Ellison Rbm Inc ....G 863 679-5283
Lake Wales *(G-7508)*
▲ Export Diesel LLC ....F 305 396-1943
Miami *(G-9547)*
◆ Fuel Solutions Distrs LLC ....G 305 528-3758
North Miami Beach *(G-11679)*
Global Gl Lc ....G 863 551-1079
Winter Haven *(G-19326)*
Got Residuals Inc ....G 775 343-9240
Naples *(G-11265)*
Indian River Biodiesel LLC ....G 321 586-7670
West Palm Beach *(G-18903)*
Ipro Force LLC ....G 603 766-8716
Windermere *(G-19229)*
Jet Fuel Catering LLC ....G 954 804-1146
Pembroke Pines *(G-14043)*
Jupiter Petroleum Inc ....G 561 622-1276
Jupiter *(G-7062)*
Kimberlyn Investments Co ....G 305 448-6328
Coral Gables *(G-2164)*
◆ Kraton Chemical LLC ....C 904 928-8700
Jacksonville *(G-6546)*
▲ Mega Power ....F 813 855-6664
Largo *(G-8009)*
Mobile 1 Inc ....F 954 283-8100
Lauderdale Lakes *(G-8091)*
Nap Impex LLC ....G 954 272-8453
Pembroke Pines *(G-14051)*
Nap Impex LLC ....G 954 589-2861
Miramar *(G-11020)*
New Energy Fuels LLC ....G 281 205-0153
Labelle *(G-7321)*
NPC&ug Inc ....G 239 694-7255
Alva *(G-89)*
Okeechobee Petroleum LLC ....G 561 478-1083
West Palm Beach *(G-18970)*
Omega Gas Inc ....G 786 277-2176
Miami *(G-10098)*
Otus Corp Intl LLC ....G 305 833-6078
Miami *(G-10122)*
Oxbow Calcining LLC ....C 580 874-2201
West Palm Beach *(G-18975)*
Petroleum Group LLC ....F 352 304-5500
Belleview *(G-374)*
Petroleum Marine LLC ....G 561 422-9018
West Palm Beach *(G-18996)*
Petrosol Processing & Refining ....F 305 442-7400
Miami *(G-10157)*
Purify Fuels Inc ....G 949 842-6159
Davie *(G-2577)*
Quality Petroleum Corp ....G 863 635-6708
Frostproof *(G-4863)*
Referral & Residual Exchange L ....G 813 655-5000
Riverview *(G-15280)*
Renewable Energy Systems Inc ....G 727 522-0286
Pinellas Park *(G-14384)*
Repco Equipment Leasing Inc ....F 727 584-3329
Largo *(G-8041)*
Residual Innovations LLC ....G 407 459-5497
Orlando *(G-13132)*
Searaven Glauben LLC ....F 727 230-8840
Saint Augustine *(G-15606)*
Sellink Aviation Fuel Div LLC ....G 305 336-6627
Miami *(G-10321)*
Sheltair Daytona Beach LLC ....E 386 255-0471
Daytona Beach *(G-2713)*
Skymo LLC ....F 305 676-6739
Cooper City *(G-2115)*
Stop-N-Go 12 ....G 386 344-5494
Lake City *(G-7388)*
Treasure Coast Sealing Co ....G 772 834-5014
Hobe Sound *(G-5729)*
Tsd Group Corp ....F 954 940-2111
Sunrise *(G-17191)*
▲ Warehouse Goods LLC ....E 877 865-2260
Boca Raton *(G-787)*

2951 Paving Mixtures & Blocks

◆ A & F Paving LLC ....G 352 359-2282
Ocala *(G-11863)*
A&D Pavers LLC ....G 954 449-0716
Pompano Beach *(G-14571)*
Advanta Asphalt Inc ....G 386 362-5580
Live Oak *(G-8226)*
Aldanas Pavers Inc ....G 305 970-5339
Miami *(G-9101)*
All In One Cmplete Hndyman Svc ....F 954 708-3463
Deerfield Beach *(G-2771)*
All Pro Pavers Hardscapes Inc ....G 954 300-6281
Pompano Beach *(G-14584)*
◆ Artistic Paver Mfg Inc ....E 305 653-7283
Miami *(G-9174)*
ASAP Brick Pavers and More ....G 850 522-7123
Panama City *(G-13866)*
Atlantic Coast Asphalt Co ....E 904 268-0274
Jacksonville *(G-6172)*
Atlantic Fence & Pavers LLC ....G 386 334-6472
Edgewater *(G-3610)*
Beauty Pavers LLC ....G 941 720-3655
Bradenton *(G-996)*
Best Pavers LLC ....G 407 259-9020
Orlando *(G-12512)*
Blacklidge Emulsions Inc ....F 954 275-7225
Pompano Beach *(G-14619)*
Blacklidge Emulsions Inc ....G 850 432-3496
Pensacola *(G-14100)*
Blacklidge Emulsions Inc ....F 813 247-5699
Tampa *(G-17473)*
Brick Pavers By Mendoza Inc ....D 772 925-1666
Vero Beach *(G-18604)*
Brick Pavers By Mendoza Inc ....F 772 408-2005
Vero Beach *(G-18605)*
Brick Pvers Drveway Big Pavers ....G 407 928-1217
Orlando *(G-12535)*
Brickland Pavers Inc ....G 561 305-0325
Pompano Beach *(G-14622)*
Btb Refining LLC ....G 561 999-9916
Boca Raton *(G-468)*
Btb Refining LLC ....G 561 347-5500
Delray Beach *(G-3054)*
Butler Pavers Inc ....G 941 423-3977
North Port *(G-11735)*
Central Florida Stone Pavers ....G 407 227-3519
Orlando *(G-12570)*
CJL Bricks & Pavers Inc ....G 305 527-4240
Miami *(G-9360)*
Clever Pavers Inc ....G 239 633-7048
Fort Myers *(G-4398)*
Colossus Pavers LLC ....G 239 601-5230
Cape Coral *(G-1405)*
Crystal River Quarries Inc ....E 352 795-2828
Crystal River *(G-2375)*
◆ Devcon International Corp ....C 954 926-5200
Boca Raton *(G-499)*
Easy Pavers Corp ....G 407 967-0511
Winter Garden *(G-19261)*
Express Pavers LLC ....G 813 408-9938
Tampa *(G-17654)*
Flamingo Pavers Inc ....E 850 974-0094
Freeport *(G-4845)*
Florida North Emulsions Inc ....G 386 328-1733
Palatka *(G-13479)*
Freedom Brick Pavers LLC ....G 863 224-6008
Lake Wales *(G-7511)*
◆ Gardner Asphalt Corporation ....D 813 248-2101
Tampa *(G-17703)*
◆ Gardner-Gibson Mfg Inc ....E 813 248-2101
Tampa *(G-17705)*
Gb Brick Pavers Inc ....G 407 453-5505
Orlando *(G-12773)*
Gem Asset Acquisition LLC ....F 904 268-6063
Jacksonville *(G-6430)*
Gem Asset Acquisition LLC ....F 407 888-2080
Orlando *(G-12775)*
Gem Asset Acquisition LLC ....F 813 630-1695
Tampa *(G-17706)*
Gemseal Pavement Products ....F 305 328-9159
Tampa *(G-17707)*
General Asphalt Co Inc ....C 305 592-6005
Miami *(G-9624)*
Group III Asphalt Inc ....F 850 983-0611
Milton *(G-10931)*
H & J Asphalt Inc ....G 305 635-8110
Miami *(G-9684)*
Impressive Pavers Inc ....G 321 508-9991
West Melbourne *(G-18775)*

J & A Big Pavers LLC ....G.... 321 948-0019
Orlando *(G-12847)*
J & V Paverscorp ....G.... 786 510-4389
Miami *(G-9779)*
JCB Brick Pavers Inc ....G.... 941 739-6089
Bradenton *(G-1065)*
JD Pavers Inc ....G.... 904 245-9183
Jacksonville Beach *(G-6946)*
Jml Pavers LLC ....G.... 239 240-0082
Fort Myers *(G-4505)*
Jr Bricks Pavers Inc ....G.... 813 516-3554
Tampa *(G-17810)*
▼ Karnak South Inc ....F.... 954 761-7606
Fort Lauderdale *(G-4084)*
La Pavers Inc ....G.... 407 209-9163
Orlando *(G-12886)*
Lcf Pavers Inc ....G.... 239 826-8177
Fort Myers *(G-4516)*
Local Pavers Inc ....G.... 954 913-6916
Deerfield Beach *(G-2864)*
Masters Block - North LLC ....G.... 407 212-7704
Saint Cloud *(G-15658)*
Melanie R Bush Pavers ....G.... 772 501-7295
Vero Beach *(G-18643)*
Mendoza Pavers Corp ....G.... 305 494-6794
Miami *(G-9974)*
Mfjr Pavers LLC ....G.... 239 440-2580
Fort Myers *(G-4529)*
Most Valuable Pavers ....G.... 239 590-5217
Cape Coral *(G-1450)*
Msh Brick Pavers Inc ....F.... 941 822-6472
Bradenton *(G-1083)*
OB Inc ....G.... 321 223-0332
Cocoa *(G-2039)*
Omega Prof Brick Pavers Inc ....G.... 727 243-4659
Largo *(G-8020)*
P&G Pavers Inc ....G.... 561 716-5113
Jupiter *(G-7089)*
Palermo Pavers Inc ....G.... 239 263-0593
Naples *(G-11353)*
Pan American Cnstr Plant ....G.... 305 477-5058
Medley *(G-8701)*
Pavemax ....G.... 386 206-3113
Daytona Beach *(G-2693)*
Pavemax ....G.... 407 494-1959
Orlando *(G-13054)*
Paver Action Inc ....G.... 954 868-1468
Pompano Beach *(G-14786)*
Paver Technologies LLC ....G.... 772 213-8905
Vero Beach *(G-18651)*
Pavers Professional Inc ....G.... 239 878-6989
Jacksonville *(G-6660)*
Pavers Solutions Inc ....G.... 754 551-1924
Deerfield Beach *(G-2883)*
Paverscape Solutions LLC ....G.... 850 497-5557
Miramar Beach *(G-11067)*
Paversealingcom Corp ....G.... 407 951-6437
Longwood *(G-8321)*
Pbc Pavers Borba Co ....G.... 407 296-7727
Orlando *(G-13056)*
Perfect Brick Pavers Inc ....G.... 727 534-2506
Port Richey *(G-15062)*
Preferred Materials ....G.... 727 573-3027
Clearwater *(G-1843)*
Prime Pavers Inc ....E.... 941 320-7878
Sarasota *(G-16547)*
Propavers LLC ....G.... 904 403-9033
Fleming Island *(G-3764)*
Quantena Energy Productgs ....F.... 352 332-6630
Gainesville *(G-4985)*
RG Groundworks LLC ....G.... 352 474-7949
Newberry *(G-11560)*
Riani Pavers Inc ....G.... 239 321-1875
Fort Myers *(G-4583)*
Riley Coatings & Pavers LLC ....G.... 352 598-9520
Ocala *(G-12038)*
Rock Brick Pavers Inc ....G.... 407 692-6816
Orlando *(G-13144)*
Southern Pavers LLC ....G.... 239 940-3671
Fort Myers *(G-4607)*
Spiegel Pavers Inc ....G.... 954 687-5797
Pompano Beach *(G-14866)*
Spiegel Pavers Inc ....G.... 954 687-5797
Coral Springs *(G-2315)*
Standard Industries Inc ....D.... 813 248-7000
Tampa *(G-18129)*
◆ Star-Seal of Florida Inc ....F.... 954 484-8402
Fort Lauderdale *(G-4259)*
Suncoast Pavers Inc ....G.... 352 754-3875
Beverly Hills *(G-379)*
Sunset Pavers Inc ....G.... 239 208-7293
Fort Myers *(G-4618)*
▲ Superior Asphalt Inc ....D.... 941 755-2850
Bradenton *(G-1123)*
Symmetry Pavers Inc ....G.... 813 340-0724
Lutz *(G-8420)*
Terra Nova Pvers Hrdscape Slto ....G.... 904 662-2999
Jacksonville *(G-6847)*
Tikal Pavers Inc ....G.... 850 892-2207
Defuniak Springs *(G-2949)*
Total Pavers Corp ....F.... 561 902-7665
Port Saint Lucie *(G-15154)*
Tremron LLC ....F.... 863 491-0990
Arcadia *(G-206)*
Tsb Emulsions LLC ....G.... 904 249-5115
Neptune Beach *(G-11478)*
Universal Paverscapes LLC ....G.... 904 428-2010
Jacksonville *(G-6887)*
Yolo Consulting LLC ....G.... 954 993-4517
Pembroke Pines *(G-14073)*
Zaragoza Pavers Inc ....G.... 239 273-6665
Fort Myers *(G-4658)*

2952 Asphalt Felts & Coatings

Acryfin Coatings LLC ....G.... 772 631-3899
Stuart *(G-16902)*
All American Sealcoating LLC ....G.... 305 961-1655
Miami *(G-9108)*
Aluminum Products ....G.... 904 829-9995
Saint Augustine *(G-15514)*
◆ American Roofing Services LLC ....G.... 305 250-7115
Coral Gables *(G-2122)*
Aristcrete Coating Experts LLC ....G.... 386 882-3660
Ormond Beach *(G-13349)*
C C Lead Inc ....F.... 863 465-6458
Lake Placid *(G-7486)*
Campen Companies ....G.... 904 388-6000
Jacksonville *(G-6250)*
Carpenters Roofg & Shtmtl Inc ....E.... 561 833-0341
Riviera Beach *(G-15310)*
▲ Chuculu LLC ....F.... 305 595-4577
Miami *(G-9353)*
Coastal Acquisitions Fla LLC ....F.... 850 769-9423
Panama City *(G-13883)*
Coatings Smples Sltons Etc LLC ....G.... 863 398-8513
Lakeland *(G-7660)*
◆ Coma Cast Corp ....E.... 305 667-6797
Miami *(G-9385)*
Dj Roof and Solar Supply LLC ....G.... 954 557-1992
Fort Lauderdale *(G-3944)*
Drexel Metals Inc ....E.... 727 572-7900
Tampa *(G-17616)*
◆ E-Z Weld Inc ....E.... 561 844-0241
Riviera Beach *(G-15323)*
Elliott Custom Coatings LLC ....G.... 407 734-5221
Orlando *(G-12706)*
◆ Gardner-Gibson Mfg Inc ....E.... 813 248-2101
Tampa *(G-17705)*
Harsco Corporation ....F.... 717 506-2071
Tampa *(G-17745)*
Hco Holding I Corporation ....F.... 863 533-0522
Bartow *(G-318)*
High Sierra Terminaling LLC ....F.... 954 764-8818
Fort Lauderdale *(G-4047)*
▼ Karnak South Inc ....F.... 954 761-7606
Fort Lauderdale *(G-4084)*
Knights Powder Coating LLC ....G.... 727 906-5130
Tarpon Springs *(G-18312)*
Lapolla Industries LLC ....F.... 954 379-0241
Deerfield Beach *(G-2857)*
▼ Marbelite International Corp ....G.... 941 378-0860
Sarasota *(G-16502)*
◆ Metro Roof Tile Inc ....F.... 863 467-0042
Medley *(G-8690)*
Miami Metal Roofing LLC ....F.... 305 749-6356
Hialeah *(G-5512)*
Monier Lifetile Inc ....G.... 561 338-8200
Boca Raton *(G-631)*
Monier Lifetile LLC ....G.... 561 338-8200
Boca Raton *(G-632)*
NP Industrial Coating Inc ....G.... 727 485-6113
Tarpon Springs *(G-18317)*
◆ Polyglass USA Inc ....D.... 954 246-8888
Deerfield Beach *(G-2888)*
Randel L Rdriguez Coatings LLC ....G.... 386 308-8120
Daytona Beach *(G-2702)*
S&L Cnstrction Specialists Inc ....G.... 407 300-5080
Orlando *(G-13153)*
Sargeant Bulk Asphalt Inc ....G.... 954 763-4796
Deerfield Beach *(G-2906)*
Standard Industries Inc ....D.... 813 248-7000
Tampa *(G-18129)*
Stormforce Jacksonville LLC ....G.... 904 288-6639
Jacksonville *(G-6817)*
◆ Super Stone Inc ....E.... 305 681-3561
Opa Locka *(G-12362)*
Thomas White LLC ....G.... 813 704-4406
Plant City *(G-14473)*
Tropical Asphalt LLC ....F.... 954 983-3434
Hallandale *(G-5164)*

2992 Lubricating Oils & Greases

Advanced Engine Tech LLC ....G.... 727 744-2935
Clearwater *(G-1565)*
Am2f Energy Inc ....G.... 407 505-1127
Winter Park *(G-19376)*
◆ Amalie Oil Company ....C.... 813 248-1988
Tampa *(G-17412)*
▲ Armor Oil Products LLC ....G.... 813 248-1988
Tampa *(G-17435)*
Bell Performance Inc ....F.... 407 831-5021
Longwood *(G-8262)*
Break-Free Inc ....E.... 800 347-1200
Jacksonville *(G-6234)*
D N L Performance Inc ....G.... 786 295-8831
Opa Locka *(G-12305)*
▲ Eng Group LLC ....G.... 954 323-2024
Fort Lauderdale *(G-3972)*
Gb Energy Management LLC ....G.... 305 792-4650
Miami *(G-9616)*
▲ Global Diversified Products ....E.... 727 209-0854
Pinellas Park *(G-14351)*
Illinois Tool Works Inc ....D.... 863 665-3338
Lakeland *(G-7708)*
Lubrexx Specialty Products LLC ....G.... 561 988-7500
Pompano Beach *(G-14748)*
Lubrication Global LLC ....F.... 954 239-9522
Doral *(G-3421)*
Ocean Bio-Chem Inc ....E.... 954 587-6280
Davie *(G-2559)*
Otus Corp Intl LLC ....G.... 305 833-6078
Miami *(G-10122)*
Pro-Tech Coatings Inc ....G.... 813 248-1477
Tampa *(G-18018)*
United Armour Products LLC ....G.... 813 767-9624
Tampa *(G-18219)*

2999 Products Of Petroleum & Coal, NEC

▲ Agrotek Services Incorporated ....G.... 305 599-3818
Miami *(G-9089)*
Bradley Indus Textiles Inc ....F.... 850 678-6111
Valparaiso *(G-18508)*
◆ Gaynor Group Inc ....G.... 954 749-1228
Sunrise *(G-17125)*
Oxbow Calcining Usa Inc ....D.... 580 874-2201
West Palm Beach *(G-18976)*
Oxbow Carbon LLC ....C.... 561 907-5400
West Palm Beach *(G-18977)*
Oxbow Enterprises Intl LLC ....G.... 561 907-5400
West Palm Beach *(G-18978)*
Panama City Petro LLC ....G.... 850 215-9146
Panama City *(G-13937)*
◆ Trigeant Ep Ltd ....F.... 561 999-9916
Boca Raton *(G-757)*

30 RUBBER AND MISCELLANEOUS PLASTICS PRODUCTS

3011 Tires & Inner Tubes

BF American Business LLC ....G.... 561 856-7094
Boca Raton *(G-446)*
BF One LLC ....F.... 239 939-5251
Fort Myers *(G-4375)*
BF Weston LLC ....D.... 561 844-5528
Weston *(G-19111)*
◆ Db Motoring Group Inc ....G.... 305 685-0707
Miami *(G-9439)*
◆ Elite Wheel Distributors Inc ....F.... 813 673-8393
Tampa *(G-17633)*
Eminel Corporation Inc ....F.... 407 900-0190
Orlando *(G-12709)*
◆ Fedan Corp ....F.... 305 885-5415
Hialeah *(G-5410)*
Jacksonville Tire Rescue Inc ....F.... 904 783-1296
Jacksonville *(G-6513)*
Jimenez Enterprises Group ....E.... 561 542-7709
Doral *(G-3403)*
Noahs MBL Tire Auto Solutions ....G.... 904 250-1502
Jacksonville *(G-6638)*

Rhino Tire Usa Llc ... F ... 407 777-5598
Orlando *(G-13135)*
Rsss 1 LLC ... G ... 941 483-3293
Venice *(G-18571)*
S N S Auto Sports LLC ... G ... 727 546-2700
Pinellas Park *(G-14386)*
Tbc Retail Group Inc ... G ... 702 395-2100
Juno Beach *(G-6984)*
▲ **Tire Experts LLC** ... G ... 305 663-3508
Medley *(G-8735)*
Vossen Wheels Inc ... F ... 305 463-7778
Doral *(G-3545)*

3021 Rubber & Plastic Footwear

◆ **Global Trading Inc** ... F ... 305 471-4455
Miami *(G-9642)*
▲ **Gold Banner USA Inc** ... F ... 305 576-2215
Miami *(G-9645)*
Protege Media LLC ... G ... 310 738-9567
Port Saint Lucie *(G-15131)*
Rebuild Globally Inc ... E ... 407 801-9936
Lake Worth *(G-7585)*

3052 Rubber & Plastic Hose & Belting

Adventry Corp ... F ... 305 582-2977
Miami Lakes *(G-10760)*
Fluid Routing Solutions LLC ... B ... 352 732-0222
Ocala *(G-11948)*
Gate Petroleum Company ... G ... 904 998-7126
Jacksonville *(G-6420)*
Hecht Rubber Corporation ... E ... 904 731-3401
Jacksonville *(G-6466)*
Hitachi Cable America Inc ... C ... 850 476-0907
Pensacola *(G-14173)*
Signature AVI US Holdings Inc ... F ... 407 648-7230
Orlando *(G-13193)*
Space Coast Distributors ... G ... 386 239-0305
Daytona Beach *(G-2718)*
Space Coast Hydraulics Inc ... F ... 321 504-6006
Rockledge *(G-15449)*
◆ **Uip International Inc** ... G ... 954 785-3539
Pompano Beach *(G-14896)*
◆ **Unaflex LLC** ... E ... 954 943-5002
Pompano Beach *(G-14898)*
Varibelt Incorporated ... G ... 305 775-1568
Miami *(G-10569)*

3053 Gaskets, Packing & Sealing Devices

▲ **Bxd Enterprises Inc** ... G ... 727 937-4100
Holiday *(G-5737)*
▲ **Construction and Elec Pdts Inc** ... F ... 954 972-9787
Pompano Beach *(G-14645)*
▲ **Fabrico Inc** ... C ... 386 736-7373
Deland *(G-2977)*
▲ **Guy Gasket Inc** ... F ... 561 703-1774
Lake Worth *(G-7555)*
Modern Silicone Tech Inc ... C ... 727 873-1805
Pinellas Park *(G-14369)*
Sanitary Prcess Components Inc ... G ... 407 650-8988
Orlando *(G-13161)*
Technetics Group LLC ... C ... 386 736-7373
Deland *(G-3019)*
Technetics Group LLC ... E ... 386 736-7373
De Land *(G-2734)*
TNT Packaging Inc ... F ... 305 769-0616
Miami *(G-10483)*

3061 Molded, Extruded & Lathe-Cut Rubber Mechanical Goods

Archimaze Logistics Inc ... G ... 954 615-7485
Fort Lauderdale *(G-3819)*
Cables and Sensors LLC ... F ... 866 373-6767
Orlando *(G-12543)*
Etco Incorporated ... C ... 941 756-8426
Bradenton *(G-1039)*
▲ **J B Nottingham & Co Inc** ... E ... 386 873-2990
Deland *(G-2986)*
Modern Silicone Tech Inc ... C ... 727 873-1805
Pinellas Park *(G-14369)*
◆ **Pompadour Products Inc** ... E ... 954 345-2700
Coral Springs *(G-2303)*
Southern Plastics & Rubber Co ... E ... 386 672-1167
Ormond Beach *(G-13401)*
◆ **T S E Industries Inc** ... C ... 727 573-7676
Clearwater *(G-1900)*

3069 Fabricated Rubber Prdts, NEC

A Clean Finish Inc ... G ... 407 516-1311
Jacksonville *(G-6109)*
◆ **Abco Products Inc** ... E ... 888 694-2226
Miami *(G-9055)*
Acuderm Inc ... D ... 954 733-6935
Fort Lauderdale *(G-3781)*
Aerial Products Corporation ... F ... 800 973-9110
Jacksonville *(G-6126)*
Aquatic Fabricators of S Fla ... G ... 954 458-0400
Hallandale *(G-5152)*
Atlantech Process Technology ... G ... 352 751-4286
Lady Lake *(G-7330)*
Babbala LLC ... G ... 844 869-5747
Boca Raton *(G-440)*
Bags Unlimited Inc ... G ... 985 868-3393
Chiefland *(G-1533)*
BF Hurley Mat Co Inc ... E ... 813 837-0616
Tampa *(G-17468)*
▲ **Bolidt Cruise Control Corp** ... G ... 305 607-4172
Opa Locka *(G-12295)*
◆ **Boulder Blimp Company Inc** ... F ... 303 664-1122
Miami *(G-9271)*
Bowsmith Inc ... G ... 863 453-6666
Avon Park *(G-284)*
Cadre Holdings Inc ... C ... 904 741-5400
Jacksonville *(G-6249)*
◆ **Eastern Aero Marine Inc** ... C ... 305 871-4050
Miami *(G-9495)*
Ffo Leesburg LLC ... G ... 352 315-0783
Leesburg *(G-8155)*
▲ **Florida Pool Products Inc** ... E ... 727 531-8913
Clearwater *(G-1690)*
Florida Tape & Labels Inc ... F ... 941 921-5788
Sarasota *(G-16438)*
Ga-MA & Associates Inc ... G ... 352 687-8840
Ocala *(G-11953)*
▲ **Gallant Inc** ... G ... 800 330-1343
Winter Garden *(G-19265)*
General Fine Machine Co Inc ... G ... 727 726-5956
Safety Harbor *(G-15494)*
General Rubber Corporation ... G ... 941 412-0001
Venice *(G-18549)*
Global Force Enterprises LLC ... G ... 786 317-8197
Miramar *(G-10998)*
Global Tire Rcycl of Smter CNT ... E ... 352 330-2213
Wildwood *(G-19194)*
▼ **Global Tire Recycling Inc** ... F ... 352 330-2213
Wildwood *(G-19195)*
Grove Medical LLC ... G ... 305 903-6402
Miami *(G-9677)*
◆ **Hernol Usa Inc** ... E ... 786 263-3341
Coral Gables *(G-2155)*
Impact Molding Clearwater LLC ... E ... 847 718-9300
Clearwater *(G-1730)*
Inspiration Foam Inc ... G ... 407 498-0040
Kissimmee *(G-7255)*
Integrity Technologies LLC ... G ... 561 768-9023
Jupiter *(G-7057)*
▲ **J & I Ventures Inc** ... E ... 561 845-0030
West Palm Beach *(G-18909)*
Lakeland Lures Inc ... G ... 863 644-3127
Lakeland *(G-7731)*
Lapolla Industries LLC ... F ... 954 379-0241
Deerfield Beach *(G-2857)*
▲ **Levita LLC** ... G ... 954 227-7468
Coral Springs *(G-2273)*
Liberty Balloons LLC ... G ... 239 947-3338
Bonita Springs *(G-843)*
Liquiguard Technologies Inc ... E ... 954 566-0996
Fort Lauderdale *(G-4101)*
▼ **Mako Hose & Rubber Co** ... G ... 561 795-6200
West Palm Beach *(G-18939)*
Marathon Engineering Corp ... E ... 239 303-7378
Lehigh Acres *(G-8198)*
Medfab Corporation ... G ... 813 854-2646
Oldsmar *(G-12247)*
Medical Defense Company Inc ... F ... 954 614-3266
Doral *(G-3429)*
Omt LLC ... F ... 954 327-1447
Fort Lauderdale *(G-4149)*
Paragon Globl Sup Slutions LLC ... G ... 813 745-9902
Tampa *(G-17975)*
Patten Co Inc ... E ... 707 826-2887
Lake Worth Beach *(G-7618)*
Polyhistor International Inc ... G ... 904 646-5666
Jacksonville *(G-6677)*
Premium Rubber Bands Inc ... G ... 305 321-0333
Miami *(G-10187)*
Professional Ctr At Gardens ... F ... 561 394-5200
Delray Beach *(G-3127)*
Proform System Inc ... G ... 305 854-2800
Miami *(G-10208)*
Put Your Name On It LLC ... G ... 813 972-1460
Tampa *(G-18026)*
Racing Shell Covers LLC ... G ... 732 236-0435
Naples *(G-11380)*
▲ **Re-Think It Inc** ... F ... 407 671-6000
Winter Park *(G-19437)*
Ready Containment LLC ... F ... 941 739-9486
Palmetto *(G-13821)*
Reliatex Inc ... E ... 813 621-6021
Tampa *(G-18051)*
Revere Manufactured Pdts Inc ... G ... 904 503-9733
Jacksonville *(G-6719)*
Rubber 2 Go Llc ... G ... 305 688-8566
Miami *(G-10286)*
◆ **Shaw Development LLC** ... C ... 239 405-6100
Bonita Springs *(G-853)*
Shredded Tire Inc ... F ... 954 970-8565
Fort Lauderdale *(G-4232)*
Southeast Gen Contrs Group Inc ... F ... 877 407-3535
Port St Lucie *(G-15179)*
Sport Products of Tampa Inc ... G ... 813 630-5552
Tampa *(G-18127)*
Stepincorp Auto Solutions LLC ... G ... 786 864-3222
Miami *(G-10413)*
Thriller Clearwater Inc ... G ... 727 389-2209
Dunedin *(G-3590)*
Throw Raft LLC ... G ... 954 366-8004
Fort Lauderdale *(G-4283)*
▲ **Tomsons Inc** ... G ... 248 646-0677
Englewood *(G-3685)*
▼ **Treadway Industries LLC** ... E ... 352 326-3313
Minneola *(G-10957)*
Veru Inc ... B ... 305 509-6897
Miami *(G-10574)*
◆ **Victus LLC** ... E ... 305 663-2129
Miami *(G-10582)*
Warfighter Fcsed Logistics Inc ... F ... 740 513-4692
Fort Lauderdale *(G-4313)*
▼ **Winslow Marine Products Corp** ... D ... 941 613-6666
Lake Suzy *(G-7497)*

3081 Plastic Unsupported Sheet & Film

▲ **American Plastic Sup & Mfg Inc** ... E ... 727 573-0636
Clearwater *(G-1581)*
Architexture LLC ... G ... 954 907-8000
Fort Lauderdale *(G-3820)*
Barco Sales & Mfg Inc ... F ... 954 563-3922
Oakland Park *(G-11784)*
Dairy-Mix Inc ... F ... 813 621-8098
Tampa *(G-17586)*
▲ **Designer Films Inc** ... F ... 305 828-0605
Hialeah *(G-5370)*
Dynamic Visions Inc ... E ... 941 497-1984
Venice *(G-18543)*
▲ **Essex Plastics Midwest LLC Lc** ... A ... 954 956-1100
Pompano Beach *(G-14683)*
◆ **Flexsol Holding Corp** ... D ... 954 941-6333
Pompano Beach *(G-14700)*
▲ **Guardian AG Plas Corp** ... G ... 813 286-8680
Tampa *(G-17732)*
▼ **Ifco Systems Us LLC** ... E ... 813 463-4103
Tampa *(G-17770)*
J & D Manufacturing Inc ... F ... 813 854-1700
Oldsmar *(G-12237)*
King Plastic Corporation ... C ... 941 423-8666
North Port *(G-11742)*
◆ **Madico Inc** ... D ... 727 327-2544
Pinellas Park *(G-14366)*
◆ **Miami Cellophane Inc** ... E ... 786 293-2212
Hialeah *(G-5508)*
◆ **Nina Plastic Bags Inc** ... D ... 407 802-6828
Orlando *(G-13003)*
Ped-Stuart Corporation ... E ... 352 754-6001
Brooksville *(G-1259)*
◆ **Processing and Packg Sups Co** ... E ... 321 723-2723
Melbourne *(G-8912)*
Protex Inc ... F ... 727 573-4665
Clearwater *(G-1850)*
Real Gold Inc ... G ... 386 873-4849
Deland *(G-3010)*
Recycled Vinyl ... G ... 727 434-1857
Sarasota *(G-16555)*
▼ **Seal-Tite Plastic Packg Co Inc** ... D ... 305 264-9015
Miami *(G-10316)*
◆ **Serv-Pak Corp** ... F ... 954 962-4262
Hollywood *(G-5907)*
Solar X ... G ... 386 673-2111
Ormond Beach *(G-13400)*
Sungraf Inc ... F ... 954 456-8500
Hallandale Beach *(G-5216)*

◆ Tape Technologies Inc ....E.... 904 284-0284
Green Cove Springs *(G-5072)*
Tropicalcreation ....G.... 941 580-8465
North Port *(G-11751)*

3082 Plastic Unsupported Profile Shapes

▲ American Plastic Sup & Mfg Inc ....E.... 727 573-0636
Clearwater *(G-1581)*
◆ Consolidated Polymer Tech ....E.... 727 531-4191
Clearwater *(G-1636)*
Daniel Bustamante ....G.... 305 779-7777
Coral Gables *(G-2137)*
Firedrake Inc ....G.... 813 713-8902
Zephyrhills *(G-19518)*
◆ Flexsol Holding Corp ....D.... 954 941-6333
Pompano Beach *(G-14700)*
King Plastic Corporation ....C.... 941 423-8666
North Port *(G-11742)*
Microlumen Inc ....D.... 813 886-1200
Oldsmar *(G-12250)*
◆ Processing and Packg Sups Co ....E.... 321 723-2723
Melbourne *(G-8912)*

3083 Plastic Laminated Plate & Sheet

AA Fiberglass Inc ....G.... 904 355-5511
Jacksonville *(G-6113)*
Acryplex Inc ....G.... 305 633-7636
Miami *(G-9066)*
American Thrmplastic Extrusion ....C.... 305 769-9566
Opa Locka *(G-12287)*
▲ Chemclad LLC ....F.... 863 967-1156
Auburndale *(G-234)*
Clear Vue Inc ....E.... 727 726-5386
Safety Harbor *(G-15490)*
Echo Plastic Systems ....F.... 305 655-1300
Deerfield Beach *(G-2820)*
▲ Enduris Extrusions Inc ....D.... 904 421-3304
Jacksonville *(G-6363)*
Fisher Cabinet Company LLC ....E.... 850 944-4171
Pensacola *(G-14151)*
Fun Marine Inc ....G.... 321 576-1100
Cocoa *(G-2024)*
Innovatier Inc ....G.... 863 688-4548
Lakeland *(G-7712)*
▲ Institutional Products Inc ....E.... 305 248-4955
Homestead *(G-5972)*
J Schor R Inc ....F.... 954 621-5279
Plantation *(G-14527)*
Neptune Tech Services Inc ....E.... 904 646-2700
Jacksonville *(G-6624)*
Protex Inc ....F.... 727 573-4665
Clearwater *(G-1850)*
Red Bud Enterprises Inc ....E.... 386 752-5696
Lake City *(G-7381)*
▼ Seal-Tite Plastic Packg Co Inc ....D.... 305 264-9015
Miami *(G-10316)*
Southern Fiberglass Inc ....F.... 904 387-2246
Jacksonville *(G-6794)*
Streamline Extrusion Inc ....F.... 727 796-4277
Safety Harbor *(G-15506)*
Suncoast Identification Tech ....G.... 239 277-9922
Fort Myers *(G-4616)*
Sungraf Inc ....F.... 954 456-8500
Hallandale Beach *(G-5216)*

3084 Plastic Pipe

◆ Accord Industries LLC ....D.... 407 671-6989
Winter Park *(G-19370)*
Advanced Drainage Systems Inc ....G.... 850 234-0004
Panama City Beach *(G-13969)*
▲ Advantage Earth Products Inc ....F.... 904 329-1430
Saint Augustine *(G-15513)*
Aei International Corp ....G.... 904 724-9771
Jacksonville *(G-6125)*
Atkore Plastic Pipe Corp ....E.... 813 884-2525
Tampa *(G-17443)*
▲ Blue Creek Holdings Inc ....G.... 814 796-1900
Plant City *(G-14410)*
C & S Plastics ....E.... 863 294-5628
Winter Haven *(G-19309)*
Cantex Inc ....C.... 863 967-4161
Auburndale *(G-231)*
Charlotte Pipe and Foundry Co ....E.... 352 748-8100
Wildwood *(G-19193)*
▲ Ciro Manufacturing Corporation ....E.... 561 988-2139
Deerfield Beach *(G-2802)*
Dixie Sptic Tank Orange Cy LLC ....F.... 386 775-3051
Orange City *(G-12375)*
Hancor Inc ....E.... 863 655-5499
Winter Garden *(G-19266)*
Maruti Technology Inc ....F.... 407 704-4775
Orlando *(G-12950)*
▼ Sanderson Pipe Corporation ....D.... 904 275-3289
Sanderson *(G-15983)*
Taylor Made Plastics Inc ....G.... 941 926-0200
Sarasota *(G-16619)*
Wellstream International Ltd ....C.... 850 636-4800
Panama City *(G-13963)*

3085 Plastic Bottles

AC Plastics LLC ....G.... 305 826-6333
Hialeah *(G-5266)*
◆ Advance Plastics Unlimited ....E.... 305 885-6266
Hialeah *(G-5270)*
▲ Altira Inc ....D.... 305 687-8074
Miami *(G-9124)*
Altium Packaging LLC ....F.... 813 248-4300
Tampa *(G-17409)*
◆ Amalie Oil Company ....C.... 813 248-1988
Tampa *(G-17412)*
Anupack LLC ....G.... 407 850-1960
Orlando *(G-12481)*
C & G Packaging LLC ....F.... 305 825-5244
Hialeah *(G-5337)*
▲ Captiva Containers LLC ....D.... 800 861-3868
Miami *(G-9310)*
CKS Packaging Inc ....D.... 407 423-0333
Orlando *(G-12586)*
CKS Packaging Inc ....D.... 954 925-9049
Hollywood *(G-5800)*
Compliance Meds Tech LLC ....G.... 786 319-9826
Miami *(G-9389)*
Florida Electromechanics Inc ....G.... 305 825-5244
Hialeah *(G-5412)*
Global Source Imports LLC ....G.... 917 213-6891
Miami *(G-9641)*
▲ Mango Bottling Inc ....E.... 321 631-1005
Cocoa *(G-2034)*
Mesa Industries Inc ....F.... 386 738-3255
Deland *(G-2995)*
Mfx Corp ....F.... 407 429-4051
Orlando *(G-12965)*
New Sentry Marketing Inc ....G.... 561 982-9599
Boca Raton *(G-640)*
▲ Rock Bottom Bottles LLC ....G.... 901 237-9929
Sarasota *(G-16287)*
US Pack Group LLC ....G.... 954 556-1840
Sunrise *(G-17193)*
W R Kershaw Inc ....G.... 386 673-0602
Ormond Beach *(G-13408)*

3086 Plastic Foam Prdts

3a Products LLC ....G.... 754 263-2968
Miramar *(G-10958)*
AAA Architectural Elements ....F.... 941 722-1910
Palmetto *(G-13782)*
Allied Aerofoam Products LLC ....F.... 731 660-2705
Fort Lauderdale *(G-3798)*
◆ Allied Aerofoam Products LLC ....D.... 813 626-0090
Fort Lauderdale *(G-3799)*
Allied Foam Fabricators LLC ....D.... 813 626-0090
Tampa *(G-17401)*
American Archtctral Foam Wrks ....F.... 813 443-0791
Tampa *(G-17414)*
Architectural Foam Supply Inc ....E.... 954 943-6949
Pompano Beach *(G-14598)*
▲ Atlantic Insulation Inc ....D.... 904 354-2217
Jacksonville *(G-6174)*
Autopax Inc ....G.... 772 563-0131
Vero Beach *(G-18596)*
Barco Sales & Mfg Inc ....F.... 954 563-3922
Oakland Park *(G-11784)*
Coastal Foam Systems LLC ....G.... 850 470-9827
Pensacola *(G-14115)*
Compsys Inc ....D.... 321 255-0399
Melbourne *(G-8795)*
Dart Container Company Fla LLC ....C.... 813 752-1990
Plant City *(G-14423)*
Dart Container Corp Florida ....F.... 813 752-6525
Plant City *(G-14424)*
Dart Container Corp Florida ....F.... 941 358-1202
Sarasota *(G-16204)*
Dart Container Corp Florida ....F.... 941 358-1202
Sarasota *(G-16404)*
◆ Design Works By Tech Pdts Inc ....E.... 941 355-2703
Sarasota *(G-16410)*
Drb Packaging LLC ....G.... 321 877-2802
Rockledge *(G-15405)*
Drb Packaging LLC ....G.... 321 877-2802
Rockledge *(G-15406)*
◆ Dyplast Products LLC ....D.... 305 921-0100
Opa Locka *(G-12311)*
East Coast Foam Supply Inc ....G.... 321 433-8231
Rockledge *(G-15408)*
Foam & Psp Inc ....G.... 954 816-5648
Fort Lauderdale *(G-4008)*
Foam By Design Inc ....E.... 727 561-7479
Clearwater *(G-1692)*
Foam Decoration Inc ....G.... 786 293-8813
Miami *(G-9591)*
◆ Foam Factory Inc ....E.... 954 485-6700
Boca Raton *(G-536)*
Foam Masters Inc ....E.... 239 403-0755
Naples *(G-11248)*
Great Magnet LLC ....F.... 407 260-0591
Winter Park *(G-19408)*
▲ Icemule Company Inc ....F.... 904 325-9012
Saint Augustine *(G-15552)*
Icorp-Ifoam Specialty Products ....G.... 407 328-8500
Sanford *(G-16064)*
▲ Imperial Foam & Insul Mfg Co ....D.... 386 673-4177
Ormond Beach *(G-13379)*
Innocor Foam Tech - Acp Inc ....D.... 305 685-6341
Miami *(G-9745)*
Italian Cast Stones Inc ....E.... 813 902-8900
Tampa *(G-17796)*
J C & A of South Florida Inc ....G.... 305 445-6665
Miami *(G-9780)*
▲ Key Packaging Company Inc ....E.... 941 355-2728
Sarasota *(G-16245)*
Kitko Corp ....G.... 786 287-8900
Doral *(G-3408)*
◆ Magna Manufacturing Inc ....E.... 850 243-1112
Fort Walton Beach *(G-4814)*
Medfab Corporation ....G.... 813 854-2646
Oldsmar *(G-12247)*
Merry Mailman Inc ....G.... 954 786-1146
Pompano Beach *(G-14758)*
◆ Nida-Core Corporation ....E.... 772 343-7300
Port Saint Lucie *(G-15124)*
Novicon Industries ....G.... 813 854-3235
Oldsmar *(G-12251)*
▲ Plastix Usa LLC ....D.... 305 891-0091
Hollywood *(G-5892)*
Pmh Homes Inc ....G.... 941 234-5121
Bradenton *(G-1099)*
Reilly Foam Corp ....F.... 561 842-8090
Riviera Beach *(G-15369)*
Republic Packaging Florida Inc ....E.... 305 685-5175
Opa Locka *(G-12355)*
Root International Inc ....F.... 813 265-1808
Clearwater *(G-1865)*
◆ Scott Sign Systems Inc ....E.... 941 355-5171
Sarasota *(G-16294)*
Seven Group USA Inc ....G.... 305 392-9193
Doral *(G-3500)*
Source of Sup In Polyurethanes ....G.... 239 573-3637
Cape Coral *(G-1473)*
Storopack Inc ....G.... 305 805-9696
Medley *(G-8731)*
Ufp Technologies Inc ....E.... 407 933-4880
Kissimmee *(G-7306)*
▲ Unity Marine Inc ....G.... 954 321-1727
Fort Lauderdale *(G-4296)*
W R Grace & Co - Conn ....F.... 561 982-7776
Boca Raton *(G-785)*
Wind Blue Technology LLC ....F.... 850 218-9398
Pensacola *(G-14288)*
Zipx Package Service Inc ....G.... 305 597-5305
Doral *(G-3553)*

3087 Custom Compounding Of Purchased Plastic Resins

Bath Junkie of Gainesville ....G.... 352 331-3012
Gainesville *(G-4884)*
City of Lakeland ....F.... 863 834-6780
Lakeland *(G-7657)*
▲ Seelye Acquisitions Inc ....G.... 407 656-6677
Apopka *(G-184)*

3088 Plastic Plumbing Fixtures

▲ AGM Orlando Inc ....G.... 407 865-9522
Altamonte Springs *(G-27)*
▼ Bathroom World Manufacturing ....G.... 954 566-0451
Oakland Park *(G-11785)*
Brian Belitz ....G.... 407 924-5543
Kissimmee *(G-7225)*
Central Fla Kit Bath Srfces In ....F.... 352 307-2333
Ocala *(G-11898)*

Coast Products LLC F 850 235-2090
Panama City Beach (G-13976)
East Coast Fixtures & Mllwk Co G 904 733-9711
Jacksonville (G-6349)
Elstons Inc G 727 527-7929
Apollo Beach (G-102)
Fountain Youth Bathrooms Inc F 772 626-9626
Port Saint Lucie (G-15110)
▲ Hale Products Inc C 352 629-5020
Ocala (G-11963)
Home & Garden Industries Inc F 305 634-0681
Miami (G-9716)
▼ Hot Tub Parts LLC G 727 573-9611
Saint Petersburg (G-15808)
▲ KDD Inc E 239 689-8402
Fort Myers (G-4509)
Lions Intl MGT Group Inc F 813 367-2517
Tampa (G-17848)
Lpi Inc F 702 403-8555
Saint Petersburg (G-15842)
▼ Martell Glass G 786 336-0142
Miami (G-9951)
Proshowmaker Inc G 813 765-2676
Land O Lakes (G-7864)
◆ Sea Products Inc D 904 781-8200
Jacksonville (G-6758)
See-Ray Plumbing Inc E 772 489-2474
Vero Beach (G-18663)
Sh Shower & Tub Enclosures LLC G 786 229-2529
Miami (G-10331)
◆ Shower Doors & More Inc G 954 358-2014
Fort Lauderdale (G-4231)
▲ Spa World Corporation D 866 588-8008
Miami (G-10390)
Tuflex Manufacturing Co E 954 781-0605
Pompano Beach (G-14895)
Two Guys Plumbing Supply LLc F 321 263-0021
Altamonte Springs (G-79)
Woodys Enterprises LLC F 407 892-1900
Saint Cloud (G-15670)

3089 Plastic Prdts

7 Plastics Inc F 407 321-5441
Longwood (G-8249)
A 1 Fabrications Inc G 352 410-0752
Weeki Wachee (G-18699)
A Crown Molding Specialist F 954 665-5640
Pembroke Pines (G-14013)
Able Closets Inc G 772 781-8250
Stuart (G-16901)
Absolute Plastic Solutions F 239 313-7779
Fort Myers (G-4342)
◆ Acacia Inc F 813 253-2789
Tampa (G-17384)
Acai Investments Llc G 305 821-8872
Hialeah (G-5267)
Accu Metal G 850 912-4855
Pensacola (G-14078)
Accu Tech LLC G 407 446-6676
Groveland (G-5091)
Acrylic Images Inc F 954 484-6633
Oakland Park (G-11773)
Action Plastics Inc G 352 342-4122
Belleview (G-365)
Advanced Air International Inc E 561 845-8212
Riviera Beach (G-15293)
Advanced Components Solutions G 813 884-1600
Lutz (G-8373)
Advanced Drainage & Hydro Inc G 813 957-3162
Lutz (G-8374)
Advantage Plastics NY Inc F 863 291-4407
Winter Haven (G-19295)
AIN Plastics of Florida Inc F 813 242-6400
Riverview (G-15264)
All Liquid Envmtl Svcs LLC E 800 767-9594
Fort Lauderdale (G-3797)
▲ Allied General Engrv & Plas F 305 626-6585
Opa Locka (G-12286)
▼ Alpha General Services Inc E 863 382-1544
Sebring (G-16680)
Altium Packaging LLC F 813 782-2695
Zephyrhills (G-19507)
Altium Packaging LLC F 813 248-4300
Tampa (G-17409)
Altium Packaging LLC F 386 246-4000
Palm Coast (G-13683)
American Composites Engrg F 352 528-5007
Williston (G-19209)
American Molding and Plas LLC E 561 676-1987
Boynton Beach (G-876)
American Moulding Corporation F 321 676-8929
Melbourne (G-8766)
American Products Inc G 813 925-0144
Tampa (G-17418)
◆ American Technical Molding Inc D 727 447-7377
Clearwater (G-1582)
American Thrmplastic Extrusion C 305 769-9566
Opa Locka (G-12287)
◆ American Tool & Mold Inc C 727 447-7377
Clearwater (G-1583)
Amerikan LLC E 863 314-9417
Sebring (G-16681)
Anupack LLC G 407 850-1960
Orlando (G-12481)
Apollo Renal Therapeutics LLC E 202 413-0963
Ocala (G-11878)
Aqua Technologies G 305 246-2125
Homestead (G-5954)
Artisan Tool & Die LLC G 765 288-6653
Sarasota (G-16178)
Arts Products LLC G 201 984-7232
Doral (G-3255)
Associated Materials LLC G 813 621-7058
Tampa (G-17439)
▼ Atlantic Molding Inc F 954 781-9340
Pompano Beach (G-14606)
Autisan International Inc G 941 349-7029
Sarasota (G-16358)
Automated Mfg Systems Inc G 561 833-9898
Mangonia Park (G-8498)
▲ Ayanna Plastics & Engrg Inc E 727 561-4329
Clearwater (G-1596)
▼ B & D Precision Tools Inc E 305 885-1583
Hialeah (G-5314)
B & R Sales Corporation G 727 571-2231
Clearwater (G-1597)
▲ Bas Plastics Inc G 954 202-9080
Fort Lauderdale (G-3840)
Bay City Window Company F 727 323-5443
Saint Petersburg (G-15718)
▼ Beachcomber Fibrgls Tech Inc G 772 283-0200
Stuart (G-16914)
Berry Global Inc G 305 887-2040
Medley (G-8622)
Better Plastics Inc G 407 480-2909
Orlando (G-12513)
BF Hurley Mat Co Inc E 813 837-0616
Tampa (G-17468)
Big Sun Plastics Inc F 352 671-1844
Ocala (G-11887)
Bingham On Site Portables LLC G 813 659-0003
Dover (G-3555)
▲ Bio Bubble Pets LLC F 561 998-5350
West Palm Beach (G-18819)
▲ Bk Plastics Industry Inc F 813 920-3628
Odessa (G-12107)
Bloem LLC G 407 889-5533
Apopka (G-118)
Blue Water Dynamics LLC D 386 957-5464
Edgewater (G-3614)
Bowen Medical Services Inc G 386 362-1345
Live Oak (G-8227)
Boyce Engineering Inc F 727 572-6318
Saint Petersburg (G-15727)
▲ Brill Hygienic Products Inc F 561 278-5600
Delray Beach (G-3052)
Brown Company G 850 455-0971
Pensacola (G-14106)
Bruce R Ely Enterprise Inc F 727 573-1643
Clearwater (G-1614)
Bucket Company LLC G 786 473-6484
Miami (G-9282)
Building Blocks Management Inc F 214 289-9737
Kissimmee (G-7227)
C & G Packaging LLC F 305 825-5244
Hialeah (G-5337)
C & J Industries Inc F 386 589-4907
Ormond Beach (G-13356)
C & S Plastics E 863 294-5628
Winter Haven (G-19309)
▼ Card Quest Inc G 813 288-0004
Tampa (G-17506)
▼ Card Usa Inc F 954 862-1300
Hollywood (G-5795)
▲ Cavaform Inc G 727 384-3676
Saint Petersburg (G-15740)
Chacho Customs G 239 369-4664
Lehigh Acres (G-8187)
Checkpoint Card Group Inc F 954 426-1331
Deerfield Beach (G-2800)
Choice Tool & Mold LLC F 941 371-6767
Sarasota (G-16383)
Chrom Industries LLC E 954 400-5135
Fort Lauderdale (G-3897)
CKS Packaging Inc D 407 423-0333
Orlando (G-12586)
CKS Packaging Inc D 407 420-9529
Orlando (G-12587)
CKS Packaging Inc D 954 925-9049
Hollywood (G-5800)
Classica & Telecard Corp G 239 354-3727
Naples (G-11210)
Coastal Awngs Hrrcane Prtction G 407 923-9482
Orlando (G-12592)
Coffee Cllloid Productions LLC F 305 424-8900
Miami (G-9375)
Commercial Stone Cab Fbrctors F 727 209-1141
Saint Petersburg (G-15749)
Commercial Stone Fbrcators Inc F 727 209-1141
Saint Petersburg (G-15750)
▲ Compak Companies LLC F 321 249-9590
Sanford (G-16019)
▲ Composite Holdings Inc E 321 268-9625
Titusville (G-18424)
Concealment Express LLC D 888 904-2722
Jacksonville (G-6282)
Conrad Plastics LLC G 954 391-9515
Hallandale Beach (G-5179)
◆ Corkcicle LLC E 866 780-0007
Orlando (G-12621)
Corrigan & Company G 904 353-5936
Jacksonville (G-6293)
County Plastics Corp G 954 971-9205
Pompano Beach (G-14649)
Covington Plastics Inc F 321 632-6775
Cocoa (G-2006)
Covocup LLC G 855 204-5106
Sarasota (G-16199)
Craemer US Corporation G 727 312-8859
Palm Harbor (G-13731)
Creative Molding Corp F 786 251-4241
Doral (G-3313)
Custom Molding & Casework Inc G 407 709-7377
Deltona (G-3167)
▲ Custom Plastic Card Company D 954 426-1331
Deerfield Beach (G-2809)
▲ Custom Plastic Developments D 407 847-3054
Kissimmee (G-7235)
Custom Plastic Fabricators G 813 884-5200
Tampa (G-17581)
Cw21 Inc E 813 754-1760
Plant City (G-14422)
D M T Inc F 321 267-3931
Cocoa (G-2008)
D&W Fine Pack LLC D 305 592-4329
Doral (G-3320)
D-Rep Plastics Inc G 407 240-4154
Clearwater (G-1648)
Daigle Tool & Die Inc G 954 785-9989
Deerfield Beach (G-2811)
◆ Darnel Inc F 954 929-0085
Hollywood (G-5809)
Dart Container Company Fla LLC C 813 752-1990
Plant City (G-14423)
▲ Dart Industries Inc B 407 826-5050
Orlando (G-12650)
▲ Delconte Packaging Inc F 305 885-2800
Hialeah (G-5368)
Delta Machine & Tool Inc E 386 738-2204
Deland (G-2969)
Diamond Precision Machine Inc F 321 729-8453
Palm Bay (G-13508)
Diemold Machine Company Inc E 239 482-1400
Fort Myers (G-4431)
Dillco Inc F 386 734-7510
Deland (G-2971)
Dixie Restorations LLC G 813 785-2159
Zephyrhills (G-19514)
Dj Plastics Inc G 407 656-6677
Apopka (G-131)
▲ Donarra Extrusions LLC F 352 369-5552
Ocala (G-11923)
Doors Molding and More F 727 498-8552
Saint Petersburg (G-15764)
▲ Doran Manufacturing Corp Fla G 904 731-3313
Jacksonville (G-6326)
Dotchi LLC F 305 477-0024
Miami (G-9483)
▼ Dura-Cast Products Inc D 863 638-3200
Lake Wales (G-7507)

▼ **Dura-Weld Inc**......G...... 561 586-0180
Lake Worth Beach *(G-7611)*
▼ **Dynotec Plastic Inc**......G...... 813 248-5335
Tampa *(G-17622)*
Ehud Industries Inc......G...... 904 803-0873
Jacksonville *(G-6357)*
▲ **Ei Global Group Llc**......G...... 561 999-8989
Boca Raton *(G-515)*
◆ **Elite Aluminum Corporation**......D...... 954 949-3200
Coconut Creek *(G-2075)*
◆ **Ellis Family Holdings Inc**......F...... 503 785-7400
Hialeah *(G-5393)*
▼ **Emmanuel Holdings Inc**......F...... 305 558-3088
Miami *(G-9524)*
Endless Oceans LLC......G...... 561 274-1990
Delray Beach *(G-3073)*
Envirosafe Technologies Inc......G...... 904 646-3456
Jacksonville *(G-6367)*
Enviroworks Inc......F...... 407 889-5533
Apopka *(G-137)*
Epic Extrusion Inc......G...... 941 378-0835
Sarasota *(G-16421)*
Estradas Fiberglass Mfg Corp......G...... 954 924-8778
Sunny Isles Beach *(G-17076)*
Euro Trim Inc......G...... 239 574-6646
Cape Coral *(G-1419)*
▲ **Eurogan-Usa Inc**......F...... 321 356-5248
Orlando *(G-12720)*
▲ **Excalibur Manufacturing Corp**......F...... 352 544-0055
Brooksville *(G-1228)*
Extreme Coatings......G...... 727 528-7998
Saint Petersburg *(G-15775)*
▼ **Faulkner Inc of Miami**......F...... 305 885-4731
Hialeah *(G-5408)*
Fellowship Enterprises Inc......G...... 727 726-5997
Safety Harbor *(G-15493)*
Fimco Manufacturing Inc......G...... 561 624-3308
Jupiter *(G-7042)*
▲ **First Shot Mold and Tool**......G...... 321 269-0031
Titusville *(G-18429)*
Firstcut......G...... 786 740-3683
Miami *(G-9573)*
Fiskars Brands Inc......G...... 407 889-5533
Apopka *(G-142)*
Florida Amico......G...... 863 688-9256
Lakeland *(G-7689)*
Florida Central Extrusion Inc......G...... 863 324-2541
Winter Haven *(G-19321)*
◆ **Florida Custom Mold Inc**......D...... 813 343-5080
Odessa *(G-12121)*
Florida Electromechanics Inc......G...... 305 825-5244
Hialeah *(G-5412)*
▲ **Florida Production Engrg Inc**......C...... 386 677-2566
Ormond Beach *(G-13372)*
Foam Molding LLC......G...... 813 434-7044
Tampa *(G-17690)*
Fuel Air Spark Technology......F...... 901 260-3278
Naples *(G-11252)*
Funder America Inc......G...... 863 655-0208
Sebring *(G-16691)*
▼ **Future Modes Inc**......G...... 305 654-9995
Miami *(G-9605)*
Gator Polymers LLC......F...... 866 292-7306
Cape Coral *(G-1427)*
Genca Corp......E...... 727 524-3622
Clearwater *(G-1701)*
Genpak LLC......F...... 863 243-1068
Lake Placid *(G-7487)*
Gerogari Display Manufacture......G...... 305 888-0993
Miami *(G-9632)*
Glass Works of Largo Inc......G...... 727 535-9808
Largo *(G-7960)*
Glasspec Corp......G...... 305 255-8444
Opa Locka *(G-12320)*
◆ **Graduate Plastics Inc**......C...... 305 687-0405
Miami *(G-9652)*
◆ **Grupo Phoenix Corp Svcs LLC**......E...... 954 241-0023
Miami *(G-9680)*
▼ **Gulf Coast Mold & Tool Corp**......F...... 239 643-1017
Bonita Springs *(G-837)*
Gulf View Plastics Inc......G...... 727 379-3072
Hudson *(G-6028)*
▲ **Hans-Mill Corp**......D...... 904 395-2288
Jacksonville *(G-6460)*
Harbortech Plastics LLC......F...... 727 944-2425
Holiday *(G-5743)*
◆ **Hardware Concepts Inc**......G...... 305 685-1337
Miami *(G-9687)*
Hc Grupo Inc......G...... 954 227-0150
Coral Springs *(G-2252)*
▲ **Hernon Manufacturing Inc**......D...... 407 322-4000
Sanford *(G-16061)*
Hippo Tampa LLC......G...... 813 391-9152
Tampa *(G-17756)*
Holmes Stamp Company......E...... 904 396-2291
Jacksonville *(G-6476)*
Holpack Corp......G...... 786 565-3969
Hialeah *(G-5448)*
▲ **Homyn Enterprises Corp**......D...... 305 870-9720
Miami *(G-9718)*
House Plastics Unlimited Inc......E...... 407 843-3290
Orlando *(G-12812)*
Idproductsource......G...... 772 336-4269
Port Saint Lucie *(G-15113)*
Idproductsource LLC......G...... 772 336-4269
Port Saint Lucie *(G-15114)*
Iis Incorporated......G...... 561 547-4297
Boynton Beach *(G-918)*
Industrial Cmpsite Systems LLC......F...... 863 646-8551
Lakeland *(G-7710)*
▲ **Industrial Plastic Pdts Inc**......E...... 305 822-3223
Miami Lakes *(G-10797)*
Industrial Plastic Systems Inc......E...... 863 646-8551
Lakeland *(G-7711)*
Innovative Base Tech LLC......G...... 727 391-9009
Saint Petersburg *(G-15816)*
Innovative PDT Solutions LLC......F...... 407 933-2029
Kissimmee *(G-7254)*
◆ **Integrated Components Corp**......F...... 305 824-0484
Hialeah *(G-5454)*
Intermas Nets USA Inc......G...... 305 442-1416
Coral Gables *(G-2160)*
International Power USA LLC......G...... 305 534-7993
Miami *(G-9760)*
▲ **J & P Deerfield Inc**......F...... 954 571-6665
Deerfield Beach *(G-2849)*
◆ **J T Walker Industries Inc**......E...... 727 461-0501
Clearwater *(G-1739)*
J W Austin Industries Inc......G...... 321 723-2422
Melbourne *(G-8853)*
◆ **Jan and Jean Inc**......G...... 813 645-0680
Ruskin *(G-15485)*
Jar-Den Llc......G...... 860 334-7539
Port Richey *(G-15056)*
Jarden LLC......D...... 561 447-2520
Boca Raton *(G-576)*
Jarden Plastic Solutions......G...... 864 879-8100
Boca Raton *(G-577)*
Jerae Inc......F...... 954 989-6665
Hollywood *(G-5853)*
Jers Group......G...... 786 953-6419
Doral *(G-3402)*
▼ **Jmh Marine Inc**......F...... 954 785-7557
Pompano Beach *(G-14736)*
Jtf Ventures LLC......G...... 305 556-5156
Miami Lakes *(G-10800)*
K & I Creative Plas & WD LLC......G...... 904 923-0409
Jacksonville *(G-6530)*
K & I Plastics Inc......G...... 904 387-0438
Jacksonville *(G-6531)*
▲ **Kasulik II LLC**......F...... 786 629-8978
Hallandale Beach *(G-5195)*
Kincaid Plastics Inc......D...... 352 754-9979
Brooksville *(G-1242)*
Kinetic Industries LLC......G...... 727 572-7604
Clearwater *(G-1750)*
Kino Sandals Inc......F...... 305 294-5044
Key West *(G-7193)*
◆ **Kramski North America Inc**......F...... 727 828-1500
Largo *(G-7995)*
▲ **L C Southwind Manufacturing**......F...... 352 687-1999
Ocala *(G-11978)*
▲ **Laser Creations Incorporated**......E...... 800 771-7151
Apopka *(G-155)*
◆ **Latam Optical LLC**......G...... 786 275-3284
Miami *(G-9865)*
Latham Plastics Inc......G...... 813 783-7212
Zephyrhills *(G-19526)*
Lean Design & Mfg Inc......F...... 727 415-3504
Lutz *(G-8395)*
Lera Plastics Inc......G...... 904 716-5421
Jacksonville *(G-6554)*
▲ **M & M Plastics Inc**......E...... 305 688-4335
Miami *(G-9923)*
M D R International Inc......F...... 305 944-5335
North Miami *(G-11644)*
M O Precision Molders Inc......F...... 727 573-4466
Clearwater *(G-1767)*
Marconi Line Inc......F...... 321 639-1130
Rockledge *(G-15434)*
Maritime Custom Designs Inc......G...... 941 716-0255
Venice *(G-18562)*
Marlon Inc......F...... 813 901-8488
Tampa *(G-17882)*
Masonways Indstrctble Plas LLC......E...... 561 478-8838
West Palm Beach *(G-18944)*
Master Mold Corp......G...... 941 486-0000
North Venice *(G-11760)*
Master Tool Co Inc......E...... 305 557-1020
Miami Lakes *(G-10815)*
Maxi-Blast of Florida Inc......G...... 727 572-0909
Saint Petersburg *(G-15851)*
▲ **Mdi Products LLC**......F...... 772 228-7371
Sebastian *(G-16669)*
Mdl Molding LLC......G...... 954 792-3104
Fort Lauderdale *(G-4114)*
Melt-Tech Polymers Inc......G...... 305 887-6148
Medley *(G-8688)*
◆ **Meltpoint Plastics Intl Inc**......E...... 305 887-8020
Medley *(G-8689)*
Mercer Products Company Inc......E...... 352 357-0057
Umatilla *(G-18499)*
Mesa Industries Inc......F...... 386 738-3255
Deland *(G-2995)*
Mid-Florida Plastics Inc......E...... 407 856-1805
Orlando *(G-12970)*
Midgard Inc......D...... 863 696-1224
Lake Wales *(G-7516)*
Mikes Precision Inc......G...... 305 558-6421
Hialeah *(G-5517)*
Modern Tchncal Molding Dev LLC......F...... 727 343-2942
Saint Petersburg *(G-15857)*
Modular Molding Intl Inc......E...... 727 541-1333
Seminole *(G-16754)*
Molded Moments Art......G...... 954 913-0793
Royal Palm Beach *(G-15475)*
Molded Poly Innovations Inc......F...... 407 314-1778
Sanford *(G-16090)*
Molding Depot Inc......E...... 813 348-4837
Tampa *(G-17915)*
◆ **Molds and Plastic Machinery**......G...... 305 828-3456
Opa Locka *(G-12340)*
Mpc Group LLC......G...... 773 927-4120
Deland *(G-3001)*
▲ **Mtng Usa Corp**......G...... 305 670-0979
Miami *(G-10051)*
▲ **MTS Medication Tech Inc**......C...... 727 576-6311
Saint Petersburg *(G-15862)*
MTS Packaging System Inc......G...... 727 812-2830
Clearwater *(G-1796)*
▼ **MTS Packaging Systems Inc**......C...... 727 576-6311
Saint Petersburg *(G-15863)*
MTS Sales & Marketing Inc......D...... 727 812-2830
Clearwater *(G-1797)*
▼ **Myton Industries Inc**......F...... 954 989-0113
Hallandale *(G-5159)*
Nanotechnovation Corporation......E...... 352 732-3244
Ocala *(G-12004)*
◆ **National Molding LLC**......C...... 305 823-5440
Miami Lakes *(G-10827)*
Nelson Plastics Inc......E...... 407 339-3570
Longwood *(G-8316)*
New Generation Packaging LLC......G...... 786 259-6670
Miami Gardens *(G-10751)*
Nfk Corporation......F...... 305 378-2116
Miami *(G-10070)*
◆ **Nida-Core Corporation**......E...... 772 343-7300
Port Saint Lucie *(G-15124)*
◆ **Noveltex Miami Inc**......E...... 305 887-8191
Hialeah *(G-5544)*
Novelty Crystal Corp......E...... 352 429-9036
Groveland *(G-5104)*
▲ **Novelty Crystal Corp**......D...... 352 429-9036
Groveland *(G-5103)*
Nursery Supplies Inc......B...... 407 846-9750
Kissimmee *(G-7278)*
Nylacarb Corp......E...... 772 569-5999
Vero Beach *(G-18649)*
◆ **Octal Ventures Inc**......F...... 727 526-9288
Pinellas Park *(G-14373)*
Octex Holdings LLC......D...... 941 371-6767
Sarasota *(G-16530)*
Onelid LLC......G...... 305 335-9730
North Miami Beach *(G-11695)*
OPif- Our Plstic Is Fntstic......G...... 954 636-4228
Lauderhill *(G-8118)*
Optical Hong Kong......F...... 305 200-5522
Hialeah *(G-5551)*
P & L Creech Inc......G...... 386 547-4182
Daytona Beach *(G-2691)*

▲ **Pacific Link Imports Inc**....G.... 954 605-6071
Parkland *(G-13997)*
Paradigm Leaders LLC....G.... 850 441-3289
Panama City Beach *(G-13982)*
▲ **Paradise Inc**....C.... 813 752-1155
Tampa *(G-17974)*
Paragon Globl Sup Slutions LLC....G.... 813 745-9902
Tampa *(G-17975)*
▼ **Paragon Plastics Inc**....E.... 321 631-6212
Titusville *(G-18448)*
Paramount Mold LLC....E.... 954 772-2333
Fort Lauderdale *(G-4157)*
▲ **Paramount Molded Products Inc**....E.... 954 772-2333
Fort Lauderdale *(G-4158)*
Parras Plastic Inc....G.... 305 972-9537
Miami *(G-10143)*
Pcm and S L Plota Co LLC....F.... 727 547-6277
Largo *(G-8024)*
▲ **Peaktop Technologies Inc**....G.... 561 598-6005
West Palm Beach *(G-18992)*
▲ **Perry Fiberglas Products Inc**....E.... 321 609-9036
Rockledge *(G-15439)*
Petroleum Containment Inc....E.... 904 358-1700
Jacksonville *(G-6669)*
◆ **Plastic Components Inc**....E.... 305 885-0561
Medley *(G-8707)*
Plastic Composites Inc....F.... 352 669-5822
Umatilla *(G-18501)*
Plastic Concepts & Designs Inc....G.... 904 396-7500
Jacksonville *(G-6676)*
Plastic Concepts Ltd Inc....F.... 727 942-6684
Tarpon Springs *(G-18320)*
Plastic Kingdom Inc....G.... 561 586-9300
Lake Worth *(G-7580)*
Plastic Parts Inc....E.... 954 974-3051
Pompano Beach *(G-14796)*
Plastic Parts Inc....G.... 954 974-3051
Margate *(G-8561)*
Plastic Solutions Inc....G.... 727 202-6815
Largo *(G-8028)*
Plastic Solutions of Pompano....G.... 800 331-7081
Pompano Beach *(G-14798)*
▲ **Plastics Dynamics Inc**....G.... 954 565-7122
Oakland Park *(G-11828)*
Plastics For Mankind Inc....F.... 305 687-5917
Opa Locka *(G-12351)*
▲ **Plastimold Products Inc**....G.... 561 869-0183
Delray Beach *(G-3118)*
Plazadoor Corp....E.... 561 578-5450
Riviera Beach *(G-15364)*
◆ **Polymer Logistics Inc**....E.... 877 462-6195
Tampa *(G-17996)*
◆ **Pompadour Products Inc**....E.... 954 345-2700
Coral Springs *(G-2303)*
Pompanette LLC....E.... 813 885-2182
Tampa *(G-17997)*
▼ **Precision Mold & Tool Inc**....E.... 407 847-5687
Kissimmee *(G-7290)*
Precision Mold Tech Inc....G.... 305 594-1789
Doral *(G-3468)*
Precision Plastics Group Inc....E.... 863 299-6639
Winter Haven *(G-19343)*
▲ **Precision Tool & Mold Inc**....F.... 727 573-4441
Clearwater *(G-1842)*
◆ **Premier Lab Supply Inc**....G.... 772 873-1700
Port Saint Lucie *(G-15130)*
Price Chpper Med Wrstbands Inc....G.... 407 505-5809
Orlando *(G-13086)*
▲ **Prime Molding Technologies Inc**....E.... 561 721-2799
Riviera Beach *(G-15366)*
▲ **Proandre Hygiene Systems Inc**....F.... 305 433-3493
Miami *(G-10204)*
◆ **Profast Corporation**....E.... 305 827-7801
Miami Lakes *(G-10844)*
Profbox of America Inc....G.... 786 454-8148
North Miami Beach *(G-11699)*
Prospect Plastics Inc....G.... 954 564-7282
Oakland Park *(G-11833)*
▲ **Protective Enclosures Co LLC**....G.... 321 441-9689
Altamonte Springs *(G-68)*
▼ **Proto Corp**....D.... 727 573-4665
Clearwater *(G-1851)*
Prototype Plastics LLC....G.... 941 371-3380
Sarasota *(G-16549)*
◆ **Prototype Plstic Extrusion Inc**....E.... 727 572-0803
Clearwater *(G-1852)*
▼ **Pvc Windoors Inc**....F.... 305 940-3608
North Miami *(G-11652)*
Quality Molds USA Inc....F.... 321 632-6066
Cocoa *(G-2044)*
Quick Cans Inc....G.... 407 415-1361
Winter Park *(G-19435)*
▲ **R P M Industries Inc**....E.... 315 255-1105
Hobe Sound *(G-5726)*
R S Design Inc....F.... 727 525-8292
Pinellas Park *(G-14383)*
Rainbow Pool Supply Inc....G.... 407 324-9616
Sanford *(G-16109)*
Rainbow Precision Mfg Corp....G.... 561 691-1658
Palm Beach Gardens *(G-13621)*
Rehrig Pacific Company....F.... 407 857-3888
Orlando *(G-13128)*
Rek Manufacturing Inc....G.... 321 269-3533
Titusville *(G-18455)*
Rosier Manufacturing Company....G.... 386 409-7223
Daytona Beach *(G-2705)*
S Gager Industries Inc....E.... 904 268-6727
Jacksonville *(G-6743)*
Safariland LLC....E.... 904 646-0141
Jacksonville *(G-6747)*
Safe Pro Inc....G.... 954 494-5768
Hialeah *(G-5609)*
Saint-Gobain Vetrotex Amer Inc....C.... 407 834-8968
Maitland *(G-8476)*
Sands Molding Inc....G.... 813 345-8646
Land O Lakes *(G-7865)*
◆ **Sargeant Marine Inc**....F.... 561 999-9916
Boca Raton *(G-702)*
Scf Processing LLC....G.... 352 377-0858
Gainesville *(G-4993)*
◆ **Scientific Plastics Ltd**....F.... 305 557-3737
Miami Lakes *(G-10856)*
◆ **Scott Sign Systems Inc**....E.... 941 355-5171
Sarasota *(G-16294)*
Sea Link Holdings LLC....F.... 727 523-8660
Largo *(G-8047)*
Seacure Inc....F.... 904 353-5353
Jacksonville *(G-6759)*
Seaway Plastics Engrg LLC....G.... 727 777-6032
Port Richey *(G-15068)*
▲ **Seaway Plastics Engrg LLC**....D.... 727 845-3235
Port Richey *(G-15069)*
Semplastics....G.... 407 353-6885
Oviedo *(G-13457)*
▼ **Shoreline Plastics LLC**....E.... 904 696-2981
Jacksonville *(G-6766)*
Shwinco Industries Inc....E.... 850 271-8900
Lynn Haven *(G-8438)*
Sibe Automation LLC....F.... 352 690-1741
Ocala *(G-12049)*
Silcar Corp....G.... 305 557-8391
Hialeah *(G-5620)*
Simco Machine and Tool Inc....F.... 863 452-1151
Avon Park *(G-295)*
▼ **Simtec Silicone Parts LLC**....E.... 954 656-4212
Miramar *(G-11043)*
Sippers By Design....G.... 305 371-5087
Miami *(G-10354)*
Soft Plastics Florida Inc....G.... 904 338-9680
Jacksonville *(G-6782)*
▲ **Sourcerers Inc**....G.... 954 530-2333
Plantation *(G-14556)*
◆ **Southast Auto Acquisition Corp**....E.... 305 885-8689
Medley *(G-8726)*
Southeast Id LLC....F.... 954 571-6665
Miami Lakes *(G-10859)*
◆ **Southern Die Casting Corp**....E.... 305 635-6571
Miami *(G-10385)*
Southern Reinforced Plastics....G.... 941 746-8793
Bradenton *(G-1118)*
Standard Injection Molding Inc....F.... 863 452-9090
Avon Park *(G-297)*
Stephen ODonnell....G.... 631 664-3594
Saint Cloud *(G-15668)*
Steven R Durante....G.... 954 564-9913
Oakland Park *(G-11844)*
Stockdale Technologies Inc....D.... 407 323-5121
Lake Mary *(G-7451)*
▼ **Stoltz Industries Inc**....F.... 954 792-3270
Davie *(G-2596)*
Structural Composites Inc....F.... 321 951-9464
Melbourne *(G-8947)*
Sumiflex LLC....G.... 954 578-6998
Sunrise *(G-17181)*
Sun Coast Industries LLC....D.... 941 355-7166
Sarasota *(G-16304)*
Sun Works Plastics Inc....G.... 727 573-2343
Clearwater *(G-1892)*
▲ **Sun-Tek Manufacturing Inc**....E.... 407 859-2117
Orlando *(G-13223)*
◆ **Sunbeam Products Inc**....B.... 561 912-4100
Boca Raton *(G-738)*
▼ **Sunco Plastics Inc**....F.... 305 238-2864
Miami *(G-10429)*
Suncoast Molders Inc....F.... 727 546-0041
Largo *(G-8063)*
▲ **Sunflex**....G.... 800 606-0756
Naples *(G-11423)*
▲ **Sunflex Wall Systems LP**....G.... 239 220-1570
Naples *(G-11424)*
Sunrise Fiberglass Inc....G.... 305 636-4111
Miami *(G-10432)*
Sunset Cadillac of Sarasota....F.... 941 922-1571
Sarasota *(G-16610)*
◆ **T S E Industries Inc**....C.... 727 573-7676
Clearwater *(G-1900)*
T S E Industries Inc....E.... 727 540-1368
Clearwater *(G-1901)*
Taco Metals Inc....F.... 727 224-4282
Seminole *(G-16767)*
Team Plastics Inc....E.... 386 740-9555
Deland *(G-3018)*
Tearepair Inc....E.... 813 948-6898
Land O Lakes *(G-7867)*
TEC Air Inc....G.... 772 335-8220
Fort Pierce *(G-4754)*
Technicraft Plastics Inc....F.... 954 927-2575
Dania *(G-2458)*
◆ **Tervis Tumbler Company**....C.... 941 966-2114
North Venice *(G-11763)*
▼ **Tiki Water Sports Inc**....G.... 305 852-9298
Key Largo *(G-7175)*
Tmf Plastic Solutions LLC....E.... 941 748-2946
Bradenton *(G-1126)*
▲ **Tomsons Inc**....G.... 248 646-0677
Englewood *(G-3685)*
Tuflex Manufacturing Co....E.... 954 781-0605
Pompano Beach *(G-14895)*
▲ **Tupperware Brands Corporation**....A.... 407 826-5050
Orlando *(G-13280)*
Tupperware Turkey Inc....D.... 407 826-5050
Orlando *(G-13282)*
▲ **Tupperware US Inc**....B.... 407 826-5050
Orlando *(G-13283)*
Tuthill Corporation....D.... 727 446-8593
Clearwater *(G-1927)*
Ultimate Containers Pro LLC....F.... 786 241-4306
Miami Gardens *(G-10757)*
◆ **Ultratech International Inc**....E.... 904 292-9019
Jacksonville *(G-6876)*
United Plastic Fabricating Inc....D.... 352 291-2477
Ocala *(G-12067)*
USA Shutter Company LLC....G.... 239 596-8883
Fort Myers *(G-4642)*
USB Plastics....G.... 727 375-8840
Odessa *(G-12163)*
Usbev Plastics LLC....F.... 813 855-0700
Oldsmar *(G-12275)*
▼ **Usbev Products Inc**....F.... 727 375-8840
Odessa *(G-12164)*
◆ **V & C Supply Ornamental Corp**....G.... 305 634-9040
Miami *(G-10558)*
Vanguard Systems Corp....G.... 727 528-0121
Saint Petersburg *(G-15950)*
Victors Trim Molding Crown Bas....G.... 727 403-6057
Saint Petersburg *(G-15953)*
▼ **Vinyl Corp**....F.... 305 477-6464
Miami *(G-10586)*
Visual Concepts In Plastic Inc....G.... 941 749-1141
Bradenton *(G-1141)*
Viterra Affordable Shutters....G.... 239 738-6364
Cape Coral *(G-1492)*
◆ **Vizco Us Inc**....E.... 941 753-3333
Bradenton *(G-1142)*
Volusia Waste Inc....G.... 386 878-3322
Deltona *(G-3181)*
W E Connery Boat Builders....G.... 239 549-8014
Cape Coral *(G-1493)*
W R Kershaw Inc....G.... 386 673-0602
Ormond Beach *(G-13408)*
Walt Dittmer and Sons Inc....E.... 407 699-1755
Winter Springs *(G-19488)*
▼ **Waterbrick International Inc**....G.... 877 420-9283
Windermere *(G-19250)*
Waterway Systems LLC....G.... 941 752-3554
Sarasota *(G-16324)*
Wattera LLC....E.... 954 400-5135
Fort Lauderdale *(G-4316)*
Wb Medical Transport LLC....G.... 561 827-8877
Port Saint Lucie *(G-15163)*

▼ **William B Rudow Inc**......G...... 941 957-4200
Sarasota *(G-16640)*
Winslow Microplastics Corp......G...... 305 493-3501
Miami *(G-10612)*
Your ID Guard......G...... 904 354-8989
Jacksonville *(G-6933)*
Z Cans LLC......G...... 941 748-6688
Bradenton *(G-1149)*
Zeus Industries......G...... 727 530-4373
Largo *(G-8081)*

31 LEATHER AND LEATHER PRODUCTS

3111 Leather Tanning & Finishing

Buonaventura Bag and Cases LLC......G...... 212 960-3442
Naples *(G-11196)*
Jdk Imports Inc......F...... 850 865-0297
Santa Rosa Beach *(G-16161)*
Leather Doctor of Doral LLC......G...... 786 367-6146
Cutler Bay *(G-2401)*
▲ **Octane Seating LLC**......E...... 888 627-6743
Fort Lauderdale *(G-4147)*
Sebring Custom Tanning Inc......G...... 863 655-1600
Sebring *(G-16707)*
Ti-Pagos Usa Inc......G...... 786 310-7423
Miami *(G-10475)*

3131 Boot & Shoe Cut Stock & Findings

Advanced Living Quarters Inc......G...... 954 684-9392
Pembroke Pines *(G-14015)*
AGM Kitchen & Bath LLC......G...... 239 300-4739
Naples *(G-11151)*
Aurum Enterprises LLC......G...... 561 921-5119
Miami Beach *(G-10646)*
Bean Counters Pro......G...... 941 504-1157
Sarasota *(G-16363)*
Counter......G...... 239 566-0644
Naples *(G-11216)*
Counter Impressions LLC......F...... 352 589-4966
Eustis *(G-3706)*
Creative Countertops Inc......F...... 904 387-2800
Jacksonville *(G-6296)*
Hospitlity Bean Cnters Plus In......G...... 954 531-1710
Deerfield Beach *(G-2846)*
Ingersoll Rand......F...... 954 391-4500
Miramar *(G-11004)*
Jmg Counters LLC......F...... 904 551-7006
Jacksonville *(G-6523)*
Pitbull Tactical LLC......G...... 866 452-4708
Orlando *(G-13069)*
Rand & London LLC......G...... 727 363-0800
Treasure Island *(G-18477)*
Rand M Rawls......G...... 904 382-4844
Jacksonville *(G-6704)*
Rand Title Corporation......G...... 407 622-7263
Winter Park *(G-19436)*
Sutherland Armour Rand......F...... 863 696-3129
Lake Wales *(G-7523)*
◆ **Tap Express Inc**......G...... 305 468-0038
Doral *(G-3523)*
Violettas LLC......G...... 305 301-3351
Miami *(G-10587)*
Winter Qarters Pasco Rv Resort......G...... 800 879-2131
Lutz *(G-8424)*

3142 House Slippers

▲ **Margarita Internl Trading Inc**......F...... 305 688-1300
Miami *(G-9946)*

3143 Men's Footwear, Exc Athletic

Kino Sandals Inc......F...... 305 294-5044
Key West *(G-7193)*
Lerness Shoe Corp......G...... 305 643-6525
Miami *(G-9885)*
Ronmar Industries Inc......F...... 561 630-8035
West Palm Beach *(G-19023)*
◆ **Zeppelin Products Inc**......F...... 954 989-8808
Hallandale Beach *(G-5226)*

3144 Women's Footwear, Exc Athletic

Cedrick McDonald......G...... 813 279-1442
Tampa *(G-17519)*
◆ **Devon-Aire Inc**......E...... 813 884-9544
Tampa *(G-17602)*
Grezzo Usa Llc......G...... 954 885-0331
Hollywood *(G-5832)*
Kino Sandals Inc......F...... 305 294-5044
Key West *(G-7193)*
▲ **Kloth Inc**......G...... 954 578-5687
Sunrise *(G-17139)*
Lerness Shoe Corp......G...... 305 643-6525
Miami *(G-9885)*
Neighborhood Property Mgmt......G...... 305 819-2361
Hialeah *(G-5536)*
Ronmar Industries Inc......F...... 561 630-8035
West Palm Beach *(G-19023)*
Stush AP USA/Stush Style LLC......F...... 404 940-3445
Sunrise *(G-17180)*
◆ **Zeppelin Products Inc**......F...... 954 989-8808
Hallandale Beach *(G-5226)*

3151 Leather Gloves & Mittens

Orbi Supply Inc......G...... 305 810-8822
Doral *(G-3451)*
Sara Glove Company Inc......G...... 866 664-7272
Naples *(G-11392)*

3161 Luggage

Agora Sales Inc......F...... 727 490-0499
Clearwater *(G-1569)*
▲ **Agora Sales Inc**......B...... 727 321-0707
Saint Petersburg *(G-15695)*
Bee Electronics Inc......D...... 772 468-7477
Fort Pierce *(G-4680)*
Fussion International Inc......G...... 305 662-4848
Coral Gables *(G-2146)*
◆ **Gar Industries Corp**......F...... 954 456-8088
Hallandale Beach *(G-5188)*
Goyard Miami LLC......E...... 305 894-9235
Bal Harbour *(G-302)*
Hontus Ltd......F...... 786 322-3022
Medley *(G-8666)*
Hut Global Inc......G...... 561 571-2523
Boca Raton *(G-560)*
◆ **Intradeco Apparel Inc**......C...... 305 264-8888
Medley *(G-8671)*
Jasmine Purkiss......F...... 386 244-7726
Edgewater *(G-3628)*
▲ **Koszegi Industries Inc**......E...... 954 419-9544
Deerfield Beach *(G-2855)*
▲ **Lug Usa LLC**......F...... 855 584-5433
Orlando *(G-12937)*
▲ **Maleta Import**......G...... 305 592-2410
Miami *(G-9938)*
◆ **My Focus Inc**......G...... 305 826-4480
Miami Lakes *(G-10826)*
Qps Companies Inc......E...... 813 246-5525
Tampa *(G-18029)*
Spires Empire LLC......G...... 305 797-0622
Key West *(G-7203)*
Stemler Corporation......E...... 727 577-1216
Saint Petersburg *(G-15927)*
Tumi Holdings Inc......G...... 941 866-6304
Sarasota *(G-16318)*
US Communications Industries......E...... 772 468-7477
Fort Pierce *(G-4767)*

3171 Handbags & Purses

◆ **Becarro International Corp**......G...... 561 737-5585
West Palm Beach *(G-18815)*
▲ **Excel Handbags Co Inc**......F...... 305 836-8800
Miami *(G-9543)*
◆ **Gar Industries Corp**......F...... 954 456-8088
Hallandale Beach *(G-5188)*
Mrkt Deux......G...... 305 603-9682
Miami *(G-10049)*

3172 Personal Leather Goods

Abco Industries LLC......G...... 813 605-5900
Tampa *(G-17383)*
Bespoke Stitchery LLC......G...... 407 412-9937
Orlando *(G-12511)*
▲ **Continental Belt Corp**......G...... 305 573-8871
Miami *(G-9395)*
Everglades Creations Inc......E...... 305 822-3344
Opa Locka *(G-12314)*
◆ **Gar Industries Corp**......F...... 954 456-8088
Hallandale Beach *(G-5188)*
▲ **Identity Stronghold LLC**......E...... 941 475-8480
Englewood *(G-3679)*
J Lea LLC......G...... 954 921-1422
Hollywood *(G-5849)*
▲ **Koszegi Industries Inc**......E...... 954 419-9544
Deerfield Beach *(G-2855)*
▲ **Leon Leather Company Inc**......F...... 386 304-1902
Edgewater *(G-3629)*
Ostrich Market Inc......G...... 954 873-1957
Melbourne *(G-8902)*
Rubber B LLC......G...... 305 771-2369
Miami Beach *(G-10707)*
◆ **Sea Link International Irb Inc**......F...... 727 523-8660
Largo *(G-8048)*
Soul Kass Boutique LLC......F...... 682 429-4323
Molino *(G-11074)*
Trimtek Leather Inc......G...... 706 577-3950
Pensacola *(G-14275)*
▲ **Winston Manufacturing Corp**......G...... 305 822-3344
Hialeah *(G-5688)*
Yvel Usa Inc......G...... 561 391-5119
Boca Raton *(G-797)*
Zpacks Corp......F...... 321 215-5658
West Melbourne *(G-18780)*

3199 Leather Goods, NEC

▼ **Allcases Reekstin & Assoc Inc**......F...... 813 891-1313
Oldsmar *(G-12200)*
American Commodity Exch Corp......G...... 904 687-0588
Jacksonville *(G-6148)*
Bully Wurld LLC......G...... 201 466-8185
Cape Coral *(G-1397)*
Cadre Holdings Inc......C...... 904 741-5400
Jacksonville *(G-6249)*
Creative Colors International......G...... 239 573-8883
Cape Coral *(G-1407)*
▲ **Dp Pet Products Inc**......F...... 407 888-4627
Orlando *(G-12681)*
E Quality Cables Inc......F...... 321 242-4820
Melbourne *(G-8817)*
Eileen Kramer Inc......G...... 315 395-3831
Aventura *(G-268)*
High Noon Unlimited Inc......G...... 727 939-2701
Holiday *(G-5744)*
Lachance Leathers LLC......G...... 407 790-6712
Orlando *(G-12887)*
Land Leather Inc......G...... 305 594-2260
Miami *(G-9857)*
Longchamp Usa Inc......E...... 305 372-1628
Miami *(G-9908)*
Mid Flrida Lthersir/Leatherboy......G...... 352 615-5851
Dade City *(G-2431)*
Milcom Services Inc......G...... 561 907-6816
Lake Worth Beach *(G-7616)*
N3xt Up Exotic LLC......G...... 863 777-3778
Tampa *(G-17928)*
▲ **Ontyte LLC**......G...... 561 880-8920
Wellington *(G-18726)*
Rally Leather & More LLC......G...... 516 643-8572
Port Orange *(G-15030)*
Roof-A-Cide West LLC......G...... 877 258-8998
Sarasota *(G-16561)*
Sarasota Leather Gallery Inc......G...... 800 741-4336
Hudson *(G-6037)*
Southern-Bartlett Intl LLC......F...... 407 374-1613
Lakeland *(G-7802)*
Summit Holsters LLC......G...... 386 383-4090
Deltona *(G-3180)*
▲ **Wellington Leather LLC**......G...... 561 790-0034
Royal Palm Beach *(G-15479)*
Zen Distributors Group II LLC......F...... 305 637-3014
Miami *(G-10629)*

32 STONE, CLAY, GLASS, AND CONCRETE PRODUCTS

3211 Flat Glass

Ad Valorem Corporation......G...... 561 488-9966
Boca Raton *(G-397)*
Advanced Impact Tech Inc......E...... 727 287-4620
Largo *(G-7886)*
◆ **Aldora Aluminum & GL Pdts Inc**......E...... 954 441-5057
Coral Springs *(G-2219)*
American Shield LLC......G...... 850 697-3066
Lanark Village *(G-7848)*
Assura Windows and Doors LLC......G...... 954 781-4430
Pompano Beach *(G-14605)*
Cardinal Lg Company......D...... 352 237-4410
Ocala *(G-11895)*
Central Florida Tinting......G...... 863 221-0185
Lake Wales *(G-7502)*
Coastal Hurricane Film LLC......G...... 941 268-9693
Port Charlotte *(G-14970)*
▲ **Commercial Insulating Glass Co**......D...... 941 378-9100
Sarasota *(G-16389)*

SIC

Cws Holding Company LLC..........D...... 352 368-6922
Ocala *(G-11915)*
Dynamic Visions Inc..........E...... 941 497-1984
Venice *(G-18543)*
Erickson International LLC..........G...... 702 853-4800
Boynton Beach *(G-904)*
◆ **Faours Mirror Corp**..........E...... 813 884-3297
Tampa *(G-17658)*
FMC/Rhyno LLC..........E...... 813 838-2264
Tampa *(G-17689)*
▼ **Giz Studio Inc**..........F...... 305 416-5001
Miami *(G-9637)*
▲ **Global Performance Windows Inc**....F...... 954 942-3322
Pompano Beach *(G-14715)*
Guardian Industries Cor..........E...... 954 525-3481
Fort Lauderdale *(G-4034)*
Impact Safe Glass Corporation..........G...... 813 247-5528
Tampa *(G-17774)*
▲ **Jsl Enterprises of Orlando**..........F...... 386 767-9653
Chuluota *(G-1553)*
Kenny Skylights LLC..........G...... 407 330-5150
Sanford *(G-16078)*
King Construction & Glass LLC..........G...... 407 508-6286
Kissimmee *(G-7261)*
Panama City Tint Center..........G...... 850 640-0167
Panama City *(G-13938)*
▼ **PGT Innovations Inc**..........A...... 941 480-1600
North Venice *(G-11762)*
Pilkington North America Inc..........F...... 407 295-8560
Orlando *(G-13068)*
Precision Auto Tint Dsign Corp..........G...... 727 385-8788
Tarpon Springs *(G-18321)*
Sick Ride LLC..........G...... 239 300-5995
Naples *(G-11402)*
Structure Glass Solutions LLC..........F...... 954 499-9450
Hialeah *(G-5635)*
▲ **Sun-Tek Manufacturing Inc**..........E...... 407 859-2117
Orlando *(G-13223)*
US Global Glass LLC..........F...... 305 651-6630
Miami *(G-10552)*
Vistamatic LLC..........E...... 866 466-9525
Coral Springs *(G-2329)*
◆ **Windoor Incorporated**..........C...... 407 481-8400
North Venice *(G-11765)*

3221 Glass Containers

◆ **Anchor Glass Container Corp**..........C...... 813 884-0000
Tampa *(G-17425)*
Anchor Glass Container Corp..........C...... 904 786-1010
Jacksonville *(G-6153)*
Anupack LLC..........G...... 407 850-1960
Orlando *(G-12481)*
Best Quality Water Sys of Fla..........C...... 407 971-2537
Oviedo *(G-13418)*
Brand You Waters LLC..........G...... 786 312-0840
Pompano Beach *(G-14621)*
Endorphin Farms Inc..........F...... 904 824-2006
Saint Augustine *(G-15541)*
Genie Cap Inc..........F...... 941 355-5730
Sarasota *(G-16448)*
◆ **Jensen Scientific Products Inc**..........E...... 954 344-2006
Coral Springs *(G-2263)*
▼ **Kiinde LLC**..........G...... 404 368-5382
Melbourne *(G-8858)*
◆ **Packaging & Resources Inc**..........G...... 954 288-9678
Weston *(G-19159)*
▲ **Rock Bottom Bottles LLC**..........G...... 901 237-9929
Sarasota *(G-16287)*
Spiker USA Corporation..........G...... 850 710-3043
Pensacola *(G-14269)*
▲ **Van Teal Inc**..........E...... 305 751-6767
Miami *(G-10566)*

3229 Pressed & Blown Glassware, NEC

A Sanborn Corporation..........E...... 727 397-3073
Madeira Beach *(G-8445)*
Allied Molded Products LLC..........E...... 941 723-3072
Palmetto *(G-13785)*
Anchor Glass Container Corp..........C...... 904 786-1010
Jacksonville *(G-6153)*
Calendar Arts LLC..........F...... 407 285-8139
Vero Beach *(G-18609)*
Charles Composites LLC..........F...... 863 357-2500
Okeechobee *(G-12173)*
Chrome Aerospace Inc..........G...... 305 506-8182
Miami Beach *(G-10655)*
Eco Cups International Corp..........F...... 407 308-1764
Orlando *(G-12696)*
Ecosoulife USA Dist LLC..........F...... 754 212-5456
Boca Raton *(G-513)*
Edmund C Miga..........G...... 941 628-5951
Port Charlotte *(G-14976)*
Flat Glass Distributors LLC..........E...... 904 354-5413
Jacksonville *(G-6394)*
◆ **Foh Inc**..........C...... 305 757-7940
Miami *(G-9592)*
Gulf Fiberoptics Inc..........E...... 813 891-1993
Oldsmar *(G-12229)*
Hoya Largo..........F...... 727 531-8964
Largo *(G-7976)*
Jga Lighting LLC..........G...... 772 408-8224
Grant *(G-5049)*
▲ **Ledradiant LLC**..........G...... 305 901-1313
Hollywood *(G-5858)*
Madart..........G...... 321 961-9264
Titusville *(G-18444)*
Merritt Precision Tech Inc..........G...... 321 453-2334
Merritt Island *(G-9003)*
▲ **Milano Worldwide Corp**..........G...... 561 266-0201
Boca Raton *(G-625)*
▲ **Miracles For Fun Usa Inc**..........F...... 561 702-8217
Hallandale Beach *(G-5199)*
Mjr Enterprises Inc..........G...... 352 483-0735
Eustis *(G-3714)*
◆ **Nebula Glass International Inc**..........E...... 954 975-3233
Pompano Beach *(G-14771)*
Owens Corning Sales LLC..........E...... 863 291-3046
Winter Haven *(G-19338)*
Perfect Reflections Inc..........G...... 813 991-4361
Zephyrhills *(G-19531)*
Perry Composites LLC..........G...... 850 584-8400
Perry *(G-14308)*
Safilo Usa Inc..........E...... 305 262-5727
Miami *(G-10297)*
Southern Lights..........G...... 727 849-4442
New Port Richey *(G-11510)*
Spectra Composites East Fla..........G...... 772 461-7747
Fort Pierce *(G-4749)*
▲ **Transitions Optical Inc**..........B...... 727 545-0400
Pinellas Park *(G-14392)*

3231 Glass Prdts Made Of Purchased Glass

Ace Mirror & Glass Works Inc..........G...... 561 792-7478
Loxahatchee *(G-8355)*
Acryplex Inc..........G...... 305 633-7636
Miami *(G-9066)*
Advent Glass Works Inc..........G...... 386 497-2050
Fort White *(G-4842)*
◆ **AGM Industries Inc**..........F...... 954 486-1112
Fort Lauderdale *(G-3789)*
Ameriglass Engineering Inc..........F...... 305 558-6227
Hialeah *(G-5298)*
◆ **Arso Enterprises Inc**..........E...... 305 681-2020
Opa Locka *(G-12290)*
◆ **Art & Frame Direct Inc**..........C...... 407 857-6000
Orlando *(G-12491)*
▼ **B & K Installations Inc**..........E...... 305 245-6968
Homestead *(G-5956)*
BT Glass & Mirror Inc..........G...... 561 841-7676
West Palm Beach *(G-18829)*
Buchelli Glass Inc..........G...... 954 695-8067
Coconut Creek *(G-2072)*
◆ **Carib Sea Inc**..........E...... 772 461-1113
Fort Pierce *(G-4683)*
▲ **Circle Redmont Inc**..........E...... 321 259-7374
Melbourne *(G-8789)*
◆ **Coastal Industries Inc**..........C...... 904 642-3970
Jacksonville *(G-6277)*
▲ **Commercial Insulating Glass Co**......D...... 941 378-9100
Sarasota *(G-16389)*
Commercial Rfrg Door Co Inc..........G...... 941 371-8110
Sarasota *(G-16390)*
▲ **Conrad Pickel Studio Inc**..........G...... 772 567-1710
Vero Beach *(G-18612)*
Crawford Glass Door Co..........F...... 954 480-6820
Deerfield Beach *(G-2805)*
▲ **Creative Glassworks**..........G...... 904 860-0865
Jacksonville *(G-6297)*
Custom Cft Windows & Doors Inc..........F...... 407 834-5400
Winter Springs *(G-19470)*
Darren Thomas Glass Co Inc..........G...... 863 655-9500
Sebring *(G-16686)*
Defenshield Inc..........G...... 904 679-3942
Saint Augustine *(G-15535)*
▼ **Dependable Shutter Service Inc**.......E...... 954 583-1411
Davie *(G-2516)*
◆ **Downey Group LLC**..........E...... 954 972-0026
Pompano Beach *(G-14668)*
Elegant Reflections..........G...... 941 627-9275
Port Charlotte *(G-14977)*
Endless Oceans LLC..........G...... 561 274-1990
Delray Beach *(G-3073)*
Enviralum Industries Inc..........F...... 305 752-4411
Miami *(G-9529)*
▼ **Flexstake Inc**..........E...... 239 481-3539
Fort Myers *(G-4450)*
▲ **Florida Glass of Tampa Bay**..........D...... 813 925-1330
Tampa *(G-17677)*
Florida Style Aluminum Inc..........G...... 239 689-8662
Fort Myers *(G-4453)*
◆ **Friedman Bros Dcrtive Arts Inc**..........D...... 800 327-1065
Medley *(G-8653)*
G F E Inc..........F...... 954 583-7005
Davie *(G-2530)*
GE Glass Inc..........G...... 305 599-7725
Miami *(G-9618)*
Geltech Inc..........D...... 407 382-4003
Orlando *(G-12774)*
▲ **Global Performance Windows Inc**....F...... 954 942-3322
Pompano Beach *(G-14715)*
Grade A Glass..........D...... 321 419-6935
Deland *(G-2980)*
Hartmans Canine Center LLC..........G...... 352 978-6592
Clermont *(G-1963)*
Jambco Millwork Inc..........F...... 954 977-4998
Margate *(G-8551)*
◆ **Jensen Scientific Products Inc**..........E...... 954 344-2006
Coral Springs *(G-2263)*
▲ **Jsl Enterprises of Orlando**..........F...... 386 767-9653
Chuluota *(G-1553)*
Justi Group Inc..........E...... 813 855-5779
Oldsmar *(G-12238)*
◆ **Kron Designs LLC**..........G...... 954 941-0800
Fort Lauderdale *(G-4091)*
◆ **Lawson Industries Inc**..........B...... 305 696-8660
Medley *(G-8678)*
Living Color Aquarium Corp..........E...... 844 522-8265
Deerfield Beach *(G-2862)*
◆ **Living Color Enterprises Inc**..........E...... 954 970-9511
Deerfield Beach *(G-2863)*
LP Auto & Home Glass..........F...... 772 335-3697
Fort Pierce *(G-4713)*
Luv Enterprises Inc..........F...... 352 867-8440
Ocala *(G-11988)*
MA Glass & Mirror LLC..........F...... 305 593-8555
Miami *(G-9930)*
▼ **Martell Glass**..........G...... 786 336-0142
Miami *(G-9951)*
Mirrors & More Inc..........G...... 954 782-7272
Pompano Beach *(G-14765)*
Neo Metal Glass LLC..........G...... 954 532-0340
Pompano Beach *(G-14772)*
◆ **Ocean Dynamics USA Inc**..........G...... 305 770-1800
Miami *(G-10088)*
Oldcastle Buildingenvelope Inc..........D...... 813 247-3184
Tampa *(G-17951)*
Omega Garage Doors Inc..........F...... 352 620-8830
Melbourne *(G-8901)*
◆ **PGT Industries Inc**..........A...... 941 480-1600
North Venice *(G-11761)*
Pompanette LLC..........E...... 813 885-2182
Tampa *(G-17997)*
◆ **Sarasota Shower Door Company**......G...... 941 378-0051
Sarasota *(G-16580)*
◆ **Sea Products Inc**..........D...... 904 781-8200
Jacksonville *(G-6758)*
▲ **Security Impact GL Hldings LLC**......G...... 561 844-3100
Riviera Beach *(G-15376)*
Shark Tooth Enterprises Inc..........E...... 904 449-8247
Green Cove Springs *(G-5071)*
▼ **Shower Doors Unlimited Inc**..........F...... 561 547-0702
Boynton Beach *(G-958)*
◆ **Smart Glass Systems Inc**..........G...... 954 801-5349
Plantation *(G-14553)*
Southeastern Aluminum Pdts LLC..........G...... 800 243-8200
Jacksonville *(G-6789)*
◆ **Square One Armoring Svcs Co**..........D...... 305 477-1109
Miami *(G-10407)*
Stony Coral Investments LLC..........F...... 941 704-5391
Myakka City *(G-11143)*
◆ **Sunoptic Technologies LLC**..........D...... 877 677-2832
Jacksonville *(G-6822)*
◆ **Sunshine Windows Mfg Inc**..........D...... 305 364-9952
Hialeah *(G-5640)*
Tallahassee Engraving & Award..........G...... 850 878-7187
Tallahassee *(G-17336)*
Tempered Glass Industries Inc..........E...... 727 499-0284
Clearwater *(G-1915)*
◆ **Terraferma USA Corporation**..........F...... 305 994-7892
Doral *(G-3528)*

Universal Alum Windows & Doors F 305 825-7900
Hialeah (G-5662)
Venture Circle Intl LLC F 407 677-6004
Sanford (G-16132)
Vision Blocks Inc F 321 254-7478
Melbourne (G-8972)
Waterbox Usa LLC G 800 674-2608
Longwood (G-8349)
Waterway Systems LLC G 941 752-3554
Sarasota (G-16324)
◆ **Windoor Incorporated** C 407 481-8400
North Venice (G-11765)
Worldglass Corporation G 813 609-2453
Tampa (G-18264)

3241 Cement, Hydraulic

◆ **Argos Cement LLC** E 813 247-4831
Tampa (G-17431)
Argos USA LLC E 352 472-4722
Newberry (G-11552)
Basecrete Technologies LLC F 941 312-5142
Sarasota (G-16362)
Basic Industries Global LLC G 850 622-5924
Santa Rosa Beach (G-16152)
Bonsal American Inc G 813 621-2427
Tampa (G-17482)
Cement Products Inc E 727 868-9226
Port Richey (G-15045)
David Sayne Masonry Inc F 386 873-4696
Deland (G-2966)
Euro Gear (usa) Inc E 518 578-1775
Miami (G-9539)
Gallop Group Inc G 813 251-6242
Tampa (G-17702)
Gulf Cast Mtls Sthwest Fla Inc F 239 790-0016
Fort Myers (G-4474)
Hco Holding I Corporation F 863 533-0522
Bartow (G-318)
Phg Kendall LLC F 954 392-8788
Hollywood (G-5891)
Titan America LLC C 305 364-2200
Medley (G-8738)

3251 Brick & Structural Clay Tile

Acme Brick Company F 850 531-0725
Tallahassee (G-17212)
American Pavers Consultants E 954 418-0000
Pompano Beach (G-14592)
◆ **Artistic Paver Mfg Inc** E 305 653-7283
Miami (G-9174)
Brick Markers USA Inc F 561 842-1338
Mangonia Park (G-8500)
Cemex Materials LLC D 941 722-4578
Palmetto (G-13790)
◆ **Dyadic International USA Inc** G 561 743-8333
Jupiter (G-7028)
◆ **Florida Brick and Clay Co Inc** F 813 754-1521
Plant City (G-14430)
◆ **HG Trading Cia Inc** G 305 986-5702
Hialeah (G-5443)
LLC Best Block E 239 789-3531
Orlando (G-12918)
LLC Best Block E 239 789-3531
Tampa (G-17855)
Masters Block - North LLC G 407 212-7704
Saint Cloud (G-15658)
Three D Products Corp G 954 971-6511
Fort Lauderdale (G-4282)

3253 Ceramic Tile

Arcana Tileworks G 407 492-0668
Winter Garden (G-19252)
Blackton Flooring Inc G 407 898-2661
Orlando (G-12522)
Casale Design Source Inc G 813 873-3653
Tampa (G-17512)
Colaianni Italian Flr Tile Mfg G 954 321-8244
Fort Lauderdale (G-3909)
▲ **Custom Mosaics Inc** G 954 610-9436
Sunrise (G-17113)
◆ **Florida Brick and Clay Co Inc** F 813 754-1521
Plant City (G-14430)
Manotiles LLC G 954 803-3303
Delray Beach (G-3104)
Mosaics Liquidation Co Inc G 772 468-8453
Fort Pierce (G-4720)
Mosch International Corp G 786 616-9108
Miami (G-10043)
Precision Ceramics Usa Inc F 727 388-5060
Saint Petersburg (G-15887)
▲ **Raskin Industries LLC** F 561 997-6658
Deerfield Beach (G-2900)
▲ **Triton Stone Holdings LLC** G 219 669-4890
Fort Lauderdale (G-4288)
◆ **Vidrepur of America LLC** F 305 468-9008
Miami (G-10584)
William Byrd & Sons Inc G 786 573-3251
Palmetto Bay (G-13858)

3255 Clay Refractories

▲ **Comimpex Group LLC** G 786 306-3204
Miami (G-9387)
◆ **Gem Paver Systems Inc** E 305 805-0000
Medley (G-8656)
◆ **Jamo Inc** D 305 885-3444
Medley (G-8676)
Oldcastle Retail Inc B 954 971-1200
Pompano Beach (G-14778)

3259 Structural Clay Prdts, NEC

▼ **Ceramica Verea USA Corp** F 305 665-3923
Miami (G-9342)
Glassarium LLC E 786 631-7080
Miami (G-9639)
Infrastructure Repair Systems G 727 327-4216
Saint Petersburg (G-15815)
James Hardie Building Pdts Inc D 813 478-1758
Plant City (G-14440)
◆ **Metro Roof Tile Inc** F 863 467-0042
Medley (G-8690)
Southeast Gen Contrs Group Inc F 877 407-3535
Port St Lucie (G-15179)

3261 China Plumbing Fixtures & Fittings

▲ **Alabama Marble Co Inc** F 305 718-8000
Doral (G-3232)
American Bidet Company F 954 981-1111
Sunrise (G-17090)
◆ **Custom Marble Works Inc** E 813 620-0475
Tampa (G-17580)
Ecotech Water LLC G 877 341-9500
St Pete Beach (G-16879)
▲ **M F B International Inc** G 305 436-6601
Miami (G-9925)
National Bidet Corp G 786 325-6593
Miami Beach (G-10696)
▲ **Rinseworks Inc** F 954 946-0070
Pompano Beach (G-14832)
Terracassa LLC G 786 581-7741
Miami (G-10468)
▼ **Wool Wholesale Plumbing Supply** D 954 763-3632
Fort Lauderdale (G-4327)

3263 Earthenware, Whiteware, Table & Kitchen Articles

Comerint Inc G 813 443-2466
Tampa (G-17547)
▲ **Kitchenista Corp** G 305 400-4992
Coral Gables (G-2165)

3264 Porcelain Electrical Splys

Famatel USA LLC G 754 217-4841
Dania (G-2445)
Insulator Seal Incorporated E 941 751-2880
Sarasota (G-16240)
Rock Intl Distributors Inc E 305 513-3314
Miami (G-10272)
Smart Material Corp F 941 870-3337
Sarasota (G-16600)

3269 Pottery Prdts, NEC

American CCC Ceramic Inc G 321 356-9317
Apopka (G-112)
Americraft Cookware LLC E 352 483-7600
Mount Dora (G-11095)
Florida Cool Ring Company F 863 858-2211
Lakeland (G-7691)
Florida Stoneware Tops Inc G 239 340-0492
Fort Myers (G-4452)
Hart S Ceramic & Stone Inc G 850 217-6145
Destin (G-3193)
Kreative Ceramics Inc G 321 278-9889
Ocoee (G-12086)
Leonard-Martin Corporation G 850 434-2203
Pensacola (G-14192)
Miy Ceramic G 305 823-5758
Miami Lakes (G-10822)
Ronald M Hart Inc G 772 600-8497
Stuart (G-17003)
Townsend Ceramics & Glass Inc F 321 269-5671
Titusville (G-18469)

3271 Concrete Block & Brick

A and A Concrete Block Inc G 305 986-5128
Miami (G-9034)
A-1 Block Corporation E 407 422-3768
Orlando (G-12424)
◆ **American Pavers Manufacturing** G 954 418-0000
Pompano Beach (G-14593)
Argos-US LLC G 407 298-1900
Orlando (G-12488)
◆ **Artistic Paver Mfg Inc** E 305 653-7283
Miami (G-9174)
Atlas Concrete Products Inc G 407 277-0841
Orlando (G-12497)
▼ **Banaszak Concrete Corp** E 954 476-1004
Davie (G-2502)
Bedrock Industries Inc F 407 859-1300
Orlando (G-12509)
▲ **Bell Concrete Products Inc** E 352 463-6103
Bell (G-341)
Blue Native of Fla Keys Inc G 305 345-5305
Big Pine Key (G-381)
Bluegrass Materials Co LLC E 919 781-4550
Jacksonville (G-6216)
Cement Products Inc E 727 868-9226
Port Richey (G-15045)
Cemex Cement Inc C 850 942-4582
Tallahassee (G-17231)
◆ **Cemex Materials LLC** C 561 833-5555
West Palm Beach (G-18841)
Cemex Materials LLC D 561 746-4556
Jupiter (G-7018)
Cemex Materials LLC E 321 636-5121
Titusville (G-18422)
Cemex Materials LLC D 352 435-0783
Okahumpka (G-12169)
Cemex Materials LLC D 305 558-0315
Miami (G-9337)
Cemex Materials LLC D 561 793-1442
West Palm Beach (G-18842)
Cemex Materials LLC D 561 743-4039
Jupiter (G-7019)
Cemex Materials LLC E 407 322-8862
Sanford (G-16008)
Cemex Materials LLC D 941 722-4578
Palmetto (G-13790)
Cemex Pacific Holdings LLC D 239 992-1400
Bonita Springs (G-824)
Central Florida Cnstr Walls F 407 448-2350
Orlando (G-12565)
◆ **Devcon International Corp** C 954 926-5200
Boca Raton (G-499)
▼ **GLC 3 & Rental Corp** G 954 916-1551
Plantation (G-14520)
Gulf Coast Ready Mix LLC E 352 621-3900
Homosassa (G-6004)
Jahna Concrete Inc F 863 453-4353
Avon Park (G-289)
Jcs Contracting Inc G 407 348-4555
Kissimmee (G-7258)
Kenton Industries LLC G 863 675-8233
Labelle (G-7318)
▲ **Labelle Brick Pavers Tile LLC** F 863 230-3100
Labelle (G-7319)
Masters Block - North LLC G 407 212-7704
Saint Cloud (G-15658)
Miami Quality Pavers Corp G 305 408-3444
Miami (G-10008)
New Line Transport LLC E 305 223-9200
Dade City (G-2432)
Paver Systems LLC E 407 859-9117
Orlando (G-13055)
PM Engraving Corp F 786 573-5292
Miami (G-10171)
Roof Tile Inc E 863 467-0042
Okeechobee (G-12190)
Ross Pivnik G 305 254-1635
Miami (G-10282)
▼ **Royal Concrete Concepts Inc** E 561 689-5398
Jupiter (G-7106)
Secure Cnstr Systems LLC G 561 687-9512
West Palm Beach (G-19027)
Shealy Revel B Inc G 352 629-1552
Ocala (G-12048)
Sunshine Driveways Inc G 954 394-7373
Hollywood (G-5918)

SIC

Titan America LLC ....C.... 305 364-2200
Medley *(G-8738)*
◆ **Tremron Inc** ....F.... 305 825-9000
Medley *(G-8741)*
Tremron LLC ....F.... 863 491-0990
Arcadia *(G-206)*
Whites Holdings Inc Centl Fla ....F.... 727 863-6072
Port Richey *(G-15078)*

3272 Concrete Prdts

A & C Concrete Products Inc ....G.... 305 232-1631
Miami *(G-9030)*
A & L Septic Tank Products ....G.... 407 273-2149
Orlando *(G-12423)*
A To Z Concrete Products Inc ....F.... 727 321-6000
Saint Petersburg *(G-15688)*
A-1 City Wide Sewer Service ....F.... 352 236-4456
Silver Springs *(G-16780)*
AAA Cast Stone Inc ....E.... 941 721-8092
Palmetto *(G-13783)*
◆ **Accord Industries LLC** ....D.... 407 671-6989
Winter Park *(G-19370)*
◆ **Aercon Florida LLC** ....D.... 863 422-6360
Haines City *(G-5137)*
Allied Precast Products Co ....E.... 407 745-5605
Orlando *(G-12460)*
Allstone Casting ....F.... 305 528-1677
Medley *(G-8607)*
▲ **American Concrete Industries** ....E.... 772 464-1187
Fort Pierce *(G-4674)*
Americast Precast Generator ....F.... 772 971-1958
Fort Pierce *(G-4675)*
Anderson Columbia Co Inc ....F.... 352 463-6342
Chiefland *(G-1531)*
Aquatectonica LLC ....F.... 941 592-3071
Bradenton *(G-990)*
Architectural Fountains Inc ....G.... 727 323-6068
Saint Petersburg *(G-15708)*
Architectural Masters LLC ....G.... 239 290-2250
Leesburg *(G-8143)*
Argos USA LLC ....E.... 678 368-4300
Newberry *(G-11551)*
Art Crete Products Inc ....F.... 386 252-5118
Daytona Beach *(G-2629)*
Artistic Columns Inc ....G.... 954 530-5537
Oakland Park *(G-11780)*
Artistic Fence Corporation ....G.... 305 805-1976
Hialeah *(G-5307)*
◆ **Artistic Statuary Inc** ....F.... 954 975-9533
Pompano Beach *(G-14602)*
Atlantic Cast Prcast S Fla LLC ....E.... 954 564-6245
Oakland Park *(G-11783)*
Atlantic Concrete Products Inc ....D.... 941 355-2988
Sarasota *(G-16356)*
Atlantic Tng LLC ....E.... 941 355-2988
Sarasota *(G-16357)*
Atlas Concrete Products Inc ....G.... 407 277-0841
Orlando *(G-12497)*
▼ **Atlas Walls LLC** ....G.... 800 951-9201
Orlando *(G-12498)*
Atm Vault Corp ....G.... 561 441-9294
Boca Raton *(G-434)*
Averett Septic Tank Co Inc ....E.... 863 665-1748
Lakeland *(G-7640)*
Bailey Sigler Inc ....G.... 386 428-5566
New Smyrna Beach *(G-11526)*
Barreiro Concrete Mtls Inc ....E.... 305 805-0095
Princeton *(G-15182)*
Bayshore Con Prdcts/Chspake In ....D.... 757 331-2300
Maitland *(G-8457)*
▲ **Bayshore Concrete Pdts Corp** ....C.... 757 331-2300
Maitland *(G-8458)*
Bayshore Concrete Products Inc ....G.... 239 543-3001
Fort Myers *(G-4373)*
Bayshore Precast Concrete Inc ....G.... 239 543-3001
Fort Myers *(G-4374)*
Bingham On-Site Sewers Inc ....D.... 813 659-0003
Dover *(G-3556)*
Bonsal American Inc ....G.... 813 621-2427
Tampa *(G-17482)*
Bonsal American Inc ....G.... 904 783-0605
Jacksonville *(G-6225)*
Bonsal American Inc ....G.... 850 476-4223
Pensacola *(G-14103)*
Bonsal American Inc ....G.... 863 967-9100
Auburndale *(G-230)*
Brothers Pavers and Precast ....G.... 561 662-9075
West Palm Beach *(G-18828)*
◆ **Brown (usa) Inc** ....F.... 305 593-9228
Miami *(G-9280)*

Building Blocks Gfrc LLC ....D.... 312 243-9960
Kissimmee *(G-7226)*
Burleys Mmrals Brial Vults LLC ....G.... 561 284-6983
Boynton Beach *(G-885)*
Cast Art International Corp ....G.... 727 807-3395
Dunedin *(G-3571)*
Cast Systems LLC ....E.... 941 625-3474
Port Charlotte *(G-14968)*
▼ **Cast-Crete Usa LLC** ....D.... 813 621-4641
Seffner *(G-16723)*
Castone Creations Inc ....F.... 305 599-3367
Doral *(G-3294)*
Cds Manufacturing Inc ....D.... 850 875-4651
Gretna *(G-5090)*
Cement Industries Inc ....D.... 239 332-1440
Fort Myers *(G-4391)*
Cement Precast Products Inc ....E.... 352 372-0953
Gainesville *(G-4894)*
Cement Products Inc ....E.... 727 868-9226
Port Richey *(G-15045)*
▲ **Cemex Cnstr Mtls ATL LLC** ....D.... 561 833-5555
West Palm Beach *(G-18837)*
Cemex Cnstr Mtls Fla LLC ....G.... 800 992-3639
Oldsmar *(G-12213)*
Cemex Cnstr Mtls Fla LLC ....F.... 800 992-3639
Sarasota *(G-16381)*
▲ **Cemex Cnstr Mtls PCF LLC** ....D.... 561 833-5555
West Palm Beach *(G-18840)*
◆ **Cemex Materials LLC** ....C.... 561 833-5555
West Palm Beach *(G-18841)*
Cemex Materials LLC ....D.... 561 746-4556
Jupiter *(G-7018)*
Cemex Materials LLC ....D.... 352 435-0783
Okahumpka *(G-12169)*
Cemex Materials LLC ....D.... 305 558-0315
Miami *(G-9337)*
Cemex Materials LLC ....D.... 561 793-1442
West Palm Beach *(G-18842)*
Cemex Materials LLC ....D.... 561 743-4039
Jupiter *(G-7019)*
Central Florida Precast Inc ....G.... 941 730-2158
Bradenton *(G-1019)*
Coastal Concrete Products LLC ....E.... 239 208-4079
Fort Myers *(G-4402)*
Coastal Precast of Florida ....E.... 239 432-0667
Fort Myers *(G-4404)*
▲ **Com Pac Filtration Inc** ....E.... 904 356-4003
Jacksonville *(G-6279)*
◆ **Coma Cast Corp** ....E.... 305 667-6797
Miami *(G-9385)*
Commercial Concrete Pdts Inc ....E.... 813 659-3707
Plant City *(G-14419)*
Concraft Inc ....G.... 561 689-0149
Greenacres *(G-5078)*
Concrete Pdts of Palm Bches In ....E.... 561 842-2743
Riviera Beach *(G-15313)*
Concrete Structures Inc ....F.... 305 597-9393
Miami *(G-9392)*
◆ **Consolidated Minerals Inc** ....F.... 352 365-6522
Leesburg *(G-8148)*
Continental Concrete Products ....G.... 904 388-1390
Jacksonville *(G-6285)*
▼ **Coral Reef Cast Stone Inc** ....F.... 561 586-1900
West Palm Beach *(G-18850)*
◆ **Coreslab Strctures Orlando Inc** ....E.... 407 855-3191
Okahumpka *(G-12170)*
▼ **Coreslab Structures Miami Inc** ....B.... 305 823-8950
Medley *(G-8635)*
Coreslab Structures Tampa Inc ....C.... 602 237-3875
Tampa *(G-17556)*
Cornerstone Interlocking Inc ....G.... 863 944-1609
Lakeland *(G-7663)*
▲ **Crom Corporation** ....B.... 352 372-3436
Gainesville *(G-4900)*
Cug LLC ....F.... 786 858-0499
Plantation *(G-14505)*
D & S Logging Inc ....G.... 850 638-5500
Chipley *(G-1543)*
D Maxwell Company Inc ....G.... 727 868-9151
Port Richey *(G-15048)*
Darkside Vault LLC ....G.... 407 353-3776
Orlando *(G-12647)*
▼ **DC Kerckhoff Company** ....F.... 239 597-7218
Naples *(G-11223)*
Decorative Precast LLC ....F.... 239 566-9503
Naples *(G-11225)*
Delzotto Products Florida Inc ....D.... 352 351-3834
Ocala *(G-11919)*
Dixie Sptic Tank Orange Cy LLC ....F.... 386 775-3051
Orange City *(G-12375)*

▲ **Dura-Stress Inc** ....C.... 352 787-1422
Leesburg *(G-8152)*
Durlach Holdings Inc ....F.... 941 751-1672
Bradenton *(G-1032)*
◆ **E T C R Inc** ....E.... 305 637-0999
Miami *(G-9490)*
◆ **E-Stone USA Corp** ....D.... 863 655-1273
Sebring *(G-16687)*
E-Stone USA Corporation ....D.... 954 266-6793
Sebring *(G-16688)*
▲ **E-Stone USA Corporation** ....D.... 863 214-8281
Miami *(G-9492)*
Earthcore Industries LLC ....E.... 904 363-3417
Jacksonville *(G-6347)*
Elite Cast Stone Inc ....G.... 305 904-3032
Ruskin *(G-15483)*
Ersion Interntnal Ctrl Systems ....G.... 800 821-7462
Tampa *(G-17648)*
F T F Construction Company ....F.... 772 571-1850
Fellsmere *(G-3725)*
Finfrock Design Inc ....E.... 407 293-4000
Apopka *(G-140)*
Finfrock Industries Inc ....C.... 407 293-4000
Apopka *(G-141)*
First Coast Concrete Pumping ....G.... 904 262-6488
Jacksonville *(G-6385)*
FL Precast LLC ....G.... 321 356-9673
Orlando *(G-12742)*
▲ **Florida Concrete Pipe Corp** ....F.... 352 742-2232
Astatula *(G-211)*
Florida Container Services ....F.... 407 302-2197
Sanford *(G-16047)*
◆ **Florida Engineered Constru** ....C.... 813 621-4641
Seffner *(G-16726)*
Florida Engineered Constru ....G.... 727 863-7451
Hudson *(G-6024)*
Florida Engineered Constru ....G.... 321 953-5161
Palm Bay *(G-13513)*
Florida Lift Stations Corp ....G.... 305 887-8485
Medley *(G-8652)*
◆ **Florida Silica Sand Company** ....E.... 954 923-8323
Fort Lauderdale *(G-4005)*
Florida Silica Sand Company ....F.... 954 923-8323
Fort Lauderdale *(G-4006)*
Florida Vault Service Inc ....G.... 727 527-4992
Saint Petersburg *(G-15787)*
▼ **Florida Wilbert Inc** ....G.... 904 765-2641
Jacksonville *(G-6405)*
Florida Wilbert Inc ....G.... 352 728-3531
Okahumpka *(G-12171)*
Forterra Pipe & Precast LLC ....E.... 863 401-6800
Winter Haven *(G-19323)*
Forterra Pipe & Precast LLC ....F.... 386 734-6228
Deland *(G-2979)*
Forterra Pressure Pipe Inc ....C.... 386 328-8841
Palatka *(G-13480)*
Freeport Fountains LLC ....E.... 407 330-1150
Sanford *(G-16050)*
◆ **Fsp-Ges Inc** ....E.... 352 799-7933
Brooksville *(G-1230)*
Gate Petroleum Company ....G.... 904 396-0517
Jacksonville *(G-6421)*
Gate Precast Company ....C.... 904 520-5795
Jacksonville *(G-6422)*
◆ **Gate Precast Company** ....G.... 904 732-7668
Jacksonville *(G-6423)*
Gate Precast Company ....C.... 407 847-5285
Kissimmee *(G-7249)*
Gate Precast Erection Co ....D.... 904 737-7220
Jacksonville *(G-6424)*
Geigel Marble & Design LLC ....G.... 305 301-0399
Key Biscayne *(G-7156)*
Granite Environmental LLC ....F.... 772 646-0597
Vero Beach *(G-18623)*
Grate Fireplace & Stone Shoppe ....E.... 239 939-7187
Fort Myers *(G-4471)*
Gulf Coast Precast Inc ....E.... 239 337-0021
Fort Myers *(G-4476)*
Gulf Coast Wilbert Inc ....G.... 850 682-8004
Crestview *(G-2350)*
Gun Vault ....G.... 850 391-7651
Tallahassee *(G-17271)*
Gunter Septic Tank Mfg ....G.... 813 654-1214
Seffner *(G-16730)*
◆ **Hall Fountains Inc** ....F.... 954 484-8530
Fort Lauderdale *(G-4039)*
Hamner Parking Lot Service ....G.... 954 328-3216
Fort Lauderdale *(G-4040)*
Hamsard Usa Inc ....C.... 386 761-1830
Daytona Beach *(G-2673)*

Hbp Pipe & Precast LLC....E.... 904 529-8228
Green Cove Springs (G-5064)
Heavy Hwy Infrastructure LLC....D.... 407 323-8853
Sanford (G-16060)
▲ Helping Adlscnts Live Optmstcl....G.... 407 257-8221
Orlando (G-12798)
Henderson Prestress Con Inc....F.... 727 938-2828
Tarpon Springs (G-18306)
▼ Heralpin Usa Inc....G.... 305 218-0174
Doral (G-3379)
▼ Herpel Inc....F.... 561 585-5573
West Palm Beach (G-18894)
Hicks Industries Inc....G.... 954 226-5148
Davie (G-2535)
I A I....G.... 561 488-6369
Boca Raton (G-561)
◆ Imperial Industries Inc....F.... 954 917-4114
Pompano Beach (G-14729)
Insteel Wire Products Company....E.... 904 275-2100
Sanderson (G-15982)
International Casting Corp....E.... 305 558-3515
Miami Lakes (G-10798)
Intrepid Precast Inc....G.... 352 347-7475
Ocala (G-11970)
J & N Stone Inc....E.... 941 924-6200
Sarasota (G-16474)
J R C Concrete Products Inc....G.... 850 456-9665
Pensacola (G-14181)
Jahna Concrete Inc....F.... 863 453-4353
Avon Park (G-289)
Janusz Art Stone Inc....G.... 305 754-7171
Miami (G-9787)
Jay Walker Enterprises Inc....G.... 850 539-7668
Tallahassee (G-17282)
Jewish Burial Society America....G.... 954 424-1899
Delray Beach (G-3096)
Johnson Bros Prcsion Prcast Pd....E.... 239 947-6734
Bonita Springs (G-842)
◆ K&T Stoneworks Inc....F.... 561 798-8486
West Palm Beach (G-18918)
Keystone Precast & Columns Cor....G.... 305 216-5375
Homestead (G-5975)
Kingman Custom Stairs & Trim L....G.... 561 547-9888
West Palm Beach (G-18921)
Kitchen & Bath Center Inc....E.... 850 244-3996
Fort Walton Beach (G-4812)
Km Precast Inc....F.... 239 438-2146
Naples (G-11306)
Knightsbridge Steel LLC....G.... 786 532-0290
Hialeah (G-5474)
Kt Properties & Dev Inc....F.... 386 253-0610
Daytona Beach (G-2677)
▼ La Moti Roof & Tile Inc....G.... 305 635-2641
Miami (G-9845)
◆ Lambert Corporation Florida....E.... 407 841-2940
Orlando (G-12889)
Landmark Precast LLC....F.... 305 242-8888
Homestead (G-5979)
Lane Construction Corporation....E.... 863 665-0457
Lakeland (G-7732)
Latteri & Sons Inc....G.... 813 876-1800
Tampa (G-17836)
Leesburg Concrete Company Inc....E.... 352 787-4177
Leesburg (G-8163)
Lewis Vault & Precast Inc....G.... 352 351-2992
Ocala (G-11982)
Lindsay Precast Inc....E.... 800 669-2278
Alachua (G-11)
▼ Lotts Concrete Products Inc....E.... 407 656-2112
Winter Garden (G-19275)
Lrg Solutions Inc....F.... 321 978-1050
Rockledge (G-15429)
Mack Concrete Industries Inc....C.... 352 742-2333
Astatula (G-213)
Mack Industries Inc....G.... 352 742-2333
Astatula (G-214)
Mancini Inc....E.... 954 583-7220
Pompano Beach (G-14752)
Marbon Inc....F.... 561 822-9999
West Palm Beach (G-18941)
▲ Marcus V Hall....G.... 352 490-9694
Chiefland (G-1536)
Mark 1 Contracting Inc....F.... 727 894-3600
New Port Richey (G-11500)
Master Construction Pdts Inc....E.... 407 857-1221
Orlando (G-12953)
Maxrodon Marble Inc....G.... 772 562-7543
Vero Beach (G-18642)
Mc Monumental Group Inc....G.... 305 651-9113
North Miami Beach (G-11691)

Metals USA Holdings Corp....A.... 954 202-4000
Fort Lauderdale (G-4118)
◆ Metro Roof Tile Inc....F.... 863 467-0042
Medley (G-8690)
Miller Brothers Contractors....F.... 941 371-4162
Sarasota (G-16510)
Monroe Concrete Products....D.... 305 296-5606
Key West (G-7197)
Monty Sanitation Inc....G.... 239 597-2486
Naples (G-11332)
Monumental Air Inc....F.... 954 383-9507
Coral Springs (G-2290)
Monumental Enterprises Inc....G.... 305 803-8493
Pembroke Pines (G-14048)
Monumental Resolutions Inc....G.... 407 973-3577
Saint Cloud (G-15662)
Mother Earth Stone LLC....F.... 407 878-2854
Sanford (G-16091)
Native Nursery....G.... 941 625-2022
Punta Gorda (G-15216)
North Florida Vault LLC....F.... 386 303-2267
Lake City (G-7372)
▲ Nuflo Inc....E.... 904 265-4001
Jacksonville (G-6642)
▲ Oldcastle Apg South Inc....A.... 813 367-9780
Palm Beach Gardens (G-13614)
▲ Oldcastle Apg South Inc....F.... 863 421-7422
Haines City (G-5144)
Oldcastle Architectural Inc....E.... 813 886-7761
Tampa (G-17950)
Oldcastle Building Produc....G.... 352 377-1699
Gainesville (G-4975)
Oldcastle Coastal Inc....G.... 813 886-7761
Tampa (G-17953)
Oldcastle Coastal Inc....G.... 813 932-1007
Tampa (G-17954)
Oldcastle Coastal Inc....G.... 813 783-1970
Zephyrhills (G-19528)
Oldcastle Coastal Inc....C.... 813 367-9780
Tampa (G-17955)
Oldcastle Infrastructure Inc....F.... 800 642-1540
Wildwood (G-19198)
Oldcastle Retail Inc....B.... 954 971-1200
Pompano Beach (G-14778)
Olde World Craftsmen Inc....G.... 239 229-3806
Fort Myers (G-4557)
Ornamental Columns and Statues....F.... 239 482-3911
Fort Myers (G-4559)
▼ Palm Beach Cast Stone Inc....E.... 561 835-4085
West Palm Beach (G-18981)
▼ Paver Systems LLC....E.... 561 844-5202
Riviera Beach (G-15359)
Paver Systems LLC....E.... 407 859-9117
Orlando (G-13055)
Pedronis Cast Stone Inc....E.... 904 783-1690
Jacksonville (G-6666)
Perl Inc....F.... 352 726-2483
Inverness (G-6095)
Perry Precast Inc....G.... 386 294-2710
Mayo (G-8597)
Pfci LLC....E.... 239 435-3575
Naples (G-11361)
Phoscrete Corporation....E.... 561 420-0595
Pompano Beach (G-14793)
Pilot Corp of Palm Beaches....F.... 561 848-2928
Riviera Beach (G-15363)
Pollak Industries....G.... 850 438-4651
Pensacola (G-14234)
Polly Concrete Products Co....F.... 850 897-3314
Niceville (G-11571)
Ponce De Leon Construction....G.... 786 554-3685
Miami (G-10178)
◆ Pre-Cast Specialties Inc....C.... 954 781-4040
Sanford (G-16104)
Pre-Cast Specialties LLC....F.... 954 781-4040
Sanford (G-16105)
Precast and Foam Works LLC....G.... 727 657-9195
Clearwater (G-1839)
Precast Designs Inc....F.... 407 856-5444
Orlando (G-13079)
Precast Solution System Inc....F.... 813 949-7929
Odessa (G-12142)
Precast Technical Assistance....F.... 850 432-8446
Pensacola (G-14236)
Precon Corporation....C.... 352 332-1200
Newberry (G-11559)
◆ Premier Stoneworks LLC....D.... 561 330-3737
Delray Beach (G-3123)
Prestressed Systems Inc....F.... 305 556-6699
Doral (G-3469)

Pro-Crete Material Corporation....E.... 352 748-1505
Orlando (G-13094)
Purifoy Construction LLC....G.... 850 206-2900
Cantonment (G-1346)
Quality Precast & Company....F.... 407 877-1000
Winter Garden (G-19282)
Quality Vaults Inc....F.... 407 656-8781
Ocoee (G-12089)
Quikrete Companies LLC....G.... 305 681-8664
Miami (G-10226)
Quikrete Companies LLC....D.... 863 665-5127
Lakeland (G-7775)
Ras Concrete Construction Inc....E.... 239 775-3709
Naples (G-11381)
Renaissance Entp Group LLC....G.... 941 284-7854
Englewood (G-3681)
Rinker Materials....F.... 305 345-4127
Medley (G-8717)
Rj Staab Stone Co....G.... 352 377-3313
Williston (G-19213)
Rj Staab Stone Company Fla LLC....G.... 352 222-5989
Williston (G-19214)
RMC Ewell Inc....E.... 850 879-0959
Niceville (G-11573)
RMC Ewell Inc....G.... 850 863-5040
Fort Walton Beach (G-4828)
RMC Ewell Inc....F.... 407 282-0984
Orlando (G-13143)
Rmmj Inc....E.... 239 597-2486
Naples (G-11386)
Roberts Vault Co Inc....E.... 352 567-0110
Dade City (G-2433)
Rocla Concrete Tie Inc....D.... 772 800-1855
Fort Pierce (G-4741)
Rogers Septic Tanks Inc....G.... 203 259-9947
Port Saint Lucie (G-15139)
▼ Rons Safe & Vault Company....G.... 305 527-2901
Plantation (G-14545)
Roof Tile Administration Inc....F.... 863 467-0042
Okeechobee (G-12189)
Roof Tile Inc....E.... 863 467-0042
Okeechobee (G-12190)
▼ Royal Concrete Concepts Inc....E.... 561 689-5398
Jupiter (G-7106)
Rudders River Rock....G.... 239 574-5656
Cape Coral (G-1462)
S & S Precast Inc....F.... 239 992-8685
Bonita Springs (G-852)
Saint Augustine Cast Stone....G.... 904 794-2626
Saint Augustine (G-15603)
Sebring Septic Tank Precast Co....E.... 863 655-2030
Sebring (G-16708)
Silk Safari Inc....G.... 561 689-3882
West Palm Beach (G-19034)
Smith Steps Inc....G.... 386 963-5655
Live Oak (G-8241)
Solar Erectors US Inc....F.... 305 823-8950
Medley (G-8724)
Solar Manufacturing Inc....E.... 954 973-8488
Pompano Beach (G-14855)
Southeastern Pipe Precast Inc....E.... 850 587-7473
Cantonment (G-1348)
Southeastern Prestressed Con....F.... 561 793-1177
West Palm Beach (G-19040)
Southern Pre Cast Structures L....G.... 352 569-1128
Bushnell (G-1321)
Spancrete Inc....E.... 305 599-8885
Miami (G-10394)
Spancrete of Florida LLC....E.... 863 655-1515
Sebring (G-16710)
Spancrete Southeast Inc....G.... 863 655-1515
Sebring (G-16711)
Stabil Concrete Products LLC....D.... 727 321-6000
Saint Petersburg (G-15925)
▲ Standard Precast Inc....D.... 904 268-0466
Jacksonville (G-6808)
Stans Septic Svc & Con Pdts....G.... 941 639-3976
Punta Gorda (G-15236)
Stone Central of Central Fla....F.... 352 689-0075
Wildwood (G-19201)
Stonecrfters Archtctral Prcast....F.... 727 544-1210
Seminole (G-16763)
Stonehardscapes Intl Inc....G.... 954 989-4050
Fort Lauderdale (G-4262)
◆ Stonexchange Inc....F.... 305 513-9795
Doral (G-3513)
◆ Structral Prestressed Inds Inc....D.... 305 556-6699
Doral (G-3514)
Structural Cnstr Orlando Inc....E.... 407 383-9719
Oviedo (G-13458)

S I C

▲ **Superior Cast Stone LLC** F 863 634-4771
Okeechobee *(G-12193)*
▼ **Superior Roof Tile Mfg** F 850 892-2299
Defuniak Springs *(G-2948)*
Suwannee American Cem Co LLC D 352 569-5393
Sumterville *(G-17069)*
Taylor Concrete Inc G 941 737-7225
Palmetto *(G-13828)*
Thompson Sales Group Inc E 239 332-0446
Fort Myers *(G-4630)*
Treasure CST Curb & Therm Plas G 772 287-0391
Palm City *(G-13676)*
Tremron LLC F 863 491-0990
Arcadia *(G-206)*
Trenwa Inc F 863 666-1680
Lakeland *(G-7825)*
True Stone Corp E 772 334-9797
Fort Pierce *(G-4760)*
True Stone Masonry LLC F 772 334-9797
Fort Pierce *(G-4761)*
▼ **United Concrete Products LLC** G 786 402-3536
Medley *(G-8747)*
◆ **Urban Stone Works** F 305 754-7171
Miami *(G-10549)*
▲ **US Bullnosing** F 954 567-0404
Oakland Park *(G-11856)*
▲ **US Concrete Products Corp** D 954 973-0368
Pompano Beach *(G-14904)*
◆ **US Paverscape LLC** D 772 223-7287
Stuart *(G-17044)*
US Precast Corp E 305 364-8253
Hialeah *(G-5667)*
▼ **US Precast Corporation** G 305 885-8471
Medley *(G-8752)*
USG International Ltd F 305 688-8744
Miami *(G-10557)*
Utilities Structures Inc F 239 334-7757
Fort Myers *(G-4643)*
Valmont Newmark Inc E 863 533-6465
Bartow *(G-335)*
◆ **VP Cast Stone Corp** G 305 691-9306
Hialeah *(G-5684)*
▲ **Wall Way Corporation** F 305 484-7600
Medley *(G-8754)*
Wesco Partners Inc E 941 484-8224
Sarasota *(G-16325)*
Wheeler Consolidated Inc F 772 464-4400
Fort Pierce *(G-4770)*
Wilbert E Beran G 813 882-0178
Tampa *(G-18258)*
Wills Prestress Inc F 239 417-9117
Naples *(G-11456)*
Wilsons Monument LLC G 850 743-8605
Quincy *(G-15257)*
Wpr Inc E 850 626-7713
Milton *(G-10948)*
▲ **Zoho Stone LLC** G 727 230-6956
Palm Harbor *(G-13770)*

3273 Ready-Mixed Concrete

A & J Ready Mix Inc G 863 228-7154
Clewiston *(G-1976)*
A L Materials G 863 551-0980
Winter Haven *(G-19293)*
A Materials Group Inc G 352 463-1254
Fanning Springs *(G-3721)*
A Materials Group Inc D 386 758-3164
Lake City *(G-7344)*
A-Mari-Mix LLC F 305 603-9134
Miami *(G-9045)*
▼ **Adonel Con Pmpg Fnshg S Fla In** D 305 392-5416
Miami *(G-9071)*
All Star Materials LLC F 352 598-7590
Ocala *(G-11869)*
Anderson Columbia Co Inc F 352 463-6342
Chiefland *(G-1531)*
Argos E 678 368-4300
Jacksonville *(G-6167)*
Argos F 352 376-6491
Gainesville *(G-4875)*
Argos Ready Mix G 941 629-7713
Port Charlotte *(G-14962)*
Argos Ready Mix LLC G 727 321-4667
Saint Petersburg *(G-15709)*
Argos USA G 863 687-1898
Lakeland *(G-7639)*
Argos USA LLC E 850 872-1209
Panama City *(G-13864)*
Argos USA LLC E 850 235-9600
Panama City Beach *(G-13970)*
Argos USA LLC G 850 576-4141
Tallahassee *(G-17223)*
Argos USA LLC E 407 299-9924
Orlando *(G-12487)*
Argos USA LLC G 866 322-4547
Sarasota *(G-16348)*
Argos USA LLC E 813 962-3213
Tampa *(G-17432)*
B M H Concrete Inc F 561 615-0011
West Palm Beach *(G-18809)*
▼ **Banaszak Concrete Corp** E 954 476-1004
Davie *(G-2502)*
▲ **Bell Concrete Products Inc** E 352 463-6103
Bell *(G-341)*
Berkshire Managment Associates G 305 883-3277
Miami *(G-9233)*
Bet Er Mix Inc G 352 799-5538
Brooksville *(G-1214)*
BET-Er Mix Holding Inc G 727 868-9226
Port Richey *(G-15043)*
Better Mix F 800 232-6833
Hudson *(G-6016)*
Brooks Welding & Concrete Shop F 850 984-5279
Panacea *(G-13859)*
C Mix Corp F 954 670-0208
Fort Lauderdale *(G-3878)*
▲ **Cement Miami Terminal** G 305 221-2502
Miami *(G-9334)*
Cement Products Inc E 727 868-9226
Port Richey *(G-15045)*
◆ **Cement-It Inc** G 954 565-7875
Fort Lauderdale *(G-3889)*
Cemex Inc E 813 663-9712
Tampa *(G-17521)*
Cemex Cement Inc C 904 296-2400
Orange Park *(G-12384)*
Cemex Cement Inc C 352 867-5794
Ocala *(G-11897)*
Cemex Cement Inc C 727 327-5730
Saint Petersburg *(G-15742)*
Cemex Cement Inc C 407 877-9623
Winter Garden *(G-19255)*
Cemex Cement Inc C 850 942-4582
Tallahassee *(G-17231)*
Cemex Cnstr Mtls Fla LLC F 305 247-3011
Homestead *(G-5957)*
Cemex Cnstr Mtls Fla LLC G 321 636-5121
Cape Canaveral *(G-1355)*
Cemex Cnstr Mtls Fla LLC F 904 880-4958
Jacksonville *(G-6257)*
Cemex Cnstr Mtls Fla LLC G 321 632-0500
Cocoa *(G-2004)*
Cemex Cnstr Mtls Fla LLC E 800 992-3639
Fort Pierce *(G-4685)*
Cemex Cnstr Mtls Fla LLC G 954 977-9222
Pompano Beach *(G-14632)*
Cemex Cnstr Mtls Fla LLC G 561 996-5249
Belle Glade *(G-346)*
Cemex Cnstr Mtls Fla LLC F 352 330-1115
Wildwood *(G-19192)*
Cemex Cnstr Mtls Fla LLC G 352 746-0136
Lecanto *(G-8131)*
Cemex Cnstr Mtls Fla LLC F 813 621-5575
Tampa *(G-17522)*
Cemex Cnstr Mtls Fla LLC F 561 745-5240
Jupiter *(G-7017)*
Cemex Cnstr Mtls Fla LLC G 352 793-3048
Bushnell *(G-1315)*
Cemex Cnstr Mtls Fla LLC F 904 213-8860
Orange Park *(G-12385)*
Cemex Cnstr Mtls Fla LLC G 904 827-0369
Saint Augustine *(G-15528)*
▼ **Cemex Cnstr Mtls Fla LLC** F 561 833-5555
West Palm Beach *(G-18839)*
Cemex Cnstr Mtls Fla LLC G 772 461-7102
Fort Pierce *(G-4686)*
Cemex Cnstr Mtls Fla LLC G 863 419-2875
Davenport *(G-2476)*
Cemex Cnstr Mtls Fla LLC G 800 992-3639
Oldsmar *(G-12213)*
Cemex Cnstr Mtls Fla LLC F 561 832-6646
West Palm Beach *(G-18838)*
Cemex Concrete Company F 305 558-0255
Medley *(G-8628)*
Cemex Corp D 561 820-8613
Miami *(G-9335)*
Cemex Materials LLC D 386 775-0790
Deland *(G-2963)*
Cemex Materials LLC D 305 223-6934
Miami *(G-9336)*
Cemex Materials LLC D 321 636-5121
Cocoa *(G-2005)*
Cemex Materials LLC D 305 821-5661
Medley *(G-8629)*
Cemex Materials LLC D 772 287-0502
Stuart *(G-16921)*
Cemex Materials LLC D 305 818-4941
Medley *(G-8630)*
Cemex Materials LLC D 904 296-2400
Jacksonville *(G-6258)*
Cemex Materials LLC D 941 722-4578
Palmetto *(G-13790)*
Cemex Materials LLC D 954 523-9978
Fort Lauderdale *(G-3890)*
Cemex Materials LLC E 407 322-8862
Sanford *(G-16008)*
Cemex Materials LLC D 850 769-2243
Panama City *(G-13878)*
Cemex Materials LLC F 863 688-2306
Lakeland *(G-7655)*
Cemex Materials LLC D 954 431-7655
Pembroke Pines *(G-14026)*
Cemex Materials LLC D 813 620-3760
Tampa *(G-17523)*
Cemex Materials LLC D 239 332-0135
Fort Myers *(G-4392)*
Cemex Materials LLC D 561 881-4472
Riviera Beach *(G-15311)*
Cemex Materials LLC E 863 678-3945
Lake Wales *(G-7501)*
◆ **Cemex Materials LLC** C 561 833-5555
West Palm Beach *(G-18841)*
Cemex Materials LLC D 561 746-4556
Jupiter *(G-7018)*
Cemex Materials LLC D 352 435-0783
Okahumpka *(G-12169)*
Cemex Materials LLC D 305 558-0315
Miami *(G-9337)*
Cemex Materials LLC D 561 793-1442
West Palm Beach *(G-18842)*
Cemex Materials LLC D 561 743-4039
Jupiter *(G-7019)*
Central Concrete Supermix Inc F 954 480-9333
Deerfield Beach *(G-2799)*
▲ **Colonial Ready Mix LLC** G 941 698-4022
Placida *(G-14395)*
Columbia Ready Mix Concrete F 386 755-2458
Lake City *(G-7350)*
Coreyco LLC G 813 469-1203
Wesley Chapel *(G-18742)*
Couch Ready Mix Usa Inc E 850 236-9042
Cantonment *(G-1337)*
Crestview Ready Mix Inc F 850 682-6117
Crestview *(G-2345)*
Crh Americas Inc D 843 672-5553
Lakeland *(G-7665)*
Cylinders On Cemex Gas G 305 818-4952
Doral *(G-3318)*
Davis Concrete Inc E 727 733-3141
Clearwater *(G-1649)*
◆ **Devcon International Corp** C 954 926-5200
Boca Raton *(G-499)*
Drake Inc F 239 590-9199
Fort Myers *(G-4436)*
Drake Ready Mix Inc D 239 590-9199
Fort Myers *(G-4437)*
Dunco Rock & Gravel Inc G 813 752-5622
Plant City *(G-14428)*
Eagle Ready Mix G 239 732-9333
Naples *(G-11233)*
Eagle Ready Mix LLC E 239 693-1500
Fort Myers *(G-4439)*
Florida Block & Ready Mix LLC E 727 585-2852
Clearwater *(G-1686)*
Florida Block & Ready Mix LLC E 813 623-3700
Tampa *(G-17672)*
Florida Concrete Recycling F 352 495-2044
Archer *(G-208)*
Florida Mining Enterprises LLC G 904 270-2646
Atlantic Beach *(G-222)*
◆ **Florida Rock** F 352 472-4722
Newberry *(G-11556)*
Florida Rock Concrete G 407 877-6180
Clermont *(G-1960)*
Florida Rock Concrete Inc G 904 355-1781
Jacksonville *(G-6401)*
Florida Rock Industries G 352 854-6468
Ocala *(G-11947)*
Fort Walton Concrete Co F 850 243-8114
Fort Walton Beach *(G-4800)*

Frako Concrete Services Inc..................G....... 305 551-8196
Miami *(G-9597)*
Frontier Ready Mix Inc..................F....... 727 544-1000
Pinellas Park *(G-14350)*
Griswold Ready Mix Con Inc..................F....... 904 751-3796
Jacksonville *(G-6453)*
Gulf Coast Ready Mix LLC..................E....... 352 621-3900
Homosassa *(G-6004)*
Hanson Lehigh Cement..................F....... 800 665-6006
Cape Canaveral *(G-1359)*
Hare Lumber & Ready Mix Inc..................F....... 863 983-8725
Clewiston *(G-1982)*
Hicks Industries Inc..................E....... 863 425-4155
Mulberry *(G-11125)*
Instacrete Mobile Concrete..................F....... 813 956-3741
Zephyrhills *(G-19523)*
Jahna Concrete Inc..................E....... 863 453-4353
Avon Park *(G-290)*
Jahna Concrete Inc..................F....... 863 453-4353
Avon Park *(G-289)*
◆ **Jamo Inc**..................D....... 305 885-3444
Medley *(G-8676)*
Kmr Concrete Inc..................E....... 863 519-9077
Bartow *(G-321)*
Kuhlman Corporation..................G....... 239 334-3111
Fort Myers *(G-4514)*
Larrys Mobilcrete Inc..................G....... 352 336-2525
Gainesville *(G-4950)*
Legacy Vulcan LLC..................G....... 407 855-9902
Orlando *(G-12903)*
Legacy Vulcan LLC..................G....... 850 914-9661
Panama City *(G-13925)*
Legacy Vulcan LLC..................G....... 407 321-5323
Sanford *(G-16080)*
Legacy Vulcan LLC..................G....... 727 321-4667
Saint Petersburg *(G-15837)*
Legacy Vulcan LLC..................G....... 352 376-2182
Gainesville *(G-4953)*
Legacy Vulcan LLC..................G....... 352 473-4258
Keystone Heights *(G-7209)*
Legacy Vulcan LLC..................G....... 850 951-0562
Defuniak Springs *(G-2944)*
Legacy Vulcan LLC..................G....... 863 687-7625
Lakeland *(G-7734)*
Legacy Vulcan LLC..................F....... 386 659-2477
Grandin *(G-5047)*
Legacy Vulcan LLC..................G....... 850 997-1490
Lloyd *(G-8244)*
Lehigh Cement Company LLC..................E....... 813 248-4000
Tampa *(G-17841)*
Lehigh Cement Company LLC..................E....... 954 581-2812
Davie *(G-2545)*
Lehigh Cement Company LLC..................E....... 321 323-5039
Cape Canaveral *(G-1363)*
▼ **Litecrete Inc**..................E....... 305 500-9373
Miami *(G-9901)*
Maschmeyer Concrete Co Fla..................F....... 386 668-7801
Debary *(G-2751)*
Maschmeyer Concrete Co Fla..................F....... 407 339-5311
Longwood *(G-8310)*
▲ **Maschmeyer Concrete Co Fla**..................E....... 561 848-9112
Lake Park *(G-7476)*
Maschmeyer Concrete Co Fla..................F....... 863 420-6800
Davenport *(G-2481)*
Metropolitan Mix..................G....... 904 242-0743
Ponte Vedra Beach *(G-14947)*
Miami Mix Corp..................G....... 954 704-9682
Miramar *(G-11016)*
Mix It Loop Inc..................G....... 407 902-9334
Orlando *(G-12973)*
Mix It Up..................G....... 251 767-1771
Fort Walton Beach *(G-4816)*
Mix Masters Inc..................G....... 386 846-9239
Port Orange *(G-15024)*
Ocala Concrete Services LLC..................G....... 352 694-4300
Ocala *(G-12009)*
Okeechobee Asphalt & Ready Mix..................G....... 863 763-7373
Okeechobee *(G-12187)*
Oldcastle Coastal..................F....... 813 621-2427
Tampa *(G-17952)*
Organizacion Marketing Mix LLC..................F....... 407 924-2709
Kissimmee *(G-7279)*
Ozinga South Florida Inc..................G....... 786 422-4694
Davie *(G-2563)*
Panama City Concrete Inc..................G....... 850 851-3637
Panama City *(G-13934)*
Pensacola Ready Mix LLC..................F....... 850 477-0343
Cantonment *(G-1345)*
Phoscrete Corporation..................E....... 561 420-0595
Pompano Beach *(G-14793)*
Polimix Usa LLC..................F....... 305 888-4752
Medley *(G-8708)*
Preferred Materials Inc..................E....... 904 288-0244
Lutz *(G-8412)*
Preferred Materials Inc..................G....... 407 578-1200
Orlando *(G-13081)*
Prestige/Ab Ready Mix LLC..................E....... 561 478-9980
West Palm Beach *(G-19006)*
Prestige/Ab Ready Mix LLC..................E....... 407 654-3330
Clermont *(G-1971)*
Prestige/Ab Ready Mix LLC..................E....... 321 751-2566
Melbourne *(G-8911)*
Prestige/Ab Ready Mix LLC..................F....... 407 847-7229
Orlando *(G-13084)*
Prestige/Ab Ready Mix LLC..................E....... 772 468-4666
Fort Pierce *(G-4736)*
Pro-Mix Inc..................G....... 305 556-6699
Medley *(G-8711)*
Quality Block & Supply Inc..................G....... 863 425-3070
Mulberry *(G-11133)*
Quality Ready Mix Inc..................B....... 561 833-5555
West Palm Beach *(G-19014)*
Ready Mix Usa LLC..................F....... 850 227-7677
Port Saint Joe *(G-15083)*
Rinker Materials Corp..................G....... 352 799-7881
Brooksville *(G-1264)*
Rinker Materials Corp..................G....... 305 386-0078
Miami *(G-10265)*
Rinker Materials Corp..................G....... 386 775-0790
Deland *(G-3012)*
▼ **Rios Con Pmpg & Rentl Inc**..................E....... 305 888-7909
Medley *(G-8718)*
RMC Ewell Inc..................E....... 850 879-0959
Niceville *(G-11573)*
RMC Ewell Inc..................G....... 850 863-5040
Fort Walton Beach *(G-4828)*
RMC Ewell Inc..................F....... 407 282-0984
Orlando *(G-13143)*
Rudys Ready Mix..................G....... 305 382-9283
Miami *(G-10287)*
South Florida Con Block LLC..................G....... 305 408-3444
Miami *(G-10382)*
South Florida Concrete & Rdymx..................E....... 305 888-0420
Medley *(G-8725)*
Superior Redi-Mix..................F....... 850 575-1532
Midway *(G-10918)*
▲ **Supermix Concrete**..................E....... 954 858-0780
Miami *(G-10439)*
Supermix Concrete..................D....... 305 265-4465
Fort Pierce *(G-4753)*
Sweet Mix LLC..................G....... 561 227-8332
West Palm Beach *(G-19054)*
Symrna Ready Mix..................F....... 352 330-1001
Wildwood *(G-19202)*
T Bower Enterprises Inc..................G....... 863 984-3050
Polk City *(G-14568)*
Taco Mix Corp..................G....... 239 498-9448
Naples *(G-11433)*
Takeria Mix Inc..................F....... 904 338-9157
Jacksonville *(G-6834)*
Tarmac Florida Inc..................F....... 954 481-2800
Deerfield Beach *(G-2923)*
Titan America LLC..................G....... 386 734-5526
Deland *(G-3022)*
Titan America LLC..................F....... 561 842-5309
Mangonia Park *(G-8514)*
Titan America LLC..................E....... 305 761-1944
Medley *(G-8736)*
Titan America LLC..................F....... 954 481-2800
Medley *(G-8737)*
Titan America LLC..................E....... 954 426-8407
Deerfield Beach *(G-2928)*
Titan America LLC..................C....... 305 364-2200
Medley *(G-8738)*
◆ **Titan Florida LLC**..................A....... 800 588-3939
Medley *(G-8739)*
Tradeland Americas Inc..................G....... 786 718-1490
South Miami *(G-16831)*
Universal Concrete & Ready Mix..................E....... 305 512-3400
Hialeah *(G-5663)*
Universal Concrete & Ready Mix..................F....... 305 888-4101
Medley *(G-8749)*
Vulcan Materials Company..................G....... 352 473-4258
Keystone Heights *(G-7212)*
Vulcan Materials Company..................F....... 205 298-3000
Tampa *(G-18248)*
Vulcan Materials Company..................G....... 863 675-5866
Moore Haven *(G-11090)*
We Mix You Match Inc..................G....... 561 615-0253
West Palm Beach *(G-19085)*
Whites Holdings Inc Centl Fla..................F....... 727 863-6072
Port Richey *(G-15078)*
Wpr Inc..................E....... 850 626-7713
Milton *(G-10948)*
Xpress Materials LLC..................F....... 352 748-2200
Wildwood *(G-19206)*

3274 Lime

Crystal River Quarries Inc..................E....... 352 795-2828
Crystal River *(G-2375)*
Key Lime Customs LLC..................G....... 407 353-9942
Windermere *(G-19233)*
Lemon Lime Catering LLC..................G....... 786 332-3636
Miami *(G-9883)*
Lhoist North America Ala LLC..................F....... 352 585-3488
Brooksville *(G-1246)*
Lhoist North America Ala LLC..................E....... 817 732-8164
Pompano Beach *(G-14744)*
Lime Street Development LLC..................G....... 239 594-7777
Naples *(G-11313)*
Marianna Lime Products Inc..................G....... 850 526-3580
Marianna *(G-8581)*
Marianna Limestone LLC..................F....... 954 581-1220
Marianna *(G-8582)*
◆ **Mineral Life Intl Inc**..................G....... 305 661-9854
Miami *(G-10026)*
Silver Star On Lime LLC..................G....... 941 312-4566
Sarasota *(G-16597)*

3275 Gypsum Prdts

▼ **Certanteed Gyps Ciling Mfg Inc**..................E....... 813 286-3900
Tampa *(G-17528)*
Continental Palatka LLC..................D....... 703 480-3800
Palatka *(G-13475)*
E2 Walls Inc..................E....... 813 374-2010
Tampa *(G-17624)*
Gypsum Bd Specialists USA Corp..................G....... 954 348-8869
Pembroke Pines *(G-14039)*
H & H Gypsum LLC..................G....... 321 972-5571
Casselberry *(G-1504)*
◆ **Lambert Corporation Florida**..................E....... 407 841-2940
Orlando *(G-12889)*
Premix-Marbletite Mfg Co..................F....... 407 327-0830
Winter Springs *(G-19480)*
United States Gypsum Company..................D....... 904 768-2501
Jacksonville *(G-6883)*
United States Gypsum Company..................D....... 305 688-8744
Miami Shores *(G-10886)*

3281 Cut Stone Prdts

Advanced Marble Products Inc..................G....... 941 485-7775
Venice *(G-18528)*
Affordable Granite Concepts..................F....... 407 332-0057
Altamonte Springs *(G-26)*
▼ **Airam Stone Designs Inc**..................G....... 305 477-8009
Miami *(G-9094)*
▲ **All Granite & Marble Corp**..................G....... 508 248-9393
Sarasota *(G-16340)*
American MBL Restoration Inc..................G....... 561 502-0764
Palm Springs *(G-13773)*
Ametrine LLC..................F....... 786 300-7946
Brandon *(G-1151)*
◆ **Ancient Mosaic Studios LLC**..................F....... 772 460-3145
Fort Pierce *(G-4676)*
▲ **Andean Stone Company LLC**..................G....... 305 460-3320
Hialeah *(G-5300)*
▲ **Architctural MBL Importers Inc**..................E....... 941 365-3552
Sarasota *(G-16347)*
Artistic Columns Inc..................G....... 954 530-5537
Oakland Park *(G-11780)*
Asv Stone Llc..................G....... 941 268-5321
Sarasota *(G-16354)*
Atlantic Marble Company Inc..................E....... 904 262-6262
Jacksonville *(G-6176)*
▼ **Bathroom World Manufacturing**..................G....... 954 566-0451
Oakland Park *(G-11785)*
Borders & Accents Inc..................F....... 305 947-6200
North Miami *(G-11629)*
▲ **Breton USA Customers Svc Corp**..................F....... 941 360-2700
Sarasota *(G-16369)*
◆ **C L Industries Inc**..................E....... 800 333-2660
Orlando *(G-12540)*
Cantor Design On Granite..................G....... 407 230-1568
Orlando *(G-12546)*
Cemex Materials LLC..................D....... 561 746-4556
Jupiter *(G-7018)*
Center Sand Mine..................G....... 800 366-7263
Clermont *(G-1951)*
Creative Curbing..................G....... 352 347-3329
Summerfield *(G-17058)*

SIC

Creta Granite & Marble Inc....G.... 954 956-9993
Pompano Beach (G-14650)
Cug LLC....F.... 786 858-0499
Plantation (G-14505)
Custom Cultered Marble Inc....G.... 239 823-8241
Spring Hill (G-16851)
◆ Custom Marble Works Inc....E.... 813 620-0475
Tampa (G-17580)
▲ D G Morrison Inc....F.... 813 865-0208
Odessa (G-12114)
Davis Kwik Kerb LLC....G.... 386 690-0058
New Smyrna Beach (G-11531)
▲ Debanie Inc....F.... 239 254-1222
Naples (G-11224)
◆ Designers Tops Inc....F.... 305 599-9973
Miami (G-9461)
◆ Devcon International Corp....C.... 954 926-5200
Boca Raton (G-499)
◆ Dyadic International USA Inc....G.... 561 743-8333
Jupiter (G-7028)
▼ Englert Arts Inc....G.... 561 241-9924
Boca Raton (G-518)
Eterna Urn Co Inc....G.... 386 258-6491
Daytona Beach (G-2663)
Exotic Countertop Inc....G.... 954 979-8188
Pompano Beach (G-14685)
F T F Construction Company....F.... 772 571-1850
Fellsmere (G-3725)
▲ Fantasy Marble & Granite Inc....G.... 954 788-0433
Pompano Beach (G-14687)
Fasulo Granite & Marble Inc....G.... 561 371-5410
Jupiter (G-7041)
Fine Surfaces and More Inc....G.... 305 691-5752
Miami (G-9568)
First Coast Granite & MBL Inc....E.... 904 388-1217
Jacksonville (G-6386)
Five Star Marble and Stone....G.... 904 887-4736
Ponte Vedra (G-14925)
Flagstone Pavers South....G.... 239 225-5646
Pompano Beach (G-14698)
Florida Amico....G.... 863 688-9256
Lakeland (G-7689)
▼ Florida Funeral Shipping Cntrs....G.... 954 957-9259
Fort Lauderdale (G-4000)
Fusion Industries Intl LLC....G.... 239 415-7554
Fort Myers (G-4462)
Galaxy Custom Granite Inc....G.... 352 220-2822
Inverness (G-6088)
Global Stone Corp....G.... 786 601-2459
Cutler Bay (G-2395)
Gold Granite & Marble....F.... 863 439-9794
Lake Hamilton (G-7390)
Granite World Inc....E.... 813 243-6556
Tampa (G-17725)
Grevan Artistic Ventures Inc....F.... 850 243-8111
Fort Walton Beach (G-4804)
HI Tech Granite and Marble....G.... 407 230-4363
Orlando (G-12802)
Highlander Stone Corp....G.... 786 333-1151
Opa Locka (G-12323)
House of Marble & Granite Inc....G.... 239 261-0099
Naples (G-11281)
▲ International Gran & Stone LLC....E.... 813 920-6500
Odessa (G-12127)
Italian Cast Stones Inc....E.... 813 902-8900
Tampa (G-17796)
Italy Tile and Marble Inc....G.... 941 488-5646
Saint Augustine (G-15559)
▲ J & J Stone Tops Inc....G.... 305 305-8993
Opa Locka (G-12328)
J & N Stone Inc....G.... 863 422-7369
Davenport (G-2480)
J V Installations Corp....E.... 407 849-0262
Orlando (G-12848)
Kadassa Inc....F.... 954 684-8361
Riviera Beach (G-15339)
◆ Keystone Products Inc....F.... 305 245-4716
Homestead (G-5976)
▲ Kusser Graniteworks Usa Inc....G.... 813 248-3428
Tampa (G-17830)
Kwik Kerb LLC....G.... 386 453-1004
Port Orange (G-15021)
Kwik Kerb By 3d....G.... 352 383-1123
Mount Dora (G-11106)
LAS & JB Inc....G.... 772 672-5315
Fort Pierce (G-4711)
▲ Luxury Stone....G.... 813 985-0850
Tampa (G-17865)
Marble Designs of FL Inc....G.... 321 269-6920
Titusville (G-18445)
Marble Doctors LLC....D.... 203 794-1000
Wellington (G-18724)
◆ Marble Lite Products Corp....E.... 305 557-8766
Miami Lakes (G-10812)
MGM Granite & Marble Company....G.... 954 894-6802
Fort Lauderdale (G-4120)
Moderno Porcelain Works LLC....F.... 954 607-3535
Sunrise (G-17147)
◆ Mont Krest Stone Inc....G.... 727 209-0864
Largo (G-8013)
Mother Earth Stone LLC....F.... 407 878-2854
Sanford (G-16091)
Naples Stone Consulting LLC....F.... 239 325-8653
Naples (G-11339)
▲ National Stoneworks LLC....E.... 954 349-1609
Weston (G-19152)
Natural Stone Sltons Fnest SRS....E.... 941 954-1100
Sarasota (G-16519)
▲ New England Granite & Marble....G.... 772 283-8667
Stuart (G-16980)
▲ Old World Marble and Gran Inc....G.... 239 596-4777
Naples (G-11350)
▲ Palm Beach Aggregates LLC....E.... 561 795-6550
Loxahatchee (G-8362)
Paver Systems LLC....E.... 407 859-9117
Orlando (G-13055)
▲ Prestige Flrg Instllations Inc....F.... 407 291-0609
Orlando (G-13083)
PSC Building Group Inc....F.... 561 756-6811
Delray Beach (G-3130)
◆ Puma Marble Co Inc....F.... 305 758-6461
Miami (G-10214)
Quartzo LLC....F.... 888 813-3442
Tampa (G-18034)
Reyes Granite & Marble Corp....F.... 305 599-7330
Miami (G-10259)
Ribeiro Stones LLC....G.... 407 723-8802
Orlando (G-13136)
Rik Enterprises Inc....G.... 239 772-9485
Cape Coral (G-1460)
Sarasotas Finest MBL Gran Inc....G.... 941 365-9697
Sarasota (G-16583)
Showcase Marble Inc....F.... 386 253-6646
Daytona Beach (G-2714)
Signature Granite Inc....F.... 813 443-5597
Tampa (G-18103)
Stone and Equipment Inc....E.... 305 665-0002
Miami (G-10416)
Stone Craft Masters LLC....F.... 786 401-7060
Doral (G-3512)
Stone Design By Santos LLC....G.... 954 366-1919
Pompano Beach (G-14873)
Stone Palace....F.... 407 896-0872
Orlando (G-13216)
▲ Stone Trend International Inc....E.... 941 927-9113
Sarasota (G-16605)
Stonecrfters Archtctral Prcast....F.... 727 544-1210
Seminole (G-16763)
◆ Stoneworks Inc....F.... 305 666-6676
Miami (G-10417)
▼ Suncoast Stone Inc....E.... 561 364-2061
Delray Beach (G-3148)
T H Stone....G.... 561 361-3966
Boca Raton (G-741)
Taken For Granite....G.... 727 235-1559
Saint Petersburg (G-15932)
◆ Terrastone Inc....G.... 305 234-8384
Miami (G-10469)
▲ Triton Stone Holdings LLC....G.... 219 669-4890
Fort Lauderdale (G-4288)
Tropix Marble Company....F.... 239 334-2371
Cape Coral (G-1488)
Unique Marble Inc....F.... 772 766-4432
Vero Beach (G-18672)
▲ Unisource Stone Inc....G.... 561 493-0660
Stuart (G-17043)
▲ Venice Granit & Marble Inc....G.... 941 483-4363
Venice (G-18585)
Yarey Inc....F.... 954 520-6015
Boca Raton (G-795)
Zachey Design Marble Inc....G.... 754 367-6261
Hollywood (G-5945)

3291 Abrasive Prdts

Abracol North America Corp....G.... 305 431-5596
Miami (G-9057)
Abrasive Dynamics Inc....F.... 860 291-0664
Pompano Beach (G-14573)
▼ All Polishing Solutions....G.... 954 505-4041
Miramar (G-10965)
Bobs Barricades Inc....E.... 813 886-0518
Tampa (G-17478)
▲ Global Diversified Products....E.... 727 209-0854
Pinellas Park (G-14351)
Harsco Corporation....F.... 717 506-2071
Tampa (G-17745)
Hone Renovation Specialists....G.... 407 202-3536
Orlando (G-12808)
Kay Diamond Products LLC....F.... 561 994-5400
Boca Raton (G-585)
Liquid Metal Products Inc....G.... 402 895-4436
Ocala (G-11986)
Maxi-Blast of Florida Inc....G.... 727 572-0909
Saint Petersburg (G-15851)
Microtool and Instrument Inc....E.... 786 242-8780
Palmetto Bay (G-13851)
Sandpaper Marketing Inc....G.... 850 939-8040
Navarre (G-11475)
▼ Sheila Shine Inc....E.... 305 557-1729
Miami (G-10335)
▲ Trident Trading Inc....G.... 561 488-0458
Boca Raton (G-756)
▼ True Grit Abrasives Inc....E.... 813 247-5219
Tampa (G-18203)
Tyrex Ore & Minerals Company....G.... 305 333-5288
Miami (G-10520)
United Abrasives Inc....F.... 239 300-0033
Naples (G-11446)
▲ Worldwide Superabrasives LLC....E.... 954 828-9650
Boynton Beach (G-976)
Wwsa Solids LLC....F.... 561 588-9299
Boynton Beach (G-978)

3292 Asbestos products

American Coatings Corporation....G.... 954 970-7820
Margate (G-8535)
Cahill Construction Services....G.... 239 369-9290
Lehigh Acres (G-8186)

3295 Minerals & Earths: Ground Or Treated

Active Minerals Intl LLC....G.... 410 825-2920
Quincy (G-15245)
◆ Atlas Peat & Soil Inc....E.... 561 734-7300
Boynton Beach (G-881)
Calcium Silicate Corp Inc....F.... 863 902-0217
Lake Harbor (G-7394)
Center American Longevity....G.... 305 777-1667
Miami (G-9338)
Chemours Company Fc LLC....C.... 904 964-1200
Starke (G-16890)
Conrad Yelvington Distrs Inc....G.... 352 336-5049
Gainesville (G-4895)
Diatomite Corp of America....G.... 305 466-0075
Miami (G-9465)
Harsco Corporation....F.... 717 506-2071
Tampa (G-17745)
Imerys Perlite Usa Inc....G.... 850 875-1282
Quincy (G-15251)
Sanborn Resources Ltd....G.... 561 551-6161
West Palm Beach (G-19025)
Terfa Litter USA Inc....F.... 416 358-4495
Sunny Isles Beach (G-17081)
Tradeland Americas Inc....G.... 786 718-1490
South Miami (G-16831)

3296 Mineral Wool

◆ Bigham Insulation & Sup Co Inc....E.... 954 522-2887
Fort Lauderdale (G-3852)
Magnum Venus Plastech....F.... 727 573-2955
Clearwater (G-1772)
Martin Gallagher LLC....G.... 407 453-1027
Kissimmee (G-7273)
Owens Corning Sales LLC....E.... 863 291-3046
Winter Haven (G-19338)
Quiet Flex....F.... 352 429-3286
Groveland (G-5106)
Rossiter Manufacturing....G.... 386 409-7223
Daytona Beach (G-2706)
Ryan Scientific LLC....F.... 904 284-6025
Green Cove Springs (G-5069)
▲ Super Sensitive String Sls Co....E.... 941 371-0016
Sarasota (G-16612)
Tubos Inc....G.... 727 504-0633
Largo (G-8070)
Tubos Inc....G.... 727 504-0633
Clearwater (G-1926)

3297 Nonclay Refractories

Matthews International Corp....C....407 886-5533
Apopka (G-158)
▼ Natures Earth Products Inc....E....561 688-8101
West Palm Beach (G-18958)
◆ Osmi Inc....F....561 330-9300
Boca Raton (G-657)

3299 Nonmetallic Mineral Prdts, NEC

Andrew Pratt Stucco & Plst Inc....F....407 501-2609
Orlando (G-12478)
Architectural Fountains Inc....G....727 323-6068
Saint Petersburg (G-15708)
Best of Orlando Pntg & Stucco....G....407 947-4174
Apopka (G-117)
▼ Best Products Mix Inc....G....305 512-9920
Hialeah (G-5324)
Bill Praus Stucco LLC....G....386 453-8400
Flagler Beach (G-3753)
Bluewater Finishing LLC....G....772 460-9457
Port Saint Lucie (G-15092)
Braden Kitchens Inc....E....321 636-4700
Cocoa (G-1999)
Custom Stucco Inc....G....941 650-5649
Englewood (G-3659)
Custom Wall Systems Inc....G....772 408-3006
Vero Beach (G-18614)
Cutting Edge Archtctral Mldngs....G....941 727-1111
Bradenton (G-1027)
Cutting Edge Moldings LLC....G....734 649-1500
Sarasota (G-16201)
▼ E T Plastering Inc....F....305 874-7082
Virginia Gardens (G-18688)
Fekel Stucco Plastering Inc....G....239 571-5464
Naples (G-11245)
◆ Fleurissima Inc....F....305 572-0203
Miami (G-9575)
◆ Florida Nonwovens Inc....F....407 241-2701
Orlando (G-12751)
▼ Florida Stucco Corp....E....561 487-1301
Boca Raton (G-534)
Florida Sunshine Stucco LLC....G....407 947-2088
Orlando (G-12757)
G & R Stucco Inc....G....941 780-1561
North Port (G-11739)
Gold Coast Plst & Stucco Inc....F....954 275-9132
Margate (G-8545)
Green Forest Industries Inc....E....941 721-0504
Palmetto (G-13801)
Imagecare Maintenance Systems....F....727 536-8646
Clearwater (G-1729)
Ipg Network Corp....F....305 681-4001
Miami (G-9766)
J&Jh Stucco Inc....G....813 482-5282
Riverview (G-15274)
Jag Stucco Inc....G....813 210-6577
Land O Lakes (G-7858)
John S Smith Stucco Inc....G....813 928-4320
New Port Richey (G-11496)
Joseph Malara....G....352 789-7646
Coral Springs (G-2266)
Juan Diaz Stucco Spc Inc....G....407 402-1912
Minneola (G-10955)
MDK Enterpises Inc....F....904 288-6855
Jacksonville (G-6586)
Pitelka Plastering Stucco....G....630 235-5611
Venice (G-18567)
◆ Pre-Mix Marble Tite Inc....E....954 917-7665
Pompano Beach (G-14806)
◆ Premix-Marbletite Mfg Co....F....954 970-6540
Pompano Beach (G-14810)
Premix-Marbletite Mfg Co....F....407 327-0830
Winter Springs (G-19480)
Q Plastering and Stucco Inc....G....239 530-1712
Naples (G-11378)
Reyes Stucco Inc....G....321 557-1319
Cocoa (G-2047)
Right Stucco Inc....G....407 468-6119
Orlando (G-13139)
River City Stucco Inc....G....904 234-9526
Jacksonville (G-6728)
S&L Cnstrction Specialists Inc....G....407 300-5080
Orlando (G-13153)
▲ Spaulding Craft Inc....F....727 726-2316
Safety Harbor (G-15505)
Sun-Rock Inc....F....727 938-0013
Tarpon Springs (G-18327)
Tim Hardy Plaster Moldings LLC....G....239 877-8434
Naples (G-11441)
Treasure Cove II Inc....F....941 966-2004
Sarasota (G-16625)
▲ Trebol Florida LLC....F....904 751-2828
Jacksonville (G-6867)
Tri Inc....F....813 267-1201
Tampa (G-18199)
Trinity Exterior Solutions LLC....G....850 393-9682
Holt (G-5950)
Unique Rabbit Studios Inc....G....954 691-1390
Pompano Beach (G-14899)
Vimar Stucco Inc....G....813 966-4831
Brandon (G-1184)

33 PRIMARY METAL INDUSTRIES

3312 Blast Furnaces, Coke Ovens, Steel & Rolling Mills

ABS Structural Corp....F....321 768-2067
Melbourne (G-8756)
▲ Advance One Wheels Inc....F....305 238-5833
Miami (G-9074)
Alpine Tool Inc....G....727 587-0407
Largo (G-7891)
▲ American Force Wheels Inc....F....786 345-6301
Hialeah (G-5291)
American Stainless Mfrs....D....786 275-4458
Miami (G-9147)
American Vinyl Company....F....813 663-0157
Tampa (G-17421)
▼ Associated Steel & Alum Co Inc....F....954 974-7890
Pompano Beach (G-14603)
Associated Steel & Alum Ltd....F....954 974-7890
Pompano Beach (G-14604)
ATI Accurate Technology....G....239 206-1240
Palmetto (G-13787)
ATI Agency Inc....F....954 895-7909
Boca Raton (G-432)
ATI By Sea Co....G....954 483-0526
Hollywood (G-5776)
ATI Pro AV LLC....G....941 322-1008
Sarasota (G-16355)
ATI Sales Inc....G....954 909-4639
Plantation (G-14493)
Ati2 Inc....G....904 396-3766
Jacksonville (G-6171)
▼ Atlantic Wire and Rigging Inc....G....321 633-1552
Cocoa (G-1997)
▲ Automotive Armor Mfg Inc....F....941 721-3335
Palmetto (G-13788)
Belt Corp....G....954 505-7400
Hollywood (G-5785)
Berg Europipe Holding Corp....C....850 769-2273
Panama City (G-13869)
Berg LLC....F....786 201-2625
Aventura (G-264)
Bigg Wills Wheels LLC....G....352 222-6170
Gainesville (G-4886)
Brewfab LLC....G....727 823-8333
Saint Petersburg (G-15729)
Calnat International Inc....G....239 839-2581
Cape Coral (G-1401)
Chemko Technical Services Inc....E....954 783-7673
Pompano Beach (G-14634)
Commercial Metals Company....G....904 781-4780
Jacksonville (G-6281)
Conc-Steel Inc....G....516 882-5551
Palm Coast (G-13689)
▼ Custom Stainless Stl Eqp Inc....E....305 627-6049
Miami (G-9419)
Defense Stamping & Engineering....E....850 438-6105
Pensacola (G-14127)
Diverse Co....F....863 425-4251
Mulberry (G-11123)
Dixie Structures & Maintenance....F....205 274-4525
Fort Myers (G-4433)
Drt Express Inc....G....305 827-5005
Hialeah (G-5378)
Durbal Inc....G....727 531-3040
Clearwater (G-1662)
◆ Elite Wheel Distributors Inc....F....813 673-8393
Tampa (G-17633)
Fabmaster Inc....G....727 216-6750
Clearwater (G-1680)
Florida Aluminum and Steel Inc....F....863 967-4191
Auburndale (G-241)
Florida Stainless Steel ACC....G....727 207-2575
Spring Hill (G-16853)
Florida Stl Frame Truss Mfg LL....G....813 460-0006
Wesley Chapel (G-18746)
Friedman & Greenberg PA....G....954 370-4774
Plantation (G-14519)
Frozen Wheels LLC....F....305 799-2258
Miami (G-9601)
Garcia Iron Works....G....305 888-0080
Hialeah (G-5425)
◆ Gerdau Ameristeel Corp....A....813 286-8383
Tampa (G-17710)
◆ Gerdau Ameristeel US Inc....B....813 286-8383
Tampa (G-17711)
Gerdau Ameristeel US Inc....E....813 752-7550
Plant City (G-14435)
◆ Gerdau USA Inc....B....813 286-8383
Tampa (G-17712)
Gulf Atlantic Culvert Company....F....850 562-2384
Tallahassee (G-17270)
H & M Steel....G....904 765-3465
Jacksonville (G-6458)
Harbor Entps Ltd Lblty Co....F....229 403-0756
Tallahassee (G-17274)
▼ Hollywood Iron Works Inc....F....954 962-0556
West Park (G-19094)
Home & Garden Industries Inc....F....305 634-0681
Miami (G-9716)
Inductoweld Tube Corp....G....646 734-7094
Fort Lauderdale (G-4057)
◆ Industrial Galvanizers Miami....E....305 681-8844
Miami (G-9738)
Industrial Spring Corp....F....954 524-2558
Davie (G-2537)
Innovative Steel Tech Inc....F....813 767-1746
Gibsonton (G-5030)
International Iron Works LLC....G....305 835-0190
Hialeah (G-5455)
Iron Sharpens Ir Training LLC....G....407 614-4500
Winter Garden (G-19271)
Just Steel Inc....F....941 755-7811
Sarasota (G-16242)
Kissimmee Iron Works Inc....G....407 870-8872
Kissimmee (G-7262)
Latham Marine Inc....E....954 462-3055
Fort Lauderdale (G-4096)
Leals Tires & Wheels....G....239 491-2214
Lehigh Acres (G-8195)
Maclan Corporation Inc....E....863 665-4814
Lakeland (G-7742)
Manna On Wheels Inc....G....813 754-2277
Dover (G-3560)
Manor Steel Fabricators....G....941 722-8077
Palmetto (G-13810)
Marilyn Jeffcoat....G....407 382-1783
Orlando (G-12949)
▲ Maschmeyer Concrete Co Fla....E....561 848-9112
Lake Park (G-7476)
Matschel of Flagler Inc....G....386 446-4595
Saint Augustine (G-15567)
Metal Culverts Inc....E....727 531-1431
Clearwater (G-1782)
Metal Processors Inc....E....813 654-0050
Tampa (G-17904)
◆ Mgl Engineering Inc....E....863 648-0320
Lakeland (G-7750)
▼ Miami Power Wheels....G....305 553-1888
Miami (G-10004)
Neo Metal Glass LLC....G....954 532-0340
Pompano Beach (G-14772)
New Bs Wheel LLC....G....309 657-4899
Saint Augustine (G-15572)
Nucor LLC....G....786 290-9328
Surfside (G-17204)
Nucor Steel Florida Inc....G....863 546-5800
Frostproof (G-4862)
Phlebotomists On Wheels Inc....G....954 873-7591
Fort Lauderdale (G-4165)
◆ Project and Cnstr Wldg Inc....F....239 772-9299
Cape Coral (G-1458)
Renaissance Steel LLC....F....941 773-7290
Temple Terrace (G-18376)
▲ Renovaship Inc....G....954 342-9062
Hallandale Beach (G-5208)
Rq Welding Inc....G....786 609-3384
Miami (G-10284)
▲ Sarasota Precision Engrg Inc....F....941 727-3444
Sarasota (G-16293)
School-On-Wheels....G....239 530-8522
Naples (G-11396)
▼ Sea Side Specialties....G....561 276-6518
Delray Beach (G-3139)
Sel West Coast Inc....E....352 373-6354
Gainesville (G-4994)

SIC

Sfa Systems Inc ....E.... 561 585-5927
Lake Worth *(G-7586)*
Sg Global LLC ....G.... 305 726-3439
Miami *(G-10329)*
Shaws Fiberglass Inc ....G.... 863 425-9176
Mulberry *(G-11136)*
▲ **Sheffield Steel Corporation** ....A.... 918 245-1335
Tampa *(G-18095)*
▲ **Skipper Wright Inc** ....F.... 904 354-4381
Jacksonville *(G-6779)*
Specialty Forged Wheels Inc ....G.... 786 332-5925
Miami *(G-10400)*
Spectrum Engineering Inc ....G.... 239 277-1182
Fort Myers *(G-4610)*
▼ **Stainless Fabricators Inc** ....E.... 813 926-7113
Odessa *(G-12155)*
Stainless Steel Guide Rods ....G.... 813 240-7616
Hudson *(G-6038)*
Stainless Steel Guide Rods ....G.... 727 207-0583
Spring Hill *(G-16877)*
Stainless Steel Kitchens Corp ....F.... 305 999-1543
North Bay Village *(G-11596)*
◆ **Starr Wheel Group Inc** ....F.... 954 935-5536
Coral Springs *(G-2316)*
Str Racing Wheels ....G.... 407 251-7171
Orlando *(G-13217)*
T&T Sons Inc ....G.... 859 576-3316
Oviedo *(G-13459)*
TK Tires & Wheels Inc ....G.... 321 473-8945
Melbourne *(G-8964)*
▲ **Uk Sales LLC** ....G.... 561 239-2980
Coconut Creek *(G-2099)*
Urban Metals LLC ....F.... 813 241-2801
Tampa *(G-18225)*
US Pipe Fabrication LLC ....E.... 860 769-6097
Orlando *(G-13299)*
Wheel Wright ....G.... 850 626-2662
Milton *(G-10946)*
Zerons Metal Designers Inc ....F.... 305 688-2240
Hialeah *(G-5696)*

3313 Electrometallurgical Prdts

Bayside Small Cap Senior Loan ....F.... 305 381-4100
Miami *(G-9227)*
Beehive3d Inc ....G.... 954 560-9513
Deerfield Beach *(G-2784)*
Chance Aluminum Corp ....F.... 407 789-1606
Orlando *(G-12574)*
Globe Specialty Metals Inc ....F.... 786 509-6900
Miami *(G-9644)*

3315 Steel Wire Drawing & Nails & Spikes

◆ **American Fence Shop LLC** ....F.... 305 681-3511
Hialeah *(G-5290)*
Antebellum Manufacturing LLC ....E.... 352 877-3888
Ocala *(G-11875)*
▲ **Baby Guard Inc** ....F.... 954 741-6351
Coral Springs *(G-2222)*
Complete Access Ctrl Centl Fla ....G.... 407 498-0067
Saint Cloud *(G-15647)*
◆ **Gerdau Ameristeel US Inc** ....B.... 813 286-8383
Tampa *(G-17711)*
◆ **Gerdau USA Inc** ....B.... 813 286-8383
Tampa *(G-17712)*
Green Mountain Specialties ....F.... 386 469-0057
Deland *(G-2982)*
▲ **Keystone Steel Products Co** ....G.... 813 248-9828
Tampa *(G-17822)*
▼ **L A Ornamental & Rack Corp** ....G.... 305 696-0419
Miami *(G-9835)*
List Manufacturing Inc ....E.... 954 429-9155
Deerfield Beach *(G-2860)*
Macias Gabions Inc ....G.... 850 910-8000
Lauderhill *(G-8114)*
Merchants Metals Inc ....D.... 813 333-5515
Tampa *(G-17901)*
Metalhouse LLC ....G.... 407 270-3000
Orlando *(G-12962)*
◆ **Nationwide Industries Inc** ....E.... 813 988-2628
Tampa *(G-17933)*
Orbital Corporation of Tampa ....G.... 813 782-7300
Zephyrhills *(G-19529)*
Peninsula Steel Inc ....G.... 956 795-1966
Plant City *(G-14456)*
Peninsula Steel Inc ....E.... 813 473-8133
Plant City *(G-14457)*
◆ **Phelps Dodge Intl Corp** ....E.... 305 648-7888
Doral *(G-3459)*
Phosco Electric Supply Co Inc ....G.... 941 708-9633
Bradenton *(G-1096)*
Pte Systems International LLC ....E.... 305 863-3409
Hialeah *(G-5582)*
Repwire LLC ....G.... 786 486-1823
Doral *(G-3483)*
Rq Welding Inc ....G.... 786 609-3384
Miami *(G-10284)*
Suncoast Post-Tension Ltd ....E.... 305 592-5075
Miami *(G-10430)*
Tecnometales Onis Cnc LLC ....G.... 786 637-8316
Pembroke Pines *(G-14065)*
◆ **Wire Products Inc of Florida** ....E.... 954 772-1477
Fort Lauderdale *(G-4326)*
Wire Tech International Inc ....G.... 786 258-5746
Bal Harbour *(G-304)*

3316 Cold Rolled Steel Sheet, Strip & Bars

Hydro Extrusion Usa LLC ....B.... 904 794-1500
Saint Augustine *(G-15550)*
◆ **Hydro Precision Tubing USA LLC** ....C.... 321 636-8147
Rockledge *(G-15420)*
Stuart Building Products LLC ....G.... 239 461-3100
Fort Myers *(G-4613)*
Suncoast Post-Tension Ltd ....E.... 305 592-5075
Miami *(G-10430)*

3317 Steel Pipe & Tubes

◆ **Accord Industries LLC** ....D.... 407 671-6989
Winter Park *(G-19370)*
Ace Mechanical Inc ....G.... 727 304-6277
Largo *(G-7884)*
Allsteel Processing LC ....F.... 954 587-1900
Fort Lauderdale *(G-3808)*
Atkore International Inc ....G.... 800 882-5543
Boca Raton *(G-433)*
◆ **Berg Pipe Panama City Corp** ....C.... 850 769-2273
Panama City *(G-13870)*
Cmn Steel Fabricators Inc ....D.... 305 592-5466
Miami *(G-9367)*
▲ **Custom Fab Inc** ....D.... 407 859-3954
Orlando *(G-12639)*
Driveshaft Power Inc ....F.... 561 433-0022
Lake Worth *(G-7547)*
Florida Steam Services Inc ....G.... 407 247-8250
Geneva *(G-5022)*
GPM Fab & Supply LLC ....G.... 813 689-7107
Seffner *(G-16729)*
Metal Culverts Inc ....E.... 727 531-1431
Clearwater *(G-1782)*
▼ **Neptune Research Inc** ....E.... 561 683-6992
Riviera Beach *(G-15352)*
Ride and Tube Inc ....F.... 352 454-8194
Summerfield *(G-17061)*
Sanitube LLC ....F.... 863 606-5960
Lakeland *(G-7787)*
Southstern Indus Fbrcators LLC ....E.... 941 776-1211
Duette *(G-3563)*
Specialty Steel Holdco Inc ....G.... 305 375-7560
Miami *(G-10402)*
Theclipcom Inc ....G.... 305 599-3871
Tavernier *(G-18363)*
Value Providers LLC ....G.... 321 567-0919
Daytona Beach *(G-2731)*
Wellstream International Ltd ....C.... 850 636-4800
Panama City *(G-13963)*

3321 Gray Iron Foundries

Custom Flange Pipe LLC ....F.... 863 353-6602
Winter Haven *(G-19316)*
Forterra Pressure Pipe Inc ....C.... 386 328-8841
Palatka *(G-13480)*
▼ **Halliday Products Inc** ....D.... 407 298-4470
Orlando *(G-12794)*
Maddox Foundry & Mch Works LLC ....E.... 352 495-2121
Archer *(G-210)*
Tld LLC ....G.... 813 927-7554
Tampa *(G-18191)*
◆ **U S Holdings Inc** ....G.... 305 885-0301
Hialeah *(G-5656)*
▼ **United States Fndry & Mfg Corp** ....C.... 305 885-0301
Medley *(G-8748)*
United States Fndry & Mfg Corp ....F.... 305 556-1661
Hialeah *(G-5661)*
Urecon Systems Inc ....E.... 904 695-3332
Winter Park *(G-19456)*

3322 Malleable Iron Foundries

▼ **United States Fndry & Mfg Corp** ....C.... 305 885-0301
Medley *(G-8748)*

3324 Steel Investment Foundries

Alm Technologies Inc ....E.... 904 849-7212
Yulee *(G-19495)*
Cloud Investment Partners Lllp ....G.... 561 266-0845
Boynton Beach *(G-891)*
Extant Cmpnnts Group Hldngs In ....G.... 321 254-1500
Melbourne *(G-8828)*
Extant Cmpnnts Group Intrmdate ....C.... 321 254-1500
Melbourne *(G-8829)*
General Pneumatics Inflation ....G.... 941 216-3500
Sarasota *(G-16219)*
Kellstrom Aerospace Group Inc ....E.... 954 538-2482
Boca Raton *(G-586)*
M Austin Forman ....E.... 954 763-8111
Fort Lauderdale *(G-4107)*
R B Casting Inc ....G.... 407 648-2005
Orlando *(G-13108)*

3325 Steel Foundries, NEC

Contemporary Carbide Tech ....F.... 386 734-0080
Deland *(G-2964)*
▲ **Hardware Parts Corporation** ....G.... 561 994-2121
Boca Raton *(G-556)*
Maddox Foundry & Mch Works LLC ....E.... 352 495-2121
Archer *(G-210)*

3331 Primary Smelting & Refining Of Copper

EJM Copper Inc ....F.... 407 447-0074
Orlando *(G-12702)*

3334 Primary Production Of Aluminum

AJs Aluminum Inc ....G.... 352 688-7631
Spring Hill *(G-16845)*
All Coast Manufacturing Inc ....G.... 813 626-2264
Tampa *(G-17398)*
▼ **Alumacart Inc** ....F.... 772 675-2158
Hobe Sound *(G-5721)*
Benchmark Aluminum Inc ....G.... 941 585-9977
Port Charlotte *(G-14964)*
Charleston Aluminum LLC ....F.... 305 628-4014
Hialeah *(G-5342)*
Eastern Metal Supply Inc ....F.... 863 682-6660
Lakeland *(G-7679)*
◆ **Florida Sales & Marketing** ....E.... 239 274-3103
Fort Myers *(G-4451)*
Glassarium LLC ....E.... 786 631-7080
Miami *(G-9639)*
Gyrosolar Corp ....G.... 954 554-9990
Weston *(G-19136)*
◆ **Ideal Deals LLC** ....C.... 386 736-1700
Saint Augustine *(G-15553)*
Jmn Aluminum ....G.... 813 325-7807
Tampa *(G-17807)*
Mary Lame Wrought Iron & Alum ....G.... 727 934-2879
Holiday *(G-5747)*
Shelmet Corp ....G.... 561 688-9700
West Palm Beach *(G-19030)*
Streamline Aluminum Inc ....F.... 239 561-7200
Fort Myers *(G-4612)*
Tru Mension Mfg Solutions ....G.... 321 255-4665
Melbourne *(G-8967)*

3339 Primary Nonferrous Metals, NEC

Allliance Precious Mtls Group ....G.... 954 480-8676
Coconut Creek *(G-2069)*
C C Lead Inc ....F.... 863 465-6458
Lake Placid *(G-7486)*
CB Precious Metals LLC ....F.... 407 790-1585
Longwood *(G-8264)*
▲ **Envirofocus Technologies LLC** ....D.... 813 620-3260
Tampa *(G-17645)*
◆ **Flotech Inc** ....D.... 904 358-1849
Jacksonville *(G-6406)*
Globe Specialty Metals Inc ....F.... 786 509-6900
Miami *(G-9644)*
I J Precious Metals Inc ....G.... 305 371-3009
Miami *(G-9724)*
Palm Beach Precious Metals ....G.... 561 662-6025
Palm Springs *(G-13779)*
Pmr Gestion Inc ....G.... 561 501-5190
Delray Beach *(G-3120)*
Precious Metal Group LLC ....G.... 904 219-8358
Jacksonville *(G-6680)*
Precious Metals Buyers LLC ....G.... 813 880-9544
Tampa *(G-18001)*
Precious Metals Buyers LLC ....F.... 813 417-7857
Tampa *(G-18002)*
Precious Metals Xchange Group ....G.... 305 556-1696
Doral *(G-3466)*

Premium Precious Metals LLC ....G....... 954 367-7513
Fort Lauderdale *(G-4178)*
◆ Republic Metals Corporation ....C....... 305 685-8505
Opa Locka *(G-12354)*
SPI LLC...C....... 786 907-4022
Miami *(G-10405)*

3341 Secondary Smelting & Refining Of Nonferrous Metals

All Metals Fabrication LLC...................G....... 904 862-6885
Jacksonville *(G-6134)*
Alliance Metals LLC..............................G....... 305 343-9536
Bay Harbor Islands *(G-337)*
▲ Enviro Focus Technology ....G....... 813 744-5000
Tampa *(G-17644)*
◆ Flotech Inc ....D....... 904 358-1849
Jacksonville *(G-6406)*
Troika Group Inc ....G....... 561 313-1119
Wellington *(G-18738)*
Wise Recycling 1 LLC............................F....... 850 477-5273
Pensacola *(G-14290)*

3351 Rolling, Drawing & Extruding Of Copper

Admiralty Industries Corp.....................G....... 305 722-7311
Doral *(G-3227)*
◆ American Wire Group Inc ....F....... 954 455-3050
Aventura *(G-260)*
Kme Amrica Mar Tube Ftting LLC ....D....... 904 265-4001
Jacksonville *(G-6541)*
Manchester Copper Tube LLC ....F....... 321 636-1477
Rockledge *(G-15433)*
Technetics Group LLC............................C....... 386 736-7373
Deland *(G-3019)*
Technetics Group LLC............................E....... 386 736-7373
De Land *(G-2734)*

3353 Aluminum Sheet, Plate & Foil

Aluminum Solutions Group Inc.............G....... 561 999-9932
Boca Raton *(G-417)*
American Aluminum Doors Corp ....F....... 305 885-4020
Hialeah *(G-5287)*
Engedi Specialities Inc..........................G....... 386 497-1010
Fort White *(G-4843)*
Perez Industries Inc...............................F....... 239 992-2444
Bonita Springs *(G-846)*
Polytech International LLC ....F....... 904 354-9355
Jacksonville *(G-6678)*
Sun Indalex LLC.....................................E....... 561 394-0550
Boca Raton *(G-734)*

3354 Aluminum Extruded Prdts

Absolute Aluminum Inc.........................D....... 941 497-7777
Venice *(G-18526)*
◆ Aldora Aluminum & GL Pdts Inc ....E....... 954 441-5057
Coral Springs *(G-2219)*
▲ Aludisc LLC...E....... 910 299-0911
Boca Raton *(G-416)*
▼ Alumacart Inc ....F....... 772 675-2158
Hobe Sound *(G-5721)*
Aluminum Products Whl Inc..................G....... 904 268-4895
Jacksonville *(G-6144)*
Alumitech Inc..F....... 407 826-5373
Orlando *(G-12463)*
American Products Inc...........................G....... 813 925-0144
Tampa *(G-17418)*
◆ American Windows Shutters Inc.......E....... 239 278-3066
Fort Myers *(G-4359)*
Anchor Aluminum Products South ....G....... 305 293-7965
Key West *(G-7177)*
Architctral Mtal Flashings LLC..............F....... 239 221-0123
Cape Coral *(G-1383)*
▼ Associated Steel & Alum Co Inc.......F....... 954 974-7890
Pompano Beach *(G-14603)*
▼ Benada Aluminum Products LLC.....C....... 407 323-3300
Sanford *(G-16002)*
▼ Cline Aluminum Doors Inc.................E....... 941 746-4104
Bradenton *(G-1021)*
Cross Key Marine Canvas Inc................G....... 305 451-1302
Key Largo *(G-7167)*
▲ Eagle Metal Distributors Inc.............G....... 407 367-0688
Orlando *(G-12693)*
Expert Shutter Services Inc...................D....... 772 871-1915
Port Saint Lucie *(G-15108)*
◆ Florida Extruders Intl Inc..................D....... 407 323-3300
Sanford *(G-16049)*
Global Aluminum Solutions LLC...........G....... 954 636-4143
Pembroke Pines *(G-14036)*
Golden Aluminum Extrusion LLC ....E....... 330 372-2300
Plant City *(G-14436)*
Gulf Electronics ....F....... 727 595-3840
Largo *(G-7967)*
Hydro Extrusion Usa LLC ....B....... 904 794-1500
Saint Augustine *(G-15550)*
◆ Hydro Precision Tubing USA LLC.....C....... 321 636-8147
Rockledge *(G-15420)*
◆ Jupiter Industries LLC ....G....... 239 225-9041
Fort Myers *(G-4508)*
▼ Karnak South Inc ....F....... 954 761-7606
Fort Lauderdale *(G-4084)*
▲ Keymark Corporation Florida ....C....... 863 858-5500
Lakeland *(G-7727)*
Largo Aluminum Inc ....F....... 305 852-2390
Islamorada *(G-6098)*
▲ Liberty Aluminum Co.........................E....... 239 369-3000
Lehigh Acres *(G-8197)*
▼ Magic Tilt Trailer Mfg Co Inc ....E....... 727 535-5561
Clearwater *(G-1769)*
Mary Lame Wrought Iron & Alum ....G....... 727 934-2879
Holiday *(G-5747)*
Metal Container Corporation ....C....... 904 695-7600
Jacksonville *(G-6596)*
Metals USA Holdings Corp ....A....... 954 202-4000
Fort Lauderdale *(G-4118)*
Naples Iron Works Inc ....E....... 239 649-7265
Naples *(G-11336)*
Nav-X LLC..E....... 954 978-9988
Fort Lauderdale *(G-4134)*
Plastic and Products Mktg LLC.............F....... 352 867-8078
Ocala *(G-12028)*
▲ RDS Manufacturing Inc ....C....... 850 584-6898
Perry *(G-14310)*
◆ Rolling Shield Incorporated ....E....... 305 436-6661
Miami Lakes *(G-10852)*
Sapa Extrsons St Augustine LLC..........A....... 904 794-1500
Saint Augustine *(G-15604)*
▲ Sapa Prcsion Tubing Adrian Inc........E....... 321 636-8147
Rockledge *(G-15446)*
▲ Sinobec Resources LLC.....................G....... 561 409-2205
Deerfield Beach *(G-2912)*
▲ Snappy Structures Inc.......................F....... 954 926-6611
Hollywood *(G-5910)*
▼ Style-View Products Inc ....F....... 305 634-9688
Miami *(G-10426)*
Super Lite Aluminum Products ....G....... 407 682-2121
Altamonte Springs *(G-78)*
T and C Sales Inc...................................G....... 321 632-0920
Rockledge *(G-15450)*
Te Olde Foundry Shoppe Inc.................G....... 239 261-3911
Naples *(G-11436)*
▲ Titan Specialty Cnstr Inc ....E....... 850 916-7660
Milton *(G-10943)*
Walt Dittmer and Sons Inc ....E....... 407 699-1755
Winter Springs *(G-19488)*

3355 Aluminum Rolling & Drawing, NEC

▲ Advanced Aluminum of Centl Fla......G....... 321 639-1451
Cocoa *(G-1992)*
▲ Aludisc LLC...E....... 910 299-0911
Boca Raton *(G-416)*
▼ Aluminium Design Products LLC.....G....... 561 894-8775
Delray Beach *(G-3045)*
◆ American Wire Group Inc ....F....... 954 455-3050
Aventura *(G-260)*
Barrows Aluminum Inc...........................F....... 386 767-3445
Port Orange *(G-15011)*
Carmacks Quality Aluminum.................G....... 727 846-0305
Port Richey *(G-15044)*
Custom Fbrications of Freeport ....F....... 850 729-0500
Valparaiso *(G-18509)*
Fabworx LLC..F....... 239 573-9353
Cape Coral *(G-1422)*
Largo Aluminum Inc ....F....... 305 852-2390
Islamorada *(G-6098)*
Poma Corporation..................................D....... 561 790-5799
West Palm Beach *(G-19001)*
Prestige Aluminum Railing Inc..............G....... 904 966-2163
Starke *(G-16896)*
Spectra Metal Sales Inc ....F....... 727 530-5435
Clearwater *(G-1887)*
◆ White Aluminum Fabrication Inc.......E....... 772 219-3245
Stuart *(G-17048)*
▲ Winrise Enterprises LLC ....F....... 786 621-6705
Miramar *(G-11061)*

3356 Rolling, Drawing-Extruding Of Nonferrous Metals

Ashtin Inc..G....... 352 867-1900
Ocala *(G-11880)*
C C Lead Inc ....F....... 863 465-6458
Lake Placid *(G-7486)*
Custom Tin Works LLC ....G....... 352 728-1788
Fruitland Park *(G-4864)*
Dons Custom Service Inc.......................G....... 954 491-4043
Fort Lauderdale *(G-3948)*
Garrett Tin & Brother Inc.......................G....... 727 236-5434
Trinity *(G-18486)*
Gold Buyers of America LLC ....C....... 877 721-8033
Greenacres *(G-5081)*
Heartland Metals Inc..............................E....... 863 465-7501
Lake Placid *(G-7488)*
Larrys Extreme Audio Tint LLC ....G....... 941 766-8468
Port Charlotte *(G-14987)*
Leadex...G....... 305 266-2028
Miami *(G-9877)*
Nickels and Associates LLC ....G....... 863 699-0180
Lake Placid *(G-7491)*
▲ Nuflo Inc...E....... 904 265-4001
Jacksonville *(G-6642)*
Shar Family Enterprises Llc..................G....... 352 365-6988
Leesburg *(G-8171)*
▼ Something In A Tin Inc ....G....... 305 785-6891
Miami *(G-10375)*
Sunrui Ttnium Prcsion Pdts Inc ....F....... 727 953-7101
Clearwater *(G-1895)*
Tin-Rez Corp Inc ....F....... 561 654-3133
Boynton Beach *(G-969)*
Titanium 22 Productions........................G....... 310 962-0937
Miami Beach *(G-10720)*
Titanium Dance Challenge LLC.............G....... 813 340-0903
Tampa *(G-18189)*
Titanium Development LLC ....G....... 407 844-8664
Orlando *(G-13257)*
Titanium Endeavors LLC........................G....... 321 728-9732
Melbourne *(G-8963)*
Titanium Fusion Tech LLC ....G....... 435 881-5742
Orlando *(G-13258)*
Titanium Gymnastics and Cheerl...........G....... 813 659-2204
Plant City *(G-14474)*
Titanium Gynmastics & Cheer...............G....... 813 689-2200
Lithia *(G-8224)*
Titanium Integration LLC ....G....... 561 775-1898
Palm Beach Gardens *(G-13632)*
Titanium Laser Tech Inc.........................G....... 956 279-0638
Niceville *(G-11575)*
Titanium Performance LLC ....G....... 407 712-5770
Winter Park *(G-19453)*
Titanium Prof Hyraulics..........................G....... 917 929-5044
Hallandale *(G-5162)*
Titanium Real Estate LLC.......................G....... 863 808-0445
Lakeland *(G-7822)*
Titanium Tech Corp ....G....... 407 912-9126
Orlando *(G-13259)*

3357 Nonferrous Wire Drawing

Advanced Magnet Lab Inc......................F....... 321 728-7543
Melbourne *(G-8758)*
▼ AGS Enterprises Inc ....G....... 305 716-7660
Doral *(G-3231)*
American Data Supply Inc......................F....... 866 650-3282
Clearwater *(G-1579)*
Amphenol Custom Cable Inc ....C....... 813 623-2232
Tampa *(G-17423)*
Amphenol Custom Cable Inc ....E....... 407 393-3886
Orlando *(G-12476)*
▲ Carlisle Interconnect Tech Inc ....A....... 904 829-5600
Saint Augustine *(G-15526)*
Commski LLC..G....... 813 501-0111
Tampa *(G-17548)*
Conduit Space Rcvery Systems L..........F....... 330 416-0887
Bradenton *(G-1023)*
◆ Dekoron Unitherm LLC ....E....... 800 633-5015
Cape Coral *(G-1411)*
▲ Diversfied Mtl Specialists Inc ....G....... 941 244-0935
North Venice *(G-11757)*
◆ Electro Technik Industries Inc...........D....... 727 530-9555
Clearwater *(G-1666)*
Equity Group Usa Inc ....G....... 407 421-6464
Winter Springs *(G-19472)*
Fibertronics Inc......................................E....... 321 473-8933
Melbourne *(G-8832)*
▲ Ford Wire and Cable Corp.................E....... 772 388-3660
Sebastian *(G-16660)*
Gulf Photonics Inc ....G....... 813 855-6618
Oldsmar *(G-12231)*
Integrated Cable Solutions ....E....... 813 769-5740
Tampa *(G-17787)*
▲ Kai Limited..C....... 954 957-8586
Fort Lauderdale *(G-4083)*

Logus Manufacturing Corp E 561 842-3550
West Palm Beach *(G-18934)*
Managed Data Assoc Inc G 386 449-8419
Palm Coast *(G-13702)*
Marathon Fiber Optics LLC G 305 902-9010
Riverview *(G-15277)*
Molex LLC F 727 521-2700
Pinellas Park *(G-14370)*
Monroe Cable LLC D 941 429-8484
North Port *(G-11744)*
◆ **Newlink Cabling Systems Inc** F 305 477-8063
Medley *(G-8697)*
Oceaneering International Inc C 985 329-3282
Panama City *(G-13933)*
◆ **Phelps Dodge Intl Corp** E 305 648-7888
Doral *(G-3459)*
Sunmaster of Naples Inc E 239 261-3581
Naples *(G-11426)*
Technlogy Integration Svcs LLC G 904 565-4050
Jacksonville *(G-6843)*
▲ **Tensolite LLC** A 904 829-5600
Saint Augustine *(G-15626)*
Times Microwave Systems Inc F 203 949-8400
West Palm Beach *(G-19064)*
Tricab (usa) Inc G 754 210-5490
Hollywood *(G-5927)*
Wireless Latin Entrmt Inc G 305 858-7740
Miami *(G-10614)*
◆ **Wiretec Ignition Inc** F 407 578-4569
Palmetto *(G-13837)*

3363 Aluminum Die Castings

▼ **Big Sun Equine Products Inc** G 352 629-9645
Ocala *(G-11886)*
◆ **Southern Die Casting Corp** E 305 635-6571
Miami *(G-10385)*
Southern Mfg Upholstery Inc F 727 573-1006
Clearwater *(G-1882)*
Strive Development Corporation F 850 689-2124
Crestview *(G-2360)*

3364 Nonferrous Die Castings, Exc Aluminum

Camp Aircraft Inc F 727 397-6076
Saint Petersburg *(G-15734)*
▲ **Fullerton 799 Inc** E 727 572-7040
Clearwater *(G-1696)*
▲ **Motor City Classics Inc** G 954 473-2201
Sunrise *(G-17149)*
◆ **Southern Die Casting Corp** E 305 635-6571
Miami *(G-10385)*
▲ **Target Manufacturing Inc** G 305 633-0361
Miami *(G-10460)*

3365 Aluminum Foundries

▼ **Broward Casting Foundry Inc** E 954 584-6400
Fort Lauderdale *(G-3869)*
Cost Cast Aluminum Corp E 863 422-5617
Haines City *(G-5140)*
Florida Machine & Casting Co G 561 655-3771
Riviera Beach *(G-15330)*
▼ **G & K Aluminum Inc** F 772 283-1297
Stuart *(G-16943)*
Gables Engineering Inc B 305 774-4400
Coral Gables *(G-2147)*
Harberson Rv Pinellas LLC E 727 937-6176
Holiday *(G-5742)*
Heroal USA Inc A 888 437-6257
Orlando *(G-12799)*
HP Preferred Ltd Partners F 407 298-4470
Orlando *(G-12813)*
Kitchen Sink Express LLC G 800 888-6604
Dunedin *(G-3583)*
Luv Enterprises Inc F 352 867-8440
Ocala *(G-11988)*
MSC Metal Fabrication G 954 344-8343
Coral Springs *(G-2292)*
RC Investment Casting G 305 801-9088
Hialeah *(G-5594)*
Rebah Fabrication Inc F 407 857-3232
Orlando *(G-13120)*
Sapa Extrsons St Augustine LLC A 904 794-1500
Saint Augustine *(G-15604)*
Simplimatic Automation G 941 360-6500
Sarasota *(G-16297)*
▲ **Sinobec Resources LLC** G 561 409-2205
Deerfield Beach *(G-2912)*
◆ **Southern Die Casting Corp** E 305 635-6571
Miami *(G-10385)*

St Judas Tadeus Foundry Inc G 305 512-3612
Hialeah *(G-5631)*
Tarvin Mobile Home Service G 727 734-3400
Palm Harbor *(G-13765)*
West Coast Castings Inc F 941 753-2969
Bradenton *(G-1146)*

3366 Copper Foundries

◆ **American Bronze Foundry Inc** F 407 328-8090
Sanford *(G-15992)*
Arte Bronce Monuments Inc G 305 477-0813
Medley *(G-8614)*
Blair Propeller MA G 772 283-1453
Stuart *(G-16917)*
▼ **Bronzart Foundry Inc** F 941 922-9106
Sarasota *(G-16370)*
Brown Dog Propeller LLC G 321 254-7767
Satellite Beach *(G-16649)*
Florida Airboat Propeller G 863 324-1653
Winter Haven *(G-19320)*
Florida Machine & Casting Co G 561 655-3771
Riviera Beach *(G-15330)*
Hawver Aluminum Foundry Inc G 813 961-1497
Tampa *(G-17748)*
Henefelt Precision Products F 727 531-0406
Largo *(G-7969)*
Loren/Wtp G 954 846-9800
Hollywood *(G-5862)*
PM Craftsman E 863 665-0815
Lakeland *(G-7768)*
Robert St Croix Sculpture Stu G 561 835-1753
West Palm Beach *(G-19021)*
S & S Propeller Co Inc G 718 359-3393
Pompano Beach *(G-14838)*
▲ **Turning Point Propellers Inc** G 904 900-7739
Jacksonville *(G-6871)*
▲ **We Bronze Wholesale LLC** G 954 922-8826
Fort Lauderdale *(G-4318)*

3369 Nonferrous Foundries: Castings, NEC

Altis Aju Kingwood LLC G 305 338-5232
Miami *(G-9125)*
Camp Company St Petersburg E 727 397-6076
Saint Petersburg *(G-15735)*
▲ **Chromalloy Castings Tampa Corp** C 561 935-3571
Palm Beach Gardens *(G-13577)*
Collins Mfg Inc D 321 322-0280
Apopka *(G-126)*
Cost Cast Aluminum Corp E 863 422-5617
Haines City *(G-5140)*
◆ **Flotech Inc** D 904 358-1849
Jacksonville *(G-6406)*
Gables Engineering Inc B 305 774-4400
Coral Gables *(G-2147)*
Gypsy Mining Inc G 772 589-5547
Roseland *(G-15459)*
Inspectech Aeroservice Inc F 954 359-6766
Fort Lauderdale *(G-4060)*
J&N Keystone of Florida G 305 528-1677
Medley *(G-8675)*
Kellstrom Aerospace Group Inc E 954 538-2482
Boca Raton *(G-586)*
Nav-X LLC E 954 978-9988
Fort Lauderdale *(G-4134)*
Shell Aerospace LLC G 786 400-2660
Miami *(G-10336)*
◆ **Southern Die Casting Corp** E 305 635-6571
Miami *(G-10385)*
▲ **Tampa Brass and Aluminum Corp** C 813 885-6064
Tampa *(G-18162)*
Xl Carts Inc G 904 277-7111
Fernandina Beach *(G-3751)*

3398 Metal Heat Treating

American Metal Processors Inc F 386 754-9367
Lake City *(G-7347)*
Braddck Mtllgl Arsp Ser Inc F 561 622-2200
Boynton Beach *(G-884)*
Braddock Metallurgical Inc F 386 267-0955
Jacksonville *(G-6229)*
Braddock Metallurgical GA Inc F 386 267-0955
Daytona Beach *(G-2632)*
Braddock Metallurgical MGT LLC E 386 267-0955
Daytona Beach *(G-2633)*
▲ **Braddock Mtllrgcal - Dytona In** G 386 267-0955
Daytona Beach *(G-2634)*
Braddock Mtllurgical Holdg Inc G 386 323-1500
Daytona Beach *(G-2635)*
Dynamic Alloy F 352 728-7600
Leesburg *(G-8153)*

Heat Treating Incorporated D 352 245-8811
Belleview *(G-370)*
Metal Improvement Company LLC G 305 592-5960
Miami *(G-9984)*
Nelco Products Inc G 727 533-8282
Clearwater *(G-1806)*
Suncoast Heat Treat Inc F 386 267-0955
Daytona Beach *(G-2721)*
Suncoast Heat Treat Inc F 561 776-7763
Boynton Beach *(G-965)*
Superheat Fgh Services Inc G 519 396-1324
Bartow *(G-334)*
Thermal Braze Inc G 561 746-6640
Jupiter *(G-7127)*
▼ **Whertec Inc** D 904 278-6503
Jacksonville *(G-6917)*

3399 Primary Metal Prdts, NEC

Accurate Metal Finshg Fla Inc F 321 636-4900
Rockledge *(G-15391)*
AP Richter Holding Co LLC G 239 732-9440
Naples *(G-11164)*
Azz Powder Coating - Tampa LLC G 813 390-2802
Tampa *(G-17451)*
B-N-J Powder Coatings LLC G 407 999-8448
Orlando *(G-12503)*
▲ **Carlisle Interconnect Tech Inc** A 904 829-5600
Saint Augustine *(G-15526)*
▼ **Ceramlock Coatings Inc** G 772 781-2141
Palm City *(G-13645)*
CMC Steel Us LLC E 904 266-4261
Jacksonville *(G-6272)*
Fk Irons Inc E 855 354-7667
Doral *(G-3352)*
Klocke of America Inc D 239 561-5800
Fort Myers *(G-4512)*
New York Nails G 904 448-6040
Jacksonville *(G-6631)*
▼ **Ogre Custom Fabrications LLC** G 321 544-2142
Melbourne *(G-8900)*
Poly Coatings of South Inc F 941 371-8555
Sarasota *(G-16546)*
Quest Manufacturing Corp F 305 513-8583
Medley *(G-8713)*
Shashy Enterprises Inc G 352 732-3904
Ocala *(G-12047)*

34 FABRICATED METAL PRODUCTS, EXCEPT MACHINERY AND TRANSPORTATION EQUIPMENT

3411 Metal Cans

Andersons Can Line Fbrction Eq F 407 889-4665
Apopka *(G-113)*
Anheuser-Busch Companies LLC D 407 251-4049
Orlando *(G-12480)*
Egd Euro Gourmet Deli Inc G 305 937-1515
Aventura *(G-267)*
La Perrada Del Gordo Boca LLC F 561 968-6978
West Palm Beach *(G-18923)*
Metal Container Corporation C 904 695-7600
Jacksonville *(G-6596)*
Nardis Enterprises LLC G 954 529-0691
Fort Lauderdale *(G-4130)*
Outstanding Events Inc F 772 463-5406
Palm City *(G-13668)*
S&J Aluminum Works Inc G 850 492-5700
Pensacola *(G-14256)*
Wastequip Manufacturing Co LLC E 863 665-6507
Lakeland *(G-7832)*
Weplenish LLC G 954 909-4183
Plantation *(G-14567)*

3412 Metal Barrels, Drums, Kegs & Pails

Extreme Coatings G 727 528-7998
Saint Petersburg *(G-15775)*
Migrandy Corp E 321 459-0044
Merritt Island *(G-9004)*
▲ **Standard Kegs LLC** F 305 454-9721
Medley *(G-8729)*
Stemler Corporation E 727 577-1216
Saint Petersburg *(G-15927)*

3421 Cutlery

Albertos On Fifth G 239 430-1060
Naples *(G-11153)*

Amami United Flavours of World ....G....... 305 397-8577
Miami Beach *(G-10639)*
▲ **American Household Inc** ....D....... 561 912-4100
Boca Raton *(G-422)*
▲ **Andritz Iggesund Tools Inc** ....E....... 813 855-6902
Oldsmar *(G-12202)*
Be Merry..G....... 772 324-8289
Stuart *(G-16913)*
Dobros Inc..G....... 386 279-0003
Deland *(G-2972)*
El Rinkon..G....... 786 332-3125
Miami *(G-9506)*
Fresh..G....... 561 330-4345
Delray Beach *(G-3080)*
Fresh Choice MA Rket.........................G....... 407 448-8956
Orlando *(G-12763)*
Gator Shack..G....... 863 381-2222
Sebring *(G-16692)*
Grecian & Company Inc ....G....... 386 344-1967
Lake City *(G-7359)*
Hammocks Plaza..................................G....... 305 380-0961
Miami *(G-9685)*
Jean La Frite..G....... 305 397-8747
Miami Beach *(G-10685)*
La Parada Criolla Inc ....G....... 321 207-7100
Longwood *(G-8304)*
Miguel Casa Corp..................................G....... 305 887-0098
Hialeah *(G-5516)*
Moyo..G....... 352 208-2770
Ocala *(G-12002)*
▲ **Novelty Crystal Corp** ....D....... 352 429-9036
Groveland *(G-5103)*
Old City Sweepstakes...........................G....... 904 808-0456
Saint Augustine *(G-15581)*
Pattys On Main LLC..............................G....... 941 650-9080
Sarasota *(G-16538)*
Pizzaros..G....... 239 390-0349
Bonita Springs *(G-847)*
Price King 2 LLC..................................G....... 786 337-8801
Hialeah *(G-5567)*
Robs Bageland Inc................................G....... 954 640-5470
Plantation *(G-14544)*
Sarasota-Manatee Originals Inc ....G....... 941 365-2800
Sarasota *(G-16582)*
Silly Grape Inc......................................G....... 407 790-7999
Maitland *(G-8478)*
Slyce Inc..G....... 727 408-5272
Indian Rocks Beach *(G-6069)*
▲ **Southern Supply and Mfg Co**...........E....... 727 323-7099
Saint Petersburg *(G-15919)*
Sunbeam Americas Holdings LLC ....C....... 561 912-4100
Boca Raton *(G-736)*
Taste of Thai LLC..................................G....... 850 581-3340
Gulf Breeze *(G-5129)*
Willies Wild..G....... 850 597-8116
Tallahassee *(G-17346)*
Yolo Las Olas LLC..................................F....... 954 522-3002
Fort Lauderdale *(G-4332)*

3423 Hand & Edge Tools

ABC Hammers.......................................G....... 708 343-9900
Sarasota *(G-16170)*
◆ **Ames Companies Inc** ....B....... 717 737-1500
Orlando *(G-12475)*
▲ **Andritz Iggesund Tools Inc** ....E....... 813 855-6902
Oldsmar *(G-12202)*
Applied Fiber Concepts Inc ....G....... 754 581-2744
Hialeah *(G-5302)*
Arca LLC..F....... 305 470-1430
Miami *(G-9162)*
Automated Production Eqp Ape...........F....... 631 654-1197
Key Largo *(G-7164)*
◆ **B & A Manufacturing Co** ....E....... 561 848-8648
Riviera Beach *(G-15300)*
Benchmark of Palm Beach....................G....... 706 258-3553
Palm Beach *(G-13549)*
▲ **Cob Industries Inc**..............................G....... 321 723-3200
West Melbourne *(G-18770)*
Conrado Salas Jr LLC ....G....... 941 587-5919
Sarasota *(G-16393)*
▲ **Daniels Manufacturing Corp** ....C....... 407 855-6161
Orlando *(G-12646)*
Daves All Around ....G....... 407 325-6693
Oviedo *(G-13426)*
▲ **Es Manufacturing Inc**..........................F....... 727 323-4040
Pinellas Park *(G-14347)*
▲ **Exit Ten Inc**..G....... 407 574-2433
Longwood *(G-8277)*
Florida Knife Co......................................E....... 941 371-2104
Sarasota *(G-16437)*

Frank Bennardello ....G....... 561 470-4838
Boca Raton *(G-539)*
George Birney Jr....................................G....... 407 851-5604
Orlando *(G-12783)*
Grip Tooling Technologies LLC...........G....... 813 654-6832
Brandon *(G-1161)*
Halex Corporation..................................G....... 239 216-4444
Naples *(G-11275)*
Imperial Photoengraving.......................G....... 772 924-1731
Stuart *(G-16957)*
Infinite Lasers LLC.................................G....... 850 424-3759
Destin *(G-3195)*
Iron Bridge Tools Inc..............................G....... 954 596-1090
Fort Lauderdale *(G-4066)*
James Reese Enterprises Inc ....F....... 727 386-5311
Clearwater *(G-1741)*
Just Door Toolz LLC...............................G....... 954 448-6872
Port Saint Lucie *(G-15116)*
La Perlelle LLC.......................................G....... 941 388-2458
Sarasota *(G-16486)*
Mayhew/Bestway LLC ....E....... 631 586-4702
Ormond Beach *(G-13385)*
◆ **Merit International Entps Inc** ....E....... 305 635-1011
Miami *(G-9980)*
Micro Jig Inc..G....... 855 747-7233
Winter Park *(G-19425)*
◆ **Nasco Industries Inc** ....E....... 954 733-8665
Fort Lauderdale *(G-4131)*
Nessmith Dye Cutting & Finshg ....G....... 904 353-6317
Jacksonville *(G-6625)*
▲ **Pettit Tools & Supplies Inc**................F....... 954 781-2640
Pompano Beach *(G-14790)*
Quality Carpet ....G....... 727 527-1359
Saint Petersburg *(G-15895)*
▲ **Round Table Tools Inc**.......................G....... 850 877-7650
Tallahassee *(G-17318)*
◆ **Skyo Industries Inc** ....E....... 631 586-4702
Ormond Beach *(G-13399)*
◆ **Steritool Inc**..F....... 904 388-3672
Jacksonville *(G-6813)*
Sykleb Inc ....G....... 305 303-9391
North Miami *(G-11657)*
Thida Thai Jewelry.................................G....... 561 455-4249
Miami *(G-10473)*
Thomas A Glassman LLC......................G....... 239 822-2219
Naples *(G-11439)*
▲ **Volpino Corp**......................................F....... 904 264-8808
Orange Park *(G-12413)*
Vs Coatings LLC....................................F....... 305 677-6224
Miami *(G-10592)*

3425 Hand Saws & Saw Blades

Blades Direct LLC..................................F....... 855 225-2337
Coral Springs *(G-2227)*
Diamond Blades 4us..............................G....... 800 659-5843
Deerfield Beach *(G-2814)*
Elliott Diamond Tool Inc.......................F....... 727 585-3839
Clearwater *(G-1669)*
▲ **Global Diversified Products**..............E....... 727 209-0854
Pinellas Park *(G-14351)*
Microtool and Instrument Inc...............E....... 786 242-8780
Palmetto Bay *(G-13851)*
▲ **Round Table Tools Inc**.......................G....... 850 877-7650
Tallahassee *(G-17318)*
▲ **RSC Industries Inc**..............................F....... 813 886-4711
Tampa *(G-18071)*

3429 Hardware, NEC

A Extend Life Inc....................................G....... 941 505-7766
Punta Gorda *(G-15188)*
▲ **Accon Marine Inc** ....F....... 727 572-9202
Clearwater *(G-1562)*
Acryplex Inc..G....... 305 633-7636
Miami *(G-9066)*
Advance Panel Corp...............................G....... 347 399-6732
Miami Lakes *(G-10759)*
Aerospace Retail Inc.............................F....... 888 918-8116
Boca Raton *(G-405)*
Alpine Engineered Products..................E....... 954 781-3333
Pompano Beach *(G-14589)*
Altum Aerospace ....F....... 954 618-6573
Sunrise *(G-17089)*
▲ **AME Triton LLC**...................................E....... 352 799-1111
Brooksville *(G-1209)*
▼ **American Marine Coverings Inc** ....F....... 305 889-5355
Hialeah *(G-5292)*
Assa Abloy Hospitality Inc....................G....... 954 920-0772
Fort Lauderdale *(G-3827)*
Automation Consulting Inc....................F....... 850 477-6477
Pensacola *(G-14095)*

Aviation Intl Solutions LLC ....G....... 305 267-7117
Hialeah *(G-5313)*
Aviation Parts & Trade Corp ....G....... 954 944-2828
Plantation *(G-14495)*
Barr Systems LLC..................................E....... 352 491-3100
Gainesville *(G-4883)*
▼ **Batech Inc**..E....... 321 784-4838
Cape Canaveral *(G-1351)*
▼ **Beachcomber Fibrgls Tech Inc**.........G....... 772 283-0200
Stuart *(G-16914)*
Bikekeeper LLC.......................................G....... 561 209-6863
Lake Worth *(G-7536)*
Biosculptor Corporation ....G....... 305 823-8300
Hialeah *(G-5326)*
▼ **Birdsall Marine Design Inc**...............E....... 561 832-7879
West Palm Beach *(G-18822)*
▲ **Bms International Inc** ....E....... 813 247-7040
Tampa *(G-17477)*
Brandon Lock & Safe Inc ....G....... 813 655-4200
Tampa *(G-17485)*
◆ **Brown (usa) Inc** ....F....... 305 593-9228
Miami *(G-9280)*
◆ **Byrd Technologies Inc**........................E....... 954 957-8333
Pompano Beach *(G-14627)*
C & S Plastics..E....... 863 294-5628
Winter Haven *(G-19309)*
Consolidated Ace Hdwr Sup Inc...........G....... 850 939-9800
Navarre *(G-11465)*
▲ **CT Hydraulics Inc**..............................F....... 724 342-3089
Sanibel *(G-16145)*
◆ **Custom Marble Works Inc** ....E....... 813 620-0475
Tampa *(G-17580)*
D I R Inc..G....... 863 661-5360
Lakeland *(G-7669)*
Dayton Superior Corporation ....G....... 407 859-4541
Orlando *(G-12657)*
Divine Dovetail ....G....... 561 245-7601
Boca Raton *(G-504)*
Dolphin Boat Lifts Inc............................G....... 239 936-1782
Fort Myers *(G-4435)*
Doorknob Discount Center LLC ....G....... 813 963-3104
Lutz *(G-8380)*
Dse Inc ....E....... 813 443-4809
Tampa *(G-17617)*
▲ **E-Z Fastening Solutions Inc**.............G....... 813 854-3937
Oldsmar *(G-12223)*
Ecs America LLC ....G....... 305 629-9599
Miami *(G-9501)*
Ellis Trap and Cage Mfg Inc..................G....... 850 969-1302
Pensacola *(G-14140)*
Filmfastener LLC....................................G....... 813 926-8721
Clearwater *(G-1681)*
▲ **Florida Pool Products Inc** ....E....... 727 531-8913
Clearwater *(G-1690)*
▲ **G G Schmitt & Sons Inc**.....................C....... 717 394-3701
Sarasota *(G-16216)*
Gaab Locks LLC.....................................G....... 305 788-8515
Fort Lauderdale *(G-4018)*
◆ **Galley Maid Marine Pdts Inc**..............F....... 863 467-6070
Okeechobee *(G-12178)*
Garelick Mfg Co.....................................D....... 727 545-4571
Largo *(G-7956)*
Gator Door East Inc ....E....... 904 824-2827
Saint Augustine *(G-15545)*
General Clamp Industries Inc ....F....... 407 859-6000
Orlando *(G-12777)*
◆ **General Hydraulic Solutions** ....G....... 727 561-0719
Clearwater *(G-1702)*
Goodrich Corporation ....C....... 904 757-3660
Jacksonville *(G-6441)*
▼ **Grate Ideas of America LLC**..............G....... 844 292-6044
Fort Lauderdale *(G-4027)*
H B Sherman Traps Inc..........................G....... 850 575-8727
Tallahassee *(G-17272)*
▼ **Halliday Products Inc** ....D....... 407 298-4470
Orlando *(G-12794)*
◆ **Hardware Concepts Inc** ....G....... 305 685-1337
Miami *(G-9687)*
Hardware Online Store ....F....... 954 565-5678
Fort Lauderdale *(G-4042)*
Hc Grupo Inc ....G....... 954 227-0150
Coral Springs *(G-2252)*
◆ **Headhunter Inc**.....................................E....... 954 462-5953
Fort Lauderdale *(G-4044)*
Inland Specialties Inc ....G....... 941 756-1234
Sarasota *(G-16237)*
Inter Gard R&D LLC...............................F....... 954 476-5574
Sunrise *(G-17129)*
◆ **International Dock Products** ....F....... 954 964-5315
Hallandale Beach *(G-5191)*

SIC

Employee Codes: A=Over 500 employees, B=251-500
C=101-250, D=51-100, E=20-50, F=10-19, G=4-9

Ipline LLC...F... 305 675-4235
Miami (G-9767)
◆ **James D Nall Co Inc**...E... 305 884-8363
Fort Lauderdale (G-4074)
Jco Metals Inc...F... 386 734-5867
Deland (G-2987)
Jefco Manufacturing Inc...E... 954 527-4220
Fort Lauderdale (G-4078)
Latham Marine Inc...E... 954 462-3055
Fort Lauderdale (G-4096)
▲ **Lenco Marine Solutions LLC**...E... 772 288-2662
Stuart (G-16970)
Longbow Marine Inc...G... 954 616-5737
Fort Lauderdale (G-4102)
Loos & Co Inc...D... 239 643-5667
Naples (G-11316)
M&C Hardware LLC...G... 305 971-9444
Miami (G-9928)
▼ **Marine Manufacturing Inc**...G... 305 885-3493
Hialeah (G-5503)
Marko Garage Doors & Gates Inc...G... 561 547-4001
Palm Springs (G-13776)
▲ **Mermaid Mfg Southwest Fla Inc**...F... 239 418-0535
Fort Myers (G-4528)
Mica Craft & Design Inc...F... 561 863-5354
West Palm Beach (G-18950)
Mirage Systems Inc...F... 386 740-9222
Deland (G-2997)
Mobile Rugged Tech Corp...G... 781 771-6743
Winter Park (G-19427)
◆ **Ocean Dynamics USA Inc**...G... 305 770-1800
Miami (G-10088)
Orbe Inc...G... 954 534-2264
Oakland Park (G-11827)
Patrick Industries Inc...C... 941 556-6311
Sarasota (G-16273)
Patrick Industries Inc...D... 239 283-0800
Cape Coral (G-1454)
Pcs Aerospace & Marketing LLC...E... 973 352-9159
Cutler Bay (G-2407)
Phg Kendall LLC...F... 954 392-8788
Hollywood (G-5891)
Pipewelders Marine Inc...D... 954 587-8400
Fort Lauderdale (G-4169)
Pompanette LLC...E... 813 885-2182
Tampa (G-17997)
▲ **Practical Design Products Co**...E... 561 995-4023
Boca Raton (G-671)
Precise Technologies Inc...F... 727 535-5594
Largo (G-8030)
Precision Shapes Inc...E... 321 269-2555
Titusville (G-18453)
Press-Rite Inc...G... 954 963-7373
Miramar (G-11030)
Proven Industries Inc...F... 813 895-4385
Palmetto (G-13819)
R J Marine Group Inc...G... 772 232-6590
Stuart (G-16995)
Rampmaster Inc...F... 305 691-9090
Miami (G-10238)
Rokey Corporation...G... 561 470-0164
Boca Raton (G-693)
▼ **Rupp Marine Inc**...F... 772 286-5300
Stuart (G-17004)
Safety Clamps Inc...F... 904 781-2809
Jacksonville (G-6749)
Savvy Associate Inc...F... 954 941-6986
Pompano Beach (G-14840)
SBs Precision Shtmtl Inc...E... 321 951-7411
Melbourne (G-8927)
Shorr Enterprises Inc...F... 954 733-9840
Lauderdale Lakes (G-8093)
▲ **Southcoast Marine Products Inc**...C... 727 573-4821
Clearwater (G-1881)
◆ **Southern Die Casting Corp**...E... 305 635-6571
Miami (G-10385)
▼ **Stainless Fabricators Inc**...E... 813 926-7113
Odessa (G-12155)
◆ **Stainless Marine Inc**...E... 305 681-7893
Opa Locka (G-12361)
◆ **Strategic Brands Inc**...F... 516 745-6100
Pompano Beach (G-14875)
Stuart Industries Inc...F... 305 651-3474
Miami (G-10425)
Super Screening Incorporated...G... 239 931-3224
Fort Myers (G-4619)
▼ **T & R Marine Corp**...G... 850 584-4261
Perry (G-14315)
▲ **Taylor Made Systems Brdnton In**...C... 941 747-1900
Oviedo (G-13461)

Td Tra -Dix Supply Inc...G... 727 869-8662
Hudson (G-6039)
◆ **Tides Marine Inc**...E... 954 420-0949
Deerfield Beach (G-2926)
U S Hardware Supply Inc...E... 407 657-1551
Winter Park (G-19454)
Uninsred Untd Prchute Tech LLC...D... 386 736-7589
Deland (G-3027)
▲ **Venture Circle Enterprises LLC**...F... 407 678-7489
Sanford (G-16131)
▲ **Ver-Val Enterprises Inc**...F... 850 244-7931
Fort Walton Beach (G-4838)
Vitsur Industries Inc...G... 561 744-1290
Jupiter (G-7141)
W D Wilson Inc...E... 813 626-6989
Tampa (G-18250)
Warfighter Fcsed Logistics Inc...F... 740 513-4692
Fort Lauderdale (G-4313)
▲ **Weehoo Inc**...G... 720 477-3700
Tarpon Springs (G-18330)
Window Craftsmen Inc...E... 941 922-1844
Sarasota (G-16641)
Woodies Inc...G... 305 266-9209
Miami (G-10618)

3431 Enameled Iron & Metal Sanitary Ware

AAA Event Services LLC...F... 386 454-0929
Newberry (G-11549)
Arya Group LLC...G... 561 792-9992
Wellington (G-18709)
▲ **Atlantis Porcelain Art Corp**...G... 305 582-8663
Miami (G-9185)
▼ **Bathroom World Manufacturing**...G... 954 566-0451
Oakland Park (G-11785)
▲ **Deco Lav Inc**...F... 561 274-2110
Boca Raton (G-496)
East Coast Fixtures & Mllwk Co...G... 904 733-9711
Jacksonville (G-6349)
Florida Custom Fabricators...F... 407 892-8538
Saint Cloud (G-15650)
Jambco Millwork Inc...F... 954 977-4998
Margate (G-8551)
▼ **Martell Glass**...G... 786 336-0142
Miami (G-9951)
▲ **Pelican International Inc**...E... 727 388-9895
Clearwater (G-1829)
Sanastar Inc...F... 954 323-2485
Oakland Park (G-11836)
▼ **Shower Doors Unlimited Inc**...F... 561 547-0702
Boynton Beach (G-958)
▼ **Wool Wholesale Plumbing Supply**...D... 954 763-3632
Fort Lauderdale (G-4327)

3432 Plumbing Fixture Fittings & Trim, Brass

AB Fire Sprinklers LLC...G... 954 973-8054
Pompano Beach (G-14572)
Apollo Retail Specialists LLC...B... 813 712-2525
Tampa (G-17428)
Averett Septic Tank Co Inc...E... 863 665-1748
Lakeland (G-7640)
Bobs Backflow & Plumbing Co...G... 904 268-8009
Jacksonville (G-6219)
C Mike Roach Inc...F... 864 882-1101
Hobe Sound (G-5723)
▲ **Coolcraft Inc**...G... 954 946-0070
Pompano Beach (G-14648)
▲ **Dakota Plumbing Products LLC**...F... 954 987-3430
Fort Lauderdale (G-3930)
Ddp Holdings LLC...C... 813 712-2515
Tampa (G-17595)
Designers Plumbing Studio Inc...G... 954 920-5997
Hollywood (G-5810)
Ecolab Inc...F... 800 931-8911
Jupiter (G-7031)
▲ **Enolgas Usa Inc**...G... 754 205-7902
Pompano Beach (G-14681)
Home & Garden Industries Inc...F... 305 634-0681
Miami (G-9716)
Johnston Archtctral Systems In...E... 904 886-9030
Jacksonville (G-6527)
◆ **K-Rain Manufacturing Corp**...D... 561 721-3936
Riviera Beach (G-15338)
M & C Assemblies Inc...A... 800 462-7779
Tarpon Springs (G-18314)
▲ **M F B International Inc**...G... 305 436-6601
Miami (G-9925)
OMalley Manufacturing Inc...G... 727 327-6817
Saint Petersburg (G-15872)
Plumb Rite of Central Florida...G... 407 292-0750
Apopka (G-172)

Star Sight Innovations...G... 307 786-2911
Crescent City (G-2343)
▲ **Target Manufacturing Inc**...G... 305 633-0361
Miami (G-10460)
True Plumbing Svc Inc...G... 941 296-5123
Bradenton (G-1134)
▲ **Ultraclenz LLC**...F... 800 931-8911
Jupiter (G-7136)
▼ **Wool Wholesale Plumbing Supply**...D... 954 763-3632
Fort Lauderdale (G-4327)

3433 Heating Eqpt

Alfa Laval Inc...G... 941 727-1900
Sarasota (G-16173)
▲ **Ameritech Energy Corporation**...F... 386 589-7501
Daytona Beach (G-2625)
Coast To Coast Solar Inc...F... 813 406-6501
Lutz (G-8376)
Duststop Filters Inc...G... 904 725-1001
Jacksonville (G-6338)
Eco Solar Technology...G... 904 219-0807
Jacksonville (G-6352)
Florida Solar Energy LLC...G... 561 206-2324
Boca Raton (G-533)
Gain Solar LLC...G... 305 933-1060
Aventura (G-270)
Gulf Associates Control Inc...E... 954 426-0536
Deerfield Beach (G-2833)
Innovative Heat Concepts LLC...G... 305 248-4971
Homestead (G-5971)
▲ **Intertech Worldwide Corp**...G... 561 395-5441
Boca Raton (G-571)
Jer-Air Manufacturing Inc...E... 352 591-2674
Micanopy (G-10902)
◆ **Leslie Controls Inc**...C... 813 978-1000
Temple Terrace (G-18371)
▲ **Micron Fiber - Tech Inc**...F... 386 668-7895
Debary (G-2752)
Parts Central Inc...F... 850 547-1660
Bonifay (G-806)
R & J Mfg of Gainesville...G... 352 375-3130
Gainesville (G-4987)
Shilpico Inc...G... 561 306-5625
Boca Raton (G-708)
Snapspeed LLC...G... 321 441-3797
Indian Harbour Beach (G-6067)
Solar Energy Specialist Corp...G... 863 514-9532
Winter Haven (G-19356)
Southland Power & Enrgy Co LLC...G... 800 217-6040
Fort Lauderdale (G-4251)
◆ **Sunset Power Inc**...F... 866 485-2757
Jacksonville (G-6824)
▼ **Thermal Conversion Tech Inc**...E... 904 358-3720
Jacksonville (G-6848)
▼ **United States Green Enrgy Corp**...E... 540 295-4843
Pensacola (G-14279)

3441 Fabricated Structural Steel

▲ **3 D F X Inc**...F... 407 237-6249
Orlando (G-12416)
3lmetals Inc...G... 305 497-4038
Miami (G-9026)
A & K Machine & Fab Shop Inc...F... 904 388-7772
Jacksonville (G-6107)
A&L Hall Investments Inc...E... 904 781-5080
Bryceville (G-1296)
A/C Cages...G... 407 446-9259
Deltona (G-3162)
AAA Steel Fabricators Inc...G... 954 570-7211
Deerfield Beach (G-2761)
Aat Omega LLC...E... 352 473-6673
Keystone Heights (G-7205)
Ace Fabricators Inc...F... 904 355-3724
Jacksonville (G-6117)
▼ **Adelman Steel Corp**...F... 305 691-7740
Miami (G-9068)
Advanced Manufacturing & Engrg...G... 352 629-1494
Ocala (G-11864)
AGIsupreme Llc...E... 818 232-6699
Hollywood (G-5765)
Air Duct Systems Inc...F... 407 839-3313
Orlando (G-12443)
Ajl Fabrication Llc...F... 407 654-1950
Kissimmee (G-7218)
Al-Mar Metals Inc...G... 386 734-3377
De Leon Springs (G-2735)
Alchemist Holdings LLC...F... 772 340-7774
Port Saint Lucie (G-15085)
Alchemist Holdings LLC...E... 772 343-1111
Port Saint Lucie (G-15086)

Alico Metal Fabricators LLC ....G....... 239 454-4766
Fort Myers *(G-4349)*
Allensteel Inc....G....... 239 454-1331
Fort Myers *(G-4351)*
Allied Steel Structures Inc ....F 877 997-8335
Fort Lauderdale *(G-3806)*
Allied-360 LLC....E....... 954 590-4940
Fort Lauderdale *(G-3807)*
Allpro Fbricators Erectors Inc ....G....... 954 797-7300
Davie *(G-2492)*
Alse Industries LLC ....F 305 688-8778
Miami Gardens *(G-10734)*
▼ **Aluma Tower Company Inc** ....E....... 772 567-3423
Vero Beach *(G-18592)*
Aluma Tower Company Inc....F 772 567-3423
Vero Beach *(G-18593)*
Aluminum Designs LLC ....G....... 239 289-3388
Naples *(G-11157)*
Ameribuilt Stl Structures LLC....G....... 407 340-9401
Oviedo *(G-13411)*
American Archtctral Mtls GL LL ....G....... 305 688-8778
Hialeah *(G-5288)*
American Metal Fab of Ctrl Fl ....G....... 813 653-2788
Brandon *(G-1150)*
American Wtrjet Fbrcation Svcs....G....... 407 826-0497
Orlando *(G-12474)*
Aminsa Corp....G....... 954 865-1289
Weston *(G-19104)*
Anthony Spagna Svc & Maint Inc....G....... 352 796-2109
Brooksville *(G-1212)*
Aog Detailing Services Inc....G....... 727 742-7321
Saint Petersburg *(G-15703)*
Apex Fabrication Inc....F 904 259-4666
Macclenny *(G-8441)*
Apex Metal Fabrication Inc ....F 386 328-2564
Palatka *(G-13473)*
ARC Transition LLC....G....... 386 626-0001
Daytona Beach *(G-2628)*
ARC-Rite Inc....E....... 386 325-3523
Jacksonville *(G-6165)*
Arcosa Trffic Ltg Strctres LLC....E....... 352 748-4258
Sumterville *(G-17067)*
▲ **Artec Metal Fabrication Inc** ....G....... 305 888-4375
Hialeah *(G-5306)*
Artemis Holdings LLC ....C 904 284-5611
Green Cove Springs *(G-5053)*
Artful Canvas Design Inc ....E....... 727 521-0212
Saint Petersburg *(G-15713)*
Artistic Gate Railing....G....... 954 348-9752
Oakland Park *(G-11781)*
Atlantic Central Entps Inc ....F 386 255-6227
Daytona Beach *(G-2630)*
Atlantic Steel Inc....E....... 407 599-3822
Longwood *(G-8258)*
Automated Metal Products Inc ....G....... 863 638-4404
Lake Wales *(G-7500)*
▼ **B & K Installations Inc**....E....... 305 245-6968
Homestead *(G-5956)*
Baker Metalworks and Sup Inc ....F 850 537-2010
Baker *(G-301)*
Banker Steel South LLC....F 407 293-0120
Orlando *(G-12505)*
▼ **Barrett Custom Designs LLC** ....G....... 321 242-2002
Melbourne *(G-8776)*
▲ **Bausch American Towers LLC** ....F 772 283-2771
Stuart *(G-16911)*
Bell Steel Company ....D....... 850 432-1545
Pensacola *(G-14097)*
Bell Steel Company ....F 850 479-2980
Pensacola *(G-14098)*
▼ **Best Fabrications Inc**....F....... 863 519-6611
Bartow *(G-310)*
▼ **Best Industries**....F 772 460-8310
Fort Pierce *(G-4681)*
Big Bend Rebar Inc....F 850 875-8000
Quincy *(G-15246)*
Big Iron Intl Inc....G....... 407 222-2573
Orlando *(G-12514)*
Blue Marlin Towers Inc....G....... 954 530-9140
Fort Lauderdale *(G-3858)*
Bostic Steel Inc ....D....... 305 592-7276
Doral *(G-3282)*
Brantley Machine & Fabrication ....F 904 359-0554
Jacksonville *(G-6232)*
▲ **Breton USA Customers Svc Corp** ....F 941 360-2700
Sarasota *(G-16369)*
Burch Welding & Fabrication....G....... 904 353-6513
Jacksonville *(G-6245)*
Calloway Barge Lines Inc....G....... 904 284-0503
Green Cove Springs *(G-5056)*
Canam Steel Corporation....G....... 386 252-3730
Daytona Beach *(G-2638)*
Canam Steel Corporation....G....... 407 295-3864
Orlando *(G-12545)*
Canam Steel Corporation....G....... 904 781-0898
Jacksonville *(G-6251)*
Capital Steel Inc ....F 352 628-1700
Homosassa *(G-6001)*
Capitol Rental Bldg Eqp Inc....F 305 633-5008
Miami *(G-9309)*
Cato Steel Co....F 407 671-3333
Winter Park *(G-19391)*
Cemex Materials LLC....D....... 941 722-4578
Palmetto *(G-13790)*
Central Fla Stl Bldg & Sup LLC ....G....... 352 266-6795
Ocala *(G-11899)*
Central Metal Fabricators Inc....E 305 261-6262
Miami *(G-9339)*
Central Steel Fabricators LLC ....G....... 904 503-1660
Jacksonville *(G-6259)*
Chism Manufacturing Svcs LLC....F 941 896-9671
Sarasota *(G-16190)*
Clarkwestern Dietrich Building....D....... 800 693-3018
Ocala *(G-11904)*
Clarkwstern Dtrich Bldg System ....E 954 772-6300
Fort Lauderdale *(G-3902)*
Classic Metal Fabrication Inc....G....... 561 305-9532
Boca Raton *(G-482)*
Coastal Acquisitions Fla LLC ....F 850 769-9423
Panama City *(G-13882)*
Coastal Mfg & Fabrication Inc ....G....... 352 799-8706
Brooksville *(G-1221)*
Coastal Sheet Mtalof S Fla LLC ....E....... 561 718-6044
Lake Worth *(G-7543)*
Complete Metal Solutions Intl....G....... 954 560-0583
Fort Lauderdale *(G-3913)*
Cornerstone Fabrication LLC ....E....... 386 310-1110
Debary *(G-2747)*
Custom Fabrication Inc....E 813 754-7571
Plant City *(G-14421)*
Custom Marine Components Inc....F 904 221-6412
Jacksonville *(G-6303)*
▲ **Custom Metal Specialties Inc** ....E 727 522-3986
Pinellas Park *(G-14341)*
Custom Wldg & Fabrication Inc....E....... 863 967-1000
Auburndale *(G-237)*
D & D MBL Wldg Fabrication Inc ....F 954 791-3385
Fort Lauderdale *(G-3927)*
D & D MBL Wldg Fabrication Inc....D....... 772 489-7900
Fort Pierce *(G-4690)*
D & D Wldg & Fabrication LLC ....F 954 791-3385
Fort Lauderdale *(G-3928)*
D & I Carbide Tool Co Inc....F 727 848-3356
Hudson *(G-6020)*
D W Allen Marine Svcs Inc ....E....... 904 358-1933
Jacksonville *(G-6306)*
Dade Engineering Group LLC....F 305 885-2766
Miami *(G-9429)*
Daytona Welding & Fabrication ....F 386 562-0093
Daytona Beach *(G-2657)*
DEC Sheet Metal Inc ....F 863 669-0707
Lakeland *(G-7672)*
◆ **Deltana Enterprises Inc** ....E....... 305 592-8188
Doral *(G-3327)*
Division 5 Florida Inc....E....... 904 964-4513
Starke *(G-16893)*
Dixie Metal Products Inc ....D....... 352 873-2554
Ocala *(G-11921)*
Dixie-Southern Arkansas LLC ....G....... 479 751-9183
Bradenton *(G-1031)*
DK International Assoc Inc ....E....... 954 828-1256
Fort Lauderdale *(G-3945)*
Domestic Custom Metals Company....G....... 239 643-2422
Naples *(G-11231)*
Dutchy Enterprises LLC....G....... 321 877-0700
Cocoa *(G-2016)*
Dynabilt Technologies Corp ....F 305 919-9800
Hialeah *(G-5381)*
▲ **E-Z Metals Inc**....E....... 239 936-7887
Fort Myers *(G-4438)*
Eagle Metal Products Inc ....G....... 561 964-4192
Lake Worth *(G-7549)*
East Coast Medal....G....... 561 619-6753
Lantana *(G-7870)*
▼ **East Coast Metal Decks Inc** ....E....... 561 433-8259
Lantana *(G-7871)*
Eastern Metal Supply NC Inc ....F 800 432-2204
West Palm Beach *(G-18859)*
Eastern Shipbuilding Group Inc....A....... 850 522-7400
Panama City *(G-13896)*
Ed Steel Fabricator Inc....G....... 305 926-4904
Hialeah *(G-5389)*
Elro Manufacturing LLC ....F 407 410-6006
Apopka *(G-133)*
Emerald Coast Fabricators ....G....... 850 554-6172
Pensacola *(G-14141)*
Emf Inc....C....... 321 453-3670
Merritt Island *(G-9000)*
▼ **Emjac Industries Inc**....D....... 305 883-2194
Hialeah *(G-5395)*
Entertainment Metals Inc ....E....... 800 817-2683
Fort Myers *(G-4444)*
▼ **Fab Rite Inc**....G....... 561 848-8181
Riviera Beach *(G-15327)*
▲ **Fabco Metal Products LLC**....D....... 386 252-3730
Daytona Beach *(G-2664)*
Fabricated Products Tampa Inc....E....... 813 247-4001
Tampa *(G-17657)*
Fabricating Technologies LLC....G....... 352 473-6673
Keystone Heights *(G-7207)*
Fabsouth LLC....D....... 954 938-5800
Oakland Park *(G-11804)*
First Class Liaisons LLC ....G....... 954 882-8634
Wellington *(G-18717)*
Fis Group Inc....G....... 786 622-3308
Opa Locka *(G-12315)*
Fitzlord Inc....D....... 904 731-2041
Jacksonville *(G-6390)*
FK Instrument Co LLC....D....... 727 472-2003
Clearwater *(G-1683)*
Florida Aluminum and Steel Inc ....F 863 967-4191
Auburndale *(G-241)*
Florida CMC Rebar....G....... 407 518-5101
Jacksonville *(G-6395)*
Florida Custom Fabricators ....F 407 892-8538
Saint Cloud *(G-15650)*
Florida Fabrication Inc ....F 407 212-0105
Apopka *(G-143)*
▲ **Florida Glass of Tampa Bay**....D....... 813 925-1330
Tampa *(G-17677)*
Fox Equipment LLC....E....... 904 531-3150
Green Cove Springs *(G-5061)*
▼ **Fsf Manufacturing Inc**....C....... 407 971-8280
Oviedo *(G-13431)*
G & A Manufacturing Inc ....F 352 473-6882
Keystone Heights *(G-7208)*
G Bauman Fabrications Inc ....G....... 954 914-8037
Pompano Beach *(G-14708)*
Gainesville Wldg & Fabrication ....G....... 352 373-0384
Gainesville *(G-4930)*
Gardner-Watson Decking Inc....E....... 813 891-9849
Oldsmar *(G-12227)*
Gem Industries Inc....E....... 321 302-8985
Cocoa *(G-2027)*
General Saw Company ....F 813 231-3167
Tampa *(G-17708)*
Georges Welding Services Inc ....D....... 305 822-2445
Medley *(G-8658)*
Gerdau Ameristeel US Inc....B 813 752-7550
Plant City *(G-14434)*
Gill Manufacturing Inc ....F....... 863 422-5711
Davenport *(G-2479)*
Greenes Wldg & Fabrication LLC....G....... 904 773-3101
Middleburg *(G-10905)*
Grizzly Products Corp ....F 813 545-3828
Tampa *(G-17730)*
Group Steel Inc ....G....... 786 319-1222
Hialeah *(G-5437)*
Group Steel Inc ....G....... 305 965-0614
Miami *(G-9676)*
Gulf Coast Fabricators Inc ....G....... 850 584-5979
Perry *(G-14301)*
Gunns Welding & Fabricating....G....... 727 393-5238
Saint Petersburg *(G-15801)*
Hall Metal Corp....G....... 772 460-0706
Fort Pierce *(G-4705)*
▲ **Hammer Haag Steel Inc** ....C....... 727 216-6903
Clearwater *(G-1710)*
Harrison Metals Inc....G....... 352 588-2436
San Antonio *(G-15973)*
Heights Tower Systems Inc ....G....... 850 455-1210
Pensacola *(G-14171)*
Henley Metal LLC....F 904 353-4770
Jacksonville *(G-6468)*
Herco Sheet Metal Inc....E....... 850 244-7424
Fort Walton Beach *(G-4808)*
Hernandez Metal Fabricators....G....... 305 970-4145
Miami *(G-9704)*
Highway Systems Incorporated ....F 813 907-7512
Lutz *(G-8389)*

S I C

Hmb Steel Corporation..........F....... 321 636-6511
Rockledge *(G-15418)*

Holbrook Metal Fabrication LLC..........G....... 386 937-5441
Palatka *(G-13483)*

▼ **Hollywood Iron Works Inc**..........F....... 954 962-0556
West Park *(G-19094)*

Imagine That Inc..........F....... 813 728-8324
Tarpon Springs *(G-18309)*

◆ **Imperial Industries Inc**..........F....... 954 917-4114
Pompano Beach *(G-14729)*

Industrial Welding & Maint..........G....... 352 799-3432
Brooksville *(G-1236)*

Innovative Fabricators Fla Inc..........G....... 941 375-8668
Nokomis *(G-11582)*

Inox Stainless Specialist LLC..........F....... 407 764-2456
Pompano Beach *(G-14731)*

Inprodelca Inc..........G....... 865 687-7921
Pembroke Pines *(G-14042)*

Interstate Wldg & Fabrication..........F....... 727 446-1449
Clearwater *(G-1735)*

Inversnes Wlldel Asociados Inc..........E....... 305 591-0931
Doral *(G-3394)*

▼ **Inversnes Wlldel Asociados Inc**..........D....... 305 591-0118
Miami *(G-9764)*

J & J Steel Services Corp..........G....... 305 878-8929
Medley *(G-8673)*

J & J Wldg Stl Fbrction Fla In..........E....... 813 754-0771
Auburndale *(G-246)*

J A Custom..........G....... 561 615-4680
West Palm Beach *(G-18910)*

J2b Industrial LLC..........G....... 904 805-0745
Jacksonville *(G-6506)*

J2b Industrial LLC..........F....... 904 574-8919
Jacksonville *(G-6507)*

Jacksonville Steel Pdts Inc..........G....... 904 268-3364
Jacksonville *(G-6512)*

Jamar Cnstr Fabrication Inc..........G....... 321 400-0333
Sanford *(G-16071)*

Jglc Enterprises LLC..........E....... 772 223-7393
Stuart *(G-16961)*

▲ **Jnc Welding & Fabricating Inc**..........E....... 954 227-9424
Coral Springs *(G-2265)*

Jomar Metal Fabrication Inc..........G....... 407 857-1259
Orlando *(G-12859)*

Juno Ironcraft..........G....... 561 352-0471
Lake Park *(G-7475)*

Just Steel Inc..........F....... 941 755-7811
Sarasota *(G-16242)*

Just-In-Time Mfg Corp..........F....... 321 752-7552
Melbourne *(G-8857)*

K&T Manufacturing Inc..........G....... 407 814-7700
Apopka *(G-152)*

Keene Metal Fabricators Inc..........E....... 813 621-2455
Tampa *(G-17817)*

▼ **Kemco Industries LLC**..........D....... 407 322-1230
Sanford *(G-16077)*

L & D Steel USA Inc..........F....... 727 538-9917
Largo *(G-7996)*

L M Industrial Inc..........G....... 407 240-8911
Orlando *(G-12879)*

Latham Marine Inc..........E....... 954 462-3055
Fort Lauderdale *(G-4096)*

▲ **Lexington Dsign + Fbrction E L**..........F....... 407 578-4720
Orlando *(G-12906)*

Locus Location Systems LLC..........E....... 321 727-3077
Melbourne *(G-8878)*

Manning Company..........G....... 954 523-9355
Fort Lauderdale *(G-4111)*

Mares Services Corp..........F....... 305 752-0093
Miami *(G-9944)*

Marlyn Steel Products Inc..........E....... 813 621-1375
Tampa *(G-17884)*

Martin & Vleminckx Rides LLC..........G....... 407 566-0036
Sarasota *(G-16504)*

▲ **Master Fabricators Inc**..........F....... 786 537-7440
Miami *(G-9954)*

McCarthy Fabrication LLC..........F....... 407 943-4909
Sanford *(G-16085)*

McDs Pro LLC..........G....... 954 302-3054
Davie *(G-2550)*

Meachem Steel Inc..........G....... 352 735-7333
Sorrento *(G-16789)*

Mechanical Dynamics Inc..........E....... 863 292-0709
Winter Haven *(G-19336)*

Merlin Industries Inc..........F....... 954 472-6891
Davie *(G-2552)*

▼ **Met-Con Inc**..........D....... 321 632-4880
Cocoa *(G-2035)*

Metal Magix Inc..........G....... 754 235-9996
Pompano Beach *(G-14759)*

▼ **Metal Supply and Machining Inc**..........F....... 561 276-4941
Delray Beach *(G-3107)*

▼ **Metal Systems Inc**..........G....... 813 752-7088
Plant City *(G-14448)*

Metalcraft Services Tampa Inc..........G....... 813 558-8700
Tampa *(G-17905)*

Metpro Supply Inc..........E....... 863 425-7155
Mulberry *(G-11130)*

Miami Fabricator Inc..........G....... 305 505-1908
Miami *(G-10000)*

Miami Fabricator Inc..........G....... 305 505-1908
Miami *(G-10001)*

Michael Valentines Inc..........F....... 239 332-0855
Fort Myers *(G-4531)*

Mid Florida Steel Corp..........E....... 321 632-8228
Cocoa *(G-2036)*

▲ **Miller-Leaman Inc**..........E....... 386 248-0500
Daytona Beach *(G-2687)*

Misc Metal Fabrication LLC..........F....... 754 264-1026
Deerfield Beach *(G-2874)*

◆ **MO Steel Fbricator Erector Inc**..........G....... 305 945-4855
Miami *(G-10031)*

Moody Construction Svcs Inc..........E....... 941 776-1542
Duette *(G-3562)*

MPH Industries Inc..........F....... 352 372-9533
Gainesville *(G-4966)*

Naples Iron Works Inc..........E....... 239 649-7265
Naples *(G-11336)*

▲ **Nautical Structures Inds Inc**..........D....... 727 541-6664
Largo *(G-8018)*

New Millennium Bldg Systems LLC..........C....... 386 466-1300
Lake City *(G-7369)*

Nextower LLC..........G....... 407 907-7984
Gainesville *(G-4972)*

Orange State Steel Cnstr Inc..........E....... 727 544-3398
Pinellas Park *(G-14374)*

Orlando Metal Fabrication Inc..........F....... 407 850-4313
Orlando *(G-13034)*

Palatka Welding Shop Inc..........E....... 386 328-1507
Palatka *(G-13488)*

▼ **Palm Beach Iron Works Inc**..........E....... 561 683-1816
West Palm Beach *(G-18983)*

Peters Structural Products..........G....... 863 229-5275
Winter Haven *(G-19341)*

Petrotech Services Inc..........D....... 813 248-0743
Tampa *(G-17987)*

▼ **Phoenix Metal Products Inc**..........E....... 772 595-6386
Fort Pierce *(G-4732)*

Piecemakers LLC..........F....... 786 517-1829
Doral *(G-3462)*

Piecemakers LLC..........F....... 786 517-1829
Brandon *(G-1173)*

◆ **Pilot Steel Inc**..........E....... 954 978-3615
Pompano Beach *(G-14794)*

Pipe Welders Inc..........D....... 954 587-8400
Fort Lauderdale *(G-4168)*

Pipewelders Marine Inc..........D....... 954 587-8400
Fort Lauderdale *(G-4169)*

Plant City Powder Coating..........G....... 813 763-6028
Plant City *(G-14459)*

▲ **Ppa Miami Corp**..........G....... 305 436-0460
Miami *(G-10181)*

Precision Metal Fabrications..........G....... 305 691-0616
Hialeah *(G-5564)*

Premier Fabricators LLC..........G....... 772 323-2042
Fort Pierce *(G-4735)*

Pro Fab..........G....... 813 545-2861
Tampa *(G-18017)*

Protek Systems Inc..........G....... 561 395-8155
Delray Beach *(G-3129)*

Quality Fbrction Mch Works Inc..........F....... 386 755-0220
Lake City *(G-7379)*

Quality Industries America Inc..........G....... 386 755-0220
Lake City *(G-7380)*

Quality Metal Fabricators Inc..........E....... 813 831-7320
Tampa *(G-18032)*

Quality Metal Worx..........G....... 863 353-6638
Haines City *(G-5147)*

Quality Steel Fabricators Inc..........F....... 813 247-7110
Tampa *(G-18033)*

Raber Industries Inc..........G....... 239 728-5527
Alva *(G-90)*

Rafab Specialty Fabrication Inc..........F....... 407 422-3750
Orlando *(G-13112)*

RDS Industrial Inc..........F....... 321 631-0121
Cocoa *(G-2045)*

Rebah Fabrication Inc..........F....... 407 857-3232
Orlando *(G-13120)*

Reeds Metal Manufacturing Inc..........E....... 352 498-0100
Cross City *(G-2366)*

Renaissance Man Incorporated..........G....... 850 432-1177
Pensacola *(G-14252)*

Renova Land and Sea LLC..........G....... 786 916-2695
Miramar *(G-11036)*

Republic Industries..........G....... 954 627-6000
Fort Lauderdale *(G-4203)*

Rev-Tech Mfg Solutions LLC..........F....... 727 577-4999
Saint Petersburg *(G-15901)*

Richland Towers Inc..........E....... 813 286-4140
Tampa *(G-18056)*

Rm Brands Inc..........G....... 904 356-0092
Jacksonville *(G-6732)*

Robert Ojeda Metalsmith Inc..........G....... 561 507-5511
Royal Palm Beach *(G-15477)*

Robotic Security Systems Inc..........E....... 850 871-9300
Panama City *(G-13946)*

Roof Hugger Inc..........G....... 813 909-4424
Lutz *(G-8414)*

▼ **Rubin Iron Works LLC**..........E....... 904 356-5635
Jacksonville *(G-6739)*

Ryder Welding Service Inc..........F....... 305 685-6630
Opa Locka *(G-12357)*

S & B Metal Products E Fla Inc..........E....... 386 274-0092
Daytona Beach *(G-2707)*

SBs Precision Shtmtl Inc..........E....... 321 951-7411
Melbourne *(G-8927)*

Sea Cast Curb Adptors Crbs LLC..........F....... 772 466-2400
Fort Pierce *(G-4745)*

Seaside Aluminum llc..........F....... 386 252-4940
Daytona Beach *(G-2710)*

Sembco Stl Erection Met Bldg..........F....... 561 863-0606
Riviera Beach *(G-15377)*

▲ **Shapes Group Ltd Co**..........D....... 321 837-0500
Palm Bay *(G-13534)*

Shaws Fiberglass Inc..........G....... 863 425-9176
Mulberry *(G-11136)*

Sheet Metal Systems Inc..........F....... 727 548-1711
Pinellas Park *(G-14387)*

▲ **Snappy Structures Inc**..........F....... 954 926-6611
Hollywood *(G-5910)*

Southern Aluminum and Stl Inc..........G....... 850 484-4700
Cantonment *(G-1349)*

Southern Custom Iron & Art LLC..........E....... 561 586-8400
Lake Worth Beach *(G-7621)*

Southern Strl Stl Fla Inc..........E....... 727 327-7123
Saint Petersburg *(G-15918)*

Southstern Stnless Fabricators..........F....... 904 354-4381
Jacksonville *(G-6800)*

Southwest Steel Group Inc..........G....... 239 283-8980
Cape Coral *(G-1477)*

Specialty Structures Inc..........F....... 386 668-0474
Debary *(G-2756)*

Spencer Fabrications Inc..........E....... 352 343-0014
Tavares *(G-18354)*

Spring Loaded Inc..........G....... 561 747-8785
Jupiter *(G-7121)*

Star Fabricators..........G....... 904 899-6569
Jacksonville *(G-6809)*

Steel City Inc..........F....... 850 785-9596
Panama City *(G-13952)*

◆ **Steel Components Inc**..........F....... 954 427-6820
Coconut Creek *(G-2097)*

◆ **Steel Fabricators LLC**..........C....... 954 772-0440
Oakland Park *(G-11843)*

Steel Monkey Dream Shop LLC..........G....... 786 356-1077
Miami *(G-10411)*

Steel Products Inc..........G....... 941 351-8128
Sarasota *(G-16604)*

Sterling Steel Fabrications..........E....... 561 366-8600
Mangonia Park *(G-8512)*

Sterling Stl Cstm Alum Fbrcton..........F....... 561 386-7166
Riviera Beach *(G-15380)*

Storage Building Company LLC..........F....... 863 738-1319
Palmetto *(G-13825)*

Structural Steel of Brevard..........G....... 321 726-0271
Melbourne *(G-8948)*

Stuart Yacht Builders..........F....... 561 747-1947
Stuart *(G-17029)*

Sunbelt Metals & Mfg Inc..........E....... 407 889-8960
Apopka *(G-189)*

Superior Swim Systems Inc..........G....... 239 566-2060
Naples *(G-11428)*

T L Sheet Metal Inc..........G....... 813 871-3780
Tampa *(G-18152)*

Tampa Amalgamated Steel Corp..........F....... 813 621-0550
Tampa *(G-18155)*

Tampa Amalgamated Steel Corp..........G....... 813 621-0550
Tampa *(G-18156)*

Tampa Marine Fabricators LLC..........G....... 813 664-1700
Tampa *(G-18165)*

Tampa Steel Erecting Company ....D....... 813 677-7184
Tampa *(G-18174)*
Tampa Tank & Welding Inc ....F....... 813 241-0123
Gibsonton *(G-5033)*
Teknifab Industries Inc ....G....... 321 722-1922
Melbourne *(G-8958)*
Tidal Wave Tanks Fabrications ....G....... 863 425-7795
Mulberry *(G-11139)*
Trinity Fabricators Inc ....E....... 904 284-9657
Green Cove Springs *(G-5073)*
Tryana LLC ....G....... 813 467-9916
Tampa *(G-18206)*
◆ **TTI Holdings Inc** ....G....... 813 623-2675
Tampa *(G-18208)*
▼ **Tuckers Machine & Stl Svc Inc** ....D....... 352 787-3157
Leesburg *(G-8179)*
United Fabrication & Maint ....G....... 863 295-9000
Eloise *(G-3656)*
United Granite Inc ....F....... 813 391-4323
Tampa *(G-18221)*
▼ **United States Fndry & Mfg Corp** ....C....... 305 885-0301
Medley *(G-8748)*
United States Fndry & Mfg Corp ....F....... 305 556-1661
Hialeah *(G-5661)*
Universal Erectors Inc ....G....... 813 621-8111
Lithia *(G-8225)*
Universal Welding Service Co ....G....... 305 898-9130
Miami Lakes *(G-10874)*
Unlimited Welding Inc ....E....... 407 327-3333
Winter Springs *(G-19487)*
US Custom Fabrication Inc ....G....... 954 917-6161
Pompano Beach *(G-14905)*
US Metal Fabricators Inc ....F....... 954 921-0800
Dania Beach *(G-2474)*
▼ **USF Fabrication Inc** ....C....... 305 556-1661
Hialeah *(G-5669)*
▼ **Van Linda Iron Works Inc** ....E....... 561 586-8400
Lake Worth Beach *(G-7622)*
Veatic ....G....... 888 474-2999
Kissimmee *(G-7309)*
Viper Communication Systems ....E....... 352 694-7030
Ocala *(G-12072)*
Vision Conveyor Inc ....F....... 352 343-3300
Tavares *(G-18359)*
Vulcan Steel ....G....... 561 945-1259
Jupiter *(G-7142)*
W D Wilson Inc ....E....... 813 626-6989
Tampa *(G-18250)*
Welding and Fabrication Inc ....G....... 973 508-7267
Hallandale Beach *(G-5224)*
West Point Industries Inc ....G....... 561 848-8381
Lake Park *(G-7481)*
Western Fabricating LLC ....G....... 239 676-5382
Fort Myers *(G-4654)*
Wheeler Consolidated Inc ....F....... 772 464-4400
Fort Pierce *(G-4770)*
Wilcox Steel Company LLC ....G....... 727 443-0461
Clearwater *(G-1939)*
Wilkinson Steel Supply LLC ....G....... 904 757-1522
Jacksonville *(G-6920)*

3442 Metal Doors, Sash, Frames, Molding & Trim

5 Day Plantation Shutters ....G....... 727 474-6130
Largo *(G-7881)*
▼ **A Curv Tech Corp** ....F....... 305 888-9631
Hialeah *(G-5256)*
A Superior Garage Door Company ....E....... 305 556-6624
Hialeah *(G-5258)*
Aabc Inc ....F....... 727 434-4444
Largo *(G-7882)*
ABC Shutters Protection Corp ....G....... 785 547-9527
Miami *(G-9054)*
Accurate Metal Door Inc ....G....... 321 305-5951
Titusville *(G-18409)*
Adams Hurricane Protection Inc ....F....... 850 434-2336
Pensacola *(G-14081)*
Addison Metal Additions Inc ....G....... 305 245-9860
Homestead *(G-5953)*
Advanced Hurricane Protection ....G....... 772 220-1200
Stuart *(G-16903)*
Aero Door International LLC ....F....... 407 654-0591
Eustis *(G-3701)*
Aim Shutters ....G....... 954 861-6666
Sunrise *(G-17084)*
Al & Sons Millwork Inc ....E....... 352 245-9191
Belleview *(G-366)*
All Flrida Hrrcane Prtction Co ....G....... 305 305-9177
Miami *(G-9109)*
▼ **Alutech Corporation** ....G....... 305 593-2080
Miami *(G-9127)*
American Cnstr Entps Inc ....G....... 941 629-2070
Port Charlotte *(G-14960)*
American Marine Mfg Inc ....G....... 305 497-7723
Hialeah *(G-5293)*
ANC Shutters LLC ....F....... 561 966-8336
Lake Worth *(G-7534)*
Anchor Aluminum Products South ....G....... 305 293-7965
Key West *(G-7177)*
Architectural Metal Systems ....F....... 407 277-1364
Orlando *(G-12486)*
Architectural Openings Inc ....F....... 407 260-7110
Longwood *(G-8256)*
◆ **Arso Enterprises Inc** ....E....... 305 681-2020
Opa Locka *(G-12290)*
Ashton Manufacturing LLC ....F....... 941 351-5529
Sarasota *(G-16350)*
Before Wind Blows LLC ....G....... 407 977-4833
Chuluota *(G-1552)*
▼ **Best Rolling Manufacturer Inc** ....D....... 305 821-4276
Miami Lakes *(G-10767)*
Blind Brothers Inc ....G....... 786 518-8938
Miami *(G-9256)*
Brevard Aluminum Cnstr Co ....G....... 321 383-9255
Titusville *(G-18417)*
Builders Door and Supply Inc ....F....... 941 955-2311
Sarasota *(G-16372)*
▲ **Building Envelope Systems Inc** ....G....... 305 693-0683
Hialeah *(G-5333)*
C & D Industrial Maint LLC ....F....... 833 776-5833
Bradenton *(G-1005)*
▼ **California Shutters Inc** ....G....... 305 827-9333
Miami Lakes *(G-10772)*
Camco Corp ....G....... 561 427-0433
Jupiter *(G-7014)*
Caribbean Shutter LLC ....G....... 305 202-0501
Miami Springs *(G-10889)*
Cat 5 Hurricane Products LLC ....F....... 941 752-4692
Bradenton *(G-1016)*
Cedrus Inc ....E....... 772 286-2082
Stuart *(G-16920)*
Cement Precast Products Inc ....E....... 352 372-0953
Gainesville *(G-4894)*
▼ **Central Florida Lbr & Sup Co** ....D....... 407 298-5600
Orlando *(G-12569)*
Centralum Usa LLC ....G....... 786 646-9756
Miami *(G-9340)*
▼ **Cline Aluminum Doors Inc** ....E....... 941 746-4104
Bradenton *(G-1021)*
Coastal Awngs Hrrcane Prtction ....G....... 407 923-9482
Orlando *(G-12592)*
Coastal Shutters Inc ....G....... 954 759-1115
Port Saint Lucie *(G-15099)*
Coastal Shutters Online LLC ....G....... 786 509-2093
Miami *(G-9368)*
Commercial Rfrg Door Co Inc ....G....... 941 371-8110
Sarasota *(G-16390)*
▲ **Cordell International Inc** ....F....... 352 694-1800
Ocala *(G-11908)*
Coyote Acquisition Co ....D....... 941 480-1600
North Venice *(G-11755)*
Custom Cft Windows & Doors Inc ....F....... 407 834-5400
Winter Springs *(G-19470)*
◆ **Custom Window Systems Inc** ....A....... 352 368-6922
Ocala *(G-11914)*
Defenshield Inc ....G....... 904 679-3942
Saint Augustine *(G-15535)*
▼ **Dependable Shutter Service Inc** ....E....... 954 583-1411
Davie *(G-2516)*
▼ **Dor A Lum Corporation** ....F....... 305 884-3922
Medley *(G-8644)*
Ds Shutters Group Inc ....G....... 772 260-6393
Wellington *(G-18715)*
Eastman Performance Films LLC ....G....... 954 920-2001
Fort Lauderdale *(G-3956)*
Eclipse Screen and Shutters ....G....... 305 216-4716
Miami *(G-9498)*
Eddy Storm Protection ....G....... 386 248-1631
Daytona Beach *(G-2661)*
Ehs Fla ....G....... 352 438-0005
Ocala *(G-11930)*
◆ **Euro-Wall Systems LLC** ....E....... 941 979-5316
North Port *(G-11738)*
Expert Shutter Services Inc ....D....... 772 871-1915
Port Saint Lucie *(G-15108)*
First Windows Incorporated ....G....... 813 508-9388
Wesley Chapel *(G-18745)*
▲ **Florida A&G Co Inc** ....A....... 800 432-8132
Tamarac *(G-17356)*
Florida Shutter Factory Inc ....G....... 954 687-4793
Fort Lauderdale *(G-4004)*
▼ **Florida Shutters Inc** ....E....... 772 569-2200
Vero Beach *(G-18619)*
Florida Storm Shutters Inc ....G....... 954 257-8365
Fort Lauderdale *(G-4007)*
Fortified Building Pdts Inc ....E....... 850 432-2485
Pensacola *(G-14158)*
Fortress Impact Wndows Dors LL ....G....... 954 621-2395
Fort Lauderdale *(G-4010)*
▼ **Future Modes Inc** ....G....... 305 654-9995
Miami *(G-9605)*
G F E Inc ....F....... 954 583-7005
Davie *(G-2530)*
◆ **Garcia Door & Window Inc** ....G....... 305 635-0644
Miami *(G-9614)*
▼ **General Impact GL Windows Corp** ......F....... 305 558-8103
Hialeah *(G-5426)*
◆ **Gopi Glass Sales & Svcs Corp** ....E....... 305 592-2089
Miami *(G-9650)*
Gotcha Shuttered ....G....... 850 450-9137
Destin *(G-3192)*
▼ **Guardian Hurricane Protection** ....F....... 305 805-7050
Miami Lakes *(G-10796)*
Gulfport Industries Inc ....F....... 813 885-1000
Tampa *(G-17736)*
▼ **Gulfstream Alum & Shutter Corp** ....E....... 772 287-6476
Stuart *(G-16950)*
▼ **Halliday Products Inc** ....D....... 407 298-4470
Orlando *(G-12794)*
Hill Enterprises LLC ....G....... 850 478-4455
Pensacola *(G-14172)*
Hollow Metal Doors & Frames ....G....... 954 993-0613
Fort Lauderdale *(G-4048)*
Hollow Metal Inc ....F....... 813 246-4112
Valrico *(G-18519)*
Hurricane Shutter & Plus Inc ....G....... 786 287-0007
Miami *(G-9721)*
Innovtive Win Cncpts Doors Inc ....F....... 561 493-2303
Boynton Beach *(G-921)*
Islandoor Company ....G....... 954 524-3667
Fort Lauderdale *(G-4069)*
◆ **J T Walker Industries Inc** ....E....... 727 461-0501
Clearwater *(G-1739)*
Jambco Millwork Inc ....F....... 954 977-4998
Margate *(G-8551)*
Jansen Shutters & Spc Ltd ....G....... 941 484-4700
North Venice *(G-11759)*
Joe Taylor Restoration ....E....... 954 972-5390
Delray Beach *(G-3097)*
John Screen Service LLC ....G....... 561 798-3132
Wellington *(G-18721)*
Johnson & Jackson Glass Pdts ....F....... 813 630-9774
Tampa *(G-17808)*
Jose Morales Hurricane Shutter ....G....... 786 315-1835
Miami *(G-9803)*
Kevco Builders Inc ....F....... 352 308-8025
Eustis *(G-3711)*
Kinco Ltd ....B....... 904 355-1476
Jacksonville *(G-6538)*
◆ **L C La Finestra** ....E....... 305 599-8093
Doral *(G-3414)*
Lake Door and Trim Inc ....F....... 352 589-5566
Eustis *(G-3712)*
Larry Johnson Inc ....F....... 305 888-2300
Hialeah *(G-5483)*
◆ **Lawson Industries Inc** ....B....... 305 696-8660
Medley *(G-8678)*
Levinson Built LLC ....F....... 561 712-9882
West Palm Beach *(G-18929)*
Loxahatchee Shutter & Alum Inc ....G....... 561 513-9581
Loxahatchee *(G-8361)*
M Bilt Enterprises Inc ....F....... 352 528-5566
Ocala *(G-11989)*
Majestic Ultimate Design Inc ....F....... 954 533-8677
Oakland Park *(G-11820)*
◆ **Masonite Holdings Inc** ....F....... 813 877-2726
Tampa *(G-17888)*
◆ **Masonite International Corp** ....D....... 800 895-2723
Tampa *(G-17889)*
Master Alum & SEC Shutter Co ....G....... 727 725-1744
Safety Harbor *(G-15498)*
Metal Fronts Inc ....G....... 727 547-6700
Seminole *(G-16752)*
◆ **Miami Wall Systems Inc** ....C....... 305 888-2300
Hialeah *(G-5515)*
Mills & Nebraska Door & Trim ....F....... 407 472-2742
Orlando *(G-12971)*
◆ **Nationwide Industries Inc** ....E....... 813 988-2628
Tampa *(G-17933)*

SIC

◆ **New Age Windows & Doors Corp** .....F 305 889-0703
Medley ***(G-8695)***
◆ **Next Door Company** .....E 954 772-6666
Hialeah ***(G-5540)***
Oliveri Woodworking Inc .....F 561 478-7233
West Palm Beach ***(G-18972)***
Omega Garage Doors Inc .....F 352 620-8830
Melbourne ***(G-8901)***
On Screen Ink .....G 724 516-4999
Pompano Beach ***(G-14779)***
Orlando Shutters LLC .....E 407 495-5250
Lake Mary ***(G-7440)***
◆ **Panelfold Inc** .....C 305 688-3501
Miami ***(G-10138)***
Patio Products Mfg LLC .....F 813 664-0158
Tampa ***(G-17978)***
Performnce Glzing Slutions LLC .....G 305 975-3717
Miami ***(G-10154)***
◆ **PGT Industries Inc** .....A 941 480-1600
North Venice ***(G-11761)***
▼ **PGT Innovations Inc** .....A 941 480-1600
North Venice ***(G-11762)***
Pinellas Blind and Shutter Inc .....G 727 481-4461
Clearwater ***(G-1833)***
▼ **Pinos Window Corporation** .....F 305 888-9903
Medley ***(G-8706)***
Pioneer Screen Inc .....G 772 260-3068
Palm City ***(G-13671)***
Plantation Shutters Inc .....G 772 208-8245
Port Saint Lucie ***(G-15129)***
Plotkowski Inc .....G 561 740-2226
Boynton Beach ***(G-940)***
Poma Corporation .....D 561 790-5799
West Palm Beach ***(G-19001)***
Powerbees Incorporated .....G 561 797-5927
Boynton Beach ***(G-941)***
▼ **Quality Engineered Products Co** .....E 813 885-1693
Tampa ***(G-18031)***
◆ **Ram Sales LLC** .....D 844 726-6382
Miami ***(G-10237)***
Rearden Steel Mfg LLC .....G 772 882-8517
Fort Pierce ***(G-4739)***
Reeds Metal Manufacturing Inc .....E 352 498-0100
Cross City ***(G-2366)***
▼ **Reich Metal Fabricators Inc** .....E 561 585-3173
West Palm Beach ***(G-19018)***
Reliable Pool Enclsres Screns .....G 407 731-3408
Orlando ***(G-13129)***
Rescue Metal Framing LLC .....F 561 660-5945
Fort Lauderdale ***(G-4204)***
Rolladen Inc .....F 954 454-4114
Longwood ***(G-8332)***
▲ **Rollertech Corp** .....F 239 645-6698
Fort Myers ***(G-4586)***
◆ **Rolling Door Parts Inc** .....F 305 888-5020
Miami ***(G-10276)***
◆ **Rolling Shield Incorporated** .....E 305 436-6661
Miami Lakes ***(G-10852)***
◆ **Rolling Shield Parts Inc** .....F 305 436-6661
Miami Lakes ***(G-10853)***
Rollshield LLC .....F 727 441-2243
Clearwater ***(G-1864)***
Rolsafe LLC .....F 239 225-2487
Fort Myers ***(G-4587)***
Russell Home Imprvmnt Ctr Inc .....G 954 436-9186
Davie ***(G-2588)***
Sano Associates Inc .....E 239 403-2650
Naples ***(G-11391)***
Screening Leon & Repair Inc .....G 850 575-2840
Tallahassee ***(G-17321)***
◆ **Sea Products Inc** .....D 904 781-8200
Jacksonville ***(G-6758)***
Sentinel Inc .....F 239 263-9888
Naples ***(G-11397)***
Sentry Protection Technology .....G 941 306-4949
Sarasota ***(G-16592)***
Shoreline Shutter Systems Inc .....G 386 299-2219
Port Orange ***(G-15033)***
Shutter Down All Weather Protc .....G 561 856-0655
Boynton Beach ***(G-959)***
Shutter Down Storm Protection .....G 813 957-8936
Plant City ***(G-14465)***
Shutter Lubrication & Service .....G 561 745-8956
Jupiter ***(G-7113)***
Shutter Southern Cross .....G 941 276-7064
North Port ***(G-11750)***
Shutter Southern Cross .....G 941 235-2620
Port Charlotte ***(G-14997)***
Shutter2think Inc .....G 850 291-8301
Palm Beach Gardens ***(G-13628)***
Shutters On Sale Inc .....G 386 756-0009
Port Orange ***(G-15034)***
Shuttertek Inc .....G 772 828-6149
Port Saint Lucie ***(G-15142)***
Simplex Inc .....E 352 357-2828
Mount Dora ***(G-11114)***
Simpson Screens Inc .....F 904 757-1498
Jacksonville ***(G-6777)***
Smart Guard Shutters LLC .....G 386 227-6295
Palm Coast ***(G-13710)***
Smart Shutters Inc .....G 786 391-1100
Miami ***(G-10364)***
Smart Tracks Inc .....G 239 938-1000
Fort Myers ***(G-4605)***
▼ **Southeastern Door Company LLC** .....F 561 746-5493
Jupiter ***(G-7119)***
Southern Cross Shutter Systems .....G 941 585-2152
Port Charlotte ***(G-14998)***
Space Coast Storm Shutters LLC .....G 410 652-5717
Cocoa Beach ***(G-2067)***
Specialty Products Inc .....G 850 438-4264
Pensacola ***(G-14267)***
Strong Hurricane Shutter .....G 786 587-3990
Miami ***(G-10421)***
▼ **Style-View Products Inc** .....F 305 634-9688
Miami ***(G-10426)***
▼ **Sun Barrier Products Inc** .....F 407 830-9085
Longwood ***(G-8341)***
◆ **Sun Metals Systems Inc** .....E 813 889-0718
Tampa ***(G-18140)***
◆ **Sunshine Windows Mfg Inc** .....D 305 364-9952
Hialeah ***(G-5640)***
Superior Storm Solutions .....G 305 638-8420
Miami ***(G-10438)***
▲ **Superior Trim & Door Inc** .....E 407 408-7624
Apopka ***(G-190)***
Swfl Hurricane Shutters Inc .....G 239 454-4944
Cape Coral ***(G-1481)***
T M Building Products Ltd .....G 954 781-4430
Pompano Beach ***(G-14882)***
Tag Media Group LLC .....G 239 288-0499
Fort Myers ***(G-4622)***
▲ **Toledo Doors Inc** .....F 305 633-4352
Miami ***(G-10487)***
◆ **Trebor USA Corp** .....F 954 922-1620
Hollywood ***(G-5925)***
Tropic Shield Inc .....F 954 731-5553
Lauderdale Lakes ***(G-8095)***
▲ **Ultimate Door of Palm Beach** .....F 561 642-2828
Lake Worth ***(G-7595)***
◆ **Unique Technology Inc** .....E 941 358-5410
Sarasota ***(G-16627)***
Universal Alum Windows & Doors .....F 305 825-7900
Hialeah ***(G-5662)***
Upright Aluminum Inc .....G 239 731-6644
North Fort Myers ***(G-11608)***
USA Aluminum .....G 305 303-9121
Hallandale Beach ***(G-5222)***
Valco Group Inc .....C 813 870-0482
Tampa ***(G-18232)***
Valiant Products Inc .....E 863 688-7998
Lakeland ***(G-7829)***
◆ **Vidco Industries Inc** .....E 305 888-0077
Medley ***(G-8753)***
Well Bilt Industries Usa LLC .....F 352 528-5566
Ocala ***(G-12074)***
West Coast Shutters Sunburst .....F 727 894-0044
Saint Petersburg ***(G-15957)***
West Palm Installers Inc .....F 305 406-3575
Doral ***(G-3548)***
Will Shutter U Inc .....G 772 285-3600
Jensen Beach ***(G-6974)***
Window Craftsmen Inc .....E 941 922-1844
Sarasota ***(G-16641)***
Windsor Window Company .....F 321 385-3880
Titusville ***(G-18473)***
◆ **Worldwide Door Components Inc** .....E 813 870-0003
Tampa ***(G-18265)***
Xterior Shutter Systems .....G 239 872-2327
Cape Coral ***(G-1496)***
▼ **Yale Ogron Mfg Co Inc** .....D 305 687-0424
Opa Locka ***(G-12372)***
YKK AP America Inc .....G 561 736-7808
Boynton Beach ***(G-979)***
YKK AP America Inc .....F 407 856-0660
Orlando ***(G-13337)***

3443 Fabricated Plate Work

▲ **A-Fabco Inc** .....E 813 677-8790
Gibsonton ***(G-5024)***
Accurate Metals Spinning Inc .....G 305 885-9988
Medley ***(G-8606)***
Admiralty Industries Corp .....G 305 722-7311
Doral ***(G-3227)***
Airlock USA LLC .....F 305 888-6454
Miami Springs ***(G-10887)***
▲ **Alfa Laval Aalborg Inc** .....D 954 435-5999
Miramar ***(G-10964)***
Aluminum Tank Industries Inc .....G 863 401-9474
Winter Haven ***(G-19298)***
Aly Fabrication Inc .....G 724 898-2990
Saint Augustine ***(G-15515)***
Ameri Produ Produ Compa of Pin .....G 813 925-0144
Tampa ***(G-17413)***
◆ **American Aluminum ACC Inc** .....E 850 277-0869
Perry ***(G-14292)***
American Mfg & Mch Inc .....D 352 728-2222
Okahumpka ***(G-12168)***
American Products Inc .....G 813 925-0144
Tampa ***(G-17418)***
American Stainless & Alum Pdts .....G 423 472-4832
Kissimmee ***(G-7219)***
◆ **Applied Cooling Technology LLC** .....G 239 217-5080
Cape Coral ***(G-1382)***
ARC-Rite Inc .....E 386 325-3523
Jacksonville ***(G-6165)***
B & F Waste Solutions Llc .....G 772 336-1113
Vero Beach ***(G-18597)***
Blackwater Truss Systems LLC .....G 850 623-1414
Milton ***(G-10923)***
Boyd Welding LLC .....G 352 447-2405
Ocala ***(G-11889)***
Brewfab LLC .....G 727 823-8333
Saint Petersburg ***(G-15729)***
Broach Process Serving .....G 727 385-9467
New Port Richey ***(G-11483)***
Central Maintenance & Wldg Inc .....B 813 229-0012
Lithia ***(G-8216)***
Central Metal Fabricators Inc .....E 305 261-6262
Miami ***(G-9339)***
CJ Mulanix Co Inc .....G 716 423-8010
Clearwater ***(G-1626)***
Coastal Machine LLC .....G 850 769-6117
Panama City ***(G-13885)***
Coastal Marine Power Inc .....G 941 322-8182
Myakka City ***(G-11141)***
College Hunks Hlg Junk & Mvg .....G 407 378-2500
Orlando ***(G-12601)***
▼ **Dixie Tank Company** .....E 904 781-9500
Jacksonville ***(G-6322)***
Dl Myers Corp .....F 609 698-8800
Jupiter ***(G-7024)***
Dumpstermaxx .....G 805 552-6299
University Park ***(G-18504)***
Dumpsterme LLC .....G 904 647-1945
Jacksonville ***(G-6334)***
Duramaster Cylinders .....F 813 882-0040
Tampa ***(G-17620)***
Durapoly Industries Inc .....G 352 622-3455
Silver Springs ***(G-16781)***
Dwi Inc .....F 321 508-9833
Malabar ***(G-8488)***
Eileen Ruth Bendis .....G 954 565-5470
Fort Lauderdale ***(G-3966)***
Elevated Dumpsters LLC .....G 813 732-6338
Zephyrhills ***(G-19515)***
Empire Dumpsters LLC .....G 407 223-8985
Apopka ***(G-134)***
Envirovault LLC .....F 904 354-1858
Jacksonville ***(G-6368)***
Formweld Fitting Inc .....E 850 626-4888
Milton ***(G-10928)***
Fuel Tanks To Go LLC .....G 865 604-4726
Ocala ***(G-11950)***
G Metal Industries Inc .....F 305 633-0300
Miami ***(G-9607)***
Gencor Industries Inc .....C 407 290-6000
Orlando ***(G-12776)***
Greenco Manufacturing Corp .....E 813 882-4400
Tampa ***(G-17728)***
Gz Dumpsters LLC .....G 407 600-0756
Altamonte Springs ***(G-49)***
▼ **Halliday Products Inc** .....D 407 298-4470
Orlando ***(G-12794)***
Heritage Manufacturing Svcs .....G 727 906-5599
Saint Petersburg ***(G-15806)***
▼ **Hutchins Co Inc** .....F 727 442-6651
Clearwater ***(G-1722)***
Interstate Recycling Waste .....F 407 812-5555
Orlando ***(G-12838)***

Jacksonville Steel Pdts Inc....G....904 268-3364
Jacksonville *(G-6512)*
Jim Appleys Tru-ARC Inc....F....727 571-3007
Clearwater *(G-1743)*
▼ Keller-Nglillis Design Mfg Inc....F....727 733-4111
Dunedin *(G-3582)*
◆ Krausz Usa Inc....F....352 509-3600
Ocala *(G-11977)*
L & D Dumpsters LLC....G....352 589-5043
Astatula *(G-212)*
Lizheng Stinless Stl Tube Coil....G....888 582-8820
Tampa *(G-17853)*
Lr Dumpsters LLC....G....321 279-0169
Winter Park *(G-19419)*
Mantua Manufacturing Co....G....813 621-3714
Tampa *(G-17878)*
Metal 2 Metal Inc....G....954 253-9450
Palmetto Bay *(G-13850)*
Mid-State Machine & Fabg Corp....B....863 665-6233
Lakeland *(G-7751)*
Midwest Mtal Fbrction Cstm Rll....E....317 769-6489
North Fort Myers *(G-11599)*
Militek Industries LLC....G....941 544-5636
Bradenton *(G-1078)*
Mitek USA Inc....G....813 906-3122
Tampa *(G-17911)*
▼ Modern Welding Company Fla Inc....D....407 843-1270
Orlando *(G-12975)*
Monitor Products Inc....D....352 544-2620
Brooksville *(G-1254)*
Mpc Containment Systems LLC....D....773 927-4121
Deland *(G-3000)*
Myrlen Inc....G....800 662-4762
Coral Springs *(G-2293)*
▲ Nautical Structures Inds Inc....D....727 541-6664
Largo *(G-8018)*
Need A Dumpster LLC....G....888 407-3867
Apopka *(G-164)*
Nelson and Affiliates Inc....F....352 316-5641
Gainesville *(G-4970)*
Ofab Inc....D....352 629-0040
Ocala *(G-12019)*
Oxigeno Nitrogeno Inc....F....954 659-3881
Weston *(G-19158)*
Platinium Rosis Inc....G....786 617-9973
Miami Beach *(G-10703)*
Pro Dumpsters Inc....F....407 910-6341
Kissimmee *(G-7291)*
Quality Fbrction Mch Works Inc....F....386 755-0220
Lake City *(G-7379)*
▲ RDS Manufacturing Inc....C....850 584-6898
Perry *(G-14310)*
Ring Power Corporation....E....904 354-1858
Jacksonville *(G-6725)*
Riw of Jacksonville Inc....F....904 356-5635
Jacksonville *(G-6730)*
Ryan Manufacturing Inc....F....386 325-3644
East Palatka *(G-3606)*
▼ Sen-Dure Products Inc....D....954 973-1260
Fort Lauderdale *(G-4230)*
◆ Serf Inc....E....850 476-8203
Cantonment *(G-1347)*
Service D N D Dumpster....G....813 989-3867
Tampa *(G-18086)*
SMI Tool & Die Inc....G....321 632-6200
Cocoa *(G-2051)*
Southern Dumpsters Inc....G....772 413-1228
Melbourne *(G-8936)*
Southern Mfg & Fabrication LLC....F....407 894-8851
Sanford *(G-16119)*
Southstern Indus Fbrcators LLC....E....941 776-1211
Duette *(G-3563)*
▼ Specialty Tank and Eqp Co....G....904 353-8761
Jacksonville *(G-6804)*
Spencer Fabrications Inc....E....352 343-0014
Tavares *(G-18354)*
◆ SPX Flow Technology Usa Inc....G....352 237-1220
Ocala *(G-12058)*
Staysealed Inc....G....866 978-2973
Lakeland *(G-7805)*
▼ Style-View Products Inc....F....305 634-9688
Miami *(G-10426)*
Sunbelt Metals & Mfg Inc....E....407 889-8960
Apopka *(G-189)*
▼ Sunshine Marine Tanks Inc....G....305 805-9898
Medley *(G-8733)*
▼ Supply Expediters Intl Inc....F....305 805-4255
Pembroke Pines *(G-14061)*
Swiss Components Inc....F....321 723-6729
Melbourne *(G-8953)*
Tampa Tank & Welding Inc....F....813 241-0123
Gibsonton *(G-5033)*
Trash Express SW Inc....G....239 340-5291
Fort Myers *(G-4638)*
Tru Simulation + Training Inc....D....813 792-9300
Odessa *(G-12161)*
◆ TTI Holdings Inc....G....813 623-2675
Tampa *(G-18208)*
U-Load Dumpsters LLC....G....352 318-3045
Ponce De Leon *(G-14919)*
United Ntons Space Crps Mltary....F....702 373-2351
Ponce De Leon *(G-14920)*
Universal Metal Works Inc....G....904 765-2600
Jacksonville *(G-6886)*
US Chutes Corp....F....860 567-4000
Boca Raton *(G-771)*
Valiant Products Inc....E....863 688-7998
Lakeland *(G-7829)*
▼ Vertarib Inc....E....877 815-8610
West Palm Beach *(G-19078)*
W D Wilson Inc....E....813 626-6989
Tampa *(G-18250)*
Walker Stainless Eqp Co LLC....G....352 343-2606
Tavares *(G-18360)*
Wastequip Manufacturing Co LLC....E....863 665-6507
Lakeland *(G-7832)*
Wes Industries Inc....F....941 371-7617
Sarasota *(G-16637)*
World Stone and Design LLC....G....850 235-0399
Panama City *(G-13965)*
Xtreme Dumpster Services Corp....G....407 272-8899
Orlando *(G-13333)*
Zahn Builders Inc....G....718 885-2202
Lighthouse Point *(G-8214)*

3444 Sheet Metal Work

A & A Sheetmetal Contr Corp....D....305 592-2217
Doral *(G-3219)*
A Certified Screen Service....F....386 673-0054
Ormond Beach *(G-13345)*
A&K Sheet Metal LLC....G....786 351-8313
Miami *(G-9044)*
Aba Engineering & Mfg Inc....F....386 672-9665
Ormond Beach *(G-13346)*
Abele Sheetmetal Works Inc....F....561 471-1134
Riviera Beach *(G-15290)*
◆ Accord Industries LLC....D....407 671-6989
Winter Park *(G-19370)*
Actron Entities Inc....D....727 531-5871
Clearwater *(G-1563)*
Adeptus Industries Inc....F....941 756-7636
Bradenton *(G-982)*
Advanced Alum Polk Cnty Inc....E....863 648-5787
Lakeland *(G-7626)*
Advanced Metals LLC....G....352 494-2476
Hawthorne *(G-5242)*
Advanced Sheet Metal & Welding....G....239 430-1155
Naples *(G-11150)*
▼ Affordable Metal Inc....F....305 691-8082
Hialeah *(G-5274)*
▲ Air Distributors Inc....E....352 522-0006
Dunnellon *(G-3592)*
Airite Air Conditioning Inc....E....813 886-0235
Tampa *(G-17395)*
AJF Sheet Metals Inc....G....305 970-6359
North Miami *(G-11623)*
▲ AL Garey & Associates Inc....C....954 975-7992
Coral Springs *(G-2218)*
Alacriant Holdings LLC....E....330 233-0523
Lake Mary *(G-7398)*
All County Sheet Metal Inc....G....561 588-0099
Lake Worth Beach *(G-7601)*
All Metal Fab Inc....E....904 570-9772
Jacksonville *(G-6133)*
All Phase Construction USA LLC....F....754 227-5605
Deerfield Beach *(G-2772)*
All Southern Fabricators Inc....E....727 573-4846
Clearwater *(G-1574)*
Alumflo Inc....G....727 527-8494
Saint Petersburg *(G-15698)*
◆ American Metal Fabricators Inc....E....561 790-5799
Mangonia Park *(G-8497)*
AMS Fabrications Inc....F....813 420-0784
Oakland Park *(G-11776)*
Anvil Iron Works Inc....E....727 375-2884
Odessa *(G-12102)*
Apache Sheet Metal....G....954 214-4468
Weston *(G-19106)*
Architctral Shtmtl Fabricators....G....407 672-9086
Winter Park *(G-19379)*
Architectural Metal Systems....F....407 277-1364
Orlando *(G-12486)*
Architectural Metals S W FL....E....239 334-7433
Fort Myers *(G-4366)*
Arrow Sheet Metal Works Inc....E....813 247-2179
Tampa *(G-17436)*
▼ B & K Installations Inc....E....305 245-6968
Homestead *(G-5956)*
B & T Metalworks Inc....E....352 236-6000
Ocala *(G-11884)*
B&B Custom Sheet Metal Inc....G....727 938-8083
Tarpon Springs *(G-18283)*
B&C Sheet Metal Duct Corp....G....305 316-9212
Miami *(G-9211)*
Badger Corporation....G....954 942-5277
Pompano Beach *(G-14611)*
Baker Metal Works & Supply LLC....E....850 537-2010
Baker *(G-300)*
▼ Barrett Custom Designs LLC....G....321 242-2002
Melbourne *(G-8776)*
▲ Bausch American Towers LLC....F....772 283-2771
Stuart *(G-16911)*
Bausch Enterprises Inc....F....772 220-6652
Stuart *(G-16912)*
Bay Harbor Sheet Metal Inc....F....813 740-8662
Tampa *(G-17457)*
Beautiful Mailbox Co....E....305 403-4820
Hialeah *(G-5318)*
Benchmark Quality Gutters Inc....G....904 759-9800
Jacksonville *(G-6204)*
▼ Birdsall Marine Design Inc....E....561 832-7879
West Palm Beach *(G-18822)*
Blackwater Folk Art Inc....G....850 623-3470
Milton *(G-10922)*
Bob Kline Quality Metal Inc....G....561 659-4245
West Palm Beach *(G-18827)*
▼ Bohnert Sheet Metal & Roofg Co....F....305 696-6851
Miami *(G-9264)*
Breiner Machine Co Inc....F....352 544-0463
Brooksville *(G-1216)*
C C Lead Inc....F....863 465-6458
Lake Placid *(G-7486)*
Camcorp Industries Inc....G....941 488-5000
Venice *(G-18536)*
Captive-Aire Systems Inc....E....407 682-9396
Altamonte Springs *(G-36)*
Captive-Aire Systems Inc....E....813 448-7884
Tampa *(G-17505)*
Carpenters Roofg & Shtmtl Inc....E....561 833-0341
Riviera Beach *(G-15310)*
Cato Steel Co....F....407 671-3333
Winter Park *(G-19391)*
Cemex Cnstr Mtls Fla LLC....F....561 832-6646
West Palm Beach *(G-18838)*
Cemex Materials LLC....D....561 746-4556
Jupiter *(G-7018)*
Central Metal Fabricators Inc....E....305 261-6262
Miami *(G-9339)*
Century Metal Products Inc....E....407 293-8871
Orlando *(G-12571)*
▲ Circle Redmont Inc....E....321 259-7374
Melbourne *(G-8789)*
◆ Cladding Systems Inc....E....813 250-0786
Tampa *(G-17537)*
Clarkwstern Dtrich Bldg System....F....800 543-7140
Dade City *(G-2426)*
Clear Vue Inc....E....727 726-5386
Safety Harbor *(G-15490)*
Coastal Awngs Hrrcane Prtction....G....407 923-9482
Orlando *(G-12592)*
Conklin Metal Industries Inc....F....407 688-0900
Orlando *(G-12614)*
Consolidated Metal Products....G....850 576-2167
Tallahassee *(G-17236)*
Cornerstone Fabrication LLC....E....386 310-1110
Debary *(G-2747)*
▼ Corrugated Industries Fla Inc....E....813 623-6606
Tampa *(G-17559)*
▲ Crown Products Company Inc....C....904 737-7144
Jacksonville *(G-6300)*
Crown Products Company Inc....D....904 924-8340
Jacksonville *(G-6301)*
Crown Seamless Gutters Inc....F....561 748-9919
West Palm Beach *(G-18852)*
Custom Cft Windows & Doors Inc....F....407 834-5400
Winter Springs *(G-19470)*
Custom Metal Fabricators Inc....G....407 841-8551
Orlando *(G-12640)*
▲ Custom Metal Specialties Inc....E....727 522-3986
Pinellas Park *(G-14341)*

Cwp Sheet Metal Inc .... E 407 349-0926
Geneva *(G-5019)*
D C Inc Prtble Wldg Fbrication .... G 863 533-4483
Frostproof *(G-4859)*
▼ **Dans Custom Sheet Metal Inc** .... E 239 594-0530
Naples *(G-11221)*
Day Metal Products LLC .... G 352 799-9258
Brooksville *(G-1225)*
Dayton Superior Corporation .... G 407 859-4541
Orlando *(G-12657)*
Daytona Sheet Metal and Air .... G 386 547-2422
Port Orange *(G-15015)*
Deans Cstm Shtmtl Fabrication .... G 813 757-6270
Dover *(G-3558)*
Decon USA .... G 440 610-5009
Tarpon Springs *(G-18292)*
◆ **Delta International Inc** .... F 305 665-6573
Miami *(G-9451)*
Dills Enterprises LLC .... G 941 493-1993
Venice *(G-18542)*
Dixie Metalcraft Incorporated .... F 239 337-4299
Fort Myers *(G-4432)*
Dolphin Sheet Metal Inc .... F 561 744-0242
Jupiter *(G-7025)*
▼ **Doral Building Supply Corp** .... F 305 471-9797
Doral *(G-3332)*
Duct Design Corporation .... E 305 827-0110
Hialeah *(G-5380)*
Dynamic Metals LLC .... F 561 629-7304
West Palm Beach *(G-18858)*
Dynamic Precision Group Inc .... E 772 287-7770
Stuart *(G-16934)*
Earnest Products Inc .... D 407 831-1588
Sanford *(G-16038)*
Electrnic Shtmtal Crftsmen Fla .... E 321 727-0633
Melbourne *(G-8823)*
Electro Mech Solutions Inc .... E 813 792-0400
Odessa *(G-12118)*
▲ **Emerald Sails** .... F 850 240-4777
Shalimar *(G-16774)*
Epic Metals Corporation .... G 863 533-7404
Bartow *(G-314)*
Europa Manufacturing Inc .... F 954 426-2965
Coconut Creek *(G-2076)*
Exact Inc .... C 904 783-6640
Jacksonville *(G-6372)*
Flamco of Texas LLC .... E 904 783-8400
Jacksonville *(G-6392)*
Flash Roofing and Shtmtl LLC .... G 786 237-9440
Miami *(G-9574)*
▲ **Flite Technology Inc** .... F 321 631-2050
Cocoa *(G-2022)*
▼ **Float-On Corporation** .... E 772 569-4440
Vero Beach *(G-18617)*
Florida Aluminum and Steel Inc .... F 863 967-4191
Auburndale *(G-241)*
▼ **Florida Metal Products LLC** .... D 904 783-8400
Jacksonville *(G-6400)*
Florida Metal-Craft Inc .... F 407 656-1100
Winter Garden *(G-19264)*
▼ **Florida Shutters Inc** .... E 772 569-2200
Vero Beach *(G-18619)*
▲ **Florida Storm Panels Inc** .... F 305 685-9000
Opa Locka *(G-12318)*
◆ **Flotech Inc** .... D 904 358-1849
Jacksonville *(G-6406)*
Fowlers Sheet Metal Inc .... F 561 659-3309
West Palm Beach *(G-18883)*
Frc Electrical Industries Inc .... G 321 676-3300
Palm Bay *(G-13514)*
Fresco Group Inc .... F 239 936-8055
Fort Myers *(G-4459)*
Ft Acquisition Company Llc .... E 904 367-0095
Jacksonville *(G-6417)*
▼ **G & K Aluminum Inc** .... F 772 283-1297
Stuart *(G-16943)*
G F E Inc .... F 954 583-7005
Davie *(G-2530)*
Gautier Fabrication Inc .... E 941 485-2464
North Venice *(G-11758)*
General Metals & Plastics Inc .... G 904 354-8224
Jacksonville *(G-6432)*
Gibson Wldg Shetmetal Vent Inc .... G 850 837-6141
Destin *(G-3190)*
Gizmos Lion Sheet Metal Inc .... F 561 684-8480
West Palm Beach *(G-18888)*
Gms Sheet Metal Inc .... F 772 221-0585
Palm City *(G-13659)*
Gulf Atlantic Culvert Company .... F 850 562-2384
Tallahassee *(G-17270)*

▲ **H Lamm Industries Inc** .... C 954 491-8929
Oakland Park *(G-11810)*
▼ **Halliday Products Inc** .... D 407 298-4470
Orlando *(G-12794)*
Hendrix Maintenance & Repr LLC .... G 863 647-3511
Lakeland *(G-7704)*
Hollywood Design & Concepts .... F 954 458-4634
Yalaha *(G-19490)*
Home & Garden Industries Inc .... F 305 634-0681
Miami *(G-9716)*
▼ **Hood Depot International Inc** .... E 954 570-9860
Deerfield Beach *(G-2844)*
Hurricane Roofing & Shtmtl Inc .... G 954 968-8155
Margate *(G-8549)*
▼ **Hurst Awning Company Inc** .... E 305 693-0600
Hollywood *(G-5847)*
Hydro Extrusion Usa LLC .... B 904 794-1500
Saint Augustine *(G-15550)*
Ice Sheet Metal LLC .... G 850 872-2129
Panama City *(G-13916)*
Impulse Air Inc .... E 904 475-1822
Jacksonville *(G-6491)*
Infinity Manufactured Inds .... F 727 532-4453
Largo *(G-7980)*
Integrated Metal Products Inc .... D 863 687-4110
Lakeland *(G-7713)*
◆ **International Dock Products** .... F 954 964-5315
Hallandale Beach *(G-5191)*
Interstate Wldg & Fabrication .... F 727 446-1449
Clearwater *(G-1735)*
J & J Steel Services Corp .... G 305 878-8929
Medley *(G-8673)*
Jax Metals LLC .... G 904 731-4655
Jacksonville *(G-6519)*
◆ **JC Industrial Mfg Corp** .... E 305 634-5280
Miami *(G-9789)*
Jer-Air Manufacturing Inc .... E 352 591-2674
Micanopy *(G-10902)*
Jim Appleys Tru-ARC Inc .... F 727 571-3007
Clearwater *(G-1743)*
◆ **JP Custom Metals** .... F 786 318-2855
Miami *(G-9806)*
Keene Metal Fabricators Inc .... E 813 621-2455
Tampa *(G-17817)*
▼ **Kemco Industries LLC** .... D 407 322-1230
Sanford *(G-16077)*
Kenco 2000 Inc .... F 386 672-1590
Daytona Beach *(G-2676)*
Kinship Precision LLC .... F 321 765-3531
Melbourne *(G-8859)*
Kling Fabrication Inc .... F 727 321-7233
Pinellas Park *(G-14359)*
Kustom Industrial Fabricators .... F 407 965-1940
Longwood *(G-8302)*
Kustom Us Inc .... F 407 965-1940
Longwood *(G-8303)*
L D F Services .... F 386 947-9256
Daytona Beach *(G-2678)*
Lajoie Investment Corp .... F 954 463-3271
Fort Lauderdale *(G-4094)*
Lapin Sheet Metal Company .... D 407 423-9897
Orlando *(G-12892)*
Largo Aluminum Inc .... F 305 852-2390
Islamorada *(G-6098)*
▲ **Liberty Aluminum Co** .... E 239 369-3000
Lehigh Acres *(G-8197)*
▼ **Lion Sheet Metal Inc** .... F 561 840-0540
West Palm Beach *(G-18931)*
Lloyd Industries Inc .... D 904 541-1655
Orange Park *(G-12399)*
▲ **LV Thompson Inc** .... C 813 248-3456
Tampa *(G-17866)*
Magnus Hitech Industries Inc .... E 321 724-9731
Melbourne *(G-8882)*
Manning Company .... G 954 523-9355
Fort Lauderdale *(G-4111)*
Marion Metal Works Inc .... E 352 351-4221
Ocala *(G-11992)*
▼ **Marlyn Steel Decks Inc** .... F 813 621-1375
Tampa *(G-17883)*
Marlyn Steel Products Inc .... E 813 621-1375
Tampa *(G-17884)*
Masseys Metals .... E 813 626-8275
Tampa *(G-17892)*
Mechanical Svcs Centl Fla Inc .... C 407 857-3510
Orlando *(G-12957)*
Memphis Metal Manufacturing Co .... F 901 276-6363
Tampa *(G-17900)*
Mercury Aircraft .... G 607 776-7002
Miami *(G-9979)*

Metal 2 Metal Inc .... G 954 253-9450
Palmetto Bay *(G-13850)*
Metal Creations Sarasota Llc .... F 941 922-7096
Sarasota *(G-16256)*
Metal Culverts Inc .... E 727 531-1431
Clearwater *(G-1782)*
▼ **Metal Essence Inc** .... G 407 478-8480
Longwood *(G-8312)*
▼ **Metal Mart Systems Inc** .... E 863 533-4040
Bartow *(G-324)*
Metal Products Company LC .... F 850 526-5593
Marianna *(G-8584)*
Metal Roof Factory Inc .... G 321 632-8300
Rockledge *(G-15436)*
Metal Sales Manufacturing Corp .... F 904 783-3660
Jacksonville *(G-6597)*
▼ **Metal Supply and Machining Inc** .... F 561 276-4941
Delray Beach *(G-3107)*
Metal Works By Gal .... G 407 486-7198
Sanford *(G-16087)*
Metalcraft Industries Inc .... E 352 680-3555
Ocala *(G-11999)*
Metalcrafters LLC .... G 904 257-9036
Jacksonville *(G-6598)*
Metalfab Inc .... F 352 588-9901
San Antonio *(G-15974)*
Metalworks Engineering Corp .... F 305 223-0011
Hialeah *(G-5507)*
◆ **Miami Tech Inc** .... E 305 693-7054
Miami *(G-10014)*
Miami Tech Inc .... F 786 354-1115
Hialeah *(G-5514)*
Mid-State Machine & Fabg Corp .... B 863 665-6233
Lakeland *(G-7751)*
▼ **Millennium Metals Inc** .... E 904 358-8366
Jacksonville *(G-6606)*
MJM Manufacturing Inc .... D 305 620-2020
Miami Lakes *(G-10823)*
▼ **Modern Metal Systems Inc** .... G 727 573-2255
Clearwater *(G-1790)*
Mr Gutter Cutter Inc .... F 772 286-7780
Stuart *(G-16978)*
▼ **N C A Manufacturing Inc** .... D 727 441-2651
Clearwater *(G-1799)*
Naples Iron Works Inc .... E 239 649-7265
Naples *(G-11336)*
▲ **Nautical Structures Inds Inc** .... D 727 541-6664
Largo *(G-8018)*
No Equal Design Inc .... G 305 971-5177
Miami *(G-10074)*
Normandin LLC .... F 941 739-8046
Sarasota *(G-16267)*
Northside Sheet Metal Inc .... G 850 769-1461
Panama City *(G-13932)*
Nova Sidera Metal Forming Corp .... G 786 717-7149
Miami *(G-10080)*
Ornamental Design Ironworks .... E 813 626-8449
Tampa *(G-17960)*
Osborne Metals .... G 727 441-1703
Clearwater *(G-1823)*
▲ **Osgood Industries LLC** .... C 813 448-9041
Oldsmar *(G-12254)*
P & M Sheet Metal Corp .... G 954 618-8513
Pembroke Pines *(G-14053)*
Parrish Inc .... G 386 985-4879
De Leon Springs *(G-2740)*
Perez Industries Inc .... F 239 992-2444
Bonita Springs *(G-846)*
Pioneer Development Entps Inc .... F 239 592-0001
Naples *(G-11367)*
Pipewelders Marine Inc .... D 954 587-8400
Fort Lauderdale *(G-4169)*
Plotkowski Inc .... G 561 740-2226
Boynton Beach *(G-940)*
Pomper Sheet Metal Inc .... G 954 492-9717
Oakland Park *(G-11829)*
Precision Fabrication Corp .... E 941 488-2474
Nokomis *(G-11587)*
▲ **Precision Metal Industries Inc** .... D 954 942-6303
Pompano Beach *(G-14808)*
Precision Metal Services Inc .... F 407 843-3682
Sorrento *(G-16791)*
Preferred Metal Products Inc .... F 407 296-4449
Orlando *(G-13082)*
Premier Archtctural Shtmtl Inc .... G 727 373-8937
Odessa *(G-12143)*
Premier Fabricating Llc .... E 813 855-4633
Oldsmar *(G-12260)*
Production Metal Stampings .... F 850 981-8240
Milton *(G-10938)*

R Townsend Rescreens Inc ....G....... 239 244-4759
Punta Gorda *(G-15226)*
Rafab Spcialty Fabrication Inc....F....... 407 422-3750
Orlando *(G-13112)*
Rainbow Precision Mfg Corp....G....... 561 691-1658
Palm Beach Gardens *(G-13621)*
Rankine-Hinman Mfg Co....F....... 904 808-0404
Saint Augustine *(G-15594)*
Rapid Metal Products Inc....E....... 863 701-0058
Lakeland *(G-7776)*
Reading Truck Body LLC....E....... 727 943-8911
Tarpon Springs *(G-18323)*
Responsive Machining Inc....F....... 321 225-4011
Titusville *(G-18457)*
Road Block Fabrication Inc....G....... 708 417-6091
Fort Myers *(G-4584)*
◆ **Rolling Shield Incorporated**....E....... 305 436-6661
Miami Lakes *(G-10852)*
◆ **Rolling Shield Parts Inc**....F....... 305 436-6661
Miami Lakes *(G-10853)*
S & B Metal Products S Fla Inc....C....... 941 727-3669
Bradenton *(G-1108)*
S & B Metal Products S Fla Inc....E....... 941 727-3669
Lakeland *(G-7783)*
S & S Welding Inc....F....... 863 533-2888
Bartow *(G-333)*
S P Sheet Metal Co Inc....F....... 609 698-8800
Jupiter *(G-7107)*
S&L Cnstrction Specialists Inc....G....... 407 300-5080
Orlando *(G-13153)*
SBs Precision Shtmtl Inc....E....... 321 951-7411
Melbourne *(G-8927)*
Scott Safety LLC....E....... 239 340-8695
Moore Haven *(G-11089)*
Seacoast Air Conditioning & Sh....F....... 772 466-2400
Fort Pierce *(G-4746)*
Sfa Systems Inc....E....... 561 585-5927
Lake Worth *(G-7586)*
Sfi Inc....E....... 407 834-2258
Orlando *(G-13177)*
Sheet Metal Unlimited....G....... 772 872-7440
Stuart *(G-17011)*
Silver Sheet Florida Inc....E....... 850 230-9711
Panama City *(G-13950)*
Simar Industries Inc....E....... 352 622-2287
Ocala *(G-12053)*
Singer Holdings Inc....F....... 321 724-0900
Melbourne *(G-8934)*
▲ **Sourcerers Inc**....G....... 954 530-2333
Plantation *(G-14556)*
South Florida Sheet Metal....F....... 954 647-6457
Pembroke Pines *(G-14060)*
Spectrum Engineering & Mfg Inc....G....... 727 376-5510
Odessa *(G-12154)*
Spencer Fabrications Inc....E....... 352 343-0014
Tavares *(G-18354)*
▼ **Stainless Fabricators Inc**....E....... 813 926-7113
Odessa *(G-12155)*
Stampco Inc....F....... 904 737-6144
Jacksonville *(G-6807)*
Stanron Corporation....E....... 954 974-8050
Fort Lauderdale *(G-4257)*
Steel City Inc....F....... 850 785-9596
Panama City *(G-13952)*
Steel Cnstr Systems Holdg Co....E....... 407 438-1664
Orlando *(G-13214)*
Sterling Industry LLC....E....... 561 845-2440
Riviera Beach *(G-15379)*
Straightline Metals....G....... 407 988-2353
Winter Springs *(G-19484)*
▼ **Style-View Products Inc**....F....... 305 634-9688
Miami *(G-10426)*
Sunbelt Metals & Mfg Inc....E....... 407 889-8960
Apopka *(G-189)*
Sunshine Metal Products Inc....G....... 407 331-1300
Altamonte Springs *(G-77)*
Superior Metal....F....... 407 522-8100
Orlando *(G-13229)*
▼ **Superior Metal Fabricators Inc**....E....... 407 295-5772
Orlando *(G-13230)*
Tampa Metal Works Inc....F....... 813 628-9223
Tampa *(G-18169)*
Tampa Multi Roll Sheet Metal....G....... 813 340-3554
Tampa *(G-18170)*
Tampa Sheet Metal Company....D....... 813 251-1845
Tampa *(G-18172)*
Tarpon Stnless Fabricators Inc....E....... 727 942-1821
Tarpon Springs *(G-18328)*
Taurus Chutes Inc....G....... 954 445-0146
Oakland Park *(G-11846)*
Tejeda Sheet Metal & Aluminum....G....... 305 609-5477
Hialeah *(G-5647)*
Telese Inc....E....... 813 752-6015
Plant City *(G-14470)*
Thomas Smith & Company Inc....F....... 863 858-2199
Lakeland *(G-7821)*
Thompson Awning & Shutter Co....E....... 904 355-1616
Jacksonville *(G-6849)*
Tibor Inc....E....... 561 272-0770
Delray Beach *(G-3150)*
Tk - Autek Inc....G....... 727 572-7473
Palm Harbor *(G-13766)*
Topline Cstm Fabrications LLC....G....... 850 295-2481
Perry *(G-14318)*
Townsend Signs Inc....G....... 386 255-1955
Holly Hill *(G-5761)*
Tri-H Metal Products Inc....G....... 941 753-7311
Bradenton *(G-1130)*
Tri-Tech of Florida Inc....F....... 727 544-8836
Saint Petersburg *(G-15944)*
Tropical Showers Inc....G....... 954 260-5196
Pompano Beach *(G-14892)*
▲ **Turbocombustor Technology Inc**....B....... 772 287-7770
Stuart *(G-17041)*
United Express Intl Corp....G....... 305 591-3292
Miami *(G-10535)*
United Fabrication Shtmtl Inc....G....... 407 826-1933
Orlando *(G-13292)*
United States Awning Company....E....... 941 955-7010
Sarasota *(G-16631)*
Upton House Cooler Corporation....G....... 305 633-2531
Miami *(G-10547)*
◆ **US Sheet Metal Inc**....F....... 305 884-7705
Miami *(G-10553)*
USA Sheet Metal Inc....G....... 786 517-3482
Hialeah *(G-5668)*
▲ **Ver-Val Enterprises Inc**....F....... 850 244-7931
Fort Walton Beach *(G-4838)*
Versatile Manufacturing Inc....E....... 954 561-8083
Oakland Park *(G-11859)*
Versatile Manufacturing Inc....F....... 954 561-8083
Oakland Park *(G-11860)*
Vertec Inc....F....... 850 478-6480
Pensacola *(G-14283)*
W D Wilson Inc....E....... 813 626-6989
Tampa *(G-18250)*
Wheeler Consolidated Inc....F....... 772 464-4400
Fort Pierce *(G-4770)*
White Rose Installation....F....... 772 562-6698
Vero Beach *(G-18683)*
Wilkinson Hi-Rise LLC....C....... 954 342-4400
Fort Lauderdale *(G-4324)*
Window Craftsmen Inc....E....... 941 922-1844
Sarasota *(G-16641)*
Worlds Columbian Exonumis....G....... 561 734-4433
Boynton Beach *(G-975)*

3446 Architectural & Ornamental Metal Work

Aarg Stairs & Raillings Corp....G....... 786 545-6465
Hialeah *(G-5262)*
Aerotec Aluminium Inc....G....... 407 324-5400
Sanford *(G-15988)*
Agri Metal Supply Inc....G....... 386 294-1720
Mayo *(G-8594)*
◆ **Airguide Manufacturing LLC**....C....... 305 888-1631
Hialeah *(G-5276)*
Alabama Metal Industries Corp....D....... 863 688-9256
Lakeland *(G-7630)*
Alenac Metals Corp....E....... 561 877-4109
Palm Springs *(G-13771)*
Alse Industries LLC....F....... 305 688-8778
Miami Gardens *(G-10734)*
▼ **Alumacart Inc**....F....... 772 675-2158
Hobe Sound *(G-5721)*
Amazon Metal Fabricators Inc....F....... 321 631-7574
Cocoa *(G-1994)*
Ambiance Interiors Mfg Corp....G....... 305 668-4995
Miami *(G-9136)*
AMD Ornamental Inc....G....... 239 458-7437
Cape Coral *(G-1378)*
American All Scure Gtes Fnce L....F....... 407 423-4962
Orlando *(G-12467)*
Anchor Aluminum Products South....G....... 305 293-7965
Key West *(G-7177)*
Architctral Designs Metalworks....G....... 954 532-1331
Pompano Beach *(G-14597)*
Architectural Metal Systems....F....... 407 277-1364
Orlando *(G-12486)*
Art Craft Metals Inc....E....... 954 946-4620
Pompano Beach *(G-14601)*
Artistic Welding Inc....G....... 954 563-3098
Oakland Park *(G-11782)*
▼ **Arts Work Unlimited Inc**....G....... 305 247-9257
Miami *(G-9175)*
▼ **Awnings of Hollywood Inc**....E....... 954 963-7717
Hollywood *(G-5780)*
Bachiller Iron Works Inc....E....... 305 751-7773
Miami *(G-9213)*
▲ **Bausch American Towers LLC**....F....... 772 283-2771
Stuart *(G-16911)*
Buchanan Signs Screen Process....E....... 904 725-5500
Jacksonville *(G-6243)*
Caballero Metals Corp....G....... 305 266-9085
Miami *(G-9298)*
Caballero Metals Corp....F....... 305 266-9085
Miami *(G-9299)*
Casco Services Inc....F....... 727 942-1888
Tarpon Springs *(G-18288)*
Cedrus Inc....E....... 772 286-2082
Stuart *(G-16920)*
Cement Precast Products Inc....E....... 352 372-0953
Gainesville *(G-4894)*
Chancey Metal Products Inc....E....... 904 260-6880
Jacksonville *(G-6261)*
Citory Solutions LLC....F....... 407 766-6533
Orlando *(G-12584)*
Classic Iron Decor Inc....F....... 904 241-5022
Jacksonville Beach *(G-6940)*
Clear Horizon Ventures Company....E....... 727 372-1100
Hudson *(G-6018)*
Comres Manufacturing Inc....F....... 813 249-0391
Tampa *(G-17550)*
Creative Metal Studio Inc....E....... 321 206-6112
Apopka *(G-127)*
Custom Metal Creations LLC....G....... 772 807-0000
Fort Pierce *(G-4689)*
▲ **Custom Metal Specialties Inc**....E....... 727 522-3986
Pinellas Park *(G-14341)*
D & D MBL Wldg Fabrication Inc....D....... 772 489-7900
Fort Pierce *(G-4690)*
▲ **D G Morrison Inc**....F....... 813 865-0208
Odessa *(G-12114)*
David Viera LLC....G....... 305 218-3401
Hialeah *(G-5365)*
Deland Metal Craft Company....G....... 386 734-0828
Deland *(G-2967)*
Edwards Ornamental Iron Inc....F....... 904 354-4282
Jacksonville *(G-6355)*
English Ironworks Inc....G....... 941 364-9120
Sarasota *(G-16420)*
Express Ornamental LLC....G....... 813 486-0344
Tampa *(G-17653)*
▼ **Fab Rite Inc**....G....... 561 848-8181
Riviera Beach *(G-15327)*
Fluid Metalworks Inc -105....G....... 850 332-0103
Pensacola *(G-14155)*
Frattle Stairs & Rails Inc....F....... 904 384-3495
Jacksonville *(G-6415)*
Gainesville Iron Works Inc....G....... 352 373-4004
Gainesville *(G-4927)*
▼ **Gelander Industries Inc**....F....... 352 343-3100
Tavares *(G-18338)*
Gj Francos Stair Co Inc....G....... 727 510-4102
Largo *(G-7959)*
Glassarium LLC....E....... 786 631-7080
Miami *(G-9639)*
Greco Alum Railings USA Inc....E....... 727 372-4545
Hudson *(G-6026)*
Greg Valentine LLC....E....... 239 332-0855
Fort Myers *(G-4473)*
Gurtan Designs....G....... 954 972-6100
Pompano Beach *(G-14719)*
▼ **Halliday Products Inc**....D....... 407 298-4470
Orlando *(G-12794)*
Hernandez Ornamental Inc....G....... 305 592-7296
Doral *(G-3381)*
Hollywood Design & Concepts....F....... 954 458-4634
Yalaha *(G-19490)*
Hueston Stair Company....G....... 314 225-4280
Clermont *(G-1964)*
Icon Welding & Fabrication....E....... 941 822-8822
Sarasota *(G-16232)*
Iron-Art & Fence Inc....F....... 407 699-1734
Longwood *(G-8293)*
Ironworks Inc of Orange Park....E....... 904 291-9330
Middleburg *(G-10907)*
J A Custom....G....... 561 615-4680
West Palm Beach *(G-18910)*
Jace Fabrication Inc....G....... 727 547-6873
Pinellas Park *(G-14355)*

JC Iron Omamental Works Inc..............G....... 561 508-5966
Mangonia Park *(G-8504)*
John R Caito..............G....... 850 612-0179
Fort Walton Beach *(G-4811)*
Kawneer Company Inc..............C....... 407 648-4511
Orlando *(G-12867)*
▼ **L & L Ornamental Iron Works**..............F....... 561 547-5605
West Palm Beach *(G-18922)*
▼ **L A Ornamental & Rack Corp**..............G....... 305 696-0419
Miami *(G-9835)*
Largo Aluminum Inc..............F....... 305 852-2390
Islamorada *(G-6098)*
▼ **Laza Iron Works Inc**..............F....... 305 754-8200
Miami *(G-9872)*
▲ **Liberty Aluminum Co**..............E....... 239 369-3000
Lehigh Acres *(G-8197)*
▼ **Litecrete Inc**..............E....... 305 500-9373
Miami *(G-9901)*
M&B Steel Fabricators Inc..............F....... 407 486-1774
Orlando *(G-12942)*
Majic Stairs Inc..............G....... 352 255-1390
The Villages *(G-18392)*
Majic Stairs Inc..............E....... 352 446-6295
Ocala *(G-11991)*
Mantua Manufacturing Co..............G....... 813 621-3714
Tampa *(G-17878)*
Mary Lame Wrought Iron & Alum..............G....... 727 934-2879
Holiday *(G-5747)*
Metal Creations Sarasota Llc..............F....... 941 922-7096
Sarasota *(G-16256)*
▼ **Metal Supply and Machining Inc**..............F....... 561 276-4941
Delray Beach *(G-3107)*
Miami Railing Design Corp..............G....... 305 926-0062
Miami *(G-10009)*
◆ **Millers Custom Metals Inc**..............F....... 561 540-6263
Lake Worth *(G-7572)*
Monumental Fabrication of Amer..............G....... 850 227-9500
Port Saint Joe *(G-15081)*
Naples Iron Works Inc..............E....... 239 649-7265
Naples *(G-11336)*
Nichols Truck Bodies LLC..............E....... 904 781-5080
Jacksonville *(G-6634)*
Ornamental Design Ironworks..............E....... 813 626-8449
Tampa *(G-17960)*
Ornamntal Metal Specialist Inc..............G....... 786 360-5727
Hialeah *(G-5552)*
Pioneer Welding & Fabrication..............G....... 407 880-4997
Apopka *(G-170)*
Quality Railings Miami Corp..............G....... 786 400-0462
Hialeah *(G-5590)*
Railtec Constructions Company..............G....... 410 795-0712
Hutchinson Island *(G-6047)*
Rampmaster Inc..............F....... 305 691-9090
Miami *(G-10238)*
RDS Industrial Inc..............F....... 321 631-0121
Cocoa *(G-2045)*
Regional Cnstr Resources Inc..............E....... 713 789-5131
Sarasota *(G-16558)*
▼ **Reich Metal Fabricators Inc**..............E....... 561 585-3173
West Palm Beach *(G-19018)*
Remior Industries Inc..............E....... 305 883-8722
Miami *(G-10250)*
Rustic Steel Creations Inc..............G....... 813 222-0016
Tampa *(G-18073)*
S & S Welding Inc..............F....... 863 533-2888
Bartow *(G-333)*
▼ **Saftron Manufacturing LLC**..............F....... 305 233-5511
Bradenton *(G-1109)*
▲ **Screenco North Inc**..............E....... 561 840-3300
Palm Beach Gardens *(G-13624)*
Sfa Systems Inc..............E....... 561 585-5927
Lake Worth *(G-7586)*
▲ **Shanker Industries Realty Inc**..............G....... 631 940-9889
West Palm Beach *(G-19029)*
▲ **Solara Industries Inc**..............E....... 863 688-3330
Lakeland *(G-7796)*
South Florida Stairs Inc..............F....... 561 822-3110
Boynton Beach *(G-962)*
▼ **Southeastern Ornamental Iron**..............E....... 904 292-0933
Jacksonville *(G-6790)*
Southern Aluminum Inc..............F....... 239 275-3367
Cape Coral *(G-1474)*
▼ **Stainless Fabricators Inc**..............E....... 813 926-7113
Odessa *(G-12155)*
Statements 2000 LLC..............G....... 561 249-1587
West Palm Beach *(G-19042)*
Sunbelt Metals & Mfg Inc..............E....... 407 889-8960
Apopka *(G-189)*
Tampa Tank & Welding Inc..............F....... 813 241-0123
Gibsonton *(G-5033)*
▲ **Toledo Doors Inc**..............F....... 305 633-4352
Miami *(G-10487)*
◆ **TTI Holdings Inc**..............G....... 813 623-2675
Tampa *(G-18208)*
US Ironworks Company..............F....... 850 588-5995
Panama City *(G-13959)*
Vasquez Custom Metals Inc..............G....... 813 248-3348
Tampa *(G-18234)*
Vintage Ironworks LLC..............G....... 407 339-2555
Altamonte Springs *(G-83)*
W D Wilson Inc..............E....... 813 626-6989
Tampa *(G-18250)*
Wesco Partners Inc..............E....... 941 484-8224
Sarasota *(G-16325)*
White Ladder Inc..............G....... 904 343-9314
Fernandina Beach *(G-3750)*
Wilcox Steel Company LLC..............G....... 727 443-0461
Clearwater *(G-1939)*
Wonderland Products Inc..............G....... 904 786-0144
Jacksonville *(G-6927)*
Ymg Iron Work & Metal Design..............G....... 305 343-2537
Pembroke Pines *(G-14072)*

3448 Prefabricated Metal Buildings & Cmp-nts

▼ **A-1 Roof Trusses Ltd Company**..............F....... 270 316-9409
Coral Springs *(G-2210)*
ABC Screen Masters Inc..............G....... 239 772-7336
Cape Coral *(G-1371)*
Adf International Inc..............F....... 954 931-5150
Pompano Beach *(G-14577)*
Advanced Alum Polk Cnty Inc..............E....... 863 648-5787
Lakeland *(G-7626)*
Affordble Qlty Drywall Screen..............G....... 561 723-0635
Lake Worth *(G-7531)*
Affordble Screen Enclosure LLC..............G....... 561 900-8868
Delray Beach *(G-3042)*
All About Screens..............G....... 239 398-1798
Bonita Springs *(G-812)*
All American Building Products..............G....... 786 718-7300
Dania *(G-2438)*
All Amrcan Bldg Strctres Contr..............G....... 407 466-4959
Apopka *(G-110)*
▼ **All Steel Bldngs Cmponents Inc**..............E....... 813 671-8044
Gibsonton *(G-5025)*
Allied Insulated Panels Inc..............G....... 800 599-3905
Fort Lauderdale *(G-3803)*
Allied Steel Buildings Inc..............E....... 800 508-2718
Fort Lauderdale *(G-3804)*
◆ **Allied Steel Buildings Inc**..............F....... 954 590-4949
Fort Lauderdale *(G-3805)*
Allstar Screen Enclosures & St..............G....... 954 266-9757
Davie *(G-2493)*
Aluma TEC Aluminun..............G....... 352 732-7362
Ocala *(G-11870)*
Alumicenter Inc..............G....... 954 674-2631
Miramar *(G-10967)*
Aluminum Creations..............F....... 386 451-0113
De Leon Springs *(G-2736)*
Amazon Sheds and Gazebos Inc..............F....... 239 498-5558
Fort Myers *(G-4355)*
Amramp North FL..............G....... 904 424-3331
Tallahassee *(G-17218)*
Amtex-Nms Holdings Inc..............D....... 352 728-2930
Leesburg *(G-8141)*
▼ **B & K Installations Inc**..............E....... 305 245-6968
Homestead *(G-5956)*
Bestway Portable Building Inc..............F....... 850 747-1984
Panama City *(G-13871)*
Blue Water Dynamics LLC..............D....... 386 957-5464
Edgewater *(G-3614)*
Bluewater Marine Systems Inc..............G....... 619 499-7507
Saint Petersburg *(G-15724)*
British Boys & Associates..............G....... 305 278-1790
Miami *(G-9277)*
C P Enterprises of Apopka Inc..............G....... 407 886-3321
Mount Dora *(G-11098)*
Carport Solution LLC..............F....... 352 789-1149
Ocala *(G-11896)*
Carports Anywhere Inc..............F....... 352 468-1116
Starke *(G-16888)*
Charles Screening & Alum LLC..............G....... 239 369-0551
Lehigh Acres *(G-8188)*
Clupper LLC..............G....... 386 956-6396
Deltona *(G-3166)*
Cmn Steel Fabricators Inc..............D....... 305 592-5466
Miami *(G-9367)*
▲ **Coastal Craftsmen Aluminum Inc**..............E....... 727 868-8802
Hudson *(G-6019)*
▼ **Coastal Screen & Rail LLC**..............G....... 321 917-4605
Delray Beach *(G-3062)*
Curvco Steel Structures Corp..............F....... 800 956-6341
Delray Beach *(G-3067)*
Custom Built Screen Enclosures..............F....... 239 242-0224
Cape Coral *(G-1408)*
◆ **Dade Engineering Corp**..............F....... 305 885-2766
Coral Gables *(G-2136)*
◆ **Dean Steel Buildings Inc**..............D....... 239 334-1051
Fort Myers *(G-4429)*
Defenshield Inc..............G....... 904 679-3942
Saint Augustine *(G-15535)*
Design Pro Screens Inc..............G....... 407 831-6541
Longwood *(G-8273)*
Df Multi Services LLC..............G....... 407 683-2223
Orlando *(G-12668)*
Eds Aluminum Buildings Inc..............G....... 850 476-2169
Pensacola *(G-14138)*
Elite Outdoor Buildings LLC..............G....... 386 364-1364
Live Oak *(G-8231)*
Ferrera Tooling Inc..............F....... 863 646-8500
Lakeland *(G-7685)*
Fertec Inc..............F....... 850 478-6480
Pensacola *(G-14150)*
▲ **Florida Floats Inc**..............E....... 904 358-3362
Jacksonville *(G-6398)*
▼ **Florida Pre-Fab Inc**..............F....... 813 247-3934
Tampa *(G-17685)*
Florida Screen Enclosures LLC..............G....... 352 398-5679
Spring Hill *(G-16852)*
Forts Services LLC..............F....... 786 942-4389
Coconut Creek *(G-2077)*
Gardners Screen Enclosures..............F....... 813 843-8527
Seffner *(G-16728)*
General Metals & Plastics Inc..............G....... 904 354-8224
Jacksonville *(G-6432)*
Grays Portable Buildings Inc..............G....... 386 755-6449
Lake City *(G-7356)*
▼ **Gulfstream Alum & Shutter Corp**..............E....... 772 287-6476
Stuart *(G-16950)*
Harper Screen Enclosures LLC..............G....... 813 417-5937
Riverview *(G-15272)*
Housmans Alum & Screening Inc..............F....... 321 255-2778
Melbourne *(G-8847)*
Hydes Screening Inc..............G....... 954 345-6743
Coral Springs *(G-2258)*
J D Aluminum..............G....... 239 543-3558
Fort Myers *(G-4500)*
Jacobsen Manufacturing Inc..............C....... 727 726-1138
Safety Harbor *(G-15496)*
Jax Enterprises LLC..............G....... 904 786-6909
Jacksonville *(G-6518)*
Jbr Exteriors Inc..............G....... 772 873-0600
Port Saint Lucie *(G-15115)*
JCs Building Sales..............G....... 386 277-2851
Deland *(G-2988)*
Jennifer Yoder Sung..............G....... 352 748-6655
Wildwood *(G-19196)*
K C Screen..............G....... 407 977-9636
Oviedo *(G-13442)*
Keens Portable Buildings Inc..............F....... 386 364-7995
Live Oak *(G-8234)*
◆ **Kingspan Insulated Panels Inc**..............C....... 386 626-6789
Deland *(G-2991)*
Kingspan Insulated Panels Inc..............D....... 386 626-6789
Deland *(G-2992)*
▼ **Kingspan-Medusa Inc**..............C....... 386 626-6789
Deland *(G-2993)*
Knox Aluminum Inc..............F....... 813 645-3529
Ruskin *(G-15486)*
Langstons Utility Buildings..............G....... 813 659-0141
Mulberry *(G-11128)*
Leslie Industries Inc..............F....... 850 422-0099
Tallahassee *(G-17290)*
M S Amtex-N Inc..............C....... 352 326-9729
Leesburg *(G-8164)*
Majestic Metals Inc..............F....... 813 380-6885
Valrico *(G-18522)*
◆ **Marinetek North America Inc**..............F....... 727 498-8741
Saint Petersburg *(G-15849)*
▲ **Mark Housman Screen RPS Inc**..............E....... 321 255-2778
Melbourne *(G-8883)*
Martin L Matthews..............G....... 904 881-3550
Jacksonville *(G-6579)*
Metal Building Kings..............G....... 412 522-4797
Tamarac *(G-17363)*
Metal Building Supplies LLC..............F....... 407 935-9714
Kissimmee *(G-7274)*
Modular Life Solutions LLC..............G....... 904 900-7965
Jacksonville *(G-6611)*

Morin Corp....G.... 386 626-6789
Deland *(G-2999)*
▼ Neopod Systems LLC....F.... 954 603-3100
Sunrise *(G-17151)*
New World Enclosures Inc....F.... 904 334-4752
Green Cove Springs *(G-5067)*
Ocala Metal Products Inc....G.... 352 861-4500
Ocala *(G-12012)*
Pace Enclosures Inc....F.... 239 275-3818
Fort Myers *(G-4561)*
Park Place Manufacturing Inc....F.... 863 382-0126
Sebring *(G-16701)*
Pioneer Development Entps Inc....F.... 239 592-0001
Naples *(G-11367)*
Precision Screen Enclosures....G.... 239 221-8465
Bonita Springs *(G-848)*
Premier Buildings of Navarre....G.... 850 684-3639
Navarre *(G-11472)*
Quality Rescreening....G.... 941 625-9765
Fort Myers *(G-4578)*
Quality Screen Enclosure LLC....G.... 954 226-1980
Hollywood *(G-5898)*
R & K Buildings Inc....E.... 850 995-9525
Milton *(G-10939)*
R & K Portable Buildings....G.... 850 857-7899
Pensacola *(G-14247)*
R Townsend Rescreens Inc....G.... 239 244-4759
Punta Gorda *(G-15226)*
Rampmaster Inc....F.... 305 691-9090
Miami *(G-10238)*
Ring Power Corporation....E.... 904 354-1858
Jacksonville *(G-6725)*
Scif Solutions Inc....F.... 904 298-0631
Jacksonville *(G-6755)*
Screen Enclosure Lighting....G.... 904 838-9786
Jacksonville Beach *(G-6958)*
Screen Enclosure Services Inc....G.... 239 334-6528
Fort Myers *(G-4600)*
Screen Savers LLC....G.... 321 299-8099
Chuluota *(G-1554)*
▲ Screenco North Inc....E.... 561 840-3300
Palm Beach Gardens *(G-13624)*
Screens Fast....G.... 239 565-1211
Fort Myers *(G-4601)*
Serenity Screen Enclosures LLC....G.... 407 692-3031
Orlando *(G-13175)*
▲ Sesolinc Grp Inc....F.... 772 287-9090
Stuart *(G-17009)*
Shed4less LLC....G.... 863 660-7300
Lakeland *(G-7790)*
Sheds Galore and More LLC....G.... 386 362-1786
Live Oak *(G-8240)*
◆ Shoreline Foundation Inc....C.... 954 985-0981
West Park *(G-19098)*
Smithbilt Industries Inc....D.... 321 690-0902
Auburndale *(G-253)*
▼ Steel Technology & Design....F.... 863 665-2525
Lakeland *(G-7806)*
Suncrest Sheds of South Fla....F.... 305 231-1990
Miami Lakes *(G-10865)*
Superior Sheds Inc....E.... 386 774-9861
Orange City *(G-12379)*
Tdse Inc....E.... 352 399-6413
Wildwood *(G-19204)*
Teds Sheds of Tampa....E.... 239 344-2900
Bonita Springs *(G-861)*
▲ Titan Specialty Cnstr Inc....E.... 850 916-7660
Milton *(G-10943)*
Tri County Aluminum Spc....G.... 727 848-4523
Hudson *(G-6042)*
Trident Building Systems Inc....C.... 941 755-7073
Sarasota *(G-16314)*
U C Fab of Florida LLC....G.... 407 614-4210
Ocoee *(G-12094)*
US Building Systems Corp....F.... 954 281-2100
Deerfield Beach *(G-2931)*
Wheel Systems Intl Inc....F.... 920 235-9888
Bradenton *(G-1147)*
Worth Metals Inc....F.... 904 626-1434
Green Cove Springs *(G-5077)*

3449 Misc Structural Metal Work

Ace Construction Management....G.... 407 704-7803
Orlando *(G-12429)*
▼ Alumacart Inc....F.... 772 675-2158
Hobe Sound *(G-5721)*
Anvil Iron Works Inc....E.... 727 375-2884
Odessa *(G-12102)*
Atlantic Steel Cnstr LLC....G.... 419 236-2200
Miami *(G-9184)*
Brunsteel Corp....G.... 305 251-7607
Miami *(G-9281)*
Capstone Cg LLC....F.... 941 371-3321
Sarasota *(G-16187)*
Davanti Doors Llc....G.... 239 842-8341
Fort Myers *(G-4426)*
Fenwall LLC....D.... 813 343-5979
Tampa *(G-17664)*
▼ Freedom Steel Building Corp....E.... 561 330-0447
Fort Lauderdale *(G-4013)*
Gerdau Ameristeel US Inc....B.... 813 752-7550
Plant City *(G-14434)*
◆ Gerdau Ameristeel US Inc....B.... 813 286-8383
Tampa *(G-17711)*
◆ Gerdau USA Inc....B.... 813 286-8383
Tampa *(G-17712)*
GMF Industries Inc....D.... 863 646-5081
Lakeland *(G-7700)*
Gulf Coast Rebar Inc....E.... 813 247-1200
Tampa *(G-17734)*
Hanaya LLC....F.... 904 285-7575
Ponte Vedra Beach *(G-14941)*
Johnson & Jackson Glass Pdts....F.... 813 630-9774
Tampa *(G-17808)*
Mid Florida Steel Corp....E.... 321 632-8228
Cocoa *(G-2036)*
Midwest Mtal Fbrction Cstm Rll....E.... 317 769-6489
North Fort Myers *(G-11599)*
R&W Distributors Inc....G.... 239 948-5735
Bonita Springs *(G-851)*
▲ Raw Energy Materials Corp....F.... 954 270-9000
Pompano Beach *(G-14825)*
S & S Welding Inc....F.... 863 533-2888
Bartow *(G-333)*
Specialty Fabrication LLC....E.... 863 683-0708
Lakeland *(G-7803)*
◆ Structall Building Systems Inc....E.... 813 855-2627
Oldsmar *(G-12269)*
Tri Tech Metal Inc....G.... 727 946-1229
New Port Richey *(G-11516)*

3451 Screw Machine Prdts

Ashley F Ward Inc....F.... 904 284-2848
Green Cove Springs *(G-5054)*
Blitz Micro Turning Inc....G.... 727 725-5005
Safety Harbor *(G-15489)*
Coastal Machine LLC....G.... 850 769-6117
Panama City *(G-13885)*
Consoldted Mch Tl Holdings LLC....G.... 888 317-9990
Flagler Beach *(G-3754)*
▲ Construction and Elec Pdts Inc....F.... 954 972-9787
Pompano Beach *(G-14645)*
D J Camco Corporation....G.... 904 355-5995
Jacksonville *(G-6305)*
Danco Machine Inc....G.... 727 501-0460
Largo *(G-7930)*
Federated Precision Inc....E.... 561 288-6500
Deerfield Beach *(G-2824)*
Forcon Precision Products LLC....F.... 239 574-4543
Cape Coral *(G-1426)*
Gti Systems Inc....E.... 863 965-2002
Auburndale *(G-245)*
Hunter Aerospace Supply LLC....G.... 954 321-8848
Fort Lauderdale *(G-4052)*
Integrated Design & Develop....G.... 407 268-4300
Sanford *(G-16068)*
Klopfer Holdings Inc....D.... 727 472-2002
Clearwater *(G-1752)*
Merit Screw....G.... 352 344-3744
Hernando *(G-5246)*
Mkm Sarasota LLC....E.... 941 358-0383
Sarasota *(G-16511)*
MSP Industries LLC....C.... 727 443-5764
Clearwater *(G-1795)*
Mtec Trailer Supply....F.... 813 659-1647
Plant City *(G-14449)*
OMalley Manufacturing Inc....G.... 727 327-6817
Saint Petersburg *(G-15872)*
Praesto Enterprises LLC....G.... 407 298-9171
Orlando *(G-13077)*
Precision Metal Parts Inc....E.... 727 526-9165
Saint Petersburg *(G-15888)*
Precision Shapes Inc....E.... 321 269-2555
Titusville *(G-18453)*
Precision Turning Corporation....F.... 386 364-5788
Live Oak *(G-8237)*
Quality Precision Pdts Co Inc....F.... 305 885-4596
Hialeah *(G-5589)*
Royal Precision Products Inc....E.... 305 685-5490
Opa Locka *(G-12356)*
Sanctuary Intl Ministries....G.... 954 955-7818
Fort Lauderdale *(G-4222)*
Sidus Space Inc....E.... 321 613-0615
Cape Canaveral *(G-1367)*
Walkup Enterprises Inc....F.... 727 571-1244
Clearwater *(G-1935)*
Weber Mfg & Supplies Inc....F.... 941 488-5185
North Venice *(G-11764)*

3452 Bolts, Nuts, Screws, Rivets & Washers

Angela Zieglers Window Washers....G.... 239 849-0310
Cape Coral *(G-1380)*
Arrowhead Global LLC....G.... 727 497-7340
Clearwater *(G-1589)*
▲ Construction and Elec Pdts Inc....F.... 954 972-9787
Pompano Beach *(G-14645)*
Dowels Pins & Shafts Inc....E.... 727 461-1255
Clearwater *(G-1656)*
▲ Edwin B Stimpson Company Inc....B.... 954 946-3500
Pompano Beach *(G-14675)*
Fire Rescue Pins Com....G.... 561 312-8423
Palm Beach Gardens *(G-13589)*
Florida Indus Solutions LLC....G.... 833 746-7347
Tampa *(G-17678)*
Grabber Construction Pdts Inc....G.... 813 249-2281
Tampa *(G-17723)*
Henefelt Precision Products....F.... 727 531-0406
Largo *(G-7969)*
Hunter Aerospace Supply LLC....G.... 954 321-8848
Fort Lauderdale *(G-4052)*
Inland Specialties....G.... 941 351-6300
Sarasota *(G-16236)*
▲ Lerner Enterprises Inc....E.... 440 323-5529
Port Charlotte *(G-14988)*
Lighthouse of Leesburg Inc....G.... 352 408-6566
Palm Bay *(G-13521)*
Migrandy Corp....E.... 321 459-0044
Merritt Island *(G-9004)*
Naples Hma LLC....F.... 239 390-2174
Estero *(G-3692)*
Osborne Metals....G.... 727 441-1703
Clearwater *(G-1823)*
Pin-N-Win Wrestling Club Inc....G.... 904 276-8038
Orange Park *(G-12403)*
Pins Fever....G.... 407 619-5314
Altamonte Springs *(G-65)*
Praesto Enterprises LLC....G.... 407 298-9171
Orlando *(G-13077)*
Precision Shapes Inc....E.... 321 269-2555
Titusville *(G-18453)*
Pressure Washers USA....G.... 561 848-7970
Lake Park *(G-7478)*
Quality Socket Screw Mfg Corp....F.... 941 475-9585
Englewood *(G-3665)*
Shamrock Mobile Detl & Pressur....G.... 941 286-3572
Punta Gorda *(G-15231)*
▲ Siligom USA LLC....F.... 786 406-6262
Doral *(G-3504)*
Sin Pin Inc....G.... 877 805-5665
Stuart *(G-17015)*
Sockets & Specials Inc....F.... 561 582-7022
West Palm Beach *(G-19036)*
Standard Rivet Company Inc....F.... 386 872-6477
South Daytona *(G-16810)*
▲ Sunpack of Pensacola Inc....F.... 850 476-9838
Pensacola *(G-14271)*
Super Brite Screw Corp....F.... 305 822-6560
Miami *(G-10436)*
U S Hardware Supply Inc....E.... 407 657-1551
Winter Park *(G-19454)*
Washers-R-Us Inc....G.... 850 573-0221
Alford *(G-23)*
Xue Wu Inc....G.... 727 532-4571
Clearwater *(G-1946)*

3462 Iron & Steel Forgings

American Professional Ir Work....G.... 305 556-9522
Hialeah *(G-5294)*
Anchor & Docking Inc....G.... 239 770-2030
Cape Coral *(G-1379)*
ARC Group Worldwide Inc....D.... 303 467-5236
Deland *(G-2959)*
Archimaze Logistics Inc....G.... 954 615-7485
Fort Lauderdale *(G-3819)*
Blue Horseshoe Pools West Inc....G.... 321 287-8758
Clermont *(G-1950)*
▲ Dieselsite Inc....G.... 888 414-3457
Homosassa *(G-6002)*
Dockside At Horseshoe Beach L....G.... 352 377-4616
Gainesville *(G-4906)*

SIC

Enstar Holdings (us) LLC......D....... 727 217-2900
Saint Petersburg *(G-15770)*
Grizzly Manufacturing Inc......E....... 386 755-0220
Lake City *(G-7360)*
Hines Energy Complex......F....... 863 519-6106
Bartow *(G-319)*
Horseshoe Knoll Lc......G....... 850 894-0824
Tallahassee *(G-17280)*
Horseshoe Picking Inc......F....... 305 345-5778
Homestead *(G-5969)*
Horseshoe Shrimp Boat LLC......G....... 352 356-1982
Horseshoe Beach *(G-6007)*
Jmg Strategies LLC......G....... 305 606-2117
Miami Beach *(G-10686)*
Lubov Manufacturing Inc......G....... 813 873-2640
Tampa *(G-17862)*
Masaka LLC......F....... 786 800-8337
Doral *(G-3426)*
Nav-X LLC......E....... 954 978-9988
Fort Lauderdale *(G-4134)*
North Amrcn Prtection Ctrl LLC......G....... 407 788-3717
Altamonte Springs *(G-58)*
◆ **Point Blank Enterprises Inc**......A....... 954 630-0900
Pompano Beach *(G-14801)*
◆ **Profast Usa Inc**......F....... 305 827-7801
Miami Lakes *(G-10845)*
▲ **Profile Racing Inc**......E....... 727 392-8307
Saint Petersburg *(G-15891)*
▲ **Riley Gear Corporation**......D....... 904 829-5652
Saint Augustine *(G-15596)*
Rosuca International LLC......G....... 305 332-5572
Doral *(G-3490)*
Scorpion Equity LLC......E....... 352 512-0800
Ocala *(G-12043)*
▲ **Sunpack of Pensacola Inc**......F....... 850 476-9838
Pensacola *(G-14271)*
▼ **Survival Armor Inc**......E....... 239 210-0891
Fort Myers *(G-4620)*
◆ **Xcessive Inc**......G....... 866 919-9527
Miami Lakes *(G-10882)*

3463 Nonferrous Forgings

Advanced Engine Tech LLC......G....... 727 744-2935
Clearwater *(G-1565)*
Bill Evans Aluminum Inc......G....... 352 400-1424
Lecanto *(G-8128)*
John Mader Enterprises Inc......E....... 239 731-5455
Fort Myers *(G-4506)*
Lawrence Commercial Systems......F....... 850 574-8723
Tallahassee *(G-17289)*
Nav-X LLC......E....... 954 978-9988
Fort Lauderdale *(G-4134)*
▲ **Sapa Prcsion Tubing Adrian Inc**......E....... 321 636-8147
Rockledge *(G-15446)*

3465 Automotive Stampings

Clever Covers Inc......G....... 407 423-5959
Orlando *(G-12590)*
Cooper-Standard Automotive Inc......E....... 407 330-3323
Sanford *(G-16024)*
Cooper-Standard Automotive Inc......D....... 407 330-3323
Sanford *(G-16025)*
Direct Sales and Design Inc......F....... 954 522-5477
Fort Lauderdale *(G-3943)*
◆ **Excellent Performance Inc**......G....... 561 296-0776
Riviera Beach *(G-15326)*
▲ **Florida Production Engrg Inc**......C....... 386 677-2566
Ormond Beach *(G-13372)*
Glennmar Supply LLC......F....... 727 536-1955
Largo *(G-7961)*
Lincoln Tactical LLC......F....... 813 419-3110
Valrico *(G-18521)*
▼ **Marquez Brothers Inc**......F....... 305 888-0090
Medley *(G-8683)*
Priko Corp......F....... 305 556-3558
Miami Lakes *(G-10843)*
Pro Trim of Central Florida......G....... 863 294-4646
Winter Haven *(G-19346)*
PSi Customs......G....... 863 661-4211
Winter Haven *(G-19350)*
▼ **Rotab Inc**......E....... 954 447-7746
Fort Lauderdale *(G-4217)*
Spicer Industries Inc......F....... 352 732-5300
Ocala *(G-12057)*
Sterling Eqp Mfg Centl Fla Inc......G....... 352 669-3255
Umatilla *(G-18503)*
▲ **Wish Inc**......F....... 305 653-9474
North Miami Beach *(G-11713)*

3469 Metal Stampings, NEC

Accurate Metal Fabricators......F....... 407 933-2666
Kissimmee *(G-7217)*
Accurate Metals Spinning Inc......G....... 305 885-9988
Medley *(G-8606)*
▼ **Aero Precision Products Inc**......D....... 305 688-2565
Opa Locka *(G-12283)*
Aero Technology Mfg Inc......F....... 305 345-7747
Miami *(G-9082)*
Aircraft Tbular Components Inc......E....... 321 757-9020
Melbourne *(G-8760)*
All Southern Fabricators Inc......E....... 727 573-4846
Clearwater *(G-1574)*
Benton Machine Works Inc......G....... 904 768-9161
Jacksonville *(G-6207)*
Blackwater Folk Art Inc......G....... 850 623-3470
Milton *(G-10922)*
Blue Water Dynamics LLC......D....... 386 957-5464
Edgewater *(G-3614)*
Boca Stone Designs......F....... 561 362-2085
Boca Raton *(G-458)*
Chasco Machine & Manufacturing......G....... 727 815-3510
Brooksville *(G-1218)*
▲ **Chasco Machine & Mfg Inc**......E....... 352 678-4188
Brooksville *(G-1219)*
Cnc Works Service Inc......F....... 813 777-8642
Clearwater *(G-1630)*
◆ **Composite Essential Mtls LLC**......G....... 772 344-0034
Port St Lucie *(G-15172)*
D & A Machine Inc......G....... 407 275-5770
Orlando *(G-12642)*
▲ **Daws Manufacturing Company Inc**......C....... 850 478-3298
Pensacola *(G-14125)*
Defense Stamping & Engineering......E....... 850 438-6105
Pensacola *(G-14127)*
▼ **Ebway LLC**......E....... 954 971-4911
Fort Lauderdale *(G-3957)*
▲ **Edwin B Stimpson Company Inc**......B....... 954 946-3500
Pompano Beach *(G-14675)*
Epare LLC......F....... 347 682-5121
Miami *(G-9531)*
▲ **ES Investments LLC**......C....... 727 536-8822
Clearwater *(G-1677)*
◆ **Eurosign Metalwerke Inc**......G....... 954 717-4426
Fort Lauderdale *(G-3975)*
Exact Inc......C....... 904 783-6640
Jacksonville *(G-6372)*
Famatel USA LLC......G....... 754 217-4841
Dania *(G-2445)*
Florida Metal Services Inc......D....... 727 541-6441
Largo *(G-7950)*
Floridian Title Group Inc......G....... 305 792-4911
Miami *(G-9588)*
Gator Stampings Intl Inc......D....... 941 753-9598
Sarasota *(G-16218)*
Global Friction Products Inc......F....... 813 241-2700
Tampa *(G-17715)*
▲ **Global Marketing Corp**......E....... 973 426-1088
Bradenton *(G-1047)*
Gregg Tool & Die Co Inc......G....... 305 685-6309
Hialeah *(G-5436)*
Griffiths Corporation......D....... 407 851-8342
Orlando *(G-12790)*
▲ **Helicopter Helmet LLC**......G....... 843 556-0405
Melbourne *(G-8841)*
▲ **Hoffstetter Tool & Die Inc**......F....... 727 573-7775
Clearwater *(G-1715)*
Hudson Tool & Die Company Inc......C....... 386 672-2000
Ormond Beach *(G-13378)*
▲ **Hycomb Usa Inc**......F....... 954 251-1691
Hallandale Beach *(G-5190)*
Icosi Manufacturing LLC......F....... 813 854-1333
Odessa *(G-12095)*
Industrial Spring Corp......F....... 954 524-2558
Davie *(G-2537)*
Interlake Industries Inc......G....... 863 688-5665
Lakeland *(G-7716)*
Interlake Stamping Florida Inc......C....... 863 688-5665
Lakeland *(G-7717)*
▼ **Iron Container LLC**......E....... 305 726-2150
Miami *(G-9771)*
◆ **Iva Parts Broker LLC**......G....... 239 222-2604
Miramar *(G-11006)*
John Trent Construction LLC......G....... 904 753-2942
Fernandina Beach *(G-3740)*
▲ **Koszegi Industries Inc**......E....... 954 419-9544
Deerfield Beach *(G-2855)*
▼ **Kwikprint Manufacturing Co Inc**......G....... 904 737-3755
Jacksonville *(G-6547)*

LAtelier Pris Hute Design LLC......F....... 800 792-3550
Miami *(G-9866)*
Leader Tech Inc......D....... 813 855-6921
Tampa *(G-17838)*
▲ **Masonite Corporation**......D....... 813 877-2726
Tampa *(G-17887)*
Metal Products Company LC......F....... 850 526-5593
Marianna *(G-8584)*
Metal Spinning Systems Inc......G....... 305 252-7778
Miami *(G-9985)*
Mikes Aluminum Products LLC......G....... 407 855-1989
Saint Cloud *(G-15660)*
Mohawk Manufacturing Company......F....... 407 849-0333
Longwood *(G-8313)*
▲ **Officine Gullo USA LLC**......F....... 800 781-7125
Miami *(G-10091)*
P&A Machine......F....... 407 275-5770
Orlando *(G-13042)*
Peterson Manufacturing Co Inc......E....... 941 371-4989
Sarasota *(G-16544)*
Plastic and Products Mktg LLC......F....... 352 867-8078
Ocala *(G-12028)*
Premier Fabricating Llc......E....... 813 855-4633
Oldsmar *(G-12260)*
Press-Rite Inc......G....... 954 963-7373
Miramar *(G-11030)*
Production Metal Stampings......F....... 850 981-8240
Milton *(G-10938)*
Professnal Kit Instller Group......F....... 954 436-1513
Miramar *(G-11033)*
R and R Brokerage Co......G....... 305 592-4329
Doral *(G-3477)*
▲ **RDS Manufacturing Inc**......C....... 850 584-6898
Perry *(G-14310)*
Rek Manufacturing Inc......G....... 321 269-3533
Titusville *(G-18455)*
▲ **Roden International Inc**......F....... 954 929-1900
Hollywood *(G-5902)*
Royal Prestige......F....... 813 464-9872
Fort Lauderdale *(G-4219)*
SBs Precision Shtmtl Inc......E....... 321 951-7411
Melbourne *(G-8927)*
Sohacki Industries Inc......E....... 904 826-0130
Saint Augustine *(G-15613)*
SOUTHERN SPRING & STAMPING INC E....... 941 488-2276
Venice *(G-18575)*
Spicer Industries Inc......F....... 352 732-5300
Ocala *(G-12057)*
Stanron Corporation......E....... 954 974-8050
Fort Lauderdale *(G-4257)*
Strictly Toolboxes......G....... 352 672-6566
Gainesville *(G-5005)*
Top Notch Diecutting Foil STA......G....... 904 346-3511
Jacksonville *(G-6863)*
▲ **Trident Trading Inc**......G....... 561 488-0458
Boca Raton *(G-756)*
U S Hardware Supply Inc......E....... 407 657-1551
Winter Park *(G-19454)*
Wastequip Manufacturing Co LLC......E....... 863 665-6507
Lakeland *(G-7832)*
▲ **Zeroll Co**......F....... 772 461-3811
Weston *(G-19180)*

3471 Electroplating, Plating, Polishing, Anodizing & Coloring

A Sotolongo Polishing Marble C......G....... 305 271-7957
Miami *(G-9043)*
Accurate Metal Finshg Fla Inc......F....... 321 636-4900
Rockledge *(G-15392)*
Accurate Metal Finshg Fla Inc......F....... 321 636-4900
Rockledge *(G-15391)*
Action Plating Corp......F....... 305 685-6313
Opa Locka *(G-12282)*
Adtec II Tampa Inc......E....... 786 588-3688
Pinellas Park *(G-14333)*
Airco Plating Company Inc......E....... 305 633-2476
Miami *(G-9095)*
Alex Robert Silversmith Inc......G....... 727 442-7333
Clearwater *(G-1573)*
Allbright Electropolishing......G....... 727 449-9353
Clearwater *(G-1575)*
AM Metal Finishing......E....... 407 843-0182
Orlando *(G-12464)*
Amado Wheel Finishing......G....... 786 732-6249
Miami *(G-9130)*
American Buffing Solid Surface......G....... 407 625-6837
Orlando *(G-12468)*
B4c Technologies Inc......G....... 772 463-1557
Palm City *(G-13643)*

Bent Chrome LLC ....G....... 813 363-3398
Riverview *(G-15265)*
▲ **Best Engineered Surfc Tech LLC** .....D....... 407 932-0008
Kissimmee *(G-7223)*
▲ **Biomedtech Laboratories Inc** ....F....... 813 558-2000
Tampa *(G-17470)*
Burn Brite Metals Co Inc ....G....... 727 360-4408
Treasure Island *(G-18474)*
Central Florida Plating Inc ....G....... 321 452-7234
Merritt Island *(G-8998)*
Certified Metal Finishing Inc ....E....... 954 979-0707
Pompano Beach *(G-14633)*
Cfu Plating ....G....... 386 795-5198
Ocala *(G-11900)*
Chem-Tek Metal Finishing Corp ....F....... 321 722-2227
Melbourne *(G-8788)*
Chrome Plating Shop ....G....... 786 527-5357
Miami *(G-9352)*
Coating Hues Inc ....G....... 786 626-9241
Naples *(G-11212)*
Coating Technology Inc ....E....... 813 854-3674
Oldsmar *(G-12216)*
Crown Plating Inc ....E....... 904 783-6640
Jacksonville *(G-6299)*
Cya Powder Coating LLC ....G....... 727 299-9832
Clearwater *(G-1646)*
D R C Industries Inc ....G....... 954 971-0699
Pompano Beach *(G-14657)*
▼ **David Russell Anodizing** ....G....... 407 302-4041
Sanford *(G-16032)*
Delta Metal Finishing Inc ....E....... 954 953-9898
Fort Lauderdale *(G-3936)*
Dhs Enterprises Inc ....G....... 727 572-9470
Clearwater *(G-1651)*
Electro Lab Inc ....F....... 813 818-7605
Oldsmar *(G-12225)*
Eps Metal Finishing ....G....... 954 782-3073
Pompano Beach *(G-14682)*
Exact Inc ....C....... 904 783-6640
Jacksonville *(G-6372)*
Exotic Marble Polishing Inc ....G....... 786 318-6568
North Miami *(G-11638)*
Ezproducts International Inc ....G....... 863 735-0813
Wauchula *(G-18691)*
Finishing Group of Florid ....G....... 954 981-2171
Hollywood *(G-5821)*
Finns Brass and Silver Polsg ....G....... 904 387-1165
Jacksonville *(G-6381)*
First Cast Strpping MBL Sndbls ....G....... 904 733-5915
Jacksonville *(G-6383)*
Florida Polishing ....G....... 305 688-2988
Opa Locka *(G-12317)*
Freedom Metal Finishing Inc ....E....... 727 573-2464
Clearwater *(G-1695)*
Gold Effects Inc ....G....... 727 573-1990
Clearwater *(G-1704)*
Gold Plating Specialties ....G....... 239 851-9323
Fort Myers *(G-4470)*
Gti Systems Inc ....E....... 863 965-2002
Auburndale *(G-245)*
Hard Chrome Enterprises Inc ....G....... 561 844-2529
Lake Park *(G-7474)*
Hard Surface Polishing LLC ....G....... 850 360-4140
Graceville *(G-5043)*
Hialeah Plating ....G....... 305 953-4143
Hialeah *(G-5445)*
Industrial Marine Inc ....F....... 904 781-4707
Jacksonville *(G-6493)*
Innovative Money Concepts ....G....... 954 748-6197
Parkland *(G-13992)*
Jssa Inc ....E....... 321 383-7798
Titusville *(G-18435)*
Kerno LLC ....F....... 954 261-5854
Fort Lauderdale *(G-4089)*
Kissimmee Polishing ....G....... 407 923-9446
Kissimmee *(G-7263)*
Marios Metalcraft ....G....... 239 649-0085
Naples *(G-11321)*
Mark Plating Co ....G....... 561 655-4370
West Palm Beach *(G-18942)*
Melmar Cstm Met Finshg Svc Inc ....G....... 954 327-5788
Davie *(G-2551)*
Metal Spray Painting Powder ....G....... 954 227-2744
Coral Springs *(G-2281)*
Mil-Spec Metal Finishing Inc ....G....... 386 426-7188
Edgewater *(G-3631)*
Millenium Engine Plating Inc ....G....... 305 688-0098
Hialeah *(G-5518)*
Ni-Chro Plating Corp ....G....... 727 327-5118
Saint Petersburg *(G-15866)*
Orlando Plating Co ....G....... 407 843-1140
Orlando *(G-13036)*
PC of Titusville Inc ....F....... 321 267-1161
Titusville *(G-18449)*
Peninsula Metal Finishing Inc ....E....... 407 291-1023
Orlando *(G-13059)*
Policrete LLC ....G....... 305 552-7026
Miami *(G-10175)*
Polishing By Wilson O ....G....... 727 203-0100
Port Richey *(G-15063)*
Poly Coatings of South Inc ....F....... 941 371-8555
Sarasota *(G-16546)*
Pozin Enterprises Inc ....E....... 727 546-8974
Clearwater *(G-1838)*
Pro-Chemicals USA Corp ....G....... 305 885-7922
Medley *(G-8710)*
Purecoat International LLC ....E....... 561 844-0100
West Palm Beach *(G-19013)*
Quality Anodizing Incorporated ....G....... 954 791-8711
Davie *(G-2578)*
Quality Finishers Inc ....G....... 954 782-3073
Pompano Beach *(G-14822)*
Quality Powder Coating Inc ....F....... 941 378-0051
Sarasota *(G-16553)*
Russell Bros Alum Andzing Ctin ....F....... 407 323-5619
Sanford *(G-16113)*
Seminole Metal Finishing Inc ....F....... 407 332-8949
Altamonte Springs *(G-72)*
Shineline Buffing & Detail ....G....... 941 268-1033
Punta Gorda *(G-15232)*
Sintavia LLC ....G....... 954 474-7800
Fort Lauderdale *(G-4238)*
Space Coast Map LLC ....G....... 321 242-4538
Melbourne *(G-8938)*
Spacecast Pltg Met Rfnshing In ....F....... 321 254-2880
Melbourne *(G-8939)*
▼ **Spectra Chrome LLC** ....G....... 727 573-1990
Clearwater *(G-1886)*
Standard Sand & Silica Company ....G....... 863 419-9673
Haines City *(G-5148)*
Stuart-Dean Co Inc ....F....... 305 652-9595
Doral *(G-3515)*
Superior Chrome Plating Inc ....F....... 832 659-0873
Naples *(G-11427)*
Techno-Coatings Inc ....C....... 305 945-2220
North Miami *(G-11659)*
▲ **Titan Specialty Cnstr Inc** ....E....... 850 916-7660
Milton *(G-10943)*
Unique Marble Polishing Inc ....G....... 305 969-1554
Miami *(G-10532)*
▲ **Universal Polishing Systems** ....G....... 407 227-9516
Orlando *(G-13297)*
World Plate ....G....... 386 597-7832
Bunnell *(G-1312)*
Z-2 Metal Artwork Inc ....G....... 305 804-4974
Hialeah *(G-5694)*

3479 Coating & Engraving, NEC

5 Star Coatings LLc ....G....... 850 628-3743
Panama City Beach *(G-13967)*
88 South Atlantic LLC ....G....... 386 253-0105
Daytona Beach *(G-2619)*
904 Powderworx LLC ....G....... 904 290-6383
Jacksonville *(G-6104)*
A J W Coatings Corp ....G....... 786 357-7580
Hialeah Gardens *(G-5697)*
A Tek Steel Industries Inc ....G....... 561 745-2858
Jupiter *(G-6992)*
A-Brevard Coatings Inc ....G....... 321 726-0322
Palm Bay *(G-13497)*
AAA Custom Powder Coating Inc ....G....... 305 531-5983
Miami Beach *(G-10634)*
Abakan Inc ....G....... 786 206-5368
Miami *(G-9052)*
Absolute Powder Coating Inc ....F....... 954 917-2715
Pompano Beach *(G-14574)*
Accurate Powder Coating Inc ....G....... 321 269-6972
Titusville *(G-18410)*
Aerospc/Dfense Coatings GA Inc ....G....... 407 843-1140
Altamonte Springs *(G-25)*
All American Coatings LLC ....G....... 941 730-9397
Valrico *(G-18514)*
Allstar Lighting & Sound Inc ....F....... 407 767-0111
Longwood *(G-8252)*
Alpha Coatings Inc ....G....... 850 324-9454
Cantonment *(G-1334)*
Alternative Coatings of SW Fla ....G....... 239 537-6153
Naples *(G-11156)*
Aluminum Powder Coating ....G....... 305 628-4155
Hialeah *(G-5285)*
Aluminum Powder Coating Lc ....F....... 305 628-4155
Hialeah *(G-5286)*
American Prtective Coating Inc ....E....... 954 561-0999
Fort Lauderdale *(G-3814)*
Americas Blasting Coatings LLC ....G....... 754 281-6738
Fort Lauderdale *(G-3815)*
Americoat Corporation ....G....... 863 667-1035
Lakeland *(G-7635)*
Ameritech Powder Coating Inc ....F....... 239 274-8000
Fort Myers *(G-4361)*
Aml Extreme Powdercoating ....G....... 904 794-4313
Saint Augustine *(G-15516)*
Arcoat Coatings Corporation ....E....... 561 422-9900
West Palm Beach *(G-18799)*
Artistic Custom Coatings Inc ....G....... 941 822-5608
Sarasota *(G-16349)*
Automated Services Inc ....F....... 772 461-3388
Fort Pierce *(G-4679)*
Azz Powder Coating - Tampa LLC ....G....... 813 390-2802
Tampa *(G-17451)*
Bacc Coatings LLC ....G....... 239 424-8843
Cape Coral *(G-1387)*
Bad Fish Powder Coat ....G....... 904 465-8888
Jacksonville *(G-6188)*
Balpro Powder Coating Inc ....F....... 954 797-0520
Fort Lauderdale *(G-3838)*
▲ **Best Engineered Surfc Tech LLC** .....D....... 407 932-0008
Kissimmee *(G-7223)*
Best Finisher ....F....... 305 688-8174
Miami *(G-9234)*
Best Powder Coatings Inc ....E....... 305 836-9460
Hialeah *(G-5323)*
Blast Ctings Powdercoating LLC ....F....... 561 635-7605
Lake Worth Beach *(G-7608)*
Bobs Custom Coatings LLC ....G....... 941 745-9659
Bradenton *(G-1001)*
Boca Coatings Inc ....G....... 561 400-8183
Boca Raton *(G-449)*
Bold City Spray Coatings LLC ....G....... 904 655-0825
Jacksonville *(G-6224)*
Bricklser Engrv Monuments Corp ....F....... 786 806-0672
Doral *(G-3285)*
Brothers Powder Coating Inc ....G....... 727 846-0717
New Port Richey *(G-11484)*
Brycoat Inc ....E....... 727 490-1000
Oldsmar *(G-12212)*
Bumper Doctor ....G....... 850 341-1771
Pensacola *(G-14109)*
C2 Powder Coating LLC ....G....... 941 404-2671
Bradenton *(G-1009)*
Caliber Coating Inc ....G....... 813 928-1461
Zephyrhills *(G-19509)*
Captivated Coatings LLC ....G....... 321 446-6619
Merritt Island *(G-8997)*
Centrex Powdercoating Inc ....G....... 813 390-2802
Tampa *(G-17524)*
Clear View Coatings LLC ....F....... 850 210-0155
Tallahassee *(G-17234)*
Cm2 Industries Inc ....G....... 305 685-4812
Opa Locka *(G-12301)*
Coastal Powder Coatings Inc ....G....... 772 283-5311
Palm City *(G-13648)*
Coating Heaven ....G....... 321 300-5464
Orlando *(G-12593)*
Continental Property LLC ....G....... 817 613-1890
Orlando *(G-12616)*
Copernicco Coatings LLC ....G....... 407 948-3434
Orlando *(G-12620)*
▲ **Corrocoat USA Inc** ....F....... 904 268-4559
Jacksonville *(G-6294)*
Coverall Aluminum Inc ....F....... 321 377-7874
Sanford *(G-16026)*
Creative Coating LLC ....G....... 407 346-5725
Kissimmee *(G-7234)*
Critical Coatings Inc ....G....... 813 515-7119
Tampa *(G-17568)*
Custom Colors Powder Coating ....G....... 941 953-7997
Sarasota *(G-16399)*
Custom Powder Coating LLC ....G....... 386 758-3973
Lake City *(G-7352)*
Cya Powder Coating LLC ....G....... 727 299-9832
Clearwater *(G-1646)*
D and I Trucking Express Inc ....G....... 786 443-3320
Miami *(G-9425)*
D and S Superior Coatings Inc ....G....... 360 388-6099
Fort Myers *(G-4424)*
Dads Powder Coating ....G....... 813 715-6561
Zephyrhills *(G-19513)*
Decortive Electro Coatings Inc ....F....... 386 255-7878
Daytona Beach *(G-2658)*

S I C

Dew It Right Coatings........G....... 504 272-4981
Edgewater *(G-3621)*
Dna Surface Concepts Inc........F....... 561 328-7302
Riviera Beach *(G-15320)*
Dps Powder Coating........G....... 727 573-2797
Clearwater *(G-1658)*
Ds Coatings Inc........F....... 321 848-4719
Avon Park *(G-286)*
Ds Powder Coating........G....... 561 660-7835
Lake Worth Beach *(G-7610)*
E G Coatings LLC........F....... 407 624-2615
Kissimmee *(G-7240)*
Ecosmart Surface & Coating TEC........G....... 402 319-1607
West Palm Beach *(G-18860)*
▲ Electrostatic Industrial Pntg........G....... 305 696-4556
Miami *(G-9511)*
Elite Powder Coating........G....... 786 616-8084
Miami *(G-9517)*
Emerald Coast Coatings LLC........F....... 850 424-5244
Fort Walton Beach *(G-4798)*
Endless Coatings Inc........G....... 813 714-5395
Zephyrhills *(G-19516)*
Every Thing Aluminum........G....... 561 202-9900
Lantana *(G-7873)*
Excell Coatings Inc........E....... 321 868-7968
Cape Canaveral *(G-1358)*
Exotic Custom Coatings........G....... 850 358-1492
Lynn Haven *(G-8432)*
Extreme Coatings........G....... 727 528-7998
Saint Petersburg *(G-15775)*
Finlayson Enterprises Inc........G....... 850 785-7953
Panama City *(G-13902)*
Finns Brass and Silver Polsg........G....... 904 387-1165
Jacksonville *(G-6381)*
Florida Pwdr Cting Shtters Inc........F....... 561 588-2410
Lantana *(G-7874)*
Florida Spcialty Coatings Corp........G....... 727 224-6883
Melbourne *(G-8834)*
Foot-In-Your-mouth Inc........F....... 850 438-0876
Pensacola *(G-14157)*
Genteel Coatings LLC........G....... 772 708-1781
Inglis *(G-6076)*
Gg Professional Painting Corp........F....... 786 716-8972
Miami *(G-9635)*
▲ Glassflake International Inc........G....... 904 268-4000
Jacksonville *(G-6436)*
Glory Sandblasting Inc........F....... 407 422-0078
Orlando *(G-12784)*
Gml Coatings LLC........F....... 941 755-2176
Bradenton *(G-1050)*
Grindhard Coatings Inc........G....... 772 221-9986
Stuart *(G-16949)*
Gwb Coatings LLC........G....... 407 271-7732
Orlando *(G-12791)*
▲ Gws Tool LLC........F....... 352 343-8778
Tavares *(G-18340)*
Hialeah Powder Coating Corp........F....... 786 275-4107
Hialeah *(G-5446)*
◆ High Performance Systems Inc........E....... 863 294-5566
Winter Haven *(G-19329)*
◆ Ideal Deals LLC........C....... 386 736-1700
Saint Augustine *(G-15553)*
Industrial Coating Solutions........G....... 813 333-8988
Tampa *(G-17780)*
Industrial Glvanizers Amer Inc........E....... 813 621-8990
Tampa *(G-17781)*
Industrial Glvanizers Amer Inc........E....... 305 681-8844
Miami *(G-9739)*
▲ Industrial Glvnzers Stheastern........D....... 813 621-8990
Miami *(G-9740)*
Industrial Marine Inc........F....... 904 781-4707
Jacksonville *(G-6493)*
Industrial Nanotech Inc........G....... 800 767-3998
Naples *(G-11286)*
Innovative Powder Coating Inc........G....... 954 537-2558
Oakland Park *(G-11813)*
JAS Powder Coating LLC........G....... 954 916-7711
Fort Lauderdale *(G-4076)*
JAS Powder Coating LLC........G....... 386 410-6675
Edgewater *(G-3627)*
JM Coatings Inc........G....... 407 312-1115
Longwood *(G-8297)*
Jmc Coatings LLC........G....... 239 260-5451
Naples *(G-11297)*
Jnr International Metals Inc........G....... 305 671-3509
North Miami Beach *(G-11687)*
Kingdom Coatings Inc........G....... 904 600-1424
Middleburg *(G-10908)*
L A Rust Inc........F....... 954 749-5009
Sunrise *(G-17140)*

Labelpro Inc........F....... 727 538-2149
Clearwater *(G-1757)*
Leisure Furniture Powder CT........F....... 239 597-4343
Naples *(G-11310)*
Leto LLC........G....... 813 486-8049
Clearwater *(G-1758)*
M and T Pro Coating Inc........G....... 727 272-4620
Clearwater *(G-1766)*
Magnum Coatings Inc........G....... 407 704-0786
Brandon *(G-1166)*
Majestic Coatings Inc........G....... 561 722-9593
Lake Worth *(G-7568)*
Marlin Coatings LLC........F....... 850 224-1370
Tallahassee *(G-17295)*
Matrix Coatings Corp........F....... 561 848-1288
West Palm Beach *(G-18945)*
Matrix Coatings Inc........G....... 561 848-1288
West Palm Beach *(G-18946)*
Metalplate Galvanizing LP........D....... 904 768-6330
Jacksonville *(G-6599)*
◆ Mineral Life Intl Inc........G....... 305 661-9854
Miami *(G-10026)*
Modern Coating System LLC........G....... 786 326-3652
Miami *(G-10033)*
Monteocha Coatings Inc........G....... 352 367-3136
Gainesville *(G-4965)*
Mpp Coatings Inc........G....... 386 334-4484
Port Orange *(G-15025)*
Nano Activated Coatings Inc........G....... 727 437-1099
Clearwater *(G-1800)*
Nano Safe Coatings Inc........G....... 561 747-5758
Jupiter *(G-7079)*
Naples Powder Coating LLC........G....... 239 352-3500
Naples *(G-11337)*
National Powdr Coating Fla Inc........G....... 941 756-1322
Bradenton *(G-1084)*
North FL Custom Coatings Inc........G....... 904 251-4462
Jacksonville *(G-6639)*
Nu-Vue Industries Inc........E....... 305 694-0397
Hialeah *(G-5546)*
Orellana Coatings Inc........G....... 305 389-4610
Miami *(G-10114)*
Palm Bay Coml Coatings Inc........G....... 321 266-2467
Melbourne *(G-8903)*
Pcm Products Inc........E....... 321 267-7500
Titusville *(G-18450)*
Performance Powder Coating........F....... 407 339-4000
Longwood *(G-8323)*
Petes Seal Coating........G....... 857 251-1912
Pompano Beach *(G-14789)*
POm Performance Coatings LLC........G....... 561 441-7611
West Palm Beach *(G-19000)*
Powder Coating Factory LLC........G....... 407 286-4550
Orlando *(G-13074)*
Powdertech Plus Inc........G....... 904 269-1719
Orange Park *(G-12404)*
Power Tek LLC........G....... 904 814-7007
Saint Augustine *(G-15590)*
Pozin Enterprises Inc........E....... 727 546-8974
Clearwater *(G-1838)*
Precision Coat of Florida........G....... 813 986-1611
Tampa *(G-18004)*
Precision Metal Services Inc........F....... 407 843-3682
Sorrento *(G-16791)*
Preferred Coatings LLC........G....... 231 499-3864
Bradenton *(G-1102)*
Premium Powder Coating........G....... 386 789-0216
Deltona *(G-3178)*
▼ Prime Tech Coatings Inc........G....... 561 844-2312
Mangonia Park *(G-8510)*
Pro Color Coating LLC........G....... 941 661-4769
Port Charlotte *(G-14994)*
Pro Powder Coating Inc........F....... 941 505-8010
Punta Gorda *(G-15221)*
Protect All Coating Inc........G....... 727 278-7454
Saint Petersburg *(G-15894)*
Protective Coatings LLC........G....... 407 535-8535
Apopka *(G-174)*
Protek Custom Coatings LLC........G....... 850 656-7923
Tallahassee *(G-17312)*
Quality Aerospace Coatings LLC........G....... 863 619-2628
Lakeland *(G-7774)*
R & H Air Coatings Inc........G....... 863 559-6021
Fort Meade *(G-4339)*
Reliable Finishes........G....... 321 723-3334
Melbourne *(G-8918)*
Rigid Coatings & Castings Inc........G....... 352 396-8738
Apopka *(G-180)*
Rigid Coatings & Castings Inc........G....... 352 396-8738
Apopka *(G-181)*

RSR Industrial Coatings Inc........F....... 863 537-1110
Bartow *(G-332)*
S&H Arcylic Coatings Inc........G....... 352 232-1249
Spring Hill *(G-16862)*
Sea Site Inc........G....... 305 403-3002
Miami *(G-10315)*
Shannon Spray Coatings Inc........G....... 850 602-7163
Pensacola *(G-14260)*
Solar Tint Inc........G....... 305 663-4663
South Miami *(G-16828)*
Southern Micro Etch Inc........F....... 954 781-5999
Pompano Beach *(G-14864)*
Southwest Custom Coatings Inc........G....... 239 682-9462
Naples *(G-11410)*
Special Coatings Inc........G....... 239 301-2714
Naples *(G-11414)*
Specialty Powder Coating LLC........G....... 813 782-2720
Zephyrhills *(G-19536)*
Steven Herranz Custom Coatings........G....... 941 915-4686
Palmetto *(G-13824)*
Superior Sealers Coatings Inc........G....... 727 807-7851
New Port Richey *(G-11513)*
Tampa Bay Powder Coating Inc........G....... 813 964-5667
Tampa *(G-18159)*
Tampa Bays Coatings Screening........G....... 813 230-1610
Temple Terrace *(G-18381)*
Taylors Indus Coatings Inc........F....... 800 932-3049
Lake Wales *(G-7525)*
Td Coating Inc........G....... 786 325-4211
North Miami *(G-11658)*
The Nanosteel Company LLC........D....... 407 838-1427
Maitland *(G-8481)*
Titans Protective Coatings LLC........F....... 561 370-2085
Jupiter *(G-7129)*
▼ Tolliver Aluminum Service Inc........F....... 561 582-8939
West Palm Beach *(G-19067)*
Top of The Line Coating Inc........G....... 407 485-8546
Orlando *(G-13262)*
Top Quality Finishers Inc........G....... 305 688-8174
Miami *(G-10493)*
Torres & Tavara Coating LLC........G....... 904 520-9910
Jacksonville *(G-6936)*
Trojan Fla Powdr Coating Inc........E....... 941 351-0500
Sarasota *(G-16316)*
Tropic Seal Industries Inc........F....... 239 543-8069
Fort Myers *(G-4639)*
Tropical Custom Coatings........G....... 941 475-3663
Port Charlotte *(G-15002)*
Tua Systems Inc........G....... 321 453-3200
Merritt Island *(G-9018)*
U S A Coatings Inc........F....... 904 477-0916
Jacksonville *(G-6874)*
▲ Uct Coatings Inc........F....... 772 872-7110
Palm City *(G-13677)*
Universal Prof Coatings Inc........G....... 954 294-5236
Middleburg *(G-10913)*
◆ V and N Advanced Auto Sys LLC........G....... 321 504-6440
Rockledge *(G-15455)*
▲ Wheelblast Inc........E....... 813 715-7117
Zephyrhills *(G-19542)*
Zps Powdercoating........G....... 727 465-8131
Largo *(G-8082)*

3482 Small Arms Ammunition

Arms East LLC........G....... 561 293-2915
Bradenton *(G-991)*
Boland Production Supply Inc........G....... 863 324-7784
Winter Haven *(G-19304)*
Degraaff Inc........G....... 305 451-4460
Key Largo *(G-7168)*
Energy Technical Systems Inc........F....... 850 223-2393
Perry *(G-14299)*
◆ General Dynmics Ord Tctcal Sys........C....... 727 578-8100
Saint Petersburg *(G-15791)*
Global Ordnance LLC........E....... 941 549-8388
Sarasota *(G-16221)*
Gti Systems Inc........E....... 863 965-2002
Auburndale *(G-245)*
Hyperion Munitions Inc........F....... 844 622-8339
Largo *(G-7977)*
Jsn Blue Thunder LLC........G....... 786 398-5222
Miami *(G-9809)*
L C Npee........E....... 888 316-3718
Hialeah *(G-5479)*
Paul Wong........G....... 863 465-1114
Lake Placid *(G-7492)*
Pcp Tactical LLC........G....... 772 473-3472
Vero Beach *(G-18652)*
▲ Precision Ammunition LLC........G....... 813 626-0077
Tampa *(G-18003)*

Wide Open Armory LLC..........G....... 727 202-5980
Seminole *(G-16771)*

3483 Ammunition, Large

Arma Holdings Inc..........E....... 813 402-0667
Tampa *(G-17434)*
Carbon Mine Supply LLC..........G....... 606 437-9905
Bradenton *(G-1013)*
Cesaroni Aerospace Inc..........E....... 941 400-1421
Bowling Green *(G-865)*
Dse Inc..........E....... 813 443-4809
Tampa *(G-17617)*
Energy Technical Systems Inc..........F....... 850 223-2393
Perry *(G-14299)*
◆ **General Dynmics Ord Tctcal Sys**......C....... 727 578-8100
Saint Petersburg *(G-15791)*
Global Ordnance LLC..........E....... 941 549-8388
Sarasota *(G-16221)*
Gti Systems Inc..........E....... 863 965-2002
Auburndale *(G-245)*
▼ **Kaman Precision Products Inc**........C....... 407 282-1000
Orlando *(G-12865)*
Syrac Ordnance Inc..........G....... 727 612-6090
New Port Richey *(G-11515)*

3484 Small Arms

Adams Arms Holdings LLC..........E....... 727 853-0550
Brooksville *(G-1205)*
Ao Precision Manufacturing LLC..........G....... 386 274-5882
Daytona Beach *(G-2626)*
Arma Holdings Inc..........E....... 813 402-0667
Tampa *(G-17434)*
Arsenal Democracy LLC..........F....... 850 296-2122
Freeport *(G-4844)*
Artisan Arms Inc..........G....... 321 299-4053
Apopka *(G-114)*
Ballista Tactical Systems..........G....... 954 260-0765
Fort Lauderdale *(G-3837)*
Blackbird Armament LLC..........F....... 833 255-2473
Melbourne *(G-8781)*
C Products Defense Inc..........E....... 941 727-0009
Bradenton *(G-1008)*
Crosstac Corporation..........G....... 406 522-9300
Medley *(G-8638)*
Dark Storm Manufacturing LLC..........G....... 516 983-3473
Merritt Island *(G-8999)*
Diamondback Firearms LLC..........F....... 321 305-5995
Cocoa *(G-2011)*
Eric Lemoine..........G....... 407 919-9783
Longwood *(G-8276)*
Global Ordnance LLC..........E....... 941 549-8388
Sarasota *(G-16221)*
Gtgjfe LLC..........G....... 904 800-6333
Jacksonville *(G-6455)*
Hitman Industries LLC..........F....... 321 735-8562
Rockledge *(G-15417)*
Kel-TEC Cnc Industries Inc..........F....... 321 631-0068
Cocoa *(G-2033)*
Khaled W Akkawi..........G....... 321 396-3108
Apopka *(G-154)*
Knights Manufacturing Company..........D....... 321 607-9900
Titusville *(G-18441)*
Mossberg Group Inc..........F....... 386 274-5882
Daytona Beach *(G-2689)*
Mwg Company Inc..........G....... 305 232-7344
Cutler Bay *(G-2405)*
Naroh Manufacturing LLC..........F....... 321 806-4875
Rockledge *(G-15437)*
◆ **O I Inc**..........E....... 321 499-3800
Melbourne *(G-8899)*
Precision Machine Tech LLC..........F....... 305 594-1789
Doral *(G-3467)*
R M Equipment Inc..........E....... 305 477-9312
Miami *(G-10232)*
▲ **Rwc Group LLC**..........E....... 754 222-1407
Pompano Beach *(G-14837)*
▲ **Sccy Industries LLC**..........C....... 386 322-6336
Daytona Beach *(G-2708)*
US Security Defense Corp..........E....... 407 979-1478
Tavares *(G-18357)*
Wide Open Armory LLC..........G....... 727 202-5980
Seminole *(G-16771)*

3489 Ordnance & Access, NEC

Ao Precision Manufacturing LLC..........G....... 386 274-5882
Daytona Beach *(G-2626)*
Avasar Corp..........E....... 321 723-3456
Melbourne *(G-8773)*
Ballista Tactical Systems..........G....... 954 260-0765
Fort Lauderdale *(G-3837)*
Break-Free Inc..........E....... 800 347-1200
Jacksonville *(G-6234)*
◆ **C4 Advnced Tctical Systems LLC**.....D....... 407 206-3886
Orlando *(G-12541)*
◆ **Cbm Trading Inc**..........G....... 954 252-7460
Davie *(G-2506)*
Dse Inc..........E....... 813 443-4809
Tampa *(G-17617)*
Elite Distributors LLC..........F....... 407 601-6665
Orlando *(G-12705)*
Energy Technical Systems Inc..........F....... 850 223-2393
Perry *(G-14299)*
Fairbanks and Fairbanks Inc..........G....... 850 293-1184
Pensacola *(G-14148)*
General Defense Corporation..........G....... 954 444-0155
Davie *(G-2532)*
◆ **General Dynmics Ord Tctcal Sys**......C....... 727 578-8100
Saint Petersburg *(G-15791)*
Global Ordnance LLC..........E....... 941 549-8388
Sarasota *(G-16221)*
Gr Dynamics LLC..........F....... 850 897-9700
Niceville *(G-11568)*
▲ **High End Defense Solutions LLC**.....G....... 305 591-7795
Doral *(G-3382)*
Integrated Design & Develop..........G....... 407 268-4300
Sanford *(G-16068)*
Iron Sight Precision LLC..........G....... 561 735-9971
Boynton Beach *(G-923)*
▼ **Kaman Precision Products Inc**........C....... 407 282-1000
Orlando *(G-12865)*
L2d Outdoors Inc..........G....... 954 757-6116
Coral Springs *(G-2271)*
Leonidas Customs Inc..........G....... 561 542-4151
Wellington *(G-18723)*
Nst Global LLC..........E....... 941 748-2270
Bradenton *(G-1088)*
Pace Launcher Casings Llc..........G....... 813 245-6570
Odessa *(G-12138)*
Slr Rifleworks LLC..........G....... 855 757-7435
Winter Garden *(G-19285)*
Syrac Ordnance Inc..........G....... 727 612-6090
New Port Richey *(G-11515)*
Tom & Company LLC..........G....... 321 917-0760
Melbourne *(G-8965)*

3491 Industrial Valves

Abbey Rogers..........G....... 813 645-1400
Tampa *(G-17382)*
Alfa Laval Inc..........G....... 941 727-1900
Sarasota *(G-16173)*
▼ **Azex Flow Technologies Inc**..........G....... 305 393-8037
Miami *(G-9206)*
Chem-TEC Equipment Co..........F....... 954 428-8259
Deerfield Beach *(G-2801)*
Chemseal Inc..........G....... 305 433-8362
Hialeah *(G-5343)*
Chicago Electronic Distrs Inc..........F....... 312 985-6175
Port Charlotte *(G-14969)*
Circor International Inc..........G....... 813 978-1000
Temple Terrace *(G-18367)*
Doch LLC..........G....... 571 491-7578
Tampa *(G-17612)*
▲ **Dresser Inc**..........E....... 318 640-2250
Jacksonville *(G-6328)*
Dresser LLC..........B....... 904 781-7071
Jacksonville *(G-6329)*
▲ **Fabco-Air Inc**..........D....... 352 373-3578
Gainesville *(G-4918)*
Gate Cfv Solutions Inc..........G....... 772 388-3387
Sebastian *(G-16661)*
▲ **Grinnell LLC**..........B....... 561 988-3658
Boca Raton *(G-552)*
Guard Dog Valves Inc..........G....... 239 793-6886
Naples *(G-11269)*
▲ **Hoerbiger Corp America Inc**..........B....... 954 974-5700
Pompano Beach *(G-14725)*
▼ **Hose Power USA**..........G....... 863 669-9333
Lakeland *(G-7706)*
Inovinox Usa LLC..........G....... 800 780-1017
Miami *(G-9749)*
Iq Valves Co..........E....... 321 729-9634
Melbourne *(G-8851)*
▲ **Jefferson Solenoid Valves USA**........D....... 305 249-8120
Miami *(G-9794)*
◆ **Leslie Controls Inc**..........C....... 813 978-1000
Temple Terrace *(G-18371)*
Merit Fastener Corporation..........G....... 813 626-3748
Tampa *(G-17903)*
◆ **Micro Matic Usa Inc**..........E....... 352 544-1081
Brooksville *(G-1252)*
Morris Valves Inc..........G....... 305 477-6525
Doral *(G-3441)*
◆ **Petroleum Equipment and Mfg Co**....F....... 305 558-9573
Hialeah *(G-5557)*
Roper Technologies Inc..........E....... 941 556-2601
Sarasota *(G-16563)*
S A Microtechnologies LLC..........F....... 954 973-6166
Pompano Beach *(G-14839)*
▲ **Target Manufacturing Inc**..........G....... 305 633-0361
Miami *(G-10460)*
Thermoval Solenoid Valves Usa..........G....... 954 835-5523
Davie *(G-2605)*
Tsm Champ LLC..........D....... 615 806-7900
Sarasota *(G-16317)*

3492 Fluid Power Valves & Hose Fittings

▼ **Awab LLC**..........G....... 954 763-3003
Fort Lauderdale *(G-3835)*
Commercial Truck & Trailer Sls..........E....... 863 968-9393
Auburndale *(G-236)*
Eem Technologies Corp..........F....... 786 606-5993
Doral *(G-3340)*
Engineered Mtls & Mfg Intl LLC..........G....... 727 546-5580
Largo *(G-7941)*
▼ **Florida Hose & Hydraulics Inc**..........G....... 305 887-9577
Miami *(G-9584)*
Helios Technologies Inc..........A....... 941 362-1200
Sarasota *(G-16227)*
▼ **Hose Power USA**..........G....... 863 669-9333
Lakeland *(G-7706)*
Ibd Industrial LLC..........G....... 786 655-7577
Coral Gables *(G-2156)*
Industrial Mobile Hydraulics..........G....... 904 866-7592
Jacksonville *(G-6494)*
Innovative Products LLC..........G....... 888 764-6478
Fort Lauderdale *(G-4059)*
Jet Research Development Inc..........D....... 954 427-0404
Deerfield Beach *(G-2850)*
▲ **Kinetics Usa Inc**..........E....... 561 988-8826
Boca Raton *(G-588)*
◆ **Leslie Controls Inc**..........C....... 813 978-1000
Temple Terrace *(G-18371)*
▼ **Mako Hose & Rubber Co**..........G....... 561 795-6200
West Palm Beach *(G-18939)*
◆ **Micro Pneumatic Logic Inc**..........C....... 954 935-6821
Pompano Beach *(G-14762)*
Moog Inc..........G....... 716 652-2000
Pembroke Pines *(G-14049)*
Space Coast Hydraulics Inc..........F....... 321 504-6006
Rockledge *(G-15449)*
STS Distribution Solutions LLC..........F....... 844 359-4673
Miramar *(G-11048)*
Teknocraft Inc..........E....... 321 729-9634
Melbourne *(G-8959)*
Zennergy LLC..........F....... 813 382-3460
Tampa *(G-18280)*

3493 Steel Springs, Except Wire

▲ **Easylift N Bansbach Amer Inc**..........E....... 321 253-1999
Melbourne *(G-8819)*
Goodrich Corporation..........C....... 904 757-3660
Jacksonville *(G-6441)*
Industrial Spring Corp..........F....... 954 524-2558
Davie *(G-2537)*
J C S Engineering & Dev..........F....... 305 888-7911
Hialeah *(G-5459)*
S N S Auto Sports LLC..........G....... 727 546-2700
Pinellas Park *(G-14386)*
SOUTHERN SPRING & STAMPING INC E....... 941 488-2276
Venice *(G-18575)*
Vette Brakes & Products Inc..........E....... 727 345-5292
Saint Petersburg *(G-15952)*

3494 Valves & Pipe Fittings, NEC

◆ **A & N Corporation**..........D....... 352 528-4100
Williston *(G-19207)*
Andersons Can Line Fbrction Eq..........F....... 407 889-4665
Apopka *(G-113)*
▼ **Azex Flow Technologies Inc**..........G....... 305 393-8037
Miami *(G-9206)*
◆ **Depend-O-Drain Inc**..........E....... 941 756-1710
Bradenton *(G-1030)*
Eagle Pneumatic Inc..........E....... 863 644-4870
Lakeland *(G-7678)*
▲ **Enolgas Usa Inc**..........G....... 754 205-7902
Pompano Beach *(G-14681)*
◆ **Flotech Inc**..........D....... 904 358-1849
Jacksonville *(G-6406)*
Formweld Fitting Inc..........E....... 850 626-4888
Milton *(G-10928)*

S I C

Gate Cfv Solutions Inc.....G..... 772 388-3387
Sebastian *(G-16661)*
Gil Industries Inc.....G..... 850 479-3400
Cantonment *(G-1340)*
▲ **Hoerbiger Compression Tech AME**..B..... 954 974-5700
Pompano Beach *(G-14724)*
◆ **K-Rain Manufacturing Corp**.....D..... 561 721-3936
Riviera Beach *(G-15338)*
◆ **Leslie Controls Inc**.....C..... 813 978-1000
Temple Terrace *(G-18371)*
Mat-Vac Technology Inc.....F..... 386 238-7017
Daytona Beach *(G-2683)*
Microflex Inc.....E..... 386 672-1945
Ormond Beach *(G-13386)*
▲ **Nuflo Inc**.....E..... 904 265-4001
Jacksonville *(G-6642)*
▲ **Precision Fabg & Clg Co Inc**.....D..... 321 635-2000
Cocoa *(G-2042)*
◆ **Serf Inc**.....E..... 850 476-8203
Cantonment *(G-1347)*
◆ **Southeast Power Group Inc**.....D..... 305 592-9745
Doral *(G-3507)*
Southern Innovative Energy Inc.....G..... 321 747-9205
Titusville *(G-18461)*
Sun Pipe and Valves LLC.....G..... 772 408-5530
Port Saint Lucie *(G-15150)*
▲ **Target Manufacturing Inc**.....G..... 305 633-0361
Miami *(G-10460)*
Teckno Corp.....G..... 305 677-3487
Doral *(G-3526)*
Teknocraft Inc.....E..... 321 729-9634
Melbourne *(G-8959)*
◆ **Tradewinds Power Corp**.....D..... 305 592-9745
Doral *(G-3531)*

3495 Wire Springs

Barnes Group Inc.....G..... 941 255-0978
Lake Suzy *(G-7496)*
Carlo Morelli.....G..... 954 241-1426
Hollywood *(G-5796)*
◆ **Cook Spring Co**.....D..... 941 377-5766
Sarasota *(G-16394)*
▼ **Forceleader Inc**.....G..... 727 521-1808
Pinellas Park *(G-14348)*
▲ **Gilco Spring of Florida Inc**.....E..... 813 855-4631
Oldsmar *(G-12228)*
Goodrich Corporation.....C..... 904 757-3660
Jacksonville *(G-6441)*
Harper Limbach LLC.....G..... 813 207-0057
Tampa *(G-17744)*
J C S Engineering & Dev.....F..... 305 888-7911
Hialeah *(G-5459)*
Militek Industries LLC.....G..... 941 544-5636
Bradenton *(G-1078)*
Optimum Spring Mfg Inc.....G..... 904 567-5999
Ponte Vedra *(G-14927)*
SOUTHERN SPRING & STAMPING INC E..... 941 488-2276
Venice *(G-18575)*
Z Haydu Manufacturing Corp.....G..... 954 925-1779
Hollywood *(G-5944)*

3496 Misc Fabricated Wire Prdts

▲ **Alp Industries Inc**.....F..... 786 845-8617
Doral *(G-3240)*
Animal Air Service Inc.....E..... 305 218-1759
Doral *(G-3250)*
▲ **Aquateko International LLC**.....G..... 904 273-7200
Ponte Vedra Beach *(G-14933)*
Artistic Fence Corporation.....G..... 305 805-1976
Hialeah *(G-5307)*
▲ **Baby Guard Inc**.....F..... 954 741-6351
Coral Springs *(G-2222)*
Belt Maintenance Group Inc.....G..... 813 907-9316
Wesley Chapel *(G-18740)*
◆ **Best Manufacturing Company**.....F..... 954 922-1443
Hollywood *(G-5786)*
Blue Water Dynamics LLC.....D..... 386 957-5464
Edgewater *(G-3614)*
Brandano Displays Inc.....E..... 954 956-7266
Margate *(G-8537)*
▲ **Central Wire Industries LLC**.....E..... 850 983-9926
Milton *(G-10926)*
Clear Vue Inc.....E..... 727 726-5386
Safety Harbor *(G-15490)*
Closetmaid LLC.....E..... 352 351-6100
Ocala *(G-11905)*
Cross City Veneer Company Inc.....D..... 352 498-3226
Cross City *(G-2364)*
D & D Manufacturing LLC.....F..... 321 890-0069
Titusville *(G-18427)*
◆ **Eastern Wire Products Inc**.....E..... 904 781-6775
Jacksonville *(G-6350)*
Ellis Trap and Cage Mfg Inc.....G..... 850 969-1302
Pensacola *(G-14140)*
Equity Group Usa Inc.....G..... 407 421-6464
Winter Springs *(G-19472)*
Fabricated Wire Products Inc.....G..... 813 802-8463
Valrico *(G-18517)*
Florida Wire & Cable.....G..... 904 275-2101
Sanderson *(G-15980)*
▼ **Florida Wire & Rigging Sup Inc**.....G..... 407 422-6218
Orlando *(G-12759)*
◆ **Grille Tech Inc**.....E..... 305 537-0053
Miami *(G-9672)*
Harpers Manufacturing Spc.....G..... 941 629-3490
Punta Gorda *(G-15209)*
▲ **Industrial Conveyor Belt**.....G..... 904 345-3046
Jacksonville *(G-6492)*
Insteel Wire Products Company.....E..... 904 275-2100
Sanderson *(G-15982)*
Jayco Screens Inc.....G..... 850 456-0673
Pensacola *(G-14182)*
John W Hock Company.....G..... 352 378-3209
Gainesville *(G-4948)*
Johnson Well Equipment Inc.....G..... 850 453-3131
Pensacola *(G-14185)*
Las Zirh Americas Inc.....G..... 305 942-7597
Miami *(G-9862)*
Load King Manufacturing Co.....C..... 904 354-8882
Jacksonville *(G-6560)*
▲ **Ludlow Fibc Corp**.....G..... 305 702-5000
Opa Locka *(G-12334)*
Mansur Industries Inc.....F..... 305 593-8015
Doral *(G-3423)*
Marmon Aerospace & Defense LLC.....D..... 239 643-6400
Naples *(G-11322)*
Merchants Metals LLC.....F..... 904 781-3920
Jacksonville *(G-6595)*
Merchants Metals LLC.....F..... 813 980-0938
Tampa *(G-17902)*
Merchants Metals LLC.....G..... 561 478-0059
West Palm Beach *(G-18949)*
◆ **Miami Cordage LLC**.....E..... 305 636-3000
Miami *(G-9996)*
Mutual Industries North Inc.....D..... 239 332-2400
Fort Myers *(G-4541)*
◆ **Octal Ventures Inc**.....F..... 727 526-9288
Pinellas Park *(G-14373)*
Rat Trap Bait Company Inc.....F..... 863 967-2148
Auburndale *(G-251)*
Roro Inc.....F..... 561 909-6220
West Palm Beach *(G-19024)*
Rowe Industries Inc.....F..... 302 855-0585
Pembroke Park *(G-14011)*
SOUTHERN SPRING & STAMPING INC E..... 941 488-2276
Venice *(G-18575)*
Southwire Company LLC.....C..... 850 423-4680
Crestview *(G-2359)*
St Judas Tadeus Foundry Inc.....G..... 305 512-3612
Hialeah *(G-5631)*
TL Fahringer Co Inc.....G..... 813 681-2373
Tampa *(G-18190)*
◆ **Vutec Corporation**.....C..... 954 545-9000
Coral Springs *(G-2330)*
Wire Experts Group Inc.....D..... 239 597-8555
Naples *(G-11458)*
Wire Mesh Corp.....E..... 706 922-5179
Jacksonville *(G-6924)*
◆ **Wire Products Inc of Florida**.....E..... 954 772-1477
Fort Lauderdale *(G-4326)*

3497 Metal Foil & Leaf

R and R Brokerage Co.....G..... 305 592-4329
Doral *(G-3477)*
Vega.....G..... 239 574-1798
Cape Coral *(G-1490)*

3498 Fabricated Pipe & Pipe Fittings

▼ **Alumacart Inc**.....F..... 772 675-2158
Hobe Sound *(G-5721)*
ARC-Rite Inc.....E..... 386 325-3523
Jacksonville *(G-6165)*
Blue Water Dynamics LLC.....D..... 386 957-5464
Edgewater *(G-3614)*
Cantex Inc.....C..... 863 967-4161
Auburndale *(G-231)*
▲ **Custom Fab Inc**.....D..... 407 859-3954
Orlando *(G-12639)*
Custom Tube Products Inc.....F..... 386 426-0670
Edgewater *(G-3620)*
Customfab Inc.....G..... 786 339-9158
Homestead *(G-5960)*
Energy Task Force LLC.....F..... 407 523-3770
Apopka *(G-135)*
Etf West LLC.....G..... 407 523-3770
Apopka *(G-139)*
Formweld Fitting Inc.....E..... 850 626-4888
Milton *(G-10928)*
Georg Fischer LLC.....G..... 305 418-9150
Doral *(G-3366)*
GPM Fab & Supply LLC.....G..... 813 689-7107
Seffner *(G-16729)*
Gulf Atlantic Culvert Company.....F..... 850 562-2384
Tallahassee *(G-17270)*
Gunns Welding & Fabricating.....G..... 727 393-5238
Saint Petersburg *(G-15801)*
▲ **Hines Bending Systems Inc**.....F..... 239 433-2132
Fort Myers *(G-4482)*
Insulation Design & Dist LLC.....G..... 850 332-7312
Cantonment *(G-1341)*
◆ **Jensen Scientific Products Inc**.....E..... 954 344-2006
Coral Springs *(G-2263)*
◆ **Marine Exhaust Systems Inc**.....D..... 561 848-1238
Riviera Beach *(G-15346)*
MPH Industries Inc.....F..... 352 372-9533
Gainesville *(G-4966)*
Peterson Manufacturing Co Inc.....E..... 941 371-4989
Sarasota *(G-16544)*
Petrotech Services Inc.....F..... 813 248-0743
Tampa *(G-17986)*
Petrotech Services Inc.....D..... 813 248-0743
Tampa *(G-17987)*
Pipeline Fabricators Inc.....F..... 863 678-0977
Lake Wales *(G-7518)*
Price Brothers Company.....G..... 386 328-8841
Palatka *(G-13490)*
▲ **S C R Precision Tube Bending**.....F..... 813 622-7091
Tampa *(G-18074)*
▲ **Shafers Classic Reproductions**.....G..... 813 622-7091
Tampa *(G-18089)*
Specialty Maintenance & Constr.....G..... 863 644-8432
Lakeland *(G-7804)*
▲ **Strongbridge International LLC**.....E..... 904 278-7499
Orange Park *(G-12407)*
Sunshine Piping Inc.....E..... 850 763-4834
Panama City *(G-13953)*
▲ **Townley Engrg & Mfg Co Inc**.....C..... 352 687-3001
Candler *(G-1332)*
Trubendz Technology Inc.....F..... 305 378-9337
Cutler Bay *(G-2417)*
Trubendz Technology Inc.....E..... 305 378-9337
Cutler Bay *(G-2418)*
US Pipe Fabrication LLC.....E..... 860 769-6097
Orlando *(G-13299)*

3499 Fabricated Metal Prdts, NEC

◆ **6 Ports LLC**.....F..... 561 743-8696
Jupiter *(G-6990)*
Abraham George Inc.....F..... 850 523-0757
Tallahassee *(G-17211)*
All American Barricades.....G..... 305 685-6124
Fort Lauderdale *(G-3796)*
▼ **All Metal Fabrication**.....G..... 305 666-3312
Pinecrest *(G-14323)*
All Metals Custom Inc.....G..... 727 709-4297
Pinellas Park *(G-14334)*
American Metal Fabrication LLC.....F..... 954 736-9819
Tamarac *(G-17350)*
Aquatectonica LLC.....F..... 941 592-3071
Bradenton *(G-990)*
ARC Group Worldwide Inc.....D..... 303 467-5236
Deland *(G-2959)*
Architectural Fountains Inc.....G..... 727 323-6068
Saint Petersburg *(G-15708)*
▲ **Argonide Corporation**.....F..... 407 322-2500
Sanford *(G-15995)*
Artcraft Stone Inc.....G..... 239 253-6696
Naples *(G-11168)*
Atlantic Central Entps Inc.....F..... 386 255-6227
Daytona Beach *(G-2630)*
Atlantic Coast Roofing & Metal.....G..... 321 449-9494
Merritt Island *(G-8991)*
▲ **Bamm Manufacturing Inc**.....G..... 239 277-0776
Fort Myers *(G-4371)*
Baxter Custom Fabrication Inc.....G..... 863 289-9819
Winter Haven *(G-19302)*
BHd Precision Products Inc.....G..... 941 753-0003
Sarasota *(G-16183)*
Blue Chip Group LLC.....G..... 305 863-9094
Doral *(G-3280)*

Bobs Barricades Inc E 813 886-0518
Tampa *(G-17478)*

Bobs Barricades Inc E 239 656-1183
Fort Myers *(G-4379)*

Brady Built Technologies Inc G 270 692-6866
Melbourne *(G-8784)*

Brandon Lock & Safe Inc G 813 655-4200
Tampa *(G-17485)*

C & J Cstm Wldg Fbrication LLC G 407 414-1739
Kissimmee *(G-7228)*

◆ **Cabus USA Inc** G 305 681-0872
North Miami *(G-11631)*

Centerline Steel LLC E 904 217-4186
Saint Augustine *(G-15529)*

▲ **Champion Shtmtl Fabrication** G 407 509-7439
Winter Park *(G-19392)*

Constrction Mtal Fbrcators LLC G 305 781-9004
Hialeah *(G-5352)*

Custom Mfg & Engrg Inc D 727 548-0522
Pinellas Park *(G-14342)*

David Gill Enterprises G 863 422-5711
Davenport *(G-2477)*

Desapro Inc E 321 674-6804
Rockledge *(G-15401)*

Dillco Inc F 386 734-7510
Deland *(G-2971)*

Dj/Pj Inc E 813 907-6359
Clearwater *(G-1653)*

Doll Marine Metal Fabrica G 954 941-5093
Fort Lauderdale *(G-3946)*

East Coast Machine Inc F 321 632-4817
Cocoa *(G-2017)*

East Coast Metalworks LLC G 321 698-0624
Cocoa *(G-2018)*

▲ **Edak Inc** F 321 674-6804
Melbourne *(G-8820)*

Ees Design LLC F 954 541-2660
Fort Lauderdale *(G-3965)*

Emerald Coast Met Fabrication G 850 465-3517
Pensacola *(G-14142)*

Endless Oceans LLC G 561 274-1990
Delray Beach *(G-3073)*

Ernies Metal Fabricating G 813 679-0816
Brandon *(G-1157)*

G and G Industries Inc G 754 701-4178
Davie *(G-2528)*

Garelick Mfg Co D 727 545-4571
Largo *(G-7956)*

▼ **Gyro-Gale Inc** G 772 283-1711
Stuart *(G-16952)*

◆ **Hayman Safe Co Inc** F 407 365-5434
Oviedo *(G-13434)*

International Vault Inc E 941 390-4505
Lakewood Ranch *(G-7839)*

J A Custom Fabricators Inc F 561 615-4680
Lake Worth *(G-7559)*

J&J Sheet Mtal Fabercation LLC G 941 752-0569
Sarasota *(G-16241)*

Jetstream Fabrication LLC G 772 287-3338
Stuart *(G-16960)*

▲ **JHK LLC** G 786 871-0150
Miami *(G-9797)*

JKS Industries Inc E 863 425-1745
Mulberry *(G-11126)*

JKS Industries Inc F 727 573-1305
Tampa *(G-17805)*

Johnston Archtctral Systems In E 904 886-9030
Jacksonville *(G-6527)*

▼ **Jose Rodriguez Met Fabrication** G 305 305-6110
Miami *(G-9805)*

JP Donvan Prcsion McHining LLC G 321 383-1171
Rockledge *(G-15424)*

Kool Ledz LLC G 561 212-5843
Boca Raton *(G-591)*

▲ **L C Acme Barricades** D 904 781-1950
Jacksonville *(G-6548)*

Lakes Metal Fabrication Inc G 954 731-2010
Oakland Park *(G-11818)*

Leesburg Concrete Company Inc E 352 787-4177
Leesburg *(G-8163)*

Lotus Containers Inc G 786 590-1056
Miami *(G-9913)*

Lrvs Barricades LLC G 305 343-6101
Miami *(G-9914)*

MA Metal Fabricators Inc G 786 343-0268
Miami *(G-9931)*

▼ **Manufacturers Inv Group LLC** F 630 285-0800
Keystone Heights *(G-7210)*

Marble Bridge Inc F 239 213-1411
Naples *(G-11319)*

Medway Hall Dev Group Inc F 904 786-0622
Jacksonville *(G-6594)*

Merritt Hollow Metal Inc G 727 656-4380
Largo *(G-8010)*

Metal Creations Sarasota Llc F 941 922-7096
Sarasota *(G-16256)*

MSC Metal Fabrication G 954 344-8343
Coral Springs *(G-2292)*

Pac Seating Systems Inc D 772 286-6670
Palm City *(G-13669)*

Pinellas Precision Laser LLC G 727 420-0388
Saint Petersburg *(G-15876)*

Pitts Fabrication LLC G 850 259-4548
Fort Walton Beach *(G-4822)*

PM Craftsman E 863 665-0815
Lakeland *(G-7768)*

Preston Works Inc G 850 932-0888
Holt *(G-5949)*

Robert James Custom Metal Fabr F 772 214-0996
Jacksonville *(G-6733)*

Rssi Barriers Llc E 850 871-9300
Panama City *(G-13948)*

▲ **Russell Hobbs Inc** D 954 883-1000
Miramar *(G-11037)*

S & J Custom Fabrication Inc F 352 246-1462
Keystone Heights *(G-7211)*

S & S Metal and Plastics Inc E 904 731-4655
Jacksonville *(G-6742)*

Safe Banks and Lock G 954 762-3565
Fort Lauderdale *(G-4221)*

Safety Systems Barricades G 407 674-8440
Orlando *(G-13154)*

Safety Zone Specialists Inc G 863 984-1385
Lakeland *(G-7784)*

Seiter Enterprises Inc F 813 728-8324
Tarpon Springs *(G-18324)*

Sfi Inc E 407 834-2258
Orlando *(G-13177)*

▼ **Sklar Bov Solutions Inc** G 352 746-6731
Hernando *(G-5247)*

Soto Metal Fabrication Inc E 786 486-7125
Miami *(G-10379)*

Spicer Industries Inc F 352 732-5300
Ocala *(G-12057)*

Spot-On Wldg Met Fbrcation LLC G 239 825-7452
Naples *(G-11416)*

Spraying Systems Co G 813 259-9400
Bradenton *(G-1119)*

Structural Metal Fabricators G 786 253-8012
Miami *(G-10422)*

Sunset Metal Fabrication Inc G 386 215-4520
Sarasota *(G-16611)*

Telese Properties Inc D 813 752-6015
Plant City *(G-14471)*

▲ **Theissen Training Systems Inc** D 352 490-8020
Gainesville *(G-5009)*

Tpi Aluminum G 239 332-3900
Fort Myers *(G-4635)*

Traffic Control Pdts Fla Inc F 813 621-8484
Fort Myers *(G-4636)*

Traffic Control Pdts Fla Inc F 407 521-6777
Orlando *(G-13267)*

Traffic Control Pdts Fla Inc F 352 372-7088
Jacksonville *(G-6865)*

Tru Mension Mfg Solutions G 321 255-4665
Melbourne *(G-8967)*

▲ **United Metal Fabrications Inc** G 305 962-1608
North Miami *(G-11661)*

Valuesafes Inc G 877 629-6214
Port Charlotte *(G-15005)*

◆ **Vault Structures Inc** E 239 332-3270
Fort Myers *(G-4644)*

Vested Metals Intl LLC G 904 495-7278
Saint Augustine *(G-15631)*

Waltzing Waters Inc G 239 574-5181
Cape Coral *(G-1494)*

Wesco Partners Inc E 941 484-8224
Sarasota *(G-16325)*

Worth Metals Inc F 904 626-1434
Green Cove Springs *(G-5077)*

Yeager Manufacturing Tech LLC F 407 573-7033
Winter Park *(G-19463)*

Zerons Metal Designers Inc F 305 688-2240
Hialeah *(G-5696)*

35 INDUSTRIAL AND COMMERCIAL MACHINERY AND COMPUTER EQUIPMENT

3511 Steam, Gas & Hydraulic Turbines & Engines

▲ **2jcp LLC** G 904 834-3818
Ponte Vedra *(G-14922)*

▼ **Alterntive Repr McHning Svcs L** E 904 861-3040
Jacksonville *(G-6142)*

Belac LLC D 813 749-3200
Oldsmar *(G-12210)*

Brady Wind LLC G 561 304-5136
Juno Beach *(G-6976)*

▲ **Chromalloy Castings Tampa Corp** C 561 935-3571
Palm Beach Gardens *(G-13577)*

Chromalloy Mtl Solutions LLC E 954 378-1999
Fort Lauderdale *(G-3899)*

▲ **Diemech Turbine Solution Inc** G 386 804-0179
Deland *(G-2970)*

Escue Energy LLC G 561 762-1486
Royal Palm Beach *(G-15466)*

Florida Hydro Power & Light Co G 386 328-2470
Palatka *(G-13478)*

Gas Turbine Efficiency Inc E 407 304-5200
Orlando *(G-12771)*

Gas Turbine Efficiency LLC E 407 304-5200
Orlando *(G-12772)*

GE G 904 570-3151
Jacksonville *(G-6428)*

GSE Jetall Inc G 305 688-2111
Opa Locka *(G-12321)*

◆ **Hoerbger Auto Cmfort Systems L** E 334 321-2292
Deerfield Beach *(G-2839)*

Hydroplus Inc F 941 479-7473
Palmetto *(G-13807)*

▲ **Jupiter Bach North America Inc** C 850 476-6304
Pensacola *(G-14187)*

Locust Usa Inc F 305 889-5410
Medley *(G-8679)*

Marajo Diesel Power Corp G 786 212-1485
Doral *(G-3424)*

◆ **Mitsubishi Power Americas Inc** D 407 688-6100
Lake Mary *(G-7436)*

Peerless Wind Systems G 516 249-6900
Boynton Beach *(G-939)*

▲ **Power Equipments Trading LLC** G 305 704-7021
Doral *(G-3464)*

Power Systems Inc E 561 354-1100
Jupiter *(G-7094)*

◆ **Power Systems Mfg LLC** B 561 354-1100
Jupiter *(G-7095)*

Powerphase LLC F 561 299-3970
Jupiter *(G-7096)*

Raytheon Technologies Corp A 858 277-7639
Jupiter *(G-7103)*

Sandpiper Turbine LLC F 407 377-7220
Kissimmee *(G-7294)*

Siemens Energy Inc D 407 736-1400
Orlando *(G-13183)*

Siemens Energy Inc D 407 206-5008
Orlando *(G-13184)*

Siemens Energy Inc D 407 736-7957
Orlando *(G-13185)*

Siemens Gmesa Rnwble Enrgy Inc A 407 736-2000
Orlando *(G-13186)*

Siemens Gmesa Rnwble Enrgy Inc D 407 721-3273
Orlando *(G-13187)*

Solar Turbines Incorporated F 305 476-6855
Miami *(G-10370)*

Southern Innovative Energy Inc G 321 747-9205
Titusville *(G-18461)*

Southstern Indus Fbrcators LLC E 941 776-1211
Duette *(G-3563)*

Southwest Turbine Inc G 305 769-1765
Hialeah *(G-5630)*

Stratgic Trbine Invntory Group G 561 427-2007
Jupiter *(G-7124)*

◆ **Turbine Generator Maint Inc** E 239 573-1233
Cape Coral *(G-1489)*

Turbine Resources Intl LLC G 850 377-0449
Pensacola *(G-14277)*

Vestas G 561 588-9933
West Palm Beach *(G-19079)*

Vonwidman Designs LLC G 727 862-5303
New Port Richey *(G-11520)*

3519 Internal Combustion Engines, NEC

◆ 2g Cenrgy Pwr Systems Tech Inc ....E 904 342-5988
Saint Augustine (G-15511)
360 Energy Solutions LLC ....E 786 348-2156
Miami (G-9025)
ABB Inc ....E 954 450-9544
Miramar (G-10960)
Advanced Engine Tech LLC ....G 727 744-2935
Clearwater (G-1565)
Alamo USA Inc ....G 954 774-3747
Hallandale Beach (G-5168)
All Keys Diesel Repair Inc ....G 305 289-2070
Marathon (G-8517)
American Diesel and Gas Inc ....F 561 447-8500
Deerfield Beach (G-2776)
Bms-Tek LLC ....G 321 727-7800
Melbourne (G-8783)
Boat Energy LLC ....G 954 501-2628
Fort Lauderdale (G-3863)
Brunswick Corporation ....G 850 769-1011
Panama City (G-13874)
◆ Cobra Power Corporation ....G 305 893-5018
North Miami (G-11633)
Cummins-Wagner-Florida LLC ....E 813 630-2220
Tampa (G-17573)
Cyclone Power Technologies Inc ....F 954 943-8721
Pompano Beach (G-14656)
▼ Diesel Machinery Intl USA ....G 305 551-4424
Miami (G-9466)
◆ Diesel Pro Power Inc ....F 305 545-5588
Miami (G-9467)
Dukane Seacom Inc ....C 941 739-3200
Sarasota (G-16209)
Emerald Coast Mfg LLC ....G 850 469-1133
Pensacola (G-14143)
Engine Lab of Tampa Inc ....F 813 630-2422
Tampa (G-17640)
Environmental Recovery Systems ....G 727 344-3301
Saint Petersburg (G-15771)
Fast Forward Race Engines Inc ....G 813 788-1794
Zephyrhills (G-19517)
▲ Fka Racing Inc ....G 386 938-4211
Jennings (G-6964)
Gem Aerospace ....G 786 464-5900
Doral (G-3359)
Gem Remotes Inc ....F 239 642-0873
Naples (G-11259)
Gfs Corp ....E 954 693-9657
Weston (G-19132)
Granite Services Intl Inc ....F 813 242-7400
Tampa (G-17724)
Gull Tool & Machine Inc ....G 727 527-0808
Saint Petersburg (G-15800)
◆ Innovation Marine Corporation ....E 941 355-7852
Sarasota (G-16238)
JRL Service Co ....G 727 243-4734
Tarpon Springs (G-18311)
Just Engines ....G 561 575-2681
Jupiter (G-7064)
Keith Eickert Power Pdts LLC ....F 386 446-0660
Palm Coast (G-13700)
◆ Man Capital Corporation ....E 732 582-8220
Pompano Beach (G-14751)
Marine Electronics Engine ....G 727 459-5593
Saint Petersburg (G-15847)
Mars Precision Products Inc ....G 727 846-0505
Port Richey (G-15061)
Megawattage LLC ....F 954 328-0232
Fort Lauderdale (G-4117)
National Diesel Engine Inc ....F 810 516-6855
Tampa (G-17931)
▼ Offshore Performance Spc ....F 239 481-2768
Fort Myers (G-4555)
PMC North America Inc ....F 727 530-0714
Largo (G-8029)
Price Rite Engines LLC ....G 727 600-8206
Largo (G-8031)
Progress Rail Services Corp ....D 239 643-3013
Naples (G-11376)
▼ Sen-Dure Products Inc ....D 954 973-1260
Fort Lauderdale (G-4230)
Spectrumit Inc ....F 850 202-5263
Pensacola (G-14268)
Topline Hy-Lift Johnson Inc ....E 352 799-4668
Brooksville (G-1281)
Turbousa Inc ....F 954 767-8631
Oakland Park (G-11850)
USA Marine Engines ....F 954 614-4810
Fort Lauderdale (G-4299)
USA Marine Engines LLC ....G 954 383-1870
Davie (G-2609)
◆ Xcessive Inc ....G 866 919-9527
Miami Lakes (G-10882)

3523 Farm Machinery & Eqpt

5 Star Builders Inc ....G 561 795-1282
Wellington (G-18707)
50 50 Parmley Envmtl Svcs LLC ....G 407 593-1165
Saint Cloud (G-15641)
▼ Agri Machinery & Parts Inc ....F 407 299-1592
Orlando (G-12442)
Agrifleet Leasing Corporation ....E 239 293-3976
Auburndale (G-229)
◆ Agro & Cnstr Solutions Inc ....F 305 593-7011
Doral (G-3230)
▲ Alpha Technology USA Corp ....F 407 571-2060
Sanford (G-15990)
▲ Amega Sciences Inc ....G 863 937-9792
Lakeland (G-7632)
Animal Air Service Inc ....E 305 218-1759
Doral (G-3250)
Atlas Metal Industries Inc ....C 305 625-2451
Miami (G-9186)
▼ Bag-A-Nut LLC ....G 904 641-3934
Jacksonville (G-6191)
Black Widow Custom Cases ....G 321 327-8058
Palm Bay (G-13504)
Bravo Inc ....G 239 471-8127
Cape Coral (G-1394)
▲ Brinsea Products Inc ....G 321 267-7009
Titusville (G-18418)
Brush Cases LLC ....G 305 340-7214
Miami Beach (G-10649)
▼ Bulk Resources Inc ....G 813 764-8420
Plant City (G-14413)
Bushhog N Blade Work ....G 904 669-2764
Saint Augustine (G-15525)
C P Enterprises of Apopka Inc ....G 407 886-3321
Mount Dora (G-11098)
Castillos Farms Inc ....G 305 232-0771
Miami (G-9323)
Chargers and Cases LLC ....G 352 587-2539
Winter Park (G-19393)
Cnh Industrial America LLC ....F 954 389-9779
Weston (G-19116)
Conibear Equipment Co Inc ....G 863 858-4414
Lakeland (G-7662)
Cory Aun ....G 407 957-1133
Saint Cloud (G-15648)
David B Case ....G 904 262-6224
Jacksonville (G-6313)
David R Case ....G 727 808-9330
Spring Hill (G-16872)
Delaney Resources Inc ....G 863 670-5924
Dade City (G-2427)
▲ Eastern Irrigation Supply ....G 352 472-3323
Newberry (G-11553)
▲ Erb Roberts Tillage LLC ....G 352 376-4888
Fort Lauderdale (G-3974)
▲ Farmco Manufacturers Inc ....F 813 645-0611
Ruskin (G-15484)
First Case Cash LLC ....G 954 200-5374
Hallandale Beach (G-5185)
Florida Sprayers Inc ....G 813 989-0500
Temple Terrace (G-18369)
▲ Fogmaster Corporation ....G 954 481-9975
Deerfield Beach (G-2825)
Foley Air LLC ....F 904 379-2243
Jacksonville (G-6411)
Franz A Ullrich Jr ....G 863 773-4653
Wauchula (G-18692)
Free Life Inc ....G 954 584-8485
Plantation (G-14518)
Golf Agronomics Sand & Hlg Inc ....G 800 626-1359
Sarasota (G-16451)
◆ Grain Machinery Mfg Corp ....F 305 620-2525
Miami (G-9654)
Hawkhead International Inc ....G 904 264-4295
Orange Park (G-12396)
Hera Cases LLC ....G 305 322-8960
Coral Gables (G-2154)
Hera Cases LLC ....G 305 714-2274
Miami (G-9703)
Home & Garden Industries Inc ....F 305 634-0681
Miami (G-9716)
I Fix & Cases LLC ....G 939 645-5252
Orlando (G-12816)
Industrial Cnveyor Systems Inc ....F 305 255-0200
Cutler Bay (G-2398)
International Packaging Mchs ....G 239 643-2020
Naples (G-11290)
Irms Inc ....F 321 631-1161
Rockledge (G-15423)
Jmp Marine LLC ....E 305 599-0009
Doral (G-3405)
John W Hock Company ....G 352 378-3209
Gainesville (G-4948)
◆ K-Rain Manufacturing Corp ....D 561 721-3936
Riviera Beach (G-15338)
Kochan Cases ....G 850 533-4190
Mary Esther (G-8591)
▲ Manley Farms Inc ....G 239 597-6416
Naples (G-11318)
Marden Industries Inc ....F 863 682-7882
Punta Gorda (G-15213)
▲ Marine Metal Products Co ....G 727 461-5575
Clearwater (G-1773)
Maxijet Inc ....E 863 439-3667
Dundee (G-3566)
Natureform Hatchery Tech LLC ....F 904 358-0355
Jacksonville (G-6619)
Neelco Industries Inc ....F 321 632-5303
Cocoa (G-2038)
Niteo Products LLC ....F 561 745-1812
Jupiter (G-7082)
Okee-B Inc ....D 561 996-3040
Belle Glade (G-350)
On Site AG Services ....F 863 382-7502
Sebring (G-16700)
OSteen Plastic Inc ....G 954 434-4921
Southwest Ranches (G-16839)
Ovipost Inc ....F 707 776-6108
Labelle (G-7322)
◆ Pas Reform North America LLC ....E 904 358-0355
Jacksonville (G-6659)
Performnce Ntrtn Solutions LLC ....G 310 435-2995
Loxahatchee Groves (G-8367)
Petersen Industries Inc ....C 863 676-1493
Lake Wales (G-7517)
Powercases Inc ....G 239 415-3846
Miromar Lakes (G-11071)
R & C Sales & Mfg Inc ....F 904 824-2223
Palm Coast (G-13707)
R & S Metalworks & Co LLC ....F 772 466-3303
Port Saint Lucie (G-15132)
Rainbow Manufacturing Company ....G 305 477-5541
Miami Lakes (G-10848)
Roccos Custom Cases Corp ....G 305 799-2841
Hialeah (G-5603)
Rugby Road Corp ....G 407 328-5474
Sanford (G-16112)
Ryan Manufacturing Inc ....F 386 325-3644
East Palatka (G-3606)
◆ Sanchelima International Inc ....F 305 591-4343
Doral (G-3495)
Sebring Septic Tank Precast Co ....E 863 655-2030
Sebring (G-16708)
Southern Fiberglass Inc ....F 904 387-2246
Jacksonville (G-6794)
Spray Box LLC ....G 850 567-2724
Tallahassee (G-17330)
St Johns Turf Case ....F 352 258-3314
East Palatka (G-3607)
◆ Tracto Parts Corp ....G 305 972-1357
Miami (G-10499)
Tru-Flo Corp ....F 561 996-5850
Belle Glade (G-354)
Turner Machine & Supply Co ....G 772 464-4550
Fort Pierce (G-4762)

3524 Garden, Lawn Tractors & Eqpt

All-Pro Equipment & Rental Inc ....F 850 656-0208
Tallahassee (G-17217)
◆ Ames Companies Inc ....B 717 737-1500
Orlando (G-12475)
Brandfx LLC ....E 321 632-2063
Cocoa (G-2000)
Bravo Inc ....G 239 471-8127
Cape Coral (G-1394)
Electrolux Professional LLC ....F 954 327-6778
Fort Lauderdale (G-3967)
Greg Franklin Enterprises Inc ....F 904 675-9129
Hilliard (G-5708)
Iceblox Inc ....F 717 697-1900
New Port Richey (G-11493)
Morning Glory Lawn Maintenance ....G 407 376-5833
Orlando (G-12980)
Mulch & Stone Emporium Inc ....G 352 237-7870
Ocala (G-12003)

◆ Oase North America Inc....G....800 365-3880
Riviera Beach (G-15354)
Peterson Enterprises LLC....G....386 456-3400
Mc Alpin (G-8600)
Pickhardt Professional Sr....G....941 737-7262
Palmetto (G-13816)
Pottre Gardening Products LLC....G....941 224-8856
Bradenton (G-1100)
▼ Precision Small Engine Company....F....954 974-1960
Pompano Beach (G-14809)
Robomow USA Inc....G....844 762-6669
Vero Beach (G-18659)
▲ Trailmate Inc....E....941 739-5743
Jacksonville (G-6866)
Woodys Hedging LLC....G....863 557-4525
Lake Hamilton (G-7393)

3531 Construction Machinery & Eqpt

A & J Pavers Inc....G....863 559-1920
Lakeland (G-7624)
A Clean Finish Inc....G....407 516-1311
Jacksonville (G-6109)
AA Casey Company....F....813 234-8831
Tampa (G-17378)
Adriano Gb Brick Pavers LLC....G....407 497-1517
Orlando (G-12432)
Advanced Infrstrcture Tech Inc....G....239 992-1700
Bonita Springs (G-810)
Altec Inc....G....813 372-0058
Tampa (G-17407)
Altec Industries Inc....F....904 647-5219
Jacksonville (G-6140)
AM Pavers Inc....G....954 275-1590
Boca Raton (G-418)
◆ Amer-Con Corp....E....786 293-8004
Palmetto Bay (G-13839)
◆ American Boom and Barrier Inc....E....321 784-2110
Cape Canaveral (G-1350)
American Mfg & Mch Inc....D....352 728-2222
Okahumpka (G-12168)
Anderson Backhoe Service Inc....G....904 759-9084
Jacksonville (G-6155)
Apogee Services Inc....F....561 441-5354
Boynton Beach (G-878)
Artistic Pavers....G....727 572-1998
Clearwater (G-1590)
Artistic Pavers LLC....F....727 573-0918
Clearwater (G-1591)
Atm Pavers Inc....G....239 322-7010
Cape Coral (G-1386)
Baju Professional Brick Pavers....G....727 234-5300
Pinellas Park (G-14336)
Baron Pavers Corp....G....786 389-2894
Miami (G-9222)
▲ Blasters Ready Jet Inc....E....813 985-4500
Tampa (G-17474)
Bogantec Corp....G....954 217-0023
Dania Beach (G-2463)
Bravo Inc....G....239 471-8127
Cape Coral (G-1394)
Brazilian Brickpavers Inc....G....850 699-7833
Fort Walton Beach (G-4785)
Brito Brick & Pavers Corp....G....727 214-8760
Clearwater (G-1613)
Brutus Roller LLC....G....609 393-0007
Bradenton (G-1003)
C&C Brick Pavers Inc....G....813 716-8291
Tampa (G-17496)
Caterpillar 2 Butterfly Corp....F....786 540-4191
Miami (G-9325)
Caterpllar 2 Bttrfly Otrach CT....G....850 515-1143
Fort Walton Beach (G-4786)
Cavo Development Inc....G....305 255-7465
Miami (G-9327)
◆ Cme Arma Inc....E....305 633-1524
Miami (G-9366)
Coastal Crane and Rigging Inc....G....850 460-1766
Santa Rosa Beach (G-16155)
Compact Brick Pavers Inc....G....727 278-1544
Bradenton (G-1022)
◆ Costex Corporation....C....305 592-9769
Miami (G-9407)
Country Man S....G....352 472-8699
Trenton (G-18482)
Cross Construction Svcs Inc....D....813 907-1013
Lutz (G-8379)
Csa International Inc....E....561 746-7946
Jupiter (G-7020)
D A B Constructors Inc....G....352 797-3537
Brooksville (G-1224)
Dave Siler Transport....G....239 348-3283
Naples (G-11222)
▼ David Thiessens Pavers Inc....G....813 516-1389
Thonotosassa (G-18400)
Destination Pavers LLC....G....850 319-6551
Panama City (G-13891)
Dhs Unlimited Inc....G....954 532-2142
Pompano Beach (G-14663)
Duncan and Sons Cnstr Eqp Inc....F....305 216-3115
Miami Gardens (G-10738)
◆ Enviro-USA American Mfr LLC....E....321 222-9551
Cape Canaveral (G-1357)
▲ Environmental Mfg & Supply Inc....F....850 547-5287
Bonifay (G-803)
Equipment Fabricators Inc....E....321 632-0990
Cocoa (G-2020)
Ficap....F....407 302-3316
Lake Mary (G-7415)
Fine Line Pavers Inc....G....561 389-9819
West Palm Beach (G-18871)
First Coast Pavers Corp....F....904 410-0278
Orange Park (G-12395)
▼ Flagship Marine Inc....G....772 781-4242
Stuart (G-16940)
▲ Florida Dragline Operation....G....305 824-9755
Hialeah (G-5411)
Florida E Coast Holdings Corp....E....904 279-3152
Jacksonville (G-6396)
▼ Florida General Trading Inc....D....813 391-2149
Ocala (G-11946)
Form-Co Inc....G....800 745-3700
Orlando (G-12762)
Frz Marine....G....941 322-2631
Sarasota (G-16440)
Fw Shoring Company....G....813 248-2495
Tampa (G-17700)
Fw Shoring Company....G....517 676-8800
Orlando (G-12767)
Gar International....G....954 704-9590
Miramar (G-10996)
Gardner Asphalt Corporation....C....813 248-2101
Tampa (G-17704)
Gencor Industries Inc....C....407 290-6000
Orlando (G-12776)
General Clamp Industries Inc....F....407 859-6000
Orlando (G-12777)
Hco Holding I Corporation....F....863 533-0522
Bartow (G-318)
Herbert Pavers Inc....G....941 447-4909
Bradenton (G-1056)
Hightec Con Pavers & Curbing....G....941 412-6077
Englewood (G-3678)
Homewood Holdings LLC....F....941 740-3655
Cape Coral (G-1438)
Iler Group Inc....F....813 600-1738
Wesley Chapel (G-18749)
Industrial Cnveyor Systems Inc....F....305 255-0200
Cutler Bay (G-2398)
Ingrams Backhoe Dumptruck Svc....G....850 718-6042
Cottondale (G-2332)
Island Paver Sealing & Prssure....G....727 641-3512
Clearwater (G-1738)
James Frncisco Backhoe Svc Inc....G....727 514-1968
New Port Richey (G-11494)
Javidco Scratch N Dent....G....727 494-7611
Port Richey (G-15057)
Jdl Surface Innovations Inc....E....239 772-0077
Cape Coral (G-1441)
Jetboatpilot LLC....F....850 960-3236
Panama City (G-13921)
Jlg Industries Inc....C....786 558-8909
Doral (G-3404)
Jones Communications Inc....G....407 448-6615
Sanford (G-16074)
Keystone Brick Paver....G....239 340-6492
Fort Myers (G-4510)
▲ Labelle Brick Pavers Tile LLC....F....863 230-3100
Labelle (G-7319)
Lentus Products LLC....G....203 913-7600
Kissimmee (G-7268)
Lg Enterprises Pavers Inc....G....813 412-9235
Tampa (G-17843)
Liebherr Cranes Inc....G....305 817-7500
Hialeah (G-5486)
▼ Mafeks International LLC....F....561 997-2080
Boca Raton (G-605)
Marine Spc Cstm Fabricator....G....813 855-0554
Oldsmar (G-12246)
Martins Pavers & Pools Corp....G....754 368-4413
Deerfield Beach (G-2869)
Masaka LLC....F....786 800-8337
Doral (G-3426)
Matao Brick Pavers Inc....G....321 663-1978
Orlando (G-12954)
Michigan Group Inc....G....954 328-6341
Coconut Creek (G-2090)
Moncada Backhoe Services LLC....G....786 269-5427
Miami (G-10039)
Naia Brick Pavers Inc....G....727 638-4734
Pinellas Park (G-14371)
Nippon Maciwumei Co....F....954 533-7747
Sunrise (G-17152)
North Florida Brick Pavers LLC....G....850 255-0336
Santa Rosa Beach (G-16164)
North Port Pavers Inc....G....941 391-7557
North Port (G-11745)
Number 1 Brick Pavers Inc....G....321 388-7889
Orlando (G-13014)
P3 Fleet LLC....F....904 549-5500
Jacksonville (G-6651)
Pacific....G....305 785-9068
Miami (G-10127)
Pacific Pavers Inc....G....941 238-7854
Bradenton (G-1090)
Pantropic Power Inc....D....954 797-7972
Fort Lauderdale (G-4156)
▲ Patriot Foundation Systems LLC....G....352 668-4842
San Antonio (G-15975)
Paver King....G....407 221-1718
Lake Mary (G-7442)
Paver Paradise LLC....G....561 843-3031
Port St Lucie (G-15178)
Paver Way LLC....F....321 303-0968
Altamonte Springs (G-63)
Pavers Inc....G....352 754-3875
Brooksville (G-1258)
Payless Brick Pavers LLC....G....904 629-7436
Jacksonville (G-6662)
▲ Pemberton Inc....E....407 831-6688
Longwood (G-8322)
Perfect Pavers South Fla LLC....F....954 779-1855
Fort Lauderdale (G-4162)
Precise Pavers Inc....F....863 528-8000
Auburndale (G-250)
◆ Premix-Marbletite Mfg Co....F....954 970-6540
Pompano Beach (G-14810)
Professonal Paver Restorations....G....352 797-8411
Spring Hill (G-16859)
Puzzled Caterpillars Inc....G....904 379-9219
Jacksonville (G-6697)
Reef Pavers Inc....G....904 471-0859
Jacksonville Beach (G-6956)
Reyes Interlocking Pavers Inc....G....863 698-9179
Plant City (G-14462)
Rio Pavers Inc....G....321 388-6757
Orlando (G-13140)
Roadsafe Traffic Systems Inc....E....386 755-0140
Lake City (G-7382)
Rockstone Brick Pavers....G....813 685-3900
Brandon (G-1175)
◆ Ronnies Welding & Machine....G....305 238-0972
Cutler Bay (G-2410)
S T Wooten Corporation....E....239 337-9486
Fort Myers (G-4591)
Scutti America Inc....F....954 384-2377
Weston (G-19167)
Shantui America Corp....F....786 491-9114
Miami (G-10334)
Shavers Pavers....G....407 350-3538
Kissimmee (G-7298)
▲ Sicoma North America Inc....G....800 921-7559
Clearwater (G-1877)
Sipp Technologies LLC....E....904 374-5606
Jacksonville (G-6778)
Sivo Brick Pavers Inc....G....813 917-3859
Palm Harbor (G-13760)
Smith Challenger Mfg Svcs Inc....F....863 248-2624
Lakeland (G-7794)
South Florida Marine....G....305 232-8788
Cutler Bay (G-2413)
South Florida Pavers Corp....G....786 517-9100
Hialeah (G-5626)
Southwest Precision AG Inc....G....863 674-5799
Felda (G-3724)
Space Coast Hydraulics Inc....F....321 504-6006
Rockledge (G-15449)
▲ Stabil Concrete Pavers LLC....E....941 739-7823
Sarasota (G-16300)
Stamp Concrete & Pavers Inc....G....561 880-1527
Merritt Island (G-9014)

SIC

Employee Codes: A=Over 500 employees, B=251-500
C=101-250, D=51-100, E=20-50, F=10-19, G=4-9

Stone Brick Pavers Inc ...G... 407 844-1455
Ocoee *(G-12090)*
Suncoast Pavers Llc ...G... 813 323-4014
Odessa *(G-12158)*
Superior Pavers and Stone LLC ...G... 904 887-7831
Jacksonville *(G-6829)*
▲ Supertrak Inc ...F... 941 505-7800
Punta Gorda *(G-15239)*
Sws Services Inc ...F... 904 802-2120
Fernandina Beach *(G-3748)*
T & E Pavers Inc ...G... 239 243-6229
Cape Coral *(G-1483)*
Tarmac America Inc ...G... 386 427-0438
Edgewater *(G-3637)*
Tecnografic Inc ...E... 954 928-1714
Fort Lauderdale *(G-4276)*
Tensik Inc ...G... 954 937-9505
Winter Haven *(G-19363)*
Timburr Express LLC ...G... 850 535-1488
Vernon *(G-18587)*
▲ Townley Engrg & Mfg Co Inc ...C... 352 687-3001
Candler *(G-1332)*
Tremron LLC ...C... 904 359-5900
Jacksonville *(G-6868)*
Tropical Paver Sealing ...G... 727 786-4011
Wesley Chapel *(G-18761)*
Tyco Machine Inc ...G... 352 544-0210
Brooksville *(G-1284)*
U Got Recovery Inc ...F... 407 343-9919
Kissimmee *(G-7305)*
◆ Uflex Usa Inc ...E... 941 351-2628
Sarasota *(G-16319)*
US Paver Co ...G... 954 292-4373
Boca Raton *(G-772)*
Villar Stone & Paver Works LLC ...G... 860 209-2907
Sarasota *(G-16633)*
Wagner Pavers Contractor ...G... 321 633-5131
Rockledge *(G-15456)*
Waller Pavers Inc ...G... 863 644-8187
Lakeland *(G-7831)*
Wanted Dead or Alive Inc ...G... 239 633-5080
North Fort Myers *(G-11609)*
◆ Waterblasting Technologies Inc ...C... 772 223-7393
Stuart *(G-17047)*
Wf Brick Pavers Inc ...G... 813 506-1941
Oldsmar *(G-12278)*
Zennergy LLC ...F... 813 382-3460
Tampa *(G-18280)*
Zinc Guy Inc ...E... 954 907-2752
Davie *(G-2618)*

3532 Mining Machinery & Eqpt

Atacama Resources Intl Inc ...G... 613 421-9733
Plantation *(G-14492)*
◆ B & A Manufacturing Co ...E... 561 848-8648
Riviera Beach *(G-15300)*
Blue Water Industries LLC ...G... 904 512-7706
Jacksonville *(G-6215)*
Bluegrass Materials Co LLC ...E... 919 781-4550
Jacksonville *(G-6216)*
Chemours Company Fc LLC ...D... 904 964-1230
Starke *(G-16889)*
Knight Industrial Eqp Inc ...G... 863 646-2997
Lakeland *(G-7729)*
Microtool and Instrument Inc ...E... 786 242-8780
Palmetto Bay *(G-13851)*
▼ Montgomery Industries Intl ...E... 904 355-4055
Jacksonville *(G-6615)*
Quality Fbrction Mch Works Inc ...F... 386 755-0220
Lake City *(G-7379)*
◆ Ronnies Welding & Machine ...G... 305 238-0972
Cutler Bay *(G-2410)*
◆ Sandvik Mining & Cnstr USA LLC ...C... 386 462-4100
Alachua *(G-18)*
◆ Technical International Corp ...G... 305 374-1054
Miami *(G-10462)*
Tmg Manufacturing Corp ...F... 813 464-2299
Tampa *(G-18192)*
▲ Townley Engrg & Mfg Co Inc ...C... 352 687-3001
Candler *(G-1332)*
▲ Townley Foundry & Mch Co Inc ...D... 352 687-3001
Candler *(G-1333)*
Vertex Precision Inc ...E... 561 582-6171
Lake Worth *(G-7597)*
Wolf Americas LLC ...G... 407 704-2051
Orlando *(G-13327)*

3533 Oil Field Machinery & Eqpt

Carib Energy (usa) LLC ...A... 904 727-2559
Jacksonville *(G-6254)*
▲ Chromalloy Gas Turbine LLC ...A... 561 935-3571
Palm Beach Gardens *(G-13578)*
▲ Enviro Petroleum Inc ...G... 713 896-6996
Jensen Beach *(G-6968)*
▼ Fred International LLC ...F... 786 539-1600
Miramar *(G-10995)*
Jayco Screens Inc ...G... 850 456-0673
Pensacola *(G-14182)*
◆ Krausz Usa Inc ...F... 352 509-3600
Ocala *(G-11977)*
▼ Logistic Systems Inc ...G... 305 477-4999
Miami *(G-9906)*
Phoenix Dewatering Inc ...F... 407 330-7015
Sanford *(G-16101)*
Rfg Petro Systems LLC ...F... 941 487-7524
Sarasota *(G-16559)*
◆ Sandvik Mining & Cnstr USA LLC ...C... 386 462-4100
Alachua *(G-18)*
Skide Llc ...F... 305 537-4275
Miami *(G-10356)*
Tecvalco USA Inc ...E... 866 427-3444
Rockledge *(G-15452)*

3534 Elevators & Moving Stairways

A1 Elevators LLC ...G... 954 773-4443
North Lauderdale *(G-11610)*
Armstrong Elevator Company ...G... 727 323-3800
Largo *(G-7900)*
Beautiful Homes Inc ...G... 800 403-1480
Spring Hill *(G-16848)*
City Elevator Service Corp ...G... 305 345-1951
Miami *(G-9356)*
◆ Concept Elevator Group LLC ...D... 786 845-8955
Miami *(G-9390)*
E M A C Inc ...E... 850 526-4111
Marianna *(G-8577)*
▼ Gunderlin Ltd Inc ...D... 305 696-6071
Hialeah *(G-5440)*
▼ International Machine Works ...F... 305 635-3585
Miami *(G-9759)*
Jonathan Mariotti Entps LLC ...G... 855 353-8280
Fort Myers *(G-4507)*
Kohtler Elevator Inds Inc ...E... 305 687-7037
Opa Locka *(G-12331)*
▼ Mobile Specialties Inc ...G... 407 878-5469
Sanford *(G-16088)*
Otis Elevator Company ...B... 561 618-4831
West Palm Beach *(G-18974)*
Precision Lift Industries LLC ...G... 877 770-5862
Pensacola *(G-14237)*
Qcab LLC ...G... 305 510-2566
Vero Beach *(G-18655)*
◆ Southeast Elevator Llc ...D... 772 461-0030
Fort Pierce *(G-4747)*
Unitech Industries Corp ...F... 305 691-0330
Miami *(G-10533)*

3535 Conveyors & Eqpt

▼ Agri Machinery & Parts Inc ...F... 407 299-1592
Orlando *(G-12442)*
American Automtn Systems Inc ...G... 305 620-0077
Miami Lakes *(G-10762)*
Anchor Machine & Fabricating ...F... 813 247-3099
Tampa *(G-17426)*
Andersons Can Line Fbrction Eq ...F... 407 889-4665
Apopka *(G-113)*
Atlas Metal Industries Inc ...C... 305 625-2451
Miami *(G-9186)*
Automated Parking Corporation ...G... 754 200-8441
Fort Lauderdale *(G-3833)*
Built Right Installers Intl ...F... 305 362-6010
Hialeah *(G-5334)*
Capitol Conveyors Inc ...G... 727 314-7474
Trinity *(G-18483)*
Chris Industries Corp ...G... 941 729-7600
Palmetto *(G-13791)*
Container Handling Solutions ...G... 941 359-2095
Sarasota *(G-16194)*
Conveyor Concepts Corporation ...G... 941 751-1200
Sarasota *(G-16196)*
◆ Conveyor Consulting & Rbr Corp ...G... 813 385-1254
Odessa *(G-12113)*
Custom Metal Designs Inc ...D... 407 656-7771
Oakland *(G-11769)*
Eagle Pneumatic Inc ...E... 863 644-4870
Lakeland *(G-7678)*
Emmeti USA LLC ...F... 813 490-6252
Safety Harbor *(G-15492)*
▼ Epperson & Company ...D... 813 626-6125
Tampa *(G-17647)*
Erie Manufacturing Inc ...F... 863 534-3743
Bartow *(G-315)*
▲ Flite Technology Inc ...F... 321 631-2050
Cocoa *(G-2022)*
Franbiz Inc ...G... 813 282-1115
Clearwater *(G-1694)*
▲ Gaemmerler (us) Corporation ...G... 941 465-4400
Palmetto *(G-13800)*
ISA Group Corp ...F... 305 748-1578
Miami *(G-9773)*
J D B Dense Flow Inc ...F... 727 785-8500
Palm Harbor *(G-13741)*
Jepsen Tool Company Inc ...F... 904 262-2793
Jacksonville *(G-6521)*
▼ Keller-Nglillis Design Mfg Inc ...F... 727 733-4111
Dunedin *(G-3582)*
▲ Lynx Products Corp Inc ...G... 941 727-9676
Bradenton *(G-1073)*
M A K Manufacturing Inc ...G... 352 343-5881
Tavares *(G-18346)*
Material Conveying Maint Inc ...E... 813 740-1111
Tampa *(G-17894)*
Multi-Flex LLC ...G... 941 360-6500
Sarasota *(G-16260)*
Novak Machining Inc ...G... 727 527-5473
Pinellas Park *(G-14372)*
Padgett Manufacturing Inc ...D... 941 756-8566
Bradenton *(G-1093)*
Quality Fbrction Mch Works Inc ...F... 386 755-0220
Lake City *(G-7379)*
Sardee Industries Inc ...E... 407 295-2114
Orlando *(G-13163)*
Sdi Industries Inc ...E... 321 733-1128
Melbourne *(G-8928)*
Sunshine Tool LLC ...G... 941 351-6330
Sarasota *(G-16306)*
Titan Service Industry Llc ...G... 678 313-4707
Deland *(G-3023)*
Tpi Engineered Systems Inc ...G... 727 233-2810
Hudson *(G-6041)*
◆ UNI-Pak Corp ...E... 407 830-9300
Longwood *(G-8346)*
US Conveyor Solutions Inc ...F... 352 343-0085
Tavares *(G-18356)*
▲ Ver-Val Enterprises Inc ...F... 850 244-7931
Fort Walton Beach *(G-4838)*
▼ William Laroque Installers Inc ...E... 305 769-1717
Hollywood *(G-5940)*

3536 Hoists, Cranes & Monorails

◆ Aci Hoist & Crane Inc ...G... 954 367-6116
Pompano Beach *(G-14575)*
Advanced Overhead Systems Inc ...E... 863 667-3757
Lakeland *(G-7627)*
◆ Beta Max Inc ...E... 321 727-3737
Palm Bay *(G-13502)*
Beta Max Inc ...G... 321 914-0918
Palm Bay *(G-13503)*
Boat Lift Pros of SW Fla Inc ...F... 239 339-7080
Fort Myers *(G-4376)*
Boat Lifts By Synergy LLC ...G... 641 676-4785
Fort Myers *(G-4377)*
Boat Lifts of South Florida ...G... 305 522-1320
Tavernier *(G-18361)*
Coastal Crane and Rigging Inc ...G... 850 460-1766
Santa Rosa Beach *(G-16155)*
▼ Davit Master Corp ...F... 727 573-4414
Clearwater *(G-1650)*
▼ Deco Power Lift Inc ...F... 727 736-4529
Safety Harbor *(G-15491)*
Deshazo LLC ...G... 863 272-3107
Lakeland *(G-7674)*
◆ Diversfied Lifting Systems Inc ...E... 813 248-2299
Tampa *(G-17609)*
Equipment Fabricators Inc ...E... 321 632-0990
Cocoa *(G-2020)*
Florida Boat Lift ...G... 813 873-1614
Tampa *(G-17673)*
◆ Golden Manufacturing Inc ...E... 239 337-4141
North Fort Myers *(G-11598)*
High Tech Hoist Corp ...G... 321 733-3387
Melbourne *(G-8843)*
▲ Hook International Inc ...G... 727 209-0855
Largo *(G-7974)*
Imm Survivor Inc ...F... 239 454-7020
Fort Myers *(G-4490)*
◆ J Herbert Corporation ...F... 407 846-0588
Kissimmee *(G-7256)*
Kone Crane Maintenance Svcs ...F... 813 707-0086
Plant City *(G-14445)*

▼ **Nautical Acquisitions Corp** ....C....... 727 541-6664
Largo *(G-8017)*
▼ **Neptune Boat Lifts Inc** ....E....... 954 524-3616
Fort Lauderdale *(G-4135)*
PM Enterprises Holdings LLC ....E....... 407 846-0588
Kissimmee *(G-7288)*
Presto Lifts ....G....... 786 615-7256
Hialeah *(G-5566)*
Qlty Alumn Boat Lifts Inc ....G....... 850 434-6446
Pensacola *(G-14244)*
Quality Alum Boat Lifts Inc ....G....... 850 434-6446
Pensacola *(G-14245)*
▼ **Quick Lift Inc** ....G....... 305 471-0147
Doral *(G-3475)*
Rocky Bayou Enterprises Inc ....G....... 850 244-4567
Fort Walton Beach *(G-4829)*
SE Custom Lift Systems Inc ....G....... 954 941-8090
Pompano Beach *(G-14844)*
◆ **Touchless Cover LLC** ....E....... 407 679-2217
Orlando *(G-13265)*
▲ **V-Bro Products LLC** ....F....... 352 267-6235
Tavares *(G-18358)*

3537 Indl Trucks, Tractors, Trailers & Stackers

A & R Material Handling Inc ....F....... 904 879-6957
Callahan *(G-1322)*
A & S Equipment Co ....F....... 305 436-8207
Doral *(G-3220)*
All Lift Solutions Inc ....G....... 786 295-3946
Miami *(G-9111)*
Alliance Commercial Eqp Inc ....G....... 772 232-8149
Pompano Beach *(G-14587)*
Alpine Systems Associates Inc ....G....... 305 262-3263
Medley *(G-8608)*
Alta Equipment Holdings Inc ....G....... 813 519-4097
Tampa *(G-17406)*
Amds Trading Inc ....G....... 305 594-6680
Doral *(G-3246)*
◆ **Amer-Con Corp** ....E....... 786 293-8004
Palmetto Bay *(G-13839)*
▼ **Amera Trail Inc** ....E....... 407 892-1100
Saint Cloud *(G-15643)*
B R Express ....G....... 904 881-2556
Jacksonville *(G-6186)*
▼ **Benitez Forklift Corp** ....G....... 786 307-3872
Hialeah *(G-5321)*
Big Man Friendly Trnsp LLC ....G....... 941 229-3454
Lakewood Ranch *(G-7837)*
▲ **Bms International Inc** ....E....... 813 247-7040
Tampa *(G-17477)*
Bravo Inc ....G....... 239 471-8127
Cape Coral *(G-1394)*
Carriers Direct Inc ....F....... 941 776-2979
Parrish *(G-14005)*
Cholift Forklift USA Co ....G....... 786 483-6930
Hialeah *(G-5344)*
Dfd Loaders Inc ....F....... 954 283-8839
Coral Springs *(G-2241)*
◆ **Dhs Power Corp** ....G....... 305 599-1022
Miami *(G-9463)*
◆ **Diversfied Lifting Systems Inc** ....E....... 813 248-2299
Tampa *(G-17609)*
Dmoney365 Logistic LLC ....F....... 954 529-8202
North Lauderdale *(G-11613)*
Earthmover Cnstr Eqp LLC ....E....... 407 401-8956
Apopka *(G-132)*
Empire Trnspt Solutions Corp ....G....... 305 439-5677
Hialeah *(G-5398)*
First Coast Cargo Inc ....F....... 844 774-7711
Jacksonville *(G-6384)*
Florida Jacksonville Forklift ....G....... 904 674-6898
Jacksonville *(G-6399)*
Forklift ....G....... 305 468-1824
Miami *(G-9594)*
▲ **Gosan Usa Inc** ....F....... 904 356-4181
Jacksonville *(G-6442)*
Grass Pro Shops Inc ....F....... 813 381-3890
Tampa *(G-17726)*
▼ **Gyro-Gale Inc** ....G....... 772 283-1711
Stuart *(G-16952)*
Iscar GSE Corp ....E....... 305 364-8886
Miami Gardens *(G-10748)*
Iscar GSE Corp ....E....... 305 364-8886
Miami Gardens *(G-10749)*
Jamco Industrial Inc ....F....... 866 848-5400
Sanford *(G-16072)*
John Bean Technologies Corp ....E....... 407 851-3377
Orlando *(G-12858)*
Lake County Forklift Solutions ....G....... 352 735-4024
Sorrento *(G-16788)*
Lit Forklift LLC ....G....... 321 271-4626
Cocoa Beach *(G-2065)*
Lite Cart Corp ....G....... 727 584-7364
Largo *(G-8002)*
LUnion Logistics LLC ....F....... 866 586-4660
Hollywood *(G-5866)*
MC Intl Transportation ....F....... 305 805-8228
Miami *(G-9959)*
Mettler-Toledo Inc ....C....... 607 257-6000
Lutz *(G-8400)*
Modest Logistics LLC ....F....... 321 314-2825
Orlando *(G-12976)*
Ocean Way Transport LLC ....G....... 407 669-3822
Orlando *(G-13018)*
On Time Loading ....F....... 877 668-4630
Miami *(G-10099)*
Onsite Rlble Forklift Svcs Inc ....F....... 305 305-8638
Hialeah *(G-5550)*
Orlandos Forklift Service LLC ....G....... 407 761-9104
Orlando *(G-13038)*
Polson Transportation LLC ....G....... 614 733-9677
Fort Myers *(G-4568)*
Rack It Truck Racks ....F....... 800 354-1900
San Antonio *(G-15977)*
Rampmaster Inc ....F....... 305 691-9090
Miami *(G-10238)*
Ring Power Corporation ....G....... 863 606-0512
Lakeland *(G-7779)*
RJ Forklift Services Inc ....G....... 786 539-6613
Miami *(G-10266)*
Rolls Rite Trailers Inc ....F....... 850 526-2290
Marianna *(G-8585)*
Runn-It LLC ....G....... 800 932-8052
Miami *(G-10289)*
Sardee Industries Inc ....E....... 407 295-2114
Orlando *(G-13163)*
Sdi Industries Inc ....E....... 321 733-1128
Melbourne *(G-8928)*
Shane Laliberte Lift LLC ....G....... 407 873-0703
Saint Cloud *(G-15666)*
Smart Miles Logistics LLC ....G....... 754 244-2656
Fort Lauderdale *(G-4239)*
South Fla Forklift Doctor Corp ....G....... 561 951-6243
Lake Worth Beach *(G-7620)*
Tampa Fork Lift Inc ....F....... 904 674-6899
Jacksonville *(G-6837)*
Terex Corporation ....G....... 352 330-4044
Wildwood *(G-19205)*
◆ **Tesco Equipment LLC** ....E....... 954 752-7994
Coral Springs *(G-2322)*
Textron Ground Support Eqp Inc ....G....... 954 359-5730
Fort Lauderdale *(G-4280)*
Tfl of Orlando ....G....... 407 936-1553
Orlando *(G-13251)*
The Forklift Company Inc ....F....... 863 595-8156
Lake Alfred *(G-7334)*
Toteum All Trckg Trnsprting L ....E....... 888 506-5890
Orlando *(G-13264)*
Windstar Express Inc ....G....... 786 252-1569
Miami *(G-10609)*
◆ **World Industrial Equipment Inc** ....E....... 772 461-6056
Fort Pierce *(G-4772)*

3541 Machine Tools: Cutting

A & L Toolings LLC ....G....... 407 242-7114
Sanford *(G-15984)*
Aerowest Mfg Corp ....G....... 786 367-6948
Hialeah *(G-5273)*
▼ **Agi-Vr/Wesson Inc** ....E....... 239 573-5132
Cape Coral *(G-1377)*
Amaya Lathing & Plaspering ....G....... 786 953-6420
Miami *(G-9131)*
Amaya Lathing & Plastering LLC ....G....... 305 216-4247
Miami *(G-9132)*
Americut of Florida Inc ....F....... 800 692-2187
Fort Myers *(G-4360)*
▲ **Andritz Iggesund Tools Inc** ....E....... 813 855-6902
Oldsmar *(G-12202)*
▼ **Armada Systems Inc** ....F....... 850 664-5197
Destin *(G-3183)*
Azt Technology LLC ....C....... 239 352-0600
Naples *(G-11179)*
◆ **Bescutter LLC** ....G....... 888 525-2897
Lehigh Acres *(G-8185)*
Chase Metals Inc ....E....... 352 669-1254
Umatilla *(G-18496)*
Coastal Machine LLC ....G....... 850 769-6117
Panama City *(G-13885)*
▼ **E T Plastering Inc** ....F....... 305 874-7082
Virginia Gardens *(G-18688)*
Elliott Diamond Tool Inc ....F....... 727 585-3839
Clearwater *(G-1669)*
Ems Technologies NA LLC ....F....... 321 259-5979
Orlando *(G-12710)*
Federated Precision Inc ....E....... 561 288-6500
Deerfield Beach *(G-2824)*
Florida Hytorc ....F....... 813 990-9470
Clearwater *(G-1689)*
Florida Knife Co ....E....... 941 371-2104
Sarasota *(G-16437)*
◆ **Gaynor Group Inc** ....G....... 954 749-1228
Sunrise *(G-17125)*
▲ **Giraldo & Donalisio Corp** ....G....... 239 567-2206
Cape Coral *(G-1429)*
Grizzly Manufacturing Inc ....E....... 386 755-0220
Lake City *(G-7360)*
Gulf Machining Inc ....F....... 727 571-1244
Clearwater *(G-1707)*
Heath Corporation ....G....... 863 638-1819
Lake Wales *(G-7513)*
High Performance Holdings Ltd ....E....... 815 874-9421
Lakeland *(G-7705)*
Highvac Co LLC ....F....... 407 969-0399
Orlando *(G-12803)*
Huff Carbide Tool Inc ....F....... 727 848-4001
Port Richey *(G-15052)*
Icosi Manufacturing LLC ....F....... 813 854-1333
Odessa *(G-12095)*
▲ **International Tool Mchs of Fla** ....E....... 386 446-0500
Palm Coast *(G-13699)*
Lathing By Estaban M Perez Inc ....G....... 352 302-8791
Lady Lake *(G-7327)*
Levil Technology Corp ....G....... 407 542-3971
Oviedo *(G-13447)*
Lexington Cutter Inc ....E....... 941 739-2726
Bradenton *(G-1070)*
LJ&j Lathing Inc ....G....... 386 325-5040
Palatka *(G-13485)*
LPs Lath Plst & Stucco Inc ....G....... 954 444-3727
Fort Lauderdale *(G-4104)*
Lundy Enterprises Inc ....F....... 727 549-1292
Largo *(G-8003)*
M Vb Industries Inc ....E....... 954 480-6448
Deerfield Beach *(G-2865)*
Machine Technology Inc ....G....... 321 254-3886
Melbourne *(G-8880)*
Martin Munive Inc ....G....... 772 318-8168
Port Saint Lucie *(G-15121)*
Maydone Ltd Liability Company ....G....... 407 399-3287
Orlando *(G-12955)*
▼ **Metal Supply and Machining Inc** ....F....... 561 276-4941
Delray Beach *(G-3107)*
▲ **Mitts and Merrill LP** ....G....... 352 343-7001
Tavares *(G-18349)*
Odyssey Fastening Systems Inc ....G....... 561 436-5570
Jupiter *(G-7086)*
Precision Metal Parts Inc ....E....... 727 526-9165
Saint Petersburg *(G-15888)*
Precision Turning Corporation ....F....... 386 364-5788
Live Oak *(G-8237)*
Prime Horizontal ....G....... 239 471-2357
Cape Coral *(G-1457)*
Rankine-Hinman Mfg Co ....F....... 904 808-0404
Saint Augustine *(G-15594)*
Reiley Tool Company LLC ....G....... 360 929-0350
Middleburg *(G-10912)*
▲ **Reinecker Grinders Corp** ....G....... 954 974-6190
Pompano Beach *(G-14827)*
▲ **Republic Drill/Apt Corp** ....D....... 305 592-7777
Miami *(G-10256)*
Rockford Ettco Procunier Inc ....F....... 863 688-0071
Lakeland *(G-7781)*
Santiago ....G....... 386 527-5822
Port Orange *(G-15031)*
Skill-Metric Machine & Tl Inc ....E....... 561 454-8900
Delray Beach *(G-3143)*
Snk America Inc ....F....... 407 831-7766
Sanford *(G-16117)*
State Lathinginc ....G....... 786 357-8404
Lake Worth *(G-7588)*
Super Tool Inc ....E....... 941 751-9677
Bradenton *(G-1122)*
Technical Ord Solutions LLC ....G....... 850 223-2393
Perry *(G-14316)*
Unbridled Technologies LLC ....G....... 888 334-8402
Brooksville *(G-1285)*
Walin Tools LLC ....G....... 850 226-8632
Fort Walton Beach *(G-4839)*

SIC

Zel Tech Trining Solutions LLC ....E 757 722-5565
Winter Park *(G-19464)*

3542 Machine Tools: Forming

◆ **Aflg Invstmnts-Industrials LLC** ....G....... 813 443-8203
Tampa *(G-17390)*
Aflg Invstmnts-Industrials LLC..............F 813 443-8203
Hernando Beach *(G-5250)*
B&M RC Racing..................................G....... 313 518-3999
Winter Haven *(G-19301)*
▲ **Bedeschi America Inc**......................D....... 954 602-2175
Boca Raton *(G-444)*
◆ **Bridgestone Hosepower LLC** ....D....... 904 264-1267
Orange Park *(G-12383)*
Coastal Machine LLC..........................G....... 850 769-6117
Panama City *(G-13885)*
Daigle Tool & Die Inc ....G....... 954 785-9989
Deerfield Beach *(G-2811)*
Delta Machine & Tool Inc....................E 386 738-2204
Deland *(G-2969)*
Double Header LLC..............................G....... 352 377-4458
Gainesville *(G-4908)*
Electro Mech Solutions Inc...................E 813 792-0400
Odessa *(G-12118)*
▲ **Fabco-Air Inc**......................................D....... 352 373-3578
Gainesville *(G-4918)*
Fuji International LLC.........................F 941 961-5472
Sarasota *(G-16442)*
G & R Machine Inc ....G....... 407 324-1600
Sanford *(G-16053)*
▲ **Hydrapower International Inc** ....A 239 642-5379
Marco Island *(G-8525)*
Jenzano Incorporated..........................F 386 761-4474
Port Orange *(G-15020)*
▲ **Lenco Holdings LLC**..........................G....... 305 360-0895
Deerfield Beach *(G-2858)*
Maydone Ltd Liability Company...........G....... 407 399-3287
Orlando *(G-12955)*
Phoenix Enterprises Fla LLC................F 813 986-9000
Temple Terrace *(G-18374)*
Production Metal Stampings ....F 850 981-8240
Milton *(G-10938)*
◆ **Sequa Corporation** ....A 561 935-3571
Palm Beach Gardens *(G-13626)*
Standard Rivet Company Inc................F 386 872-6477
South Daytona *(G-16810)*
Sunrise Manufacturing Intl Inc ....F 813 780-7369
Zephyrhills *(G-19538)*
U S Hardware Supply Inc ....E 407 657-1551
Winter Park *(G-19454)*

3543 Industrial Patterns

Cost Cast Aluminum Corp ....E 863 422-5617
Haines City *(G-5140)*
Living Pattern LLC...............................G....... 561 596-8205
Delray Beach *(G-3101)*
Pattern Grading & Marker Svcs............G....... 305 495-9963
Miramar *(G-11027)*
◆ **U S Holdings Inc**................................G....... 305 885-0301
Hialeah *(G-5656)*

3544 Dies, Tools, Jigs, Fixtures & Indl Molds

Accu Metal..G....... 850 912-4855
Pensacola *(G-14078)*
◆ **Advanced Machine and Tool Inc** ....D....... 772 465-6546
Fort Pierce *(G-4669)*
▲ **Allied General Engrv & Plas**..............F 305 626-6585
Opa Locka *(G-12286)*
American Mfg & Mch Inc ....D....... 352 728-2222
Okahumpka *(G-12168)*
American Mold Removal Inc.................G....... 561 575-7757
Loxahatchee *(G-8357)*
Ameritech Die & Mold South Inc ....G....... 386 677-1770
Ormond Beach *(G-13348)*
Apex Flood Fire Mold Clnup Inc...........G....... 305 975-1710
Boca Raton *(G-427)*
ARC Transition LLC..............................G....... 386 626-0001
Daytona Beach *(G-2628)*
Armoury Property & Mold Inspec..........G....... 813 503-9765
Port Charlotte *(G-14963)*
▲ **Ashwell Label Dies Inc** ....F 727 527-0098
Pinellas Park *(G-14335)*
▼ **B & D Precision Tools Inc** ....E 305 885-1583
Hialeah *(G-5314)*
C & C Tool & Mold...............................G....... 863 699-5337
Lake Placid *(G-7485)*
Cavaform International LLC..................D....... 727 384-3676
Saint Petersburg *(G-15741)*
Certified Mold Treatment LLC...............G....... 305 879-1839
Summerland Key *(G-17065)*
Cind-Al Inc...G....... 863 401-8700
Clermont *(G-1952)*
▲ **Cob Industries Inc**..............................G....... 321 723-3200
West Melbourne *(G-18770)*
Complete Mold Remediators Inc...........G....... 305 903-8885
Homestead *(G-5958)*
Covington Plastics Inc ....F 321 632-6775
Cocoa *(G-2006)*
Crenshaw Die & Manufacturing.............F 949 475-5505
Daytona Beach *(G-2648)*
D M T Inc...F 321 267-3931
Cocoa *(G-2008)*
Danly Corporation................................G....... 305 285-0111
Miami *(G-9434)*
Daytona Dock & Seawall Service ....G....... 386 255-7909
Daytona Beach *(G-2653)*
Delta Machine & Tool Inc....................E 386 738-2204
Deland *(G-2969)*
Destin Machine Inc ....G....... 850 837-7114
Destin *(G-3187)*
Diemold Machine Company Inc...........E 239 482-1400
Fort Myers *(G-4431)*
Dimension Machine Engrg LLC.............F 586 948-3600
Cape Coral *(G-1413)*
Dimension Machine Tool Inc..................F 586 948-3600
Cape Coral *(G-1414)*
▼ **Ebway LLC**...E 954 971-4911
Fort Lauderdale *(G-3957)*
Ebway LLC...D....... 954 971-4911
Fort Lauderdale *(G-3958)*
◆ **Eddy Floor Scraper Inc**......................G....... 954 981-0715
Hallandale *(G-5156)*
Emergency Mold Specialist LLC ....G....... 239 691-3157
Naples *(G-11236)*
Expert Mold Removal Inc.....................G....... 407 925-6443
Tavares *(G-18336)*
▲ **Ezell Precision Tool Co** ....F 727 573-3575
Clearwater *(G-1678)*
FDM of Clearwater Inc ....F 727 544-8801
Largo *(G-7944)*
Firedrake Inc.......................................G....... 813 713-8902
Zephyrhills *(G-19518)*
Florida Mold Mitigators LLC ....G....... 772 633-3415
Vero Beach *(G-18618)*
Florida Mold Stoppers Inc....................G....... 954 445-5560
Davie *(G-2526)*
FMC Marketing Inc................................G....... 201 417-1767
Hollywood *(G-5824)*
▲ **Fullerton 799 Inc** ....E 727 572-7040
Clearwater *(G-1696)*
Gama TEC Corporation ....G....... 305 362-0456
Hialeah *(G-5423)*
Greg Heyen..G....... 727 585-8555
Largo *(G-7965)*
Gregg Tool & Die Co Inc.......................G....... 305 685-6309
Hialeah *(G-5436)*
▼ **Gulf Coast Mold & Tool Corp** ....F 239 643-1017
Bonita Springs *(G-837)*
Gulf Tool Corporation............................F 850 456-0840
Pensacola *(G-14168)*
▲ **Hoffstetter Tool & Die Inc**..................F 727 573-7775
Clearwater *(G-1715)*
Huff Carbide Tool Inc.............................F 727 848-4001
Port Richey *(G-15052)*
J C S Engineering & Dev......................F 305 888-7911
Hialeah *(G-5459)*
JSB Enterprises Inc..............................E 941 723-2288
Palmetto *(G-13808)*
Kinetic Industries LLC...........................G....... 727 572-7604
Clearwater *(G-1750)*
Kirtech Enterprises Inc..........................F 352 742-7222
Tavares *(G-18344)*
Leeds Machining Co..............................G....... 407 671-3688
Orlando *(G-12901)*
M D Mold LLC.......................................G....... 941 214-0854
Port Charlotte *(G-14989)*
Miami Quality Graphics Inc...................E 305 634-9506
Miami *(G-10007)*
▲ **Mitts and Merrill LP**...........................G....... 352 343-7001
Tavares *(G-18349)*
Mold Be Gone Plus ....G....... 239 672-5321
Fort Myers *(G-4536)*
Mold Busters LLC ....G....... 786 360-6464
Miami *(G-10036)*
Mold Expert ....G....... 954 829-3102
Coral Springs *(G-2286)*
Mold Pros Franchising Inc.....................F 239 262-6653
Naples *(G-11328)*
Mold R US Inc.......................................G....... 954 850-6653
Hollywood *(G-5879)*
Moloney Die Company ....G....... 904 388-3654
Jacksonville *(G-6613)*
OSteen Plastic Inc.................................G....... 954 434-4921
Southwest Ranches *(G-16839)*
Oxygenix Mold and Odor LLC ....G....... 850 926-5421
Crawfordville *(G-2335)*
Pace Machine & Tool Inc ....F 561 747-5444
Stuart *(G-16985)*
▲ **Pacific Die Cast Inc**............................F 813 316-2221
Tampa *(G-17968)*
Papenfuss Holdings Inc ....G....... 239 775-9090
Naples *(G-11356)*
PMC Enterprises Mgmt Division............F 239 949-6566
Naples *(G-11371)*
Precision Mold Restoration LLC ....G....... 239 699-3688
Cape Coral *(G-1455)*
Precision Tl Engrg of Gnsville...............F 352 376-2533
Gainesville *(G-4982)*
Project Mold..G....... 561 213-6167
Boca Raton *(G-676)*
Rafferty Holdings LLC ....E 352 248-0906
Gainesville *(G-4989)*
Redkeys Dies..G....... 772 463-5824
Stuart *(G-17000)*
Robert Petrucci Inc................................F 954 772-2333
Fort Lauderdale *(G-4211)*
Roller Die + Forming..............................E 502 804-5571
Green Cove Springs *(G-5068)*
Savage Ventures Inc..............................E 772 335-5655
Port Saint Lucie *(G-15141)*
Schwarz Bros Manufacturing Co...........G....... 309 342-5814
Pensacola *(G-14259)*
Simplex Manufacturing Inc ....E 941 378-8700
Sarasota *(G-16598)*
Sohacki Industries Inc...........................E 904 826-0130
Saint Augustine *(G-15613)*
Southpointe Precision...........................G....... 239 225-1350
Fort Myers *(G-4608)*
▲ **Spaulding Craft Inc**............................F 727 726-2316
Safety Harbor *(G-15505)*
▼ **Sunco Plastics Inc** ....F 305 238-2864
Miami *(G-10429)*
Suncoast Tool & Gage Inds Inc ....F 727 572-8000
Clearwater *(G-1893)*
T H L Diamond Products Inc..................G....... 954 596-5012
Deerfield Beach *(G-2922)*
Technamold Inc......................................G....... 727 561-0030
Clearwater *(G-1910)*
Tennessee Tool and Fixture LLC...........F 931 954-5316
Winter Park *(G-19452)*
Tibor Inc..E 561 272-0770
Delray Beach *(G-3150)*
Triad Edm Inc ....G....... 352 489-5336
Dunnellon *(G-3601)*
Unique Tool & Die LLC ....F 772 464-5006
Fort Pierce *(G-4766)*
▼ **Universal Die Services Inc** ....G....... 863 665-6092
Lakeland *(G-7828)*
US Mold Inc ....G....... 561 748-2223
Jupiter *(G-7138)*
Versacomp Inc.......................................F 954 561-8778
Oakland Park *(G-11858)*
Versatile Manufacturing Inc ....E 954 561-8083
Oakland Park *(G-11859)*
Versatile Manufacturing Inc ....F 954 561-8083
Oakland Park *(G-11860)*
Victors Die Cutting Inc ....G....... 305 599-0255
Hialeah *(G-5679)*
West Point Industries Inc.......................G....... 561 848-8381
Lake Park *(G-7481)*

3545 Machine Tool Access

A B & B Manufacturing Inc....................F 904 378-3350
Jacksonville *(G-6108)*
▲ **Aaw Products Inc** ....G....... 305 330-6863
Miami *(G-9049)*
Advantage Drills Inc ....G....... 407 478-2487
Winter Park *(G-19373)*
▼ **Agi-Vr/Wesson Inc**..............................E 239 573-5132
Cape Coral *(G-1377)*
▲ **Andritz Iggesund Tools Inc** ....E 813 855-6902
Oldsmar *(G-12202)*
◆ **Approved Performance Tooling** ....E 305 592-7775
Miami *(G-9158)*
Armorit Precision LLC...........................F 941 751-1292
Sarasota *(G-16176)*
Axiom Automotive Technologies ....G....... 407 299-4400
Orlando *(G-12502)*
◆ **B & A Manufacturing Co** ....E 561 848-8648
Riviera Beach *(G-15300)*

B & P Motors Inc ....G.... 305 687-7337
Opa Locka (G-12292)
▲ Construction and Elec Pdts Inc ....F.... 954 972-9787
Pompano Beach (G-14645)
Creative Carbide Inc ....F.... 239 567-0041
Fort Myers (G-4414)
Dan Lipman and Associates ....G.... 561 245-8672
Delray Beach (G-3068)
◆ Delta International Inc ....F.... 305 665-6573
Miami (G-9451)
Dse Inc ....E.... 813 443-4809
Tampa (G-17617)
▲ E-Z Fastening Solutions Inc ....G.... 813 854-3937
Oldsmar (G-12223)
Elite Aero LLC ....G.... 727 244-3382
Saint Petersburg (G-15768)
Elliott Diamond Tool Inc ....F.... 727 585-3839
Clearwater (G-1669)
Florida Knife Co ....E.... 941 371-2104
Sarasota (G-16437)
Goss Inc ....E.... 386 423-0311
New Smyrna Beach (G-11534)
Gulf Tool Corporation ....F.... 850 456-0840
Pensacola (G-14168)
▲ Gws Tool LLC ....F.... 352 343-8778
Tavares (G-18340)
Gws Tool Holdings LLC ....E.... 352 343-8778
Tavares (G-18341)
Henefelt Precision Products ....F.... 727 531-0406
Largo (G-7969)
Jacksnvlle Advnced McHning LLC ....G.... 904 292-2999
Jacksonville (G-6508)
Lexington Cutter Inc ....E.... 941 739-2726
Bradenton (G-1070)
▲ Mastercut Tool Corp ....E.... 727 726-5336
Safety Harbor (G-15499)
Micro Quality Corp ....G.... 954 354-5572
Deerfield Beach (G-2872)
Microtex Electronics Inc ....G.... 386 426-1922
Weeki Wachee (G-18704)
Microtool and Instrument Inc ....E.... 786 242-8780
Palmetto Bay (G-13851)
▲ Mitts and Merrill LP ....G.... 352 343-7001
Tavares (G-18349)
◆ Nasco Industries Inc ....E.... 954 733-8665
Fort Lauderdale (G-4131)
OGrady Tool Company ....F.... 239 560-3395
Fort Myers (G-4556)
Omega One Research Inc ....G.... 561 995-9611
Boca Raton (G-654)
Outline Technologies Inc ....G.... 904 858-9933
Jacksonville (G-6650)
Polygon Solutions Inc ....G.... 239 628-4800
Fort Myers (G-4569)
Rhino Tools Inc ....F.... 305 332-7750
Hialeah (G-5598)
Rock River Tool Inc ....F.... 941 753-6343
Bradenton (G-1106)
◆ Sandar Industries Inc ....E.... 904 246-4309
Atlantic Beach (G-226)
◆ Shaw Development LLC ....C.... 239 405-6100
Bonita Springs (G-853)
Sohacki Industries Inc ....E.... 904 826-0130
Saint Augustine (G-15613)
Suncoast Tool & Gage Inds Inc ....F.... 727 572-8000
Clearwater (G-1893)
Swisstech Machinery LLC ....G.... 407 416-2383
Orlando (G-13233)
Thermocarbon Inc ....E.... 407 834-7800
Casselberry (G-1520)
Time Industries Inc ....G.... 321 676-2080
Melbourne (G-8962)
Tom Burke Services ....G.... 863 940-4504
Lakeland (G-7823)
Toolinghouse Inc ....G.... 239 424-8503
Cape Coral (G-1486)
▲ Trumeter Company Inc ....G.... 954 725-6699
Coconut Creek (G-2098)
Turbine Broach Company ....F.... 352 795-1163
Hernando (G-5248)
Widell Industries Inc ....D.... 800 237-5963
Port Richey (G-15079)

3546 Power Hand Tools

▲ Air Turbine Technology Inc ....F.... 561 994-0500
Boca Raton (G-408)
Bayou Outdoor Equipment ....F.... 850 729-2711
Valparaiso (G-18506)
Black & Decker (us) Inc ....G.... 407 657-0474
Orlando (G-12519)
▲ Daniels Manufacturing Corp ....C.... 407 855-6161
Orlando (G-12646)
◆ Delta International Inc ....F.... 305 665-6573
Miami (G-9451)
▲ Delta Regis Tools Inc ....E.... 772 465-4302
Fort Pierce (G-4692)
▲ Es Manufacturing Inc ....F.... 727 323-4040
Pinellas Park (G-14347)
▲ Fabco-Air Inc ....D.... 352 373-3578
Gainesville (G-4918)
▲ Laycock Systems Inc ....F.... 813 248-3555
Tampa (G-17837)
◆ Nasco Industries Inc ....E.... 954 733-8665
Fort Lauderdale (G-4131)
◆ Ronnies Welding & Machine ....G.... 305 238-0972
Cutler Bay (G-2410)
S I P Corporation ....F.... 813 884-8300
Tampa (G-18075)
Tct Manufacturing ....E.... 352 735-5070
Mount Dora (G-11115)
Tdk Electronics Inc ....F.... 561 509-7771
Ocean Ridge (G-12080)

3547 Rolling Mill Machinery & Eqpt

Continental Metals ....G.... 734 362-1144
Fort Myers (G-4409)
◆ Industrial Galvanizers Miami ....E.... 305 681-8844
Miami (G-9738)
Metalhouse LLC ....G.... 407 270-3000
Orlando (G-12962)
Metalplate Galvanizing LP ....D.... 904 768-6330
Jacksonville (G-6599)

3548 Welding Apparatus

Alloy Cladding Company LLC ....F.... 561 625-4550
Fort Myers (G-4353)
Alphatron Industries Inc ....G.... 954 581-1418
Davie (G-2494)
◆ American Torch Tip Company ....C.... 941 753-7557
Bradenton (G-988)
Applied Design & Fabrication ....G.... 954 524-6619
Lake Placid (G-7484)
Automated Production Eqp Ape ....F.... 631 654-1197
Key Largo (G-7164)
Goss Inc ....E.... 386 423-0311
New Smyrna Beach (G-11534)
▲ J B Nottingham & Co Inc ....E.... 386 873-2990
Deland (G-2986)
▼ Jdci Enterprises Inc ....E.... 239 768-2292
Fort Myers (G-4502)
Parodi General Group Corp ....G.... 954 306-1098
Coconut Creek (G-2092)
R & S Metalworks & Co LLC ....F.... 772 466-3303
Port Saint Lucie (G-15132)
▲ Seelye Acquisitions Inc ....G.... 407 656-6677
Apopka (G-184)
▼ Smittys Boat Tops and Mar Eqp ....G.... 305 245-0229
Homestead (G-5993)
TL Fahringer Co Inc ....G.... 813 681-2373
Tampa (G-18190)
◆ Uniweld Products Inc ....C.... 954 584-2000
Fort Lauderdale (G-4298)
◆ V & C Supply Ornamental Corp ....G.... 305 634-9040
Miami (G-10558)

3549 Metalworking Machinery, NEC

Alh Systems Inc ....G.... 727 787-6306
Palm Harbor (G-13717)
▲ Automatic Mfg Systems Inc ....E.... 954 791-1500
Plantation (G-14494)
Best Closures Inc ....G.... 305 821-6607
Miami Lakes (G-10766)
▼ Centurion Armoring Intl Inc ....F.... 813 426-3385
Tampa (G-17525)
Custom Instruments LLC ....G.... 561 735-9971
Boynton Beach (G-894)
Decoral System USA Corporation ....E.... 954 755-6021
Coral Springs (G-2239)
▼ Ebway LLC ....E.... 954 971-4911
Fort Lauderdale (G-3957)
▲ Hilton International Inds ....E.... 941 371-2600
Sarasota (G-16460)
Inen USA Corp ....G.... 305 343-6666
Opa Locka (G-12325)
Intelligent Robotics Inc ....G.... 850 728-7353
Tallahassee (G-17281)
Jrmetal Ornamental ....G.... 954 989-2607
Hollywood (G-5855)
◆ KCm Mch Sp Broward Cnty Inc ....F.... 954 475-8732
Davie (G-2540)
Marchant Machine Corporation ....G.... 301 937-4481
Sarasota (G-16503)
Mid-State Machine Company LLC ....E.... 704 636-7029
Fort Myers (G-4533)
Precision Tl Engrg of Gnsville ....F.... 352 376-2533
Gainesville (G-4982)
Prime Global Group Inc ....E.... 386 676-2200
Ormond Beach (G-13393)
Robotics Fabrication Inc ....E.... 850 896-4987
Panama City (G-13947)
Servo Tech Inc ....G.... 727 573-7998
Clearwater (G-1875)
Smith Machine Services Inc ....G.... 904 845-2002
Hilliard (G-5718)
Symme3d LLC ....F.... 321 220-1584
Orlando (G-13234)
TL Fahringer Co Inc ....G.... 813 681-2373
Tampa (G-18190)
▲ Tophet-Blyth LLC ....F.... 239 594-5477
Naples (G-11444)
United Machining Service Inc ....G.... 407 422-7710
Orlando (G-13293)
Waterjet Robotics USA LLC ....G.... 772 403-2192
Palm Beach Gardens (G-13634)
Westlund Engineering Inc ....G.... 727 572-4343
Palm Harbor (G-13769)

3552 Textile Machinery

Alpine Industries Corporation ....F.... 941 749-1900
Bradenton (G-985)
▼ B Line Apparel Inc ....F.... 305 953-8300
Hialeah (G-5315)
Baylee & Company LLC ....G.... 305 333-6464
Hialeah (G-5317)
◆ Hills Inc ....D.... 321 723-5560
Melbourne (G-8844)
Imprints International Inc ....G.... 561 202-0105
Royal Palm Beach (G-15471)
ISA Group Corp ....F.... 305 748-1578
Miami (G-9773)
ISA Group Corp ....G.... 786 201-8360
Coral Gables (G-2161)
Joni Industries Inc ....F.... 352 799-5456
Brooksville (G-1240)
Lac Inc ....G.... 407 671-6610
Winter Park (G-19417)
Levil Technology Corp ....G.... 407 542-3971
Oviedo (G-13447)
Monarch Knitting McHy Corp ....G.... 954 345-2091
Coral Springs (G-2288)
◆ Pantograms Inc ....G.... 813 839-5697
Tampa (G-17972)
▲ Pantograms Mfg Co Inc ....E.... 813 839-5697
Tampa (G-17973)
Prime Global Group Inc ....E.... 386 676-2200
Ormond Beach (G-13393)
Progressive Machine Co Inc ....F.... 386 333-6850
Ormond Beach (G-13395)
◆ Ricoma International Corp ....G.... 305 418-4421
Doral (G-3485)
Tekmatic Corp ....F.... 305 972-1300
Miami (G-10466)
◆ Unicraft Corp ....F.... 305 633-4945
Miami (G-10528)
◆ United Associates Group Inc ....F.... 561 840-0050
Riviera Beach (G-15387)

3553 Woodworking Machinery

A H Woodcrafter ....G.... 305 885-2136
Miami (G-9039)
◆ Braid Sales and Marketing Inc ....E.... 321 752-8180
Melbourne (G-8785)
Calvert Manufacturing Inc ....F.... 407 331-5522
Casselberry (G-1499)
Commercial Cabinetry LLC ....G.... 407 440-4601
Orlando (G-12604)
County of Sumter ....G.... 352 689-4460
Bushnell (G-1316)
▲ Dimar Usa Inc ....G.... 954 590-8573
Fort Lauderdale (G-3942)
Inzirillo ....G.... 954 486-0055
Oakland Park (G-11815)
Lastrada Furniture Inc ....F.... 954 485-6000
Fort Lauderdale (G-4095)
▲ Lioher Enterprise Corp ....G.... 305 685-0005
Miami Lakes (G-10807)
Pleasure Interiors LLC ....E.... 941 756-9969
Sarasota (G-16545)
Quality Fbrction Mch Works Inc ....F.... 386 755-0220
Lake City (G-7379)

S I C

▲ **Teknatool Usa Inc** ....G....... 727 954-3433
Clearwater *(G-1914)*
Thomas Mix Kitchens & Baths ....G....... 239 229-4323
Fort Myers *(G-4627)*
Up - N - Atom ....G....... 904 716-5431
Jacksonville *(G-6888)*

3554 Paper Inds Machinery

Industrial Cnstr Svcs Dsign In ....D....... 904 827-9795
Saint Augustine *(G-15555)*
Kazdin Industries Inc ....G....... 772 223-5511
Palm City *(G-13663)*
Profold Inc ....E....... 772 589-0063
Sebastian *(G-16671)*
Ronco Machine Inc ....G....... 904 827-9795
Jacksonville *(G-6735)*
Southeastern Paper Group Inc ....C....... 864 574-0440
Lakeland *(G-7798)*

3555 Printing Trades Machinery & Eqpt

Altamonte Office Supply Inc ....G....... 407 339-6911
Longwood *(G-8253)*
Amrav Inc ....G....... 407 831-1550
Altamonte Springs *(G-31)*
◆ **Apex Machine Company** ....D....... 954 563-0209
Oakland Park *(G-11778)*
CST USA Inc ....F....... 404 695-2249
Miami *(G-9415)*
▼ **EL Harley Inc** ....F....... 561 841-9887
Delray Beach *(G-3072)*
Elements of Space LLC ....G....... 407 718-9690
Orlando *(G-12704)*
Equigraph Trading Corp ....G....... 786 237-5665
Miami *(G-9534)*
Gammerlertech Corporation ....E....... 941 803-0150
Bradenton *(G-1045)*
Guided Particle Systems Inc ....G....... 727 424-8790
Pensacola *(G-14165)*
▲ **Howard Imprinting Machine Co** ....G....... 813 884-2398
Tampa *(G-17762)*
Instabook Corp ....G....... 352 332-1311
Gainesville *(G-4943)*
Iter3d Inc ....G....... 718 473-0114
Aventura *(G-274)*
Kyocera Dcment Sltons Sthast L ....F....... 772 562-0511
Fort Pierce *(G-4710)*
Man Enterprises 3 LLC ....G....... 561 655-4944
West Palm Beach *(G-18940)*
Mark/Trece Inc ....E....... 863 647-4372
Lakeland *(G-7745)*
▲ **MGI Usa Inc** ....F....... 321 751-6755
Melbourne *(G-8888)*
Palm Prnting/Printers Ink Corp ....E....... 239 332-8600
Fort Myers *(G-4562)*
Southern Graphic Machine LLC ....G....... 615 812-0778
Edgewater *(G-3636)*
Southwest Eqp For Hrnando Cnty ....G....... 352 596-5142
Brooksville *(G-1273)*
Trinity Graphic Usa Inc ....F....... 941 355-2636
Sarasota *(G-16315)*
Universal Stncling Mkg Systems ....E....... 727 894-3027
Saint Petersburg *(G-15948)*
▼ **William B Rudow Inc** ....G....... 941 957-4200
Sarasota *(G-16640)*
▲ **Zenith Rollers Llc** ....G....... 954 493-6484
Fort Lauderdale *(G-4334)*

3556 Food Prdts Machinery

▲ **Alexander Industries Inc** ....G....... 305 888-9840
Hialeah *(G-5277)*
Alvean Americas Inc ....F....... 305 606-0770
Coral Gables *(G-2121)*
Aquaback Technologies Inc ....F....... 978 863-1000
Port Saint Lucie *(G-15088)*
Authentic Trading Inc ....G....... 347 866-7241
Davie *(G-2500)*
Brain Freeze Nitrogen ....G....... 786 235-8505
Doral *(G-3284)*
BWC Equipment LLC ....G....... 239 443-9925
Cape Coral *(G-1398)*
Californo Corp ....G....... 855 553-6766
Hallandale Beach *(G-5176)*
◆ **Carter Day Holding Inc** ....D....... 239 280-0361
Naples *(G-11199)*
◆ **Cei Liquidation Inc** ....G....... 281 541-2444
Fort Pierce *(G-4684)*
Cummins-Wagner-Florida LLC ....E....... 813 630-2220
Tampa *(G-17573)*
Czarnikow Group Ltd ....G....... 786 476-0000
Miami *(G-9423)*
Defrancisci Machine Co LLC ....F....... 321 952-6600
Melbourne *(G-8801)*
Deluxe Equipment Co ....F....... 941 753-4184
Bradenton *(G-1029)*
Emerge Interactive Inc ....E....... 772 563-0570
Vero Beach *(G-18616)*
Group 32 Dev & Engrg Inc ....F....... 305 361-0463
Key Biscayne *(G-7157)*
▼ **Gruenewald Mfg Co Inc** ....F....... 978 777-0200
Ocklawaha *(G-12081)*
Hoppin Pop Kettle Stop LLC ....G....... 502 220-2372
Jacksonville *(G-6479)*
◆ **Jbt Foodtech Citrus Systems** ....D....... 863 683-5411
Lakeland *(G-7720)*
Jbt LLC ....E....... 407 463-2045
Orlando *(G-12853)*
Jbt LLC ....F....... 513 238-4218
Naples *(G-11295)*
John Bean Technologies Corp ....C....... 863 683-5411
Lakeland *(G-7722)*
John Bean Technologies Corp ....E....... 407 851-3377
Orlando *(G-12858)*
Kenfar Corporation ....G....... 813 443-5222
Tampa *(G-17818)*
◆ **Mvp Group LLC** ....F....... 786 600-4687
North Miami *(G-11647)*
Point Distillery LLC ....F....... 727 269-5588
New Port Richey *(G-11508)*
Remco Industries International ....F....... 954 462-0000
Fort Lauderdale *(G-4201)*
▲ **Rice Machinery Supply Co Inc** ....F....... 305 620-2274
Miami *(G-10263)*
◆ **Sanchelima International Inc** ....F....... 305 591-4343
Doral *(G-3495)*
Sen-Pack Inc ....E....... 386 763-3312
New Smyrna Beach *(G-11543)*
Stephen J Austin ....G....... 941 780-7842
Nokomis *(G-11588)*
▲ **Sugar Development Corp** ....G....... 561 784-0604
West Palm Beach *(G-19047)*
◆ **Thinking Foods Inc** ....G....... 305 433-8287
Miami *(G-10474)*
◆ **Union Engineering N Amer LLC** ....F....... 386 225-4952
Daytona Beach *(G-2729)*
Whigham Citrus Packing House ....G....... 772 569-7190
Vero Beach *(G-18682)*
▲ **Zumex Usa Inc** ....G....... 305 591-0061
Doral *(G-3554)*

3559 Special Ind Machinery, NEC

Adamas Instrument Corporation ....F....... 727 540-0033
Clearwater *(G-1564)*
◆ **Akj Industries Inc** ....G....... 239 939-1696
Fort Myers *(G-4348)*
▼ **Al Stein Industries LLC** ....F....... 727 329-8755
Largo *(G-7889)*
Alto Recycling LLC ....G....... 813 962-0140
Tampa *(G-17410)*
▼ **Amtec Less Lethal Systems Inc** ....D....... 850 223-4066
Perry *(G-14293)*
Andrew Martin Swift ....G....... 321 409-0509
Melbourne *(G-8767)*
Archimaze Logistics Inc ....G....... 954 615-7485
Fort Lauderdale *(G-3819)*
◆ **Atlantic Intl Distrs Inc** ....C....... 904 725-5202
Jacksonville *(G-6175)*
Automated Production Eqp Ape ....F....... 631 654-1197
Key Largo *(G-7164)*
▲ **Automated Vacuum Systems Inc** ....G....... 941 378-4565
Sarasota *(G-16359)*
Baytronics Manufacturing Inc ....G....... 813 434-0401
Tampa *(G-17460)*
BBH General Partnership ....G....... 863 425-5626
Mulberry *(G-11120)*
Beachchip Technologies LLC ....G....... 727 643-8106
Clearwater *(G-1605)*
Cisam LLC ....G....... 813 404-4180
Zephyrhills *(G-19511)*
▼ **Concrete Edge Company** ....G....... 407 658-2788
Orlando *(G-12612)*
Connectronics US Inc ....G....... 954 534-3335
Palm Beach *(G-13552)*
Demaco LLC ....G....... 321 952-6600
Miami *(G-9453)*
Dilution Solutions Inc ....G....... 800 451-6628
Clearwater *(G-1652)*
Eidschun Engineering Inc ....E....... 727 647-2300
Clearwater *(G-1664)*
Energy Technical Systems Inc ....F....... 850 223-2393
Perry *(G-14299)*
▲ **Flite Technology Inc** ....F....... 321 631-2050
Cocoa *(G-2022)*
Florida Oil Service Inc ....F....... 813 655-4753
Lithia *(G-8219)*
Force Enterprises Coatings LLC ....F....... 561 480-7298
Wellington *(G-18718)*
Fresh Mark Corporation ....F....... 352 394-7746
Clermont *(G-1961)*
Fueltec Systems LLC ....G....... 828 212-1141
Royal Palm Beach *(G-15468)*
Global Manufacturing Tech Inc ....G....... 239 657-3720
Immokalee *(G-6049)*
Gold Refinery ....G....... 813 220-5067
Tampa *(G-17721)*
Guided Particle Systems Inc ....G....... 727 424-8790
Pensacola *(G-14165)*
▲ **Hilton International Inds** ....E....... 941 371-2600
Sarasota *(G-16460)*
Industrial Shredders LLC ....F....... 941 753-2815
Sarasota *(G-16234)*
Instazorb International Inc ....G....... 561 416-7302
Boca Raton *(G-565)*
Interactive Cards Inc ....F....... 863 688-4548
Lakeland *(G-7714)*
International Ozone Svcs LLC ....G....... 352 978-9785
Mount Dora *(G-11105)*
Interplex Labs Ltd ....D....... 954 718-9953
Tamarac *(G-17358)*
Intuitos LLC ....F....... 727 522-2301
Largo *(G-7983)*
Laserstar Technologies Corp ....G....... 407 248-1142
Orlando *(G-12896)*
Lcn Incorporated ....E....... 305 461-2770
Miami *(G-9873)*
Lewa Group Corp ....G....... 305 407-9500
Miami Lakes *(G-10806)*
Lgl Group Inc ....G....... 407 298-2000
Orlando *(G-12907)*
▼ **Logistic Systems Inc** ....G....... 305 477-4999
Miami *(G-9906)*
Mec Cryo LLC ....E....... 813 644-3764
Tampa *(G-17899)*
Mid West Lettering Company ....E....... 850 477-6522
Pensacola *(G-14209)*
Midgard Inc ....D....... 863 696-1224
Lake Wales *(G-7516)*
▲ **Mold Control Systems Inc** ....G....... 561 316-5412
Palm Beach Gardens *(G-13610)*
Novena TEC LLC ....E....... 407 392-1868
Orlando *(G-13011)*
Omega Lift Corporation ....F....... 561 840-0088
Riviera Beach *(G-15358)*
Park Plus Florida Inc ....F....... 954 929-7511
Dania *(G-2456)*
Pcm and S L Plota Co LLC ....F....... 727 547-6277
Largo *(G-8024)*
Pe Manufacturing Company Fla ....E....... 727 823-8172
Clearwater *(G-1828)*
Pharmacy Automtn Systems LLC ....G....... 727 544-6522
Pinellas Park *(G-14375)*
◆ **Polyumac Inc** ....E....... 305 691-9093
Hialeah *(G-5561)*
Popstops Marketing Inc ....G....... 800 209-4571
Saint Petersburg *(G-15884)*
Poseidon Industries Inc ....G....... 305 812-2582
Punta Gorda *(G-15220)*
Prestige Service Group ....G....... 954 532-9014
Pompano Beach *(G-14811)*
Progress Rail Services Corp ....G....... 352 748-8008
Wildwood *(G-19200)*
Quik Shred ....G....... 561 841-1822
Jupiter *(G-7101)*
Rcc Conveyors Inc ....F....... 224 338-8841
Estero *(G-3694)*
Recycling Center ....G....... 386 364-5865
Live Oak *(G-8239)*
Reduction International LLC ....G....... 954 905-5999
Weston *(G-19164)*
▲ **Robotic Parking Systems Inc** ....F....... 727 539-7275
Clearwater *(G-1863)*
Rubyquartz Technology LLC ....F....... 305 406-0211
Doral *(G-3493)*
Safetarp Corp ....D....... 904 824-7277
Saint Augustine *(G-15602)*
◆ **Shirley L Jordan Company Inc** ....F....... 352 754-1117
Brooksville *(G-1268)*
Solid Start Inc ....E....... 863 937-9297
Lakeland *(G-7797)*
◆ **Somero Enterprises Inc** ....D....... 906 482-7252
Fort Myers *(G-4606)*

Southern Fabricating Machinery...........G....... 813 966-3983
Lithia *(G-8223)*
▲ **Star Envirotech Inc**...........F....... 714 427-1244
Hialeah *(G-5633)*
▲ **Sun Nation Corp**...........F....... 954 822-5460
Pompano Beach *(G-14877)*
Sunshine Tool LLC...........G....... 941 351-6330
Sarasota *(G-16306)*
Surface Finishing Tech Inc...........E....... 727 577-7777
Clearwater *(G-1898)*
◆ **Systemone Technologies Inc**...........G....... 305 593-8015
Doral *(G-3521)*
Tin Man Co...........G....... 305 365-1926
Coral Gables *(G-2198)*
◆ **Vampa Tires Supplies Inc**...........G....... 305 888-1001
Miami *(G-10564)*
Water Purification Systems...........G....... 954 467-8920
Fort Lauderdale *(G-4314)*
Wilkinson Hi-Rise LLC...........C....... 954 342-4400
Fort Lauderdale *(G-4324)*
Wolverine Advanced Mtls LLC...........G....... 352 787-3015
Leesburg *(G-8181)*
Worldwide Technology Inc...........E....... 813 855-2443
Oldsmar *(G-12279)*

3561 Pumps & Pumping Eqpt

◆ **Acme Dynamics Inc**...........F....... 813 752-3137
Winter Haven *(G-19294)*
▼ **Acme Service Corp**...........F....... 305 836-4800
Miami *(G-9065)*
Air Dimensions Inc...........E....... 954 428-7333
Deerfield Beach *(G-2770)*
▲ **Air Supply of Future Inc**...........F....... 954 977-0877
Pompano Beach *(G-14582)*
American Incinerators Corp...........E....... 321 282-7357
Orlando *(G-12470)*
American-Marsh Pumps LLC...........G....... 863 646-5689
Lakeland *(G-7634)*
◆ **Anko Products Inc**...........E....... 941 748-2307
Bradenton *(G-989)*
Awl Manufacturing Inc...........G....... 239 643-5780
Naples *(G-11178)*
◆ **Azcue Pumps USA Inc**...........G....... 954 597-7602
Tamarac *(G-17352)*
Channel Industries Inc...........F....... 561 214-0637
West Palm Beach *(G-18845)*
Custom Masters Inc...........E....... 407 331-4634
Longwood *(G-8270)*
▼ **D & D Machine & Hydraulics Inc**...........E....... 239 275-7177
Fort Myers *(G-4423)*
Delta P Systems Inc...........F....... 386 236-0950
Ormond Beach *(G-13361)*
▲ **Fluidra Usa LLC**...........E....... 904 378-0999
Jacksonville *(G-6409)*
G & F Manufacturing Inc...........F....... 239 939-7446
Fort Myers *(G-4464)*
Global Pump Daytona...........G....... 386 426-2411
Edgewater *(G-3623)*
▲ **Greylor Dynesco Co Inc**...........G....... 239 574-2011
Cape Coral *(G-1431)*
▲ **Hamworthy Inc**...........G....... 305 597-7520
Fort Lauderdale *(G-4041)*
Hisco Pump South LLC...........F....... 904 786-4488
Jacksonville *(G-6472)*
Hizer Machine Mfg Inc...........G....... 386 755-3155
White Springs *(G-19187)*
Holland Pump Company...........G....... 813 626-0599
Tampa *(G-17759)*
◆ **Holland Pump Company**...........G....... 561 697-3333
West Palm Beach *(G-18896)*
Holland Pump Company...........G....... 904 880-0010
Jacksonville *(G-6475)*
▼ **Hoover Pumping Systems Corp**...........E....... 954 971-7350
Pompano Beach *(G-14727)*
▲ **Hydrolec Inc**...........E....... 904 730-3766
Jacksonville *(G-6484)*
◆ **Innovation Marine Corporation**...........E....... 941 355-7852
Sarasota *(G-16238)*
ITT Flygt Corp...........G....... 239 633-2553
Fort Myers *(G-4497)*
▲ **Jka Pump Specialists**...........G....... 561 686-4455
West Palm Beach *(G-18912)*
John Mader Enterprises Inc...........E....... 239 731-5455
Fort Myers *(G-4506)*
Johnston Archtctral Systems In...........E....... 904 886-9030
Jacksonville *(G-6527)*
Lodex Enterprises Corp...........G....... 954 442-3843
Miramar *(G-11010)*
▲ **Marine Metal Products Co**...........G....... 727 461-5575
Clearwater *(G-1773)*
Multitrode Inc...........E....... 561 737-1210
Boca Raton *(G-633)*
◆ **Mwi Corporation**...........E....... 954 426-1500
Deerfield Beach *(G-2877)*
▲ **Osgood Industries LLC**...........C....... 813 448-9041
Oldsmar *(G-12254)*
Performance Pumps Inc...........E....... 407 339-6700
Casselberry *(G-1512)*
Phoenix Dewatering Inc...........F....... 407 330-7015
Sanford *(G-16101)*
Pioneer Dredge Inc...........G....... 904 732-2151
Jacksonville *(G-6675)*
▲ **Portable Pumping Systems Inc**...........G....... 727 518-9191
Clearwater *(G-1837)*
▲ **Power Equipments Trading LLC**...........G....... 305 704-7021
Doral *(G-3464)*
Pulsafeeder Inc...........D....... 941 575-2900
Punta Gorda *(G-15223)*
Pulsafeeder Spo Inc...........F....... 941 575-3800
Punta Gorda *(G-15224)*
Quantumflo Inc...........E....... 407 807-7050
Sanford *(G-16108)*
▲ **Reverso Pumps Inc**...........F....... 954 523-9396
Davie *(G-2584)*
RG Groundworks LLC...........G....... 352 474-7949
Newberry *(G-11560)*
Schwing Bioset...........G....... 239 237-2174
Fort Myers *(G-4598)*
◆ **Serf Inc**...........E....... 850 476-8203
Cantonment *(G-1347)*
Smith Surface Prep Systems Inc...........D....... 954 941-9744
Pompano Beach *(G-14854)*
Southern Innovative Energy Inc...........G....... 321 747-9205
Titusville *(G-18461)*
▲ **Stenner Pump Company Inc**...........C....... 904 641-1666
Jacksonville *(G-6811)*
Stinner Pump Company...........G....... 904 329-2098
Jacksonville *(G-6814)*
▲ **Townley Engrg & Mfg Co Inc**...........C....... 352 687-3001
Candler *(G-1332)*
Tradewinds Power Corp...........F....... 863 382-2166
Sebring *(G-16716)*
Tru-Flo Corp...........F....... 561 996-5850
Belle Glade *(G-354)*
Turner Machine & Supply Co...........G....... 772 464-4550
Fort Pierce *(G-4762)*
United Rentals North Amer Inc...........G....... 239 690-0600
Fort Myers *(G-4640)*
United Rentals North Amer Inc...........G....... 850 478-2833
Pensacola *(G-14278)*
United Rentals North Amer Inc...........G....... 941 755-3177
Sarasota *(G-16321)*
Vickery and Company...........F....... 813 987-2100
Tampa *(G-18244)*
Wilo USA LLC...........D....... 954 524-6776
Fort Lauderdale *(G-4325)*
Xylem Dewatering Solutions...........G....... 904 695-2131
Jacksonville *(G-6932)*

3562 Ball & Roller Bearings

Bearing Specialist Inc...........G....... 305 796-3415
Doral *(G-3265)*
Centrifugal Rebabbitting Inc...........F....... 954 522-3003
Fort Lauderdale *(G-3891)*
◆ **Debway Corporation**...........G....... 305 818-6353
Hialeah *(G-5366)*
Faro Industriale Spa Co...........G....... 941 925-3004
Sarasota *(G-16428)*
◆ **NSK Latin America Inc**...........E....... 305 477-0605
Miami *(G-10083)*
Shadow-Caster Led Lighting LLC...........E....... 727 474-2877
Clearwater *(G-1876)*

3563 Air & Gas Compressors

▲ **Aircel LLC**...........E....... 865 681-7066
Naples *(G-11152)*
▲ **America Energy Inc**...........G....... 954 762-7763
Pembroke Pines *(G-14020)*
American Mfg & Mch Inc...........D....... 352 728-2222
Okahumpka *(G-12168)*
▲ **Brownies Marine Group Inc**...........G....... 954 462-5570
Pompano Beach *(G-14624)*
Danfoss LLC...........C....... 850 504-4800
Tallahassee *(G-17240)*
Desco Manufacturing Inc...........F....... 941 925-7029
Sarasota *(G-16409)*
Graham & Company LLC...........G....... 904 281-0003
Jacksonville *(G-6444)*
Greengood Energy Corp...........G....... 954 417-6117
Hollywood *(G-5831)*
Gssc Inc...........G....... 727 461-6044
Clearwater *(G-1706)*
Hankison...........G....... 352 273-1220
Ocala *(G-11965)*
Hisco Pump South LLC...........F....... 904 786-4488
Jacksonville *(G-6472)*
▼ **Interbay Air Compressors Inc**...........G....... 813 831-8213
Tampa *(G-17789)*
Irms Inc...........F....... 321 631-1161
Rockledge *(G-15423)*
L M Compressor LLC...........G....... 352 484-0850
Ocala *(G-11979)*
Makai Marine Industries Inc...........G....... 954 425-0203
Deerfield Beach *(G-2867)*
Mat Industries LLC...........E....... 847 821-9630
Dania Beach *(G-2470)*
Mat-Vac Technology Inc...........F....... 386 238-7017
Daytona Beach *(G-2683)*
Q Industries Inc...........G....... 954 689-2263
Fort Lauderdale *(G-4187)*
Roper Technologies Inc...........E....... 941 556-2601
Sarasota *(G-16563)*
Southern Air Comprsr Svc Inc...........G....... 863 425-9111
Mulberry *(G-11137)*
Spraymation Development Corp...........E....... 954 484-9700
Fort Lauderdale *(G-4255)*
Trusco Manufacturing Company...........G....... 352 237-0311
Ocala *(G-12062)*
Ultimate Compressor LLC...........G....... 305 720-3079
Pembroke Pines *(G-14068)*
Vac Cubes Inc...........G....... 727 944-3337
Tarpon Springs *(G-18329)*

3564 Blowers & Fans

3t Corporation...........G....... 786 222-2147
Hialeah *(G-5253)*
Advanced Tech & Tstg Labs...........G....... 352 871-3802
Tampa *(G-17388)*
Air Flow Specialists...........G....... 954 727-9507
Davie *(G-2490)*
Air Purifying Systems Inc...........G....... 954 962-0450
Miami *(G-9093)*
Air Sponge Filter Company Inc...........G....... 954 752-1836
Coral Springs *(G-2217)*
▼ **Andrews Filter and Supply Corp**...........E....... 407 423-3310
Orlando *(G-12479)*
Atco Rubber Products Inc...........E....... 813 754-6678
Plant City *(G-14403)*
Atitlan Enterprises LLC...........F....... 813 362-1909
Tampa *(G-17442)*
Better Air North America LLC...........G....... 844 447-7624
Hollywood *(G-5787)*
▲ **Biozone Scientific Intl Inc**...........G....... 407 876-2000
Orlando *(G-12517)*
Boair Inc...........G....... 954 426-9226
Deerfield Beach *(G-2786)*
Breezemaker Fan Company Inc...........E....... 813 248-5552
Tampa *(G-17486)*
Central Florida Central Fla...........E....... 407 674-2626
Orlando *(G-12564)*
Certainteed Corporation...........F....... 863 294-3206
Winter Haven *(G-19313)*
Chilly Willys Heating & A Inc...........G....... 904 772-1164
Jacksonville *(G-6264)*
▲ **Cool Components Inc**...........G....... 813 322-3814
Tampa *(G-17554)*
Custom Masters Inc...........E....... 407 331-4634
Longwood *(G-8270)*
DOT Blue Trading Inc...........G....... 954 646-0448
Miami *(G-9482)*
Duststop Filters Inc...........G....... 904 725-1001
Jacksonville *(G-6338)*
Energenics Corporation...........E....... 239 643-1711
Naples *(G-11238)*
▲ **Fan America Inc**...........G....... 941 955-9788
Sarasota *(G-16426)*
▲ **Fanam Inc**...........G....... 941 955-9788
Sarasota *(G-16427)*
Filters Plus Inc...........G....... 813 232-2000
Tampa *(G-17665)*
▲ **Flaire Corporation**...........C....... 352 237-1220
Ocala *(G-11944)*
Flanders Corp...........F....... 727 822-4411
Saint Petersburg *(G-15782)*
Florida Air Cleaning Inc...........G....... 727 573-5281
Clearwater *(G-1685)*
Fresh Aire Sanitization...........G....... 407 301-9831
Kissimmee *(G-7247)*
Glasfloss Industries Inc...........F....... 904 741-9922
Jacksonville *(G-6435)*

SIC

▼ Hood Depot International Inc ....E 954 570-9860
Deerfield Beach (G-2844)
Iaire LLC ....G 407 873-2538
Orlando (G-12818)
▲ Kanalflakt Inc ....F 941 359-3267
Sarasota (G-16480)
Merritt Mfg LLC ....G 407 481-1074
Land O Lakes (G-7862)
Moffitt Corporation Inc ....F 904 241-9944
Jacksonville Beach (G-6951)
Moffitt Fan Corporation ....F 585 768-7010
Jacksonville Beach (G-6952)
Pall Aeropower Corporation ....B 727 849-9999
Deland (G-3006)
Pall Filtration and Sep ....C 386 822-8000
Deland (G-3007)
▲ Plastec Ventilation Inc ....G 941 751-7596
Bradenton (G-1098)
Polk Air Filter Sales Inc ....G 863 688-4436
Lakeland (G-7769)
Q-Pac Systems Inc ....E 229 834-2908
Elkton (G-3651)
R & J Mfg of Gainesville ....G 352 375-3130
Gainesville (G-4987)
Rainbow Eb Buenavista ....G 305 982-8153
Miami (G-10235)
Raytheon Technologies Corp ....A 858 277-7639
Jupiter (G-7103)
▲ RB Kanalflakt Inc ....E 941 359-3267
Sarasota (G-16554)
▲ Rgf Environmental Group Inc ....C 800 842-7771
Riviera Beach (G-15372)
Robinson Fans Inc ....E 724 452-6121
Lakeland (G-7780)
Rv Air Inc ....G 309 657-4300
Clearwater (G-1866)
◆ S&P USA Vntilation Systems LLC ....D 904 731-4711
Jacksonville (G-6744)
Sunshine Filters of Pinellas ....E 727 530-3884
Largo (G-8064)
Sy-Klone Company LLC ....E 904 448-6563
Jacksonville (G-6832)
Timilon Corporation ....F 239 330-9650
Bonita Springs (G-862)
▼ Triatomic Environmental Inc ....F 561 748-4864
Jupiter (G-7132)
Turner Envirologic Inc ....E 954 422-9566
Deerfield Beach (G-2930)
Upton House Cooler Corporation ....G 305 633-2531
Miami (G-10547)
Ventilex Inc ....G 954 433-1321
Pembroke Pines (G-14070)
▲ Warren Technology Inc ....C 305 556-6933
Hialeah (G-5686)
Wes Holdings Corp ....F 941 371-4995
Sarasota (G-16636)
Worldwide Technology Inc ....E 813 855-2443
Oldsmar (G-12279)
Zazz Engineering Inc ....G 561 594-0123
Stuart (G-17054)

3565 Packaging Machinery

A & B of Tarpon Corporation ....E 727 940-5333
Tarpon Springs (G-18281)
◆ Acasi Machinery Inc ....F 305 805-8533
Miami (G-9058)
B & M Industries Inc ....G 813 754-9960
Plant City (G-14404)
◆ B H Bunn Company ....F 863 647-1555
Lakeland (G-7641)
▲ Balpack Incorporated ....G 941 371-7323
Sarasota (G-16361)
Bbull Usa Inc ....G 813 855-1400
Oldsmar (G-12208)
◆ Booth Manufacturing Company ....E 772 465-4441
Fort Pierce (G-4682)
Central Florida Sales & Svc ....F 863 967-6678
Auburndale (G-233)
▼ Diamond Moba Americas Inc ....D 954 384-5828
Weston (G-19120)
▲ Emhart Glass Manufacturing Inc ....E 727 535-5502
Saint Petersburg (G-15769)
▲ Endflex LLC ....E 305 622-4070
Opa Locka (G-12313)
Fill Tech Solutions Inc 200 ....E 727 572-8550
Largo (G-7946)
Flexo Concepts Manufacturing ....G 305 233-7075
Miami (G-9576)
Gevas Pckg Converting Tech Ltd ....G 561 202-0800
Boynton Beach (G-911)
◆ Grain Machinery Mfg Corp ....F 305 620-2525
Miami (G-9654)
▼ Hdh Agri Products LLC ....G 352 343-3484
Tavares (G-18342)
Ics Inex Inspection Systems ....F 727 535-5502
Clearwater (G-1728)
Industrial Marking Eqp Co Inc ....G 561 626-8520
Palm Beach Gardens (G-13596)
◆ Inline Filling Systems LLC ....E 941 486-8800
Venice (G-18556)
Intellitech Inc ....E 727 914-7000
Saint Petersburg (G-15817)
International Packaging Mchs ....G 239 643-2020
Naples (G-11290)
ISA Group Corp ....F 305 748-1578
Miami (G-9773)
▲ K H S Inc ....D 941 359-4000
Sarasota (G-16243)
▼ Kiinde LLC ....G 404 368-5382
Melbourne (G-8858)
Kinematics and Controls Corp ....G 352 796-0300
Brooksville (G-1243)
▲ Lanfranchi North America Inc ....F 813 901-5333
Tampa (G-17835)
▲ MDC Engineering Inc ....F 941 358-0610
Sarasota (G-16505)
▲ Micron Pharmaworks LLC ....C 727 232-8200
Odessa (G-12134)
▲ MTS Medication Tech Inc ....C 727 576-6311
Saint Petersburg (G-15862)
New England Machinery ....E 941 755-5550
Bradenton (G-1085)
◆ New England Machinery Inc ....E 941 755-5550
Bradenton (G-1086)
Orkan18 ....G 855 675-2618
Lake Worth (G-7576)
▲ Osgood Industries LLC ....C 813 448-9041
Oldsmar (G-12254)
◆ Pelliconi Florida LLC ....E 407 855-6984
Orlando (G-13058)
Pepsico Inc ....G 305 593-7500
Medley (G-8703)
Plan Automation LLC ....G 786 502-1812
Miami Beach (G-10701)
▲ Pneumatic Scale Angelus ....D 727 535-4100
Clearwater (G-1836)
◆ Polypack Inc ....D 727 578-5000
Pinellas Park (G-14377)
Polypack Limited Partnership ....E 727 578-5000
Pinellas Park (G-14378)
Production System Engineering ....F 863 299-7330
Winter Haven (G-19347)
Quality Carton Inc ....G 941 921-1770
Sarasota (G-16551)
R & L Manufacturing Inc ....F 772 770-9300
Vero Beach (G-18658)
Sardee Industries Inc ....E 407 295-2114
Orlando (G-13163)
Southern Packaging McHy Corp ....E 305 245-3045
Florida City (G-3769)
Sweepy Group Products LLC ....G 305 556-3450
Miami Lakes (G-10866)
Trepko Inc ....F 813 443-0794
Tampa (G-18198)
Universal Labeling Systems Inc ....E 727 327-2123
Saint Petersburg (G-15946)
VMS Usa Inc ....F 727 434-1577
Seminole (G-16770)
Westlund Engineering Inc ....G 727 572-4343
Palm Harbor (G-13769)
White Label Liquid Inc ....E 386 256-1826
Daytona Beach (G-2732)

3566 Speed Changers, Drives & Gears

ABB Enterprise Software Inc ....C 954 752-6700
Coral Springs (G-2211)
Aerotek Gear & Spline Inc ....G 954 543-3473
Coral Springs (G-2215)
▲ Hydraulicnet LLC ....F 630 543-7630
Saint Augustine (G-15549)
▲ JW Performance Transm Inc ....E 321 632-6205
Rockledge (G-15425)
Lubov Manufacturing Inc ....G 813 873-2640
Tampa (G-17862)
PMC North America Inc ....F 727 530-0714
Largo (G-8029)
▲ Riley Gear Corporation ....D 904 829-5652
Saint Augustine (G-15596)
S I P Corporation ....F 813 884-8300
Tampa (G-18075)
▲ Snow-Nabstedt Power Transmissi ....G 603 661-5551
Bradenton (G-1116)
Spincontrol Gearing LLC ....G 863 241-9055
Lake Wales (G-7521)

3567 Indl Process Furnaces & Ovens

Air Burners Inc ....F 772 220-7303
Palm City (G-13639)
◆ Air Burners LLC ....E 772 220-7303
Palm City (G-13640)
Aruki Services LLC ....G 850 364-5206
Havana (G-5232)
Bcr Environmental Corporation ....E 904 819-9170
Jacksonville (G-6198)
Clarios LLC ....B 727 541-3531
Largo (G-7922)
▲ Intelligent Heater LLC ....G 305 248-4971
Homestead (G-5973)
Matthews International Corp ....C 407 886-5533
Apopka (G-158)
Palmetto Group LLC ....G 863 294-8070
Winter Haven (G-19339)
Pillar Inc ....G 904 545-4993
Jacksonville (G-6672)
Sardee Industries Inc ....E 407 295-2114
Orlando (G-13163)
Thermotech Systems Corporation ....G 407 290-6000
Orlando (G-13254)

3568 Mechanical Power Transmission Eqpt, NEC

Alto Products Corp Al ....G 305 892-7777
Doral (G-3242)
◆ American Vulkan Corporation ....E 863 324-2424
Winter Haven (G-19299)
Consultant MGT Group LLC ....G 352 344-4001
Inverness (G-6083)
Creative Carbide Inc ....F 239 567-0041
Fort Myers (G-4414)
Dowels Pins & Shafts Inc ....E 727 461-1255
Clearwater (G-1656)
Easy Flex Couplings LLC ....G 863 665-9374
Clermont (G-1956)
Enstar Holdings (us) LLC ....D 727 217-2900
Saint Petersburg (G-15770)
▲ Gfx Inc ....E 305 499-9789
Miami (G-9634)
Ggb1 LLC ....G 305 387-5334
Miami (G-9636)
Grizzly Manufacturing Inc ....E 386 755-0220
Lake City (G-7360)
▲ Ipts Inc ....F 561 844-8216
Riviera Beach (G-15335)
▲ JW Performance Transm Inc ....E 321 632-6205
Rockledge (G-15425)
◆ Man-Trans LLC ....F 850 222-6993
Tallahassee (G-17294)
North Amrcn Prtection Ctrl LLC ....G 407 788-3717
Altamonte Springs (G-58)
◆ NSK Latin America Inc ....E 305 477-0605
Miami (G-10083)
▲ Orion Power Systems Inc ....G 877 385-1654
Jacksonville (G-6648)
Quality Industries America Inc ....G 386 755-0220
Lake City (G-7380)
◆ Schur & Company LLC ....D 904 353-8075
Jacksonville (G-6754)
Southern Gear & Machine Inc ....D 305 691-6300
Miami (G-10386)
▲ SS White Technologies Inc ....C 727 626-2800
Saint Petersburg (G-15923)
Suncoast Rebuild Center Inc ....F 813 238-3433
Tampa (G-18144)
▲ Torque Technologies Products ....G 630 462-1188
Sarasota (G-16312)
U M P ....G 305 740-4996
Miami (G-10522)

3569 Indl Machinery & Eqpt, NEC

▼ 911 Equipment Inc ....F 954 217-1745
Weston (G-19100)
◆ Aflg Invstmnts-Industrials LLC ....G 813 443-8203
Tampa (G-17390)
Aflg Invstmnts-Industrials LLC ....F 813 443-8203
Hernando Beach (G-5250)
Airgroup Inc ....F 561 279-0680
Boca Raton (G-409)
American Recycling Systems Inc ....G 772 225-8072
Jensen Beach (G-6965)

◆ **Aquacal Autopilot Inc** .... C 727 823-5642
Saint Petersburg *(G-15705)*
▲ **Automatic Mfg Systems Inc** .... E 954 791-1500
Plantation *(G-14494)*
▼ **B & L Cremation Systems Inc** .... D 727 541-4666
Largo *(G-7903)*
◆ **B E Pressure Supply Inc** .... F 561 688-9246
West Palm Beach *(G-18807)*
Barry Resnick .... G 407 296-9999
Orlando *(G-12508)*
Bcdirect Corp .... F 305 623-3838
Miami *(G-9229)*
Buffalo Machine Manufacturing .... G 727 321-1905
Saint Petersburg *(G-15731)*
◆ **Carter Day Holding Inc** .... D 239 280-0361
Naples *(G-11199)*
▼ **Casper Engineering Corp** .... G 305 666-4046
Pinecrest *(G-14326)*
◆ **Cirven Usa LLC** .... G 305 815-2545
Doral *(G-3299)*
Custom Masters Inc .... E 407 331-4634
Longwood *(G-8270)*
Darly Filtration Inc .... G 727 318-7064
Largo *(G-7931)*
Dha Filter LLC .... G 904 269-8701
Orange Park *(G-12388)*
Done Right Fire Gear Repr Inc .... G 727 848-9019
Hudson *(G-6021)*
Eddys Filter Change Inc .... G 407 448-4498
Altamonte Springs *(G-42)*
Environmental Recovery Systems .... G 727 344-3301
Saint Petersburg *(G-15771)*
Federal Eastern Intl Inc .... F 954 533-4506
Fort Lauderdale *(G-3989)*
Gea Mechanical Eqp US Inc .... G 863 669-1500
Lakeland *(G-7696)*
▲ **Grinnell LLC** .... B 561 988-3658
Boca Raton *(G-552)*
Health Robotics Canada LLC .... F 786 388-5339
Miami *(G-9692)*
▲ **Industrial Filter Pump Mfg Co** .... G 708 656-7800
Mims *(G-10951)*
Ingelub Corp .... F 407 656-8800
Winter Garden *(G-19270)*
Innovated Industrial Svcs Inc .... F 863 701-2711
Bartow *(G-320)*
International Baler Corp .... E 904 358-3812
Jacksonville *(G-6500)*
Jenzano Incorporated .... F 386 761-4474
Port Orange *(G-15020)*
JRS Ventures LLP .... G 715 441-1051
Deltona *(G-3172)*
Keltour US Inc .... F 239 424-8901
Cape Coral *(G-1443)*
Load King Manufacturing Co .... C 904 354-8882
Jacksonville *(G-6560)*
Lodex Enterprises Corp .... G 954 442-3843
Miramar *(G-11010)*
▲ **Magenav Inc** .... G 718 551-1815
Fort Lauderdale *(G-4109)*
Matthews International Corp .... C 407 886-5533
Apopka *(G-158)*
◆ **Miami Filter LLC** .... E 772 466-1440
Fort Pierce *(G-4718)*
Muller Fire Protection Inc .... E 305 636-9780
Miami *(G-10052)*
Mustang Vacuum Systems Inc .... E 941 377-1440
Sarasota *(G-16261)*
No Flood Inc .... G 239 776-1671
Fort Myers *(G-4548)*
Onan Generators & Engines .... G 772 334-8282
Jensen Beach *(G-6972)*
◆ **Pall Aeropower Corporation** .... B 727 849-9999
New Port Richey *(G-11507)*
Pall Aeropower Corporation .... B 727 849-9999
Deland *(G-3006)*
▲ **Phantom Sales Group Inc** .... G 888 614-1232
Bartow *(G-330)*
Pneumatic Products Corporation .... G 352 873-5793
Ocala *(G-12029)*
Porous Metal Filters Inc .... G 407 682-1494
Longwood *(G-8327)*
Rz Service Group LLC .... G 904 402-2313
Jacksonville *(G-6741)*
Safetek International Inc .... G 702 558-8202
Boca Raton *(G-698)*
Sams Gas .... G 386 698-1033
Crescent City *(G-2341)*
▼ **Sealift LLC** .... F 321 638-0301
Merritt Island *(G-9012)*
◆ **Serf Inc** .... E 850 476-8203
Cantonment *(G-1347)*
Siemens Industry Inc .... G 407 650-3570
Orlando *(G-13188)*
Sims Machine & Controls Inc .... F 352 799-2405
Brooksville *(G-1270)*
Suinpla LLC .... F 786 747-4829
Medley *(G-8732)*
▼ **Supermarket Services Inc** .... G 954 525-0439
Davie *(G-2600)*
Syn-Tech Systems Inc .... C 850 878-2558
Tallahassee *(G-17332)*
▲ **Target Manufacturing Inc** .... G 305 633-0361
Miami *(G-10460)*
Travis Lh LLC .... F 863 967-0628
Winter Haven *(G-19364)*
◆ **Union Engineering N Amer LLC** .... F 386 225-4952
Daytona Beach *(G-2729)*
Vuflow Filters Co Inc .... G 352 597-2607
Brooksville *(G-1290)*
Wellstream Inc .... E 281 249-0900
Panama City *(G-13962)*
Whetstone Indus Holdings Inc .... G 904 824-0888
Saint Augustine *(G-15635)*
Wolverine Engines .... G 850 462-4160
Fort Walton Beach *(G-4841)*

3571 Electronic Computers

3nstar Inc .... F 786 233-7011
Doral *(G-3216)*
9t Technology LLC .... G 904 703-9214
Jacksonville *(G-6106)*
◆ **Acer Latin America Inc** .... G 305 392-7000
Doral *(G-3223)*
Advanced Electronics Labs Inc .... G 305 255-6401
Pinecrest *(G-14322)*
Alienware Corp .... G 786 260-9625
Miami *(G-9105)*
Appel 26 Corp .... G 305 672-8645
Miami Beach *(G-10643)*
Apple Spice - Jax .... G 904 328-6542
Jacksonville *(G-6160)*
Artex Computer Llc .... G 407 844-2253
Miami *(G-9173)*
Atlantic Multi Family I LLC .... F 301 233-1261
Parkland *(G-13988)*
Ayon Cybersecurity Inc .... E 321 953-3033
Cocoa *(G-1998)*
Best Lidar Corporation .... E 321 425-6725
Melbourne *(G-8779)*
Bio-Logic Systems Corp .... D 847 949-0456
Orlando *(G-12515)*
Black Diamond Systems Corp .... D 917 539-7309
Vero Beach *(G-18601)*
Buscar Inc .... G 813 877-7272
Tampa *(G-17491)*
C & R Designs Inc .... G 321 383-2255
Titusville *(G-18419)*
C & R Designs Printing LLC .... G 321 383-2255
Titusville *(G-18420)*
Computer Technician Inc .... G 941 479-0242
Palmetto *(G-13793)*
▲ **Contec Americas Inc** .... D 321 728-0172
Melbourne *(G-8796)*
Dakim Inc .... F 561 790-0884
Royal Palm Beach *(G-15465)*
Dell USA LP .... F 512 728-8391
Miami *(G-9450)*
Digital Scoreboards LLC .... E 888 738-4230
Venice *(G-18541)*
Energybionics LLC .... G 561 229-4985
Stuart *(G-16938)*
Enterprise Tech Partners LLC .... F 918 851-3285
Orlando *(G-12713)*
EPC Inc .... F 636 443-1999
Tampa *(G-17646)*
Essentials .... G 386 677-7444
Ormond Beach *(G-13368)*
Faratech LLC .... G 954 651-7287
Sunrise *(G-17122)*
▲ **Fun Electronics Inc** .... F 305 933-4646
Miami *(G-9603)*
Geekshive Inc .... F 888 797-4335
Miami *(G-9620)*
General Dynmics Mssion Systems .... E 407 823-7000
Orlando *(G-12779)*
Gold Network of Miami Inc .... G 305 343-7355
Hialeah *(G-5433)*
Hatalom Corporation .... E 407 567-2556
Orlando *(G-12796)*
Ibi Systems Inc .... G 954 978-9225
Fort Lauderdale *(G-4054)*
Industrial Technology LLC .... F 877 224-5534
Fort Myers *(G-4494)*
Industry Standard Technology .... G 941 355-2100
Sarasota *(G-16235)*
Integrated Dealer Systems Inc .... F 800 962-7872
Oldsmar *(G-12236)*
Jpt-Tech LLC .... G 352 219-7860
Micanopy *(G-10903)*
Konnected Inc .... F 407 286-3138
Orlando *(G-12876)*
Kos Industries Inc .... G 863 318-1511
Winter Haven *(G-19333)*
Lek Technology Consultants .... G 407 877-6505
Winter Garden *(G-19273)*
Lockheed Martin Corporation .... B 813 855-5711
Oldsmar *(G-12245)*
◆ **M & S Computer Products Inc** .... G 561 244-5400
Boynton Beach *(G-930)*
Matrix Media LLC .... G 435 313-2877
Palm Harbor *(G-13746)*
McEs LLC .... G 321 363-4977
Sanford *(G-16086)*
Morgan Technical Services .... G 772 466-5757
Fort Pierce *(G-4719)*
Motorola Solutions Inc .... G 407 562-4000
Lake Mary *(G-7437)*
Mvr Copiadoras Digitales .... G 786 366-1842
Doral *(G-3442)*
Nortech Engineering Inc .... G 508 823-8520
Port Charlotte *(G-14991)*
Oriental Red Apple LLC .... G 646 853-1468
Miami *(G-10118)*
▲ **Origin Pc LLC** .... E 305 971-1000
Miami *(G-10119)*
Orion Technologies LLC .... E 407 476-2120
Orlando *(G-13030)*
P S T Computers Inc .... G 954 566-1600
Fort Lauderdale *(G-4153)*
Palm Tree Computer Systems Inc .... F 407 359-3356
Oviedo *(G-13452)*
PC Masters Corp .... G 305 582-5595
Miami Lakes *(G-10835)*
Phintec LLC .... G 321 214-2500
Orlando *(G-13066)*
Phone Wave Inc .... G 352 683-8101
Spring Hill *(G-16858)*
Qtronics Inc .... G 850 267-0102
Santa Rosa Beach *(G-16165)*
Ra Co AMO Inc .... F 561 626-7232
Palm Beach Gardens *(G-13620)*
Refly of Miami Inc .... F 786 762-2748
Miami *(G-10246)*
Sif Technology Company LLC .... G 941 225-8363
Sarasota *(G-16295)*
▲ **Smartmatic Corporation** .... F 561 862-0747
Boca Raton *(G-721)*
Superchips Inc .... E 407 585-7000
Sanford *(G-16123)*
Syn-Tech Systems Inc .... C 850 878-2558
Tallahassee *(G-17332)*
Tactical Phaser Corp .... G 321 262-4140
Oviedo *(G-13460)*
United Wireless Tech Inc .... F 561 302-9350
Boca Raton *(G-769)*
Valor Latin Group Inc .... G 305 791-5255
Doral *(G-3540)*
Versatus Hpc Inc .... F 561 544-8862
Boca Raton *(G-777)*
▲ **Vinland International Inc** .... E 954 316-2007
Plantation *(G-14566)*

3572 Computer Storage Devices

Chiptech Imaging LLC .... G 954 827-1401
Coral Springs *(G-2230)*
Computer Technician Inc .... G 941 479-0242
Palmetto *(G-13793)*
Computers At Work Inc .... E 239 571-1050
Fort Myers *(G-4407)*
EMC Quality Group Corp .... G 786 501-5891
Miami Lakes *(G-10785)*
EMC Representations Corp .... G 305 305-1776
Hialeah *(G-5394)*
EMC Roofing LLC .... G 786 597-6604
Tampa *(G-17635)*
EMC South Florida LLC .... G 786 352-9327
South Miami *(G-16816)*
EMC Ticketing LLC .... G 813 792-1234
Land O Lakes *(G-7853)*

S I C

Gtechusa Inc...G... 786 281-1803
Hollywood *(G-5834)*
Hatalom Corporation...E... 407 567-2556
Orlando *(G-12796)*
Hill Donnelly Corporation...D... 800 525-1242
Tampa *(G-17755)*
IMC Storage...G... 305 418-0069
Doral *(G-3389)*
Lucid Technology Inc...G... 727 487-2430
Clearwater *(G-1764)*
Quality Contract Mfg Svcs LLC...F... 941 355-7787
Sarasota *(G-16280)*
Quantem Fbo Group Kssimmee LLC...G... 407 846-8001
Kissimmee *(G-7293)*
Quantum Assets LLC...G... 786 484-1187
Miami *(G-10220)*
Quantum Creations LLC...F... 786 233-6769
Miami Gardens *(G-10752)*
Quantum Limit Partners LLC...E... 954 849-3720
Fort Lauderdale *(G-4194)*
Quantum Reflex Integration Inc...E... 352 228-0766
Crystal River *(G-2380)*
Quantum Safety Services Inc...G... 786 420-0735
Miami *(G-10221)*
Quantum Servicing Corporation...G... 305 229-6675
Miami *(G-10222)*
Quantum-L/S Dna Labs Intl...G... 407 246-0484
Orlando *(G-13104)*
Quiantum Creative Group Inc...G... 954 557-6777
North Bay Village *(G-11595)*
Refly of Miami Inc...F... 786 762-2748
Miami *(G-10246)*
Rela USA LLC...G... 786 656-5069
Miami *(G-10249)*
▲ **Reliant Medical Services Inc**...G... 954 977-4224
Pompano Beach *(G-14829)*
Seagate Productions LLC...G... 561 506-7750
Boynton Beach *(G-957)*
Simply Group II LLC...G... 407 960-4690
Sanford *(G-16116)*
Totally Storage Inc...F... 407 472-6000
Lake Mary *(G-7455)*
Western Digital Corporation...G... 561 995-1496
Boca Raton *(G-789)*
Wheeler Emergency Management C...G... 850 372-4174
Marianna *(G-8587)*

3575 Computer Terminals

▲ **Aeb Technologies Inc**...G... 352 417-0009
Homosassa *(G-5999)*
Biosculptor Corporation...G... 305 823-8300
Hialeah *(G-5326)*
Comcept Solutions LLC...E... 727 535-1900
Seminole *(G-16744)*
◆ **Seal Shield LLC**...E... 877 325-7443
Orlando *(G-13172)*
Vei Technologies Inc...G... 954 653-0210
Fort Lauderdale *(G-4305)*
◆ **Verifone Inc**...C... 800 837-4366
Coral Springs *(G-2326)*

3577 Computer Peripheral Eqpt, NEC

2n USA LLC...G... 954 606-6602
Doral *(G-3214)*
Amag Technology Inc...G... 407 549-3882
Lake Mary *(G-7399)*
◆ **AMC Development Group LLC**...G... 305 597-8641
Doral *(G-3245)*
American Fibertek Inc...E... 732 302-0660
Saint Petersburg *(G-15699)*
Arco Computer Products LLC...G... 954 925-2688
Hollywood *(G-5774)*
Barrett & Company...G... 305 293-4501
Key West *(G-7179)*
▼ **Best Iproductscom LLC**...G... 386 402-7800
Edgewater *(G-3613)*
▼ **Boca Systems Inc**...C... 561 998-9600
Boca Raton *(G-459)*
Braden & Son Construction Inc...G... 239 694-8600
Fort Myers *(G-4380)*
Carlos Abascal...G... 973 696-1971
Miami *(G-9320)*
Centurion Holdings I LLC...E... 636 349-5425
Tampa *(G-17526)*
▲ **Component General Inc**...E... 727 376-6655
Odessa *(G-12112)*
Compro Solution...G... 407 733-4130
Sanford *(G-16021)*
Conduent Image Solutions Inc...C... 407 849-0279
Orlando *(G-12613)*
Crucial Collision Prod LLC...F... 321 501-1722
Melbourne *(G-8798)*
Cyipcom Inc...G... 954 727-2500
Oakland Park *(G-11794)*
▲ **Datamax International Corp**...B... 407 578-8007
Orlando *(G-12651)*
◆ **Datamax-Oneil Corporation**...C... 800 816-9649
Orlando *(G-12652)*
Donovan Home Services LLC...F... 813 644-9488
Saint Petersburg *(G-15762)*
Dtsystems Inc...G... 813 994-0030
Tampa *(G-17618)*
Eizo Rugged Solutions Inc...E... 407 262-7100
Altamonte Springs *(G-43)*
▲ **Electro-Comp Services Inc**...E... 727 532-4262
Clearwater *(G-1667)*
Electronics For Imaging Inc...G... 800 624-5999
Jacksonville Beach *(G-6943)*
▲ **Evolis Inc**...F... 954 777-9262
Fort Lauderdale *(G-3977)*
Global Mind USA LLC...D... 305 402-2190
Miami *(G-9640)*
Graphic Data Inc...G... 954 493-8003
Margate *(G-8547)*
Icloak Inc...G... 407 422-0876
Orlando *(G-12820)*
In Touch Electronics LLC...G... 813 818-9990
Tampa *(G-17776)*
Industrial Scan Inc...E... 407 322-3664
Sanford *(G-16066)*
Integrated Dealer Systems Inc...F... 800 962-7872
Oldsmar *(G-12236)*
It Manex LLC...G... 954 442-4465
Miramar *(G-11005)*
Iter3d Inc...G... 718 473-0114
Aventura *(G-274)*
Knight Bacon Associates...G... 772 388-5115
Sebastian *(G-16665)*
L3 Technologies Inc...G... 321 409-6122
Melbourne *(G-8864)*
Lexmark International Inc...C... 954 345-2442
Coral Springs *(G-2274)*
Lexmark International Inc...F... 305 467-2200
Miami *(G-9887)*
Lift Spectrum Technologies LLC...G... 407 228-8343
Orlando *(G-12910)*
Logiscenter LLC...G... 800 729-0236
Miami *(G-9905)*
McEs LLC...G... 321 363-4977
Sanford *(G-16086)*
McKenny Printing Enterprise...G... 727 420-4944
Saint Petersburg *(G-15853)*
Micro Crane Inc...G... 954 755-2225
Coral Springs *(G-2285)*
Multimedia Effects Inc...F... 800 367-3054
Plantation *(G-14536)*
▼ **Nemal Electronics Intl Inc**...E... 305 899-0900
North Miami *(G-11648)*
Nscrypt Inc...E... 407 275-4720
Orlando *(G-13012)*
OConnell Team LLC...G... 772 201-3848
Port Saint Lucie *(G-15126)*
Peripheral Services Inc...E... 813 854-1181
Oldsmar *(G-12256)*
Roberto Valverde...G... 305 324-5252
Miami *(G-10271)*
▼ **Scan Technology Inc**...G... 931 723-0304
Gainesville *(G-4992)*
▲ **Select Engineered Systems Inc**...E... 305 823-5410
Hialeah *(G-5613)*
Signature Computer Svcs Inc...G... 954 421-0950
Boca Raton *(G-710)*
▲ **Smdk Corp**...E... 239 444-1736
Naples *(G-11406)*
Speedpro Imaging St Petersburg...G... 727 266-0956
Saint Petersburg *(G-15922)*
Suncoast Identification Tech...G... 239 277-9922
Fort Myers *(G-4616)*
Suncoast Led Displays LLC...F... 727 683-2777
Palm Harbor *(G-13763)*
Synthes3d USA Inc...F... 321 946-1303
Orlando *(G-13237)*
Technetics Group Daytona Inc...C... 386 253-0628
Daytona Beach *(G-2722)*
Technologies For Tomorrow Inc...F... 850 478-5222
Pensacola *(G-14273)*
Ten In Motion LLC...F... 407 226-0204
Orlando *(G-13247)*
Thinglobal LLC...G... 561 923-8559
Boca Raton *(G-749)*
Thinktech Corporation...F... 954 501-3034
Margate *(G-8569)*
Totalprint USA...G... 855 915-1300
Tampa *(G-18196)*
Tropical Pcb Design Services...F... 561 784-9536
Loxahatchee *(G-8366)*
Uniscan LLC...F... 305 322-7669
Doral *(G-3537)*
US Barcodes Inc...G... 727 849-1196
Port Richey *(G-15074)*
Verifone Inc...C... 727 535-9200
Clearwater *(G-1932)*
◆ **Verifone Inc**...C... 800 837-4366
Coral Springs *(G-2326)*
Wau USA Corp...F... 305 361-6110
Key Biscayne *(G-7163)*
Western Microsystems Inc...E... 800 547-7082
Jacksonville *(G-6912)*
Zsno Ft Lauderdale...G... 954 792-2223
Miramar *(G-11062)*

3578 Calculating & Accounting Eqpt

Adnan Enterprises...G... 305 430-9752
Miami Gardens *(G-10731)*
◆ **American Changer Corp**...D... 954 917-3009
Fort Lauderdale *(G-3811)*
American Respiratory Solutions...F... 386 698-4446
Crescent City *(G-2338)*
Americas Atm LLC...F... 954 414-0341
Plantation *(G-14489)*
Atmcentral...G... 727 345-8460
Saint Petersburg *(G-15714)*
Atmfla Inc...G... 407 425-7708
Orlando *(G-12499)*
Blue Eagle Alliance Inc...G... 904 322-8067
Jacksonville *(G-6213)*
◆ **Bluestar Latin America Inc**...E... 800 354-9776
Miramar *(G-10975)*
Eep...F... 407 380-2828
Belle Isle *(G-357)*
General Business Services...G... 904 260-1099
Jacksonville *(G-6431)*
Greenwise Bankcard...G... 954 673-0406
Coconut Creek *(G-2078)*
▲ **Klopp International Inc**...F... 813 855-6789
Oldsmar *(G-12240)*
▲ **Klopp of Florida Inc**...G... 813 855-6789
Oldsmar *(G-12241)*
▲ **Logic Controls Inc**...E... 800 576-9647
Orlando *(G-12934)*
▼ **Metavante Holdings LLC**...G... 904 438-6000
Jacksonville *(G-6600)*
Money Tree Atm Mfg LLC...G... 850 244-5543
Fort Walton Beach *(G-4817)*
Motaz Inc...G... 239 334-7699
Fort Myers *(G-4538)*
Professional Office Svcs Inc...G... 863 967-6634
Winter Haven *(G-19348)*
▲ **R S S Partners Inc**...G... 904 241-6144
Jacksonville Beach *(G-6955)*
Sarniya Enterprises Inc...F... 352 347-6030
Ocala *(G-12042)*
Shade Saver Inc...G... 850 650-0884
Ocala *(G-12045)*
Szabo Pos Displays Inc...G... 941 778-0192
Bradenton *(G-1124)*
◆ **Verifone Inc**...C... 800 837-4366
Coral Springs *(G-2326)*
Verifone Inc...B... 727 953-4000
Clearwater *(G-1931)*
Verifone Inc...C... 727 535-9200
Clearwater *(G-1932)*
Verifone Inc...G... 754 229-4571
Coral Springs *(G-2327)*
▲ **Verifone Systems Inc**...C... 408 232-7800
Coral Springs *(G-2328)*
Zhyno Inc...G... 844 313-1900
Miami *(G-10631)*

3579 Office Machines, NEC

Barclays Business Center LLC...G... 786 260-0080
Miami *(G-9218)*
Checks Your Way Inc...G... 386 362-4044
Live Oak *(G-8228)*
▲ **Cim USA Inc**...G... 305 369-1040
Doral *(G-3298)*
Dictaphone Corporation...D... 321 255-8668
Melbourne *(G-8805)*
▲ **Diversified Performance System**...F... 904 765-7181
Jacksonville *(G-6321)*

Hth Engineering Inc ....E 727 939-8853
Tarpon Springs *(G-18308)*
▲ **Klopp International Inc** ....F 813 855-6789
Oldsmar *(G-12240)*
M C Mieth Manufacturing Inc ....F 386 767-3494
Port Orange *(G-15023)*
Naztec International Group LLC ....F 561 802-4110
West Palm Beach *(G-18959)*
▲ **Naztec International Group LLC** ....F 561 802-4110
West Palm Beach *(G-18960)*
▲ **New Market Enterprises Ltd** ....F 484 341-8004
Palm Harbor *(G-13748)*
Pitney Bowes Inc ....D 813 639-1110
Tampa *(G-17994)*
Plant Partners Inc ....F 941 752-1039
Sarasota *(G-16277)*
R & K Marketing Inc ....G 904 745-0022
Jacksonville *(G-6701)*
Simplexgrinnell Holdings LLC ....G 978 731-2500
Boca Raton *(G-716)*
▲ **Smartmatic Corporation** ....F 561 862-0747
Boca Raton *(G-721)*
Solunet ....G 321 369-9719
Palm Bay *(G-13536)*

3581 Automatic Vending Machines

Hylton & Assoc ....G 321 303-2862
Orlando *(G-12815)*
Optima Associates Inc ....F 877 371-1555
Lake City *(G-7374)*
Optimal Vending Systems ....G 301 633-2353
Alachua *(G-13)*
Rocket Vending Inc ....F 561 672-1373
Boca Raton *(G-692)*
SAP Enterprises Inc ....F 954 871-8688
North Lauderdale *(G-11621)*
Sunnypics LLC ....G 407 992-6210
Orlando *(G-13224)*
▲ **Vendapin LLC** ....F 352 796-2693
Brooksville *(G-1289)*

3582 Commercial Laundry, Dry Clean & Pressing Mchs

▼ **Coin-O-Matic Inc** ....E 305 635-4141
Miami *(G-9376)*
◆ **Kemco Systems Co LLC** ....D 727 573-2323
Clearwater *(G-1748)*
Psp Industrial Laundry Eqp LLC ....F 305 517-1421
Pompano Beach *(G-14821)*
PWS International ....G 850 432-4222
Pensacola *(G-14243)*
R&K Mehall Inc ....G 727 781-8780
Palm Harbor *(G-13754)*
Steiner-Atlantic LLC ....E 305 754-4551
Miami Gardens *(G-10756)*
▼ **Unipress Corporation** ....D 813 623-3731
Tampa *(G-18218)*

3585 Air Conditioning & Heating Eqpt

1600 Lenox LLC ....G 786 360-2553
Miami *(G-9021)*
◆ **A & V Refrigeration Corp** ....G 305 883-0733
Hialeah *(G-5255)*
A C Repairs Inc ....G 813 909-0809
Lutz *(G-8370)*
AAA Able Appliance Service ....G 954 791-5222
Fort Lauderdale *(G-3774)*
▼ **Acme Service Corp** ....F 305 836-4800
Miami *(G-9065)*
▼ **Addison Hvac LLC** ....C 407 292-4400
Orlando *(G-12430)*
▼ **Adrick Marine Group Inc** ....F 321 631-0776
Cocoa *(G-1991)*
▲ **Advanced Hermetics Inc** ....G 407 464-0539
Apopka *(G-109)*
▼ **Air & Power Solutions Inc** ....G 954 427-0019
Coconut Creek *(G-2068)*
Air Doctor of Swfl LLC ....G 239 285-8774
Lehigh Acres *(G-8184)*
Air Source 1 LLC ....G 772 626-7604
Port St Lucie *(G-15167)*
All Power Pro Inc ....G 904 310-3069
Fernandina Beach *(G-3730)*
Allied Manufacturing Inc ....G 813 502-0300
Tampa *(G-17402)*
American Hermetics Georgia Inc ....G 305 592-8958
Miami *(G-9143)*
▲ **American Panel Corporation** ....C 352 245-7055
Ocala *(G-11871)*
American Standards Inc ....G 904 683-2189
Jacksonville *(G-6150)*
◆ **Amerikooler LLC** ....C 305 884-8384
Hialeah *(G-5299)*
▼ **Andrews Filter and Supply Corp** ....E 407 423-3310
Orlando *(G-12479)*
◆ **Aquacal Autopilot Inc** ....C 727 823-5642
Saint Petersburg *(G-15705)*
◆ **Arctic Industries LLC** ....D 305 883-5581
Medley *(G-8611)*
◆ **Asbury Manufacturing Co LLC** ....E 814 453-6761
Fort Lauderdale *(G-3826)*
Baez Enterprises Corp ....F 813 317-7277
Seffner *(G-16721)*
Banks Airconditioning & Rfrgn ....G 813 917-8685
Plant City *(G-14406)*
Beam Associates LLC ....E 813 855-5695
Oldsmar *(G-12209)*
Beverage Equipment Repair Co ....F 239 573-0683
Cape Coral *(G-1389)*
Bmp Usa Inc ....D 813 443-0757
Tampa *(G-17476)*
Built Right Pool Heaters LLC ....G 941 505-1600
Punta Gorda *(G-15200)*
Calorex USA LLC ....F 239 482-0606
Fort Myers *(G-4385)*
◆ **Carrier Corporation** ....C 800 379-6484
Palm Beach Gardens *(G-13573)*
Carrier Global Corporation ....A 561 365-2000
Palm Beach Gardens *(G-13575)*
Chiller Medic Inc ....G 904 814-9446
Jacksonville *(G-6263)*
Clarios LLC ....B 727 541-3531
Largo *(G-7922)*
▲ **Classic Auto A Mnfactoring Inc** ....F 813 251-2356
Tampa *(G-17540)*
Climax Inc ....G 786 264-6082
Doral *(G-3301)*
▼ **Cold Storage Engineering Co** ....G 305 448-0099
Miami *(G-9377)*
◆ **Coldflo Inc** ....G 305 324-8555
Miami *(G-9378)*
Con-Air Industries Inc ....D 407 298-5733
Orlando *(G-12611)*
◆ **Cook Manufacturing Group Inc** ....F 863 546-6183
Frostproof *(G-4857)*
◆ **CPS Products Inc** ....G 305 687-4121
Miramar *(G-10981)*
Crown Products Company Inc ....D 904 924-8340
Jacksonville *(G-6301)*
Dade Engineering Group LLC ....F 305 885-2766
Miami *(G-9429)*
Danfoss LLC ....G 772 219-0745
Stuart *(G-16930)*
Danfoss LLC ....C 850 504-4800
Tallahassee *(G-17240)*
Data Cooling Tech Canada LLC ....E 813 865-4701
Tampa *(G-17590)*
Dcg Enterprises LLC ....G 813 931-4303
Tampa *(G-17594)*
▲ **Drinkable Air Inc** ....E 954 533-6415
Lauderdale Lakes *(G-8086)*
Duststop Filters Inc ....G 904 725-1001
Jacksonville *(G-6338)*
Eco Products Limited LLC ....G 863 337-4918
Lakeland *(G-7680)*
Electrolux Professional LLC ....F 954 327-6778
Fort Lauderdale *(G-3967)*
Energetico Inc ....G 213 550-5211
North Miami *(G-11637)*
Engineered Air Systems Inc ....F 813 881-9555
Tampa *(G-17641)*
Everest Air Corp ....F 407 319-6204
Kissimmee *(G-7243)*
Fireside Holdings Inc ....G 941 371-0300
Bradenton *(G-1041)*
First America Products ....F 904 683-1253
Orange Park *(G-12393)*
First America Products LLC ....G 904 215-8075
Miami *(G-9571)*
▼ **Flagship Marine Inc** ....G 772 781-4242
Stuart *(G-16940)*
▲ **Frascold USA Corporation** ....G 855 547-5600
Jacksonville *(G-6412)*
Fusion AC & Appl Svc LLC ....G 888 670-8435
Pompano Beach *(G-14707)*
Gate Cfv Solutions Inc ....G 772 388-3387
Sebastian *(G-16661)*
Gem 360 LLC ....E 800 436-1932
Miami *(G-9621)*
Gigvaoi Fifth and Lenox ....G 305 604-0635
Palmetto Bay *(G-13844)*
Green Air Group LLC ....D 850 608-3065
Freeport *(G-4848)*
◆ **Heat-Pipe Technology Inc** ....E 813 470-4250
Tampa *(G-17749)*
◆ **Holiday Ice Inc** ....E 407 831-2077
Longwood *(G-8287)*
Hoseline Inc ....F 407 892-2599
Saint Cloud *(G-15654)*
Hoseline Inc ....F 541 258-8984
Ocala *(G-11966)*
Ice Link 2018 LLC ....G 305 988-4023
Lake Worth Beach *(G-7613)*
Icecold2 LLC ....G 855 326-2665
Tampa *(G-17767)*
Innovative Support Systems ....G 407 682-7570
Altamonte Springs *(G-51)*
Innovative Svc Solutions LLC ....E 407 296-5211
Orlando *(G-12831)*
International H20 Inc ....G 954 854-1638
North Miami Beach *(G-11683)*
◆ **J T Walker Industries Inc** ....E 727 461-0501
Clearwater *(G-1739)*
◆ **James D Nall Co Inc** ....E 305 884-8363
Fort Lauderdale *(G-4074)*
Jer-Air Manufacturing Inc ....E 352 591-2674
Micanopy *(G-10902)*
John Bean Technologies Corp ....E 407 851-3377
Orlando *(G-12858)*
◆ **Klimaire Products Inc** ....F 305 593-8358
Doral *(G-3409)*
Kommercial Refrigeration Inc ....G 863 299-3000
Winter Haven *(G-19332)*
◆ **Kysor Industrial Corporation** ....F 727 376-8600
Trinity *(G-18487)*
Lajoie Investment Corp ....F 954 463-3271
Fort Lauderdale *(G-4094)*
◆ **Lennox Global Ltd** ....D 305 718-2921
Doral *(G-3416)*
Lennox Industries ....G 305 718-2974
Doral *(G-3417)*
Lennox International Inc ....G 352 379-9630
Gainesville *(G-4954)*
Lennox Miami Corp ....E 305 763-8655
Miami Beach *(G-10687)*
Lennox National Account S ....G 954 745-3482
Miami *(G-9884)*
Lorenze & Associates Inc ....G 407 682-7570
Altamonte Springs *(G-53)*
Mainstream Engineering Corp ....E 321 631-3550
Rockledge *(G-15432)*
Mas Hvac Inc ....F 904 531-3140
Elkton *(G-3649)*
▲ **Mermaid Mfg Southwest Fla Inc** ....F 239 418-0535
Fort Myers *(G-4528)*
◆ **Metal Industries Inc** ....C 727 441-2651
Clearwater *(G-1783)*
MI Metals Inc ....C 813 855-5695
Oldsmar *(G-12248)*
Micro Matic Usa Inc ....G 352 799-6331
Brooksville *(G-1250)*
Micro Matic Usa Inc ....G 352 544-1081
Brooksville *(G-1251)*
◆ **Micro Matic Usa Inc** ....E 352 544-1081
Brooksville *(G-1252)*
Miles of Smiles Rides Inc ....F 727 528-1227
Seminole *(G-16753)*
Monar Corporation ....G 954 650-1930
Coral Springs *(G-2287)*
Mosco Inc ....G 561 588-3880
Lake Worth Beach *(G-7617)*
◆ **Mr Winter Inc** ....E 800 327-3371
Medley *(G-8693)*
Northrich Florida LLC ....F 954 678-6602
Weston *(G-19154)*
Parker Davis Hvac Intl Inc ....E 305 513-4488
Doral *(G-3455)*
Preble Enterprises Inc ....G 954 480-6919
Deerfield Beach *(G-2889)*
Proservices Supply LLC ....F 858 254-4415
Jacksonville *(G-6696)*
Quality Marine Air Refrig ....G 954 560-0084
Fort Lauderdale *(G-4191)*
◆ **Quorum Marine & Elec Inc** ....E 772 220-0038
Stuart *(G-16994)*
R & J Mfg of Gainesville ....G 352 375-3130
Gainesville *(G-4987)*
R & Y Automotive AC Cmpsr ....E 305 919-9232
North Miami Beach *(G-11700)*

SIC

▼ **R & Y Automotive AC Cmpsr** ....F....... 305 947-1173
North Miami Beach *(G-11701)*
Re-Bus LLC ....G....... 772 418-7711
Fort Pierce *(G-4738)*
▼ **Refrigeration Panels Inc** ....F....... 305 836-6900
Miami *(G-10247)*
◆ **Refrigrtion Engnred Systems In** ....E....... 305 836-6900
Miami *(G-10248)*
▲ **Reftec International Inc** ....E....... 800 214-4883
Bradenton *(G-1104)*
Reftec Intl Systems LLC ....F....... 727 290-9830
Largo *(G-8039)*
Ross Slade Inc ....G....... 813 250-0488
Tampa *(G-18069)*
Sharing Three Inc ....F....... 305 884-8384
Hialeah *(G-5617)*
Soda Service of Florida LLC ....G....... 727 595-7632
Largo *(G-8057)*
South Florida Marine ....G....... 305 232-8788
Cutler Bay *(G-2413)*
Southern Hvac Corporation ....G....... 407 917-1800
Maitland *(G-8479)*
Southern Technologies ....E....... 904 266-2100
Jacksonville *(G-6798)*
Stan Weaver & Co Inc ....E....... 407 581-6940
Orlando *(G-13211)*
Store It Cold LLC ....G....... 720 456-1178
Medley *(G-8730)*
Total of Florida ....G....... 239 768-9400
Fort Myers *(G-4634)*
◆ **Trane Central America Inc** ....E....... 305 592-8646
Miami *(G-10502)*
Trane Technologies Company LLC ....A....... 850 873-8200
Panama City *(G-13956)*
Trane US Inc ....G....... 239 277-0344
Fort Myers *(G-4637)*
Trane US Inc ....D....... 954 499-6900
Miramar *(G-11052)*
Transport A/C Inc ....G....... 954 254-4822
Pensacola *(G-14274)*
Tsm Champ LLC ....D....... 615 806-7900
Sarasota *(G-16317)*
V & F Air Conditioning Sup LLC ....F....... 305 477-1040
Miami *(G-10559)*
Verde GSE Inc ....E....... 888 837-5221
Palmetto *(G-13832)*
▲ **Warren Technology Inc** ....C....... 305 556-6933
Hialeah *(G-5686)*
Welbilt Inc ....A....... 727 375-7010
Trinity *(G-18491)*
Westran Corporation ....G....... 727 375-7010
Trinity *(G-18492)*
Zenit Service LLC ....G....... 407 878-7840
Lake Mary *(G-7462)*

3586 Measuring & Dispensing Pumps

▲ **Stenner Pump Company Inc** ....C....... 904 641-1666
Jacksonville *(G-6811)*

3589 Service Ind Machines, NEC

A Clean Finish Inc ....G....... 407 516-1311
Jacksonville *(G-6109)*
A&M Cleaning Solutions LLC ....F....... 786 559-7093
West Palm Beach *(G-18785)*
A1 Cleaning Concepts Inc ....G....... 772 288-7214
Stuart *(G-16899)*
Accommodating Services Inc ....G....... 863 528-3231
Lake Wales *(G-7498)*
▼ **Action Manufacturing & Sup Inc** ....F....... 239 574-3443
Cape Coral *(G-1373)*
Action Mfg & Sup WPB LLC ....G....... 239 574-3443
West Palm Beach *(G-18788)*
Advatech Corporation ....G....... 732 803-8000
West Palm Beach *(G-18790)*
Aesinc Advanced Eqp & Svcs ....G....... 954 857-1895
Coral Springs *(G-2216)*
AFL Industries Inc ....G....... 561 848-1826
Riviera Beach *(G-15295)*
Agua Control LLC ....G....... 813 663-0701
Tampa *(G-17393)*
◆ **Aladdin Equipment Company** ....D....... 941 371-3732
Sarasota *(G-16338)*
◆ **American Boom and Barrier Inc** ....E....... 321 784-2110
Cape Canaveral *(G-1350)*
▲ **American Engineering Svcs Inc** ....G....... 813 621-3932
Plant City *(G-14399)*
American Pressure Systems Inc ....G....... 321 914-0827
West Melbourne *(G-18765)*
Andre T Jean ....G....... 305 647-8744
Opa Locka *(G-12288)*
Angel Fernandez ....G....... 239 580-9714
Fort Myers *(G-4363)*
Annellies Car Wash LLC ....G....... 954 990-8436
Lauderhill *(G-8101)*
▲ **Apollo Worldwide Inc** ....G....... 561 585-3865
Hypoluxo *(G-6048)*
▲ **Aqua Engineering & Equipment** ....F....... 407 599-2123
Winter Park *(G-19378)*
▼ **Aqua Wholesale Inc** ....G....... 941 341-0847
Sarasota *(G-16345)*
Aquasolve Ventures LLC ....G....... 732 570-0707
Daytona Beach *(G-2627)*
Aquatec Solutions LLC ....F....... 561 717-6933
Boca Raton *(G-428)*
▲ **Aquatech Manufacturing LLC** ....F....... 813 664-0300
Tampa *(G-17430)*
▼ **Aquathin Corp** ....E....... 800 462-7634
Pompano Beach *(G-14596)*
Ashberry Acquisition Company ....F....... 813 248-0055
Tampa *(G-17438)*
Astro Pure Incorporated ....F....... 954 422-8966
Deerfield Beach *(G-2781)*
Atlantic Drinking Water Systms ....G....... 252 255-1110
Fort Myers *(G-4369)*
Atlas Metal Industries Inc ....C....... 305 625-2451
Miami *(G-9186)*
◆ **Atmospheric Wtr Solutions Inc** ....F....... 954 306-6763
Cooper City *(G-2109)*
▲ **Bar Maid Corporation** ....F....... 954 960-1468
Pompano Beach *(G-14614)*
Bateh Networking Solutions LLC ....G....... 904 725-2282
Jacksonville *(G-6197)*
Bay Area Security Shred ....F....... 877 974-7337
Palm Harbor *(G-13723)*
Bcr Environmental Corporation ....E....... 904 819-9170
Jacksonville *(G-6198)*
▲ **Biozone Scientific Intl Inc** ....G....... 407 876-2000
Orlando *(G-12517)*
Blast Off Equipment Inc ....F....... 561 964-6199
West Palm Beach *(G-18824)*
Brake-Funderburk Entps Inc ....E....... 904 730-6788
Jacksonville *(G-6230)*
C & D Industrial Maint LLC ....F....... 833 776-5833
Bradenton *(G-1005)*
Car Wash Solutions Florida Inc ....E....... 941 323-8817
Ocala *(G-11894)*
Ce Hooton Sales LLC ....F....... 305 255-9722
Sarasota *(G-16189)*
Central Processing Corp ....G....... 352 787-3004
Leesburg *(G-8146)*
Charles Gable Inc ....G....... 239 300-0220
Naples *(G-11207)*
Chlorinators Inc ....E....... 772 288-4854
Stuart *(G-16924)*
City of Bradenton ....E....... 941 727-6360
Bradenton *(G-1020)*
City of Cocoa Beach ....F....... 321 868-3342
Cocoa Beach *(G-2061)*
City of Hollywood ....F....... 954 967-4230
Hollywood *(G-5799)*
Clearwater Enviro Tech Inc ....E....... 727 209-6400
Largo *(G-7924)*
▲ **Com Pac Filtration Inc** ....E....... 904 356-4003
Jacksonville *(G-6279)*
Consumer Engineering Inc ....F....... 321 984-8550
Palm Bay *(G-13507)*
Crane Co ....G....... 941 480-9101
Venice *(G-18538)*
▼ **Crane Environmental Inc** ....D....... 941 480-9101
Venice *(G-18539)*
Crystal Pool Service Inc ....F....... 954 444-8282
Sunrise *(G-17111)*
Dais Corp ....F....... 727 375-8484
Odessa *(G-12115)*
Defense Flight Aerospace LLC ....F....... 321 442-7255
Orlando *(G-12660)*
Dependable Water Inc ....E....... 772 563-7473
Vero Beach *(G-18615)*
◆ **Douglas Machines Corp** ....E....... 727 461-3477
Clearwater *(G-1655)*
Dyco ....G....... 941 484-9057
Sarasota *(G-16416)*
▼ **Ebco Envmtl Bins & Cntrs Inc** ....F....... 954 967-9999
West Park *(G-19092)*
Eco Water Technologies Corp ....G....... 954 599-3672
Fort Lauderdale *(G-3961)*
Ecosphere Technologies Inc ....F....... 772 287-4846
Stuart *(G-16936)*
Electrolytic Tech Svcs LLC ....G....... 305 655-2755
North Miami Beach *(G-11673)*
▲ **Electrolytic Technologies Corp** ....F....... 305 655-2755
Miami *(G-9510)*
Enodis Holdings Inc ....C....... 727 375-7010
Trinity *(G-18484)*
▼ **Enviro Water Solutions LLC** ....D....... 877 842-1635
Deland *(G-2975)*
◆ **Enviro-USA American Mfr LLC** ....E....... 321 222-9551
Cape Canaveral *(G-1357)*
Environmental Services ....E....... 727 518-3080
Clearwater *(G-1674)*
▼ **Esd Waste2water Inc** ....D....... 800 277-3279
Ocala *(G-11933)*
▲ **Esse Sales Inc** ....G....... 954 368-3900
Oakland Park *(G-11803)*
▲ **Euroasia Products Inc** ....G....... 321 221-9398
Orlando *(G-12719)*
Evoqua Water Technologies LLC ....G....... 813 620-0900
Tampa *(G-17651)*
Evoqua Water Technologies LLC ....G....... 407 650-1765
Orlando *(G-12725)*
Extra Time Solutions ....F....... 407 625-2198
Clermont *(G-1957)*
▲ **Fluidra Usa LLC** ....E....... 904 378-0999
Jacksonville *(G-6409)*
Focus On Water Inc ....G....... 239 275-1880
Fort Myers *(G-4456)*
Fovico Inc ....F....... 561 624-5400
West Palm Beach *(G-18882)*
◆ **Fshs Inc** ....G....... 941 625-5929
Port Charlotte *(G-14982)*
Gator Drain Cleaning Equipment ....G....... 954 584-4441
Davie *(G-2531)*
Genesis Systems LLC ....G....... 417 499-3301
Tampa *(G-17709)*
▲ **Genfloor LLC** ....G....... 305 477-1557
Doral *(G-3364)*
Getitcleaned ....F....... 239 331-2891
Naples *(G-11261)*
Great Lakes Wtr Trtmnt Systems ....G....... 269 381-0210
Naples *(G-11267)*
▲ **Greenlam America Inc** ....F....... 305 640-0388
Doral *(G-3373)*
▲ **H2o International Inc** ....F....... 954 570-3464
Deerfield Beach *(G-2834)*
◆ **Harmsco Inc** ....D....... 561 848-9628
Riviera Beach *(G-15331)*
▲ **Harn Ro Systems Inc** ....E....... 941 488-9671
Venice *(G-18553)*
Hydro-Dyne Engineering Inc ....E....... 727 532-0777
Oldsmar *(G-12233)*
ICI Custom Parts Inc ....E....... 813 888-7979
Tampa *(G-17768)*
Industrial Marine Inc ....F....... 904 781-4707
Jacksonville *(G-6493)*
International Food Eqp Inc ....G....... 305 785-5100
Miami Springs *(G-10891)*
J-Ko Company ....G....... 561 795-7377
Royal Palm Beach *(G-15472)*
Jamuna1 LLC ....G....... 407 313-5927
Windermere *(G-19230)*
Jiva Cubes Inc ....G....... 305 788-1200
Surfside *(G-17203)*
Johnson Well Equipment Inc ....G....... 850 453-3131
Pensacola *(G-14185)*
Jtm International Inc ....G....... 954 680-3517
Cooper City *(G-2113)*
K V Water Equipment & Krane Co ....F....... 941 723-0707
Venice *(G-18558)*
◆ **Kemco Systems Co LLC** ....D....... 727 573-2323
Clearwater *(G-1748)*
Latitude Clean Tech Group Inc ....F....... 561 417-0687
Boca Raton *(G-597)*
▲ **LDS Vacuum Products Inc** ....E....... 407 862-4643
Longwood *(G-8305)*
Lenntech USA LLC ....G....... 877 453-8095
South Miami *(G-16820)*
Lifegard Prfcation Systems LLC ....G....... 813 875-7777
Tampa *(G-17846)*
Lodex Enterprises Corp ....G....... 954 442-3843
Miramar *(G-11010)*
▼ **Louis Di Rmndo Wrldwide Invstm** ....F....... 786 536-7578
Miami Beach *(G-10689)*
▲ **Main USA Corp** ....G....... 305 499-4994
Miami *(G-9937)*
Mar Cor Purification Inc ....E....... 484 991-0220
Lakeland *(G-7744)*
Membrane Systems Corp ....G....... 239 283-8590
Cape Coral *(G-1448)*
Michael P Wahlquist ....G....... 850 643-5139
Bristol *(G-1200)*

Mold Remediation Services Inc ....G....... 904 574-5266
Jacksonville *(G-6612)*
N-Viro Inc ....G....... 904 781-4707
Jacksonville *(G-6617)*
Nilfisk Pressure-Pro LLC ....D....... 772 672-3697
Fort Pierce *(G-4722)*
Originclear Inc ....G....... 323 939-6645
Clearwater *(G-1822)*
▲ **Paragon Water Systems Inc** ....E....... 727 538-4704
Tampa *(G-17976)*
◆ **Parkson Corporation** ....G....... 954 974-6610
Fort Lauderdale *(G-4160)*
Poseidon Services Inc ....G....... 786 294-8529
Miami *(G-10179)*
◆ **Premier Water & Enrgy Tech Inc** ....E....... 904 268-1152
Jacksonville *(G-6685)*
Pressure Shine LLC ....G....... 727 216-8543
Palm Harbor *(G-13751)*
Pristine Environment LLC ....F....... 727 541-5748
Pinellas Park *(G-14380)*
Pro Water Treatment Inc ....G....... 954 650-1955
Margate *(G-8564)*
Pulsafeeder Inc ....D....... 941 575-2900
Punta Gorda *(G-15223)*
Pulsafeeder Spo Inc ....F....... 941 575-3800
Punta Gorda *(G-15224)*
Pure Water Changes Inc ....F....... 407 699-2837
Windermere *(G-19241)*
▲ **R & R Stone Industries Inc** ....G....... 888 999-4921
Miami *(G-10229)*
▲ **Randazza Enterprises Inc** ....F....... 813 677-0041
Riverview *(G-15279)*
Resource Management Associates ....G....... 239 656-0818
Fort Myers *(G-4582)*
▲ **Rgf Environmental Group Inc** ....C....... 800 842-7771
Riviera Beach *(G-15372)*
◆ **Rgf Marine Envmtl Tech Inc** ....E....... 561 848-1826
Riviera Beach *(G-15373)*
Richard Lyn ....G....... 954 326-1017
North Lauderdale *(G-11620)*
Rz Service Group LLC ....G....... 904 402-2313
Jacksonville *(G-6741)*
▲ **Sawyer Products Inc** ....E....... 727 725-1177
Safety Harbor *(G-15502)*
◆ **Seaking Inc** ....E....... 954 961-6629
Davie *(G-2589)*
Sergeant Bretts Coffee LLC ....G....... 561 451-0048
Coconut Creek *(G-2094)*
▲ **Smith Equipment & Supply Co** ....E....... 863 665-4904
Lakeland *(G-7795)*
South West Adventure Team LLC ....G....... 903 288-4739
Labelle *(G-7323)*
Southern Power Washing ....G....... 561 644-2237
Loxahatchee *(G-8365)*
Starke Waste Wtr Trtmnt Plant ....G....... 904 964-7999
Starke *(G-16897)*
Superior Waterway Services Inc ....F....... 561 799-5852
Riviera Beach *(G-15383)*
Tampa Fiberglass Inc ....F....... 813 248-6828
Tampa *(G-18164)*
◆ **Technical International Corp** ....G....... 305 374-1054
Miami *(G-10462)*
▼ **Tetra Process Technology** ....G....... 813 886-9331
Tampa *(G-18184)*
Transition of Slc Inc ....E....... 772 461-4486
Fort Pierce *(G-4757)*
Twinoxide-Usa Inc ....G....... 321 207-8524
Merritt Island *(G-9019)*
Unihold Inc ....G....... 941 966-7440
Nokomis *(G-11590)*
◆ **Vac-Con Inc** ....B....... 904 284-4200
Green Cove Springs *(G-5075)*
Vapex Environmental Tech Inc ....G....... 407 277-0900
Cocoa *(G-2055)*
Voda Technologies LLC ....G....... 727 645-6030
Palm Harbor *(G-13767)*
Wastequip Manufacturing Co LLC ....E....... 863 665-6507
Lakeland *(G-7832)*
Water Bagel Boca East Lllp ....G....... 347 661-7171
Jupiter *(G-7144)*
Waterfilterusa ....G....... 386 469-0138
Deland *(G-3032)*
◆ **Watermakers Inc** ....F....... 954 467-8920
Fort Lauderdale *(G-4315)*
Watts Water Technologies Inc ....G....... 352 465-2000
Dunnellon *(G-3602)*
Welbilt Inc ....A....... 727 375-7010
Trinity *(G-18491)*
White Mop Wringer Company ....C....... 813 971-2223
Tampa *(G-18256)*
Worldwide Technology Inc ....E....... 813 855-2443
Oldsmar *(G-12279)*
Wws Contracting LLC ....E....... 813 868-3100
Tampa *(G-18269)*
Yacht-Mate Products Inc ....G....... 954 527-0112
Fort Lauderdale *(G-4331)*
Yauchler Properties LLC ....F....... 863 662-5570
Winter Haven *(G-19369)*

3592 Carburetors, Pistons, Rings & Valves

Control Southern Inc ....D....... 904 353-0004
Jacksonville *(G-6287)*
▲ **Daytona Parts Company** ....G....... 386 427-7108
New Smyrna Beach *(G-11532)*
Florida Marine Products Inc ....F....... 813 248-2283
Tampa *(G-17683)*
Flyteone Inc ....G....... 813 421-1410
Clearwater *(G-1691)*
Innovative Products LLC ....G....... 888 764-6478
Fort Lauderdale *(G-4059)*
▲ **Mtc Engineering LLC** ....E....... 321 636-9480
Cocoa *(G-2037)*
Total Performance Inc ....G....... 203 265-5667
Palm Coast *(G-13713)*

3593 Fluid Power Cylinders & Actuators

Duramaster Cylinders ....F....... 813 882-0040
Tampa *(G-17620)*
Dynalco Controls Corporation ....E....... 323 589-6181
Fort Lauderdale *(G-3952)*
Eem Technologies Corp ....F....... 786 606-5993
Doral *(G-3340)*
Greenco Manufacturing Corp ....E....... 813 882-4400
Tampa *(G-17728)*
◆ **Leslie Controls Inc** ....C....... 813 978-1000
Temple Terrace *(G-18371)*
National Cylinder Head Exchang ....G....... 813 870-6340
Tampa *(G-17930)*

3594 Fluid Power Pumps & Motors

Eem Technologies Corp ....F....... 786 606-5993
Doral *(G-3340)*
Evo Motors LLC ....F....... 813 621-7799
Seffner *(G-16725)*
▲ **Flaire Corporation** ....C....... 352 237-1220
Ocala *(G-11944)*
▲ **Hydrolec Inc** ....E....... 904 730-3766
Jacksonville *(G-6484)*
Leading Edge Aerospace Llc ....G....... 305 608-6826
Miami Gardens *(G-10750)*
Motors Pumps and Accessories ....G....... 305 883-3181
Medley *(G-8692)*
Mwi Corporation ....F....... 239 337-4747
Fort Myers *(G-4542)*
◆ **Oase North America Inc** ....G....... 800 365-3880
Riviera Beach *(G-15354)*
Scott Industrial Systems Inc ....F....... 904 693-3318
Jacksonville *(G-6756)*

3596 Scales & Balances, Exc Laboratory

Atlas Industrial Scales Inc ....G....... 352 610-9989
Spring Hill *(G-16847)*
Intercomp ....G....... 407 637-9766
Delray Beach *(G-3092)*
Keytroller LLC ....F....... 813 877-4500
Tampa *(G-17823)*
▲ **Merrick Industries Inc** ....C....... 850 265-3611
Lynn Haven *(G-8436)*
Mettler Toledo ....F....... 607 257-6000
Lutz *(G-8399)*
Mettler-Toledo Inc ....C....... 607 257-6000
Lutz *(G-8400)*
Mettler-Toledo Inc ....F....... 407 423-3856
Orlando *(G-12964)*
Pinto Palma Sound LLC ....E....... 877 959-1815
Cutler Bay *(G-2408)*
▲ **Radwag USA LLC** ....G....... 305 651-3522
North Miami Beach *(G-11702)*
Tannehill Intl Inds Inc ....C....... 850 265-3611
Lynn Haven *(G-8439)*
▼ **US 1 Truck Sales LLC** ....G....... 904 545-1233
Jacksonville *(G-6889)*
Weightech USA LLC ....F....... 954 666-0877
Davie *(G-2613)*

3599 Machinery & Eqpt, Indl & Commercial, NEC

1842 Daily Grind & Mercantile ....G....... 352 543-5004
Cedar Key *(G-1522)*
▲ **3 D F X Inc** ....F....... 407 237-6249
Orlando *(G-12416)*
A & E Machine Inc ....F....... 321 636-3110
Cocoa *(G-1988)*
A & J Aerospace Corp ....F....... 786 564-9986
Miami *(G-9031)*
A M Tool & Engineering Company ....G....... 727 375-5002
Odessa *(G-12097)*
Aaron Tool Inc ....E....... 941 758-9369
Bradenton *(G-980)*
Aba Engineering & Mfg Inc ....F....... 386 672-9665
Ormond Beach *(G-13346)*
Absolute Technologies Inc ....G....... 954 868-9045
Parkland *(G-13987)*
Accu Right Inc ....G....... 561 586-5368
Lake Worth *(G-7528)*
Acdm-PMS Inc ....G....... 305 258-0347
Homestead *(G-5952)*
Ace Tools ....G....... 386 302-5152
Palm Coast *(G-13680)*
Acu Grind Tool Works Inc ....E....... 941 758-6963
Bradenton *(G-981)*
Addtad Partners Inc ....G....... 727 863-0847
Hudson *(G-6014)*
Adeptus Industries Inc ....F....... 941 756-7636
Bradenton *(G-982)*
Advance Hydraulic Services ....G....... 352 502-9462
Leesburg *(G-8138)*
Advance Tool Company Inc ....F....... 727 726-8907
Safety Harbor *(G-15488)*
Advanced Air West Palm Bch Inc ....E....... 561 845-8289
Riviera Beach *(G-15294)*
Advanced Cnc Machining Inc ....G....... 954 478-8369
Margate *(G-8530)*
Advanced Cnc Manufacturing ....F....... 727 372-8222
Odessa *(G-12098)*
Advanced Cylinder Heads ....G....... 407 671-2886
Winter Park *(G-19372)*
◆ **Advanced Machine and Tool Inc** ....D....... 772 465-6546
Fort Pierce *(G-4669)*
Advanced Machining Inc ....G....... 386 424-7333
New Smyrna Beach *(G-11524)*
Advanced Metal Fab Inc ....F....... 305 557-2008
Hialeah *(G-5271)*
Advanced Precision Machining ....G....... 561 243-4567
Delray Beach *(G-3041)*
Advanced Precision Mch US Inc ....F....... 239 332-2841
Fort Myers *(G-4345)*
▼ **Aero Precision Products Inc** ....D....... 305 688-2565
Opa Locka *(G-12283)*
Aero Technology Mfg Inc ....F....... 305 345-7747
Miami *(G-9082)*
Aero-Marine Technologies Inc ....G....... 941 205-5420
Englewood *(G-3658)*
Aerospace Components Inc ....F....... 727 347-9915
Saint Petersburg *(G-15693)*
AGA Machine Shop Inc ....G....... 954 522-1108
Fort Lauderdale *(G-3788)*
Agteck Inc ....E....... 321 305-5930
Cocoa *(G-1993)*
AK U TEC Machine & Tool Inc ....G....... 727 573-5211
Clearwater *(G-1572)*
▲ **AL Garey & Associates Inc** ....C....... 954 975-7992
Coral Springs *(G-2218)*
All Cut Inc No Selection ....G....... 239 789-1748
Fort Myers *(G-4350)*
Alnitak Corporation ....F....... 941 727-1122
Sarasota *(G-16174)*
Alpha Hydraulics LLC ....G....... 561 355-0318
Riviera Beach *(G-15297)*
Ames Tools ....F....... 239 693-1055
Fort Myers *(G-4362)*
Ammcon Corp ....G....... 904 863-3196
Green Cove Springs *(G-5052)*
Amteco Machine & Manufacturing ....F....... 727 573-0993
Clearwater *(G-1584)*
Anchor Machine & Fabricating ....F....... 813 247-3099
Tampa *(G-17426)*
Anco Precision Inc ....G....... 954 429-3703
Deerfield Beach *(G-2777)*
Apple Machine & Supply Co ....E....... 772 466-9353
Fort Pierce *(G-4677)*
Armorit Precison ....G....... 941 751-6635
Sarasota *(G-16177)*
Arnold Industries South Inc ....G....... 352 867-0190
Ocala *(G-11879)*
Ascent Precision Gear Corp ....G....... 386 792-3215
Jasper *(G-6959)*
Associated Machine Company Inc ....D....... 305 836-6163
Miami *(G-9180)*

S I C

Atomic Machine & EDM Inc..........G....... 239 353-9100
Naples *(G-11176)*
Attilas Machine & Welding..........G....... 305 947-0953
North Miami Beach *(G-11668)*
Automated Production Eqp Ape..........G....... 305 451-4722
Key Largo *(G-7165)*
B & D Machine and Tool Inc..........F....... 321 727-0098
Palm Bay *(G-13501)*
B & P Motor Heads Inc..........G....... 305 769-3183
Opa Locka *(G-12291)*
B G Instrument Corp..........F....... 941 485-7700
North Venice *(G-11753)*
Ba Precision Products Corp..........G....... 561 859-3400
Boca Raton *(G-439)*
Baker-Hill Industries Inc..........E....... 954 752-3090
Coral Springs *(G-2224)*
Bartow Machine Works Inc..........G....... 863 533-6361
Bartow *(G-308)*
Bay Cnc Machine LLC..........G....... 813 362-9626
Oldsmar *(G-12207)*
Bay Tech Industries Inc..........E....... 813 854-1774
Odessa *(G-12105)*
Bears Metal Works Inc..........F....... 863 537-5644
Bartow *(G-309)*
Bellowstech LLC..........G....... 386 615-7530
Ormond Beach *(G-13352)*
Bellowstech LLC..........E....... 386 615-7530
Ormond Beach *(G-13353)*
Benton Machine Works Inc..........G....... 904 768-9161
Jacksonville *(G-6207)*
Best Metal Work..........G....... 561 842-1960
West Palm Beach *(G-18818)*
Betty Engines Machine Shop Inc..........G....... 305 458-1467
Miami *(G-9237)*
Big Country Small Engine..........G....... 850 348-9022
Panama City *(G-13872)*
Big OS Stump Grinding..........G....... 904 945-5900
Jacksonville *(G-6208)*
Blair Machine & Tool Inc..........F....... 904 731-4377
Jacksonville *(G-6212)*
◆ **Bobs Space Racers Inc**..........C....... 386 677-0761
Daytona Beach *(G-2631)*
Bobs Wldg Fbrcation Maint Inc..........E....... 863 665-0135
Lakeland *(G-7648)*
Brantley Machine & Fabrication..........F....... 904 359-0554
Jacksonville *(G-6232)*
Breiner Machine Co Inc..........F....... 352 544-0463
Brooksville *(G-1216)*
Brevard Robotics..........E....... 321 637-0367
Cocoa *(G-2001)*
Broward Machine LLC..........G....... 954 920-8004
Dania *(G-2440)*
▲ **Bryan Nelco Inc**..........G....... 727 533-8282
Clearwater *(G-1615)*
Bryants Precision M F G Corp..........E....... 772 569-2319
Vero Beach *(G-18606)*
Builders Automtn McHy Co LLC..........E....... 727 538-2180
Largo *(G-7917)*
C & C Tool & Mold..........G....... 863 699-5337
Lake Placid *(G-7485)*
C W Machining Inc..........G....... 352 732-5824
Ocala *(G-11892)*
C4 Group LLC..........F....... 850 230-4541
Panama City Beach *(G-13975)*
Camcorp Industries Inc..........G....... 941 488-5000
Venice *(G-18536)*
▼ **Casper Engineering Corp**..........G....... 305 666-4046
Pinecrest *(G-14326)*
Catamount Machine Works LLC..........F....... 813 659-0505
Plant City *(G-14417)*
Catapult 13 Crtive Studios LLC..........G....... 305 788-6948
Miami *(G-9324)*
Catapult Group Inc..........G....... 904 834-7728
Ponte Vedra Beach *(G-14935)*
Catapult Lakeland Inc..........G....... 863 687-3788
Lakeland *(G-7654)*
Catapult Learning LL..........G....... 561 573-6025
Delray Beach *(G-3057)*
Causey Machine Works Inc..........F....... 407 277-7570
Orlando *(G-12555)*
Centerline Tool & Engrg Inc..........F....... 941 749-5519
Bradenton *(G-1018)*
Central Florida Sales & Svc..........F....... 863 967-6678
Auburndale *(G-233)*
▼ **Cew LLC**..........G....... 305 232-8892
Miami *(G-9344)*
Cew Technologies Inc..........G....... 305 232-8892
Miami *(G-9345)*
Charian Machine & Mfg Inc..........G....... 727 561-0150
Clearwater *(G-1624)*
Chasco Machine & Manufacturing..........G....... 727 815-3510
Brooksville *(G-1218)*
Chickasha Manufacturing Co Inc..........E....... 405 224-0229
Osprey *(G-13410)*
Cinalta Corp..........G....... 954 815-0612
Pompano Beach *(G-14635)*
Circle S Manufacturing Co Inc..........G....... 352 236-3580
Fort Mc Coy *(G-4336)*
Clearwater Machining Inc..........G....... 727 512-0337
Clearwater *(G-1628)*
Clearwater Manufacturing Co..........G....... 813 818-0959
Oldsmar *(G-12215)*
Cnc-Precision Machining Corp..........G....... 786 452-9575
Hialeah *(G-5348)*
Cnr Precision Tool Inc..........G....... 954 426-9650
Coral Springs *(G-2231)*
Cole Machine LLC..........G....... 239 571-4364
Naples *(G-11214)*
Concept Group LLC..........F....... 856 767-5506
Palm Beach Gardens *(G-13582)*
Consoldted Mch Tl Holdings LLC..........G....... 888 317-9990
Flagler Beach *(G-3754)*
Cost Cast Inc..........F....... 863 422-5617
Haines City *(G-5139)*
Crabil Manufacturing Inc..........E....... 727 209-8368
Saint Petersburg *(G-15754)*
Crankshaft Rebuilders Inc..........D....... 407 323-4870
Sanford *(G-16027)*
CT Natural..........G....... 813 996-6443
Tampa *(G-17572)*
Custom Tube Products Inc..........F....... 386 426-0670
Edgewater *(G-3620)*
Custom Watersports Eqp Inc..........G....... 941 753-9949
Bradenton *(G-1026)*
Cutting Edge Mch Fbrcation LLC..........G....... 321 626-0588
Cocoa *(G-2007)*
D & B Machine Inc..........E....... 941 355-8002
Sarasota *(G-16202)*
D & J Machinery Inc..........E....... 863 983-3171
Clewiston *(G-1978)*
D N Machining..........E....... 941 727-1684
Bradenton *(G-1028)*
Daily Grind Stumpgrinding..........G....... 954 588-4640
Sunrise *(G-17114)*
Dalane Machining Inc..........E....... 813 854-5905
Tampa *(G-17587)*
Danco Machine Inc..........G....... 727 501-0460
Largo *(G-7930)*
Daves Machine Shop Inc..........G....... 386 325-0974
Palatka *(G-13477)*
Defense Stamping & Engineering..........E....... 850 438-6105
Pensacola *(G-14127)*
Delta Machine LLC..........G....... 386 738-2204
Deland *(G-2968)*
Destin Machine Inc..........G....... 850 837-7114
Destin *(G-3187)*
Diamond Precision Machine Inc..........F....... 321 729-8453
Palm Bay *(G-13508)*
Diamondback Cnc LLC..........E....... 321 305-5995
Cocoa *(G-2010)*
Dimension Machine Tool Inc..........F....... 586 948-3600
Cape Coral *(G-1414)*
Dj/Pj Inc..........E....... 813 907-6359
Clearwater *(G-1653)*
Drake Tool Co Inc..........G....... 407 859-4221
Orlando *(G-12684)*
Dulond Tool & Engineering Inc..........F....... 941 758-4489
Sarasota *(G-16210)*
Dunrite Metal Fabricators Inc..........F....... 727 299-9242
Clearwater *(G-1660)*
◆ **E M P Inc**..........G....... 772 286-7343
Stuart *(G-16935)*
Eagle Quality Components LLC..........F....... 352 516-4838
Tavares *(G-18335)*
East Coast Machine Inc..........F....... 321 632-4817
Cocoa *(G-2017)*
Edafa Industries Inc..........G....... 954 946-0830
Pompano Beach *(G-14673)*
Edmunds Metal Works Inc..........E....... 941 755-4725
Bradenton *(G-1035)*
Electrodes Inc..........G....... 727 698-7498
Seminole *(G-16746)*
▼ **Elite Cnc Machining Inc**..........E....... 727 531-8447
Clearwater *(G-1668)*
Elite Manufacturing US..........G....... 919 757-2732
Fleming Island *(G-3762)*
Elite Manufacturing US LLC..........G....... 904 516-4796
Fleming Island *(G-3763)*
Endoscopy Rplacement Parts Inc..........G....... 352 472-5120
Newberry *(G-11554)*
Enginetics..........F....... 305 695-8000
Fernandina Beach *(G-3737)*
Entech Onsite Services LLC..........G....... 407 956-8980
Rockledge *(G-15409)*
Es Machine Shop..........G....... 850 968-9300
Cantonment *(G-1339)*
Esther Wilson Enterprises LLC..........G....... 904 634-7463
Jacksonville *(G-6370)*
Euro Gear (usa) Inc..........E....... 518 578-1775
Miami *(G-9539)*
Everglades Machine Inc..........G....... 863 983-0133
Clewiston *(G-1979)*
Excell Solutions LLC..........G....... 407 615-9330
Lakeland *(G-7683)*
Express Tools Inc..........G....... 954 663-4333
Davie *(G-2522)*
F C Machine Corporation..........G....... 407 673-9601
Winter Park *(G-19406)*
F K Instrument Co Inc..........D....... 727 461-6060
Clearwater *(G-1679)*
Fabrication Florida Venture..........G....... 954 388-5014
Fort Lauderdale *(G-3985)*
◆ **Farmer Mold and Mch Works Inc**..........E....... 727 522-0515
Saint Petersburg *(G-15776)*
First Coast Fabrication Inc..........G....... 904 849-7426
Yulee *(G-19496)*
Flc Machines Inc..........E....... 352 728-2303
Leesburg *(G-8157)*
Flex TEC Coating Services LLC..........G....... 813 481-8354
Zephyrhills *(G-19519)*
Florida Engine Rebuilders Corp..........G....... 305 232-8784
Miami *(G-9582)*
Florida Mch Works Ltd Partnr..........F....... 904 225-2090
Yulee *(G-19497)*
Florida Metal-Craft Inc..........F....... 407 656-1100
Winter Garden *(G-19264)*
Florida Metallizing Svc Inc..........E....... 863 425-1143
Mulberry *(G-11124)*
Florida Precision Mch Met Work..........G....... 813 486-5050
Tampa *(G-17686)*
Fort Walton Machining Inc..........E....... 800 223-0881
Fort Walton Beach *(G-4801)*
Fort Walton Machining Inc..........C....... 850 244-9095
Fort Walton Beach *(G-4802)*
G & S Machine Shop Corp..........G....... 305 863-7866
Medley *(G-8654)*
Gam Swiss Turning Inc..........G....... 954 428-6785
Deerfield Beach *(G-2829)*
General Fine Machine Co Inc..........G....... 727 726-5956
Safety Harbor *(G-15494)*
General Machine Company Inc..........G....... 941 756-2815
Sarasota *(G-16447)*
▼ **General Machine Shop**..........G....... 305 558-2409
Miami Lakes *(G-10794)*
◆ **Globe Trailers Florida Inc**..........E....... 941 753-6425
Bradenton *(G-1049)*
GMF Industries Inc..........D....... 863 646-5081
Lakeland *(G-7700)*
Godwin and Singer Inc..........G....... 727 896-8631
Saint Petersburg *(G-15795)*
Gondia Machine Shop Inc..........G....... 305 763-7494
Medley *(G-8660)*
Green Machine..........G....... 772 475-6832
Fort Pierce *(G-4704)*
Grind It LLC..........G....... 813 310-9710
Lutz *(G-8386)*
▲ **Grinder Wear Parts Inc**..........E....... 503 982-0881
Largo *(G-7966)*
Group E Holdings Inc..........D....... 321 724-0127
Palm Bay *(G-13515)*
Group Heros Inc..........G....... 305 635-0219
Miami *(G-9675)*
Gt Machining..........G....... 941 809-5735
Sarasota *(G-16225)*
Gulfport Grind Inc..........G....... 727 343-2785
Gulfport *(G-5135)*
Gull Tool & Machine Inc..........G....... 727 527-0808
Saint Petersburg *(G-15800)*
Gunns Welding & Fabricating..........G....... 727 393-5238
Saint Petersburg *(G-15801)*
H&S Swanson Fmly Holdings Inc..........D....... 727 541-3575
Pinellas Park *(G-14352)*
▲ **Hammer Haag Steel Inc**..........C....... 727 216-6903
Clearwater *(G-1710)*
Harbor Machine Inc..........G....... 727 772-9515
Palm Harbor *(G-13739)*
Harder Prcision Components Inc..........E....... 727 442-4212
Clearwater *(G-1711)*
Henderson Machine Inc..........G....... 954 419-9789
Deerfield Beach *(G-2837)*

Hollywood Machine Shop Inc ....G....... 954 893-6103
Hollywood *(G-5844)*
Holmes Tool & Engineering Inc ....E....... 850 547-4417
Bonifay *(G-804)*
Inclan Machine Shop ....G....... 305 846-9675
Miami *(G-9737)*
Indian River All-Fab Inc ....G....... 772 778-0032
Vero Beach *(G-18629)*
Industrial & Marine Maint ....G....... 813 622-8338
Tampa *(G-17779)*
Industrial Marine Inc ....F....... 904 781-4707
Jacksonville *(G-6493)*
Industrial Oviedo LLC ....G....... 786 350-8153
Miami Beach *(G-10682)*
Innovative Machine Inc ....F....... 386 418-8880
Gainesville *(G-4942)*
Integrated Design & Develop ....G....... 407 268-4300
Sanford *(G-16068)*
Integritrust Solutions LLC ....G....... 850 685-9801
Navarre *(G-11466)*
Intrepid Machine Inc ....E....... 352 540-9919
Brooksville *(G-1238)*
Intrepid Machine Inc ....G....... 813 854-3825
Tampa *(G-17792)*
J L M Machine Co Inc ....F....... 941 748-4288
Bradenton *(G-1064)*
J M Milling Inc ....G....... 386 546-6826
East Palatka *(G-3603)*
Jacore Technologies ....F....... 813 860-7465
Odessa *(G-12129)*
Jakobsen Tool Co Inc ....G....... 727 447-1143
Clearwater *(G-1740)*
James Caldwell Stump Grinding ....G....... 813 843-1262
Plant City *(G-14439)*
Jamison Industries Inc ....F....... 813 886-4888
Tampa *(G-17803)*
◆ **JC Industrial Mfg Corp** ....E....... 305 634-5280
Miami *(G-9789)*
JC Machine Inc ....F....... 863 644-2815
Lakeland *(G-7721)*
▲ **JC Machine Works Corp** ....E....... 305 634-5280
Miami *(G-9790)*
JC Marine Service Fabrica ....G....... 954 913-8185
Hollywood *(G-5852)*
JD Tools LLC ....F....... 407 767-5175
Longwood *(G-8295)*
Jet Helseth Manufacturing Inc ....E....... 407 324-9001
Deland *(G-2989)*
Jim Appleys Tru-ARC Inc ....F....... 727 571-3007
Clearwater *(G-1743)*
Jmg Tool LLC ....G....... 805 532-1631
Loxahatchee *(G-8360)*
JW Appley and Son Inc ....E....... 727 572-4910
Clearwater *(G-1747)*
K & K Precision Manufacturing ....G....... 850 769-9080
Panama City *(G-13923)*
K J C O Inc ....G....... 954 401-4299
Titusville *(G-18436)*
Karob Manufacturing Inc ....E....... 352 732-2414
Ocala *(G-11974)*
Karry Industries Inc ....G....... 904 398-4007
Jacksonville *(G-6533)*
Kens Stump Grinding LLC ....G....... 407 948-5031
Orlando *(G-12870)*
Kevins Machine & Engrg LLC ....G....... 850 519-6516
Crawfordville *(G-2334)*
Kinetic Industries LLC ....G....... 727 572-7604
Clearwater *(G-1750)*
Kinship Precision LLC ....F....... 321 765-3531
Melbourne *(G-8859)*
Kn Machine & Tools Inc ....F....... 561 748-3035
Jupiter *(G-7065)*
Koral Manufacturing Inc ....G....... 727 548-5040
Pinellas Park *(G-14360)*
Koral Precision LLC ....F....... 727 548-5040
Pinellas Park *(G-14361)*
Kw Products Inc ....F....... 813 855-7817
Oldsmar *(G-12242)*
La Zero Inc ....G....... 727 545-1175
Pinellas Park *(G-14363)*
Lake Park Auto Machine Inc ....G....... 561 848-6197
West Palm Beach *(G-18924)*
Larson-Burton Incorporated ....F....... 815 637-9500
Daytona Beach *(G-2680)*
Laserstar Technologies Corp ....G....... 401 438-1500
Orlando *(G-12895)*
◆ **Lawrence Factor Inc** ....E....... 305 430-9152
Miami Lakes *(G-10805)*
Liddys Machine Shop Inc ....E....... 904 354-0134
Jacksonville *(G-6556)*
Lisa Mc Call ....F....... 850 265-4241
Panama City *(G-13926)*
LMS Manufacturing LLC ....F....... 850 526-0121
Marianna *(G-8580)*
Lyons Machine Tool Co Inc ....E....... 904 797-1550
Saint Augustine *(G-15566)*
M W M Services Inc ....F....... 561 844-0955
Riviera Beach *(G-15345)*
M Z Machine Inc ....G....... 561 744-2791
Jupiter *(G-7069)*
Macgyver Machine Services Inc ....G....... 352 455-0413
Hollywood *(G-5867)*
Machine Engineers Inc ....F....... 904 353-8289
Jacksonville *(G-6571)*
Machine Shop ....G....... 786 991-6959
Orlando *(G-12944)*
Machine Technology Inc ....G....... 863 298-8001
Sebring *(G-16699)*
Machine Tool Masters Inc ....F....... 850 432-2829
Pensacola *(G-14199)*
Machine Top LLC ....F....... 786 238-8926
Dania *(G-2450)*
Madson Inc ....F....... 305 863-7390
Medley *(G-8681)*
Magnolia Machine Company ....E....... 863 965-8201
Auburndale *(G-248)*
Magnus Hitech Industries Inc ....E....... 321 724-9731
Melbourne *(G-8882)*
Majestic Machine & Engrg Inc ....F....... 904 257-9115
Jacksonville *(G-6576)*
Manatee Tool Inc ....G....... 941 355-9252
Sarasota *(G-16252)*
Mandala Tool Company Inc ....G....... 305 652-4575
Miami *(G-9941)*
Marden Industries Inc ....F....... 863 682-7882
Punta Gorda *(G-15213)*
Marion Precision Tool Inc ....F....... 352 867-0080
Ocala *(G-11993)*
Maritech Machine Inc ....E....... 850 872-0852
Panama City *(G-13928)*
▼ **Master Machine & Tool Co II** ....F....... 863 425-4902
Mulberry *(G-11129)*
Matawan Tool & Mfg Co Inc ....G....... 772 221-3706
Palm City *(G-13666)*
Matrix Machining & Mfg LLC ....F....... 908 355-1900
Clearwater *(G-1777)*
Mediscope Manufacturing Inc ....F....... 954 975-9997
Pompano Beach *(G-14757)*
Medley Machine Shop Inc ....F....... 305 884-3200
Medley *(G-8687)*
Mercury Machining Co Inc ....E....... 850 433-5017
Pensacola *(G-14206)*
◆ **Merit Fastener Corporation** ....E....... 407 331-4815
Longwood *(G-8311)*
Merit Fastener Corporation ....G....... 813 626-3748
Tampa *(G-17903)*
Merit Screw ....G....... 352 344-3744
Hernando *(G-5246)*
▼ **Metal Essence Inc** ....G....... 407 478-8480
Longwood *(G-8312)*
Metal Technologies Group Inc ....G....... 904 429-7727
Saint Augustine *(G-15569)*
▼ **Metalmaster Machine Shop Inc** ....F....... 407 423-9049
Orlando *(G-12963)*
Michigan Pmps Elc Mtrs Repr Co ....G....... 407 841-6800
Orlando *(G-12967)*
Micro Tool Engineering Inc ....F....... 561 842-7381
Riviera Beach *(G-15348)*
Microflex Inc ....E....... 386 672-1945
Ormond Beach *(G-13386)*
Mictron Inc ....E....... 941 371-6564
Sarasota *(G-16507)*
Mid-State Machine & Fabg Corp ....B....... 863 665-6233
Lakeland *(G-7751)*
Mikes Precision Inc ....G....... 305 558-6421
Hialeah *(G-5517)*
Mikes Trck Prts Mch Sp Plus I ....G....... 786 534-9608
Miami *(G-10019)*
Mil-Tec Incorporated ....E....... 239 369-2880
Lehigh Acres *(G-8199)*
◆ **Milans Machine Shop & Wldg Svc** ....E....... 305 592-2447
Doral *(G-3438)*
Mkm Sarasota LLC ....E....... 941 358-0383
Sarasota *(G-16511)*
Morey Machining & Mfg Inc ....E....... 239 693-8699
Fort Myers *(G-4537)*
Motion Machining LLC ....G....... 321 693-0999
Melbourne *(G-8891)*
Motor Service Group LLC ....G....... 305 592-2440
Miami *(G-10044)*
Motor Service Inc ....G....... 305 592-2440
Miami *(G-10045)*
Mr Bones Stump Grinding ....G....... 941 927-0790
Sarasota *(G-16515)*
MSP Industries LLC ....C....... 727 443-5764
Clearwater *(G-1795)*
Mte Inc ....G....... 352 371-3898
Gainesville *(G-4967)*
Narramore Machine Shop LLC ....F....... 863 667-1004
Lakeland *(G-7756)*
National Cylinder Head Exchang ....G....... 813 870-6340
Tampa *(G-17930)*
Nelson Mch Sp Wldg & Engrg Inc ....G....... 305 710-5029
Opa Locka *(G-12345)*
New Technology Precision Machi ....F....... 561 624-3830
Jupiter *(G-7080)*
Newmans Truck Body and Eqp Inc ....F....... 904 695-9589
Jacksonville *(G-6632)*
◆ **Nida-Core Corporation** ....E....... 772 343-7300
Port Saint Lucie *(G-15124)*
Nores Precision Inc ....E....... 954 420-0025
Deerfield Beach *(G-2879)*
Norman Engineering Corporation ....G....... 407 425-6433
Orlando *(G-13007)*
North Coast Machining Inc ....G....... 954 942-6943
Lighthouse Point *(G-8210)*
Novak Machining Inc ....G....... 727 527-5473
Pinellas Park *(G-14372)*
Nunez Machine Shop Inc ....F....... 786 615-4261
Miami Lakes *(G-10831)*
Oai Enterprises LLC ....F....... 239 225-1350
Fort Myers *(G-4553)*
Ofab Inc ....D....... 352 629-0040
Ocala *(G-12019)*
▲ **Orange Park Machine Inc** ....E....... 904 269-1935
Orange Park *(G-12401)*
P & A Welding and Machine Inc ....G....... 863 425-3198
Mulberry *(G-11132)*
P D I S Inc ....F....... 561 243-8442
Delray Beach *(G-3112)*
P&A Machine ....F....... 407 275-5770
Orlando *(G-13042)*
P&L Machine & Tool Company Inc ....G....... 727 863-0847
Hudson *(G-6035)*
Pace Machine Tool Inc ....E....... 248 960-9903
Port Charlotte *(G-14992)*
Paj Innovative Concepts Inc ....E....... 813 659-0505
Plant City *(G-14451)*
Park Central Inc ....E....... 850 547-1660
Bonifay *(G-805)*
Parker Machinery Co Inc ....G....... 904 356-5038
Jacksonville *(G-6657)*
Parts Central Inc ....F....... 850 547-1660
Bonifay *(G-806)*
Peerless Instrument Co Inc ....E....... 954 921-6006
Hollywood *(G-5888)*
Performance Machining Svcs Inc ....F....... 850 469-9106
Pensacola *(G-14229)*
Performance Sales & Service ....G....... 863 465-2814
Lake Placid *(G-7493)*
Pompano Precision Products Inc ....E....... 954 946-6059
Pompano Beach *(G-14805)*
Powder Systems Inc ....G....... 352 680-3558
Ocala *(G-12030)*
Praesto Enterprises LLC ....G....... 407 298-9171
Orlando *(G-13077)*
Pratt Cnc ....G....... 321 482-9494
Titusville *(G-18452)*
Pre-Tech Inc ....G....... 863 422-5079
Haines City *(G-5146)*
Precise Technologies Inc ....F....... 727 535-5594
Largo *(G-8030)*
Precision Ers ....E....... 813 257-0900
Tampa *(G-18006)*
Precision Machine Tech LLC ....F....... 305 594-1789
Doral *(G-3467)*
Precision Qulty Machining Inc ....G....... 407 831-7240
Casselberry *(G-1515)*
Precision Shapes Inc ....E....... 321 269-2555
Titusville *(G-18453)*
Precision Tech Machining LLC ....G....... 321 693-3469
Melbourne *(G-8910)*
Precision Tl Engrg of Gnsville ....F....... 352 376-2533
Gainesville *(G-4982)*
▲ **Premier Die Casting Company** ....D....... 732 634-3000
Coral Gables *(G-2185)*
Princeton Tool South LLC ....F....... 813 600-8143
Tampa *(G-18012)*
Pro Machine Inc ....G....... 407 296-5031
Orlando *(G-13093)*

S I C

Production Metal Stampings ....F 850 981-8240
Milton *(G-10938)*
Proto Plus Inc ....G 561 471-5325
West Palm Beach *(G-19008)*
Puch Manufacturing Corporation ....E 407 650-9926
Orlando *(G-13099)*
▲ **Qem Inc** ....E 727 545-8833
Largo *(G-8033)*
Qgistix Inc ....G 855 573-3872
Boynton Beach *(G-949)*
Qtm Inc ....E 813 891-1300
Oldsmar *(G-12266)*
Quality Components & Assembly ....G 954 792-5151
Fort Lauderdale *(G-4190)*
Quality Machine Service Inc ....G 610 554-3917
Port Charlotte *(G-14995)*
Quality Wood Machine Inc ....G 305 221-0218
Miami *(G-10218)*
Quik Tek Inc ....G 772 501-3471
Vero Beach *(G-18657)*
R & D Machine and Engrg Inc ....E 813 891-9109
Oldsmar *(G-12267)*
R and R Machine Shop ....F 941 621-8143
Punta Gorda *(G-15225)*
Race Performance Machine Shop ....G 813 443-8225
Tampa *(G-18037)*
Rafferty Holdings LLC ....E 352 248-0906
Gainesville *(G-4989)*
Ramac Inc ....G 813 962-2793
Tampa *(G-18038)*
Ramstar Corporation ....G 561 499-8488
Delray Beach *(G-3132)*
Raptor Wear Products USA Inc ....F 786 972-0326
Miami *(G-10240)*
Ray Machine Inc ....F 850 784-1116
Panama City *(G-13943)*
Ready Machine Corp ....G 850 479-1722
Pensacola *(G-14250)*
Real Fleet Solutions LLC ....E 321 631-2414
Cocoa *(G-2046)*
Reliable Tool and Machine Inc ....G 561 844-8848
Riviera Beach *(G-15370)*
Renick Enterprises Inc ....G 561 863-4183
Riviera Beach *(G-15371)*
▲ **Renzetti Inc** ....F 321 267-7705
Titusville *(G-18456)*
Responsive Machining Inc ....F 321 225-4011
Titusville *(G-18457)*
Revtech ....F 727 369-1750
Saint Petersburg *(G-15902)*
Rfg Consulting Services Inc ....G 786 498-2177
Miami *(G-10261)*
Riegl Usa Inc ....E 407 248-9927
Winter Garden *(G-19283)*
Riva Industries Inc ....G 813 573-1601
Clearwater *(G-1861)*
Riw of Jacksonville Inc ....F 904 356-5635
Jacksonville *(G-6730)*
Roan Manufacturing Inc ....G 813 510-4929
Odessa *(G-12146)*
▲ **Rodriguez Welding** ....G 305 856-3749
Miami *(G-10275)*
Rowe Manufacturing LLC ....F 407 324-5757
Sanford *(G-16111)*
Rubingers Manufacturing Co ....F 863 665-1599
Lakeland *(G-7782)*
Ryder Welding Service Inc ....F 305 685-6630
Opa Locka *(G-12357)*
S & K Prfmce Machining & Fab ....G 954 306-2214
Plantation *(G-14547)*
S and S Morris LLC ....F 404 431-7803
Sarasota *(G-16567)*
S J Turbine LLC ....G 954 804-4779
Weston *(G-19165)*
Samson Metal and Machine Inc ....E 863 665-0283
Lakeland *(G-7785)*
Sanchez Machine Shop LLC ....G 863 494-1212
Arcadia *(G-204)*
Santa Rosa Auto Parts Inc ....E 850 477-7747
Pensacola *(G-14257)*
Sasco Machining Inc ....F 561 746-8233
Jupiter *(G-7108)*
Savvy Associate Inc ....F 954 941-6986
Pompano Beach *(G-14840)*
◆ **Schur & Company LLC** ....D 904 353-8075
Jacksonville *(G-6754)*
Seaboard Manufacturing LLC ....G 727 497-3572
Clearwater *(G-1872)*
Select Machinery Inc ....G 941 960-1970
Sarasota *(G-16591)*
Selectwo Machine Company Inc ....G 407 788-3102
Longwood *(G-8334)*
Servo Tech Inc ....G 727 573-7998
Clearwater *(G-1875)*
Setty Enterprises Inc ....F 561 844-3711
West Palm Beach *(G-19028)*
Shores Automotive ....G 561 391-0260
Boca Raton *(G-709)*
Sidus Space Inc ....E 321 613-0615
Cape Canaveral *(G-1367)*
Simplex Manufacturing Inc ....E 941 378-8700
Sarasota *(G-16598)*
Sio Cnc Machining Inc ....G 727 533-8271
Clearwater *(G-1878)*
Sizemore Welding Inc ....E 386 437-4073
Bunnell *(G-1306)*
Sjg Machine Inc ....G 352 345-3656
Brooksville *(G-1271)*
Skyline Attractions LLC ....F 407 587-0080
Orlando *(G-13197)*
Sleuth Inc ....E 941 745-9903
Bradenton *(G-1114)*
SMI Tool & Die Inc ....G 321 632-6200
Cocoa *(G-2051)*
Sohacki Industries Inc ....E 904 826-0130
Saint Augustine *(G-15613)*
Southern Fiberglass Inc ....F 904 387-2246
Jacksonville *(G-6794)*
Southern Machine Tool & Rbldrs ....F 941 749-0988
Bradenton *(G-1117)*
Southern Manufacturing Inc ....F 305 267-1943
Miami *(G-10388)*
Southern Mfg Tech Inc ....D 954 953-9537
Tampa *(G-18120)*
Southridge Outdoor Storage ....G 352 516-5598
Tavares *(G-18353)*
Space Coast Hydraulics Inc ....F 321 504-6006
Rockledge *(G-15449)*
Space Manufacturing Inc ....F 727 532-9466
Clearwater *(G-1884)*
Special Tool Solutions Inc ....E 904 356-5671
Jacksonville *(G-6803)*
Speed Machine Shop Corp ....G 305 233-3299
Cutler Bay *(G-2414)*
Squared Machine & Tool Inc A ....F 678 988-2477
Gulf Breeze *(G-5127)*
Suinpla LLC ....F 786 747-4829
Medley *(G-8732)*
Sulzer Ems Inc ....E 407 858-9447
Orlando *(G-13220)*
Sun Power Diesel Inc ....G 954 522-4775
Fort Lauderdale *(G-4264)*
Sunshine Filters of Pinellas ....E 727 530-3884
Largo *(G-8064)*
Sunshine Tool LLC ....G 941 351-6330
Sarasota *(G-16306)*
Swiss Components Inc ....F 321 723-6729
Melbourne *(G-8953)*
Sy-Klone Company LLC ....E 904 448-6563
Jacksonville *(G-6832)*
System 48 Plus Inc ....G 561 844-5305
West Palm Beach *(G-19055)*
T M Tooling Inc ....E 561 712-0903
West Palm Beach *(G-19056)*
Tallahassee Welding & Mch Sp ....E 850 576-9596
Tallahassee *(G-17337)*
Talon Innovations FL Corp ....E 320 251-0390
Tampa *(G-18154)*
Tampa Bay Machining Inc ....E 813 855-8456
Tampa *(G-18158)*
▲ **Tampa Brass and Aluminum Corp** ....C 813 885-6064
Tampa *(G-18162)*
Tampa Machine Products Inc ....E 813 854-3332
Oldsmar *(G-12270)*
Tampatechnik Corporation ....G 727 823-8889
Saint Petersburg *(G-15935)*
Tavtek LLC ....G 904 907-7749
Saint Johns *(G-15681)*
Tavtek LLC ....G 904 907-7749
Saint Johns *(G-15682)*
Technical Components Inc ....G 863 646-3253
Lakeland *(G-7819)*
Techshop Int ....G 713 589-3559
Medley *(G-8734)*
Tectron ....F 904 355-5512
Jacksonville *(G-6844)*
Teknocraft Inc ....E 321 729-9634
Melbourne *(G-8959)*
Tep Manufacturing Co ....G 321 632-1417
Rockledge *(G-15453)*
Tera Industries Inc ....E 561 848-7272
Riviera Beach *(G-15384)*
Thompson Repairs Inc ....G 904 384-5175
Jacksonville *(G-6850)*
Titan Metalworks Inc ....G 904 503-2941
Jacksonville *(G-6858)*
Topline Machine & Tool LLC ....G 352 799-4668
Brooksville *(G-1282)*
Tpr Systems Inc ....F 850 983-8600
Milton *(G-10944)*
Transport PC USA Inc ....G 813 264-1700
Wesley Chapel *(G-18760)*
Treasure Coast Machines Inc ....F 772 283-2024
Stuart *(G-17037)*
Triad Edm Inc ....G 352 489-5336
Dunnellon *(G-3601)*
Troy Thompson Inc ....G 813 716-1598
Brooksville *(G-1283)*
Trurev LLC ....G 800 397-3388
Davie *(G-2608)*
▲ **Ttc-The Trading Company Inc** ....E 503 982-0880
Largo *(G-8069)*
▼ **Tuckers Machine & Stl Svc Inc** ....D 352 787-3157
Leesburg *(G-8179)*
Turbine Parts Repair Inc ....G 850 983-8600
Milton *(G-10945)*
Turbo Parts LLC ....F 352 351-4510
Ocala *(G-12064)*
Turner Machine & Supply Co ....G 772 464-4550
Fort Pierce *(G-4762)*
Tws Fabricators ....F 954 983-9749
Pembroke Pines *(G-14067)*
Tyco Machine Inc ....G 352 544-0210
Brooksville *(G-1284)*
U D T Inc ....G 850 784-0537
Panama City *(G-13958)*
Ultimate Machining Corporation ....G 954 749-9810
Sunrise *(G-17192)*
Ultimate Tool Inc ....F 954 489-9996
Oakland Park *(G-11853)*
Ultra Prcsion McHning Grnding ....F 321 725-9655
Palm Bay *(G-13545)*
◆ **Unaflex LLC** ....E 954 943-5002
Pompano Beach *(G-14898)*
Unitron Prcision Machining Inc ....F 407 299-4180
Apopka *(G-193)*
US Precision Manufacturing Inc ....E 954 332-2921
Deerfield Beach *(G-2932)*
▼ **Van Linda Iron Works Inc** ....E 561 586-8400
Lake Worth Beach *(G-7622)*
Van-Ess Manufacturing Inc ....G 352 799-1015
Brooksville *(G-1287)*
Velocity Machine Works LLC ....F 850 727-5066
Tallahassee *(G-17343)*
Verde Speed Machine Shop Corp ....G 305 233-3299
Cutler Bay *(G-2419)*
◆ **Vertical Reality Inc** ....G 305 238-4522
Palmetto Bay *(G-13856)*
▲ **Vertical Reality Mfg Inc** ....G 305 238-4522
Palmetto Bay *(G-13857)*
Vine and Grind LLC ....G 727 420-3122
Treasure Island *(G-18479)*
Water Technology of Pensacola ....E 850 477-4789
Pensacola *(G-14286)*
Watson Steel Products ....G 716 853-2233
Miami *(G-10597)*
Weber Mfg & Supplies Inc ....F 941 488-5185
North Venice *(G-11764)*
West Coast Wonderworks LLC ....G 407 351-8800
Orlando *(G-13321)*
West Florida Precision Mch LLC ....F 727 939-0030
Tarpon Springs *(G-18331)*
West Palm Machining & Welding ....G 561 841-2725
Riviera Beach *(G-15389)*
Willett Precision Machining ....F 727 573-9299
Clearwater *(G-1940)*
Wilson Machine & Welding Works ....G 904 829-3737
Saint Augustine *(G-15637)*
Wilsons Machine Products Inc ....E 407 644-2020
Winter Park *(G-19458)*
Wood Machine Corp ....G 407 851-8714
Orlando *(G-13330)*
World Class Machining Inc ....F 386 437-7036
Bunnell *(G-1311)*
Xpress Precision Products Inc ....G 305 685-2127
Hialeah *(G-5691)*
Y&D Machine Shop Inc ....F 786 717-6356
Hialeah *(G-5692)*
Yam Machine Shop and Iron Work ....G 786 246-4174
Miami *(G-10624)*

36 ELECTRONIC AND OTHER ELECTRICAL EQUIPMENT AND COMPONENTS, EXCEPT COMPUTER

3612 Power, Distribution & Specialty Transformers

ABB Inc...D... 407 732-2000
Lake Mary *(G-7396)*
ABB Inc...D... 305 471-0844
Miami *(G-9053)*
ABB Partners LLC...F... 917 843-4430
Palm Beach *(G-13547)*
Arteche USA Inc...F... 954 438-9499
Miramar *(G-10968)*
Backbone Interconnect LLC...E... 954 800-4749
Sunrise *(G-17093)*
▲ **Bright Manufacturing LLC**...G... 954 603-4950
Fort Lauderdale *(G-3868)*
◆ **Central Turbos Corp**...F... 305 406-3933
Doral *(G-3296)*
Control Solutions Inc...F... 813 247-2136
Tampa *(G-17553)*
▲ **Digitrax Inc**...E... 850 872-9890
Panama City *(G-13893)*
Discrete Electronics Inc...G... 941 575-8700
Punta Gorda *(G-15204)*
Edisonecoenergycom Corporation...G... 954 417-5326
Fort Lauderdale *(G-3964)*
Evolution Intrcnnect Systems I...F... 954 217-6223
Davie *(G-2521)*
Exxelia Usa Inc...E... 407 695-6562
Longwood *(G-8279)*
◆ **Florida Transformer Inc**...C... 850 892-2711
Defuniak Springs *(G-2942)*
Gfsf Inc...G... 727 478-7284
Odessa *(G-12123)*
▲ **Hatch Transformers Inc**...E... 813 288-8006
Tampa *(G-17746)*
▲ **Hytronics Corp**...D... 727 535-0413
Clearwater *(G-1725)*
Inductive Technologies Inc...F... 727 536-7861
Clearwater *(G-1731)*
▲ **Instrument Transformers LLC**...B... 727 461-9413
Clearwater *(G-1732)*
Lextm3 Systems LLC...F... 954 888-1024
Davie *(G-2546)*
Magnatronix Corporation Inc...F... 727 536-7861
Clearwater *(G-1770)*
◆ **Manutech Assembly Inc**...G... 305 888-2800
Miami *(G-9942)*
◆ **Miami Transformers Corp**...E... 305 257-1491
Homestead *(G-5983)*
▲ **Neubert Aero Corp**...G... 352 345-4828
Brooksville *(G-1256)*
Nwl Inc...D... 800 742-5695
Lake Hamilton *(G-7391)*
Nwl Inc...C... 561 848-9009
Riviera Beach *(G-15353)*
OHM Americas LLC...F... 800 467-7275
Fort Lauderdale *(G-4148)*
▲ **Payton America Inc**...F... 954 428-3326
Deerfield Beach *(G-2884)*
Power Quality Intl LLC...G... 727 478-7284
Odessa *(G-12141)*
Powerficient LLC...E... 800 320-2535
Fort Lauderdale *(G-4172)*
▲ **Robertson Transformer Co**...E... 708 388-2315
Sarasota *(G-16560)*
▲ **Solucnes Elctrcas Intgrles LLC**...G... 305 804-4201
Miami *(G-10373)*
▲ **Spin Magnetics**...E... 863 676-9333
Lake Wales *(G-7520)*
Sunbelt Transformer Ltd...G... 305 517-3657
Pompano Beach *(G-14878)*
▲ **Technipower LLC**...F... 954 346-2442
Coral Springs *(G-2321)*
Universal Microwave Corp...D... 352 754-2200
Brooksville *(G-1286)*
◆ **Ventex Technology Inc**...F... 561 354-6300
Jupiter *(G-7139)*
▲ **Wired Rite Systems Inc**...F... 707 838-1122
Sarasota *(G-16643)*

3613 Switchgear & Switchboard Apparatus

ABB Enterprise Software Inc...C... 954 752-6700
Coral Springs *(G-2211)*
ABB Inc...D... 407 732-2000
Lake Mary *(G-7396)*
ABB Inc...D... 305 471-0844
Miami *(G-9053)*
▲ **America Energy Inc**...G... 954 762-7763
Pembroke Pines *(G-14020)*
B & J Atlantic Inc...E... 904 338-0088
Jacksonville *(G-6185)*
▼ **Champion Controls Inc**...E... 954 318-3090
Fort Lauderdale *(G-3895)*
Consumer Engineering Inc...F... 321 984-8550
Palm Bay *(G-13507)*
Control Solutions Inc...F... 813 247-2136
Tampa *(G-17553)*
Custom Control Solutions Inc...G... 850 937-8902
Cantonment *(G-1338)*
Electrical Controls Inc...F... 954 801-6846
Tamarac *(G-17355)*
Entech Controls Corp...G... 954 613-2971
Miami *(G-9528)*
Evolution Intrcnnect Systems I...F... 954 217-6223
Davie *(G-2521)*
◆ **Ff Systems Inc**...G... 239 288-4255
Fort Myers *(G-4449)*
Gas Turbine Efficiency LLC...E... 407 304-5200
Orlando *(G-12772)*
Hallmark Nameplate Inc...D... 352 383-8142
Mount Dora *(G-11103)*
Hughes Corporation...F... 954 755-7111
Coral Springs *(G-2256)*
▲ **J B Nottingham & Co Inc**...E... 386 873-2990
Deland *(G-2986)*
Jimenez Enterprises Group...E... 561 542-7709
Doral *(G-3403)*
▼ **Kemco Industries LLC**...D... 407 322-1230
Sanford *(G-16077)*
Lextm3 Systems LLC...F... 954 888-1024
Davie *(G-2546)*
◆ **Miami Switchgear Company**...G... 786 336-5783
Miami *(G-10013)*
Motor Protection Electronics...F... 407 299-3825
Apopka *(G-163)*
▲ **National Std Parts Assoc Inc**...D... 850 456-5771
Pensacola *(G-14211)*
Paneltronics Incorporated...D... 305 823-9777
Hialeah *(G-5554)*
Power Grid Pros Inc...G... 716 378-1419
Weston *(G-19160)*
Powerficient LLC...E... 800 320-2535
Fort Lauderdale *(G-4172)*
Quality Building Controls Inc...E... 813 885-5005
Tampa *(G-18030)*
Rapid Switch Systems LLC...G... 941 720-7380
Bradenton *(G-1103)*
Ring Power Corporation...E... 904 354-1858
Jacksonville *(G-6725)*
Siemens Industry Inc...D... 954 436-8848
Pembroke Pines *(G-14059)*
Southwire Company LLC...E... 727 535-0572
Largo *(G-8059)*
Techno-Solis Inc...F... 727 823-6766
Saint Petersburg *(G-15937)*
◆ **Technology Research LLC**...D... 727 535-0572
Clearwater *(G-1912)*
▲ **TESS LLC**...F... 954 583-6262
Fort Lauderdale *(G-4278)*
◆ **Ultrapanel Marine Inc**...E... 772 285-4258
Miami *(G-10527)*

3621 Motors & Generators

360 Energy Solutions LLC...E... 786 348-2156
Miami *(G-9025)*
AB Electric Motors & Pumps...E... 954 322-6900
Hollywood *(G-5764)*
▼ **Acme Service Corp**...F... 305 836-4800
Miami *(G-9065)*
Adtec Productions Incorporated...G... 904 720-2003
Jacksonville *(G-6120)*
◆ **Advanced Manufacturing Inc**...E... 727 573-3300
Saint Petersburg *(G-15691)*
◆ **Advanced Mfg & Pwr Systems Inc**...E... 386 822-5565
Deland *(G-2953)*
All Power Pro Inc...G... 904 310-3069
Fernandina Beach *(G-3730)*
American Generator Svcs LLC...F... 954 965-1210
Davie *(G-2496)*
American Traction Systems Inc...E... 239 768-0757
Fort Myers *(G-4358)*
▲ **Amper Usa LLC**...G... 305 717-3101
Doral *(G-3248)*
◆ **Anko Products Inc**...E... 941 748-2307
Bradenton *(G-989)*
◆ **Armstrong Power Systems LLC**...F... 305 470-0058
Miami *(G-9170)*
B & I Generators LLC...G... 407 474-6216
Sanford *(G-16000)*
Bgt Holdings LLC...G... 239 643-9949
Naples *(G-11187)*
▲ **Blue Summit Wind LLC**...G... 561 691-7171
Juno Beach *(G-6975)*
Capacity Inc...E... 855 440-7825
Sarasota *(G-16186)*
Central Fla Remanufacturing...G... 407 299-9011
Orlando *(G-12563)*
Chism Manufacturing Svcs LLC...F... 941 896-9671
Sarasota *(G-16190)*
Discovery Technology Intl Inc...F... 941 907-4444
Lakewood Ranch *(G-7843)*
Emergency Standby Power LLC...F... 850 259-2304
Fort Walton Beach *(G-4799)*
◆ **Fischer Panda Generators Inc**...F... 954 462-2800
Pompano Beach *(G-14694)*
Fischer Panda Generators LLC...E... 954 462-2800
Pompano Beach *(G-14695)*
Fisher Electric Technology Inc...F... 727 345-9122
Saint Petersburg *(G-15780)*
FPL Energy Oklahoma Wind LLC...G... 561 691-7171
Juno Beach *(G-6980)*
◆ **G S Servicore Corp**...E... 305 888-0189
Hialeah *(G-5420)*
GE Aviation Systems LLC...B... 727 531-7781
Clearwater *(G-1699)*
◆ **GE Renewables North Amer LLC**...C... 850 474-4011
Pensacola *(G-14161)*
▼ **Geneforce Incorporated**...G... 786 823-0700
Miami *(G-9622)*
◆ **General Power Limited Inc**...F... 800 763-0359
Doral *(G-3362)*
Generator Supercenter Orlando...G... 407 984-5000
Orlando *(G-12780)*
Genertor Sprcnter Suthwest Fla...G... 608 765-5177
Fort Myers *(G-4468)*
Green Rhino Enrgy Slutions LLC...D... 407 925-5868
Apopka *(G-147)*
Grove Power Inc...G... 305 599-2045
Doral *(G-3375)*
Hts Controls Inc...F... 813 287-5512
Tampa *(G-17766)*
Hydrogen Diesel Prfmce Inc...G... 407 847-6064
Kissimmee *(G-7251)*
▲ **Hytronics Corp**...D... 727 535-0413
Clearwater *(G-1725)*
▲ **Innovative Power Solutions LLC**...E... 732 544-1075
Sarasota *(G-16239)*
◆ **Jat Power LLC**...F... 305 592-0103
Doral *(G-3400)*
▼ **JDM of Miami LLC**...G... 305 253-4650
Miami *(G-9792)*
K&M Power Systems LLC...G... 866 945-9100
Riviera Beach *(G-15337)*
Lithium Battery Company LLC...F... 813 504-0074
Tampa *(G-17850)*
◆ **Marine Exhaust Systems Inc**...D... 561 848-1238
Riviera Beach *(G-15346)*
Maymaan Research LLC...G... 954 374-9376
Hollywood *(G-5873)*
Megawattage LLC...F... 954 328-0232
Fort Lauderdale *(G-4117)*
Miramar Mrmids Synchro Team LL...G... 954 646-6350
Miramar *(G-11017)*
Mobile Power Generators LLC...E... 352 365-2777
Leesburg *(G-8167)*
▲ **Motor Magnetics Inc**...E... 727 873-3180
Saint Petersburg *(G-15861)*
Mtservicer LLC...G... 305 200-1254
Miami Lakes *(G-10824)*
▼ **Multi-Commercial Services Corp**...G... 305 235-1373
Miami *(G-10054)*
Nidec Motor Corporation...C... 954 346-4900
Coral Springs *(G-2297)*
One Stop Generator Shop Inc...G... 561 840-0009
West Palm Beach *(G-18973)*
Peerless Wind Systems...G... 516 249-6900
Boynton Beach *(G-939)*
◆ **Perkins Power Corp**...F... 904 278-9919
Doral *(G-3457)*
Pheasant Run Wind LLC...G... 561 691-7171
Juno Beach *(G-6982)*
Pheasant Run Wind Holdings II...E... 561 691-7171
Juno Beach *(G-6983)*

SIC

▼ **Pinnacle Central Company Inc** ....F 904 354-5746
Jacksonville *(G-6673)*
▲ **Ptse Holding Inc** ....E 800 760-0027
Leesburg *(G-8168)*
▲ **Ray Electric Outboards Inc** ....G 239 574-1948
Cape Coral *(G-1459)*
Resolver Group Inc ....G 941 387-7410
Longboat Key *(G-8246)*
Resolvers LLC ....G 954 254-7948
Deerfield Beach *(G-2904)*
▲ **Robertson Transformer Co** ....E 708 388-2315
Sarasota *(G-16560)*
◆ **Sdmo Generating Sets Inc** ....E 305 863-0012
Miramar *(G-11040)*
Silent Standby Power Sup LLC ....G 954 253-9557
West Palm Beach *(G-19033)*
▼ **Solar Stik Inc** ....E 800 793-4364
Saint Augustine *(G-15614)*
◆ **Southeast Power Group Inc** ....D 305 592-9745
Doral *(G-3507)*
Tampa Armature Works Inc ....C 813 612-2600
Tampa *(G-18157)*
Technet Corp ....G 305 582-5369
Doral *(G-3524)*
◆ **Tradewinds Power Corp** ....D 305 592-9745
Doral *(G-3531)*
Tuscola Wind II LLC ....G 561 691-7171
Juno Beach *(G-6985)*
Universal Generators LLC ....G 954 383-5394
Pompano Beach *(G-14903)*
US Generator Inc ....G 772 778-0131
Sebastian *(G-16675)*
Vasco Winds LLC ....G 561 691-7171
Juno Beach *(G-6986)*
White Oak Energy Backleverage ....E 561 691-7171
Juno Beach *(G-6987)*
White Oak Energy Holdings LLC ....G 561 691-7171
Juno Beach *(G-6988)*
Wilton Wind II LLC ....G 561 691-7171
Juno Beach *(G-6989)*
Winans Electric Motors LLC ....G 863 875-5710
Auburndale *(G-255)*
Windera Power Systems Inc ....G 407 808-1271
Sanford *(G-16140)*

3624 Carbon & Graphite Prdts

Rapid Composites LLC ....G 941 322-6647
Sarasota *(G-16284)*
Steve French Entps Ltd LLC ....G 772 692-0222
Stuart *(G-17022)*

3625 Relays & Indl Controls

ABB Enterprise Software Inc ....C 954 752-6700
Coral Springs *(G-2211)*
ABB Inc ....D 407 732-2000
Lake Mary *(G-7396)*
ABB Inc ....D 305 471-0844
Miami *(G-9053)*
Action Controls Inc ....G 253 243-7703
Aventura *(G-259)*
▲ **Advance Controls Inc** ....F 941 746-3221
Bradenton *(G-983)*
Advance Ctrl Mfg Jean Annette ....G 941 697-0846
Englewood *(G-3657)*
Alttec Corporation ....G 727 547-1622
Clearwater *(G-1578)*
Artful Arnautic Assemblies LLC ....G 727 522-0055
Saint Petersburg *(G-15712)*
Barcode Automation Inc ....F 407 327-2177
Winter Springs *(G-19468)*
Beckwith Electric Co Inc ....G 727 544-2326
Largo *(G-7905)*
CC Control Corp ....E 561 293-3975
West Palm Beach *(G-18836)*
Coast Controls Inc ....F 941 355-7555
Sarasota *(G-16192)*
Custom Controls Technology Inc ....E 305 805-3700
Hialeah *(G-5358)*
▲ **D & L Auto & Marine Supplies** ....G 305 593-0560
Doral *(G-3319)*
Dynalco Controls Corporation ....E 323 589-6181
Fort Lauderdale *(G-3952)*
E G Pump Controls Inc ....E 904 292-0110
Jacksonville *(G-6344)*
Eaton & Wolk ....G 305 249-1640
Miami *(G-9496)*
Eaton Corporation ....G 561 998-4111
Boca Raton *(G-512)*
Eaton Law ....G 813 264-4800
Tampa *(G-17629)*
Electrical Controls Inc ....F 954 801-6846
Tamarac *(G-17355)*
Entech Controls Corp ....G 954 613-2971
Miami *(G-9528)*
◆ **Faac International Inc** ....G 904 448-8952
Rockledge *(G-15411)*
▲ **Facts Engineering LLC** ....E 727 375-8888
Trinity *(G-18485)*
General Scientific Corporation ....G 850 866-9636
Panama City *(G-13908)*
▲ **Hale Products Inc** ....C 352 629-5020
Ocala *(G-11963)*
▲ **Hf Scientific Inc** ....E 888 203-7248
Fort Myers *(G-4481)*
Hts Controls Inc ....F 813 287-5512
Tampa *(G-17766)*
Hymeg Corporation ....G 800 322-1953
Clearwater *(G-1724)*
ICI Custom Parts Inc ....E 813 888-7979
Tampa *(G-17768)*
Industrial Service Solutions ....C 239 288-5230
Fort Myers *(G-4493)*
▲ **Intelligent Heater LLC** ....G 305 248-4971
Homestead *(G-5973)*
◆ **International Specialists Inc** ....G 813 631-8643
Lutz *(G-8392)*
Jenzano Incorporated ....F 386 761-4474
Port Orange *(G-15020)*
▼ **Kemco Industries LLC** ....D 407 322-1230
Sanford *(G-16077)*
Kinematics and Controls Corp ....G 352 796-0300
Brooksville *(G-1243)*
L-3 Cmmnctons Ntronix Holdings ....D 212 697-1111
Melbourne *(G-8863)*
Lextm3 Systems LLC ....F 954 888-1024
Davie *(G-2546)*
Lithium Battery Company LLC ....F 813 504-0074
Tampa *(G-17850)*
▲ **Malema Engineering Corporation** ....F 561 995-0595
Boca Raton *(G-606)*
Marine Engine Controls Inc ....F 727 518-8080
Hudson *(G-6034)*
Metal-Tech Controls Corp ....G 941 575-7677
Punta Gorda *(G-15215)*
Mia Consulting & Trading Inc ....G 305 640-9677
Miami *(G-9989)*
▲ **Micro Control Systems Inc** ....E 239 694-0089
Fort Myers *(G-4532)*
Moog Inc ....G 716 652-2000
Pembroke Pines *(G-14049)*
Motor Protection Electronics ....F 407 299-3825
Apopka *(G-163)*
Nidec Motor Corporation ....C 954 346-4900
Coral Springs *(G-2297)*
Panish Controls ....G 203 333-7371
Largo *(G-8022)*
◆ **Phasetronics Inc** ....C 727 573-1819
Clearwater *(G-1830)*
Pro Co Inc ....G 321 422-0900
Winter Springs *(G-19481)*
Quest Controls Inc ....F 941 729-4799
Palmetto *(G-13820)*
Resa Pwr Slutions Plant Cy LLC ....F 813 752-6550
Plant City *(G-14461)*
RTC Solutions Inc ....G 919 439-8680
Davie *(G-2587)*
▲ **Saminco Inc** ....E 239 561-1561
Fort Myers *(G-4594)*
▼ **Scientific Instruments Inc** ....E 561 881-8500
Mangonia Park *(G-8511)*
▲ **Seatorque Control Systems LLC** ....E 772 220-3020
Stuart *(G-17007)*
▲ **Select Engineered Systems Inc** ....E 305 823-5410
Hialeah *(G-5613)*
Sepac Corp ....F 305 718-3379
Miami *(G-10325)*
◆ **Song-Chuan USA Inc** ....F 954 788-5889
Pompano Beach *(G-14856)*
▼ **Southeastern Marine Power LLC** ....F 727 545-2700
Saint Petersburg *(G-15916)*
Southern Automated Systems ....G 863 815-7444
Lakeland *(G-7799)*
Southern Switch & Contacts ....F 727 789-0951
Palm Harbor *(G-13762)*
STA-Con Incorporated ....E 407 298-5940
Apopka *(G-187)*
Standard Technology Inc ....F 386 671-7406
Ormond Beach *(G-13402)*
Sun Electronic Systems Inc ....F 321 383-9400
Titusville *(G-18466)*
Sun State Systems Inc ....F 904 269-2544
Orange Park *(G-12408)*
T R S ....E 407 298-5490
Orlando *(G-13238)*
Taylor Electronics Inc ....F 941 925-3605
Sarasota *(G-16618)*
Technical Drive Ctrl Svcs Inc ....G 954 471-6521
Davie *(G-2601)*
Technico of Central Florida ....G 321 631-4414
Rockledge *(G-15451)*
Tel-Tron Technologies Corp ....E 386 523-1070
Daytona Beach *(G-2724)*
▲ **Tentech Corporation** ....F 305 938-0389
Miami *(G-10467)*
Tic Light Electrical Corp ....G 305 712-3499
Miami *(G-10476)*
◆ **Ultrapanel Marine Inc** ....E 772 285-4258
Miami *(G-10527)*
Universal Precision Inds Inc ....G 727 581-7097
Largo *(G-8071)*
Wolff Controls Corporation ....F 863 324-0423
Winter Haven *(G-19368)*

3629 Electrical Indl Apparatus, NEC

Air Temp of America Inc ....G 850 340-3017
Panama City *(G-13861)*
American Payment Systems ....F 407 856-8524
Orlando *(G-12472)*
▲ **Apollo Energy Systems Inc** ....G 954 969-7755
Pompano Beach *(G-14595)*
Axis Group ....F 954 580-6000
Pompano Beach *(G-14608)*
Burlakoff Manufacturing Co ....G 972 889-2502
Ocala *(G-11891)*
Chenega Manufacturing Svcs LLC ....E 850 763-6013
Panama City *(G-13880)*
Coastland Specialties LLC ....G 239 910-5401
Bonita Springs *(G-825)*
Creating Tech Solutions LLC ....E 727 914-3001
Clearwater *(G-1641)*
Creating Tech Solutions LLC ....E 727 914-3001
Clearwater *(G-1642)*
Dioxide Materials Inc ....F 217 239-1400
Boca Raton *(G-502)*
Electrnic Systems Sutheast LLC ....G 561 955-9006
Fort Myers *(G-4442)*
First Look Inc ....G 954 240-0530
Fort Lauderdale *(G-3995)*
▲ **General Capacitor LLC** ....G 510 371-2700
Tallahassee *(G-17262)*
GOTG LLC ....G 800 381-4684
Brooksville *(G-1232)*
Industry Standard Technology ....G 941 355-2100
Sarasota *(G-16235)*
Keytroller LLC ....F 813 877-4500
Tampa *(G-17823)*
▲ **Keytroller LLC** ....G 813 877-4500
Tampa *(G-17824)*
Kinetronics Corporation ....F 941 951-2432
Bradenton *(G-1067)*
Kollsman Inc ....G 407 312-1384
Orlando *(G-12875)*
◆ **Ksm Electronics Inc** ....D 954 642-7050
Tamarac *(G-17361)*
▼ **Lightning Master Corporation** ....E 800 749-6800
Clearwater *(G-1761)*
Lithium Battery Company LLC ....F 813 504-0074
Tampa *(G-17850)*
M Micro Technologies Inc ....B 954 973-6166
Pompano Beach *(G-14749)*
▲ **Mathews Associates Inc** ....C 407 323-3390
Sanford *(G-16082)*
◆ **Mitsubishi Power Americas Inc** ....D 407 688-6100
Lake Mary *(G-7436)*
OHM Americas LLC ....F 800 467-7275
Fort Lauderdale *(G-4148)*
Omniaelectronics llc ....G 631 742-5719
North Bay Village *(G-11594)*
Patlon Industries Inc ....G 305 255-7744
Miami *(G-10144)*
S&S Consulting Partners LLC ....G 850 803-8379
Niceville *(G-11574)*
◆ **Sagrad Inc** ....F 321 726-9400
Melbourne *(G-8923)*
Schneider Electric It Corp ....G 305 266-5005
Sunrise *(G-17171)*
Sepac Corp ....F 305 718-3379
Miami *(G-10325)*
▼ **Ultrasonic Technologies Inc** ....G 813 973-1702
Wesley Chapel *(G-18762)*

Universal Networking Svcs Co ....G....... 281 825-9790
Saint Petersburg *(G-15947)*
◆ **Veethree Electronics & Mar LLC** ....D....... 941 538-7775
Bradenton *(G-1140)*
Watts Technologies LLC ....F....... 407 512-5750
Sanford *(G-16135)*

3631 Household Cooking Eqpt

▲ **A&J Manufacturing Inc**....................E....... 912 638-4724
Tampa *(G-17377)*
Advanced Outdoor Concepts Inc..........G....... 954 429-1428
Deerfield Beach *(G-2765)*
▲ **American Household Inc**..................D....... 561 912-4100
Boca Raton *(G-422)*
▲ **Apollo Worldwide Inc**.......................G....... 561 585-3865
Hypoluxo *(G-6048)*
Creative Home and Kitchen LLC ....F....... 786 233-8621
Doral *(G-3312)*
Dryer Vent Wizard of Pb ....F....... 561 901-3464
Boynton Beach *(G-899)*
Firetainment Inc ....G....... 888 552-7897
Orlando *(G-12740)*
▼ **L C Ch International Inc**....................G....... 305 888-1323
Hialeah *(G-5478)*
Profire Inc ....F....... 305 665-5313
Pinecrest *(G-14331)*
Strategic Products Inc...........................G....... 321 752-0441
Melbourne *(G-8945)*
Sunbeam Americas Holdings LLC ....C....... 561 912-4100
Boca Raton *(G-736)*
◆ **Sunbeam Latin America LLC**...........E....... 786 845-2540
Boca Raton *(G-737)*
◆ **Sunbeam Products Inc** ....B....... 561 912-4100
Boca Raton *(G-738)*
▲ **Tannous Innovations LLC** ....G....... 754 220-6645
Pompano Beach *(G-14883)*

3632 Household Refrigerators & Freezers

▼ **Acme Service Corp** ....F....... 305 836-4800
Miami *(G-9065)*
GE Consumer Corporation ....D....... 904 696-9775
Jacksonville *(G-6429)*
Wine Plum Inc ....F....... 844 856-7586
Dania Beach *(G-2475)*

3633 Household Laundry Eqpt

Japan Fabricare Inc ....G....... 407 366-9986
Oviedo *(G-13441)*

3634 Electric Household Appliances

Air-Tech of Pensacola Inc......................F....... 850 433-6443
Pensacola *(G-14087)*
Airfree USA LLC....................................F....... 305 772-6577
Miami *(G-9097)*
◆ **Alton Manufacturing Inc** ....G....... 305 821-0701
Miami *(G-9126)*
▲ **American Household Inc**..................D....... 561 912-4100
Boca Raton *(G-422)*
▲ **and-Dell Corporation**........................E....... 954 523-6478
Fort Lauderdale *(G-3816)*
Avstar Systems LLC ....G....... 239 793-5511
Naples *(G-11177)*
▲ **Balla De Rodriguez Migdalia M**.........G....... 305 228-6566
Miami *(G-9216)*
Charcoal Chef Usa LLC.........................G....... 786 273-6511
Miami *(G-9349)*
Charles & Co LLC ....F....... 404 592-1190
Fort Lauderdale *(G-3896)*
▲ **Clean Cut Intl LLC**............................F....... 866 599-7066
Juno Beach *(G-6978)*
Db Tucker LLC.......................................G....... 561 301-4974
Jupiter *(G-7023)*
Eaton Corporation ....G....... 813 281-8069
Tampa *(G-17628)*
▲ **Fan America Inc** ....G....... 941 955-9788
Sarasota *(G-16426)*
◆ **Flash Sales Inc** ....G....... 954 914-2689
Miami Gardens *(G-10741)*
Grimes Aerospace Company................D....... 407 276-6083
Delray Beach *(G-3088)*
Healthquest Technologies LLC ....G....... 850 997-6300
Monticello *(G-11076)*
▲ **Intelligent Heater LLC**.......................G....... 305 248-4971
Homestead *(G-5973)*
◆ **Melitta North America Inc** ....D....... 727 535-2111
Clearwater *(G-1779)*
◆ **Melitta Usa Inc** ....D....... 727 535-2111
Clearwater *(G-1780)*

Pyure Company Inc ....E....... 561 735-3701
Boynton Beach *(G-948)*
▲ **Russell Hobbs Inc**.............................D....... 954 883-1000
Miramar *(G-11037)*
▲ **Saniflow Corporation**.........................G....... 305 424-2433
Miami *(G-10302)*
◆ **Simulated Envmt Concepts Inc**.........F....... 754 263-3184
Hollywood *(G-5908)*
Sunbeam Americas Holdings LLC ....C....... 561 912-4100
Boca Raton *(G-736)*
◆ **Sunbeam Products Inc** ....B....... 561 912-4100
Boca Raton *(G-738)*
Suns Up of Swf LLC...............................G....... 301 470-2678
Venice *(G-18579)*
Tropical Ceiling Fan Company ....G....... 877 921-3267
Miami *(G-10507)*
Uniware Houseware Corp ....E....... 305 952-4958
Miami Lakes *(G-10875)*
▲ **Van Tibolli Beauty Corp**.....................E....... 305 390-0044
Fort Lauderdale *(G-4304)*
Vapor Group Inc.....................................F....... 954 792-8450
Miami *(G-10568)*
Veltia Usa LLC.......................................G....... 305 298-8262
Coral Gables *(G-2204)*
▲ **Warehouse Goods LLC** ....E....... 877 865-2260
Boca Raton *(G-787)*

3635 Household Vacuum Cleaners

AAA Monterey Discount Vacuum..........G....... 772 288-5233
Stuart *(G-16900)*
Intelliclean Solutions LLC......................G....... 615 293-2299
Miami *(G-9753)*

3639 Household Appliances, NEC

Appliances To Go Usa Llc......................G....... 239 278-0811
Cape Coral *(G-1381)*
▲ **Clean Cut Intl LLC**............................F....... 866 599-7066
Juno Beach *(G-6978)*
Deers Holdings Inc ....G....... 805 323-6899
Bay Harbor Islands *(G-338)*
Dka Distributing LLC ....G....... 800 275-4352
Tampa *(G-17610)*
Flexshopper LLC....................................E....... 561 922-6609
Boca Raton *(G-530)*
Kappa Metal USA Inc.............................G....... 954 757-7100
Coconut Creek *(G-2087)*
◆ **La Cuisine Intl Distrs Inc** ....E....... 305 418-0010
Miami *(G-9839)*
Lean Green Enterprises LLC ....G....... 954 525-2971
Fort Lauderdale *(G-4099)*
Marey International LLC........................G....... 787 727-0277
Miami *(G-9945)*
Mia Appliances LLC...............................G....... 866 670-4860
Miami *(G-9988)*
Minea Usa Llc..F....... 800 971-3216
Coral Gables *(G-2177)*
Peralta Group Inc...................................G....... 954 502-8100
Sunrise *(G-17157)*
Unique Designs & Finishes Inc ....F....... 772 335-4884
Port Saint Lucie *(G-15159)*

3641 Electric Lamps

AMS Global Suppliers Group LLC.........G....... 305 714-9441
Miami *(G-9152)*
◆ **Bella Luna Inc**....................................E....... 305 696-0310
Hialeah *(G-5319)*
Digecon Plastics International...............F....... 850 477-5483
Pensacola *(G-14131)*
Eag-Led LLC..C....... 813 463-2420
Tampa *(G-17625)*
Energy Management Products LLC ......G....... 410 320-0200
Bradenton *(G-1038)*
Hyperbaric Treatment Assn ....G....... 804 296-4094
Saint Augustine *(G-15551)*
Johnston Archtctral Systems In.............E....... 904 886-9030
Jacksonville *(G-6527)*
Jq Green America Inc............................G....... 786 397-0999
Saint Lucie West *(G-15686)*
▲ **Kyp Go Inc**..F....... 386 736-3770
Deland *(G-2994)*
Oceanic Electrical Mfg Co Inc...............F....... 908 355-1900
Clearwater *(G-1816)*
Pearl Academy LLC ....G....... 904 619-6419
Jacksonville *(G-6663)*
▲ **Robertson Transformer Co** ....E....... 708 388-2315
Sarasota *(G-16560)*
◆ **Seal Shield LLC** ....E....... 877 325-7443
Orlando *(G-13172)*
Sun Catalina Holdings LLC....................E....... 305 558-4777
Miami Lakes *(G-10864)*

▲ **Surf Lighting Inc** ....F....... 305 888-7851
Hialeah *(G-5644)*
Vision Engineering Labs ....E....... 727 812-2000
Largo *(G-8075)*

3643 Current-Carrying Wiring Devices

123 Dollar Plus Inc.................................G....... 305 456-4561
Miami *(G-9020)*
ABB Installation Products Inc ....D....... 386 677-9110
Ormond Beach *(G-13347)*
Alico Lighting Group Inc........................G....... 305 542-2648
Hollywood *(G-5768)*
Allstate Lghtning Prtction LLC ....G....... 813 240-2736
Tampa *(G-17404)*
B G Service Company Inc ....E....... 561 659-1471
West Palm Beach *(G-18808)*
▲ **Bren Tuck Inc** ....F....... 727 561-7697
Clearwater *(G-1612)*
◆ **Broadband International Inc**..............G....... 305 882-0505
Medley *(G-8626)*
▲ **Carlisle Interconnect Tech Inc**..........A....... 904 829-5600
Saint Augustine *(G-15526)*
Certified Manufacturing Inc ....E....... 850 537-3777
Holt *(G-5948)*
Compulink Corporation..........................B....... 727 579-1500
Saint Petersburg *(G-15752)*
▲ **Cooper Crouse-Hinds Mtl Inc** ....C....... 321 725-8000
Melbourne *(G-8797)*
Data Phone Wire & Cable Corp.............F....... 954 761-7171
Fort Lauderdale *(G-3933)*
▲ **Dayton-Granger Inc** ....C....... 954 463-3451
Fort Lauderdale *(G-3935)*
Douglas Abbott ....G....... 407 422-3597
Orlando *(G-12680)*
Evolution Intrcnnect Systems I ....F....... 954 217-6223
Davie *(G-2521)*
Five Oceans Florida Inc.........................E....... 772 221-8188
Palm City *(G-13655)*
Gulf Connectors Inc...............................G....... 239 657-2986
Immokalee *(G-6050)*
▲ **Hytronics Corp**...................................D....... 727 535-0413
Clearwater *(G-1725)*
I C Probotics Inc.....................................D....... 407 339-8298
Longwood *(G-8288)*
▲ **Interconnect Cable Tech Corp**..........D....... 352 796-1716
Brooksville *(G-1237)*
▲ **J B Nottingham & Co Inc**...................E....... 386 873-2990
Deland *(G-2986)*
▲ **Kleen Wheels Corporation**................G....... 954 791-9112
Davie *(G-2541)*
Lextm3 Systems LLC..............................F....... 954 888-1024
Davie *(G-2546)*
Lightning Prtction Systems Inc...............F....... 239 643-4323
Naples *(G-11312)*
Lightning Specialists Inc........................G....... 727 938-3560
Odessa *(G-12131)*
▲ **LMI Components Inc**..........................F....... 561 994-5896
Boca Raton *(G-604)*
Logus Manufacturing Corp....................E....... 561 842-3550
West Palm Beach *(G-18934)*
Mactech Power Line and Cable ....G....... 954 895-9966
Miramar *(G-11013)*
Micro Contacts Inc.................................F....... 954 973-6166
Pompano Beach *(G-14761)*
Molex LLC..F....... 727 521-2700
Pinellas Park *(G-14370)*
Multi Contact USA.................................G....... 561 738-5637
Boynton Beach *(G-935)*
▲ **National Std Parts Assoc Inc** ....D....... 850 456-5771
Pensacola *(G-14211)*
Oceaneering International Inc ....C....... 985 329-3282
Panama City *(G-13933)*
Omega Power Systems Inc....................G....... 772 219-0045
Stuart *(G-16982)*
Panamtech Inc...F....... 954 587-3769
Plantation *(G-14541)*
Paramount Industries Inc.......................E....... 954 781-3755
Pompano Beach *(G-14784)*
▲ **Polaris Sales Co Inc**..........................C....... 727 372-1703
Odessa *(G-12140)*
S A Microtechnologies LLC ....F....... 954 973-6166
Pompano Beach *(G-14839)*
▼ **Scan Technology Inc** ....G....... 931 723-0304
Gainesville *(G-4992)*
▲ **Select Engineered Systems Inc**.........E....... 305 823-5410
Hialeah *(G-5613)*
Southern Switch & Contacts..................F....... 727 789-0951
Palm Harbor *(G-13762)*
Superior Electronics Inc.........................E....... 727 733-0700
Clearwater *(G-1896)*

S I C

Tag Heuer........G....... 954 846-2103
Sunrise *(G-17184)*
▲ **Technipower LLC**........F....... 954 346-2442
Coral Springs *(G-2321)*
▲ **Tensolite LLC**........A....... 904 829-5600
Saint Augustine *(G-15626)*
Terracassa LLC........G....... 786 581-7741
Miami *(G-10468)*
Thor Guard Inc........F....... 954 835-0900
Sunrise *(G-17188)*
Tienda Maya........G....... 561 965-0900
Lake Worth *(G-7591)*
Topflite Manufacturing Inc........F....... 800 219-2601
Miami *(G-10494)*
▲ **United Electronics Corporation**........D....... 954 888-1024
Miami *(G-10534)*
▲ **Vee Industries Inc**........G....... 561 732-1083
Boynton Beach *(G-973)*
◆ **Verifone Inc**........C....... 800 837-4366
Coral Springs *(G-2326)*

3644 Noncurrent-Carrying Wiring Devices

Afc Cable Systems Inc........G....... 813 539-0588
Largo *(G-7888)*
Alta Technologies Inc........G....... 609 538-9500
Ponte Vedra Beach *(G-14931)*
Apw........G....... 850 332-7023
Pensacola *(G-14088)*
Backbone Interconnect LLC........E....... 954 800-4749
Sunrise *(G-17093)*
Bashers RC Raceway LLC........G....... 561 889-9386
Jupiter *(G-7004)*
Camp Aircraft Inc........F....... 727 397-6076
Saint Petersburg *(G-15734)*
Cantex Inc........C....... 863 967-4161
Auburndale *(G-231)*
Etco Incorporated........C....... 941 756-8426
Bradenton *(G-1039)*
◆ **Gamma Insulators Corp**........E....... 585 302-0878
Coral Gables *(G-2149)*
Gaukaupa Raceway........G....... 904 483-3473
Jacksonville *(G-6426)*
Golden Glades Raceway LLC........G....... 305 321-9627
Miami Gardens *(G-10743)*
Holeshot Raceway Inc........G....... 407 864-1095
Oviedo *(G-13435)*
Insulator Seal Incorporated........E....... 941 751-2880
Sarasota *(G-16240)*
K-Raceway LLC........G....... 407 889-4314
Apopka *(G-153)*
▲ **LMI Components Inc**........F....... 561 994-5896
Boca Raton *(G-604)*
Mary Symon........G....... 813 986-4676
Dover *(G-3561)*
Microlumen Inc........D....... 813 886-1200
Oldsmar *(G-12250)*
Montalvos Raceway LLC........G....... 239 289-6931
Naples *(G-11331)*
Nelson Raceway LLC........G....... 904 206-1625
Fernandina Beach *(G-3744)*
Nine Mile Raceway Inc........G....... 850 937-1845
Cantonment *(G-1343)*
Nuggets Racing LLC........G....... 954 943-3561
Pompano Beach *(G-14777)*
Race Way 6800........G....... 904 329-2961
Macclenny *(G-8444)*
Raceway........G....... 850 453-9437
Pensacola *(G-14249)*
Raceway Electric LLC........G....... 772 260-6530
Port Saint Lucie *(G-15135)*
Raceway Towing LLC........G....... 754 244-9597
Oakland Park *(G-11835)*
◆ **Reditek Corporation**........F....... 954 781-1069
Pompano Beach *(G-14826)*

3645 Residential Lighting Fixtures

▲ **Allure Shades Inc**........F....... 954 543-6259
Lauderhill *(G-8100)*
Blu Sense........G....... 786 616-8628
Doral *(G-3279)*
Brian Slater & Associates LLC........F....... 561 886-7705
Boca Raton *(G-464)*
◆ **Brownlee Lighting Inc**........E....... 407 297-3677
Orlando *(G-12537)*
▲ **Capstone Industries Inc**........F....... 954 570-8889
Deerfield Beach *(G-2795)*
City Electric Supply Company........C....... 772 878-4944
Port St Lucie *(G-15171)*
▲ **Dauer Manufacturing Corp**........G....... 800 883-2590
Medley *(G-8640)*
Digecon Plastics International........F....... 850 477-5483
Pensacola *(G-14131)*
◆ **Edsun Lighting Fixtures Mfg**........F....... 305 888-8849
Hialeah *(G-5390)*
◆ **Evolution Lighting LLC**........E....... 305 558-4777
Pembroke Pines *(G-14034)*
General Metal Intl Inc........G....... 305 628-2052
Miramar *(G-10997)*
Gq Investments LLC........C....... 305 821-3850
Hialeah *(G-5435)*
Janoro Fixture Mfg Corp........G....... 305 887-2524
Hialeah *(G-5463)*
Logic Illumination LLC........F....... 407 906-0126
Kissimmee *(G-7270)*
◆ **Louis Poulsen USA Inc**........D....... 954 349-2525
Weston *(G-19148)*
Marios Metalcraft........G....... 239 649-0085
Naples *(G-11321)*
Morlee Lampshade Co Inc........E....... 305 500-9310
Miami *(G-10041)*
◆ **Papila Design Inc**........G....... 407 240-2992
Orlando *(G-13050)*
◆ **Remcraft Lighting Products Inc**........E....... 305 687-9031
Opa Locka *(G-12353)*
Smarthome-Products Inc........F....... 727 490-7260
Clearwater *(G-1880)*
Stateside Indus Solutions LLC........G....... 305 301-4052
Miramar *(G-11046)*
▲ **Studio 21 Lighting Inc**........E....... 941 355-2677
Sarasota *(G-16303)*
Sun Catalina Holdings LLC........E....... 305 558-4777
Miami Lakes *(G-10864)*
Tamlite........G....... 772 878-4944
Port St Lucie *(G-15181)*
◆ **The Natural Light Inc**........E....... 850 265-0800
Lynn Haven *(G-8440)*
▲ **Van Teal Inc**........E....... 305 751-6767
Miami *(G-10566)*
Versailles Lighting Inc........F....... 561 945-5744
Delray Beach *(G-3158)*
Vonn LLC........F....... 888 604-8666
North Miami Beach *(G-11710)*
▲ **Well Traveled Imports Inc**........F....... 904 261-5400
Amelia Island *(G-93)*

3646 Commercial, Indl & Institutional Lighting Fixtures

Affineon Lighting........F....... 407 448-3434
Weston *(G-19103)*
Alumination LLC........G....... 904 361-8174
Jacksonville *(G-6143)*
▲ **Apollo Metro Solutions Inc**........G....... 239 444-6934
Naples *(G-11165)*
◆ **Brownlee Lighting Inc**........E....... 407 297-3677
Orlando *(G-12537)*
Candela Controls Inc........E....... 407 654-2420
Winter Garden *(G-19254)*
City Electric Supply Company........C....... 772 878-4944
Port St Lucie *(G-15171)*
Commercial Energy Services........F....... 904 589-1059
Green Cove Springs *(G-5059)*
Coresential Energy & Lighting........E....... 919 602-0849
Tampa *(G-17555)*
▲ **Dauer Manufacturing Corp**........G....... 800 883-2590
Medley *(G-8640)*
Digecon Plastics International........F....... 850 477-5483
Pensacola *(G-14131)*
◆ **Edsun Lighting Fixtures Mfg**........F....... 305 888-8849
Hialeah *(G-5390)*
Elc Sales LLC........G....... 772 285-5230
Stuart *(G-16937)*
▲ **Electraled Inc**........F....... 727 561-7610
Clearwater *(G-1665)*
▲ **Energy Harness Corporation**........G....... 239 790-3300
Cape Coral *(G-1417)*
Energy Management Products LLC........G....... 410 320-0200
Bradenton *(G-1038)*
▲ **Energy Sving Solutions USA LLC**........F....... 305 735-2878
Miami *(G-9527)*
▲ **Eran Financial Services LLC**........E....... 844 411-5483
Boca Raton *(G-520)*
Eran Group Inc........F....... 561 289-5021
Boca Raton *(G-521)*
◆ **Evolution Lighting LLC**........E....... 305 558-4777
Pembroke Pines *(G-14034)*
▲ **Global Tech Led LLC**........E....... 877 748-5533
Fort Lauderdale *(G-4024)*
Green Applications LLC........E....... 954 900-2290
Fort Lauderdale *(G-4030)*
▲ **Green Creative LLC**........E....... 866 774-5433
Sanford *(G-16057)*
Green Global Energy Systems........F....... 305 253-3413
Cutler Bay *(G-2396)*
H I T Lighting Corp........G....... 772 221-1155
Palm City *(G-13662)*
◆ **Harris Manufacturing Inc**........F....... 877 204-7540
Jacksonville *(G-6461)*
Icpf Development Group LLC........F....... 727 474-9927
Clearwater *(G-1727)*
▲ **J B Nottingham & Co Inc**........E....... 386 873-2990
Deland *(G-2986)*
Janoro Fixture Mfg Corp........G....... 305 887-2524
Hialeah *(G-5463)*
Just Leds Inc........G....... 727 468-4496
Bradenton *(G-1066)*
Keylon Lighting Services Inc........G....... 352 279-3249
Brooksville *(G-1241)*
Koncept Systems LLC........E....... 786 610-0122
Homestead *(G-5977)*
Led Lghting Slutions Globl LLC........G....... 855 309-1702
Bradenton *(G-1069)*
▲ **Ledradiant LLC**........G....... 305 901-1313
Hollywood *(G-5858)*
▲ **Lighting Science Group Corp**........G....... 321 779-5520
Melbourne *(G-8874)*
Lightn Up Inc........F....... 954 797-7778
Sunrise *(G-17143)*
◆ **Louis Poulsen USA Inc**........D....... 954 349-2525
Weston *(G-19148)*
▲ **Lumastream Inc**........E....... 727 827-2805
Saint Petersburg *(G-15844)*
▲ **Lumilum LLC**........F....... 305 233-2844
Miami *(G-9918)*
Metrotech Media & Lighting Inc........G....... 844 463-8761
Pensacola *(G-14208)*
Morning Star Industries Inc........E....... 800 440-6050
Jensen Beach *(G-6971)*
Municipal Lighting Systems Inc........G....... 305 666-4210
Miami *(G-10055)*
Pioneer Led Lighting Corp........G....... 305 620-5300
Miami Lakes *(G-10839)*
R & R American Corporation........G....... 786 497-8898
Miami *(G-10228)*
◆ **Remcraft Lighting Products Inc**........E....... 305 687-9031
Opa Locka *(G-12353)*
Restoration Arts........G....... 305 953-9755
Miami Gardens *(G-10753)*
Safetogether Ltd Liability Co........G....... 954 227-2236
Parkland *(G-14000)*
Schroe Lights LLC........G....... 407 748-9300
Orlando *(G-13168)*
Sun Catalina Holdings LLC........E....... 305 558-4777
Miami Lakes *(G-10864)*
▲ **Surf Lighting Inc**........F....... 305 888-7851
Hialeah *(G-5644)*
Systematix Inc........E....... 850 983-2213
Milton *(G-10942)*
Tek-Lite Inc........G....... 410 775-7123
Melbourne *(G-8957)*
Underwater Lights Usa LLC........F....... 954 760-4447
Fort Lauderdale *(G-4292)*
Van Teal Hospitality Inc........G....... 305 751-6767
Miami *(G-10565)*
Versailles Lighting Inc........F....... 561 945-5744
Delray Beach *(G-3158)*
Violet Defense LLC........E....... 407 433-1104
Orlando *(G-13304)*
▲ **Vision Engineering Labs**........D....... 727 812-2035
Largo *(G-8076)*
Vonn LLC........F....... 888 604-8666
North Miami Beach *(G-11710)*
▲ **Xeleum Lighting LLC**........F....... 954 617-8170
Boca Raton *(G-794)*

3647 Vehicular Lighting Eqpt

▲ **Autocraft Manufacturing Co**........E....... 321 453-1850
Merritt Island *(G-8992)*
▲ **B/E Aerospace Inc**........E....... 410 266-2048
Wellington *(G-18710)*
Basewest Inc........E....... 727 573-2700
Clearwater *(G-1599)*
▲ **Brooking Industries Inc**........G....... 954 533-0765
Saint Augustine *(G-15524)*
Cobalt Aerospace Inc........G....... 305 450-0457
Hialeah *(G-5349)*
Emergency Vehicle Sup Co LLC........E....... 954 428-5201
Pompano Beach *(G-14678)*
Energy Management Products LLC........G....... 410 320-0200
Bradenton *(G-1038)*

Hg2 Emergency Lighting LLC................F....... 407 426-7700
Orlando *(G-12801)*
◆ **Light Integration Inc**........................G....... 407 681-0072
Longwood *(G-8307)*
Lumishore Usa LLC..............................G....... 941 405-3302
Sarasota *(G-16251)*
◆ **Lumitec LLC**..E....... 561 272-9840
Delray Beach *(G-3102)*
Phantom Products Inc...........................F....... 321 690-6729
Rockledge *(G-15440)*
Radiant Power Corp................................C....... 941 739-3200
Sarasota *(G-16281)*
Rontan North America Inc......................E....... 305 599-2974
Doral *(G-3489)*
◆ **Sea Link International Irb Inc**...........F....... 727 523-8660
Largo *(G-8048)*

3648 Lighting Eqpt, NEC

0energy Lighting Inc...............................F....... 855 955-1055
Orlando *(G-12415)*
A J Giammanco & Associates...................F....... 386 328-1254
Palatka *(G-13472)*
▲ **ACR Electronics Inc**..............................C....... 954 981-3333
Fort Lauderdale *(G-3779)*
▲ **Adva-Lite Inc**...E....... 727 369-5319
Seminole *(G-16735)*
▲ **Airstar America Inc**...............................F....... 407 851-7830
Orlando *(G-12447)*
▲ **Apollo Metro Solutions Inc**...................G....... 239 444-6934
Naples *(G-11165)*
Aquallsion Design Concepts LLC.............G....... 407 440-2972
Orlando *(G-12485)*
Armadillo Sounds Inc..............................G....... 305 801-7906
Miami *(G-9169)*
◆ **Bella Luna Inc**..E....... 305 696-0310
Hialeah *(G-5319)*
▲ **Bluegate Inc**...F....... 305 628-8391
Miami Gardens *(G-10736)*
▲ **Bluworld of Water LLC**..........................D....... 407 426-7674
Orlando *(G-12529)*
Brite Shot Inc..F....... 954 418-7125
Deerfield Beach *(G-2790)*
Candela Controls Inc.................................E....... 407 654-2420
Winter Garden *(G-19254)*
Capstone Companies Inc...........................G....... 954 252-3440
Deerfield Beach *(G-2794)*
CC Lighting Inc...G....... 805 302-5321
Boynton Beach *(G-888)*
Christie Lites Entps USA LLC...................C....... 407 856-0016
Orlando *(G-12581)*
▲ **Christie Lites Orlando LLC**....................F....... 206 223-7200
Orlando *(G-12582)*
Creative Lighting & Power LLC................F....... 407 967-0957
Lakeland *(G-7664)*
▲ **Cyalume Tech Holdings Inc**...................D....... 954 315-4939
Fort Lauderdale *(G-3925)*
Digital Lighting Systems Inc.....................G....... 305 264-8391
Miami *(G-9468)*
Dj Live Productions LLC...........................G....... 407 383-1740
Altamonte Springs *(G-41)*
Eag-Led LLC...C....... 813 463-2420
Tampa *(G-17625)*
Energyware LLC...G....... 540 809-5902
Davie *(G-2519)*
◆ **Evolution Lighting LLC**...........................E....... 305 558-4777
Pembroke Pines *(G-14034)*
◆ **Fanto Group LLC**.....................................F....... 407 857-5101
Orlando *(G-12733)*
First Block LLC...D....... 727 462-2526
Clearwater *(G-1682)*
Fos Led Lighting Solution..........................G....... 321 208-8174
Rockledge *(G-15412)*
▲ **Fusion Energy Solutions LLC**.................G....... 941 366-9936
Punta Gorda *(G-15206)*
Hoosier Lightening Inc...............................G....... 407 290-3323
Orlando *(G-12809)*
▲ **Illuminated Lightpanels Inc**....................G....... 954 484-6633
Oakland Park *(G-11812)*
Illuminations Holiday Ltg LLC...................G....... 813 334-4827
Tampa *(G-17771)*
▲ **IMC Lighting Inc**......................................G....... 305 373-4422
Miami *(G-9734)*
Jay Strong Lighting Inc..............................G....... 813 253-0490
Tampa *(G-17804)*
Jibe Ltg N Amer Ltd Lblty Co....................G....... 954 899-4040
Parkland *(G-13993)*
Jsm Creations Inc.......................................G....... 239 229-8746
Cape Coral *(G-1442)*
Kenneth J Manning Lighting......................G....... 561 702-0169
Boca Raton *(G-587)*
Koncept Systems LLC................................E....... 786 610-0122
Homestead *(G-5977)*
Lanai Bright LLC..G....... 239 303-4756
Lehigh Acres *(G-8194)*
Lanai Lights LLC...G....... 239 415-2561
Fort Myers *(G-4515)*
▲ **Led Surf Lighting Inc**...............................G....... 239 687-4458
Naples *(G-11309)*
Ledger 2 Ledger Inc....................................G....... 321 961-4017
Orlando *(G-12899)*
▼ **Light and Sound Equipment Inc**..............G....... 305 233-3737
Cutler Bay *(G-2402)*
▲ **Lighting Science Group Corp**..................G....... 321 779-5520
Melbourne *(G-8874)*
▲ **Lighting Technologies**............................F....... 850 462-1790
Pensacola *(G-14193)*
Lightnet Usa Inc..F....... 305 260-6444
Miami *(G-9891)*
Lit Lighting & Grip LLC...............................G....... 305 770-0272
Miami *(G-9899)*
Liteworks Lighting Productions..................G....... 407 888-8677
Orlando *(G-12916)*
Logic Illumination LLC...............................F....... 407 906-0126
Kissimmee *(G-7270)*
Lps Production LLC...................................F....... 786 208-6217
Miami Lakes *(G-10809)*
◆ **Lumitec LLC**...E....... 561 272-9840
Delray Beach *(G-3102)*
◆ **Lux Unlimited Inc**....................................G....... 305 871-8774
Miami *(G-9922)*
Mia Led Lighting Inc...................................G....... 786 440-2856
Hollywood *(G-5876)*
▲ **Neubert Aero Corp**..................................G....... 352 345-4828
Brooksville *(G-1256)*
Next Step Products LLC.............................G....... 407 857-9900
Orlando *(G-13001)*
◆ **Nightscenes Inc**......................................F....... 813 855-9416
Tampa *(G-17940)*
Platinum Ltg Productions LLC....................G....... 941 320-1906
Sarasota *(G-16278)*
Professional Holiday Lighting......................G....... 208 709-2968
Ormond Beach *(G-13394)*
◆ **Prosun International LLC**........................D....... 727 825-0400
Saint Petersburg *(G-15893)*
Pure Bright Lighting LLC.............................G....... 954 780-8700
Fort Lauderdale *(G-4185)*
Rand Search Light Advertising...................G....... 954 476-7620
Davie *(G-2580)*
Renos Led Sleds...G....... 727 593-0340
Largo *(G-8040)*
Reward Lighting Net LLC............................G....... 561 832-1819
West Palm Beach *(G-19019)*
▼ **RLS Lighting Inc**.......................................G....... 954 458-0345
Fort Lauderdale *(G-4209)*
Roth Southeast Lighting LLC......................G....... 954 423-6640
Fort Lauderdale *(G-4218)*
▲ **Russell Hobbs Inc**....................................D....... 954 883-1000
Miramar *(G-11037)*
S B Lighting LLC...G....... 850 687-1166
Ponce De Leon *(G-14918)*
Searchlight Inc..G....... 407 965-2649
Kissimmee *(G-7297)*
▲ **Sgm Lighting Inc**......................................G....... 407 440-3601
Orlando *(G-13178)*
Siglo Holdings LLC.....................................C....... 727 369-5220
Largo *(G-8051)*
Southwest Signal Inc..................................E....... 813 621-4949
Englewood *(G-3667)*
State Lighting Co Inc...................................G....... 561 371-9529
West Palm Beach *(G-19041)*
Stonelight LLC...G....... 239 514-3272
Naples *(G-11418)*
◆ **Street Lighting Equipment Corp**..............F....... 954 961-9140
Hallandale Beach *(G-5215)*
Sun Catalina Holdings LLC.........................E....... 305 558-4777
Miami Lakes *(G-10864)*
Sundown Lighting..G....... 561 254-3738
Lantana *(G-7876)*
Sweetlight Systems.....................................G....... 239 245-8159
Fort Myers *(G-4621)*
Tamlite Lighting - New Whse......................G....... 772 879-7440
Port Saint Lucie *(G-15153)*
Tantasia...G....... 239 274-5455
Fort Myers *(G-4623)*
Titans USA Ltd...F....... 727 290-9897
Clearwater *(G-1922)*
◆ **Triarch International Inc**..........................F....... 305 622-3400
Hollywood *(G-5926)*
Triple Seven Home LLC...............................G....... 321 652-5151
Grant *(G-5050)*
Underwter Fish Light Ltd Lblty....................G....... 941 391-5846
Port Charlotte *(G-15003)*
▲ **Van Teal Inc**...E....... 305 751-6767
Miami *(G-10566)*
▲ **Virginia Electronic & Ltg Corp**...................G....... 904 230-2840
Green Cove Springs *(G-5076)*
◆ **Volt Lighting**...F....... 813 978-3700
Lutz *(G-8423)*
▲ **Zaniboni Lighting LLC**...............................D....... 727 213-0410
Clearwater *(G-1947)*

3651 Household Audio & Video Eqpt

A-N-L Home Solutions LLC...........................F....... 954 648-2623
Miami *(G-9046)*
◆ **Advanced Cmmnications Tech Inc**............F....... 954 444-4119
Boca Raton *(G-403)*
Andrew Mj Inc...G....... 561 575-6032
Jupiter *(G-7000)*
Astra Products Co Inc Tampa.......................E....... 813 855-3021
Oldsmar *(G-12206)*
Attack Communications Inc..........................G....... 954 300-2716
Fort Lauderdale *(G-3831)*
Audio Video Imagineering Inc.......................G....... 305 947-6991
Biscayne Park *(G-383)*
Audioshark Inc...G....... 954 591-9252
Hollywood *(G-5778)*
▼ **AVI-Spl Holdings Inc**...................................A....... 866 708-5034
Tampa *(G-17446)*
▼ **AVI-Spl LLC**...A....... 813 884-7168
Tampa *(G-17447)*
Da Vinci Systems Inc......................................G....... 954 688-5600
Coral Springs *(G-2236)*
Dj Live Productions LLC.................................G....... 407 383-1740
Altamonte Springs *(G-41)*
Eagle Eye Global Tracking LLC......................G....... 727 399-6888
Tarpon Springs *(G-18298)*
Eminent Technology Inc.................................G....... 850 575-5655
Tallahassee *(G-17247)*
Fgmg International...F....... 305 988-7436
Deltona *(G-3169)*
Freshetech LLC...G....... 516 519-3453
Orlando *(G-12765)*
▲ **Fun Electronics Inc**.......................................F....... 305 933-4646
Miami *(G-9603)*
Gocase LLC...G....... 415 341-6248
Miami Beach *(G-10673)*
Gulf Coast Beach Cams LLC..........................G....... 850 792-4617
Miramar Beach *(G-11066)*
Hki Soundigital USA LLC................................G....... 786 600-1056
Dania *(G-2446)*
K & A Audio Inc...F....... 941 925-7648
Sarasota *(G-16478)*
Koncept Systems LLC....................................E....... 786 610-0122
Homestead *(G-5977)*
▼ **Light and Sound Equipment Inc**...................G....... 305 233-3737
Cutler Bay *(G-2402)*
Magnum Audio Group Inc...............................G....... 813 870-2857
Tampa *(G-17874)*
▲ **MD Audio Engineering Inc**............................G....... 305 593-8361
Miami *(G-9960)*
Mdt Technologies Inc......................................G....... 305 308-2902
Medley *(G-8686)*
Mpr Audio System LLC...................................G....... 305 988-8524
Miami *(G-10047)*
Nowvision Technologies Inc...........................G....... 813 943-4639
Lutz *(G-8406)*
Padgett Communications Inc.........................E....... 727 323-5800
Tampa *(G-17969)*
Perpetual Marketing Assoc Inc.......................G....... 813 949-9385
Lutz *(G-8408)*
Peter Fogel..G....... 561 245-5252
Delray Beach *(G-3115)*
Philips North America LLC.............................D....... 305 969-7447
Miami *(G-10158)*
Power Evolution Inc...G....... 305 318-8476
Orlando *(G-13075)*
Radio OEM Inc..G....... 920 564-6622
Sorrento *(G-16793)*
Raytheon Company...G....... 727 768-8468
Largo *(G-8037)*
Raytheon Company...C....... 310 647-9438
Largo *(G-8036)*
Red Microphone..G....... 818 806-8545
Miami *(G-10244)*
S N S Auto Sports LLC....................................G....... 727 546-2700
Pinellas Park *(G-14386)*
▲ **Singing Machine Company Inc**.....................F....... 954 596-1000
Fort Lauderdale *(G-4236)*
Sonobrands LLC..F....... 305 418-9367
Miami *(G-10376)*

S
I
C

▲ Sound Anchors Inc ....G 321 724-1237
Palm Bay *(G-13537)*
◆ Spirit llc ....E 954 592-0227
Miami Gardens *(G-10755)*
◆ Sun Mackie LLC ....A 561 394-0550
Boca Raton *(G-735)*
Teranex Systems Inc ....E 407 888-4300
Orlando *(G-13249)*
Time Is Money Campaign LLC ....F 352 255-5273
Clermont *(G-1975)*
Valvetrain Amplification ....G 407 886-7656
Apopka *(G-194)*
Visual Acoustics LLC ....G 786 390-6128
Miami *(G-10590)*
◆ Voxx International Corporation ....B 800 645-7750
Orlando *(G-13313)*
◆ Wireworld By David Salz Inc ....E 954 474-4464
Davie *(G-2616)*
Wizard Labs ....G 321 422-0803
Altamonte Springs *(G-84)*

3652 Phonograph Records & Magnetic Tape

▼ Akman Inc ....G 407 948-0562
Cocoa Beach *(G-2057)*
Axzes LLC ....G 786 626-1611
Doral *(G-3261)*
Bible Alliance Inc ....E 941 748-3031
Bradenton *(G-999)*
Capital Technology Solutions ....G 850 562-3321
Tallahassee *(G-17230)*
Captain Zoom Products Inc ....G 561 989-9119
Boca Raton *(G-470)*
Covis Inc ....G 954 315-3835
Fort Lauderdale *(G-3920)*
Dubhouse Inc ....G 954 524-3658
Fort Lauderdale *(G-3951)*
Enterprise Slling Slutions LLC ....G 904 655-9410
Jacksonville *(G-6366)*
Ibr LLC ....G 407 694-6748
Saint Cloud *(G-15655)*
Jazziz Magazine Inc ....E 561 893-6868
Boca Raton *(G-578)*
Mahigaming LLC ....F 561 504-1534
Deerfield Beach *(G-2866)*
Man Enterprises 3 LLC ....G 561 655-4944
West Palm Beach *(G-18940)*
Miami Tape Inc ....F 305 558-9211
Hialeah *(G-5513)*
Muscle Mixes Inc ....F 407 872-7576
Orlando *(G-12987)*
Obsolete Gamer Inc ....G 305 388-3372
Miami *(G-10087)*
Ocoa LLC ....E 407 898-1961
Orlando *(G-13019)*
Panoptex Technologies Inc ....F 407 412-0222
Orlando *(G-13048)*
Piergate LLC ....G 813 938-9170
Lutz *(G-8409)*
Runaware Inc ....F 954 907-9052
Coral Springs *(G-2308)*
▲ Singing Machine Company Inc ....F 954 596-1000
Fort Lauderdale *(G-4236)*
Synaptic Sparks Inc ....G 205 774-8324
Orlando *(G-13235)*
Workep Inc ....G 787 634-1115
North Miami *(G-11665)*

3661 Telephone & Telegraph Apparatus

Adcon Telemetry Inc ....G 561 989-5309
Boca Raton *(G-398)*
Allied Telecommunications Ltd ....F 954 370-9900
Plantation *(G-14487)*
Altanet Corporation ....G 786 228-5758
Miami *(G-9123)*
American Data Supply Inc ....F 866 650-3282
Clearwater *(G-1579)*
American Impact Media Corp ....E 954 457-9003
Hallandale Beach *(G-5169)*
▲ Antennas For Cmmnctons Ocala F ....E 352 687-4121
Ocala *(G-11876)*
Anuva Manufacturing Svcs Inc ....E 321 821-4900
Melbourne *(G-8768)*
Arden Photonics LLC ....F 727 478-2651
Clearwater *(G-1588)*
Avaya Inc ....G 239 498-2737
Bonita Springs *(G-815)*
Avaya Inc ....C 305 264-7021
Miami *(G-9193)*
Black Box Corporation ....G 407 276-3171
Orlando *(G-12520)*
C & C Multiservices Corp ....F 305 200-5851
Miami *(G-9292)*
▲ CCM Clllar Cnnection Miami Inc ....E 305 406-1656
Doral *(G-3295)*
Cellphone Parts Express LLC ....F 954 635-5525
Hallandale Beach *(G-5177)*
▲ Cellular Masters Inc ....E 305 592-7906
Miami *(G-9333)*
Ciao Group Inc ....E 347 560-5040
Boca Raton *(G-479)*
Cleartel Voice and Data LLC ....G 239 220-5545
Fort Myers *(G-4397)*
Communication Eqp & Engrg Co ....F 863 357-0798
Okeechobee *(G-12174)*
Communications Labs Inc ....F 321 701-9000
Melbourne *(G-8794)*
▲ Converlogic Inter LLC ....G 786 623-4747
Doral *(G-3305)*
Coppercom Inc ....D 561 322-4000
Boca Raton *(G-489)*
Coretek Industries Inc ....G 321 385-2860
Titusville *(G-18425)*
Cyipcom Inc ....G 954 727-2500
Oakland Park *(G-11794)*
Dasan Zhone Solutions Inc ....G 305 789-6680
Miami *(G-9436)*
Eci Telecom Inc ....E 954 772-3070
Fort Lauderdale *(G-3960)*
Florida Veex Inc ....F 727 442-6677
Largo *(G-7952)*
Hemco Industries Inc ....F 305 769-0606
North Miami *(G-11641)*
▲ Hose-Mccann Telephone Co Inc ....E 954 429-1110
Deerfield Beach *(G-2845)*
Ingeant Florida LLC ....G 954 868-2879
Coconut Creek *(G-2080)*
J I S Associates ....G 321 777-6829
Satellite Beach *(G-16652)*
L3harris Technologies Inc ....E 321 727-4255
Palm Bay *(G-13519)*
L3harris Technologies Inc ....E 321 984-0782
Melbourne *(G-8868)*
L3harris Technologies Inc ....G 321 727-9100
Melbourne *(G-8870)*
▲ L3harris Technologies Inc ....B 321 727-9100
Melbourne *(G-8865)*
▲ Medtel Services LLC ....E 941 753-5000
Palmetto *(G-13812)*
Milsav LLC ....G 407 556-5055
Orlando *(G-12972)*
Monroe Cable LLC ....D 941 429-8484
North Port *(G-11744)*
Motorola Solutions Inc ....G 407 562-4000
Lake Mary *(G-7437)*
Multicore Photonics Inc ....F 407 325-7800
Orlando *(G-12985)*
▲ Networks Assets LLC ....F 954 334-1390
Weston *(G-19153)*
Nextera Fibernet LLC ....D 866 787-2637
Juno Beach *(G-6981)*
Omnisys LLC ....E 800 325-2017
Sarasota *(G-16532)*
Photon Towers Inc ....G 305 235-7337
Miami *(G-10160)*
◆ Precision Comm Svcs Inc ....C 813 238-1000
Tampa *(G-18005)*
Prepaid Solutions LLC ....F 786 257-2714
Miami *(G-10188)*
Primal Innovation Tech LLC ....F 407 558-9366
Tampa *(G-18010)*
◆ Prime Meridian Trading Corp ....G 954 727-2152
Sunrise *(G-17161)*
Pss Communications Inc ....F 408 496-3330
Sun City Center *(G-17071)*
Raytheon Company ....C 310 647-9438
Largo *(G-8036)*
Recall Technologies Inc ....G 321 952-4422
Palm Bay *(G-13530)*
▲ Select Engineered Systems Inc ....E 305 823-5410
Hialeah *(G-5613)*
Siemens Corporation ....G 407 736-5629
Orlando *(G-13182)*
Sk Worldwide LLC ....G 786 360-4842
Surfside *(G-17206)*
▼ Smiths Interconnect Inc ....C 813 901-7200
Tampa *(G-18111)*
Steve Baie Enterprises Inc ....G 407 822-3997
Apopka *(G-188)*
Synergy Communication MGT LLC ....F 800 749-3160
Cape Canaveral *(G-1369)*
Tellabs International Inc ....E 954 492-0120
Fort Lauderdale *(G-4277)*
Tier5 Technical Services ....G 904 435-3484
Jacksonville *(G-6855)*
Touchpoint Group Holdings Inc ....G 305 420-6640
Miami *(G-10496)*
Truvoice Telecom Inc ....G 888 448-5556
Tampa *(G-18205)*
Victus Capital Enterprises Inc ....E 727 442-6677
Saint Petersburg *(G-15954)*
Wintel ....F 407 834-1188
Longwood *(G-8351)*
Wireless Coverage Group Inc ....G 561 429-5032
Hobe Sound *(G-5731)*
Zhone Technologies Inc ....G 510 777-7151
Seminole *(G-16773)*

3663 Radio & T V Communications, Systs & Eqpt, Broadcast/Studio

▲ ACR Electronics Inc ....C 954 981-3333
Fort Lauderdale *(G-3779)*
Aero-Mach TCO Manufacturing ....G 239 936-7570
Fort Myers *(G-4346)*
Airbus Onweb Stlltes N Amer LL ....C 321 522-6645
Merritt Island *(G-8989)*
Airbus Onweb Stlltes N Amer LL ....D 321 522-6645
Merritt Island *(G-8990)*
▲ Airspan Networks Inc ....E 561 893-8670
Boca Raton *(G-410)*
Alphatec Communications ....G 518 580-0520
Doral *(G-3241)*
Altelix LLC ....F 561 660-9434
Boca Raton *(G-415)*
Analog Modules Inc ....D 407 339-4355
Longwood *(G-8255)*
▲ Antennas For Cmmnctons Ocala F ....E 352 687-4121
Ocala *(G-11876)*
Antique Automobile Radio Inc ....G 727 785-8733
Palm Harbor *(G-13719)*
Anywhere Gps LLC ....G 949 468-6842
Saint Augustine *(G-15517)*
Applied Systems Integrator Inc ....G 321 259-6106
Melbourne *(G-8770)*
Artex Computer Llc ....G 407 844-2253
Miami *(G-9173)*
◆ Aska Communication Corp ....G 954 708-2387
Miami *(G-9178)*
Astrumsat Communications LLC ....G 954 368-9980
Sanford *(G-15996)*
▼ AVI-Spl Emplyee Emrgncy Rlief ....A 813 884-7168
Tampa *(G-17445)*
▼ AVI-Spl Holdings Inc ....A 866 708-5034
Tampa *(G-17446)*
▼ AVI-Spl LLC ....A 813 884-7168
Tampa *(G-17447)*
Balsys Technology Group Inc ....G 407 656-3719
Winter Garden *(G-19253)*
▼ Barco LLC ....G 305 677-9600
Miami *(G-9219)*
Becker Avionics Inc ....F 954 450-3137
Miramar *(G-10974)*
▲ Bk Technologies Inc ....F 321 984-1414
West Melbourne *(G-18767)*
Bk Technologies Corporation ....F 321 984-1414
West Melbourne *(G-18768)*
Black News Channel LLC ....D 844 262-3968
Tallahassee *(G-17228)*
Bluazu LLC ....F 386 697-3743
Gainesville *(G-4888)*
Boeing Company ....G 850 882-4912
Eglin Afb *(G-3641)*
Brightsky LLC ....F 239 919-8551
Naples *(G-11194)*
C E S Wireless Tech Corp ....E 407 681-0869
Winter Park *(G-19387)*
CF Motion Inc ....G 727 458-7092
Clearwater *(G-1623)*
Cobham Satcom ....F 407 650-9054
Sanford *(G-16017)*
Commscope Technologies LLC ....F 407 944-9116
Orlando *(G-12607)*
◆ Commstructures Inc ....D 850 968-9293
Pensacola *(G-14118)*
▲ Component General Inc ....E 727 376-6655
Odessa *(G-12112)*
▲ Componexx Corp ....G 954 236-6569
Sunrise *(G-17107)*
▼ Comtech Antenna Systems Inc ....D 407 854-1950
Orlando *(G-12609)*

▼ **Comtech Systems Inc**....D.... 407 854-1950
Orlando *(G-12610)*
▲ **Cooper Notification Inc**....D.... 941 487-2300
Sarasota *(G-16197)*
Crown Castle Intl Corp....F.... 305 552-3675
Miami *(G-9413)*
▲ **Crystal Communications Inc**....G.... 954 474-3072
Sunrise *(G-17110)*
Cybercellulars Inc....G.... 407 608-7888
Orlando *(G-12641)*
Da Vinci Systems Inc....G.... 954 688-5600
Coral Springs *(G-2236)*
Dayton Industrial Corporation....G.... 941 351-4454
Sarasota *(G-16405)*
▲ **Dayton-Granger Inc**....C.... 954 463-3451
Fort Lauderdale *(G-3935)*
Denke Laboratories Inc....E.... 941 721-0568
Palmetto *(G-13795)*
E2g Partners LLC....E.... 813 855-2251
Saint Petersburg *(G-15766)*
Ejm Broadcast Inc....G.... 321 251-5662
Orlando *(G-12701)*
◆ **Electro Technik Industries Inc**....D.... 727 530-9555
Clearwater *(G-1666)*
Ericsson Inc....G.... 856 230-6268
Orlando *(G-12716)*
▲ **Fiplex Communications Inc**....E.... 305 884-8991
Doral *(G-3351)*
First Communications Inc....D.... 850 668-7990
Tallahassee *(G-17251)*
▼ **Flagship Marine Inc**....G.... 772 781-4242
Stuart *(G-16940)*
Fleetboss Globl Pstning Sltons....E.... 407 265-9559
Fern Park *(G-3728)*
Florical Systems Inc....E.... 352 372-8326
Gainesville *(G-4920)*
Fortune Media Group Inc....F.... 954 379-4321
Coral Springs *(G-2248)*
Gap Antenna Products Inc....G.... 772 571-9922
Fellsmere *(G-3726)*
Gateway Wireless Communications....F.... 561 732-6444
Boynton Beach *(G-909)*
Global Satellite Prpts LLC....G.... 954 459-3000
Fort Lauderdale *(G-4023)*
Global Wrless Sltions Tech Inc....G.... 941 744-2511
Bradenton *(G-1048)*
Gogps USA Inc....F.... 941 751-2363
Sarasota *(G-16223)*
Gps Education LLC....G.... 386 756-7575
Port Orange *(G-15019)*
Gps Industries LLC....G.... 941 894-8030
Sarasota *(G-16452)*
Helical Communication Tech Inc....G.... 561 762-2823
Rockledge *(G-15416)*
▲ **Hilomast LLC**....G.... 386 668-6784
Debary *(G-2749)*
I-Acritas LLC....G.... 407 375-5707
Orlando *(G-12817)*
▲ **Imagik International Corp**....F.... 786 631-5003
Doral *(G-3388)*
Interface Technology Group Inc....G.... 321 433-1165
Rockledge *(G-15422)*
International Sound Corp....D.... 305 556-1000
Hialeah *(G-5456)*
Interstate Electronics Corp....D.... 321 730-0119
Cape Canaveral *(G-1362)*
Itelecom USA Inc....G.... 305 557-4660
Weston *(G-19143)*
J&B Cmmnication Solutions Corp....G.... 786 346-7449
Davie *(G-2539)*
Joe Hearn Innovative Tech LLC....F.... 850 898-3744
Pensacola *(G-14183)*
Julio Garcia Satellite....G.... 407 414-3223
Kissimmee *(G-7260)*
Keytroller LLC....F.... 813 877-4500
Tampa *(G-17823)*
L3 Technologies Inc....G.... 850 678-9444
Eglin A F B *(G-3640)*
L3 Technologies Inc....G.... 305 371-7039
Fort Lauderdale *(G-4092)*
L3 Technologies Inc....G.... 941 377-5562
Sarasota *(G-16485)*
L3harris Technologies Inc....G.... 321 309-7848
Melbourne *(G-8866)*
▲ **L3harris Technologies Inc**....B.... 321 727-9100
Melbourne *(G-8865)*
L3harris Technologies Inc....D.... 321 768-4660
Malabar *(G-8494)*
Limitless Mobile Wholesale Inc....D.... 321 710-6936
Ocoee *(G-12087)*
Locus Solutions LLC....D.... 561 575-7600
Palm Beach Gardens *(G-13605)*
▲ **M C Test Service Inc**....A.... 321 253-0541
Melbourne *(G-8879)*
Mackay Communications Inc....G.... 904 724-6101
Jacksonville *(G-6572)*
Mambo LLC....F.... 305 860-2544
Doral *(G-3422)*
Maxxfi LLC....F.... 513 289-6521
Cape Coral *(G-1447)*
Micro Systems Inc....C.... 850 244-2332
Fort Walton Beach *(G-4815)*
Mil-Sat LLC....G.... 954 862-3613
Davie *(G-2553)*
▲ **Millimeter Wave Products Inc**....E.... 727 563-0034
Saint Petersburg *(G-15854)*
Monroe Cable LLC....D.... 941 429-8484
North Port *(G-11744)*
Motorola Solutions....G.... 239 939-7717
Fort Myers *(G-4539)*
Motorola Solutions Inc....G.... 850 243-4426
Fort Walton Beach *(G-4818)*
Motorola Solutions Inc....A.... 954 723-5000
Plantation *(G-14535)*
Motorola Solutions Inc....G.... 407 562-4000
Lake Mary *(G-7437)*
Motorola Solutions Inc....G.... 561 369-7164
Boynton Beach *(G-933)*
Motorola Solutions Inc....G.... 850 651-1725
Shalimar *(G-16776)*
Motorola Solutions Center....G.... 863 665-5105
Lakeland *(G-7755)*
Myers Engineering Intl Inc....E.... 954 975-2712
Margate *(G-8558)*
Nahuel Trading Corp....F.... 305 999-9944
Miami *(G-10059)*
◆ **NC IV Inc**....F.... 941 378-9133
Sarasota *(G-16522)*
Nic4 Inc....F.... 877 455-2131
Tampa *(G-17939)*
Nxgen Brands LLC....E.... 888 315-6339
Plantation *(G-14540)*
Orbsat Corp....F.... 305 560-5355
Aventura *(G-278)*
OSI International LLC....G.... 561 394-9508
Boca Raton *(G-656)*
Parkervision Inc....F.... 904 732-6100
Jacksonville *(G-6658)*
Pax Catholic Communications....E.... 305 638-9729
Miami *(G-10146)*
▲ **Phototelesis LP**....E.... 321 254-1500
Melbourne *(G-8908)*
Pinnacle Cmmncations Group LLC....F.... 904 910-0444
Jacksonville *(G-6674)*
Quality Cable Contractors Inc....E.... 407 246-0606
Orlando *(G-13103)*
Qualitysat Corp....G.... 305 232-4211
Miami *(G-10219)*
R F Laboratories Inc....F.... 920 564-2700
Sorrento *(G-16792)*
▲ **Radiotronics Inc**....F.... 772 600-7574
Stuart *(G-16996)*
Rangevideo Laap....G.... 404 421-2574
North Miami Beach *(G-11703)*
▼ **Ravic Technologies LLC**....G.... 954 237-3241
Medley *(G-8715)*
Raytheon Company....G.... 310 647-9438
Largo *(G-8038)*
Raytheon Company....G.... 727 768-8468
Largo *(G-8037)*
Raytheon Company....G.... 321 235-6682
Orlando *(G-13116)*
Reico Inc....F.... 850 243-4400
Fort Walton Beach *(G-4827)*
▲ **Relm Communications Inc**....C.... 321 953-7800
Melbourne *(G-8919)*
▲ **RES-Net Microwave Inc**....E.... 727 530-9555
Clearwater *(G-1858)*
Rockwell Collins Inc....D.... 321 768-7303
Melbourne *(G-8921)*
▲ **RVr USA LLC**....G.... 305 471-9091
Doral *(G-3494)*
Satcom Direct Inc....G.... 321 242-6665
Melbourne *(G-8925)*
Satcom Drect Cmmunications Inc....F.... 321 777-3000
Melbourne *(G-8926)*
◆ **Satcom Scientific Inc**....F.... 407 856-1050
Orlando *(G-13164)*
Satellite Now Inc....G.... 239 945-0520
Cape Coral *(G-1465)*
Self Made Dynasty LLC....G.... 754 303-3134
Fort Lauderdale *(G-4229)*
Sidus Space Inc....E.... 321 613-0615
Cape Canaveral *(G-1367)*
Sierra Nevada Corporation....E.... 850 659-3600
Shalimar *(G-16777)*
▲ **Sky Phone LLC**....F.... 305 531-5218
Miami Beach *(G-10711)*
▼ **Smiths Interconnect Inc**....C.... 813 901-7200
Tampa *(G-18111)*
Southeastern Engineering Inc....F.... 321 984-2521
Palm Bay *(G-13538)*
▲ **Sports Radar Ltd**....G.... 352 503-6825
Homosassa *(G-6006)*
Srt Wireless LLC....G.... 954 797-7850
Sunrise *(G-17177)*
Summation Research Inc....E.... 321 254-2580
Melbourne *(G-8949)*
Tampa Microwave LLC....E.... 813 855-2251
Clearwater *(G-1904)*
Tech Comm Inc....F.... 954 712-7777
Fort Lauderdale *(G-4275)*
Techcodes LLC....G.... 321 529-4122
Titusville *(G-18467)*
Tecore Government Services LLC....G.... 410 872-6000
Melbourne *(G-8956)*
◆ **Transamerica Intl Brdcstg**....G.... 305 477-0973
Miami *(G-10503)*
Tridor Group Inc....F.... 786 707-2241
Miami *(G-10506)*
Trs Wireless Inc....E.... 407 447-7333
Orlando *(G-13277)*
TV Film International Inc....G.... 305 671-3265
Miami *(G-10515)*
TX Trading Inc....G.... 786 303-9950
Miami *(G-10518)*
U B Corp....G.... 813 884-1463
Tampa *(G-18210)*
United Wireless Tech Inc....F.... 561 302-9350
Boca Raton *(G-769)*
US Mobile Pro LLC....G.... 973 365-1812
Orlando *(G-13298)*
Vela Research LP....D.... 727 507-5300
Clearwater *(G-1930)*
Venti Group LLC....G.... 949 264-3185
Miami Beach *(G-10726)*
Vertical Bridge Towers LLC....C.... 561 948-6367
Boca Raton *(G-778)*
Viasat Inc....G.... 813 880-5000
Tampa *(G-18243)*
Viatech of Delaware Inc....E.... 321 308-6600
Melbourne *(G-8971)*
Video Display Corporation....D.... 321 784-4427
Cocoa *(G-2056)*
Visual Comm Specialists Inc....G.... 407 936-7300
Lake Mary *(G-7460)*
Vmoviles Inc....G.... 954 609-2510
Aventura *(G-282)*
◆ **Voxx International Corporation**....B.... 800 645-7750
Orlando *(G-13313)*
▲ **W & W Manufacturing Co**....E.... 516 942-0011
Tampa *(G-18249)*
Wialan Technologies LLC....E.... 954 749-3481
Sunrise *(G-17198)*
Williams Communications Inc....G.... 850 689-6651
Crestview *(G-2361)*
Wiztel USA Inc....G.... 416 457-5513
Miromar Lakes *(G-11072)*
Wpp Group Usa Inc....G.... 305 341-8132
Miami *(G-10623)*

3669 Communications Eqpt, NEC

Access Wrless Data Sltions LLC....G.... 813 751-2039
Lutz *(G-8372)*
Acoustic Communications LLC....G.... 305 463-9485
Doral *(G-3226)*
Advantor Systems Corporation....C.... 407 859-3350
Orlando *(G-12436)*
Alstom Signaling Operation LLC....C.... 781 740-8111
Melbourne *(G-8765)*
Asp Alarm & Elec Sups Inc....G.... 305 556-9047
Hialeah *(G-5309)*
▲ **Attenti Us Inc**....C.... 813 749-5454
Odessa *(G-12104)*
Automation Consulting Inc....F.... 850 477-6477
Pensacola *(G-14095)*
▼ **AVI-Spl Emplyee Emrgncy Rlief**....A.... 813 884-7168
Tampa *(G-17445)*
▼ **AVI-Spl Holdings Inc**....A.... 866 708-5034
Tampa *(G-17446)*

S I C

▼ **AVI-Spl LLC**..................A....... 813 884-7168
Tampa *(G-17447)*
Bay Design Marine Group Inc..................G....... 239 825-8094
Naples *(G-11184)*
Carrier Fire SEC Americas Corp..................G....... 828 695-4000
Palm Beach Gardens *(G-13574)*
City of Ocala..................E....... 352 622-6803
Ocala *(G-11903)*
Danas Safty Supply Inc..................F....... 305 639-6024
Doral *(G-3323)*
Ddci Inc..................D....... 407 814-0225
Orlando *(G-12659)*
Dynasystems LLC..................G....... 410 343-7759
Melbourne *(G-8816)*
First Communications Inc..................D....... 850 668-7990
Tallahassee *(G-17251)*
Gresso LLC..................G....... 305 515-8677
Miami *(G-9671)*
Heritage Medcall LLC..................F....... 813 221-1000
Tampa *(G-17753)*
Ingram Signalization Inc..................E....... 850 433-8267
Pensacola *(G-14178)*
International C & C Corp..................E....... 727 249-0675
Largo *(G-7981)*
Interrail Engineering Inc..................E....... 904 268-6411
Jacksonville *(G-6501)*
JB Custom Marine..................G....... 239 877-2784
Naples *(G-11294)*
Kaltec Electronics Inc..................F....... 813 888-9555
Tampa *(G-17814)*
Keytroller LLC..................F....... 813 877-4500
Tampa *(G-17823)*
L3 Technologies Inc..................G....... 305 371-7039
Fort Lauderdale *(G-4092)*
Lugloc LLC..................F....... 305 961-1765
Miami *(G-9916)*
Med Alert Response Inc..................G....... 407 730-3571
Orlando *(G-12958)*
Medattend LLC..................F....... 561 465-2735
Boca Raton *(G-616)*
Minuteman Industries Inc..................G....... 813 248-1776
Tampa *(G-17909)*
Morganelli & Associates Inc..................G....... 386 738-3669
Deland *(G-2998)*
N & H Construction Inc..................F....... 904 282-2224
Middleburg *(G-10910)*
Nitv Federal Services LLC..................G....... 561 798-6280
West Palm Beach *(G-18966)*
North American Signal LLC..................G....... 850 462-1790
Pensacola *(G-14212)*
North Amrcn Signal Systems LLC..................G....... 352 376-8341
Gainesville *(G-4973)*
Old Heritage Medcall Inc..................F....... 813 221-1000
Tampa *(G-17948)*
Padgett Communications Inc..................E....... 727 323-5800
Tampa *(G-17969)*
◆ **Peek Traffic Corporation**..................C....... 941 366-8770
Sarasota *(G-16275)*
Potter Roemer LLC..................G....... 786 845-0842
Doral *(G-3463)*
◆ **Prime Meridian Trading Corp**..................G....... 954 727-2152
Sunrise *(G-17161)*
▼ **Rossam Industries Inc**..................E....... 305 493-5111
Fort Lauderdale *(G-4216)*
▲ **Salt International Corp**..................G....... 305 698-8889
Pembroke Park *(G-14012)*
Security Tech Group Inc..................G....... 305 631-2228
Miami *(G-10320)*
Simplex Time Recorder Co..................G....... 561 988-7200
Boca Raton *(G-715)*
Simplexgrinnell Holdings LLC..................G....... 978 731-2500
Boca Raton *(G-716)*
▼ **Smiths Interconnect Inc**..................C....... 813 901-7200
Tampa *(G-18111)*
Southwest Signal Inc..................E....... 813 621-4949
Englewood *(G-3667)*
Spec-TEC Manufacturing Inc..................G....... 954 749-4204
Sunrise *(G-17176)*
Superior Fire & Lf Safety Inc..................F....... 850 572-0265
Cape Coral *(G-1480)*
▲ **Tectron Engineering Company**..................F....... 904 394-0683
Jacksonville *(G-6845)*
Traffic Control Pdts Fla Inc..................F....... 352 372-7088
Jacksonville *(G-6865)*
▲ **Traffipax LLC**..................B....... 561 881-7400
Jupiter *(G-7131)*
▼ **Transprtation Ctrl Systems Inc**..................E....... 813 630-2800
Tampa *(G-18197)*
▲ **Two Way Radio Gear Inc**..................F....... 800 984-1534
Fort Pierce *(G-4764)*
United Rail Inc..................F....... 904 503-9757
Jacksonville *(G-6881)*
▲ **Vanguard Products Group Inc**..................D....... 813 855-9639
Oldsmar *(G-12277)*
Vecom Usa LLC..................G....... 813 901-5300
Tampa *(G-18235)*
Viper Communication Systems..................E....... 352 694-7030
Ocala *(G-12072)*
Walkup Enterprises Inc..................F....... 727 571-1244
Clearwater *(G-1935)*
Zom Monterra LP..................G....... 407 644-6300
Orlando *(G-13344)*
▲ **Zumro Manufacturing Inc**..................E....... 954 782-7779
Pompano Beach *(G-14916)*

3671 Radio & T V Receiving Electron Tubes

◆ **Advanced Manufacturing Inc**..................E....... 727 573-3300
Saint Petersburg *(G-15691)*
Cathodic Prtection Tech of Fla..................G....... 321 799-0046
Cocoa Beach *(G-2060)*
▲ **Citel America Inc**..................F....... 954 430-6310
Miramar *(G-10979)*
L3harris Technologies Inc..................G....... 321 727-9100
Melbourne *(G-8870)*
Lextm3 Systems LLC..................F....... 954 888-1024
Davie *(G-2546)*
Passur Aerospace Inc..................G....... 631 589-6800
Orlando *(G-13051)*
Video Display Corporation..................D....... 321 784-4427
Cocoa *(G-2056)*

3672 Printed Circuit Boards

4front Solutions LLC..................D....... 814 464-2000
Deland *(G-2951)*
▲ **ACt USA International LLC**..................F....... 321 725-4200
Melbourne *(G-8757)*
◆ **Advanced Manufacturing Inc**..................E....... 727 573-3300
Saint Petersburg *(G-15691)*
Alegro Industries Inc..................D....... 702 943-0978
Tamarac *(G-17349)*
American Auto Marine Wiring..................G....... 954 782-0193
Pompano Beach *(G-14590)*
AOC Technologies Inc..................F....... 727 577-9749
Saint Petersburg *(G-15702)*
Ateei International Corp..................E....... 305 597-6408
Doral *(G-3258)*
Aw-Tronics LLC..................E....... 786 228-7835
Miami *(G-9202)*
Axon Circuit Inc..................F....... 407 265-7980
Longwood *(G-8260)*
▲ **Axon Circuit Inc**..................E....... 407 265-7980
Tampa *(G-17450)*
▲ **Bare Board Group Inc**..................E....... 727 549-2200
Largo *(G-7904)*
Board Shark Pcb Inc..................G....... 352 759-2100
Astor *(G-215)*
▲ **C K C Industries Inc**..................G....... 813 888-9468
Tampa *(G-17494)*
Calumet Electronics..................G....... 954 668-7689
Hollywood *(G-5794)*
Certified Manufacturing Inc..................E....... 850 537-3777
Holt *(G-5948)*
Circuit Works Co..................G....... 727 544-5336
Pinellas Park *(G-14338)*
Circuitronics LLC..................F....... 407 322-8300
Sanford *(G-16015)*
▲ **Circuitronix LLC**..................B....... 786 364-4458
Fort Lauderdale *(G-3900)*
Concept 2 Market Inc..................F....... 954 974-0022
Pompano Beach *(G-14643)*
Continuity Unlimited Inc..................F....... 561 358-8171
Oviedo *(G-13422)*
Creonix LLC..................F....... 941 758-3340
Brooksville *(G-1223)*
Delta Group Electronics Inc..................D....... 321 631-0799
Rockledge *(G-15400)*
Denver Elevator Systems Inc..................G....... 800 633-9788
Cape Canaveral *(G-1356)*
Diamond Mt Inc..................F....... 321 339-3377
Melbourne *(G-8804)*
Elreha Printed Circuits..................G....... 727 244-0130
Bradenton *(G-1036)*
Englander Enterprises Inc..................E....... 727 461-4755
Clearwater *(G-1673)*
▲ **Florida Elreha Corporation**..................E....... 727 327-6236
Saint Petersburg *(G-15783)*
Global Intrcnnect Slutions LLC..................G....... 239 254-0326
Naples *(G-11262)*
◆ **H & T Global Circuit Fctry LLC**..................D....... 727 327-6236
Saint Petersburg *(G-15802)*
I3 Microsystems Inc..................E....... 727 235-6532
Saint Petersburg *(G-15810)*
▲ **Icmfg & Associates Inc**..................G....... 727 258-4995
Clearwater *(G-1726)*
Infinity Pcb Inc..................G....... 321 804-8045
West Melbourne *(G-18776)*
Itct USA..................G....... 352 799-1466
Brooksville *(G-1239)*
Jabil Advnced Mech Sltions Inc..................E....... 727 577-9749
Saint Petersburg *(G-15821)*
Jabil Circuit..................G....... 727 577-9749
Saint Petersburg *(G-15822)*
▲ **Jabil Circuit LLC**..................G....... 727 577-9749
Saint Petersburg *(G-15823)*
Jabil Circuit LLC..................D....... 727 577-9749
Saint Petersburg *(G-15824)*
Jabil Def & Arospc Svcs LLC..................E....... 727 577-9749
Saint Petersburg *(G-15825)*
Jabil Def & Arospc Svcs LLC..................F....... 727 577-9749
Saint Petersburg *(G-15826)*
Jabil Inc..................A....... 727 577-9749
Saint Petersburg *(G-15827)*
Jabil Inc..................E....... 727 577-9749
Saint Petersburg *(G-15828)*
Jabil Inc..................C....... 727 803-3110
Saint Petersburg *(G-15829)*
Jabil Inc..................D....... 727 577-9749
Saint Petersburg *(G-15830)*
Jrt Manufacturing LLC..................F....... 321 363-4133
Sanford *(G-16076)*
Kimball Electronics Tampa Inc..................C....... 813 814-5229
Tampa *(G-17825)*
Laser Photo Tooling Services..................F....... 561 393-4710
Boca Raton *(G-596)*
▲ **M C Test Service Inc**..................A....... 321 253-0541
Melbourne *(G-8879)*
▲ **Mack Technologies Florida Inc**..................C....... 321 725-6993
Melbourne *(G-8881)*
Marlo Electronics Inc..................E....... 561 477-0856
Boca Raton *(G-610)*
▲ **Mathews Associates Inc**..................C....... 407 323-3390
Sanford *(G-16082)*
▲ **Mc Assembly Holdings Inc**..................G....... 321 253-0541
Melbourne *(G-8884)*
▲ **Memo Labs Inc**..................F....... 561 842-0586
West Palm Beach *(G-18948)*
Micro Engineering Inc..................E....... 407 886-4849
Apopka *(G-161)*
Nano Dimension USA Inc..................E....... 650 209-2866
Sunrise *(G-17150)*
Nypro Healthcare LLC..................E....... 727 577-9749
Saint Petersburg *(G-15868)*
Oum LLC..................F....... 407 886-1511
Apopka *(G-168)*
Paramount Industries Inc..................E....... 954 781-3755
Pompano Beach *(G-14784)*
Pica Sales and Engineering..................G....... 239 992-9079
Estero *(G-3693)*
Precision Circuits Inc..................E....... 321 632-8629
Rockledge *(G-15441)*
Prime Technological Svcs LLC..................D....... 850 539-2500
Havana *(G-5239)*
▲ **Profab Electronics Inc**..................E....... 954 917-1998
Pompano Beach *(G-14818)*
Protek Electronics Inc..................E....... 941 351-4399
Sarasota *(G-16548)*
Qualitel Inc..................E....... 954 464-3991
Hollywood *(G-5897)*
▲ **Quality Manufacturing Svcs Inc**..................D....... 407 531-6000
Lake Mary *(G-7447)*
Ra Co AMO Inc..................F....... 561 626-7232
Palm Beach Gardens *(G-13620)*
Rtp Corp..................G....... 954 597-5333
Pompano Beach *(G-14836)*
Sibex Inc..................C....... 727 726-4343
Crystal River *(G-2382)*
▼ **Smiths Interconnect Inc**..................C....... 813 901-7200
Tampa *(G-18111)*
▲ **Solutions Manufacturing Inc**..................D....... 321 848-0848
Rockledge *(G-15448)*
▲ **Sparton Corporation**..................C....... 847 762-5800
De Leon Springs *(G-2742)*
▲ **Sparton Deleon Springs LLC**..................D....... 386 985-4631
De Leon Springs *(G-2743)*
Specialty Fin Consulting Corp..................B....... 717 246-1661
Longboat Key *(G-8247)*
Superior Electronics Inc..................E....... 727 733-0700
Clearwater *(G-1896)*
▲ **Sypris Electronics LLC**..................B....... 813 972-6000
Tampa *(G-18149)*

Tms Enterprises LLC..........B....... 850 539-2500
Havana *(G-5240)*
Tropical Assemblies Inc..........D....... 954 396-9999
Oakland Park *(G-11848)*
Tropical Stencil Pcb Inc..........F....... 561 972-5133
Jupiter *(G-7133)*
United Circuits Inc..........F....... 954 971-6860
Pompano Beach *(G-14900)*
Xtreme Electronic Designs Inc..........G....... 561 557-3667
Jupiter *(G-7148)*

3674 Semiconductors

▲ Absen Inc..........D....... 407 203-8870
Orlando *(G-12426)*
◆ Adj Inc..........F....... 727 289-6173
Tierra Verde *(G-18405)*
Aerouno Llc..........F....... 561 767-5597
Margate *(G-8532)*
◆ AGS Electronics Inc..........G....... 850 471-1551
Pensacola *(G-14086)*
Akuwa Solutions Group Inc..........F....... 941 343-9947
Sarasota *(G-16337)*
Alterna Power Inc..........F....... 407 287-9148
Orlando *(G-12462)*
American All..........G....... 561 401-0885
Loxahatchee *(G-8356)*
American Led Display Solutions..........G....... 561 227-8048
Miami *(G-9145)*
American Technology Pdts Inc..........F....... 407 960-1722
Sanford *(G-15993)*
Analog Modules Inc..........D....... 407 339-4355
Longwood *(G-8255)*
▲ Apollo Metro Solutions Inc..........G....... 239 444-6934
Naples *(G-11165)*
Apure Distribution LLC..........F....... 305 351-1025
Miami *(G-9159)*
Aqualuma LLC..........G....... 954 234-2512
Deerfield Beach *(G-2778)*
Atlas Renewable Energy USA LLC..........F....... 786 358-5614
Miami *(G-9189)*
Aurora Semiconductor LLC..........E....... 727 235-6500
Saint Petersburg *(G-15716)*
B & R Profiles LLC..........E....... 305 479-8308
Bartow *(G-306)*
Baytronics Manufacturing Inc..........G....... 813 434-0401
Tampa *(G-17460)*
Boca Semiconductor Corporation..........E....... 561 226-8500
Boca Raton *(G-456)*
▲ Brightwatts Inc..........F....... 954 513-3352
Oakland Park *(G-11787)*
▲ Chip Supply Inc..........D....... 407 298-7100
Orlando *(G-12580)*
City Labs Inc..........G....... 305 909-7593
Miami *(G-9357)*
Cobham Slip Rings Naples Inc..........D....... 239 263-3102
Naples *(G-11213)*
Convergent Actuarial Svcs Inc..........G....... 561 715-4204
Delray Beach *(G-3064)*
Convergent Engineering Inc..........F....... 352 378-4899
Gainesville *(G-4896)*
Convergent Marketing LLC..........G....... 561 270-7081
Delray Beach *(G-3065)*
Convergent Technologies..........F....... 407 482-4381
Orlando *(G-12618)*
Cybortrack Solutions Inc..........G....... 805 904-5677
Longwood *(G-8271)*
▲ David S Stoyka..........G....... 561 848-2599
Riviera Beach *(G-15319)*
Drs Ntwork Imaging Systems LLC..........E....... 321 309-1500
Palm Bay *(G-13509)*
Drt Services..........G....... 321 549-1431
Palm Bay *(G-13510)*
Exalos Inc..........E....... 215 669-4488
Fort Lauderdale *(G-3980)*
Florida Micro Devices Inc..........G....... 954 973-7200
Coral Springs *(G-2245)*
Gb Energy Tech..........F....... 561 450-6047
Delray Beach *(G-3083)*
Gen-Prodics Inc..........G....... 772 221-8464
Palm City *(G-13658)*
▲ Guardian Solar LLC..........F....... 727 504-2790
Tarpon Springs *(G-18304)*
Hine Automation LLC..........G....... 813 749-7519
Saint Petersburg *(G-15807)*
▼ Hybrid Sources Inc..........F....... 772 563-9100
Vero Beach *(G-18626)*
Icamr Inc..........G....... 407 742-4253
Kissimmee *(G-7252)*
Intelbase Security Corporation..........G....... 703 371-9181
Saint Augustine *(G-15557)*
◆ Intertech Supply Inc..........G....... 786 200-0561
Miami *(G-9762)*
Itelecom USA Inc..........G....... 305 557-4660
Weston *(G-19143)*
JAs Business Solutions Inc..........E....... 954 975-0025
Pompano Beach *(G-14735)*
Keytroller LLC..........F....... 813 877-4500
Tampa *(G-17823)*
▲ L3harris Technologies Inc..........B....... 321 727-9100
Melbourne *(G-8865)*
Legacy Components LLC..........F....... 813 964-6805
Tampa *(G-17840)*
Luminoso LLC..........G....... 305 364-8099
Miami Lakes *(G-10810)*
Lumiron Inc..........G....... 305 652-2599
Miami *(G-9919)*
M P I Medical Products Inc..........G....... 321 676-1299
Palm Bay *(G-13522)*
Mercury Systems Inc..........E....... 352 371-2567
Gainesville *(G-4961)*
▲ Micro Control Systems Inc..........E....... 239 694-0089
Fort Myers *(G-4532)*
Micro Engineering Inc..........E....... 407 886-4849
Apopka *(G-161)*
Micross Components Inc..........E....... 407 298-7100
Orlando *(G-12968)*
Micross Minco LLC..........D....... 512 339-3422
Orlando *(G-12969)*
Micross Prmier Smcdtr Svcs LLC..........E....... 727 532-1777
Clearwater *(G-1785)*
Motorola Solutions Inc..........G....... 407 562-4000
Lake Mary *(G-7437)*
Multicore Photonics Inc..........G....... 407 325-7800
Orlando *(G-12984)*
Multicore Technologies LLC..........G....... 407 325-7800
Orlando *(G-12986)*
Nebula Led Lighting Systems of..........G....... 813 907-0001
Wesley Chapel *(G-18754)*
Neos Technologies Inc..........G....... 321 242-7818
Melbourne *(G-8893)*
Nor East Materials Inc..........F....... 386 478-0087
New Smyrna Beach *(G-11539)*
Northrop Grumman Systems Corp..........B....... 407 295-4010
Apopka *(G-166)*
Notice Four LLC..........G....... 954 652-1168
Fort Lauderdale *(G-4143)*
Oerlikon USA Inc..........E....... 727 577-4999
Saint Petersburg *(G-15870)*
One Resonance Sensors LLC..........F....... 407 637-0771
Sanford *(G-16095)*
Parkervision Inc..........F....... 904 732-6100
Jacksonville *(G-6658)*
Planar Energy Devices Inc..........F....... 407 459-1440
Orlando *(G-13071)*
▲ Plasma-Therm LLC..........C....... 727 577-4999
Saint Petersburg *(G-15881)*
Power Production MGT Inc..........G....... 352 263-0766
Gainesville *(G-4981)*
Premier Semiconductor Svcs LLC..........G....... 727 532-1777
Clearwater *(G-1844)*
Qorvo Us Inc..........B....... 407 886-8860
Apopka *(G-176)*
Qualcomm Atheros Inc..........F....... 407 284-7314
Orlando *(G-13102)*
Quantum Technology Inc..........G....... 407 333-9348
Lake Mary *(G-7448)*
Quartz Unlimited LLC..........G....... 561 306-1243
Boca Raton *(G-679)*
Raytheon Company..........C....... 310 647-9438
Largo *(G-8036)*
Reflectivity Inc..........F....... 386 738-1008
Deland *(G-3011)*
Renesas Electronics Amer Inc..........A....... 321 724-7000
Palm Bay *(G-13531)*
▼ Scientific Instruments Inc..........E....... 561 881-8500
Mangonia Park *(G-8511)*
Semiconductor Technology Inc..........G....... 772 341-0800
Stuart *(G-17008)*
Semilab USA LLC..........E....... 813 977-2244
Temple Terrace *(G-18378)*
Sepac Corp..........F....... 305 718-3379
Miami *(G-10325)*
▼ Smiths Interconnect Inc..........C....... 813 901-7200
Tampa *(G-18111)*
◆ Solar Electric Power Company..........F....... 772 220-6615
Stuart *(G-17018)*
Solarbeam International Inc..........G....... 305 248-8400
Homestead *(G-5994)*
Solartech Universal LLC..........E....... 561 440-8000
Riviera Beach *(G-15378)*
Solitron Devices Inc..........D....... 561 848-4311
West Palm Beach *(G-19038)*
Sollunar Energy Inc..........G....... 352 293-2347
Spring Hill *(G-16864)*
Spartronics Brooksville LLC..........D....... 352 799-6520
Brooksville *(G-1274)*
Spartronics Brooksville LLC..........B....... 352 799-6520
Brooksville *(G-1275)*
Suncoast Led Displays LLC..........F....... 727 683-2777
Palm Harbor *(G-13763)*
Sunwyre Inc..........F....... 904 631-6961
Jacksonville *(G-6827)*
Supliaereos USA LLC..........G....... 727 754-4915
Clearwater *(G-1897)*
Technology Products Design Inc..........F....... 321 432-3537
Palm Bay *(G-13543)*
Tesco of Swfl Inc..........G....... 239 234-6490
Naples *(G-11438)*
Tesseract Sensors LLC..........F....... 407 385-2498
Sanford *(G-16127)*
Tm USA Inc..........G....... 954 801-4649
Doral *(G-3529)*
Triple Play Cmmunications Corp..........G....... 321 327-8997
Melbourne *(G-8966)*
US Applied Phys Ics Group..........G....... 321 567-7270
Titusville *(G-18471)*
US Applied Physics Group LLC..........G....... 321 607-9023
Titusville *(G-18472)*
Visiontech Components LLC..........F....... 727 547-5466
Clearwater *(G-1933)*
▼ Wafer World Inc..........F....... 561 842-4441
West Palm Beach *(G-19083)*
Wbn LLC..........G....... 786 870-4172
Doral *(G-3547)*
Xilinx Inc..........F....... 407 365-8644
Oviedo *(G-13462)*

3675 Electronic Capacitors

ABB Inc..........D....... 407 732-2000
Lake Mary *(G-7396)*
ABB Inc..........D....... 305 471-0844
Miami *(G-9053)*
American Tchncal Crmics Fla In..........D....... 904 724-2000
Jacksonville *(G-6152)*
▲ Bocatech Inc..........G....... 954 397-7070
Deerfield Beach *(G-2788)*
▲ Dynamic Engrg Innovations Inc..........C....... 386 445-6000
Palm Coast *(G-13692)*
Exxelia Usa Inc..........E....... 407 695-6562
Longwood *(G-8279)*
▲ General Capacitor LLC..........G....... 510 371-2700
Tallahassee *(G-17262)*
▲ Kemet Corporation..........A....... 954 766-2800
Fort Lauderdale *(G-4086)*
Kemet Ventures LLC..........G....... 407 403-2958
Orlando *(G-12868)*
Mat-Vac Technology Inc..........F....... 386 238-7017
Daytona Beach *(G-2683)*
Nordquist Dielectrics Inc..........E....... 727 585-7990
Clearwater *(G-1809)*
Nwl Inc..........C....... 561 848-9009
Riviera Beach *(G-15353)*
Vladmir Ltd..........E....... 386 445-6000
Palm Coast *(G-13714)*

3676 Electronic Resistors

▼ Casa Del Marinero Corp..........G....... 305 374-5386
Miami *(G-9322)*
▲ Component General Inc..........E....... 727 376-6655
Odessa *(G-12112)*
◆ Electro Technik Industries Inc..........D....... 727 530-9555
Clearwater *(G-1666)*
Precision Resistor Co Inc..........E....... 727 541-5771
Seminole *(G-16756)*
Solitron Devices Inc..........D....... 561 848-4311
West Palm Beach *(G-19038)*
Vishay Americas Inc..........B....... 407 804-2567
Lake Mary *(G-7459)*

3677 Electronic Coils & Transformers

▲ Bocatech Inc..........G....... 954 397-7070
Deerfield Beach *(G-2788)*
Certified Manufacturing Inc..........E....... 850 537-3777
Holt *(G-5948)*
E3 Fluid Recovery Eng..........G....... 727 754-9792
Largo *(G-7939)*
◆ Electro Technik Industries Inc..........D....... 727 530-9555
Clearwater *(G-1666)*
Exxelia Usa Inc..........E....... 407 695-6562
Longwood *(G-8279)*

SIC

◆ **Filta Group Inc** F 407 996-5550
Orlando *(G-12738)*
Filter Research Corporation E 321 802-3444
Palm Bay *(G-13512)*
▲ **Hytronics Corp** D 727 535-0413
Clearwater *(G-1725)*
◆ **Manutech Assembly Inc** G 305 888-2800
Miami *(G-9942)*
Nordquist Dielectrics Inc E 727 585-7990
Clearwater *(G-1809)*
OHM Americas LLC F 800 467-7275
Fort Lauderdale *(G-4148)*
Paal Technologies Inc G 954 368-5000
Sunrise *(G-17156)*
Pall Filtration and Sep C 386 822-8000
Deland *(G-3007)*
Piezo Technology Inc C 407 298-2000
Orlando *(G-13067)*
Precision Econowind LLC F 239 997-3860
North Fort Myers *(G-11603)*
Renco Usa Inc F 321 637-1000
Miami *(G-10252)*
▲ **Spin Magnetics** E 863 676-9333
Lake Wales *(G-7520)*
Standard Technology Inc F 386 671-7406
Ormond Beach *(G-13402)*
▲ **Two Little Fishies Inc** G 305 623-7695
Miami *(G-10517)*
▲ **Vision Engineering Labs** D 727 812-2035
Largo *(G-8076)*
Winatic Corporation D 727 538-8917
Clearwater *(G-1942)*

3678 Electronic Connectors

Altelix LLC F 561 660-9434
Boca Raton *(G-415)*
Arrowhead Global LLC G 727 497-7340
Clearwater *(G-1589)*
Backbone Interconnect LLC E 954 800-4749
Sunrise *(G-17093)*
▲ **Benchmark Connector Corp** E 954 746-9929
Sunrise *(G-17096)*
▲ **Bocatech Inc** G 954 397-7070
Deerfield Beach *(G-2788)*
▲ **Carlisle Interconnect Tech Inc** A 904 829-5600
Saint Augustine *(G-15526)*
▲ **Diversfied Mtl Specialists Inc** G 941 244-0935
North Venice *(G-11757)*
◆ **Eagle I Tech Inc** E 772 221-8188
Palm City *(G-13651)*
▲ **Interconnect Cable Tech Corp** D 352 796-1716
Brooksville *(G-1237)*
Lextm3 Systems LLC F 954 888-1024
Davie *(G-2546)*
Logus Manufacturing Corp E 561 842-3550
West Palm Beach *(G-18934)*
Molex LLC F 727 521-2700
Pinellas Park *(G-14370)*
Rde Connectors & Cables Inc F 954 746-6400
Sunrise *(G-17168)*
▲ **Rpp Devices** G 772 807-7098
Port Saint Lucie *(G-15140)*
Stratos Light Wave Inc G 321 308-4100
Melbourne *(G-8946)*
Sv Microwave Inc C 561 840-1800
West Palm Beach *(G-19052)*
Teledyne Instruments Inc C 386 236-0780
Daytona Beach *(G-2725)*
Winchster Interconnect Rf Corp E 800 881-9689
Melbourne *(G-8975)*

3679 Electronic Components, NEC

2204 Avenue X LLC G 407 619-1410
Vero Beach *(G-18588)*
ABC Components Inc F 954 249-6286
Cooper City *(G-2106)*
ACR Family Components LLC E 352 243-0307
Groveland *(G-5092)*
Adtec Productions Incorporated G 904 720-2003
Jacksonville *(G-6120)*
◆ **Advanced Manufacturing Inc** E 727 573-3300
Saint Petersburg *(G-15691)*
Aero Electronics Systems Inc G 321 269-0478
Titusville *(G-18411)*
Akuwa Solutions Group Inc F 941 343-9947
Sarasota *(G-16337)*
▼ **All Things Digital Inc** E 305 887-9464
Miami *(G-9113)*
Allied Circuits LLC G 239 970-2299
Naples *(G-11155)*
American Data Supply Inc F 866 650-3282
Clearwater *(G-1579)*
American Fibertek Inc E 732 302-0660
Saint Petersburg *(G-15699)*
APA Wireless Technologies Inc F 954 563-8833
Oakland Park *(G-11777)*
API Tech North America Inc G 929 255-1231
Winter Park *(G-19377)*
Arcco Inc G 954 564-0827
Oakland Park *(G-11779)*
Aspen Electronics Inc E 305 863-2151
Miami *(G-9179)*
Atlas Marine Systems Inc F 954 735-6767
Fort Lauderdale *(G-3830)*
Automatic Coax and Cable Inc E 407 322-7622
Sanford *(G-15999)*
Backbone Interconnect LLC E 954 800-4749
Sunrise *(G-17093)*
Best Circuits Inc E 321 425-6725
Melbourne *(G-8778)*
▲ **Bocatech Inc** G 954 397-7070
Deerfield Beach *(G-2788)*
Built Story LLC G 305 671-3890
Miami *(G-9283)*
Capacitor and Components LLC E 954 798-8943
Sunrise *(G-17104)*
▲ **Carlisle Interconnect Tech Inc** A 904 829-5600
Saint Augustine *(G-15526)*
Concept 2 Market Inc F 954 974-0022
Pompano Beach *(G-14643)*
Concept Group LLC F 856 767-5506
Palm Beach Gardens *(G-13582)*
▲ **Concurrent Mfg Solutions LLC** E 512 637-2540
Doral *(G-3304)*
Continuity Unlimited Inc F 561 358-8171
Oviedo *(G-13422)*
Crystek Crystals Corporation E 239 561-3311
Fort Myers *(G-4418)*
Custom Mfg & Engrg Inc D 727 548-0522
Pinellas Park *(G-14342)*
Daytona Glass Works LLC F 386 274-2550
Daytona Beach *(G-2654)*
Dbi Services LLC E 239 218-5204
Fort Myers *(G-4427)*
Delta Group Electronics Inc D 321 631-0799
Rockledge *(G-15400)*
▲ **Digital Antenna Inc** F 954 747-7022
Sunrise *(G-17115)*
Digital Pixel Displays LLC G 321 948-3751
Orlando *(G-12673)*
▲ **DMC Components Intl LLC** G 407 478-4064
Winter Park *(G-19404)*
Dry Bonez Inc G 321 926-6399
Boca Raton *(G-510)*
Edge Power Solutions Inc F 321 499-1919
Melbourne *(G-8821)*
▲ **Electriduct Inc** E 954 867-9100
Pompano Beach *(G-14676)*
◆ **Electro Technik Industries Inc** D 727 530-9555
Clearwater *(G-1666)*
Electrosource Inc G 954 723-0840
Plantation *(G-14510)*
Flint LLC G 813 622-8899
Tampa *(G-17670)*
Frc Electrical Industries Inc G 321 676-3300
Palm Bay *(G-13514)*
Freshsurety Corporation G 321 209-8699
Altamonte Springs *(G-47)*
Hascall Engineering and Mfg Co F 941 723-2833
Palmetto *(G-13805)*
Hiltronics Corporation G 954 341-9100
Coral Springs *(G-2254)*
▲ **I-Con Systems Inc** D 407 365-6241
Oviedo *(G-13438)*
▲ **Intellitec Motor Vehicles LLC** E 386 738-7307
Deland *(G-2984)*
▲ **Interconnect Cable Tech Corp** D 352 796-1716
Brooksville *(G-1237)*
J and A Maintenance F 754 234-0708
Sunrise *(G-17133)*
Jfh Technologies LLC E 407 938-9336
Lake Buena Vista *(G-7336)*
Joyce Telectronics Corp F 727 461-3525
Zephyrhills *(G-19525)*
Just-In-Time Mfg Corp F 321 752-7552
Melbourne *(G-8857)*
▲ **Kai Limited** C 954 957-8586
Fort Lauderdale *(G-4083)*
KID Group Inc G 888 805-8851
Greenacres *(G-5084)*
Kimball Electronics Tampa Inc C 813 814-5229
Tampa *(G-17825)*
◆ **Ksm Electronics Inc** D 954 642-7050
Tamarac *(G-17361)*
L3 Technologies Inc G 305 371-7039
Fort Lauderdale *(G-4092)*
Leeward Tech G 305 215-4526
Homestead *(G-5980)*
Lgl Group Inc G 407 298-2000
Orlando *(G-12907)*
▲ **LMI Components Inc** F 561 994-5896
Boca Raton *(G-604)*
Logus Manufacturing Corp E 561 842-3550
West Palm Beach *(G-18934)*
Mdco Inc F 813 855-4068
Tampa *(G-17898)*
Meck Tech Corp G 888 225-9403
Orange Park *(G-12400)*
Micro Hybrids Inc G 772 225-4206
Stuart *(G-16976)*
Micro Technology of Brevard G 321 733-1766
Melbourne *(G-8889)*
◆ **Micro-Ant LLC** D 904 683-8394
Jacksonville *(G-6602)*
Microwave Electronics G 561 432-8511
Lake Worth *(G-7570)*
Mini Circuits Lab Inc D 305 558-6381
Hialeah *(G-5519)*
MN Trades Inc G 954 455-9320
Hallandale Beach *(G-5200)*
Molex LLC F 727 521-2700
Pinellas Park *(G-14370)*
Monroe Cable LLC D 941 429-8484
North Port *(G-11744)*
Mtn Government Services Inc F 954 538-4000
Miramar *(G-11019)*
New ERA Technology Corp F 352 746-3569
Beverly Hills *(G-377)*
New Vision Display Inc G 407 480-5800
Orlando *(G-12999)*
Niftys Inc F 786 878-4725
Miami *(G-10073)*
North Erie Electronics Inc F 561 839-8127
Jupiter *(G-7084)*
OHM Americas LLC F 800 467-7275
Fort Lauderdale *(G-4148)*
Paal Technologies Inc G 954 368-5000
Sunrise *(G-17156)*
▼ **Pacer Electronics Florida Inc** E 941 378-5774
Sarasota *(G-16534)*
Paradise Cable Industries F 941 488-6092
Venice *(G-18566)*
Paramount Electronic Mfg Co E 954 781-3755
Boca Raton *(G-662)*
Paramount Industries Inc E 954 781-3755
Pompano Beach *(G-14784)*
Phantom Technologies Inc E 407 265-2567
Longwood *(G-8325)*
▲ **Phil Lau** F 813 631-8643
Tampa *(G-17989)*
Piezo Technology Inc C 407 298-2000
Orlando *(G-13067)*
Powerficient LLC E 800 320-2535
Fort Lauderdale *(G-4172)*
Pro Fuse G 305 982-8457
Miami *(G-10203)*
Protek Electronics Inc E 941 351-4399
Sarasota *(G-16548)*
Quartz Unlimited Inc E 561 720-7460
Boca Raton *(G-678)*
Rami Technology USA LLC G 305 593-6033
Doral *(G-3481)*
Relcom Industries Inc G 561 304-7717
Greenacres *(G-5086)*
▲ **RES-Net Microwave Inc** E 727 530-9555
Clearwater *(G-1858)*
Sam-E-Nik Corp G 347 992-2123
Coral Gables *(G-2193)*
Sibex Inc C 727 726-4343
Crystal River *(G-2382)*
Smiths Interconnect Inc C 813 901-7200
Tampa *(G-18112)*
Smiths Interconnect Group Ltd G 805 370-5580
Stuart *(G-17016)*
Smiths Intrcnnect Americas Inc B 772 286-9300
Stuart *(G-17017)*
Soltec Electronics LLC G 321 288-5689
Rockledge *(G-15447)*
▲ **Sound Connections Intl** G 813 948-2707
Lutz *(G-8419)*

Spacecoast Cable & Harness Inc..........E....... 321 269-0377
Titusville *(G-18462)*
▲ **Sparton Deleon Springs LLC**..........D....... 386 985-4631
De Leon Springs *(G-2743)*
▲ **Spectraflex Inc**..........G....... 850 892-3900
Defuniak Springs *(G-2947)*
Spectrum Microwave Inc..........C....... 321 727-1838
Melbourne *(G-8941)*
Superior Electronics..........G....... 941 355-9500
Sarasota *(G-16307)*
Sv Microwave Inc..........C....... 561 840-1800
West Palm Beach *(G-19052)*
Syncron Ems Llc..........D....... 321 409-0025
Palm Bay *(G-13542)*
▲ **Sypris Electronics LLC**..........B....... 813 972-6000
Tampa *(G-18149)*
Tdk Electronics Inc..........F....... 561 509-7771
Ocean Ridge *(G-12080)*
Technical Service Labs Inc..........E....... 850 243-3722
Fort Walton Beach *(G-4834)*
▲ **Technipower LLC**..........F....... 954 346-2442
Coral Springs *(G-2321)*
Techtronics LLC..........G....... 407 738-4680
Kissimmee *(G-7303)*
Tekquest Inc..........F....... 321 768-6069
Palm Bay *(G-13544)*
Telematic Systems Inc..........G....... 239 217-0629
North Fort Myers *(G-11607)*
▲ **Tensolite LLC**..........A....... 904 829-5600
Saint Augustine *(G-15626)*
Trademark Components Inc..........G....... 813 948-2233
Lutz *(G-8421)*
Tri-Tech Electronics Inc..........D....... 407 277-2131
Orlando *(G-13270)*
Trinity Manufacturing Corp..........E....... 941 727-9595
Bradenton *(G-1131)*
Unique Electronics Inc..........C....... 407 422-3051
Orlando *(G-13291)*
▲ **V-Blox Corporation**..........G....... 904 425-4908
Jacksonville *(G-6890)*
▲ **Vc Displays Inc**..........E....... 352 796-0060
Brooksville *(G-1288)*
◆ **Via Optronics LLC**..........E....... 407 745-5031
Orlando *(G-13302)*
Video Display Corporation..........E....... 813 854-2259
Tampa *(G-18246)*
▲ **Vision Engineering Labs**..........D....... 727 812-2035
Largo *(G-8076)*
▲ **Winchster Intrcnnect Hrmtics L**..........D....... 321 254-4067
Melbourne *(G-8976)*
Workforce Audio Inc..........E....... 866 360-6416
Tampa *(G-18262)*

3691 Storage Batteries

▲ **Amper Usa LLC**..........G....... 305 717-3101
Doral *(G-3248)*
Authentic Trading Inc..........G....... 347 866-7241
Davie *(G-2500)*
◆ **Caliber Sales Engineering Inc**..........E....... 954 430-6234
Sunrise *(G-17103)*
Chargex LLC..........G....... 855 242-7439
Tampa *(G-17532)*
Chicago Electronic Distrs Inc..........F....... 312 985-6175
Port Charlotte *(G-14969)*
Clarios LLC..........G....... 904 786-9161
Jacksonville *(G-6265)*
Cleva Technologies LLC..........F....... 561 654-5279
Boca Raton *(G-485)*
Creating Tech Solutions LLC..........E....... 727 914-3001
Clearwater *(G-1643)*
Creating Tech Solutions LLC..........E....... 727 914-3001
Clearwater *(G-1641)*
Duracell Company..........E....... 561 494-7550
West Palm Beach *(G-18857)*
Enersys Advanced Systems Inc..........D....... 610 208-1934
Pinellas Park *(G-14346)*
Es Tudios Corp..........G....... 305 300-9262
Miami *(G-9535)*
Exide Battery..........G....... 904 783-1224
Jacksonville *(G-6373)*
▼ **Geneforce Incorporated**..........G....... 786 823-0700
Miami *(G-9622)*
◆ **Inspired Energy LLC**..........C....... 352 472-4855
Newberry *(G-11557)*
Kash Corporation..........G....... 786 368-7747
Miami *(G-9816)*
▲ **Kendoo Technology Inc**..........G....... 305 592-9688
Doral *(G-3407)*
▼ **Lithionics Battery LLC**..........F....... 727 726-4204
Clearwater *(G-1762)*
Lithium Battery Company LLC..........F....... 813 504-0074
Tampa *(G-17850)*
▲ **Mathews Associates Inc**..........C....... 407 323-3390
Sanford *(G-16082)*
Max Global North America LLC..........G....... 954 727-6656
Miramar *(G-11015)*
Palm Beach Btry Ventures LLC..........F....... 561 881-8900
Lake Park *(G-7477)*
Rainbow Storage..........F....... 386 362-1171
Live Oak *(G-8238)*
◆ **T N R Technical Inc**..........F....... 407 321-3011
Sanford *(G-16125)*
▲ **W & W Manufacturing Co**..........E....... 516 942-0011
Tampa *(G-18249)*

3692 Primary Batteries: Dry & Wet

▲ **Adva-Lite Inc**..........E....... 727 369-5319
Seminole *(G-16735)*
Creating Tech Solutions LLC..........E....... 727 914-3001
Clearwater *(G-1641)*
Creating Tech Solutions LLC..........E....... 727 914-3001
Clearwater *(G-1643)*
▲ **Empire Scientific**..........G....... 630 510-8636
Tampa *(G-17637)*
Future Plus of Florida..........G....... 612 240-7275
Tampa *(G-17698)*
JW Marketing and Consulting..........F....... 866 323-0001
Coconut Creek *(G-2086)*
Oakridge Globl Enrgy Sltons In..........E....... 321 610-7959
Palm Bay *(G-13528)*
Rayovac Corp..........G....... 727 393-0966
Largo *(G-8035)*
◆ **T N R Technical Inc**..........F....... 407 321-3011
Sanford *(G-16125)*
▲ **TAe Trans Atlantic Elec Inc**..........E....... 631 595-9206
Tampa *(G-18153)*

3694 Electrical Eqpt For Internal Combustion Engines

▲ **Advanced Automotive Designs**..........G....... 561 499-8812
Delray Beach *(G-3040)*
▲ **Alcolock FL Inc**..........G....... 407 207-3337
Orlando *(G-12450)*
American Auto Marine Wiring..........G....... 954 782-0193
Pompano Beach *(G-14590)*
▲ **Arco Marine Inc**..........E....... 850 455-5476
Pensacola *(G-14090)*
B G Service Company Inc..........E....... 561 659-1471
West Palm Beach *(G-18808)*
Battery Power Solutions Inc..........G....... 727 446-8400
Clearwater *(G-1601)*
Bobcat of Wiregrass Inc..........F....... 334 792-5121
Panama City Beach *(G-13973)*
Carbel LLC..........C....... 305 599-0832
Doral *(G-3290)*
Central Fla Remanufacturing..........G....... 407 299-9011
Orlando *(G-12563)*
◆ **Central Turbos Corp**..........F....... 305 406-3933
Doral *(G-3296)*
Cleva Technologies LLC..........F....... 561 654-5279
Boca Raton *(G-485)*
Competition Specialties Inc..........F....... 386 776-1476
Mc Alpin *(G-8599)*
Create and Company Inc..........F....... 813 393-8778
Tampa *(G-17562)*
▲ **D & L Auto & Marine Supplies**..........G....... 305 593-0560
Doral *(G-3319)*
Dynalco Controls Corporation..........E....... 323 589-6181
Fort Lauderdale *(G-3952)*
▲ **Euromotion Inc**..........G....... 954 612-0354
Delray Beach *(G-3077)*
Gml Industries LLC..........E....... 352 671-7619
Ocala *(G-11957)*
Goodman Manufacturing Co LP..........G....... 904 355-4520
Jacksonville *(G-6440)*
Ibtm Engineering Inc..........G....... 239 246-1876
Sanibel *(G-16146)*
Inglotech Usa LLC..........G....... 305 479-2770
Coral Gables *(G-2157)*
L & L Automotive Electric Inc..........F....... 631 471-5230
Melbourne *(G-8862)*
Motorola Solutions Inc..........G....... 407 562-4000
Lake Mary *(G-7437)*
Pcm and S L Plota Co LLC..........F....... 727 547-6277
Largo *(G-8024)*
Reynoso & Associates Inc..........G....... 954 360-0601
Deerfield Beach *(G-2905)*
Smartcart Ev LLC..........F....... 727 906-7001
Safety Harbor *(G-15504)*
◆ **South Florida Core Distrs**..........G....... 954 452-9091
Davie *(G-2594)*
▲ **Suncoast Automotive Pdts Inc**..........F....... 954 973-4822
Pompano Beach *(G-14879)*
◆ **T C B Products Inc**..........E....... 941 723-9820
Palmetto *(G-13827)*
T R S..........E....... 407 298-5490
Orlando *(G-13238)*
Tradewinds Power Corp..........F....... 863 382-2166
Sebring *(G-16716)*
Unia International Corp..........G....... 954 404-6076
Pembroke Pines *(G-14069)*
◆ **Wiretec Ignition Inc**..........F....... 407 578-4569
Palmetto *(G-13837)*

3695 Recording Media

Areweonlinecom Llc..........G....... 561 572-0233
Boynton Beach *(G-880)*
Barr Systems LLC..........E....... 352 491-3100
Gainesville *(G-4883)*
Biosculptor Corporation..........G....... 305 823-8300
Hialeah *(G-5326)*
Brickmed LLC..........G....... 305 774-0081
Miami *(G-9276)*
▼ **Datacore Software Corporation**..........D....... 954 377-6000
Fort Lauderdale *(G-3934)*
Digital Compositing Systems..........G....... 954 432-4988
Miramar *(G-10984)*
Horizon Duplication Inc..........G....... 407 767-5000
Winter Park *(G-19411)*
Interlink Software Inc..........G....... 407 927-0898
Orlando *(G-12835)*
Telit Iot Platforms LLC..........C....... 561 982-9898
Boca Raton *(G-744)*
Triple J Marketing LLC..........E....... 813 247-6999
Tampa *(G-18201)*
Twinstar Optics & Coatings Inc..........F....... 727 847-2300
Port Richey *(G-15073)*

3699 Electrical Machinery, Eqpt & Splys, NEC

▼ **35 Technologies Group Inc**..........E....... 407 402-2119
Longwood *(G-8248)*
5dt Inc..........E....... 407 734-5377
Orlando *(G-12420)*
905 East Hillsboro LLC..........F....... 954 480-2600
Deerfield Beach *(G-2760)*
A and J Sheet Metal Inc..........G....... 561 746-4048
Jupiter *(G-6991)*
▲ **AAA Security Depot Corp**..........E....... 305 652-8567
Opa Locka *(G-12281)*
Absolute Automation & Security..........G....... 321 505-9989
Cocoa *(G-1990)*
Abz Marketing Solutions Corp..........E....... 305 340-1887
Doral *(G-3222)*
Advance Solder Technology Inc..........F....... 321 633-4777
Rockledge *(G-15393)*
Advanced Dsign Tech Systems In..........E....... 850 462-2868
Pensacola *(G-14083)*
Advanced Metal Works Inc..........F....... 727 449-9353
Clearwater *(G-1566)*
Aero Simulation Inc..........C....... 813 628-4447
Tampa *(G-17389)*
Aero-Tel Wire Harness Corp..........E....... 407 445-1722
Orlando *(G-12439)*
▲ **Aeronautical Systems Engrg Inc**..........G....... 727 375-2520
Odessa *(G-12099)*
Airo Industries Inc..........G....... 239 229-5273
Fort Myers *(G-4347)*
Alco Advanced Technologies..........G....... 305 333-0831
Doral *(G-3234)*
Alectron Inc..........G....... 786 397-6827
Doral *(G-3236)*
◆ **Amtel Security Systems Inc**..........E....... 305 591-8200
Doral *(G-3249)*
Appointment Team Inc..........F....... 561 314-5471
Boynton Beach *(G-879)*
ARC Electric Inc..........E....... 954 583-9800
Davie *(G-2498)*
◆ **Aressco Technologies Inc**..........G....... 305 245-5854
Homestead *(G-5955)*
Argotec Inc..........F....... 954 491-6550
Fort Lauderdale *(G-3821)*
Argotec Inc..........G....... 407 331-9372
Longwood *(G-8257)*
Armalaser Inc..........G....... 954 937-6054
Pompano Beach *(G-14599)*
Asco Power Technologies LP..........G....... 727 450-2730
Clearwater *(G-1593)*
Asecure America Inc..........G....... 352 347-7951
Belleview *(G-367)*

SIC

Astronics Test Systems Inc ....C 407 381-6062
Orlando *(G-12496)*
Audio Intelligence Devices ....E 954 418-1400
Deerfield Beach *(G-2782)*
▲ **Aviation Instrument Tech Inc** ....F 813 783-3361
Zephyrhills *(G-19508)*
Bell Brothers Electric LLC ....E 954 496-0632
Coral Springs *(G-2225)*
BJ Burns Incorporated ....E 305 572-9500
Sunrise *(G-17097)*
Bluedrop USA Inc ....G 407 470-0865
Orlando *(G-12527)*
Bongiovi Aviation LLC ....F 772 879-0578
Port Saint Lucie *(G-15093)*
▲ **Boss Laser LLC** ....D 888 652-1555
Sanford *(G-16005)*
Bridge Trading Usa LLC ....F 877 848-0979
Doral *(G-3286)*
▼ **Brijot Imaging Systems Inc** ....F 407 641-4370
Boca Raton *(G-466)*
C-Note Solutions Inc ....F 321 952-2490
Indialantic *(G-6056)*
▲ **Cae Healthcare USA Inc** ....E 941 377-5562
Sarasota *(G-16378)*
◆ **Cae USA Inc** ....A 813 885-7481
Tampa *(G-17500)*
◆ **Came Americas Automation LLC** ....F 305 433-3307
Miami Lakes *(G-10773)*
Canam Electric ....G 305 534-7903
Miami Beach *(G-10651)*
Carling Technologies Inc ....G 561 745-0405
Jupiter *(G-7015)*
Centrys LLC ....E 407 476-4786
Sanford *(G-16012)*
Clare Instruments (us) Inc ....G 813 886-2775
Tampa *(G-17538)*
Coastal Electric ....G 239 245-7396
Fort Myers *(G-4403)*
Commercial Gates and Elc LLC ....F 386 454-2329
High Springs *(G-5700)*
Communcations Surveillance Inc ....F 305 377-1211
Coral Gables *(G-2132)*
Complete Access Ctrl Centl Fla ....G 407 498-0067
Saint Cloud *(G-15647)*
Control and Automtn Cons Inc ....G 305 823-8670
Hialeah *(G-5353)*
Control Investments Inc ....F 954 491-6660
Fort Lauderdale *(G-3918)*
▲ **Control Laser Corporation** ....E 407 926-3500
Orlando *(G-12617)*
▲ **Control Micro Systems Inc** ....E 407 679-9716
Winter Park *(G-19396)*
Crandon Enterprises Inc ....G 352 873-8400
Ocala *(G-11910)*
Cubic Advnced Lrng Sltions Inc ....F 407 859-7410
Orlando *(G-12632)*
◆ **Cubic Simulation Systems Inc** ....C 407 641-2037
Orlando *(G-12634)*
Custom Mfg & Engrg Inc ....D 727 548-0522
Pinellas Park *(G-14342)*
▼ **Danielle Fence Mfg Co Inc** ....D 863 425-3182
Mulberry *(G-11121)*
David Chittum ....G 386 754-6127
Saint Petersburg *(G-15756)*
▼ **Deggy Corp** ....G 305 377-2233
Miami Lakes *(G-10780)*
Del Air Electric Co ....G 407 531-1173
Sanford *(G-16035)*
◆ **Devcon International Corp** ....C 954 926-5200
Boca Raton *(G-499)*
Devcon Security Services Corp ....E 813 386-3849
Pompano Beach *(G-14661)*
▲ **DMC Components Intl LLC** ....G 407 478-4064
Winter Park *(G-19404)*
Eaton Corporation ....G 813 281-8069
Tampa *(G-17628)*
▲ **Edgewater Technologies Inc** ....F 954 565-9898
Fort Lauderdale *(G-3962)*
Edmund Optics Inc ....E 813 855-1900
Oldsmar *(G-12224)*
Elipter Corp ....G 305 593-8355
Doral *(G-3342)*
Enterprise Electric LLC ....G 407 884-0668
Apopka *(G-136)*
Environmental Tectonics Corp ....F 407 282-3378
Orlando *(G-12714)*
Etc Palm Beach LLC ....D 561 881-8118
West Palm Beach *(G-18863)*
Evolution Intrcnnect Systems I ....F 954 217-6223
Davie *(G-2521)*
Exploration Resources Intn Geo ....G 601 747-0726
Lake Mary *(G-7412)*
Extreme Digital Video Inc ....G 954 792-2818
Fort Lauderdale *(G-3984)*
Famatel USA LLC ....G 754 217-4841
Dania *(G-2445)*
Faro Technologies Inc ....E 800 736-0234
Lake Mary *(G-7413)*
First Mate Inc ....G 954 475-2750
Plantation *(G-14517)*
Fonon Technologies Inc ....E 407 477-5618
Orlando *(G-12761)*
Gadgetcat LLC ....G 802 238-3671
Cocoa Beach *(G-2063)*
Gatecrafterscom ....F 800 537-4283
Odessa *(G-12122)*
Gc Electric LLC ....G 386 842-7066
Jacksonville *(G-6427)*
Geddis Inc ....F 800 844-6792
Dunedin *(G-3579)*
General Scientific Corporation ....G 850 866-9636
Panama City *(G-13908)*
Geneva Systems Inc ....G 352 235-2990
Green Cove Springs *(G-5063)*
Gess Technologies LLC ....F 305 231-6322
Hialeah *(G-5429)*
▲ **Ground Zero Electrostatics Inc** ....G 941 751-7581
Bradenton *(G-1053)*
◆ **Gto Access Systems LLC** ....D 850 575-0176
Tallahassee *(G-17269)*
Guerilla Technologies Inc ....F 772 283-0500
Palm City *(G-13661)*
▲ **Hale Products Inc** ....C 352 629-5020
Ocala *(G-11963)*
Hayes Less Lethal LLC ....G 561 201-2186
Tequesta *(G-18385)*
Hemco Industries Inc ....F 305 769-0606
North Miami *(G-11641)*
Holly Sargent ....G 954 560-6973
Fort Lauderdale *(G-4049)*
Holovis Interna Tional ....G 407 286-3976
Orlando *(G-12807)*
Hooper Corp ....F 954 382-5711
Davie *(G-2536)*
▲ **Hose-Mccann Telephone Co Inc** ....E 954 429-1110
Deerfield Beach *(G-2845)*
Hummingbirds Ai Inc ....F 305 432-2787
Miami Beach *(G-10680)*
ICO USA Corp ....G 305 253-0871
Palmetto Bay *(G-13848)*
▲ **Indra Systems Inc** ....E 407 567-1977
Orlando *(G-12827)*
Industrial Smoke & Mirrors Inc ....E 407 299-9400
Orlando *(G-12828)*
Inrad Optics Inc ....G 941 544-8278
Sarasota *(G-16466)*
Integrated Laser Systems Inc ....F 954 489-8282
Coral Springs *(G-2261)*
Integrated Surroundings Inc ....F 850 932-0848
Gulf Breeze *(G-5120)*
Interntonal Linear Matrix Corp ....F 727 549-1808
Seminole *(G-16748)*
Interrail Power Inc ....F 904 268-6411
Jacksonville *(G-6502)*
Inviro Tek Inc ....G 215 499-1209
Orlando *(G-12840)*
Invision Auto Systems Inc ....D 407 956-5161
Orlando *(G-12841)*
Invision Auto Systems Inc ....D 407 956-5161
Orlando *(G-12842)*
Invision Industries Inc ....G 407 451-8353
Orlando *(G-12843)*
▲ **J B Nottingham & Co Inc** ....E 386 873-2990
Deland *(G-2986)*
James Taylor ....F 850 882-5148
Eglin Afb *(G-3644)*
Knight Fire & Security Inc ....F 561 471-8221
Riviera Beach *(G-15341)*
L-3 Cmmnctons Advnced Lser Sys ....D 407 295-5878
Orlando *(G-12881)*
L-3 Cmmnctons Ntronix Holdings ....D 212 697-1111
Melbourne *(G-8863)*
L3 Technologies Inc ....D 407 295-5878
Orlando *(G-12882)*
L3harris Technologies Inc ....G 321 729-2186
Melbourne *(G-8867)*
L3harris Technologies Inc ....G 321 309-7848
Melbourne *(G-8866)*
▲ **L3harris Technologies Inc** ....B 321 727-9100
Melbourne *(G-8865)*
▲ **Lap of America Lc** ....G 561 416-9250
Boynton Beach *(G-927)*
Laser Assault ....G 801 374-3400
Navarre *(G-11469)*
Laser Interceptor Usa LLC ....G 352 688-0708
Spring Hill *(G-16856)*
▼ **Laserpath Technologies LLC** ....G 407 247-3930
Oviedo *(G-13446)*
Lasersight Incorporated ....F 407 678-9900
Orlando *(G-12893)*
Laserstar Technologies Corp ....G 407 248-1142
Orlando *(G-12896)*
Lehigh Acrs Fre Cnrl & Rscue ....E 239 303-5300
Lehigh Acres *(G-8196)*
Lightworks Inc ....G 305 456-3520
Miami *(G-9892)*
Load Banks Direct LLC ....F 859 554-2522
Venice *(G-18560)*
Lockheed Martin Corporation ....A 407 306-1000
Orlando *(G-12920)*
Lui Technical Services Inc ....G 954 803-7610
Sunrise *(G-17144)*
M Micro Technologies Inc ....B 954 973-6166
Pompano Beach *(G-14749)*
Marine Digital Integrators LLC ....E 772 210-2403
Stuart *(G-16974)*
Microsemi Corp ....F 407 965-5687
Lake Mary *(G-7434)*
Microsimulators Inc ....G 407 696-8722
Winter Springs *(G-19479)*
Natures Power and Energy LLC ....F 813 907-6279
Wesley Chapel *(G-18753)*
Neat Clean Group Inc ....F 727 459-6079
Clearwater *(G-1805)*
New IEM Power Systems LLC ....C 904 365-4444
Jacksonville *(G-6626)*
New Laser Tech Inc ....G 305 450-0456
Miami Lakes *(G-10829)*
◆ **Nida Corporation** ....E 321 727-2265
Melbourne *(G-8894)*
Novena TEC LLC ....E 407 392-1868
Orlando *(G-13011)*
Nuenergy Technologies Corp ....G 866 895-6838
Clearwater *(G-1812)*
▲ **Opinicus Textron Inc** ....D 813 792-9300
Lutz *(G-8407)*
◆ **Pestwest Usa LLC** ....G 941 358-1983
Sarasota *(G-16276)*
◆ **Pfi Inc** ....G 407 822-4499
Longwood *(G-8324)*
Point Blank Enterprises Inc ....D 305 820-4270
Miami Lakes *(G-10840)*
◆ **Portalp Usa Inc** ....F 800 474-3667
Naples *(G-11373)*
▲ **Power Vac Corporation** ....G 954 491-0188
Oakland Park *(G-11830)*
Pressure Systems Innvtions LLC ....F 561 249-2708
West Palm Beach *(G-19005)*
Probotix ....G 844 472-9262
Fort Walton Beach *(G-4824)*
Protective Group Inc ....E 305 820-4266
Miami Lakes *(G-10846)*
Pulse Displays LLC ....G 314 971-8700
Wesley Chapel *(G-18757)*
Quality Door Service LLC ....G 904 588-4817
Jacksonville *(G-6698)*
Rm Brands Inc ....G 904 356-0092
Jacksonville *(G-6732)*
◆ **Sabine Inc** ....D 386 418-2000
Alachua *(G-17)*
Safeguard America Inc ....F 305 859-9000
Miami *(G-10295)*
Safety Zone Specialists Inc ....G 863 984-1385
Lakeland *(G-7784)*
Salco Industries Inc ....F 941 377-7717
Sarasota *(G-16570)*
Saltex Group Corp ....G 305 477-3187
Miami *(G-10300)*
Schwartz Electro-Optics Inc ....F 407 297-8988
Orlando *(G-13169)*
Secure Biometric Corporation ....G 813 832-1164
Tampa *(G-18082)*
Security and Fire Elec Inc ....E 904 844-0964
Saint Augustine *(G-15608)*
Segutronic International Inc ....G 305 463-8551
Doral *(G-3498)*
▲ **Select Engineered Systems Inc** ....E 305 823-5410
Hialeah *(G-5613)*
Semilab USA LLC ....E 813 977-2244
Temple Terrace *(G-18378)*

Sepronet Inc ....F 305 463-8551
Doral *(G-3499)*
◆ **Sequa Corporation** ....A 561 935-3571
Palm Beach Gardens *(G-13626)*
Servision Inc ....G 305 900-4999
Hallandale Beach *(G-5210)*
Servos and Simulation Inc ....G 407 807-0208
Longwood *(G-8336)*
Sibex Inc ....C 727 726-4343
Crystal River *(G-2382)*
Sierra Nevada Corporation ....E 850 659-3600
Shalimar *(G-16777)*
Signalvault LLC ....G 407 878-6365
Debary *(G-2755)*
Simplexgrinnell Holdings LLC ....G 978 731-2500
Boca Raton *(G-716)*
Smart Access Inc ....G 407 331-4724
Lake Mary *(G-7449)*
Somfy Systems Inc ....F 561 292-3483
Boynton Beach *(G-961)*
Southeast Security Products ....G 954 786-5900
Pompano Beach *(G-14861)*
Spaceport Corporation ....G 305 690-6885
Miami *(G-10392)*
Standard Technology Inc ....F 386 671-7406
Ormond Beach *(G-13402)*
Sunrise Financial Assoc Inc ....G 321 439-9797
Orlando *(G-13225)*
▼ **Superior Metal Fabricators Inc** ....E 407 295-5772
Orlando *(G-13230)*
▲ **Surf Lighting Inc** ....F 305 888-7851
Hialeah *(G-5644)*
◆ **Surface Engrg & Alloy Co Inc** ....D 727 528-3734
Saint Petersburg *(G-15930)*
▲ **Symetrics Industries LLC** ....C 321 254-1500
Melbourne *(G-8954)*
Symetrics Technology Group LLC ....E 321 254-1500
Melbourne *(G-8955)*
T J Sales Associates Inc ....G 407 328-0777
Sanford *(G-16124)*
T V Trac Ltd ....G 516 371-1111
Boynton Beach *(G-966)*
▲ **Technipower LLC** ....F 954 346-2442
Coral Springs *(G-2321)*
▲ **Telsec Corporation** ....G 561 998-9983
Boca Raton *(G-745)*
Tem Systems Inc ....G 407 251-7114
Orlando *(G-13246)*
Theft Protection Com Corp ....F 772 231-6677
Vero Beach *(G-18670)*
Top Sales Co ....G 561 852-4311
Boca Raton *(G-752)*
Triton II Jv LLC ....G 407 894-5575
Orlando *(G-13274)*
Tru Simulation + Training Inc ....D 813 792-9300
Odessa *(G-12161)*
United Space Coast Cables Inc ....E 321 952-1040
West Melbourne *(G-18778)*
Validsoft ....G 813 334-9745
Lutz *(G-8422)*
▲ **Vanguard Products Group Inc** ....D 813 855-9639
Oldsmar *(G-12277)*
Vapor Engineering Inc ....F 850 434-3191
Pensacola *(G-14280)*
▲ **Venco Marine Inc** ....G 954 923-0036
Hollywood *(G-5936)*
▲ **Vinland Corporation** ....E 954 475-9093
Plantation *(G-14565)*
Vos Systems LLC ....F 352 317-2954
Gainesville *(G-5016)*
Voxx Automotive Corp ....E 631 231-7750
Orlando *(G-13311)*
Walker Electric Inc ....G 941 729-5015
Palmetto *(G-13834)*
World Electronics Inc ....G 954 318-1044
Sunrise *(G-17199)*
◆ **Xpondr Corporation** ....E 727 541-4149
Seminole *(G-16772)*
▲ **Xts Corp** ....F 305 863-7779
Doral *(G-3552)*

37 TRANSPORTATION EQUIPMENT

3711 Motor Vehicles & Car Bodies

Alert Towing Inc ....E 561 586-5504
Lake Worth *(G-7532)*
Alevo Automotive Inc ....G 954 593-4215
Boca Raton *(G-411)*
◆ **Amer-Con Corp** ....E 786 293-8004
Palmetto Bay *(G-13839)*
Armour Group Inc ....F 954 767-2030
Fort Lauderdale *(G-3823)*
Arons Towing & Recovery Inc ....G 772 220-1151
Hobe Sound *(G-5722)*
Barron Boyz Auto ....F 229 403-2656
Fleming Island *(G-3760)*
Citrus Motorsports ....F 352 564-2453
Crystal River *(G-2372)*
▲ **Composite Holdings Inc** ....E 321 268-9625
Titusville *(G-18424)*
Delaware Chassis Works ....G 302 378-3013
Stuart *(G-16931)*
◆ **E-One Inc** ....B 352 237-1122
Ocala *(G-11928)*
E-One Inc ....D 352 237-1122
Ocala *(G-11929)*
Electra Automotive Corp ....G 941 623-5563
Hollywood *(G-5815)*
Elite Enclosures ....F 352 323-6005
Leesburg *(G-8154)*
Emergency Vehicle Sup Co LLC ....E 954 428-5201
Pompano Beach *(G-14678)*
◆ **Emergency Vehicles Inc** ....E 561 848-6652
Lake Park *(G-7469)*
Ev Pilotcar Inc ....G 239 243-8023
Fort Myers *(G-4446)*
F I B US Corp ....G 239 262-6070
Naples *(G-11243)*
Fea Inc ....F 407 330-3535
Sanford *(G-16046)*
Flints Wrecker Service Inc ....G 863 676-1318
Lake Wales *(G-7509)*
Florida Bus Unlimited Inc ....E 407 656-1175
Orlando *(G-12746)*
◆ **Gar-P Industries Inc** ....E 305 888-7252
Medley *(G-8655)*
▼ **Giliberti Inc** ....F 772 597-1870
Indiantown *(G-6072)*
Jade Tactical Disaster Relief ....C 850 270-4077
Tampa *(G-17801)*
Lions Intl MGT Group Inc ....F 813 367-2517
Tampa *(G-17848)*
Lippert Components Inc ....G 267 825-0665
Bradenton *(G-1071)*
Liyanarchi Design LLC ....G 954 330-5034
Windermere *(G-19235)*
Metal 2 Metal Inc ....G 954 253-9450
Palmetto Bay *(G-13850)*
Mike Cope Race Cars LLC ....G 352 585-2810
Clearwater *(G-1787)*
Moser Automotive ....E 561 881-5665
Riviera Beach *(G-15350)*
Naples Hotrods & Prfmce LLC ....G 239 653-9076
Naples *(G-11334)*
Navistar Inc ....G 305 513-2255
Doral *(G-3443)*
▲ **Nev International Inc** ....F 407 671-0045
Casselberry *(G-1511)*
Noguera Holdings LLC ....G 305 846-9144
Hialeah *(G-5543)*
Nu Trek Inc ....G 813 920-4348
Odessa *(G-12136)*
Oshkosh Corporation ....G 863 603-4080
Lakeland *(G-7760)*
Pegasus Clean Air Mtr Cars Inc ....G 954 682-2000
Fort Lauderdale *(G-4161)*
Phelps Motorsports LLC ....G 239 417-2042
Naples *(G-11362)*
Pierce Manufacturing Inc ....D 941 748-3900
Bradenton *(G-1097)*
Pierce Manufacturing Inc ....A 727 573-0400
Clearwater *(G-1832)*
◆ **Rev Amblance Group Orlando Inc** ....B 407 677-7777
Winter Park *(G-19441)*
Revology Cars LLC ....F 800 974-4463
Orlando *(G-13133)*
Rp High Performance Inc ....F 561 863-2800
Riviera Beach *(G-15374)*
Shirley Simon & Associates LLC ....G 813 247-2100
Tampa *(G-18097)*
Shyft Group Inc ....E 954 946-9955
Jupiter *(G-7114)*
Speedsource Inc ....G 954 578-7071
Key Largo *(G-7174)*
◆ **Square One Armoring Svcs Co** ....D 305 477-1109
Miami *(G-10407)*
Tesla Inc ....G 305 535-7596
Miami Beach *(G-10719)*
Tesla Inc ....G 754 816-3069
Dania Beach *(G-2473)*
Tesla Inc ....G 305 774-5965
Miami *(G-10470)*
Total Performance Inc ....G 203 265-5667
Palm Coast *(G-13713)*
▲ **Trikaroo** ....G 800 679-3415
Orlando *(G-13272)*
Uma Holdings Inc ....E 786 587-1349
Hollywood *(G-5932)*
◆ **Vac-Con Inc** ....B 904 284-4200
Green Cove Springs *(G-5075)*
Valiant Transport Group LLC ....E 855 648-7423
Boca Raton *(G-774)*
Voxx Automotive Corporation ....F 407 842-7000
Orlando *(G-13312)*
◆ **Voxx International Corporation** ....B 800 645-7750
Orlando *(G-13313)*
Worldwide Auto Systems Corp ....F 954 439-6332
Hollywood *(G-5942)*

3713 Truck & Bus Bodies

A&L Hall Investments Inc ....E 904 781-5080
Bryceville *(G-1296)*
Advanced Truck Equipment Inc ....E 561 424-0442
Boynton Beach *(G-873)*
◆ **Amer-Con Corp** ....E 786 293-8004
Palmetto Bay *(G-13839)*
Armor Supply Metals LLC ....G 305 640-9901
Medley *(G-8613)*
▼ **Bulk Manufacturing Florida Inc** ....F 813 757-2313
Plant City *(G-14412)*
Express Auto Carriers LLC ....G 352 541-0040
Ocala *(G-11935)*
Florida Truck Parts ....G 786 251-8614
Hialeah Gardens *(G-5698)*
◆ **Gar-P Industries Inc** ....E 305 888-7252
Medley *(G-8655)*
▼ **Miami Dade Truck & Eqp Svc** ....F 305 691-2932
Miami *(G-9997)*
Mickey Truck Bodies Inc ....F 352 620-0015
Ocala *(G-12001)*
Nichols Truck Bodies LLC ....E 904 781-5080
Jacksonville *(G-6634)*
Pierce Manufacturing Inc ....A 727 573-0400
Clearwater *(G-1832)*
Reading Truck Body LLC ....E 727 943-8911
Tarpon Springs *(G-18322)*
Reading Truck Body LLC ....E 727 943-8911
Tarpon Springs *(G-18323)*
Simplified Fabricators Inc ....E 561 335-3488
West Palm Beach *(G-19035)*
Southeastern Truck Tops Inc ....F 386 761-0002
Daytona Beach *(G-2717)*
T Disney Trucking & Grading ....E 813 443-6258
Tampa *(G-18151)*
Terminal Service Company ....C 850 739-5702
Tallahassee *(G-17339)*
◆ **Tesco Equipment LLC** ....E 954 752-7994
Coral Springs *(G-2322)*
Transtat Equipment Inc ....F 407 857-2040
Orlando *(G-13268)*
Tuflex Manufacturing Co ....E 954 781-0605
Pompano Beach *(G-14895)*
Warren Equipment Inc ....E 813 752-5126
Plant City *(G-14477)*
◆ **World Industrial Equipment Inc** ....E 772 461-6056
Fort Pierce *(G-4772)*

3714 Motor Vehicle Parts & Access

AA Performance ....G 772 672-1164
Vero Beach *(G-18589)*
Ach LLC ....G 727 586-4930
Largo *(G-7885)*
Ach Solution USA Inc ....G 941 355-9488
Sarasota *(G-16171)*
Addco Manufacturing Company ....E 828 733-1560
Riviera Beach *(G-15292)*
▲ **Advanced Automotive Designs** ....G 561 499-8812
Delray Beach *(G-3040)*
Aero Seating Technologies LLC ....G 321 264-5600
Titusville *(G-18412)*
Air Temp of America Inc ....G 850 340-3017
Panama City *(G-13861)*
Alper Automotive Inc ....G 561 342-1501
Delray Beach *(G-3044)*
Alpha Hydraulics LLC ....G 561 355-0318
Riviera Beach *(G-15297)*
Alto Products Corp Al ....G 305 892-7777
Doral *(G-3242)*
▼ **AM Worldwide Corp** ....F 786 313-3625
Doral *(G-3244)*

S I C

Ameraparts International LLC ....B 904 725-9700
Jacksonville *(G-6145)*
American Ignition Wire LLC ....G 954 974-6500
Fort Lauderdale *(G-3813)*
▲ Apollo Sunguard Systems Inc ....F 941 925-3000
Sarasota *(G-16343)*
ARB Optimal Inc ....G 904 487-6874
Jacksonville *(G-6163)*
▲ Autocraft Manufacturing Co ....E 321 453-1850
Merritt Island *(G-8992)*
▼ Avalanche Corporation ....D 800 708-0087
Brooksville *(G-1213)*
B & B Trailers and Accessories ....F 904 829-6855
Saint Augustine *(G-15520)*
Balls Rod & Kustom LLC ....G 888 446-2191
Gainesville *(G-4881)*
▲ Battery Usa Inc ....E 863 665-6317
Lakeland *(G-7643)*
Battery Usa Inc ....G 863 665-5401
Lakeland *(G-7644)*
Beach House Engineering ....G 941 727-4488
Bradenton *(G-995)*
Billet Technology ....G 561 582-6171
Lake Worth *(G-7537)*
Blp Racing Products LLC ....F 407 422-0394
Orlando *(G-12524)*
Boat Steering Solutions LLC ....G 727 400-4746
North Venice *(G-11754)*
Boost Lab Inc ....F 813 443-0531
Wesley Chapel *(G-18741)*
Broward Power Train Co Inc ....E 954 772-0881
Fort Lauderdale *(G-3870)*
Bulletproof Hitches LLC ....G 941 251-8110
Bradenton *(G-1004)*
Capristo USA ....G 561 882-9885
West Palm Beach *(G-18834)*
Carvizion Inc ....G 772 807-0307
Port St Lucie *(G-15170)*
▲ CC Machine Inc ....F 888 577-0144
Holly Hill *(G-5757)*
Ccp Fabrication ....G 727 946-6024
Holiday *(G-5738)*
Central Florida Driveshaft ....G 407 299-1100
Orlando *(G-12567)*
▲ Chromalloy Castings Tampa Corp ....C 561 935-3571
Palm Beach Gardens *(G-13577)*
▲ Coast Wcp ....E 727 572-4249
Odessa *(G-12111)*
Coastal RE-Manufacturing Inc ....G 727 869-4808
Port Richey *(G-15046)*
▼ Commercial Duct Systems LLC ....D 877 237-3828
Thonotosassa *(G-18399)*
Competition Specialties Inc ....F 386 776-1476
Mc Alpin *(G-8599)*
Crankshaft Rebuilders Inc ....D 407 323-4870
Sanford *(G-16027)*
Creative Auto Boutique Llc ....G 407 654-7300
Oakland *(G-11768)*
Cummins Inc ....G 407 298-2080
Orlando *(G-12636)*
Cummins Inc ....G 352 861-1122
Ocala *(G-11912)*
▲ Custom Quality Mfg Inc ....E 813 290-0805
Tampa *(G-17582)*
▲ Dashcovers Plus Depot Distrs ....G 954 961-7774
Davie *(G-2514)*
▲ Daytona Parts Company ....G 386 427-7108
New Smyrna Beach *(G-11532)*
Delphi of Florida Inc ....F 727 561-9553
Saint Petersburg *(G-15757)*
Desco Machine Company LLC ....G 954 565-2739
Oakland Park *(G-11798)*
Diaz Go Green Inc ....G 407 501-2724
Orlando *(G-12670)*
Dimple Products Inc ....G 704 320-0700
Palm Coast *(G-13691)*
Dover Cylinder Head Inc ....E 850 785-6569
Panama City *(G-13894)*
Dover Cylinder Head of Jackson ....F ....
Orange Park *(G-12390)*
Dsx Products Inc ....F 904 744-3400
Jacksonville *(G-6331)*
Dubbs Fresh Detailing LLC ....G 813 770-5194
South Bay *(G-16794)*
Dynotune Inc ....G 941 753-8899
Bradenton *(G-1033)*
Enforcement One Inc ....F 727 816-9833
Oldsmar *(G-12226)*
▲ Eng Group LLC ....G 954 323-2024
Fort Lauderdale *(G-3972)*

Ensida Energy Afs LLC ....G 954 364-2296
Hollywood *(G-5816)*
Enstar Holdings (us) LLC ....D 727 217-2900
Saint Petersburg *(G-15770)*
▲ Epower 360 LLC ....F 305 330-6684
Miami *(G-9533)*
Etco Incorporated ....C 941 756-8426
Bradenton *(G-1039)*
Evamped LLC ....G 614 205-4467
Naples *(G-11241)*
▲ Exhaust Technologies Inc ....G 561 744-9500
Jupiter *(G-7037)*
Express Brake International ....F 352 304-6263
Ocala *(G-11936)*
Extreme Brake Integration Inc ....G 352 342-9596
Ocala *(G-11937)*
Extreme Corvette Co LLC ....G 941 524-8942
Bradenton *(G-1040)*
Extreme Manufacturing LLC ....F 888 844-7734
Ocala *(G-11938)*
▲ Ezy-Glide Inc ....G 850 638-4403
Chipley *(G-1544)*
Faes Srt Inc ....G 941 960-6742
Sarasota *(G-16424)*
FCA US LLC ....G 305 597-2222
Doral *(G-3349)*
Federal-Mogul Motorparts LLC ....G 954 585-2500
Fort Lauderdale *(G-3991)*
▲ Florida Dacco/Detroit Inc ....E 813 879-4131
Tampa *(G-17674)*
Florida Motors Inc ....G 786 524-9001
Miami *(G-9585)*
Florida Pwrtrain Hydrulics Inc ....G 954 463-7711
Fort Lauderdale *(G-4003)*
Florida Pwrtrain Hydrulics Inc ....G 813 623-6713
Tampa *(G-17687)*
Florida Pwrtrain Hydrulics Inc ....G 407 291-1441
Orlando *(G-12754)*
Flowmaster Inc ....G 561 249-1145
Loxahatchee *(G-8359)*
Fluid Routing Solutions LLC ....B 352 732-0222
Ocala *(G-11948)*
◆ Forecast Trading Corporation ....E 954 979-1120
Fort Lauderdale *(G-4009)*
Fuelmatics Corp ....F 305 807-4923
Palmetto Bay *(G-13843)*
▲ G-Car Inc ....D 305 883-8223
Hialeah *(G-5421)*
Gaterman Products LLC ....G 386 253-1899
Daytona Beach *(G-2667)*
Gear Driven LLC ....G 954 681-8394
Coral Springs *(G-2250)*
Gear Dynamics Inc ....G 305 691-0151
Miami *(G-9619)*
▲ Gfx Inc ....E 305 499-9789
Miami *(G-9634)*
Gt Technologies Inc ....C 850 575-8181
Tallahassee *(G-17267)*
▲ Gt Technologies I Inc ....G 850 575-8181
Tallahassee *(G-17268)*
▲ Hale Products Inc ....C 352 629-5020
Ocala *(G-11963)*
Harry J Honan ....G 405 273-9315
Riviera Beach *(G-15332)*
◆ Hoerbger Auto Cmfort Systems L ....E 334 321-2292
Deerfield Beach *(G-2839)*
Hope Technical Sales & Svcs ....G 941 412-1204
Venice *(G-18554)*
Hornblasters Inc ....E 813 783-8058
Tampa *(G-17761)*
Hre LLC ....G 317 340-5991
Fort Myers *(G-4485)*
◆ IESC Diesel Corp ....G 305 470-9306
Medley *(G-8668)*
Improved Racing Products LLC ....G 407 705-3054
Orlando *(G-12826)*
▲ Intertek International Corp ....D 305 883-8700
Hialeah *(G-5457)*
Ionemoto Inc ....G 617 784-1401
Sebastian *(G-16663)*
Iron Strength Corp ....F 305 226-6866
Miami *(G-9772)*
Isoflex Technologies Intl LLC ....G 561 210-5170
Deerfield Beach *(G-2848)*
J & J Dynamic Products LLC ....G 863 274-5333
Lakeland *(G-7719)*
JMS Corporate Group LLC ....G 786 219-6114
Aventura *(G-275)*
Jodar Inc ....G 561 375-6277
Boca Raton *(G-583)*

Johnsons Management Group Inc ....G 904 261-4044
Fernandina Beach *(G-3741)*
Jpm Import LLC ....F 800 753-3009
Margate *(G-8553)*
▲ JW Performance Transm Inc ....E 321 632-6205
Rockledge *(G-15425)*
▲ Key Automotive Florida LLC ....B 863 668-6000
Lakeland *(G-7725)*
Key Safety Systems Inc ....G 863 668-6000
Lakeland *(G-7726)*
Kirby Acquisitions LLC ....G 850 687-8703
Santa Rosa Beach *(G-16162)*
▲ Kleen Wheels Corporation ....G 954 791-9112
Davie *(G-2541)*
◆ Kysor Industrial Corporation ....F 727 376-8600
Trinity *(G-18487)*
La Experiencia Crankshaft ....G 305 823-6161
Miami Lakes *(G-10802)*
Lambs Signs Inc ....F 941 792-4453
Bradenton *(G-1068)*
Latham Marine Inc ....E 954 462-3055
Fort Lauderdale *(G-4096)*
Lightning Connecting Rods LLC ....G 727 733-2054
Clearwater *(G-1760)*
▲ Longs Wheel & Rim Inc ....D 904 757-3710
Jacksonville *(G-6564)*
Luminar Technologies Inc ....C 407 900-5259
Orlando *(G-12938)*
Luminar Technologies Inc ....E 407 900-5259
Orlando *(G-12939)*
◆ Lusa Supplier LLC ....G 305 885-7634
Miami *(G-9921)*
Luxury Motor Cars LLC ....F 407 398-6933
Orlando *(G-12940)*
M P N Inc ....E 863 606-5999
Lakeland *(G-7741)*
◆ Man-Trans LLC ....F 850 222-6993
Tallahassee *(G-17294)*
Mann+hummel Filtration Technol ....G 305 499-5100
Medley *(G-8682)*
▲ March Inc ....E 239 593-4074
Naples *(G-11320)*
Marden Industries Inc ....F 863 682-7882
Punta Gorda *(G-15213)*
▲ Minder Research Inc ....F 772 463-6522
Stuart *(G-16977)*
▲ Mobilepower LLC ....F 843 706-6108
South Miami *(G-16823)*
Motor Coach Inds Intl Inc ....F 407 246-1414
Winter Garden *(G-19277)*
▲ Multi Parts Supply Usa Inc ....E 561 748-1515
Jupiter *(G-7078)*
▼ National Carburetors Inc ....E 904 636-9400
Jacksonville *(G-6618)*
National Cylinder Services LLC ....E 407 299-8454
Orlando *(G-12990)*
▼ Onaris ....F 305 579-0056
Miami *(G-10101)*
P4rts LLC ....G 305 396-4879
Miami *(G-10125)*
Partsvu LLC ....C 239 643-2292
Naples *(G-11359)*
Paw Inc ....E 904 724-0310
Jacksonville *(G-6661)*
Phoenix Transmission Parts Inc ....G 727 541-0269
Clearwater *(G-1831)*
Pierce Manufacturing Inc ....D 941 748-3900
Bradenton *(G-1097)*
▲ Precision Shaft Technology ....G 727 442-1711
Clearwater *(G-1841)*
Premiere Services Inc ....F 678 815-6078
Tallahassee *(G-17310)*
Professional Products ....G 323 754-1287
Tampa *(G-18021)*
▲ Profile Racing Inc ....E 727 392-8307
Saint Petersburg *(G-15891)*
Progress Rail Services Corp ....D 239 643-3013
Naples *(G-11376)*
▲ Progressive Power Products Inc ....G 904 354-1819
Jacksonville *(G-6693)*
Propglide USA Corp ....G 305 520-0150
Miami *(G-10210)*
Puradyn Filter Tech Inc ....E 561 547-9499
Boynton Beach *(G-947)*
◆ Pylon Manufacturing Corp ....E 800 626-4902
Deerfield Beach *(G-2898)*
R C Specialized International ....G 407 681-5905
Casselberry *(G-1516)*
◆ Rally Manufacturing Inc ....C 305 628-2886
Miami *(G-10236)*

▲ RDS Manufacturing Inc ....C 850 584-6898
Perry (G-14310)
◆ Reach International Inc ....E 305 863-6360
Hialeah (G-5596)
▲ Redat of North America Inc ....G 407 246-1600
Orlando (G-13122)
Rehadapt North America ....G 904 687-0130
Saint Augustine (G-15595)
Rhino Tire Usa Llc ....F 407 777-5598
Orlando (G-13135)
Road Master ....G 561 479-6450
Fort Lauderdale (G-4210)
Rod-Speed Inc ....G 786 426-3996
Doral (G-3488)
Ruke Inc ....G 239 292-2553
Windermere (G-19242)
Santa Rosa Auto Parts Inc ....E 850 477-7747
Pensacola (G-14257)
Santiago Chopper LLC ....E 813 671-9097
Gibsonton (G-5032)
▲ SCI Undercar Inc ....F 727 327-2278
Saint Petersburg (G-15906)
Screaming Banshee LLC ....G 727 744-6808
Clearwater (G-1869)
Sea Systems Group Inc ....G 434 374-9553
Largo (G-8049)
▲ Shafers Classic Reproductions ....G 813 622-7091
Tampa (G-18089)
▲ Shark Skinz ....G 772 388-9621
Sebastian (G-16672)
◆ Shaw Development LLC ....C 239 405-6100
Bonita Springs (G-853)
Shearwater Marine Fl Inc ....E 772 781-5553
Stuart (G-17010)
Shipping Depot Inc ....F 813 347-2494
Tampa (G-18096)
Signal Dynamics Corporation ....F 904 342-4008
Fort Lauderdale (G-4233)
▼ Silverhorse Racing LLC ....G 321 722-2813
Melbourne (G-8933)
Sizemore Welding Inc ....E 386 437-4073
Bunnell (G-1306)
◆ Skyo Industries Inc ....E 631 586-4702
Ormond Beach (G-13399)
▲ SMR Management Inc ....G 305 529-2488
Coral Gables (G-2196)
Southeast Carbon Works Inc ....G 561 422-1798
Wellington (G-18736)
Southeastern Engineering Inc ....F 321 984-2521
Palm Bay (G-13538)
▲ Southern Wheel & Rim Inc ....F 904 786-7542
Jacksonville (G-6799)
◆ Square One Armoring Svcs Co ....D 305 477-1109
Miami (G-10407)
Standard Motor Products Inc ....G 718 392-0200
Orlando (G-13213)
Steering & Suspension Parts ....G 786 523-3726
Miami (G-10412)
Strasse Forged LLC ....F 786 701-3649
Miami (G-10419)
Style Crest Products ....G 863 709-8735
Lakeland (G-7809)
▲ Sun Coast Converters Inc ....G 850 864-2361
Fort Walton Beach (G-4833)
Suncoast Rebuild Center Inc ....F 813 238-3433
Tampa (G-18144)
Tanks Incorporated ....G 941 320-4371
Myakka City (G-11144)
▲ Thi E-Commerce LLC ....D 352 327-4058
Ocala (G-12060)
Thule Inc ....C 850 584-3448
Perry (G-14317)
Total Performance Inc ....G 203 265-5667
Palm Coast (G-13713)
Treadstone Performance ....F 305 972-9600
Cutler Bay (G-2415)
◆ Treadstone Prfmce Engrg Inc ....G 888 789-4586
Cutler Bay (G-2416)
U S Hardware Supply Inc ....E 407 657-1551
Winter Park (G-19454)
Urban Charge LLC ....G 305 809-6625
Miami Beach (G-10724)
USA Corp Airplane ....G 954 399-8472
Hollywood (G-5935)
Vette Brakes & Products Inc ....E 727 345-5292
Saint Petersburg (G-15952)
Vista-Pro Automotive LLC ....F 352 867-7272
Ocala (G-12073)
Voodoo Fab LLC ....G 727 916-0014
Holiday (G-5752)
Voxxhirschmann Corporation ....C 866 869-7888
Orlando (G-13314)
Vpr 4x4 ....G 305 468-9818
Orlando (G-13315)
Walker Products ....D 941 723-9820
Palmetto (G-13835)
Warden Enterprises Inc ....G 954 463-4404
Fort Lauderdale (G-4312)
Webelectric Products Inc ....G 440 389-5647
The Villages (G-18397)
◆ Wetherill Associates Inc ....C 800 773-0005
Miramar (G-11060)
Wheels A Million ....G 754 444-2869
Fort Lauderdale (G-4321)
Wilson Manifolds Inc ....E 954 771-6216
Oakland Park (G-11861)
Wolverine Advanced Mtls LLC ....G 352 787-3015
Leesburg (G-8181)
Woodys Acres LLC ....G 352 345-8145
Brooksville (G-1295)
Yarbrough Tire Svc Inc ....G 863 385-1574
Sebring (G-16719)

3715 Truck Trailers

▼ All Amrcan Trlr Connection Inc ....G 561 582-1800
Palm Springs (G-13772)
Alumne Manufacturing Inc ....G 352 748-3229
Wildwood (G-19190)
Arnold Manufacturing Inc ....G 850 470-9200
Pensacola (G-14092)
Axxium Engineering LLC ....G 786 573-9808
Miami (G-9204)
Bt-Twiss Transport LLC ....G 866 584-1585
Largo (G-7915)
Cepods LLC ....G 786 520-1412
Miami Beach (G-10654)
◆ Chassis King LLC ....G 727 585-1500
Clearwater (G-1625)
Dills Enterprises LLC ....G 941 493-1993
Venice (G-18542)
Draggin Trailers Inc ....G 352 351-8790
Ocala (G-11926)
EZ Truck Services Inc ....F 239 728-3022
Alva (G-88)
Freight Train Trucking Corp ....G 407 509-0611
Saint Cloud (G-15652)
◆ Globe Trailers Florida Inc ....E 941 753-6425
Bradenton (G-1049)
▼ Interglobal Capital Inc ....G 727 585-1500
Clearwater (G-1733)
Loadmaster Alum Boat Trlrs Inc ....E 813 689-3096
Tampa (G-17856)
Nelsons Truck and Trlr Sls LLC ....F 352 732-8908
Ocala (G-12005)
Pedro Truck Parts & Trailers ....G 786 439-8652
Miami (G-10149)
Pierce Manufacturing Inc ....D 941 748-3900
Bradenton (G-1097)
Rolls Rite Trailers Inc ....F 850 526-2290
Marianna (G-8585)
RPM Co ....G 352 542-3110
Old Town (G-12199)
Shadow Trailers Inc ....E 352 529-2190
Williston (G-19215)
Terminal Service Company ....C 850 739-5702
Tallahassee (G-17339)
Thunder Bay Enterprises Inc ....E 352 796-9551
Brooksville (G-1280)
◆ U-Dump Trailers LLC ....D 352 351-8510
Ocala (G-12065)
Ultimate Cargo Services LLC ....F 954 251-1680
Jacksonville (G-6875)
Unique Custom Truck & Trlr LLC ....F 305 403-7042
Miami (G-10531)
Warren Equipment Inc ....E 813 752-5126
Plant City (G-14477)

3716 Motor Homes

▼ Interntnal Srvillance Tech Inc ....E 954 574-1100
Deerfield Beach (G-2847)

3721 Aircraft

Above Ground Level Aerospace ....F 305 713-2629
Miami (G-9056)
Aercap Inc ....E 954 760-7777
Fort Lauderdale (G-3785)
Aercap Group Services Inc ....B 954 760-7777
Fort Lauderdale (G-3786)
Aerial Products Corporation ....F 800 973-9110
Jacksonville (G-6126)
Aerion Corp ....E 775 337-6682
Fort Lauderdale (G-3787)
Aero Tech Service Assoc Inc ....F 850 286-1378
Tyndall Afb (G-18493)
Aerosmart Enterprise LLC ....E 310 499-8878
Saint Petersburg (G-15692)
Air Support Tecks ....G 386 986-5301
Palm Coast (G-13681)
Airbus Oneweb Satellites LLC ....C 321 735-8446
Merritt Island (G-8988)
Aircraft Systems Group Inc ....G 727 376-9292
Odessa (G-12100)
Altum Aerospace ....F 954 618-6573
Sunrise (G-17089)
Amxs Corp ....E 904 568-1416
Jacksonville Beach (G-6938)
ASG Aerospace LLC ....G 305 253-0802
Miami (G-9177)
Astrum Travel Intl Ltd ....F 917 779-9462
Miami (G-9181)
Aviall Inc ....G 954 625-3930
Davie (G-2501)
Aviation Intl Solutions LLC ....G 305 267-7117
Hialeah (G-5313)
Aviation Parts & Trade Corp ....G 954 944-2828
Plantation (G-14495)
Birds Eye Drones LLC ....G 321 355-3415
Windermere (G-19226)
Blue Hole Helicopters Inc ....F 561 723-0378
Jupiter (G-7012)
Bmg Aerospace ....F 786 725-4959
Miami (G-9263)
Bob Laferriere Aircraft Inc ....G 727 709-2704
Tarpon Springs (G-18284)
Boeing ....E 850 301-6635
Fort Walton Beach (G-4782)
Boeing Arospc Operations Inc ....F 850 682-2746
Crestview (G-2344)
Boeing Company ....C 407 306-8782
Orlando (G-12530)
Boeing Company ....G 321 867-6005
Cape Canaveral (G-1353)
Boeing Company ....G 904 772-1273
Jacksonville (G-6220)
Boeing Company ....G 321 867-6005
Kennedy Space Center (G-7151)
Boeing Company ....G 321 867-7380
Kennedy Space Center (G-7152)
Boeing Company ....G 786 265-9965
Virginia Gardens (G-18684)
Boeing Company ....G 904 317-2490
Jacksonville (G-6221)
Boeing Company ....G 850 301-6613
Fort Walton Beach (G-4783)
Boeing Company ....G 850 882-4912
Eglin Afb (G-3641)
Boeing Company ....G 312 544-2000
Titusville (G-18416)
Bombardier Trnsp Hldngs USA In ....G 407 450-4855
Sanford (G-16004)
Bombardiier ....G 954 622-1200
Fort Lauderdale (G-3865)
C1 Aerospace LLC ....G 786 712-9949
Miami (G-9295)
Celtic Airspares LLC ....G 727 431-0482
Clearwater (G-1622)
Climax Am LLC ....G 786 502-5757
Pembroke Pines (G-14028)
Coleman Aerospace ....E 407 354-0047
Orlando (G-12599)
CSC Aerospace Corporation ....G 203 300-9760
Doral (G-3315)
▲ Diamond Aircraft Logisctics ....G 305 456-8400
Doral (G-3328)
Diloren Inc ....G 786 618-9671
Doral (G-3330)
Discovery Aviation Inc ....E 321 752-0332
Melbourne (G-8806)
Dowe Gallagher Aerospace ....G 941 256-2179
Sarasota (G-16208)
Dreamline Aerospace ....G 954 544-2365
Pembroke Pines (G-14030)
Drone Clips By Majic ....G 407 619-3704
Orlando (G-12686)
Drone Defense Systems LLC ....G 305 607-6708
Daytona Beach (G-2659)
Drone Imaging Services LLC ....G 407 620-5258
Orlando (G-12687)
Drone Master Shots LLC ....G 407 295-7715
Orlando (G-12688)

Drone Pics and Vids Corp.....G..... 786 558-4027
Miami *(G-9487)*
ELite Intl Group LLC.....F..... 305 901-5005
Miami *(G-9516)*
Embraer Executive Aircraft Inc.....D..... 321 751-5050
Melbourne *(G-8824)*
▲ **Embraer Services Inc**.....A..... 954 359-3700
Fort Lauderdale *(G-3970)*
EMC Aerospace Inc.....E..... 954 316-6015
North Miami Beach *(G-11674)*
Estumkeda Ltd.....F..... 954 966-6300
Hollywood *(G-5817)*
Excalibur Aircraft.....G..... 863 385-9486
Sebring *(G-16690)*
Extreme Crafts LLC.....G..... 561 989-7400
Boca Raton *(G-526)*
Fl Aerospace Solutions Inc.....G..... 786 395-3289
Miami *(G-9565)*
Fix n Fly Drones LLC.....G..... 321 474-2291
Tampa *(G-17667)*
Florida Aerospace Partnership.....G..... 954 617-7700
Fort Lauderdale *(G-3998)*
Florida Sncast Helicopters LLC.....F..... 941 355-1525
Sarasota *(G-16214)*
Florida SW Drones LLC.....G..... 239 785-8337
Cape Coral *(G-1425)*
Full Circle Integration LLC.....F..... 504 615-5501
Valparaiso *(G-18511)*
Garrison Lickle Aircraft.....G..... 561 833-7111
Palm Beach *(G-13555)*
Gb Airlink Inc.....G..... 561 593-7284
Stuart *(G-16946)*
General Dynamics Corporation.....G..... 850 897-9700
Niceville *(G-11567)*
GKN Aerospace Florida LLC.....D..... 314 412-8311
Panama City *(G-13910)*
Global Aerospace.....G..... 407 721-3732
Indialantic *(G-6059)*
Gonzalez Aerospace Services.....G..... 561 227-1575
Wellington *(G-18719)*
Gulf Coast Airways Inc.....G..... 239 403-3020
Naples *(G-11270)*
Gulfstream Mses Invstmnts Grou.....G..... 305 975-6186
Miami Beach *(G-10675)*
Harris Aerial LLC.....F..... 407 725-7886
Casselberry *(G-1505)*
Heli Aviation Florida LLC.....G..... 941 355-1525
Sarasota *(G-16226)*
Heli-Tech Inc.....F..... 850 763-9000
Panama City *(G-13914)*
▲ **High Standard Aviation Inc**.....E..... 305 599-8855
Doral *(G-3383)*
Inteli Drone Inc.....G..... 954 707-9547
Coconut Creek *(G-2083)*
J Cube Inc.....F..... 407 699-6866
Casselberry *(G-1507)*
Jade Tactical Disaster Relief.....C..... 850 270-4077
Tampa *(G-17801)*
Kaman Aerospace Corporation.....E..... 904 751-5369
Jacksonville *(G-6532)*
KB Aerospace Co.....G..... 754 366-9194
Fort Lauderdale *(G-4085)*
Kiss Polymers LLC.....F..... 813 962-2703
Tampa *(G-17827)*
Landmark Aviation.....G..... 305 296-5422
Key West *(G-7194)*
Lift Aerospace Corp.....F..... 305 851-5237
Miami *(G-9890)*
Lighter Than Air Systems Corp.....F..... 904 834-4400
Jacksonville *(G-6557)*
Lockheed Martin Corporation.....G..... 904 660-6917
Jacksonville *(G-6561)*
Lockheed Martin Corporation.....G..... 407 356-2000
Orlando *(G-12927)*
Lockheed Mrtin Mllmter Tech In.....E..... 407 356-4186
Orlando *(G-12932)*
Lockheed Training Facility.....G..... 850 883-2144
Eglin Afb *(G-3646)*
Lumenier Holdco LLC.....G..... 941 444-0021
Sarasota *(G-16491)*
Lumenier LLC.....F..... 941 444-0021
Sarasota *(G-16492)*
Maris Worden Aerospace Inc.....G..... 514 895-8075
South Daytona *(G-16803)*
Max Torque LLC.....F..... 863 701-8000
Lakeland *(G-7746)*
Mc Dermott Enterprises Inc.....G..... 262 593-8612
Fort Myers *(G-4525)*
Meridian South Aviation LLC.....G..... 727 536-5387
Clearwater *(G-1781)*
Mia Aerospace LLC.....G..... 786 973-4118
Miami *(G-9987)*
Miami Hang Gliding Corp.....G..... 863 805-0440
Clewiston *(G-1984)*
Micro Systems Inc.....C..... 850 244-2332
Fort Walton Beach *(G-4815)*
▲ **Mysky Aircraft Inc**.....G..... 386 492-6908
Port Orange *(G-15026)*
Navmar Applied Sciences Corp.....C..... 904 423-0927
Jacksonville *(G-6620)*
Nobel Aerospace LLC.....F..... 786 210-0716
Doral *(G-3445)*
▲ **Northrop Grmman Feld Spport Sv**.....D..... 904 810-4665
Saint Augustine *(G-15574)*
Northrop Grumman Systems Corp.....C..... 904 825-3300
Saint Augustine *(G-15576)*
Northrop Grumman Systems Corp.....C..... 904 825-3300
Saint Augustine *(G-15578)*
Northstar Aviation USA LLC.....E..... 321 600-4557
Melbourne *(G-8898)*
Onvoi AVI Supp and Inspect Ser.....G..... 805 312-3274
Defuniak Springs *(G-2945)*
Pegasus Aerospace.....G..... 850 376-0991
Destin *(G-3201)*
Perry North Aerospace Inc.....G..... 954 295-9520
Lighthouse Point *(G-8212)*
Piper Aircraft Inc.....A..... 772 567-4361
Vero Beach *(G-18653)*
Progressive Aerodyne Inc.....G..... 352 253-0108
Tavares *(G-18351)*
Puma Aero Marine Inc.....G..... 904 638-5888
Fort Lauderdale *(G-4184)*
R4 Integration Inc.....E..... 850 226-6913
Fort Walton Beach *(G-4825)*
Riverview Drones Inc.....G..... 813 451-4744
Riverview *(G-15281)*
Rockymountain Lifenet.....G..... 863 533-5168
Bartow *(G-331)*
Ronco Aircraft and Marine Inc.....E..... 321 220-0209
Palm Bay *(G-13532)*
Southstern Arspc Svcs Ltd Lblt.....G..... 305 992-8257
Pompano Beach *(G-14865)*
Southwings Avionics and ACC.....G..... 305 825-6755
Miami Lakes *(G-10863)*
Supliaereos USA LLC.....G..... 727 754-4915
Clearwater *(G-1897)*
▲ **Tecnam US Inc**.....F..... 863 655-2400
Sebring *(G-16714)*
Tiger Composites Inc.....F..... 386 334-0941
New Smyrna Beach *(G-11547)*
TP Aerospace Technics LLC.....G..... 407 730-9988
Orlando *(G-13266)*
UAS Drone Corp.....G..... 561 693-1424
Palm Beach *(G-13562)*
Uts Systems LLC.....G..... 850 226-4301
Fort Walton Beach *(G-4837)*
Van Nevel Aerospace LLC.....G..... 337 936-2504
Cottondale *(G-2333)*
▲ **Velocity Inc**.....F..... 772 589-1860
Sebastian *(G-16678)*
▼ **Vertical Aviation Technologies**.....F..... 407 322-9488
Sanford *(G-16133)*
◆ **Veserca Group Ltd Inc**.....F..... 561 210-7400
Boca Raton *(G-779)*
Viper Drones LLC.....G..... 205 677-3700
Indialantic *(G-6062)*
Vogue Aerospace & Defense Inc.....G..... 321 289-0872
Naples *(G-11453)*
Volaero Uav Drnes Hldings Corp.....F..... 954 261-3105
Sunrise *(G-17197)*
VSI & Partners Inc.....F..... 954 205-8653
Miramar *(G-11058)*

3724 Aircraft Engines & Engine Parts

Acmt South LLC.....F..... 860 645-0592
Lynn Haven *(G-8427)*
▲ **Aero-Link Marine & Power LLC**.....G..... 561 404-8181
Boca Raton *(G-404)*
Aerojet Rocketdyne De Inc.....C..... 561 882-5150
Jupiter *(G-6996)*
Aerosync Engrg Consulting Inc.....G..... 316 208-3367
Milton *(G-10920)*
Aersale 23440 LLC.....G..... 305 764-3200
Coral Gables *(G-2119)*
Air Alliance Inc.....G..... 305 735-4864
Marathon *(G-8516)*
Air Lion Incorp.....G..... 386 748-9296
Deland *(G-2955)*
Air Marshall Inc.....F..... 954 843-0991
Hollywood *(G-5766)*
Aircraft Technology Inc.....E..... 954 744-7602
Hollywood *(G-5767)*
◆ **Airmark Overhaul Inc**.....G..... 954 970-3200
Fort Lauderdale *(G-3792)*
Airstox Inc.....G..... 954 618-6573
Sunrise *(G-17085)*
▲ **Approved Turbo Components Inc**.....F..... 559 627-3600
Vero Beach *(G-18594)*
Avstar Fuel Systems Inc.....G..... 561 575-1560
Jupiter *(G-7002)*
▲ **Bonus Aerospace Inc**.....G..... 305 887-6778
Medley *(G-8624)*
Bonus Tech Inc.....F..... 786 251-4232
Medley *(G-8625)*
Chromalloy Component Svcs Inc.....D..... 954 378-1999
Fort Lauderdale *(G-3898)*
▲ **Chromalloy Gas Turbine LLC**.....A..... 561 935-3571
Palm Beach Gardens *(G-13578)*
CIT Aerospace Inc.....F..... 954 359-2561
Plantation *(G-14499)*
Csi Aerospace Inc.....E..... 954 961-9800
Hollywood *(G-5807)*
Dynamic Precision Group Inc.....E..... 772 287-7770
Stuart *(G-16934)*
ELite Intl Group LLC.....F..... 305 901-5005
Miami *(G-9516)*
Falcon Commercial Aviation LLC.....F..... 786 340-9464
Miami *(G-9558)*
Flight Source LLC.....G..... 954 249-8449
Fort Lauderdale *(G-3997)*
Florida Aero Precision Inc.....E..... 561 848-6248
Lake Park *(G-7471)*
Florida Turbine Tech Inc.....G..... 561 427-6400
Jupiter *(G-7045)*
Fossco Inc.....G..... 850 983-1330
Milton *(G-10929)*
Global Turbine Services Inc.....F..... 786 476-2166
Medley *(G-8659)*
Goodrich Corporation.....G..... 305 622-4500
Miami Gardens *(G-10744)*
H H Terry Co Inc.....F..... 239 593-0132
Naples *(G-11274)*
Hamilton Sundstrand Corp.....G..... 860 654-6252
Pompano Beach *(G-14721)*
▲ **Heico Aerospace Corporation**.....E..... 954 987-6101
Hollywood *(G-5837)*
▲ **Heico Aerospace Holdings Corp**.....G..... 954 987-4000
Hollywood *(G-5838)*
Heico Aerospace Holdings Corp.....G..... 305 463-0455
Miami *(G-9698)*
Heico Aerospace Parts Corp.....G..... 440 995-3661
Hollywood *(G-5839)*
Heico Corporation.....G..... 305 374-1745
Miami *(G-9699)*
Heico Corporation.....G..... 305 463-0455
Miami *(G-9700)*
▲ **Heico Corporation**.....B..... 954 987-4000
Hollywood *(G-5840)*
Heico Electronic Tech Corp.....E..... 954 987-6101
Hollywood *(G-5841)*
Heico Flight Support Corp.....E..... 954 987-4000
Hollywood *(G-5842)*
Honeywell International Inc.....G..... 561 479-0639
Boca Raton *(G-558)*
Honeywell International Inc.....G..... 281 546-0993
Tallahassee *(G-17279)*
Honeywell International Inc.....G..... 305 525-1950
Miami *(G-9719)*
Honeywell International Inc.....G..... 850 243-8812
Fort Walton Beach *(G-4809)*
Honeywell International Inc.....G..... 727 539-3111
Clearwater *(G-1718)*
Honeywell International Inc.....G..... 727 539-4451
Largo *(G-7972)*
Honeywell International Inc.....G..... 877 841-2840
Oviedo *(G-13436)*
Honeywell International Inc.....G..... 904 696-5222
Jacksonville *(G-6477)*
Honeywell International Inc.....G..... 813 573-1166
Clearwater *(G-1720)*
Honeywell International Inc.....G..... 904 260-5900
Jacksonville *(G-6478)*
Honeywell International Inc.....G..... 352 372-4192
Gainesville *(G-4938)*
Honeywell US Corp.....F..... 617 955-4031
North Miami Beach *(G-11682)*
Iag Engine Center LLC.....E..... 305 591-0643
Miami *(G-9726)*
Interavia Spares and Svcs Inc.....G..... 954 794-0174
Boca Raton *(G-567)*

Interntnl Synrgy For Tchncal G 321 305-0863
Orlando *(G-12837)*
Ja Engineering II Corp G 954 744-7560
Hollywood *(G-5850)*
▲ Jet Avion Corporation D 954 987-6101
Hollywood *(G-5854)*
Magellan Aviation Group Lllp G 561 266-0845
Boynton Beach *(G-931)*
Miami Leasing Inc G 786 431-1215
Miami *(G-10003)*
▼ Miami Ndt Inc F 305 599-9393
Medley *(G-8691)*
▼ Miltechnologies Inc G 305 817-4244
Miami Lakes *(G-10821)*
MTI Aviation Inc E 305 817-4244
Opa Locka *(G-12342)*
Norris Precision Mfg Inc D 727 572-6330
Clearwater *(G-1810)*
Northwings Accessories Corp C 305 463-0455
Miami *(G-10078)*
Overall-Honeycomb LLC D 941 756-8781
Sarasota *(G-16269)*
Palladium Sales LLC G 754 423-0517
Davie *(G-2564)*
Palmer Manufacturing Co LLC F 772 287-7770
Stuart *(G-16986)*
Parker-Hannifin Corporation G 239 304-1000
Naples *(G-11358)*
Pma LLC G 407 310-2548
Orlando *(G-13073)*
Pratt & Whitney Eng Svcs Inc G 305 512-9882
Miami Lakes *(G-10841)*
Precision Shapes Inc E 321 269-2555
Titusville *(G-18453)*
Precision Turbines Inc G 561 447-0751
Boca Raton *(G-672)*
Propulsion Tech Intl LLC B 954 874-0274
Miramar *(G-11034)*
PSI Mnfacturing Operations LLC G 561 747-6107
Jupiter *(G-7100)*
Radiant-Seacom Repairs Corp G 941 739-3200
Sarasota *(G-16283)*
Raytheon Technologies Corp A 858 277-7639
Jupiter *(G-7103)*
Saf Aerospace LLC G 813 376-0883
Tampa *(G-18080)*
◆ Sequa Corporation A 561 935-3571
Palm Beach Gardens *(G-13626)*
Sidus Space Inc E 321 613-0615
Cape Canaveral *(G-1367)*
Simmonds Precision Pdts Inc E 904 757-3660
Jacksonville *(G-6776)*
Skill-Metric Machine & Tl Inc E 561 454-8900
Delray Beach *(G-3143)*
Sohacki Industries Inc E 904 826-0130
Saint Augustine *(G-15613)*
Sunshine Avionics LLC G 954 517-1294
Hialeah *(G-5638)*
Supliaereos USA LLC G 727 754-4915
Clearwater *(G-1897)*
Treasure Coast Machines Inc F 772 283-2024
Stuart *(G-17037)*
Turbine Kinetics Inc D 954 744-7526
Hollywood *(G-5931)*
Turbine Weld Industries LLC E 941 485-5113
Venice *(G-18582)*
▲ Turbocombustor Technology Inc B 772 287-7770
Stuart *(G-17041)*
United Technologies Corp E 860 565-4321
Jupiter *(G-7137)*
◆ V and N Advanced Auto Sys LLC G 321 504-6440
Rockledge *(G-15455)*
Vfm Aerosystems LLC G 786 567-2348
Doral *(G-3541)*

3728 Aircraft Parts & Eqpt, NEC

A J Assoc Mfg & Engrg Co F 727 258-0994
Clearwater *(G-1560)*
A R Components Corp F 786 703-8456
Miami *(G-9042)*
AAR Airlift Group Inc E 321 837-2345
Palm Bay *(G-13498)*
AAR Corp G 786 337-4000
Medley *(G-8604)*
AAR Government Services Inc E 904 693-7260
Jacksonville *(G-6116)*
AAR Government Services Inc E 321 361-3461
Rockledge *(G-15390)*
▲ AAR Landing Gear LLC E 305 883-1511
Medley *(G-8605)*
AAR Manufacturing Inc D 727 539-8585
Clearwater *(G-1561)*
ABC Intercargo LLC G 954 908-5200
Weston *(G-19102)*
Acmt South LLC F 860 645-0592
Lynn Haven *(G-8427)*
▲ Advanced Thermal Tech Inc E 561 791-5000
Wellington *(G-18708)*
Advent Aerospace Inc E 727 549-9600
Largo *(G-7887)*
Aero Bridgeworks Inc G 321 689-1912
Orlando *(G-12438)*
Aero Hose Corp F 904 215-9638
Orange Park *(G-12380)*
Aero Mechanical Industries G 469 645-1620
Coral Gables *(G-2118)*
Aero South Florida Inc G 954 363-2376
Deerfield Beach *(G-2767)*
Aero-Flex Corp E 561 745-2534
Jupiter *(G-6994)*
Aerobase Group Inc E 321 802-5889
Melbourne *(G-8759)*
Aerojet Rocketdyne Inc G 386 626-0001
Daytona Beach *(G-2622)*
Aeronate Inc G 954 358-7145
Pembroke Pines *(G-14017)*
Aerosonic LLC C 727 461-3000
Clearwater *(G-1568)*
▲ Aerosource Inc E 941 751-2620
Sarasota *(G-16172)*
▲ Aerospace Rotables Inc F 954 452-0056
Sunrise *(G-17083)*
Aerotools Connection LLC G 305 234-3034
Miami *(G-9083)*
Aerotools USA Inc G 305 432-4258
Miami *(G-9084)*
Aerowest Mfg Corp G 786 367-6948
Hialeah *(G-5273)*
Aerox AVI Oxgn Systems LLC F 207 637-2331
Bonita Springs *(G-811)*
Aersale 26346 LLC D 305 764-3200
Coral Gables *(G-2120)*
Agd Systems Corporation G 561 722-5561
West Palm Beach *(G-18791)*
Air Operations F 305 871-5449
Miami *(G-9092)*
Aircraft Engrg Instlltion Svcs E 407 438-4436
Orlando *(G-12445)*
Airdyne Aerospace Inc E 352 593-4163
Brooksville *(G-1206)*
Aire-Tech Rotorcraft Svcs LLC F 305 696-8001
Miami *(G-9096)*
▲ Airframe International Inc F 218 461-9305
Fort Pierce *(G-4671)*
Airind Incorporated G 954 252-0900
Southwest Ranches *(G-16836)*
Airline Support Group Inc E 954 971-4567
Fort Lauderdale *(G-3790)*
Airmark Components Inc E 954 522-5370
Fort Lauderdale *(G-3791)*
▼ Airplane Services Inc G 850 675-1252
Jay *(G-6961)*
Aj Associates F 727 258-0994
Clearwater *(G-1571)*
▼ Alaris Aerospace Systems LLC F 954 596-8736
Pompano Beach *(G-14583)*
Alco Services Inc E 954 538-2189
Miramar *(G-10963)*
▲ Allclear Aerospace & Def Inc F 954 200-9195
Miramar *(G-10966)*
Allied Aerospace Inc F 786 616-8484
Doral *(G-3239)*
Allied Aerospace International G 954 429-8600
Deerfield Beach *(G-2775)*
Alm Technologies Inc E 904 849-7212
Yulee *(G-19495)*
American Enrgy Innovations LLC F 772 221-9100
Stuart *(G-16905)*
American Science and Tech Corp G 312 898-3333
Miami Beach *(G-10641)*
American Vly Avnics Clbrtion L F 904 579-5272
Orange Park *(G-12381)*
AMP Aero Services LLC G 833 267-2376
Miami *(G-9151)*
Apex Aviation Group LLC G 305 789-6695
Miami *(G-9156)*
◆ Arcadia Aerospace Inds LLC E 941 205-5700
Punta Gorda *(G-15191)*
Arma Holdings Inc E 813 402-0667
Tampa *(G-17434)*
Arrowhead Global LLC G 727 497-7340
Clearwater *(G-1589)*
Atlantic Jet Support Inc G 954 360-7549
Coconut Creek *(G-2070)*
Atlantic Precision Inc D 772 466-1011
Port Saint Lucie *(G-15089)*
Atlas Helicopter Inc G 321 696-4342
Sanford *(G-15997)*
Avalon Aviation Inc G 954 655-0256
Fort Lauderdale *(G-3834)*
Avborne Accesory Group LLC C 305 593-6038
Miami *(G-9194)*
▲ Avborne Accessory Group Inc E 305 593-6038
Miami *(G-9195)*
Aveoengineering LLC G 631 747-6671
Palm Coast *(G-13684)*
Aviacol Usa Corp F 786 701-2152
Miami *(G-9198)*
Aviation Intl Solutions LLC G 305 267-7117
Hialeah *(G-5313)*
Aviation Worldwide Svcs LLC F 321 837-2345
Palm Bay *(G-13500)*
Avionics Support Group Inc E 305 378-9786
Miami *(G-9199)*
B & J Atlantic Inc E 904 338-0088
Jacksonville *(G-6185)*
B E Aerospace E 305 459-7000
Medley *(G-8619)*
B/E Aerospace Inc G 305 471-8800
Doral *(G-3262)*
▲ B/E Aerospace Inc E 410 266-2048
Wellington *(G-18710)*
Ballistic Recovery Systems Inc D 651 457-7491
Pompano Beach *(G-14612)*
Baron LLC G 239 691-5783
Fort Myers *(G-4372)*
Bigorre Aerospace Corp F 727 525-8115
Pinellas Park *(G-14337)*
Bischoff Aero Llc F 305 883-4410
Hialeah *(G-5328)*
Boeing Company G 850 882-4912
Eglin Afb *(G-3641)*
Borgesfs Inc G 786 210-0327
Miami *(G-9268)*
Cambridge Aeronautical LLC G 305 987-3851
Miami *(G-9303)*
Censys Technologies Corp F 850 321-2278
Daytona Beach *(G-2640)*
▲ Chase Aerospace Inc F 407 812-4545
Orlando *(G-12577)*
Choice Products Inc F 386 426-6450
Edgewater *(G-3619)*
Clero Enterprises Inc G 305 681-4877
Opa Locka *(G-12300)*
▲ Coast Wcp E 727 572-4249
Odessa *(G-12111)*
Coastal Machine LLC G 850 769-6117
Panama City *(G-13885)*
Composite-Fx Sales LLC G 352 538-1624
Trenton *(G-18481)*
Crane Electronics Inc D 850 244-0043
Fort Walton Beach *(G-4789)*
CSC Textron F 954 776-5862
Fort Lauderdale *(G-3921)*
Cte Jv LLC G 407 894-5575
Orlando *(G-12631)*
Cvg Aerospace LLC G 786 293-9923
Miami *(G-9421)*
Cygnus Aerospace Incorporated E 850 612-1618
Crestview *(G-2346)*
Daher Inc G 954 893-1400
Pompano Beach *(G-14658)*
Dalimar Corp G 727 525-8115
Pinellas Park *(G-14343)*
Dass Logistics Inc F 954 837-8339
Coconut Creek *(G-2074)*
Diagma U S LLC G 407 683-0852
Orlando *(G-12669)*
Discovery Aviation Inc E 321 752-0332
Melbourne *(G-8806)*
Don Industrial Group LLC F 305 290-4237
Hialeah *(G-5377)*
Donica International Inc F 954 217-7616
Miami *(G-9478)*
Doorway Projects Inc G 561 523-2040
Lake Worth *(G-7544)*
Drones Shop LLC G 772 224-8118
Stuart *(G-16933)*
Dukane Seacom Inc C 941 739-3200
Sarasota *(G-16209)*

Electronic Components Fas Inc .... G 407 328-8111
Sanford *(G-16040)*
ELite Intl Group LLC .... F 305 901-5005
Miami *(G-9516)*
Equs Logistics LLC .... F 954 618-6573
Sunrise *(G-17120)*
Exodus Management LLC .... G 954 995-4407
Fort Lauderdale *(G-3983)*
Firefly Aircraft Parts Inc .... G 954 505-1470
Plantation *(G-14516)*
Flight Aerotech LLC .... F 305 901-6001
Miami *(G-9578)*
Flight Velocity .... G 866 937-9371
Palm Coast *(G-13694)*
Flying Colors Air Parts .... F 352 728-1900
Leesburg *(G-8158)*
Forward Express One Llc .... F 305 234-3034
Miami *(G-9595)*
Free Wing Flight Technologies .... G 813 752-8552
Plant City *(G-14432)*
◆ **General Dynamics-Ots Inc** .... D 727 578-8100
Saint Petersburg *(G-15790)*
General Mro Aerospace Inc .... G 305 482-9903
Medley *(G-8657)*
General Scientific Corporation .... G 850 866-9636
Panama City *(G-13908)*
Gigli Enterprises Inc .... G 850 871-4777
Panama City *(G-13909)*
Global Intl Investments LLC .... G 305 825-2288
Hialeah *(G-5432)*
Gold Coast Aero Accessories .... G 561 965-7767
Lake Worth *(G-7553)*
Goodrich Corporation .... G 954 538-8900
Miramar *(G-11000)*
Goodrich Corporation .... G 305 622-4565
Miami Gardens *(G-10745)*
Goodrich Corporation .... G 305 622-4500
Miami Gardens *(G-10744)*
GSE America LLC .... G 863 583-4343
Lakeland *(G-7702)*
GSE Jetall Inc .... G 305 688-2111
Opa Locka *(G-12321)*
Halcyon Aviation Capital LLC .... G 305 615-1575
Doral *(G-3376)*
▲ **Heico Corporation** .... B 954 987-4000
Hollywood *(G-5840)*
Heli-Tech Inc .... F 850 763-9000
Panama City *(G-13914)*
Hensoldt Avionics Usa LLC .... G 941 306-1328
Sarasota *(G-16459)*
▼ **Hermes Technical Intl Inc** .... G 305 477-8993
Doral *(G-3380)*
▲ **High Standard Aviation Inc** .... E 305 599-8855
Doral *(G-3383)*
◆ **Himmel Losungen Group Hlg LLC** .... G 786 631-5531
Doral *(G-3384)*
Honeycomb Arcft Repr Ctr LLC .... E 850 610-0334
Sarasota *(G-16228)*
Honeycomb Company America Inc ...... C 941 756-8781
Sarasota *(G-16229)*
Honeywell International Inc .... G 505 358-0676
Largo *(G-7973)*
Icon Aircraft Inc .... F 813 387-6603
Tampa *(G-17769)*
Integritrust Solutions LLC .... G 850 685-9801
Navarre *(G-11466)*
Interavia Spares and Svcs Inc .... G 954 794-0174
Boca Raton *(G-567)*
Interntnal Synrgy For Tchncal .... G 321 305-0863
Orlando *(G-12837)*
Intgrated Arospc Aliance LLC .... G 469 703-7093
Lake Mary *(G-7426)*
Irvin Technologies Inc .... E 866 245-9356
Winter Springs *(G-19476)*
J F Aerospace Inc .... G 786 242-6686
Miami *(G-9781)*
▲ **Jetspares International Inc** .... G 407 876-3978
Windermere *(G-19231)*
Jormac Aerospace .... D 727 549-9600
Largo *(G-7989)*
Js2 Aerospace Corp .... G 954 840-3620
Pompano Beach *(G-14738)*
Kachemak Bay Flying Service .... F 850 398-8699
Crestview *(G-2352)*
Kaman Aerospace Corporation .... E 904 751-5369
Jacksonville *(G-6532)*
Karob Instrument Inc .... G 352 732-2414
Ocala *(G-11973)*
Kellstrom Coml Arospc Inc .... E 305 818-5400
Miami Lakes *(G-10801)*

L3harris Technologies Inc .... G 321 727-4660
Palm Bay *(G-13520)*
Laminar Flow Systems Inc .... F 386 253-8833
Daytona Beach *(G-2679)*
▲ **Landing Aerospace Inc** .... G 305 687-0100
Opa Locka *(G-12332)*
Live Aerospace Inc .... G 305 910-0091
Miami *(G-9903)*
Loos & Co Inc .... D 239 643-5667
Naples *(G-11316)*
Lopez & Company Inc .... E 305 302-3045
Miami *(G-9911)*
▼ **Lopresti Speed Merchants Inc** .... E 772 562-4757
Sebastian *(G-16666)*
Ltb Aerospace LLC .... G 954 251-1141
Doral *(G-3420)*
Mattis Aerospace .... G 305 910-2377
Homestead *(G-5982)*
Maverick Composites Inc .... G 561 601-3393
Jupiter *(G-7075)*
Miami Technics LLC .... F 754 227-5459
Deerfield Beach *(G-2871)*
Micro Systems Inc .... C 850 244-2332
Fort Walton Beach *(G-4815)*
Micro Tool Engineering Inc .... F 561 842-7381
Riviera Beach *(G-15348)*
Milspec Products Inc .... G 352 735-0065
Sorrento *(G-16790)*
Mk Aviation LLC .... F 305 825-4810
Doral *(G-3440)*
Monroy Aerospace .... G 954 344-4936
Coral Springs *(G-2289)*
Moog Inc .... G 716 652-2000
Pembroke Pines *(G-14049)*
Mro Aerospace Inc .... F 727 546-4820
Largo *(G-8015)*
MSA Aircraft Products .... F 772 562-2243
Fort Pierce *(G-4721)*
Mt-Propeller Usa Inc .... F 386 736-7762
Deland *(G-3002)*
N23d Services LLC .... G 754 217-3362
Fort Lauderdale *(G-4128)*
National Aerospace Group Inc .... G 817 226-0315
Vero Beach *(G-18646)*
Northstar Aviation USA LLC .... E 321 600-4557
Melbourne *(G-8898)*
Novo Aero Services LLC .... G 786 319-8637
West Palm Beach *(G-18968)*
Omnia Inc .... G 863 619-8100
Lakeland *(G-7758)*
Pacific Scientific Company .... E 305 477-4711
Medley *(G-8700)*
Parker-Hannifin Corporation .... G 239 304-1000
Naples *(G-11358)*
Parts Cage Inc .... F 904 373-7800
Saint Augustine *(G-15584)*
Pem-Air LLC .... F 954 321-8726
Davie *(G-2568)*
Pem-Air Turbine Eng Svcs LLC .... F 954 321-8726
Davie *(G-2569)*
Pioneer Aerospace Corporation .... F 850 623-3330
Milton *(G-10936)*
Piper Aircraft Inc .... A 772 567-4361
Vero Beach *(G-18653)*
Power Flow Systems Inc .... F 386 253-8833
Daytona Beach *(G-2696)*
Pratt & Whitney Eng Svcs Inc .... G 305 512-9882
Miami Lakes *(G-10841)*
Precision Shapes Inc .... E 321 269-2555
Titusville *(G-18453)*
Precision Tech Aero Inc .... F 305 603-8347
Miami Lakes *(G-10842)*
Precision Tl Engrg of Gnsville .... F 352 376-2533
Gainesville *(G-4982)*
▲ **Quiet Technology Aerospace Inc** ..... E 305 687-9808
Hollywood *(G-5899)*
R4 Integration Inc .... E 850 226-6913
Fort Walton Beach *(G-4825)*
Radiant Power Corp .... C 941 739-3200
Sarasota *(G-16281)*
Raytheon Technologies Corp .... A 858 277-7639
Jupiter *(G-7103)*
Redstone Corporation .... G 321 213-2135
Merritt Island *(G-9007)*
Rockwell Collins Inc .... G 321 768-7492
Melbourne *(G-8920)*
Rockwell Collins Inc .... G 305 459-7000
Medley *(G-8719)*
Rolin Industries Inc .... G 850 654-1704
Fort Walton Beach *(G-4831)*

Saf Aerospace LLC .... G 813 376-0883
Tampa *(G-18080)*
Safran Power Uk Ltd .... G 941 739-7207
Sarasota *(G-16288)*
Safran Power Usa LLC .... C 941 758-7726
Sarasota *(G-16289)*
Saint-Gobain Corporation .... C 863 425-3299
Mulberry *(G-11135)*
Sal Aerospace Engineering LLC .... F 305 791-0593
Miami *(G-10299)*
Savvy Associate Inc .... F 954 941-6986
Pompano Beach *(G-14840)*
Segers Aerospace Corporation .... E 850 689-2198
Crestview *(G-2357)*
Sensenich Technologies Inc .... G 813 703-8446
Plant City *(G-14464)*
Setty Enterprises Inc .... F 561 844-3711
West Palm Beach *(G-19028)*
▲ **Shark Skinz** .... G 772 388-9621
Sebastian *(G-16672)*
Sidus Space Inc .... E 321 613-0615
Cape Canaveral *(G-1367)*
Signature AVI US Holdings Inc .... F 407 648-7230
Orlando *(G-13193)*
Simmonds Precision Pdts Inc .... E 904 757-3660
Jacksonville *(G-6776)*
Sky Aerospace Engineering .... G 407 251-7111
Orlando *(G-13195)*
Sky Aerospace Engineering Inc .... G 407 251-7111
Orlando *(G-13196)*
Sky Capital Partners Inc .... G 305 934-8259
Miami *(G-10359)*
Sky Technics Aviation Sls Inc .... G 305 885-7499
Miami *(G-10360)*
Skyhigh Accessories Inc .... G 954 316-3936
Plantation *(G-14552)*
Skymasters Aviation LLC .... G 954 796-7622
Parkland *(G-14001)*
Skyways Technics Americas LLC .... G 786 615-2443
North Miami *(G-11655)*
Smart Material Corp .... F 941 870-3337
Sarasota *(G-16600)*
SMI Tool & Die Inc .... G 321 632-6200
Cocoa *(G-2051)*
Sohacki Industries Inc .... E 904 826-0130
Saint Augustine *(G-15613)*
Solair Group Llc .... E 786 269-0160
Cutler Bay *(G-2412)*
Southeastern Engineering Inc .... F 321 984-2521
Palm Bay *(G-13538)*
Southern Fiberglass Inc .... F 904 387-2246
Jacksonville *(G-6794)*
Southern Gear & Machine Inc .... D 305 691-6300
Miami *(G-10386)*
Southwind Aviation Supply LLC .... F 405 491-0500
Oakland *(G-11771)*
Stat Industry Inc .... F 561 826-7045
Pompano Beach *(G-14868)*
Steen Aero Lab LLC .... G 321 725-4160
Palm Bay *(G-13540)*
Sunny Skies Enterprises Inc .... E 954 316-6015
North Miami Beach *(G-11705)*
Sunstate Uav LLC .... F 904 580-4828
Saint Augustine *(G-15624)*
Superior Avionics Inc .... G 954 917-9194
Fort Lauderdale *(G-4268)*
Supliaereos USA LLC .... G 727 754-4915
Clearwater *(G-1897)*
Support Aircraft Parts Inc .... F 305 975-3767
Miami *(G-10441)*
Support Systems Associates Inc .... E 321 724-5566
Melbourne *(G-8952)*
◆ **Survival Products Inc** .... G 954 966-7329
Sunrise *(G-17182)*
Technology Research Cons Inc .... G 863 419-8860
Haines City *(G-5151)*
◆ **Tesco Equipment LLC** .... E 954 752-7994
Coral Springs *(G-2322)*
Thales Inflight Entertaiment .... G 786 777-9031
Miami *(G-10472)*
TL Fahringer Co Inc .... G 813 681-2373
Tampa *(G-18190)*
▼ **Tobruk International Corp** .... G 305 406-0263
Miami *(G-10484)*
TOMI Aircraft Inc .... G 863 446-3001
Deland *(G-3024)*
Tri-Tech Electronics Inc .... D 407 277-2131
Orlando *(G-13270)*
Tri-Tech of Florida Inc .... F 727 544-8836
Saint Petersburg *(G-15944)*

Tritech Industries LLC ....F 954 383-3545
Oakland Park (G-11847)
Triumph Aerostructures LLC ....E 772 463-8700
Stuart (G-17039)
Turbine Controls LLC ....D 954 517-1706
Miramar (G-11054)
Turbo Aerospace Corp ....G 786 218-8990
Oakland Park (G-11849)
▲ Turbocombustor Technology Inc ....B 772 287-7770
Stuart (G-17041)
◆ UDC Usa Inc ....E 813 281-0200
Tampa (G-18211)
Ultra Aerospace Inc ....F 305 728-6361
Miami (G-10525)
Unison Industries LLC ....A 904 739-4000
Jacksonville (G-6879)
United Aerospace Corporation ....E 954 364-0085
Miramar (G-11055)
United Technologies Corp ....D 954 538-8900
Miramar (G-11056)
Universal Crgo Doors & Svc LLC ....E 305 594-9175
Miami (G-10540)
UTC Aerospace Systems ....G 954 538-8971
Miramar (G-11057)
V-Raptor Aircraft LLC ....G 772 388-3334
Sebastian (G-16676)
Velocity Aerospace - Nmb Inc ....E 214 396-9030
North Miami Beach (G-11708)
Velocity Aircraft Inc ....G 772 589-1860
Sebastian (G-16677)
▲ Ver-Val Enterprises Inc ....F 850 244-7931
Fort Walton Beach (G-4838)
Viking Aircraft Engines ....G 386 416-8383
Edgewater (G-3638)
Viper Drones Inc ....F 321 427-5837
Indialantic (G-6061)
Vision Manufacturing Tech Inc ....E 904 579-5272
Orange Park (G-12412)
Vision Systems North America ....F 321 265-5110
Melbourne (G-8973)
Willis Aeronautical Svcs Inc ....F 561 272-5402
Coconut Creek (G-2103)
◆ Working Drones Inc ....G 904 647-4511
Jacksonville (G-6929)
Xcalibur Arcft Solutions LLC ....G 305 744-2830
Middleburg (G-10916)
Yellow Green Aerospace Inc ....G 954 599-4161
Coral Gables (G-2208)
Zitec Inc ....G 850 678-9747
Niceville (G-11577)

3731 Shipbuilding & Repairing

◆ Advanced Mechanical Entps Inc ....E 954 764-2678
Fort Lauderdale (G-3783)
◆ Almaco Group Inc ....F 561 558-1600
Boca Raton (G-413)
Amee Bay LLC ....E 904 553-9873
Atlantic Beach (G-216)
American Marine Mfg Inc ....G 305 497-7723
Hialeah (G-5293)
Arrow Power Boats LLC ....G 772 429-8888
Fort Pierce (G-4678)
Atlantic Dry Dock ....E 904 251-1545
Jacksonville (G-6173)
Atlantic Marine Inc ....G 904 251-1580
Jacksonville (G-6177)
◆ Bae Systems Sthast Shpyrds Amh ....D 904 251-3111
Jacksonville (G-6189)
Capt Latham LLC ....G 904 483-6118
Green Cove Springs (G-5057)
Colonna Shipyard ....G 904 246-1183
Atlantic Beach (G-218)
D W Allen Marine Svcs Inc ....E 904 358-1933
Jacksonville (G-6306)
Earl Industries ....G 904 247-1301
Atlantic Beach (G-220)
▲ Eastern Shipbuilding Group Inc ....B 850 763-1900
Panama City (G-13895)
Eastern Shipyards Inc ....D 850 763-1900
Panama City (G-13897)
◆ Fassmer Service America LLC ....E 305 557-8875
Lauderhill (G-8109)
Florida Dredge and Dock LLC ....E 727 942-7888
Tarpon Springs (G-18301)
Gable Enterprises ....F 727 455-5576
Seffner (G-16727)
Gde LLC ....G 305 458-3025
Miami Beach (G-10671)
General Dynamics Corporation ....E 407 380-9384
Orlando (G-12778)
Gulf County Ship Building Inc ....G 850 229-9300
Port Saint Joe (G-15080)
▲ Gulf Marine Repair Corporation ....C 813 247-3153
Tampa (G-17735)
Gulfstream Land Company LLC ....F 772 286-3456
Stuart (G-16951)
Gulfstream Shipbuilding LLC ....G 850 835-5125
Freeport (G-4849)
Hendry Corporation ....D 813 241-9206
Tampa (G-17750)
Hendry Marine Industries Inc ....E 813 241-9206
Tampa (G-17751)
Hendry Shipyard Joint Ventr 1 ....E 813 241-9206
Tampa (G-17752)
▲ Hydrex LLC ....G 727 443-3900
Clearwater (G-1723)
International Ship Repair & MA ....F 813 247-1118
Tampa (G-17790)
International Shipyards Ancona ....F 305 371-7722
Fort Lauderdale (G-4064)
▼ Jmh Marine Inc ....F 954 785-7557
Pompano Beach (G-14736)
Karepat Group Inc ....G 772 286-5339
Stuart (G-16964)
M/V Marine Inc ....F 904 633-7992
Jacksonville (G-6569)
Marine Transportation Svcs Inc ....E 850 215-4557
Panama City (G-13927)
Maritime SEC Strtegies Fla LLC ....G 912 704-0300
Tampa (G-17880)
Merced Industrial Corp ....G 908 309-0170
Miami (G-9977)
Metro Machine Corp ....D 904 249-7772
Jacksonville (G-6601)
Miller Marine Yacht Svc Inc ....E 850 265-6768
Panama City (G-13929)
Naiad Dynamics Us Inc ....F 954 797-7566
Davie (G-2555)
New Yachts Company ....G 754 223-5907
Fort Lauderdale (G-4138)
▲ Newcastle Shipyards LLC ....C 386 312-0000
Saint Augustine (G-15573)
Nordic Made Inc ....F 954 651-6208
Davie (G-2558)
▼ Norseman Shipbuilding Corp ....E 305 545-6815
Miami (G-10076)
Ocean Marine LLC ....F 305 549-6092
Miami (G-10089)
Old City Marine LLC ....G 904 252-6887
Saint Augustine (G-15580)
OSG America LLC ....D 813 209-0600
Tampa (G-17963)
Patti Marine Enterprises Inc ....F 850 453-1282
Pensacola (G-14221)
Port Manatee Ship Repair ....E 941 417-2613
Palmetto (G-13817)
Premier Luxury Group LLC ....E 954 358-9885
Fort Lauderdale (G-4176)
Professional Coating Systems ....G 904 477-7138
Lawtey (G-8125)
Progressive Industrial Inc ....F 941 723-0201
Palmetto (G-13818)
Propel Builders Inc ....F 407 960-5116
Maitland (G-8475)
Puma Aero Marine Inc ....G 904 638-5888
Fort Lauderdale (G-4184)
Riverhawk Fast Sea Frames LLC ....G 912 484-3112
Tampa (G-18060)
Salmi and Company Inc ....G 443 243-8537
Navarre (G-11474)
◆ Seaking Inc ....E 954 961-6629
Davie (G-2589)
Seaquest Marine LLC ....G 781 888-8850
Miami (G-10317)
Searobotics Corporation ....E 772 742-3700
Stuart (G-17006)
◆ SGS US East Coast LLC ....E 305 571-9700
Miami (G-10330)
Shearwater Marine Fl Inc ....E 772 781-5553
Stuart (G-17010)
▼ Sisco Marine LLC ....E 850 265-1383
Panama City (G-13951)
Southern Drydock Inc ....E 904 355-9945
Saint Augustine (G-15615)
▼ St Augustine Marina Inc ....E 904 824-4394
Saint Augustine (G-15619)
St Augustine Trawlers Inc ....F 904 824-4394
Saint Augustine (G-15621)
◆ St Johns Ship Building Inc ....C 386 328-6054
Palatka (G-13495)
Suncoast Kingfish Classic LLC ....G 970 708-7997
Treasure Island (G-18478)
▲ Tampa Ship LLC ....B 813 248-9310
Tampa (G-18173)
Tecnico Corporation ....F 904 853-6118
Atlantic Beach (G-227)
▼ TNT Custom Marine Inc ....G 305 931-3157
Miami (G-10482)
Trident Pontoons Inc ....G 352 253-1400
Tavares (G-18355)
◆ Triton Submarines LLC ....E 772 770-1995
Sebastian (G-16674)
Ultra Lite Tenders LLC ....G 214 215-2725
Stuart (G-17042)
◆ United Ship Service Corp ....G 954 583-4588
Fort Lauderdale (G-4295)
Unlimited Marine Mfg Inc ....G 305 420-6034
Hialeah (G-5665)
US Submarines Inc ....F 208 687-9057
Vero Beach (G-18675)
USA Maritime Enterprises Inc ....G 954 764-8360
Fort Lauderdale (G-4300)
World Container Services LLC ....E 305 400-4850
Doral (G-3550)

3732 Boat Building & Repairing

Acrylico Inc ....G 561 304-2921
Lake Worth (G-7529)
Acryplex Inc ....G 305 633-7636
Miami (G-9066)
Adler Anb Inc ....G 954 581-2572
Davie (G-2488)
Admiral ....G 305 493-4355
Miami (G-9069)
Aicon Yachts Americas LLC ....G 910 583-5299
Miami Beach (G-10638)
All Craft Marine LLC ....E 813 236-8879
Zephyrhills (G-19506)
All Tank Services LLC ....G 954 260-9443
Pompano Beach (G-14585)
Alumitech Inc ....F 407 826-5373
Orlando (G-12463)
Ameracat Inc ....G 772 882-9186
Fort Pierce (G-4672)
Americraft Enterprises Inc ....G 386 756-1100
Daytona Beach (G-2624)
Andros Boatworks Inc ....F 941 351-9702
Sarasota (G-16342)
Angler Pro Boats LLC ....G 305 525-4943
South Miami (G-16812)
Arkup Llc ....G 786 448-8635
Miami Beach (G-10644)
Arthur Cox ....G 772 286-5339
Stuart (G-16910)
▼ Atlas Boat Works Inc ....G 239 574-2628
Cape Coral (G-1385)
▲ Autocraft Manufacturing Co ....E 321 453-1850
Merritt Island (G-8992)
Bahama Boat Works LLC ....F 561 882-4069
Mangonia Park (G-8499)
Barker Boatworks LLC ....F 941 233-8640
Sarasota (G-16180)
▲ Bausch American Towers LLC ....F 772 283-2771
Stuart (G-16911)
Bausch Enterprises Inc ....F 772 220-6652
Stuart (G-16912)
Bd Xtreme Holdings LLC ....F 850 703-1793
Bonifay (G-799)
Beavertail Skiffs Inc ....G 941 705-2090
Bradenton (G-997)
Beez Worx Boats LLC ....G 850 678-6548
Niceville (G-11563)
Belzona Inc ....E 305 512-3200
Doral (G-3268)
Bertram Yachts LLC ....C 813 527-9899
Tampa (G-17465)
Big Eagle LLC ....G 305 586-8766
Fort Lauderdale (G-3850)
Big O Boats LLC ....G 863 697-6319
Sebring (G-16683)
Bill Shuda ....G 772 220-6620
Stuart (G-16916)
▼ Birdsall Marine Design Inc ....E 561 832-7879
West Palm Beach (G-18822)
◆ Blazer Boats Inc ....E 321 307-4761
Orlando (G-12523)
▲ Bms International Inc ....E 813 247-7040
Tampa (G-17477)
Boat Works ....G 904 389-0090
Jacksonville (G-6217)

SIC

Boggy Creek Boat Co LLC ....G....... 904 707-0952
Jacksonville *(G-6222)*
Bohemian Boatworks LLC ....G....... 941 321-1499
Sarasota *(G-16366)*
▼ **Bonadeo Boat Works LLC** ....G....... 772 341-9820
Stuart *(G-16918)*
Bonefish Boatworks Llc ....G....... 727 243-6767
Odessa *(G-12108)*
◆ **Boston Whaler Inc** ....B....... 386 428-0057
Edgewater *(G-3615)*
◆ **Bradford Yacht Limited Inc** ....C....... 954 791-3800
Fort Lauderdale *(G-3867)*
◆ **Broward Yard & Marine LLC** ....D....... 954 927-4119
Dania *(G-2441)*
Brunswick Boat Group ....G....... 321 449-8754
Merritt Island *(G-8996)*
◆ **Brunswick Commercial &** ....D....... 386 423-2900
Edgewater *(G-3616)*
C&A Boatworks Inc ....G....... 754 366-5549
Pompano Beach *(G-14628)*
C-Worthy Corp ....F....... 954 784-7370
Pompano Beach *(G-14629)*
Campeones Marina Corp ....G....... 305 491-5738
Miami *(G-9307)*
◆ **Camper & Nicholsons Usa Inc** ....E....... 561 655-2121
Palm Beach *(G-13550)*
▼ **Canaveral Custom Boats Inc** ....G....... 321 783-3536
Cape Canaveral *(G-1354)*
Canyon Bay Boats Llc ....G....... 850 838-1400
Perry *(G-14297)*
Carey-Dunn Inc ....F....... 561 840-1694
Riviera Beach *(G-15309)*
Catalina Yachts Inc ....C....... 727 544-6681
Largo *(G-7919)*
Cayo Custom Boats LLC ....G....... 727 698-7201
Largo *(G-7920)*
CF Boatworks Inc ....G....... 954 325-6007
Fort Lauderdale *(G-3892)*
Chardonnay Boat Works LLC ....G....... 703 981-6339
Green Cove Springs *(G-5058)*
Chittum Yachts LLC ....F....... 386 589-7224
Palm City *(G-13647)*
Chittum Yachts LLC ....E....... 386 589-7224
Stuart *(G-16923)*
◆ **Chris Craft Corporation** ....C....... 941 351-4900
Sarasota *(G-16191)*
▲ **Cigarette Racing Team LLC** ....D....... 305 769-4350
Opa Locka *(G-12299)*
CK Dockside Services Inc ....G....... 954 254-0263
Parkland *(G-13990)*
CK Prime Investments Inc ....G....... 239 574-7800
Cape Coral *(G-1403)*
◆ **Classic Yacht Refinishing Inc** ....G....... 954 760-9626
Fort Lauderdale *(G-3903)*
▲ **Composite Holdings Inc** ....E....... 321 268-9625
Titusville *(G-18424)*
▼ **Concept Boats Inc** ....E....... 305 635-8712
Opa Locka *(G-12303)*
◆ **Contender Boats Inc** ....C....... 305 230-1600
Homestead *(G-5959)*
▼ **Copalo Inc** ....C....... 941 753-7828
Sarasota *(G-16198)*
Corinthian Catamarans LLC ....F....... 813 334-1029
Palm Harbor *(G-13730)*
▼ **Craig Catamaran Corporation** ....G....... 407 290-8778
Orlando *(G-12624)*
Creative Marine ....G....... 239 437-1010
Fort Myers *(G-4416)*
Custom Marine Components Inc ....F....... 904 221-6412
Jacksonville *(G-6303)*
Custom Marine Concepts Inc ....F....... 954 782-1111
Pompano Beach *(G-14654)*
▼ **Dania Cut Holdings Inc** ....F....... 954 923-9545
Dania Beach *(G-2464)*
Dennis Boatworks ....G....... 954 260-6855
Oakland Park *(G-11797)*
Diamondback Manufacturing LLC ....F....... 321 305-5995
Cocoa *(G-2012)*
▼ **Diamondback Manufacturing LLC** ....E....... 321 633-5624
Cocoa *(G-2013)*
Diamondback Towers LLC ....F....... 800 424-5624
Cocoa *(G-2014)*
Discount Boat Tops Inc ....G....... 727 536-4412
Largo *(G-7933)*
Diversified Yacht Services Inc ....E....... 239 765-8700
Fort Myers Beach *(G-4661)*
▼ **Doller Marine Sales & Services** ....F....... 954 463-9988
Fort Lauderdale *(G-3947)*
Dorado Custom Boats LLC ....F....... 727 786-3800
Tarpon Springs *(G-18295)*
Dorado Marine Inc ....F....... 727 786-3800
Ozona *(G-13467)*
Double Down Boat Works Inc ....G....... 305 984-3000
Miami *(G-9484)*
Duckworth Steel Boats Inc ....G....... 727 934-2550
Tarpon Springs *(G-18296)*
Earl Parker Yacht Refinishing ....F....... 954 791-1811
Fort Lauderdale *(G-3955)*
Eastward Boats Inc ....G....... 772 828-1358
Port Saint Lucie *(G-15104)*
◆ **Edgewater Power Boats LLC** ....D....... 386 426-5457
Edgewater *(G-3622)*
Endeavour Catamaran Corp ....F....... 727 573-5377
Clearwater *(G-1671)*
EZ Boatworks Inc ....G....... 772 475-8721
Palm City *(G-13653)*
Fabbro Marine Group Inc ....E....... 321 701-8141
Orlando *(G-12730)*
Fiesta Marine Products Inc ....F....... 727 856-6900
Hudson *(G-6023)*
Flat Island Boatworks LLC ....G....... 850 434-8295
Pensacola *(G-14153)*
▼ **Flatsmaster Marine LLC** ....F....... 239 574-7800
Cape Coral *(G-1423)*
Floral City Airboat Co Inc ....F....... 352 637-4390
Inverness *(G-6087)*
Floral City Airboat Co Inc ....G....... 352 637-4390
Floral City *(G-3767)*
▲ **Florida Derecktor Inc** ....C....... 954 920-5756
Dania Beach *(G-2465)*
Florida Mkb Holdings LLC ....E....... 407 281-7909
Clermont *(G-1959)*
Florida Trident Trading LLC ....F....... 352 253-1400
Tavares *(G-18337)*
▲ **Frank Murray & Sons Inc** ....F....... 561 845-1366
Fort Lauderdale *(G-4012)*
G & S Boats Inc ....F....... 850 835-7700
Freeport *(G-4847)*
Gable Enterprises ....F....... 727 455-5576
Seffner *(G-16727)*
▲ **Game Fisherman Inc** ....F....... 772 220-4850
Stuart *(G-16944)*
Garlington Landeweer Marine ....E....... 772 283-7124
Stuart *(G-16945)*
Gause Built Marine Inc ....E....... 727 937-9113
Tarpon Springs *(G-18302)*
Gilbane Boatworks LLC ....G....... 561 744-2223
Tequesta *(G-18384)*
◆ **Glass Tech Corp** ....E....... 305 633-6491
Miami *(G-9638)*
Glasser Boat Works Inc ....G....... 321 626-0061
Rockledge *(G-15414)*
▼ **Good Time Outdoors Inc** ....E....... 352 401-9070
Ocala *(G-11958)*
Gulfstream Boatworks ....G....... 239 223-2628
Fort Myers *(G-4479)*
Gulfstream Unsnkable Boats LLC ....F....... 813 820-6100
Tampa *(G-17737)*
Hake Yachts Inc ....G....... 772 287-3200
Stuart *(G-16954)*
Hamant Airboats LLc ....G....... 321 259-6998
Melbourne *(G-8839)*
Harley Boat Corporation ....G....... 863 533-2800
Bartow *(G-316)*
Harley Shipbuilding Corp ....G....... 863 533-2800
Bartow *(G-317)*
◆ **Hells Bay Boatworks LLC** ....E....... 321 383-8223
Titusville *(G-18432)*
▼ **Hells Bay Marine Inc** ....E....... 321 383-8223
Titusville *(G-18433)*
Hinckley ....G....... 239 919-8142
Naples *(G-11277)*
Hohol Marine Products ....G....... 386 734-0630
Deland *(G-2983)*
▲ **Huckins Yacht Corporation** ....E....... 904 389-1125
Jacksonville *(G-6481)*
▼ **Hutchins Co Inc** ....F....... 727 442-6651
Clearwater *(G-1722)*
Hydrofoils Incorporated ....G....... 561 964-6399
Lake Worth *(G-7556)*
▲ **Intrepid Powerboats Inc** ....B....... 954 324-4196
Dania *(G-2448)*
▼ **Invincible Boat Company LLC** ....E....... 305 685-2704
Opa Locka *(G-12327)*
Islamorada Boatworks LLC ....G....... 786 393-4752
Edgewater *(G-3626)*
Island Pcket Saward Yachts LLC ....G....... 727 535-6431
Largo *(G-7984)*
▲ **Ivm Usa Inc** ....E....... 786 693-2755
Miami *(G-9778)*
Jabm Advisors Inc ....G....... 727 458-3755
Tarpon Springs *(G-18310)*
Jim Smith Boats Inc ....F....... 772 286-9049
Stuart *(G-16962)*
Jlb Enterprises Tampa Inc ....G....... 813 545-3830
Tampa *(G-17806)*
▼ **Johannsen Boat Works Inc** ....G....... 772 567-4612
Vero Beach *(G-18634)*
▼ **Jupiter Mar Intl Holdings Inc** ....D....... 941 729-5000
Palmetto *(G-13809)*
K C Marine Services Inc ....G....... 954 766-8100
Fort Lauderdale *(G-4082)*
Knowles Plastics Inc ....G....... 954 232-8756
Coral Springs *(G-2270)*
▼ **Kz Manufacturing LLC** ....G....... 305 257-2628
Princeton *(G-15185)*
L & H Boats Inc ....G....... 772 288-2291
Stuart *(G-16968)*
L & S Design & Construction ....G....... 772 220-1745
Palm City *(G-13665)*
Lake & Bay Boats LLC ....G....... 813 949-7300
Naples *(G-11307)*
Land Marine Service Inc ....G....... 561 626-2947
West Palm Beach *(G-18926)*
Larsen ....G....... 305 989-4043
Stuart *(G-16969)*
Lighthouse Boatworks Inc ....G....... 561 667-7382
Jupiter *(G-7067)*
◆ **Little River Marine** ....G....... 352 378-5025
Gainesville *(G-4955)*
Littoral Marine LLC ....E....... 352 400-4222
Wildwood *(G-19197)*
Luxury Boat Services Inc ....G....... 360 451-2888
Fort Lauderdale *(G-4105)*
▼ **Mack Sales Inc** ....G....... 772 283-2306
Stuart *(G-16971)*
▼ **Magnum Marine Corporation** ....E....... 305 931-4292
Miami *(G-9934)*
◆ **Marine Exhaust Systems Inc** ....D....... 561 848-1238
Riviera Beach *(G-15346)*
Marine Fiberglass Specialist ....G....... 305 821-6667
Hialeah *(G-5502)*
Marine Transportation Svcs Inc ....E....... 850 215-4557
Panama City *(G-13927)*
Mariner International Trvl Inc ....G....... 954 925-4150
Dania *(G-2451)*
Maritec Industries Inc ....D....... 352 429-8888
Groveland *(G-5101)*
▼ **Mark McManus Inc** ....F....... 239 454-1300
Fort Myers *(G-4522)*
Markcam Inc ....G....... 772 283-7189
Stuart *(G-16975)*
Marpro Marine Ways LLC ....G....... 727 447-4930
Clearwater *(G-1774)*
Master Marine ....G....... 904 329-1541
Jacksonville *(G-6580)*
Maverick Boat Group Inc ....C....... 772 465-0631
Fort Pierce *(G-4715)*
▼ **Maverick Boat Group Inc** ....C....... 772 465-0631
Fort Pierce *(G-4716)*
◆ **McKinna Corporation** ....G....... 386 446-8822
Palm Coast *(G-13703)*
▲ **Merrill-Stevens Dry Dock Co** ....D....... 305 640-5676
Miami *(G-9983)*
Michael Rybvich Sons Boat Wrks ....E....... 561 627-9168
Palm Beach Gardens *(G-13609)*
▼ **Midnight Express Pwr Boats Inc** ....E....... 954 745-8284
Miami *(G-10018)*
Miller Marine Yacht Svc Inc ....E....... 850 265-6768
Panama City *(G-13929)*
Mirage & Co Inc ....E....... 407 301-5850
Saint Cloud *(G-15661)*
Mirage Manufacturing Inc ....D....... 352 377-4146
Gainesville *(G-4964)*
Moores Mar of Palm Beaches Inc ....G....... 561 841-2235
Riviera Beach *(G-15349)*
Motley Enterprises Inc ....G....... 703 966-3997
Saint Augustine *(G-15571)*
Multihull Technologies Inc ....G....... 305 296-2773
Key West *(G-7198)*
National Assemblers Inc ....F....... 877 915-5505
Lake Worth *(G-7574)*
◆ **Novurania of America Inc** ....D....... 772 567-9200
Vero Beach *(G-18647)*
Ocean Master Marine Inc ....G....... 561 840-0448
Riviera Beach *(G-15357)*
OP Yacht Services Corp ....F....... 954 451-3677
Fort Lauderdale *(G-4150)*
◆ **P B C H Incorporated** ....E....... 239 567-5030
Fort Myers *(G-4560)*

Parker Boatworks F 954 585-1059
Fort Lauderdale (G-4159)
Patrick Industries Inc E 941 556-6311
Sarasota (G-16274)
Pb Holdco LLC B 772 465-6006
Fort Pierce (G-4730)
Pemberton Custom Airboats G 352 422-5597
Inverness (G-6094)
◆ Performance Boats Inc F 305 956-9549
North Miami Beach (G-11697)
Performance Sales & Service G 863 465-2814
Lake Placid (G-7493)
Perry Composites LLC G 850 584-8400
Perry (G-14308)
Peter Welchs Custom Boats G 941 575-8665
Punta Gorda (G-15219)
Pipe Welders Inc D 954 587-8400
Fort Lauderdale (G-4168)
Pitman Allen Boat Repr & Maint G 727 772-9848
Palm Harbor (G-13750)
Pompanette LLC E 813 885-2182
Tampa (G-17997)
Porta Products G 386 428-7656
Edgewater (G-3633)
▲ Premier Prfmce Interiors Inc E 941 752-6271
Sarasota (G-16279)
Premium Marine Inc E 786 903-0851
Miami (G-10186)
Progressive Industrial Inc F 941 723-0201
Palmetto (G-13818)
Promarine Boats USA G 305 450-2014
Fort Lauderdale (G-4183)
▼ R J Dougherty Associates LLC C 386 409-2202
Edgewater (G-3635)
Rabud Inc G 954 925-4199
Dania (G-2457)
▼ Ram Investments South Fla Inc C 305 759-6419
Medley (G-8714)
Ray Eaton Yacht Service Inc G 954 583-8762
Fort Lauderdale (G-4199)
◆ Regal Marine Industries Inc B 407 851-4360
Orlando (G-13127)
Resilient Group Inc F 518 434-4414
Jacksonville (G-6718)
Revere Survival Inc F 904 503-9733
Jacksonville (G-6720)
Ros Holding Corporation F 954 581-9200
Fort Lauderdale (G-4214)
Roscioli International Inc E 941 755-7411
Fort Lauderdale (G-4215)
Roscioli International Inc E 941 755-7411
Bradenton (G-1107)
▼ Rupp Marine Inc F 772 286-5300
Stuart (G-17004)
S & S Performance Inc G 305 951-9846
Islamorada (G-6099)
Sabalo Boats G 727 243-6767
Odessa (G-12148)
Sarasota Boat Works Inc G 941 366-3357
Sarasota (G-16291)
Schurr Sails Inc F 850 438-9354
Pensacola (G-14258)
Sdkc Corp G 305 469-7578
Doral (G-3497)
Sea Force Center Console LLC E 941 417-7017
Palmetto (G-13822)
Sea Force Ix Inc E 941 721-9009
Wimauma (G-19223)
▼ Sea Hawk Industries Inc G 863 385-1995
Sebring (G-16706)
Sea Ray Boats Inc C 386 439-3401
Flagler Beach (G-3757)
Sea Ray Boats Inc C 321 459-9463
Merritt Island (G-9009)
Sea Ray Boats Inc C 321 459-2930
Merritt Island (G-9010)
Sea Ray Boats Inc C 321 452-9876
Merritt Island (G-9011)
Seadreams Boat Yacht Works LLC G 727 843-0010
Port Richey (G-15067)
Seahunter Inc D 305 257-3344
Princeton (G-15186)
Sheaffer Boats Inc G 813 872-7644
Tampa (G-18093)
Sheaffer Marine Inc F 813 872-7311
Tampa (G-18094)
Shearwater Marine Fl Inc E 772 781-5553
Stuart (G-17010)
▲ Shurhold Products Company G 772 287-1313
Palm City (G-13673)
Sino Eagle Usa Inc F 727 259-3570
Dunedin (G-3588)
SLM Boats Inc G 386 738-4425
Deland (G-3014)
Smith Boat Designs Inc E 954 782-1000
Pompano Beach (G-14853)
▼ Smittys Boat Tops and Mar Eqp G 305 245-0229
Homestead (G-5993)
Snug Harbor Dinghies Inc F 727 578-0618
Saint Petersburg (G-15914)
South Florida Field Techs Inc G 954 325-6548
West Palm Beach (G-19039)
▲ Southern Cross Boatworks Inc F 954 467-5801
Fort Lauderdale (G-4250)
Southern Fiberglass Inc F 904 387-2246
Jacksonville (G-6794)
Spencer Boat Co LLC G 305 324-5211
Miami (G-10404)
Spice Island Boat Works Inc G 954 632-9453
Fort Lauderdale (G-4253)
Stamas Yacht Inc D 727 937-4118
Tarpon Springs (G-18326)
Statement Marine LLC F 727 525-5235
Clearwater (G-1888)
Stinger Fiberglass Designs Inc F 321 268-1118
Titusville (G-18465)
Streamline Performance Boats C F 305 393-8848
Hialeah (G-5634)
Stuart Boat Works Inc F 772 600-7121
Stuart (G-17023)
Stuart Composites LLC E 772 266-4285
Miami (G-10424)
Stuart Yacht Builders F 561 747-1947
Stuart (G-17029)
▲ Survitec Survivor Cft Mar Inc G 954 374-4276
Miramar (G-11050)
Talaria Company LLC D 239 261-2870
Naples (G-11435)
Talaria Company LLC D 772 403-5387
Stuart (G-17032)
Talon Marine G 941 753-7400
Sarasota (G-16308)
Tampa Yacht Manufacturing LLC F 813 792-2114
Clearwater (G-1906)
Target Marine Inc G 863 293-3592
Winter Haven (G-19361)
▲ Taylor Made Systems Brdnton In C 941 747-1900
Oviedo (G-13461)
Tecnografic Inc E 954 928-1714
Fort Lauderdale (G-4276)
Tiger Composites Inc F 386 334-0941
New Smyrna Beach (G-11547)
◆ Toledo Sales Inc G 305 389-3441
Miami (G-10488)
Tom George Yacht Group G 727 734-8707
Clearwater (G-1923)
Top Cters Ycht Restoration LLC G 561 818-9259
West Palm Beach (G-19068)
Top Quality Yacht Refinishing F 954 522-5232
Fort Lauderdale (G-4286)
▲ Trolley Boats G 727 588-1100
Largo (G-8068)
Tropical Dvrsons Mrina MGT Inc G 954 922-0387
Hollywood (G-5929)
Truesouth Marine Corp G 813 286-0716
Tampa (G-18204)
▼ Twin Vee Catamarans Inc F 772 429-2525
Fort Pierce (G-4763)
Uk Sailmakers Inc G 941 365-7245
Sarasota (G-16320)
◆ Ultrapanel Marine Inc E 772 285-4258
Miami (G-10527)
US Recreational Alliance Inc F 954 782-7279
Pompano Beach (G-14906)
◆ US Spars Inc G 386 462-3760
Gainesville (G-5014)
Vilano Interiors Inc G 904 824-3439
Saint Augustine (G-15633)
W E Connery Boat Builders G 239 549-8014
Cape Coral (G-1493)
Warbird Marine Holdings LLC G 844 341-2504
Opa Locka (G-12368)
Whitewater Boat Corp G 305 756-9191
Miami (G-10603)
Whiticar Boat Works Inc E 772 287-2883
Stuart (G-17049)
◆ Williams Tenders USA Inc F 954 648-6560
Pompano Beach (G-14914)
Willis Custom Yachts LLC C 772 221-9100
Stuart (G-17050)
Willis Marine Inc G 772 283-7189
Stuart (G-17051)
World Boat Manufacturing Inc F 863 824-0015
Okeechobee (G-12194)
▲ Yacht 10 Inc G 954 759-9929
Fort Lauderdale (G-4330)

3743 Railroad Eqpt

Adams Street Station G 904 304-7222
Jacksonville (G-6119)
CAF USA Inc G 305 753-5371
Miami (G-9300)
▲ Contemprary McHnrey Engrg Svcs E 386 439-0937
Flagler Beach (G-3755)
Coulombe Enterprises G 407 366-4387
Oviedo (G-13424)
▲ G G Schmitt & Sons Inc C 717 394-3701
Sarasota (G-16216)
Hitachi Rail STS Usa Inc D 415 397-7010
Medley (G-8662)
▲ Hitachi Rail Usa Inc F 415 397-7010
Medley (G-8663)
Jimenez Enterprises Group E 561 542-7709
Doral (G-3403)
Progress Rail Services Corp F 904 783-1143
Jacksonville (G-6692)
Railings Plus Inc F 386 437-4501
Bunnell (G-1304)
Rescar Companies Inc G 386 397-2656
White Springs (G-19188)
Silver Enterprises Assoc Inc G 239 542-0068
Cape Coral (G-1472)
Southstern Rail Svcs Mlbrry FL F 863 425-4986
Mulberry (G-11138)

3751 Motorcycles, Bicycles & Parts

A1a Sportbike LLC G 321 806-3995
Titusville (G-18407)
Adir Scooters Inc G 305 532-0019
Miami Beach (G-10636)
Choice Products Inc F 386 426-6450
Edgewater (G-3619)
Dirtbag Choppers Inc F 904 725-7600
Atlantic Beach (G-219)
Dirtrbags Chopper G 904 725-7600
Jacksonville (G-6320)
Epiccycles G 561 450-6470
Delray Beach (G-3074)
First Coast Trikkes G 904 343-1833
Atlantic Beach (G-221)
Florida Grasschoppers G 561 718-9346
Lake Worth (G-7550)
Grass Choppers G 305 253-1217
Miami (G-9659)
Grass Choppers South Fla Corp G 786 586-2767
Miami (G-9660)
Hartco International G 386 698-4668
Crescent City (G-2340)
Hawk Racing G 941 209-1790
Bradenton (G-1055)
Kjs Hot Choppers G 850 200-4860
Mary Esther (G-8590)
Nasty Choppers Inc G 941 234-7743
Venice (G-18563)
Phxtreme Corp G 305 594-2284
Miami (G-10161)
Powersports 911 Inc G 813 769-2468
Tampa (G-17998)
Pro Street Choppers Inc G 407 389-2047
Apopka (G-173)
▲ Prodeco Technologies LLC E 954 974-6730
Deerfield Beach (G-2896)
▲ Profile Racing Inc E 727 392-8307
Saint Petersburg (G-15891)
Pure Med Mobility Inc G 352 366-8008
Brooksville (G-1263)
Ride Like Bessie Inc G 904 580-3631
Jacksonville (G-6724)
Scott Fischer Enterprises LLC C 844 749-2363
Fort Myers (G-4599)
Southwest Choppers Inc F 239 242-1101
Cape Coral (G-1475)
T D R Inc G 941 505-0800
Punta Gorda (G-15241)
Tampa Bay Powersports LLC E 813 968-7888
Tampa (G-18160)
▲ Trailmate Inc E 941 739-5743
Jacksonville (G-6866)
Ventum LLC G 786 838-1113
Miami Beach (G-10727)

S I C

Vet-Equip LLC ....G 239 537-3402
Naples (G-11449)

Wmr Cycle Performance Inc ....G 772 426-3000
Stuart (G-17052)

Worldglass Corporation ....G 813 609-2453
Tampa (G-18264)

Worldwide Intl Trade LLC ....E 305 414-9774
Hollywood (G-5943)

3761 Guided Missiles & Space Vehicles

Blue Origin Florida LLC ....D 253 437-9300
Merritt Island (G-8994)

Boeing Company ....G 850 882-4912
Eglin Afb (G-3641)

Chad ....F 727 433-0404
Tampa (G-17530)

Kratos Def & SEC Solutions Inc ....G 866 606-5867
Orlando (G-12877)

Lockheed Martin Corporation ....A 407 306-1000
Orlando (G-12920)

Lockheed Martin Corporation ....G 321 853-5194
Cape Canaveral (G-1364)

Lockheed Martin Corporation ....G 850 885-3583
Eglin Afb (G-3645)

Micro Systems Inc ....C 850 244-2332
Fort Walton Beach (G-4815)

Mishaal Aerospace Corporation ....G 786 353-2685
Miami (G-10027)

Moon Express Inc ....E 650 241-8577
Cape Canaveral (G-1365)

New Source Corp ....G 407 830-7771
Altamonte Springs (G-57)

▲ Northrop Grmman Feld Spport Sv ....D 904 810-4665
Saint Augustine (G-15574)

Northrop Grumman Systems Corp ....C 904 825-3300
Saint Augustine (G-15578)

Raytheon Company ....G 321 235-6682
Orlando (G-13116)

Redwire Corporation ....G 650 701-7722
Jacksonville (G-6711)

Rocket Crafters Launch LLC ....G 321 222-0858
Cocoa (G-2049)

Space Exploration Tech Corp ....E 310 363-6000
Cape Canaveral (G-1368)

▲ Space Machine & Engrg Corp ....E 727 323-2221
Saint Petersburg (G-15920)

Space X Design LLC ....G 407 592-5147
Miami (G-10391)

Trailblazerai Inc ....G 727 859-2732
Saint Petersburg (G-15942)

United Drones LLC ....G 305 978-1480
Naples (G-11447)

Wantzloeben RES Solutions LLC ....G 972 273-0190
Summerland Key (G-17066)

3764 Guided Missile/Space Vehicle Propulsion Units & parts

Aerojet Rocketdyne Inc ....B 561 796-2000
Jupiter (G-6995)

American Maglev Tech Fla Inc ....F 404 386-4036
Amelia Island (G-92)

Atk Sales Corp ....G 954 701-0465
Hollywood (G-5777)

Boeing Company ....G 850 882-4912
Eglin Afb (G-3641)

▲ Chromalloy Gas Turbine LLC ....A 561 935-3571
Palm Beach Gardens (G-13578)

Raytheon Technologies Corp ....G 561 796-2000
Jupiter (G-7102)

Sensatek Propulsion Tech Inc ....F 850 321-5993
Daytona Beach (G-2712)

◆ Sequa Corporation ....A 561 935-3571
Palm Beach Gardens (G-13626)

Topline Hy-Lift Johnson Inc ....E 352 799-4668
Brooksville (G-1281)

3769 Guided Missile/Space Vehicle Parts & Eqpt, NEC

Atsg Logistic Support Service ....F 904 579-4596
Jacksonville (G-6179)

◆ C4 Advnced Tctical Systems LLC ....D 407 206-3886
Orlando (G-12541)

▲ Chromalloy Gas Turbine LLC ....A 561 935-3571
Palm Beach Gardens (G-13578)

H H Terry Co Inc ....F 239 593-0132
Naples (G-11274)

L3 Aviation Products Inc ....C 941 371-0811
Saint Petersburg (G-15835)

Livetv ....F 321 722-0783
Melbourne (G-8876)

Micro Systems Inc ....C 850 244-2332
Fort Walton Beach (G-4815)

Micro Tool Engineering Inc ....F 561 842-7381
Riviera Beach (G-15348)

Moog Inc ....F 321 435-8722
West Melbourne (G-18777)

Moog Inc ....G 716 652-2000
Pembroke Pines (G-14049)

Precise Technologies Inc ....F 727 535-5594
Largo (G-8030)

▲ Precision Fabg & Clg Co Inc ....D 321 635-2000
Cocoa (G-2042)

Savvy Associate Inc ....F 954 941-6986
Pompano Beach (G-14840)

Sidus Space Inc ....E 321 613-0615
Cape Canaveral (G-1367)

Stuart Industries Inc ....F 305 651-3474
Miami (G-10425)

3792 Travel Trailers & Campers

Big Time Tailgate LLC ....G 407 509-5163
Titusville (G-18414)

▼ Chariot Eagle Inc ....C 623 936-7545
Ocala (G-11901)

East 46th Auto Sales Inc ....F 407 322-3100
Sanford (G-16039)

Excalibur Coach ....G 407 302-9139
Sanford (G-16043)

Pierce Manufacturing Inc ....D 941 748-3900
Bradenton (G-1097)

Rolls Axle Lc ....F 813 764-0242
Plant City (G-14463)

Southeastern Truck Tops Inc ....F 386 761-0002
Daytona Beach (G-2717)

Stephen Shives ....G 352 454-6522
Summerfield (G-17063)

3795 Tanks & Tank Components

Aba-Con Inc ....F 321 567-4967
Titusville (G-18408)

◆ C4 Advnced Tctical Systems LLC ....D 407 206-3886
Orlando (G-12541)

Clogic LLC ....G 860 324-2227
Ponte Vedra Beach (G-14936)

Fidelity Manufacturing LLC ....E 352 414-4700
Ocala (G-11940)

▲ Florida Ordnance Corporation ....F 954 493-8691
Fort Lauderdale (G-4001)

◆ Memco Inc ....E 352 241-2302
Bushnell (G-1319)

3799 Transportation Eqpt, NEC

A Cheaper Shot LLC ....F 727 221-3237
Saint Petersburg (G-15687)

A Plus Trailers ....G 786 395-0799
Southwest Ranches (G-16835)

A&R Xpress Inc ....G 954 744-4343
Miramar (G-10959)

Advance Carts Inc ....F 561 320-8674
Boca Raton (G-402)

Agile Cargo Transportation LLC ....F 407 747-0812
Jacksonville (G-6127)

▼ Amera Trail Inc ....E 407 892-1100
Saint Cloud (G-15643)

◆ Ames Companies Inc ....B 717 737-1500
Orlando (G-12475)

Andrews 1st Choice Trckg LLC ....G 205 703-5717
Jacksonville (G-6156)

B & E Rv Service & Repair LLC ....G 352 401-7930
Ocala (G-11883)

Boat Master Aluminum Trailers ....G 239 768-2224
Fort Myers (G-4378)

Bollou Transportation LLC ....F 800 548-1768
Miami (G-9266)

Bonefish Boats and Trlrs LLC ....G 239 707-4656
Cape Coral (G-1393)

▼ Caribbean Trailers Corp ....G 305 256-1505
Miami (G-9317)

Central Florida Cstm Trlrs Inc ....E 407 851-1144
Orlando (G-12566)

Chambers Body Works Inc ....G 352 588-3072
Dade City (G-2425)

Columbia Parcar Corp ....F 352 753-0244
Leesburg (G-8147)

Cricket Mini Golf Carts Inc ....F 386 220-3536
Daytona Beach (G-2649)

◆ Cruise Car Inc ....F 941 929-1630
Sarasota (G-16200)

D & R Delivery Services of Pb ....F 561 602-6427
Riviera Beach (G-15316)

East 46th Auto Sales Inc ....F 407 322-3100
Sanford (G-16039)

Elite Enclosures ....F 352 323-6005
Leesburg (G-8154)

▼ EZ Loder Adjstble Boat Trlrs S ....G 800 323-8190
Port Saint Lucie (G-15109)

Fkp ....F 561 493-0076
Boynton Beach (G-906)

▼ Float-On Corporation ....E 772 569-4440
Vero Beach (G-18617)

▼ Florida Trailer Ranch LLC ....F 904 289-7710
Jacksonville (G-6404)

Harbor View Boat Trailers ....G 941 916-3777
Punta Gorda (G-15208)

Itnorlando Inc ....G 407 900-7572
Winter Park (G-19414)

J & J Marine Service Inc ....G 813 741-2190
Saint Petersburg (G-15820)

▼ Jdci Enterprises Inc ....E 239 768-2292
Fort Myers (G-4502)

Lakeside Recreational Inc ....G 863 467-1530
Okeechobee (G-12185)

Liles Custom Trailers ....G 352 368-2652
Ocala (G-11985)

Ljs Tops & Bottoms ....E 561 736-7868
Boynton Beach (G-929)

Lnl Logistics LLC ....G 386 977-9276
Deltona (G-3173)

Lotus Containers Inc ....G 786 590-1056
Miami (G-9913)

▼ Magic Tilt Trailer Mfg Co Inc ....E 727 535-5561
Clearwater (G-1769)

Mbf Industries Inc ....E 407 323-9414
Sanford (G-16084)

Moran Transport ....G 305 824-3366
Hialeah (G-5528)

My Custom Cart LLC ....G 904 214-3723
Middleburg (G-10909)

▲ Nivel Holdings LLC ....G 904 741-6161
Jacksonville (G-6636)

◆ Nivel Parts & Mfg Co LLC ....E 904 741-6161
Jacksonville (G-6637)

▼ Owens & Sons Marine Inc ....F 727 323-1088
Saint Petersburg (G-15873)

Pauls Twing Dsptch Cntl Fla I ....G 407 323-4446
Sanford (G-16100)

Power Sports Treasure Coast ....G 772 463-6428
Stuart (G-16992)

Precision Equipment Co Inc ....G 561 689-4400
West Palm Beach (G-19003)

River City Powersports LLC ....G 386 259-5724
Debary (G-2754)

Rocket International Inc ....G 239 275-0880
Cape Coral (G-1461)

Rolls Axle Lc ....F 813 764-0242
Plant City (G-14463)

Rvcc of Florida ....G 352 569-5870
Bushnell (G-1320)

Safecraft Rstraint Systems Inc ....F 813 758-3571
Lutz (G-8416)

▲ Sodikart USA ....G 561 493-0290
Boynton Beach (G-960)

Southern Brothers Racing LLC ....G 850 509-2223
Quincy (G-15255)

Space Coast Industries Inc ....G 321 633-9336
Cocoa (G-2053)

Streetrod Productions Inc ....G 352 751-3953
The Villages (G-18393)

▲ Tampa Bay Grand Prix ....G 727 527-8464
Clearwater (G-1902)

Thule Inc ....C 850 584-3448
Perry (G-14317)

Triumph Transport Inc ....G 863 226-7276
Lakeland (G-7826)

▲ Ver-Val Enterprises Inc ....F 850 244-7931
Fort Walton Beach (G-4838)

▼ Viper 4x4 ....F 305 468-9818
Windermere (G-19249)

Xscream Inc ....G 727 449-9353
Clearwater (G-1945)

38 MEASURING, ANALYZING AND CONTROLLING INSTRUMENTS; PHOTOGRAPHIC, MEDICAL AN

3812 Search, Detection, Navigation & Guidance Systs & Instrs

321 Cpr LLC ....G.... 321 806-3525
Cocoa *(G-1987)*
ABC Components Inc ....F.... 954 249-6286
Cooper City *(G-2106)*
Aero-Trim Control Systems Inc ....G.... 954 321-1936
Davie *(G-2489)*
Aerojet Rcktdyne Clman Arspc I ....D.... 407 354-0047
Orlando *(G-12441)*
Aerospace Automation LLC ....G.... 954 260-2844
Pembroke Pines *(G-14018)*
Alakai Defense Systems Inc ....F.... 727 541-1600
Largo *(G-7890)*
Alonso Defense Group LLC ....G.... 305 989-0927
Miami *(G-9121)*
Alti-2 Inc ....F.... 386 943-9333
Deland *(G-2957)*
American Payment Systems ....G.... 954 968-6920
North Lauderdale *(G-11611)*
ARC Group Worldwide Inc ....D.... 303 467-5236
Deland *(G-2959)*
Ares Defense Group LLC ....F.... 941 255-0559
Port Charlotte *(G-14961)*
Asrc Aerospace Corp ....C.... 321 867-1462
Kennedy Space Center *(G-7150)*
▲ Astronics Dme LLC ....C.... 954 975-2100
Fort Lauderdale *(G-3828)*
Astronics Test Systems Inc ....C.... 407 381-6062
Orlando *(G-12496)*
▼ Avalex Technologies Corp ....D.... 850 470-8464
Gulf Breeze *(G-5113)*
▲ Aviation Instrument Tech Inc ....F.... 813 783-3361
Zephyrhills *(G-19508)*
Avidyne Corporation ....D.... 321 751-8520
Melbourne *(G-8774)*
Bae Systems Info & Elec Sys ....C.... 813 979-4392
Temple Terrace *(G-18366)*
Bae Systems Tech Sltons Svcs I ....G.... 850 244-6433
Fort Walton Beach *(G-4779)*
Bae Systems Tech Sltons Svcs I ....D.... 850 344-0832
Fort Walton Beach *(G-4780)*
Bae Systems Tech Sol Srvc Inc ....F.... 850 664-6070
Fort Walton Beach *(G-4781)*
Bae Systems Tech Sol Srvc Inc ....G.... 904 241-1631
Jacksonville *(G-6190)*
Bae Systems Tech Sol Srvc Inc ....G.... 850 236-2428
Panama City Beach *(G-13971)*
Becker Avionics Inc ....F.... 954 450-3137
Miramar *(G-10974)*
◆ Bluesky Mast Inc ....F.... 877 411-6278
Largo *(G-7911)*
Boca Self Defense ....G.... 954 903-0913
Boca Raton *(G-455)*
Boeing Company ....G.... 850 882-4912
Eglin Afb *(G-3641)*
C Speed LLC ....G.... 321 336-7939
Titusville *(G-18421)*
▲ Carbonara Labs Inc ....F.... 321 952-1303
Grant *(G-5048)*
Cobham Mission System Corp ....G.... 850 226-6717
Fort Walton Beach *(G-4787)*
Coda Octopus Group Inc ....F.... 407 735-2402
Orlando *(G-12598)*
◆ CPS Products Inc ....G.... 305 687-4121
Miramar *(G-10981)*
Cubic Advnced Lrng Sltions Inc ....F.... 407 859-7410
Orlando *(G-12632)*
Cubic Corporation ....G.... 407 859-7410
Orlando *(G-12633)*
▲ Dayton-Granger Inc ....C.... 954 463-3451
Fort Lauderdale *(G-3935)*
Defense Arts & Sciences LLC ....G.... 321 768-0671
West Melbourne *(G-18771)*
Defense Leadership Forum ....G.... 202 375-9587
Santa Rosa Beach *(G-16157)*
▼ Defenstech International Inc ....F.... 202 688-1988
Boca Raton *(G-497)*
Detect Inc ....F.... 850 763-7200
Panama City *(G-13892)*
Drs Advanced Isr LLC ....F.... 321 622-1202
Melbourne *(G-8807)*
Drs Advanced Isr LLC ....F.... 850 226-4888
Fort Walton Beach *(G-4791)*
Drs C3 Systems Inc ....E.... 850 302-3909
Fort Walton Beach *(G-4792)*
Drs Cengen Llc ....B.... 321 622-1500
Melbourne *(G-8808)*
Drs Consolidated Controls ....F.... 850 302-3000
Fort Walton Beach *(G-4793)*
Drs Land Electronics ....G.... 321 622-1435
Melbourne *(G-8809)*
Drs Leonardo Inc ....G.... 850 302-3000
Fort Walton Beach *(G-4794)*
Drs Leonardo Inc ....G.... 850 302-3514
Fort Walton Beach *(G-4795)*
▲ Drs Ntwork Imaging Systems LLC ....B.... 321 309-1500
Melbourne *(G-8810)*
Drs S and T Optronics Div ....F.... 321 309-1500
Melbourne *(G-8811)*
Drs Sensors Targeting Systems ....E.... 321 309-1500
Melbourne *(G-8812)*
▲ Drs Soneticom Inc ....E.... 321 733-0400
Melbourne *(G-8813)*
Drs Systems Inc ....G.... 973 451-3525
Melbourne *(G-8814)*
Drs Tactical Systems Inc ....C.... 321 727-3672
Melbourne *(G-8815)*
Drs Training Ctrl Systems LLC ....E.... 850 302-3000
Fort Walton Beach *(G-4796)*
Edgeone LLC ....F.... 561 995-7767
Boca Raton *(G-514)*
Eltec Instruments Inc ....E.... 386 252-0411
Daytona Beach *(G-2662)*
Enki Group Inc ....G.... 305 773-3502
Coral Gables *(G-2143)*
Erapsco ....G.... 386 740-5335
De Leon Springs *(G-2739)*
Etech Simulation Corp ....E.... 561 922-9792
West Palm Beach *(G-18864)*
Fab Defense Inc ....G.... 386 263-3054
Ormond Beach *(G-13370)*
Fire Defense Centers Inc ....G.... 904 731-1833
Jacksonville *(G-6382)*
Frontier Electronics ....G.... 954 255-0911
Micanopy *(G-10900)*
Full Circle Integration LLC ....F.... 504 615-5501
Valparaiso *(G-18511)*
Gables Engineering Inc ....B.... 305 774-4400
Coral Gables *(G-2147)*
Gannet Technologies LLC ....F.... 941 870-3444
Sarasota *(G-16217)*
GE Aviation Systems LLC ....F.... 727 532-6370
Clearwater *(G-1698)*
GE Aviation Systems LLC ....F.... 727 539-1631
Clearwater *(G-1700)*
GE Aviation Systems LLC ....B.... 727 531-7781
Clearwater *(G-1699)*
◆ General Dynamics-Ots Inc ....D.... 727 578-8100
Saint Petersburg *(G-15790)*
General Dynmics Land Systems I ....G.... 850 574-4700
Tallahassee *(G-17263)*
General Scientific Corporation ....G.... 850 866-9636
Panama City *(G-13908)*
GKN Aerospace Florida LLC ....D.... 314 412-8311
Panama City *(G-13910)*
Goodrich Corporation ....C.... 904 757-3660
Jacksonville *(G-6441)*
Green Energy Enterprises Inc ....E.... 904 309-8993
Jacksonville *(G-6447)*
▲ Heico Aerospace Corporation ....E.... 954 987-6101
Hollywood *(G-5837)*
Hensoldt Avionics Usa LLC ....G.... 941 306-1328
Sarasota *(G-16459)*
Honeywell Aerospace Inc ....G.... 727 539-5197
Clearwater *(G-1716)*
Honeywell International Inc ....B.... 727 539-5080
Clearwater *(G-1717)*
Honeywell International Inc ....A.... 727 531-4611
Clearwater *(G-1719)*
Honeywell International Inc ....G.... 505 358-0676
Largo *(G-7973)*
Hyper-Sub Platform Tech Inc ....F.... 386 365-6021
Lake Butler *(G-7337)*
Ilsc Holdings Lc ....G.... 480 935-4230
Orlando *(G-12822)*
Interstate Electronics Corp ....D.... 321 730-0119
Cape Canaveral *(G-1362)*
Jade Tactical Disaster Relief ....C.... 850 270-4077
Tampa *(G-17801)*
Joe Hearn Innovative Tech LLC ....F.... 850 898-3744
Pensacola *(G-14183)*
Jormac Aerospace Inc ....F.... 727 549-9600
Clearwater *(G-1745)*
Kollsman Inc ....G.... 407 312-1384
Orlando *(G-12875)*
▲ Kus Usa Inc ....E.... 954 463-1075
Davie *(G-2542)*
L3 Crestview Aerospace ....G.... 850 682-2746
Crestview *(G-2353)*
L3 Technologies Inc ....G.... 321 409-6122
Melbourne *(G-8864)*
L3 Technologies Inc ....G.... 941 371-0811
Saint Petersburg *(G-15836)*
L3 Technologies Inc ....G.... 305 371-7039
Fort Lauderdale *(G-4092)*
▲ L3harris Technologies Inc ....B.... 321 727-9100
Melbourne *(G-8865)*
L3harris Technologies Inc ....G.... 407 581-3782
Orlando *(G-12883)*
L3harris Technologies Inc ....G.... 305 542-5441
Miami *(G-9837)*
L3harris Technologies Inc ....G.... 727 415-6592
Palm Harbor *(G-13743)*
L3harris Technologies Inc ....D.... 321 768-4660
Malabar *(G-8494)*
L3harris Technologies Inc ....G.... 321 412-6601
Palm Bay *(G-13518)*
L3harris Technologies Inc ....G.... 321 727-4000
Melbourne *(G-8869)*
L3harris Technologies Inc ....G.... 321 674-4589
Melbourne *(G-8871)*
L3harris Technologies Inc ....C.... 260 451-6814
Tampa *(G-17831)*
Linx Defense LLC ....G.... 805 233-2472
Destin *(G-3197)*
Lockheed Martin Corporation ....A.... 407 306-6405
Orlando *(G-12919)*
Lockheed Martin Corporation ....G.... 407 517-6627
Orlando *(G-12921)*
Lockheed Martin Corporation ....G.... 407 306-4758
Orlando *(G-12922)*
Lockheed Martin Corporation ....D.... 863 647-0100
Lakeland *(G-7736)*
Lockheed Martin Corporation ....G.... 561 494-2501
West Palm Beach *(G-18933)*
Lockheed Martin Corporation ....G.... 407 365-4254
Oviedo *(G-13448)*
Lockheed Martin Corporation ....C.... 727 578-6940
Pinellas Park *(G-14365)*
Lockheed Martin Corporation ....G.... 407 356-5715
Lake Mary *(G-7429)*
Lockheed Martin Corporation ....F.... 407 356-2000
Orlando *(G-12923)*
Lockheed Martin Corporation ....G.... 850 301-4155
Fort Walton Beach *(G-4813)*
Lockheed Martin Corporation ....G.... 407 356-7424
Kissimmee *(G-7269)*
Lockheed Martin Corporation ....B.... 813 855-5711
Oldsmar *(G-12245)*
Lockheed Martin Corporation ....G.... 904 392-9779
Jacksonville *(G-6562)*
Lockheed Martin Corporation ....G.... 407 306-2745
Orlando *(G-12924)*
Lockheed Martin Corporation ....G.... 866 562-2363
Doral *(G-3418)*
Lockheed Martin Corporation ....G.... 407 356-1034
Orlando *(G-12925)*
Lockheed Martin Corporation ....G.... 850 581-1427
Hurlburt Field *(G-6045)*
Lockheed Martin Corporation ....G.... 863 647-0100
Lakeland *(G-7737)*
Lockheed Martin Corporation ....B.... 863 647-0558
Lakeland *(G-7738)*
Lockheed Martin Corporation ....G.... 863 647-0100
Lakeland *(G-7739)*
Lockheed Martin Corporation ....G.... 863 647-0303
Lakeland *(G-7740)*
Lockheed Martin Corporation ....G.... 301 240-7500
Orlando *(G-12926)*
Lockheed Martin Corporation ....G.... 321 264-7924
Titusville *(G-18443)*
Lockheed Martin Corporation ....G.... 407 356-6423
Orlando *(G-12928)*
Lockheed Martin Corporation ....G.... 301 897-6000
Riviera Beach *(G-15343)*
Lockheed Martin Corporation ....G.... 850 581-5710
Hurlburt Field *(G-6046)*
Lockheed Martin Corporation ....G.... 407 356-1947
Orlando *(G-12929)*
Lockheed Martin Corporation ....G.... 321 853-5194
Cape Canaveral *(G-1364)*
Lockheed Mrtin Gyrcam Systems ....D.... 407 356-6500
Orlando *(G-12930)*

Lockheed Mrtin Intgrted System ....C 407 356-2000
Orlando *(G-12931)*
◆ **Lockheed Mrtin Trning Sltons I** ....C 856 722-3317
Orlando *(G-12933)*
Loos & Co Inc ....D 239 643-5667
Naples *(G-11316)*
▲ **Mathews Associates Inc** ....C 407 323-3390
Sanford *(G-16082)*
Maxxfi LLC ....F 513 289-6521
Cape Coral *(G-1447)*
▲ **Meads International Inc** ....D 407 356-8400
Orlando *(G-12956)*
◆ **Mercaereo Inc** ....G 305 307-0672
Doral *(G-3432)*
Metro Defense Services Inc ....G 407 285-2304
Winter Park *(G-19423)*
Micro Systems Inc ....C 850 244-2332
Fort Walton Beach *(G-4815)*
Microbial Defense Systems LLC ....G 989 964-9863
Saint Augustine *(G-15570)*
Microgerm Defense LLC ....E 561 309-0842
West Palm Beach *(G-18951)*
Moog Inc ....F 321 435-8722
West Melbourne *(G-18777)*
Moog Inc ....G 716 652-2000
Pembroke Pines *(G-14049)*
Moog-Fts ....G 407 264-0611
Orlando *(G-12978)*
Motorola Solutions Inc ....G 407 562-4000
Lake Mary *(G-7437)*
Nelver Airparts Inc ....G 305 378-0072
Miami *(G-10064)*
New Generation Aerospace Inc ....G 305 882-1410
Medley *(G-8696)*
Northrop Grmman Tchncal Svcs I ....G 321 837-7000
Melbourne *(G-8895)*
Northrop Grmman Tchncal Svcs I ....F 904 825-3300
Saint Augustine *(G-15575)*
Northrop Grumman Corporation ....G 321 951-5529
Malabar *(G-8496)*
Northrop Grumman Corporation ....G 352 759-2946
Altoona *(G-87)*
Northrop Grumman Corporation ....G 321 951-5730
Palm Bay *(G-13527)*
Northrop Grumman Corporation ....A 321 951-5000
Melbourne *(G-8896)*
Northrop Grumman Systems Corp ....G 904 810-5957
Saint Augustine *(G-15577)*
Northrop Grumman Systems Corp ....A 321 951-5000
Melbourne *(G-8897)*
Northrop Grumman Systems Corp ....E 561 515-3651
Palm Beach Gardens *(G-13613)*
Northrop Grumman Systems Corp ....C 407 737-4900
Orlando *(G-13008)*
Northrop Grumman Systems Corp ....B 407 295-4010
Apopka *(G-166)*
Nxgen Brands Inc ....E 954 329-2205
Cape Coral *(G-1452)*
O2 Defense LLC ....G 704 408-7357
Odessa *(G-12137)*
▲ **Ocean Test Equipment Inc** ....G 954 474-6603
Davie *(G-2560)*
Offensive Defense Inc ....G 786 306-8162
Miramar *(G-11022)*
Orbital Sciences LLC ....B 703 406-5474
Merritt Island *(G-9005)*
Patriot Person Defense ....G 813 470-8025
Brandon *(G-1172)*
Pinnacle Cmmncations Group LLC ....F 904 910-0444
Jacksonville *(G-6674)*
Polyhistor International Inc ....G 904 646-5666
Jacksonville *(G-6677)*
Praesto Enterprises LLC ....G 407 298-9171
Orlando *(G-13077)*
Pratt & Whitney ....E 561 796-6701
Jupiter *(G-7097)*
Radiant Power Corp ....C 941 739-3200
Sarasota *(G-16281)*
Radiant Power Idc LLC ....E 760 945-0230
Sarasota *(G-16282)*
Raytheon Company ....G 850 882-8015
Eglin Afb *(G-3647)*
Raytheon Company ....G 850 664-7993
Fort Walton Beach *(G-4826)*
Raytheon Company ....C 310 647-9438
Largo *(G-8036)*
Raytheon Company ....G 850 286-6343
Tyndall Afb *(G-18494)*
Raytheon Company ....G 727 768-8468
Largo *(G-8037)*
Raytheon Company ....G 310 647-9438
Saint Petersburg *(G-15898)*
Raytheon Company ....G 321 235-6682
Orlando *(G-13116)*
Raytheon Company ....G 321 494-3323
Patrick Afb *(G-14008)*
Raytheon Company ....D 407 207-9223
Orlando *(G-13117)*
Raytheon Company ....G 321 235-1700
Orlando *(G-13118)*
Raytheon Technologies Corp ....A 858 277-7639
Jupiter *(G-7103)*
Revolution Air Craft Services ....F 954 747-4773
Pompano Beach *(G-14831)*
Richards Aviation ....G 954 527-2623
Fort Lauderdale *(G-4205)*
Riegl Usa Inc ....E 407 248-9927
Winter Garden *(G-19283)*
Rockwell Collins Inc ....G 866 786-0290
Orlando *(G-13145)*
Rockwell Collins Inc ....D 321 768-7303
Melbourne *(G-8921)*
Rover Aerospace Inc ....G 305 594-7799
Doral *(G-3491)*
Russell Associates Inc ....G 727 815-3100
New Port Richey *(G-11509)*
Saikou Optics Incorporated ....G 407 986-4200
Orlando *(G-13157)*
▼ **Sas R & D Services Inc** ....F 954 432-2345
Miramar *(G-11039)*
▲ **Senelco Iberia Inc** ....D 561 912-6000
Deerfield Beach *(G-2909)*
Sensormatic Electronics LLC ....G 561 912-6000
Boca Raton *(G-704)*
▲ **Sentech Eas Corporation** ....F 954 426-2965
Coconut Creek *(G-2093)*
◆ **Sequa Corporation** ....A 561 935-3571
Palm Beach Gardens *(G-13626)*
Seven Defenses Corporation ....F 786 448-5701
Medley *(G-8723)*
Sextant Marketing LLC ....F 800 691-9980
Tampa *(G-18087)*
Sierra Nevada Corporation ....E 850 659-3600
Shalimar *(G-16777)*
Sikorsky Aircraft Corp ....G 772 210-0849
Stuart *(G-17014)*
▼ **Smiths Interconnect Inc** ....C 813 901-7200
Tampa *(G-18111)*
Sota Manufacturing Inc ....E 561 368-8007
Boca Raton *(G-722)*
Space Cast Intllgent Sltons In ....F 321 622-6858
Melbourne *(G-8937)*
▲ **Sparton Deleon Springs LLC** ....D 386 985-4631
De Leon Springs *(G-2743)*
Spartronics Brooksville LLC ....B 352 799-6520
Brooksville *(G-1275)*
▲ **Sports Radar Ltd** ....G 352 503-6825
Homosassa *(G-6006)*
Steele Defense LLC ....G 786 610-0857
Homestead *(G-5995)*
Steele Industries Inc ....G 800 674-7302
Sarasota *(G-16301)*
Stout Defense PA ....G 352 665-9266
Gainesville *(G-5002)*
Streamline Numerics Inc ....G 352 271-8841
Gainesville *(G-5003)*
▲ **Super Sensitive String Sls Co** ....E 941 371-0016
Sarasota *(G-16612)*
Supliaereos USA LLC ....G 727 754-4915
Clearwater *(G-1897)*
▼ **Suriparts Corp** ....G 954 639-7700
Pembroke Pines *(G-14062)*
Techcodes LLC ....G 321 529-4122
Titusville *(G-18467)*
Technologies Drs Unmanned Inc ....D 850 302-3909
Fort Walton Beach *(G-4835)*
Tef-Gel Inc ....F 561 845-1086
West Palm Beach *(G-19059)*
Teleios Manufacturing Inc ....G 904 490-0600
Jacksonville *(G-6846)*
Tf Defense LLC ....G 321 961-7596
Kissimmee *(G-7304)*
Ticket Drop Traffic Defense ....G 305 332-3186
Miami *(G-10477)*
Tk Defense Solutions Inc ....G 727 365-6823
Saint Petersburg *(G-15941)*
Trakka USA LLC ....G 505 345-0270
Bradenton *(G-1128)*
▲ **Trilectron** ....G 941 721-1000
Palmetto *(G-13830)*
Truenorth Iq Inc ....G 678 849-5000
Port Saint Lucie *(G-15157)*
▲ **Trumeter Company Inc** ....G 954 725-6699
Coconut Creek *(G-2098)*
Viewpoint Systems LLC ....F 850 450-0681
Pensacola *(G-14284)*
▼ **Waterproof Charters Inc** ....G 941 639-7626
Punta Gorda *(G-15243)*
We Love Tec LLC ....G 305 433-4453
North Miami Beach *(G-11711)*
Weibel Equipment Inc ....G 571 278-1989
Lake Worth *(G-7599)*
Willis Aeronautical Svcs Inc ....F 561 272-5402
Coconut Creek *(G-2103)*

3821 Laboratory Apparatus & Furniture

◆ **AGR of Florida Inc** ....E 904 733-9393
Jacksonville *(G-6130)*
Arj Medical Inc ....G 813 855-1557
Oldsmar *(G-12203)*
Axiom Diagnostics Inc ....G 813 902-9888
Tampa *(G-17449)*
Cbg Biotech Ltd Co ....G 239 514-1148
Naples *(G-11202)*
Colloidal Dynamics LLC ....G 904 686-1536
Ponte Vedra Beach *(G-14937)*
Etectrx Inc ....E 321 363-3020
Gainesville *(G-4915)*
Ga-MA & Associates Inc ....G 352 687-8840
Ocala *(G-11953)*
Genecell International LLC ....F 305 382-6737
Doral *(G-3360)*
Genesis Reference Laboratories ....D 407 232-7130
Orlando *(G-12781)*
◆ **Germfree Laboratories Inc** ....C 386 265-4300
Ormond Beach *(G-13374)*
▲ **Hf Scientific Inc** ....E 888 203-7248
Fort Myers *(G-4481)*
◆ **Jensen Scientific Products Inc** ....E 954 344-2006
Coral Springs *(G-2263)*
Keavys Corner LLC ....G 863 658-0235
Sebring *(G-16696)*
Lifelink Corporation ....G 813 653-3197
Brandon *(G-1165)*
Logan Laboratories LLC ....G 813 316-4824
Tampa *(G-17858)*
Mansci Inc ....F 866 763-2122
Orlando *(G-12948)*
Mrn Biologics LLC ....F 508 989-6090
Coral Springs *(G-2291)*
Nfi Masks LLC ....E 239 990-6546
Fort Myers *(G-4546)*
Oculus Surgical Inc ....E 772 236-2622
Port St Lucie *(G-15177)*
Ormond Beach Clinical RES LLC ....G 386 310-7462
Ormond Beach *(G-13388)*
Phy-Med ....G 305 925-0141
Miami *(G-10162)*
Precision Coating Rods Inc ....F 813 855-5054
Oldsmar *(G-12259)*
◆ **Premier Lab Supply Inc** ....G 772 873-1700
Port Saint Lucie *(G-15130)*
▲ **Pro Lab Supply Corporation** ....G 305 600-0444
Hialeah *(G-5576)*
Rj Capital Inc ....F 561 208-7444
Boca Raton *(G-689)*
South Bay Hospital ....B 813 634-3301
Sun City Center *(G-17072)*
South Florida Laboratory Llc ....G 954 889-0335
Palm Springs *(G-13780)*
Southeast Clinical RES LLC ....F 904 296-3260
Jacksonville *(G-6786)*
▲ **Tintometer Inc** ....F 941 756-6410
Sarasota *(G-16310)*
W & B Scientific Inc ....F 954 607-1500
Pompano Beach *(G-14911)*
Walden Consulting LLC ....G 407 563-3620
Orlando *(G-13317)*

3822 Automatic Temperature Controls

Air Authorities of Tampa Inc ....G 727 525-1575
Clearwater *(G-1570)*
Airflowbalance LLC ....F 386 871-8136
Lake Mary *(G-7397)*
Automated Buildings Inc ....F 407 857-0140
Orlando *(G-12501)*
▼ **AVw Inc** ....E 954 972-3338
Margate *(G-8536)*
C & C Services of Tampa Inc ....G 813 477-8559
Plant City *(G-14414)*

Dais Corp ....F 727 375-8484
Odessa *(G-12115)*
Dsas Air Inc ....F 954 673-5385
Lauderdale Lakes *(G-8087)*
F & J Specialty Products Inc ....F 352 680-1177
Ocala *(G-11939)*
▲ Florida Enviromental Cons ....G 407 402-2828
Clermont *(G-1958)*
Galtronics Telemetry Inc ....F 386 202-2055
Palm Coast *(G-13697)*
Gulf States Automation Inc ....E 850 475-0724
Pensacola *(G-14167)*
▲ Intelligent Heater LLC ....G 305 248-4971
Homestead *(G-5973)*
Jireh AC & Rfrgn Inc ....F 305 216-2774
Miami *(G-9798)*
JRS Ventures LLP ....G 715 441-1051
Deltona *(G-3172)*
◆ Leslie Controls Inc ....C 813 978-1000
Temple Terrace *(G-18371)*
Maintnnce Reliability Tech Inc ....E 863 533-0300
Bartow *(G-323)*
Melbourne-Tillman Wtr Ctrl Dst ....E 321 723-7233
Palm Bay *(G-13524)*
▲ Micro Control Systems Inc ....E 239 694-0089
Fort Myers *(G-4532)*
Moisttech Corp ....F 941 351-7870
Sarasota *(G-16259)*
▲ Mold Control Systems Inc ....G 561 316-5412
Palm Beach Gardens *(G-13610)*
Molekule Inc ....G 352 871-3803
Tampa *(G-17916)*
Nautical Specialists ....G 954 761-7130
Fort Lauderdale *(G-4133)*
◆ Niagara Industries Inc ....F 305 876-9010
Miami *(G-10071)*
Noxtak Corp ....G 786 586-7927
Pembroke Pines *(G-14052)*
◆ Portalp Usa Inc ....F 800 474-3667
Naples *(G-11373)*
Qci ....D 407 886-6300
Apopka *(G-175)*
R & J Mfg of Gainesville ....G 352 375-3130
Gainesville *(G-4987)*
Sacyr Environment USA LLC ....F 202 361-4568
Miami *(G-10294)*
Sampletech ....G 727 239-7055
Clearwater *(G-1868)*
Simplexgrinnell Holdings LLC ....G 978 731-2500
Boca Raton *(G-716)*
Southern Environmental Inc ....E 850 944-4475
Pensacola *(G-14263)*
Suntree Technologies Inc ....F 321 637-7552
Cocoa *(G-2054)*
Technico ....F 561 588-8300
Lake Worth *(G-7590)*
Thompson Envrmntal Mntring Ctr ....G 321 591-7300
Melbourne *(G-8961)*
Top Line Installation Inc ....F 352 636-4192
Leesburg *(G-8177)*
Triumvirate Environmental ....E 407 859-4441
Orlando *(G-13275)*
Two Tree Inc ....G 352 284-1763
Gainesville *(G-5013)*
▲ Vtronix LLC ....G 305 471-7600
Miami *(G-10594)*
Whertec Technologies Inc ....G 866 207-6503
Jacksonville *(G-6918)*

3823 Indl Instruments For Meas, Display & Control

ABB Enterprise Software Inc ....C 954 752-6700
Coral Springs *(G-2211)*
◆ Advanced Manufacturing Inc ....E 727 573-3300
Saint Petersburg *(G-15691)*
Aero American Detailing Llc ....G 850 459-7425
Tallahassee *(G-17213)*
Amci Technologies Inc ....F 561 596-6288
Boynton Beach *(G-874)*
Ametek Inc ....D 727 536-7831
Largo *(G-7896)*
AP Buck Inc ....F 407 851-8602
Orlando *(G-12482)*
Applied Technologies Group Inc ....G 813 413-7025
Tampa *(G-17429)*
Aqualogix Inc ....F 858 442-4550
Palm Beach Gardens *(G-13567)*
Atkins Technical Inc ....E 860 349-3473
Gainesville *(G-4879)*
Atlas South ....G 305 824-3900
Hialeah *(G-5312)*
Automated Sonix Corporation ....G 941 964-1361
Boca Grande *(G-391)*
◆ Axi International Corporation ....E 239 690-9589
Fort Myers *(G-4370)*
Bar Beverage Ctrl Systems Fla ....G 239 213-3301
Naples *(G-11182)*
Blue Siren Inc ....E 321 242-0300
Melbourne *(G-8782)*
C E C Controls Company Inc ....F 941 746-5700
Bradenton *(G-1007)*
Centroid Products Inc ....G 386 423-3574
Edgewater *(G-3618)*
Chem-TEC Equipment Co ....F 954 428-8259
Deerfield Beach *(G-2801)*
Chemko Technical Services Inc ....E 954 783-7673
Pompano Beach *(G-14634)*
Chicago Electronic Distrs Inc ....F 312 985-6175
Port Charlotte *(G-14969)*
Chilly Willys Heating & A Inc ....G 904 772-1164
Jacksonville *(G-6264)*
▲ Clearwater Engineering Inc ....G 727 573-2210
Clearwater *(G-1627)*
Coast Controls Inc ....F 941 355-7555
Sarasota *(G-16192)*
▲ Cobex Recorders Inc ....F 954 425-0003
Coconut Creek *(G-2073)*
Coffman Systems Inc ....F 813 891-1300
Oldsmar *(G-12218)*
Complete Instrmnttion Cntrls I ....G 813 340-8545
Lithia *(G-8217)*
Computational Systems Inc ....C 954 846-5030
Sunrise *(G-17108)*
Computational Systems Inc ....C 863 648-9044
Lakeland *(G-7661)*
Control Solutions Inc ....F 813 247-2136
Tampa *(G-17553)*
Contrologix LLC ....E 407 878-2774
Sanford *(G-16023)*
▲ Core Enterprises Incorporated ....G 954 227-0781
Coral Springs *(G-2234)*
◆ CPS Products Inc ....G 305 687-4121
Miramar *(G-10981)*
▲ Crystal Photonics Inc ....E 407 328-9111
Sanford *(G-16029)*
Cv Technology Inc ....E 561 694-9588
Jupiter *(G-7022)*
Danaher Motion ....G 727 789-0446
Palm Harbor *(G-13732)*
Digital Living ....G 407 332-9998
Altamonte Springs *(G-40)*
Dynalco Controls Corporation ....E 323 589-6181
Fort Lauderdale *(G-3952)*
Ecombustible Products LLC ....G 305 792-1952
Sunny Isles Beach *(G-17075)*
Electric Pcture Dsplay Systems ....G 321 757-8484
Melbourne *(G-8822)*
Eltec Instruments Inc ....E 386 252-0411
Daytona Beach *(G-2662)*
Emcee Electronics Inc ....E 941 485-1515
Venice *(G-18546)*
Emerson Electric Co ....E 904 741-6800
Jacksonville *(G-6362)*
Energy Control Technologies ....G 954 739-8400
Davie *(G-2518)*
Engineer Service Corporation ....G 904 268-0482
Jacksonville *(G-6364)*
▲ Facts Engineering LLC ....E 727 375-8888
Trinity *(G-18485)*
Fct-Combustion Inc ....G 610 725-8840
Fort Lauderdale *(G-3988)*
For-A Latin America Inc ....G 305 261-2345
Miami *(G-9593)*
Gas Turbine Efficiency LLC ....E 407 304-5200
Orlando *(G-12772)*
Gencor Industries Inc ....C 407 290-6000
Orlando *(G-12776)*
Gkwf Inc ....G 863 644-6925
Lakeland *(G-7699)*
H Q Inc ....F 941 721-7588
Palmetto *(G-13804)*
▲ Hf Scientific Inc ....E 888 203-7248
Fort Myers *(G-4481)*
Hughes Corporation ....F 954 755-7111
Coral Springs *(G-2256)*
I C Probotics Inc ....D 407 339-8298
Longwood *(G-8288)*
▲ Ian-Conrad Bergan LLC ....E 850 434-1286
Pensacola *(G-14175)*
▲ Infiniti Digital Equipment Inc ....G 305 477-6333
Doral *(G-3390)*
Infrared Associates Inc ....F 772 223-6670
Stuart *(G-16958)*
Instrument & Valve Services Co ....G 904 741-6800
Jacksonville *(G-6499)*
Intellgent Instrumentation Inc ....F 520 573-0887
Naples *(G-11288)*
Ipeg Corporation ....F 239 963-1470
Naples *(G-11291)*
James O Corbett Inc ....G 352 483-1222
Eustis *(G-3710)*
Jhn North LLC ....G 561 294-5613
Boynton Beach *(G-925)*
Jsi Scientific Inc ....G 732 845-1925
Naples *(G-11300)*
▲ Kinetics Usa Inc ....E 561 988-8826
Boca Raton *(G-588)*
▲ Kus Usa Inc ....E 954 463-1075
Davie *(G-2542)*
L3harris Technologies Inc ....C 260 451-6814
Tampa *(G-17831)*
▲ Malema Engineering Corporation ....F 561 995-0595
Boca Raton *(G-606)*
▲ Mmats Inc ....E 561 842-0600
Jupiter *(G-7076)*
Noxtak Corp ....G 786 586-7927
Pembroke Pines *(G-14052)*
◆ Onicon Incorporated ....E 727 447-6140
Largo *(G-8021)*
Optoelectronics Inc ....F 954 642-8997
Boca Raton *(G-655)*
▲ Outform Inc ....G 800 204-0524
Miami *(G-10123)*
Phoenix Calibration Ltd Srl ....G 786 866-5906
Doral *(G-3460)*
▲ Precision Fabg & Clg Co Inc ....D 321 635-2000
Cocoa *(G-2042)*
Precision Resources Inc ....F 321 635-2000
Cocoa *(G-2043)*
Presys Instruments Inc ....G 305 495-3335
Miami *(G-10191)*
Pulsar Process Measurement Inc ....G 850 279-4882
Largo *(G-8032)*
Pyramid Imaging Inc ....G 813 984-0125
Tampa *(G-18028)*
▲ Real-Time Laboratories LLC ....D 561 988-8826
Boca Raton *(G-683)*
Red Meters LLC ....F 407 337-0110
Orlando *(G-13121)*
Riegl Usa Inc ....E 407 248-9927
Winter Garden *(G-19283)*
Roper Industrial Pdts Inv Co ....F 941 556-2601
Sarasota *(G-16562)*
Roper Technologies Inc ....E 941 556-2601
Sarasota *(G-16563)*
Saikou Optics Incorporated ....G 407 986-4200
Orlando *(G-13157)*
▼ Scientific Instruments Inc ....E 561 881-8500
Mangonia Park *(G-8511)*
◆ Sensidyne LP ....D 727 530-3602
Saint Petersburg *(G-15909)*
Sepac Corp ....F 305 718-3379
Miami *(G-10325)*
◆ Sunoptic Technologies LLC ....D 877 677-2832
Jacksonville *(G-6822)*
Tutela Monitoring Systems LLC ....G 941 462-1067
Spring Hill *(G-16869)*
◆ Uniweld Products Inc ....C 954 584-2000
Fort Lauderdale *(G-4298)*
Utilytech Company ....F 813 778-6952
Kissimmee *(G-7308)*
Vertec Inc ....F 850 478-6480
Pensacola *(G-14283)*
Wes Holdings Corp ....F 941 371-4995
Sarasota *(G-16636)*
Wilkerson Instrument Co Inc ....F 863 647-2000
Lakeland *(G-7834)*
Xothermic Inc ....G 407 951-8008
Longwood *(G-8352)*

3824 Fluid Meters & Counters

Countwise Llc ....F 954 846-7011
Sunrise *(G-17109)*
Del Monte Fresh Production Inc ....G 863 844-5836
Mulberry *(G-11122)*
Edc Corporation ....G 386 951-4075
Deland *(G-2973)*
◆ Elster Amco Water LLC ....F 352 369-6500
Ocala *(G-11931)*

S I C

Fewtek Inc F 727 736-0533
Dunedin *(G-3576)*
Hedrick-Walker & Associates G 352 735-2600
Mount Dora *(G-11104)*
Integ Construction Inc G 305 440-9101
Doral *(G-3391)*
▲ Kus Usa Inc E 954 463-1075
Davie *(G-2542)*
Maxogen Group LLC E 305 814-0734
Hollywood *(G-5871)*
Power Plus Inc G 386 672-7579
Ormond Beach *(G-13392)*
Qualitest USA Lc F 877 884-8378
Fort Lauderdale *(G-4188)*
▲ R S S Partners Inc G 904 241-6144
Jacksonville Beach *(G-6955)*
Ronaele Mustang Inc G 954 319-7433
Tamarac *(G-17367)*
Sandale Utility Products G 863 937-5208
Lakeland *(G-7786)*
Suncoast Tool & Gage Inds Inc F 727 572-8000
Clearwater *(G-1893)*
Trak Engineering Incorporated E 850 878-4585
Tallahassee *(G-17341)*
▲ Trumeter Company Inc G 954 725-6699
Coconut Creek *(G-2098)*

3825 Instrs For Measuring & Testing Electricity

AB Ampere Industrial Panels G 904 379-4168
Yulee *(G-19494)*
Akeyma Broden G 309 428-5938
Ocala *(G-11868)*
Akuwa Solutions Group Inc F 941 343-9947
Sarasota *(G-16337)*
Alber Corp D 954 377-7101
Sunrise *(G-17086)*
▲ All-Tag Corporation E 561 998-9983
Boca Raton *(G-412)*
Amascott LLC G 352 683-4895
Spring Hill *(G-16846)*
Awl Manufacturing Inc G 239 643-5780
Naples *(G-11178)*
Baytronics Manufacturing Inc G 813 434-0401
Tampa *(G-17460)*
Belle Glade Electric Motor Svc G 561 996-3333
Belle Glade *(G-345)*
C2c Innovated Technology LLC G 251 382-2277
Bonifay *(G-800)*
◆ Ce North America LLC E 305 392-2200
Coral Gables *(G-2130)*
▲ Core Enterprises Incorporated G 954 227-0781
Coral Springs *(G-2234)*
Corporate One Hundred Inc E 352 335-0901
Gainesville *(G-4898)*
◆ CPS Products Inc G 305 687-4121
Miramar *(G-10981)*
Creating Tech Solutions LLC E 727 914-3001
Clearwater *(G-1642)*
Creating Tech Solutions LLC E 727 914-3001
Clearwater *(G-1641)*
Crumbliss Manufacturing Co F 239 693-8588
Fort Myers *(G-4417)*
Crystek Crystals Corporation E 239 561-3311
Fort Myers *(G-4418)*
Dash Air Parts LLC G 786 659-5013
Miami Lakes *(G-10779)*
Data Flow Systems Inc D 321 259-5009
Melbourne *(G-8800)*
Dynalco Controls Corporation E 323 589-6181
Fort Lauderdale *(G-3952)*
Energy Control Technologies G 954 739-8400
Davie *(G-2518)*
Finetest Inc G 386 569-6189
Palm Coast *(G-13693)*
Florida Veex Inc F 727 442-6677
Largo *(G-7952)*
Gray Information Solutions Inc G 352 684-6655
Spring Hill *(G-16854)*
High Yield AG Solutions LLC G 407 592-8089
Lake Mary *(G-7422)*
Hughes Corporation F 954 755-7111
Coral Springs *(G-2256)*
I C Probotics Inc D 407 339-8298
Longwood *(G-8288)*
ID Solutions Inc F 407 823-7710
Orlando *(G-12821)*
Ideasgt Corp G 786 370-7767
Miami *(G-9730)*
▲ Indra Systems Inc E 407 567-1977
Orlando *(G-12827)*
Interstate Electronics Corp D 321 730-0119
Cape Canaveral *(G-1362)*
Jones Mediaamerica Inc B 305 289-4524
Marathon *(G-8518)*
King Han Inc G 860 933-8574
Englewood *(G-3662)*
KLA Aventura LLC G 305 931-2322
Miami *(G-9825)*
Kobetron LLC F 850 939-5222
Navarre *(G-11468)*
Lee Net Services Inc G 904 777-4833
Jacksonville *(G-6552)*
Locus Diagnostics LLC F 321 727-3077
Melbourne *(G-8877)*
Logus Manufacturing Corp E 561 842-3550
West Palm Beach *(G-18934)*
Mc Assembly International LLC F 321 253-0541
Melbourne *(G-8885)*
MC Miller Co Inc E 772 794-9448
Sebastian *(G-16668)*
Measurements International Inc E 315 393-1323
Lake Mary *(G-7433)*
Meg Systems Inc G 239 263-5833
Naples *(G-11326)*
Nci G 813 749-1799
Tampa *(G-17935)*
▲ Next Generation Home Pdts Inc G 727 834-9400
Tampa *(G-17938)*
Omega Power Systems Inc G 772 219-0045
Stuart *(G-16982)*
Optoelectronics Inc F 954 642-8997
Boca Raton *(G-655)*
Optronic Laboratories LLC F 407 422-3171
Orlando *(G-13028)*
Parkervision Inc F 904 732-6100
Jacksonville *(G-6658)*
Pdma Corporation E 813 621-6463
Tampa *(G-17979)*
Peak Electronics Inc G 305 888-1588
Miami *(G-10148)*
Performance Technology 2000 G 772 463-1056
Stuart *(G-16987)*
Piezo Technology Inc C 407 298-2000
Orlando *(G-13067)*
Pinnacle Cmmncations Group LLC F 904 910-0444
Jacksonville *(G-6674)*
Powerficient LLC E 800 320-2535
Fort Lauderdale *(G-4172)*
Quest International Inc F 305 592-6991
Miami *(G-10225)*
Ra Co AMO Inc F 561 626-7232
Palm Beach Gardens *(G-13620)*
Rail Scale Inc E 904 302-5154
Saint Augustine *(G-15593)*
▲ Relm Communications Inc C 321 953-7800
Melbourne *(G-8919)*
Rjh Technical Services Inc G 813 655-7947
Brandon *(G-1174)*
SAI/Rf of Florida G 727 394-1012
Redington Beach *(G-15259)*
Salco Industries Inc F 941 377-7717
Sarasota *(G-16570)*
Semilab USA LLC E 813 977-2244
Temple Terrace *(G-18378)*
Servos and Simulation Inc G 407 807-0208
Longwood *(G-8336)*
Sjostrom Industries Inc F 561 368-2000
Boca Raton *(G-719)*
▼ Smartsat Inc F 727 535-6880
Largo *(G-8055)*
Sota Manufacturing Inc E 561 368-8007
Boca Raton *(G-722)*
Spectrum Bridge Inc F 407 792-1570
Lake Mary *(G-7450)*
▲ T & M Atlantic Inc G 786 332-4773
Miami *(G-10452)*
◆ Technical International Corp G 305 374-1054
Miami *(G-10462)*
Techtron Corporation F 239 513-0800
Naples *(G-11437)*
Tektronix Inc F 407 660-2727
Maitland *(G-8480)*
Testmaxx Services Corporation F 954 946-7100
Pompano Beach *(G-14886)*
Tex Onsite Inc G 386 935-4093
Branford *(G-1189)*
Tucker-Davis Technologies Inc E 386 462-9622
Alachua *(G-21)*
Universal Microwave Corp D 352 754-2200
Brooksville *(G-1286)*
Vertiv Corporation D 954 377-7101
Sunrise *(G-17196)*
Victus Capital Enterprises Inc E 727 442-6677
Saint Petersburg *(G-15954)*
▲ W & W Manufacturing Co E 516 942-0011
Tampa *(G-18249)*
Wink Streaming Llc G 312 281-5444
Miami *(G-10611)*

3826 Analytical Instruments

1982 Hayworth Avenue LLC G 772 873-1700
Port St Lucie *(G-15166)*
Analytical Research Systems F 352 466-0051
Micanopy *(G-10899)*
Anton Paar Quantatec Inc G 561 731-4999
Boynton Beach *(G-877)*
Antylia Scientific D 352 854-8080
Ocala *(G-11877)*
Awareness Technology Inc C 772 283-6540
Palm City *(G-13642)*
Beckman Coulter Inc F 305 380-2175
Miami *(G-9231)*
Beckman Coulter Inc G 954 432-4336
Pembroke Pines *(G-14022)*
Belquette Inc G 727 329-9483
Clearwater *(G-1606)*
Bowman Analytics Inc G 847 781-3523
Sarasota *(G-16367)*
Cellmic LLC G 310 443-2070
Palm Harbor *(G-13727)*
Chemplex Industries Inc F 772 283-2700
Palm City *(G-13646)*
▲ Clearwater Engineering Inc G 727 573-2210
Clearwater *(G-1627)*
◆ Data Buoy Instrumentation LLC G 239 849-7063
Cape Coral *(G-1410)*
DOE & Ingalls Florida Oper LLC G 813 347-4741
Tampa *(G-17613)*
Edgeone LLC F 561 995-7767
Boca Raton *(G-514)*
F & J Specialty Products Inc F 352 680-1177
Ocala *(G-11939)*
▼ Field Forensics Inc F 727 490-3609
Saint Petersburg *(G-15779)*
Gam Laser Inc F 407 851-8999
Orlando *(G-12770)*
Gilson Inc G 904 725-7612
Jacksonville *(G-6434)*
Glo Aesthetic & Laser Institut G 561 704-4565
Lake Worth *(G-7552)*
▲ Hf Scientific Inc E 888 203-7248
Fort Myers *(G-4481)*
Infrared Systems Dev Corp F 407 679-5101
Winter Park *(G-19413)*
Invivo Corporation E 352 336-0010
Gainesville *(G-4946)*
Jl Optical Inc G 386 428-6928
New Smyrna Beach *(G-11536)*
L and C Science and Tech Inc G 305 200-3531
Hialeah *(G-5477)*
Lablogic Systems Inc F 813 626-6848
Tampa *(G-17833)*
Lindorm Inc F 305 888-0762
Miami Springs *(G-10893)*
Marysol Technologies Inc G 727 712-1523
Clearwater *(G-1775)*
Mayn Focus LLC G 603 801-8406
Winter Garden *(G-19276)*
Medical Outfitters Inc G 305 885-4045
Miami *(G-9966)*
Medical Outfitters Inc E 305 332-9103
North Bay Village *(G-11593)*
Mip-Technology Corp G 239 221-3604
Bonita Springs *(G-845)*
Multicore Photonics Inc G 407 325-7800
Orlando *(G-12984)*
Mydor Industries Inc G 954 927-1140
Dania *(G-2453)*
National Scientific Inc G 239 262-4047
Naples *(G-11342)*
Npact America Inc G 904 755-6259
Jacksonville *(G-6641)*
▲ Ocean Optics Inc E 407 673-0041
Orlando *(G-13016)*
Ocean Optics Inc D 727 545-0741
Orlando *(G-13017)*
One Resonance Sensors G 407 323-9933
Sanford *(G-16094)*

Open Magnetic Scanning Ltd ....G....... 954 202-5097
Oakland Park *(G-11826)*
Pipette Solutions LLC............G....... 877 974-7388
Casselberry *(G-1513)*
Polygrama Inc ....G....... 305 577-9716
Miami *(G-10177)*
Professional Laboratories Inc ....E....... 954 384-4446
Weston *(G-19161)*
Radiance Radiology Inc ....G....... 727 934-5500
Palm Harbor *(G-13755)*
Rave LLC ....E....... 561 330-0411
Delray Beach *(G-3134)*
Roper Technologies Inc ....E....... 941 556-2601
Sarasota *(G-16563)*
Sea Gear Corporation............G....... 321 728-9116
Melbourne *(G-8929)*
Separation Systems Inc ....F....... 850 932-1433
Gulf Breeze *(G-5126)*
South Florida Institut............G....... 305 668-2853
South Miami *(G-16830)*
Spectrecology LLC ....G....... 727 230-1697
Saint Petersburg *(G-15921)*
ST Japan Usa Llc............G....... 239 433-5566
Fort Myers *(G-4611)*
St Johns Optical Systems LLC............G....... 407 280-3787
Sanford *(G-16120)*
Stellarnet Inc ....F....... 813 855-8687
Tampa *(G-18132)*
Sun Electronic Systems Inc............F....... 321 383-9400
Titusville *(G-18466)*
Thermo Arl US Inc............E....... 800 532-4752
West Palm Beach *(G-19060)*
Thermo Electron North Amer LLC............B....... 561 688-8700
West Palm Beach *(G-19061)*
Thermo Fisher Scientific............F....... 781 327-3261
Alachua *(G-20)*
Thermo Fisher Scientific Inc............B....... 561 688-8700
West Palm Beach *(G-19062)*
Tonbo Imaging Inc ....G....... 814 441-0475
Sunrise *(G-17190)*
Twinstar Optics & Coatings Inc ....F....... 727 847-2300
Port Richey *(G-15073)*
Ultrafast Systems LLC............F....... 941 360-2161
Sarasota *(G-16626)*
▲ **USA Scientific Inc** ....E....... 352 237-6288
Ocala *(G-12069)*
Vision Analytical Inc............G....... 305 801-7140
Miami *(G-10588)*
Windsor Imaging Delray............G....... 561 900-0300
Delray Beach *(G-3160)*
World Precision Instrs LLC............D....... 941 371-1003
Sarasota *(G-16645)*
Ysi Inc ....F....... 727 565-2201
Saint Petersburg *(G-15968)*

3827 Optical Instruments

A&C Microscopes LLC ....F....... 786 514-3967
Doral *(G-3221)*
Aldana Laser Miami Inc............F....... 786 681-7752
Doral *(G-3235)*
▲ **Align Optics Inc**............G....... 954 748-1715
Sunrise *(G-17087)*
Amphenol Custom Cable Inc............C....... 813 623-2232
Tampa *(G-17423)*
Amphenol Custom Cable Inc ....E....... 407 393-3886
Orlando *(G-12476)*
Asphericon Inc............F....... 941 564-0890
Sarasota *(G-16353)*
Benz Research and Dev LLC ....E....... 941 758-8256
Sarasota *(G-16181)*
▲ **Brain Power Incorporated**............E....... 305 264-4465
Miami *(G-9273)*
D R S Optronics Inc............F....... 321 309-1500
Melbourne *(G-8799)*
Direct Optical Research Co............G....... 727 319-9000
Largo *(G-7932)*
▲ **Discipline Marketing Inc**............F....... 305 793-7358
Homestead *(G-5963)*
▲ **Electro-Optix Inc** ....F....... 954 973-2800
Pompano Beach *(G-14677)*
▲ **En-Vision America Inc** ....F....... 309 452-3088
Palmetto *(G-13796)*
◆ **ER Precision Optical Corp**............F....... 407 292-5395
Apopka *(G-138)*
Eye Specialists Mid Florida PA............F....... 863 937-4515
Lakeland *(G-7684)*
Eyes On Go Optical LLC ....G....... 954 242-3243
Davie *(G-2523)*
Fiberoptic Engineering Corp ....F....... 850 763-2289
Panama City *(G-13901)*
Graflex Inc ....G....... 561 691-5959
Jupiter *(G-7051)*
▲ **Grampus Enterprises Inc** ....G....... 305 491-9827
Weston *(G-19135)*
Ii-VI Aerospace & Defense Inc ....C....... 727 375-8562
Port Richey *(G-15053)*
▲ **Isp Optics Corporation**............D....... 914 591-3070
Orlando *(G-12845)*
Jenoptik North America Inc ....C....... 561 881-7400
Jupiter *(G-7060)*
▲ **Jenoptik Optical Systems LLC** ....C....... 561 881-7400
Jupiter *(G-7061)*
Knight Vision Lllp ....F....... 321 607-9900
Titusville *(G-18440)*
▲ **Konus USA Corporation**............G....... 305 884-7618
Medley *(G-8677)*
▲ **Laser Lens Tek Inc**............F....... 941 752-5811
Sarasota *(G-16249)*
Lenstec Inc ....E....... 727 571-2272
Saint Petersburg *(G-15839)*
Light-Tech Inc............G....... 863 385-6000
Sebring *(G-16698)*
Lightpath Technologies Inc ....D....... 407 382-4003
Orlando *(G-12911)*
Low Vision Aids Inc............G....... 954 722-1580
Ocala *(G-11987)*
Manasota Optics Inc............G....... 941 359-1748
Sarasota *(G-16500)*
▲ **Meopta USA Inc**............C....... 631 436-5900
Trinity *(G-18488)*
◆ **Mercoframes Optical Corp** ....G....... 305 882-0120
Miami *(G-9978)*
Multicore Photonics Inc ....G....... 407 325-7800
Orlando *(G-12984)*
Oasis Alignment Services Inc............F....... 850 484-2994
Pensacola *(G-14213)*
▲ **Ocean Optics Inc**............E....... 407 673-0041
Orlando *(G-13016)*
Ocean Optics Inc............D....... 727 545-0741
Orlando *(G-13017)*
Oculus Surgical Inc ....E....... 772 236-2622
Port St Lucie *(G-15177)*
Optigrate Corporation ....E....... 407 542-7704
Oviedo *(G-13450)*
▲ **Pixelteq Inc** ....G....... 727 545-0741
Orlando *(G-13070)*
Plastics For Mankind Inc............F....... 305 687-5917
Opa Locka *(G-12351)*
Pyramid Imaging Inc............G....... 813 984-0125
Tampa *(G-18028)*
Saikou Optics Incorporated............G....... 407 986-4200
Orlando *(G-13157)*
◆ **Sunoptic Technologies LLC** ....D....... 877 677-2832
Jacksonville *(G-6822)*
▲ **Tecport Optics Inc**............F....... 407 855-1212
Orlando *(G-13244)*
Thermal Matrix Intl LLC............G....... 813 222-3274
Tampa *(G-18185)*
Thermo Arl US Inc............E....... 800 532-4752
West Palm Beach *(G-19060)*
Thunder Energies Corporation............G....... 561 560-4302
Lantana *(G-7878)*
Tower Optical Corporation............F....... 561 740-2525
Boynton Beach *(G-971)*
Twinstar Optics & Coatings Inc............F....... 727 847-2300
Port Richey *(G-15073)*
Vision Solution Technology LL ....G....... 305 477-4480
Doral *(G-3543)*
Vloc Incorporated ....C....... 727 375-8562
Port Richey *(G-15077)*

3829 Measuring & Controlling Devices, NEC

7 Holdings Group LLC............E....... 754 200-1365
Doral *(G-3217)*
◆ **Advanced Manufacturing Inc** ....E....... 727 573-3300
Saint Petersburg *(G-15691)*
Airpro Diagnostics LLC............F....... 904 717-1711
Jacksonville *(G-6131)*
Alcohol Countermeasure Systems ....F....... 407 207-3337
Orlando *(G-12449)*
Alertgy Inc ....G....... 321 914-3199
Melbourne *(G-8762)*
AMD Aero Inc ....F....... 239 561-8622
Fort Myers *(G-4356)*
◆ **American Household Inc** ....D....... 561 912-4100
Boca Raton *(G-422)*
Ametek Power Instrument Inc ....D....... 954 344-9822
Coral Springs *(G-2220)*
Anton Paar Quantatec Inc............G....... 561 731-4999
Boynton Beach *(G-877)*
Applus Laboratories USA Inc ....G....... 941 205-5700
Punta Gorda *(G-15190)*
Asset Guardian Inc............G....... 727 942-2246
Palm Harbor *(G-13720)*
▼ **AVK Industries Inc** ....F....... 904 998-8400
Jacksonville *(G-6181)*
Awe Diagnostics LLC ....E....... 786 285-0755
Miami *(G-9203)*
B & G Instruments Inc ....F....... 305 871-4445
Miami *(G-9207)*
BEI............G....... 561 488-0759
Boca Raton *(G-445)*
Brrh Corporation............E....... 954 427-9665
Deerfield Beach *(G-2792)*
▲ **C K C Industries Inc**............G....... 813 888-9468
Tampa *(G-17494)*
Co2meter Inc ....F....... 386 310-4933
Ormond Beach *(G-13358)*
Collins Research Inc............F....... 321 401-6060
Orlando *(G-12603)*
Colloidal Dynamics LLC............G....... 904 686-1536
Ponte Vedra Beach *(G-14937)*
Comten Industries Inc............G....... 727 520-1200
Pinellas Park *(G-14340)*
▲ **Core Enterprises Incorporated**............G....... 954 227-0781
Coral Springs *(G-2234)*
Crumbliss Manufacturing Co............F....... 239 693-8588
Fort Myers *(G-4417)*
Datagrid Inc............G....... 352 371-7608
Gainesville *(G-4904)*
◆ **Drew Scientific Inc** ....F....... 305 418-2320
Miami Lakes *(G-10783)*
Dynalco Controls Corporation............E....... 323 589-6181
Fort Lauderdale *(G-3952)*
▲ **Electro-Optix Inc**............F....... 954 973-2800
Pompano Beach *(G-14677)*
Embrace Telecom Inc ....F....... 866 933-8986
Fort Lauderdale *(G-3969)*
Emcee Electronics Inc............E....... 941 485-1515
Venice *(G-18546)*
Exploration Resources Intn Geo ....G....... 601 747-0726
Lake Mary *(G-7412)*
F & J Specialty Products Inc............F....... 352 680-1177
Ocala *(G-11939)*
▲ **Faro Technologies Inc** ....A....... 407 333-9911
Lake Mary *(G-7414)*
Florida Level & Transit Co Inc ....G....... 813 623-3307
Tampa *(G-17680)*
▼ **Forceleader Inc** ....G....... 727 521-1808
Pinellas Park *(G-14348)*
Gaslab............G....... 386 872-7668
Ormond Beach *(G-13373)*
▲ **General Oceanics Inc** ....F....... 305 621-2882
Miami *(G-9625)*
Geodetic Services Inc............F....... 321 724-6831
Melbourne *(G-8835)*
▲ **Giebner Enterprises Inc** ....F....... 727 520-1200
Saint Petersburg *(G-15792)*
Global Telemetry Systems Inc............G....... 850 651-3388
Shalimar *(G-16775)*
▲ **Guardian Ign Interlock Mfg Inc** ....D....... 321 205-1730
Cocoa *(G-2028)*
Homestead Diagnostic Ctr Inc............F....... 305 246-5600
Homestead *(G-5967)*
Hydroplus ....G....... 386 341-2768
Edgewater *(G-3624)*
▲ **Hytronics Corp**............D....... 727 535-0413
Clearwater *(G-1725)*
Impact Register Inc............G....... 727 585-8572
Largo *(G-7978)*
Innovative Instruments Inc ....G....... 813 727-0676
Temple Terrace *(G-18370)*
Innovative Tech By Design Inc ....F....... 321 676-3194
Palm Bay *(G-13516)*
▲ **Invivo Corporation**............B....... 301 525-9683
Gainesville *(G-4945)*
IPC Global............G....... 727 470-2134
Clearwater *(G-1736)*
James O Corbett Inc............G....... 352 483-1222
Eustis *(G-3710)*
◆ **K-Rain Manufacturing Corp**............D....... 561 721-3936
Riviera Beach *(G-15338)*
▲ **LDS Vacuum Products Inc**............E....... 407 862-4643
Longwood *(G-8305)*
Leadair Inc............E....... 407 343-7571
Kissimmee *(G-7267)*
Life Proteomics Inc............F....... 813 864-7646
Tampa *(G-17845)*
◆ **Magnetic Automation Corp**............E....... 321 635-8585
Rockledge *(G-15431)*

SIC

Marathon Technology Corp ....G....... 305 592-1340
Doral *(G-3425)*
MC Miller Co Inc ....E....... 772 794-9448
Sebastian *(G-16668)*
▲ Micro Typing Systems Inc ....E....... 954 970-9500
Pompano Beach *(G-14763)*
Molekule Inc ....G....... 352 871-3803
Tampa *(G-17916)*
Mri Depot Inc ....G....... 407 696-9822
Longwood *(G-8314)*
▲ Neubert Aero Corp ....G....... 352 345-4828
Brooksville *(G-1256)*
New World Holdings Inc ....E....... 561 888-4939
Boca Raton *(G-642)*
Oculus Surgical Inc ....E....... 772 236-2622
Port St Lucie *(G-15177)*
Oriflow ....F....... 727 400-4881
Clearwater *(G-1821)*
Parker Research Corporation ....F....... 727 796-4066
Clearwater *(G-1826)*
Pet Services of Florida LLC ....G....... 352 746-6888
Beverly Hills *(G-378)*
Pixe International Corp ....G....... 850 574-6469
Tallahassee *(G-17309)*
Potenza Services Inc ....G....... 305 400-4938
Miami *(G-10180)*
Precision Leak Detection Inc ....G....... 904 996-9290
Jacksonville *(G-6681)*
Qualitest USA Lc ....F....... 877 884-8378
Fort Lauderdale *(G-4188)*
Quest Controls Inc ....F....... 941 729-4799
Palmetto *(G-13820)*
Rae Services Inc ....G....... 727 480-9940
Palm Harbor *(G-13756)*
Redington Counters Inc ....G....... 954 725-6699
Deerfield Beach *(G-2901)*
Riegl Usa Inc ....E....... 407 248-9927
Winter Garden *(G-19283)*
Rieker LLC ....G....... 407 496-1555
Orlando *(G-13138)*
Roper Technologies Inc ....E....... 941 556-2601
Sarasota *(G-16563)*
Sanomedics Inc ....G....... 305 433-7814
Boca Raton *(G-701)*
▼ Scientific Instruments Inc ....E....... 561 881-8500
Mangonia Park *(G-8511)*
▲ Select Engineered Systems Inc ....E....... 305 823-5410
Hialeah *(G-5613)*
▼ Sensor Systems LLC ....C....... 727 347-2181
Saint Petersburg *(G-15910)*
Sepac Corp ....F....... 305 718-3379
Miami *(G-10325)*
Shain Inc ....G....... 813 889-9614
Tampa *(G-18090)*
Smart Material Corp ....F....... 941 870-3337
Sarasota *(G-16600)*
St Acquisitions LLC ....G....... 941 753-1095
Sarasota *(G-16603)*
Stay-Sealed Inc ....G....... 866 978-2973
Thonotosassa *(G-18404)*
Stellarnet Inc ....F....... 813 855-8687
Tampa *(G-18132)*
Sun Nuclear Corp ....C....... 321 259-6862
Melbourne *(G-8950)*
Sunbeam Americas Holdings LLC ....C....... 561 912-4100
Boca Raton *(G-736)*
Suncoast Tool & Gage Inds Inc ....F....... 727 572-8000
Clearwater *(G-1893)*
▲ Tectron Engineering Company ....F....... 904 394-0683
Jacksonville *(G-6845)*
Thermo Arl US Inc ....E....... 800 532-4752
West Palm Beach *(G-19060)*
Tucker-Davis Technologies Inc ....E....... 386 462-9622
Alachua *(G-21)*
Uk US Partners LLC T McCuloch ....G....... 407 217-2978
Orlando *(G-13286)*
Umbrella Buses Inc ....G....... 754 457-4004
Davenport *(G-2484)*
Veracity Tech Solutions LLC ....F....... 402 658-4113
Pensacola *(G-14281)*
▲ Veroch LLC ....G....... 954 990-7544
Sunrise *(G-17195)*
Whk Biosystems LLC ....G....... 727 209-8402
Clearwater *(G-1938)*
World Precision Instrs LLC ....D....... 941 371-1003
Sarasota *(G-16645)*

3841 Surgical & Medical Instrs & Apparatus

3d Medical Manufacturing Inc ....C....... 561 842-7175
Riviera Beach *(G-15289)*
Aaron Medical Industries Inc ....G....... 727 384-2323
Saint Petersburg *(G-15689)*
▲ Abbott Labs US Sbsdries Alere ....D....... 877 441-7440
Orlando *(G-12425)*
ABC Enterprises ....G....... 407 656-6503
Oakland *(G-11767)*
Adamas Instrument Corporation ....F....... 727 540-0033
Clearwater *(G-1564)*
Adatif Medical Incorporated ....G....... 561 840-0395
Riviera Beach *(G-15291)*
Advanced Dagnstc Solutions Inc ....F....... 352 293-2810
Port Richey *(G-15042)*
Advantage Medical Elec LLC ....F....... 954 345-9800
Coral Springs *(G-2214)*
Aesthetic MBL Laser Svcs Inc ....G....... 954 480-2600
Deerfield Beach *(G-2768)*
▼ Ahc Ventures Corp ....F....... 954 978-9290
Margate *(G-8533)*
Aiolos Group Inc ....G....... 305 496-7674
Miami *(G-9090)*
◆ Airon Corporation ....G....... 321 821-9433
Melbourne *(G-8761)*
Alicia Diagnostic Inc ....F....... 407 365-8498
Chuluota *(G-1551)*
Alpha Industries Inc ....G....... 727 443-2673
Clearwater *(G-1577)*
Amend Surgical Inc ....F....... 844 281-3169
Alachua *(G-2)*
▲ American Household Inc ....D....... 561 912-4100
Boca Raton *(G-422)*
American Surgical Mask LLC ....E....... 813 606-4510
Tampa *(G-17420)*
Anew Inc ....G....... 386 668-7785
Debary *(G-2744)*
Anew International Corporation ....G....... 386 668-7785
Debary *(G-2745)*
Apollo Renal Therapeutics LLC ....E....... 202 413-0963
Ocala *(G-11878)*
Apyx Medical Corporation ....C....... 727 384-2323
Clearwater *(G-1586)*
◆ Arthrex Inc ....C....... 239 643-5553
Naples *(G-11169)*
Arthrex Manufacturing Inc ....C....... 239 643-5553
Naples *(G-11170)*
Arthrex Trauma Inc ....F....... 239 643-5553
Naples *(G-11171)*
▲ B & M Precision Inc ....B....... 813 645-1188
Ruskin *(G-15481)*
B F Industries Inc ....F....... 561 368-6662
Boca Raton *(G-437)*
Back Lory Lee ....G....... 850 638-5430
Chipley *(G-1541)*
Betawave LLC ....F....... 954 223-8298
Fort Lauderdale *(G-3848)*
Bio Ceps Inc ....E....... 727 669-7544
Clearwater *(G-1608)*
Bio-Logic Systems Corp ....D....... 847 949-0456
Orlando *(G-12515)*
▲ Bioderm Inc ....D....... 727 507-7655
Largo *(G-7909)*
▲ Bioflex Medical Magnetics ....F....... 954 565-8500
Fort Lauderdale *(G-3855)*
Biorep Technologies Inc ....F....... 305 330-4449
Miami Lakes *(G-10770)*
Biosafe Supplies LLC ....F....... 407 281-6658
Orlando *(G-12516)*
Biosculpture Technology Inc ....E....... 561 651-7816
West Palm Beach *(G-18821)*
Bolton Medical Inc ....B....... 954 838-9699
Sunrise *(G-17100)*
▲ Brain Power Incorporated ....E....... 305 264-4465
Miami *(G-9273)*
Bravo Inc ....G....... 239 471-8127
Cape Coral *(G-1394)*
Breathing Systems Inc ....G....... 850 477-2324
Pensacola *(G-14105)*
Byomed LLC ....F....... 305 634-6763
North Miami *(G-11630)*
Cae Healthcare Inc ....C....... 941 377-5562
Sarasota *(G-16377)*
Central Fla Attrnsfsonists Inc ....G....... 321 299-6019
Orlando *(G-12562)*
◆ Clinical Chmstry Spclists Corp ....F....... 919 554-1424
West Palm Beach *(G-18847)*
Clinicon Corporation ....F....... 239 939-1345
Fort Myers *(G-4399)*
◆ CMF Medicon Surgical Inc ....G....... 904 642-7500
Jacksonville *(G-6273)*
Codman & Shurtleff Inc ....F....... 908 704-4024
Miami *(G-9374)*
◆ Command Medical Products Inc ....C....... 386 677-7775
Ormond Beach *(G-13359)*
◆ Conmed Corporation ....A....... 727 392-6464
Largo *(G-7927)*
Contract Mfg Solutions Inc ....F....... 954 424-9813
Weston *(G-19117)*
Cordis Corporation ....B....... 786 313-2000
Miami Lakes *(G-10777)*
▲ Corin USA Limited Inc ....F....... 813 977-4469
Tampa *(G-17557)*
◆ Critical Disposables Inc ....E....... 407 330-1154
Sanford *(G-16028)*
Custom Medical Products Inc ....G....... 407 865-7211
Apopka *(G-129)*
Depuy Synthes Products Inc ....C....... 305 265-6842
Miami *(G-9456)*
Derm-Buro Inc ....E....... 305 953-4025
Hialeah *(G-5369)*
Dhss LLC ....E....... 305 830-0327
Hollywood *(G-5811)*
Dhss LLC ....F....... 305 405-4001
North Miami Beach *(G-11670)*
Diabetex Care ....G....... 954 427-9510
Deerfield Beach *(G-2813)*
Diagnostic Test Group LLC ....F....... 561 347-5760
Boca Raton *(G-500)*
Digicare Biomedical Tech Inc ....G....... 561 689-0408
Boynton Beach *(G-897)*
Doctor Easy Medical Pdts LLC ....G....... 904 276-7200
Orange Park *(G-12389)*
Doral Imaging Institute LLC ....G....... 305 594-2881
Miami *(G-9481)*
◆ Drew Scientific Inc ....F....... 305 418-2320
Miami Lakes *(G-10783)*
▲ Dwyer Precision Products Inc ....F....... 904 249-3545
Jacksonville *(G-6341)*
Eagle Eye Anesthesia Inc ....G....... 817 999-9830
Jacksonville *(G-6345)*
Earth Vets Inc ....G....... 352 332-9991
Fernandina Beach *(G-3736)*
Eclipsys Corp ....G....... 404 847-5000
Riviera Beach *(G-15324)*
◆ EM Adams Inc ....D....... 772 468-6550
Fort Pierce *(G-4694)*
Emcyte Corp ....E....... 239 481-7725
Fort Myers *(G-4443)*
Endo-Gear LLC ....F....... 305 710-6662
Miami *(G-9526)*
Endo-Therapeutics Inc ....D....... 727 538-9570
Clearwater *(G-1672)*
▲ Erba Diagnostics Inc ....D....... 305 324-2300
Miami Lakes *(G-10786)*
Eusa Global LLC ....G....... 786 483-7490
Medley *(G-8649)*
Evren Technologies Inc ....G....... 352 494-0950
Newberry *(G-11555)*
Family of Smith Inc ....E....... 941 726-0873
Sarasota *(G-16212)*
First Check Diagnostics LLC ....E....... 858 805-2425
Orlando *(G-12741)*
Flospine LLC ....G....... 561 705-3080
Boca Raton *(G-535)*
Galix Bmedical Instrumentation ....F....... 305 534-5905
Doral *(G-3357)*
Gardco ....G....... 954 946-9454
Pompano Beach *(G-14710)*
Gaumard Scientific Company Inc ....E....... 305 971-3790
Miami *(G-9615)*
Geddis Inc ....F....... 800 844-6792
Dunedin *(G-3579)*
Genicon Inc ....E....... 407 657-4851
Orlando *(G-12782)*
▲ Globalink Mfg Solutions ....F....... 239 455-5166
Naples *(G-11263)*
▲ Gremed Group Corp ....E....... 305 392-5331
Doral *(G-3374)*
Gulf Coast Hyperberic Inc ....G....... 850 271-1441
Panama City *(G-13911)*
Gulf Medical Fiberoptics Inc ....G....... 813 855-6618
Oldsmar *(G-12230)*
Gyrx LLC ....F....... 904 641-2599
Jacksonville *(G-6457)*
H-Cyte Inc ....E....... 844 633-6839
Tampa *(G-17739)*
Hansa Ophthalmics LLC ....E....... 305 594-1789
Doral *(G-3378)*
Hdl Therapeutics Inc ....G....... 772 453-2770
Vero Beach *(G-18625)*
He Instruments LLC ....G....... 561 832-1249
Lake Worth Beach *(G-7612)*

Health Star Inc G 321 914-6012
Merritt Island *(G-9002)*

▲ Hnm Stainless LLC E 866 291-8498
Miami *(G-9715)*

▲ Home Aide Diagnostics Inc F 954 794-0212
Deerfield Beach *(G-2843)*

Howmedica Osteonics Corp E 954 714-7933
Fort Lauderdale *(G-4050)*

Howmedica Osteonics Corp E 813 288-0760
Tampa *(G-17764)*

Howmedica Osteonics Corp E 954 791-6078
Fort Lauderdale *(G-4051)*

Hti G 941 723-4570
Palmetto *(G-13806)*

▲ Hurricane Medical Inc E 941 753-1517
Bradenton *(G-1058)*

▲ Hydrogel Vision Corporation D 941 739-1382
Sarasota *(G-16231)*

Hygreen Inc F 352 327-9747
Gainesville *(G-4939)*

Ideal Image Brandon G 813 982-3420
Brandon *(G-1162)*

Imaging Diagnostic Systems Inc F 954 581-9800
Orlando *(G-12824)*

Inneuroco Inc F 954 742-5988
Sunrise *(G-17128)*

Innfocus Inc F 305 378-2651
Miami *(G-9744)*

▲ Innomed Technologies Inc C 800 200-9842
Coconut Creek *(G-2081)*

Innovative Designs of Sarasota G 941 752-7779
Bradenton *(G-1060)*

Innovative Mfg Solutions LLC G 904 647-5300
Jacksonville *(G-6497)*

Inspired Therapeutics LLC G 339 222-0847
Melbourne Beach *(G-8980)*

Integrity Implants Inc E 800 201-9300
Palm Beach Gardens *(G-13597)*

Intellgent Haring Systems Corp F 305 668-6102
Miami *(G-9752)*

Intermed Group Inc E 561 586-3667
Alachua *(G-10)*

◆ International Medical Inds Inc E 954 917-9570
Pompano Beach *(G-14732)*

▲ Invivo Corporation B 301 525-9683
Gainesville *(G-4945)*

Invo Bioscience Inc G 978 878-9505
Lakewood Ranch *(G-7844)*

▲ Iradimed Corporation C 407 677-8022
Winter Springs *(G-19475)*

◆ Iris International Inc D 818 709-1244
Miami *(G-9770)*

▲ Ispg Inc F 941 896-3999
Bradenton *(G-1062)*

Ivan & Ivan LLC G 305 507-8793
Doral *(G-3397)*

Jepsen Tool Company Inc F 904 262-2793
Jacksonville *(G-6521)*

Jimenez Enterprises Group F 561 391-6800
Parkland *(G-13994)*

Jimenez Enterprises Group E 561 542-7709
Doral *(G-3403)*

▲ JTL Enterprises (delaware) E 727 536-5566
Clearwater *(G-1746)*

Kalitec Direct LLC G 407 545-2063
Oviedo *(G-13443)*

▲ Kawasumi Laboratories Amer Inc F 813 630-5554
Tampa *(G-17816)*

Kerma Medical Products Inc G 954 744-3480
Miramar *(G-11009)*

Klyo Medical Systems Inc F 305 330-5025
Doral *(G-3410)*

Kms Medical LLC F 305 266-3388
Miami *(G-9827)*

Kollsut International Inc G 305 438-6877
North Miami Beach *(G-11688)*

Lane Care LLC F 727 316-3708
Palm Harbor *(G-13744)*

Laser Surgical Florida Inc G 954 609-7639
Miami *(G-9863)*

▲ Led Technologies Incorporated F 800 337-9565
Largo *(G-7998)*

Lenkbar LLC D 239 732-5915
Naples *(G-11311)*

▼ Lensar Inc E 888 536-7271
Orlando *(G-12904)*

◆ Linvatec Corporation A 727 392-6464
Largo *(G-8001)*

Lor-Ed Enterprises LLC F 352 750-1999
Lady Lake *(G-7328)*

Lumenis Ltd F 305 508-5052
Miami *(G-9917)*

▲ Marina Medical Instruments Inc E 954 924-4418
Davie *(G-2549)*

Martin-Weston Co F 727 545-8877
Largo *(G-8005)*

Marysol Technologies Inc G 727 712-1523
Clearwater *(G-1775)*

Maven Medical Mfg Inc E 727 518-0555
Largo *(G-8006)*

MC Johnson Co F 239 293-0901
Naples *(G-11324)*

McKesson Pharmaceutical F 863 616-2973
Lakeland *(G-7748)*

Medic Healthcare LLC G 954 336-1776
Fort Lauderdale *(G-4116)*

Medical Energy Inc G 850 313-6277
Pensacola *(G-14205)*

▲ Medone Surgical Inc F 941 359-3129
Sarasota *(G-16255)*

Medrx Inc E 727 584-9600
Largo *(G-8008)*

Medtrnic Sofamor Danek USA Inc G 904 645-6925
Jacksonville *(G-6590)*

Medtronic E 305 458-7260
Miami Lakes *(G-10816)*

Medtronic F 305 206-8487
Miami *(G-9969)*

Medtronic D 305 818-4100
Miami Lakes *(G-10817)*

Medtronic Usa Inc A 702 308-1302
Jacksonville *(G-6591)*

Medtronic Usa Inc A 786 709-4200
Doral *(G-3430)*

Medtronic Xomed Inc A 904 296-9600
Jacksonville *(G-6592)*

Medtronic Xomed Inc B 904 296-9600
Jacksonville *(G-6593)*

MEI Development Corporation F 954 341-3302
Coral Springs *(G-2280)*

Mergenet Medical Inc F 561 208-3770
Deerfield Beach *(G-2870)*

Merlola Industries LLC G 888 418-0408
Miami *(G-9982)*

Micro Tool Engineering Inc F 561 842-7381
Riviera Beach *(G-15348)*

Microtek Medical Inc C 904 741-2964
Jacksonville *(G-6603)*

▲ Mobilehelp LLC D 561 347-6285
Boca Raton *(G-628)*

Mobilite Corporation D 407 321-5630
Sanford *(G-16089)*

Moog Inc G 716 652-2000
Pembroke Pines *(G-14049)*

Morcent Import Export Inc G 727 442-9735
Belleair *(G-360)*

Motus Gi LLC G 954 541-8000
Fort Lauderdale *(G-4125)*

Motus GI Holdings Inc E 954 541-8000
Fort Lauderdale *(G-4126)*

N E D LLC G 610 442-1017
Boca Raton *(G-634)*

Nb Products Inc E 904 807-0140
Jacksonville *(G-6621)*

Ndh Medical Inc G 727 570-2293
Saint Petersburg *(G-15864)*

Neocis Inc D 855 963-6247
Miami *(G-10065)*

Neurotronics Inc G 352 372-9955
Gainesville *(G-4971)*

New Wave Surgical Corp F 866 346-8883
Coral Springs *(G-2296)*

New World Holdings Inc E 561 888-4939
Boca Raton *(G-642)*

Nkem Inc F 800 582-0707
Sarasota *(G-16525)*

Nouveau Cosmetique Usa Inc G 321 332-6976
Orlando *(G-13009)*

Novavision Inc F 561 558-2020
Boca Raton *(G-651)*

Nuline Sensors LLC G 407 473-0765
Sanford *(G-16092)*

Oculus Surgical Inc E 772 236-2622
Port St Lucie *(G-15177)*

One Milo Inc F 305 804-0266
Miami *(G-10102)*

Opko Curna LLC G 305 575-4100
Miami *(G-10110)*

Optima Neuroscience Inc G 352 371-8281
Alachua *(G-12)*

Orbusneich Medical Inc E 954 730-0711
Fort Lauderdale *(G-4151)*

Orthopedic Designs N Amer Inc G 813 443-4905
Tampa *(G-17962)*

◆ Oscor Inc C 727 937-2511
Palm Harbor *(G-13749)*

Pablo Surgical Solutions LLC G 904 237-4864
Ponte Vedra Beach *(G-14949)*

▲ Pace Tech Inc F 727 442-8118
Clearwater *(G-1824)*

Parallax Health Sciences Inc G 888 263-9799
West Palm Beach *(G-18987)*

Parcus Medical LLC F 941 755-7965
Sarasota *(G-16271)*

Ped-Stuart Corporation E 352 754-6001
Brooksville *(G-1259)*

Pedicraft Inc F 904 348-3170
Jacksonville *(G-6665)*

◆ Perry Baromedical Corporation E 561 840-0395
Riviera Beach *(G-15362)*

Pioneer Surgical Technology G 906 225-5629
Alachua *(G-14)*

Polyhistor International Inc G 904 646-5666
Jacksonville *(G-6677)*

Precheck Health Services Inc E 305 203-4711
Miami *(G-10182)*

Precision Machine Tech LLC F 305 594-1789
Doral *(G-3467)*

▼ Professional Pet Products Inc E 305 592-1992
Doral *(G-3471)*

Promedica Inc D 813 854-1905
Oldsmar *(G-12265)*

Quantum Storage Systems G 305 687-0405
Opa Locka *(G-12352)*

Quick-Med Technologies Inc G 352 379-0611
Gainesville *(G-4986)*

Reddress Usa Inc G 800 674-9615
Ponte Vedra Beach *(G-14953)*

Regeneration Technologies Inc F 386 418-8888
Alachua *(G-15)*

Reliant Medical Systems LLC G 954 977-4224
Pompano Beach *(G-14830)*

RM Imaging Incorporated E 561 361-8090
Boca Raton *(G-690)*

Rochester Electro-Medical Inc E 813 994-7519
Coral Springs *(G-2306)*

Rolls Axle Lc F 813 764-0242
Plant City *(G-14463)*

Rotburg Instruments Amer Inc F 954 331-8046
Sunrise *(G-17170)*

Rotech Oxygen & Medical Equip G 352 291-1070
Ocala *(G-12041)*

Rti Donor Services Inc E 321 431-2464
Melbourne *(G-8922)*

Rti Surgical Inc C 386 418-8888
Alachua *(G-16)*

Rxenergy LLC F 727 726-4204
Clearwater *(G-1867)*

S4j Manufacturing Services Inc F 239 574-9400
Cape Coral *(G-1463)*

Samark Technology Corporation G 941 955-4325
Sarasota *(G-16571)*

Savvy Associate Inc F 954 941-6986
Pompano Beach *(G-14840)*

Sensus Healthcare Inc E 561 922-5808
Boca Raton *(G-705)*

Shl Pharma LLC E 954 725-2008
Deerfield Beach *(G-2910)*

Simplified Systems Inc F 305 672-7676
Miami Beach *(G-10710)*

Sinocare Meditech Inc F 800 342-7226
Fort Lauderdale *(G-4237)*

Sky Medical Inc F 954 747-3188
Sunrise *(G-17172)*

Sleepmed Incorporated F 941 361-3035
Sarasota *(G-16599)*

Sota Manufacturing Inc E 561 368-8007
Boca Raton *(G-722)*

Spacelabs Healthcare Inc E 904 786-5113
Jacksonville *(G-6801)*

Speranza Therapeutics Corp G 844 477-3726
Boca Raton *(G-726)*

Statcorp Inc G 904 786-5113
Jacksonville *(G-6810)*

◆ Steripack (usa) Limited LLC E 863 648-2333
Lakeland *(G-7807)*

Stryker Orthopedics G 904 296-6000
Jacksonville *(G-6819)*

Summit Orthopedic Tech Inc E 203 693-2727
Naples *(G-11420)*

SIC

Sun Coast Surgical & Med Sup ....G.... 813 881-0065
Tampa *(G-18138)*

Sunbeam Americas Holdings LLC ....C.... 561 912-4100
Boca Raton *(G-736)*

◆ Sunoptic Technologies LLC ....D.... 877 677-2832
Jacksonville *(G-6822)*

Surgentec LLC ....F.... 561 990-7882
Boca Raton *(G-740)*

◆ Surgimed Corporation ....F.... 912 674-7660
Coral Springs *(G-2318)*

Syntheon LLC ....G.... 305 255-1745
Miami *(G-10451)*

Techderm LLC ....G.... 407 795-1517
Palm Beach Gardens *(G-13631)*

Technicuff Corp ....F.... 352 326-2833
Leesburg *(G-8176)*

Tequesta Community Health Ctr ....G.... 561 713-0798
Jupiter *(G-7126)*

Tni Manufacturing Inc ....G.... 954 742-5988
Sunrise *(G-17189)*

Treace Medical Concepts Inc ....C.... 904 373-5940
Ponte Vedra *(G-14928)*

Tutogen Medical Inc ....E.... 386 418-8888
Alachua *(G-22)*

Twins & Martin Equipment Corp ....G.... 954 802-0345
Miami *(G-10516)*

Ultra Clean Systems Inc ....F.... 813 925-1003
Oldsmar *(G-12272)*

Ultroid Technologies Inc ....G.... 877 858-0555
Tampa *(G-18215)*

Unimed Surgical Products Inc ....E.... 727 546-1900
Seminole *(G-16769)*

Universal HM Hlth Indus Sups I ....G.... 813 493-7904
Tampa *(G-18222)*

Universal Surgical Appliance ....F.... 305 652-0810
Miami *(G-10544)*

Uroshape LLC ....F.... 321 960-2484
Melbourne *(G-8968)*

Usaop Inc ....G.... 386 212-9514
Ormond Beach *(G-13406)*

Vapor Engineering Inc ....F.... 850 434-3191
Pensacola *(G-14280)*

Vgi Medical LLC ....F.... 727 565-1235
Largo *(G-8073)*

Vital Usa Inc ....F.... 561 282-6074
West Palm Beach *(G-19082)*

Viztek Inc ....F.... 904 448-9936
Jacksonville *(G-6903)*

Vmax Vision Inc ....G.... 321 972-1823
Maitland *(G-8485)*

Vuessence Inc ....G.... 813 792-7123
Odessa *(G-12165)*

Vycor Medical Inc ....G.... 561 558-2020
Boca Raton *(G-783)*

Wayne Metal Products Inc ....G.... 407 321-7168
Sanford *(G-16136)*

Wimbledon Health Partners LLC ....F.... 800 200-8262
Boca Raton *(G-790)*

Xhale Inc ....G.... 352 371-8488
Gainesville *(G-5017)*

Z Haydu Manufacturing Corp ....G.... 954 925-1779
Hollywood *(G-5944)*

Zimmer Biomet CMF Thoracic LLC ....C.... 574 267-6639
Jacksonville *(G-6934)*

Ziptek LLC ....F.... 941 953-5509
Sarasota *(G-16646)*

3842 Orthopedic, Prosthetic & Surgical Appliances/Splys

360 O and P Inc ....G.... 813 985-5000
Temple Terrace *(G-18365)*

A & A Orthopedics Mfg ....G.... 305 256-8119
Miami *(G-9029)*

A and A Orthopedics Inc ....G.... 305 256-8119
Miami *(G-9035)*

Ace Restoration Services LLC ....F.... 786 487-1870
Miami *(G-9062)*

▼ Ace Sales Corp ....F.... 305 835-0310
Miami *(G-9063)*

Advanced Prof Surgical Svcs ....G.... 786 326-0576
Miami *(G-9076)*

Advanced Prosthetics Amer Inc ....F.... 352 383-0396
Eustis *(G-3700)*

Affordable At Home Has Inc ....G.... 786 200-0484
Miami *(G-9085)*

Affordable Wheelchair Transprt ....G.... 727 432-4089
Saint Petersburg *(G-15694)*

All American Amputee ....G.... 352 383-0396
Eustis *(G-3702)*

All Out On A Limb LLC ....G.... 813 407-6497
Ruskin *(G-15480)*

Alloy Cladding ....E.... 561 625-4550
Jupiter *(G-6999)*

▲ Alps South LLC ....D.... 727 528-8566
Saint Petersburg *(G-15697)*

Anjon Inc ....E.... 904 730-9373
Jacksonville *(G-6157)*

Applied Mobility Devices LLC ....G.... 833 439-6266
Bonita Springs *(G-813)*

Around and About Inc ....F.... 954 584-1954
Plantation *(G-14491)*

Aso Corporation ....D.... 941 378-6600
Sarasota *(G-16351)*

◆ Aso LLC ....C.... 941 379-0300
Sarasota *(G-16352)*

Atlantic Tactical Inc ....G.... 909 923-7300
Jacksonville *(G-6178)*

Audina Hearing Instruments ....D.... 407 331-0077
Longwood *(G-8259)*

Axogen Corporation ....E.... 386 462-6800
Alachua *(G-7)*

Bader Prosthetics & Orthotics ....E.... 813 962-6100
Tampa *(G-17453)*

▼ Bathroom World Manufacturing ....G.... 954 566-0451
Oakland Park *(G-11785)*

Bay Quality Prosthetic LLC ....G.... 850 522-5343
Panama City *(G-13868)*

Baycare Home Care Inc ....F.... 727 461-5878
Clearwater *(G-1603)*

Bell Hearing Instruments Inc ....E.... 813 814-2355
Oldsmar *(G-12211)*

Best Price Mobility Inc ....F.... 321 402-5955
Kissimmee *(G-7224)*

Biosculptor Corporation ....G.... 305 823-8300
Hialeah *(G-5326)*

Blue Diamond Orthopedic LLC ....G.... 407 613-2001
Orlando *(G-12525)*

Bolt Systems Inc ....G.... 407 425-0012
Orlando *(G-12532)*

Bremer Group Company Inc ....F.... 904 645-0004
Jacksonville *(G-6235)*

Buffalo Wheelchair Inc ....G.... 941 921-6331
Sarasota *(G-16371)*

Burkhart Roentgen Intl Inc ....F.... 727 327-6950
Saint Petersburg *(G-15732)*

C C Lead Inc ....F.... 863 465-6458
Lake Placid *(G-7486)*

C Dyer Development Group LLC ....G.... 727 423-6169
Tarpon Springs *(G-18285)*

Cadre Holdings Inc ....C.... 904 741-5400
Jacksonville *(G-6249)*

▲ Cameron Textiles Inc ....G.... 954 454-6482
Palm City *(G-13644)*

Captel Inc ....D.... 407 730-3397
Orlando *(G-12549)*

Catalyst Orthoscience Inc ....F.... 239 325-9976
Naples *(G-11201)*

Comfort Brace LLC ....G.... 954 899-1563
Lighthouse Point *(G-8208)*

◆ Consolidated Polymer Tech ....E.... 727 531-4191
Clearwater *(G-1636)*

Ctm Biomedical LLC ....F.... 561 650-4027
Miami *(G-9416)*

Custom Medical Systems Inc ....G.... 941 722-3434
Palmetto *(G-13794)*

Debut Development LLC ....G.... 863 448-9081
Wauchula *(G-18690)*

Decimal LLC ....E.... 407 330-3300
Sanford *(G-16033)*

◆ Demetech Corporation ....D.... 305 824-1048
Miami Lakes *(G-10781)*

Deming Designs Inc ....F.... 850 478-5765
Pensacola *(G-14129)*

Depuy Inc ....E.... 305 412-8010
Miami *(G-9455)*

Dhb Armor Group Inc ....G.... 800 413-5155
Pompano Beach *(G-14662)*

Digital Antomy Smltons For HLT ....G.... 937 623-7377
Orlando *(G-12672)*

Dollar & Penny Stretchers LLC ....G.... 941 830-5341
Port Charlotte *(G-14973)*

Donna M Walker PA ....G.... 561 289-0437
Boca Raton *(G-507)*

▼ Dr Jills Foot Pads Inc ....F.... 954 573-6557
Deerfield Beach *(G-2818)*

Dynorthotics Ltd Partnership ....G.... 954 925-5806
Dania *(G-2443)*

Ear-Tronics Inc ....G.... 239 275-7655
Fort Myers *(G-4440)*

Eartech Inc ....G.... 941 747-8193
Bradenton *(G-1034)*

▲ Elmridge Protection Pdts LLC ....G.... 561 244-8337
Boca Raton *(G-517)*

Empowered Prosthetics Corp ....G.... 561 630-9137
Palm Beach Gardens *(G-13588)*

▲ Encore Inc ....F.... 941 359-3599
Sarasota *(G-16211)*

Energy Now LLC ....G.... 941 276-0935
Port Charlotte *(G-14978)*

Euroinsoles Incorporated ....G.... 786 206-6117
Coral Gables *(G-2144)*

Evolution Liners Inc ....G.... 407 839-6213
Orlando *(G-12723)*

▲ Evolution Orthotics Inc ....E.... 407 688-2860
Lake Mary *(G-7411)*

▲ Exactech Inc ....A.... 352 377-1140
Gainesville *(G-4916)*

Florida Best Hearing ....E.... 863 402-0094
Boynton Beach *(G-907)*

Florida North Hearing Solution ....F.... 386 466-0902
Gainesville *(G-4921)*

Florida Prsthtics Orthtics Inc ....G.... 305 553-1217
Miami *(G-9586)*

Foot Function Lab Inc ....G.... 954 753-2500
Coral Springs *(G-2246)*

Freedom Fabrication Inc ....F.... 850 539-4194
Havana *(G-5238)*

Freedom Orthotics Inc ....G.... 813 833-7871
Dunedin *(G-3577)*

▲ Grace Prsthtic Fabrication Inc ....G.... 727 842-2265
New Port Richey *(G-11491)*

Great Northern Rehab PC ....G.... 352 732-8868
Ocala *(G-11960)*

Great Northern Rehab PC ....F.... 352 732-8868
Ocala *(G-11961)*

Grobarty Inc ....F.... 786 398-5530
Miami *(G-9674)*

Gulf Coast Non Emergency Trans ....G.... 239 825-1350
Fort Myers *(G-4475)*

▲ Halkey-Roberts Corporation ....C.... 727 471-4200
Saint Petersburg *(G-15803)*

Hanger Prsthetcs & Ortho Inc ....G.... 850 216-2392
Tallahassee *(G-17273)*

Hanger Prsthtics Orthotics Inc ....F.... 239 772-4510
Cape Coral *(G-1433)*

Hans Rudolph Inc ....F.... 561 877-8775
Boynton Beach *(G-916)*

Hawk Protection Incorporated ....G.... 954 980-9631
Pembroke Pines *(G-14040)*

▲ Healthline Medical Pdts Inc ....E.... 407 656-0704
Winter Garden *(G-19267)*

Hear For You Hearing Aid Ctr ....G.... 850 316-4414
Pensacola *(G-14170)*

Hogg Wild Fabrication ....G.... 904 214-3453
Jacksonville *(G-6474)*

▲ Hoveround Corporation ....B.... 941 739-6200
Sarasota *(G-16230)*

Howmedica Osteonics Corp ....G.... 941 378-4600
Sarasota *(G-16461)*

Howmedica Osteonics Corp ....G.... 813 886-3450
Tampa *(G-17763)*

▲ Imc-Heartway LLC ....G.... 239 275-6767
Fort Myers *(G-4489)*

Innovative Mfg Solutions LLC ....G.... 904 647-5300
Jacksonville *(G-6497)*

Innovative Spine Care ....G.... 813 920-3022
Tampa *(G-17785)*

Institute For Prosthetic Advan ....G.... 850 784-0320
Panama City *(G-13918)*

Integrity Prosthetics ....G.... 863 875-7063
Winter Haven *(G-19330)*

Integrity Prsthetics Orthotics ....G.... 813 416-5905
Tampa *(G-17788)*

Intermed Group Inc ....E.... 561 586-3667
Alachua *(G-10)*

Internl Sterilization Lab LLC ....G.... 352 429-3200
Groveland *(G-5097)*

◆ Invacare Florida Corporation ....B.... 407 321-5630
Sanford *(G-16069)*

JB Effects ....G.... 727 348-1865
Pinellas Park *(G-14356)*

Johnson & Johnson ....G.... 813 972-0204
Tampa *(G-17809)*

Johnson & Johnson ....E.... 305 261-3500
Miami *(G-9801)*

Jrs Limb & Tree LLC ....G.... 407 383-4843
Sanford *(G-16075)*

Juvent Medical Inc ....G.... 732 748-8866
Fort Myers Beach *(G-4665)*

Kericure Inc ... F ... 855 888-5374
Wesley Chapel (G-18750)
Kinetic Research Inc ... F ... 813 962-6300
Tampa (G-17826)
Ko Orthotics Inc ... G ... 954 570-8096
Coconut Creek (G-2088)
Lawall Prsthtics Orthotics Inc ... G ... 407 567-5190
Orlando (G-12897)
◆ Leeder Group Inc ... E ... 305 436-5030
Miami (G-9880)
◆ Lifesaving Systems Corporation ... E ... 813 645-2748
Apollo Beach (G-105)
Limb Preservation Inst Inc ... G ... 954 755-5726
Parkland (G-13996)
Limbitless Solutions Inc ... E ... 407 494-3661
Orlando (G-12912)
◆ Linvatec Corporation ... A ... 727 392-6464
Largo (G-8001)
Mahnkes Orthtics Prsthtics of ... G ... 954 772-1299
Miami (G-9935)
Main Tape Co Inc ... G ... 561 248-8867
West Palm Beach (G-18938)
▲ Mako Surgical Corp ... B ... 866 647-6256
Weston (G-19149)
Maramed Precision Corporation ... E ... 305 823-8300
Hialeah (G-5500)
Maven Medical Mfg Inc ... E ... 727 518-0555
Largo (G-8006)
McCluneys Orthpd Prsthetis Svc ... G ... 352 373-5754
Gainesville (G-4958)
Medtronic Usa Inc ... A ... 702 308-1302
Jacksonville (G-6591)
Medtronic Xomed Inc ... A ... 904 296-9600
Jacksonville (G-6592)
Medtronic Xomed Inc ... B ... 904 296-9600
Jacksonville (G-6593)
◆ Merits Health Products Inc ... E ... 239 772-0579
Fort Myers (G-4527)
Miami ... F ... 954 874-7707
Miami (G-9991)
Mobility Freedom Inc ... G ... 407 495-1333
Orlando (G-12974)
Morton Plant Mease Health Care ... A ... 727 462-7052
Clearwater (G-1793)
N-Ear Pro Inc ... E ... 877 290-4599
Tampa (G-17926)
Neutral Guard LLC ... G ... 954 249-6600
Fort Lauderdale (G-4136)
Noa International Inc ... G ... 954 835-5258
West Palm Beach (G-18967)
Noguera Holdings LLC ... G ... 305 846-9144
Hialeah (G-5543)
◆ North Shore Hldngs Lghthuse Pt ... E ... 954 785-1055
Lighthouse Point (G-8211)
◆ Ongoing Care Solutions Inc ... E ... 727 526-0707
Clearwater (G-1818)
▼ Onyx Protective Group Inc ... F ... 305 282-4455
Miami (G-10108)
Orcom Labs Inc ... G ... 321 773-0741
Indian Harbour Beach (G-6064)
▲ Orthomerica Products Inc ... C ... 407 290-6592
Orlando (G-13039)
Orthotic Prsthtic Rhbltion As ... G ... 352 331-3399
Gainesville (G-4977)
Pensacola Orthtc & Prostetic ... G ... 850 478-7676
Pensacola (G-14225)
Physician Hearing Care ... F ... 239 261-7722
Naples (G-11364)
Physiorx LLC ... F ... 407 718-5549
Ocoee (G-12088)
◆ Point Blank Enterprises Inc ... A ... 954 630-0900
Pompano Beach (G-14801)
Point Blank Enterprises Inc ... D ... 305 820-4270
Miami Lakes (G-10840)
Potenza Services Inc ... G ... 305 400-4938
Miami (G-10180)
Ppi International Corp ... D ... 954 838-1008
Sunrise (G-17159)
Precision Laboratories Inc ... E ... 407 774-4261
Longwood (G-8328)
Pride Florida ... G ... 813 621-9262
Tampa (G-18009)
Primetime Industries LLC ... G ... 813 781-0196
Wesley Chapel (G-18756)
Primus Sterilizer Company LLC ... F ... 402 344-4200
Orlando (G-13087)
◆ Professional Products Inc ... C ... 850 892-5731
Defuniak Springs (G-2946)
Prosthetic Laboratories ... G ... 305 250-9900
Coral Gables (G-2187)
Protective Group Inc ... E ... 305 820-4266
Miami Lakes (G-10846)
◆ Protective Products Entps Inc ... E ... 954 630-0900
Pompano Beach (G-14820)
Pure Med Mobility Inc ... G ... 352 366-8008
Brooksville (G-1263)
Quick Protective Systems Inc ... G ... 772 220-3315
Stuart (G-16993)
Quirantes Orthopedics Inc ... G ... 305 261-1382
Miami (G-10227)
Restoration Medical LLC ... G ... 863 272-0250
Lakeland (G-7778)
Restorative Care America Inc ... D ... 727 573-1595
Saint Petersburg (G-15900)
Restorative Products Inc ... F ... 813 342-4432
Tampa (G-18054)
Rlcjc Inc ... G ... 407 370-3338
Orlando (G-13142)
Royal Baths Manufacturing Co ... E ... 407 854-1740
Orlando (G-13147)
RS&m Consultants ... G ... 727 323-6983
Saint Petersburg (G-15903)
Ryder Orthopedics Inc ... G ... 239 939-0009
Fort Myers (G-4589)
Safariland LLC ... F ... 904 741-5400
Jacksonville (G-6746)
▲ Safariland LLC ... B ... 904 741-5400
Jacksonville (G-6748)
Safe Workplace Inc ... G ... 813 657-7233
San Antonio (G-15979)
◆ Safety Intl Bags & Straps ... F ... 407 830-0888
Casselberry (G-1517)
Santos Group Inc ... F ... 954 605-2954
Coral Springs (G-2309)
▲ Sawyer Products Inc ... E ... 727 725-1177
Safety Harbor (G-15502)
Scooter Link ... G ... 813 985-3075
Temple Terrace (G-18377)
Shukla Medical Inc ... E ... 732 474-1769
Saint Petersburg (G-15912)
Sientra Inc ... G ... 813 751-7576
Brandon (G-1179)
Simpson Construction and Roofg ... F ... 863 443-0710
Avon Park (G-296)
Sky Medical Inc ... F ... 954 747-3188
Sunrise (G-17172)
Son Life Prsthtics Orthtics In ... F ... 352 596-2257
Hernando Beach (G-5251)
South Bch Orthtics Prsthtics I ... F ... 352 512-0262
Stuart (G-17019)
South Broward Brace Inc ... F ... 954 458-0656
Hallandale Beach (G-5213)
Southern Surgical Consultants ... G ... 904 296-7828
Jacksonville (G-6797)
Spinenet LLC ... F ... 321 439-1806
Winter Park (G-19447)
Sponge Merchant International ... G ... 727 919-3523
Tarpon Springs (G-18325)
Straw Giant Company ... G ... 561 430-0729
Delray Beach (G-3147)
▼ Structure Medical LLC ... D ... 239 262-5551
Naples (G-11419)
Superior Surgical Mfg Co ... F ... 800 727-8643
Seminole (G-16766)
Surefire Laser LLC ... G ... 305 720-7118
Miami (G-10442)
Syndaver Labs Inc ... D ... 813 600-5530
Tampa (G-18148)
Synergy Rehab Technologies Inc ... G ... 407 943-7500
Saint Cloud (G-15669)
Telenetpro Inc ... F ... 954 333-8633
Pompano Beach (G-14885)
Tendonease LLC ... G ... 888 224-0319
Palm City (G-13675)
Tidwells Orthotics and Prosthe ... G ... 954 346-5402
Coral Springs (G-2323)
Tpg Black LLC ... G ... 561 777-8989
Boynton Beach (G-972)
Trackmaster LLC ... G ... 727 333-7562
Clearwater (G-1925)
Trinity Mobility ... G ... 727 389-1438
New Port Richey (G-11517)
Truear Inc ... F ... 352 314-8805
Mount Dora (G-11117)
Universal HM Hlth Indus Sups I ... G ... 813 493-7904
Tampa (G-18222)
Universal Surgical Appliance ... F ... 305 652-0810
Miami (G-10544)
US Implant Solutions LLC ... G ... 407 971-8054
Maitland (G-8483)
US Orthotics Inc ... F ... 813 621-7797
Tampa (G-18227)
Vanlympia Inc ... G ... 727 725-5055
Safety Harbor (G-15507)
Verhi Inc ... E ... 850 477-4880
Pensacola (G-14282)
Visionare LLC ... G ... 305 989-7271
Fort Myers (G-4647)
Vy Spine LLC ... G ... 866 489-7746
Tallahassee (G-17344)
Walker Hospitality Inc ... G ... 407 927-1871
Orlando (G-13318)
Westcoast Brace & Limb Inc ... F ... 813 985-5000
Temple Terrace (G-18383)
Westcoast Brace & Limb Inc ... D ... 407 502-0024
Maitland (G-8486)
Williams Orthtc-Prosthetic Inc ... G ... 850 385-6655
Tallahassee (G-17345)
Zassi Holdings Inc ... G ... 904 432-8315
Ponte Vedra Beach (G-14958)
Zimmer Dental Inc ... D ... 561 776-6700
Palm Beach Gardens (G-13637)

3843 Dental Eqpt & Splys

▲ 3b Global LLC ... G ... 813 350-7872
Tampa (G-17373)
▼ Biomet 3i LLC ... A ... 561 775-9928
Palm Beach Gardens (G-13570)
Blitz Micro Turning Inc ... G ... 727 725-5005
Safety Harbor (G-15489)
Boca Dental Supply LLC ... G ... 800 768-5691
Boca Raton (G-451)
◆ Boyd Industries Inc ... D ... 727 561-9292
Clearwater (G-1611)
DDS Lab USA Holding ... D ... 813 249-8888
Tampa (G-17596)
Dental Partners Alliance LLC ... G ... 321 574-8003
Melbourne (G-8802)
Dentate Porcelain Inc ... G ... 917 359-7696
Pompano Beach (G-14660)
Denterprise International Inc ... F ... 386 672-0450
Ormond Beach (G-13362)
Dentsply Sirona Inc ... D ... 941 527-4450
Sarasota (G-16205)
▲ Dotamed LLC ... G ... 786 594-0144
Doral (G-3335)
Dr Worthington Orthodonti ... G ... 813 968-4040
Tampa (G-17615)
Dsg Clearwater Laboratory ... F ... 727 530-9444
Clearwater (G-1659)
Dynamic Dental Corp ... G ... 954 344-5155
Coral Springs (G-2242)
Economy Dntres Jcksonville LLC ... F ... 904 696-6767
Jacksonville (G-6353)
Florida Probe Corporation ... G ... 352 372-1142
Gainesville (G-4922)
Glenroe Technologies Inc ... F ... 941 554-5262
Sarasota (G-16220)
Hec America Inc ... G ... 786 543-9238
Miami (G-9695)
Inman Orthodontic Labs Inc ... F ... 954 340-8477
Coral Springs (G-2260)
Intralock International Inc ... G ... 561 447-8282
Boca Raton (G-572)
▲ Kottler Research Corp ... G ... 850 776-7021
Milton (G-10934)
L A R Manufacturing LLC ... G ... 727 846-7860
Port Richey (G-15059)
Med Dental Equipment (import) ... G ... 786 417-8486
Miami (G-9963)
Omnia Incorporated ... E ... 863 619-8100
Lakeland (G-7759)
Orion Dntl Sls Trning Repr LLC ... G ... 888 674-6657
Kissimmee (G-7280)
Regent Labs Inc ... G ... 954 426-4889
Deerfield Beach (G-2902)
Regent Labs Inc ... G ... 954 426-4889
Deerfield Beach (G-2903)
▲ SDS Dental Inc ... E ... 954 730-3636
Pompano Beach (G-14843)
Showerfloss Inc ... G ... 239 947-2855
Estero (G-3696)
Simplified Systems Inc ... F ... 305 672-7676
Miami Beach (G-10710)
◆ Sunoptic Technologies LLC ... D ... 877 677-2832
Jacksonville (G-6822)
▲ Sunshine Health Products Inc ... F ... 954 493-5469
Fort Lauderdale (G-4267)
Valley Surgical Inc ... G ... 954 768-9886
Fort Lauderdale (G-4302)

Vet Sonic Inc ....G 305 681-4486
Hialeah (G-5677)
Wayne Metal Products Inc ....G 407 321-7168
Sanford (G-16136)
White Square Chemical Inc ....F 302 212-4555
Tavernier (G-18364)

3844 X-ray Apparatus & Tubes

Atlantic Mobile Imaging Svcs ....G 386 239-8271
Ormond Beach (G-13350)
L and C Science and Tech Inc ....G 305 200-3531
Hialeah (G-5477)
◆ **Lead Enterprises Inc** ....F 305 635-8644
Miami (G-9876)
Omega Medical Imaging LLC ....E 407 323-9400
Sanford (G-16093)
Orlando Flores ....G 305 898-2111
Miami (G-10120)
Osko Inc ....F 305 599-7161
Medley (G-8699)
Power Wthin Cnsling Cnsltn LLC ....G 863 242-3023
Haines City (G-5145)
▲ **Ziehm Imaging Inc** ....E 407 615-8560
Orlando (G-13342)

3845 Electromedical & Electrotherapeutic Apparatus

▲ **3M Resident Monitoring Inc** ....E 813 749-5453
Odessa (G-12096)
Actigraph LLC ....G 850 332-7900
Pensacola (G-14079)
Actigraph LLC ....F 850 332-7900
Pensacola (G-14080)
Airehealth Inc ....F 407 280-4107
Winter Springs (G-19467)
Anti-Ging Asthtic Lser Ctr Inc ....G 786 539-4901
Miami Beach (G-10642)
▲ **Axogen Inc** ....C 386 462-6800
Alachua (G-6)
Bio-Logic Systems Corp ....D 847 949-0456
Orlando (G-12515)
Biofuse Medical Tech Inc ....G 877 466-2434
Melbourne (G-8780)
Channel Investments LLC ....G 727 599-1360
Tampa (G-17531)
Compliance Meds Tech LLC ....G 786 319-9826
Miami (G-9389)
◆ **Conmed Corporation** ....A 727 392-6464
Largo (G-7927)
◆ **Critical Disposables Inc** ....E 407 330-1154
Sanford (G-16028)
Curallux LLC ....E 786 888-1875
Doral (G-3316)
Endo-Gear LLC ....F 305 710-6662
Miami (G-9526)
▲ **Erchonia Corporation LLC** ....E 321 473-1251
Melbourne (G-8827)
Estetika Skin & Laser Spe ....F 262 646-9222
Sarasota (G-16422)
Evren Technologies Inc ....G 352 494-0950
Newberry (G-11555)
Geddis Inc ....F 800 844-6792
Dunedin (G-3579)
H Q Inc ....F 941 721-7588
Palmetto (G-13804)
Harbor Imaging ....E 941 883-8383
Port Charlotte (G-14985)
Home Healthcare 2000 Inc ....G 954 977-4450
Pompano Beach (G-14726)
Imaging Initiatives Inc ....G 239 936-3646
Fort Myers (G-4488)
Infopia USA LLC ....F 321 225-3620
Cocoa (G-2031)
Innovatia Medical Systems LLC ....G 908 385-2802
Tampa (G-17784)
Insightec Inc ....G 786 534-3849
Miami (G-9750)
Invivo Corporation ....E 352 336-0010
Gainesville (G-4946)
◆ **Iris International Inc** ....D 818 709-1244
Miami (G-9770)
K-O Concepts Inc ....G 407 296-7788
Titusville (G-18437)
L&R Imaging ....G 678 691-3204
Pompano Beach (G-14741)
Lasersight Incorporated ....F 407 678-9900
Orlando (G-12893)
Lasersight Technologies Inc ....G 407 678-9900
Orlando (G-12894)
▲ **Lexington International LLC** ....E 800 973-4769
Boca Raton (G-600)
Medicomp Inc ....C 321 676-0010
Melbourne (G-8886)
Meditek-Icot Inc ....F 813 909-7476
Lutz (G-8398)
Megin Us LLC ....G 954 341-2965
Coral Springs (G-2279)
▲ **Micro Audiometrics Corporation** ....G 828 644-0771
Daytona Beach (G-2684)
Motus GI Holdings Inc ....E 954 541-8000
Fort Lauderdale (G-4126)
Mri Depot Inc ....G 407 696-9822
Longwood (G-8314)
Mri Specialists ....G 561 369-2144
Boynton Beach (G-934)
Natus Medical Incorporated ....E 321 235-8213
Orlando (G-12994)
Natus Medical Incorporated ....F 847 949-5200
Orlando (G-12995)
Nova Laserlight LLC ....F 407 226-0609
Orlando (G-13010)
Nuline Sensors LLC ....G 407 473-0765
Sanford (G-16092)
Orthosensor Inc ....D 954 577-7770
Dania Beach (G-2471)
Pcm and S L Plota Co LLC ....F 727 547-6277
Largo (G-8024)
Pristine Laser Center ....G 407 389-1200
Altamonte Springs (G-66)
Renal Advantage Inc A44 ....G 772 807-7229
Port Saint Lucie (G-15136)
Respitrend Inc ....G 407 529-5888
Gainesville (G-4990)
◆ **Sequa Corporation** ....A 561 935-3571
Palm Beach Gardens (G-13626)
Shenk Enterprises LLC ....F 386 753-1959
Orange City (G-12378)
Silver Bay LLC ....F 941 306-5812
Sarasota (G-16296)
Somatics LLC ....G 847 234-6761
Venice (G-18574)
Stimwave LLC ....F 800 965-5134
Pompano Beach (G-14871)
Stimwave Technologies Inc ....G 800 965-5134
Pompano Beach (G-14872)
Supersonic Imagine Inc ....G 954 660-3528
Weston (G-19168)
Syneron ....G 407 489-3366
Orlando (G-13236)
Touchpoint Medical Inc ....B 813 854-1905
Odessa (G-12159)
Tri-Tech Electronics Inc ....D 407 277-2131
Orlando (G-13270)
Twinstar Optics & Coatings Inc ....F 727 847-2300
Port Richey (G-15073)
▲ **US Defib Medical Tech LLC** ....G 305 887-7552
Medley (G-8751)
Vertec Inc ....F 850 478-6480
Pensacola (G-14283)
Vevyan Hanania Inc ....G 800 297-8485
Jacksonville (G-6896)
Zassi Holdings Inc ....G 904 432-8315
Ponte Vedra Beach (G-14958)

3851 Ophthalmic Goods

▲ **Achievia Direct Inc** ....F 386 615-8708
Daytona Beach (G-2620)
Bajio Inc ....G 630 461-0915
New Smyrna Beach (G-11527)
Bausch Lomb Surgical Inc ....F 727 724-6600
Clearwater (G-1602)
Best Price Digital Lenses Inc ....G 850 361-4401
Pensacola (G-14099)
Bicentrics Inc ....F 813 649-0225
Ruskin (G-15482)
CL Boca Raton LLC ....G 561 660-9485
Boca Raton (G-481)
CL Dadeland LLC ....G 305 712-6825
Miami (G-9361)
CL Gardens LLC ....G 561 567-0504
Palm Beach Gardens (G-13579)
CL Waterside Naples LLC ....F 239 734-8534
Naples (G-11209)
◆ **Costa Inc** ....A 386 274-4000
Daytona Beach (G-2646)
Danker Laboratories Inc ....F 941 758-7711
Sarasota (G-16203)
East Ormond Beach Crossfit ....G 386 673-3011
Ormond Beach (G-13366)
▲ **Electro-Optix Inc** ....F 954 973-2800
Pompano Beach (G-14677)
Express Vision Care Inc ....F 786 587-7404
Hialeah (G-5401)
Eyedeal Vision Care Inc ....G 321 631-2811
Melbourne (G-8830)
For Eyes Optcal Ccnut Grove In ....C 305 557-9004
Miramar (G-10993)
Gerber Coburn Optical Inc ....E 305 592-4705
Miami (G-9630)
Hoya Largo ....F 727 531-8964
Largo (G-7976)
Icare Industries Inc ....C 727 512-3000
Saint Petersburg (G-15811)
▲ **Inspecs USA LC** ....F 727 771-7710
Palm Harbor (G-13740)
Institutional Eye Care LLC ....F 866 604-2931
Bonita Springs (G-839)
Invicta Corporation ....G 561 995-9980
Boca Raton (G-573)
◆ **Johnson Jhnson Vision Care Inc** ....A 904 443-1000
Jacksonville (G-6526)
M12 Lenses Inc ....G 407 973-4403
Altamonte Springs (G-54)
Miraflex Corporation ....G 786 380-4494
Doral (G-3439)
Ocean Waves Inc ....F 904 372-4743
Jacksonville Beach (G-6953)
Ottica Dante Americas LLC ....G 561 322-0186
Boca Raton (G-658)
Pasco Vision Center ....G 813 788-7656
Zephyrhills (G-19530)
Pixeloptics Inc ....G 954 376-1542
Fort Lauderdale (G-4170)
Premium Dynamic Lens ....F 813 891-9912
Oldsmar (G-12261)
▲ **Solidar Express Coatings LLC** ....G 727 585-2192
Largo (G-8058)
Sunglass Heaven ....G 305 302-7285
Oakland Park (G-11845)
Tan Group USA LLC ....G 954 600-8697
Miami (G-10459)
Techtran Lenses Inc ....G 561 623-5490
Jupiter (G-7125)
Top Optical Lab ....F 305 662-2893
Miami (G-10492)
▲ **Transitions Optical Inc** ....B 727 545-0400
Pinellas Park (G-14392)
Unilens Corp USA ....E 727 544-2531
Clearwater (G-1928)
Universal Cntact Lenses of Fla ....G 904 731-3410
Jacksonville (G-6885)
Veriteq Acquisition Corp ....G 561 805-8007
Delray Beach (G-3157)
Vision Benefits 4 All Inc ....G 888 317-0606
Saint Johns (G-15685)
Vision Source Inc ....G 407 435-9958
Apopka (G-196)

3861 Photographic Eqpt & Splys

Ad Valorem Corporation ....G 561 488-9966
Boca Raton (G-397)
Aigean Networks ....G 754 223-2240
Oakland Park (G-11774)
▲ **Ar2 Products LLC** ....G 800 667-1263
Saint Johns (G-15673)
▼ **AVI-Spl Emplyee Emrgncy Rlief** ....A 813 884-7168
Tampa (G-17445)
▼ **AVI-Spl Holdings Inc** ....A 866 708-5034
Tampa (G-17446)
▼ **AVI-Spl LLC** ....A 813 884-7168
Tampa (G-17447)
Bdt Concepts Inc ....G 904 730-2590
Jacksonville (G-6199)
◆ **Chez Industries LLC** ....F 386 698-4414
Crescent City (G-2339)
Cinevise Inc ....G 305 232-8182
Miami (G-9354)
Cinidyne Sales Inc ....G 941 473-3914
Englewood (G-3673)
Columbia Films Inc ....G 800 531-3238
Pompano Beach (G-14641)
Dale Photo and Digital Inc ....G 954 925-0103
Hollywood (G-5808)
Desysca Inc ....G 407 724-4148
Orlando (G-12666)
Discount Distributors Inc ....G 772 336-0092
Port Saint Lucie (G-15102)
Drs Laurel Technologies ....E 727 541-6681
Largo (G-7936)

Eastman Kodak Company....D....813 908-7910
Tampa *(G-17627)*
Eyeson Dgtal Srvllnce MGT Syst....G....305 808-3344
Miami *(G-9551)*
Florida Copier Connections....G....407 844-9690
Orlando *(G-12748)*
General Screen Service Co....G....305 226-0741
Miami *(G-9626)*
◆ **Globaltek Office Supply Inc**....G....305 477-2988
Doral *(G-3370)*
Harris Aerial LLC....F....407 725-7886
Casselberry *(G-1505)*
▼ **ID Print Inc**....G....954 923-8374
Plantation *(G-14524)*
Imperx Inc....E....561 989-0006
Boca Raton *(G-563)*
Incity Security Inc....F....561 306-9228
West Palm Beach *(G-18902)*
Ink & Toner Plus....G....813 783-1650
Dade City *(G-2429)*
Innovate Audio Visual Inc....G....561 249-1117
Wellington *(G-18720)*
Larmac Development Corp....G....904 264-5006
Orange Park *(G-12397)*
Lester A Dine Inc....G....561 624-3009
Palm Beach Gardens *(G-13603)*
Light Source Business Systems....F....772 562-5046
Port Saint Lucie *(G-15120)*
▼ **Lip Trading Co**....G....954 987-0306
Hollywood *(G-5861)*
Mac Gregor Smith Blueprinters....F....407 423-5944
Orlando *(G-12943)*
Matsu Imaging LLC....F....305 503-2906
Miami *(G-9957)*
Moog Inc....F....321 435-8722
West Melbourne *(G-18777)*
▲ **Photoengraving Inc**....E....813 253-3427
Tampa *(G-17992)*
Planet Inhouse Inc....F....321 216-2189
Melbourne *(G-8909)*
▲ **Premier Plastics LLC**....E....305 805-3333
Boynton Beach *(G-943)*
Toner City Corp....G....954 945-5392
Davie *(G-2606)*
Toners Plus LLC....G....407 756-5787
Orlando *(G-13261)*
▼ **Tonertype Inc**....E....813 915-1300
Tampa *(G-18194)*
Trap World LLC....D....305 517-5676
Miami *(G-10504)*
Uribemonica....G....305 856-3857
Miami *(G-10550)*
◆ **Vutec Corporation**....C....954 545-9000
Coral Springs *(G-2330)*
Westech Development Group Inc....G....954 505-5090
Pompano Beach *(G-14912)*
Xerox Business Services LLC....G....407 926-4228
Orlando *(G-13332)*
▲ **Zd Realty LLC**....F....866 672-1212
Saint Petersburg *(G-15970)*

3873 Watch & Clock Devices & Parts

Inbigvmyshopify LLC....F....844 689-9033
Miami *(G-9736)*
Larry Cubi....G....352 445-7435
Ocala *(G-11980)*
▲ **LP Watch Group Inc**....E....954 985-3827
Hollywood *(G-5863)*
▲ **Lucien Piccard/Arnex Watch Co**....D....954 241-2745
Hollywood *(G-5865)*
Montres Corum Usa LLC....E....954 279-1220
Sunrise *(G-17148)*
◆ **Pstein Inc**....E....305 373-0037
Pembroke Park *(G-14010)*
▲ **Russell Hobbs Inc**....D....954 883-1000
Miramar *(G-11037)*
▲ **Technomarine Usa Inc**....F....305 438-0880
Miami *(G-10464)*
◆ **TWN Industries Inc**....G....305 246-5717
Princeton *(G-15187)*
Westime....G....310 205-5555
Miami *(G-10598)*

39 MISCELLANEOUS MANUFACTURING INDUSTRIES

3911 Jewelry: Precious Metal

Accar Ltd Inc....G....305 375-0620
Miami *(G-9059)*
Amber Jewelers Corp....G....305 373-8089
Miami *(G-9135)*
American Diamond Distributors....G....954 485-7808
Fort Lauderdale *(G-3812)*
Arriaga Originals....F....850 231-0084
Panama City *(G-13966)*
Arty-Sun LLC....G....561 705-2222
Boca Raton *(G-431)*
Bashert Diamonds Inc....G....305 466-1881
Aventura *(G-263)*
Bullion International Inc....C....321 773-2727
Indian Harbour Beach *(G-6063)*
Burn By Rocky Patel....G....239 653-9013
Naples *(G-11197)*
Buvin Jewelry of Florida Inc....F....305 358-0170
Miami *(G-9290)*
Classique Style Inc....F....561 995-7557
Boca Raton *(G-483)*
Corporacion Internacional De J....G....772 343-1721
Port Saint Lucie *(G-15101)*
▲ **D Turin & Company Inc**....E....305 825-2004
Hialeah *(G-5361)*
Dolphine Jewelry Contracting....G....561 488-0355
Boca Raton *(G-506)*
Evan Lloyd Designs....G....772 286-7723
Stuart *(G-16939)*
Finger Mate Inc....E....954 458-2700
Hallandale Beach *(G-5184)*
Garvinos LLC....G....352 430-1435
The Villages *(G-18390)*
Gems Jewelry & Uniques....G....850 456-8105
Pensacola *(G-14162)*
▲ **Gnj Manufacturing Inc**....E....305 651-8644
West Park *(G-19093)*
Gold Karats Jewelry LLC....G....561 401-5935
Pompano Beach *(G-14716)*
Golden Century Inc....G....954 933-2911
Margate *(G-8546)*
Green Bullion Fincl Svcs LLC....G....954 960-7000
Hollywood *(G-5830)*
◆ **Hidalgo Corp**....G....305 379-0110
Miami *(G-9708)*
Jld Manufacturing Corp....G....877 358-5462
Sunrise *(G-17137)*
Jon Paul Inc....G....954 564-4221
Fort Lauderdale *(G-4080)*
Larter & Sons....D....732 290-1515
Jupiter *(G-7066)*
▲ **Lau International Inc**....G....305 381-9855
Miami *(G-9871)*
▼ **Marios Casting Jewelry Inc**....G....305 374-2894
Miami *(G-9950)*
▼ **Mayers Jwly Co Hollywood Inc**....D....954 921-1422
Hollywood *(G-5872)*
▲ **Merit Diamond Corporation**....E....954 883-3660
Hollywood *(G-5874)*
▲ **Metal Rock Inc**....F....407 886-6440
Apopka *(G-160)*
Moba Corp....F....305 868-3700
Bal Harbour *(G-303)*
▲ **Montesino International Corp**....G....954 767-6185
Fort Lauderdale *(G-4124)*
National Custom Insignia....G....813 781-8806
Palm Harbor *(G-13747)*
Neptune Designs Inc....G....305 294-8131
Key West *(G-7199)*
OCon Enterprise Inc....D....954 920-6700
Hollywood *(G-5885)*
Orlando Novelty LLC....G....407 858-9499
Orlando *(G-13035)*
Phoenix Jewelry Mfg Inc....F....305 477-2515
Doral *(G-3461)*
Pin Makers....G....877 825-6120
Winter Park *(G-19430)*
Reyes Jewelers Corp....G....305 431-8303
Miami *(G-10260)*
Richline Group Inc....B....954 718-3200
Tamarac *(G-17366)*
Rock My World Inc....G....727 623-4646
Redington Shores *(G-15260)*
Roma Casting Inc....G....305 577-0289
Miami *(G-10277)*
Royal Splits Inc....G....310 935-6699
Orlando *(G-13148)*
Sal Praschnik Inc....F....305 866-4323
Bay Harbor Islands *(G-339)*
Santonis Jewelry Inc....G....407 298-4994
Kissimmee *(G-7295)*
Smokersvaporcom Incorporated....G....727 258-4942
Largo *(G-8056)*
Stone Set Technologies LLC....G....954 565-4979
Wellington *(G-18737)*
Suncoast Accrdted Gmlgical Lab....G....941 756-8787
Bradenton *(G-1121)*
▼ **Sunshine Lighters**....G....386 322-1300
Port Orange *(G-15038)*
Too Many Ideas Inc....G....904 396-9245
Jacksonville *(G-6862)*
Westchester Gold Fabricators....G....941 625-0666
Port Charlotte *(G-15007)*
Williams Jewelry and Mfg Co....G....727 823-7676
Saint Petersburg *(G-15961)*

3914 Silverware, Plated & Stainless Steel Ware

▲ **A J Trophies & Awards Inc**....E....850 878-7187
Tallahassee *(G-17210)*
Accent Jewelry Inc....F....941 391-6687
Punta Gorda *(G-15189)*
American Trophy Co....G....954 782-2250
Pompano Beach *(G-14594)*
Bastinelli Creations LLC....F....407 572-8073
Kissimmee *(G-7221)*
M D R International Inc....F....305 944-5335
North Miami *(G-11644)*
▲ **Metal Rock Inc**....F....407 886-6440
Apopka *(G-160)*
▼ **Michelsons Trophies Inc**....G....305 687-9898
Miami *(G-10017)*
Parrillo Inc....G....386 767-8011
South Daytona *(G-16806)*
▲ **Roden International Inc**....F....954 929-1900
Hollywood *(G-5902)*
▲ **United Trophy Manufacturing**....E....407 841-2525
Orlando *(G-13294)*

3915 Jewelers Findings & Lapidary Work

Adamas Instrument Corporation....F....727 540-0033
Clearwater *(G-1564)*
Bach Diamonds....G....954 921-4069
Hollywood *(G-5782)*
Bashert Diamonds Inc....G....305 466-1881
Aventura *(G-263)*
Finger Mate Inc....E....954 458-2700
Hallandale Beach *(G-5184)*
▲ **Giraldo & Donalisio Corp**....G....239 567-2206
Cape Coral *(G-1429)*
▲ **Jewelnet Corp**....G....561 989-8383
Delray Beach *(G-3095)*
Jewelswebscom....G....954 993-7744
Fort Lauderdale *(G-4079)*
L and I Diamonds....G....305 603-7727
Miami *(G-9836)*
▼ **Marios Casting Jewelry Inc**....G....305 374-2894
Miami *(G-9950)*
Modern Settings LLC....G....800 645-5585
Sarasota *(G-16512)*
National Custom Insignia Inc....F....813 313-2561
Tampa *(G-17929)*
Our Warehouse Inc....G....954 786-1234
Pompano Beach *(G-14782)*
Roma Casting Inc....G....305 577-0289
Miami *(G-10277)*
Suncoast Accrdted Gmlgical Lab....G....941 756-8787
Bradenton *(G-1121)*
Vee Enterprises Inc....G....954 960-0300
Pompano Beach *(G-14908)*
Wilkins Lapidary Arts....E....386 734-8470
Deland *(G-3034)*

3931 Musical Instruments

A JS Pro Percussion Center....G....813 361-4939
Tampa *(G-17375)*
◆ **Belsnickel Enterprises Inc**....F....386 256-5367
South Daytona *(G-16798)*
Dok Solution Inc....F....727 209-1313
Largo *(G-7935)*
▼ **Englert Arts Inc**....G....561 241-9924
Boca Raton *(G-518)*
Flexshopper LLC....E....561 922-6609
Boca Raton *(G-530)*
▲ **Gatchell Violins Company Inc**....F....321 733-1499
West Melbourne *(G-18774)*
Gladium LLC....G....305 989-2720
Cutler Bay *(G-2394)*
Isla Instruments LLC....F....561 603-4685
West Palm Beach *(G-18908)*
Jatiga Inc....G....727 793-0079
Clearwater *(G-1742)*

SIC

▼ **Lan Music Corp**...G... 305 722-5842
Miami *(G-9855)*
Lewis-Riggs Custom Guitars Inc...G... 407 538-3710
Orlando *(G-12905)*
Marimba Cocina Mexicana II Inc...G... 321 268-6960
Titusville *(G-18446)*
MINd&melody Inc...G... 305 582-1006
Miami *(G-10025)*
Mode Marimba Inc...G... 561 512-5001
Jupiter *(G-7077)*
◆ **Sabine Inc**...D... 386 418-2000
Alachua *(G-17)*
▲ **Super Sensitive String Sls Co**...E... 941 371-0016
Sarasota *(G-16612)*
Variance Reynolds Mtc...G... 954 765-6320
Lauderhill *(G-8123)*

3942 Dolls & Stuffed Toys

American Girl Brands LLC...F... 407 852-9771
Orlando *(G-12469)*
Baby Abuelita Productions LLC...G... 305 662-7320
Miami *(G-9212)*
▲ **Basic Fun Inc**...D... 561 997-8901
Boca Raton *(G-442)*
▲ **Doll Maker LLC**...G... 800 851-5183
Naples *(G-11230)*
◆ **JC Toys Group Inc**...F... 305 592-3541
Doral *(G-3401)*
Mascot Factory Inc...G... 877 250-2244
Orlando *(G-12952)*
Timeless Treasures Doll Club...E... 813 854-6208
Tampa *(G-18187)*

3944 Games, Toys & Children's Vehicles

Atlantic Models Inc...F... 305 883-2012
Medley *(G-8617)*
Autism Puzzle ME Inc...G... 386 314-4310
Edgewater *(G-3611)*
▲ **Basic Fun Inc**...D... 561 997-8901
Boca Raton *(G-442)*
◆ **Benchmark Entertainment LC**...E... 561 588-5200
Lake Worth Beach *(G-7606)*
Benchmark Games Intl LLC...D... 561 588-5200
Lake Worth Beach *(G-7607)*
Blingka Inc...G... 800 485-6793
Tampa *(G-17475)*
▲ **Bob Violett Models Inc**...E... 407 327-6333
Winter Springs *(G-19469)*
▲ **Brandine Woodcraft Inc**...G... 561 266-9360
Delray Beach *(G-3051)*
Check Assist...G... 850 857-7752
Pensacola *(G-14113)*
Classic Poker Chips...G... 207 332-9999
Saint Augustine *(G-15530)*
Correll Services Inc...G... 561 358-6952
Royal Palm Beach *(G-15463)*
Daytona Magic Inc...G... 386 252-6767
Daytona Beach *(G-2655)*
Dennys Electronics Inc...E... 941 485-5400
North Venice *(G-11756)*
◆ **Ev Rider LLC**...G... 239 278-5054
Fort Myers *(G-4447)*
▲ **Florida Pool Products Inc**...E... 727 531-8913
Clearwater *(G-1690)*
◆ **Galaxy America Inc**...F... 941 697-0324
Port Charlotte *(G-14983)*
▲ **George & Company LLC**...F... 239 949-3650
Bonita Springs *(G-833)*
Getfpv LLC...E... 941 444-0021
Sarasota *(G-16449)*
◆ **Groovy Toys LLC**...G... 772 878-0790
Port Saint Lucie *(G-15111)*
GT Scale Models Inc...G... 305 310-8998
Key Biscayne *(G-7158)*
◆ **Hasbro Latin America Inc**...E... 305 931-3180
Miami *(G-9688)*
Herbko Inc...G... 305 932-3572
Aventura *(G-273)*
Iq Dominoes Corp...G... 305 967-8583
Miami *(G-9769)*
▲ **Jazwares LLC**...D... 954 845-0800
Sunrise *(G-17135)*
◆ **JC Toys Group Inc**...F... 305 592-3541
Doral *(G-3401)*
Kgb Kiteboarding Inc...F... 904 705-9235
Jacksonville *(G-6536)*
Kite Bum Inc...G... 321 267-6393
Titusville *(G-18439)*
Kite Runner LLC...G... 305 785-5056
Miami *(G-9824)*
Kite Technology Group LLC...F... 407 557-0512
Kissimmee *(G-7266)*
Kite Vn Corporation...G... 772 234-3484
Vero Beach *(G-18636)*
◆ **KNex Industries Inc**...C... 215 997-7722
Boca Raton *(G-589)*
◆ **KNex Ltd Partnership Group**...D... 215 997-7722
Boca Raton *(G-590)*
Law Offces Rbecca A Beddow LLC...G... 516 671-6566
Naples *(G-11308)*
Leisure Activities Usa LLC...G... 727 417-7128
Saint Petersburg *(G-15838)*
Lumberstak Inc...G... 386 546-3745
Palatka *(G-13486)*
Lumenier Holdco LLC...G... 941 444-0021
Sarasota *(G-16491)*
Majic Wheels Corp...G... 239 313-5672
Fort Myers *(G-4521)*
Maritime Replicas Usa LLC...E... 305 921-9690
Boca Raton *(G-607)*
Master Mold Corp...G... 941 486-0000
North Venice *(G-11760)*
Misfit Gaming...D... 954 347-0906
Boca Raton *(G-626)*
Never Wrong Toys & Games LLC...G... 941 371-0909
Sarasota *(G-16524)*
▲ **Nikiani Inc**...G... 305 606-1104
West Palm Beach *(G-18965)*
Pcp Group LLC...G... 727 388-7171
Clearwater *(G-1827)*
Performance Aircraft Unlimited...G... 808 782-7171
Orlando *(G-13064)*
▲ **Prime Pedal Karts LLC**...F... 850 475-0450
Pensacola *(G-14239)*
Puzzle Pieces Support Servic...G... 813 985-3232
Tampa *(G-18027)*
Puzzleme Now Inc...G... 386 957-4987
Edgewater *(G-3634)*
Rdd International Inc...G... 954 422-9909
Boca Raton *(G-682)*
◆ **Safari Programs Inc**...D... 305 621-1000
Jacksonville *(G-6745)*
Scale Models Arts & Tech...F... 305 949-1706
North Miami Beach *(G-11704)*
Schick LLC...F... 718 810-3804
Miami *(G-10311)*
▲ **Schoenhut LLC**...G... 904 810-1945
Saint Augustine *(G-15605)*
▲ **System Enterprises LLC**...G... 888 898-3600
Clearwater *(G-1899)*
Table Golf Llc...G... 813 435-6111
Brandon *(G-1182)*
▲ **Triops Inc**...G... 850 479-4415
Pensacola *(G-14276)*
◆ **Victory Tailgate LLC**...C... 407 704-8775
Orlando *(G-13303)*

3949 Sporting & Athletic Goods, NEC

▲ **3n2 LLC**...G... 407 862-3622
Maitland *(G-8455)*
50 Hwy 17 S Inc...G... 904 225-1077
Yulee *(G-19492)*
◆ **A Plus Marine Supply Inc**...G... 850 934-3890
Gulf Breeze *(G-5110)*
All Golf...G... 954 441-1333
Pembroke Pines *(G-14019)*
All Safe of Big Pine Key...G... 305 872-7233
Key West *(G-7176)*
All Tennis LLC...G... 561 842-0070
Lake Park *(G-7465)*
◆ **Allen Shuffleboard LLC**...G... 727 399-8877
Seminole *(G-16737)*
Alpha Sun & Sport - As & S LLC...G... 954 782-2300
Boca Raton *(G-414)*
Alternative Vision LLC...G... 904 642-3566
Jacksonville *(G-6141)*
▼ **American Quality Mfg Inc**...F... 321 636-3434
Cocoa *(G-1995)*
Anzio Ironworks Corp...G... 727 895-2019
Clearwater *(G-1585)*
Armalaser Inc...G... 800 680-5020
Gainesville *(G-4876)*
Arno Belo Inc...G... 800 734-2356
Hallandale Beach *(G-5170)*
Asb Sports Group LLC...F... 305 775-4689
Miami *(G-9176)*
Atg Specialty Products Corp...G... 888 455-5499
Doral *(G-3259)*
Aussie Boomerang Bar On Ave In...F... 561 436-9741
Lake Worth *(G-7535)*
▼ **B & D Precision Tools Inc**...E... 305 885-1583
Hialeah *(G-5314)*
▲ **Baby Guard Inc**...F... 954 741-6351
Coral Springs *(G-2222)*
Back Country Inc...G... 772 532-6174
Vero Beach *(G-18598)*
▼ **Bag-A-Nut LLC**...G... 904 641-3934
Jacksonville *(G-6191)*
Bard Sports Corp...G... 305 233-2200
Miami *(G-9220)*
Billabong Destin...G... 850 424-3553
Miramar Beach *(G-11063)*
Biomech Golf Equipment LLC...F... 401 932-0479
Naples *(G-11189)*
Biscayne Tennis LLC...G... 786 231-8372
Miami *(G-9252)*
Black Bart International LLC...G... 561 842-4045
Riviera Beach *(G-15301)*
Blue Gardenia LLC...G... 727 560-0040
Saint Petersburg *(G-15723)*
▼ **Blue Hawaiian Products Inc**...E... 727 535-5677
Largo *(G-7910)*
▲ **Boone Bait Co Inc**...F... 407 975-8775
Winter Park *(G-19384)*
Boris Skateboards Mfg Inc...G... 305 519-3544
Miami *(G-9269)*
Bote LLC...F... 888 855-4450
Miramar Beach *(G-11064)*
Bote Boards...G... 850 855-4046
Fort Walton Beach *(G-4784)*
Bote Paddle Boards...G... 850 460-2250
Destin *(G-3184)*
BRC Sports Llc...F... 904 388-8126
Jacksonville *(G-6233)*
▲ **Brownies Marine Group Inc**...G... 954 462-5570
Pompano Beach *(G-14624)*
Burn Proof Gear LLC...G... 786 634-7406
Miami *(G-9286)*
◆ **C & H Baseball Inc**...G... 941 727-1533
Bradenton *(G-1006)*
Carolina Clubs Inc...G... 561 753-6948
West Palm Beach *(G-18835)*
▲ **Caseworks International Inc**...F... 954 933-9102
Fort Lauderdale *(G-3884)*
Cayago Americas Inc...F... 754 216-4600
Fort Lauderdale *(G-3885)*
Chandler Bats...G... 484 674-7175
Boca Raton *(G-478)*
Cheezeballs LLC...G... 904 716-3709
Jacksonville *(G-6262)*
Cheval Country Club...G... 813 279-5122
Dunedin *(G-3573)*
Cind-Al Inc...G... 863 401-8700
Clermont *(G-1952)*
▲ **Classic Fishing Products Inc**...E... 407 656-6133
Clermont *(G-1953)*
▲ **Clawson Custom Cues Inc**...E... 904 448-8748
Jacksonville *(G-6266)*
Contagious Fishing Charters...G... 727 595-6277
Largo *(G-7928)*
Covert Armor LLC...F... 561 459-8077
West Palm Beach *(G-18851)*
Crowder Custom Rods Inc...G... 772 220-8108
Stuart *(G-16928)*
Custom Carts of Sarasota LLC...E... 941 953-4445
Bradenton *(G-1025)*
▲ **D G Morrison Inc**...F... 813 865-0208
Odessa *(G-12114)*
Deers Holdings Inc...G... 805 323-6899
Bay Harbor Islands *(G-338)*
Diadem Sports LLC...G... 844 434-2336
Pompano Beach *(G-14665)*
Dreams Inc...G... 954 377-0002
Miramar *(G-10986)*
Durabody Usa LLC...G... 954 357-2333
Miramar *(G-10987)*
Eagle Athletica LLC...G... 305 209-7002
Miami *(G-9493)*
◆ **Easy Picker Golf Products Inc**...E... 239 368-6600
Lehigh Acres *(G-8190)*
Ecx Online Inc...G... 407 442-6834
Orlando *(G-12697)*
Evies Golf Center...G... 941 377-2399
Sarasota *(G-16423)*
Exclusive Bats LLC...G... 305 450-3858
Hialeah *(G-5400)*
Fiik Skateboards LLC...G... 561 405-9541
Fort Lauderdale *(G-3992)*
Fiik Skateboards LLC...F... 561 316-8234
Boca Raton *(G-528)*

First Tee Miami Daga F 305 633-4583
Miami *(G-9572)*
First Tee Sarasota/Manatee G 941 685-5072
Sarasota *(G-16213)*
Fishermans Center Inc G 561 844-5150
Riviera Beach *(G-15328)*
Florida Fishing Products G 239 938-4612
Tampa *(G-17676)*
Florida North Inc G 352 606-2408
Weeki Wachee *(G-18703)*
▼ **Florida Playground & Steel Co** G 813 247-2812
Tampa *(G-17684)*
▲ **Florida Pool Products Inc** E 727 531-8913
Clearwater *(G-1690)*
▼ **Florida Stucco Corp** E 561 487-1301
Boca Raton *(G-534)*
Foil Inc G 442 233-3645
Pensacola *(G-14156)*
▼ **G & K Aluminum Inc** F 772 283-1297
Stuart *(G-16943)*
◆ **Gar Industries Corp** F 954 456-8088
Hallandale Beach *(G-5188)*
▲ **Garbo Sport International Inc** G 305 599-8797
Miami *(G-9612)*
Georgia Usssa Baseball G 678 794-1630
Melbourne *(G-8836)*
◆ **Glaspro** E 941 488-4586
Venice *(G-18550)*
Golf Shaft Deals Inc G 321 591-7824
Indialantic *(G-6060)*
Gorilla Bats LLC G 813 285-9409
Riverview *(G-15271)*
Gypsy Mining Inc G 772 589-5547
Roseland *(G-15459)*
◆ **Halcyon Manufacturing Inc** E 386 454-0811
High Springs *(G-5701)*
▲ **Halo Fishing LLC** G 321 373-2055
Malabar *(G-8489)*
Headhunter Spearfishing Co G 954 745-0747
Fort Lauderdale *(G-4045)*
Highroller Fishing Lure Co LLC G 352 215-2925
Gainesville *(G-4936)*
Homerun Derby Bats Only LLC G 813 545-3887
Riverview *(G-15273)*
Hook Fish & Chkn - Mangonia Pk G 561 855-6385
Mangonia Park *(G-8501)*
◆ **Hyperform Inc** E 321 632-6503
Rockledge *(G-15421)*
Indoor Trampoline Arena Inc F 321 222-1300
Sanford *(G-16065)*
Inspired Surf Boards G 904 347-8879
Saint Augustine *(G-15556)*
Island Fever LLC G 941 639-6400
Punta Gorda *(G-15211)*
Jawil Enterprises Corps G 954 366-4212
Margate *(G-8552)*
▲ **Jay Squared LLC** F 386 677-7700
Daytona Beach *(G-2675)*
Jrh Sport Industries Inc G 904 940-3381
Saint Augustine *(G-15563)*
▼ **Just For Nets** F 813 871-1133
Tampa *(G-17812)*
Kent Manufacturing Venice Inc F 941 485-8871
Nokomis *(G-11584)*
Kj Collections G 904 285-7745
Ponte Vedra Beach *(G-14944)*
Knightmare Surfboards LLC G 321 720-4157
Malabar *(G-8492)*
L & S Bait Co Inc E 727 584-7691
Largo *(G-7997)*
La Bodeguita De Hialeah Inc G 305 240-7421
Hialeah *(G-5482)*
▲ **Laird International Corp** F 954 532-3794
Pompano Beach *(G-14742)*
Lake Area Watersports LLC G 352 475-3434
Melrose *(G-8986)*
◆ **Lamartek Inc** E 386 752-1087
Lake City *(G-7364)*
Larrys Rigs G 561 967-7791
West Palm Beach *(G-18927)*
◆ **Lead Enterprises Inc** F 305 635-8644
Miami *(G-9876)*
Lifetime Wellness Centers Inc F 321 693-8698
Melbourne *(G-8873)*
Liquid Ed Inc G 727 943-8616
Tarpon Springs *(G-18313)*
Liquid Force G 904 813-1490
Jacksonville *(G-6558)*
Ljs Tops & Bottoms E 561 736-7868
Boynton Beach *(G-929)*

◆ **Lucas 5135 Inc** E 800 835-7665
Jacksonville *(G-6566)*
Lure Course Brevard LLC G 321 412-7143
Malabar *(G-8495)*
M P Tennis Inc G 813 961-8844
Tampa *(G-17869)*
◆ **Macho Products Inc** E 800 327-6812
Sebastian *(G-16667)*
Magneto Sports LLC G 760 593-4589
Miami *(G-9933)*
Maitland Furniture Inc G 386 677-7711
Daytona Beach *(G-2682)*
Marconi Line Inc F 321 639-1130
Rockledge *(G-15434)*
▲ **Marine Metal Products Co** G 727 461-5575
Clearwater *(G-1773)*
Mayo Plastics Mfg Inc F 386 294-1049
Mayo *(G-8595)*
McG Surfboards G 904 305-8801
Atlantic Beach *(G-224)*
McSkis G 863 513-0422
Clermont *(G-1969)*
◆ **Medx Corporation** F 352 351-2005
Ocala *(G-11997)*
▼ **Mine Survival Inc** G 850 774-0025
Panama City Beach *(G-13980)*
Mirage Systems Inc F 386 740-9222
Deland *(G-2997)*
Mor Sports LLC G 239 671-5759
Cape Coral *(G-1449)*
Netting Professionals LLC G 904 432-8987
Fernandina Beach *(G-3745)*
◆ **New World Trade Inc** F 941 205-5873
Punta Gorda *(G-15218)*
Nighthawk Running LLC F 407 443-8404
Orlando *(G-13002)*
Nitro Leisure Products Inc E 414 272-5084
Stuart *(G-16981)*
◆ **O Mustad & Son USA Inc** E 206 284-7871
Doral *(G-3447)*
Onetown Boards G 786 704-5921
Miami *(G-10106)*
Pickle Pro LLC G 844 332-7069
Naples *(G-11365)*
Play Tampa Bay Inc G 727 803-6838
Saint Petersburg *(G-15882)*
Playcore Wisconsin Inc G 800 853-5316
Saint Augustine *(G-15589)*
▲ **Pocketec Inc** G 772 692-8020
Stuart *(G-16990)*
Pompanette LLC E 813 885-2182
Tampa *(G-17997)*
▼ **Precision Paddleboards** G 954 616-8046
Fort Lauderdale *(G-4173)*
Primetime Sports Agents Inc G 561 371-4421
West Palm Beach *(G-19007)*
Pro Duffers Orlando G 407 641-7626
Orlando *(G-13092)*
◆ **Pure Global Brands Inc** G 866 498-5269
West Palm Beach *(G-19011)*
Quail Height Golf Club F 386 752-3339
Lake City *(G-7378)*
Qwikpik Golf LLC G 407 505-5546
Orlando *(G-13106)*
▼ **R & D Surf** F 321 636-4456
Rockledge *(G-15442)*
Rat Trap Bait Company Inc F 863 967-2148
Auburndale *(G-251)*
Reef Runner Charters LLC G 941 921-0560
Sarasota *(G-16557)*
▲ **Renzetti Inc** F 321 267-7705
Titusville *(G-18456)*
▼ **Rigrap LLC** G 561 200-5958
Jupiter *(G-7104)*
◆ **Robertson Billiard Sups Inc** G 813 229-2778
Tampa *(G-18065)*
▼ **Rod Biscayne Manufacturing** G 305 884-0808
Hialeah *(G-5604)*
Ryman Hospitality Prpts Inc A 904 284-2770
Green Cove Springs *(G-5070)*
Salt Life LLC G 904 595-5370
Jacksonville Beach *(G-6957)*
Seasucker LLC E 941 586-2664
Bradenton *(G-1113)*
SGF Inc G 813 996-2528
Land O Lakes *(G-7866)*
Showcase Marble Inc F 386 253-6646
Daytona Beach *(G-2714)*
Signature Athletics Inc G 561 212-9284
Jupiter *(G-7115)*

Simons Hallandale Inc E 561 468-1174
Miami *(G-10351)*
Skateboard Supercross LLC G 786 529-8187
Surfside *(G-17207)*
Ski Rixen - Quiet Waters Inc G 954 429-0215
Deerfield Beach *(G-2913)*
Sogofishing LLC G 800 308-0259
Fort Lauderdale *(G-4241)*
Sonic Leak Locator G 954 340-8924
Coral Springs *(G-2314)*
Southern Recreation Inc F 904 387-4390
Jacksonville *(G-6796)*
Southern Tennis Supplies G 850 936-1772
Pensacola *(G-14265)*
Sport Products of Tampa Inc G 813 630-5552
Tampa *(G-18127)*
▲ **Sports Radar Ltd** G 352 503-6825
Homosassa *(G-6006)*
SSE and Associates Inc E 954 973-7144
Pompano Beach *(G-14867)*
Sterling Facility Services LLC G 772 871-2161
Port Saint Lucie *(G-15148)*
Stuart Industries Inc F 305 651-3474
Miami *(G-10425)*
Stuart Yacht Builders F 561 747-1947
Stuart *(G-17029)*
◆ **Sunrise Trampolines and Nets** G 727 526-9288
Pinellas Park *(G-14390)*
Swim Buoy G 305 953-4101
Opa Locka *(G-12363)*
T W A Sports Inc G 727 541-9831
Largo *(G-8065)*
Tampa Catamarans LLC G 813 966-4640
Apollo Beach *(G-106)*
Tavarez Sporting Goods Inc G 347 441-9690
Miami *(G-10461)*
Tendonease LLC G 888 224-0319
Palm City *(G-13675)*
Tess Enterprises Inc G 727 573-9701
Clearwater *(G-1917)*
Tibor Inc E 561 272-0770
Delray Beach *(G-3150)*
Top Spec US Inc G 904 345-0814
Jacksonville *(G-6864)*
Tri-Deck LLC G 386 748-3239
Deland *(G-3025)*
Tricounty Chemical Co G 407 682-3550
Apopka *(G-192)*
True East Surfboard Inc G 407 679-6896
Orlando *(G-13278)*
◆ **Undersea Breathing Systems** G 561 588-7698
Lake Worth *(G-7596)*
Uninsured Relative Workshop E 386 736-7589
Deland *(G-3028)*
▲ **United Strings Intl LLC** G 561 790-4191
West Palm Beach *(G-19075)*
Urban Extreme LLC F 954 248-9007
Hollywood *(G-5934)*
◆ **Vertical Reality Inc** G 305 238-4522
Palmetto Bay *(G-13856)*
◆ **Vertimax LLC** G 800 699-5867
Tampa *(G-18240)*
Visor Versa G 239 249-4745
Estero *(G-3698)*
Volvox Inc Hollywood G 954 961-4942
Hollywood *(G-5938)*
Waterboy Sports LLC G 407 869-9881
Winter Park *(G-19457)*
Wayloomoto LLC G 954 636-1510
Davie *(G-2612)*
▲ **Wemi Sports** G 305 446-5178
Coral Gables *(G-2206)*

3951 Pens & Mechanical Pencils

Bic Corporation A 727 536-7895
Clearwater *(G-1607)*
◆ **Dixon Ticonderoga Company** D 407 829-9000
Lake Mary *(G-7409)*
Ross Industries Inc D 954 752-2800
Pompano Beach *(G-14834)*
Scribe Manufacturing Inc B 727 524-7482
Clearwater *(G-1870)*
Scribe Manufacturing Inc F 727 536-7895
Saint Petersburg *(G-15907)*
Scribe Opco Inc D 727 536-7895
Clearwater *(G-1871)*
◆ **Sharp Marketing LLC** G 954 565-2711
Oakland Park *(G-11838)*
▼ **Trs Industries Inc** G 561 880-0031
Lake Worth *(G-7594)*

3952 Lead Pencils, Crayons & Artist's Mtrls

◆ **Art & Frame Direct Inc**......C....... 407 857-6000
Orlando *(G-12491)*
◆ **Art & Frame Source Inc**......E....... 727 329-6502
Saint Petersburg *(G-15711)*
Bic Corporation......A....... 727 536-7895
Clearwater *(G-1607)*
◆ **Dixon Ticonderoga Company**......D....... 407 829-9000
Lake Mary *(G-7409)*
M&M Studios Inc......G....... 561 744-2754
Jupiter *(G-7070)*
▲ **Sculpture House Inc**......F....... 609 466-2986
Fort Pierce *(G-4743)*
Standard Clay Mines......G....... 609 466-2986
Fort Pierce *(G-4751)*

3953 Marking Devices

Ace Marking Devices Corp......G....... 561 833-4073
West Palm Beach *(G-18786)*
▼ **Ace Printing Inc**......F....... 305 358-2572
Miami *(G-9061)*
Burr Printing Co Inc......G....... 863 294-3166
Winter Haven *(G-19308)*
▲ **Design Services Inc**......G....... 813 949-4748
Land O Lakes *(G-7852)*
Finlayson Enterprises Inc......G....... 850 785-7953
Panama City *(G-13902)*
Four G Enterprises Inc......E....... 407 834-4143
Longwood *(G-8284)*
GBIG Corporation......G....... 866 998-8466
Miami *(G-9617)*
Holmes Stamp Company......E....... 904 396-2291
Jacksonville *(G-6476)*
Identity Holding Company LLC......C....... 941 355-5171
Sarasota *(G-16233)*
◆ **Ipg (us) Holdings Inc**......D....... 941 727-5788
Sarasota *(G-16471)*
Ipg (us) Inc......G....... 941 727-5788
Sarasota *(G-16472)*
▲ **Mark Master Inc**......D....... 813 988-6000
Tampa *(G-17881)*
Nommo International LLC......G....... 866 366-3688
Orlando *(G-13006)*
One Price Drycleaners Tampa......F....... 727 734-3353
Dunedin *(G-3586)*
▼ **Say What Screen Prtg & EMB Inc**......G....... 941 745-5822
Bradenton *(G-1112)*
Sequoia Brands Inc......E....... 813 969-2000
Odessa *(G-12150)*
Southeast Marketing Concepts......G....... 561 747-7010
Jupiter *(G-7118)*
Sun Graphic Technologies Inc......E....... 941 753-7541
Sarasota *(G-16305)*
Universal Stncling Mkg Systems......E....... 727 894-3027
Saint Petersburg *(G-15948)*
Vanlex Clothing Inc......E....... 305 431-4669
Miami Lakes *(G-10878)*
Wholesale Screen Prtg of Nples......G....... 239 263-7061
Naples *(G-11455)*

3955 Carbon Paper & Inked Ribbons

Computer Forms & Supplies......G....... 727 535-0422
Largo *(G-7926)*
▲ **Eastern Ribbon & Roll Corp**......E....... 813 676-8600
Odessa *(G-12117)*
Golden Ribbon Corporation......F....... 727 545-4499
Largo *(G-7963)*
Micromicr Corporation......F....... 954 922-8044
Dania *(G-2452)*
▼ **Replenish Ink Inc**......G....... 818 206-2424
Miami *(G-10254)*
Ribbon Wholesale Corp......F....... 786 457-0555
Miami *(G-10262)*
Sun Print Management LLC......E....... 727 945-0255
Holiday *(G-5749)*
Suncoast Toner Cartridge Inc......F....... 727 945-0255
Holiday *(G-5750)*
Team Inkjet......G....... 954 554-3250
Coral Springs *(G-2320)*
Toner Cartridge Recharge Inc......G....... 305 968-1045
Miami Lakes *(G-10868)*
Toner Technologies Inc......G....... 561 547-9710
Boynton Beach *(G-970)*
◆ **Universal Ribbon Corporation**......E....... 305 471-0828
Miami *(G-10542)*
Well Made Bus Solutions LLC......G....... 754 227-7268
Coconut Creek *(G-2101)*

3961 Costume Jewelry & Novelties

Accent Jewelry Inc......F....... 941 391-6687
Punta Gorda *(G-15189)*
Aventura Jewelry & Coin......G....... 305 933-2646
Miami *(G-9196)*
Curly Girlz Creations......G....... 386 960-3536
Ocala *(G-11913)*
▲ **D Turin & Company Inc**......E....... 305 825-2004
Hialeah *(G-5361)*
Delray Pin Factory Intl......G....... 561 994-1680
Coral Springs *(G-2240)*
Eddys Jewelry......G....... 321 236-7887
Orlando *(G-12698)*
Emoji Bracelet LLC......G....... 954 987-0515
Fort Lauderdale *(G-3971)*
Galaxy Medals Inc......G....... 321 269-0840
Titusville *(G-18430)*
Inspire ME Bracelets......F....... 404 644-7771
Fort Lauderdale *(G-4061)*
◆ **International Jewelry Designs**......G....... 954 577-9099
Oakland Park *(G-11814)*
James A De Flippo Co......G....... 407 851-2765
Orlando *(G-12849)*
Magnetic Jewellry Inc......G....... 954 975-5868
Pompano Beach *(G-14750)*
Mz Jazzy Accezzoriez......G....... 239 275-6975
Fort Myers *(G-4543)*
Patrice Inc......F....... 941 359-2577
Sarasota *(G-16537)*
Pret-EE LLC......G....... 561 839-4338
Palm Beach Gardens *(G-13617)*
Red Bay Berry LLC......G....... 954 552-9935
Davie *(G-2582)*
Sashka Co......G....... 941 764-9741
Port Charlotte *(G-14996)*
▲ **Sonnys Strings Inc**......G....... 407 862-4905
Winter Park *(G-19446)*
Swarovski North America Ltd......G....... 561 791-7757
West Palm Beach *(G-19053)*
Swatch Group Caribbean......F....... 877 839-5224
Miami *(G-10445)*

3965 Fasteners, Buttons, Needles & Pins

531 East Inc......G....... 561 249-2524
Lake Worth *(G-7526)*
Allfast Fastener T......G....... 352 727-8464
Gainesville *(G-4872)*
APC Art-Phyl Creations LLC......G....... 786 571-4665
Hialeah *(G-5301)*
Arrowhead Global LLC......G....... 727 497-7340
Clearwater *(G-1589)*
Bisi Fasteners LLC......G....... 850 913-0101
Panama City *(G-13873)*
C S Fasteners......G....... 813 242-8000
Tampa *(G-17495)*
Captains Fasteners Corp......G....... 954 533-9259
Fort Lauderdale *(G-3882)*
▲ **Ceco & Associates Inc**......G....... 727 528-0075
Riverview *(G-15266)*
Coll Builders Supply Inc......F....... 407 745-4641
Orlando *(G-12600)*
Contracting Cnc Machining Inc......G....... 561 494-0703
West Palm Beach *(G-18849)*
▲ **E-Z Fastening Solutions Inc**......G....... 813 854-3937
Oldsmar *(G-12223)*
Fastener Solutions LLC......G....... 813 324-8372
Tampa *(G-17661)*
Fastener Solutions LLC......G....... 813 867-4714
Tampa *(G-17662)*
Fastener Specialty Corp......G....... 631 903-4453
Port Charlotte *(G-14980)*
Fator Fasteners Usa LLC......G....... 941 479-8518
Palmetto *(G-13798)*
Henefelt Precision Products......F....... 727 531-0406
Largo *(G-7969)*
Ideal Fastener Corporation......D....... 201 207-6722
Miami *(G-9729)*
Innovative Fasteners LLC......F....... 561 542-2152
Coconut Creek *(G-2082)*
Lapel Pin & Button Company Inc......F....... 407 677-6144
Orlando *(G-12891)*
M D R International Inc......F....... 305 944-5335
North Miami *(G-11644)*
Maxant Button & Supply Inc......G....... 770 460-2227
Plantation *(G-14532)*
Maxant Buttons LLC......G....... 770 460-2227
Moore Haven *(G-11088)*
Peterson Manufacturing Co Inc......E....... 941 371-4989
Sarasota *(G-16544)*
Scott Slide Fasteners Inc......F....... 305 576-3328
Miami *(G-10314)*
Southeastern Fasteners......G....... 407 790-4888
Longwood *(G-8338)*
Tekk Supply Inc......G....... 954 444-5782
Pompano Beach *(G-14884)*
▲ **Zoag LLC**......G....... 862 591-2969
Palm Beach Gardens *(G-13638)*

3991 Brooms & Brushes

A J Giammanco & Associates......F....... 386 328-1254
Palatka *(G-13472)*
▲ **Boden Co Inc**......E....... 727 571-1234
Clearwater *(G-1610)*
▲ **Brawley Distributing Co Inc**......F....... 727 539-8500
Largo *(G-7913)*
◆ **Corona Brushes Inc**......D....... 813 885-2525
Tampa *(G-17558)*
Elder & Jenks LLC......G....... 727 538-5545
Largo *(G-7940)*
Industrial Brush Corporation......F....... 863 647-5643
Lakeland *(G-7709)*
Kleenbore Inc......G....... 800 347-1200
Jacksonville *(G-6540)*
Marketshare LLC......G....... 631 273-0598
Boca Raton *(G-609)*
Premier Brush Inc......G....... 850 271-5736
Panama City *(G-13942)*
▼ **Rollercoat Industries Inc**......E....... 813 621-4668
Tampa *(G-18067)*
▲ **Shurhold Products Company**......G....... 772 287-1313
Palm City *(G-13673)*
▲ **Smith Equipment & Supply Co**......E....... 863 665-4904
Lakeland *(G-7795)*
◆ **Torrington Brush Works Inc**......F....... 941 355-1499
Sarasota *(G-16622)*

3993 Signs & Advertising Displays

2u Service Corp......G....... 786 219-6564
Miami *(G-9024)*
▲ **3 D F X Inc**......F....... 407 237-6249
Orlando *(G-12416)*
A 1 A Signs & Service Inc......F....... 305 757-6950
Miami *(G-9033)*
A A A Signs Inc......G....... 813 949-8397
Lutz *(G-8369)*
▲ **A J Trophies & Awards Inc**......E....... 850 878-7187
Tallahassee *(G-17210)*
A Sign......G....... 321 264-0077
Titusville *(G-18406)*
A Sign Shop LLC......G....... 813 334-7765
Apollo Beach *(G-99)*
A World of Signs......G....... 850 267-1331
Santa Rosa Beach *(G-16151)*
A&C Signs Solutions Corp......F....... 786 953-5600
Hialeah *(G-5259)*
A1a Electric Signs & Neon Inc......G....... 305 757-6950
Hialeah *(G-5261)*
Abalux Inc......F....... 305 698-9192
Hialeah *(G-5263)*
Abby Press Inc......E....... 407 847-5565
Kissimmee *(G-7216)*
Accent Neon & Sign Company......G....... 727 784-8414
Palm Harbor *(G-13716)*
▲ **Accuform Manufacturing Inc**......B....... 352 799-5434
Brooksville *(G-1204)*
Accuform Signs......F....... 800 237-1001
Spring Hill *(G-16844)*
Accurate Signs LLC......G....... 754 779-7519
Fort Lauderdale *(G-3776)*
Ace Custom Signs of Winter Pk......G....... 407 257-6475
Winter Park *(G-19371)*
Acolite Claude Untd Sign Inc......E....... 305 362-3333
Doral *(G-3224)*
Acolite Sign Company Inc......G....... 305 362-3333
Doral *(G-3225)*
Action Signs & Graphics Inc......G....... 386 752-0121
Lake City *(G-7346)*
Ad America......G....... 904 781-5900
Jacksonville *(G-6118)*
ADM II Exhibits & Displays Inc......F....... 813 887-1960
Tampa *(G-17387)*
Adtech Electric Advertising......D....... 786 533-3210
Miami *(G-9073)*
Adwave Graphics Inc......G....... 305 643-8020
Miami *(G-9078)*
Aerial Banners Inc......F....... 954 893-0099
Pembroke Pines *(G-14016)*
Affordable Signs Clermont LLC......G....... 352 241-7645
Groveland *(G-5093)*

Agi Solutions Inc....G.... 888 987-8425
Sarasota (G-16336)
All American Signs Inc....G.... 863 665-7161
Lakeland (G-7631)
All Island Signs....G.... 631 676-3498
Hudson (G-6015)
All Miami Signs Inc....F.... 305 406-2420
Miami (G-9112)
All Signs....G.... 904 262-3795
Jacksonville (G-6136)
All Venue Graphics and Signs....G.... 954 399-7446
Pompano Beach (G-14586)
All-Brite Signs....G.... 352 628-4910
Lecanto (G-8127)
Allegra Print Signs Mail....G.... 954 963-3886
Hollywood (G-5770)
Allen Industries....G.... 561 243-8072
Delray Beach (G-3043)
Allen Industries Inc....D.... 727 573-3076
Clearwater (G-1576)
Alli Cats Inc....G.... 239 274-0744
Fort Myers (G-4352)
Allstate Signs Inc....G.... 305 885-9751
Hialeah (G-5282)
Alternative Sign Group Inc....G.... 561 722-9272
West Palm Beach (G-18795)
AM Primaclasse Corp....G.... 305 767-5918
Fort Lauderdale (G-3810)
American Led Technology Inc....F.... 850 863-8777
Naples (G-11162)
American Lw & Promo Prods LLC....G.... 954 946-5252
Pompano Beach (G-14591)
American Sign Letters....G.... 772 643-4012
Sebastian (G-16654)
◆ Annat Inc....F.... 239 262-4639
Naples (G-11163)
Anything Display....F.... 239 433-9738
Fort Myers (G-4365)
Apple Sign & Awning LLC....F.... 813 948-2220
Lutz (G-8375)
ARC Creative Inc....G.... 904 996-7773
Jacksonville (G-6164)
Architctral Sgnage Systems Inc....G.... 813 996-6777
Land O Lakes (G-7849)
Architectural Graphics Inc....F.... 757 427-1900
Clearwater (G-1587)
Architectural Signcrafters....G.... 772 600-5032
Stuart (G-16908)
Architectural Signs Inc....G.... 305 282-4427
Miami (G-9164)
Arrive Alive Traffic Ctrl LLC....F.... 407 578-5431
Orlando (G-12490)
◆ Art Sign Co Inc....D.... 954 763-4410
Fort Lauderdale (G-3825)
Art-Kraft Sign Co Inc....E.... 321 727-7324
Palm Bay (G-13499)
Artful Signs....G.... 239 431-7356
Bonita Springs (G-814)
Artistic Adventures Inc....G.... 407 297-0557
Orlando (G-12493)
ASAP Signs & Graphics of Fla....G.... 727 443-4878
Clearwater (G-1592)
Ash Signs Inc....G.... 904 724-7446
Jacksonville (G-6170)
Ataly Inc....E.... 813 880-9142
Tampa (G-17441)
▼ Atlas Sign Industries Fla LLC....C.... 561 863-6659
Riviera Beach (G-15299)
Automotive Advertising Assoc....G.... 954 389-6500
Weston (G-19109)
Avalon Sign Solutions Inc....G.... 727 398-6126
Seminole (G-16740)
B R Signs Inc....G.... 954 973-7700
Pompano Beach (G-14610)
B&C Signs....G.... 386 426-2373
Edgewater (G-3612)
B2b Sign Resource....F.... 813 855-7446
Tampa (G-17452)
Bach Sign Group Inc....G.... 561 848-3440
West Palm Beach (G-18812)
Backyard Canvas & Signs Inc....G.... 813 672-2660
Gibsonton (G-5026)
Banks Sign Systems Inc....G.... 954 979-0055
Pompano Beach (G-14613)
Banners-N-Signs Etc Inc....G.... 904 272-3395
Orange Park (G-12382)
Baron International LLC....F.... 800 531-9558
Jupiter (G-7003)
▼ Barrau & Coirin Inc....G.... 305 571-5051
Miami (G-9223)
◆ Bass Industries Inc....E.... 305 751-2716
Hialeah (G-5316)
Baxter Adventures Inc....G.... 561 439-4700
Lake Worth Beach (G-7605)
Bay Area Signs Inc....F.... 813 677-0237
Plant City (G-14407)
Bayfront Printing Company....G.... 727 823-1965
Saint Petersburg (G-15719)
Bdnz Associates Inc....G.... 305 379-7993
Miami (G-9230)
Beach Neon & Sign Co....G.... 904 479-3599
Jacksonville (G-6200)
Beautiful Mailbox Co....E.... 305 403-4820
Hialeah (G-5318)
Bengis Signs Inc....F.... 305 592-3860
Miami Lakes (G-10765)
Berry Signs Inc....G.... 321 631-6150
Rockledge (G-15394)
Big Color Output Inc....G.... 941 540-4441
Cape Coral (G-1390)
Big Digital Graphics LLC....G.... 561 844-4708
Lake Park (G-7466)
Big Sign Message LLC....G.... 954 235-5717
Fort Lauderdale (G-3851)
Binca LLC....F.... 305 698-8883
Doral (G-3274)
Binney Family of Florida Inc....F.... 727 376-5596
Odessa (G-12106)
Boardwalk Designs Inc....G.... 850 265-0988
Lynn Haven (G-8430)
Boca Signworks....G.... 561 393-6010
Boca Raton (G-457)
Bolt Signs & Marketing LLC....F.... 407 865-7446
Apopka (G-119)
BR Signs International In....G.... 954 464-7999
Coral Springs (G-2229)
▲ Brite Lite Service Company....F.... 904 398-5305
Jacksonville (G-6237)
Broward Sign Shop....G.... 305 431-2455
Hallandale Beach (G-5175)
Broward Signs....G.... 954 320-9903
Fort Lauderdale (G-3871)
Bruce R Ely Enterprise Inc....F.... 727 573-1643
Clearwater (G-1614)
Bryson of Brevard Inc....E.... 321 636-5116
Rockledge (G-15396)
Buchanan Signs Screen Process....E.... 904 725-5500
Jacksonville (G-6243)
Bucks Corporation Inc....F.... 850 894-2400
Tallahassee (G-17229)
Budget Signs Inc....F.... 954 941-5710
Pompano Beach (G-14625)
Bulldog Neon Sign Company Inc....G.... 786 277-6366
Miami (G-9284)
◆ Bullet Line LLC....B.... 305 623-9223
Hialeah (G-5335)
Bundy Signs LLC....G.... 954 296-0784
Sunrise (G-17101)
Burton Signs Inc....G.... 727 841-8927
New Port Richey (G-11485)
Business Forward Inc....G.... 954 967-6730
Hollywood (G-5792)
C & E Cabinets Design LLC....G.... 386 410-4281
Edgewater (G-3617)
C & H Sign Enterprises Inc....G.... 407 826-0155
Orlando (G-12538)
C & S Graphics Inc....G.... 813 251-4411
Tampa (G-17493)
C & S Signs Inc....G.... 850 983-9540
Milton (G-10925)
C L F Enterprises....G.... 305 643-3222
Miami (G-9293)
C&D Sign and Lighting Svcs LLC....G.... 863 937-9323
Lakeland (G-7652)
Cadillac Graphics Inc....G.... 954 772-2440
Oakland Park (G-11789)
Calmac Corporation....F.... 813 493-8700
Tampa (G-17501)
Cardinal Signs Inc....G.... 352 376-8494
Gainesville (G-4893)
Carlaron Inc....G.... 386 258-1183
Daytona Beach (G-2639)
Carter Signs Inc....G.... 239 543-4004
Fort Myers (G-4390)
Catch One Comm....G.... 772 221-0225
Port Saint Lucie (G-15096)
Central Signs LLC....F.... 386 322-7446
Daytona Beach (G-2641)
Central Signs Volusia Cnty Inc....G.... 386 341-4842
South Daytona (G-16799)
Cesco Signs Inc....G.... 407 463-6635
Orlando (G-12572)
▼ Channel Letter Network Corp....E.... 305 594-3360
Miami (G-9347)
Channel Letter USA Corp....G.... 561 243-9699
Delray Beach (G-3058)
Charles Thaggard Inc....G.... 239 936-8059
Fort Myers (G-4393)
Cheap Banners & Signs Central....G.... 727 522-7414
Saint Petersburg (G-15744)
Chiliprint LLC....G.... 863 547-6930
Dundee (G-3564)
Chilton Signs & Designs LLC....G.... 863 438-0880
Winter Haven (G-19314)
Clark Craig Enterprises....F.... 813 287-0110
Tampa (G-17539)
Clarks Electrical Signs & Svcs....G.... 561 248-5932
Lake Worth (G-7542)
Classic Design and Mfg....G.... 850 433-4981
Pensacola (G-14114)
◆ Classic Shirts Inc....F.... 850 875-2200
Quincy (G-15247)
Cns Signs Inc....G.... 904 733-4806
Jacksonville (G-6274)
Coastline Whl Sgns Led Disp LL....F.... 386 238-6200
Daytona Beach (G-2643)
Coastline Whl Signs Svcs Ltd....F.... 386 238-6200
Daytona Beach (G-2644)
Collins Media & Advg LLC....F.... 954 688-9758
Margate (G-8538)
Corporate Signs Inc....G.... 305 500-9313
Doral (G-3308)
Corporate Signs Inc....G.... 305 500-9313
Doral (G-3309)
Countdown Today Inc....G.... 415 420-2849
South Miami (G-16814)
Crazy 4 Signs LLC....G.... 813 239-3085
Zephyrhills (G-19512)
Creative Printing Bay Cnty Inc....F.... 850 784-1645
Panama City (G-13889)
▲ Creative Sign Designs LLC....D.... 813 818-7100
Tampa (G-17567)
Creative Signs....G.... 786 636-6969
Doral (G-3314)
Creative Signs Inc....E.... 407 293-9393
Apopka (G-128)
Crf Group Inc....F.... 954 428-7446
Pompano Beach (G-14651)
Cso Systems Inc....F.... 941 355-5653
Sarasota (G-16397)
Custom Cut Rubber....G.... 979 422-2511
Saint Johns (G-15675)
Custom Graphics & Sign Design....G.... 904 264-7667
Orange Park (G-12387)
Custom Illusionz....G.... 386 330-5245
Live Oak (G-8229)
Custom Mailboxes and Signs....G.... 239 738-9321
Fort Myers (G-4422)
Custom Sign & Awning....F.... 727 210-0941
Clearwater (G-1644)
Cutting Edge Sgns Grphics of P....G.... 727 546-3700
Clearwater (G-1645)
D & R Signs Inc....G.... 386 252-2777
Daytona Beach (G-2651)
D E E Custom Fabricators Inc....E.... 863 667-1850
Lakeland (G-7668)
▲ D G Morrison Inc....F.... 813 865-0208
Odessa (G-12114)
D I H Corporation....G.... 561 881-8705
Riviera Beach (G-15317)
D O B Signs LLC....G.... 772 466-4913
Fort Pierce (G-4691)
Dakim Inc....F.... 561 790-0884
Royal Palm Beach (G-15465)
Daniels Whl Sign & Plas Inc....G.... 386 736-4918
Sanford (G-16031)
Data Graphics Inc....D.... 352 589-1312
Mount Dora (G-11100)
◆ David Dobbs Enterprises Inc....D.... 904 824-6171
Saint Augustine (G-15533)
Davie Fastsigns....G.... 305 423-2332
Miami (G-9438)
Daytona Trophy Inc....F.... 386 253-2806
Daytona Beach (G-2656)
▲ Delconte Packaging Inc....F.... 305 885-2800
Hialeah (G-5368)
Delivery Signs LLC....G.... 407 362-7896
Orlando (G-12661)
Delray Pin Factory Intl....G.... 561 994-1680
Coral Springs (G-2240)

Design Communications Ltd F 407 856-9661
Orlando *(G-12662)*
Design It Wraps & Graphics LLC G 904 310-6032
Fernandina Beach *(G-3734)*
Designer Sign Systems Inc G 954 972-0707
Fort Lauderdale *(G-3937)*
Designstogo Inc G 561 432-1313
Palm Springs *(G-13774)*
Dgs Retail LLC C 727 388-4975
Saint Petersburg *(G-15760)*
Dgs Retail LLC F 727 388-4975
Saint Petersburg *(G-15761)*
Digiprint & Design Corp G 786 464-1770
Sweetwater *(G-17208)*
Digital Outdoor LLC E 305 944-7945
Doral *(G-3329)*
Digital Tech of Lakeland Inc F 863 668-8770
Lakeland *(G-7675)*
Divinitas Displays LLC F 407 660-6625
Orlando *(G-12678)*
Dixie Signs Inc E 863 644-3521
Lakeland *(G-7676)*
Don Bell Signs LLC D 800 824-0080
Port Orange *(G-15016)*
Doug Bloodworth Enterprises G 407 247-9728
Lady Lake *(G-7325)*
Dragonfire Industries Inc G 407 999-2215
Orlando *(G-12683)*
Dvc Signs LLC G 727 524-8543
Largo *(G-7937)*
Dynamic Aspects Inc G 407 322-1923
Debary *(G-2748)*
E C V Display Corp G 786 586-1034
Hialeah *(G-5385)*
E&M Pckging Llcdba Crtive Sign G 813 839-6356
Tampa *(G-17623)*
Eagle Signs G 321 863-9844
Titusville *(G-18428)*
Eastern Signs LLC G 305 542-8274
Hialeah *(G-5386)*
Easy Rent Inc G 904 443-7446
Jacksonville *(G-6351)*
▲ Easy Signs Inc G 954 673-0118
Oakland Park *(G-11801)*
▼ Econochannel Inc E 305 255-2113
Hialeah *(G-5388)*
Eidolon Analytics Inc F 239 288-6951
Fort Myers *(G-4441)*
◆ Electronic Sign Supply Corp G 305 477-0555
Medley *(G-8647)*
Elite Printing & Marketing Inc G 850 474-0894
Pensacola *(G-14139)*
◆ Ellis Family Holdings Inc F 503 785-7400
Hialeah *(G-5393)*
Emerald Coast Signs G 850 398-1712
Crestview *(G-2347)*
Ernies Signs G 239 992-0800
Bonita Springs *(G-829)*
Everything Communicates Inc G 407 578-6616
Orlando *(G-12722)*
Excellent Guarantd Elctrcl G 407 221-6234
Orlando *(G-12726)*
Exotics Car Wraps G 786 768-6798
Miami *(G-9545)*
Expert Promotions LLC F 772 643-4012
Sebastian *(G-16658)*
Express Signs & Graphics Inc F 407 889-4433
Winter Garden *(G-19263)*
F D Signworks LLC G 561 248-6323
West Palm Beach *(G-18867)*
Fast Service Signs Inc G 954 380-0451
Sunrise *(G-17123)*
Fast Signs G 813 999-4981
Tampa *(G-17660)*
Fast Signs G 239 498-7200
Bonita Springs *(G-830)*
Fast Signs of Brandon G 813 655-9036
Brandon *(G-1158)*
Fastsigns F 305 628-3278
Miami Lakes *(G-10788)*
Fastsigns G 727 341-0084
Saint Petersburg *(G-15777)*
Fastsigns G 305 747-7115
Coral Gables *(G-2145)*
Fastsigns G 903 629-7204
Orlando *(G-12734)*
Fastsigns G 813 625-1800
Valrico *(G-18518)*
Fastsigns F 305 945-4700
North Miami Beach *(G-11675)*

Fastsigns G 786 615-2179
Hialeah *(G-5407)*
Fastsigns G 954 404-8341
Fort Lauderdale *(G-3987)*
Fastsigns F 954 416-3434
Hollywood *(G-5820)*
Fastsigns G 407 542-1234
Oviedo *(G-13430)*
Fastsigns G 850 477-9744
Pensacola *(G-14149)*
Fastsigns 176101 F 321 307-2400
Melbourne *(G-8831)*
Fastsigns2043 F 305 988-5264
Boca Raton *(G-527)*
FDA Signs LLC G 904 800-1776
Saint Augustine *(G-15543)*
Federal Heath Sign Company LLC F 817 685-9075
Daytona Beach *(G-2665)*
Ferrin Signs Inc E 561 802-4242
West Palm Beach *(G-18870)*
Fiero Enterprises Inc F 954 454-5004
Hallandale Beach *(G-5183)*
Finlayson Enterprises Inc G 850 785-7953
Panama City *(G-13902)*
Firedrake Inc G 813 713-8902
Zephyrhills *(G-19518)*
▼ First Sign Corp F 954 972-7222
Pompano Beach *(G-14692)*
Flexofferscom Inc G 305 999-9940
Miami *(G-9577)*
Florida Roadway Signs Inc G 561 722-4067
Lake Park *(G-7472)*
Florida Sign Company Inc F 941 747-1000
Bradenton *(G-1042)*
Florida Sign Source G 407 316-0466
Orlando *(G-12756)*
▲ Forever Signs Inc F 305 885-3411
Hialeah *(G-5416)*
Forge Unlimited Co G 727 900-7600
Clearwater *(G-1693)*
Frames & Things G 727 815-0515
Port Richey *(G-15049)*
Freeman Electric Co Inc F 850 785-7448
Panama City *(G-13905)*
Fresh Ink Print LLC G 407 412-5905
Orlando *(G-12764)*
Fusion Signs G 407 715-6439
Kissimmee *(G-7248)*
Future Signs and Services Inc G 786 255-0868
Aventura *(G-269)*
G G Markers Inc G 813 873-8181
Tampa *(G-17701)*
Galaxy Awning and Signs Inc G 305 262-4224
Hialeah *(G-5422)*
▼ Galea Corporation G 305 663-0244
Miami *(G-9611)*
Gc Traffic Signs and Sup Inc G 352 735-8445
Sorrento *(G-16786)*
General Sign Service Inc F 904 355-5630
Jacksonville *(G-6433)*
General Signs and Service Inc G 904 372-4238
Atlantic Beach *(G-223)*
Georgia Mktg & Sign Co LLC G 800 286-8671
West Palm Beach *(G-18887)*
Gibbons Advg DBA Gai Exhibits G 954 395-2397
Oakland Park *(G-11808)*
Gillette Sign & Lighting Inc G 352 256-2225
Zephyrhills *(G-19521)*
Gjcb Signs Graphics Inc F 352 429-0803
Groveland *(G-5095)*
Glomaster Signs Inc G 772 464-0718
Fort Pierce *(G-4701)*
Glow Bench Systems Intl G 954 315-4615
Sunrise *(G-17126)*
Go Mobile Signs G 239 245-7803
Fort Myers *(G-4469)*
Gould Signs Inc G 772 221-1218
Stuart *(G-16947)*
Gpi Signs G 863 453-4888
Avon Park *(G-288)*
Graph-Plex Corp F 772 766-3866
Sebastian *(G-16662)*
Graph-Plex Inc F 954 920-0905
Hollywood *(G-5829)*
Graphic Banner LLP G 954 491-9441
Oakland Park *(G-11809)*
Graphic Designs Intl Inc F 772 287-0000
Stuart *(G-16948)*
▼ Graphic Difference Inc A F 954 748-6990
Lauderhill *(G-8110)*

Graphic Images Inc F 954 984-0015
Pompano Beach *(G-14717)*
▲ Graphic Installers Inc G 863 646-5543
Lakeland *(G-7701)*
Graphic Jet Signs LLC G 786 552-2098
Palmetto Bay *(G-13845)*
Graphic Sign Dsign Cntl Fla LL G 386 547-4569
Daytona Beach *(G-2669)*
Graphics Designer Inc F 561 687-7993
West Palm Beach *(G-18889)*
Graphics Pdts Excellence Inc F 813 884-1578
Wesley Chapel *(G-18748)*
Great Bay Signs Inc G 727 437-1091
Largo *(G-7964)*
Greathouse Signs LLC G 407 247-2668
Apopka *(G-146)*
▲ Greyfield Holdings Inc E 407 830-8861
Sanford *(G-16058)*
Greyson Corp F 407 830-7443
Longwood *(G-8286)*
Gulf Coast Business World Inc F 850 864-1511
Fort Walton Beach *(G-4806)*
Gulf Coast Signs Sarasota Inc E 941 355-8841
Sarasota *(G-16454)*
Guthman Signs LLC G 941 218-0023
Bradenton *(G-1054)*
Guthman Signs LLC G 941 218-0014
Sarasota *(G-16455)*
Guy Wingo Signs G 407 578-1132
Apopka *(G-148)*
H & H Signs Inc G 941 485-0556
Venice *(G-18552)*
Hallmark Nameplate Inc D 352 383-8142
Mount Dora *(G-11103)*
Hanes-Harris Design Cons G 813 237-0202
Tampa *(G-17742)*
Hd Signs & Lighting G 850 484-9829
Pensacola *(G-14169)*
Heritage Signs G 904 529-7446
Green Cove Springs *(G-5065)*
Hermes 7 Communications LLC F 954 426-1998
Deerfield Beach *(G-2838)*
Himes Signs Inc F 850 837-1159
Destin *(G-3194)*
◆ Hit Promotional Products Inc B 727 541-5561
Largo *(G-7971)*
HOB Corporation G 813 988-2272
Tampa *(G-17758)*
Holmes Stamp Company E 904 396-2291
Jacksonville *(G-6476)*
Honchin Inc G 305 235-3800
Cutler Bay *(G-2397)*
Human Sign F 239 573-4292
Cape Coral *(G-1439)*
Hunt RDS Inc G 813 249-7551
Oldsmar *(G-12232)*
I2k Digital Solutions LLC F 305 507-0707
Miami *(G-9725)*
Ifoxx LLC G 305 785-7130
Kissimmee *(G-7253)*
Image 360 G 561 395-0745
Boca Raton *(G-562)*
▲ Imprint Promotions LLC G 321 622-8946
Melbourne *(G-8850)*
Infinity Signs & Graphix LLC F 407 270-6733
Orlando *(G-12829)*
▼ Inflatable Design Works Corp F 786 242-1049
Miami *(G-9742)*
Inklab Signs Inc G 786 430-8100
Miami *(G-9743)*
Innovative Signs Inc G 407 830-5155
Sanford *(G-16067)*
Instasign G 561 272-2323
Delray Beach *(G-3091)*
Integrted Sign Engrg Dsign LLC G 941 379-5918
Sarasota *(G-16467)*
▼ International Quiksigns Inc F 954 462-7446
Fort Lauderdale *(G-4063)*
International Sign Design Corp E 727 541-5573
Largo *(G-7982)*
International Signs & Ltg Inc F 407 332-9663
Longwood *(G-8292)*
▼ Interstate Signcrafters LLC D 561 547-3760
Boynton Beach *(G-922)*
▲ J D M Corp G 305 947-5876
Doral *(G-3398)*
J R Wheeler Corporation G 954 585-8950
Fort Lauderdale *(G-4073)*
J T E Inc G 941 925-2605
Sarasota *(G-16475)*

▼ James Testa....F....954 962-5840
Hollywood *(G-5851)*
Jar Advertising LLC....G....844 344-4586
Orlando *(G-12851)*
Jay Berry Signs....F....352 805-4050
Leesburg *(G-8162)*
▲ Jayco Signs Inc....F....407 339-5252
Maitland *(G-8468)*
Jbjb Holdings LLC....G....239 267-1975
Fort Myers *(G-4501)*
JCP Signs Inc....G....305 790-5336
Miami *(G-9791)*
Joni Industries Inc....F....352 799-5456
Brooksville *(G-1240)*
Jpl Associates Inc....F....954 929-6024
Hallandale Beach *(G-5194)*
Jwn Family Partners LP Ltd....G....352 628-4910
Lecanto *(G-8135)*
K & I Plastics Inc....G....904 387-0438
Jacksonville *(G-6531)*
K R O Enterprises Ltd....G....309 797-2213
Naples *(G-11302)*
Kauffs Ventures LLC....G....561 775-3278
Palm Beach Gardens *(G-13600)*
▲ Kay Enterprises....G....352 732-5770
Ocala *(G-11975)*
▼ Kemp Signs Inc....F....561 840-6382
Mangonia Park *(G-8507)*
Kenco 2000 Inc....F....386 672-1590
Daytona Beach *(G-2676)*
Kenco Signs Awning LLC....F....386 672-1590
Holly Hill *(G-5759)*
Kendal Signs Inc....E....321 636-5116
Rockledge *(G-15428)*
Kendall Sign and Design Inc....G....305 595-2000
Miami *(G-9820)*
Kevin Jeffers Inc....G....352 377-2322
Gainesville *(G-4949)*
Kids Wood....G....407 332-9663
Longwood *(G-8299)*
L R Gator Corporation....G....407 578-6616
Orlando *(G-12880)*
▼ L4 Design LLC....E....407 262-8200
Maitland *(G-8471)*
L4 Design LLC....F....224 612-5045
Maitland *(G-8472)*
Labelpro Inc....F....727 538-2149
Clearwater *(G-1757)*
Lambs Signs Inc....F....941 792-4453
Bradenton *(G-1068)*
Laporte Inv Holdings Inc....G....863 294-4498
Winter Haven *(G-19335)*
▲ Laser Creations Incorporated....E....800 771-7151
Apopka *(G-155)*
Lcr Signs & Services....G....772 882-5276
Port Saint Lucie *(G-15119)*
Lee Designs Llc....F....239 278-4245
Fort Myers *(G-4518)*
Leon Sign S LLC....G....786 333-4694
Hialeah *(G-5485)*
Liquid Soul Dgtal Graphics LLC....G....407 948-6973
Orlando *(G-12915)*
Local Biz Spot Inc....G....866 446-1790
Wesley Chapel *(G-18751)*
Lords Place Thrift Store....G....561 660-7942
West Palm Beach *(G-18935)*
Lsj Corp....G....954 920-0905
Hollywood *(G-5864)*
Lucke Enterprises Inc....G....727 797-1177
Clearwater *(G-1765)*
Lucke Group Inc....G....727 525-4949
Saint Petersburg *(G-15843)*
M & M Signs....E....904 381-7353
Jacksonville *(G-6568)*
M&D Signs....G....561 296-3636
West Palm Beach *(G-18937)*
Mac Papers Inc....G....800 582-0049
Clearwater *(G-1768)*
Machin Signs Inc....G....305 694-0464
Miami *(G-9932)*
Mag-Tags Inc....G....850 294-1809
Tallahassee *(G-17293)*
Major League Signs Inc....G....954 600-5505
Hialeah *(G-5498)*
Mc Graphix....G....321 725-7243
Palm Bay *(G-13523)*
▲ McCain Sales of Florida Inc....E....772 461-0665
Fort Pierce *(G-4717)*
McColl Display Solutions....F....813 333-6613
Windermere *(G-19238)*
McGrail Signs & Graphics LLC....G....850 435-1017
Pensacola *(G-14204)*
McKenny Printing Enterprise....G....727 420-4944
Saint Petersburg *(G-15853)*
McNeill Signs Inc....F....561 737-6304
Pompano Beach *(G-14756)*
McNeill Signs Inc....G....386 586-7100
Bunnell *(G-1303)*
Metro Signs Inc....E....954 410-4343
Hollywood *(G-5875)*
MGM Cargo LLC....G....407 770-1500
Orlando *(G-12966)*
Miami Banners & Signs Inc....G....305 262-4460
Miami *(G-9992)*
Miami Sign Industry....G....305 418-0673
Opa Locka *(G-12339)*
Miami Signage LLC....G....305 877-3924
Miami *(G-10010)*
Micole Electric Sign Company....G....954 796-4293
Coral Springs *(G-2284)*
Miller Signs LLC....G....786 395-9420
Hollywood *(G-5877)*
▲ Milliken & Milliken Inc....E....941 474-0223
Englewood *(G-3680)*
Mobile Sign Service Inc....G....954 579-8628
Coconut Creek *(G-2091)*
Modular Sign....G....727 391-2423
Seminole *(G-16755)*
Modulex America LLC....F....786 424-0857
Miami *(G-10034)*
Modulex Americas Group Corp....G....877 808-8049
Miami *(G-10035)*
Morrow Technologies Corp....E....727 531-4000
Saint Petersburg *(G-15859)*
Mwr Sign Enterprises Inc....G....954 914-2709
Pembroke Pines *(G-14050)*
▼ N & N Investment Corporation....E....954 590-3800
Pompano Beach *(G-14770)*
Nation Signs....G....386 466-0043
Lake City *(G-7368)*
National Direct Signs....E....561 320-2102
West Palm Beach *(G-18957)*
National Sign Inc....F....727 572-1503
Clearwater *(G-1801)*
National Traffic Signs Inc....G....727 446-7983
Clearwater *(G-1802)*
Nauset Enterprises Inc....G....727 443-3469
Clearwater *(G-1804)*
Neon & Sign Mfg Inc....G....443 664-6419
Boca Raton *(G-638)*
New Vision Signs Corp....G....786 514-6822
Miami *(G-10067)*
Nine Enterprises Inc....G....904 998-8880
Jacksonville *(G-6635)*
Nite-Bright Sign Company Inc....E....239 466-2616
Fort Myers *(G-4547)*
Nitesol Inc....G....407 557-4042
Orlando *(G-13005)*
Novalux Signs....G....904 329-9607
Jacksonville *(G-6640)*
Novus Clip Signs & Video Prod....G....239 471-5639
Fort Myers *(G-4551)*
Nu-Art Signs Inc....G....305 531-9850
Miami *(G-10084)*
Oakhurst Marketing Inc....G....727 532-8255
Saint Petersburg *(G-15869)*
Oceanside Custom LLC....G....386 341-7507
Fort Myers *(G-4554)*
Off The Chart Inc....G....954 654-6541
Davie *(G-2561)*
Olympian Led Inc....G....321 747-3220
Titusville *(G-18447)*
Omega Sign Service Corporation....G....727 505-7833
New Port Richey *(G-11505)*
On-Site Lighting & Sign Svcs....G....256 693-1018
Pensacola *(G-14216)*
Onsight Industries....G....407 830-8861
Tampa *(G-17957)*
Outdoor Images Central Fla Inc....G....407 825-9944
Orlando *(G-13040)*
Pacheco Creative Group Inc....F....305 541-1400
Miami *(G-10126)*
Paints N Cocktails Inc....F....954 514-7383
Miami *(G-10130)*
Parrillo Inc....G....386 767-8011
South Daytona *(G-16806)*
Pensacola Sign & Graphics Inc....G....850 433-7878
Pensacola *(G-14226)*
Pete Peterson Signs Inc....G....352 625-2307
Silver Springs *(G-16783)*
Phil Rowe Signs Inc....G....561 832-8688
West Palm Beach *(G-18997)*
Pivotal Sign & Graphics Inc....G....727 462-2266
Clearwater *(G-1835)*
Pk Group Inc....F....239 643-2442
Naples *(G-11368)*
Plastic Art Sign Company Inc....F....850 455-4114
Pensacola *(G-14232)*
Platinum Signs and Design LLC....G....407 971-3640
Casselberry *(G-1514)*
Platinum Signs Inc....G....561 296-3636
West Palm Beach *(G-18999)*
Poblocki Sign Co Southeast LLC....G....407 660-3174
Winter Park *(G-19432)*
◆ Poli Group International Inc....F....305 468-8986
Miami *(G-10174)*
Pope Enterprises Inc....F....850 729-7446
Niceville *(G-11572)*
Precision Auto Tint Dsign Corp....G....727 385-8788
Tarpon Springs *(G-18321)*
Preferred Signs Inc....G....954 922-0126
Hollywood *(G-5894)*
Premier Printing Signs....G....727 849-2493
Port Richey *(G-15064)*
Premier Sign & Service Inc....G....239 258-6979
Lehigh Acres *(G-8203)*
Premier Sign Company LLC....F....850 621-4524
Destin *(G-3202)*
Print Signs & Banners....G....305 600-1349
Miami *(G-10198)*
Priority 1 Signs....F....954 971-8689
Deerfield Beach *(G-2893)*
Pro-Ad Media Inc....G....863 802-5043
Lakeland *(G-7771)*
Process Automation Corporation....G....727 541-6280
Pinellas Park *(G-14381)*
Productive Products Inc....G....904 570-5553
Saint Augustine *(G-15591)*
Professional Signs....G....305 662-5957
Miami *(G-10207)*
Promo Daddy LLC....F....877 557-2336
Melbourne *(G-8913)*
▲ Promo Daddy LLC....F....352 390-3081
Melbourne *(G-8914)*
Publi Signs....G....954 927-4411
Hollywood *(G-5896)*
Put Your Name On It LLC....G....813 972-1460
Tampa *(G-18026)*
Quality Neon Sign Company....D....904 268-4681
Jacksonville *(G-6699)*
Quality Signs....G....786 261-6242
Hialeah *(G-5591)*
Quick Advertising Inc....F....407 774-0003
Apopka *(G-177)*
Quick Signs....G....904 310-1010
Saint Augustine *(G-15592)*
R & A Power Graphics Inc....F....407 898-5770
Orlando *(G-13107)*
Raimonda Investment Group Inc....G....352 347-8899
Belleview *(G-375)*
Rapid Signs and T Shirts....G....786 486-2804
Homestead *(G-5989)*
Reddi Sign Corporation....G....904 757-0680
Jacksonville *(G-6709)*
▼ Redmont Sign LLC....D....941 378-4242
Sarasota *(G-16556)*
Richard Varney Signs....G....772 873-0454
Port Saint Lucie *(G-15138)*
Ricks Quality Prtg & Signs....G....321 504-7446
Cocoa *(G-2048)*
Rigal Ramon & Maritza....G....813 968-2380
Tampa *(G-18057)*
River City Advg Objectional....G....904 731-3452
Jacksonville *(G-6726)*
Road Runner Highway Sign Inc....G....941 753-0549
Bradenton *(G-1105)*
Road Signs Inc....G....941 321-0695
Sarasota *(G-16285)*
◆ Robson Corporation....E....941 753-6935
Sarasota *(G-16286)*
Rocket Sign Supplies LLC....G....239 995-4684
Fort Myers *(G-4585)*
Rogers Sign Corp....E....352 799-1923
Brooksville *(G-1265)*
Ross Industries Inc....D....954 752-2800
Pompano Beach *(G-14834)*
Royal Atlantic Ventures LLC....F....561 243-9699
Delray Beach *(G-3136)*
RPM Graphics Inc....G....239 275-3278
Lehigh Acres *(G-8206)*

SIC

Rush Signs G 407 308-6362
Orlando *(G-13149)*
S & S Metal and Plastics Inc E 904 731-4655
Jacksonville *(G-6742)*
Sam Weiss Woodworking Inc G 954 975-8158
Margate *(G-8566)*
Sams Led Signs & Services G 407 492-4934
Davenport *(G-2482)*
Sanbur Inc F 941 371-7446
Sarasota *(G-16572)*
Sapphire LLC G 561 346-7449
Greenacres *(G-5087)*
Sar Wholesale Sign Factory F 813 949-8397
Lutz *(G-8417)*
Sarasota Signs and Visuals G 941 355-5746
Sarasota *(G-16581)*
Saul Signs Inc F 305 266-8484
Medley *(G-8722)*
Saxton Sign FL Inc G 239 458-0845
Cape Coral *(G-1466)*
Sb Signs Inc G 561 688-9100
West Palm Beach *(G-19026)*
Screen Process Printers Inc G 904 354-8708
Jacksonville *(G-6757)*
▲ **Sdm Acquisition Corporation** G 954 462-1919
Fort Lauderdale *(G-4226)*
Sebco Industries Inc G 954 566-8500
Oakland Park *(G-11837)*
Seminole Sign Company LLC G 863 623-6600
Okeechobee *(G-12192)*
Seminole State Signs & Ltg G 954 316-6030
Davie *(G-2590)*
Sep Communications LLC F 561 998-0870
Boca Raton *(G-706)*
Sh Signs G 305 967-8964
Miami *(G-10332)*
Shark Signs of Ne Fl Inc G 904 766-6222
Jacksonville *(G-6762)*
Sheldon Sign Company Inc G 941 321-6313
North Port *(G-11749)*
Shipping + Business Svcs LLC G 904 240-1737
Jacksonville *(G-6765)*
▲ **Shirts & Caps Inc** F 813 788-7026
Tampa *(G-18098)*
Sign & Vehicle Wraps Inc G 407 859-8631
Orlando *(G-13189)*
Sign A Rama G 954 796-1644
Coral Springs *(G-2312)*
▼ **Sign A Rama** G 813 264-0022
Tampa *(G-18099)*
▼ **Sign A Rama Inc** E 561 640-5570
West Palm Beach *(G-19032)*
▲ **Sign A Rama Inc** G 904 998-8880
Jacksonville *(G-6770)*
Sign and Design Depot LLC G 239 995-7446
North Fort Myers *(G-11605)*
Sign Design and Creations G 954 724-2884
Margate *(G-8567)*
Sign Design of Florida Inc E 352 787-3882
Leesburg *(G-8172)*
Sign Development Corporation G 305 227-6250
Miami *(G-10342)*
Sign Language Interpreting G 386 681-9784
Ormond Beach *(G-13398)*
Sign Man Inc G 321 259-1703
Melbourne *(G-8932)*
Sign N Drive G 813 999-4837
Tampa *(G-18100)*
Sign On LLC G 239 800-9454
Cape Coral *(G-1471)*
Sign Pro America F 412 908-9832
Jacksonville *(G-6771)*
▼ **Sign Producers Inc** E 407 855-8864
Orlando *(G-13191)*
Sign Rockers LLC E 866 212-9697
Miami *(G-10343)*
Sign Solutions of Tampa Bay G 813 269-5990
Tampa *(G-18101)*
Sign Space G 786 360-2670
Miami *(G-10344)*
Sign Stapler G 800 775-3971
Orlando *(G-13192)*
Sign Systems Grphic Dsigns Inc G 813 281-2400
Tampa *(G-18102)*
Sign Tech Inc G 941 575-1349
Punta Gorda *(G-15233)*
Sign Up Now Sign Company LLC G 754 224-9091
Pompano Beach *(G-14850)*
Sign Works Inc G 941 894-7927
Sarasota *(G-16594)*

Sign-O-Saurus Inc G 407 677-8965
Casselberry *(G-1518)*
Sign-O-Saurus of Daytona Inc G 386 322-5222
South Daytona *(G-16809)*
Signage Plus LLC G 407 668-3567
Altamonte Springs *(G-73)*
Signarama G 239 997-1644
North Fort Myers *(G-11606)*
Signarama G 850 656-3200
Tallahassee *(G-17323)*
Signarama Clearwater G 727 784-4500
Pinellas Park *(G-14388)*
Signarama Dwntwn Fort Lderdale G 954 990-4749
Fort Lauderdale *(G-4234)*
Signarama Naples G 239 330-3737
Naples *(G-11403)*
Signarama-Sarasota G 941 554-8798
Sarasota *(G-16595)*
Signature Signs Inc F 727 725-1044
Safety Harbor *(G-15503)*
Signcorp Inc G 863 224-1331
Winter Haven *(G-19355)*
Signcraft LLC G 561 543-0034
Wellington *(G-18733)*
Signcraft & More Inc G 386 755-4754
Lake City *(G-7384)*
Signcraft Publishing Co Inc F 239 939-4644
Fort Myers *(G-4604)*
Signcrafters of Central Fla F 352 323-1862
Leesburg *(G-8173)*
Signgraphix Inc G 954 571-7131
Deerfield Beach *(G-2911)*
Signline Signs & Electrical G 904 388-9474
Jacksonville *(G-6772)*
Signmasters Inc G 352 335-7000
Gainesville *(G-4995)*
Signpost LLC G 813 334-7678
Maitland *(G-8477)*
Signs & Stripes Llc G 305 775-1174
Miramar *(G-11042)*
Signs 2 U Inc G 305 227-6250
Miami *(G-10345)*
▲ **Signs All Signs** G 786 285-7900
Opa Locka *(G-12358)*
Signs Connection Inc G 305 978-5777
Miami *(G-10346)*
Signs Factory USA Inc G 786 717-5474
Hialeah *(G-5619)*
▼ **Signs For You Inc** E 305 635-6662
Miami *(G-10347)*
Signs Galore Inc G 850 683-8010
Crestview *(G-2358)*
◆ **Signs International Distr Corp** G 305 715-0017
Miami *(G-10348)*
Signs Just For You Inc G 407 927-0226
Sanford *(G-16115)*
Signs N Stuff Inc G 904 248-8141
Orange Park *(G-12406)*
Signs Now G 386 238-5507
Daytona Beach *(G-2715)*
Signs Now F 727 524-8500
Largo *(G-8052)*
Signs Now G 850 383-6500
Tallahassee *(G-17324)*
Signs Now Inc G 407 628-2410
Winter Park *(G-19443)*
Signs Now St Augustine Inc G 904 810-5838
Saint Augustine *(G-15611)*
Signs of America Tampa Corp G 813 243-9243
Tampa *(G-18104)*
Signs of Reilly G 954 263-7829
Pompano Beach *(G-14851)*
Signs of Tampa Bay LLC E 813 526-0484
Lutz *(G-8418)*
Signs of Time Inc G 772 240-9590
Stuart *(G-17013)*
Signs of Times Ventures LLC G 772 336-4525
Port Saint Lucie *(G-15143)*
Signs Plus New IDS-New Tech In F 941 378-4262
Sarasota *(G-16596)*
▲ **Signs Supreme Inc** G 561 795-0111
Wellington *(G-18734)*
Signs Unlimited Inc G 727 845-0330
Saint Augustine *(G-15612)*
Signs Unlimited of Bay County G 850 785-1061
Panama City *(G-13949)*
Signs Unlimited Sea Inc F 352 732-7341
Ocala *(G-12052)*
Signs Usa Inc F 813 901-9333
Tampa *(G-18105)*

Signsations Inc G 561 989-1900
Boca Raton *(G-712)*
Signsharks Sign Service G 904 766-6222
Jacksonville *(G-6773)*
Signsitecom Inc G 386 487-0265
Lake City *(G-7385)*
Signway Inc G 407 696-7446
Winter Park *(G-19444)*
Site Essentials G 813 865-0208
Odessa *(G-12152)*
Sitecrafters of Florida Inc E 813 258-4696
Tampa *(G-18106)*
Sky-High Sign & Lighting Inc G 813 994-3954
Palm Harbor *(G-13761)*
Skylite Signs & Services Inc F 305 362-5015
Hialeah *(G-5621)*
Skyway Signs and Wraps LLC G 727 692-2786
Wimauma *(G-19224)*
Sneids Inc G 561 278-7446
Delray Beach *(G-3144)*
Solar Enterprises Inc E 904 724-2262
Jacksonville *(G-6783)*
South Florida Sign Co G 954 973-6649
Pompano Beach *(G-14858)*
Southeastern Ltg Solutions E 386 238-1711
Daytona Beach *(G-2716)*
Southern Exhibits and Graphics G 407 423-2860
Orlando *(G-13203)*
Sp Sign LLC F 772 562-0955
Stuart *(G-17020)*
Spectrum Signworks LLC G 239 908-0505
Naples *(G-11415)*
Speed Pro Miami G 954 534-9503
Miramar *(G-11045)*
Speedpro Imaging G 772 320-9385
Stuart *(G-17021)*
Speedpro Imaging St Petersburg G 727 266-0956
Saint Petersburg *(G-15922)*
Speedpro of Orlando West G 407 509-8956
Orlando *(G-13206)*
Speedysignscom Inc E 386 755-2006
Lake City *(G-7386)*
Sposen Signature Homes LLC F 239 244-8886
Cape Coral *(G-1478)*
Srq Sign Partners LLC F 941 357-0319
Sarasota *(G-16298)*
Srq Sign Partners LLC G 941 417-4000
Sarasota *(G-16299)*
St Lucie Signs LLC G 772 971-6363
Fort Pierce *(G-4750)*
Startek Services LLC G 631 224-9220
Palm Bay *(G-13539)*
Stellar Sign and Design LLC F 407 660-3174
Winter Park *(G-19449)*
Stellar Signs Grap G 561 721-6060
West Palm Beach *(G-19043)*
Stephens Advertising Inc G 904 354-7004
Jacksonville *(G-6812)*
Steven Chancas F 352 629-5016
Ocala *(G-12059)*
Street Signs USA Inc G 561 848-1411
Lake Park *(G-7480)*
Sun Graphic Technologies Inc E 941 753-7541
Sarasota *(G-16305)*
Suncoast Investmens of PA G 941 722-5391
Palmetto *(G-13826)*
Suncoast Sign Shop Inc F 941 448-5835
Sarasota *(G-16608)*
Suncoast Signs Inc G 813 664-0699
Tampa *(G-18145)*
Sungraf Inc F 954 456-8500
Hallandale Beach *(G-5216)*
Sunray Reflections Inc G 305 305-6350
Hollywood *(G-5917)*
Superior Signs Inc F 407 601-7964
Orlando *(G-13231)*
Superior Unlimited Enterprises G 863 294-1683
Winter Haven *(G-19360)*
Szabo Pos Displays Inc G 941 778-0192
Bradenton *(G-1124)*
T & C Godby Enterprises Inc E 407 831-6334
Casselberry *(G-1519)*
Tattoo Factory Inc E 941 923-4110
Sarasota *(G-16616)*
Taylor Sign & Design Inc F 904 396-4652
Jacksonville *(G-6839)*
▲ **Thomas Sign and Awning Co Inc** C 727 573-7757
Clearwater *(G-1919)*
Thomas United Inc G 239 561-7446
Fort Myers *(G-4628)*

▼ **Tigo Inc** ....E.... 954 935-5990
Fort Lauderdale *(G-4284)*
Tone Printing LLC ....G.... 855 505-8663
Miami *(G-10489)*
Total Sign Solutions ....G.... 561 264-2551
Riviera Beach *(G-15386)*
Townsend Signs Inc ....G.... 386 255-1955
Holly Hill *(G-5761)*
Traffic Control Pdts Fla Inc ....F.... 352 372-7088
Jacksonville *(G-6865)*
▲ **Trident Trading Inc** ....G.... 561 488-0458
Boca Raton *(G-756)*
Trinity Signs LLC ....G.... 850 502-7634
Shalimar *(G-16778)*
Tropical Signs & Graphics ....G.... 321 458-7742
Merritt Island *(G-9017)*
Tru-Art Signs &GRaphix Inc ....G.... 561 371-2388
Stuart *(G-17040)*
Ufg Group Inc ....G.... 561 425-6829
West Palm Beach *(G-19074)*
Ultimate Sign Mfg LLC ....G.... 954 864-7776
Oakland Park *(G-11852)*
Ultimate Sign Service LLC ....G.... 813 210-3166
Tampa *(G-18213)*
Unique Led Products LLC ....G.... 440 520-4959
North Port *(G-11752)*
Unisigns Usa Inc ....G.... 305 509-5232
Doral *(G-3538)*
United Advantage Signs Inc ....D.... 813 855-3300
Oldsmar *(G-12273)*
United Visual Branding LLC ....D.... 813 855-3300
Oldsmar *(G-12274)*
Universal Signs ....G.... 954 366-1535
Fort Lauderdale *(G-4297)*
US Sign and Mill Inc ....E.... 239 936-9154
Fort Myers *(G-4641)*
US Signs Inc ....E.... 727 862-7933
Port Richey *(G-15075)*
USA Sign Company ....G.... 954 497-3293
Weston *(G-19176)*
USA Signs Inc ....G.... 305 470-2333
Miami *(G-10556)*
Van Gogh Signs & Displays ....G.... 813 849-7446
Tampa *(G-18233)*
Vb Custom Signs Inc ....G.... 772 713-5678
Vero Beach *(G-18676)*
Vibrant Sign Studio LLC ....G.... 305 363-2181
Miami *(G-10577)*
Vintage Art and Sign LLC ....G.... 770 815-7887
Niceville *(G-11576)*
Vinyl Bros ....G.... 850 396-5977
Gulf Breeze *(G-5131)*
Vinyl Etchings Inc ....G.... 727 845-5300
Port Richey *(G-15076)*
◆ **Vista System LLC** ....E.... 941 365-4646
Sarasota *(G-16634)*
Visual Signs LLC ....G.... 407 693-0200
Orlando *(G-13306)*
Vital Signs of Orlando Inc ....G.... 407 297-0680
Orlando *(G-13309)*
Vivid Images USA Inc ....F.... 904 620-0303
Jacksonville *(G-6902)*
Volunteer Capital LLC ....G.... 954 366-6659
Deerfield Beach *(G-2934)*
▲ **Waterboyz Wbz Inc** ....F.... 850 433-2929
Pensacola *(G-14287)*
Watershpes By Greg Gnstrom Inc ....G.... 321 777-5432
West Melbourne *(G-18779)*
Way Bright Sign Systems ....G.... 615 480-4602
Santa Rosa Beach *(G-16169)*
We Sign It Inc ....G.... 772 800-7373
Port Saint Lucie *(G-15164)*
We Sign It Inc ....F.... 772 577-4400
Fort Pierce *(G-4769)*
▼ **West Central Signs Inc** ....E.... 813 980-6763
Tampa *(G-18255)*
West Coast Signs ....E.... 941 755-5686
Sarasota *(G-16326)*
White Sands Dmg Inc ....G.... 305 947-7731
North Miami Beach *(G-11712)*
White Sign Company LLC ....G.... 386 516-6156
Debary *(G-2757)*
White Sign Company LLC ....G.... 407 342-7887
Debary *(G-2758)*
Wholesale Sign Superstore Inc ....F.... 321 212-8458
Rockledge *(G-15457)*
Wholesale Signs Fabricators ....G.... 407 729-5599
Kissimmee *(G-7311)*
Windstone Development Intl Lc ....F.... 954 370-7201
Davie *(G-2615)*
Xtreme Signs Printing Inc ....F.... 321 438-3954
Orlando *(G-13334)*
Yesco Orlando South ....G.... 407 922-5856
Kissimmee *(G-7312)*
Yesco Sign and Lighting ....G.... 407 321-3577
Sanford *(G-16142)*
Ysl Graphics LLC ....G.... 954 916-7255
Sunrise *(G-17200)*
Z & L Partners Inc ....G.... 813 639-0066
Tampa *(G-18279)*
Zeeeees Corporation ....G.... 407 624-3796
Saint Cloud *(G-15671)*
Zoo Holdings LLC ....G.... 941 355-5653
Sarasota *(G-16647)*

3995 Burial Caskets

Service Corp International ....G.... 321 636-6041
Cocoa *(G-2050)*

3996 Linoleum & Hard Surface Floor Coverings, NEC

Amercn Cabinets Granite Floors ....F.... 727 303-0678
Palm Harbor *(G-13718)*

3999 Manufacturing Industries, NEC

1800flowerscom ....G.... 954 683-1246
Fort Lauderdale *(G-3771)*
2 Guys Company ....G.... 786 970-9275
Miami *(G-9023)*
3fdm Inc ....F.... 727 877-3336
Largo *(G-7879)*
A J M O Industries Inc ....G.... 954 587-0206
Plantation *(G-14480)*
A Morris Industries LLC ....G.... 239 308-2199
Lehigh Acres *(G-8183)*
AB Used Pallets Inc ....F.... 305 594-2776
Miami *(G-9050)*
Acroturn Industries Usa LLC ....F.... 754 205-7178
Tavares *(G-18333)*
Adma ....E.... 561 989-5800
Boca Raton *(G-399)*
Adonel Block Mfg Corp ....F.... 561 615-9500
Miami *(G-9070)*
▲ **Advanced Hair Products Inc** ....G.... 561 347-2799
Deerfield Beach *(G-2764)*
Advanced Sewing ....G.... 954 484-2100
Fort Lauderdale *(G-3784)*
Advanced Vacuum Systems LLC ....G.... 941 378-4565
Sarasota *(G-16334)*
Aesthetics Complete Inc ....G.... 610 265-3535
Venice *(G-18530)*
Agripure Cbd LLC ....G.... 561 789-3819
Boca Raton *(G-407)*
Air Technical LLC ....F.... 305 837-3274
Saint Petersburg *(G-15696)*
AK Industries LLC ....F.... 954 662-7038
West Park *(G-19091)*
Albixon USA LLC ....G.... 954 297-2000
Fort Lauderdale *(G-3794)*
Allan Industries ....F.... 407 875-0897
Orlando *(G-12456)*
Almar Industries Inc ....F.... 305 385-8284
Miami *(G-9120)*
Alta Industries LLC ....G.... 305 343-6091
Miami *(G-9122)*
Alvis Industries Inc ....G.... 941 377-7800
Sarasota *(G-16341)*
▲ **Always Flowers Inc** ....F.... 305 572-1122
Miami *(G-9128)*
American Polylactide Inds ....G.... 352 653-5963
Ocala *(G-11872)*
American Trophy Co ....G.... 954 782-2250
Pompano Beach *(G-14594)*
Anchor Industries LLC ....G.... 850 509-8344
Tallahassee *(G-17219)*
Andro Corp Industries ....G.... 917 287-5294
Ocoee *(G-12083)*
Anu Industries Inc ....E.... 813 927-7254
Weeki Wachee *(G-18700)*
Apex Grinding Inc ....G.... 386 624-7350
Deland *(G-2958)*
▼ **Aquacal** ....E.... 727 898-2412
Saint Petersburg *(G-15704)*
ARI Specialties LLC ....G.... 321 269-2244
Mims *(G-10949)*
Arm Almnum Rling Mnfctures LLC ....G.... 813 626-2264
Tampa *(G-17433)*
Armageddon Manufacturing ....G.... 772 208-5288
Stuart *(G-16909)*
▲ **Armor Holdings Forensics LLC** ....E.... 904 485-1836
Jacksonville *(G-6169)*
Armor Industries Corp ....G.... 813 240-5903
Seffner *(G-16720)*
Armour Companies LLC ....G.... 386 740-7459
Deland *(G-2961)*
Arsenal Industries LLC ....F.... 407 506-2698
Winter Park *(G-19380)*
Arsenal Venture Partners Fla ....G.... 407 838-1400
Winter Park *(G-19381)*
◆ **Art & Frame Direct Inc** ....C.... 407 857-6000
Orlando *(G-12491)*
Artec Manufacturing LLC ....G.... 305 888-4375
Hialeah *(G-5305)*
Arthrex Manufacturing Inc ....G.... 239 304-2236
Ave Maria *(G-256)*
Artistic Paver Mfg ....G.... 305 949-0000
Miramar *(G-10969)*
ASG Corp ....G.... 718 641-4500
Miami Beach *(G-10645)*
Astroted Inc ....G.... 786 220-5898
Doral *(G-3257)*
Atria Industry ....G.... 786 334-6621
Doral *(G-3260)*
Audio Excellence ....G.... 407 277-8790
Orlando *(G-12500)*
Aurel Partners LLC ....E.... 203 300-7470
Lake Mary *(G-7401)*
Axiom Manufacturing Inc ....G.... 321 223-3394
West Melbourne *(G-18766)*
Axtonne Inc ....G.... 510 755-7480
Delray Beach *(G-3048)*
Bala Industries LLC ....E.... 954 243-9804
Lakeland *(G-7642)*
Balistic 2400 LLC ....F.... 407 955-0065
Naples *(G-11180)*
Balkan Industries LLC ....F.... 727 485-3357
New Port Richey *(G-11482)*
Bam Industries Inc ....G.... 561 674-2185
Boca Raton *(G-441)*
▲ **Banyan Gaming LLC** ....F.... 954 951-7094
Deerfield Beach *(G-2783)*
Bare Arii LLC ....G.... 352 701-6625
Tampa *(G-17455)*
Barth Industries ....F.... 727 787-6392
Dunedin *(G-3569)*
Basanite Industries LLC ....F.... 954 532-1726
Pompano Beach *(G-14616)*
Bass Auto Industries LLC ....G.... 727 446-4051
Clearwater *(G-1600)*
Bdjl Enterprises LLC ....F.... 407 678-9960
Apopka *(G-116)*
Be The Solution Inc ....G.... 850 545-2043
Tallahassee *(G-17227)*
Beata Bordas ....G.... 772 349-2568
Stuart *(G-16915)*
Beauty Cosmetica ....F.... 305 406-1022
Opa Locka *(G-12293)*
Belongea Industries ....G.... 574 209-1045
Arcadia *(G-200)*
Bernat Industries Intl LLC ....G.... 727 350-5904
Gulfport *(G-5132)*
◆ **Betty Dain Creations LLC** ....D.... 305 769-3451
Medley *(G-8623)*
Biggs Industries Inc ....G.... 561 775-6944
Palm Beach Gardens *(G-13569)*
Biochem Manufacturing Inc ....G.... 786 210-1290
Miami *(G-9248)*
Biochemical Manufacturing Inc ....G.... 561 799-1590
Jupiter *(G-7011)*
Black Creek Precision LLC ....F.... 888 426-6624
Jacksonville *(G-6209)*
Black Oak Industries Inc ....G.... 863 307-1566
Winter Haven *(G-19303)*
Blackwter Metal Sls NW Fla LLC ....G.... 850 622-1414
Milton *(G-10924)*
Bld Industries ....G.... 321 207-0050
Altamonte Springs *(G-33)*
Bluum Lab LLC ....F.... 877 341-3339
Hallandale Beach *(G-5173)*
Body Chemistry Industries In C ....G.... 561 253-4438
Wellington *(G-18711)*
Body Manufactur E Inc ....G.... 386 264-6040
Palm Coast *(G-13686)*
Botanical Innovations Inc ....G.... 407 332-8733
Maitland *(G-8460)*
Brads Industries LLC ....G.... 863 646-0051
Lakeland *(G-7649)*
Brainchild Corp ....E.... 239 263-0100
Naples *(G-11193)*

SIC

Brandano Displays Inc ....E.... 954 956-7266
Margate *(G-8537)*
Brevard Achievement Center Inc ....B.... 321 632-8610
Rockledge *(G-15395)*
Brewer International Inc ....F.... 772 562-0555
Vero Beach *(G-18603)*
Bri Tin Industries ....G.... 941 580-6345
Plant City *(G-14411)*
Bruns Mfg Homes ....G.... 863 294-4949
Winter Haven *(G-19307)*
Bubblemac Industries Inc ....G.... 352 396-8043
Mc Alpin *(G-8598)*
Built Story LLC ....G.... 305 671-3890
Miami *(G-9283)*
Burr Industries LLC ....G.... 619 254-2309
Cocoa *(G-2002)*
C & M Manufacturing LLC ....G.... 407 673-9601
Winter Park *(G-19386)*
◆ **C M I Enterprises Inc** ....E.... 305 622-6410
Opa Locka *(G-12297)*
C&P Industries Inc ....G.... 813 685-3131
Dover *(G-3557)*
Cafco LLC ....G.... 240 848-5574
Miami *(G-9301)*
Campbell Manufacturing Inc ....G.... 727 443-4508
Clearwater *(G-1621)*
Candle For You LLC ....G.... 920 883-7900
Jacksonville *(G-6252)*
Cannon Industries Inc ....F.... 727 320-5040
New Port Richey *(G-11486)*
Cape Candle LLC ....G.... 239 357-6766
Cape Coral *(G-1402)*
Caribbean Basin Industries Inc ....G.... 941 726-7272
Nokomis *(G-11579)*
Cas Industries LLC ....G.... 813 986-2694
Plant City *(G-14416)*
Castle Distributing Industries ....G.... 305 336-0855
Miramar *(G-10978)*
Category 5 Manufacturing Inc ....F.... 561 777-2491
Lantana *(G-7869)*
Category 5 Manufacturing Inc ....G.... 561 502-4153
Lake Worth *(G-7540)*
Cavok Capital LLC ....F.... 727 789-0951
Palm Harbor *(G-13726)*
Cbd LLC ....F.... 305 615-1194
Fort Lauderdale *(G-3886)*
Cbd Biocare ....G.... 813 380-4376
Largo *(G-7921)*
Cbd Docs LLC ....G.... 954 868-5152
Lake Worth *(G-7541)*
Cbd Dstrbuted By Miami Cbd Inc ....G.... 561 316-7456
Boynton Beach *(G-887)*
Cbd Life Florida Inc ....G.... 352 483-8333
Eustis *(G-3705)*
Cbd-ME LLC ....G.... 847 910-0505
Boca Raton *(G-473)*
Cbdpharm LLC ....G.... 813 442-5464
Tampa *(G-17518)*
CCA Industries Inc ....F.... 813 601-6238
Dade City *(G-2424)*
CCI Hair Boutique LLC ....F.... 407 408-8649
Orlando *(G-12558)*
Celios Corporation ....G.... 833 235-4671
Tampa *(G-17520)*
Centurion Residential Inds ....E.... 561 574-1483
West Palm Beach *(G-18843)*
Cgc Industries Inc ....G.... 954 923-2428
Hollywood *(G-5797)*
Chattam Industries Inc ....G.... 727 748-2419
Palm Harbor *(G-13728)*
◆ **Chelly Cosmetics Manufacturing** ....G.... 305 471-9608
Miami *(G-9350)*
Classic Hardwood Design ....G.... 850 232-6473
Molino *(G-11073)*
Classic Industries Inc ....F.... 561 855-4609
Wellington *(G-18714)*
Clifton Studio Inc ....G.... 813 240-0286
Tampa *(G-17542)*
CLJ Industries Inc ....G.... 562 688-0508
Jacksonville *(G-6269)*
Cloud Industries ....G.... 816 213-2730
Sarasota *(G-16385)*
Cmz Industries LLC ....G.... 727 726-1443
Clearwater *(G-1629)*
Coastal Aircraft Parts LLC ....G.... 954 980-6929
Sunrise *(G-17106)*
Coastal Industries USA LLC ....G.... 954 946-5223
Pompano Beach *(G-14638)*
Codsworth Industries Inc ....G.... 203 622-5151
North Miami *(G-11634)*

▲ **Collectibles of SW Florida** ....G.... 239 332-2344
Cape Coral *(G-1404)*
Colonial Industries Centl Fla ....G.... 407 484-5239
Lake Mary *(G-7406)*
Comiskey Industries Inc ....G.... 201 925-0998
Palm Coast *(G-13688)*
Commercial Metal Photography ....G.... 407 295-8182
Orlando *(G-12605)*
▲ **Condition Culture LLC** ....F.... 786 433-8279
Boynton Beach *(G-892)*
Conquest Manufacturing Fla LLC ....F.... 954 655-0139
Pompano Beach *(G-14644)*
Costa Industries LLC ....G.... 813 453-3171
Riverview *(G-15268)*
▲ **Creative Events and Exhibits** ....G.... 407 851-4754
Orlando *(G-12625)*
◆ **Cross Match Technologies Inc** ....C.... 561 622-1650
Palm Beach Gardens *(G-13583)*
Crossroads Industries LLC ....G.... 305 967-8116
Miami *(G-9412)*
Crowe Manufacturing ....G.... 813 334-1921
Tampa *(G-17569)*
Crown Leao Industries Inc ....G.... 561 866-1218
Boca Raton *(G-493)*
▲ **Crown Products LLC** ....G.... 954 917-1118
Pompano Beach *(G-14652)*
◆ **Crystal Art of Florida Inc** ....G.... 305 885-5358
Coral Springs *(G-2235)*
Ctr Industries ....G.... 321 264-1458
Mims *(G-10950)*
Daje Industries Inc ....G.... 305 592-7711
Doral *(G-3322)*
Dar Industries Inc ....G.... 904 327-9689
Jacksonville *(G-6310)*
Daytona Magic Inc ....G.... 386 252-6767
Daytona Beach *(G-2655)*
Deal To Win Inc ....E.... 718 609-1165
Oakland Park *(G-11796)*
Debut Development LLC ....G.... 863 448-9081
Wauchula *(G-18690)*
▼ **Desco Industries** ....G.... 305 255-7744
Miami *(G-9457)*
Designer Services of ....G.... 772 286-0855
Stuart *(G-16932)*
Desind Industries Corp ....G.... 212 729-0192
Orlando *(G-12665)*
Destiny & Light Inc ....F.... 813 476-8386
Tampa *(G-17601)*
Dianthus Miami Inc ....G.... 786 800-8365
Miami *(G-9464)*
▲ **Dkm Machine Manufacturing** ....F.... 904 733-0103
Jacksonville *(G-6323)*
Dontech Industries Inc ....G.... 847 682-1776
Saint Petersburg *(G-15763)*
Double D S Tobacco ....G.... 772 871-9910
Delray Beach *(G-3070)*
Dp Industries Inc ....G.... 321 356-3352
Saint Cloud *(G-15649)*
Dr Bains Premier Cbd Oil ....G.... 727 992-5289
New Port Richey *(G-11489)*
Dragon Glassing LLC ....G.... 904 509-1860
Jacksonville Beach *(G-6942)*
Duck In The Truck Puppets Inc ....G.... 772 334-3022
Jensen Beach *(G-6967)*
Dyer Industries Inc ....G.... 954 434-9065
Southwest Ranches *(G-16837)*
Dynamic Manufacturing Inc ....G.... 727 639-8633
Longwood *(G-8275)*
◆ **Dyno LLC** ....E.... 954 971-2910
Pompano Beach *(G-14670)*
E & A Industries Inc ....F.... 954 278-2428
Fort Lauderdale *(G-3954)*
E Benton Grimsley Inc ....G.... 850 863-4064
Fort Walton Beach *(G-4797)*
E M Chadbourne Inds LLC ....G.... 850 429-1797
Pensacola *(G-14135)*
▲ **Easydrift LLC** ....G.... 352 318-3683
Gainesville *(G-4912)*
Easyturf Inc ....F.... 941 753-3312
Ellenton *(G-3653)*
Echodog Industries Inc ....G.... 407 909-1636
Orlando *(G-12695)*
Ecolab Inc ....F.... 800 931-8911
Jupiter *(G-7031)*
◆ **Ecotec Manufacturing Inc** ....E.... 863 357-4500
Okeechobee *(G-12177)*
Ecstatic Nails Inc ....G.... 305 328-9554
North Miami *(G-11636)*
Edumatics Inc ....F.... 407 656-0661
Orlando *(G-12699)*

▲ **Egm Manufacturing Corp** ....F.... 954 440-0445
Sunrise *(G-17118)*
El Teide North Industries ....G.... 786 830-7506
Miami *(G-9508)*
Elastec Inc ....F.... 618 382-2525
Cocoa *(G-2019)*
Elite Flower Services Inc ....E.... 305 436-7400
Miami *(G-9515)*
EMC Manufacturing ....G.... 305 613-9546
Miami *(G-9523)*
Emerging Mfg Tech Inc ....G.... 407 341-3476
Lake Mary *(G-7410)*
Empire Enterprises ....G.... 786 373-8003
Hialeah *(G-5396)*
Endeavor Manufacturing Inc ....F.... 954 752-6828
Deerfield Beach *(G-2822)*
Enduris Extrusions Inc ....E.... 321 914-0897
Melbourne *(G-8825)*
Engitork Industries Llc ....G.... 239 877-8499
Naples *(G-11239)*
Esther Industries Inc ....G.... 850 456-6163
Pensacola *(G-14146)*
Europe Coating Industries LLC ....G.... 786 535-4143
Medley *(G-8648)*
Evergreen Rush Industries Inc ....F.... 954 825-9291
Davie *(G-2520)*
Express Badging Services Inc ....F.... 321 784-5925
Cocoa Beach *(G-2062)*
Eye Wall Industries Inc ....G.... 850 607-2288
Pensacola *(G-14147)*
Fagerberg Industries LLC ....F.... 352 318-2254
Gainesville *(G-4919)*
▲ **Falco Industries Inc** ....G.... 407 956-0045
Longwood *(G-8281)*
Fam Industries Inc ....F.... 281 779-0650
Jacksonville *(G-6377)*
Fashionable Canes ....F.... 727 547-8866
Largo *(G-7942)*
FBI Industries Inc ....G.... 239 462-1176
Fort Myers *(G-4448)*
Fbj Engineering & Dev LLC ....G.... 754 423-1309
Coral Springs *(G-2244)*
Fcs Industries Corp ....G.... 407 947-3127
Ocoee *(G-12085)*
Fcs Industries Corp ....G.... 407 412-5642
Orlando *(G-12735)*
Ferrelli Industries Inc ....G.... 305 792-0100
North Miami Beach *(G-11677)*
◆ **Fi-Foil Company Inc** ....E.... 863 965-1846
Auburndale *(G-240)*
Field Specialties ....G.... 440 635-0282
Morriston *(G-11092)*
Fine Industries Corporation ....G.... 321 452-6956
Merritt Island *(G-9001)*
Finger Lakes Custom Mfg LLC ....G.... 315 283-4849
Ocala *(G-11941)*
First Cast Fla Mfg Support LLC ....G.... 904 434-4128
Orange Park *(G-12394)*
◆ **Five Star Quality Mfg Corp** ....G.... 954 972-4772
Fort Lauderdale *(G-3996)*
FL Industries Inc ....G.... 954 422-3766
Pompano Beach *(G-14697)*
Flex Beauty Labs LLC ....F.... 646 302-8542
Orlando *(G-12743)*
Flex Innovations Inc ....G.... 866 310-3539
Venice *(G-18548)*
Florida Elite Industries LLC ....G.... 727 223-4233
Largo *(G-7948)*
Florida Factory Agents Inc ....G.... 754 264-9432
Hollywood *(G-5822)*
Florida Freshner Corp ....G.... 954 349-0348
Weston *(G-19125)*
Florida Manufactured Home ....G.... 407 509-8262
Christmas *(G-1550)*
Florida Nbty Manufacturing ....F.... 561 922-4800
Boca Raton *(G-532)*
Floridas Finest Industries ....F.... 239 333-1777
Fort Myers *(G-4455)*
Flushing Amusement Inc ....G.... 813 780-7900
Zephyrhills *(G-19520)*
Fox Industries of Swfl Inc ....F.... 239 732-6199
Naples *(G-11249)*
Fox Manufacturing LLC ....G.... 904 531-3150
Green Cove Springs *(G-5062)*
Fraziers Fabrication ....G.... 813 928-1449
Dover *(G-3559)*
Full Throttle Cnc Inc ....G.... 248 525-1973
Fort Myers *(G-4460)*
Fuller Amusements ....G.... 352 629-2792
Ocala *(G-11951)*

Fusion Industries.....G..... 239 592-7070
Naples (G-11254)
Fusion Industries LLC.....F..... 239 415-7554
Fort Myers (G-4461)
Fuzion Digital Signs.....G..... 844 529-0505
Tampa (G-17699)
▼ Gator Dock & Marine LLC.....F..... 407 323-0190
Sanford (G-16054)
Gator Fabrications LLC.....G..... 352 245-7227
Belleview (G-369)
Gibbons Industries Inc.....G..... 352 330-0294
Lutz (G-8384)
Gilla Inc.....G..... 416 843-2881
Daytona Beach (G-2668)
Global Composite USA Inc.....E..... 813 898-7987
Tampa (G-17714)
Global Industries and Mfg Inc.....G..... 954 766-4656
Plantation (G-14521)
Global Products Group LLC.....E..... 866 320-4367
Tampa (G-17717)
◆ Global Seashell Industries LLC.....G..... 813 677-6674
Tampa (G-17718)
Gloval Displays Inc.....E..... 800 972-0353
Miami Gardens (G-10742)
▲ Goodcat LLC.....E..... 239 254-8288
Naples (G-11264)
Goodwill Industries S Fla Inc.....C..... 941 745-8459
Bradenton (G-1051)
Grafico Industries Inc.....G..... 941 473-2800
Englewood (G-3660)
Gravity Colors Usa Inc.....G..... 561 419-5272
Delray Beach (G-3086)
▲ Green Touch Industries Inc.....G..... 561 659-5525
West Palm Beach (G-18890)
Guild Mfg Solutions LLC.....G..... 407 366-5165
Oviedo (G-13433)
Gulfstream Goodwill Inds Inc.....E..... 561 362-8662
Boca Raton (G-554)
Gvi Industries Inc.....G..... 954 514-7283
Pompano Beach (G-14720)
Gvi Industries Inc.....G..... 954 818-6411
Fort Lauderdale (G-4036)
Gyrotonic Mfg Inc.....G..... 305 397-8070
Miami Beach (G-10676)
H V Payne Mfg LLC.....G..... 941 773-1112
Sarasota (G-16456)
Hall Industries Incorporated.....F..... 239 768-0372
Fort Myers (G-4480)
Halliday Industries LLC.....G..... 321 288-3979
Melbourne (G-8838)
Hardrives Industries Inc.....E..... 561 278-0456
Delray Beach (G-3090)
Hayes Ivy Manufacturing.....G..... 954 306-2647
Fort Lauderdale (G-4043)
Hbys Enterprises LLC.....F..... 855 290-9900
Winter Springs (G-19473)
Hemp Cbd Daily Inc.....G..... 904 672-7623
Jacksonville (G-6467)
◆ Higgins Group Corp.....E..... 305 681-4444
Miami (G-9709)
High Temp Industries.....G..... 215 794-0864
Cape Coral (G-1434)
Hjr Industries LLC.....G..... 706 761-1200
Gibsonton (G-5029)
▲ Hollywood Cllctibles Group LLC.....G..... 407 985-4613
Orlando (G-12806)
Homeshield Industries Corp.....G..... 239 573-0802
Cape Coral (G-1437)
▲ Honeycommcore LLC.....G..... 561 747-2678
West Palm Beach (G-18897)
Hopkins Manufacturing Co.....G..... 620 591-8229
Tarpon Springs (G-18307)
Horizon Industries Inc.....F..... 561 315-5439
Royal Palm Beach (G-15470)
Hughes Fabrication.....G..... 239 481-1376
Fort Myers (G-4487)
Hunter Industries.....G..... 561 775-3239
Palm Beach Gardens (G-13595)
Hurricane Marine Manufacturing.....F..... 772 260-3950
Stuart (G-16955)
Hydro Industries-Usa LLC.....G..... 305 440-0893
Miami (G-9722)
I-75 Industries Inc.....G..... 352 840-3155
Ocala (G-11967)
Ibs Manufacturing LLC.....G..... 352 629-9752
Ocala (G-11968)
Ice Bunker A&M Corp.....F..... 786 368-0924
Hialeah (G-5452)
Imagination Enterprises LLC.....F..... 504 289-9691
Orlando (G-12823)

In The News Inc.....D..... 813 882-8886
Tampa (G-17775)
Innevape LLC.....G..... 631 957-6500
Hudson (G-6029)
Instatech Industries Inc.....G..... 954 415-4392
Lake Worth (G-7557)
◆ International Dock Products.....F..... 954 964-5315
Hallandale Beach (G-5191)
International Greenscapes LLC.....D..... 760 631-6789
Miami (G-9758)
International Vapor Group LLC.....D..... 305 824-4027
Miami Lakes (G-10799)
Intouch Inc.....F..... 702 572-4786
Orlando (G-12839)
Inusa Manufacturing LLC.....G..... 786 451-5227
Pembroke Park (G-14009)
Invigicom Inc.....G..... 407 491-6929
Apopka (G-149)
Island Lifestyle Importers LLC.....G..... 941 378-3200
Sarasota (G-16473)
Italian Hair Extension Inc.....G..... 954 839-5366
Sunrise (G-17131)
Its A 10 Inc.....G..... 954 227-7813
Coral Springs (G-2262)
Its Technologies Logistics LLC.....C..... 904 751-1300
Jacksonville (G-6505)
Iver Services.....F..... 786 329-3018
North Miami Beach (G-11684)
J C Industries Inc.....G..... 863 773-9199
Bradenton (G-1063)
Jamali Industries LLC.....G..... 954 908-5075
Sunrise (G-17134)
Jane and George Industries.....F..... 727 698-4903
Saint Petersburg (G-15832)
Jans Ventures LLC.....F..... 352 341-1710
Inverness (G-6090)
Je TAime Fragrances.....G..... 727 581-0970
Largo (G-7987)
Jerry Metallo.....G..... 305 972-2927
Princeton (G-15184)
Jess By Inches LLC.....G..... 305 731-1387
North Miami Beach (G-11686)
Jet Factory LLC.....G..... 305 848-8846
Boynton Beach (G-924)
Jfliszo Industries Inc.....G..... 239 215-6965
Fort Myers (G-4503)
JMTM Anufacturing Inc.....G..... 727 847-7665
Port Richey (G-15058)
Joni Industries Inc.....F..... 352 799-5456
Brooksville (G-1240)
Jq Industries Inc.....G..... 407 509-3880
Longwood (G-8298)
Jsp Manufacturing Holdings LLC.....G..... 727 488-5353
Pinellas Park (G-14358)
Jta Industries LLC.....G..... 407 352-4255
Orlando (G-12863)
Jta Industries LLC.....F..... 321 663-4395
Orlando (G-12864)
Jtac Industries LLC.....G..... 813 928-0628
Plant City (G-14441)
Just Fur Fun.....G..... 561 809-6596
Boca Raton (G-584)
JW Fabrications Inc.....G..... 772 201-7097
Okeechobee (G-12184)
K & N Industries Inc.....G..... 850 939-7722
Navarre (G-11467)
K Bausch Mfg Corp.....G..... 772 485-2426
Stuart (G-16963)
▼ Kaluz LLC.....E..... 786 991-2260
Miami (G-9814)
Kamco Industries LLC.....F..... 772 299-1401
Vero Beach (G-18635)
Kcon Industries LLC.....G..... 917 250-7402
Hialeah (G-5471)
Keller Manufacturing Inc.....G..... 863 937-8928
Lakeland (G-7724)
Kent Mfg Fla Keys Inc.....F..... 941 488-0355
Venice (G-18559)
Keys Deck & Dock Supplies Inc.....G..... 305 451-8001
Key Largo (G-7172)
Keystone Rv Company.....C..... 813 228-0625
Tampa (G-17821)
King Kanine LLC.....E..... 833 546-4738
Plantation (G-14528)
Kirkland Industries LLC.....G..... 386 496-3491
Lake Butler (G-7339)
KLA Industries.....G..... 727 315-4719
Largo (G-7992)
Km Coatings Mfg Jr.....F..... 602 253-1168
Deerfield Beach (G-2854)

Knight Industries.....G..... 772 344-2053
Port Saint Lucie (G-15117)
Kos Industries Inc.....G..... 863 318-1511
Winter Haven (G-19333)
Kt Fab Inc.....G..... 863 443-0029
Lake Wales (G-7514)
L & J Cbd LLC.....G..... 904 305-9700
Macclenny (G-8443)
Laal Manufacturing Inc.....G..... 786 859-3613
Miami (G-9850)
Lakeridge Falls Art League.....G..... 941 360-1046
Sarasota (G-16247)
Lampshades of Florida Inc.....F..... 954 491-3377
Deerfield Beach (G-2856)
Lancaster Industries Inc.....G..... 954 916-9293
Davie (G-2543)
Lane Shark Usa LLC.....G..... 864 382-6892
Mc David (G-8601)
Larson Industries.....G..... 352 226-8512
Gainesville (G-4951)
Larson Industries Incorporated.....F..... 352 262-0566
Gainesville (G-4952)
Lawless Industries Ltd.....G..... 352 429-3300
Groveland (G-5099)
LDM Industries Inc.....G..... 305 216-1545
Miami (G-9874)
Le Posh Pup.....G..... 561 625-6391
Okeechobee (G-12186)
Legends Fabrications LLC.....G..... 727 642-0578
Largo (G-7999)
▼ Lemon Grass Industries Inc.....G..... 954 418-6110
Parkland (G-13995)
Lesko Industries Inc.....G..... 904 273-8293
Ponte Vedra (G-14926)
Lftd Partners Inc.....F..... 847 915-2446
Jacksonville (G-6555)
Lifetime Products Group Inc.....G..... 813 781-9182
Gibsonton (G-5031)
Lion Locs LLC.....F..... 704 802-2752
Orlando (G-12914)
Live Well Cbds.....G..... 954 723-0580
Davie (G-2547)
Load King Manufacturing.....G..... 904 633-7352
Jacksonville (G-6559)
Look Worldwide Inc.....G..... 305 662-1287
Miami (G-9910)
Lost Fabrication LLC.....G..... 772 971-3467
Fort Pierce (G-4712)
Lov Industries Inc.....G..... 407 406-8221
Kissimmee (G-7272)
Low Life Industries Inc.....G..... 813 609-5599
Tampa (G-17861)
Luther Industries LLC.....G..... 813 833-5652
Tampa (G-17864)
Luv & Luv Industries Inc.....G..... 954 826-6237
Hialeah (G-5491)
M J Boturla Industries Inc.....G..... 386 574-0811
Deltona (G-3174)
M Pet Group Corp.....G..... 954 455-5003
Aventura (G-276)
Maddox Industries Inc.....G..... 561 529-2165
Jupiter (G-7071)
Made Fur You Inc.....G..... 813 444-7707
Hudson (G-6032)
Made Fur You Inc.....G..... 813 444-7707
Hudson (G-6033)
Maher Industries Inc.....G..... 407 928-5288
Orlando (G-12946)
MAKM Anufacturing Inc.....G..... 352 343-5881
Tavares (G-18347)
Manns Diversified Industries.....G..... 407 310-5938
Altamonte Springs (G-56)
Manufacturing Inc Sp.....G..... 305 362-0456
Hialeah (G-5499)
Manufacturing Martin LLC Kls.....F..... 904 641-0421
Jacksonville (G-6578)
Marcela Creations Inc.....G..... 813 253-0556
Tampa (G-17879)
Margoth Manufacturing Co.....G..... 954 200-3894
Miami Lakes (G-10813)
▼ Maritime Replicas America Inc.....G..... 305 386-1958
Hialeah (G-5504)
Marker Industries LLC.....G..... 954 907-2647
Pompano Beach (G-14753)
Marvelleth Industries Corp.....G..... 754 263-7197
Miramar (G-11014)
Maskco Technologies Inc.....F..... 877 261-6405
Miami Beach (G-10690)
Massimo Roma LLC.....G..... 561 302-5998
Miami (G-9953)

SIC

Matchless Manufacturing.....G..... 352 390-3010
Ocala *(G-11995)*
Matry Group LLC.....F..... 407 461-9797
Kissimmee *(G-7314)*
Matt Talbot Industries LLC.....G..... 407 718-7636
Sanford *(G-16083)*
▲ **Maxeff Industries Inc**.....G..... 941 893-5804
Sarasota *(G-16254)*
McM Industries Inc.....G..... 727 259-9894
Clearwater *(G-1778)*
Meath Industries Inc.....G..... 954 818-0593
Coral Springs *(G-2276)*
Mediawrite LLC.....G..... 239 344-9988
Fort Myers *(G-4526)*
Medical Waste Industries Inc.....E..... 407 325-4832
New Smyrna Beach *(G-11538)*
Metalco Mfg Inc.....G..... 305 592-0704
Hialeah *(G-5506)*
Metropolis Corp.....E..... 954 951-1011
Fort Lauderdale *(G-4119)*
Mft Stamps.....G..... 352 360-5797
Eustis *(G-3713)*
Miami Tbr LLC.....G..... 786 275-4773
Doral *(G-3437)*
Michael Moore LLC.....G..... 407 716-7325
Deltona *(G-3175)*
Milbank Manufacturing Co.....F..... 813 623-2681
Tampa *(G-17907)*
Mitten Manufacturing.....G..... 941 722-1818
Palmetto *(G-13813)*
Mjk Industries Inc.....G..... 954 788-7494
Pompano Beach *(G-14766)*
Mjr Manufacturing LLC.....G..... 727 460-0636
Clearwater *(G-1788)*
Mmo Industries Inc.....G..... 727 452-8665
Tampa *(G-17912)*
Mmx Manufacturing LLC.....F..... 786 456-5072
Miami *(G-10030)*
Motion Industries Inc.....G..... 727 536-5521
Largo *(G-8014)*
Mt Distributors LLC.....G..... 954 802-2161
Lauderhill *(G-8116)*
Multifix Cbd LLC.....G..... 786 487-0792
Hialeah *(G-5529)*
Mumford Micro Mch Works LLC.....G..... 814 720-7291
Sarasota *(G-16517)*
Munro International Inc.....E..... 352 337-1535
Gainesville *(G-4968)*
Mytek Industries.....F..... 727 536-7891
Largo *(G-8016)*
Nailboutique of WPB LLC.....G..... 954 756-2699
West Palm Beach *(G-18956)*
Namro Industries Inc.....G..... 561 704-8063
Boynton Beach *(G-936)*
Natures Gift Cbd.....G..... 954 405-1000
Hallandale Beach *(G-5201)*
Nava Pets Inc.....F..... 407 982-7256
Longwood *(G-8315)*
Navarre Industries Inc.....G..... 850 554-6682
Navarre *(G-11471)*
◆ **Nearly Natural LLC**.....F..... 800 711-0544
Hialeah *(G-5535)*
Newvida Products LLC.....G..... 863 781-9232
Zolfo Springs *(G-19547)*
Ngf Distributors Inc.....F..... 407 816-7554
Oviedo *(G-13449)*
▼ **Niagratech Industries Inc**.....G..... 305 876-9010
Miami *(G-10072)*
Nigella Industries Inc.....G..... 813 404-7923
Treasure Island *(G-18476)*
Nivel Parts and Mfg Co LLC.....G..... 904 421-3004
Tampa *(G-17941)*
◆ **No 1 Beauty Salon Furniture**.....G..... 954 981-0403
Oakland Park *(G-11825)*
Norton Manufacturing & Svc Inc.....G..... 352 225-1225
Morriston *(G-11093)*
Nova Solid Surfaces Inc.....G..... 239 888-0975
Fort Myers *(G-4550)*
NRG Industries Inc.....G..... 850 510-7174
Tallahassee *(G-17307)*
Nrnb LLC.....G..... 203 769-5995
Hialeah *(G-5545)*
NTS Industries Inc.....F..... 317 847-6675
Orlando *(G-13013)*
Nxgen Brands LLC.....E..... 888 315-6339
Plantation *(G-14540)*
Oberon Industries Inc.....G..... 321 245-7338
Orlando *(G-13015)*
Ocala Manufacturing.....G..... 352 433-6643
Ocala *(G-12011)*

Odyssey Manufacturing Co.....G..... 407 582-9051
Orlando *(G-13020)*
Omz Industries LLC.....F..... 786 210-6763
Doral *(G-3449)*
One Source Industries Inc.....G..... 813 855-3440
Oldsmar *(G-12253)*
Ontic Engineering & Mfg.....G..... 407 206-8459
Orlando *(G-13023)*
Orattac Industries LLC.....G..... 904 415-2162
Jacksonville *(G-6647)*
Oria Lab LLC.....E..... 888 329-4298
Miami *(G-10116)*
Oxzgen Inc.....G..... 844 569-9436
Tarpon Springs *(G-18318)*
Panagenics Inc.....G..... 888 773-0700
Miami *(G-10136)*
Panel Armor Products LLC.....G..... 407 960-5946
Longwood *(G-8320)*
Pap-Cap Industries LLC.....G..... 850 209-7377
Grand Ridge *(G-5046)*
Paradise Building Mtls LLC.....G..... 407 267-3378
Altamonte Springs *(G-61)*
Parrillo Inc.....G..... 386 767-8011
South Daytona *(G-16806)*
Patio Products Mfg Inc.....G..... 813 681-3806
Brandon *(G-1170)*
Patrick German Industries Inc.....G..... 727 251-3015
Brandon *(G-1171)*
Paveway Systems Inc.....F..... 386 659-1316
Florahome *(G-3765)*
Peace Love & Cbd.....G..... 386 409-0910
Edgewater *(G-3632)*
Ped-Stuart Corporation.....E..... 352 754-6001
Brooksville *(G-1259)*
Peeke Industries Inc.....G..... 954 796-1938
Parkland *(G-13998)*
Pembroke Office Industries LLC.....G..... 954 589-1329
Hollywood *(G-5889)*
Pemsum Industries Inc.....G..... 561 623-3151
West Palm Beach *(G-18993)*
Pepper Shark Llc.....F..... 305 849-0104
Key West *(G-7201)*
Pet Declaration Inc.....G..... 772 215-1607
Tampa *(G-17984)*
Pet Supplies Plus.....G..... 248 824-4676
North Port *(G-11746)*
Petainer Manufacturing US.....F..... 786 999-2019
Miami *(G-10156)*
Peterson Manufacturing LLC.....F..... 941 371-4989
Sarasota *(G-16543)*
Petlift Sb Manufacturing Inc.....F..... 941 346-2211
Lakeland *(G-7766)*
Pets2go International Inc.....E..... 404 625-9606
Homestead *(G-5987)*
Phlintrock Industries Inc.....G..... 904 579-3334
Orange Park *(G-12402)*
Plane It Safe LLC.....G..... 888 840-0499
Apopka *(G-171)*
Platinum Mfg Intl Inc.....F..... 727 544-4555
Pinellas Park *(G-14376)*
PNC Manufacturing Leather.....G..... 407 201-2069
Kissimmee *(G-7289)*
Pond Industries Inc.....G..... 727 526-5483
Saint Petersburg *(G-15883)*
Poseidon Boat Manufacturing.....F..... 239 362-3736
Fort Myers *(G-4570)*
Power Foam Manufacturing Inc.....G..... 305 303-2956
Hialeah *(G-5562)*
▲ **Powers Industries LLC**.....F..... 786 444-3616
Wilton Manors *(G-19219)*
Precision Manufacturing I.....G..... 786 547-2683
Miami *(G-10184)*
▲ **Premier Plastics LLC**.....E..... 305 805-3333
Boynton Beach *(G-943)*
Premier Plastics LLC.....G..... 305 805-3333
Hallandale Beach *(G-5203)*
◆ **Prestige Spas Inc**.....D..... 727 576-8600
Pinellas Park *(G-14379)*
▲ **Prime Manufacturing Canada**.....G..... 850 332-7193
Pensacola *(G-14238)*
Printing Services Plus LLC.....F..... 813 279-1903
Tampa *(G-18016)*
▼ **Professional Pet Products Inc**.....E..... 305 592-1992
Doral *(G-3471)*
Promed Biosciences Inc.....F..... 888 655-9155
Pinellas Park *(G-14382)*
Promo Daddy LLC.....F..... 877 557-2336
Melbourne *(G-8913)*
Prowin Industries Inc.....G..... 954 584-5686
Sunrise *(G-17165)*

Puppet Workshop Inc.....E..... 305 666-2655
Miami *(G-10215)*
▼ **Quality Aluminum Manufacturing**.....G..... 850 434-6446
Pensacola *(G-14246)*
Queen B Hair Collection LLC.....F..... 954 393-2791
Miami *(G-10224)*
R & A Industries Inc.....F..... 352 307-6655
Oviedo *(G-13455)*
R C R Manufacturing Inc.....G..... 786 499-9245
Miami *(G-10231)*
R&R Assembly Services.....G..... 407 797-8325
Titusville *(G-18454)*
Rapid Industries Inc.....F..... 772 287-0651
Stuart *(G-16997)*
Rapidspoolindustries Inc.....G..... 954 850-5300
Davie *(G-2581)*
Rar Industries LLC.....G..... 561 213-7876
Boynton Beach *(G-953)*
RCA Machine & Mfg Inc.....G..... 727 561-0150
Clearwater *(G-1857)*
Rdc Manufacturing Inc.....G..... 772 286-6921
Stuart *(G-16998)*
◆ **RDt Business Enterprises Inc**.....F..... 954 525-1133
Fort Lauderdale *(G-4200)*
Reachtv.....G..... 772 934-6349
Stuart *(G-16999)*
Real Gold Inc.....G..... 386 873-4849
Deland *(G-3010)*
Red Hawk Industries LLC.....G..... 303 779-6272
Boca Raton *(G-686)*
Rederick Metal Industries.....E..... 305 396-3396
Miami *(G-10245)*
◆ **Reflection Manufacturing**.....D..... 407 297-5727
Orlando *(G-13126)*
Resharp Industries.....G..... 352 362-1730
Ocala *(G-12037)*
Rev-Tech Mfg Solutions LLC.....F..... 727 577-4999
Saint Petersburg *(G-15901)*
Richard K Pratt LLC.....G..... 321 482-9494
Titusville *(G-18459)*
Richter Industries Inc.....G..... 239 732-9440
Naples *(G-11384)*
Riley & Company Inc.....F..... 407 265-9963
Sanford *(G-16110)*
Rm Industries.....G..... 386 428-4454
New Smyrna *(G-11523)*
Rogue Industries LLC.....G..... 850 797-9228
Fort Walton Beach *(G-4830)*
Ronca Industries LLC.....G..... 407 839-0440
Orlando *(G-13146)*
Rossiter Manufacturing.....G..... 386 409-7223
Daytona Beach *(G-2706)*
Royal Canes.....G..... 727 474-0792
Largo *(G-8043)*
RSD Industries Inc.....G..... 954 240-3660
Hollywood *(G-5903)*
Rugged Industries Inc.....G..... 239 565-2723
Estero *(G-3695)*
Ruiz Industries.....G..... 305 218-6258
Miami *(G-10288)*
Rytex Industries Inc.....F..... 727 557-7450
Largo *(G-8044)*
S & B Industries Inc.....G..... 305 367-1068
Miami *(G-10291)*
▲ **S A Feather Co Inc**.....F..... 239 693-6363
Fort Myers *(G-4590)*
S P Manufacturing LLC.....G..... 305 362-0456
Hialeah *(G-5607)*
Safe Strap LLC.....F..... 239 461-0033
Fort Myers *(G-4592)*
Salty Industries LLC.....G..... 321 626-6331
Melbourne Beach *(G-8984)*
▲ **Sb Mfg LLC**.....G..... 352 458-0137
Dade City *(G-2434)*
SBC International Group Inc.....F..... 305 506-5638
Hialeah *(G-5611)*
Sbm Beauty LLC.....F..... 850 567-7338
Quincy *(G-15253)*
Scale Models Arts & Tech.....F..... 305 949-1706
North Miami Beach *(G-11704)*
Scarb Industries Inc.....G..... 772 597-3898
Indiantown *(G-6074)*
Scents of Nature Enterprises.....E..... 305 547-2334
Miami Lakes *(G-10855)*
Scentsability Candles.....G..... 954 234-4405
Coral Springs *(G-2311)*
▲ **Scentstional Soaps Candles Inc**.....F..... 941 485-1443
Venice *(G-18572)*
Schneidder Industries LLC.....G..... 850 207-0929
Daytona Beach *(G-2709)*

◆ **Schnupp Manufacturing Co Inc** ....G....... 305 325-0520
Miami *(G-10312)*
Schoen Industries Inc........G....... 305 491-5993
Saint Cloud *(G-15665)*
◆ **Science First LLC** ....E....... 904 225-5558
Yulee *(G-19500)*
Scully Industries........G....... 941 349-5561
Sarasota *(G-16588)*
Sdm Industries Inc........G....... 904 814-2814
Palm Coast *(G-13708)*
◆ **Sea Creations Inc** ....G....... 407 857-2000
Orlando *(G-13171)*
Seaboard Manufacturing LLC........G....... 727 497-3572
Clearwater *(G-1872)*
Sebastian Sea Products In........G....... 772 321-3997
Vero Beach *(G-18662)*
Seimens Industries Inc........G....... 954 364-6600
Hollywood *(G-5906)*
Self Industries Incorporated ....G....... 386 882-3644
Ormond Beach *(G-13397)*
Seneca Industries ....G....... 561 626-4999
Palm Beach Gardens *(G-13625)*
Serenity Hair Extensions LLC........F....... 407 917-1788
Deltona *(G-3179)*
Service Industry Consultant ....G....... 561 775-4782
Palm Beach Gardens *(G-13627)*
Sexy Winks LLC........G....... 407 949-2981
Orlando *(G-13176)*
▲ **Seyer - Tech Industries Inc** ....G....... 305 233-2672
Miami *(G-10328)*
Shade Experts USA LLC ....F....... 561 422-3200
Wellington *(G-18730)*
Shelleys Cushions Mfg Inc ....E....... 305 633-1790
Miami *(G-10337)*
Shifted Industries........G....... 561 302-8915
Groveland *(G-5108)*
Siding Industries of Nthrn FL ....G....... 904 814-7923
Saint Augustine *(G-15610)*
◆ **Significant Solutions Corp** ....G....... 561 703-7703
Boca Raton *(G-711)*
Sike Usa Inc........G....... 786 331-4020
Doral *(G-3503)*
Simetri Inc........E....... 321 972-9980
Winter Park *(G-19445)*
Sinclair Industries LLC........F....... 305 215-0990
Key Largo *(G-7173)*
Smokers Video IV........G....... 904 646-1324
Jacksonville *(G-6781)*
Snook Industries........G....... 352 447-0735
Yankeetown *(G-19491)*
Sota Manufacturing LLC ....E....... 561 251-3389
Oakland Park *(G-11841)*
Soto Industries LLC........G....... 941 830-6000
Punta Gorda *(G-15235)*
South Florida Fabricators LLC ....G....... 954 802-6782
Cooper City *(G-2116)*
South Florida Rodents ....G....... 954 410-5635
Southwest Ranches *(G-16842)*
South Florida Technology Svcs ....F....... 786 286-2882
Hialeah *(G-5627)*
Southeastern Assemblies Inc........G....... 727 376-1411
Trinity *(G-18489)*
Southernunderground Industries........G....... 954 650-4699
Miami *(G-10389)*
Sox LLC ....G....... 561 501-0057
Boca Raton *(G-725)*
▼ **Spa Cover Inc**........F....... 954 923-8801
Hollywood *(G-5913)*
Spector Manufacturing Inc........G....... 860 559-6068
Palm City *(G-13674)*
Spliffpuff LLC ....F....... 786 493-4529
Doral *(G-3510)*
Squire Industries Inc ....G....... 813 523-1505
Plant City *(G-14467)*
Ss & S Industries Inc ....F....... 321 327-2500
Melbourne *(G-8944)*
State of Florida........E....... 850 488-1234
Tallahassee *(G-17331)*
Stealth Industries........G....... 561 747-1471
Jupiter *(G-7122)*
Steeda Engineering and Mfg LLC........G....... 954 960-0774
Pompano Beach *(G-14870)*
▼ **Stitching Around Inc**........G....... 305 665-1600
Miami *(G-10415)*
▲ **Stocking Factory**........G....... 305 745-2681
Big Pine Key *(G-382)*
Stover Manufacturing LLC ....G....... 386 238-3775
Daytona Beach *(G-2719)*
Stover Manufacturing LLC ....F....... 386 235-7060
Port Orange *(G-15037)*
Strap Shade Inc........G....... 239 450-5844
Bonita Springs *(G-858)*
Straw Life Inc........G....... 386 935-2850
O Brien *(G-11766)*
Strictly Ecommerce ....G....... 352 672-6566
Gainesville *(G-5004)*
Stump Industries LLC........D....... 239 940-5754
Fort Myers *(G-4614)*
Stylors Inc........F....... 904 765-4453
Jacksonville *(G-6820)*
Sun Krafts of Volusia County ....G....... 386 441-1961
Ormond Beach *(G-13403)*
▼ **Sun-Art Designs Inc**........E....... 954 929-6622
Hollywood *(G-5916)*
Sunciti Industries Inc........G....... 407 877-8081
Winter Garden *(G-19286)*
Suncoast Assemblers LLC ....G....... 407 947-8835
Belle Isle *(G-359)*
Suncoast Idntfction Sltons LLC ....F....... 239 277-9922
Fort Myers *(G-4617)*
Sundown Manufacturing Inc........F....... 727 828-0826
Clearwater *(G-1894)*
Sunglow Industries........G....... 304 554-2552
The Villages *(G-18394)*
Sunnman Inc ....G....... 305 505-6615
Hialeah *(G-5637)*
Sunshine Nylon Products Inc........G....... 352 754-9932
Brooksville *(G-1277)*
Suntyx LLC........F....... 786 558-2233
Miramar *(G-11049)*
◆ **Superior Group Companies Inc** ....A....... 727 397-9611
Seminole *(G-16764)*
Surfskate Industries LLC ....G....... 954 349-1116
Fort Lauderdale *(G-4269)*
Sustainable Casework Inds LLC ....G....... 954 980-6506
Deerfield Beach *(G-2920)*
Sweet Industries LLC ....G....... 904 228-9655
Stuart *(G-17031)*
◆ **Synergylabs LLC** ....E....... 954 525-1133
Fort Lauderdale *(G-4272)*
Szabo Pos Displays Inc........G....... 941 778-0192
Bradenton *(G-1124)*
T & M Industries Inc........F....... 954 778-2238
Deerfield Beach *(G-2921)*
Tactical Prchute Dlvry Systems........F....... 813 782-7482
Zephyrhills *(G-19540)*
Talent Assessment Inc ....G....... 904 260-4102
Jacksonville *(G-6835)*
Talon Industries Inc........G....... 727 517-0052
Belleair Beach *(G-362)*
Tayco Industries Inc ....G....... 863 318-9264
Winter Haven *(G-19362)*
Tdt Manufacturing LLC........G....... 239 573-7498
Cape Coral *(G-1484)*
Team Solutions Dental LLC ....D....... 407 542-1552
Sanford *(G-16126)*
Techniflex LLC ....E....... 561 235-0844
Boca Raton *(G-743)*
◆ **Techno-Spa Manufacturing Inc** ....G....... 386 239-8980
Daytona Beach *(G-2723)*
◆ **Tekna Manufacturing LLC**........G....... 813 782-6700
Zephyrhills *(G-19541)*
Tesco Equipment ....G....... 954 791-9470
Davie *(G-2603)*
The Caldwell Manufacturing Co ....E....... 386 418-3525
Alachua *(G-19)*
Thebestcandlescom ....G....... 732 608-5081
Margate *(G-8568)*
Themeworks Incorporated........C....... 386 454-7500
High Springs *(G-5702)*
Thompson Manufacturing Inc........G....... 239 332-0446
Fort Myers *(G-4629)*
Thor Manufacturing Inc ....F....... 866 955-8467
Boca Raton *(G-750)*
Thriv Industries LLC........F....... 404 436-3230
Delray Beach *(G-3149)*
Tifco Industries Freedom Alloy ....G....... 407 474-6747
Longwood *(G-8342)*
Tikore Industries LLC ....G....... 954 616-5902
Miami *(G-10478)*
Timberwolf Organics Ltd Lblty ....F....... 407 877-8779
Windermere *(G-19246)*
Titan Industries ....G....... 904 608-3905
Orange Park *(G-12409)*
Titan Trailers LLC........G....... 813 298-8597
Valrico *(G-18525)*
Toogle Industries LLC ....G....... 863 688-8975
Lakeland *(G-7824)*
Traincat Model Sales Inc ....G....... 954 385-8999
Weston *(G-19172)*
Treetop Industries LLC........G....... 904 471-4412
Saint Augustine *(G-15627)*
Tri-Edge Industries LLC ....G....... 561 703-5961
Lake Worth *(G-7593)*
Trial Exhibits Inc........F....... 813 258-6153
Tampa *(G-18200)*
Trividia Meditech LLC........F....... 954 677-9201
Fort Lauderdale *(G-4290)*
Tropic Guard Industries LLC ....G....... 813 447-3938
Apollo Beach *(G-107)*
▼ **Tropical Mfg Inc**........G....... 305 394-6280
Hialeah *(G-5651)*
Tropichem Research Labs LLC ....D....... 561 804-7603
Jupiter *(G-7134)*
Trost Industries LLC........G....... 407 690-8603
Orlando *(G-13276)*
Troy Industries LLC ....G....... 401 241-4231
Englewood *(G-3669)*
True Blue Metal LLC ....G....... 352 444-9596
Ocala *(G-12061)*
True Line Industries Inc........G....... 561 745-4828
Jupiter *(G-7135)*
Trulieve Cannabis Corp........F....... 844 878-5438
Quincy *(G-15256)*
Tsn Manufacturing ....F....... 813 740-1876
Tampa *(G-18207)*
Tsn Manufacturing Inc........F....... 727 709-9802
Seffner *(G-16734)*
TST Industries LLC........G....... 973 865-1998
Deland *(G-3026)*
TST Industries LLC........G....... 386 868-2011
Lake Helen *(G-7395)*
Turn Key Industries ....G....... 813 671-3446
Gibsonton *(G-5034)*
Tzh Industries Inc ....G....... 727 807-3000
Trinity *(G-18490)*
◆ **Ultimate Umbrella Company Inc** ....B....... 305 634-5116
Hialeah *(G-5657)*
▲ **Ultraclenz LLC**........F....... 800 931-8911
Jupiter *(G-7136)*
Union Pvc Industries Inc........G....... 305 883-1640
Hialeah *(G-5658)*
Unique Fbrctions Unlimited LLC........G....... 352 229-8511
Ocala *(G-12066)*
United Manufacturing Services ....G....... 941 224-1692
Bradenton *(G-1137)*
US Hemp and Oil LLC........G....... 352 817-2455
Ocala *(G-12068)*
US Patriot Industries Inc........G....... 954 802-7402
Hallandale Beach *(G-5221)*
USA Manufacturing Group LLC........G....... 786 253-3152
Coral Gables *(G-2203)*
V & G Industries Inc........F....... 786 853-1265
Hialeah *(G-5670)*
Vandalay Inds Manatee Cnty LLC........G....... 941 756-6028
Bradenton *(G-1139)*
Vanity Furs of Avondale LLC ....G....... 904 387-9900
Jacksonville *(G-6893)*
Vdh Worldwide LLC........G....... 866 304-2388
Wesley Chapel *(G-18763)*
Venancio Usa Inc........G....... 321 418-9489
Hallandale *(G-5166)*
Vicx LLC........F....... 407 674-2073
Winter Garden *(G-19288)*
Vidacann LLC........F....... 772 672-1178
Saint Johns *(G-15684)*
Virag Distribution LLC........G....... 844 448-4724
West Palm Beach *(G-19080)*
Virco Mfg Corporation ....G....... 772 834-8261
Stuart *(G-17046)*
◆ **Vision Candles Inc**........G....... 305 836-8650
Miami *(G-10589)*
Visual Magic ....G....... 727 271-2702
New Port Richey *(G-11519)*
Volcano Industries Inc........F....... 770 300-0041
Sarasota *(G-16323)*
▼ **Vplenish Nutritionals Inc**........F....... 954 304-4000
Boca Raton *(G-782)*
Wallace Industries Inc ....G....... 561 833-8554
West Palm Beach *(G-19084)*
Wallace Industries Inc ....F....... 561 301-0811
Lake Worth *(G-7598)*
Wcm Group Inc........G....... 516 238-4261
Flagler Beach *(G-3758)*
West Texas Protein Inc........F....... 806 250-5959
Jacksonville *(G-6911)*
Westrock Lake Mary ....G....... 407 936-1277
Lake Mary *(G-7461)*
Whitman Industries LLC........G....... 239 216-6171
Marco Island *(G-8528)*

Wholly Hemp Inc..........G....... 813 785-6231
Sanford (G-16139)
Whyte Power Industries Corp..........G....... 786 200-6033
Miami (G-10605)
Wicks Unlimited Inc..........G....... 631 472-2010
Pompano Beach (G-14913)
Williams Jewelry and Mfg Co..........G....... 727 823-7676
Saint Petersburg (G-15961)
Willis Industries Inc..........G....... 954 830-6163
Davie (G-2614)
Wiltcher Industries Inc..........G....... 704 907-9838
Ormond Beach (G-13409)
Woodham Industries Inc..........G....... 561 863-6666
Lake Park (G-7483)
World Indus Resources Corp..........E....... 727 572-9991
Clearwater (G-1944)
World Manufacturing LLC..........G....... 843 751-9375
Summerfield (G-17064)
Worldwide Building Intl Inc..........C....... 786 744-7076
Miami (G-10622)
Worthington Industries LLC..........G....... 813 979-1000
Tampa (G-18266)
Wrobel Industries Inc..........G....... 727 560-6850
Holiday (G-5753)
WW Timber LLC..........G....... 352 584-4550
Perry (G-14321)
◆ **Xikar Inc**..........E....... 816 474-7555
Weston (G-19179)
Xoxo Beauty Studio LLC..........G....... 407 476-7172
Altamonte Springs (G-85)
Yeager Manufacturing Tech LLC..........F....... 407 573-7033
Winter Park (G-19463)
Yetman Industries Inc..........G....... 239 561-7808
Fort Myers (G-4656)
You Lucky Dog Inc..........G....... 954 428-4648
Deerfield Beach (G-2938)
Z & N Manufacturing Corp..........G....... 407 518-1114
Kissimmee (G-7313)
Zel Custom Manufacturing LLC..........G....... 303 880-8701
Odessa (G-12167)
Zenithtech Industries Inc..........G....... 386 454-7630
High Springs (G-5704)
Zepsa Industries..........G....... 754 307-2173
Pompano Beach (G-14915)
Zpx LLC..........G....... 888 943-8849
Gainesville (G-5018)

73 BUSINESS SERVICES

7372 Prepackaged Software

1425 N Washington Street LLC..........G....... 904 680-6600
Jacksonville (G-6100)
180bytwo..........G....... 202 403-7097
Clearwater (G-1558)
24/7 Software Inc..........F....... 954 514-8988
Coral Springs (G-2209)
5nine Software Inc..........E....... 561 898-1100
West Palm Beach (G-18783)
Abawi Fit LLC..........G....... 813 215-1833
Tampa (G-17381)
Above Property LLC..........E....... 239 263-7406
Naples (G-11146)
Accenius Inc..........G....... 415 205-6444
Boca Raton (G-396)
Accounting & Computer Systems..........G....... 407 353-1570
Orlando (G-12428)
Accuware Inc..........G....... 305 894-6874
Miami Beach (G-10635)
Aci Worldwide Inc..........A....... 239 403-4600
Naples (G-11147)
Actionable Quality Assurance..........F....... 352 562-0005
Gainesville (G-4867)
Acucall LLC..........F....... 855 799-7905
North Palm Beach (G-11715)
Adaptive Insights Inc..........G....... 800 303-6346
Winter Springs (G-19466)
Ademero Inc..........F....... 863 937-0272
Lakeland (G-7625)
Advanced Public Safety LLC..........G....... 954 354-3000
Deerfield Beach (G-2766)
Advanced Services Intl Inc..........G....... 954 889-1366
Miramar (G-10961)
Advanced Software Engineering..........G....... 305 387-0112
Miami (G-9077)
Advanced Software Inc..........F....... 215 369-7800
Jacksonville Beach (G-6937)
Advantage Software Inc..........E....... 772 288-3266
Stuart (G-16904)
Adventurous Entertainment LLC..........F....... 407 483-4057
Orlando (G-12437)
Advtravl Inc..........G....... 978 549-5013
Ocala (G-11865)
◆ **Afina Systems Inc**..........G....... 305 261-1433
Miramar (G-10962)
Agile Risk Management LLC..........G....... 800 317-5497
Tampa (G-17392)
Ai2 Inc..........G....... 407 645-3234
Winter Park (G-19374)
Alchiba Inc..........G....... 561 832-9292
West Palm Beach (G-18792)
Alliance Rsrvations Netwrk LLC..........G....... 602 889-5505
Orlando (G-12459)
American Optimal Decisions Inc..........G....... 352 278-2034
Gainesville (G-4874)
Applied Neuroscience Inc..........G....... 727 324-8922
Seminole (G-16739)
Applied Software Inc..........G....... 215 297-9441
West Palm Beach (G-18797)
Appo Group Inc..........G....... 410 992-5500
Aventura (G-261)
Aptum Technologies (usa) Inc..........D....... 877 504-0091
Doral (G-3253)
Archangel Tablets LLC..........F....... 703 981-7732
North Miami Beach (G-11667)
ASG Federal Inc..........G....... 239 435-2200
Naples (G-11174)
Asure Software Inc..........G....... 702 733-9007
Tampa (G-17440)
Asysco Inc..........G....... 850 383-2522
Tallahassee (G-17224)
Atris Technology LLC..........F....... 352 331-3100
Gainesville (G-4880)
Audio Storage Technologies..........G....... 954 229-5050
Fort Lauderdale (G-3832)
Authority Software LLC..........G....... 877 603-9653
Tamarac (G-17351)
Automated Accounting Assoc Inc..........G....... 512 669-1000
Pensacola (G-14094)
Avt Technology Solutions LLC..........G....... 727 539-7429
Clearwater (G-1594)
Axiom Services Inc..........E....... 727 442-7774
Clearwater (G-1595)
Azure Computing Inc..........G....... 407 359-8787
Oviedo (G-13416)
B-Scada Inc..........F....... 352 564-9610
Crystal River (G-2370)
B2 Integrations LLC..........G....... 727 871-7025
Parrish (G-14004)
Backstage Software Inc..........G....... 407 925-8751
Ocoee (G-12084)
Backtocad Technologies LLC..........G....... 727 303-0383
Clearwater (G-1598)
Bankingly Inc..........E....... 734 201-0007
North Miami (G-11627)
Bca Technologies Inc..........F....... 407 659-0653
Maitland (G-8459)
Belatrix Software Inc..........E....... 801 673-8331
Naples (G-11185)
Bellini Systems Inc..........G....... 813 264-9252
Tampa (G-17464)
Best Choice Software Inc..........F....... 941 747-5858
Bradenton (G-998)
Big Star Systems LLC..........G....... 954 243-7209
Lauderhill (G-8102)
Bigbyte Software Systems Inc..........F....... 917 370-1733
Pembroke Pines (G-14023)
Bio-Tech Medical Software Inc..........D....... 800 797-4711
Fort Lauderdale (G-3854)
Biosculptor Corporation..........G....... 305 823-8300
Hialeah (G-5326)
Bitvisory Inc..........G....... 801 336-6626
Vero Beach (G-18600)
Bla Software Inc..........G....... 407 355-0800
Orlando (G-12518)
Black Bean Software LLC..........G....... 727 420-6916
Land O Lakes (G-7850)
Black Ice Software LLC..........G....... 561 757-4107
Boca Raton (G-448)
Black Knight Inc..........B....... 904 854-5100
Jacksonville (G-6210)
Black Knight Fincl Svcs Inc..........A....... 904 854-5100
Jacksonville (G-6211)
Blackcloak Inc..........F....... 833 882-5625
Lake Mary (G-7403)
Blue Shoe Software LLC..........G....... 321 438-5708
Orlando (G-12526)
Bohemia Intrctive Smltions Inc..........F....... 407 608-7000
Orlando (G-12531)
Bond Medical Group Inc..........E....... 813 264-5951
Tampa (G-17479)
Bond-Pro Inc..........C....... 888 789-4985
Tampa (G-17480)
Bond-Pro LLC..........F....... 813 413-7576
Tampa (G-17481)
Brainchild Corp..........E....... 239 263-0100
Naples (G-11193)
C Horse Software Inc..........G....... 321 952-0692
Palm Bay (G-13506)
Ca Inc..........C....... 305 559-4640
Miami (G-9296)
Cadcam Software Co..........G....... 727 450-6440
Clearwater (G-1620)
Cafm..........F....... 407 658-6531
Cocoa Beach (G-2059)
Capstorm LLC..........G....... 314 403-2143
Santa Rosa Beach (G-16153)
Carpediem LLC..........F....... 229 230-1453
Destin (G-3185)
Castle Software Inc..........G....... 800 345-7606
Sebastian (G-16657)
Cellec Games Inc..........G....... 407 476-3590
Apopka (G-120)
Central Fla Bus Solutions Inc..........G....... 863 297-9293
Winter Haven (G-19312)
Cerp Software Inc..........G....... 954 607-1417
Pembroke Pines (G-14027)
Certek Software Designs Inc..........G....... 727 738-8188
Dunedin (G-3572)
Certusview Technologies LLC..........G....... 844 533-1258
Palm Beach Gardens (G-13576)
▼ **CFS Inc**..........F....... 850 386-2902
Tallahassee (G-17232)
Channel Logistics LLC..........E....... 856 614-5441
Miami (G-9348)
Checksum Software LLC..........G....... 786 375-8091
Doral (G-3297)
Chicago Soft Ltd..........F....... 863 940-2066
Lakeland (G-7656)
Cirrus Software LLC..........G....... 727 450-7804
Palm Harbor (G-13729)
Citrix Systems Inc..........A....... 954 267-3000
Fort Lauderdale (G-3901)
Clinigence Holdings Inc..........G....... 678 607-6393
Fort Lauderdale (G-3904)
Cloud Business Florida LLC..........G....... 954 306-3597
Fort Lauderdale (G-3905)
Cloud Veneer LLC..........G....... 305 230-7379
Miami (G-9364)
Cloudfactors LLC..........G....... 866 779-9974
Plantation (G-14501)
CMA Interactive Corporation..........F....... 954 336-6403
Fort Lauderdale (G-3906)
Collaborative Sftwr Solutions..........G....... 954 753-2025
Coral Springs (G-2233)
Collegefrog Inc..........G....... 850 696-1500
Pensacola (G-14116)
Colorproof Software Inc..........G....... 813 963-0241
Lutz (G-8377)
Comcept Solutions LLC..........E....... 727 535-1900
Seminole (G-16744)
Community MGT Systems LLC..........F....... 561 214-4780
Palm Beach Gardens (G-13581)
Comp U Netcom Inc..........F....... 407 539-1800
Maitland (G-8462)
Comply Arm..........G....... 772 249-0345
Port Saint Lucie (G-15100)
Concept Software Inc..........G....... 321 250-6670
Winter Garden (G-19258)
Connect Slutions Worldwide LLC..........G....... 407 492-9370
Vero Beach (G-18611)
Connected Life Solutions LLC..........F....... 407 745-1952
Altamonte Springs (G-38)
Connectyx Technologies Corp..........G....... 772 221-8240
Stuart (G-16926)
Construction Software Inc..........G....... 888 801-0675
Fort Lauderdale (G-3916)
Consumer Information Bureau..........G....... 954 971-5079
Pompano Beach (G-14646)
Contact Center Solutions Inc..........E....... 305 499-0163
Miami (G-9394)
Cookie App LLC..........G....... 305 330-5099
Miami (G-9398)
Cooltech Holding Corp..........G....... 786 675-5236
Doral (G-3306)
Corellium LLC..........G....... 561 502-2420
Boynton Beach (G-893)
Coresystems Software USA Inc..........F....... 786 497-4477
Miami (G-9403)
Cornerstone Software Inc..........G....... 727 443-5557
Clearwater (G-1640)

Creative Data Solutions Inc ....F 407 333-4770
Lake Mary *(G-7407)*
Creative Vtran Productions LLC ....F 407 656-2743
Maitland *(G-8463)*
◆ **Crichlow Data Sciences Inc** ....G 863 616-1222
Lakeland *(G-7666)*
Cubic Advnced Lrng Sltions Inc ....F 407 859-7410
Orlando *(G-12632)*
Customer Success LLC ....F 386 265-4882
Port Orange *(G-15014)*
Cyber Manufacturing Inc ....G 786 457-1973
Miami *(G-9422)*
Cybertek Computer Systems Inc ....G 352 373-9923
Gainesville *(G-4901)*
Daniel Lampert Communications ....F 407 327-7000
Winter Springs *(G-19471)*
Darcy Stephen ....F 813 645-3375
Apollo Beach *(G-101)*
Dark Lake Software Inc ....F 407 602-8046
Winter Park *(G-19401)*
Dashclicks LLC ....F 866 600-3369
Fort Lauderdale *(G-3932)*
Data Access International Inc ....D 305 238-0012
Miami *(G-9437)*
Data Pro Accounting Sftwr Inc ....F 727 803-1500
Saint Petersburg *(G-15755)*
▼ **Datacore Software Corporation** ....D 954 377-6000
Fort Lauderdale *(G-3934)*
Datamentors LLC ....E 813 960-7800
Wesley Chapel *(G-18743)*
Dealer It Group LLC ....F 904 518-3379
Jacksonville *(G-6315)*
Dealerups Inc ....F 407 557-5368
Lake Mary *(G-7408)*
Devclan Inc ....G 407 933-8212
Kissimmee *(G-7238)*
Didna Inc ....G 239 851-0966
Orlando *(G-12671)*
Digi-Net Technologies Inc ....E 352 505-7450
Gainesville *(G-4905)*
Dnt Software Corp ....G 407 323-0987
Sanford *(G-16037)*
Dpi Information Inc ....F 813 258-8004
Tampa *(G-17614)*
Drsingh Technologies Inc ....F 352 334-7270
Gainesville *(G-4911)*
Duenas Mobile Applications LLC ....E 305 851-3397
Homestead *(G-5964)*
Duos Technologies Inc ....D 904 652-1601
Jacksonville *(G-6335)*
Duos Technologies Group Inc ....G 904 652-1616
Jacksonville *(G-6336)*
Dynamic Glucose Hlth Ctrs LLC ....G 800 610-6422
Fort Lauderdale *(G-3953)*
Eclipse Ehr Solutions LLC ....F 352 488-0081
Weeki Wachee *(G-18702)*
Ecoprintq Inc ....F 305 681-7445
Miami Lakes *(G-10784)*
Edashop Inc ....G 786 565-9197
Winter Garden *(G-19262)*
Educational Networks Inc ....F 866 526-0200
Coral Gables *(G-2142)*
Ei Interactive LLC ....G 407 579-0993
Orlando *(G-12700)*
Electronic Arts Inc ....F 407 838-8000
Orlando *(G-12703)*
Ellis & Associates of Sanford ....G 407 322-1128
Sanford *(G-16041)*
Elogic Learning LLC ....E 813 901-8600
Tampa *(G-17634)*
Emerald Technologies Corp ....G 773 244-0092
St Pete Beach *(G-16881)*
Emerson Prcess MGT Pwr Wtr Slt ....E 941 748-8100
Bradenton *(G-1037)*
Emphasys Cmpt Solutions Inc ....E 305 599-2531
Pembroke Pines *(G-14032)*
Encore Analytics LLC ....G 866 890-4331
Destin *(G-3189)*
Engineerica Systems Inc ....F 407 542-4982
Oviedo *(G-13428)*
Enter Your Hours LLC ....G 561 337-7785
Boynton Beach *(G-902)*
Enterprise System Assoc Inc ....F 407 275-0220
Orlando *(G-12712)*
Erwin Inc ....F 813 933-3323
Tampa *(G-17649)*
Esterel Technologies Inc ....F 724 746-3304
Orlando *(G-12717)*
Estimator Software LLC ....G 203 682-6436
Weston *(G-19122)*

Etas Timeadmin Corporation ....G 813 464-4175
Tampa *(G-17650)*
Evolution Voice Inc ....G 407 204-1614
Orlando *(G-12724)*
Evolve Technologies Inc ....G 239 963-8037
Marco Island *(G-8524)*
Excelor LLC ....F 321 300-3315
Orlando *(G-12727)*
Extralink Corporation ....G 305 804-1100
Miami Beach *(G-10665)*
Eze Castle Software Llc ....G 407 692-9699
Orlando *(G-12729)*
Ezverify & Validate LLC ....G 855 398-3981
Sunrise *(G-17121)*
Factorfox Software LLC ....G 305 671-9526
Miami *(G-9557)*
Fanwise LLC ....G 954 874-9000
Fort Lauderdale *(G-3986)*
Fcbn LLC ....G 408 505-1324
Pompano Beach *(G-14688)*
Feick Corporation ....D 305 271-8550
Miami *(G-9561)*
Finastra USA Corporation ....C 800 989-9009
Lake Mary *(G-7416)*
Finastra USA Corporation ....D 800 394-8778
Orlando *(G-12739)*
Fis Avantgard LLC ....E 484 582-2000
Jacksonville *(G-6388)*
Fis Kiodex LLC ....F 904 438-6000
Jacksonville *(G-6389)*
Flagshipmd LLC ....G 904 302-6160
Jacksonville *(G-6391)*
Fleetmatics ....F 727 483-9016
Tampa *(G-17669)*
Flexiinternational Sftwr Inc ....G 239 298-5700
Naples *(G-11247)*
Fluenz Inc ....G 305 209-1695
Miami Beach *(G-10668)*
Forewarn LLC ....G 561 757-4550
Boca Raton *(G-538)*
Fyi Software Inc ....E 239 272-6016
Naples *(G-11255)*
Gbi Intralogistics Solutions ....E 954 596-5000
Deerfield Beach *(G-2830)*
Genel/Landec Inc ....G 305 591-9990
Doral *(G-3361)*
Genensys LLC ....F 407 701-4158
Oviedo *(G-13432)*
Genius Central Systems Inc ....E 800 360-2231
Bradenton *(G-1046)*
Geocommand Inc ....G 561 347-9215
Boca Raton *(G-543)*
Georgesoft Inc ....G 850 329-5517
Tallahassee *(G-17264)*
◆ **Gleim Publications Inc** ....D 352 375-0772
Gainesville *(G-4931)*
Global Recash LLC ....D 818 297-4437
Coral Gables *(G-2151)*
Gold-Rep Corporation ....G 954 892-5868
Weston *(G-19134)*
Goodrich Corporation ....G 305 622-4500
Miami Gardens *(G-10744)*
Gooee LLC ....F 727 510-0663
Clearwater *(G-1705)*
Gorilladesk Llc ....G 561 245-8614
Boca Raton *(G-549)*
Gotobilling Inc ....F 800 305-1534
Tampa *(G-17722)*
Govpay Network LLC ....G 866 893-9678
Miami *(G-9651)*
Graphic Center Group Corp ....G 305 961-1649
Coral Gables *(G-2152)*
Green Power Systems LLC ....G 904 545-1311
Jacksonville *(G-6448)*
Green Shades Software Inc ....F 904 807-0160
Jacksonville *(G-6449)*
Grom Social Enterprises Inc ....C 561 287-5776
Boca Raton *(G-553)*
GSM Software Technologies Inc ....G 813 907-2124
Tampa *(G-17731)*
Guardia LLC ....E 954 670-2900
Fort Lauderdale *(G-4033)*
Gulf Coast Program ....G 727 945-1402
Palm Harbor *(G-13738)*
Hazmat Software LLC ....F 407 416-5434
Lake Mary *(G-7421)*
Hcr Software Solutions Inc ....E 904 638-6177
Jacksonville *(G-6464)*
Hilton Software LLC ....F 954 323-2244
Coral Springs *(G-2253)*

Himgc Limited ....D 213 443-8729
Daytona Beach *(G-2674)*
Hipaat International Inc ....F 905 405-6299
Naples *(G-11278)*
Hispacom Inc ....F 954 255-2622
Coral Springs *(G-2255)*
Hopscotch Technology Group Inc ....F 305 846-0942
Oviedo *(G-13437)*
Hr Ease Inc ....G 813 414-0040
Tampa *(G-17765)*
Hydrogen Technology Corp ....E 800 315-9554
Miami Beach *(G-10681)*
I T Pacs Pro Software Inc ....G 954 678-1270
West Park *(G-19095)*
▼ **Icarecom LLC** ....F 954 616-5604
Fort Lauderdale *(G-4055)*
Ichosen1 Inc ....F 844 403-4055
Miami *(G-9727)*
Igovsolutions LLC ....E 407 574-3056
Lake Mary *(G-7423)*
Ils Management LLC ....E 321 252-0100
Melbourne *(G-8849)*
Image One Corporation ....D 813 888-8288
Tampa *(G-17773)*
Imagicle Inc ....F 206 201-2042
Miami *(G-9733)*
Imago Products ....G 888 400-4122
Boynton Beach *(G-919)*
Impact Education Inc ....G 239 482-0202
Fort Myers *(G-4491)*
Inceptra LLC ....E 954 442-5400
Weston *(G-19141)*
Industry Weapon Inc ....E 877 344-8450
Oldsmar *(G-12235)*
Infor Public Sector Inc ....E 813 207-6911
Tampa *(G-17783)*
Information Builders Inc ....E 407 804-8000
Lake Mary *(G-7424)*
Information Mgt Svcs Inc ....F 386 677-5073
Ormond Beach *(G-13380)*
Informulate LLC ....G 866 222-2307
Oviedo *(G-13439)*
Innergy ....G 941 815-8655
Punta Gorda *(G-15210)*
Innquest Corporation ....F 813 288-4900
Tampa *(G-17786)*
Inperium Corp ....E 305 901-5650
Miami Beach *(G-10683)*
Insight Risk Technologies LLC ....G 863 804-6038
Indian Shores *(G-6070)*
Insight Software LLC ....D 305 495-0022
Weston *(G-19142)*
Integra Connect LLC ....F 800 742-3069
West Palm Beach *(G-18907)*
Inteliathlete Corp ....G 305 987-1355
Doral *(G-3392)*
Interactyx Americas Inc ....E 888 575-2266
Bonita Springs *(G-840)*
Intermedix Corporation ....D 954 308-8700
Fort Lauderdale *(G-4062)*
Intouch Gps LLC ....E 877 593-2981
Lakeland *(G-7718)*
Iomartcloud Inc ....G 954 880-1680
Vero Beach *(G-18632)*
Ipvision Software LLC ....F 813 728-3175
Tampa *(G-17793)*
▲ **Iq Formulations Llc** ....D 954 533-9256
Tamarac *(G-17359)*
▲ **Iris Inc** ....G 561 921-0847
Delray Beach *(G-3093)*
Ironwifi LLC ....F 800 963-6221
Orlando *(G-12844)*
It Labs LLC ....D 310 490-6142
Palm Beach Gardens *(G-13598)*
Iter3d Inc ....G 718 473-0114
Aventura *(G-274)*
Itqlick Inc ....G 855 487-5425
Hallandale Beach *(G-5192)*
Ityx Solutions Inc ....F 407 474-4383
Orlando *(G-12846)*
Ivengo Software Inc ....G 321 480-3155
Melbourne *(G-8852)*
Jade Software Corporation USA ....G 904 677-5133
Jacksonville *(G-6514)*
Jonas Software USA Inc ....G 800 476-0094
Pensacola *(G-14186)*
Jupiter Compass LLC ....G 561 444-6740
Palm Beach Gardens *(G-13599)*
Juritis USA LLC ....G 954 529-2168
Weston *(G-19145)*

SIC

Kamel Software Inc..............G...... 407 672-0202
Oviedo *(G-13444)*
Keith Dennis Markham..............G...... 239 353-4122
Naples *(G-11303)*
Kenexa Learning Inc..............G...... 407 562-1905
Maitland *(G-8470)*
Kenexa Learning Inc..............G...... 407 548-0434
Lake Mary *(G-7428)*
Kirchman Corporation..............D...... 877 384-0936
Orlando *(G-12871)*
Kodiak Software Inc..............G...... 727 599-8839
Clearwater *(G-1754)*
Koho Software Inc..............G...... 813 390-1309
Tampa *(G-17829)*
Kommander Software LLC..............G...... 407 906-2121
Inverness *(G-6092)*
Kreateck International Corp..............F...... 772 925-1216
Vero Beach *(G-18637)*
Lamb Tec Inc..............G...... 305 798-6266
Cutler Bay *(G-2399)*
Landtech Data Corporation..............F...... 561 790-1265
Royal Palm Beach *(G-15474)*
Launcher Solutions LLC..............F...... 904 479-0762
Jacksonville *(G-6549)*
Lawex Corporation..............F...... 305 259-9755
Coral Gables *(G-2171)*
Ld Telecommunications Inc..............D...... 954 628-3029
Fort Lauderdale *(G-4097)*
Levitech Services LLC..............G...... 904 576-0562
Jacksonville Beach *(G-6949)*
Lidarit Inc..............E...... 407 632-2622
Orlando *(G-12908)*
Lightning Phase II Inc..............G...... 727 539-1800
Seminole *(G-16749)*
Linenmaster LLC..............E...... 772 212-2710
Vero Beach *(G-18639)*
Linga Pos LLC..............E...... 800 619-5931
Naples *(G-11314)*
Linqs Inc..............F...... 321 244-2626
Winter Springs *(G-19478)*
Live Source..............G...... 561 573-2994
Boca Raton *(G-603)*
Lobby Docs LLC..............G...... 850 294-0013
Tallahassee *(G-17292)*
Logical Data Solutions Inc..............F...... 561 694-9229
Palm Beach Gardens *(G-13606)*
Logs Group LLC..............G...... 904 733-6594
Jacksonville *(G-6563)*
Lott Qa Group Inc..............G...... 201 693-2224
Bonita Springs *(G-844)*
Low Code Ip Holding LLC..............G...... 833 260-2151
Fort Lauderdale *(G-4103)*
Lps Group LLC..............G...... 305 668-8780
South Miami *(G-16821)*
Management Hlth Solutions Inc..............B...... 888 647-4621
Tampa *(G-17876)*
Manufcturing Systems Group LLC..............G...... 727 642-4677
Cape Coral *(G-1444)*
Marquis Software Dev Inc..............D...... 850 877-8864
Tallahassee *(G-17296)*
▲ **Marware Inc**..............E...... 954 927-6031
Dania Beach *(G-2468)*
Mas Editorial Corp..............G...... 305 748-0124
Hollywood *(G-5870)*
◆ **Matchware Inc**..............G...... 800 880-2810
Tampa *(G-17893)*
Mau Mau Corporation..............E...... 305 440-5203
Miami Beach *(G-10691)*
Maxit Corporation..............G...... 904 998-9520
Ponte Vedra Beach *(G-14946)*
Mc Software LLC..............G...... 801 621-3900
West Palm Beach *(G-18947)*
McAfee LLC..............G...... 561 477-6626
Boca Raton *(G-612)*
Mdintouch Us Inc..............G...... 786 268-1161
Miami *(G-9961)*
Med X Change Inc..............E...... 941 746-0538
Bradenton *(G-1077)*
Medaffinity Corporation..............F...... 850 254-9690
Tallahassee *(G-17299)*
Medelite Solutions..............G...... 850 348-0468
Lynn Haven *(G-8435)*
Mediaops Inc..............E...... 516 857-7409
Boca Raton *(G-618)*
Mediware Info Systems Inc..............F...... 904 281-0467
Jacksonville *(G-6589)*
Melodon Software Inc..............G...... 407 654-1234
Orlando *(G-12959)*
Mendeleyes Corp..............G...... 305 597-7370
Doral *(G-3431)*
Mercury Systems Inc..............E...... 352 371-2567
Gainesville *(G-4961)*
Merkari Group Inc..............G...... 305 748-3260
Coral Gables *(G-2175)*
Method Merchant Inc..............E...... 954 745-7998
Plantation *(G-14533)*
Microsoft Corporation..............C...... 425 882-8080
Fort Lauderdale *(G-4122)*
Microvision Technology Corp..............F...... 407 333-2943
Lake Mary *(G-7435)*
Mills & Murphy Sftwr Systems..............E...... 727 577-1236
Saint Petersburg *(G-15855)*
Mobilebits Holdings Corp..............G...... 941 225-6115
Sarasota *(G-16258)*
Mobvious Corp..............G...... 786 497-6620
Miami *(G-10032)*
Modernizing Medicine..............C...... 561 880-2998
Boca Raton *(G-629)*
Modernizing Medicine Inc..............B...... 561 880-2998
Boca Raton *(G-630)*
Momenry Inc..............F...... 318 668-0888
Tampa *(G-17917)*
Montague Enterprises Inc..............G...... 239 631-5292
Naples *(G-11330)*
Moore Solutions Inc..............G...... 772 337-4005
Port St Lucie *(G-15175)*
Morrissy & Co..............G...... 850 934-4243
Gulf Breeze *(G-5121)*
Motionvibe Innovations LLC..............F...... 202 285-0235
Bradenton *(G-1082)*
Motorsport Games Inc..............D...... 305 507-8799
Miami *(G-10046)*
Ms Software Inc..............G...... 813 258-1735
Tampa *(G-17920)*
Multi Soft II Inc..............F...... 305 579-8000
Miami *(G-10053)*
My Clone Solution..............F...... 813 442-9925
Tampa *(G-17922)*
My Reviewers LLC..............G...... 813 404-9734
Tampa *(G-17923)*
N2w Software Inc..............F...... 561 225-2483
West Palm Beach *(G-18955)*
Navizon Inc..............G...... 305 501-2409
Miami Beach *(G-10697)*
Ncg Medical Systems Inc..............E...... 407 788-1906
Orlando *(G-12996)*
Networked Solutions Inc..............G...... 321 259-3242
Rockledge *(G-15438)*
New Generation Computing Inc..............D...... 800 690-0642
Miami Lakes *(G-10828)*
Nex Software LLC..............G...... 786 200-3396
Homestead *(G-5986)*
Nexogy Inc..............E...... 305 358-8952
Coral Gables *(G-2181)*
Ngweb Solutions LLC..............G...... 904 332-9001
Jacksonville *(G-6633)*
Nicraf Software & Creations..............G...... 813 842-9648
Odessa *(G-12135)*
Niftys Inc..............F...... 786 878-4725
Miami *(G-10073)*
Northpointe Bank..............G...... 239 308-4532
Fort Myers *(G-4549)*
Note Bin Inc..............F...... 727 642-8530
Clearwater *(G-1811)*
Nuevo Mundo Company..............F...... 305 207-8155
Miami *(G-10085)*
Oaktree Software Inc..............F...... 407 339-5855
Altamonte Springs *(G-59)*
Obitx Inc..............G...... 904 748-9750
Jacksonville *(G-6643)*
Oceana Software Corp..............G...... 813 335-6966
Tampa *(G-17944)*
Omnivore Technologies Inc..............D...... 800 293-4058
Clearwater *(G-1817)*
On-Q Software Inc..............G...... 305 553-6566
Miami *(G-10100)*
Openkm Usa LLC..............G...... 407 257-2640
Orlando *(G-13025)*
Opie Choice LLC..............G...... 352 331-3741
Gainesville *(G-4976)*
Opie Choice LLC..............F...... 727 726-5157
Clearwater *(G-1819)*
Optimus-Fleet LLC..............F...... 407 590-5060
Orlando *(G-13027)*
Oracle America Inc..............E...... 407 458-1200
Orlando *(G-13029)*
Oracle America Inc..............G...... 305 260-7200
Miami *(G-10112)*
Oracle Balloon Decor Inc..............G...... 386 866-0878
Jacksonville *(G-6646)*
Oracle Corporation..............C...... 772 337-4141
Port Saint Lucie *(G-15128)*
Oracle Corporation..............B...... 772 466-0704
Fort Pierce *(G-4725)*
Oracle Elevator Company..............G...... 954 391-5835
Miami *(G-10113)*
Oracle Essence Inc..............F...... 786 258-8153
Weston *(G-19155)*
Ordercounter Inc..............F...... 850 332-5540
Pensacola *(G-14217)*
Orion Travel Technologies Inc..............F...... 407 574-6649
Celebration *(G-1524)*
Orizon 360..............F...... 888 979-0360
Weston *(G-19157)*
Outreach Corporation..............F...... 888 938-7356
Tampa *(G-17966)*
Pacemate LLC..............G...... 305 322-5074
Bradenton *(G-1089)*
Painassist Inc..............G...... 248 875-4222
Saint Petersburg *(G-15874)*
Panther Software Inc..............F...... 800 856-8729
Miami *(G-10140)*
Paper Free Technology Inc..............G...... 515 270-1505
Lehigh Acres *(G-8202)*
Patient Portal Tech Inc..............E...... 877 779-6627
North Palm Beach *(G-11724)*
Peeks Mobile App Corp..............F...... 407 931-3878
Kissimmee *(G-7284)*
Pepper Tree..............G...... 941 922-2662
Sarasota *(G-16540)*
Perch Security Inc..............E...... 844 500-1810
Tampa *(G-17983)*
Perii Inc..............G...... 321 253-2269
Merritt Island *(G-9006)*
Phase Integration LLC..............G...... 877 778-8885
Jacksonville *(G-6670)*
Phocas Software..............F...... 863 738-9107
Maitland *(G-8474)*
Platesmart Technologies..............F...... 813 749-0892
Oldsmar *(G-12257)*
Playoff Technologies LLC..............G...... 407 497-2202
Winter Park *(G-19431)*
Pogi Beauty LLC..............G...... 305 600-1305
Miami *(G-10173)*
Posm Software LLC..............G...... 859 274-0041
Cape Canaveral *(G-1366)*
Powerchord Inc..............D...... 727 823-1530
Saint Petersburg *(G-15886)*
Powerdms Inc..............D...... 407 992-6000
Orlando *(G-13076)*
Powerline Group Inc..............C...... 631 828-1183
Delray Beach *(G-3122)*
Praxis Software Inc..............F...... 407 226-5691
Orlando *(G-13078)*
Precision Infinity Systems Inc..............G...... 407 490-2320
Orlando *(G-13080)*
Prekcom LLC..............G...... 877 773-5669
Miami Beach *(G-10704)*
Premieretrade Forex LLC..............G...... 407 287-4149
Lake Mary *(G-7445)*
Prestashop Inc..............F...... 888 947-6543
Miami *(G-10190)*
Primal Innovation Tech LLC..............F...... 407 558-9366
Tampa *(G-18010)*
Prism Venture Partners LLC..............F...... 561 427-6565
Jupiter *(G-7098)*
Privi LLC..............G...... 863 294-0373
Winter Haven *(G-19345)*
Professional Sftwr Consortium..............F...... 407 909-9168
Windermere *(G-19240)*
Professor Software Company..............G...... 561 691-5455
Jupiter *(G-7099)*
Profitsword LLC..............E...... 407 909-8822
Orlando *(G-13095)*
Program Works Inc..............F...... 407 489-4140
Winter Springs *(G-19482)*
Projstream LLC..............F...... 407 476-1084
Lake Mary *(G-7446)*
Prolink Software Corporation..............G...... 860 659-5928
Naples *(G-11377)*
Provictus Inc..............E...... 561 437-0232
Palm Beach Gardens *(G-13619)*
Qgiv Inc..............E...... 888 855-9595
Lakeland *(G-7773)*
Quality Software LLC..............E...... 561 714-2314
Delray Beach *(G-3131)*
Queuelogix LLC..............F...... 404 721-3928
Fort Lauderdale *(G-4195)*
Radial Inc..............F...... 561 737-5151
Boynton Beach *(G-951)*

Radixx Solutions Intl Inc ....E.... 407 856-9009
Orlando (G-13111)
Ranorex Inc ....E.... 727 835-5570
Clearwater (G-1856)
Raynetcrm LLC ....F.... 813 489-9565
Venice (G-18568)
Razient LLC ....G.... 855 747-5911
Miami (G-10242)
Recon Group LLP ....G.... 855 874-8741
Miami (G-10243)
Recordsone LLC ....F.... 301 440-8119
Naples (G-11382)
Reliable Business Technologies ....G.... 386 561-9944
Longwood (G-8330)
Restoration Games LLC ....G.... 954 937-1970
Sunrise (G-17169)
Retail Cloud Technologies LLC ....D.... 727 210-1700
Clearwater (G-1859)
Riley Risk Inc ....G.... 202 601-0500
Saint Augustine (G-15597)
Rperf Technologies Corp ....F.... 954 629-2359
Coral Springs (G-2307)
RTC Software LLC ....G.... 407 765-7462
Winter Garden (G-19284)
Ruvos LLC ....F.... 850 254-7270
Tallahassee (G-17320)
S2 Pass Holdings LLC ....G.... 706 773-4097
Santa Rosa Beach (G-16166)
Saas Transportation Inc ....F.... 850 650-7709
Destin (G-3204)
Sachi Tech Inc ....F.... 813 649-8028
Tampa (G-18079)
Safco Software ....G.... 561 750-7879
Boca Raton (G-697)
Safeboot Corp ....E.... 239 298-7000
Naples (G-11388)
Sage Implementations LLC ....G.... 407 290-6952
Orlando (G-13155)
SAI Super Software Solutions ....G.... 407 445-2520
Orlando (G-13156)
SC Elearning LLC ....D.... 561 293-2543
Deerfield Beach (G-2907)
SC Parent Corporation ....D.... 703 351-0200
Miami (G-10308)
SC Purchaser Corporation ....D.... 703 351-0200
Miami (G-10309)
Scanid Inc ....G.... 305 607-3523
Miami (G-10310)
Scope Worker LLC ....E.... 917 855-5379
Miami (G-10313)
Scs Software Inc ....F.... 727 871-8366
Belleair Bluffs (G-364)
Sebring Software LLC ....E.... 941 377-0715
Sarasota (G-16590)
Security Oracle Inc ....F.... 352 988-5985
Clermont (G-1974)
Seniors Vent Mgmt Inc ....G.... 305 266-0988
Miami (G-10324)
Seronix Corporation ....G.... 352 406-1698
Mount Dora (G-11113)
Servdata Inc ....G.... 305 269-7374
Palmetto Bay (G-13854)
Seven Hlls Slution Specialists ....G.... 850 575-0566
Tallahassee (G-17322)
Shopworks LLC ....G.... 561 491-6000
West Palm Beach (G-19031)
Sibling Group Holdings Inc ....D.... 786 618-1472
Miami (G-10341)
Sighthound Inc ....F.... 650 564-4364
Winter Park (G-19442)
Silco Software Technology Inc ....F.... 813 475-4591
Odessa (G-12151)
Silvershore Partners LLC ....F.... 904 562-0812
Jacksonville (G-6775)
Silverstar Holdings Ltd ....G.... 561 479-0040
Boca Raton (G-713)
Simplepin LLC ....F.... 800 727-4136
Hobe Sound (G-5727)
Simplicity Esports LLC ....F.... 855 345-9467
Boca Raton (G-717)
Simply Reliable Inc ....G.... 800 209-9332
Saint Petersburg (G-15913)
Singular Grape Inc ....G.... 305 508-4000
Orlando (G-13194)
Sipradius LLC ....G.... 954 290-2434
Coral Springs (G-2313)
Slappey Communications LLC ....G.... 863 619-5600
Lakeland (G-7792)
Sleepy Dragon Studios Inc ....G.... 561 714-6156
Cutler Bay (G-2411)

Smart Guides ....G.... 813 534-0940
Tampa (G-18109)
Smartadvocate LLC ....E.... 239 390-1000
Bonita Springs (G-854)
Smartbear Software ....G.... 954 312-0188
Coconut Creek (G-2096)
Smartcop Inc ....E.... 850 429-0082
Pensacola (G-14262)
▲ Smartmatic Corporation ....F.... 561 862-0747
Boca Raton (G-721)
▲ Smdk Corp ....E.... 239 444-1736
Naples (G-11406)
Smx-US Inc ....E.... 914 840-5631
Miami (G-10367)
Sna Software LLC ....F.... 866 389-6750
Orlando (G-13199)
Soe Software Corporation ....E.... 813 490-7150
Tampa (G-18113)
Soft Tech America Inc ....F.... 954 563-3198
Fort Lauderdale (G-4240)
Softech International Inc ....F.... 305 233-4813
Miami (G-10369)
Software Nuggets Inc ....G.... 904 687-9778
Ponte Vedra Beach (G-14954)
Software Product Solutions LLC ....G.... 561 798-6727
West Palm Beach (G-19037)
Software Teacher Inc ....G.... 954 593-3333
Jupiter (G-7117)
Solidexperts Inc ....F.... 954 772-1903
Fort Lauderdale (G-4243)
Sophio Software Inc ....F.... 323 446-2172
Fort Lauderdale (G-4244)
Sophix Solutions Inc ....G.... 813 837-9555
Tampa (G-18115)
Sophtech Ba Solutions LLC ....G.... 407 389-4011
Altamonte Springs (G-75)
Soren Technologies Inc ....F.... 954 236-9998
Plantation (G-14555)
SOS Software Corp ....G.... 786 237-4903
Miami (G-10378)
Southeastern Marketing Associa ....G.... 954 421-7388
Deerfield Beach (G-2916)
Sphere Access Inc ....F.... 336 501-6159
Tampa (G-18126)
SRS Software LLC ....F.... 201 802-1300
Tampa (G-18128)
Stadium 1 Software LLC ....E.... 561 498-8356
Miami Beach (G-10716)
Stadson Technology Corporation ....E.... 561 372-2648
Boca Raton (G-729)
Stallion King LLC ....G.... 321 503-7368
Saint Petersburg (G-15926)
Starboard Consulting LLC ....E.... 407 622-6414
Longwood (G-8340)
Starmark International Inc ....G.... 954 874-9000
Fort Lauderdale (G-4260)
Stature Software LLC ....G.... 888 782-8881
Saint Augustine (G-15623)
Stay Smart Care LLC ....G.... 321 682-7113
Winter Park (G-19448)
Stayfilm Inc ....G.... 786 961-1007
Miami (G-10410)
Steelgate Global LLC ....G.... 610 909-8509
Fort Lauderdale (G-4261)
Strands Inc ....G.... 415 398-4333
Miami (G-10418)
Strata Analytics Holdg US LLC ....D.... 954 349-4630
Sunrise (G-17179)
Stratonet Inc ....G.... 863 382-8503
Sebring (G-16712)
Streamline Technologies Inc ....G.... 407 679-1696
Winter Springs (G-19485)
Stress Nuts LLC ....G.... 787 675-3042
Orlando (G-13218)
Sun Valley Tech Solutions Inc ....G.... 480 463-4101
Wesley Chapel (G-18759)
Sundog Software LLC ....G.... 425 635-8683
Merritt Island (G-9015)
Sunshine Software ....G.... 407 297-6253
Orlando (G-13226)
Superion LLC ....A.... 407 304-3235
Lake Mary (G-7452)
Swoogo LLC ....G.... 212 655-9810
Sarasota (G-16613)
Synergistic Office Solutions ....F.... 352 242-9100
Minneola (G-10956)
Synkt Games Inc ....F.... 305 779-5611
Miami (G-10450)
System Data Resource ....G.... 954 213-8008
Port Saint Lucie (G-15152)

Tahoe Interactive Systems Inc ....G.... 614 891-2323
Punta Gorda (G-15242)
Take A Bed LLC ....G.... 407 734-8857
Hollywood (G-5921)
Tapinfluence Inc ....E.... 720 726-4071
Winter Park (G-19451)
Team Cymru Inc ....C.... 847 378-3300
Lake Mary (G-7454)
Tech Data Education Inc ....F.... 727 539-7429
Clearwater (G-1907)
Tech Data Resources LLC ....E.... 727 539-7429
Clearwater (G-1908)
Tech Data Tennessee Inc ....E.... 727 539-7429
Clearwater (G-1909)
Technisys LLC ....B.... 305 728-5372
Miami (G-10463)
Technolgy Training Associates ....E.... 813 249-0303
Tampa (G-18179)
Telephony Partners LLC ....E.... 813 769-4690
Tampa (G-18181)
Thales E-Security Inc ....F.... 954 888-6200
Plantation (G-14557)
Thales Esecurity Inc ....E.... 954 888-6200
Plantation (G-14558)
Thalo Assist LLC ....G.... 786 340-6892
Weston (G-19169)
That Software Guy Inc ....G.... 727 533-8109
Largo (G-8066)
Theater Ears Inc ....G.... 561 305-0519
Boca Raton (G-747)
Threattrack Security Inc ....C.... 855 885-5566
Clearwater (G-1920)
Timus Inc ....G.... 904 614-4342
Jacksonville (G-6857)
Titan Tools LLC ....E.... 818 984-1001
Clearwater (G-1921)
Tops Software ....F.... 813 960-8300
Clearwater (G-1924)
Touche Software LLC ....G.... 786 241-9907
Miami (G-10495)
Tracking Solutions Corp ....E.... 877 477-2922
Doral (G-3530)
Tradestation Technologies Inc ....C.... 954 652-7000
Plantation (G-14560)
Transaction Data Systems Inc ....E.... 407 295-5050
Ocoee (G-12093)
Trendy Entertainment Inc ....E.... 814 384-7123
Gainesville (G-5012)
▲ Trivantis Corporation ....D.... 513 929-0188
Deerfield Beach (G-2929)
Tropical MBC LLC ....G.... 727 498-6511
St Pete Beach (G-16884)
Trx Integration Inc ....F.... 727 797-4707
Belleair (G-361)
Two Roads Consulting LLC ....G.... 305 395-8821
Dunedin (G-3591)
U2 Cloud LLC ....E.... 888 370-5433
Green Cove Springs (G-5074)
Ukg Inc ....D.... 954 331-7000
Weston (G-19173)
Ultimate Software ....F.... 305 559-3052
Miami (G-10524)
Unfoldingword Corporation ....F.... 407 900-3005
Orlando (G-13289)
Unicomp Corp of America ....G.... 954 755-1710
Coral Springs (G-2325)
Unique Recording Software Inc ....G.... 917 854-5403
Boca Raton (G-768)
Unite Parent Corp ....D.... 800 432-1729
Weston (G-19174)
Unitime Systems Inc ....G.... 407 233-2050
Maitland (G-8482)
Universal Software Solutions ....G.... 727 298-8877
Clearwater (G-1929)
Universal Training Sftwr Inc ....F.... 561 981-6421
Boca Raton (G-770)
Universalms Inc ....G.... 786 285-7531
Hollywood (G-5933)
Utilitech Inc ....F.... 863 767-0600
Wauchula (G-18695)
Vanguardistas LLC ....G.... 386 868-2919
Ormond Beach (G-13407)
Vector-Solutionscom Inc ....E.... 813 207-0012
Tampa (G-18236)
Veeam Software Corporation ....G.... 614 339-8200
Davie (G-2610)
Veedis Clinical Systems ....G.... 954 344-0498
Plantation (G-14562)
Vendornet ....G.... 954 767-8228
Fort Lauderdale (G-4306)

SIC

◆ **Vensoft Corp** F 786 991-2080
Miami *(G-10573)*
◆ **Verifone Inc** C 800 837-4366
Coral Springs *(G-2326)*
▲ **Verifone Systems Inc** C 408 232-7800
Coral Springs *(G-2328)*
Vertaeon LLC G 404 823-6232
Gainesville *(G-5015)*
Vfinity Inc F 239 244-2555
Naples *(G-11450)*
Vice Alliance Corp G 954 792-4240
Plantation *(G-14564)*
Vinbillingcom LLC G 904 549-5461
Jacksonville *(G-6899)*
VIP Software Corporation F 813 837-4347
Lakeland *(G-7830)*
Visible Results USA Inc F 913 706-8248
Reunion *(G-15261)*
Visions Sky Corp G 888 788-8609
Orlando *(G-13305)*
Vkidz Inc F 954 771-0914
Fort Lauderdale *(G-4310)*
Voicethread LLC E 919 724-4486
Boca Raton *(G-781)*
Vuaant Inc F 407 701-6975
Orlando *(G-13316)*
Vuram Inc F 813 421-8000
Temple Terrace *(G-18382)*
Waterfall LLC G 941 342-7417
Sarasota *(G-16635)*
▲ **Webcom Group Inc** A 904 680-6600
Jacksonville *(G-6907)*
Webidcard Inc G 443 280-1577
Saint Augustine *(G-15634)*
Webvoip Inc G 305 793-2061
Fort Lauderdale *(G-4319)*
Western Microsystems Inc E 800 547-7082
Jacksonville *(G-6912)*
Westrom Software G 866 480-1879
Vero Beach *(G-18681)*
Whole Tomato Software Inc G 408 323-1590
Sarasota *(G-16639)*
Willsonet Inc E 813 336-8175
Tampa *(G-18259)*
Wind River Systems Inc G 321 726-9463
Melbourne *(G-8977)*
Windermere Nannies LLC F 407 782-2057
Windermere *(G-19251)*
Windowware Pro G 904 584-9191
Saint Augustine *(G-15638)*
World Hlth Enrgy Holdings Inc F 561 870-0440
Boca Raton *(G-791)*
Xcape Solutions Inc E 813 369-5261
Lutz *(G-8425)*
Yihong Software Inc G 407 391-8450
Oviedo *(G-13463)*
Yippy Inc G 877 947-7901
Miami *(G-10626)*
Yourmembershipcom Inc E 727 827-0046
Saint Petersburg *(G-15967)*
Zerion Group LLC G 877 872-1726
Maitland *(G-8487)*
Zeroc Inc G 561 283-1480
Jupiter *(G-7149)*

76 MISCELLANEOUS REPAIR SERVICES

7692 Welding Repair

4f Mobile Welding LLC G 850 537-2290
Baker *(G-299)*
5571 Halifax Inc E 239 454-4999
Fort Myers *(G-4340)*
A & E Machine Inc F 321 636-3110
Cocoa *(G-1988)*
A Mobile Mechanic & Wldg Svc G 813 900-8764
Riverview *(G-15262)*
A Plus Trailers G 786 395-0799
Southwest Ranches *(G-16835)*
Aarons Equipment Repair Inc G 904 879-3249
Callahan *(G-1323)*
Able Railing & Welding LLC G 850 243-5444
Fort Walton Beach *(G-4774)*
Accurate Wldg Fabrication LLC G 727 483-3125
Tampa *(G-17386)*
Ace-Pipe Welding LLC G 561 727-6345
Palm Beach Gardens *(G-13564)*
◆ **Advanced Machine and Tool Inc** D 772 465-6546
Fort Pierce *(G-4669)*
Advanced Wldg Fbrction Dsign L G 352 237-9800
Summerfield *(G-17056)*
Ajs Fabrication Llc G 863 514-9630
Winter Haven *(G-19296)*
Alexis Welding Express Corp G 786 626-4090
Opa Locka *(G-12284)*
Alfredo Welding Service LLC G 954 770-8744
Winter Haven *(G-19297)*
All Phase Welding LLC G 772 834-2980
Vero Beach *(G-18591)*
All Weld Inc G 239 348-9550
Naples *(G-11154)*
Allied Welding & Maint Inc G 863 634-7718
Okeechobee *(G-12172)*
Amax Welding & Fabrication G 352 544-8484
Brooksville *(G-1208)*
◆ **American Fence Shop LLC** F 305 681-3511
Hialeah *(G-5290)*
American Wldg & Installation G 786 391-4800
Miami *(G-9148)*
Anthony Wright Welding G 850 544-1831
Tallahassee *(G-17220)*
ARC Dimensions Inc G 727 524-6139
Largo *(G-7898)*
ARC-Rite Inc E 386 325-3523
Jacksonville *(G-6165)*
Armor Supply Metals LLC G 305 640-9901
Medley *(G-8613)*
Arnold Industries South Inc G 352 867-0190
Ocala *(G-11879)*
Art of Iron Inc G 850 819-1500
Panama City *(G-13865)*
Atlas Innovative Services Inc F 617 259-4529
Punta Gorda *(G-15192)*
Attila Services Corp G 305 255-6776
Miami *(G-9191)*
B & B of Saint Augustine Inc G 904 829-6855
Saint Augustine *(G-15519)*
B & N Wldg & Fabrication Inc E 813 719-3956
Plant City *(G-14405)*
Badger Welding Orlando LLC G 407 648-1100
Orlando *(G-12504)*
Barrs Equipment Service Inc F 407 999-5214
Orlando *(G-12507)*
Bartow Machine Works Inc G 863 533-6361
Bartow *(G-308)*
Baxley Services Inc G 850 675-4459
Jay *(G-6962)*
Beasley Welding LLC G 352 595-4086
Anthony *(G-95)*
▲ **Bee Welding Inc** F 561 616-9003
West Palm Beach *(G-18816)*
Beyers Welding Inc G 407 892-2834
Saint Cloud *(G-15645)*
Billys Welding Inc G 239 229-8723
Cape Coral *(G-1391)*
Bjb Marine Welding & Svcs Inc G 954 909-4967
Fort Lauderdale *(G-3856)*
Blackies Weldng & Boiler Svc G 954 961-5777
Hallandale Beach *(G-5172)*
Blaine E Taylor Welding Inc G 386 931-1242
Bunnell *(G-1298)*
Blane E Taylor Welding Inc G 386 931-1240
Ormond Beach *(G-13354)*
Bluepoint Fabrication Inc F 321 269-0073
Titusville *(G-18415)*
Blunts Welding LLC G 352 274-6014
Citra *(G-1556)*
Bob Kline Quality Metal Inc G 561 659-4245
West Palm Beach *(G-18827)*
Bobs Wldg Fbrcation Maint Inc E 863 665-0135
Lakeland *(G-7648)*
Boyd Welding LLC G 352 447-2405
Ocala *(G-11889)*
Brannen Wldg & Fabrication Inc G 352 583-4849
Dade City *(G-2423)*
Brownsville Orna Ir Works Inc G 850 433-0521
Pensacola *(G-14107)*
Burton JC Companies Inc G 239 992-2377
Bonita Springs *(G-821)*
Cannons of Jack LLC G 904 733-3524
Jacksonville *(G-6253)*
Central Florida Weld & Fab LLC G 407 919-8706
Orange City *(G-12373)*
Central Maintenance & Wldg Inc F 352 795-2817
Crystal River *(G-2371)*
Central Maintenance & Wldg Inc B 813 229-0012
Lithia *(G-8216)*
Certified Wldg Fbrction Svcs L G 813 323-4090
Tampa *(G-17529)*
Champagne Welding Inc G 585 738-8611
Jacksonville *(G-6260)*
Champion Welding Services LLC G 786 262-5727
Miami Lakes *(G-10775)*
Channel Industries Inc F 561 214-0637
West Palm Beach *(G-18845)*
Chviek G 239 567-1511
North Fort Myers *(G-11597)*
Ciron Custom Welding Inc G 786 259-7589
Hialeah *(G-5345)*
Coastal Wldg Fabrications Inc F 954 938-7933
Oakland Park *(G-11791)*
Copeland Welding & Muffler Sp G 904 355-6383
Jacksonville *(G-6290)*
Cornelius Welding Inc E 863 635-3668
Frostproof *(G-4858)*
Crown Welding & Fabg Inc G 941 737-6844
Myakka City *(G-11142)*
D & D MBL Wldg Fabrication Inc F 954 791-3385
Fort Lauderdale *(G-3927)*
D & D Welding Inc G 850 438-9011
Pensacola *(G-14123)*
D & S Steel G 352 489-8791
Dunnellon *(G-3595)*
D B Welding Fabrication G 941 379-2319
Sarasota *(G-16400)*
Dade Made G 305 846-9482
Hialeah *(G-5363)*
Dcwfab LLC G 941 320-6095
Sarasota *(G-16406)*
Diligent Services Inc G 561 368-1478
Boca Raton *(G-501)*
Discount Welds LLC G 305 637-3939
Miami *(G-9470)*
Diversified Welding Inc G 561 996-9398
Belle Glade *(G-347)*
Docs Welding LLC G 813 846-5022
Plant City *(G-14425)*
Doll Marine Metal Fabrication G 954 941-5093
Pompano Beach *(G-14667)*
▲ **Double R Mfg Ocala Inc** F 352 873-1441
Ocala *(G-11924)*
Dumont Welder Services Inc G 863 969-7498
Winter Haven *(G-19318)*
Dynamic Welding & Fab LLC G 904 669-4682
Saint Augustine *(G-15540)*
◆ **E M P Inc** G 772 286-7343
Stuart *(G-16935)*
East Coast Metalworks LLC G 321 698-0624
Cocoa *(G-2018)*
East Coast Ornamental Welding F 386 672-4340
Daytona Beach *(G-2660)*
Electron Beam Development F 772 219-4600
Palm City *(G-13652)*
Elkins Welding Inc G 352 362-4577
Dunnellon *(G-3597)*
Emf Inc C 321 453-3670
Merritt Island *(G-9000)*
ENG Manufacturing Inc G 727 942-3868
Tarpon Springs *(G-18299)*
Escambia Welding and Fab Inc G 850 477-3901
Pensacola *(G-14145)*
Exact Inc C 904 783-6640
Jacksonville *(G-6372)*
F P General Welding G 786 812-6673
Miami *(G-9552)*
First Coast Fabrication Inc G 904 849-7426
Yulee *(G-19496)*
Floyd Fabrication LLC G 330 289-7351
Haines City *(G-5143)*
Franz A Ullrich Jr G 863 773-4653
Wauchula *(G-18692)*
Friendly Welding Inc F 786 953-8413
Hialeah *(G-5417)*
Fusion Welding F 239 288-6530
Fort Myers *(G-4463)*
G B Welding & Fabrication LLC F 954 967-2573
Davie *(G-2529)*
G Welding Contractor Corp G 305 896-0311
Miami Lakes *(G-10793)*
Gator Welding Inc F 561 746-0049
Jupiter *(G-7047)*
General Welding Svc Entps Inc G 305 592-9483
Doral *(G-3363)*
Grahams Welding Fabrication G 850 865-0899
Fort Walton Beach *(G-4803)*
Greenes Wldg & Fabrication LLC G 904 773-3101
Middleburg *(G-10905)*
Greg Clark Welding Inc G 904 226-2952
Jacksonville *(G-6451)*

Griffiths Corporation ....D.... 407 851-8342
Orlando (G-12790)
Gunns Welding & Fabricating....G.... 727 393-5238
Saint Petersburg (G-15801)
Hay Tech ....G.... 850 592-2424
Bascom (G-336)
Hernandez Mobile Welding Inc....G.... 954 347-4071
Okeechobee (G-12181)
Hi Tech Aviation Welding LLC....G.... 305 591-3393
Miami (G-9707)
Hialeah Welding & Ornamental....G.... 305 685-3196
Hialeah (G-5447)
Holmes Tool & Engineering Inc....E.... 850 547-4417
Bonifay (G-804)
Hot Shot Welding Inc....F.... 727 585-1900
Largo (G-7975)
House of Metal LLC....G.... 727 540-0637
Clearwater (G-1721)
Hudsons Wldg & Fabrication Inc....G.... 941 355-4858
Bradenton (G-1057)
Immokalee Fabrication and Wldg....G.... 239 675-8299
Immokalee (G-6051)
Industrial & Marine Maint....G.... 813 622-8338
Tampa (G-17779)
Industrial Repair Inc....F.... 239 368-7435
Lehigh Acres (G-8192)
Interstate Wldg & Fabrication....F.... 727 446-1449
Clearwater (G-1735)
Ironclad Welding Inc....G.... 954 925-7987
Dania (G-2449)
J L M Machine Co Inc....F.... 941 748-4288
Bradenton (G-1064)
Jackson Equipment Inc....G.... 904 845-3696
Jacksonville (G-6509)
Jam Welding Service Inc....F.... 305 662-3787
South Miami (G-16818)
◆ JC Industrial Mfg Corp....E.... 305 634-5280
Miami (G-9789)
Jim Appleys Tru-ARC Inc....F.... 727 571-3007
Clearwater (G-1743)
JL Welding Inc....F.... 786 442-4319
South Miami (G-16819)
Just Steel Inc....F.... 941 755-7811
Sarasota (G-16242)
K & D Welding LLC....G.... 941 586-0258
Sarasota (G-16479)
Kevin Murray Welding Proj DBA....G.... 813 323-3543
Spring Hill (G-16875)
Key West Wldg Fabrication Inc....G.... 305 296-5555
Key West (G-7192)
Kickin It LLC....G.... 954 648-1405
Oakland Park (G-11817)
Kinetic Fusion Corp....G.... 561 352-1670
West Palm Beach (G-18920)
King Mobile Welding Andrew....G.... 386 437-1007
Bunnell (G-1301)
Kingston Automotive & Wldg LLC....G.... 727 378-4881
Hudson (G-6031)
Knight Welding Supply LLC....G.... 561 889-5342
Stuart (G-16967)
L & C Metals LLC....G.... 407 859-2600
Orlando (G-12878)
L T Weld II LLC....G.... 352 454-2735
Clermont (G-1966)
Leeroys Fabrication & Wldg LLC....G.... 850 398-1997
Crestview (G-2354)
Lynn Industrial Welding Inc....G.... 850 584-4494
Perry (G-14306)
M&S Strong Welding Inc....G.... 623 299-5336
Dundee (G-3565)
Madson Inc....F.... 305 863-7390
Medley (G-8681)
Mag Cleaning Solutions LLC....G.... 321 317-3298
Altamonte Springs (G-55)
Matlocks Welding & Fab....G.... 305 942-9201
Marathon (G-8520)
MB Welding Inc....G.... 727 548-0923
Saint Petersburg (G-15852)
Metal Craft of Pensacola Inc....E.... 850 478-8333
Pensacola (G-14207)
Metal Fabrication and....G.... 850 205-2300
Tallahassee (G-17300)
Mid-State Machine & Fabg Corp....B.... 863 665-6233
Lakeland (G-7751)
Mike Blackburn Welding LLC....G.... 850 643-8464
Blountstown (G-386)
◆ Milans Machine Shop & Wldg Svc....E.... 305 592-2447
Doral (G-3438)
Mims Welding Incorporated....G.... 863 612-9819
Labelle (G-7320)
MPH Industries Inc....F.... 352 372-9533
Gainesville (G-4966)
Ms Mobile Wldg & Fabrication....F.... 904 591-1488
Jacksonville (G-6616)
Ms Welding....G.... 941 629-2597
Port Charlotte (G-14990)
National Pipe Welding Inc....F.... 904 588-2589
Glen Saint Mary (G-5037)
Native Welding....G.... 561 348-0100
Palm City (G-13667)
O R Welding Service LLC....G.... 561 707-4325
Belle Glade (G-349)
Omni Marine Enterprises LLC....G.... 941 474-4614
Englewood (G-3663)
On Site Svcs of Mid FL....G.... 407 444-2951
Deland (G-3004)
Ornamental Alasco Iron & Wldg....G.... 813 254-4883
Brandon (G-1168)
P & A Welding and Machine Inc....G.... 863 425-3198
Mulberry (G-11132)
Paire Jr Weld Inc....G.... 754 281-1803
North Lauderdale (G-11619)
Palatka Welding Shop Inc....E.... 386 328-1507
Palatka (G-13488)
Paradise Wldg Cstm Fabrication....G.... 239 961-8864
Naples (G-11357)
Parts Central Inc....F.... 850 547-1660
Bonifay (G-806)
Patriot Welding Inc....G.... 954 798-8819
Pompano Beach (G-14785)
Pena General Welding Inc....G.... 786 255-2153
Miami (G-10150)
Phillip & Roger Inc....G.... 850 763-6415
Panama City (G-13941)
Pk Welding Inc....G.... 407 694-9403
Kissimmee (G-7287)
Precision Brazing Inc....G.... 954 942-8971
Pompano Beach (G-14807)
Precision Svcs Jcksonville Inc....F.... 904 781-3770
Jacksonville (G-6682)
Pro Weld of South Florida Inc....G.... 954 984-0104
Margate (G-8565)
Pro-Weld Inc....G.... 863 453-9353
Avon Park (G-294)
Production Metal Stampings....F.... 850 981-8240
Milton (G-10938)
Promax Welding Inc....G.... 305 962-5033
Hialeah (G-5580)
Quality Metal Worx....G.... 863 353-6638
Haines City (G-5147)
R & K Welding and Fabrication....G.... 863 422-8728
Lake Hamilton (G-7392)
Ramsay Marine Services LLC....F.... 561 881-1234
Riviera Beach (G-15368)
Rankine-Hinman Mfg Co....F.... 904 808-0404
Saint Augustine (G-15594)
RB Custom Welding LLC....G.... 813 280-9860
Tampa (G-18040)
Real Pro Welding Inc....G.... 850 939-3469
Navarre (G-11473)
Responsive Machining Inc....F.... 321 225-4011
Titusville (G-18457)
Richards Mobile Welding....G.... 954 913-0487
Coral Springs (G-2305)
Right Way Wldg Fabrication LLC....G.... 850 212-9672
Monticello (G-11082)
RLC Building Inc....G.... 904 704-5614
Jacksonville (G-6731)
▲ Rodriguez Welding....G.... 305 856-3749
Miami (G-10275)
Rq Inc....G.... 305 879-1773
Hialeah (G-5606)
Rudd & Son Welding Inc....F.... 850 476-2110
Pensacola (G-14255)
Ryder Welding Service Inc....F.... 305 685-6630
Opa Locka (G-12357)
S & S Welding Inc....F.... 863 533-2888
Bartow (G-333)
SDr Specialties Services LLC....G.... 386 878-6771
De Leon Springs (G-2741)
◆ Serf Inc....E.... 850 476-8203
Cantonment (G-1347)
Shawn William Shumake LLC....G.... 813 374-2469
Tampa (G-18092)
Shaws Welding Inc....F.... 850 584-7197
Perry (G-14313)
Shermans Welding & Maintence....F.... 904 731-3460
Jacksonville (G-6764)
Signature Metal Fab LLC....G.... 954 214-1161
Plantation (G-14551)
▼ Smittys Boat Tops and Mar Eqp....G.... 305 245-0229
Homestead (G-5993)
Smittys Welding Shop....G.... 321 723-4533
Melbourne (G-8935)
Southern Awning Inc....E.... 561 586-0464
Lake Worth (G-7587)
Southern Welding & Mechanics....F.... 305 772-0961
Hialeah (G-5629)
Specialty Fabrication Wldg Inc....G.... 352 669-9353
Umatilla (G-18502)
St Cloud Wldg Fabrication Inc....E.... 407 957-2344
Saint Cloud (G-15667)
Steel Plus Service Center Inc....G.... 407 328-7169
Sanford (G-16121)
Steel Products Inc....G.... 941 351-8128
Sarasota (G-16604)
Straight Polarity Welding Inc....G.... 727 530-7224
Largo (G-8061)
Suncoast Welding & Fabrication....G.... 254 537-3611
Lakeland (G-7811)
Superior Fabrication Inc....G.... 941 639-2966
Punta Gorda (G-15238)
Sureweld Welding Inc....E.... 813 918-1857
Lakeland (G-7813)
T & S Mobile Welding LLC....G.... 727 505-9407
Spring Hill (G-16867)
Tallahassee Welding & Mch Sp....E.... 850 576-9596
Tallahassee (G-17337)
Tampa Amalgamated Steel Corp....F.... 813 621-0550
Tampa (G-18155)
Tarin Services LLC....G.... 803 526-9643
Tampa (G-18175)
Tera Industries Inc....E.... 561 848-7272
Riviera Beach (G-15384)
Terry M Griffin Welding....G.... 407 209-8317
Orlando (G-13250)
Tes America LLC....G.... 786 393-2544
Homestead (G-5996)
Thermal Braze Inc....G.... 561 746-6640
Jupiter (G-7127)
Tig Technologies Inc....G.... 561 691-3633
Fort Pierce (G-4755)
Tin Man Mobile Welding LLC....G.... 239 465-9058
Naples (G-11443)
Titan Metalworks LLC....G.... 904 574-9828
Jacksonville (G-6859)
Titan Mfg Inc....F.... 239 939-5152
Fort Myers (G-4631)
Titan Service Industry Llc....G.... 678 313-4707
Deland (G-3023)
Top Torch Wldg & Fabrication....G.... 352 835-1174
Spring Hill (G-16868)
Triple H Cstm Wldg Fbrction LL....G.... 850 851-5097
Panama City (G-13957)
Unlimited Welding Inc....E.... 407 327-3333
Winter Springs (G-19487)
Viking Welding and Fabrication....G.... 904 234-5964
Orange Park (G-12411)
Voyager Offroad LLC....G.... 941 235-7225
Port Charlotte (G-15006)
▼ Weimer Mechanical Services Inc....G.... 813 645-2258
Ruskin (G-15487)
Welding Anything Anywhere LLC....G.... 561 762-1404
Palm Beach Gardens (G-13635)
Welding LLC....G.... 386 478-0323
Edgewater (G-3639)
West Palm Machining & Welding....G.... 561 841-2725
Riviera Beach (G-15389)
West Point Industries Inc....G.... 561 848-8381
Lake Park (G-7481)
Westcoast Metalworks Inc....G.... 941 920-3201
Palmetto (G-13836)
Whitley Welding Company L....G.... 904 576-3410
Middleburg (G-10915)
Wilson Machine & Welding Works....G.... 904 829-3737
Saint Augustine (G-15637)
World Class Machining Inc....F.... 386 437-7036
Bunnell (G-1311)
Xpress Precision Products Inc....G.... 305 685-2127
Hialeah (G-5691)
Y C Aluminum Welding Corp....G.... 786 255-7186
Homestead (G-5997)
Ym Welding Services Inc....G.... 502 905-4651
Homestead (G-5998)

7694 Armature Rewinding Shops

▲ A & A Electric Mtrs & Pump Svc....G.... 407 843-5005
Orlando (G-12422)
Aap Industrial Inc....E.... 941 377-4373
Sarasota (G-16331)

SIC

◆ **AC Industrial Service Inc**..........F....... 305 887-5541
Hialeah ***(G-5265)***
Aircraft Electric Motors Inc..........D....... 305 885-9476
Miami Lakes ***(G-10761)***
AL Covell Electric Inc..........G....... 352 544-0680
Brooksville ***(G-1207)***
Allapattah Electric Motor Repr..........G....... 305 325-0330
Miami ***(G-9115)***
American International Mtr Svc..........G....... 727 573-9501
Clearwater ***(G-1580)***
Belle Glade Electric Motor Svc..........G....... 561 996-3333
Belle Glade ***(G-345)***
Beltech Generator & Rewinding..........G....... 954 588-2255
Fort Lauderdale ***(G-3845)***
▼ **Biscayne Electric Motor & Pump**......G....... 305 681-8171
Miami ***(G-9251)***
▼ **Blueocean Marine Services LLC**......F....... 954 583-9888
Fort Lauderdale ***(G-3861)***
Central Electric Motor Service..........F....... 863 422-4721
Haines City ***(G-5138)***
◆ **Condo Electric Motor Repr Corp**.......E....... 305 691-5400
Hialeah ***(G-5351)***
◆ **Dade Pump & Supply Co**..........G....... 305 235-5000
Miami ***(G-9430)***
Done Rite Pumps..........G....... 305 953-3380
Opa Locka ***(G-12308)***
Electrcal Systems Cmmnications..........G....... 813 248-4275
Tampa ***(G-17631)***
Electric Motors Lift Stn Svcs..........G....... 727 538-4778
Pinellas Park ***(G-14345)***
Electro Mechanical South Inc..........E....... 941 342-9111
Sarasota ***(G-16417)***
▲ **Florida Elc Mtr Co Miami Inc**..........E....... 305 759-3835
Miami ***(G-9581)***
Genesis Electric Motors Inc..........G....... 727 572-1414
Largo ***(G-7957)***
Gulf Coast Elc Mtr Svc Inc..........E....... 850 433-5134
Pensacola ***(G-14166)***
Indian River Armature Inc..........G....... 772 461-2067
Fort Pierce ***(G-4708)***
Industrial Service Solutions..........C....... 239 288-5230
Fort Myers ***(G-4493)***
John Mader Enterprises Inc..........E....... 239 731-5455
Fort Myers ***(G-4506)***
Kcw Electric Company Inc..........G....... 850 878-2051
Tallahassee ***(G-17287)***
Kolich Electric Motor Co Inc..........G....... 954 969-8605
Pompano Beach ***(G-14740)***
M & W Electric Motors Inc..........G....... 850 433-0400
Pensacola ***(G-14198)***
▼ **Miami Compressor Rbldrs Inc**..........F....... 305 303-2251
Miami ***(G-9995)***
◆ **Miami Industrial Motors Inc**..........G....... 305 593-2370
Doral ***(G-3434)***
Michigan Pmps Elc Mtrs Repr Co..........G....... 407 841-6800
Orlando ***(G-12967)***
Morgans Elc Mtr & Pump Svc..........G....... 321 960-2209
Cocoa Beach ***(G-2066)***
New Generation Aerospace Inc..........G....... 305 882-1410
Medley ***(G-8696)***
▲ **Pinellas Electric Motor Repair**..........G....... 727 572-0777
Clearwater ***(G-1834)***
Quality Driven..........G....... 941 923-3322
Sarasota ***(G-16552)***
Robert E Weissenborn Sr..........G....... 239 262-1771
Naples ***(G-11387)***
Rusch Electric Motor Repair Co..........G....... 727 319-3388
Seminole ***(G-16760)***
▲ **Southern Winding Service Inc**..........E....... 813 621-6555
Tampa ***(G-18121)***
St Agustine Elc Mtr Works Inc..........F....... 904 829-8211
Saint Augustine ***(G-15617)***
Stewarts Elc Mtr Works Inc..........E....... 407 859-1837
Orlando ***(G-13215)***
▼ **Suncoast Electric Motor Svc**..........F....... 813 247-4104
Tampa ***(G-18143)***
▲ **T A C Armatures & Pumps Corp**..........F....... 305 835-8845
Miami ***(G-10454)***
Tampa Armature Works Inc..........D....... 904 757-7790
Jacksonville ***(G-6836)***
Tampa Armature Works Inc..........C....... 813 612-2600
Tampa ***(G-18157)***
Taw Payroll Inc..........F....... 813 621-5661
Tampa ***(G-18176)***
TEam Service Corp New York..........E....... 410 365-1574
Marco Island ***(G-8527)***
Tri County Aerospace Inc..........F....... 305 639-3356
Doral ***(G-3532)***
▼ **Tripp Electric Motors Inc**..........G....... 561 996-3333
Belle Glade ***(G-353)***
TSA Rewinds Florida Inc..........G....... 305 681-2030
Opa Locka ***(G-12366)***
United Electric Motor Inc..........G....... 813 238-7872
Tampa ***(G-18220)***
▼ **V A Electrical Motors Center**..........G....... 305 825-3327
Hialeah ***(G-5671)***

ALPHABETIC SECTION

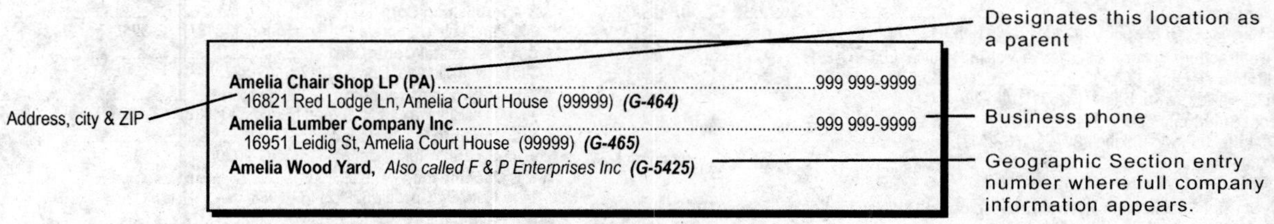

See footnotes for symbols and codes identification.

* Companies listed alphabetically.

* Complete physical or mailing address.

0energy Lighting Inc 855 955-1055
1110 Sligh Blvd Orlando (32806) ***(G-12415)***
10 Roof Cottage LLC 888 667-6961
5809 St 1st St Tampa (33611) ***(G-17371)***
100 Feet Deep, Pensacola *Also called Localtoolbox Inc* ***(G-14195)***
12 Volt USA, Kissimmee *Also called Techtronics LLC* ***(G-7303)***
123 Dollar Plus Inc 305 456-4561
7181 Sw 8th St Miami (33144) ***(G-9020)***
1425 N Washington Street LLC 904 680-6600
12808 Gran Bay Pkwy W Jacksonville (32258) ***(G-6100)***
1506 N Florida LLC 813 229-0900
1505 N Florida Ave Tampa (33602) ***(G-17372)***
1565 Woodworks LLC 904 347-7664
17 Linda Mar Dr Saint Augustine (32080) ***(G-15510)***
1600 Lenox LLC 786 360-2553
7350 Biscayne Blvd Miami (33138) ***(G-9021)***
1800flowerscom 954 683-1246
5350 Nw 35th Ter Fort Lauderdale (33309) ***(G-3771)***
180bytwo 202 403-7097
600 Cleveland St Clearwater (33755) ***(G-1558)***
1842 Daily Grind & Mercantile 352 543-5004
598 2nd St Cedar Key (32625) ***(G-1522)***
1982 Hayworth Avenue LLC 772 873-1700
1982 Sw Hayworth Ave Port St Lucie (34953) ***(G-15166)***
1concier, Medley *Also called Harbor Linen LLC* ***(G-8661)***
1source Biotechnology LLC 305 668-5888
4300 Sw 73rd Ave Miami (33155) ***(G-9022)***
1st Call For Install, Port Richey *Also called Frames & Things* ***(G-15049)***
1st Chice Hrrcane Prtction LLC 239 325-3400
25241 Bernwood Dr Ste 6 Bonita Springs (34135) ***(G-809)***
1st Choice Windows and Doors, Bonita Springs *Also called 1st Chice Hrrcane Prtction LLC* ***(G-809)***
1st Enviro-Safety Inc 239 283-1222
10200 Betsy Pkwy Saint James City (33956) ***(G-15672)***
1st Vertical Blind Company 352 343-3363
207 E Burleigh Blvd Tavares (32778) ***(G-18332)***
1st Vertical Blind Factory, Tavares *Also called 1st Vertical Blind Company* ***(G-18332)***
2 Guys Company 786 970-9275
9315 Sw 77th Ave Apt 228 Miami (33156) ***(G-9023)***
21st Century Chemical Inc 954 689-7111
2960 Sw 23rd Ter Ste 108 Fort Lauderdale (33312) ***(G-3772)***
2204 Avenue X LLC 407 619-1410
1275 Us Highway 1 Unit 2 Vero Beach (32960) ***(G-18588)***
24/7 Software Inc 954 514-8988
12411 Nw 35th St Coral Springs (33065) ***(G-2209)***
24hour Printing Inc 954 247-9575
7431 Nw 57th St Lauderhill (33319) ***(G-8097)***
2g - Cenergy, Saint Augustine *Also called 2g Cenrgy Pwr Systems Tech Inc* ***(G-15511)***
2g Cenrgy Pwr Systems Tech Inc (HQ) 904 342-5988
205 Commercial Dr Saint Augustine (32092) ***(G-15511)***
2jcp LLC 904 834-3818
101 Marketside Ave Ponte Vedra (32081) ***(G-14922)***
2klife LLC 954 316-9866
2755 W Atl Blvd Ste 104 Pompano Beach (33069) ***(G-14569)***
2leaf Press Inc 646 801-4227
1200 S Pine Island Rd Plantation (33324) ***(G-14479)***
2n USA LLC 954 606-6602
8200 Nw 27th St Ste 107 Doral (33122) ***(G-3214)***
2u Service Corp 786 219-6564
7255 Nw 68th St Ste 1 Miami (33166) ***(G-9024)***
3 D F X Inc 407 237-6249
279 N Texas Ave Orlando (32805) ***(G-12416)***
3 Miracles Corporation 407 796-9292
6843 Conway Rd Ste 120 Orlando (32812) ***(G-12417)***
3 Stars Kitchen Cabinets Corp 786 285-7147
529 W 28th St Hialeah (33010) ***(G-5252)***
3-Dimension Graphics Inc 305 599-3277
8031 Nw 14th St Doral (33126) ***(G-3215)***
305 Media Solutions, Hollywood *Also called Mas Editorial Corp* ***(G-5870)***
321 Cpr LLC 321 806-3525
29 Riverside Dr Ph 601 Cocoa (32922) ***(G-1987)***
321webprint 321 285-6771
2788 Algonquin Dr Melbourne (32935) ***(G-8755)***
33 Wraps, Boynton Beach *Also called Clear Copy Inc* ***(G-890)***
35 Technologies Group Inc 407 402-2119
2280 N Ronald Reagan Blvd Longwood (32750) ***(G-8248)***
3522091611 (PA) 352 671-1909
27206 Sw 22nd Pl Newberry (32669) ***(G-11548)***
352ink Corp 352 373-7547
327 Nw 23rd Ave Ste 1-4 Gainesville (32609) ***(G-4866)***
360 Energy Solutions LLC 786 348-2156
7650 Nw 50th St Miami (33166) ***(G-9025)***
360 O and P Inc 813 985-5000
5311 E Fletcher Ave Temple Terrace (33617) ***(G-18365)***
365 Sun LLC 208 357-8062
515 15th Ave W Palmetto (34221) ***(G-13781)***
386 Nanotech Inc 727 252-9580
6860 Gulfport Blvd S South Pasadena (33707) ***(G-16833)***
3a Products LLC 754 263-2968
2737 N Commerce Pkwy Miramar (33025) ***(G-10958)***
3b Global LLC (PA) 813 350-7872
1202 Race Track Rd Tampa (33626) ***(G-17373)***
3d Machining, Riviera Beach *Also called 3d Medical Manufacturing Inc* ***(G-15289)***
3d Medical Manufacturing Inc 561 842-7175
2001 N Congress Ave Ste F Riviera Beach (33404) ***(G-15289)***
3dmt, Daytona Beach *Also called ARC Transition LLC* ***(G-2628)***
3dmt, Daytona Beach *Also called Aerojet Rocketdyne Inc* ***(G-2622)***
3fdm Inc 727 877-3336
10600 Endeavour Way Largo (33777) ***(G-7879)***
3g Enterprises Inc 754 366-7643
1530 Via De Pepi Boynton Beach (33426) ***(G-870)***
3g Grpahics Design & Printing, Boynton Beach *Also called 3g Enterprises Inc* ***(G-870)***
3i Implant Innovations, Palm Beach Gardens *Also called Biomet 3i LLC* ***(G-13570)***
3lions Publishing Inc 727 744-8683
3958 Talah Dr Palm Harbor (34684) ***(G-13715)***
3lmetals Inc 305 497-4038
12987 Sw 19th Ter Miami (33175) ***(G-9026)***
3M Resident Monitoring Inc 813 749-5453
1838 Gunn Hwy Odessa (33556) ***(G-12096)***
3miracles, Orlando *Also called 3 Miracles Corporation* ***(G-12417)***
3n2 LLC 407 862-3622
111 Atlantic Annex Pt # 1 Maitland (32751) ***(G-8455)***
3n2 Sports, Maitland *Also called 3n2 LLC* ***(G-8455)***
3nstar Inc 786 233-7011
10813 Nw 30th St Ste 100 Doral (33172) ***(G-3216)***
3t Corporation 786 222-2147
7377 Nw 174th Ter Apt 100 Hialeah (33015) ***(G-5253)***
3tissue LLC 904 540-4335
8286 Wstn Way Cir C9 C10 Jacksonville (32256) ***(G-6101)***
4 C Timber Inc 386 937-0806
130 Odom Rd Palatka (32177) ***(G-13471)***
4 Fuel LLC 954 929-5803
2004 Grant St Hollywood (33020) ***(G-5762)***
4 Horsemen Publications Inc 727 698-0476
1768 Carlisle St Clearwater (33755) ***(G-1559)***
4 Over LLC 818 246-1170
16500 Nw 15th Ave Miami (33169) ***(G-9027)***
4 Power International Stones 407 286-4677
2704 Hazelhurst Ave Orlando (32804) ***(G-12418)***
4303 Silverwood LLC 904 900-1702
4401 San Jose Ln Jacksonville (32207) ***(G-6102)***
4714 Foods Inc 813 787-8911
4714 Causeway Blvd Tampa (33619) ***(G-17374)***
4biddenknowledge Inc 954 245-0086
2645 Executive Park Dr Weston (33331) ***(G-19099)***

4elementum LLC 305 989-1106
9149 Sw 157th Ct Miami (33196) *(G-9028)*
4ever Music LLC 407 490-0977
618 E South St Ste 500 Orlando (32801) *(G-12419)*
4f Contracting, Baker *Also called 4f Mobile Welding LLC* *(G-299)*
4f Mobile Welding LLC 850 537-2290
6289 Holloway Rd Baker (32531) *(G-299)*
4front Solutions LLC 814 464-2000
3045 Tech Pkwy Deland (32724) *(G-2951)*
4k Cabinets 727 507-0444
13565 65th St Largo (33771) *(G-7880)*
4th St Print Shack, Saint Petersburg *Also called M Victoria Enterprises Inc* *(G-15845)*
5 01 Fridays 754 444-3561
2605 E Atl Blvd Ste 210b Pompano Beach (33062) *(G-14570)*
5 Cents T-Shirt Design, Doral *Also called Baru Agency Incorporated* *(G-3264)*
5 Day Plantation Shutters 727 474-6130
1876 Lake Ave Se Ste G Largo (33771) *(G-7881)*
5 Star Builders Inc 561 795-1282
3180 Frlane Frms Rd Ste 2 Wellington (33414) *(G-18707)*
5 Star Coatings LLc 850 628-3743
126 Escanaba Ave Panama City Beach (32413) *(G-13967)*
50 50 Parmley Envmtl Svcs LLC 407 593-1165
913 Robinson Ave Saint Cloud (34769) *(G-15641)*
50 Hwy 17 S Inc 904 225-1077
850822 Us Highway 17 Yulee (32097) *(G-19492)*
525 Prnting Prmtional Pdts Inc 904 580-5943
3107 Spring Glen Rd # 211 Jacksonville (32207) *(G-6103)*
5301 Realty LLC 305 633-9779
950 Se 8th St Hialeah (33010) *(G-5254)*
531 East Inc 561 249-2524
712 Lake Ave Lake Worth (33460) *(G-7526)*
5571 Halifax Inc 239 454-4999
5571 Halifax Ave Fort Myers (33912) *(G-4340)*
5d Bio Gold LLC 561 756-8291
1725 Avenida Del Sol Boca Raton (33432) *(G-394)*
5dt Inc 407 734-5377
12249 Science Dr Ste 135 Orlando (32826) *(G-12420)*
5hp Investments LLC 561 655-5355
2822 S Dixie Hwy West Palm Beach (33405) *(G-18782)*
5nine Software Inc 561 898-1100
1555 Palm Bch Lkes Blvd S West Palm Beach (33401) *(G-18783)*
5th Element Inc 321 331-7028
3848 Shoreview Dr Kissimmee (34744) *(G-7214)*
5thelement Indian Cuisine LLC 386 302-0202
101 Palm Harbor Pkwy Palm Coast (32137) *(G-13679)*
6 Ports LLC 561 743-8696
250 S Central Blvd # 207 Jupiter (33458) *(G-6990)*
6425 Hollywood Blvd LLC 941 923-2954
6430 Hollywood Blvd Sarasota (34231) *(G-16327)*
681 Seafood & Southern Bites 954 573-7320
681 Sw 14th Ct Deerfield Beach (33441) *(G-2759)*
7 Holdings Group LLC 754 200-1365
10450 Nw 29th Ter Doral (33172) *(G-3217)*
7 Plastics Inc 407 321-5441
1680 Timocuan Way Longwood (32750) *(G-8249)*
7 Up Snapple Southeast 407 839-1706
1181 Tradeport Dr Orlando (32824) *(G-12421)*
7-Up, Boynton Beach *Also called 7up Snapple* *(G-871)*
7up Snapple 561 732-7395
4895 Park Ridge Blvd Boynton Beach (33426) *(G-871)*
8 Girls & A Guy Printing LLC 386 492-5976
31 Sun Dunes Cir Ponce Inlet (32127) *(G-14921)*
808 Island Treats, Spring Hill *Also called Romeo Ohana LLC* *(G-16861)*
850 Screen Printing LLC 850 549-7861
698 E Heinberg St Ste 101 Pensacola (32502) *(G-14074)*
88 South Atlantic LLC 386 253-0105
835 N Beach St Daytona Beach (32114) *(G-2619)*
90-Minute Books LLC 863 318-0464
302 Martinique Dr Winter Haven (33884) *(G-19292)*
904 Powderworx LLC 904 290-6383
4208 Reservoir Ln S Jacksonville (32223) *(G-6104)*
904 Sweet Treatz Street LLC 800 889-3298
7643 Gate Pkwy Ste 104 Jacksonville (32256) *(G-6105)*
905 East Hillsboro LLC 954 480-2600
905 E Hillsboro Blvd Deerfield Beach (33441) *(G-2760)*
911 Equipment Inc (PA) 954 217-1745
2645 Executive Park Dr Weston (33331) *(G-19100)*
925 Nuevos Cubanos Inc 954 806-8375
925 N Andrews Ave Fort Lauderdale (33311) *(G-3773)*
954 Savings Magazine 954 900-4649
405 Sailboat Cir Weston (33326) *(G-19101)*
9t Technology LLC 904 703-9214
3125 Double Oaks Dr Jacksonville (32226) *(G-6106)*
A & A Central Florida 407 648-5666
540 N State Road 434 # 53 Altamonte Springs (32714) *(G-24)*
A & A Electric Mtrs & Pump Svc 407 843-5005
1320 W Central Blvd Orlando (32805) *(G-12422)*
A & A Orthopedics Mfg 305 256-8119
12250 Sw 129th Ct Ste 101 Miami (33186) *(G-9029)*
A & A Printing Services LLC 786 597-6022
10482 Nw 31st Ter Doral (33172) *(G-3218)*
A & A Publishing Corp 561 982-8960
950 Peninsula Corporate C Boca Raton (33487) *(G-395)*
A & A Sheetmetal Contr Corp 305 592-2217
3067 Nw 107th Ave Doral (33172) *(G-3219)*
A & B of Tarpon Corporation 727 940-5333
40200 Us Highway 19 N Tarpon Springs (34689) *(G-18281)*
A & C Concrete Products Inc 305 232-1631
9741 Sw 168th Ter Miami (33157) *(G-9030)*
A & E Machine Inc 321 636-3110
1445 Lake Dr Cocoa (32922) *(G-1988)*
A & F Paving LLC 352 359-2282
4802 Sw 44th Cir Ocala (34474) *(G-11863)*
A & J Aerospace Corp 786 564-9986
8356 Nw 66th St Miami (33166) *(G-9031)*
A & J Boatworks, Stuart *Also called Arthur Cox* *(G-16910)*
A & J Commercial Seating Inc 352 288-2022
10485 Se 158th Pl Summerfield (34491) *(G-17055)*
A & J Mugs, Pensacola *Also called Leonard-Martin Corporation* *(G-14192)*
A & J Pavers Inc 863 559-1920
1420 Shirley Dr Lakeland (33810) *(G-7624)*
A & J Ready Mix Inc 863 228-7154
Even Rnge 300 398 W El Clewiston (33440) *(G-1976)*
A & K Machine & Fab Shop Inc 904 388-7772
3451 W Beaver St Jacksonville (32254) *(G-6107)*
A & L Septic Tank Products 407 273-2149
9304 E Colonial Dr Orlando (32817) *(G-12423)*
A & L Toolings LLC 407 242-7114
349 Fairfield Dr Sanford (32771) *(G-15984)*
A & N Corporation 352 528-4100
707 Sw 19th Ave Williston (32696) *(G-19207)*
A & R Material Handling Inc 904 879-6957
540439 Us Highway 1 Callahan (32011) *(G-1322)*
A & S Entertainment LLC 305 627-3456
250 Ne 183rd St Miami (33179) *(G-9032)*
A & S Equipment Co 305 436-8207
1900 Nw 95th Ave Doral (33172) *(G-3220)*
A & V Refrigeration Corp 305 883-0733
997 Se 12th St Hialeah (33010) *(G-5255)*
A 1 A Signs & Service Inc 305 757-6950
8965 Ne 10th Ave Miami (33138) *(G-9033)*
A 1 Fabrications Inc 352 410-0752
12440 Charlton Dr Weeki Wachee (34614) *(G-18699)*
A 1a Displays, Miami *Also called A 1 A Signs & Service Inc* *(G-9033)*
A 2 Z of Lake City Inc 386 755-0235
628 Se Allison Ct Lake City (32025) *(G-7343)*
A A A Able Air Conditioning, Fort Lauderdale *Also called AAA Able Appliance Service* *(G-3774)*
A A A Architectural Materials, Palmetto *Also called AAA Architectural Elements* *(G-13782)*
A A A Cabinets 850 438-8337
6435 Ard Rd Pensacola (32526) *(G-14075)*
A A A Signs Inc 813 949-8397
1911 Passero Ave Lutz (33559) *(G-8369)*
A Albrtini Cstm Win Treatments 941 925-2556
4023 Sawyer Rd Ofc Sarasota (34233) *(G-16328)*
A Albrtini Cstm Wndows Trtmnts, Sarasota *Also called A Albrtini Cstm Win Treatments* *(G-16328)*
A and A Concrete Block Inc 305 986-5128
4410 Sw 115th Ave Miami (33165) *(G-9034)*
A and A Orthopedics Inc 305 256-8119
12250 Sw 129th Ct Ste 101 Miami (33186) *(G-9035)*
A and D Printing & Mailing LLC 850 244-2400
105 Eglin Pkwy Se Fort Walton Beach (32548) *(G-4773)*
A and H Logging Inc 352 528-3868
333 Se 4th Ave Williston (32696) *(G-19208)*
A and J Sheet Metal Inc 561 746-4048
1567 Cypress Dr Jupiter (33469) *(G-6991)*
A B & B Manufacturing Inc 904 378-3350
2141 Lane Ave N Jacksonville (32254) *(G-6108)*
A B B Automation Technolgy Div, Coral Springs *Also called ABB Enterprise Software Inc* *(G-2211)*
A B B Power Technolgies Div, Miami *Also called ABB Inc* *(G-9053)*
A B C Canvas Inc 239 542-0909
714 Se 47th Ter Cape Coral (33904) *(G-1370)*
A B G, Melbourne *Also called Aerobase Group Inc* *(G-8759)*
A B Survey Supply Entps Inc 772 464-9500
2603 Industrial Avenue 2 Fort Pierce (34946) *(G-4667)*
A Bar Code Business Inc 352 750-0077
505 Sunbelt Rd Ste 8 The Villages (32159) *(G-18388)*
A Better Kitchen Cabinets Inc 786 234-1897
28501 Sw 152nd Ave Homestead (33033) *(G-5951)*
A C I, Bradenton *Also called Advance Controls Inc* *(G-983)*
A C Master Motors & Controls, Hialeah *Also called AC Industrial Service Inc* *(G-5265)*
A C Repairs Inc 813 909-0809
1519 Camphor Cove Dr Lutz (33549) *(G-8370)*
A Cappela Publishing Inc (PA) 941 351-2050
913 Tennessee Ln Sarasota (34234) *(G-16329)*

A Certified Screen Service 386 673-0054
560 S Yonge St Ormond Beach (32174) *(G-13345)*
A Cheaper Shot LLC 727 221-3237
4604 49th St N Saint Petersburg (33709) *(G-15687)*
A Clean Finish Inc 407 516-1311
8848 Quail Roost Ct Jacksonville (32220) *(G-6109)*
A Crown Molding Specialist 954 665-5640
9714 Nw 24th Ct Pembroke Pines (33024) *(G-14013)*
A Curv Tech Corp 305 888-9631
930 W 23rd St Hialeah (33010) *(G-5256)*
A Custom Fabrication, Lake Worth *Also called J A Custom Fabricators Inc (G-7559)*
A D Coaches Corner Inc 786 242-2229
13365 Sw 135th Ave # 102 Miami (33186) *(G-9036)*
A Developmental Stage Company, Boca Raton *Also called Invicta Corporation (G-573)*
A E T, Clearwater *Also called Advanced Engine Tech LLC (G-1565)*
A Extend Life Inc 941 505-7766
29061 Tortoise Trl Punta Gorda (33982) *(G-15188)*
A F T, Miami *Also called Azex Flow Technologies Inc (G-9206)*
A Fine Affair Dj 319 899-2071
1007 Celebration Ave # 304 Kissimmee (34747) *(G-7215)*
A Fine Print of Miami LLC 305 441-5263
2420 Sw 27th Ave Miami (33145) *(G-9037)*
A G A Electronics Corp 305 592-1860
7209 Nw 41st St Miami (33166) *(G-9038)*
A H Woodcrafter 305 885-2136
7313 Nw 56th St Miami (33166) *(G-9039)*
A Izquierdo Enterprises LLC 786 558-6657
12691 Nw 9th Way Miami (33182) *(G-9040)*
A J Assoc Mfg & Engrg Co 727 258-0994
5300 115th Ave N Clearwater (33760) *(G-1560)*
A J Giammanco & Associates 386 328-1254
115 Rachel Rd Palatka (32177) *(G-13472)*
A J M O Industries Inc 954 587-0206
1741 Sw 54th Ter Plantation (33317) *(G-14480)*
A J Trophies & Awards Inc (PA) 850 878-7187
1387 E Lafayette St Tallahassee (32301) *(G-17210)*
A J W Coatings Corp 786 357-7580
3408 W 84th St Ste 210 Hialeah Gardens (33018) *(G-5697)*
A JS Pro Percussion Center 813 361-4939
4340 W Hillsborough Ave # 208 Tampa (33614) *(G-17375)*
A L Baxley & Sons Inc 352 629-5137
1542 E Highway 329 Citra (32113) *(G-1555)*
A L Custom Wood Corp 305 557-2434
950 W 22nd St Hialeah (33010) *(G-5257)*
A L Materials 863 551-0980
1380 42nd St Nw Winter Haven (33881) *(G-19293)*
A Living Testimony LLC 352 406-0249
2119 Bates Ave Eustis (32726) *(G-3699)*
A M Coplan Associates 904 737-6996
4251 University Blvd S # 201 Jacksonville (32216) *(G-6110)*
A M P, Orlando *Also called Agri Machinery & Parts Inc (G-12442)*
A M Rayonier Products Inc 904 261-3611
1 Rayonier Way Yulee (32097) *(G-19493)*
A M Tool & Engineering Company 727 375-5002
2343 Destiny Way Odessa (33556) *(G-12097)*
A Materials Group Inc 352 463-1254
8191 Nw 160th St Fanning Springs (32693) *(G-3721)*
A Materials Group Inc (PA) 386 758-3164
871 Nw Guerdon St Lake City (32055) *(G-7344)*
A Means To A Vend Inc 954 533-8330
4700 N Dixie Hwy Oakland Park (33334) *(G-11772)*
A Mining Group LLC 386 752-7585
871 Nw Guerdon St Lake City (32055) *(G-7345)*
A Mobile Mechanic & Wldg Svc 813 900-8764
12504 Balm Riverview Rd Riverview (33579) *(G-15262)*
A Morris Industries LLC 239 308-2199
3824 23rd St W Lehigh Acres (33971) *(G-8183)*
A New World Production 321 636-6886
767 Clearlake Rd Cocoa (32922) *(G-1989)*
A P E, Key Largo *Also called Automated Production Eqp Ape (G-7164)*
A Pallet Co Inc 561 798-1564
9750 Galleon Dr West Palm Beach (33411) *(G-18784)*
A Plus Construction Svcs Inc 904 612-0597
165 Oakhill St Jacksonville (32227) *(G-6111)*
A Plus Kitchen & Bath 754 200-4207
4432 N University Dr Lauderhill (33351) *(G-8098)*
A Plus Lamination & Finshg Inc 305 636-9888
5559 Nw 36th Ave Miami (33142) *(G-9041)*
A Plus Marine Supply Inc (PA) 850 934-3890
212 Mcclure Dr Gulf Breeze (32561) *(G-5110)*
A Plus Trailers 786 395-0799
5801 Sw 210th Ter Southwest Ranches (33332) *(G-16835)*
A Quallity Pallet Company 239 245-0900
5896 Enterprise Pkwy Fort Myers (33905) *(G-4341)*
A R Components Corp 786 703-8456
8544 Nw 66th St Miami (33166) *(G-9042)*
A RE Door Cabinets Inc 813 419-0007
2502 W Carmen St Apt 1 Tampa (33609) *(G-17376)*
A S I, Fort Pierce *Also called Automated Services Inc (G-4679)*
A S O, Sarasota *Also called Aso LLC (G-16352)*
A Sanborn Corporation 727 397-3073
15019 Madeira Way Madeira Beach (33708) *(G-8445)*
A Sign 321 264-0077
3670 S Hopkins Ave Titusville (32780) *(G-18406)*
A Sign Shop LLC 813 334-7765
235 Apollo Beach Blvd # 119 Apollo Beach (33572) *(G-99)*
A Sotolongo Polishing Marble C 305 271-7957
5435 Sw 99th Ct Miami (33165) *(G-9043)*
A Superior Garage Door Company 305 556-6624
12195 Nw 98th Ave Hialeah (33018) *(G-5258)*
A T B Systems, Pensacola *Also called Water Technology of Pensacola (G-14286)*
A T C, Pompano Beach *Also called Adhesives Technology Corp (G-14578)*
A T M, Clearwater *Also called American Technical Molding Inc (G-1582)*
A T S, Fort Myers *Also called American Traction Systems Inc (G-4358)*
A Tek Steel Industries Inc 561 745-2858
3 Turtle Creek Dr Jupiter (33469) *(G-6992)*
A To Z Concrete Products Inc 727 321-6000
4451 8th Ave S Saint Petersburg (33711) *(G-15688)*
A V E Parts & Accesories, Miami *Also called P4rts LLC (G-10125)*
A W C, Plant City *Also called American Water Chemicals Inc (G-14400)*
A W R Cabinets Inc 407 323-1415
4155 Saint Johns Pkwy # 1800 Sanford (32771) *(G-15985)*
A Ward Design, Winter Haven *Also called KR Ward Inc (G-19334)*
A World of Signs 850 267-1331
77 Shannon Ln Santa Rosa Beach (32459) *(G-16151)*
A World of Wipes, Boca Raton *Also called Unico International Trdg Corp (G-765)*
A Z Printing Delray 561 330-4154
645 E Atlantic Ave Delray Beach (33483) *(G-3037)*
A&C Microscopes LLC 786 514-3967
7925 Nw 12th St Ste 112 Doral (33126) *(G-3221)*
A&C Signs Solutions Corp 786 953-5600
1745 W 37th St Hialeah (33012) *(G-5259)*
A&D Pavers LLC 954 449-0716
341 Avondale Dr Apt 3 Pompano Beach (33060) *(G-14571)*
A&H Logging Inc 352 528-3868
2752 Se 174th Ct Morriston (32668) *(G-11091)*
A&I Aluminum Shutters 561 223-5877
4614 Vespasian Ct Lake Worth (33463) *(G-7527)*
A&J Manufacturing Inc 912 638-4724
5001 W Cypress St Tampa (33607) *(G-17377)*
A&K Sheet Metal LLC 786 351-8313
9720 Nw 4th Ln Miami (33172) *(G-9044)*
A&L Hall Investments Inc 904 781-5080
1384 Cortez Rd Bryceville (32009) *(G-1296)*
A&M Cleaning Solutions LLC 786 559-7093
4400 N Terrace Dr West Palm Beach (33407) *(G-18785)*
A&R Xpress Inc 954 744-4343
9997 Nandina St Miramar (33025) *(G-10959)*
A' Nue Miami, Miami *Also called ANue Ligne Inc (G-9155)*
A-1 Block Corporation 407 422-3768
1617 S Division Ave Orlando (32805) *(G-12424)*
A-1 City Wide Sewer Service 352 236-4456
6342 E Highway 326 Silver Springs (34488) *(G-16780)*
A-1 Door Systems Inc 904 327-7206
11555 Central Pkwy # 804 Jacksonville (32224) *(G-6112)*
A-1 Roof Trusses Ltd Company (PA) 270 316-9409
11555 Heron Bay Blvd # 2 Coral Springs (33076) *(G-2210)*
A-1 Roof Trusses Ltd Company 772 409-1010
4451 Saint Lucie Blvd Fort Pierce (34946) *(G-4668)*
A-1 Sportswear Inc 305 773-7028
18820 Nw 84th Ave Hialeah (33015) *(G-5260)*
A-Brevard Coatings Inc 321 726-0322
1921 Roc Rosa Dr Ne Palm Bay (32905) *(G-13497)*
A-Fabco Inc 813 677-8790
11550 S Us Highway 41 Gibsonton (33534) *(G-5024)*
A-Mari-Mix LLC 305 603-9134
9700 Sw 24th St Miami (33165) *(G-9045)*
A-N-L Home Solutions LLC 954 648-2623
1000 Ne 196th St Miami (33179) *(G-9046)*
A-Plus Prtg & Graphic Ctr Inc 954 327-7315
6561 Nw 18th Ct Plantation (33313) *(G-14481)*
A. M. Metal Finishing, Orlando *Also called AM Metal Finishing (G-12464)*
A/C Cages 407 446-9259
890 Merrimac St Deltona (32725) *(G-3162)*
A1 Building Components, Fort Pierce *Also called A-1 Roof Trusses Ltd Company (G-4668)*
A1 Cleaning Concepts Inc 772 288-7214
173 Se Norfolk Blvd Stuart (34997) *(G-16899)*
A1 Custom Mica Inc 954 893-0063
5805 Plunkett St Hollywood (33023) *(G-5763)*
A1 Elevators LLC 954 773-4443
8185 S Coral Cir North Lauderdale (33068) *(G-11610)*
A1 Pallets LLC 813 598-9165
11802 N Us Highway 301 Thonotosassa (33592) *(G-18398)*
A1a Electric Signs & Neon Inc 305 757-6950
3655 W 16th Ave Ste 1 Hialeah (33012) *(G-5261)*
A1a Raw LLC 321 777-2526
2372 N Hwy A1a Indialantic (32903) *(G-6055)*

ALPHABETIC

A1a Signs & Svc., Hialeah *Also called A1a Electric Signs & Neon Inc* ***(G-5261)***
A1a Sportbike LLC.....321 806-3995
1500 Shepard Dr Titusville (32780) ***(G-18407)***
A1cm.....954 716-3216
5521 Nw 7th Ave Miami (33127) ***(G-9047)***
A2f LLC.....305 984-9205
2010 Nw Miami Ct Unit A Miami (33127) ***(G-9048)***
A2z Uniforms Inc.....941 254-3194
999 Cattlemen Rd Unit G Sarasota (34232) ***(G-16330)***
A360 Media, Boca Raton *Also called Worldwide Media Svcs Group Inc* ***(G-793)***
AA Casey Company.....813 234-8831
5124 N Nebraska Ave Tampa (33603) ***(G-17378)***
AA Fiberglass Inc.....904 355-5511
9378 Arlington Expy 358 Jacksonville (32225) ***(G-6113)***
AA Fiberglass Inc.....904 355-5511
521 Copeland St Jacksonville (32204) ***(G-6114)***
AA Florida Pallets.....305 805-1522
7611 Nw 74th Ave Medley (33166) ***(G-8603)***
AA Oldco Inc (PA).....215 659-5300
1625 S Congress Ave # 400 Delray Beach (33445) ***(G-3038)***
AA Performance.....772 672-1164
955 13th Ln Vero Beach (32960) ***(G-18589)***
AAA Able Appliance Service.....954 791-5222
430 N Andrews Ave Fort Lauderdale (33301) ***(G-3774)***
AAA Architectural Elements.....941 722-1910
1751 12th St E Palmetto (34221) ***(G-13782)***
AAA Cast Stone Inc.....941 721-8092
1470 12th St E Palmetto (34221) ***(G-13783)***
AAA Custom Cabinets, Pensacola *Also called A A A Cabinets* ***(G-14075)***
AAA Custom Powder Coating Inc.....305 531-5983
2625 Collins Ave Apt 803 Miami Beach (33140) ***(G-10634)***
AAA Event Services LLC.....386 454-0929
25370 Nw 8th Ln Newberry (32669) ***(G-11549)***
AAA Monterey Discount Vacuum.....772 288-5233
514 Se Monterey Rd Stuart (34994) ***(G-16900)***
AAA Porta Serve, Newberry *Also called AAA Event Services LLC* ***(G-11549)***
AAA Security Depot Corp.....305 652-8567
12815 Nw 45th Ave Ste 2 Opa Locka (33054) ***(G-12281)***
AAA Steel Fabricators Inc.....954 570-7211
1669 Sw 45th Way Deerfield Beach (33442) ***(G-2761)***
Aaa-Affordable Pallets & Reels.....813 740-8009
2811 N 76th St Tampa (33619) ***(G-17379)***
Aabc Inc.....727 434-4444
12722 62nd St Ste 206 Largo (33773) ***(G-7882)***
Aacecorp Inc.....904 353-7878
245 Riverside Ave Ste 200 Jacksonville (32202) ***(G-6115)***
Aadi Inc.....407 957-4557
190 E 12th St Saint Cloud (34769) ***(G-15642)***
Aafw-Kimco, Tampa *Also called American Archtctral Foam Wrks* ***(G-17414)***
Aap Industrial Inc.....941 377-4373
1634 Barber Rd Sarasota (34240) ***(G-16331)***
Aap Pump and Motor Works, Sarasota *Also called Aap Industrial Inc* ***(G-16331)***
AAR Airlift Group, Palm Bay *Also called Aviation Worldwide Svcs LLC* ***(G-13500)***
AAR Airlift Group Inc (HQ).....321 837-2345
2301 Commerce Park Dr Ne # 11 Palm Bay (32905) ***(G-13498)***
AAR Composites, Clearwater *Also called AAR Manufacturing Inc* ***(G-1561)***
AAR Corp.....786 337-4000
9270 Nw 100th St Medley (33178) ***(G-8604)***
AAR Defense Systems Logistics, Jacksonville *Also called AAR Government Services Inc* ***(G-6116)***
AAR Government Services Inc.....904 693-7260
8001 Westside Indus Dr Jacksonville (32219) ***(G-6116)***
AAR Government Services Inc.....321 361-3461
Aar Way Ste 101 Rockledge (32955) ***(G-15390)***
AAR Landing Gear LLC.....305 883-1511
9371 Nw 100th St Medley (33178) ***(G-8605)***
AAR Landing Gear Services, Medley *Also called AAR Landing Gear LLC* ***(G-8605)***
AAR Manufacturing Inc.....727 539-8585
14201 Myerlake Cir Clearwater (33760) ***(G-1561)***
AAR Wass, Rockledge *Also called AAR Government Services Inc* ***(G-15390)***
AAR Wheel & Brake Services, Medley *Also called AAR Corp* ***(G-8604)***
Aarg Stairs & Raillings Corp.....786 545-6465
2384 W 80th St Ste 7 Hialeah (33016) ***(G-5262)***
Aaron Best Pita, Opa Locka *Also called Universal Bakery LLC* ***(G-12367)***
Aaron Medical Industries Inc.....727 384-2323
7100 30th Ave N Saint Petersburg (33710) ***(G-15689)***
Aaron Tool Inc.....941 758-9369
2819 62nd Ave E Bradenton (34203) ***(G-980)***
Aaron's Welding & Repair, Callahan *Also called Aarons Equipment Repair Inc* ***(G-1323)***
Aarons Equipment Repair Inc.....904 879-3249
45417 Zidell Rd Callahan (32011) ***(G-1323)***
Aarons Pallets.....813 627-3225
5006 S 50th St Tampa (33619) ***(G-17380)***
Aas, Miami Lakes *Also called American Automtn Systems Inc* ***(G-10762)***
Aat Omega LLC.....352 473-6673
6670 Spring Lake Rd Keystone Heights (32656) ***(G-7205)***
Aaw Products Inc.....305 330-6863
825 Brckhllday Dr Ste 246 Miami (33130) ***(G-9049)***
Aawareness Mktg Prtg & Pubg.....352 422-3953
2659 E Gulf To Lake Hwy Inverness (34453) ***(G-6080)***
AB Ampere Industrial Panels.....904 379-4168
96266 Dowling Dr Yulee (32097) ***(G-19494)***
AB Electric Motors & Pumps.....954 322-6900
6013 Johnson St Hollywood (33024) ***(G-5764)***
AB Enzymes Inc.....954 278-3975
150 S Pine Island Rd # 270 Plantation (33324) ***(G-14482)***
AB Fire Sprinklers LLC.....954 973-8054
2759 Nw 19th St Pompano Beach (33069) ***(G-14572)***
AB Transportation, Medley *Also called Arte Bronce Monuments Inc* ***(G-8614)***
AB Used Pallets Inc.....305 594-2776
6350 Nw 72nd Ave Miami (33166) ***(G-9050)***
AB Vista Inc (HQ).....954 278-3965
150 S Pine Island Rd Plantation (33324) ***(G-14483)***
AB Vista Inc.....954 278-3965
8151 Peters Rd Plantation (33324) ***(G-14484)***
AB Wood Work Inc.....786 701-3611
13365 Sw 135th Ave Ste 10 Miami (33186) ***(G-9051)***
Aba Engineering & Mfg Inc.....386 672-9665
5 Aviator Way Ormond Beach (32174) ***(G-13346)***
Aba-Con Inc.....321 567-4967
11 S Brown Ave Titusville (32796) ***(G-18408)***
Abakan Inc (PA).....786 206-5368
2665 S Byshr Dr Ste 450 Miami (33133) ***(G-9052)***
Abalux Inc.....305 698-9192
8000 W 26th Ave Hialeah (33016) ***(G-5263)***
Abam Export, Doral *Also called Jers Group* ***(G-3402)***
Abawi Fit LLC.....813 215-1833
1327 E 7th Ave Ste 204 Tampa (33605) ***(G-17381)***
Abaxial Elevator, Fort Myers *Also called Jonathan Mariotti Entps LLC* ***(G-4507)***
ABB Enterprise Software Inc.....954 752-6700
4300 Coral Ridge Dr Coral Springs (33065) ***(G-2211)***
ABB Inc.....407 732-2000
680 Century Pt Lake Mary (32746) ***(G-7396)***
ABB Inc.....305 471-0844
8785 Sw 165th Ave Ste 302 Miami (33193) ***(G-9053)***
ABB Inc.....954 450-9544
10004 Premier Pkwy Miramar (33025) ***(G-10960)***
ABB Installation Products Inc.....386 677-9110
12 Southland Rd Ormond Beach (32174) ***(G-13347)***
ABB Partners LLC.....917 843-4430
340 Royal Poinciana Way # 3 Palm Beach (33480) ***(G-13547)***
ABB Power Distribution, Lake Mary *Also called ABB Inc* ***(G-7396)***
Abbco, Cape Canaveral *Also called American Boom and Barrier Inc* ***(G-1350)***
Abbey Rogers.....813 645-1400
10150 Highland Manor Dr Tampa (33610) ***(G-17382)***
Abbott Citrus Ladders Inc.....863 773-6322
4060 State Road 62 Bowling Green (33834) ***(G-864)***
Abbott Communications Group, Maitland *Also called Abbott Printing Co* ***(G-8456)***
Abbott Diabetes Care.....863 385-7910
6928 Matanzas Dr Sebring (33872) ***(G-16679)***
Abbott Labs US Sbsdries Alere (HQ).....877 441-7440
30 S Keller Rd Ste 100 Orlando (32810) ***(G-12425)***
Abbott Printing Co.....407 831-2999
110 Atlantic Dr Ste 110 # 110 Maitland (32751) ***(G-8456)***
Abbott Rapid Dx North Amer LLC, Orlando *Also called Abbott Labs US Sbsdries Alere* ***(G-12425)***
Abby Press Inc.....407 847-5565
929 W Oak St Kissimmee (34741) ***(G-7216)***
ABc Awning & Canvas Co Inc.....321 253-1960
244 Avenue L Delray Beach (33483) ***(G-3039)***
ABC Book Publishers Inc.....904 230-0737
4940 Blackhawk Dr Jacksonville (32259) ***(G-6935)***
ABC Components Inc.....954 249-6286
8963 Stirling Rd Ste 5 Cooper City (33328) ***(G-2106)***
ABC Enterprises.....407 656-6503
16274 Lake Johns Cir Oakland (34787) ***(G-11767)***
ABC Fence Systems Inc (PA).....850 638-8876
963 Industrial Dr Chipley (32428) ***(G-1540)***
ABC Hammers.....708 343-9900
7216 21st St E Sarasota (34243) ***(G-16170)***
ABC Imaging of Washington.....954 759-2037
714 N Federal Hwy Fort Lauderdale (33304) ***(G-3775)***
ABC Intercargo LLC.....954 908-5200
2800 Glades Cir Ste 137 Weston (33327) ***(G-19102)***
ABC Recyclers Collier Cnty Inc.....239 643-2302
4930 21st Pl Sw Naples (34116) ***(G-11145)***
ABC Screen Masters Inc.....239 772-7336
1110 Ne Pine Island Rd # 23 Cape Coral (33909) ***(G-1371)***
ABC Shutters Protection Corp.....785 547-9527
7420 Sw 38th St Miami (33155) ***(G-9054)***
Abco Graphics & Printing, Odessa *Also called Kmg Marketing LLC* ***(G-12130)***
Abco Industries LLC.....813 605-5900
5604 W Linebaugh Ave Tampa (33624) ***(G-17383)***
Abco Products Inc.....888 694-2226
6800 Nw 36th Ave Miami (33147) ***(G-9055)***
Abdiversified LLC.....954 791-6050
6825 W Sunrise Blvd Plantation (33313) ***(G-14485)***

Abe Paints, Tampa *Also called Gulf Coast Paint & Supplies* ***(G-17733)***
Abeka Print Shop Inc 850 478-8496
118 Saint John St Pensacola (32503) ***(G-14076)***
Abele Sheetmetal Works Inc 561 471-1134
1964 W 9th St Ste 3 Riviera Beach (33404) ***(G-15290)***
Abhai LLC 215 579-1842
194 Inlet Dr Saint Augustine (32080) ***(G-15512)***
Abide Family Winery Inc 850 258-0743
8401 N Lagoon Dr Panama City Beach (32408) ***(G-13968)***
Able Closets Inc 772 781-8250
218 Sw Federal Hwy Ste B Stuart (34994) ***(G-16901)***
Able Railing & Welding LLC 850 243-5444
170 Park Dr Fort Walton Beach (32548) ***(G-4774)***
About Face Cabinetry & Refacin 813 777-4088
110 Crenshaw Lake Rd Lutz (33548) ***(G-8371)***
Above LLC 850 469-9028
140 Industrial Blvd Pensacola (32505) ***(G-14077)***
Above Ground Level Aerospace 305 713-2629
13420 Sw 131st St Miami (33186) ***(G-9056)***
Above Property LLC 239 263-7406
3555 Kraft Rd Unit 400 Naples (34105) ***(G-11146)***
Abraaham Rosa Seasonings Inc 386 453-4827
813a Flight Line Blvd Deland (32724) ***(G-2952)***
Abracol North America Corp 305 431-5596
5220 Nw 72nd Ave Ste 22 Miami (33166) ***(G-9057)***
Abraham George Inc 850 523-0757
1410 Market St Tallahassee (32312) ***(G-17211)***
Abrasive Dynamics Inc 860 291-0664
1531 Se 24th Ter Pompano Beach (33062) ***(G-14573)***
ABS Structural Corp 321 768-2067
700 E Melbourne Ave Melbourne (32901) ***(G-8756)***
Absen Inc (HQ) 407 203-8870
7120 Lake Ellenor Dr Orlando (32809) ***(G-12426)***
Absolute Aluminum Inc 941 497-7777
1220 Ogden Rd Venice (34285) ***(G-18526)***
Absolute Aluminum & Cnstr, Venice *Also called Absolute Aluminum Inc* ***(G-18526)***
Absolute Automation & Security 321 505-9989
3815 N Highway 1 Ste 101 Cocoa (32926) ***(G-1990)***
Absolute Graphics Inc 954 792-3488
3721 Sw 47th Ave Ste 302 Davie (33314) ***(G-2486)***
Absolute Plastic Solutions 239 313-7779
2178 Andrea Ln Fort Myers (33912) ***(G-4342)***
Absolute Powder Coating Inc 954 917-2715
1254 Nw 21st St Pompano Beach (33069) ***(G-14574)***
Absolute Technologies Inc 954 868-9045
6320 Nw 61st Ave Parkland (33067) ***(G-13987)***
Absolute Window and Door Inc 941 485-7774
177 Center Rd Venice (34285) ***(G-18527)***
Absolute Wood Creations LLC 954 251-2202
200 S Dixie Hwy Hallandale Beach (33009) ***(G-5167)***
Absolutely Amazing Ebooks, Key West *Also called Whiz Bang LLC* ***(G-7204)***
Absolutely Suitable 561 653-6380
1 S County Rd Palm Beach (33480) ***(G-13548)***
Abyde, Clearwater *Also called Note Bin Inc* ***(G-1811)***
Abz Marketing Solutions Corp 305 340-1887
9716 Nw 29th St Doral (33172) ***(G-3222)***
AC Dob Led, Doral *Also called Wbn LLC* ***(G-3547)***
AC Graphics Inc 305 691-3778
1056 E 24th St Hialeah (33013) ***(G-5264)***
AC Industrial Service Inc 305 887-5541
268 W 23rd St Hialeah (33010) ***(G-5265)***
AC Pharma Corp 954 773-9735
3241 Holiday Springs Blvd Margate (33063) ***(G-8529)***
AC Plastics LLC 305 826-6333
1627 W 31st Pl Hialeah (33012) ***(G-5266)***
Acacia Inc 813 253-2789
904 N Rome Ave Tampa (33606) ***(G-17384)***
Academic Publication Svcs Inc 941 925-4474
3131 Clark Rd Ste 102 Sarasota (34231) ***(G-16332)***
Academy Publishing Inc 407 736-0100
210 S Semoran Blvd Orlando (32807) ***(G-12427)***
Acai Investments Llc 305 821-8872
7803 W 25th Ct Hialeah (33016) ***(G-5267)***
Acai To Go, Key Biscayne *Also called Organic Amazon Corp* ***(G-7161)***
Acasi Machinery Inc 305 805-8533
7085 Nw 46th St Miami (33166) ***(G-9058)***
ACC Holdco Inc 863 578-1206
4800 State Road 60 E Mulberry (33860) ***(G-11118)***
Accar Ltd Inc 305 375-0620
56 Ne 1st St Miami (33132) ***(G-9059)***
Accendo Tobacco LLC 305 407-2222
7575 Nw 70th St Miami (33166) ***(G-9060)***
Accenius Inc 415 205-6444
3651 Fau Blvd Ste 400 Boca Raton (33431) ***(G-396)***
Accent Casting, Punta Gorda *Also called Accent Jewelry Inc* ***(G-15189)***
Accent Jewelry Inc 941 391-6687
2373 Talbrook Ter Punta Gorda (33983) ***(G-15189)***
Accent Neon & Sign Company (PA) 727 784-8414
1179 Ridgecrest Ct Palm Harbor (34683) ***(G-13716)***
Accent Signs, Niceville *Also called Pope Enterprises Inc* ***(G-11572)***
Accent Woodworking Inc 727 522-2700
2233 34th Way Largo (33771) ***(G-7883)***
Accentia Biopharmaceuticals (PA) 813 864-2554
324 S Hyde Park Ave # 350 Tampa (33606) ***(G-17385)***
Access Able Technologies Inc 407 834-2999
360 Old Sanford Oviedo Rd Winter Springs (32708) ***(G-19465)***
Access Tools, Miami *Also called Merit International Entps Inc* ***(G-9980)***
Access Wrless Data Sltions LLC 813 751-2039
21756 State Road 54 # 101 Lutz (33549) ***(G-8372)***
Accommodating Services Inc 863 528-3231
19456 State Road 60 E Lake Wales (33898) ***(G-7498)***
Accon Marine Inc 727 572-9202
13665 Automobile Blvd Clearwater (33762) ***(G-1562)***
Accord Industries LLC (HQ) 407 671-6989
4001 Forsyth Rd Winter Park (32792) ***(G-19370)***
Accordance Bible Software, Altamonte Springs *Also called Oaktree Software Inc* ***(G-59)***
Accountble Drctional Drillillc 239 226-1606
2511 Palm Ave Fort Myers (33916) ***(G-4343)***
Accounting & Computer Systems 407 353-1570
810 Alameda St Orlando (32804) ***(G-12428)***
Accu Metal 850 912-4855
3987 N W St Ste 13 Pensacola (32505) ***(G-14078)***
Accu Right Inc 561 586-5368
1012 7th Ave S Ste 1 Lake Worth (33460) ***(G-7528)***
Accu Tech LLC 407 446-6676
1506 Max Hooks Rd Ste E Groveland (34736) ***(G-5091)***
Accu-Span Truss Co 407 321-1440
1891 High St Longwood (32750) ***(G-8250)***
Accudock, Pompano Beach *Also called Jmh Marine Inc* ***(G-14736)***
Accuform Manufacturing Inc 352 799-5434
16228 Flight Path Dr Brooksville (34604) ***(G-1204)***
Accuform Signs, Brooksville *Also called Accuform Manufacturing Inc* ***(G-1204)***
Accuform Signs 800 237-1001
11119 Holbrook St Spring Hill (34609) ***(G-16844)***
Accuplace, Plantation *Also called Automatic Mfg Systems Inc* ***(G-14494)***
Accuprint Corporation 954 973-9369
1061 Sw 30th Ave Deerfield Beach (33442) ***(G-2762)***
Accuprint My Print Shop 954 973-9369
1061 Sw 30th Ave Deerfield Beach (33442) ***(G-2763)***
Accurate Cabinet Refacing Co, Naples *Also called Gannon Charles Berchman III* ***(G-11258)***
Accurate Metal Door Inc 321 305-5951
1355 White Dr Ste 103 Titusville (32780) ***(G-18409)***
Accurate Metal Fabricators 407 933-2666
3718 Grissom Ln Kissimmee (34741) ***(G-7217)***
Accurate Metal Finishing Fla, Rockledge *Also called Accurate Metal Finshg Fla Inc* ***(G-15391)***
Accurate Metal Finshg Fla Inc (PA) 321 636-4900
500 Gus Hipp Blvd Rockledge (32955) ***(G-15391)***
Accurate Metal Finshg Fla Inc 321 636-4900
500 Gus Hipp Blvd Rockledge (32955) ***(G-15392)***
Accurate Metals Spinning Inc 305 885-9988
9001 Nw 97th Ter Ste K Medley (33178) ***(G-8606)***
Accurate Powder Coating Inc 321 269-6972
1417 Chaffee Dr Ste 10 Titusville (32780) ***(G-18410)***
Accurate Reproductions Inc 407 814-1622
2060 Apopka Blvd Apopka (32703) ***(G-108)***
Accurate Signs LLC 754 779-7519
2831 Ne 29th St Fort Lauderdale (33306) ***(G-3776)***
Accurate Wldg Fabrication LLC 727 483-3125
11029 Clay Pit Rd Tampa (33610) ***(G-17386)***
Accuware Inc 305 894-6874
235 Lincoln Rd Ste 306 Miami Beach (33139) ***(G-10635)***
Acdm-PMS Inc 305 258-0347
25331 Sw 142nd Ave Homestead (33032) ***(G-5952)***
Ace Blueprinting Inc 954 771-0104
1770 Nw 64th St Ste 500 Fort Lauderdale (33309) ***(G-3777)***
Ace Construction Management 407 704-7803
801 N Pine Hills Rd Orlando (32808) ***(G-12429)***
Ace Custom Signs of Winter Pk 407 257-6475
922 Orange Ave Winter Park (32789) ***(G-19371)***
Ace Door Co, Port Charlotte *Also called American Cnstr Entps Inc* ***(G-14960)***
Ace Fabricators Inc 904 355-3724
1705 E 30th St Jacksonville (32206) ***(G-6117)***
Ace High Printing LLC 727 542-3897
3801 16th St N Ste B Saint Petersburg (33703) ***(G-15690)***
Ace Industries, Miami *Also called Ace Printing Inc* ***(G-9061)***
Ace Marking Devices Corp 561 833-4073
3308 S Dixie Hwy West Palm Beach (33405) ***(G-18786)***
Ace Mechanical Inc 727 304-6277
6801 114th Ave Ste C Largo (33773) ***(G-7884)***
Ace Mirror & Glass Works Inc 561 792-7478
14083 85th Rd N Loxahatchee (33470) ***(G-8355)***
Ace Press Inc 239 334-1118
2133 Broadway Fort Myers (33901) ***(G-4344)***
Ace Printing Inc 305 358-2572
2846 Nw 79th Ave Miami (33122) ***(G-9061)***
Ace Restoration Services LLC 786 487-1870
11921 Sw 130th St Ste 402 Miami (33186) ***(G-9062)***

ALPHABETIC

Ace Rubber Stamp, West Palm Beach *Also called Ace Marking Devices Corp* ***(G-18786)***
Ace Sales Corp....305 835-0310
8085 Nw 68th St Miami (33166) ***(G-9063)***
Ace Shutter & Shelves LLC....239 314-9136
422 Sw 2nd Ter Cape Coral (33991) ***(G-1372)***
Ace Tools....386 302-5152
17 Lee Dr Palm Coast (32137) ***(G-13680)***
Ace Window & Door, Loxahatchee *Also called Ace Mirror & Glass Works Inc* ***(G-8355)***
Ace-Pipe Welding LLC....561 727-6345
305 Camellia St Palm Beach Gardens (33410) ***(G-13564)***
Acec, Jacksonville *Also called American Commodity Exch Corp* ***(G-6148)***
Acek9.com, Stuart *Also called Radiotronics Inc* ***(G-16996)***
Acer Latin America Inc....305 392-7000
3750 Nw 87th Ave Ste 450 Doral (33178) ***(G-3223)***
Acg Materials....405 366-9500
5160 Vermont Rd Marianna (32448) ***(G-8574)***
Ach LLC....727 586-4930
12318 Keyridge Loop Largo (33778) ***(G-7885)***
Ach Solution USA Inc....941 355-9488
1165 Commerce Blvd N Sarasota (34243) ***(G-16171)***
Achei USA Newspaper, Deerfield Beach *Also called Brazilian Clssfied ADS-Chei In* ***(G-2789)***
Achievia Direct Inc....386 615-8708
1440 N Nova Rd Unit 311 Daytona Beach (32117) ***(G-2620)***
Achievia Optical Solutions, Daytona Beach *Also called Achievia Direct Inc* ***(G-2620)***
Achsahs Delight Bakery LLC....954 533-1843
3075 Nw 19th St Fort Lauderdale (33311) ***(G-3778)***
Aci, Aventura *Also called Action Controls Inc* ***(G-259)***
Aci Hoist & Crane Inc....954 367-6116
2721 Ne 4th Ave Pompano Beach (33064) ***(G-14575)***
Aci Worldwide Inc (PA)....239 403-4600
3520 Kraft Rd Ste 300 Naples (34105) ***(G-11147)***
Acic Pharmaceuticals Inc....954 341-0795
11772 W Sample Rd Ste 103 Coral Springs (33065) ***(G-2212)***
Ackue International LLC....407 323-8688
5305 Pen Ave Sanford (32773) ***(G-15986)***
Acm Screen Printing Inc....305 547-1552
2106 Nw 22nd Ct Miami (33142) ***(G-9064)***
Acme, Brooksville *Also called Med-Nap LLC* ***(G-1249)***
Acme Brick Company....850 531-0725
660 Capital Cir Ne Tallahassee (32301) ***(G-17212)***
Acme Cap & Branding, Sanford *Also called Acme Cap & Clothing Inc* ***(G-15987)***
Acme Cap & Clothing Inc....407 321-5100
221 Bellagio Cir Sanford (32771) ***(G-15987)***
Acme Dynamics Inc (PA)....813 752-3137
545 Avenue K Se Winter Haven (33880) ***(G-19294)***
Acme Miami, Miami *Also called Acme Service Corp* ***(G-9065)***
Acme Service Corp....305 836-4800
1290 Nw 74th St Miami (33147) ***(G-9065)***
Acmt South LLC....860 645-0592
1006 Arthur Dr Lynn Haven (32444) ***(G-8427)***
Acne Seal Coating and Paving, Cape Coral *Also called Homewood Holdings LLC* ***(G-1438)***
Acolite Claude Untd Sign Inc (PA)....305 362-3333
2555 Nw 102nd Ave Ste 216 Doral (33172) ***(G-3224)***
Acolite Sign Company Inc....305 362-3333
2555 Nw 102nd Ave Ste 216 Doral (33172) ***(G-3225)***
Acore Shelving & Products Inc....904 964-4320
1460 Ne State Road 16 Starke (32091) ***(G-16886)***
Acoustic Communications LLC (PA)....305 463-9485
5049 Nw 114th Ct Doral (33178) ***(G-3226)***
ACR Custom Trailer Products, Ocala *Also called Liles Custom Trailers* ***(G-11985)***
ACR Electronics Inc (HQ)....954 981-3333
5757 Ravenswood Rd Fort Lauderdale (33312) ***(G-3779)***
ACR Family Components LLC....352 243-0307
19900 Independence Blvd Groveland (34736) ***(G-5092)***
Acrocrete Inc (HQ)....954 917-4114
1259 Nw 21st St Pompano Beach (33069) ***(G-14576)***
Acroturn Industries Usa LLC....754 205-7178
4640 Lake Industrial Blvd Tavares (32778) ***(G-18333)***
Acryfin Coatings LLC....772 631-3899
901 Nw New Providence Rd Stuart (34994) ***(G-16902)***
Acrylic Fabrication, Oakland Park *Also called Steven R Durante* ***(G-11844)***
Acrylic Images Inc....954 484-6633
2011 Nw 29th St Oakland Park (33311) ***(G-11773)***
Acrylico Inc....561 304-2921
2633 Lantana Rd Ste 6 Lake Worth (33462) ***(G-7529)***
Acrylux Paint Mfg Co Inc....954 772-0300
6010 Powerline Rd Fort Lauderdale (33309) ***(G-3780)***
Acryplex Inc....305 633-7636
2380 Nw 21st Ter Unit A Miami (33142) ***(G-9066)***
ACS, Orlando *Also called Conduent Image Solutions Inc* ***(G-12613)***
ACS of West Palm Beach Inc....561 844-5790
1300 N Florida Mango Rd # 34 West Palm Beach (33409) ***(G-18787)***
Act USA Int'l, Melbourne *Also called ACt USA International LLC* ***(G-8757)***
ACt USA International LLC....321 725-4200
3962 W Eau Gallie Blvd C Melbourne (32934) ***(G-8757)***
Actavis Laboratories Fl Inc (PA)....954 305-4414
4955 Orange Dr Davie (33314) ***(G-2487)***
Actigraph LLC....850 332-7900
102 E Garden St Pensacola (32502) ***(G-14079)***
Actigraph LLC....850 332-7900
49 E Chase St Pensacola (32502) ***(G-14080)***
Action Controls Inc....253 243-7703
3701 N Country Club Dr # 201 Aventura (33180) ***(G-259)***
Action Craft, Cape Coral *Also called Flatsmaster Marine LLC* ***(G-1423)***
Action Craft Boats, Cape Coral *Also called CK Prime Investments Inc* ***(G-1403)***
Action Label, Sanford *Also called J & J International Corp* ***(G-16070)***
Action Manufacturing & Sup Inc (PA)....239 574-3443
2602 Ne 9th Ave Cape Coral (33909) ***(G-1373)***
Action Mfg & Sup WPB LLC....239 574-3443
2711 Vista Pkwy Ste B5 West Palm Beach (33411) ***(G-18788)***
Action Plastics Inc....352 342-4122
11665 Se Us Highway 301 Belleview (34420) ***(G-365)***
Action Plating Corp....305 685-6313
1220 Ali Baba Ave Opa Locka (33054) ***(G-12282)***
Action Printers Inc....772 567-4377
2571 Stockbridge Sq Sw Vero Beach (32962) ***(G-18590)***
Action Printing Inc....305 592-4646
612 Nw 134th Ave Miami (33182) ***(G-9067)***
Action Signs & Graphics Inc....386 752-0121
4180 S Us Highway 441 Lake City (32025) ***(G-7346)***
Action Weekly Corp....561 586-8699
3708 Georgia Ave West Palm Beach (33405) ***(G-18789)***
Actionable Quality Assurance....352 562-0005
747 Sw 2nd Ave Ste 170 Gainesville (32601) ***(G-4867)***
Active Line Corp....786 766-1944
915 W 18th St Hialeah (33010) ***(G-5268)***
Active Minerals Intl LLC....410 825-2920
1130 Dade St Quincy (32351) ***(G-15245)***
Active Radiator Supply Company, Lakeland *Also called M P N Inc* ***(G-7741)***
Active Thunderboats, Pompano Beach *Also called Custom Marine Concepts Inc* ***(G-14654)***
Activedata, Naples *Also called Montague Enterprises Inc* ***(G-11330)***
Actron Engineering, Clearwater *Also called Actron Entities Inc* ***(G-1563)***
Actron Entities Inc....727 531-5871
13089 60th St N Clearwater (33760) ***(G-1563)***
Actual Woodworking Inc....305 606-7849
668 104th Ave N Naples (34108) ***(G-11148)***
Acu Grind Tool Works Inc....941 758-6963
2118 58th Ave E Bradenton (34203) ***(G-981)***
Acucall LLC....855 799-7905
824 Us Highway 1 Ste 335 North Palm Beach (33408) ***(G-11715)***
Acuderm Inc....954 733-6935
5370 Nw 35th Ter Ste 106 Fort Lauderdale (33309) ***(G-3781)***
Acuity Technologies, Tampa *Also called Telephony Partners LLC* ***(G-18181)***
Acusigns, Doral *Also called Acolite Claude Untd Sign Inc* ***(G-3224)***
Ad America....904 781-5900
8679 W Beaver St Jacksonville (32220) ***(G-6118)***
Ad Valorem Corporation....561 488-9966
2695 Nw 31st St Boca Raton (33434) ***(G-397)***
Ad-Co Printing, Tampa *Also called Disbrow Corporation* ***(G-17608)***
Ad-Tar....561 732-2055
26 Bristol Ln Boynton Beach (33436) ***(G-872)***
Adamas Instrument Corporation....727 540-0033
13247 38th St N Ste B Clearwater (33762) ***(G-1564)***
Adams Arms Holdings LLC....727 853-0550
21228 Powell Rd Brooksville (34604) ***(G-1205)***
Adams Bros Cabinetry Inc....941 639-7188
2221 Murphy Ct North Port (34289) ***(G-11731)***
Adams Bros Cabinetry Inc....863 993-0501
9300 Sw Ft Winder St Arcadia (34269) ***(G-198)***
Adams Group, North Port *Also called Adams Bros Cabinetry Inc* ***(G-11731)***
Adams Hurricane Protection Inc....850 434-2336
2302 Whaley Ave Pensacola (32503) ***(G-14081)***
Adams Street Station....904 304-7222
1738 E Adams St Jacksonville (32202) ***(G-6119)***
Adaptive Insights Inc....800 303-6346
1401 Town Plaza Ct Winter Springs (32708) ***(G-19466)***
Adapto Storage Products....305 887-9563
625 E 10th Ave Hialeah (33010) ***(G-5269)***
Adaro Envirocoal Americas, Bradenton *Also called Carbon Resources of Florida* ***(G-1015)***
Adatif Medical Incorporated (HQ)....561 840-0395
3660 Interstate Park Way Riviera Beach (33404) ***(G-15291)***
Adcon Telemetry Inc (PA)....561 989-5309
1001 Nw 51st St Ste 305 Boca Raton (33431) ***(G-398)***
Add Helium....239 300-0913
3590 Nw 54th St Ste 1 Fort Lauderdale (33309) ***(G-3782)***
Add Some Pop, Plantation *Also called Shasta Beverages Intl Inc* ***(G-14549)***
Add-V LLC....305 496-2445
1801 Nw 38th Ave Ste H Lauderhill (33311) ***(G-8099)***
Addco Industries, Riviera Beach *Also called Addco Manufacturing Company* ***(G-15292)***
Addco Manufacturing Company....828 733-1560
131 Riviera Dr Riviera Beach (33404) ***(G-15292)***
Addison Hvac LLC....407 292-4400
7050 Overland Rd Orlando (32810) ***(G-12430)***
Addison Metal Additions Inc....305 245-9860
20231 Sw 321st St Homestead (33030) ***(G-5953)***

Address-O-Lite, Pensacola *Also called Digecon Plastics International* ***(G-14131)***
Addtad Partners Inc 727 863-0847
9704 Katy Dr Ste 2 Hudson (34667) ***(G-6014)***
Adelheidis Commercial Inc 239 384-8642
3847 Tamiami Trl E Naples (34112) ***(G-11149)***
Adelman Steel Corp 305 691-7740
12040 Sw 113th Ave Miami (33176) ***(G-9068)***
Ademero Inc 863 937-0272
4685 E County Road 540a Lakeland (33813) ***(G-7625)***
Adeptus Industries Inc 941 756-7636
6224 17th St E Bradenton (34203) ***(G-982)***
Adf Group, Pompano Beach *Also called Adf International Inc* ***(G-14577)***
Adf International Inc 954 931-5150
1925 Nw 15th St Ste A Pompano Beach (33069) ***(G-14577)***
Adhesive Manufacturers Inc 305 495-8018
1572 Nw 182nd Way Pembroke Pines (33029) ***(G-14014)***
Adhesive Technologies Fla LLC 941 228-0295
411 Pheasant Way Sarasota (34236) ***(G-16333)***
Adhesives Technology Corp 754 399-1684
450 E Copans Rd Pompano Beach (33064) ***(G-14578)***
ADI, Deerfield Beach *Also called Air Dimensions Inc* ***(G-2770)***
Adidas North America Inc 321 677-0078
8200 Vineland Ave Ste 350 Orlando (32821) ***(G-12431)***
Adidas Outlet Store Orlando, Orlando *Also called Adidas North America Inc* ***(G-12431)***
Adir Scooters Inc 305 532-0019
739 5th St Miami Beach (33139) ***(G-10636)***
Adirondack Meat Company Inc 518 585-2333
5335 Mayfair Ct Cape Coral (33904) ***(G-1374)***
Adj Inc 727 289-6173
860 Pinellas Bayway S Tierra Verde (33715) ***(G-18405)***
Adj Marketing, Tierra Verde *Also called Adj Inc* ***(G-18405)***
Adjust-A-Brush, Clearwater *Also called Boden Co Inc* ***(G-1610)***
Adler Anb Inc 954 581-2572
3721 Sw 47th Ave Ste 306 Davie (33314) ***(G-2488)***
ADM II Exhibits & Displays Inc 813 887-1960
5690 W Crenshaw St Tampa (33634) ***(G-17387)***
Adma 561 989-5800
5800 Pk Of Commerce Blvd Boca Raton (33487) ***(G-399)***
Adma Biologics Inc 561 989-5800
5800 Pk Of Cmmrce Blvd Nw Boca Raton (33487) ***(G-400)***
Adma Biomanufacturing LLC 201 478-5552
5800 Pk Of Commerce Blvd Boca Raton (33487) ***(G-401)***
Admask Inc 954 962-2040
6531 Nw 13th Ct Plantation (33313) ***(G-14486)***
Admiral 305 493-4355
1690 Ne 205th Ter Miami (33179) ***(G-9069)***
Admiral Printing Inc 727 938-9589
5412 Provost Dr Unit 12 Holiday (34690) ***(G-5732)***
Admiralty Industries Corp 305 722-7311
2654 Nw 97th Ave Doral (33172) ***(G-3227)***
Adnan Enterprises 305 430-9752
4699 Nw 183rd St Miami Gardens (33055) ***(G-10731)***
Adonel Block Mfg Corp 561 615-9500
2101 Nw 110th Ave Miami (33172) ***(G-9070)***
Adonel Con Pmpg Fnshg S Fla In (PA) 305 392-5416
2101 Nw 110th Ave Miami (33172) ***(G-9071)***
Adoracion Visual, Orlando *Also called Ejm Broadcast Inc* ***(G-12701)***
Adorgraf Corp 786 752-1680
7770 Nw 64th St Miami (33166) ***(G-9072)***
Adrian Lucas Aluminum, Ocala *Also called Luv Enterprises Inc* ***(G-11988)***
Adriana Hoyos, Miami Gardens *Also called Ahus Inc* ***(G-10732)***
Adriano Gb Brick Pavers LLC 407 497-1517
9851 Cypress Park Dr Orlando (32824) ***(G-12432)***
Adrick Marine Group Inc 321 631-0776
581 Cidco Rd Cocoa (32926) ***(G-1991)***
Adsil Inc 386 274-1382
1901 Mason Ave Ste 101 Daytona Beach (32117) ***(G-2621)***
Adtec Digital, Jacksonville *Also called Adtec Productions Incorporated* ***(G-6120)***
Adtec II Tampa Inc 786 588-3688
5440 70th Ave N Pinellas Park (33781) ***(G-14333)***
Adtec Productions Incorporated 904 720-2003
2231 Corporate Sq Blvd Jacksonville (32216) ***(G-6120)***
Adtech Electric Advertising 786 533-3210
1840 Coral Way Miami (33145) ***(G-9073)***
Adultfriendfinder, Delray Beach *Also called Medleycom Incorporated* ***(G-3105)***
Adv1, Miami *Also called Advance One Wheels Inc* ***(G-9074)***
Adva-Lite Inc 727 369-5319
8285 Bryan Dairy Rd Seminole (33777) ***(G-16735)***
Advak Techologies, Miami Lakes *Also called Jtf Ventures LLC* ***(G-10800)***
Advance Carts Inc 561 320-8674
4160 Nw 1st Ave Ste 18 Boca Raton (33431) ***(G-402)***
Advance Controls Inc (PA) 941 746-3221
4505 18th St E Bradenton (34203) ***(G-983)***
Advance Ctrl Mfg Jean Annette 941 697-0846
9161 Cherry Dr Englewood (34224) ***(G-3657)***
Advance Driveline, Orlando *Also called Central Florida Driveshaft* ***(G-12567)***
Advance Green Energy Inc 352 765-3850
523 S Us Highway 41 Inverness (34450) ***(G-6081)***
Advance Hydraulic Services 352 502-9462
1511 South St Leesburg (34748) ***(G-8138)***
Advance One Wheels Inc 305 238-5833
14397 Sw 143rd Ct Ste 105 Miami (33186) ***(G-9074)***
Advance Panel Corp 347 399-6732
7877 Nw 165th Ter Miami Lakes (33016) ***(G-10759)***
Advance Plastics Unlimited 305 885-6266
905 W 19th St Hialeah (33010) ***(G-5270)***
Advance Solder Technology Inc 321 633-4777
315 Gus Hipp Blvd Rockledge (32955) ***(G-15393)***
Advance Tool Company Inc 727 726-8907
940 Harbor Lake Ct Safety Harbor (34695) ***(G-15488)***
Advanced Air International Inc 561 845-8212
6461 Garden Rd Ste 103 Riviera Beach (33404) ***(G-15293)***
Advanced Air West Palm Bch Inc 561 845-8289
6461 Garden Rd Ste 102 Riviera Beach (33404) ***(G-15294)***
Advanced Alum Polk Cnty Inc 863 648-5787
2941 Parkway St Lakeland (33811) ***(G-7626)***
Advanced Aluminum of Centl Fla 321 639-1451
155 N Range Rd Ste 13 Cocoa (32926) ***(G-1992)***
Advanced Automotive Designs 561 499-8812
6685 Dana Point Cv Delray Beach (33446) ***(G-3040)***
Advanced Awning & Design LLC 904 724-5567
2155 Corp Sq Blvd Ste 100 Jacksonville (32216) ***(G-6121)***
Advanced Bioprocess LLC 305 927-3661
3200 Nw 67th Ave Bldg 3 Miami (33166) ***(G-9075)***
Advanced Bioservices LLC 850 476-7999
5401 Corp Wds Dr Ste 500 Pensacola (32504) ***(G-14082)***
Advanced Cabinetry Inventions 305 866-1160
7601 E Treasure Dr # 2120 North Bay Village (33141) ***(G-11592)***
Advanced Cabinetry Systems, Port Charlotte *Also called Woods Distinctive Designs* ***(G-15008)***
Advanced Cabinets LLC 954 515-2675
1500 Nw 15th Ave Ste 12 Pompano Beach (33069) ***(G-14579)***
Advanced Cable Communications, Coral Springs *Also called Advanced Cmmncations Holdg Inc* ***(G-2213)***
Advanced Cmmncations Holdg Inc (HQ) 954 753-0100
12409 Nw 35th St Coral Springs (33065) ***(G-2213)***
Advanced Cmmnications Tech Inc 954 444-4119
108 Nw 20th St Boca Raton (33431) ***(G-403)***
Advanced Cnc Machining Inc 954 478-8369
6135 Nw 20th Ct Margate (33063) ***(G-8530)***
Advanced Cnc Manufacturing 727 372-8222
2313 Destiny Way Odessa (33556) ***(G-12098)***
Advanced Color Graphics Group, Hollywood *Also called R R H Inc* ***(G-5900)***
Advanced Components Solutions 813 884-1600
22652 Laureldale Dr Lutz (33549) ***(G-8373)***
Advanced Composite Systems 904 765-6502
10615 New Kings Rd Jacksonville (32219) ***(G-6122)***
Advanced Cylinder Heads 407 671-2886
2830 Forsyth Rd Ste 450 Winter Park (32792) ***(G-19372)***
Advanced Dagnstc Solutions Inc 352 293-2810
6125 Sherwin Dr Port Richey (34668) ***(G-15042)***
Advanced Design & Packg Inc 904 356-6063
2212 N Pearl St Jacksonville (32206) ***(G-6123)***
Advanced Door Concepts, Sebring *Also called Hucke Manufacturing Inc* ***(G-16695)***
Advanced Drainage & Hydro Inc 813 957-3162
19805 Deer Lake Rd Lutz (33548) ***(G-8374)***
Advanced Drainage Systems Inc 850 234-0004
12405 Panama Cy Bch Pkwy Panama City Beach (32407) ***(G-13969)***
Advanced Dsign Tech Systems In 850 462-2868
1300 E Olive Rd Pensacola (32514) ***(G-14083)***
Advanced Elctronic Diagnostics, Royal Palm Beach *Also called Nilsson Nils* ***(G-15476)***
Advanced Electronics Labs Inc 305 255-6401
7375 Sw 114th St Pinecrest (33156) ***(G-14322)***
Advanced Engine Tech LLC 727 744-2935
3087 Cherry Ln Clearwater (33759) ***(G-1565)***
Advanced Equipment and Svcs, Coral Springs *Also called Aesinc Advanced Eqp & Svcs* ***(G-2216)***
Advanced Fuel Injection 561 248-6793
211 S Hampton Dr Jupiter (33458) ***(G-6993)***
Advanced Furniture Svcs Inc 850 390-3442
8631 Match St Pensacola (32514) ***(G-14084)***
Advanced Graphics & Prtg Inc 954 966-1209
5615 Sw 88th Ave Cooper City (33328) ***(G-2107)***
Advanced Hair Products Inc 561 347-2799
1287 E Nwport Ctr Dr Ste Deerfield Beach (33442) ***(G-2764)***
Advanced Hermetics Inc 407 464-0539
2052 Platinum Rd Apopka (32703) ***(G-109)***
Advanced Hurricane Protection 772 220-1200
4517 Se Commerce Ave Stuart (34997) ***(G-16903)***
Advanced Impact Tech Inc 727 287-4620
2310 Starkey Rd Largo (33771) ***(G-7886)***
Advanced Infrstrcture Tech Inc 239 992-1700
25110 Bernwood Dr # 101 Bonita Springs (34135) ***(G-810)***
Advanced Kitchen & Cabinet 305 251-9344
21368 Sw 112th Ave Cutler Bay (33189) ***(G-2383)***
Advanced Laser Systems, Orlando *Also called L3 Technologies Inc* ***(G-12882)***

(PA)=Parent Co (HQ)=Headquarters (DH)=Div Headquarters

Advanced Living Quarters Inc...954 684-9392
426 Sw 191st Ter Pembroke Pines (33029) ***(G-14015)***
Advanced Lser Systems Tech Div, Orlando *Also called L-3 Cmmnctons Advnced Lser Sys* ***(G-12881)***
Advanced Machine and Tool Inc...772 465-6546
3900 Selvitz Rd Fort Pierce (34981) ***(G-4669)***
Advanced Machining Inc...386 424-7333
1500 Airway Cir New Smyrna Beach (32168) ***(G-11524)***
Advanced Magnet Lab Inc...321 728-7543
1604 S Hbr Cy Blvd Ste 10 Melbourne (32901) ***(G-8758)***
Advanced Manufacturing & Engrg...352 629-1494
3220 Ne 24th St Ocala (34470) ***(G-11864)***
Advanced Manufacturing Inc...727 573-3300
12205 28th St N Saint Petersburg (33716) ***(G-15691)***
Advanced Marble Products Inc (PA)...941 485-7775
177 James St Venice (34285) ***(G-18528)***
Advanced Mdular Structures Inc...954 960-1550
1911 Nw 15th St Pompano Beach (33069) ***(G-14580)***
Advanced Mechanical Entps Inc...954 764-2678
217 Sw 28th St Fort Lauderdale (33315) ***(G-3783)***
Advanced Metal Fab Inc...305 557-2008
2247 W 77th St Hialeah (33016) ***(G-5271)***
Advanced Metal Works Inc...727 449-9353
1780 Calumet St Clearwater (33765) ***(G-1566)***
Advanced Metals LLC...352 494-2476
158 Hour Glass Cir Hawthorne (32640) ***(G-5242)***
Advanced Mfg & Pwr Systems Inc...386 822-5565
1965 Bennett Ave Deland (32724) ***(G-2953)***
Advanced Millwork Inc...407 294-1927
2645 Regent Ave Orlando (32804) ***(G-12433)***
Advanced Modular Systems, Pompano Beach *Also called Advanced Mdular Structures Inc* ***(G-14580)***
Advanced Outdoor Concepts Inc...954 429-1428
3840 W Hillsboro Blvd Deerfield Beach (33442) ***(G-2765)***
Advanced Overhead Systems Inc...863 667-3757
3510 Craftsman Blvd Lakeland (33803) ***(G-7627)***
Advanced Pallets Inc...954 785-1215
2151 N State Road 7 Margate (33063) ***(G-8531)***
Advanced Pharma Research Inc...786 234-3709
10700 Caribbean Blvd # 30 Cutler Bay (33189) ***(G-2384)***
Advanced Pharmaceutical Inc...866 259-7122
1065 Ne 125th St Ste 211 North Miami (33161) ***(G-11622)***
Advanced Powder Coating Fla, Longwood *Also called Allstar Lighting & Sound Inc* ***(G-8252)***
Advanced Precision Machining...561 243-4567
1035 Nw 17th Ave Ste 3 Delray Beach (33445) ***(G-3041)***
Advanced Precision Mch US Inc...239 332-2841
3791 Edison Ave Fort Myers (33916) ***(G-4345)***
Advanced Printing...727 545-9000
7245 Bryan Dairy Rd Seminole (33777) ***(G-16736)***
Advanced Printing Finshg Inc...305 836-8581
1061 E 32nd St Hialeah (33013) ***(G-5272)***
Advanced Prof Surgical Svcs...786 326-0576
2237 Sw 63rd Ave Miami (33155) ***(G-9076)***
Advanced Prosthetics Amer Inc (HQ)...352 383-0396
601 Mount Homer Rd Eustis (32726) ***(G-3700)***
Advanced Prosthetics America, Eustis *Also called Advanced Prosthetics Amer Inc* ***(G-3700)***
Advanced Public Safety LLC...954 354-3000
400 Fairway Dr Ste 101 Deerfield Beach (33441) ***(G-2766)***
Advanced Screen Printing & EMB...863 648-1268
3635 Ventura Dr W Lakeland (33811) ***(G-7628)***
Advanced Services Intl Inc...954 889-1366
3600 Caldwell Rd Ste 406 Miramar (33027) ***(G-10961)***
Advanced Sewing...954 484-2100
3619 Nw 19th St Fort Lauderdale (33311) ***(G-3784)***
Advanced Sheet Metal & Welding...239 430-1155
4443 Arnold Ave Naples (34104) ***(G-11150)***
Advanced Software Engineering...305 387-0112
9601 Sw 142nd Ave Miami (33186) ***(G-9077)***
Advanced Software Inc...215 369-7800
1902 2nd Ave N Jacksonville Beach (32250) ***(G-6937)***
Advanced Tech & Tstg Labs...352 871-3802
3802 Spectrum Blvd # 143 Tampa (33612) ***(G-17388)***
Advanced Thermal Tech Inc (HQ)...561 791-5000
1400 Corporate Center Way Wellington (33414) ***(G-18708)***
Advanced Truck Equipment Inc...561 424-0442
1315 Neptune Dr Boynton Beach (33426) ***(G-873)***
Advanced Typesetting...407 834-1741
207 Obrien Rd Ste 101 Fern Park (32730) ***(G-3727)***
Advanced Vacuum Systems LLC...941 378-4565
2025d Porter Lake Dr Sarasota (34240) ***(G-16334)***
Advanced Wldg Fbrction Dsign L...352 237-9800
13540 Se 31st Ave Summerfield (34491) ***(G-17056)***
Advanced Xrgrphics Imging Syst...407 351-0232
6851 Tpc Dr Ofc Ofc Orlando (32822) ***(G-12434)***
Advanta Asphalt Inc...386 362-5580
1400 Howard St E Live Oak (32064) ***(G-8226)***
Advantage Drills Inc...407 478-2487
7039 Pecan Ct Winter Park (32792) ***(G-19373)***
Advantage Earth Products Inc...904 329-1430
317 Vicki Towers Dr Saint Augustine (32092) ***(G-15513)***

Advantage Enterprise Ameila Is, Lakeland *Also called Co-Edikit* ***(G-7658)***
Advantage Medical Elec LLC (HQ)...954 345-9800
11705 Nw 39th St Coral Springs (33065) ***(G-2214)***
Advantage Plastics NY Inc...863 291-4407
654 Post Ave Sw Winter Haven (33880) ***(G-19295)***
Advantage Prtg Lminating Signs, Jacksonville *Also called Advantage Prtg Lmnting Fla Inc* ***(G-6124)***
Advantage Prtg Lmnting Fla Inc...904 737-1613
4618 Sunbeam Rd Jacksonville (32257) ***(G-6124)***
Advantage Software Inc...772 288-3266
925 Se Central Pkwy Stuart (34994) ***(G-16904)***
Advantagecare Inc...407 345-8877
7081 Grand National Dr # 113 Orlando (32819) ***(G-12435)***
Advantor Systems Corporation...407 859-3350
12612 Challenger Pkwy # 3 Orlando (32826) ***(G-12436)***
Advatech Corporation...732 803-8000
250 S Australian Ave # 1504 West Palm Beach (33401) ***(G-18790)***
Advent Aerospace Inc (PA)...727 549-9600
11221 69th St Largo (33773) ***(G-7887)***
Advent Glass Works Inc...386 497-2050
242 Sw George Gln Fort White (32038) ***(G-4842)***
Adventry Corp...305 582-2977
8190 Commerce Way Miami Lakes (33016) ***(G-10760)***
Adventurous Entertainment LLC...407 483-4057
6424 Milner Blvd 4 Orlando (32809) ***(G-12437)***
Adver-T Screen Printing Inc...727 443-5525
408 S Saturn Ave Clearwater (33755) ***(G-1567)***
Advermarket Corp...239 541-1144
954 Country Club Blvd Cape Coral (33990) ***(G-1375)***
Advermarket Corp...239 542-1020
4720 Se 15th Ave Ste 205 Cape Coral (33904) ***(G-1376)***
Advocate House, Sarasota *Also called A Cappela Publishing Inc* ***(G-16329)***
Advtravl Inc...978 549-5013
116 S Magnolia Ave Ste 2 Ocala (34471) ***(G-11865)***
Adwave Graphics Inc...305 643-8020
35 Nw 27th Ave Miami (33125) ***(G-9078)***
Ae Tent LLC...305 691-0191
2995 Nw 75th St Miami (33147) ***(G-9079)***
Aeb Technologies Inc...352 417-0009
9619 W Yulee Dr Homosassa (34448) ***(G-5999)***
Aegle Therapeutics Corporation...305 608-9705
1951 Nw 7th Ave Fl 3 Miami (33136) ***(G-9080)***
Aei International Corp...904 724-9771
7709 Alton Ave Jacksonville (32211) ***(G-6125)***
Aenova Doral Manufacturing Inc (HQ)...305 463-2270
10400 Nw 29th Ter Doral (33172) ***(G-3228)***
Aenova Doral Manufacturing Inc...305 463-2263
10655 Nw 29th Ter Doral (33172) ***(G-3229)***
AEP Group, Saint Augustine *Also called Advantage Earth Products Inc* ***(G-15513)***
Aer-Flo Canvas Products Inc...941 747-4151
4455 18th St E Bradenton (34203) ***(G-984)***
Aercap Inc...954 760-7777
100 Ne 3rd Ave Ste 800 Fort Lauderdale (33301) ***(G-3785)***
Aercap Group Services Inc (HQ)...954 760-7777
100 Ne 3rd Ave Ste 800 Fort Lauderdale (33301) ***(G-3786)***
Aercon Florida LLC...863 422-6360
3701 State Road 544 E Haines City (33844) ***(G-5137)***
Aerial Banners Inc...954 893-0099
601 Sw 77th Way Pembroke Pines (33023) ***(G-14016)***
Aerial Flags, Largo *Also called Custom Grafix Industries Inc* ***(G-7929)***
Aerial Products Corporation...800 973-9110
11653 Central Pkwy # 209 Jacksonville (32224) ***(G-6126)***
Aerialife Inc...561 990-9299
1319 S L St Fl 334 Lake Worth (33460) ***(G-7530)***
Aerion Corp (PA)...775 337-6682
500 Nw 62nd St Ste 400 Fort Lauderdale (33309) ***(G-3787)***
Aero American Detailing Llc...850 459-7425
3254 Capital Cir Sw Tallahassee (32310) ***(G-17213)***
Aero Bridgeworks Inc...321 689-1912
1209 E Landstreet Rd Orlando (32824) ***(G-12438)***
Aero Door International LLC...407 654-0591
2770 Dillard Rd Eustis (32726) ***(G-3701)***
Aero Electronics Systems Inc...321 269-0478
411 S Park Ave Titusville (32796) ***(G-18411)***
Aero Fuel LLC...352 728-2018
9595 Silver Lake Dr Leesburg (34788) ***(G-8139)***
Aero Hose Corp...904 215-9638
1845 Town Center Blvd # 140 Orange Park (32003) ***(G-12380)***
Aero Mechanical Industries...469 645-1620
121 Alhambra Plz Ste 1700 Coral Gables (33134) ***(G-2118)***
Aero Precision Products Inc...305 688-2565
14000 Nw 19th Ave Opa Locka (33054) ***(G-12283)***
Aero Seating Technologies LLC...321 264-5600
1600 Armstrong Dr Titusville (32780) ***(G-18412)***
Aero Shade Technologies Inc...772 562-2243
3104 Industrial Avenue 3 # 3106 Fort Pierce (34946) ***(G-4670)***
Aero Simulation Inc...813 628-4447
8720 E Sligh Ave Tampa (33610) ***(G-17389)***
Aero South Florida Inc...954 363-2376
101 Nw 42nd Way Deerfield Beach (33442) ***(G-2767)***

Aero Stitch Inc 305 978-3446
18264 Sw 143rd Pl Miami (33177) ***(G-9081)***
Aero Supply USA, Clearwater *Also called Supliaereos USA LLC* ***(G-1897)***
Aero Tech Service Assoc Inc 850 286-1378
1311 Florida Ave Tyndall Afb (32403) ***(G-18493)***
Aero Technology Mfg Inc 305 345-7747
7735 Nw 64th St Ste 1 Miami (33166) ***(G-9082)***
Aero-Flex Corp 561 745-2534
3147 Jupiter Park Cir # 2 Jupiter (33458) ***(G-6994)***
Aero-Link Marine & Power LLC (PA) 561 404-8181
2295 Nw Corp Blvd Ste 110 Boca Raton (33431) ***(G-404)***
Aero-Mach TCO Manufacturing 239 936-7570
604 Danley Dr Fort Myers (33907) ***(G-4346)***
Aero-Marine Technologies Inc 941 205-5420
2800 Placida Rd Ste 103 Englewood (34224) ***(G-3658)***
Aero-Tel Wire Harness Corp 407 445-1722
3788 Silver Star Rd Orlando (32808) ***(G-12439)***
Aero-Trim Control Systems Inc 954 321-1936
4680 Sw 61st Ave Davie (33314) ***(G-2489)***
Aerobase Group Inc 321 802-5889
145 East Dr Ste B Melbourne (32904) ***(G-8759)***
Aerobotics Technologies Inc 407 658-9864
4514 Saddleworth Cir Orlando (32826) ***(G-12440)***
Aerodyne Research LLC 813 891-6300
1725 Lexington Ave Deland (32724) ***(G-2954)***
Aerojet Rcktdyne Clman Arspc I 407 354-0047
7675 Municipal Dr Orlando (32819) ***(G-12441)***
Aerojet Rocketdyne Inc 561 796-2000
15270 Endeavor Dr Jupiter (33478) ***(G-6995)***
Aerojet Rocketdyne Inc 386 626-0001
790 Fentress Blvd Daytona Beach (32114) ***(G-2622)***
Aerojet Rocketdyne De Inc 561 882-5150
17900 Bee Line Hwy Jupiter (33478) ***(G-6996)***
Aeronate Inc 954 358-7145
20851 Johnson St Ste 109 Pembroke Pines (33029) ***(G-14017)***
Aeronautical Systems Engrg Inc 727 375-2520
2448 Destiny Way Odessa (33556) ***(G-12099)***
Aerontics Customer Support Ctr, Lakeland *Also called Lockheed Martin Corporation* ***(G-7740)***
Aerosmart Enterprise LLC 310 499-8878
7901 4th St N Ste 300 Saint Petersburg (33702) ***(G-15692)***
Aerosonic LLC 727 461-3000
1212 N Hercules Ave Clearwater (33765) ***(G-1568)***
Aerosource Inc (HQ) 941 751-2620
2250 Whitfield Ave Sarasota (34243) ***(G-16172)***
Aerospace Automation LLC 954 260-2844
830 Sw 174th Ter Pembroke Pines (33029) ***(G-14018)***
Aerospace Components Inc 727 347-9915
2625 75th St N Saint Petersburg (33710) ***(G-15693)***
Aerospace Manufacturing, Lynn Haven *Also called Acmt South LLC* ***(G-8427)***
Aerospace Retail Inc 888 918-8116
433 Plaza Real Ste 275 Boca Raton (33432) ***(G-405)***
Aerospace Rotables Inc 954 452-0056
5151 Nw 109th Ave Sunrise (33351) ***(G-17083)***
Aerospace Tech Group Inc 561 244-7400
620 Nw 35th St Boca Raton (33431) ***(G-406)***
Aerospc/Dfense Coatings GA Inc 407 843-1140
378 Centerpointe Cir # 1272 Altamonte Springs (32701) ***(G-25)***
Aerosync Engrg Consulting Inc 316 208-3367
5848 Moors Oaks Dr Milton (32583) ***(G-10920)***
Aerosync Support, Milton *Also called Aerosync Engrg Consulting Inc* ***(G-10920)***
Aerotec Aluminium Inc 407 324-5400
1696 N Beardall Ave Sanford (32771) ***(G-15988)***
Aerotek Gear & Spline Inc 954 543-3473
11020 Nw 38th St Coral Springs (33065) ***(G-2215)***
Aerotools Connection, Miami *Also called Forward Express One Llc* ***(G-9595)***
Aerotools Connection LLC 305 234-3034
12625 Sw 134th Ct Ste 208 Miami (33186) ***(G-9083)***
Aerotools USA Inc 305 432-4258
12591 Sw 134th Ct Ste 105 Miami (33186) ***(G-9084)***
Aerouno Llc 561 767-5597
3090 Holiday Springs Blvd Margate (33063) ***(G-8532)***
Aerowest Mfg Corp 786 367-6948
8835 Nw 117th St Hialeah (33018) ***(G-5273)***
Aerox AVI Oxgn Systems LLC 207 637-2331
25190 Bernwood Dr Bonita Springs (34135) ***(G-811)***
Aersale 23440 LLC 305 764-3200
121 Alhambra Plz Ste 1700 Coral Gables (33134) ***(G-2119)***
Aersale 26346 LLC 305 764-3200
121 Alhambra Plz Ste 1700 Coral Gables (33134) ***(G-2120)***
Aersale Component Solutions, Miami *Also called Avborne Accessory Group Inc* ***(G-9195)***
AES, Plant City *Also called American Engineering Svcs Inc* ***(G-14399)***
AES Services Inc 941 237-1446
575 Bluebell Rd Venice (34293) ***(G-18529)***
Aesinc Advanced Eqp & Svcs (PA) 954 857-1895
12070 Nw 40th St Ste 2 Coral Springs (33065) ***(G-2216)***
Aesthetic MBL Laser Svcs Inc 954 480-2600
905 E Hillsboro Blvd Deerfield Beach (33441) ***(G-2768)***
Aesthetic Mobile Laser Svcs, Deerfield Beach *Also called 905 East Hillsboro LLC* ***(G-2760)***
Aesthetic Print & Design Inc 352 278-3714
2618 Ne 18th Ter Gainesville (32609) ***(G-4868)***
Aesthetics Complete Inc 610 265-3535
1164 Ponderosa Rd Venice (34293) ***(G-18530)***
Aether Media USA Inc 863 647-5500
4175 S Pipkin Rd Ste 108 Lakeland (33811) ***(G-7629)***
Aetiquetas Araragua, Miami *Also called Eti-Label Inc* ***(G-9538)***
Afab Enterprises, Eustis *Also called James O Corbett Inc* ***(G-3710)***
Afc Cable Systems Inc 813 539-0588
2000 Tall Pines Dr Largo (33771) ***(G-7888)***
Affineon Lighting 407 448-3434
16709 Amber Lk Weston (33331) ***(G-19103)***
Affordable At Home Has Inc 786 200-0484
8870 Sw 40th St Ste 7 Miami (33165) ***(G-9085)***
Affordable Boat Cushions Inc 877 350-2628
6515 Riverview Dr Riverview (33578) ***(G-15263)***
Affordable Displays, Clearwater *Also called Nauset Enterprises Inc* ***(G-1804)***
Affordable Granite Concepts 407 332-0057
1025 Miller Dr Ste 139 Altamonte Springs (32701) ***(G-26)***
Affordable Med Scrubs LLC (PA) 419 222-1088
888 Brickell Ave Ste 100 Miami (33131) ***(G-9086)***
Affordable Metal Inc 305 691-8082
3522 E 10th Ct Hialeah (33013) ***(G-5274)***
Affordable Quality Blinds Inc 786 412-4840
7345 Sw 32nd St Miami (33155) ***(G-9087)***
Affordable Signs Clermont LLC 352 241-7645
1502 Max Hooks Rd Ste C Groveland (34736) ***(G-5093)***
Affordable Wheelchair Transprt 727 432-4089
6192 39th Ave N Saint Petersburg (33709) ***(G-15694)***
Affordble Prsrvtion Rstoration 941 527-1416
2647 Britannia Rd Sarasota (34231) ***(G-16335)***
Affordble Qlty Drywall Screen 561 723-0635
3841 7th Ave N Lake Worth (33461) ***(G-7531)***
Affordble Screen Enclosure LLC 561 900-8868
5480 Palm Ridge Blvd Delray Beach (33484) ***(G-3042)***
Afi, Saint Petersburg *Also called American Fibertek Inc* ***(G-15699)***
Afina Systems Inc (HQ) 305 261-1433
3350 Sw 148th Ave Ste 401 Miramar (33027) ***(G-10962)***
AFL Industries Inc 561 848-1826
1101 W 13th St Riviera Beach (33404) ***(G-15295)***
Aflg Invstmnts-Industrials LLC (PA) 813 443-8203
701 Suth Hward Ave 106 Tampa (33606) ***(G-17390)***
Aflg Invstmnts-Industrials LLC 813 443-8203
5000 Calienta St Hernando Beach (34607) ***(G-5250)***
AGA, Miami *Also called A G A Electronics Corp* ***(G-9038)***
AGA Machine Shop Inc 954 522-1108
277 Sw 33rd St Fort Lauderdale (33315) ***(G-3788)***
Agape Graphics & Printing Inc 305 252-9147
14255 Sw 119th Ave Miami (33186) ***(G-9088)***
Agarose Unlimited Inc 800 850-0659
707 Nw 13th St Gainesville (32601) ***(G-4869)***
Agd Systems Corporation 561 722-5561
10130 Northlake Blvd # 2 West Palm Beach (33412) ***(G-18791)***
Agent Advantage, Tallahassee *Also called Homes Media Solutions LLC* ***(G-17278)***
Agg International, Hollywood *Also called Snappy Structures Inc* ***(G-5910)***
Agg Trading-W Ft Pierce Term, Fort Pierce *Also called Cemex Cnstr Mtls Fla LLC* ***(G-4685)***
Aggressive Box Inc 813 901-9600
5444 Pioneer Park Blvd A Tampa (33634) ***(G-17391)***
Agi Solutions Inc 888 987-8425
4023 Sawyer Rd Unit 140 Sarasota (34233) ***(G-16336)***
Agi-Vr/Wesson Inc 239 573-5132
2673 Ne 9th Ave Cape Coral (33909) ***(G-1377)***
Agile Cargo Transportation LLC 407 747-0812
1601-1 N Main St Jacksonville (32206) ***(G-6127)***
Agile Risk Management LLC 800 317-5497
3333 W Kennedy Blvd # 201 Tampa (33609) ***(G-17392)***
Agility Press Inc 904 731-8989
3060 Mercury Rd Jacksonville (32207) ***(G-6128)***
AGlsupreme Llc 818 232-6699
2252 Hayes St Hollywood (33020) ***(G-5765)***
Agl Aerospace, Miami *Also called Above Ground Level Aerospace* ***(G-9056)***
AGM Industries Inc 954 486-1112
1560 Nw 23rd Ave Fort Lauderdale (33311) ***(G-3789)***
AGM Kitchen & Bath LLC 239 300-4739
4384 Progress Ave Naples (34104) ***(G-11151)***
AGM Orlando Inc 407 865-9522
223 Altamonte Commerce Bl Altamonte Springs (32714) ***(G-27)***
AGM Publishing Inc 727 934-9993
3049 Coldwell Dr Holiday (34691) ***(G-5733)***
Agner Timber Services Inc 850 251-6615
2450 W Fair Rd Perry (32347) ***(G-14291)***
Agnus Distributors, Miami *Also called Dextrum Laboratories Inc* ***(G-9462)***
Agora Leather Products, Clearwater *Also called Agora Sales Inc* ***(G-1569)***
Agora Leather Products, Saint Petersburg *Also called Agora Sales Inc* ***(G-15695)***
Agora Sales Inc 727 490-0499
4215 E Bay Dr Apt 802 Clearwater (33764) ***(G-1569)***
Agora Sales Inc (PA) 727 321-0707
2101 28th St N Saint Petersburg (33713) ***(G-15695)***

ALPHABETIC

Agp Holding Corp (PA)....850 668-0006
2935 Kerry Forest Pkwy Tallahassee (32309) ***(G-17214)***
Agpb LLC....561 935-4147
800 W Indiantown Rd Jupiter (33458) ***(G-6997)***
AGR Fabricators Inc....904 733-9393
4879 Clydo Rd S Ste 1 Jacksonville (32207) ***(G-6129)***
AGR of Florida Inc....904 733-9393
4879 Clydo Rd S Jacksonville (32207) ***(G-6130)***
Agra Chem Sales Co Inc....863 453-6450
959 S Angelo Lake Rd Avon Park (33825) ***(G-283)***
Agranco Corp (usa)....877 592-0031
5966 S Dixie Hwy Ste 300 South Miami (33143) ***(G-16811)***
Agri Machinery & Parts Inc....407 299-1592
3489 All American Blvd Orlando (32810) ***(G-12442)***
Agri Metal Supply Inc....386 294-1720
232 Se Indus Pk Cir Ste C Mayo (32066) ***(G-8594)***
Agri-Products Inc (HQ)....850 668-0006
3015 N Shnnon Lkes Dr Ste Tallahassee (32309) ***(G-17215)***
Agri-Source Inc....352 351-2700
4001 Ne 35th St Ocala (34479) ***(G-11866)***
Agri-Source Fuels LLC....352 521-3460
120 E Main St Ste A Pensacola (32502) ***(G-14085)***
Agrifleet Leasing Corporation....239 293-3976
100 Thornhill Rd Auburndale (33823) ***(G-229)***
Agripure Cbd LLC....561 789-3819
12314 Melrose Way Boca Raton (33428) ***(G-407)***
Agrium Advanced Tech US Inc....407 302-2024
2451 Old Lake Mary Rd Sanford (32771) ***(G-15989)***
Agro & Cnstr Solutions Inc....305 593-7011
3630 Nw 115th Ave Doral (33178) ***(G-3230)***
Agrosource Inc....908 251-3500
166 Beacon Ln Jupiter (33469) ***(G-6998)***
Agrotek Services Incorporated....305 599-3818
6414 Nw 82nd Ave Miami (33166) ***(G-9089)***
AGS Electronics Inc....850 471-1551
4400 Bayou Blvd Ste 53b Pensacola (32503) ***(G-14086)***
AGS Enterprises Inc....305 716-7660
10305 Nw 41st St Ste 210 Doral (33178) ***(G-3231)***
Agteck Inc....321 305-5930
150 N Wilson Ave Ste 101 Cocoa (32922) ***(G-1993)***
Agua Bucha, Saint Petersburg *Also called Mother Kombucha LLC* ***(G-15860)***
Agua Control LLC....813 663-0701
5609 E Adamo Dr Ste D Tampa (33619) ***(G-17393)***
Agua Viva LLC....954 802-3255
1111 Lincoln Rd Miami Beach (33139) ***(G-10637)***
Agustin Reyes Inc....305 558-8870
2307 W 77th St Hialeah (33016) ***(G-5275)***
Ahc Ventures Corp....954 978-9290
5415 Nw 24th St Ste 103 Margate (33063) ***(G-8533)***
Ahus Inc....305 572-9052
3371 Nw 168th St Miami Gardens (33056) ***(G-10732)***
Ai Thomas LLC....904 553-6202
220 Pnte Vdra Pk Dr Ste 1 Ponte Vedra Beach (32082) ***(G-14929)***
Ai-R.com Got-Leads.com, Boca Raton *Also called Significant Solutions Corp* ***(G-711)***
Ai2 Inc....407 645-3234
1400 Bonnie Burn Cir Winter Park (32789) ***(G-19374)***
Aicon Yachts Americas LLC....910 583-5299
1801 West Ave Miami Beach (33139) ***(G-10638)***
AIG Technologies Inc....954 433-0618
5001 Nw 13th Ave Ste B Deerfield Beach (33064) ***(G-2769)***
Aigean Networks....754 223-2240
3496 Ne 12th Ter Oakland Park (33334) ***(G-11774)***
Aim, Jacksonville *Also called R & K Marketing Inc* ***(G-6701)***
Aim Immunotech Inc (PA)....352 448-7797
2117 Sw Highway 484 Ocala (34473) ***(G-11867)***
Aim Shutters....954 861-6666
5054 N Hiatus Rd Sunrise (33351) ***(G-17084)***
Aims Printing LLC....813 313-9574
1302 Cherrywood Ave Tampa (33613) ***(G-17394)***
AIN Plastics of Florida Inc....813 242-6400
6317 Pelican Creek Cir Riverview (33578) ***(G-15264)***
Aiolos Group Inc....305 496-7674
2529 Nw 74th Ave Miami (33122) ***(G-9090)***
Air & Power Solutions Inc....954 427-0019
6810 Lyons Tech Pkwy # 125 Coconut Creek (33073) ***(G-2068)***
Air Alliance Inc....305 735-4864
13369 Overseas Hwy Marathon (33050) ***(G-8516)***
Air Authorities of Tampa Inc....727 525-1575
4810 110th Ave N Ste 1a Clearwater (33762) ***(G-1570)***
Air Burners Inc....772 220-7303
4390 Sw Cargo Way Palm City (34990) ***(G-13639)***
Air Burners LLC....772 220-7303
4390 Sw Cargo Way Palm City (34990) ***(G-13640)***
Air Dimensions Inc....954 428-7333
1371 W Newport Center Dr # 101 Deerfield Beach (33442) ***(G-2770)***
Air Distributors Inc....352 522-0006
2541 W Dunnellon Rd Dunnellon (34433) ***(G-3592)***
Air Doctor of Swfl LLC....239 285-8774
1020 Jackson Ave Lehigh Acres (33972) ***(G-8184)***
Air Duct Systems Inc....407 839-3313
2106 W Central Blvd Orlando (32805) ***(G-12443)***
Air Esscentials Inc....305 446-1670
7055 Sw 47th St Miami (33155) ***(G-9091)***
Air Essentials, Miami *Also called Air Esscentials Inc* ***(G-9091)***
Air Flow Specialists....954 727-9507
5400 S University Dr 206a Davie (33328) ***(G-2490)***
Air Lion Incorp....386 748-9296
2609 Old Church Pl Deland (32720) ***(G-2955)***
Air Liquide Large Inds US LP....321 452-2214
7007 N Courtenay Pkwy Merritt Island (32953) ***(G-8987)***
Air Marshall Inc....954 843-0991
2870 Stirling Rd Ste 110 Hollywood (33020) ***(G-5766)***
Air Operations....305 871-5449
4000 Nw 28th St Miami (33142) ***(G-9092)***
Air Purifying Systems Inc....954 962-0450
3750 Nw 28th St Unit 206 Miami (33142) ***(G-9093)***
Air Shelters USA LLC (PA)....215 957-6128
650 Sw 16th Ter Pompano Beach (33069) ***(G-14581)***
Air Source 1 LLC....772 626-7604
585 Nw Merc Pl Ste 103 Port St Lucie (34986) ***(G-15167)***
Air Sponge Filter Company Inc....954 752-1836
4224 Nw 120th Ave Coral Springs (33065) ***(G-2217)***
Air Supply of Future Inc....954 977-0877
1950 Nw 15th St Ste A Pompano Beach (33069) ***(G-14582)***
Air Support Tecks....386 986-5301
14 Bird Haven Pl Palm Coast (32137) ***(G-13681)***
Air Technical LLC....305 837-3274
7901 4th St N Ste 4612 Saint Petersburg (33702) ***(G-15696)***
Air Temp of America Inc....850 340-3017
423 E 16th St Panama City (32405) ***(G-13861)***
Air Turbine Technology Inc....561 994-0500
1225 Broken Sound Pkwy Nw D Boca Raton (33487) ***(G-408)***
Air-Flite Containers Inc....407 679-1200
2699 N Forsyth Rd Ste 101 Orlando (32807) ***(G-12444)***
Air-Flo/Erwood Heating and A/C, Seminole *Also called Miles of Smiles Rides Inc* ***(G-16753)***
Air-Tech of Pensacola Inc....850 433-6443
2317 Town St Pensacola (32505) ***(G-14087)***
Air-Trac, Gainesville *Also called R & J Mfg of Gainesville* ***(G-4987)***
Air2 G2 Machine, Jacksonville *Also called Foley Air LLC* ***(G-6411)***
Airam Stone Designs Inc....305 477-8009
8900 Sw 104th St Miami (33176) ***(G-9094)***
Airbus Oneweb Satellites LLC (PA)....321 735-8446
8301 Newspace Dr Merritt Island (32953) ***(G-8988)***
Airbus Onweb Stlltes N Amer LL (HQ)....321 522-6645
8301 Newspace Dr Merritt Island (32953) ***(G-8989)***
Airbus Onweb Stlltes N Amer LL....321 522-6645
8301 Newspace Dr Merritt Island (32953) ***(G-8990)***
Aircel LLC....865 681-7066
3033 Riviera Dr Ste 101 Naples (34103) ***(G-11152)***
Airco Plating Company Inc....305 633-2476
3650 Nw 46th St Miami (33142) ***(G-9095)***
Aircraft Electric Motors Inc....305 885-9476
5800 Nw 163rd St Miami Lakes (33014) ***(G-10761)***
Aircraft Engrg Instlltion Svcs....407 438-4436
101 W Landstreet Rd Orlando (32824) ***(G-12445)***
Aircraft Systems Group Inc....727 376-9292
11528 Perpetual Dr Odessa (33556) ***(G-12100)***
Aircraft Tbular Components Inc....321 757-9020
3939 Dow Rd Melbourne (32934) ***(G-8760)***
Aircraft Technology Inc....954 744-7602
3000 Taft St Hollywood (33021) ***(G-5767)***
Airdyne Aerospace Inc....352 593-4163
3160 Premier Dr Brooksville (34604) ***(G-1206)***
Aire-Tech Rotorcraft Svcs LLC....305 696-8001
6270 Nw 37th Ave Miami (33147) ***(G-9096)***
Airehealth Inc (PA)....407 280-4107
1511 E State Road 434 # 2 Winter Springs (32708) ***(G-19467)***
Airflowbalance LLC....386 871-8136
4273 Regal Town Ln Lake Mary (32746) ***(G-7397)***
Airframe International Inc....218 461-9305
3150 Airmans Dr Fort Pierce (34946) ***(G-4671)***
Airfree USA LLC....305 772-6577
25 Se 2nd Ave Ste 1235 Miami (33131) ***(G-9097)***
Airgas Puritan Medical, Orlando *Also called Airgas Usa LLC* ***(G-12446)***
Airgas Usa LLC....407 293-6630
3100 Silver Star Rd Orlando (32808) ***(G-12446)***
Airgroup Inc....561 279-0680
9858 Glades Rd Boca Raton (33434) ***(G-409)***
Airguide Manufacturing LLC....305 888-1631
795 W 20th St Hialeah (33010) ***(G-5276)***
Airind Incorporated....954 252-0900
6511 Melaleuca Rd Southwest Ranches (33330) ***(G-16836)***
Airite Air Conditioning Inc....813 886-0235
5321 W Crenshaw St Tampa (33634) ***(G-17395)***
Airline Support Group Inc....954 971-4567
2700 W Cypress Creek Rd Fort Lauderdale (33309) ***(G-3790)***
Airlock USA LLC....305 888-6454
145 Curtiss Pkwy Miami Springs (33166) ***(G-10887)***

Airmark Components Inc....954 522-5370
2701 Sw 2nd Ave Fort Lauderdale (33315) ***(G-3791)***
Airmark Engines, Inc., Fort Lauderdale *Also called Airmark Overhaul Inc* ***(G-3792)***
Airmark Overhaul Inc....954 970-3200
6001 Nw 29th Ave Fort Lauderdale (33309) ***(G-3792)***
Airo Industries Inc....239 229-5273
2837 Fowler St Fort Myers (33901) ***(G-4347)***
Airon Corporation....321 821-9433
751 North Dr Ste 6 Melbourne (32934) ***(G-8761)***
Airplane Services Inc....850 675-1252
1817 Mineral Springs Rd Jay (32565) ***(G-6961)***
Airpro Diagnostics LLC....904 717-1711
6873 Phillips Ind Blvd Jacksonville (32256) ***(G-6131)***
Airrenu LLC....386 246-8694
6 Poinette Pl Palm Coast (32164) ***(G-13682)***
Airspan Networks Inc (PA)....561 893-8670
777 W Yamato Rd Ste 310 Boca Raton (33431) ***(G-410)***
Airstar America Inc (HQ)....407 851-7830
9603 Satellite Blvd # 150 Orlando (32837) ***(G-12447)***
Airstar Orlando, Orlando *Also called Airstar America Inc* ***(G-12447)***
Airstox Inc....954 618-6573
13680 Nw 5th St Ste 140 Sunrise (33325) ***(G-17085)***
Aishwarya Tari Apparels, Mount Dora *Also called Ata Group of Companies Inc* ***(G-11097)***
Ait Environmental Technology, Ponte Vedra Beach *Also called Ai Thomas LLC* ***(G-14929)***
Ait Group, Largo *Also called Advanced Impact Tech Inc* ***(G-7886)***
Ait USA Corp....786 953-5918
8485 Nw 74th St Miami (33166) ***(G-9098)***
Aj Associates, Clearwater *Also called A J Assoc Mfg & Engrg Co* ***(G-1560)***
Aj Associates....727 258-0994
11346 53rd St N Clearwater (33760) ***(G-1571)***
AJ AZ Woodwork Inc....561 859-4963
1917 Mears Pkwy Margate (33063) ***(G-8534)***
Aj Originals Inc....954 563-9911
1710 Ne 63rd Ct Fort Lauderdale (33334) ***(G-3793)***
Ajb Enterprises of Florida....352 331-9569
9332 Nw 15th Pl Gainesville (32606) ***(G-4870)***
AJF Sheet Metals Inc....305 970-6359
7495 Nw 7th St Ste 10 North Miami (33181) ***(G-11623)***
Ajl Fabrication Llc (PA)....407 654-1950
1436 Wendy Ct Kissimmee (34744) ***(G-7218)***
AJs Aluminum Inc....352 688-7631
5441 Spring Hill Dr Spring Hill (34606) ***(G-16845)***
Ajs Fabrication Llc....863 514-9630
5754 State Road 542 W # 2 Winter Haven (33880) ***(G-19296)***
AK Industries LLC....954 662-7038
3530 Sw 47th Ave West Park (33023) ***(G-19091)***
AK U TEC Machine & Tool Inc....727 573-5211
13191 Automobile Blvd Clearwater (33762) ***(G-1572)***
Akashic Spirit Publishing LLC....850 974-4944
610 Rio Ranchero Rd Defuniak Springs (32433) ***(G-2939)***
Akers Media Group Inc....352 787-4112
108 S 5th St Ste 201 Leesburg (34748) ***(G-8140)***
Akeyma Broden....309 428-5938
10 Sw 49th Ave Bldg 100 Ocala (34474) ***(G-11868)***
Akiknav Inc....561 842-8091
6667 42nd Ter N Ste 3 Riviera Beach (33407) ***(G-15296)***
Akira Wood Inc....352 375-0691
619 S Main St Ste A Gainesville (32601) ***(G-4871)***
Akj Industries Inc (PA)....239 939-1696
10175 6 Mile Cypress Pkwy Fort Myers (33966) ***(G-4348)***
Akman Inc....407 948-0562
2023 N Atl Ave Ste 201 Cocoa Beach (32931) ***(G-2057)***
Aksa's Generator, Doral *Also called Jat Power LLC* ***(G-3400)***
Akt, Orlando *Also called Playlist Live Inc* ***(G-13072)***
Akt Enterprises, Orlando *Also called Merchspin Inc* ***(G-12960)***
Akua Rage Entertainment Inc....904 627-5312
10960 Beach Blvd Lot 494 Jacksonville (32246) ***(G-6132)***
Akuwa Solutions Group Inc (PA)....941 343-9947
6431 Porter Rd Ste 1 Sarasota (34240) ***(G-16337)***
Al & Sons Millwork Inc....352 245-9191
6323 Se 113th St Belleview (34420) ***(G-366)***
AL Covell Electric Inc....352 544-0680
600 S Main St Brooksville (34601) ***(G-1207)***
AL Garey & Associates Inc....954 975-7992
4300 Coral Ridge Dr Coral Springs (33065) ***(G-2218)***
Al Stein Industries LLC....727 329-8755
6911 Bryan Dairy Rd # 280 Largo (33777) ***(G-7889)***
Al-FA Cabinets Inc....813 876-4205
4803 N Grady Ave Tampa (33614) ***(G-17396)***
Al-Mar Metals Inc....386 734-3377
1725 Arredondo Grant Rd De Leon Springs (32130) ***(G-2735)***
Al-Rite Fruits and Syrups Inc....305 652-2540
18524 Ne 2nd Ave Miami (33179) ***(G-9099)***
Alabama Marble Co Inc....305 718-8000
3435 Nw 79th Ave Doral (33122) ***(G-3232)***
Alabama Metal Industries Corp....863 688-9256
1033 Pine Chase Ave Lakeland (33815) ***(G-7630)***
Alachua Today Inc....386 462-3355
14804 Main St Alachua (32615) ***(G-1)***
Alacriant Holdings LLC....330 233-0523
1051 Sand Pond Rd Ste 101 Lake Mary (32746) ***(G-7398)***
Aladdin Equipment Company....941 371-3732
900 Sarasota Center Blvd Sarasota (34240) ***(G-16338)***
Alakai Defense Systems Inc....727 541-1600
8285 Bryan Dairy Rd # 125 Largo (33777) ***(G-7890)***
Alamo USA Inc....954 774-3747
1117 Ne 10th St Hallandale Beach (33009) ***(G-5168)***
Alaris Aerospace Systems LLC....954 596-8736
1721 Blount Rd Ste 1 Pompano Beach (33069) ***(G-14583)***
Albasol LLC....830 334-3280
325 S Biscayne Blvd Miami (33131) ***(G-9100)***
Alber Corp....954 377-7101
7775 W Oakland Park Blvd Sunrise (33351) ***(G-17086)***
Albertos On Fifth....239 430-1060
868 5th Ave S Naples (34102) ***(G-11153)***
Albireo Energy, Tampa *Also called Quality Building Controls Inc* ***(G-18030)***
Albixon USA LLC....954 297-2000
5820 Ne 22nd Way Apt 602 Fort Lauderdale (33308) ***(G-3794)***
Albrecht Consulting Inc....941 377-7755
1350 Global Ct Sarasota (34240) ***(G-16339)***
ALC Group Corp....786 409-7167
5900 Nw 99th Ave Doral (33178) ***(G-3233)***
Alcas USA Corp....305 591-3325
5347 Nw 35th Ave Fort Lauderdale (33309) ***(G-3795)***
Alcee Industries Inc....407 468-4573
1701 Acme St 32805 Orlando (32805) ***(G-12448)***
Alchemist Holdings LLC....772 340-7774
8283 S Us Highway 1 Port Saint Lucie (34952) ***(G-15085)***
Alchemist Holdings LLC (PA)....772 343-1111
10482 Sw Tibre Ct Port Saint Lucie (34987) ***(G-15086)***
Alchiba Inc....561 832-9292
505 S Flagler Dr Ste 900 West Palm Beach (33401) ***(G-18792)***
Alco Advanced Technologies....305 333-0831
10773 Nw 58th St Ste 3707 Doral (33178) ***(G-3234)***
Alco Services Inc....954 538-2189
15501 Sw 29th St Miramar (33027) ***(G-10963)***
Alcohol Countermeasure Systems (PA)....407 207-3337
5776 Hoffner Ave Ste 303 Orlando (32822) ***(G-12449)***
Alcolock FL Inc....407 207-3337
5776 Hoffner Ave Ste 303 Orlando (32822) ***(G-12450)***
Alcolock USA, Orlando *Also called Alcohol Countermeasure Systems* ***(G-12449)***
Alda Stevens Woodworking....850 897-4967
1537 Catmar Rd Niceville (32578) ***(G-11562)***
Aldali Inc....877 384-9494
4821 N Hale Ave Tampa (33614) ***(G-17397)***
Aldana Laser Miami Inc....786 681-7752
10201 Nw 58th St Ste 308 Doral (33178) ***(G-3235)***
Aldanas Pavers Inc....305 970-5339
3281 Nw 18th St Miami (33125) ***(G-9101)***
Aldema Services Inc....561 860-0693
4895 Royal Ct N West Palm Beach (33415) ***(G-18793)***
Aldora Aluminum & GL Pdts Inc (PA)....954 441-5057
12350 Nw 39th St Ste 102 Coral Springs (33065) ***(G-2219)***
Aleavia Brands LLC....407 289-2632
3025 Middlesex Rd Orlando (32803) ***(G-12451)***
Aleavia LLC....407 898-5800
3025 Middlesex Rd Orlando (32803) ***(G-12452)***
Alectron Inc....786 397-6827
8810 Nw 24th Ter Doral (33172) ***(G-3236)***
Alegro Industries Inc....702 943-0978
7880 N University Dr # 200 Tamarac (33321) ***(G-17349)***
Alenac & Associates, Palm Springs *Also called Alenac Metals Corp* ***(G-13771)***
Alenac Metals Corp....561 877-4109
2180 S Congress Ave A Palm Springs (33406) ***(G-13771)***
Aleph Graphics Inc....305 994-9933
1723 Nw 82nd Ave Doral (33126) ***(G-3237)***
Alert Manufacturing, Lake Worth *Also called Alert Towing Inc* ***(G-7532)***
Alert Towing Inc....561 586-5504
331 S H St Lake Worth (33460) ***(G-7532)***
Alertgy Inc....321 914-3199
2401 S Harbor City Blvd Melbourne (32901) ***(G-8762)***
Alessi Bakery, Tampa *Also called Phils Cake Box Bakeries Inc* ***(G-17991)***
Alevo Automotive Inc....954 593-4215
301 Ne 51st St Ste 1240 Boca Raton (33431) ***(G-411)***
Alex Robert Silversmith Inc....727 442-7333
625 Pinellas St Unit C Clearwater (33756) ***(G-1573)***
Alexander Industries Inc....305 888-9840
905 W 23rd St Hialeah (33010) ***(G-5277)***
Alexis Welding Express Corp....786 626-4090
12900 Nw 30th Ave Opa Locka (33054) ***(G-12284)***
Alfa Laval Aalborg Inc (HQ)....954 435-5999
3118 Commerce Pkwy Miramar (33025) ***(G-10964)***
Alfa Laval Inc....941 727-1900
2359 Trailmate Dr Sarasota (34243) ***(G-16173)***
Alfa Manufacturing LLC....305 436-8150
4701 Nw 77th Ave Miami (33166) ***(G-9102)***
Alfa Manufacturing Group LLC....305 979-7344
17401 Nw 2nd Ave Ste 7 Miami Gardens (33169) ***(G-10733)***

ALPHABETIC

Alfa Products LLC 901 218-0802
425 Nowell Loop Deland (32724) ***(G-2956)***
Alfaparf Milano, Tampa *Also called Pure-Chlor Systems Florida Inc* ***(G-18025)***
Alfred Angelo Bridals, Delray Beach *Also called AA Oldco Inc* ***(G-3038)***
Alfredo Welding Service LLC 954 770-8744
5599 Commercial Blvd Winter Haven (33880) ***(G-19297)***
Alfresco Air 786 275-5111
690 Sw 1st Ct Unit Cui Miami (33130) ***(G-9103)***
Algoma Hardwoods Inc 865 471-6300
7630 Currency Dr Orlando (32809) ***(G-12453)***
Algy Dance Costumes, Miami *Also called Algy Trimmings Co Inc* ***(G-9104)***
Algy Trimmings Co Inc 954 457-8100
7478 Nw 54th St Miami (33166) ***(G-9104)***
Alh Systems Inc 727 787-6306
1862 Eagle Ridge Blvd Palm Harbor (34685) ***(G-13717)***
Ali Kamakhi 850 405-8591
5663 Tecumseh Dr Tallahassee (32312) ***(G-17216)***
Alicia Diagnostic Inc 407 365-8498
150 W 11th St Chuluota (32766) ***(G-1551)***
Alicia Studio, Hialeah *Also called Mac D&D Inc* ***(G-5495)***
Alico Lighting Group Inc 305 542-2648
140 S Dixie Hwy Unit 101 Hollywood (33020) ***(G-5768)***
Alico Metal Fabricators LLC 239 454-4766
16750 Link Ct Ste 205 Fort Myers (33912) ***(G-4349)***
Alienware Corp 786 260-9625
13462 Sw 131st St Miami (33186) ***(G-9105)***
Align Kpital Usa LLC 305 423-7100
2500 Sw 107th Ave Ste 8 Miami (33165) ***(G-9106)***
Align Optics Inc 954 748-1715
4700 N Hiatus Rd Ste 144a Sunrise (33351) ***(G-17087)***
Aligned Global 305 731-2117
8370 W Flagler St Ste 125 Miami (33144) ***(G-9107)***
Alive By Nature Inc 800 810-1935
130 Corridor Rd Ste 3333 Ponte Vedra Beach (32082) ***(G-14930)***
All About Her 954 559-5175
12401 Orange Dr Davie (33330) ***(G-2491)***
All About Screens 239 398-1798
10111 Sunshine Dr Bonita Springs (34135) ***(G-812)***
All Amercian Hot Dog Cart Co, Miami Beach *Also called Louis Di Rmndo Wrldwide Invstm* ***(G-10689)***
All American Amputee 352 383-0396
601 Mount Homer Rd Eustis (32726) ***(G-3702)***
All American Barricades 305 685-6124
2300 Sw 41st Ave Fort Lauderdale (33317) ***(G-3796)***
All American Building Products 786 718-7300
401 Se 10th St Dania (33004) ***(G-2438)***
All American Coatings LLC 941 730-9397
2512 Gotham Way Valrico (33596) ***(G-18514)***
All American Kit & Bath LLC 305 599-9000
2900 Nw 77th Ct Doral (33122) ***(G-3238)***
All American Lube 561 432-0476
5865 S State Road 7 Lake Worth (33449) ***(G-7533)***
All American Pet Company Inc 561 337-5340
3801 Pga Blvd Ste 600 Palm Beach Gardens (33410) ***(G-13565)***
All American Sealcoating LLC 305 961-1655
1200 Brickell Ave # 1950 Miami (33131) ***(G-9108)***
All American Signs Inc 863 665-7161
206 N Eastside Dr Lakeland (33801) ***(G-7631)***
All American Woodwork 727 210-5214
1621 Gulf Blvd Ph D Clearwater Beach (33767) ***(G-1948)***
All Amrcan Bldg Strctres Contr 407 466-4959
401 E Cleveland St Apopka (32703) ***(G-110)***
All Amrcan Trlr Connection Inc 561 582-1800
3531 Lake Worth Rd Palm Springs (33461) ***(G-13772)***
All Because LLC 407 884-6700
2098 Sprint Blvd Apopka (32703) ***(G-111)***
All Binders & Indexes Inc 305 889-9983
860 W 20th St Hialeah (33010) ***(G-5278)***
All Coast Manufacturing Inc 813 626-2264
2433 S 86th St Ste F Tampa (33619) ***(G-17398)***
All County Sheet Metal Inc 561 588-0099
1930 7th Ct N Lake Worth Beach (33461) ***(G-7601)***
All Craft Marine LLC 813 236-8879
40047 County Road 54 Zephyrhills (33540) ***(G-19506)***
All Cut Inc No Selection 239 789-1748
2910 Hunter St Fort Myers (33916) ***(G-4350)***
All Elements Mechanical Corp (PA) 866 306-0359
776 Bennett Dr Unit 101 Longwood (32750) ***(G-8251)***
All Florida Engraving 352 213-4572
17728 S County Road 325 Hawthorne (32640) ***(G-5243)***
All Florida Marketing 813 281-4641
3001 N Rocky Point Dr E Rocky Point (33607) ***(G-15458)***
All Flrida Hrrcane Prtction Co 305 305-9177
22840 S Dixie Hwy Ste 2 Miami (33170) ***(G-9109)***
All Golf 954 441-1333
950 N Flamingo Rd Pembroke Pines (33028) ***(G-14019)***
All Granite & Marble Corp 508 248-9393
1909 N Washington Blvd Sarasota (34234) ***(G-16340)***
All Green Recycling Inc 754 204-3707
811 Se 16th St Ste 105 Hollywood (33024) ***(G-5769)***
All In One Cmplete Hndyman Svc 954 708-3463
177 Sw 5th Ct Deerfield Beach (33441) ***(G-2771)***
All In One Drect Mktg Slutions, Miami *Also called All In One Mail Shop Inc* ***(G-9110)***
All In One Mail Shop Inc 305 233-6100
11950 Sw 128th St Miami (33186) ***(G-9110)***
All Island Signs 631 676-3498
14803 Us Highway 19 Hudson (34667) ***(G-6015)***
All Keys Diesel Repair Inc 305 289-2070
531 107th Street Gulf Marathon (33050) ***(G-8517)***
All Lift Solutions Inc 786 295-3946
261 Sw 63rd Ct Miami (33144) ***(G-9111)***
All Liquid Envmtl Svcs LLC 800 767-9594
4600 Powerline Rd Fort Lauderdale (33309) ***(G-3797)***
All Metal Fab Inc 904 570-9772
2021 Dennis St Jacksonville (32204) ***(G-6133)***
All Metal Fabrication 305 666-3312
9621 S Dixie Hwy Pinecrest (33156) ***(G-14323)***
All Metal Roofing, Panama City *Also called Coastal Acquisitions Fla LLC* ***(G-13883)***
All Metals Custom Inc 727 709-4297
7200 59th St N Pinellas Park (33781) ***(G-14334)***
All Metals Fabrication LLC 904 862-6885
4235 Saint Augustine Rd Jacksonville (32207) ***(G-6134)***
All Miami Signs Inc 305 406-2420
7508 Nw 55th St Miami (33166) ***(G-9112)***
All Modular Service Inc 352 429-0868
861 W Myers Blvd Mascotte (34753) ***(G-8593)***
All Moldings Inc 305 556-6171
7950 W 26th Ave Hialeah (33016) ***(G-5279)***
All Naturals Direct 813 792-3777
12191 W Linebaugh Ave Tampa (33626) ***(G-17399)***
All Out On A Limb LLC 813 407-6497
1109 15th St Se Ruskin (33570) ***(G-15480)***
All Phase Construction USA LLC 754 227-5605
590 Goolsby Blvd Deerfield Beach (33442) ***(G-2772)***
All Phase Custom Mill Shop Inc 941 474-0903
7471 Sawyer Cir Port Charlotte (33981) ***(G-14959)***
All Phase Welding LLC 772 834-2980
8356 E 98th Ave Vero Beach (32967) ***(G-18591)***
All Polishing Solutions 954 505-4041
3056 S State Road 7 Miramar (33023) ***(G-10965)***
All Power Pro Inc 904 310-3069
995 Egans Creek Ln Fernandina Beach (32034) ***(G-3730)***
All Pro Chelo Corp 786 317-3914
11750 Nw 87th Pl Hialeah (33018) ***(G-5280)***
All Pro Ink 305 252-7644
10878 Sw 188th St Cutler Bay (33157) ***(G-2385)***
All Pro Pavers Hardscapes Inc 954 300-6281
430 S Dixie Hwy E Pompano Beach (33060) ***(G-14584)***
All Purpose Prtg Graphics Inc 904 346-0999
3521 Saint Augustine Rd Jacksonville (32207) ***(G-6135)***
All Safe of Big Pine Key 305 872-7233
1301 1st St Key West (33040) ***(G-7176)***
All Service Graphics Inc 321 259-8957
1020 W Eau Gallie Blvd I Melbourne (32935) ***(G-8763)***
All Signs 904 262-3795
5277 Alloaks Ct Jacksonville (32258) ***(G-6136)***
All Southern Fabricators Inc 727 573-4846
5010 126th Ave N Clearwater (33760) ***(G-1574)***
All Spring Manufacturing Inds, Hollywood *Also called Carlo Morelli* ***(G-5796)***
All Star Graphix Inc 954 772-1972
5055 Ne 12th Ave Oakland Park (33334) ***(G-11775)***
All Star Materials LLC 352 598-7590
6760 Nw 27th Avenue Rd Ocala (34475) ***(G-11869)***
All Star Printing Intl 954 974-0333
2001 W Sample Rd Ste 100 Deerfield Beach (33064) ***(G-2773)***
All Star Pvc Products, Cooper City *Also called South Florida Fabricators LLC* ***(G-2116)***
All State Pallets, Orlando *Also called Floor Tech LLC* ***(G-12745)***
All State Pallets Company LLC 407 855-8087
9801 Recycle Center Rd Orlando (32824) ***(G-12454)***
All Steel Bldngs Cmponents Inc 813 671-8044
10159 S Us Highway 41 Gibsonton (33534) ***(G-5025)***
All Stitched Up LLC 352 316-4859
1909 Sw 186th St Newberry (32669) ***(G-11550)***
All Tank Services LLC 954 260-9443
1903 W Mcnab Rd B Pompano Beach (33069) ***(G-14585)***
All Tennis LLC 561 842-0070
1434 10th St Lake Park (33403) ***(G-7465)***
All Things Digital Inc 305 887-9464
7213 Nw 54th St Miami (33166) ***(G-9113)***
All US Mold Rmval Jcksnvlle FL, Jacksonville *Also called Mold Remediation Services Inc* ***(G-6612)***
All Venue Graphics and Signs 954 399-7446
1700 Nw 15th Ave Ste 360 Pompano Beach (33069) ***(G-14586)***
All Weld Inc 239 348-9550
4416 18th Pl Sw Naples (34116) ***(G-11154)***
All Wood Cabinetry LLC 866 367-2516
210 Century Blvd Bartow (33830) ***(G-305)***
All-Bright Signs, Lecanto *Also called Jwn Family Partners LP Ltd* ***(G-8135)***

All-Brite Signs ...352 628-4910
3376 W Pennington Ct Lecanto (34461) *(G-8127)*
All-Jer Construction Usa Inc ...305 257-0225
12225 Sw 217th St Miami (33170) *(G-9114)*
All-Pro Accnting Bkkeeping LLC ...561 212-8418
1947 10th Ave N Lake Worth Beach (33461) *(G-7602)*
All-Pro Equipment & Rental Inc ...850 656-0208
2800 Mahan Dr Tallahassee (32308) *(G-17217)*
All-Star Sales Inc ...904 396-1653
5921 Richard St Jacksonville (32216) *(G-6137)*
All-Tag Corporation (PA) ...561 998-9983
1155 Broken Sound Pkwy Nw E Boca Raton (33487) *(G-412)*
All-Tag Security Americas, Boca Raton *Also called All-Tag Corporation (G-412)*
All-Weather Coatings LLC ...888 405-8904
4409 Hoffner Ave Orlando (32812) *(G-12455)*
Allan Industries ...407 875-0897
1901 Summit Tower Blvd Orlando (32810) *(G-12456)*
Allapattah Electric Motor Repr ...305 325-0330
1746 Nw 21st Ter Miami (33142) *(G-9115)*
Allapattah Industries Inc ...305 324-5900
1035 Nw 21st Ter Miami (33127) *(G-9116)*
Allay Pharmaceutical LLC (PA) ...954 336-1136
16600 Nw 54th Ave Unit 23 Hialeah (33014) *(G-5281)*
Allbright Electropolishing ...727 449-9353
5100 Ulmerton Rd Ste 7 Clearwater (33760) *(G-1575)*
Allcases Reekstin & Assoc Inc ...813 891-1313
300 Mears Blvd Oldsmar (34677) *(G-12200)*
Allclear Aerospace & Def Inc (HQ) ...954 200-9195
15501 Sw 29th St Ste 101 Miramar (33027) *(G-10966)*
Allcoffee, Opa Locka *Also called Coffee Unlimited LLC (G-12302)*
Allcoffee LLC ...305 685-6856
12815 Nw 45th Ave Ste 6b Opa Locka (33054) *(G-12285)*
Allegra Direct - South Inc ...586 226-1400
2420 Lakemont Ave Orlando (32814) *(G-12457)*
Allegra Gainesville, Gainesville *Also called 352ink Corp (G-4866)*
Allegra Marketing ...813 664-1129
2705 N Falkenburg Rd Tampa (33619) *(G-17400)*
Allegra Marketing Print Design ...407 848-1721
620 Douglas Ave Ste 1308 Altamonte Springs (32714) *(G-28)*
ALLEGRA NAPLES, Naples *Also called Pk Group Inc (G-11368)*
Allegra Print & Imaging, Orlando *Also called Csmc Inc (G-12630)*
Allegra Print & Imaging Center, Tampa *Also called Manci Graphics Corp (G-17877)*
Allegra Print and Imaging ...407 246-1567
6220 Masters Blvd Apt 301 Orlando (32819) *(G-12458)*
Allegra Print Imging Dwntwn Tm, Tampa *Also called Output Printing Corp (G-17965)*
Allegra Print Signs Mail ...954 963-3886
5846 Stirling Rd Hollywood (33021) *(G-5770)*
Allegra-Rockledge, Cocoa Beach *Also called B2b Printing Corp (G-2058)*
Allegro Nutrition Inc ...732 364-3777
6111 Horse Mill Pl Palmetto (34221) *(G-13784)*
Allen Custom Cabinetry Inc ...850 625-4713
6545 Bayline Dr Panama City (32404) *(G-13862)*
Allen Industries ...561 243-8072
220 Congress Park Dr Delray Beach (33445) *(G-3043)*
Allen Industries Inc ...727 573-3076
11351 49th St N Clearwater (33762) *(G-1576)*
Allen Shuffleboard LLC ...727 399-8877
6595 Seminole Blvd Seminole (33772) *(G-16737)*
Allendale Hunting Management, Leesburg *Also called Dura-Stress Inc (G-8152)*
Allensteel Inc ...239 454-1331
16281 Pine Ridge Rd Fort Myers (33908) *(G-4351)*
Allergan Sales LLC ...787 406-1203
13800 Nw 2nd St Ste 190 Sunrise (33325) *(G-17088)*
Allez Partnership, Fort Myers *Also called Gulf Coast Printing (G-4477)*
Allfast Fastener T ...352 727-8464
3464 Nw 49th Ave Gainesville (32605) *(G-4872)*
Allgeo & Yerkes Entps Inc ...321 255-9030
397 Pineda Ct Melbourne (32940) *(G-8764)*
Allgolf, Pembroke Pines *Also called All Golf (G-14019)*
Alli Cats Inc ...239 274-0744
12211 S Cleveland Ave Fort Myers (33907) *(G-4352)*
Alliance Cabinets & Millwork ...407 802-9921
3231 Sw 3rd St Deerfield Beach (33442) *(G-2774)*
Alliance Commercial Eqp Inc ...772 232-8149
2460 Nw 17th Ln Ste 1 Pompano Beach (33064) *(G-14587)*
Alliance Contractors Supply, Tampa *Also called Tampa Contractors Supply Inc (G-18163)*
Alliance Metals LLC ...305 343-9536
1111 Kane Concourse # 518 Bay Harbor Islands (33154) *(G-337)*
Alliance Rsrvations Netwrk LLC (HQ) ...602 889-5505
7380 W Sand Lake Rd # 360 Orlando (32819) *(G-12459)*
Allied Aerofoam Products LLC ...731 660-2705
1883 W State Road 84 # 106 Fort Lauderdale (33315) *(G-3798)*
Allied Aerofoam Products LLC (HQ) ...813 626-0090
1883 W State Road 84 # 106 Fort Lauderdale (33315) *(G-3799)*
Allied Aerospace Inc ...786 616-8484
2223 Nw 79th Ave Doral (33122) *(G-3239)*
Allied Aerospace International ...954 429-8600
1022 E Newport Center Dr Deerfield Beach (33442) *(G-2775)*
Allied Binders, Fort Lauderdale *Also called Allied Decals-Fla Inc (G-3801)*
Allied Business Service, Clearwater *Also called Coeur De Lion Inc (G-1631)*
Allied Circuits LLC ...239 970-2299
18018 Royal Tree Pkwy Naples (34114) *(G-11155)*
Allied Decals Fla Inc ...800 940-2233
1001 W Cypress Creek Rd # 320 Fort Lauderdale (33309) *(G-3800)*
Allied Decals-Fla Inc ...800 940-2233
5225 Nw 35th Ave Fort Lauderdale (33309) *(G-3801)*
Allied Foam Fabricators LLC (PA) ...813 626-0090
216 Kelsey Ln Tampa (33619) *(G-17401)*
Allied General Engrv & Plas ...305 626-6585
3485 Nw 167th St Opa Locka (33056) *(G-12286)*
Allied Graphics, Jacksonville *Also called Allied Printing Inc (G-6139)*
Allied Graphics Inc ...954 327-8559
1220 Nw 23rd Ave Fort Lauderdale (33311) *(G-3802)*
Allied Insulated Panels Inc ...800 599-3905
6451 N Federal Hwy # 1204 Fort Lauderdale (33308) *(G-3803)*
Allied Manufacturing Inc (PA) ...813 502-0300
203 Kelsey Ln Ste G Tampa (33619) *(G-17402)*
Allied Metals LLC ...305 635-3360
2902 Nw 32nd Ave Miami (33142) *(G-9117)*
Allied Molded Products LLC ...941 723-3072
1145 13th Ave E Palmetto (34221) *(G-13785)*
Allied Plastics Co Inc ...904 359-0386
2001 Walnut St Jacksonville (32206) *(G-6138)*
Allied Precast Products Co ...407 745-5605
5640 Carder Rd Orlando (32810) *(G-12460)*
Allied Printing Inc ...800 749-7683
7403 Philips Hwy Jacksonville (32256) *(G-6139)*
Allied Steel Buildings Inc ...800 508-2718
6451 N Federal Hwy # 1202 Fort Lauderdale (33308) *(G-3804)*
Allied Steel Buildings Inc (PA) ...954 590-4949
6451 N Federal Hwy # 411 Fort Lauderdale (33308) *(G-3805)*
Allied Steel Structures Inc ...877 997-8335
6400 N Andrews Ave # 200 Fort Lauderdale (33309) *(G-3806)*
Allied Telecommunications Ltd ...954 370-9900
1500 Nw 65th Ave Plantation (33313) *(G-14487)*
Allied USA Incorporated ...305 235-3950
2824 Sw 138th Path Miami (33175) *(G-9118)*
Allied Welding & Maint Inc ...863 634-7718
2912 Nw 35th Dr Okeechobee (34972) *(G-12172)*
Allied-360 LLC ...954 590-4940
101 Ne 3rd Ave Ste 300 Fort Lauderdale (33301) *(G-3807)*
Allliance Precious Mtls Group ...954 480-8676
6820 Lyons Tech Pkwy Coconut Creek (33073) *(G-2069)*
Alloy Cladding ...561 625-4550
15850 Guild Ct Jupiter (33478) *(G-6999)*
Alloy Cladding Company LLC ...561 625-4550
16170 Old Us 41 Fort Myers (33912) *(G-4353)*
Alloy Fabricators Inc ...813 925-0222
13925 Monroes Business Pa Tampa (33635) *(G-17403)*
Allpro Fbricators Erectors Inc ...954 797-7300
3595 Burris Rd Davie (33314) *(G-2492)*
Allstar Lighting & Sound Inc ...407 767-0111
754 Fleet Fin Ct Ste 102 Longwood (32750) *(G-8252)*
Allstar Printing International, Deerfield Beach *Also called All Star Printing Intl (G-2773)*
Allstar Screen Enclosures & St ...954 266-9757
9460 Poinciana Pl Apt 308 Davie (33324) *(G-2493)*
Allstate Lghtning Prtction LLC ...813 240-2736
7201 Sheldon Rd Tampa (33615) *(G-17404)*
Allstate Signs Inc ...305 885-9751
651 E 17th St Hialeah (33010) *(G-5282)*
Allsteel Processing LC ...954 587-1900
1250 Nw 23rd Ave Fort Lauderdale (33311) *(G-3808)*
Allstone Casting ...305 528-1677
6900 Nw 77th Ter Medley (33166) *(G-8607)*
Allure Shades Inc ...954 543-6259
3714 Nw 16th St Lauderhill (33311) *(G-8100)*
Alluring Design LLC ...305 582-3481
2657 W 76th St Hialeah (33016) *(G-5283)*
Alm Media LLC ...954 468-2600
633 S Andrews Ave Ste 100 Fort Lauderdale (33301) *(G-3809)*
Alm Technologies Inc ...904 849-7212
850816 Us Highway 17 Yulee (32097) *(G-19495)*
Almaco Group Inc ...561 558-1600
7900 Glades Rd Ste 630 Boca Raton (33434) *(G-413)*
Almanac LLC (PA) ...415 310-5143
1457 Sw 14th Ter Miami (33145) *(G-9119)*
Almar Industries Inc ...305 385-8284
6301 Sw 157th Pl Miami (33193) *(G-9120)*
Almi Intl Plastic Inds Inc ...954 920-6836
2227 N Federal Hwy Hollywood (33020) *(G-5771)*
Alnitak Corporation ...941 727-1122
6791 Whitfield Indus Ave Sarasota (34243) *(G-16174)*
Alnoor Import Inc ...954 683-9897
6851 W Sunrise Blvd Plantation (33313) *(G-14488)*
Aloha Screen Printing Inc ...850 934-4716
2635 Gulf Breeze Pkwy Gulf Breeze (32563) *(G-5111)*
Alonso Defense Group LLC ...305 989-0927
5076 Nw 74th Ave Miami (33166) *(G-9121)*

ALPHABETIC

Alp Industries Inc ...786 845-8617
1828 Nw 82nd Ave Doral (33126) ***(G-3240)***
Alper Automotive Inc ...561 342-1501
335 E Linton Blvd Delray Beach (33483) ***(G-3044)***
Alpha Card Compact Media LLC ...407 698-3592
941 W Morse Blvd Ste 100 Winter Park (32789) ***(G-19375)***
Alpha Coatings Inc ...850 324-9454
3040 Ashfield Estates Rd Cantonment (32533) ***(G-1334)***
Alpha Commercial Printing ...561 841-1415
838 Northlake Blvd North Palm Beach (33408) ***(G-11716)***
Alpha General Services Inc ...863 382-1544
1578 Alpha Rd E Sebring (33870) ***(G-16680)***
Alpha Hydraulics LLC ...561 355-0318
999 W 17th St Ste 5 Riviera Beach (33404) ***(G-15297)***
Alpha Industries Inc ...727 443-2673
701 N Mlk Jr Ave Clearwater (33755) ***(G-1577)***
Alpha Omega Commercial Limited (PA) ...407 925-7913
5820 Nature View Dr Windermere (34786) ***(G-19225)***
Alpha Press Inc ...407 299-2121
4333 Silver Star Rd # 19 Orlando (32808) ***(G-12461)***
Alpha Sun & Sport - As & S LLC ...954 782-2300
2851 S Ocean Blvd Apt 6v Boca Raton (33432) ***(G-414)***
Alpha Sun and Sport, Suite 150, Boca Raton *Also called Alpha Sun & Sport - As & S LLC* ***(G-414)***
Alpha Technology USA Corp ...407 571-2060
5401 Penn Ave Sanford (32773) ***(G-15990)***
Alpha To Omega, Ormond Beach *Also called Edgewell Personal Care Company* ***(G-13367)***
Alpha Woodwork Inc ...954 347-6251
2840 Ne 9th Ter Pompano Beach (33064) ***(G-14588)***
AlphaGraphics, Boca Raton *Also called W H L Business Communications* ***(G-784)***
AlphaGraphics, Lake Mary *Also called Jjaz Enterprises Inc* ***(G-7427)***
AlphaGraphics, Tampa *Also called Reimink Printing Inc* ***(G-18050)***
AlphaGraphics, Jupiter *Also called Agpb LLC* ***(G-6997)***
AlphaGraphics, Fort Lauderdale *Also called South Florida Graphics Corp* ***(G-4245)***
AlphaGraphics Us658 ...813 689-7788
105 N Falkenburg Rd Ste D Tampa (33619) ***(G-17405)***
Alphatec Communications ...518 580-0520
10570 Nw 27th St Ste 102 Doral (33172) ***(G-3241)***
Alphatron Industries Inc ...954 581-1418
3411 Sw 49th Way Ste 3 Davie (33314) ***(G-2494)***
Alpine Engineered Products ...954 781-3333
1200 Park Central Blvd S Pompano Beach (33064) ***(G-14589)***
Alpine Industries Corporation ...941 749-1900
2908 29th Ave E Ste A Bradenton (34208) ***(G-985)***
Alpine Systems Associates Inc ...305 262-3263
11725 Nw 100th Rd Ste 1 Medley (33178) ***(G-8608)***
Alpine Tool Inc ...727 587-0407
13070 90th St Largo (33773) ***(G-7891)***
Alps Orthotics, Saint Petersburg *Also called Alps South LLC* ***(G-15697)***
Alps South LLC ...727 528-8566
2895 42nd Ave N Saint Petersburg (33714) ***(G-15697)***
Alq Business Development, Pembroke Pines *Also called Advanced Living Quarters Inc* ***(G-14015)***
Alse Industries LLC ...305 688-8778
16201 Nw 49th Ave Miami Gardens (33014) ***(G-10734)***
Alstom Signaling Operation LLC ...781 740-8111
1990 W Nasa Blvd Melbourne (32904) ***(G-8765)***
Alt Thuyan ...407 302-3655
2025 Wp Ball Blvd Sanford (32771) ***(G-15991)***
Alta Equipment Holdings Inc ...813 519-4097
8418 Palm River Rd Tampa (33619) ***(G-17406)***
Alta Graphics, Miami *Also called Butler Graphics Inc* ***(G-9289)***
Alta Industries LLC ...305 343-6091
9930 Sw 164th Ter Miami (33157) ***(G-9122)***
Alta Labs, New Port Richey *Also called Ocean Global Inc* ***(G-11503)***
Alta Pharma LLC ...727 942-7645
1245 N Florida Ave Tarpon Springs (34689) ***(G-18282)***
Alta Systems Inc ...352 372-2534
6825 Nw 18th Dr Gainesville (32653) ***(G-4873)***
Alta Technologies Inc ...609 538-9500
285 Plantation Cir S Ponte Vedra Beach (32082) ***(G-14931)***
Altadis USA, Fort Lauderdale *Also called Itg Cigars Inc* ***(G-4071)***
Altamonte Office Supply Inc ...407 339-6911
1983 Corporate Sq # 101 Longwood (32750) ***(G-8253)***
Altamonte Woodworking Co Inc ...407 331-0020
318 Broadview Ave Altamonte Springs (32701) ***(G-29)***
Altanet Corporation ...786 228-5758
7950 Nw 53rd St Ste 337 Miami (33166) ***(G-9123)***
Altec Inc ...813 372-0058
1041 S 86th St Tampa (33619) ***(G-17407)***
Altec Industries Inc ...904 647-5219
2750 Imeson Rd Jacksonville (32220) ***(G-6140)***
Altec Service Center, Tampa *Also called Altec Inc* ***(G-17407)***
Altelix LLC ...561 660-9434
1201 Clint Moore Rd Boca Raton (33487) ***(G-415)***
Altered Media Inc ...813 397-3892
100 S Ashley Dr Ste 600 Tampa (33602) ***(G-17408)***
Alterna Power Inc ...407 287-9148
390 N Orange Ave Orlando (32801) ***(G-12462)***
Alternative Coatings of SW Fla ...239 537-6153
3411 1st Ave Nw Naples (34120) ***(G-11156)***
Alternative Daily ...561 628-4711
400 Clematis St Ste 203 West Palm Beach (33401) ***(G-18794)***
Alternative Laboratories LLC (PA) ...239 692-9160
4740 S Cleveland Ave Fort Myers (33907) ***(G-4354)***
Alternative Medical Entps LLC ...941 702-9955
6944 N Us Highway 41 Apollo Beach (33572) ***(G-100)***
Alternative Sign Group Inc ...561 722-9272
8955 120th Ave N West Palm Beach (33412) ***(G-18795)***
Alternative Vision LLC ...904 642-3566
2915 Anniston Rd Jacksonville (32246) ***(G-6141)***
Alterntive Repr McHning Svcs L ...904 861-3040
6555 Trade Center Dr Jacksonville (32254) ***(G-6142)***
Alti-2 Inc ...386 943-9333
1200 Flight Line Blvd # 5 Deland (32724) ***(G-2957)***
Altima Technology Devices, Doral *Also called Rover Aerospace Inc* ***(G-3491)***
Altira Inc ...305 687-8074
3225 Nw 112th St Miami (33167) ***(G-9124)***
Altis Aju Kingwood LLC ...305 338-5232
175 Sw 7th St Ste 1106 Miami (33130) ***(G-9125)***
Altium Packaging LLC ...813 782-2695
4330 20th St Zephyrhills (33542) ***(G-19507)***
Altium Packaging LLC ...813 248-4300
4961 Distribution Dr Tampa (33605) ***(G-17409)***
Altium Packaging LLC ...386 246-4000
71 Hargrove Grade Palm Coast (32137) ***(G-13683)***
Altmed Enterprises, Apollo Beach *Also called Alternative Medical Entps LLC* ***(G-100)***
Alto Products Corp Al ...305 892-7777
6301 Nw 99th Ave Doral (33178) ***(G-3242)***
Alto Recycling LLC ...813 962-0140
5701 W Linebaugh Ave Tampa (33624) ***(G-17410)***
Alton Manufacturing Inc ...305 821-0701
9511 Fontnbleau Blvd # 402 Miami (33172) ***(G-9126)***
Alttec Corporation ...727 547-1622
4260 114th Ter N Clearwater (33762) ***(G-1578)***
Altum Aerospace, Sunrise *Also called Equs Logistics LLC* ***(G-17120)***
Altum Aerospace ...954 618-6573
13680 Nw 5th St Ste 140 Sunrise (33325) ***(G-17089)***
Aludisc LLC ...910 299-0911
2127 Nw 53rd St Boca Raton (33496) ***(G-416)***
Aluma Craft Products, Miami *Also called Style-View Products Inc* ***(G-10426)***
Aluma TEC Aluminun ...352 732-7362
4412 Ne 2nd St Ocala (34470) ***(G-11870)***
Aluma Tower Company Inc (HQ) ...772 567-3423
1639 Old Dixie Hwy Vero Beach (32960) ***(G-18592)***
Aluma Tower Company Inc ...772 567-3423
926 Old Dixie Hwy Vero Beach (32960) ***(G-18593)***
Alumacart Inc ...772 675-2158
12968 Se Suzanne Dr Hobe Sound (33455) ***(G-5721)***
Alumatech Manufacturing Inc ...941 748-8880
6063 17th St E Bradenton (34203) ***(G-986)***
Alumco, Clearwater *Also called Spectra Metal Sales Inc* ***(G-1887)***
Alumflo Inc ...727 527-8494
2445 51st Ave N Saint Petersburg (33714) ***(G-15698)***
Alumicenter Inc ...954 674-2631
3160 Sw 176th Way Miramar (33029) ***(G-10967)***
Alumination LLC ...904 361-8174
2718 Townsend Blvd Jacksonville (32211) ***(G-6143)***
Aluminium Design Products LLC ...561 894-8775
1055 Sw 15th Ave Ste 1 Delray Beach (33444) ***(G-3045)***
Aluminum Creations ...386 451-0113
155 Dawson Brown Rd De Leon Springs (32130) ***(G-2736)***
Aluminum Designs LLC ...239 289-3388
3573 Entp Ave Ste 75 Naples (34104) ***(G-11157)***
Aluminum Express Inc ...954 868-2628
2745 W 78th St Hialeah (33016) ***(G-5284)***
Aluminum Powder Coating ...305 628-4155
16200 Nw 49th Ave Hialeah (33014) ***(G-5285)***
Aluminum Powder Coating Lc ...305 628-4155
16200 Nw 49th Ave Hialeah (33014) ***(G-5286)***
Aluminum Products ...904 829-9995
1701 Lakeside Ave Unit 12 Saint Augustine (32084) ***(G-15514)***
Aluminum Products Whl Inc ...904 268-4895
6963 Bus Pk Blvd N Ste 2 Jacksonville (32256) ***(G-6144)***
Aluminum Slide-On Trailers, Saint Petersburg *Also called Owens & Sons Marine Inc* ***(G-15873)***
Aluminum Solutions Group Inc ...561 999-9932
1090 Holland Dr Ste 3 Boca Raton (33487) ***(G-417)***
Aluminum Tank Industries Inc ...863 401-9474
36 Spirit Lake Rd Winter Haven (33880) ***(G-19298)***
Alumitech Inc ...407 826-5373
5104 S Orange Ave Orlando (32809) ***(G-12463)***
Alumne Manufacturing Inc ...352 748-3229
801 Industrial Dr Wildwood (34785) ***(G-19190)***
Alutech Corporation ...305 593-2080
8548 Nw 64th St Miami (33166) ***(G-9127)***

Alvean Americas Inc ...305 606-0770
2525 Ponce De Leon Blvd Coral Gables (33134) ***(G-2121)***
Alvis Industries Inc ...941 377-7800
3300 Linden Dr Sarasota (34232) ***(G-16341)***
Alvita Pharma Usa Inc ...305 961-1623
8180 Nw 36th St Ste 100 Doral (33166) ***(G-3243)***
Always Flowers Inc ...305 572-1122
6955 Nw 52nd St Miami (33166) ***(G-9128)***
Always Fun Inc ...954 258-4377
5660 Sw 99th Ln Cooper City (33328) ***(G-2108)***
Aly Fabrication Inc ...724 898-2990
31 N Saint Augustine Blvd Saint Augustine (32080) ***(G-15515)***
Alzamend Neuro Inc ...844 722-6333
3802 Spectrum Blvd # 112 Tampa (33612) ***(G-17411)***
AM Cabinets LLC ...321 663-4319
628 Alpine St Altamonte Springs (32701) ***(G-30)***
AM Metal Finishing ...407 843-0182
7594 Chancellor Dr Orlando (32809) ***(G-12464)***
AM Pavers Inc ...954 275-1590
19722 Black Olive Ln Boca Raton (33498) ***(G-418)***
AM Primaclasse Corp ...305 767-5918
3015 Ravenswood Rd # 101 Fort Lauderdale (33312) ***(G-3810)***
AM Worldwide Corp ...786 313-3625
7800 Nw 32nd St Doral (33122) ***(G-3244)***
Am2f Energy Inc ...407 505-1127
501 N Orlando Ave 313-256 Winter Park (32789) ***(G-19376)***
AMA Waters LLC ...786 400-1630
6701 Nw 7th St Ste 175 Miami (33126) ***(G-9129)***
Amado Wheel Finishing ...786 732-6249
15050 Sw 137th St Miami (33196) ***(G-9130)***
Amag Technology Inc ...407 549-3882
858 Bright Meadow Dr Lake Mary (32746) ***(G-7399)***
Amalie Oil Company (PA) ...813 248-1988
1601 Mcclosky Blvd Tampa (33605) ***(G-17412)***
Amami United Flavours of World ...305 397-8577
224 Espanola Way Miami Beach (33139) ***(G-10639)***
Amani, Tampa *Also called Elite Wheel Distributors Inc* ***(G-17633)***
Amaranth Lf Sciences Phrm Inc ...561 756-8291
1731 Avenida Del Sol Boca Raton (33432) ***(G-419)***
Amascott LLC ...352 683-4895
4142 Mariner Blvd Spring Hill (34609) ***(G-16846)***
Amax Welding & Fabrication ...352 544-8484
19496 Fort Dade Ave Brooksville (34601) ***(G-1208)***
Amaya Lathing & Plaspering ...786 953-6420
2301 Nw 7th St Miami (33125) ***(G-9131)***
Amaya Lathing & Plastering LLC ...305 216-4247
3475 W Flagler St Miami (33135) ***(G-9132)***
Amaya Solutions Inc ...813 246-5448
1802 Corporate Center Ln Plant City (33563) ***(G-14398)***
Amazin Publishing Inc ...954 445-6303
10810 Waterford Ct Orlando (32821) ***(G-12465)***
Amazing Cabinet Store LLC ...407 270-7865
4639 Ligustrum Way Orlando (32839) ***(G-12466)***
Amazon Cleaning & More Inc ...239 594-1733
2015 Morning Sun Ln Naples (34119) ***(G-11158)***
Amazon Metal Fabricators Inc ...321 631-7574
600 Cox Rd Ste C Cocoa (32926) ***(G-1994)***
Amazon Origins Inc ...239 404-1818
5911 Livermore Ln Naples (34119) ***(G-11159)***
Amazon Printers, Miami *Also called Amazon Services Inc* ***(G-9133)***
Amazon Services Inc ...305 663-0585
7186 Sw 47th St Miami (33155) ***(G-9133)***
Amazon Sheds and Gazebos Inc (PA) ...239 498-5558
17300 Jean St Fort Myers (33967) ***(G-4355)***
Amazonia Beverages, Miami *Also called AMA Waters LLC* ***(G-9129)***
Amazonia Marine Products, Orlando *Also called Highvac Co LLC* ***(G-12803)***
Amb Trucks, Medley *Also called Armor Supply Metals LLC* ***(G-8613)***
Amba Ham Company Inc ...305 754-0001
6863 Ne 3rd Ave Miami (33138) ***(G-9134)***
Ambassador Marketing Group, Delray Beach *Also called Ambassador Printing Company* ***(G-3046)***
Ambassador Printing Company ...561 330-3668
1025 Nw 17th Ave Ste C Delray Beach (33445) ***(G-3046)***
Amber Jewelers Corp ...305 373-8089
36 Ne 1st St Ste 1002 Miami (33132) ***(G-9135)***
Ambiance Interiors Mfg Corp ...305 668-4995
7456 Sw 48th St Miami (33155) ***(G-9136)***
Ambo Foods LLC ...941 485-4400
727 Commerce Dr Unit C Venice (34292) ***(G-18531)***
Ambo Health LLC ...866 414-0188
727 Commerce Dr Venice (34292) ***(G-18532)***
AMC, Coral Springs *Also called Advantage Medical Elec LLC* ***(G-2214)***
AMC Development Group LLC ...305 597-8641
10825 Nw 33rd St Doral (33172) ***(G-3245)***
Amci Technologies Inc ...561 596-6288
9772 El Clair Ranch Rd Boynton Beach (33437) ***(G-874)***
Amco Polymers, Orlando *Also called Ravago Americas LLC* ***(G-13114)***
AMD Aero Inc ...239 561-8622
14230 Jetport Loop W Fort Myers (33913) ***(G-4356)***
AMD Ornamental Inc ...239 458-7437
918 Se 9th Ln Unit A Cape Coral (33990) ***(G-1378)***
Amds Trading Inc ...305 594-6680
12301 Nw 116th Ave # 101 Doral (33178) ***(G-3246)***
AME, Ocala *Also called Advanced Manufacturing & Engrg* ***(G-11864)***
AME International, Brooksville *Also called AME Triton LLC* ***(G-1209)***
AME Triton LLC ...352 799-1111
2347 Circuit Way Brooksville (34604) ***(G-1209)***
Amee Bay LLC ...904 553-9873
1701 Mayport Rd Atlantic Beach (32233) ***(G-216)***
Amega Sciences Inc ...863 937-9792
6550 New Tampa Hwy Ste A Lakeland (33815) ***(G-7632)***
Amelia Island Graphics ...904 261-0740
2244 S 8th St Fernandina Beach (32034) ***(G-3731)***
Amend Surgical Inc ...844 281-3169
14000 Nw 126th Ter Alachua (32615) ***(G-2)***
Amendar Printing Inc ...786 287-5189
10207 Nw 10th St Miami (33172) ***(G-9137)***
Amer-Con Corp ...786 293-8004
18001 Old Cutler Rd # 401 Palmetto Bay (33157) ***(G-13839)***
Amera Trail Inc ...407 892-1100
4840 E I Bronson Memrl Saint Cloud (34771) ***(G-15643)***
Ameracat Inc ...772 882-9186
3340 N Us Highway 1 Ste 1 Fort Pierce (34946) ***(G-4672)***
Amerada Stores, Saint Cloud *Also called Hess Station 09307* ***(G-15653)***
Ameraparts International LLC ...904 725-9700
103 Century 21 Dr Ste 201 Jacksonville (32216) ***(G-6145)***
Amercn Cabinets Granite Floors ...727 303-0678
32140 Us Highway 19 N Palm Harbor (34684) ***(G-13718)***
Ameri Food & Fuel Inc ...727 584-0120
790 East Bay Dr Largo (33770) ***(G-7892)***
Ameri Produ Produ Compa of Pin ...813 925-0144
12157 W Linebaugh Ave # 335 Tampa (33626) ***(G-17413)***
Ameri-Fax, Hialeah *Also called Amerifax Acquisition Corp* ***(G-5297)***
Ameribuilt Stl Structures LLC ...407 340-9401
1016 Moccasin Run Rd Oviedo (32765) ***(G-13411)***
America Energy Inc ...954 762-7763
20861 Johnson St Ste 115 Pembroke Pines (33029) ***(G-14020)***
America Marine & Fuel Inc ...239 261-3715
895 10th St S Ste 100 Naples (34102) ***(G-11160)***
America Mia, Cooper City *Also called Always Fun Inc* ***(G-2108)***
America Solutions For Business ...305 971-5400
12943 Sw 133rd Ct Miami (33186) ***(G-9138)***
America Trading Inc ...305 256-0101
9355 Sw 144th St Miami (33176) ***(G-9139)***
American Accounting Assn ...941 921-7747
9009 Town Center Pkwy # 104 Lakewood Ranch (34202) ***(G-7836)***
American Acrylic Adhesives LLC ...877 422-4583
2020 Wild Acres Rd Unit D Largo (33771) ***(G-7893)***
American Adhesives LLC ...877 422-4583
12350 Belcher Rd S 1b Largo (33773) ***(G-7894)***
American Aggregates LLC ...813 352-2124
9040 Kimberly Blvd Ste 61 Boca Raton (33434) ***(G-420)***
American All ...561 401-0885
16079 70th St N Loxahatchee (33470) ***(G-8356)***
American All Scure Gtes Fnce L ...407 423-4962
1316 29th St Orlando (32805) ***(G-12467)***
American Aluminum ACC Inc ...850 277-0869
3291 S Us Highway 19 Perry (32348) ***(G-14292)***
American Aluminum Doors Corp ...305 885-4020
2214 W 8th Ct Hialeah (33010) ***(G-5287)***
American Architectural Mtls GL, Miami Gardens *Also called Alse Industries LLC* ***(G-10734)***
American Archtctral Foam Wrks ...813 443-0791
7810 Professional Pl Tampa (33637) ***(G-17414)***
American Archtctral Mtls GL LL ...305 688-8778
16201 Nw 49th Ave Hialeah (33014) ***(G-5288)***
American Archtctural Mllwk LLC ...844 307-9571
248 James St Venice (34285) ***(G-18533)***
American Assn Clncal Endcrnlgs, Jacksonville *Also called Aacecorp Inc* ***(G-6115)***
American Athletic Uniforms Inc ...850 729-1205
90 Eastview Ave Valparaiso (32580) ***(G-18505)***
American Atlas Corp ...904 273-6090
2309 Sawgrass Village Dr Ponte Vedra Beach (32082) ***(G-14932)***
American Auto Marine Wiring ...954 782-0193
1414 Sw 13th Ct Pompano Beach (33069) ***(G-14590)***
American Automtn Systems Inc ...305 620-0077
5471 Nw 159th St Miami Lakes (33014) ***(G-10762)***
American Awning Company Inc ...561 832-7123
537 Pine Ter West Palm Beach (33405) ***(G-18796)***
American Bhvioral RES Inst LLC ...888 353-1205
1515 N Federal Hwy # 300 Boca Raton (33432) ***(G-421)***
American Bidet Company ...954 981-1111
10821 Nw 50th St Sunrise (33351) ***(G-17090)***
American Blind Corporation ...305 262-2009
4232 Sw 75th Ave Miami (33155) ***(G-9140)***
American Boom and Barrier Inc ...321 784-2110
720 Mullet Rd Ste M Cape Canaveral (32920) ***(G-1350)***
American Bottling Company ...813 806-2931
5266 Eagle Trail Dr Tampa (33634) ***(G-17415)***

ALPHABETIC

American Bottling Company 561 732-7395
4895 Park Ridge Blvd Boynton Beach (33426) *(G-875)*
American Bottling Company 772 461-3383
3700 Avenue F Fort Pierce (34947) *(G-4673)*
American Bottling Company 941 758-7010
2919 62nd Ave E Bradenton (34203) *(G-987)*
American Bottling Company 863 665-6128
3520 Waterfield Rd Lakeland (33803) *(G-7633)*
American Bottling Company 239 489-0838
2236 Hemingway Dr Fort Myers (33912) *(G-4357)*
American Bottling Company 904 739-1000
6001 Bowdendale Ave Jacksonville (32216) *(G-6146)*
American Bronze Foundry Inc (PA) 407 328-8090
1650 E Lake Mary Blvd Sanford (32773) *(G-15992)*
American Buffing Solid Surface 407 625-6837
4407 Fairlawn Dr Orlando (32809) *(G-12468)*
American Business Cards Inc 314 739-0800
16475 Seneca Way Naples (34110) *(G-11161)*
American Cabinet Mill & Supply, Merritt Island *Also called Trasport John (G-9016)*
American Cabinet Works Inc 904 672-6649
863 Duskin Dr Jacksonville (32216) *(G-6147)*
American Carbons Inc 850 265-4214
104 New York Ave Lynn Haven (32444) *(G-8428)*
American CCC Ceramic Inc 321 356-9317
805 Largo Ct Apopka (32703) *(G-112)*
American Changer Corp 954 917-3009
1400 Nw 65th Pl Fort Lauderdale (33309) *(G-3811)*
American Chiropractor 305 434-8865
8619 Nw 68th St Ste C0138 Miami (33166) *(G-9141)*
American City Bus Journals Inc 813 873-8225
4890 W Kennedy Blvd # 85 Tampa (33609) *(G-17416)*
American Classifieds 850 747-1155
1522 Chestnut Ave Panama City (32405) *(G-13863)*
American Cnstr Entps Inc 941 629-2070
1232 Market Cir Unit 2b Port Charlotte (33953) *(G-14960)*
American Coatings Corporation 954 970-7820
1457 Banks Rd Margate (33063) *(G-8535)*
American Commodity Exch Corp (HQ) 904 687-0588
7825 Baymeadows Way No Jacksonville (32256) *(G-6148)*
American Composites Engrg 352 528-5007
20751 Ne Highway 27 Williston (32696) *(G-19209)*
American Computer & Tech Corp 786 738-3220
1775 Washington Ave 3f Miami Beach (33139) *(G-10640)*
American Concrete Industries 772 464-1187
350 N Rock Rd Fort Pierce (34945) *(G-4674)*
American Data Supply Inc 866 650-3282
10870 49th St N Clearwater (33762) *(G-1579)*
American Diamond Distributors 954 485-7808
3600 W Coml Blvd Ste 101 Fort Lauderdale (33309) *(G-3812)*
American Diesel and Gas Inc 561 447-8500
1911 Nw 40th Ct Deerfield Beach (33064) *(G-2776)*
American Elastic & Tape Inc 305 888-0303
1675 E 11th Ave Hialeah (33010) *(G-5289)*
American Engineering Svcs Inc (PA) 813 621-3932
1802 Corporate Center Ln Plant City (33563) *(G-14399)*
American Enrgy Innovations LLC 772 221-9100
6800 Sw Jack James Dr Stuart (34997) *(G-16905)*
American Epoxy Coatings LLC 954 850-1169
1340 Stirling Rd Ste 1a Dania Beach (33004) *(G-2462)*
American Fence Shop LLC 305 681-3511
4790 E 11th Ave Hialeah (33013) *(G-5290)*
American Fibertek Inc 732 302-0660
745 43rd St S Saint Petersburg (33711) *(G-15699)*
American Fine Woodwork LLC 954 261-9793
35 Seville Cir Davie (33324) *(G-2495)*
American Force Wheels Inc 786 345-6301
2310 W 76th St Hialeah (33016) *(G-5291)*
American Frame Furniture Inc 305 548-3018
1857 Nw 21st Ter Miami (33142) *(G-9142)*
American Generator Svcs LLC 954 965-1210
14820 Sw 21st St Davie (33326) *(G-2496)*
American Girl Brands LLC 407 852-9771
8001 S Orange Blossom Trl # 1460 Orlando (32809) *(G-12469)*
American Heritage Press, Winter Park *Also called T Beattie Enterprises (G-19450)*
American Hermetics Georgia Inc 305 592-8958
7478 Nw 55th St Miami (33166) *(G-9143)*
American Household Inc (HQ) 561 912-4100
2381 Nw Executive Ctr Dr Boca Raton (33431) *(G-422)*
American Hygenic Laboratories 305 891-9518
1800 Ne 114th St Ste J Miami (33181) *(G-9144)*
American Ignition Wire LLC 954 974-6500
2760 Nw 63rd Ct Fort Lauderdale (33309) *(G-3813)*
American Impact Media Corp 954 457-9003
413 Se 1st Ave Hallandale Beach (33009) *(G-5169)*
American Incinerators Corp 321 282-7357
2814 Silver Star Rd # 20 Orlando (32808) *(G-12470)*
American Industrial Group Inc 703 757-7683
3363 Ne 163rd St Ste 611 North Miami Beach (33160) *(G-11666)*
American Injectables Inc 813 435-6014
15261 Telcom Dr Brooksville (34604) *(G-1210)*

American International Mtr Svc 727 573-9501
5150 Ulmerton Rd Ste 5 Clearwater (33760) *(G-1580)*
American Lab Test & Engrg, Coral Gables *Also called Ecosan LLC (G-2140)*
American Label Group Inc 386 274-5234
705 Fentress Blvd Daytona Beach (32114) *(G-2623)*
American Led Display Solutions 561 227-8048
8060 Nw 71st St Miami (33166) *(G-9145)*
American Led Technology, Naples *Also called Tesco of Swfl Inc (G-11438)*
American Led Technology Inc 850 863-8777
1210 Wildwood Lakes Blvd # 202 Naples (34104) *(G-11162)*
American Lifting Products, Doral *Also called Alp Industries Inc (G-3240)*
American Louvered Products Co 813 884-1441
4910 W Knollwood St Tampa (33634) *(G-17417)*
American Lw & Promo Prods LLC 954 946-5252
100 Sw 5th St Pompano Beach (33060) *(G-14591)*
American Made Awnings, Hollywood *Also called Awnings of Hollywood Inc (G-5780)*
American Maglev Tech Fla Inc 404 386-4036
8030 Frst Cast Hwy Apt 10 Amelia Island (32034) *(G-92)*
American Marine Coverings Inc 305 889-5355
1065 Se 9th Ct Hialeah (33010) *(G-5292)*
American Marine Mfg Inc 305 497-7723
2637 W 76th St Hialeah (33016) *(G-5293)*
American MBL Restoration Inc 561 502-0764
43 Barbados Dr Palm Springs (33461) *(G-13773)*
American Mentality Inc 407 599-7255
210 E Palmetto Ave Longwood (32750) *(G-8254)*
American Metal Fab of Ctrl Fl 813 653-2788
1018 W Brandon Blvd 11b Brandon (33511) *(G-1150)*
American Metal Fabrication LLC 954 736-9819
5476 Nw 59th Pl Tamarac (33319) *(G-17350)*
American Metal Fabricators Inc 561 790-5799
1501 53rd St Mangonia Park (33407) *(G-8497)*
American Metal Processors Inc 386 754-9367
186 Se Newell Dr Lake City (32025) *(G-7347)*
American Metal Products Inc 407 293-0090
4026 Silver Star Rd Ste A Orlando (32808) *(G-12471)*
American Mfg & Mch Inc 352 728-2222
27137 County Road 33 Okahumpka (34762) *(G-12168)*
American Mold Removal Inc 561 575-7757
17462 37th Pl N Loxahatchee (33470) *(G-8357)*
American Molding and Plas LLC 561 676-1987
870 W Industrial Ave # 8 Boynton Beach (33426) *(G-876)*
American Moulding Corporation 321 676-8929
710 Atlantis Rd Melbourne (32904) *(G-8766)*
American Name Plate, Pompano Beach *Also called American Trophy Co (G-14594)*
American Natural Pdts Lab Inc 305 261-5152
7350 Nw 7th St Ste 101 Miami (33126) *(G-9146)*
American Optimal Decisions Inc 352 278-2034
4014 Sw 98th Ter Gainesville (32608) *(G-4874)*
American Panel Corporation 352 245-7055
5800 Se 78th St Ocala (34472) *(G-11871)*
American Pavers Consultants 954 418-0000
1251 Ne 48th St Pompano Beach (33064) *(G-14592)*
American Pavers Manufacturing, Pompano Beach *Also called American Pavers Consultants (G-14592)*
American Pavers Manufacturing (PA) 954 418-0000
1251 Ne 48th St Pompano Beach (33064) *(G-14593)*
American Payment Systems 407 856-8524
11500 S Ornge Blossom Trl Orlando (32837) *(G-12472)*
American Payment Systems 954 968-6920
1655 S State Road 7 North Lauderdale (33068) *(G-11611)*
American Pharmaceutical Svcs 407 704-5937
6001 Silver Star Rd Ste 2 Orlando (32808) *(G-12473)*
American Photonics, Sarasota *Also called Laser Lens Tek Inc (G-16249)*
American Pipes and Tubes Co, Sunny Isles Beach *Also called Inox LLC (G-17079)*
American Plastic Sup & Mfg Inc (PA) 727 573-0636
11601 56th Ct N Clearwater (33760) *(G-1581)*
American Polylactide Inds 352 653-5963
3666 Ne 25th St Ocala (34470) *(G-11872)*
American Powder Coating, Fort Lauderdale *Also called American Prtective Coating Inc (G-3814)*
American Pressure Systems Inc 321 914-0827
7608 Emerald Dr West Melbourne (32904) *(G-18765)*
American Products Inc 813 925-0144
13909 Lynmar Blvd Tampa (33626) *(G-17418)*
American Professional Ir Work 305 556-9522
8320 Nw 103rd St Hialeah (33016) *(G-5294)*
American Prtective Coating Inc 954 561-0999
6795 Nw 17th Ave Fort Lauderdale (33309) *(G-3814)*
American Quality Mfg Inc 321 636-3434
310 Shearer Blvd Cocoa (32922) *(G-1995)*
American R&R, Miami *Also called R & R American Corporation (G-10228)*
American Recycling Systems Inc 772 225-8072
1125 Ne Savannah Oaks Way Jensen Beach (34957) *(G-6965)*
American Refrigerants, Bradenton *Also called Fireside Holdings Inc (G-1041)*
American Reprographics Co LLC 813 286-8300
5005 W Laurel St Ste 102 Tampa (33607) *(G-17419)*

American Respiratory Solutions (PA)...386 698-4446
1125 N Summit St Ste C Crescent City (32112) *(G-2338)*
American Roofing Services LLC...305 250-7115
95 Merrick Way Ste 514 Coral Gables (33134) *(G-2122)*
American S-Shore Plting Sttchi...305 978-9934
1085 E 31st St Hialeah (33013) *(G-5295)*
American Sani Partition Corp...407 656-0611
300 Enterprise St Ocoee (34761) *(G-12082)*
American Science and Tech Corp...312 898-3333
1330 West Ave Apt 3305 Miami Beach (33139) *(G-10641)*
American Screen Print Inc...904 443-0071
4122 Spring Park Rd Jacksonville (32207) *(G-6149)*
American Shield LLC...850 697-3066
644 Oak St Lanark Village (32323) *(G-7848)*
American Shipper, Jacksonville *Also called Howard Publications Inc (G-6480)*
American Shutter Products Inc, Fort Myers *Also called American Windows Shutters Inc (G-4359)*
American Sign, Sebastian *Also called Expert Promotions LLC (G-16658)*
American Sign Letters...772 643-4012
8140 Evernia St Unit 1 Sebastian (32976) *(G-16654)*
American Silica Holdings LLC...352 796-8855
24060 Deer Run Rd Brooksville (34601) *(G-1211)*
American Specialty Sales Corp...305 947-9700
14286 Biscayne Blvd North Miami (33181) *(G-11624)*
American Speedy Printing, Pompano Beach *Also called Lmb Consultants Inc (G-14746)*
American Sperior Compounds Inc...716 873-1209
17409 Chelsea Downs Cir Lithia (33547) *(G-8215)*
American Stainless & Alum Pdts...423 472-4832
315 Industrial Way Kissimmee (34746) *(G-7219)*
American Stainless Mfrs (PA)...786 275-4458
8390 Nw 68th St Miami (33166) *(G-9147)*
American Stairs, Stuart *Also called Cedrus Inc (G-16920)*
American Standards Inc...904 683-2189
4744 Kingsbury St Jacksonville (32205) *(G-6150)*
American Stock LLC...904 641-2055
3225 Anniston Rd Jacksonville (32246) *(G-6151)*
American Sugar Refining Inc...561 962-8106
3998 Fau Blvd Ste 100 Boca Raton (33431) *(G-423)*
American Surgical Mask Co, Tampa *Also called American Surgical Mask LLC (G-17420)*
American Surgical Mask LLC...813 606-4510
5508 N 50th St Ste 1000 Tampa (33610) *(G-17420)*
American Tchncal Crmics Fla In...904 724-2000
2201 Corporate Sq Blvd Jacksonville (32216) *(G-6152)*
American Technical Furn LLC...866 239-4204
831 Carswell Ave Holly Hill (32117) *(G-5755)*
American Technical Molding, Clearwater *Also called American Tool & Mold Inc (G-1583)*
American Technical Molding Inc...727 447-7377
1700 Sunshine Dr Clearwater (33765) *(G-1582)*
American Technology Pdts Inc...407 960-1722
211 Northstar Ct Sanford (32771) *(G-15993)*
American Teledata, Clearwater *Also called American Data Supply Inc (G-1579)*
American Thrmplastic Extrusion...305 769-9566
4851 Nw 128th Street Rd Opa Locka (33054) *(G-12287)*
American Tool & Mold Inc...727 447-7377
1700 Sunshine Dr Clearwater (33765) *(G-1583)*
American Torch Tip Company (PA)...941 753-7557
6212 29th St E Bradenton (34203) *(G-988)*
American Traction Systems Inc...239 768-0757
10030 Amberwood Rd Ste 1 Fort Myers (33913) *(G-4358)*
American Traffic Safety Mtls...904 284-0284
1272 Harbor Rd Green Cove Springs (32043) *(G-5051)*
American Trophy Co...954 782-2250
831 W Mcnab Rd Pompano Beach (33060) *(G-14594)*
American Truss...352 493-9700
6760 Nw 138th Pl Chiefland (32626) *(G-1529)*
American Truss Chiefland LL...352 493-9700
6750 Nw 138th Pl Chiefland (32626) *(G-1530)*
American Vet Sciences LLC...727 471-0850
6911 Bryan Dairy Rd Largo (33777) *(G-7895)*
American Vinyl Company (PA)...305 687-1863
600 W 83rd St Hialeah (33014) *(G-5296)*
American Vinyl Company...813 663-0157
6715 N 53rd St Tampa (33610) *(G-17421)*
American Vly Avnics Clbrtion L...904 579-5272
137 Industrial Loop W Orange Park (32073) *(G-12381)*
American Vulkan Corporation (HQ)...863 324-2424
2525 Dundee Rd Winter Haven (33884) *(G-19299)*
American Water Chemicals, Plant City *Also called Amaya Solutions Inc (G-14398)*
American Water Chemicals Inc...813 246-5448
1802 Corporate Center Ln Plant City (33563) *(G-14400)*
American Welding Society Inc (PA)...305 443-9353
8669 Nw 36th St Ste 130 Doral (33166) *(G-3247)*
American Windows Shutters Inc...239 278-3066
11600 Adelmo Ln Fort Myers (33966) *(G-4359)*
American Wire Group Inc (PA)...954 455-3050
2980 Ne 207th St Ste 901 Aventura (33180) *(G-260)*
American Wldg & Installation...786 391-4800
4851 Nw 36th Ave Miami (33142) *(G-9148)*
American Wtrjet Fbrcation Svcs...407 826-0497
5104 S Orange Ave Orlando (32809) *(G-12474)*
American-Marsh Pumps LLC...863 646-5689
2805 Badger Rd Lakeland (33811) *(G-7634)*
Americas Atm LLC...954 414-0341
8751 W Broward Blvd # 30 Plantation (33324) *(G-14489)*
Americas Blasting Coatings LLC...754 281-6738
2020 Sw 36th Ave Fort Lauderdale (33312) *(G-3815)*
Americast Precast Generator...772 971-1958
3204 Ohio Ave Fort Pierce (34947) *(G-4675)*
Americoat Corporation...863 667-1035
2935 Barneys Pumps Pl Lakeland (33812) *(G-7635)*
Americraft Cookware LLC...352 483-7600
4129 United Ave Mount Dora (32757) *(G-11095)*
Americraft Enterprises Inc...386 756-1100
2800 S Nova Rd Ste H3 Daytona Beach (32119) *(G-2624)*
Americut of Florida Inc...800 692-2187
1941 Custom Dr Fort Myers (33907) *(G-4360)*
Amerifax Acquisition Corp...305 828-1701
7290 W 18th Ln Hialeah (33014) *(G-5297)*
Amerifood Corp...305 305-5951
1717 Nw 22nd St 6 Miami (33142) *(G-9149)*
Ameriglass Engineering Inc...305 558-6227
2246 W 79th St Hialeah (33016) *(G-5298)*
Amerikan, Sebring *Also called The Hc Companies Inc (G-16715)*
Amerikan LLC...863 314-9417
2006 Fortune Blvd Sebring (33870) *(G-16681)*
Amerikooler LLC...305 884-8384
575 E 10th Ave Hialeah (33010) *(G-5299)*
Ameriseam, Tampa *Also called J W L Trading Company Inc (G-17800)*
Ameritech Die & Mold & South, Ormond Beach *Also called Ameritech Die & Mold South Inc (G-13348)*
Ameritech Die & Mold South Inc...386 677-1770
1 E Tower Cir Ormond Beach (32174) *(G-13348)*
Ameritech Energy Corporation...386 589-7501
1500 Beville Rd Ste 606 Daytona Beach (32114) *(G-2625)*
Ameritech Powder Coating Inc...239 274-8000
502 South Rd Unit D Fort Myers (33907) *(G-4361)*
Amerx Health Care Corp...727 443-0530
164 Douglas Rd E Oldsmar (34677) *(G-12201)*
Ames Companies Inc (HQ)...717 737-1500
13485 Veterans Way # 200 Orlando (32827) *(G-12475)*
Ames Tools...239 693-1055
5011 Luckett Rd Fort Myers (33905) *(G-4362)*
Ametek Inc...727 536-7831
8600 Somerset Dr Largo (33773) *(G-7896)*
Ametek Power Instrument Inc...954 344-9822
4050 Nw 121st Ave Coral Springs (33065) *(G-2220)*
Ametrine LLC...786 300-7946
127 Barrington Dr Brandon (33511) *(G-1151)*
AMF Building Products, Mangonia Park *Also called American Metal Fabricators Inc (G-8497)*
Amgen USA Inc...805 447-1000
2202 N West Shore Blvd # 2 Tampa (33607) *(G-17422)*
Amglo Halogen, Largo *Also called Vision Engineering Labs (G-8075)*
Amglo Kemlite Laboratories, Largo *Also called Vision Engineering Labs (G-8076)*
AMI Celebrity Publications LLC...561 997-7733
1000 American Media Way Boca Raton (33464) *(G-424)*
AMI Digital Inc...561 997-7733
1000 American Media Way Boca Raton (33464) *(G-425)*
AMI Graphics Inc...352 629-4455
1302 Sw 42nd Ave Ocala (34474) *(G-11873)*
Amicitia Pharma Llc...941 722-0172
5919 60th Pl E Palmetto (34221) *(G-13786)*
Amick Cstm Woodcraft & Design...407 324-8525
1450 Kastner Pl Ste 112 Sanford (32771) *(G-15994)*
Amigo Pallets Inc...305 631-2452
7650 Nw 69th Ave Medley (33166) *(G-8609)*
Amigo Pallets Inc...305 302-9751
10251 Sw 109th St Miami (33176) *(G-9150)*
Amino Cell Inc...352 291-0200
5640 Sw 6th Pl Ste 500 Ocala (34474) *(G-11874)*
Aminsa Corp...954 865-1289
612 Bald Cypress Rd Weston (33327) *(G-19104)*
Amizetta Vineyards...707 963-1460
525 Hernando Dr Marco Island (34145) *(G-8523)*
Amj DOT LLC...646 249-0273
22304 Calibre Ct Apt 1304 Boca Raton (33433) *(G-426)*
Aml Extreme Powdercoating...904 794-4313
7750 Us Highway 1 S Saint Augustine (32086) *(G-15516)*
Ammcon Corp...904 863-3196
1503 County Road 315 # 204 Green Cove Springs (32043) *(G-5052)*
Ammo-Up, Jacksonville *Also called Bag-A-Nut LLC (G-6191)*
AMP Aero Services LLC...833 267-2376
13806 Sw 145th Ct Miami (33186) *(G-9151)*
Amper Usa LLC...305 717-3101
4447 Nw 98th Ave Doral (33178) *(G-3248)*
Ampersand Graphics Inc...772 283-1359
553 Se Monterey Rd Stuart (34994) *(G-16906)*

Ampersand Shirt Shack.....772 600-8743
553 Se Monterey Rd Stuart (34994) ***(G-16907)***
Amphenol Custom Cable Inc (HQ).....813 623-2232
3221 Cherry Palm Dr Tampa (33619) ***(G-17423)***
Amphenol Custom Cable Inc.....407 393-3886
7461 Currency Dr Orlando (32809) ***(G-12476)***
Amps, Deland *Also called Advanced Mfg & Pwr Systems Inc* ***(G-2953)***
Amrad, Palm Coast *Also called Vladmir Ltd* ***(G-13714)***
Amramp North FL.....904 424-3331
3025 Southshore Cir Tallahassee (32312) ***(G-17218)***
Amrav Inc.....407 831-1550
1026 Miller Dr Altamonte Springs (32701) ***(G-31)***
Amrob Inc.....813 238-6041
4719 N Thatcher Ave Tampa (33614) ***(G-17424)***
Amrob Incorporated.....813 237-5891
16101 Carden Dr Odessa (33556) ***(G-12101)***
AMS, Merritt Island *Also called Tua Systems Inc* ***(G-9018)***
AMS Fabrications Inc.....813 420-0784
2816 Nw 30th Ave Oakland Park (33311) ***(G-11776)***
AMS Global Suppliers Group LLC.....305 714-9441
200 S Biscayne Blvd Miami (33131) ***(G-9152)***
AMS Uniforms, Miami *Also called Affordable Med Scrubs LLC* ***(G-9086)***
Amtec Less Lethal Systems Inc.....850 223-4066
4700 Providence Rd Perry (32347) ***(G-14293)***
Amtec Sales Inc.....800 994-3318
1594 Nw 159th St Miami (33169) ***(G-9153)***
Amteco Machine & Manufacturing.....727 573-0993
4652 107th Cir N Clearwater (33762) ***(G-1584)***
Amtel Security Systems Inc.....305 591-8200
1691 Nw 107th Ave Doral (33172) ***(G-3249)***
Amtex-Nms Holdings Inc (PA).....352 728-2930
2500 Industrial St Leesburg (34748) ***(G-8141)***
Amxs Corp.....904 568-1416
524 Patricia Ln Jacksonville Beach (32250) ***(G-6938)***
Amy Cabinetry.....561 842-8091
6667 42nd Ter N Riviera Beach (33407) ***(G-15298)***
Anacom Electronica, Winter Garden *Also called Edashop Inc* ***(G-19262)***
Anaiah Press LLC.....727 692-0025
6921 39th Ave N Saint Petersburg (33709) ***(G-15700)***
Analili Analili, Miami *Also called Olian Inc* ***(G-10094)***
Analog Modules Inc.....407 339-4355
126 Baywood Ave Longwood (32750) ***(G-8255)***
Analytical Research Systems.....352 466-0051
12109 Highway 441 S Micanopy (32667) ***(G-10899)***
Anavini, Miami *Also called La Providencia Express Co* ***(G-9846)***
ANC Shutters LLC.....561 966-8336
3386 Pony Run Lake Worth (33449) ***(G-7534)***
Anchor & Docking Inc.....239 770-2030
830 Ne 24th Ln Unit G Cape Coral (33909) ***(G-1379)***
Anchor Aluminum Products South.....305 293-7965
2807 Staples Ave Key West (33040) ***(G-7177)***
Anchor Coatings Leesburg Inc.....352 728-0777
2280 Talley Rd Leesburg (34748) ***(G-8142)***
Anchor Glass Container Corp.....904 786-1010
2121 Huron St Jacksonville (32254) ***(G-6153)***
Anchor Glass Container Corp (PA).....813 884-0000
3001 N Rocky Point Dr E # 300 Tampa (33607) ***(G-17425)***
Anchor Industries LLC.....850 509-8344
2305 Braeburn Cir Tallahassee (32309) ***(G-17219)***
Anchor Machine & Fabricating.....813 247-3099
3905 E 7th Ave Tampa (33605) ***(G-17426)***
Anchor Screen Printing LLC.....850 243-4200
808 South Dr Fort Walton Beach (32547) ***(G-4775)***
Ancient Language Inc.....413 344-4042
10524 Moss Park Rd # 204 Orlando (32832) ***(G-12477)***
Ancient Mosaic Studios LLC.....772 460-3145
4106 Mariah Cir Fort Pierce (34947) ***(G-4676)***
Anco Precision Inc.....954 429-3703
3191 Sw 11th St Ste 200 Deerfield Beach (33442) ***(G-2777)***
Ancorp, Williston *Also called A & N Corporation* ***(G-19207)***
and Services.....850 805-6455
1295 Beverly St Fort Walton Beach (32547) ***(G-4776)***
and Tees LLC.....904 745-0773
7272 Crescent Oaks Ct Jacksonville (32277) ***(G-6154)***
and-Dell Corporation.....954 523-6478
245 Sw 33rd St Fort Lauderdale (33315) ***(G-3816)***
Andean Stone Company LLC.....305 460-3320
1050 E 17th St Hialeah (33010) ***(G-5300)***
Anderson Advanta Asphalt, Live Oak *Also called Advanta Asphalt Inc* ***(G-8226)***
Anderson Backhoe Service Inc.....904 759-9084
5715 Cisco Dr W Jacksonville (32219) ***(G-6155)***
Anderson Columbia Co Inc.....352 463-6342
8191 Nw 160th St Chiefland (32626) ***(G-1531)***
Anderson Materials, Chiefland *Also called Anderson Columbia Co Inc* ***(G-1531)***
Anderson Mfg & Upholstery Inc.....321 267-7028
1427 Chaffee Dr Ste 4 Titusville (32780) ***(G-18413)***
Anderson Mining Corporation (HQ).....352 542-7942
624 Ne Highway 349 Old Town (32680) ***(G-12195)***
Anderson Printing Services Inc.....727 545-9000
7245 Bryan Dairy Rd Seminole (33777) ***(G-16738)***
Anderson Truss LLC.....386 752-3103
1730 Nw Oakland Ave Lake City (32055) ***(G-7348)***
Andersons Can Line Fbrction Eq.....407 889-4665
2208 Stillwater Ave Apopka (32703) ***(G-113)***
Andre T Jean.....305 647-8744
2306 Ali Baba Ave Opa Locka (33054) ***(G-12288)***
Andrew Martin Swift.....321 409-0509
620 Atlantis Rd Ste A Melbourne (32904) ***(G-8767)***
Andrew Mj Inc.....561 575-6032
10152 Indiantown Rd Jupiter (33478) ***(G-7000)***
Andrew Pratt Stucco & Plst Inc.....407 501-2609
8048 Bridgestone Dr Orlando (32835) ***(G-12478)***
Andrews 1st Choice Trckg LLC.....205 703-5717
4532 Lane Ave S Jacksonville (32210) ***(G-6156)***
Andrews Cabinet.....850 994-0836
4025 Bell Ln Milton (32571) ***(G-10921)***
Andrews Filter and Supply Corp (PA).....407 423-3310
2309 Coolidge Ave Orlando (32804) ***(G-12479)***
Andrews Warehouse Partnership.....954 524-3330
1512 E Broward Blvd Fort Lauderdale (33301) ***(G-3817)***
Andritz Iggesund Tools Inc (HQ).....813 855-6902
220 Scarlet Blvd Oldsmar (34677) ***(G-12202)***
Andro Corp Industries.....917 287-5294
3496 Meadow Breeze Loop Ocoee (34761) ***(G-12083)***
Andros Boatworks Inc.....941 351-9702
202 Industrial Blvd Sarasota (34234) ***(G-16342)***
Andrx Corporation.....954 217-4500
2915 Weston Rd Weston (33331) ***(G-19105)***
Andrx Corporation.....954 585-1770
13900 Nw 2nd St Ste 100 Sunrise (33325) ***(G-17091)***
Andrx Corporation (HQ).....954 585-1400
4955 Orange Dr Davie (33314) ***(G-2497)***
Anesthesia Service & Equipment, Jacksonville *Also called Eagle Eye Anesthesia Inc* ***(G-6345)***
Anew Inc.....386 668-7785
32 Cunningham Rd Debary (32713) ***(G-2744)***
Anew International Corporation.....386 668-7785
32 Cunningham Rd Debary (32713) ***(G-2745)***
Angel Fernandez.....239 580-9714
17601 Laurel Valley Rd Fort Myers (33967) ***(G-4363)***
Angela Zieglers Window Washers.....239 849-0310
628 Se 23rd St Cape Coral (33990) ***(G-1380)***
Angery American Enterprises.....352 669-2198
22741 Will Murphy Rd Umatilla (32784) ***(G-18495)***
Angle Truss Co Inc.....352 343-7477
29652 State Road 19 Tavares (32778) ***(G-18334)***
Angler Pro Boats LLC.....305 525-4943
7755 Sw 66th St South Miami (33143) ***(G-16812)***
Anglo Silver Liner Co.....508 943-1440
7019 Indus Valley Cir Parrish (34219) ***(G-14003)***
Anheuser-Busch Incorporated.....863 646-7357
3907 Aero Pl Lakeland (33811) ***(G-7636)***
Anheuser-Busch Companies LLC.....407 251-4049
10928 Florida Crown Dr Orlando (32824) ***(G-12480)***
Animal Agrclture Advrsries Ame, Miami *Also called Whyte Power Industries Corp* ***(G-10605)***
Animal Air Service Inc.....305 218-1759
1952 Nw 93rd Ave Doral (33172) ***(G-3250)***
Animal Business Concepts LLC.....727 641-6176
3235 Fairfield Ave S Saint Petersburg (33712) ***(G-15701)***
Anjon Inc.....904 730-9373
4801 Dawin Rd Jacksonville (32207) ***(G-6157)***
Anko Products Inc.....941 748-2307
6012 33rd St E Bradenton (34203) ***(G-989)***
Anmapec Corporation.....786 897-5389
5210 Nw 5th St Miami (33126) ***(G-9154)***
Anna Andres.....239 335-0233
2442 Dr M L King Blvd Martin Fort Myers (33901) ***(G-4364)***
Annat Inc.....239 262-4639
6203 Janes Ln Ste D Naples (34109) ***(G-11163)***
Annellies Car Wash LLC.....954 990-8436
6420 Nw 50th St Lauderhill (33319) ***(G-8101)***
Annette M Wellington Hall Inc.....954 437-9880
5830 Sheridan St Hollywood (33021) ***(G-5772)***
Annona Biosciences Inc.....888 204-4980
2401 Pga Blvd Ste 196 Palm Beach Gardens (33410) ***(G-13566)***
Antebellum Manufacturing LLC.....352 877-3888
1120 N Magnolia Ave Ocala (34475) ***(G-11875)***
Antennas For Cmmnctons Ocala F.....352 687-4121
2499 Sw 60th Ave Ocala (34474) ***(G-11876)***
Antennas.us, Margate *Also called Myers Engineering Intl Inc* ***(G-8558)***
Anthem South LLC.....973 779-1982
9710 Nw 110th Ave Unit 10 Medley (33178) ***(G-8610)***
Anthony Spagna Svc & Maint Inc.....352 796-2109
3335 Mustang Dr Brooksville (34604) ***(G-1212)***
Anthony Wright Welding.....850 544-1831
311 Ross Rd Tallahassee (32305) ***(G-17220)***
Anti-Ging Asthtic Lser Ctr Inc.....786 539-4901
4401 Collins Ave Miami Beach (33140) ***(G-10642)***

Antique & Modern Cabinets Inc 904 393-9055
2384 Vans Ave Jacksonville (32207) **(G-6158)**
Antique Automobile Radio Inc 727 785-8733
700 Tampa Rd Palm Harbor (34683) **(G-13719)**
Antiquo Stone By F T F, Fellsmere *Also called F T F Construction Company* **(G-3725)**
Anton Paar Quantatec Inc 561 731-4999
1900 Corporate Dr Boynton Beach (33426) **(G-877)**
Antonyo Denard Llc 904 290-1579
1408 San Marco Blvd Jacksonville (32207) **(G-6159)**
Antylia Scientific 352 854-8080
5350 Sw 1st Ln Ocala (34474) **(G-11877)**
Anu Industries Inc (PA) 813 927-7254
8123 River Country Dr Weeki Wachee (34607) **(G-18700)**
ANue Ligne Inc 305 638-7979
3300 Nw 41st St Miami (33142) **(G-9155)**
Anupack LLC 407 850-1960
2501 Principal Row Orlando (32837) **(G-12481)**
Anuva Manufacturing Svcs Inc 321 821-4900
7801 Ellis Rd Ste 101 Melbourne (32904) **(G-8768)**
Anuvia Florida LLC 352 720-7070
6751 Jones Ave Mount Dora (32757) **(G-11096)**
Anuvia Plant City LLC 407 719-7798
660 E County Line Rd Plant City (33565) **(G-14401)**
Anuvia Plant Ntrnts Hldngs LLC 352 720-7070
6751 W Jones Ave Zellwood (32798) **(G-19502)**
Anvil Iron Works Inc 727 375-2884
11607 Perpetual Dr Odessa (33556) **(G-12102)**
Anvil Paints & Coatings Inc 727 535-1411
1255 Starkey Rd Ste A Largo (33771) **(G-7897)**
Anvil Paints and Coating, Largo *Also called Anvil Paints & Coatings Inc* **(G-7897)**
Anything Display 239 433-9738
6225 Presidential Ct Fort Myers (33919) **(G-4365)**
Anytime Waste, Vero Beach *Also called B & F Waste Solutions Llc* **(G-18597)**
Anywhere Gps LLC 949 468-6842
43 Sierras Loop Saint Augustine (32086) **(G-15517)**
Anzio Ironworks Corp 727 895-2019
14605 49th St N Ste 8 Clearwater (33762) **(G-1585)**
Ao Precision Manufacturing LLC 386 274-5882
1870 Mason Ave Daytona Beach (32117) **(G-2626)**
AOC Technologies Inc 727 577-9749
10560 Dr Martin L Kng Jr Saint Petersburg (33716) **(G-15702)**
Aoclsc Inc (PA) 813 248-1988
1601 Mcclosky Blvd Tampa (33605) **(G-17427)**
Aocusa, Tampa *Also called Aoclsc Inc* **(G-17427)**
Aog Detailing Services Inc 727 742-7321
6798 Crosswinds Dr N B203 Saint Petersburg (33710) **(G-15703)**
AP Buck Inc 407 851-8602
7101 Presidents Dr # 110 Orlando (32809) **(G-12482)**
AP Lifesciences LLC 954 300-7469
12085 Research Dr Ste 155 Alachua (32615) **(G-3)**
AP Richter Holding Co LLC 239 732-9440
1617 Gulfstar Dr S Naples (34112) **(G-11164)**
APA Wireless Technologies Inc 954 563-8833
4066 Ne 5th Ave Oakland Park (33334) **(G-11777)**
Apache Sheet Metal 954 214-4468
631 Stanton Ln Weston (33326) **(G-19106)**
Apakus Inc 305 403-2603
75 Valencia Ave Ste 701 Coral Gables (33134) **(G-2123)**
Apalachee Pole Company Inc (PA) 850 263-4457
1820 Highway 2 Graceville (32440) **(G-5042)**
Apalachee Pole Company Inc 850 643-2121
18601 Nw County Road 379a Bristol (32321) **(G-1191)**
Apara Productions, Miami *Also called Armadillo Sounds Inc* **(G-9169)**
Apartment Guide, Orlando *Also called Consumer Source Inc* **(G-12615)**
APC Art-Phyl Creations LLC 786 571-4665
345 W 75th Pl Hialeah (33014) **(G-5301)**
Ape South, Key Largo *Also called Automated Production Eqp Ape* **(G-7165)**
Apellix, Jacksonville *Also called Working Drones Inc* **(G-6929)**
Apex Aviation Group LLC 305 789-6695
801 Brickell Ave Ste 900 Miami (33131) **(G-9156)**
Apex Color, Jacksonville *Also called Arlington Prtg Stationers Inc* **(G-6168)**
Apex Fabrication Inc 904 259-4666
710 Griffin Ct Macclenny (32063) **(G-8441)**
Apex Flood Fire Mold Clnup Inc 305 975-1710
1340 Sw 19th Ave Boca Raton (33486) **(G-427)**
Apex Grinding Inc 386 624-7350
1857 Patterson Ave Unit 4 Deland (32724) **(G-2958)**
Apex Machine Company (PA) 954 563-0209
3000 Ne 12th Ter Oakland Park (33334) **(G-11778)**
Apex Metal Fabrication Inc 386 328-2564
177 Comfort Rd Palatka (32177) **(G-13473)**
Apexeon Biomedical LLC 850 878-2150
3075 Hawks Landing Dr Tallahassee (32309) **(G-17221)**
API, Tampa *Also called American Products Inc* **(G-17418)**
API Tech North America Inc 929 255-1231
941 W Morse Blvd Ste 100 Winter Park (32789) **(G-19377)**
Apical Pharmaceutical Corp 786 331-7200
10460 Nw 37th Ter Doral (33178) **(G-3251)**

Apis Cor Inc 347 404-1481
3060 Venture Ln Ste 101 Melbourne (32934) **(G-8769)**
Apogee Services Inc 561 441-5354
703 Sw 24th Ave Boynton Beach (33435) **(G-878)**
Apollo Energy Systems Inc (PA) 954 969-7755
4100 N Powerline Rd D3 Pompano Beach (33073) **(G-14595)**
Apollo Metro Solutions Inc 239 444-6934
2975 Horseshoe Dr S # 500 Naples (34104) **(G-11165)**
Apollo Renal Therapeutics LLC 202 413-0963
2811 Ne 14th St Ocala (34470) **(G-11878)**
Apollo Retail Specialists LLC (HQ) 813 712-2525
4450 E Adamo Dr Ste 501 Tampa (33605) **(G-17428)**
Apollo Shade Systems, Sarasota *Also called Apollo Sunguard Systems Inc* **(G-16343)**
Apollo Sunguard Systems Inc 941 925-3000
4487 Ashton Rd Sarasota (34233) **(G-16343)**
Apollo Worldwide Inc 561 585-3865
158 Las Brisas Cir Hypoluxo (33462) **(G-6048)**
Apopka Chief, The, Apopka *Also called Foliage Enterprises Inc* **(G-144)**
Apotex Corp (HQ) 954 384-8007
2400 N Commerce Pkwy # 400 Weston (33326) **(G-19107)**
Apparel Expressions LLC 850 314-0100
209b Lang Rd Fort Walton Beach (32547) **(G-4777)**
Apparel Imports Inc 800 428-6849
10893 Nw 17th St Unit 126 Miami (33172) **(G-9157)**
Apparel Industries 786 362-5958
5550 Nw 79th Ave Doral (33166) **(G-3252)**
Apparel Machinery Services Inc 772 335-5350
1545 Se S Niemeyer Cir Port Saint Lucie (34952) **(G-15087)**
Apparel Printers 352 463-8850
13201 Rachael Blvd Alachua (32615) **(G-4)**
Appel 26 Corp 305 672-8645
4101 Pine Tree Dr Apt 111 Miami Beach (33140) **(G-10643)**
Appi, Opa Locka *Also called Aero Precision Products Inc* **(G-12283)**
Appi, Miami Lakes *Also called Assocated Prtg Productions Inc* **(G-10763)**
Apple A Day Inc 941 377-5404
803 Bell Rd Sarasota (34240) **(G-16344)**
Apple Machine & Supply Co 772 466-9353
5900 Orange Ave Fort Pierce (34947) **(G-4677)**
Apple Printing & Advg Spc Inc 954 524-0493
5055 Nw 10th Ter Fort Lauderdale (33309) **(G-3818)**
Apple Sign & Awning LLC 813 948-2220
1635 Dale Mabry Hwy Ste 7 Lutz (33548) **(G-8375)**
Apple Spice - Jax 904 328-6542
3061 Philips Hwy Unit 102 Jacksonville (32207) **(G-6160)**
Apple Spice Box Lnch Dlvry Ctr, Tampa *Also called J Squared Management II LLC* **(G-17799)**
Appliances To Go Usa Llc 239 278-0811
741 Del Prado Blvd N # 160 Cape Coral (33909) **(G-1381)**
Applied Cooling Technology LLC 239 217-5080
75 Mid Cape Ter 23 Cape Coral (33991) **(G-1382)**
Applied Design & Fabrication 954 524-6619
3525 Northern Blvd Lake Placid (33852) **(G-7484)**
Applied Fiber Concepts Inc 754 581-2744
2425 W 8th Ln Hialeah (33010) **(G-5302)**
Applied Fiber Holdings LLC 850 539-7720
25 Garrett Dr Havana (32333) **(G-5230)**
Applied Fiber Mfg LLC 850 539-7720
25 Garrett Dr Havana (32333) **(G-5231)**
Applied Genetic Tech Corp 386 462-2204
14193 Nw 119th Ter Ste 10 Alachua (32615) **(G-5)**
Applied Mobility Devices LLC (PA) 833 439-6266
8951 Bonita Beach Rd Se Bonita Springs (34135) **(G-813)**
Applied Neuroscience Inc 727 324-8922
8200 Bryan Dairy Rd # 315 Seminole (33777) **(G-16739)**
Applied Software Inc 215 297-9441
737 Sandy Point Ln West Palm Beach (33410) **(G-18797)**
Applied Systems Integrator Inc 321 259-6106
746 North Dr Ste B Melbourne (32934) **(G-8770)**
Applied Technologies Group Inc 813 413-7025
333 N Falkenburg Rd B227 Tampa (33619) **(G-17429)**
Applus Laboratories USA Inc (HQ) 941 205-5700
27256 Mooney Ave Bldg 10 Punta Gorda (33982) **(G-15190)**
Appo Group Inc 410 992-5500
7000 Island Blvd Apt 2309 Aventura (33160) **(G-261)**
Appointment Team Inc 561 314-5471
1530 W Boynton Beach Blvd Boynton Beach (33436) **(G-879)**
Approved Performance Tooling 305 592-7775
8405 Nw 66th St Miami (33166) **(G-9158)**
Approved Turbo Components Inc 559 627-3600
663 2nd Ln Vero Beach (32962) **(G-18594)**
APRU LLC 888 741-3777
3125 Lake George Cove Dr Orlando (32812) **(G-12483)**
APS Promotional Solutions Inc 904 721-4977
7121 Beach Blvd Jacksonville (32216) **(G-6161)**
APT, Miami *Also called Approved Performance Tooling* **(G-9158)**
Aptum Technologies (usa) Inc 877 504-0091
2300 Nw 89th Pl Doral (33172) **(G-3253)**
Apure Distribution LLC 305 351-1025
5555 Biscayne Blvd Fl 3 Miami (33137) **(G-9159)**

ALPHABETIC

Apw..........850 332-7023
911 N 63rd Ave Pensacola (32506) *(G-14088)*
Apw Wholesale, Jacksonville *Also called Aluminum Products Whl Inc (G-6144)*
Apyelen Curves LLC..........904 434-8768
13000 City Station Dr Jacksonville (32218) *(G-6162)*
Apyx Medical Corporation (PA)..........727 384-2323
5115 Ulmerton Rd Clearwater (33760) *(G-1586)*
Aqua Engineering & Equipment..........407 599-2123
7206 Aloma Ave Winter Park (32792) *(G-19378)*
Aqua Finishing Solutions, Fort Pierce *Also called Faux Effects International Inc (G-4697)*
Aqua Pulsar LLC..........772 320-9691
3275 Sw 42nd Ave Palm City (34990) *(G-13641)*
Aqua Pure LLC..........407 521-3055
6541 N Orange Blossom Trl Orlando (32810) *(G-12484)*
Aqua Pure of SW Florida Lc, Naples *Also called Keith Dennis Markham (G-11303)*
Aqua Pure Water Co Inc..........954 744-4210
1246 Funston St Hollywood (33019) *(G-5773)*
Aqua Solutions, West Palm Beach *Also called Fovico Inc (G-18882)*
Aqua Technologies..........305 246-2125
815 N Homestead Blvd Homestead (33030) *(G-5954)*
Aqua Wholesale Inc..........941 341-0847
1155 Cattlemen Rd Ste B Sarasota (34232) *(G-16345)*
Aqua-Air Manufacturing, Fort Lauderdale *Also called James D Nall Co Inc (G-4074)*
Aquaback Technologies Inc..........978 863-1000
9300 Scarborough Ct Port Saint Lucie (34986) *(G-15088)*
Aquacal (PA)..........727 898-2412
2730 24th St N Saint Petersburg (33713) *(G-15704)*
Aquacal Autopilot Inc..........727 823-5642
2737 24th St N Saint Petersburg (33713) *(G-15705)*
Aquaflex Printing LLC..........727 914-4922
3349 118th Ave N Saint Petersburg (33716) *(G-15706)*
Aquallsion Design Concepts LLC..........407 440-2972
991 Juel St Orlando (32814) *(G-12485)*
Aqualogix Inc (PA)..........858 442-4550
4440 Pga Blvd Ste 600 Palm Beach Gardens (33410) *(G-13567)*
Aqualuma LLC..........954 234-2512
3251 Sw 13th Dr Ste A Deerfield Beach (33442) *(G-2778)*
Aquarian Bath Inc..........310 919-0220
46 High Ridge Rd Holly Hill (32117) *(G-5756)*
Aquarius Press Inc..........305 688-0066
13795 Nw 19th Ave Opa Locka (33054) *(G-12289)*
Aquarius Silk Screen Inc..........941 377-3059
5931 Palmer Blvd Sarasota (34232) *(G-16346)*
Aquasolve Ventures LLC..........732 570-0707
601 Innovation Way # 115 Daytona Beach (32114) *(G-2627)*
Aquatec Solutions LLC..........561 717-6933
140 Nw 11th St Boca Raton (33432) *(G-428)*
Aquatech Manufacturing LLC..........813 664-0300
7455 E Adamo Dr Tampa (33619) *(G-17430)*
Aquatectonica LLC..........941 592-3071
809 Tallgrass Ln Bradenton (34212) *(G-990)*
Aquateko International LLC..........904 273-7200
140 Deer Haven Dr Ponte Vedra Beach (32082) *(G-14933)*
Aquatherm Heat Pumps, Fort Myers *Also called Calorex USA LLC (G-4385)*
Aquathin Corp..........800 462-7634
950 S Andrews Ave Pompano Beach (33069) *(G-14596)*
Aquatic Fabricators of S Fla..........954 458-0400
2930 Sw 30th Ave Ste A Hallandale (33009) *(G-5152)*
Aquatic Technologies Inc..........772 225-4389
1820 Ne Jensen Beach Blvd Jensen Beach (34957) *(G-6966)*
Aquatic Wetsuits, Hallandale *Also called Aquatic Fabricators of S Fla (G-5152)*
Aqueous Concepts, Odessa *Also called Amrob Incorporated (G-12101)*
Aquinas Inc..........727 842-2254
4936 Us Highway 19 New Port Richey (34652) *(G-11480)*
Ar2 Products LLC..........800 667-1263
1820 State Road 13 Ste 11 Saint Johns (32259) *(G-15673)*
ARA Food Corporation..........305 592-5558
8001 Nw 60th St Miami (33166) *(G-9160)*
Araya Inc..........305 229-6868
9582 Sw 40th St Ste 5 Miami (33165) *(G-9161)*
ARB Optimal Inc..........904 487-6874
13783 Devan Lee Dr E Jacksonville (32226) *(G-6163)*
Arban & Associates Inc..........850 836-4362
1464 Line Rd Ponce De Leon (32455) *(G-14917)*
Arborossa Leather, Royal Palm Beach *Also called Wellington Leather LLC (G-15479)*
ARC, Tampa *Also called American Reprographics Co LLC (G-17419)*
ARC Creative Inc..........904 996-7773
2683 St Jhns Bluff Rd S S Jacksonville (32246) *(G-6164)*
ARC Dimensions Inc..........727 524-6139
7545 124th Ave Unit Stef Largo (33773) *(G-7898)*
ARC Electric Inc..........954 583-9800
3328 Burris Rd Davie (33314) *(G-2498)*
ARC Group Worldwide Inc (PA)..........303 467-5236
810 Flight Line Blvd Deland (32724) *(G-2959)*
ARC Stone III LLC..........561 478-8805
1800 4th Ave N Unit A Lake Worth Beach (33461) *(G-7603)*
ARC Transition LLC (HQ)..........386 626-0001
790 Fentress Blvd Daytona Beach (32114) *(G-2628)*
ARC United Electric Motor, Tampa *Also called United Electric Motor Inc (G-18220)*

ARC-Rite Inc..........386 325-3523
569 Edgewood Ave S Jacksonville (32205) *(G-6165)*
Arca Knitting Inc (PA)..........305 836-0155
1060 E 23rd St Hialeah (33013) *(G-5303)*
Arca LLC..........305 470-1430
1220 Nw 7th St Miami (33125) *(G-9162)*
Arcadia Aerospace Inds LLC (HQ)..........941 205-5700
27256 Mooney Ave Bldg 110 Punta Gorda (33982) *(G-15191)*
Arcadia Thrift LLC..........863 993-2004
129 S Mills Ave Arcadia (34266) *(G-199)*
Arcana Tileworks..........407 492-0668
1226 Wntr Gdn Vnlnd Rd Winter Garden (34787) *(G-19252)*
Arcco Inc..........954 564-0827
939 Nw 35th Ct Oakland Park (33309) *(G-11779)*
Arch Mirror North, Tamarac *Also called Florida A&G Co Inc (G-17356)*
Archangel Tablets LLC..........703 981-7732
15421 W Dixie Hwy Unit 11 North Miami Beach (33162) *(G-11667)*
Archer Ellison Inc..........800 449-4095
7025 County Road 46a # 1071 Lake Mary (32746) *(G-7400)*
Archer Pharmaceuticals Inc..........941 752-2949
2040 Whitfield Ave Sarasota (34243) *(G-16175)*
Archimaze Logistics Inc..........954 615-7485
1776 Nw 38th Ave Fort Lauderdale (33311) *(G-3819)*
Architctral Designs Metalworks..........954 532-1331
1773 Blount Rd Ste 307 Pompano Beach (33069) *(G-14597)*
Architctral Mlding Mllwrks Inc..........305 638-8900
3545 Nw 50th St Miami (33142) *(G-9163)*
Architctral Mllwk Slutions Inc..........727 441-1409
13090 Starkey Rd Largo (33773) *(G-7899)*
Architctral Mtal Flashings LLC..........239 221-0123
2659 Ne 9th Ave Cape Coral (33909) *(G-1383)*
Architctral Sgnage Systems Inc..........813 996-6777
6812 Land O Lakes Blvd Land O Lakes (34638) *(G-7849)*
Architctral Shtmtl Fabricators..........407 672-9086
2720 Forsyth Rd Ste 200 Winter Park (32792) *(G-19379)*
Architctral WD Wkg Mlding Div..........727 527-7400
3291 40th Ave N Saint Petersburg (33714) *(G-15707)*
Architctral Wdwkg Concepts Inc..........239 434-0549
3863 Entp Ave Unit 2 Naples (34104) *(G-11166)*
Architctral Wdwrks Cbnetry Inc..........561 848-8595
219 Coral Cay Ter Palm Beach Gardens (33418) *(G-13568)*
Architctural MBL Importers Inc..........941 365-3552
2560 12th St Sarasota (34237) *(G-16347)*
Architctural WD Pdts of Naples..........239 260-7156
2154 J And C Blvd Naples (34109) *(G-11167)*
Architechtural Foam Systems, Bradenton *Also called Pmh Homes Inc (G-1099)*
Architectural and Woodworking, Saint Petersburg *Also called William Leupold Sr (G-15960)*
Architectural Detail & Wdwkg..........561 835-4005
2617 Pinewood Ave West Palm Beach (33407) *(G-18798)*
Architectural Foam Supply Inc..........954 943-6949
100 Sw 12th Ave Pompano Beach (33069) *(G-14598)*
Architectural Fountains Inc..........727 323-6068
2010 28th St N Saint Petersburg (33713) *(G-15708)*
Architectural Graphics Inc..........757 427-1900
5500 Rio Vista Dr Clearwater (33760) *(G-1587)*
Architectural Masters LLC..........239 290-2250
2319 Griffin Rd Leesburg (34748) *(G-8143)*
Architectural Metal Systems..........407 277-1364
4881 Distribution Ct Orlando (32822) *(G-12486)*
Architectural Metal Works, Tarpon Springs *Also called Imagine That Inc (G-18309)*
Architectural Metal Works, Tarpon Springs *Also called Casco Services Inc (G-18288)*
Architectural Metals S W FL..........239 334-7433
4700 Laredo Ave Fort Myers (33905) *(G-4366)*
Architectural Openings Inc..........407 260-7110
1975 Corporate Sq Longwood (32750) *(G-8256)*
Architectural Signcrafters..........772 600-5032
3195 Se Gran Park Way Stuart (34997) *(G-16908)*
Architectural Signs Inc..........305 282-4427
14200 Sw 161st Pl Miami (33196) *(G-9164)*
Architectural Spc Trdg Co..........850 435-2507
310 Hickory St Pensacola (32505) *(G-14089)*
Architecture Wood Products, Naples *Also called Architctural WD Pdts of Naples (G-11167)*
Architexture LLC..........954 907-8000
1008 Guava Isle Fort Lauderdale (33315) *(G-3820)*
Arco Automotive Products, Pensacola *Also called Arco Marine Inc (G-14090)*
Arco Computer Products LLC..........954 925-2688
3100 N 29th Ct Ste 100 Hollywood (33020) *(G-5774)*
Arco Globas International, De Leon Springs *Also called Arco Globas Trading LLC (G-2737)*
Arco Globas Trading LLC..........305 707-7702
6111 Lake Winona Rd De Leon Springs (32130) *(G-2737)*
Arco Marine Inc..........850 455-5476
3921 W Navy Blvd Pensacola (32507) *(G-14090)*
Arcoat Coatings Corporation..........561 422-9900
2351 Vista Pkwy Ste 500 West Palm Beach (33411) *(G-18799)*
Arcosa Trffic Ltg Strctres LLC..........352 748-4258
1749 Cr 525e Sumterville (33585) *(G-17067)*
Arcpoint of Tallahassee Inc (PA)..........850 201-2500
3520 N Monroe St Tallahassee (32303) *(G-17222)*

Arctic Industries LLC 305 883-5581
9731 Nw 114th Way Medley (33178) ***(G-8611)***
Arctic-Temp Ice Makers, Longwood *Also called Holiday Ice Inc* ***(G-8287)***
Ard Printing Solutions LL 305 785-7200
14016 Sw 140th St Miami (33186) ***(G-9165)***
Arde Apparel Inc 305 326-0861
1852 Nw 21st St Miami (33142) ***(G-9166)***
Arden Photonics LLC 727 478-2651
4500 140th Ave N Ste 101 Clearwater (33762) ***(G-1588)***
Ardmore Farms LLC 386 734-4634
1915 N Woodland Blvd Deland (32720) ***(G-2960)***
Ards Awning & Upholstery Inc 863 293-2442
503 5th St Sw Winter Haven (33880) ***(G-19300)***
Area Litho Inc 863 687-4656
238 N Wabash Ave Lakeland (33815) ***(G-7637)***
Area Rugs Mfg Inc 904 398-5481
3674 Saint Augustine Rd Jacksonville (32207) ***(G-6166)***
Ares Defense Group LLC 941 255-0559
861 Jarvis St Port Charlotte (33948) ***(G-14961)***
Ares Distributors Inc 305 858-0163
2601 S Bayshore Dr # 1150 Miami (33133) ***(G-9167)***
Aresco Manufacturing & Safety, Palm City *Also called Cameron Textiles Inc* ***(G-13644)***
Aressco Technologies Inc 305 245-5854
15600 Sw 288th St Ste 307 Homestead (33033) ***(G-5955)***
Arete Industries, Odessa *Also called D G Morrison Inc* ***(G-12114)***
Areweonlinecom Llc 561 572-0233
1101 N Congress Ave # 202 Boynton Beach (33426) ***(G-880)***
Arfona Printing LLC 312 339-0215
1121 Bel Air Dr Apt 4 Highland Beach (33487) ***(G-5705)***
Argen Foods 305 884-0037
9220 Nw 102nd St Medley (33178) ***(G-8612)***
Argenal Cabinets Inc 863 670-7973
911 Hammock Shade Dr Lakeland (33809) ***(G-7638)***
Argo Crates & Containers 786 487-4607
10461 Nw 26th St Doral (33172) ***(G-3254)***
Argonide Corporation 407 322-2500
291 Power Ct Sanford (32771) ***(G-15995)***
Argos 678 368-4300
700 Palmetto St Jacksonville (32202) ***(G-6167)***
Argos 305 592-3501
12201 Nw 25th St Miami (33182) ***(G-9168)***
Argos 352 376-6491
924 S Main St Gainesville (32601) ***(G-4875)***
Argos Cement LLC 813 247-4831
2001 Maritime Blvd Tampa (33605) ***(G-17431)***
Argos Ready Mix 941 629-7713
580 Prineville St Port Charlotte (33954) ***(G-14962)***
Argos Ready Mix LLC 727 321-4667
1020 31st St S Saint Petersburg (33712) ***(G-15709)***
Argos USA 863 687-1898
2300 Mershon St Lakeland (33815) ***(G-7639)***
Argos USA LLC 850 872-1209
1601 Maple Ave Panama City (32405) ***(G-13864)***
Argos USA LLC 850 235-9600
17800 Ashley Dr Panama City Beach (32413) ***(G-13970)***
Argos USA LLC 850 576-4141
1005 Kissimmee St Tallahassee (32310) ***(G-17223)***
Argos USA LLC 407 299-9924
2858 Sidney Ave Orlando (32810) ***(G-12487)***
Argos USA LLC 678 368-4300
4000 Nw County Road 235 Newberry (32669) ***(G-11551)***
Argos USA LLC 866 322-4547
6000 Deacon Pl Sarasota (34238) ***(G-16348)***
Argos USA LLC 352 472-4722
4000 Nw County Road 235 Newberry (32669) ***(G-11552)***
Argos USA LLC 813 962-3213
5609 N 50th St Tampa (33610) ***(G-17432)***
Argos-US LLC 407 298-1900
5109 Carder Rd Orlando (32810) ***(G-12488)***
Argotec Inc (PA) 954 491-6550
2432 Ne 27th Ave Fort Lauderdale (33305) ***(G-3821)***
Argotec Inc 407 331-9372
225 Pineda St Unit 103 Longwood (32750) ***(G-8257)***
Argus International Inc 305 888-4881
318 Indian Trce Weston (33326) ***(G-19108)***
ARI Specialties LLC 321 269-2244
3660 Us Highway 1 Mims (32754) ***(G-10949)***
Arise Prints LLC 561 371-6959
12217 Coconut Row Rd West Palm Beach (33410) ***(G-18800)***
Aristcrete Coating Experts LLC 386 882-3660
1264 Riverbreeze Blvd Ormond Beach (32176) ***(G-13349)***
Arizona Chemical, Jacksonville *Also called Kraton Chemical LLC* ***(G-6546)***
Arj Art Inc 727 535-8633
517 35th Ave N Saint Petersburg (33704) ***(G-15710)***
Arj Medical Inc 813 855-1557
209 State St E Oldsmar (34677) ***(G-12203)***
Arjay Printing Company Inc 904 764-6070
131 Burbank Rd Oldsmar (34677) ***(G-12204)***
Ark Natural Product For Pets, Tampa *Also called S&J 34102 Inc* ***(G-18077)***
Ark Woodwork Inc 561 809-7957
11184 Mohawk St Boca Raton (33428) ***(G-429)***
Arkay Distributing Inc 954 536-8413
401 E Las Olas Blvd # 1400 Fort Lauderdale (33301) ***(G-3822)***
Arkup Llc 786 448-8635
2100 Park Ave Apt 211s Miami Beach (33139) ***(G-10644)***
Arlington Prtg Stationers Inc 904 358-2928
200 N Lee St Jacksonville (32204) ***(G-6168)***
Arm Almnum Rling Mnfctures LLC 813 626-2264
2433 S 86th St Ste F Tampa (33619) ***(G-17433)***
Arma Holdings Inc 813 402-0667
3030 N Rocky Point Dr W # 800 Tampa (33607) ***(G-17434)***
Armada Systems Inc (PA) 850 664-5197
508 Mountain Dr Destin (32541) ***(G-3183)***
Armadillo Sounds Inc 305 801-7906
4246 Nw 37th Ave Miami (33142) ***(G-9169)***
Armageddon Manufacturing 772 208-5288
3170 Se Dominica Ter Stuart (34997) ***(G-16909)***
Armalaser Inc 800 680-5020
5200 Nw 43rd St Gainesville (32606) ***(G-4876)***
Armalaser Inc 954 937-6054
4699 N Federal Hwy # 110 Pompano Beach (33064) ***(G-14599)***
Armbrust Aviation Group Inc 561 355-8488
8895 N Military Trl # 201 West Palm Beach (33410) ***(G-18801)***
Armen Co Inc 305 206-1601
12140 Nw 12th St Plantation (33323) ***(G-14490)***
Armor Holdings Forensics LLC 904 485-1836
13386 International Pkwy Jacksonville (32218) ***(G-6169)***
Armor Industries Corp 813 240-5903
6703 Pemberton View Dr Seffner (33584) ***(G-16720)***
Armor Oil Products LLC 813 248-1988
1601 Mcclosky Blvd Tampa (33605) ***(G-17435)***
Armor Products Mfg Inc 813 764-8844
2610 Airport Rd Plant City (33563) ***(G-14402)***
Armor Supply Metals LLC 305 640-9901
12690 Nw South River Dr Medley (33178) ***(G-8613)***
Armored Frog Inc 850 418-2048
6404 Rambler Dr Pensacola (32505) ***(G-14091)***
Armorit Precision LLC 941 751-1292
2280 Trailmate Dr Ste 103 Sarasota (34243) ***(G-16176)***
Armorit Precison 941 751-6635
6423 Parkland Dr Sarasota (34243) ***(G-16177)***
Armour Companies LLC 386 740-7459
1370 Saratoga St Deland (32724) ***(G-2961)***
Armour Group Inc 954 767-2030
6700 Powerline Rd Fort Lauderdale (33309) ***(G-3823)***
Armoury Property & Mold Inspec 813 503-9765
18682 Fort Smith Cir Port Charlotte (33948) ***(G-14963)***
Arms, Jacksonville *Also called Alterntive Repr McHning Svcs L* ***(G-6142)***
Arms East LLC 561 293-2915
2335 63rd Ave E Ste M Bradenton (34203) ***(G-991)***
Armstrong Elevator Company 727 323-3800
9225 Ulmerton Rd Ste 318 Largo (33771) ***(G-7900)***
Armstrong Power Systems LLC (PA) 305 470-0058
5100 Nw 72nd Ave Miami (33166) ***(G-9170)***
Armstrongs Printing & Graphics (PA) 850 243-6923
30 Walter Martin Rd Ne Fort Walton Beach (32548) ***(G-4778)***
Arnet Pharmaceutical Corp 954 236-9053
2525 Davie Rd Ste 330 Davie (33317) ***(G-2499)***
Arno Belo Inc 800 734-2356
221 W Hllndale Bch Blvd P Hallandale Beach (33009) ***(G-5170)***
Arnold Industries South Inc 352 867-0190
1601 Ne 6th Ave Ocala (34470) ***(G-11879)***
Arnold Lumber Company Inc 850 547-5733
3185 Thomas Dr Bonifay (32425) ***(G-798)***
Arnold Manufacturing Inc 850 470-9200
2300 Town St Pensacola (32505) ***(G-14092)***
Arnold Mnfacturing-A M C Trlrs, Pensacola *Also called Arnold Manufacturing Inc* ***(G-14092)***
Aroma Chemicals, Jacksonville *Also called Symrise Inc* ***(G-6833)***
Aroma Coffee Service Inc 239 481-7262
2168 Andrea Ln Fort Myers (33912) ***(G-4367)***
AROMAR, Miami *Also called Mar Company Distributors LLC* ***(G-9943)***
Aromatech Flavorings Inc 407 277-5727
7001 Mccoy Rd Ste 200 Orlando (32822) ***(G-12489)***
Aromavalue Inc 866 223-7561
720 Brooker Creek Blvd # 210 Oldsmar (34677) ***(G-12205)***
Arons Towing & Recovery Inc 772 220-1151
12872 Se Suzanne Dr Hobe Sound (33455) ***(G-5722)***
Around and About Inc 954 584-1954
450 N State Road 7 Plantation (33317) ***(G-14491)***
Around House Publishing Inc 561 969-7412
5405 Okchobee Blvd # 305 West Palm Beach (33417) ***(G-18802)***
Arr-Maz Products, L.P., Mulberry *Also called Arrmaz Products Inc* ***(G-11119)***
Arriaga Originals 850 231-0084
10343 E County Highway 30 # 112 Panama City (32461) ***(G-13966)***
Arribas Bindery Services Inc 954 978-8886
6701 Nw 15th Way B Fort Lauderdale (33309) ***(G-3824)***
Arrive Alive Traffic Ctrl LLC 407 578-5431
3165 N John Young Pkwy Orlando (32804) ***(G-12490)***

ALPHABETIC

Arrmaz Products Inc (HQ).....863 578-1206
4800 State Road 60 E Mulberry (33860) ***(G-11119)***
Arrow Power Boats LLC.....772 429-8888
309 Angle Rd Fort Pierce (34947) ***(G-4678)***
Arrow Sheet Metal Works Inc.....813 247-2179
2710 N 36th St Tampa (33605) ***(G-17436)***
Arrowhead Global LLC.....727 497-7340
22033 Us Highway 19 N Clearwater (33765) ***(G-1589)***
ARS, Micanopy *Also called Analytical Research Systems* ***(G-10899)***
Arsenal Democracy LLC.....850 296-2122
48 Commerce Ln Ste 7 Freeport (32439) ***(G-4844)***
Arsenal Industries LLC.....407 506-2698
750 S Orlando Ave Ste 200 Winter Park (32789) ***(G-19380)***
Arsenal Venture Partners Fla.....407 838-1400
750 S Orlando Ave Ste 200 Winter Park (32789) ***(G-19381)***
Arsenex Inc.....407 256-3490
2229 Blossomwood Dr Oviedo (32765) ***(G-13412)***
Arso Enterprises Inc.....305 681-2020
4101 Nw 132nd St Opa Locka (33054) ***(G-12290)***
Art & Frame Direct Inc (PA).....407 857-6000
11423 Satellite Blvd Orlando (32837) ***(G-12491)***
Art & Frame Drct/Timeless Inds.....407 857-6000
11423 Satellite Blvd Orlando (32837) ***(G-12492)***
Art & Frame Source Inc (PA).....727 329-6502
4251 34th St N Saint Petersburg (33714) ***(G-15711)***
Art and Orchid Gallery, The, Jupiter *Also called Inter Cell Technologies Inc* ***(G-7058)***
Art Connection Usa LLC.....954 781-0125
2860 Center Port Cir Pompano Beach (33064) ***(G-14600)***
Art Craft Metals Inc.....954 946-4620
1630 Sw 13th Ct Pompano Beach (33069) ***(G-14601)***
Art Crete Products Inc.....386 252-5118
1231 S Ridgewood Ave Daytona Beach (32114) ***(G-2629)***
Art Edibles Inc.....407 603-4043
428 Wilmington Cir Oviedo (32765) ***(G-13413)***
Art In Print Inc (PA).....561 877-0995
8640 Valhalla Dr Delray Beach (33446) ***(G-3047)***
Art of Iron Inc.....850 819-1500
311 W 35th Ct Panama City (32405) ***(G-13865)***
Art of Printing Inc.....561 640-7344
1500 N Fl Mango Rd Ste 4 West Palm Beach (33409) ***(G-18803)***
Art On Paper LLC.....305 615-9096
9550 Sw 73rd Ave Pinecrest (33156) ***(G-14324)***
Art Printing Miami.....786 581-9889
13234 Sw 131st St Miami (33186) ***(G-9171)***
Art Sign & Neon, Fort Lauderdale *Also called Art Sign Co Inc* ***(G-3825)***
Art Sign Co Inc.....954 763-4410
835 Nw 6th Ave Fort Lauderdale (33311) ***(G-3825)***
Art Signs The, Orlando *Also called Delivery Signs LLC* ***(G-12661)***
Art Staircase & Woodwork LLC.....239 440-6591
4229 Sw 14th Pl Cape Coral (33914) ***(G-1384)***
Art Wood Cabinets Corp.....754 367-0742
1533 Sw 1st Way Deerfield Beach (33441) ***(G-2779)***
Art-Kraft Sign Co Inc.....321 727-7324
2675 Kirby Cir Ne Palm Bay (32905) ***(G-13499)***
Artco Group Inc.....305 638-1785
5851 Nw 35th Ave Miami (33142) ***(G-9172)***
Artcraft Engraving & Prtg Inc.....305 557-9449
7921 W 26th Ave Hialeah (33016) ***(G-5304)***
Artcraft Stone Inc.....239 253-6696
2806 Aintree Ln Apt H101 Naples (34112) ***(G-11168)***
Arte Bronce Monuments Inc.....305 477-0813
8600 Nw S Rver Dr Ste 109 Medley (33166) ***(G-8614)***
Artec Manufacturing LLC.....305 888-4375
699 W 17th St Hialeah (33010) ***(G-5305)***
Artec Metal Fabrication Inc.....305 888-4375
699 W 17th St Hialeah (33010) ***(G-5306)***
Arteche USA Inc.....954 438-9499
3401 Sw 160th Ave Ste 430 Miramar (33027) ***(G-10968)***
Artemis Holdings LLC (HQ).....904 284-5611
4630 County Road 209 S Green Cove Springs (32043) ***(G-5053)***
Artemis Plastics, Ocala *Also called Apollo Renal Therapeutics LLC* ***(G-11878)***
Artemisa Luxury Mill Work.....305 439-3246
10147 Nw 87th Ave Medley (33178) ***(G-8615)***
Artex Computer Llc.....407 844-2253
4737 Nw 72nd Ave Miami (33166) ***(G-9173)***
Artex Publishing Inc.....727 944-4117
3130 Westridge Dr Holiday (34691) ***(G-5734)***
Artful Arnautic Assemblies LLC.....727 522-0055
2877 47th Ave N Saint Petersburg (33714) ***(G-15712)***
Artful Canvas Design Inc.....727 521-0212
2877 47th Ave N Saint Petersburg (33714) ***(G-15713)***
Artful Signs.....239 431-7356
9520 Bonita Beach Rd Se Bonita Springs (34135) ***(G-814)***
Arthrex Inc (PA).....239 643-5553
1370 Creekside Blvd Naples (34108) ***(G-11169)***
Arthrex Manufacturing Inc.....239 304-2236
6875 Arthrex Commerce Dr Ave Maria (34142) ***(G-256)***
Arthrex Manufacturing Inc.....239 643-5553
1370 Creekside Blvd Naples (34108) ***(G-11170)***
Arthrex Trauma Inc.....239 643-5553
1370 Creekside Blvd Naples (34108) ***(G-11171)***
Arthur Cox.....772 286-5339
4800 Se Anchor Ave Stuart (34997) ***(G-16910)***
Arthur Printing, Cape Coral *Also called Detailed Services Inc* ***(G-1412)***
Artificial Turf Supply LLC (PA).....877 525-8873
830-13 A1a N 160 Ponte Vedra Beach (32082) ***(G-14934)***
Artios, Orlando *Also called Richard Bryan Ingram LLC* ***(G-13137)***
Artisan Arms Inc.....321 299-4053
2516 Jmt Industrial Dr # 105 Apopka (32703) ***(G-114)***
Artisan Tool & Die LLC.....765 288-6653
2305 72nd Ave E Sarasota (34243) ***(G-16178)***
Artisan Wood Works Inc.....239 321-9122
701 Grove Dr Naples (34120) ***(G-11172)***
Artisanis Guild.....239 591-3203
1510 Rail Head Blvd Naples (34110) ***(G-11173)***
Artistic Adventures Inc.....407 297-0557
2517 Shader Rd Unit 2 Orlando (32804) ***(G-12493)***
Artistic Columns Inc.....954 530-5537
533 Ne 33rd St Oakland Park (33334) ***(G-11780)***
Artistic Custom Coatings Inc.....941 822-5608
5606 Nutmeg Ave Sarasota (34231) ***(G-16349)***
Artistic Doors Inc.....561 582-0348
2223 2nd Ave N Lake Worth Beach (33461) ***(G-7604)***
Artistic Elements Inc.....561 750-1554
400 E Palmetto Park Rd Boca Raton (33432) ***(G-430)***
Artistic Fence Corporation.....305 805-1976
1070 Se 9th Ter Ste B Hialeah (33010) ***(G-5307)***
Artistic Gate Railing.....954 348-9752
5100 Ne 12th Ave Oakland Park (33334) ***(G-11781)***
Artistic Label Company Inc.....401 737-0666
20050 Sgrove St Unit 1703 Estero (33928) ***(G-3686)***
Artistic Paver Mfg.....305 949-0000
10111 Business Dr Miramar (33025) ***(G-10969)***
Artistic Paver Mfg Inc.....305 653-7283
120 Ne 179th St Ste 1 Miami (33162) ***(G-9174)***
Artistic Pavers.....727 572-1998
13195 49th St N Clearwater (33762) ***(G-1590)***
Artistic Pavers LLC.....727 573-0918
12700 Automobile Blvd Clearwater (33762) ***(G-1591)***
Artistic Services Kit & Bath, Wellington *Also called Marble Doctors LLC* ***(G-18724)***
Artistic Statuary Inc.....954 975-9533
1490 N Powerline Rd Pompano Beach (33069) ***(G-14602)***
Artistic Stoneworks, Fort Walton Beach *Also called Grevan Artistic Ventures Inc* ***(G-4804)***
Artistic Welding Inc.....954 563-3098
802 Ne 40th Ct Oakland Park (33334) ***(G-11782)***
Artnexus Online Inc.....305 891-7270
12500 Ne 8th Ave North Miami (33161) ***(G-11625)***
Arts Products LLC (PA).....201 984-7232
8333 Nw 53rd St Ste 450 Doral (33166) ***(G-3255)***
Arts Work Unlimited Inc.....305 247-9257
22150 Sw 154th Ave Miami (33170) ***(G-9175)***
Artscase, Doral *Also called Arts Products LLC* ***(G-3255)***
Artworks International.....561 833-9165
420 6th St West Palm Beach (33401) ***(G-18804)***
Artworks Printing Enterprises.....954 893-7984
5922 Liberty St Hollywood (33021) ***(G-5775)***
Arty-Sun LLC.....561 705-2222
9045 La Fontana Blvd Boca Raton (33434) ***(G-431)***
Aruki Services LLC.....850 364-5206
102 Sw 3rd St Havana (32333) ***(G-5232)***
Arya Group LLC.....561 792-9992
11858 Forest Hill Blvd Wellington (33414) ***(G-18709)***
ASAP Brick Pavers and More.....850 522-7123
2320 N East Ave Panama City (32405) ***(G-13866)***
ASAP Magazine & Newspaper.....813 238-0184
106 W Haya St Tampa (33603) ***(G-17437)***
ASAP Screen Printing Inc.....352 505-7574
4641 Nw 6th St Ste A Gainesville (32609) ***(G-4877)***
ASAP Signs & Graphics of Fla.....727 443-4878
509 D St Clearwater (33756) ***(G-1592)***
Asb Sports Group LLC.....305 775-4689
801 Brickell Bay Dr Miami (33131) ***(G-9176)***
Asbury Manufacturing Co LLC.....814 453-6761
3355 Entp Ave Ste 160 Fort Lauderdale (33331) ***(G-3826)***
Ascend Prfmce Mtls Oprtons LLC.....734 819-0656
200 Pensacola Beach Rd B3 Gulf Breeze (32561) ***(G-5112)***
Ascend Prfmce Mtls Oprtons LLC.....850 968-7000
3000 Old Chemstrand Rd Cantonment (32533) ***(G-1335)***
Ascendants Publishing LLC.....813 391-2745
626 Se 2nd Pl Apt 3 Gainesville (32601) ***(G-4878)***
Ascent Precision Gear Corp.....386 792-3215
12180 Se County Road 137 Jasper (32052) ***(G-6959)***
Asco Power Technologies LP.....727 450-2730
14550 58th St N Clearwater (33760) ***(G-1593)***
Asecure America Inc.....352 347-7951
10080 Se 67th Ter Belleview (34420) ***(G-367)***
Asemblu Inc.....800 827-4419
18520 Nw 67th Ave 208 Hialeah (33015) ***(G-5308)***

ASG Aerospace LLC 305 253-0802
12906 Sw 139th Ave Miami (33186) *(G-9177)*
ASG Corp 718 641-4500
5235 N Bay Rd Miami Beach (33140) *(G-10645)*
ASG Federal Inc 239 435-2200
708 Goodlette-Frank Rd N Naples (34102) *(G-11174)*
Ash Grove, Sumterville *Also called Suwannee American Cem Co LLC (G-17069)*
Ash Signs Inc 904 724-7446
2141 St Johns Bluff Rd S Jacksonville (32246) *(G-6170)*
Ashberry Acquisition Company (PA) 813 248-0055
2405 E 4th Ave Tampa (33605) *(G-17438)*
Ashberry Water Conditioning, Tampa *Also called Ashberry Acquisition Company (G-17438)*
Ashley Bryan International Inc 954 351-1199
1432 E Nwport Ctr Dr Ste Deerfield Beach (33442) *(G-2780)*
Ashley F Ward Inc 904 284-2848
3525 Enterprise Way Green Cove Springs (32043) *(G-5054)*
Ashley Ward, Green Cove Springs *Also called Ashley F Ward Inc (G-5054)*
Ashtin Inc 352 867-1900
1800 Sw College Rd Ocala (34471) *(G-11880)*
Ashton Manufacturing LLC 941 351-5529
1633 Northgate Blvd Sarasota (34234) *(G-16350)*
Ashwell Die, Pinellas Park *Also called Ashwell Label Dies Inc (G-14335)*
Ashwell Label Dies Inc 727 527-0098
6545 44th St N Ste 4003 Pinellas Park (33781) *(G-14335)*
Asi, Destin *Also called Armada Systems Inc (G-3183)*
Asi Chemical Inc 863 678-1814
1901 State Road 60 W Lake Wales (33859) *(G-7499)*
Asian Food Solutions, Oviedo *Also called International Fd Solutions Inc (G-13440)*
Asian Food Solutions Inc 888 499-6888
5600 Elmhurst Cir Oviedo (32765) *(G-13414)*
Asieei, Largo *Also called Al Stein Industries LLC (G-7889)*
Aska Communication Corp 954 708-2387
2020 Nw 129th Ave Ste 205 Miami (33182) *(G-9178)*
Asmf, Winter Park *Also called Architctral Shtmtl Fabricators (G-19379)*
Aso Corporation (HQ) 941 378-6600
300 Sarasota Center Blvd Sarasota (34240) *(G-16351)*
Aso LLC (HQ) 941 379-0300
300 Sarasota Center Blvd Sarasota (34240) *(G-16352)*
Asottu Inc 626 627-6021
1317 Edgewater Dr # 3455 Orlando (32804) *(G-12494)*
Asp Alarm & Elec Sups Inc 305 556-9047
7535 W 20th Ave Hialeah (33014) *(G-5309)*
Aspen Electronics Inc 305 863-2151
7288 Nw 54th St Miami (33166) *(G-9179)*
Aspen Products Inc 904 579-4366
1857 Inlet Cove Ct Fleming Island (32003) *(G-3759)*
Asphericon Inc 941 564-0890
2601 Cattlemen Rd Ste 301 Sarasota (34232) *(G-16353)*
Aspirations Winery, Clearwater *Also called Tampa Wines LLC (G-1905)*
Asrc Aerospace Corp 321 867-1462
Bldg M6-744 Kennedy Space Center (32899) *(G-7150)*
Assa Abloy Hospitality Inc 954 920-0772
5601 Powerline Rd Ste 305 Fort Lauderdale (33309) *(G-3827)*
Asset Guardian Inc 727 942-2246
2706 Alt 19 Ste 254 Palm Harbor (34683) *(G-13720)*
Assistrx Inc (PA) 855 421-4607
4700 Millenia Blvd # 500 Orlando (32839) *(G-12495)*
Assocate Cbinetmakers Palm Bch 561 743-9566
134 Toney Penna Dr Jupiter (33458) *(G-7001)*
Assocated Prtg Productions Inc 305 623-7600
13925 Nw 60th Ave Miami Lakes (33014) *(G-10763)*
Associated Interior Desgr Svc 561 655-4926
4300 Georgia Ave West Palm Beach (33405) *(G-18805)*
Associated Machine Company Inc 305 836-6163
6540 Nw 35th Ave Miami (33147) *(G-9180)*
Associated Materials LLC 813 621-7058
933 Chad Ln Tampa (33619) *(G-17439)*
Associated Paint Inc 305 885-1964
10160 Nw South River Dr Medley (33178) *(G-8616)*
Associated Steel & Alum Co Inc 954 974-7890
3017 Nw 25th Ave Pompano Beach (33069) *(G-14603)*
Associated Steel & Alum Ltd 954 974-7890
3017 Nw 25th Ave Pompano Beach (33069) *(G-14604)*
Assoction Hspnic Hritg Fstival 305 885-5613
3430 E 1st Ave Hialeah (33013) *(G-5310)*
Assura Windows and Doors LLC (PA) 954 781-4430
1543 N Powerline Rd Pompano Beach (33069) *(G-14605)*
Astec, Rockledge *Also called Advance Solder Technology Inc (G-15393)*
Asterion Beverages Inc 866 335-2672
3357 Nw 97th Ave Doral (33172) *(G-3256)*
Astra Products Co Inc Tampa 813 855-3021
3675 Tampa Rd Oldsmar (34677) *(G-12206)*
Astro Pure Incorporated 954 422-8966
1441 Sw 1st Way Deerfield Beach (33441) *(G-2781)*
Astro-Pure Water Purifiers, Deerfield Beach *Also called Astro Pure Incorporated (G-2781)*
Astronics Dme LLC 954 975-2100
6830 Nw 16th Ter Fort Lauderdale (33309) *(G-3828)*
Astronics Test Systems Inc 407 381-6062
12889 Ingenuity Dr Orlando (32826) *(G-12496)*

Astroted Inc 786 220-5898
3320 Nw 67th Ave Unit 980 Doral (33122) *(G-3257)*
Astrum Helicopters, Miami *Also called Astrum Travel Intl Ltd (G-9181)*
Astrum Travel Intl Ltd 917 779-9462
1 Aeropost Way 12658 Miami (33206) *(G-9181)*
Astrumsat Communications LLC 954 368-9980
1919 W 1st St Sanford (32771) *(G-15996)*
Asure Software Inc 702 733-9007
5100 W Kennedy Blvd # 300 Tampa (33609) *(G-17440)*
Asv Stone Llc 941 268-5321
6664 Duck Pond Ln Sarasota (34240) *(G-16354)*
Asysco Inc 850 383-2522
1424 Piedmont Dr E # 100 Tallahassee (32308) *(G-17224)*
At Work Uniforms 850 435-3133
2211 N Pace Blvd Pensacola (32505) *(G-14093)*
Ata Group of Companies Inc 352 735-1588
8020 Arcadian Ct Mount Dora (32757) *(G-11097)*
Atacama Resources Intl Inc (PA) 613 421-9733
1200 S Pine Island Rd Plantation (33324) *(G-14492)*
Ataly Inc 813 880-9142
5828 Johns Rd Tampa (33634) *(G-17441)*
Ataly Graphics, Tampa *Also called Ataly Inc (G-17441)*
Atco Rubber Products Inc 813 754-6678
2407 Police Center Dr Plant City (33566) *(G-14403)*
Atdsat, Miami *Also called All Things Digital Inc (G-9113)*
Ateco, Opa Locka *Also called American Thrmplastic Extrusion (G-12287)*
Ateei International Corp (PA) 305 597-6408
8284 Nw 56th St Doral (33166) *(G-3258)*
Atelier Woodworking 561 386-0811
587 105th Ave N Unit 28 Royal Palm Beach (33411) *(G-15461)*
Atg, Boca Raton *Also called Aerospace Tech Group Inc (G-406)*
Atg Specialty Products Corp 888 455-5499
1725 Nw 97th Ave Doral (33172) *(G-3259)*
Athco Inc (PA) 941 351-1600
1009 Tallevast Rd Sarasota (34243) *(G-16179)*
Athena Group, The, Gainesville *Also called Mercury Systems Inc (G-4961)*
Athletic Guide Publishing 386 439-2250
509 S Central Ave Flagler Beach (32136) *(G-3752)*
ATI, Hollywood *Also called Aircraft Technology Inc (G-5767)*
ATI, North Port *Also called Monroe Cable LLC (G-11744)*
ATI Accurate Technology 239 206-1240
1180 8th Ave W Palmetto (34221) *(G-13787)*
ATI Agency Inc 954 895-7909
123 Nw 13th St Ste 305b Boca Raton (33432) *(G-432)*
ATI By Sea Co 954 483-0526
11251 Rockinghorse Rd Hollywood (33026) *(G-5776)*
ATI Pro AV LLC 941 322-1008
3764 Lena Ln Sarasota (34240) *(G-16355)*
ATI Sales Inc 954 909-4639
351 Sw 63rd Ter Plantation (33317) *(G-14493)*
Ati2 Inc 904 396-3766
10448 Atlantic Blvd Jacksonville (32225) *(G-6171)*
Atitlan Enterprises LLC 813 362-1909
16116 Lake Magdalene Blvd Tampa (33613) *(G-17442)*
Atk Sales Corp 954 701-0465
121 S 61st Ter Ste B Hollywood (33023) *(G-5777)*
Atkins Technical Inc 860 349-3473
6911 Nw 22nd St Ste B Gainesville (32653) *(G-4879)*
Atkore International Inc 800 882-5543
1 Town Center Rd Boca Raton (33486) *(G-433)*
Atkore Plastic Pipe Corp 813 884-2525
5128 W Hanna Ave Tampa (33634) *(G-17443)*
Atlantech Process Technology 352 751-4286
1953 Lake Miona Dr Lady Lake (32162) *(G-7330)*
Atlantic Bev Group USA Inc 239 334-3016
2711 1st St Apt 102 Fort Myers (33916) *(G-4368)*
Atlantic Book Bindery, Jacksonville *Also called Knopf & Sons Bindery Inc (G-6542)*
Atlantic Candy Company 904 429-7250
115 Whetstone Pl Saint Augustine (32086) *(G-15518)*
Atlantic Cast Prcast S Fla LLC 954 564-6245
533 Ne 33rd St Oakland Park (33334) *(G-11783)*
Atlantic Central Entps Inc 386 255-6227
336 Lpga Blvd Daytona Beach (32117) *(G-2630)*
Atlantic Coast Asphalt Co 904 268-0274
10382 Florida Min Blvd E Jacksonville (32257) *(G-6172)*
Atlantic Coast Roofing & Metal 321 449-9494
350 Myrtice Ave Ste 201 Merritt Island (32953) *(G-8991)*
Atlantic Coastal Bakery, Opa Locka *Also called Kellys Bakery Corp (G-12330)*
Atlantic Concrete Products Inc 941 355-2988
1701 Myrtle St Sarasota (34234) *(G-16356)*
Atlantic Custom Woodcraft Corp 727 645-6905
11146 Challenger Ave # 101 Odessa (33556) *(G-12103)*
Atlantic Drinking Water Systms 252 255-1110
2700 Parker Ave Fort Myers (33905) *(G-4369)*
Atlantic Dry Dock 904 251-1545
8500 Heckscher Dr Jacksonville (32226) *(G-6173)*
Atlantic Dry Ice Corportion 305 592-7000
6950 Nw 12th St Miami (33126) *(G-9182)*

Atlantic Earth Materials....321 631-0600
2185 W King St Cocoa (32926) ***(G-1996)***
Atlantic Fence & Pavers LLC....386 334-6472
3311 Victory Palm Dr Edgewater (32141) ***(G-3610)***
Atlantic Gas Services LLC....386 957-3668
2948 Meleto Blvd New Smyrna Beach (32168) ***(G-11525)***
Atlantic Insulation Inc....904 354-2217
325 Dennard Ave Jacksonville (32254) ***(G-6174)***
Atlantic Intl Distrs Inc....904 725-5202
5061 Shawland Rd Ste A Jacksonville (32254) ***(G-6175)***
Atlantic Island Trading, Miami *Also called Ait USA Corp* ***(G-9098)***
Atlantic Jet Center Inc....321 255-7111
1401 Gen Avi Dr Melbourne (32935) ***(G-8771)***
Atlantic Jet Support Inc....954 360-7549
4801 Johnson Rd Ste 11 Coconut Creek (33073) ***(G-2070)***
Atlantic Marble Company Inc....904 262-6262
11303 Bus Pk Blvd Ste 100 Jacksonville (32256) ***(G-6176)***
Atlantic Marine Inc....904 251-1580
8500 Heckscher Dr Jacksonville (32226) ***(G-6177)***
Atlantic Medical Products LLC....727 535-0022
13191 Starkey Rd Ste 11 Largo (33773) ***(G-7901)***
Atlantic Mobile Imaging Svcs....386 239-8271
1400 Hand Ave Ste A Ormond Beach (32174) ***(G-13350)***
Atlantic Models Inc....305 883-2012
10631 Nw 123rd Street Rd Medley (33178) ***(G-8617)***
Atlantic Molding Inc (PA)....954 781-9340
2750 Ne 4th Ave Pompano Beach (33064) ***(G-14606)***
Atlantic Multi Family I LLC....301 233-1261
9045 Vista Way Parkland (33076) ***(G-13988)***
Atlantic Precision Inc....772 466-1011
1461 Nw Commerce Ctr Pkwy Port Saint Lucie (34986) ***(G-15089)***
Atlantic Printing Ink Company, Tampa *Also called Amrob Inc* ***(G-17424)***
Atlantic Pro-Nutrients, Orlando *Also called Xymogen Inc* ***(G-13335)***
Atlantic Publishing Group Inc (PA)....352 622-6220
1396 Ne 20th Ave Ste 300 Ocala (34470) ***(G-11881)***
Atlantic Quality Parts, Jacksonville *Also called Atlantic Intl Distrs Inc* ***(G-6175)***
Atlantic Sails Makers....305 567-1773
2801 Sw 31st Ave Ste 2a Miami (33133) ***(G-9183)***
Atlantic Ship Supply Inc....954 961-8885
2050 Sw 31st Ave Hallandale (33009) ***(G-5153)***
Atlantic Steel Inc....407 599-3822
131 Sheridan Ct Longwood (32750) ***(G-8258)***
Atlantic Steel Cnstr LLC....419 236-2200
18851 Ne 29th Ave Ste 700 Miami (33180) ***(G-9184)***
Atlantic Steel Fabricators, Sarasota *Also called Atlantic Concrete Products Inc* ***(G-16356)***
Atlantic Sugar Association....561 996-6541
26400 County Rd 880 Belle Glade (33430) ***(G-344)***
Atlantic Tactical Inc....909 923-7300
13386 International Pkwy Jacksonville (32218) ***(G-6178)***
Atlantic Tng LLC....941 355-2988
1701 Myrtle St Sarasota (34234) ***(G-16357)***
Atlantic West Molding & Mllwk....239 261-2874
4530 Arnold Ave Ste 3 Naples (34104) ***(G-11175)***
Atlantic Wire and Rigging Inc....321 633-1552
330 Williams Point Blvd A Cocoa (32927) ***(G-1997)***
Atlantis Porcelain Art Corp....305 582-8663
4241 Sw 154th Ct Miami (33185) ***(G-9185)***
Atlas Boat Works Inc....239 574-2628
2404 Andalusia Blvd Cape Coral (33909) ***(G-1385)***
Atlas Concrete Products Inc....407 277-0841
6452 E Colonial Dr Orlando (32807) ***(G-12497)***
Atlas Embroidery LLC....954 625-2411
2300 Sw 34th St Fort Lauderdale (33312) ***(G-3829)***
Atlas Embroidery & Screen Prtg, Fort Lauderdale *Also called Atlas Embroidery LLC* ***(G-3829)***
Atlas Helicopter Inc....321 696-4342
1000 S Park Ave Apt 3 Sanford (32771) ***(G-15997)***
Atlas Industrial Scales Inc....352 610-9989
3715 Commercial Way Spring Hill (34606) ***(G-16847)***
Atlas Innovative Services Inc....617 259-4529
220 Shreve St Punta Gorda (33950) ***(G-15192)***
Atlas Marine Systems Inc....954 735-6767
1801 S Perimeter Rd # 150 Fort Lauderdale (33309) ***(G-3830)***
Atlas Metal Industries Inc....305 625-2451
1135 Nw 159th Dr Miami (33169) ***(G-9186)***
Atlas Operations Inc....954 788-1200
325 Sw 15th Ave Pompano Beach (33069) ***(G-14607)***
Atlas Orgnics Indian River LLC....772 563-9336
925 74th Ave Sw Vero Beach (32968) ***(G-18595)***
Atlas Paper Mills LLC (HQ)....800 562-2860
3301 Nw 107th St Miami (33167) ***(G-9187)***
Atlas Paper Mills LLC....305 835-8046
3725 E 10th Ct Hialeah (33013) ***(G-5311)***
Atlas Peat & Soil Inc (PA)....561 734-7300
9621 S State Road 7 Boynton Beach (33472) ***(G-881)***
Atlas Polymers Corp....786 312-2131
1809 Micanopy Ave Miami (33133) ***(G-9188)***
Atlas Renewable Energy USA LLC....786 358-5614
1221 Brickell Ave # 1400 Miami (33131) ***(G-9189)***
Atlas Screen Printing, Gainesville *Also called Paul Wales Inc* ***(G-4979)***
Atlas Sign Industries Fla LLC....561 863-6659
1077 W Blue Heron Blvd Riviera Beach (33404) ***(G-15299)***
Atlas South....305 824-3900
17301 W Okeechobee Rd Hialeah (33018) ***(G-5312)***
Atlas Southeast Papers Inc....407 330-9118
3401 Saint Johns Pkwy Sanford (32771) ***(G-15998)***
Atlas Tissue A Resolute Bus, Miami *Also called Resolute Tissue LLC* ***(G-10258)***
Atlas Walls LLC....800 951-9201
10500 Rocket Ct Orlando (32824) ***(G-12498)***
Atm Pavers Inc....239 322-7010
2710 Del Prado Blvd S Cape Coral (33904) ***(G-1386)***
Atm Vault Corp....561 441-9294
2151 Nw Boca Raton Blvd Boca Raton (33431) ***(G-434)***
Atmcentral....727 345-8460
6468 5th Ave S Saint Petersburg (33707) ***(G-15714)***
Atmfla Inc (PA)....407 425-7708
4601 Sw 34th St Ste 100 Orlando (32811) ***(G-12499)***
Atmospheric Wtr Solutions Inc....954 306-6763
12260 Sw 53rd St Ste 603 Cooper City (33330) ***(G-2109)***
Atomic Machine & EDM Inc....239 353-9100
9950 Business Cir Ste 13 Naples (34112) ***(G-11176)***
Atria Industry....786 334-6621
1866 Nw 82nd Ave Doral (33126) ***(G-3260)***
Atris Technology LLC....352 331-3100
3417 Nw 97th Blvd Ste 30 Gainesville (32606) ***(G-4880)***
Atsg Logistic Support Service....904 579-4596
10142 103rd St Ste 102 Jacksonville (32210) ***(G-6179)***
Attack Communications Inc....954 300-2716
1314 E Las Olas Blvd Fort Lauderdale (33301) ***(G-3831)***
Attenti Us Inc (PA)....813 749-5454
1838 Gunn Hwy Odessa (33556) ***(G-12104)***
Attesa Holdings Group LLC....305 777-3567
2949 Coconut Ave Unit 20 Miami (33133) ***(G-9190)***
Atticus Screen Printing T....407 365-9911
159 N Central Ave Ste I Oviedo (32765) ***(G-13415)***
Attila Services Corp....305 255-6776
12250 Sw 129th Ct Ste 108 Miami (33186) ***(G-9191)***
Attilas Machine & Welding....305 947-0953
2143 Ne 161st St North Miami Beach (33162) ***(G-11668)***
Attitude Drinks Incorporated (PA)....561 227-2727
712 Us Highway 1 Ste 200 North Palm Beach (33408) ***(G-11717)***
Attraction Center Pubg LLC....814 422-5683
970 Lake Carillon Dr # 3 Saint Petersburg (33716) ***(G-15715)***
Aubrey Organics, Tampa *Also called Nutraceutical Corporation* ***(G-17943)***
Audacity Audio, Fort Lauderdale *Also called Audio Storage Technologies* ***(G-3832)***
Audina Hearing Instruments....407 331-0077
165 E Wildmere Ave Longwood (32750) ***(G-8259)***
Audio Excellence (PA)....407 277-8790
477 N Semoran Blvd Orlando (32807) ***(G-12500)***
Audio Intelligence Devices....954 418-1400
637 Jim Moran Blvd Deerfield Beach (33442) ***(G-2782)***
Audio Storage Technologies....954 229-5050
1540 Ne 60th St Fort Lauderdale (33334) ***(G-3832)***
Audio Video Imagineering Inc....305 947-6991
11853 Griffing Blvd Biscayne Park (33161) ***(G-383)***
Audioshark Inc....954 591-9252
2635 Sherman St Hollywood (33020) ***(G-5778)***
Aurafin-Oroamerica, Tamarac *Also called Richline Group Inc* ***(G-17366)***
Aurel Partners LLC....203 300-7470
7025 County Road 46a # 1071380 Lake Mary (32746) ***(G-7401)***
Aurora Semiconductor LLC....727 235-6500
9900 16th St N Saint Petersburg (33716) ***(G-15716)***
Aurora Stone & Gravel LLC....321 253-4808
2699 Aurora Rd Melbourne (32935) ***(G-8772)***
Aurum Chemicals Corp....305 412-4141
9485 Sw 72nd St Ste A190 Miami (33173) ***(G-9192)***
Aurum Enterprises LLC....561 921-5119
5601 Collins Ave Apt 515 Miami Beach (33140) ***(G-10646)***
Aus Manufacturing, Bonifay *Also called Park Central Inc* ***(G-805)***
Aus Manufacturing, Bonifay *Also called Parts Central Inc* ***(G-806)***
Ausoil International Corp (PA)....954 249-8060
4612 N Hiatus Rd Sunrise (33351) ***(G-17092)***
Aussie Boomerang Bar On Ave In....561 436-9741
621 Lake Ave Lake Worth (33460) ***(G-7535)***
Austin Powder Company....352 690-7060
5299 Ne 97th Street Rd Anthony (32617) ***(G-94)***
Austin Powder Company....863 674-0504
6051 Fort Denaud Rd Fort Denaud (33935) ***(G-3770)***
Autek Spray Booths, Palm Harbor *Also called Tk - Autek Inc* ***(G-13766)***
Autek Spray Booths....727 709-4373
6145 126th Ave Unit E Largo (33773) ***(G-7902)***
Authentic Trading Inc....347 866-7241
11107 Sw 15th Mnr Davie (33324) ***(G-2500)***
Authority Software LLC....877 603-9653
7154 N University Dr # 211 Tamarac (33321) ***(G-17351)***
Autisan International Inc....941 349-7029
612 Lotus Ln Sarasota (34242) ***(G-16358)***

Autism Puzzle ME Inc....386 314-4310
2945 Lime Tree Dr Edgewater (32141) *(G-3611)*
Auto Gard Qmi Inc....727 847-5441
5318 Lemon St New Port Richey (34652) *(G-11481)*
Auto Kare, Zellwood *Also called Goho Enterprises Inc (G-19503)*
Auto Labe, Fort Pierce *Also called Booth Manufacturing Company (G-4682)*
Auto Shopper, Lakeland *Also called Showcase Publications Inc (G-7791)*
Auto Tag of America Inc (PA)....941 739-8841
6015 31st St E Bradenton (34203) *(G-992)*
Autocraft Manufacturing Co....321 453-1850
810 Kemp St Merritt Island (32952) *(G-8992)*
Automated Accounting Assoc Inc....512 669-1000
1665 Governors Dr Pensacola (32514) *(G-14094)*
Automated Buildings Inc....407 857-0140
5520 Hansel Ave Orlando (32809) *(G-12501)*
Automated Integration, Tampa *Also called Applied Technologies Group Inc (G-17429)*
Automated Metal Products Inc....863 638-4404
16070 Hwy 27 Lake Wales (33859) *(G-7500)*
Automated Mfg Systems Inc....561 833-9898
5700 Columbia Cir Mangonia Park (33407) *(G-8498)*
Automated Paper Converters....954 925-0721
400 S Dixie Hwy Hollywood (33020) *(G-5779)*
Automated Parking Corporation....754 200-8441
6555 Nw 9th Ave Ste 106 Fort Lauderdale (33309) *(G-3833)*
Automated Printing Services....904 731-3244
7124 Glendyne Dr N Jacksonville (32216) *(G-6180)*
Automated Production Eqp Ape....631 654-1197
2 N Blackwater Ln Key Largo (33037) *(G-7164)*
Automated Production Eqp Ape....305 451-4722
2 N Blackwater Ln Key Largo (33037) *(G-7165)*
Automated Services Inc....772 461-3388
2700 Industrial Avenue 3 Fort Pierce (34946) *(G-4679)*
Automated Sonix Corporation....941 964-1361
5800 Gasparilla Rd Boca Grande (33921) *(G-391)*
Automated Vacuum Systems Inc....941 378-4565
2228b Industrial Blvd Sarasota (34234) *(G-16359)*
Automatic Business Products Co....888 742-7639
4480 Eastport Park Way Port Orange (32127) *(G-15009)*
Automatic Coax and Cable Inc....407 322-7622
4060 Saint Johns Pkwy Sanford (32771) *(G-15999)*
Automatic Mfg Systems Inc....954 791-1500
1800 Nw 69th Ave Ste 102 Plantation (33313) *(G-14494)*
Automation Consulting Inc....850 477-6477
7100 Plantation Rd Ste 17 Pensacola (32504) *(G-14095)*
Automotive Advertising Assoc....954 389-6500
1045 Woodfall Ct Weston (33326) *(G-19109)*
Automotive Armor Mfg Inc....941 721-3335
1150 13th Ave E Palmetto (34221) *(G-13788)*
Automotive Mfg & Indus PDT, Ormond Beach *Also called Florida Production Engrg Inc (G-13372)*
Automundo Magazine, Coral Gables *Also called Automundo Productions Inc (G-2124)*
Automundo Productions Inc....305 541-4198
2520 Coral Way Ste 2 Coral Gables (33145) *(G-2124)*
Autopax Inc....772 563-0131
6602 Liberty Pl Vero Beach (32966) *(G-18596)*
Avacs, Orange Park *Also called American Vly Avnics Clbrtion L (G-12381)*
Avalanche Corporation....800 708-0087
17109 Old Ayers Rd Brooksville (34604) *(G-1213)*
Avalex Technologies Corp....850 470-8464
2665 Gulf Breeze Pkwy Gulf Breeze (32563) *(G-5113)*
Avalon Aviation Inc....954 655-0256
1323 Se 17th St Unit 344 Fort Lauderdale (33316) *(G-3834)*
Avalon Sign Solutions Inc....727 398-6126
11125 Park Blvd Seminole (33772) *(G-16740)*
Avanti Nutritional Labs LLC....305 822-3880
14101 Commerce Way Miami Lakes (33016) *(G-10764)*
Avasar Corp....321 723-3456
435 West Dr Melbourne (32904) *(G-8773)*
Avatar Packaging Inc....813 888-9141
5110 W Idlewild Ave Tampa (33634) *(G-17444)*
Avaya Inc....239 498-2737
25798 Old Gaslight Dr Bonita Springs (34135) *(G-815)*
Avaya Inc....305 264-7021
1000 Nw 57th Ct Ste 100 Miami (33126) *(G-9193)*
Avborne Accesory Group LLC (HQ)....305 593-6038
7500 Nw 26th St Miami (33122) *(G-9194)*
Avborne Accessory Group Inc (HQ)....305 593-6038
7600 Nw 26th St Miami (33122) *(G-9195)*
Avc Plastics, Hialeah *Also called American Vinyl Company (G-5296)*
Avema Pharma Solutions, Miami *Also called PLD Acquisitions LLC (G-10170)*
Aventura Cookies Inc....954 447-4525
1868 Nw 140th Ter Pembroke Pines (33028) *(G-14021)*
Aventura Custom Woodwork....305 891-9093
1450 Ne 130th St North Miami (33161) *(G-11626)*
Aventura Jewelry & Coin....305 933-2646
19275 Biscayne Blvd # 22 Miami (33180) *(G-9196)*
Aventura Magazine, Miami *Also called Stern Bloom Media Inc (G-10414)*
Aveoengineering LLC....631 747-6671
1200 Cinnamon Beach Way # 1122 Palm Coast (32137) *(G-13684)*
Aveotech International, Palm Coast *Also called Aveoengineering LLC (G-13684)*
Averett Septic Tank Co Inc....863 665-1748
2610 Longhorn Ave Lakeland (33801) *(G-7640)*
Avery Dennison Corporation....305 228-8740
5200 Blue Lagoon Dr # 130 Miami (33126) *(G-9197)*
Avery Dennison Corporation....727 787-1651
720 Sandy Hook Rd Palm Harbor (34683) *(G-13721)*
Avery Dennison Corporation....727 785-6995
2706 Altmate 19 N Ste 314 Palm Harbor (34683) *(G-13722)*
Avesani Music, Cutler Bay *Also called Gladium LLC (G-2394)*
Aveva Drug Dlvry Systems Inc....954 430-3340
3250 Commerce Pkwy Miramar (33025) *(G-10970)*
AVI-Spl Emplyee Emrgncy Rlief (HQ)....813 884-7168
6301 Benjamin Rd Ste 101 Tampa (33634) *(G-17445)*
AVI-Spl Holdings Inc (PA)....866 708-5034
6301 Benjamin Rd Ste 101 Tampa (33634) *(G-17446)*
AVI-Spl LLC (HQ)....813 884-7168
6301 Benjamin Rd Ste 101 Tampa (33634) *(G-17447)*
AVI-Spl Tampa Service, Tampa *Also called AVI-Spl Emplyee Emrgncy Rlief (G-17445)*
Aviacol Usa Corp....786 701-2152
2299 Nw 108th Ave Miami (33172) *(G-9198)*
Aviall Inc....954 625-3930
3350 Davie Rd Davie (33314) *(G-2501)*
Aviation Instrument Tech Inc (PA)....813 783-3361
39520 Aviation Ave Zephyrhills (33542) *(G-19508)*
Aviation Intl Solutions LLC....305 267-7117
6043 Nw 167th St Ste A16 Hialeah (33015) *(G-5313)*
Aviation Parts & Trade Corp....954 944-2828
12331 Nw 7th St Plantation (33325) *(G-14495)*
Aviation Worldwide Svcs LLC (HQ)....321 837-2345
2301 Commerce Park Dr Ne Palm Bay (32905) *(G-13500)*
Avidyne Corporation (PA)....321 751-8520
710 North Dr Melbourne (32934) *(G-8774)*
Avionics Support Group Inc....305 378-9786
13155 Sw 132nd Ave # 200 Miami (33186) *(G-9199)*
AVK Industries Inc....904 998-8400
2052 St Johns Bluff Rd S Jacksonville (32246) *(G-6181)*
Avl Systems Inc....352 854-1170
5540 Sw 6th Pl Ocala (34474) *(G-11882)*
Avon Assoc....561 391-7188
4101 N Ocean Blvd Boca Raton (33431) *(G-435)*
Avon Cabinet Corporation....941 755-2866
5821 24th St E Bradenton (34203) *(G-993)*
Avon Company....386 405-7208
11757 Beach Blvd Ste 14 Jacksonville (32246) *(G-6182)*
Avon Corrugated/Florida Corp....305 770-3439
15600 Nw 15th Ave Miami (33169) *(G-9200)*
Avro Arms, Bradenton *Also called Arms East LLC (G-991)*
Avrora Inc....386 246-9112
7 Richfield Pl Palm Coast (32164) *(G-13685)*
Avstar Fuel Systems Inc....561 575-1560
1365 Park Ln S Jupiter (33458) *(G-7002)*
Avstar Systems LLC....239 793-5511
4025 Skyway Dr Naples (34112) *(G-11177)*
Avt Technology Solutions LLC....727 539-7429
5350 Tech Data Dr Clearwater (33760) *(G-1594)*
AVw Inc....954 972-3338
541 S State Road 7 Ste 2 Margate (33068) *(G-8536)*
Aw Gates Inc....954 341-2180
11285 Sw 1st St Coral Springs (33071) *(G-2221)*
Aw Publishing....305 856-7000
3135 Sw 3rd Ave Miami (33129) *(G-9201)*
Aw-Tronics LLC....786 228-7835
100 Biscayne Blvd # 1315 Miami (33132) *(G-9202)*
Awab LLC....954 763-3003
245 Sw 32nd St Fort Lauderdale (33315) *(G-3835)*
Awards 4u, Tallahassee *Also called A J Trophies & Awards Inc (G-17210)*
Awareness Technology Inc (PA)....772 283-6540
2325 Sw Martin Hwy Palm City (34990) *(G-13642)*
Awe Diagnostics LLC....786 285-0755
3401 N Miami Ave Ste 230 Miami (33127) *(G-9203)*
Awg, Aventura *Also called American Wire Group Inc (G-260)*
Awl Manufacturing Inc....239 643-5780
4406 Exchange Ave Ste 109 Naples (34104) *(G-11178)*
Awl Manufactuting, Bonita Springs *Also called Gulf Coast Mold & Tool Corp (G-837)*
Awnings By Coversol....813 251-4774
5211 W Hillsborough Ave Tampa (33634) *(G-17448)*
Awnings of Hollywood Inc....954 963-7717
5828 Washington St Hollywood (33023) *(G-5780)*
Aws, Doral *Also called American Welding Society Inc (G-3247)*
Axi International Corporation (PA)....239 690-9589
5400 Division Dr Ste 1 Fort Myers (33905) *(G-4370)*
Axiom Automotive Technologies....407 299-4400
4290 Seaboard Rd Orlando (32808) *(G-12502)*
Axiom Diagnostics Inc....813 902-9888
4309 W Tyson Ave Tampa (33611) *(G-17449)*
Axiom International, Clearwater *Also called Axiom Services Inc (G-1595)*
Axiom Manufacturing Inc....321 223-3394
962 Hailey St West Melbourne (32904) *(G-18766)*

Axiom Services Inc 727 442-7774
1805 Drew St Clearwater (33765) *(G-1595)*
Axis, Orlando *Also called Advanced Xrgrphics Imging Syst* *(G-12434)*
Axis Group 954 580-6000
4701 N Federal Hwy # 440 Pompano Beach (33064) *(G-14608)*
Axis Phrm Partners LLC 407 936-2949
550 Technology Park Lake Mary (32746) *(G-7402)*
Axogen Inc (PA) 386 462-6800
13631 Progress Blvd # 400 Alachua (32615) *(G-6)*
Axogen Corporation 386 462-6800
13631 Progress Blvd # 400 Alachua (32615) *(G-7)*
Axon Circuit Inc 407 265-7980
155 National Pl Unit 105 Longwood (32750) *(G-8260)*
Axon Circuit Inc (PA) 407 265-7980
424 S Ware Blvd Ste A Tampa (33619) *(G-17450)*
Axrdham Corp 813 653-9588
2134 Ridgemore Dr Valrico (33594) *(G-18515)*
Axtonne Inc 510 755-7480
350 Se 1st St Delray Beach (33483) *(G-3048)*
Axxionflex, Coral Gables *Also called Ibd Industrial LLC* *(G-2156)*
Axxium Engineering LLC 786 573-9808
14032 Sw 140th St 16 Miami (33186) *(G-9204)*
Axzes LLC 786 626-1611
3401 Nw 82nd Ave Ste 370 Doral (33122) *(G-3261)*
Ayam Beautycare LLC 305 318-2598
19495 Biscayne Blvd # 608 Aventura (33180) *(G-262)*
Ayanna Plastics & Engrg Inc 727 561-4329
4701 110th Ave N Clearwater (33762) *(G-1596)*
Ayers Office Supply, Trenton *Also called Ayers Publishing Inc* *(G-18480)*
Ayers Publishing Inc 352 463-7135
207 N Main St Trenton (32693) *(G-18480)*
Ayon Cybersecurity Inc 321 953-3033
5155 King St Cocoa (32926) *(G-1998)*
Ayurdevas Natural Products LLC 786 322-0909
2076 Nw 21st St Miami (33142) *(G-9205)*
AZ Chem Holdings LP 800 526-5294
4600 Touchton Rd E # 1200 Jacksonville (32246) *(G-6183)*
Azar & Company, Jacksonville *Also called Azar Industries Inc* *(G-6184)*
Azar Industries Inc 904 358-2354
719 E Union St Jacksonville (32206) *(G-6184)*
Azcue Pumps USA Inc 954 597-7602
10308 W Mcnab Rd Tamarac (33321) *(G-17352)*
Azex Flow Technologies Inc 305 393-8037
13431 Nw 19th Ln Miami (33182) *(G-9206)*
Azopharma Inc 954 536-4738
6137 Sw 19th St Miramar (33023) *(G-10971)*
Azt Technology LLC 239 352-0600
10130 Market St Ste 7 Naples (34112) *(G-11179)*
Aztlan Foods Corp 786 202-8301
9110 Nw 106th St Medley (33178) *(G-8618)*
Azul Stone LLC 561 655-9385
920 Fern St West Palm Beach (33401) *(G-18806)*
Azure Computing Inc 407 359-8787
5700 Dot Com Ct Ste 1010 Oviedo (32765) *(G-13416)*
Azurrx, Boca Raton *Also called First Wave Biopharma Inc* *(G-529)*
Azz Powder Coating - Tampa LLC (HQ) 813 390-2802
4901 Distribution Dr Tampa (33605) *(G-17451)*
B & A Manufacturing Co 561 848-8648
3665 E Industrial Way Riviera Beach (33404) *(G-15300)*
B & B Bons LLC 954 940-4900
401 E Las Olas Blvd Fl 8 Fort Lauderdale (33301) *(G-3836)*
B & B Industries of Orlando 407 366-1800
3008 Kananwood Ct Ste 124 Oviedo (32765) *(G-13417)*
B & B of Saint Augustine Inc 904 829-6855
2875 Us Highway 1 S Saint Augustine (32086) *(G-15519)*
B & B Timber Company 904 284-5541
4880 Highway 17 S Green Cove Springs (32043) *(G-5055)*
B & B Trailers and Accessories, Saint Augustine *Also called B & B of Saint Augustine Inc* *(G-15519)*
B & B Trailers and Accessories 904 829-6855
2875 Us Highway 1 S Saint Augustine (32086) *(G-15520)*
B & D Machine and Tool Inc 321 727-0098
1720 Main St Ne Ste 3 Palm Bay (32905) *(G-13501)*
B & D Precision Tools Inc 305 885-1583
2367 W 8th Ln Hialeah (33010) *(G-5314)*
B & E Rv Service & Repair LLC 352 401-7930
6028 Ne 26th Ave Ocala (34479) *(G-11883)*
B & F Waste Solutions Llc 772 336-1113
4901 Bethel Creek Dr F Vero Beach (32963) *(G-18597)*
B & G Instruments Inc 305 871-4445
5000 Nw 36th St Bldg 875 Miami (33166) *(G-9207)*
B & I Generators LLC 407 474-6216
2100 S Park Ave Sanford (32771) *(G-16000)*
B & J Atlantic Inc 904 338-0088
5164 Shawland Rd Jacksonville (32254) *(G-6185)*
B & K Discount Cabinets LLC (PA) 321 254-2322
280 N Wickham Rd Melbourne (32935) *(G-8775)*
B & K Installations Inc 305 245-6968
246 Sw 4th Ave Homestead (33030) *(G-5956)*
B & L Cremation Systems Inc 727 541-4666
7205 114th Ave Ste A Largo (33773) *(G-7903)*
B & M Industries Inc 813 754-9960
2401 Airport Rd Plant City (33563) *(G-14404)*
B & M Precision Inc 813 645-1188
1225 4th St Sw Ruskin (33570) *(G-15481)*
B & N Wldg & Fabrication Inc 813 719-3956
4200 National Guard Dr Plant City (33563) *(G-14405)*
B & P Motor Heads Inc 305 769-3183
1815 Opa Locka Blvd Opa Locka (33054) *(G-12291)*
B & P Motors Inc 305 687-7337
1815 Opa Locka Blvd Opa Locka (33054) *(G-12292)*
B & R Products Inc (PA) 305 238-1592
18721 Sw 104th Ave Cutler Bay (33157) *(G-2386)*
B & R Profiles LLC (PA) 305 479-8308
216 Homeland Cemetery Rd Bartow (33830) *(G-306)*
B & R Sales Corporation 727 571-2231
11551 43rd St N Clearwater (33762) *(G-1597)*
B & T Metalworks Inc 352 236-6000
4630 Ne 35th St Ocala (34479) *(G-11884)*
B & T Pallets Inc 941 360-0562
7952 Fruitville Rd Sarasota (34240) *(G-16360)*
B and B Roof and Floor Trusses 850 265-4119
1808 Tennessee Ave Lynn Haven (32444) *(G-8429)*
B and M Sugar Products LLC 305 897-8427
936 Sw 1st Ave 345 Miami (33130) *(G-9208)*
B B J Environmental Solutions, Tampa *Also called Bbj Environmental LLC* *(G-17461)*
B C Cabinetry 561 393-8937
10625 Mendocino Ln Boca Raton (33428) *(G-436)*
B C T, Fort Lauderdale *Also called Business Cards Tomorrow Inc* *(G-3877)*
B C T, Fort Lauderdale *Also called BCT International Inc* *(G-3844)*
B D D International Corp 305 573-2416
203 Nw 36th St Ste 2 Miami (33127) *(G-9209)*
B E Aerospace 305 459-7000
9100 Nw 105th Cir Medley (33178) *(G-8619)*
B E Pressure Supply Inc 561 688-9246
5483 Leaper Dr West Palm Beach (33407) *(G-18807)*
B F E, Jacksonville *Also called Brake-Funderburk Entps Inc* *(G-6230)*
B F Industries Inc 561 368-6662
4201 Oak Cir Ste 29 Boca Raton (33431) *(G-437)*
B Finch Logging, Wausau *Also called Bernice I Finch* *(G-18696)*
B G Cabinets Llc 941 485-0040
177 S Jackson Rd Venice (34292) *(G-18534)*
B G Instrument Corp 941 485-7700
112 Morse Ct North Venice (34275) *(G-11753)*
B G Service Company Inc 561 659-1471
1400 Alabama Ave Ste 15 West Palm Beach (33401) *(G-18808)*
B H Bunn Company 863 647-1555
2730 Drane Field Rd Lakeland (33811) *(G-7641)*
B H Med Supplies, Miami *Also called Frozen Wheels LLC* *(G-9601)*
B J and ME Inc 561 368-5470
2284 N Dixie Hwy Fl 1 Boca Raton (33431) *(G-438)*
B Line Apparel Inc 305 953-8300
4671 E 11th Ave Hialeah (33013) *(G-5315)*
B M H Concrete Inc 561 615-0011
6811 Belvedere Rd West Palm Beach (33413) *(G-18809)*
B M I Properties, Jacksonville *Also called Florida Floats Inc* *(G-6398)*
B O C Industrial Gases Div, Orlando *Also called Messer LLC* *(G-12961)*
B P I, Miami *Also called Brain Power Incorporated* *(G-9273)*
B R Express 904 881-2556
221 Arlington Rd N Jacksonville (32211) *(G-6186)*
B R Q Grossmans Inc 954 971-1077
2087 N Powerline Rd Ste 1 Pompano Beach (33069) *(G-14609)*
B R Signs Inc 954 973-7700
1301 W Copans Rd Ste B6 Pompano Beach (33064) *(G-14610)*
B Squared of Chiefland LLC 352 507-2195
710 Nw 17th Ave Chiefland (32626) *(G-1532)*
B T G, Alachua *Also called Back To Godhead Inc* *(G-8)*
B T I, West Palm Beach *Also called Setty Enterprises Inc* *(G-19028)*
B V M, Winter Springs *Also called Bob Violett Models Inc* *(G-19469)*
B&B Custom Sheet Metal Inc 727 938-8083
770 N Grosse Ave Ste B Tarpon Springs (34689) *(G-18283)*
B&C Publishing Inc 305 385-8216
13010 N Calusa Club Dr Miami (33186) *(G-9210)*
B&C Sheet Metal Duct Corp 305 316-9212
1025 Sw 82nd Ave Miami (33144) *(G-9211)*
B&C Signs 386 426-2373
2525 Guava Dr Edgewater (32141) *(G-3612)*
B&K Country Feeds LLC 561 701-1852
912 Jamaican Dr West Palm Beach (33415) *(G-18810)*
B&M, Miami *Also called B and M Sugar Products LLC* *(G-9208)*
B&M Logging Inc 386 397-1145
10616 Se County Road 135 White Springs (32096) *(G-19185)*
B&M RC Racing 313 518-3999
4336 Shadow Wood Way Winter Haven (33880) *(G-19301)*
B-N-J Powder Coatings LLC 407 999-8448
111 W Pineloch Ave Ste 2 Orlando (32806) *(G-12503)*

B-Scada Inc (PA)......352 564-9610
9030 W Fort Island Trl 9a Crystal River (34429) *(G-2370)*
B/E Aerospace Inc (HQ)......410 266-2048
1400 Corporate Center Way Wellington (33414) *(G-18710)*
B/E Aerospace Inc......305 471-8800
9835 Nw 14th St Doral (33172) *(G-3262)*
B2 Integrations LLC......727 871-7025
5315 105th Ter E Parrish (34219) *(G-14004)*
B224 USA Co......786 598-8805
2508 Baywood Dr Holiday (34690) *(G-5735)*
B2b Printing Corp......312 953-7446
241 Curacau Dr Cocoa Beach (32931) *(G-2058)*
B2b Sign Resource......813 855-7446
13359 W Hillsborough Ave Tampa (33635) *(G-17452)*
B4c Technologies Inc......772 463-1557
4306 Sw Cargo Way Palm City (34990) *(G-13643)*
Ba Precision Products Corp......561 859-3400
2920 Nw 2nd Ave Ste 3 Boca Raton (33431) *(G-439)*
Baa LLC......954 292-9449
16482 Sw 18th St Miramar (33027) *(G-10972)*
Babbala LLC......844 869-5747
2901 Clint Moore Rd Boca Raton (33496) *(G-440)*
Babicakes LLC......561 507-0331
1279 Summit Run Cir West Palm Beach (33415) *(G-18811)*
Baby Abuelita Productions LLC......305 662-7320
6619 S Dixie Hwy Ste 139 Miami (33143) *(G-9212)*
Baby Beef USA, Miami *Also called Latin Amercn Meats & Foods USA (G-9867)*
Baby Food Chef LLC......305 335-5990
2905 W Aviary Dr Hollywood (33026) *(G-5781)*
Baby Guard Inc......954 741-6351
11947 W Sample Rd Coral Springs (33065) *(G-2222)*
Baby Guard Pool Fence Co, Coral Springs *Also called Baby Guard Inc (G-2222)*
Babys Coffee LLC......305 744-9866
3178 Us Highway 1 Key West (33040) *(G-7178)*
Bacardi Bottling Corporation......904 757-1290
12200 N Main St Jacksonville (32218) *(G-6187)*
Bacc Coatings LLC......239 424-8843
926 Se 9th St Cape Coral (33990) *(G-1387)*
Bach Diamonds......954 921-4069
2910 Oakwood Blvd Hollywood (33020) *(G-5782)*
Bach Sign Group Inc......561 848-3440
2289 Carambola Rd West Palm Beach (33406) *(G-18812)*
Bach Woodworking LLC......651 329-1220
11170 Sunset Ridge Cir Boynton Beach (33473) *(G-882)*
Bachiller Iron Works Inc......305 751-7773
295 Ne 71st St Miami (33138) *(G-9213)*
Baci By Remcraft, Opa Locka *Also called Remcraft Lighting Products Inc (G-12353)*
Back Lory Lee......850 638-5430
403 Cutchins Mill Rd Chipley (32428) *(G-1541)*
Back Country Inc......772 532-6174
636 34th Ter Vero Beach (32968) *(G-18598)*
Back To Godhead Inc......386 462-0481
13921 Nw 146th Ave Alachua (32615) *(G-8)*
Backbone Interconnect LLC......954 800-4749
10501 Nw 50th St 104-3 Sunrise (33351) *(G-17093)*
Backoff Products, Fort Lauderdale *Also called Signal Dynamics Corporation (G-4233)*
Backstage Software Inc......407 925-8751
2582 Maguire Rd Pmb 2 Ocoee (34761) *(G-12084)*
Backtocad Technologies LLC......727 303-0383
601 Cleveland St Ste 380 Clearwater (33755) *(G-1598)*
Backwoods Crossing Llc......850 765-3753
6725 Mahan Dr Tallahassee (32308) *(G-17225)*
Backyard Canvas & Signs Inc......813 672-2660
11225 Restwood Dr Gibsonton (33534) *(G-5026)*
Backyard Feed LLC......813 846-5995
6400 County Road 214 Saint Augustine (32092) *(G-15521)*
Bad Fish Powder Coat......904 465-8888
2071 Emerson St Jacksonville (32207) *(G-6188)*
Badaro Group, Clearwater *Also called Pelican International Inc (G-1829)*
Bader Prosthetics & Orthotics......813 962-6100
5513 W Sligh Ave Tampa (33634) *(G-17453)*
Badger Corporation......954 942-5277
3450 Ne 6th Ter Pompano Beach (33064) *(G-14611)*
Badger Welding Orlando LLC......407 648-1100
806 W Landstreet Rd Orlando (32824) *(G-12504)*
Bae Systems Info & Elec Sys......813 979-4392
12906 Tampa Oaks Blvd # 101 Temple Terrace (33637) *(G-18366)*
Bae Systems Sthast Shpyrds Amh (HQ)......904 251-3111
8500 Heckscher Dr Jacksonville (32226) *(G-6189)*
Bae Systems Tech Sltons Svcs I......850 244-6433
715 Hollywood Blvd Nw Fort Walton Beach (32548) *(G-4779)*
Bae Systems Tech Sltons Svcs I......850 344-0832
70 Ready Ave Nw Fort Walton Beach (32548) *(G-4780)*
Bae Systems Tech Sol Srvc Inc......850 664-6070
557 Mary Esthr Cut Off Nw Fort Walton Beach (32548) *(G-4781)*
Bae Systems Tech Sol Srvc Inc......904 241-1631
2292 Mayport Rd Jacksonville (32233) *(G-6190)*
Bae Systems Tech Sol Srvc Inc......850 236-2428
600 Grand Panama Blvd Panama City Beach (32407) *(G-13971)*

Baer Family Woodworking......954 297-2991
5815 Buchanan St Hollywood (33021) *(G-5783)*
Baez Enterprises Corp......813 317-7277
6315 Morning Star Dr Seffner (33584) *(G-16721)*
Bag of Ice, Lake City *Also called Optima Associates Inc (G-7374)*
Bag-A-Nut LLC......904 641-3934
10601 Theresa Dr Jacksonville (32246) *(G-6191)*
Bageland, Pompano Beach *Also called OPelle Enterprises Inc (G-14780)*
Bagindd Prints......954 971-9000
1843 Nw 83rd Dr Coral Springs (33071) *(G-2223)*
Bags Express Inc......305 500-9849
1555 Nw 97th Ave Doral (33172) *(G-3263)*
Bags Unlimited Inc......985 868-3393
9805 Nw 55th St Chiefland (32626) *(G-1533)*
Bahama Boat Works LLC......561 882-4069
5490 Dexter Way Mangonia Park (33407) *(G-8499)*
Bahamas Uphl & Mar Canvas Inc......305 992-4346
4782 Sw 75th Ave Miami (33155) *(G-9214)*
Bailey Industries......352 326-2898
2414 S Gelman Pl Tampa (33619) *(G-17454)*
Bailey Industries Inc (PA)......352 326-2898
1107 Thomas Ave Leesburg (34748) *(G-8144)*
Bailey Sigler Inc......386 428-5566
1050 Fremont St New Smyrna Beach (32168) *(G-11526)*
Bailey Timber Co Inc......850 674-2080
19872 State Road 20 W # 2 Blountstown (32424) *(G-384)*
Baird, West Palm Beach *Also called Thermo Arl US Inc (G-19060)*
Bajio Inc......630 461-0915
1674 Tionia Rd New Smyrna Beach (32168) *(G-11527)*
Baju Professional Brick Pavers......727 234-5300
5511 110th Ave N Pinellas Park (33782) *(G-14336)*
Baker County Press Inc......904 259-2400
104 S 5th St Macclenny (32063) *(G-8442)*
Baker Metal Works & Supply LLC (PA)......850 537-2010
5846 Highway 189 N Baker (32531) *(G-300)*
Baker Metalworks and Sup Inc......850 537-2010
5846 Highway 189 N Baker (32531) *(G-301)*
Baker Norton US Inc......305 575-6000
74 Nw 176th St Miami (33169) *(G-9215)*
Baker's Sporting Goods, Jacksonville *Also called Bakers Sports Inc (G-6192)*
Baker-Hill Industries Inc......954 752-3090
3850 Nw 118th Ave Coral Springs (33065) *(G-2224)*
Bakerly LLC (HQ)......305 608-4479
2600 S Douglas Rd Ste 410 Coral Gables (33134) *(G-2125)*
Bakers Sports Inc (PA)......904 388-8126
3600 Beachwood Ct Jacksonville (32224) *(G-6192)*
Bala Industries LLC (PA)......954 243-9804
7528 Locksley Ln Lakeland (33809) *(G-7642)*
Balistic 2400 LLC......407 955-0065
2338 Immokalee Rd Ste 177 Naples (34110) *(G-11180)*
Balkan Industries LLC (PA)......727 485-3357
7100 Maclura Dr New Port Richey (34653) *(G-11482)*
Ball Busines Products, Port Saint Lucie *Also called Discount Distributors Inc (G-15102)*
Balla De Rodriguez Migdalia M......305 228-6566
14493 Sw 27th St Miami (33175) *(G-9216)*
Ballard Printing Inc......904 783-4430
1233 Lane Ave S Ste 11 Jacksonville (32205) *(G-6193)*
Ballista Tactical Systems......954 260-0765
2881 E Oakland Park Blvd Fort Lauderdale (33306) *(G-3837)*
Ballistic Recovery Systems Inc......651 457-7491
1543 N Powerline Rd # 3 Pompano Beach (33069) *(G-14612)*
Balls Rod & Kustom LLC......888 446-2191
5118 Nw 24th Dr Gainesville (32605) *(G-4881)*
Balpack Incorporated......941 371-7323
5438 Ashton Ct Sarasota (34233) *(G-16361)*
Balpro Powder Coating Inc......954 797-0520
1624 Nw 38th Ave Fort Lauderdale (33311) *(G-3838)*
Balsys Technology Group Inc......407 656-3719
930 Carter Rd Ste 228 Winter Garden (34787) *(G-19253)*
Balzarano John......239 455-1231
781 14th St Se Naples (34117) *(G-11181)*
Bam Building and More, Lake City *Also called Grays Portable Buildings Inc (G-7356)*
Bam Core, Ocala *Also called Global Bamboo Technologies Inc (G-11956)*
Bam Enterprises Inc......850 469-8872
2906 N Davis Hwy Pensacola (32503) *(G-14096)*
Bam Industries Inc......561 674-2185
250 Nw 46th St Boca Raton (33431) *(G-441)*
Bama Printing LLC......561 855-7641
2257 Vista Pkwy Ste 11 West Palm Beach (33411) *(G-18813)*
Bamm Manufacturing Inc......239 277-0776
1222 Hemingway Dr Fort Myers (33912) *(G-4371)*
Banaghan Wood Products Inc......386 788-6114
741 Tarry Town Trl Port Orange (32127) *(G-15010)*
Banana Bag Solutions LLC......321 917-4334
450 Sherwood Ave Satellite Beach (32937) *(G-16648)*
Banaszak Concrete Corp......954 476-1004
2401 College Ave Davie (33317) *(G-2502)*
Bandart Enterprises Inc......954 564-1224
5303 Nw 35th Ter Fort Lauderdale (33309) *(G-3839)*

ALPHABETIC

Banker Steel South LLC......407 293-0120
6635 Edgewater Dr Orlando (32810) *(G-12505)*
Bankingly Inc......734 201-0007
1942 Ne 148th St North Miami (33181) *(G-11627)*
Banks Airconditioning & Rfrgn......813 917-8685
5001 Miley Rd Plant City (33565) *(G-14406)*
Banks Sails, Miami *Also called Delisser Enterprises Inc (G-9449)*
Banks Sign Systems Inc......954 979-0055
1791 Blount Rd Ste 1001 Pompano Beach (33069) *(G-14613)*
Banks, Roy Sign Systems, Pompano Beach *Also called Banks Sign Systems Inc (G-14613)*
Banners & Signs, Orange Park *Also called Banners-N-Signs Etc Inc (G-12382)*
Banners-N-Signs Etc Inc......904 272-3395
1970 Solomon St Orange Park (32073) *(G-12382)*
Banyan Biomarkers Inc (PA)......760 710-0460
132 Nw 76th Dr Ste B Gainesville (32607) *(G-4882)*
Banyan Gaming LLC......954 951-7094
245 Ne 21st Ave Ste 300 Deerfield Beach (33441) *(G-2783)*
Banyan Hill......561 455-9045
98 Se 6th Ave Ste 2 Delray Beach (33483) *(G-3049)*
Banyan Printing, Lake Worth *Also called Midds Inc (G-7571)*
Banyan Printing, Lake Worth Beach *Also called Midds Inc (G-7615)*
Baptist Communications Mission (HQ)......954 981-2271
3400 Raleigh St Hollywood (33021) *(G-5784)*
Baptist Mid-Missions Inc......863 382-6350
3417 Kenilworth Blvd Sebring (33870) *(G-16682)*
Bar Beverage Ctrl Systems Fla......239 213-3301
3427 Exchange Ave Ste 7 Naples (34104) *(G-11182)*
Bar Maid Corporation (PA)......954 960-1468
2950 Nw 22nd Ter Pompano Beach (33069) *(G-14614)*
Barbecue Superstore......305 635-4427
3800 Nw 59th St Miami (33142) *(G-9217)*
Barber Fertilizer Company......850 263-6324
5221 Highway 231 Campbellton (32426) *(G-1330)*
Barbes Publishing Inc......904 992-9945
13500 Sutton Park Dr S # 105 Jacksonville (32224) *(G-6194)*
Barcelona Dr Phillips LLC......407 352-9733
7600 Dr Phillips Blvd Orlando (32819) *(G-12506)*
Barclays Business Center LLC......786 260-0080
555 Ne 15th St Ste 200 Miami (33132) *(G-9218)*
Barco LLC......305 677-9600
475 Brickell Ave Miami (33131) *(G-9219)*
Barco Sales & Mfg Inc......954 563-3922
4201 Ne 6th Ave Oakland Park (33334) *(G-11784)*
Barcode Automation Inc......407 327-2177
207 N Moss Rd Ste 105 Winter Springs (32708) *(G-19468)*
Barcode Distributor, Miami *Also called Logiscenter LLC (G-9905)*
Bard Sports Corp (PA)......305 233-2200
14516 Sw 119th Ave Miami (33186) *(G-9220)*
Bare Arii LLC......352 701-6625
10610 N 30th St Apt 13g Tampa (33612) *(G-17455)*
Bare Board Group Inc (PA)......727 549-2200
8565 Somerset Dr Ste B Largo (33773) *(G-7904)*
Bari Millwork & Supply LLC......954 969-9440
1975 Nw 18th St Ste C Pompano Beach (33069) *(G-14615)*
Barjo Printing and Sign......786 332-2661
7911 Nw 72nd Ave Medley (33166) *(G-8620)*
Barjor Baking Group LLC......239 325-8591
6215 Taylor Rd Naples (34109) *(G-11183)*
Barker Boatworks LLC......941 233-8640
7910 25th Ct E Unit 115 Sarasota (34243) *(G-16180)*
Barnard Nut Company Inc......305 836-9999
2801 Nw 125th St Miami (33167) *(G-9221)*
Barnes & Sons Wood Producers......386 935-2229
105 Suwannee Ave Nw Branford (32008) *(G-1185)*
Barnes Group Inc......941 255-0978
12144 Sw Egret Cir Apt 13 Lake Suzy (34269) *(G-7496)*
Barnett & Pugliano Inc......727 826-6075
200 2nd Ave S Saint Petersburg (33701) *(G-15717)*
Baron LLC......239 691-5783
4784 Skates Cir Fort Myers (33905) *(G-4372)*
Baron International LLC......800 531-9558
17180 Innovation Dr Jupiter (33478) *(G-7003)*
Baron Manufacturing, Pompano Beach *Also called N & N Investment Corporation (G-14770)*
Baron Pavers Corp......786 389-2894
3281 Nw 18th St Miami (33125) *(G-9222)*
Baron Sign Manufacturing, Jupiter *Also called Baron International LLC (G-7003)*
Barr Systems LLC......352 491-3100
6241 Nw 23rd St Ste 401 Gainesville (32653) *(G-4883)*
Barrau & Coirin Inc......305 571-5051
250 Ne 61st St Miami (33137) *(G-9223)*
Barreiro Concrete Mtls Inc......305 805-0095
25440 Sw 140th Ave Princeton (33032) *(G-15182)*
Barrett & Company......305 293-4501
3201 Flagler Ave Ste 501 Key West (33040) *(G-7179)*
Barrett Custom Designs LLC......321 242-2002
6430 Anderson Way Ste A Melbourne (32940) *(G-8776)*
Barron Boyz Auto......229 403-2656
1324 Fairway Village Dr Fleming Island (32003) *(G-3760)*
Barrows Aluminum Inc......386 767-3445
630 Oak Pl Ste H Port Orange (32127) *(G-15011)*
Barrs Equipment Service Inc......407 999-5214
2506 Taylor Ave Orlando (32806) *(G-12507)*
Barry Resnick......407 296-9999
480 27th St Orlando (32806) *(G-12508)*
Barstool Comforts LLC......610 737-5856
623 Front St Apt 5305 Kissimmee (34747) *(G-7220)*
Barth Industries......727 787-6392
1701 Hickory Gate Dr S Dunedin (34698) *(G-3569)*
Bartman Enterprises Inc......321 259-4898
2735 Center Pl Ste 101 Melbourne (32940) *(G-8777)*
Barton & Guestier Usa Inc......305 895-9757
4700 Biscayne Blvd # 503 Miami (33137) *(G-9224)*
Bartow Ethanol Florida LC......863 533-2498
1705 E Mann Rd Bartow (33830) *(G-307)*
Bartow Machine Works Inc......863 533-6361
441 W Vine St Bartow (33830) *(G-308)*
Baru Agency Incorporated......305 259-8800
8400 Nw 36th St Ste 450 Doral (33166) *(G-3264)*
Bas Plastics Inc......954 202-9080
1000 Nw 56th St Fort Lauderdale (33309) *(G-3840)*
Basanite Industries LLC......954 532-1726
2041 Nw 15th Ave Pompano Beach (33069) *(G-14616)*
Baseball Digest, Orlando *Also called Grandstand Publishing LLC (G-12787)*
Basecrete Technologies LLC......941 312-5142
7969 Moyer Ave Sarasota (34240) *(G-16362)*
Basewest Inc......727 573-2700
4240 116th Ter N Clearwater (33762) *(G-1599)*
Bashers RC Raceway LLC......561 889-9386
155 Galicia Way Apt 103 Jupiter (33458) *(G-7004)*
Bashert Diamonds Inc......305 466-1881
3201 Ne 183rd St Apt 408 Aventura (33160) *(G-263)*
Basic Elements LLC......386 673-3100
300 N Nova Rd Ormond Beach (32174) *(G-13351)*
Basic Fun Inc (PA)......561 997-8901
301 E Yamato Rd Ste 4200 Boca Raton (33431) *(G-442)*
Basic Industries Global LLC......850 622-5924
108 Woodward Dr Santa Rosa Beach (32459) *(G-16152)*
Bass Auto Industries LLC......727 446-4051
2084 Range Rd Clearwater (33765) *(G-1600)*
Bass Bulletin and Directory, Hialeah *Also called Bass Industries Inc (G-5316)*
Bass Industries Inc......305 751-2716
604 W 18th St Hialeah (33010) *(G-5316)*
Bastech Inc......904 737-1722
3211 Powers Ave Jacksonville (32207) *(G-6195)*
Bastech LLC......904 737-1722
3035 Powers Ave Ste 3 Jacksonville (32207) *(G-6196)*
Bastinelli Creations LLC......407 572-8073
109 Hangar Rd Kissimmee (34741) *(G-7221)*
Batech Inc......321 784-4838
760 Mullet Rd Cape Canaveral (32920) *(G-1351)*
Bateh Networking Solutions LLC......904 725-2282
1107 Montego Rd W Jacksonville (32216) *(G-6197)*
Bath Junkie of Gainesville......352 331-3012
7529 Nw 136th St Gainesville (32653) *(G-4884)*
Bathroom World Manufacturing......954 566-0451
4160 Ne 6th Ave Oakland Park (33334) *(G-11785)*
Batista Cabinets Inc......407 922-3459
2747 Portchester Ct Kissimmee (34744) *(G-7222)*
Batter Co. Dessert Collection, Sanford *Also called Batter To Platter LLC (G-16001)*
Batter To Platter LLC......203 309-7632
2660 Jewett Ln Sanford (32771) *(G-16001)*
Batteries Plus, Lake Park *Also called Palm Beach Btry Ventures LLC (G-7477)*
Battery Assemblers, Sanford *Also called Mathews Associates Inc (G-16082)*
Battery On The Go, Coconut Creek *Also called JW Marketing and Consulting (G-2086)*
Battery Power Solutions Inc......727 446-8400
936 Cleveland St Ste A Clearwater (33755) *(G-1601)*
Battery Savers, Riviera Beach *Also called David S Stoyka (G-15319)*
Battery Usa Inc (PA)......863 665-6317
1840 S Combee Rd Lakeland (33801) *(G-7643)*
Battery Usa Inc......863 665-5401
1930 S Combee Rd Lakeland (33801) *(G-7644)*
Bauducco Manufacturing Inc......305 477-9270
1705 Nw 133rd Ave Ste 101 Miami (33182) *(G-9225)*
Bauducco USA Holding Company (HQ)......305 477-9270
1705 Nw 133rd Ave Ste 101 Miami (33182) *(G-9226)*
Bauer Compressors Inc......757 855-6006
10052 Nw 53rd St Sunrise (33351) *(G-17094)*
Bauformat South-East LLC......201 693-6635
1511 E Las Olas Blvd Fort Lauderdale (33301) *(G-3841)*
Bausch American Towers LLC......772 283-2771
6800 Sw Jack James Dr # 3 Stuart (34997) *(G-16911)*
Bausch Enterprises Inc......772 220-6652
3171 Se Waaler St Stuart (34997) *(G-16912)*
Bausch Lomb Surgical Inc......727 724-6600
21 N Park Place Blvd Clearwater (33759) *(G-1602)*
Bava Inc......850 893-4799
1403 Maclay Commerce Dr Tallahassee (32312) *(G-17226)*

Bavaria Corp International, Apopka *Also called Bavaria Corporation* ***(G-115)***
Bavaria Corporation.....407 880-0322
515 Cooper Commerce Dr # 10 Apopka (32703) ***(G-115)***
Baxley Services Inc.....850 675-4459
13451 Highway 89 Jay (32565) ***(G-6962)***
Baxter Adventures Inc.....561 439-4700
2001 10th Ave N Ste 2 Lake Worth Beach (33461) ***(G-7605)***
Baxter Custom Fabrication Inc.....863 289-9819
133 Browning Cir Winter Haven (33884) ***(G-19302)***
Bay Area Graphics.....813 247-2400
4040 E Adamo Dr Tampa (33605) ***(G-17456)***
Bay Area Prosthetics, Clearwater *Also called Baycare Home Care Inc* ***(G-1603)***
Bay Area Security Shred.....877 974-7337
301 Bear Ridge Cir Palm Harbor (34683) ***(G-13723)***
Bay Area Signs Inc.....813 677-0237
3858 E Knights Griffin Rd Plant City (33565) ***(G-14407)***
Bay Armature and Supply, Tampa *Also called Electrcal Systems Cmmnications* ***(G-17631)***
Bay Cabinets and Millworks.....850 215-1485
20679 Panama Cy Bch Pkwy Panama City Beach (32413) ***(G-13972)***
Bay City Window Company.....727 323-5443
3220 Bennett St N Ste A Saint Petersburg (33713) ***(G-15718)***
Bay City X-Press Signs & Prtg, Tampa *Also called Ljk & TS Partners Inc* ***(G-17854)***
Bay Cnc Machine LLC.....813 362-9626
305 Scarlet Blvd Oldsmar (34677) ***(G-12207)***
Bay County Bullet.....850 640-0855
1714 W 23rd St Panama City (32405) ***(G-13867)***
Bay Design Marine Group Inc.....239 825-8094
2319 J And C Blvd Ste 1 Naples (34109) ***(G-11184)***
Bay Diecutting, Oldsmar *Also called Digital Direct Corporation* ***(G-12220)***
Bay Eight Studios, North Miami Beach *Also called Palm Pheon Music Publishing* ***(G-11696)***
Bay Harbor Sheet Metal Inc.....813 740-8662
7909 Professional Pl Tampa (33637) ***(G-17457)***
Bay Meadow Architectural Mllwk.....407 332-7992
400 Bay Meadow Rd Longwood (32750) ***(G-8261)***
Bay Networks Inc.....813 249-8103
6601 Memorial Hwy 200 Tampa (33615) ***(G-17458)***
Bay Quality Prosthetic LLC.....850 522-5343
2195 Jenks Ave Ste C Panama City (32405) ***(G-13868)***
Bay State Milling Company.....772 597-2056
19150 Sw Warfield Blvd Indiantown (34956) ***(G-6071)***
Bay Tech Industries Inc.....813 854-1774
13275 Byrd Dr Odessa (33556) ***(G-12105)***
Baycare Home Care Inc.....727 461-5878
1237 S Myrtle Ave Clearwater (33756) ***(G-1603)***
Bayfront Printing Company.....727 823-1965
2235 16th Ave N Saint Petersburg (33713) ***(G-15719)***
Baylee & Company LLC.....305 333-6464
605 W 17th St Hialeah (33010) ***(G-5317)***
Baylee Nasco, Hialeah *Also called Baylee & Company LLC* ***(G-5317)***
Bayou Outdoor Equipment.....850 729-2711
489 Valparaiso Pkwy Valparaiso (32580) ***(G-18506)***
Bayou Printing Inc.....850 678-5444
113 S John Sims Pkwy Valparaiso (32580) ***(G-18507)***
Bayshore Brand Group Inc.....813 384-8275
10315 Newport Cir Tampa (33612) ***(G-17459)***
Bayshore Brands, Tampa *Also called Bayshore Brand Group Inc* ***(G-17459)***
Bayshore Con Prdcts/Chspake In.....757 331-2300
2600 Mtland Ctr Pkwy Ste Maitland (32751) ***(G-8457)***
Bayshore Concrete & Ldscp Mtls, Fort Myers *Also called Bayshore Concrete Products Inc* ***(G-4373)***
Bayshore Concrete & Ldscp Mtls, Fort Myers *Also called Bayshore Precast Concrete Inc* ***(G-4374)***
Bayshore Concrete Pdts Corp (HQ).....757 331-2300
2600 Mtland Ctr Pkwy Ste Maitland (32751) ***(G-8458)***
Bayshore Concrete Products Inc.....239 543-3001
8100 Bayshore Rd Fort Myers (33917) ***(G-4373)***
Bayshore Precast Concrete Inc.....239 543-3001
8100 Bayshore Rd Fort Myers (33917) ***(G-4374)***
Bayside Canvas Yacht Interiors.....954 792-8535
2830 W State Road 84 # 11 Fort Lauderdale (33312) ***(G-3842)***
Bayside Small Cap Senior Loan.....305 381-4100
1450 Brickell Ave Fl 31 Miami (33131) ***(G-9227)***
Baytronics Manufacturing Inc.....813 434-0401
620 E Twiggs St Ste 110 Tampa (33602) ***(G-17460)***
Bb & T, Miami *Also called Van Teal Inc* ***(G-10566)***
BBA Aviation Group, Orlando *Also called Signature AVI US Holdings Inc* ***(G-13193)***
BBH General Partnership.....863 425-5626
610 N Industrial Park Rd Mulberry (33860) ***(G-11120)***
Bbj Environmental LLC.....813 622-8550
9416 E Broadway Ave Tampa (33619) ***(G-17461)***
Bbpco, Boca Raton *Also called Brownbag Popcorn Company LLC* ***(G-467)***
Bbts Logging LLC.....850 997-2436
2182 S Jefferson Hwy Monticello (32344) ***(G-11075)***
Bbull Usa Inc.....813 855-1400
260 Scarlet Blvd Oldsmar (34677) ***(G-12208)***
Bbx Sweet Holdings LLC (HQ).....954 940-4000
401 E Las Olas Blvd Fort Lauderdale (33301) ***(G-3843)***
Bc Sales.....941 708-2727
3003 29th Ave E Bradenton (34208) ***(G-994)***
Bca Technologies Inc.....407 659-0653
1051 Winderley Pl Ste 310 Maitland (32751) ***(G-8459)***
Bcb International Inc.....727 754-4911
12010 Nw 29th Pl Sunrise (33323) ***(G-17095)***
Bcc-Bgle Cmmnctons Crp-Clrin L.....305 270-3333
8900 Sw 107th Ave Ste 30 Miami (33176) ***(G-9228)***
Bcdirect Corp.....305 623-3838
15625 Nw 15th Ave Miami (33169) ***(G-9229)***
Bce of Tampa Bay Inc.....727 535-7768
14000 63rd Way N Clearwater (33760) ***(G-1604)***
BCI, Miami *Also called Beverage Canners International* ***(G-9240)***
Bcr Environmental Corporation (PA).....904 819-9170
4063 Salisbury Rd Ste 203 Jacksonville (32216) ***(G-6198)***
BCT, Longwood *Also called Four G Enterprises Inc* ***(G-8284)***
BCT International Inc (HQ).....305 563-1224
2810 E Oklnd Prk Blvd # 308 Fort Lauderdale (33306) ***(G-3844)***
Bd Xtreme Holdings LLC.....850 703-1793
2460 Development Cir Bonifay (32425) ***(G-799)***
Bdc Florida LLC.....561 249-0900
1300 N Florida Mango Rd # 30 West Palm Beach (33409) ***(G-18814)***
Bdc Shell & Aggregate LLC.....941 875-6615
2000 State Road 31 Punta Gorda (33982) ***(G-15193)***
Bdjl Enterprises LLC.....407 678-9960
2591 Clark St Ste 208 Apopka (32703) ***(G-116)***
Bdnz Associates Inc.....305 379-7993
9481 Sw 134th St Miami (33176) ***(G-9230)***
Bdt Concepts Inc.....904 730-2590
5105 Philips Hwy Ste 205 Jacksonville (32207) ***(G-6199)***
Be Aerospace, Wellington *Also called Advanced Thermal Tech Inc* ***(G-18708)***
Be Merry.....772 324-8289
320 Se Denver Ave Stuart (34994) ***(G-16913)***
Be Pressure Supply, West Palm Beach *Also called B E Pressure Supply Inc* ***(G-18807)***
Be The Solution Inc.....850 545-2043
1400 Village Square Blvd Tallahassee (32312) ***(G-17227)***
Be Whole Nutrition LLC.....813 420-3057
5840 Highway 60 E Plant City (33567) ***(G-14408)***
Bea Sue Vineyards Inc.....352 446-5204
11025 Se Highway 42 Summerfield (34491) ***(G-17057)***
Beach Access, Pinecrest *Also called Nrz Inc* ***(G-14329)***
Beach Beacon.....727 397-5563
9911 Seminole Blvd Seminole (33772) ***(G-16741)***
Beach Embroidery & Screen Ptg.....386 478-3931
806 E 3rd Ave New Smyrna Beach (32169) ***(G-11528)***
Beach House Engineering.....941 727-4488
1625 50th Avenue Dr E Bradenton (34203) ***(G-995)***
Beach King, Orlando *Also called Alcee Industries Inc* ***(G-12448)***
Beach Neon & Sign Co, Atlantic Beach *Also called General Signs and Service Inc* ***(G-223)***
Beach Neon & Sign Co.....904 479-3599
1940 Spearing St Jacksonville (32206) ***(G-6200)***
Beach Pharmaceuticals, Tampa *Also called Beach Products Inc* ***(G-17462)***
Beach Products Inc.....813 839-6565
3010 W De Leon St Ste 100 Tampa (33609) ***(G-17462)***
Beachchip Technologies LLC.....727 643-8106
2655 Ulmerton Rd Clearwater (33762) ***(G-1605)***
Beachcomber Fibrgls Tech Inc.....772 283-0200
3355 Se Lionel Ter Stuart (34997) ***(G-16914)***
Beaches Leader, The, Jacksonville Beach *Also called Leader Group* ***(G-6947)***
Beaches Woodcraft Inc.....904 249-0785
14 Dutton Island Rd E Atlantic Beach (32233) ***(G-217)***
Beacon Phrm Jupiter LLC.....212 991-8988
210 Military Trl Jupiter (33458) ***(G-7005)***
Beacon Publishing Inc.....888 618-5253
631 Us Highway 1 Ste 201 North Palm Beach (33408) ***(G-11718)***
Beam Associates LLC (PA).....813 855-5695
301 Commerce Blvd Ste 2 Oldsmar (34677) ***(G-12209)***
Bean Counters Pro.....941 504-1157
5602 Marquesas Cir # 102 Sarasota (34233) ***(G-16363)***
Beano Publishing LLC.....954 689-8339
1575 N Park Dr Ste 100 Weston (33326) ***(G-19110)***
Beard Booze LLC.....352 424-0687
5761 Deer Flag Dr Lakeland (33811) ***(G-7645)***
Bearded Mohawk LLC.....913 680-9829
2916 Maldive Ct Deltona (32738) ***(G-3163)***
Bearing Specialist Inc.....305 796-3415
1908 Nw 94th Ave Doral (33172) ***(G-3265)***
Bears Metal Works Inc.....863 537-5644
320 S 1st Ave Bartow (33830) ***(G-309)***
Beasley Welding LLC.....352 595-4086
14291 Ne 47th Ave Anthony (32617) ***(G-95)***
Beast Row Inc.....727 787-2710
3430 E Lake Rd Ste 1 Palm Harbor (34685) ***(G-13724)***
Beata Bordas.....772 349-2568
6172 Se Riverboat Dr Stuart (34997) ***(G-16915)***
Beautiful Cabinets Corp.....813 486-9034
1903 W Skagway Ave Tampa (33604) ***(G-17463)***
Beautiful Deluxe Inc.....305 498-4995
9379 Dominican Dr Cutler Bay (33189) ***(G-2387)***

ALPHABETIC

Beautiful Homes Inc 800 403-1480
471 Mariner Blvd Spring Hill (34609) *(G-16848)*
Beautiful Mailbox Co 305 403-4820
2360 W 76th St Hialeah (33016) *(G-5318)*
Beautiko, Hialeah *Also called Niefeld Group LLC (G-5541)*
Beauty & Health Corporation 305 259-8181
10871 Sw 188th St Unit 24 Cutler Bay (33157) *(G-2388)*
Beauty Awaits Cosmetics LLC 754 226-5800
13021 Sw 20th St Miramar (33027) *(G-10973)*
Beauty Cosmetica 305 406-1022
3406 Nw 151st Ter Opa Locka (33054) *(G-12293)*
Beauty Lab Inc 305 687-0071
2360 Nw 150th St Opa Locka (33054) *(G-12294)*
Beauty Pavers LLC 941 720-3655
3600 Lk Byshore Dr Unit 1 Bradenton (34205) *(G-996)*
Beauty With Kelley Inc 786 757-6485
9845 E Fern St Palmetto Bay (33157) *(G-13840)*
Beautyge Brands Usa Inc 904 693-1200
5344 Overmyer Dr Jacksonville (32254) *(G-6201)*
Beavertail Skiffs Inc 941 705-2090
4601 15th St E Bradenton (34203) *(G-997)*
Becarro International Corp (PA) 561 737-5585
917 S Military Trl Ste C3 West Palm Beach (33415) *(G-18815)*
Beck Graphics, Saint Petersburg *Also called Colorgraphx Inc (G-15747)*
Beck Graphics Inc 727 443-3803
1114 Florida Ave Ste B Palm Harbor (34683) *(G-13725)*
Becker Avionics Inc 954 450-3137
10376 Usa Today Way Miramar (33025) *(G-10974)*
Becker Designs Inc 386 760-2280
4188 Dairy Ct Ste C Port Orange (32127) *(G-15012)*
Becker Microbial Products Inc 954 345-9321
11146 Nw 69th Pl Parkland (33076) *(G-13989)*
Becker USA, Miramar *Also called Becker Avionics Inc (G-10974)*
Beckman Coulter Inc 305 380-2175
11800 Sw 147th Ave Miami (33196) *(G-9231)*
Beckman Coulter Inc 954 432-4336
1 Sw 129th Ave Ste 201 Pembroke Pines (33027) *(G-14022)*
Beckwith Electric Co Inc 727 544-2326
11811 62nd St Largo (33773) *(G-7905)*
Bedbug Supply, Coral Springs *Also called Levita LLC (G-2273)*
Bedding Acquisition LLC (HQ) 561 997-6900
901 W Yamato Rd Ste 250 Boca Raton (33431) *(G-443)*
Bedeschi America Inc (HQ) 954 602-2175
2600 N Military Trl # 245 Boca Raton (33431) *(G-444)*
Bedrock Industries Inc 407 859-1300
10500 Rocket Ct Orlando (32824) *(G-12509)*
Bedrock Resources LLC 352 369-8600
2441 E Fort King St 202 Ocala (34471) *(G-11885)*
Bee Access Products, West Palm Beach *Also called Bee Welding Inc (G-18816)*
Bee Electronics Inc 772 468-7477
2733 Peters Rd Fort Pierce (34945) *(G-4680)*
Bee Inspired Handmade, Hollywood *Also called Note It (G-5884)*
Bee Welding Inc 561 616-9003
2145 Indian Rd West Palm Beach (33409) *(G-18816)*
Beehive3d Inc 954 560-9513
1027 Sw 30th Ave Deerfield Beach (33442) *(G-2784)*
Beer Bread Company, Boca Raton *Also called Big L Brands Inc (G-447)*
Bees Brothers LLC 305 529-5789
2990 Ponce De Leon Blvd # 202 Coral Gables (33134) *(G-2126)*
Bees Vita Plus, West Palm Beach *Also called Beesfree Inc (G-18817)*
Beesfree Inc 561 939-4860
2101 Vista Pkwy Ste 122 West Palm Beach (33411) *(G-18817)*
Beez Worx Boats LLC 850 678-6548
1000 Coral Dr Niceville (32578) *(G-11563)*
Before Wind Blows LLC 407 977-4833
282 Osprey Lakes Cir Chuluota (32766) *(G-1552)*
Beginmyprinting Com 772 828-2026
430 Sw Fairway Lndg Port Saint Lucie (34986) *(G-15090)*
Behrs, Orlando *Also called P B C Central (G-13041)*
Behrs Chocolates By Design 407 648-2020
3450 Vineland Rd Ste B Orlando (32811) *(G-12510)*
BEI 561 488-0759
19657 Waters End Dr # 20 Boca Raton (33434) *(G-445)*
Belac LLC 813 749-3200
420 Commerce Blvd Oldsmar (34677) *(G-12210)*
Belatrix Software Inc 801 673-8331
9128 Strada Pl Ste 10115 Naples (34108) *(G-11185)*
Belcher Gear Manufacturing, Tampa *Also called Lubov Manufacturing Inc (G-17862)*
Belcher Holdings Inc (PA) 727 530-1585
12393 Belcher Rd S # 420 Largo (33773) *(G-7906)*
Belcher Holdings Inc 727 471-0850
6911 Bryan Dairy Rd Largo (33777) *(G-7907)*
Belcher Pharm Acquisition, Largo *Also called Belcher Holdings Inc (G-7906)*
Belcher Pharmaceuticals LLC (PA) 727 471-0850
6911 Bryan Dairy Rd # 210 Largo (33777) *(G-7908)*
Belets Millwork Inc 904 353-8600
505 N Myrtle Ave Jacksonville (32204) *(G-6202)*
Belgium Co Inc 407 957-1886
1100 Grape Ave Ste 1 Saint Cloud (34769) *(G-15644)*
Bell Brothers Electric LLC 954 496-0632
5222 Nw 110th Ave Coral Springs (33076) *(G-2225)*
Bell Concrete Products Inc (PA) 352 463-6103
2480 N Us Highway 129 Bell (32619) *(G-341)*
Bell Hearing Instruments Inc (PA) 813 814-2355
700 Stevens Ave Ste B Oldsmar (34677) *(G-12211)*
Bell Performance Inc 407 831-5021
1340 Bennett Dr Longwood (32750) *(G-8262)*
Bell Steel Company (PA) 850 432-1545
530 S C St Pensacola (32502) *(G-14097)*
Bell Steel Company 850 479-2980
8788 Paul Starr Dr Pensacola (32514) *(G-14098)*
Bella Blsmic Pressed Olive Inc 941 505-1707
439 Ridgecrest Dr Punta Gorda (33982) *(G-15194)*
Bella Blsmic Pressed Olive Inc (PA) 941 249-3571
1200 W Retta Esplanade Punta Gorda (33950) *(G-15195)*
Bella Luna Inc 305 696-0310
3650 E 10th Ct Hialeah (33013) *(G-5319)*
Bella Slata Spclty Drssngs Sce, Rockledge *Also called Cranco Industries Inc (G-15399)*
Bella Vista Bakery Inc 954 759-1920
2220 Nw 82nd Ave Doral (33122) *(G-3266)*
Belladonna Hair Bar, Miramar *Also called The Alluring Group Inc (G-11051)*
Bellak Color Corporation 305 854-8525
9730 Nw 25th St Doral (33172) *(G-3267)*
Belle Glade Electric Motor Svc 561 996-3333
900 Nw 13th St Belle Glade (33430) *(G-345)*
Belle Glade FL Block, Belle Glade *Also called Cemex Cnstr Mtls Fla LLC (G-346)*
Belle Isle Furniture LLC (PA) 407 408-1266
7210 Seminole Dr Apt 1 Belle Isle (32812) *(G-356)*
Belleaire Press LLC 352 377-1870
10000 Sw 52nd Ave Apt 171 Gainesville (32608) *(G-4885)*
Bellini Systems Inc 813 264-9252
4925 Indpdnc Pkwy Ste 400 Tampa (33634) *(G-17464)*
Bellowstech LLC 386 615-7530
1289 N Us Highway 1 Ormond Beach (32174) *(G-13352)*
Bellowstech LLC 386 615-7530
115 Business Center Dr Ormond Beach (32174) *(G-13353)*
BellSouth, Melbourne *Also called Yp Advrtising Pubg LLC Not LLC (G-8978)*
Belocal Pro Inc 727 379-9576
12717 Flamingo Pkwy Spring Hill (34610) *(G-16870)*
Belongea Industries 574 209-1045
6837 Ne Cubitis Ave # 583 Arcadia (34266) *(G-200)*
Belquette Inc 727 329-9483
3634 131st Ave N Clearwater (33762) *(G-1606)*
Belsnickel Enterprises Inc 386 256-5367
901 Valencia Rd South Daytona (32119) *(G-16798)*
Belt Corp 954 505-7400
4032 N 29th Ave Hollywood (33020) *(G-5785)*
Belt Maintenance Group Inc (PA) 813 907-9316
27658 Cashford Cir # 102 Wesley Chapel (33544) *(G-18740)*
Beltech Generator & Rewinding 954 588-2255
850 E Coml Blvd Apt 252 Fort Lauderdale (33334) *(G-3845)*
Beltran Construction, Fort Pierce *Also called LAS & JB Inc (G-4711)*
Belts Inc 714 572-3636
2500 W 84th St Unit 8 Hialeah (33016) *(G-5320)*
Belvoir Media Group, Sarasota *Also called Belvoir Publications Inc (G-16364)*
Belvoir Publications Inc 941 929-1720
7820 Holiday Dr Sarasota (34231) *(G-16364)*
Belzona Inc 305 512-3200
2000 Nw 88th Ct Doral (33172) *(G-3268)*
Belzona Inc (HQ) 305 594-4994
2000 Nw 88th Ct Doral (33172) *(G-3269)*
Bema Inc 954 761-1919
2301 S Andrews Ave Fort Lauderdale (33316) *(G-3846)*
Bematech, Orlando *Also called Logic Controls Inc (G-12934)*
Bemeals, Hallandale Beach *Also called Qsrr Corporation (G-5205)*
Ben Hill Griffin Inc (PA) 863 635-2281
700 S Scenic Hwy Fl 33843 Frostproof (33843) *(G-4855)*
Ben Hill Griffin Inc 863 635-2281
72 North Ave Frostproof (33843) *(G-4856)*
Ben Jammin Island Jerky Llc 904 220-2067
12424 Gately Rd S Jacksonville (32225) *(G-6203)*
Ben Kaufman Sales Co Inc 305 688-2144
10025 Nw 116th Way Ste 14 Medley (33178) *(G-8621)*
Benada Aluminum Products LLC 407 323-3300
2540 Jewett Ln Sanford (32771) *(G-16002)*
Benchmark Aluminum Inc 941 585-9977
125 Justine St Port Charlotte (33954) *(G-14964)*
Benchmark Blueprinting, Sarasota *Also called Maki Printing LLC (G-16499)*
Benchmark Connector Corp 954 746-9929
4501 Nw 103rd Ave Sunrise (33351) *(G-17096)*
Benchmark Contract Furniture, Jacksonville Beach *Also called Benchmark Design Group Inc (G-6939)*
Benchmark Design Group Inc (PA) 904 246-5060
456 Osceola Ave Jacksonville Beach (32250) *(G-6939)*
Benchmark Entertainment LC 561 588-5200
2201 4th Ave N Lake Worth Beach (33461) *(G-7606)*
Benchmark Games, Lake Worth Beach *Also called Benchmark Entertainment LC (G-7606)*

Benchmark Games Intl LLC.....561 588-5200
2201 4th Ave N Lake Worth Beach (33461) ***(G-7607)***
Benchmark Metals Inc.....239 699-0802
1003 Se 12th Ave Unit 2 Cape Coral (33990) ***(G-1388)***
Benchmark of Florida, Sanford *Also called Waterfall Industries Inc* ***(G-16134)***
Benchmark of Palm Beach (PA).....706 258-3553
205 Worth Ave Ste 315 Palm Beach (33480) ***(G-13549)***
Benchmark Quality Gutters Inc.....904 759-9800
9526 Argyle Frest Blvd St Jacksonville (32222) ***(G-6204)***
Bengal Industries, Odessa *Also called Coast Wcp* ***(G-12111)***
Bengis Signs Inc.....305 592-3860
9821 Nw 80th Ave Unit 5t Miami Lakes (33016) ***(G-10765)***
Benitez Forklift Corp.....786 307-3872
18820 Nw 57th Ave Apt 301 Hialeah (33015) ***(G-5321)***
Benjamin Moore Authorized Ret, Panama City Beach *Also called Panhandle Paint & Dctg LLC* ***(G-13981)***
Benjamin Moore Authorized Ret, Navarre *Also called Consolidated Ace Hdwr Sup Inc* ***(G-11465)***
Benner China and Glwr of Fla.....904 733-4620
5329 Powers Ave Jacksonville (32207) ***(G-6205)***
Bennett Company, Gainesville *Also called Fabco-Air Inc* ***(G-4918)***
Bennetts Custom Cabinets Inc.....904 751-1455
9897 Sisson Dr Jacksonville (32218) ***(G-6206)***
Bent Chrome LLC.....813 363-3398
9506 Glenpointe Dr Riverview (33569) ***(G-15265)***
Bent Pine Publishing Corp.....772 708-0490
1402 Sw Bent Pine Cv Port Saint Lucie (34986) ***(G-15091)***
Benton Machine Works Inc.....904 768-9161
740 Carlton St Jacksonville (32208) ***(G-6207)***
Benz Research and Dev LLC.....941 758-8256
6447 Parkland Dr Sarasota (34243) ***(G-16181)***
Berco, Cape Coral *Also called Beverage Equipment Repair Co* ***(G-1389)***
Berg Europipe Holding Corp (HQ).....850 769-2273
5315 W 19th St Panama City (32401) ***(G-13869)***
Berg LLC.....786 201-2625
3201 Ne 183rd St Apt 704 Aventura (33160) ***(G-264)***
Berg Pipe Panama City Corp (HQ).....850 769-2273
5315 W 19th St Panama City (32401) ***(G-13870)***
Bergan Tank Control, Pensacola *Also called Ian-Conrad Bergan LLC* ***(G-14175)***
Bergeron Properties & Inv, Fort Lauderdale *Also called Bergeron Sand & Rock Min Inc* ***(G-3847)***
Bergeron Sand & Rock Min Inc (PA).....954 680-6100
19612 Sw 69th Pl Fort Lauderdale (33332) ***(G-3847)***
Berkant Corp.....305 771-5578
6370 Nw 82nd Ave Miami (33166) ***(G-9232)***
Berkshire Managment Associates.....305 883-3277
12841 Sw 117th St Miami (33186) ***(G-9233)***
Berman Products LLC.....561 743-5197
19558 Red Gum Trl Jupiter (33458) ***(G-7006)***
Bermont Excavating LLC.....866 367-9557
37390 Bermont Rd Punta Gorda (33982) ***(G-15196)***
Bernard Cap LLC.....305 822-4800
620 W 27th St Hialeah (33010) ***(G-5322)***
Bernat Industries Intl LLC.....727 350-5904
5133 Gulfport Blvd S Gulfport (33707) ***(G-5132)***
Bernice I Finch.....850 638-0082
1867 6th Ave Wausau (32463) ***(G-18696)***
Berry Best Stitching and EMB.....813 763-7716
3913 Sparky Ln Plant City (33565) ***(G-14409)***
Berry Global Inc.....305 887-2040
9016 Nw 105th Way Medley (33178) ***(G-8622)***
Berry Signs Inc.....321 631-6150
1740 Huntington Ln Rockledge (32955) ***(G-15394)***
Bertram Yachts LLC (HQ).....813 527-9899
5250 W Tyson Ave Tampa (33611) ***(G-17465)***
Bescutter LLC.....888 525-2897
2225 Carnaby Ct Lehigh Acres (33973) ***(G-8185)***
Beson 4 Media Group, Jacksonville *Also called Barbes Publishing Inc* ***(G-6194)***
Bespoke Stitchery LLC.....407 412-9937
2437 E Landstreet Rd Orlando (32824) ***(G-12511)***
Bessie Barnie, Doral *Also called Miami Tbr LLC* ***(G-3437)***
Best Bindery Corp.....941 505-1779
3181 Aloe St Punta Gorda (33982) ***(G-15197)***
Best Brand Bottlers Inc.....941 755-1941
6620 19th St E Unit 109 Sarasota (34243) ***(G-16182)***
Best Bubble Mailers, Hialeah *Also called Holpack Corp* ***(G-5448)***
Best Buy Awnings, Miami *Also called Business World Trading Inc* ***(G-9288)***
Best Choice Printing, Jacksonville *Also called Ballard Printing Inc* ***(G-6193)***
Best Choice Software Inc.....941 747-5858
1117 30th Ave W Bradenton (34205) ***(G-998)***
Best Circuits Inc.....321 425-6725
300 North Dr Ste 106 Melbourne (32934) ***(G-8778)***
Best Closures Inc.....305 821-6607
9780 Nw 79th Ave Miami Lakes (33016) ***(G-10766)***
Best Community Magazine.....407 571-2980
260 Maitland Ave Ste 2000 Altamonte Springs (32701) ***(G-32)***
Best Custom Tape, Miami *Also called Rela USA LLC* ***(G-10249)***
Best Door, Miami Lakes *Also called Best Rolling Manufacturer Inc* ***(G-10767)***
Best Engineered Surfc Tech LLC (PA).....407 932-0008
1820 Avenue A Kissimmee (34758) ***(G-7223)***
Best Fabrications Inc.....863 519-6611
2145 Bravo Ave Bartow (33830) ***(G-310)***
Best Finisher.....305 688-8174
2780 Nw 122nd St Miami (33167) ***(G-9234)***
Best Global Source, Apopka *Also called Oum LLC* ***(G-168)***
Best Industries.....772 460-8310
15860 W Park Ln Fort Pierce (34945) ***(G-4681)***
Best Iproductscom LLC.....386 402-7800
111 N Ridgewood Ave Edgewater (32132) ***(G-3613)***
Best Lidar Corporation.....321 425-6725
300 North Dr Ste 106 Melbourne (32934) ***(G-8779)***
Best Made Flags, Hollywood *Also called Keystone 75 Inc* ***(G-5856)***
Best Manufacturing Company.....954 922-1443
3282 N 29th Ct Hollywood (33020) ***(G-5786)***
Best Metal Work.....561 842-1960
3301 Elec Way Ste A West Palm Beach (33407) ***(G-18818)***
Best of Orlando Pntg & Stucco.....407 947-4174
3000 Clarcona Rd Lot 763 Apopka (32703) ***(G-117)***
Best Pallets of FL LLC.....386 624-5575
1830 Patterson Ave Unit D Deland (32724) ***(G-2962)***
Best Pavers LLC.....407 259-9020
8730 Hastings Beach Blvd Orlando (32829) ***(G-12512)***
Best Powder Coatings Inc.....305 836-9460
3970 E 10th Ct Hialeah (33013) ***(G-5323)***
Best Price Digital Lenses Inc.....850 361-4401
2013 W Yonge St Pensacola (32501) ***(G-14099)***
Best Price Mobility Inc.....321 402-5955
941 Armstrong Blvd Ste B Kissimmee (34741) ***(G-7224)***
Best Products Mix Inc.....305 512-9920
17541 Nw 89th Ct Hialeah (33018) ***(G-5324)***
Best Publishing Company.....561 776-6066
631 Us Highway 1 Ste 307 North Palm Beach (33408) ***(G-11719)***
Best Quality Water Sys of Fla (PA).....407 971-2537
2200 Winter Springs Blvd # 106 Oviedo (32765) ***(G-13418)***
Best Rolling Manufacturer Inc.....305 821-4276
9780 Nw 79th Ave Miami Lakes (33016) ***(G-10767)***
Best Supplier, Hialeah *Also called H Goicoechea Inc* ***(G-5441)***
Best Truss Company (PA).....305 667-6797
7035 Sw 44th St Miami (33155) ***(G-9235)***
Bestcanvas Inc.....305 759-7800
3343 Nw 107th St Miami (33167) ***(G-9236)***
Bestprintingonlinecom LLC.....239 263-2106
4408 Corporate Sq Naples (34104) ***(G-11186)***
Bestway Portable Building Inc.....850 747-1984
2919 N Highway 231 Panama City (32405) ***(G-13871)***
Bet Er Mix Inc.....352 799-5538
21101 Cortez Blvd Brooksville (34601) ***(G-1214)***
BET-Er Mix Holding Inc (PA).....727 868-9226
9301 Denton Ave Port Richey (34667) ***(G-15043)***
Beta Max Inc.....321 727-3737
1895 Rbert J Cnlan Blvd N Palm Bay (32905) ***(G-13502)***
Beta Max Hoist, Palm Bay *Also called Beta Max Inc* ***(G-13502)***
Beta Max Inc.....321 914-0918
2750 Hudson Ave Ne Palm Bay (32905) ***(G-13503)***
Betancourt Sports Ntrtn LLC (HQ).....305 593-9296
14700 Nw 60th Ave Miami Lakes (33014) ***(G-10768)***
Betawave LLC.....954 223-8298
2968 Nw 60th St Fort Lauderdale (33309) ***(G-3848)***
Betrock Information Systems.....954 981-2821
12330 Sw 53rd St Ste 712 Cooper City (33330) ***(G-2110)***
Better Air North America LLC.....844 447-7624
4651 Sheridan St Ste 335 Hollywood (33021) ***(G-5787)***
Better Built, Pensacola *Also called Daws Manufacturing Company Inc* ***(G-14125)***
Better Built Group Inc.....850 803-4044
66 N Holiday Rd Destin (32550) ***(G-3212)***
Better Copy Center, West Palm Beach *Also called Man Enterprises 3 LLC* ***(G-18940)***
Better Mix.....800 232-6833
9301 Denton Ave Hudson (34667) ***(G-6016)***
Better Plastics Inc.....407 480-2909
780 Central Florida Pkwy Orlando (32824) ***(G-12513)***
Better Sourcing Worldwide, Hallandale Beach *Also called Miracles For Fun Usa Inc* ***(G-5199)***
Betty Dain Creations LLC.....305 769-3451
9701 Nw 112th Ave Ste 10 Medley (33178) ***(G-8623)***
Betty Engines Machine Shop Inc.....305 458-1467
7120 Sw 44th St Ste A Miami (33155) ***(G-9237)***
Betwell Oil & Gas Company (PA).....305 821-8300
8083 Nw 103rd St Hialeah (33016) ***(G-5325)***
Beutlich Pharmaceuticals LLC (PA).....386 263-8860
7775 S Us Highway 1 H Bunnell (32110) ***(G-1297)***
Bev-Co Enterprises Inc (PA).....786 362-6368
2761 Nw 82nd Ave Miami (33122) ***(G-9238)***
Bev-Co Enterprises Inc.....786 953-7109
9533 Nw 41st St Doral (33178) ***(G-3270)***
Bevel Express & Tops Lac.....813 887-3174
6026 Benjamin Rd Tampa (33634) ***(G-17466)***

Beverage Blocks Inc...813 309-8711
218 E Bearss Ave Ste 332 Tampa (33613) ***(G-17467)***
Beverage Canners Inc...305 714-7000
3550 Nw 110th St Miami (33167) ***(G-9239)***
Beverage Canners International...305 714-7000
3505 Nw 107th St Miami (33167) ***(G-9240)***
Beverage Corp Intl Inc...305 714-7000
3505 Nw 107th St Miami (33167) ***(G-9241)***
Beverage Depot, Hialeah *Also called Hialeah Distribution Corp* ***(G-5444)***
Beverage Equipment Repair Co...239 573-0683
1020 Ne Pine Island Rd # 201 Cape Coral (33909) ***(G-1389)***
Beverely's, Fort Lauderdale *Also called American Diamond Distributors* ***(G-3812)***
Beverly Acquisitions Inc (PA)...561 746-3827
240 W Indiantown Rd # 101 Jupiter (33458) ***(G-7007)***
Bevolution Group, Frostproof *Also called Lemon-X Corporation* ***(G-4861)***
Bevolution Group, Frostproof *Also called Juice Tyme Inc* ***(G-4860)***
Beyers Welding Inc...407 892-2834
4950 Canoe Creek Rd Saint Cloud (34772) ***(G-15645)***
Beyette Woodworking LLC...727 254-8705
8584 Mockingbird Ln Seminole (33777) ***(G-16742)***
Beyond White Spa LLC...866 399-8867
3200 Nw 67th Ave Unit 600 Miami (33166) ***(G-9242)***
Beyondclean LLC...561 799-5710
601 Heritage Dr Ste 422 Jupiter (33458) ***(G-7008)***
Bezels For Watches, Miami *Also called Accar Ltd Inc* ***(G-9059)***
BF American Business LLC...561 856-7094
22285 Sw 66th Ave Apt 200 Boca Raton (33428) ***(G-446)***
BF Hurley Mat Co Inc...813 837-0616
6824 S Manhattan Ave # 105 Tampa (33616) ***(G-17468)***
BF One LLC...239 939-5251
5661 Independence Cir Fort Myers (33912) ***(G-4375)***
BF Weston LLC...561 844-5528
2810 Weston Rd Weston (33331) ***(G-19111)***
Bg Expo Group LLC...305 428-3576
11231 Nw 20th St Unit 140 Doral (33172) ***(G-3271)***
Bgt Holdings LLC...239 643-9949
200 Aviation Dr N Ste 5 Naples (34104) ***(G-11187)***
BHd Precision Products Inc...941 753-0003
2120 Whitfield Park Loop Sarasota (34243) ***(G-16183)***
Bi-Ads Inc...954 525-1489
545 Nw 7th Ter Fort Lauderdale (33311) ***(G-3849)***
Bible Alliance Inc (PA)...941 748-3031
12108 10th Ave E Bradenton (34212) ***(G-999)***
Bic Corporation...727 536-7895
14421 Myerlake Cir Clearwater (33760) ***(G-1607)***
Bic Graphic USA, Clearwater *Also called Bic Corporation* ***(G-1607)***
Bicentrics Inc...813 649-0225
319 1st St Ne Ruskin (33570) ***(G-15482)***
Bid Excellence Co LLC...609 929-9019
20404 Ne 16th Pl Miami (33179) ***(G-9243)***
Bid Uniforms.com, Miami *Also called Bid Excellence Co LLC* ***(G-9243)***
Biddiscombe International LLC...727 299-9287
11961 31st Ct N Saint Petersburg (33716) ***(G-15720)***
Biddiscombe Labs Stylz Pdts, Saint Petersburg *Also called Biddiscombe International LLC* ***(G-15720)***
Big Bend Fuel Inc...727 946-8727
6912 Big Bend Rd Gibsonton (33534) ***(G-5027)***
Big Bend Ice Cream Co...850 539-7778
138 Staghorn Trl Havana (32333) ***(G-5233)***
Big Bend Rebar Inc...850 875-8000
1 Corporate Ct Quincy (32351) ***(G-15246)***
Big Bend Truss Components Inc...850 539-5351
52 Salem Rd Havana (32333) ***(G-5234)***
Big Biz Direct...813 978-0584
13922 Monroes Business Pa Tampa (33635) ***(G-17469)***
Big Color Output Inc...941 540-4441
1327 Lafayette St Cape Coral (33904) ***(G-1390)***
Big Country Small Engine...850 348-9022
5412 E Highway 22 Panama City (32404) ***(G-13872)***
Big Cypress Distillery LLC...786 228-9740
13995 Sw 144th Ave # 207 Miami (33186) ***(G-9244)***
Big Digital Graphics LLC...561 844-4708
1335 Old Dixie Hwy Unit 4 Lake Park (33403) ***(G-7466)***
Big Eagle LLC...305 586-8766
3051 W State Road 84 Fort Lauderdale (33312) ***(G-3850)***
Big Fish Co Custom Creations...727 525-5010
3128 Dr M L K Jr St N Mlk Saint Petersburg (33704) ***(G-15721)***
Big Iron Intl Inc...407 222-2573
3936 S Semoran Blvd Ste 2 Orlando (32822) ***(G-12514)***
Big L Brands Inc (PA)...888 552-9768
7750 Ne Spanish Trail Ct Boca Raton (33487) ***(G-447)***
Big League Cards, Casselberry *Also called Instant Locate Inc* ***(G-1506)***
Big Man Friendly Trnsp LLC...941 229-3454
11161 State Road 70 E # 1 Lakewood Ranch (34202) ***(G-7837)***
Big O Boats LLC...863 697-6319
1350 Industrial Way E Sebring (33870) ***(G-16683)***
Big O Tires, Juno Beach *Also called Tbc Retail Group Inc* ***(G-6984)***
Big OS Stump Grinding...904 945-5900
101 Baisden Rd Apt 2 Jacksonville (32218) ***(G-6208)***
Big Red Q Printing Services...305 477-7848
2100 Nw 94th Ave Doral (33172) ***(G-3272)***
Big Rhino Screen Printing, Pensacola *Also called Above LLC* ***(G-14077)***
Big River Cypress & Hardwood...850 674-5991
19431 State Rte 71 N Blountstown (32424) ***(G-385)***
Big Sign Media Group, Fort Lauderdale *Also called Big Sign Message LLC* ***(G-3851)***
Big Sign Message LLC...954 235-5717
770 Nw 57th Ct Fort Lauderdale (33309) ***(G-3851)***
Big Star Systems LLC...954 243-7209
2061 Nw 47th Ter Apt 200 Lauderhill (33313) ***(G-8102)***
Big Sun Equine Products Inc (PA)...352 629-9645
2001 Nw 1st Ave Ocala (34475) ***(G-11886)***
Big Sun Plastics Inc...352 671-1844
2615 Nw Old Blitchton Rd Ocala (34475) ***(G-11887)***
Big Sun Products, Ocala *Also called Big Sun Equine Products Inc* ***(G-11886)***
Big T Printing, Saint Petersburg *Also called Solseen LLC* ***(G-15915)***
Big Time Tailgate LLC...407 509-5163
805 Marina Rd Titusville (32796) ***(G-18414)***
Big Top Manufacturing Inc...850 584-7786
3255 Us Highway 19 N Perry (32347) ***(G-14294)***
Big Wood Millwork Sales Inc...305 471-1155
10842 Nw 27th St Doral (33172) ***(G-3273)***
Bigbyte Software Systems Inc...917 370-1733
2214 Nw 171st Ter Pembroke Pines (33028) ***(G-14023)***
Bigg D Entertainment LLC...917 204-0292
904 Stillwater Ct Weston (33327) ***(G-19112)***
Bigg Publishing...772 563-0425
5082 4th Ln Vero Beach (32968) ***(G-18599)***
Bigg Wills Wheels LLC...352 222-6170
125 Nw 23rd Ave Ste D Gainesville (32609) ***(G-4886)***
Biggs Industries Inc...561 775-6944
11426 88th Rd N Palm Beach Gardens (33412) ***(G-13569)***
Bigham Insulation & Sup Co Inc...954 522-2887
2816 Sw 3rd Ave Fort Lauderdale (33315) ***(G-3852)***
Bighill Corporation...786 497-1875
1111 Lincoln Rd Fl 4 Miami Beach (33139) ***(G-10647)***
Bigorre Aerospace Corp...727 525-8115
6295 42nd St N Pinellas Park (33781) ***(G-14337)***
Bijol & Spices, Miami *Also called Bijol and Spices Inc* ***(G-9245)***
Bijol and Spices Inc...305 634-9030
2154 Nw 22nd Ct Miami (33142) ***(G-9245)***
Bikekeeper LLC...561 209-6863
8461 Lake Worth Rd # 173 Lake Worth (33467) ***(G-7536)***
Biking Boat Works Company, The, Saint Petersburg *Also called Snug Harbor Dinghies Inc* ***(G-15914)***
Bill & Renee Enterprises...321 452-2800
275 Magnolia Ave Ste 2 Merritt Island (32952) ***(G-8993)***
Bill Evans Aluminum Inc...352 400-1424
5831 S Gray Oak Ter Lecanto (34461) ***(G-8128)***
Bill Praus Stucco LLC...386 453-8400
625 Cumberland Dr Flagler Beach (32136) ***(G-3753)***
Bill Shuda...772 220-6620
6088 Se Woodfield Ct Stuart (34997) ***(G-16916)***
Billabong Destin...850 424-3553
500 Grand Blvd Ste 102 Miramar Beach (32550) ***(G-11063)***
Billet Technology...561 582-6171
714 S East Coast St Lake Worth (33460) ***(G-7537)***
Billiards & Barstools, Tampa *Also called Robertson Billiard Sups Inc* ***(G-18065)***
Bills Prestige Printing Inc...352 589-5833
640 S Bay St Eustis (32726) ***(G-3703)***
Billys Welding Inc...239 229-8723
16260 Saddlewood Ln Cape Coral (33991) ***(G-1391)***
Bimbo Bakeries USA...941 875-5945
2625 Commerce Pkwy # 112 North Port (34289) ***(G-11732)***
Bimbo Bakeries USA...954 968-7684
6783 Nw 17th Ave Fort Lauderdale (33309) ***(G-3853)***
Binca LLC...305 698-8883
10680 Nw 37th Ter Doral (33178) ***(G-3274)***
Bindels Custom Woodwork Inc...727 776-5233
7514 Tasco Dr North Port (34291) ***(G-11733)***
Bindery LLC...407 647-7777
611 N Wymore Rd Ste 100 Winter Park (32789) ***(G-19382)***
Bingham On Site Portables LLC...813 659-0003
3640 Sumner Rd Dover (33527) ***(G-3555)***
Bingham On-Site Sewers Inc...813 659-0003
3640 Sumner Rd Dover (33527) ***(G-3556)***
Bingo Bakery Inc...305 545-9993
2125 Nw 8th Ave Miami (33127) ***(G-9246)***
Binney Family of Florida Inc...727 376-5596
11232 Challenger Ave Odessa (33556) ***(G-12106)***
Bio Bubble Pets LLC...561 998-5350
1400 Centrepark Blvd # 860 West Palm Beach (33401) ***(G-18819)***
Bio Ceps Inc...727 669-7544
15251 Roosevelt Blvd # 204 Clearwater (33760) ***(G-1608)***
Bio Fuel Professionals...239 591-3835
25 Mentor Dr Naples (34110) ***(G-11188)***
Bio Nucleonics, Miami *Also called Bio-Nucleonics Pharma Inc* ***(G-9247)***
Bio Therapeutics Inc...954 321-5553
1850 Nw 69th Ave Ste 1 Plantation (33313) ***(G-14496)***

Bio-Lab Inc 863 709-1411
3125 Drane Field Rd # 10 Lakeland (33811) ***(G-7646)***
Bio-Logic Systems, Orlando *Also called Natus Medical Incorporated* ***(G-12995)***
Bio-Logic Systems Corp 847 949-0456
12301 Lake Underhill Rd # 201 Orlando (32828) ***(G-12515)***
Bio-Nucleonics Pharma Inc 305 576-0996
1 Ne 19th St Miami (33132) ***(G-9247)***
Bio-Pharm LLC 973 223-7163
409 W Hallandale Beach Bl Hallandale Beach (33009) ***(G-5171)***
Bio-Revival LLC 561 667-3990
661 Maplewood Dr Ste 21 Jupiter (33458) ***(G-7009)***
Bio-Tech Medical Software Inc 800 797-4711
6750 N Andrews Ave # 325 Fort Lauderdale (33309) ***(G-3854)***
Biobag Americas Inc 727 789-1646
1059 Broadway Ste F Dunedin (34698) ***(G-3570)***
Biobotanical LLC 239 458-4534
889 Ne 27th Ln Cape Coral (33909) ***(G-1392)***
Biochem Manufacturing Inc 561 799-1590
15074 Pk Of Commerce Blvd Jupiter (33478) ***(G-7010)***
Biochem Manufacturing Inc 786 210-1290
7300 N Kendall Dr Ste 640 Miami (33156) ***(G-9248)***
Biochemical Manufacturing Inc 561 799-1590
15074 Pk Of Commerce Blvd Jupiter (33478) ***(G-7011)***
Biochrom, Hialeah *Also called Pro Lab Supply Corporation* ***(G-5576)***
Biodegradable Packaging Corp 305 824-1164
9775 Nw 80th Ave Miami Lakes (33016) ***(G-10769)***
Bioderm Inc 727 507-7655
12320 73rd Ct Largo (33773) ***(G-7909)***
Bioenergetics Press 386 462-5155
19802 Old Bellamy Rd Alachua (32615) ***(G-9)***
Bioflex Medical Magnetics 954 565-8500
5970 Sw 32nd Ter Fort Lauderdale (33312) ***(G-3855)***
Biofuse Medical Tech Inc 877 466-2434
200 S Hbr Cy Blvd Ste 402 Melbourne (32901) ***(G-8780)***
Biogaia Biologics Inc 786 762-4000
8333 Nw 53rd St Ste 469 Doral (33166) ***(G-3275)***
Bioivt LLC 516 876-7902
7500 Nw 5th St Plantation (33317) ***(G-14497)***
Biolife LLC 941 360-1300
8163 25th Ct E Sarasota (34243) ***(G-16184)***
Biolife Plasma Services 407 388-1052
1385 State Road 436 Casselberry (32707) ***(G-1498)***
Biomar Products LLC 800 216-2080
9441 Nw 47th Ter Doral (33178) ***(G-3276)***
Biomech Golf Equipment LLC 401 932-0479
711 5th Ave S Ste 212 Naples (34102) ***(G-11189)***
Biomedtech Laboratories Inc (PA) 813 558-2000
3802 Spectrum Blvd # 154 Tampa (33612) ***(G-17470)***
Biomet 3i LLC 561 775-9928
4555 Riverside Dr Palm Beach Gardens (33410) ***(G-13570)***
Bionitrogen Holdings Corp (PA) 561 600-9550
1400 Centrepark Blvd # 860 West Palm Beach (33401) ***(G-18820)***
Bioquem USA, Pompano Beach *Also called W & B Scientific Inc* ***(G-14911)***
Biorep Technologies Inc 305 330-4449
15804 Nw 57th Ave Miami Lakes (33014) ***(G-10770)***
Bioresource Technology 954 792-5222
1800 N Commerce Pkwy # 1 Weston (33326) ***(G-19113)***
Biosafe Supplies LLC 407 281-6658
9436 Southridge Park Ct # 400 Orlando (32819) ***(G-12516)***
Biosculptor Corporation 305 823-8300
2480 W 82nd St Unit 1 Hialeah (33016) ***(G-5326)***
Biosculpture Technology Inc (PA) 561 651-7816
1701 S Flagler Dr Apt 607 West Palm Beach (33401) ***(G-18821)***
Bioseb, Pinellas Park *Also called Forceleader Inc* ***(G-14348)***
Biostem Technologies Inc 954 380-8342
2836 Center Port Cir Pompano Beach (33064) ***(G-14617)***
Biotest Plasma Center, Boca Raton *Also called Bpc Plasma Inc* ***(G-462)***
Biotoxins Inc 407 892-6905
5705 E I Bronson Memrl Saint Cloud (34771) ***(G-15646)***
Biotrackthc, Fort Lauderdale *Also called Bio-Tech Medical Software Inc* ***(G-3854)***
Biozone Scientific Intl Inc (PA) 407 876-2000
7616 Southland Blvd # 114 Orlando (32809) ***(G-12517)***
Birdie Publishing LLC 561 332-1826
701 Se 6th Ave Ste 102 Delray Beach (33483) ***(G-3050)***
Birdiebox LLC 786 762-2975
2129 Nw 86th Ave Miami (33122) ***(G-9249)***
Birds Eye Drones LLC 321 355-3415
6174 Louise Cove Dr Windermere (34786) ***(G-19226)***
Birdsall Marine Design Inc 561 832-7879
530 Nottingham Blvd West Palm Beach (33405) ***(G-18822)***
Biscayne Awning & Shade Co 305 638-7933
2333 Nw 8th Ave Miami (33127) ***(G-9250)***
Biscayne Bedding Intl LLC 305 633-4634
3925 E 10th Ct Hialeah (33013) ***(G-5327)***
Biscayne Electric Motor & Pump 305 681-8171
830 Nw 144th St Miami (33168) ***(G-9251)***
Biscayne Tennis LLC 786 231-8372
19021 Biscayne Blvd Miami (33180) ***(G-9252)***
Bischoff Aero Llc 305 883-4410
2583 W 6th Ln Hialeah (33010) ***(G-5328)***
Biscotti Gourment Bakery, Miami *Also called La Mansion Latina LLC* ***(G-9843)***
Bishop Pharma LLC 954 292-7325
1000 W Mcnab Rd Ste 234 Pompano Beach (33069) ***(G-14618)***
Bisi Fasteners LLC 850 913-0101
2009 Poplar Pl 302 Panama City (32405) ***(G-13873)***
Bisk Education Inc (PA) 813 621-6200
9417 Princess Palm Ave # 400 Tampa (33619) ***(G-17471)***
Bisk Publishing Company, Tampa *Also called Bisk Education Inc* ***(G-17471)***
Bitvisory Inc 801 336-6626
601 21st St Ste 300 Vero Beach (32960) ***(G-18600)***
BIW, Miami *Also called Bachiller Iron Works Inc* ***(G-9213)***
Bizcard Xpress, Orange City *Also called MRM Creative LLC* ***(G-12376)***
Bizcard Xpress Sanford LLC 407 688-8902
1744 Rinehart Rd Sanford (32771) ***(G-16003)***
Bizzspot, Wesley Chapel *Also called Local Biz Spot Inc* ***(G-18751)***
BJ Burns Incorporated 305 572-9500
1411 Sawgrs Corp Pkwy Sunrise (33323) ***(G-17097)***
Bjb Marine Welding & Svcs Inc 954 909-4967
244 Sw 31st St Fort Lauderdale (33315) ***(G-3856)***
Bjm Enterprises Inc 941 746-4171
1104 9th St W Bradenton (34205) ***(G-1000)***
Bjmjrx Inc 941 505-9036
540 Islamorada Blvd Punta Gorda (33955) ***(G-15198)***
Bk Cabinets, Melbourne *Also called B & K Discount Cabinets LLC* ***(G-8775)***
Bk Naturals LLC 561 870-0592
2611 Mercer Ave 4 West Palm Beach (33401) ***(G-18823)***
Bk Plastics Industry Inc 813 920-3628
13414 Byrd Dr Odessa (33556) ***(G-12107)***
BK Stainless Inc 786 474-0203
13899 Sw 140th St Miami (33186) ***(G-9253)***
Bk Technologies, Melbourne *Also called Relm Communications Inc* ***(G-8919)***
Bk Technologies Inc (HQ) 321 984-1414
7100 Technology Dr West Melbourne (32904) ***(G-18767)***
Bk Technologies Corporation (PA) 321 984-1414
7100 Technology Dr West Melbourne (32904) ***(G-18768)***
Bkbl Holdings Ltd 954 920-6772
5031 N Hiatus Rd Sunrise (33351) ***(G-17098)***
Bkn International Inc 301 518-7153
1100 Biscayne Blvd # 290 Miami (33132) ***(G-9254)***
Bkr Printing Inc 813 951-8609
3837 Northdale Blvd 179 Tampa (33624) ***(G-17472)***
Bks Bakery Inc 386 216-0540
2531 Dumas Dr Deltona (32738) ***(G-3164)***
Bl Acquisition, Hialeah *Also called Bullet Line LLC* ***(G-5335)***
Bl Bio Lab LLC 727 900-2707
2021 Sunnydale Blvd # 14 Clearwater (33765) ***(G-1609)***
Bl Brandhouse LLC 305 600-7181
8375 Nw 30th Ter Doral (33122) ***(G-3277)***
Bla Software Inc 407 355-0800
10424 Sparkle Ct Orlando (32836) ***(G-12518)***
Black & Decker (us) Inc 407 657-0474
6100 Hanging Moss Rd # 520 Orlando (32807) ***(G-12519)***
Black Aces Tactical, Longwood *Also called Eric Lemoine* ***(G-8276)***
Black Bart International LLC 561 842-4045
155 E Blue Heron Blvd R2 Riviera Beach (33404) ***(G-15301)***
Black Bean Software LLC 727 420-6916
21652 Cormorant Cove Dr Land O Lakes (34637) ***(G-7850)***
Black Box Corporation 407 276-3171
19 Fanfair Ave Orlando (32811) ***(G-12520)***
Black College Monthly Inc 352 335-5771
901 Se 18th Ter Gainesville (32641) ***(G-4887)***
Black College Today Inc 954 344-4469
4973 Nw 115th Ter Coral Springs (33076) ***(G-2226)***
Black Coral Rum LLC (PA) 561 766-2493
1231 W 13th St Bldg 15 Riviera Beach (33404) ***(G-15302)***
Black Creek Logging 904 591-9681
4159 County Road 218 Middleburg (32068) ***(G-10904)***
Black Creek Precision LLC 888 426-6624
5151 Sunbeam Rd Ste 10 Jacksonville (32257) ***(G-6209)***
Black Diamond Coatings Inc 800 270-4050
6036 Nature Coast Blvd Brooksville (34602) ***(G-1215)***
Black Diamond Systems Corp (PA) 917 539-7309
1305 Cape Pointe Cir Vero Beach (32963) ***(G-18601)***
Black Ice Software LLC (PA) 561 757-4107
950 Peninsula Corporate C Boca Raton (33487) ***(G-448)***
Black Knight Inc (PA) 904 854-5100
601 Riverside Ave Jacksonville (32204) ***(G-6210)***
Black Knight Fincl Svcs Inc (HQ) 904 854-5100
601 Riverside Ave Jacksonville (32204) ***(G-6211)***
Black Label Group LLC 407 917-1255
51 E Jefferson St # 1242 Orlando (32802) ***(G-12521)***
Black Mountain Apparel Inc 727 216-6419
10490 75th St Ste A Seminole (33777) ***(G-16743)***
Black News Channel LLC 844 262-3968
2320 Killearn Center Blvd Tallahassee (32309) ***(G-17228)***
Black Oak Industries Inc 863 307-1566
9518 Waterford Oaks Blvd Winter Haven (33884) ***(G-19303)***
Black Ops LLC 305 450-0127
7815 W 4th Ave Hialeah (33014) ***(G-5329)***

ALPHABETIC

Black Pearl Woodworks LLC 954 214-0899
16142 E Burns Dr Loxahatchee (33470) ***(G-8358)***
Black Tie Publishing Inc 954 472-6003
10131 Nw 14th St Plantation (33322) ***(G-14498)***
Black Widow Custom Cases 321 327-8058
1720 Main St Ne Palm Bay (32905) ***(G-13504)***
Blackbird Armament LLC 833 255-2473
150 East Dr Ste B Melbourne (32904) ***(G-8781)***
Blackbox Gps, Fort Lauderdale *Also called Embrace Telecom Inc* ***(G-3969)***
Blackcloak Inc 833 882-5625
7025 Cty Rd 46a Ste 1071 46 A Lake Mary (32746) ***(G-7403)***
Blackfist Magazine LLC (PA) 904 864-8695
382 Ne 191st St Ste 73388 Miami (33179) ***(G-9255)***
Blackhawk Construction Co Inc (PA) 321 258-4957
3060 Airport West Dr Vero Beach (32960) ***(G-18602)***
Blackhawk Quarry Co of Fla, Vero Beach *Also called Blackhawk Construction Co Inc* ***(G-18602)***
Blackies Weldng & Boiler Svc 954 961-5777
3101 Sw 25th St Hallandale Beach (33009) ***(G-5172)***
Blacklidge Emulsions Inc 954 275-7225
2501 Wiles Rd Pompano Beach (33073) ***(G-14619)***
Blacklidge Emulsions Inc 850 432-3496
4375 Mccoy Dr Pensacola (32503) ***(G-14100)***
Blacklidge Emulsions Inc 813 247-5699
2701 E 2nd Ave Tampa (33605) ***(G-17473)***
Blackstone Legal Supplies Inc (PA) 305 945-3450
3732 Nw 16th St Lauderhill (33311) ***(G-8103)***
Blackstone Legal Supply, Lauderhill *Also called Blackstone Legal Supplies Inc* ***(G-8103)***
Blackton Flooring Inc 407 898-2661
1714 Alden Rd Orlando (32803) ***(G-12522)***
Blackwater Folk Art Inc 850 623-3470
4917 Glover Ln Milton (32570) ***(G-10922)***
Blackwater Truss Systems LLC 850 623-1414
6603 Old Bagdad Hwy Milton (32583) ***(G-10923)***
Blackwell Family Corporation 941 639-0200
1869 Manzana Ave Punta Gorda (33950) ***(G-15199)***
Blackwter Metal Sls NW Fla LLC 850 622-1414
8736 Highway 87 N Milton (32570) ***(G-10924)***
Blades Direct LLC 855 225-2337
5645 Coral Ridge Dr Coral Springs (33076) ***(G-2227)***
Bladorn Investments Inc 941 627-0014
1264 Market Cir Unit 6 Port Charlotte (33953) ***(G-14965)***
Blaine E Taylor Welding Inc 386 931-1242
75 County Road 125 Bunnell (32110) ***(G-1298)***
Blair Machine & Tool Inc 904 731-4377
1301 Riverplace Blvd # 800 Jacksonville (32207) ***(G-6212)***
Blair Propeller MA 772 283-1453
3009 Se Monroe St Stuart (34997) ***(G-16917)***
Blane E Taylor Welding Inc 386 931-1240
1760 N Us Highway 1 Ormond Beach (32174) ***(G-13354)***
Blast Ctings Powdercoating LLC 561 635-7605
1847 Aragon Ave Unit 2 Lake Worth Beach (33461) ***(G-7608)***
Blast Off Equipment Inc 561 964-6199
2350 S Military Trl West Palm Beach (33415) ***(G-18824)***
Blasters Ready Jet Inc 813 985-4500
7815 Professional Pl Tampa (33637) ***(G-17474)***
Blazedpath, Fort Lauderdale *Also called Low Code Ip Holding LLC* ***(G-4103)***
Blazer Boats Inc 321 307-4761
12001 Res Pkwy Ste 236 Orlando (32826) ***(G-12523)***
Bld Industries 321 207-0050
987 Josiane Ct Ste 1064 Altamonte Springs (32701) ***(G-33)***
Blind and Drapery Gallery Inc 239 948-7611
24830 S Tamiami Trl # 170 Bonita Springs (34134) ***(G-816)***
Blind Brothers Inc 786 518-8938
7038 Sw 46th St Miami (33155) ***(G-9256)***
Blind Monkey 954 533-3090
2601 W Broward Blvd Fort Lauderdale (33312) ***(G-3857)***
Blind Mouth Brewing Co LLC 727 318-7664
3701 50th Ave S Saint Petersburg (33711) ***(G-15722)***
Blind Wizard Too Inc 954 755-3828
9146 Nw 21st St Coral Springs (33071) ***(G-2228)***
Blinds 321 Inc 305 336-9221
12335 Nw 7th St Miami (33182) ***(G-9257)***
Blinds By Randy LLC 305 300-1147
3274 Nw 181st St Miami Gardens (33056) ***(G-10735)***
Blinds Dr LLC 305 394-4808
2220 Sw 84th Ave Miami (33155) ***(G-9258)***
Blinds Express 954 826-6185
3000 Ne 16th Ave Apt D105 Oakland Park (33334) ***(G-11786)***
Blinds Plus Shutters & Shades 352 430-7200
2315 Griffin Rd Ste 8 Leesburg (34748) ***(G-8145)***
Blinds R Us Corp 305 303-2072
5946 Sw 162nd Path Miami (33193) ***(G-9259)***
Blinds Shades Industries Corp 786 445-2144
245 Ne 183rd St Ste 2b Miami (33179) ***(G-9260)***
Blinds Side 888 610-8366
5801 N Atlantic Ave Cape Canaveral (32920) ***(G-1352)***
Blingka Inc 800 485-6793
3911 Americana Dr Tampa (33634) ***(G-17475)***
Blitz Micro Turning Inc 727 725-5005
945 Harbor Lake Ct Safety Harbor (34695) ***(G-15489)***
Blix Corporate Image LLC 305 572-9001
1352 Nw 78th Ave Doral (33126) ***(G-3278)***
Blix Graphics, Doral *Also called Blix Corporate Image LLC* ***(G-3278)***
Bloem LLC 407 889-5533
3000 Orange Ave Apopka (32703) ***(G-118)***
Bloomingdale Gazette Inc 813 681-2051
3244 Lithia Pinecrest Rd # 101 Valrico (33596) ***(G-18516)***
Blow Off, Margate *Also called AVw Inc* ***(G-8536)***
Blp Racing Products LLC 407 422-0394
1015 W Church St Orlando (32805) ***(G-12524)***
Blu Sense 786 616-8628
7855 Nw 29th St Doral (33122) ***(G-3279)***
Blu Sleep Products LLC (PA) 866 973-7614
1501 Green Rd Ste B Deerfield Beach (33064) ***(G-2785)***
Bluazu LLC 386 697-3743
101 Se 2nd Pl Ste 201b Gainesville (32601) ***(G-4888)***
Blue Biofuels Inc 561 693-1943
3710 Buckeye St Ste 120 Palm Beach Gardens (33410) ***(G-13571)***
Blue Butterfly Hair Extensions, Sunrise *Also called Italian Hair Extension Inc* ***(G-17131)***
Blue Chip Group LLC 305 863-9094
3400 Nw 113th Ct Doral (33178) ***(G-3280)***
Blue Coast Bakers LLC 386 944-0800
1899 N Us Highway 1 Ormond Beach (32174) ***(G-13355)***
Blue Creek Holdings Inc (PA) 814 796-1900
6628 N Dormany Rd Plant City (33565) ***(G-14410)***
Blue Diamond Orthopedic LLC 407 613-2001
6439 Milner Blvd Ste 4 Orlando (32809) ***(G-12525)***
Blue Eagle Alliance Inc 904 322-8067
4651 Salisbury Rd # 4028 Jacksonville (32256) ***(G-6213)***
Blue Earth Solutions Inc 352 729-0150
13511 Granville Ave Clermont (34711) ***(G-1949)***
Blue Gardenia LLC 727 560-0040
661 Central Ave Saint Petersburg (33701) ***(G-15723)***
Blue Hawaiian Fiberglass Pools, Largo *Also called Blue Hawaiian Products Inc* ***(G-7910)***
Blue Hawaiian Products Inc (PA) 727 535-5677
2055 Blue Hawaiian Dr Largo (33771) ***(G-7910)***
Blue Hole Helicopters Inc 561 723-0378
3161 Se Chandelle Rd Jupiter (33478) ***(G-7012)***
Blue Horseshoe Pools West Inc 321 287-8758
16334 Arrowhead Trl Clermont (34711) ***(G-1950)***
Blue Leaf Hospitality Inc 305 668-3000
4405 Sw 74th Ave Miami (33155) ***(G-9261)***
Blue Light USA Corp 954 766-4308
4625 Nw 103rd Ave Sunrise (33351) ***(G-17099)***
Blue Marlin Towers Inc 954 530-9140
3100 W State Road 84 # 20 Fort Lauderdale (33312) ***(G-3858)***
Blue Native of Fla Keys Inc 305 345-5305
197 Industrial Rd Big Pine Key (33043) ***(G-381)***
Blue Ocean Press Inc 954 973-1819
6299 Nw 27th Way Fort Lauderdale (33309) ***(G-3859)***
Blue Origin Florida LLC (HQ) 253 437-9300
8082 Space Commerce Way Merritt Island (32953) ***(G-8994)***
Blue Planet Envmtl Systems 321 255-1931
2600 Kingswood Dr Ne Palm Bay (32905) ***(G-13505)***
Blue Planet Holdings LLC (PA) 863 559-1236
1738 Clarendon Pl Lakeland (33803) ***(G-7647)***
Blue Point Fabrication, Titusville *Also called Bluepoint Fabrication Inc* ***(G-18415)***
Blue Ribbon Tag & Label Corp (PA) 954 922-9292
4035 N 29th Ave Hollywood (33020) ***(G-5788)***
Blue Ribbon Tag & Label of PR 787 858-5300
4035 N 29th Ave Hollywood (33020) ***(G-5789)***
Blue Rock Inc (PA) 850 584-4324
4010 Olan Davis Rd Perry (32347) ***(G-14295)***
Blue Shoe Software LLC 321 438-5708
424 E Central Blvd # 720 Orlando (32801) ***(G-12526)***
Blue Siren Inc 321 242-0300
3030 Venture Ln Ste 103 Melbourne (32934) ***(G-8782)***
Blue Sky Die Company, Tavares *Also called Kirtech Enterprises Inc* ***(G-18344)***
Blue Sky Labs LLC 901 268-6988
3811 University Blvd W # 4 Jacksonville (32217) ***(G-6214)***
Blue Stone Usa LLC 305 494-1141
1172 S Dixie Hwy 301 Coral Gables (33146) ***(G-2127)***
Blue Summit Wind LLC (HQ) 561 691-7171
700 Universe Blvd Juno Beach (33408) ***(G-6975)***
Blue Sun International, Doral *Also called Kayva Distribution LLC* ***(G-3406)***
Blue Tarpon Construction LLC 251 223-3630
119 W Garden St Pensacola (32502) ***(G-14101)***
Blue Water Chairs Inc 954 318-0840
240 Sw 33rd Ct Fort Lauderdale (33315) ***(G-3860)***
Blue Water Dynamics LLC 386 957-5464
308 S Old County Rd Edgewater (32132) ***(G-3614)***
Blue Water Industries - FL LLC, Jacksonville *Also called Blue Water Industries LLC* ***(G-6215)***
Blue Water Industries LLC (PA) 904 512-7706
200 W Forsyth St Ste 1200 Jacksonville (32202) ***(G-6215)***
Blue Water Spa Covers, Apopka *Also called Bdjl Enterprises LLC* ***(G-116)***
Bluedrop USA Inc 407 470-0865
2603 Challenger Tech Ct Orlando (32826) ***(G-12527)***

Bluegate Inc 305 628-8391
16409 Nw 8th Ave Miami Gardens (33169) *(G-10736)*
Bluegator Ground Protection, Ocala *Also called Donarra Extrusions LLC (G-11923)*
Bluegrass Materials Co LLC (HQ) 919 781-4550
200 W Forsyth St Ste 1200 Jacksonville (32202) *(G-6216)*
Blueocean Marine Services LLC 954 583-9888
340 Sw 21st Ter Fort Lauderdale (33312) *(G-3861)*
Bluepoint Fabrication Inc 321 269-0073
3340 Lillian Blvd Titusville (32780) *(G-18415)*
Blues Design Group LLC 305 586-3630
3724 Nw 43rd St Miami (33142) *(G-9262)*
Bluesky Mast Inc 877 411-6278
2080 Wild Acres Rd Largo (33771) *(G-7911)*
Bluestar Latin America Inc 800 354-9776
3541-3561 Enterprise Way Miramar (33025) *(G-10975)*
Bluetoad Inc 407 992-8744
2225 Lake Nally Woods Dr Gotha (34734) *(G-5040)*
Bluewater Finishing LLC 772 460-9457
1913 Sw South Macedo Blvd Port Saint Lucie (34984) *(G-15092)*
Bluewater Marine Systems Inc 619 499-7507
360 Central Ave Ste 800 Saint Petersburg (33701) *(G-15724)*
Bluewaterpress LLC (PA) 888 247-0793
52 Tuscan Way Ste 202-309 Saint Augustine (32092) *(G-15522)*
Blumer & Stanton Enterprises (PA) 561 585-2525
5112 Georgia Ave West Palm Beach (33405) *(G-18825)*
Blumer & Stanton Inc 561 585-2525
5112 Georgia Ave West Palm Beach (33405) *(G-18826)*
Blunts Welding LLC 352 274-6014
2843 Nw 142nd Pl Citra (32113) *(G-1556)*
Blutec Glass Fabrication LLC 941 232-1600
5342 Clark Rd Unit 125 Sarasota (34233) *(G-16365)*
Bluum Lab LLC 877 341-3339
470 Ansin Blvd Ste Aa Hallandale Beach (33009) *(G-5173)*
Bluworld Innovations LLC 888 499-5433
635 W Michigan St Orlando (32805) *(G-12528)*
Bluworld of Water LLC 407 426-7674
3093 Caruso Ct Ste 40-A Orlando (32806) *(G-12529)*
BMC Services Inc 954 587-6337
2351 Sw 34th St Fort Lauderdale (33312) *(G-3862)*
Bmg Aerospace 786 725-4959
245 Ne 14th St Apt 3701 Miami (33132) *(G-9263)*
Bmp Usa Inc 813 443-0757
8105 Anderson Rd Tampa (33634) *(G-17476)*
Bms International Inc 813 247-7040
8802 E Broadway Ave Tampa (33619) *(G-17477)*
Bms-Tek LLC 321 727-7800
2896 Harper Rd Melbourne (32904) *(G-8783)*
BMW & Associates Inc 352 694-2300
4380 Se 53rd Ave Ocala (34480) *(G-11888)*
BMW Entertainment LLC 850 502-4590
136 Fishermans Cv Destin (32550) *(G-3213)*
BMW Window Coverings, Ocala *Also called BMW & Associates Inc (G-11888)*
Bn Biofuels LLC 312 239-2680
1 E 11th St Ste 202 Riviera Beach (33404) *(G-15303)*
Bnb Business Systems Inc 954 538-0669
18623 Sw 7th St Pembroke Pines (33029) *(G-14024)*
Bnj Noble Inc 954 987-1040
5408 Stirling Rd Davie (33314) *(G-2503)*
Boair Inc 954 426-9226
210 S Military Trl Deerfield Beach (33442) *(G-2786)*
Board Shark Pcb Inc 352 759-2100
53717 Rivertrace Rd Astor (32102) *(G-215)*
Boardwalk Designs Inc 850 265-0988
1312 Louisiana Ave Lynn Haven (32444) *(G-8430)*
Boat Doctor, The, Tampa *Also called Sheaffer Marine Inc (G-18094)*
Boat Energy LLC 954 501-2628
714 Nw 57th St Fort Lauderdale (33309) *(G-3863)*
Boat International Media Inc 954 522-2628
1800 Se 10th Ave Ste 340 Fort Lauderdale (33316) *(G-3864)*
Boat Lift Pros of SW Fla Inc 239 339-7080
2559 4th St Fort Myers (33901) *(G-4376)*
Boat Lifts By Synergy LLC 641 676-4785
15864 Brothers Ct Ste B Fort Myers (33912) *(G-4377)*
Boat Lifts of South Florida 305 522-1320
89170 Overseas Hwy Tavernier (33070) *(G-18361)*
Boat Master Aluminum Trailers 239 768-2224
11950 Amedicus Ln Unit 2 Fort Myers (33907) *(G-4378)*
Boat Steering Solutions LLC 727 400-4746
1070 Endeavor Ct North Venice (34275) *(G-11754)*
Boat Works 904 389-0090
1282 Belmont Ter Jacksonville (32207) *(G-6217)*
Boatmaster/J D C I Enterprises, Fort Myers *Also called Jdci Enterprises Inc (G-4502)*
Boatswains Locker Inc 904 388-0231
4565 Lakeside Dr Jacksonville (32210) *(G-6218)*
Bob & Lees Cabinets 352 748-3553
4386 Warm Springs Ave Wildwood (34785) *(G-19191)*
Bob Kline Quality Metal Inc 561 659-4245
2511 Division Ave West Palm Beach (33407) *(G-18827)*
Bob Laferriere Aircraft Inc 727 709-2704
2769 Saint Andrews Blvd Tarpon Springs (34688) *(G-18284)*
Bob S Busy Bee Printing, Tampa *Also called Printer S Pride Inc (G-18015)*
Bob Violett Models Inc 407 327-6333
3481 State Road 419 Winter Springs (32708) *(G-19469)*
Bob's Machine Shop, Tampa *Also called Bms International Inc (G-17477)*
Bob's Printing, Boynton Beach *Also called Bobs Quick Prtg & Copy Ctr (G-883)*
Bob's Top End, Fort Myers *Also called DNE Pot Sbob Inc (G-4434)*
Bobbie Weiner Enterprises LLC 817 615-8610
12355 Ne 13th Ave Unit 40 North Miami (33161) *(G-11628)*
Bobcat of Wiregrass Inc (PA) 334 792-5121
127 Griffin Blvd Panama City Beach (32413) *(G-13973)*
Bobs Backflow & Plumbing Co 904 268-8009
4640 Sub Chaser Ct # 113 Jacksonville (32244) *(G-6219)*
Bobs Barricades Inc 813 886-0518
5018 24th Ave S Tampa (33619) *(G-17478)*
Bobs Barricades Inc 239 656-1183
8031 Mainline Pkwy Fort Myers (33912) *(G-4379)*
Bobs Custom Coatings LLC 941 745-9659
3716 Highland Ave W Bradenton (34205) *(G-1001)*
Bobs Quick Prtg & Copy Ctr 561 278-0203
812 Chapel Hill Blvd Boynton Beach (33435) *(G-883)*
Bobs Space Racers Inc 386 677-0761
427 Whac A Mole Way Daytona Beach (32117) *(G-2631)*
Bobs Twist N Shake 941 485-5152
420 Us Highway 41 Byp N Venice (34285) *(G-18535)*
Bobs Wldg Fbrcation Maint Inc 863 665-0135
542 S Combee Rd Lakeland (33801) *(G-7648)*
Boca Beacon Co, Boca Grande *Also called Hopkins & Daughter Inc (G-393)*
Boca Coatings Inc 561 400-8183
6135 Belleza Ln Boca Raton (33433) *(G-449)*
Boca Color Graphics Inc 561 391-2229
139 Nw 3rd St Boca Raton (33432) *(G-450)*
Boca Dental Supply LLC 800 768-5691
3401 N Federal Hwy # 211 Boca Raton (33431) *(G-451)*
Boca Raton Commercial Printing 561 549-0126
801 N Federal Hwy Boca Raton (33432) *(G-452)*
Boca Raton Magazine, Boca Raton *Also called Jes Publishing Corp (G-580)*
Boca Raton Observer 561 702-3086
4290 Nw 66th Pl Boca Raton (33496) *(G-453)*
Boca Raton Observer Magazine, Boca Raton *Also called A & A Publishing Corp (G-395)*
Boca Raton Printing Co 561 395-8404
1000 Clint Moore Rd # 205 Boca Raton (33487) *(G-454)*
Boca Self Defense 954 903-0913
500 S Ocean Blvd Apt 306 Boca Raton (33432) *(G-455)*
Boca Semiconductor Corporation 561 226-8500
4260 Nw 1st Ave Ste 50 Boca Raton (33431) *(G-456)*
Boca Signworks 561 393-6010
174 Glades Rd Boca Raton (33432) *(G-457)*
Boca Smoothies LLC 772 323-2117
935 Military Trl Ste 102 Jupiter (33458) *(G-7013)*
Boca Stone Designs 561 362-2085
3601 N Dixie Hwy Ste 5 Boca Raton (33431) *(G-458)*
Boca Systems Inc 561 998-9600
1065 S Rogers Cir Boca Raton (33487) *(G-459)*
Boca Terry LLC 954 312-4400
3000 Sw 15th St Ste G Deerfield Beach (33442) *(G-2787)*
Bocadelray Life Magazine 954 421-9797
4611 Johnson Rd Coconut Creek (33073) *(G-2071)*
Bocatech Inc 954 397-7070
1020 Nw 6th St Ste A Deerfield Beach (33442) *(G-2788)*
Boden Co Inc 727 571-1234
10445 49th St N Ste B Clearwater (33762) *(G-1610)*
Bodhi Tree Woodwork Inc 904 540-2655
60 N Saint Augustine Blvd Saint Augustine (32080) *(G-15523)*
Bodman Oil & Gas LLC 239 430-8545
3007 Rum Row Naples (34102) *(G-11190)*
Bodolay Packaging Machine Div, Plant City *Also called B & M Industries Inc (G-14404)*
Bodree Printing Company Inc 850 455-8511
3310 N W St Pensacola (32505) *(G-14102)*
Body Action Products, Land O Lakes *Also called Product Max Group Inc (G-7863)*
Body Chemistry Industries In C 561 253-4438
2247 Stotesbury Way Wellington (33414) *(G-18711)*
Body Fuel LLC 386 566-1855
1155 Greenbriar Ave Port Orange (32127) *(G-15013)*
Body LLC 850 888-2639
2950 47th Ave N Saint Petersburg (33714) *(G-15725)*
Body Manufactur E Inc 386 264-6040
4982 Palm Coast Pkwy Nw Palm Coast (32137) *(G-13686)*
Body Nutrition, Saint Petersburg *Also called Body LLC (G-15725)*
Boeing 850 301-6635
20 Hill Ave Nw Fort Walton Beach (32548) *(G-4782)*
Boeing Arospc Operations Inc 850 682-2746
5486 Fairchild Rd Hngr 3 Crestview (32539) *(G-2344)*
Boeing Company 407 306-8782
13501 Ingenuity Dr # 204 Orlando (32826) *(G-12530)*
Boeing Company 321 867-6005
620 Magellan Rd Cape Canaveral (32920) *(G-1353)*
Boeing Company 904 772-1273
6222 Pow Mia Memorial Pkw Jacksonville (32221) *(G-6220)*

ALPHABETIC

Boeing Company 321 867-6005
O & C Building Rm 1090 Kennedy Space Center (32815) ***(G-7151)***
Boeing Company 321 867-7380
Nasa Cswy Kennedy Space Center (32815) ***(G-7152)***
Boeing Company 786 265-9965
6601 Nw 36th St Virginia Gardens (33166) ***(G-18684)***
Boeing Company 904 317-2490
6211 Aviation Ave Jacksonville (32221) ***(G-6221)***
Boeing Company 850 301-6613
626 Anchors St Nw Fort Walton Beach (32548) ***(G-4783)***
Boeing Company 850 882-4912
305 W Choctawhatchee Ave Eglin Afb (32542) ***(G-3641)***
Boeing Company 312 544-2000
100 Boeing Way Titusville (32780) ***(G-18416)***
Bogantec Corp 954 217-0023
1300 Stirling Rd Dania Beach (33004) ***(G-2463)***
Boggy Creek Boat Co LLC 904 707-0952
14476 Duval Pl W Ste 203 Jacksonville (32218) ***(G-6222)***
Bohemia Intrctive Smltions Inc 407 608-7000
3050 Tech Pkwy Ste 110 Orlando (32826) ***(G-12531)***
Bohemian Boatworks LLC 941 321-1499
5140 Jungle Plum Rd Sarasota (34242) ***(G-16366)***
Bohnert Sheet Metal & Roofg Co 305 696-6851
2225 Nw 76th St Miami (33147) ***(G-9264)***
Boiler Inspection Services, Jacksonville *Also called Whertec Inc* ***(G-6917)***
Boland Production Supply Inc 863 324-7784
507 Burns Ln Winter Haven (33884) ***(G-19304)***
Boland Timber Company Inc 850 997-5270
3616 S Byron Butler Pkwy Perry (32348) ***(G-14296)***
Bolbox, Miami *Also called Worldbox Corporation* ***(G-10621)***
Bold City Braves LLC 904 545-3480
3385 Intl Vlg Dr W Jacksonville (32277) ***(G-6223)***
Bold City Spray Coatings LLC 904 655-0825
2612 Arlex Dr E Jacksonville (32211) ***(G-6224)***
Bold Look Inc 305 687-8725
6721 Nw 36th Ave Miami (33147) ***(G-9265)***
Bolidt Cruise Control Corp 305 607-4172
14501 Nw 57th Ave Ste 111 Opa Locka (33054) ***(G-12295)***
Bollou Transportation LLC 800 548-1768
11626 Ne 2nd Ave Miami (33161) ***(G-9266)***
Bolt Lightning Protection, Clearwater *Also called Lightning Master Corporation* ***(G-1761)***
Bolt Signs & Marketing LLC (PA) 407 865-7446
151 Smran Cmmrce Pl Ste A Apopka (32703) ***(G-119)***
Bolt Systems Inc 407 425-0012
1700 Silver Star Rd Orlando (32804) ***(G-12532)***
Bolton Medical Inc 954 838-9699
799 International Pkwy Sunrise (33325) ***(G-17100)***
Bombardier Aircraft Services, Fort Lauderdale *Also called Bombardiier* ***(G-3865)***
Bombardier Trnsp Hldngs USA In 407 450-4855
801 Sunrail Dr Sanford (32771) ***(G-16004)***
Bombardiier 954 622-1200
4100 Sw 11th Ter Fort Lauderdale (33315) ***(G-3865)***
Bon Appetit French Bakery, Fort Walton Beach *Also called Palanjian Enterprises Inc* ***(G-4820)***
Bon Brands Inc 800 590-7911
10299 Sthrn Blvd Unit 21 Royal Palm Beach (33411) ***(G-15462)***
Bon Vivant Custom Woodworking, Opa Locka *Also called Bon Vivant Interiors Inc* ***(G-12296)***
Bon Vivant Interiors Inc 305 576-8066
4400 Nw 135th St Opa Locka (33054) ***(G-12296)***
Bona Enterprises Inc (PA) 954 927-4889
255 E Dania Beach Blvd Dania (33004) ***(G-2439)***
Bonadeo Boat Works LLC 772 341-9820
4431 Se Commerce Ave Stuart (34997) ***(G-16918)***
Bond Medical Group Inc 813 264-5951
3837 Northdale Blvd # 36 Tampa (33624) ***(G-17479)***
Bond-Pro Inc 888 789-4985
1501 E 2nd Ave Tampa (33605) ***(G-17480)***
Bond-Pro LLC 813 413-7576
302 Knights Run Ave # 11 Tampa (33602) ***(G-17481)***
Bonefish Boats and Trlrs LLC 239 707-4656
1121 Se 12th Pl Ste C Cape Coral (33990) ***(G-1393)***
Bonefish Boatworks Llc 727 243-6767
1005 Gunn Hwy Odessa (33556) ***(G-12108)***
Bongiovi Aviation LLC 772 879-0578
649 Sw Whitmore Dr Port Saint Lucie (34984) ***(G-15093)***
Bonita Daily News 239 213-6060
1100 Immokalee Rd Naples (34110) ***(G-11191)***
Bonita Gente Magazine 239 331-7952
2840 29th Ave Ne Naples (34120) ***(G-11192)***
Bonita Grande Aggregates, Bonita Springs *Also called Bonita Grande Mining LLC* ***(G-817)***
Bonita Grande Mining LLC 239 947-6402
25501 Bonita Grande Dr Bonita Springs (34135) ***(G-817)***
Bonita Print Shop, Bonita Springs *Also called Bonita Printshop Inc* ***(G-818)***
Bonita Print Shop, Bonita Springs *Also called I-Partner Group Inc* ***(G-838)***
Bonita Printshop Inc 239 992-8522
28210 Old 41 Rd Unit 305 Bonita Springs (34135) ***(G-818)***
Bonito & Company LLC 561 451-7494
1000 Nw 1st Ave Ste 14 Boca Raton (33432) ***(G-460)***
Bonne Sante Group, Miami *Also called Smart For Life Inc* ***(G-10363)***
Bonne Sante Natural Mfg Inc 305 594-4990
10575 Nw 37th Ter Doral (33178) ***(G-3281)***
Bonnier Corporation 954 830-4460
705 Sw 16th St Fort Lauderdale (33315) ***(G-3866)***
Bonnier Corporation (HQ) 407 628-4802
480 N Orlando Ave Ste 236 Winter Park (32789) ***(G-19383)***
Bonsai American, Pensacola *Also called Bonsal American Inc* ***(G-14103)***
Bonsal American, Pompano Beach *Also called Oldcastle Retail Inc* ***(G-14778)***
Bonsal American Inc 813 621-2427
5455 N 59th St Tampa (33610) ***(G-17482)***
Bonsal American Inc 904 783-0605
6659 Highway Ave Jacksonville (32254) ***(G-6225)***
Bonsal American Inc 850 476-4223
150 E Olive Rd Pensacola (32514) ***(G-14103)***
Bonsal American Inc 863 967-9100
1511 1st St W Auburndale (33823) ***(G-230)***
Bonus Aerospace Inc 305 887-6778
8545 Nw 79th Ave Medley (33166) ***(G-8624)***
Bonus Tech Inc 786 251-4232
8575 Nw 79th Ave Ste 4d Medley (33166) ***(G-8625)***
Booklocker Com Inc 727 483-4540
200 2nd Ave S Saint Petersburg (33701) ***(G-15726)***
Books-A-Million Inc 813 571-2062
839 Brandon Town Ctr Mall Brandon (33511) ***(G-1152)***
Boomer Times & Senior Life, Boca Raton *Also called Lf Senior Communications Group* ***(G-602)***
Boone Bait Co Inc 407 975-8775
1501 Minnesota Ave Winter Park (32789) ***(G-19384)***
Boone Welding, Gainesville *Also called MPH Industries Inc* ***(G-4966)***
Boost Lab Inc 813 443-0531
31050 Chatterly Dr Wesley Chapel (33543) ***(G-18741)***
Boostan Inc 305 223-5981
8300 W Flagler St Ste 155 Miami (33144) ***(G-9267)***
Boostane LLC 239 908-1615
10981 Harmony Park Dr # 5 Bonita Springs (34135) ***(G-819)***
Booth Manufacturing Company 772 465-4441
3101 Industrial Ave Ste 2 Fort Pierce (34946) ***(G-4682)***
Borden Dairy Company Fla LLC 863 298-9742
1000 6th St Sw Winter Haven (33880) ***(G-19305)***
Borden, Ben Talent Assessment, Jacksonville *Also called Talent Assessment Inc* ***(G-6835)***
Borders & Accents Inc 305 947-6200
1890 Ne 144th St North Miami (33181) ***(G-11629)***
Bore Tech Inc 904 262-0752
5333 Skylark Ct Jacksonville (32257) ***(G-6226)***
Borgesfs Inc 786 210-0327
14920 Sw 137th St Unit 2 Miami (33196) ***(G-9268)***
Borgzinner Inc 561 848-2538
1160 W 13th St Ste 10 Riviera Beach (33404) ***(G-15304)***
Boris Skateboards Mfg Inc 305 519-3544
695 Ne 77th St Miami (33138) ***(G-9269)***
Bornt Enterprises Inc 813 623-1492
9824 Currie Davis Dr Tampa (33619) ***(G-17483)***
Boss Laser LLC 888 652-1555
608 Trestle Pt Sanford (32771) ***(G-16005)***
Bossa Hospitality 305 394-3994
7389 Universal Blvd Orlando (32819) ***(G-12533)***
Bosshardt Realty 352 494-1400
5111 Sw 94th St Gainesville (32608) ***(G-4889)***
Bossy Princess LLC 786 285-4435
18117 Biscayne Blvd # 1194 Aventura (33160) ***(G-265)***
Bostic Steel Inc 305 592-7276
7740 Nw 34th St Doral (33122) ***(G-3282)***
Boston Ntrceutical Science LLC 617 848-4560
801 Brickell Ave Miami (33131) ***(G-9270)***
Boston Whaler Inc 386 428-0057
100 Whaler Way Edgewater (32141) ***(G-3615)***
Boswell JM & Associates Inc 239 949-2311
270 3rd St Bonita Springs (34134) ***(G-820)***
Bosworth Millwork LLC 305 942-9017
329 Mahogany Dr Key Largo (33037) ***(G-7166)***
Bot International Inc 407 366-6547
1320 Tall Maple Loop Oviedo (32765) ***(G-13419)***
Botanica Odomiwale Corp 305 381-5834
1301 Palm Ave Hialeah (33010) ***(G-5330)***
Botanical Innovations Inc 407 332-8733
100 Candace Dr Unit 120 Maitland (32751) ***(G-8460)***
Botanical Scents Nature Entps, Miami Lakes *Also called Scents Nature Enterprises Corp* ***(G-10854)***
Bote LLC 888 855-4450
12598 Emerald Coast Pkwy Miramar Beach (32550) ***(G-11064)***
Bote Boards, Miramar Beach *Also called Bote LLC* ***(G-11064)***
Bote Boards 850 855-4046
630 Anchors St Nw Fort Walton Beach (32548) ***(G-4784)***
Bote Paddle Boards 850 460-2250
383 Harbor Blvd Destin (32541) ***(G-3184)***
Boulder Blimp Company Inc 303 664-1122
13350 Sw 131st St # 106 Miami (33186) ***(G-9271)***
Bowen Medical Services Inc 386 362-1345
709 Industrial Ave Sw Live Oak (32064) ***(G-8227)***

Bowman Analytics Inc 847 781-3523
5824 Bee Ridge Rd Sarasota (34233) *(G-16367)*
Bowsmith Inc 863 453-6666
100 W Monroe St Avon Park (33825) *(G-284)*
Box Seat Clothing Company 800 787-7792
5555 W 1st St Jacksonville (32254) *(G-6227)*
Boxrus.com, Hialeah *Also called Advanced Printing Finshg Inc (G-5272)*
Boxseat Inc 850 656-1223
5245 Commonwealth Ave Jacksonville (32254) *(G-6228)*
Boyce Engineering Inc 727 572-6318
11861 31st Ct N Saint Petersburg (33716) *(G-15727)*
Boyd Industries Inc 727 561-9292
12900 44th St N Clearwater (33762) *(G-1611)*
Boyd Welding LLC 352 447-2405
802 Nw 27th Ave Ocala (34475) *(G-11889)*
Boyett Timber Inc 352 583-2138
45260 Lcchee Clay Sink Rd Webster (33597) *(G-18697)*
Boyle Publications Inc 941 255-0187
1039 Tamiami Trl Port Charlotte (33953) *(G-14966)*
Bpc LLC 305 987-9517
1717 N Byshore Dr Apt 313 Miami (33132) *(G-9272)*
Bpc Plasma Inc 561 989-5800
901 W Yamato Rd Ste 101 Boca Raton (33431) *(G-461)*
Bpc Plasma Inc (HQ) 561 569-3100
901 W Yamato Rd Ste 101 Boca Raton (33431) *(G-462)*
Bpg, Maitland *Also called Builders Publishing Group LLC (G-8461)*
Bpi Labs LLC 727 471-0850
12393 Belcher Rd S # 450 Largo (33773) *(G-7912)*
Bpj International LLC 305 507-8971
11091 Nw 27th St Ste 204 Doral (33172) *(G-3283)*
BR Signs International In 954 464-7999
5944 Coral Ridge Dr Coral Springs (33076) *(G-2229)*
Brace Integrated Services Inc 813 248-6248
8205 E Adamo Dr Tampa (33619) *(G-17484)*
Braddck Mtllgl Arsp Ser Inc 561 622-2200
507 Industrial Way Boynton Beach (33426) *(G-884)*
Braddock Metallurgical Inc (HQ) 386 267-0955
14600 Duval Pl W Jacksonville (32218) *(G-6229)*
Braddock Metallurgical GA Inc 386 267-0955
400 Fentress Blvd Daytona Beach (32114) *(G-2632)*
Braddock Metallurgical MGT LLC 386 267-0955
400 Fentress Blvd Daytona Beach (32114) *(G-2633)*
Braddock Mtllrgcal - Dytona In 386 267-0955
400 Fentress Blvd Daytona Beach (32114) *(G-2634)*
Braddock Mtllurgical Holdg Inc (PA) 386 323-1500
400 Fentress Blvd Daytona Beach (32114) *(G-2635)*
Braden & Son Construction Inc 239 694-8600
6730 Circle Dr Fort Myers (33905) *(G-4380)*
Braden Kitchens Inc 321 636-4700
515 Industry Rd S Cocoa (32926) *(G-1999)*
Bradford County Telegraph Inc (PA) 904 964-6305
135 W Call St Starke (32091) *(G-16887)*
Bradford Septic Tank Company, Riviera Beach *Also called Pilot Corp of Palm Beaches (G-15363)*
Bradford Yacht Limited Inc 954 791-3800
3051 W State Road 84 Fort Lauderdale (33312) *(G-3867)*
Bradley Indus Textiles Inc 850 678-6111
101 S John Sims Pkwy Valparaiso (32580) *(G-18508)*
Brads Industries LLC 863 646-0051
5723 Buck Run Dr Lakeland (33811) *(G-7649)*
Brady Builders, Melbourne *Also called Brady Built Technologies Inc (G-8784)*
Brady Built Technologies Inc 270 692-6866
3661 Waynesboro Way Melbourne (32934) *(G-8784)*
Brady Wind LLC 561 304-5136
700 Universe Blvd Juno Beach (33408) *(G-6976)*
Braid Sales and Marketing Inc (PA) 321 752-8180
320 North Dr Melbourne (32934) *(G-8785)*
Brain Freeze Nitrogen 786 235-8505
3905 Nw 107th Ave Ste 106 Doral (33178) *(G-3284)*
Brain Power Incorporated 305 264-4465
4470 Sw 74th Ave Miami (33155) *(G-9273)*
Brainchild Corp 239 263-0100
3050 Horseshoe Dr N # 210 Naples (34104) *(G-11193)*
Brainchild Nutritionals, Miami *Also called Maxam Group LLC (G-9958)*
Brake-Funderburk Entps Inc 904 730-6788
8383 Baycenter Rd Jacksonville (32256) *(G-6230)*
Brambier's Windows & Walls, Port Orange *Also called Drapery Control Systems Inc (G-15017)*
Brambier's Windows & Walls, Fort Lauderdale *Also called Drapery Control Systems Inc (G-3949)*
Branch Properties Inc (PA) 352 732-4143
335 Ne Watula Ave Ocala (34470) *(G-11890)*
Brand Bros., Pensacola *Also called Deluna Toole LLC (G-14128)*
Brand Builders Rx LLC 727 576-4013
9843 18th St N Ste 150 Saint Petersburg (33716) *(G-15728)*
Brand Label Inc 904 737-6433
8295 Western Way Cir Jacksonville (32256) *(G-6231)*
Brand Labs USA 954 532-5390
325 Sw 15th Ave Pompano Beach (33069) *(G-14620)*
Brand You Waters LLC 786 312-0840
2402 Bay Dr Pompano Beach (33062) *(G-14621)*
Brandano Displays Inc (PA) 954 956-7266
1473 Banks Rd Margate (33063) *(G-8537)*
Brandcomet, Maitland *Also called Grand Cypress Group Inc (G-8467)*
Brandfx LLC 321 632-2063
605 Townsend Rd Cocoa (32926) *(G-2000)*
Brandine Woodcraft Inc 561 266-9360
601 N Congress Ave # 203 Delray Beach (33445) *(G-3051)*
Brandon Brown Newsom, Ponce De Leon *Also called U-Load Dumpsters LLC (G-14919)*
Brandon Lock & Safe Inc 813 655-4200
4630 Eagle Falls Pl Tampa (33619) *(G-17485)*
Brannen Wldg & Fabrication Inc 352 583-4849
34117 Ridge Manor Blvd Dade City (33523) *(G-2423)*
Brantley Machine & Fabrication 904 359-0554
4003 N Canal St Jacksonville (32209) *(G-6232)*
Brasileiras & Brasileiros Inc 407 855-9541
4847 Lake Milly Dr Orlando (32839) *(G-12534)*
Braswell Custom Cabinets 850 436-2645
9 Clarinda Ln Pensacola (32505) *(G-14104)*
Bravo Inc 239 471-8127
1811 Se 5th Ave Cape Coral (33990) *(G-1394)*
Bravo Construction Materials, Cape Coral *Also called Bravo Inc (G-1394)*
Brawley Distributing Co Inc 727 539-8500
7162 123rd Cir Largo (33773) *(G-7913)*
Brazil America Srones Inc 305 915-0123
723 Sw 6th St Unit 4 Hallandale Beach (33009) *(G-5174)*
Brazilian Brickpavers Inc 850 699-7833
200 Racetrack Rd Ne Fort Walton Beach (32547) *(G-4785)*
Brazilian Clssfied ADS-Chei In 954 570-7568
2001 W Sample Rd Ste 422 Deerfield Beach (33064) *(G-2789)*
Brazilian Smoothie Inc 305 233-5543
13255 Sw 83rd Ave Pinecrest (33156) *(G-14325)*
Brazilian Wood Works Inc 786 468-5712
3000 Sw 3rd Ave Miami (33129) *(G-9274)*
BRC Sports Llc 904 388-8126
3600 Beachwood Ct Jacksonville (32224) *(G-6233)*
Break-Free Inc 800 347-1200
13386 International Pkwy Jacksonville (32218) *(G-6234)*
Breakthrough Clean Tech, Doral *Also called Atg Specialty Products Corp (G-3259)*
Breast Thermgrphy of BRWrd&plm 561 852-5789
10831 Bal Harbor Dr Boca Raton (33498) *(G-463)*
Breathing Systems Inc 850 477-2324
8800 Grow Dr Pensacola (32514) *(G-14105)*
Breeden Pulpwood Inc 352 528-5243
Off Hwy 41 Williston (32696) *(G-19210)*
Breeze Boat Lifts, Fort Walton Beach *Also called Rocky Bayou Enterprises Inc (G-4829)*
Breeze Corporation (HQ) 239 574-1110
2510 Del Prado Blvd S Cape Coral (33904) *(G-1395)*
Breeze Corporation 239 765-0400
19260 San Carlos Blvd Fort Myers Beach (33931) *(G-4660)*
Breeze Corporation 239 425-8860
14051 Jetport Loop Fort Myers (33913) *(G-4381)*
Breeze Newspapers 239 574-1116
14051 Jetport Loop Fort Myers (33913) *(G-4382)*
Breeze Newspapers 239 574-1110
2510 Del Prado Blvd S Cape Coral (33904) *(G-1396)*
Breeze Printing, Fort Myers *Also called Breeze Corporation (G-4381)*
Breeze Products Inc 727 521-4482
7207 114th Ave Ste B Largo (33773) *(G-7914)*
Breezemaker Fan Company Inc 813 248-5552
1608 N 24th St Tampa (33605) *(G-17486)*
Breezy Swimwear 305 763-9570
8762 Sw 133rd St Miami (33176) *(G-9275)*
Brefaros Nobile Food LLC 305 621-0074
5340 Nw 163rd St Miami Lakes (33014) *(G-10771)*
Breiner Machine Co Inc 352 544-0463
15373 Flight Path Dr Brooksville (34604) *(G-1216)*
Breitburn Operating LP 713 452-2266
5415 Oil Plant Rd Jay (32565) *(G-6963)*
Bremer Group Company Inc 904 645-0004
11243-5 Saint Johns Jacksonville (32246) *(G-6235)*
Bren Tuck Inc 727 561-7697
12929 44th St N Clearwater (33762) *(G-1612)*
Brenda Naused 352 344-4729
2043 S Atlantic Ave Daytona Beach (32118) *(G-2636)*
Bresee Woodwork Inc 941 355-2591
1795 Desoto Rd Sarasota (34234) *(G-16368)*
Breton USA Customers Svc Corp 941 360-2700
1753 Northgate Blvd Sarasota (34234) *(G-16369)*
Brevard Achievement Center Inc 321 632-8610
1845 Cogswell St Rockledge (32955) *(G-15395)*
Brevard Aluminum Cnstr Co 321 383-9255
4655 Calle Corto Titusville (32780) *(G-18417)*
Brevard Business News 321 951-7777
4300 Fortune Pl Ste D Melbourne (32904) *(G-8786)*
Brevard Robotics 321 637-0367
1485 Cox Rd Cocoa (32926) *(G-2001)*
Brevard Softball Magazine Inc 321 453-3711
400 Nora Ave Merritt Island (32952) *(G-8995)*

Brew Central LLC 936 714-3402
1024 Park St Jacksonville (32204) **(G-6236)**
Brew Hub LLC 863 698-7600
3900 Frontage Rd S Lakeland (33815) **(G-7650)**
Brew Hub, The, Lakeland *Also called Brew Hub LLC* **(G-7650)**
Brewer International Inc 772 562-0555
605 90th Ave Vero Beach (32968) **(G-18603)**
Brewfab LLC 727 823-8333
2300 31st St N Saint Petersburg (33713) **(G-15729)**
Bri Tin Industries 941 580-6345
3112 Emerson Pl Plant City (33566) **(G-14411)**
Brian Belitz 407 924-5543
3130 Winding Trl Kissimmee (34746) **(G-7225)**
Brian Slater & Associates LLC 561 886-7705
5301 N Federal Hwy # 195 Boca Raton (33487) **(G-464)**
Brianas Salad LLC 954 608-0953
5400 N Dixie Hwy Ste 7 Boca Raton (33487) **(G-465)**
Brick Markers USA Inc 561 842-1338
4430 W Tiffany Dr Ste 2 Mangonia Park (33407) **(G-8500)**
Brick Pavers By Mendoza Inc (PA) 772 925-1666
1235 S Us Highway 1 Vero Beach (32962) **(G-18604)**
Brick Pavers By Mendoza Inc 772 408-2005
1986 21st St Sw Vero Beach (32962) **(G-18605)**
Brick Pvers Drveway Big Pavers 407 928-1217
6111 Metrowest Blvd Orlando (32835) **(G-12535)**
Brickland Pavers Inc 561 305-0325
1259 Sw 46th Ave Apt 1910 Pompano Beach (33069) **(G-14622)**
Bricklser Engrv Monuments Corp 786 806-0672
7964 Nw 14th St Doral (33126) **(G-3285)**
Brickmed LLC 305 774-0081
1800 Sw 27th Ave Ste 505 Miami (33145) **(G-9276)**
Bridg, Kissimmee *Also called Icamr Inc* **(G-7252)**
Bridge Trading Usa LLC 877 848-0979
2855 Nw 112th Ave Ste 2 Doral (33172) **(G-3286)**
Bridgeport Chemical 941 753-2520
10516 Firestone Dr Bradenton (34202) **(G-1002)**
Bridgestone Hosepower LLC (HQ) 904 264-1267
50 Industrial Loop N Orange Park (32073) **(G-12383)**
Briemad Inc 561 626-4377
2401 Pga Blvd Ste 136 Palm Beach Gardens (33410) **(G-13572)**
Bright Manufacturing LLC (PA) 954 603-4950
2933 W Cypress Creek Rd # 202 Fort Lauderdale (33309) **(G-3868)**
Brightman 386 752-4883
417 Sw Aloe Ct Lake City (32024) **(G-7349)**
Brightsky LLC 239 919-8551
1004 Collier Center Way # 2 Naples (34110) **(G-11194)**
Brightwatts Inc 954 513-3352
1967 Nw 22nd St Oakland Park (33311) **(G-11787)**
Brijot Imaging Systems Inc 407 641-4370
951 W Yamato Rd Ste 205 Boca Raton (33431) **(G-466)**
Brill Hygienic Products Inc 561 278-5600
601 N Congress Ave Delray Beach (33445) **(G-3052)**
Brinsea Products Inc 321 267-7009
704 N Dixie Ave Titusville (32796) **(G-18418)**
Bristol Venture Service LLC 407 844-8629
16121 Bristol Lake Cir Orlando (32828) **(G-12536)**
Bristols Elite 954 651-3574
3326 Garfield St Hollywood (33021) **(G-5790)**
Brite Lite Service Company 904 398-5305
5300 Shad Rd Jacksonville (32257) **(G-6237)**
Brite Lite Signs, Jacksonville *Also called Brite Lite Service Company* **(G-6237)**
Brite Shot Inc 954 418-7125
600 W Hillsboro Blvd Deerfield Beach (33441) **(G-2790)**
British Boys & Associates 305 278-1790
14480 Sw 151st Ter Miami (33186) **(G-9277)**
Brito Brick & Pavers Corp 727 214-8760
6262 142nd Ave N Clearwater (33760) **(G-1613)**
Britvic North America LLC 786 641-5041
360 Nw 27th St Miami (33127) **(G-9278)**
Broach Process Serving 727 385-9467
4720 Wolfram Ln New Port Richey (34653) **(G-11483)**
Broadband International Inc (PA) 305 882-0505
11650 Nw 102nd Rd Medley (33178) **(G-8626)**
Broadcast Tech Inc (PA) 786 351-4227
10100 Nw 116th Way Ste 6 Medley (33178) **(G-8627)**
Broit Builders Inc 239 300-6900
1588 Vizcaya Ln Naples (34113) **(G-11195)**
Broit Lifting, Naples *Also called Broit Builders Inc* **(G-11195)**
Bromide Mining LLC 786 477-6229
2335 Nw 107th Ave Ste 127 Doral (33172) **(G-3287)**
Bronzart Foundry Inc 941 922-9106
5415 Ashton Ct Unit H Sarasota (34233) **(G-16370)**
Brookhaven Beverage Company, Saint Petersburg *Also called St Petersburg Dist Co LLC* **(G-15924)**
Brooking Industries Inc 954 533-0765
104 Liberty Center Pl Saint Augustine (32092) **(G-15524)**
Brooklands New Media LLC 305 901-9674
1000 5th St Ste 200 Miami Beach (33139) **(G-10648)**
Brooklyn Stitch Inc 786 280-1730
20213 Ne 16th Pl Miami (33179) **(G-9279)**
Brooklyn Water Enterprises Inc 877 224-3580
1615 S Congress Ave # 103 Delray Beach (33445) **(G-3053)**
Brooks Concrete Service, Panacea *Also called Brooks Welding & Concrete Shop* **(G-13859)**
Brooks Welding & Concrete Shop 850 984-5279
1532 Coastal Hwy Panacea (32346) **(G-13859)**
Brooksville Printing Inc 352 848-0016
712 S Main St Brooksville (34601) **(G-1217)**
Brooksville Terminal Us11, Brooksville *Also called Lhoist North America Ala LLC* **(G-1246)**
Bros Williams Printing 305 769-9925
4716 E 10th Ct Hialeah (33013) **(G-5331)**
Bros Williams Printing Inc 305 769-9925
4716 E 10th Ct Hialeah (33013) **(G-5332)**
Broski Ciderworks LLC 954 657-8947
1465 Sw 6th Ct Pompano Beach (33069) **(G-14623)**
Brothers Pallets 863 944-5278
2410 Mcjunkin Rd Lakeland (33803) **(G-7651)**
Brothers Pavers and Precast 561 662-9075
1008 Mcintosh St West Palm Beach (33405) **(G-18828)**
Brothers Powder Coating Inc 727 846-0717
7721 Rutillio Ct Ste D New Port Richey (34653) **(G-11484)**
Brothers Wholesale Inc 631 831-8484
534 Nw Mercantile Pl Port St Lucie (34986) **(G-15168)**
Broward Armature and Generator, Fort Lauderdale *Also called Blueocean Marine Services LLC* **(G-3861)**
Broward Casting Foundry Inc 954 584-6400
2240 Sw 34th St Fort Lauderdale (33312) **(G-3869)**
Broward Custom Woodwork LLC 352 376-4732
401 Jim Moran Blvd Deerfield Beach (33442) **(G-2791)**
Broward Machine LLC 954 920-8004
2070 Tigertail Blvd Ste D Dania (33004) **(G-2440)**
Broward Marine, Dania *Also called Broward Yard & Marine LLC* **(G-2441)**
Broward Power Train Co Inc 954 772-0881
5300 Nw 12th Ave Ste 3 Fort Lauderdale (33309) **(G-3870)**
Broward Print 954 272-2272
1560 N University Dr Pembroke Pines (33024) **(G-14025)**
Broward Sign Shop 305 431-2455
1001 N Federal Hwy # 341 Hallandale Beach (33009) **(G-5175)**
Broward Signs 954 320-9903
1901 S Federal Hwy Fort Lauderdale (33316) **(G-3871)**
Broward Yard & Marine LLC 954 927-4119
750 Ne 7th Ave Dania (33004) **(G-2441)**
Brown (usa) Inc 305 593-9228
2245 Nw 72nd Ave Miami (33122) **(G-9280)**
Brown Company 850 455-0971
Aileron Ave Ste N.10102 Pensacola (32506) **(G-14106)**
Brown Dog Propeller LLC 321 254-7767
405 Dove Ln Satellite Beach (32937) **(G-16649)**
Brown Dog Publishing Inc 904 262-2114
8802 Corporate Square Ct Jacksonville (32216) **(G-6238)**
Brown Enterprises, Jacksonville *Also called Solar Enterprises Inc* **(G-6783)**
Brown Fabrication, Pensacola *Also called Brown Company* **(G-14106)**
Brown International Corp LLC 863 299-2111
333 Avenue M Nw Winter Haven (33881) **(G-19306)**
Brown's Septics, Silver Springs *Also called A-1 City Wide Sewer Service* **(G-16780)**
Brownbag Popcorn Company LLC 561 212-5664
900 Ne 4th St Apt A Boca Raton (33432) **(G-467)**
Brownie Lady LLC 954 989-0630
3925 Hyde Park Cir Hollywood (33021) **(G-5791)**
Brownies Marine Group Inc (PA) 954 462-5570
3001 Nw 25th Ave Ste 1 Pompano Beach (33069) **(G-14624)**
Browning Communications, Debary *Also called Hoffman Brothers Inc* **(G-2750)**
Brownlee Lighting Inc 407 297-3677
4600 Dardanelle Dr Orlando (32808) **(G-12537)**
Brownsugarbae LLC 954 554-0318
515 E Las Olas Blvd Ste 1 Fort Lauderdale (33301) **(G-3872)**
Brownsville Orna Ir Works Inc 850 433-0521
3520 Mobile Hwy Pensacola (32505) **(G-14107)**
Brownsville Welding, Pensacola *Also called Brownsville Orna Ir Works Inc* **(G-14107)**
Brrh Corporation 954 427-9665
3313 W Hillsboro Blvd # 101 Deerfield Beach (33442) **(G-2792)**
BRT Oakleaf Pet Inc 904 563-1212
1619 Leon Rd Jacksonville (32246) **(G-6239)**
Bru Bottling Inc 561 324-5053
1507 Villa Juno Dr N Juno Beach (33408) **(G-6977)**
Bru Fl LLC 813 431-6815
8709 Imperial Ct Tampa (33635) **(G-17487)**
Bruce Component Systems Inc 352 628-0522
3409 W Pennington Ct Lecanto (34461) **(G-8129)**
Bruce R Ely Enterprise Inc 727 573-1643
12880 Auto Blvd Ste G Clearwater (33762) **(G-1614)**
Bruce Roland 850 775-1497
8000 Front Beach Rd Panama City Beach (32407) **(G-13974)**
Brumate LLC 317 474-7352
201 Nw 22nd Ave Fort Lauderdale (33311) **(G-3873)**
Brunken Manufacturing Co Inc 850 438-2478
4205 W Jackson St Pensacola (32505) **(G-14108)**
Bruno Danger Custom Cabinets 754 366-1302
761 S Easy St Sebastian (32958) **(G-16656)**

Bruno Publishing.......561 333-7682
873 Lake Wellington Dr Wellington (33414) **(G-18712)**
Bruns Mfg Homes.......863 294-4949
10 Spirit Lake Rd Winter Haven (33880) **(G-19307)**
Brunsteel Corp.......305 251-7607
14065 Sw 142nd St Miami (33186) **(G-9281)**
Brunswick Boat Group.......321 449-8754
100 Sea Ray Dr Merritt Island (32953) **(G-8996)**
Brunswick Commercial &.......386 423-2900
100 Whaler Way Edgewater (32141) **(G-3616)**
Brunswick Corporation.......850 769-1011
11 College Ave Panama City (32401) **(G-13874)**
Brush Cases LLC.......305 340-7214
1007 Meridian Ave Apt 9 Miami Beach (33139) **(G-10649)**
Bruss Company.......904 693-0688
5441 W 5th St Jacksonville (32254) **(G-6240)**
Brut Printing Co Inc.......904 354-5055
503 Parker St Jacksonville (32202) **(G-6241)**
Brutus Roller LLC.......609 393-0007
3007 29th Ave E Bradenton (34208) **(G-1003)**
Bryan Ashley Inc.......954 351-1199
1432 E Newport Center Dr Deerfield Beach (33442) **(G-2793)**
Bryan Nelco Inc.......727 533-8282
15251 Roosevelt Blvd # 202 Clearwater (33760) **(G-1615)**
Bryant Machine Shop, Vero Beach *Also called Bryants Precision M F G Corp* **(G-18606)**
Bryants Precision M F G Corp.......772 569-2319
1803 Wilbur Ave Vero Beach (32960) **(G-18606)**
Bryce Foster Inc.......800 371-0395
215 Rollingwood Trl Altamonte Springs (32714) **(G-34)**
Brycoat Inc.......727 490-1000
207 Vollmer Ave Oldsmar (34677) **(G-12212)**
Bryson of Brevard Inc.......321 636-5116
580 Gus Hipp Blvd Rockledge (32955) **(G-15396)**
BSC Ventures, Gainesville *Also called Double Envelope Corporation* **(G-4907)**
BT Glass & Mirror Inc.......561 841-7676
3748 Prospect Ave Ste 4 West Palm Beach (33404) **(G-18829)**
Bt-Twiss Transport LLC (HQ).......866 584-1585
1501 Lake Ave Se Largo (33771) **(G-7915)**
Btb Refining LLC.......561 999-9916
925 S Federal Hwy Ste 375 Boca Raton (33432) **(G-468)**
Btb Refining LLC.......561 347-5500
25 Seabreeze Ave Ste 300 Delray Beach (33483) **(G-3054)**
BTR Logging Inc.......386 397-0730
10249 Se 161st Ave White Springs (32096) **(G-19186)**
Btu Reps LLC (PA).......727 235-3591
185 23rd Ave N Saint Petersburg (33704) **(G-15730)**
Bubba Foods LLC (PA).......904 482-1900
4339 Roosevelt Blvd # 400 Jacksonville (32210) **(G-6242)**
Bubba Rope LLC.......877 499-8494
998 Explorer Cv Ste 130 Altamonte Springs (32701) **(G-35)**
Bubble Bath Detailing Car Wash, Opa Locka *Also called Andre T Jean* **(G-12288)**
Bubblemac Industries Inc.......352 396-8043
11932 156th St Mc Alpin (32062) **(G-8598)**
Bubbles Body Wear, Miami *Also called Sweet and Vicious LLC* **(G-10446)**
Buchanan Sign & Flag, Jacksonville *Also called Buchanan Signs Screen Process* **(G-6243)**
Buchanan Signs Screen Process.......904 725-5500
6755 Beach Blvd Jacksonville (32216) **(G-6243)**
Buchelli Glass Inc.......954 695-8067
5417 Nw 50th Ct Coconut Creek (33073) **(G-2072)**
Buck Pile Inc.......772 492-1056
2801 Ocean Dr Ste 101 Vero Beach (32963) **(G-18607)**
Bucket Company LLC.......786 473-6484
641 Nw 7th Street Rd Miami (33136) **(G-9282)**
Buckeye Cleaning Center, Tampa *Also called Buckeye International Inc* **(G-17488)**
Buckeye International Inc.......813 621-6260
4644 Eagle Falls Pl Tampa (33619) **(G-17488)**
Buckeye Office Intrors Instllt, Largo *Also called Buckeye Used Office Furn Inc* **(G-7916)**
Buckeye Used Office Furn Inc.......727 457-5287
6166 126th Ave Largo (33773) **(G-7916)**
Buckley Pallets.......727 415-4497
2409 Laurelwood Dr Clearwater (33763) **(G-1616)**
Buckley Pallets LLC.......727 415-4497
14550 62nd St N 2 Clearwater (33760) **(G-1617)**
Bucks Corporation Inc.......850 894-2400
1920 N Monroe St Tallahassee (32303) **(G-17229)**
Buddy Bridge Inc (PA).......941 488-0799
350 Sorrento Ranches Dr Nokomis (34275) **(G-11578)**
Buddy Custard Inc.......561 715-3785
1451 W Cypress Creek Rd Fort Lauderdale (33309) **(G-3874)**
Buddy Pauls Inc.......561 578-9813
301 Clematis St Ste 300 West Palm Beach (33401) **(G-18830)**
Buddy Ward & Sons Seafood.......850 653-8522
3022 C 30 13 Mile Rd Apalachicola (32320) **(G-97)**
Buddy Ward Sons Seafood Trckg, Apalachicola *Also called Buddy Ward & Sons Seafood* **(G-97)**
Buddy's Pizza, Venice *Also called Richard Meer Investments Inc* **(G-18570)**
Budget Print Center, Ocala *Also called Keithco Inc* **(G-11976)**
Budget Printing Center LLC.......561 848-5700
4152 Blue Heron Blvd W # 109 Riviera Beach (33404) **(G-15305)**
Budget Signs Inc.......954 941-5710
1820 Sw 7th Ave Pompano Beach (33060) **(G-14625)**
Buena Cepa Wines LLC.......310 621-2566
951 Crandon Blvd Key Biscayne (33149) **(G-7154)**
Buena Vista Construction Co.......407 828-2104
3291 Wed Way Lake Buena Vista (32830) **(G-7335)**
Buenavida Imports LLC.......305 988-5992
3508 Nw 114th Ave Ste 205 Doral (33178) **(G-3288)**
Bufalinda USA LLC.......305 979-9258
2000 Bay Dr Miami Beach (33141) **(G-10650)**
Buffalo Machine Manufacturing.......727 321-1905
3140 39th Ave N Saint Petersburg (33714) **(G-15731)**
Buffalo Wheelchair Inc.......941 921-6331
4130 S Tamiami Trl Sarasota (34231) **(G-16371)**
Buggy Guard, West Palm Beach *Also called Nikiani Inc* **(G-18965)**
Builders Automtn McHy Co LLC.......727 538-2180
12775 Starkey Rd Ste B Largo (33773) **(G-7917)**
Builders Door and Supply Inc.......941 955-2311
2022 12th St Sarasota (34237) **(G-16372)**
Builders Notice Corporation.......954 764-1322
708 S Andrews Ave Fort Lauderdale (33316) **(G-3875)**
Builders Publishing Group LLC.......407 539-2938
500 N Maitland Ave # 313 Maitland (32751) **(G-8461)**
Building Blocks Gfrc LLC.......312 243-9960
1150 Joelson Rd Fl 3 Kissimmee (34744) **(G-7226)**
Building Blocks Management Inc.......214 289-9737
1150 Joelson Rd Kissimmee (34744) **(G-7227)**
Building Envelope Systems Inc.......305 693-0683
3121 E 11th Ave Hialeah (33013) **(G-5333)**
Built LLC.......813 512-6250
602 N Newport Ave Tampa (33606) **(G-17489)**
Built Rght Ktchens of Palm Cas.......386 437-7077
7755 S Us Highway 1 Bunnell (32110) **(G-1299)**
Built Right Installers Intl.......305 362-6010
7930 W 26th Ave Unit 2 Hialeah (33016) **(G-5334)**
Built Right Pool Heaters LLC.......941 505-1600
28110 Challenger Blvd Punta Gorda (33982) **(G-15200)**
Built Rite Cabinets Inc.......352 447-2238
438 Highway 40 E Inglis (34449) **(G-6075)**
Built Story LLC.......305 671-3890
1581 Brickell Ave # 2207 Miami (33129) **(G-9283)**
Bukkehave Inc.......954 525-9788
6750 N Andrews Ave # 200 Fort Lauderdale (33309) **(G-3876)**
Bulk Food Grocers, Saint Petersburg *Also called Great Amercn Natural Pdts Inc* **(G-15796)**
Bulk Manufacturing Florida Inc.......813 757-2313
3106 Central Dr Plant City (33566) **(G-14412)**
Bulk Resources Inc (PA).......813 764-8420
1507 S Alexander St # 102 Plant City (33563) **(G-14413)**
Bulldog Neon Sign Company Inc.......786 277-6366
5728 Ne 4th Ave Miami (33137) **(G-9284)**
Bullet Line LLC (HQ).......305 623-9223
6301 E 10th Ave Ste 110 Hialeah (33013) **(G-5335)**
Bulletin Net Inc.......941 468-2569
6000 S Tamiami Trl Sarasota (34231) **(G-16373)**
Bulletproof Hitches LLC.......941 251-8110
3145 Lakewood Ranch Blvd # 106 Bradenton (34211) **(G-1004)**
Bullion International Inc.......321 773-2727
4100 N Riverside Dr Indian Harbour Beach (32937) **(G-6063)**
Bully Wurld LLC.......201 466-8185
1103 Country Club Blvd Cape Coral (33990) **(G-1397)**
Bumper Doctor.......850 341-1771
95 Airport Blvd Pensacola (32503) **(G-14109)**
Bundy Signs LLC.......954 296-0784
4556 N Hiatus Rd Sunrise (33351) **(G-17101)**
Bunkys Raw Bar, Indialantic *Also called A1a Raw LLC* **(G-6055)**
Buonaventura Bag and Cases LLC.......212 960-3442
4795 Enterprise Ave Naples (34104) **(G-11196)**
Burbank Sport Nets, Jacksonville *Also called Burbank Trawl Makers Inc* **(G-6244)**
Burbank Sports Nets, Jacksonville *Also called BRC Sports Llc* **(G-6233)**
Burbank Trawl Makers Inc.......904 321-0976
13913 Duval Rd Ste 100 Jacksonville (32218) **(G-6244)**
Burch Welding & Fabrication.......904 353-6513
2324 Phoenix Ave Jacksonville (32206) **(G-6245)**
Burke Brands LLC.......305 249-5628
521 Ne 189th St Miami (33179) **(G-9285)**
Burke Printing.......813 549-9886
10203 Thicket Point Way Tampa (33647) **(G-17490)**
Burkhart Roentgen Intl Inc.......727 327-6950
3232 Bennett St N Saint Petersburg (33713) **(G-15732)**
Burkley Case, Naples *Also called Buonaventura Bag and Cases LLC* **(G-11196)**
Burlakoff Manufacturing Co.......972 889-2502
826 Se 9th Ter Ocala (34471) **(G-11891)**
Burleys Mmrals Brial Vults LLC.......561 284-6983
7111 Ivy Crossing Ln Boynton Beach (33436) **(G-885)**
Burma Spice Inc.......863 254-0960
133 Florida Ave Nw Moore Haven (33471) **(G-11085)**
Burn Brite Metals Co Inc.......727 360-4408
425 Capri Blvd Treasure Island (33706) **(G-18474)**
Burn By Rocky Patel.......239 653-9013
9110 Strada Pl Ste 6160 Naples (34108) **(G-11197)**

ALPHABETIC

Burn Proof Gear LLC......786 634-7406
7121 N Miami Ave Miami (33150) ***(G-9286)***
Burnett Industrial Sales, Saint Augustine *Also called St Agustine Elc Mtr Works Inc* ***(G-15617)***
Burnham Woods Untd Civic Group......954 532-2675
8211 Sw 19th St North Lauderdale (33068) ***(G-11612)***
Burr Industries LLC......619 254-2309
4360 Ponds Dr Cocoa (32927) ***(G-2002)***
Burr Printing Co Inc......863 294-3166
4212 Hammond Dr Winter Haven (33881) ***(G-19308)***
Burris Investment Group Inc......850 623-3845
10648 Mac Gregor Dr Pensacola (32514) ***(G-14110)***
Burton JC Companies Inc......239 992-2377
24241 Production Cir Bonita Springs (34135) ***(G-821)***
Burton Signs Inc......727 841-8927
7349 Walnut St New Port Richey (34652) ***(G-11485)***
Bus Bulletin Inc......850 271-0017
3822 Patrick Rd Panama City (32409) ***(G-13875)***
Buscar Inc......813 877-7272
3403 W Morrison Ave Tampa (33629) ***(G-17491)***
Busch Canvas......561 881-1605
2428 Broadway Riviera Beach (33404) ***(G-15306)***
Busch Canvas & Interiors......561 881-1605
2428 Broadway Riviera Beach (33404) ***(G-15307)***
Bush Brothers, Pompano Beach *Also called Fred M Bush LLC* ***(G-14705)***
Bush Brothers Provision Co......561 832-6666
1931 N Dixie Hwy West Palm Beach (33407) ***(G-18831)***
Bushhog N Blade Work......904 669-2764
2846 Usina Road Ext Saint Augustine (32084) ***(G-15525)***
Bushnell Saw Mill Inc......352 793-2740
5178 W C 48 Bushnell (33513) ***(G-1313)***
Bushnell Truss Enterprises LLC......352 793-6090
5240 W C 476 Bushnell (33513) ***(G-1314)***
Business Card Ex Tampa Bay Inc......727 535-7768
14000 63rd Way N Clearwater (33760) ***(G-1618)***
Business Cards Tomorrow Inc (PA)......954 563-1224
2810 E Oklnd Prk Blvd # 308 Fort Lauderdale (33306) ***(G-3877)***
Business Center & Printshop......786 547-6681
815 Nw 119th St Miami (33168) ***(G-9287)***
Business Clinic Inc......786 473-4573
1475 W Okeechobee Rd # 3 Hialeah (33010) ***(G-5336)***
Business Forward Inc......954 967-6730
3286 N 29th Ct Hollywood (33020) ***(G-5792)***
Business Jrnl Publications Inc......904 396-3502
112 W Adams St Ste 200 Jacksonville (32202) ***(G-6246)***
Business Jrnl Publications Inc (HQ)......813 342-2472
4350 W Cypress St Ste 800 Tampa (33607) ***(G-17492)***
Business Report of N Cntrl FL......352 275-9469
1314 S Main St Gainesville (32601) ***(G-4890)***
Business World Trading Inc......305 238-0724
13275 Sw 136th St Unit 22 Miami (33186) ***(G-9288)***
Bust Out Promotions LLC......561 305-8313
1375 Sw 12th Ave Pompano Beach (33069) ***(G-14626)***
Busy Bee Cabinets Inc......941 628-2025
2845 Commerce Pkwy North Port (34289) ***(G-11734)***
Busy Bee Printer......772 621-3683
1902 Se Manth Ln Port Saint Lucie (34983) ***(G-15094)***
Butler Graphics Inc......305 477-1344
5055 Nw 74th Ave Unit 5 Miami (33166) ***(G-9289)***
Butler Logging Inc......386 963-2720
5570 Bulb Farm Rd Wellborn (32094) ***(G-18706)***
Butler Pavers Inc......941 423-3977
6862 Van Camp St North Port (34291) ***(G-11735)***
Buttercream Cpcakes Cof Sp Inc......305 669-8181
1411 Sunset Dr Coral Gables (33143) ***(G-2128)***
Butterfield Press......813 634-3940
1504 N Lake Dr Sun City Center (33573) ***(G-17070)***
Butterkrust Bakeries, Lakeland *Also called Southern Bakeries Inc* ***(G-7800)***
Buvin Jewelry of Florida Inc......305 358-0170
36 Ne 1st St Ste 217 Miami (33132) ***(G-9290)***
Buzz Pop Cocktails Corporation (PA)......727 275-9848
4407 Buena Vista Ln Holiday (34691) ***(G-5736)***
BWC Equipment LLC......239 443-9925
715 Ne 19th Pl Unit 41 Cape Coral (33909) ***(G-1398)***
Bxd Enterprises Inc......727 937-4100
4148 Louis Ave Holiday (34691) ***(G-5737)***
By Dancers For Dancers, Miami *Also called Lan Designs Inc* ***(G-9853)***
By Invitation Only Pubg Inc......954 922-7100
850 Ne 3rd St Ste 209 Dania (33004) ***(G-2442)***
Byblos Group Inc......305 662-6666
7175 Sw 47th St Ste 210 Miami (33155) ***(G-9291)***
Byerly Custom Design Inc......941 371-7498
743 Gantt Ave Sarasota (34232) ***(G-16374)***
Byomed LLC......305 634-6763
1555 Ne 123rd St North Miami (33161) ***(G-11630)***
Byoscience......754 240-4052
1305 Shotgun Rd Sunrise (33326) ***(G-17102)***
Byrd Technologies Inc......954 957-8333
3100 Sw 10th St Pompano Beach (33069) ***(G-14627)***
Byte Size It LLC......386 785-9311
670 Stallings Ave Deltona (32738) ***(G-3165)***
Bythenet Publishing......407 691-2806
2500 Lee Rd Winter Park (32789) ***(G-19385)***
C & C Multiservices Corp......305 200-5851
2849 Nw 7th St Miami (33125) ***(G-9292)***
C & C Services of Tampa Inc......813 477-8559
1007 Robinson Rd Plant City (33563) ***(G-14414)***
C & C Tool & Mold......863 699-5337
3417 Paso Fino Dr Lake Placid (33852) ***(G-7485)***
C & D Industrial Maint LLC......833 776-5833
2208 58th Ave E Bradenton (34203) ***(G-1005)***
C & D Printing Company......727 572-9999
12150 28th St N Saint Petersburg (33716) ***(G-15733)***
C & E Cabinets Design LLC......386 410-4281
137 W Marion Ave Edgewater (32132) ***(G-3617)***
C & E Innovative MGT LLC......727 408-5146
2454 N Mcmullen Booth Rd Clearwater (33759) ***(G-1619)***
C & G Packaging LLC......305 825-5244
7305 W 19th Ct Hialeah (33014) ***(G-5337)***
C & G Timber Harvesters Inc......850 643-1340
10213 Nw Dan Jacobs Ln Bristol (32321) ***(G-1192)***
C & H Baseball Inc (PA)......941 727-1533
10615 Tech Ter Ste 100 Bradenton (34211) ***(G-1006)***
C & H Printing Inc......904 620-8444
11315-1 St Jhns Indus Pkw Jacksonville (32246) ***(G-6247)***
C & H Sign Enterprises Inc......407 826-0155
9900 Universal Blvd # 114 Orlando (32819) ***(G-12538)***
C & J Cstm Wldg Fbrication LLC......407 414-1739
2784 East Lake Rd Kissimmee (34744) ***(G-7228)***
C & J Industries Inc......386 589-4907
105 John Anderson Dr Ormond Beach (32176) ***(G-13356)***
C & M Manufacturing LLC......407 673-9601
4212 Metric Dr Winter Park (32792) ***(G-19386)***
C & M Millwork Inc......352 588-5050
30450 Commerce Dr San Antonio (33576) ***(G-15971)***
C & M Products Division, Doral *Also called R and R Brokerage Co* ***(G-3477)***
C & R Designs Inc......321 383-2255
1227 Garden St Titusville (32796) ***(G-18419)***
C & R Designs Printing LLC......321 383-2255
415 Main St Titusville (32796) ***(G-18420)***
C & S Foliage......352 357-4847
34910 County Road 439 Eustis (32736) ***(G-3704)***
C & S Graphics Inc......813 251-4411
1335 W North B St Tampa (33606) ***(G-17493)***
C & S GRAPHICS, INC. DBA ELECTRIC SIGN COMPANY, Tampa *Also called C & S Graphics Inc* ***(G-17493)***
C & S Plastics, Winter Haven *Also called Precision Plastics Group Inc* ***(G-19343)***
C & S Plastics......863 294-5628
1550 5th St Sw Winter Haven (33880) ***(G-19309)***
C & S Press Inc......407 841-3000
405 27th St Orlando (32806) ***(G-12539)***
C & S Signs Inc......850 983-9540
8895 S Lynn Rd Milton (32583) ***(G-10925)***
C C Calhoun Inc......863 292-9511
3750 W Lake Hamilton Dr Winter Haven (33881) ***(G-19310)***
C C Lead Inc......863 465-6458
127 Ranier Dr Lake Placid (33852) ***(G-7486)***
C Dyer Development Group LLC......727 423-6169
1125 Lake St Tarpon Springs (34689) ***(G-18285)***
C E C Controls Company Inc......941 746-5700
5306 4th Avenue Cir E Bradenton (34208) ***(G-1007)***
C E M, Port St Lucie *Also called Composite Essential Mtls LLC* ***(G-15172)***
C E S Wireless Tech Corp......407 681-0869
931 S Semoran Blvd # 200 Winter Park (32792) ***(G-19387)***
C F Print Ltd Inc......631 567-2110
3174 Dressendorfer Dr The Villages (32163) ***(G-18389)***
C F Webb and Sons Logging LLC......850 971-5565
625 Se Old Logging Trl Lee (32059) ***(G-8137)***
C Horse Software Inc......321 952-0692
1510 Charles Blvd Ne Palm Bay (32907) ***(G-13506)***
C I G, Sarasota *Also called Commercial Insulating Glass Co* ***(G-16389)***
C K C Industries Inc (PA)......813 888-9468
4908 Savarese Cir Tampa (33634) ***(G-17494)***
C K S, Orlando *Also called Charles K Sewell* ***(G-12576)***
C L F Enterprises......305 643-3222
111 Sw 17th Ave Miami (33135) ***(G-9293)***
C L Industries Inc......800 333-2660
8188 S Orange Ave Orlando (32809) ***(G-12540)***
C M E, Pinellas Park *Also called Custom Mfg & Engrg Inc* ***(G-14342)***
C M I Enterprises Inc (PA)......305 622-6410
13145 Nw 45th Ave Opa Locka (33054) ***(G-12297)***
C M P G, Orlando *Also called Commercial Metal Photography* ***(G-12605)***
C M W, Lithia *Also called Central Maintenance & Wldg Inc* ***(G-8216)***
C Mike Roach Inc......864 882-1101
4847 Se Longleaf Pl Hobe Sound (33455) ***(G-5723)***
C Mix Corp......954 670-0208
5600 Nw 12th Ave Ste 306 Fort Lauderdale (33309) ***(G-3878)***

C P Enterprises of Apopka Inc...407 886-3321
3351 Laughlin Rd Mount Dora (32757) ***(G-11098)***
C P T, Cocoa Beach *Also called Cathodic Prtection Tech of Fla* ***(G-2060)***
C P Vegetable Oil Inc...954 584-0420
601 Sw 21st Ter Ste 1 Fort Lauderdale (33312) ***(G-3879)***
C Products Defense Inc...941 727-0009
4555 18th St E Bradenton (34203) ***(G-1008)***
C Q M, Tampa *Also called Custom Quality Mfg Inc* ***(G-17582)***
C S Fasteners...813 242-8000
4739 Transport Dr Tampa (33605) ***(G-17495)***
C Speed LLC...321 336-7939
6855 Tico Rd Ste 103 Titusville (32780) ***(G-18421)***
C W Machining Inc...352 732-5824
2820 Nw 8th Pl Ocala (34475) ***(G-11892)***
C&A Boatworks Inc...754 366-5549
1711 N Powerline Rd Pompano Beach (33069) ***(G-14628)***
C&A Lozaro Inc...407 671-8809
3000 N Goldenrod Rd Winter Park (32792) ***(G-19388)***
C&C Brick Pavers Inc...813 716-8291
8513 N Otis Ave Tampa (33604) ***(G-17496)***
C&C Diversified Services LLC...772 597-1022
7954 Sw Jack James Dr Stuart (34997) ***(G-16919)***
C&C Industries, Doral *Also called Cosmetics & Cleaners Intl LLC* ***(G-3310)***
C&D Canvas Inc...954 924-3433
6110 W Falcons Lea Dr Davie (33331) ***(G-2504)***
C&D Purveyors Inc...305 562-8541
7274 Nw 70th St Miami (33166) ***(G-9294)***
C&D Sign and Lighting Svcs LLC...863 937-9323
2175 E Edgewood Dr Lakeland (33803) ***(G-7652)***
C&L Technologies, Port Saint Lucie *Also called Savage Ventures Inc* ***(G-15141)***
C&P Industries Inc...813 685-3131
5021 Durant Rd Dover (33527) ***(G-3557)***
C&S Ostomy Pouch Covers Inc...941 423-8542
2214 Cloras St North Port (34287) ***(G-11736)***
C-Note Solutions Inc...321 952-2490
334 4th Ave Indialantic (32903) ***(G-6056)***
C-Worthy Corp...954 784-7370
241 Sw 5th Ct Pompano Beach (33060) ***(G-14629)***
C-Worthy Custom Yacht Canvas, Pompano Beach *Also called C-Worthy Corp* ***(G-14629)***
C.A.c Custom Artisan Cabinetry, Boca Raton *Also called Integral WD Cstm Cabinetry LLC* ***(G-566)***
C1 Aerospace LLC...786 712-9949
14519 Sw 138th Pl Miami (33186) ***(G-9295)***
C2 Image & Printing Inc...310 892-8316
7665 Nw 182nd Ter Hialeah (33015) ***(G-5338)***
C2 Powder Coating LLC...941 404-2671
6060 28th St E Ste 1 Bradenton (34203) ***(G-1009)***
C2c Innovated Technology LLC...251 382-2277
3371 Highway 90 Bonifay (32425) ***(G-800)***
C4 Advnced Tctical Systems LLC...407 206-3886
243 Wetherbee Rd Orlando (32824) ***(G-12541)***
C4 Group LLC...850 230-4541
7510 Holley Cir Panama City Beach (32408) ***(G-13975)***
C4ats, Orlando *Also called C4 Advnced Tctical Systems LLC* ***(G-12541)***
Ca Inc...305 559-4640
15298 Sw 17th Ter Miami (33185) ***(G-9296)***
CA Pipeline Inc...305 969-4655
15621 Sw 209th Ave Miami (33187) ***(G-9297)***
Caamacosta Inc...954 987-5895
5400 N 35th St Hollywood (33021) ***(G-5793)***
Caballero Metals Corp...305 266-9085
7315 Sw 45th St Miami (33155) ***(G-9298)***
Caballero Metals Corp...305 266-9085
7315 Sw 45th St Ste 4 Miami (33155) ***(G-9299)***
Cabinet and Stone, Tampa *Also called Kitchen and Bath Universe Inc* ***(G-17828)***
Cabinet Cnnction of Trsure Cas (PA)...772 621-4882
740 Nw Enterprise Dr Port Saint Lucie (34986) ***(G-15095)***
Cabinet Collection Inc...239 478-0359
24830 S Tamiami Trl Bonita Springs (34134) ***(G-822)***
Cabinet Design and Cnstr LLC...850 393-9724
101 S Pace Blvd Pensacola (32502) ***(G-14111)***
Cabinet Designs of Central Fla...321 636-1101
596 International Pl Rockledge (32955) ***(G-15397)***
Cabinet Designs of Sarasota...941 739-1607
6208 B 17th St E Bradenton (34203) ***(G-1010)***
Cabinet Dreams & Things Inc...727 514-0847
13954 Sand Oak Ct Hudson (34669) ***(G-6017)***
Cabinet Factory Outlet...386 323-0778
1595 N Nova Rd Ste A Daytona Beach (32117) ***(G-2637)***
Cabinet Genies...239 458-8563
1114 Cape Coral Pkwy E Cape Coral (33904) ***(G-1399)***
Cabinet Guy 2012 Inc...305 796-5242
14721 Sw 21st St Davie (33325) ***(G-2505)***
Cabinet Guy of Englewood Inc...941 475-9454
150 S Mccall Rd Englewood (34223) ***(G-3670)***
Cabinet Kings LLC...239 288-6740
11595 Kelly Rd Ste 322 Fort Myers (33908) ***(G-4383)***
Cabinet Market LLC...321 203-2598
3413 Forsyth Rd Ste B Winter Park (32792) ***(G-19389)***
Cabinet Masters Inc...727 535-0020
7168 123rd Cir Largo (33773) ***(G-7918)***
Cabinet Mechanics LLC...941 626-0735
468 Cicero St Nw Port Charlotte (33948) ***(G-14967)***
Cabinet Options Inc...904 434-1564
1170 Executive Cove Dr Saint Johns (32259) ***(G-15674)***
Cabinet Specialist Inc...239 641-6931
1520 21st St Sw Naples (34117) ***(G-11198)***
Cabinet Systems of Central Fla...407 678-0994
2716 Forsyth Rd Ste 114 Winter Park (32792) ***(G-19390)***
Cabinetree Collection Inc...772 569-4761
860 35th Ct Sw Vero Beach (32968) ***(G-18608)***
Cabinetry Masters LLC...954 549-8646
4193 Oldfield Crossing Dr Jacksonville (32223) ***(G-6248)***
Cabinets & Counters...561 444-3083
2373 Florida St West Palm Beach (33406) ***(G-18832)***
Cabinets -N- More Inc...321 355-9548
6023 Elgin Rd Cocoa (32927) ***(G-2003)***
Cabinets By Design...954 829-2923
4815 Ne 12th Ave Oakland Park (33334) ***(G-11788)***
Cabinets By Marylin Inc...954 729-3995
696 Sw 15th St Pompano Beach (33060) ***(G-14630)***
Cabinets By Wfc Inc...941 355-2703
6092 Clark Center Ave Sarasota (34238) ***(G-16375)***
Cabinets Direct USA...862 704-6138
16107 Via Monteverde Delray Beach (33446) ***(G-3055)***
Cabinets Extraordinaire, Sarasota *Also called Location 3 Holdings LLC* ***(G-16489)***
Cabinets Extraordinaire Inc...618 925-0515
6150 State Road 70 E # 31 Bradenton (34203) ***(G-1011)***
Cabinets Moreunlimited Inc...813 789-4203
11802 Spanish Lake Dr Tampa (33635) ***(G-17497)***
Cabinets One LLC...407 227-1147
4502 Old Winter Garden Rd Orlando (32811) ***(G-12542)***
Cabinets Plus Inc...239 574-7020
1056 Ne Pine Island Rd G Cape Coral (33909) ***(G-1400)***
Cabinets Plus of America Inc...813 408-0433
3853 S Lake Dr Unit 164 Tampa (33614) ***(G-17498)***
Cabinets Unlimited, Bradenton *Also called Manatee Cabinets Inc* ***(G-1075)***
Cabinetscapes LLC...941 539-0013
8455 Midnight Pass Rd Sarasota (34242) ***(G-16376)***
Cabinetsplusfl.com, Cape Coral *Also called Cabinets Plus Inc* ***(G-1400)***
Cabinetsync Inc...239 690-6122
11350 Metro Pkwy Ste 107 Fort Myers (33966) ***(G-4384)***
Cable USA, Naples *Also called Marmon Aerospace & Defense LLC* ***(G-11322)***
Cables and Sensors LLC...866 373-6767
5874 S Semoran Blvd Orlando (32822) ***(G-12543)***
Cableware Technology Division, Naples *Also called Loos & Co Inc* ***(G-11316)***
Cabreras Spanish Sausages LLC...305 882-1040
765 W 27th St Hialeah (33010) ***(G-5339)***
Cabus USA Inc...305 681-0872
12300 Nw 7th Ave North Miami (33168) ***(G-11631)***
Cacao Fruit Company...954 449-8704
1500 Weston Rd Ste 200 Weston (33326) ***(G-19114)***
Cadcam Software Co...727 450-6440
28200 Us Highway 19 N E Clearwater (33761) ***(G-1620)***
Caddie Company Inc...267 332-0976
4104 Causeway Vista Dr Tampa (33615) ***(G-17499)***
Cadence Keen Innovations Inc...561 249-2219
1655 Palm Bch Lkes Blvd S West Palm Beach (33401) ***(G-18833)***
Cadillac Graphics Inc...954 772-2440
4521 Ne 5th Ter Oakland Park (33334) ***(G-11789)***
Cadre Holdings Inc (PA)...904 741-5400
13386 International Pkwy Jacksonville (32218) ***(G-6249)***
Caduceus International Pubg...866 280-2900
100 Sw 75th St Ste 206 Gainesville (32607) ***(G-4891)***
Cae Healthcare Inc (HQ)...941 377-5562
6300 Edgelake Dr Sarasota (34240) ***(G-16377)***
Cae Healthcare USA Inc...941 377-5562
6300 Edgelake Dr Sarasota (34240) ***(G-16378)***
Cae USA Inc (HQ)...813 885-7481
4908 Tampa West Blvd Tampa (33634) ***(G-17500)***
Cae USA Products, Tampa *Also called Cae USA Inc* ***(G-17500)***
CAF Bustelo, Medley *Also called J M Smucker Company* ***(G-8674)***
CAF USA Inc...305 753-5371
9400 Nw 37th Ave Miami (33147) ***(G-9300)***
Cafco LLC...240 848-5574
3370 Ne 190th St Apt 2206 Miami (33180) ***(G-9301)***
Cafe Don Pablo, Miami *Also called Burke Brands LLC* ***(G-9285)***
Cafm...407 658-6531
2023 N Atlantic Ave 223 Cocoa Beach (32931) ***(G-2059)***
Cahill Construction Services...239 369-9290
212 Lake Dr Lehigh Acres (33936) ***(G-8186)***
Cal Air Forwarding...305 871-4552
3000 Nw 74th Ave Miami (33122) ***(G-9302)***
Calcium Silicate Corp Inc...863 902-0217
601 Watson Farm Rd Lake Harbor (33459) ***(G-7394)***
Calendar Arts LLC...407 285-8139
1191 Us Highway 1 Vero Beach (32960) ***(G-18609)***

Calev Systems Inc (PA)....786 837-2343
5575 Nw 36th St Miami Springs (33166) ***(G-10888)***
Caliber Coating Inc....813 928-1461
39615 Dawson Chase Dr Zephyrhills (33540) ***(G-19509)***
Caliber Elements LLC....352 697-1415
9020 W Veterans Dr Homosassa (34448) ***(G-6000)***
Caliber Sales Engineering Inc (PA)....954 430-6234
5373 N Hiatus Rd Sunrise (33351) ***(G-17103)***
California Shutters Inc....305 827-9333
16480 Nw 48th Ave Miami Lakes (33014) ***(G-10772)***
Californo Corp....855 553-6766
217 Nw 2nd Ave Hallandale Beach (33009) ***(G-5176)***
Caligiuri Corporation....407 324-4441
518 Central Park Dr Sanford (32771) ***(G-16006)***
Calkins Harbor Publishing Inc....561 906-4642
441 Marlin Rd North Palm Beach (33408) ***(G-11720)***
Calle Ocho News, Miami *Also called Pressnet Corp* ***(G-10189)***
Calloway Barge Lines Inc....904 284-0503
967 Bulkhead Rd Pier 5 Green Cove Springs (32043) ***(G-5056)***
Calmac Corporation....813 493-8700
1801 E Fowler Ave Tampa (33612) ***(G-17501)***
Calnat International Inc....239 839-2581
2118 Se 1st St Cape Coral (33990) ***(G-1401)***
Calorex USA LLC....239 482-0606
2213 Andrea Ln Ste 110 Fort Myers (33912) ***(G-4385)***
Calumet Electronics....954 668-7689
2500 Hollywood Blvd # 309 Hollywood (33020) ***(G-5794)***
Calvert Manufacturing Inc....407 331-5522
228 Colombo Dr Casselberry (32707) ***(G-1499)***
Calvert Solutions, Casselberry *Also called Calvert Manufacturing Inc* ***(G-1499)***
CAM Broc Sports Inc....407 933-6524
3726 Grissom Ln Kissimmee (34741) ***(G-7229)***
Camara Industries LLC....407 879-2549
9927 Dean Cove Ln Orlando (32825) ***(G-12544)***
Cambra Soap Company....321 525-7575
209 Ellwood Ave Satellite Beach (32937) ***(G-16650)***
Cambria, Fort Myers *Also called Cianos Tile & Marble Inc* ***(G-4395)***
Cambridge Aeronautical LLC....305 987-3851
4890 Sw 74th Ct Miami (33155) ***(G-9303)***
Cambridge Diagnostic Pdts Inc....954 971-4040
6880 Nw 17th Ave Fort Lauderdale (33309) ***(G-3880)***
Cambroc Sports, Kissimmee *Also called CAM Broc Sports Inc* ***(G-7229)***
Camco Chemical....239 992-4100
3635 Bonita Beach Rd # 3 Bonita Springs (34134) ***(G-823)***
Camco Corp....561 427-0433
1829 Park Ln S Ste 9 Jupiter (33458) ***(G-7014)***
Camcorp Industries Inc....941 488-5000
170 Rich St Venice (34292) ***(G-18536)***
Came Americas Automation LLC....305 433-3307
5863 Nw 159th St Miami Lakes (33014) ***(G-10773)***
Camel Enterprises Corp....954 234-2559
2120 Ne 203rd Ter Miami (33179) ***(G-9304)***
Camel Power Drinks, Miami *Also called Camel Enterprises Corp* ***(G-9304)***
Camelot Cabinets Inc....813 876-9150
6903 Conaty Dr Tampa (33634) ***(G-17502)***
Camera2canvas LLC....850 276-6990
2500 Minnesota Ave Lynn Haven (32444) ***(G-8431)***
Cameron Textiles Inc....954 454-6482
2740 Sw Martin Downs Blvd Palm City (34990) ***(G-13644)***
Camilo Muebles, Miami *Also called Camilo Office Furniture Inc* ***(G-9305)***
Camilo Office Furniture Inc (PA)....305 261-5366
7344 Sw 48th St Ste 202 Miami (33155) ***(G-9305)***
Camilo Office Furniture Inc....305 261-5366
18360 Sw 224th St Miami (33170) ***(G-9306)***
Camp Aircraft Inc....727 397-6076
5300 95th St N Saint Petersburg (33708) ***(G-15734)***
Camp Company St Petersburg....727 397-6076
5300 95th St N Saint Petersburg (33708) ***(G-15735)***
Campbell Manufacturing Inc....727 443-4508
2151 Logan St Clearwater (33765) ***(G-1621)***
Campbellton Farm Service, Campbellton *Also called Barber Fertilizer Company* ***(G-1330)***
Campen Companies....904 388-6000
2160 Park St Jacksonville (32204) ***(G-6250)***
Campeones Marina Corp....305 491-5738
600 Nw 7th Ave Miami (33136) ***(G-9307)***
Camper & Nicholsons Usa Inc (PA)....561 655-2121
450 Royal Palm Way # 100 Palm Beach (33480) ***(G-13550)***
Campos Chemicals....727 412-2774
3244 44th Ave N Saint Petersburg (33714) ***(G-15736)***
Campus Publications Inc....941 780-1326
2975 Bee Ridge Rd Ste D Sarasota (34239) ***(G-16379)***
Can Can Concealment LLC....727 841-6930
2521b Success Dr Odessa (33556) ***(G-12109)***
Can-America, Tampa *Also called Vigo Importing Company* ***(G-18247)***
Canac Kitchens Northwest Fla, Santa Rosa Beach *Also called Emerald Coast Cabinets Inc* ***(G-16158)***
Canada Dry of Florida, Fort Pierce *Also called American Bottling Company* ***(G-4673)***
Canada Dry of Florida....941 758-7010
2919 62nd Ave E Bradenton (34203) ***(G-1012)***
Canal Creamery....386 410-4703
323 Canal St New Smyrna Beach (32168) ***(G-11529)***
Canam Electric....305 534-7903
4835 Collins Ave Miami Beach (33140) ***(G-10651)***
Canam Steel Corporation....386 252-3730
1490 Frances Dr Daytona Beach (32124) ***(G-2638)***
Canam Steel Corporation....407 295-3864
2536 Hansrob Rd Orlando (32804) ***(G-12545)***
Canam Steel Corporation....904 781-0898
140 Ellis Rd S Jacksonville (32254) ***(G-6251)***
Canarchy Craft....813 348-6363
3924 W Spruce St Tampa (33607) ***(G-17503)***
Canaveral Custom Boats Inc....321 783-3536
774 Mullet Rd Cape Canaveral (32920) ***(G-1354)***
Candela Controls Inc....407 654-2420
751 Business Park Blvd # 101 Winter Garden (34787) ***(G-19254)***
Candi-Lyn Cabinetry....863 860-2505
1655 Verona Dr Bartow (33830) ***(G-311)***
Candies and Beyond Inc....954 828-2255
14100 Nw 60th Ave Miami Lakes (33014) ***(G-10774)***
Candle For You LLC....920 883-7900
6190 Riviera Ln Jacksonville (32216) ***(G-6252)***
Canine Chronicle, The, Ocala *Also called Endeavor Publications Inc* ***(G-11932)***
Canna Construction LLC....239 450-2141
1942 Dana Dr Fort Myers (33907) ***(G-4386)***
Cannida Co LLC....727 642-3709
2411 Union St S Saint Petersburg (33712) ***(G-15737)***
Cannon Industries Inc....727 320-5040
5349 Seafoam Dr New Port Richey (34652) ***(G-11486)***
Cannons of Jack LLC....904 733-3524
6150 Richard St Jacksonville (32216) ***(G-6253)***
Canopy Specialist LLC....813 703-6844
3301 State Road 574 Plant City (33563) ***(G-14415)***
Cansortium Charities Inc....305 902-2720
82 Ne 26th St Miami (33137) ***(G-9308)***
Canterbury House Publishing....941 312-6912
6928 W Country Club Dr N Sarasota (34243) ***(G-16185)***
Cantex Inc....863 967-4161
101 Gandy Rd Auburndale (33823) ***(G-231)***
Cantor Design On Granite....407 230-1568
4180 Player Cir Orlando (32808) ***(G-12546)***
Cantor Granite & Marble, Orlando *Also called Cantor Design On Granite* ***(G-12546)***
Canvas....727 317-5572
1535 4th St N Saint Petersburg (33704) ***(G-15738)***
Canvas Clinical Research (PA)....561 229-0002
3898 Via Poinciana Lake Worth (33467) ***(G-7538)***
Canvas Designers Inc....561 881-7663
1500 Australian Ave Ste 1 Riviera Beach (33404) ***(G-15308)***
Canvas Foods Corp....786 529-8041
19266 Seneca Ave Weston (33332) ***(G-19115)***
Canvas Freaks LLC....407 978-6224
11300 Space Blvd Ste 4 Orlando (32837) ***(G-12547)***
Canvas Land Surveying LLC....321 689-5330
1650 Oak Valley Dr Longwood (32750) ***(G-8263)***
Canvas Shop Inc....407 898-6001
635 Wilmer Ave Orlando (32808) ***(G-12548)***
Canvas Studio Inc....305 987-5895
8877 Collins Ave Apt 502 Surfside (33154) ***(G-17201)***
Canvas Tattoo LLC....561 870-7929
8872 Maple Hill Ct Boynton Beach (33473) ***(G-886)***
Canvas West Inc....941 355-0780
1470 12th St Sarasota (34236) ***(G-16380)***
Canyon Bay Boats Llc....850 838-1400
1290 Houck Rd Perry (32348) ***(G-14297)***
Capacitor and Components LLC....954 798-8943
11841 Nw 38th Pl Sunrise (33323) ***(G-17104)***
Capacity Inc....855 440-7825
2240 72nd Ave E Sarasota (34243) ***(G-16186)***
Cape Candle LLC....239 357-6766
2011 Ne 10th Ter Cape Coral (33909) ***(G-1402)***
Cape Horn Boats, Orlando *Also called Fabbro Marine Group Inc* ***(G-12730)***
Capital Contracting & Design (PA)....908 561-8411
817 Sw 10th St Fort Lauderdale (33315) ***(G-3881)***
Capital Outlook Newspaper, Tallahassee *Also called Syndicated Programming Inc* ***(G-17333)***
Capital Publishing Inc....813 286-8444
7341 Spring Hill Dr Spring Hill (34606) ***(G-16849)***
Capital Signs, Apopka *Also called Guy Wingo Signs* ***(G-148)***
Capital Steel Inc....352 628-1700
6260 S Tex Pt Homosassa (34448) ***(G-6001)***
Capital Steel Structures, Miami *Also called Capitol Rental Bldg Eqp Inc* ***(G-9309)***
Capital Technology Solutions....850 562-3321
3920 Monterey Pines Trl Tallahassee (32309) ***(G-17230)***
Capitol Conveyors Inc....727 314-7474
1429 Warrington Way Trinity (34655) ***(G-18483)***
Capitol Furniture Mfg LLC....954 485-5000
850 Broken Sound Pkwy Nw Boca Raton (33487) ***(G-469)***
Capitol Rental Bldg Eqp Inc....305 633-5008
2188 Nw 25th Ave Miami (33142) ***(G-9309)***
Capra Graphics Inc....305 418-4582
1625 Nw 79th Ave Doral (33126) ***(G-3289)***

Capri Kitchens Inc 813 623-1424
9507 E Us Highway 92 Tampa (33610) ***(G-17504)***
Capris Furniture Inds Inc 352 629-8889
1401 Nw 27th Ave Ocala (34475) ***(G-11893)***
Capristo USA 561 882-9885
4188 Westroads Dr # 130 West Palm Beach (33407) ***(G-18834)***
Capsmith Inc (PA) 407 328-7660
2240 Old Lake Mary Rd Sanford (32771) ***(G-16007)***
Capstone Cg LLC 941 371-3321
6348 17th Street Cir E Sarasota (34243) ***(G-16187)***
Capstone Companies Inc (PA) 954 252-3440
431 Fairway Dr Ste 200 Deerfield Beach (33441) ***(G-2794)***
Capstone Industries Inc 954 570-8889
431 Fairway Dr Ste 200 Deerfield Beach (33441) ***(G-2795)***
Capstorm LLC 314 403-2143
3906 Us Highway 98 W # 1159 Santa Rosa Beach (32459) ***(G-16153)***
Capt Latham LLC 904 483-6118
967 Bulkhead Rd Green Cove Springs (32043) ***(G-5057)***
Captain Cabinets LLC 813 685-7179
6705 Pemberton View Dr Seffner (33584) ***(G-16722)***
Captain Canvas & More 561 881-2278
700 Old Dixie Hwy Ste 109 Lake Park (33403) ***(G-7467)***
Captain Foods Inc 386 428-5833
207 Sapphire Rd New Smyrna Beach (32169) ***(G-11530)***
Captain Max 954 987-8552
3700 S State Road 7 Miramar (33023) ***(G-10976)***
Captain Rustys 813 244-2799
1958 Us Highway 98 Lorida (33857) ***(G-8354)***
Captain Rustys Smoked Fish Dip, Lorida *Also called Captain Rustys* ***(G-8354)***
Captain Zoom Products Inc 561 989-9119
4976 Bocaire Blvd Boca Raton (33487) ***(G-470)***
Captains Custom Tees Inc 239 424-8206
2417 Lkwood Rnch Blvd N U Lakewood Ranch (34240) ***(G-7842)***
Captains Fasteners Corp 954 533-9259
3706 Sw 30th Ave Fort Lauderdale (33312) ***(G-3882)***
Captel Inc 407 730-3397
2602 Challenger Tech Ct Orlando (32826) ***(G-12549)***
Captiva Containers LLC 800 861-3868
95 Ne 179th St Miami (33162) ***(G-9310)***
Captiva Current Inc 239 574-1110
2340 Periwinkle Way Sanibel (33957) ***(G-16143)***
Captivated Coatings LLC 321 446-6619
310 Manor Dr Merritt Island (32952) ***(G-8997)***
Captive-Aire Systems Inc 407 682-9396
311 Altamonte Commerce Bl Altamonte Springs (32714) ***(G-36)***
Captive-Aire Systems Inc 813 448-7884
4519 George Rd Ste 150 Tampa (33634) ***(G-17505)***
Capzerpharma Manufacturing LLC 561 493-4000
3677 23rd Ave S Ste B107 Lake Worth Beach (33461) ***(G-7609)***
Caq International LLC 305 744-1472
900 Biscayne Blvd # 4906 Miami (33132) ***(G-9311)***
Caquin Group Llc 786 303-2700
18851 Ne 29th Ave Ste 700 Aventura (33180) ***(G-266)***
Car Care Haven LLC 855 464-2836
505 Paul Morris Dr Englewood (34223) ***(G-3671)***
Car City Engine and Machine, Pensacola *Also called Santa Rosa Auto Parts Inc* ***(G-14257)***
Car Wash Solutions Florida Inc 941 323-8817
3310 Sw 7th St Unit 2 Ocala (34474) ***(G-11894)***
Caraustar Indus Cnsmr Pdts Gro 386 328-8335
188 Comfort Rd Palatka (32177) ***(G-13474)***
Caravaggio Cabinetry Inc 561 609-3355
119 S H St Lake Worth (33460) ***(G-7539)***
Carbel LLC 305 599-0832
2323 Nw 82nd Ave Doral (33122) ***(G-3290)***
Carbon Mine Supply LLC 606 437-9905
11023 Gatewood Dr Ste 103 Bradenton (34211) ***(G-1013)***
Carbon Press LLC 239 689-4406
1635 Hendry St Fort Myers (33901) ***(G-4387)***
Carbon Resources Inc 941 746-8089
9030 58th Dr E Ste 102 Bradenton (34202) ***(G-1014)***
Carbon Resources of Florida (PA) 941 746-8089
9030 58th Dr E Ste 102 Bradenton (34202) ***(G-1015)***
Carbonara Labs Inc 321 952-1303
4550 S Us Highway 1 Grant (32949) ***(G-5048)***
Carbonxt Inc 352 378-4950
3951 Nw 48th Ter Ste 111 Gainesville (32606) ***(G-4892)***
Card Quest Inc 813 288-0004
7902 W Waters Ave Ste C Tampa (33615) ***(G-17506)***
Card Usa Inc 954 862-1300
201 N Ocean Dr Ste 200 Hollywood (33019) ***(G-5795)***
Cardboard Only Inc 352 345-5060
11080 Wdlnd Waters Blvd Weeki Wachee (34613) ***(G-18701)***
Cardenas Roberto Blinds of Fla 315 807-6878
13301 Sw 132nd Ave Unit 2 Miami (33186) ***(G-9312)***
Cardinal Health 414 LLC 954 202-1883
5601 Powerline Rd Ste 108 Fort Lauderdale (33309) ***(G-3883)***
Cardinal Health 414 LLC 813 972-1351
3016 Usf Hawthorn Dr Tampa (33612) ***(G-17507)***
Cardinal Lg Company 352 237-4410
1300 Sw 44th Ave Ocala (34474) ***(G-11895)***
Cardinal Signs Inc 352 376-8494
6342 Nw 18th Dr Ste 1 Gainesville (32653) ***(G-4893)***
Cardinal Straws, Jacksonville *Also called CU Holdings LLC* ***(G-6302)***
Care and Love Publishing LLC 254 462-9134
1110 E 139th Ave Tampa (33613) ***(G-17508)***
Care-Metix Products Inc 813 628-8801
121 Kelsey Ln Ste F Tampa (33619) ***(G-17509)***
Care.ai, Orlando *Also called Vuaant Inc* ***(G-13316)***
Caregivercom Inc 954 893-0550
1871e W Oakland Park Blvd Oakland Park (33311) ***(G-11790)***
Careptrol Bradenton Southshore, Riverview *Also called Kuhn Family Enterprises Inc* ***(G-15275)***
Carey-Dunn Inc 561 840-1694
2001 Broadway Ste 301 Riviera Beach (33404) ***(G-15309)***
Carfore Ltd 239 415-2275
11650 Chitwood Dr Fort Myers (33908) ***(G-4388)***
Cargill Food Distribution, Hialeah *Also called Cargill Meat Solutions Corp* ***(G-5340)***
Cargill Meat Solutions Corp 305 826-3699
4220 W 91st Pl Unit 100 Hialeah (33018) ***(G-5340)***
Carib Energy (usa) LLC 904 727-2559
9487 Regency Square Blvd Jacksonville (32225) ***(G-6254)***
Carib Sea Inc 772 461-1113
3434 Industrial 31st St Fort Pierce (34946) ***(G-4683)***
Caribbean Basin Industries Inc 941 726-7272
2407 Casey Key Rd Nokomis (34275) ***(G-11579)***
Caribbean Box Company 305 667-4900
3123 Nw 73rd St Miami (33147) ***(G-9313)***
Caribbean Breeze Inc 904 261-7831
1438 E Oak St Fernandina Beach (32034) ***(G-3732)***
Caribbean Canvas and Mari 786 972-6377
7296 Sw 42nd Ter Miami (33155) ***(G-9314)***
Caribbean Cbinets Counters Inc 239 292-8073
11575 Marshwood Ln Fort Myers (33908) ***(G-4389)***
Caribbean Discount Ptg Inc 954 961-5015
6314 Pembroke Rd Ste A Miramar (33023) ***(G-10977)***
Caribbean Distillers LLC 863 508-1175
2200 3rd St Nw Winter Haven (33881) ***(G-19311)***
Caribbean Emblems 305 593-8183
3555 Nw 79th Ave Doral (33122) ***(G-3291)***
Caribbean Embroidery Designs, Doral *Also called Vyp Services LLC* ***(G-3546)***
Caribbean Fiberglass Products 305 888-0774
5445 Nw 72nd Ave Miami (33166) ***(G-9315)***
Caribbean Fuels Inc 305 233-3016
15001 Sw 141st Ter Miami (33196) ***(G-9316)***
Caribbean Global Group Corp 786 449-2767
5475 Nw Saint James Dr Port St Lucie (34983) ***(G-15169)***
Caribbean Interior Design Ctr, Boynton Beach *Also called Ceco Inc* ***(G-889)***
Caribbean Paint Company Inc 305 594-4500
5295 Nw 79th Ave Doral (33166) ***(G-3292)***
Caribbean Publishing Service, Palmetto Bay *Also called Caribbean Today News Magazine* ***(G-13841)***
Caribbean Shutter LLC 305 202-0501
633 De Soto Dr Miami Springs (33166) ***(G-10889)***
Caribbean Today News Magazine 305 238-2868
9020 Sw 152nd St Palmetto Bay (33157) ***(G-13841)***
Caribbean Trailers Corp 305 256-1505
12240 Sw 130th St Miami (33186) ***(G-9317)***
Caribe Express Associates Inc 305 222-9057
7320 Nw 12th St Ste 111 Miami (33126) ***(G-9318)***
Caribongo 727 944-5200
735 Ddecanese Blvd Ste 35 Tarpon Springs (34689) ***(G-18286)***
Carillon Publishing LLC 407 363-0375
9775 Bohart Ct Orlando (32836) ***(G-12550)***
Carlaron Inc 386 258-1183
421 Ridgewood Ave Daytona Beach (32117) ***(G-2639)***
Carlees Creations Inc 786 232-0050
12275 Sw 129th Ct Miami (33186) ***(G-9319)***
Carley Nigel Holdings LLC 407 212-9341
1041 Cascade Cir Apt 103 Rockledge (32955) ***(G-15398)***
Carling Technologies Inc 561 745-0405
120 Intracoastal Cir # 100 Jupiter (33469) ***(G-7015)***
Carlisle Interconnect Tech, Saint Augustine *Also called Tensolite LLC* ***(G-15626)***
Carlisle Interconnect Tech Inc (HQ) 904 829-5600
100 Tensolite Dr Saint Augustine (32092) ***(G-15526)***
Carlo Morelli 954 241-1426
1926 Hollywood Blvd Hollywood (33020) ***(G-5796)***
Carlos Abascal 973 696-1971
3640 Yacht Club Dr # 1703 Miami (33180) ***(G-9320)***
Carlos Velez Cabinets & Instal 407 929-3402
5314 Ira St Orlando (32807) ***(G-12551)***
Carloss Cabinets Inc 863 853-4255
120 Fulton Rd Lakeland (33809) ***(G-7653)***
Carlton Funeral Service, Mulberry *Also called Hicks Industries Inc* ***(G-11125)***
Carlton Mfg Inc (PA) 352 465-2153
20093 E Penn Ave Ste 3 Dunnellon (34432) ***(G-3594)***
Carlton Mfg Associates, Dunnellon *Also called Carlton Mfg Inc* ***(G-3594)***
Carmacks Quality Aluminum 727 846-0305
8052 Leo Kidd Ave Ste 1 Port Richey (34668) ***(G-15044)***

ALPHABETIC

Carne Asada Tortilleria Nicas.....305 221-7001
10404 W Flagler St Ste 5 Miami (33174) ***(G-9321)***
Carol City Opa Locka News.....305 669-7355
6796 Sw 62nd Ave South Miami (33143) ***(G-16813)***
Carol Printing Corporation.....631 315-5061
373 Wood Dove Ave Tarpon Springs (34689) ***(G-18287)***
Carolina Clubs Inc.....561 753-6948
11064 68th St N West Palm Beach (33412) ***(G-18835)***
Carolina Woodworks Inc.....954 692-4662
714 Nw 44th Ter Apt 203 Deerfield Beach (33442) ***(G-2796)***
Carotex, Estero *Also called Imported Yarns LLC* ***(G-3691)***
Carpe Diem Ice Cream Key West, Key West *Also called Carpe Diem Ice Cream LLC* ***(G-7180)***
Carpe Diem Ice Cream LLC.....305 504-4469
300 Front St Key West (33040) ***(G-7180)***
Carpe Diem Sales & Mktg Inc (PA).....407 682-1400
4560 36th St Orlando (32811) ***(G-12552)***
Carpediem LLC.....229 230-1453
618 Gulf Shore Dr Destin (32541) ***(G-3185)***
Carpenters Roofg & Shtmtl Inc.....561 833-0341
1701 W 10th St Riviera Beach (33404) ***(G-15310)***
Carpentree Creation.....904 300-4008
11058 Percheron Dr Jacksonville (32257) ***(G-6255)***
Carpet Clinic LLC.....850 232-1170
6927 Kelvin Ter Pensacola (32503) ***(G-14112)***
Carport Solution LLC.....352 789-1149
8975 Sw Highway 200 Ocala (34481) ***(G-11896)***
Carports Anywhere Inc.....352 468-1116
10858 Se County Road 221 Starke (32091) ***(G-16888)***
Carrier & Tech Solutions LLC, Fort Lauderdale *Also called Guardia LLC* ***(G-4033)***
Carrier Corporation (HQ).....800 379-6484
13995 Pasteur Blvd Palm Beach Gardens (33418) ***(G-13573)***
Carrier Fire SEC Americas Corp.....828 695-4000
13995 Pasteur Blvd Palm Beach Gardens (33418) ***(G-13574)***
Carrier Global Corporation (PA).....561 365-2000
13995 Pasteur Blvd Palm Beach Gardens (33418) ***(G-13575)***
Carriers Direct Inc.....941 776-2979
2623 Little Country Rd Parrish (34219) ***(G-14005)***
Carrollwood Creamery.....813 926-2023
13168 N Dale Mabry Hwy Tampa (33618) ***(G-17510)***
Carsons Cabinetry and Design.....352 373-8292
13411 Sw County Road 346 Archer (32618) ***(G-207)***
Carter Day Holding Inc (PA).....239 280-0361
27 Casa Mar Ln Naples (34103) ***(G-11199)***
Carter Signs Inc.....239 543-4004
6350 Slater Mill Way Fort Myers (33917) ***(G-4390)***
Carter Signs Scott, Fort Myers *Also called Carter Signs Inc* ***(G-4390)***
Carter-Health Disposables LLC.....407 296-6689
4201 Vinelnd Rd I-13 Orlando (32811) ***(G-12553)***
Carters Cabinetry Inc.....386 677-4192
4 Aviator Way Ormond Beach (32174) ***(G-13357)***
Carvalho Naturals LLC.....813 833-8229
5806 Cay Cove Ct Tampa (33615) ***(G-17511)***
Carvizion Inc.....772 807-0307
881 Sw Harvard Rd Port St Lucie (34953) ***(G-15170)***
Cary's Kitchen Cabinets, Hialeah *Also called Jam Cabinets & Investments LLC* ***(G-5462)***
Cas Industries LLC.....813 986-2694
2914 Appling Woods Pl Plant City (33565) ***(G-14416)***
Casa Blinds Interior Corp.....786 219-7157
8300 Nw 53rd St Doral (33166) ***(G-3293)***
Casa Del Marinero Corp.....305 374-5386
288 Ne 2nd St Miami (33132) ***(G-9322)***
Casale Design Source Inc.....813 873-3653
4002 W State St Ste 100 Tampa (33609) ***(G-17512)***
Casco Services Inc.....727 942-1888
153 E Oakwood St Tarpon Springs (34689) ***(G-18288)***
Casebriefs LLC.....646 240-4401
2234 N Federal Hwy 413 Boca Raton (33431) ***(G-471)***
Cases2go, Clearwater *Also called Root International Inc* ***(G-1865)***
Casework of America Inc (PA).....904 695-0996
1030 Ellis Rd N Jacksonville (32254) ***(G-6256)***
Caseworks Factory Store.com, Fort Lauderdale *Also called Caseworks International Inc* ***(G-3884)***
Caseworks International Inc.....954 933-9102
1883 W State Road 84 # 10 Fort Lauderdale (33315) ***(G-3884)***
Casey Research LLC.....561 455-9043
55 Ne 5th Ave Ste 300 Delray Beach (33483) ***(G-3056)***
Casey Weston LLC.....239 229-8375
4754 1st Ave Sw Naples (34119) ***(G-11200)***
Casino Bakery Inc.....813 242-0311
2726 N 36th St Tampa (33605) ***(G-17513)***
Casmin Inc.....352 253-5000
2255 Crescent Dr Mount Dora (32757) ***(G-11099)***
Casons Quality Care Svcs LLC.....386 365-1016
226 Se Lee Dr Lulu (32061) ***(G-8368)***
Casper Engineering Corp.....305 666-4046
7695 Sw 133rd St Pinecrest (33156) ***(G-14326)***
Cast Art International Corp.....727 807-3395
762 Marjon Ave Dunedin (34698) ***(G-3571)***
Cast Crete Tampa, Seffner *Also called Florida Engineered Constru* ***(G-16726)***
Cast Systems LLC.....941 625-3474
19400 Peachland Blvd Port Charlotte (33948) ***(G-14968)***
Cast-Crete, Palm Bay *Also called Florida Engineered Constru* ***(G-13513)***
Cast-Crete Usa LLC.....813 621-4641
6324 County Road 579 Seffner (33584) ***(G-16723)***
Cast-One, Doral *Also called Castone Creations Inc* ***(G-3294)***
Castcrete, Hudson *Also called Florida Engineered Constru* ***(G-6024)***
Castillo's Farm Equipment, Miami *Also called Castillos Farms Inc* ***(G-9323)***
Castillos Farms Inc.....305 232-0771
19744 Sw 177th Ave Miami (33187) ***(G-9323)***
Castle Distributing Industries.....305 336-0855
6506 Sw 19th St Miramar (33023) ***(G-10978)***
Castle Publishing LLC.....904 794-0112
4255 Us Highway 1 S Saint Augustine (32086) ***(G-15527)***
Castle Software Inc.....800 345-7606
626 Layport Dr Sebastian (32958) ***(G-16657)***
Castone Creations Inc.....305 599-3367
8309 Nw 70th St Doral (33166) ***(G-3294)***
Castor Inc.....813 254-1171
1701 W Green St Tampa (33607) ***(G-17514)***
Casual Tone Inc.....941 722-5643
509 9th St W Palmetto (34221) ***(G-13789)***
Casualcraft, Palmetto *Also called Casual Tone Inc* ***(G-13789)***
Cat 5 Hurricane Products LLC.....941 752-4692
6112 33rd St E Unit 105 Bradenton (34203) ***(G-1016)***
Cat5hp, Bradenton *Also called Cat 5 Hurricane Products LLC* ***(G-1016)***
Catalent Inc.....727 803-2832
2725 Scherer Dr N Saint Petersburg (33716) ***(G-15739)***
Catalent St Petersburg, Saint Petersburg *Also called Catalent Inc* ***(G-15739)***
Catalina Finer Food Corp.....813 872-6359
4709 N Lauber Way Tampa (33614) ***(G-17515)***
Catalina Finer Foods, Tampa *Also called Catalina Finer Meat Corp* ***(G-17516)***
Catalina Finer Meat Corp.....813 876-3910
4710 W Cayuga St Tampa (33614) ***(G-17516)***
Catalina Yachts Inc.....727 544-6681
7200 Bryan Dairy Rd Largo (33777) ***(G-7919)***
Catalyst Fabric Solutions LLC.....850 396-4325
3595 Industrial Park Dr Marianna (32446) ***(G-8575)***
Catalyst Orthoscience Inc.....239 325-9976
14710 Tamiami Trl N # 102 Naples (34110) ***(G-11201)***
Catalyst Pharmaceuticals Inc (PA).....305 420-3200
355 Alhambra Cir Ste 801 Coral Gables (33134) ***(G-2129)***
Catamont Machine Works, Plant City *Also called Paj Innovative Concepts Inc* ***(G-14451)***
Catamount Machine Works LLC.....813 659-0505
2804 Sydney Rd Plant City (33566) ***(G-14417)***
Catanias Winery LLC.....941 321-9650
524 Paul Morris Dr Ste B Englewood (34223) ***(G-3672)***
Catapult 13 Crtive Studios LLC.....305 788-6948
5 Nw 39th St Street1 Miami (33127) ***(G-9324)***
Catapult Group Inc.....904 834-7728
183 Landrum Ln Ste 104 Ponte Vedra Beach (32082) ***(G-14935)***
Catapult Lakeland Inc.....863 687-3788
226 N Kentucky Ave Lakeland (33801) ***(G-7654)***
Catapult Learning LL.....561 573-6025
501 Nw 8th Ave Delray Beach (33444) ***(G-3057)***
Catapult Print and Packg LLC (PA).....407 717-4323
5945 Hazeltine Nat Dr Orlando (32822) ***(G-12554)***
Catch One Comm.....772 221-0225
1850 Sw Fountainview Blvd # 103 Port Saint Lucie (34986) ***(G-15096)***
Category 5 Manufacturing Inc.....561 777-2491
7150 Seacrest Blvd Lantana (33462) ***(G-7869)***
Category 5 Manufacturing Inc.....561 502-4153
6662 Hillside Ln Lake Worth (33462) ***(G-7540)***
Caterpillar 2 Butterfly Corp.....786 540-4191
1153 Nw 47th Ter Miami (33127) ***(G-9325)***
Caterpillar Authorized Dealer, Fort Lauderdale *Also called Pantropic Power Inc* ***(G-4156)***
Caterpllar 2 Bttrfly Otrach CT.....850 515-1143
248 Hollywood Blvd Se Fort Walton Beach (32548) ***(G-4786)***
Catharine E Armstrong.....321 704-5042
137 1st Ave Indialantic (32903) ***(G-6057)***
Cathodic Prtection Tech of Fla.....321 799-0046
2023 N Atl Ave Ste 251 Cocoa Beach (32931) ***(G-2060)***
Cato Steel Co.....407 671-3333
3928 Forsyth Rd Winter Park (32792) ***(G-19391)***
Catskill Express LLC.....954 784-5151
1249 Hammondville Rd Pompano Beach (33069) ***(G-14631)***
Causey Machine Works Inc.....407 277-7570
12131 Science Dr Orlando (32826) ***(G-12555)***
Cavadas Ruben & Trisha Wagner.....407 248-2659
3125 Crystal Creek Blvd Orlando (32837) ***(G-12556)***
Cavaform Inc (PA).....727 384-3676
2700 72nd St N Saint Petersburg (33710) ***(G-15740)***
Cavaform International LLC.....727 384-3676
2700 72nd St N Saint Petersburg (33710) ***(G-15741)***
Cavallo Estate Winery LLC.....352 500-9463
8123 S Lecanto Hwy Lecanto (34461) ***(G-8130)***
Cavastone By Connie Davalos, Boca Raton *Also called Cavastone LLC* ***(G-472)***
Cavastone LLC.....561 994-9100
506 Nw 77th St Boca Raton (33487) ***(G-472)***

Caveat...305 501-4646
448 Nw 28th St Miami (33127) ***(G-9326)***
Cavo Development Inc...305 255-7465
16380 Sw 137th Ave Miami (33177) ***(G-9327)***
Cavok Capital LLC...727 789-0951
855 Virginia Ave Palm Harbor (34683) ***(G-13726)***
Cawy Bottling Co Inc...305 634-8669
2440 Nw 21st Ter Miami (33142) ***(G-9328)***
Caxton Newspapers Inc...305 538-9700
1688 Meridian Ave Ste 404 Miami Beach (33139) ***(G-10652)***
Cayago Americas Inc...754 216-4600
1881 W State Road 84 # 104 Fort Lauderdale (33315) ***(G-3885)***
Caylex, Orlando *Also called Lexington Dsign + Fbrction E L* ***(G-12906)***
Cayman Manufacturing Inc...954 421-1170
1301 Sw 34th Ave Deerfield Beach (33442) ***(G-2797)***
Cayman Nat Mfg & Installation...954 421-1170
1301 Sw 34th Ave Deerfield Beach (33442) ***(G-2798)***
Cayo Custom Boats LLC...727 698-7201
2055 34th Way Largo (33771) ***(G-7920)***
Cayo Hueso Enterprises Inc...305 747-0020
5750 2nd Ave Key West (33040) ***(G-7181)***
CB Designing Inc...407 927-1808
812 Plaza Ct Orlando (32803) ***(G-12557)***
CB Precious Metals LLC...407 790-1585
1237 Bella Vista Cir Longwood (32779) ***(G-8264)***
Cbc Biotechnologies Inc...813 803-6300
12005 Whitmarsh Ln Tampa (33626) ***(G-17517)***
Cbd LLC...305 615-1194
3531 Griffin Rd Ste 100 Fort Lauderdale (33312) ***(G-3886)***
Cbd Biocare...813 380-4376
7381 114th Ave Ste 406 Largo (33773) ***(G-7921)***
Cbd Brands Inc...561 325-0482
725 N Highway A1a C106 Jupiter (33477) ***(G-7016)***
Cbd Docs LLC...954 868-5152
7343 Lake Worth Rd Lake Worth (33467) ***(G-7541)***
Cbd Dstrbuted By Miami Cbd Inc...561 316-7456
416 E Boynton Beach Blvd A Boynton Beach (33435) ***(G-887)***
Cbd Life Florida Inc...352 483-8333
3109 Kurt St Eustis (32726) ***(G-3705)***
Cbd-ME LLC...847 910-0505
4075 Nw 58th Ln Boca Raton (33496) ***(G-473)***
Cbdpharm LLC...813 442-5464
13529 Westshire Dr Tampa (33618) ***(G-17518)***
Cbg Biotech Ltd Co (PA)...239 514-1148
100 Glenview Pl Apt 1003 Naples (34108) ***(G-11202)***
CBI Industries Inc...305 796-9346
13225 Sw 95th Ave Miami (33176) ***(G-9329)***
Cbm Trading Inc...954 252-7460
10620 Griffin Rd Ste 104 Davie (33328) ***(G-2506)***
CC Control Corp...561 293-3975
5760 Corporate Way West Palm Beach (33407) ***(G-18836)***
CC Kitchen Cabinets Corp...786 457-1494
521 Sw 127th Ave Miami (33184) ***(G-9330)***
CC Lighting Inc...805 302-5321
11138 Green Lake Dr Boynton Beach (33437) ***(G-888)***
CC Machine Inc (PA)...888 577-0144
618 Ridgewood Ave Ste B Holly Hill (32117) ***(G-5757)***
CC Sportswear Inc...941 351-4205
2331 Whtfeld Indus Way Un Sarasota (34243) ***(G-16188)***
CCA Industries Inc...813 601-6238
13010 Us Highway 301 Dade City (33525) ***(G-2424)***
Ccbcc Operations LLC...850 785-6171
300 W 5th St Panama City (32401) ***(G-13876)***
Ccf Holdco LLC...800 714-9215
1528 Sw Highway 17 Arcadia (34266) ***(G-201)***
CCI Hair Boutique LLC...407 408-8649
400 N Pine Hills Rd Ste C Orlando (32811) ***(G-12558)***
CCM Clllar Cnnection Miami Inc...305 406-1656
1825 Nw 79th Ave Doral (33126) ***(G-3295)***
Ccp Bayou Printing, Valparaiso *Also called Bayou Printing Inc* ***(G-18507)***
Ccp Fabrication...727 946-6024
2100 Peggy Dr Holiday (34690) ***(G-5738)***
Ccp of Miami Inc...305 233-6534
13601 Sw 143rd Ct Miami (33186) ***(G-9331)***
CD Greeting LLC...954 530-1301
3260 Ne 32nd St Fort Lauderdale (33308) ***(G-3887)***
Cda Group, Miami Beach *Also called Cda Ventures Inc* ***(G-10653)***
Cda Ventures Inc...305 428-2857
270 N Shore Dr Miami Beach (33141) ***(G-10653)***
Cdc Woodworking, Pensacola *Also called Cabinet Design and Cnstr LLC* ***(G-14111)***
Cds Manufacturing Inc...850 875-4651
106 Charles Hayes Sr Dr Gretna (32332) ***(G-5090)***
Ce Hooton Sales LLC...305 255-9722
1901 Whitfield Park Loop Sarasota (34243) ***(G-16189)***
Ce North America LLC...305 392-2200
2600 S Douglas Rd Ph 7 Coral Gables (33134) ***(G-2130)***
Ceautamed Worldwide LLC...866 409-6262
1289 Clint Moore Rd Boca Raton (33487) ***(G-474)***
Cebev LLC...918 830-4417
2424 N Federal Hwy # 101 Boca Raton (33431) ***(G-475)***
Ceco & Associates Inc...727 528-0075
6508 S 78th St Riverview (33578) ***(G-15266)***
Ceco Coated Fasteners, Riverview *Also called Ceco & Associates Inc* ***(G-15266)***
Ceco Inc...561 265-1111
2951 Sw 14th Pl Ste 39 Boynton Beach (33426) ***(G-889)***
Cedar Creek Logging Inc...850 832-0133
4138 Harry Wells Rd Panama City (32409) ***(G-13877)***
Cedar Fresh Home Products LLC (PA)...305 975-8524
4207 University Dr Miami (33146) ***(G-9332)***
Cedar Key Beacon...352 493-4796
624 W Park Ave Chiefland (32626) ***(G-1534)***
Cedars Bakery Group Inc...407 476-6593
4704 L B Mcleod Rd Orlando (32811) ***(G-12559)***
Cedars Food Inc...321 724-2624
2110 Dairy Rd Ste 101 West Melbourne (32904) ***(G-18769)***
Cedena Carmenn...305 681-1222
2310 Nw 150th St Opa Locka (33054) ***(G-12298)***
Cedrick McDonald...813 279-1442
4205 N Florida Ave Tampa (33603) ***(G-17519)***
Cedrus Inc...772 286-2082
9011 Sw Old Kansas Ave Stuart (34997) ***(G-16920)***
Ceeco, Okeechobee *Also called Communication Eqp & Engrg Co* ***(G-12174)***
Ceh Llc (PA)...941 518-6747
5510 Tdwter Preserve Blvd Bradenton (34208) ***(G-1017)***
Ceh Seafood, Bradenton *Also called Ceh Llc* ***(G-1017)***
Cei Liquidation Inc...281 541-2444
3495 S Us Highway 1 Ste A Fort Pierce (34982) ***(G-4684)***
Celeb Luxury LLC...954 763-0333
6545 Nova Dr Ste 201 Davie (33317) ***(G-2507)***
Celebration Cup, Sanford *Also called Compak Companies LLC* ***(G-16019)***
Celigenex Inc...954 957-1058
3233 Ne 34th St Apt 912a Fort Lauderdale (33308) ***(G-3888)***
Celios Corporation...833 235-4671
1228 E 7th Ave Ste 313 Tampa (33605) ***(G-17520)***
Cellec Games Inc...407 476-3590
2736 Candlewood Ct Apopka (32703) ***(G-120)***
Cellmic LLC...310 443-2070
34266 Us Highway 19 N Palm Harbor (34684) ***(G-13727)***
Cellofoam North America Inc...407 888-4667
11237 Astronaut Blvd Orlando (32837) ***(G-12560)***
Cellphone Parts Express LLC...954 635-5525
2633 Park Ln Hallandale Beach (33009) ***(G-5177)***
Cellular Masters Inc...305 592-7906
10900 Nw 21st St Ste 210 Miami (33172) ***(G-9333)***
Celmark International, Orlando *Also called Cemi International Inc* ***(G-12561)***
Celsius Inc...561 276-2239
2424 N Federal Hwy # 208 Boca Raton (33431) ***(G-476)***
Celsius Holdings Inc (PA)...561 276-2239
2424 N Federal Hwy # 208 Boca Raton (33431) ***(G-477)***
Celtic Airspares LLC...727 431-0482
28870 Us Highway 19 N # 328 Clearwater (33761) ***(G-1622)***
Cement Industries Inc...239 332-1440
2925 Hanson St Fort Myers (33916) ***(G-4391)***
Cement Miami Terminal...305 221-2502
1200 Nw 137th Ave Miami (33182) ***(G-9334)***
Cement Plant, Newberry *Also called Argos USA LLC* ***(G-11551)***
Cement Precast Products Inc...352 372-0953
2033 Ne 27th Ave Gainesville (32609) ***(G-4894)***
Cement Products Inc...727 868-9226
9301 Denton Ave Port Richey (34667) ***(G-15045)***
Cement-It Inc...954 565-7875
2455 E Sunrise Blvd # 11 Fort Lauderdale (33304) ***(G-3889)***
Cemex Inc...813 663-9712
5503 E Diana St Tampa (33610) ***(G-17521)***
Cemex Cement Inc...904 296-2400
340 Corporate Way Ste 100 Orange Park (32073) ***(G-12384)***
Cemex Cement Inc...352 867-5794
619 Sw 17th Loop Ocala (34471) ***(G-11897)***
Cemex Cement Inc...850 942-4582
3440 Weems Rd Tallahassee (32317) ***(G-17231)***
Cemex Cement Inc...727 327-5730
601 24th St S Saint Petersburg (33712) ***(G-15742)***
Cemex Cement Inc...407 877-9623
201 Hennis Rd Winter Garden (34787) ***(G-19255)***
Cemex Cnstr Mtls ATL LLC (HQ)...561 833-5555
1501 Belvedere Rd West Palm Beach (33406) ***(G-18837)***
Cemex Cnstr Mtls Fla LLC...305 247-3011
15900 Sw 408th St Homestead (33034) ***(G-5957)***
Cemex Cnstr Mtls Fla LLC...321 636-5121
209 George King Blvd Cape Canaveral (32920) ***(G-1355)***
Cemex Cnstr Mtls Fla LLC...904 880-4958
14770 Old St Augustine Rd Jacksonville (32258) ***(G-6257)***
Cemex Cnstr Mtls Fla LLC...321 632-0500
3365 E Industry Rd Cocoa (32926) ***(G-2004)***
Cemex Cnstr Mtls Fla LLC...800 992-3639
1290 Foxmoor St Moore Haven (33471) ***(G-11086)***
Cemex Cnstr Mtls Fla LLC...855 292-8453
3728 Prospect Ave Naples (34104) ***(G-11203)***
Cemex Cnstr Mtls Fla LLC...800 992-3639
Glades Cut Off Rd Fort Pierce (34981) ***(G-4685)***

Cemex Cnstr Mtls Fla LLC...954 977-9222
1150 Nw 24th St Pompano Beach (33064) ***(G-14632)***
Cemex Cnstr Mtls Fla LLC...561 996-5249
State Rd 80 & Fec Rr Belle Glade (33430) ***(G-346)***
Cemex Cnstr Mtls Fla LLC...352 330-1115
4270 County Road 124a Wildwood (34785) ***(G-19192)***
Cemex Cnstr Mtls Fla LLC...352 746-0136
2975 S Lecanto Hwy Lecanto (34461) ***(G-8131)***
Cemex Cnstr Mtls Fla LLC...813 621-5575
9609 Palm River Rd Tampa (33619) ***(G-17522)***
Cemex Cnstr Mtls Fla LLC...561 832-6646
1021 N Railroad Ave West Palm Beach (33401) ***(G-18838)***
Cemex Cnstr Mtls Fla LLC...800 992-3639
501 Douglas Rd E Oldsmar (34677) ***(G-12213)***
Cemex Cnstr Mtls Fla LLC...561 745-5240
1557 Jupiter Park Dr # 1 Jupiter (33458) ***(G-7017)***
Cemex Cnstr Mtls Fla LLC...352 793-3048
7388 Cr 745 Bushnell (33513) ***(G-1315)***
Cemex Cnstr Mtls Fla LLC...904 213-8860
340 Corporate Way Ste 100 Orange Park (32073) ***(G-12385)***
Cemex Cnstr Mtls Fla LLC...904 827-0369
233 Industry Pl Saint Augustine (32095) ***(G-15528)***
Cemex Cnstr Mtls Fla LLC (HQ)...561 833-5555
1501 Belvedere Rd West Palm Beach (33406) ***(G-18839)***
Cemex Cnstr Mtls Fla LLC...800 992-3639
622 Cattlemen Rd Sarasota (34232) ***(G-16381)***
Cemex Cnstr Mtls Fla LLC...772 461-7102
514 S 3rd St Fort Pierce (34950) ***(G-4686)***
Cemex Cnstr Mtls Fla LLC...863 419-2875
100 Lem Carnes Rd Davenport (33837) ***(G-2476)***
Cemex Cnstr Mtls PCF LLC (HQ)...561 833-5555
1501 Belvedere Rd West Palm Beach (33406) ***(G-18840)***
Cemex Concrete Company...305 558-0255
11100 Nw 138th St Medley (33178) ***(G-8628)***
Cemex Corp...561 820-8613
1200 Nw 137th Ave Miami (33182) ***(G-9335)***
Cemex Materials LLC...386 775-0790
2170 State Road 472 Deland (32724) ***(G-2963)***
Cemex Materials LLC (HQ)...561 833-5555
1501 Belvedere Rd West Palm Beach (33406) ***(G-18841)***
Cemex Materials LLC...305 223-6934
1200 Nw 137th Ave Miami (33182) ***(G-9336)***
Cemex Materials LLC...321 636-5121
3365 E Industry Rd Cocoa (32926) ***(G-2005)***
Cemex Materials LLC...305 821-5661
13292 Nw 118th Ave Medley (33178) ***(G-8629)***
Cemex Materials LLC...561 746-4556
282 Old Dixie Hwy Jupiter (33469) ***(G-7018)***
Cemex Materials LLC...772 287-0502
1232 Se Dixie Cutoff Rd Stuart (34994) ***(G-16921)***
Cemex Materials LLC...305 818-4941
13292 Nw 118th Ave Medley (33178) ***(G-8630)***
Cemex Materials LLC...904 296-2400
4807 Collins Rd Jacksonville (32244) ***(G-6258)***
Cemex Materials LLC...941 722-4578
600 9th St W Palmetto (34221) ***(G-13790)***
Cemex Materials LLC...954 523-9978
29 Sw 33rd St Fort Lauderdale (33315) ***(G-3890)***
Cemex Materials LLC...407 322-8862
2210 W 25th St Sanford (32771) ***(G-16008)***
Cemex Materials LLC...850 769-2243
714 Transmitter Rd Panama City (32401) ***(G-13878)***
Cemex Materials LLC...321 636-5121
511 Garden St Titusville (32796) ***(G-18422)***
Cemex Materials LLC...863 688-2306
801 Mccue Rd Lakeland (33815) ***(G-7655)***
Cemex Materials LLC...954 431-7655
17301 Pines Blvd Pembroke Pines (33029) ***(G-14026)***
Cemex Materials LLC...352 435-0783
27111 County Road 33 Okahumpka (34762) ***(G-12169)***
Cemex Materials LLC...813 620-3760
6302 N 56th St Tampa (33610) ***(G-17523)***
Cemex Materials LLC...305 558-0315
2201 Nw 38th Ct Miami (33142) ***(G-9337)***
Cemex Materials LLC...561 793-1442
9111 Southern Blvd West Palm Beach (33411) ***(G-18842)***
Cemex Materials LLC...561 743-4039
1001 Jupiter Park Dr # 108 Jupiter (33458) ***(G-7019)***
Cemex Materials LLC...239 332-0135
2040 Ortiz Ave Fort Myers (33905) ***(G-4392)***
Cemex Materials LLC...561 881-4472
501 Avenue S Riviera Beach (33404) ***(G-15311)***
Cemex Materials LLC...863 678-3945
534 Story Rd Lake Wales (33898) ***(G-7501)***
Cemex Pacific Holdings LLC...239 992-1400
25061 Old 41 Rd Bonita Springs (34135) ***(G-824)***
Cemi International Inc...407 859-7701
2600 Titan Row Orlando (32809) ***(G-12561)***
Censys Technologies Corp...850 321-2278
1511 Avi Ctr Pkwy Ste 220 Daytona Beach (32114) ***(G-2640)***
Center American Longevity...305 777-1667
2627 Ne 203rd St Ste 118 Miami (33180) ***(G-9338)***
Center For Business Ownership...239 455-9393
956 Glen Lake Cir Naples (34119) ***(G-11204)***
Center For Vital Living DBA...239 213-2222
2132 Tamiami Trl N Naples (34102) ***(G-11205)***
Center Sand Mine...800 366-7263
16375 Hartwood Marsh Rd Clermont (34711) ***(G-1951)***
Center Seal Inc...863 965-7124
2714 K Ville Ave Auburndale (33823) ***(G-232)***
Center Technologies, Saint Petersburg *Also called Millimeter Wave Products Inc* ***(G-15854)***
Centerline Brackets, Saint Augustine *Also called Centerline Steel LLC* ***(G-15529)***
Centerline Drctnal Drlg Srvcin, Labelle *Also called Centerline Drctnal Drlg Svc In* ***(G-7317)***
Centerline Drctnal Drlg Svc In...863 674-0913
900 S Elm St Labelle (33935) ***(G-7317)***
Centerline Steel LLC...904 217-4186
208 W Davis Industrial Dr Saint Augustine (32084) ***(G-15529)***
Centerline Tool & Engrg Inc...941 749-5519
3107 29th Ave E Ste A Bradenton (34208) ***(G-1018)***
Centerpoint Meats and Prov, Saint Petersburg *Also called Pinellas Provision Corporation* ***(G-15877)***
Central Beef Ind LLC...352 793-3671
571 W Kings Hwy Center Hill (33514) ***(G-1525)***
Central Concrete Supermix Inc...954 480-9333
1817 S Powerline Rd Deerfield Beach (33442) ***(G-2799)***
Central Electric Motor Service...863 422-4721
313 N 12th St Haines City (33844) ***(G-5138)***
Central Fla Attrnsfsonists Inc...321 299-6019
3791 Half Moon Dr Orlando (32812) ***(G-12562)***
Central Fla Bus Solutions Inc...863 297-9293
150 3rd St Sw Winter Haven (33880) ***(G-19312)***
Central Fla Kit Bath Srfces In...352 307-2333
2800 Se 62nd St Ocala (34480) ***(G-11898)***
Central Fla Prtg Graphics LLC...321 752-8753
772 Washburn Rd Ste A Melbourne (32934) ***(G-8787)***
Central Fla Remanufacturing...407 299-9011
2526 W Washington St Orlando (32805) ***(G-12563)***
Central Fla Stl Bldg & Sup LLC...352 266-6795
4750 S Pine Ave Ocala (34480) ***(G-11899)***
Central Florida Box Corp...407 936-1277
2950 Lake Emma Rd # 1000 Lake Mary (32746) ***(G-7404)***
Central Florida Central Fla...407 674-2626
4157 Seaboard Rd Orlando (32808) ***(G-12564)***
Central Florida Cnstr Walls...407 448-2350
5923 Bamboo Dr Orlando (32807) ***(G-12565)***
Central Florida Cstm Trlrs Inc (PA)...407 851-1144
2136 4th St Orlando (32824) ***(G-12566)***
Central Florida Driveshaft...407 299-1100
5512 Carder Rd Orlando (32810) ***(G-12567)***
Central Florida Ice Services...407 779-0161
410 27th St Orlando (32806) ***(G-12568)***
Central Florida Lbr & Sup Co...407 298-5600
2721 Regent Ave Orlando (32804) ***(G-12569)***
Central Florida Plating Inc...321 452-7234
675 Cypress Dr Merritt Island (32952) ***(G-8998)***
Central Florida Precast Inc...941 730-2158
1910 1st Ave E Bradenton (34208) ***(G-1019)***
Central Florida Publishing Inc...407 682-1221
300 N French Ave Sanford (32771) ***(G-16009)***
Central Florida Publishing Inc (PA)...407 323-5204
700 W Fulton St Sanford (32771) ***(G-16010)***
Central Florida Remanufactory, Orlando *Also called Central Fla Remanufacturing* ***(G-12563)***
Central Florida Sales & Svc...863 967-6678
307 Mckean St Auburndale (33823) ***(G-233)***
Central Florida Stone Pavers...407 227-3519
4560 Saint Brides Ct Orlando (32812) ***(G-12570)***
Central Florida Tinting...863 221-0185
1827 Canal Rd Lake Wales (33898) ***(G-7502)***
Central Florida Truss Inc (PA)...863 533-0821
1500 Us Highway 17 N Bartow (33830) ***(G-312)***
Central Florida Weld & Fab LLC...407 919-8706
259 N Industrial Dr Orange City (32763) ***(G-12373)***
Central Maintenance & Wldg Inc (PA)...813 229-0012
2620 E Keysville Rd Lithia (33547) ***(G-8216)***
Central Maintenance & Wldg Inc...352 795-2817
6040 N Suncoast Blvd Crystal River (34428) ***(G-2371)***
Central Metal Fabricators Inc...305 261-6262
900 Sw 70th Ave Miami (33144) ***(G-9339)***
Central Printers Inc...727 527-5879
4101 35th St N Saint Petersburg (33714) ***(G-15743)***
Central Processing Corp...352 787-3004
304 Richey Rd Leesburg (34748) ***(G-8146)***
Central Sand Inc...321 632-0308
6855 Tico Rd Unit 8 Titusville (32780) ***(G-18423)***
Central Signs LLC...386 322-7446
517 Mason Ave Daytona Beach (32117) ***(G-2641)***
Central Signs Volusia Cnty Inc...386 341-4842
497 Buchanan Way South Daytona (32119) ***(G-16799)***
Central Signs, LLC, Daytona Beach *Also called Central Signs LLC* ***(G-2641)***

Central State Aggregates LLC...813 788-0454
41150 Yonkers Blvd Zephyrhills (33541) ***(G-19510)***
Central Steel Fabricators LLC...904 503-1660
2144 Soutel Dr Jacksonville (32208) ***(G-6259)***
Central Turbos Corp (PA)...305 406-3933
1951 Nw 97th Ave Doral (33172) ***(G-3296)***
Central Wire Industries LLC...850 983-9926
5881 Commerce Rd Milton (32583) ***(G-10926)***
Centralsquare Technologies, Lake Mary *Also called Superion LLC* ***(G-7452)***
Centralsquare Technologies, Deerfield Beach *Also called Advanced Public Safety LLC* ***(G-2766)***
Centralum Usa LLC...786 646-9756
175 Sw 7th St Ste 1706 Miami (33130) ***(G-9340)***
Centrex Powdercoating Inc...813 390-2802
4901 Distribution Dr Tampa (33605) ***(G-17524)***
Centrifugal Rebabbitting Inc...954 522-3003
234 Sw 29th St Fort Lauderdale (33315) ***(G-3891)***
Centro Ddgnstico Y Tratamiento, Sanford *Also called Centro De Diagnostico* ***(G-16011)***
Centro De Diagnostico...407 865-7020
253 Bellagio Cir Sanford (32771) ***(G-16011)***
Centroid Products Inc...386 423-3574
2104 Hibiscus Dr Edgewater (32141) ***(G-3618)***
Centrys LLC...407 476-4786
750 Monroe Rd Sanford (32771) ***(G-16012)***
Centurion Armoring Intl Inc...813 426-3385
3911 W Eden Roc Cir Tampa (33634) ***(G-17525)***
Centurion Holdings I LLC...636 349-5425
324 N Dale Mabry Hwy Tampa (33609) ***(G-17526)***
Centurion Residential Inds...561 574-1483
3819 Heath Cir N West Palm Beach (33407) ***(G-18843)***
Centurion Technologies, Tampa *Also called Centurion Holdings I LLC* ***(G-17526)***
Century Boats, Zephyrhills *Also called All Craft Marine LLC* ***(G-19506)***
Century Metal Products Inc...407 293-8871
3108 Friendly Ave Orlando (32808) ***(G-12571)***
Century Millworks...850 256-2565
6082 Industrial Blvd Century (32535) ***(G-1527)***
Cenveo Worldwide Limited...321 207-0403
1955 Corporate Sq Longwood (32750) ***(G-8265)***
Cepero Remodeling Inc...305 265-1888
6972 Sw 4th St Miami (33144) ***(G-9341)***
Cepods LLC...786 520-1412
1348 Washington Ave # 257 Miami Beach (33139) ***(G-10654)***
Ceramica Verea USA Corp...305 665-3923
7035 Sw 44th St Miami (33155) ***(G-9342)***
Ceramlock Coatings Inc...772 781-2141
3912 Sw Bruner Ter Palm City (34990) ***(G-13645)***
Cerberus Craft Distillery LLC...813 789-1556
6608 Anderson Rd Tampa (33634) ***(G-17527)***
Cerenovus, Miami *Also called Depuy Synthes Products Inc* ***(G-9456)***
Cerex Advanced Fabrics Inc...850 968-0100
610 Chemstrand Rd Cantonment (32533) ***(G-1336)***
Cerno Pharmaceuticals LLC...786 763-2766
6714 Nw 72nd Ave Miami (33166) ***(G-9343)***
Cerp Software Inc...954 607-1417
17411 Nw 8th St Pembroke Pines (33029) ***(G-14027)***
Certainteed Corporation (HQ)...863 294-3206
101 Hatfield Rd Winter Haven (33880) ***(G-19313)***
Certainteed Machine Works, Winter Haven *Also called Certainteed Corporation* ***(G-19313)***
Certanteed Gyps Ciling Mfg Inc (HQ)...813 286-3900
4300 W Cypress St Ste 500 Tampa (33607) ***(G-17528)***
Certapro Painters Centl Miami, Doral *Also called Sdkc Corp* ***(G-3497)***
Certek Software Designs Inc...727 738-8188
507 S Paula Dr Dunedin (34698) ***(G-3572)***
Certified Manufacturing Inc...850 537-3777
583 Armistead Blvd Holt (32564) ***(G-5948)***
Certified Metal Finishing Inc...954 979-0707
1420 Sw 28th Ave Pompano Beach (33069) ***(G-14633)***
Certified Mold Free Corp...954 614-7100
2881 W Lake Vista Cir Davie (33328) ***(G-2508)***
Certified Mold Treatment LLC...305 879-1839
17277 Allamanda Dr Summerland Key (33042) ***(G-17065)***
Certified Whl Exterior Pdts...407 654-7170
902 Carter Rd Ste 300 Winter Garden (34787) ***(G-19256)***
Certified Wldg Fbrction Svcs L...813 323-4090
5116 Springwood Dr Tampa (33624) ***(G-17529)***
Certusview Technologies LLC...844 533-1258
3980 Rca Blvd Ste 8000 Palm Beach Gardens (33410) ***(G-13576)***
Cesaroni Aerospace Inc...941 400-1421
2280 Commerce Ct Bowling Green (33834) ***(G-865)***
Cesco Signs Inc...407 463-6635
6631 E Colonial Dr Orlando (32807) ***(G-12572)***
Cesibon...239 682-5028
8807 Tamiami Trl N Naples (34108) ***(G-11206)***
Ceva Animal Health LLC...727 548-8345
4027 Tampa Rd Ste 3000 Oldsmar (34677) ***(G-12214)***
Cew LLC...305 232-8892
14008 Sw 140th St Miami (33186) ***(G-9344)***
Cew Technologies Inc...305 232-8892
14008 Sw 140th St Miami (33186) ***(G-9345)***
CF Boatworks Inc...954 325-6007
3340 Sw 2nd Ave Fort Lauderdale (33315) ***(G-3892)***
CF Motion Inc...727 458-7092
4625 E Bay Dr Ste 306 Clearwater (33764) ***(G-1623)***
CF Sign and Stamp Company, Panama City *Also called Finlayson Enterprises Inc* ***(G-13902)***
Cfb Display Group, Lake Mary *Also called Central Florida Box Corp* ***(G-7404)***
CFM&d LLC...772 220-8938
2550 Se Willoughby Blvd Stuart (34994) ***(G-16922)***
CFS Inc...850 386-2902
2151 Delta Blvd Ste 101 Tallahassee (32303) ***(G-17232)***
Cfu Plating...386 795-5198
7575 S Us Highway 441 # 118 Ocala (34480) ***(G-11900)***
Cfuel Energy Corp...561 336-4084
2601 Biscayne Blvd Miami (33137) ***(G-9346)***
Cg Burgers (PA)...954 618-6450
1732 N Federal Hwy Fort Lauderdale (33305) ***(G-3893)***
CG Quality Woodworks Inc...305 231-3480
7530 W 19th Ct Hialeah (33014) ***(G-5341)***
Cg Roxane LLC...407 241-1640
2224 Hazelhurst Ave Orlando (32804) ***(G-12573)***
Cg Solutionsgroup, Apopka *Also called Cellec Games Inc* ***(G-120)***
Cgc Industries Inc...954 923-2428
200 N Dixie Hwy Hollywood (33020) ***(G-5797)***
Cgi Printers LLC...561 969-9999
2820 Tennis Club Dr # 202 West Palm Beach (33417) ***(G-18844)***
Chacho Customs...239 369-4664
2401 Gretchen Ave S F Lehigh Acres (33973) ***(G-8187)***
Chad...727 433-0404
817 S Macdill Ave Tampa (33609) ***(G-17530)***
Chadwick S Fuel Co Inc...754 224-8773
2600 Miami Rd Fort Lauderdale (33316) ***(G-3894)***
Chalet Suzanne Rest Cntry Inn, Lake Wales *Also called Suzanne Chalet Foods Inc* ***(G-7524)***
Chambers Body Works Inc...352 588-3072
16556 Old Johnston Rd Dade City (33523) ***(G-2425)***
Chambers Truss Inc (PA)...772 465-2012
3105 Oleander Ave Fort Pierce (34982) ***(G-4687)***
Champagne Welding Inc...585 738-8611
2910 W Beaver St Jacksonville (32254) ***(G-6260)***
Champion Controls Inc (PA)...954 318-3090
811 Nw 57th Pl Fort Lauderdale (33309) ***(G-3895)***
Champion Nutrition Inc...954 233-3300
1301 Sawgrs Corp Pkwy Sunrise (33323) ***(G-17105)***
Champion Performance Products, Sunrise *Also called Champion Nutrition Inc* ***(G-17105)***
Champion Seal, Wesley Chapel *Also called Kericure Inc* ***(G-18750)***
Champion Shtmtl Fabrication...407 509-7439
6450 University Blvd B2 Winter Park (32792) ***(G-19392)***
Champion Welding Services LLC...786 262-5727
5608 Nw 161st St Miami Lakes (33014) ***(G-10775)***
Chance Aluminum Corp...407 789-1606
11616 Landstar Blvd Orlando (32824) ***(G-12574)***
Chancey Metal Products Inc...904 260-6880
5130 Sunbeam Rd Jacksonville (32257) ***(G-6261)***
Chandler Bats...484 674-7175
2401 Nw 2nd Ave Ste 100 Boca Raton (33431) ***(G-478)***
Change This World...407 900-8840
6790 Edgwtr Cmmerce Pkwy Orlando (32810) ***(G-12575)***
Channel Industries Inc...561 214-0637
511 29th St West Palm Beach (33407) ***(G-18845)***
Channel Investments LLC...727 599-1360
4221 W Boy Scout Blvd # 300 Tampa (33607) ***(G-17531)***
Channel Letter Network Corp...305 594-3360
7204 Nw 31st St Miami (33122) ***(G-9347)***
Channel Letter USA, Delray Beach *Also called Royal Atlantic Ventures LLC* ***(G-3136)***
Channel Letter USA Corp...561 243-9699
2275 S Federal Hwy # 350 Delray Beach (33483) ***(G-3058)***
Channel Logistics LLC...856 614-5441
888 Biscayne Blvd Ste 505 Miami (33132) ***(G-9348)***
Channel Microwave, Tampa *Also called Smiths Interconnect Inc* ***(G-18112)***
Charcoal Chef Usa LLC...786 273-6511
680 Ne 50th Ter Miami (33137) ***(G-9349)***
Chardonnay Boat Works LLC...703 981-6339
411 Walnut St Green Cove Springs (32043) ***(G-5058)***
Chargers and Cases LLC...352 587-2539
2281 Lee Rd Ste 105 Winter Park (32789) ***(G-19393)***
Chargex LLC...855 242-7439
4020 W Kennedy Blvd # 10 Tampa (33609) ***(G-17532)***
Chargriller, Tampa *Also called A&J Manufacturing Inc* ***(G-17377)***
Charian Machine & Mfg Inc...727 561-0150
4652 107th Cir N Clearwater (33762) ***(G-1624)***
Chariot Eagle Inc (PA)...623 936-7545
931 Nw 37th Ave Ocala (34475) ***(G-11901)***
Charisma Media...407 333-0600
1051 Sand Pond Rd Lake Mary (32746) ***(G-7405)***
Charitees LLC...561 542-4616
3475 Sheridan St Ste 310 Hollywood (33021) ***(G-5798)***
Charles & Co LLC...404 592-1190
909 Nw 10th Ter Fort Lauderdale (33311) ***(G-3896)***
Charles Bryant Enterprises...850 785-3604
2700 Whisperwood Ln Panama City (32405) ***(G-13879)***

ALPHABETIC

Charles Composites LLC....863 357-2500
1252 Ne 12th St Okeechobee (34972) ***(G-12173)***
Charles Gable Inc....239 300-0220
18511 Royal Hammock Blvd Naples (34114) ***(G-11207)***
Charles Industries, Okeechobee *Also called Charles Composites LLC* ***(G-12173)***
Charles K Sewell....407 423-1870
333 W Michigan St Orlando (32806) ***(G-12576)***
Charles Screening & Alum LLC....239 369-0551
848 Theodore Vail St E Lehigh Acres (33974) ***(G-8188)***
Charles Thaggard Inc....239 936-8059
1951 Collier Ave Ste A Fort Myers (33901) ***(G-4393)***
Charleston Aluminum LLC....305 628-4014
1150 Nw 159th Dr Hialeah (33016) ***(G-5342)***
Charleston Winery....843 425-1265
465 18th St Vero Beach (32960) ***(G-18610)***
Charlie S Logging Inc....850 643-1145
17586 Nw County Road 12 Bristol (32321) ***(G-1193)***
Charlotte County Min & Mtl Inc....239 567-1800
16070 Tamiami Trl Punta Gorda (33955) ***(G-15201)***
Charlotte Pipe and Foundry Co....352 748-8100
4149 County Road 124a Wildwood (34785) ***(G-19193)***
Charuvil Oil Inc DBA Valero....772 871-9050
815 E Prima Vista Blvd Port Saint Lucie (34952) ***(G-15097)***
Chasco Machine & Manufacturing....727 815-3510
5071 Cedar Ridge Dr Brooksville (34601) ***(G-1218)***
Chasco Machine & Mfg Inc....352 678-4188
5071 Cedar Ridge Dr Brooksville (34601) ***(G-1219)***
Chase Aerospace Inc....407 812-4545
5342 Greenside Ct Orlando (32819) ***(G-12577)***
Chase Metals Inc....352 669-1254
38051 State Road 19 Umatilla (32784) ***(G-18496)***
Chassis King, Clearwater *Also called Interglobal Capital Inc* ***(G-1733)***
Chassis King LLC....727 585-1500
1016 Pnc De Leon Blvd Clearwater (33756) ***(G-1625)***
Chattam Industries Inc....727 748-2419
36181 E Lake Rd Ste 144 Palm Harbor (34685) ***(G-13728)***
Chautuqua Vineyards Winery Inc (PA)....850 892-5887
364 Hugh Adams Rd Defuniak Springs (32435) ***(G-2940)***
Cheany Inc....813 443-5271
119 E Tarpon Ave Tarpon Springs (34689) ***(G-18289)***
Cheap Banners & Signs Central....727 522-7414
5502 Haines Rd N Saint Petersburg (33714) ***(G-15744)***
Check Assist....850 857-7752
9270 University Pkwy # 105 Pensacola (32514) ***(G-14113)***
Checkpoint Card Group Inc....954 426-1331
1801 Green Rd Deerfield Beach (33064) ***(G-2800)***
Checks Your Way Inc....386 362-4044
621 Ohio Ave N Live Oak (32064) ***(G-8228)***
Checksum Software LLC....786 375-8091
7979 Nw 21st St Doral (33122) ***(G-3297)***
Cheesecake Etc Desserts, Miami Springs *Also called Obem Foods Inc* ***(G-10896)***
Cheesecake, Etc, Miami Springs *Also called T & W Inc* ***(G-10898)***
Cheezeballs LLC....904 716-3709
3759 Cascade Ct Jacksonville (32207) ***(G-6262)***
Chef Distilled LLC....305 747-8236
107 Simonton St Key West (33040) ***(G-7182)***
Chef Philippe, Hollywood *Also called Gourmet Parisien Inc* ***(G-5828)***
Chefs Commissary LLC....321 303-2947
6929 Narcoossee Rd # 509 Orlando (32822) ***(G-12578)***
Chelle Walton Publishing....239 699-4754
936 Main St Sanibel (33957) ***(G-16144)***
Chelly Cosmetics Manufacturing....305 471-9608
7172 Sw 30th Rd Miami (33155) ***(G-9350)***
Cheltec Inc....941 355-1045
2215 Industrial Blvd Sarasota (34234) ***(G-16382)***
Chem Guard Inc....407 402-2798
3964 Buglers Rest Pl Casselberry (32707) ***(G-1500)***
Chem TEC, Deerfield Beach *Also called Chem-TEC Equipment Co* ***(G-2801)***
Chem-Free System Inc....954 258-5415
7168 Cataluna Cir Delray Beach (33446) ***(G-3059)***
Chem-TEC Equipment Co....954 428-8259
3077 Sw 13th Dr Deerfield Beach (33442) ***(G-2801)***
Chem-Tek Metal Finishing Corp....321 722-2227
636 Atlantis Rd Melbourne (32904) ***(G-8788)***
Chem-Tek Plating Industries, Melbourne *Also called Chem-Tek Metal Finishing Corp* ***(G-8788)***
Chemclad LLC....863 967-1156
1701 Hobbs Rd Auburndale (33823) ***(G-234)***
Chemco Corp....305 623-4445
4920 Nw 165th St Miami Lakes (33014) ***(G-10776)***
Chemical Dynamics Inc....813 752-4950
4206 Business Ln Plant City (33566) ***(G-14418)***
Chemko Technical Services Inc....954 783-7673
1000 E Atl Blvd Ste 115 Pompano Beach (33060) ***(G-14634)***
Chemline Inc....407 847-4181
1662 Broad St Kissimmee (34746) ***(G-7230)***
Chemours Company Fc LLC....904 964-1230
Florida Plant Starke (32091) ***(G-16889)***
Chemours Company Fc LLC....904 964-1200
5222 Treat Rd Starke (32091) ***(G-16890)***
Chemplex Industries Inc....772 283-2700
2820 Sw 42nd Ave Palm City (34990) ***(G-13646)***
Chemseal Inc....305 433-8362
7891 W 25th Ct Hialeah (33016) ***(G-5343)***
Chen, Chao Ming Company, Jacksonville *Also called Sunshine Packing & Noodle Co* ***(G-6826)***
Chenega Manufacturing Svcs LLC....850 763-6013
1509 Saint Andrews Blvd Panama City (32405) ***(G-13880)***
Cheney Ofs Inc....407 292-3223
3875 Bengert St Orlando (32808) ***(G-12579)***
Chernin Beef Industries, Center Hill *Also called Central Beef Ind LLC* ***(G-1525)***
Chervo USA Inc....561 510-2458
1201 Us Highway 1 Ste 435 North Palm Beach (33408) ***(G-11721)***
Cheval Country Club....813 279-5122
545 Frederica Ln Dunedin (34698) ***(G-3573)***
Chez Industries LLC....386 698-4414
2167 S Us Highway 17 Crescent City (32112) ***(G-2339)***
Chhaya Corporation....407 348-9400
1988 E Osceola Pkwy Kissimmee (34743) ***(G-7231)***
Chiantis....407 484-6510
685 Towne Center Blvd Sanford (32771) ***(G-16013)***
Chicago Electronic Distrs Inc....312 985-6175
17097 Glenview Ave Port Charlotte (33954) ***(G-14969)***
Chicago Soft Ltd....863 940-2066
1820 E Edgewood Dr # 105 Lakeland (33803) ***(G-7656)***
Chickasha Manufacturing Co Inc....405 224-0229
277 Saratoga Ct Osprey (34229) ***(G-13410)***
Chidsey Custom Woodworks....561 632-9728
4327 Willow Pond Cir West Palm Beach (33417) ***(G-18846)***
Chief Cabinets LLC....850 545-5055
4329 W Pensacola St Ste 3 Tallahassee (32304) ***(G-17233)***
Chiefland Crab Company Inc....352 493-4887
1606 Sw 4th Pl Chiefland (32626) ***(G-1535)***
Chili Produkt Kft....954 655-4111
9850 Scribner Ln Wellington (33414) ***(G-18713)***
Chiliprint LLC....863 547-6930
28597 Hwy 27 Dundee (33838) ***(G-3564)***
Chiller Medic Inc....904 814-9446
8933 Western Way Ste 18 Jacksonville (32256) ***(G-6263)***
Chilly Willys Heating & A Inc....904 772-1164
8006 Renault Dr Jacksonville (32244) ***(G-6264)***
Chilton Signs & Designs LLC....863 438-0880
549 Pope Ave Nw Winter Haven (33881) ***(G-19314)***
Chin & Chin Enterprises Inc....407 478-8726
3580 Aloma Ave Ste 5 Winter Park (32792) ***(G-19394)***
Chip Supply Inc (HQ)....407 298-7100
7725 N Orange Blossom Trl Orlando (32810) ***(G-12580)***
Chipico South, Palmetto *Also called Vienna Beef Ltd* ***(G-13833)***
Chipley Newspapers Inc....850 638-0212
112 E Virginia Ave Bonifay (32425) ***(G-801)***
Chiptech Inc (PA)....954 454-3554
2885 Sw 30th Ave Hallandale (33009) ***(G-5154)***
Chiptech Imaging LLC....954 827-1401
4613 N University Dr # 576 Coral Springs (33067) ***(G-2230)***
Chiptronics, Miami *Also called Sonobrands LLC* ***(G-10376)***
Chism Manufacturing Svcs LLC....941 896-9671
6416 Parkland Dr Sarasota (34243) ***(G-16190)***
Chittum Yachts LLC (PA)....386 589-7224
4577 Sw Cargo Way Palm City (34990) ***(G-13647)***
Chittum Yachts LLC....386 589-7224
4953 Se Pine Knoll Way Stuart (34997) ***(G-16923)***
Chlorinators Inc....772 288-4854
1044 Se Dixie Cutoff Rd Stuart (34994) ***(G-16924)***
Chocolate Compass LLC....407 600-0145
5899 Pearl Estates Ln Sanford (32771) ***(G-16014)***
Chocolate Guys LLC....561 278-5889
2875 S Congress Ave Ste G Delray Beach (33445) ***(G-3060)***
Choctaw Trading Co Inc....407 905-9917
99 W Plant St Winter Garden (34787) ***(G-19257)***
Choctaw Willy, Winter Garden *Also called Choctaw Trading Co Inc* ***(G-19257)***
Choice ADS, Deerfield Beach *Also called Forum Publishing Group Inc* ***(G-2827)***
Choice Cabinets LLC....352 629-1556
3826 Nw Gainesville Rd Ocala (34475) ***(G-11902)***
Choice Products Inc....386 426-6450
143 W Palm Way Edgewater (32132) ***(G-3619)***
Choice Tool & Mold LLC....941 371-6767
901 Sarasota Center Blvd Sarasota (34240) ***(G-16383)***
Cholados Y Mas....813 935-9262
6729 N Armenia Ave Tampa (33604) ***(G-17533)***
Cholift Forklift USA Co....786 483-6930
1390 W 42nd St Apt 204 Hialeah (33012) ***(G-5344)***
Chris Craft Corporation....941 351-4900
8161 15th St E Sarasota (34243) ***(G-16191)***
Chris Industries Corp....941 729-7600
1118 8th Ave W Palmetto (34221) ***(G-13791)***
Chris-Craft, Sarasota *Also called Chris Craft Corporation* ***(G-16191)***

Christian L International Inc 305 947-1722
2297 Ne 164th St Miami (33160) *(G-9351)*
Christian Publishing Inc 813 920-5664
8807 Bys Run Odessa (33556) *(G-12110)*
Christie Lites Entps USA LLC (PA) 407 856-0016
6990 Lake Ellenor Dr Orlando (32809) *(G-12581)*
Christie Lites Orlando LLC (HQ) 206 223-7200
2479 Eunice Ave Orlando (32808) *(G-12582)*
Chrom Industries LLC 954 400-5135
3131 Sw 42nd St Fort Lauderdale (33312) *(G-3897)*
Chromalloy Castings Tampa Corp (HQ) 561 935-3571
3999 Rca Blvd Palm Beach Gardens (33410) *(G-13577)*
Chromalloy Component Svcs Inc 954 378-1999
3600 Nw 54th St Fort Lauderdale (33309) *(G-3898)*
Chromalloy Gas Turbine LLC (HQ) 561 935-3571
4100 Rca Blvd Palm Beach Gardens (33410) *(G-13578)*
Chromalloy Mtl Solutions LLC 954 378-1999
3600 Nw 54th St Fort Lauderdale (33309) *(G-3899)*
Chromatech Digital Inc 727 528-4711
4301 31st St N Saint Petersburg (33714) *(G-15745)*
Chromatech Printing, Saint Petersburg *Also called Chromatech Digital Inc* *(G-15745)*
Chrome Aerospace Inc 305 506-8182
345 85th St Miami Beach (33141) *(G-10655)*
Chrome Connection Corp 305 947-9191
15405 W Dixie Hwy North Miami Beach (33162) *(G-11669)*
Chrome Plating Shop 786 527-5357
18680 Ne 2nd Ave Ste 1 Miami (33179) *(G-9352)*
Chuculu LLC 305 595-4577
9455 Sw 78th St Miami (33173) *(G-9353)*
Chunky Plates LLC 321 746-3346
2550 W Colonial Dr Orlando (32804) *(G-12583)*
Churrico Factory LLC 239 989-7616
4125 Cleveland Ave # 1370 Fort Myers (33901) *(G-4394)*
Chviek 239 567-1511
6650 Rich Rd North Fort Myers (33917) *(G-11597)*
Cianos Tile & Marble Inc 239 267-8453
5680 Halifax Ave Fort Myers (33912) *(G-4395)*
Ciao Group Inc (PA) 347 560-5040
951 W Yamato Rd Ste 101 Boca Raton (33431) *(G-479)*
CIC Conveyors, Palmetto *Also called Chris Industries Corp* *(G-13791)*
Ciega Inc 727 526-9048
4410 35th St N Saint Petersburg (33714) *(G-15746)*
Cienfuegos Pallets Corp 786 703-3686
7781 Nw 73rd Ct Medley (33166) *(G-8631)*
Cigar City Brewing, Tampa *Also called Canarchy Craft* *(G-17503)*
Cigar City Brewpub LLC (PA) 813 348-6363
3924 W Spruce St Tampa (33607) *(G-17534)*
Cigar City Smoked Salsa LLC 813 421-3340
5106 N 30th St Tampa (33610) *(G-17535)*
Cigarette Racing Team LLC 305 769-4350
4355 Nw 128th St Opa Locka (33054) *(G-12299)*
Cim USA Inc 305 369-1040
10813 Nw 30th St Ste 108 Doral (33172) *(G-3298)*
Cima Activewear LLC 239 273-6055
23124 Marsh Landing Blvd Estero (33928) *(G-3687)*
Cinalta Corp 954 815-0612
1700 Nw 15th Ave Ste 305 Pompano Beach (33069) *(G-14635)*
Cincinnati Printing Service 239 455-0960
174 Via Perignon Naples (34119) *(G-11208)*
Cind-Al Inc 863 401-8700
13518 Granville Ave Clermont (34711) *(G-1952)*
Cinega Custom Framing & Design (PA) 904 495-1846
490 Hillside Dr Orange Park (32073) *(G-12386)*
Cinema Crafters Inc 305 891-6121
12564 Ne 14th Ave North Miami (33161) *(G-11632)*
Cinevise Inc 305 232-8182
12457 Sw 130th St Miami (33186) *(G-9354)*
Cinidyne Sales Inc 941 473-3914
1811 Englewood Rd Englewood (34223) *(G-3673)*
Cintas Corporation 813 874-1401
3601 W Swann Ave Ste 107 Tampa (33609) *(G-17536)*
Cintas Corporation 239 693-8722
12771 Westlinks Dr Ste 1 Fort Myers (33913) *(G-4396)*
Cintas Fire Protection, Fort Myers *Also called Cintas Corporation* *(G-4396)*
Cioreview, Fort Lauderdale *Also called Valleymedia Inc* *(G-4303)*
Circle C Timber Inc 863 735-0383
2086 Fish Branch Rd Zolfo Springs (33890) *(G-19544)*
Circle Redmont Inc 321 259-7374
2760 Business Center Blvd Melbourne (32940) *(G-8789)*
Circle S Manufacturing Co Inc 352 236-3580
13650 Ne 110th St Fort Mc Coy (32134) *(G-4336)*
Circor, Temple Terrace *Also called Leslie Controls Inc* *(G-18371)*
Circor International Inc 813 978-1000
12501 Telecom Dr Temple Terrace (33637) *(G-18367)*
Circuit Works Co 727 544-5336
6405 49th St N Ste B Pinellas Park (33781) *(G-14338)*
Circuitronics LLC 407 322-8300
223 Hickman Dr Ste 101 Sanford (32771) *(G-16015)*
Circuitronix LLC (PA) 786 364-4458
3131 Sw 42nd St Fort Lauderdale (33312) *(G-3900)*
Ciro Manufacturing Corporation 561 988-2139
692 S Military Trl Deerfield Beach (33442) *(G-2802)*
Ciron Custom Welding Inc 786 259-7589
2954 W 84th St Hialeah (33018) *(G-5345)*
Cirrus Software LLC 727 450-7804
34125 Us Highway 19 N # 310 Palm Harbor (34684) *(G-13729)*
Cirven Usa LLC 305 815-2545
9681 Nw 45th Ln Doral (33178) *(G-3299)*
Cisam LLC 813 404-4180
32789 Eiland Blvd Zephyrhills (33545) *(G-19511)*
CIT Aerospace Inc 954 359-2561
1000 S Pine Island Rd # 500 Plantation (33324) *(G-14499)*
Citel America Inc 954 430-6310
10108 Usa Today Way Miramar (33025) *(G-10979)*
Citilube Inc 305 681-6064
3300 Nw 112th St Miami (33167) *(G-9355)*
Citory Solutions LLC 407 766-6533
10524 Moss Park Rd # 204 Orlando (32832) *(G-12584)*
Citrix Systems Inc (PA) 954 267-3000
851 W Cypress Creek Rd Fort Lauderdale (33309) *(G-3901)*
Citrus County Chronicle, The, Crystal River *Also called Citrus Publishing LLC* *(G-2373)*
Citrus County Life Magazine 352 341-4769
305 S Salisbury Ter Lecanto (34461) *(G-8132)*
Citrus Extracts LLC 772 464-9800
3495 S Us Highway 1 Ste A Fort Pierce (34982) *(G-4688)*
Citrus Industry Magazine, Newberry *Also called 3522091611* *(G-11548)*
Citrus Motorsports 352 564-2453
7800 W Gulf & Lake Hwy Crystal River (34429) *(G-2372)*
Citrus Publishing LLC (HQ) 352 563-6363
1624 N Meadowcrest Blvd Crystal River (34429) *(G-2373)*
Citrus Times Edition, Inverness *Also called Times Publishing Company* *(G-6097)*
Citrus World Inc (PA) 863 676-1411
20205 Hwy 27 Lake Wales (33853) *(G-7503)*
Citrus World ADM Svcs Inc 863 676-1411
20205 Hwy 27 Lake Wales (33853) *(G-7504)*
Citrus World Services Inc 863 676-1411
20205 Hwy 27 Lake Wales (33853) *(G-7505)*
City Clors Dgital Prtg Ctr Inc 305 471-0816
1470 Nw 79th Ave Doral (33126) *(G-3300)*
City Debate Publishing Company 305 868-1161
6538 Collins Ave Miami Beach (33141) *(G-10656)*
City Electric Supply Company 772 878-4944
660 Nw Peacock Blvd Port St Lucie (34986) *(G-15171)*
City Elevator Service Corp 305 345-1951
15107 Sw 138th Pl Miami (33186) *(G-9356)*
City Fashion, The, Boca Raton *Also called Amj DOT LLC* *(G-426)*
City Labs Inc 305 909-7593
12491 Sw 134th Ct Ste 23 Miami (33186) *(G-9357)*
City News Publishing LLC 305 332-9101
12364 Clearfalls Dr Boca Raton (33428) *(G-480)*
City of Bradenton 941 727-6360
5600 Natalie Way E Bradenton (34203) *(G-1020)*
City of Cocoa Beach 321 868-3342
1600 Minutemen Cswy Cocoa Beach (32931) *(G-2061)*
City of Hollywood 954 967-4230
3441 Hollywood Blvd Fl 2 Hollywood (33021) *(G-5799)*
City of Lakeland 863 834-6780
1140 E Parker St Lakeland (33801) *(G-7657)*
City of Largo, Clearwater *Also called Environmental Services* *(G-1674)*
City of Ocala 352 622-6803
1307 Nw 4th Ave Ocala (34475) *(G-11903)*
City of Winter Haven 863 291-5858
125 N Lake Silver Dr Nw Winter Haven (33881) *(G-19315)*
City Prints LLC 407 409-0509
200 E Colonial Dr Orlando (32801) *(G-12585)*
City Prints Signs & Flyers 407 532-6078
2131 W Fairbanks Ave Winter Park (32789) *(G-19395)*
City Publications South FL 305 495-3311
6501 Nw 36th St Ste 300 Virginia Gardens (33166) *(G-18685)*
Citygrader LLC 305 635-2686
2990 Nw 40th Street Miami Miami (33142) *(G-9358)*
Citypavers, Pembroke Pines *Also called Yolo Consulting LLC* *(G-14073)*
CJ Labs Inc 305 234-9644
12245 Sw 128th St Unit 30 Miami (33186) *(G-9359)*
CJ Mulanix Co Inc 716 423-8010
2803 Gulf To Bay Blvd Clearwater (33759) *(G-1626)*
CJ Publishers Inc 727 521-6277
4940 72nd Ave N Ste 200 Pinellas Park (33781) *(G-14339)*
Cjb Industries Inc 941 552-8397
23 N Blvd Of Presidents Sarasota (34236) *(G-16384)*
Cjks Deluxe Inc 786 657-8726
8920 Nw 187th St Hialeah (33018) *(G-5346)*
CJL Bricks & Pavers Inc 305 527-4240
9301 Nw 33rd Ct Miami (33147) *(G-9360)*
CK Dockside Services Inc 954 254-0263
6141 Nw 80th Ter Parkland (33067) *(G-13990)*
CK Prime Investments Inc 239 574-7800
830 Ne 24th Ln Unit C Cape Coral (33909) *(G-1403)*
Cki Solutions, West Palm Beach *Also called Cadence Keen Innovations Inc* *(G-18833)*

ALPHABETIC

CKS Packaging Inc...407 423-0333
333 W Michigan St Orlando (32806) ***(G-12586)***
CKS Packaging Inc...407 420-9529
7400 S Orange Ave Orlando (32809) ***(G-12587)***
CKS Packaging Inc...954 925-9049
4020 N 29th Ter Hollywood (33020) ***(G-5800)***
CL Boca Raton LLC...561 660-9485
6000 Glades Rd Ste 1234 Boca Raton (33431) ***(G-481)***
CL Dadeland LLC...305 712-6825
Dadeland Mall 7535 N Kend Miami (33156) ***(G-9361)***
CL Gardens LLC...561 567-0504
3101 Pga Blvd Palm Beach Gardens (33410) ***(G-13579)***
CL Waterside Naples LLC...239 734-8534
5455 Tamiami Trl N Naples (34108) ***(G-11209)***
Claddah Corp...407 834-8881
207 Reece Way Ste 1625 Casselberry (32707) ***(G-1501)***
Cladding Systems Inc...813 250-0786
3218 E 4th Ave Tampa (33605) ***(G-17537)***
Claims Pages, Deltona *Also called Nationwide Publishing Company* ***(G-3176)***
Clairson Plastics, Ocala *Also called Nanotechnovation Corporation* ***(G-12004)***
Clare Instruments (us) Inc...813 886-2775
6304 Benjamin Rd Ste 506 Tampa (33634) ***(G-17538)***
Clarios LLC...904 786-9161
6973 Highway Ave Ste 301 Jacksonville (32254) ***(G-6265)***
Clarios LLC...727 541-3531
8575 Largo Lakes Dr Largo (33773) ***(G-7922)***
Clarity Diagnostics, Boca Raton *Also called Diagnostic Test Group LLC* ***(G-500)***
Clark Craig Enterprises (PA)...813 287-0110
3901 W Kennedy Blvd Tampa (33609) ***(G-17539)***
Clarks Electrical Signs & Svcs...561 248-5932
108 W Cypress Rd Lake Worth (33467) ***(G-7542)***
Clarkwestern Dietrich Building...800 693-3018
331 Sw 57th Ave Ocala (34474) ***(G-11904)***
Clarkwstern Dtrich Bldg System...954 772-6300
1001 Nw 58th Ct Fort Lauderdale (33309) ***(G-3902)***
Clarkwstern Dtrich Bldg System...800 543-7140
38020 Pulp Dr Dade City (33523) ***(G-2426)***
Clasic Fishing Products, Clermont *Also called Cind-Al Inc* ***(G-1952)***
Class 1, Ocala *Also called Hale Products Inc* ***(G-11963)***
Class A Printing LLC...386 447-0520
11 Industry Dr Palm Coast (32137) ***(G-13687)***
Classb.com, Tampa *Also called Shirts & Caps Inc* ***(G-18098)***
Classic Architecutal, Oakland Park *Also called Cadillac Graphics Inc* ***(G-11789)***
Classic Auto A Mnfactoring Inc...813 251-2356
4901 W Rio Vista Ave A Tampa (33634) ***(G-17540)***
Classic Cabinets and More LLC...727 239-8869
8187 Wild Oaks Cir Largo (33773) ***(G-7923)***
Classic Canvas & Upholstery...954 850-4994
1934 Cleveland St Hollywood (33020) ***(G-5801)***
Classic Design and Mfg...850 433-4981
909 N Tarragona St Pensacola (32501) ***(G-14114)***
Classic Fishing Products Inc (PA)...407 656-6133
13518 Granville Ave Clermont (34711) ***(G-1953)***
Classic Hardwood Design...850 232-6473
3895 Highway 97 Molino (32577) ***(G-11073)***
Classic Industries Inc...561 855-4609
3111 Fortune Way Wellington (33414) ***(G-18714)***
Classic Iron Decor Inc...904 241-5022
1004 10th Ave S Jacksonville Beach (32250) ***(G-6940)***
Classic Kitchens Brevard Inc...321 327-5972
670 S Wickham Rd Melbourne (32904) ***(G-8790)***
Classic Mail Corp...386 290-0309
1027 N Nova Rd Ste 109 Daytona Beach (32117) ***(G-2642)***
Classic Metal Fabrication Inc...561 305-9532
121 Nw 11th St Boca Raton (33432) ***(G-482)***
Classic Motor Sport, Holly Hill *Also called Motorsport Marketing Inc* ***(G-5760)***
Classic Pizza Crusts Inc...954 570-8383
1741 Nw 33rd St Pompano Beach (33064) ***(G-14636)***
Classic Poker Chips...207 332-9999
121 Lancaster Pl Saint Augustine (32080) ***(G-15530)***
Classic Printing & Finish LLC...305 817-4242
3140 W 84th St Unit 7 Hialeah (33018) ***(G-5347)***
Classic Screen Prtg Design Inc...407 850-0112
1353 Pine Ave Orlando (32824) ***(G-12588)***
Classic Shirts Inc...850 875-2200
110 Zeta St Quincy (32351) ***(G-15247)***
Classic Sign & Mirror, Pensacola *Also called Classic Design and Mfg* ***(G-14114)***
Classic Stars Inc...305 871-6767
2355 Nw 35th Ave Miami (33142) ***(G-9362)***
Classic Trim Wtp Inc...305 258-3090
25400 Sw 141st Ave Ste B Princeton (33032) ***(G-15183)***
Classic Uniforms, Hialeah *Also called Fashion Connection Miami Inc* ***(G-5405)***
Classic Woodworks LLC (PA)...772 398-6258
513 Se Maple Ter Port Saint Lucie (34983) ***(G-15098)***
Classic Yacht Refinishing Inc...954 760-9626
1881 W State Road 84 # 10 Fort Lauderdale (33315) ***(G-3903)***
Classica & Telecard Corp...239 354-3727
12355 Collier Blvd Ste C Naples (34116) ***(G-11210)***
Classica Tlcard Comm Srervices, Naples *Also called Classica & Telecard Corp* ***(G-11210)***
Classics Reborn Publishing LLC...727 232-6739
9954 Sweet Bay Ct New Port Richey (34654) ***(G-11487)***
Classique Style Inc...561 995-7557
6590 W Rogers Cir Ste 8 Boca Raton (33487) ***(G-483)***
Clawson Custom Cues Inc...904 448-8748
7255 Salisbury Rd Ste 1 Jacksonville (32256) ***(G-6266)***
Clayton Homes Inc...850 785-3302
2310 E 15th St Panama City (32405) ***(G-13881)***
Clayton Industries, Lake City *Also called Linman Inc* ***(G-7365)***
CLC, Orlando *Also called Control Laser Corporation* ***(G-12617)***
Clean & Shine Auto Marine...239 261-6563
4451 Gulf Shore Blvd N Naples (34103) ***(G-11211)***
Clean Cut Intl LLC...866 599-7066
14255 Us Highway 1 Juno Beach (33408) ***(G-6978)***
Clean Energy ESb Inc...202 905-6726
600 Biltmore Way Apt 508 Coral Gables (33134) ***(G-2131)***
Clean Pack Products, Tampa *Also called Cleanpak Products LLC* ***(G-17541)***
Cleanpak Products LLC...813 740-8611
221 Hobbs St Ste 108 Tampa (33619) ***(G-17541)***
Clear Choice Inc...407 830-6968
1045 Miller Dr Altamonte Springs (32701) ***(G-37)***
Clear Copy Inc...561 369-3900
1304 N Federal Hwy Boynton Beach (33435) ***(G-890)***
Clear Distribution Inc...904 330-5624
6611 Sthpint Pkwy Ste C30 Jacksonville (32216) ***(G-6267)***
Clear Horizon Ventures Company...727 372-1100
9410 Eden Ave Hudson (34667) ***(G-6018)***
Clear View Coatings LLC...850 210-0155
4514 Deslin Ct Tallahassee (32305) ***(G-17234)***
Clear Vision Signs and Systems, Wesley Chapel *Also called Graphics Pdts Excellence Inc* ***(G-18748)***
Clear Vue Inc (PA)...727 726-5386
905 Delaware St Safety Harbor (34695) ***(G-15490)***
Clear Water Plasma, Palm City *Also called Aqua Pulsar LLC* ***(G-13641)***
Clearant Inc (PA)...407 876-3134
6001 Lexington Park Orlando (32819) ***(G-12589)***
Clearly Derm LLC (PA)...561 353-3376
7050 W Palmetto Park Rd # 30 Boca Raton (33433) ***(G-484)***
Cleartel Voice and Data LLC...239 220-5545
5433 Harbour Castle Dr Fort Myers (33907) ***(G-4397)***
Clearwater Engineering Inc...727 573-2210
14605 49th St N Ste 19 Clearwater (33762) ***(G-1627)***
Clearwater Enviro Tech Inc...727 209-6400
8767 115th Ave Largo (33773) ***(G-7924)***
Clearwater Machining Inc...727 512-0337
11551 43rd St N Clearwater (33762) ***(G-1628)***
Clearwater Manufacturing Co...813 818-0959
203 Tower Dr Oldsmar (34677) ***(G-12215)***
Clero Enterprises Inc...305 681-4877
3881 Nw 125th St Opa Locka (33054) ***(G-12300)***
Cleva Power, Boca Raton *Also called Cleva Technologies LLC* ***(G-485)***
Cleva Technologies LLC...561 654-5279
1951 Nw 19th St Ste 101 Boca Raton (33431) ***(G-485)***
Cleveland Diabetes Care Inc (PA)...904 394-2620
10752 Deerwood Park Blvd Jacksonville (32256) ***(G-6268)***
Clever Cabinetry LLC...813 992-0020
10513 Anglecrest Dr Riverview (33569) ***(G-15267)***
Clever Covers Inc...407 423-5959
524 W Winter Park St Orlando (32804) ***(G-12590)***
Clever Pavers Inc...239 633-7048
2727 Clnl Blvd Apt 204 Fort Myers (33907) ***(G-4398)***
Clewiston News, Okeechobee *Also called Independent Newsmedia Inc USA* ***(G-12182)***
Clewiston Water Btlg Co LLC...863 902-1317
615 Commerce Ct Clewiston (33440) ***(G-1977)***
Clifton Studio Inc...813 240-0286
4710 Eisenhower Blvd D Tampa (33634) ***(G-17542)***
Climax Am LLC...786 502-5757
7201 S Arprt Rd Hngar 303 Hangar Pembroke Pines (33023) ***(G-14028)***
Climax Inc...786 264-6082
10401 Nw 28th St Doral (33172) ***(G-3301)***
Climb Your Mountain Inc...571 571-8623
11345 Nw 122nd St Medley (33178) ***(G-8632)***
Cline Aluminum Doors Inc...941 746-4104
112 32nd Ave W Bradenton (34205) ***(G-1021)***
Cline Group, Palm Beach Gardens *Also called Cline Resource and Dev Co* ***(G-13580)***
Cline Resource and Dev Co (PA)...561 626-4999
3825 Pga Blvd Ste 1101 Palm Beach Gardens (33410) ***(G-13580)***
Clinical Chmstry Spclists Corp...919 554-1424
6901 Okeechobee Blvd D5-L3 West Palm Beach (33411) ***(G-18847)***
Clinical Dagnstc Solutions Inc...954 791-1773
1800 Nw 65th Ave Plantation (33313) ***(G-14500)***
Clinical Refractions Perfected, Fort Myers *Also called Clinicon Corporation* ***(G-4399)***
Clinicon Corporation...239 939-1345
3949 Evans Ave Ste 107 Fort Myers (33901) ***(G-4399)***
Clinigence Holdings Inc (PA)...678 607-6393
2455 E Sunrise Blvd # 1204 Fort Lauderdale (33304) ***(G-3904)***
CLJ Industries Inc...562 688-0508
6015 Chester Cir Ste 213 Jacksonville (32217) ***(G-6269)***

Cljp Inc 850 678-8819
200 Hart St Niceville (32578) *(G-11564)*
Clock Spring Company Inc 561 683-6992
3875 Fiscal Ct Riviera Beach (33404) *(G-15312)*
Clogic Defense, Ponte Vedra Beach *Also called Clogic LLC (G-14936)*
Clogic LLC (PA) 860 324-2227
135 Deer Estates Ln Ponte Vedra Beach (32082) *(G-14936)*
Clondalkin LLC 866 545-8703
10950 Belcher Rd S Largo (33777) *(G-7925)*
Clonts Groves Inc 407 359-4103
285 Howard Ave Oviedo (32765) *(G-13420)*
Clorox Healthcare Holdings LLC 904 996-7758
3611 Saint Johns Ave 1 Jacksonville (32205) *(G-6270)*
Closet Pros 305 240-7775
1103 Truman Ave Key West (33040) *(G-7183)*
Closet Systems, Clearwater *Also called Wall Bed Systems Inc (G-1936)*
Closetmaid LLC (HQ) 352 401-6000
13485 Veterans Way # 200 Orlando (32827) *(G-12591)*
Closetmaid LLC 352 351-6100
720 Sw 17th Pl Ocala (34471) *(G-11905)*
Closets By Design, Fort Lauderdale *Also called Riverstone Snctary - Cbd - Inc (G-4207)*
Closeup Inc 650 284-8831
8400 Nw 25th St Miami (33198) *(G-9363)*
Clothesline Inc 850 877-9171
1369 E Lafayette St Ste A Tallahassee (32301) *(G-17235)*
Clothing Warehouse 904 354-9002
1010 Park St Jacksonville (32204) *(G-6271)*
Cloud Business Florida LLC 954 306-3597
4101 Ravenswood Rd # 325 Fort Lauderdale (33312) *(G-3905)*
Cloud Industries 816 213-2730
8275 Shadow Pine Way Sarasota (34238) *(G-16385)*
Cloud Investment Partners Lllp 561 266-0845
1811 Corporate Dr Boynton Beach (33426) *(G-891)*
Cloud Veneer LLC 305 230-7379
1001 Brickell Bay Dr # 2700 Miami (33131) *(G-9364)*
Cloudfactors LLC 866 779-9974
1200 S Pine Island Rd Plantation (33324) *(G-14501)*
Cloudkiss Beverages Inc 407 324-8500
3031 S Mellonville Ave Sanford (32773) *(G-16016)*
Clover Interior Systems Inc 941 484-1300
505 Lyons Bay Rd Nokomis (34275) *(G-11580)*
Clr Roasters LLC 305 591-0040
2131 Nw 72nd Ave Miami (33122) *(G-9365)*
Cls Holdings Usa Inc (PA) 888 438-9132
11767 S Dixie Hwy Ste 115 Pinecrest (33156) *(G-14327)*
Club Information Systems, Tampa *Also called Technolgy Training Associates (G-18179)*
Clupper LLC 386 956-6396
2386 Pavillion Ter Deltona (32738) *(G-3166)*
Clutch House, Fort Lauderdale *Also called Warden Enterprises Inc (G-4312)*
Clx Engineering, Sanford *Also called Contrologix LLC (G-16023)*
Cm2 Industries Inc 305 685-4812
1769 Opa Locka Blvd Opa Locka (33054) *(G-12301)*
CMA Interactive Corporation 954 336-6403
5011 Neptune Ln Fort Lauderdale (33312) *(G-3906)*
CMC Bakery LLC 978 682-2382
4100 N Powerline Rd M2 Pompano Beach (33073) *(G-14637)*
CMC Steel Fabricators, Jacksonville *Also called Commercial Metals Company (G-6281)*
CMC Steel Florida, Jacksonville *Also called CMC Steel Us LLC (G-6272)*
CMC Steel Us LLC 904 266-4261
16770 Rebar Rd Jacksonville (32234) *(G-6272)*
Cme Arma Inc 305 633-1524
4500 Nw 36th Ave Miami (33142) *(G-9366)*
CMF, Pompano Beach *Also called Certified Metal Finishing Inc (G-14633)*
CMF Medicon Surgical Inc 904 642-7500
11200 St Jhns Indus Pkwy Jacksonville (32246) *(G-6273)*
CMF Truss Inc 352 796-5805
13521 Ponce De Leon Blvd Brooksville (34601) *(G-1220)*
CMI, Opa Locka *Also called C M I Enterprises Inc (G-12297)*
CMI, Leesburg *Also called Consolidated Minerals Inc (G-8148)*
CMI International, Sanford *Also called Gator Dock & Marine LLC (G-16054)*
CMI Microclimates, Inverness *Also called Custom Manufacturing Inc (G-6084)*
CMI Microclimates Inc 607 569-2738
1720 S Tranquil Ave Inverness (34450) *(G-6082)*
Cmk, Roseland *Also called Gypsy Mining Inc (G-15459)*
Cmn Steel Fabricators Inc 305 592-5466
7993 Nw 60th St Miami (33166) *(G-9367)*
CMR FL Solutions LLC 586 206-2517
2532 Oneida Rd Venice (34293) *(G-18537)*
CMS, Sarasota *Also called Chism Manufacturing Svcs LLC (G-16190)*
Cmsi, Weston *Also called Contract Mfg Solutions Inc (G-19117)*
Cmz Industries LLC 727 726-1443
27232 Us Highway 19 N Clearwater (33761) *(G-1629)*
Cnc Cabinet Components Inc 321 956-3470
560 Distribution Dr Melbourne (32904) *(G-8791)*
Cnc Works Service Inc 813 777-8642
13584 49th St N Ste 5 Clearwater (33762) *(G-1630)*
Cnc-Precision Machining Corp 786 452-9575
1055 E 26th St Hialeah (33013) *(G-5348)*
Cngas Group, Hollywood *Also called Greengood Energy Corp (G-5831)*
Cnh Industrial America LLC 954 389-9779
3265 Meridian Pkwy # 124 Weston (33331) *(G-19116)*
Cnr Precision Tool Inc 954 426-9650
8480 Nw 29th Ct Coral Springs (33065) *(G-2231)*
Cns Millworks Inc 850 259-9206
164 N Brookwood Dr Santa Rosa Beach (32459) *(G-16154)*
Cns Signs Inc 904 733-4806
3539 W Beaver St Jacksonville (32254) *(G-6274)*
Co-Edikit 863 802-1000
307 W Main St Ste 2 Lakeland (33815) *(G-7658)*
Co2meter Inc 386 310-4933
131 Business Center Dr A3 Ormond Beach (32174) *(G-13358)*
Coale Industries, Miami *Also called TNT Packaging Inc (G-10483)*
Coast Controls Inc 941 355-7555
7500 Commerce Ct Sarasota (34243) *(G-16192)*
Coast Laser Center, Sarasota *Also called Family of Smith Inc (G-16212)*
Coast Products LLC 850 235-2090
169 Griffin Blvd Unit 106 Panama City Beach (32413) *(G-13976)*
Coast To Coast Designs, Miami *Also called One World Resource LLC (G-10105)*
Coast To Coast Solar Inc 813 406-6501
19209 N Us Highway 41 Lutz (33549) *(G-8376)*
Coast Wcp 727 572-4249
1806 Gunn Hwy Odessa (33556) *(G-12111)*
Coastal, Palm Beach Gardens *Also called Oldcastle Apg South Inc (G-13614)*
Coastal Acquisitions Fla LLC (PA) 850 769-9423
2120 E Business 98 Panama City (32401) *(G-13882)*
Coastal Acquisitions Fla LLC 850 769-9423
2120 E 5th St Panama City (32401) *(G-13883)*
Coastal Aircraft Parts LLC 954 980-6929
2999 Nw 115th Ter Sunrise (33323) *(G-17106)*
Coastal and Mainland Cabinets, Fort Myers *Also called Mobius Business Group Inc (G-4535)*
Coastal Angler Magazine 850 586-3474
1296 Highway A1a Satellite Beach (32937) *(G-16651)*
Coastal Awngs Hrrcane Prtction 407 923-9482
14438 Avalon Reserve Blvd Orlando (32828) *(G-12592)*
Coastal Cabinets & Countertops 850 424-3940
12889 Us Highway 98 W 109a Miramar Beach (32550) *(G-11065)*
Coastal Canvas and Awning Co 239 433-1114
5761 Independence Cir # 1 Fort Myers (33912) *(G-4400)*
Coastal Closet Co of Fla LLC 239 826-3807
6361 Mtro Plntn Rd Unit B Fort Myers (33966) *(G-4401)*
Coastal Communications Corp 561 989-0600
2700 N Military Trl # 120 Boca Raton (33431) *(G-486)*
Coastal Concrete Products LLC 239 208-4079
7742 Alico Rd Fort Myers (33912) *(G-4402)*
Coastal Craftsmen Aluminum Inc (PA) 727 868-8802
15046 Labor Pl Hudson (34667) *(G-6019)*
Coastal Crane and Rigging Inc 850 460-1766
54 Pisces Dr Santa Rosa Beach (32459) *(G-16155)*
Coastal Custom Woodwork LLC 904 945-2299
1435 W Church St Ofc C Jacksonville (32204) *(G-6275)*
Coastal Dewatering, Clearwater *Also called Portable Pumping Systems Inc (G-1837)*
Coastal Directory Company 321 777-7076
1900 S Hbr Cy Blvd Ste 30 Melbourne (32901) *(G-8792)*
Coastal Door & Mllwk Svcs LLC 561 266-3716
1300 Sw 10th St Delray Beach (33444) *(G-3061)*
Coastal Electric 239 245-7396
5760 Youngquist Rd Ste 9 Fort Myers (33912) *(G-4403)*
Coastal Films of Florida, Jacksonville *Also called Sigma Extruding Corp (G-6769)*
Coastal Films of Florida 904 786-2031
627 Lane Ave N Jacksonville (32254) *(G-6276)*
Coastal Foam Systems LLC 850 470-9827
3276 W Scott St Pensacola (32505) *(G-14115)*
Coastal Forest Resources Co (PA) 850 539-6432
8007 Fl Ga Hwy Havana (32333) *(G-5235)*
Coastal Fuels Mktg Inc 941 722-7753
804 N Dock St Palmetto (34221) *(G-13792)*
Coastal Hurricane Film LLC 941 268-9693
807 Thornton Ave Nw Port Charlotte (33948) *(G-14970)*
Coastal Imprinting 321 543-4169
3091 Ohio St Melbourne (32904) *(G-8793)*
Coastal Industries Inc (PA) 904 642-3970
3700 St Jhns Indus Pkwy W Jacksonville (32246) *(G-6277)*
Coastal Industries USA LLC 954 946-5223
560 Sw 6th Ct Pompano Beach (33060) *(G-14638)*
Coastal Kitchen Interiors, Naples *Also called Jfaure LLC (G-11296)*
Coastal Logging Inc 850 832-0133
4138 Harry Wells Rd Panama City (32409) *(G-13884)*
Coastal Machine LLC 850 769-6117
7424 Coastal Dr Panama City (32404) *(G-13885)*
Coastal Marine Power Inc 941 322-8182
30710 Saddlebag Trl Myakka City (34251) *(G-11141)*
Coastal Mfg & Fabrication Inc 352 799-8706
16208 Cortez Blvd Brooksville (34601) *(G-1221)*
Coastal Millworks Inc 561 881-7755
3810 Consumer St Ste 2 West Palm Beach (33404) *(G-18848)*
Coastal Millworks & More LLC 850 250-6672
1714 Wolfrun Ln Panama City (32405) *(G-13886)*

ALPHABETIC

Coastal Observer, Lake Worth *Also called Lake Worth Herald Press* ***(G-7564)***
Coastal Paddle Co LLC 850 916-1600
848 Gulf Breeze Pkwy Gulf Breeze (32561) ***(G-5114)***
Coastal Plywood Company 800 359-6432
8007 Fl Ga Hwy Havana (32333) ***(G-5236)***
Coastal Powder Coatings Inc 772 283-5311
2049 Sw Poma Dr Palm City (34990) ***(G-13648)***
Coastal Precast of Florida 239 432-0667
7291 Pennsylvania St # 3 Fort Myers (33912) ***(G-4404)***
Coastal Printing Inc Sarasota 941 351-1515
4391 Independence Ct Sarasota (34234) ***(G-16386)***
Coastal Promotions Inc 850 460-2270
128 Indian Bayou Dr Destin (32541) ***(G-3186)***
Coastal RE-Manufacturing Inc 727 869-4808
7620 Valencia Ave Port Richey (34668) ***(G-15046)***
Coastal Reign Inc 863 940-4082
2068 Indian Sky Cir Lakeland (33813) ***(G-7659)***
Coastal Screen & Rail LLC 321 917-4605
1127 Poinsettia Dr Delray Beach (33444) ***(G-3062)***
Coastal Sheet Mtalof S Fla LLC 561 718-6044
8927 Hypoluxo Rd Ste A4 Lake Worth (33467) ***(G-7543)***
Coastal Shutters Inc 954 759-1115
303 Nw Hibiscus St Port Saint Lucie (34983) ***(G-15099)***
Coastal Shutters Online LLC 786 509-2093
1300 S Miami Ave # 3907 Miami (33130) ***(G-9368)***
Coastal Site Development, Fort Myers *Also called Coastal Concrete Products LLC* ***(G-4402)***
Coastal Timberlands, Havana *Also called Coastal Forest Resources Co* ***(G-5235)***
Coastal Wipers Inc (PA) 813 628-4464
5705 E Hanna Ave Tampa (33610) ***(G-17543)***
Coastal Wldg Fabrications Inc 954 938-7933
740 Ne 45th St Oakland Park (33334) ***(G-11791)***
Coastal Woodwork Inc 561 218-3353
380 Sw 12th Ave Pompano Beach (33069) ***(G-14639)***
Coastland Specialties LLC 239 910-5401
28340 Trails Edge Blvd Bonita Springs (34134) ***(G-825)***
Coastline Cbntry Cstm Mllwk LL 239 208-2876
6440 Metro Plantation Rd Fort Myers (33966) ***(G-4405)***
Coastline Marine, Pompano Beach *Also called US Recreational Alliance Inc* ***(G-14906)***
Coastline Whl Sgns Led Disp LL 386 238-6200
532 N Segrave St Daytona Beach (32114) ***(G-2643)***
Coastline Whl Signs Svcs Ltd 386 238-6200
532 N Segrave St Daytona Beach (32114) ***(G-2644)***
Coating Application Tech Inc 781 850-5080
1851 67th Ave E Sarasota (34243) ***(G-16193)***
Coating Heaven 321 300-5464
2555 N Forsyth Rd Ste E Orlando (32807) ***(G-12593)***
Coating Hues Inc 786 626-9241
747 Pine Crest Ln Naples (34104) ***(G-11212)***
Coating Laminating Converting, Green Cove Springs *Also called Tape Technologies Inc* ***(G-5072)***
Coating Technology Inc 813 854-3674
360 Scarlet Blvd Oldsmar (34677) ***(G-12216)***
Coatings Smples Sltons Etc LLC 863 398-8513
5515 Summerland Hills Dr Lakeland (33812) ***(G-7660)***
Cob Industries Inc 321 723-3200
6909 Vickie Cir West Melbourne (32904) ***(G-18770)***
Cobalt Aerospace Inc 305 450-0457
2550 W 78th St Unit 8 Hialeah (33016) ***(G-5349)***
Cobalt Laser 407 855-2833
965 W Taft Vineland Rd # 107 Orlando (32824) ***(G-12594)***
Cobb America, Deerfield Beach *Also called Advanced Outdoor Concepts Inc* ***(G-2765)***
Cobex Recorders Inc 954 425-0003
6601 Lyons Rd Ste F8 Coconut Creek (33073) ***(G-2073)***
Cobham Mission System Corp 850 226-6717
706 Anchors St Nw Fort Walton Beach (32548) ***(G-4787)***
Cobham Satcom 407 650-9054
1538 Tropic Park Dr Sanford (32773) ***(G-16017)***
Cobham Slip Rings Naples Inc (HQ) 239 263-3102
3030 Horseshoe Dr S Naples (34104) ***(G-11213)***
Cobra Power Corporation 305 893-5018
13353 Ne 17th Ave North Miami (33181) ***(G-11633)***
Coca Cola Bottling Co 813 569-3030
599 Lake Kathy Dr Brandon (33510) ***(G-1153)***
Coca Cola Enterprises Inc 305 256-3628
16569 Sw 117th Ave Miami (33177) ***(G-9369)***
Coca-Cola, Miami *Also called Coca Cola Enterprises Inc* ***(G-9369)***
Coca-Cola, Panama City *Also called Ccbcc Operations LLC* ***(G-13876)***
Coca-Cola Beverages Fla LLC 813 623-5411
9102 Sabal Indus Blvd Tampa (33619) ***(G-17544)***
Coca-Cola Beverages Fla LLC (PA) 800 438-2653
10117 Princess Palm Ave # 100 Tampa (33610) ***(G-17545)***
Coca-Cola Beverages Fla LLC 407 295-9290
2900 Mercy Dr Orlando (32808) ***(G-12595)***
Coca-Cola Beverages Fla LLC 904 786-2720
1411 Huron St Jacksonville (32254) ***(G-6278)***
Coca-Cola Bottling Co 305 378-1073
16569 Sw 117th Ave Miami (33177) ***(G-9370)***
Coca-Cola Bottling Co 844 863-2653
1126 N Lime Ave Sarasota (34237) ***(G-16387)***
Coca-Cola Btlg Centl Fla LLC 832 260-0462
235 W Brandon Blvd Brandon (33511) ***(G-1154)***
Coca-Cola Co 407 287-4527
16603 Bay Club Dr Clermont (34711) ***(G-1954)***
Coca-Cola Company 407 886-1568
2659 Orange Ave Apopka (32703) ***(G-121)***
Coca-Cola Company 941 351-4695
2150 47th St Sarasota (34234) ***(G-16388)***
Coca-Cola Company 954 985-5000
3350 Pembroke Rd Hollywood (33021) ***(G-5802)***
Coca-Cola Company 404 676-2121
2651 Orange Ave Apopka (32703) ***(G-122)***
Coca-Cola Company 407 565-2465
2651 Orange Ave Apopka (32703) ***(G-123)***
Coca-Cola Company 904 342-5609
90 S Dixie Hwy Saint Augustine (32084) ***(G-15531)***
Coca-Cola Company 407 560-0107
1512 E Buena Vista Dr Orlando (32830) ***(G-12596)***
Coca-Cola Company 727 736-7101
427 San Christopher Dr Dunedin (34698) ***(G-3574)***
Coca-Cola Company 407 295-9290
2900 Mercy Dr Orlando (32808) ***(G-12597)***
Coca-Cola Company 407 358-6758
2501 Orange Ave Apopka (32703) ***(G-124)***
Coca-Cola Company 954 961-8564
2700 Sw 32nd Ave Hollywood (33023) ***(G-5803)***
Coca-Cola Company Distribution 407 814-1327
1451 Ocoee Apopka Rd Apopka (32703) ***(G-125)***
Coca-Cola Enterprises 954 917-1108
2351 Blount Rd Pompano Beach (33069) ***(G-14640)***
Coca-Cola Refreshments USA Inc 863 551-3700
705 Main St Auburndale (33823) ***(G-235)***
Coco Cosmetics Inc 305 622-3488
20325 Ne 15th Ct Miami (33179) ***(G-9371)***
Coco Gelato Corp (PA) 786 621-2444
3514 Nw 36th St Miami (33142) ***(G-9372)***
Coco Lopez Inc (PA) 954 450-3100
3401 Sw 160th Ave Ste 350 Miramar (33027) ***(G-10980)***
Cocoa Bch Wtr Reclamation Dept, Cocoa Beach *Also called City of Cocoa Beach* ***(G-2061)***
Cocoa Customs RC, Cocoa *Also called Cutting Edge Mch Fbrcation LLC* ***(G-2007)***
Coconut Tree Btq & Gallery, Seminole *Also called Preferred Custom Printing LLC* ***(G-16757)***
Cocrystal Pharma Inc 877 262-7123
4400 Biscayne Blvd Miami (33137) ***(G-9373)***
Coda Octopus Group Inc (PA) 407 735-2402
3300 S Hiawassee Rd # 104 Orlando (32835) ***(G-12598)***
Coding Institute, The, Naples *Also called National Subscription Bureau* ***(G-11343)***
Codman & Shurtleff Inc 908 704-4024
6303 Blue Lagoon Dr Miami (33126) ***(G-9374)***
Codsworth Industries Inc 203 622-5151
12864 Biscayne Blvd Ste 3 North Miami (33181) ***(G-11634)***
Coeur De Lion Inc 727 442-4808
1610 N Myrtle Ave Clearwater (33755) ***(G-1631)***
Coffee Candy Store, The, Miami Lakes *Also called Candies and Beyond Inc* ***(G-10774)***
Coffee Cllloid Productions LLC 305 424-8900
12240 Sw 132nd Ct Miami (33186) ***(G-9375)***
Coffee News Clearwater 727 789-6677
160 Lisa Ln Oldsmar (34677) ***(G-12217)***
Coffee Unlimited LLC 305 685-6366
12815 Nw 45th Ave Ste 6b Opa Locka (33054) ***(G-12302)***
Coffin Cabinetry & Trim Michae 352 217-3729
91 S Pine Ave Umatilla (32784) ***(G-18497)***
Coffman Systems Inc 813 891-1300
300 Stevens Ave Oldsmar (34677) ***(G-12218)***
Cofran International Corp 305 592-2644
1540 Nw 94th Ave Doral (33172) ***(G-3302)***
Cogswell Innovations Inc 954 245-8877
2000 E Oakland Park Blvd # 106 Fort Lauderdale (33306) ***(G-3907)***
Cohen Capital LLC 954 661-8270
3020 E Commercial Blvd Fort Lauderdale (33308) ***(G-3908)***
Coin-O-Matic Inc 305 635-4141
3950 Nw 31st Ave Miami (33142) ***(G-9376)***
Coinweek LLC 407 786-5555
306 N Swetwater Cove Blvd Longwood (32779) ***(G-8266)***
Cojali Usa Inc 305 960-7651
2200 Nw 102nd Ave Ste 4b Doral (33172) ***(G-3303)***
Cola Construction Inc 305 218-3985
1111 Lincoln Rd Ste 800 Miami Beach (33139) ***(G-10657)***
Cola Group Riverside LLC 305 940-0277
16047 Collins Ave # 2103 Sunny Isles Beach (33160) ***(G-17073)***
Colaianni Italian Flr Tile Mfg 954 321-8244
700 Sw 21st Ter Fort Lauderdale (33312) ***(G-3909)***
Cold Fire Direct, Miami Beach *Also called Stuntwear LLC* ***(G-10718)***
Cold Stone Creamery-Parkland 954 341-8033
6230 Coral Ridge Dr # 110 Coral Springs (33076) ***(G-2232)***
Cold Storage Engineering Co (PA) 305 448-0099
703 Nw 62nd Ave Ste 650 Miami (33126) ***(G-9377)***
Coldflo Inc 305 324-8555
1050 Nw 21st St Miami (33127) ***(G-9378)***
Cole Enterprises Inc 727 441-4101
436 E Shore Dr Clearwater (33767) ***(G-1632)***

Cole Machine LLC 239 571-4364
5740 Shirley St Naples (34109) *(G-11214)*
Cole Machine Naples, Naples *Also called Cole Machine LLC (G-11214)*
Coleman Aerospace 407 354-0047
5950 Lakehurst Dr Orlando (32819) *(G-12599)*
Coleo LLC 215 436-0902
1198 Champions Dr Daytona Beach (32124) *(G-2645)*
Colitz Mining Co Inc 352 795-2409
7040 N Suncoast Blvd Crystal River (34428) *(G-2374)*
Coll Builders Supply Inc 407 745-4641
6663 Narcoossee Rd # 178 Orlando (32822) *(G-12600)*
Collaborative Sftwr Solutions 954 753-2025
4721 Nw 115th Ave Coral Springs (33076) *(G-2233)*
Collectibles of SW Florida 239 332-2344
1502 Ne 11th Ter Cape Coral (33909) *(G-1404)*
Collectors International Pubg 561 845-7156
1285 N Lake Way Palm Beach (33480) *(G-13551)*
College Hunks Hlg Junk & Mvg 407 378-2500
4484 Sw 34th St Orlando (32811) *(G-12601)*
Collegefrog Inc 850 696-1500
418 W Garden St Pensacola (32502) *(G-14116)*
Collidecom LLC 407 903-5626
4700 Millnia Blvdn Ste 400 Orlando (32839) *(G-12602)*
Collier Business Systems 239 649-5554
2280 Linwood Ave Naples (34112) *(G-11215)*
Collier Parkway Fuel LLC 732 492-4791
3402 Sheehan Dr Land O Lakes (34638) *(G-7851)*
Collins Aerospace, Miramar *Also called United Technologies Corp (G-11056)*
Collins Aerospace, Miami Gardens *Also called Goodrich Corporation (G-10745)*
Collins and Dupont Interiors 239 694-3400
5711 Corporation Cir Fort Myers (33905) *(G-4406)*
Collins Media & Advg LLC 954 688-9758
5453 Nw 24th St Ste 2 Margate (33063) *(G-8538)*
Collins Mfg Inc 321 322-0280
672 Johns Rd Apopka (32703) *(G-126)*
Collins Research Inc 321 401-6060
6790 Edgwter Cmmerce Pkwy Orlando (32810) *(G-12603)*
Colloidal Dynamics LLC 904 686-1536
5150 Palm Valley Rd # 303 Ponte Vedra Beach (32082) *(G-14937)*
Colonial Industries Centl Fla 407 484-5239
462 Mohave Ter Lake Mary (32746) *(G-7406)*
Colonial Press Intl Inc 305 633-1581
3690 Nw 50th St Miami (33142) *(G-9379)*
Colonial Ready Mix LLC 941 698-4022
5250 Linwood Rd Placida (33946) *(G-14395)*
Colonna Shipyard 904 246-1183
1701 Mayport Rd Atlantic Beach (32233) *(G-218)*
Color Concepts Prtg Design Co 813 623-2921
2602 Tampa East Blvd Tampa (33619) *(G-17546)*
Color Express Inc 305 558-2061
7990 W 25th Ct Hialeah (33016) *(G-5350)*
Color K Graphics, Miami *Also called K Color Corp (G-9813)*
Color Press Corp 786 621-8491
1835 Nw 112th Ave Ste 184 Miami (33172) *(G-9380)*
Color Press Print Inc 850 763-9884
3430 Highway 77 Ste D Panama City (32405) *(G-13887)*
Color Touch Inc 954 444-1999
3701 Nw 16th St Lauderhill (33311) *(G-8104)*
Color-Chrome Technologies Inc 954 335-0127
2345 Sw 34th St Fort Lauderdale (33312) *(G-3910)*
Coloramax Printing Inc 305 541-0322
3215 Nw 7th St Miami (33125) *(G-9381)*
Colorbyte Software, Lutz *Also called Colorproof Software Inc (G-8377)*
Colorfast Coml Prtg Grphics Sv, Clearwater *Also called Colorfast Printing & Graphics (G-1633)*
Colorfast Printing & Graphics 727 531-9506
14114 63rd Way N Clearwater (33760) *(G-1633)*
Colorgraphx Inc 727 572-6364
1551 102nd Ave N Ste A Saint Petersburg (33716) *(G-15747)*
Colormet Foods LLC 888 775-3966
3610 Ne 1st Ave Miami (33137) *(G-9382)*
Colorprint Design 305 229-8880
1220 Sw 78th Ct Miami (33144) *(G-9383)*
Colorproof Software Inc 813 963-0241
234 Crystal Grove Blvd Lutz (33548) *(G-8377)*
Colortone Inc 954 455-0200
226 Nw 4th Ave Hallandale Beach (33009) *(G-5178)*
Colossus Pavers LLC 239 601-5230
2118 Sw 39th St Cape Coral (33914) *(G-1405)*
Columbia Care Florida, Arcadia *Also called Ccf Holdco LLC (G-201)*
Columbia Films Inc 800 531-3238
43 S Pompano Pkwy Ste 461 Pompano Beach (33069) *(G-14641)*
Columbia Parcar Corp 352 753-0244
2505 Industrial St Leesburg (34748) *(G-8147)*
Columbia Ready Mix Concrete (PA) 386 755-2458
516 Nw Waldo St Lake City (32055) *(G-7350)*
Com Miami Corporation 305 376-5040
3832 Ne 199th Ter Miami (33180) *(G-9384)*
Com Pac Filtration Inc 904 356-4003
2020 W Beaver St Jacksonville (32209) *(G-6279)*
Com-Ten Industries, Saint Petersburg *Also called Giebner Enterprises Inc (G-15792)*
Coma Cast Corp 305 667-6797
4383 Sw 70th Ct Miami (33155) *(G-9385)*
Comcept Solutions LLC 727 535-1900
13799 Park Blvd Ste 307 Seminole (33776) *(G-16744)*
Comep Usa Inc (PA) 786 554-2211
1301 Ne 13th Ct Ste 220 Miami (33172) *(G-9386)*
Comerint Inc 813 443-2466
5125 W Rio Vista Ave Tampa (33634) *(G-17547)*
Comex Systems Inc 908 881-6301
9380 Nastrand Cir Port Charlotte (33981) *(G-14971)*
Comfort Brace LLC 954 899-1563
1971 Ne 31st St Lighthouse Point (33064) *(G-8208)*
Comida Vida Inc 855 720-7663
5600 Elmhurst Cir Oviedo (32765) *(G-13421)*
Comimpex Flooring and Finishes, Miami *Also called Comimpex Group LLC (G-9387)*
Comimpex Group LLC 786 306-3204
844 Sw 154th Ct Miami (33194) *(G-9387)*
Comiskey Industries Inc 201 925-0998
18 Eastlake Dr Palm Coast (32137) *(G-13688)*
Comlabs, Melbourne *Also called Communications Labs Inc (G-8794)*
Comm Dots LLC Connecting 305 505-6009
3890 Coco Grove Ave Miami (33133) *(G-9388)*
Command Medical Products Inc 386 677-7775
15 Signal Ave Ormond Beach (32174) *(G-13359)*
Command Print LLC 716 583-5175
3250 Bonita Beach Rd # 205 Bonita Springs (34134) *(G-826)*
Commercial Acoustics, Tampa *Also called Residential Acoustics LLC (G-18053)*
Commercial Cabinetry LLC 407 440-4601
6135 Cyril Ave Orlando (32809) *(G-12604)*
Commercial Casework Inc (PA) 904 264-4222
1030 Ellis Rd N Jacksonville (32254) *(G-6280)*
Commercial Concrete Pdts Inc 813 659-3707
2705 Sammonds Rd Plant City (33563) *(G-14419)*
Commercial Door Systems Fla LL 850 466-5906
612 W Romana St Pensacola (32502) *(G-14117)*
Commercial Duct Systems LLC 877 237-3828
9707 Williams Rd Thonotosassa (33592) *(G-18399)*
Commercial Energy Services 904 589-1059
1528 Virgils Way Ste 14 Green Cove Springs (32043) *(G-5059)*
Commercial Gates and Elc LLC 386 454-2329
27317 Nw 78th Ave High Springs (32643) *(G-5700)*
Commercial Instllation Systems 727 525-2372
6175 Wdrow Wilson Blvd Ne Saint Petersburg (33703) *(G-15748)*
Commercial Insulating Glass Co (PA) 941 378-9100
6200 Porter Rd Sarasota (34240) *(G-16389)*
Commercial Metal Photography 407 295-8182
1934a Silver Star Rd Orlando (32804) *(G-12605)*
Commercial Metals Company 904 781-4780
10483 General Ave Jacksonville (32220) *(G-6281)*
Commercial Millworks Inc 407 648-2787
1120 S Hughey Ave Ste A Orlando (32806) *(G-12606)*
Commercial Printer Phrm Prtr, Doral *Also called Vista Color Corporation (G-3544)*
Commercial Printers Inc (PA) 954 781-3737
6600 Nw 15th Ave Fort Lauderdale (33309) *(G-3911)*
Commercial Printing, Tallahassee *Also called Bava Inc (G-17226)*
Commercial Rfrg Door Co Inc 941 371-8110
6200 Porter Rd Sarasota (34240) *(G-16390)*
Commercial Stone Cab Fbrctors 727 209-1141
3120 46th Ave N Saint Petersburg (33714) *(G-15749)*
Commercial Stone Fbrcators Inc 727 209-1141
3120 46th Ave N Saint Petersburg (33714) *(G-15750)*
Commercial Truck & Trailer Sls 863 968-9393
507 Us Highway 92 E Auburndale (33823) *(G-236)*
Commercial Wood Designs Inc 407 302-9063
257 Power Ct Sanford (32771) *(G-16018)*
Common Sense Publishing LLC 561 510-1713
55 Ne 5th Ave Ste 100 Delray Beach (33483) *(G-3063)*
Commonwealth Brands Inc (HQ) 800 481-5814
5900 N Andrews Ave Ste 11 Fort Lauderdale (33309) *(G-3912)*
Commscope Technologies LLC 407 944-9116
11310 Satellite Blvd Orlando (32837) *(G-12607)*
Commski LLC 813 501-0111
7853 Gunn Hwy 252 Tampa (33626) *(G-17548)*
Commstructures Inc 850 968-9293
101 E Roberts Rd Pensacola (32534) *(G-14118)*
Communcations Surveillance Inc 305 377-1211
4000 Ponce De Leon Blvd Coral Gables (33146) *(G-2132)*
Communicate 360, Orlando *Also called Open Market Enterprises LLC (G-13024)*
Communication Eqp & Engrg Co 863 357-0798
519 Sw Park St Okeechobee (34972) *(G-12174)*
Communications Labs Inc 321 701-9000
4005 Opportunity Dr Melbourne (32934) *(G-8794)*
Community MGT Systems LLC 561 214-4780
4650 Donald Ross Rd # 220 Palm Beach Gardens (33418) *(G-13581)*
Community News Papers Inc 386 752-1293
180 E Duval St Lake City (32055) *(G-7351)*

ALPHABETIC

Community News Publications, Land O Lakes *Also called Manatee Media Inc (G-7861)*
Community News Publications 813 909-2800
3632 Land O Lkes Blvd Ste Lutz (33549) *(G-8378)*
Community Pharmacy Svcs LLC 727 431-8261
19387 Us Highway 19 N Clearwater (33764) *(G-1634)*
Comoderm Corp 561 756-2929
2175 N Andrews Ave Ste 4 Pompano Beach (33069) *(G-14642)*
Comp U Netcom Inc 407 539-1800
331 N Maitland Ave D10 Maitland (32751) *(G-8462)*
Compact Brick Pavers Inc 727 278-1544
1019 Pine Lily Pl Bradenton (34201) *(G-1022)*
Compact Container Systems LLC 561 392-6910
2500 N Military Trl # 400 Boca Raton (33431) *(G-487)*
Compact Contract Inc 352 817-8058
1822 Sw 34th Ct Ocala (34474) *(G-11906)*
Compak Companies LLC 321 249-9590
751 Cornwall Rd Sanford (32773) *(G-16019)*
Compass Banners & Printing LLC 727 522-7414
5502 Haines Rd N Saint Petersburg (33714) *(G-15751)*
Compass Printing and Marketing 954 856-8331
5218 Nw 15th St Margate (33063) *(G-8539)*
Compass Publishing LLC 407 328-0970
671 Progress Way Sanford (32771) *(G-16020)*
Compass Service 954 900-4462
7822 Nw 44th St Lauderhill (33351) *(G-8105)*
Competition Specialties Inc 386 776-1476
16936 County Road 252 Mc Alpin (32062) *(G-8599)*
Competitor Group Inc 858 450-6510
3407 W Dr Ml King Jr 10 Tampa (33607) *(G-17549)*
Complementary Coatings Corp 386 428-6461
9592 Parksouth Ct Orlando (32837) *(G-12608)*
Complete Access Ctrl Centl Fla 407 498-0067
2013 Jaffa Dr Saint Cloud (34771) *(G-15647)*
Complete Instrmnttion Cntrls I 813 340-8545
11524 Hammock Oaks Ct Lithia (33547) *(G-8217)*
Complete Metal Solutions Intl 954 560-0583
107 Nw 5th Ave Fort Lauderdale (33311) *(G-3913)*
Complete Mold Remediators Inc 305 903-8885
31800 Sw 195th Ave Homestead (33030) *(G-5958)*
Complete Printing Solutions, Jacksonville *Also called WJS Printing Partners Inc (G-6925)*
Compliance Meds Tech LLC 786 319-9826
20855 Ne 16th Ave Ste C13 Miami (33179) *(G-9389)*
Comply Arm 772 249-0345
1680 Sw St Lucie W Blvd Port Saint Lucie (34986) *(G-15100)*
Component General Inc 727 376-6655
2445 Success Dr Odessa (33556) *(G-12112)*
Componexx Corp 954 236-6569
789 Shotgun Rd Sunrise (33326) *(G-17107)*
Composite Essential Mtls LLC 772 344-0034
315 Nw Peacock Blvd Port St Lucie (34986) *(G-15172)*
Composite Holdings Inc (PA) 321 268-9625
805 Marina Rd Titusville (32796) *(G-18424)*
Composite-Fx Sales LLC 352 538-1624
9069 Se County Road 319 Trenton (32693) *(G-18481)*
Compost Jax, Jacksonville *Also called Sunshine Organics Compost LLC (G-6825)*
COMPOUND MIAMI THE, Miami *Also called A2f LLC (G-9048)*
Comprehensive Grants MGT, Lutz *Also called Gibbons Industries Inc (G-8384)*
Compro Solution 407 733-4130
1670 Tropic Park Dr Sanford (32773) *(G-16021)*
Compsys Inc 321 255-0399
4255 Dow Rd Melbourne (32934) *(G-8795)*
Comptech Global Solutions Inc 941 766-8100
775 Tamiami Trl Unit B Port Charlotte (33953) *(G-14972)*
Compuclamp, Vero Beach *Also called Theft Protection Com Corp (G-18670)*
Compulink Corporation (HQ) 727 579-1500
1205 Gandy Blvd N Saint Petersburg (33702) *(G-15752)*
Computational Systems Inc 954 846-5030
1300 Concord Ter Ste 400 Sunrise (33323) *(G-17108)*
Computational Systems Inc 863 648-9044
5030 Gateway Blvd Ste 11 Lakeland (33811) *(G-7661)*
Computer Center of Sanford, Sanford *Also called Ellis & Associates of Sanford (G-16041)*
Computer Forms & Supplies 727 535-0422
1198 Hickory Dr Largo (33770) *(G-7926)*
Computer Technician Inc 941 479-0242
829 8th Ave W Palmetto (34221) *(G-13793)*
Computers At Work Inc 239 571-1050
3033 Winkler Ave Ste 210 Fort Myers (33916) *(G-4407)*
Comres Manufacturing Inc 813 249-0391
7211 Anderson Rd Tampa (33634) *(G-17550)*
Comtech Antenna Systems Inc 407 854-1950
212 Outlook Point Dr # 100 Orlando (32809) *(G-12609)*
Comtech Systems Inc 407 854-1950
212 Outlook Point Dr # 100 Orlando (32809) *(G-12610)*
Comten Industries Inc 727 520-1200
6405 49th St N Ste A Pinellas Park (33781) *(G-14340)*
Comtronix US, Fort Myers *Also called Industrial Technology LLC (G-4494)*
Con Serv Manufacturing, Lakeland *Also called Gkwf Inc (G-7699)*
Con-Air Industries Inc 407 298-5733
4157 Seaboard Rd Orlando (32808) *(G-12611)*
Conagra Brands Inc 904 417-0964
3660 Deerpark Blvd Elkton (32033) *(G-3648)*
Conagra Snack Foods, Elkton *Also called Conagra Brands Inc (G-3648)*
Conali Express Corp 954 531-9573
3281 Nw 65th St Fort Lauderdale (33309) *(G-3914)*
Conc-Steel Inc 516 882-5551
250 Palm Coast Pkwy Ne Palm Coast (32137) *(G-13689)*
Concealment Express LLC 888 904-2722
10066 103rd St Ste 103 Jacksonville (32210) *(G-6282)*
Concentrated Aloe Corp 386 673-7566
20 W Tower Cir Ormond Beach (32174) *(G-13360)*
Concept 2 Market Inc 954 974-0022
3000 Nw 25th Ave Ste 11 Pompano Beach (33069) *(G-14643)*
Concept Boats Inc 305 635-8712
2410 Nw 147th St Opa Locka (33054) *(G-12303)*
Concept Design and Printing 813 516-9798
7402 N 56th St Ste 810 Tampa (33617) *(G-17551)*
Concept Elevator Group LLC (PA) 786 845-8955
8027 Nw 71st St Miami (33166) *(G-9390)*
Concept Group LLC 856 767-5506
350 Hiatt Dr Ste 120 Palm Beach Gardens (33418) *(G-13582)*
Concept One Custom Cabine 954 829-3505
5807 Dawson St Hollywood (33023) *(G-5804)*
Concept Software Inc 321 250-6670
1319 Green Frest Ct Ste 4 Winter Garden (34787) *(G-19258)*
Conchita Foods Inc (PA) 305 888-9703
10051 Nw 99th Ave Ste 3 Medley (33178) *(G-8633)*
Concord Print Shops, Ocala *Also called Ocala Print Quick Inc (G-12014)*
Concordia Pharmaceuticals Inc 786 304-2083
2600 Sw 3rd Ave Ste 950 Miami (33129) *(G-9391)*
Concraft Inc (PA) 561 689-0149
353 Swain Blvd Greenacres (33463) *(G-5078)*
Concraft Patio Products, Greenacres *Also called Concraft Inc (G-5078)*
Concrete Edge Company 407 658-2788
1952 Saturn Blvd Orlando (32837) *(G-12612)*
Concrete Pdts of Palm Bches In 561 842-2743
460 Avenue S Riviera Beach (33404) *(G-15313)*
Concrete Products-Division, Winter Park *Also called Accord Industries LLC (G-19370)*
Concrete Structures Inc 305 597-9393
12100 Nw 58th St Miami (33010) *(G-9392)*
Concrete Systems, Port Richey *Also called D Maxwell Company Inc (G-15048)*
Concurrent Mfg Solutions LLC (HQ) 512 637-2540
10773 Nw 58th St Ste 100 Doral (33178) *(G-3304)*
Condition Culture LLC 786 433-8279
123 Harbors Way Boynton Beach (33435) *(G-892)*
Condo Electric Motor Repr Corp 305 691-5400
3615 E 10th Ct Hialeah (33013) *(G-5351)*
Conduent Image Solutions Inc 407 849-0279
4209 Vineland Rd Ste J2 Orlando (32811) *(G-12613)*
Conduit Space Rcvery Systems L 330 416-0887
5204 Lena Rd Bradenton (34211) *(G-1023)*
Coneheads Frozen Custards 772 600-7730
43 Sw Flagler Ave Stuart (34994) *(G-16925)*
Conexus Technologies Inc 513 779-5448
1145 Horizon View Dr Sarasota (34242) *(G-16391)*
Conglobal Industries, Jacksonville *Also called Its Technologies Logistics LLC (G-6505)*
Conibear Equipment Co Inc (PA) 863 858-4414
8910 Us Highway 98 N Lakeland (33809) *(G-7662)*
Conibear Recreational Vehicles, Lakeland *Also called Conibear Equipment Co Inc (G-7662)*
Conklin Metal Industries Inc 407 688-0900
3060 Pennington Dr Orlando (32804) *(G-12614)*
Conmed Corporation (PA) 727 392-6464
11311 Concept Blvd Largo (33773) *(G-7927)*
Conmed Linvatec, Largo *Also called Linvatec Corporation (G-8001)*
Connect Slutions Worldwide LLC 407 492-9370
1602 Indian Bay Dr Vero Beach (32963) *(G-18611)*
Connected Life Solutions LLC 407 745-1952
153 Dahlia Dr Altamonte Springs (32714) *(G-38)*
Connectpress Ltd 505 629-0695
2015 S Tuttle Ave Ste A Sarasota (34239) *(G-16392)*
Connectronics US Inc 954 534-3335
101 Bradley Pl Ste 202 Palm Beach (33480) *(G-13552)*
Connectsure, Leesburg *Also called Top Line Installation Inc (G-8177)*
Connectyx Technologies Corp 772 221-8240
850 Nw Federal Hwy # 411 Stuart (34994) *(G-16926)*
Conopco Inc 727 573-1591
5400 118th Ave N Clearwater (33760) *(G-1635)*
Conquest Financial Management 305 630-8950
11451 Nw 36th Ave Miami (33167) *(G-9393)*
Conquest Manufacturing Fla LLC 954 655-0139
1121 Nw 31st Ave Pompano Beach (33069) *(G-14644)*
Conquistador Management Group, Homestead *Also called Pets2go International Inc (G-5987)*
Conrad Markle Bldr & Cbnt 904 744-4569
1120 Romney St Jacksonville (32211) *(G-6283)*
Conrad Pickel Studio Inc 772 567-1710
7777 20th St Vero Beach (32966) *(G-18612)*
Conrad Plastics LLC 954 391-9515
1904 S Ocean Dr Apt 1703 Hallandale Beach (33009) *(G-5179)*

Conrad Yelvington Distrs Inc 352 336-5049
7605 Nw 13th St Gainesville (32653) ***(G-4895)***
Conrado Salas Jr LLC 941 587-5919
125 Avenida Veneccia Sarasota (34242) ***(G-16393)***
Conric Holdings LLC 239 690-9840
8770 Paseo De Valencia St Fort Myers (33908) ***(G-4408)***
Conric PR & Marketing, Fort Myers *Also called Conric Holdings LLC* ***(G-4408)***
Consoldted Mch Tl Holdings LLC (PA) 888 317-9990
712 S Ocean Shore Blvd Flagler Beach (32136) ***(G-3754)***
Consoldted Rsurce Recovery Inc 813 262-8404
1502 N 50th St Tampa (33619) ***(G-17552)***
Consolidated Ace Hdwr Sup Inc 850 939-9800
8188 Navarre Pkwy Navarre (32566) ***(G-11465)***
Consolidated Box, Fort Lauderdale *Also called Mas Entrprses of Ft Lauderdale* ***(G-4113)***
Consolidated Cigr Holdings Inc 954 772-9000
5900 N Andrews Ave # 1100 Fort Lauderdale (33309) ***(G-3915)***
Consolidated Cordage Corp 561 347-7247
1707 Avenida Del Sol Boca Raton (33432) ***(G-488)***
Consolidated Forest Pdts Inc 407 830-7723
320 Millinor Rd Perry (32347) ***(G-14298)***
Consolidated Forest Pdts Inc (PA) 407 830-7723
375 Commerce Way Longwood (32750) ***(G-8267)***
Consolidated Label Co 407 339-2626
2001 E Lake Mary Blvd Sanford (32773) ***(G-16022)***
Consolidated Metal Products 850 576-2167
3416 Garber Dr Tallahassee (32303) ***(G-17236)***
Consolidated Minerals Inc (PA) 352 365-6522
8500 Us Highway 441 Leesburg (34788) ***(G-8148)***
Consolidated Parking Equipment, Miami *Also called Lcn Incorporated* ***(G-9873)***
Consolidated Polymer Tech 727 531-4191
4451 110th Ave N Clearwater (33762) ***(G-1636)***
Consolidated Tech Solutions, Pensacola *Also called Smartcop Inc* ***(G-14262)***
Constrction Mtal Fbrcators LLC 305 781-9004
15913 Nw 49th Ave Hialeah (33014) ***(G-5352)***
Construccion-Pan Americana, Miami *Also called International Cnstr Pubg* ***(G-9757)***
Constructconnect Inc 772 770-6003
2001 9th Ave Ste 204 Vero Beach (32960) ***(G-18613)***
Construction and Elec Pdts Inc 954 972-9787
1800 Nw 15th Ave Ste 155 Pompano Beach (33069) ***(G-14645)***
Construction Bulletin Inc 904 388-0336
7033 Commwl Ave Ste 1 Jacksonville (32220) ***(G-6284)***
Construction Collections, Fort Lauderdale *Also called Builders Notice Corporation* ***(G-3875)***
Construction Journal Ltd (PA) 772 781-2144
400 Sw 7th St Stuart (34994) ***(G-16927)***
Construction Software Inc 888 801-0675
515 E Las Olas Blvd Ste 1 Fort Lauderdale (33301) ***(G-3916)***
Consulier Engineering Inc (PA) 561 842-2492
2391 President Barack Oba Riviera Beach (33404) ***(G-15314)***
Consultant MGT Group LLC 352 344-4001
200 W Main St Inverness (34450) ***(G-6083)***
Consulting, Altamonte Springs *Also called Connected Life Solutions LLC* ***(G-38)***
Consumer Engineering Inc 321 984-8550
1240 Clearmont St Ne # 1 Palm Bay (32905) ***(G-13507)***
Consumer Information Bureau 954 971-5079
2301 W Sample Rd Ste 4-2a Pompano Beach (33073) ***(G-14646)***
Consumer Source Inc 407 888-0745
8026 Sunport Dr Ste 304 Orlando (32809) ***(G-12615)***
Contact Center Solutions Inc 305 499-0163
66 W Flagler St Miami (33130) ***(G-9394)***
Contact Enterprises Inc 561 900-5134
3170 N Federal Hwy # 100 Pompano Beach (33064) ***(G-14647)***
Contagious Fishing Charters 727 595-6277
14481 Starboard Ln Largo (33774) ***(G-7928)***
Container Handling Solutions 941 359-2095
1349 W University Pkwy Sarasota (34243) ***(G-16194)***
Container Mfg Solutions 888 805-8785
10460 Sw 186th St Cutler Bay (33157) ***(G-2389)***
Contec Americas Inc 321 728-0172
3991 Sarno Rd Melbourne (32934) ***(G-8796)***
Contemporary Cabinets Gulf CST 941 758-3060
2245 Whitfield Indus Way Sarasota (34243) ***(G-16195)***
Contemporary Carbide Tech 386 734-0080
1730 Patterson Ave Unit B Deland (32724) ***(G-2964)***
Contemporary Interiors Inc 352 620-8686
2626 Nw 35th St Ocala (34475) ***(G-11907)***
Contemprary McHnrey Engrg Svcs 386 439-0937
551 Roberts Rd Flagler Beach (32136) ***(G-3755)***
Contender Boats Inc 305 230-1600
1820 Se 38th Ave Homestead (33035) ***(G-5959)***
Continental Belt & Tie, Miami *Also called Continental Belt Corp* ***(G-9395)***
Continental Belt Corp 305 573-8871
2267 Nw 20th St Miami (33142) ***(G-9395)***
Continental Blood Bank, Miami *Also called Continental Services Group* ***(G-9396)***
Continental Concrete, Miami *Also called Supermix Concrete* ***(G-10439)***
Continental Concrete Materials, Davie *Also called Lehigh Cement Company LLC* ***(G-2545)***
Continental Concrete Products 904 388-1390
2251 Urban Rd Jacksonville (32210) ***(G-6285)***
Continental Marketing Group, Miami *Also called GBIG Corporation* ***(G-9617)***
Continental Metals 734 362-1144
11921 Wedge Dr Fort Myers (33913) ***(G-4409)***
Continental Palatka LLC 703 480-3800
886 N Highway 17 Palatka (32177) ***(G-13475)***
Continental Printing Svcs Inc 904 743-6718
4929 Toproyal Ln Jacksonville (32277) ***(G-6286)***
Continental Property LLC 817 613-1890
901 Central Florida Pkwy A3 Orlando (32824) ***(G-12616)***
Continental Services Group (PA) 305 633-7700
1300 Nw 36th St Miami (33142) ***(G-9396)***
Continental Services Group 954 327-0809
2901 W Broward Blvd Fort Lauderdale (33312) ***(G-3917)***
Continuity Unlimited Inc 561 358-8171
1750 W Broadway St # 112 Oviedo (32765) ***(G-13422)***
Contours Rx LLC 727 827-7321
200 2nd Ave S Ste 701 Saint Petersburg (33701) ***(G-15753)***
Contract Mfg Solutions Inc 954 424-9813
1880 N Commerce Pkwy # 1 Weston (33326) ***(G-19117)***
Contracting Cnc Machining Inc 561 494-0703
8360 Currency Dr Ste 7 West Palm Beach (33404) ***(G-18849)***
Contractors Cabinet Company 786 492-7118
5512 W Sample Rd Margate (33073) ***(G-8540)***
Control and Automtn Cons Inc 305 823-8670
11300 Nw 87th Ct Ste 125 Hialeah (33018) ***(G-5353)***
Control Investments Inc (PA) 954 491-6660
6001 Ne 14th Ave Fort Lauderdale (33334) ***(G-3918)***
Control Laser Corporation 407 926-3500
8251 Presidents Dr # 1688 Orlando (32809) ***(G-12617)***
Control Micro Systems Inc 407 679-9716
4420 Metric Dr Ste A Winter Park (32792) ***(G-19396)***
Control Solutions Inc 813 247-2136
1406 N 16th St Tampa (33605) ***(G-17553)***
Control Southern Inc 904 353-0004
4133 N Canal St Jacksonville (32209) ***(G-6287)***
Contrologix LLC 407 878-2774
361 S White Cedar Rd Sanford (32771) ***(G-16023)***
Convergent Actuarial Svcs Inc 561 715-4204
510 Lavers Cir Delray Beach (33444) ***(G-3064)***
Convergent Engineering Inc 352 378-4899
100 Sw 75th St Ste 106 Gainesville (32607) ***(G-4896)***
Convergent Marketing LLC 561 270-7081
701 Nw 2nd Ave Delray Beach (33444) ***(G-3065)***
Convergent Technologies 407 482-4381
14764 Sapodilla Dr Orlando (32828) ***(G-12618)***
Converlogic Americas, Doral *Also called Converlogic Inter LLC* ***(G-3305)***
Converlogic Inter LLC (PA) 786 623-4747
2254 Nw 93rd Ave Doral (33172) ***(G-3305)***
Converpack Inc 786 304-1680
9230 9250 Nw 102th St 9 Medley (33178) ***(G-8634)***
Conveyor Concepts Corporation 941 751-1200
2323 Whitfield Park Ave Sarasota (34243) ***(G-16196)***
Conveyor Consulting & Rbr Corp 813 385-1254
2511 Destiny Way Odessa (33556) ***(G-12113)***
Convicted Printing LLC 813 304-5568
3005 Rosebud Ln Brandon (33511) ***(G-1155)***
Convivium Press Inc 305 889-0489
7661 Nw 68th St Unit 108 Miami (33166) ***(G-9397)***
Conway Bldg Cstm Woodworks LLC 407 738-9266
3001 Viscount Cir Kissimmee (34747) ***(G-7232)***
Cook Manufacturing Group Inc 863 546-6183
100 E 7th St Frostproof (33843) ***(G-4857)***
Cook Spring Co 941 377-5766
233 Sarasota Center Blvd Sarasota (34240) ***(G-16394)***
Cooke Communications Fla LLC (PA) 305 292-7777
3140 Flagler Ave Key West (33040) ***(G-7184)***
Cookie App LLC 305 330-5099
2 S Biscayne Blvd # 2680 Miami (33131) ***(G-9398)***
Cool Components Inc 813 322-3814
904 E Chelsea St Tampa (33603) ***(G-17554)***
Cool Cow 229 272-5495
2819 Mahan Dr Ste 110 Tallahassee (32308) ***(G-17237)***
Cool Flex, Palm Coast *Also called Total Performance Inc* ***(G-13713)***
Cool Ocean LLC 954 848-4060
9810 Sw 4th St Plantation (33324) ***(G-14502)***
Cool Pet Holistics, Saint Petersburg *Also called Animal Business Concepts LLC* ***(G-15701)***
Cool Treat 407 248-0743
7001 International Dr Orlando (32819) ***(G-12619)***
Coolcraft Inc 954 946-0070
1700 Nw 15th Ave Ste 330 Pompano Beach (33069) ***(G-14648)***
Coolhead Helmet LLC 786 292-4829
999 Brickell Bay Dr Miami (33131) ***(G-9399)***
Cooltech Holding Corp (HQ) 786 675-5236
2100 Nw 84th Ave Doral (33122) ***(G-3306)***
Cooper, Sanibel *Also called CT Hydraulics Inc* ***(G-16145)***
Cooper Crouse-Hinds Mtl Inc (HQ) 321 725-8000
4325 Wdlnd Pk Dr Ste 101 Melbourne (32904) ***(G-8797)***
Cooper Notification Inc 941 487-2300
7246 16th St E Unit 105 Sarasota (34243) ***(G-16197)***
Cooper Timber Harvesting Inc 863 494-0240
2056 Ne Newberry Dr Arcadia (34266) ***(G-202)***

ALPHABETIC

Cooper-Standard Automotive Inc 407 330-3323
3551 W 1st St Sanford (32771) ***(G-16024)***
Cooper-Standard Automotive Inc 407 330-3323
501 Cornwall Rd Ste 2773 Sanford (32773) ***(G-16025)***
Coopers Hawk Intrmdate Hldg LL 904 996-2466
4850 Big Island Dr Jacksonville (32246) ***(G-6288)***
Cooppa News Reporter 954 437-8864
13550 Sw 10th St Pembroke Pines (33027) ***(G-14029)***
Coosa LLC 904 268-1187
12811 Helm Dr Jacksonville (32258) ***(G-6289)***
Copaco Inc 407 333-3041
366 E Graves Ave Ste B Orange City (32763) ***(G-12374)***
Copalo Inc 941 753-7828
6510 19th St E Sarasota (34243) ***(G-16198)***
Copans Quick Print, Pompano Beach *Also called B R Q Grossmans Inc* ***(G-14609)***
Copeland Welding & Muffler Sp 904 355-6383
484 Lime St Jacksonville (32204) ***(G-6290)***
Copernicco Coatings LLC 407 948-3434
2624 Pisces Dr Orlando (32837) ***(G-12620)***
Coplan Composition Service, Jacksonville *Also called A M Coplan Associates* ***(G-6110)***
Copper Bottom Craft Distillery, Apollo Beach *Also called Four Seas Distilling Co LLC* ***(G-104)***
Coppercom Inc 561 322-4000
3600 Fau Blvd Ste 100 Boca Raton (33431) ***(G-489)***
Coppercom, A Heico, Boca Raton *Also called Coppercom Inc* ***(G-489)***
Copy Cat Printing LLC 850 438-5566
3636 N L St Ste D-A Pensacola (32505) ***(G-14119)***
Copy Right Bgmd Inc 904 680-0343
5569 Bowden Rd Ste 6 Jacksonville (32216) ***(G-6291)***
Copy Right Printing, Bradenton *Also called W D H Enterprises Inc* ***(G-1143)***
Copy Systems Business Center 850 650-0886
4821 Us Highway 98 W # 102 Santa Rosa Beach (32459) ***(G-16156)***
Copy Van of Florida Inc 407 366-7126
2224 Andrew Ln Oviedo (32765) ***(G-13423)***
Copy Van Printing, Oviedo *Also called Copy Van of Florida Inc* ***(G-13423)***
Copy Well Inc 850 222-9777
927 N Monroe St Tallahassee (32303) ***(G-17238)***
Copy-Flow Inc 305 592-0930
4727 Orange Dr Davie (33314) ***(G-2509)***
Coqui Pharma, Doral *Also called Coqui Rdo Pharmaceuticals Corp* ***(G-3307)***
Coqui Rdo Pharmaceuticals Corp 787 685-5046
3125 Nw 84th Ave Doral (33122) ***(G-3307)***
Cor International (not Inc) 850 766-2866
3204 Hastie Rd Tallahassee (32305) ***(G-17239)***
Cor Label LLC 407 402-6633
901 S Chrles Rchard Ball Debary (32713) ***(G-2746)***
Coral Cabinet Inc 305 484-8702
14378 Sw 98th Ter Miami (33186) ***(G-9400)***
Coral Club Tee Shirts Inc 305 828-6939
3192 W 81st St Hialeah (33018) ***(G-5354)***
Coral Gables Custom Design Inc 305 591-7575
4038 Nw 32nd Ave Miami (33142) ***(G-9401)***
Coral Gables Living 786 552-6464
400 University Dr Fl 2 Coral Gables (33134) ***(G-2133)***
Coral Reef Cast Stone Inc 561 586-1900
6100 Georgia Ave West Palm Beach (33405) ***(G-18850)***
Coraldom Usa LLC 305 716-0200
4434 Nw 74th Ave Miami (33166) ***(G-9402)***
Corbin Sand and Clay Inc 850 638-8462
1177 Jackson Ave Chipley (32428) ***(G-1542)***
Cordaroys Wholesale Inc (PA) 352 332-1837
3421 W University Ave Gainesville (32607) ***(G-4897)***
Cordell International Inc 352 694-1800
1056 Ne 16th St Ocala (34470) ***(G-11908)***
Cordis Corporation 786 313-2000
14201 Nw 60th Ave Miami Lakes (33014) ***(G-10777)***
Cordoba Foods LLC 305 733-4768
4477 E 11th Ave Hialeah (33013) ***(G-5355)***
Core Enterprises Incorporated 954 227-0781
3650 Coral Ridge Dr # 101 Coral Springs (33065) ***(G-2234)***
Core Label LLC 772 287-2141
4313 Sw Port Way Palm City (34990) ***(G-13649)***
Core Moto, Titusville *Also called A1a Sportbike LLC* ***(G-18407)***
Core Outdoors Inc 904 215-6866
134 Poole Blvd Saint Augustine (32095) ***(G-15532)***
Corelite Inc (PA) 305 921-4292
1060 E 30th St Hialeah (33013) ***(G-5356)***
Corellium LLC 561 502-2420
1301 N Congress Ave # 41 Boynton Beach (33426) ***(G-893)***
Corerx Inc 727 259-6950
5733 Myerlake Cir Clearwater (33760) ***(G-1637)***
Corerx Inc (PA) 727 259-6950
14205 Myerlake Cir Clearwater (33760) ***(G-1638)***
Corerx Pharmaceuticals Inc 727 259-6950
14205 Myerlake Cir Clearwater (33760) ***(G-1639)***
Coresential Energy & Lighting 919 602-0849
1201 N 50th St Tampa (33619) ***(G-17555)***
Coreslab Strctures Orlando Inc 407 855-3191
2720 County Road 470 Okahumpka (34762) ***(G-12170)***
Coreslab Structures Miami Inc 305 823-8950
10501 Nw 121st Way Medley (33178) ***(G-8635)***
Coreslab Structures Tampa Inc 602 237-3875
6301 N 56th St Tampa (33610) ***(G-17556)***
Coresystems Software USA Inc 786 497-4477
801 Brickell Ave Ste 1400 Miami (33131) ***(G-9403)***
Coresystems USA, Miami *Also called Coresystems Software USA Inc* ***(G-9403)***
Coretek Industries Inc 321 385-2860
1300 White Dr Ste A Titusville (32780) ***(G-18425)***
Coreyco LLC 813 469-1203
6253 Candlewood Dr Wesley Chapel (33544) ***(G-18742)***
Corin USA Limited Inc (HQ) 813 977-4469
12750 Citrus Park Ln # 120 Tampa (33625) ***(G-17557)***
Corines Frsh Fruits/Vegetbles 352 708-6247
2530 Citrus Tower Blvd Clermont (34711) ***(G-1955)***
Corinthian Catamarans LLC 813 334-1029
4338 Auston Way Palm Harbor (34685) ***(G-13730)***
Cork Industries Inc 904 695-2400
5555 W Beaver St Jacksonville (32254) ***(G-6292)***
Corkcicle LLC 866 780-0007
1300 Brookhaven Dr Ste 2 Orlando (32803) ***(G-12621)***
Corkscrew Winery 352 751-1787
205 Se Sanchez Ave Ocala (34471) ***(G-11909)***
Corn-E-Lee Woodcrafts 239 574-2414
1201 Se 9th Ter Cape Coral (33990) ***(G-1406)***
Cornelius Welding Inc 863 635-3668
221 N Scenic Hwy Frostproof (33843) ***(G-4858)***
Cornerstone Builders S W Fla, Fort Myers *Also called Cornerstone Kitchens Inc* ***(G-4410)***
Cornerstone Fabrication LLC 386 310-1110
291 Sprngview Commerce Dr Debary (32713) ***(G-2747)***
Cornerstone Interlocking Inc 863 944-1609
5915 Walt Loop Rd Lakeland (33809) ***(G-7663)***
Cornerstone Kitchens Inc 239 332-3020
3150 Old Metro Pkwy Fort Myers (33916) ***(G-4410)***
Cornerstone Software Inc 727 443-5557
1356 Hibiscus St Clearwater (33755) ***(G-1640)***
Cornwell, Palm Bay *Also called Walters Tools LLC* ***(G-13546)***
Corona Brushes Inc 813 885-2525
5065 Savarese Cir Tampa (33634) ***(G-17558)***
Corona Printing Company Inc 754 263-2914
1833 Sw 31st Ave Hallandale (33009) ***(G-5155)***
Coronado Paint Co Inc 386 428-6461
9592 Parksouth Ct Orlando (32837) ***(G-12622)***
Coronet Industries Inc 813 752-1161
4082 Coronet Rd Plant City (33566) ***(G-14420)***
Corpdesign 866 323-6055
6695 Nw 36th Ave Miami (33147) ***(G-9404)***
Corporacion Internacional De J 772 343-1721
2868 Sw Port St Lcie Blvd Port Saint Lucie (34953) ***(G-15101)***
Corporate & Incentive Travel, Boca Raton *Also called Coastal Communications Corp* ***(G-486)***
Corporate It, Deerfield Beach *Also called Hoerbiger America Holding Inc* ***(G-2841)***
Corporate One Hundred Inc 352 335-0901
605 Nw 53rd Ave Ste A17 Gainesville (32609) ***(G-4898)***
Corporate Print Resources Inc 305 968-2037
7900 Sw 160th St Palmetto Bay (33157) ***(G-13842)***
Corporate Printing & Advg Inc 305 273-6000
13515 Sw 99th St Miami (33186) ***(G-9405)***
Corporate Printing Svcs Inc 305 273-6000
13288 Sw 114th Ter Miami (33186) ***(G-9406)***
Corporate Signs Inc 305 500-9313
1375 Nw 97th Ave Ste 12 Doral (33172) ***(G-3308)***
Corporate Signs Inc 305 500-9313
5960 Nw 99th Ave Unit 8 Doral (33178) ***(G-3309)***
Corporate Sports & Entrmt, Tampa *Also called Total Spcalty Publications LLC* ***(G-18195)***
Correll Services Inc 561 358-6952
260 Crestwood Cir Apt 106 Royal Palm Beach (33411) ***(G-15463)***
Corrigan & Company 904 353-5936
119 Sewald St Jacksonville (32204) ***(G-6293)***
Corrocoat USA Inc 904 268-4559
6525 Greenland Rd Jacksonville (32258) ***(G-6294)***
Corrugated Help LLC 904 874-7285
1219 W Madison St Starke (32091) ***(G-16891)***
Corrugated Industries Fla Inc 813 623-6606
1920 N Us Highway 301 Tampa (33619) ***(G-17559)***
Corrugating Division, Dundee *Also called Pratt Industries Inc* ***(G-3568)***
Corry Cabinet Company Inc 850 539-6455
811 N Main St Havana (32333) ***(G-5237)***
Corsicana Bedding LLC 863 519-5905
450 Polk St Bartow (33830) ***(G-313)***
Corvatsch Corp 305 775-2831
1894 Bay Rd Miami Beach (33139) ***(G-10658)***
Cory Aun 407 957-1133
3275 Burberry Pl Saint Cloud (34772) ***(G-15648)***
Cosmesis Skincare Inc 954 963-5090
3816 Hollywood Blvd Hollywood (33021) ***(G-5805)***
Cosmetic Corp of America Inc 305 883-8434
9750 Nw 91st Ct Medley (33178) ***(G-8636)***
Cosmetic Creations Inc 904 261-7831
1438 E Oak St Fernandina Beach (32034) ***(G-3733)***

Cosmetic Solutions LLC 561 226-8600
6101 Pk Of Commerce Blvd Boca Raton (33487) ***(G-490)***
Cosmetics, Lauderdale Lakes *Also called Kookie Kllection Kosmetics LLC* ***(G-8090)***
Cosmetics & Cleaners Intl LLC 305 592-5504
6000 Nw 97th Ave Unit 9 Doral (33178) ***(G-3310)***
Cosmo International Corp (PA) 954 798-4500
1341 W Newport Center Dr Deerfield Beach (33442) ***(G-2803)***
Cosmo International Corp 954 798-4500
1341 W Newport Center Dr Deerfield Beach (33442) ***(G-2804)***
Cosmo International Fragrances, Deerfield Beach *Also called Cosmo International Corp* ***(G-2803)***
Cosmo International Fragrances, Deerfield Beach *Also called Cosmo International Corp* ***(G-2804)***
Cosmo Leather Co, Miami *Also called Mario Kenny* ***(G-9949)***
Cosmo Pro, Daytona Beach *Also called Techno-Spa Manufacturing Inc* ***(G-2723)***
Cosner Manufacturing LLC 863 676-2579
511 N Scenic Hwy Lake Wales (33853) ***(G-7506)***
Cost Cast Inc 863 422-5617
1301 W Commerce Ave Haines City (33844) ***(G-5139)***
Cost Cast Aluminum Corp 863 422-5617
1301 W Commerce Ave Haines City (33844) ***(G-5140)***
Costa Del Mar, Daytona Beach *Also called Costa Inc* ***(G-2646)***
Costa Inc (HQ) 386 274-4000
2361 Mason Ave Ste 100 Daytona Beach (32117) ***(G-2646)***
Costa Industries LLC 813 453-3171
10312 Bloomngdale Ave # 1 Riverview (33578) ***(G-15268)***
Costal Fuels Marketing 904 358-6725
3425 Talleyrand Ave Jacksonville (32206) ***(G-6295)***
Costex Corporation (PA) 305 592-9769
5800 Nw 74th Ave Miami (33166) ***(G-9407)***
Costex Tractor Parts, Miami *Also called Costex Corporation* ***(G-9407)***
Coterie Care Inc 850 325-0422
701 Ferguson Dr Fort Walton Beach (32547) ***(G-4788)***
Cott Beverage, Tampa *Also called Refresco Beverages US Inc* ***(G-18048)***
Cotton Pickin Shirts Plus 850 435-3133
2211 N Pace Blvd Pensacola (32505) ***(G-14120)***
Cottonimagescom Inc 305 251-2560
10481 Nw 28th St Doral (33172) ***(G-3311)***
Couch Ready Mix Usa Inc 850 236-9042
3008 S Highway 95a Cantonment (32533) ***(G-1337)***
Couchman Printing Company 386 756-3052
1634 S Ridgewood Ave South Daytona (32119) ***(G-16800)***
Coughlan Products Corp 973 904-1500
3043 Perdue Ter Punta Gorda (33983) ***(G-15202)***
Coulombe Enterprises 407 366-4387
1293 N County Road 426 # 121 Oviedo (32765) ***(G-13424)***
Countdown Today Inc 415 420-2849
6001 Sw 70th St Apt 532 South Miami (33143) ***(G-16814)***
Counter 239 566-0644
9110 Strada Pl Ste 6130 Naples (34108) ***(G-11216)***
Counter Active Inc 813 626-0022
87 Sanchez Dr E Ponte Vedra (32082) ***(G-14923)***
Counter Impressions LLC 352 589-4966
12 S Bay St Eustis (32726) ***(G-3706)***
Counter Productions Inc 386 673-6500
1052 N Beach St Daytona Beach (32117) ***(G-2647)***
Counter Top Publishing Inc 941 321-5811
3715 35th St W Bradenton (34205) ***(G-1024)***
Countertop Solutions Inc 239 961-0663
3930 Domestic Ave Ste B Naples (34104) ***(G-11217)***
Country Cabinets 850 547-5477
1915 Adolph Whitaker Rd Bonifay (32425) ***(G-802)***
Country Club Concierge Mag Inc 904 223-0204
830-13 A1a N Ste 496 Ponte Vedra Beach (32082) ***(G-14938)***
Country Frits Juices Nurs Corp 786 302-8487
12100 Sw 177th Ave Miami (33196) ***(G-9408)***
Country Malt Group, Plant City *Also called Great Western Malting Co* ***(G-14437)***
Country Man S 352 472-8699
7100 Se State Road 26 Trenton (32693) ***(G-18482)***
Country Prime Meats USA Inc 250 396-4111
9695 W Broward Blvd Plantation (33324) ***(G-14503)***
Country Pure Foods Inc 904 734-4634
1915 N Woodland Blvd Deland (32720) ***(G-2965)***
Country Side T-Shirt 352 372-1015
2025 Ne County Road 234 Gainesville (32641) ***(G-4899)***
Country Store Interiors, Sarasota *Also called D W A Inc* ***(G-16401)***
Country Tees, Jupiter *Also called Southeast Marketing Concepts* ***(G-7118)***
Countryside Publishing Co Inc 813 925-0195
477 Commerce Blvd Oldsmar (34677) ***(G-12219)***
Countrywide Screen Printing 239 333-4020
14261 Jetport Loop W Fort Myers (33913) ***(G-4411)***
Countwise Llc (PA) 954 846-7011
1149 Sawgrs Corp Pkwy Sunrise (33323) ***(G-17109)***
County of Broward 954 357-7120
151 Sw 2nd St Fl 1 Fort Lauderdale (33301) ***(G-3919)***
County of Hernando 352 754-4042
238 Howell Ave Brooksville (34601) ***(G-1222)***
County of Orange 407 649-0076
400 E South St Orlando (32801) ***(G-12623)***
County of Sumter 352 689-4460
910 N Main St Ste 308 Bushnell (33513) ***(G-1316)***
County Plastics Corp 954 971-9205
1801 Nw 22nd St Pompano Beach (33069) ***(G-14649)***
Cover Publishing 239 482-4814
1385 Sautern Dr Fort Myers (33919) ***(G-4412)***
Cover Style, Doral *Also called Earth & Sea Wear LLC* ***(G-3338)***
Coverall Aluminum Inc 321 377-7874
1980 Dolgner Pl Ste 1068 Sanford (32771) ***(G-16026)***
Coverall Interiors 813 961-8261
5102 W Linebaugh Ave Tampa (33624) ***(G-17560)***
Covert Armor LLC 561 459-8077
1101 Clare Ave Ste 2 West Palm Beach (33401) ***(G-18851)***
Covington Plastics Inc 321 632-6775
427 Shearer Blvd Cocoa (32922) ***(G-2006)***
Covis Inc 954 315-3835
110 E Broward Blvd # 170 Fort Lauderdale (33301) ***(G-3920)***
Covocup LLC 855 204-5106
6621 19th St E Sarasota (34243) ***(G-16199)***
Cows USA, Cutler Bay *Also called Container Mfg Solutions* ***(G-2389)***
Cox Designer Windows Inc 727 847-1046
6810 Commerce Ave Port Richey (34668) ***(G-15047)***
Coyote Acquisition Co (HQ) 941 480-1600
1070 Technology Dr North Venice (34275) ***(G-11755)***
Cozy Bar 305 532-2699
500 S Pointe Dr Miami Beach (33139) ***(G-10659)***
CP Logging Inc 850 379-8698
20688 Ne Burlington Rd Hosford (32334) ***(G-6008)***
CP Royalties LLC 888 694-9265
301 W Platt St Tampa (33606) ***(G-17561)***
CP Vegetable Oil, Fort Lauderdale *Also called C P Vegetable Oil Inc* ***(G-3879)***
Cpc-Cryolab, Temple Terrace *Also called Circor International Inc* ***(G-18367)***
CPD BOTTLING CLOSURE, Boca Raton *Also called New Sentry Marketing Inc* ***(G-640)***
CPS Products Inc (HQ) 305 687-4121
3600 Enterprise Way Miramar (33025) ***(G-10981)***
Crabil Manufacturing Inc 727 209-8368
9600 18th St N Saint Petersburg (33716) ***(G-15754)***
Craemer US Corporation 727 312-8859
2927 Pinewood Run Palm Harbor (34684) ***(G-13731)***
Craig Armstrong 786 319-6514
1770 Normandy Dr Apt 2 Miami Beach (33141) ***(G-10660)***
Craig Catamaran Corporation 407 290-8778
4333 Silver Star Rd # 1 Orlando (32808) ***(G-12624)***
Crain Ventures Inc 407 933-1820
2775 Old Dixie Hwy Ste C Kissimmee (34744) ***(G-7233)***
Cramco Inc 305 634-7500
5600 Nw 36th Ave Miami (33142) ***(G-9409)***
Cranco Industries Inc 321 690-2695
1710 Baldwin St Rockledge (32955) ***(G-15399)***
Crandon Electric Co, Ocala *Also called Crandon Enterprises Inc* ***(G-11910)***
Crandon Enterprises Inc 352 873-8400
255 Sw 96th Ln Ocala (34476) ***(G-11910)***
Crane Co 941 480-9101
730 Commerce Dr Venice (34292) ***(G-18538)***
Crane Electronics Inc 850 244-0043
84 Hill Ave Nw Fort Walton Beach (32548) ***(G-4789)***
Crane Environmental Inc 941 480-9101
730 Commerce Dr Venice (34292) ***(G-18539)***
Crane Environmental Products, Venice *Also called Crane Environmental Inc* ***(G-18539)***
Crankshaft Rebuilders Inc 407 323-4870
1200 Albright Rd Sanford (32771) ***(G-16027)***
Crawford Glass Door Co 954 480-6820
3301 Sw 13th Dr Ste B Deerfield Beach (33442) ***(G-2805)***
Crawfords Custom Woodwork 904 782-1375
21535 Us Highway 301 N Lawtey (32058) ***(G-8124)***
Crazy 4 Signs LLC 813 239-3085
4819 Allen Rd Zephyrhills (33541) ***(G-19512)***
CRC Press LLC (HQ) 561 994-0555
6000 Broken Sound Pkwy Nw # 300 Boca Raton (33487) ***(G-491)***
CRC Press LLC 561 361-6000
3848 Fau Blvd Ste 310 Boca Raton (33431) ***(G-492)***
Creaction Industry Llc 305 779-4851
8710 Nw 100th St Medley (33178) ***(G-8637)***
Creaction Organize, Medley *Also called Creaction Industry Llc* ***(G-8637)***
Creamer Corp 850 265-2700
338 W Highway 388 Panama City (32409) ***(G-13888)***
Creaprint Usa Corp 786 369-7398
8950 Sw 74th Ct Ste 1406 Miami (33156) ***(G-9410)***
Create and Company Inc 813 393-8778
1023 E Columbus Dr Tampa (33605) ***(G-17562)***
Createch Machine & Design, Lakeland *Also called High Performance Holdings Ltd* ***(G-7705)***
Createco, Tampa *Also called Create and Company Inc* ***(G-17562)***
Creating Tech Solutions LLC (PA) 727 914-3001
5250 140th Ave N Clearwater (33760) ***(G-1641)***
Creating Tech Solutions LLC 727 914-3001
5250 140th Ave N Clearwater (33760) ***(G-1642)***

ALPHABETIC

Creating Tech Solutions LLC 727 914-3001
5250 140th Ave N Clearwater (33760) ***(G-1643)***
Creations In Cabinetry Inc 386 237-3082
2 Market Pl Palm Coast (32137) ***(G-13690)***
Creative Auto Boutique Llc 407 654-7300
17949 W Colonial Dr Oakland (34787) ***(G-11768)***
Creative Biz Center Inc 954 918-7322
7860 W Commercial Blvd Lauderhill (33351) ***(G-8106)***
Creative Builder Services Inc 813 818-7100
6422 Harney Rd Ste F Tampa (33610) ***(G-17563)***
Creative Cabinet Concepts Inc 239 939-1313
7947 Drew Cir Fort Myers (33967) ***(G-4413)***
Creative Canvas Centl Fla Inc 407 661-1211
436 Wekiva Rapids Dr Altamonte Springs (32714) ***(G-39)***
Creative Car Coats 813 886-2589
5553 W Waters Ave Tampa (33634) ***(G-17564)***
Creative Carbide Inc (PA) 239 567-0041
7880 Interstate Ct Unit A Fort Myers (33917) ***(G-4414)***
Creative Clture Mdia Group LLC 786 237-0206
5740 Sw 116th St Coral Gables (33156) ***(G-2134)***
Creative Coating LLC 407 346-5725
1058 Soaring Eagle Ln Kissimmee (34746) ***(G-7234)***
Creative Color Printing Inc 954 701-6763
3721 Sw 47th Ave Ste 302 Davie (33314) ***(G-2510)***
Creative Colors International, Brandon *Also called Patrick German Industries Inc* ***(G-1171)***
Creative Colors International 239 573-8883
1221 Se 9th Ter Cape Coral (33990) ***(G-1407)***
Creative Concepts Intl LLC 888 530-7904
16960 Alico Mission Way Fort Myers (33908) ***(G-4415)***
Creative Concepts Orlando Inc 407 260-1435
1650 Forest Ave Ste 100 Longwood (32750) ***(G-8268)***
Creative Counters, Jacksonville *Also called Creative Countertops Inc* ***(G-6296)***
Creative Countertops Inc 904 387-2800
4768 Highway Ave Jacksonville (32254) ***(G-6296)***
Creative Curbing 352 347-3329
15340 Se 73rd Ave Summerfield (34491) ***(G-17058)***
Creative Custom Stairs 941 505-0336
3857 Acline Rd Unit 104 Punta Gorda (33950) ***(G-15203)***
Creative Data Solutions Inc 407 333-4770
1540 Intl Pkwy Ste 2000 Lake Mary (32746) ***(G-7407)***
Creative Design and Print 239 325-9163
809 Walkerbilt Rd Ste 4 Naples (34110) ***(G-11218)***
Creative Energies Inc 352 351-9448
1805 Ne 19th Ave Ocala (34470) ***(G-11911)***
Creative Events and Exhibits (PA) 407 851-4754
405 Fairlane Ave Orlando (32809) ***(G-12625)***
Creative Glassworks 904 860-0865
2062 Saint Martins Dr W Jacksonville (32246) ***(G-6297)***
Creative Home and Kitchen LLC 786 233-8621
2000 Nw 97th Ave Ste 112 Doral (33172) ***(G-3312)***
Creative Images Embrodiery 904 730-5660
2989 Philips Hwy Jacksonville (32207) ***(G-6298)***
Creative Lighting & Power LLC 407 967-0957
330 Winston Creek Pkwy G Lakeland (33810) ***(G-7664)***
Creative Lighting & Solar, Lakeland *Also called Creative Lighting & Power LLC* ***(G-7664)***
Creative Loafing Inc (HQ) 813 739-4800
1911 N 13th St Ste W200 Tampa (33605) ***(G-17565)***
Creative Loafing Inc 941 365-6776
1911 N 13th St Fl 1 Tampa (33605) ***(G-17566)***
Creative Loafing Sarasota, Tampa *Also called Weekly Planet of Sarasota Inc* ***(G-18252)***
Creative Mailbox Designs, Tampa *Also called Creative Builder Services Inc* ***(G-17563)***
Creative Mailbox Sign Designs, Tampa *Also called Creative Sign Designs LLC* ***(G-17567)***
Creative Marine 239 437-1010
6261 Arc Way Fort Myers (33966) ***(G-4416)***
Creative Metal Products, Boynton Beach *Also called Natural Beauty Wood Products* ***(G-937)***
Creative Metal Studio Inc (PA) 321 206-6112
2312 Clark St Ste 3 Apopka (32703) ***(G-127)***
Creative Metal Works, Holt *Also called Preston Works Inc* ***(G-5949)***
Creative Millwork Inc 305 885-5474
7635 W 28th Ave Bay 3 Hialeah (33016) ***(G-5357)***
Creative Molding Corp 786 251-4241
2949 Nw 97th Ct Doral (33172) ***(G-3313)***
Creative Monogramming, Clearwater *Also called John & Betsy Hovland* ***(G-1744)***
Creative Printing, Sebring *Also called Creative Services of Centl Fla* ***(G-16684)***
Creative Printing, Pompano Beach *Also called FGA Printing* ***(G-14689)***
Creative Printing & Publishing, Sanford *Also called Paragon Products Inc* ***(G-16099)***
Creative Printing Bay Cnty Inc 850 784-1645
1328 Harrison Ave Panama City (32401) ***(G-13889)***
Creative Promotional Products 407 383-7114
1325 E Harding St Orlando (32806) ***(G-12626)***
Creative Prtg & Screen Designs, Panama City *Also called Creative Printing Bay Cnty Inc* ***(G-13889)***
Creative Prtg Grphic Dsign Inc 407 855-0202
1009 Pine St Orlando (32824) ***(G-12627)***
Creative Routes Press 561 213-9800
2815 Hampton Cir E Delray Beach (33445) ***(G-3066)***
Creative Services of Centl Fla 863 385-8383
2023 Us Highway 27 N Sebring (33870) ***(G-16684)***
Creative Shirts Intl Inc 954 351-0909
5214 Ne 12th Ave Oakland Park (33334) ***(G-11792)***
Creative Sign Designs LLC (PA) 813 818-7100
12801 Commodity Pl Tampa (33626) ***(G-17567)***
Creative Signs 786 636-6969
2340 Nw 102nd Pl Doral (33172) ***(G-3314)***
Creative Signs Inc 407 293-9393
2301 N Hiawassee Rd Apopka (32703) ***(G-128)***
Creative Solid Surfacing, Fort Myers *Also called Creative Cabinet Concepts Inc* ***(G-4413)***
Creative Teaching Cabinets 754 205-0886
4340 Nw 19th Ave Deerfield Beach (33064) ***(G-2806)***
Creative Tech Sarasota Inc 941 371-2743
5959 Palmer Blvd Sarasota (34232) ***(G-16395)***
Creative Vtran Productions LLC 407 656-2743
2400 Mtland Ctr Pkwy Ste Maitland (32751) ***(G-8463)***
Creative Wood Graphics, Safety Harbor *Also called Signature Signs Inc* ***(G-15503)***
Creative Woodwork Miami Inc 305 634-3100
6001 Nw 37th Ave Miami (33142) ***(G-9411)***
Creative Woodworking Concepts 727 937-4165
905 Rivo Pl Tarpon Springs (34689) ***(G-18290)***
Crenshaw Die & Manufacturing 949 475-5505
100 Zaharias Cir Daytona Beach (32124) ***(G-2648)***
Creonix LLC 941 758-3340
30167 Power Line Rd Brooksville (34602) ***(G-1223)***
Crescent Garden, Miami *Also called Dotchi LLC* ***(G-9483)***
Crescent Garden, Hollywood *Also called Darnel Inc* ***(G-5809)***
Cress Chemical & Equipment Co 407 425-2846
519 19th St Orlando (32805) ***(G-12628)***
Crestview Ready Mix, Fort Walton Beach *Also called Fort Walton Concrete Co* ***(G-4800)***
Crestview Ready Mix Inc 850 682-6117
1070 Farmer St Crestview (32539) ***(G-2345)***
Creta Granite & Marble Inc 954 956-9993
1900 Nw 33rd St Ste 10 Pompano Beach (33064) ***(G-14650)***
Crevalle Boats, Wildwood *Also called Littoral Marine LLC* ***(G-19197)***
Crf Group Inc 954 428-7446
4716 N Powerline Rd Pompano Beach (33073) ***(G-14651)***
Crh Americas Inc 843 672-5553
500 S Florida Ave Ste 240 Lakeland (33801) ***(G-7665)***
Crichlow Data Sciences Inc 863 616-1222
2500 Drane Feld Rd Ste 10 Lakeland (33811) ***(G-7666)***
Cricket Mini Golf Carts Inc 386 220-3536
1575 Avi Ctr Pkwy Ste 432 Daytona Beach (32114) ***(G-2649)***
Critical Coatings Inc 813 515-7119
1307 E Clifton St Tampa (33604) ***(G-17568)***
Critical Disposables Inc 407 330-1154
700 Martin L King Jr Blvd Sanford (32771) ***(G-16028)***
Critical Review Journals, Crj, Boca Raton *Also called CRC Press LLC* ***(G-491)***
Croft Publishing Inc 352 473-3159
5006 County Road 214 Keystone Heights (32656) ***(G-7206)***
Crofton & Sons, Tampa *Also called Uncle Johns Pride LLC* ***(G-18216)***
Crom Corporation (PA) 352 372-3436
250 Sw 36th Ter Gainesville (32607) ***(G-4900)***
Cromer International Press, Haines City *Also called Cromer Printing Inc* ***(G-5141)***
Cromer Printing Inc 863 422-8651
24 N 6th St Haines City (33844) ***(G-5141)***
Crompco Inc 954 584-8488
6531 Nw 13th Ct Plantation (33313) ***(G-14504)***
Cronus Litho LLC 239 325-4846
9010 Strada Stell Ct # 103 Naples (34109) ***(G-11219)***
Crop LLC 941 923-8640
2320 Gulf Gate Dr Sarasota (34231) ***(G-16396)***
Cross Atlantic Commodities Inc (PA) 954 678-0698
4581 Weston Rd Ste 273 Weston (33331) ***(G-19118)***
Cross City Lumber LLC 352 578-8078
59 Ne 132nd Ave Cross City (32628) ***(G-2363)***
Cross City Veneer Company Inc 352 498-3226
106 Ne 180th St Cross City (32628) ***(G-2364)***
Cross Construction Svcs Inc 813 907-1013
25221 Wesley Chapel Blvd Lutz (33559) ***(G-8379)***
Cross Key Marine Canvas Inc 305 451-1302
103761 Overseas Hwy Key Largo (33037) ***(G-7167)***
Cross Match Technologies Inc (HQ) 561 622-1650
3950 Rca Blvd Ste 5001 Palm Beach Gardens (33410) ***(G-13583)***
Crossroads Industries LLC 305 967-8116
12807 Sw 42nd St Miami (33175) ***(G-9412)***
Crosstac Corporation 406 522-9300
12605 Nw 115th Ave B-104 Medley (33178) ***(G-8638)***
Crowder Custom Rods Inc 772 220-8108
3040 Se Dominica Ter Stuart (34997) ***(G-16928)***
Crowder Rods, Stuart *Also called Crowder Custom Rods Inc* ***(G-16928)***
Crowe Manufacturing 813 334-1921
5203 S Lois Ave Tampa (33611) ***(G-17569)***
Crowell Companies, Tampa *Also called Crowell Marine Inc* ***(G-17570)***
Crowell Marine Inc 813 236-3625
7305 N Florida Ave Tampa (33604) ***(G-17570)***
Crown Building Systems, Jacksonville *Also called Crown Products Company Inc* ***(G-6301)***
Crown Castle Intl Corp 305 552-3675
9250 W Flagler St Miami (33174) ***(G-9413)***

Crown Leao Industries Inc...561 866-1218
150 E Palmetto Park Rd # 80 Boca Raton (33432) ***(G-493)***
Crown Plating Inc...904 783-6640
5285 Ramona Blvd Jacksonville (32205) ***(G-6299)***
Crown Printing Inc...863 682-4881
1303 E Main St Lakeland (33801) ***(G-7667)***
Crown Products LLC (PA)...954 917-1118
935 Nw 31st Ave Ste 4 Pompano Beach (33069) ***(G-14652)***
Crown Products Company Inc (PA)...904 737-7144
6390 Philips Hwy Jacksonville (32216) ***(G-6300)***
Crown Products Company Inc...904 924-8340
3545 New Kings Rd Jacksonville (32209) ***(G-6301)***
Crown Seamless Gutters Inc...561 748-9919
7880 Coconut Blvd West Palm Beach (33412) ***(G-18852)***
Crown Welding & Fabg Inc...941 737-6844
6030 Wauchula Rd Myakka City (34251) ***(G-11142)***
Crucial Collision Prod LLC...321 501-1722
3334 Henry St Melbourne (32901) ***(G-8798)***
Cruise Car Inc...941 929-1630
1227 Hardin Ave Sarasota (34243) ***(G-16200)***
Cruising Gide Publications Inc...727 733-5322
2418 Summerwood Ct Dunedin (34698) ***(G-3575)***
Crumbliss Manufacturing Co...239 693-8588
5812 Enterprise Pkwy Fort Myers (33905) ***(G-4417)***
Crumbliss Test Equipment, Fort Myers *Also called Crumbliss Manufacturing Co* ***(G-4417)***
Crunchi LLC...772 600-8082
7671 Sw Ellipse Way Stuart (34997) ***(G-16929)***
Crusellas & Co Inc...305 261-9580
7014 Sw 4th St Miami (33144) ***(G-9414)***
Crustys Bread Bakery...727 937-9041
438 Athens St Tarpon Springs (34689) ***(G-18291)***
Cryntel Enterprises Ltd Inc...954 577-7844
10412 W State Road 84 # 1 Davie (33324) ***(G-2511)***
Cryoderm, Margate *Also called Ahc Ventures Corp* ***(G-8533)***
Cryothrapy Pain Rlief Pdts Inc...954 364-8192
3460 Laurel Oaks Ln Hollywood (33021) ***(G-5806)***
Crystal Art of Florida Inc...305 885-5358
11555 Heron Bay Blvd # 2 Coral Springs (33076) ***(G-2235)***
Crystal Communications Inc...954 474-3072
5600 Nw 102nd Ave Ste M Sunrise (33351) ***(G-17110)***
Crystal Geyser, Orlando *Also called Cg Roxane LLC* ***(G-12573)***
Crystal Panepinto Inc...941 475-9235
667 Palomino Trl Englewood (34223) ***(G-3674)***
Crystal Photonics Inc...407 328-9111
5525 Benchmark Ln Sanford (32773) ***(G-16029)***
Crystal Pool Service Inc...954 444-8282
10718 Nw 53rd St Sunrise (33351) ***(G-17111)***
Crystal River Quarries, Crystal River *Also called Colitz Mining Co Inc* ***(G-2374)***
Crystal River Quarries Inc...352 795-2828
7040 N Suncoast Blvd Crystal River (34428) ***(G-2375)***
Crystal River Water Pollution...352 795-3199
302 Nw 11th St Crystal River (34428) ***(G-2376)***
Crystek Crystals Corporation...239 561-3311
16850 Oriole Rd Ste 3 Fort Myers (33912) ***(G-4418)***
Csa International Inc...561 746-7946
759 Parkway Jupiter (33477) ***(G-7020)***
Csba Digital Printing...813 482-1608
3601 Bay Heights Way Tampa (33611) ***(G-17571)***
CSC Aerospace Corporation...203 300-9760
9737 Nw 41st St Doral (33178) ***(G-3315)***
CSC Racing Corporation...248 548-5727
15819 Guild Ct B Jupiter (33478) ***(G-7021)***
CSC Textron...954 776-5862
2011 S Perimeter Rd Fort Lauderdale (33309) ***(G-3921)***
Csg, Orlando *Also called Ddci Inc* ***(G-12659)***
Csi Aerospace Inc...954 961-9800
3000 Taft St Hollywood (33021) ***(G-5807)***
Csi Home Decor Inc...754 301-2147
5365 N Hiatus Rd Sunrise (33351) ***(G-17112)***
Csl of America Inc...407 849-7070
1900 S Orange Blossom Trl Orlando (32805) ***(G-12629)***
Csmc Inc...407 246-1567
4498 Vineland Rd Orlando (32811) ***(G-12630)***
Cso Systems Inc...941 355-5653
4139 N Washington Blvd Sarasota (34234) ***(G-16397)***
CSR Enterprise Ltd...954 624-2284
370 Nw 123rd St North Miami (33168) ***(G-11635)***
Csr Performance Products, Mc Alpin *Also called Competition Specialties Inc* ***(G-8599)***
CST USA Inc...404 695-2249
20533 Biscayne Blvd # 565 Miami (33180) ***(G-9415)***
Csw Cabinet Services Inc...727 267-1767
17711 Overstreet Ln Spring Hill (34610) ***(G-16871)***
CT Hydraulics Inc...724 342-3089
1845 Ardsley Way Sanibel (33957) ***(G-16145)***
CT Natural...813 996-6443
2908 W Arch St Tampa (33607) ***(G-17572)***
Cte Jv LLC...407 894-5575
12802 Science Dr Ste 300 Orlando (32826) ***(G-12631)***
CTI Group Worldwide Svcs Inc...954 568-5900
2455 E Sunrise Blvd # 1100 Fort Lauderdale (33304) ***(G-3922)***
Ctm Biomedical LLC...561 650-4027
78 Sw 7th St Ste 500 Miami (33130) ***(G-9416)***
Ctr Industries...321 264-1458
3980 Hammock Rd Mims (32754) ***(G-10950)***
Ctts, Auburndale *Also called Commercial Truck & Trailer Sls* ***(G-236)***
CU Holdings LLC...904 483-5700
5515 W 5th St Jacksonville (32254) ***(G-6302)***
Cuban Press...305 304-9419
526 Sw 98th Ct Miami (33174) ***(G-9417)***
Cubco Inc...386 254-2706
605 Commercial Dr Daytona Beach (32117) ***(G-2650)***
Cubic Advnced Lrng Sltions Inc...407 859-7410
2001 W Oak Ridge Rd Orlando (32809) ***(G-12632)***
Cubic Corporation...407 859-7410
3862 Quadrangle Blvd # 100 Orlando (32817) ***(G-12633)***
Cubic Simulation Systems Inc...407 641-2037
2001 W Oak Ridge Rd # 100 Orlando (32809) ***(G-12634)***
Cubic Transportation Systems, Orlando *Also called Cubic Simulation Systems Inc* ***(G-12634)***
Cubos LLC...786 299-2671
13832 Sw 142nd Ave Miami (33186) ***(G-9418)***
Cue & Case, Jacksonville *Also called Lucas 5135 Inc* ***(G-6566)***
Cug LLC...786 858-0499
950 S Pine Island Rd Plantation (33324) ***(G-14505)***
Culinary Concepts Inc...407 228-0069
2215 Tradeport Dr Orlando (32824) ***(G-12635)***
Culture Cartel Media Inc...407 680-8923
105 Rockwood Way Sanford (32771) ***(G-16030)***
Cummins Inc...407 298-2080
4820 N Orange Blossom Trl Orlando (32810) ***(G-12636)***
Cummins Inc...352 861-1122
321 Sw 52nd Ave Ocala (34474) ***(G-11912)***
Cummins-Wagner-Florida LLC (HQ)...813 630-2220
9834 Currie Davis Dr Tampa (33619) ***(G-17573)***
Cup Plus USA...321 972-1968
4440 Metric Dr Winter Park (32792) ***(G-19397)***
Cupcake Inc...407 644-7800
105 Candace Dr Unit 109 Maitland (32751) ***(G-8464)***
Cupcake Girls Dessert Company...904 372-4579
1516 3rd St N Jacksonville Beach (32250) ***(G-6941)***
Cupcake Heaven...352 610-4433
2721 Forest Rd Spring Hill (34606) ***(G-16850)***
Cupcakes Frsting Sprinkles LLC...305 769-3393
2301 Nw 155th St Opa Locka (33054) ***(G-12304)***
Cupcakes On Main...321 693-7236
3065 Westwood Dr Titusville (32796) ***(G-18426)***
Curallux LLC...786 888-1875
1715 Nw 82nd Ave Doral (33126) ***(G-3316)***
Curly Girlz Creations...386 960-3536
10410 Sw 98th Ter Ocala (34481) ***(G-11913)***
Current...954 262-8455
3301 College Ave Asa105 Davie (33314) ***(G-2512)***
Current Products Company LLC...850 435-4994
1995 Hollywood Ave Pensacola (32505) ***(G-14121)***
Curry & Sons Inc...305 296-8781
3201 Flagler Ave Ste 504 Key West (33040) ***(G-7185)***
Curry & Sons Prtg & Off Sup, Key West *Also called Curry & Sons Inc* ***(G-7185)***
Curry Cabinetry Inc...813 321-3650
4831 E Broadway Ave Tampa (33605) ***(G-17574)***
Curtis K Foulks...239 454-9663
2240 Hemingway Dr Ste J Fort Myers (33912) ***(G-4419)***
Curvco Steel Structures Corp...800 956-6341
14545 S Military Trl H Delray Beach (33484) ***(G-3067)***
Cusano's Baking Co., Orlando *Also called Cusanos Italian Bakery Inc* ***(G-12637)***
Cusanos Italian Bakery Inc...786 506-4281
1904 Premier Row Orlando (32809) ***(G-12637)***
Cushion Solutions Incorporated...813 253-2131
802 N Rome Ave Tampa (33606) ***(G-17575)***
Cushybeds, Pompano Beach *Also called Cyber Group USA LLC* ***(G-14655)***
Custom Aerospace Machine, Palm Bay *Also called Group E Holdings Inc* ***(G-13515)***
Custom Agronomics Inc...772 223-0775
2300 Sw Poma Dr Palm City (34990) ***(G-13650)***
Custom Bag Designs, Miami Beach *Also called Brush Cases LLC* ***(G-10649)***
Custom Beach Huts LLC...305 439-3991
800 S Douglas Rd Ste 300 Coral Gables (33134) ***(G-2135)***
Custom Built Screen Enclosures...239 242-0224
765 Ne 19th Pl Unit 2 Cape Coral (33909) ***(G-1408)***
Custom Button Company, Melbourne *Also called Promo Daddy LLC* ***(G-8914)***
Custom Cabinet Doors & More In...954 318-1881
1530 Nw 23rd Ave Fort Lauderdale (33311) ***(G-3923)***
Custom Cabinet Factory Inc...352 429-7722
642 W Broad St Groveland (34736) ***(G-5094)***
Custom Cabinets...727 392-1676
11060 70th Ave Seminole (33772) ***(G-16745)***
Custom Cabinets By Jensen LLC...813 250-0286
1704 W Fig St Tampa (33606) ***(G-17576)***
Custom Cabinets Design Inc...561 210-3423
5000 Nw 3rd Ave Deerfield Beach (33064) ***(G-2807)***

ALPHABETIC

Custom Cabinets Inc...941 366-0428
7350 Deer Crossing Ct Sarasota (34240) ***(G-16398)***
Custom Cabinets SW Florida LLC...239 415-3350
5929 Youngquist Rd Fort Myers (33912) ***(G-4420)***
Custom Cable Crafters, Palm Coast *Also called Managed Data Assoc Inc* ***(G-13702)***
Custom Cable Industries, Tampa *Also called Amphenol Custom Cable Inc* ***(G-17423)***
Custom Canvas and Cushions...561 800-8541
176 E 21st St Riviera Beach (33404) ***(G-15315)***
Custom Carpentry Plus LLC...305 972-3735
9801 Bel Aire Dr Cutler Bay (33157) ***(G-2390)***
Custom Carts of Lakewood Ranch, Bradenton *Also called Custom Carts of Sarasota LLC* ***(G-1025)***
Custom Carts of Sarasota LLC...941 953-4445
4515 15th St E Bradenton (34203) ***(G-1025)***
Custom Cft Windows & Doors Inc...407 834-5400
1436 Northern Way Winter Springs (32708) ***(G-19470)***
Custom Colors Powder Coating...941 953-7997
1930 21st St Sarasota (34234) ***(G-16399)***
Custom Comfort Medtek LLC...407 332-0062
3939 Forsyth Rd Ste A Winter Park (32792) ***(G-19398)***
Custom Control Solutions Inc...850 937-8902
1520 Power Blvd Cantonment (32533) ***(G-1338)***
Custom Controls Technology Inc...305 805-3700
2230 W 77th St Hialeah (33016) ***(G-5358)***
Custom Cornhole Boards Inc...407 203-6886
6169 Cyril Ave Orlando (32809) ***(G-12638)***
Custom Craft Laminates Inc...813 877-7100
4705 N Manhattan Ave Tampa (33614) ***(G-17577)***
Custom Crafters...954 792-6119
170 Sw 5th St Pompano Beach (33060) ***(G-14653)***
Custom Crate & Logistics Co...954 527-5742
280 Sw 33rd St Fort Lauderdale (33315) ***(G-3924)***
Custom Cultered Marble Inc...239 823-8241
3052 Commerce Ave Spring Hill (34609) ***(G-16851)***
Custom Cut Rubber...979 422-2511
617 Acorn Ct Saint Johns (32259) ***(G-15675)***
Custom Door Direct Llc...813 248-5757
1100 N 50th St Bldg 2 Tampa (33619) ***(G-17578)***
Custom Doors & Specialties...954 763-4214
2637 N Andrews Ave Wilton Manors (33311) ***(G-19217)***
Custom Drawers of Swfl LLC...239 226-1699
2861 Work Dr Fort Myers (33916) ***(G-4421)***
Custom Engraving Company, Melbourne *Also called Imprint Promotions LLC* ***(G-8850)***
Custom Fab Inc (HQ)...407 859-3954
109 5th St Orlando (32824) ***(G-12639)***
Custom Fabrication Inc...813 754-7571
2604 E Us Highway 92 Plant City (33566) ***(G-14421)***
Custom Fbrications of Freeport...850 729-0500
479 Old Florida Sr 10 Rd Valparaiso (32580) ***(G-18509)***
Custom Flange Pipe LLC...863 353-6602
3700 W Lake Hamilton Dr Winter Haven (33881) ***(G-19316)***
Custom Grafix Industries Inc...727 530-7300
12571 66th St Largo (33773) ***(G-7929)***
Custom Graphics & Sign Design...904 264-7667
230 Industrial Loop S Orange Park (32073) ***(G-12387)***
Custom Graphics and Plates Inc...407 696-5448
782 Big Tree Dr Unit 100 Longwood (32750) ***(G-8269)***
Custom Graphics Inc...954 563-6756
1801 Green Rd Ste B Deerfield Beach (33064) ***(G-2808)***
Custom Illusionz...386 330-5245
319 Howard St E Live Oak (32064) ***(G-8229)***
Custom Install Solutions Inc...916 601-1190
3632 Nw 5th Ter Boca Raton (33431) ***(G-494)***
Custom Instruments LLC...561 735-9971
711 N Railroad Ave Unit 3 Boynton Beach (33435) ***(G-894)***
Custom Klosets & Cabinets Inc...813 246-4806
6403 N 50th St Tampa (33610) ***(G-17579)***
Custom Mailboxes and Signs...239 738-9321
13319 5th St Fort Myers (33905) ***(G-4422)***
Custom Manufacturing Corp...305 863-1001
9324 Nw 102nd St Medley (33178) ***(G-8639)***
Custom Manufacturing Inc...607 569-2738
1720 S Tranquil Ave Inverness (34450) ***(G-6084)***
Custom Marble Works Inc...813 620-0475
1905 N 43rd St Tampa (33605) ***(G-17580)***
Custom Marine Components Inc...904 221-6412
13755 Atlantic Blvd Jacksonville (32225) ***(G-6303)***
Custom Marine Concepts Inc (PA)...954 782-1111
2500 Ne 5th Ave Pompano Beach (33064) ***(G-14654)***
Custom Marine Joinery Inc...954 822-6057
4032 Ne 5th Ter Oakland Park (33334) ***(G-11793)***
Custom Masters Inc...407 331-4634
401 Lake Bennett Ct Longwood (32750) ***(G-8270)***
Custom Medical Products Inc...407 865-7211
3909 E Semrn Blvd Ste 599 Apopka (32703) ***(G-129)***
Custom Medical Systems Inc...941 722-3434
404 10th Ave W Palmetto (34221) ***(G-13794)***
Custom Metal Building Products, Tampa *Also called Corrugated Industries Fla Inc* ***(G-17559)***
Custom Metal Creations LLC...772 807-0000
3106 S Brocksmith Rd Fort Pierce (34945) ***(G-4689)***
Custom Metal Designs Inc...407 656-7771
921 W Oakland Ave Oakland (34760) ***(G-11769)***
Custom Metal Fabricators Inc...407 841-8551
1415 Long St Orlando (32805) ***(G-12640)***
Custom Metal Specialties Inc...727 522-3986
3921 69th Ave N Pinellas Park (33781) ***(G-14341)***
Custom Mfg & Engrg Inc...727 548-0522
3690 70th Ave N Pinellas Park (33781) ***(G-14342)***
Custom Mica Furniture Inc...305 888-8480
575 W 28th St Hialeah (33010) ***(G-5359)***
Custom Molding & Casework Inc...407 709-7377
1650 Travers Ln Deltona (32738) ***(G-3167)***
Custom Mosaics Inc...954 610-9436
11110 W Oakland Park Blvd Sunrise (33351) ***(G-17113)***
Custom Plastic Card Company...954 426-1331
1801 Green Rd Ste A Deerfield Beach (33064) ***(G-2809)***
Custom Plastic Developments...407 847-3054
2710 N John Young Pkwy Kissimmee (34741) ***(G-7235)***
Custom Plastic Fabricators...813 884-5200
6201 Johns Rd Ste 8 Tampa (33634) ***(G-17581)***
Custom Powder Coating LLC...386 758-3973
1129 Se Ormond Witt Rd Lake City (32025) ***(G-7352)***
Custom Production, Crestview *Also called Strive Development Corporation* ***(G-2360)***
Custom Quality Mfg Inc...813 290-0805
5015 Tampa West Blvd Tampa (33634) ***(G-17582)***
Custom Screen Printing Florida, Opa Locka *Also called John M Caldwell Distrg Co Inc* ***(G-12329)***
Custom Sign & Awning...727 210-0941
4502 107th Cir N Ste D Clearwater (33762) ***(G-1644)***
Custom Stainless Stl Eqp Inc...305 627-6049
16215 Nw 15th Ave Miami (33169) ***(G-9419)***
Custom Stucco Inc...941 650-5649
1921 Michigan Ave Englewood (34224) ***(G-3659)***
Custom Tin Works LLC...352 728-1788
5318 James Rd Fruitland Park (34731) ***(G-4864)***
Custom Trade Printing.com, Auburndale *Also called Di Jam Holdings Inc* ***(G-239)***
Custom Truss LLC...561 266-3451
510 Industrial Ave Boynton Beach (33426) ***(G-895)***
Custom Tube Products Inc...386 426-0670
317 Base Leg Dr Edgewater (32132) ***(G-3620)***
Custom Wall Systems Inc...772 408-3006
9495 22nd St Vero Beach (32966) ***(G-18614)***
Custom Watersports Eqp Inc...941 753-9949
1218 50th Avenue Plz W Bradenton (34207) ***(G-1026)***
Custom WD Architectural Mllwk...786 290-5412
13119 Sw 122nd Ave Miami (33186) ***(G-9420)***
Custom WD Designs of Pensacola...850 476-9663
3335 Addison Dr Pensacola (32514) ***(G-14122)***
Custom Wheel, Holly Hill *Also called CC Machine Inc* ***(G-5757)***
Custom Window Systems, Ocala *Also called Cws Holding Company LLC* ***(G-11915)***
Custom Window Systems Inc...352 368-6922
1900 Sw 44th Ave Ocala (34474) ***(G-11914)***
Custom Wldg & Fabrication Inc...863 967-1000
364 Recker Hwy Auburndale (33823) ***(G-237)***
Custom Wood Products Inc...904 737-6906
3811 University Blvd W # 10 Jacksonville (32217) ***(G-6304)***
Custom Woodworking...850 319-4440
4312 Brewton Ln Panama City (32404) ***(G-13890)***
Customer First Inc Naples...239 949-8518
10940 Harmony Park Dr Bonita Springs (34135) ***(G-827)***
Customer Success LLC...386 265-4882
1892 Clubhouse Dr Port Orange (32128) ***(G-15014)***
Customfab Inc...786 339-9158
23601 Sw 133rd Ave Homestead (33032) ***(G-5960)***
Cut Services LLC...305 560-0905
8264 Nw 58th St Doral (33166) ***(G-3317)***
Cutler Hammer, Tampa *Also called Eaton Corporation* ***(G-17628)***
Cutoutz.com, Riviera Beach *Also called D I H Corporation* ***(G-15317)***
Cutrale Citrus Juices, Auburndale *Also called Cutrale Farms Inc* ***(G-238)***
Cutrale Citrus Juices USA Inc...352 728-7800
11 Cloud St Leesburg (34748) ***(G-8149)***
Cutrale Farms Inc...863 965-5000
602 Mckean St Auburndale (33823) ***(G-238)***
Cutting Edge Archtctral Mldngs, Sarasota *Also called Cutting Edge Moldings LLC* ***(G-16201)***
Cutting Edge Archtctral Mldngs...941 727-1111
7282 55th Ave E Pmb 176 Bradenton (34203) ***(G-1027)***
Cutting Edge Mch Fbrcation LLC...321 626-0588
534 Saint Johns St Bldg C Cocoa (32922) ***(G-2007)***
Cutting Edge Moldings LLC...734 649-1500
7116 24th Ct E Sarasota (34243) ***(G-16201)***
Cutting Edge Sgns Grphics of P...727 546-3700
12795 49th St N Clearwater (33762) ***(G-1645)***
Cv Technology Inc...561 694-9588
15852 Mercantile Ct # 100 Jupiter (33478) ***(G-7022)***
Cve Reporter Inc...954 421-5566
3501 West Dr Deerfield Beach (33442) ***(G-2810)***
Cvg Aerospace LLC...786 293-9923
13500 Sw 134th Ave Ste 6 Miami (33186) ***(G-9421)***

Cvista LLC....813 405-3000
4333 Garden Vista Dr Riverview (33578) *(G-15269)*
Cw21 Inc....813 754-1760
3404 E Us Highway 92 Plant City (33566) *(G-14422)*
Cwac Custom Woodworking & Cabi....407 343-7774
2420 Smith St Ste I Kissimmee (34744) *(G-7236)*
Cwi Industrial Services, Frostproof *Also called Cornelius Welding Inc* *(G-4858)*
Cwp Sheet Metal Inc....407 349-0926
1661 Bandit Way Geneva (32732) *(G-5019)*
Cws Holding Company LLC....352 368-6922
1900 Sw 44th Ave Ocala (34474) *(G-11915)*
Cx1 Miami Mobile Mix, Homestead *Also called Cemex Cnstr Mtls Fla LLC* *(G-5957)*
Cxac, Weston *Also called Cross Atlantic Commodities Inc* *(G-19118)*
CXR Strategies LLC....516 998-0400
1128 Ryal Palm Bch Blvd Royal Palm Beach (33411) *(G-15464)*
Cya Powder Coating LLC....727 299-9832
12099 44th St N Clearwater (33762) *(G-1646)*
Cyalume Tech Holdings Inc (HQ)....954 315-4939
910 Se 17th St Ste 300 Fort Lauderdale (33316) *(G-3925)*
Cyber Group USA LLC....888 574-9555
3770 Park Central Blvd N Pompano Beach (33064) *(G-14655)*
Cyber Manufacturing Inc....786 457-1973
14440 Sw 110th St Miami (33186) *(G-9422)*
Cyber Security Solutions, Tampa *Also called Willsonet Inc* *(G-18259)*
Cybercellulars Inc....407 608-7888
12981 S Ornge Blossom Trl Orlando (32837) *(G-12641)*
Cybertek Computer Solutions, Gainesville *Also called Cybertek Computer Systems Inc* *(G-4901)*
Cybertek Computer Systems Inc....352 373-9923
607 Nw 13th St Gainesville (32601) *(G-4901)*
Cybortrack Solutions Inc....805 904-5677
657 Florida Central Pkwy Longwood (32750) *(G-8271)*
Cyclelogic Products, Stuart *Also called Wmr Cycle Performance Inc* *(G-17052)*
Cycling Quarterly LLC....786 367-2497
1007 N Federal Hwy 383 Fort Lauderdale (33304) *(G-3926)*
Cyclo Industries, Jupiter *Also called Niteo Products LLC* *(G-7082)*
Cyclo Therapeutics Inc (PA)....386 418-8060
6714 Nw 16th St Ste B Gainesville (32653) *(G-4902)*
Cyclone Belt Washer, Clearwater *Also called Douglas Machines Corp* *(G-1655)*
Cyclone Power Technologies Inc (PA)....954 943-8721
601 Ne 26th Ct Pompano Beach (33064) *(G-14656)*
Cygnus Aerospace Incorporated....850 612-1618
1001 Industrial Dr Crestview (32539) *(G-2346)*
Cyipcom Inc....954 727-2500
300 E Oakland Park Blvd # 358 Oakland Park (33334) *(G-11794)*
Cylinders On Cemex Gas....305 818-4952
12155 Nw 136th St Doral (33178) *(G-3318)*
Cymed, Sarasota *Also called Nkem Inc* *(G-16525)*
Cypress Folding Cartons Inc....813 884-5418
6025 Jet Port Indus Blvd Tampa (33634) *(G-17583)*
Cypress Signs, Winter Haven *Also called Superior Unlimited Enterprises* *(G-19360)*
Czarnikow Group Ltd....786 476-0000
333 Se 2nd Ave Ste 3410 Miami (33131) *(G-9423)*
D & A Machine Inc....407 275-5770
7220 Old Cheney Hwy Orlando (32807) *(G-12642)*
D & B Bookbinders, Hialeah *Also called Dobbs & Brodeur Bookbinders* *(G-5376)*
D & B Machine Inc....941 355-8002
1855 61st St Sarasota (34243) *(G-16202)*
D & D Building Contractors....954 791-2075
3380 Sw 50th Ave Davie (33314) *(G-2513)*
D & D Machine & Hydraulics Inc....239 275-7177
10945 Metro Pkwy Fort Myers (33966) *(G-4423)*
D & D Manufacturing LLC....321 890-0069
2655 Cherrywood Ln Titusville (32780) *(G-18427)*
D & D MBL Wldg Fabrication Inc (PA)....954 791-3385
222 Sw 21st Ter Fort Lauderdale (33312) *(G-3927)*
D & D MBL Wldg Fabrication Inc....772 489-7900
5300 Steel Blvd Fort Pierce (34946) *(G-4690)*
D & D Millwork Distributors, Davie *Also called D & D Building Contractors* *(G-2513)*
D & D Welding, Fort Lauderdale *Also called D & D MBL Wldg Fabrication Inc* *(G-3927)*
D & D Welding, Fort Pierce *Also called D & D MBL Wldg Fabrication Inc* *(G-4690)*
D & D Welding Inc....850 438-9011
2715 N W St Pensacola (32505) *(G-14123)*
D & D Wldg & Fabrication LLC (PA)....954 791-3385
222 Sw 21st Ter Fort Lauderdale (33312) *(G-3928)*
D & G Custom Cabinetry Inc....954 561-8822
5712 Coco Palm Dr Tamarac (33319) *(G-17353)*
D & G Millwork & Cabinetry LLC....305 830-3000
2618 Ne 191st St Miami (33180) *(G-9424)*
D & I Carbide Tool Co Inc....727 848-3356
12104 Parkwood St Hudson (34669) *(G-6020)*
D & J Logos, Tampa *Also called Image Depot* *(G-17772)*
D & J Machinery Inc....863 983-3171
728 E Trinidad Ave Clewiston (33440) *(G-1978)*
D & L Auto & Marine Supplies....305 593-0560
5601 Nw 79th Ave Doral (33166) *(G-3319)*
D & M Truss Co....850 944-4864
2620 W Michigan Ave Pensacola (32526) *(G-14124)*
D & N Cabinetry Inc....863 471-1500
2920 Kenilworth Blvd Sebring (33870) *(G-16685)*
D & R Delivery Services of Pb....561 602-6427
312 Canterbury Dr W Riviera Beach (33407) *(G-15316)*
D & R Signs Inc....386 252-2777
133 Thomasson Ave Daytona Beach (32117) *(G-2651)*
D & S Hauling, Clearwater *Also called D & S Pallets Inc* *(G-1647)*
D & S Logging Inc....850 638-5500
261 Highway 273 Chipley (32428) *(G-1543)*
D & S Pallet Recycle Center....352 351-0070
2640 Nw 35th St Ocala (34475) *(G-11916)*
D & S Pallets Inc....727 540-0061
12195 46th St N Clearwater (33762) *(G-1647)*
D & S Steel....352 489-8791
19450 Sw 5th Pl Dunnellon (34431) *(G-3595)*
D A B Constructors Inc....352 797-3537
3300 Northeast Pkwy Brooksville (34609) *(G-1224)*
D and I Trucking Express Inc....786 443-3320
21009 Nw 14th Pl Apt 353 Miami (33169) *(G-9425)*
D and S Superior Coatings Inc....360 388-6099
6150 Metro Plantation Rd Fort Myers (33966) *(G-4424)*
D B Welding Fabrication....941 379-2319
6292 Tower Ln Unit 2 Sarasota (34240) *(G-16400)*
D C Inc Prtble Wldg Fbrication....863 533-4483
3971 Mammoth Grove Rd Frostproof (33843) *(G-4859)*
D C S, Fort Lauderdale *Also called Dons Custom Service Inc* *(G-3948)*
D D B Corporation....305 721-9506
7340 Nw 35th Ave Miami (33147) *(G-9426)*
D E B Printing & Graphics Inc....954 968-0060
6500 Nw 15th Ave Ste 100 Fort Lauderdale (33309) *(G-3929)*
D E E Custom Fabricators Inc....863 667-1850
3545 Waterfield Pkwy Lakeland (33803) *(G-7668)*
D F S, Melbourne *Also called Data Flow Systems Inc* *(G-8800)*
D G, Fort Lauderdale *Also called Dayton-Granger Inc* *(G-3935)*
D G Morrison Inc (PA)....813 865-0208
13209 Byrd Dr Odessa (33556) *(G-12114)*
D G Steel Rule Die Mfg, Miami Lakes *Also called Maq Investments Group Inc* *(G-10811)*
D G Yuengling and Son Inc....813 972-8500
11111 N 30th St Tampa (33612) *(G-17584)*
D I H Corporation....561 881-8705
1750 Australian Ave Ste 3 Riviera Beach (33404) *(G-15317)*
D I R Inc....863 661-5360
3430 Flightline Dr Lakeland (33811) *(G-7669)*
D I Y Yogert....239 471-2177
1327 Cape Coral Pkwy E Cape Coral (33904) *(G-1409)*
D J Camco Corporation....904 355-5995
2426 Dennis St Jacksonville (32204) *(G-6305)*
D J Trusses Unlimited Inc....863 687-4796
3125 Reynolds Rd Lakeland (33803) *(G-7670)*
D L S Electronics, Miami *Also called Digital Lighting Systems Inc* *(G-9468)*
D M C Industries Inc....352 620-9322
13530 N Jacksonville Rd Sparr (32192) *(G-16843)*
D M P, Ocala *Also called Dixie Metal Products Inc* *(G-11921)*
D M S I, North Venice *Also called Diversfied Mtl Specialists Inc* *(G-11757)*
D M T Inc....321 267-3931
817 N Cocoa Blvd Cocoa (32922) *(G-2008)*
D Mahan Cabinets, Cutler Bay *Also called Mahan Cabinets* *(G-2403)*
D Maxwell Company Inc....727 868-9151
8323 Arcola Ave Port Richey (34667) *(G-15048)*
D N L Performance Inc....786 295-8831
1797 Opa Locka Blvd Opa Locka (33054) *(G-12305)*
D N Machining....941 727-1684
2211 60th Dr E Bradenton (34203) *(G-1028)*
D O B Signs LLC....772 466-4913
4475 N Old Dixie Hwy Fort Pierce (34946) *(G-4691)*
D R C Industries Inc....954 971-0699
4100 N Powerline Rd Z1 Pompano Beach (33073) *(G-14657)*
D R Nickelson & Company Inc....386 755-6565
229 Nw Wilks Ln Ste 1 Lake City (32055) *(G-7353)*
D R P, Boca Raton *Also called Direct Response Publication* *(G-503)*
D R S Optronics Inc....321 309-1500
100 N Babcock St Melbourne (32935) *(G-8799)*
D T Woodcrafters Corp....305 556-3771
1677 W 31st Pl Hialeah (33012) *(G-5360)*
D Turin & Company Inc....305 825-2004
8045 W 26th Ct Hialeah (33016) *(G-5361)*
D V M Pharmaceuticals Inc....305 575-6950
3040 Universal Blvd Weston (33331) *(G-19119)*
D W A Inc (PA)....941 444-1134
5401 Palmer Blvd Sarasota (34232) *(G-16401)*
D W Allen Marine Svcs Inc....904 358-1933
1841 Wambolt St Jacksonville (32202) *(G-6306)*
D& R Printing LLC....941 378-3311
6569 Tarawa Dr Sarasota (34241) *(G-16402)*
D&D Wood Working Inc....407 427-0106
8622 Brackenwood Dr Orlando (32829) *(G-12643)*
D&R Printing LLC....941 378-3311
4281 Clark Rd Sarasota (34233) *(G-16403)*

ALPHABETIC

D&W Fine Pack LLC...305 592-4329
7740 Nw 55th St Doral (33166) ***(G-3320)***
D' Lanerg, Miami *Also called American Hygenic Laboratories* ***(G-9144)***
D-R Media and Investments LLC...941 207-1602
300 Tamiami Trl S Venice (34285) ***(G-18540)***
D-Rep Plastics Inc...407 240-4154
11345 53rd St N Clearwater (33760) ***(G-1648)***
D1 Locker LLC...305 446-9041
4880 Nw 4th St Miami (33126) ***(G-9427)***
Da Vinci Cabinetry LLC...239 633-7957
25241 Bernwood Dr Ste 7 Bonita Springs (34135) ***(G-828)***
Da Vinci Systems Inc...954 688-5600
124 Th Ave Coral Springs (33065) ***(G-2236)***
Daby Products Carisen...305 559-3018
5757 Sw 8th St West Miami (33144) ***(G-18781)***
DAccord Shirts & Guayaberas...305 576-0926
7320 Nw 12th St Miami (33126) ***(G-9428)***
Dackor Inc...407 654-5013
310 E Crown Point Rd Winter Garden (34787) ***(G-19259)***
Dackor 3d Laminates, Winter Garden *Also called Dackor Inc* ***(G-19259)***
Dade Doors Inc...305 556-8980
1707 W 32nd Pl Hialeah (33012) ***(G-5362)***
Dade Engineering Corp...305 885-2766
6855 Edgewater Dr Apt 1e Coral Gables (33133) ***(G-2136)***
Dade Engineering Group LLC...305 885-2766
7700 Nw 37th Ave Miami (33147) ***(G-9429)***
Dade Made...305 846-9482
478 W 28th St Hialeah (33010) ***(G-5363)***
Dade Pump & Supply Co...305 235-5000
14261 S Dixie Hwy Miami (33176) ***(G-9430)***
Dade Truss Company Inc...305 592-8245
6401 Nw 74th Ave Miami (33166) ***(G-9431)***
Dads Powder Coating...813 715-6561
40420 Free Fall Ave Zephyrhills (33542) ***(G-19513)***
Daeco, Coral Gables *Also called Dade Engineering Corp* ***(G-2136)***
Dagher & Sons Inc...904 998-0911
11775 Marco Beach Dr Jacksonville (32224) ***(G-6307)***
DAGHER PRINTING, Jacksonville *Also called Dagher & Sons Inc* ***(G-6307)***
Daher Inc (PA)...954 893-1400
601 Ne 10th St Pompano Beach (33060) ***(G-14658)***
Dahlquist Enterprises Inc...407 896-2294
1315 N Mills Ave Orlando (32803) ***(G-12644)***
Dahlquists Printing & Graphics, Orlando *Also called Dahlquist Enterprises Inc* ***(G-12644)***
Daigle Tool & Die Inc...954 785-9989
764 Ne 42nd St Deerfield Beach (33064) ***(G-2811)***
Daily Buzz...407 673-5400
3260 University Blvd Winter Park (32792) ***(G-19399)***
Daily Commercial, Leesburg *Also called Harborpoint Media LLC* ***(G-8161)***
Daily Green...352 226-8288
436 Se 2nd St Gainesville (32601) ***(G-4903)***
Daily Grind Stumpgrinding...954 588-4640
10330 Nw 31st Ct Sunrise (33351) ***(G-17114)***
Daily Melt...305 519-2585
3401 N Miami Ave Miami (33127) ***(G-9432)***
Daily Melt...305 573-9700
98 Ne 2nd Ave Miami (33132) ***(G-9433)***
Daily Multiservices Inc...786 286-3817
6763 Nw 182nd St Apt 105 Hialeah (33015) ***(G-5364)***
Daily News Inc...386 312-5200
1825 Saint Johns Ave Palatka (32177) ***(G-13476)***
Daily Room...754 200-5153
1000 S Pine Island Rd # 160 Plantation (33324) ***(G-14506)***
Daily Therapy Services Inc...954 649-3620
8040 Nw 54th St Lauderhill (33351) ***(G-8107)***
Daily Trnsfrmtion Mnstries Inc...727 847-5152
12563 Leatherleaf Dr Tampa (33626) ***(G-17585)***
Dailychew LLC...954 849-0553
9355 Nw 18th Pl Plantation (33322) ***(G-14507)***
Dailys...904 448-0562
9143 Baymeadows Rd Jacksonville (32256) ***(G-6308)***
Dailys...904 880-4784
13800 Old St Augustine Rd Jacksonville (32258) ***(G-6309)***
Dailys 1113 Shell...904 608-0219
40 Settlement Dr Ponte Vedra (32081) ***(G-14924)***
Dain M Bayer...407 647-0679
2333 Chantilly Ave Winter Park (32789) ***(G-19400)***
Dairy Fairy LLC...305 865-1506
9457 Harding Ave Surfside (33154) ***(G-17202)***
Dairy Feeds Inc (PA)...863 763-0258
1901 Nw 9th St Okeechobee (34972) ***(G-12175)***
Dairy-Mix Inc...813 621-8098
9314 Princess Palm Ave Tampa (33619) ***(G-17586)***
Dais Corp...727 375-8484
11552 Prosperous Dr Odessa (33556) ***(G-12115)***
Daisies Closets...863 838-5056
6720 Bordeaux Blvd Lakeland (33811) ***(G-7671)***
Daisy Crazy Inc...305 300-5144
3902 Estepona Ave Doral (33178) ***(G-3321)***
Daisy V Castillo Vendor...305 254-1427
10418 Sw 210th Ter Cutler Bay (33189) ***(G-2391)***
Daje Industries Inc...305 592-7711
6020 Nw 99th Ave Doral (33178) ***(G-3322)***
Dakim Inc...561 790-0884
11420 Okeechobee Blvd D Royal Palm Beach (33411) ***(G-15465)***
Dakota Plumbing Products LLC (PA)...954 987-3430
800 Nw 65th St Ste B Fort Lauderdale (33309) ***(G-3930)***
Dalane Machining Inc...813 854-5905
13530 Wright Cir Tampa (33626) ***(G-17587)***
Dale Mabry Heating & Metal Co...813 877-1574
4313 W South Ave Tampa (33614) ***(G-17588)***
Dale Photo and Digital Inc...954 925-0103
2960 Simms St Hollywood (33020) ***(G-5808)***
Dale Smith Cabinetry LLC...407 625-2274
6598 S Goldenrod Rd Orlando (32822) ***(G-12645)***
Daleo Fuels Inc...954 931-3331
2901 W Oakland Park Blvd Oakland Park (33311) ***(G-11795)***
Dalian Platinum Chem Ltd Corp...954 501-0564
200 S Andrews Ave Ste 200 # 200 Fort Lauderdale (33301) ***(G-3931)***
Dalimar Corp...727 525-8115
6295 42nd St N Pinellas Park (33781) ***(G-14343)***
Dalpro Commercial Rfrgn, Tampa *Also called Allied Manufacturing Inc* ***(G-17402)***
Dan Boudreau Inc...407 491-7611
3325 Red Ash Cir Oviedo (32766) ***(G-13425)***
Dan Frame & Trim Inc...352 726-4567
7770 E Rustic Trl Inverness (34453) ***(G-6085)***
Dan Lipman and Associates...561 245-8672
15852 Corintha Ter Delray Beach (33446) ***(G-3068)***
Dana Andrews Woodworking...561 882-0444
1748 Australian Ave Riviera Beach (33404) ***(G-15318)***
Danaher Motion...727 789-0446
2112 Mary Ln Palm Harbor (34685) ***(G-13732)***
Danam Electronics, Miami Lakes *Also called Drew Scientific Inc* ***(G-10783)***
Danas Safty Supply Inc...305 639-6024
1622 Nw 82nd Ave Doral (33126) ***(G-3323)***
Danco Machine Inc...727 501-0460
13131 92nd St Ste 608a Largo (33773) ***(G-7930)***
Dandee Foods, Lakeland *Also called ME Thompson Inc* ***(G-7749)***
Dandee Sandwich, Jacksonville *Also called ME Thompson Inc* ***(G-6587)***
Dandy Media Corporation...954 616-6800
1380 Nw 65th Ave Ste A Plantation (33313) ***(G-14508)***
Dandyprint.com, Plantation *Also called Dandy Media Corporation* ***(G-14508)***
Danfoss LLC...772 219-0745
7560 Sw Jack James Dr Stuart (34997) ***(G-16930)***
Danfoss LLC...850 504-4800
1769 E Paul Dirac Dr Tallahassee (32310) ***(G-17240)***
Danfoss Turbocor Compressors, Tallahassee *Also called Danfoss LLC* ***(G-17240)***
Dania Cut Holdings Inc...954 923-9545
760 Ne 7th Ave Dania Beach (33004) ***(G-2464)***
Dania Cut Super Yacht Repair, Dania Beach *Also called Dania Cut Holdings Inc* ***(G-2464)***
Daniel Bustamante...305 779-7777
1210 Placetas Ave Coral Gables (33146) ***(G-2137)***
Daniel Lampert Communications...407 327-7000
101 Brookshire Ct Winter Springs (32708) ***(G-19471)***
Danielle Fence Mfg Co Inc...863 425-3182
4855 State Road 60 W Mulberry (33860) ***(G-11121)***
Daniels Manufacturing Corp...407 855-6161
526 Thorpe Rd Orlando (32824) ***(G-12646)***
Daniels Offset Printing Inc...305 261-3263
8541 Franjo Rd Cutler Bay (33189) ***(G-2392)***
Daniels Whl Sign & Plas Inc...386 736-4918
5224 W State Road 46 Sanford (32771) ***(G-16031)***
Danifer Printing Inc...727 849-5883
7117 Us Highway 19 New Port Richey (34652) ***(G-11488)***
Danker Laboratories Inc...941 758-7711
1144 Tallevast Rd Ste 106 Sarasota (34243) ***(G-16203)***
Danker Labs, Sarasota *Also called Danker Laboratories Inc* ***(G-16203)***
Danly Corporation (PA)...305 285-0111
3121 Commodore Plz Ph 5 Miami (33133) ***(G-9434)***
Danny Brawley...239 597-0084
5790 Waxmyrtle Way Naples (34109) ***(G-11220)***
Dannys Prtg Svc Sups & Eqp Inc...305 757-2282
7233 Biscayne Blvd Miami (33138) ***(G-9435)***
Dans Custom Sheet Metal Inc...239 594-0530
5700 Washington St Naples (34109) ***(G-11221)***
Dapp Embroidery Inc...407 260-1600
1075 Fla Cntl Pkwy Ste 25 Longwood (32750) ***(G-8272)***
Dar Industries Inc...904 327-9689
5570 Fl Min Blvd S Jacksonville (32257) ***(G-6310)***
Darcy Stephen...813 645-3375
922 Allegro Ln Apollo Beach (33572) ***(G-101)***
Darifair Foods Inc...904 268-8999
4131 Sunbeam Rd Jacksonville (32257) ***(G-6311)***
Dark Horse Signs and Prtg LLC...850 684-3833
6476 Starfish Cv Gulf Breeze (32563) ***(G-5115)***
Dark Lake Software Inc...407 602-8046
1229 Wading Waters Cir Winter Park (32792) ***(G-19401)***
Dark Lake Systems, Winter Park *Also called Dark Lake Software Inc* ***(G-19401)***
Dark Storm Manufacturing LLC...516 983-3473
3390 N Courtenay Pkwy Merritt Island (32953) ***(G-8999)***

Darkside Vault LLC 407 353-3776
207 N Goldenrod Rd # 200 Orlando (32807) ***(G-12647)***
Darland Bakery Inc 407 894-1061
42 Cardamon Dr Orlando (32825) ***(G-12648)***
Darling Ingredients Inc 904 964-8083
11313 Se 52nd Ave Starke (32091) ***(G-16892)***
Darling Ingredients Inc 407 856-7667
408 W Landstreet Rd Orlando (32824) ***(G-12649)***
Darling Ingredients Inc 863 425-0065
1001 Orient Rd Tampa (33619) ***(G-17589)***
Darling Ingredients Inc 239 693-2300
8181 Katanga Ct Fort Myers (33916) ***(G-4425)***
Darly Filtration Inc 727 318-7064
8094 118th Ave Largo (33773) ***(G-7931)***
Darmar Cabinets Inc 786 556-5784
5273 Nw 161st St Miami Lakes (33014) ***(G-10778)***
Darmerica LLC 321 219-9111
198 Wilshire Blvd Casselberry (32707) ***(G-1502)***
Darmiven Inc 305 871-1157
6355 Nw 36th St Ste 506 Virginia Gardens (33166) ***(G-18686)***
Darnel Inc 954 929-0085
2331 Thomas St Hollywood (33020) ***(G-5809)***
Darren Thomas Glass Co Inc 863 655-9500
251 Commercial Ct Sebring (33876) ***(G-16686)***
Dart Container Company Fla LLC 813 752-1990
4610 Airport Rd Plant City (33563) ***(G-14423)***
Dart Container Corp Florida 813 752-6525
1605 Turkey Creek Rd Plant City (33566) ***(G-14424)***
Dart Container Corp Florida 941 358-1202
8010 15th St E Sarasota (34243) ***(G-16204)***
Dart Container Corp Florida 941 358-1202
1952 Field Rd Ste B3 Sarasota (34231) ***(G-16404)***
Dart Industries Inc (HQ) 407 826-5050
14901 S Ornge Blssom Trl Orlando (32837) ***(G-12650)***
Dasan Zhone Solutions Inc 305 789-6680
801 Brickell Ave Fl 9 Miami (33131) ***(G-9436)***
Dash Air Parts LLC 786 659-5013
6625 Mami Lkes Dr Ste 525 Miami Lakes (33014) ***(G-10779)***
Dashclicks LLC 866 600-3369
2901 Stirling Rd Ste 210 Fort Lauderdale (33312) ***(G-3932)***
Dashcovers Plus Depot Distrs 954 961-7774
4431 Sw 64th Ave Ste 104 Davie (33314) ***(G-2514)***
Dasops Inc 386 258-6230
2425 Dodge Dr Daytona Beach (32118) ***(G-2652)***
Dass & Associates, Coconut Creek *Also called Dass Logistics Inc* ***(G-2074)***
Dass Logistics Inc 954 837-8339
6601 Lyons Rd Ste B1 Coconut Creek (33073) ***(G-2074)***
Data Access International Inc 305 238-0012
14000 Sw 119th Ave Miami (33186) ***(G-9437)***
Data Buoy Instrumentation LLC 239 849-7063
75 Mid Cape Ter Ste 8 Cape Coral (33991) ***(G-1410)***
Data Cooling Tech Canada LLC 813 865-4701
5110 W Clifton St Tampa (33634) ***(G-17590)***
Data Flow Systems Inc 321 259-5009
605 N John Rodes Blvd Melbourne (32934) ***(G-8800)***
Data Graphics Inc 352 589-1312
3800 Progress Blvd Mount Dora (32757) ***(G-11100)***
Data Image, Winter Park *Also called DMC Components Intl LLC* ***(G-19404)***
Data Line, Sun City Center *Also called Pss Communications Inc* ***(G-17071)***
Data Phone Wire & Cable Corp 954 761-7171
3420 Sw 14th St Fort Lauderdale (33312) ***(G-3933)***
Data Pro Accounting Sftwr Inc 727 803-1500
111 2nd Ave Ne Ste 1200 Saint Petersburg (33701) ***(G-15755)***
Data Protection Solutions, Hollywood *Also called Arco Computer Products LLC* ***(G-5774)***
Data Publishers Inc 954 752-2332
9602 Nw 36th Mnr Coral Springs (33065) ***(G-2237)***
Datacore Software Corporation (PA) 954 377-6000
1901 W Cypress Creek Rd # 200 Fort Lauderdale (33309) ***(G-3934)***
Datagrid Inc 352 371-7608
4111 Nw 6th St Ste D Gainesville (32609) ***(G-4904)***
Datamax International Corp (HQ) 407 578-8007
4501 Pkwy Commerce Blvd Orlando (32808) ***(G-12651)***
Datamax-Oneil Corporation (HQ) 800 816-9649
4501 Pkwy Commerce Blvd Orlando (32808) ***(G-12652)***
Datamentors LLC (PA) 813 960-7800
2319 Oak Myrtle Ln Wesley Chapel (33544) ***(G-18743)***
Datum Metal Products, Mangonia Park *Also called Hoover Canvas Products Co* ***(G-8502)***
Dauer Manufacturing Corp 800 883-2590
10100 Nw 116th Way U Medley (33178) ***(G-8640)***
Dauntless Usa Inc 904 996-8800
9995 Gate Pkwy N Ste 400 Jacksonville (32246) ***(G-6312)***
Davanti Doors Llc 239 842-8341
2840 South St Fort Myers (33916) ***(G-4426)***
Dave Siler Transport 239 348-3283
111 14th St Se Naples (34117) ***(G-11222)***
Davenport -Block Manufacturing, Davenport *Also called Cemex Cnstr Mtls Fla LLC* ***(G-2476)***
Daves All Around 407 325-6693
3530 Hollow Oak Run Oviedo (32766) ***(G-13426)***
Daves Machine Shop Inc 386 325-0974
644 W Peniel Rd Palatka (32177) ***(G-13477)***
Daves Super Smoothies LLC 407 293-7334
2505 Monte Carlo Trl Orlando (32805) ***(G-12653)***
David B Case 904 262-6224
10358 Sylvan Ln W Jacksonville (32257) ***(G-6313)***
David Chittum 386 754-6127
1800 Bonita Way S Saint Petersburg (33712) ***(G-15756)***
David Delights LLC 407 648-2020
4677 L B Mcleod Rd Ste J Orlando (32811) ***(G-12654)***
David Dobbs Enterprises Inc (PA) 904 824-6171
4600 Us 1 N Saint Augustine (32095) ***(G-15533)***
David E Ashe Sawmill 904 377-4800
5440 State Road 13 N Saint Augustine (32092) ***(G-15534)***
David Gill Enterprises 863 422-5711
110 Hwy 17 92 Davenport (33837) ***(G-2477)***
David Jacobs Pubg Group LLC 813 321-4119
14497 N D Mabry Hwy 135 Tampa (33618) ***(G-17591)***
David R Case 727 808-9330
18519 Floralton Dr Spring Hill (34610) ***(G-16872)***
David R Nassivera Inc 352 351-1176
2250 Ne 70th St Ocala (34479) ***(G-11917)***
David Russell Anodizing 407 302-4041
2501 Mccracken Rd Sanford (32771) ***(G-16032)***
David S Stoyka 561 848-2599
8125 Monetary Dr Ste H6 Riviera Beach (33404) ***(G-15319)***
David Sayne Masonry Inc 386 873-4696
1010 Geryl Way Deland (32724) ***(G-2966)***
David Thiessens Pavers Inc 813 516-1389
12203 Floral Ln Thonotosassa (33592) ***(G-18400)***
David Viera LLC 305 218-3401
7828 W 29th Ln Apt 101 Hialeah (33018) ***(G-5365)***
David's Novelties, Pensacola *Also called Kenneth S Jarrell Inc* ***(G-14189)***
Davie Embroidme 954 452-0600
2471 S University Dr Davie (33324) ***(G-2515)***
Davie Fastsigns 305 423-2332
40 Nw 3rd St Ste 1 Miami (33128) ***(G-9438)***
Davila Woodworking Inc 954 458-0460
214 Nw 1st Ave Hallandale Beach (33009) ***(G-5180)***
Davis Concrete Inc (PA) 727 733-3141
1670 Sunshine Dr Clearwater (33765) ***(G-1649)***
Davis Franklin Printing Co 813 259-2500
520 N Willow Ave Tampa (33606) ***(G-17592)***
Davis Kwik Kerb LLC 386 690-0058
656 S State Road 415 New Smyrna Beach (32168) ***(G-11531)***
Davis Mail Services Inc 904 477-7970
13464 Grover Rd Jacksonville (32226) ***(G-6314)***
Davis-Wick Talent MGT LLC 407 369-1614
5400 Nw 27th Ct Margate (33063) ***(G-8541)***
Davison Publishing Co Inc 407 657-3710
3452 Lake Lynda Dr # 363 Orlando (32817) ***(G-12655)***
Davison Publishing Company LLC 407 380-8900
2860 Delaney Ave Orlando (32806) ***(G-12656)***
Davit Master Corp 727 573-4414
5560 Ulmerton Rd Clearwater (33760) ***(G-1650)***
Dawn Foods Inc 866 218-3801
8035 Nw 84th St Medley (33166) ***(G-8641)***
Daws Manufacturing Company Inc (PA) 850 478-3298
8811 Grow Dr Pensacola (32514) ***(G-14125)***
Dax Copying and Printing Inc 954 236-3000
1868 N University Dr # 106 Plantation (33322) ***(G-14509)***
Day Metal Products LLC 352 799-9258
119 E Dr M L King Jr Blvd Brooksville (34601) ***(G-1225)***
Dayoris Doors 954 374-8538
2114 Sw 60th Ter Miramar (33023) ***(G-10982)***
Daystar International Inc 813 281-0200
917 Terra Mar Dr Tampa (33613) ***(G-17593)***
Dayton Industrial Corporation 941 351-4454
2237 Industrial Blvd Sarasota (34234) ***(G-16405)***
Dayton Superior Corporation 407 859-4541
7415 Emerald Dunes Dr # 1200 Orlando (32822) ***(G-12657)***
Dayton-Granger Inc 954 463-3451
3299 Sw 9th Ave Fort Lauderdale (33315) ***(G-3935)***
Daytona Beach Jet Center, Daytona Beach *Also called Sheltair Daytona Beach LLC* ***(G-2713)***
Daytona Cooling Systems, Doral *Also called Daytona Rubber Company Inc* ***(G-3324)***
Daytona Dock & Seawall Service 386 255-7909
862 Terrace Ave Daytona Beach (32114) ***(G-2653)***
Daytona Glass Works LLC 386 274-2550
843 Bill France Blvd Daytona Beach (32117) ***(G-2654)***
Daytona Helmets International, Daytona Beach *Also called Jay Squared LLC* ***(G-2675)***
Daytona Magic Inc 386 252-6767
136 S Beach St Daytona Beach (32114) ***(G-2655)***
Daytona Parts Company 386 427-7108
1191 Turnbull Bay Rd New Smyrna Beach (32168) ***(G-11532)***
Daytona Rubber Company Inc 305 513-4105
10460 Nw 29th Ter Doral (33172) ***(G-3324)***
Daytona Sheet Metal and Air 386 547-2422
14 Woodlake Dr Port Orange (32129) ***(G-15015)***
Daytona Trophy Inc 386 253-2806
2413 Bellevue Ave Daytona Beach (32114) ***(G-2656)***

ALPHABETIC

Daytona Welding & Fabrication 386 562-0093
837 Pinewood St Daytona Beach (32117) ***(G-2657)***
Dazmed Inc 561 571-2020
508 Nw 77th St Boca Raton (33487) ***(G-495)***
Dazmed Pharmaceuticals, Boca Raton *Also called Dazmed Inc* ***(G-495)***
Db Motoring Group Inc 305 685-0707
6834 Nw 77th Ct Miami (33166) ***(G-9439)***
Db Tucker LLC 561 301-4974
126 S Village Way Jupiter (33458) ***(G-7023)***
Dbi Services LLC 239 218-5204
5893 Entp Pkwy Ste A Fort Myers (33905) ***(G-4427)***
Dbn Investment LLC 407 917-2525
3300 S Hiawassee Rd # 107 Orlando (32835) ***(G-12658)***
Dbt Marine Products, Largo *Also called Discount Boat Tops Inc* ***(G-7933)***
DC Apparel Inc 863 325-9273
3260 Dundee Rd Winter Haven (33884) ***(G-19317)***
DC Kerckhoff Company 239 597-7218
1901 Elsa St Naples (34109) ***(G-11223)***
DC Style Corp 786 391-3780
1835 Nw 112th Ave Miami (33172) ***(G-9440)***
Dcg Enterprises LLC 813 931-4303
2702 N 35th St Tampa (33605) ***(G-17594)***
DCS Pharma USA LLC 248 979-8866
801 Brickell Ave Ste 900 Miami (33131) ***(G-9441)***
Dcsm, Naples *Also called Dans Custom Sheet Metal Inc* ***(G-11221)***
Dcwfab LLC 941 320-6095
3374 Howell Pl Sarasota (34232) ***(G-16406)***
Ddci Inc 407 814-0225
995 W Kennedy Blvd Ste 35 Orlando (32810) ***(G-12659)***
Ddd Hams Inc 850 205-1426
1519 Capital Cir Ne Tallahassee (32308) ***(G-17241)***
Ddp Holdings LLC (HQ) 813 712-2515
4450 E Adamo Dr Ste 501 Tampa (33605) ***(G-17595)***
DDS Lab USA Holding 813 249-8888
6015 Benjamin Rd Ste 310 Tampa (33634) ***(G-17596)***
DDy Martinez LLC 786 263-2672
3105 Nw 107th Ave Ste 400 Doral (33172) ***(G-3325)***
De Funiak Springs Yard, Defuniak Springs *Also called Legacy Vulcan LLC* ***(G-2944)***
De La Mer Originals, Jacksonville *Also called Regency Cap & Gown Company* ***(G-6713)***
De La Rosa, Lauderdale Lakes *Also called Delarosa Real Foods LLC* ***(G-8085)***
De Lima Consultants Group Inc 954 933-7030
4216 Nw 120th Ave Coral Springs (33065) ***(G-2238)***
De Loach Industries, Sarasota *Also called Wes Holdings Corp* ***(G-16636)***
De Luna Coffee Intl Inc 850 478-6371
1014 Underwood Ave Ste D Pensacola (32504) ***(G-14126)***
De Ruiter Electric Motor, Miami *Also called Dade Pump & Supply Co* ***(G-9430)***
De Todos Tortillas Inc 305 248-4402
820 N Krome Ave Homestead (33030) ***(G-5961)***
De Vinco Company 941 722-1100
435 Canning Plant Rd Seffner (33584) ***(G-16724)***
Deako Coating & Chemical Inc 305 634-5162
2540 Nw 29th Ave Ste 105 Miami (33142) ***(G-9442)***
Deako Coatings Chemical 305 323-9914
10459 Sw 185th Ter Cutler Bay (33157) ***(G-2393)***
Deal To Win Inc 718 609-1165
4050 Ne 9th Ave Oakland Park (33334) ***(G-11796)***
Dealer It Group LLC 904 518-3379
5220 Belfort Rd Ste 400 Jacksonville (32256) ***(G-6315)***
Dealer Printing Service, Tampa *Also called Ed Vance Printing Company Inc* ***(G-17630)***
Dealerups Inc 407 557-5368
4185 W Lake Mary Blvd # 2 Lake Mary (32746) ***(G-7408)***
Dean Dairy Holdings LLC 239 334-1114
3579 Work Dr Fort Myers (33916) ***(G-4428)***
Dean Steel Buildings Inc (PA) 239 334-1051
2929 Industrial Ave Fort Myers (33901) ***(G-4429)***
Deans Cstm Shtmtl Fabrication 813 757-6270
5106 Varnadore Ln Dover (33527) ***(G-3558)***
Debanie Inc 239 254-1222
5450 Taylor Rd Naples (34109) ***(G-11224)***
Debruyne Enterprise Inc 850 562-0491
5186 Woodlane Cir Tallahassee (32303) ***(G-17242)***
Debut Development LLC 863 448-9081
897 S 6th Ave Ste 1 Wauchula (33873) ***(G-18690)***
Debway Corporation 305 818-6353
2343 W 76th St Hialeah (33016) ***(G-5366)***
Dec Metals, Lakeland *Also called DEC Sheet Metal Inc* ***(G-7672)***
DEC Sheet Metal Inc 863 669-0707
3015 Waterfield Cir Lakeland (33803) ***(G-7672)***
Decimal LLC 407 330-3300
121 Central Park Pl Sanford (32771) ***(G-16033)***
Decimal Engineering, Coral Springs *Also called AL Garey & Associates Inc* ***(G-2218)***
Deco Abrusci International LLC 305 406-3401
8485 Nw 29th St Doral (33122) ***(G-3326)***
Deco Boat Lifts, Safety Harbor *Also called Deco Power Lift Inc* ***(G-15491)***
Deco Lav Inc (PA) 561 274-2110
4920 Bocaire Blvd Boca Raton (33487) ***(G-496)***
Deco Power Lift Inc 727 736-4529
1041 Harbor Lake Dr Safety Harbor (34695) ***(G-15491)***
Deco Shades Solutions Inc 305 558-9800
3155 W Okeechobee Rd Hialeah (33012) ***(G-5367)***
Deco Truss Company Inc 305 257-1910
13980 Sw 252nd St Homestead (33032) ***(G-5962)***
Deco Wraps, Doral *Also called Hammer Head Group Inc* ***(G-3377)***
Decocandles, Miami *Also called Kaluz LLC* ***(G-9814)***
Decon USA 440 610-5009
15 Central Ct Tarpon Springs (34689) ***(G-18292)***
Decor Custom Woodwork LLC 561 631-3240
925 Pine Cir Greenacres (33463) ***(G-5079)***
Decoral System USA Corporation 954 755-6021
12477 Nw 44th St Coral Springs (33065) ***(G-2239)***
Decorative Precast LLC 239 566-9503
420 Sharwood Dr Naples (34110) ***(G-11225)***
Decorators Resource Centl Fla, Sanford *Also called American Bronze Foundry Inc* ***(G-15992)***
Decortive Electro Coatings Inc 386 255-7878
501 Kingston Ave Daytona Beach (32114) ***(G-2658)***
Decosta Woodworking LLC 508 802-7765
763 Home Grove Dr Winter Garden (34787) ***(G-19260)***
Decowall 813 886-5226
6001 Johns Rd Ste 342 Tampa (33634) ***(G-17597)***
Decoy Inc 305 633-6384
2480 Nw 20th St Unit D Miami (33142) ***(G-9443)***
Decoy Next Level In Apparel, Miami *Also called Decoy Inc* ***(G-9443)***
Deeja Foods Inc 321 402-8300
1770 Business Center Ln Kissimmee (34758) ***(G-7237)***
Deep Ocean Woodworks Inc 407 687-2773
6289 Bordeaux Cir Sanford (32771) ***(G-16034)***
Deepstream Designs Inc 305 857-0466
2699 Tigertail Ave Apt 54 Miami (33133) ***(G-9444)***
Deers Holdings Inc 805 323-6899
1108 Kane Cncurse Ste 206 Bay Harbor Islands (33154) ***(G-338)***
Defend-X, Boca Raton *Also called Defenstech International Inc* ***(G-497)***
Defender Screens International 866 802-0400
5330 Pinkney Ave Bldg 6 Sarasota (34233) ***(G-16407)***
Defender SD Manufacturing LLC (PA) 813 864-2570
324 S Hyde Park Ave # 350 Tampa (33606) ***(G-17598)***
Defense Arts & Sciences LLC 321 768-0671
2240 Pine Meadow Ave West Melbourne (32904) ***(G-18771)***
Defense Flight Aerospace LLC 321 442-7255
5448 Hoffner Ave Ste 105 Orlando (32812) ***(G-12660)***
Defense Leadership Forum 202 375-9587
174 Watercolor Way Santa Rosa Beach (32459) ***(G-16157)***
Defense Stamping & Engineering (PA) 850 438-6105
3911 Mobile Hwy Pensacola (32505) ***(G-14127)***
Defenshield Inc 904 679-3942
7000 Us Highway 1 N # 401 Saint Augustine (32095) ***(G-15535)***
Defenstech International Inc 202 688-1988
1080 Holland Dr Ste 1 Boca Raton (33487) ***(G-497)***
Definitive Design, Yulee *Also called Alm Technologies Inc* ***(G-19495)***
Defrancisci Machine Co LLC 321 952-6600
2681 Aurora Rd Melbourne (32935) ***(G-8801)***
Defuniak Springs Herald Breeze 850 892-3232
740 Baldwin Ave Defuniak Springs (32435) ***(G-2941)***
Deggy Corp 305 377-2233
15485 Eagle Nest Ln # 100 Miami Lakes (33014) ***(G-10780)***
Degraaff Inc 305 451-4460
99264 Overseas Hwy Key Largo (33037) ***(G-7168)***
Dekoron Unitherm LLC (HQ) 800 633-5015
1531 Commerce Creek Blvd Cape Coral (33909) ***(G-1411)***
Dekscape 239 278-3325
17051 Alico Commerce Ct # 3 Fort Myers (33967) ***(G-4430)***
Del Air Electric Co 407 531-1173
201 Tech Dr Sanford (32771) ***(G-16035)***
Del Mar Hollywood LLC 786 325-8335
1680 Michigan Ave Ste 910 Miami Beach (33139) ***(G-10661)***
Del Monte Fresh Produce NA Inc (HQ) 305 520-8400
241 Sevilla Ave Coral Gables (33134) ***(G-2138)***
Del Monte Fresh Production Inc 863 844-5836
5050 State Rte 60w Mulberry (33860) ***(G-11122)***
Del Rosario Enterprises Inc 786 547-6812
7339 Nw 79th Ter Medley (33166) ***(G-8642)***
Delacom Detection Systems LLC 941 544-6636
7463 Roxye Ln Sarasota (34240) ***(G-16408)***
Deland Beacon Newspaper, Deland *Also called West Bolusia Beacon* ***(G-3033)***
Deland Metal Craft Company 386 734-0828
300 W Beresford Ave Deland (32720) ***(G-2967)***
Delaney Resources Inc 863 670-5924
8831 Janmar Rd Dade City (33525) ***(G-2427)***
Delarosa Real Foods LLC 718 333-0333
2648 Nw 31st Ave Lauderdale Lakes (33311) ***(G-8085)***
Delaware Chassis Works 302 378-3013
3513 Se Gran Park Way Stuart (34997) ***(G-16931)***
Delconte Packaging Inc 305 885-2800
757 W 26th St Hialeah (33010) ***(G-5368)***
Delet Doors Inc 786 250-4506
9250 Sw 117th Ter Miami (33176) ***(G-9445)***
Deli Fresh Foods Inc 305 652-2848
18630 Ne 2nd Ave Miami (33179) ***(G-9446)***

Delicae Gourmet LLC 727 942-2502
1310 E Lake Dr Tarpon Springs (34688) ***(G-18293)***
Delicate Designs Event Plg Inc 305 833-8725
12080 Ne 16th Ave Apt 201 Miami (33161) ***(G-9447)***
Delicio Baking Company Inc 305 865-5664
300 71st St Ste 450 Miami Beach (33141) ***(G-10662)***
Deliciosa Food Group Inc 954 492-6131
1177 Nw 81st St Miami (33150) ***(G-9448)***
Delisser Enterprises Inc 305 649-6001
3470 Nw 7th St Miami (33125) ***(G-9449)***
Delivery Signs LLC 407 362-7896
40 W Crystal Lake St # 100 Orlando (32806) ***(G-12661)***
Dell USA LP 512 728-8391
14591 Sw 120th St Miami (33186) ***(G-9450)***
Delphi of Florida Inc 727 561-9553
12425 28th S N Ste 100 Saint Petersburg (33716) ***(G-15757)***
Delran Business Products, Hialeah *Also called All Binders & Indexes Inc* ***(G-5278)***
Delray Awning Inc 561 276-5381
80 N Congress Ave Delray Beach (33445) ***(G-3069)***
Delray Pin Factory Intl 561 994-1680
5304 Nw 84th Ter Coral Springs (33067) ***(G-2240)***
Delray's Screens, Boynton Beach *Also called Plotkowski Inc* ***(G-940)***
Delta Doors, Medley *Also called Vidco Industries Inc* ***(G-8753)***
Delta Fountains, Jacksonville *Also called Johnston Archtctral Systems In* ***(G-6527)***
Delta Group Elec Inc Fla, Rockledge *Also called Delta Group Electronics Inc* ***(G-15400)***
Delta Group Electronics Inc 321 631-0799
395 Gus Hipp Blvd Rockledge (32955) ***(G-15400)***
Delta Industries, Fort Walton Beach *Also called John R Caito* ***(G-4811)***
Delta International Inc 305 665-6573
4856 Sw 72nd Ave Miami (33155) ***(G-9451)***
Delta Laboratories Inc (PA) 305 887-4393
3710 W Highway 326 Ocala (34475) ***(G-11918)***
Delta Machine LLC 386 738-2204
1501 Lexington Ave Deland (32724) ***(G-2968)***
Delta Machine & Tool Inc 386 738-2204
1212 N Mcdonald Ave Deland (32724) ***(G-2969)***
Delta Metal Finishing Inc 954 953-9898
101 Ne 3rd Ave Ste 1500 Fort Lauderdale (33301) ***(G-3936)***
Delta Mg 561 840-0577
4440 S Tiffany Dr Ste 8 West Palm Beach (33407) ***(G-18853)***
Delta Oil 813 323-3113
823 Bayou Dr Brandon (33510) ***(G-1156)***
Delta P Systems Inc 386 236-0950
3 E Tower Cir Ormond Beach (32174) ***(G-13361)***
Delta Regis Tools Inc 772 465-4302
7370 Commercial Cir Fort Pierce (34951) ***(G-4692)***
Deltana Enterprises Inc 305 592-8188
10820 Nw 29th St Doral (33172) ***(G-3327)***
Deluna Toole LLC 850 435-4063
6565 N W St Ste 260 Pensacola (32505) ***(G-14128)***
Deluxe Clsets Cabinets Stn LLC 786 879-3371
15290 Sw 36th Ter Miami (33185) ***(G-9452)***
Deluxe Equipment Co 941 753-4184
7817 Alhambra Dr Bradenton (34209) ***(G-1029)***
Deluxe Stone Inc 561 236-2322
6129 Country Fair Cir Boynton Beach (33437) ***(G-896)***
Delzotto Products Florida Inc 352 351-3834
4575 W Highway 40 Ocala (34482) ***(G-11919)***
Demaco, Melbourne *Also called Defrancisci Machine Co LLC* ***(G-8801)***
Demaco LLC 321 952-6600
121 Sw 109th Ave Apt M2 Miami (33174) ***(G-9453)***
Demelle Biopharma LLC 908 240-8939
1245 N Florida Ave Tarpon Springs (34689) ***(G-18294)***
Demerx Inc 954 607-3670
1951 Nw 7th Ave Ste 300 Miami (33136) ***(G-9454)***
Demetech Corporation (PA) 305 824-1048
14175 Nw 60th Ave Miami Lakes (33014) ***(G-10781)***
Deming Designs Inc 850 478-5765
1090 Cobblestone Dr Pensacola (32514) ***(G-14129)***
Demoss Cabinetry LLC 863 738-0080
3003 Brooks St Ste 1 Lakeland (33803) ***(G-7673)***
Denali Investments Inc 386 364-2979
140 Palm St Ne Live Oak (32064) ***(G-8230)***
Denim Lily LLC 754 264-9331
2785 Se 11th St Pompano Beach (33062) ***(G-14659)***
Denise Marie, Miami *Also called Arde Apparel Inc* ***(G-9166)***
Denke Laboratories Inc 941 721-0568
12285 Us Highway 41 N Palmetto (34221) ***(G-13795)***
Denke Labratories, Palmetto *Also called Hascall Engineering and Mfg Co* ***(G-13805)***
Dennis Boatworks 954 260-6855
2207 Nw 29th St Oakland Park (33311) ***(G-11797)***
Dennis Hernandez & Assoc PA 813 470-4545
410 S Cedar Ave Tampa (33606) ***(G-17599)***
Dennys Electronics Inc 941 485-5400
1044 Endeavor Ct North Venice (34275) ***(G-11756)***
Dental Partners Alliance LLC (PA) 321 574-8003
7341 Office Park Pl # 101 Melbourne (32940) ***(G-8802)***
Dentate Porcelain Inc 917 359-7696
2722 Ne 1st St Ste 1 Pompano Beach (33062) ***(G-14660)***
Denterprise International Inc 386 672-0450
100 E Granada Blvd # 219 Ormond Beach (32176) ***(G-13362)***
Dentsply Raintree Glenroe, Sarasota *Also called Dentsply Sirona Inc* ***(G-16205)***
Dentsply Sirona Inc 941 527-4450
7290 26th Ct E Sarasota (34243) ***(G-16205)***
Dentz Design Screen Prtg LLC 609 303-0827
56 S Dixie Hwy Ste 3 Saint Augustine (32084) ***(G-15536)***
Denver Elevator Systems Inc 800 633-9788
7073 N Atlantic Ave Cape Canaveral (32920) ***(G-1356)***
Depend-O-Drain Inc 941 756-1710
6012 33rd St E Bradenton (34203) ***(G-1030)***
Dependable Shutter & Glass, Davie *Also called Dependable Shutter Service Inc* ***(G-2516)***
Dependable Shutter Service Inc 954 583-1411
4741 Orange Dr Davie (33314) ***(G-2516)***
Dependable Water Inc 904 599-0560
320 W Blackjack Br Way Saint Johns (32259) ***(G-15676)***
Dependable Water Inc (PA) 772 563-7473
7956 102nd Ct Vero Beach (32967) ***(G-18615)***
Depuy Inc 305 412-8010
6303 Blue Lagoon Dr Miami (33126) ***(G-9455)***
Depuy Synthes Products Inc 305 265-6842
6303 Blue Lagoon Dr Miami (33126) ***(G-9456)***
Derecktor of Florida, Dania Beach *Also called Florida Derecktor Inc* ***(G-2465)***
Derm-Buro Inc 305 953-4025
4675 E 10th Ct Hialeah (33013) ***(G-5369)***
Dermaccina Dossier, Miami *Also called Nac USA Corporation* ***(G-10058)***
Dermatonus 305 229-3923
5262 Sw 158th Ave Miramar (33027) ***(G-10983)***
Dermazone Solutions Inc 727 446-6882
2440 30th Ave N Saint Petersburg (33713) ***(G-15758)***
Desapro Inc 321 674-6804
435 Gus Hipp Blvd Rockledge (32955) ***(G-15401)***
Desco Industries 305 255-7744
13937 Sw 119th Ave Miami (33186) ***(G-9457)***
Desco Machine Company LLC 954 565-2739
3000 Ne 12th Ter Oakland Park (33334) ***(G-11798)***
Desco Manufacturing Inc 941 925-7029
4561 Samuel St Sarasota (34233) ***(G-16409)***
Desert Micro, Jacksonville *Also called Western Microsystems Inc* ***(G-6912)***
Desh-Videsh Media Group Inc 954 784-8100
10088 W Mcnab Rd Tamarac (33321) ***(G-17354)***
Deshazo LLC 863 272-3107
3525 Reynolds Rd Ste 10 Lakeland (33803) ***(G-7674)***
Design & Print 561 361-8299
199 W Palmetto Park Rd Boca Raton (33432) ***(G-498)***
Design & Print Solutions Inc 407 703-7861
553 Sheeler Ave Apopka (32703) ***(G-130)***
Design Cncepts/Marine Concepts, Sarasota *Also called Patrick Industries Inc* ***(G-16273)***
Design Cncpts By Amrcn Plitics, Clearwater *Also called American Plastic Sup & Mfg Inc* ***(G-1581)***
Design Communications Ltd 407 856-9661
10611 Satellite Blvd Orlando (32837) ***(G-12662)***
Design Containers Inc 904 764-6541
2913 Westside Blvd Jacksonville (32209) ***(G-6316)***
Design Cores and Tubes, Jacksonville *Also called Design Containers Inc* ***(G-6316)***
Design Custom Millwork Inc 407 878-1267
130 Tech Dr Sanford (32771) ***(G-16036)***
Design Furnishings Inc 407 294-0507
3647 All American Blvd Orlando (32810) ***(G-12663)***
Design It Wraps & Graphics LLC 904 310-6032
2873 Jamestown Rd Fernandina Beach (32034) ***(G-3734)***
Design Litho Inc 813 238-7494
5205 N Florida Ave Tampa (33603) ***(G-17600)***
Design NS Leather Furniture, Boca Raton *Also called Nordic Line Inc* ***(G-648)***
Design Pro Screens Inc 407 831-6541
1287 S Oleander St Longwood (32750) ***(G-8273)***
Design Services Inc 813 949-4748
2200 Knight Rd Land O Lakes (34639) ***(G-7852)***
Design Systems South Inc 850 293-1905
4765 Baywind Dr Pensacola (32514) ***(G-14130)***
Design Works By Tech Pdts Inc (HQ) 941 355-2703
4500 Carmichael Ave Sarasota (34234) ***(G-16410)***
Design Your Kit Clset More Inc 786 227-6412
13400 Sw 134th Ave Ste 5 Miami (33186) ***(G-9458)***
Design-A-Rug Inc (PA) 954 943-7487
200 N Federal Hwy Deerfield Beach (33441) ***(G-2812)***
Designated Diver, Saint Augustine *Also called Designated Sports Inc* ***(G-15537)***
Designated Sports Inc 904 797-9469
3545 Us 1 S Ste A9 Saint Augustine (32086) ***(G-15537)***
Designer Door Products Inc 786 800-3855
17852 State Road 9 Miami (33162) ***(G-9459)***
Designer Films Inc 305 828-0605
7485 W 19th Ct Hialeah (33014) ***(G-5370)***
Designer Lifestyles LLC 904 631-8954
619 Cassat Ave Jacksonville (32205) ***(G-6317)***
Designer Services of 772 286-0855
3241 Se Slater St Stuart (34997) ***(G-16932)***
Designer Sign Systems Inc 954 972-0707
3540 Nw 56th St Ste 201 Fort Lauderdale (33309) ***(G-3937)***

Designer Speciality Millwork, Miami *Also called Designers Specialty Cab Co Inc* ***(G-9460)***
Designer's Choice Cabinetry, Rockledge *Also called Designers Choice Cabinetry Inc* ***(G-15403)***
Designer's Specialty Millwork, Fort Lauderdale *Also called Designers Specialty Cab Co Inc* ***(G-3938)***
Designers Choice Cabinetry..........321 632-0772
285 Barnes Blvd Rockledge (32955) ***(G-15402)***
Designers Choice Cabinetry Inc (HQ)..........321 632-0772
100 Tgk Cir Rockledge (32955) ***(G-15403)***
Designers Plastics, Clearwater *Also called Bruce R Ely Enterprise Inc* ***(G-1614)***
Designers Plumbing Studio Inc..........954 920-5997
3040 N 29th Ave Ste F Hollywood (33020) ***(G-5810)***
Designers Press Inc..........407 843-3141
6305 Chancellor Dr Orlando (32809) ***(G-12664)***
Designers Specialty Cab Co Inc..........954 776-4500
1730 Biscayne Blvd 201g Miami (33132) ***(G-9460)***
Designers Specialty Cab Co Inc (PA)..........954 868-3440
1320 Nw 65th Pl Fort Lauderdale (33309) ***(G-3938)***
Designers Top Shop Inc..........863 453-3855
12 N Anoka Ave Avon Park (33825) ***(G-285)***
Designers Tops Inc..........305 599-9973
4725 Nw 36th Ave Miami (33142) ***(G-9461)***
Designers Wholesale Workroom..........239 434-7633
1035 Industrial Blvd Naples (34104) ***(G-11226)***
Designs In Rugs, Lutz *Also called Hanteri Enterprises Corp* ***(G-8388)***
Designs To Shine..........727 525-4297
1033 34th St N Saint Petersburg (33713) ***(G-15759)***
Designstogo Inc..........561 432-1313
4317 10th Ave N Palm Springs (33461) ***(G-13774)***
Desind Industries Corp..........212 729-0192
150 E Robinson St # 1009 Orlando (32801) ***(G-12665)***
Deskrafters, Sanford *Also called TOS Manufacturing Inc* ***(G-16129)***
Desoto Sun, Punta Gorda *Also called Sun Coast Media Group Inc* ***(G-15237)***
Desperado Leather, Edgewater *Also called Leon Leather Company Inc* ***(G-3629)***
Desserts2go Inc..........941 379-0488
3960 Bellwood Dr Sarasota (34232) ***(G-16411)***
Destin Engraving, Destin *Also called Infinite Lasers LLC* ***(G-3195)***
Destin Log..........850 837-2828
2 Eglin Pkwy Ne Fort Walton Beach (32548) ***(G-4790)***
Destin Machine Inc..........850 837-7114
600 Fourth St Destin (32541) ***(G-3187)***
Destination Athlete Broward FL, Pompano Beach *Also called Lion Press Inc* ***(G-14745)***
Destination Bvi II Inc..........850 699-9551
36120 Emerald Coast Pkwy Destin (32541) ***(G-3188)***
Destination Pavers LLC..........850 319-6551
2827 Cynthia Ct Panama City (32405) ***(G-13891)***
Destiny & Light Inc..........813 476-8386
5911 Sheldon Rd Tampa (33615) ***(G-17601)***
Desysca Inc..........407 724-4148
9528 Silver Buttonwood St Orlando (32832) ***(G-12666)***
Detailed Services Inc..........239 542-2452
1518 Se 46th Ln Cape Coral (33904) ***(G-1412)***
Detect Inc (PA)..........850 763-7200
2817 Highway 77 Panama City (32405) ***(G-13892)***
DEUX MAINS, Lake Worth *Also called Rebuild Globally Inc* ***(G-7585)***
Devatis Inc..........954 316-4844
2800 W State Road 84 # 11 Fort Lauderdale (33312) ***(G-3939)***
Devclan Inc..........407 933-8212
808 N Main St Kissimmee (34744) ***(G-7238)***
Devcon International Corp (HQ)..........954 926-5200
595 S Federal Hwy Ste 500 Boca Raton (33432) ***(G-499)***
Devcon Security Services Corp..........813 386-3849
2801 Gateway Dr Pompano Beach (33069) ***(G-14661)***
Devine Cabinetry LLC..........941 716-0339
6315 Ruff St North Port (34291) ***(G-11737)***
Devon Chase & Company..........407 438-6466
2814 Silver Star Rd # 5 Orlando (32808) ***(G-12667)***
Devon-Aire Inc..........813 884-9544
8505 Sunstate St Tampa (33634) ***(G-17602)***
Dew It Right Coatings..........504 272-4981
3122 Umbrella Tree Dr Edgewater (32141) ***(G-3621)***
Dewalt Service Center 076, Orlando *Also called Black & Decker (us) Inc* ***(G-12519)***
Dextrum Laboratories Inc..........305 594-4020
6993 Nw 82nd Ave Ste 20 Miami (33166) ***(G-9462)***
Df Multi Services LLC..........407 683-2223
845 N Garland Ave Orlando (32801) ***(G-12668)***
Dfa Dairy Brands Fluid LLC..........352 754-1750
16235 Aviation Loop Dr Brooksville (34604) ***(G-1226)***
Dfa Dairy Brands Fluid LLC..........386 775-6700
11231 Phillips Ind Blvd E Jacksonville (32256) ***(G-6318)***
Dfa Dairy Brands Fluid LLC..........386 775-6700
650 S Wickham Rd Melbourne (32904) ***(G-8803)***
Dfa Dairy Brands Fluid LLC..........813 621-7805
4219 E 19th Ave Tampa (33605) ***(G-17603)***
Dfd Loaders Inc..........954 283-8839
11820 Nw 37th St Coral Springs (33065) ***(G-2241)***
Dg Design and Print Co LLC..........321 446-6435
4290 Us Highway 1 Ste A Rockledge (32955) ***(G-15404)***
Dg Promotions, Mount Dora *Also called Data Graphics Inc* ***(G-11100)***
Dgp Enterprises Inc..........941 729-2373
1130 Commerce Blvd N Sarasota (34243) ***(G-16206)***
Dgs Retail LLC..........727 388-4975
4400 34th St N Ste L Saint Petersburg (33714) ***(G-15760)***
Dgs Retail LLC..........727 388-4975
307044th Avenuene N Saint Petersburg (33714) ***(G-15761)***
Dha Filter LLC..........904 269-8701
38 Knight Boxx Rd Orange Park (32065) ***(G-12388)***
Dhb Armor Group Inc (PA)..........800 413-5155
2102 Sw 2nd St Pompano Beach (33069) ***(G-14662)***
Dhf Marketing Inc..........305 884-8077
685 W 25th St Hialeah (33010) ***(G-5371)***
Dhs Enterprises Inc..........727 572-9470
5150 Ulmerton Rd Ste 14 Clearwater (33760) ***(G-1651)***
Dhs Equiptment, Pompano Beach *Also called Dhs Unlimited Inc* ***(G-14663)***
Dhs Power Corp..........305 599-1022
8061 Nw 67th St Miami (33166) ***(G-9463)***
Dhs Unlimited Inc..........954 532-2142
4100 N Powerline Rd G3 Pompano Beach (33073) ***(G-14663)***
Dhss LLC..........305 830-0327
2035 Harding St Ste 200 Hollywood (33020) ***(G-5811)***
Dhss LLC..........305 405-4001
16830 Ne 19th Ave North Miami Beach (33162) ***(G-11670)***
Di Di Designs Inc..........305 836-0266
13376 Nw 42nd Ave Opa Locka (33054) ***(G-12306)***
Di Jam Holdings Inc..........863 967-6949
123 Main St Auburndale (33823) ***(G-239)***
Diabetex Care..........954 427-9510
1525 Nw 3rd St Deerfield Beach (33442) ***(G-2813)***
Diabetic Care Rx LLC (PA)..........866 348-0441
3890 Park Central Blvd N Pompano Beach (33064) ***(G-14664)***
Diadem Sports LLC (PA)..........844 434-2336
200 Park Central Blvd S Pompano Beach (33064) ***(G-14665)***
Diageo North America Inc..........305 476-7761
396 Alhambra Cir Coral Gables (33134) ***(G-2139)***
Diagma U S LLC..........407 683-0852
255 S Orange Ave Ste 745 Orlando (32801) ***(G-12669)***
Diagnostic Test Group LLC..........561 347-5760
1060 Holland Dr Ste A Boca Raton (33487) ***(G-500)***
Diamond Advertising & Mktg..........561 833-5129
1200 S Flagler Dr Apt 106 West Palm Beach (33401) ***(G-18854)***
Diamond Aircraft Logisctics..........305 456-8400
11003 Nw 33rd St Doral (33172) ***(G-3328)***
Diamond Blades 4us..........800 659-5843
2150 Sw 10th St Deerfield Beach (33442) ***(G-2814)***
Diamond Cbd, Fort Lauderdale *Also called Cbd LLC* ***(G-3886)***
Diamond Moba Americas Inc..........954 384-5828
2731 Executive Park Dr # 4 Weston (33331) ***(G-19120)***
Diamond Mt Inc..........321 339-3377
4200 Dow Rd Ste Cd Melbourne (32934) ***(G-8804)***
Diamond Precision Machine Inc..........321 729-8453
2300 Commerce Park Dr Ne Palm Bay (32905) ***(G-13508)***
Diamond R Fertilizer, Fort Pierce *Also called Pioneer Ag-Chem Inc* ***(G-4734)***
Diamond R Fertilizer Co Inc..........863 763-2158
710 Ne 5th Ave Okeechobee (34972) ***(G-12176)***
Diamond-Mt, Melbourne *Also called Diamond Mt Inc* ***(G-8804)***
Diamondback Airboats, Cocoa *Also called Diamondback Manufacturing LLC* ***(G-2013)***
Diamondback Barrels LLC..........321 305-5995
4135 Pine Tree Pl Cocoa (32926) ***(G-2009)***
Diamondback Cnc LLC..........321 305-5995
3400 Grissom Pkwy Cocoa (32926) ***(G-2010)***
Diamondback Firearms LLC..........321 305-5995
3400 Grissom Pkwy Cocoa (32926) ***(G-2011)***
Diamondback Manufacturing LLC..........321 305-5995
1060 Cox Rd Bldg A Cocoa (32926) ***(G-2012)***
Diamondback Manufacturing LLC..........321 633-5624
1060 Cox Rd Cocoa (32926) ***(G-2013)***
Diamondback Towers LLC..........800 424-5624
1060 Cox Rd Bldg B Cocoa (32926) ***(G-2014)***
Diana Food Group, Pompano Beach *Also called Prima Food Corp* ***(G-14812)***
Diane Dal Lago Limited Company..........813 374-2473
5915 Memorial Hwy Ste 115 Tampa (33615) ***(G-17604)***
Dianthus Miami Inc (PA)..........786 800-8365
7635 Nw 27th Ave Miami (33147) ***(G-9464)***
Diario Las Americas, Miami *Also called Las Amrcas Mltimedia Group LLC* ***(G-9861)***
Diatomite Corp of America..........305 466-0075
19925 Ne 39th Pl Miami (33180) ***(G-9465)***
Diaz Brothers Corp..........305 364-4911
7750 W 24th Ave Hialeah (33016) ***(G-5372)***
Diaz Go Green Inc..........407 501-2724
413 Brailiff Ct Orlando (32824) ***(G-12670)***
Dictaphone Corporation..........321 255-8668
3984 Pepsi Cola Dr Melbourne (32934) ***(G-8805)***
Diction Wear LLC..........954 696-5490
2851 Nw 11th Pl Apt 3 Fort Lauderdale (33311) ***(G-3940)***
Didna Inc..........239 851-0966
206 Hillcrest St Orlando (32801) ***(G-12671)***
Die Verse Tool & Manufacturing, Palmetto *Also called JSB Enterprises Inc* ***(G-13808)***

Diemech Turbine Solution Inc....386 804-0179
1200 Flight Line Blvd # 1 Deland (32724) ***(G-2970)***
Diemold Machine Company Inc....239 482-1400
2350 Bruner Ln Fort Myers (33912) ***(G-4431)***
Diesel Machinery Intl USA....305 551-4424
4121 Sw 90th Ct Miami (33165) ***(G-9466)***
Diesel Pro Power Inc....305 545-5588
760 Nw 4th St Ste 100 Miami (33128) ***(G-9467)***
Diesel Pro Power USA, Miami *Also called Diesel Pro Power Inc* ***(G-9467)***
Dieselsite Inc....888 414-3457
7400 W Industrial Ln # 6 Homosassa (34448) ***(G-6002)***
Dietzgen Corporation (PA)....813 286-4767
121 Kelsey Ln Ste G Tampa (33619) ***(G-17605)***
Dievac Plastics, Hialeah *Also called Acai Investments Llc* ***(G-5267)***
Digecon Plastics International....850 477-5483
3255 Potter St Pensacola (32514) ***(G-14131)***
Digi-Net Technologies Inc (PA)....352 505-7450
4420 Nw 36th Ave Ste A Gainesville (32606) ***(G-4905)***
Digicare Biomedical Tech Inc....561 689-0408
107 Commerce Rd Boynton Beach (33426) ***(G-897)***
Digichat, Gainesville *Also called Digi-Net Technologies Inc* ***(G-4905)***
Digiprint & Design Corp....786 464-1770
1460 Nw 107th Ave Ste R Sweetwater (33172) ***(G-17208)***
Digital Antenna Inc....954 747-7022
5325 Nw 108th Ave Sunrise (33351) ***(G-17115)***
Digital Antomy Smltons For HLT....937 623-7377
1720 S Orange Ave Ste 300 Orlando (32806) ***(G-12672)***
Digital Color Publications LLC....813 886-0065
6103 Johns Rd Ste 5 Tampa (33634) ***(G-17606)***
Digital Compositing Systems....954 432-4988
3309 Onyx Rd Miramar (33025) ***(G-10984)***
Digital Control Company, Clearwater *Also called Alltec Corporation* ***(G-1578)***
Digital Direct Corporation....813 448-9071
131 Burbank Rd Oldsmar (34677) ***(G-12220)***
Digital Graphics, Orlando *Also called Linographics Inc* ***(G-12913)***
Digital Lighting Systems Inc....305 264-8391
7588 Nw 8th St Fl 2 Miami (33126) ***(G-9468)***
Digital Lightwave, Largo *Also called Florida Veex Inc* ***(G-7952)***
Digital Living....407 332-9998
4303 Vineland Rd Altamonte Springs (32714) ***(G-40)***
Digital Outdoor LLC....305 944-7945
8405 Nw 29th St Doral (33122) ***(G-3329)***
Digital Output....904 285-9944
5150 Palm Valley Rd # 103 Ponte Vedra Beach (32082) ***(G-14939)***
Digital Pixel Displays LLC (PA)....321 948-3751
111 N Orange Ave Orlando (32801) ***(G-12673)***
Digital Press....407 421-3131
12002 Philbrook Ct Orlando (32825) ***(G-12674)***
Digital Printing Solutions Inc....407 671-8715
6438 University Blvd # 12 Winter Park (32792) ***(G-19402)***
Digital Propaganda Inc....407 644-8444
997 W Kennedy Blvd A12 Orlando (32810) ***(G-12675)***
Digital Publishing of Florida....813 749-8640
131 Burbank Rd Oldsmar (34677) ***(G-12221)***
Digital Scoreboards LLC....888 738-4230
333 Suth Tmami Trail Ste Venice (34285) ***(G-18541)***
Digital Tech of Lakeland Inc....863 668-8770
3020 Winter Lake Rd Lakeland (33803) ***(G-7675)***
Digital Watchdog, Tampa *Also called Kaltec Electronics Inc* ***(G-17814)***
Digitech Graphics Group, Lakeland *Also called Digital Tech of Lakeland Inc* ***(G-7675)***
Digitrax Inc....850 872-9890
2443 Transmitter Rd Panama City (32404) ***(G-13893)***
Diji Integrated Press, Tampa *Also called Jak Corporate Holdings Inc* ***(G-17802)***
Dilan Enterprises Inc....305 887-3051
2339 W 9th Ct Hialeah (33010) ***(G-5373)***
Diligent Services Inc....561 368-1478
2730 Nw 1st Ave Boca Raton (33431) ***(G-501)***
Dillco Inc....386 734-7510
1842 Patterson Ave Deland (32724) ***(G-2971)***
Dillon Yarn Corporation (PA)....973 684-1600
3250 W Coml Blvd Ste 320 Fort Lauderdale (33309) ***(G-3941)***
Dills Enterprises LLC....941 493-1993
301 Seaboard Ave Venice (34285) ***(G-18542)***
Dilo Direct, Odessa *Also called Dilo Production Inc* ***(G-12116)***
Dilo Production Inc (PA)....727 376-5593
11642 Pyramid Dr Odessa (33556) ***(G-12116)***
Diloren Inc....786 618-9671
8800 Nw 13th Ter Doral (33172) ***(G-3330)***
Dilution Solutions Inc....800 451-6628
2090 Sunnydale Blvd Clearwater (33765) ***(G-1652)***
Dimar Usa Inc (PA)....954 590-8573
1332 W Mcnab Rd Fort Lauderdale (33309) ***(G-3942)***
Dimension Machine Engrg LLC....586 948-3600
5201 Sw 28th Pl Cape Coral (33914) ***(G-1413)***
Dimension Machine Tool Inc....586 948-3600
5201 Sw 28th Pl Cape Coral (33914) ***(G-1414)***
Dimension Photo Engrv Co Inc....813 251-0244
1507 W Cass St Tampa (33606) ***(G-17607)***
Dimple Products Inc....704 320-0700
7 Clear Ct Palm Coast (32137) ***(G-13691)***
Dinner Belle Inc....747 210-6284
4214 Inverrary Blvd # 89 Lauderhill (33319) ***(G-8108)***
Dion Fuels LLC (PA)....305 296-2000
5300 Overseas Hwy 2 Key West (33040) ***(G-7186)***
Dion Money Management LLC....413 458-4700
3101 Green Dolphin Ln Naples (34102) ***(G-11227)***
Diora Professionnel LLC....954 628-5163
1037 Nw 3rd St Hallandale Beach (33009) ***(G-5181)***
Dioxide Materials Inc....217 239-1400
3998 Fau Blvd Ste 300 Boca Raton (33431) ***(G-502)***
Dioxyme, Fort Myers *Also called Taylor L Max L C* ***(G-4625)***
Dip-A-Dee Donuts....352 460-4266
1376 W North Blvd Leesburg (34748) ***(G-8150)***
Direcly, Coral Gables *Also called Merkari Group Inc* ***(G-2175)***
Direct Impressions Inc....239 549-4484
1335 Miramar St Cape Coral (33904) ***(G-1415)***
Direct Media Solutions Inc....904 419-3675
11555 Central Pkwy # 804 Jacksonville (32224) ***(G-6319)***
Direct Optical Research Co....727 319-9000
8725 115th Ave Largo (33773) ***(G-7932)***
Direct Response Publication....561 620-3010
315 Se Mizner Blvd # 208 Boca Raton (33432) ***(G-503)***
Direct Sales and Design Inc....954 522-5477
1140 Ne 7th Ave Unit 3 Fort Lauderdale (33304) ***(G-3943)***
Dirtbag Choppers Inc....904 725-7600
27 W 11th St Atlantic Beach (32233) ***(G-219)***
Dirtrbags Chopper....904 725-7600
2426 Mayport Rd Ste 5 Jacksonville (32233) ***(G-6320)***
Disbrow Corporation (PA)....813 621-9444
8412 Sabal Indus Blvd Tampa (33619) ***(G-17608)***
Discipline Marketing Inc....305 793-7358
21230 Sw 246th St Homestead (33031) ***(G-5963)***
Discos Y Empanadas Argentina....305 326-9300
2181 Nw 10th Ave Miami (33127) ***(G-9469)***
Discount Awnings Inc....941 753-5700
6620 19th St E Unit 111 Sarasota (34243) ***(G-16207)***
Discount Boat Tops Inc....727 536-4412
14000 66th St Ste A Largo (33771) ***(G-7933)***
Discount Distributors Inc....772 336-0092
725 Se Port St Lucie Blvd # 106 Port Saint Lucie (34984) ***(G-15102)***
Discount Metal Mart, Plant City *Also called Metal Systems Inc* ***(G-14448)***
Discount Printing, Fort Lauderdale *Also called V P Press Inc* ***(G-4301)***
Discount Welds LLC....305 637-3939
2745 Nw 21st St Miami (33142) ***(G-9470)***
Discovery Aviation Inc....321 752-0332
100 Aerospace Dr Unit 4 Melbourne (32901) ***(G-8806)***
Discovery Canvas East Coast Co....786 487-8897
1386 Nw 54th St Miami (33142) ***(G-9471)***
Discovery Tank Testing Inc....561 840-1666
1209 Gateway Rd Ste 203 West Palm Beach (33403) ***(G-18855)***
Discovery Technology Intl Inc (HQ)....941 907-4444
6700 Professional Pkwy Lakewood Ranch (34240) ***(G-7843)***
Discrete Electronics Inc....941 575-8700
1205 Elizabeth St Ste I Punta Gorda (33950) ***(G-15204)***
Distant Shores Media, Orlando *Also called Unfoldingword Corporation* ***(G-13289)***
Distinct Dsgns Cstm Coml Case....727 530-0119
1135 Starkey Rd Largo (33771) ***(G-7934)***
Distinct.ink, Winter Park *Also called Chargers and Cases LLC* ***(G-19393)***
Distinctive Cabinet Designs....239 641-5165
5556 Yahl St Ste A Naples (34109) ***(G-11228)***
Distinctive Creat Intr Wkshp I....954 921-1861
2126 Pierce St Hollywood (33020) ***(G-5812)***
Distingshed Gntlman MBL Dtling....321 200-4331
7512 Dr Phillips Blvd 50-1 Orlando (32819) ***(G-12676)***
Distribuidora Continental SA....305 374-4474
6355 Nw 36th St Ste 506 Virginia Gardens (33166) ***(G-18687)***
Distribuidora Giorgio Usa LLC....305 685-6366
12815 Nw 45th Ave Opa Locka (33054) ***(G-12307)***
District 95 Wood Working Inc....888 400-3136
1040 Sw 10th Ave Ste 4 Pompano Beach (33069) ***(G-14666)***
Dittmer Architectural Aluminum, Winter Springs *Also called Walt Dittmer and Sons Inc* ***(G-19488)***
Diva Stuff....386 256-2521
1368 N Us Highway 1 # 406 Ormond Beach (32174) ***(G-13363)***
Divas Fashion....786 717-7039
8382 Bird Rd Miami (33155) ***(G-9472)***
Divatti & Co LLC....786 354-1888
1050 E 17th St Miramar (33027) ***(G-10985)***
Dive Rite, Lake City *Also called Lamartek Inc* ***(G-7364)***
Divers Den, Panama City *Also called Gigli Enterprises Inc* ***(G-13909)***
Diverse Co....863 425-4251
1950 Industrial Park Rd Mulberry (33860) ***(G-11123)***
Diverse Transport Systems, Mulberry *Also called Diverse Co* ***(G-11123)***
Diversfied Lifting Systems Inc....813 248-2299
4702 Distribution Dr Tampa (33605) ***(G-17609)***
Diversfied Mtl Specialists Inc....941 244-0935
105 Triple Dmd Blvd Ste 1 North Venice (34275) ***(G-11757)***

ALPHABETIC

Diversified Graphics Inc 407 425-9443
720 Franklin Ln Orlando (32801) *(G-12677)*
Diversified Mining Inc 407 923-3194
2178 Crandon Ave Winter Park (32789) *(G-19403)*
Diversified Pallets Inc 904 491-6800
1894 S 14th St Ste 2 Fernandina Beach (32034) *(G-3735)*
Diversified Performance System 904 765-7181
6800 N Main St Jacksonville (32208) *(G-6321)*
Diversified Products Mfg, Jacksonville *Also called Paw Inc (G-6661)*
Diversified Pubg & Design 239 598-4826
975 Imperl Golf Cours Bld Naples (34110) *(G-11229)*
Diversified Sales Company, Oldsmar *Also called DSC Sales of SC Inc (G-12222)*
Diversified Welding Inc 561 996-9398
714 Nw Avenue L Belle Glade (33430) *(G-347)*
Diversified Woodworks LLC 321 591-9935
26 North Ct Indialantic (32903) *(G-6058)*
Diversified Yacht Services Inc 239 765-8700
751 Fishermans Wharf Fort Myers Beach (33931) *(G-4661)*
Diversity Best Practices, Winter Park *Also called Working Mother Media Inc (G-19461)*
Diversityinc Media LLC 973 494-0539
111 Reef Rd Palm Beach (33480) *(G-13553)*
Diversitypro Corp 305 691-2348
6632 Sw 64th Ave South Miami (33143) *(G-16815)*
Divine Coffee Roasters, Sarasota *Also called Neat Print Inc (G-16523)*
Divine Dovetail 561 245-7601
1050 Nw 1st Ave Ste 7 Boca Raton (33432) *(G-504)*
Divinitas Displays LLC 407 660-6625
7598 Currency Dr Orlando (32809) *(G-12678)*
Division 5 Florida Inc 904 964-4513
417 E Weldon St Starke (32091) *(G-16893)*
Division 5 Steel, Starke *Also called Division 5 Florida Inc (G-16893)*
Divitae Inc 786 585-5556
570 E 65th St Hialeah (33013) *(G-5374)*
Diwi Jewelry, Oakland Park *Also called International Jewelry Designs (G-11814)*
Dixie Lime Andstone Co 352 512-0180
2441 E Fort King St Ocala (34471) *(G-11920)*
Dixie Metal Products Inc (PA) 352 873-2554
442 Sw 54th Ct Ocala (34474) *(G-11921)*
Dixie Metalcraft Incorporated 239 337-4299
3050 Warehouse Rd Fort Myers (33916) *(G-4432)*
Dixie Restorations LLC 813 785-2159
2212 Hilda Ann Rd Zephyrhills (33540) *(G-19514)*
Dixie Signs Inc 863 644-3521
2930 Drane Field Rd Lakeland (33811) *(G-7676)*
Dixie Southern, Duette *Also called Southstern Indus Fbrcators LLC (G-3563)*
Dixie Sptic Tank Orange Cy LLC 386 775-3051
1200 S Leavitt Ave Orange City (32763) *(G-12375)*
Dixie Structures & Maintenance (PA) 205 274-4525
1216 Hopedale Dr Fort Myers (33919) *(G-4433)*
Dixie Tank Company 904 781-9500
5349 Highway Ave Jacksonville (32254) *(G-6322)*
Dixie Workshop Inc 352 629-4699
2350 Nw 42nd St Ocala (34475) *(G-11922)*
Dixie-Southern Arkansas LLC 479 751-9183
9135 58th Dr E Bradenton (34202) *(G-1031)*
Dixon Screen Printing LLC 850 476-3924
312 W Detroit Blvd Pensacola (32534) *(G-14132)*
Dixon Ticonderoga Company (HQ) 407 829-9000
615 Crscent Exec Ct Ste 5 Lake Mary (32746) *(G-7409)*
Diy Blinds Inc 305 692-8877
19515 Presidential Way North Miami Beach (33179) *(G-11671)*
Dizenzo Manufacturing Intl 954 978-4624
4400 Nw 19th Ave Ste J Deerfield Beach (33064) *(G-2815)*
Dj Cabinet Factory Inc 786 483-8868
2552 W 3rd Ct Hialeah (33010) *(G-5375)*
Dj DK, Orlando *Also called Unique Designs Prof Svcs Inc (G-13290)*
Dj Live Productions LLC 407 383-1740
999 Douglas Ave Altamonte Springs (32714) *(G-41)*
Dj Plastics Inc 407 656-6677
946 Century Ln Apopka (32703) *(G-131)*
Dj Roof and Solar Supply LLC 954 557-1992
2009 Admirals Way Fort Lauderdale (33316) *(G-3944)*
Dj/Pj Inc 813 907-6359
13215 38th St N Clearwater (33762) *(G-1653)*
DK Events LLC 305 760-2963
1565 Ne 150th St Miami (33161) *(G-9473)*
DK International Assoc Inc 954 828-1256
1417 Sw 1st Ave Fort Lauderdale (33315) *(G-3945)*
Dka Distributing LLC 800 275-4352
5010 Tampa West Blvd Tampa (33634) *(G-17610)*
Dkia, Fort Lauderdale *Also called DK International Assoc Inc (G-3945)*
Dkm Machine Manufacturing 904 733-0103
3811 University Blvd W # 26 Jacksonville (32217) *(G-6323)*
Dl Cabinetry Orlando LLC 504 669-7847
7025 W Colonial Dr Orlando (32818) *(G-12679)*
Dl Myers Corp 609 698-8800
5500 Military Trl Ste 22 Jupiter (33458) *(G-7024)*
Dla Document Services 813 828-4646
2617 Florida Keys Ave # 25 Tampa (33621) *(G-17611)*
Dlc, Winter Springs *Also called Daniel Lampert Communications (G-19471)*
Dlp Industries, Miramar *Also called Press-Rite Inc (G-11030)*
Dlux Printing & Publishing, Pensacola *Also called Dlux Printing Inc (G-14133)*
Dlux Printing Inc 850 457-8494
3320 N W St Pensacola (32505) *(G-14133)*
Dlz Holdings South Inc (PA) 352 344-8741
956 S Us Highway 41 Inverness (34450) *(G-6086)*
Dm Stratton LLC 904 342-7063
564 Magnolia Ave Saint Johns (32259) *(G-15677)*
Dma Cabinets Inc 352 249-8147
1653b W Gulf To Lake Hwy Lecanto (34461) *(G-8133)*
DMC Components Intl LLC 407 478-4064
4202 Metric Dr Winter Park (32792) *(G-19404)*
Dmoney365 Logistic LLC 954 529-8202
1331 S State Road 7 North Lauderdale (33068) *(G-11613)*
Dmr Creative Marketing LLC 954 725-3750
321 Goolsby Blvd Deerfield Beach (33442) *(G-2816)*
Dmr Woodworks LLC 850 969-9261
1161 W Detroit Blvd Pensacola (32534) *(G-14134)*
Dna Brands Inc (PA) 561 654-5722
275 E Coml Blvd Ste 208 Lauderdale By The SE (33308) *(G-8084)*
Dna Surface Concepts Inc 561 328-7302
1980 Avenue L Riviera Beach (33404) *(G-15320)*
DNE Pot Sbob Inc 239 936-8880
11000 Metro Pkwy Ste 10 Fort Myers (33966) *(G-4434)*
Dnt Software Corp 407 323-0987
1710 Beacon Dr Sanford (32771) *(G-16037)*
Do You Remember Inc 305 987-9111
36 Island Ave Apt 45 Miami Beach (33139) *(G-10663)*
Dobbs & Brodeur Bookbinders 305 885-5215
1030 E 14th St Hialeah (33010) *(G-5376)*
Dobros Inc 386 279-0003
803 W New York Ave Deland (32720) *(G-2972)*
Doch LLC 571 491-7578
14630 Grenadine Dr Apt 7 Tampa (33613) *(G-17612)*
Dock Builders Supply, Gibsonton *Also called W R Williams Enterprises Inc (G-5035)*
Dockside At Horseshoe Beach L 352 377-4616
6809 Nw 48th Ln Gainesville (32653) *(G-4906)*
Docs Welding LLC 813 846-5022
4708 Schield Ct Plant City (33566) *(G-14425)*
Doctor Easy Medical Pdts LLC 904 276-7200
1029 Blanding Blvd # 701 Orange Park (32065) *(G-12389)*
Doctor Granite and Cabinets 321 368-1779
3532 Chica Cir West Melbourne (32904) *(G-18772)*
Doctor Pickle LLC 772 985-5919
1279 W Palmetto Park Rd Boca Raton (33427) *(G-505)*
Doctor Scientific Organica, Riviera Beach *Also called Lavi Enterprises LLC (G-15342)*
Doctors Scientific Organica LLC (HQ) 888 455-9031
1210 W 13th St Riviera Beach (33404) *(G-15321)*
Doctorxs Allergy Formula 904 758-2088
2375 St Johns Bluff Rd S Jacksonville (32246) *(G-6324)*
Docuprint Corporation 305 639-8618
7950 Nw 53rd St Ste 337 Miami (33166) *(G-9474)*
Docuvision Incorporated 954 791-0091
3650 Hacienda Blvd Ste F Davie (33314) *(G-2517)*
DOE & Ingalls Florida Oper LLC 813 347-4741
9940 Currie Davis Dr # 13 Tampa (33619) *(G-17613)*
Doerfler Manufacturing Inc 763 772-3728
235 N Central Ave Umatilla (32784) *(G-18498)*
Doerrs Cstm Cabinets Trim LLC 904 540-7024
1300 Wildwood Dr Saint Augustine (32086) *(G-15538)*
Doerrs Custom Cabinets & Trim 904 540-7024
1761 Dobbs Rd Saint Augustine (32084) *(G-15539)*
Dok Solution Inc 727 209-1313
12253 62nd St Largo (33773) *(G-7935)*
Dolci Peccati LLC 954 632-8551
1900 N Bayshore Dr Miami (33132) *(G-9475)*
Dole 305 925-7900
10055 Nw 12th St Doral (33172) *(G-3331)*
Doll Maker LLC 800 851-5183
11330 Tamiami Trl E Naples (34113) *(G-11230)*
Doll Maker, The, Naples *Also called Doll Maker LLC (G-11230)*
Doll Marine Metal Fabrica 954 941-5093
6800 Nw 15th Way Fort Lauderdale (33309) *(G-3946)*
Doll Marine Metal Fabrication 954 941-5093
250 S Dixie Hwy E Pompano Beach (33060) *(G-14667)*
Dollar & Penny Stretchers LLC 941 830-5341
13100 S Mccall Rd Port Charlotte (33981) *(G-14973)*
Doller Marine Sales & Services 954 463-9988
100 Sw 28th St Fort Lauderdale (33315) *(G-3947)*
Dolmar Foods Inc 262 303-6026
5920 Se Hames Rd Belleview (34420) *(G-368)*
Dolomite Inc 850 482-4962
1321 Highway 71 Marianna (32448) *(G-8576)*
Dolph Map Company Inc 954 763-4732
1600 E Commercial Blvd Oakland Park (33334) *(G-11799)*
Dolphin Boat Lifts Inc 239 936-1782
6440 Topaz Ct Fort Myers (33966) *(G-4435)*
Dolphin Boats, Princeton *Also called Kz Manufacturing LLC (G-15185)*

Dolphin Kitchen & Bath 305 482-9486
2051 Nw 112th Ave Ste 123 Miami (33172) *(G-9476)*
Dolphin Paddlesports Inc 941 924-2785
6018 S Tamiami Trl Sarasota (34231) *(G-16412)*
Dolphin Publishing, Miami Springs *Also called Dolphin/Curtis Publishing Co (G-10890)*
Dolphin Sheet Metal Inc 561 744-0242
142 Jupiter St Jupiter (33458) *(G-7025)*
Dolphin/Curtis Publishing Co (PA) 305 594-0508
53 Curtiss Pkwy Miami Springs (33166) *(G-10890)*
Dolphine Jewelry Contracting 561 488-0355
9064 Villa Portofino Cir Boca Raton (33496) *(G-506)*
Domestic Custom Metals Company 239 643-2422
4275 Progress Ave Naples (34104) *(G-11231)*
Domestic Metals, Naples *Also called Domestic Custom Metals Company (G-11231)*
Dominion Printers Inc 757 340-1300
5393 Kennel St Port Charlotte (33981) *(G-14974)*
Domrey Cigar Ltd Company 941 360-8200
3001 Gateway Ctr Pkwy N Pinellas Park (33782) *(G-14344)*
Domtar Industries Inc 727 421-6919
2598 Lakeside Ct Palm Harbor (34684) *(G-13733)*
Don and Kathy Kesler 305 793-9216
3897 Kumquat Ave Miami (33133) *(G-9477)*
Don Bell Signs LLC 800 824-0080
365 Oak Pl Port Orange (32127) *(G-15016)*
Don Industrial Group LLC 305 290-4237
7760 W 20th Ave Ste 7 Hialeah (33016) *(G-5377)*
Don Schick LLC 954 491-9042
4741 Ne 13th Ave Oakland Park (33334) *(G-11800)*
Donald Art Company Inc 407 831-2525
713 Industry Rd Longwood (32750) *(G-8274)*
Donald Ross Gas Inc 561 776-1324
225 Skylark Pt Jupiter (33458) *(G-7026)*
Donald Smith Logging Inc 850 697-3975
127 Cora Mae Rd Carrabelle (32322) *(G-1497)*
Donarra Extrusions LLC 352 369-5552
1811 Sw 42nd Ave Ocala (34474) *(G-11923)*
Donau Carbon US Lcc 352 465-5959
551 N Us Highway 41 Dunnellon (34432) *(G-3596)*
Done Right Fire Gear Repr Inc 727 848-9019
7621 Maryland Ave Hudson (34667) *(G-6021)*
Done Rite Pumps 305 953-3380
4240 Nw 133rd St Opa Locka (33054) *(G-12308)*
Dongili Investment Group Inc 941 927-3003
5563 Marquesas Cir Sarasota (34233) *(G-16413)*
Donica International Inc 954 217-7616
7500 Nw 52nd St Miami (33166) *(G-9478)*
Donna Lynn Enterprises Inc 772 286-2812
10358 Rverside Dr Ste 130 Palm Beach Gardens (33410) *(G-13584)*
Donna M Walker PA 561 289-0437
11137 Harbour Springs Cir Boca Raton (33428) *(G-507)*
Donnelley Financial LLC 305 371-3900
200 S Biscayne Blvd # 1750 Miami (33131) *(G-9479)*
Donoso Printing Corp 786 508-9426
9811 Nw 80th Ave Miami Lakes (33016) *(G-10782)*
Donovan Home Services LLC 813 644-9488
3390 Gandy Blvd N Saint Petersburg (33702) *(G-15762)*
Dons Cabinets and Woodworking 727 863-3404
15801 Archer St Hudson (34667) *(G-6022)*
Dons Custom Service Inc 954 491-4043
900 Ne 3rd Ave Fort Lauderdale (33304) *(G-3948)*
Dont Fade Rehydrade, Boca Raton *Also called Rehydrade LLC (G-687)*
Dontech Industries Inc 847 682-1776
9 Jefferson Ct S Saint Petersburg (33711) *(G-15763)*
Donzi Yachts, Fort Lauderdale *Also called Roscioli International Inc (G-4215)*
Donzi Yachts, Bradenton *Also called Roscioli International Inc (G-1107)*
Door Shop, The, Hollywood *Also called Trebor USA Corp (G-5925)*
Door Styles Inc 305 653-4447
1178 Nw 163rd Dr Miami (33169) *(G-9480)*
Doorknob Discount Center LLC 813 963-3104
18404 Bittern Ave Lutz (33558) *(G-8380)*
Doormark Inc 954 418-4700
430 Goolsby Blvd Deerfield Beach (33442) *(G-2817)*
Doors 4 U Inc 786 400-2298
7322 Nw 79th Ter Medley (33166) *(G-8643)*
Doors and Hardware Tampa Bay, Largo *Also called Architctral Mllwk Slutions Inc (G-7899)*
Doors Molding and More 727 498-8552
2894 22nd Ave N Saint Petersburg (33713) *(G-15764)*
Doorway Projects Inc 561 523-2040
6484 Kirsten Way Lake Worth (33467) *(G-7544)*
Dor A Lum Corporation 305 884-3922
7040 Nw 77th Ter Medley (33166) *(G-8644)*
Dorado Custom Boats LLC 727 786-3800
1400 L And R Indus Blvd Tarpon Springs (34689) *(G-18295)*
Dorado Graphix LLC 904 751-4500
10592 Balmoral Cir E # 9 Jacksonville (32218) *(G-6325)*
Dorado Marine Inc 727 786-3800
270 Hedden Ct Ozona (34660) *(G-13467)*
Doral Building Supply Corp 305 471-9797
5095 Nw 79th Ave Doral (33166) *(G-3332)*
Doral Dgtal Reprographics Corp 305 704-3194
5701 Nw 79th Ave Doral (33166) *(G-3333)*
Doral Family Journal LLC 305 300-4594
10773 Nw 58th St Ste 96 Doral (33178) *(G-3334)*
Doral Imaging Institute LLC 305 594-2881
2760 Sw 97th Ave Apt 101 Miami (33165) *(G-9481)*
Doralum, Medley *Also called Dor A Lum Corporation (G-8644)*
Doran Manufacturing Corp Fla 904 731-3313
6261 Powers Ave Jacksonville (32217) *(G-6326)*
Dorward Energy Corporation 727 490-1778
447 3rd Ave N Ste 400 Saint Petersburg (33701) *(G-15765)*
Dosal Tobacco Corporation (PA) 305 685-2949
4775 Nw 132nd St Opa Locka (33054) *(G-12309)*
DOT Blue Trading Inc 954 646-0448
3100 Nw 72nd Ave Ste 126 Miami (33122) *(G-9482)*
DOT Green Energy Inc 717 505-8686
100 Hampton Rd Lot 84 Clearwater (33759) *(G-1654)*
Dotamed LLC 786 594-0144
6332 Nw 99th Ave Doral (33178) *(G-3335)*
Dotchi LLC 305 477-0024
6807 Biscayne Blvd Miami (33138) *(G-9483)*
Dotrailings.com, Cocoa *Also called Amazon Metal Fabricators Inc (G-1994)*
Double D S Tobacco 772 871-9910
7560 Us Hwy 1 Delray Beach (33446) *(G-3070)*
Double Down Boat Works Inc 305 984-3000
8204 Sw 103rd Ave Miami (33173) *(G-9484)*
Double Envelope Corporation 352 375-0738
2500 Ne 39th Ave Gainesville (32609) *(G-4907)*
Double H Enterprises Inc 972 562-8588
170 Bear Foot Trl Ormond Beach (32174) *(G-13364)*
Double Header LLC 352 377-4458
3015 Nw 38th St Gainesville (32606) *(G-4908)*
Double J of Broward Inc (PA) 954 659-8880
1800 N Commerce Pkwy # 2 Weston (33326) *(G-19121)*
Double R Mfg Ocala Inc 352 873-1441
5529 Sw 1st Ln Ocala (34474) *(G-11924)*
Double R Publishing 305 525-3573
621 Nw 10th Ct Boynton Beach (33426) *(G-898)*
Doug Bloodworth Enterprises 407 247-9728
3211 Lake Griffin Rd Lady Lake (32159) *(G-7325)*
Dougherty Manufacturing, Edgewater *Also called Blue Water Dynamics LLC (G-3614)*
Douglas A Fisher Inc 941 951-0189
957 N Lime Ave Sarasota (34237) *(G-16414)*
Douglas Abbott 407 422-3597
3708 S John Young Pkwy Orlando (32839) *(G-12680)*
Douglas Fuel II Inc 305 620-0707
3701 Nw 167th St Miami Gardens (33055) *(G-10737)*
Douglas Machines Corp 727 461-3477
4500 110th Ave N Clearwater (33762) *(G-1655)*
Douglas Marine, Hollywood *Also called Spa Cover Inc (G-5913)*
Douglass Screen Printers Inc 863 687-8545
2710 New Tampa Hwy Lakeland (33815) *(G-7677)*
Dover Cylinder Head Inc (PA) 850 785-6569
2704 W 15th St 98 Panama City (32401) *(G-13894)*
Dover Cylinder Head of Jackson ....
80 Industrial Loop N A Orange Park (32073) *(G-12390)*
Dowe Gallagher Aerospace 941 256-2179
7425 16th St E Sarasota (34243) *(G-16208)*
Dowels Pins & Shafts Inc 727 461-1255
1975 Calumet St Clearwater (33765) *(G-1656)*
Dowling Graphics Inc 727 573-5997
12920 Automobile Blvd Clearwater (33762) *(G-1657)*
Down Shift LLC 813 431-2389
4504 Scott Rd Lutz (33558) *(G-8381)*
Downes Trading Co 813 855-7122
5730 Stag Thicket Ln Palm Harbor (34685) *(G-13734)*
Downey & Associates, Altamonte Springs *Also called Bld Industries (G-33)*
Downey Group LLC 954 972-0026
1100 Nw 15th Ave Pompano Beach (33069) *(G-14668)*
Downtown Projects I LLC 352 226-8288
702 Nw 12th Ave Gainesville (32601) *(G-4909)*
Doyle Ploch Sailmakers, Saint Petersburg *Also called Southern Interest Co Inc (G-15917)*
Doyles Fine Wood Working Inc 813 763-7800
1019 Redbud Cir Plant City (33563) *(G-14426)*
DP EMB & Screen Prints Inc 954 245-5902
3485 N Hiatus Rd Sunrise (33351) *(G-17116)*
Dp Industries Inc 321 356-3352
6375 Carroll Cir Saint Cloud (34771) *(G-15649)*
Dp Pet Products Inc 407 888-4627
5340 Young Pine Rd 8 Orlando (32829) *(G-12681)*
Dpdm Inc 561 327-4150
10444 White Pinto Ct Lake Worth (33449) *(G-7545)*
Dpf Solutions Group LLC 904 580-5343
6100 Philips Hwy Jacksonville (32216) *(G-6327)*
Dpi Information Inc 813 258-8004
8402 Laurel Fair Cir # 209 Tampa (33610) *(G-17614)*
Dpr Print & Promotional, Deerfield Beach *Also called Print Basics Inc (G-2891)*
Dprint, Lakeland *Also called Douglass Screen Printers Inc (G-7677)*

Dps Powder Coating 727 573-2797
4980 110th Ave N Clearwater (33760) ***(G-1658)***
Dr Bains Premier Cbd Oil 727 992-5289
6121 Fjord Way New Port Richey (34652) ***(G-11489)***
Dr Jills Foot Pads Inc 954 573-6557
384 S Military Trl Deerfield Beach (33442) ***(G-2818)***
Dr Pepper Bottling Co 407 354-5800
1700 Directors Row Orlando (32809) ***(G-12682)***
Dr Pepper/Seven Up Inc 321 433-3622
1313 W King St Cocoa (32922) ***(G-2015)***
Dr Pepper/Seven Up Inc 352 732-9777
3337 Sw 7th St Ocala (34474) ***(G-11925)***
Dr Pepper/Seven Up Inc 561 995-6260
7251 W Plmtt Prk Rd Ste 3 Boca Raton (33433) ***(G-508)***
Dr Spirits Company LLC 561 349-5005
604 Lake Ave Lake Worth (33460) ***(G-7546)***
Dr Worthington Orthodonti 813 968-4040
3640 Madaca Ln Tampa (33618) ***(G-17615)***
Dr. Botanicals, Miami Beach *Also called F&J USA LLC* ***(G-10666)***
Dr. Pepper Snapple, Boca Raton *Also called Dr Pepper/Seven Up Inc* ***(G-508)***
Drab To Fab 941 475-7700
136 S Mccall Rd Englewood (34223) ***(G-3675)***
Draggin Trailers Inc 352 351-8790
3100 Se 50th Pl Ocala (34480) ***(G-11926)***
Dragon Factory, Jacksonville Beach *Also called Dragon Glassing LLC* ***(G-6942)***
Dragon Flower Winery, Summerfield *Also called Bea Sue Vineyards Inc* ***(G-17057)***
Dragon Glassing LLC 904 509-1860
1378 Eastwind Dr Jacksonville Beach (32250) ***(G-6942)***
Dragonfire Industries Inc 407 999-2215
4065 L B Mcleod Rd Ste G1 Orlando (32811) ***(G-12683)***
Dragonfly Graphics 772 879-9800
861 Sw Lakehurst Dr Ste B Port Saint Lucie (34983) ***(G-15103)***
Dragonfly Graphics Inc 352 375-2144
319 Sw 3rd Ave Gainesville (32601) ***(G-4910)***
Dragons Miracle LLC 561 670-5546
160 W Camino Real Ste 154 Boca Raton (33432) ***(G-509)***
Drake Inc 239 590-9199
2920 Rockfill Rd Fort Myers (33916) ***(G-4436)***
Drake Ready Mix Inc 239 590-9199
2920 Rockfill Rd Fort Myers (33916) ***(G-4437)***
Drake Tool Co Inc 407 859-4221
10211 General Dr Orlando (32824) ***(G-12684)***
Drapery Control Systems Inc 386 756-0101
3817 S Nova Rd Ste 104 Port Orange (32127) ***(G-15017)***
Drapery Control Systems Inc (PA) 305 653-1712
5545 Nw 35th Ave D Fort Lauderdale (33309) ***(G-3949)***
Drapery Masters LLC 407 448-6898
3718 Grissom Ln Kissimmee (34741) ***(G-7239)***
Drb Packaging LLC 321 877-2802
386 Commerce Pkwy Rockledge (32955) ***(G-15405)***
Drb Packaging LLC 321 877-2802
386 Commerce Pkwy Rockledge (32955) ***(G-15406)***
Dream Cuizine 727 943-8289
4952 Ridgemoor Blvd Palm Harbor (34685) ***(G-13735)***
Dreamboat Canvas LLC 954 536-2415
3710 Harrison St Apt 3 Hollywood (33021) ***(G-5813)***
Dreamline Aerospace 954 544-2365
7649 Pines Blvd Pembroke Pines (33024) ***(G-14030)***
Dreams Inc 954 377-0002
15701 Sw 29th St Miramar (33027) ***(G-10986)***
Dreamspinner Press LLC 800 970-3759
10800 Kilcrease Way Tallahassee (32305) ***(G-17243)***
Drench Khari LLC 561 507-4723
331 W 19th St Riviera Beach (33404) ***(G-15322)***
Dresser Inc 318 640-2250
12970 Normandy Blvd Jacksonville (32221) ***(G-6328)***
Dresser LLC 904 781-7071
12970 Normandy Blvd Jacksonville (32221) ***(G-6329)***
Drew Estate LLC (PA) 786 581-1800
12415 Sw 136th Ave Ste 7 Miami (33186) ***(G-9485)***
Drew Scientific Inc (HQ) 305 418-2320
14100 Nw 57th Ct Miami Lakes (33014) ***(G-10783)***
Drewlu Enterprises Inc 407 478-7872
3412 Aloma Ave Ste 1 Winter Park (32792) ***(G-19405)***
Drexel Metals Inc 727 572-7900
8641 Elm Fair Blvd Tampa (33610) ***(G-17616)***
Drinkable Air Inc 954 533-6415
2944 Nw 27th St Bldg 14 Lauderdale Lakes (33311) ***(G-8086)***
Drinks On ME 305 LLC 786 488-2356
6118 Nw 7th Ave Miami (33127) ***(G-9486)***
Drip Communication LLC 407 730-5519
6831 Edgwter Cmmerce Pkwy Orlando (32810) ***(G-12685)***
Driveshaft Power Inc 561 433-0022
10101 Lantana Rd Ste K Lake Worth (33449) ***(G-7547)***
Drone Aviation, Jacksonville *Also called Lighter Than Air Systems Corp* ***(G-6557)***
Drone Clips By Majic 407 619-3704
4772 Lonsdale Cir Orlando (32817) ***(G-12686)***
Drone Defense Systems LLC 305 607-6708
172 Gray Dove Ct Daytona Beach (32119) ***(G-2659)***
Drone Imaging Services LLC 407 620-5258
8540 Summerville Pl Orlando (32819) ***(G-12687)***
Drone Master Shots LLC 407 295-7715
3603 N Pine Hills Rd Orlando (32808) ***(G-12688)***
Drone Pics and Vids Corp 786 558-4027
13237 Sw 45th Ln Miami (33175) ***(G-9487)***
Drones Shop LLC 772 224-8118
4406 Se Graham Dr Stuart (34997) ***(G-16933)***
Drs Advanced Isr LLC 321 622-1202
100 N Babcock St Melbourne (32935) ***(G-8807)***
Drs Advanced Isr LLC 850 226-4888
654 Anchors St Nw Ste 1 Fort Walton Beach (32548) ***(G-4791)***
Drs Allergy, Jacksonville *Also called Doctorxs Allergy Formula* ***(G-6324)***
Drs C3 Systems Inc 850 302-3909
645 Anchors St Nw Fort Walton Beach (32548) ***(G-4792)***
Drs Cengen Llc (HQ) 321 622-1500
100 Babcock St Melbourne Melbourne (32935) ***(G-8808)***
Drs Consolidated Controls 850 302-3000
645 Anchors St Nw Fort Walton Beach (32548) ***(G-4793)***
Drs Land Electronics 321 622-1435
100 N Babcock St Melbourne (32935) ***(G-8809)***
Drs Laurel Technologies (HQ) 727 541-6681
6200 118th Ave Largo (33773) ***(G-7936)***
Drs Leonardo Inc 850 302-3000
645 Anchors St Nw Fort Walton Beach (32548) ***(G-4794)***
Drs Leonardo Inc 850 302-3514
640 Lovejoy Rd Nw Fort Walton Beach (32548) ***(G-4795)***
Drs Ntwork Imaging Systems LLC 321 309-1500
3520 Dixie Hwy Ne Palm Bay (32905) ***(G-13509)***
Drs Ntwork Imaging Systems LLC (HQ) 321 309-1500
100 N Babcock St Melbourne (32935) ***(G-8810)***
Drs S and T Optronics Div 321 309-1500
100 N Babcock St Melbourne (32935) ***(G-8811)***
Drs Sensors Targeting Systems 321 309-1500
100 N Babcock St Melbourne (32935) ***(G-8812)***
Drs Soneticom Inc 321 733-0400
100 N Babcock St Melbourne (32935) ***(G-8813)***
Drs Systems Inc 973 451-3525
100 N Babcock St Melbourne (32935) ***(G-8814)***
Drs Tactical Systems Inc 321 727-3672
100 N Babcock St Melbourne (32935) ***(G-8815)***
Drs Technologies, Fort Walton Beach *Also called Drs Training Ctrl Systems LLC* ***(G-4796)***
Drs Technology, Melbourne *Also called Drs Soneticom Inc* ***(G-8813)***
Drs Training Ctrl Systems LLC (HQ) 850 302-3000
645 Anchors St Nw Fort Walton Beach (32548) ***(G-4796)***
Drsingh Technologies Inc 352 334-7270
1912 Nw 67th Pl Gainesville (32653) ***(G-4911)***
Drt Express Inc 305 827-5005
7855 W 2nd Ct Ste 4 Hialeah (33014) ***(G-5378)***
Drt Services 321 549-1431
861 Young Ave Nw Palm Bay (32907) ***(G-13510)***
Drum Circle Distilling LLC 941 358-1900
2212 Industrial Blvd Sarasota (34234) ***(G-16415)***
Drummond Press Inc (PA) 904 354-2818
2472 Dennis St Jacksonville (32204) ***(G-6330)***
Dry Bonez Inc 321 926-6399
22180 Woodset Ln Boca Raton (33428) ***(G-510)***
Dry Color USA LLC 407 856-7788
8701 S Ct Skinner Orlando (32824) ***(G-12689)***
Dryer Vent Wizard of Pb 561 901-3464
22 Las Flores Boynton Beach (33426) ***(G-899)***
Drywall Elements 407 454-7293
1700 35th St Ste 110 Orlando (32839) ***(G-12690)***
Ds Coatings Inc 321 848-4719
18 S Butler Ave Avon Park (33825) ***(G-286)***
Ds Healthcare Group Inc (HQ) 888 404-7770
1850 Nw 84th Ave Ste 108 Doral (33126) ***(G-3336)***
Ds Laboratories, Doral *Also called Ds Healthcare Group Inc* ***(G-3336)***
Ds Powder Coating 561 660-7835
1800 4th Ave N Unit B Lake Worth Beach (33461) ***(G-7610)***
Ds Shutters Group Inc 772 260-6393
13278 Moonstone Ter Wellington (33414) ***(G-18715)***
Ds18, Miami Gardens *Also called Spirit llc* ***(G-10755)***
Dsas Air Inc 954 673-5385
4509 Nw 39th St Lauderdale Lakes (33319) ***(G-8087)***
DSC Sales of SC Inc (PA) 813 854-3131
455 Commerce Blvd Oldsmar (34677) ***(G-12222)***
Dse Inc (PA) 813 443-4809
5201 S West Shore Blvd Tampa (33611) ***(G-17617)***
Dsg Clearwater Laboratory 727 530-9444
14333 58th St N Clearwater (33760) ***(G-1659)***
DSM Lake City LLC 352 861-5843
8100 Sw 54th Ct Ocala (34476) ***(G-11927)***
Dsx Products Inc 904 744-3400
4430 Palmetto Inlt W Jacksonville (32277) ***(G-6331)***
Dtc Stairs, Miami *Also called Dade Truss Company Inc* ***(G-9431)***
DTF Woodworks 954 317-6443
4481 Sw 38th Ter Fort Lauderdale (33312) ***(G-3950)***
Dti Design Trend Inc 954 680-8370
496 W 18th St Hialeah (33010) ***(G-5379)***

Dtsystems Inc 813 994-0030
4834 W Gandy Blvd Tampa (33611) *(G-17618)*
Dubbs Fresh Detailing LLC 813 770-5194
235 Nw 1st Ave South Bay (33493) *(G-16794)*
Dubhouse Inc 954 524-3658
404 Se 15th St Fort Lauderdale (33316) *(G-3951)*
Duck In The Truck Puppets Inc 772 334-3022
1649 Ne Sunview Ter Jensen Beach (34957) *(G-6967)*
Duck Walk, Fort Lauderdale *Also called Boat International Media Inc (G-3864)*
Ducksteins Services 352 449-5678
3 Morgan Ave Leesburg (34748) *(G-8151)*
Duckworth Steel Boats Inc 727 934-2550
1051 Island Ave Tarpon Springs (34689) *(G-18296)*
Duct Design Corporation 305 827-0110
7850 W 22nd Ave Unit 1 Hialeah (33016) *(G-5380)*
Duct Dynasty 407 730-9081
465 Mandalay Rd Orlando (32809) *(G-12691)*
Dudley Blake LLC 904 866-2829
4141 Spring Park Cir Jacksonville (32207) *(G-6332)*
Duenas Mobile Applications LLC (PA) 305 851-3397
15600 Sw 288th St Ste 402 Homestead (33033) *(G-5964)*
Dugout Sportswear 386 615-0024
488 Parque Dr Ormond Beach (32174) *(G-13365)*
Dukane Seacom Inc 941 739-3200
7135 16th St E Ste 101 Sarasota (34243) *(G-16209)*
Dukeman Custom Woodwork, Jacksonville *Also called Dukemans Custom Woodworking (G-6333)*
Dukemans Custom Woodworking 904 355-5188
141 N Myrtle Ave Fl 2 Jacksonville (32204) *(G-6333)*
Dukes Brewhouse Inc 813 758-9309
1808 James L Redman Pkwy Plant City (33563) *(G-14427)*
Duley Truss Inc 352 465-0964
2591 W Dunnellon Rd 488 Dunnellon (34433) *(G-3593)*
Dulond Tool & Engineering Inc 941 758-4489
2306 Whitfield Park Loop Sarasota (34243) *(G-16210)*
Dumont Welder Services Inc 863 969-7498
143 Argentina Dr Winter Haven (33880) *(G-19318)*
Dumpster Company, Fort Myers *Also called Majic Wheels Corp (G-4521)*
Dumpstermaxx 805 552-6299
5265 University Pkwy # 101 University Park (34201) *(G-18504)*
Dumpsterme LLC 904 647-1945
13255 Lanier Rd Jacksonville (32226) *(G-6334)*
Duncan and Sons Cnstr Eqp Inc 305 216-3115
2750 Nw 209th Ter Miami Gardens (33056) *(G-10738)*
Duncanmatthews LLC 813 466-8290
7019 Silvermill Dr Tampa (33635) *(G-17619)*
Duncanson Dynasty Inc 561 288-1349
723 39th St West Palm Beach (33407) *(G-18856)*
Dunco Materials, Plant City *Also called Dunco Rock & Gravel Inc (G-14428)*
Dunco Rock & Gravel Inc 813 752-5622
3115 Sammonds Rd Plant City (33563) *(G-14428)*
Dunnellon Discount Drugs, Dunnellon *Also called Kashiben Say LLC (G-3598)*
Dunrite Metal Fabricators Inc 727 299-9242
12099 44th St N Clearwater (33762) *(G-1660)*
Duos Technologies Inc (PA) 904 652-1601
6622 Sthpint Dr S Ste 310 Jacksonville (32216) *(G-6335)*
Duos Technologies Group Inc (PA) 904 652-1616
6622 Sthpint Dr S Ste 310 Jacksonville (32216) *(G-6336)*
DUOSTECH, Jacksonville *Also called Duos Technologies Group Inc (G-6336)*
Dupont Fine Homes Inc 850 934-8545
4371 Marilyn Ct Gulf Breeze (32563) *(G-5116)*
Dupont Publishing Inc (PA) 727 573-9339
4707 140th Ave N Ste 302 Clearwater (33762) *(G-1661)*
Dupont Registry, Clearwater *Also called Dupont Publishing Inc (G-1661)*
Dupree Logging, Westville *Also called Woodie L Dupree (G-19182)*
Dupuy Silo Facility LLC (PA) 904 899-7200
1520 Edgewood Ave N Jacksonville (32254) *(G-6337)*
Dura-Cast Products Inc 863 638-3200
16160 Hwy 27 Lake Wales (33859) *(G-7507)*
Dura-Stress Inc (PA) 352 787-1422
11325 County Road 44 Leesburg (34788) *(G-8152)*
Dura-Weld Inc 561 586-0180
3599 23rd Ave S Ste 9 Lake Worth Beach (33461) *(G-7611)*
Durabody Usa LLC 954 357-2333
12068 Miramar Pkwy Miramar (33025) *(G-10987)*
Duracell Company 561 494-7550
515 N Flagler Dr Ste 1600 West Palm Beach (33401) *(G-18857)*
Duraguard Products, Tampa *Also called Pacific Die Cast Inc (G-17968)*
Duraline, Deland *Also called J B Nottingham & Co Inc (G-2986)*
Duramaster, Tampa *Also called Greenco Manufacturing Corp (G-17728)*
Duramaster Cylinders 813 882-0040
5688 W Crenshaw St Tampa (33634) *(G-17620)*
Durapoly Industries Inc 352 622-3455
191 N Highway 314a Silver Springs (34488) *(G-16781)*
Durbal Inc 727 531-3040
14115 63rd Way N Ste A Clearwater (33760) *(G-1662)*
Durisan, Sarasota *Also called Sanit Technologies LLC (G-16290)*
Durlach Holdings Inc 941 751-1672
6008 28th St E Ste A Bradenton (34203) *(G-1032)*
Durra Print Inc 850 222-4768
3044 W Tharpe St Tallahassee (32303) *(G-17244)*
Durra Quick Print Inc 850 681-2900
1334 N Monroe St Tallahassee (32303) *(G-17245)*
Dusobox Corporation 407 855-5120
2501 Investors Row # 500 Orlando (32837) *(G-12692)*
Dusobox Creative Packg Group, Orlando *Also called Dusobox Corporation (G-12692)*
Duststop Air Filters, Jacksonville *Also called Duststop Filters Inc (G-6338)*
Duststop Filters Inc 904 725-1001
165 Tresca Rd Jacksonville (32225) *(G-6338)*
Dutch Packing Co Inc 305 871-3640
74 Sw Coral Ter Ste 101 Miami (33155) *(G-9488)*
Dutchy Enterprises LLC 321 877-0700
600 Cox Rd Ste A Cocoa (32926) *(G-2016)*
Duval Bakery Products Inc 904 354-7878
1733 Evergreen Ave Jacksonville (32206) *(G-6339)*
Duval Fixtures Inc 904 757-3964
3600 Saint Augustine Rd Jacksonville (32207) *(G-6340)*
Duvo Websites, Riverview *Also called Costa Industries LLC (G-15268)*
Duy Drugs Inc 305 594-3667
1730 Nw 79th Ave Doral (33126) *(G-3337)*
DVC Marketing 727 442-7125
1313 N Howard Ave Tampa (33607) *(G-17621)*
Dvc Signs LLC 727 524-8543
12350 Belcher Rd S 14b Largo (33773) *(G-7937)*
Dvh Macleod Corp 850 224-6760
1100 N Monroe St Ste A Tallahassee (32303) *(G-17246)*
Dwi Inc 321 508-9833
1960 Howell Ln Malabar (32950) *(G-8488)*
Dwyer Precision Products Inc 904 249-3545
266 20th St N Jacksonville (32250) *(G-6341)*
Dxm Marketing Group LLC 904 332-6490
9485 Rgncy Sq Blvd # 460 Jacksonville (32225) *(G-6342)*
Dyadic Industries Intl, Jupiter *Also called Dyadic International USA Inc (G-7028)*
Dyadic International Inc (PA) 561 743-8333
140 Intrcostal Pt Dr # 404 Jupiter (33477) *(G-7027)*
Dyadic International USA Inc (HQ) 561 743-8333
140 Intrcostal Pt Dr # 404 Jupiter (33477) *(G-7028)*
Dyco 941 484-9057
6222 Tower Ln Unit A10 Sarasota (34240) *(G-16416)*
Dyer Industries Inc 954 434-9065
5501 Sw 163rd Ave Southwest Ranches (33331) *(G-16837)*
Dyn-O-Mat Inc 561 747-2301
1201 Jupiter Park Dr # 1 Jupiter (33458) *(G-7029)*
Dynabilt Technologies Corp 305 919-9800
180 W 22nd St Hialeah (33010) *(G-5381)*
Dynacolor Graphics Inc 305 625-5388
950 Se 8th St Hialeah (33010) *(G-5382)*
Dynalco Controls Corporation (HQ) 323 589-6181
5450 Nw 33rd Ave Ste 104 Fort Lauderdale (33309) *(G-3952)*
Dynamd, Bonita Springs *Also called Applied Mobility Devices LLC (G-813)*
Dynamic Alloy 352 728-7600
1018 W North Blvd Ste A Leesburg (34748) *(G-8153)*
Dynamic Aspects Inc 407 322-1923
108 Fox Chase Ct Debary (32713) *(G-2748)*
Dynamic Color Inc 954 462-0261
200 Park Central Blvd S Pompano Beach (33064) *(G-14669)*
Dynamic Dental Corp 954 344-5155
3760 Nw 126th Ave Coral Springs (33065) *(G-2242)*
Dynamic Engrg Innovations Inc 386 445-6000
32 Hargrove Grade Palm Coast (32137) *(G-13692)*
Dynamic Glucose Hlth Ctrs LLC 800 610-6422
515 E Las Olas Blvd Ste 1 Fort Lauderdale (33301) *(G-3953)*
Dynamic Manufacturing Inc 727 639-8633
2280 N Ronald Reagan Blvd Longwood (32750) *(G-8275)*
Dynamic Material Systems LLC 407 353-6885
269 Aulin Ave Ste 1003 Oviedo (32765) *(G-13427)*
Dynamic Metals LLC 561 629-7304
340 Pike Rd West Palm Beach (33411) *(G-18858)*
Dynamic Precision Group Inc (PA) 772 287-7770
3651 Se Commerce Ave Stuart (34997) *(G-16934)*
Dynamic Printing of Brandon 813 664-6880
6014 Tealside Ct Lithia (33547) *(G-8218)*
Dynamic Visions Inc 941 497-1984
355 Center Ct Venice (34285) *(G-18543)*
Dynamic Welding & Fab LLC 904 669-4682
2190 Tocoi Ter Saint Augustine (32092) *(G-15540)*
Dynamis Epoxy LLC 941 488-3999
415 E Venice Ave Venice (34285) *(G-18544)*
Dynamis Inc 941 488-3999
415 E Venice Ave Venice (34285) *(G-18545)*
Dynamo Shredder Company, Palm Harbor *Also called New Market Enterprises Ltd (G-13748)*
Dynasel Incorporated 972 733-4447
114 Grantham A Deerfield Beach (33442) *(G-2819)*
Dynasty Apparel Corp (PA) 305 685-3490
13000 Nw 42nd Ave Opa Locka (33054) *(G-12310)*

ALPHABETIC

Dynasystems LLC 410 343-7759
3445 Spring Branch Trl # 360 Melbourne (32935) ***(G-8816)***
Dyno LLC (PA) 954 971-2910
1571 W Copans Rd Ste 105 Pompano Beach (33064) ***(G-14670)***
Dyno Merchandise, Pompano Beach *Also called Dyno LLC* ***(G-14670)***
Dyno Nobel Inc 352 796-9018
14200 Brooksville Rock Rd Brooksville (34614) ***(G-1227)***
Dynofresh, Davie *Also called Hac International Inc* ***(G-2534)***
Dynomat Inc 561 747-2301
1201 Jupiter Park Dr Jupiter (33458) ***(G-7030)***
Dynorthotics Ltd Partnership 954 925-5806
1916 Tigertail Blvd Dania (33004) ***(G-2443)***
Dynotec Plastic Inc 813 248-5335
2211 N 38th St Ste A Tampa (33605) ***(G-17622)***
Dynotune Inc 941 753-8899
515 27th St E Ste 4 Bradenton (34208) ***(G-1033)***
Dyplast Products LLC 305 921-0100
12501 Nw 38th Ave Opa Locka (33054) ***(G-12311)***
E & A Industries Inc 954 278-2428
16 Ne 4th St Ste 110e Fort Lauderdale (33301) ***(G-3954)***
E & D Kitchen Cabinet Inc 786 343-8558
6790 W 6th Ct Hialeah (33012) ***(G-5383)***
E & E Woodcraft Corp 305 556-1443
1619 W 33rd Pl Hialeah (33012) ***(G-5384)***
E & M Recycling Inc 561 718-1092
630 S Palmway Lake Worth (33460) ***(G-7548)***
E & P Printing Corp 305 715-9545
7882 Nw 64th St Miami (33166) ***(G-9489)***
E 3 Maintenance 904 708-7208
13720 Old St Agstine Rd S Jacksonville (32258) ***(G-6343)***
E A S I, Tampa *Also called Engineered Air Systems Inc* ***(G-17641)***
E Benton Grimsley Inc 850 863-4064
909 Mar Walt Dr Fort Walton Beach (32547) ***(G-4797)***
E C I, Tamarac *Also called Electrical Controls Inc* ***(G-17355)***
E C I, Hialeah *Also called Environmental Contractors Inc* ***(G-5399)***
E C V Display Corp 786 586-1034
2336 W 77th St Hialeah (33016) ***(G-5385)***
E G Coatings LLC 407 624-2615
1751 Covey Ct Kissimmee (34744) ***(G-7240)***
E G Controls, Jacksonville *Also called E G Pump Controls Inc* ***(G-6344)***
E G Pump Controls Inc 904 292-0110
11790 Philips Hwy Jacksonville (32256) ***(G-6344)***
E J M Gutter, Orlando *Also called EJM Copper Inc* ***(G-12702)***
E L I T E Intergroup, Miami *Also called ELite Intl Group LLC* ***(G-9516)***
E M A C Inc (PA) 850 526-4111
4518 Lafayette St Marianna (32446) ***(G-8577)***
E M Chadbourne Inds LLC 850 429-1797
192 Hewitt St Pensacola (32503) ***(G-14135)***
E M P Inc 772 286-7343
4340 Se Commerce Ave Stuart (34997) ***(G-16935)***
E M S, Odessa *Also called Electro Mech Solutions Inc* ***(G-12118)***
E M S, Melbourne *Also called Envirnmental Mfg Solutions LLC* ***(G-8826)***
E Quality Cables Inc 321 242-4820
4450 Enterprise Ct Ste G Melbourne (32934) ***(G-8817)***
E S A I, Orlando *Also called Enterprise System Assoc Inc* ***(G-12712)***
E T C R Inc 305 637-0999
3181 Nw 36th Ave Miami (33142) ***(G-9490)***
E T I Incorporated 727 546-6472
10610 75th St Largo (33777) ***(G-7938)***
E T Plastering Inc 305 874-7082
3831 Nw 58th Ct Virginia Gardens (33166) ***(G-18688)***
E&M Innovative Forager LLC (PA) 954 923-0056
2649 S Park Rd Hallandale Beach (33009) ***(G-5182)***
E&M Pckging Llcdba Crtive Sign 813 839-6356
3001 W Granada St Tampa (33629) ***(G-17623)***
E&P Solutions and Services Inc 305 715-9545
7884 Nw 64th St Miami (33166) ***(G-9491)***
E&T Horizons Ltd Liability Co 321 704-1244
2623 Chapel Bridge Ln Melbourne (32940) ***(G-8818)***
E-Direct Oil Inc 518 366-2208
1675 Persimmon Dr Naples (34109) ***(G-11232)***
E-Libro Corporation 305 466-0155
16699 Collins Ave # 1002 Sunny Isles Beach (33160) ***(G-17074)***
E-Liquids Investment Group LLC 954 507-6060
591 Swgrss Corp Pkwy Sunrise (33325) ***(G-17117)***
E-One Inc (HQ) 352 237-1122
1601 Sw 37th Ave Ocala (34474) ***(G-11928)***
E-One Inc 352 237-1122
1701 Sw 37th Ave Ocala (34474) ***(G-11929)***
E-One Parts Central, Ocala *Also called E-One Inc* ***(G-11928)***
E-Sea Rider LLC 727 863-3333
4054 Louis Ave Holiday (34691) ***(G-5739)***
E-Sea Rider Marine Bean Bags, Holiday *Also called E-Sea Rider LLC* ***(G-5739)***
E-Stone USA Corp 863 655-1273
8041 Haywood Taylor Blvd Sebring (33870) ***(G-16687)***
E-Stone USA Corporation 954 266-6793
472 Webster Turn Dr Sebring (33870) ***(G-16688)***
E-Stone USA Corporation (HQ) 863 214-8281
1565 Nw 36th St Miami (33142) ***(G-9492)***
E-Tag, Boca Raton *Also called Telsec Corporation* ***(G-745)***
E-Z Fastening Solutions Inc 813 854-3937
640 Brooker Creek Blvd # 425 Oldsmar (34677) ***(G-12223)***
E-Z Metals Inc 239 936-7887
6133 Idlewild St Fort Myers (33966) ***(G-4438)***
E-Z Weld Inc 561 844-0241
1661 Pres Barack Obama Hw Riviera Beach (33404) ***(G-15323)***
E1w Games Llc 561 255-7370
14545 S Military Trl J Delray Beach (33484) ***(G-3071)***
E2 Walls Inc 813 374-2010
5692 W Crenshaw St Tampa (33634) ***(G-17624)***
E2g Partners LLC 813 855-2251
11200 Dr Mrtn Lther King Saint Petersburg (33716) ***(G-15766)***
E3 Fluid Recovery Eng (PA) 727 754-9792
13517 65th St Largo (33771) ***(G-7939)***
E3 Graphics Inc 954 510-1302
9868 W Sample Rd Coral Springs (33065) ***(G-2243)***
Eag-Led LLC (PA) 813 463-2420
12918 Commodity Pl Tampa (33626) ***(G-17625)***
Eagle Artistic Printing Inc 973 476-6301
10277 Shireoaks Ln Boca Raton (33498) ***(G-511)***
Eagle Athletic Wear Inc (PA) 727 937-6147
720 E Tarpon Ave Tarpon Springs (34689) ***(G-18297)***
Eagle Athletica LLC 305 209-7002
1000 Brickell Ave Ste 715 Miami (33131) ***(G-9493)***
Eagle Aviation Maintenance, Defuniak Springs *Also called Onvoi AVI Supp and Inspect Ser* ***(G-2945)***
Eagle Engrg & Land Dev Inc 913 948-4320
302 Sw 3rd Ave Boynton Beach (33435) ***(G-900)***
Eagle Eye Anesthesia Inc 817 999-9830
11233 St Jhns Indus Pkwy Jacksonville (32246) ***(G-6345)***
Eagle Eye Global Tracking LLC 727 399-6888
39620 Us Highway 19 N Tarpon Springs (34689) ***(G-18298)***
Eagle I Tech Inc 772 221-8188
4529 Sw Cargo Way Palm City (34990) ***(G-13651)***
Eagle Insulation Fabrication, Jacksonville *Also called Atlantic Insulation Inc* ***(G-6174)***
Eagle Labs Incorporated 727 548-1816
5000 Park St N Ste 1202 Saint Petersburg (33709) ***(G-15767)***
Eagle Manufacturing Group, Hialeah *Also called U S Holdings Inc* ***(G-5656)***
Eagle Metal Distributors Inc 407 367-0688
603 W Landstreet Rd Ste B Orlando (32824) ***(G-12693)***
Eagle Metal Products Inc 561 964-4192
100 N Country Club Blvd Lake Worth (33462) ***(G-7549)***
Eagle Painting, Sunrise *Also called J & J Inc* ***(G-17132)***
Eagle Pneumatic Inc 863 644-4870
3902 Industry Blvd Lakeland (33811) ***(G-7678)***
Eagle Printing 727 469-8622
12223 N Florida Ave Tampa (33612) ***(G-17626)***
Eagle Prof Flrg Removal 813 520-3027
11548 Bay Gardens Loop Riverview (33569) ***(G-15270)***
Eagle Quality Components LLC 352 516-4838
280 Hummer Way Tavares (32778) ***(G-18335)***
Eagle Ready Mix 239 732-9333
9210 Collier Blvd Naples (34114) ***(G-11233)***
Eagle Ready Mix LLC 239 693-1500
16576 Gator Rd Fort Myers (33912) ***(G-4439)***
Eagle Signs 321 863-9844
1250 Cheney Hwy Unit B Titusville (32780) ***(G-18428)***
Eagle View Windows Inc 904 647-8221
13340 International Pkwy Jacksonville (32218) ***(G-6346)***
Eagled Global Lights, Tampa *Also called Eag-Led LLC* ***(G-17625)***
Eaglelithocom Inc 786 521-7211
2725 Nw 17th Ave Miami (33142) ***(G-9494)***
Eam Worldwide, Miami *Also called Eastern Aero Marine Inc* ***(G-9495)***
Ear-Tronics Inc (PA) 239 275-7655
7181 College Pkwy Ste 14 Fort Myers (33907) ***(G-4440)***
Earl Industries 904 247-1301
1543 Main St Atlantic Beach (32233) ***(G-220)***
Earl Parker Yacht Refinishing 954 791-1811
1915 Sw 21st Ave Fort Lauderdale (33312) ***(G-3955)***
Early Foods LLC 850 791-3319
1630 E Lee St Pensacola (32503) ***(G-14136)***
Earnest Metal Fabrication, Sanford *Also called Earnest Products Inc* ***(G-16038)***
Earnest Products Inc 407 831-1588
2000 E Lake Mary Blvd Sanford (32773) ***(G-16038)***
Eartech Inc 941 747-8193
3904 9th Ave W Bradenton (34205) ***(G-1034)***
Earth & Sea Wear LLC 786 332-2236
8785 Nw 13th Ter Doral (33172) ***(G-3338)***
Earth Group Inc 954 979-8444
2200 N Andrews Ave Pompano Beach (33069) ***(G-14671)***
Earth Vets Inc 352 332-9991
96093 Marsh Lakes Dr Fernandina Beach (32034) ***(G-3736)***
Earthcore Industries LLC (PA) 904 363-3417
6899 Phillips Ind Blvd Jacksonville (32256) ***(G-6347)***
Earthmover Cnstr Eqp LLC 407 401-8956
2325 Clark St Apopka (32703) ***(G-132)***

Earthsoil Inc 888 282-1920
5000-18 Us Hwy 17 S 107 Fleming Island (32003) **(G-3761)**
Earthtnes In Hrmony With Nture, Stuart *Also called Ronald M Hart Inc* **(G-17003)**
East 46th Auto Sales Inc 407 322-3100
3710 E State Road 46 Sanford (32771) **(G-16039)**
East 46th Trailor Sales, Sanford *Also called East 46th Auto Sales Inc* **(G-16039)**
East Coast Cabinet Co 321 392-4686
100 Eyster Blvd Rockledge (32955) **(G-15407)**
East Coast Cooling Tower Inc 904 551-5527
9850 Interstate Center Dr Jacksonville (32218) **(G-6348)**
East Coast Door Inc 954 868-4700
1297 Se 5th Ave Pompano Beach (33060) **(G-14672)**
East Coast Fixtures & Mllwk Co 904 733-9711
4880 Clydo Rd S Jacksonville (32207) **(G-6349)**
East Coast Floats LLC 407 203-5628
4832 New Broad St Orlando (32814) **(G-12694)**
East Coast Foam Supply Inc 321 433-8231
392 Richard Rd Rockledge (32955) **(G-15408)**
East Coast Machine Inc 321 632-4817
3022 Oxbow Cir Cocoa (32926) **(G-2017)**
East Coast Medal 561 619-6753
860 N 8th St Lantana (33462) **(G-7870)**
East Coast Metal Decks Inc 561 433-8259
620 Whitney Ave Lantana (33462) **(G-7871)**
East Coast Metalworks LLC 321 698-0624
6615 Bethel St Cocoa (32927) **(G-2018)**
East Coast Ornamental Welding 386 672-4340
1794 State Ave Daytona Beach (32117) **(G-2660)**
East Coast Truss, Fort Pierce *Also called Martinez Builders Supply LLC* **(G-4714)**
East Ft. Pierce FL Readymix, Fort Pierce *Also called Cemex Cnstr Mtls Fla LLC* **(G-4686)**
East Ormond Beach Crossfit 386 673-3011
1474 W Granada Blvd Ormond Beach (32174) **(G-13366)**
East Side Printing & Pubg 239 369-1244
27 Homestead Rd N Ste 53 Lehigh Acres (33936) **(G-8189)**
Eastburn Woodworks Inc 850 456-8090
2620 Hollywood Ave Pensacola (32505) **(G-14137)**
Eastern Aero Marine Inc 305 871-4050
5502 Nw 37th Ave Miami (33142) **(G-9495)**
Eastern Irrigation Supply 352 472-3323
5328 Nw State Road 45 Newberry (32669) **(G-11553)**
Eastern Metal Supply Inc 863 682-6660
4675 Drane Field Rd Lakeland (33811) **(G-7679)**
Eastern Metal Supply NC Inc 800 432-2204
4268 Westroads Dr West Palm Beach (33407) **(G-18859)**
Eastern Ribbon & Roll Corp (PA) 813 676-8600
1920 Gunn Hwy Odessa (33556) **(G-12117)**
Eastern Shipbuilding Group Inc (PA) 850 763-1900
2200 Nelson Ave Panama City (32401) **(G-13895)**
Eastern Shipbuilding Group Inc 850 522-7400
13300 Allanton Rd Panama City (32404) **(G-13896)**
Eastern Shipyards Inc 850 763-1900
2200 Nelson Ave Panama City (32401) **(G-13897)**
Eastern Shores Printing (PA) 305 685-8976
4476 Nw 128th St Opa Locka (33054) **(G-12312)**
Eastern Shres Prtg Woven Label, Opa Locka *Also called Eastern Shores Printing* **(G-12312)**
Eastern Signs LLC 305 542-8274
13408 Nw 38th Ct Hialeah (33014) **(G-5386)**
Eastern Wire Products Inc 904 781-6775
5301 W 5th St Jacksonville (32254) **(G-6350)**
Eastgate Publishing Inc 772 286-0101
9015 Se Athena St Hobe Sound (33455) **(G-5724)**
Eastman Kodak Company 813 908-7910
5364 Ehrlich Rd Tampa (33624) **(G-17627)**
Eastman Performance Films LLC 954 920-2001
5553 Ravenswood Rd # 104 Fort Lauderdale (33312) **(G-3956)**
Eastward Boats Inc 772 828-1358
1520 Se S Nmyer Cir Ste 6 Port Saint Lucie (34952) **(G-15104)**
Easy Flex Couplings LLC 863 665-9374
4327 S Highway 27 Clermont (34711) **(G-1956)**
Easy Foam Inc 970 927-0209
4 Calendula Ct W Homosassa (34446) **(G-6003)**
Easy Foods Inc 321 300-1104
1965 Avenue A Kissimmee (34758) **(G-7241)**
Easy Foods Inc (PA) 305 599-0357
5900 Nw 97th Ave Unit 14 Doral (33178) **(G-3339)**
Easy Pavers Corp 407 967-0511
334 Windford Ct Winter Garden (34787) **(G-19261)**
Easy Picker Golf Products Inc 239 368-6600
415 Leonard Blvd N Lehigh Acres (33971) **(G-8190)**
Easy Rent Inc 904 443-7446
8535 Baymeadows Rd Ste 7 Jacksonville (32256) **(G-6351)**
Easy Signs Inc 954 673-0118
4860 N Dixie Hwy Oakland Park (33334) **(G-11801)**
Easydrift LLC 352 318-3683
13100 Nw 50th Ave Gainesville (32606) **(G-4912)**
Easylife Tech, Dania *Also called Famatel USA LLC* **(G-2445)**
Easylift N Bansbach Amer Inc 321 253-1999
50 West Dr Melbourne (32904) **(G-8819)**
Easyturf Inc 941 753-3312
3203 Us Highway 301 N Ellenton (34222) **(G-3653)**
Eaton & Wolk 305 249-1640
2665 S Byshr Dr Ste 609 Miami (33133) **(G-9496)**
Eaton Corporation 813 281-8069
1511 N West Shore Blvd # 1111 Tampa (33607) **(G-17628)**
Eaton Corporation 561 998-4111
1225 Broken Sound Pkwy Nw F Boca Raton (33487) **(G-512)**
Eaton Law 813 264-4800
14812 N Florida Ave Tampa (33613) **(G-17629)**
Ebco Envmtl Bins & Cntrs Inc 954 967-9999
2101 Sw 56th Ter West Park (33023) **(G-19092)**
Ebella Magazine 239 431-7231
5647 Naples Blvd Naples (34109) **(G-11234)**
Ebs Quality Service Inc 305 595-4048
13210 Sw 132nd Ave Ste 1 Miami (33186) **(G-9497)**
Ebway LLC 954 971-4911
6600 Nw 21st Ave Ste A Fort Lauderdale (33309) **(G-3957)**
Ebway LLC 954 971-4911
6601 Nw 20th Ave Fort Lauderdale (33309) **(G-3958)**
EC Cabinets Inc 305 887-2091
1511 E 11th Ave Hialeah (33010) **(G-5387)**
ECB Publishing, Monticello *Also called Monticello News* **(G-11080)**
Ecc, Saint Petersburg *Also called Evolving Coal Corp* **(G-15773)**
Ecco Doors LLC 561 392-3533
505 Industrial Way Boynton Beach (33426) **(G-901)**
Echo Plastic Systems 305 655-1300
1801 Green Rd Ste B Deerfield Beach (33064) **(G-2820)**
Echodog Industries Inc 407 909-1636
9350 Bentley Park Cir Orlando (32819) **(G-12695)**
Eci Pharmaceuticals LLC (PA) 954 486-8181
5311 Nw 35th Ter Fort Lauderdale (33309) **(G-3959)**
Eci Telecom Inc (HQ) 954 772-3070
5100 Nw 33rd Ave Ste 150 Fort Lauderdale (33309) **(G-3960)**
Ecleris, Medley *Also called Eusa Global LLC* **(G-8649)**
Eclipse Ehr Solutions LLC 352 488-0081
11242 Commercial Way Weeki Wachee (34614) **(G-18702)**
Eclipse Magazine, Tampa *Also called Creative Loafing Inc* **(G-17566)**
Eclipse Screen and Shutters 305 216-4716
3120 Sw 114th Ave Miami (33165) **(G-9498)**
Eclipsys Corp 404 847-5000
8017 Via Hacienda Riviera Beach (33418) **(G-15324)**
Eco Concepts Inc 954 920-9700
3607 N 29th Ave Hollywood (33020) **(G-5814)**
Eco Cups International Corp 407 308-1764
2814 Silver Star Rd Apt 4 Orlando (32808) **(G-12696)**
Eco Informativo 786 362-6789
1901 Brickell Ave B201 Miami (33129) **(G-9499)**
Eco Products Limited LLC 863 337-4918
3536 Dmg Dr Lakeland (33811) **(G-7680)**
Eco Solar Technology 904 219-0807
12334 Hidden Hills Ln Jacksonville (32225) **(G-6352)**
Eco Water Technologies Corp 954 599-3672
150 N Federal Hwy Ste 200 Fort Lauderdale (33301) **(G-3961)**
Eco Window Systems LLC 305 885-5299
8502 Nw 80th St Unit 100 Medley (33166) **(G-8645)**
Eco Woodwork and Design Inc 954 326-8806
3761 Ne 4th Ave Oakland Park (33334) **(G-11802)**
Ecolab Inc 561 207-6278
100 Vllage Sq Xing Ste 10 Palm Beach Gardens (33410) **(G-13585)**
Ecolab Inc 800 931-8911
1201 Jupiter Park Dr # 1 Jupiter (33458) **(G-7031)**
Ecological Laboratories Inc 239 573-6650
2525 Ne 9th Ave Cape Coral (33909) **(G-1416)**
Ecombustible Products LLC 305 792-1952
15901 Collins Ave Apt 901 Sunny Isles Beach (33160) **(G-17075)**
Econo-Blast, Saint Petersburg *Also called Maxi-Blast of Florida Inc* **(G-15851)**
Econochannel Inc 305 255-2113
213 Se 10th Ave Hialeah (33010) **(G-5388)**
Economy Dntres Jcksonville LLC 904 696-6767
1680 Dunn Ave Ste 6 Jacksonville (32218) **(G-6353)**
Economy Printing Co 904 786-4070
14413 Christen Dr S Jacksonville (32218) **(G-6354)**
Economy Tent International, Miami *Also called Ae Tent LLC* **(G-9079)**
Economy Tent International Inc 305 691-0191
2995 Nw 75th St Miami (33147) **(G-9500)**
Ecopod, Miami *Also called Sltons Envirnmntal Group Assoc* **(G-10362)**
Ecoprintq Inc 305 681-7445
14261 Commerce Way # 101 Miami Lakes (33016) **(G-10784)**
Ecosan LLC 954 446-5929
2520 Coral Way Ste 2 Coral Gables (33145) **(G-2140)**
Ecosmart 561 328-6488
1313 S Killian Dr Lake Park (33403) **(G-7468)**
Ecosmart Surface & Coating TEC 402 319-1607
1313 S Killian Dr West Palm Beach (33403) **(G-18860)**
Ecosoulife USA Dist LLC 754 212-5456
3651 Fau Blvd Ste 400 Boca Raton (33431) **(G-513)**
Ecosphere Technologies Inc (PA) 772 287-4846
3491 Se Gran Park Way Stuart (34997) **(G-16936)**
Ecotec Manufacturing Inc 863 357-4500
312 Sw 7th Ave Okeechobee (34974) **(G-12177)**

ALPHABETIC

Ecotech Water LLC.....877 341-9500
7121 Gulf Blvd St Pete Beach (33706) ***(G-16879)***
Ecs America LLC.....305 629-9599
7253 Nw 12th St Miami (33126) ***(G-9501)***
Ecstatic Nails Inc.....305 328-9554
13224 W Dixie Hwy North Miami (33161) ***(G-11636)***
Ecx Online Inc.....407 442-6834
11208 Taeda Dr Orlando (32832) ***(G-12697)***
Ed Allen Inc.....941 743-2646
1312 Market Cir Unit 9 Port Charlotte (33953) ***(G-14975)***
ED Publications Inc.....727 726-3592
2431 Estancia Blvd Bldg B Clearwater (33761) ***(G-1663)***
Ed Steel Fabricator Inc.....305 926-4904
4807 E 10th Ln Hialeah (33013) ***(G-5389)***
Ed Vance Printing Company Inc.....813 882-8888
6107 Memorial Hwy Ste E7 Tampa (33615) ***(G-17630)***
Ed-Gar Leasing Company Inc.....904 284-1900
1306 Idlewild Ave Green Cove Springs (32043) ***(G-5060)***
Edafa Industries Inc.....954 946-0830
1460 Sw 3rd St Ste 6 Pompano Beach (33069) ***(G-14673)***
Edak Inc (HQ).....321 674-6804
630 Distribution Dr Melbourne (32904) ***(G-8820)***
Edashop Inc.....786 565-9197
15388 Arcadia Bluff Loop Winter Garden (34787) ***(G-19262)***
Edc Corporation.....386 951-4075
1701 Lexington Ave Deland (32724) ***(G-2973)***
Edca Bakery Corporation.....305 448-7843
5236 W Flagler St Coral Gables (33134) ***(G-2141)***
Eddy Floor Scraper Inc.....954 981-0715
1806 Sw 31st Ave Hallandale (33009) ***(G-5156)***
Eddy Storm Protection.....386 248-1631
1000 N Nova Rd Daytona Beach (32117) ***(G-2661)***
Eddys Filter Change Inc.....407 448-4498
822 Keystone Ave Altamonte Springs (32701) ***(G-42)***
Eddys Jewlelry.....321 236-7887
2148 Whisper Lakes Blvd Orlando (32837) ***(G-12698)***
Eden Fast Frozen Dessert LLC.....787 375-0826
107 Broadway Kissimmee (34741) ***(G-7242)***
Edens Garden Natural H.....585 353-8547
3237 Kings Ridge Ter Deltona (32725) ***(G-3168)***
Edge of Humanity LLC.....954 425-0540
1801 Ne 51st St Pompano Beach (33064) ***(G-14674)***
Edge Power Solutions Inc.....321 499-1919
5131 Industry Dr Ste 107 Melbourne (32940) ***(G-8821)***
Edgeline Industries LLC (PA).....954 727-5272
1319 E Hillsboro Blvd # 514 Deerfield Beach (33441) ***(G-2821)***
Edgeone LLC.....561 995-7767
1141 Holland Dr Ste 1 Boca Raton (33487) ***(G-514)***
Edgetech, Boca Raton *Also called Edgeone LLC* ***(G-514)***
Edgewater Power Boats LLC.....386 426-5457
211 Dale St Edgewater (32132) ***(G-3622)***
Edgewater Technologies Inc.....954 565-9898
1200 Ne 7th Ave Ste 4 Fort Lauderdale (33304) ***(G-3962)***
Edgewell Personal Care Company.....386 673-2024
1190 N Us Highway 1 Ormond Beach (32174) ***(G-13367)***
Edible Flair Inc.....954 321-3608
220 Florida Ave Fort Lauderdale (33312) ***(G-3963)***
Edigitalprintingcom Inc.....305 378-2325
11950 Sw 128th St Miami (33186) ***(G-9502)***
Edisonecoenergycom Corporation.....954 417-5326
528 Sw 5th Ave Apt 3 Fort Lauderdale (33315) ***(G-3964)***
Editorial Bautista Independent, Sebring *Also called Baptist Mid-Missions Inc* ***(G-16682)***
Editorial Televisa Publishing, Virginia Gardens *Also called Et Publishing International* ***(G-18689)***
Editorial Unilit, Medley *Also called Spanish House Inc* ***(G-8728)***
Edmund C Miga.....941 628-5951
23040 Bradford Ave Port Charlotte (33952) ***(G-14976)***
Edmund Optics Inc.....813 855-1900
141 Burbank Rd Oldsmar (34677) ***(G-12224)***
Edmund Optics Florida, Oldsmar *Also called Edmund Optics Inc* ***(G-12224)***
Edmunds Metal Works Inc.....941 755-4725
6111 15th St E Ste A Bradenton (34203) ***(G-1035)***
Eds Aluminum Buildings Inc (PA).....850 476-2169
9555 Pensacola Blvd Pensacola (32534) ***(G-14138)***
Eds Delight LLC.....305 632-3051
2080 Ne 186th Dr North Miami Beach (33179) ***(G-11672)***
Edsun Lighting Fixtures Mfg.....305 888-8849
569 W 17th St Hialeah (33010) ***(G-5390)***
Educational Networks Inc (PA).....866 526-0200
901 Ponce De Leon Blvd Coral Gables (33134) ***(G-2142)***
Educational Pubg Centl Fla LLC.....407 234-4401
1551 Cobble Ln Mount Dora (32757) ***(G-11101)***
Edumatics Inc.....407 656-0661
7649 W Clnl Dr Ste 120 Orlando (32818) ***(G-12699)***
Eduself, Sarasota *Also called Techpubs Ltd* ***(G-16620)***
Edward Thomas Company.....561 746-1441
185 E Indiantown Rd # 114 Jupiter (33477) ***(G-7032)***
Edwards Manufacturing, Tampa *Also called EMI Industries LLC* ***(G-17636)***
Edwards Ornamental Iron Inc.....904 354-4282
1252 W Beaver St Jacksonville (32204) ***(G-6355)***
Edwin B Stimpson Company Inc (PA).....954 946-3500
1515 Sw 13th Ct Pompano Beach (33069) ***(G-14675)***
Eei Manufacturing Services, Clearwater *Also called Englander Enterprises Inc* ***(G-1673)***
Eem Technologies Corp (PA).....786 606-5993
9590 Nw 40th Street Rd Doral (33178) ***(G-3340)***
Eep.....407 380-2828
3307 Trentwood Blvd Belle Isle (32812) ***(G-357)***
Ees Design LLC.....954 541-2660
2801 Nw 55th Ct Ste 5e Fort Lauderdale (33309) ***(G-3965)***
Ef Enterprises of North Fla.....904 739-5995
4381 Gadsden Ct Jacksonville (32207) ***(G-6356)***
Effearredi Usa Inc.....786 725-4948
123 Nw 23rd St Miami (33127) ***(G-9503)***
Egd Euro Gourmet Deli Inc.....305 937-1515
18650 Ne 28th Ct Aventura (33180) ***(G-267)***
Egea Food LLC.....833 353-6637
4313 Sw 75th Ave Miami (33155) ***(G-9504)***
Egg Roll Skins Inc.....305 836-0571
3251 E 11th Ave Hialeah (33013) ***(G-5391)***
Eggplant and Dough, Brooksville *Also called Mr GS Foods* ***(G-1255)***
Eglin Aero Club, Eglin Afb *Also called James Taylor* ***(G-3644)***
Eglin Air Force Base.....850 882-5422
205 W D Ave Ste 433 Eglin Afb (32542) ***(G-3642)***
Eglin Air Force Base (PA).....850 882-3315
207 W D Ave Ste 125 Eglin Afb (32542) ***(G-3643)***
Eglin Flyer.....850 678-4581
1181 John Sims Pkwy E Niceville (32578) ***(G-11565)***
Egm Manufacturing Corp.....954 440-0445
10032 Nw 53rd St Sunrise (33351) ***(G-17118)***
Egmont Press, Boca Raton *Also called Spett Printing Co Inc* ***(G-727)***
Ehs Fla.....352 438-0005
3159 Se 6th St Ocala (34471) ***(G-11930)***
Ehud Industries Inc.....904 803-0873
9782 Nimitz Ct S Jacksonville (32246) ***(G-6357)***
Ei Global Group Llc.....561 999-8989
1515 N Federal Hwy # 200 Boca Raton (33432) ***(G-515)***
Ei Interactive LLC.....407 579-0993
121 S Orange Ave Ste 1400 Orlando (32801) ***(G-12700)***
Eidolon Analytics Inc.....239 288-6951
2487 N Airport Rd Fort Myers (33907) ***(G-4441)***
Eidschun Engineering Inc.....727 647-2300
2899 Heron Pl Clearwater (33762) ***(G-1664)***
Eiff Aerodynamics Inc.....386 734-3958
1405 Flight Line Blvd # 18 Deland (32724) ***(G-2974)***
Eighteen Degrees Eighteen.....904 686-1892
3787 Palm Valley Rd # 101 Ponte Vedra Beach (32082) ***(G-14940)***
Eileen Kramer Inc.....315 395-3831
19955 Ne 38th Ct Apt 504 Aventura (33180) ***(G-268)***
Eileen Ruth Bendis.....954 565-5470
3850 Galt Ocean Dr Fort Lauderdale (33308) ***(G-3966)***
Eiq Mobility Inc.....561 691-7171
700 Universe Blvd Juno Beach (33408) ***(G-6979)***
Eizo Rugged Solutions Inc.....407 262-7100
442 Northlake Blvd # 1008 Altamonte Springs (32701) ***(G-43)***
Ejco Inc.....352 375-0797
927 Nw 13th St Gainesville (32601) ***(G-4913)***
Ejcon, Jacksonville *Also called Medway Hall Dev Group Inc* ***(G-6594)***
Ejm Broadcast Inc.....321 251-5662
12854 Boggy Pointe Dr Orlando (32824) ***(G-12701)***
EJM Copper Inc.....407 447-0074
1911 Ellman St Orlando (32804) ***(G-12702)***
El Clarin, Miami *Also called Bcc-Bgle Cmmnctons Crp-Clrin L* ***(G-9228)***
El Colusa News.....786 845-6868
2550 Nw 72nd Ave Ste 308 Miami (33122) ***(G-9505)***
El Custom Wood Creations Inc.....786 337-0014
2004 Tigertail Blvd Dania (33004) ***(G-2444)***
El Equisteo Sabor, Hialeah *Also called Miami Foods Distrs USA Inc* ***(G-5510)***
El Global News.....305 212-1361
3785 Nw 82nd Ave Doral (33166) ***(G-3341)***
EL Harley Inc.....561 841-9887
2885 S Congress Ave Ste F Delray Beach (33445) ***(G-3072)***
El Hispano.....772 878-6488
102 Nw Airoso Blvd Port Saint Lucie (34983) ***(G-15105)***
El Jaliciense Inc.....850 481-1232
232 S Tyndall Pkwy Panama City (32404) ***(G-13898)***
El Latino Newspaper.....561 835-4913
4404 Georgia Ave Ste A West Palm Beach (33405) ***(G-18861)***
El Mira Sol Inc (PA).....813 754-5857
4008 Airport Rd Plant City (33563) ***(G-14429)***
El Molino Coffee, Tampa *Also called Naviera Coffee Mills Inc* ***(G-17934)***
El Quijote, Miami *Also called Elore Holdings Inc* ***(G-9520)***
El Rinkon.....786 332-3125
3105 Nw 27th Ave Miami (33142) ***(G-9506)***
El Sabor Spices Inc.....305 691-2300
3501 Nw 67th St Miami (33147) ***(G-9507)***
El Teide North Industries.....786 830-7506
7763 Nw 64th St Ste 4 Miami (33166) ***(G-9508)***

El Toro Meat Packing Corp 305 836-4461
738 Nw 72nd St Miami (33150) ***(G-9509)***
El Trigal International 305 594-6610
10740 Nw 74th St Medley (33178) ***(G-8646)***
Elaine Smith Inc 561 863-3333
7740 Byron Dr Riviera Beach (33404) ***(G-15325)***
Elana Kattan, Opa Locka *Also called Di Di Designs Inc* ***(G-12306)***
Elastec Inc 618 382-2525
401 Shearer Blvd Cocoa (32922) ***(G-2019)***
Elc Sales LLC 772 285-5230
4699 Se Bywood Ter Stuart (34997) ***(G-16937)***
Elc Security Products, Doral *Also called Starlock Inc* ***(G-3511)***
Elder & Jenks LLC 727 538-5545
12595 71st Ct Largo (33773) ***(G-7940)***
Eldorado Stone, Fort Lauderdale *Also called Florida Silica Sand Company* ***(G-4006)***
Electra Automotive Corp 941 623-5563
1001 N 21st Ave Hollywood (33020) ***(G-5815)***
Electraled Inc 727 561-7610
10990 49th St N Clearwater (33762) ***(G-1665)***
Electrcal Systems Cmmnications 813 248-4275
1601 N 43rd St Tampa (33605) ***(G-17631)***
Electric Motors Lift Stn Svcs 727 538-4778
4480 126th Ave N Pinellas Park (33782) ***(G-14345)***
Electric Pcture Dsplay Systems 321 757-8484
6425 Anderson Way Melbourne (32940) ***(G-8822)***
Electrical Controls Inc 954 801-6846
9510 Bradshaw Ln Tamarac (33321) ***(G-17355)***
Electriduct Inc 954 867-9100
1650 Nw 18th St Unit 801 Pompano Beach (33069) ***(G-14676)***
Electrnic Shtmtal Crftsmen Fla 321 727-0633
3675 W New Haven Ave Melbourne (32904) ***(G-8823)***
Electrnic Systems Sutheast LLC 561 955-9006
5840 Halifax Ave Fort Myers (33912) ***(G-4442)***
Electro Lab Inc 813 818-7605
369 Douglas Rd E Oldsmar (34677) ***(G-12225)***
Electro Mech Solutions Inc 813 792-0400
1555 Gunn Hwy Odessa (33556) ***(G-12118)***
Electro Mechanical South Inc 941 342-9111
1575 Cattlemen Rd Ste 133 Sarasota (34232) ***(G-16417)***
Electro Technik Industries Inc (PA) 727 530-9555
5410 115th Ave N Clearwater (33760) ***(G-1666)***
Electro-Comp Services Inc 727 532-4262
11437 43rd St N Clearwater (33762) ***(G-1667)***
Electro-Optical Imaging, West Melbourne *Also called Moog Inc* ***(G-18777)***
Electro-Optix Inc 954 973-2800
2181 N Powerline Rd Ste 1 Pompano Beach (33069) ***(G-14677)***
Electrodes Inc 727 698-7498
10350 62nd Ter Seminole (33772) ***(G-16746)***
Electrolux Professional LLC 954 327-6778
3225 Sw 42nd St Fort Lauderdale (33312) ***(G-3967)***
Electrolytic Tech Svcs LLC 305 655-2755
19501 Ne 10th Ave Ste 203 North Miami Beach (33179) ***(G-11673)***
Electrolytic Technologies Corp (PA) 305 655-2755
19597 Ne 10th Ave Ste G Miami (33179) ***(G-9510)***
Electron Beam Development 772 219-4600
3591 Sw Deggeller Ct Palm City (34990) ***(G-13652)***
Electronic Arts Inc 407 838-8000
1950 Summit Park Dr Orlando (32810) ***(G-12703)***
Electronic Components Fas Inc 407 328-8111
1305 Hstric Gldsboro Blvd Sanford (32771) ***(G-16040)***
Electronic Manufacturing Co, Tampa *Also called Mdco Inc* ***(G-17898)***
Electronic Monitoring, Odessa *Also called Attenti Us Inc* ***(G-12104)***
Electronic Sign Supply Corp 305 477-0555
12601 Nw 115th Ave 106a Medley (33178) ***(G-8647)***
Electronics For Imaging Inc 800 624-5999
1902 2nd Ave N Jacksonville Beach (32250) ***(G-6943)***
Electrosource Inc 954 723-0840
11785 Nw 5th St Plantation (33325) ***(G-14510)***
Electrostatic Industrial Pntg 305 696-4556
6801 Nw 25th Ave Miami (33147) ***(G-9511)***
Elega Fam FL More Drect Axic, Minneola *Also called Treadway Industries LLC* ***(G-10957)***
Elegant House Intl LLC 954 457-8836
1960 Sw 30th Ave Hallandale (33009) ***(G-5157)***
Elegant Reflections 941 627-9275
168 Waterside St Port Charlotte (33954) ***(G-14977)***
Element 26 LLC 413 519-1146
1810 S Ocean Dr Fort Pierce (34949) ***(G-4693)***
Element Aircraft Sales LLC 954 494-2242
1001 Sw 20th St Boca Raton (33486) ***(G-516)***
Element E-Liquid, Miramár *Also called Element Eliquid LLC* ***(G-10988)***
Element Eliquid LLC 754 260-5500
11411 Interchange Cir S Miramar (33025) ***(G-10988)***
Element Inc Co 786 208-5693
6606 Sw 52nd Ter Miami (33155) ***(G-9512)***
Element Mdterranean Steakhouse 407 873-6829
1413 Main St Sarasota (34236) ***(G-16418)***
Element Melbourne, West Melbourne *Also called Element Mtls Tech Jupiter LLC* ***(G-18773)***
Element Mtls Tech Jupiter LLC 321 327-8985
7780 Technology Dr West Melbourne (32904) ***(G-18773)***
Element Outdoors LLC 888 589-9589
5412 Covered Bridge Ln Pace (32571) ***(G-13468)***
Element Solutions Inc (PA) 561 207-9600
500 E Broward Blvd # 1860 Fort Lauderdale (33394) ***(G-3968)***
Element-M LLC 954 288-8683
9835 Nw 5th Pl Plantation (33324) ***(G-14511)***
Elemental Energy Inc 352 589-5703
4400 N Highway 19a Ste 5 Mount Dora (32757) ***(G-11102)***
Elemental Mobile Services LLC 904 768-9840
3435 Japonica Rd N Jacksonville (32209) ***(G-6358)***
Elements Accounting Inc 305 662-4448
7344 Sw 48th St Ste 301 Miami (33155) ***(G-9513)***
Elements of Space LLC 407 718-9690
10142 Pink Carnation Ct Orlando (32825) ***(G-12704)***
Elements of Stylez 813 575-8416
30040 State Road 54 Wesley Chapel (33543) ***(G-18744)***
Elements Restoration LLC 813 330-2035
401 N Ashley Dr Tampa (33602) ***(G-17632)***
Elevated Dumpsters LLC 813 732-6338
37550 Phelps Rd Zephyrhills (33541) ***(G-19515)***
Elicar Printing 305 324-5252
1929 Nw 22nd St Miami (33142) ***(G-9514)***
Eligius Metal Works, Jacksonville *Also called Henley Metal LLC* ***(G-6468)***
Elipter Corp 305 593-8355
3900 Nw 79th Ave Ste 482 Doral (33166) ***(G-3342)***
Elisa Technologies Inc 352 337-3929
2501 Nw 66th Ct Gainesville (32653) ***(G-4914)***
Elite Aero LLC 727 244-3382
4828 Queen Palm Ter Ne Saint Petersburg (33703) ***(G-15768)***
Elite Aluminum Corporation 954 949-3200
4650 Lyons Tech Pkwy Coconut Creek (33073) ***(G-2075)***
Elite Awnings, Altamonte Springs *Also called A & A Central Florida* ***(G-24)***
Elite Cabinet Coatings 352 795-2655
7170 N Ira Martin Ave Crystal River (34428) ***(G-2377)***
Elite Cabinetry Inc 239 262-1144
5435 Jaeger Rd Ste 100 Naples (34109) ***(G-11235)***
Elite Cast Stone Inc 305 904-3032
1023 Windton Oak Dr Ruskin (33570) ***(G-15483)***
Elite Cnc Machining Inc 727 531-8447
6399 142nd Ave N Ste 122 Clearwater (33760) ***(G-1668)***
Elite Distributors LLC 407 601-6665
1716 Premier Row A Orlando (32809) ***(G-12705)***
Elite Enclosures 352 323-6005
2505 Industrial St Leesburg (34748) ***(G-8154)***
Elite Fitforever LLC 305 902-2358
4302 Alton Rd Ste 300 Miami Beach (33140) ***(G-10664)***
Elite Flower Services Inc 305 436-7400
6755 Nw 36th St Unit 180 Miami (33166) ***(G-9515)***
Elite Graphics 305 331-2678
18710 W Oakmont Dr Hialeah (33015) ***(G-5392)***
ELite Intl Group LLC 305 901-5005
7950 Nw 53rd St Ste 337 Miami (33166) ***(G-9516)***
Elite Manufacturing US 919 757-2732
1860 Indian River Dr Fleming Island (32003) ***(G-3762)***
Elite Manufacturing US LLC 904 516-4796
1860 Indian River Dr Fleming Island (32003) ***(G-3763)***
Elite Outdoor Buildings LLC 386 364-1364
2008 Ohio Ave N Live Oak (32064) ***(G-8231)***
Elite Panel Products, Coconut Creek *Also called Elite Aluminum Corporation* ***(G-2075)***
Elite Powder Coating 786 616-8084
8298 Nw 64th St Miami (33166) ***(G-9517)***
Elite Power Prtg Solutions Inc 786 387-7164
10103 Sw 166th Ct Miami (33196) ***(G-9518)***
Elite Printing & Marketing Inc 850 474-0894
3636 N L St Ste D-A Pensacola (32505) ***(G-14139)***
Elite Simulation Solutions, Oviedo *Also called Azure Computing Inc* ***(G-13416)***
Elite Wheel Distributors Inc (PA) 813 673-8393
3901 Riga Blvd Tampa (33619) ***(G-17633)***
Elite Woodwork, Sarasota *Also called Bresee Woodwork Inc* ***(G-16368)***
Elizabeth Arden Inc (HQ) 954 364-6900
880 Sw 145th Ave Ste 200 Pembroke Pines (33027) ***(G-14031)***
Elk Creek Wine 561 529-2822
4392 Nicole Cir Jupiter (33469) ***(G-7033)***
Elkins Welding Inc 352 362-4577
1620 N Us Highway 41 Dunnellon (34432) ***(G-3597)***
Elliott Custom Coatings LLC 407 734-5221
14128 Rensselaer Rd Orlando (32826) ***(G-12706)***
Elliott Diamond Tool Inc 727 585-3839
1835 Bough Ave Unit 1 Clearwater (33760) ***(G-1669)***
Ellipsis Brewing 407 556-3241
7500 Tpc Blvd Ste 8 Orlando (32822) ***(G-12707)***
Ellis & Associates of Sanford 407 322-1128
915 W 1st St Ste B Sanford (32771) ***(G-16041)***
Ellis Family Holdings Inc 503 785-7400
6301 E 10th Ave Ste 110 Hialeah (33013) ***(G-5393)***
Ellis Trap and Cage Mfg Inc 850 969-1302
9601 N Palafox St Ste 6b Pensacola (32534) ***(G-14140)***
Ellis Wood Collection Ltd 610 372-2880
420 64th Ave Apt 302 St Pete Beach (33706) ***(G-16880)***

Ellison Graphics Corp.......561 746-9256
1400 W Indiantown Rd Jupiter (33458) ***(G-7034)***
Ellison Rbm Inc.......863 679-5283
4865 State Road 60 E Lake Wales (33898) ***(G-7508)***
Elmridge Protection Pdts LLC.......561 244-8337
1200 Clint Moore Rd Ste 1 Boca Raton (33487) ***(G-517)***
Elogic Learning LLC.......813 901-8600
14934 N Florida Ave Tampa (33613) ***(G-17634)***
Elore Enterprises LLC.......305 477-1650
1055 Nw 159th Dr Miami (33169) ***(G-9519)***
Elore Holdings Inc (HQ).......305 477-1650
1055 Nw 159th Dr Miami (33169) ***(G-9520)***
Elreha Printed Circuits.......727 244-0130
7522 Plantation Cir Bradenton (34201) ***(G-1036)***
Elro Manufacturing LLC.......407 410-6006
516 Cooper Commerce Dr Apopka (32703) ***(G-133)***
Elster Amco Water LLC.......352 369-6500
10 Sw 49th Ave Ste 101 Ocala (34474) ***(G-11931)***
Elster Amco Wtr Mtring Systems, Ocala *Also called Elster Amco Water LLC* ***(G-11931)***
Elstons Inc.......727 527-7929
703 Islebay Dr Apollo Beach (33572) ***(G-102)***
Elstons Lmnted Toil Partitions, Apollo Beach *Also called Elstons Inc* ***(G-102)***
Eltec Instruments Inc (PA).......386 252-0411
350 Fentress Blvd Daytona Beach (32114) ***(G-2662)***
Elton Foil Embossing Inc.......904 399-1510
3414 Galilee Rd Jacksonville (32207) ***(G-6359)***
Elyse Installations LLC.......904 322-4754
1848 Ector Rd Jacksonville (32211) ***(G-6360)***
EM Adams Inc.......772 468-6550
7496 Commercial Cir Fort Pierce (34951) ***(G-4694)***
Emac, Marianna *Also called E M A C Inc* ***(G-8577)***
EMB Supplies, Tampa *Also called Pantograms Mfg Co Inc* ***(G-17973)***
EMB Wholesale.......904 452-4362
7749 Normandy Blvd 145-408 Jacksonville (32221) ***(G-6361)***
Embrace Telecom Inc.......866 933-8986
333 Las Olas Way Cu1 Fort Lauderdale (33301) ***(G-3969)***
Embraer, Boca Raton *Also called Veserca Group Ltd Inc* ***(G-779)***
Embraer Aero Seating Tech, Titusville *Also called Aero Seating Technologies LLC* ***(G-18412)***
Embraer Executive Aircraft Inc (HQ).......321 751-5050
1111 General Aviation Dr Melbourne (32935) ***(G-8824)***
Embraer Executive Jets, Melbourne *Also called Embraer Executive Aircraft Inc* ***(G-8824)***
Embraer Services Inc.......954 359-3700
276 Sw 34th St Fort Lauderdale (33315) ***(G-3970)***
Embroid ME.......941 312-5494
5931 Palmer Blvd Sarasota (34232) ***(G-16419)***
Embroidered Stitches.......702 751-2770
686 Se Keyes St Port St Lucie (34983) ***(G-15173)***
Embroidertoo LLC.......813 909-0239
17230 Chinaberry Rd Lutz (33558) ***(G-8382)***
Embroidery Chimp LLC.......561 775-9195
3954 Northlake Blvd Palm Beach Gardens (33403) ***(G-13586)***
Embroidery Plus.......561 439-8943
824 W Lantana Rd Lantana (33462) ***(G-7872)***
Embroidery Solutions Inc.......407 438-8188
6001 S Orange Ave Orlando (32809) ***(G-12708)***
Embroidery USA Inc.......305 477-9973
6900 Nw 50th St Miami (33166) ***(G-9521)***
Embroidme - North Miami Beach.......954 434-2191
10518 Sw 53rd St Cooper City (33328) ***(G-2111)***
Embroidme Clearwater Co.......813 803-0763
26248 Us Highway 19 N Clearwater (33761) ***(G-1670)***
Embroservice LLC.......305 267-2323
7003 N Waterway Dr # 222 Miami (33155) ***(G-9522)***
EMC Aerospace Inc.......954 316-6015
570 Ne 185th St North Miami Beach (33179) ***(G-11674)***
EMC Manufacturing.......305 613-9546
3032 Nw 72nd Ave Miami (33122) ***(G-9523)***
EMC Quality Group Corp.......786 501-5891
6625 Mami Lkes Dr E Ste 2 Miami Lakes (33014) ***(G-10785)***
EMC Representations Corp.......305 305-1776
1198 W 23rd St Hialeah (33010) ***(G-5394)***
EMC Roofing LLC.......786 597-6604
8822 Thomas Oaks Dr # 40 Tampa (33626) ***(G-17635)***
EMC South Florida LLC.......786 352-9327
6075 Sunset Dr Ste 201 South Miami (33143) ***(G-16816)***
EMC Ticketing LLC.......813 792-1234
8409 Land O Lakes Blvd Land O Lakes (34638) ***(G-7853)***
Emcee Electronics Inc (PA).......941 485-1515
520 Cypress Ave Venice (34285) ***(G-18546)***
Emcyte Corp.......239 481-7725
4331 Veronica S Shoemaker Fort Myers (33916) ***(G-4443)***
Emerald Coast Cabinets Inc.......850 267-2290
5597 Us Highway 98 W # 101 Santa Rosa Beach (32459) ***(G-16158)***
Emerald Coast Coatings LLC.......850 424-5244
705 Anchors St Nw Fort Walton Beach (32548) ***(G-4798)***
Emerald Coast Fabrication.......850 235-1174
53o Gulf View Dr Panama City (32413) ***(G-13899)***
Emerald Coast Fabricators.......850 554-6172
2120 W Wright St Pensacola (32505) ***(G-14141)***
Emerald Coast Media & Mktg.......850 267-4555
790 N County Highway 393 Santa Rosa Beach (32459) ***(G-16159)***
Emerald Coast Met Fabrication.......850 465-3517
9215 Latham St Pensacola (32514) ***(G-14142)***
Emerald Coast Mfg LLC.......850 469-1133
4121 Warehouse Ln Pensacola (32505) ***(G-14143)***
Emerald Coast Signs.......850 398-1712
4563 Rainbird Rise Rd Crestview (32539) ***(G-2347)***
Emerald Coast Truss LLC.......850 623-1967
5817 Commerce Rd Milton (32583) ***(G-10927)***
Emerald Coast Wine Cellars, Defuniak Springs *Also called Chautuqua Vineyards Winery Inc* ***(G-2940)***
Emerald Prints LLC.......850 460-5532
1169 John Sims Pkwy E Niceville (32578) ***(G-11566)***
Emerald Sails.......850 240-4777
100 Old Ferry Rd Shalimar (32579) ***(G-16774)***
Emerald Technologies Corp.......773 244-0092
3807 Belle Vista Dr E St Pete Beach (33706) ***(G-16881)***
Emerald Transformer, Defuniak Springs *Also called Florida Transformer Inc* ***(G-2942)***
Emerge Interactive Inc (PA).......772 563-0570
5375 Sol Rue Cir Vero Beach (32967) ***(G-18616)***
Emergency Mold Specialist LLC.......239 691-3157
1344 Park Lake Dr Naples (34110) ***(G-11236)***
Emergency Standby Power LLC.......850 259-2304
17 Duval St Fort Walton Beach (32547) ***(G-4799)***
Emergency Vehicle Sup Co LLC.......954 428-5201
2251 Hammondville Rd Pompano Beach (33069) ***(G-14678)***
Emergency Vehicles Inc (PA).......561 848-6652
705 13th St Lake Park (33403) ***(G-7469)***
Emerging Mfg Tech Inc.......407 341-3476
108 Commerce St Ste 102 Lake Mary (32746) ***(G-7410)***
Emerson Electric Co.......904 741-6800
13350 International Pkwy # 102 Jacksonville (32218) ***(G-6362)***
Emerson Instr & Valve Svcs, Jacksonville *Also called Instrument & Valve Services Co* ***(G-6499)***
Emerson Latin America, Sunrise *Also called Computational Systems Inc* ***(G-17108)***
Emerson Prcess MGT Pwr Wtr Slt.......941 748-8100
1401 Manatee Ave W # 400 Bradenton (34205) ***(G-1037)***
Emerson Process Management, Jacksonville *Also called Emerson Electric Co* ***(G-6362)***
Emf Inc.......321 453-3670
124 Imperial St Merritt Island (32952) ***(G-9000)***
Emhart Glass Manufacturing Inc.......727 535-5502
9875 18th St N Saint Petersburg (33716) ***(G-15769)***
Emhart Inex, Saint Petersburg *Also called Emhart Glass Manufacturing Inc* ***(G-15769)***
EMI Filter Company, Clearwater *Also called Nordquist Dielectrics Inc* ***(G-1809)***
EMI Industries LLC (PA).......813 626-3166
1316 Tech Blvd Tampa (33619) ***(G-17636)***
Eminel Corporation Inc.......407 900-0190
8600 Com Cir Unit 148 Orlando (32819) ***(G-12709)***
Eminent Technology Inc.......850 575-5655
225 E Palmer Ave Tallahassee (32301) ***(G-17247)***
EMJ Pharma Inc.......973 600-9087
133 Playa Rienta Way Palm Beach Gardens (33418) ***(G-13587)***
Emjac Industries Inc.......305 883-2194
1075 Hialeah Dr Hialeah (33010) ***(G-5395)***
Emmanuel Holdings Inc.......305 558-3088
2190 Nw 46th St Miami (33142) ***(G-9524)***
Emmeti USA LLC.......813 490-6252
202 10th Ave N Ste A Safety Harbor (34695) ***(G-15492)***
Emmi, Largo *Also called Engineered Mtls & Mfg Intl LLC* ***(G-7941)***
Emoji Bracelet LLC.......954 987-0515
3531 Griffin Rd Fort Lauderdale (33312) ***(G-3971)***
Empanada Lady Co.......786 271-6460
6732 Ne 4th Ave Miami (33138) ***(G-9525)***
Emphasys Cmpt Solutions Inc.......305 599-2531
1200 Sw 145th Ave Ste 301 Pembroke Pines (33027) ***(G-14032)***
Emphasys Software, Pembroke Pines *Also called Emphasys Cmpt Solutions Inc* ***(G-14032)***
Empire Central, Tampa *Also called Empire Scientific* ***(G-17637)***
Empire Corp Kit of.......800 432-3028
2846 Nw 79th Ave Doral (33122) ***(G-3343)***
Empire Dumpsters LLC.......407 223-8985
927 E Semoran Blvd Apopka (32703) ***(G-134)***
Empire Enterprises.......786 373-8003
2980 W 84th St Unit 11 Hialeah (33018) ***(G-5396)***
Empire Scientific, Tampa *Also called TAe Trans Atlantic Elec Inc* ***(G-18153)***
Empire Scientific.......630 510-8636
4504 E Hillsborough Ave Tampa (33610) ***(G-17637)***
Empire Stone and Cabinets.......305 885-7092
720 W 27th St Hialeah (33010) ***(G-5397)***
Empire Trnspt Solutions Corp.......305 439-5677
228 W 18th St Hialeah (33010) ***(G-5398)***
Empirica.......727 403-0399
904 Old Mill Pond Rd Palm Harbor (34683) ***(G-13736)***
Empower Software Solutions, Maitland *Also called Unitime Systems Inc* ***(G-8482)***
Empowered Diagnostics LLC.......206 228-5990
3341 W Mcnab Rd Pompano Beach (33069) ***(G-14679)***
Empowered Prosthetics Corp.......561 630-9137
392 Prestwick Cir Apt 4 Palm Beach Gardens (33418) ***(G-13588)***

Empress Sissi, Sanford *Also called Caligiuri Corporation* ***(G-16006)***
Empyre Music Publishing LLC....813 873-7700
1101 N Himes Ave Ste B Tampa (33607) ***(G-17638)***
Ems Technologies NA LLC....321 259-5979
121 S Orange Ave Ste 1500 Orlando (32801) ***(G-12710)***
En-Vision America Inc....309 452-3088
825 4th St W Palmetto (34221) ***(G-13796)***
Enchanting Creations....305 978-2828
210 Ne 98th St Miami Shores (33138) ***(G-10884)***
Enchanting Elements....321 663-9521
8261 Lucello Ter W Naples (34114) ***(G-11237)***
Encompass Mktg & Dev Group Inc....407 420-7777
102 Drennen Rd Orlando (32806) ***(G-12711)***
Encore Analytics LLC....866 890-4331
86 Shirah St Destin (32541) ***(G-3189)***
Encore Brandz Company....813 282-7073
8815 N 15th St Tampa (33604) ***(G-17639)***
Encore Inc....941 359-3599
6487 Parkland Dr Ste 111 Sarasota (34243) ***(G-16211)***
Endeavor Manufacturing Inc....954 752-6828
510 Goolsby Blvd Deerfield Beach (33442) ***(G-2822)***
Endeavor Publications Inc....352 369-1104
4727 Nw 80th Ave Ocala (34482) ***(G-11932)***
Endeavour Catamaran Corp....727 573-5377
3703 131st Ave N Clearwater (33762) ***(G-1671)***
Endevours Together LLC....850 274-2641
2211 Orleans Dr Tallahassee (32308) ***(G-17248)***
Endflex LLC....305 622-4070
4760 Nw 128th St Opa Locka (33054) ***(G-12313)***
Endless Coatings Inc....813 714-5395
8607 Gall Blvd Zephyrhills (33541) ***(G-19516)***
Endless Oceans LLC....561 274-1990
3125 S Federal Hwy Delray Beach (33483) ***(G-3073)***
Endo-Gear LLC....305 710-6662
4390 Sw 74th Ave Miami (33155) ***(G-9526)***
Endo-Therapeutics Inc....727 538-9570
15251 Roosevelt Blvd # 204 Clearwater (33760) ***(G-1672)***
Endorphin Farms Inc....904 824-2006
3255 Parker Dr Saint Augustine (32084) ***(G-15541)***
Endoscopy Rplacement Parts Inc....352 472-5120
25430 Nw 8th Ln Newberry (32669) ***(G-11554)***
Enduris Extrusions Inc (PA)....904 421-3304
7167 Old Kings Rd Jacksonville (32219) ***(G-6363)***
Enduris Extrusions Inc....321 914-0897
605 Distribution Dr Ste 1 Melbourne (32904) ***(G-8825)***
Energenics Corporation....239 643-1711
1470 Don St Naples (34104) ***(G-11238)***
Energetico Inc....213 550-5211
2260 Ne 123rd St North Miami (33181) ***(G-11637)***
Energy Control Technologies....954 739-8400
10220 W State Road 84 # 9 Davie (33324) ***(G-2518)***
Energy Harness Corporation (PA)....239 790-3300
71 Mid Cape Ter Ste 8 Cape Coral (33991) ***(G-1417)***
Energy Harness Led Lighting, Cape Coral *Also called Energy Harness Corporation* ***(G-1417)***
Energy Management Products LLC (PA)....410 320-0200
6118 Riverview Blvd Bradenton (34209) ***(G-1038)***
Energy Now LLC....941 276-0935
757 Clearview Dr Port Charlotte (33953) ***(G-14978)***
Energy Services Providers Inc (HQ)....305 947-7880
3700 Lakeside Dr 6 Miramar (33027) ***(G-10989)***
Energy Sving Solutions USA LLC....305 735-2878
1031 Ives Dairy Rd # 228 Miami (33179) ***(G-9527)***
Energy Task Force LLC (HQ)....407 523-3770
2501 Clark St Ste 101 Apopka (32703) ***(G-135)***
Energy Technical Systems Inc....850 223-2393
9319 Puckett Rd Perry (32348) ***(G-14299)***
Energybionics LLC....561 229-4985
519 Sw Glen Crest Way Stuart (34997) ***(G-16938)***
Energycontrol.com, Davie *Also called Energy Control Technologies* ***(G-2518)***
Energyware LLC....540 809-5902
17120 Reserve Ct Davie (33331) ***(G-2519)***
Enersys Advanced Systems Inc....610 208-1934
5430 70th Ave N Pinellas Park (33781) ***(G-14346)***
Enforcement One Inc....727 816-9833
381 Roberts Rd Oldsmar (34677) ***(G-12226)***
Enforty, Boca Raton *Also called Mark Benton* ***(G-608)***
Eng Group LLC....954 323-2024
5309 Sw 34th Ave Fort Lauderdale (33312) ***(G-3972)***
Eng Group LLC Teg , The, Fort Lauderdale *Also called Eng Group LLC* ***(G-3972)***
ENG Manufacturing Inc....727 942-3868
773 Wesley Ave Tarpon Springs (34689) ***(G-18299)***
Engead Gb Design & Prtg Inc....954 783-5161
414 E Sample Rd Pompano Beach (33064) ***(G-14680)***
Engedi Specialities Inc....386 497-1010
429 Sw Greenwood Ter Fort White (32038) ***(G-4843)***
Engelhard Corp....850 627-7688
1101 N Madison St Quincy (32352) ***(G-15248)***
Engine Armour Products, Tampa *Also called Armor Oil Products LLC* ***(G-17435)***
Engine Lab of Tampa Inc....813 630-2422
201 S 78th St Tampa (33619) ***(G-17640)***
Engineer Service Corporation....904 268-0482
2950 Halcyon Ln Ste 601 Jacksonville (32223) ***(G-6364)***
Engineered Air Systems Inc....813 881-9555
6605 Walton Way Tampa (33610) ***(G-17641)***
Engineered Equipment Corp....561 839-4008
777 S Flagler Dr Ste 800 West Palm Beach (33401) ***(G-18862)***
Engineered Mtls & Mfg Intl LLC....727 546-5580
10860 76th Ct Ste A Largo (33777) ***(G-7941)***
Engineered Plastic Specialists, Orlando *Also called Mid-Florida Plastics Inc* ***(G-12970)***
Engineerica Systems Inc....407 542-4982
7250 Red Bug Lake Rd # 1036 Oviedo (32765) ***(G-13428)***
Engineering, Longwood *Also called Servos and Simulation Inc* ***(G-8336)***
Engineering & Met Fabrication, Merritt Island *Also called Emf Inc* ***(G-9000)***
Engineering Analysis Group LLC....813 523-7377
13902 N Dale Mabry Hwy # 230 Tampa (33618) ***(G-17642)***
Enginetics....305 695-8000
5142 Sea Chase Dr Unit 5 Fernandina Beach (32034) ***(G-3737)***
Engitork Industries Llc....239 877-8499
222 Industrial Blvd # 13 Naples (34104) ***(G-11239)***
England Trading Company LLC....888 969-4190
1407 Atlantic Blvd Jacksonville (32207) ***(G-6365)***
Englander Enterprises Inc....727 461-4755
703 Grand Central St Clearwater (33756) ***(G-1673)***
Englert Arts Inc....561 241-9924
1021 S Rogers Cir Ste 18 Boca Raton (33487) ***(G-518)***
Englewood Sun Herald, Englewood *Also called Sun Coast Media Group Inc* ***(G-3684)***
English Ironworks Inc....941 364-9120
1960 21st St Sarasota (34234) ***(G-16420)***
Enki Group Inc....305 773-3502
11555 Sw 82nd Avenue Rd Coral Gables (33156) ***(G-2143)***
Enodis Holdings Inc (HQ)....727 375-7010
2227 Welbilt Blvd Trinity (34655) ***(G-18484)***
Enolgas Usa Inc....754 205-7902
2530 N Powerline Rd # 401 Pompano Beach (33069) ***(G-14681)***
Enozo Technologies Inc....512 944-7772
8470 Enterprise Cir Lakewood Ranch (34202) ***(G-7838)***
Ensida Energy Afs LLC....954 364-2296
2315 Sw 32nd Ave Hollywood (33023) ***(G-5816)***
Enstar Holdings (us) LLC (HQ)....727 217-2900
150 2nd Ave N Fl 3 Saint Petersburg (33701) ***(G-15770)***
Entech Controls Corp....954 613-2971
1031 Ives Dairy Rd Bldg 4 Miami (33179) ***(G-9528)***
Entech Onsite Services LLC....407 956-8980
280 Gus Hipp Blvd Rockledge (32955) ***(G-15409)***
Entegra Roof Tile, Okeechobee *Also called Roof Tile Inc* ***(G-12190)***
Enter Your Hours LLC....561 337-7785
2447 Quantum Blvd Boynton Beach (33426) ***(G-902)***
Enterprise Electric LLC....407 884-0668
2100 Ocoee Apopka Rd Apopka (32703) ***(G-136)***
Enterprise Slling Slutions LLC....904 655-9410
12627 San Jose Blvd Ste 1 Jacksonville (32223) ***(G-6366)***
Enterprise System Assoc Inc (PA)....407 275-0220
3259 Progress Dr Orlando (32826) ***(G-12712)***
Enterprise Tech Partners LLC....918 851-3285
37 N Orange Ave Ste 616 Orlando (32801) ***(G-12713)***
Enterra Inc....813 514-0531
2801 W Busch Blvd Tampa (33618) ***(G-17643)***
Entertainment Metals Inc....800 817-2683
13351 Saddle Rd Ste 205 Fort Myers (33913) ***(G-4444)***
Entertainment Mfg Group, Fort Myers *Also called Entertainment Metals Inc* ***(G-4444)***
Entire Select Inc....954 674-2368
10857 Nw 50th St Sunrise (33351) ***(G-17119)***
Enveric Biosciences Inc (PA)....239 302-1707
4851 Tamiami Trl N # 200 Naples (34103) ***(G-11240)***
Enviralum Industries Inc....305 752-4411
5100 Nw 72nd Ave Unit C Miami (33166) ***(G-9529)***
Envirnmental Mfg Solutions LLC (PA)....321 837-0050
7705 Progress Cir Melbourne (32904) ***(G-8826)***
Enviro Focus Technology....813 744-5000
6505 Jewel Ave Tampa (33619) ***(G-17644)***
Enviro Petroleum Inc....713 896-6996
10072 S Ocean Dr Apt 7n Jensen Beach (34957) ***(G-6968)***
Enviro Water Solutions LLC....877 842-1635
3060 Prfmce Cir Ste 2 Deland (32724) ***(G-2975)***
Enviro-USA American Mfr LLC....321 222-9551
151 Center St Ste 101 Cape Canaveral (32920) ***(G-1357)***
Envirofocus Technologies LLC....813 620-3260
1901 N 66th St Tampa (33619) ***(G-17645)***
Environmental Aborbent Pdts, Jupiter *Also called Dynomat Inc* ***(G-7030)***
Environmental Contractors Inc....305 556-6942
2648 W 78th St Hialeah (33016) ***(G-5399)***
Environmental Graphics, Odessa *Also called Binney Family of Florida Inc* ***(G-12106)***
Environmental Mfg & Supply Inc....850 547-5287
3255 Highway 90 Bonifay (32425) ***(G-803)***
Environmental Recovery Systems....727 344-3301
7001 Mango Ave S Saint Petersburg (33707) ***(G-15771)***
Environmental Services....727 518-3080
5100 150th Ave N Clearwater (33760) ***(G-1674)***

A L P H A B E T I C

Environmental Tectonics Corp....407 282-3378
2100 N Alafaya Trl # 900 Orlando (32826) ***(G-12714)***
Envirosafe Technologies Inc....904 646-3456
11201 St Johns Indstrl Pk Jacksonville (32246) ***(G-6367)***
Enviroseal Corporation....772 335-8225
1019 Se Hlbrook Ct 1021 Port Saint Lucie (34952) ***(G-15106)***
Envirovault LLC....904 354-1858
1727 Bennett St Jacksonville (32206) ***(G-6368)***
Enviroworks Inc....407 889-5533
3000 Orange Ave Apopka (32703) ***(G-137)***
Envision Graphics Inc....305 470-0083
7335 Nw 35th St Miami (33122) ***(G-9530)***
Enviva Pellets Cottondale LLC....850 557-7357
2500 Green Circle Pkwy Cottondale (32431) ***(G-2331)***
Envoy Therapeutics Inc....561 210-7705
555 Heritage Dr Ste 150 Jupiter (33458) ***(G-7035)***
Enzymedica Inc....941 505-5565
771 Commerce Dr Ste 3 Venice (34292) ***(G-18547)***
EO Painter Printing Company....386 985-4877
4900 Us Highway 17 De Leon Springs (32130) ***(G-2738)***
Ep6 Group Inc....772 332-9100
1150 Bell Ave Fort Pierce (34982) ***(G-4695)***
Epare LLC....347 682-5121
117 Ne 1st Ave Miami (33132) ***(G-9531)***
EPC Inc....636 443-1999
3629 Queen Palm Dr Tampa (33619) ***(G-17646)***
Ephs Holdings Inc....212 321-0091
7694 Colony Palm Dr Boynton Beach (33436) ***(G-903)***
Epi Cabinets....850 665-0659
2632 Hollywood Ave Pensacola (32505) ***(G-14144)***
Epic Extrusion Inc....941 378-0835
8141 Blaikie Ct Ste 3 Sarasota (34240) ***(G-16421)***
Epic Harvests LLC....904 503-5143
5215 Philips Hwy Ste 3 Jacksonville (32207) ***(G-6369)***
Epic Metals Corporation....863 533-7404
1930 State Road 60 W Bartow (33830) ***(G-314)***
Epic Promos LLC....561 479-8055
6451 E Rogers Cir Ste 3 Boca Raton (33487) ***(G-519)***
Epiccycles....561 450-6470
14851 Lyons Rd Delray Beach (33446) ***(G-3074)***
Epigenetix Inc....561 543-7569
1004 Brooks Ln Delray Beach (33483) ***(G-3075)***
Epigram Publishing Co....941 391-5296
151 Tillman St Port Charlotte (33954) ***(G-14979)***
Epitomi Inc....305 971-5370
12201 Sw 128th Ct Ste 108 Miami (33186) ***(G-9532)***
Epoc CNG LLC....561 706-4140
1300 Nw 65th Pl Fort Lauderdale (33309) ***(G-3973)***
Epower 360 LLC (PA)....305 330-6684
7780 Sw 71st Ave Miami (33143) ***(G-9533)***
Epoxy Floor Coatings LLC....920 471-6913
1544 Toledo St Holiday (34690) ***(G-5740)***
Epoxy2u of Florida Inc....239 772-0899
922 Se 14th Pl Cape Coral (33990) ***(G-1418)***
Epperson & Company....813 626-6125
5202 Shadowlawn Ave Tampa (33610) ***(G-17647)***
Eprint Inc....407 930-5870
14 E Washington St Orlando (32801) ***(G-12715)***
Eps Metal Finishing....954 782-3073
640 Ne 26th Ct Pompano Beach (33064) ***(G-14682)***
Equigraph Trading Corp....786 237-5665
13331 Sw 132nd Ave Miami (33186) ***(G-9534)***
Equipment Fabricators Inc....321 632-0990
655 Cidco Rd Cocoa (32926) ***(G-2020)***
Equipment Sales & Service Inc (HQ)....727 572-9197
12707 44th St N Clearwater (33762) ***(G-1675)***
Equity Group Usa Inc....407 421-6464
1129 Citrus Oaks Run Winter Springs (32708) ***(G-19472)***
Equs Logistics LLC....954 618-6573
13680 Nw 5th St Ste 140 Sunrise (33325) ***(G-17120)***
ER Jahna Industries Inc....863 675-3942
Highway 78 E La Belle (33935) ***(G-7316)***
ER Jahna Industries Inc....863 424-0730
4949 Sand Mine Rd Davenport (33897) ***(G-2478)***
ER Jahna Industries Inc....863 422-7617
4910 State Road 544 E Haines City (33844) ***(G-5142)***
ER Precision Optical Corp....407 292-5395
1676 E Semoran Blvd Apopka (32703) ***(G-138)***
ERA Organics Inc....800 579-9817
33 N Garden Ave Ste 120 Clearwater (33755) ***(G-1676)***
Eran Financial Services LLC....844 411-5483
3500 Nw Boca Raton Blvd Boca Raton (33431) ***(G-520)***
Eran Group Inc....561 289-5021
3500 Nw 2nd Ave Boca Raton (33431) ***(G-521)***
Erapsco....386 740-5335
C 0 5612 Johnson Lake Rd De Leon Springs (32130) ***(G-2739)***
Erb Roberts Tillage LLC....352 376-4888
401 E Las Olas Blvd Fort Lauderdale (33301) ***(G-3974)***
Erba Diagnostics Inc (HQ)....305 324-2300
14100 Nw 57th Ct Miami Lakes (33014) ***(G-10786)***
Erchonia Corporation LLC....321 473-1251
650 Atlantis Rd Melbourne (32904) ***(G-8827)***
Eric Lemoine....407 919-9783
1355 Bennett Dr Unit 129 Longwood (32750) ***(G-8276)***
Erickson International LLC....702 853-4800
161 Commerce Rd Ste 2 Boynton Beach (33426) ***(G-904)***
Ericsson Inc....856 230-6268
360 S Lake Destiny Dr Orlando (32810) ***(G-12716)***
Erie Manufacturing Inc....863 534-3743
1520 Centennial Blvd Bartow (33830) ***(G-315)***
Ernies Metal Fabricating....813 679-0816
406 E Windhorst Rd Brandon (33510) ***(G-1157)***
Ernies Signs....239 992-0800
3901 Bonita Beach Rd Bonita Springs (34134) ***(G-829)***
Errico Custom Woodworks Inc....561 306-0046
11637 153rd Ct N Jupiter (33478) ***(G-7036)***
Ersion Interntnal Ctrl Systems....800 821-7462
3030 N Rocky Point Dr W # 1 Tampa (33607) ***(G-17648)***
Erwad Real Estate, Hollywood *Also called Volvox Inc Hollywood* ***(G-5938)***
Erwin Inc....813 933-3323
201 N Franklin St # 2200 Tampa (33602) ***(G-17649)***
ES Investments LLC (PA)....727 536-8822
14055 Us Highway 19 N Clearwater (33764) ***(G-1677)***
Es Machine Shop....850 968-9300
235 Petty Dr Cantonment (32533) ***(G-1339)***
Es Manufacturing Inc....727 323-4040
4590 62nd Ave N Pinellas Park (33781) ***(G-14347)***
Es Tudios Corp....305 300-9262
5483 Nw 72nd Ave Miami (33166) ***(G-9535)***
Escambia Welding and Fab Inc....850 477-3901
2474 W Nine Mile Rd B Pensacola (32534) ***(G-14145)***
Esco Equipment Supply Co, Brooksville *Also called Shirley L Jordan Company Inc* ***(G-1268)***
Esco Industries Inc....863 666-3696
2001 Lasso Ln Lakeland (33801) ***(G-7681)***
Escue Energy LLC....561 762-1486
11903 Southern Blvd Royal Palm Beach (33411) ***(G-15466)***
Esd Waste2water Inc....800 277-3279
495 Oak Rd Ocala (34472) ***(G-11933)***
ESP Printing....386 263-2949
4601 E Moody Blvd Ste D5 Bunnell (32110) ***(G-1300)***
Esperanto Inc....305 513-8980
8725 Nw 18th Ter Ste 312 Doral (33172) ***(G-3344)***
Espresso Disposition Corp 1 (HQ)....305 594-9062
6262 Bird Rd Ste 2i Miami (33155) ***(G-9536)***
Esquadro Inc....754 367-3098
217 Se 1st Ter Deerfield Beach (33441) ***(G-2823)***
Esse Sales Inc....954 368-3900
2725 Nw 30th Ave Oakland Park (33311) ***(G-11803)***
Essential Oil University LLC....502 498-8804
6150 Manasota Key Rd Englewood (34223) ***(G-3676)***
Essential Publishing Group LLC (PA)....410 440-5777
1140 Holland Dr Ste 21 Boca Raton (33487) ***(G-522)***
Essential Publishing Group LLC....561 570-7165
5319 Lake Worth Rd Greenacres (33463) ***(G-5080)***
Essentialnet Solutions, Rockledge *Also called Networked Solutions Inc* ***(G-15438)***
Essentials....386 677-7444
150a W Granada Blvd Ormond Beach (32174) ***(G-13368)***
Essex Plastics Midwest LLC Lc....954 956-1100
1531 Nw 12th Ave Pompano Beach (33069) ***(G-14683)***
Essona Organics Inc....716 481-0183
14773 Cumberland Dr # 107 Delray Beach (33446) ***(G-3076)***
Estal Usa Inc....305 728-3272
150 Se 2nd Ave Miami (33131) ***(G-9537)***
Esteemed Brands Inc....954 442-3923
3450 Lakeside Dr Ste 120 Miramar (33027) ***(G-10990)***
Esterel Technologies Inc....724 746-3304
1082 N Alsaya Trl Ste 124 Orlando (32826) ***(G-12717)***
Estero FL....239 289-9511
23191 Fashion Dr Unit 309 Estero (33928) ***(G-3688)***
Estetika Skin & Laser Spe....262 646-9222
1463 Tangier Way Sarasota (34239) ***(G-16422)***
Esther Industries Inc....850 456-6163
107 Industrial Blvd Pensacola (32505) ***(G-14146)***
Esther Wilson Enterprises LLC....904 634-7463
2303 Rogero Rd Jacksonville (32211) ***(G-6370)***
Estimator Software LLC....203 682-6436
16102 Emerald Estates Dr Weston (33331) ***(G-19122)***
Estradas Fiberglass Mfg Corp....954 924-8778
16900 N Bay Rd Apt 803 Sunny Isles Beach (33160) ***(G-17076)***
Estumkeda Ltd....954 966-6300
6300 Stirling Rd Hollywood (33024) ***(G-5817)***
Et Publishing International (PA)....305 871-6400
6355 Nw 36th St Virginia Gardens (33166) ***(G-18689)***
Etas Timeadmin Corporation....813 464-4175
307 S Boulevard Ste A Tampa (33606) ***(G-17650)***
Etc Palm Beach LLC....561 881-8118
1800 Okeechobee Rd # 100 West Palm Beach (33409) ***(G-18863)***
Etchart LLC....321 504-4060
3732 N Highway 1 Ste 5 Cocoa (32926) ***(G-2021)***
Etco Automotive Products Div, Bradenton *Also called Etco Incorporated* ***(G-1039)***

Etco Incorporated 941 756-8426
3004 62nd Ave E Bradenton (34203) ***(G-1039)***
Etech Simulation Corp (PA) 561 922-9792
2721 Vista Pkwy Ste C13 West Palm Beach (33411) ***(G-18864)***
Etectrx Inc 321 363-3020
747 Sw 2nd Ave Ste 365ti Gainesville (32601) ***(G-4915)***
Eterna Urn Co Inc 386 258-6491
126 Carswell Ave Daytona Beach (32117) ***(G-2663)***
Eternal Elements LLC 407 830-6968
1045 Miller Dr Altamonte Springs (32701) ***(G-44)***
Eternal Smoke Inc 407 984-5090
1321 Edgewater Dr Ste 1 Orlando (32804) ***(G-12718)***
Eternity Cabinets 239 482-7172
17000 Alico Commerce Ct Fort Myers (33967) ***(G-4445)***
Etf West LLC 407 523-3770
2501 Clark St Apopka (32703) ***(G-139)***
Ethnergy International Inc 954 499-1582
1524 Sw 59 Ln Pembroke Pines (33027) ***(G-14033)***
Eti-Label Inc 305 716-0094
6961 Nw 82nd Ave Miami (33166) ***(G-9538)***
Euclid Chemical Company 813 886-8811
19215 Redwood Rd Odessa (33556) ***(G-12119)***
Euramerica Gas and Oil Corp 954 858-5714
1333 S University Dr # 202 Plantation (33324) ***(G-14512)***
Euro Gear (usa) Inc (PA) 518 578-1775
1395 Brickell Ave Ste 800 Miami (33131) ***(G-9539)***
Euro Trim Inc 239 574-6646
17200 Primavera Cir Cape Coral (33909) ***(G-1419)***
Euro-Wall Systems LLC 941 979-5316
2200 Murphy Ct North Port (34289) ***(G-11738)***
Euroasia Products Inc 321 221-9398
3956 W Town Center Blvd # 166 Orlando (32837) ***(G-12719)***
Eurocraft Cabinets Inc 561 948-3034
1217 Clint Moore Rd Boca Raton (33487) ***(G-523)***
Eurogan-Usa Inc 321 356-5248
502 Sunport Ln Ste 350 Orlando (32809) ***(G-12720)***
Euroinsoles Incorporated 786 206-6117
75 Valencia Ave Ste 201 Coral Gables (33134) ***(G-2144)***
Euroker LLC 305 477-0096
3287 Nw 78th Ave Doral (33122) ***(G-3345)***
Euromotion Inc 954 612-0354
7194 Skyline Dr Delray Beach (33446) ***(G-3077)***
Europa Manufacturing Inc 954 426-2965
4900 Lyons Tech Pkwy # 7 Coconut Creek (33073) ***(G-2076)***
Europe Coating Industries LLC 786 535-4143
8213 Nw 74th Ave Medley (33166) ***(G-8648)***
European Cabinets & Design LLC 561 684-1440
4050 Westgate Ave West Palm Beach (33409) ***(G-18865)***
Europrint Inc 407 869-9955
620 Douglas Ave Ste 1308 Altamonte Springs (32714) ***(G-45)***
Eurosign Metalwerke Inc 954 717-4426
5301 Nw 35th Ave Fort Lauderdale (33309) ***(G-3975)***
Euroteam Wax Center, Fort Lauderdale *Also called Ft Lauderdale Wax* ***(G-4014)***
Eusa Global LLC 786 483-7490
11801 Nw 100th Rd Ste 17 Medley (33178) ***(G-8649)***
Ev Pilotcar Inc 239 243-8023
6293 Thomas Rd Fort Myers (33912) ***(G-4446)***
Ev Rider LLC 239 278-5054
6410 Arc Way Ste A Fort Myers (33966) ***(G-4447)***
Evamped LLC 614 205-4467
13751 Luna Dr Naples (34109) ***(G-11241)***
Evan Lloyd Designs 772 286-7723
3576 Se Dixie Hwy Stuart (34997) ***(G-16939)***
Evans Custom Cabinetry LLC 904 829-1973
3595 Fortner Rd Saint Augustine (32084) ***(G-15542)***
Eve Corporation (PA) 305 599-3832
23085 Addison Lakes Cir Boca Raton (33433) ***(G-524)***
Everest Air Corp 407 319-6204
3830 Golden Feather Way Kissimmee (34746) ***(G-7243)***
Everest Cabinets Inc 407 790-7819
6100 Hanging Moss Rd # 5 Orlando (32807) ***(G-12721)***
Everett Pubg - Tampa Bay LLC 727 534-3425
6044 Grand Blvd New Port Richey (34652) ***(G-11490)***
Everett-Morrison Motorcars, Odessa *Also called Nu Trek Inc* ***(G-12136)***
Everfresh Juice Co Inc 954 581-0922
8100 Sw 10th St Ste 4000 Plantation (33324) ***(G-14513)***
Everglades Boats, Edgewater *Also called R J Dougherty Associates LLC* ***(G-3635)***
Everglades Creations Inc 305 822-3344
2335 Nw 149th St Opa Locka (33054) ***(G-12314)***
Everglades Envelope Co Inc 954 783-7920
6650 Nw 15th Ave Fort Lauderdale (33309) ***(G-3976)***
Everglades Foods Inc 863 655-2214
6120 State Road 66 Sebring (33875) ***(G-16689)***
Everglades Machine Inc 863 983-0133
1816 Red Rd Clewiston (33440) ***(G-1979)***
Everglades Pro Painters Corp 786 444-5024
2200 Sw 59th Ave Miami (33155) ***(G-9540)***
Evergreen Rush Industries Inc 954 825-9291
473 Sw 126th Ave Davie (33325) ***(G-2520)***
Evergreen Sweeteners Inc 305 835-6907
3601 Nw 62nd St Miami (33147) ***(G-9541)***
Evergreen Sweeteners Inc (PA) 954 381-7776
1936 Hollywood Blvd # 20 Hollywood (33020) ***(G-5818)***
Evergreen Sweeteners Inc 407 323-4250
2200 Country Club Rd Sanford (32771) ***(G-16042)***
Eversafe, Sarasota *Also called Matrix24 Laboratories LLC* ***(G-16253)***
Every Thing Aluminum 561 202-9900
615 Whitney Ave Ste 15 Lantana (33462) ***(G-7873)***
Everyday Feminism LLC 202 643-1001
75 N Woodward Ave Tallahassee (32313) ***(G-17249)***
Everything Communicates Inc 407 578-6616
4380 L B Mcleod Rd Orlando (32811) ***(G-12722)***
Everything Printing Inc 239 541-2679
202 Se 44th St Cape Coral (33904) ***(G-1420)***
Evies Golf Center 941 377-2399
4735 Bee Ridge Rd Sarasota (34233) ***(G-16423)***
Evm Woodwork Corp 954 970-4352
971 Sw 70th Way North Lauderdale (33068) ***(G-11614)***
Evm Woodworks Corp 954 655-6414
7542 W Mcnab Rd North Lauderdale (33068) ***(G-11615)***
Evo Motors LLC 813 621-7799
11809 E Us Highway 92 Seffner (33584) ***(G-16725)***
Evolis Inc (HQ) 954 777-9262
3201 W Coml Blvd Ste 110 Fort Lauderdale (33309) ***(G-3977)***
Evolution Intrcnnect Systems I 954 217-6223
11870 W State Road 84 C Davie (33325) ***(G-2521)***
Evolution Lighting LLC (PA) 305 558-4777
880 Sw 145th Ave Ste 100 Pembroke Pines (33027) ***(G-14034)***
Evolution Liners Inc 407 839-6213
40 W Illiana St Orlando (32806) ***(G-12723)***
Evolution Metals Corp 561 531-2314
516 S Dixie Hwy West Palm Beach (33401) ***(G-18866)***
Evolution Orthotics Inc 407 688-2860
156 Harston Ct Lake Mary (32746) ***(G-7411)***
Evolution Signs and Print Inc 904 634-5666
11672 Philips Hwy Ste 3 Jacksonville (32256) ***(G-6371)***
Evolution Voice Inc 407 204-1614
5728 Major Blvd Ste 720 Orlando (32819) ***(G-12724)***
Evolution Woodworking 407 221-5031
670 Coffee Trl Geneva (32732) ***(G-5020)***
Evolutionary Screen Printing L 863 248-2692
3521 Waterfield Pkwy Lakeland (33803) ***(G-7682)***
Evolutions - Graphics Designs-, Miami *Also called Pacheco Creative Group Inc* ***(G-10126)***
Evolve E-Learning Solutions, Marco Island *Also called Evolve Technologies Inc* ***(G-8524)***
Evolve Technologies Inc 239 963-8037
950 N Collier Blvd # 400 Marco Island (34145) ***(G-8524)***
Evolvegene LLC 727 623-4052
12105 28th St N Ste A Saint Petersburg (33716) ***(G-15772)***
Evolving Coal Corp 813 944-3100
200 2nd Ave S Ste 733 Saint Petersburg (33701) ***(G-15773)***
Evoqua Water Technologies LLC 813 620-0900
4711 Oak Fair Blvd Tampa (33610) ***(G-17651)***
Evoqua Water Technologies LLC 407 650-1765
4506 L B Mcleod Rd Orlando (32811) ***(G-12725)***
Evora Enterprises Inc 305 261-4522
2608 Nw 6th St Ocala (34475) ***(G-11934)***
Evren Technologies Inc 352 494-0950
404 Sw 140th Ter Ste 50 Newberry (32669) ***(G-11555)***
Ew Publishing LLC 305 358-1100
2820 Ne 30th St Apt 10 Fort Lauderdale (33306) ***(G-3978)***
EW Scripps Company 772 408-5300
1939 Se Federal Hwy Port Saint Lucie (34986) ***(G-15107)***
Ewh Press 386 405-5069
1796 Ocean Shore Blvd Ormond Beach (32176) ***(G-13369)***
Ewhite LLC 954 530-3382
2633 Bayview Dr Fort Lauderdale (33306) ***(G-3979)***
Exact Inc 904 783-6640
5285 Ramona Blvd Jacksonville (32205) ***(G-6372)***
Exactech Inc (HQ) 352 377-1140
2320 Nw 66th Ct Gainesville (32653) ***(G-4916)***
Exactus Pharmacy Solutions Inc 888 314-3874
8715 Henderson Rd Tampa (33634) ***(G-17652)***
Exalos Inc 215 669-4488
824 Se 12th St Fort Lauderdale (33316) ***(G-3980)***
Excaliber Printing Inc 877 542-1699
45 S Pompano Pkwy Pompano Beach (33069) ***(G-14684)***
Excalibur Aircraft 863 385-9486
6439 Tractor Rd Sebring (33876) ***(G-16690)***
Excalibur Coach 407 302-9139
1830 Bobby Lee Pt Sanford (32771) ***(G-16043)***
Excalibur Manufacturing Corp (PA) 352 544-0055
16186 Flight Path Dr Brooksville (34604) ***(G-1228)***
Excel Converting Inc 786 318-2222
6950 Nw 37th Ct Miami (33147) ***(G-9542)***
Excel Fuel Inc 727 547-5511
6201 54th Ave N Saint Petersburg (33709) ***(G-15774)***
Excel Handbags Co Inc 305 836-8800
3651 Nw 81st St Miami (33147) ***(G-9543)***

ALPHABETIC

Excel Millwork & Moulding Inc 850 576-7228
7001 Fortune Blvd Midway (32343) *(G-10917)*
Excelag Corp (PA) 305 670-0145
7300 N Kendall Dr Ste 640 Miami (33156) *(G-9544)*
Excell Coatings Inc 321 868-7968
745 Scallop Dr Cape Canaveral (32920) *(G-1358)*
Excell Solutions LLC 407 615-9330
5115 N Socrum Loop Rd Lakeland (33809) *(G-7683)*
Excell Woodwork Corp 954 461-0465
1917 Mears Pkwy Margate (33063) *(G-8542)*
Excellent Guarantd Elctrcl 407 221-6234
1625 Red Clover Ct Orlando (32825) *(G-12726)*
Excellent Performance Inc 561 296-0776
4650 Dyer Blvd Riviera Beach (33407) *(G-15326)*
Excelor LLC 321 300-3315
7380 W Sand Lake Rd # 500 Orlando (32819) *(G-12727)*
Exces International LLC 561 880-8920
3460 Frlane Frms Rd Ste 1 Wellington (33414) *(G-18716)*
Excess Liquidator LLC 407 247-9105
3012 Kananwood Ct Ste 132 Oviedo (32765) *(G-13429)*
Exclusive Apparel LLC 800 859-6260
2598 E Sunrise Blvd # 2104 Fort Lauderdale (33304) *(G-3981)*
Exclusive Bats LLC 305 450-3858
10930 Nw 138th St Unit 1 Hialeah (33018) *(G-5400)*
Executive Label Inc 954 978-6983
5447 Nw 24th St Ste 5 Margate (33063) *(G-8543)*
Executive Printers of Florida, Medley *Also called Hobby Press Inc (G-8664)*
Executive Prtg & Mailing Svcs, Pompano Beach *Also called Leila K Moavero (G-14743)*
Exelan Pharmaceuticals Inc 561 287-6631
370 W Cmino Grdns Blvd St Boca Raton (33432) *(G-525)*
Exhaust Technologies Inc 561 744-9500
851 Jupiter Park Ln Jupiter (33458) *(G-7037)*
Exide Battery 904 783-1224
600 Suemac Rd Ste 1 Jacksonville (32254) *(G-6373)*
Exist Inc 954 739-7030
1650 Nw 23rd Ave Ste A Fort Lauderdale (33311) *(G-3982)*
Exist Clothing & Embroidery, Fort Lauderdale *Also called Exist Inc (G-3982)*
Exit Ten Inc 407 574-2433
100 Highline Dr Unit 116 Longwood (32750) *(G-8277)*
Exodus Aviation, Fort Lauderdale *Also called Exodus Management LLC (G-3983)*
Exodus Management LLC 954 995-4407
6750 N Andrews Ave Ste 20 Fort Lauderdale (33309) *(G-3983)*
Exotic Countertop Inc 954 979-8188
2160 Nw 22nd St Pompano Beach (33069) *(G-14685)*
Exotic Custom Coatings 850 358-1492
605 New York Ave Lynn Haven (32444) *(G-8432)*
Exotic Interiors, Lauderdale Lakes *Also called Tropic Shield Inc (G-8095)*
Exotic Marble Polishing Inc 786 318-6568
12325 Ne 9th Ave Apt 4 North Miami (33161) *(G-11638)*
Exotics By Cedrick, Tampa *Also called Cedrick McDonald (G-17519)*
Exotics Car Wraps 786 768-6798
245 Ne 183rd St Ste 3a Miami (33179) *(G-9545)*
Expandothane, Yulee *Also called Soythane Technologies Inc (G-19501)*
Expert Mold Removal Inc 407 925-6443
14929 Lenze Dr Tavares (32778) *(G-18336)*
Expert Printing and Graphics, Palmetto Bay *Also called Inkpressions Inc (G-13849)*
Expert Promotions LLC 772 643-4012
434 Georgia Blvd Sebastian (32958) *(G-16658)*
Expert Shutter Services Inc 772 871-1915
668 Sw Whitmore Dr Port Saint Lucie (34984) *(G-15108)*
Expert Subjects LLC 786 877-8531
4775 Collins Ave Miami (33140) *(G-9546)*
Expert TS of Jacksonville 904 387-2500
711 Cassat Ave Jacksonville (32205) *(G-6374)*
Exploration Resources Intn Geo 601 747-0726
1130 Business Center Dr Lake Mary (32746) *(G-7412)*
Exploration Services LLC 352 505-3578
4440 Ne 41st Ter Gainesville (32609) *(G-4917)*
Export Diesel LLC (PA) 305 396-1943
1835 Nw 112th Ave Ste 173 Miami (33172) *(G-9547)*
Expose Yourself USA, Fort Lauderdale *Also called Tigo Inc (G-4284)*
Express, Tarpon Springs *Also called Marrakech Inc (G-18315)*
Express Auto Carriers LLC 352 541-0040
5551 Se 44th Cir Ocala (34480) *(G-11935)*
Express Badging Services Inc 321 784-5925
1980 N Atl Ave Ste 525 Cocoa Beach (32931) *(G-2062)*
Express Brake International 352 304-6263
4376 Ne 35th St Ocala (34479) *(G-11936)*
Express Care of Tampa Bay (PA) 813 641-0068
6015 Rex Hall Ln Apollo Beach (33572) *(G-103)*
Express Fuel Systems Inc 904 525-4052
8351 Highgate Dr Jacksonville (32216) *(G-6375)*
Express Ironing Inc 305 261-1072
4707 Sw 75th Ave Miami (33155) *(G-9548)*
Express Ironing of Miami, Miami *Also called Express Ironing Inc (G-9548)*
Express Label Co Inc 407 332-4774
1955 Corp Sq Ste 1001 Longwood (32750) *(G-8278)*
Express Ornamental LLC 813 486-0344
9211 Maybury Ct Tampa (33615) *(G-17653)*
Express Paper Company Inc 305 685-4929
5590 Nw 163rd St Miami Lakes (33014) *(G-10787)*
Express Pavers LLC 813 408-9938
7716 Winging Way Dr Tampa (33615) *(G-17654)*
Express Press Inc 813 884-3310
107 N Jefferson St Tampa (33602) *(G-17655)*
Express Printing, Tallahassee *Also called Copy Well Inc (G-17238)*
Express Printing & Office Sups 904 765-9696
9840 Interstate Center Dr Jacksonville (32218) *(G-6376)*
Express Printing Center Inc 813 909-1085
2355 Raden Dr Land O Lakes (34639) *(G-7854)*
Express Printing Corporation 305 546-6369
7024 Sw 46th St Miami (33155) *(G-9549)*
Express Prtg Winter Haven Inc 863 294-3286
757 Cypress Gardens Blvd Winter Haven (33880) *(G-19319)*
Express Removal Service LLC 305 303-8249
15950 Bunche Park Schl Dr Miami Gardens (33054) *(G-10739)*
Express Signs & Graphics Inc 407 889-4433
547 Garden Heights Dr Winter Garden (34787) *(G-19263)*
Express Tools Inc 954 663-4333
14521 Sw 21st St Davie (33325) *(G-2522)*
Express Vision Care Inc 786 587-7404
1550 W 84th St Ste 15 Hialeah (33014) *(G-5401)*
Expressions In Wood 954 956-0005
4270 Nw 19th Ave Ste A Pompano Beach (33064) *(G-14686)*
Expressway Oil Corp 786 302-9534
7391 Nw 78th St Medley (33166) *(G-8650)*
Exquisite Wood Works By Al 321 634-5398
5565 Schenck Ave Ste 5 Rockledge (32955) *(G-15410)*
Extant Aerospace, Melbourne *Also called Symetrics Industries LLC (G-8954)*
Extant Aerospace, Melbourne *Also called Extant Cmpnnts Group Hldngs In (G-8828)*
Extant Cmpnnts Group Hldngs In 321 254-1500
1615 W Nasa Blvd Melbourne (32901) *(G-8828)*
Extant Cmpnnts Group Intrmdate (PA) 321 254-1500
1615 W Nasa Blvd Melbourne (32901) *(G-8829)*
Extra Time Solutions 407 625-2198
3695 Peaceful Valley Dr Clermont (34711) *(G-1957)*
Extract Downtown Orlando LLC 407 722-7379
101 S Garland Ave Orlando (32801) *(G-12728)*
Extralink Corporation 305 804-1100
6538 Collins Ave Miami Beach (33141) *(G-10665)*
Extreme Brake Integration Inc 352 342-9596
5817 Nw 44th Ave Ocala (34482) *(G-11937)*
Extreme Care Inc 239 898-3709
11997 Princess Grace Ct Cape Coral (33991) *(G-1421)*
Extreme Coatings, Saint Petersburg *Also called Surface Engrg & Alloy Co Inc (G-15930)*
Extreme Coatings 727 528-7998
2895 46th Ave N Saint Petersburg (33714) *(G-15775)*
Extreme Corvette Co LLC 941 524-8942
6015 28th St E Unit F1 Bradenton (34203) *(G-1040)*
Extreme Crafts LLC 561 989-7400
999 Nw 51st St Ste 100 Boca Raton (33431) *(G-526)*
Extreme Digital Video Inc 954 792-2818
3784 Sw 30th Ave Fort Lauderdale (33312) *(G-3984)*
Extreme H2o, Sarasota *Also called Hydrogel Vision Corporation (G-16231)*
Extreme Iron & Wood Work Inc 407 925-2448
535 Sellars Dr Lake Alfred (33850) *(G-7331)*
Extreme Manufacturing LLC 888 844-7734
1909 Ne 25th Ave Ocala (34470) *(G-11938)*
Extreme Wood Works S Fla Inc 305 463-8614
1520 Nw 79th Ave Doral (33126) *(G-3346)*
Exxelia Usa Inc (PA) 407 695-6562
1221 N Us Highway 17 92 Longwood (32750) *(G-8279)*
Eye Specialists Mid Florida PA 863 937-4515
2004 E County Road 540a Lakeland (33813) *(G-7684)*
Eye Wall Industries Inc 850 607-2288
3920 W Navy Blvd Pensacola (32507) *(G-14147)*
Eye-Dye, Pensacola *Also called Bam Enterprises Inc (G-14096)*
Eyedeal Vision Care Inc 321 631-2811
5500 Stadium Pkwy Ste 102 Melbourne (32940) *(G-8830)*
Eyedose Inc 786 853-6194
66 W Flagler St Ste 900 Miami (33130) *(G-9550)*
Eyes On Go Optical LLC 954 242-3243
4715 Sw 62nd Ave Davie (33314) *(G-2523)*
Eyeson Dgtal Srvllnce MGT Syst 305 808-3344
64 Ne 1st St Miami (33132) *(G-9551)*
EZ Boatworks Inc 772 475-8721
10602 Sw Corey Pl Palm City (34990) *(G-13653)*
EZ Loder Adjstble Boat Trlrs S 800 323-8190
1462 Commerce Centre Dr Port Saint Lucie (34986) *(G-15109)*
EZ Neon Inc 561 262-7813
12179 179th Ct N Jupiter (33478) *(G-7038)*
EZ Truck Services Inc 239 728-3022
19595 N River Rd Alva (33920) *(G-88)*
Ezassi, Ponte Vedra Beach *Also called Zassi Holdings Inc (G-14958)*
Eze Castle Software Llc 407 692-9699
3501 Quadrangle Blvd # 200 Orlando (32817) *(G-12729)*
Ezell Precision Tool Co 727 573-3575
4733 122nd Ave N Clearwater (33762) *(G-1678)*

Ezproducts International Inc 863 735-0813
612 N Florida Ave Wauchula (33873) ***(G-18691)***
Ezverify & Validate LLC 855 398-3981
1401 Nw 136th Ave Ste 400 Sunrise (33323) ***(G-17121)***
Ezy Wrap, Defuniak Springs *Also called Professional Products Inc* ***(G-2946)***
Ezy-Glide Inc 850 638-4403
715 7th St Chipley (32428) ***(G-1544)***
Ezywipe of America, Miami *Also called Beyond White Spa LLC* ***(G-9242)***
F & J Specialty Products Inc 352 680-1177
404 Cypress Rd Ocala (34472) ***(G-11939)***
F & J Woodworking Inc 239 455-8823
1311 Wildwood Lakes Blvd Naples (34104) ***(G-11242)***
F & R General Interiors Corp 305 635-4747
480 W 20th St Hialeah (33010) ***(G-5402)***
F & S Cabinets Inc 386 822-9525
1307 Yorktown St Deland (32724) ***(G-2976)***
F & S Mill Works 407 349-9948
522 Cemetery Rd Geneva (32732) ***(G-5021)***
F C Machine Corporation 407 673-9601
4212 Metric Dr Winter Park (32792) ***(G-19406)***
F D Signworks LLC 561 248-6323
941 S Military Trl F5 West Palm Beach (33415) ***(G-18867)***
F I B US Corp 239 262-6070
3966 Arnold Ave Naples (34104) ***(G-11243)***
F I M C O, Tampa *Also called Florida Ink Mfg Co Inc* ***(G-17679)***
F K Instrument, Clearwater *Also called F K Instrument Co Inc* ***(G-1679)***
F K Instrument Co Inc 727 461-6060
2134 Sunnydale Blvd Clearwater (33765) ***(G-1679)***
F L F Corp 561 747-7077
810 Saturn St Ste 28 Jupiter (33477) ***(G-7039)***
F O F Plastics Inc 727 937-2144
1614 Tallahassee Dr Tarpon Springs (34689) ***(G-18300)***
F P G, Fort Lauderdale *Also called Florida Packg & Graphics Inc* ***(G-4002)***
F P General Welding 786 812-6673
3131 Sw 120th Ct Miami (33175) ***(G-9552)***
F S View Fla Flambeau Newsppr 850 561-6653
277 N Magnolia Dr Tallahassee (32301) ***(G-17250)***
F T F Construction Company 772 571-1850
25 N Myrtle St Fellsmere (32948) ***(G-3725)***
F W I Inc 407 509-9739
1388 S Ronald Reagan Blvd Longwood (32750) ***(G-8280)***
F&J USA LLC 800 406-6190
1111 Lincoln Rd Ste 500 Miami Beach (33139) ***(G-10666)***
F-Response, Tampa *Also called Agile Risk Management LLC* ***(G-17392)***
F3 Analytics LLC 404 551-2600
16040 Gulf Shores Dr Boca Grande (33921) ***(G-392)***
Faac International Inc (HQ) 904 448-8952
3160 Murrell Rd Rockledge (32955) ***(G-15411)***
Fab Defense Inc 386 263-3054
873 Hull Rd Unit 5 Ormond Beach (32174) ***(G-13370)***
Fab Rite Inc 561 848-8181
4636 Dyer Blvd Riviera Beach (33407) ***(G-15327)***
Faba Cabinets & Such LLC 813 871-1529
7029 W Hillsborough Ave Tampa (33634) ***(G-17656)***
Fabbro Marine Group Inc 321 701-8141
100 E Pine St Ste 110 Orlando (32801) ***(G-12730)***
Fabco Metal Products LLC 386 252-3730
1490 Frances Dr Daytona Beach (32124) ***(G-2664)***
Fabco-Air Inc 352 373-3578
3716 Ne 49th Ave Gainesville (32609) ***(G-4918)***
Fabio Napoleoni Artworks 207 952-1561
2701 Gretagreen Ct Orlando (32835) ***(G-12731)***
Fabis Group Corporation 305 718-3638
8025 Nw 68th St Miami (33166) ***(G-9553)***
Fabis Group Corporation 305 718-3638
8231 Nw 66th St Miami (33166) ***(G-9554)***
Fabmaster Inc 727 216-6750
2100 Palmetto St Ste A Clearwater (33765) ***(G-1680)***
Fabric Innovations Inc 305 860-5757
7318 Sw 48th St Miami (33155) ***(G-9555)***
Fabricated Products Tampa Inc 813 247-4001
1100 S 56th St Tampa (33619) ***(G-17657)***
Fabricated Wire Products Inc 813 802-8463
401 Lutie Dr Valrico (33594) ***(G-18517)***
Fabricating Technologies LLC 352 473-6673
6670 Spring Lake Rd Keystone Heights (32656) ***(G-7207)***
Fabrication Florida Venture 954 388-5014
1201 Nw 65th Pl Fort Lauderdale (33309) ***(G-3985)***
Fabrico Inc 386 736-7373
1700 E Intl Speedway Blvd Deland (32724) ***(G-2977)***
Fabrox LLC 904 342-4048
2 Sunshine Blvd Ormond Beach (32174) ***(G-13371)***
Fabsouth LLC (HQ) 954 938-5800
721 Ne 44th St Oakland Park (33334) ***(G-11804)***
Fabtech Supply, Jacksonville *Also called Ft Acquisition Company Llc* ***(G-6417)***
Fabworx LLC 239 573-9353
848 Se 9th St Cape Coral (33990) ***(G-1422)***
Facelove Cosmetics Inc (PA) 786 346-7357
18202 Homestead Ave Miami (33157) ***(G-9556)***
Factorfox Software LLC 305 671-9526
14221 Sw 120th St Miami (33186) ***(G-9557)***
Factory Direct Cab Refacing 954 445-6635
1060 Scarlet Oak St Hollywood (33019) ***(G-5819)***
Factorymart Inc 561 202-9820
3875 Fiscal Ct Ste 400 West Palm Beach (33404) ***(G-18868)***
Facts Engineering LLC 727 375-8888
8049 Photonics Dr Trinity (34655) ***(G-18485)***
Faes Srt Inc 941 960-6742
7619 Trillium Blvd Sarasota (34241) ***(G-16424)***
Fagerberg Industries LLC 352 318-2254
100 Sw 75th St Ste 206 Gainesville (32607) ***(G-4919)***
Fairbanks and Fairbanks Inc 850 293-1184
405 S K St Pensacola (32502) ***(G-14148)***
Fairing Xchange LLC 904 589-5253
144 Industrial Loop E Orange Park (32073) ***(G-12391)***
Faithful Heart Froyo LLC 407 325-3052
2405 Whitehall Cir Winter Park (32792) ***(G-19407)***
Fajas Colombianas USA LLC 786 326-0002
18850 Nw 57th Ave Hialeah (33015) ***(G-5403)***
Falco Industries Inc 407 956-0045
1550 Dixon Rd Longwood (32779) ***(G-8281)***
Falcon Commercial Aviation LLC 786 340-9464
13500 Sw 134th Ave Ste 3 Miami (33186) ***(G-9558)***
Falconpro Industries Inc 305 556-4456
1690 W 40th St Hialeah (33012) ***(G-5404)***
Falcons Castl Blinds Globl Fla 561 727-4332
3316 Lake Ave West Palm Beach (33405) ***(G-18869)***
Falfas Cabinet & Stone LLC 941 960-2065
1705 Cattlemen Rd Sarasota (34232) ***(G-16425)***
Fam Industries Inc 281 779-0650
7039 Mirabelle Dr Jacksonville (32258) ***(G-6377)***
Famatel USA LLC 754 217-4841
1221 Stirling Rd Ste 120 Dania (33004) ***(G-2445)***
Family Magazines, Sarasota *Also called Florida Family Magazine* ***(G-16434)***
Family of Smith Inc (PA) 941 726-0873
5899 Whitfield Ave # 104 Sarasota (34243) ***(G-16212)***
Family Reading Club, Clearwater *Also called Publishers Prmotional Svcs Inc* ***(G-1853)***
Fan America Inc 941 955-9788
2235 6th St Sarasota (34237) ***(G-16426)***
Fanam Inc 941 955-9788
2043 Global Ct Sarasota (34240) ***(G-16427)***
Fanatics Mounted Memories Inc 866 578-9115
8100 Nations Way Jacksonville (32256) ***(G-6378)***
Fanning Springs Ice Company 352 463-1999
3080 Pine Ave Old Town (32680) ***(G-12196)***
Fantasy Brewmasters LLC 239 206-3247
950 Commercial Blvd Naples (34104) ***(G-11244)***
Fantasy Chocolates Inc 561 276-9007
1815 Cypress Lake Dr Orlando (32837) ***(G-12732)***
Fantasy Escapes, Holiday *Also called Admiral Printing Inc* ***(G-5732)***
Fantasy Marble & Granite Inc 954 788-0433
400 Sw 12th Ave Ste 4/5 Pompano Beach (33069) ***(G-14687)***
Fanto Group LLC (PA) 407 857-5101
7022 Tpc Dr Ste 550 Orlando (32822) ***(G-12733)***
Fanwise LLC 954 874-9000
210 S Andrews Ave Fort Lauderdale (33301) ***(G-3986)***
Faour Glass Technologies, Tampa *Also called Faours Mirror Corp* ***(G-17658)***
Faours Mirror Corp 813 884-3297
5119 W Knox St Ste A Tampa (33634) ***(G-17658)***
Far Chemical, Palm Bay *Also called Far Research Inc* ***(G-13511)***
Far Research Inc 321 723-6160
2210 Wilhelmina Ct Ne Palm Bay (32905) ***(G-13511)***
Faraday Inc 813 536-6104
802 E Whiting St Tampa (33602) ***(G-17659)***
Farartis LLC 305 594-5704
12050 Nw 28th Ave Miami (33167) ***(G-9559)***
Faratech LLC 954 651-7287
5373 N Nob Hill Rd Sunrise (33351) ***(G-17122)***
Farma International Inc 305 670-4416
9400 S Ddland Blvd Ste 60 Miami (33156) ***(G-9560)***
Farmco Manufacturers Inc 813 645-0611
1110 4th St Sw Ruskin (33570) ***(G-15484)***
Farmer Mold and Mch Works Inc 727 522-0515
2904 44th Ave N Saint Petersburg (33714) ***(G-15776)***
Farmers Cooperative Inc (PA) 386 362-1459
1841 Howard St W Live Oak (32064) ***(G-8232)***
Faro Industriale Spa Co 941 925-3004
6208 Clark Center Ave Sarasota (34238) ***(G-16428)***
Faro Technologies Inc 800 736-0234
125 Technology Park Lake Mary (32746) ***(G-7413)***
Faro Technologies Inc (PA) 407 333-9911
250 Technology Park Lake Mary (32746) ***(G-7414)***
Fasco Epoxies Inc 772 464-0808
2550 N Us Highway 1 Fort Pierce (34946) ***(G-4696)***
Fashion Connection Miami Inc 305 882-0782
900 W 19th St Hialeah (33010) ***(G-5405)***
Fashion Pool USA Inc 970 367-4797
6111 Linton St Jupiter (33458) ***(G-7040)***

ALPHABETIC

Fashionable Canes.....727 547-8866
7381 114th Ave Ste 402b Largo (33773) ***(G-7942)***
Fassi Equipment Inc.....954 385-6555
2800 Glades Cir Ste 127 Weston (33327) ***(G-19123)***
Fassidigitalcom Inc.....954 385-6555
2800 Gldes Crcles Ste 127 Weston (33327) ***(G-19124)***
Fassiequipment.com, Weston *Also called Fassi Equipment Inc* ***(G-19123)***
Fassmer Service America LLC (HQ).....305 557-8875
3650 Nw 15th St Lauderhill (33311) ***(G-8109)***
Fast Forward Race Engines Inc.....813 788-1794
2610 Paul S Buchman Hwy Zephyrhills (33540) ***(G-19517)***
Fast Frontier Printing.....407 538-5621
7360 Ulmerton Rd Apt 19d Largo (33771) ***(G-7943)***
Fast Fuel Corp.....786 251-0373
2274 W 80th St Unit 4 Hialeah (33016) ***(G-5406)***
Fast Labels.....904 626-0508
8680 Bandera Cir S Jacksonville (32244) ***(G-6379)***
Fast Service Signs Inc.....954 380-0451
10257 Nw 53rd St Sunrise (33351) ***(G-17123)***
Fast Signs.....813 999-4981
14618 N Dale Mabry Hwy Tampa (33618) ***(G-17660)***
Fast Signs.....239 498-7200
28440 Old 41 Rd Bonita Springs (34135) ***(G-830)***
Fast Signs of Brandon.....813 655-9036
2020 Brandon Crossing Cir Brandon (33511) ***(G-1158)***
Fastener Solutions LLC.....813 324-8372
333 N Falkenburg Rd Tampa (33619) ***(G-17661)***
Fastener Solutions LLC.....813 867-4714
2420 W Stroud Ave Tampa (33629) ***(G-17662)***
Fastener Specialties Mfg Co, West Palm Beach *Also called Sockets & Specials Inc* ***(G-19036)***
Fastener Specialty Corp.....631 903-4453
24100 Tiseo Blvd Unit 14 Port Charlotte (33980) ***(G-14980)***
Fastglas.....904 765-2222
4226 Spring Grove Rd Jacksonville (32209) ***(G-6380)***
Fastkit Corp.....305 599-0839
11250 Nw 25th St Ste 100 Doral (33172) ***(G-3347)***
Fastkit Corp.....754 227-8234
11250 Nw 25th St Ste 100 Doral (33172) ***(G-3348)***
Fastsigns, Brandon *Also called Fast Signs of Brandon* ***(G-1158)***
Fastsigns, Tallahassee *Also called Bucks Corporation Inc* ***(G-17229)***
Fastsigns, Saint Petersburg *Also called Lucke Group Inc* ***(G-15843)***
Fastsigns, Oldsmar *Also called Hunt RDS Inc* ***(G-12232)***
Fastsigns, Deerfield Beach *Also called Hermes 7 Communications LLC* ***(G-2838)***
Fastsigns, Pembroke Pines *Also called Mwr Sign Enterprises Inc* ***(G-14050)***
Fastsigns, Tampa *Also called Fast Signs* ***(G-17660)***
Fastsigns, Jacksonville *Also called Easy Rent Inc* ***(G-6351)***
Fastsigns, Bonita Springs *Also called Fast Signs* ***(G-830)***
Fastsigns, Miami *Also called Signs 2 U Inc* ***(G-10345)***
Fastsigns, Orlando *Also called MGM Cargo LLC* ***(G-12966)***
Fastsigns, Fort Myers *Also called Alli Cats Inc* ***(G-4352)***
Fastsigns, Orlando *Also called R & A Power Graphics Inc* ***(G-13107)***
Fastsigns, Tampa *Also called Calmac Corporation* ***(G-17501)***
Fastsigns, Miami *Also called Bdnz Associates Inc* ***(G-9230)***
Fastsigns, Orlando *Also called C & H Sign Enterprises Inc* ***(G-12538)***
Fastsigns, Sarasota *Also called Sarasota Signs and Visuals* ***(G-16581)***
Fastsigns, Casselberry *Also called T & C Godby Enterprises Inc* ***(G-1519)***
Fastsigns, Jacksonville *Also called Ash Signs Inc* ***(G-6170)***
Fastsigns, Miami *Also called Sign Development Corporation* ***(G-10342)***
Fastsigns, Lake Worth Beach *Also called Baxter Adventures Inc* ***(G-7605)***
Fastsigns, Davie *Also called Windstone Development Intl Lc* ***(G-2615)***
Fastsigns, Oakland Park *Also called Sebco Industries Inc* ***(G-11837)***
Fastsigns, Clearwater *Also called Lucke Enterprises Inc* ***(G-1765)***
Fastsigns, Apopka *Also called Quick Advertising Inc* ***(G-177)***
Fastsigns, Tampa *Also called Clark Craig Enterprises* ***(G-17539)***
Fastsigns.....305 628-3278
15925 Nw 57th Ave Miami Lakes (33014) ***(G-10788)***
Fastsigns.....727 341-0084
4058 Park St N Saint Petersburg (33709) ***(G-15777)***
Fastsigns.....305 747-7115
146 Madeira Ave Coral Gables (33134) ***(G-2145)***
Fastsigns.....903 629-7204
5125 The Oaks Cir Orlando (32809) ***(G-12734)***
Fastsigns.....813 625-1800
1110 Lakemont Dr Valrico (33594) ***(G-18518)***
Fastsigns.....305 945-4700
15405 W Dixie Hwy North Miami Beach (33162) ***(G-11675)***
Fastsigns.....786 615-2179
118 Hialeah Dr Hialeah (33010) ***(G-5407)***
Fastsigns.....954 404-8341
3328 Griffin Rd Fort Lauderdale (33312) ***(G-3987)***
Fastsigns.....954 416-3434
2841 Hollywood Blvd Hollywood (33020) ***(G-5820)***
Fastsigns.....407 542-1234
2200 Winter Springs Blvd # 118 Oviedo (32765) ***(G-13430)***
Fastsigns.....850 477-9744
6060 Tippin Ave Pensacola (32504) ***(G-14149)***
Fastsigns 176101.....321 307-2400
7640 N Wickham Rd Melbourne (32940) ***(G-8831)***
Fastsigns 176501, Saint Augustine *Also called FDA Signs LLC* ***(G-15543)***
Fastsigns2043.....305 988-5264
2401 N Federal Hwy Boca Raton (33431) ***(G-527)***
Fasulo Granite & Marble Inc.....561 371-5410
368 River Edge Rd Jupiter (33477) ***(G-7041)***
Fat and Weird Cookie Co LLC.....850 832-9150
2540 Jenks Ave Panama City (32405) ***(G-13900)***
Fatezzi Inc.....407 323-8688
5305 Pen Ave Sanford (32773) ***(G-16044)***
Father's Table, The, Sanford *Also called Fathers Table LLC* ***(G-16045)***
Fathers Table LLC (PA).....407 324-1200
2100 Country Club Rd Sanford (32771) ***(G-16045)***
Fathym Inc.....303 905-4402
2303 14th St W Palmetto (34221) ***(G-13797)***
Fator Fasteners Usa LLC.....941 479-8518
1905 Intermodal Cir Palmetto (34221) ***(G-13798)***
Fatovich Technologies LLC.....772 597-1326
2159 Sw Cameron Ln Palm City (34990) ***(G-13654)***
Faulkner Inc of Miami.....305 885-4731
7275 W 20th Ave Hialeah (33014) ***(G-5408)***
Faulkner Plastics, Hialeah *Also called Faulkner Inc of Miami* ***(G-5408)***
Faux Effects International Inc.....772 778-9044
2700 Industrial Avenue 2 Fort Pierce (34946) ***(G-4697)***
FB Beer Company, Naples *Also called Fantasy Brewmasters LLC* ***(G-11244)***
FBI Industries Inc.....239 462-1176
11020 Yellow Poplar Dr Fort Myers (33913) ***(G-4448)***
Fbj Engineering & Dev LLC.....754 423-1309
4346 Nw 120th Ave Coral Springs (33065) ***(G-2244)***
Fbr 1804 Inc.....305 340-3114
18320 Ne 21st Ct North Miami Beach (33179) ***(G-11676)***
FCA US LLC.....305 597-2222
9975 Nw 12th St Doral (33172) ***(G-3349)***
Fcbn LLC.....408 505-1324
2637 E Atl Blvd 22868 Pompano Beach (33062) ***(G-14688)***
Fcm, Odessa *Also called Florida Custom Mold Inc* ***(G-12121)***
Fcs Holdings Inc.....352 793-5151
530 W Kings Hwy Center Hill (33514) ***(G-1526)***
Fcs Industries Corp.....407 947-3127
406 Anessa Rose Loop Ocoee (34761) ***(G-12085)***
Fcs Industries Corp.....407 412-5642
6996 Piazza Grande Ave # 314 Orlando (32835) ***(G-12735)***
Fct-Combustion Inc.....610 725-8840
5049 Sw 35th Ter Tce Fort Lauderdale (33312) ***(G-3988)***
FDA Signs LLC.....904 800-1776
2303 N Ponce De Leon Blvd Saint Augustine (32084) ***(G-15543)***
Fdc Print LLC.....305 885-8707
950 Se 8th St Hialeah (33010) ***(G-5409)***
Fdc Vitamins LLC (HQ).....305 468-1600
14620 Nw 60th Ave Miami Lakes (33014) ***(G-10789)***
FDM of Clearwater Inc.....727 544-8801
10850 75th St Largo (33777) ***(G-7944)***
Fea Inc.....407 330-3535
5333 Pen Ave Sanford (32773) ***(G-16046)***
Feagle Logging LLC.....386 365-2689
805 Ne Indigo Dr Lake City (32055) ***(G-7354)***
Featherlite Exhibits.....800 229-5533
1715 E Sewaha St Tampa (33612) ***(G-17663)***
Featherlocks, Boynton Beach *Also called Condition Culture LLC* ***(G-892)***
Fedan Corp.....305 885-5415
2280 W 1st Ave Hialeah (33010) ***(G-5410)***
Fedan Tire Co, Hialeah *Also called Fedan Corp* ***(G-5410)***
Federal Eastern Intl Inc.....954 533-4506
3516 W Broward Blvd Fort Lauderdale (33312) ***(G-3989)***
Federal Heath Sign Company LLC.....817 685-9075
1128 Beville Rd Ste E Daytona Beach (32114) ***(G-2665)***
Federal Millwork Corp.....954 522-0653
3300 Se 6th Ave Fort Lauderdale (33316) ***(G-3990)***
Federal Suppliers Guide, Oldsmar *Also called Countryside Publishing Co Inc* ***(G-12219)***
Federal-Mogul Motorparts LLC.....954 585-2500
3499 Sw 42nd St Fort Lauderdale (33312) ***(G-3991)***
Federated Precision Inc.....561 288-6500
692 S Military Trl Deerfield Beach (33442) ***(G-2824)***
Feds Apparel.....954 932-0685
2230 Sw 70th Ave Ste 1 Davie (33317) ***(G-2524)***
Feick Corporation.....305 271-8550
8869 Sw 131st St Miami (33176) ***(G-9561)***
Fekel Stucco Plastering Inc.....239 571-5464
3780 29th Ave Sw Naples (34117) ***(G-11245)***
Fekkai Brands LLC.....954 791-6050
6825 W Sunrise Blvd Plantation (33313) ***(G-14514)***
Fekkai Retail LLC (PA).....866 514-8048
6825 W Sunrise Blvd Plantation (33313) ***(G-14515)***
Feldenkreis Holdings LLC (PA).....305 592-2830
3000 Nw 107th Ave Doral (33172) ***(G-3350)***

Felix Reynoso...954 497-2330
3062 Nw 23rd Ter Oakland Park (33311) ***(G-11805)***
Fellowship Enterprises Inc...727 726-5997
995 Harbor Lake Dr Ste 10 Safety Harbor (34695) ***(G-15493)***
Femmescience LLC...305 361-0994
280 Woodcrest Rd Key Biscayne (33149) ***(G-7155)***
Fenix Wester Corp...305 324-9105
2006 Nw 20th St Miami (33142) ***(G-9562)***
Fenwall LLC (PA)...813 343-5979
12850 Commodity Pl Tampa (33626) ***(G-17664)***
Fermatex Enterprises Inc...407 332-8320
685 S Rnald Reagan Blvd Orlando (32808) ***(G-12736)***
Fernandina Observer Inc...904 261-4372
205 Lighthouse Cir Fernandina Beach (32034) ***(G-3738)***
Ferrari Express Inc...305 374-5003
36 Ne 1st St Ste 1049 Miami (33132) ***(G-9563)***
Ferrelli Industries Inc...305 792-0100
2058 Ne 183rd St North Miami Beach (33179) ***(G-11677)***
Ferrera Embroidery & Prtg Ser...786 667-2680
331 Ne 167th St Miami (33162) ***(G-9564)***
Ferrera Tooling Inc...863 646-8500
3960 Air Park Dr Lakeland (33811) ***(G-7685)***
Ferrin Signs Inc...561 802-4242
945 26th St West Palm Beach (33407) ***(G-18870)***
Ferris Groves...352 860-0366
7607 S Florida Ave Floral City (34436) ***(G-3766)***
Ferris Stahl-Meyers Packing, Madison *Also called Prg Packing Corp* ***(G-8453)***
Fertec Inc...850 478-6480
141 Terry Dr Pensacola (32503) ***(G-14150)***
Fetco, Clearwater *Also called Magnatronix Corporation Inc* ***(G-1770)***
Fewtek Inc...727 736-0533
2539 Gary Cir Apt 201 Dunedin (34698) ***(G-3576)***
Ff Systems Inc...239 288-4255
2840 Hunter St Fort Myers (33916) ***(G-4449)***
Ffo Leesburg LLC...352 315-0783
9917 Us Highway 441 Leesburg (34788) ***(G-8155)***
Ffutter Fetti, Largo *Also called Parti Line International Inc* ***(G-8023)***
FGA Printing...954 763-1122
2550 N Powerline Rd # 105 Pompano Beach (33069) ***(G-14689)***
Fgmg International...305 988-7436
2820 Lightwood St Deltona (32738) ***(G-3169)***
Fgt Cabinetry LLC...321 800-2036
1031 Crews Comm Dr Ste 13 Orlando (32837) ***(G-12737)***
Fhs Enterprises LLC...754 214-9379
2875 S Congress Ave Ste D Delray Beach (33445) ***(G-3078)***
Fl Aerospace Solutions Inc...786 395-3289
7938 Nw 66th St Miami (33166) ***(G-9565)***
Fl Foil Co, Auburndale *Also called Fi-Foil Company Inc* ***(G-240)***
Fi-Foil Company Inc...863 965-1846
612 W Bridgers Ave Auburndale (33823) ***(G-240)***
Fiberbuilt Umbrellas Inc...954 484-9139
2201 W Atlantic Blvd Pompano Beach (33069) ***(G-14690)***
Fiberflon Usa Inc...786 953-7329
1835 Nw 112th Ave Miami (33172) ***(G-9566)***
Fiberglass Fabrication, Cocoa *Also called Fun Marine Inc* ***(G-2024)***
Fiberoptic Engineering Corp...850 763-2289
6541 Bayline Dr Panama City (32404) ***(G-13901)***
Fibertronics Inc...321 473-8933
2900 Dusa Dr Melbourne (32934) ***(G-8832)***
Fibre Tech Inc...727 539-0844
2323 34th Way Largo (33771) ***(G-7945)***
Ficap...407 302-3316
705 Remington Oak Dr Lake Mary (32746) ***(G-7415)***
Fidelity Manufacturing LLC...352 414-4700
1900 Ne 25th Ave Ocala (34470) ***(G-11940)***
Fidelity Printing Corporation...727 522-9557
3662 Morris St N Saint Petersburg (33713) ***(G-15778)***
Field Forensics Inc...727 490-3609
1601 3rd St S Saint Petersburg (33701) ***(G-15779)***
Field Office, Tampa *Also called Viasat Inc* ***(G-18243)***
Field Service Office, Lake Buena Vista *Also called Jfh Technologies LLC* ***(G-7336)***
Field Specialties...440 635-0282
4750 Se 220th Ave Morriston (32668) ***(G-11092)***
Fiero Enterprises Inc...954 454-5004
203 Nw 5th Ave Hallandale Beach (33009) ***(G-5183)***
Fiesta Marine Products Inc...727 856-6900
11016 State Road 52 Hudson (34669) ***(G-6023)***
Fiesta Pontoon Boats, Hudson *Also called Fiesta Marine Products Inc* ***(G-6023)***
Fifo Wireless, Miami *Also called Cellular Masters Inc* ***(G-9333)***
Fiik Skateboards LLC...561 405-9541
5300 Powerline Rd Ste 209 Fort Lauderdale (33309) ***(G-3992)***
Fiik Skateboards LLC (PA)...561 316-8234
7050 W Palmetto Park Rd Boca Raton (33433) ***(G-528)***
Fill Tech Solutions Inc 200...727 572-8550
11401 Belcher Rd S # 230 Largo (33773) ***(G-7946)***
Filmfastener LLC...813 926-8721
12052 49th St N C Clearwater (33762) ***(G-1681)***
Filorga Americas Inc...786 266-7429
429 Lenox Ave Miami Beach (33139) ***(G-10667)***
Filta Group Inc (PA)...407 996-5550
7075 Kingspointe Pkwy # 1 Orlando (32819) ***(G-12738)***
Filter Research Corporation...321 802-3444
1270 Clearmont St Ne # 15 Palm Bay (32905) ***(G-13512)***
Filters Plus Inc...813 232-2000
6708 Benjamin Rd Ste 200 Tampa (33634) ***(G-17665)***
Filthy Food LLC...786 916-5556
16500 Nw 15th Ave Miami (33169) ***(G-9567)***
Fimco Manufacturing Inc...561 624-3308
15795 Corporate Rd N Jupiter (33478) ***(G-7042)***
Final Touch Molding Cabinetry...239 948-7856
25070 Bernwood Dr Bonita Springs (34135) ***(G-831)***
Finastra USA Corporation...800 989-9009
744 Primera Blvd Ste 2000 Lake Mary (32746) ***(G-7416)***
Finastra USA Corporation...800 394-8778
8010 Sunport Dr Ste 101 Orlando (32809) ***(G-12739)***
Find A Friend LLC...813 293-1584
3318 Russett Pl Land O Lakes (34638) ***(G-7855)***
Findexcom Inc (PA)...561 328-6488
1313 S Killian Dr Lake Park (33403) ***(G-7470)***
Fine Archtctral Mllwk Shutters...954 491-2055
800 Nw 57th Pl Fort Lauderdale (33309) ***(G-3993)***
Fine Art Connoisseur, Boca Raton *Also called Stream Line Publishing Inc* ***(G-732)***
Fine Art Lamps, Hialeah *Also called Gq Investments LLC* ***(G-5435)***
Fine D-Zign Signs, Saint Cloud *Also called Zeeeees Corporation* ***(G-15671)***
Fine Industries Corporation...321 452-6956
1591 Stafford Ave Merritt Island (32952) ***(G-9001)***
Fine Line Custom Millwork LLC...941 628-9611
1683 Ne Bishop St Arcadia (34266) ***(G-203)***
Fine Line Pavers Inc...561 389-9819
6480 Bischoff Rd West Palm Beach (33413) ***(G-18871)***
Fine Line Printing & Graphics, Titusville *Also called Integrity Business Svcs Inc* ***(G-18434)***
Fine Surfaces and More Inc...305 691-5752
8860 Nw 15th Ave Miami (33147) ***(G-9568)***
Fine Wood Design Inc...727 531-8000
12087 62nd St Unit 8 Largo (33773) ***(G-7947)***
Fine Wood Work, Pensacola *Also called Southern Woodworks Fine Wdwkg* ***(G-14266)***
Fine Woodworking...941 957-0863
2243 Valencia Dr Sarasota (34239) ***(G-16429)***
Fine Woodworks...954 448-9206
15145 Se 175th St Weirsdale (32195) ***(G-18705)***
Finecraft Cabinetry, Bradenton *Also called Sarasota Kitchens and Closets* ***(G-1111)***
Finecraft Custom Cabinetry...941 378-1901
6209 Clarity Ct Sarasota (34240) ***(G-16430)***
Finecraft Custom Cabinets...941 312-6598
4333 S Tamiami Trl Sarasota (34231) ***(G-16431)***
Finest Global Products. Com, Sarasota *Also called S and S Morris LLC* ***(G-16567)***
Finesta Inc...786 439-1647
12650 Nw 25th St Ste 112 Miami (33182) ***(G-9569)***
Finetest Inc (PA)...386 569-6189
1 Industry Dr Ste C Palm Coast (32137) ***(G-13693)***
Finfrock Design Inc...407 293-4000
2400 Apopka Blvd Apopka (32703) ***(G-140)***
Finfrock Industries Inc...407 293-4000
2400 Apopka Blvd Apopka (32703) ***(G-141)***
Finger Lakes Custom Mfg LLC...315 283-4849
1211 Ne 17th Rd Ocala (34470) ***(G-11941)***
Finger Mate Inc...954 458-2700
2500 E Hallandale Beach B Hallandale Beach (33009) ***(G-5184)***
Finishing Group of Florid...954 981-2171
3997 Pembroke Rd Hollywood (33021) ***(G-5821)***
Finlayson Enterprises Inc...850 785-7953
1802 Beck Ave Panama City (32405) ***(G-13902)***
Finns Brass and Silver Polsg...904 387-1165
2025 Hamilton St Jacksonville (32210) ***(G-6381)***
Finotex USA Corp (PA)...305 593-1102
6942 Nw 50th St Miami (33166) ***(G-9570)***
Finyl Products Inc...352 351-4033
8657 Nw 80th Ave Ocala (34482) ***(G-11942)***
Fiori Bruna Pasta Products, Miami Lakes *Also called Brefaros Nobile Food LLC* ***(G-10771)***
Fiplex Communications Inc (PA)...305 884-8991
2101 Nw 79th Ave Doral (33122) ***(G-3351)***
Fire Defense Centers Inc...904 731-1833
3919 Morton St Jacksonville (32217) ***(G-6382)***
Fire Fly Fuels Inc...941 404-6820
1550 Global Ct Sarasota (34240) ***(G-16432)***
Fire Rescue Pins Com...561 312-8423
4292 Osha St Palm Beach Gardens (33410) ***(G-13589)***
Firebird Scrubs and More LLC...904 258-7514
805 Glendale Ln Orange Park (32065) ***(G-12392)***
Firedrake Inc...813 713-8902
39309 Air Park Rd Zephyrhills (33542) ***(G-19518)***
Firefly Aircraft Parts Inc...954 505-1470
150 S Pine Island Rd Plantation (33324) ***(G-14516)***
Firehouse Promotions Inc...407 990-1600
2450 Maitland Center Pkwy Maitland (32751) ***(G-8465)***
Fireside Holdings Inc...941 371-0300
2053 58th Avenue Cir E Bradenton (34203) ***(G-1041)***

ALPHABETIC

Firetainment Inc...888 552-7897
2475 N John Young Pkwy Orlando (32804) *(G-12740)*
Firmenich Lakeland...863 646-0165
3919 Kidron Rd Lakeland (33811) *(G-7686)*
First America Products...904 683-1253
153 Industrial Loop S Orange Park (32073) *(G-12393)*
First America Products LLC...904 215-8075
9710 E Indigo St Ste 203 Miami (33157) *(G-9571)*
First Block LLC...727 462-2526
615 Drew St Clearwater (33755) *(G-1682)*
First Case Cash LLC...954 200-5374
225 Holiday Dr Hallandale Beach (33009) *(G-5185)*
First Cast Fla Mfg Support LLC...904 434-4128
1884 Chatham Village Dr Orange Park (32003) *(G-12394)*
First Cast Strpping MBL Sndbls...904 733-5915
4846 Philips Hwy Jacksonville (32207) *(G-6383)*
First Check Diagnostics LLC...858 805-2425
30 S Keller Rd Ste 100 Orlando (32810) *(G-12741)*
First Class Liaisons LLC...954 882-8634
2470 Wellington Green Dr Wellington (33414) *(G-18717)*
First Class Media Inc...561 719-3433
1003 Jupiter Park Ln # 5 Jupiter (33458) *(G-7043)*
First Coast Cargo Inc...844 774-7711
7643 Gate Pkwy 104-31 Jacksonville (32256) *(G-6384)*
First Coast Concrete Pumping...904 262-6488
6115 Earline Cir N Jacksonville (32258) *(G-6385)*
First Coast Continuous Forms, Orange Park *Also called Zilla Inc (G-12414)*
First Coast Fabrication Inc...904 849-7426
96144 Nassau Pl Yulee (32097) *(G-19496)*
First Coast Granite & MBL Inc...904 388-1217
6860 Phillips Ind Blvd Jacksonville (32256) *(G-6386)*
First Coast Pavers Corp...904 410-0278
204 Blairmore Blvd Orange Park (32073) *(G-12395)*
First Coast Tee Shirt Co Inc...904 737-1985
5971 Powers Ave Ste 104 Jacksonville (32217) *(G-6387)*
First Coast Trikkes...904 343-1833
510 Mayport Rd Atlantic Beach (32233) *(G-221)*
First Communications Inc...850 668-7990
2910 Krry Frest Pkwy Ste Tallahassee (32309) *(G-17251)*
First Edition Design Inc...941 921-2607
5202 Old Ashwood Dr Sarasota (34233) *(G-16433)*
First Edition Design Pubg, Sarasota *Also called First Edition Design Inc (G-16433)*
First Grade Food Corporation...813 886-6118
5134 W Hanna Ave Tampa (33634) *(G-17666)*
First Impression Design MGT, North Miami *Also called Cinema Crafters Inc (G-11632)*
First Impression Graphic Svcs, Fort Lauderdale *Also called Walruss Enterprises Inc (G-4311)*
First Impressions Industries, North Miami *Also called J M Interiors Inc (G-11642)*
First Impressions Printing...352 237-6141
1847 Sw 27th Ave Ocala (34471) *(G-11943)*
First Imprseesion South Flo...954 525-0342
1509 Sw 1st Ave Fort Lauderdale (33315) *(G-3994)*
First Imprssion Dors Mllwk Inc...561 798-6684
346 Pike Rd Ste 6 West Palm Beach (33411) *(G-18872)*
First Imprssons Prtg Cmmnctons...407 831-6100
851 E State Road 434 Longwood (32750) *(G-8282)*
First Look Display Group, Tampa *Also called Caddie Company Inc (G-17499)*
First Look Inc...954 240-0530
757 Se 17th St 986 Fort Lauderdale (33316) *(G-3995)*
First Marketing Company (PA)...954 979-0700
3300 Gateway Dr Pompano Beach (33069) *(G-14691)*
First Mate Inc...954 475-2750
11950 Nw 27th St Plantation (33323) *(G-14517)*
First Shot Mold and Tool...321 269-0031
1125 White Dr Titusville (32780) *(G-18429)*
First Sign Corp...954 972-7222
2085 N Powerline Rd Ste 1 Pompano Beach (33069) *(G-14692)*
First Tee Miami Daga...305 633-4583
1802 Nw 37th Ave Miami (33125) *(G-9572)*
First Tee Sarasota/Manatee...941 685-5072
7741 15th St E Sarasota (34243) *(G-16213)*
First Wave Biopharma Inc...561 589-7020
777 W Yamato Rd Ste 502 Boca Raton (33431) *(G-529)*
First Windows Incorporated...813 508-9388
27524 Cashford Cir Wesley Chapel (33544) *(G-18745)*
Firstcut...786 740-3683
3030 Virginia St Miami (33133) *(G-9573)*
Firstpath Laboratory Svcs LLC...954 977-6977
3141 W Mcnab Rd Pompano Beach (33069) *(G-14693)*
Fis Avantgard LLC (HQ)...484 582-2000
601 Riverside Ave Jacksonville (32204) *(G-6388)*
Fis Group Inc...786 622-3308
3820 Nw 125th St Opa Locka (33054) *(G-12315)*
Fis Kiodex LLC...904 438-6000
601 Riverside Ave Jacksonville (32204) *(G-6389)*
Fischer Panda Generators Inc...954 462-2800
351 S Andrews Ave Pompano Beach (33069) *(G-14694)*
Fischer Panda Generators LLC...954 462-2800
351 S Andrews Ave Pompano Beach (33069) *(G-14695)*
Fisher Cabinet Company LLC...850 944-4171
3900 N Palafox St Pensacola (32505) *(G-14151)*
Fisher Electric Technology Inc...727 345-9122
2801 72nd St N Saint Petersburg (33710) *(G-15780)*
Fishermans Center Inc...561 844-5150
56 E Blue Heron Blvd Riviera Beach (33404) *(G-15328)*
Fiskars Brands Inc...407 889-5533
3000 Orange Ave Apopka (32703) *(G-142)*
Fit Canvas Inc...954 258-9352
870 Sw 50th Ave Margate (33068) *(G-8544)*
Fit Like Foots, Clearwater *Also called C & E Innovative MGT LLC (G-1619)*
Fitletic Sports LLC...305 907-6663
1049 Nw 1st Ct Hallandale Beach (33009) *(G-5186)*
Fitteam Global LLC...586 260-1487
4440 Pga Blvd Ste 600 Palm Beach Gardens (33410) *(G-13590)*
Fitusa Manufacturing, Ormond Beach *Also called Fabrox LLC (G-13371)*
Fitzlord Inc...904 731-2041
650 E 27th St Jacksonville (32206) *(G-6390)*
Five Oceans Florida Inc...772 221-8188
4529 Sw Cargo Way Palm City (34990) *(G-13655)*
Five Sports Inc...727 209-1750
11880 28th St N Ste 100 Saint Petersburg (33716) *(G-15781)*
Five Star Bakery...954 983-6133
6847 Miramar Pkwy Miramar (33023) *(G-10991)*
Five Star Builders W Palm Bch, Wellington *Also called 5 Star Builders Inc (G-18707)*
Five Star Field Services...347 446-6816
3539 S Federal Hwy Apt L Boynton Beach (33435) *(G-905)*
Five Star Gurmet Foods Fla Inc...239 280-0336
3600 Shaw Blvd Naples (34117) *(G-11246)*
Five Star Marble and Stone...904 887-4736
117 Taylor Ridge Ave Ponte Vedra (32081) *(G-14925)*
Five Star Measurement, Boynton Beach *Also called Five Star Field Services (G-905)*
Five Star Millwork Inc...954 956-7665
4100 N Powerline Rd Y4 Pompano Beach (33073) *(G-14696)*
Five Star Quality Mfg Corp...954 972-4772
2200 Ne 62nd Ct Fort Lauderdale (33308) *(G-3996)*
Five Star Shutters, Fort Lauderdale *Also called Five Star Quality Mfg Corp (G-3996)*
Five Star Sports Tickets...440 899-2000
1755 E Hallandale Bch Hallandale Beach (33009) *(G-5187)*
Five Stones Mine LLC (PA)...813 967-2123
18500 Us Highway 441 Canal Point (33438) *(G-1331)*
Fix n Fly Drones LLC...321 474-2291
2105 N Jamaica St Tampa (33607) *(G-17667)*
Fj Cabinets & Woodworking LLC...850 433-3925
509 N K St Pensacola (32501) *(G-14152)*
Fjh Music Company Inc...954 382-6061
2525 Davie Rd Ste 360 Davie (33317) *(G-2525)*
FK Instrument Co LLC...727 472-2003
2134 Sunnydale Blvd Clearwater (33765) *(G-1683)*
Fk Irons Inc...855 354-7667
1771 Nw 79th Ave Doral (33126) *(G-3352)*
Fka Enroute Emergency Systems, Tampa *Also called Infor Public Sector Inc (G-17783)*
Fka Racing Inc...386 938-4211
3994 Nw 36th Loop Jennings (32053) *(G-6964)*
Fkp...561 493-0076
2950 Commerce Park Dr # 6 Boynton Beach (33426) *(G-906)*
FL Central Cnstr & Rmdlg...863 701-3548
8120 Timberidge Loop W Lakeland (33809) *(G-7687)*
FL Industries Inc...954 422-3766
2930 Ne 8th Ave Pompano Beach (33064) *(G-14697)*
FL Precast LLC...321 356-9673
12679 Maribou Cir Orlando (32828) *(G-12742)*
Fla Property Holdings Inc...813 888-8796
13980 Nw 58th Ct Miami Lakes (33014) *(G-10790)*
Flagship Marine Inc...772 781-4242
3211 Se Gran Park Way Stuart (34997) *(G-16940)*
Flagshipmd LLC...904 302-6160
7800 Belfort Pkwy Ste 230 Jacksonville (32256) *(G-6391)*
Flagstone Pavers, Brooksville *Also called Fsp-Ges Inc (G-1230)*
Flagstone Pavers South...239 225-5646
1251 Ne 48th St Pompano Beach (33064) *(G-14698)*
Flaire Corporation...352 237-1220
4647 Sw 40th Ave Ocala (34474) *(G-11944)*
Flamco of Texas LLC (HQ)...904 783-8400
6940 Stuart Ave Jacksonville (32254) *(G-6392)*
Flame Boss, Orlando *Also called Collins Research Inc (G-12603)*
Flamingo Crossing, Key West *Also called McConnell Corp (G-7196)*
Flamingo Graphics, Opa Locka *Also called Pasa Services Inc (G-12350)*
Flamingo Pavers Inc...850 974-0094
289 Tropical Way Freeport (32439) *(G-4845)*
Flamingo Printing of Brevard...321 723-2771
1785 Waverly Pl Melbourne (32901) *(G-8833)*
Flamingo Travel, Saint Augustine *Also called Jls of St Augustine Inc (G-15560)*
Flamm Industries Inc...904 356-2876
1313 Haines St Jacksonville (32206) *(G-6393)*
Flanders Corp...727 822-4411
2399 26th Ave N Saint Petersburg (33713) *(G-15782)*
Flare Clothing Inc...863 859-1800
3800 Us Highway 98 N # 746 Lakeland (33809) *(G-7688)*

Flash Prints LLC 786 422-3195
19401 Nw 23rd Ave Miami Gardens (33056) ***(G-10740)***
Flash Roofing and Shtmtl LLC 786 237-9440
17425 Sw 109th Ct Miami (33157) ***(G-9574)***
Flash Sales Inc 954 914-2689
4401 Nw 167th St Miami Gardens (33055) ***(G-10741)***
Flat Glass Distributors LLC 904 354-5413
5355 Shawland Rd Jacksonville (32254) ***(G-6394)***
Flat Island Boatworks LLC 850 434-8295
700 Myrick St Pensacola (32505) ***(G-14153)***
Flatsmaster Marine LLC 239 574-7800
830 Ne 24th Ln Unit C Cape Coral (33909) ***(G-1423)***
Flatwoods Forest Products Inc 352 787-1161
240 State Road 44 Leesburg (34748) ***(G-8156)***
Flavana LLC 561 285-7034
1480 S Dixie Hwy E Pompano Beach (33060) ***(G-14699)***
Flavor Right Foods SE, Tampa *Also called Southeast Dairy Processors Inc* ***(G-18117)***
Flavorworks Inc 561 588-8246
10130 Northlake Blvd West Palm Beach (33412) ***(G-18873)***
Flayco Products Inc 813 879-1356
4821 N Hale Ave Tampa (33614) ***(G-17668)***
Flc Machines Inc 352 728-2303
8010 Us Highway 441 Leesburg (34788) ***(G-8157)***
Fleabusters, Fort Lauderdale *Also called Rx For Fleas Inc* ***(G-4220)***
Fleaworld Div, Orlando *Also called United Trophy Manufacturing* ***(G-13294)***
Fleda Pharmaceuticals Corp 813 920-9882
13231 Byrd Legg Dr Odessa (33556) ***(G-12120)***
Fleet Spc An Enforcement One, Oldsmar *Also called Enforcement One Inc* ***(G-12226)***
Fleetboss Globl Pstning Sltons 407 265-9559
241 Obrien Rd Fern Park (32730) ***(G-3728)***
Fleetistics, Wesley Chapel *Also called Iler Group Inc* ***(G-18749)***
Fleetmatics 727 483-9016
4211 W Boy Scout Blvd # 4 Tampa (33607) ***(G-17669)***
Fleurissima Inc (PA) 305 572-0203
4242 Ne 2nd Ave Miami (33137) ***(G-9575)***
Flex Beauty Labs LLC 646 302-8542
7512 Dr Phillips Blvd Orlando (32819) ***(G-12743)***
Flex Innovations Inc 866 310-3539
313 Seaboard Ave Unit B Venice (34285) ***(G-18548)***
Flex Pack USA LLC 407 704-0800
1205 Pine Ave Orlando (32824) ***(G-12744)***
Flex TEC Coating Services LLC 813 481-8354
3348 Anata Dr Zephyrhills (33541) ***(G-19519)***
Flexfield Express, Orlando *Also called Sage Implementations LLC* ***(G-13155)***
Flexible Prtg Solutions LLC 727 446-3014
2070 Weaver Park Dr Clearwater (33765) ***(G-1684)***
Flexiinternational Sftwr Inc 239 298-5700
856 3rd Ave S Ste 200 Naples (34102) ***(G-11247)***
Flexo Concepts Manufacturing 305 233-7075
13552 Sw 129th St Miami (33186) ***(G-9576)***
Flexofferscom Inc 305 999-9940
990 Biscayne Blvd Miami (33132) ***(G-9577)***
Flexshopper LLC 561 922-6609
2700 N Military Trl # 200 Boca Raton (33431) ***(G-530)***
Flexsol Holding Corp (PA) 954 941-6333
1531 Nw 12th Ave Pompano Beach (33069) ***(G-14700)***
Flexstake Inc 239 481-3539
2150 Andrea Ln Fort Myers (33912) ***(G-4450)***
Flight Aerotech LLC 305 901-6001
7241 Nw 54th St Miami (33166) ***(G-9578)***
Flight Management, Sarasota *Also called Dart Container Corp Florida* ***(G-16204)***
Flight Source LLC 954 249-8449
2011 S Perimeter Rd Fort Lauderdale (33309) ***(G-3997)***
Flight Specialties Components, Hollywood *Also called Heico Aerospace Parts Corp* ***(G-5839)***
Flight Velocity 866 937-9371
279 Old Moody Blvd Palm Coast (32164) ***(G-13694)***
Flint LLC 813 622-8899
1212 Maydell Dr Tampa (33619) ***(G-17670)***
Flints Wrecker Service Inc 863 676-1318
6442 State Road 60 E Lake Wales (33898) ***(G-7509)***
Flite Rite Industries, Fort Lauderdale *Also called Florida Funeral Shipping Cntrs* ***(G-4000)***
Flite Technology Inc 321 631-2050
2511 Friday Rd Cocoa (32926) ***(G-2022)***
Flo King Filter Systems, Longwood *Also called Custom Masters Inc* ***(G-8270)***
Flo Sun Land Corporation 561 655-6303
340 Royal Poinciana Way # 316 Palm Beach (33480) ***(G-13554)***
Float-On Corporation 772 569-4440
1925 98th Ave Vero Beach (32966) ***(G-18617)***
Floor Tech LLC 407 855-8087
9801 Recycle Center Rd Orlando (32824) ***(G-12745)***
Floors Inc 813 879-5720
6205 Johns Rd Ste 1 Tampa (33634) ***(G-17671)***
Floral City Airboat Co Inc (PA) 352 637-4390
5098 S Florida Ave Inverness (34450) ***(G-6087)***
Floral City Airboat Co Inc 352 637-4390
12080 S Hewitt Pt Floral City (34436) ***(G-3767)***
Floribbean Inc 844 282-8459
6800 Bird Rd Miami (33155) ***(G-9579)***
Floribbean Grill The, Orlando *Also called West Development Group LLC* ***(G-13322)***
Florical Systems Inc (PA) 352 372-8326
4500 Nw 27th Ave Ste B1 Gainesville (32606) ***(G-4920)***
Florida A&G Co Inc 800 432-8132
10200 Nw 67th St Tamarac (33321) ***(G-17356)***
Florida AA Pallets Inc 305 805-1522
7611 Nw 74th Ave Medley (33166) ***(G-8651)***
Florida Aero Precision Inc (HQ) 561 848-6248
120 Reed Rd Lake Park (33403) ***(G-7471)***
Florida Aerospace Partnership 954 617-7700
4019 Sw 30th Ave Fort Lauderdale (33312) ***(G-3998)***
Florida Air Cleaning Inc 727 573-5281
13584 49th St N Ste 17 Clearwater (33762) ***(G-1685)***
Florida Airboat Propeller 863 324-1653
404 Burns Ln Winter Haven (33884) ***(G-19320)***
Florida Algae LLC 954 213-2693
540 Sw 11th Ave Fort Lauderdale (33312) ***(G-3999)***
Florida Aluminum and Steel Inc 863 967-4191
100 Thornhill Rd Auburndale (33823) ***(G-241)***
Florida Amico 863 688-9256
1033 Pine Chase Ave Lakeland (33815) ***(G-7689)***
Florida Applied Films, Lakeland *Also called SMC Diversified Services Inc* ***(G-7793)***
Florida Beef Inc 912 632-1183
441 State Road 64 E Zolfo Springs (33890) ***(G-19545)***
Florida Best Hearing 863 402-0094
4739 N Congress Ave Boynton Beach (33426) ***(G-907)***
Florida Bid Reporting Service 850 539-7522
313 Williams St Ste 11 Tallahassee (32303) ***(G-17252)***
Florida Block & Ready Mix LLC (PA) 727 585-2852
12795 49th St N Clearwater (33762) ***(G-1686)***
Florida Block & Ready Mix LLC 813 623-3700
5208 36th Ave S Tampa (33619) ***(G-17672)***
Florida Boat Lift 813 873-1614
4821 N Manhattan Ave Tampa (33614) ***(G-17673)***
Florida Brewery Inc 305 621-0099
6303 Blue Lagoon Dr # 280 Miami (33126) ***(G-9580)***
Florida Brewery Inc 863 965-1825
202 Gandy Rd Auburndale (33823) ***(G-242)***
Florida Brick and Clay Co Inc 813 754-1521
1708 Turkey Creek Rd Plant City (33566) ***(G-14430)***
Florida Bus Unlimited Inc 407 656-1175
1925 W Princeton St Orlando (32804) ***(G-12746)***
Florida Candy Factory Inc 727 446-0024
721 Lakeview Rd Clearwater (33756) ***(G-1687)***
Florida Cane Distillery, The, Tampa *Also called Florida Distillery LLC* ***(G-17675)***
Florida Caribbean Distillers, Auburndale *Also called Florida Distillers Co* ***(G-243)***
Florida Catholic Media Inc 407 373-0075
50 E Robinson St Orlando (32801) ***(G-12747)***
Florida Cental Logging Inc 863 272-5364
7328 Us Highway 98 N Lakeland (33809) ***(G-7690)***
Florida Central Extrusion Inc 863 324-2541
3700 Dundee Rd Unit 9 Winter Haven (33884) ***(G-19321)***
Florida Christn Conference Inc 407 460-8259
1500 E Vine St Kissimmee (34744) ***(G-7244)***
Florida CMC Rebar 407 518-5101
1395 Chaffee Rd S 2 Jacksonville (32221) ***(G-6395)***
Florida Coast Lighting Systems, Miami *Also called Municipal Lighting Systems Inc* ***(G-10055)***
Florida Coca-Cola Bottling Co 561 848-0055
6553 Garden Rd Riviera Beach (33404) ***(G-15329)***
Florida Coca-Cola Bottling Co (HQ) 813 569-2600
521 Lake Kathy Dr Brandon (33510) ***(G-1159)***
Florida Coca-Cola Bottling Co 772 461-3636
3939 Saint Lucie Blvd Fort Pierce (34946) ***(G-4698)***
Florida Coca-Cola Bottling Co 850 678-9370
647 Valparaiso Pkwy Valparaiso (32580) ***(G-18510)***
Florida Coca-Cola Bottling Co 850 478-4800
7330 N Davis Hwy Pensacola (32504) ***(G-14154)***
Florida Coca-Cola Bottling Co 850 575-6122
2050 Maryland Cir Tallahassee (32303) ***(G-17253)***
Florida Color Printing Inc 772 286-7264
1501 Se Decker Ave # 110 Stuart (34994) ***(G-16941)***
Florida Columns, Safety Harbor *Also called Spaulding Craft Inc* ***(G-15505)***
Florida Concrete Pipe Corp 352 742-2232
25750 C R 561 Astatula (34705) ***(G-211)***
Florida Concrete Recycling 352 495-2044
18515 Sw Archer Rd Archer (32618) ***(G-208)***
Florida Container Depot, Brooksville *Also called GOTG LLC* ***(G-1232)***
Florida Container Services 407 302-2197
3795 S Sanford Ave Sanford (32773) ***(G-16047)***
Florida Cool Ring Company 863 858-2211
2220 Gator Creek Ranch Rd Lakeland (33809) ***(G-7691)***
Florida Copier Connections 407 844-9690
8022 Office Ct Ste 100 Orlando (32809) ***(G-12748)***
Florida Craft Distributors LLC 813 528-7902
2650 Jewett Ln Sanford (32771) ***(G-16048)***
Florida Crystal Refinery Inc (HQ) 561 366-5200
1 N Clematis St Ste 200 West Palm Beach (33401) ***(G-18874)***
Florida Crystals, Palm Beach *Also called Flo Sun Land Corporation* ***(G-13554)***
Florida Crystals, West Palm Beach *Also called Okeelanta Corporation* ***(G-18971)***

ALPHABETIC

Florida Crystals Corporation (HQ)....561 655-6303
1 N Clematis St Ste 200 West Palm Beach (33401) ***(G-18875)***
Florida Crystals Corporation....561 366-5000
626 N Dixie Hwy West Palm Beach (33401) ***(G-18876)***
Florida Crystals Corporation....561 992-5635
8501 S Us Hwy 27 Ave South Bay (33493) ***(G-16795)***
Florida Crystals Corporation....561 515-8080
1 N Clematis St Ste 400 West Palm Beach (33401) ***(G-18877)***
Florida Crystals Food, South Bay *Also called Florida Crystals Corporation* ***(G-16795)***
Florida Crystals Food Corp....561 366-5100
1 N Clematis St Ste 200 West Palm Beach (33401) ***(G-18878)***
Florida Custom Cabinets Inc....850 769-4781
3536 E Orlando Rd Panama City (32404) ***(G-13903)***
Florida Custom Fabricators....407 892-8538
2315 Tyson Rd Saint Cloud (34771) ***(G-15650)***
Florida Custom Mold Inc (PA)....813 343-5080
1806 Gunn Hwy Odessa (33556) ***(G-12121)***
Florida Cypress & Fence Co....561 392-3011
3922 Sw Saint Lucie Ln Palm City (34990) ***(G-13656)***
Florida Dacco/Detroit Inc....813 879-4131
3611 W Chestnut St Tampa (33607) ***(G-17674)***
Florida Derecktor Inc (PA)....954 920-5756
775 Taylor Ln Dania Beach (33004) ***(G-2465)***
Florida Design Inc....561 997-1660
621 Nw 53rd St Ste 370 Boca Raton (33487) ***(G-531)***
Florida Design Mfg Assoc Inc....561 533-0733
7430 Pine Tree Ln West Palm Beach (33406) ***(G-18879)***
Florida Designer Cabinets Inc....352 793-8555
1034 S Us 301 Sumterville (33585) ***(G-17068)***
Florida Discharge Machine, Largo *Also called FDM of Clearwater Inc* ***(G-7944)***
Florida Distillers Co....863 967-4481
425 Recker Hwy Auburndale (33823) ***(G-243)***
Florida Distillery LLC....813 347-6565
501 S Falkenburg Rd C5 Tampa (33619) ***(G-17675)***
Florida Dragline Operation....305 824-9755
3163 W 81st St Hialeah (33018) ***(G-5411)***
Florida Dragline Operations, Miami *Also called North American Coal Corp* ***(G-10077)***
Florida Dredge and Dock LLC....727 942-7888
1040 Island Ave Tarpon Springs (34689) ***(G-18301)***
Florida E Coast Holdings Corp....904 279-3152
6140 Philips Hwy Jacksonville (32216) ***(G-6396)***
Florida E Coast Supersonics Tc....386 689-2367
712 Cherry St New Smyrna Beach (32168) ***(G-11533)***
Florida East Coast Railway, Jacksonville *Also called Florida E Coast Holdings Corp* ***(G-6396)***
Florida Elc Mtr Co Miami Inc....305 759-3835
6350 Ne 4th Ct Miami (33138) ***(G-9581)***
Florida Electromechanics Inc....305 825-5244
7305 W 19th Ct Hialeah (33014) ***(G-5412)***
Florida Elite Industries LLC....727 223-4233
1185 Gooden Xing Bldg B Largo (33778) ***(G-7948)***
Florida Elreha Corporation....727 327-6236
2510 Terminal Dr S Saint Petersburg (33712) ***(G-15783)***
Florida Embroidered Patch &....561 748-9356
1095 Jupiter Park Dr # 8 Jupiter (33458) ***(G-7044)***
Florida Embroidme Jacksonville....904 309-9535
540 Commerce Center Dr # 1 Jacksonville (32225) ***(G-6397)***
Florida Emrgncy Eqp Upfitters, Hialeah *Also called South Florida Technology Svcs* ***(G-5627)***
Florida Engine Rebuilders Corp....305 232-8784
12500 Sw 130th St Ste 13 Miami (33186) ***(G-9582)***
Florida Engineered Constru (PA)....813 621-4641
6324 County Road 579 Seffner (33584) ***(G-16726)***
Florida Engineered Constru....727 863-7451
16835 Us Highway 19 Hudson (34667) ***(G-6024)***
Florida Engineered Constru....321 953-5161
2590 Kirby Cir Ne Palm Bay (32905) ***(G-13513)***
Florida Enviromental Cons....407 402-2828
9734 Crenshaw Cir Clermont (34711) ***(G-1958)***
Florida Eqine Publications Inc....352 732-8686
801 Sw 60th Ave Ocala (34474) ***(G-11945)***
Florida Extracts, Tavares *Also called Palmate LLC* ***(G-18350)***
Florida Extruders Intl Inc....407 323-3300
2540 Jewett Ln Sanford (32771) ***(G-16049)***
Florida Fabrication Inc....407 212-0105
800 Johns Rd Apopka (32703) ***(G-143)***
Florida Factory Agents Inc....754 264-9432
5701 Sheridan St Hollywood (33021) ***(G-5822)***
Florida Family Magazine....941 922-5437
4851 Hoyer Dr Sarasota (34241) ***(G-16434)***
Florida Fence Post Co Inc (PA)....863 735-1361
5251 State Road 64 W Ona (33865) ***(G-12280)***
Florida Finisher Inc....941 722-5643
509 9th St W Palmetto (34221) ***(G-13799)***
Florida Fishing Products....239 938-4612
205 W Ohio Ave Tampa (33603) ***(G-17676)***
Florida Flexible....305 512-2222
2699 W 79th St Unit 1 Hialeah (33016) ***(G-5413)***
Florida Floats Inc (HQ)....904 358-3362
1813 Dennis St Jacksonville (32204) ***(G-6398)***
Florida Flvors Cncentrates Inc....561 775-5714
205 Sedona Way Palm Beach Gardens (33418) ***(G-13591)***
Florida Food Products LLC (PA)....352 357-4141
2231 W County Road 44 # 1 Eustis (32726) ***(G-3707)***
Florida Forest Products LLC....727 585-2067
1975 20th Ave Se Largo (33771) ***(G-7949)***
Florida Frames Inc....727 572-4064
12880 Auto Blvd Ste B Clearwater (33762) ***(G-1688)***
Florida Freedom Newspapers Inc, Panama City *Also called Panama City News Herald* ***(G-13935)***
Florida Fresh Seafood Corp....305 694-1733
7337 Nw 37th Ave Unit 7 Miami (33147) ***(G-9583)***
Florida Freshner Corp....954 349-0348
1138 Sunflower Cir Weston (33327) ***(G-19125)***
Florida Froyo Inc....407 977-4911
725 Primera Blvd Lake Mary (32746) ***(G-7417)***
Florida Funeral Shipping Cntrs....954 957-9259
1321c Nw 65th Pl Ste C Fort Lauderdale (33309) ***(G-4000)***
Florida General Trading Inc (PA)....813 391-2149
6195 N Us Highway 441 Ocala (34475) ***(G-11946)***
Florida Georgia Welding Supply, Jacksonville *Also called Southstern Stnless Fabricators* ***(G-6800)***
Florida Glass of Tampa Bay....813 925-1330
13929 Lynmar Blvd Tampa (33626) ***(G-17677)***
Florida Glsd Holdings Inc....321 633-4644
851 Greensboro Rd Cocoa (32926) ***(G-2023)***
Florida Gold Foods LLC....347 595-1983
1770 Business Center Ln Kissimmee (34758) ***(G-7245)***
Florida Graphic Printing Inc....386 253-4532
503 Mason Ave Daytona Beach (32117) ***(G-2666)***
Florida Graphic Supply, Clearwater *Also called Mac Papers Inc* ***(G-1768)***
Florida Grasschoppers....561 718-9346
75 Ohio Rd Lake Worth (33467) ***(G-7550)***
Florida Handrail & Fabrication, Gainesville *Also called Gainesville Wldg & Fabrication* ***(G-4930)***
Florida Harbor Homes Inc....941 284-8363
850 Bayshore Dr Englewood (34223) ***(G-3677)***
Florida Health Care News Inc....813 989-1330
215 Bullard Pkwy Temple Terrace (33617) ***(G-18368)***
Florida Health Publishing LLC....847 506-2925
125 Sw 3rd Pl Ste 205 Cape Coral (33991) ***(G-1424)***
Florida Heritage Wdwkg LLC....941 705-9980
2237 Industrial Blvd Sarasota (34234) ***(G-16435)***
Florida Homes Magazine....941 227-7331
1900 Main St Ste 312 Sarasota (34236) ***(G-16436)***
Florida Hose & Hydraulics Inc....305 887-9577
7128 Nw 72nd Ave Ste 336 Miami (33166) ***(G-9584)***
Florida Hospital Assn MGT Corp....407 841-6230
827 Highland Ave Orlando (32803) ***(G-12749)***
Florida Hydro Power & Light Co....386 328-2470
171 Comfort Rd Palatka (32177) ***(G-13478)***
Florida Hytorc....813 990-9470
22131 Hwy Us19 Clearwater (33765) ***(G-1689)***
Florida Ice Corporation....305 685-9377
13401 Nw 38th Ct Opa Locka (33054) ***(G-12316)***
Florida Indus Solutions LLC....833 746-7347
13773 N Nebraska Ave Tampa (33613) ***(G-17678)***
Florida Ink Mfg Co Inc....813 247-2911
1715 Temple St Tampa (33619) ***(G-17679)***
Florida International Firm Inc....305 450-5920
1750 Nw 107th Ave P408 Sweetwater (33172) ***(G-17209)***
Florida Jacksonville Forklift....904 674-6898
1063 Haines St Jacksonville (32206) ***(G-6399)***
Florida Jerky Enterprises Inc....256 682-2959
14025 Budworth Cir Orlando (32832) ***(G-12750)***
Florida Keys Keylime Products....305 853-0378
95231 Overseas Hwy Key Largo (33037) ***(G-7169)***
Florida Keys Keynoter, Marathon *Also called Keynoter Publishing Co Inc* ***(G-8519)***
Florida Kit Cbnets Amercn Corp....305 828-2830
9325 W Okeechobee Rd Hialeah (33016) ***(G-5414)***
Florida Knife Co....941 371-2104
1735 Apex Rd Sarasota (34240) ***(G-16437)***
Florida Kolmiami Corporation....305 582-0114
6491 Cow Pen Rd Apt H102 Miami Lakes (33014) ***(G-10791)***
Florida Laminated Tempered GL, Miami *Also called US Global Glass LLC* ***(G-10552)***
Florida Laminating & Uv Svcs, Saint Petersburg *Also called Florida Print Solutions Inc* ***(G-15784)***
Florida Law Weekly, Tallahassee *Also called Judicial & ADM RES Assoc* ***(G-17285)***
Florida Level & Transit Co Inc....813 623-3307
5468 56th Cmmrce Pk Blvd Tampa (33610) ***(G-17680)***
Florida Lift Stations Corp....305 887-8485
9498 Nw South River Dr Medley (33166) ***(G-8652)***
Florida Living LLC....352 556-9691
7410 Dent St Brooksville (34601) ***(G-1229)***
Florida Machine & Casting Co....561 655-3771
8011 Monetary Dr Ste A6 Riviera Beach (33404) ***(G-15330)***
Florida Machining Center, Clearwater *Also called Riva Industries Inc* ***(G-1861)***
Florida Made Door Co (PA)....352 742-1000
1 N Dale Mabry Hwy # 950 Tampa (33609) ***(G-17681)***

Florida Manufactured Home 407 509-8262
1722 Duthie Ln Christmas (32709) ***(G-1550)***
Florida Marine, Riviera Beach *Also called Carey-Dunn Inc* ***(G-15309)***
Florida Marine Joiner Svc Inc 813 514-1125
4917 Hartford St Tampa (33619) ***(G-17682)***
Florida Marine Products Inc 813 248-2283
2001 E 5th Ave Tampa (33605) ***(G-17683)***
Florida Marking Products LLC 407 834-3000
1205 Sarah Ave Ste 171 Longwood (32750) ***(G-8283)***
Florida Mch Works Ltd Partnr 904 225-2090
86412 Gene Lassere Blvd Yulee (32097) ***(G-19497)***
Florida Media Inc 407 816-9596
1888 Brackenhurst Pl Lake Mary (32746) ***(G-7418)***
Florida Metal Products LLC (HQ) 904 783-8400
6940 Stuart Ave Jacksonville (32254) ***(G-6400)***
Florida Metal Services Inc 727 541-6441
6951 108th Ave Largo (33777) ***(G-7950)***
Florida Metal-Craft Inc 407 656-1100
47 S Dillard St Winter Garden (34787) ***(G-19264)***
Florida Metallizing Svc Inc 863 425-1143
1810 State Road 37 S Mulberry (33860) ***(G-11124)***
Florida Micro Devices Inc 954 973-7200
4676 Nw 60th Ln Coral Springs (33067) ***(G-2245)***
Florida Mining Enterprises LLC 904 270-2646
2207 Alicia Ln Atlantic Beach (32233) ***(G-222)***
Florida Mkb Holdings LLC 407 281-7909
16212 Sr 50 Clermont (34711) ***(G-1959)***
Florida Mold Mitigators LLC 772 633-3415
7025 29th Ct Vero Beach (32967) ***(G-18618)***
Florida Mold Stoppers Inc 954 445-5560
5520 S University Dr Davie (33328) ***(G-2526)***
Florida Monthly, Lake Mary *Also called Florida Media Inc* ***(G-7418)***
Florida Motors Inc 786 524-9001
1515 Nw 167th St Ste 300 Miami (33169) ***(G-9585)***
Florida Natural Flavors Inc 407 834-5979
170 Lyman Rd Casselberry (32707) ***(G-1503)***
Florida Nbty Manufacturing 561 922-4800
901 Broken Sound Pkwy Nw Boca Raton (33487) ***(G-532)***
Florida Nonwovens Inc 407 241-2701
1111 Central Florida Pkwy Orlando (32837) ***(G-12751)***
Florida North Inc 352 606-2408
10294 Maybird Ave Weeki Wachee (34613) ***(G-18703)***
Florida North Emulsions Inc 386 328-1733
701 N Moody Rd Ste 151 Palatka (32177) ***(G-13479)***
Florida North Hearing Solution 386 466-0902
2228 Nw 44th Pl Gainesville (32605) ***(G-4921)***
Florida North Lumber Co Inc 850 643-2238
Hwy 12 S Bristol (32321) ***(G-1194)***
Florida North Lumber Inc 850 263-4457
18601 Nw County Road 12 Bristol (32321) ***(G-1195)***
Florida Nutri Labs LLC 863 607-6708
2715 Badger Rd Lakeland (33811) ***(G-7692)***
Florida Oil Service Inc 813 655-4753
16220 Ternglade Dr Lithia (33547) ***(G-8219)***
Florida Orange Groves Inc 727 347-4025
1500 Pasadena Ave S South Pasadena (33707) ***(G-16834)***
Florida Ordnance Corporation 954 493-8691
4740 Nw 15th Ave Fort Lauderdale (33309) ***(G-4001)***
Florida Packg & Graphics Inc 954 781-1440
6680 Nw 16th Ter Fort Lauderdale (33309) ***(G-4002)***
Florida Pallet LLC 772 562-4900
14325 78th Ave Sebastian (32958) ***(G-16659)***
Florida Phosphate Council Inc 863 904-0641
215 S Monroe St Ste 730 Tallahassee (32301) ***(G-17254)***
Florida Phosphorus 561 983-3208
6 Abaco Rd Key Largo (33037) ***(G-7170)***
Florida Pillow Company 407 648-9121
1012 Sligh Blvd Orlando (32806) ***(G-12752)***
Florida Playground & Steel Co 813 247-2812
4701 S 50th St Tampa (33619) ***(G-17684)***
Florida Plntn Shutters LLC 386 788-7766
1725 S Nova Rd Ste A1 South Daytona (32119) ***(G-16801)***
Florida Plywoods Inc 850 948-2211
1228 Nw Us 221 Greenville (32331) ***(G-5088)***
Florida Pole Setters & Crane 772 283-6820
4157 Sw Moore St Palm City (34990) ***(G-13657)***
Florida Polishing 305 688-2988
2163 Opa Locka Blvd Opa Locka (33054) ***(G-12317)***
Florida Pool Products Inc 727 531-8913
14550 62nd St N Clearwater (33760) ***(G-1690)***
Florida Power Systems, Jacksonville *Also called V-Blox Corporation* ***(G-6890)***
Florida Pre-Fab Inc 813 247-3934
2907 Sagasta St Tampa (33619) ***(G-17685)***
Florida Precision Mch Met Work 813 486-5050
5904 Lynn Rd Tampa (33624) ***(G-17686)***
Florida Precision Tool, Clearwater *Also called James Reese Enterprises Inc* ***(G-1741)***
Florida Print Finishers Inc 850 877-8503
1621 Capital Cir Ne Ste F Tallahassee (32308) ***(G-17255)***
Florida Print Solutions Inc (PA) 727 327-5500
432 31st St N Saint Petersburg (33713) ***(G-15784)***
Florida Printing Group Inc 954 956-8570
1850 S Ocean Blvd Apt 904 Pompano Beach (33062) ***(G-14701)***
Florida Prnts Blind Chldren In 407 257-7637
1431 Spring Fest Ln Orlando (32828) ***(G-12753)***
Florida Probe Corporation 352 372-1142
3700 Nw 91st St Ste C100 Gainesville (32606) ***(G-4922)***
Florida Production Engrg Inc (HQ) 386 677-2566
2 E Tower Cir Ormond Beach (32174) ***(G-13372)***
Florida Prsthtics Orthtics Inc 305 553-1217
9981 Sw 12th St Miami (33174) ***(G-9586)***
Florida Prtctive Coatings Cons 407 322-1243
482 Cardinal Oaks Ct Lake Mary (32746) ***(G-7419)***
Florida Pwdr Cting Shtters Inc 561 588-2410
854 N Dixie Hwy Lantana (33462) ***(G-7874)***
Florida Pwrtrain Hydrulics Inc 954 463-7711
917 Nw 1st St Fort Lauderdale (33311) ***(G-4003)***
Florida Pwrtrain Hydrulics Inc 813 623-6713
6501 E Adamo Dr Tampa (33619) ***(G-17687)***
Florida Pwrtrain Hydrulics Inc 407 291-1441
4455 Dardanelle Dr Orlando (32808) ***(G-12754)***
Florida Quality Truss Inc 954 975-3384
3635 Park Central Blvd N Pompano Beach (33064) ***(G-14702)***
Florida Quality Truss Inds Inc (PA) 954 971-3167
3635 Park Central Blvd N Pompano Beach (33064) ***(G-14703)***
Florida Refresco Inc 863 665-5515
2090 Bartow Rd Lakeland (33801) ***(G-7693)***
Florida Research, Clearwater *Also called Cole Enterprises Inc* ***(G-1632)***
Florida Roadway Signs Inc 561 722-4067
1137 Silver Beach Rd Lake Park (33403) ***(G-7472)***
Florida Rock 352 472-4722
4000 Nw County Road 235 Newberry (32669) ***(G-11556)***
Florida Rock Concrete 407 877-6180
15150 Pine Valley Blvd Clermont (34711) ***(G-1960)***
Florida Rock Concrete Inc 904 355-1781
700 Palmetto St Jacksonville (32202) ***(G-6401)***
Florida Rock Industries (HQ) 904 355-1781
4707 Gordon St Jacksonville (32216) ***(G-6402)***
Florida Rock Industries 352 854-6468
3599 Sw 74th Ave Ocala (34474) ***(G-11947)***
Florida Rs Technology, Palm City *Also called Five Oceans Florida Inc* ***(G-13655)***
Florida Rs Technology, Palm City *Also called Eagle I Tech Inc* ***(G-13651)***
Florida Rum Company LLC 305 791-1221
2901 Simms St Unit D Hollywood (33020) ***(G-5823)***
Florida Rust 386 259-9940
618 Tradewinds Dr Deltona (32738) ***(G-3170)***
Florida Sales & Marketing 239 274-3103
11840 Metro Pkwy Fort Myers (33966) ***(G-4451)***
Florida Salt Scrubs, Delray Beach *Also called Fhs Enterprises LLC* ***(G-3078)***
Florida Screen Enclosures LLC 352 398-5679
1451 Alameda Dr Spring Hill (34609) ***(G-16852)***
Florida Screen Enterprise, Opa Locka *Also called Yale Ogron Mfg Co Inc* ***(G-12372)***
Florida Screen Services Inc 407 316-0466
805 W Central Blvd Orlando (32805) ***(G-12755)***
Florida Sentinel Bulletin, Tampa *Also called Florida Sentinel Publishing Co* ***(G-17688)***
Florida Sentinel Publishing Co 813 248-1921
2207 E 21st Ave Tampa (33605) ***(G-17688)***
Florida Shed Company Inc (PA) 727 524-9191
3865 Tyrone Blvd N Saint Petersburg (33709) ***(G-15785)***
Florida Sheet Metal, Melbourne *Also called Singer Holdings Inc* ***(G-8934)***
Florida Shutter Factory Inc 954 687-4793
3069 Nw 26th St Fort Lauderdale (33311) ***(G-4004)***
Florida Shutters Inc 772 569-2200
1055 Commerce Ave Vero Beach (32960) ***(G-18619)***
Florida Sign Company Inc 941 747-1000
1101 29th Ave W Bradenton (34205) ***(G-1042)***
Florida Sign Source 407 316-0466
505 W Robinson St Orlando (32801) ***(G-12756)***
Florida Silica Sand Company (PA) 954 923-8323
2962 Trivium Cir Ste 106 Fort Lauderdale (33312) ***(G-4005)***
Florida Silica Sand Company 954 923-8323
2962 Trivium Cir Ste 105 Fort Lauderdale (33312) ***(G-4006)***
Florida Sncast Helicopters LLC 941 355-1525
8191 N Tamiami Trl # 104 Sarasota (34243) ***(G-16214)***
Florida Sncast Trism Prmotions 727 544-1212
10750 75th St Largo (33777) ***(G-7951)***
Florida Solar Energy LLC 561 206-2324
7999 N Federal Hwy # 400 Boca Raton (33487) ***(G-533)***
Florida Spcialty Coatings Corp 727 224-6883
3270 Suntree Blvd Ste 214 Melbourne (32940) ***(G-8834)***
Florida Specifier, Orlando *Also called National Tchncal Cmmunications* ***(G-12991)***
Florida Sprayers Inc (PA) 813 989-0500
8808 Venture Cv Ste 101 Temple Terrace (33637) ***(G-18369)***
Florida Stainless Steel ACC 727 207-2575
5601 Cactus Cir Spring Hill (34606) ***(G-16853)***
Florida Star & News, Jacksonville *Also called Florida Star Inc* ***(G-6403)***
Florida Star Inc 904 766-8834
1257 Edgewood Ave W Jacksonville (32208) ***(G-6403)***
Florida State Graphics Inc 727 328-0733
2828 20th Ave N Saint Petersburg (33713) ***(G-15786)***

ALPHABETIC

Florida Steam Services Inc 407 247-8250
349 Whitcomb Dr Geneva (32732) *(G-5022)*
Florida Stl Frame Truss Mfg LL 813 460-0006
2312 Cypress Cv Ste 101 Wesley Chapel (33544) *(G-18746)*
Florida Stoneware Tops Inc 239 340-0492
11251 Orange River Blvd Fort Myers (33905) *(G-4452)*
Florida Storm Panels Inc 305 685-9000
14475 Nw 26th Ave Opa Locka (33054) *(G-12318)*
Florida Storm Shutters Inc 954 257-8365
4898 Sw 24th Ave Fort Lauderdale (33312) *(G-4007)*
Florida Stucco Corp 561 487-1301
21195 Boca Rio Rd Boca Raton (33433) *(G-534)*
Florida Style Aluminum Inc 239 689-8662
15481 Old Wedgewood Ct Fort Myers (33908) *(G-4453)*
Florida Sugar Distributors (HQ) 561 655-6303
1 N Clematis St Ste 310 West Palm Beach (33401) *(G-18880)*
Florida Sugar Farmers 863 983-7276
111 Ponce De Leon Ave Clewiston (33440) *(G-1980)*
Florida Sun Printing, Callahan *Also called Southern Company Entp Inc (G-1329)*
Florida Sunshine Stucco LLC 407 947-2088
9484 Boggy Creek Rd Orlando (32824) *(G-12757)*
Florida SW Drones LLC 239 785-8337
1425 Sw 43rd Ter Cape Coral (33914) *(G-1425)*
Florida Tape & Labels Inc 941 921-5788
5717b Lawton Dr Sarasota (34233) *(G-16438)*
Florida Tees, Tallahassee *Also called Florida Print Finishers Inc (G-17255)*
Florida Thread & Trimming 954 240-2474
7395 W 18th Ln Hialeah (33014) *(G-5415)*
Florida Trading Company, Tavares *Also called Florida Trident Trading LLC (G-18337)*
Florida Trailer Ranch LLC 904 289-7710
14770 Normandy Blvd Jacksonville (32234) *(G-6404)*
Florida Transformer Inc (HQ) 850 892-2711
4509 St Hwy 83 N Defuniak Springs (32433) *(G-2942)*
Florida Trend Magazine, Saint Petersburg *Also called Trend Magazines Inc (G-15943)*
Florida Trident Trading LLC 352 253-1400
3801 State Road 19 Tavares (32778) *(G-18337)*
Florida Truck Parts 786 251-8614
13115 W Okeechobee Rd # 101 Hialeah Gardens (33018) *(G-5698)*
Florida Truss Corporation 407 438-2553
1302 Abberton Dr Orlando (32837) *(G-12758)*
Florida Turbine Tech Inc (HQ) 561 427-6400
1701 Military Trl Ste 110 Jupiter (33458) *(G-7045)*
Florida Vault Service Inc 727 527-4992
3007 47th Ave N Saint Petersburg (33714) *(G-15787)*
Florida Veex Inc 727 442-6677
2100 Tall Pines Dr Largo (33771) *(G-7952)*
Florida Weekly 239 333-2135
2891 Center Pointe Dr # 300 Fort Myers (33916) *(G-4454)*
Florida West Poggenpohl 239 948-9005
10800 Corkscrew Rd # 105 Estero (33928) *(G-3689)*
Florida Wilbert Inc (PA) 904 765-2641
5050 New Kings Rd Jacksonville (32209) *(G-6405)*
Florida Wilbert Inc 352 728-3531
27439 Hayward Worm Frm Rd Okahumpka (34762) *(G-12171)*
Florida Winery Inc 727 362-0008
12945 Village Blvd Madeira Beach (33708) *(G-8446)*
Florida Wire & Cable 904 275-2101
1 Wiremil Rd Sanderson (32087) *(G-15980)*
Florida Wire & Rigging Sup Inc 407 422-6218
4524 36th St Orlando (32811) *(G-12759)*
Florida Wire and Rigging Works, Miami *Also called Miami Cordage LLC (G-9996)*
Florida Wood, Longwood *Also called F W I Inc (G-8280)*
Florida Wood Creations Inc 239 561-5411
42881 Lake Babcock Dr # 200 Punta Gorda (33982) *(G-15205)*
Florida's Natural Growers, Lake Wales *Also called Citrus World Inc (G-7503)*
Floridahorse, The, Ocala *Also called Florida Eqine Publications Inc (G-11945)*
Floridas Best Inc 407 682-9570
839 Sunshine Ln Altamonte Springs (32714) *(G-46)*
Floridas Finest Industries 239 333-1777
5294 Summerlin Fort Myers (33907) *(G-4455)*
Floridas Hotspots Publishing 954 928-1862
5090 Ne 12th Ave Oakland Park (33334) *(G-11806)*
Floridas Natural Food Svc Inc 888 657-6600
20205 Hwy 27 Lake Wales (33853) *(G-7510)*
Floridian Blinds Llc 786 250-4697
10735 Sw 216th St Unit 40 Miami (33170) *(G-9587)*
Floridian Title Group Inc 305 792-4911
20801 Biscayne Blvd # 306 Miami (33180) *(G-9588)*
Flospine LLC 561 705-3080
3651 Fau Blvd Ste 400 Boca Raton (33431) *(G-535)*
Flotech Inc (PA) 904 358-1849
136 Eastport Rd Jacksonville (32218) *(G-6406)*
Flottec LLC (PA) 973 588-4717
19100 Se Reach Island Ln Jupiter (33458) *(G-7046)*
Flowers Bakeries LLC 850 875-4997
321 W Jefferson St Quincy (32351) *(G-15249)*
Flowers Bakery, Sarasota *Also called Flowers Bkg Co Bradenton LLC (G-16215)*
Flowers Baking, Pensacola *Also called Franklin Baking Company LLC (G-14159)*
Flowers Baking Co LLC 850 763-2541
2133 Transmitter Rd Panama City (32404) *(G-13904)*
Flowers Baking Co Lakeland Inc 863 682-1155
3355 W Memorial Blvd Lakeland (33815) *(G-7694)*
Flowers Baking Co Miami LLC 772 778-3990
3215 Aviation Blvd Vero Beach (32960) *(G-18620)*
Flowers Baking Co Miami LLC 305 599-8457
2681 Nw 104th Ct Doral (33172) *(G-3353)*
Flowers Baking Co Miami LLC (HQ) 305 652-3416
17800 Nw Miami Ct Miami (33169) *(G-9589)*
Flowers Baking Company, Quincy *Also called Flowers Bakeries LLC (G-15249)*
Flowers Baking Company, Lakeland *Also called Flowers Bkg Co Bradenton LLC (G-7695)*
Flowers Baking Company, Avon Park *Also called Flowers Bkg Co Bradenton LLC (G-287)*
Flowers Baking Company, Orlando *Also called Flowers Bkg Co Bradenton LLC (G-12760)*
Flowers Baking Company, Hudson *Also called Flowers Bkg Co Bradenton LLC (G-6025)*
Flowers Baking Company, Kissimmee *Also called Flowers Bkg Co Bradenton LLC (G-7246)*
Flowers Baking Company, Bonita Springs *Also called Flowers Bkg Co Bradenton LLC (G-832)*
Flowers Baking Company, Bradenton *Also called Flowers Bkg Co Bradenton LLC (G-1043)*
Flowers Bkg Co Bradenton LLC 941 627-0752
23240 Bayshore Rd Port Charlotte (33980) *(G-14981)*
Flowers Bkg Co Bradenton LLC 941 758-5656
2610 Mine And Mill Rd 4-9 Lakeland (33801) *(G-7695)*
Flowers Bkg Co Bradenton LLC 941 758-5656
1202 State Road 64 W Avon Park (33825) *(G-287)*
Flowers Bkg Co Bradenton LLC 941 758-5656
4301 N Pine Hills Rd Orlando (32808) *(G-12760)*
Flowers Bkg Co Bradenton LLC 941 758-5656
16721 Us Highway 19 Hudson (34667) *(G-6025)*
Flowers Bkg Co Bradenton LLC 941 758-5656
4990 S Orange Blossom Trl Kissimmee (34758) *(G-7246)*
Flowers Bkg Co Bradenton LLC 941 758-5656
26240 Old 41 Rd Bonita Springs (34135) *(G-832)*
Flowers Bkg Co Bradenton LLC 941 758-5656
720 9th St E Bradenton (34208) *(G-1043)*
Flowers Bkg Co Bradenton LLC (HQ) 941 758-5656
6490 Parkland Dr Sarasota (34243) *(G-16215)*
Flowers Bkg Co Thomasville LLC 229 226-5331
3385 S Monroe St Tallahassee (32301) *(G-17256)*
Flowers Bkg Jacksonville LLC (HQ) 904 354-3771
2261 W 30th St Jacksonville (32209) *(G-6407)*
Flowers Logging Co Inc 850 639-2856
5644 Sw Odeen Flowers Rd Kinard (32449) *(G-7213)*
Flowhance Inc 305 690-0784
1951 Nw 7th Ave Miami (33136) *(G-9590)*
Flowmaster Inc 561 249-1145
14231 83rd Ln N Loxahatchee (33470) *(G-8359)*
Flowmatic, Dunnellon *Also called Watts Water Technologies Inc (G-3602)*
Floyd Fabrication LLC 330 289-7351
2821 Sanderling St Haines City (33844) *(G-5143)*
Floyd Publications Inc 813 707-8783
702 W Dr Mrtn Lther King Plant City (33563) *(G-14431)*
Flt Geosystems, Tampa *Also called Florida Level & Transit Co Inc (G-17680)*
Fluenz Inc 305 209-1695
1000 5th St Ste 200 Miami Beach (33139) *(G-10668)*
Fluid Designs Inc 904 737-1557
4357 Habana Ave Jacksonville (32217) *(G-6408)*
Fluid Handling Support Corp 786 623-2105
6030 Nw 99th Ave Unit 409 Doral (33178) *(G-3354)*
Fluid Metalworks Inc -105 ....850 332-0103
55 S A St Pensacola (32502) *(G-14155)*
Fluid Routing Solutions LLC 352 732-0222
3100 Se Maricamp Rd Ocala (34471) *(G-11948)*
Fluid Wings LLC 888 245-5843
1636 Old Daytona St Deland (32724) *(G-2978)*
Fluidra Usa LLC (PA) 904 378-0999
8525 Mallory Rd Jacksonville (32220) *(G-6409)*
Flushing Amusement Inc 813 780-7900
40423 Air Time Ave Zephyrhills (33542) *(G-19520)*
Fluxxer, Pompano Beach *Also called Lubrexx Specialty Products LLC (G-14748)*
Flyer Studios Inc 786 402-9596
13740 Sw 33rd Ct Davie (33330) *(G-2527)*
Flying Colors Air Parts 352 728-1900
2727 W Main St Leesburg (34748) *(G-8158)*
Flying W Plastics Fl Inc 904 800-2451
109 Stevens St Jacksonville (32254) *(G-6410)*
Flyrite Banner Makers Inc 352 873-7501
3459 Sw 74th Ave Ste 100 Ocala (34474) *(G-11949)*
Flyteone Inc 813 421-1410
2687 Westchester Dr N Clearwater (33761) *(G-1691)*
FM Meat Products Ltd Partnr 352 546-3000
19798 Ne Highway 315 Fort Mc Coy (32134) *(G-4337)*
FMC Marketing Inc 201 417-1767
2001 N 32nd Ave Hollywood (33021) *(G-5824)*
FMC/Rhyno LLC 813 838-2264
5115 W Knox St Tampa (33634) *(G-17689)*
Foam & Psp Inc 954 816-5648
3325 Griffin Rd Ste 208 Fort Lauderdale (33312) *(G-4008)*

Foam By Design Inc 727 561-7479
10606 49th St N Clearwater (33762) *(G-1692)*
Foam Decoration Inc 786 293-8813
13800 Sw 142nd Ave Miami (33186) *(G-9591)*
Foam Factory Inc 954 485-6700
10137 Spyglass Way Boca Raton (33498) *(G-536)*
Foam Masters Inc 239 403-0755
4506 Mercantile Ave Naples (34104) *(G-11248)*
Foam Molding LLC 813 434-7044
3211 W Beach St Tampa (33607) *(G-17690)*
Foamseal Hurricane Adhesive 850 766-2000
2017 Chatsworth Way Tallahassee (32309) *(G-17257)*
Focal Point Publishing LLC 877 469-9530
4131 Nw 13th St Ste 200 Gainesville (32609) *(G-4923)*
Focus Community Publications 407 892-0019
980 Orange Ave Saint Cloud (34769) *(G-15651)*
Focus On Water Inc 239 275-1880
10160 Mcgregor Blvd Fort Myers (33919) *(G-4456)*
Fogmaster Corporation (PA) 954 481-9975
1051 Sw 30th Ave Deerfield Beach (33442) *(G-2825)*
Foh Inc 305 757-7940
7630 Biscayne Blvd Miami (33138) *(G-9592)*
Foil Inc 442 233-3645
201 E Wright St Pensacola (32501) *(G-14156)*
Foilmania, Doral *Also called Bellak Color Corporation* *(G-3267)*
Folders Tabs Et Cetera 813 884-3651
4906 Savarese Cir Tampa (33634) *(G-17691)*
Foley Air LLC 904 379-2243
136 Ellis Rd N Jacksonville (32254) *(G-6411)*
Foley Cellulose LLC 850 584-1121
3510 Contractors Rd Perry (32348) *(G-14300)*
Foley Publishing LLC 908 766-6006
7530 15th Ln Vero Beach (32966) *(G-18621)*
Foliage Enterprises Inc 407 886-2777
400 N Park Ave Apopka (32712) *(G-144)*
Fonon Technologies Inc (PA) 407 477-5618
1101 N Keller Rd Ste G Orlando (32810) *(G-12761)*
Food Marketing Consultants Inc 954 322-2668
2805 N Commerce Pkwy Miramar (33025) *(G-10992)*
Food Partners Inc 863 298-8771
340 W Central Ave Ste 200 Winter Haven (33880) *(G-19322)*
Food Spot 59, Miami *Also called Millenium Oil & Gas Distrs Inc* *(G-10022)*
Foods Div, Leesburg *Also called Cutrale Citrus Juices USA Inc* *(G-8149)*
Foot Function Lab Inc 954 753-2500
11540 Wiles Rd Ste 1 Coral Springs (33076) *(G-2246)*
Foot-In-Your-mouth Inc 850 438-0876
9721 Fowler Ave Pensacola (32534) *(G-14157)*
Foote Woodworking Inc 941 923-6553
8347 Midnight Pass Rd Sarasota (34242) *(G-16439)*
For Eyes Optcal Ccnut Grove In (HQ) 305 557-9004
3601 Sw 160th Ave Ste 400 Miramar (33027) *(G-10993)*
For Life Products LLC 954 747-3300
2301 Sw 145th Ave Ste 301 Miramar (33027) *(G-10994)*
For Rent Media Solutions, Altamonte Springs *Also called United Advg Publications Inc* *(G-81)*
For-A Latin America Inc 305 261-2345
5200 Blue Lagoon Dr # 130 Miami (33126) *(G-9593)*
Force Enterprises Coatings LLC 561 480-7298
12302 Sannenwood Ln Wellington (33414) *(G-18718)*
Force Imaging Group LLC 888 406-2120
1936 Bruce B Downs Blvd Wesley Chapel (33544) *(G-18747)*
Forceleader Inc 727 521-1808
6405 49th St N Ste A Pinellas Park (33781) *(G-14348)*
Forcon Precision Products LLC 239 574-4543
1110 Ne Pine Island Rd Cape Coral (33909) *(G-1426)*
Ford Press Inc 352 787-4650
305 S Canal St Leesburg (34748) *(G-8159)*
Ford Wire and Cable Corp 772 388-3660
7756 130th St Sebastian (32958) *(G-16660)*
Forecast Products, Fort Lauderdale *Also called Forecast Trading Corporation* *(G-4009)*
Forecast Trading Corporation 954 979-1120
2760 Nw 63rd Ct Fort Lauderdale (33309) *(G-4009)*
Forest Research Institute Inc 631 436-4600
2915 Weston Rd Weston (33331) *(G-19126)*
Forest Research Institute Inc 954 622-5600
13800 Nw 2nd St Ste 190 Sunrise (33325) *(G-17124)*
Forestry Resources Inc (PA) 239 332-3966
4353 Michigan Link Fort Myers (33916) *(G-4457)*
Forestry Resources Ecological, Fort Myers *Also called Forestry Resources Inc* *(G-4457)*
Forever Current Music LLC 213 458-2880
20749 Waters Edge Ct Boca Raton (33498) *(G-537)*
Forever Signs Inc 305 885-3411
2400 W 3rd Ct Hialeah (33010) *(G-5416)*
Forever Yung Altrntive Hlthcar, South Miami *Also called EMC South Florida LLC* *(G-16816)*
Forewarn LLC 561 757-4550
2650 N Military Trl # 300 Boca Raton (33431) *(G-538)*
Forge Unlimited Co 727 900-7600
10880 49th St N Clearwater (33762) *(G-1693)*
Forklift 305 468-1824
2365 Nw 70th Ave Miami (33122) *(G-9594)*
Form Script - Form Print LLC 954 345-3727
9101 W Sample Rd Apt 101 Coral Springs (33065) *(G-2247)*
Form-Co Inc 800 745-3700
2487 Tradeport Dr Ste 200 Orlando (32824) *(G-12762)*
Formal Wear International, Miami *Also called Apparel Imports Inc* *(G-9157)*
Formulated Solutions LLC (PA) 727 373-3970
11775 Starkey Rd Largo (33773) *(G-7953)*
Formulated Solutions LLC 727 456-0302
1776 11th Ave N Saint Petersburg (33713) *(G-15788)*
Formweld Fitting Inc 850 626-4888
8118 Progress Dr Milton (32583) *(G-10928)*
Forno De Minas Usa Inc 954 840-6533
242 Sw 12th Ave Deerfield Beach (33442) *(G-2826)*
Fort Lauderdale Molding, Delray Beach *Also called Plastimold Products Inc* *(G-3118)*
Fort Lauderdale Woodworking 954 935-0366
3001 Sw 10th St Pompano Beach (33069) *(G-14704)*
Fort Meyers Beach Bulletin, Cape Coral *Also called Breeze Corporation* *(G-1395)*
Fort Myers Asphalt Plant, Fort Myers *Also called S T Wooten Corporation* *(G-4591)*
Fort Myers Bch Soccer Leag Inc 239 353-7567
108 Bay Mar Dr Fort Myers Beach (33931) *(G-4662)*
Fort Myers Beach Shopg Guide, Fort Myers Beach *Also called Breeze Corporation* *(G-4660)*
Fort Myers Digital LLC 239 482-3086
6381 Corp Pk Cir Ste 2 Fort Myers (33966) *(G-4458)*
Fort Walton Co, Crestview *Also called Crestview Ready Mix Inc* *(G-2345)*
Fort Walton Concrete Co 850 243-8114
26 Industrial St Nw Fort Walton Beach (32548) *(G-4800)*
Fort Walton Machining Inc 800 223-0881
635 Anchors St Nw Fort Walton Beach (32548) *(G-4801)*
Fort Walton Machining Inc (PA) 850 244-9095
43 Jet Dr Nw Fort Walton Beach (32548) *(G-4802)*
Forterra Pipe & Precast LLC 863 401-6800
1285 Lucerne Loop Rd Ne Winter Haven (33881) *(G-19323)*
Forterra Pipe & Precast LLC 386 734-6228
840 West Ave Deland (32720) *(G-2979)*
Forterra Pressure Pipe Inc 386 328-8841
245 Comfort Rd Palatka (32177) *(G-13480)*
Fortified Building Pdts Inc 850 432-2485
2001 W Government St Pensacola (32502) *(G-14158)*
Fortified Shutters, Pensacola *Also called Fortified Building Pdts Inc* *(G-14158)*
Fortress Impact Wndows Dors LL 954 621-2395
6788 Nw 17th Ave Fort Lauderdale (33309) *(G-4010)*
Fortress Marine Anchors, Fort Lauderdale *Also called Nav-X LLC* *(G-4134)*
Forts Services LLC 786 942-4389
4650 Lyons Tech Pkwy Coconut Creek (33073) *(G-2077)*
Fortune Canvas Company Inc 941 740-4296
210 Green Dolphin Dr Placida (33946) *(G-14396)*
Fortune Media Group Inc 954 379-4321
6250 Coral Ridge Dr # 100 Coral Springs (33076) *(G-2248)*
Forum Publishing Group Inc (HQ) 954 698-6397
1701 Green Rd Ste B Deerfield Beach (33064) *(G-2827)*
Forum Publishing Group Inc 954 596-5650
333 Sw 12th Ave Deerfield Beach (33442) *(G-2828)*
Forward Defuniak Incorporated 850 830-7663
504 Circle Dr Defuniak Springs (32435) *(G-2943)*
Forward Express One Llc 305 234-3034
12625 Sw 134th Ct Ste 208 Miami (33186) *(G-9595)*
Fos Led Lighting Solution 321 208-8174
5595 Schenck Ave Ste 2ro Rockledge (32955) *(G-15412)*
Fossco Inc 850 983-1330
3948 Garcon Point Rd Milton (32583) *(G-10929)*
Foster & Foster Worldwide LLC 352 362-9102
635 Lexington Pkwy Apopka (32712) *(G-145)*
Foulks Forest, Fort Myers *Also called Curtis K Foulks* *(G-4419)*
Foundation Art Services, Fort Lauderdale *Also called Frametastic Inc* *(G-4011)*
Fountain Youth Bathrooms Inc 772 626-9626
2559 Sw Kenilworth St Port Saint Lucie (34953) *(G-15110)*
Four G Enterprises Inc 407 834-4143
1150 Florida Central Pkwy Longwood (32750) *(G-8284)*
Four Purls 863 293-6261
1226 7th St Nw Winter Haven (33881) *(G-19324)*
Four Seas Distilling Co LLC 813 645-0057
915 Bunker View Dr Apollo Beach (33572) *(G-104)*
Four Seas Trading Corp 813 221-0895
1542 N Franklin St Tampa (33602) *(G-17692)*
Four Star Products Inc 941 727-6161
6110 33rd St E Bradenton (34203) *(G-1044)*
Four WD Consulting & Pubg LLC 216 533-2203
5405 Okchobee Blvd # 201 West Palm Beach (33417) *(G-18881)*
Fournies Associates 561 445-5102
1226 Nw 19th Ter Delray Beach (33445) *(G-3079)*
Fovico Inc 561 624-5400
15908 77th Trl N West Palm Beach (33418) *(G-18882)*
Fowlers Sheet Metal Inc 561 659-3309
4716 Georgia Ave West Palm Beach (33405) *(G-18883)*
Fox Equipment LLC (PA) 904 531-3150
965 Bunker Ave Green Cove Springs (32043) *(G-5061)*
Fox Furniture, Daytona Beach *Also called Rex Fox Enterprises Inc* *(G-2704)*

ALPHABETIC

Fox Industries of Swfl Inc ... 239 732-6199
3951 Mercantile Ave Naples (34104) ***(G-11249)***
Fox Manufacturing LLC ... 904 531-3150
965 Bunker Ave Green Cove Springs (32043) ***(G-5062)***
Fpc Printing Inc ... 813 626-9430
201 Kelsey Ln Tampa (33619) ***(G-17693)***
FPL Energy Oklahoma Wind LLC ... 561 691-7171
700 Universe Blvd Juno Beach (33408) ***(G-6980)***
Fragrance Expresscom LLC ... 800 372-4726
1221 Nw 165th St Miami (33169) ***(G-9596)***
Fragrance Health and Buty Aids, Miami *Also called Fragrance Expresscom LLC* ***(G-9596)***
Frako Concrete Services Inc ... 305 551-8196
10312 Sw 3rd St Miami (33174) ***(G-9597)***
Frame Tech of Orlando, Altamonte Springs *Also called Amrav Inc* ***(G-31)***
Frames & Things ... 727 815-0515
6137 Ridge Rd Port Richey (34668) ***(G-15049)***
Frametastic Inc ... 954 567-2800
5470 Nw 10th Ter Fort Lauderdale (33309) ***(G-4011)***
Franbiz Inc ... 813 282-1115
2841 Executive Dr Ste 100 Clearwater (33762) ***(G-1694)***
Franja Corp ... 954 659-1950
1515 Veracruz Ln Weston (33327) ***(G-19127)***
Frank Bennardello ... 561 470-4838
8121 Glades Rd Boca Raton (33434) ***(G-539)***
Frank Murray & Sons Inc ... 561 845-1366
1515 Se 16th St Fort Lauderdale (33316) ***(G-4012)***
Frank The Kit Exprt Palm Coast ... 386 264-6105
28 Farmbrook Ln Palm Coast (32137) ***(G-13695)***
Franklin Baking Company LLC ... 850 478-8360
9201 N Davis Hwy Pensacola (32514) ***(G-14159)***
Franklin Dodd Communications, Hialeah *Also called Fdc Print LLC* ***(G-5409)***
Franklin Equipment, Hilliard *Also called Greg Franklin Enterprises Inc* ***(G-5708)***
Franklin Trade Graphics, Hialeah *Also called 5301 Realty LLC* ***(G-5254)***
Franz A Ullrich Jr ... 863 773-4653
514 N Florida Ave Wauchula (33873) ***(G-18692)***
Frascold USA Corporation ... 855 547-5600
5343 Bowden Rd 2 Jacksonville (32216) ***(G-6412)***
Fraser Millworks Inc ... 904 768-7710
9424 Sisson Dr Jacksonville (32218) ***(G-6413)***
Fraser West Inc ... 901 620-4200
6640 County Road 218 Jacksonville (32234) ***(G-6414)***
Frattle Stairs & Rails Inc ... 904 384-3495
465 Tresca Rd Jacksonville (32225) ***(G-6415)***
Fraziers Fabrication ... 813 928-1449
4730 Durant Rd Dover (33527) ***(G-3559)***
Frc Electrical Industries Inc (PA) ... 321 676-3300
1260 Clearmont St Ne Palm Bay (32905) ***(G-13514)***
Fred International LLC ... 786 539-1600
3350 Sw 148th Ave Ste 120 Miramar (33027) ***(G-10995)***
Fred M Bush LLC ... 561 394-7292
1961 Hammondville Rd Pompano Beach (33069) ***(G-14705)***
Freddie Glenns Woodwork LLC ... 850 556-7163
819 Brighton Rd Tallahassee (32301) ***(G-17258)***
Frederic Thomas USA Inc ... 239 593-8000
5621 Strand Blvd Ste 301 Naples (34110) ***(G-11250)***
Free Life Inc ... 954 584-8485
320 Nw 69th Ave Apt 150 Plantation (33317) ***(G-14518)***
Free Press ... 305 853-7277
100430 Overseas Hwy # 300 Key Largo (33037) ***(G-7171)***
Free Press Publishing Company ... 813 254-5888
1010 W Cass St Tampa (33606) ***(G-17694)***
Free Wing Flight Technologies ... 813 752-8552
607 S Alexander St Ste Plant City (33563) ***(G-14432)***
Freedom Brick Pavers LLC ... 863 224-6008
2625 Shiner Dr Lake Wales (33898) ***(G-7511)***
Freedom Enterprise & Associate, Sanford *Also called Fea Inc* ***(G-16046)***
Freedom Fabrication Inc ... 850 539-4194
815 N Main St Ste B Havana (32333) ***(G-5238)***
Freedom Fittings, Melbourne *Also called Kinship Precision LLC* ***(G-8859)***
Freedom Metal Finishing Inc ... 727 573-2464
5095 113th Ave N Clearwater (33760) ***(G-1695)***
Freedom Orthotics Inc ... 813 833-7871
1714 County Road 1 Ste 23 Dunedin (34698) ***(G-3577)***
Freedom Steel Building Corp ... 561 330-0447
1883 W State Road 84 # 106 Fort Lauderdale (33315) ***(G-4013)***
Freeman Electric Co Inc ... 850 785-7448
534 Oak Ave Panama City (32401) ***(G-13905)***
Freeman Pallets Inc ... 352 328-9326
3530 Se Hawthorne Rd Gainesville (32641) ***(G-4924)***
Freeport Ammonia LLC ... 813 222-3813
100 N Tampa St Ste 3200 Tampa (33602) ***(G-17695)***
Freeport Fountains LLC ... 407 330-1150
1510 Kastner Pl Ste 3 Sanford (32771) ***(G-16050)***
Freeport Truss Company Inc ... 850 835-4541
16676 Us Highway 331 S Freeport (32439) ***(G-4846)***
Freezetone Products LLC ... 305 640-0414
7986 Nw 14th St Doral (33126) ***(G-3355)***
Freight Train Trucking Corp ... 407 509-0611
2503 Bross Dr Saint Cloud (34771) ***(G-15652)***
Freon & Fabric ... 386 801-5096
2885 W Huron Dr Deltona (32738) ***(G-3171)***
Fresco Group Inc ... 239 936-8055
13300 S Clevlnd Ave Ste 5 Fort Myers (33907) ***(G-4459)***
Fresenius Kabi Usa LLC ... 847 550-2300
1733 Nw 79th Ave Doral (33191) ***(G-3356)***
Fresh ... 561 330-4345
4801 Linton Blvd Delray Beach (33445) ***(G-3080)***
Fresh Aire Sanitization ... 407 301-9831
1107 Mabbette St Kissimmee (34741) ***(G-7247)***
Fresh Blends North America Inc ... 531 665-8200
955 Nw 17th Ave Ste J Delray Beach (33445) ***(G-3081)***
Fresh Brandz LLC ... 813 880-7110
6201 Johns Rd Ste 11 Tampa (33634) ***(G-17696)***
Fresh Choice MA Rket ... 407 448-8956
10249 S John Young Pkwy Orlando (32837) ***(G-12763)***
Fresh Ink Print LLC ... 407 412-5905
4729 Patch Rd Ste 200 Orlando (32822) ***(G-12764)***
Fresh Ink Signs & Graphics, Orlando *Also called Fresh Ink Print LLC* ***(G-12764)***
Fresh Mark Corporation ... 352 394-7746
12518 El Viento Rd Clermont (34711) ***(G-1961)***
Fresh On Fifth ... 305 234-5678
448 Ocean Dr Ste 2 Miami Beach (33139) ***(G-10669)***
Fresh Press ... 305 942-8571
15334 W Dixie Hwy North Miami Beach (33162) ***(G-11678)***
Fresh Prints ... 813 992-1655
19514 French Lace Dr Lutz (33558) ***(G-8383)***
Fresh Start Beverage Company (PA) ... 561 757-6541
4001 N Ocean Blvd Apt B30 Boca Raton (33431) ***(G-540)***
Fresh Thread Llc ... 904 677-9505
2823 State Road A1a Jacksonville (32233) ***(G-6416)***
Freshco Ltd ... 772 287-2111
7929 Sw Jack James Dr Stuart (34997) ***(G-16942)***
Freshetech LLC ... 516 519-3453
1211 Pine Ave Orlando (32824) ***(G-12765)***
Freshsurety Corporation ... 321 209-8699
277 Douglas Ave Ste 1002 Altamonte Springs (32714) ***(G-47)***
Fretto Prints Inc ... 904 687-1985
255 Se Us Highway 19 # 1 Crystal River (34429) ***(G-2378)***
Frida's Bakery and Cafe, Largo *Also called Rouzbeh Inc* ***(G-8042)***
Friedman & Greenberg PA ... 954 370-4774
9675 W Broward Blvd Plantation (33324) ***(G-14519)***
Friedman Bros Dcrtive Arts Inc ... 800 327-1065
9015 Nw 105th Way Medley (33178) ***(G-8653)***
Friendfinder.com, Delray Beach *Also called Various Inc* ***(G-3155)***
Friendly Welding Inc ... 786 953-8413
4600 E 10th Ln Hialeah (33013) ***(G-5417)***
Friends Professional Sty ... 561 734-4660
1521 Neptune Dr Boynton Beach (33426) ***(G-908)***
Frieze, The, Miami Beach *Also called Worlds Greatest Ice Cream Inc* ***(G-10730)***
Frio Distributors Inc ... 813 567-1493
1406 Mercantile Ct Plant City (33563) ***(G-14433)***
Fritanga Y Tortilla Modra ... 305 649-9377
1885 W Flagler St Miami (33135) ***(G-9598)***
Frito-Lay North America Inc ... 407 295-1810
2800 Silver Star Rd Orlando (32808) ***(G-12766)***
Frito-Lay North America Inc ... 972 334-7000
10255 Kay Dr Seminole (33772) ***(G-16747)***
Fritz Commercial Printing Inc ... 561 585-6869
5401 S Dixie Hwy West Palm Beach (33405) ***(G-18884)***
Fritz Duane L Sr Tre Frit ... 727 576-1584
8701 40th Way N Pinellas Park (33782) ***(G-14349)***
Frog Publications Inc ... 352 588-2082
11820 Uradco Pl Ste 105 San Antonio (33576) ***(G-15972)***
From Trees Inc ... 813 431-8285
6030 Springer Dr Port Richey (34668) ***(G-15050)***
Fromkin Energy LLC ... 954 683-2509
4630 N University Dr Coral Springs (33067) ***(G-2249)***
Front Line Publishing Inc ... 813 480-8033
719 Regent Cir S Brandon (33511) ***(G-1160)***
Front of House Inc ... 305 757-7940
7630 Biscayne Blvd # 105 Miami (33138) ***(G-9599)***
Front of House Rm 360 By Foh, Miami *Also called Foh Inc* ***(G-9592)***
Frontier Communications, Micanopy *Also called Frontier Electronics* ***(G-10900)***
Frontier Electronics ... 954 255-0911
255 W Smith Ave Micanopy (32667) ***(G-10900)***
Frontier Ready Mix Inc ... 727 544-1000
8311 63rd Way N Pinellas Park (33781) ***(G-14350)***
Frostbite Nitrogen Ice Cream ... 305 933-5482
2305 Ne 197th St Miami (33180) ***(G-9600)***
Frosting ... 772 234-2915
2915 Cardinal Dr Vero Beach (32963) ***(G-18622)***
Froyolicious Inc ... 561 753-4890
11081 Sthrn Blvd Ste 110 Royal Palm Beach (33411) ***(G-15467)***
Frozen Wheels LLC ... 305 799-2258
16565 Nw 15th Ave Miami (33169) ***(G-9601)***
Fruit Dynamics LLC ... 239 643-7373
4206 Mercantile Ave Naples (34104) ***(G-11251)***
Fruitful International, Miami Lakes *Also called Fruitful LLC* ***(G-10792)***

Fruitful LLC 954 534-9828
10030 Nw 79th Ave Hleahg Miami Lakes (33016) *(G-10792)*
Fruselva Usa LLC 949 798-0061
801 Brickell Ave Ste 800 Miami (33131) *(G-9602)*
Fry Trim Works Inc 772 260-8486
4626 Ne Dudley Cir Jensen Beach (34957) *(G-6969)*
Frz Marine 941 322-2631
3152 Lena Ln Sarasota (34240) *(G-16440)*
Fsbc, Boca Raton *Also called Fresh Start Beverage Company (G-540)*
Fsf Manufacturing Inc 407 971-8280
575 Econ River Pl Oviedo (32765) *(G-13431)*
Fshs Inc 941 625-5929
4210 Whidden Blvd Port Charlotte (33980) *(G-14982)*
Fsp-Ges Inc 352 799-7933
9070 Old Cobb Rd Brooksville (34601) *(G-1230)*
Fss Company, Fort Lauderdale *Also called Florida Silica Sand Company (G-4005)*
Ft Acquisition Company Llc 904 367-0095
11315 Distribution Ave E Jacksonville (32256) *(G-6417)*
Ft Lauderdale Wax 954 256-9291
1912 N Sederal Hwy Fort Lauderdale (33305) *(G-4014)*
Fuel Air Spark Technology 901 260-3278
160 10th St N Naples (34102) *(G-11252)*
Fuel Connection 305 354-8115
14290 W Dixie Hwy North Miami (33161) *(G-11639)*
Fuel Life 1 LLC 954 652-1735
869 Falling Water Rd Weston (33326) *(G-19128)*
Fuel Medics, North Miami Beach *Also called Fuel Solutions Distrs LLC (G-11679)*
Fuel N Go LLC 239 656-1072
10351 Corkscrew Rd Estero (33928) *(G-3690)*
Fuel Productions LLC 904 342-7826
1960 Us Highway 1 S 199 Saint Augustine (32086) *(G-15544)*
Fuel Reformation Inc 954 800-4289
1451 W Cypress Creek Rd # 300 Fort Lauderdale (33309) *(G-4015)*
Fuel Solutions LLC 813 969-2506
14213 Banbury Way Tampa (33624) *(G-17697)*
Fuel Solutions Distrs LLC 305 528-3758
3777 Ne 163rd St Pmb 148 North Miami Beach (33160) *(G-11679)*
Fuel Tanks To Go LLC 865 604-4726
13 Cypress Road Pass Ocala (34472) *(G-11950)*
Fuel U Fast Inc 561 654-0212
5660 Wind Drift Ln Boca Raton (33433) *(G-541)*
Fuelmatics Corp 305 807-4923
17641 Sw 87th Ave Palmetto Bay (33157) *(G-13843)*
Fuelmyschool 407 952-1030
4344 Indian Deer Rd Windermere (34786) *(G-19227)*
Fuels Unlimited Inc 407 302-3193
509 S French Ave Sanford (32771) *(G-16051)*
Fueltec Systems LLC 828 212-1141
11388 Okeechobee Blvd Royal Palm Beach (33411) *(G-15468)*
Fuentes Custom Woodwork LLC 941 232-0635
1490 Blvd Of The Arts Sarasota (34236) *(G-16441)*
Fuji International LLC 941 961-5472
6259 Sturbridge Ct Sarasota (34238) *(G-16442)*
Full Bore Directional Inc 727 327-7784
4921 15th Ave S Gulfport (33707) *(G-5133)*
Full Circle Directional Inc 352 568-0639
2161 Sw 83rd Pl Bushnell (33513) *(G-1317)*
Full Circle Integration LLC 504 615-5501
127b N John Sims Pkwy Valparaiso (32580) *(G-18511)*
Full Cut Tabs LLC 941 316-1510
2153 10th St Sarasota (34237) *(G-16443)*
Full House, Melbourne *Also called Braid Sales and Marketing Inc (G-8785)*
Full Lf Natural Hlth Pdts LLC 954 889-4019
1932 Hollywood Blvd Hollywood (33020) *(G-5825)*
Full Life Direct LLC 800 305-3043
1932 Hollywood Blvd Hollywood (33020) *(G-5826)*
Full Press Apparel Inc 850 222-1003
3445 Garber Dr Tallahassee (32303) *(G-17259)*
Full Throttle Cnc Inc 248 525-1973
3550 Work Dr Unit A2 Fort Myers (33916) *(G-4460)*
Fuller Amusements 352 629-2792
2250 Se 52nd St Ocala (34480) *(G-11951)*
Fullerton 799 Inc 727 572-7040
5300 115th Ave N Clearwater (33760) *(G-1696)*
Fully Promoted, Clearwater *Also called Embroidme Clearwater Co (G-1670)*
Fully Promoted 239 593-2193
1410 Pine Ridge Rd Ste 9 Naples (34108) *(G-11253)*
Fully Promoted 561 615-8655
1369 N Military Trl West Palm Beach (33409) *(G-18885)*
Fun Electronics Inc 305 933-4646
2999 Ne 191st St Ph 2 Miami (33180) *(G-9603)*
Fun Marine Inc 321 576-1100
682 Industry Rd S Cocoa (32926) *(G-2024)*
Function Please LLC (PA) 305 792-7900
2001 Tyler St Ste 5 Hollywood (33020) *(G-5827)*
Fundacion Educativa Carlos M 305 859-9617
1925 Brickell Ave D1108 Miami (33129) *(G-9604)*
Funder America Inc 863 655-0208
12 Crosley Ln Sebring (33870) *(G-16691)*
Funsparks, Clearwater *Also called System Enterprises LLC (G-1899)*
Fuqua Sawmill Inc 352 236-3456
1751 Nw 33rd Ave Ocala (34475) *(G-11952)*
Furniture Concepts 2000 Inc 954 946-0310
454 Ne 28th St Pompano Beach (33064) *(G-14706)*
Furniture Concepts Inc 727 535-0093
2180 34th Way Ste D Largo (33771) *(G-7954)*
Furniture Design Gallery, Sanford *Also called Furniture Design of Centl Fla (G-16052)*
Furniture Design of Centl Fla 407 330-4430
219 Hickman Dr Sanford (32771) *(G-16052)*
Furnival Cabinetry LLC 321 638-1223
7235 Camilo Rd Cocoa (32927) *(G-2025)*
Furnival Construction LLC 321 638-1223
7235 Camilo Rd Cocoa (32927) *(G-2026)*
Furst-Mcness Company 386 755-5605
3830 Nw Brown Rd Lake City (32055) *(G-7355)*
Fury Surf Shack 305 747-0799
201 Front St Ste 109 Key West (33040) *(G-7187)*
Fusion AC & Appl Svc LLC 888 670-8435
2637 E Atlantic Blvd Pompano Beach (33062) *(G-14707)*
Fusion Energy Solutions LLC 941 366-9936
5506 Independence Ct B Punta Gorda (33982) *(G-15206)*
Fusion Industries 239 592-7070
1998 Trade Center Way Naples (34109) *(G-11254)*
Fusion Industries LLC 239 415-7554
16710 Gator Rd Fort Myers (33912) *(G-4461)*
Fusion Industries Intl LLC 239 415-7554
16710 Gator Rd Fort Myers (33912) *(G-4462)*
Fusion Signs 407 715-6439
720 N John Young Pkwy Kissimmee (34741) *(G-7248)*
Fusion Signs & Graphics, Kissimmee *Also called Fusion Signs (G-7248)*
Fusion Welding 239 288-6530
15865 Brothers Ct Fort Myers (33912) *(G-4463)*
Fussion International Inc 305 662-4848
446 Loretto Ave Coral Gables (33146) *(G-2146)*
Futch Printing & Mailing Inc 904 388-3995
4606 Shirley Ave Jacksonville (32210) *(G-6418)*
Futura International, Clearwater *Also called Opie Choice LLC (G-1819)*
Future Designs By Lahijani, Miami *Also called Lux Unlimited Inc (G-9922)*
Future Foods LLC 786 390-5226
1005 Lake Ave Lake Worth (33460) *(G-7551)*
Future Kitchen Corp 786 356-3746
5841 W 3rd Ave Hialeah (33012) *(G-5418)*
Future Modes Inc 305 654-9995
1910 Ne 206th St Miami (33179) *(G-9605)*
Future Plus of Florida 612 240-7275
138 S Dale Mabry Hwy Tampa (33609) *(G-17698)*
Future Signs and Services Inc 786 255-0868
3530 Mystic Pointe Dr Aventura (33180) *(G-269)*
Futurecow, Sanford *Also called Alpha Technology USA Corp (G-15990)*
Futurescape Inc 386 679-4120
6119 Del Mar Dr Port Orange (32127) *(G-15018)*
Fuzion Digital Signs 844 529-0505
4409 N Clark Ave Tampa (33614) *(G-17699)*
Fw Shoring Company 813 248-2495
7532 Malta Ln Tampa (33637) *(G-17700)*
Fw Shoring Company 517 676-8800
11128 Boggy Creek Rd Orlando (32824) *(G-12767)*
Fws Distributors LLC (PA) 561 312-3318
14501 Nw 57th Ave Ste 113 Miami (33014) *(G-9606)*
Fws Distributors LLC 305 677-9663
4653 L B Mcleod Rd Ste B Orlando (32811) *(G-12768)*
Fyi Software Inc 239 272-6016
4850 Tamiami Trl N # 301 Naples (34103) *(G-11255)*
G & A Manufacturing Inc 352 473-6882
6587 State Road 21 Keystone Heights (32656) *(G-7208)*
G & B Trading Imports, Miami *Also called Valentina Signa Inc (G-10562)*
G & F Manufacturing Inc 239 939-7446
7902 Interstate Ct Fort Myers (33917) *(G-4464)*
G & G Latin Business Inc 954 385-8085
16668 Saddle Club Rd Weston (33326) *(G-19129)*
G & H Reclaim LLC 904 879-2091
45321 Green Ave Callahan (32011) *(G-1324)*
G & K Aluminum Inc 772 283-1297
3110 Se Slater St Stuart (34997) *(G-16943)*
G & R Machine Inc 407 324-1600
701 Cornwall Rd Ste A Sanford (32773) *(G-16053)*
G & R Stucco Inc 941 780-1561
7234 Belcrest Ct North Port (34287) *(G-11739)*
G & S Boats Inc 850 835-7700
143 Yacht Dr Freeport (32439) *(G-4847)*
G & S Machine Shop Corp 305 863-7866
7715 Nw 74th Ave Medley (33166) *(G-8654)*
G A C Inc/Gulf Associates, Deerfield Beach *Also called Gulf Associates Control Inc (G-2833)*
G A Food Services, Fort Lauderdale *Also called GA Fd Svcs Pinellas Cnty LLC (G-4017)*
G and G Industries Inc 754 701-4178
5910 Sw 43rd St Davie (33314) *(G-2528)*
G and W Craftsman LLC 440 453-2770
2249 Kirkwood Ave Naples (34112) *(G-11256)*

ALPHABETIC

G B Welding & Fabrication LLC 954 967-2573
2397 College Ave Davie (33317) ***(G-2529)***
G Bauman Fabrications Inc 954 914-8037
281 Nw 16th St Pompano Beach (33060) ***(G-14708)***
G Black Logging LLC 850 379-8747
15698 Ne Moore St Hosford (32334) ***(G-6009)***
G E Generators, Pensacola *Also called GE Renewables North Amer LLC* ***(G-14161)***
G F C, Belle Glade *Also called Glades Formulating Corporation* ***(G-348)***
G F E Inc 954 583-7005
3030 Burris Rd Davie (33314) ***(G-2530)***
G G Markers Inc 813 873-8181
4815 N Coolidge Ave Tampa (33614) ***(G-17701)***
G G Schmitt & Sons Inc 717 394-3701
7230 15th St E Sarasota (34243) ***(G-16216)***
G Haddock Rowland Inc 904 845-2725
376488 Kings Ferry Rd Hilliard (32046) ***(G-5706)***
G J Embroidery Inc 407 284-8036
6839 Narcoossee Rd Ste 33 Orlando (32822) ***(G-12769)***
G J V Inc 727 584-7136
12509 Ulmerton Rd Largo (33774) ***(G-7955)***
G K Window Treatments Inc 954 786-2927
231 Sw 5th St Pompano Beach (33060) ***(G-14709)***
G K Woodworks 941 232-3910
5365 Matthew Ct Sarasota (34231) ***(G-16444)***
G L E M Inc 727 461-5300
1878 Drew St Clearwater (33765) ***(G-1697)***
G M F, Lakeland *Also called GMF Industries Inc* ***(G-7700)***
G M R, Tampa *Also called Gulf Marine Repair Corporation* ***(G-17735)***
G Metal Industries Inc 305 633-0300
3670 Nw 49th St Miami (33142) ***(G-9607)***
G Phillips and Sons LLC 248 705-5873
8987 Wildlife Loop Sarasota (34238) ***(G-16445)***
G Print Inc 305 316-2266
2392 W 80th St Ste 1 Hialeah (33016) ***(G-5419)***
G S C, Hialeah *Also called General Stair Corporation* ***(G-5428)***
G S Printers Inc 305 931-2755
1239 N Flagler Dr Fort Lauderdale (33304) ***(G-4016)***
G S Servicore Corp 305 888-0189
3630 E 10th Ct Hialeah (33013) ***(G-5420)***
G Welding Contractor Corp 305 896-0311
10226 Nw 80th Ave Miami Lakes (33016) ***(G-10793)***
G&F Mnfctring Mfr Glfstream He, Fort Myers *Also called G & F Manufacturing Inc* ***(G-4464)***
G&G Quality Services Inc 386 566-0309
72 Wynnfield Dr Palm Coast (32164) ***(G-13696)***
G-Car Inc (PA) 305 883-8223
235 W 75th Pl Hialeah (33014) ***(G-5421)***
G-Forces Div, Hialeah *Also called Derm-Buro Inc* ***(G-5369)***
G.A. Foods, Saint Petersburg *Also called GA Fd Svcs Pinellas Cnty LLC* ***(G-15789)***
G.A. International, Fort Lauderdale *Also called L3 Technologies Inc* ***(G-4092)***
G2c Enterprises Inc 850 398-5368
695 Sioux Cir Crestview (32536) ***(G-2348)***
G2c Enterprises Inc 850 585-4166
695 Sioux Cir Crestview (32536) ***(G-2349)***
G2pn.com, Saint Petersburg *Also called Go 2 Print Now Inc* ***(G-15794)***
G6 Embroidery LLC 904 729-1191
6001 Argyle Frest Blvd St Jacksonville (32244) ***(G-6419)***
GA Fd Svcs Pinellas Cnty LLC (PA) 727 388-0075
12200 32nd Ct N Saint Petersburg (33716) ***(G-15789)***
GA Fd Svcs Pinellas Cnty LLC 954 972-8884
1750 W Mcnab Rd Fort Lauderdale (33309) ***(G-4017)***
GA Fd Svcs Pinellas Cnty LLC 239 693-5090
5501 Division Dr Fort Myers (33905) ***(G-4465)***
Ga-MA & Associates Inc (PA) 352 687-8840
404 Cypress Rd Ocala (34472) ***(G-11953)***
Gaab Locks LLC 305 788-8515
21014 Sheridan St Fort Lauderdale (33332) ***(G-4018)***
Gable Enterprises 727 455-5576
1008 Lenna Ave Seffner (33584) ***(G-16727)***
Gables Engineering Inc 305 774-4400
247 Greco Ave Coral Gables (33146) ***(G-2147)***
Gabol Screen Printing Co 305 681-3882
12815 Nw 45th Ave Opa Locka (33054) ***(G-12319)***
Gabrielas Memoirs Inc 305 666-9991
5750 Sw 45th Ter Miami (33155) ***(G-9608)***
Gadal Laboratories Inc 786 732-2571
12178 Sw 128th St Miami (33186) ***(G-9609)***
Gaddie Construction Co 850 215-8421
3391 State Ave Panama City (32405) ***(G-13906)***
Gadgetcat LLC 802 238-3671
465 North Shore Dr Cocoa Beach (32931) ***(G-2063)***
Gadsden County Times Inc 850 627-7649
9 W King St Quincy (32351) ***(G-15250)***
Gaemmerler (us) Corporation 941 465-4400
2906 Corporate Way Palmetto (34221) ***(G-13800)***
GAF Materials, Tampa *Also called Standard Industries Inc* ***(G-18129)***
Gaias Formula 954 655-8095
827 Sw 17th Ave Delray Beach (33444) ***(G-3082)***
Gail P Scherer DBA/Flag Lady O 941 926-9460
4539 Winners Cir Sarasota (34238) ***(G-16446)***
Gain Solar LLC 305 933-1060
18205 Biscayne Blvd Aventura (33160) ***(G-270)***
Gainesville 352 339-0294
8039 Sw 67th Rd Gainesville (32608) ***(G-4925)***
Gainesville Ice Company 352 378-2604
508 Se 11th Ave Gainesville (32601) ***(G-4926)***
Gainesville Iron Works Inc 352 373-4004
2341 Nw 66th Ct Gainesville (32653) ***(G-4927)***
Gainesville Ironworks, Gainesville *Also called Gainesville Iron Works Inc* ***(G-4927)***
Gainesville Sun 352 374-5000
2700 Sw 13th St Gainesville (32608) ***(G-4928)***
Gainesville Sun Publishing Co (HQ) 352 378-1411
2700 Sw 13th St Gainesville (32608) ***(G-4929)***
Gainesville Wldg & Fabrication 352 373-0384
2327 Ne 19th Dr Gainesville (32609) ***(G-4930)***
Gainesville/Ocala Business, Ocala *Also called Ocala Magazine* ***(G-12010)***
Galactic News Service 239 431-7470
6809 Wellington Dr Naples (34109) ***(G-11257)***
Galan Express Inc 305 438-8738
1150 Sw 154th Ave Miami (33194) ***(G-9610)***
Galaxy America Inc 941 697-0324
7431 Sawyer Cir Port Charlotte (33981) ***(G-14983)***
Galaxy Awning and Signs Inc 305 262-4224
1620 W 33rd Pl Hialeah (33012) ***(G-5422)***
Galaxy Custom Granite Inc 352 220-2822
5388 E Jasmine Ln Inverness (34453) ***(G-6088)***
Galaxy Medals Inc 321 269-0840
1125 White Dr Titusville (32780) ***(G-18430)***
Galea Corporation 305 663-0244
4679 Sw 72nd Ave Miami (33155) ***(G-9611)***
Galileo, Homestead *Also called Discipline Marketing Inc* ***(G-5963)***
Galix Bmedical Instrumentation 305 534-5905
8205 Nw 30th Ter Doral (33122) ***(G-3357)***
Gallant Inc 800 330-1343
1267 Wntr Gdn Vnlnd Rd # 230 Winter Garden (34787) ***(G-19265)***
Gallery Industries, Hollywood *Also called Stanley Industries of S Fla* ***(G-5915)***
Galletas La Unica, Miami *Also called Star Bakery Inc* ***(G-10409)***
Galletas Yeya, Miami *Also called Tuly Corporation* ***(G-10512)***
Galley Maid Marine Pdts Inc 863 467-6070
60 Ne 110th St Okeechobee (34972) ***(G-12178)***
Gallop Group Inc 813 251-6242
2402 S Ardson Pl Tampa (33629) ***(G-17702)***
Galloway Foods Inc 305 670-7600
1430 S Dixie Hwy Ste 311 Coral Gables (33146) ***(G-2148)***
Galtronics Telemetry Inc 386 202-2055
1 Hargrove Grade Ste 5 Palm Coast (32137) ***(G-13697)***
Gam Laser Inc (PA) 407 851-8999
7100 Tpc Dr Ste 200 Orlando (32822) ***(G-12770)***
Gam Swiss Turning Inc 954 428-6785
355 Sw 33rd Ave Deerfield Beach (33442) ***(G-2829)***
Gama TEC Corporation 305 362-0456
2208 W 79th St Hialeah (33016) ***(G-5423)***
Gambler Bass Boats, Groveland *Also called Maritec Industries Inc* ***(G-5101)***
Game Fisherman Inc 772 220-4850
1384 Nw Coconut Point Ln Stuart (34994) ***(G-16944)***
Gamma Insulators Corp (PA) 585 302-0878
2121 Ponce De Leon Blvd Coral Gables (33134) ***(G-2149)***
Gammerler US, Bradenton *Also called Gammerlertech Corporation* ***(G-1045)***
Gammerlertech Corporation 941 803-0150
3135 Lakewood Ranch Blvd # 107 Bradenton (34211) ***(G-1045)***
Gand Inc 240 575-0622
119 Wshington Ave Ste 618 Miami Beach (33139) ***(G-10670)***
Gandy Printers Inc 850 222-5847
1800 S Monroe St Tallahassee (32301) ***(G-17260)***
Gannet Technologies LLC 941 870-3444
7135 16th St E Ste 115 Sarasota (34243) ***(G-16217)***
Gannon Charles Berchman III 239 514-0243
1290 Oakes Blvd Naples (34119) ***(G-11258)***
Gap Antenna Products Inc 772 571-9922
99 N Willow St Fellsmere (32948) ***(G-3726)***
Gapv 786 257-1681
7800 Sw 57th Ave Ste 219c South Miami (33143) ***(G-16817)***
Gar Business Group LLC 321 632-5133
386 Commerce Pkwy Rockledge (32955) ***(G-15413)***
Gar Industries Corp 954 456-8088
224 Nw 6th Ave Hallandale Beach (33009) ***(G-5188)***
Gar International 954 704-9590
3315 Commerce Pkwy Miramar (33025) ***(G-10996)***
Gar-P Industries Inc 305 888-7252
10890 Nw South River Dr Medley (33178) ***(G-8655)***
Garbo Sport International Inc 305 599-8797
11231 Nw 20th St Unit 122 Miami (33172) ***(G-9612)***
Garcia Armando Custom Cabinets 305 775-5674
220 Sw 30th Rd Miami (33129) ***(G-9613)***
Garcia Deluxe Services Corp 786 291-4329
1240 W 34th St Hialeah (33012) ***(G-5424)***
Garcia Door & Window Inc 305 635-0644
2787 Nw 34th St Miami (33142) ***(G-9614)***

Garcia Iron Works...305 888-0080
365 W 21st St Hialeah (33010) ***(G-5425)***
Garcia Mining Company LLC (PA)...863 902-9777
6605 Garcia Dr Clewiston (33440) ***(G-1981)***
Garcia Woodwork Entps Inc...954 226-3906
1961 Nw 29th St Oakland Park (33311) ***(G-11807)***
Garco Manufacturing Co Inc...321 868-3778
1400 S Orlando Ave Cocoa Beach (32931) ***(G-2064)***
Gardber-Gibson, Tampa *Also called Gardner Asphalt Corporation* ***(G-17704)***
Gardco...954 946-9454
316 Ne 1st St Pompano Beach (33060) ***(G-14710)***
Gardner Asphalt Corporation (HQ)...813 248-2101
4161 E 7th Ave Tampa (33605) ***(G-17703)***
Gardner Asphalt Corporation...813 248-2101
4001 E 7th Ave Tampa (33605) ***(G-17704)***
Gardner-Gibson Mfg Inc (HQ)...813 248-2101
4161 E 7th Ave Tampa (33605) ***(G-17705)***
Gardner-Watson Decking Inc...813 891-9849
305 Scarlet Blvd Ste A Oldsmar (34677) ***(G-12227)***
Gardners Screen Enclosures...813 843-8527
1113 Lake Shore Ranch Dr Seffner (33584) ***(G-16728)***
Garelick Mfg Co...727 545-4571
7151 114th Ave Largo (33773) ***(G-7956)***
Garflex Inc (PA)...305 436-8915
9594 Nw 41st St Ste 209 Doral (33178) ***(G-3358)***
Garlington Landeweer Marine...772 283-7124
3370 Se Slater St Stuart (34997) ***(G-16945)***
Garment Gear Inc...850 215-2121
1522 Degama Ave Panama City (32405) ***(G-13907)***
Garrett Tin & Brother Inc...727 236-5434
2536 Palesta Dr Trinity (34655) ***(G-18486)***
Garrison Lickle Aircraft...561 833-7111
400 S Ocean Blvd Ofc Palm Beach (33480) ***(G-13555)***
Garvin Management Company Inc (PA)...850 893-4719
4042 Sawgrass Cir Tallahassee (32309) ***(G-17261)***
Garvinos LLC (PA)...352 430-1435
1081 Canal St The Villages (32162) ***(G-18390)***
Garys Cabinets and More LLC...941 585-8001
1945 Custom Dr Fort Myers (33907) ***(G-4466)***
Gas One Inc (PA)...561 483-0504
19688 Oakbrook Cir Boca Raton (33434) ***(G-542)***
Gas Turbine Efficiency Inc...407 304-5200
300 Sunport Ln Ste 100 Orlando (32809) ***(G-12771)***
Gas Turbine Efficiency LLC...407 304-5200
300 Sunport Ln Ste 100 Orlando (32809) ***(G-12772)***
Gaseous Fuel Systems Corp...954 693-9475
3360 Entp Ave Ste 180 Weston (33331) ***(G-19130)***
Gaslab...386 872-7668
131 Business Center Dr Ormond Beach (32174) ***(G-13373)***
Gaspari Nutrition, Palmetto *Also called Allegro Nutrition Inc* ***(G-13784)***
Gatchell Violins Company Inc...321 733-1499
1377 W New Haven Ave West Melbourne (32904) ***(G-18774)***
Gate Access Systems, Jacksonville *Also called Edwards Ornamental Iron Inc* ***(G-6355)***
Gate Cfv Solutions Inc...772 388-3387
100 Sebastian Indus Pl Sebastian (32958) ***(G-16661)***
Gate Petroleum Company...904 998-7126
11040 Mccormick Rd Jacksonville (32225) ***(G-6420)***
Gate Petroleum Company...904 396-0517
4100 Heckscher Dr Jacksonville (32226) ***(G-6421)***
Gate Precast Company...904 520-5795
402 Zoo Pkwy Jacksonville (32226) ***(G-6422)***
Gate Precast Company (HQ)...904 732-7668
9540 San Jose Blvd Jacksonville (32257) ***(G-6423)***
Gate Precast Company...407 847-5285
1018 Sawdust Trl Kissimmee (34744) ***(G-7249)***
Gate Precast Concrete, Kissimmee *Also called Gate Precast Company* ***(G-7249)***
Gate Precast Erection Co...904 737-7220
9540 San Jose Blvd Jacksonville (32257) ***(G-6424)***
Gatecrafterscom...800 537-4283
13100 State Road 54 Odessa (33556) ***(G-12122)***
Gatehouse Media LLC...863 401-6900
455 6th St Nw Winter Haven (33881) ***(G-19325)***
Gater Custom Cabinet & Doors...904 778-2300
4621 Wesconnett Blvd Jacksonville (32210) ***(G-6425)***
Gaterman Products LLC...386 253-1899
114 Meadowbrook Cir Daytona Beach (32114) ***(G-2667)***
Gateway Wireless Communications...561 732-6444
3600 S Congress Ave Boynton Beach (33426) ***(G-909)***
Gatlin Group LLC...850 941-0959
6979 Raburn Rd Pensacola (32526) ***(G-14160)***
Gator Blinds & Shutters...352 375-1995
3035 Se Maricmp Rd104 234 Ocala (34471) ***(G-11954)***
Gator Custom Blinds...352 867-0448
1871 Ne 23rd St Ocala (34470) ***(G-11955)***
Gator Dock & Marine LLC...407 323-0190
2880 S Mellonville Ave Sanford (32773) ***(G-16054)***
Gator Door East Inc...904 824-2827
2150 Dobbs Rd Saint Augustine (32086) ***(G-15545)***
Gator Drain Cleaning Equipment...954 584-4441
5411 Orange Dr Davie (33314) ***(G-2531)***
Gator Fabrications LLC...352 245-7227
3450 Se 132nd Ln Belleview (34420) ***(G-369)***
Gator Feed Co Inc...863 763-3337
1205 Us Highway 98 N Okeechobee (34972) ***(G-12179)***
Gator Freds, Wesley Chapel *Also called Transport PC USA Inc* ***(G-18760)***
Gator Polymers LLC...866 292-7306
3302 Se 22nd Ave Cape Coral (33904) ***(G-1427)***
Gator Printing & Design LLC...352 593-4168
18628 Cortez Blvd Brooksville (34601) ***(G-1231)***
Gator Shack...863 381-2222
4651 Us Highway 98 Sebring (33876) ***(G-16692)***
Gator Stampings Intl Inc...941 753-9598
6610 33rd St E Sarasota (34243) ***(G-16218)***
Gator Telecom, Pompano Beach *Also called Devcon Security Services Corp* ***(G-14661)***
Gator Welding Inc...561 746-0049
201 Jupiter St Jupiter (33458) ***(G-7047)***
Gattas Corp...727 733-5886
745 Main St Ste B Dunedin (34698) ***(G-3578)***
Gattas Marine Services, Dunedin *Also called Gattas Corp* ***(G-3578)***
Gatto Furniture, Fort Lauderdale *Also called Broward Casting Foundry Inc* ***(G-3869)***
Gaukaupa Raceway...904 483-3473
8405 Beach Blvd Jacksonville (32216) ***(G-6426)***
Gaumard Scientific Company Inc...305 971-3790
14700 Sw 136th St Miami (33196) ***(G-9615)***
Gause Built Marine Inc...727 937-9113
728 Wesley Ave Ste 10 Tarpon Springs (34689) ***(G-18302)***
Gautier Fabrication Inc...941 485-2464
1049 Endeavor Ct North Venice (34275) ***(G-11758)***
Gaynor Group Inc...954 749-1228
5030 N Hiatus Rd Sunrise (33351) ***(G-17125)***
Gb Airlink Inc...561 593-7284
2524 Se Wtham Feld Dr Uni Stuart (34996) ***(G-16946)***
Gb Brick Pavers Inc...407 453-5505
4409 S Kirkman Rd Apt 303 Orlando (32811) ***(G-12773)***
Gb Cabinets Incorporated...863 446-0676
3907 Palazzo St Sebring (33872) ***(G-16693)***
Gb Energy Management LLC...305 792-4650
2875 Ne 191st St Ste 901 Miami (33180) ***(G-9616)***
Gb Energy Tech...561 450-6047
2875 S Congress Ave Ste B Delray Beach (33445) ***(G-3083)***
Gb Printing...954 941-3778
414 E Sample Rd Pompano Beach (33064) ***(G-14711)***
Gbi Intralogistics Solutions...954 596-5000
1143 W Newport Center Dr Deerfield Beach (33442) ***(G-2830)***
GBIG Corporation...866 998-8466
8744 Sw 133rd St Miami (33176) ***(G-9617)***
GBS, Pembroke Pines *Also called Gypsum Bd Specialists USA Corp* ***(G-14039)***
Gc Cabinet Express LLC...561 662-0369
1335 Old Dixie Hwy # 20 Lake Park (33403) ***(G-7473)***
Gc Electric LLC...386 842-7066
9101 Tobias Rd E Jacksonville (32234) ***(G-6427)***
Gc Signs and Supply, Sorrento *Also called Gc Traffic Signs and Sup Inc* ***(G-16786)***
Gc Traffic Signs and Sup Inc...352 735-8445
31713 Long Acres Dr Sorrento (32776) ***(G-16786)***
Gcato 1959 Enterprises LLC...954 937-6282
2750 Nw 11th St Pompano Beach (33069) ***(G-14712)***
Gce, Clearwater *Also called Skinny Mixes LLC* ***(G-1879)***
Gcn Media Services, Pompano Beach *Also called Gcn Publishing Inc* ***(G-14713)***
Gcn Publishing Inc...203 665-6211
49 N Federal Hwy 338 Pompano Beach (33062) ***(G-14713)***
Gde LLC...305 458-3025
430 W 37th St Miami Beach (33140) ***(G-10671)***
Gds...305 764-0920
11900 Biscayne Blvd # 262 North Miami (33181) ***(G-11640)***
GE...904 570-3151
12079 Normandy Blvd Jacksonville (32221) ***(G-6428)***
GE Aviation Systems LLC...727 532-6370
14100 Roosevelt Blvd Clearwater (33762) ***(G-1698)***
GE Aviation Systems LLC...727 531-7781
14200 Roosevelt Blvd Clearwater (33762) ***(G-1699)***
GE Aviation Systems LLC...727 539-1631
14200 Roosevelt Blvd Clearwater (33762) ***(G-1700)***
GE Consumer Corporation...904 696-9775
600 Whittaker Rd Jacksonville (32218) ***(G-6429)***
GE Consumer Distribution, Jacksonville *Also called GE Consumer Corporation* ***(G-6429)***
GE Glass Inc...305 599-7725
4455 Nw 73rd Ave Miami (33166) ***(G-9618)***
GE Renewables North Amer LLC (HQ)...850 474-4011
8301 Scenic Hwy Pensacola (32514) ***(G-14161)***
Gea Mechanical Eqp US Inc...863 669-1500
4725 Lakeland Commerce Pa Lakeland (33805) ***(G-7696)***
Gear Driven LLC...954 681-8394
4613 N University Dr Coral Springs (33067) ***(G-2250)***
Gear Dynamics Inc...305 691-0151
3685 Nw 106th St Miami (33147) ***(G-9619)***
Geat Lakes Water Cond Systems, Naples *Also called Great Lakes Wtr Trtmnt Systems* ***(G-11267)***
Gecko Woodworks...239 738-8283
5654 Natoma Dr Fort Myers (33919) ***(G-4467)***

ALPHABETIC

Geddis Inc 800 844-6792
2221 Paddock Cir Dunedin (34698) ***(G-3579)***
Geekshive Inc 888 797-4335
9100 S Ddland Blvd Ste 15 Miami (33156) ***(G-9620)***
Gei Works, Vero Beach *Also called Granite Environmental LLC* ***(G-18623)***
Geigel Marble & Design LLC 305 301-0399
199 Ocean Lane Dr # 1202 Key Biscayne (33149) ***(G-7156)***
Geiger Logging Inc 904 845-7534
28714 Yellow Rose Ln Hilliard (32046) ***(G-5707)***
Gelander Industries Inc 352 343-3100
611 Southridge Indl Dr Tavares (32778) ***(G-18338)***
Gelateria Milani LLC 305 532-8562
436 Espanola Way Miami Beach (33139) ***(G-10672)***
Gelato Petrini LLC 561 600-4088
1205 Sw 4th Ave Delray Beach (33444) ***(G-3084)***
Geltech Inc 407 382-4003
2603 Challenger Tech Ct # 100 Orlando (32826) ***(G-12774)***
Geltech Solutions Inc 561 427-6144
1460 Park Ln S Ste 1 Jupiter (33458) ***(G-7048)***
Gem 360 LLC 800 436-1932
7650 Nw 50th St Miami (33166) ***(G-9621)***
Gem Aerospace 786 464-5900
10300 Nw 19th St Doral (33172) ***(G-3359)***
Gem Asset Acquisition LLC 904 268-6063
9556 Historic Kings Rd S Jacksonville (32257) ***(G-6430)***
Gem Asset Acquisition LLC 407 888-2080
6441 Pinecastle Blvd Orlando (32809) ***(G-12775)***
Gem Asset Acquisition LLC 813 630-1695
5050 Denver St Tampa (33619) ***(G-17706)***
Gem Freshco LLC 772 595-0070
3586 Oleander Ave Fort Pierce (34982) ***(G-4699)***
Gem Inc of Capri, Naples *Also called Gem Remotes Inc* ***(G-11259)***
Gem Industries, Sunrise *Also called Gaynor Group Inc* ***(G-17125)***
Gem Industries Inc 321 302-8985
370 Cox Rd Cocoa (32926) ***(G-2027)***
Gem Paver Systems Inc (PA) 305 805-0000
9845 Nw 118th Way Medley (33178) ***(G-8656)***
Gem Remotes Inc 239 642-0873
3527 Plover Ave Unit 2 Naples (34117) ***(G-11259)***
Gemoco Division, Palm Beach Gardens *Also called Chromalloy Gas Turbine LLC* ***(G-13578)***
Gems Jewelry & Uniques 850 456-8105
306 Bremen Ave Pensacola (32507) ***(G-14162)***
Gemseal Pavement Products 305 328-9159
5050 Denver St Tampa (33619) ***(G-17707)***
Gemseal Pavements Pdts - Tampa, Tampa *Also called Gem Asset Acquisition LLC* ***(G-17706)***
Gemseal Pvments Pdts - Jackson, Jacksonville *Also called Gem Asset Acquisition LLC* ***(G-6430)***
Gemseal Pvments Pdts - Orlando, Orlando *Also called Gem Asset Acquisition LLC* ***(G-12775)***
Gemstone Cabinetry LLC 941 426-5656
2845 Commerce Pkwy North Port (34289) ***(G-11740)***
Gen-Prodics Inc 772 221-8464
2029 Sw Oak Ridge Rd Palm City (34990) ***(G-13658)***
Genca Corp 727 524-3622
13805 58th St N Clearwater (33760) ***(G-1701)***
Gencor Industries, Orlando *Also called Thermotech Systems Corporation* ***(G-13254)***
Gencor Industries Inc (PA) 407 290-6000
5201 N Orange Blossom Trl Orlando (32810) ***(G-12776)***
Genecell International LLC 305 382-6737
2664 Nw 97th Ave Doral (33172) ***(G-3360)***
Geneforce Incorporated 786 823-0700
2635 Nw 20th St Miami (33142) ***(G-9622)***
Genel/Landec Inc 305 591-9990
10845 Nw 29th St Doral (33172) ***(G-3361)***
Genensys LLC 407 701-4158
7269 Winding Lake Cir Oviedo (32765) ***(G-13432)***
General & Duplicating Services 305 541-2116
2057 Nw 27th Ave Miami (33142) ***(G-9623)***
General Asphalt Co Inc 305 592-6005
4850 Nw 72nd Ave Miami (33166) ***(G-9624)***
General Business Services 904 260-1099
12412 San Jose Blvd # 101 Jacksonville (32223) ***(G-6431)***
General Cabinets Inc 727 863-3404
15801 Archer St Port Richey (34667) ***(G-15051)***
General Cabinets Pasco County, Hudson *Also called Dons Cabinets and Woodworking* ***(G-6022)***
General Capacitor LLC 510 371-2700
132-1 Hamilton Park Dr Tallahassee (32304) ***(G-17262)***
General Catagraphy Inc 561 455-4398
4 Estate Dr Boynton Beach (33436) ***(G-910)***
General Clamp Industries Inc 407 859-6000
1155 Central Florida Pkwy Orlando (32837) ***(G-12777)***
General Defense Corporation 954 444-0155
4960 Sw 52nd St Ste 413 Davie (33314) ***(G-2532)***
General Dynamics Corporation 407 380-9384
3275 Progress Dr Orlando (32826) ***(G-12778)***
General Dynamics Corporation 850 897-9700
115 Hart St Niceville (32578) ***(G-11567)***
General Dynamics-Ots Inc (HQ) 727 578-8100
11399 16th Ct N Ste 200 Saint Petersburg (33716) ***(G-15790)***
General Dynmics Land Systems I 850 574-4700
2930 Commonwealth Blvd Tallahassee (32303) ***(G-17263)***
General Dynmics Mssion Systems 407 823-7000
12001 Res Pkwy Ste 500 Orlando (32826) ***(G-12779)***
General Dynmics Nassco Mayport, Jacksonville *Also called Metro Machine Corp* ***(G-6601)***
General Dynmics Ord Tctcal Sys (HQ) 727 578-8100
11399 16th Ct N Ste 200 Saint Petersburg (33716) ***(G-15791)***
General Fine Machine Co Inc 727 726-5956
1010 Park Ct Ste F Safety Harbor (34695) ***(G-15494)***
General Floors, Doral *Also called Genfloor LLC* ***(G-3364)***
General Hydraulic Solutions 727 561-0719
10601 47th St N Clearwater (33762) ***(G-1702)***
General Impact GL Windows Corp 305 558-8103
290 W 78th Rd Hialeah (33014) ***(G-5426)***
General Machine Company Inc 941 756-2815
5207 Malaga Ave Sarasota (34235) ***(G-16447)***
General Machine Shop 305 558-2409
9820 Nw 80th Ave Miami Lakes (33016) ***(G-10794)***
General Metal Intl Inc 305 628-2052
13580 Sw 51st St Miramar (33027) ***(G-10997)***
General Metals & Plastics Inc 904 354-8224
2727 Waller St Jacksonville (32205) ***(G-6432)***
General Mro Aerospace Inc 305 482-9903
10990 Nw 92nd Ter Medley (33178) ***(G-8657)***
General Oceanics Inc 305 621-2882
1295 Nw 163rd St Miami (33169) ***(G-9625)***
General Pillows & Fiber Inc 305 884-8300
605 W 17th St Hialeah (33010) ***(G-5427)***
General Pneumatics Inflation 941 216-3500
2236 72nd Ave E Sarasota (34243) ***(G-16219)***
General Power Limited Inc 800 763-0359
9930 Nw 21st St Fl 1 Doral (33172) ***(G-3362)***
General Rubber Corporation 941 412-0001
405 Commercial Ct Ste C Venice (34292) ***(G-18549)***
General Saw Company 813 231-3167
2902 E Sligh Ave Tampa (33610) ***(G-17708)***
General Scientific Corporation 850 866-9636
1300 Thomas Dr Panama City (32408) ***(G-13908)***
General Scientific Mfg, Panama City *Also called General Scientific Corporation* ***(G-13908)***
General Screen Service Co 305 226-0741
5033 Sw 151st Pl Miami (33185) ***(G-9626)***
General Sign, Miami *Also called C L F Enterprises* ***(G-9293)***
General Sign Service Inc 904 355-5630
1940 Spearing St Jacksonville (32206) ***(G-6433)***
General Signs and Service Inc 904 372-4238
20 Donner Rd Atlantic Beach (32233) ***(G-223)***
General Stair Corporation 305 769-9900
690 W 83rd St Hialeah (33014) ***(G-5428)***
General Welding Svc Entps Inc 305 592-9483
8115 Nw 56th St Doral (33166) ***(G-3363)***
Generations Metier Inc (PA) 239 283-9209
2818 Nw 43rd Pl Cape Coral (33993) ***(G-1428)***
Generator Supercenter Orlando 407 984-5000
3071 N Orange Blossom Trl Orlando (32804) ***(G-12780)***
Generex Laboratories LLC 239 592-7255
1915 Trade Center Way Naples (34109) ***(G-11260)***
Generex Labs, Naples *Also called Generex Laboratories LLC* ***(G-11260)***
Genertor Sprcnter Suthwest Fla 608 765-5177
16243 S Tamiami Trl Fort Myers (33908) ***(G-4468)***
Genesis 50 20 LLC 954 860-8175
16682 Royal Poinciana Dr Weston (33326) ***(G-19131)***
Genesis Electric Motors Inc 727 572-1414
6330 118th Ave Unit A Largo (33773) ***(G-7957)***
Genesis Health Institute Inc 954 561-3175
1001 Ne 26th St Wilton Manors (33305) ***(G-19218)***
Genesis II Systems Inc 954 489-1124
2425 E Coml Blvd Ste 101 Fort Lauderdale (33308) ***(G-4019)***
Genesis Reference Laboratories 407 232-7130
7924 Forest Cy Rd Ste 210 Orlando (32810) ***(G-12781)***
Genesis Systems LLC 417 499-3301
3108 N Boundary Blvd # 9 Tampa (33621) ***(G-17709)***
Geneva Foods LLC (PA) 407 302-4751
2664 Jewett Ln Sanford (32771) ***(G-16055)***
Geneva Systems Inc 352 235-2990
712 Simmons Trl Green Cove Springs (32043) ***(G-5063)***
Genfloor LLC 305 477-1557
6312 Nw 99th Ave Doral (33178) ***(G-3364)***
Genicon Inc 407 657-4851
2455 Ridgemoor Dr Orlando (32828) ***(G-12782)***
Genie Cap Inc 941 355-5730
4410 Independence Ct Sarasota (34234) ***(G-16448)***
Genie Publishing 863 937-7769
5111 Fernbrook Ln Lakeland (33811) ***(G-7697)***
Genie Shelf 305 213-4382
10935 Sw 138th Ct Miami (33186) ***(G-9627)***
Genius Central Systems Inc 800 360-2231
2025 Lakewood Ranch Blvd # 202 Bradenton (34211) ***(G-1046)***
Genos Construction Inc 234 303-3427
12421 Us Highway 301 # 228 Dade City (33525) ***(G-2428)***

Genpak LLC 863 243-1068
55 Pine Ridge Dr Lake Placid (33852) **(G-7487)**
Gensco Laboratories LLC....754 263-2898
8550 Nw 33rd St Ste 200 Doral (33122) **(G-3365)**
Gensco Pharma, Doral *Also called Gensco Laboratories LLC* **(G-3365)**
Genteel Coatings LLC....772 708-1781
10151 Se 195th St Inglis (34449) **(G-6076)**
Gentry Printing Company LLC 727 441-1914
2070 Gentry St Clearwater (33765) **(G-1703)**
Genuine Ad Inc....786 399-6484
17600 N Bay Rd Apt 406 Sunny Isles Beach (33160) **(G-17077)**
Genuine Denim....305 491-1326
851 Ne 182nd Ter North Miami Beach (33162) **(G-11680)**
Genzyme Corporation....800 245-4363
1031 Ives Dairy Rd # 228 Miami (33179) **(G-9628)**
Genzyme Genetics, Miami *Also called Genzyme Corporation* **(G-9628)**
Geo Environmental, Miami *Also called General Oceanics Inc* **(G-9625)**
Geocommand Inc 561 347-9215
3700 Airport Rd Ste 410 Boca Raton (33431) **(G-543)**
Geodetic Services Inc....321 724-6831
1511 Riverview Dr Melbourne (32901) **(G-8835)**
Georg Fischer LLC (HQ) 305 418-9150
10540 Nw 26th St Doral (33172) **(G-3366)**
George & Company LLC....239 949-3650
28771 S Diesel Dr Ste 3 Bonita Springs (34135) **(G-833)**
George Birney Jr 407 851-5604
6714 Bouganvillea Cres Dr Orlando (32809) **(G-12783)**
George Gillespie Cabinets....561 744-6191
15611 78th Dr N West Palm Beach (33418) **(G-18886)**
George's Metal Fab, Medley *Also called Georges Welding Services Inc* **(G-8658)**
Georges Welding Services Inc....305 822-2445
11400 Nw 134th St Medley (33178) **(G-8658)**
Georgesoft Inc....850 329-5517
207 W Park Ave Ste B Tallahassee (32301) **(G-17264)**
Georgia Coast Publications, Stuart *Also called Treasure Coast Publishing Inc* **(G-17038)**
Georgia Mktg & Sign Co LLC 800 286-8671
2121 Vista Pkwy West Palm Beach (33411) **(G-18887)**
Georgia Usssa Baseball....678 794-1630
5610 Rusack Dr Melbourne (32940) **(G-8836)**
Georgia-Florida Bark and Mulch, Monticello *Also called Randy Wheeler* **(G-11081)**
Georgia-Pacific LLC 386 328-8826
County Rd 216 E Palatka (32177) **(G-13481)**
Georgia-Pacific LLC 404 652-4000
5240 Ne 64th Ave Silver Springs (34488) **(G-16782)**
Georgian American Alloys Inc (PA)....305 375-7560
200 Suth Bscyne Blvd Ste Miami (33131) **(G-9629)**
Gerber Coburn Optical Inc....305 592-4705
2585 Nw 74th Ave Miami (33122) **(G-9630)**
Gerdau Ameristeel, Tampa *Also called Sheffield Steel Corporation* **(G-18095)**
Gerdau Ameristeel Corp (HQ)....813 286-8383
4221 W Boy Scout Blvd # 600 Tampa (33607) **(G-17710)**
Gerdau Ameristeel US Inc (HQ)....813 286-8383
4221 W Boy Scout Blvd # 600 Tampa (33607) **(G-17711)**
Gerdau Ameristeel US Inc....813 752-7550
4006 Paul Buchman Hwy Plant City (33565) **(G-14434)**
Gerdau Ameristeel US Inc....813 752-7550
2100 Joe Mcintosh Rd Plant City (33565) **(G-14435)**
Gerdau Long Steel America, Tampa *Also called Gerdau USA Inc* **(G-17712)**
Gerdau Long Steel North Amer, Tampa *Also called Gerdau Ameristeel US Inc* **(G-17711)**
Gerdau USA Inc (HQ)....813 286-8383
4221 W Boy Scout Blvd Tampa (33607) **(G-17712)**
Germain Awning Center, Miami *Also called Germain Canvas & Awning Co* **(G-9631)**
Germain Canvas & Awning Co....305 751-4963
921 Belle Meade Island Dr Miami (33138) **(G-9631)**
Germfree Laboratories Inc....386 265-4300
4 Sunshine Blvd Ormond Beach (32174) **(G-13374)**
Germkleen LLC....954 947-5602
716 Nw 6th Ave Fort Lauderdale (33311) **(G-4020)**
Gerogari Display Manufacture....305 888-0993
5517 Nw 72nd Ave Miami (33166) **(G-9632)**
Gesco Ice Cream Vending Corp (PA)....718 782-3232
17555 Collins Ave # 2903 Sunny Isles Beach (33160) **(G-17078)**
Gess Technologies LLC....305 231-6322
7292 W 20th Ave Hialeah (33016) **(G-5429)**
Get Hams Inc....850 386-7123
3396 Lakeshore Dr Tallahassee (32312) **(G-17265)**
Get Salted LLC....954 826-3947
120 Nw 11th St Boca Raton (33432) **(G-544)**
Getabstract Inc....305 936-2626
20900 Ne 30th Ave Ste 315 Miami (33180) **(G-9633)**
Getfpv LLC 941 444-0021
1060 Goodrich Ave Sarasota (34236) **(G-16449)**
Getitcleaned....239 331-2891
3520 6th Ave Ne Naples (34120) **(G-11261)**
Gevas Pckg Converting Tech Ltd 561 202-0800
3553 High Ridge Rd Boynton Beach (33426) **(G-911)**
GF Piping Systems, Doral *Also called Georg Fischer LLC* **(G-3366)**
GF Woodworks 407 716-3712
1306 Pressview Ave Altamonte Springs (32701) **(G-48)**
Gfoodz LLC 561 703-4505
10356 Willow Oaks Trl Boynton Beach (33473) **(G-912)**
GFS, Weston *Also called Gaseous Fuel Systems Corp* **(G-19130)**
Gfs Corp 954 693-9657
3360 Entp Ave Ste 180 Weston (33331) **(G-19132)**
Gfsf Inc....727 478-7284
2404 Merchant Ave Odessa (33556) **(G-12123)**
Gfx Inc (PA) 305 499-9789
4810 Nw 74th Ave Miami (33166) **(G-9634)**
Gg Professional Painting Corp 786 716-8972
2001 Ludlam Rd Apt 317 Miami (33155) **(G-9635)**
Ggb1 LLC 305 387-5334
9828 Sw 146th Pl Miami (33186) **(G-9636)**
GI, Gainesville *Also called Gainesville Ice Company* **(G-4926)**
Gibbons Advg DBA Gai Exhibits....954 395-2397
4050 Ne 6th Ave Oakland Park (33334) **(G-11808)**
Gibbons Industries Inc....352 330-0294
1927 Passero Ave Lutz (33559) **(G-8384)**
Gibson Wldg Shetmetal Vent Inc 850 837-6141
335 Mountain Dr Destin (32541) **(G-3190)**
Giebner Enterprises Inc....727 520-1200
4760 Brittany Dr S Apt 20 Saint Petersburg (33715) **(G-15792)**
Gift Giving Creations Corp 786 239-0229
7221 Nw 174th Ter Apt 102 Hialeah (33015) **(G-5430)**
Gift Wrap My Face LLC 305 788-1473
16791 Royal Poinciana Dr Weston (33326) **(G-19133)**
Giggle Magazine, Gainesville *Also called Irving Publications LLC* **(G-4947)**
Gigli Enterprises Inc (PA) 850 871-4777
4833 E Business Hwy 98 Panama City (32404) **(G-13909)**
Gigliola Inc....954 564-7871
3341 E Oakland Park Blvd Fort Lauderdale (33308) **(G-4021)**
Gigvaoi Fifth and Lenox....305 604-0635
18001 Old Cutler Rd # 307 Palmetto Bay (33157) **(G-13844)**
Gil Industries Inc....850 479-3400
3060 S Highway 95a Cantonment (32533) **(G-1340)**
Gilbane Boatworks LLC....561 744-2223
19137 Se Federal Hwy # 1 Tequesta (33469) **(G-18384)**
Gilco Spring of Florida Inc....813 855-4631
3991 Tampa Rd Oldsmar (34677) **(G-12228)**
Gilda Industries Inc 305 887-8286
2525 W 4th Ave Hialeah (33010) **(G-5431)**
Giliberti Inc....772 597-1870
16015 Sw Farm Rd Indiantown (34956) **(G-6072)**
Gill Manufacturing Inc 863 422-5711
110 S Hwy 17 92 Davenport (33837) **(G-2479)**
Gilla Inc (PA) 416 843-2881
475 Fentress Blvd Ste L Daytona Beach (32114) **(G-2668)**
Gillette Sign & Lighting Inc....352 256-2225
1609 Warbler St Zephyrhills (33540) **(G-19521)**
Gilman Building Products, Jacksonville *Also called Maxville LLC* **(G-6582)**
Gilman Building Products LLC 904 548-1000
581705 White Oak Rd Yulee (32097) **(G-19498)**
Gilman's Cabinets, Lecanto *Also called Gilmans Custom Furn & Cabinets* **(G-8134)**
Gilmans Custom Furn & Cabinets....352 746-3532
4625 W Homosassa Trl Lecanto (34461) **(G-8134)**
Gilson Inc....904 725-7612
730 Trinidad Rd Jacksonville (32216) **(G-6434)**
Gingham Gator LLC 352 475-1985
8136 Alderman Rd Melrose (32666) **(G-8985)**
Gioia Sails South LLC....386 597-2876
14 Commerce Blvd Palm Coast (32164) **(G-13698)**
Giovanni Art In Custom Furn....954 698-1008
1478 Sw 1st Way Deerfield Beach (33441) **(G-2831)**
Giovannis Bakery Inc....727 536-2253
299 Keene Rd Largo (33771) **(G-7958)**
Giraldo & Donalisio Corp....239 567-2206
3909 Ne 19th Ave Cape Coral (33909) **(G-1429)**
Givaudan Fragrances Corp 863 667-0821
4705 Us Highway 92 E Lakeland (33801) **(G-7698)**
Givaudan Roure Flavors, Lakeland *Also called Givaudan Fragrances Corp* **(G-7698)**
Giz Studio Inc....305 416-5001
601 Nw 11th St Miami (33136) **(G-9637)**
Gizmos Lion Sheet Metal Inc....561 684-8480
1648 Donna Rd West Palm Beach (33409) **(G-18888)**
Gj Francos Stair Co Inc....727 510-4102
1079 Woodbrook Dr S Largo (33770) **(G-7959)**
Gjcb Signs Graphics Inc 352 429-0803
136 S Main Ave Groveland (34736) **(G-5095)**
Gk Inc (PA)....215 223-7207
2724 Ne 35th Dr Fort Lauderdale (33308) **(G-4022)**
GK Hair, Fort Lauderdale *Also called Van Tibolli Beauty Corp* **(G-4304)**
GKN Aerospace Florida LLC....314 412-8311
6051 Ventr Crossings Blvd Panama City (32409) **(G-13910)**
Gkwf Inc....863 644-6925
520 W Brannen Rd Lakeland (33813) **(G-7699)**
GL Shavings LLC....352 360-0063
26444 County Road 33 Groveland (34736) **(G-5096)**
Glades Formulating Corporation 561 996-4200
909 Nw 13th St Belle Glade (33430) **(G-348)**

Glades Sugar House, Belle Glade *Also called Sugar Cane Growers Coop Fla* ***(G-351)***
Gladium LLC 305 989-2720
18944 Sw 93rd Ct Cutler Bay (33157) ***(G-2394)***
Glamer Medspa LLC 305 744-6908
2114 N Flamingo Rd Pembroke Pines (33028) ***(G-14035)***
Glasfloss Industries Inc 904 741-9922
1310 Tradeport Dr Jacksonville (32218) ***(G-6435)***
Glaspro 941 488-4586
101 Pond Cypress Rd Venice (34292) ***(G-18550)***
Glasrite Inc 863 967-8151
627 W Bridgers Ave Auburndale (33823) ***(G-244)***
Glass Pros of Tampa, Tampa *Also called Johnson & Jackson Glass Pdts* ***(G-17808)***
Glass Tech Corp 305 633-6491
3103 Nw 20th St Miami (33142) ***(G-9638)***
Glass Works, Chuluota *Also called Jsl Enterprises of Orlando* ***(G-1553)***
Glass Works of Largo Inc 727 535-9808
2020 Wild Acres Rd Unit D Largo (33771) ***(G-7960)***
Glassarium LLC 786 631-7080
444 Ne 30th St Unit 804 Miami (33137) ***(G-9639)***
Glasser Boat Works Inc 321 626-0061
1670 Barrett Dr Rockledge (32955) ***(G-15414)***
Glassflake International Inc 904 268-4000
6525 Greenland Rd Jacksonville (32258) ***(G-6436)***
Glasslam, Pompano Beach *Also called Nebula Glass International Inc* ***(G-14771)***
Glasspec Corp 305 255-8444
2385 Nw 149th St Opa Locka (33054) ***(G-12320)***
GLC 3 & Rental Corp 954 916-1551
11490 Nw 20th Ct Plantation (33323) ***(G-14520)***
GLC 3 Concrete, Plantation *Also called GLC 3 & Rental Corp* ***(G-14520)***
Gleim Publications Inc 352 375-0772
4201 Nw 95th Blvd Gainesville (32606) ***(G-4931)***
Gleman Sons Cstm Woodworks LLC 407 314-9638
110 Tech Dr Sanford (32771) ***(G-16056)***
Glennmar Supply LLC 727 536-1955
6265 118th Ave Largo (33773) ***(G-7961)***
Glenny Stone Works Inc 786 502-3918
3000 Nw 77th Ct Doral (33122) ***(G-3367)***
Glenroe Technologies Inc 941 554-5262
7290 26th Ct E Sarasota (34243) ***(G-16220)***
Glidden Professional Paint Ctr, Tampa *Also called PPG Architectural Finishes Inc* ***(G-17999)***
Glider Printing LLC 813 601-8907
13377 W Hillsborough Ave Uni Tampa (33635) ***(G-17713)***
GLM Publishing LLC 561 409-7696
2165 Nw 30th Rd Boca Raton (33431) ***(G-545)***
Glo Aesthetic & Laser Institut 561 704-4565
5919 Ithaca Cir W Lake Worth (33463) ***(G-7552)***
Global Aerospace 407 721-3732
1515 N Hwy A1a Apt 202 Indialantic (32903) ***(G-6059)***
Global Agriculture Tech Engrg, Sebastian *Also called Gate Cfv Solutions Inc* ***(G-16661)***
Global Aliment Inc 786 536-5261
7791 Nw 46th St Ste 308 Doral (33166) ***(G-3368)***
Global Aluminum Solutions LLC 954 636-4143
13558 Nw 9th Ct Pembroke Pines (33028) ***(G-14036)***
Global Bamboo Technologies Inc 707 730-0288
310 Cypress Rd Ocala (34472) ***(G-11956)***
Global Biometric, Tampa *Also called Secure Biometric Corporation* ***(G-18082)***
Global Cabinet Distributors 305 625-9814
16355 Nw 48th Ave Miami Lakes (33014) ***(G-10795)***
Global Composite USA Inc 813 898-7987
6608 S West Shore Blvd Tampa (33616) ***(G-17714)***
Global Custom Cabinets LLC 407 738-0146
289 Beckenham Dr Kissimmee (34758) ***(G-7250)***
Global Directories Inc 954 571-8283
450 Fairway Dr Ste 204 Deerfield Beach (33441) ***(G-2832)***
Global Diversified Products 727 209-0854
5195 102nd Ave N Pinellas Park (33782) ***(G-14351)***
Global Force Enterprises LLC 786 317-8197
2331 W Lake Miramar Cir Miramar (33025) ***(G-10998)***
Global Friction Products Inc 813 241-2700
2003 S 50th St Tampa (33619) ***(G-17715)***
Global Galan Logistics Inc 754 263-2708
3132 Sw 173rd Ter Miramar (33029) ***(G-10999)***
Global Gl Lc 863 551-1079
343 Hamilton Shores Dr Ne Winter Haven (33881) ***(G-19326)***
Global Holdings and Dev LLC 949 500-4997
3850 Oaks Clubhouse Dr Pompano Beach (33069) ***(G-14714)***
Global Impressions Inc 727 531-1290
1299 Starkey Rd Ste 103 Largo (33771) ***(G-7962)***
Global Industries and Mfg Inc 954 766-4656
10781 Cleary Blvd Apt 112 Plantation (33324) ***(G-14521)***
Global Intl Investments LLC 305 825-2288
6175 Nw 167th St Ste G32 Hialeah (33015) ***(G-5432)***
Global Intrcnnect Slutions LLC 239 254-0326
4522 Executive Dr Ste 103 Naples (34119) ***(G-11262)***
Global Manufacturing Tech Inc 239 657-3720
160 Airpark Blvd Unit 101 Immokalee (34142) ***(G-6049)***
Global Marketing Corp 973 426-1088
3752 Summerwind Cir Bradenton (34209) ***(G-1047)***
Global Media Press Corp 813 857-5898
6723 N Armenia Ave Tampa (33604) ***(G-17716)***
Global Mind USA LLC 305 402-2190
250 Nw 23rd St Unit 212 Miami (33127) ***(G-9640)***
Global Ordnance LLC (PA) 941 549-8388
2150 Whitfield Ave Sarasota (34243) ***(G-16221)***
Global Performance Windows Inc 954 942-3322
1881 Sw 3rd St Pompano Beach (33069) ***(G-14715)***
Global Personalized Academics, Miami *Also called Sibling Group Holdings Inc* ***(G-10341)***
Global Pharma Analytics LLC 701 491-7770
225 Chimney Corner Ln # 30 Jupiter (33458) ***(G-7049)***
Global Phrm Compliance 239 949-4958
4324 Sanctuary Way Bonita Springs (34134) ***(G-834)***
Global Prime Wood LLC 770 292-9200
2875 Ne 191st St Ste 500 Aventura (33180) ***(G-271)***
Global Printing Services Inc 305 446-7628
3150 Ponce De Leon Blvd Coral Gables (33134) ***(G-2150)***
Global Printing Solutions Inc 727 458-3483
2569 25th Ave N Saint Petersburg (33713) ***(G-15793)***
Global Products Group LLC (PA) 866 320-4367
13760 Reptron Blvd Tampa (33626) ***(G-17717)***
Global Publishing Inc 904 262-0491
9799 Old St Augustine Rd Jacksonville (32257) ***(G-6437)***
Global Pump Daytona 386 426-2411
411 Timaquan Trl Edgewater (32132) ***(G-3623)***
Global Quality Brands, West Palm Beach *Also called Pure Global Brands Inc* ***(G-19011)***
Global Reach Rx Pbf LLC 786 703-1988
10560 Nw 27th St Ste 101a Doral (33172) ***(G-3369)***
Global Recash LLC 818 297-4437
3191 Coral Way Coral Gables (33145) ***(G-2151)***
Global Satellite Prpts LLC 954 459-3000
1901 S Andrews Ave Fort Lauderdale (33316) ***(G-4023)***
Global Seashell Industries LLC 813 677-6674
4930 Distribution Dr Tampa (33605) ***(G-17718)***
Global Seven Inc 973 664-1900
1936 Grove St Sarasota (34239) ***(G-16450)***
Global Source Imports LLC 917 213-6891
175 Sw 7th St Ste 1518 Miami (33130) ***(G-9641)***
Global Stone Collection LLC (PA) 772 467-1924
1405 N Us Highway 1 Fort Pierce (34950) ***(G-4700)***
Global Stone Corp 786 601-2459
10780 Sw 188th St Cutler Bay (33157) ***(G-2395)***
Global Stone Project Entp, Saint Petersburg *Also called Commercial Stone Fbrcators Inc* ***(G-15750)***
Global Tech Led LLC 877 748-5533
1883 W State Road 84 # 106 Fort Lauderdale (33315) ***(G-4024)***
Global Telemetry Systems Inc 850 651-3388
70 6th Ave Shalimar (32579) ***(G-16775)***
Global Tire Rcycl of Smter CNT 352 330-2213
1201 Industrial Dr Wildwood (34785) ***(G-19194)***
Global Tire Recycling Inc (PA) 352 330-2213
1201 Industrial Dr Wildwood (34785) ***(G-19195)***
Global Tissue Group Jax, Jacksonville *Also called Gtg-Jax LLC* ***(G-6454)***
Global Tissue Group Jax 904 861-3290
11801 Central Pkwy Jacksonville (32224) ***(G-6438)***
Global Trading Inc (PA) 305 471-4455
7500 Nw 25th St Unit 12 Miami (33122) ***(G-9642)***
Global Turbine Services Inc 786 476-2166
9374 Nw 102nd St Medley (33178) ***(G-8659)***
Global Village Ventures 813 453-6199
5415 W Sligh Ave Ste 102 Tampa (33634) ***(G-17719)***
Global Windows, Pompano Beach *Also called Global Performance Windows Inc* ***(G-14715)***
Global Wrless Sltions Tech Inc 941 744-2511
101 Riverfront Blvd # 400 Bradenton (34205) ***(G-1048)***
Globalink Mfg Solutions 239 455-5166
3893 Mannix Dr Ste 514 Naples (34114) ***(G-11263)***
Globaltek Art & Design, Doral *Also called Globaltek Office Supply Inc* ***(G-3370)***
Globaltek Office Supply Inc 305 477-2988
11200 Nw 25th St Ste 123 Doral (33172) ***(G-3370)***
Globe Boyz International LLC 305 308-8160
1365 Nw 84th Ter Miami (33147) ***(G-9643)***
Globe Specialty Metals Inc (HQ) 786 509-6900
600 Brickell Ave Ste 3100 Miami (33131) ***(G-9644)***
Globe Trailers Florida Inc 941 753-6425
3101 59th Avenue Dr E Bradenton (34203) ***(G-1049)***
Glodea Kitchens, Jacksonville *Also called Glodea Store Corp* ***(G-6439)***
Glodea Store Corp 888 400-4937
521 Copeland St Jacksonville (32204) ***(G-6439)***
Glomaster Signs Inc 772 464-0718
4141 Bandy Blvd Fort Pierce (34981) ***(G-4701)***
Glory Company, Orlando *Also called Glory Sandblasting Inc* ***(G-12784)***
Glory Sandblasting Inc 407 422-0078
2922 38th St Orlando (32839) ***(G-12784)***
Gloval Displays Inc 800 972-0353
1100 Nw 159th Dr Miami Gardens (33169) ***(G-10742)***
Glow Bench Systems Intl (PA) 954 315-4615
1580 Sawgrs Corp Pkwy # 13 Sunrise (33323) ***(G-17126)***
GLS Assoc Inc 561 451-1999
9170 Long Lake Palm Dr Boca Raton (33496) ***(G-546)***

Glu, Miami Beach *Also called Craig Armstrong* ***(G-10660)***
Glucorell Inc......407 384-3388
130 White Oak Cir Maitland (32751) ***(G-8466)***
Gma-Food LLC......646 469-8599
24756 State Road 54 Lutz (33559) ***(G-8385)***
Gmed, Boca Raton *Also called Modernizing Medicine* ***(G-629)***
GMF Industries Inc......863 646-5081
4600 Drane Field Rd Lakeland (33811) ***(G-7700)***
Gml Coatings LLC......941 755-2176
10315 Technology Ter Bradenton (34211) ***(G-1050)***
Gml Industries LLC......352 671-7619
5542 Sw 6th Pl Ocala (34474) ***(G-11957)***
Gms Sheet Metal Inc......772 221-0585
3377 Sw 42nd Ave Ste D Palm City (34990) ***(G-13659)***
Gmv Holdings LLC......561 747-7864
4905 Midtown Ln Apt 2414 Palm Beach Gardens (33418) ***(G-13592)***
Gnd Publishing LLC......561 625-1242
72 Saint James Ter Palm Beach Gardens (33418) ***(G-13593)***
Gnj Manufacturing Inc......305 651-8644
5811 Hallandale Bch Blvd West Park (33023) ***(G-19093)***
Gnr Orthopedic Designs, Ocala *Also called Great Northern Rehab PC* ***(G-11960)***
Gns Embroidery......850 775-1147
1713 Moylan Rd Panama City Beach (32407) ***(G-13977)***
Gns Technologies LLC......561 367-3774
5612 Pacific Blvd Apt 704 Boca Raton (33433) ***(G-547)***
Go 2 Print Now Inc......800 500-4276
2390 26th Ave N Saint Petersburg (33713) ***(G-15794)***
Go Green Marine Inc......850 499-5137
1234 Arprt Rd Ste 109-110 Destin (32541) ***(G-3191)***
Go Latinos Magazine LLC......786 601-7693
13345 Sw 264th Ter Homestead (33032) ***(G-5965)***
Go Lighting Service, Weston *Also called Itelecom USA Inc* ***(G-19143)***
Go Mobile Signs......239 245-7803
13468 Palm Beach Blvd C Fort Myers (33905) ***(G-4469)***
Go Puck, Sarasota *Also called Capacity Inc* ***(G-16186)***
Goal Line Embroidery......305 295-7585
3255 Flagler Ave Ste 301 Key West (33040) ***(G-7188)***
Gobczynskis Printery Inc......941 758-5734
6452 Parkland Dr Sarasota (34243) ***(G-16222)***
Gocase LLC......415 341-6248
125 Jefferson Ave Apt 121 Miami Beach (33139) ***(G-10673)***
Godatafeed, Plantation *Also called Method Merchant Inc* ***(G-14533)***
Godawa Septic Tank Service, Daytona Beach *Also called P & L Creech Inc* ***(G-2691)***
Godwin and Singer Inc......727 896-8631
1415 Burlington Ave N Saint Petersburg (33705) ***(G-15795)***
Goen3 Corporation (PA)......407 601-6000
6555 Sanger Rd Ste 100 Orlando (32827) ***(G-12785)***
Goforit Inc......727 785-7616
34034 Us Highway 19 N Palm Harbor (34684) ***(G-13737)***
Gogps USA Inc......941 751-2363
7152 15th St E Sarasota (34243) ***(G-16223)***
Goho Enterprises Inc......407 884-0770
3351 Laughlan Rd Zellwood (32798) ***(G-19503)***
Goizper USA, Sarasota *Also called Torque Technologies Products* ***(G-16312)***
Gold Banner USA Inc......305 576-2215
2660 Nw 3rd Ave Miami (33127) ***(G-9645)***
Gold Bond Building Pdts LLC......813 672-8269
12949 S Us Highway 41 Gibsonton (33534) ***(G-5028)***
Gold Buyers of America LLC......877 721-8033
2001 20th Ln Greenacres (33463) ***(G-5081)***
Gold Coast Aero Accessories......561 965-7767
2633 Lantana Rd Ste 23 Lake Worth (33462) ***(G-7553)***
Gold Coast Plst & Stucco Inc......954 275-9132
1815 Nw 64th Way Margate (33063) ***(G-8545)***
Gold Coast Printing Inc......813 853-2219
401 E Jackson St Ste 2340 Tampa (33602) ***(G-17720)***
Gold Coffee Roasters Inc......561 746-8110
1425 Park Ln S Jupiter (33458) ***(G-7050)***
Gold Eagle, Miami *Also called Bard Sports Corp* ***(G-9220)***
Gold Effects Inc......727 573-1990
13130 56th Ct Ste 609 Clearwater (33760) ***(G-1704)***
Gold Granite & Marble......863 439-9794
930 Robert Rd Unit 47 Lake Hamilton (33851) ***(G-7390)***
Gold Karats Jewelry LLC......561 401-5935
1000 E Atl Blvd Ste 217 Pompano Beach (33060) ***(G-14716)***
Gold Network of Miami Inc......305 343-7355
17620 Nw 63rd Ct Hialeah (33015) ***(G-5433)***
Gold Plating Specialties......239 851-9323
17560 Allentown Rd Fort Myers (33967) ***(G-4470)***
Gold Refinery......813 220-5067
18019 Palm Breeze Dr Tampa (33647) ***(G-17721)***
Gold Seal Cutlery, Saint Petersburg *Also called Southern Supply and Mfg Co* ***(G-15919)***
Gold Star Printers, Fort Lauderdale *Also called G S Printers Inc* ***(G-4016)***
Gold-Rep Corporation......954 892-5868
750 Heritage Dr Weston (33326) ***(G-19134)***
Golden Aluminum Extrusion LLC......330 372-2300
1650 Alumax Cir Plant City (33566) ***(G-14436)***
Golden Boar Product Corp......305 500-9392
7224 Nw 25th St Miami (33122) ***(G-9646)***
Golden Boatlifts, North Fort Myers *Also called Golden Manufacturing Inc* ***(G-11598)***
Golden Century Inc......954 933-2911
1935 Banks Rd Margate (33063) ***(G-8546)***
Golden Glades Raceway LLC......305 321-9627
17021 Nw 27th Ave Miami Gardens (33056) ***(G-10743)***
Golden Manufacturing Inc......239 337-4141
17611 East St Unit B North Fort Myers (33917) ***(G-11598)***
Golden Print Inc......561 833-9661
2701 Sw 6th St Boynton Beach (33435) ***(G-913)***
Golden Ribbon Corporation......727 545-4499
10321 72nd St Largo (33777) ***(G-7963)***
Golden Wood Works LLC......239 677-8540
2529 Sw 26th Pl Cape Coral (33914) ***(G-1430)***
Goldfaden Skincare, Hollywood *Also called Cosmesis Skincare Inc* ***(G-5805)***
Goldfield Cnsld Mines Co (HQ)......321 724-1700
100 Rialto Pl Ste 500 Melbourne (32901) ***(G-8837)***
Goldys Box Co......954 648-1623
3267 Trussler Ter The Villages (32163) ***(G-18391)***
Golf Agronomics Sand & Hlg Inc......800 626-1359
2165 17th St Sarasota (34234) ***(G-16451)***
Golf America Southwest Fla Inc......904 688-0280
2049 Crown Dr Saint Augustine (32092) ***(G-15546)***
Golf Shaft Deals Inc......321 591-7824
529 Franklyn Ave Indialantic (32903) ***(G-6060)***
Golfweek, Orlando *Also called Turnstile Publishing Company* ***(G-13284)***
Goloso Food Llc......321 277-2055
1700 35th St Ste 107 Orlando (32839) ***(G-12786)***
Gondia Machine Shop, Medley *Also called Medley Machine Shop Inc* ***(G-8687)***
Gondia Machine Shop Inc......305 763-7494
9452 Nw 109th St Medley (33178) ***(G-8660)***
Gontech Custom Wood Corp......305 323-0765
2005 Sw 129th Ct Miami (33175) ***(G-9647)***
Gonzalez Aerospace Services......561 227-1575
1035 S State Road 7 # 313 Wellington (33414) ***(G-18719)***
Good 4 Tklc Inc......321 632-4340
5020 Nova Ave Rockledge (32955) ***(G-15415)***
Good Catch Inc......305 757-7700
6713 Ne 3rd Ave Miami (33138) ***(G-9648)***
Good Chance Inc......754 263-2792
20851 Johnson St Ste 107 Pembroke Pines (33029) ***(G-14037)***
Good Chance Textile Inc......754 263-2792
20851 Johnson St Ste 107 Pembroke Pines (33029) ***(G-14038)***
Good Feet, Orlando *Also called Rlcjc Inc* ***(G-13142)***
Good Gal Storage G.G.s, Fort Lauderdale *Also called Kron Designs LLC* ***(G-4091)***
Good Impressions......305 336-0318
12434 Sw 27th St Miami (33175) ***(G-9649)***
Good Jams LLC......702 379-5551
6450 N Federal Hwy Boca Raton (33487) ***(G-548)***
Good Life Publishing Inc......352 317-6903
6906 Sw 134th Ave Archer (32618) ***(G-209)***
Good Neighbor Pharmacy, Largo *Also called St Mary Pharmacy LLC* ***(G-8060)***
Good Rep Inc......407 869-6531
100 Bay Hammock Ln Longwood (32779) ***(G-8285)***
Good Time Outdoors Inc......352 401-9070
4600 W Highway 326 Ocala (34482) ***(G-11958)***
Good Time Printing Inc......352 629-8838
1522 E Silver Sprng Blvd Ocala (34470) ***(G-11959)***
Good Times Sports Bar and Gril......239 369-7000
700 Leeland Hts Blvd W Lehigh Acres (33936) ***(G-8191)***
Goodcat LLC......239 254-8288
1440 Rail Head Blvd Ste 5 Naples (34110) ***(G-11264)***
Goodman Manufacturing Co LP......904 355-4520
1934 W Beaver St Jacksonville (32209) ***(G-6440)***
Goodpress Publishing LLC......561 865-8101
4731 W Atlantic Ave Ste 5 Delray Beach (33445) ***(G-3085)***
Goodrich Corporation......305 622-4500
3201 Nw 167th St Miami Gardens (33056) ***(G-10744)***
Goodrich Corporation......954 538-8900
3601 S Flamingo Rd Miramar (33027) ***(G-11000)***
Goodrich Corporation......305 622-4565
3201 Nw 167th St Miami Gardens (33056) ***(G-10745)***
Goodrich Corporation......904 757-3660
6061 Goodrich Blvd Jacksonville (32226) ***(G-6441)***
Goodwater Albemarle Co, Delray Beach *Also called Worrell Water Technologies LLC* ***(G-3161)***
Goodwill Industries S Fla Inc......941 745-8459
2563 Lakewood Ranch Blvd Bradenton (34211) ***(G-1051)***
Goodwin Heart Pine Company, Micanopy *Also called Goodwin Lumber Company Inc* ***(G-10901)***
Goodwin Lumber Company Inc......352 466-0339
106 Sw 109th Pl Micanopy (32667) ***(G-10901)***
Goodyear Belts, Miami Lakes *Also called Adventry Corp* ***(G-10760)***
Gooee LLC......727 510-0663
1444 S Belcher Rd Clearwater (33764) ***(G-1705)***
Gopi Glass Sales & Svcs Corp......305 592-2089
7450 Nw 41st St Miami (33166) ***(G-9650)***
Gopole, Saint Johns *Also called Ar2 Products LLC* ***(G-15673)***

ALPHABETIC

Gorilla Bats LLC 813 285-9409
11223 Saint Andrews Ct Riverview (33579) ***(G-15271)***
Gorilla Boost, Fort Lauderdale *Also called Two Brothers Cultivation LLC* ***(G-4291)***
Gorilladesk Llc 561 245-8614
7370 E Country Club Blvd Boca Raton (33487) ***(G-549)***
Goruck LLC (HQ) 904 708-2081
415 Pablo Ave Ste 140 Jacksonville Beach (32250) ***(G-6944)***
Goruck Holdings LLC (PA) 904 708-2081
415 Pablo Ave Ste 140 Jacksonville Beach (32250) ***(G-6945)***
Gosan Usa Inc 904 356-4181
1926 Spearing St Jacksonville (32206) ***(G-6442)***
Gosimplyconnect, Fort Lauderdale *Also called Simply45 LLC* ***(G-4235)***
Gospel Journal 904 389-9635
3491 Pall Mall Dr Ste 125 Jacksonville (32257) ***(G-6443)***
Goss Inc 386 423-0311
1419 Industrial Dr New Smyrna Beach (32168) ***(G-11534)***
Got It Inc 954 899-0001
107 E Palmetto Park Rd Boca Raton (33432) ***(G-550)***
Got Residuals Inc 775 343-9240
2614 Tamiami Trl N # 704 Naples (34103) ***(G-11265)***
Gotcha Shuttered 850 450-9137
4151 Cmmons Dr W Apt 5406 Destin (32541) ***(G-3192)***
GOTG LLC 800 381-4684
19182 Powell Rd 1 Brooksville (34604) ***(G-1232)***
Gotobilling Inc 800 305-1534
218 E Bearss Ave Ste 368 Tampa (33613) ***(G-17722)***
Gotrg, Miami *Also called Recon Group LLP* ***(G-10243)***
Gould Signs Inc 772 221-1218
3035 Se Waaler St Stuart (34997) ***(G-16947)***
Gourmet 3005 Inc 786 334-6250
2315 W 77th St Hialeah (33016) ***(G-5434)***
Gourmet Cup, Valrico *Also called Rae Launo Corporation* ***(G-18524)***
Gourmet Food Solutions LLC 413 687-3285
19950 W Country Club Dr # 101 Aventura (33180) ***(G-272)***
Gourmet Parisien Inc 305 778-0756
1943 Sherman St Hollywood (33020) ***(G-5828)***
Govpay Network LLC 866 893-9678
12855 Sw 132nd St Ste 204 Miami (33186) ***(G-9651)***
Goyard Miami LLC 305 894-9235
9700 Collins Ave Ste 118 Bal Harbour (33154) ***(G-302)***
Gpi Signs 863 453-4888
500 S Lake Ave Avon Park (33825) ***(G-288)***
GPM Fab & Supply LLC 813 689-7107
1504 Lenna Ave Seffner (33584) ***(G-16729)***
Gps Education LLC 386 756-7575
2463 Old Samsula Rd Port Orange (32128) ***(G-15019)***
Gps Industries LLC 941 894-8030
1358 Fruitville Rd # 210 Sarasota (34236) ***(G-16452)***
Gq Investments LLC 305 821-3850
3840 W 104th St Unit 20 Hialeah (33018) ***(G-5435)***
Gr Dynamics LLC 850 897-9700
115 Hart St Niceville (32578) ***(G-11568)***
Grabber Construction Pdts Inc 813 249-2281
5835 Barry Rd Ste 107 Tampa (33634) ***(G-17723)***
Graber Cabinets, Sarasota *Also called Morning Star of Sarasota Inc* ***(G-16514)***
Graber Cabinets, Bradenton *Also called Woodtech Global Inc* ***(G-1148)***
Grace Bible Church 850 623-4671
6331 Chestnut St Milton (32570) ***(G-10930)***
Grace Prsthtic Fabrication Inc 727 842-2265
7928 Rutillio Ct New Port Richey (34653) ***(G-11491)***
Grade A Glass (PA) 321 419-6935
1640 Patterson Ave Deland (32724) ***(G-2980)***
Graduate Plastics Inc (PA) 305 687-0405
15800 Nw 15th Ave Miami (33169) ***(G-9652)***
Grafico Industries Inc 941 473-2800
7211 Waters Way Englewood (34224) ***(G-3660)***
Grafix, Clearwater *Also called Labelpro Inc* ***(G-1757)***
Graflex Inc 561 691-5959
15855 Assembly Loop # 100 Jupiter (33478) ***(G-7051)***
Grafton Cosmetics, Boynton Beach *Also called Grafton Products Corp* ***(G-914)***
Grafton Furniture Company 305 696-3811
3401 Nw 71st St Miami (33147) ***(G-9653)***
Grafton Products Corp 561 738-2886
1801 Corporate Dr Boynton Beach (33426) ***(G-914)***
Grafx By Caz (fort Pierce) 772 284-9258
492 Maple Ave Fort Pierce (34982) ***(G-4702)***
Graham & Company LLC 904 281-0003
9440 Philips Hwy Ste 1 Jacksonville (32256) ***(G-6444)***
Grahams Welding Fabrication 850 865-0899
622 Fairway Ave Ne Fort Walton Beach (32547) ***(G-4803)***
Grain Machinery Mfg Corp 305 620-2525
1130 Nw 163rd Dr Miami (33169) ***(G-9654)***
Grainman, Miami *Also called Grain Machinery Mfg Corp* ***(G-9654)***
Grampus Enterprises Inc 305 491-9827
2800 Glades Cir Ste 109 Weston (33327) ***(G-19135)***
Grampus Tech, Weston *Also called Grampus Enterprises Inc* ***(G-19135)***
Gran Savana USA, Orlando *Also called Goloso Food Llc* ***(G-12786)***
Granada Art Service, Miami *Also called Granada Prtg & Graphics Corp* ***(G-9655)***
Granada Prtg & Graphics Corp 305 593-5266
8693 Nw 66th St Miami (33166) ***(G-9655)***
Grand Band, Hollywood *Also called J Lea LLC* ***(G-5849)***
Grand Buffet 941 752-3388
4848 14th St W Bradenton (34207) ***(G-1052)***
Grand Cypress Group Inc 407 622-1993
151 N Maitland Ave Maitland (32751) ***(G-8467)***
Grand Havana Inc 305 297-2207
407 Lincoln Rd Ste 2a Miami Beach (33139) ***(G-10674)***
Grand Products International 386 736-3528
1601 Essex Ave Deland (32724) ***(G-2981)***
Grand Western, Orlando *Also called Cheney Ofs Inc* ***(G-12579)***
Grand Woodworking Llc 239 594-9663
663 Hickory Rd Naples (34108) ***(G-11266)***
Grandstand Publishing LLC 847 491-6440
390 N Orange Ave Ste 2300 Orlando (32801) ***(G-12787)***
Granite Environmental LLC 772 646-0597
5400 85th St Vero Beach (32967) ***(G-18623)***
Granite Imports Inc 732 500-2549
1500 Gateway Blvd Ste 250 Boynton Beach (33426) ***(G-915)***
Granite Services Intl Inc 813 242-7400
201 N Franklin St # 1000 Tampa (33602) ***(G-17724)***
Granite Tampa Bay, Odessa *Also called International Gran & Stone LLC* ***(G-12127)***
Granite World Inc 813 243-6556
7024 Benjamin Rd Tampa (33634) ***(G-17725)***
Grannys Cheesecake & More Inc 561 847-6599
17003 Nw 32nd Ave Okeechobee (34972) ***(G-12180)***
Grant Printing, Fort Lauderdale *Also called Jrg Systems Inc* ***(G-4081)***
Grapevine Usa Inc 786 510-9122
333 Las Olas Way Fort Lauderdale (33301) ***(G-4025)***
Graph-Plex Corp 772 766-3866
5240 95th St Sebastian (32958) ***(G-16662)***
Graph-Plex Inc 954 920-0905
2830 N 28th Ter Hollywood (33020) ***(G-5829)***
Graphic and Printing Svcs Corp 954 486-8868
5035 Nw 37th Ave Tamarac (33309) ***(G-17357)***
Graphic Banner LLP 954 491-9441
1330 E Commercial Blvd Oakland Park (33334) ***(G-11809)***
Graphic Center Group Corp 305 961-1649
2150 Coral Way Fl 1 Coral Gables (33145) ***(G-2152)***
Graphic Data Inc 954 493-8003
7378 W Atlantic Blvd Margate (33063) ***(G-8547)***
Graphic Designs Intl Inc 772 287-0000
3161 Se Slater St Stuart (34997) ***(G-16948)***
Graphic Difference Inc A 954 748-6990
7362 W Commercial Blvd Lauderhill (33319) ***(G-8110)***
Graphic Dynamics Inc 954 728-8452
735 Nw 7th Ter Fort Lauderdale (33311) ***(G-4026)***
Graphic Images Inc 954 984-0015
2301 Nw 33rd Ct Ste 105 Pompano Beach (33069) ***(G-14717)***
Graphic Installers Inc 863 646-5543
4403 Holden Rd Lakeland (33811) ***(G-7701)***
Graphic Jet Signs LLC 786 552-2098
17358 S Dixie Hwy Palmetto Bay (33157) ***(G-13845)***
Graphic Masters Inc 800 230-3873
801 Brickell Ave Ste 300 Miami (33131) ***(G-9656)***
Graphic Press, Titusville *Also called Graphic Reproductions Inc* ***(G-18431)***
Graphic Press Corporation 850 562-2262
5123a Woodlane Cir Ste A Tallahassee (32303) ***(G-17266)***
Graphic Printing Corp 561 994-3586
751 Park Of Commerce Dr Boca Raton (33487) ***(G-551)***
Graphic Reproductions Inc 321 267-1111
2214 Garden St Ste B Titusville (32796) ***(G-18431)***
Graphic Sign Dsign Cntl Fla LL 386 547-4569
529 Ridgewood Ave Daytona Beach (32117) ***(G-2669)***
Graphica Services Inc 305 232-5333
12943 Sw 133rd Ct Miami (33186) ***(G-9657)***
Graphics Arts Bindery Inc 352 394-4077
3023 Pinnacle Ct Clermont (34711) ***(G-1962)***
Graphics Designer Inc 561 687-7993
1367 N Military Trl West Palm Beach (33409) ***(G-18889)***
Graphics Pdts Excellence Inc 813 884-1578
5335 Emory Dr Wesley Chapel (33543) ***(G-18748)***
Graphics Screen Printing & EMB, Tarpon Springs *Also called Eagle Athletic Wear Inc* ***(G-18297)***
Graphics Type Color Entps Inc 305 591-7600
2300 Nw 7th Ave Miami (33127) ***(G-9658)***
Graphink Incorporated 305 468-9463
8850 Nw 13th Ter Unit 103 Doral (33172) ***(G-3371)***
Graphix Screen Printing 727 937-6147
720 E Tarpon Ave Tarpon Springs (34689) ***(G-18303)***
Graphix Solutions of America 727 898-6744
12015 Major Turner Run Parrish (34219) ***(G-14006)***
Grass Choppers 305 253-1217
11861 Sw 180th St Miami (33177) ***(G-9659)***
Grass Choppers South Fla Corp 786 586-2767
9240 Sw 16th St Miami (33165) ***(G-9660)***
Grass Pro Shops Inc 813 381-3890
303 S Falkenburg Rd Tampa (33619) ***(G-17726)***

Grass River Publshing ... 954 974-7383
5510 Sw 7th St Margate (33068) **(G-8548)**
Grate Fireplace & Stone Shoppe ... 239 939-7187
16611 S Tamiami Trl Fort Myers (33908) **(G-4471)**
Grate Ideas of America LLC ... 844 292-6044
1417 Sw 1st Ave Fort Lauderdale (33315) **(G-4027)**
Graves Company, Pompano Beach *Also called Vee Enterprises Inc* **(G-14908)**
Gravity Colors Usa Inc ... 561 419-5272
2428 Bloods Grove Cir Delray Beach (33445) **(G-3086)**
Gravity Ink & Stitch Inc ... 954 558-0119
2910 Nw 130th Ave Apt 112 Sunrise (33323) **(G-17127)**
Gravity Produce LLC ... 269 471-9463
4401 Bay Beach Ln Apt 844 Fort Myers Beach (33931) **(G-4663)**
Gravitystorm Inc ... 772 519-3009
7402 Fort Walton Ave Fort Pierce (34951) **(G-4703)**
Gray Information Solutions Inc ... 352 684-6655
12812 Coronado Dr Spring Hill (34609) **(G-16854)**
Gray Logging LLC ... 850 973-3863
811 Ne Oats Ave Madison (32340) **(G-8449)**
Gray Logging LLC ... 850 973-3863
665 Sw Harvey Greene Dr Madison (32340) **(G-8450)**
Grays Portable Buildings Inc ... 386 755-6449
792 Sw Bascom Norris Dr Lake City (32025) **(G-7356)**
Grease TEC Holding LLC ... 352 742-2440
28615 Lake Indus Blvd Tavares (32778) **(G-18339)**
Greased Lightning, Winter Haven *Also called Global Gl Lc* **(G-19326)**
Great Amercn Natural Pdts Inc ... 727 521-4372
4121 16th St N Saint Petersburg (33703) **(G-15796)**
Great America Beverage Co LLC ... 786 763-2027
8515 Sw 139th Ter Palmetto Bay (33158) **(G-13846)**
Great American Imports Llc ... 786 524-4120
3758 Nw 54th St Miami (33142) **(G-9661)**
Great American Rolling Ppr Co ... 813 928-9166
5015 W Nassau St Tampa (33607) **(G-17727)**
Great American Woodworks Inc ... 727 375-1212
11445 Pyramid Dr Odessa (33556) **(G-12124)**
Great Atlantic Outfitters ... 904 722-0196
803 North St Jacksonville (32211) **(G-6445)**
Great Bay Distributors Inc ... 727 584-8626
2310 Starkey Rd Holiday (34690) **(G-5741)**
Great Bay Signs Inc ... 727 437-1091
7381 114th Ave Ste 403a Largo (33773) **(G-7964)**
Great Cir Vntures Holdings LLC (PA) ... 305 638-2650
2105 Nw 86th Ave Doral (33122) **(G-3372)**
Great Escape Publishing ... 561 860-8266
101 Se 6th Ave Ste A Delray Beach (33483) **(G-3087)**
Great Hse Mdia Group of Pbls I ... 407 779-3846
4449 Riverton Dr Orlando (32817) **(G-12788)**
Great Lakes Wtr Trtmnt Systems ... 269 381-0210
1000 Wiggins Pass Rd Naples (34110) **(G-11267)**
Great Locations Inc (PA) ... 954 943-1188
2745 E Atl Blvd Ste 305 Pompano Beach (33062) **(G-14718)**
Great Magnet LLC ... 407 260-0591
1701 Winter Green Blvd Winter Park (32792) **(G-19408)**
Great Northern Corporation ... 920 739-3671
1420 Vantage Way S # 100 Jacksonville (32218) **(G-6446)**
Great Northern Rehab PC (PA) ... 352 732-8868
2620 Se Merrycamp Rd Ocala (34471) **(G-11960)**
Great Northern Rehab PC ... 352 732-8868
2620 Se Maricamp Rd Ocala (34471) **(G-11961)**
Great South Timber & Lbr Inc ... 386 752-3774
1135 Se State Road 100 Lake City (32025) **(G-7357)**
Great South Timber & Lbr Inc (PA) ... 386 755-3046
517 Se Baya Dr Lake City (32025) **(G-7358)**
Great Southern Wood Prsv Inc ... 352 793-9410
194 Cr 527a Lake Panasoffkee (33538) **(G-7463)**
Great Virtualworks LLC ... 800 606-6518
4100 Sw 28th Way Fort Lauderdale (33312) **(G-4028)**
Great Western Malting Co ... 360 991-0888
225 S County Line Rd Plant City (33566) **(G-14437)**
Greater 7th Digital Press Inc ... 305 681-2412
14627 Nw 7th Ave Miami (33168) **(G-9662)**
Greater Miami Elks Lodge Inc ... 305 754-5899
5150 Nw 2nd Ave Miami (33127) **(G-9663)**
Greathouse Signs LLC ... 407 247-2668
156 Holly St Apopka (32712) **(G-146)**
Greatwoodworks ... 239 200-4848
19057 Dogwood Rd Fort Myers (33967) **(G-4472)**
Grecian & Company Inc ... 386 344-1967
2988 Nw Us Highway 41 Lake City (32055) **(G-7359)**
Greco Alum Railings USA Inc ... 727 372-4545
9410 Eden Ave Hudson (34667) **(G-6026)**
Greek Island Spice Inc ... 954 761-7161
2905 Sw 2nd Ave Fort Lauderdale (33315) **(G-4029)**
Green Air Controls, Freeport *Also called Green Air Group LLC* **(G-4848)**
Green Air Group LLC ... 850 608-3065
902 State Highway 20 E # 104 Freeport (32439) **(G-4848)**
Green Applications LLC ... 954 900-2290
3233 Sw 2nd Ave Ste 200 Fort Lauderdale (33315) **(G-4030)**
Green Bench Monthly ... 813 417-3944
3018 Jackson St N Saint Petersburg (33704) **(G-15797)**
Green Biofuels LLC ... 305 639-3030
3123 Nw 73rd St Miami (33147) **(G-9664)**
Green Biofuels Miami LLC ... 305 639-3030
3123 Nw 73rd St Ste A-C Miami (33147) **(G-9665)**
Green Bull Products Inc ... 386 402-0409
310 Washington St New Smyrna (32168) **(G-11522)**
Green Bullion Fincl Svcs LLC ... 954 960-7000
3613 N 29th Ave Hollywood (33020) **(G-5830)**
Green Creative LLC ... 866 774-5433
519 Codisco Way Sanford (32771) **(G-16057)**
Green Energy Enterprises Inc (PA) ... 904 309-8993
9300 Normandy Blvd # 511 Jacksonville (32221) **(G-6447)**
Green Essentials LLC ... 786 584-4377
7480 Bird Rd Ste 810 Miami (33155) **(G-9666)**
Green Forest Industries Inc ... 941 721-0504
1365 12th St E Palmetto (34221) **(G-13801)**
Green Forest Products LLC ... 352 341-5500
105 N Apopka Ave Inverness (34450) **(G-6089)**
Green Fuel Systems LLC ... 352 483-5005
24745 Lester Way Eustis (32736) **(G-3708)**
Green Gas America Inc (PA) ... 772 220-0717
2740 Sw Martin Downs Blvd Palm City (34990) **(G-13660)**
Green Global Energy Systems ... 305 253-3413
18868 Sw 80th Ct Cutler Bay (33157) **(G-2396)**
Green Holness, Orlando *Also called Florida Copier Connections* **(G-12748)**
Green Leaf Foods LLC ... 305 308-9167
4050 Sw 145th Ter Miramar (33027) **(G-11001)**
Green Light Printing Inc ... 305 576-5858
151 Nw 36th St Miami (33127) **(G-9667)**
Green Machine ... 772 475-6832
5110 La Salle St Apt A Fort Pierce (34951) **(G-4704)**
Green Marine Fuels Inc ... 305 775-3546
3220 S Dixie Hwy Ste 201 Miami (33133) **(G-9668)**
Green Mountain Specialties ... 386 469-0057
2004 Brunswick Ln 5 Deland (32724) **(G-2982)**
Green Papers Inc ... 305 956-3535
15660 W Dixie Hwy North Miami Beach (33162) **(G-11681)**
Green Plant LLC ... 305 397-9394
3600 Nw 59th St Miami (33142) **(G-9669)**
Green Power Systems LLC ... 904 545-1311
4155 Lakeside Dr Jacksonville (32210) **(G-6448)**
Green Rhino Enrgy Slutions LLC (PA) ... 407 925-5868
1451 Ocoee Apopka Rd Apopka (32703) **(G-147)**
Green Roads of Florida ... 954 626-0574
5150 Sw 48th Way Davie (33314) **(G-2533)**
Green Shades Software Inc ... 904 807-0160
7020 A C Skinner Pkwy Jacksonville (32256) **(G-6449)**
Green Sheet, The, Port Charlotte *Also called Sun Coast Media Group Inc* **(G-15001)**
Green Surfaces, Miami *Also called Blues Design Group LLC* **(G-9262)**
Green Toad Printers, North Miami Beach *Also called Green Papers Inc* **(G-11681)**
Green Touch Industries Inc ... 561 659-5525
100 Us Highway 1 West Palm Beach (33403) **(G-18890)**
Greenco Manufacturing Corp ... 813 882-4400
5688 W Crenshaw St Frnt Tampa (33634) **(G-17728)**
Greencore LLC ... 727 251-9837
970 Tyrone Blvd N Saint Petersburg (33710) **(G-15798)**
Greene Publishing Inc ... 850 973-6397
1695 S State Road 53 Madison (32340) **(G-8451)**
Greenes Reserve Inc ... 954 304-0791
500 Nw 27th Ave Ocala (34475) **(G-11962)**
Greenes Wldg & Fabrication LLC ... 904 773-3101
32 Mink Ave Middleburg (32068) **(G-10905)**
Greengood Energy Corp ... 954 417-6117
3389 Sheridan St Ste 410 Hollywood (33021) **(G-5831)**
Greenie Tots Inc ... 888 316-6126
772 Nw 132nd Ave Plantation (33325) **(G-14522)**
Greenlam America Inc ... 305 640-0388
8750 Nw 36th St Ste 635 Doral (33178) **(G-3373)**
Greenlam Laminates, Doral *Also called Greenlam America Inc* **(G-3373)**
Greens First, Boca Raton *Also called Ceautamed Worldwide LLC* **(G-474)**
Greenscape Laboratories Inc ... 850 723-7496
1311 E La Rua St Pensacola (32501) **(G-14163)**
Greentechnologies LLC (PA) ... 352 379-7780
3926 Nw 34th Dr Gainesville (32605) **(G-4932)**
Greentex America LLC ... 305 908-8580
520 S Dixie Hwy Ofc 120 Hallandale Beach (33009) **(G-5189)**
Greentree Marketing Svcs Inc ... 800 557-9567
1828 Sw 24th Ave Fort Lauderdale (33312) **(G-4031)**
Greenwave Biodiesel LLC ... 239 682-7700
420 W Mcnab Rd Fort Lauderdale (33309) **(G-4032)**
Greenwise Bankcard ... 954 673-0406
4400 W Sample Rd Coconut Creek (33073) **(G-2078)**
Greenwood Lake News Inc (PA) ... 845 477-2575
13032 Pinnacle Ln Hudson (34669) **(G-6027)**
Greenwood Lk & W Milford News, Hudson *Also called Greenwood Lake News Inc* **(G-6027)**
Greg Allens Inc (PA) ... 904 262-8912
7071 Davis Creek Rd Jacksonville (32256) **(G-6450)**

Greg Clark Welding Inc 904 226-2952
6108 Arlington Rd Jacksonville (32211) *(G-6451)*
Greg Franklin Enterprises Inc 904 675-9129
551797 Us Highway 1 Hilliard (32046) *(G-5708)*
Greg Heyen 727 585-8555
8950 131st Ave Largo (33773) *(G-7965)*
Greg Pyle Enterprises, High Springs *Also called Commercial Gates and Elc LLC (G-5700)*
Greg Valentine LLC 239 332-0855
3590 Old Metro Pkwy Fort Myers (33916) *(G-4473)*
Greg Valley 941 739-6628
2010 Whitfield Park Loop Sarasota (34243) *(G-16224)*
Gregg Tool & Die Co Inc 305 685-6309
4725 E 10th Ct Hialeah (33013) *(G-5436)*
Gregomarc LLC 305 559-9777
9772 Sw 8th St Miami (33174) *(G-9670)*
Gregory Michael Genung 850 572-4407
11520 Aruba Dr Pensacola (32506) *(G-14164)*
Gregorys Cabinets Inc 239 450-8840
3470 27th Ave Sw Naples (34117) *(G-11268)*
Gremed Group Corp 305 392-5331
8040 Nw 14th St Doral (33126) *(G-3374)*
Gresso LLC 305 515-8677
495 Brickell Ave Apt 3902 Miami (33131) *(G-9671)*
Grevan Artistic Ventures Inc (PA) 850 243-8111
622 Lovejoy Rd Nw Fort Walton Beach (32548) *(G-4804)*
Greyfield Holdings Inc (PA) 407 830-8861
900 Central Park Dr Sanford (32771) *(G-16058)*
Greylor Dynesco Co Inc 239 574-2011
2340 Andalusia Blvd Cape Coral (33909) *(G-1431)*
Greyson Corp 407 830-7443
726 N Us Highway 17 92 Longwood (32750) *(G-8286)*
Grezzo Usa Llc 954 885-0331
1109 Pelican Ln Hollywood (33019) *(G-5832)*
Gribetz International, Sunrise *Also called Leggett & Platt Incorporated (G-17142)*
Griffin & Holman Inc 904 781-4531
1855 Cassat Ave Ste 8 Jacksonville (32210) *(G-6452)*
GRIFFIN FERTILIZER CO, Frostproof *Also called Ben Hill Griffin Inc (G-4855)*
Griffin Industries LLC 904 964-8083
11313 Se 52nd Ave Starke (32091) *(G-16894)*
Griffin Industries LLC 407 857-5474
408 W Landstreet Rd Orlando (32824) *(G-12789)*
Griffin Industries LLC 813 626-1135
1001 Orient Rd Tampa (33619) *(G-17729)*
Griffin Sawmill & Woodworking 863 241-5180
845 W Lake Wales Rd N Lake Wales (33859) *(G-7512)*
Griffis Lumber LLC 352 372-9965
9333 Nw 13th St Gainesville (32653) *(G-4933)*
Griffis Timber Inc 904 275-2372
11625 Willie Griffis Rd Sanderson (32087) *(G-15981)*
Griffiths Corporation 407 851-8342
10659 Rocket Blvd Orlando (32824) *(G-12790)*
Griffon Graphics Inc 954 922-1800
2117 Hollywood Blvd Hollywood (33020) *(G-5833)*
Grille Tech Inc 305 537-0053
5101 Nw 36th Ave Miami (33142) *(G-9672)*
Grimes Aerospace Company 407 276-6083
12807 Lake Drive Ext Delray Beach (33444) *(G-3088)*
Grind It LLC 813 310-9710
17002 Hanna Rd Lutz (33549) *(G-8386)*
Grinder Wear Parts Inc 503 982-0881
2062 20th Ave Se Largo (33771) *(G-7966)*
Grindhard Coatings Inc 772 221-9986
7850 Sw Ellipse Way Stuart (34997) *(G-16949)*
Grinnell Fire Prtction Systems, Boca Raton *Also called Grinnell LLC (G-552)*
Grinnell LLC (HQ) 561 988-3658
1501 Nw 51st St Boca Raton (33431) *(G-552)*
Grip Tooling Technologies LLC 813 654-6832
1202 Telfair Rd Brandon (33510) *(G-1161)*
Griswold Ready Mix Con Inc 904 751-3796
11660 Camden Rd Jacksonville (32218) *(G-6453)*
Grizzly Manufacturing Inc 386 755-0220
174 Ne Cortez Ter Lake City (32055) *(G-7360)*
Grizzly Printing Parlour LLC 786 416-2494
14244 Sw 90th Ter Miami (33186) *(G-9673)*
Grizzly Products Corp 813 545-3828
4406 W Virginia Ave Tampa (33614) *(G-17730)*
Grms Servicing LLC 850 278-1000
249 Mack Byou Loop Ste 30 Santa Rosa Beach (32459) *(G-16160)*
Grobarty Inc (PA) 786 398-5530
10891 Nw 17th St Unit 133 Miami (33172) *(G-9674)*
Grom Social Enterprises Inc (PA) 561 287-5776
2060 Nw Boca Raton Blvd Boca Raton (33431) *(G-553)*
Groovy Toys LLC 772 878-0790
585 Nw Merc Pl Ste 108 Port Saint Lucie (34986) *(G-15111)*
Grooyi, Port Saint Lucie *Also called Groovy Toys LLC (G-15111)*
Ground Zero Electrostatics Inc (PA) 941 751-7581
8015 34th Ave E Bradenton (34211) *(G-1053)*
Group 32 Dev & Engrg Inc (PA) 305 361-0463
200 Ocean Lane Dr Apt 806 Key Biscayne (33149) *(G-7157)*
Group E Holdings Inc 321 724-0127
2144 Franklin Dr Ne Palm Bay (32905) *(G-13515)*
Group Heros Inc 305 635-0219
5720 Nw 35th Ave Miami (33142) *(G-9675)*
Group III Asphalt Inc 850 983-0611
6108 Wastle Rd Milton (32583) *(G-10931)*
Group Steel Inc (PA) 786 319-1222
3492 W 84th St Hialeah (33018) *(G-5437)*
Group Steel Inc 305 965-0614
2437 Sw 138th Ave Miami (33175) *(G-9676)*
Grove Medical LLC 305 903-6402
11926 Sw 8th St Miami (33184) *(G-9677)*
Grove Power Inc 305 599-2045
158 Doral (33122) *(G-3375)*
Growers Fertilizer Corporation (PA) 863 956-1101
312 N Buena Vista Dr Lake Alfred (33850) *(G-7332)*
Growhealthy Holdings LLC 863 223-8882
324 Datura St West Palm Beach (33401) *(G-18891)*
Growve, Saint Petersburg *Also called Viva 5 LLC (G-15955)*
Grub Company 347 464-9770
6 Fernwood Trl Ormond Beach (32174) *(G-13375)*
Gruenewald Mfg Co Inc 978 777-0200
9800 Se 176th Court Rd Ocklawaha (32179) *(G-12081)*
Grunenthal Services Inc 786 364-6308
1005 Sw 87th Ave Miami (33174) *(G-9678)*
Grupo De Diarios America LLC 305 577-0094
848 Brickell Ave Ste 600 Miami (33131) *(G-9679)*
Grupo Editorial Expansion 305 374-9003
2800 Ponce De Leon Blvd # 1160 Coral Gables (33134) *(G-2153)*
Grupo Erik USA LLC 305 447-2611
3355 W 68th St Apt 120 Hialeah (33018) *(G-5438)*
Grupo Phoenix Corp Svcs LLC (PA) 954 241-0023
2980 Ne 207th St Ste 705 Miami (33180) *(G-9680)*
Gs Cabinets Inc 305 986-4768
3054b Nw 15th St Miami (33125) *(G-9681)*
GS Gelato and Desserts Inc 850 243-5455
1785 Fim Blvd Fort Walton Beach (32547) *(G-4805)*
GSE America LLC (PA) 863 583-4343
3928 Anchuca Dr Ste 3 Lakeland (33811) *(G-7702)*
GSE Jetall Inc 305 688-2111
4821 Nw 128th St Opa Locka (33054) *(G-12321)*
GSM Software Technologies Inc 813 907-2124
20020 Tamiami Ave Tampa (33647) *(G-17731)*
Gssc Inc 727 461-6044
11692 56th Ct N Clearwater (33760) *(G-1706)*
Gt Grandstands Inc 813 305-1415
2810 Sydney Rd Plant City (33566) *(G-14438)*
Gt Ice LLC, Ponte Vedra *Also called 2jcp LLC (G-14922)*
Gt Machining 941 809-5735
1400 Commerce Blvd Ste G Sarasota (34243) *(G-16225)*
Gt Pallets LLC 786 541-6532
958 Nw 73rd St Miami (33150) *(G-9682)*
GT Scale Models Inc 305 310-8998
166 Harbor Dr Key Biscayne (33149) *(G-7158)*
Gt Technologies Inc 850 575-8181
2919 Commonwealth Blvd Tallahassee (32303) *(G-17267)*
Gt Technologies I Inc 850 575-8181
2919 Commonwealth Blvd Tallahassee (32303) *(G-17268)*
GTC Media, Miami *Also called Graphics Type Color Entps Inc (G-9658)*
GTE, Orlando *Also called Gas Turbine Efficiency LLC (G-12772)*
GTE, Orlando *Also called Gas Turbine Efficiency Inc (G-12771)*
Gtechusa Inc 786 281-1803
3390 N 40th St Hollywood (33021) *(G-5834)*
Gtg-Jax LLC 904 861-3290
11801 Central Pkwy Jacksonville (32224) *(G-6454)*
Gtgjfe LLC 904 800-6333
5570 Fl Min Blvd S Ste 1 Jacksonville (32257) *(G-6455)*
Gti Systems Inc (PA) 863 965-2002
1250 Hobbs Rd Auburndale (33823) *(G-245)*
Gto Access Systems LLC 850 575-0176
3121 Hartsfield Rd Tallahassee (32303) *(G-17269)*
Gto Performance Air Boats, Ocala *Also called Good Time Outdoors Inc (G-11958)*
GTS, Shalimar *Also called Global Telemetry Systems Inc (G-16775)*
Guanabana & Co LLC 904 891-5256
8802 Corporate Square Ct # 306 Jacksonville (32216) *(G-6456)*
Guanabana Artisan Ice Pops, Jacksonville *Also called Guanabana & Co LLC (G-6456)*
Guard Dog Valves Inc 239 793-6886
14500 Tamiami Trl E Naples (34114) *(G-11269)*
Guardia LLC (PA) 954 670-2900
5900 N Andrews Ave Ste 10 Fort Lauderdale (33309) *(G-4033)*
Guardian AG Plas Corp 813 286-8680
5401 W Kennedy Blvd # 75 Tampa (33609) *(G-17732)*
Guardian Essentials LLC 817 401-0200
137 Nw 1st Ave Delray Beach (33444) *(G-3089)*
Guardian Fire Equipment, Miami *Also called Target Manufacturing Inc (G-10460)*
Guardian Hurricane Protection 305 805-7050
5729 Nw 159th St Miami Lakes (33014) *(G-10796)*
Guardian Ign Interlock Mfg Inc 321 205-1730
2971 Oxbow Cir Ste A Cocoa (32926) *(G-2028)*

Guardian Industries Cor 954 525-3481
3060 Sw 2nd Ave Fort Lauderdale (33315) ***(G-4034)***
Guardian Manufacturing, Cocoa *Also called Guardian Ign Interlock Mfg Inc* ***(G-2028)***
Guardian Solar LLC 727 504-2790
764 Anclote Rd Ste A Tarpon Springs (34689) ***(G-18304)***
Guerilla Technologies Inc 772 283-0500
4203 Sw High Meadows Ave Palm City (34990) ***(G-13661)***
Guerra Universal Cabinet I 561 317-4079
3324 Sierra Dr Ste A Lake Worth (33461) ***(G-7554)***
Guerrilla Press 352 281-7420
302 Nw 2nd Ave Gainesville (32601) ***(G-4934)***
Guerrilla Prtg Solutions LLC 352 394-7770
304 Mohawk Rd Minneola (34715) ***(G-10954)***
Guest Service Publications Inc 516 333-3474
28026 Pisces Ln Bonita Springs (34135) ***(G-835)***
Guided Particle Systems Inc 727 424-8790
1000 College Blvd Bldg 11 Pensacola (32504) ***(G-14165)***
Guideline Central, Lake Mary *Also called International Guidelines Ctr* ***(G-7425)***
Guild Mfg Solutions LLC 407 366-5165
1005 Lingo Cir Oviedo (32765) ***(G-13433)***
Guimar Inc 305 888-1547
1224 E 4th Ave Hialeah (33010) ***(G-5439)***
Gulf Associates Control Inc 954 426-0536
231 Se 1st Ter Deerfield Beach (33441) ***(G-2833)***
Gulf Atlantic Culvert Company 850 562-2384
5344 Gateway Dr Tallahassee (32303) ***(G-17270)***
Gulf Breeze Apparel LLC 941 488-8337
616 Cypress Ave Venice (34285) ***(G-18551)***
Gulf Breeze News Inc 850 932-8986
913 Gulf Breeze Pkwy # 35 Gulf Breeze (32561) ***(G-5117)***
Gulf Cable LLC 201 720-2417
5700 Industrial Blvd Milton (32583) ***(G-10932)***
Gulf Cast Mtls Sthwest Fla Inc 239 790-0016
16121 Lee Rd Fort Myers (33912) ***(G-4474)***
Gulf Coast Airways Inc 239 403-3020
526 Terminal Dr Naples (34104) ***(G-11270)***
Gulf Coast Aluminum, Fort Myers *Also called Tag Media Group LLC* ***(G-4622)***
Gulf Coast Beach Cams LLC 850 792-4617
12273 Us Highway 98 W Miramar Beach (32550) ***(G-11066)***
Gulf Coast Business Review 941 906-9386
650 Central Ave Ste 5 Sarasota (34236) ***(G-16453)***
Gulf Coast Business World Inc 850 864-1511
3 Racetrack Rd Nw Fort Walton Beach (32547) ***(G-4806)***
Gulf Coast Cabinetry Inc 850 769-3799
22200 Panama Cy Bch Pkwy Panama City Beach (32413) ***(G-13978)***
Gulf Coast Custom Wdwkg Inc 941 343-7883
21301 Washburn Ave Port Charlotte (33952) ***(G-14984)***
Gulf Coast Elc Mtr Svc Inc 850 433-5134
3810 Hopkins St Pensacola (32505) ***(G-14166)***
Gulf Coast Fabricators Inc 850 584-5979
3480 S Byron Butler Pkwy Perry (32348) ***(G-14301)***
Gulf Coast Growers Florida LLC 941 737-2532
2105 S Dock St Palmetto (34221) ***(G-13802)***
Gulf Coast Hyperbarics, Panama City *Also called Gulf Coast Hyperberic Inc* ***(G-13911)***
Gulf Coast Hyperberic Inc 850 271-1441
215 Forest Park Cir Panama City (32405) ***(G-13911)***
Gulf Coast Installers LLC 239 273-4663
28720 S Diesel Dr Bonita Springs (34135) ***(G-836)***
Gulf Coast Mold & Tool Corp 239 643-1017
25190 Bernwood Dr Bonita Springs (34135) ***(G-837)***
Gulf Coast Monuments, Crestview *Also called Gulf Coast Wilbert Inc* ***(G-2350)***
Gulf Coast Non Emergency Trans 239 825-1350
17531 Boat Club Dr Fort Myers (33908) ***(G-4475)***
Gulf Coast Paint & Supplies 813 932-3093
1910 N Us Highway 301 Tampa (33619) ***(G-17733)***
Gulf Coast Pavers, Labelle *Also called Labelle Brick Pavers Tile LLC* ***(G-7319)***
Gulf Coast Precast Inc 239 337-0021
2506 Precast Ct Fort Myers (33916) ***(G-4476)***
Gulf Coast Printing, Largo *Also called Sun Coast Paper & Envelope Inc* ***(G-8062)***
Gulf Coast Printing 239 482-5555
11000 Panther Printing Wa Fort Myers (33908) ***(G-4477)***
Gulf Coast Program 727 945-1402
3515 Alt 19 Ste B Palm Harbor (34683) ***(G-13738)***
Gulf Coast Ready Mix LLC 352 621-3900
8778 W Jump Ct Homosassa (34448) ***(G-6004)***
Gulf Coast Rebar Inc 813 247-1200
1301 E 4th Ave Tampa (33605) ***(G-17734)***
Gulf Coast Shades & Blinds LLC 850 332-2100
714 Roanoke Ct Gulf Breeze (32561) ***(G-5118)***
Gulf Coast Signs Sarasota Inc 941 355-8841
1713 Northgate Blvd Sarasota (34234) ***(G-16454)***
Gulf Coast Timber Company 850 271-8818
8206 S Holland Rd Panama City (32409) ***(G-13912)***
Gulf Coast Truss Co Inc 239 278-1819
6115 Idlewild St Fort Myers (33966) ***(G-4478)***
Gulf Coast Wilbert Inc (PA) 850 682-8004
100 Martin St Crestview (32536) ***(G-2350)***
Gulf Connectors Inc 239 657-2986
160 Airpark Blvd Unit 104 Immokalee (34142) ***(G-6050)***
Gulf Contours Inc 941 639-3933
7500 Golf Course Blvd Punta Gorda (33982) ***(G-15207)***
Gulf County Ship Building Inc 850 229-9300
1550 Old Dynamite Dock Rd Port Saint Joe (32456) ***(G-15080)***
Gulf Electronics 727 595-3840
12155 Meadowbrook Ln Largo (33774) ***(G-7967)***
Gulf Fiberoptics Inc 813 891-1993
448 Commerce Blvd Oldsmar (34677) ***(G-12229)***
Gulf Glo Banners and Signs LLC 850 234-0952
8808 Front Beach Rd Panama City (32407) ***(G-13913)***
Gulf Machining, Clearwater *Also called Walkup Enterprises Inc* ***(G-1935)***
Gulf Machining Inc 727 571-1244
5040 110th Ave N Clearwater (33760) ***(G-1707)***
Gulf Marine Repair Corporation (PA) 813 247-3153
1800 Grant St Tampa (33605) ***(G-17735)***
Gulf Medical Fiberoptics Inc 813 855-6618
448 Commerce Blvd Oldsmar (34677) ***(G-12230)***
Gulf Packaging Co 727 441-1117
1756 Emerald Dr Clearwater (33756) ***(G-1708)***
Gulf Photonics Inc 813 855-6618
448 Commerce Blvd Oldsmar (34677) ***(G-12231)***
Gulf Publishing Company Inc (PA) 727 596-2863
11470 Oakhurst Rd Largo (33774) ***(G-7968)***
Gulf Shore Press LLC 727 641-2920
1997 Timberline Dr Naples (34109) ***(G-11271)***
Gulf South Distributors Inc 850 244-1522
707 Anchors St Nw Fort Walton Beach (32548) ***(G-4807)***
Gulf States Automation Inc 850 475-0724
245 W Airport Blvd Ste B Pensacola (32505) ***(G-14167)***
Gulf Stream Gear, Boca Raton *Also called Super Grafix Inc* ***(G-739)***
Gulf Tool Corporation 850 456-0840
8470 Gulf Beach Hwy Pensacola (32507) ***(G-14168)***
Gulf View Plastics Inc 727 379-3072
18816 Oak Way Dr Hudson (34667) ***(G-6028)***
Gulfcoast Gabber Inc 727 321-6965
1419 49th St S Gulfport (33707) ***(G-5134)***
Gulfcoast Sailing Inc 727 823-1968
1354 20th St N Saint Petersburg (33713) ***(G-15799)***
Gulfport Grind Inc 727 343-2785
5825 20th Ave S Gulfport (33707) ***(G-5135)***
Gulfport Industries Inc 813 885-1000
6308 Benjamin Rd Ste 714 Tampa (33634) ***(G-17736)***
Gulfshore Business 239 887-1930
1421 Pine Ridge Rd # 100 Naples (34109) ***(G-11272)***
Gulfshore Clothier LLC 239 450-8437
201 8th St S Ste 101 Naples (34102) ***(G-11273)***
Gulfshore Custom Woodworks LLC 239 205-0777
1012 Nw 36th Ave Cape Coral (33993) ***(G-1432)***
Gulfstream Alum & Shutter Corp 772 287-6476
1673 Se Pomeroy St Stuart (34997) ***(G-16950)***
Gulfstream Boatworks 239 223-2628
1811 Rhonda St Fort Myers (33901) ***(G-4479)***
Gulfstream Goodwill Inds Inc 561 362-8662
1662 N Federal Hwy Boca Raton (33432) ***(G-554)***
Gulfstream Land Company LLC 772 286-3456
200 Sw Monterey Rd Stuart (34994) ***(G-16951)***
Gulfstream Media Group Inc 954 462-4488
1401 E Broward Blvd # 206 Fort Lauderdale (33301) ***(G-4035)***
Gulfstream Mses Invstmnts Grou 305 975-6186
1535 Biarritz Dr Miami Beach (33141) ***(G-10675)***
Gulfstream Natural Gas Sys LLC 941 723-7000
4610 Buckeye Rd Palmetto (34221) ***(G-13803)***
Gulfstream Shipbuilding LLC 850 835-5125
116 Shipyard Rd Freeport (32439) ***(G-4849)***
Gulfstream Unsnkable Boats LLC 813 820-6100
5251 W Tyson Ave Tampa (33611) ***(G-17737)***
Gulfstream Woodwork LLC 561 231-1810
4901 Georgia Ave West Palm Beach (33405) ***(G-18892)***
Gulfstream Yachts, Tampa *Also called Gulfstream Unsnkable Boats LLC* ***(G-17737)***
Gull Tool & Machine Inc 727 527-0808
3033 47th Ave N Frnt Saint Petersburg (33714) ***(G-15800)***
Gun Drilling of Florida, Largo *Also called Lundy Enterprises Inc* ***(G-8003)***
Gun Vault 850 391-7651
3305 Capital Cir Ne # 103 Tallahassee (32308) ***(G-17271)***
Gunderlin Ltd Inc 305 696-6071
3625 E 11th Ave Hialeah (33013) ***(G-5440)***
Gunn Prtg & Lithography Inc 813 870-6010
4415 W Dr Martin L King Martin Luther Tampa (33614) ***(G-17738)***
Gunns Welding & Fabricating 727 393-5238
4729 96th St N Saint Petersburg (33708) ***(G-15801)***
Gunter Septic Tank Mfg 813 654-1214
1434 E Dr Mrtn Lther King Seffner (33584) ***(G-16730)***
Gurtan Designs 954 972-6100
1048 Sw 4th Ter Pompano Beach (33060) ***(G-14719)***
Gut Armor, Sunrise *Also called Byoscience* ***(G-17102)***
Gutcher's Quickprint, Tampa *Also called Mad Inc* ***(G-17871)***
Guthman Signs LLC 941 218-0023
15777 High Bell Pl Bradenton (34212) ***(G-1054)***
Guthman Signs LLC 941 218-0014
519 Interstate Ct Sarasota (34240) ***(G-16455)***

ALPHABETIC

Gutters Unlimited Plus, Naples *Also called Fox Industries of Swfl Inc* ***(G-11249)***
Guy Gasket Inc......561 703-1774
4446 Carver St Lake Worth (33461) ***(G-7555)***
Guy Wingo Signs......407 578-1132
2682 Pemberton Dr Apopka (32703) ***(G-148)***
Guygiene Group, The, Winter Park *Also called Peter Marcus Paradigm LLC* ***(G-19429)***
Guyton Industries LLC......772 208-3019
14601 Sw 168th Ave Indiantown (34956) ***(G-6073)***
Guyton's Custom Design, Indiantown *Also called Guyton Industries LLC* ***(G-6073)***
Gvi Industries Inc......954 514-7283
620 Ne 24th St Pompano Beach (33064) ***(G-14720)***
Gvi Industries Inc......954 818-6411
350 Nw 55th St Fort Lauderdale (33309) ***(G-4036)***
Gvj Corp......786 224-2808
15120 Sw 159th Ct Miami (33196) ***(G-9683)***
Gw Schultz Tool, Tavares *Also called Gws Tool LLC* ***(G-18340)***
Gwa Alper, Delray Beach *Also called Alper Automotive Inc* ***(G-3044)***
Gwb Coatings LLC......407 271-7732
3612 Danby Ct Orlando (32812) ***(G-12791)***
Gws Tool LLC......352 343-8778
595 County Road 448 Tavares (32778) ***(G-18340)***
Gws Tool Group, Tavares *Also called Gws Tool Holdings LLC* ***(G-18341)***
Gws Tool Holdings LLC (PA)......352 343-8778
595 County Road 448 Tavares (32778) ***(G-18341)***
Gypsum Bd Specialists USA Corp......954 348-8869
241 Nw 217th Way Pembroke Pines (33029) ***(G-14039)***
Gypsum Supply - Tampa, Tampa *Also called Cemex Cnstr Mtls Fla LLC* ***(G-17522)***
Gypsum Supply - Wildwood, Wildwood *Also called Cemex Cnstr Mtls Fla LLC* ***(G-19192)***
Gypsy Mining Inc......772 589-5547
12855 79th Ave Roseland (32957) ***(G-15459)***
Gyro-Gale Inc......772 283-1711
2981 Se Dominica Ter # 4 Stuart (34997) ***(G-16952)***
Gyrosolar Corp......954 554-9990
2655 Edgewater Dr Weston (33332) ***(G-19136)***
Gyrotonic Mfg Inc......305 397-8070
1370 Washington Ave # 307 Miami Beach (33139) ***(G-10676)***
Gyrx LLC......904 641-2599
11222 St Johns Indus Pkwy Jacksonville (32246) ***(G-6457)***
Gz Dumpsters LLC......407 600-0756
1231 Woodridge Ct Altamonte Springs (32714) ***(G-49)***
H & H Gypsum LLC......321 972-5571
371 Oleander Way Ste 1325 Casselberry (32707) ***(G-1504)***
H & H Printing Inc......407 422-2932
1406 W Washington St Orlando (32805) ***(G-12792)***
H & H Products Company......407 299-5410
6600 Magnolia Homes Rd Orlando (32810) ***(G-12793)***
H & H Publishing Co Inc......727 442-7760
1231 Kapp Dr Clearwater (33765) ***(G-1709)***
H & H Signs Inc......941 485-0556
426 E Venice Ave Venice (34285) ***(G-18552)***
H & J Asphalt Inc......305 635-8110
4310 Nw 35th Ave Miami (33142) ***(G-9684)***
H & M Printing Inc......407 831-8030
104 Loren Ct Sanford (32771) ***(G-16059)***
H & M Steel......904 765-3465
9843 Evans Rd Jacksonville (32208) ***(G-6458)***
H & T Global Circuit Fctry LLC......727 327-6236
2510 Terminal Dr S Saint Petersburg (33712) ***(G-15802)***
H & W Creative Colors, Cape Coral *Also called Creative Colors International* ***(G-1407)***
H B Sherman Traps Inc......850 575-8727
3731 Peddie Dr Tallahassee (32303) ***(G-17272)***
H B Tutun Jr Logging Inc......850 584-9324
2930 Old Foley Rd Perry (32348) ***(G-14302)***
H D Quickprint & Disc Off Sups......407 678-1355
2721 Forsyth Rd Ste 101 Winter Park (32792) ***(G-19409)***
H D Quikprint & Disc Off Sups, Winter Park *Also called H D Quickprint & Disc Off Sups* ***(G-19409)***
H Goicoechea Inc......305 805-3333
695 E 10th Ave Hialeah (33010) ***(G-5441)***
H H Terry Co Inc......239 593-0132
4445 Dunlin Ct Naples (34119) ***(G-11274)***
H I T Lighting Corp......772 221-1155
3399 Sw 42nd Ave Palm City (34990) ***(G-13662)***
H Jones Timber LLC......386 312-0603
546 W Peniel Rd Palatka (32177) ***(G-13482)***
H Lamm Industries Inc......954 491-8929
4425 Ne 6th Ter Oakland Park (33334) ***(G-11810)***
H M D, Sanford *Also called Alt Thuyan* ***(G-15991)***
H M J Corporation......954 229-1873
81 Bay Colony Dr Fort Lauderdale (33308) ***(G-4037)***
H Q Inc......941 721-7588
210 9th Street Dr W Palmetto (34221) ***(G-13804)***
H Sixto Distributors Inc......305 688-5242
13301 Nw 38th Ct Opa Locka (33054) ***(G-12322)***
H T I, Belleview *Also called Heat Treating Incorporated* ***(G-370)***
H V Payne Mfg LLC......941 773-1112
164 Cowpen Ln Sarasota (34240) ***(G-16456)***
H&J Asphalt Plant, Miami *Also called H & J Asphalt Inc* ***(G-9684)***
H&K Home Supplies Distrs LLC......786 308-6024
10818 Sw 240th St Homestead (33032) ***(G-5966)***
H&M Phillips Inc......727 797-4600
12772 Burns Dr Odessa (33556) ***(G-12125)***
H&S Swanson Fmly Holdings Inc (HQ)......727 541-3575
9000 68th St N Pinellas Park (33782) ***(G-14352)***
H&T Global Circuits, Saint Petersburg *Also called H & T Global Circuit Fctry LLC* ***(G-15802)***
H-Cyte Inc (PA)......844 633-6839
201 E Kennedy Blvd # 700 Tampa (33602) ***(G-17739)***
H.A.L.o, Orlando *Also called Helping Adlscnts Live Optmstcl* ***(G-12798)***
H2 Home Collection Inc......714 916-9513
1601-1 N Main St # 3159 Jacksonville (32206) ***(G-6459)***
H20logy Inc......904 829-6098
3233 County Road 208 Saint Augustine (32092) ***(G-15547)***
H2c Brands LLC (PA)......904 342-7485
110 Cumberland Park Dr # 205 Saint Augustine (32095) ***(G-15548)***
H2o International Inc......954 570-3464
3001 Sw 15th St Ste C Deerfield Beach (33442) ***(G-2834)***
H2ocean LLC (PA)......866 420-2326
7938 Sw Jack James Dr Stuart (34997) ***(G-16953)***
H2r Corp (PA)......727 541-3444
3921 76th Ave N Pinellas Park (33781) ***(G-14353)***
H317 Logistics LLC......404 307-1621
9019 Somerset Bay Ln # 402 Vero Beach (32963) ***(G-18624)***
Habibco Woodworks LLC......954 659-8501
1049 Nautica Dr Weston (33327) ***(G-19137)***
Hac International Inc......954 584-4530
3911 Sw 47th Ave Ste 914 Davie (33314) ***(G-2534)***
Hailey Cian LLC......954 895-7143
201 Sw 2nd St Fort Lauderdale (33301) ***(G-4038)***
Haines City Mine, Haines City *Also called ER Jahna Industries Inc* ***(G-5142)***
Hairmax Lasercomb, Boca Raton *Also called Lexington International LLC* ***(G-600)***
Haitian Community Yellow Pages, Hollywood *Also called Vive Creole LLC* ***(G-5937)***
Hake Yachts Inc......772 287-3200
4550 Se Hampton Ct Stuart (34997) ***(G-16954)***
Halcyon Aviation Capital LLC......305 615-1575
8350 Nw 52nd Ter Ste 301 Doral (33166) ***(G-3376)***
Halcyon Manufacturing Inc......386 454-0811
24587 Nw 178th Pl High Springs (32643) ***(G-5701)***
Hale Products Inc......352 629-5020
607 Nw 27th Ave Ocala (34475) ***(G-11963)***
Halex Corporation......239 216-4444
2059 Trade Center Way Naples (34109) ***(G-11275)***
Halifax Media Group LLC (HQ)......386 265-6700
2339 Beville Rd Daytona Beach (32119) ***(G-2670)***
Halifax Media Group LLC......941 361-4800
1777 Main St Ste 200 Sarasota (34236) ***(G-16457)***
Halifax Media Holdings LLC (PA)......386 681-2404
901 6th St Daytona Beach (32117) ***(G-2671)***
Halifax Plastic Inc......386 252-2442
221 Fentress Blvd Daytona Beach (32114) ***(G-2672)***
Halkey-Roberts Corporation (HQ)......727 471-4200
2700 Halkey Roberts Pl N Saint Petersburg (33716) ***(G-15803)***
Hall Fountains Inc......954 484-8530
5500 Nw 22nd Ave Fort Lauderdale (33309) ***(G-4039)***
Hall Industries Incorporated......239 768-0372
11850 Regional Ln Unit 6 Fort Myers (33913) ***(G-4480)***
Hall Metal Corp......772 460-0706
4700 Magnum Dr Fort Pierce (34981) ***(G-4705)***
Halldale Media Inc......407 322-5605
735 Primera Blvd Ste 220 Lake Mary (32746) ***(G-7420)***
Halliday Industries LLC......321 288-3979
7715 Ellis Rd Ste A Melbourne (32904) ***(G-8838)***
Halliday Product, Orlando *Also called HP Preferred Ltd Partners* ***(G-12813)***
Halliday Products Inc......407 298-4470
6401 Edgewater Dr Orlando (32810) ***(G-12794)***
Hallmark Emblems Inc......813 223-5427
2401 N Tampa St Tampa (33602) ***(G-17740)***
Hallmark Nameplate Inc......352 383-8142
1717 Lincoln Ave Mount Dora (32757) ***(G-11103)***
Halo Fishing LLC......321 373-2055
520 Atz Rd Malabar (32950) ***(G-8489)***
Haman Industries Inc......813 626-5700
2402 S 54th St Tampa (33619) ***(G-17741)***
Hamant Airboats LLc......321 259-6998
108 E Hibiscus Blvd Melbourne (32901) ***(G-8839)***
Hamburg House Inc......305 557-9913
6157 Nw 167th St Ste F20 Hialeah (33015) ***(G-5442)***
Hamilton Printing Inc......772 334-0151
779 Ne Dixie Hwy Jensen Beach (34957) ***(G-6970)***
Hamilton Sundstrand Corp......860 654-6252
2901 Nw 27th Ave Pompano Beach (33069) ***(G-14721)***
Hammer Haag Steel Inc......727 216-6903
12707 Us Highway 19 N Clearwater (33764) ***(G-1710)***
Hammer Head Group Inc......305 436-5691
8900 Nw 33rd St Ste 100 Doral (33172) ***(G-3377)***
Hammill Post......352 304-8675
8400 Sw 90th St Unit B Ocala (34481) ***(G-11964)***
Hammocks Plaza......305 380-0961
11735 Sw 147th Ave Miami (33196) ***(G-9685)***

Hammond Enterprises......386 575-2402
1460 William St Leesburg (34748) *(G-8160)*
Hammond Kitchens & Bath LLC......321 768-9549
7618 Silver Sands Rd Melbourne (32904) *(G-8840)*
Hamner Parking Lot Service......954 328-3216
2151 Ne 55th St Fort Lauderdale (33308) *(G-4040)*
Hampton Hexane Transfer Stn, Starke *Also called Darling Ingredients Inc (G-16892)*
Hamsard Usa Inc......386 761-1830
2330 S Nova Rd Ste A Daytona Beach (32119) *(G-2673)*
Hamworthy Inc (HQ)......305 597-7520
2900 Sw 42nd St Fort Lauderdale (33312) *(G-4041)*
Hanaya LLC......904 285-7575
543 Le Master Dr Ponte Vedra Beach (32082) *(G-14941)*
Hancor Inc......863 655-5499
115 N West Crown Point Rd Winter Garden (34787) *(G-19266)*
Hand Carved Creations......561 893-0292
5331 N Dixie Hwy Ste 3 Boca Raton (33487) *(G-555)*
Handal Foods LLC......954 753-0649
11822 Nw 30th Ct Coral Springs (33065) *(G-2251)*
Handcraft Woodworking Inc......954 418-6356
1498 Nw 3rd St Deerfield Beach (33442) *(G-2835)*
Handcrafted Pewter, Fort Myers *Also called Bamm Manufacturing Inc (G-4371)*
Hanes-Harris Design Cons......813 237-0202
6106 N Nebraska Ave Ste A Tampa (33604) *(G-17742)*
Hanger Clinic, Tallahassee *Also called Hanger Prsthetcs & Ortho Inc (G-17273)*
Hanger Clinic, Cape Coral *Also called Hanger Prsthtics Orthotics Inc (G-1433)*
Hanger Prsthetcs & Ortho Inc......850 216-2392
2717 Mahan Dr Ste 2 Tallahassee (32308) *(G-17273)*
Hanger Prsthtics Orthotics Inc......239 772-4510
323 Del Prado Blvd S Cape Coral (33990) *(G-1433)*
Hankison......352 273-1220
4647 Sw 40th Ave Ocala (34474) *(G-11965)*
Hanna Pharmaceuticals LLC......813 409-9327
1451 Kensington Woods Dr Lutz (33549) *(G-8387)*
Hans Rudolph Inc......561 877-8775
7185 Briella Dr Boynton Beach (33437) *(G-916)*
Hans-Mill Corp......904 395-2288
5406 W 1st St Jacksonville (32254) *(G-6460)*
Hansa Ophthalmics LLC......305 594-1789
4083 Nw 79th Ave Doral (33166) *(G-3378)*
Hansen Plastics Division, Clearwater *Also called Tuthill Corporation (G-1927)*
Hanson and Bringle Cabinets, Key West *Also called Cayo Hueso Enterprises Inc (G-7181)*
Hanson Lehigh Cement......800 665-6006
575 Cargo Rd Cape Canaveral (32920) *(G-1359)*
Hanson Pipe & Products, Deland *Also called Forterra Pipe & Precast LLC (G-2979)*
Hanteri Enterprises Corp......813 949-8729
1915 Vandervort Rd Lutz (33549) *(G-8388)*
Happy Endings of Miami Inc......305 759-4467
651 Nw 106th St Miami (33150) *(G-9686)*
Happy Kids For Kids Inc......954 730-7922
3722 Nw 16th St Lauderhill (33311) *(G-8111)*
Happy Mix LLC......954 880-0160
8747 Stirling Rd Cooper City (33328) *(G-2112)*
Harberson Rv Pinellas LLC......727 937-6176
2112 Us Highway 19 Holiday (34691) *(G-5742)*
Harbinger, Jacksonville *Also called Quality Neon Sign Company (G-6699)*
Harbor Entps Ltd Lblty Co......229 403-0756
2417 Fleischmann Rd Ste 4 Tallahassee (32308) *(G-17274)*
Harbor Homes......941 320-2670
2624 Marlette St Sarasota (34231) *(G-16458)*
Harbor Imaging......941 883-8383
3430 Tamiami Trl Ste B Port Charlotte (33952) *(G-14985)*
Harbor Linen LLC (HQ)......305 805-8085
10800 Nw 106th St Ste 12 Medley (33178) *(G-8661)*
Harbor Machine Inc......727 772-9515
374 Foxcroft Dr E Palm Harbor (34683) *(G-13739)*
Harbor View Boat Trailers......941 916-3777
17 Callao St Punta Gorda (33983) *(G-15208)*
Harbor Woodworks......727 669-0808
1010 Park Ct Bldg A Safety Harbor (34695) *(G-15495)*
Harborpoint Media LLC (PA)......352 365-8200
212 E Main St Leesburg (34748) *(G-8161)*
Harbortech Plastics LLC......727 944-2425
3151 Grand Blvd Holiday (34690) *(G-5743)*
Harcros Chemicals Inc......813 247-4531
5132 Trenton St Tampa (33619) *(G-17743)*
Hard Chrome Enterprises Inc......561 844-2529
220 10th St Lake Park (33403) *(G-7474)*
Hard Surface Polishing LLC......850 360-4140
5361 Huckleberry Ln Graceville (32440) *(G-5043)*
Harder Prcision Components Inc......727 442-4212
1123 Seminole St Clearwater (33755) *(G-1711)*
Hardie Pipe, Plant City *Also called James Hardie Building Pdts Inc (G-14440)*
Hardrives Industries Inc......561 278-0456
2101 S Congress Ave Delray Beach (33445) *(G-3090)*
Hardware Concepts Inc......305 685-1337
3758 Nw 54th St Miami (33142) *(G-9687)*
Hardware Online Store......954 565-5678
4343 N Andrews Ave Fort Lauderdale (33309) *(G-4042)*
Hardware Parts Corporation......561 994-2121
5030 Champion Blvd 6250 Boca Raton (33496) *(G-556)*
Hardy Logging Company Inc......850 994-1955
3901 Willard Norris Rd Pace (32571) *(G-13469)*
Hare Lumber & Ready Mix Inc......863 983-8725
425 E Haiti Ave Clewiston (33440) *(G-1982)*
Harlen S Woodworking......850 774-2224
1709 Tennessee Ave Lynn Haven (32444) *(G-8433)*
Harley Boat, Bartow *Also called Harley Shipbuilding Corp (G-317)*
Harley Boat Corporation......863 533-2800
300 S 1st Ave Bartow (33830) *(G-316)*
Harley Boats, Bartow *Also called Harley Boat Corporation (G-316)*
Harley Shipbuilding Corp......863 533-2800
300 S 1st Ave Bartow (33830) *(G-317)*
Harmsco Filtration Products, Riviera Beach *Also called Harmsco Inc (G-15331)*
Harmsco Inc (PA)......561 848-9628
7169 49th Ter N Riviera Beach (33407) *(G-15331)*
Harn Ro Systems Inc......941 488-9671
310 Center Ct Venice (34285) *(G-18553)*
Harper Limbach LLC......813 207-0057
9051 Fla Min Blvd Ste 103 Tampa (33634) *(G-17744)*
Harper Screen Enclosures LLC......813 417-5937
11217 Rice Creek Rd Riverview (33569) *(G-15272)*
Harpers Manufacturing Spc......941 629-3490
24730 Sandhill Blvd # 902 Punta Gorda (33983) *(G-15209)*
Harrells LLC (HQ)......863 687-2774
5105 New Tampa Hwy Lakeland (33815) *(G-7703)*
Harris Aerial LLC (PA)......407 725-7886
1043 Seminola Blvd Casselberry (32707) *(G-1505)*
Harris Corporation, Gcsd, Melbourne *Also called L3harris Technologies Inc (G-8869)*
Harris Letterpress, Clearwater *Also called Ironhorse Pressworks Inc (G-1737)*
Harris Lighting, Jacksonville *Also called Harris Manufacturing Inc (G-6461)*
Harris Manufacturing Inc......877 204-7540
9143 Philips Hwy Ste 420 Jacksonville (32256) *(G-6461)*
Harris Woodworks LLC......561 543-3265
4078 Jonquil Cir S Palm Beach Gardens (33410) *(G-13594)*
Harrison Gypsum LLC......850 762-4315
5160 Vermont Rd Marianna (32448) *(G-8578)*
Harrison Logging......352 591-2779
17701 Nw 133rd Court Rd Williston (32696) *(G-19211)*
Harrison Metals Inc......352 588-2436
11640 Corporate Lake Blvd San Antonio (33576) *(G-15973)*
Harry J Honan......405 273-9315
1051 Singer Dr Riviera Beach (33404) *(G-15332)*
Harry Pickett......904 845-4643
37752 Kings Ferry Rd Hilliard (32046) *(G-5709)*
Harsco Corporation......717 506-2071
5950 Old 41a Hwy Tampa (33619) *(G-17745)*
Hart Graphics......727 938-7018
1307 E Lemon St Tarpon Springs (34689) *(G-18305)*
Hart S Ceramic & Stone Inc......850 217-6145
981 Highway 98 E Ste 3 Destin (32541) *(G-3193)*
Hartco Inc......904 353-5259
25 E Beaver St Jacksonville (32202) *(G-6462)*
Hartco International......386 698-4668
2288 S Us Highway 17 Crescent City (32112) *(G-2340)*
Hartley Press Inc......904 398-5141
4250 Saint Augustine Rd Jacksonville (32207) *(G-6463)*
Hartman Windows and Doors LLC......561 296-9600
2107 Blue Heron Blvd W Riviera Beach (33404) *(G-15333)*
Hartmans Canine Center LLC......352 978-6592
6242 Oil Well Rd Clermont (34714) *(G-1963)*
Hartmans Print Center Inc......941 475-2220
2828 S Mccall Rd Ste 37 Englewood (34224) *(G-3661)*
Hartsock Sawmill Inc......352 753-3581
2939 Hartsock Sawmill Rd Lady Lake (32159) *(G-7326)*
Harvest Day Press......727 822-4961
585 Dolphin Ave Se Saint Petersburg (33705) *(G-15804)*
Harvest Moon Distributors LLC......321 297-7942
3450 Parkway Center Ct Orlando (32808) *(G-12795)*
Harvest Print & Bus Svcs Inc......850 681-2488
1613 Capital Cir Ne Tallahassee (32308) *(G-17275)*
Harvest Print Mktg Sltions LLC......850 681-2488
1613 Capital Cir Ne Tallahassee (32308) *(G-17276)*
Harvest Printing, Tallahassee *Also called Harvest Print Mktg Sltions LLC (G-17276)*
Harvest Prtg & Copy Ctr Inc......850 681-2488
1613 Capital Cir Ne Tallahassee (32308) *(G-17277)*
Harvey Branker and Assoc PA......954 966-4445
3816 Hollywood Blvd # 203 Hollywood (33021) *(G-5835)*
Harvey Covington Thomas S Fla, Hollywood *Also called Harvey Branker and Assoc PA (G-5835)*
Harwil Fixtures Inc......904 692-1051
103 W Saint Johns Ave Hastings (32145) *(G-5228)*
Hasbro Latin America Inc (HQ)......305 931-3180
5200 Blue Lagoon Dr Fl 10 Miami (33126) *(G-9688)*
Hascall Engineering and Mfg Co......941 723-2833
1608 20th Ave E Palmetto (34221) *(G-13805)*
Hascall-Denke, Palmetto *Also called Denke Laboratories Inc (G-13795)*

ALPHABETIC

Hatalom Corporation...407 567-2556
3505 Lake Lynda Dr # 200 Orlando (32817) ***(G-12796)***
Hatch Enterprises Inc...386 935-1419
8199 Us Highway 27 Branford (32008) ***(G-1186)***
HATCH LIGHTING, Tampa *Also called Hatch Transformers Inc* ***(G-17746)***
Hatch Transformers Inc...813 288-8006
7821 Woodland Center Blvd Tampa (33614) ***(G-17746)***
Hathaspace, Tampa *Also called Atitlan Enterprises LLC* ***(G-17442)***
Haute Living Inc...305 798-1373
999 Brickell Ave Ste 520 Miami (33131) ***(G-9689)***
Havana Dream Cigars, Miami *Also called Havana Dreams LLC* ***(G-9690)***
Havana Dreams LLC...305 322-7599
2621 Sw 132nd Ave Miami (33175) ***(G-9690)***
Haven Coffee Roasters LLC...863 251-9619
140 3rd St Sw Winter Haven (33880) ***(G-19327)***
Hawk Protection Incorporated...954 980-9631
1020 Sw 98th Ave Pembroke Pines (33025) ***(G-14040)***
Hawk Racing...941 209-1790
6060 28th St E Ste 5 Bradenton (34203) ***(G-1055)***
Hawkhead International Inc...904 264-4295
90 Industrial Loop N Orange Park (32073) ***(G-12396)***
Hawks Nuts Inc...813 872-0900
4713 N Hale Ave Tampa (33614) ***(G-17747)***
Hawks Orgnal Jmbo Bled Peanuts, Tampa *Also called Hawks Nuts Inc* ***(G-17747)***
Hawver Aluminum Foundry Inc...813 961-1497
9526 N Trask St Tampa (33624) ***(G-17748)***
Hay Tech...850 592-2424
6468 Wolf Pond Rd Bascom (32423) ***(G-336)***
Hayes Ivy Manufacturing...954 306-2647
200 Sw 1st Ave Ste 960 Fort Lauderdale (33301) ***(G-4043)***
Hayes Less Lethal LLC...561 201-2186
18955 Se Homewood Ave Tequesta (33469) ***(G-18385)***
Hayman Safe Co Inc...407 365-5434
1291 N County Road 426 Oviedo (32765) ***(G-13434)***
Hazmat Software LLC...407 416-5434
760 Heather Glen Cir Lake Mary (32746) ***(G-7421)***
HB Fuller Cnstr Pdts Inc...352 372-3931
1913 Nw 60th Ln Gainesville (32653) ***(G-4935)***
HB Sealing Products Inc (HQ)...727 796-1300
420 Park Place Blvd # 100 Clearwater (33759) ***(G-1712)***
HB Tuten Jr Logging Inc...850 584-9324
3870 S Byron Butler Pkwy Perry (32348) ***(G-14303)***
Hbp Pipe & Precast LLC...904 529-8228
4210 Highway 17 S Us Green Cove Springs (32043) ***(G-5064)***
Hbt Forestry Services Inc...850 584-9324
2930 Old Foley Rd Perry (32348) ***(G-14304)***
Hbys Enterprises LLC...855 290-9900
1170 Tree Swallow Dr # 347 Winter Springs (32708) ***(G-19473)***
Hc Grupo Inc...954 227-0150
2929 N University Dr # 105 Coral Springs (33065) ***(G-2252)***
Hci Books, Deerfield Beach *Also called Health Communications Inc* ***(G-2836)***
Hco Holding I Corporation...863 533-0522
2701 State Road 60 W Bartow (33830) ***(G-318)***
Hcr Software Solutions Inc...904 638-6177
13400 Sutton Park Dr S # 1101 Jacksonville (32224) ***(G-6464)***
HCW Biologics Inc...954 842-2024
2929 N Commerce Pkwy Miramar (33025) ***(G-11002)***
HCW Therapeutics, Miramar *Also called HCW Biologics Inc* ***(G-11002)***
Hd Kit, Medley *Also called IESC Diesel Corp* ***(G-8668)***
Hd Signs & Lighting...850 484-9829
9400 N Davis Hwy Pensacola (32514) ***(G-14169)***
Hdd LLC...561 346-9054
412 Clematis St West Palm Beach (33401) ***(G-18893)***
Hdh Agri Products LLC...352 343-3484
27536 County Road 561 Tavares (32778) ***(G-18342)***
Hdl Therapeutics Inc...772 453-2770
601 21st St Ste 300 Vero Beach (32960) ***(G-18625)***
He Instruments LLC...561 832-1249
3677 23rd Ave S Ste B107 Lake Worth Beach (33461) ***(G-7612)***
Headhunter Inc...954 462-5953
3380 Sw 11th Ave Fort Lauderdale (33315) ***(G-4044)***
Headhunter Spearfishing Co...954 745-0747
1140 Ne 7th Ave Unit 6 Fort Lauderdale (33304) ***(G-4045)***
Headwaters Management LLC...608 209-3111
1160 N Federal Hwy # 214 Fort Lauderdale (33304) ***(G-4046)***
Headwaters Wine and Spirits, Fort Lauderdale *Also called Headwaters Management LLC* ***(G-4046)***
Headwear International, Miami Lakes *Also called Ladove Inc* ***(G-10803)***
Heal and Shine Inc...561 801-3423
11648 Orange Grove Blvd Royal Palm Beach (33411) ***(G-15469)***
Health & Muscles...305 225-2929
14144 Sw 8th St Miami (33184) ***(G-9691)***
Health Communications Inc...954 360-0909
3201 Sw 15th St Deerfield Beach (33442) ***(G-2836)***
Health Robotics Canada LLC...786 388-5339
6303 Blue Lagoon Dr # 310 Miami (33126) ***(G-9692)***
Health Star Inc...321 914-6012
625 E Merritt Ave Ste I Merritt Island (32953) ***(G-9002)***
Healtheintentions Inc (PA)...954 394-8867
500 Ne 185th St Unit 8 Miami (33179) ***(G-9693)***
Healthier Choices MGT Corp (PA)...305 600-5004
3800 N 28th Way Hollywood (33020) ***(G-5836)***
Healthline Medical Pdts Inc...407 656-0704
1065 E Story Rd Winter Garden (34787) ***(G-19267)***
Healthlink, Jacksonville *Also called Clorox Healthcare Holdings LLC* ***(G-6270)***
Healthquest Technologies LLC...850 997-6300
1817 W Capps Hwy Monticello (32344) ***(G-11076)***
Healthy Schools LLC...904 887-4540
3546 Saint Johns Bluff Rd Jacksonville (32224) ***(G-6465)***
Hear For You Hearing Aid Ctr...850 316-4414
1805 Creighton Rd Ste 1 Pensacola (32504) ***(G-14170)***
Heara Inc...305 651-5200
19595 Ne 10th Ave Ste H Miami (33179) ***(G-9694)***
Heartland Metals Inc...863 465-7501
127 Ranier Dr Lake Placid (33852) ***(G-7488)***
Heartway USA, Fort Myers *Also called Imc-Heartway LLC* ***(G-4489)***
Heat Treating Incorporated...352 245-8811
6740 Se 110th St Unit 508 Belleview (34420) ***(G-370)***
Heat-Pipe Technology Inc...813 470-4250
6904 Parke East Blvd Tampa (33610) ***(G-17749)***
Heath Corporation...863 638-1819
1303 Meyers Rd Lake Wales (33859) ***(G-7513)***
Heavy Hwy Infrastructure LLC...407 323-8853
2210 W 25th St Sanford (32771) ***(G-16060)***
Hec America Inc...786 543-9238
4919 Sw 147th Pl Miami (33185) ***(G-9695)***
Hecht Rubber Corporation...904 731-3401
6161 Philips Hwy Jacksonville (32216) ***(G-6466)***
Hector & Hector Inc...305 629-8864
6790 Nw 84th Ave Miami (33166) ***(G-9696)***
Hector Corporation...786 308-5853
2127 Nw 88th St Miami (33147) ***(G-9697)***
Hedrick-Walker & Associates...352 735-2600
3425 Lake Center Dr Ste 2 Mount Dora (32757) ***(G-11104)***
Heet, Palm Beach Gardens *Also called Pret-EE LLC* ***(G-13617)***
Heico Aerospace Corporation (HQ)...954 987-6101
3000 Taft St Hollywood (33021) ***(G-5837)***
Heico Aerospace Holdings Corp (HQ)...954 987-4000
3000 Taft St Hollywood (33021) ***(G-5838)***
Heico Aerospace Holdings Corp...305 463-0455
7875 Nw 64th St Miami (33166) ***(G-9698)***
Heico Aerospace Parts Corp...440 995-3661
300 Taft St Hollywood (33019) ***(G-5839)***
Heico Company, Tampa *Also called Leader Tech Inc* ***(G-17838)***
Heico Component Repair Group, Miami *Also called Northwings Accessories Corp* ***(G-10078)***
Heico Corporation...305 374-1745
825 Brickell Bay Dr # 1643 Miami (33131) ***(G-9699)***
Heico Corporation...305 463-0455
7900 Nw 64th St Miami (33166) ***(G-9700)***
Heico Corporation (PA)...954 987-4000
3000 Taft St Hollywood (33021) ***(G-5840)***
Heico Electronic Tech Corp (HQ)...954 987-6101
3000 Taft St Hollywood (33021) ***(G-5841)***
Heico Electronic Tech Group, Hollywood *Also called Heico Electronic Tech Corp* ***(G-5841)***
Heico Flight Support Corp (HQ)...954 987-4000
3000 Taft St Hollywood (33021) ***(G-5842)***
Heico Parts Group, Hollywood *Also called Jet Avion Corporation* ***(G-5854)***
Heights Tower Systems Inc...850 455-1210
1529 Gulf Beach Hwy Pensacola (32507) ***(G-14171)***
Heisler Hardwood Inc...727 410-0401
1838 N Washington Ave Clearwater (33755) ***(G-1713)***
Heli Aviation Florida LLC...941 355-1525
8191 N Tamiami Trl Sarasota (34243) ***(G-16226)***
Heli-Tech Inc...850 763-9000
3621 Frankford Ave Panama City (32405) ***(G-13914)***
Helical Communication Tech Inc...561 762-2823
634 Barnes Blvd Ste 206 Rockledge (32955) ***(G-15416)***
Helicopter Helmet LLC (PA)...843 556-0405
274 West Dr Melbourne (32904) ***(G-8841)***
Helicopter Helmets.com, Melbourne *Also called Helicopter Helmet LLC* ***(G-8841)***
Helios Technologies Inc (PA)...941 362-1200
1500 W University Pkwy Sarasota (34243) ***(G-16227)***
Hell's Bay Boatworks, Titusville *Also called Hells Bay Marine Inc* ***(G-18433)***
Heller Cabinetry Inc...321 729-9690
415 Stan Dr Melbourne (32904) ***(G-8842)***
Hells Bay Boatworks LLC...321 383-8223
1520 Chaffee Dr Titusville (32780) ***(G-18432)***
Hells Bay Marine Inc...321 383-8223
1520 Chaffee Dr Titusville (32780) ***(G-18433)***
Helms Hauling & Materials Llc...850 218-6895
1423 Pine St Niceville (32578) ***(G-11569)***
Helms Hauling and Materials, Niceville *Also called Helms Hauling & Materials Llc* ***(G-11569)***
Helou Regino Publisher LLC...407 370-7300
7061 Grand National Dr 105b Orlando (32819) ***(G-12797)***
Helping Adlscnts Live Optmstcl...407 257-8221
4844 Cason Cove Dr # 204 Orlando (32811) ***(G-12798)***

Hemarus Llc-Jcksnvle Plsma Ctr ... 904 642-1005
601 Heritage Dr 118 Jupiter (33458) *(G-7052)*
Hemco Industries Inc (PA) ... 305 769-0606
2500 Ne 135th St Ph 5 North Miami (33181) *(G-11641)*
Hemingway Rum Company LLC (PA) ... 305 414-8754
201 Simonton St Key West (33040) *(G-7189)*
Hemp Cbd Daily Inc ... 904 672-7623
13724 Shady Woods St N Jacksonville (32224) *(G-6467)*
Hemp Pantry, Inverness *Also called Jans Ventures LLC (G-6090)*
Henderson Machine Inc ... 954 419-9789
1809 S Powerline Rd # 110 Deerfield Beach (33442) *(G-2837)*
Henderson Prestress Con Inc ... 727 938-2828
822 Anclote Rd Tarpon Springs (34689) *(G-18306)*
Hendrix Maintenance & Repr LLC ... 863 647-3511
3705 Century Blvd Ste 6 Lakeland (33811) *(G-7704)*
Hendry Corporation ... 813 241-9206
1800 Grant St Tampa (33605) *(G-17750)*
Hendry Marine Industries Inc ... 813 241-9206
1800 Grant St Tampa (33605) *(G-17751)*
Hendry Shipyard Joint Ventr 1 ... 813 241-9206
1800 Grant St Tampa (33605) *(G-17752)*
Henefelt Precision Products ... 727 531-0406
8475 Ulmerton Rd Largo (33771) *(G-7969)*
Henjaty Publishing Co ... 305 633-9993
3824 Nw 15th Ave Miami (33142) *(G-9701)*
Henley Metal LLC ... 904 353-4770
6593 Powers Ave Ste 23 Jacksonville (32217) *(G-6468)*
Henry W Long ... 352 542-7068
264 Se 752nd Ave Old Town (32680) *(G-12197)*
Henrys Hickory House Inc ... 904 493-4420
249 Copeland St Jacksonville (32204) *(G-6469)*
Henscratch Farms Inc ... 863 699-2060
980 Henscratch Rd Lake Placid (33852) *(G-7489)*
Henscratch Farms Winery, Lake Placid *Also called Henscratch Farms Inc (G-7489)*
Hensoldt Avionics Usa LLC ... 941 306-1328
2480 Fruitville Rd Ste 6 Sarasota (34237) *(G-16459)*
Hentzen Coatings Inc ... 727 572-4474
5182 126th Ave N Clearwater (33760) *(G-1714)*
Hepburn Industries Inc ... 305 757-6688
300 Ne 59th St Miami (33137) *(G-9702)*
Hera Cases LLC ... 305 322-8960
6901 Edgewater Dr Apt 315 Coral Gables (33133) *(G-2154)*
Hera Cases LLC ... 305 714-2274
10 Nw 42nd Ave Ste 700 Miami (33126) *(G-9703)*
Herald-Advocate Publishing Co ... 863 773-3255
115 S 7th Ave Wauchula (33873) *(G-18693)*
Heralpin Usa Inc ... 305 218-0174
10570 Nw 27th St Ste H101 Doral (33172) *(G-3379)*
Herbert Pavers Inc ... 941 447-4909
3031 46th Ave E Bradenton (34203) *(G-1056)*
Herbko Inc ... 305 932-3572
3000 Island Blvd Ph 5 Aventura (33160) *(G-273)*
Herco Sheet Metal Inc ... 850 244-7424
201 Northampton Cir Fort Walton Beach (32547) *(G-4808)*
Herco Sheet Metal., Fort Walton Beach *Also called Herco Sheet Metal Inc (G-4808)*
Hercules Sealing Products, Clearwater *Also called HB Sealing Products Inc (G-1712)*
Herff Jones, Winter Park *Also called Herff Jones Inc (G-19410)*
Herff Jones Inc ... 407 647-4373
112 N Wymore Rd Winter Park (32789) *(G-19410)*
Herff Jones LLC ... 904 641-4060
12086 Fort Caroline Rd # 201 Jacksonville (32225) *(G-6470)*
Herff Jones LLC ... 727 527-0696
4200 31st St N Saint Petersburg (33714) *(G-15805)*
Heritage Centl Fla Jewish News ... 407 834-8277
207 Obrien Rd Ste 101 Fern Park (32730) *(G-3729)*
Heritage Manufacturing Svcs ... 727 906-5599
4365 22nd St N Saint Petersburg (33714) *(G-15806)*
Heritage Medcall LLC ... 813 221-1000
202 E Virginia Ave Tampa (33603) *(G-17753)*
Heritage Newspaper, Fern Park *Also called Heritage Centl Fla Jewish News (G-3729)*
Heritage Plastics, Tampa *Also called Atkore Plastic Pipe Corp (G-17443)*
Heritage Publishing Inc ... 904 296-1304
6620 Sthpint Dr S Ste 310 Jacksonville (32216) *(G-6471)*
Heritage Signs ... 904 529-7446
1282 Energy Cove Ct Green Cove Springs (32043) *(G-5065)*
Heritage Skin Care Inc ... 305 757-9264
180 Ne 99th St Miami Shores (33138) *(G-10885)*
Herman Cabinets Inc ... 727 459-6730
1000 Belcher Rd S Largo (33771) *(G-7970)*
Herman Group, Bradenton *Also called Spraying Systems Co (G-1119)*
Hermes 7 Communications LLC ... 954 426-1998
430 W Hillsboro Blvd Deerfield Beach (33441) *(G-2838)*
Hermes Technical Intl Inc ... 305 477-8993
8227 Nw 54th St Doral (33166) *(G-3380)*
Hernandez Metal Fabricators ... 305 970-4145
15062 Sw 9th Way Miami (33194) *(G-9704)*
Hernandez Mobile Welding Inc ... 954 347-4071
20320 Nw 258th St Okeechobee (34972) *(G-12181)*
Hernandez Ornamental Inc ... 305 592-7296
1910 Nw 96th Ave Doral (33172) *(G-3381)*
Hernandez Printing Service ... 305 642-0483
1771 W Flagler St Miami (33135) *(G-9705)*
Hernando Litho Printing, Brooksville *Also called Hernando Lithoprinting Inc (G-1233)*
Hernando Lithoprinting Inc ... 352 796-4136
969 Hale Ave Brooksville (34601) *(G-1233)*
Hernol Usa Inc ... 786 263-3341
201 Alhambra Cir Ste 6 Coral Gables (33134) *(G-2155)*
Hernon Manufacturing Inc ... 407 322-4000
121 Tech Dr Sanford (32771) *(G-16061)*
Heroal USA Inc ... 888 437-6257
7022 Tpc Dr Ste 100 Orlando (32822) *(G-12799)*
Herpel Inc (PA) ... 561 585-5573
6400 Georgia Ave West Palm Beach (33405) *(G-18894)*
Hes Products Inc ... 407 834-0741
87 Old Wiggins Ln Ormond Beach (32174) *(G-13376)*
Hess Express ... 772 335-9975
10453 S Us Highway 1 Port Saint Lucie (34952) *(G-15112)*
Hess Station 09307 ... 407 891-7156
4500 13th St Saint Cloud (34769) *(G-15653)*
Hexskin LLC ... 305 901-1573
1901 Brickell Ave B201 Miami (33129) *(G-9706)*
Hey Day ... 305 763-8660
1825 West Ave Miami Beach (33139) *(G-10677)*
Hf Scientific Inc ... 888 203-7248
16260 Arprt Pk Dr Ste 140 Fort Myers (33913) *(G-4481)*
Hg Brokerage Services Inc ... 407 294-3507
2813 S Hiawassee Rd # 301 Orlando (32835) *(G-12800)*
HG Trading Cia Inc ... 305 986-5702
1055 Se 9th Ter Hialeah (33010) *(G-5443)*
Hg2 Emergency Lighting LLC ... 407 426-7700
477 N Semoran Blvd Orlando (32807) *(G-12801)*
HGP Industries, Tampa *Also called Oldcastle Buildingenvelope Inc (G-17951)*
HI Tech Aviation Welding LLC ... 305 591-3393
8060 Nw 67th St Miami (33166) *(G-9707)*
HI Tech Construction Svc Inc ... 863 968-0731
5540 Commercial Blvd Winter Haven (33880) *(G-19328)*
HI Tech Granite and Marble ... 407 230-4363
11362 Space Blvd Orlando (32837) *(G-12802)*
HI Tech Printing Systems Inc ... 954 933-9155
3411 Ne 6th Ter Pompano Beach (33064) *(G-14722)*
HI Tech Welding, Miami *Also called HI Tech Aviation Welding LLC (G-9707)*
Hi-TEC Laboratories Inc ... 850 835-6822
9646 State Highway 20 W Freeport (32439) *(G-4850)*
Hialeah Distribution Corp ... 786 200-2498
270 W 25th St Hialeah (33010) *(G-5444)*
Hialeah Plating ... 305 953-4143
4335 E 10th Ave Hialeah (33013) *(G-5445)*
Hialeah Powder Coating Corp ... 786 275-4107
1690 W 33rd Pl Hialeah (33012) *(G-5446)*
Hialeah Welding & Ornamental ... 305 685-3196
4295 E 11th Ave Hialeah (33013) *(G-5447)*
Hicks Industries Inc (PA) ... 863 425-4155
2005 Industrial Park Rd Mulberry (33860) *(G-11125)*
Hicks Industries Inc ... 954 226-5148
2257 Sw 66th Ter Davie (33317) *(G-2535)*
Hidalgo Corp ... 305 379-0110
14 Ne 1st Ave Ste 805 Miami (33132) *(G-9708)*
Hidalgo Jewelry, Miami *Also called Hidalgo Corp (G-9708)*
Hidenet Scrities Architectures, West Palm Beach *Also called Bionitrogen Holdings Corp (G-18820)*
Higgins Group Corp ... 305 681-4444
3198 Nw 125th St Miami (33167) *(G-9709)*
High End Cabinets LLC ... 561 469-8237
4715 Georgia Ave West Palm Beach (33405) *(G-18895)*
High End Defense Solutions LLC ... 305 591-7795
2201 Nw 102nd Pl Ste 4 Doral (33172) *(G-3382)*
High Export, Doral *Also called AMC Development Group LLC (G-3245)*
High Five Products Inc ... 239 449-9268
7361 Lantana Way Naples (34119) *(G-11276)*
High Noon Holsters, Holiday *Also called High Noon Unlimited Inc (G-5744)*
High Noon Unlimited Inc ... 727 939-2701
4339 Buena Vista Ln Holiday (34691) *(G-5744)*
High Performance Boats & Cars, Fort Myers *Also called P B C H Incorporated (G-4560)*
High Performance Holdings Ltd ... 815 874-9421
625 Mccue Rd Ste 1 Lakeland (33815) *(G-7705)*
High Performance Systems Inc ... 863 294-5566
1201 Amercn Superior Blvd Winter Haven (33880) *(G-19329)*
High Power Services, Saint Petersburg *Also called David Chittum (G-15756)*
High Sierra Terminaling LLC ... 954 764-8818
1200 Se 20th St Fort Lauderdale (33316) *(G-4047)*
High Standard Aviation Inc ... 305 599-8855
5900 Nw 97th Ave Unit 3 Doral (33178) *(G-3383)*
High Tech Hoist Corp ... 321 733-3387
3682 N Wickham Rd 225 Melbourne (32935) *(G-8843)*
High Temp Industries ... 215 794-0864
3808 Sw 6th Ter Cape Coral (33991) *(G-1434)*

High Top Products Corp 305 633-3287
8187 Nw 8th St Apt 108 Miami (33126) *(G-9710)*
High Velocity, Naples *Also called Sano Associates Inc (G-11391)*
High Yield AG Solutions LLC 407 592-8089
735 Primera Blvd Ste 200 Lake Mary (32746) *(G-7422)*
Highland Cabinet Inc 863 385-4396
739 Glenwood Ave Sebring (33870) *(G-16694)*
Highland Cabinet Shop, Sebring *Also called Highland Cabinet Inc (G-16694)*
Highland Mint, Indian Harbour Beach *Also called Bullion International Inc (G-6063)*
Highlander Stone Corp 786 333-1151
14105 Nw 19th Ave Opa Locka (33054) *(G-12323)*
Highlands Ethanol LLC 813 421-1090
2202 N West Shore Blvd Tampa (33607) *(G-17754)*
Highroller Fishing Lure Co LLC 352 215-2925
4630 Nw 30th St Gainesville (32605) *(G-4936)*
Highseer.com, Doral *Also called Parker Davis Hvac Intl Inc (G-3455)*
Hightec Con Pavers & Curbing 941 412-6077
290 E Langsner St Englewood (34223) *(G-3678)*
Highvac Co LLC 407 969-0399
3842 Commerce Loop Orlando (32808) *(G-12803)*
Highway Systems Incorporated 813 907-7512
4450 Pet Ln Lutz (33559) *(G-8389)*
Hilcraft Engraving Inc 305 871-6100
3960 Nw 26th St Miami (33142) *(G-9711)*
Hill Dermaceuticals Inc 407 323-1887
2650 S Mellonville Ave Sanford (32773) *(G-16062)*
Hill Donnelly Corporation (PA) 800 525-1242
10126 Windhorst Rd Tampa (33619) *(G-17755)*
Hill Enterprises LLC 850 478-4455
125 Terry Dr Pensacola (32503) *(G-14172)*
Hill Labs Inc 407 323-1887
2650 S Mellonville Ave Sanford (32773) *(G-16063)*
Hill Printing Inc 407 654-4282
1220 Wntr Gdn Vnlnd Rd # 104 Winter Garden (34787) *(G-19268)*
Hilliard Bruce Vineyards LLC 305 979-2601
1521 Alton Rd Ste 842 Miami Beach (33139) *(G-10678)*
Hills Inc 321 723-5560
7785 Ellis Rd Melbourne (32904) *(G-8844)*
Hillshire Brands Company 321 637-9765
3860 Curtis Blvd Ste 614 Cocoa (32927) *(G-2029)*
Hilomast LLC 386 668-6784
402 Chairman Ct Ste 100 Debary (32713) *(G-2749)*
Hilton International Inds 941 371-2600
6055 Porter Way Sarasota (34232) *(G-16460)*
Hilton Software LLC 954 323-2244
2730 N University Dr Coral Springs (33065) *(G-2253)*
Hiltronics Corporation 954 341-9100
3979 Nw 126th Ave Coral Springs (33065) *(G-2254)*
Himes Signs Inc 850 837-1159
4 Commerce Dr Ste 4 # 4 Destin (32541) *(G-3194)*
Himgc Limited 213 443-8729
1301 Beville Rd Daytona Beach (32119) *(G-2674)*
Himmel Losungen Group Hlg LLC 786 631-5531
4711 Nw 79th Ave Ste 12l Doral (33166) *(G-3384)*
Hinckley 239 919-8142
535 5th Ave S Naples (34102) *(G-11277)*
Hine Automation LLC 813 749-7519
12495 34th St N Ste B Saint Petersburg (33716) *(G-15807)*
Hines Bending Systems Inc 239 433-2132
6441 Metro Plantation Rd Fort Myers (33966) *(G-4482)*
Hines Energy Complex 863 519-6106
7700 County Road 555 S Bartow (33830) *(G-319)*
Hinsilblon Ltd Inc 239 418-1133
12381 S Cleveland Ave Fort Myers (33907) *(G-4483)*
Hinsilblon Laboratories, Fort Myers *Also called Hinsilblon Ltd Inc (G-4483)*
Hipaat International Inc 905 405-6299
340 9th St N Naples (34102) *(G-11278)*
Hippo Tampa LLC 813 391-9152
605 Bosphorous Ave Tampa (33606) *(G-17756)*
Hire Authority 561 477-6663
8445 Miller Dr Miami (33155) *(G-9712)*
His, Pinellas Park *Also called HIS Cabinetry Inc (G-14354)*
HIS Cabinetry Inc 727 527-7262
6200 49th St N Pinellas Park (33781) *(G-14354)*
Hisco Pump South LLC 904 786-4488
2664 Robert St Jacksonville (32207) *(G-6472)*
Hispacom Inc 954 255-2622
9900 W Sample Rd Ste 200 Coral Springs (33065) *(G-2255)*
Hispanic Certified Foods Inc 305 772-6815
1741 Nw 33rd St Pompano Beach (33064) *(G-14723)*
Hit Promotional Products Inc (PA) 727 541-5561
7150 Bryan Dairy Rd Largo (33777) *(G-7971)*
Hitachi Cable America Inc 850 476-0907
9101 Ely St Pensacola (32514) *(G-14173)*
Hitachi Rail STS Usa Inc 415 397-7010
11150 Nw 122nd St Medley (33178) *(G-8662)*
Hitachi Rail Usa Inc (PA) 415 397-7010
11150 Nw 122nd St Medley (33178) *(G-8663)*
Hitech Truss Inc 352 797-0877
6179 Nature Coast Blvd Brooksville (34602) *(G-1234)*
Hitek Property LLC 352 797-0877
6179 Nature Coast Blvd Brooksville (34602) *(G-1235)*
Hitek Truss, Brooksville *Also called Hitech Truss Inc (G-1234)*
Hitex Marketing Group Inc 305 406-1150
1566 Nw 108th Ave Miami (33172) *(G-9713)*
Hitking Sports LLC 941 661-2753
10100 Paradise Blvd Treasure Island (33706) *(G-18475)*
Hitman Industries LLC 321 735-8562
185 Gus Hipp Blvd Rockledge (32955) *(G-15417)*
Hitmaster Graphics LLC 813 250-0555
1706 W Fig St Tampa (33606) *(G-17757)*
Hizer Machine Mfg Inc 386 755-3155
12137 Se Us Highway 41 White Springs (32096) *(G-19187)*
Hjr Industries LLC 706 761-1200
12726 Kings Lake Dr Gibsonton (33534) *(G-5029)*
Hki Soundigital USA LLC 786 600-1056
345 Bryan Rd Dania (33004) *(G-2446)*
HM Factory LLC 305 897-0004
2952 Nw 72nd Ave Miami (33122) *(G-9714)*
HM Froyos LLC 561 339-0603
8204 Firenze Blvd Orlando (32836) *(G-12804)*
Hmb Steel Corporation 321 636-6511
4080 Pines Industrial Ave Rockledge (32955) *(G-15418)*
Hmh Publishing Co Inc 617 351-5000
9400 Southpark Ctr Loop Orlando (32819) *(G-12805)*
Hnm Medical, Miami *Also called Hnm Stainless LLC (G-9715)*
Hnm Stainless LLC 866 291-8498
20855 Ne 16th Ave Ste C15 Miami (33179) *(G-9715)*
HOB Corporation 813 988-2272
5604 E 122nd Ave Tampa (33617) *(G-17758)*
Hobbs Trucking LLC 904 463-5681
15616 County Road 108 Hilliard (32046) *(G-5710)*
Hobby Press Inc 305 887-4333
8001 Nw 74th Ave Medley (33166) *(G-8664)*
Hock, John W Co, Gainesville *Also called John W Hock Company (G-4948)*
Hoerbger Auto Cmfort Systems L 334 321-2292
1191 E Nwport Ctr Dr Ste Deerfield Beach (33442) *(G-2839)*
Hoerbiger America Holding Inc (PA) 954 422-9850
1432 E Nwport Ctr Dr Ste Deerfield Beach (33442) *(G-2840)*
Hoerbiger America Holding Inc 954 422-9850
1191 E Newport Center Dr Deerfield Beach (33442) *(G-2841)*
Hoerbiger Compression Tech AME (HQ) 954 974-5700
3350 Gateway Dr Pompano Beach (33069) *(G-14724)*
Hoerbiger Compression Technolo, Pompano Beach *Also called Hoerbiger Corp America Inc (G-14725)*
Hoerbiger Corp America Inc (HQ) 954 974-5700
3350 Gateway Dr Pompano Beach (33069) *(G-14725)*
Hoerndler Inc 239 643-2008
4165 Corporate Sq Naples (34104) *(G-11279)*
Hoffman Brothers Inc 407 563-5004
275 S Chrles Rchard Ball Debary (32713) *(G-2750)*
Hoffman Commercial Group Inc (HQ) 561 967-2213
5190 Lake Worth Rd Greenacres (33463) *(G-5082)*
Hoffman Mint, Fort Lauderdale *Also called American Changer Corp (G-3811)*
Hoffman's Chocolates, Greenacres *Also called Hoffman Commercial Group Inc (G-5082)*
Hoffstetter Tool & Die Inc 727 573-7775
4371 112th Ter N Clearwater (33762) *(G-1715)*
Hofmann & Leavy Inc 954 698-0000
3251 Sw 13th Dr Ste 3 Deerfield Beach (33442) *(G-2842)*
Hog Technologies, Stuart *Also called Waterblasting Technologies Inc (G-17047)*
Hogan Assessment Systems Inc 904 992-0302
13500 Sutton Park Dr S # 401 Jacksonville (32224) *(G-6473)*
Hogenkamp Research Inc 850 677-1072
308 Plantation Hill Rd Gulf Breeze (32561) *(G-5119)*
Hogg Wild Fabrication 904 214-3453
5737 Arlington Rd Jacksonville (32211) *(G-6474)*
Hohol Marine Products 386 734-0630
2741 W New York Ave Deland (32720) *(G-2983)*
Hoipong Customs Inc 954 684-9232
18331 Pines Blvd Pembroke Pines (33029) *(G-14041)*
Holbrook Metal Fabrication LLC 386 937-5441
341 N Highway 17 Palatka (32177) *(G-13483)*
Holeshot Performance Wheels, Bunnell *Also called World Class Machining Inc (G-1311)*
Holeshot Raceway Inc 407 864-1095
434 Terrace Dr Oviedo (32765) *(G-13435)*
Holiday Cleaners Inc 727 842-6989
3640 Calera Dr New Port Richey (34652) *(G-11492)*
Holiday Ice Inc 407 831-2077
204 Short Ave Longwood (32750) *(G-8287)*
Holland Pump Company 813 626-0599
6426 Causeway Blvd Tampa (33619) *(G-17759)*
Holland Pump Company (PA) 561 697-3333
7312 Westport Pl West Palm Beach (33413) *(G-18896)*
Holland Pump Company 904 880-0010
2720 Lane Ave N Jacksonville (32254) *(G-6475)*
Hollander HM Fshons Hldngs LLC (HQ) 212 302-6571
6501 Congress Ave Ste 300 Boca Raton (33487) *(G-557)*
Hollander Sleep Products, Boca Raton *Also called Bedding Acquisition LLC (G-443)*

Hollow Metal Doors & Frames 954 993-0613
1947 Sw 28th Ave Fort Lauderdale (33312) ***(G-4048)***
Hollow Metal Inc 813 246-4112
2803 Park Meadow Dr Valrico (33594) ***(G-18519)***
Holly Sargent 954 560-6973
1000 Se 4th St Apt 315 Fort Lauderdale (33301) ***(G-4049)***
Hollywood Cllctibles Group LLC 407 985-4613
11491 Rocket Blvd Orlando (32824) ***(G-12806)***
Hollywood Design & Concepts 954 458-4634
26534 Bloomfield Ave Yalaha (34797) ***(G-19490)***
Hollywood Houndz LLC 407 614-2108
4101 Briar Gate Ln Winter Garden (34787) ***(G-19269)***
Hollywood Iron Works Inc 954 962-0556
2313 Sw 57th Ter West Park (33023) ***(G-19094)***
Hollywood Lodging Inc 305 803-7455
2601 N 29th Ave Hollywood (33020) ***(G-5843)***
Hollywood Machine Shop Inc 954 893-6103
5835 Rodman St Hollywood (33023) ***(G-5844)***
Hollywood Water Trtmnt Plant, Hollywood *Also called City of Hollywood* ***(G-5799)***
Hollywood Woodwork Inc 954 920-5009
2951 Pembroke Rd Hollywood (33020) ***(G-5845)***
Hollywood Woodwork LLC 954 920-5009
2951 Pembroke Rd Hollywood (33020) ***(G-5846)***
Holmes Stamp Company (PA) 904 396-2291
2021 Saint Augustine Rd E Jacksonville (32207) ***(G-6476)***
Holmes Tool & Engineering Inc 850 547-4417
1019 N Waukesha St Bonifay (32425) ***(G-804)***
Holovis Interna Tional 407 286-3976
7380 W Sand Lake Rd Orlando (32819) ***(G-12807)***
Holpack Corp 786 565-3969
3840 W 104th St Unit 7 Hialeah (33018) ***(G-5448)***
Holtec International (PA) 561 745-7772
1001 N Us Highway 1 Jupiter (33477) ***(G-7053)***
Holyland Tapestries Inc 305 255-7955
14565 Sw 75th Ave Palmetto Bay (33158) ***(G-13847)***
Hom Ade Foods Inc 850 444-4740
10648 Mac Gregor Dr Pensacola (32514) ***(G-14174)***
Hom/Ade Food Sales Inc 850 623-3845
4641 Forsyth St Bagdad (32530) ***(G-298)***
Homac Manufacturing, Ormond Beach *Also called ABB Installation Products Inc* ***(G-13347)***
Home & Garden Industries Inc 305 634-0681
5700 Nw 32nd Ave Miami (33142) ***(G-9716)***
Home Aide Diagnostics Inc 954 794-0212
1072 S Powerline Rd Deerfield Beach (33442) ***(G-2843)***
Home and Design Magazine 239 598-4826
809 Walkerbilt Rd Ste 4 Naples (34110) ***(G-11280)***
Home Art Corporation 352 326-3337
2408 Us Highway 441/27 Fruitland Park (34731) ***(G-4865)***
Home Bistro Inc (PA) 561 227-2727
4014 Chase Ave Ste 212 Miami Beach (33140) ***(G-10679)***
Home County Times Advertiser, Bonifay *Also called Chipley Newspapers Inc* ***(G-801)***
Home Design Group Corp 305 888-5836
220 W 21st St Hialeah (33010) ***(G-5449)***
Home Examiner Inc 786 897-8349
1690 Ne 191st St Apt 308 Miami (33179) ***(G-9717)***
Home Fashion Source, Chipley *Also called Westpoint Home Inc* ***(G-1549)***
Home Healthcare 2000 Inc 954 977-4450
1290 Sw 30th Ave Pompano Beach (33069) ***(G-14726)***
Home Improver Inc 239 549-6901
1732 Se 47th Ter Cape Coral (33904) ***(G-1435)***
Home Mag, The, Saint Augustine *Also called Old Port Group LLC* ***(G-15582)***
Home Mag, The, Longwood *Also called Samjay Media Group Orlando LLC* ***(G-8333)***
Home Pride Cabinets Inc 813 887-3782
8503 Sunstate St Tampa (33634) ***(G-17760)***
Home Protection Team, Miami *Also called Security Tech Group Inc* ***(G-10320)***
Home Source Manufacturing Inc 404 663-0647
3595 Industrial Park Dr Marianna (32446) ***(G-8579)***
Home Town Journal 904 259-9141
9915 River Oak Dr Glen Saint Mary (32040) ***(G-5036)***
Home Town News, South Miami *Also called Miller Publishing Co Inc* ***(G-16822)***
Home Works Bay County Inc 850 215-7880
4902 E Highway 98 Panama City (32404) ***(G-13915)***
Homemag Inc 239 549-6960
1732 Se 47th Ter Cape Coral (33904) ***(G-1436)***
Homerun Derby Bats Only LLC 813 545-3887
6931 Potomac Cir Riverview (33578) ***(G-15273)***
Homes & Land Magazine, Melbourne *Also called Shelton Group LLC* ***(G-8931)***
Homes & Land Magazine, Bonita Springs *Also called Boswell JM & Associates Inc* ***(G-820)***
Homes & Land of Emerald Coast, Destin *Also called North Metro Media* ***(G-3199)***
Homes Devoted Inc 321 473-8567
694 Hammock Rd Melbourne (32904) ***(G-8845)***
Homes Magazine Inc 239 334-7168
2133 Broadway Fort Myers (33901) ***(G-4484)***
Homes Media Solutions LLC (HQ) 850 350-7800
325 John Knox Rd Bldg 200 Tallahassee (32303) ***(G-17278)***
Homes Real Estate Magazine, Fort Myers *Also called Homes Magazine Inc* ***(G-4484)***
Homeshield Industries Corp 239 573-0802
765 Ne 19th Pl Cape Coral (33909) ***(G-1437)***
Homestead Diagnostic Ctr Inc 305 246-5600
650 Ne 22nd Ter Ste 100 Homestead (33033) ***(G-5967)***
Homestead Newspapers Inc 305 245-2311
125 Ne 8th St Ste 2 Homestead (33030) ***(G-5968)***
Hometown Foods Usa LLC 305 887-5200
11800 Nw 102nd Rd Ste 6 Medley (33178) ***(G-8665)***
Hometown News LC (PA) 772 465-5656
1102 S Us Highway 1 Fort Pierce (34950) ***(G-4706)***
Hometown News LC 321 242-1013
380 N Wickham Rd Ste F Melbourne (32935) ***(G-8846)***
Homewood Holdings LLC 941 740-3655
745 Ne 19th Pl Cape Coral (33909) ***(G-1438)***
Homyn Enterprises Corp 305 870-9720
4050 Nw 29th St Miami (33142) ***(G-9718)***
Honchin Inc 305 235-3800
10397 Sw 186th St Cutler Bay (33157) ***(G-2397)***
Honda Generators of Tampa, Tampa *Also called Interbay Air Compressors Inc* ***(G-17789)***
Honduras Food Services Inc 310 940-2071
2337 Sw Archer Rd Apt 302 Gainesville (32608) ***(G-4937)***
Hone Renovation Specialists 407 202-3536
10760 Emerald Chase Dr Orlando (32836) ***(G-12808)***
Honeycomb Arcft Repr Ctr LLC 850 610-0334
1950 Limbus Ave Sarasota (34243) ***(G-16228)***
Honeycomb Company America Inc 941 756-8781
1950 Limbus Ave Sarasota (34243) ***(G-16229)***
Honeycommcore LLC (PA) 561 747-2678
15771 80th Dr N West Palm Beach (33418) ***(G-18897)***
Honeywell Aerospace Inc 727 539-5197
13350 Us Highway 19 N Clearwater (33764) ***(G-1716)***
Honeywell Authorized Dealer, Jacksonville *Also called Southern Technologies* ***(G-6798)***
Honeywell Authorized Dealer, Tampa *Also called Airite Air Conditioning Inc* ***(G-17395)***
Honeywell Authorized Dealer, Maitland *Also called Southern Hvac Corporation* ***(G-8479)***
Honeywell Authorized Dealer, Orlando *Also called Mechanical Svcs Centl Fla Inc* ***(G-12957)***
Honeywell Authorized Dealer, Orlando *Also called Innovative Svc Solutions LLC* ***(G-12831)***
Honeywell Authorized Dealer, Plant City *Also called C & C Services of Tampa Inc* ***(G-14414)***
Honeywell Authorized Dealer, Largo *Also called Straight Polarity Welding Inc* ***(G-8061)***
Honeywell International Inc 561 479-0639
21911 Pine Bark Way Boca Raton (33428) ***(G-558)***
Honeywell International Inc 281 546-0993
1531 Commonwealth Bus Dr Tallahassee (32303) ***(G-17279)***
Honeywell International Inc 727 539-5080
13350 Us Highway 19 N Clearwater (33764) ***(G-1717)***
Honeywell International Inc 305 525-1950
5783 Sw 40th St 308 Miami (33155) ***(G-9719)***
Honeywell International Inc 850 243-8812
15 Industrial St Nw Fort Walton Beach (32548) ***(G-4809)***
Honeywell International Inc 727 539-3111
1221 Us 19 N Clearwater (33763) ***(G-1718)***
Honeywell International Inc 727 539-4451
13051 66th St Largo (33773) ***(G-7972)***
Honeywell International Inc 877 841-2840
1006 Lingo Ct Oviedo (32765) ***(G-13436)***
Honeywell International Inc 904 696-5222
6200 Flagship Cir N Jacksonville (32226) ***(G-6477)***
Honeywell International Inc 505 358-0676
13051 66th St Largo (33773) ***(G-7973)***
Honeywell International Inc 727 531-4611
13350 Us Highway 19 N Clearwater (33764) ***(G-1719)***
Honeywell International Inc 813 573-1166
13190 56th Ct Ste 403 Clearwater (33760) ***(G-1720)***
Honeywell International Inc 904 260-5900
9440 Philips Hwy Ste 4 Jacksonville (32256) ***(G-6478)***
Honeywell International Inc 352 372-4192
1225 Sw 25th Pl Gainesville (32601) ***(G-4938)***
Honeywell US Corp 617 955-4031
3545 Ne 166th St Apt 304 North Miami Beach (33160) ***(G-11682)***
Hontus Ltd (PA) 786 322-3022
11450 Nw 122nd St Ste 100 Medley (33178) ***(G-8666)***
Hontus, Ltd., Inc., Medley *Also called Hontus Ltd* ***(G-8666)***
Hood Depot International Inc 954 570-9860
710 S Powerline Rd Ste H Deerfield Beach (33442) ***(G-2844)***
Hook Fish & Chkn - Mangonia Pk 561 855-6385
5701 N Australian Ave Mangonia Park (33407) ***(G-8501)***
Hook International, Pinellas Park *Also called Global Diversified Products* ***(G-14351)***
Hook International Inc 727 209-0855
6795 114th Ave Largo (33773) ***(G-7974)***
Hooper Corp 954 382-5711
6900 Sw 21st Ct Davie (33317) ***(G-2536)***
Hoosier Lightening Inc 407 290-3323
2415 N John Young Pkwy Orlando (32804) ***(G-12809)***
Hoot/Wisdom Music Pubg LLC 561 297-3205
777 Glades Rd Boca Raton (33431) ***(G-559)***
Hoover Canvas Products, Oakland Park *Also called Major Canvas Products Inc* ***(G-11821)***
Hoover Canvas Products Co (PA) 954 764-1711
4351 Ne 12th Ter Oakland Park (33334) ***(G-11811)***
Hoover Canvas Products Co 954 541-9745
5107 N Australian Ave Mangonia Park (33407) ***(G-8502)***
Hoover Canvas Products Co 561 844-4444
5107 N Australian Ave Mangonia Park (33407) ***(G-8503)***

ALPHABETIC

Hoover Pumping Systems Corp.....954 971-7350
2801 N Powerline Rd Pompano Beach (33069) *(G-14727)*
Hope Technical Sales & Svcs.....941 412-1204
692 Sawgrass Bridge Rd Venice (34292) *(G-18554)*
Hopkins & Daughter Inc.....941 964-2995
431 Park Ave Boca Grande (33921) *(G-393)*
Hopkins Manufacturing Co.....620 591-8229
855 Pine St Tarpon Springs (34689) *(G-18307)*
Hoppin Pop Kettle Stop LLC (PA).....502 220-2372
1850 Emerson St Jacksonville (32207) *(G-6479)*
Hopscotch Technology Group Inc.....305 846-0942
1288 Sanctuary Dr Oviedo (32766) *(G-13437)*
Horizon Duplication Inc.....407 767-5000
841 Nicolet Ave Ste 5 Winter Park (32789) *(G-19411)*
Horizon Industries Inc.....561 315-5439
180 Business Park Way B1 Royal Palm Beach (33411) *(G-15470)*
Horizon Media Express, Winter Park *Also called Horizon Duplication Inc (G-19411)*
Horizon Publications Inc.....386 427-1000
508 Tanal St New Smyrna Beach (32168) *(G-11535)*
Hornblasters Inc.....813 783-8058
6511 N 54th St Tampa (33610) *(G-17761)*
Horse & Pony.....813 986-1003
11819 Hazen Ave Thonotosassa (33592) *(G-18401)*
Horseshoe Knoll Lc.....850 894-0824
2982 Giverny Cir Tallahassee (32309) *(G-17280)*
Horseshoe Picking Inc.....305 345-5778
21400 Sw 392nd St Homestead (33034) *(G-5969)*
Horseshoe Shrimp Boat LLC.....352 356-1982
77 Main St Horseshoe Beach (32648) *(G-6007)*
Hose McCann Communications, Deerfield Beach *Also called Hose-Mccann Telephone Co Inc (G-2845)*
Hose Power USA.....863 669-9333
3110 Winter Lake Rd Lakeland (33803) *(G-7706)*
Hose-Mccann Telephone Co Inc (PA).....954 429-1110
1241 W Newport Center Dr Deerfield Beach (33442) *(G-2845)*
Hoseline Inc.....407 892-2599
1619 Park Commerce Ct Saint Cloud (34769) *(G-15654)*
Hoseline Inc.....541 258-8984
701 Nw 37th Ave Ocala (34475) *(G-11966)*
Hospitlity Bean Cnters Plus In.....954 531-1710
1011 Se 4th Ct Deerfield Beach (33441) *(G-2846)*
Hot Action Sportswear Inc.....386 677-5680
307 Division Ave Ormond Beach (32174) *(G-13377)*
Hot Dog Shoppe LLC.....850 682-3649
1308 N Ferdon Blvd Crestview (32536) *(G-2351)*
Hot Off Press.....386 238-8700
952 Big Tree Rd South Daytona (32119) *(G-16802)*
Hot Sauce Harrys Inc.....941 423-7092
1077 Innovation Ave # 10 North Port (34289) *(G-11741)*
Hot Shot Welding Inc.....727 585-1900
1135 Starkey Rd Ste 10 Largo (33771) *(G-7975)*
Hot Tub Parts LLC.....727 573-9611
6190 45th St N Ste A Saint Petersburg (33714) *(G-15808)*
Hotspot Magazine of Florida, Wilton Manors *Also called Venice Quarters Inc (G-19221)*
Hotspray Industrial Coatings.....407 658-5700
1932 N Goldenrod Rd Orlando (32807) *(G-12810)*
Hotsy Cleaning Systems, Orlando *Also called Lee Chemical Corporation (G-12900)*
Houghton Mifflin Harcourt.....407 345-2000
9400 S Park Loop Orlando (32819) *(G-12811)*
House Doctair Inc.....239 349-7497
5438 Ferrari Ave Ave Maria (34142) *(G-257)*
House of Cabinets Ltd Inc.....352 795-5300
4107 N Citrus Ave Crystal River (34428) *(G-2379)*
House of Llull Atlier.....305 964-7921
13850 Sw 143rd Ct Ste 19 Miami (33186) *(G-9720)*
House of Marble & Granite Inc (PA).....239 261-0099
440 Tamiami Trl N Naples (34102) *(G-11281)*
House of Metal LLC.....727 540-0637
4161 114th Ter N Clearwater (33762) *(G-1721)*
House of Wood, Mangonia Park *Also called Terry D Triplett Inc (G-8513)*
House Plastics Unlimited Inc.....407 843-3290
2580 S Orange Blossom Trl Orlando (32805) *(G-12812)*
Housmans Alum & Screening Inc.....321 255-2778
2911 Dusa Dr Ste E Melbourne (32934) *(G-8847)*
Hoveround Corporation (PA).....941 739-6200
2151 Whitfield Indus Way Sarasota (34243) *(G-16230)*
Howard Imprinting Machine Co.....813 884-2398
5013 Tampa West Blvd Tampa (33634) *(G-17762)*
Howard Publications Inc (HQ).....904 355-2601
501 W Bay St Ste 200 Jacksonville (32202) *(G-6480)*
Howard Scripts Inc.....561 746-5111
800 W Indiantown Rd Jupiter (33458) *(G-7054)*
Howell Logging & Land Clearing.....352 528-2698
20253 Ne 20th St Williston (32696) *(G-19212)*
Howies Instant Printing Inc.....561 686-8699
1572 Palm Bch Lakes Blvd West Palm Beach (33401) *(G-18898)*
Howmedica Osteonics Corp.....941 378-4600
8235 Blaikie Ct Sarasota (34240) *(G-16461)*
Howmedica Osteonics Corp.....954 714-7933
505 Nw 65th Ct Ste 102 Fort Lauderdale (33309) *(G-4050)*
Howmedica Osteonics Corp.....813 886-3450
8731 Florida Mining Blvd Tampa (33634) *(G-17763)*
Howmedica Osteonics Corp.....813 288-0760
405 N Reo St Ste 310 Tampa (33609) *(G-17764)*
Howmedica Osteonics Corp.....954 791-6078
2944 Trivium Cir Fort Lauderdale (33312) *(G-4051)*
Hoya Largo.....727 531-8964
12345 Starkey Rd Ste E Largo (33773) *(G-7976)*
Hoyles Logging.....813 782-1164
40430 Jerry Rd Zephyrhills (33540) *(G-19522)*
HP Preferred Ltd Partners.....407 298-4470
6401 Edgewater Dr Orlando (32810) *(G-12813)*
Hps, Miami *Also called Hernandez Printing Service (G-9705)*
Hr Ease Inc.....813 414-0040
2002 N Lois Ave Ste 220 Tampa (33607) *(G-17765)*
Hre LLC.....317 340-5991
15860 Pine Ridge Rd Fort Myers (33908) *(G-4485)*
HRF Exploration & Prod LLC (PA).....561 847-4743
250 El Dorado Ln Palm Beach (33480) *(G-13556)*
Hsc, Jacksonville *Also called Holmes Stamp Company (G-6476)*
Hte, Bonifay *Also called Holmes Tool & Engineering Inc (G-804)*
Hth Engineering Inc.....727 939-8853
825 Cypress Trails Dr Tarpon Springs (34688) *(G-18308)*
Hti.....941 723-4570
210 9th Street Dr W Palmetto (34221) *(G-13806)*
Hts Controls Inc.....813 287-5512
4918 W Grace St Tampa (33607) *(G-17766)*
Hucke Manufacturing Inc.....863 655-3667
222 Commercial Pl Sebring (33876) *(G-16695)*
Huckins Yacht Corporation.....904 389-1125
3482 Lake Shore Blvd Jacksonville (32210) *(G-6481)*
Hudson Cabinets & Millwork LLC.....239 218-0451
6261 Metro Plantation Rd Fort Myers (33966) *(G-4486)*
Hudson Do It Best Hardware, Hudson *Also called Td Tra -Dix Supply Inc (G-6039)*
Hudson Technologies, Ormond Beach *Also called Hudson Tool & Die Company Inc (G-13378)*
Hudson Tool & Die Company Inc.....386 672-2000
1327 N Us Highway 1 Ormond Beach (32174) *(G-13378)*
Hudsons Wldg & Fabrication Inc.....941 355-4858
10845 Forest Run Dr Bradenton (34211) *(G-1057)*
Hueston Stair Company.....314 225-4280
836 W Montrose St Ste 5 Clermont (34711) *(G-1964)*
Huff Carbide Tool Inc.....727 848-4001
6541 Industrial Ave Port Richey (34668) *(G-15052)*
Hugh Robinson Inc.....954 484-0660
2718 Nw 31st Ave Lauderdale Lakes (33311) *(G-8088)*
Hughes Consolidated Services.....904 438-5710
4712 Royal Ave Jacksonville (32205) *(G-6482)*
Hughes Corporation.....954 755-7111
4000 Nw 121st Ave Coral Springs (33065) *(G-2256)*
Hughes Fabrication.....239 481-1376
2304 Bruner Ln Ste 1 Fort Myers (33912) *(G-4487)*
Hughes Trim Llc.....863 206-6048
7613 Currency Dr Orlando (32809) *(G-12814)*
Hulas Market Place LLC.....941 704-3305
1508 Stickney Point Rd Sarasota (34231) *(G-16462)*
Human Rights Defense Center, Lake Worth *Also called Prison Legal News (G-7583)*
Human Sign.....239 573-4292
1830 Del Prado Blvd S Cape Coral (33990) *(G-1439)*
Humic Growth Solutions Inc (PA).....904 392-7201
709 Eastport Rd Jacksonville (32218) *(G-6483)*
Humic Growth Solutions Inc.....904 329-1012
938 Hall Park Rd Green Cove Springs (32043) *(G-5066)*
Humic Growth Solutions Inc.....904 329-1012
112 Badger Park Dr Saint Johns (32259) *(G-15678)*
Hummingbirds Ai Inc.....305 432-2787
8140 Hawthorne Ave Miami Beach (33141) *(G-10680)*
Humo E-Liquids, Sunrise *Also called E-Liquids Investment Group LLC (G-17117)*
Hunt Enterprises Inc.....863 682-6187
1224 E Lime St Lakeland (33801) *(G-7707)*
Hunt RDS Inc.....813 249-7551
3898 Tampa Rd Oldsmar (34677) *(G-12232)*
Hunt Ventures Inc.....941 375-3699
232 Bahama St Venice (34285) *(G-18555)*
Hunted Tees LLC.....407 260-2138
606 Hattaway Dr Altamonte Springs (32701) *(G-50)*
Hunter Aerospace Supply LLC.....954 321-8848
3331 Nw 55th St Fort Lauderdale (33309) *(G-4052)*
Hunter Green Group Inc.....954 753-9914
4613 N University Dr # 277 Coral Springs (33067) *(G-2257)*
Hunter Green Group, The, Coral Springs *Also called Hunter Green Group Inc (G-2257)*
Hunter Industries.....561 775-3239
10235 Allamanda Cir Palm Beach Gardens (33410) *(G-13595)*
Hunter Wood Products, Deland *Also called Island Shutter Co Inc (G-2985)*
Hunting Report The, Miami *Also called Oxpecker Enterprise Inc (G-10124)*
Huntley Stemwood Inc.....904 237-4005
2785 Black Creek Dr Middleburg (32068) *(G-10906)*
Huntsman Properties LLC (PA).....954 282-1797
2145 Davie Blvd Ste 101 Fort Lauderdale (33312) *(G-4053)*

Hurricane Graphics Inc 305 760-9154
3331 Nw 168th St Miami Gardens (33056) ***(G-10746)***
Hurricane Marine Manufacturing 772 260-3950
3301 Se Slater St Stuart (34997) ***(G-16955)***
Hurricane Medical Inc 941 753-1517
5315 Lena Rd Bradenton (34211) ***(G-1058)***
Hurricane Roofing & Shtmtl Inc 954 968-8155
1905 Mears Pkwy Margate (33063) ***(G-8549)***
Hurricane Shtters Cntl Fla Inc 321 639-2622
3460 Us Highway 1 Rockledge (32955) ***(G-15419)***
Hurricane Shutter & Plus Inc 786 287-0007
8004 Sw 149th Ave Miami (33193) ***(G-9721)***
Hurst Awning Company Inc (PA) 305 693-0600
3613 N 29th Ave Hollywood (33020) ***(G-5847)***
Hut Global Inc 561 571-2523
131 S Federal Hwy Apt 721 Boca Raton (33432) ***(G-560)***
Hutchins Co Inc 727 442-6651
1195 Kapp Dr Clearwater (33765) ***(G-1722)***
Hvac, Pompano Beach *Also called Fusion AC & Appl Svc LLC* ***(G-14707)***
Hvac Genius, The, Deltona *Also called JRS Ventures LLP* ***(G-3172)***
Hy-Tech Thermal Solutions LLC 321 984-9777
159 Park Hill Blvd Melbourne (32904) ***(G-8848)***
Hyas, Lake Mary *Also called High Yield AG Solutions LLC* ***(G-7422)***
Hybrid Impressions Inc (PA) 305 392-5029
8020 W 30th Ct Hialeah (33018) ***(G-5450)***
Hybrid Sources Inc 772 563-9100
2950 43rd Ave Vero Beach (32960) ***(G-18626)***
Hyco, Clearwater *Also called Hytronics Corp* ***(G-1725)***
Hycomb Usa Inc 954 251-1691
311 W Ansin Blvd Hallandale Beach (33009) ***(G-5190)***
Hydes Screening Inc 954 345-6743
3700 Nw 124th Ave Ste 126 Coral Springs (33065) ***(G-2258)***
Hydra Hair Care, Sunrise *Also called Lawton LLC* ***(G-17141)***
Hydrapower International Inc 239 642-5379
950 N Collier Blvd # 202 Marco Island (34145) ***(G-8525)***
Hydraulic Net, Saint Augustine *Also called Hydraulicnet LLC* ***(G-15549)***
Hydraulicnet LLC 630 543-7630
6980 Us Highway 1 N # 107 Saint Augustine (32095) ***(G-15549)***
Hydrex LLC 727 443-3900
627 Pinellas St Unit C Clearwater (33756) ***(G-1723)***
Hydro Extrusion Usa LLC 904 794-1500
200 Riviera Blvd Saint Augustine (32086) ***(G-15550)***
Hydro Industries-Usa LLC 305 440-0893
3401 Ne 1st Ave Miami (33137) ***(G-9722)***
Hydro Precision Tubing USA LLC (HQ) 321 636-8147
100 Gus Hipp Blvd Rockledge (32955) ***(G-15420)***
Hydro-Dyne Engineering Inc 727 532-0777
4750 118th Ave N Oldsmar (34677) ***(G-12233)***
Hydrofoils Incorporated 561 964-6399
4151 Lake Worth Rd Lake Worth (33466) ***(G-7556)***
Hydrogel Vision Corporation 941 739-1382
7575 Commerce Ct Sarasota (34243) ***(G-16231)***
Hydrogen Diesel Prfmce Inc 407 847-6064
2410 Sabra Ct Kissimmee (34744) ***(G-7251)***
Hydrogen Inc 239 436-6668
383 Harbour Dr Apt 111 Naples (34103) ***(G-11282)***
Hydrogen One Inc 352 361-6974
6880 Se 104th St Belleview (34420) ***(G-371)***
Hydrogen Technology Corp 800 315-9554
900 West Ave Apt 501 Miami Beach (33139) ***(G-10681)***
Hydrolec Inc 904 730-3766
5050 Stepp Ave Jacksonville (32216) ***(G-6484)***
Hydromassage, Clearwater *Also called JTL Enterprises (delaware)* ***(G-1746)***
Hydron Technologies Inc 727 342-5050
9843 18th St N Ste 150 Saint Petersburg (33716) ***(G-15809)***
Hydroplus 386 341-2768
1712 Fern Palm Dr Ste 7 Edgewater (32132) ***(G-3624)***
Hydroplus Inc 941 479-7473
615 Riviera Dunes Way # 207 Palmetto (34221) ***(G-13807)***
Hygenator Pillow Service, Hialeah *Also called General Pillows & Fiber Inc* ***(G-5427)***
Hygenator Pillow Service Inc 305 325-0250
10100 E Calusa Club Dr Miami (33186) ***(G-9723)***
Hygreen Inc 352 327-9747
3630 Sw 47th Ave Ste 100 Gainesville (32608) ***(G-4939)***
Hyland Custom Cabinetry, Naples *Also called Thomas Rley Artisans Guild Inc* ***(G-11440)***
Hylton & Assoc 321 303-2862
1449 Sackett Cir Orlando (32818) ***(G-12815)***
Hymeg Corporation 800 322-1953
5410 115th Ave N Clearwater (33760) ***(G-1724)***
Hyper-Sub Platform Tech Inc 386 365-6021
4661 W State Road 238 Lake Butler (32054) ***(G-7337)***
Hyperbaric Treatment Assn 804 296-4094
129 Sea Grove Main St # 202 Saint Augustine (32080) ***(G-15551)***
Hyperform Inc (HQ) 321 632-6503
5440 Schenck Ave Rockledge (32955) ***(G-15421)***
Hyperion Managing LLC 904 612-3987
2751-2 Larsen Rd Jacksonville (32207) ***(G-6485)***
Hyperion Munitions Inc 844 622-8339
2150 34th Way Largo (33771) ***(G-7977)***
Hytronics Corp 727 535-0413
5410 115th Ave N Clearwater (33760) ***(G-1725)***
I A I 561 488-6369
21362 Placida Ter Boca Raton (33433) ***(G-561)***
I ABC Corp 904 645-6000
11711 Marco Beach Dr Jacksonville (32224) ***(G-6486)***
I C Probotics Inc 407 339-8298
122 E Lake Ave Longwood (32750) ***(G-8288)***
I C T S America Inc 786 307-2993
8400 Nw 36th St Ste 450 Doral (33166) ***(G-3385)***
I Fix & Cases LLC 939 645-5252
11068 Smmrspring Lakes Dr Orlando (32825) ***(G-12816)***
I Found It 561 557-2881
9339 Highway A1a Alt West Palm Beach (33403) ***(G-18899)***
I I S, Boynton Beach *Also called Innovative Indus Solutions Inc* ***(G-920)***
I J Precious Metals Inc 305 371-3009
22 Ne 1st St Miami (33132) ***(G-9724)***
I M I Publishing Inc 615 957-9288
425 Cove Twr Dr Apt 1204 Naples (34110) ***(G-11283)***
I M S, Ormond Beach *Also called Information Mgt Svcs Inc* ***(G-13380)***
I P G, Sarasota *Also called Intertape Polymer Corp* ***(G-16469)***
I P M, Naples *Also called International Packaging Mchs* ***(G-11290)***
I P S, Floral City *Also called Instant Printing Services Inc* ***(G-3768)***
I P Team Inc 772 398-4664
701 Nw Federal Hwy # 301 Stuart (34994) ***(G-16956)***
I R Bowen & Sons, Jacksonville *Also called Skipper Wright Inc* ***(G-6779)***
I S M, Orlando *Also called Industrial Smoke & Mirrors Inc* ***(G-12828)***
I S T, Sarasota *Also called Industry Standard Technology* ***(G-16235)***
I T Pacs Pro Software Inc 954 678-1270
5612 Pembroke Rd Ste A West Park (33023) ***(G-19095)***
I Wed Today, Miami *Also called Carlees Creations Inc* ***(G-9319)***
I Wentworth Inc 561 231-7544
645 Beachland Blvd Vero Beach (32963) ***(G-18627)***
I-75 Industries Inc 352 840-3155
1466 Nw 38th Ave Ocala (34482) ***(G-11967)***
I-Acritas LLC 407 375-5707
118 E Jefferson St Fl 3 Orlando (32801) ***(G-12817)***
I-Con Systems Inc 407 365-6241
3100 Camp Rd Oviedo (32765) ***(G-13438)***
I-Partner Group Inc (PA) 239 449-4749
28200 Old 41 Rd Unit 204 Bonita Springs (34135) ***(G-838)***
I-Pop Inc 561 567-9000
475 N Cleary Rd Unit 4 West Palm Beach (33413) ***(G-18900)***
I.T.S. USA, Maitland *Also called US Implant Solutions LLC* ***(G-8483)***
I2k Digital Solutions LLC 305 507-0707
7884 Nw 64th St Miami (33166) ***(G-9725)***
I3, Naples *Also called Intellgent Instrumentation Inc* ***(G-11288)***
I3 Microsystems Inc 727 235-6532
9900 16th St N Saint Petersburg (33716) ***(G-15810)***
Iag Engine Center LLC 305 591-0643
6929 Nw 46th St Miami (33166) ***(G-9726)***
Iaire LLC 407 873-2538
2100 Consulate Dr Ste 102 Orlando (32837) ***(G-12818)***
Iamgold Purchasing Svcs Inc 713 671-5973
2000 Nw 97th Ave Ste 114 Doral (33172) ***(G-3386)***
Ian-Conrad Bergan LLC (PA) 850 434-1286
1001 E Belmont St Pensacola (32501) ***(G-14175)***
Ianorod JB LLC 954 217-3014
4579 Weston Rd Weston (33331) ***(G-19138)***
IB Furniture Inc 941 371-5764
1236 Porter Rd Unit 4 Sarasota (34240) ***(G-16463)***
Ibd Industrial LLC 786 655-7577
1825 Ponce De Leon Blvd Coral Gables (33134) ***(G-2156)***
Ibi Systems Inc 954 978-9225
6842 Nw 20th Ave Fort Lauderdale (33309) ***(G-4054)***
Ibiley School Uniforms, Miami *Also called Uniform Authority Inc* ***(G-10529)***
Ibr LLC 407 694-6748
1580 Lake Parkway Dr Saint Cloud (34771) ***(G-15655)***
Ibs Manufacturing LLC 352 629-9752
18 Ne 16th St Ocala (34470) ***(G-11968)***
Ibs Partners Ltd (PA) 954 581-0922
1 N University Dr Ut400a Plantation (33324) ***(G-14523)***
Ibtm Engineering Inc 239 246-1876
1291 Par View Dr Sanibel (33957) ***(G-16146)***
Ic Industries Inc 305 696-8330
1101 E 33rd St Fl 2 Hialeah (33013) ***(G-5451)***
Icamr Inc 407 742-4253
200 Neocity Way Kissimmee (34744) ***(G-7252)***
Icare Industries Inc (PA) 727 512-3000
4399 35th St N Ste 100 Saint Petersburg (33714) ***(G-15811)***
Icarecom LLC 954 616-5604
401 E Las Olas Blvd Ste 1 Fort Lauderdale (33301) ***(G-4055)***
ICC, Miami Lakes *Also called International Casting Corp* ***(G-10798)***
Icco, Coral Springs *Also called Hispacom Inc* ***(G-2255)***
Ice Bunker A&M Corp 786 368-0924
717 W 27th St Hialeah (33010) ***(G-5452)***
Ice Cream & Gifts LLC 352 237-2660
6160 Sw Highway 200 # 116 Ocala (34476) ***(G-11969)***

ALPHABETIC

Ice Cream Club Inc (PA).......561 731-3331
1580 High Ridge Rd Boynton Beach (33426) **(G-917)**
Ice Link 2018 LLC.......305 988-4023
1963 10th Ave N Lake Worth Beach (33461) **(G-7613)**
Ice Magic Holdings, Orlando *Also called Ice Magic-Orlando Inc* **(G-12819)**
Ice Magic-Orlando Inc (PA).......407 816-1905
9468 American Eagle Way # 100 Orlando (32837) **(G-12819)**
Ice Pop Factory, Plant City *Also called Frio Distributors Inc* **(G-14433)**
Ice Sheet Metal LLC.......850 872-2129
29 E 10th St Panama City (32401) **(G-13916)**
Iceblox Inc.......717 697-1900
7436 Evesborough Ln New Port Richey (34655) **(G-11493)**
Icecapade Frozen Treats Inc.......904 314-4190
1833 N Pearl St Jacksonville (32206) **(G-6487)**
Icecold2 LLC.......855 326-2665
10004 N Dale Mabry Hwy Tampa (33618) **(G-17767)**
Icecool World, Tampa *Also called Icecold2 LLC* **(G-17767)**
ICEE Company.......954 966-7502
11 Sw 12th Ave Ste 108 Dania (33004) **(G-2447)**
Icemule Company Inc.......904 325-9012
601 S Ponce De Leon Blvd Saint Augustine (32084) **(G-15552)**
Ichosen1 Inc.......844 403-4055
1441 Brickell Ave Ste 17 Miami (33131) **(G-9727)**
ICI Custom Parts Inc.......813 888-7979
13911 Bittersweet Way Tampa (33625) **(G-17768)**
Icloak Inc.......407 422-0876
37 N Orange Ave Ste 1025 Orlando (32801) **(G-12820)**
ICM Printing Co Inc.......352 377-7468
5510 Sw 41st Blvd Ste 101 Gainesville (32608) **(G-4940)**
Icmfg & Associates Inc.......727 258-4995
3734 131st Ave N Ste 11 Clearwater (33762) **(G-1726)**
ICO USA Corp.......305 253-0871
15815 Sw 89th Ave Palmetto Bay (33157) **(G-13848)**
Icome2fix LLC.......954 789-4102
400 Nw 26th St Miami (33127) **(G-9728)**
Icon, Saint Augustine *Also called Industrial Cnstr Svcs Dsign In* **(G-15555)**
Icon Aircraft Inc.......813 387-6603
825 Severn Ave Tampa (33606) **(G-17769)**
Icon Embroidery Inc.......407 858-0886
2833 Butler Bay Dr N Windermere (34786) **(G-19228)**
Icon Welding & Fabrication.......941 822-8822
8145 27th St E Sarasota (34243) **(G-16232)**
Icorp-Ifoam Specialty Products.......407 328-8500
250 Power Ct Sanford (32771) **(G-16064)**
Icosi Manufacturing LLC.......813 854-1333
11134 Challenger Ave Odessa (33556) **(G-12095)**
ICP Adhesives Sealants.......954 905-0531
12505 Nw 44th St Coral Springs (33065) **(G-2259)**
Icpf Development Group LLC (PA).......727 474-9927
514 N Betty Ln Clearwater (33755) **(G-1727)**
Ics Inex Inspection Systems.......727 535-5502
13075 Us Highway 19 N Clearwater (33764) **(G-1728)**
Ictc USA, Brooksville *Also called Interconnect Cable Tech Corp* **(G-1237)**
ID Print Inc.......954 923-8374
6561 Nw 18th Ct Plantation (33313) **(G-14524)**
ID Solutions Inc.......407 823-7710
9609 Pacific Pines Ct Orlando (32832) **(G-12821)**
Idaho Timber LLC.......386 758-8111
176 Sw Midtown Pl Ste 101 Lake City (32025) **(G-7361)**
Idea Design Studio Inc.......305 823-6008
8562 Nw 56th St Doral (33166) **(G-3387)**
Ideal Aluminum, Saint Augustine *Also called Ideal Deals LLC* **(G-15553)**
Ideal Cabinetry, Bartow *Also called All Wood Cabinetry LLC* **(G-305)**
Ideal Deals LLC.......386 736-1700
3200 Parker Dr Saint Augustine (32084) **(G-15553)**
Ideal Fastener Corporation.......201 207-6722
10800 Biscayne Blvd Miami (33161) **(G-9729)**
Ideal Gas LLC.......904 417-6470
3200 Parker Dr Saint Augustine (32084) **(G-15554)**
Ideal Helicopter Service, Fort Myers *Also called Mc Dermott Enterprises Inc* **(G-4525)**
Ideal Image Brandon.......813 982-3420
1602 Oakfield Dr Ste 105 Brandon (33511) **(G-1162)**
Ideal Publishing Co Inc.......727 321-0785
3063 Lown St N Saint Petersburg (33713) **(G-15812)**
Ideasgt Corp.......786 370-7767
7510 Sw 153rd Pl Apt 101 Miami (33193) **(G-9730)**
Ideasphere, Boca Raton *Also called Twinlab Holdings Inc* **(G-762)**
Identifire Safety, West Palm Beach *Also called F D Signworks LLC* **(G-18867)**
Identity Holding Company LLC.......941 355-5171
7525 Pennsylvania Ave # 101 Sarasota (34243) **(G-16233)**
Identity Stronghold LLC.......941 475-8480
563 Paul Morris Dr Unit B Englewood (34223) **(G-3679)**
Idex International, Tampa *Also called Island Designs Outlet Inc* **(G-17794)**
IDI, Bradenton *Also called Innovative Designs of Sarasota* **(G-1060)**
Idproductsource.......772 336-4269
645 Nw Entp Driv Ste Port Saint Lucie (34986) **(G-15113)**
Idproductsource LLC.......772 336-4269
651 Nw Enterprise Dr Port Saint Lucie (34986) **(G-15114)**
Idsolution Inc.......305 603-9835
10302 Nw S Rver Dr Ste 15 Medley (33178) **(G-8667)**
Ies Sales and Service LLC.......305 687-9400
2340 Nw 147th St Opa Locka (33054) **(G-12324)**
Ies Sales and Service LLC.......305 525-6079
2233 Nw 77th Ter Miami (33147) **(G-9731)**
IESC Diesel Corp.......305 470-9306
7817 Nw 72nd Ave Medley (33166) **(G-8668)**
Ifco Systems Us LLC (PA).......813 463-4103
3030 N Rocky Point Dr W # 300 Tampa (33607) **(G-17770)**
Iff Chemical Holdings Inc.......904 783-2180
2051 Lane Ave N Jacksonville (32254) **(G-6488)**
Ifoxx LLC.......305 785-7130
3051 Greystone Loop # 302 Kissimmee (34741) **(G-7253)**
Igbo Network LLC.......352 727-4113
5021 Nw 34th Blvd Ste D Gainesville (32605) **(G-4941)**
Igovsolutions LLC.......407 574-3056
1307 S Intl Pkwy Ste 2061 Lake Mary (32746) **(G-7423)**
Igs LLC.......800 419-3014
27901 Sw 129th Ct Homestead (33032) **(G-5970)**
Iguana Graphics Inc.......813 657-7800
1345 Oakfield Dr Brandon (33511) **(G-1163)**
Ii-VI Aerospace & Defense Inc.......727 375-8562
6716 Industrial Ave Port Richey (34668) **(G-15053)**
Iis Incorporated.......561 547-4297
3020 High Ridge Rd Boynton Beach (33426) **(G-918)**
Ijkb LLC.......941 953-9046
502 N Spoonbill Dr Sarasota (34236) **(G-16464)**
Ike Behar, Miramar *Also called Regina Behar Enterprises Inc* **(G-11035)**
IL Mobile, Deerfield Beach *Also called Ramos Woodwork LLC* **(G-2899)**
IL Nuts Inc.......786 366-4536
19098 W Dixie Hwy Miami (33180) **(G-9732)**
Ilan Custom Woodwork LLC (PA).......727 272-5364
42 Ventura Dr Dunedin (34698) **(G-3580)**
Iler Group Inc.......813 600-1738
2604 Cypress Ridge Blvd # 102 Wesley Chapel (33544) **(G-18749)**
Ilex Organics LLC.......386 566-3826
1814 Fern Palm Dr Ste B Edgewater (32132) **(G-3625)**
Iliad Biotechnologies LLC.......954 336-0777
4581 Weston Rd Ste 260 Weston (33331) **(G-19139)**
Illinois Tool Works Inc.......863 665-3338
3606 Craftsman Blvd Lakeland (33803) **(G-7708)**
Illuminated Lightpanels Inc.......954 484-6633
2011 Nw 29th St Oakland Park (33311) **(G-11812)**
Illuminations Holiday Ltg LLC.......813 334-4827
8708 Elmdale Pl Tampa (33637) **(G-17771)**
Ils Management LLC.......321 252-0100
930 S Hbr Cy Blvd Ste 505 Melbourne (32901) **(G-8849)**
Ilsc Holdings Lc.......480 935-4230
12001 Science Dr Ste 160 Orlando (32826) **(G-12822)**
Image 360, Jacksonville *Also called ARC Creative Inc* **(G-6164)**
Image 360.......561 395-0745
6560 E Rogers Cir Boca Raton (33487) **(G-562)**
Image Depot.......813 685-7116
2017 E Fowler Ave Tampa (33612) **(G-17772)**
Image Experts Inc.......727 488-7556
4556 36th Ave N Saint Petersburg (33713) **(G-15813)**
Image Graphics 2000 Inc.......954 332-3380
2450 W Sample Rd Ste 20 Pompano Beach (33073) **(G-14728)**
Image Impressions, Tamarac *Also called Graphic and Printing Svcs Corp* **(G-17357)**
Image International Inc.......561 793-9560
8040 Belvedere Rd Ste 1 West Palm Beach (33411) **(G-18901)**
Image One Corporation.......813 888-8288
6202 Benjamin Rd Ste 103 Tampa (33634) **(G-17773)**
Image Printing & Graphics LLC.......321 783-5555
8649 Villanova Dr Cape Canaveral (32920) **(G-1360)**
Image Prtg & Digital Svcs Inc.......850 244-3380
315 E Hollywood Blvd # 3 Mary Esther (32569) **(G-8589)**
Image360 - Lauderhill, Lauderhill *Also called Graphic Difference Inc A* **(G-8110)**
Image360 South Tampa, Tampa *Also called Z & L Partners Inc* **(G-18279)**
Image360 St Petersburg Central, Saint Petersburg *Also called Bayfront Printing Company* **(G-15719)**
Imagecare Maintenance Systems.......727 536-8646
14055 46th St N Ste 1108 Clearwater (33762) **(G-1729)**
Imagicle Inc.......206 201-2042
66 W Flagler St Ste 1002 Miami (33130) **(G-9733)**
Imagik International Corp.......786 631-5003
8390 Nw 25th St Doral (33122) **(G-3388)**
Imagination Creations Inc.......561 744-7802
2895 Jupiter Park Dr # 300 Jupiter (33458) **(G-7055)**
Imagination Enterprises LLC.......504 289-9691
7616 Southland Blvd # 102 Orlando (32809) **(G-12823)**
Imagine That Inc.......813 728-8324
155 E Oakwood St Tarpon Springs (34689) **(G-18309)**
Imaging Diagnostic Systems Inc.......954 581-9800
1221 E Robinson St Orlando (32801) **(G-12824)**
Imaging For Life, Bradenton *Also called US Pet Imaging LLC* **(G-1138)**
Imaging For Life, Sarasota *Also called US Pet Imaging LLC* **(G-16632)**

Imaging Initiatives Inc 239 936-3646
5291 Smmrland Commons Way Fort Myers (33907) ***(G-4488)***
Imago Products 888 400-4122
1500 Gateway Blvd Ste 220 Boynton Beach (33426) ***(G-919)***
IMC Agrico, Mulberry *Also called Mos Holdings Inc* ***(G-11131)***
IMC Lighting Inc 305 373-4422
2915 Biscayne Blvd # 301 Miami (33137) ***(G-9734)***
IMC Storage 305 418-0069
3955 Adra Ave Doral (33178) ***(G-3389)***
Imc-Heartway LLC (PA) 239 275-6767
5681 Independence Cir A Fort Myers (33912) ***(G-4489)***
Imerys Perlite Usa Inc 850 875-1282
612 S Shelfer St Quincy (32351) ***(G-15251)***
Imh, Jacksonville *Also called Industrial Mobile Hydraulics* ***(G-6494)***
IMI, Pompano Beach *Also called International Medical Inds Inc* ***(G-14732)***
IMI, Gainesville *Also called Innovative Machine Inc* ***(G-4942)***
IMI Publishing Inc 239 529-5081
640 21st St Nw Naples (34120) ***(G-11284)***
Imm Survivor Inc 239 454-7020
17030 Alico Center Rd Fort Myers (33967) ***(G-4490)***
Immokalee Fabrication and Wldg 239 675-8299
891 Arthur Ct Immokalee (34142) ***(G-6051)***
Immokalee Ranch 239 657-2000
4451 County Road 846 Immokalee (34142) ***(G-6052)***
Immudyne Nutritional LLC 914 714-8901
1301 Riverplace Blvd # 80 Jacksonville (32207) ***(G-6489)***
Immune Therapeutics Inc 888 613-8802
2431 Aloma Ave 124 Winter Park (32792) ***(G-19412)***
Immunotek Bio Centers LLC 337 500-1175
825 9th St W Bradenton (34205) ***(G-1059)***
Immunotek Bio Centers LLC 561 270-6712
4560 Lake Worth Rd Greenacres (33463) ***(G-5083)***
Immunotek Bio Centers LLC 772 577-7194
2710 S Us Highway 1 Fort Pierce (34982) ***(G-4707)***
Immunotek Bio Centers LLC 404 345-3570
1225 W King St Cocoa (32922) ***(G-2030)***
Impact Design Group Inc 904 636-8989
4613 Philips Hwy Ste 207 Jacksonville (32207) ***(G-6490)***
Impact Education Inc 239 482-0202
18180 Old Dominion Ct Fort Myers (33908) ***(G-4491)***
Impact Molding Clearwater LLC 847 718-9300
2050 Sunnydale Blvd Clearwater (33765) ***(G-1730)***
Impact Promotional Pubg LLC 727 736-6228
1546 Main St Dunedin (34698) ***(G-3581)***
Impact Register Inc 727 585-8572
1870 Starkey Rd Ste 1 Largo (33771) ***(G-7978)***
Impact Safe Glass Corporation 813 247-5528
2705 N 35th St Tampa (33605) ***(G-17774)***
Imperial Foam & Insul Mfg Co 386 673-4177
2360 Old Tomoka Rd W Ormond Beach (32174) ***(G-13379)***
Imperial Imprinting LLC 772 633-8256
8815 92nd Ct Vero Beach (32967) ***(G-18628)***
Imperial Industries Inc (HQ) 954 917-4114
1259 Nw 21st St Pompano Beach (33069) ***(G-14729)***
Imperial Kitchens Inc 239 208-9359
12541 Metro Pkwy Ste 14 Fort Myers (33966) ***(G-4492)***
Imperial Motor Parts, Lakeland *Also called Battery Usa Inc* ***(G-7644)***
Imperial Motor Parts-Division, Lakeland *Also called Battery Usa Inc* ***(G-7643)***
Imperial Photoengraving 772 924-1731
11013 Sw Redwing Dr Stuart (34997) ***(G-16957)***
Imperial Privacy Systems LLC 954 782-7130
1400 Sw 8th St Pompano Beach (33069) ***(G-14730)***
Imperx Inc (PA) 561 989-0006
6421 Congress Ave Ste 204 Boca Raton (33487) ***(G-563)***
Impex of Doral Inc 305 470-0041
7850 Nw 80th St Medley (33166) ***(G-8669)***
Imported Yarns LLC 239 405-2974
21561 Pelican Sound Dr # 101 Estero (33928) ***(G-3691)***
Impremedia LLC 407 767-0070
685 S Ronald Reagan Blvd Longwood (32750) ***(G-8289)***
Impress Ink LLC (PA) 407 982-5646
540 N Goldenrod Rd Ste A Orlando (32807) ***(G-12825)***
Impress Ink Screen Prtg & EMB, Orlando *Also called Impress Ink LLC* ***(G-12825)***
Impressing Design Print 786 615-3695
17699 Nw 78th Ave Hialeah (33015) ***(G-5453)***
Impressions Dry Cleaners Inc 561 988-3030
6201 N Federal Hwy Ste 1 Boca Raton (33487) ***(G-564)***
Impressions of Miami Inc 305 666-0277
6960 Sw 47th St Miami (33155) ***(G-9735)***
Impressive Pavers Inc 321 508-9991
2883 Glasbern Cir West Melbourne (32904) ***(G-18775)***
Imprint 941 484-5151
3449 Tech Dr Unit 212 Nokomis (34275) ***(G-11581)***
Imprint Promotions LLC 321 622-8946
405 N Wickham Rd Ste A Melbourne (32935) ***(G-8850)***
Imprints International Inc 561 202-0105
150 Businefl Pk Way Ste 2 Royal Palm Beach (33411) ***(G-15471)***
Improved Racing Products LLC 407 705-3054
4855 Dist Ct Ste 1 Orlando (32822) ***(G-12826)***
Impulse Air Inc 904 475-1822
2126 W 21st St Jacksonville (32209) ***(G-6491)***
IMS, Cape Coral *Also called Project and Cnstr Wldg Inc* ***(G-1458)***
IMS Publishing Inc 954 761-8777
1850 Se 17th St Ste 107 Fort Lauderdale (33316) ***(G-4056)***
In Diversified Plant Services 813 453-7025
22528 Laureldale Dr Lutz (33549) ***(G-8390)***
In Focus Interactive Magazine 954 966-1233
3001 Sw 64th Ter Miramar (33023) ***(G-11003)***
In Gear Fashions Inc (PA) 305 830-2900
4401 Nw 167th St Miami Gardens (33055) ***(G-10747)***
In Press Marketing 954 659-9332
2487 Quail Roost Dr Weston (33327) ***(G-19140)***
In Stock Printers Inc 727 447-2515
725 Stevens Ave Oldsmar (34677) ***(G-12234)***
In The Bite 561 529-3940
342 Toney Penna Dr Jupiter (33458) ***(G-7056)***
In The Loop Brewing Inc 813 857-0111
3338 Land O Lakes Blvd Land O Lakes (34639) ***(G-7856)***
In The News Inc 813 882-8886
3706 N Ridge Ave Tampa (33603) ***(G-17775)***
In Touch Electronics LLC 813 818-9990
13944 Lynmar Blvd Bldg 2 Tampa (33626) ***(G-17776)***
In-O-Vate Technologies, Jupiter *Also called 6 Ports LLC* ***(G-6990)***
Inbigvmyshopify LLC 844 689-9033
12030 Sw 129th Ct Ste 105 Miami (33186) ***(G-9736)***
Inceptra LLC (PA) 954 442-5400
1900 N Commerce Pkwy Weston (33326) ***(G-19141)***
Incity Property Management, West Palm Beach *Also called Incity Security Inc* ***(G-18902)***
Incity Security Inc 561 306-9228
3560 Inv Ln Ste 102 West Palm Beach (33404) ***(G-18902)***
Inclan Machine Shop 305 846-9675
4401 Sw 75th Ave Miami (33155) ***(G-9737)***
Increte Systems, Odessa *Also called Euclid Chemical Company* ***(G-12119)***
Increte Systems 813 886-8811
1725 Gunn Hwy Odessa (33556) ***(G-12126)***
Independent Florida Sun 850 438-8115
226 Palafox Pl Pensacola (32502) ***(G-14176)***
Independent Newsmedia Inc USA 863 983-9148
107 Sw 17th St Ste D Okeechobee (34974) ***(G-12182)***
Independent Printing, Daytona Beach *Also called Tiffany and Associates Inc* ***(G-2727)***
Independent Resources Inc (PA) 813 237-0945
5010 N Nebraska Ave Tampa (33603) ***(G-17777)***
Indian River All-Fab Inc 772 778-0032
1119 18th Pl Vero Beach (32960) ***(G-18629)***
Indian River Armature Inc 772 461-2067
120 Lakes End Dr Apt A Fort Pierce (34982) ***(G-4708)***
Indian River Biodiesel LLC 321 586-7670
1810 Okeechobee Rd Ste A West Palm Beach (33409) ***(G-18903)***
Indian River Brewery Corp 321 728-4114
200 Imperial Blvd Cape Canaveral (32920) ***(G-1361)***
Indian River Select, Stuart *Also called Freshco Ltd* ***(G-16942)***
Indian Rver Brwing C/Flrida Be, Cape Canaveral *Also called Indian River Brewery Corp* ***(G-1361)***
Indian Toners USA Company 954 600-5483
10625 Nw 69th Pl Parkland (33076) ***(G-13991)***
Indicali Inc 831 905-4780
15310 Amberly Dr Ste 250 Tampa (33647) ***(G-17778)***
Indigo Mountain Inc 239 947-0023
4280 Mourning Dove Dr Naples (34119) ***(G-11285)***
Indigo River Publishing 256 404-5884
3 W Garden St Ste 718 Pensacola (32502) ***(G-14177)***
Indoor Trampoline Arena Inc 321 222-1300
605 Hickman Cir Sanford (32771) ***(G-16065)***
Indra Systems Inc 407 567-1977
3505 Lake Lynda Dr # 200 Orlando (32817) ***(G-12827)***
Inductive Technologies Inc 727 536-7861
5410 115th Ave N Clearwater (33760) ***(G-1731)***
Inductoweld Tube Corp 646 734-7094
3350 Ne 33rd Ave Fort Lauderdale (33308) ***(G-4057)***
Industrial & Marine Maint 813 622-8338
5511 24th Ave S Tampa (33619) ***(G-17779)***
Industrial Brush Corporation 863 647-5643
4000 Drane Field Rd Lakeland (33811) ***(G-7709)***
Industrial Cmpsite Systems LLC 863 646-8551
4225 Drane Field Rd Lakeland (33811) ***(G-7710)***
Industrial Cnstr Svcs Dsign In (PA) 904 827-9795
4405 Sartillo Rd Ste A Saint Augustine (32095) ***(G-15555)***
Industrial Cnveyor Systems Inc 305 255-0200
18693 Sw 103rd Ct Cutler Bay (33157) ***(G-2398)***
Industrial Coating Solutions 813 333-8988
7307 Yardley Way Tampa (33647) ***(G-17780)***
Industrial Conveyor Belt 904 345-3046
2475 Lloyd Rd Jacksonville (32254) ***(G-6492)***
Industrial Filter Pump Mfg Co 708 656-7800
2680 Us Highway 1 Mims (32754) ***(G-10951)***
Industrial Galvanizers Miami, Miami *Also called Industrial Glvanizers Amer Inc* ***(G-9739)***
Industrial Galvanizers Miami 305 681-8844
3350 Nw 119th St Miami (33167) ***(G-9738)***

Industrial Galvanizers Tampa, Tampa *Also called Industrial Glvanizers Amer Inc* ***(G-17781)***
Industrial Glvanizers Amer Inc.......813 621-8990
9520 E Broadway Ave Tampa (33619) ***(G-17781)***
Industrial Glvanizers Amer Inc.......305 681-8844
3350 Nw 119th St Miami (33167) ***(G-9739)***
Industrial Glvnzers Stheastern.......813 621-8990
3350 Nw 119th St Miami (33167) ***(G-9740)***
Industrial Marine Inc.......904 781-4707
7259 Old Plank Rd Jacksonville (32254) ***(G-6493)***
Industrial Marking Eqp Co Inc.......561 626-8520
4152 Lazy Hammock Rd Palm Beach Gardens (33410) ***(G-13596)***
Industrial Marking Svcs Inc.......727 541-7622
10830 Canal St Ste C Largo (33777) ***(G-7979)***
Industrial Mobile Hydraulics.......904 866-7592
1180 Lane Ave N Jacksonville (32254) ***(G-6494)***
Industrial Nanotech Inc.......800 767-3998
1415 Panther Ln Naples (34109) ***(G-11286)***
Industrial Oviedo LLC.......786 350-8153
7601 E Trsore Dr Unit 121 Miami Beach (33141) ***(G-10682)***
Industrial Plastic Pdts Inc.......305 822-3223
14025 Nw 58th Ct Miami Lakes (33014) ***(G-10797)***
Industrial Plastic Systems, Lakeland *Also called Industrial Cmpsite Systems LLC* ***(G-7710)***
Industrial Plastic Systems Inc.......863 646-8551
4225 Drane Field Rd Lakeland (33811) ***(G-7711)***
Industrial Products Div, Fort Lauderdale *Also called Nasco Industries Inc* ***(G-4131)***
Industrial Projects Services.......813 265-2957
4102 W Linebaugh Ave # 103 Tampa (33624) ***(G-17782)***
Industrial Repair, Jacksonville *Also called Liddys Machine Shop Inc* ***(G-6556)***
Industrial Repair Inc.......239 368-7435
551 Westgate Blvd Ste 111 Lehigh Acres (33971) ***(G-8192)***
Industrial Scan Inc.......407 322-3664
223 Hickman Dr Ste 109 Sanford (32771) ***(G-16066)***
Industrial Service Solutions (PA).......239 288-5230
10070 Dnels Intrstate Ct Fort Myers (33913) ***(G-4493)***
Industrial Shadeports Inc.......954 755-0661
6600 Nw 12th Ave Ste 220 Fort Lauderdale (33309) ***(G-4058)***
Industrial Shredders LLC.......941 753-2815
1920 Whitfield Ave Sarasota (34243) ***(G-16234)***
Industrial Smoke & Mirrors Inc.......407 299-9400
3024 Shader Rd Orlando (32808) ***(G-12828)***
Industrial Spring Corp.......954 524-2558
3129 Peachtree Cir Davie (33328) ***(G-2537)***
Industrial Technology, Riviera Beach *Also called Tera Industries Inc* ***(G-15384)***
Industrial Technology LLC.......877 224-5534
6310 Techster Blvd Ste 3 Fort Myers (33966) ***(G-4494)***
Industrial Welding & Maint.......352 799-3432
10080 Cobb Rd Brooksville (34601) ***(G-1236)***
Industrias De Aslntes Y Acero, Miami *Also called Agrotek Services Incorporated* ***(G-9089)***
Industry Standard Technology.......941 355-2100
1868 University Pkwy Sarasota (34243) ***(G-16235)***
Industry Weapon Inc.......877 344-8450
4033 Tampa Rd Ste 103 Oldsmar (34677) ***(G-12235)***
Industry West, Jacksonville *Also called England Trading Company LLC* ***(G-6365)***
Inen USA Corp.......305 343-6666
12750 Cairo Ln Opa Locka (33054) ***(G-12325)***
Ineos New Planet Bioenergy LLC.......772 794-7900
925 74th Ave Sw Vero Beach (32968) ***(G-18630)***
Infinite Lasers LLC.......850 424-3759
45 Harbor Blvd Destin (32541) ***(G-3195)***
Infinite Print LLC.......727 942-2121
1014 Us Highway 19 # 114 Holiday (34691) ***(G-5745)***
Infinite Ret Design & Mfg Corp.......305 967-8339
7320 Nw 36th Ave Miami (33147) ***(G-9741)***
Infiniti Digital Equipment Inc.......305 477-6333
10500 Nw 29th Ter Doral (33172) ***(G-3390)***
Infiniti Paint & Coatings, Deerfield Beach *Also called Lapolla Industries LLC* ***(G-2857)***
Infinity Embroidery, Miami *Also called VSF Corp* ***(G-10593)***
Infinity Manufactured Inds.......727 532-4453
12450 Enterprise Blvd Largo (33773) ***(G-7980)***
Infinity Manufacturing LLC.......954 531-6918
4811 Lyons Tech Pkwy Coconut Creek (33073) ***(G-2079)***
Infinity Pcb Inc.......321 804-8045
4195 W New Haven Ave Rear West Melbourne (32904) ***(G-18776)***
Infinity Signs & Graphix LLC.......407 270-6733
1887 Central Florida Pkwy Orlando (32837) ***(G-12829)***
Infinty Genome Sciences Inc.......321 327-7365
301 Riverside Dr Melbourne Beach (32951) ***(G-8979)***
Inflatable Design Works Corp.......786 242-1049
13350 Sw 131st St Unit 10 Miami (33186) ***(G-9742)***
Infopia USA LLC.......321 225-3620
7160 Bright Ave Cocoa (32927) ***(G-2031)***
Infor Public Sector Inc.......813 207-6911
3501 E Frontage Rd # 350 Tampa (33607) ***(G-17783)***
Informa Usa Inc.......561 361-6017
101 Paramount Dr Ste 100 Sarasota (34232) ***(G-16465)***
Information Builders Inc.......407 804-8000
300 Primera Blvd Ste 300 Lake Mary (32746) ***(G-7424)***
Information Mgt Svcs Inc.......386 677-5073
107 Sundance Trl Ormond Beach (32176) ***(G-13380)***
Informulate LLC.......866 222-2307
7437 Winding Lake Cir Oviedo (32765) ***(G-13439)***
Infotek Groups Inc.......612 666-0535
11150 4th St N Apt 3013 Saint Petersburg (33716) ***(G-15814)***
Infrared Associates Inc.......772 223-6670
2851 Se Monroe St Stuart (34997) ***(G-16958)***
Infrared Systems Dev Corp.......407 679-5101
7319 Sandscove Ct Ste 4 Winter Park (32792) ***(G-19413)***
Infrastructure Repair Systems.......727 327-4216
3113 Lown St N Saint Petersburg (33713) ***(G-15815)***
Infupharma LLC.......305 301-3389
6720 Tyler St Hollywood (33024) ***(G-5848)***
Ing Phrmctcal Pdts Prvate Lbel, Sunrise *Also called Interntnal Ntrctcals Group Inc* ***(G-17130)***
Ingeant Florida LLC.......954 868-2879
5163 Woodfield Way Coconut Creek (33073) ***(G-2080)***
Ingear, Miami Gardens *Also called In Gear Fashions Inc* ***(G-10747)***
Ingelub Corp.......407 656-8800
12935 W Colonial Dr Winter Garden (34787) ***(G-19270)***
Ingenus Pharmaceuticals LLC (PA).......407 354-5365
4190 Millenia Blvd Orlando (32839) ***(G-12830)***
Ingersoll Rand.......954 391-4500
2884 Corporate Way Miramar (33025) ***(G-11004)***
Ingersoll-Rand, Panama City *Also called Trane Technologies Company LLC* ***(G-13956)***
Inglotech Usa LLC.......305 479-2770
2020 Ponce De Leon Blvd # 1108 Coral Gables (33134) ***(G-2157)***
Ingram Signalization Inc.......850 433-8267
4522 N Davis Hwy Pensacola (32503) ***(G-14178)***
Ingrams Backhoe Dumptruck Svc.......850 718-6042
2155 Roark Rd Cottondale (32431) ***(G-2332)***
Ink & Toner Plus.......813 783-1650
10149 Connerly Rd Dade City (33525) ***(G-2429)***
Ink Bros Printing LLC.......407 494-9585
1372 Bennett Dr Unit 164 Longwood (32750) ***(G-8290)***
Ink Master Graphics, Jacksonville *Also called Time Printing Co Inc* ***(G-6856)***
Ink Publishing Corporation.......786 206-9867
806 S Douglas Rd Ste 300 Coral Gables (33134) ***(G-2158)***
Ink Publishing Corporation (HQ).......786 482-2065
800 Suth Dglas Rd Ste 250 Coral Gables (33134) ***(G-2159)***
Ink Trax Inc.......850 235-4849
238 W 5th St Panama City (32401) ***(G-13917)***
Inklab Signs Inc.......786 430-8100
12324 Sw 117th Ct Miami (33186) ***(G-9743)***
Inkpressions Inc.......305 261-0872
13804 Sw 83rd Ct Palmetto Bay (33158) ***(G-13849)***
Inky Fingers Printing Inc.......904 384-1900
2752 Park St Jacksonville (32205) ***(G-6495)***
Inland Specialties.......941 351-6300
7655 Matoaka Rd Sarasota (34243) ***(G-16236)***
Inland Specialties Inc.......941 756-1234
6424 Parkland Dr Sarasota (34243) ***(G-16237)***
Inline Filling Systems LLC.......941 486-8800
216 Seaboard Ave Venice (34285) ***(G-18556)***
Inman Orthodontic Labs Inc.......954 340-8477
3953 Nw 126th Ave Coral Springs (33065) ***(G-2260)***
Innergy.......941 815-8655
315 E Olympia Ave # 251 Punta Gorda (33950) ***(G-15210)***
Inneuroco Inc (PA).......954 742-5988
4635 Nw 103rd Ave Sunrise (33351) ***(G-17128)***
Innevape LLC.......631 957-6500
9718 Katy Dr Ste 2 Hudson (34667) ***(G-6029)***
Innfocus Inc.......305 378-2651
12415 Sw 136th Ave Ste 3 Miami (33186) ***(G-9744)***
Innocor Foam Tech - Acp Inc.......305 685-6341
3225 Nw 107th St Miami (33167) ***(G-9745)***
Innomed Technologies Inc (HQ).......800 200-9842
6601 Lyons Rd Ste B1 Coconut Creek (33073) ***(G-2081)***
Innova Eco Bldg Systems LLC.......305 455-7707
3300 Nw 110th St Miami (33167) ***(G-9746)***
Innova Gel, Miami *Also called Innova Softgel LLC* ***(G-9747)***
Innova Home LLC.......561 855-2450
6200 S Dixie Hwy West Palm Beach (33405) ***(G-18904)***
Innova Softgel LLC.......855 536-8872
14193 Sw 119th Ave Miami (33186) ***(G-9747)***
Innovate Audio Visual Inc.......561 249-1117
3460 Frlane Frms Rd Ste 1 Wellington (33414) ***(G-18720)***
Innovated Industrial Svcs Inc.......863 701-2711
1416 Chamber Dr Bartow (33830) ***(G-320)***
Innovatia Medical Systems LLC.......908 385-2802
450 Knights Run Ave # 1003 Tampa (33602) ***(G-17784)***
Innovatier Inc.......863 688-4548
2769 New Tampa Hwy Lakeland (33815) ***(G-7712)***
Innovation Marine Corporation.......941 355-7852
8011 15th St E Sarasota (34243) ***(G-16238)***
Innovations By Mirart, Pompano Beach *Also called Mirart Inc* ***(G-14764)***
Innovations Cabinets Corp.......305 458-9395
8887 Fontainebleau Blvd # 406 Miami (33172) ***(G-9748)***
Innovative Acquisition Co LLC, Jacksonville *Also called Innovative Cnstr Group LLC* ***(G-6496)***

Innovative Base Tech LLC 727 391-9009
5030 Seminole Blvd Saint Petersburg (33708) *(G-15816)*
Innovative Cabinet & Case Work, Clearwater *Also called Rich Maid Cabinets Inc (G-1860)*
Innovative Cnstr Group LLC (HQ) 904 398-5690
5216 Shad Rd Jacksonville (32257) *(G-6496)*
Innovative Contractors, Nokomis *Also called Innovative Fabricators Fla Inc (G-11582)*
Innovative Data Solutions, Orlando *Also called Powerdms Inc (G-13076)*
Innovative Designs of Sarasota 941 752-7779
6224 31st St E Ste 8 Bradenton (34203) *(G-1060)*
Innovative Fabricators Fla Inc 941 375-8668
104 Palmetto Rd W Nokomis (34275) *(G-11582)*
Innovative Fasteners LLC 561 542-2152
6601 Lyons Rd Ste I5 Coconut Creek (33073) *(G-2082)*
Innovative Flare LLC 561 247-2776
7750 Okeechobee Blvd 4-7 West Palm Beach (33411) *(G-18905)*
Innovative Heat Concepts LLC 305 248-4971
127 Sw 5th Ave Homestead (33030) *(G-5971)*
Innovative Indus Solutions Inc (PA) 561 733-1548
3020 High Ridge Rd Boynton Beach (33426) *(G-920)*
Innovative Ink, Lakeland *Also called Parkinson Enterprises Inc (G-7762)*
Innovative Instruments Inc 813 727-0676
8533 Queen Brooks Ct Temple Terrace (33637) *(G-18370)*
Innovative Machine Inc 386 418-8880
6115 Nw 123rd Pl Gainesville (32653) *(G-4942)*
Innovative Mfg Solutions LLC 904 647-5300
7949 Atl Blvd Unit 209 Jacksonville (32211) *(G-6497)*
Innovative Money Concepts 954 748-6197
12560 Nw 83rd Ct Parkland (33076) *(G-13992)*
Innovative PDT Solutions LLC 407 933-2029
2710 N John Young Pkwy Kissimmee (34741) *(G-7254)*
Innovative Powder Coating Inc 954 537-2558
550 Ne 33rd St Oakland Park (33334) *(G-11813)*
Innovative Power Solutions LLC 732 544-1075
2250 Whitfield Ave Sarasota (34243) *(G-16239)*
Innovative Products LLC 888 764-6478
1632 Ne 12th Ter Fort Lauderdale (33305) *(G-4059)*
Innovative Signs Inc 407 830-5155
957 Penfield Cv Sanford (32773) *(G-16067)*
Innovative Spine Care 813 920-3022
8333 Gunn Hwy Tampa (33626) *(G-17785)*
Innovative Steel Tech Inc 813 767-1746
12620 S Us Highway 41 Gibsonton (33534) *(G-5030)*
Innovative Support Systems 407 682-7570
1030 Sunshine Ln Ste 1000 Altamonte Springs (32714) *(G-51)*
Innovative Svc Solutions LLC 407 296-5211
3144 N John Young Pkwy Orlando (32804) *(G-12831)*
Innovative Tech By Design Inc 321 676-3194
2469 Palm Bay Rd Ne 9 Palm Bay (32905) *(G-13516)*
Innovtive Cabinets Closets Inc 904 475-2336
5772 Mining Ter Jacksonville (32257) *(G-6498)*
Innovtive Win Cncpts Doors Inc 561 493-2303
4336 Juniper Ter Boynton Beach (33436) *(G-921)*
Innquest Corporation 813 288-4900
500 N West Shore Blvd # 950 Tampa (33609) *(G-17786)*
Innquest Software, Tampa *Also called Innquest Corporation (G-17786)*
Inovart Inc 941 751-2324
2304 58th Ave E Bradenton (34203) *(G-1061)*
Inovinox Usa LLC 800 780-1017
7875 Sw 104th St Miami (33156) *(G-9749)*
Inox LLC 305 409-2764
19201 Collins Ave Ste 131 Sunny Isles Beach (33160) *(G-17079)*
Inox Stainless Specialist LLC 407 764-2456
1336 Sw 8th St Pompano Beach (33069) *(G-14731)*
Inperium Corp 305 901-5650
1111 Lincoln Rd Ste 760 Miami Beach (33139) *(G-10683)*
Inprodelca Inc 865 687-7921
702 Nw 170th Ter Pembroke Pines (33028) *(G-14042)*
Inprovit Vital Health, Orlando *Also called Vital Health Corporation (G-13308)*
Inquirer Newspapers Inc 772 257-6230
2046 Treasure Coast Plz Vero Beach (32960) *(G-18631)*
Inrad Optics Inc 941 544-8278
2935 51st St Sarasota (34234) *(G-16466)*
Insanejournalcom 561 315-9311
2372 Pinewood Ln West Palm Beach (33415) *(G-18906)*
Inseco Inc 239 939-1072
2897 South St Fort Myers (33916) *(G-4495)*
Inshore Power Boats, Odessa *Also called Bonefish Boatworks Llc (G-12108)*
Insight Cabinetry LLC 352 818-9708
2210 Grant Ave Eustis (32726) *(G-3709)*
Insight Risk Technologies LLC 863 804-6038
19455 Gulf Blvd Ste 5 Indian Shores (33785) *(G-6070)*
Insight Software LLC (HQ) 305 495-0022
3265 Meridian Pkwy # 112 Weston (33331) *(G-19142)*
Insightec Inc (HQ) 786 534-3849
801 Brickell Ave Ste 1600 Miami (33131) *(G-9750)*
Insl-X Coronado Lenmar, Orlando *Also called Complementary Coatings Corp (G-12608)*
Inspec Solutions LLC (PA) 866 467-7320
330 Carswell Ave Holly Hill (32117) *(G-5758)*
Inspecs USA LC 727 771-7710
30798 Us Highway 19 N Palm Harbor (34684) *(G-13740)*
Inspectech Aeroservice Inc 954 359-6766
902 Sw 34th St Fort Lauderdale (33315) *(G-4060)*
Inspiration Foam Inc 407 498-0040
2860 Nicole Ave Kissimmee (34744) *(G-7255)*
Inspire Inc 321 557-3247
137 Wishing Well Cir Sw Palm Bay (32908) *(G-13517)*
Inspire ME Bracelets 404 644-7771
3333 Ne 16th Pl Fort Lauderdale (33305) *(G-4061)*
Inspired Energy LLC 352 472-4855
25440 Nw 8th Pl Newberry (32669) *(G-11557)*
Inspired Surf Boards 904 347-8879
2310 Dobbs Rd Saint Augustine (32086) *(G-15556)*
Inspired Therapeutics LLC 339 222-0847
7309 S Highway A1a Melbourne Beach (32951) *(G-8980)*
Instabook Corp 352 332-1311
12300 Nw 56th Ave Gainesville (32653) *(G-4943)*
Instacrete Mobile Concrete 813 956-3741
6253 Candlewood Dr Zephyrhills (33544) *(G-19523)*
Instanatural LLC 800 290-6932
12001 Res Pkwy Ste 244 Orlando (32826) *(G-12832)*
Instant Call Center LLC 321 356-1587
126 Ingram Cir Longwood (32779) *(G-8291)*
Instant Imprints 224 764-2198
1915 Crown Hill Blvd Orlando (32828) *(G-12833)*
Instant Imprints 850 474-9184
570 Pheasant Ct Pensacola (32514) *(G-14179)*
Instant Locate Inc 800 431-0812
920 State Road 436 Casselberry (32707) *(G-1506)*
Instant Printing & Copy Center 727 849-1199
3307 Us Highway 19 Holiday (34691) *(G-5746)*
Instant Printing Services Inc 727 546-8036
8885 E Haines Ct Floral City (34436) *(G-3768)*
Instant Ps LLC 786 278-5007
8415 Sw 107th Ave Miami (33173) *(G-9751)*
Instant Signs of South Florida, Miami *Also called Galea Corporation (G-9611)*
Instasign 561 272-2323
155 Avenue L Delray Beach (33483) *(G-3091)*
Instatech Industries Inc 954 415-4392
9835 Lake Worth Rd Ste 16 Lake Worth (33467) *(G-7557)*
Instazorb International Inc 561 416-7302
500 Ne Spanish River Blvd Boca Raton (33431) *(G-565)*
Insteel Wire Products Company 904 275-2100
1 Wiremill Rd Sanderson (32087) *(G-15982)*
Institute For Prosthetic Advan 850 784-0320
2315 Ruth Hentz Ave Panama City (32405) *(G-13918)*
Institutional Eye Care LLC 866 604-2931
27499 Rvrview Ctr Blvd St Bonita Springs (34134) *(G-839)*
Institutional Products Inc 305 248-4955
1011 Nw 6th St Homestead (33030) *(G-5972)*
Instorescreen LLC 646 301-4690
2338 Immokalee Rd Naples (34110) *(G-11287)*
Instrument & Valve Services Co 904 741-6800
13350 Intl Pkwy Ste 102 Jacksonville (32218) *(G-6499)*
Instrument Publication 352 542-7716
521 Ne 452nd St Old Town (32680) *(G-12198)*
Instrument Transformers LLC 727 461-9413
1907 Calumet St Clearwater (33765) *(G-1732)*
Insty-Prints, Tallahassee *Also called Garvin Management Company Inc (G-17261)*
Insty-Prints, Boca Raton *Also called B J and ME Inc (G-438)*
Insty-Prints, Mary Esther *Also called Image Prtg & Digital Svcs Inc (G-8589)*
Insty-Prints 352 373-7547
327 Nw 23rd Ave Gainesville (32609) *(G-4944)*
Insulation Design & Dist LLC 850 332-7312
1879 Ziglar Rd Cantonment (32533) *(G-1341)*
Insulator Seal Incorporated (HQ) 941 751-2880
6460 Parkland Dr Sarasota (34243) *(G-16240)*
Insulow, Maitland *Also called Glucorell Inc (G-8466)*
Insurance Plus 904 567-1553
820 A1a N Ste W18 Ponte Vedra Beach (32082) *(G-14942)*
Intec Printing Solutions Corp 813 949-7799
16011 N Nebraska Ave Lutz (33549) *(G-8391)*
Intech Graphics, Naples *Also called Ngp Corporate Square Inc (G-11345)*
Intech Printing & Direct Mail, Naples *Also called Sosumi Holdings Inc (G-11407)*
Integ Construction Inc 305 440-9101
2451 Nw 109th Ave Unit 5 Doral (33172) *(G-3391)*
Integra Connect LLC (PA) 800 742-3069
501 S Flagler Dr Ste 600 West Palm Beach (33401) *(G-18907)*
Integral WD Cstm Cabinetry LLC 561 361-5111
176 Glades Rd Ste A Boca Raton (33432) *(G-566)*
Integrated Cable Solutions 813 769-5740
5905 Johns Rd Ste 101 Tampa (33634) *(G-17787)*
Integrated Components Corp 305 824-0484
2592 W 78th St Hialeah (33016) *(G-5454)*
Integrated Dealer Systems Inc 800 962-7872
640 Brooker Creek Blvd Oldsmar (34677) *(G-12236)*
Integrated Design & Develop 407 268-4300
410 W 4th St Sanford (32771) *(G-16068)*

ALPHABETIC

Integrated Diagnostics Group, Miami *Also called Sanzay Corporation* ***(G-10304)***
Integrated Laser Systems Inc...954 489-8282
11383 Lakeview Dr Coral Springs (33071) ***(G-2261)***
Integrated Metal Products Inc...863 687-4110
2923 Old Tampa Hwy Lakeland (33803) ***(G-7713)***
Integrated Surroundings Inc...850 932-0848
4333 Gulf Breeze Pkwy Gulf Breeze (32563) ***(G-5120)***
Integrated Systems & Services, Saint Petersburg *Also called Ysi Inc* ***(G-15968)***
Integritrust Solutions LLC...850 685-9801
2078 Bahama Dr Navarre (32566) ***(G-11466)***
Integrity Business Svcs Inc (PA)...321 267-9294
3700 S Hopkins Ave Ste E Titusville (32780) ***(G-18434)***
Integrity Implants Inc...800 201-9300
354 Hiatt Dr Ste 100 Palm Beach Gardens (33418) ***(G-13597)***
Integrity Medical, Jupiter *Also called Integrity Technologies LLC* ***(G-7057)***
Integrity Prosthetics...863 875-7063
135 1st St S Winter Haven (33880) ***(G-19330)***
Integrity Prsthetics Orthotics...813 416-5905
12206 Bruce B Downs Blvd Tampa (33612) ***(G-17788)***
Integrity Technologies LLC...561 768-9023
5270 Pennock Point Rd Jupiter (33458) ***(G-7057)***
Integrted Sign Engrg Dsign LLC...941 379-5918
7007 Webber Rd Sarasota (34240) ***(G-16467)***
Intelbase Security Corporation...703 371-9181
400 Night Hawk Ln Saint Augustine (32080) ***(G-15557)***
Inteli Drone Inc...954 707-9547
7141 Nw 48th Way Coconut Creek (33073) ***(G-2083)***
Inteliathlete Corp...305 987-1355
5501 Nw 105th Ct Doral (33178) ***(G-3392)***
Intellgent Haring Systems Corp (PA)...305 668-6102
6860 Sw 81st St Miami (33143) ***(G-9752)***
Intellgent Instrumentation Inc (PA)...520 573-0887
1421 Pine Ridge Rd # 120 Naples (34109) ***(G-11288)***
Intelliclean Solutions LLC (PA)...615 293-2299
444 Brickell Ave Ste 800 Miami (33131) ***(G-9753)***
Intelligent Heater LLC...305 248-4971
127 Sw 5th Ave Homestead (33030) ***(G-5973)***
Intelligent Robotics Inc...850 728-7353
3697 Longfellow Rd Tallahassee (32311) ***(G-17281)***
Intellitec Motor Vehicles LLC (HQ)...386 738-7307
1455 Jacobs Rd Deland (32724) ***(G-2984)***
Intellitech Inc...727 914-7000
11801 28th St N Ste 5 Saint Petersburg (33716) ***(G-15817)***
Inteplast Engineered Films Inc...407 851-6620
7549 Brokerage Dr Orlando (32809) ***(G-12834)***
Inter Cell Technologies Inc...561 575-6868
6671 W Indiantown Rd # 56439 Jupiter (33458) ***(G-7058)***
Inter Gard R&D LLC...954 476-5574
15491 Sw 12th St Sunrise (33326) ***(G-17129)***
Interactive Cards Inc...863 688-4548
2787 New Tampa Hwy Lakeland (33815) ***(G-7714)***
Interactive Legal, Melbourne *Also called Ils Management LLC* ***(G-8849)***
Interactyx Americas Inc...888 575-2266
3461 Bonita Bay Blvd # 2 Bonita Springs (34134) ***(G-840)***
Interamericas Beverages Inc...561 881-1340
1726 Avenue L Riviera Beach (33404) ***(G-15334)***
Interavia Spares and Svcs Inc...954 794-0174
746 Saint Albans Dr Boca Raton (33486) ***(G-567)***
Interbay Air Compressors Inc...813 831-8213
5110 S West Shore Blvd Tampa (33611) ***(G-17789)***
Interbeverage LLC...305 961-1110
3100 Nw 74th Ave Miami (33122) ***(G-9754)***
Intercit Inc...863 646-0165
4330 Drane Field Rd Lakeland (33811) ***(G-7715)***
Intercomp...407 637-9766
5910 Morningstar Cir Delray Beach (33484) ***(G-3092)***
Interconnect Cable Tech Corp...352 796-1716
16090 Flight Path Dr Brooksville (34604) ***(G-1237)***
Interface Technology Group Inc...321 433-1165
2107 Us Highway 1 Rockledge (32955) ***(G-15422)***
Interfries Inc (PA)...786 427-1427
18800 Ne 29th Ave Apt 426 Miami (33180) ***(G-9755)***
Interglobal Capital Inc...727 585-1500
1016 Pnc De Leon Blvd Clearwater (33756) ***(G-1733)***
Interior Design...646 805-0200
3651 Fau Blvd Ste 200 Boca Raton (33431) ***(G-568)***
Interior Dsign Media Group LLC...561 750-0151
3731 Fau Blvd Ste 1 Boca Raton (33431) ***(G-569)***
Interlachen Cabinets Inc...352 481-6078
2010 State Road 20 Hawthorne (32640) ***(G-5244)***
Interlake Industries Inc...863 688-5665
1022 County Line Rd Lakeland (33815) ***(G-7716)***
Interlake Stamping Florida Inc...863 688-5665
1022 County Line Rd Lakeland (33815) ***(G-7717)***
Interlink Software Inc...407 927-0898
8946 Leeland Archer Blvd Orlando (32836) ***(G-12835)***
Intermas Nets USA Inc...305 442-1416
2655 S Le Jeune Rd # 810 Coral Gables (33134) ***(G-2160)***
Intermed Group Inc (PA)...561 586-3667
13301 Nw Us Highway 441 Alachua (32615) ***(G-10)***
Intermedix Corporation (HQ)...954 308-8700
6451 N Federal Hwy # 1000 Fort Lauderdale (33308) ***(G-4062)***
Internano, Delray Beach *Also called Rave LLC* ***(G-3134)***
International Baler Corp...904 358-3812
5400 Rio Grande Ave Jacksonville (32254) ***(G-6500)***
International C & C Corp...727 249-0675
10831 Canal St Largo (33777) ***(G-7981)***
International Casting Corp...305 558-3515
6187 Miami Lakes Dr E Miami Lakes (33014) ***(G-10798)***
International Closet Center...305 883-6551
7330 Nw 79th Ter Medley (33166) ***(G-8670)***
International Clothiers Inc...914 715-5600
4000 Twrside Ter Ste 2412 Miami (33138) ***(G-9756)***
International Cnstr Pubg...305 668-4999
4913 Sw 75th Ave Miami (33155) ***(G-9757)***
International Composite...206 349-7468
1468 Northgate Blvd Sarasota (34234) ***(G-16468)***
International Dock Products...954 964-5315
3101 Sw 25th St Ste 106 Hallandale Beach (33009) ***(G-5191)***
International Draperies Inc...954 590-3897
1471 Banks Rd Margate (33063) ***(G-8550)***
International Epoxies Sealers, San Antonio *Also called S & R Fastener Co Inc* ***(G-15978)***
International Fd Solutions Inc (PA)...888 499-6888
5600 Elmhurst Cir Oviedo (32765) ***(G-13440)***
International Finishes Inc...561 948-1066
7777 Glades Rd Boca Raton (33434) ***(G-570)***
International Food Eqp Inc...305 785-5100
1280 Partridge Ave Miami Springs (33166) ***(G-10891)***
International Gran & Stone LLC...813 920-6500
1842 Gunn Hwy Odessa (33556) ***(G-12127)***
International Greenscapes LLC...760 631-6789
20855 Ne 16th Ave Ste C4 Miami (33179) ***(G-9758)***
International Guidelines Ctr...407 878-7606
106 Commerce St Ste 105 Lake Mary (32746) ***(G-7425)***
International H20 Inc...954 854-1638
18387 Ne 4th Ct North Miami Beach (33179) ***(G-11683)***
International Imaging Mtls Inc...727 834-8200
2300 Destiny Way Odessa (33556) ***(G-12128)***
International Iron Works LLC (PA)...305 835-0190
3585 E 10th Ct Hialeah (33013) ***(G-5455)***
International Jewelry Designs...954 577-9099
4750 N Dixie Hwy Ste 3 Oakland Park (33334) ***(G-11814)***
International Keg Rental LLC...407 900-9992
10450 Trkey Lk Rd Unit 69 Orlando (32819) ***(G-12836)***
International Machine Shop, Miami *Also called International Machine Works* ***(G-9759)***
International Machine Works...305 635-3585
3631 Nw 48th Ter Miami (33142) ***(G-9759)***
International Mdse Sources Inc (PA)...239 430-9993
4551 Gulf Shore Blvd N Naples (34103) ***(G-11289)***
International Medical Inds Inc...954 917-9570
2981 Gateway Dr Pompano Beach (33069) ***(G-14732)***
International Ozone Svcs LLC...352 978-9785
320924 Sunnygo Dr Ste 210 Mount Dora (32757) ***(G-11105)***
International Packaging Mchs...239 643-2020
3963 Enterprise Ave Naples (34104) ***(G-11290)***
International Paint LLC...321 636-9722
3062 Oxbow Cir Cocoa (32926) ***(G-2032)***
International Paint LLC...305 620-9220
3489 Nw 167th St Opa Locka (33056) ***(G-12326)***
International Polymer Svcs LLC...401 529-6855
3431 Mai Kai Dr Pensacola (32526) ***(G-14180)***
International Power USA LLC...305 534-7993
2091 Nw 139th St Miami (33015) ***(G-9760)***
International Printing & Copyi...954 295-5239
5379 Lyons Rd Coconut Creek (33073) ***(G-2084)***
International Prtg Ad Spc Inc...772 398-4664
701 Nw Federal Hwy # 301 Stuart (34994) ***(G-16959)***
International Quiksigns Inc...954 462-7446
804 Se 17th St Fort Lauderdale (33316) ***(G-4063)***
International Ship Repair & MA...813 247-1118
1601 Sahlman Dr Tampa (33605) ***(G-17790)***
International Shipyards Ancona...305 371-7722
1850 Se 17th St Ste 200 Fort Lauderdale (33316) ***(G-4064)***
International Sign Design Corp...727 541-5573
10831 Canal St Largo (33777) ***(G-7982)***
International Signs & Ltg Inc...407 332-9663
714 Commerce Cir Longwood (32750) ***(G-8292)***
International Sound Corp...305 556-1000
1550 W 35th Pl Hialeah (33012) ***(G-5456)***
International Specialist, Tampa *Also called Phil Lau* ***(G-17989)***
International Specialists Inc (PA)...813 631-8643
15424 N Nebraska Ave Lutz (33549) ***(G-8392)***
International Tool Mchs of Fla...386 446-0500
5 Industry Dr Palm Coast (32137) ***(G-13699)***
International Trading Company, Opa Locka *Also called Lear Investors Inc* ***(G-12333)***
International Treescapes, Miami *Also called International Greenscapes LLC* ***(G-9758)***
International Uniform, Miami *Also called Interntnal Export Uniforms Inc* ***(G-9761)***
International Vapor Group LLC (HQ)...305 824-4027
14300 Commerce Way Miami Lakes (33016) ***(G-10799)***

International Vault Inc 941 390-4505
16227 Daysailor Trl Lakewood Ranch (34202) ***(G-7839)***
International Weatherization 954 818-3288
500 E Broward Blvd # 1710 Fort Lauderdale (33394) ***(G-4065)***
Internl Sterilization Lab LLC 352 429-3200
217 Sampey Rd Groveland (34736) ***(G-5097)***
Interntnal Export Uniforms Inc 305 869-9900
4000 Nw 29th St Miami (33142) ***(G-9761)***
Interntnal Ntrctcals Group Inc 786 518-2903
771 Shotgun Rd Sunrise (33326) ***(G-17130)***
Interntnal Pckg Athntic Cisine, Winter Springs *Also called Ipac Inc* ***(G-19474)***
Interntnal Srvillance Tech Inc (PA) 954 574-1100
160 Sw 12th Ave Deerfield Beach (33442) ***(G-2847)***
Interntnal Synrgy For Tchncal 321 305-0863
12001 Res Pkwy Ste 236 Orlando (32826) ***(G-12837)***
Interntnal Tech Sltons Sup LLC 305 364-5229
2636 Nw 97th Ave Doral (33172) ***(G-3393)***
Interntonal Linear Matrix Corp 727 549-1808
10831 Canal St Seminole (33777) ***(G-16748)***
Interplex Labs Ltd 954 718-9953
6690 N Hiatus Rd Tamarac (33321) ***(G-17358)***
Interprint Incorporated (HQ) 727 531-8957
12350 Us 19 N Clearwater (33764) ***(G-1734)***
Interprint Web Printing, Clearwater *Also called Interprint Incorporated* ***(G-1734)***
Interrail Engineering Inc 904 268-6411
12443 San Jose Blvd # 1103 Jacksonville (32223) ***(G-6501)***
Interrail Power Inc 904 268-6411
12443 San Jose Blvd Jacksonville (32223) ***(G-6502)***
Interstate Electronics Corp 321 730-0119
Air Force Sta Bldg 54815 Cape Canaveral (32920) ***(G-1362)***
Interstate Recycling Waste 407 812-5555
5232 Laval Dr Orlando (32839) ***(G-12838)***
Interstate Signcrafters LLC 561 547-3760
130 Commerce Rd Boynton Beach (33426) ***(G-922)***
Interstate Wldg & Fabrication 727 446-1449
1939 Sherwood St Clearwater (33765) ***(G-1735)***
Intertape Polymer Corp (HQ) 888 898-7834
100 Paramount Dr Ste 300 Sarasota (34232) ***(G-16469)***
Intertape Polymer Corp 813 621-8410
9940 Currie Davis Dr Tampa (33619) ***(G-17791)***
Intertape Polymer Group, Sarasota *Also called Ipg (us) Holdings Inc* ***(G-16471)***
Intertape Polymr Woven USA Inc (HQ) 800 474-8273
100 Paramount Dr Ste 300 Sarasota (34232) ***(G-16470)***
Intertech Supply Inc 786 200-0561
13334 Sw 9th Ter Miami (33184) ***(G-9762)***
Intertech Worldwide Corp (PA) 561 395-5441
4400 N Federal Hwy # 125 Boca Raton (33431) ***(G-571)***
Intertek Auto-Sun-Shade, Hialeah *Also called Intertek International Corp* ***(G-5457)***
Intertek International Corp 305 883-8700
401 Se 11th Ave Hialeah (33010) ***(G-5457)***
Intertex Miami LLC 305 627-3536
50 Ne 179th St Bay 1-2 Miami (33162) ***(G-9763)***
Intgrated Arospc Aliance LLC 469 703-7093
188 E Crystal Lake Ave # 132 Lake Mary (32746) ***(G-7426)***
Intouch Inc 702 572-4786
5036 Dr Phillips Blvd Orlando (32819) ***(G-12839)***
Intouch Gps LLC 877 593-2981
439 S Florida Ave 100b Lakeland (33801) ***(G-7718)***
Intradeco Apparel Inc (HQ) 305 264-8888
9500 Nw 108th Ave Medley (33178) ***(G-8671)***
Intralock International Inc 561 447-8282
6560 W Rogers Cir Ste 24 Boca Raton (33487) ***(G-572)***
Intratab Labs Inc 305 887-5850
424 Hunting Lodge Dr Miami Springs (33166) ***(G-10892)***
Intrepid Machine Inc 352 540-9919
2305 Circuit Way Brooksville (34604) ***(G-1238)***
Intrepid Machine Inc 813 854-3825
12020 Race Track Rd Tampa (33626) ***(G-17792)***
Intrepid Powerboats Inc (PA) 954 324-4196
805 Ne E 3rd St Dania (33004) ***(G-2448)***
Intrepid Precast Inc 352 347-7475
470 Se 123rd Street Rd Ocala (34480) ***(G-11970)***
Intrinsic Interventions Inc 614 205-8465
223 Dolphin Cove Ct Bonita Springs (34134) ***(G-841)***
Intuition Ale Works, Jacksonville *Also called Rpd Management LLC* ***(G-6738)***
Intuitos LLC 727 522-2301
2300 Tall Pines Dr # 120 Largo (33771) ***(G-7983)***
Inusa Manufacturing LLC 786 451-5227
2500 Sw 32nd Ave Pembroke Park (33023) ***(G-14009)***
Invacare Florida Corporation 407 321-5630
2101 E Lake Mary Blvd Sanford (32773) ***(G-16069)***
Invel, Orlando *Also called Goen3 Corporation* ***(G-12785)***
Inversiones Medicas SIS, Doral *Also called Ivan & Ivan LLC* ***(G-3397)***
Inversnes Wlldel Asociados Inc 305 591-0931
8250 Nw 58th St Doral (33166) ***(G-3394)***
Inversnes Wlldel Asociados Inc (PA) 305 591-0118
4700 Nw 72nd Ave Miami (33166) ***(G-9764)***
Invicta Corporation (PA) 561 995-9980
1160 S Rogers Cir Boca Raton (33487) ***(G-573)***
Invigicom Inc 407 491-6929
205 N Park Ave Ste 110 Apopka (32703) ***(G-149)***
Invincible Boat Company LLC 305 685-2704
4700 Nw 132nd St Opa Locka (33054) ***(G-12327)***
Inviro Tek Inc 215 499-1209
11334 Boggy Creek Rd # 1 Orlando (32824) ***(G-12840)***
Invision Auto Systems Inc 407 956-5161
3001 Directors Row Orlando (32809) ***(G-12841)***
Invision Auto Systems Inc (HQ) 407 956-5161
2351 J Lawson Blvd Orlando (32824) ***(G-12842)***
Invision Industries Inc 407 451-8353
2351 J Lawson Blvd Orlando (32824) ***(G-12843)***
Invivo Corporation (HQ) 301 525-9683
3545 Sw 47th Ave Gainesville (32608) ***(G-4945)***
Invivo Corporation 352 336-0010
3600 Sw 47th Ave Gainesville (32608) ***(G-4946)***
Invo Bioscience Inc 978 878-9505
5582 Broadcast Ct Lakewood Ranch (34240) ***(G-7844)***
Invoinet Inc (HQ) 305 432-5366
1111 Brickell Ave # 1860 Miami (33131) ***(G-9765)***
Inzirillo 954 486-0055
2051 Nw 29th St Oakland Park (33311) ***(G-11815)***
Iomartcloud Inc 954 880-1680
601 21st St Vero Beach (32960) ***(G-18632)***
Ionemoto Inc 617 784-1401
300 Industrial Cir Sebastian (32958) ***(G-16663)***
IPA Prosthetics & Orthotics, Panama City *Also called Institute For Prosthetic Advan* ***(G-13918)***
Ipac Inc 407 699-7507
1270 Belle Ave Unit 115 Winter Springs (32708) ***(G-19474)***
IPC Global 727 470-2134
1062 Cephas Rd Clearwater (33765) ***(G-1736)***
Ipeg Corporation 239 963-1470
5400 Jaeger Rd Ste 2 Naples (34109) ***(G-11291)***
Ipg (us) Holdings Inc (HQ) 941 727-5788
100 Paramount Dr Ste 300 Sarasota (34232) ***(G-16471)***
Ipg (us) Inc (HQ) 941 727-5788
100 Paramount Dr Ste 300 Sarasota (34232) ***(G-16472)***
Ipg Network Corp 305 681-4001
3155 Nw 40th St Miami (33142) ***(G-9766)***
Ipline LLC 305 675-4235
18152 Sw 144th Ct Miami (33177) ***(G-9767)***
Ipq Trade Corp 786 522-2310
488 Ne 18th St Ste Cu1 Miami (33132) ***(G-9768)***
Iprint 3d USA 888 868-7329
2550 N Powerline Rd # 103 Pompano Beach (33069) ***(G-14733)***
Ipro Force LLC 603 766-8716
6929 Corley Ave Windermere (34786) ***(G-19229)***
Ips, Lakeland *Also called Industrial Plastic Systems Inc* ***(G-7711)***
Ips, Sarasota *Also called Innovative Power Solutions LLC* ***(G-16239)***
Ipts Inc 561 844-8216
7221 Hvrhill Bus Pkwy # 103 Riviera Beach (33407) ***(G-15335)***
Ipvision Software LLC 813 728-3175
5905 Johns Rd Tampa (33634) ***(G-17793)***
Iq Dominoes Corp 305 967-8583
11740 Sw 14th St Miami (33184) ***(G-9769)***
Iq Formulations Llc 954 533-9256
10151 Nw 67th St Tamarac (33321) ***(G-17359)***
Iq Valves Co 321 729-9634
425 West Dr Melbourne (32904) ***(G-8851)***
Ir Clinical, West Palm Beach *Also called Clinical Chmstry Spclists Corp* ***(G-18847)***
Iradimed Corporation 407 677-8022
1025 Willa Springs Dr Winter Springs (32708) ***(G-19475)***
Ireco Inc 239 593-3749
9929 Clear Lake Cir Naples (34109) ***(G-11292)***
Iris Inc 561 921-0847
955 Nw 17th Ave Ste D Delray Beach (33445) ***(G-3093)***
Iris Diagnostics, Miami *Also called Beckman Coulter Inc* ***(G-9231)***
Iris International Inc (HQ) 818 709-1244
11800 Sw 147th Ave Miami (33196) ***(G-9770)***
Irms Inc 321 631-1161
2191 Rockledge Dr Rockledge (32955) ***(G-15423)***
Iron Bridge Tools Inc 954 596-1090
101 Ne 3rd Ave Ste 1800 Fort Lauderdale (33301) ***(G-4066)***
Iron Container LLC (PA) 305 726-2150
8505 Nw 74th St Miami (33166) ***(G-9771)***
Iron Sharpens Ir Training LLC 407 614-4500
2038 Black Lake Blvd Winter Garden (34787) ***(G-19271)***
Iron Sight Precision LLC 561 735-9971
711 N Railroad Ave Boynton Beach (33435) ***(G-923)***
Iron Strength Corp 305 226-6866
9568 Sw 40th St Miami (33165) ***(G-9772)***
Iron-Art & Fence Inc 407 699-1734
731 N Us Highway 17 92 # 201 Longwood (32750) ***(G-8293)***
Ironbeer Soft Drink, Doral *Also called Sunshine Bottling Co* ***(G-3517)***
Ironclad Impact Wndows Dors LL 954 743-4321
3701 Sw 47th Ave Ste 106 Davie (33314) ***(G-2538)***
Ironclad Welding Inc 954 925-7987
1205 Sw 4th Ave Dania (33004) ***(G-2449)***

ALPHABETIC

Ironhorse Pressworks Inc....727 462-9988
406 S Jupiter Ave Clearwater (33755) ***(G-1737)***
Ironwifi LLC....800 963-6221
3071 N Orange Blossom Trl C Orlando (32804) ***(G-12844)***
Ironworks Inc of Orange Park....904 291-9330
1701 Blanding Blvd Middleburg (32068) ***(G-10907)***
Irvin Technologies Inc....866 245-9356
1081 Willa Springs Dr Winter Springs (32708) ***(G-19476)***
Irving Publications LLC....352 219-4688
5745 Sw 75th St Unit 286 Gainesville (32608) ***(G-4947)***
Is4ts, Orlando *Also called Interntnal Synrgy For Tchncal* ***(G-12837)***
ISA Group Corp....305 748-1578
2665 S Byshr Dr Ste 710 Miami (33133) ***(G-9773)***
ISA Group Corp....786 201-8360
1204 Placetas Ave Coral Gables (33146) ***(G-2161)***
Iscar Ground Services Eqp, Miami Gardens *Also called Iscar GSE Corp* ***(G-10749)***
Iscar GSE Corp....305 364-8886
1182 Nw 159th Dr Miami Gardens (33169) ***(G-10748)***
Iscar GSE Corp....305 364-8886
1180 Nw 159th Dr Miami Gardens (33169) ***(G-10749)***
Isl, Groveland *Also called Internl Sterilization Lab LLC* ***(G-5097)***
Isla Instruments LLC....561 603-4685
13884 71st Pl N West Palm Beach (33412) ***(G-18908)***
Islamorada Boatworks LLC....786 393-4752
4501 S Ridgewood Ave Edgewater (32141) ***(G-3626)***
Island Designs Outlet Inc....813 855-0020
14501 Mccormick Dr Tampa (33626) ***(G-17794)***
Island Dream Itln Ice Dssrts L....904 778-6839
9501 Arlington Expy Fc4 Jacksonville (32225) ***(G-6503)***
Island Fever LLC....941 639-6400
1200 W Retta Esplanade # 19 Punta Gorda (33950) ***(G-15211)***
Island Joys....561 201-6005
3679 Nw 19th St Fort Lauderdale (33311) ***(G-4067)***
Island Lifestyle Importers LLC....941 378-3200
426 Interstate Ct Sarasota (34240) ***(G-16473)***
Island Media Publishing LLC....904 556-3002
120 N 15th St Fernandina Beach (32034) ***(G-3739)***
Island Millwork Inc....352 694-5565
3621 Ne 36th Ave Ocala (34479) ***(G-11971)***
Island Park Custom Woodworking....239 437-9670
16270 Old Us 41 Fort Myers (33912) ***(G-4496)***
Island Paver Sealing & Prssure....727 641-3512
13584 49th St N Ste 2 Clearwater (33762) ***(G-1738)***
Island Pcket Saward Yachts LLC....727 535-6431
1979 Wild Acres Rd Largo (33771) ***(G-7984)***
Island Print Shop....239 642-0077
3888 Mannix Dr Ste 301 Naples (34114) ***(G-11293)***
Island Salt Company LLC....954 610-2590
900 Se 6th St Fort Lauderdale (33301) ***(G-4068)***
Island Sand Paper....239 290-4038
450 Old San Carlos Blvd Fort Myers Beach (33931) ***(G-4664)***
Island Shutter Co Inc....386 738-9455
1838 Patterson Ave Deland (32724) ***(G-2985)***
Island Style Homes Inc....772 464-6259
4275 Mariah Cir Fort Pierce (34947) ***(G-4709)***
Island Sun Newspaper, Sanibel *Also called Lorken Publications Inc* ***(G-16147)***
Island The Reporter Inc....727 631-4730
1331 Sea Gull Dr S Saint Petersburg (33707) ***(G-15818)***
Island Tops, Jacksonville *Also called Fastglas* ***(G-6380)***
Islander, Key Biscayne *Also called Samara Publishing* ***(G-7162)***
Islandoor Company....954 524-3667
951 Nw 9th Ave Fort Lauderdale (33311) ***(G-4069)***
Isle of Luxe Inc....352 745-0515
701 Market St Ste 111 Saint Augustine (32095) ***(G-15558)***
ISO Panel, Medley *Also called Mr Winter Inc* ***(G-8693)***
Isoaid LLC....727 815-3262
7824 Clark Moody Blvd Port Richey (34668) ***(G-15054)***
Isocialmedia Digital Marketing....561 510-1124
433 Plaza Real Ste 275 Boca Raton (33432) ***(G-574)***
Isoflex Technologies Intl LLC....561 210-5170
3434 Sw 15th St B Deerfield Beach (33442) ***(G-2848)***
Isolyser, Jacksonville *Also called Microtek Medical Inc* ***(G-6603)***
Isp Optics Corporation (HQ)....914 591-3070
2603 Challenger Tech Ct # 100 Orlando (32826) ***(G-12845)***
Ispg Inc....941 896-3999
10504 Technology Ter Bradenton (34211) ***(G-1062)***
Ispy Equities....813 731-0676
12309 Field Point Way Spring Hill (34610) ***(G-16873)***
It Busness Solutions Group Inc....407 260-0116
800 Waterway Pl Longwood (32750) ***(G-8294)***
It Had To Be Told Pubg LLC....813 810-5961
330 Inner Harbour Cir Tampa (33602) ***(G-17795)***
It Is Finished Inc....813 598-9585
24851 Ravello St Land O Lakes (34639) ***(G-7857)***
It Labs LLC....310 490-6142
1810 Flower Dr Palm Beach Gardens (33410) ***(G-13598)***
It Manex LLC....954 442-4465
16140 Sw 51st St Miramar (33027) ***(G-11005)***

It Smells Good....904 899-2818
1705 W 4th St Jacksonville (32209) ***(G-6504)***
It's A "10" Haircare, Coral Springs *Also called Its A 10 Inc* ***(G-2262)***
Ita Inc....386 301-5172
9 W Tower Cir Ste C Ormond Beach (32174) ***(G-13381)***
Italfloor Tile, Fort Lauderdale *Also called Colaianni Italian Flr Tile Mfg* ***(G-3909)***
Italian Cabinetry Inc....786 534-2742
3250 Ne 1st Ave Ste 305 Miami (33137) ***(G-9774)***
Italian Cast Stones Inc....813 902-8900
5418 W Ingraham St Tampa (33616) ***(G-17796)***
Italian Hair Extension Inc....954 839-5366
10770 Nw 53rd St Sunrise (33351) ***(G-17131)***
Italian Moonshiners Inc....954 687-4500
8300 Nw 53rd St Ste 350 Doral (33166) ***(G-3395)***
Italian Rose Garlic Pdts LLC (HQ)....561 863-5556
1380 W 15th St Riviera Beach (33404) ***(G-15336)***
Italkraft LLC (PA)....305 406-1301
2900 Nw 77th Ct Doral (33122) ***(G-3396)***
Italy Tile and Marble Inc (PA)....941 488-5646
2085 A1a S Ste 304 Saint Augustine (32080) ***(G-15559)***
Itct USA....352 799-1466
16090 Flight Path Dr Brooksville (34604) ***(G-1239)***
Itd Food Safety, Palm Bay *Also called Innovative Tech By Design Inc* ***(G-13516)***
Iteg LLC....305 399-2510
333 Las Olas Way Cu1 Fort Lauderdale (33301) ***(G-4070)***
Itelecom USA Inc....305 557-4660
1422 Canary Island Dr Weston (33327) ***(G-19143)***
Iter3d Inc....718 473-0114
2221 Ne 164th St Ste 296 Aventura (33160) ***(G-274)***
Itg Cigars Inc (HQ)....954 772-9000
5900 N Andrews Ave Ste 11 Fort Lauderdale (33309) ***(G-4071)***
ITM, Palm Coast *Also called International Tool Mchs of Fla* ***(G-13699)***
Itnorlando Inc....407 900-7572
1201 S Orlando Ave # 205 Winter Park (32789) ***(G-19414)***
Itqlick Inc....855 487-5425
2100 E Hlnd Bch Blvd # 203 Hallandale Beach (33009) ***(G-5192)***
Its A 10 Inc....954 227-7813
4613 N University Dr # 478 Coral Springs (33067) ***(G-2262)***
Its Technologies Logistics LLC....904 751-1300
8831 Moncrief Dinsmore Rd Jacksonville (32219) ***(G-6505)***
ITT Flygt Corp....239 633-2553
5771 Country Lakes Dr Fort Myers (33905) ***(G-4497)***
ITW Professional Auto Pdts, Lakeland *Also called Illinois Tool Works Inc* ***(G-7708)***
Ityx Solutions Inc....407 474-4383
2915 Musselwhite Ave Orlando (32804) ***(G-12846)***
Iva Parts Broker LLC....239 222-2604
2708 Sw 165th Ave Miramar (33027) ***(G-11006)***
Ivan & Ivan LLC....305 507-8793
1465 Nw 97th Ave Doral (33172) ***(G-3397)***
Ivax Corporation (HQ)....305 329-3795
4400 Biscayne Blvd Miami (33137) ***(G-9775)***
Ivax Pharmaceuticals LLC (HQ)....305 575-6000
74 Nw 176th St Miami (33169) ***(G-9776)***
Ivax Research Inc (HQ)....305 668-7688
4400 Biscayne Blvd Miami (33137) ***(G-9777)***
Ivax Teva....954 384-5316
2945 W Corp Lks Blvd A Weston (33331) ***(G-19144)***
Ivengo Software Inc....321 480-3155
1378 Tipperary Dr Melbourne (32940) ***(G-8852)***
Iver Services....786 329-3018
2381 Ne 135th Ter North Miami Beach (33181) ***(G-11684)***
Iverica Industrial Inc....305 691-1659
1044 E 29th St Hialeah (33013) ***(G-5458)***
Ivm Usa Inc....786 693-2755
800 Brickell Ave Ste 550 Miami (33131) ***(G-9778)***
Ivory International Inc (HQ)....305 687-2244
9500 Nw 108th Ave Medley (33178) ***(G-8672)***
Izzycue, Miami *Also called Bkn International Inc* ***(G-9254)***
J & A Big Pavers LLC....321 948-0019
6214 W Robinson St Orlando (32835) ***(G-12847)***
J & A Custom Cabinetry Inc....786 255-4181
15825 Sw 285th St Homestead (33033) ***(G-5974)***
J & D Manufacturing Inc....813 854-1700
375 Mears Blvd Oldsmar (34677) ***(G-12237)***
J & D Oldja LLC....727 526-3240
4424 34th St N Saint Petersburg (33714) ***(G-15819)***
J & E Custom Cabinets....727 868-2820
9926 Denton Ave Port Richey (34667) ***(G-15055)***
J & G Explosives LLC....407 883-0734
413 Idlewyld Dr Fort Lauderdale (33301) ***(G-4072)***
J & H Supply Co Inc....561 582-3346
825 N Dixie Hwy Lake Worth (33460) ***(G-7558)***
J & I Ventures Inc....561 845-0030
4390 Westroads Dr Ste 2 West Palm Beach (33407) ***(G-18909)***
J & J Custom Mica Inc....239 433-2828
9971 Bavaria Rd Fort Myers (33913) ***(G-4498)***
J & J Door Manufacturing Inc....850 769-2554
2325 Transmitter Rd Panama City (32404) ***(G-13919)***
J & J Dynamic Products LLC....863 274-5333
2730 Drane Field Rd Lakeland (33811) ***(G-7719)***

J & J Inc...954 746-7300
10062 Nw 50th St Sunrise (33351) ***(G-17132)***
J & J International Corp...407 349-7114
240 Power Ct Ste 132 Sanford (32771) ***(G-16070)***
J & J Litho Enterprises Inc (PA)...239 433-2311
6835 Intl Ctr Blvd Ste 8 Fort Myers (33912) ***(G-4499)***
J & J Marine Service Inc...813 741-2190
2922 46th Ave N Saint Petersburg (33714) ***(G-15820)***
J & J Refregrator, Miami *Also called Coldflo Inc* ***(G-9378)***
J & J Steel Services Corp...305 878-8929
9401 Nw 109th St Unit 5 Medley (33178) ***(G-8673)***
J & J Stone Tops Inc...305 305-8993
13760 Nw 19th Ave Opa Locka (33054) ***(G-12328)***
J & J Wldg Stl Fbrction Fla In...813 754-0771
364 Recker Hwy Auburndale (33823) ***(G-246)***
J & K 8 Inc...954 984-8585
1591 N Powerline Rd Pompano Beach (33069) ***(G-14734)***
J & N Stone Inc...941 924-6200
6111 Clark Center Ave Sarasota (34238) ***(G-16474)***
J & N Stone Inc (PA)...863 422-7369
135 Bargain Barn Rd Davenport (33837) ***(G-2480)***
J & P Deerfield Inc...954 571-6665
1191 W Newport Center Dr Deerfield Beach (33442) ***(G-2849)***
J & R Metal Fabrications, Jupiter *Also called Spring Loaded Inc* ***(G-7121)***
J & S Cypress Inc...352 383-3864
28625 Cypress Mill Rd Sorrento (32776) ***(G-16787)***
J & V Paverscorp...786 510-4389
2614 Sw 36th Ave Miami (33133) ***(G-9779)***
J A Custom...561 615-4680
3042 Ike Rd Ste 17 West Palm Beach (33411) ***(G-18910)***
J A Custom Fabricators Inc...561 615-4680
1230 Wingfield St Lake Worth (33460) ***(G-7559)***
J and A Maintenance...754 234-0708
6220 Nw 15th St Sunrise (33313) ***(G-17133)***
J B Nottingham & Co Inc...386 873-2990
1731 Patterson Ave Deland (32724) ***(G-2986)***
J B Woodworking Inc...850 362-6362
625 Valparaiso Pkwy # 202 Valparaiso (32580) ***(G-18512)***
J Bristol LLC...407 488-6744
2715 Norris Ave Winter Park (32789) ***(G-19415)***
J C & A of South Florida Inc...305 445-6665
3109 Grand Ave Miami (33133) ***(G-9780)***
J C Industries Inc...863 773-9199
6105 33rd St E Bradenton (34203) ***(G-1063)***
J C M I, Lakeland *Also called JC Machine Inc* ***(G-7721)***
J C Machine Shop, Miami *Also called JC Industrial Mfg Corp* ***(G-9789)***
J C Newman Cigar Co (PA)...813 248-2124
2701 N 16th St Tampa (33605) ***(G-17797)***
J C S Engineering & Dev...305 888-7911
211 W 22nd St Hialeah (33010) ***(G-5459)***
J Cube Inc...407 699-6866
180 E Trade Winds Rd Casselberry (32708) ***(G-1507)***
J D Aluminum...239 543-3558
18161 Sandy Pines Cir Fort Myers (33917) ***(G-4500)***
J D B Dense Flow Inc...727 785-8500
1004 Bee Pond Rd Palm Harbor (34683) ***(G-13741)***
J D M Corp...305 947-5876
1551 Nw 93rd Ave Doral (33172) ***(G-3398)***
J F Aerospace Inc...786 242-6686
12242 Sw 132nd Ct Miami (33186) ***(G-9781)***
J F V Designs Inc...321 228-7469
220 Southridge Indus Dr Tavares (32778) ***(G-18343)***
J Herbert Corporation...407 846-0588
1751 S John Young Pkwy Kissimmee (34741) ***(G-7256)***
J I S Associates...321 777-6829
445 Cardinal Dr Satellite Beach (32937) ***(G-16652)***
J J Cabinets Appliances...786 573-0300
8833 Sw 129th St Miami (33176) ***(G-9782)***
J J M Services Inc...954 437-1880
12004 Miramar Pkwy Miramar (33025) ***(G-11007)***
J J Taylor Distributing Fla, Fort Myers *Also called JJ Taylor Distrg Fla Inc* ***(G-4504)***
J K & M Ink Corporation...813 875-3106
4714 N Thatcher Ave Tampa (33614) ***(G-17798)***
J L Finish Woodwork Inc...954 609-4387
2003 Sw 70th Way North Lauderdale (33068) ***(G-11616)***
J L M Machine Co Inc...941 748-4288
2704 29th Ave E Bradenton (34208) ***(G-1064)***
J Lea LLC...954 921-1422
916 N 20th Ave Hollywood (33020) ***(G-5849)***
J M Econo-Print Inc...305 591-3620
303 Camilo Ave Coral Gables (33134) ***(G-2162)***
J M Interiors Inc...305 891-6121
12564 Ne 14th Ave North Miami (33161) ***(G-11642)***
J M Milling Inc...386 546-6826
120 Dog Branch Rd East Palatka (32131) ***(G-3603)***
J M Smucker Company...305 594-2886
9290 Nw 112th Ave Ste 15 Medley (33178) ***(G-8674)***
J N C Investments, Coral Springs *Also called Jnc Habitat Investments Inc* ***(G-2264)***
J Q Bell & Sons...904 879-1597
44247 Bell Ln Callahan (32011) ***(G-1325)***
J R C Concrete Products Inc...850 456-9665
994 S Fairfield Dr Lot 2 Pensacola (32506) ***(G-14181)***
J R Wheeler Corporation...954 585-8950
3748 Sw 30th Ave Fort Lauderdale (33312) ***(G-4073)***
J Ross Publishing Inc...954 727-9333
300 S Pine Island Rd # 305 Plantation (33324) ***(G-14525)***
J S Trading Inc...954 791-9035
6524 Nw 13th Ct Plantation (33313) ***(G-14526)***
J Schor R Inc...954 621-5279
1776 N Pine Island Rd Plantation (33322) ***(G-14527)***
J Squared Management II LLC...813 373-5359
5909 Breckenridge Pkwy F Tampa (33610) ***(G-17799)***
J T E Inc...941 925-2605
3959 Sawyer Rd Sarasota (34233) ***(G-16475)***
J T S Woodworking Inc...561 272-7996
75 Nw 18th Ave Delray Beach (33444) ***(G-3094)***
J T Walker Industries Inc (PA)...727 461-0501
1310 N Hercules Ave Ste A Clearwater (33765) ***(G-1739)***
J Turner & Co, Ponte Vedra Beach *Also called Jt Enterprises Group LLC* ***(G-14943)***
J V Installations Corp...407 849-0262
1310 W Central Blvd Orlando (32805) ***(G-12848)***
J W Austin Industries Inc...321 723-2422
7713 Ellis Rd Melbourne (32904) ***(G-8853)***
J W Dawson Co Inc...305 634-8618
3739 Nw 43rd St Miami (33142) ***(G-9783)***
J W L Trading Company Inc...813 854-1128
13801 W Hillsborough Ave Tampa (33635) ***(G-17800)***
J&B Cmmnication Solutions Corp...786 346-7449
6555 Stirling Rd Davie (33314) ***(G-2539)***
J&D Oil Field Intl Inc...305 436-0024
3785 Nw 82nd Ave Ste 206 Doral (33166) ***(G-3399)***
J&D Oilfield International, Doral *Also called J&D Oil Field Intl Inc* ***(G-3399)***
J&J Sheet Mtal Fabercation LLC...941 752-0569
728 Winter Garden Dr Sarasota (34243) ***(G-16241)***
J&J Suwannee Enterprises LLC...386 658-1721
6835 River Rd Live Oak (32060) ***(G-8233)***
J&Jh Stucco Inc...813 482-5282
12713 Lovers Ln Riverview (33579) ***(G-15274)***
J&K Kitchen, Bath and Stone, Pompano Beach *Also called J & K 8 Inc* ***(G-14734)***
J&N Keystone of Florida...305 528-1677
6900 Nw 77th Ter Medley (33166) ***(G-8675)***
J&S Inks LLC...305 999-0304
1212 Ne 176th Ter North Miami Beach (33162) ***(G-11685)***
J-Coast Woodworks LLC...561 262-6144
1312 Commerce Ln Jupiter (33458) ***(G-7059)***
J-Ko Company...561 795-7377
200 Business Park Way D Royal Palm Beach (33411) ***(G-15472)***
J-Kup Corp...352 683-5629
1260 Lori Dr Spring Hill (34606) ***(G-16855)***
J. C. Mch Sp & Met Fabrication, Miami *Also called JC Machine Works Corp* ***(G-9790)***
J.W. Appley and Son, Clearwater *Also called Dj/Pj Inc* ***(G-1653)***
J2b Industrial LLC...904 805-0745
1134 Ovington Rd S Jacksonville (32216) ***(G-6506)***
J2b Industrial LLC...904 574-8919
5941 Richard St Unit 19 Jacksonville (32216) ***(G-6507)***
Ja Engineering II Corp (HQ)...954 744-7560
3000 Taft St Hollywood (33021) ***(G-5850)***
JA Uniforms Inc...305 234-1231
12323 Sw 132nd Ct Miami (33186) ***(G-9784)***
Jab-B-Inc...813 803-3995
18125 N Us Highway 41 # 104 Lutz (33549) ***(G-8393)***
Jabberwocky LLC...310 717-3343
2 S Biscayne Blvd # 2680 Miami (33131) ***(G-9785)***
Jabil Advnced Mech Sltions Inc...727 577-9749
10560 Dr M Lth Kng Jr St Martin Saint Petersburg (33716) ***(G-15821)***
Jabil Circuit...727 577-9749
9700 18th St N Saint Petersburg (33716) ***(G-15822)***
Jabil Circuit LLC (HQ)...727 577-9749
10560 Dr Mrtn Lther King Saint Petersburg (33716) ***(G-15823)***
Jabil Circuit LLC...727 577-9749
3201 34th St S Saint Petersburg (33711) ***(G-15824)***
Jabil Def & Arospc Svcs LLC (HQ)...727 577-9749
10500 Dr Mrtn Lther King Saint Petersburg (33716) ***(G-15825)***
Jabil Def & Arospc Svcs LLC (HQ)...727 577-9749
10560 Dr Mlk Jr St N Saint Petersburg (33716) ***(G-15826)***
Jabil Inc (PA)...727 577-9749
10560 Dr Mrtn Lther King Saint Petersburg (33716) ***(G-15827)***
Jabil Inc...727 577-9749
10500 Dr Mlk Jr St N Dock Saint Petersburg (33716) ***(G-15828)***
Jabil Inc...727 803-3110
1300 Dr Marti Luthe King Saint Petersburg (33705) ***(G-15829)***
Jabil Inc...727 577-9749
10500 Dr Mrtn Lther King Saint Petersburg (33716) ***(G-15830)***
Jabil Luxembourg Manufacturing, Saint Petersburg *Also called Jabil Inc* ***(G-15829)***
Jabm Advisors Inc...727 458-3755
2839 Grey Oaks Blvd Tarpon Springs (34688) ***(G-18310)***
Jabs Investors Corp...561 540-2693
1815 10th Ave N Ste A Lake Worth Beach (33461) ***(G-7614)***
Jace Fabrication Inc...727 547-6873
9930 62nd St N Pinellas Park (33782) ***(G-14355)***

ALPHABETIC

Jack W Dixon, Pensacola *Also called Dixon Screen Printing LLC* ***(G-14132)***
Jack's Magic, Largo *Also called Jacks Magic Products Inc* ***(G-7985)***
Jackie Z Style Co St Pete LLC.....727 258-4849
113 2nd Ave N Saint Petersburg (33701) ***(G-15831)***
Jackiezstyleco, Saint Petersburg *Also called Jackie Z Style Co St Pete LLC* ***(G-15831)***
Jacks Magic Products Inc.....727 536-4500
12435 73rd Ct Largo (33773) ***(G-7985)***
Jacksnvlle Advnced McHning LLC.....904 292-2999
9655 Fl Min Blvd W Jacksonville (32257) ***(G-6508)***
Jackson County Times, Marianna *Also called Woody Hatcher* ***(G-8588)***
Jackson Equipment Inc.....904 845-3696
2310 Shipwreck Cir W Jacksonville (32224) ***(G-6509)***
Jacksonville Box & Woodwork Co.....904 354-1441
5011 Buffalo Ave Jacksonville (32206) ***(G-6510)***
Jacksonville Business Journal, Jacksonville *Also called Business Jrnl Publications Inc* ***(G-6246)***
Jacksonville Cyber Defense, Jacksonville *Also called Tier5 Technical Services* ***(G-6855)***
Jacksonville Free Press.....904 634-1993
1122 Edgewood Ave W Jacksonville (32208) ***(G-6511)***
Jacksonville Magazine, Jacksonville *Also called White Publishing Co Inc* ***(G-6919)***
Jacksonville Steel Pdts Inc.....904 268-3364
6085 Greenland Rd Jacksonville (32258) ***(G-6512)***
Jacksonville Tire Rescue Inc.....904 783-1296
7010 Lenox Ave Jacksonville (32205) ***(G-6513)***
Jacobsen Factory Outlet.....386 438-8458
3973 W Us Highway 90 Lake City (32055) ***(G-7362)***
Jacobsen Homes, Safety Harbor *Also called Jacobsen Manufacturing Inc* ***(G-15496)***
Jacobsen Manufacturing Inc (PA).....727 726-1138
600 Packard Ct Safety Harbor (34695) ***(G-15496)***
Jacore Technologies.....813 860-7465
1346 Osceola Hollow Rd Odessa (33556) ***(G-12129)***
Jada Foods LLC.....305 319-0263
3126 John P Curci Dr # 1 Hallandale Beach (33009) ***(G-5193)***
Jade Software Corporation USA.....904 677-5133
10151 Deerwood Park Blvd Jacksonville (32256) ***(G-6514)***
Jade Tactical Disaster Relief.....850 270-4077
3816 W Sligh Ave Tampa (33614) ***(G-17801)***
Jafar On Fifth, Miami Beach *Also called Fresh On Fifth* ***(G-10669)***
Jaffer Wll Drllng A Div of AC.....954 523-6669
1451 Se 9th Ct Hialeah (33010) ***(G-5460)***
Jag Stucco Inc.....813 210-6577
4047 Marlow Loop Land O Lakes (34639) ***(G-7858)***
Jahna Concrete Inc (PA).....863 453-4353
103 County Road 17a W Avon Park (33825) ***(G-289)***
Jahna Concrete Inc.....863 453-4353
104 S Railroad Ave Avon Park (33825) ***(G-290)***
Jaiba Cabinets Inc.....305 364-3646
8125 W 20th Ave Hialeah (33014) ***(G-5461)***
Jak Corporate Holdings Inc.....813 289-1660
4920 W Cypress St Ste 100 Tampa (33607) ***(G-17802)***
Jakobsen Tool Co Inc.....727 447-1143
805 Pierce St Clearwater (33756) ***(G-1740)***
Jam Cabinets & Investments LLC.....305 823-9020
2795 W 78th St Hialeah (33016) ***(G-5462)***
Jam Welding Service Inc.....305 662-3787
5818 Sw 68th St South Miami (33143) ***(G-16818)***
Jamali Industries LLC.....954 908-5075
1455 Nw 126th Ln Sunrise (33323) ***(G-17134)***
Jamar Cnstr Fabrication Inc.....321 400-0333
119 Commerce Way Sanford (32771) ***(G-16071)***
Jambco Millwork Inc.....954 977-4998
101 S State Road 7 Margate (33068) ***(G-8551)***
Jamco Industrial Inc.....866 848-5400
3800 Entp Way Ste 1110 Sanford (32771) ***(G-16072)***
Jamerica Inc.....561 488-6247
11188 Jasmine Hill Cir Boca Raton (33498) ***(G-575)***
James A De Flippo Co.....407 851-2765
4665 Gatlin Oaks Ln Orlando (32806) ***(G-12849)***
James Caldwell Stump Grinding.....813 843-1262
1310 Whitehurst Rd Plant City (33563) ***(G-14439)***
James D Nall Co Inc (PA).....305 884-8363
1883 W State Road 84 # 106 Fort Lauderdale (33315) ***(G-4074)***
James Frncisco Backhoe Svc Inc.....727 514-1968
7833 Griswold Loop New Port Richey (34655) ***(G-11494)***
James G Dowling.....407 509-9484
1375 Palm Way Sanford (32773) ***(G-16073)***
James Hardie Building Pdts Inc.....813 478-1758
809 S Woodrow Wilson St Plant City (33563) ***(G-14440)***
James Hines Printing.....904 398-5110
1650 Art Museum Dr Ste 18 Jacksonville (32207) ***(G-6515)***
James O Corbett Inc.....352 483-1222
2151 W County Road 44 Eustis (32726) ***(G-3710)***
James R Kontorchik LLC.....904 962-0597
3265 Net Ct Jacksonville (32277) ***(G-6516)***
James Reese Enterprises Inc.....727 386-5311
1714 Misty Plateau Trl Clearwater (33765) ***(G-1741)***
James Simmons Cabinets Inc.....407 468-1802
4835 Berrywood Dr Orlando (32812) ***(G-12850)***
James Spear Design Inc.....727 592-9600
12253 62nd St Ste A Largo (33773) ***(G-7986)***
James Taylor.....850 882-5148
200 W Escambia Rd Eglin Afb (32542) ***(G-3644)***
James Testa.....954 962-5840
5621 Johnson St Hollywood (33021) ***(G-5851)***
Jamestown Kitchens Inc.....941 359-1166
4050 N Washington Blvd Sarasota (34234) ***(G-16476)***
Jamison Industries Inc.....813 886-4888
7710 N Ola Ave Tampa (33604) ***(G-17803)***
Jamison Paints, Tampa *Also called Jamison Industries Inc* ***(G-17803)***
Jammin Jams USA LLC.....305 494-5617
9351 Sw 56th St Miami (33165) ***(G-9786)***
Jamo Inc.....305 885-3444
8850 Nw 79th Ave Medley (33166) ***(G-8676)***
Jamuna1 LLC.....407 313-5927
4654 River Gem Ave Windermere (34786) ***(G-19230)***
Jan and Jean Inc.....813 645-0680
1010 E Shell Point Rd Ruskin (33570) ***(G-15485)***
Jane and George Industries.....727 698-4903
4197 49th Ave S Saint Petersburg (33711) ***(G-15832)***
Janine of London Inc.....954 772-3593
45 Fort Royal Is Fort Lauderdale (33308) ***(G-4075)***
Janoro Fixture Mfg Corp.....305 887-2524
249 W 29th St Hialeah (33012) ***(G-5463)***
Jans Ventures LLC.....352 341-1710
2044 Highway 44 W Inverness (34453) ***(G-6090)***
Jansen Shutters & Spc Ltd.....941 484-4700
115 Morse Ct North Venice (34275) ***(G-11759)***
Janus Displays, Saint Petersburg *Also called Morrow Technologies Corp* ***(G-15859)***
Janusz Art Stone Inc.....305 754-7171
7025 Ne 2nd Ave Miami (33138) ***(G-9787)***
Japan Fabricare Inc.....407 366-9986
9 Alafaya Woods Blvd Oviedo (32765) ***(G-13441)***
Jar Advertising LLC.....844 344-4586
8601 Commodity Cir Orlando (32819) ***(G-12851)***
Jar-Den Llc.....860 334-7539
7400 Castanea Dr Port Richey (34668) ***(G-15056)***
Jarden Consumer Solutions, Boca Raton *Also called Jarden LLC* ***(G-576)***
Jarden LLC.....561 447-2520
2381 Nw Executive Ctr Dr Boca Raton (33431) ***(G-576)***
Jarden Plastic Solutions.....864 879-8100
2381 Nw Executive Ctr Dr Boca Raton (33431) ***(G-577)***
Jareed Online Publishing LLC, Tallahassee *Also called Ali Kamakhi* ***(G-17216)***
JAs Business Solutions Inc.....954 975-0025
200 Park Central Blvd S Pompano Beach (33064) ***(G-14735)***
JAS Interconnect Solutions, Pompano Beach *Also called JAs Business Solutions Inc* ***(G-14735)***
JAS Powder Coating LLC.....954 916-7711
219 Sw 21st Ter Fort Lauderdale (33312) ***(G-4076)***
JAS Powder Coating LLC.....386 410-6675
1710 Industrial Ave Edgewater (32132) ***(G-3627)***
Jasmine Purkiss.....386 244-7726
2526 Hibiscus Dr 108-08 Edgewater (32141) ***(G-3628)***
Jat Power LLC.....305 592-0103
8000 Nw 29th St Doral (33122) ***(G-3400)***
Jatiga Inc.....727 793-0079
2660 Enterprise Rd Clearwater (33763) ***(G-1742)***
Javalution Coffee Company.....954 568-1747
2485 E Sunrise Blvd # 20 Fort Lauderdale (33304) ***(G-4077)***
Javidco Scratch N Dent.....727 494-7611
6302 Ridge Rd Port Richey (34668) ***(G-15057)***
Jawil Enterprises Corps.....954 366-4212
205 S State Road 7 Margate (33068) ***(G-8552)***
Jax Embroidery.....904 367-4335
8110 Cypress Plaza Dr # 203 Jacksonville (32256) ***(G-6517)***
Jax Enterprises LLC.....904 786-6909
7042 Wiley Rd Jacksonville (32210) ***(G-6518)***
Jax Metals LLC.....904 731-4655
3740 Morton St Jacksonville (32217) ***(G-6519)***
Jax Tire Rescue, Jacksonville *Also called Jacksonville Tire Rescue Inc* ***(G-6513)***
Jay Berry Signs.....352 805-4050
125 Montclair Rd Ste 1 Leesburg (34748) ***(G-8162)***
Jay Robinson Cabinet Sales Inc.....954 298-3009
683 Ne 42nd St Oakland Park (33334) ***(G-11816)***
Jay Squared LLC.....386 677-7700
1810 Mason Ave Daytona Beach (32117) ***(G-2675)***
Jay Strong Lighting Inc.....813 253-0490
2007 W Dekle Ave Tampa (33606) ***(G-17804)***
Jay Walker Enterprises Inc.....850 539-7668
1934 Iron Bridge Rd Tallahassee (32318) ***(G-17282)***
Jayco International LLC.....407 855-8880
7451 Brokerage Dr Orlando (32809) ***(G-12852)***
Jayco Screens Inc.....850 456-0673
9131 W Highway 98 Pensacola (32506) ***(G-14182)***
Jayco Signs Inc.....407 339-5252
149 Atlantic Dr Maitland (32751) ***(G-8468)***
Jayco Woodworks Inc.....850 814-3041
9338 Resota Beach Rd Panama City (32409) ***(G-13920)***

Jaynor Furnishings Inc...954 973-8446
1603 Abaco Dr Coconut Creek (33066) ***(G-2085)***
Jayshree Holdings Inc...352 429-1000
18830 State Road 19 Groveland (34736) ***(G-5098)***
Jazanique Wickson...815 221-7155
8135 Crespi Blvd Apt 4 Miami Beach (33141) ***(G-10684)***
Jazwares LLC (HQ)...954 845-0800
1067 Shotgun Rd Sunrise (33326) ***(G-17135)***
Jazziz Magazine Inc...561 893-6868
2650 N Military Trl # 140 Boca Raton (33431) ***(G-578)***
Jazzy Dogs Publishing...941 726-0343
204 Millet Pl Nokomis (34275) ***(G-11583)***
JB Custom Marine...239 877-2784
3461 18th Ave Ne Naples (34120) ***(G-11294)***
JB Effects...727 348-1865
7682 49th St N Pinellas Park (33781) ***(G-14356)***
JB Thome & Co Inc...727 642-0588
1110 Boca Ciega Isle Dr St Pete Beach (33706) ***(G-16882)***
JB Wood Werks LLC...239 314-4462
2550 Sw 27th Ave Cape Coral (33914) ***(G-1440)***
Jbjb Holdings LLC...239 267-1975
14110 Clear Water Ln Fort Myers (33907) ***(G-4501)***
Jblaze Inc...954 680-3962
4910 Sw 172nd Ave Southwest Ranches (33331) ***(G-16838)***
Jbr Exteriors Inc...772 873-0600
1201 Sw Biltmore St Port Saint Lucie (34983) ***(G-15115)***
Jbt Aerotech-Military Programs, Orlando *Also called John Bean Technologies Corp* ***(G-12858)***
Jbt Food Tech, Lakeland *Also called Jbt Foodtech Citrus Systems* ***(G-7720)***
Jbt Foodtech, Lakeland *Also called John Bean Technologies Corp* ***(G-7722)***
Jbt Foodtech Citrus Systems...863 683-5411
400 Fairway Ave Lakeland (33801) ***(G-7720)***
Jbt LLC (PA)...407 463-2045
528 W Yale St Orlando (32804) ***(G-12853)***
Jbt LLC...513 238-4218
2875 Citrus Lake Dr # 205 Naples (34109) ***(G-11295)***
JC 323 Media Pubg Group Inc...772 940-3510
7186 Ontario Shores Pl Lake Worth (33467) ***(G-7560)***
JC Best Finish Cabinet Inc...786 216-5571
2150 Nw 35th St Miami (33142) ***(G-9788)***
JC Industrial Mfg Corp...305 634-5280
5700 Nw 32nd Ct Miami (33142) ***(G-9789)***
JC Iron Omamental Works Inc...561 508-5966
1213 50th St Mangonia Park (33407) ***(G-8504)***
JC Machine Inc...863 644-2815
3620 Airport Rd Lakeland (33811) ***(G-7721)***
JC Machine Works Corp...305 634-5280
5700 Nw 32nd Ct Miami (33142) ***(G-9790)***
JC Marine Service Fabrica...954 913-8185
3000 N 22nd Ave Hollywood (33020) ***(G-5852)***
JC Publishers LLC...863 875-6071
4844 Osprey Way Winter Haven (33881) ***(G-19331)***
JC Santos Embroidery...407 201-8617
3557 Forest Park Dr Kissimmee (34746) ***(G-7257)***
JC Toys Group Inc...305 592-3541
2841 Nw 107th Ave Doral (33172) ***(G-3401)***
JC Voyage LLC...603 686-0065
2403 Nw 30th Rd Boca Raton (33431) ***(G-579)***
JCB Brick Pavers Inc...941 739-6089
6148 42nd Street Cir E Bradenton (34203) ***(G-1065)***
Jci Jones Chemicals Inc...904 355-0779
1433 Talleyrand Ave Jacksonville (32206) ***(G-6520)***
Jco Metals Inc...386 734-5867
1665 Lexington Ave # 106 Deland (32724) ***(G-2987)***
JCP Signs Inc...305 790-5336
20483 Sw 127th Pl Miami (33177) ***(G-9791)***
JCs Building Sales...386 277-2851
4070 N Us Highway 17 Deland (32720) ***(G-2988)***
Jcs Contracting Inc...407 348-4555
731 Duncan Ave Kissimmee (34744) ***(G-7258)***
Jcs Limited Corporation...954 822-2887
7611 Nw 70th Ave Tamarac (33321) ***(G-17360)***
JD Pavers Inc...904 245-9183
1304 8th St N Jacksonville Beach (32250) ***(G-6946)***
JD Tools LLC...407 767-5175
786 Big Tree Dr Longwood (32750) ***(G-8295)***
JD Wine Concepts LLC...407 730-3082
1312 Wilfred Dr Orlando (32803) ***(G-12854)***
Jdci Enterprises, Fort Myers *Also called Boat Master Aluminum Trailers* ***(G-4378)***
Jdci Enterprises Inc...239 768-2292
11950 Amedicus Ln Unit 2 Fort Myers (33907) ***(G-4502)***
Jde Distributors LLC...727 498-7886
6553 46th St N Ste 905 Pinellas Park (33781) ***(G-14357)***
Jdjsis Inc...561 732-2388
8645 N Military Trl # 501 West Palm Beach (33410) ***(G-18911)***
Jdk Imports Inc (PA)...850 865-0297
87 Whispering Lake Dr Santa Rosa Beach (32459) ***(G-16161)***
Jdl Surface Innovations Inc...239 772-0077
922 Se 14th Pl Cape Coral (33990) ***(G-1441)***
JDM of Miami LLC...305 253-4650
14195 Sw 139th Ct Miami (33186) ***(G-9792)***
Jds Uniforms, Groveland *Also called Gjcb Signs Graphics Inc* ***(G-5095)***
Jdt Servicing LLC...813 909-8640
24310 Breezy Oak Ct Lutz (33559) ***(G-8394)***
Je TAime Fragrances (PA)...727 581-0970
1299 Starkey Rd Ste 103 Largo (33771) ***(G-7987)***
JEAN ARCHIBALD DBA JGA ASSOC, Grant *Also called Jga Lighting LLC* ***(G-5049)***
Jean La Frite...305 397-8747
1520 Washington Ave Miami Beach (33139) ***(G-10685)***
Jean Richard Kitchen Cabinets...786 285-5506
18342 Ne 2nd Ave Miami (33179) ***(G-9793)***
Jeanius Publishing LLC...239 560-5229
108 Airview Ave Lehigh Acres (33936) ***(G-8193)***
Jeb Thermofoil of South Fla...305 887-6214
1065 E 16th St Hialeah (33010) ***(G-5464)***
Jefco Manufacturing Inc...954 527-4220
718 Nw 1st St Fort Lauderdale (33311) ***(G-4078)***
Jeffcoat Signs, Gainesville *Also called Kevin Jeffers Inc* ***(G-4949)***
Jefferson Solenoid Valves USA...305 249-8120
20225 Ne 15th Ct Miami (33179) ***(G-9794)***
Jeffrey Bowden Cabinets LLC...727 992-9187
12437 Banbury Ave New Port Richey (34654) ***(G-11495)***
Jehova Jireh Wood Work Prof...850 862-7131
939 Beal Pkwy Nw Fort Walton Beach (32547) ***(G-4810)***
Jem Art Inc...954 966-7078
801 Shotgun Rd Sunrise (33326) ***(G-17136)***
Jenard Fresh Incorporated...407 851-9432
8101 Presidents Dr Orlando (32809) ***(G-12855)***
Jencor Publishing Inc...772 589-5578
104 Miller Dr Sebastian (32958) ***(G-16664)***
Jennifer Yoder Sung...352 748-6655
9235 County Road 128d Wildwood (34785) ***(G-19196)***
Jennings Mobile HM Set Up LLC...863 965-0883
1048 Us Highway 92 W Auburndale (33823) ***(G-247)***
Jenoptik North America Inc (HQ)...561 881-7400
16490 Innovation Dr Jupiter (33478) ***(G-7060)***
Jenoptik Optical Systems LLC (HQ)...561 881-7400
16490 Innovation Dr Ste A Jupiter (33478) ***(G-7061)***
Jensen Inert Products, Coral Springs *Also called Jensen Scientific Products Inc* ***(G-2263)***
Jensen Scientific Products Inc...954 344-2006
3773 Nw 126th Ave Coral Springs (33065) ***(G-2263)***
Jenzano Incorporated...386 761-4474
820 Oak St Port Orange (32127) ***(G-15020)***
Jepsen Tool Company Inc...904 262-2793
6864 Phillips Pkwy Dr S Jacksonville (32256) ***(G-6521)***
Jer-Air Manufacturing Inc...352 591-2674
22750 Highway 441 N Micanopy (32667) ***(G-10902)***
Jerae Inc...954 989-6665
6031 Hollywood Blvd Hollywood (33024) ***(G-5853)***
Jeremiahs Original Italian Ice, Winter Park *Also called Jeremiahs Original Water Ice* ***(G-19416)***
Jeremiahs Original Water Ice (PA)...407 679-2665
6864 Aloma Ave Winter Park (32792) ***(G-19416)***
Jerry Metallo...305 972-2927
25490 Sw 141st Ave Princeton (33032) ***(G-15184)***
Jers Group...786 953-6419
8625 Nw 54th St Doral (33166) ***(G-3402)***
Jes Publishing Corp...561 997-8683
1000 Clint Moore Rd # 103 Boca Raton (33487) ***(G-580)***
Jess By Inches LLC...305 731-1387
2185 Ne 169th St North Miami Beach (33162) ***(G-11686)***
Jessups Specialty Products...407 332-7574
910 Waterway Pl Longwood (32750) ***(G-8296)***
Jesus Cabinets Corp...786 285-1088
1701 W 42nd Pl Hialeah (33012) ***(G-5465)***
Jesus Cabinets Corp...786 237-6299
10641 Sw 20th Ter Miami (33165) ***(G-9795)***
Jet Avion Corporation...954 987-6101
3000 Taft St Hollywood (33021) ***(G-5854)***
Jet Factory LLC...305 848-8846
147 Sw 25th Ave Boynton Beach (33435) ***(G-924)***
Jet Fuel Catering LLC...954 804-1146
1920 Nw 137th Way Pembroke Pines (33028) ***(G-14043)***
Jet Graphics Inc...305 264-4333
4101 Sw 73rd Ave Miami (33155) ***(G-9796)***
Jet Helseth Manufacturing Inc...407 324-9001
1730 Patterson Ave Deland (32724) ***(G-2989)***
Jet Press, Cape Canaveral *Also called Image Printing & Graphics LLC* ***(G-1360)***
Jet Research Development Inc...954 427-0404
1215 W Newport Center Dr Deerfield Beach (33442) ***(G-2850)***
Jet Set Printing Inc...407 339-1900
130 N Cypress Way Casselberry (32707) ***(G-1508)***
Jetboatpilot LLC...850 960-3236
3825b W Highway 390 Panama City (32405) ***(G-13921)***
Jetspares International Inc...407 876-3978
10650 Chase Rd Bldg 5 Windermere (34786) ***(G-19231)***
Jetstream Fabrication LLC...772 287-3338
1880 Se Federal Hwy Stuart (34994) ***(G-16960)***

ALPHABETIC

Jewelnet Corp 561 989-8383
72 Se 6th Ave Apt K Delray Beach (33483) *(G-3095)*
Jewelry Tray Factory, The, Sunrise *Also called Jld Manufacturing Corp (G-17137)*
Jewels Handmade LLC 407 283-9951
2648 Renegade Dr Apt 101 Orlando (32818) *(G-12856)*
Jewelswebscom 954 993-7744
3500 N Sr 7 Ste 103-3 Fort Lauderdale (33319) *(G-4079)*
Jewish Burial Society America 954 424-1899
15310 Strathearn Dr # 11505 Delray Beach (33446) *(G-3096)*
Jewish Press Group of Tmpa Bay 727 535-4400
1101 Belcher Rd S Ste H Largo (33771) *(G-7988)*
Jewish Press Group Tampa Bay, Largo *Also called Jewish Press Group of Tmpa Bay (G-7988)*
Jfaure LLC 239 631-5324
22758 J&C Blvd Naples (34109) *(G-11296)*
Jfe Compost 863 532-9629
11000 Red Barn Rd Ne Okeechobee (34974) *(G-12183)*
Jfh Technologies LLC 407 938-9336
1500 W Buena Vista Dr Lake Buena Vista (32830) *(G-7336)*
Jfliszo Industries Inc 239 215-6965
17051 Alico Commerce Ct # 3 Fort Myers (33967) *(G-4503)*
Jga Lighting LLC 772 408-8224
3869 Garden Wood Cir Grant (32949) *(G-5049)*
Jglc Enterprises LLC 772 223-7393
3920 Se Commerce Ave Stuart (34997) *(G-16961)*
Jhi Technology, Pensacola *Also called Joe Hearn Innovative Tech LLC (G-14183)*
JHK LLC 786 871-0150
7950 Nw 53rd St Ste 215 Miami (33166) *(G-9797)*
Jhn North LLC 561 294-5613
3554 Lothair Ave Boynton Beach (33436) *(G-925)*
Jhr Management, West Palm Beach *Also called Coral Reef Cast Stone Inc (G-18850)*
Jibe Ltg N Amer Ltd Lblty Co 954 899-4040
5917 Nw 63rd Way Parkland (33067) *(G-13993)*
Jiffi Print, Coral Springs *Also called Media Systems Inc (G-2277)*
Jim Appleys Tru-ARC Inc 727 571-3007
5140 110th Ave N Clearwater (33760) *(G-1743)*
Jim Baird Cabinets 772 569-0936
1020 11th Pl Ste 1 Vero Beach (32960) *(G-18633)*
Jim Rinaldos Cabinetry Inc 813 788-2715
37828 Sky Ridge Cir Dade City (33525) *(G-2430)*
Jim Smith Boats Inc 772 286-9049
4396 Se Commerce Ave Stuart (34997) *(G-16962)*
Jimbob Printing Inc 850 973-2633
482 Sw Range Ave Madison (32340) *(G-8452)*
Jimenez Enterprises Group 561 391-6800
5851 Holmberg Rd Apt 3723 Parkland (33067) *(G-13994)*
Jimenez Enterprises Group (PA) 561 542-7709
10855 Nw 50th St Apt 204 Doral (33178) *(G-3403)*
Jimmy & Toons Icecream Sp LLC 850 752-2291
104 E Washington St Quincy (32351) *(G-15252)*
Jireh AC & Rfrgn Inc 305 216-2774
5001 Sw 142nd Pl Miami (33175) *(G-9798)*
Jireh Woodwork Inc 954 515-8041
3821 Nw 9th Ave Deerfield Beach (33064) *(G-2851)*
Jita Press Inc 850 329-0884
3283 Sugar Berry Way Tallahassee (32303) *(G-17283)*
Jiva Cubes Inc 305 788-1200
9264 Dickens Ave Surfside (33154) *(G-17203)*
Jj Screenprint LLC 941 587-1801
1850 Porter Lake Dr Ste 1 Sarasota (34240) *(G-16477)*
JJ Taylor Distrg Fla Inc 239 267-1006
2440 Park 82 Dr 82nd Fort Myers (33905) *(G-4504)*
Jjaz Enterprises Inc 407 330-0245
1061 S Sun Dr Ste 1033 Lake Mary (32746) *(G-7427)*
Jjc Woodworks Inc 954 461-0088
4796 Nw 67th Ave Lauderhill (33319) *(G-8112)*
Jjj & H Inc 904 389-1130
4237 Salisbury Rd Ste 200 Jacksonville (32216) *(G-6522)*
JK&m Ink, Tampa *Also called J K & M Ink Corporation (G-17798)*
Jk2 Scenic LLC 407 703-2977
541 Live Pine Cir Apopka (32703) *(G-150)*
Jka Pump Specialists 561 686-4455
5407 N Haverhill Rd 344-345 West Palm Beach (33407) *(G-18912)*
Jkg Group 561 866-2850
160 Nw 51st St Boca Raton (33431) *(G-581)*
JKS Industries Inc 863 425-1745
2701 Cozart Rd Mulberry (33860) *(G-11126)*
JKS Industries Inc (PA) 727 573-1305
4644 W Gandy Blvd Tampa (33611) *(G-17805)*
Jl Optical Inc 386 428-6928
2908 Palma Ln New Smyrna Beach (32168) *(G-11536)*
Jl Optical Microscopes, New Smyrna Beach *Also called Jl Optical Inc (G-11536)*
JL Welding Inc 786 442-4319
6510 Sw 64th Ct South Miami (33143) *(G-16819)*
Jlb Enterprises Tampa Inc 813 545-3830
4508 Grainary Ave Tampa (33624) *(G-17806)*
Jld Manufacturing Corp 877 358-5462
4747 N Nob Hill Rd Ste 8 Sunrise (33351) *(G-17137)*
Jlg Industries Inc 786 558-8909
10974 Nw 63rd St Doral (33178) *(G-3404)*
Jls Dairy Holdings, Miami *Also called Latin Dairy Foods LLC (G-9869)*
Jls of St Augustine Inc 904 797-6098
3161 Mac Rd Saint Augustine (32086) *(G-15560)*
Jlt Custom Works Inc 863 245-3371
2239 Greenleaf Rd Wauchula (33873) *(G-18694)*
JM Coatings Inc 407 312-1115
1910 Longwood Lk Mary Rd Longwood (32750) *(G-8297)*
JM Custom Millworks Inc 561 582-5600
1113 48th St Ste 2 Mangonia Park (33407) *(G-8505)*
JM Custom Woodworking 561 582-5600
1113 48th St Ste 2 Mangonia Park (33407) *(G-8506)*
JM Ocean Mar Canvas & Uphl Inc 786 473-7143
1825 Sw 31st Ave Hallandale (33009) *(G-5158)*
Jmc Coatings LLC 239 260-5451
2025 J And C Blvd Naples (34109) *(G-11297)*
Jmf Dgital Print Solutions Inc 954 362-4929
19150 Sw 16th St Pembroke Pines (33029) *(G-14044)*
Jmg Counters LLC 904 551-7006
5120 W Beaver St Jacksonville (32254) *(G-6523)*
Jmg Strategies LLC 305 606-2117
300 S Pointe Dr Apt 907 Miami Beach (33139) *(G-10686)*
Jmg Tool LLC 805 532-1631
14282 76th Rd N Loxahatchee (33470) *(G-8360)*
Jmh Marine Inc 954 785-7557
1790 Sw 13th Ct Pompano Beach (33069) *(G-14736)*
Jml Pavers LLC 239 240-0082
18657 Holly Rd Fort Myers (33967) *(G-4505)*
Jmn Aluminum 813 325-7807
8503 Westridge Dr Tampa (33615) *(G-17807)*
JMP Fashion Inc (PA) 305 633-9920
2199 Nw 20th St Unit 2 Miami (33142) *(G-9799)*
Jmp Marine LLC 305 599-0009
2000 Nw 84th Ave Ste 244 Doral (33122) *(G-3405)*
Jmp USA, Doral *Also called Jmp Marine LLC (G-3405)*
JMS Corporate Group LLC 786 219-6114
21205 Ne 37th Ave Aventura (33180) *(G-275)*
JMS Designs of Florida Inc 954 572-6100
4550 N Hiatus Rd Sunrise (33351) *(G-17138)*
JMTM Anufacturing Inc 727 847-7665
6651 Industrial Ave Port Richey (34668) *(G-15058)*
Jnc Habitat Investments Inc 954 249-7469
645 Nw 112th Way Coral Springs (33071) *(G-2264)*
Jnc Welding & Fabricating Inc 954 227-9424
3769 Nw 126th Ave Coral Springs (33065) *(G-2265)*
Jne Candy Co LLC (PA) 407 622-6292
11767 Chateaubriand Ave Orlando (32836) *(G-12857)*
Jnr International Metals Inc 305 671-3509
17071 W Dixie Hwy Ste 301 North Miami Beach (33160) *(G-11687)*
Jo MO Enterprises Inc 708 599-8098
20966 Estada Ln Boca Raton (33433) *(G-582)*
Job News 904 296-3006
6620 S Sthpint Dr Ste 300 Jacksonville (32256) *(G-6524)*
Jockey International Inc 561 689-7646
1781 Palmbeachlakes West Palm Beach (33401) *(G-18913)*
Jockey Outl - Palm Bch Outlets, West Palm Beach *Also called Jockey International Inc (G-18913)*
Jodan Technology Inc 561 515-5556
7708 Coral Colony Way Lake Worth (33467) *(G-7561)*
Jodar Inc 561 375-6277
354 Ne 5th St Boca Raton (33432) *(G-583)*
Jode Corporation 321 684-1769
9565 Riverview Dr Sebastian (32976) *(G-16655)*
Joe Hearn Innovative Tech LLC 850 898-3744
600 Univ Ofc Blvd 17c Pensacola (32504) *(G-14183)*
Joe Taylor Restoration (PA) 954 972-5390
855 Nw 17th Ave Ste C Delray Beach (33445) *(G-3097)*
Johannsen Boat Works Inc 772 567-4612
690 4th Pl Ste D Vero Beach (32962) *(G-18634)*
John & Betsy Hovland 727 449-2032
2073 Range Rd Clearwater (33765) *(G-1744)*
John A Cruce Jr Inc 850 584-9755
311 Glenridge Rd Perry (32348) *(G-14305)*
John A Pulling Jr 239 593-5247
5610 Yahl St Ste 6 Naples (34109) *(G-11298)*
John Andersen 407 702-4891
923 Ridgeside Ct Apopka (32712) *(G-151)*
John Bean Technologies Corp 863 683-5411
400 Fairway Ave Lakeland (33801) *(G-7722)*
John Bean Technologies Corp 407 851-3377
7300 Presidents Dr Orlando (32809) *(G-12858)*
John Deere Authorized Dealer, Fort Walton Beach *Also called Emergency Standby Power LLC (G-4799)*
John Deere Authorized Dealer, Sebring *Also called Tradewinds Power Corp (G-16716)*
John Deere Authorized Dealer, Doral *Also called Tradewinds Power Corp (G-3531)*
John Deere Authorized Dealer, Fort Myers *Also called Mwi Corporation (G-4542)*
John E Anderson 305 741-8400
505 16th St 1 West Palm Beach (33407) *(G-18914)*

John Eric Madden....813 395-3314
34811 Arbor Green Pl Zephyrhills (33541) *(G-19524)*
John Franklin Mowery....202 468-8644
100 W Venice Ave Ste E Venice (34285) *(G-18557)*
John Hurst Outdoor Svcs LLC....850 556-7459
3694 Corinth Dr Tallahassee (32308) *(G-17284)*
John L Shadd Enterprises....386 496-3989
Us Hwy 121 Lake Butler (32054) *(G-7338)*
John Lacquey Enterprises Inc....386 935-1705
8125 264th St Branford (32008) *(G-1187)*
John M Caldwell Distrg Co Inc....305 685-9822
1150 Ali Baba Ave Opa Locka (33054) *(G-12329)*
John Mader Enterprises Inc....239 731-5455
18161 N Tamiami Trl Fort Myers (33903) *(G-4506)*
John Measel Cabinets, Sarasota *Also called Midnite Son II of Sarasota* *(G-16508)*
John P Cooksey LLC....850 997-8426
205 Oma Rd Monticello (32344) *(G-11077)*
John R Caito....850 612-0179
91 Ready Ave Nw Fort Walton Beach (32548) *(G-4811)*
John S Smith Stucco Inc....813 928-4320
10041 Orland St New Port Richey (34654) *(G-11496)*
John S Wilson Inc....410 442-2400
6222 Parkers Hammock Rd Naples (34112) *(G-11299)*
John Screen Service LLC....561 798-3132
1210 Mystic Way Wellington (33414) *(G-18721)*
John Stewart Enterprises Inc....904 356-9392
502 N Hogan St Jacksonville (32202) *(G-6525)*
John Trent Construction LLC....904 753-2942
1831 Windswept Oak Ln Fernandina Beach (32034) *(G-3740)*
John W Hock Company....352 378-3209
7409 Nw 23rd Ave Gainesville (32606) *(G-4948)*
Johnny Devil Inc....305 634-0700
7301 Nw 36th Ct Miami (33147) *(G-9800)*
Johnny Heaven, Miami *Also called Johnny Devil Inc* *(G-9800)*
Johnny Sellers Logging Inc....850 643-5214
Turkey Creek Rd Bristol (32321) *(G-1196)*
Johnny Under Pressure LLC....850 530-8763
7250 Frank Reeder Rd Pensacola (32526) *(G-14184)*
Johns & Conner Inc....904 845-4430
15924 County Road 108 Hilliard (32046) *(G-5711)*
Johns & Conner Logging Inc....904 845-4430
15924 County Road 108 Hilliard (32046) *(G-5712)*
Johns & Connor Inc....904 845-4541
28244 Pond View Cir Hilliard (32046) *(G-5713)*
Johns Pass Winery....727 362-0008
12945 Village Blvd Madeira Beach (33708) *(G-8447)*
Johnson & Jackson Glass Pdts....813 630-9774
4912 N Manhattan Ave Tampa (33614) *(G-17808)*
Johnson & Johnson....954 534-1141
1024 Se 3rd Ave Apt 304 Dania Beach (33004) *(G-2466)*
Johnson & Johnson....813 972-0204
8800 Grand Oak Cir # 500 Tampa (33637) *(G-17809)*
Johnson & Johnson....305 261-3500
6303 Blue Lagoon Dr # 450 Miami (33126) *(G-9801)*
Johnson and Johnson, Miami *Also called Codman & Shurtleff Inc* *(G-9374)*
Johnson Bros Prcsion Prcast Pd....239 947-6734
24263 Production Cir Bonita Springs (34135) *(G-842)*
Johnson Brothers Whl Meats Inc....850 763-2828
1640 Martin Luther King J Panama City (32405) *(G-13922)*
Johnson Controls, Jacksonville *Also called Clarios LLC* *(G-6265)*
Johnson Environmental Services, Fort Lauderdale *Also called All Liquid Envmtl Svcs LLC* *(G-3797)*
Johnson Jhnson Vision Care Inc (HQ)....904 443-1000
7500 Centurion Pkwy Jacksonville (32256) *(G-6526)*
Johnson Printing, Bradenton *Also called Bjm Enterprises Inc* *(G-1000)*
Johnson Well Equipment Inc....850 453-3131
8480 Gulf Beach Hwy Pensacola (32507) *(G-14185)*
Johnson Woodworking....772 473-1404
3470 Leghorn Rd Malabar (32950) *(G-8490)*
Johnsons Management Group Inc....904 261-4044
1485 S 8th St Fernandina Beach (32034) *(G-3741)*
Johnsons Woodwork Incorporated....904 826-4100
175 Cumberland Park Dr Saint Augustine (32095) *(G-15561)*
Johnston Archtctral Systems In....904 886-9030
11494 Columbia Park Dr W Jacksonville (32258) *(G-6527)*
Joiner Land Clearing LLC....850 997-5729
1417 Government Farm Rd Monticello (32344) *(G-11078)*
Joiners Enterprises Inc....850 623-5593
4973 Joiner Cir Milton (32583) *(G-10933)*
Joint Force Enterprises, Jacksonville *Also called Gtgjfe LLC* *(G-6455)*
Jomar Metal Fabrication Inc....407 857-1259
1239 Spruce Ave Orlando (32824) *(G-12859)*
Jon Paul Inc....954 564-4221
3353 Galt Ocean Dr 55 Fort Lauderdale (33308) *(G-4080)*
Jon Paul Jewelers, Fort Lauderdale *Also called Jon Paul Inc* *(G-4080)*
Jonas Software USA Inc....800 476-0094
9295 Scenic Hwy Pensacola (32514) *(G-14186)*
Jonathan Mariotti Entps LLC....855 353-8280
608 Danley Dr Unit C Fort Myers (33907) *(G-4507)*
Jonel Knitting Mills Inc....305 887-7333
7130 W 12th Ln Hialeah (33014) *(G-5466)*
Jones Awnings & Canvas Inc....954 784-6966
127 Nw 16th St Pompano Beach (33060) *(G-14737)*
Jones Awnings & Canvas Inc....407 845-9400
372 W Grant St Orlando (32806) *(G-12860)*
Jones Communications Inc....407 448-6615
312 W 1st St Ste 503 Sanford (32771) *(G-16074)*
Jones Field Services Pamela....904 368-9777
9904 Nw County Road 229 Starke (32091) *(G-16895)*
Jones Mediaamerica Inc....305 289-4524
11399 Overseas Hwy 5sw Marathon (33050) *(G-8518)*
Joni Industries Inc....352 799-5456
16230 Aviation Loop Dr Brooksville (34604) *(G-1240)*
Jordan Brown Inc (PA)....904 495-0717
475 W Town Pl Ste 200 Saint Augustine (32092) *(G-15562)*
Jordan Norris Inc....407 846-1400
997 W Kennedy Blvd Ste A1 Orlando (32810) *(G-12861)*
Jorges Finest Woodworks Inc....305 491-4380
2471 Nw 95th St Miami (33147) *(G-9802)*
Jormac Aerospace....727 549-9600
11221 69th St Largo (33773) *(G-7989)*
Jormac Aerospace Inc....727 549-9600
13130 56th Ct Ste 604 Clearwater (33760) *(G-1745)*
Joro Fashions Florida Inc....305 888-8110
6650 Sw 123rd St Pinecrest (33156) *(G-14328)*
Jose Leal Enterprises Inc....305 887-9611
705 W 20th St Hialeah (33010) *(G-5467)*
Jose Morales Hurricane Shutter....786 315-1835
13271 Sw 17th Ln Miami (33175) *(G-9803)*
Jose Polanco....305 631-1784
614 Sw 22nd Ave Miami (33135) *(G-9804)*
Jose Rodriguez Met Fabrication....305 305-6110
2451 Brickell Ave Miami (33129) *(G-9805)*
Joseph J Taylor Truss....321 482-4039
2599 Larry Ct Melbourne (32935) *(G-8854)*
Joseph Malara....352 789-7646
5944 Coral Ridge Dr Coral Springs (33076) *(G-2266)*
Josper Chef USA, Miami *Also called Charcoal Chef Usa LLC* *(G-9349)*
Journal Housing Science, Coral Gables *Also called Ural Associates Inc* *(G-2200)*
Joy's Gourmet, Melbourne *Also called Joys International Foods Inc* *(G-8855)*
Joya Essentials LLC....407 865-0880
9918 Hatton Cir Orlando (32832) *(G-12862)*
Joyce Telectronics Corp....727 461-3525
40421 Chancey Rd Ste 101 Zephyrhills (33542) *(G-19525)*
Joyner Inc....850 832-6326
9740 Steel Field Rd Panama City Beach (32413) *(G-13979)*
Joys International Foods Inc....321 242-6520
2600 Aurora Rd Ste Q Melbourne (32935) *(G-8855)*
Joyson Safety Systems, Lakeland *Also called Key Automotive Florida LLC* *(G-7725)*
JP Cosmetics Inc....305 231-4963
1687 W 32nd Pl Hialeah (33012) *(G-5468)*
JP Custom Metals....786 318-2855
7200 Nw 29th Ct Miami (33147) *(G-9806)*
JP Donvan Prcsion McHining LLC....321 383-1171
201 Paint St Rockledge (32955) *(G-15424)*
Jpl Associates Inc....954 929-6024
1250 E Hallandale Beach B Hallandale Beach (33009) *(G-5194)*
Jpm Import LLC....800 753-3009
7350 Nw 1st St Apt 207 Margate (33063) *(G-8553)*
JPS Digital LLC....813 501-6040
4860 S Marsh Hawk Ter Inverness (34452) *(G-6091)*
Jpt-Tech LLC....352 219-7860
11094 Nw 188th Street Rd Micanopy (32667) *(G-10903)*
Jq Green America Inc....786 397-0999
651 Nw Entp Dr Ste 109 Saint Lucie West (34986) *(G-15686)*
Jq Industries Inc....407 509-3880
2070 Terrace Blvd Longwood (32779) *(G-8298)*
Jr Boarts Packaging, Rockledge *Also called Gar Business Group LLC* *(G-15413)*
Jr Bricks Pavers Inc....813 516-3554
207 Jason Dr Tampa (33615) *(G-17810)*
Jr Electronics, Miami *Also called Iron Strength Corp* *(G-9772)*
Jr Embroidery Inc....305 253-6968
12321 Sw 133rd Ct Miami (33186) *(G-9807)*
Jr Plastics Corporation....352 401-0880
5111 S Pine Ave Ste G Ocala (34480) *(G-11972)*
Jr Wood Works Inc....305 401-6056
7954 Ne 4th Ave Miami (33138) *(G-9808)*
Jrf Technology LLC....813 443-5273
9830 Currie Davis Dr Tampa (33619) *(G-17811)*
Jrg Systems Inc....954 962-1020
1239 N Flagler Dr Fort Lauderdale (33304) *(G-4081)*
Jrh Sport Industries Inc....904 940-3381
6550 State Road 16 Saint Augustine (32092) *(G-15563)*
JRL Service Co....727 243-4734
332 Anclote Rd Tarpon Springs (34689) *(G-18311)*
Jrmetal Ornamental....954 989-2607
3725 Pembroke Rd Ste A11 Hollywood (33021) *(G-5855)*
JRP Screen Printing Inc....305 333-4244
8416 Nw 201st Ter Hialeah (33015) *(G-5469)*

ALPHABETIC

Jrs Limb & Tree LLC...407 383-4843
297 Grant Line Rd Sanford (32771) *(G-16075)*
JRS Ventures LLP...715 441-1051
915 Doyle Rd Ste 303-356 Deltona (32725) *(G-3172)*
Jrt Manufacturing LLC...321 363-4133
421 Cornwall Rd Sanford (32773) *(G-16076)*
Js2 Aerospace Corp...954 840-3620
1888 Nw 21st St Pompano Beach (33069) *(G-14738)*
JSB Enterprises Inc...941 723-2288
1650 12th St E Palmetto (34221) *(G-13808)*
Jsi Scientific Inc...732 845-1925
862 105th Ave N Ste 18 Naples (34108) *(G-11300)*
Jsl Enterprises of Orlando...386 767-9653
1434 Circle Ln Chuluota (32766) *(G-1553)*
Jsm Creations Inc...239 229-8746
16260 Saddlewood Ln Cape Coral (33991) *(G-1442)*
Jsn Blue Thunder LLC...786 398-5222
1876 Nw 7th St Miami (33125) *(G-9809)*
Jsp Manufacturing Holdings LLC...727 488-5353
6203 80th Ave N Pinellas Park (33781) *(G-14358)*
Jsr Wellness Inc...561 748-2477
5500 Village Blvd Ste 202 West Palm Beach (33407) *(G-18915)*
Jssa Inc...321 383-7798
895 Buffalo Rd Titusville (32796) *(G-18435)*
Jt Enterprises Group LLC (PA)...904 803-9338
280 Village Main St Ponte Vedra Beach (32082) *(G-14943)*
Jt Enterprises Group LLC...904 551-2680
6100 Philips Hwy Jacksonville (32216) *(G-6528)*
Jta Industries LLC (PA)...407 352-4255
9165 Phillips Grove Ter Orlando (32836) *(G-12863)*
Jta Industries LLC...321 663-4395
3391 S Kirkman Rd # 1223 Orlando (32811) *(G-12864)*
Jtac Industries LLC...813 928-0628
2509 Trkey Creek Rd Ste 1 Plant City (33566) *(G-14441)*
Jtf Ventures LLC...305 556-5156
7889 Nw 98th St Miami Lakes (33016) *(G-10800)*
Jti Duty-Free USA Inc...305 377-3922
501 Brickell Dr Ste 402 Miami (33131) *(G-9810)*
JTL Enterprises (delaware)...727 536-5566
15395 Roosevelt Blvd Clearwater (33760) *(G-1746)*
Jtm International Inc...954 680-3517
5560 Sw 98th Way Cooper City (33328) *(G-2113)*
Juan Alemany Woodwork...407 350-4072
2108 Winding Ridge Ave S Kissimmee (34741) *(G-7259)*
Juan Bermudez, Sunrise *Also called Neopod Systems LLC* ***(G-17151)***
Juan Diaz Stucco Spc Inc...407 402-1912
825 High Pointe Cir Minneola (34715) *(G-10955)*
Juan F Montano...305 274-0512
7895 Sw 57th Ter Miami (33143) *(G-9811)*
Juan Pampanas Designs Inc...305 573-7550
32 Nw 20th St Miami (33127) *(G-9812)*
Juan Rodriguez Cabinetry Corp...305 467-3878
221 W 41st St Hialeah (33012) *(G-5470)*
Judicial & ADM RES Assoc...850 222-3171
1327 N Adams St Tallahassee (32303) *(G-17285)*
Juice Tyme Inc...631 424-2850
500 S Lake Reedy Blvd Frostproof (33843) *(G-4860)*
Juiceblendz, Weston *Also called Ianorod JB LLC* ***(G-19138)***
Juiceco, Vero Beach *Also called United Jice Companies Amer Inc* ***(G-18673)***
Juicera, Miami *Also called Healtheintentions Inc* ***(G-9693)***
Julio Garcia Satellite...407 414-3223
1248 S John Young Pkwy Kissimmee (34741) *(G-7260)*
Juniors Bait and Seafood Inc...321 480-5492
1500 Maple Ave Melbourne (32935) *(G-8856)*
Junk Cars Broward County, Oakland Park *Also called Raceway Towing LLC* ***(G-11835)***
Juno Ironcraft...561 352-0471
1233 Old Dixie Hwy Lake Park (33403) *(G-7475)*
Jupiter Bach North America Inc...850 476-6304
3301 Bill Metzger Ln Pensacola (32514) *(G-14187)*
Jupiter Compass LLC...561 444-6740
600 S Entrada Way Apt 204 Palm Beach Gardens (33410) *(G-13599)*
Jupiter Courier, Jupiter *Also called Howard Scripts Inc* ***(G-7054)***
Jupiter Courier, Stuart *Also called Stuart News* ***(G-17025)***
Jupiter Industries LLC...239 225-9041
9373 Laredo Ave Fort Myers (33905) *(G-4508)*
Jupiter Mar Intl Holdings Inc (PA)...941 729-5000
1103 12th Ave E Palmetto (34221) *(G-13809)*
Jupiter Petroleum Inc...561 622-1276
5490 Military Trl Jupiter (33458) *(G-7062)*
Jupiter Wellness Inc...561 462-2700
1061 E Indiantown Rd # 110 Jupiter (33477) *(G-7063)*
Juracsik, Ted Tool & Die, Delray Beach *Also called Tibor Inc* ***(G-3150)***
Juritis USA LLC...954 529-2168
2500 Weston Rd Ste 105 Weston (33331) *(G-19145)*
Just Counters Other Stuff Inc...941 235-1300
1489 Market Cir Bldg 309 Port Charlotte (33953) *(G-14986)*
Just Door Toolz LLC...954 448-6872
1552 Sw Abingdon Ave Port Saint Lucie (34953) *(G-15116)*
Just Engines...561 575-2681
209 Circle W Jupiter (33458) *(G-7064)*
Just For Nets, Tampa *Also called Lee Fisher International Inc* ***(G-17839)***
Just For Nets...813 871-1133
4817 N Lois Ave Ste 104 Tampa (33614) *(G-17812)*
Just Fur Fun...561 809-6596
8951 Old Pine Rd Boca Raton (33433) *(G-584)*
Just Leds Inc...727 468-4496
1515 Rye Rd E Bradenton (34212) *(G-1066)*
Just Now Jennings LLC...239 331-0315
6542 Chestnut Cir Naples (34109) *(G-11301)*
Just Say Print Inc...954 254-7793
1500 Nw 112th Way Coral Springs (33071) *(G-2267)*
Just Steel Inc...941 755-7811
3100 Whitfield Ave Ste B Sarasota (34243) *(G-16242)*
Just-In-Time Mfg Corp...321 752-7552
3153 Skyway Cir Ste 101 Melbourne (32934) *(G-8857)*
Justi Group Inc...813 855-5779
305 Marlborough St Oldsmar (34677) *(G-12238)*
Justice Government Supply Inc...954 559-3038
555 Pacific Grove Dr # 2 West Palm Beach (33401) *(G-18916)*
Juvent Medical Inc...732 748-8866
3111 Shell Mound Blvd Fort Myers Beach (33931) *(G-4665)*
JVI Minerals Inc...561 894-1022
15108 Ashland Dr Apt F196 Delray Beach (33484) *(G-3098)*
JW Appley and Son Inc...727 572-4910
13215 38th St N Clearwater (33762) *(G-1747)*
JW Fabrications Inc...772 201-7097
32801 Us Highway 441 N # 171 Okeechobee (34972) *(G-12184)*
JW Machine, Orlando *Also called Praesto Enterprises LLC* ***(G-13077)***
JW Marketing and Consulting...866 323-0001
6574 N State Road 7 # 27 Coconut Creek (33073) *(G-2086)*
JW Performance Transm Inc...321 632-6205
1826 Baldwin St Rockledge (32955) *(G-15425)*
Jwn Family Partners LP Ltd...352 628-4910
6198 S Lecanto Hwy Lecanto (34461) *(G-8135)*
K & A Audio Inc...941 925-7648
4604 Ashton Rd Sarasota (34233) *(G-16478)*
K & B Landscape Supplies Inc...800 330-8816
3900 E State Road 44 Deland (32724) *(G-2990)*
K & C The Printer, North Miami *Also called American Specialty Sales Corp* ***(G-11624)***
K & D Welding LLC...941 586-0258
848 Gantt Ave Sarasota (34232) *(G-16479)*
K & G Box Inc...904 356-6063
2212 N Pearl St Jacksonville (32206) *(G-6529)*
K & G Creations, Delray Beach *Also called Jewelnet Corp* ***(G-3095)***
K & I Creative Plas & WD LLC...904 923-0409
582 Nixon St Jacksonville (32204) *(G-6530)*
K & I Plastics Inc...904 387-0438
582 Nixon St Jacksonville (32204) *(G-6531)*
K & K Precision Manufacturing...850 769-9080
2307 Industrial Dr Panama City (32405) *(G-13923)*
K & M Custom Cabinetry Inc...727 791-3993
977 Withlacoochee St A Safety Harbor (34695) *(G-15497)*
K & M Truss Inc...407 880-4551
2844 N Ornge Blssom Trl Zellwood (32798) *(G-19504)*
K & N Industries Inc...850 939-7722
9218 Navarre Pkwy Navarre (32566) *(G-11467)*
K and G Food Services LLC...954 857-9283
9500 Sandhill Crane Dr West Palm Beach (33412) *(G-18917)*
K Bausch Mfg Corp...772 485-2426
2813 Se Monroe St Stuart (34997) *(G-16963)*
K C I Kone Crane, Plant City *Also called Kone Crane Maintenance Svcs* ***(G-14445)***
K C Industries LLC...863 425-1195
2420 Old Highway 60 Mulberry (33860) *(G-11127)*
K C Marine Services Inc...954 766-8100
1111 Sw 21st Ave Ste 20 Fort Lauderdale (33312) *(G-4082)*
K C Screen...407 977-9636
1705 Evans St Oviedo (32765) *(G-13442)*
K Color Corp...305 579-2290
7255 Nw 68th St Ste 1 Miami (33166) *(G-9813)*
K H S Inc...941 359-4000
5501 N Washington Blvd Sarasota (34243) *(G-16243)*
K J C O Inc (PA)...954 401-4299
481 Ambleside Dr Titusville (32780) *(G-18436)*
K K Woodworking...321 724-1298
2300 Kahler Ln Malabar (32950) *(G-8491)*
K L Distributing Inc...415 800-2158
7425 Sailfish Dr Hudson (34667) *(G-6030)*
K P Kitchens Corp...954 322-9087
6412 Pembroke Rd Miramar (33023) *(G-11008)*
K Pro Supply Co Inc...941 758-1226
2135 Whitfield Park Ave Sarasota (34243) *(G-16244)*
K R C, Milton *Also called Kottler Research Corp* ***(G-10934)***
K R O Enterprises Ltd...309 797-2213
7950 Preserve Cir Apt 816 Naples (34119) *(G-11302)*
K Rain, Riviera Beach *Also called K-Rain Manufacturing Corp* ***(G-15338)***
K V Water Equipment & Krane Co...941 723-0707
730 Commerce Dr Venice (34292) *(G-18558)*

K&M Power Systems LLC......866 945-9100
7641 Central Indus Dr Riviera Beach (33404) ***(G-15337)***
K&T Manufacturing Inc......407 814-7700
557 Cooper Indus Pkwy Apopka (32703) ***(G-152)***
K&T Stoneworks Inc......561 798-8486
101 N Benoist Farms Rd West Palm Beach (33411) ***(G-18918)***
K-Kraft Cabinets Inc......321 632-8800
1751 Cogswell St Rockledge (32955) ***(G-15426)***
K-Kraft Industries Inc......321 632-8800
1751 Cogswell St Rockledge (32955) ***(G-15427)***
K-O Concepts Inc......407 296-7788
1200 White Dr Ste D Titusville (32780) ***(G-18437)***
K-Raceway LLC......407 889-4314
1549 Madison Ivy Cir Apopka (32712) ***(G-153)***
K-Rain Manufacturing Corp (PA)......561 721-3936
1640 Australian Ave Riviera Beach (33404) ***(G-15338)***
K-Technologies Inc......863 940-4815
4306 Wallace Rd Lakeland (33812) ***(G-7723)***
K12 Print Inc......800 764-7600
3875 Fiscal Ct Ste 400 West Palm Beach (33404) ***(G-18919)***
K20 Oil LLC......954 421-1735
1201 S Military Trl Deerfield Beach (33442) ***(G-2852)***
Kabinets By Kinsey Inc......813 222-0460
3815 N Florida Ave Tampa (33603) ***(G-17813)***
Kabrit Repair Services LLC......407 714-1470
9118 Panzani Pl Windermere (34786) ***(G-19232)***
Kachemak Bay Flying Service......850 398-8699
5545 John Givens Rd Crestview (32539) ***(G-2352)***
Kadassa Inc......954 684-8361
3541 Dr Martin Luther Kin Riviera Beach (33404) ***(G-15339)***
Kai Limited......954 957-8586
1650 W Mcnab Rd Fort Lauderdale (33309) ***(G-4083)***
Kalashnikov USA, Pompano Beach *Also called Rwc Group LLC* ***(G-14837)***
Kalitec Direct LLC......407 545-2063
865 Oviedo Blvd Ste 1017 Oviedo (32765) ***(G-13443)***
Kalitec Medical, Oviedo *Also called Kalitec Direct LLC* ***(G-13443)***
Kaltec Electronics Inc......813 888-9555
5436 W Crenshaw St Tampa (33634) ***(G-17814)***
Kaluz LLC......786 991-2260
7105 Nw 41st St Miami (33166) ***(G-9814)***
Kam Tatonetti, Delray Beach *Also called Kc & B Custom Inc* ***(G-3099)***
Kamaj Business Group Inc......813 863-9967
601 N Ashley Dr Ste 1 Tampa (33602) ***(G-17815)***
Kaman Aerospace Corporation......904 751-5369
9410 Parker Ave Jacksonville (32218) ***(G-6532)***
Kaman Precision Products Inc (HQ)......407 282-1000
6655 E Colonial Dr Orlando (32807) ***(G-12865)***
Kamco Industries LLC......772 299-1401
5720 Us Highway 1 Vero Beach (32967) ***(G-18635)***
Kamel Software Inc......407 672-0202
1809 E Broadway St # 134 Oviedo (32765) ***(G-13444)***
Kameleon Press Inc......850 566-2522
1925 Benjamin Chaires Rd Tallahassee (32317) ***(G-17286)***
Kamsa, Doral *Also called Asterion Beverages Inc* ***(G-3256)***
Kamtex USA Incorporated......954 733-1044
2916 Nw 28th St Lauderdale Lakes (33311) ***(G-8089)***
Kanalflakt Inc (PA)......941 359-3267
1712 Northgate Blvd Sarasota (34234) ***(G-16480)***
Kane-Miller Corp (PA)......941 346-2003
1515 Ringling Blvd # 840 Sarasota (34236) ***(G-16481)***
Kappa Metal USA Inc......954 757-7100
5497 Wiles Rd Ste 202 Coconut Creek (33073) ***(G-2087)***
Karepat Group Inc......772 286-5339
4800 Se Anchor Ave Stuart (34997) ***(G-16964)***
Karigam Enterprises Inc......305 358-7755
1110 Brickell Ave Ste 702 Miami (33131) ***(G-9815)***
Karmanos Printing & Graphics, Tallahassee *Also called Oompha Inc* ***(G-17308)***
Karnak Corporation......352 481-4145
147 Pine Tree Rd East Palatka (32131) ***(G-3604)***
Karnak South Inc......954 761-7606
1010 Se 20th St Fort Lauderdale (33316) ***(G-4084)***
Karob Instrument Inc......352 732-2414
1644 Ne 22nd Ave Ocala (34470) ***(G-11973)***
Karob Manufacturing Inc......352 732-2414
1644 Ne 22nd Ave Bldg Ste Ocala (34470) ***(G-11974)***
Karry Industries Inc......904 398-4007
4007 Saint Augustine Rd Jacksonville (32207) ***(G-6533)***
Kash Corporation......786 368-7747
7450 Sw 82nd Ave Miami (33143) ***(G-9816)***
Kashiben Say LLC......352 489-4960
11150 N Williams St Dunnellon (34432) ***(G-3598)***
Kasse Cabinets Inc......407 285-2738
9781 S Orange Blossom Trl # 8 Orlando (32837) ***(G-12866)***
Kasulik II LLC......786 629-8978
1170 E Hllndale Bch Blvd Hallandale Beach (33009) ***(G-5195)***
Katmai Electronic Systems, Orlando *Also called Ilsc Holdings Lc* ***(G-12822)***
Kauffs Ventures LLC......561 775-3278
3587 Northlake Blvd Palm Beach Gardens (33403) ***(G-13600)***
Kavi Skin Solutions Inc......415 839-5156
3520 South St Titusville (32780) ***(G-18438)***
Kawasumi Laboratories Amer Inc......813 630-5554
10002 Princess Palm Ave # 324 Tampa (33619) ***(G-17816)***
Kawneer Architectural Products, Orlando *Also called Kawneer Company Inc* ***(G-12867)***
Kawneer Company Inc......407 648-4511
4645 L B Mcleod Rd Orlando (32811) ***(G-12867)***
Kay Diamond Products LLC......561 994-5400
1080 Holland Dr Ste 2 Boca Raton (33487) ***(G-585)***
Kay Enterprises......352 732-5770
2026 Se 3rd Pl Ocala (34471) ***(G-11975)***
Kay Peak Group Inc......754 307-5400
6510 W Atlantic Blvd Margate (33063) ***(G-8554)***
Kayva Distribution LLC......305 428-2816
2201 Nw 102nd Pl Ste 4a Doral (33172) ***(G-3406)***
Kazdin Industries Inc......772 223-5511
5258 Sw Anhinga Ave Palm City (34990) ***(G-13663)***
KB Aerospace Co......754 366-9194
401 E Las Olas Blvd Fort Lauderdale (33301) ***(G-4085)***
KB Electronics, Coral Springs *Also called Nidec Motor Corporation* ***(G-2297)***
Kbf Design Gallery Inc......407 830-7703
1295 S Orlando Ave Maitland (32751) ***(G-8469)***
Kbfs, Crestview *Also called Kachemak Bay Flying Service* ***(G-2352)***
Kc & B Custom Inc......561 276-1887
2413 N Federal Hwy Unit A Delray Beach (33483) ***(G-3099)***
Kci......352 572-2873
24 S Ponder Ave Lecanto (34461) ***(G-8136)***
KCm Mch Sp Broward Cnty Inc......954 475-8732
2394 Sw 66th Ter Davie (33317) ***(G-2540)***
Kcon Industries LLC......917 250-7402
6538 Nw 170th Ter Hialeah (33015) ***(G-5471)***
Kcw Cnc and Laser Engraving, Palm Harbor *Also called Kevins Custom Woodworking* ***(G-13742)***
Kcw Electric Company Inc......850 878-2051
4765 Shelfer Rd Tallahassee (32305) ***(G-17287)***
Kd-Pharma Usa Inc......786 345-5500
14193 Sw 119th Ave Ste 10 Miami (33186) ***(G-9817)***
Kdavid Woodwork & Design Inc......754 205-2433
7546 W Mcnab Rd North Lauderdale (33068) ***(G-11617)***
KDD Inc (PA)......239 689-8402
16431 Domestic Ave Fort Myers (33912) ***(G-4509)***
Keavys Corner LLC......863 658-0235
12413 Us Highway 98 Sebring (33876) ***(G-16696)***
Kee Kreative LLC......954 931-2579
3405 Nw 14th Ct Lauderhill (33311) ***(G-8113)***
Keel & Curley Winery LLC......813 752-9100
5210 Thonotosassa Rd Plant City (33565) ***(G-14442)***
Keels & Wheels, Sarasota *Also called Mio Publication Inc* ***(G-16257)***
Keene Metal Fabricators Inc......813 621-2455
5912 E Broadway Ave Tampa (33619) ***(G-17817)***
Keens Portable Buildings Inc......386 364-7995
620 Howard St W Live Oak (32064) ***(G-8234)***
Keepit Neat......352 867-0541
11630 Ne Jacksonville Rd Anthony (32617) ***(G-96)***
Keepmefresh......502 407-7902
614 E Highway 50 Ste 122 Clermont (34711) ***(G-1965)***
Keith Dennis Markham......239 353-4122
220 24th Ave Ne Naples (34120) ***(G-11303)***
Keith Eickert Power Pdts LLC......386 446-0660
11 Industry Dr Palm Coast (32137) ***(G-13700)***
Keithco Enterprises, Ocala *Also called Steven Chancas* ***(G-12059)***
Keithco Inc......352 351-4741
1519 S Pine Ave Ocala (34471) ***(G-11976)***
Kel Glo Corp......305 751-5641
54 Ne 73rd St Miami (33138) ***(G-9818)***
Kel-TEC Cnc Industries Inc......321 631-0068
1505 Cox Rd Cocoa (32926) ***(G-2033)***
Keller Manufacturing Inc......863 937-8928
4442 Holden Rd Lakeland (33811) ***(G-7724)***
Keller-Nglillis Design Mfg Inc......727 733-4111
655 San Christopher Dr Dunedin (34698) ***(G-3582)***
Kelleys Krafts and Kreations......813 508-1051
12224 Hamlin Rd Spring Hill (34610) ***(G-16874)***
Kellstrom Aerospace Group Inc (HQ)......954 538-2482
2500 N Military Trl Ste 4 Boca Raton (33431) ***(G-586)***
Kellstrom Coml Arospc Inc......305 818-5400
14400 Nw 77th Ct Ste 306 Miami Lakes (33016) ***(G-10801)***
Kellstrom Defense Arospc Inc, Miramar *Also called Allclear Aerospace & Def Inc* ***(G-10966)***
Kelly Foods......904 354-7600
2240 Dennis St Jacksonville (32204) ***(G-6534)***
Kellys Bakery Corp......305 685-4622
3990 Nw 132nd St Unit A Opa Locka (33054) ***(G-12330)***
KELSIES BLINDS, Oviedo *Also called Kelsies Blinds* ***(G-13445)***
Kelsies Blinds......407 977-0827
2464 W State Rd Ste 1028 Oviedo (32765) ***(G-13445)***
Keltec, Cocoa *Also called Kel-TEC Cnc Industries Inc* ***(G-2033)***
Kelton Company LLC......850 434-6830
220 W Garden St Ste 605 Pensacola (32502) ***(G-14188)***
Keltour US Inc......239 424-8901
71 Mid Cape Ter Unit 1/2 Cape Coral (33991) ***(G-1443)***

ALPHABETIC

Kemco Industries LLC 407 322-1230
70 Keyes Ave Sanford (32773) ***(G-16077)***
Kemco Systems Co LLC (PA) 727 573-2323
11500 47th St N Clearwater (33762) ***(G-1748)***
Kemet Corporation (HQ) 954 766-2800
1 E Broward Blvd Ste 200 Fort Lauderdale (33301) ***(G-4086)***
Kemet Ventures LLC 407 403-2958
10524 Moss Park Rd Orlando (32832) ***(G-12868)***
Kemp, Ocala *Also called Flaire Corporation* ***(G-11944)***
Kemp, Ocala *Also called SPX Flow Technology Usa Inc* ***(G-12058)***
Kemp Signs Inc 561 840-6382
1740 Hill Ave Mangonia Park (33407) ***(G-8507)***
Kempfer Sawmill Inc 407 892-2955
6254 Kempfer Rd Saint Cloud (34773) ***(G-15656)***
Kempharm Inc (PA) 321 939-3416
1180 Celebration Blvd # 10 Celebration (34747) ***(G-1523)***
Ken Clearys Two LLC 727 573-0700
10900 47th St N Clearwater (33762) ***(G-1749)***
Ken R Avery Painting Inc 813 855-5037
3704 State Road 580 W Oldsmar (34677) ***(G-12239)***
Kenart Holdings Llc 561 863-5556
1380 W 15th St Riviera Beach (33404) ***(G-15340)***
Kenco 2000 Inc 386 672-1590
1539 Garden Ave Daytona Beach (32117) ***(G-2676)***
Kenco Hospitality Inc 954 921-5434
1000 Nw 56th St Fort Lauderdale (33309) ***(G-4087)***
Kenco Quilting & Textiles Inc 954 921-5434
1000 Nw 56th St Fort Lauderdale (33309) ***(G-4088)***
Kenco Signs Awning LLC 386 672-1590
1538 Garden Ave Holly Hill (32117) ***(G-5759)***
Kendal Signs, Rockledge *Also called Bryson of Brevard Inc* ***(G-15396)***
Kendal Signs Inc 321 636-5116
580 Gus Hipp Blvd Rockledge (32955) ***(G-15428)***
Kendall Fuel Inc 305 270-7735
9949 N Kendall Dr Miami (33176) ***(G-9819)***
Kendall News, South Miami *Also called Your Hometown Newspaper Inc* ***(G-16832)***
Kendall Sign and Design Inc 305 595-2000
12558 Sw 88th St Miami (33186) ***(G-9820)***
Kendoo Technology Inc 305 592-9688
1950 Nw 94th Ave Lowr Doral (33172) ***(G-3407)***
Kenexa Learning Inc 407 562-1905
601 S Lake Destiny Rd # 30 Maitland (32751) ***(G-8470)***
Kenexa Learning Inc 407 548-0434
100 Colonial Center Pkwy # 1 Lake Mary (32746) ***(G-7428)***
Kenfar Corporation 813 443-5222
5926 Jet Port Industrial Tampa (33634) ***(G-17818)***
Kennedy Craft Cabinets Inc 239 598-1566
5790 Washington St Naples (34109) ***(G-11304)***
Kennesaw Fruit & Juice, Pompano Beach *Also called R & Z Ventures Inc* ***(G-14824)***
Kenneth E Keller 239 649-7579
4110 Entp Ave Ste 116 Naples (34116) ***(G-11305)***
Kenneth J Manning Lighting 561 702-0169
11170 Malayan St Boca Raton (33428) ***(G-587)***
Kenneth P Green 850 643-5851
12977 Nw Pea Ridge Rd Bristol (32321) ***(G-1197)***
Kenneth P Green Logging, Bristol *Also called Kenneth P Green* ***(G-1197)***
Kenneth S Jarrell Inc 334 215-7774
9859 N Palafox St Pensacola (32534) ***(G-14189)***
Kenney Communications Inc (PA) 407 859-3113
1215 Spruce Ave Orlando (32824) ***(G-12869)***
Kenny Skylights LLC 407 330-5150
5294 Tower Way Sanford (32773) ***(G-16078)***
Kenny-Ts Inc 850 575-6644
1471 Capital Cir Nw # 10 Tallahassee (32303) ***(G-17288)***
Kens Gas Piping Inc 850 897-4149
419 Adams Ave Ste A Valparaiso (32580) ***(G-18513)***
Kens Stump Grinding LLC 407 948-5031
3848 Beachman Dr Orlando (32810) ***(G-12870)***
Kent Manufacturing Venice Inc 941 485-8871
155 Toscavilla Blvd Nokomis (34275) ***(G-11584)***
Kent Mfg Fla Keys Inc 941 488-0355
248 James St Venice (34285) ***(G-18559)***
Kenton Industries LLC 863 675-8233
1477 Forestry Division Rd Labelle (33935) ***(G-7318)***
Keralis Inter Inc (PA) 305 345-0849
2539 S Byshr Dr Apt 117 Miami (33133) ***(G-9821)***
Keratherapy, Hallandale Beach *Also called Diora Professionnel LLC* ***(G-5181)***
Keratin Cure, Opa Locka *Also called Beauty Cosmetica* ***(G-12293)***
Keratin Salon Direct, Royal Palm Beach *Also called CXR Strategies LLC* ***(G-15464)***
Keratronix Inc 954 753-5741
4377 Nw 124th Ave Coral Springs (33065) ***(G-2268)***
Kericure Inc 855 888-5374
26620 Easy St Wesley Chapel (33544) ***(G-18750)***
Kerma Medical Products Inc 954 744-3480
3371 Executive Way Miramar (33025) ***(G-11009)***
Kerno LLC 954 261-5854
20958 Sheridan St Fort Lauderdale (33332) ***(G-4089)***
Kerry Consulting Corp 561 364-9969
30 Lawrence Lake Dr Boynton Beach (33436) ***(G-926)***
Kerry Inc 813 359-5182
1111 W Dr Mlk Jr Blvd Plant City (33563) ***(G-14443)***
Kerry Inc 813 359-5181
1111 W Dr Mrtn Lther King Plant City (33563) ***(G-14444)***
Kerry Ingredients & Flavours, Plant City *Also called Kerry Inc* ***(G-14444)***
Keurig Dr Pepper Inc 561 227-1424
5266 Eagle Trail Dr Tampa (33634) ***(G-17819)***
Kevco Builders Inc 352 308-8025
2104 S Bay St Eustis (32726) ***(G-3711)***
Kevin Jeffers Inc 352 377-2322
1611 S Main St Gainesville (32601) ***(G-4949)***
Kevin Murray Welding Proj DBA 813 323-3543
18151 Bosley Dr Spring Hill (34610) ***(G-16875)***
Kevins Custom Woodworking 727 804-8422
246 Arbor Dr E Palm Harbor (34683) ***(G-13742)***
Kevins Machine & Engrg LLC 850 519-6516
2709 Crawfordville Hwy Crawfordville (32327) ***(G-2334)***
Key Automotive Florida LLC 863 668-6000
5300 Allen K Breed Hwy Lakeland (33811) ***(G-7725)***
Key Biscayne Smoothie Company 305 441-7882
249 Catalonia Ave Coral Gables (33134) ***(G-2163)***
Key Largo Canvas, Key Largo *Also called Cross Key Marine Canvas Inc* ***(G-7167)***
Key Lime Customs LLC 407 353-9942
1040 W 2nd Ave Windermere (34786) ***(G-19233)***
Key Logging 386 328-6984
229 Lynn Dr Hollister (32147) ***(G-5754)***
Key Packaging Company Inc 941 355-2728
7350 15th St E Sarasota (34243) ***(G-16245)***
Key Safety Systems Inc 863 668-6000
5300 Allen K Breed Hwy Lakeland (33811) ***(G-7726)***
Key West Citizen, Key West *Also called Cooke Communications Fla LLC* ***(G-7184)***
Key West Multihull, Key West *Also called Multihull Technologies Inc* ***(G-7198)***
Key West Printing LLC 305 517-6711
5585 2nd Ave Ste 1 Key West (33040) ***(G-7190)***
Key West Smuggler Co 916 995-1873
1107 Key Plz Key West (33040) ***(G-7191)***
Key West Wldg Fabrication Inc 305 296-5555
5650 1st Ave Key West (33040) ***(G-7192)***
Keylon Lighting Services Inc 352 279-3249
6931 Remington Rd Brooksville (34602) ***(G-1241)***
Keymark Corporation Florida 863 858-5500
2540 Knights Station Rd Lakeland (33810) ***(G-7727)***
Keynoter Publishing Co Inc 305 743-5551
3015 Overseas Hwy Marathon (33050) ***(G-8519)***
Keyplex, Miami *Also called Morse Enterprises Limited Inc* ***(G-10042)***
Keys Deck & Dock Supplies Inc 305 451-8001
100151 Overseas Hwy Key Largo (33037) ***(G-7172)***
Keystone 75 Inc 954 430-1880
5620 Dewey St Hollywood (33023) ***(G-5856)***
Keystone Brick Paver 239 340-6492
11495 Ranchette Rd Fort Myers (33966) ***(G-4510)***
Keystone Color Works Inc 813 250-1313
2411 S Hesperides St Tampa (33629) ***(G-17820)***
Keystone Development, Jacksonville *Also called Keystone Industries LLC* ***(G-6535)***
Keystone Industries LLC (PA) 239 337-7474
1915 Wigmore St Jacksonville (32206) ***(G-6535)***
Keystone Precast & Columns Cor 305 216-5375
29630 Sw 183rd Ct Homestead (33030) ***(G-5975)***
Keystone Products Inc 305 245-4716
1414 Nw 3rd Ave Homestead (33034) ***(G-5976)***
Keystone Rv Company 813 228-0625
1201 Old Hopewell Rd # 9 Tampa (33619) ***(G-17821)***
Keystone Steel Products Co 813 248-9828
3101 E 2nd Ave Tampa (33605) ***(G-17822)***
Keystone Water Company LLC 863 465-1932
200 Turner Rd Lake Placid (33852) ***(G-7490)***
Keytag1 LLC 203 982-8448
265 S Federal Hwy Deerfield Beach (33441) ***(G-2853)***
Keytroller LLC 813 877-4500
3907 W Martin Luther King Tampa (33614) ***(G-17823)***
Keytroller LLC 813 877-4500
3907 W Dr Mart Luth Kng B Martin Luther King Tampa (33614) ***(G-17824)***
Kgb Kiteboarding Inc (PA) 904 705-9235
9378 Arlington Expy Jacksonville (32225) ***(G-6536)***
Khaled W Akkawi 321 396-3108
1349 S Orange Blossom Trl Apopka (32703) ***(G-154)***
Kibby Foods LLC 305 456-3635
2315 W 77th St Hialeah (33016) ***(G-5472)***
Kickin It LLC 954 648-1405
3560 Lloyd Dr Oakland Park (33309) ***(G-11817)***
KID Group Inc 888 805-8851
4010 S 57th Ave Ste 104 Greenacres (33463) ***(G-5084)***
Kid-U-Not Inc 407 324-2112
1201 Central Park Dr Sanford (32771) ***(G-16079)***
Kiddidoo USA, Miami Beach *Also called Sports Structure Intl LLC* ***(G-10715)***
Kids Wood 407 332-9663
714 Commerce Cir Longwood (32750) ***(G-8299)***
Kights Printing & Office Pdts 904 731-7990
8505-1 Baymeadows Rd Jacksonville (32256) ***(G-6537)***

Kiinde LLC......404 368-5382
6300 N Wickham Rd Ste 130 Melbourne (32940) ***(G-8858)***
Kik Custom Products, Auburndale *Also called Sewell Products Florida LLC* ***(G-252)***
Kikinaz Screen Printing Inc......561 512-3134
336 Sandpiper Ave Royal Palm Beach (33411) ***(G-15473)***
Kikisteescom LLC......954 314-7147
762 Verona Lake Dr Weston (33326) ***(G-19146)***
Kimball Electronics Tampa Inc......813 814-5229
13750 Reptron Blvd Tampa (33626) ***(G-17825)***
Kimberlyn Investments Co......305 448-6328
2828 Coral Way Ste 309 Coral Gables (33145) ***(G-2164)***
Kimera Koffee, Coral Gables *Also called Kraken Koffee LLC* ***(G-2169)***
Kinane Corp......772 288-6580
310 Se Denver Ave Stuart (34994) ***(G-16965)***
Kincaid Plastics Inc......352 754-9979
2400 Corporate Blvd Brooksville (34604) ***(G-1242)***
Kinco Ltd (HQ)......904 355-1476
5245 Old Kings Rd Jacksonville (32254) ***(G-6538)***
Kinematics and Controls Corp......352 796-0300
15151 Technology Dr Brooksville (34604) ***(G-1243)***
Kinetic Fusion Corp......561 352-1670
12781 56th Pl N West Palm Beach (33411) ***(G-18920)***
Kinetic Industries LLC......727 572-7604
10445 49th St N Ste A Clearwater (33762) ***(G-1750)***
Kinetic Research, Tampa *Also called Bader Prosthetics & Orthotics* ***(G-17453)***
Kinetic Research Inc......813 962-6300
5513 W Sligh Ave Tampa (33634) ***(G-17826)***
Kinetics Usa Inc......561 988-8826
990 S Rogers Cir Ste 5 Boca Raton (33487) ***(G-588)***
Kinetronics Corporation......941 951-2432
5316 Lena Rd Bradenton (34211) ***(G-1067)***
King & Grube Advg & Prtg LLC......727 327-6033
1211 10th St Sw Largo (33770) ***(G-7990)***
King & Grube Inc......727 327-6033
1211 10th St Sw Largo (33770) ***(G-7991)***
King Arthur's Tools, Tallahassee *Also called Round Table Tools Inc* ***(G-17318)***
King Brands LLC......239 313-2057
9910 Bavaria Rd Fort Myers (33913) ***(G-4511)***
King Construction & Glass LLC......407 508-6286
1414 Grandview Blvd Kissimmee (34744) ***(G-7261)***
King Han Inc......860 933-8574
3725 S Access Rd Ste C Englewood (34224) ***(G-3662)***
King Kanine LLC (PA)......833 546-4738
150 S Pine Island Rd # 115 Plantation (33324) ***(G-14528)***
King Mobile Welding Andrew......386 437-1007
1645 County Road 302 Bunnell (32110) ***(G-1301)***
King of Socks......772 204-3286
2085 Se N Blackwell Dr Port St Lucie (34952) ***(G-15174)***
King Pharmaceuticals LLC......954 575-7085
2814 N University Dr Coral Springs (33065) ***(G-2269)***
King Pharmaceuticals LLC......423 989-8000
2540 26th Ave N Saint Petersburg (33713) ***(G-15833)***
King Plastic Corporation......941 423-8666
1100 N Toledo Blade Blvd North Port (34288) ***(G-11742)***
King Printing & Graphics Inc......813 681-5060
634 Oakfield Dr Brandon (33511) ***(G-1164)***
King Tech Print LLC......786 362-6249
7205 Nw 44th St Miami (33166) ***(G-9822)***
King's Office Supply & Prtg Co, Crescent City *Also called Scott Brevard Inc* ***(G-2342)***
Kingdom Coatings Inc......904 600-1424
2779 Indigo Cir Middleburg (32068) ***(G-10908)***
Kingman Custom Stairs & Trim L......561 547-9888
436 Lytle St West Palm Beach (33405) ***(G-18921)***
Kings & Queens Cabinets......863 646-6972
841 Windsor St Lakeland (33803) ***(G-7728)***
Kings Creek Flowers, Miami *Also called Ebs Quality Service Inc* ***(G-9497)***
Kings Han Manufacturing, Englewood *Also called King Han Inc* ***(G-3662)***
Kings Pharmacy, Coral Springs *Also called King Pharmaceuticals LLC* ***(G-2269)***
Kingspan - Asi, Deland *Also called Kingspan Insulated Panels Inc* ***(G-2991)***
Kingspan Deland Plant, Deland *Also called Kingspan Insulated Panels Inc* ***(G-2992)***
Kingspan Insulated Panels Inc (HQ)......386 626-6789
726 Summerhill Dr Deland (32724) ***(G-2991)***
Kingspan Insulated Panels Inc......386 626-6789
725 Summerhill Dr Deland (32724) ***(G-2992)***
Kingspan-Medusa Inc (HQ)......386 626-6789
726 Summerhill Dr Deland (32724) ***(G-2993)***
Kingston Automotive & Wldg LLC......727 378-4881
8039 Palatine Dr Hudson (34667) ***(G-6031)***
Kino Sandals Inc......305 294-5044
107 Fitzpatrick St Key West (33040) ***(G-7193)***
Kino Shoe Factory, Key West *Also called Kino Sandals Inc* ***(G-7193)***
Kinship Precision LLC......321 765-3531
435 West Dr Melbourne (32904) ***(G-8859)***
Kira Labs Inc......954 978-4549
3400 Gateway Dr Ste 100 Pompano Beach (33069) ***(G-14739)***
Kirby Acquisitions LLC......850 687-8703
294 Hunters Rd Santa Rosa Beach (32459) ***(G-16162)***
Kirchman Corporation (PA)......877 384-0936
2001 Summit Park Dr # 100 Orlando (32810) ***(G-12871)***
Kirkland Industries LLC......386 496-3491
4638 Sw 150th Rd Lake Butler (32054) ***(G-7339)***
Kirtech Enterprises Inc......352 742-7222
28210 Lake Indus Blvd Tavares (32778) ***(G-18344)***
Kiskeya Minerals Usa LLC......305 328-5082
8249 Nw 70th St Miami (33166) ***(G-9823)***
Kiss Polymers LLC......813 962-2703
12515 Sugar Pine Way Tampa (33624) ***(G-17827)***
Kissimmee Iron Works Inc......407 870-8872
2741 Old Dixie Hwy Kissimmee (34744) ***(G-7262)***
Kissimmee Polishing......407 923-9446
805 Prkway Plz Blvd Ste A Kissimmee (34744) ***(G-7263)***
Kissimmee Printing......407 518-2514
1230 Simpson Rd Kissimmee (34744) ***(G-7264)***
Kissimmee Smoke Shop......407 952-6181
7551 W Irlo Brnsn Mem Hwy Kissimmee (34747) ***(G-7265)***
Kit Residential Designs Inc......305 796-5940
5921 Nw 176th St Unit 2 Hialeah (33015) ***(G-5473)***
Kitchen & Bath Center Inc (PA)......850 244-3996
20 Ready Ave Nw Fort Walton Beach (32548) ***(G-4812)***
Kitchen and Bath Universe Inc......813 887-5658
6606 N 56th St Tampa (33610) ***(G-17828)***
Kitchen Counter Connections......386 677-9471
123 N Orchard St Ste 3e Ormond Beach (32174) ***(G-13382)***
Kitchen Design Center, Fort Walton Beach *Also called Gulf South Distributors Inc* ***(G-4807)***
Kitchen Dsgns By Joan E Rbbins......321 727-0012
7690 Industrial Rd Melbourne (32904) ***(G-8860)***
Kitchen Sink Express LLC......800 888-6604
1986 Brae Moor Dr Dunedin (34698) ***(G-3583)***
Kitchen USA Inc......904 714-1970
6965 Philips Hwy Jacksonville (32216) ***(G-6539)***
Kitchenest, Doral *Also called Creative Home and Kitchen LLC* ***(G-3312)***
Kitchenista Corp......305 400-4992
2332 Galiano St Fl 2 Coral Gables (33134) ***(G-2165)***
Kitchenpro, Miami *Also called Hec America Inc* ***(G-9695)***
Kitchens By US, Pembroke Pines *Also called M X Corporation* ***(G-14046)***
Kitchens By US......407 745-4923
4201 L B Mcleod Rd Orlando (32811) ***(G-12872)***
Kitchens Crafters Inc......407 788-0560
302 Black Gum Trl Longwood (32779) ***(G-8300)***
Kitchens Rta LLC......407 969-0902
2467 N John Young Pkwy Orlando (32804) ***(G-12873)***
Kitchens Xtreme LLC......941 387-5181
4181 Taggart Cay S # 301 Sarasota (34233) ***(G-16482)***
Kitchens, Baths & Closets, Boca Raton *Also called Got It Inc* ***(G-550)***
Kite Bum Inc......321 267-6393
2575 Shady Oaks Dr Titusville (32796) ***(G-18439)***
Kite Runner LLC......305 785-5056
6031 Sw 85th St Miami (33143) ***(G-9824)***
Kite Technology Group LLC......407 557-0512
2642 Michigan Ave Ste C Kissimmee (34744) ***(G-7266)***
Kite Vn Corporation......772 234-3484
1045 Winding River Rd Vero Beach (32963) ***(G-18636)***
Kiteman Productions Inc......407 943-8480
5200 Ridgeway Dr Orlando (32819) ***(G-12874)***
Kitko Corp......786 287-8900
10773 Nw 58th St Ste 87 Doral (33178) ***(G-3408)***
Kizable LLC......727 600-3469
1125 Ne 16th Ter Fort Lauderdale (33304) ***(G-4090)***
Kj Collections......904 285-7745
12350 Arbor Dr Ponte Vedra Beach (32082) ***(G-14944)***
Kj Reynolds Inc......904 829-6488
3520 Ag Ctr Dr Ste 306 Saint Augustine (32092) ***(G-15564)***
Kjs Hot Choppers......850 200-4860
1652 W Highway 98 Mary Esther (32569) ***(G-8590)***
KLA Aventura LLC......305 931-2322
600 Sw 1st Ave Miami (33130) ***(G-9825)***
KLA Industries......727 315-4719
801 West Bay Dr Ste 203 Largo (33770) ***(G-7992)***
Klasmann-Deilmann Americas Inc......305 397-8498
1300 S Miami Ave # 1905 Miami (33130) ***(G-9826)***
Kleen Wheels Corporation......954 791-9112
5000 Oakes Rd Ste H Davie (33314) ***(G-2541)***
Kleenbore Inc......800 347-1200
13386 International Pkwy Jacksonville (32218) ***(G-6540)***
Kleids Enterprises Inc......727 796-7900
22023 Us Highway 19 N Clearwater (33765) ***(G-1751)***
Klimaire Products Inc......305 593-8358
2190 Nw 89th Pl Doral (33172) ***(G-3409)***
Kling Fabrication Inc......727 321-7233
6563 46th St N Ste 705 Pinellas Park (33781) ***(G-14359)***
Klocke of America Inc......239 561-5800
16260 Arprt Pk Dr Ste 125 Fort Myers (33913) ***(G-4512)***
Klopfer Holdings Inc......727 472-2002
2134 Sunnydale Blvd Clearwater (33765) ***(G-1752)***
Klopp Coin Counters, Oldsmar *Also called Klopp International Inc* ***(G-12240)***
Klopp International Inc......813 855-6789
237 Dunbar Ct Oldsmar (34677) ***(G-12240)***
Klopp of Florida Inc......813 855-6789
251 Dunbar Ave Oldsmar (34677) ***(G-12241)***

ALPHABETIC

Kloth Inc 954 578-5687
10111 Nw 46th St Sunrise (33351) ***(G-17139)***
Klp Investments LLC 401 762-4357
1424 Se Macarthur Blvd Stuart (34996) ***(G-16966)***
Klugman Enterprises LLC 352 318-9623
7410 Linden Ln Sarasota (34243) ***(G-16246)***
Klyo Medical Systems Inc 305 330-5025
1464 Nw 82nd Ave Doral (33126) ***(G-3410)***
Km Coatings Mfg Jr 602 253-1168
1111 W Newport Center Dr Deerfield Beach (33442) ***(G-2854)***
Km Industrial Racking Inc 813 900-7457
8989 Ulmerton Rd Largo (33771) ***(G-7993)***
Km Precast Inc 239 438-2146
7701 Gardner Dr Unit 101 Naples (34109) ***(G-11306)***
KMA Pharma LLC 754 220-6936
4151 Ne 30th Ter Lighthouse Point (33064) ***(G-8209)***
Kme Amrica Mar Tube Ftting LLC 904 265-4001
3440 Evergreen Ave Jacksonville (32206) ***(G-6541)***
Kmg Marketing LLC 727 376-7200
11515 Pyramid Dr Odessa (33556) ***(G-12130)***
Kmi International Inc 561 588-5514
2501 Park St Lake Worth (33460) ***(G-7562)***
Kmr Concrete Inc 863 519-9077
2835 State Road 60 E Bartow (33830) ***(G-321)***
Kms Medical LLC 305 266-3388
13755 Sw 119th Ave Miami (33186) ***(G-9827)***
Kmss Products Inc 800 646-3005
9225 Ulmerton Rd Ste D Largo (33771) ***(G-7994)***
Kn Machine & Tools Inc 561 748-3035
3125 Jupiter Park Cir # 4 Jupiter (33458) ***(G-7065)***
KNex Industries Inc 215 997-7722
301 E Yamato Rd Ste 4200 Boca Raton (33431) ***(G-589)***
KNex Ltd Partnership Group 215 997-7722
301 E Yamato Rd Ste 4200 Boca Raton (33431) ***(G-590)***
Knight Bacon Associates 772 388-5115
9577 Gator Dr Unit 1 Sebastian (32958) ***(G-16665)***
Knight Fire & Security Inc 561 471-8221
7513 Central Indus Dr Riviera Beach (33404) ***(G-15341)***
Knight Industrial Eqp Inc 863 646-2997
3701 Airfield Dr W Lakeland (33811) ***(G-7729)***
Knight Industries 772 344-2053
1001 Sw Cornelia Ave Port Saint Lucie (34953) ***(G-15117)***
Knight Vision Lllp 321 607-9900
701 Columbia Blvd Titusville (32780) ***(G-18440)***
Knight Welding Supply LLC 561 889-5342
3131 Se Waaler St Stuart (34997) ***(G-16967)***
Knight-Rddr/Miami Herald Cr Un 305 376-2181
1 Herald Plz Fl 2 Miami (33132) ***(G-9828)***
Knightmare Surfboards LLC 321 720-4157
3525 Corey Rd Malabar (32950) ***(G-8492)***
Knights Farm Fresh Feeds Inc 352 793-2242
5376 Cr 316a Bushnell (33513) ***(G-1318)***
Knights Manufacturing Company 321 607-9900
701 Columbia Blvd Titusville (32780) ***(G-18441)***
Knights Powder Coating LLC 727 906-5130
712 Wesley Ave Tarpon Springs (34689) ***(G-18312)***
Knightsbridge Steel LLC 786 532-0290
507 W 17th St Hialeah (33010) ***(G-5474)***
Knopf & Sons Bindery Inc (PA) 904 353-5115
1817 Florida Ave Jacksonville (32206) ***(G-6542)***
Knopf & Sons Bindery Inc 904 355-4411
1817 Florida Ave Jacksonville (32206) ***(G-6543)***
Knothole Creations Inc 727 561-9107
13205 40th St N Clearwater (33762) ***(G-1753)***
Knowles Plastics Inc 954 232-8756
10301 Nw 16th Ct Coral Springs (33071) ***(G-2270)***
Knowles' Mobile Marine, Coral Springs *Also called Knowles Plastics Inc* ***(G-2270)***
Knox Aluminum Inc 813 645-3529
720 4th St Sw Ste B Ruskin (33570) ***(G-15486)***
Ko Orthotics Inc 954 570-8096
5130 Heron Ct Coconut Creek (33073) ***(G-2088)***
Koala Tee Inc (usa) 941 954-7700
2160 17th St Sarasota (34234) ***(G-16483)***
Kobalt Music Pubg Amer Inc 305 200-5682
2100 Ponce De Leon Blvd Coral Gables (33134) ***(G-2166)***
Kobetron LLC 850 939-5222
1778 Sea Lark Ln Navarre (32566) ***(G-11468)***
Kochan Cases 850 533-4190
740 Bryn Mawr Blvd Mary Esther (32569) ***(G-8591)***
Kodiak Software Inc 727 599-8839
832 Narcissus Ave Clearwater (33767) ***(G-1754)***
Kohler Sdmo, Miramar *Also called Sdmo Generating Sets Inc* ***(G-11040)***
Koho Software Inc 813 390-1309
6030 Printery St Unit 103 Tampa (33616) ***(G-17829)***
Kohtler Elevator Inds Inc (PA) 305 687-7037
4115 Nw 132nd St Unit B Opa Locka (33054) ***(G-12331)***
Koki Interiors Furn Mfg Inc 305 558-6573
7680 W 7th Ave Hialeah (33014) ***(G-5475)***
Kold Draft International, LLC, Fort Lauderdale *Also called Asbury Manufacturing Co LLC* ***(G-3826)***
Kolich Electric Motor Co Inc 954 969-8605
3420 Nw 25th Ave Pompano Beach (33069) ***(G-14740)***
Kollsman Inc 407 312-1384
12600 Challenger Pkwy Orlando (32826) ***(G-12875)***
Kollsman Instrument Division, Palm Beach Gardens *Also called Sequa Corporation* ***(G-13626)***
Kollsut International Inc 305 438-6877
1763 Ne 162nd St North Miami Beach (33162) ***(G-11688)***
Kombucha 221b.c., Sarasota *Also called Mad At SAD LLC* ***(G-16495)***
Kommander Software LLC 407 906-2121
2271 E Steven St Inverness (34453) ***(G-6092)***
Kommercial Refrigeration Inc 863 299-3000
810 Hillside Ct N Winter Haven (33881) ***(G-19332)***
Kona Gold LLC 844 714-2224
746 North Dr Ste A Melbourne (32934) ***(G-8861)***
Konadocks LLC 407 909-0606
230 Deer Island Rd Winter Garden (34787) ***(G-19272)***
Koncept Systems LLC 786 610-0122
10755 Sw 244th Ter Homestead (33032) ***(G-5977)***
Kone Crane Maintenance Svcs 813 707-0086
2007 Wood Ct Ste 5 Plant City (33563) ***(G-14445)***
Konnected Inc 407 286-3138
5718 Old Cheney Hwy Orlando (32807) ***(G-12876)***
Konus USA Corporation 305 884-7618
7530 Nw 79th St Medley (33166) ***(G-8677)***
Kookie Kllection Kosmetics LLC 954 218-4302
3601 Nw 44th Ave Lauderdale Lakes (33319) ***(G-8090)***
Kool Ledz LLC 561 212-5843
21238 Stonewood Dr Boca Raton (33428) ***(G-591)***
Koozie Group, Clearwater *Also called Scribe Opco Inc* ***(G-1871)***
Koral Manufacturing Inc 727 548-5040
8720 66th Ct N Pinellas Park (33782) ***(G-14360)***
Koral Precision LLC 727 548-5040
8720 66th Ct N Pinellas Park (33782) ***(G-14361)***
Korangy Publishing Inc 786 334-5052
6318 Biscayne Blvd Miami (33138) ***(G-9829)***
Korasana, Gainesville *Also called Zpx LLC* ***(G-5018)***
Kos Industries Inc 863 318-1511
3056 Cypress Gardens Rd Winter Haven (33884) ***(G-19333)***
Koszegi Industries Inc 954 419-9544
1801 Green Rd Ste E Deerfield Beach (33064) ***(G-2855)***
Kottler Research Corp 850 776-7021
2000 Garcon Point Rd Milton (32583) ***(G-10934)***
Kova Laboratories Inc 954 978-8730
1711 Banks Rd Margate (33063) ***(G-8555)***
Kover Corp 305 888-0146
1375 Nw 97th Ave Ste 12 Doral (33172) ***(G-3411)***
Kozuba & Sons Distillery Inc 813 857-8197
1960 5th Ave S Saint Petersburg (33712) ***(G-15834)***
Kr Solutions Group US LLC 305 307-8353
1500 Nw 89th Ct Ste 115 Doral (33172) ***(G-3412)***
KR Ward Inc 863 325-9070
1000 Hoover Rd Winter Haven (33884) ***(G-19334)***
Kraft Foods, Coral Gables *Also called Mondelez Global LLC* ***(G-2179)***
Kraft Heinz Foods Company 904 632-3400
735 E Bay St Jacksonville (32202) ***(G-6544)***
Kraft Heinz Foods Company 407 786-8157
2180 W State Road 434 # 2112 Longwood (32779) ***(G-8301)***
Kraft Heinz Foods Company 813 810-5298
5806 Peach Heather Trl Valrico (33596) ***(G-18520)***
Kraft Heinz Foods Company 305 428-7152
355 Alhambra Cir Ste 1350 Coral Gables (33134) ***(G-2167)***
Kraft Heinz Foods Company 305 476-7000
255 Alhambra Cir Ste 1010 Coral Gables (33134) ***(G-2168)***
Kraft Heinz Foods Company 239 694-3663
5521 Division Dr Fort Myers (33905) ***(G-4513)***
Kraft Heinz Foods Company 904 695-1300
7500 Forshee Dr Jacksonville (32219) ***(G-6545)***
Kraken Koffee LLC 833 546-3725
2555 Ponce De Leon Blvd Coral Gables (33134) ***(G-2169)***
Kramer Pharmacal Inc 305 226-0641
8900 Sw 24th St Miami (33165) ***(G-9830)***
Kramski North America Inc 727 828-1500
8222 118th Ave Ste 650 Largo (33773) ***(G-7995)***
Krane Environmental, Venice *Also called K V Water Equipment & Krane Co* ***(G-18558)***
Kraton Chemical LLC (HQ) 904 928-8700
4600 Touchton Rd E # 1200 Jacksonville (32246) ***(G-6546)***
Kraton Chemical LLC 850 438-9222
411 S Pace Blvd Pensacola (32502) ***(G-14190)***
Kraton Chemical LLC 850 785-8521
2 S Everitt Ave Panama City (32401) ***(G-13924)***
Kratos Def & SEC Solutions Inc 866 606-5867
8601 Transport Dr Orlando (32832) ***(G-12877)***
Krausz Usa Inc 352 509-3600
331 Sw 57th Ave Ocala (34474) ***(G-11977)***
Kreateck International Corp 772 925-1216
1707 20th St Vero Beach (32960) ***(G-18637)***
Kreative Ceramics Inc 321 278-9889
2165 Twisted Pine Rd Ocoee (34761) ***(G-12086)***

Kreative Drive Inc 786 845-8605
8953 Nw 23rd St Doral (33172) **(G-3413)**
Kreyol Essence LLC 786 453-8287
8325 Ne 2nd Ave Ste 117 Miami (33138) **(G-9831)**
Krieger Publishing Co Inc 321 724-9542
1725 Krieger Ln Malabar (32950) **(G-8493)**
Kristine Window Treatments LLC 305 623-8302
15998 Nw 49th Ave Hialeah (33014) **(G-5476)**
Krome Brewing Company LLC 786 601-9337
17480 Sw 232nd St Miami (33170) **(G-9832)**
Kron Designs LLC 954 941-0800
6818 Nw 20th Ave Fort Lauderdale (33309) **(G-4091)**
Krs Global Biotechnology Inc 888 502-2050
791 Park Of Commerce Blvd # 600 Boca Raton (33487) **(G-592)**
Krs Global Biotechnology Mfg, Boca Raton *Also called Krs Global Biotechnology Inc* **(G-592)**
Krs MSA LLC 727 264-7605
1324 Seven Springs Blvd New Port Richey (34655) **(G-11497)**
Krunchy Krisps LLC 561 309-7049
2740 Sw Martin Downs Blvd Palm City (34990) **(G-13664)**
Krunchy Melts, Hallandale Beach *Also called Jada Foods LLC* **(G-5193)**
Ksm Electronics Inc (PA) 954 642-7050
5607 N Hiatus Rd Ste 600 Tamarac (33321) **(G-17361)**
Ksr Publishing Inc 941 388-7050
2477 Stickney Point Rd 315b Sarasota (34231) **(G-16484)**
Kt Fab Inc 863 443-0029
1057 Lancelot Dr Lake Wales (33853) **(G-7514)**
Kt Properties & Dev Inc 386 253-0610
500 Walker St Daytona Beach (32117) **(G-2677)**
Kuando Trading Corp 786 603-3772
1001 Brickell Bay Dr Miami (33131) **(G-9833)**
Kuhlman Corporation 239 334-3111
2690 Rockfill Rd Fort Myers (33916) **(G-4514)**
Kuhn Family Enterprises Inc 813 671-5353
11920 Timberhill Dr Riverview (33569) **(G-15275)**
Kulfi LLC 855 488-4273
1100 Holland Dr Boca Raton (33487) **(G-593)**
Kurts Custom Woodworks 352 693-5407
13636 Se 33rd Ct Summerfield (34491) **(G-17059)**
Kus Usa Inc 954 463-1075
3350 Davie Rd Ste 203 Davie (33314) **(G-2542)**
Kusser Fountainworks, Tampa *Also called Kusser Graniteworks Usa Inc* **(G-17830)**
Kusser Graniteworks Usa Inc 813 248-3428
3109 E 4th Ave Tampa (33605) **(G-17830)**
Kustom Industrial Fabricators 407 965-1940
265 Hunt Park Cv Longwood (32750) **(G-8302)**
Kustom Us Inc (PA) 407 965-1940
640 E State Road 434 # 1000 Longwood (32750) **(G-8303)**
Kw Products Inc 813 855-7817
305 Mears Blvd Oldsmar (34677) **(G-12242)**
Kwik Kerb LLC 386 453-1004
844 Williams Ln Port Orange (32127) **(G-15021)**
Kwik Kerb By 3d 352 383-1123
814 Liberty Ave Mount Dora (32757) **(G-11106)**
Kwik Kopy Printing, Fort Myers *Also called J & J Litho Enterprises Inc* **(G-4499)**
Kwikie Dup Ctr of Pinellas Pk 727 544-7788
8520 49th St N Pinellas Park (33781) **(G-14362)**
Kwikie Printing, Pinellas Park *Also called Kwikie Dup Ctr of Pinellas Pk* **(G-14362)**
Kwikprint Manufacturing Co Inc 904 737-3755
4868 Victor St Jacksonville (32207) **(G-6547)**
Kyaeto Systems, Saint Petersburg *Also called Donovan Home Services LLC* **(G-15762)**
Kyocera Dcment Sltons Sthast L 772 562-0511
480 Okeechobee Rd Ste 101 Fort Pierce (34947) **(G-4710)**
Kyp Go Inc 386 736-3770
1551 Lakeside Dr Deland (32720) **(G-2994)**
Kysor Industrial Corporation (HQ) 727 376-8600
2227 Welbilt Blvd Trinity (34655) **(G-18487)**
Kysor Warren, Trinity *Also called Kysor Industrial Corporation* **(G-18487)**
Kz Manufacturing LLC 305 257-2628
24601 Packinghouse Rd # 1 Princeton (33032) **(G-15185)**
L & A Quality Products Inc 305 326-9300
2181 Nw 10th Ave Miami (33127) **(G-9834)**
L & C Metals LLC 407 859-2600
711 Central Florida Pkwy Orlando (32824) **(G-12878)**
L & D Dumpsters LLC 352 589-5043
25207 Jefferson St Astatula (34705) **(G-212)**
L & D Steel USA Inc 727 538-9917
13240 Belcher Rd S Largo (33773) **(G-7996)**
L & H Boats Inc 772 288-2291
3350 Se Slater St Stuart (34997) **(G-16968)**
L & J Cbd LLC 904 305-9700
14176 Camelot Pl Macclenny (32063) **(G-8443)**
L & L Automotive Electric Inc 631 471-5230
4575 Carolwood Dr Melbourne (32934) **(G-8862)**
L & L Ornamental Iron Works 561 547-5605
5601 Georgia Ave West Palm Beach (33405) **(G-18922)**
L & M Pallet Services Inc 863 519-3502
1190 Us Highway 17 S Bartow (33830) **(G-322)**
L & N Label Company Inc 727 442-5400
2051 Sunnydale Blvd Clearwater (33765) **(G-1755)**
L & S Bait Co Inc 727 584-7691
1415 E Bay Dr Largo (33771) **(G-7997)**
L & S Design & Construction 772 220-1745
3561 Sw Corporate Pkwy Palm City (34990) **(G-13665)**
L A Ornamental & Rack Corp 305 696-0419
3708 Nw 82nd St Miami (33147) **(G-9835)**
L A R Manufacturing LLC 727 846-7860
6828 Commerce Ave Port Richey (34668) **(G-15059)**
L A Rust Inc 954 749-5009
10231 Nw 53rd St Sunrise (33351) **(G-17140)**
L and C Science and Tech Inc 305 200-3531
2205 W 80th St Ste 1 Hialeah (33016) **(G-5477)**
L and D Logging 850 859-1013
701 Sandspur Rd Westville (32464) **(G-19181)**
L and I Diamonds 305 603-7727
36 Ne 1st St Miami (33132) **(G-9836)**
L and TW Oodwork LLC 305 742-4362
17420 Sw 236th St Homestead (33031) **(G-5978)**
L C Acme Barricades (PA) 904 781-1950
9800 Normandy Blvd Jacksonville (32221) **(G-6548)**
L C Ch International Inc 305 888-1323
7395 W 18th Ln Hialeah (33014) **(G-5478)**
L C Clark Publishing Inc 561 627-3393
600 Sandtree Dr Ste 107 Palm Beach Gardens (33403) **(G-13601)**
L C Industries Inc 850 581-0117
125 Bennett Ave Hurlburt Field (32544) **(G-6044)**
L C La Finestra 305 599-8093
2790 Nw 104th Ct Doral (33172) **(G-3414)**
L C Npee 888 316-3718
451 E 10th Ct Hialeah (33010) **(G-5479)**
L C Southwind Manufacturing 352 687-1999
415 Cypress Rd Ocala (34472) **(G-11978)**
L D F Services 386 947-9256
1111 State Ave Daytona Beach (32117) **(G-2678)**
L J'S Tops & Bottoms, Boynton Beach *Also called Ljs Tops & Bottoms* **(G-929)**
L M Compressor LLC 352 484-0850
5800 Sw 25th St Ocala (34474) **(G-11979)**
L M Industrial Inc 407 240-8911
1429 Central Florida Pkwy Orlando (32837) **(G-12879)**
L R Gator Corporation 407 578-6616
4380 L B Mcleod Rd Orlando (32811) **(G-12880)**
L R M, Rockledge *Also called Lrm Industries Intl Inc* **(G-15430)**
L R P, Palm Beach Gardens *Also called Lrp Publications Inc* **(G-13608)**
L S I, Miami *Also called Logistic Systems Inc* **(G-9906)**
L T Weld II LLC 352 454-2735
1200 Whitewood Way Clermont (34714) **(G-1966)**
L W Timber Co Inc 850 592-2597
3830 Highway 69 Greenwood (32443) **(G-5089)**
L&R Imaging 678 691-3204
2450 W Sample Rd Ste 8 Pompano Beach (33073) **(G-14741)**
L-3 Cmmnctons Advnced Lser Sys 407 295-5878
2500 N Orange Blossom Trl Orlando (32804) **(G-12881)**
L-3 Cmmnctons Ntronix Holdings 212 697-1111
1025 W Nasa Blvd Melbourne (32919) **(G-8863)**
L2d Outdoors Inc 954 757-6116
4300 Nw 120th Ave Coral Springs (33065) **(G-2271)**
L3 Aviation Products Inc 941 371-0811
490 1st Ave S Ste 600 Saint Petersburg (33701) **(G-15835)**
L3 Crestview Aerospace 850 682-2746
5486 Fairchild Rd Crestview (32539) **(G-2353)**
L3 Technologies, Saint Petersburg *Also called L3 Aviation Products Inc* **(G-15835)**
L3 Technologies Inc 321 409-6122
1200 Woody Burke Rd Melbourne (32901) **(G-8864)**
L3 Technologies Inc 941 371-0811
490 1st Ave S Saint Petersburg (33701) **(G-15836)**
L3 Technologies Inc 407 295-5878
2500 N Orange Blossom Trl Orlando (32804) **(G-12882)**
L3 Technologies Inc 850 678-9444
8th St Bldg 968 Eglin A F B (32542) **(G-3640)**
L3 Technologies Inc 305 371-7039
2900 Sw 42nd St Fort Lauderdale (33312) **(G-4092)**
L3 Technologies Inc 941 377-5562
6300 Edgelake Dr Sarasota (34240) **(G-16485)**
L3harris Technologies Inc (PA) 321 727-9100
1025 W Nasa Blvd Melbourne (32919) **(G-8865)**
L3harris Technologies Inc 321 309-7848
407 N John Rodes Blvd Melbourne (32934) **(G-8866)**
L3harris Technologies Inc 407 581-3782
7022 Tpc Dr Ste 500 Orlando (32822) **(G-12883)**
L3harris Technologies Inc 305 542-5441
7508 Nw 54th St Miami (33166) **(G-9837)**
L3harris Technologies Inc 727 415-6592
2330 Grove Valley Ave Palm Harbor (34683) **(G-13743)**
L3harris Technologies Inc 260 451-6814
5690 W Cypress St Ste B Tampa (33607) **(G-17831)**
L3harris Technologies Inc 321 768-4660
2800 Jordan Blvd Malabar (32950) **(G-8494)**

A L P H A B E T I C

L3harris Technologies Inc 321 729-2186
2571 Kirby Cir Ne Melbourne (32905) ***(G-8867)***
L3harris Technologies Inc 321 412-6601
1282 Roslyn Ave Nw Palm Bay (32907) ***(G-13518)***
L3harris Technologies Inc 321 727-4255
Plant 16 Troutman Blvd Palm Bay (32905) ***(G-13519)***
L3harris Technologies Inc 321 727-4660
1000 Charles J Herbert Dr Palm Bay (32905) ***(G-13520)***
L3harris Technologies Inc 321 984-0782
150 S Wickham Rd Melbourne (32904) ***(G-8868)***
L3harris Technologies Inc 321 727-4000
1025 W Nasa Blvd Melbourne (32902) ***(G-8869)***
L3harris Technologies Inc 321 727-9100
1025 W Nasa Blvd Melbourne (32919) ***(G-8870)***
L3harris Technologies Inc 321 674-4589
1025 W Nasa Blvd D11d Melbourne (32919) ***(G-8871)***
L4 Design LLC (PA) 407 262-8200
2701 Mtland Ctr Pkwy Ste Maitland (32751) ***(G-8471)***
L4 Design LLC 224 612-5045
2701 Mtland Ctr Pkwy Ste Maitland (32751) ***(G-8472)***
L7 Apparel & Denim Company LLC 954 867-8124
1900 Taylor St Hollywood (33020) ***(G-5857)***
La Autentica 786 409-3779
2294 W 78th St Hialeah (33016) ***(G-5480)***
La Autentica Foods Inc 305 888-6727
2294 W 78th St Hialeah (33016) ***(G-5481)***
La Bodeguita De Hialeah Inc 305 240-7421
1044 W 23rd St Hialeah (33010) ***(G-5482)***
La Caja China, Hialeah *Also called L C Ch International Inc* ***(G-5478)***
La Chiquita Tortilla Mfr 407 251-8290
6918 Presidents Dr Orlando (32809) ***(G-12884)***
La Ciudad En Sus Manos LLC 813 770-4973
555 Forest Lake Dr Altamonte Springs (32714) ***(G-52)***
La Coronella Meat Processing 305 691-2630
9566 Nw 7th Ave Miami (33150) ***(G-9838)***
La Cuisine Intl Distrs Inc 305 418-0010
2005 Nw 115th Ave Miami (33172) ***(G-9839)***
La Esquina Del Le Billto 305 477-4225
8601 Nw 58th St Unit 101 Doral (33166) ***(G-3415)***
La Esquina Del Lechon, Doral *Also called La Esquina Del Le Billto* ***(G-3415)***
La Experiencia Crankshaft 305 823-6161
9910 Nw 80th Ave Unit 2m Miami Lakes (33016) ***(G-10802)***
La Fabrika Retail Services LLC 786 525-4491
6303 Blue Lagoon Dr Ste 4 Miami (33126) ***(G-9840)***
La Gaceta Publishing Inc 813 248-3921
3210 E 7th Ave Tampa (33605) ***(G-17832)***
La Gaceta Tri-Lingual Weekly, Tampa *Also called La Gaceta Publishing Inc* ***(G-17832)***
La Genomics LLC 407 909-1120
5939 Blakeford Dr Windermere (34786) ***(G-19234)***
La Glass, Miami *Also called MA Glass & Mirror LLC* ***(G-9930)***
La Lechonera Media, Miami *Also called La Lechonera Products Inc* ***(G-9841)***
La Lechonera Products Inc 305 635-2303
2161 Nw 22nd Ct Miami (33142) ***(G-9841)***
La Luna Ltd 305 644-0444
1638 Sw 8th St Miami (33135) ***(G-9842)***
La Mansion Latina LLC 305 406-1606
9183 Sw 152nd Path Miami (33196) ***(G-9843)***
La Mar Orlando LLC 407 423-2051
621 Commonwealth Ave Orlando (32803) ***(G-12885)***
La Montina Inc 305 324-0083
1445 Nw 22nd St Miami (33142) ***(G-9844)***
La Moti Roof & Tile Inc 305 635-2641
1360 Nw 29th St Miami (33142) ***(G-9845)***
La Parada Criolla Inc 321 207-7100
254 W State Road 434 Longwood (32750) ***(G-8304)***
La Pavers Inc 407 209-9163
2349 Lake Debra Dr Orlando (32835) ***(G-12886)***
La Perle Memorials, Inverness *Also called Perl Inc* ***(G-6095)***
La Perlelle LLC 941 388-2458
17 Fillmore Dr Sarasota (34236) ***(G-16486)***
La Perrada Del Gordo Boca LLC 561 968-6978
2650 S Military Trl West Palm Beach (33415) ***(G-18923)***
La Physique', Eustis *Also called A Living Testimony LLC* ***(G-3699)***
La Prensa, Longwood *Also called Impremedia LLC* ***(G-8289)***
La Providencia Express Co 305 409-9894
4728 Sw 74th Ave Miami (33155) ***(G-9846)***
La Province Inc 305 538-2406
2106 Nw 13th Ave Miami (33142) ***(G-9847)***
La Real Foods Inc 305 232-6449
13013 Sw 122nd Ave Miami (33186) ***(G-9848)***
La Real Tortillas, Miami *Also called La Real Foods Inc* ***(G-9848)***
La Sin Rival, Miami *Also called Gregomarc LLC* ***(G-9670)***
La Tropical Brewing Co LLC 786 362-5429
1825 Ponce De Leon Blvd Coral Gables (33134) ***(G-2170)***
La Villarena Meat & Pork Inc (PA) 305 759-0555
6455 Ne 3rd Ave Miami (33138) ***(G-9849)***
La Voz De La Calle, Hialeah *Also called Voice Publishing Co Inc* ***(G-5683)***
La Zero Inc 727 545-1175
8100 Park Blvd N Ste 41 Pinellas Park (33781) ***(G-14363)***

Laal Manufacturing Inc 786 859-3613
55 Ne 1st St Ste 55 # 55 Miami (33132) ***(G-9850)***
Lab Kingz LLC 561 808-4216
514 Sw 15th Ter Delray Beach (33444) ***(G-3100)***
Label Company 850 438-7334
680 E Heinberg St Pensacola (32502) ***(G-14191)***
Label Graphics Inc 561 798-8180
11298 Roselynn Way Lake Worth (33449) ***(G-7563)***
Label Printing Service 727 820-1226
1245 N Hercules Ave Clearwater (33765) ***(G-1756)***
Label Tape Systems, Sarasota *Also called Dongili Investment Group Inc* ***(G-16413)***
Labelclick Inc 727 548-8345
630 Brooker Creek Blvd # 340 Oldsmar (34677) ***(G-12243)***
Labelflex, Miami *Also called Tradingflex Inc* ***(G-10501)***
Labelle Brick Pavers Tile LLC 863 230-3100
1515 Forestry Division Rd Labelle (33935) ***(G-7319)***
Labelpro Inc 727 538-2149
14409 60th St N Clearwater (33760) ***(G-1757)***
Labinal Power Systems, Sarasota *Also called Safran Power Uk Ltd* ***(G-16288)***
Lablogic Systems Inc 813 626-6848
1911 N Us Highway 301 # 140 Tampa (33619) ***(G-17833)***
Lac Inc 407 671-6610
3580 Aloma Ave Ste 1 Winter Park (32792) ***(G-19417)***
Lachance Leathers LLC 407 790-6712
4017 Moorings Ln Orlando (32810) ***(G-12887)***
Lactalogics Inc 772 202-0407
8883 S Us Highway 1 Port Saint Lucie (34952) ***(G-15118)***
Ladove Inc 305 823-8051
5701 Miami Lakes Dr E Miami Lakes (33014) ***(G-10803)***
Ladove Industries Inc 305 624-2456
5701 Miami Lakes Dr E Miami Lakes (33014) ***(G-10804)***
Lagaci Inc 954 929-1395
2201 Stirling Rd Ste 101 Fort Lauderdale (33312) ***(G-4093)***
Lagaci Sport, Fort Lauderdale *Also called Lagaci Inc* ***(G-4093)***
Lahia America Corp 305 254-6212
12401 Sw 134th Ct Miami (33186) ***(G-9851)***
Laird International Corp 954 532-3794
2300 Nw 30th Pl Bldg 9 Pompano Beach (33069) ***(G-14742)***
Lajoie Investment Corp 954 463-3271
819 Nw 7th Ter Fort Lauderdale (33311) ***(G-4094)***
Lakay Vita LLC 786 985-7552
419 N Federal Hwy Apt 209 Hallandale Beach (33009) ***(G-5196)***
Lake & Bay Boats LLC 813 949-7300
5770 Shirley St Naples (34109) ***(G-11307)***
Lake Aerospace Services, Miramar *Also called VSI & Partners Inc* ***(G-11058)***
Lake Area Watersports LLC 352 475-3434
829 N State Road 21 Melrose (32666) ***(G-8986)***
Lake City Mediplex LLC 386 752-2209
162 Nw Birdie Pl Lake City (32055) ***(G-7363)***
Lake City Reporter, Lake City *Also called Community News Papers Inc* ***(G-7351)***
Lake County Forklift Solutions 352 735-4024
25808 Eufaula Way Sorrento (32776) ***(G-16788)***
Lake Door and Trim Inc 352 589-5566
1589 Pine Grove Rd Eustis (32726) ***(G-3712)***
Lake News, Mount Dora *Also called Triangle Shopping Guide Inc* ***(G-11116)***
Lake News LLC 407 251-1314
9836 Sweetleaf St Orlando (32827) ***(G-12888)***
Lake Park Auto Machine Inc 561 848-6197
404 Foresta Ter West Palm Beach (33415) ***(G-18924)***
Lake Point Restoration LLC 561 924-9100
12012 South Shore Blvd # 10 Wellington (33414) ***(G-18722)***
Lake Sentinel, Tavares *Also called Sentinel Cmmnctons News Vntres* ***(G-18352)***
Lake Worth Herald Press 561 585-9387
1313 Central Ter Lake Worth (33460) ***(G-7564)***
Lakeland Digital Printing Co 863 509-8049
3264 Merlot Dr Lakeland (33811) ***(G-7730)***
Lakeland Lures Inc 863 644-3127
955 Oak Ln Lakeland (33811) ***(G-7731)***
Lakeland Outdoor Advertising, Coral Gables *Also called Outdoor Media Inc* ***(G-2183)***
Lakeridge Falls Art League 941 360-1046
4200 Lakeridge Blvd Sarasota (34243) ***(G-16247)***
Lakeridge Winery & Vineyards, Clermont *Also called Seavin Inc* ***(G-1973)***
Lakes Metal Fabrication Inc 954 731-2010
2350 Nw 30th Ct Oakland Park (33311) ***(G-11818)***
Lakeshore Custom Wood Products 813 623-2790
5210 Shadowlawn Ave Tampa (33610) ***(G-17834)***
Lakeside Publishing Co LLC 847 491-6440
3180 Burgundy Dr N Palm Beach Gardens (33410) ***(G-13602)***
Lakeside Recreational Inc 863 467-1530
4074 Us Highway 441 Se Okeechobee (34974) ***(G-12185)***
Lakeview Dirt Co Inc 904 824-2586
497 S Holmes Blvd Saint Augustine (32084) ***(G-15565)***
Lakewood Juices, Miami *Also called Allapattah Industries Inc* ***(G-9116)***
Lakewood Manufacturing Co Inc 443 398-5015
10696 Grande Blvd West Palm Beach (33412) ***(G-18925)***
Lakewood Manufacutring, West Palm Beach *Also called Lakewood Manufacturing Co Inc* ***(G-18925)***

Lakewood Organics LLC 305 324-5900
2125 Nw 10th Ct Miami (33127) ***(G-9852)***
Lamartek Inc 386 752-1087
175 Nw Washington St Lake City (32055) ***(G-7364)***
Lamb Tec Inc 305 798-6266
7755 Sw 193rd Ln Cutler Bay (33157) ***(G-2399)***
Lambert Corporation Florida 407 841-2940
20 Coburn Ave Orlando (32805) ***(G-12889)***
Lambs Signs Inc 941 792-4453
4230 26th St W Bradenton (34205) ***(G-1068)***
Laminar Flow Systems Inc 386 253-8833
1585 Avi Ctr Pkwy Ste 605 Daytona Beach (32114) ***(G-2679)***
Laminations Southeast, Jacksonville *Also called Great Northern Corporation* ***(G-6446)***
Lampshade Direct, Deerfield Beach *Also called Lampshades of Florida Inc* ***(G-2856)***
Lampshades of Florida Inc 954 491-3377
4280 Nw 5th Dr Deerfield Beach (33442) ***(G-2856)***
Lan Designs Inc 305 661-7878
7169 Sw 44th St Miami (33155) ***(G-9853)***
Lan Industries LLC 305 889-2087
5413 Nw 74th Ave Miami (33166) ***(G-9854)***
Lan Music Corp 305 722-5842
13611 S Dixie Hwy Miami (33176) ***(G-9855)***
Lanai Bright LLC 239 303-4756
200 Waldo Ave Unit 1 Lehigh Acres (33971) ***(G-8194)***
Lanai Lights LLC 239 415-2561
3411 Hanson St Unit A Fort Myers (33916) ***(G-4515)***
Lancaster Industries Inc 954 916-9293
13974 N Cypress Cove Cir Davie (33325) ***(G-2543)***
Lance Lashelle (PA) 425 820-8888
6231 Nw 4th Ave Boca Raton (33487) ***(G-594)***
Lance Printers Service Inc 305 256-7982
13934 Sw 154th St Miami (33177) ***(G-9856)***
Lanco & Harris Corp 407 240-4000
600 Mid Florida Dr Orlando (32824) ***(G-12890)***
Land Leather Inc 305 594-2260
1927 Nw 135th Ave Miami (33182) ***(G-9857)***
Land Marine Service Inc 561 626-2947
2590 W Edgewater Dr West Palm Beach (33410) ***(G-18926)***
Land O Lakes Winery LLC 813 995-9463
3901 Land O Lakes Blvd Land O Lakes (34639) ***(G-7859)***
Landing Aerospace Inc 305 687-0100
4604 Nw 133rd St Opa Locka (33054) ***(G-12332)***
Landis Service Company, Tampa *Also called Coastal Wipers Inc* ***(G-17543)***
Landmark Aviation 305 296-5422
3471 S Roosevelt Blvd Key West (33040) ***(G-7194)***
Landmark Precast LLC 305 242-8888
438 Nw 10th Ave Homestead (33030) ***(G-5979)***
Landslide Publishing Inc 561 392-4717
201 Plaza Real Ste 140 Boca Raton (33432) ***(G-595)***
Landtech Data Corporation 561 790-1265
1460 Royal Palm Bch Blvd Royal Palm Beach (33411) ***(G-15474)***
Landtech Software Co., Royal Palm Beach *Also called Landtech Data Corporation* ***(G-15474)***
Lane Care LLC 727 316-3708
3241 Fox Chase Cir N Palm Harbor (34683) ***(G-13744)***
Lane Construction Corporation 863 665-0457
3350 Reynolds Rd Lakeland (33803) ***(G-7732)***
Lane Shark Usa LLC 864 382-6892
4600 Highway 97a Mc David (32568) ***(G-8601)***
Lanfranchi North America Inc 813 901-5333
8401 Benjamin Rd Ste A Tampa (33634) ***(G-17835)***
Langstons Utility Buildings 813 659-0141
4298 State Road 60 W Mulberry (33860) ***(G-11128)***
Lanzas Distributor Inc 305 885-5966
7251 Nw 54th St Miami (33166) ***(G-9858)***
Lanzas Foods, Miami *Also called Lanzas Distributor Inc* ***(G-9858)***
Lap of Amer Laser Applications, Boynton Beach *Also called Lap of America Lc* ***(G-927)***
Lap of America Lc 561 416-9250
161 Commerce Rd Ste 3 Boynton Beach (33426) ***(G-927)***
Lapel Pin & Button Company Inc (PA) 407 677-6144
10151 University Blvd Orlando (32817) ***(G-12891)***
Lapin Sheet Metal Company 407 423-9897
3825 Gardenia Ave Orlando (32839) ***(G-12892)***
Lapolla Industries LLC 954 379-0241
720 S Military Trl Deerfield Beach (33442) ***(G-2857)***
Laporte Inv Holdings Inc 863 294-4498
512 6th St Nw Winter Haven (33881) ***(G-19335)***
Largent Fuels USA LLC 786 431-5981
1200 Brickell Ave Ste 240 Miami (33131) ***(G-9859)***
Largo Aluminum Inc 305 852-2390
86500 Overseas Hwy Islamorada (33036) ***(G-6098)***
Larmac Development Corp 904 264-5006
879 Camp Frncis Jhnson Rd Orange Park (32065) ***(G-12397)***
Larrick Group Inc 941 351-2700
1845 57th St Sarasota (34243) ***(G-16248)***
Larry Burr Printing Co, Winter Haven *Also called Burr Printing Co Inc* ***(G-19308)***
Larry C Cribb 904 845-2804
28145 Enterprise Dr Hilliard (32046) ***(G-5714)***
Larry Cubi 352 445-7435
9772 Sw 46th Ct Ocala (34476) ***(G-11980)***
Larry Johnson Inc 305 888-2300
701 W 25th St Hialeah (33010) ***(G-5483)***
Larrys Extreme Audio Tint LLC 941 766-8468
19360 Strathcona Ave Port Charlotte (33954) ***(G-14987)***
Larrys Mobilcrete Inc 352 336-2525
1104 Nw 50th Ave Ste A Gainesville (32609) ***(G-4950)***
Larrys Rigs 561 967-7791
2460 Sunset Dr West Palm Beach (33415) ***(G-18927)***
Larsen 305 989-4043
3 Melody Ln Stuart (34996) ***(G-16969)***
Larsen Cabinetmaker Co 305 252-1212
14374 Sw 142nd Ave Miami (33186) ***(G-9860)***
Larson Industries 352 226-8512
409 Sw 4th Ave Gainesville (32601) ***(G-4951)***
Larson Industries Incorporated (PA) 352 262-0566
409 Sw 4th Ave Gainesville (32601) ***(G-4952)***
Larson-Burton Incorporated 815 637-9500
1010 N Nova Rd Daytona Beach (32117) ***(G-2680)***
Larter & Sons 732 290-1515
83 River Dr Jupiter (33469) ***(G-7066)***
LAS & JB Inc 772 672-5315
4840 S Us Highway 1 Fort Pierce (34982) ***(G-4711)***
Las Amrcas Mltimedia Group LLC 305 633-3341
888 Brickell Ave Ste 500 Miami (33131) ***(G-9861)***
Las Zirh Americas Inc 305 942-7597
2792 Nw 24th St Miami (33142) ***(G-9862)***
Lase, Cutler Bay *Also called Light and Sound Equipment Inc* ***(G-2402)***
Laser, Orlando *Also called Superior Metal* ***(G-13229)***
Laser Assault 801 374-3400
9863 Creet Cir Navarre (32566) ***(G-11469)***
Laser Creations Incorporated 800 771-7151
946 Century Ln Apopka (32703) ***(G-155)***
Laser Interceptor Usa LLC 352 688-0708
5769 Greystone Dr Spring Hill (34609) ***(G-16856)***
Laser Lens Tek Inc 941 752-5811
6621 19th St E Sarasota (34243) ***(G-16249)***
Laser Light Litho Corp 305 899-0713
1440 Ne 131st St North Miami (33161) ***(G-11643)***
Laser Magic, Apopka *Also called Laser Creations Incorporated* ***(G-155)***
Laser Photo Tooling Services 561 393-4710
5081 N Dixie Hwy Boca Raton (33431) ***(G-596)***
Laser Productions Network, Miami *Also called Spaceport Corporation* ***(G-10392)***
Laser Surgical Florida Inc 954 609-7639
900 Biscayne Blvd # 2001 Miami (33132) ***(G-9863)***
Laserpath Technologies LLC 407 247-3930
2789 Wrights Rd Ste 1021 Oviedo (32765) ***(G-13446)***
Lasersight Incorporated (PA) 407 678-9900
10244 E Clnl Dr Ste 201 Orlando (32817) ***(G-12893)***
Lasersight Technologies Inc 407 678-9900
10244 E Clnl Dr Ste 201 Orlando (32817) ***(G-12894)***
Laserstar Technologies Corp 401 438-1500
2461 Orlando Central Pkwy Orlando (32809) ***(G-12895)***
Laserstar Technologies Corp 407 248-1142
2453 Orlando Central Pkwy Orlando (32809) ***(G-12896)***
Lastrada Furniture Inc (PA) 954 485-6000
1785 Nw 38th Ave Fort Lauderdale (33311) ***(G-4095)***
Lastrada Furniture & Interiors, Fort Lauderdale *Also called Lastrada Furniture Inc* ***(G-4095)***
Latam Group Corp 305 793-8961
12453 Sw 124th Ter Miami (33186) ***(G-9864)***
Latam Optical LLC 786 275-3284
2585 Nw 74th Ave Miami (33122) ***(G-9865)***
LAtelier Pris Hute Design LLC 800 792-3550
6151 Biscayne Blvd Miami (33137) ***(G-9866)***
Latham Marine Inc 954 462-3055
280 Sw 32nd Ct Fort Lauderdale (33315) ***(G-4096)***
Latham Plastics Inc 813 783-7212
40119 County Road 54 Zephyrhills (33540) ***(G-19526)***
Lathing By Estaban M Perez Inc 352 302-8791
38321 Groveview Ave Lady Lake (32159) ***(G-7327)***
Latin Amercn Meats & Foods USA (PA) 305 477-2700
6939 Nw 82nd Ave Miami (33166) ***(G-9867)***
Latin Amrcn Fncl Pblctions Inc (HQ) 305 416-5261
1101 Brickell Ave # 1200 Miami (33131) ***(G-9868)***
Latin Dairy Foods LLC 305 888-1788
2175 Nw 24th Ave Miami (33142) ***(G-9869)***
Latin Goddess Press Inc 917 703-1356
872 Leopard Trl Winter Springs (32708) ***(G-19477)***
Latin Press Inc 305 285-3133
600 Sw 22nd Ave Miami (33135) ***(G-9870)***
Latinfinance, Miami *Also called Latin Amrcn Fncl Pblctions Inc* ***(G-9868)***
Latino Cabinet Center Plus LLC 786 663-0909
487 Ne 167th St North Miami Beach (33162) ***(G-11689)***
Latitude 235 Coffee and Tea (PA) 941 556-2600
7245 21st St E Sarasota (34243) ***(G-16250)***
Latitude 27 Canvas 772 321-6361
2306 7th Ave Vero Beach (32960) ***(G-18638)***
Latitude Clean Tech Group Inc 561 417-0687
190 Nw Spanish River Blvd # 101 Boca Raton (33431) ***(G-597)***
Latteri & Sons Inc 813 876-1800
305 N Glen Ave Tampa (33609) ***(G-17836)***

ALPHABETIC

Latteri & Sons Vault and Monu, Tampa *Also called Latteri & Sons Inc* ***(G-17836)***
Lau International Inc 305 381-9855
36 Ne 1st St Ste 438 Miami (33132) ***(G-9871)***
Lauderdale Graphics Corp (PA) 954 450-0800
1625 Sw 117th Ave Davie (33325) ***(G-2544)***
Laughing Mermaid The, Melbourne *Also called Pure Wave Organics Inc* ***(G-8915)***
Launcher Solutions LLC 904 479-0762
10752 Deerwood Park Blvd # 100 Jacksonville (32256) ***(G-6549)***
Laundromart 561 487-4343
23182 Sandalfoot Plaza Dr Boca Raton (33428) ***(G-598)***
Laura Knit Collection Inc (PA) 305 945-8222
3224 Ne 167th St North Miami Beach (33160) ***(G-11690)***
Laurey Co, Pompano Beach *Also called Strategic Brands Inc* ***(G-14875)***
Lavi Enterprises LLC 561 721-7170
1210 W 13th St Riviera Beach (33404) ***(G-15342)***
Lavish Blinds Corp 786 229-8134
9822 Sw 222nd Ter Cutler Bay (33190) ***(G-2400)***
Law Offces Rbecca A Beddow LLC 516 671-6566
2500 Airport Rd S Ste 208 Naples (34112) ***(G-11308)***
Lawall Prsthtics Orthotics Inc 407 567-5190
6535 Nemours Pkwy Orlando (32827) ***(G-12897)***
Lawex Corporation (PA) 305 259-9755
1550 Madruga Ave Ste 508 Coral Gables (33146) ***(G-2171)***
Lawko Inc 904 389-2850
5126 Ortega Blvd Jacksonville (32210) ***(G-6550)***
Lawless Industries Ltd 352 429-3300
19994 Independence Blvd Groveland (34736) ***(G-5099)***
Lawrence Commercial Systems 850 574-8723
451 Geddie Rd Tallahassee (32304) ***(G-17289)***
Lawrence Factor Inc 305 430-9152
4740 Nw 157th St Miami Lakes (33014) ***(G-10805)***
Lawrenceville Press Inc 609 737-1148
820 N 8th St Lantana (33462) ***(G-7875)***
Lawson Industries Inc (PA) 305 696-8660
8501 Nw 90th St Medley (33166) ***(G-8678)***
Lawton LLC 833 493-7226
10001 W Oklnd Pk Blvd Sunrise (33351) ***(G-17141)***
Lawton Connect, Orlando *Also called Lawton Printers Inc* ***(G-12898)***
Lawton Printers Inc 407 260-0400
649 Triumph Ct Orlando (32805) ***(G-12898)***
Laycock Systems Inc 813 248-3555
1601 N 43rd St Tampa (33605) ***(G-17837)***
Laza Iron Works Inc 305 754-8200
7251 N Miami Ave Miami (33150) ***(G-9872)***
Lcf Pavers Inc 239 826-8177
1825 Linhart Ave Lot 25 Fort Myers (33901) ***(G-4516)***
LCI, Orlando *Also called C L Industries Inc* ***(G-12540)***
LCI DISTRIBUTORS, Miami *Also called La Cuisine Intl Distrs Inc* ***(G-9839)***
LCI-leu, Hurlburt Field *Also called L C Industries Inc* ***(G-6044)***
Lcn Incorporated 305 461-2770
6949 Nw 82nd Ave Miami (33166) ***(G-9873)***
Lcr Signs & Services 772 882-5276
2862 Se Buccaneer Cir Port Saint Lucie (34952) ***(G-15119)***
Ld Telecommunications Inc 954 628-3029
2101 W Commercial Blvd Fort Lauderdale (33309) ***(G-4097)***
Ldc, Saint Augustine *Also called Lakeview Dirt Co Inc* ***(G-15565)***
LDM Industries Inc 305 216-1545
12904 Sw 132nd Ct Miami (33186) ***(G-9874)***
LDS Vacuum Products Inc (PA) 407 862-4643
773 Big Tree Dr Longwood (32750) ***(G-8305)***
Le Atelier Paris Haute Design, Miami *Also called Officine Gullo USA LLC* ***(G-10091)***
Le Mundo Vino LLC 786 369-5232
12323 Sw 130th St Miami (33186) ***(G-9875)***
Le Posh Pup 561 625-6391
14625 Nw 298th St Okeechobee (34972) ***(G-12186)***
Le Publications Inc 954 766-8433
3600 W Commercial Blvd Fort Lauderdale (33309) ***(G-4098)***
Le Soleil De La Floride, Hollywood *Also called Griffon Graphics Inc* ***(G-5833)***
Lead 2 Design 954 757-6116
4302 Nw 120th Ave Coral Springs (33065) ***(G-2272)***
Lead Enterprises Inc 305 635-8644
3300 Nw 29th St Miami (33142) ***(G-9876)***
Leadair Inc 407 343-7571
113 Hangar Rd Kissimmee (34741) ***(G-7267)***
Leader Group (PA) 904 249-7475
1372 Beach Blvd Jacksonville Beach (32250) ***(G-6947)***
Leader Mulch, Miami *Also called Rubber 2 Go Llc* ***(G-10286)***
Leader Tech Inc 813 855-6921
12420 Race Track Rd Tampa (33626) ***(G-17838)***
Leaderinprint Inc 561 200-9412
8927 Hypoluxo Rd Ste A4 Lake Worth (33467) ***(G-7565)***
Leadex 305 266-2028
4731 Sw 75th Ave Miami (33155) ***(G-9877)***
Leading Edge Aerospace Llc 305 608-6826
16115 Nw 52nd Ave Miami Gardens (33014) ***(G-10750)***
LEAFYWELL, Plantation *Also called Nxgen Brands LLC* ***(G-14540)***
Leals Tires & Wheels 239 491-2214
1585 Gretchen Ave S # 1 Lehigh Acres (33973) ***(G-8195)***
Lean Design & Mfg Inc 727 415-3504
19412 Livingston Ave Lutz (33559) ***(G-8395)***
Lean Green Enterprises LLC 954 525-2971
2125 S Andrews Ave Fort Lauderdale (33316) ***(G-4099)***
Lear Investors Inc (PA) 305 681-8582
4154 Nw 132nd St Opa Locka (33054) ***(G-12333)***
Leather Doctor of Doral LLC 786 367-6146
18739 Sw 107th Ave Cutler Bay (33157) ***(G-2401)***
Leatherjacket4, Lakeland *Also called Shaikh Rizwan* ***(G-7789)***
Leblon Cachaca, Miami *Also called Leblon LLC* ***(G-9878)***
Leblon LLC 954 649-0148
2701 S Le Jeune Rd Miami (33134) ***(G-9878)***
Lecanto Ready Mix Con Plant, Lecanto *Also called Cemex Cnstr Mtls Fla LLC* ***(G-8131)***
Lectora, Deerfield Beach *Also called Trivantis Corporation* ***(G-2929)***
Led Lghting Slutions Globl LLC 855 309-1702
6118 Riverview Blvd Bradenton (34209) ***(G-1069)***
Led Lighting, Miami Lakes *Also called Luminoso LLC* ***(G-10810)***
Led Lighting Solutions, Bradenton *Also called Energy Management Products LLC* ***(G-1038)***
Led Pro Services, Clearwater *Also called Icpf Development Group LLC* ***(G-1727)***
Led Supply, The, Kissimmee *Also called Logic Illumination LLC* ***(G-7270)***
Led Surf Lighting Inc 239 687-4458
3425 Radio Rd Ste 202 Naples (34104) ***(G-11309)***
Led Technologies Incorporated 800 337-9565
12821 Starkey Rd Ste 4900 Largo (33773) ***(G-7998)***
Leda Printing Inc 941 922-1563
3939 S Tamiami Trl Sarasota (34231) ***(G-16487)***
Ledger (HQ) 863 802-7000
300 W Lime St Lakeland (33815) ***(G-7733)***
Ledger 2 Ledger Inc 321 961-4017
4700 Millenia Blvd # 175 Orlando (32839) ***(G-12899)***
Ledger Publishing Company, Lakeland *Also called Ledger* ***(G-7733)***
Ledradiant LLC 305 901-1313
615 N 21st Ave Hollywood (33020) ***(G-5858)***
Lee Cabinets Corp 786 291-5871
11260 Sw 50th St Miami (33165) ***(G-9879)***
Lee Chemical Corporation 407 843-6950
2800 Taft Ave Orlando (32804) ***(G-12900)***
Lee County Fuels Inc 239 349-5322
16272 Cutters Ct Fort Myers (33908) ***(G-4517)***
Lee Designs Llc 239 278-4245
3300 Palm Ave Fort Myers (33901) ***(G-4518)***
Lee Fisher International Inc 813 875-6296
3922 W Osborne Ave Tampa (33614) ***(G-17839)***
Lee Lowsky 904 470-4110
4651 Salisbury Rd Jacksonville (32256) ***(G-6551)***
Lee McCullough Inc 352 796-7100
Hud Brooksville (34606) ***(G-1244)***
Lee Net Services Inc 904 777-4833
8216 Cheryl Ann Ln Jacksonville (32244) ***(G-6552)***
Lee Printing Inc (PA) 904 396-5715
2653 Isabella Blvd Unit 4 Jacksonville Beach (32250) ***(G-6948)***
Leeder Group Inc 305 436-5030
8508 Nw 66th St Miami (33166) ***(G-9880)***
Leeds Machining Co 407 671-3688
4025 Bibb Ln Orlando (32817) ***(G-12901)***
Leeroys Fabrication & Wldg LLC 850 398-1997
5834 White Oak Dr Crestview (32539) ***(G-2354)***
Leesburg Concrete Company Inc 352 787-4177
1335 Thomas Ave Leesburg (34748) ***(G-8163)***
Leeward Tech 305 215-4526
815 N Homestead Blvd # 405 Homestead (33030) ***(G-5980)***
Lefab Commercial LLC 305 456-1306
76 Miracle Mile Coral Gables (33134) ***(G-2172)***
Legacy Building Supply Company 850 729-5901
109 Kelly Rd Niceville (32578) ***(G-11570)***
Legacy Cabinet Company, The, Niceville *Also called Cljp Inc* ***(G-11564)***
Legacy Cnstr Rmdlg Clg Svcs LL 800 638-9646
500 N Federal Hwy Ste 631 Hallandale Beach (33009) ***(G-5197)***
Legacy Components LLC 813 964-6805
4613 N Clark Ave Tampa (33614) ***(G-17840)***
Legacy Publishing Group 407 290-8414
3878 N Lake Orlando Pkwy Orlando (32808) ***(G-12902)***
Legacy Publishing Services 407 647-3787
1883 Lee Rd Winter Park (32789) ***(G-19418)***
Legacy Sports Inc 352 732-6759
1417 Sw 17th St Ocala (34471) ***(G-11981)***
Legacy Vulcan LLC 407 855-9902
8500 Florida Rock Rd Orlando (32824) ***(G-12903)***
Legacy Vulcan LLC 850 914-9661
2 Edwards Dr Panama City (32405) ***(G-13925)***
Legacy Vulcan LLC 407 321-5323
4150 Maverick Ct Sanford (32771) ***(G-16080)***
Legacy Vulcan LLC 352 796-5690
14556 Ponce De Leon Blvd Brooksville (34601) ***(G-1245)***
Legacy Vulcan LLC 727 321-4667
1020 31st St S Saint Petersburg (33712) ***(G-15837)***
Legacy Vulcan LLC 352 376-2182
924 S Main St Gainesville (32601) ***(G-4953)***

Legacy Vulcan LLC 352 473-4258
6547 State Road 21 Keystone Heights (32656) ***(G-7209)***
Legacy Vulcan LLC 352 394-6196
3310 Green Swamp Rd Clermont (34714) ***(G-1967)***
Legacy Vulcan LLC 850 951-0562
104 Lee S Pl Defuniak Springs (32435) ***(G-2944)***
Legacy Vulcan LLC 863 687-7625
2300 Mershon St Lakeland (33815) ***(G-7734)***
Legacy Vulcan LLC 386 659-2477
1 Mile W On Hwy 100 Grandin (32138) ***(G-5047)***
Legacy Vulcan LLC 850 997-1490
2792 Gamble Rd Lloyd (32337) ***(G-8244)***
Legacy Vulcan Corp 352 742-2122
27222 County Road 561 Tavares (32778) ***(G-18345)***
Legal Components, Clearwater *Also called Ezell Precision Tool Co* ***(G-1678)***
Legar Inc 561 635-5882
303 E Woolbright Rd # 103 Boynton Beach (33435) ***(G-928)***
Legend Design and Production 305 270-1156
9765 Sw 84th St Miami (33173) ***(G-9881)***
Legend Moto LLC 863 946-2002
1100 Us Highway 27 Moore Haven (33471) ***(G-11087)***
Legend Printing Company LLC 904 268-7079
9816 Beach Blvd Jacksonville (32246) ***(G-6553)***
Legends Fabrications LLC 727 642-0578
10298 110th St Largo (33778) ***(G-7999)***
Leggett & Platt Incorporated 954 846-0300
13800 Nw 4th St Sunrise (33325) ***(G-17142)***
Lehigh Acrs Fre Cnrl & Rscue 239 303-5300
636 Thomas Sherwin Ave S Lehigh Acres (33974) ***(G-8196)***
Lehigh Cement Company LLC 813 248-4000
3920 Pendola Point Rd Tampa (33619) ***(G-17841)***
Lehigh Cement Company LLC 954 581-2812
3575 Sw 49th Way Davie (33314) ***(G-2545)***
Lehigh Cement Company LLC 321 323-5039
9012 Marlin St Cape Canaveral (32920) ***(G-1363)***
Lehigh White Cement Co LLC (HQ) 561 812-7439
1601 Forum Pl Ste 1110 West Palm Beach (33401) ***(G-18928)***
Lehigh White Cement Co LLC 561 812-7441
3920 Pendola Point Rd Tampa (33619) ***(G-17842)***
Leila K Moavero 954 978-0018
1800 Nw 15th Ave Ste 140 Pompano Beach (33069) ***(G-14743)***
Leisure Activities Usa LLC 727 417-7128
2399 26th Ave N Saint Petersburg (33713) ***(G-15838)***
Leisure Furniture Powder CT 239 597-4343
1076 Business Ln Ste 7 Naples (34110) ***(G-11310)***
Leisurelay365, Miami *Also called Eyedose Inc* ***(G-9550)***
Leiton Decor & Design 786 286-4776
4237 Nw 37th Ct Miami (33142) ***(G-9882)***
Lek Technology Consultants 407 877-6505
12788 Gillard Rd Winter Garden (34787) ***(G-19273)***
Lemon Bay Truss & Supply Co 941 698-0800
5300 Linwood Rd Placida (33946) ***(G-14397)***
Lemon Grass Industries Inc 954 418-6110
5920 Nw 59th Ave Parkland (33067) ***(G-13995)***
Lemon Lime Catering LLC 786 332-3636
425 Nw 100th Ter Miami (33150) ***(G-9883)***
Lemon-X Corporation 863 635-8400
500 S Lake Reedy Blvd Frostproof (33843) ***(G-4861)***
Lenco Holdings LLC 305 360-0895
1223 Sw 1st Way Deerfield Beach (33441) ***(G-2858)***
Lenco Marine Solutions LLC 772 288-2662
4700 Se Municipal Ct Stuart (34997) ***(G-16970)***
Lenkbar LLC 239 732-5915
2705 Corporate Flight Dr Naples (34104) ***(G-11311)***
Lennox Global Ltd (HQ) 305 718-2921
2335 Nw 107th Ave Ste 132 Doral (33172) ***(G-3416)***
Lennox Industries 305 718-2974
2335 Nw 107th Ave Ste 132 Doral (33172) ***(G-3417)***
Lennox International Inc 352 379-9630
605 Nw 53rd Ave Ste A4 Gainesville (32609) ***(G-4954)***
Lennox Miami Corp 305 763-8655
1900 Collins Ave Miami Beach (33139) ***(G-10687)***
Lennox National Account S 954 745-3482
4418 Sw 74th Ave Miami (33155) ***(G-9884)***
Lenntech USA LLC 877 453-8095
5975 Sunset Dr Ste 802 South Miami (33143) ***(G-16820)***
Lenoc Chemical Solutions Inc 229 499-0665
2970 Manuel Rd Bowling Green (33834) ***(G-866)***
Lensar Inc 888 536-7271
2800 Discovery Dr Ste 100 Orlando (32826) ***(G-12904)***
Lenstec Inc (PA) 727 571-2272
1765 Commerce Ave N Saint Petersburg (33716) ***(G-15839)***
Lentus Products LLC 203 913-7600
215 Celebration Pl # 520 Kissimmee (34747) ***(G-7268)***
Leo Fashions Inc 305 887-1032
230 W 23rd St Hialeah (33010) ***(G-5484)***
Leo Manufacturing, Fort Lauderdale *Also called Lajoie Investment Corp* ***(G-4094)***
Leon Leather Company Inc 386 304-1902
3735 Us Highway 1 Edgewater (32141) ***(G-3629)***
Leon Sign S LLC 786 333-4694
2330 W 80th St Hialeah (33016) ***(G-5485)***
Leonard-Martin Corporation 850 434-2203
24 N Palafox St Pensacola (32502) ***(G-14192)***
Leonidas Customs Inc 561 542-4151
1054 Larch Way Wellington (33414) ***(G-18723)***
Leopard Brands Inc 954 794-0007
6800 E Rogers Cir Boca Raton (33487) ***(G-599)***
Lera Plastics Inc 904 716-5421
9216 Haydon Rd Jacksonville (32218) ***(G-6554)***
Lerner Enterprises Inc 440 323-5529
19367 Abhenry Cir Port Charlotte (33948) ***(G-14988)***
Lerness Shoe Corp 305 643-6525
2155 Sw 8th St Miami (33135) ***(G-9885)***
Lesco Inc 863 655-2424
425 Haywood Taylor Blvd Sebring (33870) ***(G-16697)***
Lesko Industries Inc 904 273-8293
104 Twin Cedar Ct Ponte Vedra (32082) ***(G-14926)***
Leslie Controls Inc (HQ) 813 978-1000
12501 Telecom Dr Temple Terrace (33637) ***(G-18371)***
Leslie Industries Inc 850 422-0099
2454 Centerville Rd Tallahassee (32308) ***(G-17290)***
Less Frtnate Mus Pubg Ltd Lblt 786 663-0385
10724 Nw 18th Ave Miami (33167) ***(G-9886)***
Lester A Dine Inc 561 624-3009
351 Hiatt Dr Palm Beach Gardens (33418) ***(G-13603)***
Leto LLC 813 486-8049
14483 62nd St N Clearwater (33760) ***(G-1758)***
Levatas 561 622-4511
11701 Lk Vctr Grdn Ave Palm Beach Gardens (33410) ***(G-13604)***
Levil Technology Corp 407 542-3971
1704 Kennedy Pt Ste 1124 Oviedo (32765) ***(G-13447)***
Levinson Built LLC 561 712-9882
1638 Donna Rd West Palm Beach (33409) ***(G-18929)***
Levita LLC 954 227-7468
12410 Nw 39th St Coral Springs (33065) ***(G-2273)***
Levitech Services LLC 904 576-0562
112 5th Ave S Apt 301 Jacksonville Beach (32250) ***(G-6949)***
Lewa Group Corp 305 407-9500
6001 Nw 153rd St Miami Lakes (33014) ***(G-10806)***
Lewis Vault & Precast Inc 352 351-2992
1731 Sw 7th Ave Ocala (34471) ***(G-11982)***
Lewis-Riggs Custom Guitars Inc 407 538-3710
1001 Lake Sherwood Dr Orlando (32818) ***(G-12905)***
Lexington Cutter Inc 941 739-2726
2951 63rd Ave E Bradenton (34203) ***(G-1070)***
Lexington Dsign + Fbrction E L 407 578-4720
613 Triumph Ct Ste 1 Orlando (32805) ***(G-12906)***
Lexington International LLC 800 973-4769
1040 Holland Dr Boca Raton (33487) ***(G-600)***
Lexmark International Inc 954 345-2442
10866 Nw 14th St Coral Springs (33071) ***(G-2274)***
Lexmark International Inc 305 467-2200
5201 Blue Lagoon Dr # 87 Miami (33126) ***(G-9887)***
Lexprint LLC 305 661-2424
4255 Sw 72nd Ave Miami (33155) ***(G-9888)***
Lextm3 Systems LLC 954 888-1024
15751 Sw 41st St Ste 300 Davie (33331) ***(G-2546)***
Lf of America Corp 561 988-0303
7700 Congress Ave # 1120 Boca Raton (33487) ***(G-601)***
Lf Senior Communications Group 561 392-4550
1515 N Federal Hwy # 300 Boca Raton (33432) ***(G-602)***
Lfh Southernstone LLC 727 538-0123
12520 Automobile Blvd Clearwater (33762) ***(G-1759)***
Lftd Partners Inc (PA) 847 915-2446
4227 Habana Ave Jacksonville (32217) ***(G-6555)***
Lg Enterprises Pavers Inc 813 412-9235
8711 Lindenhurst Pl Tampa (33634) ***(G-17843)***
Lg Hausys America Inc 813 249-7658
1820 Massaro Blvd Ste 300 Tampa (33619) ***(G-17844)***
Lg-TEC Corporation 305 770-4005
2021 Coolidge St Hollywood (33020) ***(G-5859)***
Lgl Group Inc (PA) 407 298-2000
2525 Shader Rd Orlando (32804) ***(G-12907)***
Lgl Latin America Operations, Doral *Also called Lennox Global Ltd* ***(G-3416)***
Lh Travis, Winter Haven *Also called Travis Lh LLC* ***(G-19364)***
Lhoist North America Ala LLC 352 585-3488
10245 Cement Plant Rd Brooksville (34601) ***(G-1246)***
Lhoist North America Ala LLC 817 732-8164
1263 Hammondville Rd Pompano Beach (33069) ***(G-14744)***
Lhoist North America Tenn Inc 352 629-7990
11661 Nw Gainesville Rd Ocala (34482) ***(G-11983)***
Liberty Aluminum Co 239 369-3000
5613a 6th St W Lehigh Acres (33971) ***(G-8197)***
Liberty Balloons LLC 239 947-3338
10401 Morningside Ln Bonita Springs (34135) ***(G-843)***
Liberty Calhoun Journal Inc 850 643-3333
11493 Nw Summers Rd Bristol (32321) ***(G-1198)***
Liberty Crtive - Coml Prtg Prm 407 960-4270
800 Waterway Pl Longwood (32750) ***(G-8306)***

ALPHABETIC

Liberty Printing, Odessa *Also called H&M Phillips Inc (G-12125)*
Liberty Woodworking Inc...727 642-9652
6563 46th St N Ste 702 Pinellas Park (33781) ***(G-14364)***
Libre...305 267-2000
2700 Sw 8th St Miami (33135) ***(G-9889)***
Lidarit Inc...407 632-2622
7208 W Sand Lake Rd Orlando (32819) ***(G-12908)***
Liddys Machine Shop Inc...904 354-0134
7621 Holiday Rd S Jacksonville (32216) ***(G-6556)***
Lidias Embroidery...386 447-2293
29 Old Kings Rd N Ste 1a Palm Coast (32137) ***(G-13701)***
Liebherr Cranes Inc...305 817-7500
15101 Nw 112th Ave Hialeah (33018) ***(G-5486)***
Liebherr Nenzing Crane, Hialeah *Also called Liebherr Cranes Inc (G-5486)*
Lifdek Corporation...321 759-3422
1620 Tangerine St Ste 1 Melbourne (32901) ***(G-8872)***
Life All Natural, Miami *Also called Lan Industries LLC (G-9854)*
Life Extension, Fort Lauderdale *Also called Le Publications Inc (G-4098)*
Life In A Tee Shirt Prtg LLC...941 927-0116
2905 Woodpine Cir Sarasota (34231) ***(G-16488)***
Life Proteomics Inc...813 864-7646
8875 Hidden River Pkwy Tampa (33637) ***(G-17845)***
Life Spice and Ingredients LLC...708 301-0447
300 Cherry Ln Palm Beach (33480) ***(G-13557)***
Life Wear Technologies, Pompano Beach *Also called Modular Thermal Tech LLC (G-14767)*
Lifecell, Hallandale Beach *Also called South Beach Skin Care Inc (G-5212)*
Lifeco Foods North America...321 348-5896
855 E Plant St Ste 1700 Winter Garden (34787) ***(G-19274)***
Lifegard Prfcation Systems LLC...813 875-7777
7028 W Waters Ave Ste 228 Tampa (33634) ***(G-17846)***
Lifelink Corporation...813 653-3197
525 E Sadie St Brandon (33510) ***(G-1165)***
Lifelink Foundation Inc...407 218-8783
1739 S Orange Ave Orlando (32806) ***(G-12909)***
Lifes A Bch Publications LLC...850 650-2780
124 Benning Dr Ste 7 Destin (32541) ***(G-3196)***
Lifes A Stitch...386 385-3079
2510 Crill Ave Palatka (32177) ***(G-13484)***
Lifesaving Systems Corporation...813 645-2748
220 Elsberry Rd Apollo Beach (33572) ***(G-105)***
Lifestyle Magazine...386 423-2772
1210 S Riverside Dr New Smyrna Beach (32168) ***(G-11537)***
Lifestyle Media Group LLC...954 377-9470
3511 W Commercial Blvd Fort Lauderdale (33309) ***(G-4100)***
Lifestyle Printworks Inc...321 604-1531
1300 Armstrong Dr Ste 10 Titusville (32780) ***(G-18442)***
Lifestyle Publications LLC...954 217-1165
1675 Market St Ste 203 Weston (33326) ***(G-19147)***
Lifetime Environmental Designs...352 237-7177
3550 Sw 74th Ave Ocala (34474) ***(G-11984)***
Lifetime Products Group Inc...813 781-9182
7215 Nundy Ave Gibsonton (33534) ***(G-5031)***
Lifetime Wellness Centers Inc...321 693-8698
618 Washburn Rd Ste A Melbourne (32934) ***(G-8873)***
Lift Aerospace Corp...305 851-5237
6960 Nw 50th St Miami (33166) ***(G-9890)***
Lift Spectrum Technologies LLC...407 228-8343
4700 Millenia Blvd # 175 Orlando (32839) ***(G-12910)***
Light Age Press Inc...352 242-4530
5660 County Road 561 Clermont (34714) ***(G-1968)***
Light and Sound Equipment Inc...305 233-3737
10777 Sw 188th St Cutler Bay (33157) ***(G-2402)***
Light Integration Inc...407 681-0072
477 Commerce Way Ste 105 Longwood (32750) ***(G-8307)***
Light Source Business Systems...772 562-5046
582 Nw Mercantile Pl Port Saint Lucie (34986) ***(G-15120)***
Light-Tech Inc...863 385-6000
8880 W Josephine Rd Sebring (33875) ***(G-16698)***
Lightening Print, Saint Petersburg *Also called Ideal Publishing Co Inc (G-15812)*
Lighter Than Air Systems Corp (HQ)...904 834-4400
11651 Central Pkwy # 118 Jacksonville (32224) ***(G-6557)***
Lighthouse Boatworks Inc...561 667-7382
512 N Hepburn Ave Jupiter (33458) ***(G-7067)***
Lighthouse Express World Inc...754 210-6196
3880 N 28th Ter Hollywood (33020) ***(G-5860)***
Lighthouse of Leesburg Inc...352 408-6566
420 Calamondin Ave Nw Palm Bay (32907) ***(G-13521)***
Lighting Science Group Corp (HQ)...321 779-5520
3905 W Eau Gallie Blvd # 101 Melbourne (32934) ***(G-8874)***
Lighting Technologies...850 462-1790
1810 Barrancas Ave Pensacola (32502) ***(G-14193)***
Lightking Outdoor, Doral *Also called Digital Outdoor LLC (G-3329)*
Lightn Up Inc...954 797-7778
10401 Nw 53rd St Sunrise (33351) ***(G-17143)***
Lightnet Usa Inc...305 260-6444
123 Nw 23rd St Miami (33127) ***(G-9891)***
Lightning Connecting Rods LLC...727 733-2054
1630 N Hercules Ave Ste B Clearwater (33765) ***(G-1760)***
Lightning Master Corporation...800 749-6800
2100 Palmetto St Ste A Clearwater (33765) ***(G-1761)***
Lightning Phase II Inc...727 539-1800
10700 76th Ct Seminole (33777) ***(G-16749)***
Lightning Prtction Systems Inc...239 643-4323
38818 Exchange Ave Naples (34104) ***(G-11312)***
Lightning Prtg & Graphics Inc...321 242-7766
2330 N Wickham Rd Ste 12 Melbourne (32935) ***(G-8875)***
Lightning Specialists Inc...727 938-3560
11498 Prosperous Dr Odessa (33556) ***(G-12131)***
Lightpath Technologies Inc (PA)...407 382-4003
2603 Challenger Tech Ct Orlando (32826) ***(G-12911)***
Lightsource Imaging Solutions, Port Saint Lucie *Also called Light Source Business Systems (G-15120)*
Lightstone Woodworking LLC...727 424-2660
8842 Commodore Dr Seminole (33776) ***(G-16750)***
Lightworks Inc...305 456-3520
7035 Sw 47th St Ste A Miami (33155) ***(G-9892)***
Ligi Tool and Engineering, Deerfield Beach *Also called US Precision Manufacturing Inc (G-2932)*
Lignotech Florida LLC...904 577-9077
6 Gum St Fernandina Beach (32034) ***(G-3742)***
Lilas Desserts Inc...305 252-1441
12309 Sw 130th St Miami (33186) ***(G-9893)***
Liles Custom Trailers...352 368-2652
4940 N Us Highway 441 Ocala (34475) ***(G-11985)***
Liles Oil Company...407 739-2083
201 Kraft Dr Casselberry (32707) ***(G-1509)***
Lilian Oils On Canvas Inc...941 320-6263
13215 Fawn Lily Dr Riverview (33579) ***(G-15276)***
Lillian Bay Medical Inc...941 815-7373
300 10th St S Apt 346 Saint Petersburg (33705) ***(G-15840)***
Lillys Gastronomia Italiana FL, Hallandale Beach *Also called Lillys Gstrnmia Itlana Fla Inc (G-5198)*
Lillys Gstrnmia Itlana Fla Inc...305 655-2111
370 Ansin Blvd Hallandale Beach (33009) ***(G-5198)***
Lily Ann Cabinets - Tampa Bay...727 877-8180
8601 Somerset Dr Ste C Largo (33773) ***(G-8000)***
Limb Preservation Inst Inc...954 755-5726
11529 Nw 72nd Pl Parkland (33076) ***(G-13996)***
Limbitless Solutions Inc (PA)...407 494-3661
4217 E Plaza Dr Orlando (32816) ***(G-12912)***
Lime Street Development LLC...239 594-7777
808 Wiggins Pass Rd # 201 Naples (34110) ***(G-11313)***
Limelight Publishing LLC...727 384-5999
6677 13th Ave N Ste 3a Saint Petersburg (33710) ***(G-15841)***
Limestone Products Company...352 472-2116
3107 Nw County Road 235 Newberry (32669) ***(G-11558)***
Limited Designs LLC...305 547-9909
382 Ne 191st St 87394 Miami (33179) ***(G-9894)***
Limitless Mobile Wholesale Inc (PA)...321 710-6936
885 Sedalia St Ocoee (34761) ***(G-12087)***
Lincoln Smith Ventures LLC...863 337-6670
2058 E Edgewood Dr Lakeland (33803) ***(G-7735)***
Lincoln Tactical LLC...813 419-3110
1319 Brahma Dr Valrico (33594) ***(G-18521)***
Lincoln-Marti Cmnty Agcy Inc (PA)...305 643-4888
2700 Sw 8th St Miami (33135) ***(G-9895)***
Lincoln-Marti Cmnty Agcy Inc...646 463-6120
450 Sw 16th Ave Miami (33135) ***(G-9896)***
Lindley Foods LLC...407 884-9433
2023 Apex Ct Apopka (32703) ***(G-156)***
Lindorm Inc...305 888-0762
601 Plover Ave Miami Springs (33166) ***(G-10893)***
Lindsay Precast Inc...800 669-2278
13365 Southern Precast Dr Alachua (32615) ***(G-11)***
Lindsey Macke Bindery Printing...727 514-3570
11626 Prosperous Dr Odessa (33556) ***(G-12132)***
Linenmaster LLC...772 212-2710
601 21st St Ste 300 Vero Beach (32960) ***(G-18639)***
Linenwood Home LLC...850 607-7445
24 E Brainerd St Pensacola (32501) ***(G-14194)***
Liners of Legend, Hialeah *Also called Maritime Replicas America Inc (G-5504)*
Linga Pos LLC (PA)...800 619-5931
4501 Tamiami Trl N # 400 Naples (34103) ***(G-11314)***
Linkpoint LLC...305 903-9191
137 E Enid Dr Key Biscayne (33149) ***(G-7159)***
Linman Inc...904 755-6800
Us Hwy 100 Lake City (32055) ***(G-7365)***
Linographics Inc...407 422-8700
617 N Magnolia Ave Orlando (32801) ***(G-12913)***
Linpharma Inc...888 989-3237
601 S Fremont Ave Tampa (33606) ***(G-17847)***
Linqs Inc...321 244-2626
1511 E State Road 434 # 2 Winter Springs (32708) ***(G-19478)***
Linvatec Corporation (HQ)...727 392-6464
11311 Concept Blvd Largo (33773) ***(G-8001)***
Linville Enterprises LLC...813 782-1558
38333 5th Ave Zephyrhills (33542) ***(G-19527)***

Linx Defense LLC 805 233-2472
4507 Furling Ln Ste 205 Destin (32541) *(G-3197)*
Lioher Enterprise Corp 305 685-0005
13939 Nw 60th Ave Miami Lakes (33014) *(G-10807)*
Lion Ink Print Inc 561 358-8925
8091 N Military Trl Ste 7 West Palm Beach (33410) *(G-18930)*
Lion Locs LLC 704 802-2752
1002 Lucerne Ter Orlando (32806) *(G-12914)*
Lion Pool Products, Palatka *Also called A J Giammanco & Associates (G-13472)*
Lion Press Inc 954 971-6193
1913 W Copans Rd Pompano Beach (33064) *(G-14745)*
Lion Sheet Metal Inc 561 840-0540
1648 Donna Rd West Palm Beach (33409) *(G-18931)*
Lioness Publication House 561 670-4645
5612 56th Way West Palm Beach (33409) *(G-18932)*
Lionheart Printers LLC 561 781-8300
1312 Commerce Ln Ste A15 Jupiter (33458) *(G-7068)*
Lions Intl MGT Group Inc 813 367-2517
8875 Hidden River Pkwy # 304 Tampa (33637) *(G-17848)*
Lip Trading Co 954 987-0306
3460 N 34th Ave Hollywood (33021) *(G-5861)*
Lippert Components Inc 267 825-0665
1900 47th Ter E Bradenton (34203) *(G-1071)*
Liquid Ed Inc 727 943-8616
740 Wesley Ave Tarpon Springs (34689) *(G-18313)*
Liquid Edge LLC 904 637-1494
178 Industrial Loop S Orange Park (32073) *(G-12398)*
Liquid Force 904 813-1490
3921 Hickory Grove Dr S Jacksonville (32277) *(G-6558)*
Liquid Metal Products Inc 402 895-4436
901 Sw 73rd Street Rd Ocala (34476) *(G-11986)*
Liquid Soul Dgtal Graphics LLC 407 948-6973
3628 E Esther St Orlando (32812) *(G-12915)*
Liquid Technolgy Corp 832 804-8650
340 Scarlet Blvd Oldsmar (34677) *(G-12244)*
Liquidcapsule Mfg LLC 813 431-0532
9216 Palm River Rd # 203 Tampa (33619) *(G-17849)*
Liquiguard Technologies Inc 954 566-0996
5807 N Andrews Way Fort Lauderdale (33309) *(G-4101)*
Lisa Bakery Inc 305 888-8431
2460 W 1st Ave Hialeah (33010) *(G-5487)*
Lisa Mc Call 850 265-4241
1740 Sherman Ave Panama City (32405) *(G-13926)*
Lisa Todd International LLC 305 445-2632
1441 Nw N River Dr 3a Miami (33125) *(G-9897)*
List + Beisler Corp 646 866-6960
200 Suth Bscyne Blvd Lvel Level Miami (33131) *(G-9898)*
List Distillery LLC 239 208-7214
3680 Evans Ave Fort Myers (33901) *(G-4519)*
List Industries Inc (PA) 954 429-9155
401 Jim Moran Blvd Deerfield Beach (33442) *(G-2859)*
List Manufacturing Inc 954 429-9155
401 Jim Moran Blvd Deerfield Beach (33442) *(G-2860)*
List Plymouth LLC 954 429-9155
401 Jim Moran Blvd Deerfield Beach (33442) *(G-2861)*
Lit Forklift LLC 321 271-4626
151 W Gadsden Ln Cocoa Beach (32931) *(G-2065)*
Lit Lighting & Grip LLC 305 770-0272
19599 Ne 10th Ave Miami (33179) *(G-9899)*
Lit Prints Inc 305 456-0150
2181 Sw 1st St Miami (33135) *(G-9900)*
Lit Prints Inc 305 951-5122
4460 Sw 5th St Coral Gables (33134) *(G-2173)*
Lite Cart Corp 727 584-7364
1950 Lake Ave Se Unit A Largo (33771) *(G-8002)*
Lite Crete Insulated Concrete, Miami *Also called Litecrete Inc (G-9901)*
Litecrete Inc 305 500-9373
8095 Nw 64th St Miami (33166) *(G-9901)*
Liteworks Lighting Productions 407 888-8677
752 Palm Dr Orlando (32803) *(G-12916)*
Lithionics Battery LLC 727 726-4204
1770 Calumet St Clearwater (33765) *(G-1762)*
Lithium Battery Company LLC 813 504-0074
4912 W Knox St Ste 100 Tampa (33634) *(G-17850)*
Litho Art Inc 305 232-7098
12190 Sw 131st Ave Miami (33186) *(G-9902)*
Litho Haus Printers Inc (PA) 850 671-6600
2843 Industrial Plaza Dr A1 Tallahassee (32301) *(G-17291)*
Lithocraft Inc 386 761-3584
4460 S Ridgewood Ave Port Orange (32127) *(G-15022)*
Lithographing Art, Miami *Also called Litho Art Inc (G-9902)*
Lithohaus Printers, Tallahassee *Also called Litho Haus Printers Inc (G-17291)*
Lithotec Commercial Printing 727 541-4614
12350 Us Highway 19 N Clearwater (33764) *(G-1763)*
Litterbin LLC 772 633-7184
669 2nd Ln Vero Beach (32962) *(G-18640)*
Little Pickle LLC 850 231-1290
38 Clayton Ln Ste 19 Santa Rosa Beach (32459) *(G-16163)*
Little River Marine 352 378-5025
250 Se 10th Ave Gainesville (32601) *(G-4955)*
Little Steps Daycare, Miami *Also called B&C Sheet Metal Duct Corp (G-9211)*
Littoral Marine LLC 352 400-4222
1520 Industrial Dr Wildwood (34785) *(G-19197)*
Liv LLC 321 276-5302
8004 Nw 154th St Ste 261 Miami Lakes (33016) *(G-10808)*
Live Aerospace Inc 305 910-0091
7205 Nw 68th St Ste 11 Miami (33166) *(G-9903)*
Live Oak Feed Mill, Live Oak *Also called Pilgrims Pride Corporation (G-8236)*
Live Source 561 573-2994
10037 Country Brook Rd Boca Raton (33428) *(G-603)*
Live Ultimate Inc 305 532-6882
1691 Michigan Ave Miami Beach (33139) *(G-10688)*
Live Well Cbds 954 723-0580
12640 Sw 7th Pl Davie (33325) *(G-2547)*
Live Wise Naturals LLC 866 866-0075
13502 4th Plz E Bradenton (34212) *(G-1072)*
Lively Company LLC 617 737-1199
501 E Jackson St Ste 301 Tampa (33602) *(G-17851)*
Livetv 321 722-0783
1333 Gateway Dr Ste 1007 Melbourne (32901) *(G-8876)*
Livie Water, Orlando *Also called Aqua Pure LLC (G-12484)*
Living Color Aquarium Corp 844 522-8265
740 S Porwerline Rd Ste E Deerfield Beach (33442) *(G-2862)*
Living Color Enterprises Inc 954 970-9511
720 S Powerline Rd Ste D Deerfield Beach (33442) *(G-2863)*
Living Fuel Inc 813 254-0777
1409 W Swann Ave Tampa (33606) *(G-17852)*
Living Parables 407 488-6201
1823 Antigua Dr Orlando (32806) *(G-12917)*
Living Pattern LLC 561 596-8205
101 Avocado Rd Delray Beach (33444) *(G-3101)*
Living Well Spending Less Inc 941 209-1811
307 Taylor St Punta Gorda (33950) *(G-15212)*
Liyanarchi Design LLC 954 330-5034
13433 Sunkiss Loop Windermere (34786) *(G-19235)*
Lizheng Stinless Stl Tube Coil 888 582-8820
3902 Henderson Blvd # 207 Tampa (33629) *(G-17853)*
LJ&j Lathing Inc 386 325-5040
402 N 16th St B6 Palatka (32177) *(G-13485)*
Ljk & TS Partners Inc 941 661-5675
7031 Benjamin Rd Ste E Tampa (33634) *(G-17854)*
Ljs Tops & Bottoms 561 736-7868
3050 Sw 14th Pl Ste 11 Boynton Beach (33426) *(G-929)*
Lk Industries, Jacksonville *Also called Load King Manufacturing Co (G-6560)*
LLC Best Block (PA) 239 789-3531
2858 Sidney Ave Orlando (32810) *(G-12918)*
LLC Best Block 239 789-3531
5609 N 50th St Tampa (33610) *(G-17855)*
Llc, Clondalkin, Largo *Also called Clondalkin LLC (G-7925)*
Llorens Phrm Intl Div Inc 305 716-0595
7080 Nw 37th Ct Miami (33147) *(G-9904)*
Lloyd Industries Inc 904 541-1655
138 Industrial Loop W Orange Park (32073) *(G-12399)*
Llumina Press, Fort Lauderdale *Also called Media Creations Inc (G-4115)*
Lmb Consultants Inc 954 537-9590
1280 S Powerline Rd # 17 Pompano Beach (33069) *(G-14746)*
LMI Components Inc 561 994-5896
1181 S Rogers Cir Ste 25 Boca Raton (33487) *(G-604)*
Lmn Printing Co Inc 386 428-9928
118 N Ridgewood Ave Edgewater (32132) *(G-3630)*
LMS Manufacturing LLC 850 526-0121
4430 Magnolia Rd Marianna (32448) *(G-8580)*
Lnl Logistics LLC 386 977-9276
915 Doyle Rd Ste 303-150 Deltona (32725) *(G-3173)*
Load Banks Direct LLC 859 554-2522
309 Nassau St N Venice (34285) *(G-18560)*
Load King Manufacturing 904 633-7352
14001 Atlantic Blvd Jacksonville (32225) *(G-6559)*
Load King Manufacturing Co (PA) 904 354-8882
1357 W Beaver St Jacksonville (32209) *(G-6560)*
Loadmaster Alum Boat Trlrs Inc 813 689-3096
10105 Cedar Run Tampa (33619) *(G-17856)*
Lobby Docs LLC 850 294-0013
3472 Weems Rd Tallahassee (32317) *(G-17292)*
Loboy, Fort Walton Beach *Also called Magna Manufacturing Inc (G-4814)*
Local Biz Spot Inc (PA) 866 446-1790
26747 Saxony Way Wesley Chapel (33544) *(G-18751)*
Local Community News Inc 904 886-4919
54024 Cravey Rd Callahan (32011) *(G-1326)*
Local Pavers Inc 954 913-6916
670 Ne 43rd St Deerfield Beach (33064) *(G-2864)*
Local Value Magazine 813 421-6781
301 W Platt St Tampa (33606) *(G-17857)*
Local Wood Inc 561 410-2113
336 Golfview Rd Apt 810 North Palm Beach (33408) *(G-11722)*
Local Woodwork LLC 954 551-1515
5491 Nw 15th St Margate (33063) *(G-8556)*
Localtoolbox Inc 415 250-3232
2720 Bayou Grande Blvd Pensacola (32507) *(G-14195)*

ALPHABETIC

Location 3 Holdings LLC 941 342-3443
5686 Fruitville Rd Sarasota (34232) ***(G-16489)***
Lockheed Martin Aeronautics, Pinellas Park *Also called Lockheed Martin Corporation* ***(G-14365)***
Lockheed Martin Corporation 407 306-6405
100 Global Innovation Cir Orlando (32825) ***(G-12919)***
Lockheed Martin Corporation 407 306-1000
12506 Lake Underhill Rd Orlando (32825) ***(G-12920)***
Lockheed Martin Corporation 407 517-6627
1700 Tradeport Dr Orlando (32824) ***(G-12921)***
Lockheed Martin Corporation 407 306-4758
6429 Marlberry Dr Orlando (32819) ***(G-12922)***
Lockheed Martin Corporation 863 647-0100
1040 S Pkwy Frontage Rd Lakeland (33813) ***(G-7736)***
Lockheed Martin Corporation 561 494-2501
1400 Nrthpint Pkwy Ste 10 West Palm Beach (33407) ***(G-18933)***
Lockheed Martin Corporation 407 365-4254
568 Carrigan Ave Oviedo (32765) ***(G-13448)***
Lockheed Martin Corporation 727 578-6940
9300 28th St N Ste A Pinellas Park (33782) ***(G-14365)***
Lockheed Martin Corporation 407 356-5715
1190 Gatwick Loop Lake Mary (32746) ***(G-7429)***
Lockheed Martin Corporation 407 356-2000
5600 W Sand Lake Rd Orlando (32819) ***(G-12923)***
Lockheed Martin Corporation 904 660-6917
2629 Port Industrial Dr # 311 Jacksonville (32226) ***(G-6561)***
Lockheed Martin Corporation 850 301-4155
91 Hill Ave Nw Fort Walton Beach (32548) ***(G-4813)***
Lockheed Martin Corporation 407 356-7424
4909 Fells Cove Ave Kissimmee (34744) ***(G-7269)***
Lockheed Martin Corporation 813 855-5711
3655 Tampa Rd Oldsmar (34677) ***(G-12245)***
Lockheed Martin Corporation 321 853-5194
Pier Rd Cape Canaveral (32920) ***(G-1364)***
Lockheed Martin Corporation 904 392-9779
13618 Lake Fretwell St Jacksonville (32221) ***(G-6562)***
Lockheed Martin Corporation 407 306-2745
100 Global Innovation Cir Orlando (32825) ***(G-12924)***
Lockheed Martin Corporation 866 562-2363
8669 Nw 36th St Ste 200 Doral (33166) ***(G-3418)***
Lockheed Martin Corporation 850 885-3583
1404 Nomad Way Eglin Afb (32542) ***(G-3645)***
Lockheed Martin Corporation 407 356-1034
8751 Lockheed Martin Blvd Orlando (32819) ***(G-12925)***
Lockheed Martin Corporation 850 581-1427
945 Tully St Bldg 90028 Hurlburt Field (32544) ***(G-6045)***
Lockheed Martin Corporation 863 647-0100
1040 S Pkwy Frontage Rd Lakeland (33813) ***(G-7737)***
Lockheed Martin Corporation 863 647-0558
1040 South Blvd Lakeland (33803) ***(G-7738)***
Lockheed Martin Corporation 863 647-0100
1040 S Pkwy Frontage Rd Lakeland (33813) ***(G-7739)***
Lockheed Martin Corporation 863 647-0303
1040 S Pkwy Frontage Rd Lakeland (33813) ***(G-7740)***
Lockheed Martin Corporation 301 240-7500
5600 W Sand Lake Rd Orlando (32819) ***(G-12926)***
Lockheed Martin Corporation 321 264-7924
1100 Lockheed Way Titusville (32780) ***(G-18443)***
Lockheed Martin Corporation 407 356-2000
5600 W Sand Lake Rd Orlando (32819) ***(G-12927)***
Lockheed Martin Corporation 407 356-6423
733 Saxby Ave Orlando (32835) ***(G-12928)***
Lockheed Martin Corporation 301 897-6000
100 E 17th St Riviera Beach (33404) ***(G-15343)***
Lockheed Martin Corporation 850 581-5710
589 Independence Rd Hurlburt Field (32544) ***(G-6046)***
Lockheed Martin Corporation 407 356-1947
9556 Turkey Oak Bnd Orlando (32817) ***(G-12929)***
Lockheed Martin Government, Lakeland *Also called Lockheed Martin Corporation* ***(G-7736)***
Lockheed Martin Mis Fire Ctrl, Orlando *Also called Lockheed Martin Corporation* ***(G-12923)***
Lockheed Martin Mis Fire Ctrl, Orlando *Also called Lockheed Martin Corporation* ***(G-12925)***
Lockheed Mrtin Gyrcam Systems 407 356-6500
5600 W Sand Lake Rd Mp-265 Orlando (32819) ***(G-12930)***
Lockheed Mrtin Intgrted System 407 356-2000
5600 W Sand Lake Rd Orlando (32819) ***(G-12931)***
Lockheed Mrtin Mllmter Tech In 407 356-4186
5600 W Sand Lake Rd Orlando (32819) ***(G-12932)***
Lockheed Mrtin Rtary Mssion Sy, Orlando *Also called Lockheed Mrtin Trning Sltons I* ***(G-12933)***
Lockheed Mrtin Trning Sltons I (HQ) 856 722-3317
100 Global Innovation Cir Orlando (32825) ***(G-12933)***
Lockheed Training Facility 850 883-2144
1001 Nomad Way Bldg 1404 Eglin Afb (32542) ***(G-3646)***
Locksmith Killers, Miami *Also called Ecs America LLC* ***(G-9501)***
Locus Diagnostics LLC 321 727-3077
1055 S John Rodes Blvd Melbourne (32904) ***(G-8877)***
Locus Location Systems LLC 321 727-3077
1055 S John Rodes Blvd Melbourne (32904) ***(G-8878)***

Locus Solutions LLC 561 575-7600
7121 Fairway Dr Ste 400 Palm Beach Gardens (33418) ***(G-13605)***
Locus Traxx Worlwide, Palm Beach Gardens *Also called Locus Solutions LLC* ***(G-13605)***
Locust Usa Inc 305 889-5410
8312 Nw 74th Ave Medley (33166) ***(G-8679)***
Locust Power, Medley *Also called Locust Usa Inc* ***(G-8679)***
Locususa, Melbourne *Also called Locus Diagnostics LLC* ***(G-8877)***
Lodex Enterprises Corp 954 442-3843
17048 Sw 38th Dr Miramar (33027) ***(G-11010)***
Logan Laboratories LLC 813 316-4824
4919 Memorial Hwy Ste 200 Tampa (33634) ***(G-17858)***
Loggerhead Distillery LLC 321 800-8566
124 W 2nd St Sanford (32771) ***(G-16081)***
Logic Controls Inc 800 576-9647
404 Sunport Ln Ste 550 Orlando (32809) ***(G-12934)***
Logic Illumination LLC 407 906-0126
3600 Commerce Blvd 102b Kissimmee (34741) ***(G-7270)***
Logic Springs Technologies, Lake Mary *Also called Microvision Technology Corp* ***(G-7435)***
Logical Data Solutions Inc 561 694-9229
31 Windward Isle Palm Beach Gardens (33418) ***(G-13606)***
Logiscenter LLC 800 729-0236
5201 Blue Lagoon Dr Fl 8 Miami (33126) ***(G-9905)***
Logistic Systems Inc (PA) 305 477-4999
2175 Nw 115th Ave Miami (33172) ***(G-9906)***
Logoi Inc 305 232-5880
12900 Sw 128th St Ste 204 Miami (33186) ***(G-9907)***
Logos Promote Inc 407 447-5646
3804 N John Young Pkwy Orlando (32804) ***(G-12935)***
Logoxpress Inc 954 973-4994
2520 N Powerline Rd # 303 Pompano Beach (33069) ***(G-14747)***
Logs Group LLC 904 733-6594
7785 Bymadows Way Ste 104 Jacksonville (32256) ***(G-6563)***
Logsdon and Associates Inc 407 292-0084
13049 Lake Roper Ct Windermere (34786) ***(G-19236)***
Logus Manufacturing Corp 561 842-3550
1711 Longwood Rd Ste A West Palm Beach (33409) ***(G-18934)***
Logus Microwave, West Palm Beach *Also called Logus Manufacturing Corp* ***(G-18934)***
Loksak Inc 239 331-5550
6507 Marbella Dr Naples (34105) ***(G-11315)***
Lollipop Children Center Inc 386 755-3953
416 Se Ermine Ave Lake City (32025) ***(G-7366)***
Lombardis Woodworking 305 439-7208
1000 Oriole Ave Miami Springs (33166) ***(G-10894)***
Londos Fine Cabinetry LLC 727 544-2929
6901 Bryan Dairy Rd # 130 Seminole (33777) ***(G-16751)***
Lone Star Beef Jerky LLC 806 241-4188
724 Glengary Ln Palm Harbor (34683) ***(G-13745)***
Long, H W Logging, Old Town *Also called Henry W Long* ***(G-12197)***
Longboat Key News Inc 941 387-2200
5370 Gulf Of Mexico Dr Longboat Key (34228) ***(G-8245)***
Longboat Observer, Sarasota *Also called Observer Group Inc* ***(G-16528)***
Longbow Marine Inc 954 616-5737
1305 Sw 1st Ave Fort Lauderdale (33315) ***(G-4102)***
Longchamp Usa Inc 305 372-1628
1450 Brickell Ave # 2140 Miami (33131) ***(G-9908)***
Longeveron Inc 305 909-0840
1951 Nw 7th Ave Ste 520 Miami (33136) ***(G-9909)***
Longs Wheel & Rim Inc 904 757-3710
940 Eastport Rd Jacksonville (32218) ***(G-6564)***
Lonza 727 608-6802
5709 Johns Rd Ste 1209 Tampa (33634) ***(G-17859)***
Look Worldwide Inc 305 662-1287
6851 Sw 31st St Miami (33155) ***(G-9910)***
Looper Sports Connection Inc 352 796-7974
19225 Cortez Blvd Brooksville (34601) ***(G-1247)***
Loos & Co Inc 239 643-5667
901 Industrial Blvd Naples (34104) ***(G-11316)***
Lopco Aviation, Miami *Also called Lopez & Company Inc* ***(G-9911)***
Lopez & Company Inc (PA) 305 302-3045
2221 Ne 164th St Miami (33160) ***(G-9911)***
Lopresti Aviation, Sebastian *Also called Lopresti Speed Merchants Inc* ***(G-16666)***
Lopresti Speed Merchants Inc 772 562-4757
210 Airport Dr E Sebastian (32958) ***(G-16666)***
Lor-Ed Enterprises LLC 352 750-1999
309 Lagrande Blvd Lady Lake (32159) ***(G-7328)***
Lords Place Thrift Store 561 660-7942
750 S Military Trl West Palm Beach (33415) ***(G-18935)***
Loren/Wtp 954 846-9800
3040 N 29th Ave Hollywood (33020) ***(G-5862)***
Lorenze & Associates Inc 407 682-7570
1030 Sunshine Ln Ste 1000 Altamonte Springs (32714) ***(G-53)***
Lori Roberts Print Shop I 813 882-8456
6101 Johns Rd Ste 9 Tampa (33634) ***(G-17860)***
Lorina Inc 305 779-3085
8750 Nw 36th St Ste 260 Doral (33178) ***(G-3419)***
Loris 1 Inc 727 847-4499
3544 Grand Blvd New Port Richey (34652) ***(G-11498)***
Lorken Publications Inc (PA) 239 395-1213
1640 Periwinkle Way Ste 2 Sanibel (33957) ***(G-16147)***

Los Atntcos Sndwich Cuban Cafe....407 282-2322
7339 E Colonial Dr Ste 1 Orlando (32807) ***(G-12936)***
Los Coquitos....407 289-9315
1319 E Vine St Kissimmee (34744) ***(G-7271)***
Los Latinos Magazine Inc....305 882-9074
138 Hialeah Dr Hialeah (33010) ***(G-5488)***
Los Primos Express Service....786 701-3297
12039 Sw 132nd Ct Miami (33186) ***(G-9912)***
Losobe LLC....850 748-3162
943 Candlestick Ct Pensacola (32514) ***(G-14196)***
Lost Fabrication LLC....772 971-3467
3811 Crossroads Pkwy Fort Pierce (34945) ***(G-4712)***
Lost Key Publishing LLC....850 380-6680
7166 Sharp Reef Rd Pensacola (32507) ***(G-14197)***
Lott Qa Group Inc....201 693-2224
27499 Riverview Center Bl Bonita Springs (34134) ***(G-844)***
Lotts Concrete Products Inc....407 656-2112
429 Hennis Rd Winter Garden (34787) ***(G-19275)***
Lotus Containers Inc....786 590-1056
1000 Brickell Ave Ste 640 Miami (33131) ***(G-9913)***
Lotus Stress Relief LLC....941 706-2778
2965 Bee Ridge Rd Sarasota (34239) ***(G-16490)***
Louis Chocolates, Jacksonville *Also called Louis Sherry Company LLC* ***(G-6565)***
Louis Di Rmndo Wrldwide Invstm....786 536-7578
2410 N Shore Ter Miami Beach (33141) ***(G-10689)***
Louis Poulsen USA Inc....954 349-2525
3260 Meridian Pkwy Weston (33331) ***(G-19148)***
Louis Sherry Company LLC....904 482-1900
4339 Rosevlt Blvd Ste 400 Jacksonville (32210) ***(G-6565)***
Louvers Window Fashions....941 275-2655
1233 Waterside Ln Venice (34285) ***(G-18561)***
Lov Industries Inc....407 406-8221
742 Royal Palm Dr Kissimmee (34743) ***(G-7272)***
Love Homes, Panama City *Also called Clayton Homes Inc* ***(G-13881)***
Love Is In The Air Corp....305 828-8181
2284 W 77th St Hialeah (33016) ***(G-5489)***
Low Code Ip Holding LLC....833 260-2151
401 E Las Olas Blvd Ste 1 Fort Lauderdale (33301) ***(G-4103)***
Low Life Industries Inc....813 609-5599
5004 W Linebaugh Ave A Tampa (33624) ***(G-17861)***
Low Vision Aids Inc (PA)....954 722-1580
2125 Sw Highway 484 Ocala (34473) ***(G-11987)***
Lowe Gear Printing....866 714-9965
15510 N Nebraska Ave B Lutz (33549) ***(G-8396)***
Lowell Plant Usf5, Ocala *Also called Lhoist North America Tenn Inc* ***(G-11983)***
Loxahatchee Shutter & Alum Inc....561 513-9581
16758 67th Ct N Loxahatchee (33470) ***(G-8361)***
LP Auto & Home Glass....772 335-3697
2471 Se Sapelo Ave Fort Pierce (34952) ***(G-4713)***
LP Express Services, Miami *Also called Los Primos Express Service* ***(G-9912)***
LP Watch Group Inc....954 985-3827
101 S State Road 7 # 201 Hollywood (33023) ***(G-5863)***
Lpi Inc....702 403-8555
6101 45th St N Saint Petersburg (33714) ***(G-15842)***
Lps, Boca Raton *Also called Laser Photo Tooling Services* ***(G-596)***
Lps Group LLC (PA)....305 668-8780
7900 Sw 57th Ave Ph 23 South Miami (33143) ***(G-16821)***
LPs Lath Plst & Stucco Inc....954 444-3727
513 Nw 16th Ave Fort Lauderdale (33311) ***(G-4104)***
Lps Lighting Sound Video Prod, Miami Lakes *Also called Lps Production LLC* ***(G-10809)***
Lps Production LLC....786 208-6217
15915 Nw 59th Ave Miami Lakes (33014) ***(G-10809)***
Lr Dumpsters LLC....321 279-0169
1950 Aster Dr Winter Park (32792) ***(G-19419)***
Lrg Solutions Inc....321 978-1050
1950 Murrell Rd Ste 3 Rockledge (32955) ***(G-15429)***
Lrm Industries Intl Inc....321 635-9797
135 Gus Hipp Blvd Rockledge (32955) ***(G-15430)***
Lrp Conferences LLC (HQ)....215 784-0860
360 Hiatt Dr Palm Beach Gardens (33418) ***(G-13607)***
Lrp Publications Inc (PA)....215 784-0860
360 Hiatt Dr Palm Beach Gardens (33418) ***(G-13608)***
Lrvs Barricades LLC....305 343-6101
8461 Nw 61st St Miami (33166) ***(G-9914)***
Lsj Corp....954 920-0905
2301 N 21st Ave Hollywood (33020) ***(G-5864)***
Lst, Orlando *Also called Lift Spectrum Technologies LLC* ***(G-12910)***
Ltb Aerospace LLC....954 251-1141
2250 Nw 102nd Pl Doral (33172) ***(G-3420)***
LTSC LLC....863 678-0011
28 W Park Ave Lake Wales (33853) ***(G-7515)***
Lubov Manufacturing Inc....813 873-2640
4747 N West Shore Blvd Tampa (33614) ***(G-17862)***
Lubrexx Specialty Products LLC....561 988-7500
4100 N Powerline Rd O1 Pompano Beach (33073) ***(G-14748)***
Lubrication Global LLC....954 239-9522
8450 Nw 56th St Doral (33166) ***(G-3421)***
Lucas 5135 Inc....800 835-7665
8130 Bymdws Way W Ste 10 Jacksonville (32256) ***(G-6566)***
Lucas Construction Inc....386 623-0088
5 Echo Woods Way Ormond Beach (32174) ***(G-13383)***
Lucid Technology Inc....727 487-2430
2380 Drew St Ste 1 Clearwater (33765) ***(G-1764)***
Lucien Piccard, Hollywood *Also called LP Watch Group Inc* ***(G-5863)***
Lucien Piccard/Arnex Watch Co....954 241-2745
101 S State Road 7 # 201 Hollywood (33023) ***(G-5865)***
Lucke Enterprises Inc....727 797-1177
2781 Gulf To Bay Blvd Clearwater (33759) ***(G-1765)***
Lucke Group Inc....727 525-4949
408 33rd Ave N Ste A Saint Petersburg (33704) ***(G-15843)***
Lucky Blinds Shutters LLC....352 239-8475
9390 Se 163rd Ln Summerfield (34491) ***(G-17060)***
Lucky Dog Printing Inc....407 346-1663
1404 Hamlin Ave Saint Cloud (34771) ***(G-15657)***
Lucky Dog Screen Printing Mg....407 629-8838
2716 Forsyth Rd Ste 105 Winter Park (32792) ***(G-19420)***
Lucky Fortune Cookie, Tampa *Also called First Grade Food Corporation* ***(G-17666)***
Lucky Pig, Miami *Also called Golden Boar Product Corp* ***(G-9646)***
Lucy Print, Miami *Also called A Fine Print of Miami LLC* ***(G-9037)***
Ludaca Printing Corp....305 300-4355
13339 Sw 42nd St Miami (33175) ***(G-9915)***
Ludlow Fibc Corp....305 702-5000
13260 Nw 45th Ave Opa Locka (33054) ***(G-12334)***
Lufemor Inc....305 557-2162
5392 W 16th Ave Hialeah (33012) ***(G-5490)***
Lug Usa LLC....855 584-5433
8546 Palm Pkwy Ste 305 Orlando (32836) ***(G-12937)***
Lugloc LLC....305 961-1765
550 Nw 29th St Miami (33127) ***(G-9916)***
Lui Technical Services Inc....954 803-7610
11821 Nw 34th Pl Sunrise (33323) ***(G-17144)***
Luis Martinez Cigar Co....800 822-4427
2701 N 16th St Tampa (33605) ***(G-17863)***
Lujotex LLC....954 322-1001
14359 Miramar Pkwy # 290 Miramar (33027) ***(G-11011)***
Lukes Ice Cream....561 588-5853
1025 W 17th St Riviera Beach (33404) ***(G-15344)***
Lululemon....813 973-3879
28211 Paseo Dr Ste 160 Wesley Chapel (33543) ***(G-18752)***
Lumastream Inc (PA)....727 827-2805
2201 1st Ave S Saint Petersburg (33712) ***(G-15844)***
Lumber Unlimited, Ponte Vedra Beach *Also called Trusses Unlimited Inc* ***(G-14955)***
Lumberstak Inc....386 546-3745
125 Underwood Dr Palatka (32177) ***(G-13486)***
Lumenier Holdco LLC (PA)....941 444-0021
1060 Goodrich Ave Sarasota (34236) ***(G-16491)***
Lumenier LLC....941 444-0021
1060 Goodrich Ave Sarasota (34236) ***(G-16492)***
Lumenis Ltd....305 508-5052
6800 Sw 40th St Ste 102 Miami (33155) ***(G-9917)***
Lumilum LLC....305 233-2844
12400 Sw 134th Ct Ste 1 Miami (33186) ***(G-9918)***
Luminar Technologies Inc (PA)....407 900-5259
2603 Discovery Dr Ste 100 Orlando (32826) ***(G-12938)***
Luminar Technologies Inc....407 900-5259
12601 Research Pkwy Orlando (32826) ***(G-12939)***
Luminoso LLC....305 364-8099
9800 Nw 78th Ave Miami Lakes (33016) ***(G-10810)***
Lumiron Inc....305 652-2599
20725 Ne 16th Ave Ste A33 Miami (33179) ***(G-9919)***
Lumishore Usa LLC....941 405-3302
7127 24th Ct E Sarasota (34243) ***(G-16251)***
Lumitec LLC....561 272-9840
1405 Poinsettia Dr Ste 10 Delray Beach (33444) ***(G-3102)***
Lumo Print Inc....305 246-0003
27750 S Dixie Hwy Homestead (33032) ***(G-5981)***
Lumos Diagnostics Inc....941 556-1850
7040 Prof Pkwy Ste B Lakewood Ranch (34240) ***(G-7845)***
Luna Negra Productions Inc....786 247-1215
3110 Sw 129th Ave Miami (33175) ***(G-9920)***
Lunasea Lighting, Homosassa *Also called Aeb Technologies Inc* ***(G-5999)***
Lundy Enterprises Inc....727 549-1292
6951 114th Ave Largo (33773) ***(G-8003)***
LUnion Logistics LLC....866 586-4660
4000 Hollywood Blvd 555s Hollywood (33021) ***(G-5866)***
Luong Moc III Inc....407 478-8726
3580 Aloma Ave Ste 5 Winter Park (32792) ***(G-19421)***
Lupin Research Inc....800 466-1450
4006 Nw 124th Ave Coral Springs (33065) ***(G-2275)***
Lure Course Brevard LLC....321 412-7143
2955 Lett Ln Malabar (32950) ***(G-8495)***
Lusa Supplier LLC....305 885-7634
7339 Nw 66th St Miami (33166) ***(G-9921)***
Lush Fresh Handmade Cosmetics....850 650-2434
4127 Legendary Dr Destin (32541) ***(G-3198)***
Luther Industries LLC....813 833-5652
3101 River Grove Dr Tampa (33610) ***(G-17864)***
Lutimi Nr Corp....954 245-7986
3190 S State Road 7 # 18 Miramar (33023) ***(G-11012)***

ALPHABETIC

Lutz Radiology, Lutz *Also called Meditek-Icot Inc* ***(G-8398)***
Luv & Luv Industries Inc....954 826-6237
3149 W 80th St Hialeah (33018) ***(G-5491)***
Luv Enterprises Inc....352 867-8440
141 Sw 71st Pl Ocala (34476) ***(G-11988)***
Lux Unlimited Inc....305 871-8774
4121 Nw 27th St Miami (33142) ***(G-9922)***
Luxe Brands Inc (PA)....954 791-6050
6825 W Sunrise Blvd Plantation (33313) ***(G-14529)***
Luxe Prints LLC....941 484-4500
329 Central Ave Sarasota (34236) ***(G-16493)***
Luxe Vintages LLC....561 558-7399
14545 S Military Trl J Delray Beach (33484) ***(G-3103)***
Luxebrands LLC....866 514-8048
6825 W Sunrise Blvd Plantation (33313) ***(G-14530)***
Luxurable Kitchen & Bath Llc....727 286-8927
11601 66th St Largo (33773) ***(G-8004)***
Luxury Boat Services Inc....360 451-2888
1990 Sw 9th St 2 Fort Lauderdale (33312) ***(G-4105)***
Luxury Motor Cars LLC....407 398-6933
420 S Orange Ave Ste 220 Orlando (32801) ***(G-12940)***
Luxury Stone....813 985-0850
10020 Us Highway 301 N Tampa (33637) ***(G-17865)***
Luxury Woodworking Soluti....786 398-1785
3468 W 84th St Unit 108 Hialeah (33018) ***(G-5492)***
Luxury World LLC....954 746-8776
4667 Nw 103rd Ave Sunrise (33351) ***(G-17145)***
Luz General Services, Pompano Beach *Also called Neo Metal Glass LLC* ***(G-14772)***
LV Thompson Inc....813 248-3456
5015 E Hillsborough Ave Tampa (33610) ***(G-17866)***
LW Rozzo Inc....954 435-8501
17200 Pines Blvd Pembroke Pines (33029) ***(G-14045)***
Lykes Memorial Co Library, Brooksville *Also called County of Hernando* ***(G-1222)***
Lyndan Inc....813 977-6683
5402 E Hanna Ave Tampa (33610) ***(G-17867)***
Lynn Industrial Welding Inc....850 584-4494
182 E Park St Perry (32348) ***(G-14306)***
Lynx Products Corp Inc....941 727-9676
2424 Manatee Ave W # 203 Bradenton (34205) ***(G-1073)***
Lyons Machine Tool Co Inc....904 797-1550
5115 Cres Technical Ct Saint Augustine (32086) ***(G-15566)***
Lyric Choir Gown Company....904 725-7977
6801 Beach Blvd Jacksonville (32216) ***(G-6567)***
Lytron Print....954 683-1291
919 Ne 20th Ave Fort Lauderdale (33304) ***(G-4106)***
M & B Products Inc (PA)....813 988-2211
8601 Harney Rd Temple Terrace (33637) ***(G-18372)***
M & C Assemblies Inc....800 462-7779
904 Live Oak St Tarpon Springs (34689) ***(G-18314)***
M & E Kitchen Cabinets Inc....786 346-9987
7237 W 29th Ln Hialeah (33018) ***(G-5493)***
M & H Enterprises Inc....305 885-5945
589 W 27th St Hialeah (33010) ***(G-5494)***
M & L Timber Inc....386 437-0895
Sr 11 Bunnell (32110) ***(G-1302)***
M & M Enterprises Daytona LLC (PA)....386 672-1554
1502 State Ave Daytona Beach (32117) ***(G-2681)***
M & M Industries, Seminole *Also called Modular Molding Intl Inc* ***(G-16754)***
M & M Plastics Inc....305 688-4335
15800 Nw 15th Ave Miami (33169) ***(G-9923)***
M & M Rehabilitation, Gainesville *Also called Orthotic Prsthtic Rhblttion As* ***(G-4977)***
M & M Signs....904 381-7353
524 Stockton St Jacksonville (32204) ***(G-6568)***
M & N Capital Enterprises LLC....800 865-5064
5160 W Clifton St Tampa (33634) ***(G-17868)***
M & R Seafood Inc....352 498-5150
Hwy 351a Cross City (32628) ***(G-2365)***
M & R Technologies, Bartow *Also called Maintnnce Reliability Tech Inc* ***(G-323)***
M & S Computer Products Inc....561 244-5400
11419 Wingfoot Dr Boynton Beach (33437) ***(G-930)***
M & W Electric Motors Inc....850 433-0400
1250 Barrancas Ave Pensacola (32502) ***(G-14198)***
M A K Manufacturing Inc....352 343-5881
13742 County Road 448 Tavares (32778) ***(G-18346)***
M and P Plating, Saint Petersburg *Also called Ni-Chro Plating Corp* ***(G-15866)***
M and T Pro Coating Inc....727 272-4620
2200 Euclid Cir N Clearwater (33764) ***(G-1766)***
M Austin Forman....954 763-8111
888 Se 3rd Ave Ste 501 Fort Lauderdale (33316) ***(G-4107)***
M Bilt Enterprises Inc....352 528-5566
1821 Sw 28th St Ocala (34471) ***(G-11989)***
M C Assembly, Melbourne *Also called M C Test Service Inc* ***(G-8879)***
M C Mieth Manufacturing Inc....386 767-3494
665 Herbert St Port Orange (32129) ***(G-15023)***
M C Test Service Inc (HQ)....321 253-0541
425 North Dr Melbourne (32934) ***(G-8879)***
M Cabinets....305 968-8188
18955 Ne 4th Ct Miami (33179) ***(G-9924)***
M D H Graphic Services Inc....561 533-9000
5001 Georgia Ave West Palm Beach (33405) ***(G-18936)***
M D Mold LLC....941 214-0854
20439 Stardust Ave Port Charlotte (33952) ***(G-14989)***
M D R International Inc....305 944-5335
14861 Ne 20th Ave North Miami (33181) ***(G-11644)***
M E C I, Hudson *Also called Marine Engine Controls Inc* ***(G-6034)***
M F B International Inc....305 436-6601
8323 Nw 64th St Miami (33166) ***(G-9925)***
M G I USA Inc Mastercarte, Melbourne *Also called MGI Usa Inc* ***(G-8888)***
M J Boturla Industries Inc....386 574-0811
1885 S Lehigh Dr Deltona (32738) ***(G-3174)***
M J Embroidery Screen Prtg LLC....407 239-0246
8651 8th St Orlando (32836) ***(G-12941)***
M L Solutions Inc....305 506-5113
1395 Brckwell Ave Ste 800 Miami (33132) ***(G-9926)***
M Micro Technologies Inc....954 973-6166
2901 Gateway Dr Pompano Beach (33069) ***(G-14749)***
M O Precision Molders Inc....727 573-4466
13750 49th St N Clearwater (33762) ***(G-1767)***
M P E, Apopka *Also called Motor Protection Electronics* ***(G-163)***
M P I Medical Products Inc....321 676-1299
1631 Elmhurst Cir Se Palm Bay (32909) ***(G-13522)***
M P N Inc....863 606-5999
815 Pear St Lakeland (33815) ***(G-7741)***
M P Tennis Inc (PA)....813 961-8844
14843 N Dale Mabry Hwy Tampa (33618) ***(G-17869)***
M Pet Group Corp....954 455-5003
2980 Ne 207th St Ste 701 Aventura (33180) ***(G-276)***
M R M S Inc....305 576-3000
571 Nw 29th St Miami (33127) ***(G-9927)***
M S Amtex-N Inc....352 326-9729
2500 Industrial St Leesburg (34748) ***(G-8164)***
M Vb Industries Inc....954 480-6448
510 Goolsby Blvd 5 Deerfield Beach (33442) ***(G-2865)***
M Victoria Enterprises Inc....727 576-8090
9109 4th St N Saint Petersburg (33702) ***(G-15845)***
M W M Services Inc....561 844-0955
7655 Enterprise Dr Ste 4 Riviera Beach (33404) ***(G-15345)***
M Wegener Inc....561 848-2408
24 Springdale Cir Palm Springs (33461) ***(G-13775)***
M X Corporation....305 597-9881
1531 Nw 180th Way Pembroke Pines (33029) ***(G-14046)***
M Z Machine Inc....561 744-2791
3046 Jupiter Park Cir Jupiter (33458) ***(G-7069)***
M&B Steel Fabricators Inc....407 486-1774
2536 Hansrob Rd Orlando (32804) ***(G-12942)***
M&C Hardware LLC....305 971-9444
13720 Sw 152nd St Miami (33177) ***(G-9928)***
M&D Signs....561 296-3636
2898 Forest Hill Blvd West Palm Beach (33406) ***(G-18937)***
M&E Timber Inc....850 584-6650
2451 E Ellison Rd Perry (32347) ***(G-14307)***
M&L Cabinets Inc....941 761-8100
7320 Manatee Ave W Bradenton (34209) ***(G-1074)***
M&M Studios Inc....561 744-2754
1445 Jupiter Park Dr # 1 Jupiter (33458) ***(G-7070)***
M&S Strong Welding Inc....623 299-5336
410 Florida Ave Dundee (33838) ***(G-3565)***
M-Biolabs Inc....239 571-0435
1415 Panther Ln Naples (34109) ***(G-11317)***
M.T.s Pavers & Pools, Deerfield Beach *Also called Martins Pavers & Pools Corp* ***(G-2869)***
M/V Marine Inc....904 633-7992
609 Talleyrand Ave Jacksonville (32202) ***(G-6569)***
M12 Lenses Inc....407 973-4403
350 Pinestraw Cir Altamonte Springs (32714) ***(G-54)***
M3 Biopharma Inc....858 603-8296
5437 Manchini St Sarasota (34238) ***(G-16494)***
M30 Freedom Inc....813 433-1776
4018 Stornoway Dr Land O Lakes (34638) ***(G-7860)***
MA Fine Foods LLC....305 878-6277
13280 Sw 131st St Ste 106 Miami (33186) ***(G-9929)***
MA Glass & Mirror LLC....305 593-8555
7116 Nw 42nd St Miami (33166) ***(G-9930)***
MA Metal Fabricators Inc....786 343-0268
937 Nw 97th Ave Apt 104 Miami (33172) ***(G-9931)***
Mac D&D Inc....305 821-9452
971 W 53rd St Hialeah (33012) ***(G-5495)***
Mac Directory, Miami Beach *Also called American Computer & Tech Corp* ***(G-10640)***
MAc Entps Tampa Bay Inc....813 363-2601
4928 Ladyfish Ct New Port Richey (34652) ***(G-11499)***
Mac Gregor Smith Blueprinters....407 423-5944
1500 S Division Ave Orlando (32805) ***(G-12943)***
Mac Pallets....813 340-3246
2805 Sabina Ct Tampa (33610) ***(G-17870)***
Mac Paper Converters LLC....800 334-7026
8370 Philips Hwy Jacksonville (32256) ***(G-6570)***
Mac Papers Inc....800 582-0049
1351 N Arcturas Ave Clearwater (33765) ***(G-1768)***

Mac Papers Envelope Converters, Jacksonville *Also called Mac Paper Converters LLC* ***(G-6570)***
Macbonner Computer Services, Holmes Beach *Also called Macbonner Inc* ***(G-5946)***
Macbonner Inc 941 778-7978
315 58th St Unit J Holmes Beach (34217) ***(G-5946)***
Macgyver Machine Services Inc 352 455-0413
1722 Sheridan St Hollywood (33020) ***(G-5867)***
Machin Signs Inc 305 694-0464
2530 Nw 77th St Miami (33147) ***(G-9932)***
Machine Engineers Inc 904 353-8289
651 E 8th St Jacksonville (32206) ***(G-6571)***
Machine Shop, Deerfield Beach *Also called Anco Precision Inc* ***(G-2777)***
Machine Shop 786 991-6959
11609 Malverns Loop Orlando (32832) ***(G-12944)***
MACHINE SHOP / DBA B&R SALES, Clearwater *Also called Clearwater Machining Inc* ***(G-1628)***
Machine Tech Services, Melbourne *Also called Machine Technology Inc* ***(G-8880)***
Machine Technology Inc 321 254-3886
2495 Jen Dr Ste 1 Melbourne (32940) ***(G-8880)***
Machine Technology Inc 863 298-8001
108 Investment Ct Sebring (33876) ***(G-16699)***
Machine Tool Masters Inc 850 432-2829
3947 Stoddard Rd Pensacola (32526) ***(G-14199)***
Machine Top LLC 786 238-8926
720 Sw 4th Ct Dania (33004) ***(G-2450)***
Macho Products Inc 800 327-6812
10045 102nd Ter Sebastian (32958) ***(G-16667)***
Macias Gabions Inc 850 910-8000
3801 Environ Blvd Apt 519 Lauderhill (33319) ***(G-8114)***
Mack Concrete, Astatula *Also called Mack Industries Inc* ***(G-214)***
Mack Concrete Industries Inc 352 742-2333
23902 County Road 561 Astatula (34705) ***(G-213)***
Mack Industries Inc 352 742-2333
23902 County Road 561 Astatula (34705) ***(G-214)***
Mack Sales Inc 772 283-2306
3129 Se Dominica Ter Stuart (34997) ***(G-16971)***
Mack Technologies Florida Inc 321 725-6993
7505 Technology Dr Melbourne (32904) ***(G-8881)***
Mackay Communications Inc 904 724-6101
9655 Florida Mining Blvd Jacksonville (32257) ***(G-6572)***
Mackay Marine, Jacksonville *Also called Mackay Communications Inc* ***(G-6572)***
Maclan Corporation Inc (PA) 863 665-4814
1808 S Combee Rd Lakeland (33801) ***(G-7742)***
Macpac Inc 904 315-6457
830-13 A1a N 477 Ponte Vedra Beach (32082) ***(G-14945)***
Macrocap Labs Inc (PA) 321 234-6282
975 Bennett Dr Longwood (32750) ***(G-8308)***
Mactech Power Line and Cable 954 895-9966
15120 Sw 49th St Miramar (33027) ***(G-11013)***
Mad Inc 813 251-9334
3805 W San Nicholas St Tampa (33629) ***(G-17871)***
Mad At SAD LLC 941 203-8854
4050 Middle Ave Sarasota (34234) ***(G-16495)***
Mad Chiller Extracts LLC 813 304-1664
118 S Howard Ave Tampa (33606) ***(G-17872)***
Madan Corporation (PA) 954 925-0077
130 Sw 3rd Ave Dania Beach (33004) ***(G-2467)***
Madan Kosher Foods, Dania Beach *Also called Madan Corporation* ***(G-2467)***
Madart 321 961-9264
3635 S Ridge Cir Titusville (32796) ***(G-18444)***
Madden Millworks 310 514-2640
1650 Margaret St 116 Jacksonville (32204) ***(G-6573)***
Maddox Foundry & Mch Works LLC 352 495-2121
13370 Sw 170th St Archer (32618) ***(G-210)***
Maddox Industries Inc 561 529-2165
16401 134th Ter N Jupiter (33478) ***(G-7071)***
Maddys Print Shop LLC 954 749-0440
5450 Nw 33rd Ave Ste 108 Fort Lauderdale (33309) ***(G-4108)***
Made Fur You Inc (PA) 813 444-7707
18112 Thomas Blvd Hudson (34667) ***(G-6032)***
Made Fur You Inc 813 444-7707
12121 Little Rd Hudson (34667) ***(G-6033)***
Made In America Plastic Inc 786 310-7816
9949 Nw 89th Ave Unit 11 Medley (33178) ***(G-8680)***
Made To Match Clothing Company, Clearwater *Also called Kleids Enterprises Inc* ***(G-1751)***
Mader Electric Motors, Fort Myers *Also called John Mader Enterprises Inc* ***(G-4506)***
Madewell Kitchens Inc 727 856-1014
11619 State Road 52 Port Richey (34669) ***(G-15060)***
Madico Inc (HQ) 727 327-2544
9251 Belcher Rd N Ste A Pinellas Park (33782) ***(G-14366)***
Madison Avenue Furniture, Sarasota *Also called Studio 21 Lighting Inc* ***(G-16303)***
Madison Millwork & Cabinet Co 954 966-7551
5746 Dawson St Ste A Hollywood (33023) ***(G-5868)***
Madson Inc 305 863-7390
10925 Nw South River Dr Medley (33178) ***(G-8681)***
Madson Meat, Medley *Also called Madson Inc* ***(G-8681)***
Maestro Winery 308 627-6436
8241 Pelican Landing Rd Jacksonville (32256) ***(G-6574)***
Maestroshield, Fort Myers *Also called USA Shutter Company LLC* ***(G-4642)***
Mafeks International LLC 561 997-2080
4755 Tech Way Ste 208 Boca Raton (33431) ***(G-605)***
Mag Cleaning Solutions LLC 321 317-3298
428 Los Altos Way Apt 204 Altamonte Springs (32714) ***(G-55)***
Mag Works Inc 305 823-4440
7725 W 2nd Ct Hialeah (33014) ***(G-5496)***
Mag-Tags Inc 850 294-1809
4446 Sierra Ct Tallahassee (32309) ***(G-17293)***
Magazine Morris 561 963-0231
6108 Royal Birkdale Dr Lake Worth (33463) ***(G-7566)***
Magellan Aviation Group Lllp 561 266-0845
1811 Corporate Dr Boynton Beach (33426) ***(G-931)***
Magellan Pharmaceuticals Inc 813 623-6800
1202 Tech Blvd Ste 106 Tampa (33619) ***(G-17873)***
Magenav Inc 718 551-1815
3530 Nw 53rd St Fort Lauderdale (33309) ***(G-4109)***
Maggac Corporation 561 439-2707
7629 Santee Ter Lake Worth (33467) ***(G-7567)***
Magic Candle, Orlando *Also called Imagination Enterprises LLC* ***(G-12823)***
Magic Faucet Bidet, Miami *Also called M F B International Inc* ***(G-9925)***
Magic Magazine 407 420-6080
633 N Orange Ave Orlando (32801) ***(G-12945)***
Magic Print Copy Center 239 332-4456
2133 Broadway Fort Myers (33901) ***(G-4520)***
Magic Tilt Trailer Mfg Co Inc 727 535-5561
2161 Lions Club Rd Clearwater (33764) ***(G-1769)***
Magic Trailers, Clearwater *Also called Magic Tilt Trailer Mfg Co Inc* ***(G-1769)***
Magical Creamery LLC 407 719-6866
965 Helmsley Ct Apt 101 Lake Mary (32746) ***(G-7430)***
Magna Manufacturing Inc 850 243-1112
85 Hill Ave Nw Fort Walton Beach (32548) ***(G-4814)***
Magnaprint Corp 954 376-8416
1522 E Commercial Blvd Oakland Park (33334) ***(G-11819)***
Magnatronix Corporation Inc 727 536-7861
5410 115th Ave N Clearwater (33760) ***(G-1770)***
Magnetic Automation Corp 321 635-8585
3160 Murrell Rd Rockledge (32955) ***(G-15431)***
Magnetic Bookmarks, Cape Coral *Also called Collectibles of SW Florida* ***(G-1404)***
Magnetic Jewellry Inc 954 975-5868
2900 W Sample Rd Pompano Beach (33073) ***(G-14750)***
Magneto Sports LLC 760 593-4589
360 Nw 27th St Miami (33127) ***(G-9933)***
Magnificat Holdings LLC 727 798-0512
1125 Eldridge St Clearwater (33755) ***(G-1771)***
Magnifying America, Ocala *Also called Low Vision Aids Inc* ***(G-11987)***
Magnolia Bakery, Ocala *Also called Magnolias Gurmet Bky Itln Deli* ***(G-11990)***
Magnolia Custom Cabinetry 941 906-8744
1830 S Osprey Ave Ste 107 Sarasota (34239) ***(G-16496)***
Magnolia Machine Company 863 965-8201
1088 Us Highway 92 W Auburndale (33823) ***(G-248)***
Magnolia Millwork Intl Inc 407 585-3470
231 Plaza Oval Casselberry (32707) ***(G-1510)***
Magnolia Press, Sanford *Also called H & M Printing Inc* ***(G-16059)***
Magnolias Gurmet Bky Itln Deli 352 207-2667
1412 N Magnolia Ave Ocala (34475) ***(G-11990)***
Magnum Audio Group Inc 813 870-2857
4504 W Spruce St Apt 112 Tampa (33607) ***(G-17874)***
Magnum Coatings Inc 407 704-0786
802 Lumsden Reserve Dr Brandon (33511) ***(G-1166)***
Magnum Marine Corporation 305 931-4292
2900 Ne 188th St Miami (33180) ***(G-9934)***
Magnum Venus Plastech 727 573-2955
5148 113th Ave N Clearwater (33760) ***(G-1772)***
Magnus Hitech Industries Inc 321 724-9731
1605 Lake St Melbourne (32901) ***(G-8882)***
Magruders Woodworking Inc 954 649-0861
5861 Woodland Point Dr Tamarac (33319) ***(G-17362)***
Mahan Cabinets 305 255-3325
10471 Sw 184th Ter Cutler Bay (33157) ***(G-2403)***
Maher Industries Inc 407 928-5288
5434 Osprey Isle Ln Orlando (32819) ***(G-12946)***
Mahigaming LLC 561 504-1534
245 Ne 21st Ave Ste 200 Deerfield Beach (33441) ***(G-2866)***
Mahnkes Orthtics Prsthtics of (PA) 954 772-1299
4990 Sw 72nd Ave Ste 107 Miami (33155) ***(G-9935)***
Mailbox Publishing Inc 772 334-2121
3727 Se Ocean Blvd Ste 20 Stuart (34996) ***(G-16972)***
Mailing & Bindery Systems Inc 813 416-8965
3959 Van Dyke Rd Lutz (33558) ***(G-8397)***
Main & Six Brewing Company LLC 904 673-0144
1636 N Main St Jacksonville (32206) ***(G-6575)***
Main Packaging Supply 305 863-7176
7317 Nw 61st St Miami (33166) ***(G-9936)***
Main Tape Co Inc 561 248-8867
521 27th St West Palm Beach (33407) ***(G-18938)***
Main USA Corp 305 499-4994
8549 Nw 68th St Miami (33166) ***(G-9937)***

ALPHABETIC

Mainstream Engineering Corp 321 631-3550
200 Yellow Pl Rockledge (32955) ***(G-15432)***
Mainstream Fiber Networks....941 807-6100
5124 Redbriar Ct Sarasota (34238) ***(G-16497)***
Maintnnce Reliability Tech Inc....863 533-0300
1421 Chamber Dr Bartow (33830) ***(G-323)***
Maison Goyard, Bal Harbour *Also called Goyard Miami LLC* ***(G-302)***
Maitland Furniture Inc....386 677-7711
1711 State Ave Daytona Beach (32117) ***(G-2682)***
Maiweave, Sarasota *Also called Intertape Polymr Woven USA Inc* ***(G-16470)***
Majestic Coatings Inc....561 722-9593
9936 Cross Pine Ct Lake Worth (33467) ***(G-7568)***
Majestic Foods, Hialeah *Also called Majesty Foods LLC* ***(G-5497)***
Majestic Machine & Engrg Inc....904 257-9115
570 Us Highway 90 E Jacksonville (32234) ***(G-6576)***
Majestic Metals Inc....813 380-6885
1807 N Waterman Dr Valrico (33594) ***(G-18522)***
Majestic Ultimate Design Inc....954 533-8677
4431 Ne 6th Ave Oakland Park (33334) ***(G-11820)***
Majestic Unsc Spcial Intllgnce, Ponce De Leon *Also called United Ntons Space Crps Mltary* ***(G-14920)***
Majestic Woodworks....352 429-2520
156 Groveland Farms Rd Groveland (34736) ***(G-5100)***
Majestics Business USA LLC....305 713-9773
11077 Biscayne Blvd # 201 North Miami (33161) ***(G-11645)***
Majesty Foods LLC....305 817-1888
2740 W 81st St Hialeah (33016) ***(G-5497)***
Majic Nails, Winter Garden *Also called Vicx LLC* ***(G-19288)***
Majic Stairs Inc....352 255-1390
744 Abaco Path The Villages (32163) ***(G-18392)***
Majic Stairs Inc (PA)....352 446-6295
120 Cypress Rd Ocala (34472) ***(G-11991)***
Majic Wheels Corp (PA)....239 313-5672
1950 Custom Dr Fort Myers (33907) ***(G-4521)***
Major Canvas Products Inc....954 764-1711
4351 Ne 12th Ter Oakland Park (33334) ***(G-11821)***
Major League Signs Inc....954 600-5505
9103 Nw 171st Ln Hialeah (33018) ***(G-5498)***
Major Partitions Ltd Corp....813 286-8634
405 S Dale Mabry Hwy # 260 Tampa (33609) ***(G-17875)***
Major Products Company....386 673-8381
841 Buena Vista Ave Ormond Beach (32174) ***(G-13384)***
Mak Food Service, Miami *Also called Deli Fresh Foods Inc* ***(G-9446)***
Makai Marine Industries Inc....954 425-0203
730 S Deerfield Ave Ste 8 Deerfield Beach (33441) ***(G-2867)***
Make A Statement Gifts, Boca Raton *Also called Sep Communications LLC* ***(G-706)***
Make Your Mark Promo .com, Bradenton *Also called Say What Screen Prtg & EMB Inc* ***(G-1112)***
Maki Printing LLC....941 809-7574
1173 Palmer Wood Ct Sarasota (34236) ***(G-16498)***
Maki Printing LLC (PA)....941 925-4802
4130 Boca Pointe Dr Sarasota (34238) ***(G-16499)***
MAKM Anufacturing Inc....352 343-5881
13742 County Road 448 Tavares (32778) ***(G-18347)***
Mako Hose & Rubber Co....561 795-6200
8331 Mc Allister Way 100a West Palm Beach (33411) ***(G-18939)***
Mako Surgical Corp (HQ)....866 647-6256
3365 Enterprise Ave Weston (33331) ***(G-19149)***
Malema Engineering Corporation (PA)....561 995-0595
1060 S Rogers Cir Boca Raton (33487) ***(G-606)***
Malema Flow Sensors, Boca Raton *Also called Malema Engineering Corporation* ***(G-606)***
Maleta Import....305 592-2410
6928 Nw 12th St Miami (33126) ***(G-9938)***
Mama Asian Noodle Bar....954 973-1670
4437 Lyons Rd Coconut Creek (33073) ***(G-2089)***
Mama Bear Lawn Care Press....863 517-5322
30290 Josie Billie Hwy Clewiston (33440) ***(G-1983)***
Mamalu Wood LLC....305 261-6332
7003 N Waterway Dr # 207 Miami (33155) ***(G-9939)***
Mambi Cheese Company Inc....305 324-5282
2151 Nw 10th Ave Miami (33127) ***(G-9940)***
Mambo LLC....305 860-2544
1800 Nw 94th Ave Doral (33172) ***(G-3422)***
Man Capital Corporation (HQ)....732 582-8220
591 Sw 13th Ter Pompano Beach (33069) ***(G-14751)***
Man Enterprises 3 LLC....561 655-4944
3845 Investment Ln Ste 1 West Palm Beach (33404) ***(G-18940)***
Man-Trans LLC....850 222-6993
4920 Woodlane Cir Tallahassee (32303) ***(G-17294)***
Managed Data Assoc Inc....386 449-8419
12 Walla Pl Palm Coast (32164) ***(G-13702)***
Management Hlth Solutions Inc (PA)....888 647-4621
5701 E Hillsborough Ave Tampa (33610) ***(G-17876)***
Management International Inc....954 763-8811
1828 Se 1st Ave Fort Lauderdale (33316) ***(G-4110)***
Manasota Optics Inc....941 359-1748
1743 Northgate Blvd Sarasota (34234) ***(G-16500)***
Manasota Pallets....941 360-0562
7952 Fruitville Rd Sarasota (34240) ***(G-16501)***
Manatee Bay Enterprises Inc....407 245-3600
2234 W Taft Vnlnd Rd A Orlando (32837) ***(G-12947)***
Manatee Cabinets Inc....941 792-8656
8700 Cortez Rd W Bradenton (34210) ***(G-1075)***
Manatee Media Inc....813 909-2800
3632 Land O Lakes Blvd Land O Lakes (34639) ***(G-7861)***
Manatee Printers Inc....941 746-9100
1007 30th Ave W Bradenton (34205) ***(G-1076)***
Manatee Shirts and Graphics, Saint Petersburg *Also called Arj Art Inc* ***(G-15710)***
Manatee Smoothies LLC....985 640-3088
1161 E State Road 70 Lakewood Ranch (34202) ***(G-7840)***
Manatee Tool Inc....941 355-9252
1400 Commerce Blvd Ste Cd Sarasota (34243) ***(G-16252)***
Manchester Copper Tube LLC....321 636-1477
435 Gus Hipp Blvd Rockledge (32955) ***(G-15433)***
Manci Graphics Corp....813 664-1129
2705 N Falkenburg Rd Tampa (33619) ***(G-17877)***
Mancini Inc....954 583-7220
1878 Nw 21st St Pompano Beach (33069) ***(G-14752)***
Mancini Packing Company....863 735-2000
3500 Mancini Pl Zolfo Springs (33890) ***(G-19546)***
Mandala Tool Company Inc....305 652-4575
18588 Ne 2nd Ave Miami (33179) ***(G-9941)***
Mandrel Exhaust Systems, Cutler Bay *Also called Trubendz Technology Inc* ***(G-2418)***
Mangiamo, Miami Beach *Also called Bighill Corporation* ***(G-10647)***
Mango Bang, Bonita Springs *Also called Winds* ***(G-863)***
Mango Bottling Inc....321 631-1005
767 Clearlake Rd Cocoa (32922) ***(G-2034)***
Mango Publications....863 583-4773
715 S New York Ave Lakeland (33815) ***(G-7743)***
Mangrove Navada, Tampa *Also called Asure Software Inc* ***(G-17440)***
Manicini Foods, Zolfo Springs *Also called Mancini Packing Company* ***(G-19546)***
Manifest Distilling LLC....904 619-1479
960 E Forsyth St Jacksonville (32202) ***(G-6577)***
Manley Farms Inc (PA)....239 597-6416
1040 Collier Center Way # 12 Naples (34110) ***(G-11318)***
Manley Farms North, Naples *Also called Manley Farms Inc* ***(G-11318)***
Mann+hummel Filtration Technol....305 499-5100
10505 Nw 112th Ave Ste 22 Medley (33178) ***(G-8682)***
Manna On Wheels Inc....813 754-2277
2217 Bogaert Rd Dover (33527) ***(G-3560)***
Manning Company....954 523-9355
223 Sw 28th St Fort Lauderdale (33315) ***(G-4111)***
Manns Diversified Industries....407 310-5938
380 S State Road 434 # 10 Altamonte Springs (32714) ***(G-56)***
Manor Steel Fabricators....941 722-8077
1507 18th Avenue Dr E Palmetto (34221) ***(G-13810)***
Manotiles LLC....954 803-3303
14364 Canalview Dr Apt A Delray Beach (33484) ***(G-3104)***
Mansci Inc....866 763-2122
6925 Lake Ellenor Dr # 136 Orlando (32809) ***(G-12948)***
Mansfield International Inc....954 632-3280
3561 N 55th Fort Lauderdale (33301) ***(G-4112)***
Mansur Industries Inc....305 593-8015
8305 Nw 27th St Ste 107 Doral (33122) ***(G-3423)***
Mantua Manufacturing Co....813 621-3714
8108 Krauss Blvd B Tampa (33619) ***(G-17878)***
Manufacturer, Hallandale Beach *Also called Arno Belo Inc* ***(G-5170)***
Manufacturer, Melbourne *Also called Edge Power Solutions Inc* ***(G-8821)***
Manufacturer, Live Oak *Also called Smith Steps Inc* ***(G-8241)***
Manufacturer, Miami Lakes *Also called Texene LLC* ***(G-10867)***
Manufacturer - Distributor, Eustis *Also called Rcd Corporation* ***(G-3716)***
Manufacturers Inv Group LLC....630 285-0800
6670 Spring Lake Rd Keystone Heights (32656) ***(G-7210)***
Manufacturing, Palmetto Bay *Also called Metal 2 Metal Inc* ***(G-13850)***
Manufacturing, Sanford *Also called Quantumflo Inc* ***(G-16108)***
Manufacturing By Skema Inc....954 797-7325
3801 Sw 47th Ave Ste 501 Davie (33314) ***(G-2548)***
Manufacturing Facility, Flagler Beach *Also called Sea Ray Boats Inc* ***(G-3757)***
Manufacturing Inc Sp....305 362-0456
2200 W 77th St Hialeah (33016) ***(G-5499)***
Manufacturing Martin LLC Kls....904 641-0421
11228 St Jhns Indus Pkwy Jacksonville (32246) ***(G-6578)***
Manufctring Prcess Ctrl Instrs, Orlando *Also called Red Meters LLC* ***(G-13121)***
Manufctring Sls Pipe Bnding Eq, Fort Myers *Also called Hines Bending Systems Inc* ***(G-4482)***
Manufcturers Metal Forming Mch, Sarasota *Also called Marchant Machine Corporation* ***(G-16503)***
Manufcturing Systems Group LLC....727 642-4677
1826 Se 5th St Cape Coral (33990) ***(G-1444)***
Manutech Assembly Inc (PA)....305 888-2800
7901 Nw 67th St Miami (33166) ***(G-9942)***
Map & Globe LLC (PA)....407 898-0757
113 Candace Dr Ste 3 Maitland (32751) ***(G-8473)***
Map and Globe Store, The, Maitland *Also called Map & Globe LLC* ***(G-8473)***
Mapei Corporation (HQ)....954 246-8888
1144 E Newport Center Dr Deerfield Beach (33442) ***(G-2868)***

Maq Investments Group Inc 305 691-1468
14312 Commerce Way Miami Lakes (33016) **(G-10811)**
Mar Company Distributors LLC 786 477-4174
6750 Nw 79th Ave Miami (33166) **(G-9943)**
Mar Cor Purification Inc 484 991-0220
5001 Gateway Blvd Ste 21 Lakeland (33811) **(G-7744)**
Mar-Co Gas Services Inc 561 745-0085
11138 161st St N Jupiter (33478) **(G-7072)**
Mar-Quipt, Pompano Beach *Also called Byrd Technologies Inc* **(G-14627)**
Maracom Marine, Doral *Also called Marathon Technology Corp* **(G-3425)**
Marajo Diesel Power Corp 786 212-1485
1950 Nw 93rd Ave Doral (33172) **(G-3424)**
Maramed Orthopedic Systems, Hialeah *Also called Maramed Precision Corporation* **(G-5500)**
Maramed Precision Corporation 305 823-8300
2480 W 82nd St Unit 1 Hialeah (33016) **(G-5500)**
Marathon Engineering Corp 239 303-7378
5615 2nd St W Lehigh Acres (33971) **(G-8198)**
Marathon Fiber Optics LLC 305 902-9010
12303 Edgeknoll Dr Riverview (33579) **(G-15277)**
Marathon Ribbon Co, Largo *Also called Golden Ribbon Corporation* **(G-7963)**
Marathon Technology Corp 305 592-1340
8280 Nw 56th St Doral (33166) **(G-3425)**
Marbelite International Corp 941 378-0860
1500 Global Ct Sarasota (34240) **(G-16502)**
Marble Bridge Inc 239 213-1411
3827 Arnold Ave Naples (34104) **(G-11319)**
Marble Crafters, Daytona Beach *Also called Showcase Marble Inc* **(G-2714)**
Marble Designs, Naples *Also called Debanie Inc* **(G-11224)**
Marble Designs of FL Inc 321 269-6920
1975 Silver Star Rd Titusville (32796) **(G-18445)**
Marble Doctors LLC (PA) 203 794-1000
1198 Mulberry Pl Wellington (33414) **(G-18724)**
Marble Lite Products Corp 305 557-8766
9920 Nw 79th Ave Miami Lakes (33016) **(G-10812)**
Marble Works Kit & Bath Ctr, Fort Walton Beach *Also called Kitchen & Bath Center Inc* **(G-4812)**
Marblue, Dania Beach *Also called Marware Inc* **(G-2468)**
Marbon Inc 561 822-9999
10723 Ibis Reserve Cir West Palm Beach (33412) **(G-18941)**
Marcela Creations Inc 813 253-0556
1802 W Kennedy Blvd Tampa (33606) **(G-17879)**
March Inc 239 593-4074
16160 Performance Way Naples (34110) **(G-11320)**
March Performance, Naples *Also called March Inc* **(G-11320)**
Marchant Machine Corporation 301 937-4481
8713 Amaretto Ave Sarasota (34238) **(G-16503)**
Marco Polo Publications Inc 866 610-9441
360 Central Ave Ste 1260 Saint Petersburg (33701) **(G-15846)**
Marconi Line Inc 321 639-1130
1870 Huntington Ln Rockledge (32955) **(G-15434)**
Marcus V Hall 352 490-9694
14271 Nw 66th Ave Chiefland (32626) **(G-1536)**
Marden Industries Inc 863 682-7882
26855 Airport Rd Punta Gorda (33982) **(G-15213)**
Mares Services Corp 305 752-0093
14758 Sw 56th St Miami (33185) **(G-9944)**
Marex, Plantation *Also called Maritime Executive LLC* **(G-14531)**
Marey International LLC 787 727-0277
8113 Nw 68th St Miami (33166) **(G-9945)**
Margarita International, Miami *Also called Margarita Internl Trading Inc* **(G-9946)**
Margarita Internl Trading Inc 305 688-1300
5601 Nw 72nd Ave Miami (33166) **(G-9946)**
Margoth Manufacturing Co 954 200-3894
9910 Nw 80th Ave Unit 2u Miami Lakes (33016) **(G-10813)**
Maria E Acosta 305 231-5543
4004 W 11th Ln Hialeah (33012) **(G-5501)**
Maria Fuentes LLC 305 717-3404
10130 Sw 32nd St Miami (33165) **(G-9947)**
Marianna Lime Products Inc 850 526-3580
3333 Valley View Rd Marianna (32446) **(G-8581)**
Marianna Limestone LLC 954 581-1220
3333 Valley View Rd Marianna (32446) **(G-8582)**
Marianna Truss Inc 850 594-5420
3644 Highway 71 Marianna (32446) **(G-8583)**
Marilyn Jeffcoat 407 382-1783
1198 Paladin Ct Orlando (32812) **(G-12949)**
Marimba Cocina Mexicana II Inc 321 268-6960
3758 S Washington Ave Titusville (32780) **(G-18446)**
Marina Medical Instruments Inc 954 924-4418
8190 W State Road 84 Davie (33324) **(G-2549)**
Marine Canvas Inc 305 325-1830
471 Ne 79th St Miami (33138) **(G-9948)**
Marine Concepts, Sarasota *Also called Patrick Industries Inc* **(G-16274)**
Marine Concepts 239 283-0800
2443 Sw Pine Island Rd Cape Coral (33991) **(G-1445)**
Marine Customs Unlimited 772 223-8005
3355 Se Dixie Hwy Stuart (34997) **(G-16973)**
Marine Digital Integrators LLC 772 210-2403
7667 Sw Ellipse Way Stuart (34997) **(G-16974)**
Marine Electrical Engineer, Fort Lauderdale *Also called Luxury Boat Services Inc* **(G-4105)**
Marine Electronics Engine 727 459-5593
4801 96th St N Saint Petersburg (33708) **(G-15847)**
Marine Engine Controls Inc 727 518-8080
9035 Wister Ln Hudson (34669) **(G-6034)**
Marine Exhaust Systems Inc (PA) 561 848-1238
3640 Fiscal Ct Ste D Riviera Beach (33404) **(G-15346)**
Marine Fiberglass Specialist 305 821-6667
8600 Nw 174th St Hialeah (33015) **(G-5502)**
Marine Industrial Paint Co 727 527-3382
4590 60th Ave N Saint Petersburg (33714) **(G-15848)**
Marine Inland Fabricators, Panama City *Also called Sisco Marine LLC* **(G-13951)**
Marine Manufacturing Inc 305 885-3493
295 W 23rd St Hialeah (33010) **(G-5503)**
Marine Metal Products Co 727 461-5575
2154 Calumet St Clearwater (33765) **(G-1773)**
Marine Pleasure Craft, Cutler Bay *Also called South Florida Marine* **(G-2413)**
Marine Spc Cstm Fabricator 813 855-0554
360 Mears Blvd Oldsmar (34677) **(G-12246)**
Marine Transportation Svcs Inc 850 215-4557
3615 Calhoun Ave Panama City (32405) **(G-13927)**
Mariner International Trvl Inc 954 925-4150
850 Ne 3rd St Ste 201 Dania (33004) **(G-2451)**
Marinetek North America Inc 727 498-8741
111 2nd Ave Ne Ste 360 Saint Petersburg (33701) **(G-15849)**
Marinize Products Corp 954 989-7990
3986 Pembroke Rd Hollywood (33021) **(G-5869)**
Mario Kenny 786 274-0527
789 Ne 83rd St Miami (33138) **(G-9949)**
Marion Metal Works Inc 352 351-4221
4750 S Pine Ave Ocala (34480) **(G-11992)**
Marion Nature Park 352 817-3077
12888 Se Us Highway 441 Belleview (34420) **(G-372)**
Marion Precision Tool Inc 352 867-0080
1800 Nw 10th St Ocala (34475) **(G-11993)**
Marion Rock Inc 352 687-2023
5979 Se Maricamp Rd Ocala (34472) **(G-11994)**
Marios Casting Jewelry Inc 305 374-2894
36 Ne 1st St Ste 851 Miami (33132) **(G-9950)**
Marios Metalcraft 239 649-0085
4227 Mercantile Ave Ste A Naples (34104) **(G-11321)**
Marios Mtalcraft Powdr Coating, Naples *Also called Marios Metalcraft* **(G-11321)**
Maris Worden Aerospace Inc 514 895-8075
2001 S Ridgewood Ave South Daytona (32119) **(G-16803)**
Maritec Industries Inc 352 429-8888
20150 Independence Blvd Groveland (34736) **(G-5101)**
Maritech Machine Inc 850 872-0852
1740 Sherman Ave Panama City (32405) **(G-13928)**
Maritime Custom Designs Inc 941 716-0255
170 Rich St Venice (34292) **(G-18562)**
Maritime Executive LLC 954 848-9955
7473 Nw 4th St Plantation (33317) **(G-14531)**
Maritime Replicas America Inc 305 386-1958
1275 W 47th Pl Ste 423 Hialeah (33012) **(G-5504)**
Maritime Replicas Usa LLC 305 921-9690
70 Dorset B Boca Raton (33434) **(G-607)**
Maritime SEC Strtegies Fla LLC 912 704-0300
5251 W Tyson Ave Tampa (33611) **(G-17880)**
Marizyme Inc (PA) 561 935-9955
555 Heritage Dr Ste 205 Jupiter (33458) **(G-7073)**
Mark 1 Contracting Inc 727 894-3600
10656 Casey Dr New Port Richey (34654) **(G-11500)**
Mark Benton 754 203-9377
900 N Federal Hwy Boca Raton (33432) **(G-608)**
Mark Housman Screen RPS Inc 321 255-2778
2911 Dusa Dr Ste E Melbourne (32934) **(G-8883)**
Mark Master Inc 813 988-6000
11111 N 46th St Tampa (33617) **(G-17881)**
Mark McManus Inc 239 454-1300
15821 Chief Ct Fort Myers (33912) **(G-4522)**
Mark Plating Co 561 655-4370
441 25th St West Palm Beach (33407) **(G-18942)**
Mark Trece, Lakeland *Also called Mark/Trece Inc* **(G-7745)**
Mark V Printing LLC 954 563-2505
140 Ne 32nd Ct Oakland Park (33334) **(G-11822)**
Mark Walters LLC 727 742-3091
1126 15th Ave N Saint Petersburg (33704) **(G-15850)**
Mark Wayne Adams Inc 407 756-5862
490 Wekiva Cove Rd Longwood (32779) **(G-8309)**
Mark Weisser Productions, Boynton Beach *Also called Mark Wsser Graphic Productions* **(G-932)**
Mark Wsser Graphic Productions 305 888-7445
8941 Golden Mountain Cir Boynton Beach (33473) **(G-932)**
Mark/Trece Inc 863 647-4372
5385 Gateway Blvd Lakeland (33811) **(G-7745)**
Markcam Inc 772 283-7189
4361 Se Commerce Ave Stuart (34997) **(G-16975)**

ALPHABETIC

Marker Industries LLC....954 907-2647
3980 Oaks Clubhouse Dr Pompano Beach (33069) ***(G-14753)***

Market Ink Usa Inc....561 502-3438
1000 S Military Trl Ste D West Palm Beach (33415) ***(G-18943)***

Market Logic, Doral *Also called Esperanto Inc* ***(G-3344)***

Marketing Bar, The, Pensacola *Also called Mc Squared Group Inc* ***(G-14202)***

Marketshare LLC....631 273-0598
6790 E Rogers Cir Boca Raton (33487) ***(G-609)***

Marko Garage Doors & Gates Inc....561 547-4001
248 Davis Rd Palm Springs (33461) ***(G-13776)***

Marlin & Barrel Distillery LLC....321 230-4755
115 S 2nd St Fernandina Beach (32034) ***(G-3743)***

Marlin Coatings LLC....850 224-1370
3666 Peddie Dr Tallahassee (32303) ***(G-17295)***

Marlin Darlin Air LLC....727 726-1136
2819 West Bay Dr Belleair Bluffs (33770) ***(G-363)***

Marlin Graphics Inc....561 743-5220
1251 Jupiter Park Dr # 7 Jupiter (33458) ***(G-7074)***

Marlo Electronics Inc....561 477-0856
2412 Nw 35th St Boca Raton (33431) ***(G-610)***

Marlon Inc....813 901-8488
8513 Sunstate St Tampa (33634) ***(G-17882)***

Marlyn Steel Decks Inc....813 621-1375
6808 Harney Rd Tampa (33610) ***(G-17883)***

Marlyn Steel Products Inc....813 621-1375
6808 Harney Rd Tampa (33610) ***(G-17884)***

Marmon Aerospace & Defense LLC....239 643-6400
2584 Horseshoe Dr S Naples (34104) ***(G-11322)***

Marnis Dolce....407 915-7607
2928 Rapollo Ln Apopka (32712) ***(G-157)***

Marpro Marine Ways LLC....727 447-4930
1822 N Belcher Rd Clearwater (33765) ***(G-1774)***

Marquez Brothers Inc....305 888-0090
9115 Nw 93rd St Medley (33178) ***(G-8683)***

Marquez Custom Cabinets Inc....813 352-8027
9222 Lazy Ln Tampa (33614) ***(G-17885)***

Marquis Software Dev Inc....850 877-8864
1625 Summit Lake Dr # 105 Tallahassee (32317) ***(G-17296)***

Marrakech Inc....727 942-2218
720 Wesley Ave Ste 10 Tarpon Springs (34689) ***(G-18315)***

Mars Precision Products Inc....727 846-0505
8526 Leo Kidd Ave Port Richey (34668) ***(G-15061)***

Martell Glass....786 336-0142
7246 Nw 25th St Miami (33122) ***(G-9951)***

Marti Lincoln Community Agency, Miami *Also called Lincoln-Marti Cmnty Agcy Inc* ***(G-9896)***

Martin & Vleminckx Rides LLC (HQ)....407 566-0036
253 Cosmopolitan Ct Sarasota (34236) ***(G-16504)***

Martin County Hometown News, Fort Pierce *Also called Hometown News LC* ***(G-4706)***

Martin Gallagher LLC....407 453-1027
4443 Philadelphia Cir Kissimmee (34746) ***(G-7273)***

Martin L Matthews....904 881-3550
120 Velvet Dr Jacksonville (32220) ***(G-6579)***

Martin Lithograph Inc....813 254-1553
505 N Rome Ave Tampa (33606) ***(G-17886)***

Martin Marietta....850 432-8112
271 S Pace Blvd Pensacola (32502) ***(G-14200)***

Martin Munive Inc....772 318-8168
19200 Glades Cut Off Rd Port Saint Lucie (34987) ***(G-15121)***

Martin-Weston Co....727 545-8877
10860 76th Ct Ste B Largo (33777) ***(G-8005)***

Martinez Builders Supply LLC....772 466-2480
5285 Saint Lucie Blvd Fort Pierce (34946) ***(G-4714)***

Martinez Distributors Corp....305 882-8282
3081 Nw 74th Ave Miami (33122) ***(G-9952)***

Martinez Truss Company Inc....305 883-6261
9280 Nw S River Dr Medley (33166) ***(G-8684)***

Martins Fmous Pstry Shoppe Inc....800 548-1200
297 Nw Brown Rd Lake City (32055) ***(G-7367)***

Martins Fmous Pstry Shoppe Inc....800 548-1200
3000 S Highway 77 Lynn Haven (32444) ***(G-8434)***

Martins Fmous Pstry Shoppe Inc....800 548-1200
195 E Fairfield Dr Pensacola (32503) ***(G-14201)***

Martins Fmous Pstry Shoppe Inc....800 548-1200
4525 Capital Cir Nw Tallahassee (32303) ***(G-17297)***

Martins Pavers & Pools Corp....754 368-4413
220 Nw 40th Ct Deerfield Beach (33064) ***(G-2869)***

Martinson Mica Wood Pdts Inc....305 688-4445
13740 Nw 19th Ave Opa Locka (33054) ***(G-12335)***

Maruti Fence, Orlando *Also called Maruti Technology Inc* ***(G-12950)***

Maruti Technology Inc....407 704-4775
1775 Colton Dr Orlando (32822) ***(G-12950)***

Marvelleth Industries Corp....754 263-7197
6661 Sw 26th St Miramar (33023) ***(G-11014)***

Marvelous Mushrooms, Medley *Also called Idsolution Inc* ***(G-8667)***

Marvin J Dericho....407 290-0109
4618 Dutton Dr Orlando (32808) ***(G-12951)***

Marware Inc....954 927-6031
1206 Stirling Rd Bay 9a-B Dania Beach (33004) ***(G-2468)***

Marx Brothers Cabinets Inc....813 695-1473
1935 Erin Brooke Dr Valrico (33594) ***(G-18523)***

Mary Angel....772 299-1392
6700 37th St Vero Beach (32966) ***(G-18641)***

Mary Lake Life Mag Inc....407 324-2644
881 Silversmith Cir Lake Mary (32746) ***(G-7431)***

Mary Lake Life Magazine Inc....407 324-2644
3232 W Lake Mary Blvd # 1420 Lake Mary (32746) ***(G-7432)***

Mary Lame Wrought Iron & Alum....727 934-2879
1022 Us Highway 19 Holiday (34691) ***(G-5747)***

Mary Symon....813 986-4676
13206 Emerald Acres Ave Dover (33527) ***(G-3561)***

Marysol Technologies Inc....727 712-1523
1444c S Belcher Rd 136 Clearwater (33764) ***(G-1775)***

Mas Editorial Corp....305 748-0124
1596 Trailhead Ter Hollywood (33021) ***(G-5870)***

Mas Entrprses of Ft Lauderdale....904 356-9606
1883 W State Road 84 # 10 Fort Lauderdale (33315) ***(G-4113)***

Mas Hvac Inc....904 531-3140
4010 Deerpark Blvd Elkton (32033) ***(G-3649)***

Masa Trading LLC....561 729-3293
1454 Sw 11th Ter Pompano Beach (33069) ***(G-14754)***

Masaka LLC....786 800-8337
3105 Nw 107th Ave Ste 601 Doral (33172) ***(G-3426)***

Masc Aspen Partners LLC....212 545-1076
17639 Lake Estates Dr Boca Raton (33496) ***(G-611)***

Maschmeyer Concrete Co Fla....386 668-7801
275 Benson Junction Rd Debary (32713) ***(G-2751)***

Maschmeyer Concrete Co Fla....407 339-5311
1601 S Ronald Reagan Blvd Longwood (32750) ***(G-8310)***

Maschmeyer Concrete Co Fla (PA)....561 848-9112
1142 Watertower Rd Lake Park (33403) ***(G-7476)***

Maschmeyer Concrete Co Fla....863 420-6800
4949 Sand Mine Rd Davenport (33897) ***(G-2481)***

Mascot Factory Inc....877 250-2244
4376 L B Mcleod Rd Orlando (32811) ***(G-12952)***

Mask Giant, Delray Beach *Also called Straw Giant Company* ***(G-3147)***

Maskco Technologies Inc....877 261-6405
1348 Washington Ave Miami Beach (33139) ***(G-10690)***

Masking Systems of America....813 920-2271
13221 Byrd Dr Odessa (33556) ***(G-12133)***

Mason Vitamins Inc....800 327-6005
15750 Nw 59th Ave Miami Lakes (33014) ***(G-10814)***

Mason-Florida LLC....352 638-9003
2415 Griffin Rd Leesburg (34748) ***(G-8165)***

Masonite Architectural, Tampa *Also called Masonite Corporation* ***(G-17887)***

Masonite Corporation (HQ)....813 877-2726
1242 E 5th Ave Tampa (33605) ***(G-17887)***

Masonite Holdings Inc....813 877-2726
201 N Franklin St Ste 300 Tampa (33602) ***(G-17888)***

Masonite International, Tampa *Also called Masonite US Corporation* ***(G-17890)***

Masonite International Corp (PA)....800 895-2723
1242 E 5th Ave Tampa (33605) ***(G-17889)***

Masonite US Corporation....813 877-2726
1242 E 5th Ave Tampa (33605) ***(G-17890)***

Masonways Indstrctble Plas LLC....561 478-8838
580 Village Blvd Ste 330 West Palm Beach (33409) ***(G-18944)***

Massachusetts Bay Clam Co Inc....813 855-4599
13605 W Hillsborough Ave Tampa (33635) ***(G-17891)***

Masseys Metals....813 626-8275
2251 Massaro Blvd Tampa (33619) ***(G-17892)***

Massimo & Umberto Inc....954 993-0842
132 Sw 3rd Ave Dania Beach (33004) ***(G-2469)***

Massimo Roma LLC....561 302-5998
1395 Brickell Ave Ste 900 Miami (33131) ***(G-9953)***

Masso Estate Winery LLC (PA)....305 707-7749
3150 Sw 38th Ave Ste 1303 Coral Gables (33146) ***(G-2174)***

Master Alum & SEC Shutter Co....727 725-1744
950 Harbor Lake Ct Safety Harbor (34695) ***(G-15498)***

Master Cabinet Maker Inc....941 723-0278
5004 Us Highway 41 N A Palmetto (34221) ***(G-13811)***

Master Cabinets LLC....239 324-9701
5462 Ferrari Ave Ave Maria (34142) ***(G-258)***

Master Construction Pdts Inc (PA)....407 857-1221
501 Thorpe Rd Orlando (32824) ***(G-12953)***

Master Fabricators Inc....786 537-7440
12101 Sw 114th Pl Miami (33176) ***(G-9954)***

Master Kitchen Cabinets....239 225-9668
12960 Commerce Lk Dr # 8 Fort Myers (33913) ***(G-4523)***

Master Machine & Tool Co II....863 425-4902
2010 Moores Ln Mulberry (33860) ***(G-11129)***

Master Marine....904 329-1541
14255 Beach Blvd Jacksonville (32250) ***(G-6580)***

Master Mold Corp....941 486-0000
123 Morse Ct North Venice (34275) ***(G-11760)***

Master Nutrition Labs Inc....786 847-2000
13165 Nw 47th Ave Opa Locka (33054) ***(G-12336)***

Master Painting & Sealants LLC....305 910-5104
480 Ne 112th St Miami (33161) ***(G-9955)***

Master Syrup Makers, Miami *Also called Al-Rite Fruits and Syrups Inc* ***(G-9099)***

Master Tool Co Inc....305 557-1020
6115 Nw 153rd St Miami Lakes (33014) ***(G-10815)***

Master-Kraft Cabinetry......863 661-2083
305 Keystone Rd Auburndale (33823) *(G-249)*
Mastercraft Shtters Blinds LLC......904 379-7544
1700 E Church St Jacksonville (32202) *(G-6581)*
Mastercut Tool Corp......727 726-5336
965 Harbor Lake Dr Safety Harbor (34695) *(G-15499)*
Masters Block - North LLC......407 212-7704
1037 New York Ave Saint Cloud (34769) *(G-15658)*
Mastertaste Inc......813 754-7392
205 E Terrace Dr Plant City (33563) *(G-14446)*
Mat Div-Cocoa Maintenance Shop, Cocoa *Also called Cemex Cnstr Mtls Fla LLC (G-2004)*
Mat Div-Ft Lauder Maint Shop, Pompano Beach *Also called Cemex Cnstr Mtls Fla LLC (G-14632)*
Mat Div-Palm Beach Maint Shop, West Palm Beach *Also called Cemex Cnstr Mtls Fla LLC (G-18838)*
Mat Industries LLC......847 821-9630
1815 Griffin Rd Ste 400 Dania Beach (33004) *(G-2470)*
Mat-Vac Technology Inc......386 238-7017
410 Arroyo Ln Daytona Beach (32114) *(G-2683)*
Matao Brick Pavers Inc......321 663-1978
4348 S Kirkman Rd Apt 801 Orlando (32811) *(G-12954)*
Matawan Tool & Mfg Co Inc......772 221-3706
2861 Sw Brighton Way Palm City (34990) *(G-13666)*
Matchless Manufacturing......352 390-3010
10709 Sw 55th Ave Ocala (34476) *(G-11995)*
Matchware Inc (PA)......800 880-2810
511 W Bay St Ste 460 Tampa (33606) *(G-17893)*
Matco Tools, Davie *Also called Express Tools Inc (G-2522)*
Matco Transload Us06, Pompano Beach *Also called Lhoist North America Ala LLC (G-14744)*
Material Conveying Maint Inc (PA)......813 740-1111
4901 30th Ave S Tampa (33619) *(G-17894)*
Materials Div-Jacksonville ADM, Orange Park *Also called Cemex Cnstr Mtls Fla LLC (G-12385)*
Materials Div-Jupiter Lab, Jupiter *Also called Cemex Cnstr Mtls Fla LLC (G-7017)*
Matherson Organics LLC......850 792-4007
75 N Woodward Ave 85899 Tallahassee (32313) *(G-17298)*
Matheson Treigas......850 679-3024
2898 Old Chemstrand Rd Cantonment (32533) *(G-1342)*
Matheson Tri-Gas Inc......561 615-3000
1800 Bee Line Hwy Riviera Beach (33404) *(G-15347)*
Matheson Tri-Gas Inc......727 572-8737
12650 49th St N Clearwater (33762) *(G-1776)*
Mathews Associates Inc......407 323-3390
220 Power Ct Sanford (32771) *(G-16082)*
Matlocks Welding & Fab......305 942-9201
799 106th Street Ocean Marathon (33050) *(G-8520)*
Matrix Coatings Corp......561 848-1288
3575 Investment Ln West Palm Beach (33404) *(G-18945)*
Matrix Coatings Inc......561 848-1288
3575 Investment Ln West Palm Beach (33404) *(G-18946)*
Matrix Composites Inc......321 633-4480
275 Barnes Blvd Rockledge (32955) *(G-15435)*
Matrix Machining & Mfg LLC (PA)......908 355-1900
1904 Calumet St Clearwater (33765) *(G-1777)*
Matrix Marketing Solutions......407 654-5736
13629 Lake Cawood Dr Windermere (34786) *(G-19237)*
Matrix Media LLC......435 313-2877
989 Georgia Ave Palm Harbor (34683) *(G-13746)*
Matrix Packaging of Florida (HQ)......305 358-9696
1001 Brickell Bay Dr Miami (33131) *(G-9956)*
Matrix24 Laboratories LLC......941 879-3048
1453 Tallevast Rd Sarasota (34243) *(G-16253)*
Matry Group LLC......407 461-9797
10 S Flag Dr Kissimmee (34759) *(G-7314)*
Matschel of Flagler Inc......386 446-4595
239 Marshside Dr Saint Augustine (32080) *(G-15567)*
Matsu Imaging LLC......305 503-2906
2125 Nw 115th Ave Miami (33172) *(G-9957)*
Matt Talbot Industries LLC......407 718-7636
218 S Oak Ave Sanford (32771) *(G-16083)*
Matteo Graphics Inc......239 652-1002
160 Hunter Blvd Ste A1 Cape Coral (33909) *(G-1446)*
Mattheessons......305 296-1616
106 Duval St Key West (33040) *(G-7195)*
Matthews International Corp......407 886-5533
2045 Sprint Blvd Apopka (32703) *(G-158)*
Mattis Aerospace......305 910-2377
26085 S Dixie Hwy Homestead (33032) *(G-5982)*
Matusalem & Company, Miami *Also called Ron Matusalem & Matusa Fla Inc (G-10279)*
Mau Mau Corporation......305 440-5203
555 Jefferson Ave Miami Beach (33139) *(G-10691)*
Mauer Sports Nutrition Inc......888 609-2489
11309 Wine Palm Rd Fort Myers (33966) *(G-4524)*
Maui Holdings LLC......904 741-5400
250 Royal Palm Way # 201 Palm Beach (33480) *(G-13558)*
Maupin House Publishing Inc......800 524-0634
2300 Nw 71st Pl Gainesville (32653) *(G-4956)*
Maven Medical Mfg Inc......727 518-0555
2250 Lake Ave Se Largo (33771) *(G-8006)*
Maverick Boat Group Inc......772 465-0631
4551 Saint Lucie Blvd Fort Pierce (34946) *(G-4715)*
Maverick Boat Group Inc (HQ)......772 465-0631
3207 Industrial 29th St Fort Pierce (34946) *(G-4716)*
Maverick Composites Inc......561 601-3393
6105 Francis St Jupiter (33458) *(G-7075)*
Maverick Natural Resources LLC......239 657-2171
909 County Road 846 Immokalee (34142) *(G-6053)*
Maverick Press Inc......239 331-8379
975 6th Ave S Ste 200 Naples (34102) *(G-11323)*
Max Avw Professional LLC......954 972-3338
441 S State Road 7 Ste 4 Margate (33068) *(G-8557)*
Max Global North America LLC......954 727-6656
6137 Sw 33rd St Miramar (33023) *(G-11015)*
Max Torque LLC......863 701-8000
3360 Flightline Dr Lakeland (33811) *(G-7746)*
Max-Pak Inc (HQ)......863 682-0123
2808 New Tampa Hwy Lakeland (33815) *(G-7747)*
Maxam Group LLC......305 952-3227
20725 Ne 16th Ave Ste A1 Miami (33179) *(G-9958)*
Maxant Button & Supply Inc......770 460-2227
5901 Plantation Rd Plantation (33317) *(G-14532)*
Maxant Buttons LLC......770 460-2227
213 Florida Ave Nw Moore Haven (33471) *(G-11088)*
Maxeff Industries Inc......941 893-5804
1251 Commerce Blvd S Sarasota (34243) *(G-16254)*
Maxi-Blast of Florida Inc......727 572-0909
11000 Gandy Blvd N Saint Petersburg (33702) *(G-15851)*
Maxigraphics Inc......954 978-0740
2201 W Sample Rd Ste 8-2a Pompano Beach (33073) *(G-14755)*
Maxijet Inc......863 439-3667
8400 Lake Trask Rd Dundee (33838) *(G-3566)*
Maximilian Zenho & Co Inc......352 875-1190
2775 Nw 49th Ave Unit 205 Ocala (34482) *(G-11996)*
Maxit Corporation......904 998-9520
1102 A1a N Ste 206 Ponte Vedra Beach (32082) *(G-14946)*
Maxogen Group LLC......305 814-0734
2719 Hollywood Blvd Hollywood (33020) *(G-5871)*
Maxpak, Lakeland *Also called Max-Pak Inc (G-7747)*
Maxrodon Marble Inc......772 562-7543
2250 Old Dixie Hwy Se Vero Beach (32962) *(G-18642)*
Maxville LLC......904 289-7261
6640 County Road 218 Jacksonville (32234) *(G-6582)*
Maxwells Sanibel Lime-Elo Inc......239 472-8618
392 Raintree Pl Sanibel (33957) *(G-16148)*
Maxxfi LLC......513 289-6521
3428 Sw 25th Pl Cape Coral (33914) *(G-1447)*
May & Well Inc......813 333-5806
8907 Regents Park Dr # 390 Tampa (33647) *(G-17895)*
Mayaca Materials, Canal Point *Also called Five Stones Mine LLC (G-1331)*
Maydone Ltd Liability Company......407 399-3287
6233 Westgate Dr Apt 613 Orlando (32835) *(G-12955)*
Mayers Jwly Co Hollywood Inc (PA)......954 921-1422
2002 Grant St Hollywood (33020) *(G-5872)*
Mayhew/Bestway LLC......631 586-4702
2a Sunshine Blvd Ormond Beach (32174) *(G-13385)*
Maymaan Research LLC......954 374-9376
3904 N 29th Ave Hollywood (33020) *(G-5873)*
Mayn Focus LLC......603 801-8406
2057 Harbor Cove Way Winter Garden (34787) *(G-19276)*
Mayo Clinic......904 953-2000
14225 Zumbro Dr Jacksonville (32224) *(G-6583)*
Mayo Clinic......904 953-2000
4500 San Pablo Rd S Jacksonville (32224) *(G-6584)*
Mayo Clnic Pet Rdchmstry Fclty, Jacksonville *Also called Mayo Clinic (G-6583)*
Mayo Clnic Pet Rdchmstry Fclty, Jacksonville *Also called Mayo Clinic (G-6584)*
Mayo Plastics Mfg Inc......386 294-1049
232 Se Indus Cir S B Mayo (32066) *(G-8595)*
Mayo Truss Co Inc......386 294-3988
845 E Us 27 Mayo (32066) *(G-8596)*
Mayworth Showcase Works Inc......813 251-1558
1711 W State St Tampa (33606) *(G-17896)*
MB Welding Inc......727 548-0923
7360 46th Ave N Saint Petersburg (33709) *(G-15852)*
Mbf Industries Inc......407 323-9414
210 Tech Dr Sanford (32771) *(G-16084)*
MBL, Naples *Also called M-Biolabs Inc (G-11317)*
Mc Assembly Holdings Inc (HQ)......321 253-0541
425 North Dr Melbourne (32934) *(G-8884)*
Mc Assembly International LLC (HQ)......321 253-0541
425 North Dr Melbourne (32934) *(G-8885)*
Mc Connie Enterprises Inc......813 247-3827
4707 30th Ave S Tampa (33619) *(G-17897)*
Mc Connie Fence, Tampa *Also called Mc Connie Enterprises Inc (G-17897)*
Mc Dermott Enterprises Inc......262 593-8612
6720 Cadet Ave Fort Myers (33905) *(G-4525)*
Mc Graphix......321 725-7243
1390 Ashboro Cir Se Palm Bay (32909) *(G-13523)*
MC Intl Transportation......305 805-8228
8321 Nw 68th St Miami (33166) *(G-9959)*

ALPHABETIC

MC Johnson Co...239 293-0901
2037 J And C Blvd Naples (34109) ***(G-11324)***
MC Miller Co Inc...772 794-9448
11640 Us Highway 1 Sebastian (32958) ***(G-16668)***
Mc Monumental Group Inc...305 651-9113
281 Ne 168th Ter North Miami Beach (33162) ***(G-11691)***
Mc Software LLC...801 621-3900
12300 South Shore Blvd West Palm Beach (33414) ***(G-18947)***
Mc Squared Group Inc...850 435-4600
260 S Tarragona St # 140 Pensacola (32502) ***(G-14202)***
McAfee LLC...561 477-6626
19496 Island Court Dr Boca Raton (33434) ***(G-612)***
McCabinet Inc (PA)...727 608-5929
7273 112th Ave N Largo (33773) ***(G-8007)***
McCain Mills Inc...813 752-6478
5605 Paul Buchman Hwy Plant City (33565) ***(G-14447)***
McCain Sales of Florida Inc...772 461-0665
3001 Orange Ave Fort Pierce (34947) ***(G-4717)***
McCallum Cabinets Inc...352 372-2344
3004 Ne 21st Way Gainesville (32609) ***(G-4957)***
McCarthy Fabrication LLC...407 943-4909
201 N Maple Ave Ste 2 Sanford (32771) ***(G-16085)***
McClatchy Shared Services Ctr...305 740-8800
3511 Nw 91st Ave Doral (33172) ***(G-3427)***
McClellan Logging Inc...352 468-1856
State Rd 325 Hampton (32044) ***(G-5227)***
McCluneys Orthpd Prsthetis Svc...352 373-5754
2930 Nw 16th Ave Gainesville (32605) ***(G-4958)***
McCluneys Orthpd Prsthtic Srvi, Gainesville *Also called McCluneys Orthpd Prsthetis Svc* ***(G-4958)***
McColl Display Solutions...813 333-6613
8416 Iron Mountain Trl Windermere (34786) ***(G-19238)***
McConnell Corp...305 296-6124
1107 Duval St Key West (33040) ***(G-7196)***
McCord Holding, Melbourne *Also called Fastsigns 176101* ***(G-8831)***
McCormick & Company Inc...904 247-7773
1020 10th St N Jacksonville Beach (32250) ***(G-6950)***
McCormick Restaurant Services...561 706-5554
7682 Solimar Cir Boca Raton (33433) ***(G-613)***
McCullough Bottled Water, Brooksville *Also called Lee McCullough Inc* ***(G-1244)***
McDirt Industries Inc...850 944-0112
5570 Bellview Ave Pensacola (32526) ***(G-14203)***
McDs Pro LLC...954 302-3054
2021 Sw 70th Ave Bay 15 Davie (33317) ***(G-2550)***
McEs LLC...321 363-4977
2499 Old Lake Mary Rd # 102 Sanford (32771) ***(G-16086)***
McG Surfboards...904 305-8801
97 Levy Rd Atlantic Beach (32233) ***(G-224)***
McGee Enterprises Inc...904 328-3226
8535 Baymeadows Rd Ste 28 Jacksonville (32256) ***(G-6585)***
McGrail Signs & Graphics LLC...850 435-1017
1011 N P St Pensacola (32505) ***(G-14204)***
McIlpack Inc...561 988-8545
7614 Nw 6th Ave Boca Raton (33487) ***(G-614)***
McKenny Printing Enterprise...727 420-4944
2748 25th St N Saint Petersburg (33713) ***(G-15853)***
McKenzie Cabinetry Fine Wdwkg...727 424-3707
5695 70th Ave N Pinellas Park (33781) ***(G-14367)***
McKesson Pharmaceutical...863 616-2973
1515 Kendrick Ln Lakeland (33805) ***(G-7748)***
McKinna Corporation...386 446-8822
17 S Waterview Dr Palm Coast (32137) ***(G-13703)***
McKinna Yachts, Palm Coast *Also called McKinna Corporation* ***(G-13703)***
McKinney Woodworking Inc...904 591-1233
105 Greenbriar Estates Dr Saint Johns (32259) ***(G-15679)***
McM Food Corp...305 885-9254
7385 Nw 78th St Medley (33166) ***(G-8685)***
McM Industries Inc...727 259-9894
1721 Penny Ln Clearwater (33756) ***(G-1778)***
McManus Superboats, Fort Myers *Also called Mark McManus Inc* ***(G-4522)***
McMill LLC...561 279-3232
4800 N Federal Hwy 302d Boca Raton (33431) ***(G-615)***
McMillan Logging Inc...850 643-4819
15405 Nw Pea Ridge Rd Bristol (32321) ***(G-1199)***
McNeill Signs Inc (PA)...561 737-6304
555 S Dixie Hwy E Pompano Beach (33060) ***(G-14756)***
McNeill Signs Inc...386 586-7100
400 Ninth St Bunnell (32110) ***(G-1303)***
MCP, Orlando *Also called Master Construction Pdts Inc* ***(G-12953)***
MCR Amrcan Pharmaceuticals Inc...352 754-8587
16255 Aviation Loop Dr Brooksville (34604) ***(G-1248)***
MCR Compression Services LLC (PA)...432 552-8720
1261 S Haberland Blvd North Port (34288) ***(G-11743)***
McSkis...863 513-0422
10411 Carlson Cir Clermont (34711) ***(G-1969)***
McStar Revenue Solutions, Lakeland *Also called Bala Industries LLC* ***(G-7642)***
McT, Safety Harbor *Also called Mastercut Tool Corp* ***(G-15499)***
McW Parts, Sunrise *Also called Nippon Maciwumei Co* ***(G-17152)***
MD Audio Engineering Inc...305 593-8361
6941 Nw 42nd St Miami (33166) ***(G-9960)***
MDC Engineering Inc (PA)...941 358-0610
1701 Desoto Rd Sarasota (34234) ***(G-16505)***
Mdco Inc...813 855-4068
13440 Wright Cir Tampa (33626) ***(G-17898)***
Mdg Tools, Miami *Also called Aaw Products Inc* ***(G-9049)***
Mdi Products LLC...772 228-7371
10055 102nd Ter Sebastian (32958) ***(G-16669)***
Mdintouch Us Inc...786 268-1161
11735 Sw 103rd Ave Miami (33176) ***(G-9961)***
MDK Enterpises Inc...904 288-6855
11623 Columbia Park Dr E Jacksonville (32258) ***(G-6586)***
Mdl Molding LLC...954 792-3104
1112 Sw 22nd Ter Fort Lauderdale (33312) ***(G-4114)***
Mdr LLC...954 845-9500
14101 Nw 4th St Sunrise (33325) ***(G-17146)***
Mdso Security Office, Palm Bay *Also called L3harris Technologies Inc* ***(G-13519)***
Mdt Technologies Inc...305 308-2902
10619 Nw 122nd St Medley (33178) ***(G-8686)***
Mdz Publishing...954 680-9956
5063 Sweetwater Ter Cooper City (33330) ***(G-2114)***
ME Thompson Inc (PA)...904 356-6258
2178 W 21st St Jacksonville (32209) ***(G-6587)***
ME Thompson Inc...863 667-3732
1840 Fairbanks St Lakeland (33805) ***(G-7749)***
Meachem Steel Inc...352 735-7333
25546 High Hampton Cir Sorrento (32776) ***(G-16789)***
Meadowbrook Inc...800 338-2232
970 Egrets Run Apt 102 Naples (34108) ***(G-11325)***
Meadowbrook Press, Naples *Also called Meadowbrook Inc* ***(G-11325)***
Meads International Inc (HQ)...407 356-8400
5600 W Sand Lake Rd Orlando (32819) ***(G-12956)***
Measurements International Inc...315 393-1323
343 Clermont Ave Lake Mary (32746) ***(G-7433)***
Meath Industries Inc...954 818-0593
1440 Coral Ridge Dr Coral Springs (33071) ***(G-2276)***
Mec Cryo LLC...813 644-3764
4430 E Adamo Dr Ste 305 Tampa (33605) ***(G-17899)***
Mechanical Air Concepts, Doral *Also called Climax Inc* ***(G-3301)***
Mechanical Design Corp...772 388-8782
100 Industrial Park Blvd Sebastian (32958) ***(G-16670)***
Mechanical Dynamics Inc...863 292-0709
1116 5th St Sw Winter Haven (33880) ***(G-19336)***
Mechanical Svcs Centl Fla Inc (HQ)...407 857-3510
9820 Satellite Blvd Orlando (32837) ***(G-12957)***
Meck Tech Corp...888 225-9403
747 Park Ave Ste 2m Orange Park (32073) ***(G-12400)***
Mecol Oil Tools Corp...305 638-7686
1741 Nw 21st St Miami (33142) ***(G-9962)***
Mecox Gardens & Pottery Inc...561 805-8611
3900 S Dixie Hwy Palm Beach (33480) ***(G-13559)***
Med Alert Response Inc...407 730-3571
6239 Edgewater Dr Ste N1 Orlando (32810) ***(G-12958)***
Med Dental Equipment (import)...786 417-8486
7795 Sw 161st Ave Miami (33193) ***(G-9963)***
Med X Change Inc (HQ)...941 746-0538
525 8th St W Bradenton (34205) ***(G-1077)***
Med-Nap LLC...352 796-6020
301 Marianne St Brooksville (34601) ***(G-1249)***
Medaffinity Corporation...850 254-9690
2350 Phillips Rd Apt 1110 Tallahassee (32308) ***(G-17299)***
Medallion Leisure Furniture...305 626-0000
800 Nw 166th St Miami (33169) ***(G-9964)***
Medattend LLC...561 465-2735
1200 Clint Moore Rd Ste 5 Boca Raton (33487) ***(G-616)***
Medeiros Custom Wood Work...305 970-0472
8000 Nw 37th Ave Miami (33147) ***(G-9965)***
Medelite Solutions...850 348-0468
1804 Scarlett Blvd Lynn Haven (32444) ***(G-8435)***
Medfab Corporation...813 854-2646
210 Douglas Rd E Oldsmar (34677) ***(G-12247)***
Medfare LLC...561 998-9444
6560 W Rogers Cir Ste 13 Boca Raton (33487) ***(G-617)***
Media Creations Inc...954 726-0902
7101 W Coml Blvd Ste 4e Fort Lauderdale (33319) ***(G-4115)***
Media Digittal LLC...305 506-0470
8410 Nw 53rd Ter Ste 107 Doral (33166) ***(G-3428)***
Media Edge Communications LLC...352 313-6700
3951 Nw 48th Ter Ste 219 Gainesville (32606) ***(G-4959)***
Media Edge Publishing, Gainesville *Also called Media Edge Communications LLC* ***(G-4959)***
Media Publishing, Orlando *Also called Great Hse Mdia Group of Pbls I* ***(G-12788)***
Media Systems Inc...954 427-4411
3859 Nw 124th Ave Coral Springs (33065) ***(G-2277)***
Media Works Inc...904 398-5518
1451 Louisa St Jacksonville (32207) ***(G-6588)***
Mediaops Inc...516 857-7409
21455 Halstead Dr Boca Raton (33428) ***(G-618)***
Mediawrite LLC...239 344-9988
6835 Intl Ctr Blvd Ste 9 Fort Myers (33912) ***(G-4526)***

Medic Healthcare LLC 954 336-1776
6750 N Andrews Ave # 200 Fort Lauderdale (33309) **(G-4116)**
Medical Concepts, Chipley *Also called Back Lory Lee* **(G-1541)**
Medical Defense Company Inc 954 614-3266
1300 Nw 84th Ave Doral (33126) **(G-3429)**
Medical Education Technologies, Sarasota *Also called L3 Technologies Inc* **(G-16485)**
Medical Energy Inc 850 313-6277
8806 Paul Starr Dr Pensacola (32514) **(G-14205)**
Medical Examiners Office Dst 1, Pensacola *Also called P A Vivid Pathology* **(G-14218)**
Medical ID Solutions, Orlando *Also called Price Chpper Med Wrstbands Inc* **(G-13086)**
Medical Outfitters Inc (PA) 305 885-4045
8062 Nw 66th St Miami (33166) **(G-9966)**
Medical Outfitters Inc 305 332-9103
1666 J F Kennedy Cswy # 409 North Bay Village (33141) **(G-11593)**
Medical Waste Industries Inc 407 325-4832
612 Downing St New Smyrna Beach (32168) **(G-11538)**
Medicomp Inc (PA) 321 676-0010
600 Atlantis Rd Melbourne (32904) **(G-8886)**
Medipharma Inc (PA) 305 858-7332
2001 Sw 27th Ave Miami (33145) **(G-9967)**
Mediscope Manufacturing Inc 954 975-9997
401 Briny Ave Apt 405 Pompano Beach (33062) **(G-14757)**
Meditek-Icot Inc 813 909-7476
1916 Highland Oaks Blvd Lutz (33559) **(G-8398)**
Mediware BCT, Jacksonville *Also called Mediware Info Systems Inc* **(G-6589)**
Mediware Info Systems Inc 904 281-0467
7800 Belfort Pkwy Ste 291 Jacksonville (32256) **(G-6589)**
Medley Machine Shop Inc 305 884-3200
9452 Nw 109th St Medley (33178) **(G-8687)**
Medleycom Incorporated 408 745-5418
1615 S Congress Ave # 10 Delray Beach (33445) **(G-3105)**
Medone Surgical Inc 941 359-3129
670 Tallevast Rd Sarasota (34243) **(G-16255)**
MEDOVEX, Tampa *Also called H-Cyte Inc* **(G-17739)**
Medrx Inc 727 584-9600
1200 Starkey Rd Ste 105 Largo (33771) **(G-8008)**
Medtek Medical Solutions LLC 786 458-8080
6961 Nw 82nd Ave Miami (33166) **(G-9968)**
Medtel Services LLC (PA) 941 753-5000
2511 Corporate Way Palmetto (34221) **(G-13812)**
Medtrnic Sofamor Danek USA Inc 904 645-6925
10245 Centurion Pkwy N Jacksonville (32256) **(G-6590)**
Medtronic 305 458-7260
14420 Nw 60th Ave Miami Lakes (33014) **(G-10816)**
Medtronic 305 206-8487
8501 Sw 84th Ct Miami (33143) **(G-9969)**
Medtronic (HQ) 305 818-4100
14400 Nw 60th Ave Miami Lakes (33014) **(G-10817)**
Medtronic Usa Inc 702 308-1302
6743 Southpoint Dr N Jacksonville (32216) **(G-6591)**
Medtronic Usa Inc 786 709-4200
9850 Nw 41st St Ste 450 Doral (33178) **(G-3430)**
Medtronic Xomed Inc (HQ) 904 296-9600
6743 Southpoint Dr N Jacksonville (32216) **(G-6592)**
Medtronic Xomed Inc 904 296-9600
4102 Southpoint Blvd Jacksonville (32216) **(G-6593)**
Medway Hall Dev Group Inc (PA) 904 786-0622
590 Beautyrest Ave Jacksonville (32254) **(G-6594)**
Medx Corporation 352 351-2005
839 Nw 25th Ave Ocala (34475) **(G-11997)**
Meek Chic Queen Inc 407 920-8135
9257 Ramblewood Dr # 1332 Coral Springs (33071) **(G-2278)**
Meektees LLC 786 424-8491
3606 Nw 5th Ave Miami (33127) **(G-9970)**
Meelko Co 845 600-3379
3890 Nw 132nd St Unit F Opa Locka (33054) **(G-12337)**
Meg Systems Inc 239 263-5833
2030 River Reach Dr # 138 Naples (34104) **(G-11326)**
Mega 4s Bottling Company LLC 305 815-3775
5144 Sw 163rd Pl Miami (33185) **(G-9971)**
Mega Book Inc 352 378-4567
2937 Ne 19th Dr Gainesville (32609) **(G-4960)**
Mega Power 813 855-6664
211 Violet St Ste 100 Largo (33773) **(G-8009)**
Megabooks, Gainesville *Also called Mega Book Inc* **(G-4960)**
Megacolor Print LLC 305 499-9395
221 Meridian Ave Apt 413 Miami Beach (33139) **(G-10692)**
Megafend Mooring Products, Fort Lauderdale *Also called Yacht 10 Inc* **(G-4330)**
Megamalls Inc 407 891-2111
2432 13th St Saint Cloud (34769) **(G-15659)**
Megatron Equity Partners Inc 305 789-6688
801 Brickell Ave Ste 900 Miami (33131) **(G-9972)**
Megawattage LLC (PA) 954 328-0232
850 Sw 21st Ter Fort Lauderdale (33312) **(G-4117)**
Megawattage.com Generators, Fort Lauderdale *Also called Megawattage LLC* **(G-4117)**
Meggitt Aftermarket Services, Medley *Also called Pacific Scientific Company* **(G-8700)**
Megin Us LLC (PA) 954 341-2965
11772 W Sample Rd Coral Springs (33065) **(G-2279)**

MEI Companies Inc 352 361-6895
12150 Ne 7th Ave Citra (32113) **(G-1557)**
MEI Development Corporation 954 341-3302
11772 W Sample Rd Ste 101 Coral Springs (33065) **(G-2280)**
Meishboy Productions Inc 407 949-1464
433 Ashley Brooke Ct Apopka (32712) **(G-159)**
Meister Media Worldwide Inc 407 539-6552
2431 Aloma Ave 124 Winter Park (32792) **(G-19422)**
Mel Ray Industries, Crescent City *Also called Chez Industries LLC* **(G-2339)**
Melanie R Bush Pavers 772 501-7295
8316 106th Ave Vero Beach (32967) **(G-18643)**
Melbourne Architectural Mllwk 321 308-3297
325 East Dr Melbourne (32904) **(G-8887)**
Melbourne-Tillman Wtr Ctrl Dst 321 723-7233
5990 Minton Rd Nw Palm Bay (32907) **(G-13524)**
Melitta North America Inc (HQ) 727 535-2111
13925 58th St N Clearwater (33760) **(G-1779)**
Melitta USA, Clearwater *Also called Melitta North America Inc* **(G-1779)**
Melitta Usa Inc (HQ) 727 535-2111
13925 58th St N Clearwater (33760) **(G-1780)**
Melmar Cstm Met Finshg Svc Inc 954 327-5788
5990 Sw 42nd Pl Davie (33314) **(G-2551)**
Melodon Software Inc 407 654-1234
2813 S Hiawassee Rd # 302 Orlando (32835) **(G-12959)**
Melt-Tech Polymers Inc 305 887-6148
7570 Nw 79th St Medley (33166) **(G-8688)**
Meltpoint Plastics Intl Inc 305 887-8020
7570 Nw 79th St Medley (33166) **(G-8689)**
Membrane Systems Corp 239 283-8590
3227 Old Burnt Store Rd N Cape Coral (33993) **(G-1448)**
Memco Inc 352 241-2302
1789 Ec 48 Bushnell (33513) **(G-1319)**
Memco Enviro Safe, Bushnell *Also called Memco Inc* **(G-1319)**
Memo Labs Inc 561 842-0586
8390 Currency Dr Ste 4 West Palm Beach (33404) **(G-18948)**
Memphis Metal Manufacturing Co 901 276-6363
10811 Barbados Isle Dr Tampa (33647) **(G-17900)**
Mendeleyes Corp 305 597-7370
5401 Nw 110th Ave Doral (33178) **(G-3431)**
Mendez Brothers LLC 305 685-3490
13000 Nw 42nd Ave Opa Locka (33054) **(G-12338)**
Mendez Fuel 305 227-0470
11870 Sw 40th St Miami (33175) **(G-9973)**
Mendoza Pavers Corp 305 494-6794
1137 Nw 2nd St Apt 3 Miami (33128) **(G-9974)**
Menscience-Mk 305 361-0994
2199 Nw 22nd Ct Miami (33142) **(G-9975)**
Menu Design, Saint Augustine *Also called David Dobbs Enterprises Inc* **(G-15533)**
Menu Men Inc 305 633-7925
1301 Nw 27th Ave Miami (33125) **(G-9976)**
Meopta USA Inc 631 436-5900
7826 Photonics Dr Trinity (34655) **(G-18488)**
Mercaereo Inc 305 307-0672
6346 Nw 99th Ave Doral (33178) **(G-3432)**
Mercantile Two 941 388-0059
28 S Blvd Of Presidents Sarasota (34236) **(G-16506)**
Mercaworld and CIA LLC 786 212-5905
20871 Johnson St Ste 115 Pembroke Pines (33029) **(G-14047)**
Merced Industrial Corp 908 309-0170
230 Nw 107th Ave Apt 106 Miami (33172) **(G-9977)**
Mercer Products Company Inc 352 357-0057
37235 State Road 19 Umatilla (32784) **(G-18499)**
Mercers Fresh Roasted Coffees 941 286-7054
4678 Tamiami Trl Unit 109 Punta Gorda (33980) **(G-15214)**
Merchants Metals Inc 813 333-5515
2835 Overpass Rd Ste 100 Tampa (33619) **(G-17901)**
Merchants Metals LLC 904 781-3920
5918-1 Lane Cir S Jacksonville (32254) **(G-6595)**
Merchants Metals LLC 813 980-0938
4921 Joanne Kearney Blvd Tampa (33619) **(G-17902)**
Merchants Metals LLC 561 478-0059
1601 Hill Ave Ste B West Palm Beach (33407) **(G-18949)**
Merchspin Inc 877 306-3651
6424 Forest City Rd Orlando (32810) **(G-12960)**
Merck Sharp & Dohme Corp 305 512-6062
14240 Plmetto Frontage Rd Miami Lakes (33016) **(G-10818)**
Merco Frame, Miami *Also called Mercoframes Optical Corp* **(G-9978)**
Mercoframes Optical Corp 305 882-0120
5555 Nw 74th Ave Miami (33166) **(G-9978)**
Mercury Aircraft 607 776-7002
1135 Nw 159th Dr Miami (33169) **(G-9979)**
Mercury Machining Co Inc (PA) 850 433-5017
1085 W Gimble St Pensacola (32502) **(G-14206)**
Mercury Marine Power Division, Panama City *Also called Brunswick Corporation* **(G-13874)**
Mercury Printing, Sarasota *Also called Seapress Inc* **(G-16589)**
Mercury Printing, Sarasota *Also called D&R Printing LLC* **(G-16403)**
Mercury Systems Inc 352 371-2567
800 Sw 2nd Ave Ste 300 Gainesville (32601) **(G-4961)**

ALPHABETIC

Merenguitoscom LLC....305 685-2709
4847 E 10th Ct Hialeah (33013) ***(G-5505)***
Mergenet Medical Inc....561 208-3770
1701 W Hillsboro Blvd # 303 Deerfield Beach (33442) ***(G-2870)***
Meridian Cable LLC....847 847-1128
345 Vale Dr Saint Augustine (32095) ***(G-15568)***
Meridian Centre....253 620-4542
6531 Park Of Commerce Blv Boca Raton (33487) ***(G-619)***
Meridian Life Science Inc....561 241-0223
1121 Holland Dr Ste 27 Boca Raton (33487) ***(G-620)***
Meridian South Aviation LLC....727 536-5387
15875 Fairchild Dr Clearwater (33762) ***(G-1781)***
Merit Diamond Corporation....954 883-3660
1900 Tyler St Fl 3 Hollywood (33020) ***(G-5874)***
Merit Fastener Corporation (PA)....407 331-4815
2510 N Ronald Reagan Blvd Longwood (32750) ***(G-8311)***
Merit Fastener Corporation....813 626-3748
5416 56th Cmmerce Pk Blvd Tampa (33610) ***(G-17903)***
Merit International Entps Inc....305 635-1011
1628 Nw 28th St Miami (33142) ***(G-9980)***
Merit Screw....352 344-3744
3484 E Hartley Ct Hernando (34442) ***(G-5246)***
Merit Screw Products, Hernando *Also called Merit Screw* ***(G-5246)***
Merits Health Products Inc....239 772-0579
4245 Evans Ave Fort Myers (33901) ***(G-4527)***
Merkari Group Inc....305 748-3260
2222 Ponce De Leon Blvd Coral Gables (33134) ***(G-2175)***
Merkavah International Inc....305 909-6798
201 S Biscayne Blvd Miami (33131) ***(G-9981)***
Merle Harris Enterprises Inc....386 677-7060
724 Big Tree Rd South Daytona (32119) ***(G-16804)***
Merlin Industries Inc....954 472-6891
2201 College Ave Davie (33317) ***(G-2552)***
Merlola Industries LLC....888 418-0408
7950 Nw 53rd St Ste 341 Miami (33166) ***(G-9982)***
Mermaid Marine Air, Fort Myers *Also called Mermaid Mfg Southwest Fla Inc* ***(G-4528)***
Mermaid Mfg Southwest Fla Inc....239 418-0535
2651 Park Windsor Dr # 203 Fort Myers (33901) ***(G-4528)***
Merrick Industries Inc....850 265-3611
10 Arthur Dr Lynn Haven (32444) ***(G-8436)***
Merrill-Stevens Dry Dock Co (PA)....305 640-5676
1270 Nw 11th St Miami (33125) ***(G-9983)***
Merrill-Stevens Yachts, Miami *Also called Merrill-Stevens Dry Dock Co* ***(G-9983)***
Merritt Hollow Metal Inc....727 656-4380
10822 124th Ave Largo (33778) ***(G-8010)***
Merritt Island Plant, Merritt Island *Also called Sea Ray Boats Inc* ***(G-9009)***
Merritt Mfg LLC....407 481-1074
2347 Foggy Ridge Pkwy Land O Lakes (34639) ***(G-7862)***
Merritt Precision Tech Inc....321 453-2334
3425 N Courtenay Pkwy Merritt Island (32953) ***(G-9003)***
Merry Mailman Inc....954 786-1146
3907 N Federal Hwy Pompano Beach (33064) ***(G-14758)***
Mesa Industries Inc....386 738-3255
1560 Lexington Ave Deland (32724) ***(G-2995)***
Messer LLC....407 851-3311
1134 Central Florida Pkwy Orlando (32837) ***(G-12961)***
Messer LLC....925 606-2000
430 S Congress Ave Ste 7 Delray Beach (33445) ***(G-3106)***
Messner Printing, Winter Haven *Also called Messner Publications Inc* ***(G-19337)***
Messner Publications Inc....863 318-1595
3250 Dundee Rd Winter Haven (33884) ***(G-19337)***
Mestizo Foods LLC....352 414-4900
3031 W Silver Sprng Blvd Ocala (34475) ***(G-11998)***
Met-Con Inc....321 632-4880
465 Canaveral Groves Blvd Cocoa (32926) ***(G-2035)***
Metabolic Nutrition, Tamarac *Also called Iq Formulations Llc* ***(G-17359)***
Metal 2 Metal Inc....954 253-9450
17040 Sw 87th Ct Palmetto Bay (33157) ***(G-13850)***
Metal Aire, Clearwater *Also called Metal Industries Inc* ***(G-1783)***
Metal Building Erection, Jacksonville *Also called Jax Enterprises LLC* ***(G-6518)***
Metal Building Kings....412 522-4797
8050 N University Dr Tamarac (33321) ***(G-17363)***
Metal Building Supplies LLC....407 935-9714
800 E Donegan Ave Kissimmee (34744) ***(G-7274)***
Metal Container Corporation....904 695-7600
1100 Ellis Rd N Jacksonville (32254) ***(G-6596)***
Metal Craft of Pensacola Inc....850 478-8333
4 E Hannah St Pensacola (32534) ***(G-14207)***
Metal Creations Sarasota Llc....941 922-7096
1235 Tallevast Rd Sarasota (34243) ***(G-16256)***
Metal Culverts Inc....727 531-1431
2148 Pine Forest Dr Clearwater (33764) ***(G-1782)***
Metal Essence Inc....407 478-8480
910 Waterway Pl Longwood (32750) ***(G-8312)***
Metal Fabrication and....850 205-2300
3600 Weems Rd Ste D Tallahassee (32317) ***(G-17300)***
Metal Fabricators, De Leon Springs *Also called Al-Mar Metals Inc* ***(G-2735)***
Metal Fronts Inc....727 547-6700
10930 75th St Seminole (33777) ***(G-16752)***
Metal Improvement Company LLC....305 592-5960
1940 Nw 70th Ave Miami (33126) ***(G-9984)***
Metal Industries Inc (HQ)....727 441-2651
1985 Carroll St Clearwater (33765) ***(G-1783)***
Metal Magix Inc....754 235-9996
3711 Ne 11th Ave Ste 4 Pompano Beach (33064) ***(G-14759)***
Metal Mart Systems Inc....863 533-4040
255 Century Blvd Bartow (33830) ***(G-324)***
Metal Processors Inc....813 654-0050
200 S Falkenburg Rd Tampa (33619) ***(G-17904)***
Metal Products Company LC....850 526-5593
3787 Industrial Park Dr Marianna (32446) ***(G-8584)***
Metal Rock Inc....407 886-6440
174a Semoran Commerce Pl # 103 Apopka (32703) ***(G-160)***
Metal Roof Factory Inc....321 632-8300
599 Gus Hipp Blvd Rockledge (32955) ***(G-15436)***
Metal Sales Manufacturing Corp....904 783-3660
7110 Stuart Ave Jacksonville (32254) ***(G-6597)***
Metal Shop, The, Dunnellon *Also called Air Distributors Inc* ***(G-3592)***
Metal Spinning Systems Inc....305 252-7778
14250 Sw 136th St Ste 2 Miami (33186) ***(G-9985)***
Metal Spray Painting Powder....954 227-2744
3701 Nw 126th Ave Ste 4 Coral Springs (33065) ***(G-2281)***
Metal Supply and Machining Inc....561 276-4941
1304 Gwenzell Ave Ste B Delray Beach (33444) ***(G-3107)***
Metal Systems Inc....813 752-7088
3301 Paul Buchman Hwy Plant City (33565) ***(G-14448)***
Metal Technologies Group Inc....904 429-7727
1105 Registry Blvd Saint Augustine (32092) ***(G-15569)***
Metal Works By Gal....407 486-7198
5650 S Sanford Ave Sanford (32773) ***(G-16087)***
Metal-Tech Controls Corp....941 575-7677
3441 Saint Croix Ct Punta Gorda (33950) ***(G-15215)***
Metalco Mfg Inc....305 592-0704
700 W 20th St Hialeah (33010) ***(G-5506)***
Metalcraft, Pensacola *Also called Metal Craft of Pensacola Inc* ***(G-14207)***
Metalcraft Industries Inc....352 680-3555
120 Cypress Rd Ocala (34472) ***(G-11999)***
Metalcraft Services Tampa Inc....813 558-8700
10706 Nh 46th St Tampa (33617) ***(G-17905)***
Metalcrafters LLC....904 257-9036
10759 Grayson St Jacksonville (32220) ***(G-6598)***
Metalex LLC....941 918-4431
3816 Cutlass Byu Nokomis (34275) ***(G-11585)***
Metalfab Inc (PA)....352 588-9901
28212 Rice Rd San Antonio (33576) ***(G-15974)***
Metalhouse LLC....407 270-3000
4705 S Apk Vnlnd Rd # 140 Orlando (32819) ***(G-12962)***
Metalmaster Machine Shop Inc....407 423-9049
4549 L B Mcleod Rd Orlando (32811) ***(G-12963)***
Metalmaster Manufacturing Svcs, Orlando *Also called Metalmaster Machine Shop Inc* ***(G-12963)***
Metalplate Galvanizing LP....904 768-6330
7123 Moncrief Rd W Jacksonville (32219) ***(G-6599)***
Metals & Mining, West Palm Beach *Also called Evolution Metals Corp* ***(G-18866)***
Metals Supermarket, Tampa *Also called Tryana LLC* ***(G-18206)***
Metals USA Holdings Corp (HQ)....954 202-4000
4901 Nw 17th Way Ste 405 Fort Lauderdale (33309) ***(G-4118)***
Metalworks Engineering Corp....305 223-0011
1745 W 32nd Pl Hialeah (33012) ***(G-5507)***
Metavante Banking Solutions, Orlando *Also called Kirchman Corporation* ***(G-12871)***
Metavante Holdings LLC (HQ)....904 438-6000
601 Riverside Ave Jacksonville (32204) ***(G-6600)***
Methapharm Inc....954 341-0795
11772 W Sample Rd Ste 101 Coral Springs (33065) ***(G-2282)***
Method Merchant Inc....954 745-7998
150 S Pine Island Rd # 530 Plantation (33324) ***(G-14533)***
Metpro Supply Inc....863 425-7155
5070 State Road 60 E Mulberry (33860) ***(G-11130)***
Metritek Corporation (PA)....561 995-2414
849 Nw 126th Ave Coral Springs (33071) ***(G-2283)***
Metritek Group LLC....561 995-2414
370 Camino Gardens Blvd Boca Raton (33432) ***(G-621)***
Metro Defense Services Inc....407 285-2304
3001 Aloma Ave 227 Winter Park (32792) ***(G-19423)***
Metro Door Brickell LLC....786 326-4748
2660 Ne 189th St Miami (33180) ***(G-9986)***
Metro Life Media Inc....813 745-3658
3404 S Omar Ave Tampa (33629) ***(G-17906)***
Metro Machine Corp....904 249-7772
599 Wonderwood Dr Jacksonville (32233) ***(G-6601)***
Metro Roof Tile Inc....863 467-0042
9845 Nw 118th Way Medley (33178) ***(G-8690)***
Metro Signs Inc....954 410-4343
1220 S State Road 7 Hollywood (33023) ***(G-5875)***
Metronow, Orlando *Also called Milsav LLC* ***(G-12972)***
Metropolis Corp....954 951-1011
2455 E Sunrise Blvd # 909 Fort Lauderdale (33304) ***(G-4119)***

Metropolis Graphics Inc...407 740-5455
805 S Orlando Ave Ste D Winter Park (32789) *(G-19424)*
Metropolis Iron By Design, Fort Myers *Also called Alico Metal Fabricators LLC (G-4349)*
Metropolitan Mix...904 242-0743
3108 Sawgrass Village Cir Ponte Vedra Beach (32082) *(G-14947)*
Metrotech Media & Lighting Inc...844 463-8761
38 S Blue Angel Pkwy # 108 Pensacola (32506) *(G-14208)*
Mettler Toledo...607 257-6000
1571 Northpointe Pkwy Lutz (33558) *(G-8399)*
Mettler-Toledo Inc...607 257-6000
1571 Northpointe Pkwy Lutz (33558) *(G-8400)*
Mettler-Toledo Inc...407 423-3856
45 N Magnolia Ave Orlando (32801) *(G-12964)*
Mezcal Hub LLC...561 373-7972
748 Muirfield Cir Lake Worth (33462) *(G-7569)*
MFA, Port Saint Joe *Also called Monumental Fabrication of Amer (G-15081)*
Mfjr Pavers LLC...239 440-2580
1621 Red Cedar Dr Fort Myers (33907) *(G-4529)*
Mft Stamps...352 360-5797
132 E Magnolia Ave Eustis (32726) *(G-3713)*
Mfx Corp...407 429-4051
7065 Westpointe Blvd # 205 Orlando (32835) *(G-12965)*
Mg Cabinet Installers LLC...561 530-7961
3860 Miller Rd Apt B Palm Springs (33461) *(G-13777)*
Mg Coating and Sealantsllc...305 409-0915
1280 Ne 137th Ter North Miami (33161) *(G-11646)*
Mg Woodwork Inc...561 459-7552
5540 Nw 76th Pl Ste A Pompano Beach (33073) *(G-14760)*
MGI Usa Inc...321 751-6755
3143 Skyway Cir Melbourne (32934) *(G-8888)*
Mgl Engineering Inc...863 648-0320
2740 Parkway St Lakeland (33811) *(G-7750)*
MGM Cargo LLC...407 770-1500
7154 W Colonial Dr Orlando (32818) *(G-12966)*
MGM Granite & Marble Company...954 894-6802
5937 Ravenswood Rd Bldg H Fort Lauderdale (33312) *(G-4120)*
Mgo America, Miami *Also called Innova Eco Bldg Systems LLC (G-9746)*
Mhkap LLC...239 919-0786
2059 Tamiami Trl E Naples (34112) *(G-11327)*
Mhms Corp...813 948-0504
142 Whitaker Rd Ste A Lutz (33549) *(G-8401)*
Ml Metals Inc (HQ)...813 855-5695
301 Commerce Blvd Oldsmar (34677) *(G-12248)*
Mia Aerospace LLC...786 973-4118
12560 Nw 11th Ln Miami (33182) *(G-9987)*
Mia Appliances LLC...866 670-4860
3650 N Miami Ave Fl 2 Miami (33127) *(G-9988)*
Mia Consulting & Trading Inc...305 640-9677
7806 Nw 71st St Ste 209 Miami (33166) *(G-9989)*
Mia Led Lighting Inc...786 440-2856
2925 Adams St Hollywood (33020) *(G-5876)*
Miacucina LLC...305 792-9494
3650 N Miami Ave Miami (33127) *(G-9990)*
Miacucina LLC...305 444-7383
105 Miracle Mile Coral Gables (33134) *(G-2176)*
Miami...954 874-7707
3661 S Miami Ave Ste 407 Miami (33133) *(G-9991)*
Miami Awning, Miami *Also called Miami Beach Awning Co (G-9993)*
Miami Balloons & Signs, Miami *Also called Miami Banners & Signs Inc (G-9992)*
Miami Banners & Signs Inc...305 262-4460
6335 Nw 74th Ave Miami (33166) *(G-9992)*
Miami Beach Awning Co...305 576-2029
3905 Nw 31st Ave Miami (33142) *(G-9993)*
Miami Cellophane Inc...786 293-2212
7485 W 19th Ct Hialeah (33014) *(G-5508)*
Miami Cocktail Company Inc...305 482-1974
2750 Nw 3rd Ave Ste 14 Miami (33127) *(G-9994)*
Miami Compressor Rbldrs Inc...305 303-2251
3230 Nw 38th St Miami (33142) *(G-9995)*
Miami Cordage LLC...305 636-3000
2475 Nw 38th St Miami (33142) *(G-9996)*
Miami Dade Truck & Eqp Svc...305 691-2932
3294 Nw 69th St Miami (33147) *(G-9997)*
Miami Daily Business Review, Fort Lauderdale *Also called Alm Media LLC (G-3809)*
Miami Decor Inc...800 235-2197
7351 Nw 61st St Miami (33166) *(G-9998)*
Miami Diver, Miami *Also called SGS US East Coast LLC (G-10330)*
Miami Engrv Co-Oxford Prtg Co...305 371-9595
54 Nw 11th St Miami (33136) *(G-9999)*
Miami Epic Tees Corp...305 224-3465
10990 Nw 138th St Unit 16 Hialeah (33018) *(G-5509)*
Miami Fabricator Inc...305 505-1908
5323 Sw 159th Ct Miami (33185) *(G-10000)*
Miami Fabricator Inc...305 505-1908
2235 Nw 41st St Miami (33142) *(G-10001)*
Miami Filter LLC...772 466-1440
7384 Commercial Cir Fort Pierce (34951) *(G-4718)*
Miami Foods Distrs USA Inc...305 512-3246
2761 W 77th Pl Hialeah (33016) *(G-5510)*
Miami Grandstand Entertainment...305 636-9665
2330 W 79th St Hialeah (33016) *(G-5511)*
Miami Hang Gliding Corp...863 805-0440
12655 E State Road 80 Clewiston (33440) *(G-1984)*
Miami Herald...305 269-7768
4302 Sw 73rd Ave Miami (33155) *(G-10002)*
Miami Herald...800 843-4372
3500 Nw 89th Ct Doral (33172) *(G-3433)*
Miami Industrial Motors Inc...305 593-2370
8252 Nw 58th St Doral (33166) *(G-3434)*
Miami Leasing Inc...786 431-1215
14532 Sw 129th St Miami (33186) *(G-10003)*
Miami Metal Deck, Hialeah *Also called Miami Metal Roofing LLC (G-5512)*
Miami Metal Roofing LLC...305 749-6356
16000 Nw 49th Ave A Hialeah (33014) *(G-5512)*
Miami Mix Corp...954 704-9682
15014 Sw 21st St Miramar (33027) *(G-11016)*
Miami Ndt Inc...305 599-9393
8050 Nw 90th St Medley (33166) *(G-8691)*
Miami News 24 Inc...786 331-8141
6874 Nw 113th Pl Doral (33178) *(G-3435)*
Miami Offset, Hollywood *Also called Ter Prints Usa Inc (G-5922)*
Miami Oliveoil & Beyond Llc...954 632-2762
1783 Nw 79th Ave Doral (33126) *(G-3436)*
Miami Power Wheels...305 553-1888
9500 Sw 40th St Ste 305 Miami (33165) *(G-10004)*
Miami Prestige Interiors Inc...305 685-3343
3000 Nw 125th St Unit C Miami (33167) *(G-10005)*
Miami Publicity LLC...561 215-5189
8300 Sw 8th St Ste 101 Miami (33144) *(G-10006)*
Miami Quality Graphics Inc...305 634-9506
3701 Nw 51st St Miami (33142) *(G-10007)*
Miami Quality Pavers Corp...305 408-3444
5800 Sw 177th Ave Ste 101 Miami (33193) *(G-10008)*
Miami Railing Design Corp...305 926-0062
4401 Sw 75th Ave Ste 10 Miami (33155) *(G-10009)*
Miami Screenprint Supply...305 622-7532
5566 Nw 161st St Miami Lakes (33014) *(G-10819)*
Miami Sign Industry...305 418-0673
13454 Nw 38th Ct Opa Locka (33054) *(G-12339)*
Miami Signage LLC...305 877-3924
8311 Sw 157th Ave Miami (33193) *(G-10010)*
Miami Slice LLC...786 200-2723
3177 Nw 7th Ave Miami (33127) *(G-10011)*
Miami Stitch and Print Center...305 770-4285
20213 Ne 16th Pl Miami (33179) *(G-10012)*
Miami Sublimation, Hialeah *Also called Active Line Corp (G-5268)*
Miami Switchgear Company...786 336-5783
7060 Nw 52nd St Miami (33166) *(G-10013)*
Miami Tank, Fort Pierce *Also called Miami Filter LLC (G-4718)*
Miami Tape Inc...305 558-9211
6175 Nw 167th St Ste G38 Hialeah (33015) *(G-5513)*
Miami Tbr LLC...786 275-4773
1919 Nw 82nd Ave Doral (33126) *(G-3437)*
Miami Tech Inc (PA)...305 693-7054
3611 Nw 74th St Miami (33147) *(G-10014)*
Miami Tech Inc...786 354-1115
1725 W 39th Pl Hialeah (33012) *(G-5514)*
Miami Technics LLC...754 227-5459
457 Goolsby Blvd Deerfield Beach (33442) *(G-2871)*
Miami Tees Inc...305 623-3908
5120 Nw 165th St Ste 101 Miami Lakes (33014) *(G-10820)*
Miami Times...305 694-6210
900 Nw 54th St Miami (33127) *(G-10015)*
Miami Transformers Corp...305 257-1491
13935 Sw 252nd St Homestead (33032) *(G-5983)*
Miami Trucolor Offset Svc Co...954 962-5230
2211 Sw 57th Ter West Park (33023) *(G-19096)*
Miami Wall, Hialeah *Also called Larry Johnson Inc (G-5483)*
Miami Wall Systems Inc...305 888-2300
701 W 25th St Hialeah (33010) *(G-5515)*
Mica Craft & Design Inc...561 863-5354
3905 Investment Ln Ste 15 West Palm Beach (33404) *(G-18950)*
Mica Pdts & WD of Boca Raton...561 395-4686
150 Glades Rd Boca Raton (33432) *(G-622)*
Mica Visions Inc...727 712-3213
2650 Enterprise Rd Ste D Clearwater (33763) *(G-1784)*
Mica Works Cabinetry, Gainesville *Also called Micaworks Cabinetry Inc (G-4962)*
Micaworks Cabinetry Inc...352 336-1707
4440 Sw 35th Ter Gainesville (32608) *(G-4962)*
Micco Aircraft Company, Hollywood *Also called Estumkeda Ltd (G-5817)*
Michael Kors...813 413-3310
909 Brandon Town Ctr Mall Brandon (33511) *(G-1167)*
Michael L Larviere Inc...239 267-2738
17537 Braddock Rd Fort Myers (33967) *(G-4530)*
Michael Moore LLC...407 716-7325
1266 Gage Ave Deltona (32738) *(G-3175)*
Michael P Wahlquist...850 643-5139
13036 Nw Freeman Rd Bristol (32321) *(G-1200)*

ALPHABETIC

Michael Rybvich Sons Boat Wrks....561 627-9168
2175 Idlewild Rd Palm Beach Gardens (33410) ***(G-13609)***
Michael Valentines Inc....239 332-0855
10660 Clear Lake Loop # 234 Fort Myers (33908) ***(G-4531)***
Michelle Lynn Solutions Inc....786 413-0455
1395 Brickell Ave Ste 800 Miami (33131) ***(G-10016)***
Michelsons Trophies Inc....305 687-9898
14730 Nw 7th Ave Miami (33168) ***(G-10017)***
Michigan Avenue Bridge Inc....352 236-4044
4690 Ne 35th St Ocala (34479) ***(G-12000)***
Michigan Drill, Miami *Also called Republic Drill/Apt Corp* ***(G-10256)***
Michigan Group Inc....954 328-6341
5481 Wiles Rd Coconut Creek (33073) ***(G-2090)***
Michigan Pmps Elc Mtrs Repr Co....407 841-6800
1210 W Michigan St Orlando (32805) ***(G-12967)***
Michigan St Pump & Electric, Orlando *Also called Michigan Pmps Elc Mtrs Repr Co* ***(G-12967)***
Mickey Truck Bodies Inc....352 620-0015
601 Nw 24th Ct Ocala (34475) ***(G-12001)***
Micole Electric Sign Company....954 796-4293
10840 Sw 1st Ct Coral Springs (33071) ***(G-2284)***
Micon Packaging Inc....813 855-4651
301 Commerce Blvd Bldg 1 Oldsmar (34677) ***(G-12249)***
Micro Audiometrics Corporation....828 644-0771
1901 Mason Ave Ste 104 Daytona Beach (32117) ***(G-2684)***
Micro Contacts Inc....954 973-6166
2901 Gateway Dr Pompano Beach (33069) ***(G-14761)***
Micro Control Systems Inc....239 694-0089
5580 Enterprise Pkwy Fort Myers (33905) ***(G-4532)***
Micro Crane Inc....954 755-2225
3610 Nw 118th Ave Ste 4 Coral Springs (33065) ***(G-2285)***
Micro Design International, Lake Mary *Also called Totally Storage Inc* ***(G-7455)***
Micro Engineering Inc....407 886-4849
1428 E Semrn Blvd Ste 120 Apopka (32703) ***(G-161)***
Micro Hybrids Inc (PA)....772 225-4206
2600 Se Ocean Blvd Apt D5 Stuart (34996) ***(G-16976)***
Micro Jig Inc....855 747-7233
7212 Sandscove Ct Winter Park (32792) ***(G-19425)***
Micro Matic Usa Inc....352 799-6331
15111 Dispense Ln Brooksville (34604) ***(G-1250)***
Micro Matic Usa Inc....352 544-1081
16121 Flight Path Dr Brooksville (34604) ***(G-1251)***
Micro Matic Usa Inc (HQ)....352 544-1081
2386 Simon Ct Brooksville (34604) ***(G-1252)***
Micro Pneumatic Logic Inc....954 935-6821
2901 Gateway Dr Pompano Beach (33069) ***(G-14762)***
Micro Printing Inc....954 676-5757
2571 Nw 4th Ct Fort Lauderdale (33311) ***(G-4121)***
Micro Quality Corp....954 354-5572
438 S Military Trl Deerfield Beach (33442) ***(G-2872)***
Micro Systems Inc (HQ)....850 244-2332
35 Hill Ave Nw Fort Walton Beach (32548) ***(G-4815)***
Micro Technology of Brevard....321 733-1766
255 West Dr Melbourne (32904) ***(G-8889)***
Micro Tool Engineering Inc....561 842-7381
7575 Centl Indus Dr Ste A Riviera Beach (33404) ***(G-15348)***
Micro Typing Systems Inc....954 970-9500
1295 Sw 29th Ave Pompano Beach (33069) ***(G-14763)***
Micro-Ant LLC....904 683-8394
4722 Wesconnett Blvd Jacksonville (32210) ***(G-6602)***
Microbial Defense Systems LLC....989 964-9863
404 Bostwick Cir Saint Augustine (32092) ***(G-15570)***
Microblack Enterprise, Orlando *Also called Black Box Corporation* ***(G-12520)***
Microcomputer Services....561 988-7000
1200 S Rogers Cir Ste 8 Boca Raton (33487) ***(G-623)***
Microflex Inc....386 672-1945
1810 N Us Highway 1 Ormond Beach (32174) ***(G-13386)***
Microflex Automotive, Ormond Beach *Also called Microflex Inc* ***(G-13386)***
Microgerm Defense LLC....561 309-0842
2257 Vista Pk Way Ste 22 West Palm Beach (33411) ***(G-18951)***
Microguard....386 274-1382
1901 Mason Ave Daytona Beach (32117) ***(G-2685)***
Microlumen Inc....813 886-1200
1 Microlumen Way Oldsmar (34677) ***(G-12250)***
Micromicr Corporation....954 922-8044
35 Sw 12th Ave Ste 112 Dania (33004) ***(G-2452)***
Micron Fiber - Tech Inc....386 668-7895
230 Sprngview Commerce Dr Debary (32713) ***(G-2752)***
Micron Pharmaworks LLC....727 232-8200
2346 Success Dr Odessa (33556) ***(G-12134)***
Micron Pharmaworks, Inc., Odessa *Also called Micron Pharmaworks LLC* ***(G-12134)***
Microsalt Inc....877 825-0655
515 N Flagler Dr Ste P300 West Palm Beach (33401) ***(G-18952)***
Microseal International, Boca Raton *Also called Lance Lashelle* ***(G-594)***
Microsemi Corp....407 965-5687
1064 Greenwood Blvd # 124 Lake Mary (32746) ***(G-7434)***
Microsimulators Inc....407 696-8722
1612 White Dove Dr Winter Springs (32708) ***(G-19479)***
Microsoft Corporation....425 882-8080
6750 N Andrews Ave # 400 Fort Lauderdale (33309) ***(G-4122)***
Micross Components, Clearwater *Also called Micross Prmier Smcdtr Svcs LLC* ***(G-1785)***
Micross Components, Orlando *Also called Chip Supply Inc* ***(G-12580)***
Micross Components Inc (PA)....407 298-7100
7725 N Orange Blossom Trl Orlando (32810) ***(G-12968)***
Micross Minco LLC....512 339-3422
7725 N Orange Blossom Trl Orlando (32810) ***(G-12969)***
Micross Prmier Smcdtr Svcs LLC....727 532-1777
4400 140th Ave N Ste 140 Clearwater (33762) ***(G-1785)***
Microtechnologies, Pompano Beach *Also called Micro Pneumatic Logic Inc* ***(G-14762)***
Microtechnologies, Pompano Beach *Also called M Micro Technologies Inc* ***(G-14749)***
Microtek Medical Inc....904 741-2964
13500 Tradeport Cir E Jacksonville (32218) ***(G-6603)***
Microtex Electronics Inc....386 426-1922
13191 Kingfisher Rd Weeki Wachee (34614) ***(G-18704)***
Microtool and Instrument Inc....786 242-8780
15203 Sw 87th Ave Palmetto Bay (33157) ***(G-13851)***
Microvision Technology Corp....407 333-2943
43 Skyline Dr Ste 3051 Lake Mary (32746) ***(G-7435)***
Microwave Electronics....561 432-8511
6314 Dornich Ln Lake Worth (33463) ***(G-7570)***
Mictron Inc....941 371-6564
8130 Fruitville Rd Sarasota (34240) ***(G-16507)***
Mid Florida Signs, Leesburg *Also called Sign Design of Florida Inc* ***(G-8172)***
Mid Florida Steel Corp....321 632-8228
870 Cidco Rd Cocoa (32926) ***(G-2036)***
Mid Flrida Lthersir/Leatherboy....352 615-5851
21710 Us Highway 98 Dade City (33523) ***(G-2431)***
Mid State Machine & Fabg, Lakeland *Also called Mid-State Machine & Fabg Corp* ***(G-7751)***
Mid State Plastics, Ruskin *Also called Jan and Jean Inc* ***(G-15485)***
Mid State Screen Graphics LLC....727 573-2299
13183 38th St N Clearwater (33762) ***(G-1786)***
Mid West Lettering Company....850 477-6522
7800 Sears Blvd Pensacola (32514) ***(G-14209)***
Mid-Florida Plastics Inc....407 856-1805
780 Central Florida Pkwy Orlando (32824) ***(G-12970)***
Mid-Florida Publications Inc (PA)....352 589-8811
4645 N Highway 19a Mount Dora (32757) ***(G-11107)***
Mid-Florida Sportswear LLC....386 258-5632
2415 Bellevue Ave Daytona Beach (32114) ***(G-2686)***
Mid-Flrida Lbr Acqisitions Inc....863 533-0155
4281 Echo Ave Bartow (33830) ***(G-325)***
Mid-State Machine & Fabg Corp (PA)....863 665-6233
2730 Mine And Mill Rd Lakeland (33801) ***(G-7751)***
Mid-State Machine Company LLC....704 636-7029
4516 Longboat Ln Fort Myers (33919) ***(G-4533)***
Midds Inc....561 586-6220
128 S Dixie Hwy Lake Worth (33460) ***(G-7571)***
Midds Inc....561 586-6220
1937 10th Ave N Lake Worth Beach (33461) ***(G-7615)***
Midgard Inc....863 696-1224
6402 State Road 60 E Lake Wales (33898) ***(G-7516)***
Midnight Express Pwr Boats Inc....954 745-8284
351 Ne 185th St Miami (33179) ***(G-10018)***
Midnite Son II of Sarasota....941 377-6029
1257 Porter Rd Sarasota (34240) ***(G-16508)***
Midway Labs Usa LLC....561 571-6252
6401 Congress Ave Ste 100 Boca Raton (33487) ***(G-624)***
Midwest Mtal Fbrction Cstm Rll....317 769-6489
13331 Seaside Harbour Dr North Fort Myers (33903) ***(G-11599)***
Mightees LLC....201 450-7470
18518 Flamingo Rd Fort Myers (33967) ***(G-4534)***
Migrandy Corp....321 459-0044
675 Cypress Dr Merritt Island (32952) ***(G-9004)***
Miguel Casa Corp....305 887-0098
2005 W 4th Ave Hialeah (33010) ***(G-5516)***
Mll Oil Holding Inc....321 200-0039
1201 Hays St Tallahassee (32301) ***(G-17301)***
Mike and Val Tupper Ind....904 757-7566
14171 Denton Rd Jacksonville (32226) ***(G-6604)***
Mike Blackburn Welding LLC....850 643-8464
19983 Ne Hentz Ave Blountstown (32424) ***(G-386)***
Mike Cope Race Cars LLC....352 585-2810
14152 63rd Way N Clearwater (33760) ***(G-1787)***
Mike Pulver LLC....386 747-8951
703 Deerfoot Rd Deland (32720) ***(G-2996)***
Mikes Aluminum Products LLC....407 855-1989
4445 Story Rd Saint Cloud (34772) ***(G-15660)***
Mikes Precision Inc....305 558-6421
1929 W 76th St Hialeah (33014) ***(G-5517)***
Mikes Print Shop Inc....407 718-4964
2118 Poinciana Rd Winter Park (32792) ***(G-19426)***
Mikes Trck Prts Mch Sp Plus I....786 534-9608
7337 Nw 54th St Miami (33166) ***(G-10019)***
Mil-Sat LLC....954 862-3613
12555 Orange Dr Davie (33330) ***(G-2553)***
Mil-Spec Metal Finishing Inc....386 426-7188
706 W Park Ave Ste A Edgewater (32132) ***(G-3631)***

Mil-Tec Incorporated 239 369-2880
5578 6th St W Lehigh Acres (33971) ***(G-8199)***
Milano Worldwide Corp....561 266-0201
222 W Yamato Rd Ste 106 Boca Raton (33431) ***(G-625)***
Milans Machine Shop & Wldg Svc....305 592-2447
8052 Nw 56th St Doral (33166) ***(G-3438)***
Milbank Manufacturing Co....813 623-2681
3214 Queen Palm Dr Tampa (33619) ***(G-17907)***
Milca Bottling Company....305 365-0044
620 Harbor Cir Key Biscayne (33149) ***(G-7160)***
Milcom Services Inc....561 907-6816
1963 10th Ave N Lake Worth Beach (33461) ***(G-7616)***
Mile Marker News, Key West *Also called Overseas Radio LLC* ***(G-7200)***
Milenium Publishing LLC....786 573-9974
12742 Sw 103rd Ct Miami (33176) ***(G-10020)***
Miles of Smiles Rides Inc....727 528-1227
10530 72nd St Ste 705 Seminole (33777) ***(G-16753)***
Miles of Wood Inc....305 300-6370
5951 Sw 44th Ter Miami (33155) ***(G-10021)***
Miles Partnership II LLC (PA)....941 342-2300
6751 Prof Pkwy W Ste 200 Sarasota (34240) ***(G-16509)***
Military One Click LLC....904 390-7100
815 S Main St Jacksonville (32207) ***(G-6605)***
Militek Industries LLC....941 544-5636
5727 23rd St W Bradenton (34207) ***(G-1078)***
Mill-Rite Woodworking Co Inc....727 527-7808
6401 47th St N Pinellas Park (33781) ***(G-14368)***
Millcreek Fine Cabinetry Inc....954 801-8595
1700 Nw 65th Ave Ste 9 Plantation (33313) ***(G-14534)***
Millenia Froyo LLC....407 694-9938
9066 Harbor Isle Dr Windermere (34786) ***(G-19239)***
Millenium Engine Plating Inc....305 688-0098
600 W 84th St Hialeah (33014) ***(G-5518)***
Millenium Natural Health Pdts, Doral *Also called Bonne Sante Natural Mfg Inc* ***(G-3281)***
Millenium Oil & Gas Distrs Inc....305 220-3669
12801 Sw 42nd St Miami (33175) ***(G-10022)***
Millenium Wood Boxes Inc....305 969-5510
13139 Sw 122nd Ave Miami (33186) ***(G-10023)***
Millennium Glass Inc....305 638-1785
5851 Nw 35th Ave Miami (33142) ***(G-10024)***
Millennium Metals Inc....904 358-8366
10200 Eastport Rd Jacksonville (32218) ***(G-6606)***
Miller Brothers Contractors....941 371-4162
990 Cattlemen Rd Sarasota (34232) ***(G-16510)***
Miller Creative Graphics....904 771-5855
8725 Youngerman Ct # 101 Jacksonville (32244) ***(G-6607)***
Miller Creative Works Inc....904 504-3212
710 9th Ave N Jacksonville (32250) ***(G-6608)***
Miller Marine Yacht Svc Inc....850 265-6768
7141 Grassy Point Rd Panama City (32409) ***(G-13929)***
Miller Publishing Co Inc....305 669-7355
6796 Sw 62nd Ave South Miami (33143) ***(G-16822)***
Miller Signs LLC....786 395-9420
2501 N 69th Ave Hollywood (33024) ***(G-5877)***
Miller-Leaman Inc....386 248-0500
800 Orange Ave Daytona Beach (32114) ***(G-2687)***
Millers Custom Metals Inc....561 540-6263
1224 Pope Ln Lake Worth (33460) ***(G-7572)***
Milliken & Company....352 244-2267
5002 Ne 54th Pl Gainesville (32609) ***(G-4963)***
Milliken & Milliken Inc....941 474-0223
101 S Mccall Rd Englewood (34223) ***(G-3680)***
Milliken Industries, Englewood *Also called Milliken & Milliken Inc* ***(G-3680)***
Millimeter Wave Products Inc....727 563-0034
2007 Gandy Blvd N # 1310 Saint Petersburg (33702) ***(G-15854)***
Millionaire Publishing LLC....305 763-8184
110 Wshngton Ave Apt 1524 Miami Beach (33139) ***(G-10693)***
Mills & Murphy Sftwr Systems....727 577-1236
618 94th Ave N Saint Petersburg (33702) ***(G-15855)***
Mills & Nebraska, Orlando *Also called Central Florida Lbr & Sup Co* ***(G-12569)***
Mills & Nebraska Door & Trim....407 472-2742
2721 Regent Ave Orlando (32804) ***(G-12971)***
Millwork 360 LLC....813 854-3100
12941 Memorial Hwy Tampa (33635) ***(G-17908)***
Millwork and Design Inc....352 544-0444
22309 Rodeo Dr Brooksville (34602) ***(G-1253)***
Millwork Masters LLC....727 807-6221
7013 Us Highway 19 New Port Richey (34652) ***(G-11501)***
Millwork Plus Inc....352 343-2121
262 Hummer Way Tavares (32778) ***(G-18348)***
Milpro Publications LLC....321 613-2250
559 Edward Rd Melbourne (32904) ***(G-8890)***
Milsav LLC....407 556-5055
10542 Wittenberg Way Orlando (32832) ***(G-12972)***
Milspec Products Inc....352 735-0065
31537 Long Acres Dr Sorrento (32776) ***(G-16790)***
Miltechnologies Inc....305 817-4244
13980 Nw 58th Ct Miami Lakes (33014) ***(G-10821)***
Milton Newspapers Inc....850 623-2120
6576 Caroline St Milton (32570) ***(G-10935)***
Milton Truss Company, Milton *Also called Emerald Coast Truss LLC* ***(G-10927)***
Mimi's Ravioli, Hollywood *Also called Termine Ravioli Manufacturing* ***(G-5923)***
Mims Welding Incorporated....863 612-9819
90 Evans Rd Labelle (33935) ***(G-7320)***
Mimzy Froyo Delights LLC....917 862-9520
600 S Rosemary Ave # 162 West Palm Beach (33401) ***(G-18953)***
MINA MAR GROUP, Lantana *Also called Thunder Energies Corporation* ***(G-7878)***
MINd&melody Inc....305 582-1006
12905 Sw 132nd St Miami (33186) ***(G-10025)***
Minder Research Inc....772 463-6522
3000 Se Waaler St Stuart (34997) ***(G-16977)***
Mine Survival Inc....850 774-0025
9210 Pnama Cy Bch Pkwy St Panama City Beach (32407) ***(G-13980)***
Minea Usa Llc....800 971-3216
1550 S Dixie Hwy Ste 216 Coral Gables (33146) ***(G-2177)***
Mineral Life Intl Inc....305 661-9854
6732 Sw 71st Ct Miami (33143) ***(G-10026)***
Mini Circuits Lab Inc....305 558-6381
2160 W 80th St Hialeah (33016) ***(G-5519)***
Mini Truckin, Tampa *Also called Hornblasters Inc* ***(G-17761)***
Minisportsballs.com, Tampa *Also called Put Your Name On It LLC* ***(G-18026)***
Mint Prints....561 900-5432
805 Se 1st Way Ste 8 Deerfield Beach (33441) ***(G-2873)***
Minute Man Press....727 791-1115
1425 Main St Ste C Dunedin (34698) ***(G-3584)***
Minuteman, Orlando *Also called Zetma LLC* ***(G-13341)***
Minuteman Industries Inc....813 248-1776
1407 E 5th Ave Tampa (33605) ***(G-17909)***
Minuteman Press, Coral Springs *Also called E3 Graphics Inc* ***(G-2243)***
Minuteman Press, Boca Raton *Also called Spinnaker Holding Company* ***(G-728)***
Minuteman Press, Hialeah *Also called Semprun & Morales Corporation* ***(G-5615)***
Minuteman Press, Minneola *Also called Guerrilla Prtg Solutions LLC* ***(G-10954)***
Minuteman Press, Orlando *Also called Pamatian Group Inc* ***(G-13046)***
Minuteman Press, Jacksonville *Also called Sonshine Digital Graphics Inc* ***(G-6784)***
Minuteman Press, Naples *Also called Just Now Jennings LLC* ***(G-11301)***
Minuteman Press, West Palm Beach *Also called 5hp Investments LLC* ***(G-18782)***
Minuteman Press, Orlando *Also called Relion Enterprises LLC* ***(G-13130)***
Minuteman Press, Fort Lauderdale *Also called Bema Inc* ***(G-3846)***
Minuteman Press, Jupiter *Also called Tiba Enterprises Inc* ***(G-7128)***
Minuteman Press, Hollywood *Also called Taie Inc* ***(G-5920)***
Minuteman Press, Sunrise *Also called Printrust Inc* ***(G-17164)***
Minuteman Press, Lakeland *Also called Lincoln Smith Ventures LLC* ***(G-7735)***
Minuteman Press, North Palm Beach *Also called Universal Graphics & Prtg Inc* ***(G-11729)***
Minuteman Press, Dunedin *Also called Minute Man Press* ***(G-3584)***
Minuteman Press, New Port Richey *Also called Danifer Printing Inc* ***(G-11488)***
Minuteman Press, Miramar *Also called J J M Services Inc* ***(G-11007)***
Minuteman Press, Stuart *Also called Kinane Corp* ***(G-16965)***
Minuteman Press, Miami *Also called Boostan Inc* ***(G-9267)***
Minuteman Press, Longwood *Also called It Busness Solutions Group Inc* ***(G-8294)***
Minuteman Press, Jacksonville *Also called Ra Printing Inc* ***(G-6703)***
Minuteman Press, Vero Beach *Also called Spinnaker Vero Inc* ***(G-18667)***
Minuteman Press, Miami *Also called Orellana Investments Inc* ***(G-10115)***
Minuteman Press....727 535-3800
2475 E Bay Dr Ste A Largo (33771) ***(G-8011)***
Minuteman Press....813 884-2476
5519 Hanley Rd Tampa (33634) ***(G-17910)***
Minuteman Press....904 733-5578
1370 Marsh Harbor Dr Jacksonville (32225) ***(G-6609)***
Minuteman Press....305 242-6800
22469 Sw 103rd Ave Cutler Bay (33190) ***(G-2404)***
Minuteman Press....863 337-6670
2058 E Edgewood Dr Ste C Lakeland (33803) ***(G-7752)***
Minuteman Press....503 789-5741
3 S John Young Pkwy # 17 Kissimmee (34741) ***(G-7275)***
Minuteman Press....386 255-2767
201 N Ridgewood Ave Daytona Beach (32114) ***(G-2688)***
Minuteman Press....352 728-6333
1417 E Main St Leesburg (34748) ***(G-8166)***
Minuteman Press....772 301-0222
6967 Hancock Dr Port Saint Lucie (34952) ***(G-15122)***
Minuteman Press....954 804-8304
6677 Lake Worth Rd Lake Worth (33467) ***(G-7573)***
Minuteman Systems & Alarms, Tampa *Also called Minuteman Industries Inc* ***(G-17909)***
Minutemen Printing, Pompano Beach *Also called United Printing Sales Inc* ***(G-14902)***
Mio Gourment Products LLC....305 219-0253
616 W 27th St Hialeah (33010) ***(G-5520)***
Mio Publication Inc....941 351-2411
1864 University Pkwy Sarasota (34243) ***(G-16257)***
Mip-Technology Corp....239 221-3604
28100 Bonita Grande Dr # 101 Bonita Springs (34135) ***(G-845)***
Mipe Corp....305 825-1195
3960 W 16th Ave Ste 208 Hialeah (33012) ***(G-5521)***
Miracle Noodle, Miami *Also called Strumba Media LLC* ***(G-10423)***

ALPHABETIC

Miracle Seafood Manufacturers 850 653-2114
610 Us Highway 98 Apalachicola (32320) ***(G-98)***
Miracles For Fun Usa Inc 561 702-8217
1835 E Hllndale Bch Blvd Hallandale Beach (33009) ***(G-5199)***
Miraflex Corporation 786 380-4494
7950 Nw 53rd St Ste 324 Doral (33166) ***(G-3439)***
Mirage & Co Inc 407 301-5850
3826 Cedar Hammock Trl Saint Cloud (34772) ***(G-15661)***
Mirage Manufacturing Inc 352 377-4146
3001 Ne 20th Way Gainesville (32609) ***(G-4964)***
Mirage Systems Inc 386 740-9222
1501a Lexington Ave Deland (32724) ***(G-2997)***
Mirage Woodworking Inc 305 606-7043
6875 W 7th Ave Apt 608 Hialeah (33014) ***(G-5522)***
Miramar Mrmids Synchro Team LL 954 646-6350
4944 Sw 164th Ave Miramar (33027) ***(G-11017)***
Miramar Publishing Inc 305 695-0639
1030 14th St Miami Beach (33139) ***(G-10694)***
Miranda Eldorado Mfg Co 727 586-0707
1744 12th St Se Ofc Ofc Largo (33771) ***(G-8012)***
Mirandas Woodcraft LLC 954 306-3568
3764 Nw 16th St Lauderhill (33311) ***(G-8115)***
Mirart Inc 954 974-5230
2707 Gateway Dr Pompano Beach (33069) ***(G-14764)***
Mircalear, Gainesville *Also called Florida North Hearing Solution* ***(G-4921)***
Mirrolure, Largo *Also called L & S Bait Co Inc* ***(G-7997)***
Mirrors & More Inc 954 782-7272
3390 Ne 6th Ter Pompano Beach (33064) ***(G-14765)***
Mirrors 2 Go, Miami *Also called Italian Cabinetry Inc* ***(G-9774)***
Misc Metal Fabrication LLC 754 264-1026
3001 Sw 15th St Ste A Deerfield Beach (33442) ***(G-2874)***
Misfit Gaming 954 347-0906
6401 Congress Ave Boca Raton (33487) ***(G-626)***
Mishaal Aerospace Corporation 786 353-2685
31 Se 5th St Apt 3415 Miami (33131) ***(G-10027)***
Mishas Cupcakes Inc (PA) 786 200-6153
5616 Sunset Dr Miami (33143) ***(G-10028)***
Miss BS Inc 305 981-9900
13899 Biscayne Blvd # 309 North Miami Beach (33181) ***(G-11692)***
Missing Galaxy Publishing, Largo *Also called Silly Dandelions Inc* ***(G-8053)***
Mister Cabinet Deluxe Inc 305 205-3601
2280 W 77th St Hialeah (33016) ***(G-5523)***
Mitcham Media Group LLC 850 893-9624
4032 Mclaughlin Dr Tallahassee (32309) ***(G-17302)***
Mitchell Wood Works Inc 727 321-7586
4726 15th Ave S Saint Petersburg (33711) ***(G-15856)***
Mitek USA Inc 813 906-3122
6904 Parke East Blvd Tampa (33610) ***(G-17911)***
Mitsubishi Power Americas Inc (HQ) 407 688-6100
400 Colonial Center Pkwy # 500 Lake Mary (32746) ***(G-7436)***
Mitsubshi Htchi Pwr Systems Am, Lake Mary *Also called Mitsubishi Power Americas Inc* ***(G-7436)***
Mitten Manufacturing 941 722-1818
1614 20th St E Unit 102 Palmetto (34221) ***(G-13813)***
Mittera, Jacksonville *Also called Trend Offset Printing Svcs Inc* ***(G-6869)***
Mitts and Merrill LP 352 343-7001
28623 Lake Indus Blvd Tavares (32778) ***(G-18349)***
Mityflex, Bradenton *Also called Anko Products Inc* ***(G-989)***
Mix It At Loop 407 201-8948
2617 W Osceola Pkwy Kissimmee (34741) ***(G-7276)***
Mix It Loop Inc 407 902-9334
12517 Greco Dr Orlando (32824) ***(G-12973)***
Mix It Up 251 767-1771
909 Santa Rosa Blvd # 551 Fort Walton Beach (32548) ***(G-4816)***
Mix Masters Inc 386 846-9239
523 Virginia Ave Unit B Port Orange (32127) ***(G-15024)***
Mixers Bar & Grille, Palm Harbor *Also called Beast Row Inc* ***(G-13724)***
Miy Ceramic 305 823-5758
7000 Gleneagle Dr Miami Lakes (33014) ***(G-10822)***
Mizkan America Inc 863 956-0391
445 N Dakota Ave Lake Alfred (33850) ***(G-7333)***
Mjk Industries Inc 954 788-7494
201 Se 3rd Ct Pompano Beach (33060) ***(G-14766)***
MJM Cabinet Inc 786 953-5000
226 W 23rd St Hialeah (33010) ***(G-5524)***
MJM Manufacturing Inc 305 620-2020
5205 Nw 161st St Miami Lakes (33014) ***(G-10823)***
Mjr Enterprises Inc 352 483-0735
1895 Irma Rd Eustis (32726) ***(G-3714)***
Mjr Manufacturing LLC 727 460-0636
2519 N Mcmullen Booth Rd Clearwater (33761) ***(G-1788)***
Mjr Woodworks LLC 407 403-5430
552 Cooper Indus Pkwy Apopka (32703) ***(G-162)***
Mk Aviation LLC 305 825-4810
9471 Nw 12th St Doral (33172) ***(G-3440)***
Mk Brothers Inc 407 847-9547
2790 Michigan Ave Ste 318 Kissimmee (34744) ***(G-7277)***
Mk Monomers LLC 732 928-5800
905 Brickell Bay Dr # 23 Miami (33131) ***(G-10029)***
Mkm Sarasota LLC 941 358-0383
2363 Industrial Blvd Sarasota (34234) ***(G-16511)***
Mli Intgrted Graphic Solutions, Tampa *Also called Martin Lithograph Inc* ***(G-17886)***
Mlxl Productions Inx 904 350-0048
2935 Dawn Rd Jacksonville (32207) ***(G-6610)***
Mm Wildwood LLC 917 609-7128
10126 Lake Miona Way Oxford (34484) ***(G-13464)***
Mm Wood Designs Inc 561 602-2775
2859 Cormorant Rd Delray Beach (33444) ***(G-3108)***
Mmats Inc 561 842-0600
15132 Pk Of Commerce Blvd Jupiter (33478) ***(G-7076)***
Mmats Professional Audio, Jupiter *Also called Mmats Inc* ***(G-7076)***
Mmo Industries Inc 727 452-8665
4710 Eisenhower Blvd A1 Tampa (33634) ***(G-17912)***
Mmp-Boca Raton LLC 561 392-8626
1609 Nw 2nd Ave Boca Raton (33432) ***(G-627)***
Mmt Technologies Inc 863 619-2926
4302 Holden Rd Lakeland (33811) ***(G-7753)***
Mmx Manufacturing LLC 786 456-5072
6508 Nw 77th Ct Miami (33166) ***(G-10030)***
MN Trades Inc 954 455-9320
200 Leslie Dr Ofc Hallandale Beach (33009) ***(G-5200)***
MO Steel Fbricator Erector Inc 305 945-4855
353 Ne 185th St Miami (33179) ***(G-10031)***
Moba Corp 305 868-3700
10155 Collins Ave # 1807 Bal Harbour (33154) ***(G-303)***
Mobica Center, Hialeah *Also called Mister Cabinet Deluxe Inc* ***(G-5523)***
Mobil Boat Fuel Inc 941 718-3781
616 49th St E Bradenton (34208) ***(G-1079)***
Mobile 1 Inc 954 283-8100
3680 W Oakland Park Blvd Lauderdale Lakes (33311) ***(G-8091)***
Mobile Auto Solutions LLC 561 903-5328
1578 Quail Dr Apt 10 West Palm Beach (33409) ***(G-18954)***
Mobile Meals 813 907-6325
8909 Magnolia Chase Cir Tampa (33647) ***(G-17913)***
Mobile Power Generators LLC 352 365-2777
634 State Road 44 Leesburg (34748) ***(G-8167)***
Mobile Rugged Tech Corp 781 771-6743
931 S Semoran Blvd # 204 Winter Park (32792) ***(G-19427)***
Mobile Rving 954 870-7095
2150 Sw 10th St Ste A Deerfield Beach (33442) ***(G-2875)***
Mobile Sign Service Inc 954 579-8628
4381 Nw 4th St Coconut Creek (33066) ***(G-2091)***
Mobile Specialties Inc 407 878-5469
1683 N Beardall Ave # 117 Sanford (32771) ***(G-16088)***
Mobile Walkways, Sanford *Also called Mobile Specialties Inc* ***(G-16088)***
Mobilebits Holdings Corp (PA) 941 225-6115
5901 N Honore Ave Ste 120 Sarasota (34243) ***(G-16258)***
Mobilehelp LLC (PA) 561 347-6285
5050 Conference Way N # 125 Boca Raton (33431) ***(G-628)***
Mobilepower LLC 843 706-6108
5975 Sunset Dr South Miami (33143) ***(G-16823)***
Mobilite Corporation 407 321-5630
2101 E Lake Mary Blvd Sanford (32773) ***(G-16089)***
Mobility Freedom Inc 407 495-1333
7260 Narcoossee Rd Orlando (32822) ***(G-12974)***
Mobius Business Group Inc 239 274-8900
1961 Dana Dr Fort Myers (33907) ***(G-4535)***
Mobvious Corp 786 497-6620
2100 Coral Way Ste 200 Miami (33145) ***(G-10032)***
Mode Marimba Inc 561 512-5001
19960 Earlwood Dr Jupiter (33458) ***(G-7077)***
Model Screw Products, Clearwater *Also called MSP Industries LLC* ***(G-1795)***
Modern Cabinetry and AMP Mllwk (PA) 813 426-6941
5330 Ehrlich Rd Ste 102 Tampa (33624) ***(G-17914)***
Modern Coating System LLC 786 326-3652
3201 Nw 13th Ave Miami (33142) ***(G-10033)***
Modern Digital Imaging Inc 850 222-7514
519 N Monroe St Tallahassee (32301) ***(G-17303)***
Modern Display, Doral *Also called J D M Corp* ***(G-3398)***
Modern Graphic Arts, Saint Petersburg *Also called Sandy-Alexander Inc* ***(G-15905)***
Modern Happy Home Llc 954 436-0055
1201 E Sunrise Blvd # 305 Fort Lauderdale (33304) ***(G-4123)***
Modern Mail Print Slutions Inc 727 572-6245
14201 58th St N Clearwater (33760) ***(G-1789)***
Modern Metal Systems Inc (PA) 727 573-2255
4530 126th Ave N Clearwater (33762) ***(G-1790)***
Modern Settings LLC 800 645-5585
6331 Porter Rd Unit 8 Sarasota (34240) ***(G-16512)***
Modern Silicone Tech Inc 727 873-1805
10601 Us Highway 19 N Pinellas Park (33782) ***(G-14369)***
Modern Tchncal Molding Dev LLC 727 343-2942
2600 72nd St N Saint Petersburg (33710) ***(G-15857)***
Modern Welding Company Fla Inc 407 843-1270
1801 Atlanta Ave Orlando (32806) ***(G-12975)***
Modernizing Medicine 561 880-2998
4850 Network Way Ste 200 Boca Raton (33431) ***(G-629)***
Modernizing Medicine Inc (PA) 561 880-2998
4850 Network Way Ste 200 Boca Raton (33431) ***(G-630)***

Moderno Porcelain Works LLC 954 607-3535
13807 Nw 4th St Sunrise (33325) **(G-17147)**
Modest Logistics LLC 321 314-2825
2295 S Hiawassee Rd Orlando (32835) **(G-12976)**
Modular Life Solutions LLC 904 900-7965
6622 Sthpint Dr S Ste 250 Jacksonville (32216) **(G-6611)**
Modular Molding Intl Inc 727 541-1333
10521 75th St Ste B Seminole (33777) **(G-16754)**
Modular Sign 727 391-2423
8287 138th St Seminole (33776) **(G-16755)**
Modular Thermal Tech LLC (PA) 954 785-1055
1520 Sw 5th Ct Pompano Beach (33069) **(G-14767)**
Modulex America LLC 786 424-0857
14 Ne 1st Ave Ste 707 Miami (33132) **(G-10034)**
Modulex Americas Group Corp 877 808-8049
14 Ne 1st Ave Ste 707 Miami (33132) **(G-10035)**
Moffitt Corporation Inc (PA) 904 241-9944
1351 13th Ave S Ste 130 Jacksonville Beach (32250) **(G-6951)**
Moffitt Fan Corporation 585 768-7010
1351 13th Ave S Ste 130 Jacksonville Beach (32250) **(G-6952)**
Mohamed Lamrana Jalloh 347 305-5556
811 Jefferson Ave Apt 205 Miami Beach (33139) **(G-10695)**
Mohawk Industries Inc 918 272-0184
2500 Sw 32nd Ave Hollywood (33023) **(G-5878)**
Mohawk Manufacturing Company 407 849-0333
963 N Ronald Reagan Blvd Longwood (32750) **(G-8313)**
Mohnark Pharmaceuticals Inc 954 607-4559
5150 Sw 48th Way Ste 604 Davie (33314) **(G-2554)**
Moi, Sarasota *Also called Manasota Optics Inc* **(G-16500)**
Moisttech Corp 941 351-7870
6408 Parkland Dr Ste 104 Sarasota (34243) **(G-16259)**
Mojowax Media Inc 805 550-6013
1100 Yale Ave Bradenton (34207) **(G-1080)**
Mold Be Gone Plus 239 672-5321
14120 Carlotta St Fort Myers (33905) **(G-4536)**
Mold Busters LLC 786 360-6464
12900 Sw 80th St Miami (33183) **(G-10036)**
Mold Control Systems Inc 561 316-5412
2000 Pga Blvd Ste 4440 Palm Beach Gardens (33408) **(G-13610)**
Mold Expert 954 829-3102
2812 Nw 87th Ave Coral Springs (33065) **(G-2286)**
Mold Pros Franchising Inc 239 262-6653
3428 Runaway Ln Ste 106 Naples (34114) **(G-11328)**
Mold R US Inc 954 850-6653
6596 Taft St Hollywood (33024) **(G-5879)**
Mold Remediation Services Inc 904 574-5266
7643 Gate Pkwy 104-57 Jacksonville (32256) **(G-6612)**
Molded Container, Hialeah *Also called Ellis Family Holdings Inc* **(G-5393)**
Molded Moments Art 954 913-0793
1477 Running Oak Ln Royal Palm Beach (33411) **(G-15475)**
Molded Poly Innovations Inc 407 314-1778
2635 S French Ave Sanford (32773) **(G-16090)**
Molding Depot Inc 813 348-4837
3707 W Carmen St Tampa (33609) **(G-17915)**
Molds and Plastic Machinery 305 828-3456
13145 Nw 47th Ave Opa Locka (33054) **(G-12340)**
Molekule Inc 352 871-3803
3802 Spectrum Blvd # 143 Tampa (33612) **(G-17916)**
Molex LLC 727 521-2700
4650 62nd Ave N Pinellas Park (33781) **(G-14370)**
Molex Tampa Bay Operations, Pinellas Park *Also called Molex LLC* **(G-14370)**
Molly & Friends, Gainesville *Also called Munro International Inc* **(G-4968)**
Mollys Marine Service LLC 239 262-2628
895 10th St S Naples (34102) **(G-11329)**
Mollys Suds LLC 678 361-5456
7490 30th Ave N A Saint Petersburg (33710) **(G-15858)**
Moloney Die Company 904 388-3654
5002 Palmer Ave Jacksonville (32210) **(G-6613)**
Moloney Wire Dies, Jacksonville *Also called Moloney Die Company* **(G-6613)**
Molson Coors Brewing Company 305 792-6620
5200 Blue Lagoon Dr # 220 Miami (33126) **(G-10037)**
Momenry Inc 318 668-0888
100 S Ashley Dr Ste 600 Tampa (33602) **(G-17917)**
Momentum Comfort Gear Inc 305 653-5050
470 Ne 185th St Miami (33179) **(G-10038)**
Mon Reve, Sunrise *Also called Entire Select Inc* **(G-17119)**
Monadnock Paper Mills Inc 603 588-8672
1439 Kensington Woods Dr Lutz (33549) **(G-8402)**
Monar Corporation 954 650-1930
9825 W Sample Rd Ste 202 Coral Springs (33065) **(G-2287)**
Monarch Knitting McHy Corp 954 345-2091
9871 Nw 57th Mnr Coral Springs (33076) **(G-2288)**
Monarch Printing & Design, Port Charlotte *Also called Bladorn Investments Inc* **(G-14965)**
Monarch Safety Products Inc 407 442-0269
121 S Orange Ave Ste 1500 Orlando (32801) **(G-12977)**
Monarq Americas LLC 305 632-7448
55 Merrick Way Ste 202 Coral Gables (33134) **(G-2178)**
Monarq Group, Coral Gables *Also called Monarq Americas LLC* **(G-2178)**
Moncada Backhoe Services LLC 786 269-5427
11427 Nw 4th Ter Miami (33172) **(G-10039)**
Mondelez Global LLC 305 774-6273
396 Alhambra Cir Ste 1000 Coral Gables (33134) **(G-2179)**
Money Tree Atm Mfg LLC 850 244-5543
130 Staff Dr Ne Fort Walton Beach (32548) **(G-4817)**
Money Tree Publishing, Crestview *Also called Wrongs Without Wremedies LLC* **(G-2362)**
Monier Lifetile Inc 561 338-8200
135 Nw 20th St Boca Raton (33431) **(G-631)**
Monier Lifetile LLC 561 338-8200
2910 N Federal Hwy Boca Raton (33431) **(G-632)**
Monin Inc 727 461-3033
2100 Range Rd Clearwater (33765) **(G-1791)**
Monin Gourmet Flavorings, Clearwater *Also called Monin Inc* **(G-1791)**
Monison Pallets Inc 904 359-0235
3160 W 45th St Jacksonville (32209) **(G-6614)**
Monison Pallets Inc (PA) 305 637-1600
5420 Nw 37th Ave Miami (33142) **(G-10040)**
Monitor Products Inc 352 544-2620
15400 Flight Path Dr Brooksville (34604) **(G-1254)**
Monkey Shack 850 234-0082
11840 Front Beach Rd A Panama City (32407) **(G-13930)**
Monogram Online, Oakland Park *Also called Deal To Win Inc* **(G-11796)**
Monroe Cable LLC 941 429-8484
2529 Commerce Pkwy North Port (34289) **(G-11744)**
Monroe Concrete Products 305 296-5606
Mile Mark 8 5 # 85 Key West (33040) **(G-7197)**
Monroy Aerospace 954 344-4936
10908 Nw 17th Mnr Coral Springs (33071) **(G-2289)**
Monster Transmission & Prfmce, Brooksville *Also called Avalanche Corporation* **(G-1213)**
Mont Krest Stone Inc (PA) 727 209-0864
6795 114th Ave Largo (33773) **(G-8013)**
Montague Enterprises Inc 239 631-5292
1004 Collier Center Way # 206 Naples (34110) **(G-11330)**
Montalvos Raceway LLC 239 289-6931
280 35th Ave Ne Naples (34120) **(G-11331)**
Montedana Fuels 305 887-6754
2090 Palm Ave Hialeah (33010) **(G-5525)**
Monteocha Coatings Inc 352 367-3136
2607 Ne 56th Ter Gainesville (32609) **(G-4965)**
Montesino International Corp 954 767-6185
1816 N Dixie Hwy Fort Lauderdale (33305) **(G-4124)**
Montevista Greetings LLC 305 888-9797
545 W 17th St Hialeah (33010) **(G-5526)**
Montgomery Industries Intl 904 355-4055
2017 Thelma St Jacksonville (32206) **(G-6615)**
Monthly Media, Largo *Also called Village Scribe Printing Co* **(G-8074)**
Monticello Milling Co Inc 850 997-5521
500 S Jefferson St Monticello (32344) **(G-11079)**
Monticello News 850 997-3568
180 W Washington St Monticello (32344) **(G-11080)**
Montres Corum Usa LLC 954 279-1220
14050 Nw 14th St Ste 110 Sunrise (33323) **(G-17148)**
Monty Sanitation, Naples *Also called Rmmj Inc* **(G-11386)**
Monty Sanitation Inc 239 597-2486
5545 Shirley St Naples (34109) **(G-11332)**
Monument Pharmacy, Jacksonville *Also called Shriji Swami LLC* **(G-6767)**
Monumental Air Inc 954 383-9507
4333 Nw 64th Ave Coral Springs (33067) **(G-2290)**
Monumental Enterprises Inc 305 803-8493
7958 Pines Blvd Ste 242 Pembroke Pines (33024) **(G-14048)**
Monumental Fabrication of Amer 850 227-9500
950 W Rutherford St Port Saint Joe (32456) **(G-15081)**
Monumental Resolutions Inc 407 973-3577
1253 Hancock Cir Saint Cloud (34769) **(G-15662)**
Moody Construction Svcs Inc 941 776-1542
12450 County Road 39 Duette (34219) **(G-3562)**
Moog Inc 321 435-8722
4300 Fortune Pl Ste A West Melbourne (32904) **(G-18777)**
Moog Inc 716 652-2000
9000 Sheridan St Ste 168 Pembroke Pines (33024) **(G-14049)**
Moog-Fts 407 264-0611
7455 Emerald Dunes Dr # 2 Orlando (32822) **(G-12978)**
Moon Express Inc 650 241-8577
100 Space Port Way Cape Canaveral (32920) **(G-1365)**
Moonex, Cape Canaveral *Also called Moon Express Inc* **(G-1365)**
Moore & Bode Group LLC 786 615-9389
2221 Se 27th Dr Homestead (33035) **(G-5984)**
Moore Computer Consultants, Miramar *Also called Digital Compositing Systems* **(G-10984)**
Moore Solutions Inc 772 337-4005
1680 Se Lyngate Dr # 202 Port St Lucie (34952) **(G-15175)**
Moores Mar of Palm Beaches Inc 561 841-2235
1410 Avenue E Riviera Beach (33404) **(G-15349)**
Mooring Yacht Brokerage, Dania *Also called Mariner International Trvl Inc* **(G-2451)**
Moose Tracts Inc 407 491-1412
2325 Ohio Dr Orlando (32803) **(G-12979)**
MOR Printing Inc 954 377-1197
610 Sw 12th Ave Pompano Beach (33069) **(G-14768)**
Mor Printing & Envelopes, Pompano Beach *Also called MOR Printing Inc* **(G-14768)**

ALPHABETIC

Mor Sports LLC...239 671-5759
1242 Sw Pine Island Rd Cape Coral (33991) *(G-1449)*
Moralmar Kitchen Cabinets...305 819-8402
3130 W 15th Ave Hialeah (33012) *(G-5527)*
Moran Transport...305 824-3366
9829 Nw 129th Ter Hialeah (33018) *(G-5528)*
Moran Woodworking LLC...941 600-8842
275 Herons Run Dr Apt 707 Sarasota (34232) *(G-16513)*
Morcent Import Export Inc...727 442-9735
1702 Indian Rocks Rd Belleair (33756) *(G-360)*
More Woodturning Magazine...508 838-1933
12728 Fontana Loop Bradenton (34211) *(G-1081)*
Morelia Paletas Gourmet, Coral Gables *Also called Lefab Commercial LLC (G-2172)*
Morey Machining & Mfg Inc...239 693-8699
9350 Workmen Way Fort Myers (33905) *(G-4537)*
Morgan Cabinet Restylers LLC...813 931-4663
15915 N Florida Ave Lutz (33549) *(G-8403)*
Morgan Technical Services...772 466-5757
5512 Silver Oak Dr Fort Pierce (34982) *(G-4719)*
Morganelli & Associates Inc...386 738-3669
1401 Saratoga St Deland (32724) *(G-2998)*
Morgannas Alchemy LLC...727 505-8376
10347 Palladio Dr New Port Richey (34655) *(G-11502)*
Morgans Elc Mtr & Pump Svc, Cocoa Beach *Also called Morgans Elc Mtr & Pump Svc (G-2066)*
Morgans Elc Mtr & Pump Svc...321 960-2209
157 N Orlando Ave Cocoa Beach (32931) *(G-2066)*
Mori Lee LLC (PA)...954 418-6165
3155 Sw 10th St Ste 6a1 Deerfield Beach (33442) *(G-2876)*
Morin Corp...386 626-6789
1975 Eidson Dr Deland (32724) *(G-2999)*
Morlee Lampshade Co Inc...305 500-9310
6915 Nw 43rd St Miami (33166) *(G-10041)*
Morning Glory Lawn Maintenance...407 376-5833
4750 Nantucket Ln Orlando (32808) *(G-12980)*
Morning Star Industries Inc...800 440-6050
630 Ne Jensen Beach Blvd Jensen Beach (34957) *(G-6971)*
Morning Star of Sarasota Inc...941 371-0392
1985 Cattlemen Rd Unit A Sarasota (34232) *(G-16514)*
Morning Star Personalized AP...772 569-8412
621 2nd Ln Vero Beach (32962) *(G-18644)*
Moroccan Khlii Inc...813 699-0096
808 N Macdill Ave Tampa (33609) *(G-17918)*
Morris Mica Cabinets Inc...954 979-6838
1920 Nw 22nd Ct Pompano Beach (33069) *(G-14769)*
Morris Valves Inc...305 477-6525
5590 Nw 84th Ave Ste C Doral (33166) *(G-3441)*
Morris Visitor Publications...407 423-0618
801 N Magnolia Ave # 201 Orlando (32803) *(G-12981)*
Morrison Meat Packers, Miami *Also called El Toro Meat Packing Corp (G-9509)*
Morrissy & Co...850 934-4243
204 Fairpoint Dr Gulf Breeze (32561) *(G-5121)*
Morrow Technologies Corp...727 531-4000
12000 28th St N Fl 1 Saint Petersburg (33716) *(G-15859)*
Morse Enterprises Limited Inc...407 682-6500
400 N Ny Ave Ste 200 Miami (33129) *(G-10042)*
Morten Enterprises Inc (PA)...727 531-8957
12350 Us Highway 19 N Clearwater (33764) *(G-1792)*
Morton Plant Mease Health Care...727 462-7052
430 Pinellas St Clearwater (33756) *(G-1793)*
Mos Holdings Inc...763 577-2700
5000 Old Highway 37 Mulberry (33860) *(G-11131)*
Mosaic...863 860-1328
5810 Deer Flag Dr Lakeland (33811) *(G-7754)*
Mosaic Company (PA)...813 775-4200
101 E Kennedy Blvd # 2500 Tampa (33602) *(G-17919)*
Mosaic Crop Nutrition LLC...813 500-6800
13830 Circa Crossing Dr Lithia (33547) *(G-8220)*
Mosaic Fertilizer LLC (HQ)...813 500-6300
13830 Circa Crossing Dr Lithia (33547) *(G-8221)*
Mosaics Liquidation Co Inc...772 468-8453
901 S 3rd St Fort Pierce (34950) *(G-4720)*
Mosch International Corp...786 616-9108
6400 Nw 72nd Ave Miami (33166) *(G-10043)*
Mosco Inc...561 588-3880
2200 4th Ave N Ste 10 Lake Worth Beach (33461) *(G-7617)*
Moser Automotive...561 881-5665
2391 President Barack Oba Riviera Beach (33404) *(G-15350)*
Mossberg Group Inc...386 274-5882
1870 Mason Ave Daytona Beach (32117) *(G-2689)*
Most Valuable Pavers...239 590-5217
224 Sw 22nd Pl Cape Coral (33991) *(G-1450)*
Motaz Inc...239 334-7699
2441 Hanson St Fort Myers (33901) *(G-4538)*
Mother Earth Stone LLC...407 878-2854
4035 Maronda Way Sanford (32771) *(G-16091)*
Mother Kombucha LLC...727 767-0408
4360 28th St N Saint Petersburg (33714) *(G-15860)*
Motherkin Cleaners, Oviedo *Also called Japan Fabricare Inc (G-13441)*
Motion Industries Inc...727 536-5521
6480 126th Ave Largo (33773) *(G-8014)*
Motion Machining LLC...321 693-0999
1568 Maeve Cir Melbourne (32904) *(G-8891)*
Motionvibe Innovations LLC...202 285-0235
4031 Caddie Dr E Bradenton (34203) *(G-1082)*
Motley Enterprises Inc...703 966-3997
701 Market St Ste 111 Saint Augustine (32095) *(G-15571)*
Motor City Classics Inc...954 473-2201
12717 W Sunrise Blvd Sunrise (33323) *(G-17149)*
Motor Coach Inds Intl Inc...407 246-1414
1155 Elboc Way Winter Garden (34787) *(G-19277)*
Motor Magnetics Inc...727 873-3180
2801 72nd St N Saint Petersburg (33710) *(G-15861)*
Motor Protection Electronics...407 299-3825
2464 Vulcan Rd Apopka (32703) *(G-163)*
Motor Service Group LLC...305 592-2440
6600 Nw 77th Ct Miami (33166) *(G-10044)*
Motor Service Inc...305 592-2440
6600 Nw 77th Ct Miami (33166) *(G-10045)*
Motorola Solutions...239 939-7717
13891 Jetport Loop Ste 9 Fort Myers (33913) *(G-4539)*
Motorola Solutions Inc...850 243-4426
73 Eglin Pkwy Ne Unit 302 Fort Walton Beach (32548) *(G-4818)*
Motorola Solutions Inc...954 723-5000
8000 W Sunrise Blvd Plantation (33322) *(G-14535)*
Motorola Solutions Inc...407 562-4000
1064 Greenwood Blvd # 400 Lake Mary (32746) *(G-7437)*
Motorola Solutions Inc...561 369-7164
2009 Corporate Dr Boynton Beach (33426) *(G-933)*
Motorola Solutions Inc...850 651-1725
60 2nd St Shalimar (32579) *(G-16776)*
Motorola Solutions Center...863 665-5105
2352 Old Combee Rd # 101 Lakeland (33805) *(G-7755)*
Motors For Less, Pembroke Pines *Also called Ventilex Inc (G-14070)*
Motors Pumps and Accessories...305 883-3181
7530 Nw 77th St Medley (33166) *(G-8692)*
Motorsport Games Inc (HQ)...305 507-8799
5972 Ne 4th Ave Miami (33137) *(G-10046)*
Motorsport Marketing Inc...386 239-0523
915 Ridgewood Ave Holly Hill (32117) *(G-5760)*
Motortronics, Clearwater *Also called Phasetronics Inc (G-1830)*
Motus Gi LLC...954 541-8000
1301 E Broward Blvd # 31 Fort Lauderdale (33301) *(G-4125)*
Motus GI Holdings Inc (PA)...954 541-8000
1301 E Broward Blvd Fl 3 Fort Lauderdale (33301) *(G-4126)*
Motus Gi, Inc., Fort Lauderdale *Also called Motus Gi LLC (G-4125)*
Moulton Publications Inc...772 234-8871
956 20th St Ste 101 Vero Beach (32960) *(G-18645)*
Mounted Memories Inc...866 236-2541
15701 Sw 29th St Miramar (33027) *(G-11018)*
Moyo...352 208-2770
6027 Sw 54th St Ste 201 Ocala (34474) *(G-12002)*
Mp 93 Screen Print and EMB LLC...407 592-3657
3330 Vineland Rd Ste C Orlando (32811) *(G-12982)*
Mpact Sales Solutions...630 669-5937
622 Largovista Dr Oakland (34787) *(G-11770)*
Mpalacios Blinds Inc...239 601-4864
810 Hillside St Lehigh Acres (33936) *(G-8200)*
Mpc Containment Systems LLC (HQ)...773 927-4121
880 N Spring Garden Ave Deland (32720) *(G-3000)*
Mpc Group LLC (PA)...773 927-4120
880 N Spring Garden Ave Deland (32720) *(G-3001)*
MPH Industries Inc...352 372-9533
2406 Ne 19th Dr Gainesville (32609) *(G-4966)*
Mpp Coatings Inc...386 334-4484
3837 Long Grove Ln Port Orange (32129) *(G-15025)*
Mpr Audio System LLC...305 988-8524
3465 Nw 71st Ter Miami (33147) *(G-10047)*
Mr Americas 2 LLC...407 217-2282
15771 State Road 535 K Orlando (32821) *(G-12983)*
Mr Bills Fine Foods...727 581-9850
1115 Ponce De Leon Blvd Clearwater (33756) *(G-1794)*
Mr Bones Stump Grinding...941 927-0790
5590 Swift Rd Sarasota (34231) *(G-16515)*
Mr Cool Waters Inc (PA)...305 234-6311
12009 Sw 129th Ct Unit 5 Miami (33186) *(G-10048)*
Mr Foamy, Fort Myers *Also called Mr Foamy Southwest Fl LLC (G-4540)*
Mr Foamy Southwest Fl LLC...239 461-3110
3411 Hanson St Unit A Fort Myers (33916) *(G-4540)*
Mr Goodwood Inc...941 961-4478
4643 Meadowview Cir Sarasota (34233) *(G-16516)*
Mr GS Foods...352 799-1806
15402 Aviation Loop Dr Brooksville (34604) *(G-1255)*
Mr Gummy Vitamins LLC...855 674-8669
12845 Nw 45th Ave Opa Locka (33054) *(G-12341)*
Mr Gutter Cutter Inc...772 286-7780
3102 Se Dixie Hwy Stuart (34997) *(G-16978)*
Mr Mica Wood Inc...561 278-5821
1300 Sw 10th St Ste 3 Delray Beach (33444) *(G-3109)*

Mr Rach, Coral Springs *Also called Foot Function Lab Inc* ***(G-2246)***
Mr Real Deal barbque LLC...561 271-8749
1050 Dotterel Rd Apt 200 Delray Beach (33444) ***(G-3110)***
Mr Shower Door, Fort Myers *Also called KDD Inc* ***(G-4509)***
Mr Tango Sausages, Miami *Also called Special Americas Bbq Inc* ***(G-10399)***
Mr Winter Inc...800 327-3371
8800 Nw 77th Ct Medley (33166) ***(G-8693)***
Mri Depot Inc...407 696-9822
1075 Fla Cntl Pkwy Ste 20 Longwood (32750) ***(G-8314)***
Mri Specialists...561 369-2144
1800 W Woolbright Rd # 100 Boynton Beach (33426) ***(G-934)***
Mrkt Deux...305 603-9682
140 Ne 39th St Miami (33137) ***(G-10049)***
Mrl Industries, Keystone Heights *Also called Manufacturers Inv Group LLC* ***(G-7210)***
MRM Creative LLC...386 218-5940
1209 Saxon Blvd Ste 4 Orange City (32763) ***(G-12376)***
Mrn Biologics LLC...508 989-6090
3732 Nw 126th Ave Coral Springs (33065) ***(G-2291)***
Mro Aerospace Inc...727 546-4820
10530 72nd St Ste 701 Largo (33777) ***(G-8015)***
Mrs Traylors Plntn Style Foods, Panama City *Also called Charles Bryant Enterprises* ***(G-13879)***
Mrs. Pasta, Dania Beach *Also called Massimo & Umberto Inc* ***(G-2469)***
Ms Mobile Wldg & Fabrication...904 591-1488
1929 Logging Ln Jacksonville (32221) ***(G-6616)***
Ms Software Inc...813 258-1735
5101 Vinson Dr Tampa (33610) ***(G-17920)***
Ms Welding...941 629-2597
2222 Tea St Port Charlotte (33948) ***(G-14990)***
MSA Aircraft Products...772 562-2243
3106 Industrial Avenue 3 Fort Pierce (34946) ***(G-4721)***
MSC Metal Fabrication...954 344-8343
7600 Wiles Rd Ste B Coral Springs (33067) ***(G-2292)***
Msh Brick Pavers Inc...941 822-6472
5640 Fountain Lake Cir Bradenton (34207) ***(G-1083)***
Msm Outdoors, Fernandina Beach *Also called Sws Services Inc* ***(G-3748)***
MSP Industries LLC...727 443-5764
1500 N Belcher Rd Clearwater (33765) ***(G-1795)***
Msquared Publishing...786 399-0607
3200 Mary St Miami (33133) ***(G-10050)***
Mt Distributors LLC...954 802-2161
7818 Nw 44th St Lauderhill (33351) ***(G-8116)***
Mt-Propeller Usa Inc...386 736-7762
1180 Airport Terminal Dr Deland (32724) ***(G-3002)***
Mtc Engineering LLC...321 636-9480
428 Shearer Blvd Cocoa (32922) ***(G-2037)***
Mte Inc...352 371-3898
8930 Nw 13th St Gainesville (32653) ***(G-4967)***
Mtec Trailer Supply...813 659-1647
3804 Sydney Rd Plant City (33566) ***(G-14449)***
MTI Aviation Inc...305 817-4244
13150 Nw 45th Ave Opa Locka (33054) ***(G-12342)***
Mtm, Pensacola *Also called Machine Tool Masters Inc* ***(G-14199)***
MTM&d, Saint Petersburg *Also called Modern Tchncal Molding Dev LLC* ***(G-15857)***
Mtn Government Services Inc...954 538-4000
3044 N Commerce Pkwy Miramar (33025) ***(G-11019)***
Mtng Usa Corp...305 670-0979
11334 Sw 157th Pl Miami (33196) ***(G-10051)***
Mtronpti, Orlando *Also called Piezo Technology Inc* ***(G-13067)***
MTS Medication Tech Inc (HQ)...727 576-6311
2003 Gandy Blvd N Ste 800 Saint Petersburg (33702) ***(G-15862)***
MTS Packaging System Inc...727 812-2830
12920 Automobile Blvd Clearwater (33762) ***(G-1796)***
MTS Packaging Systems Inc (PA)...727 576-6311
2003 Gandy Blvd N Ste 800 Saint Petersburg (33702) ***(G-15863)***
MTS Sales & Marketing Inc...727 812-2830
12920 Automobile Blvd Clearwater (33762) ***(G-1797)***
Mtservicer LLC...305 200-1254
8140 Nw 155th St Miami Lakes (33016) ***(G-10824)***
Muchochos Saw Mill & Pallets...786 899-0535
356 Palmetto Dr A Miami Springs (33166) ***(G-10895)***
Muelby Construction Services...561 376-7614
378 Northlake Blvd North Palm Beach (33408) ***(G-11723)***
Mulberry Railcar, Mulberry *Also called Southstern Rail Svcs Mlbrry FL* ***(G-11138)***
Mulch & Stone Emporium Inc...352 237-7870
7699 Sw Highway 200 Ocala (34476) ***(G-12003)***
Muller Fire Protection Inc...305 636-9780
2311 Sw 98th Pl Miami (33165) ***(G-10052)***
Multi Contact USA...561 738-5637
3814 Lace Vine Ln Boynton Beach (33436) ***(G-935)***
Multi Parts Supply Usa Inc...561 748-1515
1649 Park Ln S Jupiter (33458) ***(G-7078)***
Multi Soft II Inc...305 579-8000
4400 Biscayne Blvd Fl 10 Miami (33137) ***(G-10053)***
Multi-Commercial Services Corp...305 235-1373
15420 Sw 136th St Unit 26 Miami (33196) ***(G-10054)***
Multi-Flex LLC...941 360-6500
8046 36th Street Cir E Sarasota (34243) ***(G-16260)***
Multicolor Printing Inc...772 287-1676
1249 Se Dixie Cutoff Rd Stuart (34994) ***(G-16979)***
Multicore Photonics Inc...407 325-7800
5832 N Dean Rd Orlando (32817) ***(G-12984)***
Multicore Photonics Inc...407 325-7800
319 N Crystal Lake Dr Orlando (32803) ***(G-12985)***
Multicore Technologies LLC...407 325-7800
319 N Crystal Lake Dr Orlando (32803) ***(G-12986)***
Multifix Cbd LLC...786 487-0792
3740 E 10th Ct Hialeah (33013) ***(G-5529)***
Multihull Technologies Inc...305 296-2773
6811 Shrimp Rd Key West (33040) ***(G-7198)***
Multimedia Effects Inc...800 367-3054
9715 W Broward Blvd Ste 3 Plantation (33324) ***(G-14536)***
Multiparts, Jupiter *Also called Multi Parts Supply Usa Inc* ***(G-7078)***
Multitrode Inc...561 737-1210
6560 E Rogers Cir Boca Raton (33487) ***(G-633)***
Mumford Micro Mch Works LLC...814 720-7291
1882 Porter Lake Dr # 103 Sarasota (34240) ***(G-16517)***
Mundi Intl Trading Corp...305 205-0062
1971 Landing Way Weston (33326) ***(G-19150)***
Mundy Kitchen Cabinet Inc...786 298-0131
9921 Nw 80th Ave Unit 1p Miami Lakes (33016) ***(G-10825)***
Municipal Code Corporation (HQ)...850 576-3171
1700 Capital Cir Sw Tallahassee (32310) ***(G-17304)***
Municipal Lighting Systems Inc (PA)...305 666-4210
7035 Sw 47th St Ste A Miami (33155) ***(G-10055)***
Municipal Supply & Sign, Naples *Also called Annat Inc* ***(G-11163)***
Munro International Inc...352 337-1535
1030 Se 4th St Gainesville (32601) ***(G-4968)***
Murphy Bed USA Inc (PA)...954 493-9001
4330 N Federal Hwy Fort Lauderdale (33308) ***(G-4127)***
Murray Products, Fort Lauderdale *Also called Frank Murray & Sons Inc* ***(G-4012)***
Murse Properties LLC...941 966-3380
6650 S Tammy Amy Trl Sarasota (34231) ***(G-16518)***
Muscle Fx LLC...305 514-0061
2221 Ne 164th St Ste 1267 North Miami Beach (33160) ***(G-11693)***
Muscle Mixes Inc...407 872-7576
1617 Hillcrest St Orlando (32803) ***(G-12987)***
Muse Gelato Inc...407 363-1443
7362 Futures Dr Ste 20 Orlando (32819) ***(G-12988)***
Mustang Vacuum Systems Inc...941 377-1440
7135 16th St E Ste 115 Sarasota (34243) ***(G-16261)***
Mutual Industries North Inc...239 332-2400
2940 Walpear St Unit 1 Fort Myers (33916) ***(G-4541)***
Muv, Miami *Also called Wpp Group Usa Inc* ***(G-10623)***
Mvp Group LLC...786 600-4687
2175 Ne 120th St North Miami (33181) ***(G-11647)***
Mvr Copiadoras Digitales...786 366-1842
9649 Nw 33rd St Doral (33172) ***(G-3442)***
Mvs International Inc...954 727-3383
702 Willow Bend Rd Weston (33327) ***(G-19151)***
Mwg Company Inc...305 232-7344
10665 Sw 185th Ter Cutler Bay (33157) ***(G-2405)***
Mwi Corporation (PA)...954 426-1500
33 Nw 2nd St Deerfield Beach (33441) ***(G-2877)***
Mwi Corporation...239 337-4747
4945 Kim Ln Fort Myers (33905) ***(G-4542)***
Mwi Pumps, Deerfield Beach *Also called Mwi Corporation* ***(G-2877)***
Mwr Sign Enterprises Inc...954 914-2709
9909 Pines Blvd Pembroke Pines (33024) ***(G-14050)***
Mws Drapery Inc...305 794-3811
496 W 18th St Hialeah (33010) ***(G-5530)***
Mxn Inc...813 654-3173
10120 Woodberry Rd Tampa (33619) ***(G-17921)***
My Blank Canvas...386 747-5254
970 N Spring Garden Ave Deland (32720) ***(G-3003)***
My Clone Solution...813 442-9925
4532 W Kennedy Blvd 183 Tampa (33609) ***(G-17922)***
My Custom Cart LLC...904 214-3723
2581 Blanding Blvd Middleburg (32068) ***(G-10909)***
My Drone Services, Indialantic *Also called Viper Drones LLC* ***(G-6062)***
My Familys Seasonings LLC...863 698-7968
15301 Roosevelt Blvd # 303 Clearwater (33760) ***(G-1798)***
My Favorite Things, Eustis *Also called Mft Stamps* ***(G-3713)***
My Focus Inc...305 826-4480
5395 Nw 165th St Ste 102 Miami Lakes (33014) ***(G-10826)***
My Glam Choice Inc...786 586-7927
6910 Nw 84th Ave Miami (33166) ***(G-10056)***
My Passion On A Plate LLC...954 857-6382
7901 Southgate Blvd C3 North Lauderdale (33068) ***(G-11618)***
My Print Shop, Deerfield Beach *Also called Accuprint Corporation* ***(G-2762)***
My Print Shop Inc...954 973-9369
1061 Sw 30th Ave Deerfield Beach (33442) ***(G-2878)***
My Reviewers LLC...813 404-9734
3802 Spectrum Blvd 8 Tampa (33612) ***(G-17923)***
My Vision Express, Weston *Also called Insight Software LLC* ***(G-19142)***
My Wild Life Press LLC...515 203-9728
2155 S Ocean Blvd Apt 1 Delray Beach (33483) ***(G-3111)***

ALPHABETIC

Mydor Industries Inc...954 927-1140
470 Sw 9th St Dania (33004) ***(G-2453)***
Myers Engineering Intl Inc...954 975-2712
5425 Nw 24th St Ste 202 Margate (33063) ***(G-8558)***
Myers Printing Inc...813 237-0288
5601 N Florida Ave Tampa (33604) ***(G-17924)***
Mymd Pharmaceuticals Inc...813 864-2566
324 S Hyde Park Ave # 350 Tampa (33606) ***(G-17925)***
Myreviewers, Tampa *Also called My Reviewers LLC* ***(G-17923)***
Myriam Interiors Inc (PA)...305 626-9898
16301 Nw 49th Ave Hialeah (33014) ***(G-5531)***
Myrlen Inc...800 662-4762
3814 Nw 126th Ave Coral Springs (33065) ***(G-2293)***
Mysky Aircraft Inc...386 492-6908
205 Cessna Blvd Ste 1 Port Orange (32128) ***(G-15026)***
Mytek Industries...727 536-7891
11910 62nd St Largo (33773) ***(G-8016)***
Myton Industries Inc...954 989-0113
1981 S Park Rd Hallandale (33009) ***(G-5159)***
Mz Jazzy Accezzoriez...239 275-6975
3598 Fowler St Fort Myers (33901) ***(G-4543)***
N & H Construction Inc...904 282-2224
1708 Nolan Rd Middleburg (32068) ***(G-10910)***
N & N Investment Corporation...954 590-3800
3001 Nw 16th Ter Pompano Beach (33064) ***(G-14770)***
N A Comandulli LLC...941 870-2878
6935 15th St E Units105 Sarasota (34243) ***(G-16262)***
N A Whittenburg, Sarasota *Also called Design Works By Tech Pdts Inc* ***(G-16410)***
N C A Manufacturing Inc...727 441-2651
1985 Carroll St Clearwater (33765) ***(G-1799)***
N E D LLC...610 442-1017
902 Clint Moore Rd # 206 Boca Raton (33487) ***(G-634)***
N Ear Pro, Tampa *Also called N-Ear Pro Inc* ***(G-17926)***
N Media Group LLC (PA)...239 594-1322
4500 Executive Dr Ste 320 Naples (34119) ***(G-11333)***
N R I, Riviera Beach *Also called Neptune Research Inc* ***(G-15352)***
N V Texpack Group...305 358-9696
3225 Aviation Ave Ste 303 Miami (33133) ***(G-10057)***
N-Ear Pro Inc...877 290-4599
4821 N Grady Ave Tampa (33614) ***(G-17926)***
N-Viro Inc...904 781-4707
7259 Old Plank Rd Jacksonville (32254) ***(G-6617)***
N23d Services LLC...754 217-3362
20974 Sheridan St Fort Lauderdale (33332) ***(G-4128)***
N2w Software Inc...561 225-2483
1555 Palm Beach Lakes Blv West Palm Beach (33401) ***(G-18955)***
N3xt L3vel 2 Point 0 LLC...863 777-3778
1248 E Hillsborough Ave Tampa (33604) ***(G-17927)***
N3xt Up Exotic LLC...863 777-3778
1248 E Hillsborough Ave Tampa (33604) ***(G-17928)***
Nabi...561 989-5800
5800 Pk Of Commerce Blvd Boca Raton (33487) ***(G-635)***
Nac USA Corporation...800 396-0149
9000 Sw 137th Ave Miami (33186) ***(G-10058)***
Nadco Tapes & Labels Inc...941 751-6693
2240 72nd Ter E Sarasota (34243) ***(G-16263)***
Nahuel Trading Corp...305 999-9944
17838 State Road 9 Miami (33162) ***(G-10059)***
Nai Print Solutions LLC...850 637-1260
457 Strandview Dr Pensacola (32534) ***(G-14210)***
Naia Brick Pavers Inc...727 638-4734
8216 43rd Way N Pinellas Park (33781) ***(G-14371)***
Naiad Dynamics Us Inc...954 797-7566
3750 Hacienda Blvd Ste A Davie (33314) ***(G-2555)***
Nailboutique of WPB LLC...954 756-2699
1225 N Military Trl 4d West Palm Beach (33409) ***(G-18956)***
Nakasawa Mining and Energy LLC...305 302-4980
175 Sw 7th St Ste 1812 Miami (33130) ***(G-10060)***
Naked Whey Inc...352 246-7294
382 Ne 191st St Miami (33179) ***(G-10061)***
Namro Industries Inc...561 704-8063
4336 Juniper Ter Boynton Beach (33436) ***(G-936)***
Nana Foods Inc...407 363-7183
5219 Timberview Ter Orlando (32819) ***(G-12989)***
Nanas Original Stromboli Inc...954 771-6262
5421 Ne 14th Ave Fort Lauderdale (33334) ***(G-4129)***
Nani Sweets LLC (PA)...305 793-1077
8140 W 30th Ct Hialeah (33018) ***(G-5532)***
Nanni Usa LLC...305 450-4853
306 Alcazar Ave Coral Gables (33134) ***(G-2180)***
Nano Activated Coatings Inc...727 437-1099
507 S Prospect Ave Clearwater (33756) ***(G-1800)***
Nano Dimension 3d, Sunrise *Also called Nano Dimension USA Inc* ***(G-17150)***
Nano Dimension USA Inc...650 209-2866
13798 Nw 4th St Ste 315 Sunrise (33325) ***(G-17150)***
Nano Liquitec LLC...813 447-1742
5627 Terrain De Golf Dr Lutz (33558) ***(G-8404)***
Nano Safe Coatings Inc...561 747-5758
5500 Military Trl Ste 22 Jupiter (33458) ***(G-7079)***
Nanobiotech Pharma Inc...866 568-0178
5944 Coral Ridge Dr Coral Springs (33076) ***(G-2294)***
Nanotechnovation Corporation...352 732-3244
2811 Ne 14th St Ocala (34470) ***(G-12004)***
Nap Impex LLC...954 272-8453
622 Sw 158th Ter Pembroke Pines (33027) ***(G-14051)***
Nap Impex LLC...954 589-2861
18592 Sw 55th St Miramar (33029) ***(G-11020)***
Naple Daily News, The, Naples *Also called Bonita Daily News* ***(G-11191)***
Naples Armature Works, Naples *Also called Robert E Weissenborn Sr* ***(G-11387)***
Naples C&D Recycling Facility, Naples *Also called Yahl Mulching & Recycling Inc* ***(G-11462)***
Naples Hang Gliding, Clewiston *Also called Miami Hang Gliding Corp* ***(G-1984)***
Naples Hma LLC...239 390-2174
24231 Walden Center Dr # 201 Estero (34134) ***(G-3692)***
Naples Hotrods & Prfmce LLC...239 653-9076
6122 Janes Ln Naples (34109) ***(G-11334)***
Naples Illustrated, Naples *Also called Palm Beach Media Group Inc* ***(G-11355)***
Naples Illustrated, West Palm Beach *Also called Palm Beach Liquidation Company* ***(G-18984)***
Naples Illustrated...239 434-6966
3066 Tamiami Trl Mre 10 Moore Ste 102 Naples (34102) ***(G-11335)***
Naples Iron Works Inc...239 649-7265
4551 Arnold Ave Naples (34104) ***(G-11336)***
Naples Powder Coating LLC...239 352-3500
3960 Domestic Ave Ste A Naples (34104) ***(G-11337)***
Naples Printing Inc...239 643-2442
1100 Coml Blvd Ste 114 Naples (34104) ***(G-11338)***
Naples Stone Consulting LLC...239 325-8653
1881 Trade Center Way Naples (34109) ***(G-11339)***
Naples Team Sports Center, Naples *Also called Synergy Sports LLC* ***(G-11432)***
Naples Woodworks Inc...239 287-1632
6080 Golden Oaks Ln Naples (34119) ***(G-11340)***
Nardis Enterprises LLC...954 529-0691
2831 Ne 56th Ct Fort Lauderdale (33308) ***(G-4130)***
Naroh Manufacturing LLC...321 806-4875
185 Gus Hipp Blvd Rockledge (32955) ***(G-15437)***
Narramore Machine Shop LLC...863 667-1004
2770 Industrial Park Dr Lakeland (33801) ***(G-7756)***
Nasco Industries Inc...954 733-8665
3541 Nw 53rd St Fort Lauderdale (33309) ***(G-4131)***
Nassau Printing & Off Sup Inc...904 879-2305
542028 Us Highway 1 Callahan (32011) ***(G-1327)***
Nasty Choppers Inc...941 234-7743
5010 Linda St Venice (34293) ***(G-18563)***
Natalia Likhacheva, Palmetto *Also called 365 Sun LLC* ***(G-13781)***
Natalies Orchid Island Juice, Fort Pierce *Also called Orchid Island Juice Co Inc* ***(G-4727)***
Nation Signs...386 466-0043
162 Sw Spencer Ct Ste 101 Lake City (32024) ***(G-7368)***
National Aerospace Group Inc...817 226-0315
928 36th Ct Sw Vero Beach (32968) ***(G-18646)***
National Assemblers Inc...877 915-5505
6586 Hypoluxo Rd Ste 145 Lake Worth (33467) ***(G-7574)***
National Bedding Company LLC...561 840-8491
3774 Interstate Park Rd N Riviera Beach (33404) ***(G-15351)***
National Beverage Corp (PA)...954 581-0922
8100 Sw 10th St Ste 4000 Plantation (33324) ***(G-14537)***
National Beverage Corp...352 357-7130
2221 W Highway 44 Eustis (32726) ***(G-3715)***
National Bidet Corp...786 325-6593
7150 Indian Creek Dr # 404 Miami Beach (33141) ***(G-10696)***
National Carburetors Inc...904 636-9400
2461 Rolac Rd Jacksonville (32207) ***(G-6618)***
National Chemical Sply...800 515-9938
4151 Sw 47th Ave Davie (33314) ***(G-2556)***
National Chemical Supply Inc...954 683-1645
6930 Sw 16th St Plantation (33317) ***(G-14538)***
National Custom Insignia...813 781-8806
1676 Arabian Ln Palm Harbor (34685) ***(G-13747)***
National Custom Insignia Inc...813 313-2561
8875 Hdden Rver Pkwy Ste Tampa (33637) ***(G-17929)***
National Custom Table Pads...239 596-6805
6030 English Oaks Ln Naples (34119) ***(G-11341)***
National Cylinder Head Exchang...813 870-6340
4408 N Thatcher Ave Tampa (33614) ***(G-17930)***
National Cylinder Services LLC (PA)...407 299-8454
4601 Dardanelle Dr Orlando (32808) ***(G-12990)***
National Diesel Engine Inc...810 516-6855
253 S 78th St Tampa (33619) ***(G-17931)***
National Direct Signs...561 320-2102
777 S Flagler Dr West Palm Beach (33401) ***(G-18957)***
National Health Alliance LLC...727 504-3915
500 N West Shore Blvd # 640 Tampa (33609) ***(G-17932)***
National Indexing Systems, Orlando *Also called Nis Print Inc* ***(G-13004)***
National Intelligence Academy, Deerfield Beach *Also called Interntnal Srvillance Tech Inc* ***(G-2847)***
National Jewellers, Hallandale Beach *Also called Finger Mate Inc* ***(G-5184)***
National Molding LLC (PA)...305 823-5440
14427 Nw 60th Ave Miami Lakes (33014) ***(G-10827)***

National Multiple Listing Inc (PA)...954 772-8880
6511 Bay Club Dr Apt 2 Fort Lauderdale (33308) *(G-4132)*
National Newspaper Placem...866 404-5913
766 N Sun Dr Ste 2090 Lake Mary (32746) *(G-7438)*
National Pallets...305 324-1021
2160 Nw 8th Ave Miami (33127) *(G-10062)*
National Pipe Welding Inc...904 588-2589
9473 Smokey Rd Glen Saint Mary (32040) *(G-5037)*
National Police Ammunition, Hialeah *Also called L C Npee (G-5479)*
National Powdr Coating Fla Inc...941 756-1322
6004 31st St E Bradenton (34203) *(G-1084)*
National Print & Design, Delray Beach *Also called Art In Print Inc (G-3047)*
National Saw Company, Largo *Also called Brawley Distributing Co Inc (G-7913)*
National Scientific Inc...239 262-4047
3838 Tamiami Trl N Ste 31 Naples (34103) *(G-11342)*
National Sign Inc...727 572-1503
5651 116th Ave N Clearwater (33760) *(G-1801)*
National Std Parts Assoc Inc...850 456-5771
1301 E Belmont St Pensacola (32501) *(G-14211)*
National Stoneworks LLC...954 349-1609
3360 Entp Ave Ste 100 Weston (33331) *(G-19152)*
National Subscription Bureau...800 508-1311
2272 Airport Rd S Ste 301 Naples (34112) *(G-11343)*
National Tchncal Cmmunications...407 671-7777
8645 Port Said St Orlando (32817) *(G-12991)*
National Traffic Signs Inc...727 446-7983
14521 60th St N Clearwater (33760) *(G-1802)*
National Woodworks Inc...407 489-3572
4122 Mercy Industrial Ct Orlando (32808) *(G-12992)*
Nationwide Coils & Coatings, Weston *Also called Northrich Florida LLC (G-19154)*
Nationwide Industries Inc (PA)...813 988-2628
3505 Cragmont Dr Tampa (33619) *(G-17933)*
Nationwide Prtctive Cting Mfrs...941 753-7500
7106 24th Ct E Sarasota (34243) *(G-16264)*
Nationwide Publishing Company (PA)...352 253-0017
537 Deltona Blvd Deltona (32725) *(G-3176)*
Native Nursery...941 625-2022
4735 Tamiami Trl Punta Gorda (33980) *(G-15216)*
Native Outfitters, West Palm Beach *Also called Bdc Florida LLC (G-18814)*
Native Sun Sports, Pinellas Park *Also called Rock N Roll Custom Screened S (G-14385)*
Native Welding...561 348-0100
3371 Sw 42nd Ave Ste D Palm City (34990) *(G-13667)*
Natura-Vigor, Davie *Also called Arnet Pharmaceutical Corp (G-2499)*
Natural Beauty Wood Products...561 732-0224
1120 Se 1st St Boynton Beach (33435) *(G-937)*
Natural Crvings Pet Treats LLC...786 404-8099
1100 Nw 7th St Homestead (33030) *(G-5985)*
Natural Ethercom...954 274-6801
10600 Nw 43rd St Coral Springs (33065) *(G-2295)*
Natural Fruit Corp...305 887-7525
770 W 20th St Hialeah (33010) *(G-5533)*
Natural Hats and More LLC...954 549-0819
5801 Wiley St Hollywood (33023) *(G-5880)*
Natural Light, The, Lynn Haven *Also called The Natural Light Inc (G-8440)*
Natural Organic Products Intl...352 383-8252
710 S Rossiter St Mount Dora (32757) *(G-11108)*
Natural Stone Sltons Fnest SRS (PA)...941 954-1100
2303 17th St Sarasota (34234) *(G-16519)*
Natural Vitamins Lab Corp...305 265-1660
12845 Nw 45th Ave Opa Locka (33054) *(G-12343)*
Natural Vitamins Lab Corp...305 265-1660
12845 Nw 45th Ave Opa Locka (33054) *(G-12344)*
Natural Vitamins Labs, Opa Locka *Also called Natural Vitamins Lab Corp (G-12344)*
Natural Wood Works LLC...954 445-1493
2382 W 77th St Hialeah (33016) *(G-5534)*
Natural-Immunogenics Corp...888 328-8840
7504 Pennsylvania Ave Sarasota (34243) *(G-16265)*
Natural4naturalz LLC...561 621-1546
561 Old Farm Pl Clewiston (33440) *(G-1985)*
Nature Cast Ant-Vnom Index LLC...352 683-0647
9204 Chase St Spring Hill (34606) *(G-16857)*
Nature Medrx Inc...239 215-8557
1342 Clnl Blvd Unit C20 Fort Myers (33907) *(G-4544)*
Naturecity LLC...800 593-2563
990 S Rogers Cir Ste 11 Boca Raton (33487) *(G-636)*
Natureform Hatchery Systems, Jacksonville *Also called Pas Reform North America LLC (G-6659)*
Natureform Hatchery Tech LLC...904 358-0355
2550 Cabot Commerce Dr # 22 Jacksonville (32226) *(G-6619)*
Natures Bioscience LLC...800 570-7450
5020 Clark Rd Sarasota (34233) *(G-16520)*
Natures Botanicals Inc...727 443-4524
2101 Sunnydale Blvd Ste C Clearwater (33765) *(G-1803)*
Natures Clear LLC...561 503-1751
2328 10th Ave N Ste 501d Lake Worth (33461) *(G-7575)*
Natures Earth Products Inc...561 688-8101
2200 N Fl Mango Rd # 403 West Palm Beach (33409) *(G-18958)*
Natures Fuel Inc...407 808-4272
2254 Saw Palmetto Ln Orlando (32828) *(G-12993)*
Natures Gift Cbd...954 405-1000
320 Ne 12th Ave Apt 506 Hallandale Beach (33009) *(G-5201)*
Natures Heathy Gourmet...772 873-0180
1260 Sw Biltmore St Port St Lucie (34983) *(G-15176)*
Natures Own Pest Control Inc...941 378-3334
1899 Porter Lake Dr # 103 Sarasota (34240) *(G-16521)*
Natures Power and Energy LLC...813 907-6279
30131 Clearview Dr Wesley Chapel (33545) *(G-18753)*
Natus Medical Incorporated...321 235-8213
12301 Lake Underhill Rd # 201 Orlando (32828) *(G-12994)*
Natus Medical Incorporated...847 949-5200
12301 Lake Underhill Rd # 201 Orlando (32828) *(G-12995)*
Nauset Enterprises Inc...727 443-3469
2120 Calumet St Ste 1 Clearwater (33765) *(G-1804)*
Nautical Acquisitions Corp...727 541-6664
7301 114th Ave Largo (33773) *(G-8017)*
Nautical Flair, Riviera Beach *Also called Canvas Designers Inc (G-15308)*
Nautical Specialists...954 761-7130
2841 Ne 36th St Fort Lauderdale (33308) *(G-4133)*
Nautical Structures, Largo *Also called Nautical Acquisitions Corp (G-8017)*
Nautical Structures Inds Inc (PA)...727 541-6664
7301 114th Ave Largo (33773) *(G-8018)*
Nautiloft LLC...801 712-6692
3192 Matecumbe Key Rd Punta Gorda (33955) *(G-15217)*
Nauttyboiz Extreme Printing, West Palm Beach *Also called John E Anderson (G-18914)*
Nav-X LLC...954 978-9988
1386 W Mcnab Rd Fort Lauderdale (33309) *(G-4134)*
Nava Pets Inc...407 982-7256
400 North St Unit 184 Longwood (32750) *(G-8315)*
Navarre Beach Woodworks...850 781-7884
1713 Shellfish Dr Navarre (32566) *(G-11470)*
Navarre Fishing Rodeo, Navarre *Also called Sandpaper Marketing Inc (G-11475)*
Navarre Industries Inc...850 554-6682
2056 Sundown Dr Navarre (32566) *(G-11471)*
Naviera Coffee Mills Inc...813 248-2521
2012 E 7th Ave Tampa (33605) *(G-17934)*
Navinta III Inc...561 997-6959
1003 Clint Moore Rd Boca Raton (33487) *(G-637)*
Navistar Inc...305 513-2255
8600 Nw 36th St Ste 304 Doral (33166) *(G-3443)*
Navizon Inc...305 501-2409
235 Lincoln Rd Ste 306 Miami Beach (33139) *(G-10697)*
Navmar Applied Sciences Corp...904 423-0927
7254 Golden Wings Rd Jacksonville (32244) *(G-6620)*
Naylor LLC (PA)...800 369-6220
5950 Nw 1st Pl Gainesville (32607) *(G-4969)*
Naylor Association Solutions, Gainesville *Also called Naylor LLC (G-4969)*
Naztec International Group LLC...561 802-4110
263 N Jog Rd West Palm Beach (33413) *(G-18959)*
Naztec International Group LLC (PA)...561 802-4110
8983 Okeechobee Blvd # 202 West Palm Beach (33411) *(G-18960)*
Nb Products Inc...904 807-0140
1551 Atl Blvd Ste 105 Jacksonville (32207) *(G-6621)*
Nbk Maintenance, Saint Augustine *Also called Old City Marine LLC (G-15580)*
NC II, Sarasota *Also called NC IV Inc (G-16522)*
NC IV Inc...941 378-9133
1788 Barber Rd Sarasota (34240) *(G-16522)*
NC Printing & Accounting Co...904 327-7701
6110 Powers Ave Ste 11 Jacksonville (32217) *(G-6622)*
Ncc Promotional, Groveland *Also called Novelty Crystal Corp (G-5104)*
Ncdi, Doral *Also called New Concepts Distrs Intl LLC (G-3444)*
Ncg Medical Systems Inc (PA)...407 788-1906
1402 Edgewater Dr Ste 101 Orlando (32804) *(G-12996)*
NCH FL Funding LLC...321 777-7777
525 N Harbor City Blvd Melbourne (32935) *(G-8892)*
NCH Marine LLC...754 422-4237
13325 Sw 28th St Davie (33330) *(G-2557)*
Nci...813 749-1799
11327 Countryway Blvd Tampa (33626) *(G-17935)*
Ncp Solutions LLC...205 849-5200
841 Prudential Dr # 1200 Jacksonville (32207) *(G-6623)*
Ndh Medical Inc...727 570-2293
11001 Roosevelt Blvd N # 150 Saint Petersburg (33716) *(G-15864)*
Ne Media Group Inc...954 733-8393
2880 W Oklnd Prk Blvd # 207 Oakland Park (33311) *(G-11823)*
Nearly Natural LLC...800 711-0544
3870 W 108th St Unit 20 Hialeah (33018) *(G-5535)*
Neat Clean Group Inc...727 459-6079
2523 Marina Key Ln Clearwater (33763) *(G-1805)*
Neat Print Inc...941 545-1517
2147 Porter Lake Dr Ste G Sarasota (34240) *(G-16523)*
Nebraska Printing Inc...813 870-6871
3849 W Azeele St Tampa (33609) *(G-17936)*
Nebula Glass International Inc...954 975-3233
1601 Blount Rd Pompano Beach (33069) *(G-14771)*
Nebula Led Lighting Systems of...813 907-0001
28832 Falling Leaves Way Wesley Chapel (33543) *(G-18754)*
Need A Dumpster LLC...888 407-3867
1733 Benbow Ct Ste 5 Apopka (32703) *(G-164)*

Need Printing, Pompano Beach *Also called Gb Printing* ***(G-14711)***
Neelco Industries Inc 321 632-5303
420 Shearer Blvd Cocoa (32922) ***(G-2038)***
Neglex Inc 305 551-4177
300 Sw 107th Ave Ste 114 Miami (33174) ***(G-10063)***
Neighborhood News & Lifestyles 727 943-0551
220 S Safford Ave Tarpon Springs (34689) ***(G-18316)***
Neighborhood Property Mgmt 305 819-2361
2150 W 68th St Ste 205 Hialeah (33016) ***(G-5536)***
Nelco Products Inc 727 533-8282
15251 Roosevelt Blvd # 202 Clearwater (33760) ***(G-1806)***
Nelson and Affiliates Inc 352 316-5641
3324 W University Ave Gainesville (32607) ***(G-4970)***
Nelson Mch Sp Wldg & Engrg Inc 305 710-5029
13990 Nw 22nd Ave Opa Locka (33054) ***(G-12345)***
Nelson Plastics Inc 407 339-3570
578 North St Longwood (32750) ***(G-8316)***
Nelson Raceway LLC 904 206-1625
96321 Bay View Dr Fernandina Beach (32034) ***(G-3744)***
Nelsons Truck and Trlr Sls LLC 352 732-8908
4131 Nw Blitchton Rd Ocala (34482) ***(G-12005)***
Nelver Airparts Inc 305 378-0072
12360 Sw 132nd Ct Ste 205 Miami (33186) ***(G-10064)***
Nem, Bradenton *Also called New England Machinery Inc* ***(G-1086)***
Nemal Electronics Intl Inc (PA) 305 899-0900
12240 Ne 14th Ave North Miami (33161) ***(G-11648)***
Nemec 407 829-2679
1534 Cherry Lake Way Lake Mary (32746) ***(G-7439)***
Nenem Inc 561 389-2010
1287 Waterway Cove Dr West Palm Beach (33414) ***(G-18961)***
Neo Metal Glass LLC 954 532-0340
2101 Nw 33rd St Ste 1400 Pompano Beach (33069) ***(G-14772)***
Neocabinet Inc 310 927-1008
1623 Plunkett St Hollywood (33020) ***(G-5881)***
Neocis Inc 855 963-6247
2800 Biscayne Blvd # 600 Miami (33137) ***(G-10065)***
Neon & Sign Mfg Inc 443 664-6419
7870 Lago Del Mar Dr Boca Raton (33433) ***(G-638)***
Neon Cowboys LLC 949 514-5557
2312 Clark St Ste 5 Apopka (32703) ***(G-165)***
Neon Sleevz LLC 239 348-0520
4437 54th Ave Ne Naples (34120) ***(G-11344)***
Neon Workforce Technologies 305 458-8244
2300 W 84th St Ste 601 Hialeah (33016) ***(G-5537)***
Neopod Systems LLC (PA) 954 603-3100
1329 Shotgun Rd Sunrise (33326) ***(G-17151)***
Neos Technologies Inc (PA) 321 242-7818
4300 Fortune Pl Ste C Melbourne (32904) ***(G-8893)***
Nephron Pharmaceuticals 407 913-3142
1162 Bella Vida Blvd Orlando (32828) ***(G-12997)***
Nephron Pharmaceuticals Corp 407 999-2225
4121 Sw 34th St Orlando (32811) ***(G-12998)***
Neptune Boat Lifts Inc 954 524-3616
280 Sw 6th St Fort Lauderdale (33301) ***(G-4135)***
Neptune Designs Inc 305 294-8131
301 Duval St Key West (33040) ***(G-7199)***
Neptune Petroleum LLC 561 684-2844
3974 Okeechobee Blvd # 2 West Palm Beach (33409) ***(G-18962)***
Neptune Precision Composites, Jacksonville *Also called Neptune Tech Services Inc* ***(G-6624)***
Neptune Research Inc (PA) 561 683-6992
3875 Fiscal Ct Ste 100 Riviera Beach (33404) ***(G-15352)***
Neptune Tech Services Inc (PA) 904 646-2700
11657 Central Pkwy # 405 Jacksonville (32224) ***(G-6624)***
Nessmith Dye Cutting & Finshg 904 353-6317
536 E 4th St Jacksonville (32206) ***(G-6625)***
Nestle Professional, Thonotosassa *Also called Nestle Usa Inc* ***(G-18402)***
Nestle Professional Vitality, Thonotosassa *Also called Nestle Usa Inc* ***(G-18403)***
Nestle Usa Inc 813 273-5355
11471 N Us Highway 301 # 10 Thonotosassa (33592) ***(G-18402)***
Nestle Usa Inc 813 301-4638
11441 N Us Highway 301 Thonotosassa (33592) ***(G-18403)***
Netexpressusa Inc (PA) 888 575-1245
8991 Daniels Center Dr # 105 Fort Myers (33912) ***(G-4545)***
Nets Depot Inc 305 215-5579
9949 Nw 89th Ave Unit 13 Medley (33178) ***(G-8694)***
Netting Professionals LLC 904 432-8987
1600 N 14th St Fernandina Beach (32034) ***(G-3745)***
Network USA, Bradenton *Also called Inovart Inc* ***(G-1061)***
Networked Solutions Inc 321 259-3242
7145 Turner Rd Ste 102 Rockledge (32955) ***(G-15438)***
Networking Dynamics, Clearwater *Also called Universal Software Solutions* ***(G-1929)***
Networks Assets LLC 954 334-1390
3265 Meridian Pkwy # 134 Weston (33331) ***(G-19153)***
Neubert Aero Corp 352 345-4828
16110 Flight Path Dr Brooksville (34604) ***(G-1256)***
Neuro Pharmalogics Inc 240 476-4491
901 Nw 35th St Boca Raton (33431) ***(G-639)***
Neurotronics Inc 352 372-9955
4500 Nw 27th Ave Ste C2 Gainesville (32606) ***(G-4971)***
Neutral Guard LLC 954 249-6600
1401 Sw 34th Ave Fort Lauderdale (33312) ***(G-4136)***
Nev International Inc 407 671-0045
1211 State Road 436 # 141 Casselberry (32707) ***(G-1511)***
Never Wrong Toys & Games LLC 941 371-0909
2201 Cantu Ct Ste 100 Sarasota (34232) ***(G-16524)***
New Age Windows & Doors Corp 305 889-0703
7196 Nw 77th Ter Medley (33166) ***(G-8695)***
New Best Packers Inc 386 328-5127
1122 Bronson St Palatka (32177) ***(G-13487)***
New Breed Clothing llc 941 773-7406
1120 Magellan Dr Sarasota (34243) ***(G-16266)***
New Bs Wheel LLC 309 657-4899
321 Ocean Forest Dr Saint Augustine (32080) ***(G-15572)***
New Century 305 670-3510
7950 Sunset Dr Miami (33143) ***(G-10066)***
New Choices, Boca Raton *Also called Raytash Inc* ***(G-681)***
New Concepts Distrs Intl LLC 305 463-8735
2315 Nw 107th Ave Ste 1b5 Doral (33172) ***(G-3444)***
New Dairy Opco LLC 305 652-3720
501 Ne 181st St North Miami Beach (33162) ***(G-11694)***
New Dawn Coffee Company 727 321-5155
2336 5th Ave S Saint Petersburg (33712) ***(G-15865)***
New Design Furniture Mfg, Lauderdale Lakes *Also called Shorr Enterprises Inc* ***(G-8093)***
New Dimensions, Riviera Beach *Also called Pendulum One Inc* ***(G-15360)***
New Energy Fuels LLC 281 205-0153
259 Ford Ave Labelle (33935) ***(G-7321)***
New England Granite & Marble 772 283-8667
890 Sw Enterprise Way Stuart (34997) ***(G-16980)***
New England Machinery 941 755-5550
6204 29th St E Bradenton (34203) ***(G-1085)***
New England Machinery Inc 941 755-5550
2820 62nd Ave E Bradenton (34203) ***(G-1086)***
New ERA Technology Corp 352 746-3569
620 W Sunset Strip Dr Beverly Hills (34465) ***(G-377)***
New Generation Aerospace Inc 305 882-1410
8004 Nw 90th St Medley (33166) ***(G-8696)***
New Generation Computing Inc (HQ) 800 690-0642
14900 Nw 79th Ct Ste 100 Miami Lakes (33016) ***(G-10828)***
New Generation Packaging LLC 786 259-6670
16542 Nw 54th Ave Miami Gardens (33014) ***(G-10751)***
New Gnrtion Abndant Mssion Ch 772 497-5871
2017 Sw Tropical Ter Port Saint Lucie (34953) ***(G-15123)***
New Gnrtion Jews Abndant Mssio, Port Saint Lucie *Also called New Gnrtion Abndant Mssion Ch* ***(G-15123)***
New Hope Sugar Company 561 366-5120
1 N Clematis St West Palm Beach (33401) ***(G-18963)***
New IEM Power Systems LLC (HQ) 904 365-4444
11902 Central Pkwy Jacksonville (32224) ***(G-6626)***
New Image Printing Promotion 904 240-1516
9556 Historic Kings Rd S Jacksonville (32257) ***(G-6627)***
New Kitchen Concepts, Daytona Beach *Also called Counter Productions Inc* ***(G-2647)***
New Laser Tech Inc 305 450-0456
7003 Greentree Ln Miami Lakes (33014) ***(G-10829)***
New Line Transport LLC 305 223-9200
9931 Old Lakeland Hwy Dade City (33525) ***(G-2432)***
New Marco Foods Inc 305 836-0571
3251 E 11th Ave Hialeah (33013) ***(G-5538)***
New Market Enterprises Ltd 484 341-8004
392 Harbor Ridge Dr Palm Harbor (34683) ***(G-13748)***
New Mix Products 904 292-1920
4465 Crooked Oak Ct Jacksonville (32257) ***(G-6628)***
New Millennium Bldg Systems LLC 386 466-1300
1992 Nw Bascom Norris Dr Lake City (32055) ***(G-7369)***
New Nautical Coatings Inc (HQ) 727 523-8053
14805 49th St N Clearwater (33762) ***(G-1807)***
New Pelican LLC 954 783-8700
1636 E Atlantic Blvd Pompano Beach (33060) ***(G-14773)***
New River Cabinet & Fix Inc 954 938-9200
750 Nw 57th Ct Fort Lauderdale (33309) ***(G-4137)***
New Sentry Marketing Inc 561 982-9599
878 Nafa Dr Boca Raton (33487) ***(G-640)***
New Smyrna Beach Plas Plant, New Smyrna Beach *Also called Sonoco Products Company* ***(G-11545)***
New Smyrna Daily Journal, Daytona Beach *Also called News-Journal Corporation* ***(G-2690)***
New Source Corp 407 830-7771
107 Hilltop Pl Altamonte Springs (32701) ***(G-57)***
New Style Wood Work Corp 305 989-9665
2735 W 61st St Apt 104 Hialeah (33016) ***(G-5539)***
New T Management Inc 954 927-4889
255 E Dania Beach Blvd # 2 Dania (33004) ***(G-2454)***
New Tampa Embroidme of 813 994-0118
1917 Passero Ave Lutz (33559) ***(G-8405)***
New Technology Precision Machi 561 624-3830
15300 Pk Of Commerce Blvd Jupiter (33478) ***(G-7080)***
New Underground RR Pubg Co 305 825-1444
14411 Commerce Way # 320 Miami Lakes (33016) ***(G-10830)***

New Vbb LLC 904 631-5978
3044 Mercury Rd S Jacksonville (32207) *(G-6629)*
New Vision Display Inc 407 480-5800
135 W Central Blvd # 330 Orlando (32801) *(G-12999)*
New Vision Furniture Inc 305 562-9428
4115 Nw 132nd St Unit I Opa Locka (33054) *(G-12346)*
New Vision Signs Corp 786 514-6822
15446 Sw 25th Ter Miami (33185) *(G-10067)*
New Wave Designs, Vero Beach *Also called Morning Star Personalized AP (G-18644)*
New Wave Surgical Corp 866 346-8883
3700 Nw 124th Ave Ste 135 Coral Springs (33065) *(G-2296)*
New Woodworks Inc 954 520-4812
4140 Ne 5th Ave Oakland Park (33334) *(G-11824)*
New World Enclosures Inc 904 334-4752
1350 Riviera Dr Green Cove Springs (32043) *(G-5067)*
New World Gold Corporation (PA) 561 962-4139
350 Cmino Grdns Blvd Ste Boca Raton (33432) *(G-641)*
New World Holdings Inc 561 888-4939
1080 Holland Dr Ste 1 Boca Raton (33487) *(G-642)*
New World Medicinals, Boca Raton *Also called New World Holdings Inc (G-642)*
New World Publications Inc 904 737-6558
1861 Cornell Rd Jacksonville (32207) *(G-6630)*
New World Trade Inc 941 205-5873
8249 Skylane Way Ste 111 Punta Gorda (33982) *(G-15218)*
New Yachts Company 754 223-5907
2890 W State Road 84 # 103 Fort Lauderdale (33312) *(G-4138)*
New York Deli Express 954 572-1442
4630 N University Dr Lauderhill (33351) *(G-8117)*
New York Intl Bread Co 407 843-9744
1500 W Church St Orlando (32805) *(G-13000)*
New York Mri Management, Fort Myers *Also called Imaging Initiatives Inc (G-4488)*
New York Nails 904 448-6040
5869 University Blvd W Jacksonville (32216) *(G-6631)*
New You Media LLC 800 606-6518
4150 Sw 28th Way Fort Lauderdale (33312) *(G-4139)*
Newbeauty Media Group LLC 561 961-7600
3651 Nw 8th Ave Ste 400 Boca Raton (33431) *(G-643)*
Newbeauty Media Group, Lllp, Boca Raton *Also called Newbeauty Media Group LLC (G-643)*
Newbevco Inc (HQ) 954 581-0922
8100 Sw 10th St Plantation (33324) *(G-14539)*
Newcastle Shipyards LLC 386 312-0000
106 Dory Rd Saint Augustine (32086) *(G-15573)*
Newer Spreader, Sanford *Also called Rugby Road Corp (G-16112)*
Newlink Cabling Systems Inc (PA) 305 477-8063
11701 Nw 102nd Rd Ste 21 Medley (33178) *(G-8697)*
Newmans Truck Body and Eqp Inc 904 695-9589
6880 W 12th St Jacksonville (32254) *(G-6632)*
Newmark International, Bartow *Also called Valmont Newmark Inc (G-335)*
Newmil Inc 954 444-4471
2029 Sw 20th St Fort Lauderdale (33315) *(G-4140)*
News & Sun Sentinel Company, Fort Lauderdale *Also called Sun-Sentinel Company LLC (G-4265)*
News Chief, Winter Haven *Also called Gatehouse Media LLC (G-19325)*
News Features USA Inc 305 298-5313
6301 Collins Ave Miami Beach (33141) *(G-10698)*
News Herald 850 785-6550
221 E 23rd St Ste B Panama City (32405) *(G-13931)*
News Leader Inc 352 242-9818
637 8th St Clermont (34711) *(G-1970)*
News-Journal Corporation (PA) 386 252-1511
901 6th St Daytona Beach (32117) *(G-2690)*
News-Journal Corporation 386 283-5664
4984 Palm Coast Pkwy Nw # 5 Palm Coast (32137) *(G-13704)*
Newsmax Media Inc 561 686-1165
1501 Nrthpint Pkwy Ste 10 West Palm Beach (33407) *(G-18964)*
Newsnotes LLC 407 949-8185
610 Ocean St Satellite Beach (32937) *(G-16653)*
Newspaper Printing Company 727 572-7488
12198 44th St N Clearwater (33762) *(G-1808)*
Newspaper Printing Company 813 839-0035
5210 S Lois Ave Tampa (33611) *(G-17937)*
Newspaper Publishers Inc 561 793-7606
12794 Frest Hl Blvd Ste 3 Wellington (33414) *(G-18725)*
Newvida Products LLC 863 781-9232
4757 Sweetwater Rd Zolfo Springs (33890) *(G-19547)*
Nex Software LLC 786 200-3396
29690 Sw 183rd Ct Homestead (33030) *(G-5986)*
Nex-Xos Worldwide LLC (PA) 305 433-8376
3922 Pembroke Rd Hollywood (33021) *(G-5882)*
Nexgen Framing System LLC 321 508-6763
2288 Wilhelmina Ct Ne Palm Bay (32905) *(G-13525)*
Nexogy Inc 305 358-8952
2121 Ponce De Leon Blvd # 200 Coral Gables (33134) *(G-2181)*
Nexogy Sac, Fort Lauderdale *Also called Ld Telecommunications Inc (G-4097)*
Nexpub, Miramar *Also called Print Factory LLC (G-11031)*
Nexpub Inc 954 392-5889
3820 Executive Way Miramar (33025) *(G-11021)*

Nexstar Broadcasting Inc 863 683-6531
223 S Florida Ave Lakeland (33801) *(G-7757)*
Next Door Company 954 772-6666
4005 E 10th Ct Hialeah (33013) *(G-5540)*
Next Gen Web Solutions, Jacksonville *Also called Ngweb Solutions LLC (G-6633)*
Next Generation Home Pdts Inc 727 834-9400
701 S Howard Ave Tampa (33606) *(G-17938)*
Next Level, Pompano Beach *Also called SC Capital Ventures Inc (G-14841)*
Next Step Products LLC 407 857-9900
9400 Southridge Park Ct # 200 Orlando (32819) *(G-13001)*
Nextera Fibernet LLC 866 787-2637
700 Universe Blvd Juno Beach (33408) *(G-6981)*
Nextgen, Tampa *Also called Next Generation Home Pdts Inc (G-17938)*
Nextower LLC 407 907-7984
11895 Sw 33rd Ln Gainesville (32608) *(G-4972)*
Nextreef Systems, Myakka City *Also called Stony Coral Investments LLC (G-11143)*
Nextsource Biotechnology LLC 305 753-6360
80 Sw 8th St Miami (33130) *(G-10068)*
Nexus Alliance Corp 321 945-4283
160 Vista Oak Dr Longwood (32779) *(G-8317)*
Nfi Masks LLC 239 990-6546
16140 Lee Rd Unit 120 Fort Myers (33912) *(G-4546)*
Nfjb Inc 954 771-1100
60 Nw 60th St Fort Lauderdale (33309) *(G-4141)*
Nfk Corporation 305 791-2044
8150 Sw 118th Pl Miami (33183) *(G-10069)*
Nfk Corporation 305 378-2116
13456 Sw 131st St Miami (33186) *(G-10070)*
Ngf Distributors Inc 407 816-7554
3035 Turkey Ave Oviedo (32765) *(G-13449)*
Ngp Corporate Square Inc 239 643-3430
4408 Corporate Sq Naples (34104) *(G-11345)*
Ngweb Solutions LLC 904 332-9001
6821 Sthpint Dr N Ste 220 Jacksonville (32216) *(G-6633)*
Ni-Chro Plating Corp 727 327-5118
700 37th St S Saint Petersburg (33711) *(G-15866)*
Niagara Bottling LLC 352 429-3611
7633 American Way Groveland (34736) *(G-5102)*
Niagara Industries Inc 305 876-9010
4120 Nw 28th St Miami (33142) *(G-10071)*
Niagratech Industries Inc 305 876-9010
2540 Nw 38th Ct Miami (33142) *(G-10072)*
Niba Collections, Hollywood *Also called Niba Designs Inc (G-5883)*
Niba Designs Inc (PA) 305 456-6230
3609 N 29th Ave Hollywood (33020) *(G-5883)*
Nic4 Inc 877 455-2131
111 Kelsey Ln Ste D Tampa (33619) *(G-17939)*
Niche Digital Media Corp 561 768-9793
900 E Indiantown Rd # 312 Jupiter (33477) *(G-7081)*
Nichols Truck Bodies LLC 904 781-5080
1168 Cahoon Rd S Jacksonville (32221) *(G-6634)*
Nickels and Associates LLC 863 699-0180
133 Lavender Ave Lake Placid (33852) *(G-7491)*
Nickols Cbinetry Woodworks Inc 941 485-7894
765 U S 41 Byp S Bypass S Venice (34285) *(G-18564)*
Nicolette Mayer Collection Inc 561 241-6906
3750 Ne 6th Dr Boca Raton (33431) *(G-644)*
Nicraf Software & Creations 813 842-9648
17413 Equestrian Trl Odessa (33556) *(G-12135)*
Nida Corporation (PA) 321 727-2265
300 S John Rodes Blvd Melbourne (32904) *(G-8894)*
Nida-Core Corporation (HQ) 772 343-7300
541 Nw Interpark Pl Port Saint Lucie (34986) *(G-15124)*
Nidec Motor Corporation 954 346-4900
12095 Nw 39th St Coral Springs (33065) *(G-2297)*
Niefeld Group LLC 786 587-7423
2420 W 80th St Unit 5 Hialeah (33016) *(G-5541)*
Nielsen Publishing 941 539-7579
2504 Tamiami Trl N Nokomis (34275) *(G-11586)*
Niftys Inc 786 878-4725
78 Sw 7th St Miami (33130) *(G-10073)*
Nigella Industries Inc 813 404-7923
11975 3rd St E Apt 1 Treasure Island (33706) *(G-18476)*
Nighthawk Running LLC 407 443-8404
1623 Wycliff Dr Orlando (32803) *(G-13002)*
Nighthawk Safety, Orlando *Also called Nighthawk Running LLC (G-13002)*
Nightingale Corp 800 363-8954
11380 Prosperity Farms Rd Palm Beach Gardens (33410) *(G-13611)*
Nightmoves Magazine, Oldsmar *Also called PA C Publishing Inc (G-12255)*
Nightscenes Inc 813 855-9416
12802 Commodity Pl Tampa (33626) *(G-17940)*
Nik Public Safety, Jacksonville *Also called Armor Holdings Forensics LLC (G-6169)*
Nikiani Inc 305 606-1104
717 Maritime Way West Palm Beach (33410) *(G-18965)*
Nilfisk Pressure-Pro LLC 772 672-3697
7300 Commercial Cir Fort Pierce (34951) *(G-4722)*
Nilsson Nils 561 790-2400
1128 Royal Palm Bch Royal Palm Beach (33411) *(G-15476)*

ALPHABETIC

Nina Plastic Bags Inc (PA)....407 802-6828
1903 Cypress Lake Dr Orlando (32837) ***(G-13003)***
Nina Plastics, Orlando *Also called Nina Plastic Bags Inc* ***(G-13003)***
Nine Enterprises Inc....904 998-8880
3633 Southside Blvd Jacksonville (32216) ***(G-6635)***
Nine Mile Raceway Inc....850 937-1845
1281 Lear Ct Cantonment (32533) ***(G-1343)***
Nippon Maciwumei Co....954 533-7747
4500 N Hiatus Rd Ste 214 Sunrise (33351) ***(G-17152)***
Nis Print Inc....407 423-7575
1809 S Division Ave Orlando (32805) ***(G-13004)***
Nissi Elastic Corp....305 968-3812
961 E 17th St Hialeah (33010) ***(G-5542)***
Nite-Bright Sign Company Inc....239 466-2616
16061 Pine Ridge Rd Fort Myers (33908) ***(G-4547)***
Niteo Products LLC....561 745-1812
902 S Us Highway 1 Jupiter (33477) ***(G-7082)***
Nitesol Inc....407 557-4042
1831 Tallokas Ave Orlando (32805) ***(G-13005)***
Nitro Gulf, Stuart *Also called Nitro Leisure Products Inc* ***(G-16981)***
Nitro Leisure Products Inc....414 272-5084
4490 Se Cheri Ct Stuart (34997) ***(G-16981)***
Nitrogen Jupiter LLC....561 662-2150
6779 W Indiantown Rd Jupiter (33458) ***(G-7083)***
Nitv Federal Services LLC....561 798-6280
11400 Fortune Cir West Palm Beach (33414) ***(G-18966)***
Nivcoe International Dev....321 282-3666
2020 W Fairbanks Ave # 102 Winter Park (32789) ***(G-19428)***
Nivel Holdings LLC (PA)....904 741-6161
3510 Pt Jacksonville Park Jacksonville (32226) ***(G-6636)***
Nivel Parts & Mfg Co LLC (HQ)....904 741-6161
3510-1 Port Jcksnvlle Pkw Jacksonville (32226) ***(G-6637)***
Nivel Parts and Mfg Co LLC....904 421-3004
3608 Queen Palm Dr Ste A Tampa (33619) ***(G-17941)***
Nivel Parts Manufacturing, Jacksonville *Also called Nivel Holdings LLC* ***(G-6636)***
Nkem Inc....800 582-0707
1451 Sarasota Center Blvd Sarasota (34240) ***(G-16525)***
Nml, Boca Raton *Also called Mmp-Boca Raton LLC* ***(G-627)***
No 1 Beauty Salon Furniture....954 981-0403
4712 Ne 12th Ave Oakland Park (33334) ***(G-11825)***
No Equal Design Inc....305 971-5177
6995 Nw 46th St A Miami (33166) ***(G-10074)***
No Flood Inc....239 776-1671
17061 Alico Commerce Ct Fort Myers (33967) ***(G-4548)***
No Limit TS and Prints LLC....813 933-3424
11811 Pasco Trails Blvd Spring Hill (34610) ***(G-16876)***
No No-See-Um, Fort Myers *Also called Velmaxxx Enterprises Inc* ***(G-4645)***
No. 1 Bsf, Oakland Park *Also called No 1 Beauty Salon Furniture* ***(G-11825)***
Noa International Inc....954 835-5258
2361 Vista Pkwy Ste 1 West Palm Beach (33411) ***(G-18967)***
Noahs MBL Tire Auto Solutions....904 250-1502
5119 Cemetery Rd Jacksonville (32210) ***(G-6638)***
Nobel Aerospace LLC....786 210-0716
1532 Nw 89th Ct Doral (33172) ***(G-3445)***
Nobility Homes Inc (PA)....352 732-5157
3741 Sw 7th St Ocala (34474) ***(G-12006)***
Nobility Homes Inc....352 245-5126
6432 Se 115th Ln Belleview (34420) ***(G-373)***
Nobility Plant 8, Belleview *Also called Nobility Homes Inc* ***(G-373)***
Noble Wood Works....561 702-2889
225 Nw 16th St Pompano Beach (33060) ***(G-14774)***
Noble Woodworks Inc....561 702-2889
22053 Palms Way Apt 106 Boca Raton (33433) ***(G-645)***
Noble Worldwide Fla Citrus Sls, Winter Haven *Also called Wm G Roe & Sons Inc* ***(G-19367)***
Noble's Jockey Apparel, Davie *Also called Bnj Noble Inc* ***(G-2503)***
Noell Design Group Inc....561 391-9942
1050 Nw 1st Ave Ste 16 Boca Raton (33432) ***(G-646)***
NOGHOLD, Hialeah *Also called Noguera Holdings LLC* ***(G-5543)***
Noguera Holdings LLC....305 846-9144
1635 W 32nd Pl Hialeah (33012) ***(G-5543)***
Nohbo Labs LLC....321 345-5319
1581 Robert J Conlan Blvd Palm Bay (32905) ***(G-13526)***
Nommo International LLC....866 366-3688
1317 Edgewater Dr Orlando (32804) ***(G-13006)***
Noodle Time Inc....305 593-0770
8685 Nw 53rd Ter Miami (33166) ***(G-10075)***
Nopetro LLC....305 441-9059
1152 Capital Cir Nw Tallahassee (32304) ***(G-17305)***
Nopi, Mount Dora *Also called Natural Organic Products Intl* ***(G-11108)***
Nor East Materials Inc....386 478-0087
3459 Velona Ave New Smyrna Beach (32168) ***(G-11539)***
Norco, Deland *Also called Delta Machine & Tool Inc* ***(G-2969)***
Nordic Group LLC (PA)....561 789-8676
2220 Sw 11th Pl Boca Raton (33486) ***(G-647)***
Nordic Line Inc (PA)....561 338-5545
1080 Nw 1st Ave Boca Raton (33432) ***(G-648)***
Nordic Made Inc....954 651-6208
3801 Sw 47th Ave Ste 503 Davie (33314) ***(G-2558)***
Nordquist Dielectrics Inc....727 585-7990
12750 59th Way N Clearwater (33760) ***(G-1809)***
Nores Precision Inc....954 420-0025
44 Se 9th St Deerfield Beach (33441) ***(G-2879)***
Norjac Oil & Gas Inc or J....954 779-3192
2525 Barcelona Dr Fort Lauderdale (33301) ***(G-4142)***
Norman Engineering Corporation....407 425-6433
2579 N Orange Blossom Trl Orlando (32804) ***(G-13007)***
Normandin LLC....941 739-8046
2206 72nd Dr E Sarasota (34243) ***(G-16267)***
Norris Precision Mfg Inc....727 572-6330
4680 110th Ave N Clearwater (33762) ***(G-1810)***
Norseman Shipbuilding Corp....305 545-6815
437 Nw South River Dr Miami (33128) ***(G-10076)***
Nortech Engineering Inc....508 823-8520
13001 Cedar Creek Dr Port Charlotte (33953) ***(G-14991)***
North America Bio Fuel Corp....877 877-9279
1767 Lakewood Ranch Blvd # 210 Bradenton (34211) ***(G-1087)***
North America Wireline LLC....870 365-5401
6057 Clay Cir Gulf Breeze (32563) ***(G-5122)***
North American Coal Corp....305 824-9018
18300 Sw 122nd St Miami (33196) ***(G-10077)***
North American Mining....305 824-3181
10025 Nw 116th Way Ste 1 Medley (33178) ***(G-8698)***
North American Operations, Orlando *Also called Esterel Technologies Inc* ***(G-12717)***
North American Signal LLC....850 462-1790
1810 Barrancas Ave Pensacola (32502) ***(G-14212)***
North Amrcn Adhesives Coatings, Deerfield Beach *Also called Mapei Corporation* ***(G-2868)***
North Amrcn Prtection Ctrl LLC....407 788-3717
190 N Westmonte Dr Altamonte Springs (32714) ***(G-58)***
North Amrcn Signal Systems LLC....352 376-8341
605 Nw 53rd Ave Ste A17 Gainesville (32609) ***(G-4973)***
North Central Advertiser Inc....386 755-2917
358 Nw Main Blvd Lake City (32055) ***(G-7370)***
North Coast Machining Inc....954 942-6943
2311 Ne 26th St Lighthouse Point (33064) ***(G-8210)***
North Erie Electronics Inc....561 839-8127
1001 N Us Highway 1 # 506 Jupiter (33477) ***(G-7084)***
North FL Custom Coatings Inc....904 251-4462
2896 Cortez Rd Jacksonville (32246) ***(G-6639)***
North Florida AG Services Inc....352 494-3978
3151 Sw Custom Made Cir Lake City (32024) ***(G-7371)***
North Florida Brick Pavers LLC....850 255-0336
664 E Shipwreck Rd Santa Rosa Beach (32459) ***(G-16164)***
North Florida Lumber, Bristol *Also called North Florida Woodlands Inc* ***(G-1201)***
North Florida Printing Inc....386 362-1080
109 Tuxedo Ave Ne Live Oak (32064) ***(G-8235)***
North Florida Vault LLC....386 303-2267
561 Nw Hilton Ave Lake City (32055) ***(G-7372)***
North Florida Woodlands Inc....850 643-2238
18601 Nw County Road 12 Bristol (32321) ***(G-1201)***
North Fort Myers Prescr Sp....239 599-4120
16251 N Cleveland Ave # 13 North Fort Myers (33903) ***(G-11600)***
North Metro Media....850 650-1014
4507 Furling Ln Ste 106 Destin (32541) ***(G-3199)***
North Palm Printing Center....561 622-2839
4588 Juniper Ln Palm Beach Gardens (33418) ***(G-13612)***
North Port Pavers Inc....941 391-7557
6099 Estates Dr North Port (34291) ***(G-11745)***
North Shore Hldngs Lghthuse Pt....954 785-1055
4130 Ne 24th Ave Lighthouse Point (33064) ***(G-8211)***
North W Fla Cncil of Blind Cor....850 982-7867
2807 Sandy Ridge Rd Gulf Breeze (32563) ***(G-5123)***
Northast Wtr Rclmtion Fclities, Saint Petersburg *Also called Northeast Water Reclamation* ***(G-15867)***
Northeast Pro-Tech Inc....772 489-8762
7219 Reserve Creek Dr Port Saint Lucie (34986) ***(G-15125)***
Northeast Water Reclamation....727 893-7779
1160 62nd Ave Ne Saint Petersburg (33702) ***(G-15867)***
Northern Litho Inc....239 653-9645
9486 Gulf Shore Dr Naples (34108) ***(G-11346)***
Northland Manufacturing Inc....850 878-5149
3485 S Monroe St Tallahassee (32301) ***(G-17306)***
Northpointe Bank....239 308-4532
8660 College Pkwy Ste 150 Fort Myers (33919) ***(G-4549)***
Northrich Florida LLC....954 678-6602
2111 N Commerce Pkwy Weston (33326) ***(G-19154)***
Northrop Grmman Feld Spport Sv (HQ)....904 810-4665
5000 Us Highway 1 N B02-60 Saint Augustine (32095) ***(G-15574)***
Northrop Grmman Mssion Systems, Orlando *Also called Northrop Grumman Systems Corp* ***(G-13008)***
Northrop Grmman Tchncal Svcs I....321 837-7000
1235 Evans Rd Melbourne (32904) ***(G-8895)***
Northrop Grmman Tchncal Svcs I....904 825-3300
5000 Us Highway 1 N Saint Augustine (32095) ***(G-15575)***
Northrop Grumman Corporation, Melbourne *Also called Northrop Grumman Systems Corp* ***(G-8897)***
Northrop Grumman Corporation....321 951-5529
2880 Pomello Rd Malabar (32950) ***(G-8496)***

Northrop Grumman Corporation 352 759-2946
18510 Nfs 524 Altoona (32702) ***(G-87)***
Northrop Grumman Corporation 321 951-5730
811 Gabriel Ave Ne Palm Bay (32907) ***(G-13527)***
Northrop Grumman Corporation 321 951-5000
2000 W Nasa Blvd Melbourne (32904) ***(G-8896)***
Northrop Grumman Systems Corp 904 825-3300
5000 Us Highway 1 N Saint Augustine (32095) ***(G-15576)***
Northrop Grumman Systems Corp 904 810-5957
125 International Golf Saint Augustine (32095) ***(G-15577)***
Northrop Grumman Systems Corp 407 295-4010
2787 S Orange Blossom Trl Apopka (32703) ***(G-166)***
Northrop Grumman Systems Corp 321 951-5000
2000 W Nasa Blvd Melbourne (32904) ***(G-8897)***
Northrop Grumman Systems Corp 904 825-3300
5000 Us Highway 1 N Saint Augustine (32095) ***(G-15578)***
Northrop Grumman Systems Corp 561 515-3651
348 Hiatt Dr Ste 100 Palm Beach Gardens (33418) ***(G-13613)***
Northrop Grumman Systems Corp 407 737-4900
11474 Corp Blvd Ste 120 Orlando (32817) ***(G-13008)***
Northside Pharmacy LLC 256 398-7500
36474c Emerald Coast Pkwy Destin (32541) ***(G-3200)***
Northside Sheet Metal Inc 850 769-1461
2836 Transmitter Rd Panama City (32404) ***(G-13932)***
Northstar Aviation USA LLC 321 600-4557
1431 General Aviation Dr Melbourne (32935) ***(G-8898)***
Northwest Florida Daily News, Fort Walton Beach *Also called Panama City News Herald* ***(G-4821)***
Northwest Florida Daily News (HQ) 850 863-1111
2 Eglin Pkwy Ne Fort Walton Beach (32548) ***(G-4819)***
Northwings Accessories Corp (HQ) 305 463-0455
7875 Nw 64th St Miami (33166) ***(G-10078)***
Norton Manufacturing & Svc Inc 352 225-1225
11590 Se 30th St Morriston (32668) ***(G-11093)***
Norwood Promotional Products, Clearwater *Also called Scribe Manufacturing Inc* ***(G-1870)***
Nosta Carpenter Shop, Miami *Also called Nosta Inc* ***(G-10079)***
Nosta Inc 305 634-1435
1235 Nw 29th St Miami (33142) ***(G-10079)***
Nostalgic America Inc 561 585-1724
102 Ne 2nd St Ste 172 Boca Raton (33432) ***(G-649)***
Nostalgic Specialty Foods Inc 561 391-8600
399 S Federal Hwy Boca Raton (33432) ***(G-650)***
Note Bin Inc 727 642-8530
29399 Us 19 N Ste 360 Clearwater (33761) ***(G-1811)***
Note It 954 593-8616
915 Weeping Willow Way Hollywood (33019) ***(G-5884)***
Notice Four LLC 954 652-1168
2775 Nw 62nd St Fort Lauderdale (33309) ***(G-4143)***
Notice That Tee Inc 954 971-1018
2501 Nw 34th Pl Ste 27 Pompano Beach (33069) ***(G-14775)***
Notions, Miami *Also called Scott Slide Fasteners Inc* ***(G-10314)***
Noumenon Corporation 302 296-5460
1616 Cape Coral Pkwy W Cape Coral (33914) ***(G-1451)***
Nouveau Cosmetique Usa Inc 321 332-6976
189 S Orange Ave Ste 1110 Orlando (32801) ***(G-13009)***
Nova Laserlight LLC 407 226-0609
7600 Dr Phillips Blvd Orlando (32819) ***(G-13010)***
Nova Sidera Metal Forming Corp 786 717-7149
14341 Sw 120th St Ste 105 Miami (33186) ***(G-10080)***
Nova Solid Surfaces Inc 239 888-0975
12350 Crystal Commerce Lo Fort Myers (33966) ***(G-4550)***
Novak Machining Inc 727 527-5473
3921 69th Ave N Pinellas Park (33781) ***(G-14372)***
Novalux Signs 904 329-9607
8550 Argyle Business Loop Jacksonville (32244) ***(G-6640)***
Novaphos Inc 863 285-8607
3200 County Rte 630 W Fort Meade (33841) ***(G-4338)***
Novavision Inc (HQ) 561 558-2020
951 Broken Sound Pkwy Nw # 320 Boca Raton (33487) ***(G-651)***
Noveltex Miami Inc 305 887-8191
151 E 10th Ave Hialeah (33010) ***(G-5544)***
Novelty Crystal Corp 352 429-9036
21005 Obrien Rd Groveland (34736) ***(G-5103)***
Novelty Crystal Corp 352 429-9036
21005 Obrien Rd Groveland (34736) ***(G-5104)***
Noven Pharmaceuticals Inc (HQ) 305 964-3393
11960 Sw 144th St Miami (33186) ***(G-10081)***
Noven Therapeutics LLC 212 682-4420
11960 Sw 144th St Miami (33186) ***(G-10082)***
Novena TEC LLC (PA) 407 392-1868
4767 New Broad St Orlando (32814) ***(G-13011)***
Novicon Industries 813 854-3235
400 Roberts Rd Oldsmar (34677) ***(G-12251)***
Novo Aero Services LLC 786 319-8637
6965 Vista Pkwy N Ste 16 West Palm Beach (33411) ***(G-18968)***
Novurania of America Inc 772 567-9200
2105 S Us Highway 1 Vero Beach (32962) ***(G-18647)***
Novus Clip Signs & Video Prod 239 471-5639
12771 Metro Pkwy Ste 1 Fort Myers (33966) ***(G-4551)***
Nowvision Technologies Inc 813 943-4639
618 De Buel Rd Bldng A Lutz (33549) ***(G-8406)***
Noxtak Corp 786 586-7927
21011 Johnson St Ste 110 Pembroke Pines (33029) ***(G-14052)***
NP Industrial Coating Inc 727 485-6113
631 Baynard Dr Tarpon Springs (34689) ***(G-18317)***
Npact America Inc 904 755-6259
14476 Duval Pl W Ste 109 Jacksonville (32218) ***(G-6641)***
Npc of Tampa Inc 813 839-0035
5210 S Lois Ave Tampa (33611) ***(G-17942)***
NPC&ug Inc 239 694-7255
22021 Luckey Lee Ln Alva (33920) ***(G-89)***
NRG Industries Inc 850 510-7174
10631 Lake Iamonia Dr Tallahassee (32312) ***(G-17307)***
Nrnb LLC 203 769-5995
8520 Nw 174th St Hialeah (33015) ***(G-5545)***
Nrz Inc 305 345-7303
12885 Sw 82nd Ave Pinecrest (33156) ***(G-14329)***
Nscrypt Inc 407 275-4720
12151 Res Pkwy Ste 150 Orlando (32826) ***(G-13012)***
NSK Latin America Inc (HQ) 305 477-0605
11601 Nw 107th St Ste 200 Miami (33178) ***(G-10083)***
Nspa, Pensacola *Also called National Std Parts Assoc Inc* ***(G-14211)***
Nst Global LLC 941 748-2270
3145 Lakewood Ranch Blvd Bradenton (34211) ***(G-1088)***
NTS Industries Inc 317 847-6675
1218 W New Hampshire St Orlando (32804) ***(G-13013)***
Nu Earth Labs LLC 727 648-4787
150 Douglas Ave Dunedin (34698) ***(G-3585)***
Nu Trek Inc 813 920-4348
16708 Hutchison Rd Odessa (33556) ***(G-12136)***
Nu-Art Signs Inc 305 531-9850
3343 Nw 7th Ave Miami (33127) ***(G-10084)***
Nu-Element Inc 561 322-8904
240 Ne 8th Ave Deerfield Beach (33441) ***(G-2880)***
Nu-Pac Industries, Pompano Beach *Also called Ross Industries Inc* ***(G-14834)***
Nu-Trend Container, Jacksonville *Also called Corrigan & Company* ***(G-6293)***
Nu-Vue Industries Inc 305 694-0397
1055 E 29th St Hialeah (33013) ***(G-5546)***
Nubo Bottle Company LLC 954 283-9057
526 Bayfront Dr Boynton Beach (33435) ***(G-938)***
Nucor LLC 786 290-9328
8835 Harding Ave Surfside (33154) ***(G-17204)***
Nucor Steel Florida Inc 863 546-5800
22 Nucor Dr Frostproof (33843) ***(G-4862)***
Nucycle Energy of Tampa LLC 813 848-0509
2067 S County Line Rd Plant City (33566) ***(G-14450)***
Nuenergy Technologies Corp 866 895-6838
601 Cleveland St Ste 501 Clearwater (33755) ***(G-1812)***
Nuevo Mundo Company 305 207-8155
9702 Sw 40th St Miami (33165) ***(G-10085)***
Nuflo Inc 904 265-4001
3440 Evergreen Ave Ste 1 Jacksonville (32206) ***(G-6642)***
Nuform Cabinetry 954 532-2746
1745 N Powerline Rd Pompano Beach (33069) ***(G-14776)***
Nuggets Racing LLC 954 943-3561
3441 Ne 13th Ave Pompano Beach (33064) ***(G-14777)***
Nulab Inc 727 446-1126
519 Cleveland St Ste 101 Clearwater (33755) ***(G-1813)***
Nuline Sensors LLC 407 473-0765
210 Specialty Pt Sanford (32771) ***(G-16092)***
Number 1 Brick Pavers Inc 321 388-7889
3406 Soho St Apt 101 Orlando (32835) ***(G-13014)***
Numerator Technologies Inc 941 807-5333
862 Freeling Dr Sarasota (34242) ***(G-16526)***
Nunez Machine Shop Inc 786 615-4261
9809 Nw 80th Ave Miami Lakes (33016) ***(G-10831)***
Nupress of Miami Inc 305 594-2100
2050 Nw 94th Ave Doral (33172) ***(G-3446)***
Nursery Supplies Inc 407 846-9750
2050 Avenue A Kissimmee (34758) ***(G-7278)***
Nurserymens Sure-Gro Corp 772 770-0462
4390 Us Highway 1 Vero Beach (32967) ***(G-18648)***
Nutop International LLC 954 909-0010
2601 E Oklnd Prk Blvd # 601 Fort Lauderdale (33306) ***(G-4144)***
Nutra Pharma Corp 954 509-0911
4001 Nw 73rd Way Coral Springs (33065) ***(G-2298)***
Nutra-Lift Skin Care, Fort Lauderdale *Also called Younger You Inc* ***(G-4333)***
Nutra-Luxe MD LLC 239 561-9699
12801 Commwl Dr Ste 1 Fort Myers (33913) ***(G-4552)***
Nutraceutical Corporation 813 877-4186
5046 W Linebaugh Ave Tampa (33624) ***(G-17943)***
Nutrakey LLC 321 234-6282
975 Bennett Dr Longwood (32750) ***(G-8318)***
Nutramedix LLC 561 745-2917
2885 Jupiter Park Dr # 1600 Jupiter (33458) ***(G-7085)***
Nutrasource LLC (PA) 786 427-4305
1395 Brickell Ave Ste 800 Miami (33131) ***(G-10086)***
Nutri D'Light, Hialeah *Also called Productos Las Delicias Inc* ***(G-5577)***
Nutri-Force Nutrition, Miami Lakes *Also called Fdc Vitamins LLC* ***(G-10789)***

ALPHABETIC

Nutricorp LLC 305 680-4896
671 W 18th St Hialeah (33010) ***(G-5547)***
Nutrifusion LLC 404 240-0030
10641 Airport Pulling Rd Naples (34109) ***(G-11347)***
Nutrition Laboratories Inc 915 496-7531
2151 Logan St Clearwater (33765) ***(G-1814)***
Nutrition Laboratories Inc 727 442-2747
2141 Logan St Clearwater (33765) ***(G-1815)***
Nutrition World Health Market, Palm Beach Gardens *Also called Briemad Inc* ***(G-13572)***
Nutritious You LLC 941 203-5203
6583 Midnight Pass Rd Sarasota (34242) ***(G-16527)***
Nuts About Florida, Miami *Also called Barnard Nut Company Inc* ***(G-9221)***
Nutty Scoopz, Jacksonville *Also called Hoppin Pop Kettle Stop LLC* ***(G-6479)***
Nv5geospatial, Saint Petersburg *Also called Quantum Spatial Inc* ***(G-15897)***
Nvip LLC 972 435-4097
2231 Linwood Ave Naples (34112) ***(G-11348)***
Nwgc, Boca Raton *Also called New World Gold Corporation* ***(G-641)***
Nwh Publishing Llc 904 217-3911
659 Los Caminos St Saint Augustine (32095) ***(G-15579)***
Nwi, Sarasota *Also called Genie Cap Inc* ***(G-16448)***
Nwl Inc 800 742-5695
4701 Crump Rd Lake Hamilton (33851) ***(G-7391)***
Nwl Inc 561 848-9009
8050 Monetary Dr Riviera Beach (33404) ***(G-15353)***
Nxgen Brands Inc (PA) 954 329-2205
2322 Se 8th St Cape Coral (33990) ***(G-1452)***
Nxgen Brands LLC 888 315-6339
8032 Lakepointe Dr Plantation (33322) ***(G-14540)***
Nylacarb Corp 772 569-5999
1725 98th Ave Vero Beach (32966) ***(G-18649)***
Nypro Healthcare LLC 727 577-9749
10560 Dr Martin Luther Saint Petersburg (33716) ***(G-15868)***
Nyrstar Us Inc 954 400-6464
350 E Las Olas Blvd # 800 Fort Lauderdale (33301) ***(G-4145)***
O I Inc 321 499-3800
295 North Dr Ste A Melbourne (32934) ***(G-8899)***
O Mustad & Son USA Inc 206 284-7871
2315 Nw 107th Ave Ste 88 Doral (33172) ***(G-3447)***
O Neill Industries Intl Inc (PA) 850 754-0312
8 E Quintette Rd Ste B Cantonment (32533) ***(G-1344)***
O R Welding Service LLC 561 707-4325
841 Ne 24th St Apt 2 Belle Glade (33430) ***(G-349)***
O'Malley Valve Co., Saint Petersburg *Also called OMalley Manufacturing Inc* ***(G-15872)***
O2 Defense LLC 704 408-7357
13501 Lunker Ct Odessa (33556) ***(G-12137)***
Oai, Tampa *Also called Outdoor America Images Inc* ***(G-17964)***
Oai Enterprises LLC 239 225-1350
12960 Commerce Lakes Dr Fort Myers (33913) ***(G-4553)***
Oakbrook Sales Inc 800 773-0979
2200 Butts Rd Ste 200 Boca Raton (33431) ***(G-652)***
Oakhurst Marketing Inc 727 532-8255
2392 31st St S Saint Petersburg (33712) ***(G-15869)***
Oakhurst Signs, Saint Petersburg *Also called Oakhurst Marketing Inc* ***(G-15869)***
Oakland Park Exxon, Oakland Park *Also called Daleo Fuels Inc* ***(G-11795)***
Oakland Park Smoothie Inc 954 567-0871
2765 Ne 19th St Fort Lauderdale (33305) ***(G-4146)***
Oakley Signs, Maitland *Also called L4 Design LLC* ***(G-8471)***
Oakridge Globl Enrgy Sltons In 321 610-7959
3520 Dixie Hwy Ne Palm Bay (32905) ***(G-13528)***
Oaktree Software Inc 407 339-5855
222 S Westmonte Dr # 251 Altamonte Springs (32714) ***(G-59)***
Oase North America Inc 800 365-3880
7241 Hvrhill Bus Pkwy # 105 Riviera Beach (33407) ***(G-15354)***
Oasis Alignment Services Inc 850 484-2994
7501 Sears Blvd Pensacola (32514) ***(G-14213)***
OB Inc (PA) 321 223-0332
5020 Scott Rd Cocoa (32926) ***(G-2039)***
Obem Foods Inc 305 887-0258
400 Swallow Dr Miami Springs (33166) ***(G-10896)***
Oberon Industries Inc 321 245-7338
1900 Stanley St Orlando (32803) ***(G-13015)***
Obitx Inc 904 748-9750
4720 Salisbury Rd Jacksonville (32256) ***(G-6643)***
Observer Group, Sarasota *Also called Observer Media Group Inc* ***(G-16529)***
Observer Group 407 654-5500
446 N Dillard St Winter Garden (34787) ***(G-19278)***
Observer Group and Gulf Coast 239 263-0122
2960 Immokalee Rd Naples (34110) ***(G-11349)***
Observer Group Inc 941 383-5509
1970 Main St Fl 3 Sarasota (34236) ***(G-16528)***
Observer Media Group Inc (PA) 941 366-3468
1970 Main St Fl 3 Sarasota (34236) ***(G-16529)***
Observer, The, New Smyrna Beach *Also called Horizon Publications Inc* ***(G-11535)***
Obsolete Gamer Inc 305 388-3372
13501 Sw 80th St Miami (33183) ***(G-10087)***
Ocala Bedrock, Ocala *Also called Bedrock Resources LLC* ***(G-11885)***
Ocala Breeders Sales Co Inc (PA) 352 237-4667
1701 Sw 60th Ave Ocala (34474) ***(G-12007)***
Ocala Breeders' Feed & Supply, Ocala *Also called Ocala Breeders Sales Co Inc* ***(G-12007)***
Ocala Centre 6 .... 305 322-7365
3075 Sw 53rd St Ocala (34471) ***(G-12008)***
Ocala Concrete Services LLC 352 694-4300
3498 W Highway 326 Ocala (34475) ***(G-12009)***
Ocala Engineering-Traffic Div, Ocala *Also called City of Ocala* ***(G-11903)***
Ocala Magazine 352 622-2995
743 E Fort King St Ocala (34471) ***(G-12010)***
Ocala Manufacturing 352 433-6643
10245 N Us Highway 27 Ocala (34482) ***(G-12011)***
Ocala Metal Products Inc 352 861-4500
800 N Pine Ave Ocala (34475) ***(G-12012)***
Ocala Pharmacy LLC 352 509-7890
8290 Sw Highway 200 Ocala (34481) ***(G-12013)***
Ocala Print Quick Inc 352 629-0736
600 S Magnolia Ave Ocala (34471) ***(G-12014)***
Ocala Publication Incorported 352 732-0073
908 Se 16th St Ocala (34471) ***(G-12015)***
Ocala Star Banner Corporation 352 867-4010
2121 Sw 19th Avenue Rd Ocala (34471) ***(G-12016)***
Ocala Style Magazine, Ocala *Also called Ocala Publication Incorported* ***(G-12015)***
Ocala Swamp LLC 352 732-4260
1900 Se 18th Ave Ocala (34471) ***(G-12017)***
Ocalanow Com 352 433-2497
126 Se 41st Ave Ocala (34471) ***(G-12018)***
OCC My Stone LLC 786 352-1567
10090 Nw 80th Ct Apt 1238 Miami Lakes (33016) ***(G-10832)***
Ocean Bio-Chem Inc (PA) 954 587-6280
4041 Sw 47th Ave Davie (33314) ***(G-2559)***
Ocean Blue Graphics Inc 561 881-2022
1841 W 10th St Ste 1 Riviera Beach (33404) ***(G-15355)***
Ocean Blue Graphics Design Inc 561 881-2022
1841 W 10th St Ste 1 Riviera Beach (33404) ***(G-15356)***
Ocean Breeze, Stuart *Also called Quorum Marine & Elec Inc* ***(G-16994)***
Ocean Dynamics USA Inc 305 770-1800
18377 Ne 4th Ct Miami (33179) ***(G-10088)***
Ocean Global Inc 727 842-7544
4925 Southshore Dr New Port Richey (34652) ***(G-11503)***
Ocean Insight, Orlando *Also called Ocean Optics Inc* ***(G-13016)***
Ocean Kitchen Cabinets 352 745-7110
4445 Sw 35th Ter Ste 200 Gainesville (32608) ***(G-4974)***
Ocean Marine LLC 305 549-6092
3109 Grand Ave 408 Miami (33133) ***(G-10089)***
Ocean Master Marine Inc 561 840-0448
837 W 13th St Unit C Riviera Beach (33404) ***(G-15357)***
Ocean Media, Stuart *Also called Mailbox Publishing Inc* ***(G-16972)***
Ocean Optics Inc (HQ) 407 673-0041
3500 Quadrangle Blvd Orlando (32817) ***(G-13016)***
Ocean Optics Inc 727 545-0741
3500 Quadrangle Blvd Orlando (32817) ***(G-13017)***
Ocean Pharmaceuticals Inc 954 473-4717
5373 N Hiatus Rd Sunrise (33351) ***(G-17153)***
Ocean Potion, Cocoa *Also called Florida Glsd Holdings Inc* ***(G-2023)***
Ocean Tech, West Palm Beach *Also called J & I Ventures Inc* ***(G-18909)***
Ocean Test Equipment Inc 954 474-6603
2021 Sw 70th Ave Ste B1 Davie (33317) ***(G-2560)***
Ocean Waves Inc 904 372-4743
525 3rd St N Ste 105 Jacksonville Beach (32250) ***(G-6953)***
Ocean Way Transport LLC 407 669-3822
4529 Piedmont St Orlando (32811) ***(G-13018)***
Ocean Woodworks Inc 904 246-7178
1701 Mayport Rd Ste 1 Atlantic Beach (32233) ***(G-225)***
Oceana Software Corp 813 335-6966
5202 Quarrystone Ln Tampa (33624) ***(G-17944)***
Oceaneering International Inc 985 329-3282
1700 C Ave Panama City (32401) ***(G-13933)***
Oceangrown 941 921-2401
7453 Commercial Cir Fort Pierce (34951) ***(G-4723)***
Oceanic Electrical Mfg Co Inc 908 355-1900
1904 Calumet St Clearwater (33765) ***(G-1816)***
Oceanic Resturant Equipment, Tampa *Also called Four Seas Trading Corp* ***(G-17692)***
Oceanside Custom LLC 386 341-7507
4125 Cleveland Ave # 1035 Fort Myers (33901) ***(G-4554)***
Oceanstyle By Burgess, Miami Beach *Also called Oceanstyle LLC* ***(G-10699)***
Oceanstyle LLC 305 672-9400
390 Alton Rd Ste 2 Miami Beach (33139) ***(G-10699)***
Oceanvista Publishing LLC 561 547-5730
6605 S Dixie Hwy West Palm Beach (33405) ***(G-18969)***
Ocoa LLC 407 898-1961
800 N Magnolia Ave # 1400 Orlando (32803) ***(G-13019)***
OCon Enterprise Inc 954 920-6700
821 N 21st Ave Hollywood (33020) ***(G-5885)***
OConnell Team LLC 772 201-3848
152 Sw Milburn Cir Port Saint Lucie (34953) ***(G-15126)***
Ocoos, Ocala *Also called Advtravl Inc* ***(G-11865)***
Ocoow LLC 805 266-7616
2340 Sopchoppy Hwy Sopchoppy (32358) ***(G-16785)***
Octal Ventures Inc 727 526-9288
6544 44th St N Ste 1205 Pinellas Park (33781) ***(G-14373)***

Octametro LLC....305 715-9713
8539 Nw 56th St Doral (33166) ***(G-3448)***
Octane Seating LLC....888 627-6743
401 E Las Olas Blvd Ste 1 Fort Lauderdale (33301) ***(G-4147)***
Octex Holdings LLC (PA)....941 371-6767
901 Sarasota Center Blvd Sarasota (34240) ***(G-16530)***
Oculus Surgical Inc....772 236-2622
562 Nw Merc Pl Ste 104 Port St Lucie (34986) ***(G-15177)***
Odara Kanvas Cosmetics....239 785-8013
1126 Homer Ave S Lehigh Acres (33973) ***(G-8201)***
Odhams Press, Tampa *Also called 10 Roof Cottage LLC* ***(G-17371)***
Odyssey, Jacksonville *Also called Benner China and Glwr of Fla* ***(G-6205)***
Odyssey Fastening Systems Inc....561 436-5570
516 Commerce Way Ste 5 Jupiter (33458) ***(G-7086)***
Odyssey Manufacturing Co....407 582-9051
250 Central Florida Pkwy Orlando (32824) ***(G-13020)***
Odyssey Manufacturing Co (PA)....813 635-0339
1484 Massaro Blvd Tampa (33619) ***(G-17945)***
Odyssey Manufacturing Co....813 635-0339
5361 Hartford St Tampa (33619) ***(G-17946)***
Oerlikon USA Inc....727 577-4999
10050 16th St N Saint Petersburg (33716) ***(G-15870)***
Ofab Inc....352 629-0040
1909 Ne 25th Ave Ocala (34470) ***(G-12019)***
Off The Chart Inc....954 654-6541
5400 S University Dr Davie (33328) ***(G-2561)***
Off The Wall Screen Printing, Lynn Haven *Also called Rinehart Corp* ***(G-8437)***
Offensive Defense Inc....786 306-8162
5444 Sw 186th Way Miramar (33029) ***(G-11022)***
Office Express Corp....786 503-6800
1835 Nw 112th Ave Ste 174 Miami (33172) ***(G-10090)***
Office Furniture By Tempo Inc....305 685-3077
4136 E 10th Ln Hialeah (33013) ***(G-5548)***
Office Graphic Design, Coral Gables *Also called Graphic Center Group Corp* ***(G-2152)***
Office of Medical Examiner....772 464-7378
2500 S 35th St Fort Pierce (34981) ***(G-4724)***
Office, The, Miami *Also called A & S Entertainment LLC* ***(G-9032)***
Official Gear Company Inc....407 721-9110
106 Deer Run Lake Dr Ormond Beach (32174) ***(G-13387)***
Officine Gullo USA LLC....800 781-7125
6151 Biscayne Blvd Miami (33137) ***(G-10091)***
Offshore Inland Mar Olfld Svcs....251 443-5550
640 S Barracks St Pensacola (32502) ***(G-14214)***
Offshore Performance Spc....239 481-2768
15881 Chief Ct Fort Myers (33912) ***(G-4555)***
OGrady Tool Company....239 560-3395
7721 Hidden Pond Ln Fort Myers (33917) ***(G-4556)***
Ogre Custom Fabrications LLC....321 544-2142
2495 Jen Dr Ste 10 Melbourne (32940) ***(G-8900)***
OH Catering Inc....305 903-9271
3006 Sw 155th Ave Miami (33185) ***(G-10092)***
Ohana Liquids LLC....888 642-6244
900 N Atlantic Ave New Smyrna Beach (32169) ***(G-11540)***
OHanrahan Consultants Inc....727 531-3375
6414 125th Ave Largo (33773) ***(G-8019)***
OHM Americas LLC....800 467-7275
3736 Sw 30th Ave Fort Lauderdale (33312) ***(G-4148)***
OHM Power Solutions, Fort Lauderdale *Also called OHM Americas LLC* ***(G-4148)***
Ohmac Chemical Group, Largo *Also called OHanrahan Consultants Inc* ***(G-8019)***
Oi Distribution, Weston *Also called Original Impressions LLC* ***(G-19156)***
Oils R US 1 800....305 681-0909
3300 Nw 112th St Miami (33167) ***(G-10093)***
Ojm, Miami *Also called Lau International Inc* ***(G-9871)***
Okay Pure Naturals, Opa Locka *Also called Xtreme Tools International Inc* ***(G-12371)***
Okee-B Inc....561 996-3040
1125 Ne 18th St Belle Glade (33430) ***(G-350)***
Okeechobee Asphalt & Ready Mix....863 763-7373
503 Nw 9th St Okeechobee (34972) ***(G-12187)***
Okeechobee Petroleum LLC....561 478-1083
6970 Okeechobee Blvd West Palm Beach (33411) ***(G-18970)***
Okeelanta Corporation....561 996-9072
6 Mile S Of S Bay Hwy 27 South Bay (33493) ***(G-16796)***
Okeelanta Corporation (HQ)....561 366-5100
1 N Clematis St Ste 200 West Palm Beach (33401) ***(G-18971)***
Okeelanta Sugar, South Bay *Also called Okeelanta Corporation* ***(G-16796)***
OL Products Inc....813 854-3575
100 Mount Vernon St Oldsmar (34677) ***(G-12252)***
Olas Foods Specialty Mkt Inc....813 447-5127
5791 54th Ave N Kenneth City (33709) ***(G-7153)***
Old 97 Company (HQ)....813 246-4180
4829 E 7th Ave Tampa (33605) ***(G-17947)***
Old Castle Coastal, Gainesville *Also called Oldcastle Building Produc* ***(G-4975)***
Old City Building....850 432-7723
201 E Government St Pensacola (32502) ***(G-14215)***
Old City Marine LLC....904 252-6887
76 Dockside Dr Ste 112 Saint Augustine (32084) ***(G-15580)***
Old City Sweepstakes....904 808-0456
2303 N Ponce De Leon Blvd Saint Augustine (32084) ***(G-15581)***
Old Heritage Medcall Inc....813 221-1000
202 E Virginia Ave Tampa (33603) ***(G-17948)***
Old Meeting House Home Made Ic....813 254-0977
901 S Howard Ave Tampa (33606) ***(G-17949)***
Old Oak Truss Company....813 689-6597
1460 State Rd 574 Seffner (33584) ***(G-16731)***
Old Port Group LLC....904 819-5812
1301 Plntn Is Dr S 206b Saint Augustine (32080) ***(G-15582)***
Old Town Timber LLC....904 217-7046
205 C St Saint Augustine (32080) ***(G-15583)***
Old World Marble and Gran Inc....239 596-4777
1998 Trade Center Way # 1 Naples (34109) ***(G-11350)***
Oldcastle Apg South Inc....813 367-9780
3801 Pga Blvd Ste 806 Palm Beach Gardens (33410) ***(G-13614)***
Oldcastle Apg South Inc....863 421-7422
1980 Marley Dr Haines City (33844) ***(G-5144)***
Oldcastle Architectural Inc....813 886-7761
5603 Anderson Rd Tampa (33614) ***(G-17950)***
Oldcastle Building Produc....352 377-1699
3302 Ne 2nd St Gainesville (32609) ***(G-4975)***
Oldcastle Buildingenvelope Inc....813 247-3184
5115 Hartford St Tampa (33619) ***(G-17951)***
Oldcastle Coastal, Riviera Beach *Also called Paver Systems LLC* ***(G-15359)***
Oldcastle Coastal....813 621-2427
5455 N 59th St Tampa (33610) ***(G-17952)***
Oldcastle Coastal Inc....813 886-7761
5603 Anderson Rd Tampa (33614) ***(G-17953)***
Oldcastle Coastal Inc....813 932-1007
8910 N 12th St Tampa (33604) ***(G-17954)***
Oldcastle Coastal Inc....813 783-1970
3749 Copeland Dr Zephyrhills (33542) ***(G-19528)***
Oldcastle Coastal Inc (HQ)....813 367-9780
4630 Woodland Corporate B Tampa (33614) ***(G-17955)***
Oldcastle Infrastructure Inc....800 642-1540
1410 Industrial Dr Wildwood (34785) ***(G-19198)***
Oldcastle Lawn & Garden, Lakeland *Also called Crh Americas Inc* ***(G-7665)***
Oldcastle Retail Inc....954 971-1200
1200 Nw 18th St Pompano Beach (33069) ***(G-14778)***
Olde Hearth Bread Company, Casselberry *Also called Claddah Corp* ***(G-1501)***
Olde World Craftsmen Inc....239 229-3806
15970 Lake Candlewood Dr Fort Myers (33908) ***(G-4557)***
Oldja Enterprises Inc....727 526-3240
4424 34th St N Saint Petersburg (33714) ***(G-15871)***
Oldsmar Ready Mix Con Plant, Oldsmar *Also called Cemex Cnstr Mtls Fla LLC* ***(G-12213)***
Oldsmar Service Center, Oldsmar *Also called Structall Building Systems Inc* ***(G-12269)***
Olevin Compounds LLC....954 993-5148
12758 Sw 47th St Miramar (33027) ***(G-11023)***
Olian Inc....305 233-9116
13011 Sw 132nd St Miami (33186) ***(G-10094)***
Olive 30a Oil Inc....850 909-0099
12805 Us Highway 98 E N1 Inlet Beach (32461) ***(G-6077)***
Olive Amelia LLC....904 310-3603
206 Centre St Fernandina Beach (32034) ***(G-3746)***
Olive Naples Oil Company (PA)....239 596-3000
2368 Immokalee Rd Naples (34110) ***(G-11351)***
Olive Oil Co of Fort Myers....239 821-4630
2960 39th St Sw Naples (34117) ***(G-11352)***
Olive Tree II....813 991-8781
2653 Bruce B Downs Blvd Wesley Chapel (33544) ***(G-18755)***
Oliveira Services Corp....772 834-4803
972 Sw Paar Dr Port Saint Lucie (34953) ***(G-15127)***
Oliveri Woodworking Inc....561 478-7233
3001 Tuxedo Ave West Palm Beach (33405) ***(G-18972)***
Ollie Pippa International Inc....888 851-6533
21733 Old Bridge Trl Boca Raton (33428) ***(G-653)***
Ollo Usa LLC....941 366-0600
1223 S Tamiami Trl Sarasota (34239) ***(G-16531)***
Olmedo Printing Corp....305 262-4666
710 Sw 73rd Ct Miami (33144) ***(G-10095)***
Olmstead Publishing LLC....954 559-0192
2629 Grassmoor Loop Apopka (32712) ***(G-167)***
Oly Custom Cabinets Miami Inc....305 216-3947
13285 Sw 39th St Miami (33175) ***(G-10096)***
Olympian Led Inc....321 747-3220
3620 S Hopkins Ave Titusville (32780) ***(G-18447)***
Olympic Case Co, Tampa *Also called Qps Companies Inc* ***(G-18029)***
Olympus Group Inc....407 851-6229
2100 Principal Row # 407 Orlando (32837) ***(G-13021)***
OMalley Manufacturing Inc....727 327-6817
4228 8th Ave S Saint Petersburg (33711) ***(G-15872)***
Omax Home Inc....239 980-2755
1946 Dana Dr Fort Myers (33907) ***(G-4558)***
Omb America, Miami *Also called Transamerica Intl Brdcstg* ***(G-10503)***
Omega Energy Usa LLC....786 245-0642
600 Brickell Ave Ste 1530 Miami (33131) ***(G-10097)***
Omega Garage Doors Inc....352 620-8830
7751 Industrial Rd Melbourne (32904) ***(G-8901)***
Omega Gas Inc....786 277-2176
18401 Sw 115th Ave Miami (33157) ***(G-10098)***

ALPHABETIC

Omega Lift Corporation...561 840-0088
6701 Garden Rd Ste 1 Riviera Beach (33404) ***(G-15358)***
Omega Medical Imaging LLC...407 323-9400
3400 Saint Johns Pkwy # 1020 Sanford (32771) ***(G-16093)***
Omega One Research Inc...561 995-9611
6458 E Rogers Cir Boca Raton (33487) ***(G-654)***
Omega Power Systems Inc...772 219-0045
4443 Se Commerce Ave Stuart (34997) ***(G-16982)***
Omega Prof Brick Pavers Inc...727 243-4659
3679 141st Ave Apt B Largo (33771) ***(G-8020)***
Omega Publishing...727 815-0402
6014 Us Highway 19 # 305 New Port Richey (34652) ***(G-11504)***
Omega Sign Service Corporation...727 505-7833
11301 Biddeford Pl New Port Richey (34654) ***(G-11505)***
Omega3 Innovations, Venice *Also called Ambo Health LLC* ***(G-18532)***
OMI of Lake City LLC...386 288-5632
4066 Nw Wisteria Dr Lake City (32055) ***(G-7373)***
Omni Displays LLC...352 799-9997
15261 Telcom Dr Brooksville (34604) ***(G-1257)***
Omni Dsgns Ldscp Mngements LLC...561 339-4800
18155 Jupiter Landings Dr Jupiter (33458) ***(G-7087)***
Omni Marine Enterprises LLC...941 474-4614
2640 S Mccall Rd Englewood (34224) ***(G-3663)***
Omnia Inc...863 619-8100
3125 Drane Feld Rd Ste 29 Lakeland (33811) ***(G-7758)***
Omnia Incorporated...863 619-8100
3125 Drane Feld Rd Ste 29 Lakeland (33811) ***(G-7759)***
Omniaelectronics llc...631 742-5719
7945 East Dr Apt 204 North Bay Village (33141) ***(G-11594)***
Omnifund, Tampa *Also called Gotobilling Inc* ***(G-17722)***
Omnimark Enterprises LLC...516 351-9075
6843 Narcoossee Rd Orlando (32822) ***(G-13022)***
Omnireliant Corporation...813 909-9191
4218 W Linebaugh Ave Tampa (33624) ***(G-17956)***
Omnisys LLC...800 325-2017
551 N Cattlemen Rd Sarasota (34232) ***(G-16532)***
Omnivore Technologies Inc...800 293-4058
13577 Feather Sound Dr # 390 Clearwater (33762) ***(G-1817)***
Omt Inc...772 287-3762
648 Se Monterey Rd Stuart (34994) ***(G-16983)***
Omt LLC...954 327-1447
3848 Sw 30th Ave Fort Lauderdale (33312) ***(G-4149)***
Omz Industries LLC...786 210-6763
6010 Nw 99th Ave Unit 102 Doral (33178) ***(G-3449)***
On A Roll Distributors Inc...352 726-3420
1626 E Saint James Loop Inverness (34453) ***(G-6093)***
On Base Foods Group LLC...248 672-7659
3179 E Pebble Creek Dr Avon Park (33825) ***(G-291)***
On Demand Envelopes, Hallandale Beach *Also called Services On Demand Print Inc* ***(G-5209)***
On Demand Printing, Oldsmar *Also called Ronecker Holdings LLC* ***(G-12268)***
On Demand Spclty Envelope Corp...305 681-5345
917 Sw 10th St Hallandale Beach (33009) ***(G-5202)***
On Screen Ink...724 516-4999
1360 Hammondville Rd Pompano Beach (33069) ***(G-14779)***
On Site AG Services...863 382-7502
359 S Commerce Ave Sebring (33870) ***(G-16700)***
On Site Svcs of Mid FL...407 444-2951
265 Damascus Rd Deland (32724) ***(G-3004)***
On The Go Food & Fuel Inc...727 815-0823
6444 Massachusetts Ave New Port Richey (34653) ***(G-11506)***
On The Run Printing...305 733-2619
7141 Dilido Blvd Miramar (33023) ***(G-11024)***
On Time Loading...877 668-4630
4300 Biscayne Blvd Miami (33137) ***(G-10099)***
On-Board Media Inc...305 673-0400
8400 Nw 36th St Ste 500 Doral (33166) ***(G-3450)***
On-Q Software Inc...305 553-6566
13764 Sw 11th St Miami (33184) ***(G-10100)***
On-Site Lighting & Sign Svcs...256 693-1018
5925 Flaxman St Pensacola (32506) ***(G-14216)***
Onan Generators & Engines...772 334-8282
883 Ne Dixie Hwy Jensen Beach (34957) ***(G-6972)***
Onaris...305 579-0056
14 Ne 1st Ave Ste 607 Miami (33132) ***(G-10101)***
Onboard Media, Doral *Also called On-Board Media Inc* ***(G-3450)***
Onca Gear LLC...857 253-8207
2372 W 77th St Hialeah (33016) ***(G-5549)***
One Bio Corp...305 328-8662
19950 W Country Club Dr Aventura (33180) ***(G-277)***
One Biotechnology Company...941 355-8451
1833 57th St Ste A Sarasota (34243) ***(G-16268)***
One Group...305 604-6999
2311 Collins Ave Miami Beach (33139) ***(G-10700)***
One Hour Printing...386 763-3111
661 Beville Rd Ste 109 South Daytona (32119) ***(G-16805)***
One Hundred Ten Percent, Ponte Vedra Beach *Also called Recover Gear LLC* ***(G-14952)***
One Milo Inc...305 804-0266
1010 Brickell Ave # 2709 Miami (33131) ***(G-10102)***
One Nugget LLc...904 527-3218
2206 Osprey Point Dr W Jacksonville (32224) ***(G-6644)***
One Nursing Care LLC...954 441-6644
3351 Executive Way Miramar (33025) ***(G-11025)***
One Price Drycleaners Tampa (PA)...727 734-3353
1850 Main St Dunedin (34698) ***(G-3586)***
One Resonance Sensors...407 323-9933
101 Gordon St Sanford (32771) ***(G-16094)***
One Resonance Sensors LLC...407 637-0771
101 Gordon St Sanford (32771) ***(G-16095)***
One Source Industries Inc...813 855-3440
200 Pine Ave N Ste A Oldsmar (34677) ***(G-12253)***
One Source Technology, Largo *Also called Computer Forms & Supplies* ***(G-7926)***
One Step Papers LLC (PA)...305 238-2296
12105 Sw 130th St Ste 202 Miami (33186) ***(G-10103)***
One Stop Generator Shop Inc...561 840-0009
3600 Inv Ln Ste 104 West Palm Beach (33404) ***(G-18973)***
One World Media LLC...786 762-3030
3390 Mary St Ste 116 Miami (33133) ***(G-10104)***
One World Resource LLC...305 445-9199
4608 Sw 74th Ave Miami (33155) ***(G-10105)***
Onelid LLC...305 335-9730
2100 Ne 211th Ter North Miami Beach (33179) ***(G-11695)***
Onesource Information Services, Tampa *Also called Hill Donnelly Corporation* ***(G-17755)***
Onesource of Florida Inc...904 620-0003
6720 Arlington Expy Jacksonville (32211) ***(G-6645)***
Onetown Boards...786 704-5921
580 Nw 120th St Miami (33168) ***(G-10106)***
Ongoing Care Solutions Inc...727 526-0707
11721 Us Highway 19 N Clearwater (33764) ***(G-1818)***
Onicon Incorporated (HQ)...727 447-6140
11451 Belcher Rd S Largo (33773) ***(G-8021)***
Online German Publisher LLC...239 344-8953
1000 Nw 37th Pl Cape Coral (33993) ***(G-1453)***
Online Labels LLC (PA)...407 936-3900
2001 E Lake Mary Blvd Sanford (32773) ***(G-16096)***
Onnow.fm, Jacksonville Beach *Also called Levitech Services LLC* ***(G-6949)***
Onpoint Global...651 788-1274
8325 Ne 2nd Ave Ste 100 Miami (33138) ***(G-10107)***
Onsight Industries...407 830-8861
221 Hobbs St Tampa (33619) ***(G-17957)***
Onsite Rlble Forklift Svcs Inc...305 305-8638
714 E 28th St Hialeah (33013) ***(G-5550)***
Ontic Engineering & Mfg...407 206-8459
13485 Veterans Way # 600 Orlando (32827) ***(G-13023)***
Ontyte LLC...561 880-8920
3460 Fairlane Farms Rd # 15 Wellington (33414) ***(G-18726)***
Onvoi AVI Supp and Inspect Ser...805 312-3274
619 Airpark Rd Defuniak Springs (32435) ***(G-2945)***
Onyx Armor, Miami *Also called Onyx Protective Group Inc* ***(G-10108)***
Onyx Protective Group Inc...305 282-4455
7359 Nw 34th St Miami (33122) ***(G-10108)***
Oompha Inc...850 222-7210
1754 Thomasville Rd Tallahassee (32303) ***(G-17308)***
OP Yacht Services Corp...954 451-3677
2015 Sw 20th St Ste 220 Fort Lauderdale (33315) ***(G-4150)***
Opa-Locka Pallets Inc...305 681-8212
3180 Nw 131st St Opa Locka (33054) ***(G-12347)***
OPC News...904 686-3938
1102 A1a N Ste 108 Ponte Vedra Beach (32082) ***(G-14948)***
OPelle Enterprises Inc...954 942-7338
1471 Sw 5th Ct Pompano Beach (33069) ***(G-14780)***
Open House Magazine Inc...305 576-6011
505 Ne 30th St Apt 405 Miami (33137) ***(G-10109)***
Open Magnetic Scanning Ltd...954 202-5097
4805 N Dixie Hwy Oakland Park (33334) ***(G-11826)***
Open Market Enterprises LLC...407 322-5434
3461 Parkway Center Ct Orlando (32808) ***(G-13024)***
Open Palm Press Inc...813 870-3839
3839 W Kennedy Blvd Tampa (33609) ***(G-17958)***
Openkm Usa LLC...407 257-2640
1715 Branchwater Trl Orlando (32825) ***(G-13025)***
Openwater Seafood LLC...407 440-0656
13435 S Orange Ave Orlando (32824) ***(G-13026)***
Opie Choice LLC (PA)...352 331-3741
3870 Nw 83rd St Gainesville (32606) ***(G-4976)***
Opie Choice LLC...727 726-5157
22047 Us Highway 19 N Clearwater (33765) ***(G-1819)***
Opie Choice Network, Gainesville *Also called Opie Choice LLC* ***(G-4976)***
OPif- Our Plstic Is Fntstic...954 636-4228
698 1/2 Nw 16 Stunits E F Lauderhill (33311) ***(G-8118)***
Opinicus Textron Inc...813 792-9300
1827 Northpointe Pkwy Lutz (33558) ***(G-8407)***
Opko Curna LLC...305 575-4100
4400 Biscayne Blvd Miami (33137) ***(G-10110)***
Opko Health Inc (PA)...305 575-4100
4400 Biscayne Blvd Miami (33137) ***(G-10111)***
Opreme Beverage Corp...954 699-0669
5151 Corporate Way Jupiter (33458) ***(G-7088)***
Optek International, Largo *Also called Intuitos LLC* ***(G-7983)***

Optical Hong Kong...305 200-5522
6073 Nw 167th St Ste C20 Hialeah (33015) ***(G-5551)***
Optigrate Corporation...407 542-7704
562 S Econ Cir Oviedo (32765) ***(G-13450)***
Optima Associates Inc...877 371-1555
2469 W Us Highway 90 # 130 Lake City (32055) ***(G-7374)***
Optima Neuroscience Inc...352 371-8281
11930 Research Cir Alachua (32615) ***(G-12)***
Optimal Station, Alachua *Also called Optimal Vending Systems* ***(G-13)***
Optimal Vending Systems...301 633-2353
22806 Nw County Road 241 Alachua (32615) ***(G-13)***
Optimum Power & Envmt Fla, Deerfield Beach *Also called Reynoso & Associates Inc* ***(G-2905)***
Optimum Spring Mfg Inc...904 567-5999
150 Hilden Rd Ste 316 Ponte Vedra (32081) ***(G-14927)***
Optimus-Fleet LLC...407 590-5060
7550 Futures Dr Orlando (32819) ***(G-13027)***
Optoelectronics Inc...954 642-8997
160 W Camino Real Boca Raton (33432) ***(G-655)***
Optronic Laboratories LLC...407 422-3171
4632 36th St Orlando (32811) ***(G-13028)***
Oracle America Inc...407 458-1200
7453 T G Lee Blvd Orlando (32822) ***(G-13029)***
Oracle America Inc...305 260-7200
6505 Blue Lagoon Dr # 40 Miami (33126) ***(G-10112)***
Oracle Balloon Decor Inc...386 866-0878
9951 Atl Blvd Ste 429 Jacksonville (32225) ***(G-6646)***
Oracle Corporation...772 337-4141
1701 Se Hillmoor Dr D16 Port Saint Lucie (34952) ***(G-15128)***
Oracle Corporation...772 466-0704
2100 Nebraska Ave Fort Pierce (34950) ***(G-4725)***
Oracle Elevator Company...954 391-5835
8000 Nw 25th St Ste 400 Miami (33122) ***(G-10113)***
Oracle Essence Inc...786 258-8153
1341 St Tropez Cir Weston (33326) ***(G-19155)***
Oragenics Inc (PA)...813 286-7900
4902 Eisenhower Blvd # 125 Tampa (33634) ***(G-17959)***
Oral Stericlean, Tampa *Also called 3b Global LLC* ***(G-17373)***
Orange Park Machine Inc...904 269-1935
84 Industrial Loop N Orange Park (32073) ***(G-12401)***
Orange Peel Gazette...407 312-7335
760 Mahogany Ln Altamonte Springs (32714) ***(G-60)***
Orange Peel Gazette Inc...407 892-5556
145 E 13th St Saint Cloud (34769) ***(G-15663)***
Orange Peel Gazette Treasur...772 489-8005
2721 S 10th St Fort Pierce (34982) ***(G-4726)***
Orange Peel Gztte of Oscola CN (PA)...407 892-5556
145 E 13th St Saint Cloud (34769) ***(G-15664)***
Orange State Steel Cnstr Inc...727 544-3398
6201 80th Ave N Pinellas Park (33781) ***(G-14374)***
Orange Sunshine Graphics Inc...954 797-7425
5051 S State Road 7 # 517 Davie (33314) ***(G-2562)***
Orattac Industries LLC...904 415-2162
15501 Shellcracker Rd Jacksonville (32226) ***(G-6647)***
Orbe Inc...954 534-2264
2310 Nw 30th Ct Oakland Park (33311) ***(G-11827)***
Orbeco-Hellige, Sarasota *Also called Tintometer Inc* ***(G-16310)***
Orbi Supply Inc...305 810-8822
8760 Nw 36st Ste 425 Doral (33178) ***(G-3451)***
Orbital Corporation of Tampa...813 782-7300
40421 Chancey Rd Ste 101 Zephyrhills (33542) ***(G-19529)***
Orbital Sciences LLC...703 406-5474
5335 N Courtenay Pkwy Merritt Island (32953) ***(G-9005)***
Orbsat Corp (PA)...305 560-5355
18851 Ne 29th Ave Ste 700 Aventura (33180) ***(G-278)***
Orbusneich Medical Inc...954 730-0711
5363 Nw 35th Ave Fort Lauderdale (33309) ***(G-4151)***
Orca Composites LLC...206 349-5300
1468 Northgate Blvd Sarasota (34234) ***(G-16533)***
Orchid Island Juice Co Inc...772 465-1122
330 N Us Highway 1 Fort Pierce (34950) ***(G-4727)***
Orchid Printing Inc...786 523-3324
20225 Sw 90th Avenue Rd Cutler Bay (33189) ***(G-2406)***
Orcom Labs Inc...321 773-0741
131 Tomahawk Dr Ste 9b Indian Harbour Beach (32937) ***(G-6064)***
Ord of Ahepa Ch 356 Daily & T...727 791-1040
2555 Enterprise Rd Ste 10 Clearwater (33763) ***(G-1820)***
Order Counter Com Point Svc S, Pensacola *Also called Ordercounter Inc* ***(G-14217)***
Ordercounter Inc...850 332-5540
9270 University Pkwy # 102 Pensacola (32514) ***(G-14217)***
Orellana Coatings Inc...305 389-4610
9447 Fontainebleau Blvd Miami (33172) ***(G-10114)***
Orellana Investments Inc...305 477-2817
2818 Nw 79th Ave Miami (33122) ***(G-10115)***
Organabio LLC...305 676-2586
7800 Sw 57th Ave Ste 225 South Miami (33143) ***(G-16824)***
Organic Amazon Corp...305 365-7811
104 Crandon Blvd Key Biscayne (33149) ***(G-7161)***
Organic Cane Company Inc...561 385-4081
923 Se Lincoln Ave Stuart (34994) ***(G-16984)***
Organic Laboratories Inc (PA)...772 286-5581
5520 Glades Cut Off Rd Fort Pierce (34981) ***(G-4728)***
Organizacion Marketing Mix LLC...407 924-2709
1006 Verona St Kissimmee (34741) ***(G-7279)***
Oria Lab LLC...888 329-4298
7064 Sw 44th St Miami (33155) ***(G-10116)***
Oriental Packing Company Inc...305 235-1829
12221 Sw 104th Ter Miami (33186) ***(G-10117)***
Oriental Red Apple LLC...646 853-1468
255 Park Blvd Miami (33126) ***(G-10118)***
Oriflow...727 400-4881
2125 Range Rd Ste B Clearwater (33765) ***(G-1821)***
Origin Pc LLC...305 971-1000
12400 Sw 134th Ct Ste 8 Miami (33186) ***(G-10119)***
Original Impressions LLC...305 233-1322
2965 W Corp Lks Blvd Weston (33331) ***(G-19156)***
Original Pnguin Drect Oprtions...305 592-2830
3000 Nw 107th Ave Doral (33172) ***(G-3452)***
Original Seat Sack Company., Naples *Also called Youthful Innovations LLC* ***(G-11463)***
Originates Inc...954 233-2500
20900 Ne 30th Ave Ste 707 Aventura (33180) ***(G-279)***
Originclear Inc (PA)...323 939-6645
13575 58th St N Ste 200 Clearwater (33760) ***(G-1822)***
Orion Dntl Sls Trning Repr LLC...888 674-6657
4721 Rockvale Dr Kissimmee (34758) ***(G-7280)***
Orion Power Systems Inc (PA)...877 385-1654
2939 W Beaver St Jacksonville (32254) ***(G-6648)***
Orion Press, Miami *Also called Print Bold Corp* ***(G-10193)***
Orion Repair, Kissimmee *Also called Orion Dntl Sls Trning Repr LLC* ***(G-7280)***
Orion Technologies LLC...407 476-2120
12605 Challenger Pkwy # 130 Orlando (32826) ***(G-13030)***
Orion Travel Technologies Inc (PA)...407 574-6649
200 Celebration Pl # 840 Celebration (34747) ***(G-1524)***
Orion Visual Group, Miami *Also called Print Pro Shop Inc* ***(G-10196)***
Orizon 360...888 979-0360
1840 N Commerce Pkwy # 3 Weston (33326) ***(G-19157)***
Orka Cabinets Inc...954 907-2456
12022 Nw 47th St Coral Springs (33076) ***(G-2299)***
Orkan18...855 675-2618
9835 Lake Worth Rd Ste 16 Lake Worth (33467) ***(G-7576)***
Orlando Blinds Factory...407 697-0521
210 N Goldenrod Rd Ste 1 Orlando (32807) ***(G-13031)***
Orlando Branding Agency LLC...407 692-8868
1035 Covington St Oviedo (32765) ***(G-13451)***
Orlando Brewing Partners...407 843-6783
1401 W Gore St Ste 3 Orlando (32805) ***(G-13032)***
Orlando Commercial Millwork...407 549-2679
5054 Hidden Path Way Sanford (32771) ***(G-16097)***
Orlando Donut Mfg LLC...407 933-7111
2550 Michigan Ave Ste G Kissimmee (34744) ***(G-7281)***
Orlando Doughnut Mfg Co, Kissimmee *Also called Orlando Donut Mfg LLC* ***(G-7281)***
Orlando Flores...305 898-2111
3841 Sw 92nd Ave Miami (33165) ***(G-10120)***
Orlando Ice Cream Company, Orlando *Also called Muse Gelato Inc* ***(G-12988)***
Orlando Ice Servive Corp...407 999-4940
2640 Kunze Ave Orlando (32806) ***(G-13033)***
Orlando Metal Fabrication Inc...407 850-4313
11516 Satellite Blvd Orlando (32837) ***(G-13034)***
Orlando Metro Magazine, Tampa *Also called Metro Life Media Inc* ***(G-17906)***
Orlando Novelty LLC (PA)...407 858-9499
1624 Premier Row Orlando (32809) ***(G-13035)***
Orlando Novelty Wholesale, Orlando *Also called Orlando Novelty LLC* ***(G-13035)***
Orlando Plating Co...407 843-1140
601 N Orange Blossom Trl Orlando (32805) ***(G-13036)***
Orlando Post, Margate *Also called Trading Post of Central Fla* ***(G-8570)***
Orlando Sentinnel Media Group, Orlando *Also called Sentinel Communicatns News Ven* ***(G-13174)***
Orlando Shutters Blinds & More, Lake Mary *Also called Orlando Shutters LLC* ***(G-7440)***
Orlando Shutters LLC (PA)...407 495-5250
4300 W Lake Mary Blvd # 1 Lake Mary (32746) ***(G-7440)***
Orlando Times Inc...407 841-3052
4403 Vineland Rd Ste B5 Orlando (32811) ***(G-13037)***
Orlando Weekly, Orlando *Also called The Scranton Times L P* ***(G-13253)***
Orlandos Forklift Service LLC...407 761-9104
3138 Natoma Way Orlando (32825) ***(G-13038)***
Ormond Beach Clinical RES LLC...386 310-7462
1400 Hand Ave Ste L Ormond Beach (32174) ***(G-13388)***
Ormond Beach Observer...386 492-2784
310 Wilmette Ave Ste 3 Ormond Beach (32174) ***(G-13389)***
Ormond Beach Olive Oil...386 333-9236
203 E Granada Blvd Ormond Beach (32176) ***(G-13390)***
Ornamental Alasco Iron & Wldg...813 254-4883
733 Camrose Dr Brandon (33510) ***(G-1168)***
Ornamental Columns and Statues...239 482-3911
16179 S Tamiami Trl Fort Myers (33908) ***(G-4559)***
Ornamental Design Ironworks...813 626-8449
4706 N Falkenburg Rd Tampa (33610) ***(G-17960)***

ALPHABETIC

Ornamntal Metal Specialist Inc 786 360-5727
7889 Nw 173rd St Hialeah (33015) ***(G-5552)***
Ortega & Velazco Cabinet Inc 305 726-9097
8346 Nw D South River Dr Miami (33116) ***(G-10121)***
Ortega Custom Cabinets Inc 813 403-7101
7006 Hazelhurst Ct Tampa (33615) ***(G-17961)***
Ortega Industries and Mfg 305 688-0090
13281 Nw 43rd Ave Opa Locka (33054) ***(G-12348)***
Orthomerica Products Inc 407 290-6592
6333 N Orange Blossom Trl Orlando (32810) ***(G-13039)***
Orthopedic Designs N Amer Inc 813 443-4905
5912 Breckenridge Pkwy F Tampa (33610) ***(G-17962)***
Orthosensor Inc (HQ) 954 577-7770
1855 Griffin Rd Ste A310 Dania Beach (33004) ***(G-2471)***
Orthotic Prsthtic Rhbltion As 352 331-3399
6608 Nw 9th Blvd Gainesville (32605) ***(G-4977)***
Orvino Imports & Distrg Inc 954 785-3100
11927 W Sample Rd Coral Springs (33065) ***(G-2300)***
Oryza Pharmaceuticals Inc 954 881-5481
4117 Nw 124th Ave Coral Springs (33065) ***(G-2301)***
Osborn Publications 305 899-0501
2365 Biscayne Bay Dr North Miami (33181) ***(G-11649)***
Osborne Metals 727 441-1703
324 S Madison Ave Clearwater (33756) ***(G-1823)***
Oscars Woodworks Inc 786 543-9200
2431 W 80th St Unit 7 Hialeah (33016) ***(G-5553)***
Osceola Farms Co (HQ) 561 655-6303
340 Royal Poinciana Way # 315 Palm Beach (33480) ***(G-13560)***
Osceola Farms Co 561 924-7156
Us Highway 98 Hatton Hwy Pahokee (33476) ***(G-13470)***
Osceola Press, Kissimmee *Also called Crain Ventures Inc* ***(G-7233)***
Osceola Shopper, Kissimmee *Also called Sun Publications Florida Inc* ***(G-7299)***
Osceola Shopper, Lakeland *Also called Sun Publications Florida Inc* ***(G-7810)***
Osceola Star 407 933-0174
921 Emmett St Kissimmee (34741) ***(G-7282)***
Osceola Woman Newspaper LLC 407 891-9771
111 E Monu Ave Unit 401 Kissimmee (34741) ***(G-7283)***
Oscor Inc (PA) 727 937-2511
3816 Desoto Blvd Palm Harbor (34683) ***(G-13749)***
Osd Display, Orlando *Also called New Vision Display Inc* ***(G-12999)***
OSG America LLC 813 209-0600
302 Knights Run Ave # 1200 Tampa (33602) ***(G-17963)***
Osgood Industries LLC 813 448-9041
601 Burbank Rd Oldsmar (34677) ***(G-12254)***
Osgood Industries LLC, Oldsmar *Also called Osgood Industries LLC* ***(G-12254)***
Oshkosh Corporation 863 603-4080
4950 Frontage Rd S Lakeland (33815) ***(G-7760)***
OSI International LLC 561 394-9508
164 W Royal Palm Rd Boca Raton (33432) ***(G-656)***
Osko Inc 305 599-7161
8085 Nw 90th St Medley (33166) ***(G-8699)***
Osler Incorporated (PA) 954 767-6339
200 Sw 1st Ave Ste 1250 Fort Lauderdale (33301) ***(G-4152)***
Osmi Inc (PA) 561 330-9300
7777 Glades Rd Ste 200 Boca Raton (33434) ***(G-657)***
Ostara Usa LLC (PA) 813 666-8123
2720 S Falkenburg Rd Riverview (33578) ***(G-15278)***
OSteen Plastic Inc 954 434-4921
17539 Sw 59th Ct Southwest Ranches (33331) ***(G-16839)***
Ostrich Market Inc 954 873-1957
381 Dayton Blvd Melbourne (32904) ***(G-8902)***
Otis Elevator Company 561 618-4831
5500 Village Blvd Ste 101 West Palm Beach (33407) ***(G-18974)***
Otr Wheel Engineering, Jacksonville *Also called Longs Wheel & Rim Inc* ***(G-6564)***
Ott Welding, Bonita Springs *Also called Burton JC Companies Inc* ***(G-821)***
Ottica Dante Americas LLC 561 322-0186
10890 Haydn Dr Boca Raton (33498) ***(G-658)***
Otus Corp Intl LLC 305 833-6078
8306 Mills Dr 222 Miami (33183) ***(G-10122)***
Ouality Precast, Mulberry *Also called Quality Block & Supply Inc* ***(G-11133)***
Ouhlala Gourmet Corp 305 774-7332
2655 S Le Jeune Rd # 1011 Coral Gables (33134) ***(G-2182)***
Oum LLC 407 886-1511
531 Cooper Indus Pkwy Apopka (32703) ***(G-168)***
Oumph, Lake Worth *Also called Future Foods LLC* ***(G-7551)***
Our City Media of Florida LLC 954 306-1007
400 Swgrss Corp Pkwy 200c Sunrise (33325) ***(G-17154)***
Our Florida Publishing 904 859-2805
9581 Sunrise Lakes Blvd # 312 Sunrise (33322) ***(G-17155)***
Our Seniors Guidecom Inc 904 655-2130
14286-19 Bch Blvd Ste 335 Jacksonville (32246) ***(G-6649)***
Our Town News 954 979-0991
3665 Park Central Blvd N Pompano Beach (33064) ***(G-14781)***
Our Village Okeechobee Inc 863 467-0158
325 Se 15th Ave Okeechobee (34974) ***(G-12188)***
Our Warehouse Inc 954 786-1234
2749 E Atlantic Blvd Pompano Beach (33062) ***(G-14782)***
Ouro Custom Woodwork Inc 954 428-0735
12 Sw 9th St Deerfield Beach (33441) ***(G-2881)***

Outback Series, The, Deland *Also called Pain Away LLC* ***(G-3005)***
Outdoor America Images Inc (PA) 813 888-8796
4545 W Hillsborough Ave Tampa (33614) ***(G-17964)***
Outdoor America Images Inc 813 888-8796
13982 Nw 58th Ct Miami Lakes (33014) ***(G-10833)***
Outdoor Images Central Fla Inc 407 825-9944
4061 Forrestal Ave Unit 2 Orlando (32806) ***(G-13040)***
Outdoor Media Inc 305 529-1400
3195 Ponce De Leon Blvd # 300 Coral Gables (33134) ***(G-2183)***
Outdoor Products LLC 352 473-0886
125 Sw 284th Ave Steinhatchee (32359) ***(G-16898)***
Outform Inc (HQ) 800 204-0524
82 Ne 26th St Unit 103 Miami (33137) ***(G-10123)***
Outlaw Oyster Company LLC 850 841-9344
16 Chickasaw St Panacea (32346) ***(G-13860)***
Outline Technologies Inc 904 858-9933
9920 Blakeford Mill Rd Jacksonville (32256) ***(G-6650)***
Outlook International Electric, Sunrise *Also called BJ Burns Incorporated* ***(G-17097)***
Outpost 30a LLC 850 909-0138
11 N Castle Harbour Dr F Inlet Beach (32461) ***(G-6078)***
Outpost North Lake 352 669-2430
131 N Central Ave Umatilla (32784) ***(G-18500)***
Output Printing Corp 813 228-8800
107 N Jefferson St Tampa (33602) ***(G-17965)***
Outreach Corporation 888 938-7356
1208 E Kennedy Blvd Tampa (33602) ***(G-17966)***
Outstanding Events Inc 772 463-5406
5380 Sw Landing Creek Dr Palm City (34990) ***(G-13668)***
Overall-Honeycomb LLC (HQ) 941 756-8781
1950 Limbus Ave Sarasota (34243) ***(G-16269)***
Overseas Publishing Management, Virginia Gardens *Also called Distribuidora Continental SA* ***(G-18687)***
Overseas Radio LLC 305 296-1630
3732 Flagler Ave Key West (33040) ***(G-7200)***
Ovipost Inc 707 776-6108
635 A Rd Labelle (33935) ***(G-7322)***
Owens & Sons Marine Inc 727 323-1088
3601 8th Ave S Saint Petersburg (33711) ***(G-15873)***
Owens Corning Sales LLC 863 291-3046
3327 Queens Cove Loop Winter Haven (33880) ***(G-19338)***
Owens Distributors Inc 407 302-8602
2850 W Airport Blvd Sanford (32771) ***(G-16098)***
Oxbow Activated Carbon LLC, West Palm Beach *Also called Puragen LLC* ***(G-19010)***
Oxbow Calcining LLC 580 874-2201
1601 Forum Pl Ph 2 West Palm Beach (33401) ***(G-18975)***
Oxbow Calcining Usa Inc (HQ) 580 874-2201
1601 Forum Pl Ste 1400 West Palm Beach (33401) ***(G-18976)***
Oxbow Carbon LLC (HQ) 561 907-5400
1601 Forum Pl Ste 1400 West Palm Beach (33401) ***(G-18977)***
Oxbow Enterprises Intl LLC 561 907-5400
1601 Forum Pl Ste 1400 West Palm Beach (33401) ***(G-18978)***
Oxendine Publishing Inc 352 373-6907
412 Nw 16th Ave Gainesville (32601) ***(G-4978)***
Oxford Acquisition, Miami *Also called Miami Engrv Co-Oxford Prtg Co* ***(G-9999)***
Oxigeno Nitrogeno Inc 954 659-3881
16200 Golf Club Rd Weston (33326) ***(G-19158)***
Oxpecker Enterprise Inc 305 253-5301
12182 Sw 128th St Miami (33186) ***(G-10124)***
Oxygen Development LLC (PA) 954 480-2675
1525 S Congress Ave Palm Springs (33406) ***(G-13778)***
Oxygenix Mold and Odor LLC 850 926-5421
467 Parkside Cir Crawfordville (32327) ***(G-2335)***
Oxzgen Inc 844 569-9436
40180 Us Highway 19 N Tarpon Springs (34689) ***(G-18318)***
Oz Naturals LLC 561 602-2932
319 Clematis St Ste 700 West Palm Beach (33401) ***(G-18979)***
Ozinga South Florida Inc 786 422-4694
2401 College Ave Davie (33317) ***(G-2563)***
P & A Welding and Machine Inc 863 425-3198
2811 State Road 60 W Mulberry (33860) ***(G-11132)***
P & G Printing Group Inc 954 971-2511
2034 Mears Pkwy Margate (33063) ***(G-8559)***
P & J Graphics Inc 813 626-3243
11407 Cerca Del Rio Pl Temple Terrace (33617) ***(G-18373)***
P & L Creech Inc 386 547-4182
2960 S Nova Rd Daytona Beach (32119) ***(G-2691)***
P & M Sheet Metal Corp 954 618-8513
134 Nw 109th Ave Apt 304 Pembroke Pines (33026) ***(G-14053)***
P & S Logging Inc 904 845-4256
15864 County Road 108 Hilliard (32046) ***(G-5715)***
P A Vivid Pathology (PA) 850 416-7780
5149 N 9th Ave Ste 122 Pensacola (32504) ***(G-14218)***
P B C Central 407 648-2020
3450 Vineland Rd Ste B Orlando (32811) ***(G-13041)***
P B C Cultural Counsel 561 471-2903
1555 Palm Bch Lakes Blvd West Palm Beach (33401) ***(G-18980)***
P B C H Incorporated 239 567-5030
7941 Mercantile St Fort Myers (33917) ***(G-4560)***
P D I S Inc 561 243-8442
2855 S Congress Ave Ste C Delray Beach (33445) ***(G-3112)***

P D P, Boca Raton *Also called Practical Design Products Co* ***(G-671)***
P D Services, Oakland Park *Also called Powless Drapery Service Inc* ***(G-11831)***
P P P, Doral *Also called Professional Pet Products Inc* ***(G-3471)***
P S Research Corp 954 558-8727
3702 Nw 16th St Lauderhill (33311) ***(G-8119)***
P S T Computers Inc 954 566-1600
2808 N Federal Hwy Fort Lauderdale (33306) ***(G-4153)***
P T I, Miramar *Also called Propulsion Tech Intl LLC* ***(G-11034)***
P&A Machine 407 275-5770
7220 Old Cheney Hwy Orlando (32807) ***(G-13042)***
P&G Pavers Inc 561 716-5113
6671 W Indiantown Rd 50-2 Jupiter (33458) ***(G-7089)***
P&L Machine & Tool Company Inc 727 863-0847
9704 Katy Dr Ste 2 Hudson (34667) ***(G-6035)***
P&L Machine and Tool Co, Hudson *Also called Addtad Partners Inc* ***(G-6014)***
P'Kolino Studio, Miami *Also called PKolino LLC* ***(G-10167)***
P3 Fleet LLC 904 549-5500
11950 New Kings Rd Jacksonville (32219) ***(G-6651)***
P4rts LLC 305 396-4879
11601 Nw 107th St Ste 300 Miami (33178) ***(G-10125)***
PA C Publishing Inc 813 814-1505
850 Dunbar Ave Oldsmar (34677) ***(G-12255)***
Paal Technologies Inc 954 368-5000
5387 N Nob Hill Rd Sunrise (33351) ***(G-17156)***
Paas, Ocala *Also called Signature Brands LLC* ***(G-12050)***
Pablo Surgical Solutions LLC 904 237-4864
816 A1a N Ste 200 Ponte Vedra Beach (32082) ***(G-14949)***
Pac Printing, Pinellas Park *Also called Process Automation Corporation* ***(G-14381)***
Pac Seating Systems Inc 772 286-6670
3370 Sw 42nd Ave Palm City (34990) ***(G-13669)***
Paca Foods LLC 813 628-8228
5212 Cone Rd Tampa (33610) ***(G-17967)***
Pace Defense, Odessa *Also called Pace Launcher Casings Llc* ***(G-12138)***
Pace Enclosures Inc 239 275-3818
12101 Crystal Condo Rd Fort Myers (33966) ***(G-4561)***
Pace Launcher Casings Llc 813 245-6570
2445 Merchant Ave Unit B Odessa (33556) ***(G-12138)***
Pace Machine & Tool Inc 561 747-5444
7986 Sw Jack James Dr Stuart (34997) ***(G-16985)***
Pace Machine Tool Inc 248 960-9903
13564 Ingraham Blvd Port Charlotte (33981) ***(G-14992)***
Pace Tech Inc 727 442-8118
2040 Calumet St Clearwater (33765) ***(G-1824)***
Pacem Defense, Perry *Also called Amtec Less Lethal Systems Inc* ***(G-14293)***
Pacemate LLC 305 322-5074
518 13th St W Bradenton (34205) ***(G-1089)***
Pacer Electronics Florida Inc (PA) 941 378-5774
1555 Apex Rd Sarasota (34240) ***(G-16534)***
Pacheco Creative Group Inc 305 541-1400
2164 Nw 19th Ave Miami (33142) ***(G-10126)***
Pacific 305 785-9068
8526 Nw 70th St Miami (33166) ***(G-10127)***
Pacific Arches Corporation 352 236-7787
1740 Se 18th St Ste 1302 Ocala (34471) ***(G-12020)***
Pacific Coast Feather LLC (PA) 206 624-1057
901 W Yamato Rd Ste 250 Boca Raton (33431) ***(G-659)***
Pacific Die Cast Inc (PA) 813 316-2221
12802 Commodity Pl Tampa (33626) ***(G-17968)***
Pacific Limited, Miami *Also called Pacific Ltd Corp* ***(G-10129)***
Pacific Limited Intl Corp 305 358-1900
825 Brickell Bay Dr # 17 Miami (33131) ***(G-10128)***
Pacific Link Imports Inc 954 605-6071
11497 Nw 81st Pl Parkland (33076) ***(G-13997)***
Pacific Ltd Corp 305 358-1900
825 Brickell Bay Dr # 17 Miami (33131) ***(G-10129)***
Pacific Pavers Inc 941 238-7854
6326 5th Street Cir E Bradenton (34203) ***(G-1090)***
Pacific Scientific Company 305 477-4711
11700 Nw 102nd Rd Ste 6 Medley (33178) ***(G-8700)***
Pack4u LLC 407 857-2871
7531 Currency Dr Orlando (32809) ***(G-13043)***
Packaging & Resources Inc 954 288-9678
19245 S Gardenia Ave Weston (33332) ***(G-19159)***
Packaging Alternatives Corp (PA) 352 867-5050
4130 Sw 13th St Ocala (34474) ***(G-12021)***
Packaging Corporation America 386 792-0810
5939 Se Us Highway 41 Jasper (32052) ***(G-6960)***
Packaging Machines, Sarasota *Also called MDC Engineering Inc* ***(G-16505)***
Packard Company Inc 941 451-8201
787 Commerce Dr Venice (34292) ***(G-18565)***
Pad Printing Technology Corp 941 739-8667
2145 63rd Ave E Bradenton (34203) ***(G-1091)***
Pad Printing Technology Group 941 739-8667
2145 63rd Ave E Bradenton (34203) ***(G-1092)***
Padgett Communications Inc 727 323-5800
5005 W Laurel St Ste 103 Tampa (33607) ***(G-17969)***
Padgett Manufacturing Inc 941 756-8566
2915 62nd Ave E Bradenton (34203) ***(G-1093)***
Padgetts Pulpwood Inc 904 282-5112
3745 Old Jennings Rd Middleburg (32068) ***(G-10911)***
Page Golfs Yellow Directory 305 378-8038
7251 Sw 152nd St Palmetto Bay (33157) ***(G-13852)***
Page One LLC 833 467-2431
1231 Stirling Rd Ste 107 Dania (33004) ***(G-2455)***
Pageantry Magazine, Longwood *Also called Pageantry Tlent Entrmt Svcs In* ***(G-8319)***
Pageantry Tlent Entrmt Svcs In 407 260-2262
1855 W State Road 434 Longwood (32750) ***(G-8319)***
Pagnifique, Miami *Also called Farartis LLC* ***(G-9559)***
Pagnifique USA, Miramar *Also called Panamerican Food LLC* ***(G-11026)***
Pain Away LLC 800 215-8739
1515 Detrick Ave Deland (32724) ***(G-3005)***
Painassist Inc 248 875-4222
6199 54th St S Saint Petersburg (33715) ***(G-15874)***
Painting & Specialty Coatings, Bartow *Also called RSR Industrial Coatings Inc* ***(G-332)***
Paints & Coatings Inc 239 997-6645
17660 East St North Fort Myers (33917) ***(G-11601)***
Paints N Cocktails Inc 954 514-7383
14710 Ne 2nd Ct Miami (33161) ***(G-10130)***
Pair ODice Brewing Co LLC 727 755-3423
4400 118th Ave N Ste 205 Clearwater (33762) ***(G-1825)***
Paire Jr Weld Inc 754 281-1803
7540 W Mcnab Rd Ste E13 North Lauderdale (33068) ***(G-11619)***
Paj Innovative Concepts Inc 813 659-0505
2804 Sydney Rd Plant City (33566) ***(G-14451)***
Pal-King Inc 904 334-8797
1300 W Beaver St Jacksonville (32209) ***(G-6652)***
Palafox Marine Inc 850 438-9354
490 S L St Pensacola (32502) ***(G-14219)***
Palama, Miami Beach *Also called Mohamed Lamrana Jalloh* ***(G-10695)***
Palanjian Enterprises Inc 850 244-2848
420 Mary Esther Cut Off N Fort Walton Beach (32548) ***(G-4820)***
Palatka Daily News, Palatka *Also called Daily News Inc* ***(G-13476)***
Palatka Tube Plant, Palatka *Also called Caraustar Indus Cnsmr Pdts Gro* ***(G-13474)***
Palatka Welding Shop Inc 386 328-1507
1301 Madison St Palatka (32177) ***(G-13488)***
Paleo Simplified LLC 813 446-5969
605 S Bayshore Blvd Safety Harbor (34695) ***(G-15500)***
Palermo Pavers Inc 239 263-0593
4001 Estey Ave Naples (34104) ***(G-11353)***
Pall Aeropower Corporation (HQ) 727 849-9999
10540 Ridge Rd Ste 100 New Port Richey (34654) ***(G-11507)***
Pall Aeropower Corporation 727 849-9999
1750 Filter Dr Deland (32724) ***(G-3006)***
Pall Filtration and Sep 386 822-8000
1750 Filter Dr Deland (32724) ***(G-3007)***
Palladio Beauty Group, Hollywood *Also called Pb Group LLC* ***(G-5887)***
Palladio Beauty Group LLC 954 922-4311
3912 Pembroke Rd Hollywood (33021) ***(G-5886)***
Palladium Graphics, Tampa *Also called HOB Corporation* ***(G-17758)***
Palladium Sales LLC 754 423-0517
5081 S State Road 7 # 810 Davie (33314) ***(G-2564)***
Pallet Consultants Corp (PA) 954 946-2212
810 Nw 13th Ave Pompano Beach (33069) ***(G-14783)***
Pallet Depot LLC 863 686-6245
6300 New Tampa Hwy Lakeland (33815) ***(G-7761)***
Pallet Direct Inc 888 433-1727
5660 Cypress Hollow Way Naples (34109) ***(G-11354)***
Pallet Doctor Inc 904 444-2514
221 N Hogan St Ste 371 Jacksonville (32202) ***(G-6653)***
Pallet Dude LLC 941 720-1667
7952 Fruitville Rd Sarasota (34240) ***(G-16535)***
Pallet Enterprises of Florida 305 836-3204
7525 Nw 37th Ave Unit D Miami (33147) ***(G-10131)***
Pallet Enterprises Orlando Inc 407 888-3200
10694 Cosmonaut Blvd Orlando (32824) ***(G-13044)***
Pallet Ex Jacksonville Inc 904 781-2500
7779 Hammond Blvd Jacksonville (32220) ***(G-6654)***
Pallet Exchange Inc 386 734-0133
1219 Doris St Orange City (32763) ***(G-12377)***
Pallet Express Inc 813 752-1600
1503 Turkey Creek Rd Plant City (33566) ***(G-14452)***
Pallet Express of Jkvl Inc 904 781-2500
7779 Hammond Blvd Jacksonville (32220) ***(G-6655)***
Pallet Holdings LLC (PA) 561 367-0009
1200 N Federal Hwy # 207 Boca Raton (33432) ***(G-660)***
Pallet Industries Inc (HQ) 954 935-5804
1815 S Powerline Rd Deerfield Beach (33442) ***(G-2882)***
Pallet One of Mobile LLC 251 960-1107
6001 Foxtrot Ave Bartow (33830) ***(G-326)***
Pallet Racks Plus LLC 321 203-6634
20445 Nettleton St Orlando (32833) ***(G-13045)***
Pallet Recall Inc 941 727-1944
6755 33rd St E Sarasota (34243) ***(G-16270)***
Pallet Services Inc (PA) 813 754-7719
1705 Turkey Creek Rd Plant City (33566) ***(G-14453)***
Pallet Services of Plant City, Plant City *Also called Pallet Services Inc* ***(G-14453)***

ALPHABETIC

Pallet Solutions Inc 305 801-8314
7525 Nw 37th Ave Unit D Miami (33147) *(G-10132)*
Palletone Inc (HQ) 800 771-1147
6001 Foxtrot Ave Bartow (33830) *(G-327)*
Palletone of Texas LP (HQ) 903 628-5695
1470 Us Highway 17 S Bartow (33830) *(G-328)*
Palletone of Texas LP 863 533-1147
1470 Us Highway 17 S Bartow (33830) *(G-329)*
Pallets Inc 407 492-0857
640 Majestic Oak Dr Apopka (32712) *(G-169)*
Pallets Plus Inc 813 759-6355
2606 N Airport Rd Plant City (33563) *(G-14454)*
Pallets To Go Inc 305 654-0303
1691 Nw 23rd St Miami (33142) *(G-10133)*
Palm Bay Coml Coatings Inc 321 266-2467
615 Palmetto Ave Melbourne (32901) *(G-8903)*
Palm Bch Pssport Pblctons Mdia, West Palm Beach *Also called Passport Pblcations Media Corp (G-18988)*
Palm Beach Aggregates LLC 561 795-6550
20125 Southern Blvd Loxahatchee (33470) *(G-8362)*
Palm Beach Btry Ventures LLC (PA) 561 881-8900
1250 Northlake Blvd Lake Park (33403) *(G-7477)*
Palm Beach Cast Stone Inc 561 835-4085
809 N Railroad Ave West Palm Beach (33401) *(G-18981)*
Palm Beach Cstm Cabinetry Inc 561 859-9071
5363 Plains Dr Lake Worth (33463) *(G-7577)*
Palm Beach Cstm Woodworks LLC 561 575-5335
1315 53rd St Ste 5 Mangonia Park (33407) *(G-8508)*
Palm Beach Daily News, West Palm Beach *Also called Palm Beach Newspapers Inc (G-18985)*
Palm Beach Embroidery USA Inc 561 506-6307
8645 N Military Trl West Palm Beach (33410) *(G-18982)*
Palm Beach Gardens Fla Wkly 561 904-6443
11380 Prosperity Farms Rd Palm Beach Gardens (33410) *(G-13615)*
Palm Beach Iron Works Inc 561 683-1816
7768 Belvedere Rd West Palm Beach (33411) *(G-18983)*
Palm Beach Junior Clg Prnt Shp 561 969-0122
4200 S Congress Ave Lake Worth (33461) *(G-7578)*
Palm Beach Limestone, West Palm Beach *Also called Palm Beach Cast Stone Inc (G-18981)*
Palm Beach Liquidation Company (PA) 561 659-0210
1000 N Dixie Hwy Ste C West Palm Beach (33401) *(G-18984)*
Palm Beach Media Group Inc 239 434-6966
3066 Tamiami Trl N # 102 Naples (34103) *(G-11355)*
Palm Beach Newspapers Inc 561 820-3800
2751 S Dixie Hwy West Palm Beach (33405) *(G-18985)*
Palm Beach Post, West Palm Beach *Also called Pathfnders Palm Bch-Mrtin Cnty (G-18989)*
Palm Beach Precious Metals 561 662-6025
3200 Frost Rd Palm Springs (33406) *(G-13779)*
Palm Beach Smoothies Com Inc 561 379-8647
150 N Us Highway 1 Ste 5 Tequesta (33469) *(G-18386)*
Palm Beach Trim Inc 561 588-8746
6900 W State Road 84 Davie (33317) *(G-2565)*
Palm Beach Woodwork Co Inc 561 844-8818
1101 53rd Ct S Ste B Mangonia Park (33407) *(G-8509)*
Palm Coast Crush 2 ....386 447-2768
135 London Dr Palm Coast (32137) *(G-13705)*
Palm Coast Observer LLC 386 447-9723
1 Florida Park Dr N # 104 Palm Coast (32137) *(G-13706)*
Palm Labs Adhesives LLC 321 710-4850
3063 Enterprise Rd Ste 31 Debary (32713) *(G-2753)*
Palm Pheon Music Publishing 305 705-2405
15421 W Dixie Hwy North Miami Beach (33162) *(G-11696)*
Palm Print Inc 561 833-9661
919 N Dixie Hwy West Palm Beach (33401) *(G-18986)*
Palm Printing, Lakewood Ranch *Also called Stewart-Hedrick Inc (G-7847)*
Palm Prnting/Printers Ink Corp 239 332-8600
2400 First St Ste 102 Fort Myers (33901) *(G-4562)*
Palm Prtg Strgc Solutions LLC 239 332-8600
2306 Dr Mrtn Luther King Fort Myers (33901) *(G-4563)*
Palm Springs Printing, Sanford *Also called Central Florida Publishing Inc (G-16009)*
Palm Tree Computer Systems Inc (PA) 407 359-3356
19 E Broadway St Oviedo (32765) *(G-13452)*
Palmas Printing Inc (PA) 321 984-4451
200 East Dr Melbourne (32904) *(G-8904)*
Palmate LLC 352 508-7800
200 County Road 448 Tavares (32778) *(G-18350)*
Palmer Manufacturing Co LLC 772 287-7770
3651 Se Commerce Ave Stuart (34997) *(G-16986)*
Palmetto Canning Company 941 722-1100
3601 Us Highway 41 N Palmetto (34221) *(G-13814)*
Palmetto Group LLC 863 294-8070
1530 Drexel Ave Ne Winter Haven (33881) *(G-19339)*
Palmetto Printing Inc 305 253-2444
3065 Ohio St Miami (33133) *(G-10134)*
Palmland Paper Co Inc 954 764-6910
708 Ne 2nd Ave Fort Lauderdale (33304) *(G-4154)*
Pamatian Group Inc (PA) 407 291-8387
997 W Kennedy Blvd Ste A1 Orlando (32810) *(G-13046)*
Pamplona Foods Inc 305 970-4120
9600 Sw 122nd Ct Miami (33186) *(G-10135)*
Pan American Chemical Co., Miami *Also called Sheila Shine Inc (G-10335)*
Pan American Cnstr Plant 305 477-5058
8000 Nw 74th St Medley (33166) *(G-8701)*
Pan American Graphic Inc 305 885-1962
9745 Nw 80th Ave Miami Lakes (33016) *(G-10834)*
Panagenics Inc 888 773-0700
10711 Sw 216th St Unit 10 Miami (33170) *(G-10136)*
Panama City Concrete Inc 850 851-3637
1119 Lindenwood Dr Panama City (32405) *(G-13934)*
Panama City News Herald (HQ) 850 747-5000
501 W 11th St Panama City (32401) *(G-13935)*
Panama City News Herald 850 863-1111
2 Eglin Pkwy Ne Fort Walton Beach (32548) *(G-4821)*
Panama City Pallet Inc 850 769-1040
1706 Maple Ave Panama City (32405) *(G-13936)*
Panama City Petro LLC 850 215-9146
7409 E Highway 22 Panama City (32404) *(G-13937)*
Panama City Tint Center 850 640-0167
526 E 6th St Panama City (32401) *(G-13938)*
Panama City Yard, Panama City *Also called Legacy Vulcan LLC (G-13925)*
Panama Jack Inc 407 843-8110
230 Ernestine St Orlando (32801) *(G-13047)*
Panama Pallets Co Inc 850 769-1040
1706 Maple Ave Panama City (32405) *(G-13939)*
Panamco LLC 305 856-7100
701 Nw 62nd Ave Ste 800 Miami (33126) *(G-10137)*
Panamerican Food LLC (PA) 305 594-5704
10491 N Commerce Pkwy Miramar (33025) *(G-11026)*
Panamtech Inc (PA) 954 587-3769
700 Nw 70th Ter Plantation (33317) *(G-14541)*
Panapastry LLC 305 883-1557
9001 Nw 97th Ter Ste M Medley (33178) *(G-8702)*
Pandia Press Inc 352 789-8156
312 Forest Rd Mount Dora (32757) *(G-11109)*
Pane Rustica Bakery & Cafe 813 902-8828
3225 S Macdill Ave Tampa (33629) *(G-17970)*
Panel Armor Products LLC 407 960-5946
1970 Corporate Sq Unit B Longwood (32750) *(G-8320)*
Panelfold Inc 305 688-3501
10700 Nw 36th Ave Miami (33167) *(G-10138)*
Paneltronics Incorporated 305 823-9777
11960 Nw 87th Ct Ste 1 Hialeah (33018) *(G-5554)*
Pangenex Corporation (PA) 352 346-4045
9950 Princess Palm Ave Tampa (33619) *(G-17971)*
Panhandle Paint & Dctg LLC 850 596-9248
8103 Panama City Bch Pkwy Panama City Beach (32407) *(G-13981)*
Panish Controls 203 333-7371
12553 66th St Largo (33773) *(G-8022)*
Panoff Publishing Inc 954 377-7777
6261 Nw 6th Way Ste 100 Fort Lauderdale (33309) *(G-4155)*
Panoptex Technologies Inc 407 412-0222
6555 Sanger Rd Ste 100 Orlando (32827) *(G-13048)*
Pantaleon Commodities Corp 786 542-6333
601 Brickell Key Dr # 60 Miami (33131) *(G-10139)*
Panther Printing Inc 239 936-5050
11580 Marshwood Ln Fort Myers (33908) *(G-4564)*
Panther Software Inc 800 856-8729
10800 Biscayne Blvd # 201 Miami (33161) *(G-10140)*
Pantograms Inc 813 839-5697
4537 S Dale Mabry Hwy Tampa (33611) *(G-17972)*
Pantograms Mfg Co Inc 813 839-5697
4537 S Dale Mabry Hwy Tampa (33611) *(G-17973)*
Pantropic Power Inc 954 797-7972
1881 W State Road 84 # 103 Fort Lauderdale (33315) *(G-4156)*
Pap-Cap Industries LLC 850 209-7377
3235 Wisteria Ln Grand Ridge (32442) *(G-5046)*
Papa Johns Peanuts Inc 904 389-2511
2555 W Beaver St Jacksonville (32254) *(G-6656)*
Papenfuss Holdings Inc 239 775-9090
11430 Tamiami Trl E Naples (34113) *(G-11356)*
Paper Bag Manufacturers Inc 305 685-1100
4131 Nw 132nd St Opa Locka (33054) *(G-12349)*
Paper Box 407 415-7262
500 Amethyst Way Lake Mary (32746) *(G-7441)*
Paper Chase 561 641-5319
6626 Via Rienzo Lake Worth (33467) *(G-7579)*
Paper Converter, Odessa *Also called Eastern Ribbon & Roll Corp (G-12117)*
Paper Fish Printing Inc 239 481-3555
17251 Alico Center Rd # 5 Fort Myers (33967) *(G-4565)*
Paper Free Technology Inc 515 270-1505
10626 Windsmont Ct Lehigh Acres (33936) *(G-8202)*
Paper Palm LLC 407 647-3328
621 Commonwealth Ave Orlando (32803) *(G-13049)*
Paper Pushers of America Inc 386 872-7025
2430 S Atlantic Ave Ste C Daytona Beach (32118) *(G-2692)*
Papers Unlimited Plus Inc (PA) 215 947-1155
161 Remo Pl Palm Beach Gardens (33418) *(G-13616)*

Papila Design Inc...407 240-2992
701 W Landstreet Rd Orlando (32824) ***(G-13050)***
Papous Craft Distillery LLC...813 766-9539
605 N Pinellas Ave Tarpon Springs (34689) ***(G-18319)***
Papsco, Melbourne *Also called Processing and Packg Sups Co* ***(G-8912)***
Par, Lutz *Also called Psychlgcal Asssment Rsrces In* ***(G-8413)***
Parabel Inc...321 409-7415
1901 S Hbr Cy Blvd Ste 60 Melbourne (32901) ***(G-8905)***
Parabel USA Inc...978 905-0958
1991 74th Ave Ste B Vero Beach (32966) ***(G-18650)***
Parachute Laboratories, Deland *Also called Jco Metals Inc* ***(G-2987)***
Paradigm Leaders LLC...850 441-3289
7946 Front Beach Rd Panama City Beach (32407) ***(G-13982)***
Paradigm Parachute and Defense...928 580-9013
4040 Ashland Ave Pensacola (32534) ***(G-14220)***
Paradigm Plastics, Panama City Beach *Also called Paradigm Leaders LLC* ***(G-13982)***
Paradigm Plastics Inc...727 797-3555
912 3rd St N Ste D Safety Harbor (34695) ***(G-15501)***
Paradigm Precision, Stuart *Also called Turbocombustor Technology Inc* ***(G-17041)***
Paradise Inc (PA)...813 752-1155
5110 W Poe Ave Tampa (33629) ***(G-17974)***
Paradise Air Fresh LLC...561 972-0375
3029 Sw 42nd Ave Palm City (34990) ***(G-13670)***
Paradise Archtctral Panels Stl, Miami *Also called Paradise Awnings Corporation* ***(G-10141)***
Paradise Awnings Corporation...305 597-5714
4310 Nw 36th Ave Miami (33142) ***(G-10141)***
Paradise Building Mtls LLC...407 267-3378
665 Youngstown Pkwy # 268 Altamonte Springs (32714) ***(G-61)***
Paradise Cable Industries...941 488-6092
723 Commerce Dr Unit H Venice (34292) ***(G-18566)***
Paradise Cstm Screening & EMB...954 566-9096
2180 Sw 71st Ter Davie (33317) ***(G-2566)***
Paradise EMB & Silkscreen Inc...305 595-6441
8801 Sw 129th St Miami (33176) ***(G-10142)***
Paradise Label Inc...863 860-8779
4021 S Frontage Rd Plant City (33566) ***(G-14455)***
Paradise Publishing Group Inc...941 306-2166
6618 Seven Pines Dr Bradenton (34203) ***(G-1094)***
Paradise Wldg Cstm Fabrication...239 961-8864
3888 Mannix Dr Ste 310 Naples (34114) ***(G-11357)***
Paradox Marine, Fort Lauderdale *Also called Edgewater Technologies Inc* ***(G-3962)***
Paraflow Energy Solutions LLC...713 239-0336
6501 Congress Ave Ste 100 Boca Raton (33487) ***(G-661)***
Paragon Globl Sup Slutions LLC...813 745-9902
301 W Platt St Ste 98 Tampa (33606) ***(G-17975)***
Paragon Plastics Inc...321 631-6212
1401 Armstrong Dr Titusville (32780) ***(G-18448)***
Paragon Printers, Melbourne *Also called Q P Consulting Inc* ***(G-8916)***
Paragon Products Inc...407 302-9147
2300 Old Lake Mary Rd Sanford (32771) ***(G-16099)***
Paragon Water Systems Inc...727 538-4704
13805 Monroe Park Tampa (33635) ***(G-17976)***
Parallax Health Sciences Inc (PA)...888 263-9799
2054 Vsta Pkwy Emrald Vw West Palm Beach (33411) ***(G-18987)***
Parallel Florida LLC...404 920-4890
2203 N Lois Ave Ste M275 Tampa (33607) ***(G-17977)***
Paramount Depot LLC...786 275-0107
7975 Nw 56th St Doral (33166) ***(G-3453)***
Paramount Digital Pubg LLC...813 489-5029
123 W Bloomingdale Ave # 3 Brandon (33511) ***(G-1169)***
Paramount Electronic Mfg Co...954 781-3755
1551 Sw 6th Ter Boca Raton (33486) ***(G-662)***
Paramount Industries Inc (PA)...954 781-3755
1020 Sw 10th Ave Ste 6 Pompano Beach (33069) ***(G-14784)***
Paramount Marketing Inc...352 608-8801
138 Juniper Loop Cir Ocala (34480) ***(G-12022)***
Paramount Mold LLC...954 772-2333
1701 W Cypress Creek Rd Fort Lauderdale (33309) ***(G-4157)***
Paramount Molded Products Inc...954 772-2333
1701 W Cypress Creek Rd Fort Lauderdale (33309) ***(G-4158)***
Paramount Sales & Consulting, Pompano Beach *Also called Paramount Industries Inc* ***(G-14784)***
Parasol Films Inc...954 478-8661
9503 Nw 73rd St Tamarac (33321) ***(G-17364)***
Parcus Medical LLC...941 755-7965
6423 Parkland Dr Sarasota (34243) ***(G-16271)***
Parinto Global Enterprises LLC...305 606-3107
5213 Nw 79th Ave Doral (33166) ***(G-3454)***
Paris Ink Inc...561 990-1194
1020 Holland Dr Ste 119 Boca Raton (33487) ***(G-663)***
Park Central Inc...850 547-1660
704 W Highway 90 Bonifay (32425) ***(G-805)***
Park Lake Printers, Orlando *Also called Florida Hospital Assn MGT Corp* ***(G-12749)***
Park Place Manufacturing Inc...863 382-0126
454 Park St Sebring (33870) ***(G-16701)***
Park Place Truss Inc...863 382-0126
500 Park St Sebring (33870) ***(G-16702)***
Park Place Truss & Design Inc...863 382-0126
206 W Center Ave Sebring (33870) ***(G-16703)***
Park Plus Florida Inc...954 929-7511
1111 Old Griffin Rd Dania (33004) ***(G-2456)***
Park Row Printing, Plantation *Also called Crompco Inc* ***(G-14504)***
Parker Boatworks...954 585-1059
617 Nw 7th Ave Fort Lauderdale (33311) ***(G-4159)***
Parker Davis Hvac Intl Inc...305 513-4488
3250 Nw 107th Ave Doral (33172) ***(G-3455)***
Parker Machinery Co Inc...904 356-5038
424 Copeland St Jacksonville (32204) ***(G-6657)***
Parker Plastics, Hallandale Beach *Also called Gar Industries Corp* ***(G-5188)***
Parker Protective Products LLC...800 879-0329
1965 Ne 148th St North Miami (33181) ***(G-11650)***
Parker Research Corporation...727 796-4066
2642 Enterprise Rd Clearwater (33763) ***(G-1826)***
Parker-Hannifin Corporation...239 304-1000
3580 Shaw Blvd Naples (34117) ***(G-11358)***
Parkervision Inc (PA)...904 732-6100
9446 Philips Hwy Ste 5a Jacksonville (32256) ***(G-6658)***
Parkinson Enterprises Inc...863 688-7900
1840 Harden Blvd Lakeland (33803) ***(G-7762)***
Parklanders, Coral Springs *Also called Data Publishers Inc* ***(G-2237)***
Parkside Publishing LLC...888 386-1115
1633 W Classical Blvd Delray Beach (33445) ***(G-3113)***
Parkson Corporation (HQ)...954 974-6610
1401 W Cypress Creek Rd # 100 Fort Lauderdale (33309) ***(G-4160)***
Parkway Printing Inc...239 936-6970
6371 Arc Way Ste 1 Fort Myers (33966) ***(G-4566)***
Parodi General Group Corp...954 306-1098
5431 Nw 50th Ct Coconut Creek (33073) ***(G-2092)***
Parras Plastic Inc...305 972-9537
13894 Sw 139th Ct Miami (33186) ***(G-10143)***
Parrillo Inc...386 767-8011
1644 S Ridgewood Ave South Daytona (32119) ***(G-16806)***
Parrish Inc...386 985-4879
5498 Aragon Ave De Leon Springs (32130) ***(G-2740)***
Parthenon Prints Inc...850 769-8321
909 W 39th St Panama City (32405) ***(G-13940)***
Parti Line International Inc...504 522-0300
9219 133rd Ave Unit 1e Largo (33773) ***(G-8023)***
Parts Cage Inc...904 373-7800
280 Business Park Cir # 412 Saint Augustine (32095) ***(G-15584)***
Parts Central Inc...850 547-1660
704 W Highway 90 Bonifay (32425) ***(G-806)***
Partsvu LLC...239 643-2292
829 Airport Pulling Rd N Naples (34104) ***(G-11359)***
Pas Reform North America LLC...904 358-0355
2550 Cabot Commerce Dr Jacksonville (32226) ***(G-6659)***
Pasa Services Inc...305 594-8662
13015 Nw 38th Ave Opa Locka (33054) ***(G-12350)***
Pasco Vision Center...813 788-7656
38038 North Ave Zephyrhills (33542) ***(G-19530)***
Passion Labels & Packaging...941 312-5003
1223 Tallevast Rd Sarasota (34243) ***(G-16272)***
Passport Pblcations Media Corp...561 615-3900
1555 Palm Beach Lakes Blv West Palm Beach (33401) ***(G-18988)***
Passur Aerospace Inc...631 589-6800
5750 Major Blvd Ste 530 Orlando (32819) ***(G-13051)***
Pastrana Prime LLC...407 470-9339
524 Madrigal Ct Orlando (32825) ***(G-13052)***
Pat Clark Custom Woodworking L...941 376-1387
5180 Island Date St Sarasota (34232) ***(G-16536)***
Pat Cobb Printing...772 465-5484
1201 Palm Walk Ln Fort Pierce (34950) ***(G-4729)***
Patco Electronics, Clearwater *Also called Creating Tech Solutions LLC* ***(G-1643)***
Pathfinder Shirts...407 865-6530
865 Sunshine Ln Altamonte Springs (32714) ***(G-62)***
Pathfnders Palm Bch-Mrtin Cnty...561 820-4262
2751 S Dixie Hwy West Palm Beach (33405) ***(G-18989)***
Pathway Holdings LLC...813 514-7899
5002 Us Highway 41 N Palmetto (34221) ***(G-13815)***
Patient Care America, Pompano Beach *Also called Diabetic Care Rx LLC* ***(G-14664)***
Patient Portal Tech Inc (PA)...877 779-6627
2000 Pga Blvd Ste 4440 North Palm Beach (33408) ***(G-11724)***
Patients First Products, Fort Myers *Also called Safe Strap LLC* ***(G-4592)***
Patio Products Mfg LLC...813 664-0158
9706 E Us Highway 92 Tampa (33610) ***(G-17978)***
Patio Products Mfg Inc...813 681-3806
509 S Larry Cir Brandon (33511) ***(G-1170)***
Patlon Industries Inc...305 255-7744
13913 Sw 119th Ave Miami (33186) ***(G-10144)***
Patrice Inc...941 359-2577
1747 Independence Blvd E Sarasota (34234) ***(G-16537)***
Patrick German Industries Inc...727 251-3015
1302 Wallwood Dr Brandon (33510) ***(G-1171)***
Patrick Industries Inc...941 556-6311
6805 15th St E Sarasota (34243) ***(G-16273)***
Patrick Industries Inc...941 556-6311
6805 15th St E Sarasota (34243) ***(G-16274)***
Patrick Industries Inc...352 732-8841
1609 Sw 17th St Ocala (34471) ***(G-12023)***

ALPHABETIC

Patrick Industries Inc......239 283-0800
2443 Sw Pine Island Rd Cape Coral (33991) ***(G-1454)***
Patriot Foundation Systems LLC......352 668-4842
30427 Commerce Dr San Antonio (33576) ***(G-15975)***
Patriot Person Defense......813 470-8025
1604 White Dove Ct Brandon (33510) ***(G-1172)***
Patriot Press Inc......407 625-7516
14141 Lake Price Dr Orlando (32826) ***(G-13053)***
Patriot Publishing USA LLC......904 217-7632
2286 W Clovelly Ln Saint Augustine (32092) ***(G-15585)***
Patriot Welding Inc......954 798-8819
151 Sw 5th St W Pompano Beach (33060) ***(G-14785)***
Patten Co Inc......707 826-2887
1803 Madrid Ave Lake Worth Beach (33461) ***(G-7618)***
Patten Group, Lake Worth Beach *Also called Patten Co Inc* ***(G-7618)***
Pattern Grading & Marker Svcs......305 495-9963
3650 Sw 141st Ave Miramar (33027) ***(G-11027)***
Patterson Publishing......863 701-2707
214 Traders Aly Lakeland (33801) ***(G-7763)***
Patterson Publishing LLC......863 701-2707
214 Traders Aly Lakeland (33801) ***(G-7764)***
Patti Marine Enterprises Inc......850 453-1282
306 S Pinewood Ln Pensacola (32507) ***(G-14221)***
Patticakes Cupcakery LLC......386 383-1782
964 Reed Canal Rd South Daytona (32119) ***(G-16807)***
Patty King Inc......305 817-1888
2740 W 81st St Hialeah (33016) ***(G-5555)***
Patty King Production Plant, Hialeah *Also called Patty King Inc* ***(G-5555)***
Pattys On Main LLC......941 650-9080
1400 Main St Sarasota (34236) ***(G-16538)***
Paul Himber Inc......561 586-3741
5324 Georgia Ave West Palm Beach (33405) ***(G-18990)***
Paul Tinsley Engraving......407 656-4344
236 Virginia Dr Winter Garden (34787) ***(G-19279)***
Paul Wales Inc......352 371-2120
131 Se 10th Ave Gainesville (32601) ***(G-4979)***
Paul White Logging Inc......850 379-8651
65 South Hosford (32334) ***(G-6010)***
Paul Wong......863 465-1114
1475 Jersey St Ne Lake Placid (33852) ***(G-7492)***
Pauls Pallets......850 474-1920
8928 Abbington Dr Pensacola (32534) ***(G-14222)***
Pauls Twing Dsptch Cntl Fla I......407 323-4446
1919 W 1st St Sanford (32771) ***(G-16100)***
Pavemax......386 206-3113
1120 Enterprise Ct Daytona Beach (32117) ***(G-2693)***
Pavemax......407 494-1959
5401 S Kirkman Rd 310a Orlando (32819) ***(G-13054)***
Paver Action Inc......954 868-1468
3741 Ne 18th Ave Pompano Beach (33064) ***(G-14786)***
Paver King......407 221-1718
1472 Farrindon Cir Lake Mary (32746) ***(G-7442)***
Paver Paradise LLC......561 843-3031
2468 Sw Cameo Blvd Port St Lucie (34953) ***(G-15178)***
Paver Systems LLC (HQ)......561 844-5202
7167 Interpace Rd Riviera Beach (33407) ***(G-15359)***
Paver Systems LLC......407 859-9117
39 E Landstreet Rd Orlando (32824) ***(G-13055)***
Paver Technologies LLC......772 213-8905
2110 Captains Walk Vero Beach (32963) ***(G-18651)***
Paver Way LLC......321 303-0968
160 N Spring Trl Altamonte Springs (32714) ***(G-63)***
Pavers Inc......352 754-3875
14497 Ponce De Leon Blvd Brooksville (34601) ***(G-1258)***
Pavers Professional Inc......239 878-6989
4086 Stillwood Dr Jacksonville (32257) ***(G-6660)***
Pavers Solutions Inc......754 551-1924
201 Nw 43rd St Deerfield Beach (33064) ***(G-2883)***
Paverscape Solutions LLC......850 497-5557
21 Professional Ct Miramar Beach (32550) ***(G-11067)***
Paversealingcom Corp......407 951-6437
1225 Windsor Ave Longwood (32750) ***(G-8321)***
Paveway Systems Inc......386 659-1316
114 Indian Lakes Ln Florahome (32140) ***(G-3765)***
Paw Inc......904 724-0310
8330 Atlantic Blvd Jacksonville (32211) ***(G-6661)***
Paw Print Co......561 753-5588
1593 Trotter Ct West Palm Beach (33414) ***(G-18991)***
Paws Off Prime K9 Cuisine LLC......305 546-7475
7415 Nw 54th St Miami (33166) ***(G-10145)***
Pawtitas, Miami *Also called Cafco LLC* ***(G-9301)***
Pax Catholic Communications......305 638-9729
1779 Nw 28th St Miami (33142) ***(G-10146)***
Paxen Publishing LLC (PA)......321 425-3030
2194 Highway A1a Ste 208 Indian Harbour Beach (32937) ***(G-6065)***
Payless Brick Pavers LLC......904 629-7436
6873 Plum Lake Ln E Jacksonville (32222) ***(G-6662)***
Payo LLC......786 368-8655
12481 N Stonebrook Cir Davie (33330) ***(G-2567)***
Payton America Inc......954 428-3326
1805 S Powerline Rd # 109 Deerfield Beach (33442) ***(G-2884)***
Payton Group International, Deerfield Beach *Also called Payton America Inc* ***(G-2884)***
Pb Group LLC......954 922-4311
3912 Pembroke Rd Hollywood (33021) ***(G-5887)***
Pb Holdco LLC......772 465-6006
3901 Saint Lucie Blvd Fort Pierce (34946) ***(G-4730)***
Pbc Pavers Borba Co......407 296-7727
1841 S Kirkman Rd # 1311 Orlando (32811) ***(G-13056)***
Pbcw Shutters and More, Mangonia Park *Also called Palm Beach Cstm Woodworks LLC* ***(G-8508)***
Pbg Golf Restaurant, West Palm Beach *Also called K and G Food Services LLC* ***(G-18917)***
Pbi/Gordon Corp......850 478-2770
8809 Ely St Pensacola (32514) ***(G-14223)***
PC Masters Corp......305 582-5595
5951 Nw 151st St Ste 35 Miami Lakes (33014) ***(G-10835)***
PC of Titusville Inc......321 267-1161
701 Columbia Blvd Titusville (32780) ***(G-18449)***
PCA, Pompano Beach *Also called Printing Corp of Americas Inc* ***(G-14815)***
Pca/Valdosta 645a, Jasper *Also called Packaging Corporation America* ***(G-6960)***
PCC Print Shop, Inc., Pensacola *Also called Abeka Print Shop Inc* ***(G-14076)***
PCF, Pensacola *Also called Publishers Crcltion Fflllment* ***(G-14242)***
Pcg, Jacksonville *Also called Pinnacle Cmmncations Group LLC* ***(G-6674)***
PCI, Rockledge *Also called Precision Circuits Inc* ***(G-15441)***
PCI Communications Inc......941 729-5202
1202 Gary Ave Unit 113 Ellenton (34222) ***(G-3654)***
Pcm and S L Plota Co LLC......727 547-6277
8016 118th Ave Largo (33773) ***(G-8024)***
Pcm Products Inc......321 267-7500
1225 White Dr Titusville (32780) ***(G-18450)***
Pcp Group LLC......727 388-7171
13590 Automobile Blvd Clearwater (33762) ***(G-1827)***
Pcp Tactical LLC......772 473-3472
3895 39th Sq Vero Beach (32960) ***(G-18652)***
Pcs Aerospace & Marketing LLC......973 352-9159
7736 Sw 193rd Ln Cutler Bay (33157) ***(G-2407)***
Pcs Phosphate/White Springs, White Springs *Also called White Springs AG Chem Inc* ***(G-19189)***
Pcsi, Sanford *Also called Pre-Cast Specialties Inc* ***(G-16104)***
Pd Partners, Tampa *Also called Product Dev Partners LLC* ***(G-18020)***
Pd Wire & Cable Sales Corp (HQ)......305 648-7790
9850 Nw 41st St Ste 200 Doral (33178) ***(G-3456)***
PDC......386 322-2808
4480 Eastport Park Way Port Orange (32127) ***(G-15027)***
Pdma Corporation......813 621-6463
5909 Hampton Oaks Pkwy C Tampa (33610) ***(G-17979)***
PDR OF THE GABLES, Doral *Also called Relu Co* ***(G-3482)***
Pe Manufacturing Company Fla......727 823-8172
11400 47th St N Ste A Clearwater (33762) ***(G-1828)***
Peace Love & Cbd......386 409-0910
110 Silver Cir Edgewater (32141) ***(G-3632)***
Peace Millwork Co Inc......305 573-6222
3535 Nw 50th St Miami (33142) ***(G-10147)***
Peace River Deli Provs Inc......941 426-4846
18480 Paulson Dr Port Charlotte (33954) ***(G-14993)***
Peak Electronics Inc......305 888-1588
7255 Nw 68th St Ste 8 Miami (33166) ***(G-10148)***
Peak Nutritional Products LLC......813 884-4989
5525 Johns Rd Ste 905 Tampa (33634) ***(G-17980)***
Peak Performance Nutrients Inc......561 266-1038
1505 Poinsettia Dr Ste 4 Delray Beach (33444) ***(G-3114)***
Peaktop Technologies Inc......561 598-6005
1727 Okeechobee Rd West Palm Beach (33409) ***(G-18992)***
Pearce Logging LLC......386 365-1880
9335 Nw 148th Trl Lake Butler (32054) ***(G-7340)***
Pearcey Enterprise......904 235-3096
7806 N 52nd St Tampa (33617) ***(G-17981)***
Pearl Academy LLC......904 619-6419
450 Busch Dr Unit 6 Jacksonville (32218) ***(G-6663)***
Pearsons Refacing and Refacing......904 591-3850
67 Carrera St Saint Augustine (32084) ***(G-15586)***
Peartree Cabinets and Design......941 377-7655
1635 12th St Sarasota (34236) ***(G-16539)***
Pecky Cypress & More LLC......772 215-0430
5500 Military Trl 22-12 Jupiter (33458) ***(G-7090)***
Ped-Stuart Corporation......352 754-6001
15351 Flight Path Dr Brooksville (34604) ***(G-1259)***
Pedano Custom Furniture Inc......904 704-9329
10617 Coleman Rd Jacksonville (32257) ***(G-6664)***
Pedicraft Inc......904 348-3170
4134 Saint Augustine Rd Jacksonville (32207) ***(G-6665)***
Pedro Truck Parts & Trailers......786 439-8652
9140 Fontnbleau Blvd # 5 Miami (33172) ***(G-10149)***
Pedronis Cast Stone Inc......904 783-1690
5169 Edgewood Ct Jacksonville (32254) ***(G-6666)***
Peek Traffic Corporation......941 366-8770
6408 Parkland Dr Ste 102 Sarasota (34243) ***(G-16275)***

Peekaboo Organics LLC 305 527-7162
8918 Abbott Ave Surfside (33154) ***(G-17205)***
Peeke Industries Inc 954 796-1938
6529 Nw 99th Ave Parkland (33076) ***(G-13998)***
Peeks Mobile App Corp 407 931-3878
3955 Golden Finch Way Kissimmee (34746) ***(G-7284)***
Peerless Instrument Co Inc 954 921-6006
2030 Coolidge St Hollywood (33020) ***(G-5888)***
Peerless Wind Systems 516 249-6900
8681 Hawkwood Bay Dr Boynton Beach (33473) ***(G-939)***
Pegasus Aerospace 850 376-0991
290 Vinings Way Blvd # 6103 Destin (32541) ***(G-3201)***
Pegasus Clean Air Mtr Cars Inc 954 682-2000
2400 W Cypress Creek Rd Fort Lauderdale (33309) ***(G-4161)***
Pegasus Laboratories Inc (HQ) 850 478-2770
8809 Ely St Pensacola (32514) ***(G-14224)***
Pegasus Resources Corp 561 575-2393
224 Commodore Dr Jupiter (33477) ***(G-7091)***
Pegasus Water Systems, Cape Coral *Also called Action Manufacturing & Sup Inc* ***(G-1373)***
Pegbroad Data System, Jacksonville *Also called Southeastern Pegboard Printers* ***(G-6792)***
Peggy Jennings Design, Saint Petersburg *Also called PJ Designs Inc* ***(G-15879)***
Pei Shores Inc 407 523-2899
4100 Silver Star Rd Ste C Orlando (32808) ***(G-13057)***
Peixoto, Miami *Also called Rme Studio Inc* ***(G-10268)***
Pelican Bay Publishing 954 610-7787
934 N University Dr Coral Springs (33071) ***(G-2302)***
Pelican International Inc 727 388-9895
6140 Ulmerton Rd Clearwater (33760) ***(G-1829)***
Pelican Pumps, West Palm Beach *Also called Channel Industries Inc* ***(G-18845)***
Pelican Water Systems, Deland *Also called Enviro Water Solutions LLC* ***(G-2975)***
Pelican Wire, Naples *Also called Wire Experts Group Inc* ***(G-11458)***
Pelliccione Builders Sup Inc 941 334-3014
17056 Wayzata Ct North Fort Myers (33917) ***(G-11602)***
Pelliconi Florida LLC (HQ) 407 855-6984
2501 Principal Row Orlando (32837) ***(G-13058)***
Pem-Air LLC 954 321-8726
5921 Sw 44th Ct Davie (33314) ***(G-2568)***
Pem-Air Turbine Eng Svcs LLC 954 321-8726
5921 Sw 44th Ct Davie (33314) ***(G-2569)***
Pemberton Inc 407 831-6688
103 Highline Dr Longwood (32750) ***(G-8322)***
Pemberton Custom Airboats 352 422-5597
8009 E Pemberton Path Inverness (34450) ***(G-6094)***
Pembroke Office Industries LLC 954 589-1329
1500 S 66th Ave Hollywood (33023) ***(G-5889)***
Pembroke Pines FL Readymix, Pembroke Pines *Also called Cemex Materials LLC* ***(G-14026)***
Pemco, Clearwater *Also called Pe Manufacturing Company Fla* ***(G-1828)***
Pemco, Boca Raton *Also called Paramount Electronic Mfg Co* ***(G-662)***
Pemco, Hialeah *Also called Petroleum Equipment and Mfg Co* ***(G-5557)***
Pemsum Industries Inc 561 623-3151
120 S Olive Ave Ste 311 West Palm Beach (33401) ***(G-18993)***
Pen Power, Tampa *Also called Granite Services Intl Inc* ***(G-17724)***
Pena General Welding Inc 786 255-2153
4788 Sw 75th Ave Miami (33155) ***(G-10150)***
Pencil Printing 407 346-4952
3004 Michigan Ave Kissimmee (34744) ***(G-7285)***
Pendulum One Inc 561 844-8169
6555 Garden Rd Ste 13 Riviera Beach (33404) ***(G-15360)***
Penek Chemical Industries Inc 954 978-6501
4100 N Powerline Rd Z5 Pompano Beach (33073) ***(G-14787)***
Peniel Inc 305 594-2739
11844 Sw 27th St Miramar (33025) ***(G-11028)***
Peninsula Metal Finishing Inc 407 291-1023
2550 Dinneen Ave Orlando (32804) ***(G-13059)***
Peninsula Steel Inc (PA) 956 795-1966
4504 Sydney Rd Plant City (33566) ***(G-14456)***
Peninsula Steel Inc 813 473-8133
4504 Sydney Rd Plant City (33566) ***(G-14457)***
Peninsula Tissue Corporation 305 863-0704
2630 Nw 72nd Ave Miami (33122) ***(G-10151)***
Penny Hoarder, The, Saint Petersburg *Also called Taylor Media LLC* ***(G-15936)***
Pennysaver 718 986-6437
245 S Woodland Blvd Deland (32720) ***(G-3008)***
Pensacola Orthtc & Prostetic 850 478-7676
5855 Creek Station Dr Pensacola (32504) ***(G-14225)***
Pensacola Ready Mix LLC 850 477-0343
Pc 3008 Hwy 95 A S Cantonment (32533) ***(G-1345)***
Pensacola Sign & Graphics Inc 850 433-7878
3711 N Palafox St Pensacola (32505) ***(G-14226)***
Pensacola Voice Inc 850 434-6963
213 E Yonge St Pensacola (32503) ***(G-14227)***
Pensacola Wood Treating Co 850 433-1300
1813 E Gadsden St Pensacola (32501) ***(G-14228)***
Penstripe Graphics 904 726-0200
4251 University Blvd S # 402 Jacksonville (32216) ***(G-6667)***
Pentacles Energy GP LLC 786 552-9931
1600 Ponce De Leon Blvd Coral Gables (33134) ***(G-2184)***
Pentair Union Engineering N.A., Daytona Beach *Also called Union Engineering N Amer LLC* ***(G-2729)***
Pepper Shark Llc (PA) 305 849-0104
6 Havana Ln Key West (33040) ***(G-7201)***
Pepper Tree 941 922-2662
1269 1st St Ste 7 Sarasota (34236) ***(G-16540)***
Peppertree Press LLC 941 922-2662
6341 Yellow Wood Pl Sarasota (34241) ***(G-16541)***
Pepsi Beverages Company 407 241-4110
7701 Southland Blvd Orlando (32809) ***(G-13060)***
Pepsi Bottling Group 863 452-9920
1006 W Cornell St Avon Park (33825) ***(G-292)***
Pepsi Bottling Group Inc 863 687-7605
4100 Frontage Rd S Lakeland (33815) ***(G-7765)***
Pepsi St Pete 727 527-8113
4451 34th St N Saint Petersburg (33714) ***(G-15875)***
Pepsi-Cola, Lakeland *Also called Pepsi Bottling Group Inc* ***(G-7765)***
Pepsi-Cola, Medley *Also called Pepsico Inc* ***(G-8703)***
Pepsi-Cola Bottling Co Tampa 239 643-4642
1171 Industrial Blvd Naples (34104) ***(G-11360)***
Pepsi-Cola Bottling Co Tampa (HQ) 813 971-2550
11315 N 30th St Tampa (33612) ***(G-17982)***
Pepsi-Cola Bottling Co Tampa 941 378-1058
7881 Fruitville Rd Sarasota (34240) ***(G-16542)***
Pepsi-Cola Bottling Co Tampa 407 857-3301
1700 Directors Row Orlando (32809) ***(G-13061)***
Pepsi-Cola Bottling Co Tampa 239 337-2011
3625 Mrtin Lther King Blv Fort Myers (33916) ***(G-4567)***
Pepsi-Cola Bottling Co Tampa 727 942-3664
5406 Whippoorwill Dr Holiday (34690) ***(G-5748)***
Pepsi-Cola Bottling Co Tampa 407 826-5929
7501 Monetary Dr Orlando (32809) ***(G-13062)***
Pepsi-Cola Btlg Ft Ldrdl-Palm 561 848-1000
7305 Garden Rd Riviera Beach (33404) ***(G-15361)***
Pepsi-Cola Metro Btlg Co Inc 904 733-1627
5829 Pepsi Pl Jacksonville (32216) ***(G-6668)***
Pepsi-Cola Metro Btlg Co Inc 407 354-5800
7380 W Sand Lake Rd # 230 Orlando (32819) ***(G-13063)***
Pepsi-Cola Metro Btlg Co Inc 386 752-8956
619 Sw Arrowhead Ter Lake City (32024) ***(G-7375)***
Pepsi-Cola Metro Btlg Co Inc 352 376-8276
6335 Nw 18th Dr Gainesville (32653) ***(G-4980)***
Pepsi-Cola Metro Btlg Co Inc 863 551-4500
5023 Recker Hwy Winter Haven (33880) ***(G-19340)***
Pepsi-Cola Metro Btlg Co Inc 352 629-8911
525 Sw 16th St Ocala (34471) ***(G-12024)***
Pepsi-Cola Metro Btlg Co Inc 321 242-2984
3951 Sarno Rd Melbourne (32934) ***(G-8906)***
Pepsi-Cola Metro Btlg Co Inc 352 797-1160
490 Champion Dr Brooksville (34601) ***(G-1260)***
Pepsi-Cola Metro Btlg Co Inc 772 464-6150
3620 Crossroads Pkwy Fort Pierce (34945) ***(G-4731)***
Pepsico, Jacksonville *Also called Pepsi-Cola Metro Btlg Co Inc* ***(G-6668)***
Pepsico, Saint Petersburg *Also called Pepsi St Pete* ***(G-15875)***
Pepsico, Naples *Also called Pepsi-Cola Bottling Co Tampa* ***(G-11360)***
Pepsico, Avon Park *Also called Pepsi Bottling Group* ***(G-292)***
Pepsico, Fort Pierce *Also called Pepsi-Cola Metro Btlg Co Inc* ***(G-4731)***
Pepsico, Tallahassee *Also called Refreshment Services Inc* ***(G-17315)***
Pepsico Inc 305 593-7500
8701 Nw 93rd St Medley (33178) ***(G-8703)***
Pepsico Inc 407 933-5542
1650 S Poinciana Blvd Kissimmee (34758) ***(G-7286)***
Pepsico Inc 800 433-2652
800 Fairway Dr Ste 400 Deerfield Beach (33441) ***(G-2885)***
Pepsico Beverage Distributors 305 537-4477
1000 Nw 57th Ct Miami (33126) ***(G-10152)***
Pepsico Latin America Beverage 305 537-4477
1000 Nw 57th Ct Ste 800 Miami (33126) ***(G-10153)***
Peralta Group Inc 954 502-8100
4566 N Hiatus Rd Sunrise (33351) ***(G-17157)***
Perch Security Inc 844 500-1810
4110 George Rd Ste 200 Tampa (33634) ***(G-17983)***
Perez Industries Inc 239 992-2444
26364 Old 41 Rd Bonita Springs (34135) ***(G-846)***
Perfect Brick Pavers Inc 727 534-2506
5626 Quist Dr Port Richey (34668) ***(G-15062)***
Perfect Care, Orlando *Also called Ncg Medical Systems Inc* ***(G-12996)***
Perfect Oil Inc 954 984-8944
2900 W Sample Rd Pompano Beach (33073) ***(G-14788)***
Perfect Pavers South Fla LLC 954 779-1855
528 Nw 1st Ave Fort Lauderdale (33301) ***(G-4162)***
Perfect Reflections Inc 813 991-4361
7708 Avocet Dr Zephyrhills (33544) ***(G-19531)***
Perfectus Pet Food LLC 800 774-3296
3300 Oakwood Blvd Hollywood (33020) ***(G-5890)***
Performance Aircraft Unlimited 808 782-7171
4918 Sudbury Ct Orlando (32826) ***(G-13064)***
Performance Boats Inc 305 956-9549
2050 Ne 153rd St North Miami Beach (33162) ***(G-11697)***

ALPHABETIC

Performance Designs Inc ...386 738-2224
1300 E Intl Speedway Blvd Deland (32724) ***(G-3009)***
Performance Machining Svcs Inc ...850 469-9106
4161 Warehouse Ln Pensacola (32505) ***(G-14229)***
Performance Powder Coating ...407 339-4000
416 Commerce Way Longwood (32750) ***(G-8323)***
Performance Pumps Inc ...407 339-6700
321 Oleander Way Casselberry (32707) ***(G-1512)***
Performance Sales & Service ...863 465-2814
1130 Us Highway 27 N Lake Placid (33852) ***(G-7493)***
Performance Technology 2000 ...772 463-1056
1501 Se Decker Ave # 129 Stuart (34994) ***(G-16987)***
Performance USA Battery, Miami *Also called Mia Consulting & Trading Inc* ***(G-9989)***
Performnce Glzing Slutions LLC ...305 975-3717
7239 Nw 54th St Miami (33166) ***(G-10154)***
Performnce Ntrtn Solutions LLC ...310 435-2995
14895 22nd Rd N Loxahatchee Groves (33470) ***(G-8367)***
Perfumeland ...407 354-3342
5216 Vanguard St Orlando (32819) ***(G-13065)***
Perfumery, The, Englewood *Also called Essential Oil University LLC* ***(G-3676)***
Perii Inc ...321 253-2269
2755 N Bnana Rver Dr Ste Merritt Island (32952) ***(G-9006)***
Perii Software, Merritt Island *Also called Perii Inc* ***(G-9006)***
Periodic Elements LLC ...561 972-7791
19115 Se Coral Reef Ln Jupiter (33458) ***(G-7092)***
Peripheral Services Inc ...813 854-1181
103 Pine Ave S Oldsmar (34677) ***(G-12256)***
Perkins Power, Doral *Also called Southeast Power Group Inc* ***(G-3507)***
Perkins Power Corp ...904 278-9919
5820 Nw 84th Ave Doral (33166) ***(G-3457)***
Perl Inc ...352 726-2483
5009 S Florida Ave Inverness (34450) ***(G-6095)***
Perma Cap, Davie *Also called Kleen Wheels Corporation* ***(G-2541)***
Permacraft Sign & Trophies Co, South Daytona *Also called Parrillo Inc* ***(G-16806)***
Permatile Roofing, Lakeland *Also called Advanced Alum Polk Cnty Inc* ***(G-7626)***
Perpetual Marketing Assoc Inc (PA) ...813 949-9385
25126 State Road 54 Lutz (33559) ***(G-8408)***
Perri Brothers and Associates ...305 887-8686
9001 Nw 97th Ter Medley (33178) ***(G-8704)***
Perry Baromedical Corporation (HQ) ...561 840-0395
3750 Prospect Ave Riviera Beach (33404) ***(G-15362)***
Perry Composites LLC ...850 584-8400
1290 Houck Rd Perry (32348) ***(G-14308)***
Perry Ellis International Inc (HQ) ...305 592-2830
3000 Nw 107th Ave Doral (33172) ***(G-3458)***
Perry Fiberglas Products Inc ...321 609-9036
5415 Village Dr Rockledge (32955) ***(G-15439)***
Perry Newspapers Inc ...850 584-5513
123 S Jefferson St Perry (32347) ***(G-14309)***
Perry North Aerospace Inc ...954 295-9520
2764 Ne 25th St Lighthouse Point (33064) ***(G-8212)***
Perry Precast Inc ...386 294-2710
232 Se Industrial Pk Cir Mayo (32066) ***(G-8597)***
Personal Brands LLC ...855 426-7765
508 Sw 12th Ave Deerfield Beach (33442) ***(G-2886)***
Pestanos Woodworking LLC ...954 448-3932
15332 Sw 53rd Ln Miami (33185) ***(G-10155)***
Pestwest Usa LLC ...941 358-1983
7135 16th St E Ste 124 Sarasota (34243) ***(G-16276)***
Pet & Feed Store, Jacksonville *Also called BRT Oakleaf Pet Inc* ***(G-6239)***
Pet Declaration Inc ...772 215-1607
13915 River Willow Pl Tampa (33637) ***(G-17984)***
Pet Doc FL LLC ...407 437-6614
1630 Sand Key Cir Oviedo (32765) ***(G-13453)***
Pet Pages, Sarasota *Also called T V HI Lites Penny Saver Inc* ***(G-16614)***
Pet Services of Florida LLC ...352 746-6888
3404 N Lecanto Hwy Beverly Hills (34465) ***(G-378)***
Pet Supplies Plus ...248 824-4676
1045 Front Pl North Port (34287) ***(G-11746)***
Petainer Manufacturing US ...786 999-2019
5901 Sw 74th St 311 Miami (33143) ***(G-10156)***
Pete Peterson Signs Inc ...352 625-2307
11094 Ne Highway 314 Silver Springs (34488) ***(G-16783)***
Peter Flagg Woodwork ...561 307-4200
103 E Chandler Rd West Palm Beach (33406) ***(G-18994)***
Peter Fogel ...561 245-5252
8108 Summer Shores Dr Delray Beach (33446) ***(G-3115)***
Peter Marcus Paradigm LLC ...877 887-8696
1331 Lakeview Dr Winter Park (32789) ***(G-19429)***
Peter Printer Inc ...305 558-0147
1355 W 49th St Hialeah (33012) ***(G-5556)***
Peter T Amann ...561 848-2770
8111 Garden Rd Ste G West Palm Beach (33404) ***(G-18995)***
Peter Welchs Custom Boats ...941 575-8665
8446 Alfred Blvd Punta Gorda (33982) ***(G-15219)***
Peterbrooke Choclat Fctry LLC ...904 273-7878
880 State Rd A1a Ste 4 1 A Ponte Vedra Beach (32082) ***(G-14950)***
Peters Structural Products ...863 229-5275
1320 Hidden Creek Ct Winter Haven (33880) ***(G-19341)***
Petersen Industries Inc ...863 676-1493
4000 State Road 60 W Lake Wales (33859) ***(G-7517)***
Petersen Metals, Hudson *Also called Clear Horizon Ventures Company* ***(G-6018)***
Peterson Enterprises LLC ...386 456-3400
12502 158th Ter Mc Alpin (32062) ***(G-8600)***
Peterson Manufacturing LLC ...941 371-4989
155 Cattlemen Rd Sarasota (34232) ***(G-16543)***
Peterson Manufacturing Co Inc ...941 371-4989
155 Cattlemen Rd Sarasota (34232) ***(G-16544)***
Petes Seal Coating ...857 251-1912
2300 Ne 15th Ter Pompano Beach (33064) ***(G-14789)***
Petit Custom Wood Works ...954 200-3111
3673 W Valley Green Dr Davie (33328) ***(G-2570)***
Petlift Sb Manufacturing Inc ...941 346-2211
5301 Gateway Blvd Lakeland (33811) ***(G-7766)***
Petnet Solutions Inc ...813 627-0022
9204 Florida Palm Dr Tampa (33619) ***(G-17985)***
Petroheral, Doral *Also called Heralpin Usa Inc* ***(G-3379)***
Petroimage, Belleview *Also called Petroleum Group LLC* ***(G-374)***
Petroleum Containment Inc ...904 358-1700
8873 Western Way Jacksonville (32256) ***(G-6669)***
Petroleum Equipment and Mfg Co ...305 558-9573
2185 W 76th St Hialeah (33016) ***(G-5557)***
Petroleum Group LLC ...352 304-5500
6432 Se 115th Ln Belleview (34420) ***(G-374)***
Petroleum Marine LLC ...561 422-9018
15985 Meadow Wood Dr West Palm Beach (33414) ***(G-18996)***
Petrosol Processing & Refining ...305 442-7400
2655 S Le Jeune Rd # 1003 Miami (33134) ***(G-10157)***
Petrotech Services Inc ...813 248-0743
1807 E 2nd Ave Tampa (33605) ***(G-17986)***
Petrotech Services Inc (PA) ...813 248-0743
4041 Maritime Blvd Tampa (33605) ***(G-17987)***
Petruj Chemical Corp ...305 556-1271
8055 Nw 98th St Miami Lakes (33016) ***(G-10836)***
Pets2go International Inc ...404 625-9606
2301 Se 23rd Ter Homestead (33035) ***(G-5987)***
Petti, Vince, Hallandale Beach *Also called South Broward Brace Inc* ***(G-5213)***
Pettit Racing, Riviera Beach *Also called Excellent Performance Inc* ***(G-15326)***
Pettit Tools & Supplies Inc ...954 781-2640
4391 Ne 11th Ave Pompano Beach (33064) ***(G-14790)***
Pfa Publishing ...727 512-5814
6020 Shore Blvd S Gulfport (33707) ***(G-5136)***
Pfaff Engraving, Miami Lakes *Also called Pfaffco Inc* ***(G-10837)***
Pfaffco Inc ...305 635-0986
14329 Commerce Way Miami Lakes (33016) ***(G-10837)***
Pfci LLC ...239 435-3575
4610 Enterprise Ave Naples (34104) ***(G-11361)***
Pfi, Lake Wales *Also called Pipeline Fabricators Inc* ***(G-7518)***
Pfi Inc ...407 822-4499
607 Savage Ct Longwood (32750) ***(G-8324)***
Pg Express Inc ...954 788-3263
1000 W Mcnab Rd Ste 104 Pompano Beach (33069) ***(G-14791)***
Pgms, Miramar *Also called Pattern Grading & Marker Svcs* ***(G-11027)***
PGT Custom Windows Doors, North Venice *Also called PGT Industries Inc* ***(G-11761)***
PGT Industries Inc (HQ) ...941 480-1600
1070 Technology Dr North Venice (34275) ***(G-11761)***
PGT Innovations Inc (PA) ...941 480-1600
1070 Technology Dr North Venice (34275) ***(G-11762)***
Phantom Products Inc ...321 690-6729
474 Barnes Blvd Rockledge (32955) ***(G-15440)***
Phantom Sales Group Inc ...888 614-1232
1550 Centennial Blvd Bartow (33830) ***(G-330)***
Phantom Technologies Inc ...407 265-2567
2280 N Ronald Reagan Blvd # 103 Longwood (32750) ***(G-8325)***
Phantom USA LLC ...863 353-5972
101 Shepard Ave Dundee (33838) ***(G-3567)***
Pharma Formulations Labs Inc ...786 985-1254
12601 Nw 115th Ave # 103 Medley (33178) ***(G-8705)***
Pharma Nature LLC ...305 395-4723
2271 Dorado Ave Davie (33324) ***(G-2571)***
Pharma Resources Inc ...973 780-5241
380 S State Road 434 Altamonte Springs (32714) ***(G-64)***
Pharmachem, Opa Locka *Also called World Perfumes Inc* ***(G-12370)***
Pharmacy Automation Systems, Largo *Also called Qem Inc* ***(G-8033)***
Pharmacy Automtn Systems LLC ...727 544-6522
8790 66th Ct N Pinellas Park (33782) ***(G-14375)***
Pharmalab Enterprises Inc (PA) ...305 821-4002
14501 Nw 60th Ave Miami Lakes (33014) ***(G-10838)***
Pharmalink Inc ...800 257-3527
8285 Bryan Dairy Rd # 200 Largo (33777) ***(G-8025)***
Pharmamed Global Distributors, Fort Lauderdale *Also called Pharmamed USA Inc* ***(G-4163)***
Pharmamed USA Inc ...954 533-4462
3778 Sw 30th Ave Fort Lauderdale (33312) ***(G-4163)***
Pharmatech LLC (PA) ...954 581-7881
4131 Sw 47th Ave Ste 1403 Davie (33314) ***(G-2572)***
Pharmatech LLC ...954 629-2444
4131 Sw 47th Ave Ste 1405 Davie (33314) ***(G-2573)***

Pharmatech Pharmatech LLC 954 583-8778
3597 Nw 19th St Fort Lauderdale (33311) ***(G-4164)***
Pharmco Laboratories Inc 321 268-1313
3520 South St Titusville (32780) ***(G-18451)***
Phase Integration LLC 877 778-8885
815 S Main St Jacksonville (32207) ***(G-6670)***
Phasetronics Inc (PA) 727 573-1819
1600 Sunshine Dr Clearwater (33765) ***(G-1830)***
Pheasant Run Wind LLC 561 691-7171
700 Universe Blvd Juno Beach (33408) ***(G-6982)***
Pheasant Run Wind Holdings II (HQ) 561 691-7171
700 Universe Blvd Juno Beach (33408) ***(G-6983)***
Phelps Dodge Intl Corp (HQ) 305 648-7888
9850 Nw 41st St Ste 200 Doral (33178) ***(G-3459)***
Phelps Motorsports LLC 239 417-2042
2255 Linwood Ave Naples (34112) ***(G-11362)***
Phg Kendall LLC 954 392-8788
4651 Sheridan St Ste 480 Hollywood (33021) ***(G-5891)***
PHI CHI Foundation Inc 561 526-3401
740 Sw 50th Ter Margate (33068) ***(G-8560)***
Phil & Brenda Johnson Inc 813 623-5478
5609 E Hillsborough Ave Tampa (33610) ***(G-17988)***
Phil Buckner Woodworks Inc 904 339-4475
118 Jackson Rd Ste 4 Jacksonville (32225) ***(G-6671)***
Phil Lau 813 631-8643
16309 Millan De Avila Tampa (33613) ***(G-17989)***
Phil Rowe Signs Inc 561 832-8688
805 N Dixie Hwy West Palm Beach (33401) ***(G-18997)***
Philip Stein, Pembroke Park *Also called Pstein Inc* ***(G-14010)***
Philips North America LLC 305 969-7447
13305 Sw 106th Ave Miami (33176) ***(G-10158)***
Phillip & Roger Inc 850 763-6415
2201 N East Ave Panama City (32405) ***(G-13941)***
Phillip Roy Inc 727 593-2700
13064 Indian Rocks Rd Largo (33774) ***(G-8026)***
Phillips Energy Inc (HQ) 850 682-5127
806 W James Lee Blvd Crestview (32536) ***(G-2355)***
Phillips Graphics Inc 352 622-1776
1711 Sw 17th St Ocala (34471) ***(G-12025)***
Phillips Printing Services LLC 941 526-6570
5103 Lena Rd Unit 107 Bradenton (34211) ***(G-1095)***
Philly Swirl, Tampa *Also called Phillys Famous Water Ice Inc* ***(G-17990)***
Phillys Famous Water Ice Inc 813 248-8644
1102 N 28th St Tampa (33605) ***(G-17990)***
Phils Cake Box Bakeries Inc 813 348-0128
4705 W Cayuga St Tampa (33614) ***(G-17991)***
Phintec LLC 321 214-2500
618 E South St Ste 500 Orlando (32801) ***(G-13066)***
Phl Pool Services, Ormond Beach *Also called Professional Holiday Lighting* ***(G-13394)***
Phlebotomists On Wheels Inc 954 873-7591
1451 W Cypress Creek Rd # 300 Fort Lauderdale (33309) ***(G-4165)***
Phlexapeel LLC 407 990-1854
100 Rialto Pl Ste 743 Melbourne (32901) ***(G-8907)***
Phlintrock Industries Inc 904 579-3334
2117 Foxwood Dr Orange Park (32073) ***(G-12402)***
Phocas Software 863 738-9107
235 S Maitland Ave Maitland (32751) ***(G-8474)***
Phoenix Calibration Ltd Srl 786 866-5906
1733 Nw 79th Ave Doral (33191) ***(G-3460)***
Phoenix Coating Resources, Mulberry *Also called Saint-Gobain Corporation* ***(G-11135)***
Phoenix Custom Gear LLC 561 808-7181
1730 S Federal Hwy # 242 Delray Beach (33483) ***(G-3116)***
Phoenix Dewatering Inc 407 330-7015
1980 Cameron Ave Sanford (32771) ***(G-16101)***
Phoenix Enterprises Fla LLC 813 986-9000
7616 Industrial Ln Temple Terrace (33637) ***(G-18374)***
Phoenix Group Florida Inc (PA) 954 563-1224
3000 Ne 30th Pl Fl 5 Fort Lauderdale (33306) ***(G-4166)***
Phoenix Jewelry Mfg Inc 305 477-2515
1499 Nw 79th Ave Doral (33126) ***(G-3461)***
Phoenix Media Network Inc 561 994-1118
6531 Pk Of Commerce Blvd Boca Raton (33487) ***(G-664)***
Phoenix Metal Products Inc 772 595-6386
3000 Industrial Avenue 3 Fort Pierce (34946) ***(G-4732)***
Phoenix Publications 954 609-7586
777 S Federal Hwy Pompano Beach (33062) ***(G-14792)***
Phoenix Tanks, Jacksonville *Also called Envirovault LLC* ***(G-6368)***
Phoenix Trans Parts, Clearwater *Also called Phoenix Transmission Parts Inc* ***(G-1831)***
Phoenix Transmission Parts Inc (PA) 727 541-0269
12550 44th St N Ste A Clearwater (33762) ***(G-1831)***
Phoenix Wood Products Inc (PA) 888 304-1131
3761 Ne 36th Ave Ocala (34479) ***(G-12026)***
Phone Wave Inc 352 683-8101
178 Mariner Blvd Spring Hill (34609) ***(G-16858)***
Phosco Electric Supply Co Inc 941 708-9633
1734 5th St W Bradenton (34205) ***(G-1096)***
Phoscrete Corporation (PA) 561 420-0595
1800 Nw 15th Ave Ste 130 Pompano Beach (33069) ***(G-14793)***
Photo Finishing News Inc 239 992-4421
11618 Quail Village Way Naples (34119) ***(G-11363)***
Photo Graphics 772 220-1430
1601 Nw Federal Hwy Stuart (34994) ***(G-16988)***
Photo Offset Inc 305 666-1067
4824 Sw 72nd Ave Miami (33155) ***(G-10159)***
Photoengraving Inc (PA) 813 253-3427
502 N Willow Ave Tampa (33606) ***(G-17992)***
Photofinishing News, Naples *Also called Photo Finishing News Inc* ***(G-11363)***
Photon Towers Inc 305 235-7337
17290 Sw 192nd St Miami (33187) ***(G-10160)***
Phototelesis LP 321 254-1500
1615 W Nasa Blvd Melbourne (32901) ***(G-8908)***
Phxtreme Corp 305 594-2284
1835 Nw 112th Ave Ste 166 Miami (33172) ***(G-10161)***
Phy-Med 305 925-0141
8905 Sw 87th Ave Ste 200 Miami (33176) ***(G-10162)***
Phylomed, Plantation *Also called Bio Therapeutics Inc* ***(G-14496)***
Physician Hearing Care 239 261-7722
11121 Health Park Blvd # 700 Naples (34110) ***(G-11364)***
Physicians Imaging LLC (PA) 352 383-3716
3615 Lake Center Dr Mount Dora (32757) ***(G-11110)***
Physicians Regional - Pine, Estero *Also called Naples Hma LLC* ***(G-3692)***
Physiorx LLC 407 718-5549
2706 Rew Cir Ocoee (34761) ***(G-12088)***
Pica Sales and Engineering 239 992-9079
19771 Chapel Trce Estero (33928) ***(G-3693)***
Picasso Embroidery Systems 305 827-9666
6043 Nw 167th St Ste A25 Hialeah (33015) ***(G-5558)***
Piccionis Frozen Desserts 561 633-5759
489 Goldenwood Way Wellington (33414) ***(G-18727)***
Picket Fence Childrens 813 713-8589
4931 Allen Rd Zephyrhills (33541) ***(G-19532)***
Pickett Logging, Hilliard *Also called Harry Pickett* ***(G-5709)***
Pickhardt Professional Sr 941 737-7262
4329 14th Street Cir Palmetto (34221) ***(G-13816)***
Pickle Factory, Santa Rosa Beach *Also called Little Pickle LLC* ***(G-16163)***
Pickle Pro LLC 844 332-7069
3527 Plover Ave Unit 2 Naples (34117) ***(G-11365)***
Pickled Art Inc 954 635-7370
1495 N Federal Hwy Fort Lauderdale (33304) ***(G-4167)***
Pickles Plus 941 661-6139
6196 Tidwell St North Port (34291) ***(G-11747)***
Pictures and Mirrors, Orlando *Also called Total Vision Design Group* ***(G-13263)***
Piecemakers LLC 786 517-1829
5521 Nw 78th Ave Doral (33166) ***(G-3462)***
Piecemakers LLC 786 517-1829
120 N Knights Ave Brandon (33510) ***(G-1173)***
Pierce Manufacturing Inc 727 573-0400
12770 44th St N Clearwater (33762) ***(G-1832)***
Pierce Manufacturing Inc 941 748-3900
1512 38th Ave E Bradenton (34208) ***(G-1097)***
Pierced Ciderworks 772 302-3863
411 N 2nd St Fort Pierce (34950) ***(G-4733)***
Piergate LLC 813 938-9170
4450 Pet Ln Ste 105 Lutz (33559) ***(G-8409)***
Piezo Technology Inc (HQ) 407 298-2000
2525 Shader Rd Orlando (32804) ***(G-13067)***
Pigments Black Diamond 904 241-2533
1316 Barrington Cir Saint Augustine (32092) ***(G-15587)***
Pike Pole Press 407 474-7453
1506 Magnolia Ave Sanford (32771) ***(G-16102)***
Pikmykid, Kidio, Tampa *Also called Sachi Tech Inc* ***(G-18079)***
Pilgrims Pride Corporation 386 362-4171
1306 Howard St W Live Oak (32064) ***(G-8236)***
Pilkington North America Inc 407 295-8560
4500 Seaboard Rd Ste A Orlando (32808) ***(G-13068)***
Pillar Inc 904 545-4993
2232 Corporate Sq Blvd Jacksonville (32216) ***(G-6672)***
Pillow Plus Manufacturing Inc 305 652-2218
515 Ne 189th St Miami (33179) ***(G-10163)***
Pilot Corp of Palm Beaches 561 848-2928
7117 49th Ter N Riviera Beach (33407) ***(G-15363)***
Pilot Steel Inc 954 978-3615
1950 W Copans Rd Pompano Beach (33064) ***(G-14794)***
Piloto Music Publisher Corp 321 348-0638
13660 Sw 32nd St Miami (33175) ***(G-10164)***
Pin Creator, The, Winter Springs *Also called Hbys Enterprises LLC* ***(G-19473)***
Pin Hsiao & Associates LLC 425 637-3357
4470 Eastport Park Way Port Orange (32127) ***(G-15028)***
Pin Makers 877 825-6120
803 S Orlando Ave Winter Park (32789) ***(G-19430)***
Pin-N-Win Wrestling Club Inc 904 276-8038
117 Suzanne Ave Orange Park (32073) ***(G-12403)***
Pine Top Logging LLC 386 365-0857
27687 65th Rd Branford (32008) ***(G-1188)***
Pineapple Grove Woodworks 561 676-1287
3740 Prospect Ave West Palm Beach (33404) ***(G-18998)***
Pinecrest Tribune 305 662-2277
6796 Sw 62nd Ave South Miami (33143) ***(G-16825)***

Pinellas Blind and Shutter Inc 727 481-4461
5100 Ulmerton Rd Ste 22 Clearwater (33760) ***(G-1833)***
Pinellas Custom Cabinets Inc 727 864-4263
8800 126th Ave Largo (33773) ***(G-8027)***
Pinellas Electric Motor Repair 727 572-0777
12990 44th St N Clearwater (33762) ***(G-1834)***
Pinellas Precision Laser LLC 727 420-0388
4185 35th St N Saint Petersburg (33714) ***(G-15876)***
Pinellas Provision Corporation 727 822-2701
201 16th St S Saint Petersburg (33705) ***(G-15877)***
Pink Inc Publishing 904 834-3118
124 Mills Ln Jacksonville Beach (32250) ***(G-6954)***
Pinnacle Cabinets Closets LLC 850 477-5402
9900b N Palafox St Pensacola (32534) ***(G-14230)***
Pinnacle Central Company Inc (PA) 904 354-5746
103 Bryan St Jacksonville (32202) ***(G-6673)***
Pinnacle Cmmncations Group LLC 904 910-0444
10151 Deerwood Park Blvd Jacksonville (32256) ***(G-6674)***
Pinnacle Foods Inc 321 952-7926
5905 S Highway A1a Melbourne Beach (32951) ***(G-8981)***
Pinocho Bakery, Coral Gables *Also called Edca Bakery Corporation* ***(G-2141)***
Pinos Window Corporation 305 888-9903
6860 Nw 75th St Medley (33166) ***(G-8706)***
Pins Fever 407 619-5314
161 Willow Ave Altamonte Springs (32714) ***(G-65)***
Pinstripe Magazine LLC 201 310-5398
3770 58th Ave Ne Naples (34120) ***(G-11366)***
Pinto Palma Sound LLC 877 959-1815
10665 Sw 190th St # 3103 Cutler Bay (33157) ***(G-2408)***
Pinzon Caramel Syrup 305 591-2472
6937 Nw 52nd St Miami (33166) ***(G-10165)***
Pioneer Aerospace Corporation 850 623-3330
8101 Opportunity Dr Milton (32583) ***(G-10936)***
Pioneer Ag-Chem Inc (PA) 772 464-9300
4100 Glades Cut Off Rd Fort Pierce (34981) ***(G-4734)***
Pioneer Announcements Inc 305 573-7000
20324 Ne 16th Pl Miami (33179) ***(G-10166)***
Pioneer Casework LLC 305 404-3490
7901 4th St N Ste 4616 Saint Petersburg (33702) ***(G-15878)***
Pioneer Development Entps Inc 239 592-0001
5901 Shirley St Naples (34109) ***(G-11367)***
Pioneer Dredge Inc 904 732-2151
8515 Baymeadows Way # 201 Jacksonville (32256) ***(G-6675)***
Pioneer Led Lighting Corp 305 620-5300
4980 Nw 165th St Unit A1 Miami Lakes (33014) ***(G-10839)***
Pioneer Metals, Jacksonville *Also called Goodman Manufacturing Co LP* ***(G-6440)***
Pioneer Printing and Signs, Cape Coral *Also called Everything Printing Inc* ***(G-1420)***
Pioneer Screen Inc 772 260-3068
2740 Sw Martin Downs Blvd Palm City (34990) ***(G-13671)***
Pioneer Surgical Technology 906 225-5629
11621 Research Cir Alachua (32615) ***(G-14)***
Pioneer Welding & Fabrication 407 880-4997
532 Hillend Ct Apopka (32712) ***(G-170)***
Pioneer Woodworking, Saint Petersburg *Also called Pioneer Casework LLC* ***(G-15878)***
PIP Marketing Signs Print 904 825-2372
248 State Road 312 Saint Augustine (32086) ***(G-15588)***
PIP Printing, Port Richey *Also called Premier Printing Signs* ***(G-15064)***
PIP Printing, Kissimmee *Also called Abby Press Inc* ***(G-7216)***
PIP Printing, Palm Beach Gardens *Also called Donna Lynn Enterprises Inc* ***(G-13584)***
PIP Printing, Fort Lauderdale *Also called Bandart Enterprises Inc* ***(G-3839)***
PIP Printing, Merritt Island *Also called Bill & Renee Enterprises* ***(G-8993)***
PIP Printing 352 622-3224
11 Sw 1st Ave Ocala (34471) ***(G-12027)***
PIP Printing 386 258-3326
133 W Intl Speedway Blvd Daytona Beach (32114) ***(G-2694)***
PIP Printing 622 Inc 813 935-8113
10428 N Florida Ave Tampa (33612) ***(G-17993)***
Pipco, Fort Lauderdale *Also called Wool Wholesale Plumbing Supply* ***(G-4327)***
Pipe Welders Inc (PA) 954 587-8400
2965 W State Road 84 Fort Lauderdale (33312) ***(G-4168)***
Pipeline Fabricators Inc 863 678-0977
733 Carlton Ave Lake Wales (33853) ***(G-7518)***
Piper Aircraft Inc (PA) 772 567-4361
2926 Piper Dr Vero Beach (32960) ***(G-18653)***
Pipette Solutions LLC 877 974-7388
1749 Grand Rue Dr Casselberry (32707) ***(G-1513)***
Pipewelders Marine Inc 954 587-8400
2965 W State Road 84 Fort Lauderdale (33312) ***(G-4169)***
Pitbull Tactical LLC 866 452-4708
3564 Avalon Park Blvd E Orlando (32828) ***(G-13069)***
Pitelka Plastering Stucco 630 235-5611
4951 Summertree Rd Venice (34293) ***(G-18567)***
Pitman Allen Boat Repr & Maint 727 772-9848
970 Cortland Way Palm Harbor (34683) ***(G-13750)***
Pitney Bowes Inc 813 639-1110
5310 Cypress Center Dr # 110 Tampa (33609) ***(G-17994)***
Pitts Fabrication LLC 850 259-4548
617 James Lee Rd Fort Walton Beach (32547) ***(G-4822)***
Pivotal Sign & Graphics Inc 727 462-2266
2140 Sunnydale Blvd Ste D Clearwater (33765) ***(G-1835)***
Pivotal Therapeutics US Inc 905 856-9797
3651 Fau Blvd Ste 400 Boca Raton (33431) ***(G-665)***
Pixe International Corp 850 574-6469
2306 Domingo Dr Tallahassee (32304) ***(G-17309)***
Pixeloptics Inc 954 376-1542
6750 N Andrews Ave Fort Lauderdale (33309) ***(G-4170)***
Pixelteq Inc (HQ) 727 545-0741
3500 Quadrangle Blvd Orlando (32817) ***(G-13070)***
Pixie Dusted Stitches 207 776-3277
3318 Royal Ascot Run Gotha (34734) ***(G-5041)***
Pixotine Products Inc 305 479-1335
1095 Jupiter Park Dr # 12 Jupiter (33458) ***(G-7093)***
Pizza Packet, Boca Raton *Also called Pizza Spice Packet LLC* ***(G-666)***
Pizza Spice Packet LLC 718 831-7036
170 Ne 2nd St Unit 491 Boca Raton (33429) ***(G-666)***
Pizzaros 239 390-0349
24611 Production Cir Bonita Springs (34135) ***(G-847)***
PJ Designs Inc (PA) 727 525-0599
1515 Park St N Saint Petersburg (33710) ***(G-15879)***
Pjm, Doral *Also called Phoenix Jewelry Mfg Inc* ***(G-3461)***
Pk Graphicz 305 534-2184
1000 W Mcnab Rd Pompano Beach (33069) ***(G-14795)***
Pk Group Inc 239 643-2442
3930 Domestic Ave Ste A Naples (34104) ***(G-11368)***
Pk Welding Inc 407 694-9403
830 N John Young Pkwy Kissimmee (34741) ***(G-7287)***
Pki Group, Miramar *Also called Professnal Kit Instller Group* ***(G-11033)***
PKolino LLC 888 403-8992
7300 Nw 35th Ave Miami (33147) ***(G-10167)***
Pl Smoothie LLC 954 554-0450
10234 Sw 26th St Davie (33324) ***(G-2574)***
Placetas Pallet Corp 305 633-4262
195 W 19th St Hialeah (33010) ***(G-5559)***
Plan Automation LLC 786 502-1812
350 Lincoln Rd Miami Beach (33139) ***(G-10701)***
Planar Energy Devices Inc 407 459-1440
653 W Michigan St Orlando (32805) ***(G-13071)***
Plane It Safe LLC 888 840-0499
1135 Ocoee Apopka Rd Apopka (32703) ***(G-171)***
Planet, Sunrise *Also called Kloth Inc* ***(G-17139)***
Planet Fiat of West Miami, Doral *Also called FCA US LLC* ***(G-3349)***
Planet Inhouse Inc 321 216-2189
3000 N Wickham Rd Melbourne (32935) ***(G-8909)***
Plant 2, Havana *Also called Tms Enterprises LLC* ***(G-5240)***
Plant City Observer LLC 813 704-6850
110 E Reynolds St 100b Plant City (33563) ***(G-14458)***
Plant City Powder Coating 813 763-6028
4604 Us Highway 92 W Plant City (33563) ***(G-14459)***
Plant Foods Inc 772 567-5741
5051 41st St Vero Beach (32967) ***(G-18654)***
Plant Partners Inc 941 752-1039
6691 33rd St E Ste B3 Sarasota (34243) ***(G-16277)***
Plant Solutions Inc 305 242-3103
15901 Sw 272nd St Homestead (33031) ***(G-5988)***
Plant Theory Botanical CAF, Miami Beach *Also called Plant Theory LLC* ***(G-10702)***
Plant Theory LLC 305 672-5785
1525 Meridian Ave Apt 210 Miami Beach (33139) ***(G-10702)***
Plantain Products Company (PA) 800 477-2447
2440 Nw 116th St Ste 100 Miami (33167) ***(G-10168)***
Plantation Botanicals Inc 863 675-2984
1401 County Rd Ste 830 Felda (33930) ***(G-3722)***
Plantation Journal Corporation 954 226-6170
7860 Peters Rd Ste F110 Plantation (33324) ***(G-14542)***
Plantation Medicinals Inc 863 675-2984
1401 County Rd Ste 830 Felda (33930) ***(G-3723)***
Plantation Shutters Inc 772 208-8245
1388 Commerce Ctr Dr Port Saint Lucie (34986) ***(G-15129)***
Plantfinder, Cooper City *Also called Betrock Information Systems* ***(G-2110)***
Plantogen Skin Care, Boca Raton *Also called Ollie Pippa International Inc* ***(G-653)***
Plasma Cutting LLC 954 558-1371
3140 W Hllandale Bch Blvd Hallandale (33009) ***(G-5160)***
Plasma Energy Group LLC 813 760-6385
17402 Isbell Ln Odessa (33556) ***(G-12139)***
Plasma-Therm Inc 856 753-8111
1150 16th St N Saint Petersburg (33705) ***(G-15880)***
Plasma-Therm LLC (PA) 727 577-4999
10050 16th St N Saint Petersburg (33716) ***(G-15881)***
Plasmine Technology Inc (HQ) 850 438-8550
3298 Summit Blvd Ste 35 Pensacola (32503) ***(G-14231)***
Plastec Ventilation Inc 941 751-7596
2012 58th Avenue Cir E Bradenton (34203) ***(G-1098)***
Plasti-Card Corporation 305 944-2726
7901 Clay Mica Ct Delray Beach (33446) ***(G-3117)***
Plastic and Products Mktg LLC 352 867-8078
3445 Sw 6th St Ocala (34474) ***(G-12028)***
Plastic Art Sign Company Inc 850 455-4114
3931 W Navy Blvd Pensacola (32507) ***(G-14232)***

Plastic Coated Papers Inc...850 968-6100
1701 E Kingsfield Rd Pensacola (32534) ***(G-14233)***
Plastic Components Inc (PA)...305 885-0561
9051 Nw 97th Ter Medley (33178) ***(G-8707)***
Plastic Composites Inc...352 669-5822
630 Goodbar Ave Umatilla (32784) ***(G-18501)***
Plastic Concepts & Designs Inc...904 396-7500
880 Us Highway 301 S # 1 Jacksonville (32234) ***(G-6676)***
Plastic Concepts Ltd Inc...727 942-6684
1456 L And R Indus Blvd Tarpon Springs (34689) ***(G-18320)***
Plastic International, Medley *Also called Plastic Components Inc* ***(G-8707)***
Plastic Kingdom Inc...561 586-9300
407 N Dixie Hwy Lake Worth (33460) ***(G-7580)***
Plastic Masters International...386 312-9775
327 State Road 207 East Palatka (32131) ***(G-3605)***
Plastic Parts Inc...954 974-3051
4100 N Powerline Rd Z5 Pompano Beach (33073) ***(G-14796)***
Plastic Parts Inc...954 974-3051
6222 Flores Del Mar Margate (33063) ***(G-8561)***
Plastic Sealing Company Inc...954 956-9797
1940 Nw 18th St Ste 1 Pompano Beach (33069) ***(G-14797)***
Plastic Solutions Inc...727 202-6815
801 West Bay Dr Ste 308 Largo (33770) ***(G-8028)***
Plastic Solutions of Pompano...800 331-7081
4100 N Powerline Rd Z5 Pompano Beach (33073) ***(G-14798)***
Plastic Specialties Inc...239 643-0933
3573 Arnold Ave Ste B Naples (34104) ***(G-11369)***
Plastic Trading Intl Inc...863 688-1983
3612 Ventura Dr E Lakeland (33811) ***(G-7767)***
Plastics America Incorporated...813 620-3711
8501 E Adamo Dr Tampa (33619) ***(G-17995)***
Plastics Dynamics Inc...954 565-7122
4301 Ne 11th Ave Oakland Park (33334) ***(G-11828)***
Plastics For Mankind Inc (PA)...305 687-5917
13050 Nw 47th Ave Opa Locka (33054) ***(G-12351)***
Plastiform, Opa Locka *Also called Plastics For Mankind Inc* ***(G-12351)***
Plastimold Products Inc...561 869-0183
250 N Congress Ave Delray Beach (33445) ***(G-3118)***
Plastirex LLC...305 471-1111
1552 Sun Pure Rd Avon Park (33825) ***(G-293)***
Plastix Usa LLC...305 891-0091
900 N Federal Hwy Ste 104 Hollywood (33020) ***(G-5892)***
Platecrafters Corporation...215 997-1990
782 Big Tree Dr Longwood (32750) ***(G-8326)***
Platesmart Technologies...813 749-0892
640 Brooker Creek Blvd # 465 Oldsmar (34677) ***(G-12257)***
Plating Resources Inc...321 632-2435
2845 W King St Ste 108 Cocoa (32926) ***(G-2040)***
Plating Technologies Inc...772 220-4201
2971 Se Dominica Ter # 12 Stuart (34997) ***(G-16989)***
Platinium Rosis Inc...786 617-9973
1602 Alton Rd 602 Miami Beach (33139) ***(G-10703)***
Platinum Group Usa Inc...561 274-7553
75 N Congress Ave Delray Beach (33445) ***(G-3119)***
Platinum Ltg Productions LLC...941 320-1906
8051 N Tamiami Trl D10 Sarasota (34243) ***(G-16278)***
Platinum Mfg Intl Inc...727 544-4555
10166 66th St N Pinellas Park (33782) ***(G-14376)***
Platinum Signs and Design LLC (PA)...407 971-3640
352 W Melody Ln Casselberry (32707) ***(G-1514)***
Platinum Signs Inc...561 296-3636
2898 Forest Hill Blvd West Palm Beach (33406) ***(G-18999)***
Plattsco Inc...954 744-4099
1343 Shotgun Rd Sunrise (33326) ***(G-17158)***
Play Tampa Bay Inc...727 803-6838
7925 4th St N Ste B Saint Petersburg (33702) ***(G-15882)***
Playbill Magazine, Miami *Also called Playbill Southern Publishing* ***(G-10169)***
Playbill Southern Publishing...305 595-1984
10001 Sw 54th St Miami (33165) ***(G-10169)***
Playcore Wisconsin Inc...800 853-5316
405 Golfway West Dr # 302 Saint Augustine (32095) ***(G-15589)***
Players Media Group Inc...509 254-4949
5267 Zenith Garden Loop Brooksville (34601) ***(G-1261)***
Playlist Live Inc...877 306-3651
6424 Forest City Rd Orlando (32810) ***(G-13072)***
Playoff Technologies LLC...407 497-2202
1430 Elizabeth Dr Winter Park (32789) ***(G-19431)***
Playtex Manufacturing Inc...386 677-9559
1190 N Us Highway 1 Ormond Beach (32174) ***(G-13391)***
Plaza Materials Corp...813 788-0454
41150 Yonkers Blvd Zephyrhills (33541) ***(G-19533)***
Plazadoor Corp...561 578-5450
1500 Avenue R Ste 200 Riviera Beach (33404) ***(G-15364)***
PLC Cabinets Installed Ltd...239 641-7565
1408 Rail Head Blvd Naples (34110) ***(G-11370)***
PLD Acquisitions LLC...305 463-2270
10400 Nw 29th Ter Miami Miami (33172) ***(G-10170)***
Pleasure Interiors LLC...941 756-9969
2207 Industrial Blvd Sarasota (34234) ***(G-16545)***
Plotkowski Inc (PA)...561 740-2226
210 Se 12th Ave Ste 1 Boynton Beach (33435) ***(G-940)***
Pls Print, Clearwater *Also called Precision Litho Service Inc* ***(G-1840)***
Plumb Rite of Central Florida...407 292-0750
2850 Overland Rd Apopka (32703) ***(G-172)***
Plus Communication, Lake Mary *Also called Charisma Media* ***(G-7405)***
Plus Communications Inc (PA)...407 333-0600
600 Rinehart Rd Lake Mary (32746) ***(G-7443)***
Plus Communications Inc...407 333-0600
600 Rinehart Rd Lake Mary (32746) ***(G-7444)***
Plushbeds Inc...888 449-5738
17076 Boca Club Blvd # 4 Boca Raton (33487) ***(G-667)***
Plywood Express Inc...954 956-7576
2601 Gateway Dr Ste B Pompano Beach (33069) ***(G-14799)***
PM Craftsman...863 665-0815
3525 Craftsman Blvd Lakeland (33803) ***(G-7768)***
PM Engraving Corp...786 573-5292
18425 Sw 200th St Miami (33187) ***(G-10171)***
PM Enterprises Holdings LLC...407 846-0588
1751 S John Young Pkwy Kissimmee (34741) ***(G-7288)***
Pma LLC...407 310-2548
4646 Patricia Ann Ct Orlando (32839) ***(G-13073)***
PMC Enterprises Mgmt Division...239 949-6566
11216 Tamiami Trl N Naples (34110) ***(G-11371)***
PMC North America Inc...727 530-0714
2060 34th Way Largo (33771) ***(G-8029)***
Pmh Homes Inc...941 234-5121
14705 21st Ave E Bradenton (34212) ***(G-1099)***
Pmr Gestion Inc...561 501-5190
1100 Sw 10th St Delray Beach (33444) ***(G-3120)***
PNC Manufacturing Leather...407 201-2069
4107 S Orange Blossom Trl Kissimmee (34746) ***(G-7289)***
Pneumatic Products Corporation...352 873-5793
4647 Sw 40th Ave Ocala (34474) ***(G-12029)***
Pneumatic Scale Angelus...727 535-4100
5320 140th Ave N Clearwater (33760) ***(G-1836)***
Pneumatic Scale Clearwater, Clearwater *Also called Pneumatic Scale Angelus* ***(G-1836)***
Poblocki Sign Co Southeast LLC...407 660-3174
7005 Stapoint Ct Winter Park (32792) ***(G-19432)***
Poc Archer's Arrow Joint, Tampa *Also called Titan Petroleum Corporation* ***(G-18188)***
Pocketec Inc...772 692-8020
50 Ne Dixie Hwy Ste E7 Stuart (34994) ***(G-16990)***
Pod Crane Services and Rentals...805 291-2675
5203 Sw 159th Ct Miami (33185) ***(G-10172)***
Podgo Printing LLC...954 874-9100
3810 N 29th Ave Hollywood (33020) ***(G-5893)***
Poggesi USA, Miramar *Also called Suntyx LLC* ***(G-11049)***
Pogi Beauty LLC...305 600-1305
3800 Ne 1st Ave Miami (33137) ***(G-10173)***
Point Blank Enterprises Inc...954 846-8222
2102 Sw 2nd St Pompano Beach (33069) ***(G-14800)***
Point Blank Enterprises Inc (HQ)...954 630-0900
2102 Sw 2nd St Pompano Beach (33069) ***(G-14801)***
Point Blank Enterprises Inc...305 820-4270
14100 Nw 58th Ct Miami Lakes (33014) ***(G-10840)***
Point Blank Intrmdate Hldg LLC...954 630-0900
2102 Sw 2nd St Pompano Beach (33069) ***(G-14802)***
Point Blank Protective Apprl (PA)...954 630-0900
2102 Sw 2nd St Pompano Beach (33069) ***(G-14803)***
Point Distillery LLC...727 269-5588
11807 Little Rd New Port Richey (34654) ***(G-11508)***
Polaris Electrical Connectors, Odessa *Also called Polaris Sales Co Inc* ***(G-12140)***
Polaris Sales Co Inc...727 372-1703
11625 Prosperous Dr Odessa (33556) ***(G-12140)***
Polenghi Usa Inc...954 637-4900
720 S Powerline Rd Ste C Deerfield Beach (33442) ***(G-2887)***
Poli Group International Inc...305 468-8986
1574 Nw 108th Ave Miami (33172) ***(G-10174)***
Poli Sign Supplies, Miami *Also called Poli Group International Inc* ***(G-10174)***
Policrete LLC...305 552-7026
3399 Nw 72nd Ave Ste 108 Miami (33122) ***(G-10175)***
Polimix Usa LLC...305 888-4752
11750 Nw South River Dr Medley (33178) ***(G-8708)***
Polishing By Wilson O...727 203-0100
5521 Bay Blvd Apt 102 Port Richey (34668) ***(G-15063)***
Polk Air Filter Sales Inc...863 688-4436
1851 E Gary Rd Lakeland (33801) ***(G-7769)***
Polk County Democrat (PA)...863 533-4183
99 3rd St Nw Winter Haven (33881) ***(G-19342)***
Polks Meat Products Inc...813 961-2881
18104 Muncie Pl Lutz (33558) ***(G-8410)***
Pollak Industries...850 438-4651
2313 Truman Ave Pensacola (32505) ***(G-14234)***
Polly Concrete Products Co...850 897-3314
1495 Cedar St Niceville (32578) ***(G-11571)***
Polo Players Edition...561 968-5208
9011 Lake Worth Rd B Lake Worth (33467) ***(G-7581)***
Polson Transportation LLC...614 733-9677
9032 Pomelo Rd W Fort Myers (33967) ***(G-4568)***

ALPHABETIC

Poly Coatings of South Inc....941 371-8555
5944 Sandphil Rd Sarasota (34232) *(G-16546)*
Poly Plastic Packaging Co Inc....561 498-9040
18800 Long Lake Dr Boca Raton (33496) *(G-668)*
Poly Systems Co, West Palm Beach *Also called Peter T Amann (G-18995)*
Poly-Chem Corp....305 593-1928
3039 Ne Quayside Ln Miami (33138) *(G-10176)*
Polyglass Roofg Watering Svcs, Deerfield Beach *Also called Polyglass USA Inc (G-2888)*
Polyglass USA Inc (HQ)....954 246-8888
1111 W Newport Center Dr Deerfield Beach (33442) *(G-2888)*
Polygon Solutions Inc....239 628-4800
6461 Metro Plantation Rd Fort Myers (33966) *(G-4569)*
Polygrama Inc....305 577-9716
245 Se 1st St Ste 234 Miami (33131) *(G-10177)*
Polyhistor International Inc....904 646-5666
11200 Saint Johns Jacksonville (32246) *(G-6677)*
Polymatics Plastic Processing, Clearwater *Also called Kinetic Industries LLC (G-1750)*
Polymer Logistics Inc (HQ)....877 462-6195
4630 Woodlnd Corp Blvd # 209 Tampa (33614) *(G-17996)*
Polymersan LLC....305 887-3824
1181 Se 9th Ter Ste B Hialeah (33010) *(G-5560)*
Polypack Inc (PA)....727 578-5000
3301 Gateway Ctr Blvd N Pinellas Park (33782) *(G-14377)*
Polypack Limited Partnership....727 578-5000
3301 Gateway Ctr Blvd N Pinellas Park (33782) *(G-14378)*
Polyplastics, Boca Raton *Also called Poly Plastic Packaging Co Inc (G-668)*
Polytech International LLC....904 354-9355
6635 Highway Ave Jacksonville (32254) *(G-6678)*
Polyumac Inc....305 691-9093
1060 E 30th St Hialeah (33013) *(G-5561)*
POm Performance Coatings LLC....561 441-7611
2264 S Wallen Dr West Palm Beach (33410) *(G-19000)*
Poma Corporation....561 790-5799
9040 Belvedere Rd West Palm Beach (33411) *(G-19001)*
Pompadour Products Inc....954 345-2700
1197 Nw 83rd Ave Coral Springs (33071) *(G-2303)*
Pompanette Kitchen's, Riviera Beach *Also called Akiknav Inc (G-15296)*
Pompanette LLC....813 885-2182
7712 Cheri Ct Tampa (33634) *(G-17997)*
Pompano Pelican Inc....954 783-8700
1500 E Atl Blvd Ste A Pompano Beach (33060) *(G-14804)*
Pompano Precision Products Inc (PA)....954 946-6059
1100 Sw 12th Ave Pompano Beach (33069) *(G-14805)*
Pomper Sheet Metal Inc....954 492-9717
4444 Ne 11th Ave Oakland Park (33334) *(G-11829)*
Poms Enterprises Inc....954 358-1359
5425 Nw 24th St Ste 210 Margate (33063) *(G-8562)*
Ponce De Leon Construction....786 554-3685
440 Nw 132nd Ave Miami (33182) *(G-10178)*
Pond Industries Inc....727 526-5483
1942 Iowa Ave Ne Saint Petersburg (33703) *(G-15883)*
Ponte Vedra Wns Civic Aliance....904 834-3543
359 San Juan Dr Ponte Vedra Beach (32082) *(G-14951)*
Pool Cleaning Service, Labelle *Also called South West Adventure Team LLC (G-7323)*
Pop Em Sock Ems....850 287-3778
675 Gulf Breeze Pkwy Gulf Breeze (32561) *(G-5124)*
Popcorn Cellar LLC....239 272-8494
651 5th Ave S Naples (34102) *(G-11372)*
Pope Enterprises Inc....850 729-7446
516 John Sims Pkwy E Niceville (32578) *(G-11572)*
Poppin Box LLC....904 484-7030
116 Bartram Oaks Walk Saint Johns (32259) *(G-15680)*
Popstops Marketing Inc....800 209-4571
111 2nd Ave Ne Ste 1201 Saint Petersburg (33701) *(G-15884)*
Porath Fine Cabinetry Inc....561 616-9400
3101 Tuxedo Ave West Palm Beach (33405) *(G-19002)*
Porche Systems, Pensacola *Also called Automation Consulting Inc (G-14095)*
Porous Metal Filters Inc....407 682-1494
112 Wheatland Ct Longwood (32779) *(G-8327)*
Port Canaveral FL Canaveral Rm, Cape Canaveral *Also called Cemex Cnstr Mtls Fla LLC (G-1355)*
Port Canaveral Yard, Tampa *Also called Vgcm LLC (G-18242)*
Port Manatee Ship Repair....941 417-2613
2114 Piney Point Rd Palmetto (34221) *(G-13817)*
Port of Palm Cold Storage Inc....386 328-5127
1122 Bronson St Palatka (32177) *(G-13489)*
Port Printing Co....561 848-1402
3532 Broadway Riviera Beach (33404) *(G-15365)*
Port St Lucie News....772 287-1550
1939 Se Federal Hwy Stuart (34994) *(G-16991)*
Port St. Lucie News, Port Saint Lucie *Also called EW Scripps Company (G-15107)*
Porta Products....386 428-7656
200 Dale St Edgewater (32132) *(G-3633)*
Portable Pumping Systems Inc....727 518-9191
4760 Spring Ave Clearwater (33762) *(G-1837)*
Portable-Shade USA LLC....321 704-8100
428 Shearer Blvd Cocoa (32922) *(G-2041)*
Portalp Usa Inc....800 474-3667
1030 Collier Center Way # 10 Naples (34110) *(G-11373)*
Porter Pizza Box Florida Inc (PA)....800 626-0828
6094 Us Highway 98 S Lakeland (33812) *(G-7770)*
Poseidon Boat Manufacturing....239 362-3736
5826 Corporation Cir Fort Myers (33905) *(G-4570)*
Poseidon Industries Inc....305 812-2582
5462 Williamsburg Dr Punta Gorda (33982) *(G-15220)*
Poseidon Services Inc....786 294-8529
12685 Nw 11th Ln Miami (33182) *(G-10179)*
Poseidon Window Treatments LLC....954 920-1112
1942 Tigertail Blvd Dania Beach (33004) *(G-2472)*
Posh Cabinets....954 444-5441
9640 Parkview Ave Boca Raton (33428) *(G-669)*
Positive Note Network....712 259-1381
116 Maurice Ave Nw Fort Walton Beach (32548) *(G-4823)*
Positive Screenprint....904 381-0963
2808 W Beaver St Jacksonville (32254) *(G-6679)*
Positiveid Corporation (PA)....561 805-8000
1690 S Congress Ave # 201 Delray Beach (33445) *(G-3121)*
Posm Software LLC....859 274-0041
8010 N Atl Ave Ste 12 Cape Canaveral (32920) *(G-1366)*
Post Mortem Publications Inc....352 429-1133
146 E Broad St Groveland (34736) *(G-5105)*
Potenza Hrc, Miami *Also called Potenza Services Inc (G-10180)*
Potenza Services Inc....305 400-4938
10711 Sw 216th St Miami (33170) *(G-10180)*
Potnetwork Holdings Inc (PA)....800 433-0127
3531 Griffin Rd Fort Lauderdale (33312) *(G-4171)*
Potter Roemer LLC....786 845-0842
8306 Nw 14th St Doral (33126) *(G-3463)*
Potters Coffee Company....850 525-1793
1727 Creighton Rd Pensacola (32504) *(G-14235)*
Pottre Gardening Products LLC....941 224-8856
1115 76th St Nw Bradenton (34209) *(G-1100)*
Pouchfill Packaging LLC....386 274-1600
811 Fentress Ct Daytona Beach (32117) *(G-2695)*
Poulsen Lighting, Weston *Also called Louis Poulsen USA Inc (G-19148)*
Povia Paints Inc (PA)....239 791-0011
2897 South St Fort Myers (33916) *(G-4571)*
Powder Coating Factory LLC....407 286-4550
635 Wilmer Ave Orlando (32808) *(G-13074)*
Powder Systems Inc....352 680-3558
120 Cypress Rd Ocala (34472) *(G-12030)*
Powdertech Plus Inc....904 269-1719
98 Industrial Loop N Orange Park (32073) *(G-12404)*
Powell Woodworking LLC....407 883-9181
5150 Sage Cedar Pl Sanford (32771) *(G-16103)*
Power Bright Technologies, Fort Lauderdale *Also called Bright Manufacturing LLC (G-3868)*
Power Equipments Trading LLC (PA)....305 704-7021
8300 Nw 53rd St Ste 350 Doral (33166) *(G-3464)*
Power Evolution Inc....305 318-8476
14163 Sapphire Bay Cir Orlando (32828) *(G-13075)*
Power Flow Systems Inc....386 253-8833
795 Fentress Blvd Ste A Daytona Beach (32114) *(G-2696)*
Power Foam Manufacturing Inc....305 303-2956
4595 E 10th Ct Hialeah (33013) *(G-5562)*
Power Grid Pros Inc....716 378-1419
618 Heritage Dr Weston (33326) *(G-19160)*
Power Kleen Corporation....813 854-2648
101 S Bayview Blvd Oldsmar (34677) *(G-12258)*
Power Plus Inc....386 672-7579
550 Parque Dr Ormond Beach (32174) *(G-13392)*
Power Point Graphics Inc....561 351-5599
19528 Sedgefield Ter Boca Raton (33498) *(G-670)*
Power Printing of Florida....727 823-1162
956 1st Ave N Saint Petersburg (33705) *(G-15885)*
Power Production MGT Inc....352 263-0766
408 W University Ave 600b Gainesville (32601) *(G-4981)*
Power Quality International, Odessa *Also called Gfsf Inc (G-12123)*
Power Quality Intl LLC....727 478-7284
2404 Merchant Ave Odessa (33556) *(G-12141)*
Power Sports Treasure Coast....772 463-6428
2212 Se Indian St Stuart (34997) *(G-16992)*
Power Systems Inc....561 354-1100
1440 W Indiantown Rd # 200 Jupiter (33458) *(G-7094)*
Power Systems Mfg LLC....561 354-1100
1440 W Indiantown Rd # 200 Jupiter (33458) *(G-7095)*
Power Technology Southeast, Leesburg *Also called Mobile Power Generators LLC (G-8167)*
Power Tek LLC....904 814-7007
154 Cornell Rd Saint Augustine (32086) *(G-15590)*
Power Vac Corporation....954 491-0188
4811 Ne 12th Ave Oakland Park (33334) *(G-11830)*
Power Wthin Cnsling Cnsltn LLC....863 242-3023
280 Patterson Rd Ste 1 Haines City (33844) *(G-5145)*
Powerbees Incorporated....561 797-5927
1375 Gateway Blvd Boynton Beach (33426) *(G-941)*
Powercases Inc....239 415-3846
18281 Via Caprini Dr Miromar Lakes (33913) *(G-11071)*
Powerchord Inc....727 823-1530
360 Central Ave Fl 5 Saint Petersburg (33701) *(G-15886)*

Powerdms Inc...407 992-6000
101 S Garland Ave Ste 300 Orlando (32801) ***(G-13076)***
Powerficient LLC...800 320-2535
6250 Nw 27th Way Fort Lauderdale (33309) ***(G-4172)***
Powerful Foods LLC...305 779-2449
9171 S Dixie Hwy Pinecrest (33156) ***(G-14330)***
Powerful Yogurt, Pinecrest *Also called Powerful Foods LLC* ***(G-14330)***
Powerlift Hydraulic Doors Fla, Fort Pierce *Also called Rearden Steel Mfg LLC* ***(G-4739)***
Powerline Group Inc...631 828-1183
8406 Hawks Gully Ave Delray Beach (33446) ***(G-3122)***
Powerphase LLC...561 299-3970
1001 N Us Highway 1 # 206 Jupiter (33477) ***(G-7096)***
Powers Industries LLC (PA)...786 444-3616
2715 Ne 6th Ln Wilton Manors (33334) ***(G-19219)***
Powersports 911 Inc...813 769-2468
5911 Benjamin Center Dr Tampa (33634) ***(G-17998)***
Powertech Generators, Leesburg *Also called Ptse Holding Inc* ***(G-8168)***
Powless Drapery Service Inc...954 566-7863
4029 Ne 10th Ave Oakland Park (33334) ***(G-11831)***
Pozin Enterprises Inc...727 546-8974
14493 62nd St N Clearwater (33760) ***(G-1838)***
Ppa Miami Corp...305 436-0460
8620 Nw 64th St Ste 10 Miami (33166) ***(G-10181)***
PPG Architectural Finishes Inc...813 877-5841
3102 W Kennedy Blvd Tampa (33609) ***(G-17999)***
PPG Inc...813 831-9902
5133 W Cypress St Tampa (33607) ***(G-18000)***
PPG Industries Inc...305 477-0541
1376 Nw 78th Ave Doral (33126) ***(G-3465)***
Ppi, Sarasota *Also called Premier Prfmce Interiors Inc* ***(G-16279)***
Ppi Group, Fort Lauderdale *Also called Panoff Publishing Inc* ***(G-4155)***
Ppi International Corp...954 838-1008
1649 Nw 136th Ave Sunrise (33323) ***(G-17159)***
Practical Design Products Co...561 995-4023
1101 Holland Dr Boca Raton (33487) ***(G-671)***
Practicepanther, Miami *Also called Panther Software Inc* ***(G-10140)***
Pradere Manufacturing Corp...305 823-0190
7655 W 20th Ave Hialeah (33014) ***(G-5563)***
Pradere Office Products, Hialeah *Also called Pradere Manufacturing Corp* ***(G-5563)***
Praesto Enterprises LLC...407 298-9171
2525 Industrial Blvd Orlando (32804) ***(G-13077)***
Prana Organic Plant Oils Inc...216 288-2054
174 Dove Creek Dr Tavernier (33070) ***(G-18362)***
Pratt & Whitney...561 796-6701
15270 Endeavor Dr Jupiter (33478) ***(G-7097)***
Pratt & Whitney Eng Svcs Inc...305 512-9882
14100 Palmetto Frntg Rd Miami Lakes (33016) ***(G-10841)***
Pratt & Whitney Military Engs, Jupiter *Also called United Technologies Corp* ***(G-7137)***
Pratt Cnc...321 482-9494
1325 White Dr Titusville (32780) ***(G-18452)***
Pratt Industries Inc...863 439-4184
331 Frederick Ave Dundee (33838) ***(G-3568)***
Pratt Plastics, Titusville *Also called Richard K Pratt LLC* ***(G-18459)***
Pratt Whitney Rockettdyne, Jupiter *Also called Raytheon Technologies Corp* ***(G-7102)***
Praxis Software Inc...407 226-5691
7575 Kingspointe Pkwy # 9 Orlando (32819) ***(G-13078)***
Pre-Cast Specialties Inc...954 781-4040
3850 E Lake Mary Blvd Sanford (32773) ***(G-16104)***
Pre-Cast Specialties LLC (PA)...954 781-4040
3850 E Lake Mary Blvd Sanford (32773) ***(G-16105)***
Pre-Mix Marble Tite Inc...954 917-7665
1259 Nw 21st St Pompano Beach (33069) ***(G-14806)***
Pre-Tech Inc...863 422-5079
3052 Us Highway 17 92 N Haines City (33844) ***(G-5146)***
Preble Enterprises Inc...954 480-6919
1339 Sw 1st Way Deerfield Beach (33441) ***(G-2889)***
Precast and Foam Works LLC...727 657-9195
29757 66th Way N Clearwater (33761) ***(G-1839)***
Precast Designs Inc...407 856-5444
10305 Rocket Ct Orlando (32824) ***(G-13079)***
Precast Keystone, Naples *Also called Pfci LLC* ***(G-11361)***
Precast Solution System Inc...813 949-7929
2045 Chesapeake Dr Ste 2 Odessa (33556) ***(G-12142)***
Precast Specialties, Sanford *Also called Pre-Cast Specialties LLC* ***(G-16105)***
Precast Technical Assistance...850 432-8446
21 S Tarragona St Ste 101 Pensacola (32502) ***(G-14236)***
Precheck Health Services Inc (PA)...305 203-4711
848 Brickell Ave Ph 5 Miami (33131) ***(G-10182)***
Precious Metal Group LLC...904 219-8358
5410 Blanding Blvd Jacksonville (32244) ***(G-6680)***
Precious Metals Buyers LLC (PA)...813 880-9544
6201 Johns Rd Ste 5 Tampa (33634) ***(G-18001)***
Precious Metals Buyers LLC...813 417-7857
7028 W Waters Ave Tampa (33634) ***(G-18002)***
Precious Metals Xchange Group...305 556-1696
1890 Nw 95th Ave Doral (33172) ***(G-3466)***
Precious Prints Inc...786 346-7740
7670 Sw 82nd Ave Miami (33143) ***(G-10183)***
Precise Pavers Inc...863 528-8000
2581 Nelson St Auburndale (33823) ***(G-250)***
Precise Print Florida...813 960-4958
410 W Chapman Rd Lutz (33548) ***(G-8411)***
Precise Technologies Inc...727 535-5594
12395 75th St Largo (33773) ***(G-8030)***
Precision Aluminum Products, Deerfield Beach *Also called Preble Enterprises Inc* ***(G-2889)***
Precision Ammunition LLC...813 626-0077
5402 E Diana St Tampa (33610) ***(G-18003)***
Precision Auto Tint Dsign Corp...727 385-8788
746 Haven Pl Tarpon Springs (34689) ***(G-18321)***
Precision Brazing Inc...954 942-8971
471 Ne 28th St Pompano Beach (33064) ***(G-14807)***
Precision Cabinetry LLC...386 218-3340
2240 E Old Mill Dr Deltona (32725) ***(G-3177)***
Precision Ceramics Usa Inc...727 388-5060
9843 18th St N Ste 120 Saint Petersburg (33716) ***(G-15887)***
Precision Circuits Inc...321 632-8629
550 Gus Hipp Blvd Rockledge (32955) ***(G-15441)***
Precision Coat of Florida...813 986-1611
10410 Canary Isle Dr Tampa (33647) ***(G-18004)***
Precision Coating Rods Inc...813 855-5054
600 Mount Vernon St Oldsmar (34677) ***(G-12259)***
Precision Comm Svcs Inc (HQ)...813 238-1000
7710 N 30th St Tampa (33610) ***(G-18005)***
Precision Directional Drlg LLC...941 320-8308
5010 60th Dr E Bradenton (34203) ***(G-1101)***
Precision Econowind LLC...239 997-3860
8940 N Fork Dr North Fort Myers (33903) ***(G-11603)***
Precision Equipment Co Inc...561 689-4400
197 65th Ter N West Palm Beach (33413) ***(G-19003)***
Precision Ers...813 257-0900
7710 N 30th St Tampa (33610) ***(G-18006)***
Precision Fabg & Clg Co Inc...321 635-2000
3975 E Railroad Ave Cocoa (32926) ***(G-2042)***
Precision Fabrication Corp...941 488-2474
510 Church St Nokomis (34275) ***(G-11587)***
Precision Infinity Systems Inc...407 490-2320
14569 Jamaica Dogwood Dr Orlando (32828) ***(G-13080)***
Precision Laboratories Inc...407 774-4261
165 E Wildmere Ave Longwood (32750) ***(G-8328)***
Precision Leak Detection Inc...904 996-9290
84 Autumn Springs Ct W Jacksonville (32225) ***(G-6681)***
Precision Lift Industries LLC...877 770-5862
3605 N Davis Hwy Pensacola (32503) ***(G-14237)***
Precision Litho Service Inc...727 573-1763
4250 118th Ave N Clearwater (33762) ***(G-1840)***
Precision Machine Tech LLC...305 594-1789
4083 Nw 79th Ave Doral (33166) ***(G-3467)***
Precision Manufacturing, Fort Myers *Also called OGrady Tool Company* ***(G-4556)***
Precision Manufacturing I...786 547-2683
8760 Sw 131st St Miami (33176) ***(G-10184)***
Precision Metal Fabrications...305 691-0616
3600 E 10th Ct 20 Hialeah (33013) ***(G-5564)***
Precision Metal Industries Inc...954 942-6303
1408 Sw 8th St Pompano Beach (33069) ***(G-14808)***
Precision Metal Parts Inc...727 526-9165
4725 28th St N Saint Petersburg (33714) ***(G-15888)***
Precision Metal Services Inc...407 843-3682
33243 Equestrian Trl Sorrento (32776) ***(G-16791)***
Precision Mold & Tool Inc...407 847-5687
2780 N John Young Pkwy Kissimmee (34741) ***(G-7290)***
Precision Mold Restoration LLC...239 699-3688
204 Ne 23rd Ter Cape Coral (33909) ***(G-1455)***
Precision Mold Tech Inc...305 594-1789
4083 Nw 79th Ave Doral (33166) ***(G-3468)***
Precision Paddleboards...954 616-8046
429 Seabreeze Blvd 214 Fort Lauderdale (33316) ***(G-4173)***
Precision Plastics, Delray Beach *Also called Axtonne Inc* ***(G-3048)***
Precision Plastics Group Inc...863 299-6639
1635 7th St Sw Winter Haven (33880) ***(G-19343)***
Precision Press LLC...386 872-1639
3 Oak Glen Dr Daytona Beach (32119) ***(G-2697)***
Precision Printing of Columbus...561 509-7269
11831 Fox Hill Cir Boynton Beach (33473) ***(G-942)***
Precision Qulty Machining Inc...407 831-7240
207 Reece Way Ste 1601 Casselberry (32707) ***(G-1515)***
Precision Resistor Co Inc...727 541-5771
9442 Laura Anne Dr Seminole (33776) ***(G-16756)***
Precision Resources Inc (PA)...321 635-2000
3975 E Railroad Ave Cocoa (32926) ***(G-2043)***
Precision Screen Enclosures...239 221-8465
28790 S Diesel Dr Bonita Springs (34135) ***(G-848)***
Precision Shaft Technology...727 442-1711
1717 Overbrook Ave Clearwater (33755) ***(G-1841)***
Precision Shapes Inc (PA)...321 269-2555
8835 Grissom Pkwy Titusville (32780) ***(G-18453)***
Precision Small Engine Company...954 974-1960
2510 Nw 16th Ln Pompano Beach (33064) ***(G-14809)***
Precision Stone, Delray Beach *Also called PSC Building Group Inc* ***(G-3130)***

A L P H A B E T I C

Precision Svcs Jcksonville Inc...904 781-3770
5201 W Beaver St Jacksonville (32254) *(G-6682)*
Precision Tech Aero Inc...305 603-8347
6051 Nw 153rd St Miami Lakes (33014) *(G-10842)*
Precision Tech Machining LLC...321 693-3469
1421 Albert Dr Melbourne (32935) *(G-8910)*
Precision Tl Engrg of Gnsville...352 376-2533
2709 Ne 20th Way Gainesville (32609) *(G-4982)*
Precision Tool & Mold Inc...727 573-4441
12050 44th St N Clearwater (33762) *(G-1842)*
Precision Turbines Inc (PA)...561 447-0751
4710 Nw Boca Raton Blvd Boca Raton (33431) *(G-672)*
Precision Turning Corporation...386 364-5788
715 Goldkist Blvd Sw Live Oak (32064) *(G-8237)*
Precision Window Films, Tarpon Springs *Also called Precision Auto Tint Dsign Corp (G-18321)*
Precision Woodcraft, Lake Worth *Also called Maggac Corporation (G-7567)*
Precon Corporation...352 332-1200
115 Sw 140th Ter Newberry (32669) *(G-11559)*
Predator Products, Jacksonville *Also called Clawson Custom Cues Inc (G-6266)*
Preferred Coatings LLC...231 499-3864
212 Fairway Isles Ln Bradenton (34212) *(G-1102)*
Preferred Custom Printing LLC...727 443-1900
7000 Bryan Dairy Rd B2 Seminole (33777) *(G-16757)*
Preferred Materials...727 573-3027
12955 40th St N Clearwater (33762) *(G-1843)*
Preferred Materials Inc (HQ)...904 288-0244
4636 Scarborough Dr Lutz (33559) *(G-8412)*
Preferred Materials Inc...407 578-1200
7120 Overland Rd Orlando (32810) *(G-13081)*
Preferred Metal Products Inc...407 296-4449
3614 Princeton Oaks St Orlando (32808) *(G-13082)*
Preferred Pallets Llc...863 401-9517
4353 Fussell Ln Winter Haven (33880) *(G-19344)*
Preferred Pcks Pblications Inc...954 377-8000
1335 Shotgun Rd Sunrise (33326) *(G-17160)*
Preferred Printing & Graphics, West Palm Beach *Also called Sunshine Printing Inc (G-19050)*
Preferred Signs Inc...954 922-0126
1906 N Dixie Hwy Hollywood (33020) *(G-5894)*
Preferred Stitching Inc...813 737-3996
10552 Lithia Pinecrest Rd Lithia (33547) *(G-8222)*
Preform LLC...888 826-5161
3845 Deerpark Blvd Elkton (32033) *(G-3650)*
Prege...954 908-1535
1475 W Cypress Creek Rd Fort Lauderdale (33309) *(G-4174)*
Prekcom LLC...877 773-5669
429 Lenox Ave Miami Beach (33139) *(G-10704)*
Premdor Finance LLC...813 877-2726
1 N Dale Mabry Hwy # 950 Tampa (33609) *(G-18007)*
Premier Archtctural Shtmtl Inc...727 373-8937
8501 Northton Groves Blvd Odessa (33556) *(G-12143)*
Premier Brush Inc...850 271-5736
2230 Industrial Dr Panama City (32405) *(G-13942)*
Premier Buildings of Navarre...850 684-3639
2617 Hidden Creek Dr Navarre (32566) *(G-11472)*
Premier Cabinets LLC...407 760-9060
3036 Kananwood Ct # 1024 Oviedo (32765) *(G-13454)*
Premier Coatings LLC...954 797-9275
450 Nw 27th Ave Fort Lauderdale (33311) *(G-4175)*
Premier Corporate Printing...305 378-8480
3414 Galilee Rd Jacksonville (32207) *(G-6683)*
Premier Corporate Printing LLC...305 378-8480
3414 Galilee Rd Jacksonville (32207) *(G-6684)*
Premier Die Casting Company...732 634-3000
47 S Prospect Dr Coral Gables (33133) *(G-2185)*
Premier Distributor of Miami...305 821-9671
1635 W 40th St Hialeah (33012) *(G-5565)*
Premier Fabricating Llc...813 855-4633
232 Dunbar Ct Oldsmar (34677) *(G-12260)*
Premier Fabricators LLC...772 323-2042
7413 Commercial Cir Fort Pierce (34951) *(G-4735)*
Premier Global Enterprises...561 747-7303
133 N Us Highway 1 Tequesta (33469) *(G-18387)*
Premier Lab Supply Inc...772 873-1700
691 Nw Enterprise Dr Port Saint Lucie (34986) *(G-15130)*
Premier Luxury Group LLC...954 358-9885
2860 W State Road 84 Ste Fort Lauderdale (33312) *(G-4176)*
Premier Manufacturing Pdts LLC...239 542-0260
730 Ne 19th Pl Cape Coral (33909) *(G-1456)*
Premier Pallet Recycler LLC...561 722-0457
1230 Gateway Rd Ste 1 West Palm Beach (33403) *(G-19004)*
Premier Pallets Inc...813 986-4889
5805 Breckenridge Pkwy A Tampa (33610) *(G-18008)*
Premier Parties Entertainment...352 375-6122
805 Nw 13th St Gainesville (32601) *(G-4983)*
Premier Plastics LLC (PA)...305 805-3333
1500 Gateway Blvd Ste 250 Boynton Beach (33426) *(G-943)*
Premier Plastics LLC...305 805-3333
500 S Federal Hwy # 2715 Hallandale Beach (33009) *(G-5203)*
Premier Prfmce Interiors Inc...941 752-6271
6304 17th Street Cir E Sarasota (34243) *(G-16279)*
Premier Printing Signs...727 849-2493
6520 Industrial Ave Ste 1 Port Richey (34668) *(G-15064)*
Premier Printing Solutions Inc...305 490-0244
6600 Nw 15th Ave Fort Lauderdale (33309) *(G-4177)*
Premier Publishing Inc...561 394-9066
3350 Nw 2nd Ave Ste B38 Boca Raton (33431) *(G-673)*
Premier Semiconductor Svcs LLC...727 532-1777
4400 140th Ave N Ste 140 Clearwater (33762) *(G-1844)*
Premier Sign & Service Inc...239 258-6979
7716 6th Pl Lehigh Acres (33936) *(G-8203)*
Premier Sign Company LLC...850 621-4524
216 Mountain Dr Ste 100 Destin (32541) *(G-3202)*
Premier Stoneworks LLC...561 330-3737
1455 Sw 4th Ave Delray Beach (33444) *(G-3123)*
Premier Tees...941 681-2688
2780 Worth Ave Englewood (34224) *(G-3664)*
Premier Water & Enrgy Tech Inc...904 268-1152
11481 Columbia Park Dr W Jacksonville (32258) *(G-6685)*
Premiere Plastering, Jacksonville *Also called MDK Enterpises Inc (G-6586)*
Premiere Services Inc...678 815-6078
2305 Garland Ct 1 Tallahassee (32303) *(G-17310)*
Premieretrade Forex LLC...407 287-4149
103 Commerce St Ste 140 Lake Mary (32746) *(G-7445)*
Premium Absrbent Dspsables LLC...561 737-6377
3030 Sw 13th Pl Ste A Boynton Beach (33426) *(G-944)*
Premium Auto Sealant Usa LLC...786 637-2573
12450 Nw South River Dr Medley (33178) *(G-8709)*
Premium Dynamic Lens...813 891-9912
640 Brooker Creek Blvd # 435 Oldsmar (34677) *(G-12261)*
Premium Latin Music Inc...212 873-1472
1545 Sw 14th Ter Miami (33145) *(G-10185)*
Premium Marine Inc...786 903-0851
777 Brickell Ave Ste 500 Miami (33131) *(G-10186)*
Premium Powder Coating...386 789-0216
1872 Sweetwater Bnd Deltona (32738) *(G-3178)*
Premium Precious Metals LLC...954 367-7513
1883 W State Road 84 # 106 Fort Lauderdale (33315) *(G-4178)*
Premium Quality Meats Inc...239 309-4418
7979 Riviera Blvd Miramar (33023) *(G-11029)*
Premium Rubber Bands Inc...305 321-0333
9430 Sw 136th St Miami (33176) *(G-10187)*
Premix-Marbletite Mfg Co (HQ)...954 970-6540
1259 Nw 21st St Pompano Beach (33069) *(G-14810)*
Premix-Marbletite Mfg Co...407 327-0830
325 Old Sanford Oviedo Rd Winter Springs (32708) *(G-19480)*
Prepaid Solutions LLC...786 257-2714
601 Brickell Key Dr # 70 Miami (33131) *(G-10188)*
Presage Analytics Inc...800 309-1704
27500 Rvrview Ctr Blvd St Bonita Springs (34134) *(G-849)*
Prescient Logistics LLC...407 547-2680
576 Monroe Rd Ste 1304 Sanford (32771) *(G-16106)*
Presidium, Lakeland *Also called Slappey Communications LLC (G-7792)*
Press Beauty Facial Bar...561 281-0631
3475 Fargo Ave Lake Worth (33467) *(G-7582)*
Press Gourmet Sandwiches...954 440-0422
6206 N Federal Hwy Fort Lauderdale (33308) *(G-4179)*
Press Print Graphics LLC...850 249-3700
106 N Gulf Blvd Ste C Panama City Beach (32413) *(G-13983)*
Press Printing Company, Fort Myers *Also called Press Printing Enterprises Inc (G-4572)*
Press Printing Enterprises Inc...239 598-1500
3601 Hanson St Fort Myers (33916) *(G-4572)*
Press Room Inc...954 792-6729
619 Sw 159th Ter Pembroke Pines (33027) *(G-14054)*
Press-Rite Inc...954 963-7373
2125 Sw 60th Way Miramar (33023) *(G-11030)*
Pressex Inc...727 299-8500
12910 Automobile Blvd Clearwater (33762) *(G-1845)*
Pressnet Corp...786 728-1369
321 Nw 63rd Ct Miami (33126) *(G-10189)*
Presstige Printing, Bonita Springs *Also called Customer First Inc Naples (G-827)*
Pressure Point Water Proofing...352 337-9905
11922 Se 225th Dr Hawthorne (32640) *(G-5245)*
Pressure Shine LLC...727 216-8543
2665 Walnut Dr Palm Harbor (34683) *(G-13751)*
Pressure Systems Innvtions LLC...561 249-2708
3750 Investment Ln Ste 4 West Palm Beach (33404) *(G-19005)*
Pressure Washers USA...561 848-7970
1440 10th Ct Bay A Lake Park (33403) *(G-7478)*
Prestashop Inc...888 947-6543
1001 Brickell Bay Dr # 2502 Miami (33131) *(G-10190)*
Prestige A B Ready Mix, Clermont *Also called Prestige/Ab Ready Mix LLC (G-1971)*
Prestige Aluminum Railing Inc...904 966-2163
4778 Se 142nd Way Starke (32091) *(G-16896)*
Prestige Brands International...914 524-6800
26811 S Bay Dr Ste 300 Bonita Springs (34134) *(G-850)*
Prestige Concrete, Melbourne *Also called Prestige/Ab Ready Mix LLC (G-8911)*
Prestige Entertainment, North Miami *Also called Codsworth Industries Inc (G-11634)*

Prestige Flrg Instllations Inc.....407 291-0609
3065 Pennington Dr Orlando (32804) *(G-13083)*
Prestige Granite & Marble, Orlando *Also called Prestige Flrg Instllations Inc (G-13083)*
Prestige Publication Group.....305 538-9700
1688 Meridian Ave Ste 404 Miami Beach (33139) *(G-10705)*
Prestige Service Group.....954 532-9014
2520 Nw 16th Ln Pompano Beach (33064) *(G-14811)*
Prestige Spa Covers, Pinellas Park *Also called Prestige Spas Inc (G-14379)*
Prestige Spas Inc.....727 576-8600
2875 Mci Dr N Pinellas Park (33782) *(G-14379)*
Prestige/Ab Ready Mix LLC (PA).....561 478-9980
7228 Westport Pl Ste C West Palm Beach (33413) *(G-19006)*
Prestige/Ab Ready Mix LLC.....407 654-3330
17600 State Road 50 Clermont (34711) *(G-1971)*
Prestige/Ab Ready Mix LLC.....321 751-2566
2585 Avocado Ave Melbourne (32935) *(G-8911)*
Prestige/Ab Ready Mix LLC.....407 847-7229
8529 Suthpark Cir Ste 320 Orlando (32819) *(G-13084)*
Prestige/Ab Ready Mix LLC.....772 468-4666
4190 Selvitz Rd Fort Pierce (34981) *(G-4736)*
Presto Lifts.....786 615-7256
1840 W 49th St Ste 403 Hialeah (33012) *(G-5566)*
Presto Print II Inc.....203 627-2528
7785 Silver Lake Dr Delray Beach (33446) *(G-3124)*
Preston Works Inc.....850 932-0888
599 Armistead Blvd Holt (32564) *(G-5949)*
Prestressed Systems Inc.....305 556-6699
11405 Nw 112th Ct Doral (33178) *(G-3469)*
Presys Instruments Inc.....305 495-3335
14453 Sw 84th St Miami (33183) *(G-10191)*
Pret-EE LLC.....561 839-4338
4440 Pga Blvd Ste 600 Palm Beach Gardens (33410) *(G-13617)*
Pretec Directional Drlg LLC.....786 220-7667
800 S Douglas Rd Ste 1200 Coral Gables (33134) *(G-2186)*
Pretty Vulgar LLC.....561 465-8831
1141 S Rogers Cir Ste 7 Boca Raton (33487) *(G-674)*
Pretz Snacks Corp.....718 869-2762
9755 Nw 46th Ter Doral (33178) *(G-3470)*
Prevail Solutions LLC.....727 210-6600
19321 Us Highway 19 N # 605 Clearwater (33764) *(G-1846)*
Prg Packing Corp (PA).....201 242-5500
294 Sw Harvey Greene Dr Madison (32340) *(G-8453)*
Price Brothers Company.....386 328-8841
245 Comfort Rd Palatka (32177) *(G-13490)*
Price Chopper Inc.....407 679-1600
6325 Mccoy Rd Orlando (32822) *(G-13085)*
Price Chopper Wristbands, Orlando *Also called Price Chopper Inc (G-13085)*
Price Chpper Med Wrstbands Inc.....407 505-5809
6325 Mccoy Rd Orlando (32822) *(G-13086)*
Price King 2 LLC.....786 337-8801
495 W 29th St Hialeah (33012) *(G-5567)*
Price Rite Engines LLC.....727 600-8206
8152 Candlewoode Dr Largo (33773) *(G-8031)*
Pride Florida.....813 621-9262
1913 N Us Highway 301 # 100 Tampa (33619) *(G-18009)*
Pride Straws LLC.....407 754-5833
3246 N Miami Ave Miami (33127) *(G-10192)*
Priko Corp.....305 556-3558
16500 Nw 86th Ct Miami Lakes (33016) *(G-10843)*
Prima Food Corp.....954 788-0411
4020 Ne 10th Way Pompano Beach (33064) *(G-14812)*
Prima Foods International Inc.....352 732-9148
2140 Ne 36th Ave Ocala (34470) *(G-12031)*
Primal Innovation Tech LLC.....407 558-9366
10150 Highland Manor Dr # 200 Tampa (33610) *(G-18010)*
Prime Custom Cabinets & Design, Pompano Beach *Also called District 95 Wood Working Inc (G-14666)*
Prime Enterprises LLC.....305 625-4929
16363 Nw 49th Ave Hialeah (33014) *(G-5568)*
Prime Flexible Products, Panama City *Also called Wellstream Inc (G-13962)*
Prime Global Group Inc.....386 676-2200
3 Aviator Way Ormond Beach (32174) *(G-13393)*
Prime Horizontal.....239 471-2357
5317 Sw 9th Pl Cape Coral (33914) *(G-1457)*
Prime Hotel Group US, Hollywood *Also called Phg Kendall LLC (G-5891)*
Prime Karts, Pensacola *Also called Prime Pedal Karts LLC (G-14239)*
Prime Life Ntrtn Companyllc.....754 307-7137
1239 E Nwport Ctr Dr Ste Deerfield Beach (33442) *(G-2890)*
Prime Manufacturing Canada.....850 332-7193
9235 Roe St Pensacola (32514) *(G-14238)*
Prime Matter Labs, Hialeah *Also called Prime Enterprises LLC (G-5568)*
Prime Meridian Trading Corp.....954 727-2152
4624 N Hiatus Rd Sunrise (33351) *(G-17161)*
Prime Molding Technologies Inc.....561 721-2799
3765 Investment Ln Ste A Riviera Beach (33404) *(G-15366)*
Prime Packaging Inc.....305 625-6737
16363 Nw 49th Ave Hialeah (33014) *(G-5569)*
Prime Pavers Inc.....941 320-7878
7235 Mauna Loa Blvd Sarasota (34241) *(G-16547)*
Prime Pedal Karts LLC.....850 475-0450
9235 Roe St Pensacola (32514) *(G-14239)*
Prime Tech Coatings Inc.....561 844-2312
1135 53rd Ct N Mangonia Park (33407) *(G-8510)*
Prime Technical Coatings, Mangonia Park *Also called Prime Tech Coatings Inc (G-8510)*
Prime Technological Svcs LLC.....850 539-2500
102 Technology Way Havana (32333) *(G-5239)*
Prime Topco LLC.....305 625-4929
16363 Nw 49th Ave Hialeah (33014) *(G-5570)*
Prime Woodwork Inc.....786 226-5646
17309 Nw 63rd Ave Hialeah (33015) *(G-5571)*
Primetime Industries LLC.....813 781-0196
32671 Natural Bridge Rd Wesley Chapel (33543) *(G-18756)*
Primetime Sports Agents Inc.....561 371-4421
500 Pacific Grove Dr West Palm Beach (33401) *(G-19007)*
Primo Water Corporation.....844 237-7466
4221 W Boy Scout Blvd Tampa (33607) *(G-18011)*
Primus Sterilizer Company LLC (HQ).....402 344-4200
7936 Forest City Rd Orlando (32810) *(G-13087)*
Prince Minerals Inc.....832 241-2169
710 S Rossiter St Mount Dora (32757) *(G-11111)*
Princeton Custom Cabinetry, Margate *Also called Princeton Industries Inc (G-8563)*
Princeton Custom Cabinetry.....954 755-7614
12550 Nw 39th St Pompano Beach (33065) *(G-14813)*
Princeton Industries Inc (PA).....954 344-9155
1790 Mears Pkwy Margate (33063) *(G-8563)*
Princeton Machine Shop, Homestead *Also called Acdm-PMS Inc (G-5952)*
Princeton Tool South LLC.....813 600-8143
9009 King Palm Dr Tampa (33619) *(G-18012)*
Print Administrate.....407 877-5923
1273 Winter Gdn Winter Garden (34787) *(G-19280)*
Print All Promotions LLC.....800 971-3209
18202 Sandalwood Dr 18 Wildwood (34785) *(G-19199)*
Print Art Screen Printing Inc.....386 258-5186
340 Marion St Daytona Beach (32114) *(G-2698)*
Print Avenue, Naples *Also called American Business Cards Inc (G-11161)*
Print Basics Inc.....954 354-0700
1059 Sw 30th Ave Deerfield Beach (33442) *(G-2891)*
Print Big Inc.....305 398-8898
1680 W 33rd Pl Hialeah (33012) *(G-5572)*
Print Bold Corp.....305 517-1281
13995 Sw 144th Ave Ste 20 Miami (33186) *(G-10193)*
Print Direct Inc.....772 545-9191
8183 Se Cumberland Cir Hobe Sound (33455) *(G-5725)*
Print Dynamics.....954 524-9294
1223 N Flagler Dr Fort Lauderdale (33304) *(G-4180)*
Print E-Solution Inc.....954 588-5454
409 Goolsby Blvd Deerfield Beach (33442) *(G-2892)*
Print Esolutions, Deerfield Beach *Also called Print E-Solution Inc (G-2892)*
Print Etc Inc.....813 972-2800
13121 Canopy Creek Dr Tampa (33625) *(G-18013)*
Print Express.....904 737-6641
1889 Southampton Rd Jacksonville (32207) *(G-6686)*
Print Factory LLC.....954 392-5889
3820 Executive Way Miramar (33025) *(G-11031)*
Print Farm Inc (PA).....305 592-2895
3511 Nw 74th Ave Miami (33122) *(G-10194)*
Print Headquarters.....772 286-2812
10358 Rverside Dr Ste 130 Palm Beach Gardens (33410) *(G-13618)*
Print Hopper.....954 770-3007
4634 N Hiatus Rd Sunrise (33351) *(G-17162)*
Print Idea Center LLC.....954 682-6369
7788 Centl Indus Dr Ste 3 Riviera Beach (33404) *(G-15367)*
Print It 4 Less.....800 370-5591
601 N Congress Ave # 208 Delray Beach (33445) *(G-3125)*
Print It Plus, Royal Palm Beach *Also called Dakim Inc (G-15465)*
Print It Usacom Inc.....954 370-2200
13660 W State Road 84 Davie (33325) *(G-2575)*
Print Mart Inc.....727 796-0064
1430 Main St Dunedin (34698) *(G-3587)*
Print Media, Miami *Also called Amtec Sales Inc (G-9153)*
Print Motion Inc (PA).....305 851-7206
1501 Sw 118th Ct Miami (33184) *(G-10195)*
Print My Atm LLC.....866 292-6179
100 W Lucerne Cir Ste 200 Orlando (32801) *(G-13088)*
Print Now-Business Cards Today, Pensacola *Also called Printnow Inc (G-14241)*
Print One Inc.....813 273-0240
3898 Tampa Rd Ste B Oldsmar (34677) *(G-12262)*
Print Pelican, Riviera Beach *Also called Topline Prtg & Graphics Inc (G-15385)*
Print Pro Shop Inc.....305 859-8282
660 Nw 85th St Miami (33150) *(G-10196)*
Print Rite Co.....305 757-0611
748 Ne 79th St Miami (33138) *(G-10197)*
Print Shack.....813 885-4152
5011 W Hillsborough Ave C Tampa (33634) *(G-18014)*
Print Shack.....352 799-2972
210 W Jefferson St Brooksville (34601) *(G-1262)*
Print Shop of Chiefland Inc.....352 493-0322
208 N Main St Chiefland (32626) *(G-1537)*

ALPHABETIC

Print Shop, The, Fort Myers *Also called Proprint of Naples Inc* ***(G-4574)***
Print Shop, The, Chiefland *Also called Print Shop of Chiefland Inc* ***(G-1537)***
Print Signs & Banners...305 600-1349
4244 Sw 73rd Ave Miami (33155) ***(G-10198)***
Print Solution Digital LLC...305 819-7420
6540 W 20th Ave Unit 3 Hialeah (33016) ***(G-5573)***
Print Store LLC...727 656-1376
4722 Kylemore Ct Palm Harbor (34685) ***(G-13752)***
Print This and That LLC (PA)...386 752-5905
167 Sw Mossy Oak Way Lake City (32024) ***(G-7376)***
Print This and That LLC...386 344-4420
231 Nw Burk Ave Ste 101 Lake City (32055) ***(G-7377)***
Print123.com, Titusville *Also called C & R Designs Printing LLC* ***(G-18420)***
Print123.com, Titusville *Also called C & R Designs Inc* ***(G-18419)***
Printec Inc...813 854-1075
241 Douglas Rd E Ste 1 Oldsmar (34677) ***(G-12263)***
Printed Systems Inc...904 281-0909
1309 Saint Johns Bluff Rd Jacksonville (32225) ***(G-6687)***
Printer S Pride Inc...813 932-8683
7211 N Dale Mabry Hwy # 10 Tampa (33614) ***(G-18015)***
Printerbazaar Usa Inc...954 730-3473
15321 S Dixie Hwy Ste 309 Miami (33157) ***(G-10199)***
Printerpix, Lake Mary *Also called Treasured Photo Gifts LLC* ***(G-7456)***
Printers Edge LLC...407 294-8542
6229 Edgewater Dr Ste 400 Orlando (32810) ***(G-13089)***
Printers For Less LLC...954 647-0051
1217 Ne 12th Ave Fort Lauderdale (33304) ***(G-4181)***
Printers of Pensacola LLC...850 434-2588
1207 W Garden St Pensacola (32502) ***(G-14240)***
Printers Printer Inc...954 917-2773
2681 W Mcnab Rd Pompano Beach (33069) ***(G-14814)***
Printers, The, Apopka *Also called All Because LLC* ***(G-111)***
Printery, The, Sarasota *Also called Gobczynskis Printery Inc* ***(G-16222)***
Printex Worldwide Inc...954 518-0722
2037 Sw 31st Ave Hallandale (33009) ***(G-5161)***
Printfarm, Miami *Also called Print Farm Inc* ***(G-10194)***
Printfast & Office Supplies, Indian Harbour Beach *Also called Steven M Roessler LLC* ***(G-6068)***
Printhouseusacom Inc...305 231-0202
450 W 28th St Ste 2 Hialeah (33010) ***(G-5574)***
Printing and Labels Inc...954 578-4411
5405 Nw 102nd Ave Ste 218 Sunrise (33351) ***(G-17163)***
Printing and Promotion Svcs...201 612-0800
7320 Amberly Ln Apt 103 Delray Beach (33446) ***(G-3126)***
Printing Center LLC...305 513-9114
6740 Sw 155th Ave Miami (33193) ***(G-10200)***
Printing Connection Too Inc...954 584-4197
4960 Sw 52nd St Ste 409 Davie (33314) ***(G-2576)***
Printing Corp of Americas Inc...954 943-6087
620 Sw 12th Ave Pompano Beach (33069) ***(G-14815)***
Printing Department LLC...386 253-7990
176 Carswell Ave Daytona Beach (32117) ***(G-2699)***
Printing Depot Inc...813 855-6758
3898 Tampa Rd Ste B Oldsmar (34677) ***(G-12264)***
Printing Edge Inc...904 399-3343
2205 Emerson St Jacksonville (32207) ***(G-6688)***
Printing Express...305 512-0900
1608 W 68th St Hialeah (33014) ***(G-5575)***
Printing For A Cause LLC...786 496-0637
360 Central Ave Ste 800 Saint Petersburg (33701) ***(G-15889)***
Printing Grphics Cnnection Inc...305 222-6144
823 Nw 133rd Ct Miami (33182) ***(G-10201)***
Printing Impressions Prom...904 465-2223
1762 Singing Bird Ln Jacksonville (32223) ***(G-6689)***
Printing Mart Inc...954 753-0323
1951 W Copans Rd Ste 2 Pompano Beach (33064) ***(G-14816)***
Printing Mart Inc South Fla...954 753-0323
1951 W Copans Rd Ste 2 Pompano Beach (33064) ***(G-14817)***
Printing Online, Miami *Also called Tag & Label of Florida Inc* ***(G-10457)***
Printing Place, The, New Port Richey *Also called Aquinas Inc* ***(G-11480)***
Printing Sensations, Miami Gardens *Also called Hurricane Graphics Inc* ***(G-10746)***
Printing Services Plus LLC...813 279-1903
100 S Ashley Dr Tampa (33602) ***(G-18016)***
Printing Unlimited, Naples *Also called K R O Enterprises Ltd* ***(G-11302)***
Printing USA, Winter Park *Also called Drewlu Enterprises Inc* ***(G-19405)***
Printing Usa Inc...407 857-7468
4732 S Orange Blossom Trl Orlando (32839) ***(G-13090)***
Printing.com, Tampa *Also called Suncoast Specialty Prtg Inc* ***(G-18146)***
Printing.com, South Daytona *Also called Couchman Printing Company* ***(G-16800)***
Printing.com, Tallahassee *Also called Modern Digital Imaging Inc* ***(G-17303)***
Printing.com, Jacksonville *Also called Media Works Inc* ***(G-6588)***
Printing.com, Jacksonville *Also called Miller Creative Graphics* ***(G-6607)***
Printing.com 5point, Jacksonville *Also called Wingard LLC* ***(G-6923)***
Printmaster Inc...954 771-6104
5220 Ne 12th Ave Oakland Park (33334) ***(G-11832)***
Printmor...954 247-9405
3941 Nw 126th Ave Coral Springs (33065) ***(G-2304)***
Printmor Large Format Printing, Coral Springs *Also called Printmor* ***(G-2304)***
Printnovations Inc...305 322-4041
125 Sw 4th Ave Hallandale Beach (33009) ***(G-5204)***
Printnow Inc...850 435-1149
5555 N Davis Hwy Ste H Pensacola (32503) ***(G-14241)***
Printrust Inc...954 572-0790
4617 Nw 103rd Ave Sunrise (33351) ***(G-17164)***
Prints 2 Go Inc...727 725-1700
24129 Us Highway 19 N Clearwater (33763) ***(G-1847)***
Prints Hope International Inc...305 528-1593
2353 Sw 130th Ter Miramar (33027) ***(G-11032)***
Prints The Ppr of Wnter Pk LLC...407 740-0989
1597 Hillcrest Ave Winter Park (32789) ***(G-19433)***
Printshaqcom Inc...954 678-7286
1654 Jackson St Hollywood (33020) ***(G-5895)***
Printworks...850 681-6909
4753 Blountstown Hwy Tallahassee (32304) ***(G-17311)***
Printworld...754 312-5908
4150 Nw 10th Ave Fort Lauderdale (33309) ***(G-4182)***
Priority 1 Signs...954 971-8689
1911 Nw 40th Ct Deerfield Beach (33064) ***(G-2893)***
Priority Manufacturing, Miami *Also called M R M S Inc* ***(G-9927)***
Priority One Signs, Deerfield Beach *Also called Volunteer Capital LLC* ***(G-2934)***
Priority Printing Inc...727 446-6605
2125 Range Rd Ste B Clearwater (33765) ***(G-1848)***
Prism Music Inc...954 718-6850
9905 Nw 71st St Tamarac (33321) ***(G-17365)***
Prism Venture Partners LLC...561 427-6565
675 W Indiantown Rd # 103 Jupiter (33458) ***(G-7098)***
Prisna Latino...305 525-9292
7455 Nw 50th St Miami (33166) ***(G-10202)***
Prison Legal News...561 360-2523
1013 Lucerne Ave Ste 206 Lake Worth (33460) ***(G-7583)***
Pristine Environment LLC...727 541-5748
6575 80th Ave N Pinellas Park (33781) ***(G-14380)***
Pristine Laser Center...407 389-1200
1180 Spring Cntre S Blvd Altamonte Springs (32714) ***(G-66)***
Privacy Glass Solutions, Coral Springs *Also called Vistamatic LLC* ***(G-2329)***
Privacy Window Design Inc...386 761-7306
600 Oak St Ste 2b Port Orange (32127) ***(G-15029)***
Private Label Express, Coral Springs *Also called De Lima Consultants Group Inc* ***(G-2238)***
Private Label Skin Na LLC...877 516-2200
2260 118th Ave N Saint Petersburg (33716) ***(G-15890)***
Prive International Inc...888 750-5850
19597 Ne 10th Ave Ste F North Miami Beach (33179) ***(G-11698)***
Prive Porter LLC...561 479-9200
980 N Federal Hwy Boca Raton (33432) ***(G-675)***
Privi LLC...863 294-0373
141 E Central Ave Ste 300 Winter Haven (33880) ***(G-19345)***
Pro Art America Inc...863 385-4242
620 Red Oak Ave Sebring (33870) ***(G-16704)***
Pro Chem Products Inc...407 425-5533
1340 W Central Blvd Orlando (32805) ***(G-13091)***
Pro Co Inc...321 422-0900
910 Belle Ave Ste 1000 Winter Springs (32708) ***(G-19481)***
Pro Color Coating LLC...941 661-4769
244 Macarthur Dr Port Charlotte (33954) ***(G-14994)***
Pro Duffers Orlando...407 641-7626
1144 Ballyshannon Pkwy Orlando (32828) ***(G-13092)***
Pro Dumpsters Inc...407 910-6341
3864 Wood Thrush Dr Kissimmee (34744) ***(G-7291)***
Pro Edge Cutlery LLC...239 304-8000
4484 Arnold Ave Naples (34104) ***(G-11374)***
Pro Edge Paper, Naples *Also called Pro Edge Cutlery LLC* ***(G-11374)***
Pro Fab...813 545-2861
11910 Dietz Dr Tampa (33626) ***(G-18017)***
Pro Fuse...305 982-8457
11231 Nw 20th St Miami (33172) ***(G-10203)***
Pro Horizons Inc...813 764-8844
2610 Airport Rd Plant City (33563) ***(G-14460)***
Pro Kitchen Cabinets Corp...786 768-4291
10675 Sw 190th St Ste 110 Cutler Bay (33157) ***(G-2409)***
Pro Lab Supply Corporation...305 600-0444
5921 Nw 176th St Unit 5 Hialeah (33015) ***(G-5576)***
Pro Machine Inc...407 296-5031
6150 Edgewater Dr Ste H Orlando (32810) ***(G-13093)***
Pro Millwork Installations...561 302-5869
1420 Sw 30th Ave Boynton Beach (33426) ***(G-945)***
Pro Pak Enterprises Inc...888 375-2275
741 Nw 42nd Way Deerfield Beach (33442) ***(G-2894)***
Pro Pet Distributors, Orlando *Also called Dp Pet Products Inc* ***(G-12681)***
Pro Poly of America Inc...352 629-1414
230 Ne 25th Ave Ste 300 Ocala (34470) ***(G-12032)***
Pro Poly of America Inc (PA)...352 629-1414
1821 Nw 57th St Ocala (34475) ***(G-12033)***
Pro Powder Coating Inc...941 505-8010
5474 Williamsburg Dr Punta Gorda (33982) ***(G-15221)***
Pro Publishing Inc...954 888-7726
18020 Sw 66th St Southwest Ranches (33331) ***(G-16840)***

Pro Street Choppers Inc 407 389-2047
917 Suwannee Dr Apopka (32703) *(G-173)*
Pro Tech Custom Cabinet 727 863-5143
9100 Bolton Ave Port Richey (34667) *(G-15065)*
Pro Trim Millwork Inc 239 592-5454
3995 Upolo Ln Naples (34119) *(G-11375)*
Pro Trim of Central Florida 863 294-4646
2456 Hartridge Point Dr W Winter Haven (33881) *(G-19346)*
Pro Water Sports, Melrose *Also called Lake Area Watersports LLC* *(G-8986)*
Pro Water Treatment Inc 954 650-1955
1935 Mears Pkwy Frnt Margate (33063) *(G-8564)*
Pro Weld of South Florida Inc 954 984-0104
3101 Vista Del Mar Margate (33063) *(G-8565)*
Pro-Ad Media Inc 863 802-5043
115 Allamanda Dr Lakeland (33803) *(G-7771)*
Pro-Chemicals USA Corp 305 885-7922
7575 Nw 82nd St Medley (33166) *(G-8710)*
Pro-Copy Inc 813 988-5900
5219 E Fowler Ave Temple Terrace (33617) *(G-18375)*
Pro-Crete Material Corporation 352 748-1505
1617 S Division Ave Orlando (32805) *(G-13094)*
Pro-Lab, Weston *Also called Professional Laboratories Inc* *(G-19161)*
Pro-Mix Inc 305 556-6699
11405 Nw 138th St Medley (33178) *(G-8711)*
Pro-Tech Coatings Inc 813 248-1477
3201 E 3rd Ave Tampa (33605) *(G-18018)*
Pro-Tools, Temple Terrace *Also called Phoenix Enterprises Fla LLC* *(G-18374)*
Pro-Weld Inc 863 453-9353
222 S Forest Ave Unit 1 Avon Park (33825) *(G-294)*
Proandre Hygiene Systems Inc 305 433-3493
1200 Brickell Ave # 1950 Miami (33131) *(G-10204)*
Probag Inc 305 883-3266
9955 Nw 88th Ave Medley (33178) *(G-8712)*
Probiora Health LLC 214 559-2994
6302 Benjamin Rd Ste 409 Tampa (33634) *(G-18019)*
Probotix 844 472-9262
628 Lovejoy Rd Nw Unit 3e Fort Walton Beach (32548) *(G-4824)*
Process Automation Corporation 727 541-6280
5260 87th Ave N Pinellas Park (33782) *(G-14381)*
Process Solutions, Riviera Beach *Also called United Associates Group Inc* *(G-15387)*
Processing and Packg Sups Co 321 723-2723
700 S John Rodes Blvd Melbourne (32904) *(G-8912)*
Procorp LLC 904 477-6762
8535 Baymeadows Rd Ste 58 Jacksonville (32256) *(G-6690)*
Procraft Cabinetry Florida LLC 754 212-2277
1850 S Powerline Rd Ste A Deerfield Beach (33442) *(G-2895)*
Procyon Corporation (PA) 727 447-2998
1300 S Highland Ave Clearwater (33756) *(G-1849)*
Prodair Corporation (HQ) 850 994-5511
4575 Highway 90 Milton (32571) *(G-10937)*
Prodalim USA Inc 407 656-1000
355 9th St Winter Garden (34787) *(G-19281)*
Prodeco Technologies LLC 954 974-6730
1601 Green Rd Deerfield Beach (33064) *(G-2896)*
Prodigy Customs 407 832-1752
527 Little Wekiva Rd Altamonte Springs (32714) *(G-67)*
Produce Business Magazine, Boca Raton *Also called Phoenix Media Network Inc* *(G-664)*
Product Dev Partners LLC 813 908-6775
6291 W Linebaugh Ave Tampa (33625) *(G-18020)*
Product Max Group Inc 813 949-5061
8011 Land O Lakes Blvd Land O Lakes (34638) *(G-7863)*
Production Metal Stampings 850 981-8240
8133 Opportunity Dr Milton (32583) *(G-10938)*
Production System Engineering 863 299-7330
3204 E Lake Hamilton Dr Winter Haven (33881) *(G-19347)*
Productive Products Inc 904 570-5553
321 Valverde Ln Saint Augustine (32086) *(G-15591)*
Productos Las Delicias Inc 305 760-4223
2954 W 84th St Unit 11 Hialeah (33018) *(G-5577)*
Products By O2 Inc 561 392-1892
3020 High Ridge Rd # 300 Boynton Beach (33426) *(G-946)*
Profab Corporation (PA) 352 369-5515
4901 Nw 5th St Ocala (34482) *(G-12034)*
Profab Electronics Inc 954 917-1998
2855 W Mcnab Rd Pompano Beach (33069) *(G-14818)*
Profab Plastics, Ocala *Also called Profab Corporation* *(G-12034)*
Profast Corporation 305 827-7801
5854 Miami Lakes Dr E Miami Lakes (33014) *(G-10844)*
Profast Usa Inc 305 827-7801
5854 Miami Lakes Dr E Miami Lakes (33014) *(G-10845)*
Profbox of America Inc 786 454-8148
17071 W Dixie Hwy Ste 116 North Miami Beach (33160) *(G-11699)*
Professional Bindery Inc 305 633-3761
3668 Nw 48th Ter Miami (33142) *(G-10205)*
Professional Coating Systems 904 477-7138
2187 Nw 247th St Lawtey (32058) *(G-8125)*
Professional Ctr At Gardens 561 394-5200
190 Se 5th Ave Delray Beach (33483) *(G-3127)*
Professional Engrv & Trophy, North Miami *Also called Cabus USA Inc* *(G-11631)*
Professional Holiday Lighting 208 709-2968
181 Royal Dunes Cir Ormond Beach (32176) *(G-13394)*
Professional Kitchen Cabinets 305 888-5660
1035 E 13th St Hialeah (33010) *(G-5578)*
Professional Laboratories Inc 954 384-4446
1675 N Commerce Pkwy Weston (33326) *(G-19161)*
Professional Office Svcs Inc 863 967-6634
64 Industrial Blvd Winter Haven (33880) *(G-19348)*
Professional Office Svcs Inc 305 756-8632
176 Ne 82nd St Miami (33138) *(G-10206)*
Professional Pet Products Inc 305 592-1992
1873 Nw 97th Ave Doral (33172) *(G-3471)*
Professional Printing 561 845-0514
120 Us Highway 1 Ste 1 North Palm Beach (33408) *(G-11725)*
Professional Products 323 754-1287
4949 Marbrisa Dr Apt 102 Tampa (33624) *(G-18021)*
Professional Products Inc 850 892-5731
54 Hugh Adams Rd Defuniak Springs (32435) *(G-2946)*
Professional Prtg For Less Inc 954 977-3737
3907 N Federal Hwy # 242 Pompano Beach (33064) *(G-14819)*
Professional Sftwr Consortium 407 909-9168
5040 Down Point Ln Windermere (34786) *(G-19240)*
Professional Shoring & Supply, Tampa *Also called Fw Shoring Company* *(G-17700)*
Professional Shoring & Supply, Orlando *Also called Fw Shoring Company* *(G-12767)*
Professional Signs 305 662-5957
6460 Sw 35th St Miami (33155) *(G-10207)*
Professional Site & Trnspt Inc 386 239-6800
3728 W Intl Spwy Blvd Daytona Beach (32124) *(G-2700)*
Professnal Kit Instller Group 954 436-1513
1892 Sw 152nd Ter Miramar (33027) *(G-11033)*
Professnal Reproduction of Jax 904 389-4141
7029 Commonwealth Ave Jacksonville (32220) *(G-6691)*
Professonal Paver Restorations 352 797-8411
3259 Dothan Ave Spring Hill (34609) *(G-16859)*
Professor Software Company 561 691-5455
268 Barbados Dr Jupiter (33458) *(G-7099)*
Profile Racing Inc 727 392-8307
4803 95th St N Saint Petersburg (33708) *(G-15891)*
Profile Tool & Gear, Saint Petersburg *Also called Profile Racing Inc* *(G-15891)*
Profilegorilla, Jacksonville *Also called Silvershore Partners LLC* *(G-6775)*
Profire Inc 305 665-5313
9621 S Dixie Hwy Pinecrest (33156) *(G-14331)*
Profitsword LLC 407 909-8822
7512 Dr Phillips Blvd Orlando (32819) *(G-13095)*
Profold Inc 772 589-0063
10300 99th Way Sebastian (32958) *(G-16671)*
Proform System Inc 305 854-2800
2665 S Bayshore Dr Miami (33133) *(G-10208)*
Profounda Health & Beauty 407 270-7792
10501 S Orange Ave # 124 Orlando (32824) *(G-13096)*
Program Works Inc 407 489-4140
1511 E State Road 434 # 2001 Winter Springs (32708) *(G-19482)*
Prographix Inc 863 298-8081
2614 Avenue G Nw Winter Haven (33880) *(G-19349)*
Progress Fuels Corporation (HQ) 727 824-6600
1 Progress Plz Fl 11 Saint Petersburg (33701) *(G-15892)*
Progress House 321 298-4652
1097 Sandy Ln Ne Palm Bay (32905) *(G-13529)*
Progress Rail Services Corp 352 748-8008
4198 E County Road 462 Wildwood (34785) *(G-19200)*
Progress Rail Services Corp 239 643-3013
3581 Mercantile Ave Naples (34104) *(G-11376)*
Progress Rail Services Corp 904 783-1143
420 Agmac Ave Jacksonville (32254) *(G-6692)*
Progress Wine Group, Miami *Also called Fws Distributors LLC* *(G-9606)*
Progress Wine Group, Orlando *Also called Fws Distributors LLC* *(G-12768)*
Progressive Aerodyne Inc 352 253-0108
3801 State Road 19 Tavares (32778) *(G-18351)*
Progressive Industrial Inc 941 723-0201
1412 18th Avenue Dr E Palmetto (34221) *(G-13818)*
Progressive Machine Co Inc 386 333-6850
3 Aviator Way Ormond Beach (32174) *(G-13395)*
Progressive Power Products Inc 904 354-1819
4062 N Liberty St Jacksonville (32206) *(G-6693)*
Progressive Printing Co Inc 904 388-0746
4505 Lexington Ave Jacksonville (32210) *(G-6694)*
Progressive Printing Services, Delray Beach *Also called Progressive Printing Solutions* *(G-3128)*
Progressive Printing Solutions 800 370-5591
601 N Congress Ave # 208 Delray Beach (33445) *(G-3128)*
Project and Cnstr Wldg Inc 239 772-9299
2603 Andalusia Blvd Cape Coral (33909) *(G-1458)*
Project Mold 561 213-6167
7666 Cypress Cres Boca Raton (33433) *(G-676)*
Project Pros Woodworking Inc 239 454-6800
17051 Jean St Ste 12 Fort Myers (33967) *(G-4573)*
Projstream LLC 407 476-1084
1540 Intl Pkwy 2000 Lake Mary (32746) *(G-7446)*

Prolabel Inc...305 620-2202
621 W 20th St Hialeah (33010) ***(G-5579)***
Prolific Cabinetry & More Inc...904 448-6575
7660 Philips Hwy Ste 5 Jacksonville (32256) ***(G-6695)***
Prolific Resource Inc...727 868-9341
12045 Cobble Stone Dr Port Richey (34667) ***(G-15066)***
Proline Chemical & Plastics LL...850 835-6822
9646 State Highway 20 W Freeport (32439) ***(G-4851)***
Prolink Software Corporation...860 659-5928
999 Vanderbilt Beach Rd Naples (34108) ***(G-11377)***
Prologo Branding LLC...407 730-9831
5508 Commerce Dr Orlando (32839) ***(G-13097)***
Promarine Boats USA...305 450-2014
2111 Sw 31st St Fort Lauderdale (33312) ***(G-4183)***
Promax Welding Inc...305 962-5033
8055 W 23rd Ave Hialeah (33016) ***(G-5580)***
Promed Biosciences Inc...888 655-9155
9375 Us Highway 19 N A Pinellas Park (33782) ***(G-14382)***
Promedica Inc...813 854-1905
114 Douglas Rd E Oldsmar (34677) ***(G-12265)***
Promex LLC...305 884-2400
1415 E 11th Ave Hialeah (33010) ***(G-5581)***
Promo Daddy LLC...877 557-2336
812 N Apollo Blvd Melbourne (32935) ***(G-8913)***
Promo Daddy LLC (PA)...352 390-3081
800 N Apollo Blvd Melbourne (32935) ***(G-8914)***
Promo Printing Group, Tampa *Also called PPG Inc* ***(G-18000)***
Promoitalia LLC...305 347-5178
1221 Brickell Ave Miami (33131) ***(G-10209)***
Promotional Concepts Team, Hallandale Beach *Also called Jpl Associates Inc* ***(G-5194)***
Promotional Mktg Online LLC...941 347-8564
17377 Ophir Ln Punta Gorda (33955) ***(G-15222)***
Promowear...561 372-0505
9547 Cinnamon Ct Parkland (33076) ***(G-13999)***
Propak Software, Winter Haven *Also called Central Fla Bus Solutions Inc* ***(G-19312)***
Propavers LLC...904 403-9033
1337 Fairway Village Dr Fleming Island (32003) ***(G-3764)***
Propel Builders Inc...407 960-5116
111 S Maitland Ave # 200 Maitland (32751) ***(G-8475)***
Property Armor, Jacksonville *Also called Rm Brands Inc* ***(G-6732)***
Property Solutions and Cnstr, Jacksonville *Also called A Clean Finish Inc* ***(G-6109)***
Propglide USA Corp...305 520-0150
4769 Nw 72nd Ave Miami (33166) ***(G-10210)***
Proplus Products Inc...863 375-2487
149 County Line Rd E Bowling Green (33834) ***(G-867)***
Proprint of Naples Inc (PA)...239 775-3553
5900 Enterprise Pkwy Fort Myers (33905) ***(G-4574)***
Propulsion Tech Intl LLC...954 874-0274
15301 Sw 29th St Ste 100 Miramar (33027) ***(G-11034)***
Prosegur Eas Usa LLC...561 900-2744
598 Hillsboro Tech Dr Deerfield Beach (33441) ***(G-2897)***
Proservices Supply LLC...858 254-4415
12620 Beach Blvd Ste 3304 Jacksonville (32246) ***(G-6696)***
Proshowmaker Inc...813 765-2676
2310 Foggy Ridge Pkwy Land O Lakes (34639) ***(G-7864)***
Prosolus Inc (HQ)...305 514-0270
6701 Nw 7th St Ste 165 Miami (33126) ***(G-10211)***
Prospect Avenue Rm, Naples *Also called Cemex Cnstr Mtls Fla LLC* ***(G-11203)***
Prospect Plastics Inc...954 564-7282
836 Ne 44th St Oakland Park (33334) ***(G-11833)***
Prospects Plastics, Oakland Park *Also called Prospect Plastics Inc* ***(G-11833)***
Prosthetic Laboratories...305 250-9900
1270 Bird Rd Coral Gables (33146) ***(G-2187)***
Prosun International LLC...727 825-0400
2442 23rd St N Saint Petersburg (33713) ***(G-15893)***
Protech Nutraceuticals Inc...727 466-0770
10321 72nd St Seminole (33777) ***(G-16758)***
Protect All Coating Inc...727 278-7454
2458 36th Ave N Saint Petersburg (33713) ***(G-15894)***
Protective Coatings LLC...407 535-8535
344 Longhorn Dr Apopka (32712) ***(G-174)***
Protective Enclosures Co LLC...321 441-9689
385 Centerpointe Cir # 1319 Altamonte Springs (32701) ***(G-68)***
Protective Group A Point Blank, Pompano Beach *Also called Point Blank Enterprises Inc* ***(G-14801)***
Protective Group A Pt Blank Co, Miami Lakes *Also called Point Blank Enterprises Inc* ***(G-10840)***
Protective Group Inc...305 820-4266
14100 Nw 58th Ct Miami Lakes (33014) ***(G-10846)***
Protective Products Entps, Pompano Beach *Also called Point Blank Enterprises Inc* ***(G-14800)***
Protective Products Entps Inc...954 630-0900
2102 Sw 2nd St Pompano Beach (33069) ***(G-14820)***
Protege Media LLC...310 738-9567
5945 Nw Dowell Ct Port Saint Lucie (34986) ***(G-15131)***
Protek Custom Coatings LLC...850 656-7923
1320 Gateshead Cir Tallahassee (32317) ***(G-17312)***
Protek Electronics Inc...941 351-4399
1781 Independence Blvd Sarasota (34234) ***(G-16548)***
Protek Systems Inc...561 395-8155
1250 Wallace Dr Ste B Delray Beach (33444) ***(G-3129)***
Protex Inc...727 573-4665
10500 47th St N Clearwater (33762) ***(G-1850)***
Protexin...786 310-7233
1833 Nw 79th Ave Doral (33126) ***(G-3472)***
Proto Corp...727 573-4665
10500 47th St N Clearwater (33762) ***(G-1851)***
Proto Plus Inc...561 471-5325
350 Tall Pines Rd Ste B West Palm Beach (33413) ***(G-19008)***
Prototype Plastics LLC...941 371-3380
1523 Edgar Pl Sarasota (34240) ***(G-16549)***
Prototype Plstic Extrusion Inc...727 572-0803
3637 131st Ave N Clearwater (33762) ***(G-1852)***
Proud Tshirts Corp...305 769-3300
62 Ne 167th St Miami (33162) ***(G-10212)***
Proven Industries Inc...813 895-4385
2310 S Dock St Ste 111 Palmetto (34221) ***(G-13819)***
Provictus Inc...561 437-0232
4440 Pga Blvd Ste 635 Palm Beach Gardens (33410) ***(G-13619)***
Prowin Industries Inc...954 584-5686
6120 Nw 11th St Sunrise (33313) ***(G-17165)***
Proximity Mills LLC...813 251-3060
4020 W Kennedy Blvd # 10 Tampa (33609) ***(G-18022)***
Prs Taco Place...407 440-2803
717 W Smith St Orlando (32804) ***(G-13098)***
PS & QS Custom Prints LLC...352 231-3961
4024 Ne 1st Dr Gainesville (32609) ***(G-4984)***
PS Cabinet Works Inc...239 850-2162
217 Jefferson Ave Lehigh Acres (33936) ***(G-8204)***
PSC Building Group Inc...561 756-6811
900 Sw 15th Ave Delray Beach (33444) ***(G-3130)***
PSI, Oldsmar *Also called Peripheral Services Inc* ***(G-12256)***
PSi Customs...863 661-4211
132 Argentina Dr Winter Haven (33880) ***(G-19350)***
PSI Mnfacturing Operations LLC (PA)...561 747-6107
831 Jupiter Park Dr Jupiter (33458) ***(G-7100)***
PSI Printing, Jacksonville *Also called Printed Systems Inc* ***(G-6687)***
PSM, Jupiter *Also called Power Systems Mfg LLC* ***(G-7095)***
Psp Industrial Laundry Eqp LLC...305 517-1421
2700 Gateway Dr Pompano Beach (33069) ***(G-14821)***
Pspc Escrow II Corp...561 207-9600
1450 Centrepark Blvd # 21 West Palm Beach (33401) ***(G-19009)***
Pss Communications Inc...408 496-3330
309 Bryce Ct Sun City Center (33573) ***(G-17071)***
PST, Clearwater *Also called Precision Shaft Technology* ***(G-1841)***
PST Computers, Fort Lauderdale *Also called P S T Computers Inc* ***(G-4153)***
Pstein Inc...305 373-0037
4350 W Hllandale Bch Blvd Pembroke Park (33023) ***(G-14010)***
Psychlgcal Assssment Rsrces In (PA)...813 968-3003
16204 N Florida Ave Lutz (33549) ***(G-8413)***
Pte Systems International LLC (PA)...305 863-3409
1950 W 8th Ave Hialeah (33010) ***(G-5582)***
Ptse Holding Inc...800 760-0027
634 State Road 44 Leesburg (34748) ***(G-8168)***
Publi Signs...954 927-4411
250 N Dixie Hwy Unit 5 Hollywood (33020) ***(G-5896)***
Public Communications Office P, Fort Lauderdale *Also called County of Broward* ***(G-3919)***
Public Image Printing Inc...727 363-1800
5050 Gulf Blvd Ste C St Pete Beach (33706) ***(G-16883)***
Publicaciones Internacional, Doral *Also called Spanish Peri & Bk Sls Inc* ***(G-3508)***
Publishers Crcltion Flflment...877 723-6668
3351b Mclemore Dr Pensacola (32514) ***(G-14242)***
Publishers Direct Choice LLC...305 264-5998
1440 Sw 78th Ave Miami (33144) ***(G-10213)***
Publishers of Seniors Today, South Daytona *Also called Merle Harris Enterprises Inc* ***(G-16804)***
Publishers Prmotional Svcs Inc...303 431-4080
1383 S Missouri Ave Clearwater (33756) ***(G-1853)***
Publishers Whse Sanibel Island...239 267-6151
20350 Summerlin Rd # 2140 Fort Myers (33908) ***(G-4575)***
Publishing, Venice *Also called D-R Media and Investments LLC* ***(G-18540)***
Publishing Research Inc...954 921-4026
1313 Ne 125th St North Miami (33161) ***(G-11651)***
Puch Manufacturing Corporation...407 650-9926
3701 Saint Valentine Way Orlando (32811) ***(G-13099)***
Pulling Inc...305 224-2469
12797 Nw 13th St Sunrise (33323) ***(G-17166)***
Pulsaderm LLC...877 474-4038
12801 Commwl Dr Ste 2 Fort Myers (33913) ***(G-4576)***
Pulsafeeder Inc...941 575-2900
27101 Airport Rd Punta Gorda (33982) ***(G-15223)***
Pulsafeeder Spo Inc...941 575-3800
27101 Airport Rd Punta Gorda (33982) ***(G-15224)***
Pulsar Process Measurement Inc...850 279-4882
11451 Belcher Rd S Largo (33773) ***(G-8032)***

Pulse Displays LLC 314 971-8700
27334 Bonterra Loop Wesley Chapel (33544) ***(G-18757)***
Puma Aero Marine Inc 904 638-5888
622 Ne 14th Ave Apt 10 Fort Lauderdale (33304) ***(G-4184)***
Puma Marble Co Inc 305 758-6461
5445 Nw 2nd Ave Miami (33127) ***(G-10214)***
Punta Gorda Sun Herald, Port Charlotte *Also called Sun Coast Media Group Inc* ***(G-15000)***
Puppet Workshop Inc (PA) 305 666-2655
295 E 10th Ct Hialeah (33010) ***(G-5583)***
Puppet Workshop Inc 305 666-2655
7040 Sw 47th St Fl 2 Miami (33155) ***(G-10215)***
Pura Vida Dairy Inc 305 817-1762
3130 W 84th St U1 Hialeah (33018) ***(G-5584)***
Puradyn Filter Tech Inc 561 547-9499
2017 High Ridge Rd Boynton Beach (33426) ***(G-947)***
Puragen LLC (HQ) 561 907-5400
1601 Forum Pl Ste 1400 West Palm Beach (33401) ***(G-19010)***
Puragen LLC 760 630-5724
11300 Us Highway 1 # 203 North Palm Beach (33408) ***(G-11726)***
Puraglobe Florida LLC 813 247-1754
4420 Pendola Point Rd Tampa (33619) ***(G-18023)***
Purchasing Department, West Palm Beach *Also called Florida Crystals Corporation* ***(G-18877)***
Purchasing Dept, Doral *Also called Cylinders On Cemex Gas* ***(G-3318)***
Pure 32 LLC 813 792-9219
17633 Gunn Hwy Ste 132 Odessa (33556) ***(G-12144)***
Pure Bright Lighting LLC 954 780-8700
711 Bayshore Dr Apt 302 Fort Lauderdale (33304) ***(G-4185)***
Pure Canvas Inc 561 818-2655
4849 Lake Worth Rd Greenacres (33463) ***(G-5085)***
Pure Essential 407 732-7225
6788 Sylvan Woods Dr Sanford (32771) ***(G-16107)***
Pure Global Brands Inc (PA) 866 498-5269
500 S Australian Ave West Palm Beach (33401) ***(G-19011)***
Pure Labs LLC 561 659-2229
240 10th St 1 West Palm Beach (33401) ***(G-19012)***
Pure Lead Products, Lake Placid *Also called Heartland Metals Inc* ***(G-7488)***
Pure Life Products LLC 321 578-2060
3380 Nw 114th St Bldg C Miami (33167) ***(G-10216)***
Pure Life Soap Company, Miami *Also called Pure Life Products LLC* ***(G-10216)***
Pure Med Mobility Inc 352 366-8008
1125 W Jefferson St Brooksville (34601) ***(G-1263)***
Pure Postcards Inc 877 446-2434
1938 Byram Dr Clearwater (33755) ***(G-1854)***
Pure Solutions Inc 813 925-1098
14100 Mccormick Dr Tampa (33626) ***(G-18024)***
Pure Source LLC 305 477-8111
9750 Nw 17th St Doral (33172) ***(G-3473)***
Pure Source, The, Doral *Also called Pure Source LLC* ***(G-3473)***
Pure Water Changes Inc 407 699-2837
7775 Maslin St Windermere (34786) ***(G-19241)***
Pure Water Sulotins LLC 727 784-7400
35168 Us Highway 19 N Palm Harbor (34684) ***(G-13753)***
Pure Wave Organics Inc 321 368-7002
2861 Saint James Ln Melbourne (32935) ***(G-8915)***
Pure-Chlor Systems Florida Inc 305 437-9937
8200 Nw 33rd St Ste 109 Tampa (33614) ***(G-18025)***
Purecoat International LLC (PA) 561 844-0100
3301 Elec Way Ste B West Palm Beach (33407) ***(G-19013)***
Purecycle Technologies Inc (PA) 877 648-3565
5950 Hazeltine National D Orlando (32822) ***(G-13100)***
Purifoy Construction LLC 850 206-2900
1425 Muscogee Rd Cantonment (32533) ***(G-1346)***
Purify Fuels Inc 949 842-6159
14113 N Cypress Cove Cir Davie (33325) ***(G-2577)***
Purina Animal Nutrition LLC 863 262-4332
2815 Drane Field Rd Lakeland (33811) ***(G-7772)***
Puritair LLC 954 281-5105
1320 Nw 65th Pl Ste 201 Fort Lauderdale (33309) ***(G-4186)***
Puromax, Port Charlotte *Also called Fshs Inc* ***(G-14982)***
Purovite Inc 305 364-5727
7347 Sw 45th St Miami (33155) ***(G-10217)***
Purox Brands Corp 305 392-0738
5801 E 10th Ave Unit 108 Hialeah (33013) ***(G-5585)***
Purple Dove 904 261-5227
474311 E State Road 200 Fernandina Beach (32034) ***(G-3747)***
Purpleglassboutique LLC 407 601-2641
6337 W Colonial Dr Orlando (32818) ***(G-13101)***
Pursuit Boats, Fort Pierce *Also called Pb Holdco LLC* ***(G-4730)***
Pusateri, Thomas J MD, Zephyrhills *Also called Pasco Vision Center* ***(G-19530)***
Put Your Name On It LLC 813 972-1460
16057 Tampa Palms Blvd W # 4 Tampa (33647) ***(G-18026)***
Putnam Paper & Packaging Inc 904 328-5101
109 Jax Ln Palatka (32177) ***(G-13491)***
Puzzle Pieces Support Servic 813 985-3232
4809 E Busch Blvd Ste 205 Tampa (33617) ***(G-18027)***
Puzzled Caterpillars Inc 904 379-9219
5230 Anisa Ct Jacksonville (32209) ***(G-6697)***
Puzzleme Now Inc 386 957-4987
2230 Hibiscus Dr Edgewater (32141) ***(G-3634)***
Pvc Spiral Supply, Tampa *Also called Marlon Inc* ***(G-17882)***
Pvc Windoors Inc 305 940-3608
1815 Ne 144th St North Miami (33181) ***(G-11652)***
Pvh Corp 850 269-0482
10746 Us Highway 98 W # 158 Miramar Beach (32550) ***(G-11068)***
PWS International 850 432-4222
5 Clarinda Ln Pensacola (32505) ***(G-14243)***
Pylon Manufacturing Corp (HQ) 800 626-4902
600 W Hillsboro Blvd # 4 Deerfield Beach (33441) ***(G-2898)***
Pyramid Imaging Inc 813 984-0125
945 E 11th Ave Tampa (33605) ***(G-18028)***
Pyramid Mouldings, Green Cove Springs *Also called Artemis Holdings LLC* ***(G-5053)***
Pyramideye Print Corp 786 663-1157
1350 W 34th St Hialeah (33012) ***(G-5586)***
Pyrolyzer LLC 561 400-1608
750 Ne Spanish River Blvd Boca Raton (33431) ***(G-677)***
Pyrotecnico of Florida LLC 352 588-5086
30435 Commerce Dr Ste 102 San Antonio (33576) ***(G-15976)***
Pyure Company Inc 561 735-3701
2055 High Ridge Rd Boynton Beach (33426) ***(G-948)***
Q & O Custom Woodwork Inc 954 391-8281
5939 Sw 23rd St West Park (33023) ***(G-19097)***
Q Industries Inc 954 689-2263
401 E Las Olas Blvd # 130 Fort Lauderdale (33301) ***(G-4187)***
Q P Consulting Inc 321 727-2442
2110 Dairy Rd Ste 102 Melbourne (32904) ***(G-8916)***
Q Plastering and Stucco Inc 239 530-1712
5422 Texas Ave Naples (34113) ***(G-11378)***
Q Sea, Tampa *Also called Ultrasonics and Magnetics* ***(G-18214)***
Q-Pac Systems Inc 229 834-2908
4010 Deerpark Blvd Elkton (32033) ***(G-3651)***
Qcab LLC 305 510-2566
281 53rd Cir Vero Bch Fl Vero Beach (32968) ***(G-18655)***
Qci 407 886-6300
2152 Sprint Blvd Apopka (32703) ***(G-175)***
Qci Britannic Inc (PA) 305 860-0102
1600 Ponce De Leon Blvd # 907 Coral Gables (33134) ***(G-2188)***
Qcms, Sarasota *Also called Quality Contract Mfg Svcs LLC* ***(G-16280)***
Qem Inc 727 545-8833
6513 116th Ave Largo (33773) ***(G-8033)***
Qgistix Inc 855 573-3872
2019 Corporate Dr Boynton Beach (33426) ***(G-949)***
Qgiv Inc 888 855-9595
53 Lake Morton Dr Lakeland (33801) ***(G-7773)***
Qlty Alumn Boat Lifts Inc 850 434-6446
2375 W Herman Ave Pensacola (32505) ***(G-14244)***
Qol Medical LLC (PA) 772 584-3640
3405 Ocean Dr Vero Beach (32963) ***(G-18656)***
Qorvo Us Inc 407 886-8860
1818 S Orange Blossom Trl Apopka (32703) ***(G-176)***
Qps Companies Inc (PA) 813 246-5525
9110 King Palm Dr Ste 101 Tampa (33619) ***(G-18029)***
Qrpetcodes.com, Land O Lakes *Also called Find A Friend LLC* ***(G-7855)***
Qsrr Corporation 305 322-9867
3126 John P Curci Dr # 4 Hallandale Beach (33009) ***(G-5205)***
Qssi, Tampa *Also called Nightscenes Inc* ***(G-17940)***
Qtm Inc 813 891-1300
300 Stevens Ave Oldsmar (34677) ***(G-12266)***
Qtronics Inc 850 267-0102
279 Santa Rosa St Santa Rosa Beach (32459) ***(G-16165)***
Quad Intl Incorporated 305 662-5959
1629 Nw 84th Ave Doral (33126) ***(G-3474)***
Quail Height Golf Club 386 752-3339
161 Sw Quail Heights Ter Lake City (32025) ***(G-7378)***
Quaker Oats Company 407 846-5926
1650 S Poinciana Blvd Kissimmee (34758) ***(G-7292)***
Qualcomm Atheros Inc 407 284-7314
5955 T G Lee Blvd Ste 600 Orlando (32822) ***(G-13102)***
Qualitel Inc 954 464-3991
2414 N Federal Hwy Hollywood (33020) ***(G-5897)***
Qualitest USA Lc 877 884-8378
401 E Las Olas Blvd Ste 1 Fort Lauderdale (33301) ***(G-4188)***
Quality 1 Appraisal Inc 786 859-4085
18831 Nw 78th Pl Hialeah (33015) ***(G-5587)***
Quality Aerospace Coatings LLC 863 619-2628
3610 Airport Rd Lakeland (33811) ***(G-7774)***
Quality Alum Boat Lifts Inc 850 434-6446
2375 W Herman Ave Pensacola (32505) ***(G-14245)***
Quality Aluminum Manufacturing 850 434-6446
2375 W Herman Ave Pensacola (32505) ***(G-14246)***
Quality Anodizing Incorporated 954 791-8711
5990 Sw 42nd Pl Davie (33314) ***(G-2578)***
Quality Arts Lcp LLC 305 735-2310
7880 W 25th Ct Hialeah (33016) ***(G-5588)***
Quality Bakery Products LLC (HQ) 954 779-3663
888 E Las Olas Blvd # 700 Fort Lauderdale (33301) ***(G-4189)***
Quality Banner Company, Ocala *Also called AMI Graphics Inc* ***(G-11873)***

ALPHABETIC

Quality Beverage Services, Tampa *Also called Dcg Enterprises LLC* ***(G-17594)***
Quality Block & Supply Inc........863 425-3070
1590 Industrial Park Rd Mulberry (33860) ***(G-11133)***
Quality Building Controls Inc........813 885-5005
10011 Williams Rd Tampa (33624) ***(G-18030)***
Quality Cabinet Recovering........941 378-1715
3316 Bay Oaks Dr Sarasota (34234) ***(G-16550)***
Quality Cabinets & Counters........239 948-5364
7869 Drew Cir Unit 1 Fort Myers (33967) ***(G-4577)***
Quality Cable & Communications, Orlando *Also called Quality Cable Contractors Inc* ***(G-13103)***
Quality Cable Contractors Inc........407 246-0606
1936 Premier Row Orlando (32809) ***(G-13103)***
Quality Carpet........727 527-1359
4420 44th St N Saint Petersburg (33714) ***(G-15895)***
Quality Carton Inc........941 921-1770
4686 Ashton Rd Sarasota (34233) ***(G-16551)***
Quality Carton of Florida, Sarasota *Also called Quality Carton Inc* ***(G-16551)***
Quality Cbinets By Stewart LLC........954 624-6877
3120 Sw 19th St Ste 160 Hallandale Beach (33009) ***(G-5206)***
Quality Cmpnents Tampa Bay LLC........727 623-4909
6801 114th Ave Largo (33773) ***(G-8034)***
Quality Components & Assembly........954 792-5151
440 Nw 27th Ave Fort Lauderdale (33311) ***(G-4190)***
Quality Contract Mfg Svcs LLC........941 355-7787
1905 72nd Dr E Sarasota (34243) ***(G-16280)***
Quality Creations Inc........727 571-4332
10550 47th St N Clearwater (33762) ***(G-1855)***
Quality Custom Cabinet Design........352 728-4292
2215 Griffin Rd Leesburg (34748) ***(G-8169)***
Quality Door Service LLC........904 588-4817
4223 Key Largo Dr Jacksonville (32218) ***(G-6698)***
Quality Driven........941 923-3322
4023 Sawyer Rd Unit 216 Sarasota (34233) ***(G-16552)***
Quality Enclosures, Sarasota *Also called Sarasota Shower Door Company* ***(G-16580)***
Quality Engineered Products Co........813 885-1693
4506 Quality Ln Tampa (33634) ***(G-18031)***
Quality Fabrication Mch Works, Lake City *Also called Quality Industries America Inc* ***(G-7380)***
Quality Fbrction Mch Works Inc........386 755-0220
3631 E Us Highway 90 Lake City (32055) ***(G-7379)***
Quality Finishers Inc........954 782-3073
640 Ne 26th Ct Pompano Beach (33064) ***(G-14822)***
Quality Forms & Printing Co........407 671-8026
3071 Autumn Ct Winter Park (32792) ***(G-19434)***
Quality Images, Jacksonville *Also called Impact Design Group Inc* ***(G-6490)***
Quality Industrial Chem Inc........727 573-5760
3161 118th Ave N Saint Petersburg (33716) ***(G-15896)***
Quality Industries America Inc (PA)........386 755-0220
3631 E Us Highway 90 Lake City (32055) ***(G-7380)***
Quality Life Publishing Co........239 513-9907
6210 Shirley St Ste 112 Naples (34109) ***(G-11379)***
Quality Machine Service Inc........610 554-3917
2199 Fernwood St Port Charlotte (33948) ***(G-14995)***
Quality Manufacturing Svcs Inc........407 531-6000
400 Caring Dr Ste 1010 Lake Mary (32746) ***(G-7447)***
Quality Marine Air Refrig........954 560-0084
248 Sw 31st St Fort Lauderdale (33315) ***(G-4191)***
Quality Metal Fabricators Inc........813 831-7320
2610 E 5th Ave Tampa (33605) ***(G-18032)***
Quality Metal Works, Plant City *Also called Telese Properties Inc* ***(G-14471)***
Quality Metal Works, Plant City *Also called Telese Inc* ***(G-14470)***
Quality Metal Worx........863 353-6638
1306 Melbourne Ave Haines City (33844) ***(G-5147)***
Quality Mills, Lake City *Also called Grizzly Manufacturing Inc* ***(G-7360)***
Quality Molds USA Inc........321 632-6066
2402 Cherbourg Rd Cocoa (32926) ***(G-2044)***
Quality Neon Sign Company (PA)........904 268-4681
5300 Shad Rd Jacksonville (32257) ***(G-6699)***
Quality Petroleum Corp........863 635-6708
301 Hwy 630 E Frostproof (33843) ***(G-4863)***
Quality Powder Coating Inc........941 378-0051
2025 Porter Lake Dr F Sarasota (34240) ***(G-16553)***
Quality Precast & Company........407 877-1000
416 E Bay St Winter Garden (34787) ***(G-19282)***
Quality Precision Pdts Co Inc........305 885-4596
678 W 27th St Hialeah (33010) ***(G-5589)***
Quality Printing Inc........386 255-1565
705 W Intl Speedway Blvd Daytona Beach (32114) ***(G-2701)***
Quality Railings Miami Corp........786 400-0462
460 W 18th St Hialeah (33010) ***(G-5590)***
Quality Ready Mix Inc (PA)........561 833-5555
1501 Belvedere Rd West Palm Beach (33406) ***(G-19014)***
Quality Rescreening........941 625-9765
17221 Alico Center Rd # 2 Fort Myers (33967) ***(G-4578)***
Quality Screen Enclosure LLC........954 226-1980
3800 Hillcrest Dr Apt 210 Hollywood (33021) ***(G-5898)***
Quality Shavings South Florida........561 433-9955
10191 Lantana Rd Lake Worth (33449) ***(G-7584)***
Quality Signs........786 261-6242
2736 W 54th St Hialeah (33016) ***(G-5591)***
Quality Socket Screw Mfg Corp........941 475-9585
2790 Worth Ave Englewood (34224) ***(G-3665)***
Quality Software LLC........561 714-2314
55 Se 2nd Ave 1 Delray Beach (33444) ***(G-3131)***
Quality Steel Fabricators Inc........813 247-7110
4544 Hartford St Tampa (33619) ***(G-18033)***
Quality Stones R US LLC........904 551-5619
10475 Fortune Pkwy St Jacksonville (32256) ***(G-6700)***
Quality Vaults Inc (PA)........407 656-8781
751 S Bluford Ave Ocoee (34761) ***(G-12089)***
Quality Wood Machine Inc........305 221-0218
8410 Sw 33rd Ter Miami (33155) ***(G-10218)***
Qualitysat Corp........305 232-4211
13355 Sw 135th Ave Miami (33186) ***(G-10219)***
Quantachrome Instruments, Boynton Beach *Also called Anton Paar Quantatec Inc* ***(G-877)***
Quantem Fbo Group Kssimmee LLC........407 846-8001
3950 Merlin Dr Kissimmee (34741) ***(G-7293)***
Quantena Energy Productgs........352 332-6630
1720 Sw 78th St Gainesville (32607) ***(G-4985)***
Quantoro Publishing, Miami *Also called Quanturo Publishing Inc* ***(G-10223)***
Quantum Assets LLC........786 484-1187
638 Nw 11th St Miami (33136) ***(G-10220)***
Quantum Creations LLC........786 233-6769
15705 Nw 13th Ave Miami Gardens (33169) ***(G-10752)***
Quantum Development LLC........954 587-4205
3685 Sw 30th Ave Fort Lauderdale (33312) ***(G-4192)***
Quantum Envmtl Slutions St Inc........800 975-8721
2699 Stirling Rd Ste C Fort Lauderdale (33312) ***(G-4193)***
Quantum Leap Winery, Orlando *Also called JD Wine Concepts LLC* ***(G-12854)***
Quantum Limit Partners LLC (PA)........954 849-3720
1037 Se 2nd Ct Fort Lauderdale (33301) ***(G-4194)***
Quantum Pharmaceuticals LLC........321 724-0625
429 Riverview Ln Melbourne Beach (32951) ***(G-8982)***
Quantum Reflex Integration Inc........352 228-0766
716 Sw Kings Bay Dr Crystal River (34429) ***(G-2380)***
Quantum Safety Services Inc........786 420-0735
20280 Sw 190th St Miami (33187) ***(G-10221)***
Quantum Servicing Corporation........305 229-6675
790 Nw 107th Ave Ste 400 Miami (33172) ***(G-10222)***
Quantum Spatial Inc (HQ)........920 457-3631
10033 Dr Mrtn Lther King Saint Petersburg (33716) ***(G-15897)***
Quantum Storage Systems, Miami *Also called Graduate Plastics Inc* ***(G-9652)***
Quantum Storage Systems........305 687-0405
4820 Nw 128th St Opa Locka (33054) ***(G-12352)***
Quantum Technology Inc........407 333-9348
108 Commerce St Ste 101 Lake Mary (32746) ***(G-7448)***
Quantum-L/S Dna Labs Intl........407 246-0484
511 Shady Lane Dr Orlando (32804) ***(G-13104)***
Quantumflo Inc........407 807-7050
2664 Jewett Ln Sanford (32771) ***(G-16108)***
Quanturo Publishing Inc........305 373-3700
4141 Ne 2nd Ave Ste 202 Miami (33137) ***(G-10223)***
Quartz Unlimited Inc........561 720-7460
2255 Glades Rd Ste 324 Boca Raton (33431) ***(G-678)***
Quartz Unlimited LLC........561 306-1243
5030 Champion Blvd Boca Raton (33496) ***(G-679)***
Quartzo LLC........888 813-3442
5115 Shadowlawn Ave Tampa (33610) ***(G-18034)***
Quasar Light Therapy, Sarasota *Also called Silver Bay LLC* ***(G-16296)***
Queen B Hair Collection LLC........954 393-2791
17111 Nw 10th Ct Miami (33169) ***(G-10224)***
Queen Craft, Panama City *Also called Marine Transportation Svcs Inc* ***(G-13927)***
Quest Controls Inc (PA)........941 729-4799
208 9th Street Dr W Palmetto (34221) ***(G-13820)***
Quest Desk Solutions, Tampa *Also called Koho Software Inc* ***(G-17829)***
Quest Drape, Sunrise *Also called Bkbl Holdings Ltd* ***(G-17098)***
Quest Drape........407 888-8164
10003 Satellite Blvd # 210 Orlando (32837) ***(G-13105)***
Quest Environmental Products........321 984-4423
6928 Sonny Dale Dr Ste A Melbourne (32904) ***(G-8917)***
Quest International Inc........305 592-6991
8127 Nw 29th St Miami (33122) ***(G-10225)***
Quest Manufacturing Corp........305 513-8583
11200 Nw 138th St Medley (33178) ***(G-8713)***
Queteq, Sanford *Also called Watts Technologies LLC* ***(G-16135)***
Queuelogix LLC........404 721-3928
1200 E Las Olas Blvd # 201 Fort Lauderdale (33301) ***(G-4195)***
Quiantum Creative Group Inc........954 557-6777
7935 East Dr North Bay Village (33141) ***(G-11595)***
Quick Advertising Inc........407 774-0003
3030 E Semrn Blvd Ste 236 Apopka (32703) ***(G-177)***
Quick Cans Inc........407 415-1361
7034 Arbor Ct Winter Park (32792) ***(G-19435)***
Quick Lift Inc........305 471-0147
8491 Nw 54th St Doral (33166) ***(G-3475)***
Quick Press........305 418-8744
2600 Nw 87th Ave Ste 16 Doral (33172) ***(G-3476)***

Quick Print 954 974-2820
1231 S Powerline Rd Pompano Beach (33069) *(G-14823)*
Quick Print Center, Hialeah *Also called Lufemor Inc (G-5490)*
Quick Prints LLC 954 526-9013
3145 Davie Blvd Fort Lauderdale (33312) *(G-4196)*
Quick Prints LLC 954 594-9415
8201 Peters Rd Ste 1000 Plantation (33324) *(G-14543)*
Quick Protective Systems Inc 772 220-3315
421 Sw California Ave # 101 Stuart (34994) *(G-16993)*
Quick Signs 904 310-1010
4425 Us Highway 1 S # 101 Saint Augustine (32086) *(G-15592)*
Quick-Med Technologies Inc 352 379-0611
902 Nw 4th St Gainesville (32601) *(G-4986)*
Quickload Custom Built Trlrs, Saint Petersburg *Also called J & J Marine Service Inc (G-15820)*
Quickprint Business Center, Punta Gorda *Also called Blackwell Family Corporation (G-15199)*
Quickprint Line 561 740-9930
2015 Corporate Dr Boynton Beach (33426) *(G-950)*
Quickseries Publishing Inc 954 584-1606
5100 Nw 33rd Ave Ste 247 Fort Lauderdale (33309) *(G-4197)*
Quicksilver Prtg & Copying Inc 813 888-6811
3816a W Sligh Ave Tampa (33614) *(G-18035)*
Quiet Flex 352 429-3286
7730 American Way Groveland (34736) *(G-5106)*
Quiet Technology Aerospace Inc 305 687-9808
4100 N 29th Ter Hollywood (33020) *(G-5899)*
Quik Shred 561 841-1822
1070 E Indiantown Rd # 308 Jupiter (33477) *(G-7101)*
Quik Tek Inc 772 501-3471
2046 Treasure Coast Plz Vero Beach (32960) *(G-18657)*
Quikrete Companies LLC 305 681-8664
3700 Nw 123rd St Miami (33167) *(G-10226)*
Quikrete Companies LLC 863 665-5127
4230 Maine Ave Lakeland (33801) *(G-7775)*
Quirantes Orthopedics Inc 305 261-1382
5840 W Flagler St Miami (33144) *(G-10227)*
Quorum Marine & Elec Inc 772 220-0038
2951 Se Dominica Ter Stuart (34997) *(G-16994)*
Qwikpik Golf LLC 407 505-5546
10096 Tavistock Rd Orlando (32827) *(G-13106)*
R & A Industries Inc 352 307-6655
306 Aulin Ave Oviedo (32765) *(G-13455)*
R & A Performance Fuel Inc 954 237-9824
12951 Nw 1st St Pembroke Pines (33028) *(G-14055)*
R & A Power Graphics Inc 407 898-5770
5000 E Colonial Dr Orlando (32803) *(G-13107)*
R & C Sales & Mfg Inc 904 824-2223
18 Hargrove Grade Ste 101 Palm Coast (32137) *(G-13707)*
R & D Machine and Engrg Inc 813 891-9109
130 Scarlet Blvd Oldsmar (34677) *(G-12267)*
R & D Sleeves Llc (PA) 407 886-9010
520 W Orange Blossom Trl Apopka (32712) *(G-178)*
R & D Surf 321 636-4456
488 Gus Hipp Blvd Rockledge (32955) *(G-15442)*
R & H Air Coatings Inc 863 559-6021
524 Water Oak Ct Fort Meade (33841) *(G-4339)*
R & H Platting, Oakland Park *Also called Felix Reynoso (G-11805)*
R & J Custom Cabinets Inc 813 871-5779
3907 W Cayuga St Tampa (33614) *(G-18036)*
R & J Enterprises, Green Cove Springs *Also called Shark Tooth Enterprises Inc (G-5071)*
R & J Mfg of Gainesville 352 375-3130
2001 Ne 31st Ave Gainesville (32609) *(G-4987)*
R & K Builders, Pensacola *Also called R & K Portable Buildings (G-14247)*
R & K Buildings Inc 850 995-9525
4213 Avalon Blvd Milton (32583) *(G-10939)*
R & K Marketing Inc 904 745-0022
11657 Central Pkwy # 401 Jacksonville (32224) *(G-6701)*
R & K Portable Builders, Milton *Also called R & K Buildings Inc (G-10939)*
R & K Portable Buildings 850 857-7899
8120 Pensacola Blvd Pensacola (32534) *(G-14247)*
R & K Welding and Fabrication 863 422-8728
4709 Crump Rd Lake Hamilton (33851) *(G-7392)*
R & L Manufacturing Inc 772 770-9300
5021 41st St Unit 2 Vero Beach (32967) *(G-18658)*
R & R American Corporation (PA) 786 497-8898
7222 Nw 56th St Miami (33166) *(G-10228)*
R & R Designer Cabinets Inc 954 735-6435
3063 Nw 23rd Way Oakland Park (33311) *(G-11834)*
R & R Door and Trim Inc 561 844-5496
8111 Garden Rd Ste J West Palm Beach (33404) *(G-19015)*
R & R Doors Corp 305 982-8106
1660 W 33rd Pl Hialeah (33012) *(G-5592)*
R & R Mica Works Inc 305 231-1887
6541 Lake Blue Dr Miami Lakes (33014) *(G-10847)*
R & R Stone Industries Inc 888 999-4921
7941 Nw 67th St Miami (33166) *(G-10229)*
R & S Metalworks & Co LLC 772 466-3303
5690 Carlton Rd Port Saint Lucie (34987) *(G-15132)*
R & S Snacks LLC 954 839-5482
1660 Sw Buttercup Ave Port Saint Lucie (34953) *(G-15133)*
R & W Distributors, Bonita Springs *Also called R&W Distributors Inc (G-851)*
R & Y Automotive AC Cmpsr 305 919-9232
15315 Ne 21st Ave North Miami Beach (33162) *(G-11700)*
R & Y Automotive AC Cmpsr (PA) 305 947-1173
15315 Ne 21st Ave North Miami Beach (33162) *(G-11701)*
R & Z Ventures Inc 954 532-7938
1300 Sw 1st Ct Pompano Beach (33069) *(G-14824)*
R and D Kitchen Cabinets Corp 305 305-2390
14863 Sw 139th St Miami (33196) *(G-10230)*
R and R Brokerage Co 305 592-4329
7740 Nw 55th St Doral (33166) *(G-3477)*
R and R Machine Shop 941 621-8143
6601 Taylor Rd Punta Gorda (33950) *(G-15225)*
R and R Rebar, Winter Garden *Also called Quality Precast & Company (G-19282)*
R B Casting Inc 407 648-2005
637 22nd St Orlando (32805) *(G-13108)*
R C R Manufacturing Inc 786 499-9245
9279 Sw 38th St Miami (33165) *(G-10231)*
R C Specialized International 407 681-5905
1436 State Road 436 Casselberry (32707) *(G-1516)*
R Dorian Millworks LLC 561 863-9125
2361 Vista Pkwy Ste 7 West Palm Beach (33411) *(G-19016)*
R F Laboratories Inc 920 564-2700
31355 Bear Pond Dr # 46 Sorrento (32776) *(G-16792)*
R G Management Inc 407 889-3100
3640 Princeton Oaks St Orlando (32808) *(G-13109)*
R J Dougherty Associates LLC 386 409-2202
544 Air Park Rd Edgewater (32132) *(G-3635)*
R J Marine Group Inc 772 232-6590
619 Nw Baker Rd Stuart (34994) *(G-16995)*
R J Reynolds Tobacco Company 772 873-6955
2687 Sw Domina Rd Port Saint Lucie (34953) *(G-15134)*
R K Constructors of Centl Fla 407 222-5376
4630 S Kirkman Rd Ste 221 Orlando (32811) *(G-13110)*
R K L Enterprises of Pensacola 850 432-2335
3740 N Pace Blvd Pensacola (32505) *(G-14248)*
R M A, Fort Myers *Also called Resource Management Associates (G-4582)*
R M Equipment Inc 305 477-9312
6975 Nw 43rd St Miami (33166) *(G-10232)*
R P M Industries Inc 315 255-1105
8505 Se Gulfstream Pl Hobe Sound (33455) *(G-5726)*
R P Welding, Navarre *Also called Real Pro Welding Inc (G-11473)*
R R H Inc 954 966-1209
5900 Johnson St Hollywood (33021) *(G-5900)*
R S Apparel Inc 305 599-4939
8454 Nw 58th St Doral (33166) *(G-3478)*
R S Design Inc 727 525-8292
6351 46th St N Pinellas Park (33781) *(G-14383)*
R S S Partners Inc 904 241-6144
1301 1st St S Apt 1501 Jacksonville Beach (32250) *(G-6955)*
R Smith Printing Inc 518 827-7700
4820 Joseph St Hastings (32145) *(G-5229)*
R T Publishing Inc 904 886-4919
12443 San Jose Blvd # 403 Jacksonville (32223) *(G-6702)*
R Townsend Rescreens Inc 239 244-4759
30390 Cedar Rd Punta Gorda (33982) *(G-15226)*
R Y D Enterprises Inc 305 655-1045
20815 Ne 16th Ave Ste B7 Miami (33179) *(G-10233)*
R&D, Oldsmar *Also called R & D Machine and Engrg Inc (G-12267)*
R&K Mehall Inc 727 781-8780
211 Whisper Lake Rd Palm Harbor (34683) *(G-13754)*
R&R Assembly Services 407 797-8325
448 N Dixie Ave Titusville (32796) *(G-18454)*
R&R Racing Engines, Punta Gorda *Also called R and R Machine Shop (G-15225)*
R&S Itrnational Inv Group LLC 305 576-3000
571 Nw 29th St Miami (33127) *(G-10234)*
R&W Distributors Inc 239 948-5735
10919 Enterprise Ave Bonita Springs (34135) *(G-851)*
R-Da Trading LLC 954 278-6983
2893 Executive Park Dr Weston (33331) *(G-19162)*
R-Lines LLC 954 457-7777
201 Ansin Blvd Hallandale Beach (33009) *(G-5207)*
R.S.T., Coral Gables *Also called Radiation Shield Tech Inc (G-2189)*
R4 Integration Inc 850 226-6913
45 Beal Pkwy Ne Fort Walton Beach (32548) *(G-4825)*
Ra Co AMO Inc 561 626-7232
4100 Burns Rd Palm Beach Gardens (33410) *(G-13620)*
Ra Printing Inc 904 733-5578
4185 Sunbeam Rd Ste 100 Jacksonville (32257) *(G-6703)*
Raaw, Coral Gables *Also called Raw Foods International Llc (G-2190)*
Raber Industries Inc 239 728-5527
2190 Sebastian Ct Alva (33920) *(G-90)*
Rabud Inc 954 925-4199
110 N Bryan Rd Dania (33004) *(G-2457)*
Race Performance Machine Shop 813 443-8225
4707 N Lois Ave Tampa (33614) *(G-18037)*

ALPHABETIC

Race Way 6800.....904 329-2961
1651 S 6th St Macclenny (32063) ***(G-8444)***
Racestar Manufacturing, Altamonte Springs *Also called Super Lite Aluminum Products* ***(G-78)***
Raceway.....850 453-9437
3530 Barrancas Ave Pensacola (32507) ***(G-14249)***
Raceway Electric LLC.....772 260-6530
208 Sw Aubudon Ave Port Saint Lucie (34984) ***(G-15135)***
Raceway Towing LLC.....754 244-9597
480 Ne 35th Ct Unit 4 Oakland Park (33334) ***(G-11835)***
Rachel Ally.....727 804-9596
9437 Debbie Ln Hudson (34669) ***(G-6036)***
Racing Shell Covers LLC.....732 236-0435
3899 Mannix Dr Ste 409 Naples (34114) ***(G-11380)***
Rack It Truck Racks.....800 354-1900
30904 State Road 52 San Antonio (33576) ***(G-15977)***
RAD Wear Inc.....352 727-4498
2135 Nw 40th Ter Ste A Gainesville (32605) ***(G-4988)***
Radchen USA Inc.....786 270-7628
8389 Nw 115th Ct Doral (33178) ***(G-3479)***
Radial Inc.....561 737-5151
1903 S Congress Ave # 460 Boynton Beach (33426) ***(G-951)***
Radiance Radiology Inc.....727 934-5500
37566 Us Highway 19 N Palm Harbor (34684) ***(G-13755)***
Radiant Power Corp (HQ).....941 739-3200
7135 16th St E Ste 101 Sarasota (34243) ***(G-16281)***
Radiant Power Idc LLC.....760 945-0230
7135 16th St E Ste 101 Sarasota (34243) ***(G-16282)***
Radiant Printing, Lakeland *Also called William Burns* ***(G-7835)***
Radiant-Seacom Repairs Corp.....941 739-3200
7135 16th St E Ste 101 Sarasota (34243) ***(G-16283)***
Radiation Shield Tech Inc.....866 733-6766
6 Aragon Ave Coral Gables (33134) ***(G-2189)***
Radica LLC.....954 383-0089
10471 Nw 36th St Doral (33178) ***(G-3480)***
Radio OEM Inc.....920 564-6622
31355 State Road 46 Sorrento (32776) ***(G-16793)***
Radio Paz, Miami *Also called Pax Catholic Communications* ***(G-10146)***
Radiotronics Inc.....772 600-7574
1315 Sw Commerce Way Stuart (34997) ***(G-16996)***
Radixx Solutions Intl Inc (HQ).....407 856-9009
20 N Orange Ave Ste 150 Orlando (32801) ***(G-13111)***
Radwag USA LLC.....305 651-3522
19599 Ne 10th Ave Ste E North Miami Beach (33179) ***(G-11702)***
Rae Launo Corporation.....813 242-4281
2606 Durant Oaks Dr Valrico (33596) ***(G-18524)***
Rae Services Inc.....727 480-9940
1700 Arabian Ln Palm Harbor (34685) ***(G-13756)***
Rafab Spcialty Fabrication Inc.....407 422-3750
2116 W Central Blvd Orlando (32805) ***(G-13112)***
Rafael Moreaun, Miami *Also called Amber Jewelers Corp* ***(G-9135)***
Rafaella, Doral *Also called Supreme International LLC* ***(G-3519)***
Rafferty Holdings LLC.....352 248-0906
2722 Nw 74th Pl Gainesville (32653) ***(G-4989)***
Rafferty Machine and Tool, Gainesville *Also called Rafferty Holdings LLC* ***(G-4989)***
Rafi Publications LLC.....954 384-4166
885 Crestview Cir Weston (33327) ***(G-19163)***
Ragalta, Hallandale Beach *Also called Kasulik II LLC* ***(G-5195)***
Ragz.....850 656-1223
2827 Industrial Plaza Dr Tallahassee (32301) ***(G-17313)***
Rail Scale Inc.....904 302-5154
111 Nature Walk Pkwy # 105 Saint Augustine (32092) ***(G-15593)***
Railings Plus Inc.....386 437-4501
1150 State Rd 11 Ste 201 Bunnell (32110) ***(G-1304)***
Railtec Constructions Company.....410 795-0712
4949 N Hwy A1a Apt 182 Hutchinson Island (34949) ***(G-6047)***
Railtech Construction, Hutchinson Island *Also called Railtec Constructions Company* ***(G-6047)***
Raimonda Investment Group Inc.....352 347-8899
5911 Se Hames Rd Belleview (34420) ***(G-375)***
Rainbow Cabinets, Ocala *Also called Michigan Avenue Bridge Inc* ***(G-12000)***
Rainbow Cabinets Inc.....352 236-4044
4690 Ne 35th St Ocala (34479) ***(G-12035)***
Rainbow Eb Buenavista.....305 982-8153
8554 Sw 8th St Miami (33144) ***(G-10235)***
Rainbow Ink Products Inc.....954 252-6030
15640 Lancelot Ct Davie (33331) ***(G-2579)***
Rainbow Irrigation, Miami Lakes *Also called Rainbow Manufacturing Company* ***(G-10848)***
Rainbow Lght Ntrtnal Systems I (HQ).....954 233-3300
1301 Sawgrs Corp Pkwy Sunrise (33323) ***(G-17167)***
Rainbow Manufacturing Company.....305 477-5541
16541 Nw 84th Ave Miami Lakes (33016) ***(G-10848)***
Rainbow Pool Supply Inc.....407 324-9616
2920 W Airport Blvd Sanford (32771) ***(G-16109)***
Rainbow Precision Mfg Corp.....561 691-1658
4371 Northlake Blvd Palm Beach Gardens (33410) ***(G-13621)***
Rainbow Printing Inc.....561 364-9000
3300 S Congress Ave # 12 Boynton Beach (33426) ***(G-952)***
Rainbow Storage.....386 362-1171
7434 County Road 795 Live Oak (32060) ***(G-8238)***
Rainbows End.....727 733-8572
1450 Wetherington Way Palm Harbor (34683) ***(G-13757)***
Rainbows End Quilt Shoppe, Palm Harbor *Also called Rainbows End* ***(G-13757)***
Raintree Graphics, Jacksonville *Also called All-Star Sales Inc* ***(G-6137)***
Rally Leather & More LLC.....516 643-8572
1066 Chelsea Way Port Orange (32129) ***(G-15030)***
Rally Manufacturing Inc.....305 628-2886
7200 Nw 19th St Ste 308 Miami (33126) ***(G-10236)***
Rally Point Publications LLC (PA).....863 221-6304
234 Ruby Lake Ln Winter Haven (33884) ***(G-19351)***
Ralph & Llerena Pallets Inc.....305 446-2651
495 E 47th St Hialeah (33013) ***(G-5593)***
Ralph Santore & Sons Inc.....386 437-2242
2546 County Road 305 Bunnell (32110) ***(G-1305)***
Raltron Electronics, Doral *Also called Rami Technology USA LLC* ***(G-3481)***
Ram Investments South Fla Inc (PA).....305 759-6419
11102 Nw South River Dr Medley (33178) ***(G-8714)***
Ram Sales LLC.....844 726-6382
7400 Nw 37th Ave Miami (33147) ***(G-10237)***
Ram Steel Framing, Miami *Also called Ram Sales LLC* ***(G-10237)***
Ram-Lin, Orlando *Also called Central Florida Cstm Trlrs Inc* ***(G-12566)***
Ramac Inc.....813 962-2793
16503 Cayman Dr Tampa (33624) ***(G-18038)***
Rami Technology USA LLC (PA).....305 593-6033
10400 Nw 33rd St Ste 290 Doral (33172) ***(G-3481)***
Rammo, Destin *Also called Go Green Marine Inc* ***(G-3191)***
Ramos Woodwork LLC.....954 861-7679
1955 Sw 15th Pl Deerfield Beach (33442) ***(G-2899)***
Rampell Software.....561 628-5102
122 N County Rd Palm Beach (33480) ***(G-13561)***
Rampmaster Inc.....305 691-9090
11098 Biscayne Blvd # 401 Miami (33161) ***(G-10238)***
Ramsay Marine Services LLC.....561 881-1234
999 W 17th St Ste 1 Riviera Beach (33404) ***(G-15368)***
Ramseys Printing & Office Pdts.....850 227-7468
209 Reid Ave Port Saint Joe (32456) ***(G-15082)***
Ramstar Corporation.....561 499-8488
5304 Ventura Dr Delray Beach (33484) ***(G-3132)***
Rancheritos.....561 479-0046
8903 Glades Rd Ste A10 Boca Raton (33434) ***(G-680)***
Rand & London LLC.....727 363-0800
279 104th Ave Treasure Island (33706) ***(G-18477)***
Rand M Rawls.....904 382-4844
4495 Glen Kernan Pkwy E Jacksonville (32224) ***(G-6704)***
Rand Search Light Advertising.....954 476-7620
11330 Sw 17th St Davie (33325) ***(G-2580)***
Rand Title Corporation.....407 622-7263
400 N New York Ave Winter Park (32789) ***(G-19436)***
Randall Birge.....850 373-6131
2579 Lilly Dr Bonifay (32425) ***(G-807)***
Randazza Enterprises Inc.....813 677-0041
8824 Van Fleet Rd Riverview (33578) ***(G-15279)***
Randel L Rdriguez Coatings LLC.....386 308-8120
1227 David Dr Daytona Beach (32117) ***(G-2702)***
Randolph Cnstr Group Inc.....954 276-2889
1191 N Federal Hwy Ste 1 Delray Beach (33483) ***(G-3133)***
Randy Morris Logging Inc.....850 773-9010
4259 Highway 77 Chipley (32428) ***(G-1545)***
Randy Wheeler.....850 997-1248
1560 Spring Hollow Dr Monticello (32344) ***(G-11081)***
Ranger Associates Inc.....407 869-0024
688 Florida Central Pkwy Longwood (32750) ***(G-8329)***
Ranger Prtg & Promotional Pdts, Longwood *Also called Ranger Associates Inc* ***(G-8329)***
Rangevideo Laap.....404 421-2574
15101 Ne 21st Ave North Miami Beach (33162) ***(G-11703)***
Rankine-Hinman Mfg Co.....904 808-0404
6980 Us Highway 1 N # 108 Saint Augustine (32095) ***(G-15594)***
Ranorex Inc.....727 835-5570
28050 Us Highway 19 N # 303 Clearwater (33761) ***(G-1856)***
Rap Snacks Inc.....305 926-9594
150 Se 2nd Ave Ph 6 Miami (33131) ***(G-10239)***
Rapha Pharmaceuticals Inc.....727 946-9444
7208 W Sand Lake Rd Orlando (32819) ***(G-13113)***
Rapid Composites LLC.....941 322-6647
2216 72nd Dr E Sarasota (34243) ***(G-16284)***
Rapid Genomics LLC.....352 213-4741
5 W Forsyth St Ste 200 Jacksonville (32202) ***(G-6705)***
Rapid Graphix Inc.....941 639-2043
10251 Tamiami Trl Punta Gorda (33950) ***(G-15227)***
Rapid Industries Inc.....772 287-0651
3100 Se Waaler St Stuart (34997) ***(G-16997)***
Rapid Metal Products Inc.....863 701-0058
4257 Holden Rd Lakeland (33811) ***(G-7776)***
Rapid Press, Tallahassee *Also called Rapid Rater Company* ***(G-17314)***
Rapid Print, Jacksonville *Also called Professnal Reproduction of Jax* ***(G-6691)***
Rapid Print Southwest Fla Inc.....239 590-9797
12244 Treeline Ave Ste 4 Fort Myers (33913) ***(G-4579)***

Rapid Printer Solutions..........954 769-9553
851 Eller Dr Fort Lauderdale (33316) *(G-4198)*
Rapid Rater Company..........850 893-7346
3626 Cagney Dr Tallahassee (32309) *(G-17314)*
Rapid Reproductions LLC..........607 843-2221
108 Seagrape Rd Melbourne Beach (32951) *(G-8983)*
Rapid Response..........407 774-9877
250 Altmnte Commerce 10 Altamonte Springs (32714) *(G-69)*
Rapid Signs and T Shirts..........786 486-2804
27466 S Dixie Hwy Homestead (33032) *(G-5989)*
Rapid Switch Systems LLC..........941 720-7380
4601 15th St E Bradenton (34203) *(G-1103)*
Rapidspoolindustries Inc..........954 850-5300
3150 Sw 148th Ave Davie (33331) *(G-2581)*
Raptor Wear Products USA Inc..........786 972-0326
7842 Nw 71st St Miami (33166) *(G-10240)*
Rar Industries LLC..........561 213-7876
9558 Equus Cir Boynton Beach (33472) *(G-953)*
RARe Cabinets Inc..........407 415-3730
613 Majorca Ave Altamonte Springs (32714) *(G-70)*
Ras Concrete Construction Inc..........239 775-3709
5501 Cynthia Ln Naples (34112) *(G-11381)*
Raskin Industries LLC..........561 997-6658
710 S Powerline Rd Ste G Deerfield Beach (33442) *(G-2900)*
Rass Fast Pallet Inc..........786 877-2854
4214 Nw 11th Pl Miami (33127) *(G-10241)*
Rat Trap Bait Company Inc..........863 967-2148
106 Adams St Auburndale (33823) *(G-251)*
Ravago Americas LLC (HQ)..........407 773-7777
1900 Smmit Twr Blvd Ste 9 Orlando (32810) *(G-13114)*
Ravago Holdings America Inc (HQ)..........407 875-9595
1900 Smmit Twr Blvd Ste 9 Orlando (32810) *(G-13115)*
Rave LLC (HQ)..........561 330-0411
430 S Congress Ave Ste 7 Delray Beach (33445) *(G-3134)*
Raven Forest Operating LLC..........727 497-2727
13014 N Dale Mbry Hwy # 736 Tampa (33618) *(G-18039)*
Ravenswood Import Export Ltd L..........863 800-0210
204 S Main Ave Ste 5 Lake Placid (33852) *(G-7494)*
Ravic Technologies LLC..........954 237-3241
7939 Nw 84th St Ste 101 Medley (33166) *(G-8715)*
Raw Energy Materials Corp..........954 270-9000
170 Se 13th St Pompano Beach (33060) *(G-14825)*
Raw Foods International Llc..........305 856-1991
2600 S Douglas Rd Ste 410 Coral Gables (33134) *(G-2190)*
Ray Eaton Yacht Service Inc..........954 583-8762
2311 Sw 33rd Ter Fort Lauderdale (33312) *(G-4199)*
Ray Electric Outboards Inc..........239 574-1948
908 Ne 24th Ln Unit 6 Cape Coral (33909) *(G-1459)*
Ray Graphics Inc..........863 325-0911
1895 Executive Rd Winter Haven (33884) *(G-19352)*
Ray Machine Inc..........850 784-1116
3711 N Highway 231 Panama City (32404) *(G-13943)*
Raygraphics, Winter Haven *Also called Ray Graphics Inc* *(G-19352)*
Raymond Newkirk..........772 359-0237
920 Angle Rd Fort Pierce (34947) *(G-4737)*
Raynetcrm LLC..........813 489-9565
121 Ginger Rd Venice (34293) *(G-18568)*
Rayonier A M Products Inc (HQ)..........904 357-9100
1301 Riverplace Blvd Jacksonville (32207) *(G-6706)*
Rayonier Advanced Materials, Jacksonville *Also called Rayonier AM Sales and Tech Inc* *(G-6708)*
Rayonier Advanced Mtls Inc (PA)..........904 357-4600
1301 Riverplace Blvd # 23 Jacksonville (32207) *(G-6707)*
Rayonier AM Sales and Tech Inc (HQ)..........904 357-4600
1301 Riverplace Blvd # 23 Jacksonville (32207) *(G-6708)*
Rayonier Inc..........904 277-1343
1 Rayonier Way Yulee (32097) *(G-19499)*
Rayovac Corp..........727 393-0966
7636 91st St Largo (33777) *(G-8035)*
Rays Pallets, Fort Pierce *Also called Raymond Newkirk* *(G-4737)*
Raytash Inc (PA)..........561 347-8863
1420 Sw 1st St Boca Raton (33486) *(G-681)*
Raytheon Company..........850 882-8015
1003 N 2nd St Bldg 130 Eglin Afb (32542) *(G-3647)*
Raytheon Company..........850 664-7993
91 Hill Ave Nw Ste 201 Fort Walton Beach (32548) *(G-4826)*
Raytheon Company..........310 647-9438
7887 Bryan Dairy Rd # 110 Largo (33777) *(G-8036)*
Raytheon Company..........850 286-6343
1279 Florida Ave Tyndall Afb (32403) *(G-18494)*
Raytheon Company..........727 768-8468
7887 Bryan Dairy Rd # 110 Largo (33777) *(G-8037)*
Raytheon Company..........310 647-9438
7401 22nd Ave N Bldg D Saint Petersburg (33710) *(G-15898)*
Raytheon Company..........321 235-6682
13501 Ingenuity Dr # 100 Orlando (32826) *(G-13116)*
Raytheon Company..........321 494-3323
1034 S Patrick Dr Patrick Afb (32925) *(G-14008)*
Raytheon Company..........407 207-9223
12792 Research Pkwy # 100 Orlando (32826) *(G-13117)*
Raytheon Company..........321 235-1700
2603 Challenger Tech Ct Orlando (32826) *(G-13118)*
Raytheon Company..........310 647-9438
7887 Bryan Dairy Rd # 110 Largo (33777) *(G-8038)*
Raytheon Technologies Corp..........561 796-2000
17900 Bee Line Hwy Jupiter (33478) *(G-7102)*
Raytheon Technologies Corp..........858 277-7639
17900 Bee Line Hwy Jupiter (33478) *(G-7103)*
Razient LLC..........855 747-5911
990 Biscayne Blvd Ste 503 Miami (33132) *(G-10242)*
RB Cabinetry LLC..........850 685-5316
408 Evergreen Dr Ste A Destin (32541) *(G-3203)*
RB Custom Welding LLC..........813 280-9860
5210 E 10th Ave Tampa (33619) *(G-18040)*
RB Kanalflakt Inc..........941 359-3267
1712 Northgate Blvd Sarasota (34234) *(G-16554)*
Rbj Timber Inc..........904 879-1597
44247 Bell Ln Callahan (32011) *(G-1328)*
Rbs Woodwork Corp (PA)..........754 214-7682
378 Nw 153rd Ave Pembroke Pines (33028) *(G-14056)*
RC Investment Casting..........305 801-9088
4570 E 11th Ave Hialeah (33013) *(G-5594)*
RCA Machine & Mfg Inc..........727 561-0150
4652 107th Cir N Clearwater (33762) *(G-1857)*
Rcai, Saint Petersburg *Also called Restorative Care America Inc* *(G-15900)*
Rcc Conveyors Inc (PA)..........224 338-8841
21569 Oaks Of Estero Cir Estero (33928) *(G-3694)*
Rcd Corporation..........352 589-0099
2850 Dillard Rd Eustis (32726) *(G-3716)*
Rcr Coffee Company Inc (PA)..........813 248-6264
402 N 22nd St Tampa (33605) *(G-18041)*
RCS Wood Crafters LLC..........305 836-0120
1051 E 24th St Hialeah (33013) *(G-5595)*
Rdc Manufacturing Inc..........772 286-6921
3353 Se Gran Park Way Stuart (34997) *(G-16998)*
Rdd International Inc..........954 422-9909
301 Ne 51st St Ste 1240 Boca Raton (33431) *(G-682)*
Rde Connectors & Cables Inc..........954 746-6400
5277 Nw 108th Ave Sunrise (33351) *(G-17168)*
RDS Industrial Inc..........321 631-0121
436 Shearer Blvd Cocoa (32922) *(G-2045)*
RDS Manufacturing Inc..........850 584-6898
300 Industrial Park Dr Perry (32348) *(G-14310)*
RDt Business Enterprises Inc..........954 525-1133
3333 Se 14th Ave Fort Lauderdale (33316) *(G-4200)*
Re-Bus LLC..........772 418-7711
5015 Saint Lucie Blvd Fort Pierce (34946) *(G-4738)*
Re-Think It Inc..........407 671-6000
6869 Stapoint Ct Ste 107 Winter Park (32792) *(G-19437)*
Reach Cooling Group, Hialeah *Also called Reach International Inc* *(G-5596)*
Reach International Inc..........305 863-6360
625 E 10th Ave Hialeah (33010) *(G-5596)*
Reachtv..........772 934-6349
1976 Nw Fork Rd Stuart (34994) *(G-16999)*
Readers Drect Publications Inc..........727 643-8616
9404 94th St Seminole (33777) *(G-16759)*
Reading Truck Body LLC..........727 943-8911
1476 L And R Indus Blvd Tarpon Springs (34689) *(G-18322)*
Reading Truck Body LLC..........727 943-8911
1476 L&R Industrial Blvd Tarpon Springs (34689) *(G-18323)*
Ready Building Products Inc..........941 639-6222
7000 Progress Dr Punta Gorda (33982) *(G-15228)*
Ready Containment LLC..........941 739-9486
2300 S Dock St Ste 101 Palmetto (34221) *(G-13821)*
Ready Machine Corp..........850 479-1722
6155 Drexel Rd Pensacola (32504) *(G-14250)*
Ready Mix Usa LLC..........850 227-7677
1001 Ccil G Cstin Sr Blvd Port Saint Joe (32456) *(G-15083)*
Ready Set Mount, Fort Myers *Also called Creative Concepts Intl LLC* *(G-4415)*
Readymix, Saint Augustine *Also called Cemex Cnstr Mtls Fla LLC* *(G-15528)*
Readymix - Moore Haven Rm, Moore Haven *Also called Cemex Cnstr Mtls Fla LLC* *(G-11086)*
Readymix - Port St Joe, Port Saint Joe *Also called Ready Mix Usa LLC* *(G-15083)*
Reagan H Fox III Inc..........850 584-9229
Woods Creek Rd Perry (32347) *(G-14311)*
Reah Group LLC..........727 423-0668
2721 W Gray St Tampa (33609) *(G-18042)*
Real Extract Ventures Inc..........561 371-3532
2200 Merriweather Way Wellington (33414) *(G-18728)*
Real Fleet Solutions LLC..........321 631-2414
605 Townsend Rd Cocoa (32926) *(G-2046)*
Real Gold Inc..........386 873-4849
1853 Patterson Ave Unit 4 Deland (32724) *(G-3010)*
Real Ketones LLC..........801 244-8610
111 2nd Ave Ne Ste 1401 Saint Petersburg (33701) *(G-15899)*
Real News Real Fast..........727 485-6055
9365 Northcliffe Blvd Spring Hill (34606) *(G-16860)*
Real Print & Ship Inc..........727 787-1949
4047 Carlyle Lakes Blvd Palm Harbor (34685) *(G-13758)*

ALPHABETIC

Real Pro Welding Inc...850 939-3469
8285 East Bay Blvd Navarre (32566) ***(G-11473)***
Real Producers, Land O Lakes *Also called M30 Freedom Inc* ***(G-7860)***
Real Producers, Oviedo *Also called Orlando Branding Agency LLC* ***(G-13451)***
Real Solutions, Melbourne *Also called Alstom Signaling Operation LLC* ***(G-8765)***
Real Thread Inc...407 679-3895
1101 N Keller Rd Ste A Orlando (32810) ***(G-13119)***
Real Time Labratories, Boca Raton *Also called Kinetics Usa Inc* ***(G-588)***
Real-Time Laboratories LLC (HQ)...561 988-8826
990 S Rogers Cir Ste 5 Boca Raton (33487) ***(G-683)***
Realm Labs LLC...561 549-9099
7700 Congress Ave # 3110 Boca Raton (33487) ***(G-684)***
Realstargps, Orlando *Also called Sunrise Financial Assoc Inc* ***(G-13225)***
Realty Systems Inc...386 439-0460
3165 Old Kings Rd S Flagler Beach (32136) ***(G-3756)***
Rearden Steel Mfg LLC...772 882-8517
5350 Steel Blvd Fort Pierce (34946) ***(G-4739)***
Rebah Fabrication Inc...407 857-3232
12081 Stone Bark Trl Orlando (32824) ***(G-13120)***
Rebar Alchemist, Port Saint Lucie *Also called Alchemist Holdings LLC* ***(G-15086)***
Reboundersz Purchasing Dev, Sanford *Also called Indoor Trampoline Arena Inc* ***(G-16065)***
Rebuild Globally Inc...407 801-9936
810 S K St Lake Worth (33460) ***(G-7585)***
Recall Technologies Inc...321 952-4422
1651 Seabury Point Rd Nw Palm Bay (32907) ***(G-13530)***
Recommend Magazine, Miami Lakes *Also called Worth Intl Media Group* ***(G-10881)***
Recommend Travel Publications...305 826-4763
5979 Nw 151st St Ste 120 Miami Lakes (33014) ***(G-10849)***
Recon Group LLP...855 874-8741
20200 W Dixie Hwy # 1005 Miami (33180) ***(G-10243)***
Recordsone LLC...301 440-8119
10641 Airport Pulling R Naples (34109) ***(G-11382)***
Recover Gear LLC...904 280-9660
822 A1a N Ponte Vedra Beach (32082) ***(G-14952)***
Recreational Screen Printing...561 757-5479
707 E Palmetto Park Rd Boca Raton (33432) ***(G-685)***
Recycled Vinyl...727 434-1857
848 Myrtle St Sarasota (34234) ***(G-16555)***
Recycling Center...386 364-5865
700 Houston Ave Nw Live Oak (32064) ***(G-8239)***
Red 7 Tees LLC...305 793-1440
189 W Oakdale Ave Crestview (32536) ***(G-2356)***
Red Bay Berry LLC...954 552-9935
2983 E Lake Vista Cir Davie (33328) ***(G-2582)***
Red Brick Publishing LLC...718 208-3600
6647 Conch Ct Boynton Beach (33437) ***(G-954)***
Red Bud Enterprises Inc...386 752-5696
1435 Nw County Road 25a Lake City (32055) ***(G-7381)***
Red Diamond Salsa LLC...813 672-7707
18632 S Us Highway 301 Wimauma (33598) ***(G-19222)***
Red Hawk Industries LLC...303 779-6272
5100 Town Center Cir # 350 Boca Raton (33486) ***(G-686)***
Red Hot Trends Inc...305 888-6951
7911 Nw 72nd Ave Ste 107 Medley (33166) ***(G-8716)***
Red Level Dolomite, Crystal River *Also called Crystal River Quarries Inc* ***(G-2375)***
Red Meters LLC...407 337-0110
6520 Pinecastle Blvd Orlando (32809) ***(G-13121)***
Red Microphone...818 806-8545
3312 N Miami Ave Miami (33127) ***(G-10244)***
Red Phoenix Extracts, Fort Pierce *Also called Cei Liquidation Inc* ***(G-4684)***
Red Smith Foods Inc...954 581-1996
4145 Sw 47th Ave Davie (33314) ***(G-2583)***
Redat of North America Inc...407 246-1600
120 Bonnie Loch Ct Orlando (32806) ***(G-13122)***
Redberd Printing...407 622-2292
803 S Orlando Ave Winter Park (32789) ***(G-19438)***
Redbird Printing...904 654-8371
803 S Orlando Ave Ste J Winter Park (32789) ***(G-19439)***
Reddi Sign Corporation...904 757-0680
107 Mott St Jacksonville (32254) ***(G-6709)***
Reddress Usa Inc...800 674-9615
822 A1a N Ste 310 Ponte Vedra Beach (32082) ***(G-14953)***
Reddy Ice Corporation...772 461-5046
2901 Industrial Avenue 2 Fort Pierce (34946) ***(G-4740)***
Reddy Ice Corporation...850 433-2191
1511 W Government St Pensacola (32502) ***(G-14251)***
Reddy Ice Corporation...904 388-2653
5849 Commonwealth Ave Jacksonville (32254) ***(G-6710)***
Reddy Ice Corporation...850 233-0128
1225 Moylan Rd Panama City (32407) ***(G-13944)***
Reddy Ice Corporation...561 881-9501
7719 Garden Rd West Palm Beach (33404) ***(G-19017)***
Reddy Ice Inc...407 296-8300
1920 Commerce Oak Ave Orlando (32808) ***(G-13123)***
Redeag Le, Lakeland *Also called Redeagle International LLC* ***(G-7777)***
Redeagle International LLC...863 682-6698
5143 S Lakeland Dr Ste 4 Lakeland (33813) ***(G-7777)***
Rederick Metal Industries (PA)...305 396-3396
1933 Nw 21st Ter Miami (33142) ***(G-10245)***
Redington Counters Inc...954 725-6699
702 S Military Trl Deerfield Beach (33442) ***(G-2901)***
Reditek Corporation...954 781-1069
2826 Center Port Cir Pompano Beach (33064) ***(G-14826)***
Redkeys Dies...772 463-5824
1680 Sw Wildcat Trl Stuart (34997) ***(G-17000)***
Redline Wheels Florida, Orlando *Also called Str Racing Wheels* ***(G-13217)***
Redmont Sign LLC (PA)...941 378-4242
2201 Cantu Ct Ste 215 Sarasota (34232) ***(G-16556)***
Redquin Publishing LLC...813 314-4500
201 E Kennedy Blvd # 600 Tampa (33602) ***(G-18043)***
Redsled DBA Bulldog Equipment...954 448-5221
2691 Sw Windship Way Stuart (34997) ***(G-17001)***
Redstone Corporation...321 213-2135
606 Gladiola St Hngr 255 Merritt Island (32952) ***(G-9007)***
Reduction International LLC...954 905-5999
2700 Glades Cir Ste 116 Weston (33327) ***(G-19164)***
Redwire Corporation (PA)...650 701-7722
8226 Philips Hwy Ste 101 Jacksonville (32256) ***(G-6711)***
Redwood Custom Woodworking (PA)...407 529-9877
1409 Murdock Blvd Orlando (32825) ***(G-13124)***
Reed Brenan, Orlando *Also called Reed Brennan Media Associates* ***(G-13125)***
Reed Brennan Media Associates...407 894-7300
628 Virginia Dr Orlando (32803) ***(G-13125)***
Reed Minerals Division, Tampa *Also called Harsco Corporation* ***(G-17745)***
Reeds Metal Manufacturing Inc...352 498-0100
16454 Se Highway 19 Cross City (32628) ***(G-2366)***
Reef Pavers Inc...904 471-0859
604 Barbara Ln Jacksonville Beach (32250) ***(G-6956)***
Reef Runner Charters LLC...941 921-0560
2561 Marblehead Dr Sarasota (34231) ***(G-16557)***
Referral & Residual Exchange L...813 655-5000
9376 Balm Riverview Rd Riverview (33569) ***(G-15280)***
Reflection Manufacturing...407 297-5727
10336 Pointview Ct Orlando (32836) ***(G-13126)***
Reflections Beach & Resortwear...954 776-1230
104 Commercial Blvd Laud By Sea (33308) ***(G-8083)***
Reflectivity Inc...386 738-1008
320 S Spring Garden Ave E Deland (32720) ***(G-3011)***
Reflex Pubg Eric Reflex Co...813 314-8810
777 S Harbour Island Blvd Tampa (33602) ***(G-18044)***
Refly of Miami Inc...786 762-2748
7360 Nw 35th St Miami (33122) ***(G-10246)***
Refresco Beverages US Inc...813 313-1711
8112 Woodland Center Blvd Tampa (33614) ***(G-18045)***
Refresco Beverages US Inc...813 241-0147
4506 Acline Dr E Tampa (33605) ***(G-18046)***
Refresco Beverages US Inc (HQ)...813 313-1800
8112 Woodland Center Blvd Tampa (33614) ***(G-18047)***
Refresco Beverages US Inc...314 994-7545
8112 Woodland Center Blvd Tampa (33614) ***(G-18048)***
Refresco US Holding Inc (PA)...813 313-1863
8118 Woodland Center Blvd Tampa (33614) ***(G-18049)***
Refreshed Traveler, Apopka *Also called Plane It Safe LLC* ***(G-171)***
Refreshing Smoothie...904 549-5366
9550 Baymeadows Rd Jacksonville (32256) ***(G-6712)***
Refreshment Services Inc...850 574-0281
3919 W Pensacola St Tallahassee (32304) ***(G-17315)***
Refrigeration Panels, Miami *Also called Refrigrtion Engnred Systems In* ***(G-10248)***
Refrigeration Panels Inc...305 836-6900
7215 Nw 36th Ave Miami (33147) ***(G-10247)***
Refrigrtion Engnred Systems In...305 836-6900
7215 Nw 36th Ave Miami (33147) ***(G-10248)***
Reftec International Inc...800 214-4883
10530 Portal Xing Ste 104 Bradenton (34211) ***(G-1104)***
Reftec Intl Systems LLC...727 290-9830
6950 112th Cir Largo (33773) ***(G-8039)***
Regal Boats, Orlando *Also called Regal Marine Industries Inc* ***(G-13127)***
Regal Cabinets Inc...407 678-1003
3903 Forsyth Rd Winter Park (32792) ***(G-19440)***
Regal Marine Industries Inc (PA)...407 851-4360
2300 Jetport Dr Orlando (32809) ***(G-13127)***
Regency Cap & Gown Company...904 724-3500
7534 Atlantic Blvd Jacksonville (32211) ***(G-6713)***
Regency Custom Cabinets Inc...239 332-7977
8207 Katanga Ct Fort Myers (33916) ***(G-4580)***
Regeneration Technologies Inc...386 418-8888
11621 Research Cir Alachua (32615) ***(G-15)***
Regenerative Proc Plant LLC...727 781-0818
34176 Us Highway 19 N Palm Harbor (34684) ***(G-13759)***
Regent Cabinetry and More Inc...239 693-2207
5610 Zip Dr Fort Myers (33905) ***(G-4581)***
Regent Labs Inc (PA)...954 426-4889
700 W Hillsboro Blvd 2-206 Deerfield Beach (33441) ***(G-2902)***
Regent Labs Inc...954 426-4889
473 Goolsby Blvd Deerfield Beach (33442) ***(G-2903)***
Regina Behar Enterprises Inc...305 557-5212
11440 Interchange Cir N Miramar (33025) ***(G-11035)***
Regional Cnstr Resources Inc...713 789-5131
66 N Washington Dr Sarasota (34236) ***(G-16558)***

Regional Trailer Repair Inc.........912 484-7729
1048 Escambia St Jacksonville (32208) ***(G-6714)***
Rehadapt North America.........904 687-0130
7619 A1a S Saint Augustine (32080) ***(G-15595)***
Rehrig Pacific Company.........407 857-3888
7452 Presidents Dr Orlando (32809) ***(G-13128)***
Rehydrade LLC.........561 419-5656
131 S Federal Hwy Apt 418 Boca Raton (33432) ***(G-687)***
Reich Metal Fabricators Inc.........561 585-3173
5405 Webster Ave West Palm Beach (33405) ***(G-19018)***
Reico Inc.........850 243-4400
95 Ready Ave Nw Fort Walton Beach (32548) ***(G-4827)***
Reiley Tool Company LLC.........360 929-0350
3950 Equestrian Ct Middleburg (32068) ***(G-10912)***
Reilly Foam Corp.........561 842-8090
3896 Westroads Dr Riviera Beach (33407) ***(G-15369)***
Reimink Printing Inc.........813 289-4663
4209 W Kennedy Blvd Tampa (33609) ***(G-18050)***
Reinecker Grinders Corp.........954 974-6190
1700 Nw 15th Ave Ste 310 Pompano Beach (33069) ***(G-14827)***
Rek Design & Print LLC.........407 331-5100
1306 Winter Springs Blvd Winter Springs (32708) ***(G-19483)***
Rek Manufacturing Inc.........321 269-3533
1419 Chaffee Dr Ste 4 Titusville (32780) ***(G-18455)***
Rela USA LLC.........786 656-5069
8398 Nw 70th St Miami (33166) ***(G-10249)***
Relaxium, Boca Raton *Also called American Bhvioral RES Inst LLC* ***(G-421)***
Relcom Industries Inc.........561 304-7717
3900 Woodlake Blvd # 200 Greenacres (33463) ***(G-5086)***
Reliabilityweb.com, Fort Myers *Also called Netexpressusa Inc* ***(G-4545)***
Reliable Business Technologies.........386 561-9944
285 W Pine Ave Longwood (32750) ***(G-8330)***
Reliable Cabinet Designs.........941 473-3403
6900 San Casa Dr Unit 1 Englewood (34224) ***(G-3666)***
Reliable Custom Imprints Corp.........407 834-0571
448 Commerce Way Unit 100 Longwood (32750) ***(G-8331)***
Reliable Finishes.........321 723-3334
7730 Industrial Rd Melbourne (32904) ***(G-8918)***
Reliable Pool Enclsres Screens, Orlando *Also called Reliable Pool Enclsres Screns* ***(G-13129)***
Reliable Pool Enclsres Screns.........407 731-3408
5558 Force Four Pkwy Orlando (32839) ***(G-13129)***
Reliable Tool and Machine Inc.........561 844-8848
328 W 11th St Riviera Beach (33404) ***(G-15370)***
Reliance Media Inc.........505 243-1821
515 Cooper Commerce Dr # 140 Apopka (32703) ***(G-179)***
Reliance Petro Holdings LLC.........352 390-8039
1820 Se 18th Ave Ste 3 Ocala (34471) ***(G-12036)***
Reliance Supply Co USA LLC.........954 971-9111
1880 Nw 18th St Pompano Beach (33069) ***(G-14828)***
Reliant Medical Services Inc.........954 977-4224
3081 W Mcnab Rd Pompano Beach (33069) ***(G-14829)***
Reliant Medical Systems LLC.........954 977-4224
3081 W Mcnab Rd Pompano Beach (33069) ***(G-14830)***
Reliatex Inc.........813 621-6021
6004 Bonacker Dr Tampa (33610) ***(G-18051)***
Relion Enterprises LLC.........321 287-4225
13526 Village Park Dr # 202 Orlando (32837) ***(G-13130)***
Reliox Corporation.........904 729-5097
8475 Western Way Ste 155 Jacksonville (32256) ***(G-6715)***
Relm Communications Inc.........321 953-7800
7100 Technology Dr Melbourne (32904) ***(G-8919)***
Relu Co.........786 717-5665
7827 Nw 15th St Doral (33126) ***(G-3482)***
Remas Draperies Etc Inc.........904 845-9300
27777 Conner Nelson Rd Hilliard (32046) ***(G-5716)***
Remco Industries International.........954 462-0000
917 Nw 8th Ave Fort Lauderdale (33311) ***(G-4201)***
Remco Specialty Products Co, Fort Lauderdale *Also called Remco Industries International* ***(G-4201)***
Remcraft Lighting Products Inc.........305 687-9031
12870 Nw 45th Ave Opa Locka (33054) ***(G-12353)***
Remior Industries Inc.........305 883-8722
9165 Nw 96th St Miami (33178) ***(G-10250)***
Remodeling Guys, The, Lakeland *Also called Solara Industries Inc* ***(G-7796)***
Renacer Bros LLC.........305 935-6777
18839 Biscayne Blvd # 150 Miami (33180) ***(G-10251)***
Renaissance Custom Woodworking.........561 212-9885
307 W Mallory Cir Delray Beach (33483) ***(G-3135)***
Renaissance Entp Group LLC.........941 284-7854
155 W Dearborn St Englewood (34223) ***(G-3681)***
Renaissance Fabrication, Pensacola *Also called Renaissance Man Incorporated* ***(G-14252)***
Renaissance Man Incorporated.........850 432-1177
2203 N Pace Blvd Pensacola (32505) ***(G-14252)***
Renaissance Steel LLC.........941 773-7290
6508 E Fowler Ave Temple Terrace (33617) ***(G-18376)***
Renal Advantage Inc A44.........772 807-7229
8661 S Us Highway 1 Port Saint Lucie (34952) ***(G-15136)***
Renco Usa Inc.........321 637-1000
5959 Blue Lagoon Dr Miami (33126) ***(G-10252)***
Renesas Electronics Amer Inc.........321 724-7000
1650 Rbert J Cnlan Blvd N Palm Bay (32905) ***(G-13531)***
Renewable Energy Systems Inc.........727 522-0286
6531 43rd St N Ste 1604 Pinellas Park (33781) ***(G-14384)***
Renewable Fuels Group LLC.........305 388-3028
15184 Sw 111th St Miami (33196) ***(G-10253)***
Renick Enterprises Inc.........561 863-4183
1211 W 13th St Riviera Beach (33404) ***(G-15371)***
Rennak Inc.........305 558-0144
6161 Miami Lakes Dr E Miami Lakes (33014) ***(G-10850)***
Renos Led Sleds.........727 593-0340
14548 Sioux Ave Largo (33774) ***(G-8040)***
Renova Land and Sea LLC.........786 916-2695
4954 Sw 128th Ave Miramar (33027) ***(G-11036)***
Renovaship Inc.........954 342-9062
2700 S Park Rd Hallandale Beach (33009) ***(G-5208)***
Renovatec Enterprise Inc.........954 444-8694
2590 Nw 4th Ct Fort Lauderdale (33311) ***(G-4202)***
Renovation Concrete, Jacksonville *Also called Outline Technologies Inc* ***(G-6650)***
Renue Systems South East Fla, Aventura *Also called Services NS 18 LLC* ***(G-280)***
Renzetti Inc.........321 267-7705
8800 Grissom Pkwy Titusville (32780) ***(G-18456)***
Repair Electrical Motors Ac/DC, Opa Locka *Also called Done Rite Pumps* ***(G-12308)***
Repco Equipment Leasing Inc.........727 584-3329
1550 Starkey Rd Largo (33771) ***(G-8041)***
Replenish Ink Inc.........818 206-2424
701 Brickell Ave Key Blvd Miami (33131) ***(G-10254)***
Reporgraphics Unlimited Inc.........386 253-7990
124 Bay St Daytona Beach (32114) ***(G-2703)***
Repro Plus Inc.........407 843-1492
850 S Hughey Ave Orlando (32801) ***(G-13131)***
Reprographic Services Inc.........305 859-8282
1036 Sw 8th St Miami (33130) ***(G-10255)***
Reprographic Solutions Inc (PA).........772 340-3430
234 Sw Port St Lucie Blvd Port Saint Lucie (34984) ***(G-15137)***
Repscrubs, Sanford *Also called Prescient Logistics LLC* ***(G-16106)***
Reptile World, Saint Cloud *Also called Biotoxins Inc* ***(G-15646)***
Republic Drill/Apt Corp (PA).........305 592-7777
7840 Nw 62nd St Miami (33166) ***(G-10256)***
Republic Industries.........954 627-6000
450 E Las Olas Blvd # 1200 Fort Lauderdale (33301) ***(G-4203)***
Republic Metals Corporation.........305 685-8505
12900 Nw 38th Ave Opa Locka (33054) ***(G-12354)***
Republic Newspapers Inc.........813 782-1558
38333 5th Ave Zephyrhills (33542) ***(G-19534)***
Republic Newspapers Inc.........352 394-2183
732 W Montrose St Clermont (34711) ***(G-1972)***
Republic Packaging Florida Inc.........305 685-5175
4570 Nw 128th St Opa Locka (33054) ***(G-12355)***
Repwire LLC.........786 486-1823
5500 Nw 106th Ct Doral (33178) ***(G-3483)***
RES Textiles Inc.........813 476-5524
4511 N Himes Ave Ste 200 Tampa (33614) ***(G-18052)***
RES-Net Microwave, Clearwater *Also called Electro Technik Industries Inc* ***(G-1666)***
RES-Net Microwave Inc.........727 530-9555
5410 115th Ave N Clearwater (33760) ***(G-1858)***
Resa Pwr Slutions Plant Cy LLC.........813 752-6550
1401 Mercantile Ct Plant City (33563) ***(G-14461)***
Rescar Companies Inc.........386 397-2656
16950 Se County Road 137 White Springs (32096) ***(G-19188)***
Rescue Metal Framing LLC.........561 660-5945
2601 Delmar Pl Fort Lauderdale (33301) ***(G-4204)***
Research II, Ormond Beach *Also called Hes Products Inc* ***(G-13376)***
Reserveage.........561 443-5301
4800 T Rex Ave Boca Raton (33431) ***(G-688)***
Resharp Industries.........352 362-1730
5101 Se 11th Ave Ocala (34480) ***(G-12037)***
Resident Cmnty News Group Inc.........904 962-6876
1650 Margaret St 31 Jacksonville (32204) ***(G-6716)***
Resident Community News.........904 388-8839
2973 Fitzgerald St Jacksonville (32254) ***(G-6717)***
Residential Acoustics LLC.........813 922-2390
6122 Benjamin Rd Tampa (33634) ***(G-18053)***
Residual Innovations LLC.........407 459-5497
7253 Pleasant Dr Orlando (32818) ***(G-13132)***
Resilient Group Inc.........518 434-4414
3114 Double Oaks Dr Jacksonville (32226) ***(G-6718)***
Resolute Cross City LLC.........352 498-3363
40 Sw 10th St Cross City (32628) ***(G-2367)***
Resolute Cross Cy RE Hldngs LL.........352 498-3363
40 Sw 10th St Cross City (32628) ***(G-2368)***
Resolute FP Florida Inc (HQ).........800 562-2860
3301 Nw 107th St Miami (33167) ***(G-10257)***
Resolute Tissue LLC.........305 636-5741
3301 Nw 107th St Miami (33167) ***(G-10258)***
Resolute Tissue Sales.........800 562-2860
3725 E 10th Ct Hialeah (33013) ***(G-5597)***

ALPHABETIC

Resolver Group Inc 941 387-7410
20 Lighthouse Point Dr Longboat Key (34228) *(G-8246)*
Resolvers LLC 954 254-7948
711 Se 1st Way Apt 6 Deerfield Beach (33441) *(G-2904)*
Resort Poolside Shops Inc 407 256-5853
2912 Nela Ave Belle Isle (32809) *(G-358)*
Resort Window Treatments Inc 813 355-4877
5157 Gall Blvd Zephyrhills (33542) *(G-19535)*
Resource Management Associates 239 656-0818
1675 Temple Ter Ste 2 Fort Myers (33917) *(G-4582)*
Respect Foods 561 557-2832
4731 Cadiz Cir Palm Beach Gardens (33418) *(G-13622)*
Respitrend Inc 407 529-5888
3630 Sw 47th Ave Gainesville (32608) *(G-4990)*
Responsive Machining Inc 321 225-4011
1650 Chaffee Dr Titusville (32780) *(G-18457)*
Restifo Investments LLC 305 468-0013
1424 Nw 82nd Ave Doral (33126) *(G-3484)*
Restonic/San Francisco, Boca Raton *Also called Sleeprite Industries Inc (G-720)*
Restoration Arts 305 953-9755
15301 Nw 34th Ave Miami Gardens (33054) *(G-10753)*
Restoration Games LLC 954 937-1970
12717 W Sunrise Blvd Sunrise (33323) *(G-17169)*
Restoration Medical LLC 863 272-0250
5235 Nichols Dr E Lakeland (33812) *(G-7778)*
Restorative Care America Inc (PA) 727 573-1595
12221 33rd St N Saint Petersburg (33716) *(G-15900)*
Restorative Products Inc 813 342-4432
13560 Wright Cir Tampa (33626) *(G-18054)*
Retail Cloud Technologies LLC 727 210-1700
380 Park Place Blvd # 250 Clearwater (33759) *(G-1859)*
Retreat 813 254-2014
123 S Hyde Park Ave Tampa (33606) *(G-18055)*
Reuse Salvage Inc 772 485-3248
40668 Se Russell Way Port Salerno (34992) *(G-15165)*
Rev Amblance Group Orlando Inc (HQ) 407 677-7777
2737 Forsyth Rd Winter Park (32792) *(G-19441)*
Rev Personal Care LLC 832 217-8585
2905 Payson Way Wellington (33414) *(G-18729)*
Rev-Tech Mfg Solutions LLC 727 577-4999
9900 18th St N Ste 105 Saint Petersburg (33716) *(G-15901)*
Revere Manufactured Pdts Inc 904 503-9733
323 Hwy Ave Jacksonville (32254) *(G-6719)*
Revere Survival Inc 904 503-9733
5323 Highway Ave Jacksonville (32254) *(G-6720)*
Reverso Pumps Inc 954 523-9396
4001 Sw 47th Ave Ste 201 Davie (33314) *(G-2584)*
Review Newspapers 941 474-4351
370 W Dearborn St Ste B Englewood (34223) *(G-3682)*
Revive Light Therapy, Largo *Also called Led Technologies Incorporated (G-7998)*
Revlon Inc 904 693-1254
540 Beautyrest Ave Jacksonville (32254) *(G-6721)*
Revlon Consumer Products Corp 904 378-4167
5344 Overmyer Dr Jacksonville (32254) *(G-6722)*
Revlon Professional Products, Jacksonville *Also called Roux Laboratories Inc (G-6737)*
Revology Cars LLC 800 974-4463
6756 Edgwter Cmmrce Pkwy Orlando (32810) *(G-13133)*
Revolution Air Craft Services 954 747-4773
2511 Nw 16th Ln Ste 3 Pompano Beach (33064) *(G-14831)*
Revtech 727 369-1750
10050 16th St N Saint Petersburg (33716) *(G-15902)*
Reward Lighting Net LLC 561 832-1819
6000 Georgia Ave Ste 10 West Palm Beach (33405) *(G-19019)*
Rex 3, Davie *Also called Rex Three Inc (G-2585)*
Rex Fox Enterprises Inc 386 677-3752
1966 N Nova Rd Daytona Beach (32117) *(G-2704)*
Rex Lumber Graceville LLC (HQ) 850 263-2056
5299 Alabama St Graceville (32440) *(G-5044)*
Rex Lumber LLC 850 643-2172
Highway 12 S Bristol (32321) *(G-1202)*
Rex Lumber LLC (PA) 850 263-4457
5381 Cliff St Graceville (32440) *(G-5045)*
Rex Three Inc 954 452-8301
15431 Sw 14th St Davie (33326) *(G-2585)*
Rexpro Services 561 328-6488
1313 S Killian Dr Lake Park (33403) *(G-7479)*
Reyes Granite & Marble Corp 305 599-7330
7905 Nw 60th St Miami (33166) *(G-10259)*
Reyes Interlocking Pavers Inc 863 698-9179
1317 E Calhoun St Plant City (33563) *(G-14462)*
Reyes Jewelers Corp 305 431-8303
36 Ne 1st St Ste 734 Miami (33132) *(G-10260)*
Reyes Limitless Nutrition, Brandon *Also called Twisted Fusion Nutrition (G-1183)*
Reyes Stucco Inc 321 557-1319
1515 Peachtree St Lot 3 Cocoa (32922) *(G-2047)*
Reynolds Aluminum Recycl Div, Pensacola *Also called Wise Recycling 1 LLC (G-14290)*
Reynoso & Associates Inc 954 360-0601
434 Sw 12th Ave Deerfield Beach (33442) *(G-2905)*
Rezolin LLC 386 677-8238
131 Business Center Dr A7 Ormond Beach (32174) *(G-13396)*
Rfg Consulting Services Inc 786 498-2177
801 Brickell Ave Ste 900 Miami (33131) *(G-10261)*
Rfg Petro Systems LLC (PA) 941 487-7524
32 S Osprey Ave Ste 1 Sarasota (34236) *(G-16559)*
Rfis Security Solutions, Lake Mary *Also called Microsemi Corp (G-7434)*
Rfl & Figlio LLC 904 765-2222
4226 Spring Grove Ave Jacksonville (32209) *(G-6723)*
RG Groundworks LLC 352 474-7949
5915 Nw 210th St Newberry (32669) *(G-11560)*
Rgf Environmental, Riviera Beach *Also called Rgf Marine Envmtl Tech Inc (G-15373)*
Rgf Environmental Group Inc 800 842-7771
1101 W 13th St Riviera Beach (33404) *(G-15372)*
Rgf Marine Envmtl Tech Inc 561 848-1826
1101 W 13th St Riviera Beach (33404) *(G-15373)*
Rgu Color Inc 386 252-9979
3133 S Ridgewood Ave # 1 South Daytona (32119) *(G-16808)*
Rhinestntransfersdirectcom Inc 484 254-6410
1821 Verde Way Orlando (32835) *(G-13134)*
Rhino Tire Usa Llc 407 777-5598
11423 Satellite Blvd Orlando (32837) *(G-13135)*
Rhino Tools Inc 305 332-7750
18844 Nw 89th Ct Hialeah (33018) *(G-5598)*
Rhodes Brothers Miami Inc 305 456-9682
37 Deer Run Miami Springs (33166) *(G-10897)*
Rhonda Clanton 305 502-7050
6133 Nw 181st Ter Cir S Hialeah (33015) *(G-5599)*
Rhyno Glass, Tampa *Also called FMC/Rhyno LLC (G-17689)*
Riani Pavers Inc 239 321-1875
1735 Brantley Rd Apt 2015 Fort Myers (33907) *(G-4583)*
Ribbon Printers Unlimited 888 546-3310
12104 Oakvista Dr Boynton Beach (33437) *(G-955)*
Ribbon Wholesale Corp 786 457-0555
219 Sw 21st Ct Miami (33135) *(G-10262)*
Ribeiro Stones LLC 407 723-8802
2207 Silver Star Rd Orlando (32804) *(G-13136)*
Rice Machinery Supply Co Inc 305 620-2274
1130 Nw 163rd Dr Miami (33169) *(G-10263)*
Rich Haven Interiors, Davenport *Also called J & N Stone Inc (G-2480)*
Rich Ice Cream Co 561 833-7585
2915 S Dixie Hwy West Palm Beach (33405) *(G-19020)*
Rich Maid Cabinets Inc 727 572-4857
12706 Daniels Dr Clearwater (33762) *(G-1860)*
Rich Woodturning Inc 305 573-9142
5626 Nw 161st St Miami Lakes (33014) *(G-10851)*
Richard Appelbaum & Associates 813 920-0300
18412 Keystone Grove Blvd Odessa (33556) *(G-12145)*
Richard Brown Logging Inc 850 379-8674
18534 Ne State Road 65 Hosford (32334) *(G-6011)*
Richard Bryan Ingram LLC 407 677-7779
2454 N Forsyth Rd Orlando (32807) *(G-13137)*
Richard C Good 321 639-6383
1125 White Dr Titusville (32780) *(G-18458)*
Richard Griggs Custom Woodwork 941 223-9376
1008 Mohawk Rd Venice (34293) *(G-18569)*
Richard K Pratt LLC 321 482-9494
1325 White Dr Titusville (32780) *(G-18459)*
Richard Lyn 954 326-1017
7944 Forest Blvd North Lauderdale (33068) *(G-11620)*
Richard Meer Investments Inc 941 484-6551
822 Pinebrook Rd Venice (34285) *(G-18570)*
Richard Varney Signs 772 873-0454
3031 Sw Lucerne St Port Saint Lucie (34953) *(G-15138)*
Richard Wagner LLC 239 450-1721
9601 Campbell Cir Naples (34109) *(G-11383)*
Richards Aviation 954 527-2623
1350 River Reach Dr # 506 Fort Lauderdale (33315) *(G-4205)*
Richards Brazilian Sausage LLC 786 609-3554
18503 Pines Blvd Ste 310 Pembroke Pines (33029) *(G-14057)*
Richards Mobile Welding 954 913-0487
3541 Nw 73rd Way Coral Springs (33065) *(G-2305)*
Richards Paint Mfg Co Inc (PA) 321 636-6200
200 Paint St Rockledge (32955) *(G-15443)*
Richardson Family Products LLC 239 896-3595
8596 Athena Ct Lehigh Acres (33971) *(G-8205)*
Richardsons Cabinet Works 850 832-8298
3724 Chandler Fenn Dr Panama City (32404) *(G-13945)*
Richland Towers Inc 813 286-4140
400 N Ashley Dr Ste 2500 Tampa (33602) *(G-18056)*
Richline Group Inc 954 718-3200
6701 Nob Hill Rd Tamarac (33321) *(G-17366)*
Richter Industries Inc 239 732-9440
1617 Gulfstar Dr S Naples (34112) *(G-11384)*
Rick's Quality Printing & Sign, Cocoa *Also called Ricks Quality Prtg & Signs (G-2048)*
Rickeys World Famous Sauce Inc 954 829-9464
4799 Hollywood Blvd Hollywood (33021) *(G-5901)*
Ricks Pallet Co Inc 305 884-4896
2420 W 3rd Ave Hialeah (33010) *(G-5600)*
Ricks Quality Prtg & Signs 321 504-7446
681 Industry Rd S Ste A Cocoa (32926) *(G-2048)*

Ricoma International Corp..........305 418-4421
3450 Nw 114th Ave Doral (33178) ***(G-3485)***
Ricordea Publishing, Miami *Also called Two Little Fishies Inc* ***(G-10517)***
Ricos Candy Snack & Bakery, Hialeah *Also called Ricos Tostaditos Inc* ***(G-5601)***
Ricos Tostaditos Inc..........305 885-7392
740 W 28th St Hialeah (33010) ***(G-5601)***
Ride and Tube Inc..........352 454-8194
16625 Se 19th Ct Summerfield (34491) ***(G-17061)***
Ride Like Bessie Inc..........904 580-3631
7643 Gate Pkwy Unit 104-1 Jacksonville (32256) ***(G-6724)***
Ridgeway Timber Inc..........352 463-6013
3949 Nw County Road 341 Bell (32619) ***(G-342)***
Ridgway Roof Truss Company..........352 376-4436
235 Sw 11th Pl Gainesville (32601) ***(G-4991)***
Riegl Usa Inc..........407 248-9927
14707 W Colonial Dr Winter Garden (34787) ***(G-19283)***
Rieker LLC..........407 496-1555
5337 Foxshire Ct Orlando (32819) ***(G-13138)***
Rigal Ramon & Maritza..........813 968-2380
4917 Rockledge Cir Tampa (33624) ***(G-18057)***
Right Stucco Inc..........407 468-6119
7585 Stidham Dr Orlando (32818) ***(G-13139)***
Right Way Wldg Fabrication LLC..........850 212-9672
1605 Cherry Tree Rd Monticello (32344) ***(G-11082)***
Rigid Coatings & Castings Inc..........352 396-8738
3290 Overland Rd Apopka (32703) ***(G-180)***
Rigid Coatings & Castings Inc..........352 396-8738
2585 Clark St Apopka (32703) ***(G-181)***
Rigrap LLC..........561 200-5958
2818 28th Ct Jupiter (33477) ***(G-7104)***
Rik Enterprises Inc..........239 772-9485
954 Ne Pine Island Rd G Cape Coral (33909) ***(G-1460)***
Rika Bakeries Inc..........305 691-5673
1025 E 24th St Hialeah (33013) ***(G-5602)***
Riks Cabinetry Inc..........561 929-5260
5011 W Oakland Park Blvd Lauderdale Lakes (33313) ***(G-8092)***
Riley & Company Inc (PA)..........407 265-9963
5491 Benchmark Ln Sanford (32773) ***(G-16110)***
Riley Coatings & Pavers LLC..........352 598-9520
4402 Ne 18th Ter Ocala (34479) ***(G-12038)***
Riley Gear Corporation (PA)..........904 829-5652
1 Precision Dr Saint Augustine (32092) ***(G-15596)***
Riley Risk Inc..........202 601-0500
1301 Plntn Is Dr S Saint Augustine (32080) ***(G-15597)***
Rima Cargo LLC..........305 477-8002
8375 Nw 68th St Miami (33166) ***(G-10264)***
Rinaldi Printing & Packaging, Tampa *Also called Rinaldi Printing Company* ***(G-18058)***
Rinaldi Printing Company..........813 569-0033
4514 E Adamo Dr Tampa (33605) ***(G-18058)***
Rinehart Corp..........850 271-5600
1515 Ohio Ave Lynn Haven (32444) ***(G-8437)***
Ring Lift, Lakeland *Also called Ring Power Corporation* ***(G-7779)***
Ring of Fire Radio LLC..........866 666-6114
316 S Baylen St Pensacola (32502) ***(G-14253)***
Ring Power Corporation..........863 606-0512
3425 Reynolds Rd Lakeland (33803) ***(G-7779)***
Ring Power Corporation..........904 354-1858
1727 Bennett St Jacksonville (32206) ***(G-6725)***
Rinker Materials, Bushnell *Also called Cemex Cnstr Mtls Fla LLC* ***(G-1315)***
Rinker Materials, Lake Wales *Also called Cemex Materials LLC* ***(G-7501)***
Rinker Materials..........305 345-4127
13100 Nw 118th Ave Medley (33178) ***(G-8717)***
Rinker Materials Corp..........352 799-7881
10311 Cement Plant Rd Brooksville (34601) ***(G-1264)***
Rinker Materials Corp..........305 386-0078
8800 Sw 177th Ave Miami (33196) ***(G-10265)***
Rinker Materials Corp..........386 775-0790
2170 State Road 472 Deland (32724) ***(G-3012)***
Rinker Materials Corp Con..........305 818-4952
12155 Nw 136th St Doral (33178) ***(G-3486)***
Rinker Portland Cement, Miami *Also called Cemex Materials LLC* ***(G-9336)***
Rinseworks Inc..........954 946-0070
1700 Nw 15th Ave Ste 330 Pompano Beach (33069) ***(G-14832)***
Rio Pavers Inc..........321 388-6757
7297 Mardell Ct Orlando (32835) ***(G-13140)***
Rio's Concrete Equipment, Medley *Also called Rios Con Pmpg & Rentl Inc* ***(G-8718)***
Rios Con Pmpg & Rentl Inc..........305 888-7909
8750 Nw 93rd St Medley (33178) ***(G-8718)***
Ripa & Associates Inc..........813 623-6777
1409 Tech Blvd Ste 1 Tampa (33619) ***(G-18059)***
Rippee Construction Inc..........850 668-6805
2107 Delta Way Tallahassee (32303) ***(G-17316)***
Ritchie Swimwear, Weston *Also called Double J of Broward Inc* ***(G-19121)***
Ritetest, Pompano Beach *Also called Firstpath Laboratory Svcs LLC* ***(G-14693)***
Ritter Kit Bath & Closet LLC..........239 272-4551
4870 Tallowood Way Naples (34116) ***(G-11385)***
Riva Industries Inc..........813 573-1601
4986 113th Ave N Clearwater (33760) ***(G-1861)***
River City Advg Objectional..........904 731-3452
3514 Morton St Jacksonville (32217) ***(G-6726)***
River City Cstm Cabinetry Inc..........904 247-0807
1863 Mayport Rd Jacksonville (32233) ***(G-6727)***
River City Powersports LLC..........386 259-5724
895 Diplomat Dr Unit E Debary (32713) ***(G-2754)***
River City Stucco Inc..........904 234-9526
117 Magnolia Ave Jacksonville (32218) ***(G-6728)***
River Craft LLC..........407 867-0584
2148 Orinoco Dr Ste 356 Orlando (32837) ***(G-13141)***
River Printing, Jacksonville *Also called John Stewart Enterprises Inc* ***(G-6525)***
Riverhawk Fast Sea Frames LLC..........912 484-3112
5251 W Tyson Ave Tampa (33611) ***(G-18060)***
Riverhead Housing Inc..........630 688-6791
3044 Sw 42nd St Fort Lauderdale (33312) ***(G-4206)***
Riverland Logging Inc..........904 845-4326
25190 County Road 121 Hilliard (32046) ***(G-5717)***
Riverstone Snctary - Cbd - Inc..........954 473-1254
2101 W Coml Blvd Ste 3500 Fort Lauderdale (33309) ***(G-4207)***
Riverview Community News, Lutz *Also called Community News Publications* ***(G-8378)***
Riverview Drones Inc..........813 451-4744
11326 Lake Lucaya Dr Riverview (33579) ***(G-15281)***
Riverview Millworks Inc..........904 764-9571
9157 Lem Turner Rd Jacksonville (32208) ***(G-6729)***
Riverwatch Marina & Boatyard, Stuart *Also called Gulfstream Land Company LLC* ***(G-16951)***
Riviera Beach FL Warehouse Bm, Riviera Beach *Also called Cemex Materials LLC* ***(G-15311)***
Riw of Jacksonville Inc..........904 356-5635
608 Carmen St Jacksonville (32206) ***(G-6730)***
Rizzo Management, Lake Worth *Also called Polo Players Edition* ***(G-7581)***
Rj Capital Inc..........561 208-7444
2200 Glades Rd Ste 305b Boca Raton (33431) ***(G-689)***
Rj Foods..........863 425-3282
104 N Church Ave Mulberry (33860) ***(G-11134)***
RJ Forklift Services Inc..........786 539-6613
8567 Coral Way Miami (33155) ***(G-10266)***
Rj Staab Stone Co..........352 377-3313
824 N Main St Williston (32696) ***(G-19213)***
Rj Staab Stone Company Fla LLC..........352 222-5989
824 N Main St Williston (32696) ***(G-19214)***
Rj Unique Cabinets..........954 708-0893
2600 Hammondville Rd Pompano Beach (33069) ***(G-14833)***
Rjh Technical Services Inc..........813 655-7947
517 Gornto Lake Rd Brandon (33510) ***(G-1174)***
Rjs Racing Equipment, Jupiter *Also called CSC Racing Corporation* ***(G-7021)***
RL Schreiber Inc (PA)..........954 972-7102
2745 W Cypress Creek Rd Fort Lauderdale (33309) ***(G-4208)***
RLC Building Inc..........904 704-5614
11190 Hendon Dr Jacksonville (32246) ***(G-6731)***
Rlcjc Inc..........407 370-3338
4684 Millenia Plaza Way Orlando (32839) ***(G-13142)***
Rls (usa) Inc..........561 596-0556
7802 Woodland Center Blvd Tampa (33614) ***(G-18061)***
RLS Lighting Inc..........954 458-0345
205 Ansin Blvd Fort Lauderdale (33311) ***(G-4209)***
Rm Brands Inc..........904 356-0092
2910 W Beaver St Jacksonville (32254) ***(G-6732)***
Rm Custom Woodcraft Inc..........786 355-7387
10400 Nw 36th Ct Miami (33147) ***(G-10267)***
RM Imaging Incorporated..........561 361-8090
2499 Glades Rd Ste 206 Boca Raton (33431) ***(G-690)***
Rm Industries..........386 428-4454
424 Luna Bella Ln Apt 318 New Smyrna (32168) ***(G-11523)***
RMC, Opa Locka *Also called Republic Metals Corporation* ***(G-12354)***
RMC Ewell Inc..........850 879-0959
16040 State Highway 20 Niceville (32578) ***(G-11573)***
RMC Ewell Inc..........850 863-5040
1787 F I M Rd Fort Walton Beach (32547) ***(G-4828)***
RMC Ewell Inc..........407 282-0984
7400 Narcoossee Rd Orlando (32822) ***(G-13143)***
Rme Studio Inc..........305 409-0856
7245 Ne 4th Ave Ste 102 Miami (33138) ***(G-10268)***
Rmf Printing Technologies Inc..........716 683-7500
21200 Ne 38th Ave # 1501 Miami (33180) ***(G-10269)***
RMM Cabinets LLC..........954 588-6353
1616 Nw 2nd Ave Boca Raton (33432) ***(G-691)***
Rmmj Inc..........239 597-2486
5545 Shirley St Naples (34109) ***(G-11386)***
RMR Distributors Inc..........813 908-1141
9610 Norwood Dr Tampa (33624) ***(G-18062)***
Rnn Productions LLC..........437 238-9501
7700 Biscayne Blvd # 200 Miami (33138) ***(G-10270)***
Road Block Fabrication Inc..........708 417-6091
16140 Lee Rd Unit 100 Fort Myers (33912) ***(G-4584)***
Road Master..........561 479-6450
203 W State Road 84 Fort Lauderdale (33315) ***(G-4210)***
Road Runner Highway Sign Inc..........941 753-0549
4421 12th Street Ct E Bradenton (34203) ***(G-1105)***

Road Signs Inc...941 321-0695
2017 Whitfield Park Dr Sarasota (34243) ***(G-16285)***
Roadsafe Traffic Systems Inc...386 755-0140
2118 Nw County Road 25a Lake City (32055) ***(G-7382)***
Roan Manufacturing Inc...813 510-4929
1834 Gunn Hwy Odessa (33556) ***(G-12146)***
Rob Dinic Interiors, Lakeland *Also called D I R Inc* ***(G-7669)***
Robba, Emilio, Miami *Also called Fleurissima Inc* ***(G-9575)***
Robbins Lumber, Tampa *Also called Robbins Manufacturing Company* ***(G-18063)***
Robbins Manufactuing Co...352 793-2443
12904 Sr 471 Webster (33597) ***(G-18698)***
Robbins Manufacturing Company (PA)...813 971-3030
1003 E 131st Ave Tampa (33612) ***(G-18063)***
Robbins Manufacturing Company...888 558-8199
1003 E 131st Ave Tampa (33612) ***(G-18064)***
Roberlo Usa Inc...786 334-6191
8501 Nw 17th St Ste 103 Doral (33126) ***(G-3487)***
Robert Duffy Cabinets Inc...239 777-0372
161 Tahiti Rd Marco Island (34145) ***(G-8526)***
Robert E Weissenborn Sr (PA)...239 262-1771
1101 5th Ave S Naples (34102) ***(G-11387)***
Robert Gomes Publishing Inc...941 637-6080
8512 Alan Blvd Punta Gorda (33982) ***(G-15229)***
Robert James Custom Metal Fabr...772 214-0996
2900 N Canal St Jacksonville (32209) ***(G-6733)***
Robert McKee Enterprises Inc...772 291-2159
7481 Sw Jack James Dr Stuart (34997) ***(G-17002)***
Robert Ojeda Metalsmith Inc...561 507-5511
10151 Yeoman Ln Royal Palm Beach (33411) ***(G-15477)***
Robert Petrucci Inc...954 772-2333
1701 W Cypress Creek Rd Fort Lauderdale (33309) ***(G-4211)***
Robert St Croix Sculpture Stu...561 835-1753
1400 Alabama Ave Ste 6 West Palm Beach (33401) ***(G-19021)***
Robert's Saw Company, Tampa *Also called RSC Industries Inc* ***(G-18071)***
Roberto Valverde...305 324-5252
1929 Nw 22nd St Miami (33142) ***(G-10271)***
Roberts Lumber Company Inc...850 584-4573
3655 E Us 27 Hwy Perry (32347) ***(G-14312)***
Roberts Printing, Clearwater *Also called Roberts Quality Printing Inc* ***(G-1862)***
Roberts Quality Printing Inc...727 442-4011
2049 Calumet St Clearwater (33765) ***(G-1862)***
Roberts Vault Co Inc...352 567-0110
14621 Roberts Barn Rd Dade City (33523) ***(G-2433)***
Robertson Billiard Sups Inc...813 229-2778
1721 N Franklin St Tampa (33602) ***(G-18065)***
Robertson Transformer Co...708 388-2315
4152 Independence Ct C2 Sarasota (34234) ***(G-16560)***
Robertson Worldwide, Sarasota *Also called Robertson Transformer Co* ***(G-16560)***
Robinson Fans Inc...724 452-6121
3955 Drane Field Rd Lakeland (33811) ***(G-7780)***
Robomow USA Inc...844 762-6669
9050 16th Pl Ste 1 Vero Beach (32966) ***(G-18659)***
Robot-Costumes Technologies...904 535-0074
120 Cumberland Park Dr # 305 Saint Augustine (32095) ***(G-15598)***
Robotic Parking Systems Inc...727 539-7275
12812 60th St N Clearwater (33760) ***(G-1863)***
Robotic Security Systems Inc...850 871-9300
6530 E Highway 22 Panama City (32404) ***(G-13946)***
Robotics Fabrication Inc...850 896-4987
5835 Bay Line Dr Panama City (32404) ***(G-13947)***
Robotray, Miami *Also called Bcdirect Corp* ***(G-9229)***
Robs Bageland Inc...954 640-5470
8201 W Sunrise Blvd Plantation (33322) ***(G-14544)***
Robson Corporation...941 753-6935
2231 Whitfield Park Loop Sarasota (34243) ***(G-16286)***
Roccos Custom Cases Corp...305 799-2841
6965 W 2nd Ln Hialeah (33014) ***(G-5603)***
Rochester Electro-Medical Inc...813 994-7519
11711 Nw 39th St Coral Springs (33065) ***(G-2306)***
Rock & Roll, West Palm Beach *Also called Noa International Inc* ***(G-18967)***
Rock Bottom Bottles LLC...901 237-9929
1447 Tallevast Rd Sarasota (34243) ***(G-16287)***
Rock Brick Pavers Inc...407 692-6816
344 S Hart Blvd Orlando (32835) ***(G-13144)***
Rock Brothers Brewing LLC...917 324-8175
1901 N 15th St Tampa (33605) ***(G-18066)***
Rock Intl Distributors Inc...305 513-3314
8279 Nw 66th St Miami (33166) ***(G-10272)***
Rock My World Inc...727 623-4646
17733 Long Point Dr Redington Shores (33708) ***(G-15260)***
Rock N Roll Custom Screened S...727 528-2111
4590 62nd Ave N Pinellas Park (33781) ***(G-14385)***
Rock Ridge Materials Inc...321 268-8455
1525 White Dr Titusville (32780) ***(G-18460)***
Rock River Tool Inc...941 753-6343
2953 63rd Ave E Bradenton (34203) ***(G-1106)***
Rockers Stone Inc...305 447-1231
3615 Plaza St Miami (33133) ***(G-10273)***
Rocket Crafters Launch LLC...321 222-0858
305 Brevard Ave Cocoa (32922) ***(G-2049)***
Rocket International Inc...239 275-0880
2803 Sw 33rd St Cape Coral (33914) ***(G-1461)***
Rocket Sign Supplies LLC...239 995-4684
3587 Vrnica S Shmker Blvd Fort Myers (33916) ***(G-4585)***
Rocket Towne Inc...561 478-1274
412 Tall Pines Rd West Palm Beach (33413) ***(G-19022)***
Rocket Vending Inc...561 672-1373
19234 S Creekshore Ct Boca Raton (33498) ***(G-692)***
Rockford Ettco Procunier Inc...863 688-0071
304 Winston Creek Pkwy Lakeland (33810) ***(G-7781)***
Rockledge Phrm Mfg LLC...321 636-0717
417 Richard Rd Rockledge (32955) ***(G-15444)***
Rockpack Inc...407 757-0798
2549 Clark St Apopka (32703) ***(G-182)***
Rockstone Brick Pavers...813 685-3900
401 S Parsons Ave Ste F Brandon (33511) ***(G-1175)***
Rockwell Cllins Vsual Dsplay S, Orlando *Also called Rockwell Collins Inc* ***(G-13145)***
Rockwell Collins, Wellington *Also called B/E Aerospace Inc* ***(G-18710)***
Rockwell Collins Inc...321 768-7492
795 W Nasa Blvd Melbourne (32901) ***(G-8920)***
Rockwell Collins Inc...305 459-7000
9100 Nw 105th Cir Medley (33178) ***(G-8719)***
Rockwell Collins Inc...866 786-0290
12600 Challenger Pkwy # 130 Orlando (32826) ***(G-13145)***
Rockwell Collins Inc...321 768-7303
1100 W Hibiscus Blvd Melbourne (32901) ***(G-8921)***
Rocky Bayou Enterprises Inc...850 244-4567
630 Lovejoy Rd Nw Fort Walton Beach (32548) ***(G-4829)***
Rockymountain Lifenet...863 533-5168
5581 Airport Blvd Bartow (33830) ***(G-331)***
Rocla Concrete Tie Inc...772 800-1855
600 S 3rd St Fort Pierce (34950) ***(G-4741)***
Rod Biscayne Manufacturing...305 884-0808
425 E 9th St Hialeah (33010) ***(G-5604)***
Rod-Speed Inc...786 426-3996
8901 Nw 109th Ct Unit 903 Doral (33178) ***(G-3488)***
Roden International Inc (PA)...954 929-1900
2806 N 29th Ave Hollywood (33020) ***(G-5902)***
Rodents On The Road, East Palatka *Also called Karnak Corporation* ***(G-3604)***
Rodes Printing Corp...305 559-5263
8369 Bird Rd Miami (33155) ***(G-10274)***
Rodriguez Welding...305 856-3749
220 Sw 6th St Miami (33130) ***(G-10275)***
Roebic Laboratories Inc...561 799-3380
1213 Ocean Dunes Cir Jupiter (33477) ***(G-7105)***
Rogers Holster Co, Jacksonville *Also called Safariland LLC* ***(G-6747)***
Rogers Septic Tanks Inc...203 259-9947
10603 Sw Capraia Way Port Saint Lucie (34986) ***(G-15139)***
Rogers Sign Corp...352 799-1923
701 S Lemon Ave Brooksville (34601) ***(G-1265)***
Rogue Industries LLC...850 797-9228
217 Miracle Strip Pkwy Se Fort Walton Beach (32548) ***(G-4830)***
Rokey Corporation...561 470-0164
18188 Blue Lake Way Boca Raton (33498) ***(G-693)***
Rolin Industries Inc...850 654-1704
94 Ready Ave Nw Unit A1 Fort Walton Beach (32548) ***(G-4831)***
Roll A Way, Tampa *Also called Valco Group Inc* ***(G-18232)***
Roll-A-Guard, Largo *Also called Aabc Inc* ***(G-7882)***
Rolladen Inc...954 454-4114
1328 Bennett Dr Longwood (32750) ***(G-8332)***
Roller Coat Industries, Tampa *Also called Rollercoat Industries Inc* ***(G-18067)***
Roller Die + Forming...502 804-5571
4630 County Road 209 S Green Cove Springs (32043) ***(G-5068)***
Rollercoat Industries Inc...813 621-4668
10135 E Us Highway 92 Tampa (33610) ***(G-18067)***
Rollertech Corp...239 645-6698
5845 Corporation Cir Fort Myers (33905) ***(G-4586)***
Rolling Door Parts Inc...305 888-5020
8187 Nw 71st St Miami (33166) ***(G-10276)***
Rolling Greens Mobile Home Pk...352 624-0022
1899 Se 58th Ave Ocala (34480) ***(G-12039)***
Rolling Greens News...352 236-0007
1720 Ne 49th Ave Ocala (34470) ***(G-12040)***
Rolling Shield Incorporated...305 436-6661
9875 Nw 79th Ave Miami Lakes (33016) ***(G-10852)***
Rolling Shield Parts Inc...305 436-6661
9875 Nw 79th Ave Miami Lakes (33016) ***(G-10853)***
Rolls Axle Lc...813 764-0242
702 Hitchcock St Plant City (33563) ***(G-14463)***
Rolls Rite Trailers Inc...850 526-2290
3741 Industrial Park Dr Marianna (32446) ***(G-8585)***
Rollshield LLC...727 441-2243
1151 Kapp Dr Clearwater (33765) ***(G-1864)***
Rolltech Hurricanes Shutters, Pensacola *Also called Adams Hurricane Protection Inc* ***(G-14081)***
Rolsafe LLC...239 225-2487
12801 Commwl Dr Ste 7 Fort Myers (33913) ***(G-4587)***

Rolu Woodcraft Inc...305 685-0914
4733 E 11th Ave Hialeah (33013) ***(G-5605)***
Roma Casting Inc...305 577-0289
14 Ne 1st Ave Ste 306 Miami (33132) ***(G-10277)***
Romano Group LLC...305 255-4242
12253 Sw 130th St Miami (33186) ***(G-10278)***
Romark Laboratories LC...813 282-8544
3000 Bayport Dr Ste 200 Tampa (33607) ***(G-18068)***
Romco Fuels Inc...954 474-5392
10835 Sw 38th Dr Davie (33328) ***(G-2586)***
Rome Supply, Pompano Beach *Also called Bari Millwork & Supply LLC* ***(G-14615)***
Romeo Ohana LLC...808 500-3420
138 Mariner Blvd Spring Hill (34609) ***(G-16861)***
Romeo Roseau Ecommerce...561 633-1352
245 Ne 6th Ave Boynton Beach (33435) ***(G-956)***
Romeros Pallets of Jax...904 329-2962
3151 W Beaver St Jacksonville (32254) ***(G-6734)***
Romine Reprographics Svcs, Apopka *Also called Design & Print Solutions Inc* ***(G-130)***
Ron Matusalem & Matusa Fla Inc...305 448-8255
1205 Sw 37th Ave Ste 300 Miami (33135) ***(G-10279)***
Ronaele Mustang Inc...954 319-7433
5965 Manchester Way Tamarac (33321) ***(G-17367)***
Ronald A Ferguson...786 488-4019
710 Nw 5th Ave Fort Lauderdale (33311) ***(G-4212)***
Ronald M Hart Inc...772 600-8497
43 Sw Osceola St Stuart (34994) ***(G-17003)***
Ronca Industries LLC...407 839-0440
719 Peachtree Rd Ste 100 Orlando (32804) ***(G-13146)***
Ronco Aircraft and Marine Inc (PA)...321 220-0209
1774 Plantation Cir Se Palm Bay (32909) ***(G-13532)***
Ronco Machine Inc...904 827-9795
2100 Dennis St Jacksonville (32204) ***(G-6735)***
Ronecker Holdings LLC...813 855-5559
303 Mears Blvd Oldsmar (34677) ***(G-12268)***
Ronmar Industries Inc...561 630-8035
8990 Lakes Blvd West Palm Beach (33412) ***(G-19023)***
Ronnie & Moes Italian Ice LLC...786 970-1805
7900 Nw 27th Ave Ste 602a Miami (33147) ***(G-10280)***
Ronnies Welding & Machine...305 238-0972
18640 Sw 104th Ct Cutler Bay (33157) ***(G-2410)***
Rons Safe & Vault Company...305 527-2901
5541 W Broward Blvd Plantation (33317) ***(G-14545)***
Rontan North America Inc...305 599-2974
7859 Nw 46th St Ste 5b Doral (33166) ***(G-3489)***
Roof Hugger Inc...813 909-4424
142 Whitaker Rd Ste B Lutz (33549) ***(G-8414)***
Roof Tile Administration Inc...863 467-0042
1289 Ne 9th Ave Okeechobee (34972) ***(G-12189)***
Roof Tile Inc...863 467-0042
1289 Ne 9th Ave Okeechobee (34972) ***(G-12190)***
Roof-A-Cide West LLC...877 258-8998
1640 Field Rd Sarasota (34231) ***(G-16561)***
Roorda Buiders Inc...727 410-7776
15115 Race Track Rd Odessa (33556) ***(G-12147)***
Root International Inc (PA)...813 265-1808
4910 Creekside Dr Ste B Clearwater (33760) ***(G-1865)***
Rope Works Inc...954 525-6575
262 Sw 33rd St Fort Lauderdale (33315) ***(G-4213)***
Roper Industrial Pdts Inv Co...941 556-2601
6901 Prof Pkwy E Ste 200 Sarasota (34240) ***(G-16562)***
Roper Technologies Inc (PA)...941 556-2601
6901 Prof Pkwy E Ste 200 Sarasota (34240) ***(G-16563)***
Roque Brothers Corp...305 885-6995
5646 Nw 35th Ct Miami (33142) ***(G-10281)***
Roro Inc...561 909-6220
300 S Australian Ave # 16 West Palm Beach (33401) ***(G-19024)***
Ros Holding Corporation...954 581-9200
3201 W State Road 84 Fort Lauderdale (33312) ***(G-4214)***
Roscioli International Inc (PA)...941 755-7411
3201 W State Road 84 Fort Lauderdale (33312) ***(G-4215)***
Roscioli International Inc...941 755-7411
6111 21st St E Bradenton (34203) ***(G-1107)***
Rose Poster Printing, Miami Lakes *Also called Outdoor America Images Inc* ***(G-10833)***
Rose Printing Co Inc...850 339-8093
2504 Harriman Cir Tallahassee (32308) ***(G-17317)***
Rosebandits LLC (PA)...305 778-6370
740 San Esteban Ave Coral Gables (33146) ***(G-2191)***
Rosebel Gold Mines NV, Doral *Also called Iamgold Purchasing Svcs Inc* ***(G-3386)***
Roselle Publishing...813 907-5250
6415 Gentle Ben Cir Wesley Chapel (33544) ***(G-18758)***
Rosier Manufacturing Company...386 409-7223
409 W Intl Speedway Blvd Daytona Beach (32114) ***(G-2705)***
Ross Industries Inc...954 752-2800
11440 W Sample Rd Pompano Beach (33065) ***(G-14834)***
Ross Pivnik...305 254-1635
9380 Sw 125th Ter Miami (33176) ***(G-10282)***
Ross Slade Inc...813 250-0488
205 N Armenia Ave Ste 101 Tampa (33609) ***(G-18069)***
Rossam Industries Inc...305 493-5111
811 Nw 57th Pl Fort Lauderdale (33309) ***(G-4216)***
Rossiter Manufacturing...386 409-7223
409 W Intl Speedway Blvd Daytona Beach (32114) ***(G-2706)***
Rosuca International LLC...305 332-5572
5639 Nw 113th Ct Doral (33178) ***(G-3490)***
Rotab Inc...954 447-7746
20950 Sheridan St Fort Lauderdale (33332) ***(G-4217)***
Rotary Manufacturing LLC...941 564-8038
3276 Commerce Pkwy North Port (34289) ***(G-11748)***
Rotburg Instruments Amer Inc...954 331-8046
1560 Sawgrass Corporate Sunrise (33323) ***(G-17170)***
Rotech Oxygen & Medical Equip...352 291-1070
3300 Sw 34th Ave Ste 116 Ocala (34474) ***(G-12041)***
Roth Lighting, Fort Lauderdale *Also called Roth Southeast Lighting LLC* ***(G-4218)***
Roth Southeast Lighting LLC...954 423-6640
204 Sw 21st Ter Fort Lauderdale (33312) ***(G-4218)***
Rotor Works, Sarasota *Also called Florida Sncast Helicopters LLC* ***(G-16214)***
Round Table Tools Inc...850 877-7650
3645 Hartsfield Rd Tallahassee (32303) ***(G-17318)***
Rourke Educational Media LLC...772 234-6001
2066 14th Ave Ste 101 Vero Beach (32960) ***(G-18660)***
Rourke Publishing Group, Vero Beach *Also called Rourke Ray Publishing Co Inc* ***(G-18661)***
Rourke Ray Publishing Co Inc...772 234-6001
1701 Highway A1a Ste 300 Vero Beach (32963) ***(G-18661)***
Roux Laboratories Inc (HQ)...904 366-2602
5344 Overmyer Dr Jacksonville (32254) ***(G-6736)***
Roux Laboratories Inc...904 378-4167
5344 Overmyer Dr Jacksonville (32254) ***(G-6737)***
Rouzbeh Inc...727 587-7077
9700 Ulmerton Rd Largo (33771) ***(G-8042)***
Rover Aerospace Inc...305 594-7799
2254 Nw 94th Ave Doral (33172) ***(G-3491)***
Rowe Industries Inc...302 855-0585
2525 Sw 32nd Ave Pembroke Park (33023) ***(G-14011)***
Rowe Manufacturing LLC...407 324-5757
722 Golden Spike Ln Sanford (32771) ***(G-16111)***
Rowell Laboratories Inc...407 929-9445
174 Semoran Commerce Pl # 110 Apopka (32703) ***(G-183)***
Rowell Labs, Apopka *Also called Rowell Laboratories Inc* ***(G-183)***
Rowland Publishing Inc...850 878-0554
1932 Miccosukee Rd Tallahassee (32308) ***(G-17319)***
Rowland Specialists, Fort Lauderdale *Also called Florida Pwrtrain Hydrulics Inc* ***(G-4003)***
Rox Volleyball...877 769-2121
3520 Ag Ctr Dr Ste 310 Saint Augustine (32092) ***(G-15599)***
Roy Smith S Screen...561 792-3381
16648 71st Ln N Loxahatchee (33470) ***(G-8363)***
Royal Ancient Superfoods...305 600-1747
10530 Nw 37th Ter Doral (33178) ***(G-3492)***
Royal Atlantic Ventures LLC...561 243-9699
1505 Poinsettia Dr H-9 Delray Beach (33444) ***(G-3136)***
Royal Baths Manufacturing Co...407 854-1740
1920 Premier Row Orlando (32809) ***(G-13147)***
Royal Blinds LLC...786 253-8126
13006 Sw 50th St Miami (33175) ***(G-10283)***
Royal Canes...727 474-0792
12399 Belcher Rd S # 160 Largo (33773) ***(G-8043)***
Royal Concrete Concepts Inc (PA)...561 689-5398
1410 Park Ln S Ste 2 Jupiter (33458) ***(G-7106)***
Royal Crown Developers LLC...561 305-4588
9880 Marina Blvd Apt 1513 Boca Raton (33428) ***(G-694)***
Royal Cup Coffee, Pensacola *Also called Royal Cup Inc* ***(G-14254)***
Royal Cup Inc...813 664-8902
3502 Queen Palm Dr Ste A Tampa (33619) ***(G-18070)***
Royal Cup Inc...850 436-4435
3741 N Davis Hwy 78 Pensacola (32503) ***(G-14254)***
Royal Headwear & EMB Inc...305 889-8480
7675 Nw 80th Ter Medley (33166) ***(G-8720)***
Royal Identity Incorporated...813 405-4940
522 Oakfield Dr Brandon (33511) ***(G-1176)***
Royal Manor Vineyard & Winery...386 684-6270
224 Royal Ave Interlachen (32148) ***(G-6079)***
Royal Palm Press Inc...941 575-4299
25560 Technology Blvd Punta Gorda (33950) ***(G-15230)***
Royal Patio Mfg, Sarasota *Also called Dgp Enterprises Inc* ***(G-16206)***
Royal Precision Products Inc (PA)...305 685-5490
13171 Nw 43rd Ave Opa Locka (33054) ***(G-12356)***
Royal Press, Orlando *Also called Fermatex Enterprises Inc* ***(G-12736)***
Royal Prestige...813 464-9872
5221 Nw 33rd Ave Fort Lauderdale (33309) ***(G-4219)***
Royal Splits Inc (PA)...310 935-6699
6633 Voltaire Dr Orlando (32809) ***(G-13148)***
Royal Tees Inc...941 366-0056
5556 Palmer Blvd Sarasota (34232) ***(G-16564)***
Royal Truss Corp...786 222-1100
10900 Nw South River Dr Medley (33178) ***(G-8721)***
Royalty Enterprises LLC...786 380-7774
221 Meridian Ave Apt 508 Miami Beach (33139) ***(G-10706)***
Royce, Sarasota *Also called Rp International LLC* ***(G-16566)***
Royce International LLC (HQ)...941 894-1228
3400 S Tamiami Trl # 300 Sarasota (34239) ***(G-16565)***

Rozar Logging Inc 352 267-0829
847 Crawford Rd Groveland (34736) ***(G-5107)***
Rp High Performance Inc 561 863-2800
2391 President Barack Oba Riviera Beach (33404) ***(G-15374)***
Rp International LLC (PA) 941 894-1228
3400 S Tamiami Trl # 300 Sarasota (34239) ***(G-16566)***
Rpd Management LLC 904 710-8911
720 King St Jacksonville (32204) ***(G-6738)***
Rperf Technologies Corp 954 629-2359
6584 Nw 56th Dr Coral Springs (33067) ***(G-2307)***
RPM, Rockledge *Also called Rockledge Phrm Mfg LLC* ***(G-15444)***
RPM Co 352 542-3110
27908 Se Hwy 19 Old Town (32680) ***(G-12199)***
RPM Displays, Hobe Sound *Also called R P M Industries Inc* ***(G-5726)***
RPM Graphics Inc 239 275-3278
508 Owen Ave N Lehigh Acres (33971) ***(G-8206)***
Rpp Devices 772 807-7098
625 Nw Commodity Cv Port Saint Lucie (34986) ***(G-15140)***
Rq Inc 305 879-1773
2443 W 4th Ct Hialeah (33010) ***(G-5606)***
Rq Welding Inc 786 609-3384
6011 Sw 109th Ave Miami (33173) ***(G-10284)***
Rrhill Printing Solutions Inc 786 897-2432
16637 Sw 81st Ter Miami (33193) ***(G-10285)***
RS&m Consultants 727 323-6983
2350 34th St N Ste 140 Saint Petersburg (33713) ***(G-15903)***
RSC Industries Inc 813 886-4711
5451 W Waters Ave Tampa (33634) ***(G-18071)***
RSD Industries Inc 954 240-3660
1612 Funston St Hollywood (33020) ***(G-5903)***
RSR Industrial Coatings Inc 863 537-1110
1577 Centennial Blvd Bartow (33830) ***(G-332)***
Rssi Barriers Llc 850 871-9300
6530 E Highway 22 Panama City (32404) ***(G-13948)***
Rsss 1 LLC 941 483-3293
224 Pensacola Rd Venice (34285) ***(G-18571)***
Rt22 Creations Inc 954 254-8258
1305 Ne 3rd Ave Pompano Beach (33060) ***(G-14835)***
Rta Cabinets & More LLC 321 288-3068
222 E Eau Gallie Blvd Indian Harbour Beach (32937) ***(G-6066)***
RTC Software LLC 407 765-7462
14602 Black Cherry Trl Winter Garden (34787) ***(G-19284)***
RTC Solutions Inc 919 439-8680
4370 Oakes Rd Ste 700 Davie (33314) ***(G-2587)***
Rti Donor Services Inc 321 431-2464
401 N Wickham Rd Ste 143 Melbourne (32935) ***(G-8922)***
Rti Surgical Inc 386 418-8888
11621 Research Cir Alachua (32615) ***(G-16)***
Rtp Corp 954 597-5333
2832 Center Port Cir Pompano Beach (33064) ***(G-14836)***
Rubber 2 Go Llc 305 688-8566
3551 Nw 116th St Miami (33167) ***(G-10286)***
Rubber B LLC 305 771-2369
605 Lincoln Rd Ste 210 Miami Beach (33139) ***(G-10707)***
Rubens Custom Cabinets Inc 813 510-8397
1310 W Termino St Tampa (33612) ***(G-18072)***
Rubin Iron Works LLC 904 356-5635
608 Carmen St Jacksonville (32206) ***(G-6739)***
Rubinelli Woodwork Inc 954 445-0537
8891 Sw 16th St Boca Raton (33433) ***(G-695)***
Rubingers Manufacturing Co 863 665-1599
2626 Mine And Mill Ln Lakeland (33801) ***(G-7782)***
Ruby Vanrum 850 643-5155
12167 Nw Freeman Rd Bristol (32321) ***(G-1203)***
Rubyquartz Technology LLC 305 406-0211
10400 Nw 33rd St Ste 290 Doral (33172) ***(G-3493)***
Rudd & Son Welding Inc 850 476-2110
81 E Ten Mile Rd Pensacola (32534) ***(G-14255)***
Rudd Welding, Pensacola *Also called Rudd & Son Welding Inc* ***(G-14255)***
Rudders River Rock 239 574-5656
1901 Se 15th Pl Apt A Cape Coral (33990) ***(G-1462)***
Rudolph & ME, Port Charlotte *Also called Edmund C Miga* ***(G-14976)***
Rudys Ready Mix 305 382-9283
5800 Sw 122nd Ave Miami (33183) ***(G-10287)***
Rugby Road Corp 407 328-5474
3941 Saint Johns Pkwy Sanford (32771) ***(G-16112)***
Rugged Industries Inc 239 565-2723
20041 Legacy Ct Estero (33928) ***(G-3695)***
Ruiz Industries 305 218-6258
10752 Sw 143rd Ave Miami (33186) ***(G-10288)***
Ruke Inc 239 292-2553
1226 Main St Windermere (34786) ***(G-19242)***
Rulon Company of Georgia 904 584-1400
2000 Ring Way Saint Augustine (32092) ***(G-15600)***
Runaware Inc 954 907-9052
5440 Nw 108th Way Coral Springs (33076) ***(G-2308)***
Runn-It LLC 800 932-8052
66 W Flagler St Ste 900 Miami (33130) ***(G-10289)***
Running Board Warehouse, Ocala *Also called Thi E-Commerce LLC* ***(G-12060)***
Rupp Marine Inc 772 286-5300
4761 Se Anchor Ave Stuart (34997) ***(G-17004)***
Rusch Electric Motor Repair Co 727 319-3388
13000 Lois Ave Seminole (33776) ***(G-16760)***
Rush Flyers 954 332-0509
6561 Nw 18th Ct Plantation (33313) ***(G-14546)***
Rush Signs 407 308-6362
1612 Prgrine Flcons Way A Orlando (32837) ***(G-13149)***
Rush To Excellence Prtg Inc 904 367-0100
4204 Spring Park Rd Jacksonville (32207) ***(G-6740)***
Russanos Express LLC 772 220-3329
2946 Sw Mapp Rd Palm City (34990) ***(G-13672)***
Russell Associates Inc (HQ) 727 815-3100
10540 Ridge Rd Ste 300 New Port Richey (34654) ***(G-11509)***
Russell Bindery, Saint Augustine *Also called Russells Bindery Inc* ***(G-15601)***
Russell Bros Alum Andzing Ctin 407 323-5619
1001 Cornwall Rd Sanford (32773) ***(G-16113)***
Russell Bros Alum Anodizing, Sanford *Also called Russell Bros Alum Andzing Ctin* ***(G-16113)***
Russell Hobbs Inc (HQ) 954 883-1000
3633 S Flamingo Rd Miramar (33027) ***(G-11037)***
Russell Home Imprvmnt Ctr Inc 954 436-9186
3250 Sw 131st Ter Davie (33330) ***(G-2588)***
Russells Bindery Inc 904 829-3100
90 Palmer St Saint Augustine (32084) ***(G-15601)***
Rustic Steel Creations Inc 813 222-0016
3919 N Highland Ave Tampa (33603) ***(G-18073)***
Ruvos LLC (PA) 850 254-7270
2252 Klarn Ctr Blvd Tallahassee (32309) ***(G-17320)***
Rv Air Inc (PA) 309 657-4300
628 Cleveland St Apt 1407 Clearwater (33755) ***(G-1866)***
Rvcc of Florida 352 569-5870
2540 W C 48 Bushnell (33513) ***(G-1320)***
Rvr Elettronica, Doral *Also called RVr USA LLC* ***(G-3494)***
RVr USA LLC 305 471-9091
7782 Nw 46th St 20 Doral (33166) ***(G-3494)***
Rwc Group LLC 754 222-1407
3901 Ne 12th Ave Ste 400 Pompano Beach (33064) ***(G-14837)***
Rwla Enterprises LLC 772 334-1248
2810 Se Dune Dr Apt 1104 Stuart (34996) ***(G-17005)***
Rx For Fleas Inc 954 351-9244
6555 Powerline Rd Ste 412 Fort Lauderdale (33309) ***(G-4220)***
Rxenergy LLC 727 726-4204
2449 N Mcmullen Booth Rd Clearwater (33759) ***(G-1867)***
Rxgenesys LLC 786 220-8366
175 Sw 7th St Ste 2417 Miami (33130) ***(G-10290)***
Rxprinting and Graphics LLC 407 965-3039
4909 S Orange Ave Orlando (32806) ***(G-13150)***
Ryan Manufacturing Inc 386 325-3644
339b State Road 207 East Palatka (32131) ***(G-3606)***
Ryan Petroleum, Fort Myers *Also called Ryan Tire & Petroleum Inc* ***(G-4588)***
Ryan Scientific LLC 904 284-6025
4035a Reynolds Blvd Green Cove Springs (32043) ***(G-5069)***
Ryan Tire & Petroleum Inc 239 334-1351
2650 Edison Ave Fort Myers (33916) ***(G-4588)***
Ryd Enterprises, Miami *Also called R Y D Enterprises Inc* ***(G-10233)***
Ryder Orthopedics Inc (PA) 239 939-0009
1500 Royal Palm Square Bl Fort Myers (33919) ***(G-4589)***
Ryder Welding Service Inc 305 685-6630
350 Ali Baba Ave Opa Locka (33054) ***(G-12357)***
Ryman Hospitality Prpts Inc 904 284-2770
625 Oak St Green Cove Springs (32043) ***(G-5070)***
Rytex Industries Inc 727 557-7450
12855 Belcher Rd S Largo (33773) ***(G-8044)***
Rz Service Group LLC 904 402-2313
12574 Flagler Center Blvd Jacksonville (32258) ***(G-6741)***
S & B Industries Inc 305 367-1068
11052 Sw 162nd Ter Miami (33157) ***(G-10291)***
S & B Metal Products E Fla Inc 386 274-0092
1811 Holsonback Dr Daytona Beach (32117) ***(G-2707)***
S & B Metal Products S Fla Inc 941 727-3669
6012 31st St E Bradenton (34203) ***(G-1108)***
S & B Metal Products S Fla Inc (PA) 941 727-3669
5301 Gateway Blvd Lakeland (33811) ***(G-7783)***
S & J Custom Fabrication Inc 352 246-1462
5955 Indian Trl Keystone Heights (32656) ***(G-7211)***
S & K Prfmce Machining & Fab 954 306-2214
11911 Nw 27th Ct Plantation (33323) ***(G-14547)***
S & R Fastener Co Inc 352 588-0768
30241 Commerce Dr San Antonio (33576) ***(G-15978)***
S & S Enterprises, Summerfield *Also called Stephen Shives* ***(G-17063)***
S & S Metal and Plastics Inc 904 731-4655
3740 Morton St Jacksonville (32217) ***(G-6742)***
S & S Performance Inc 305 951-9846
80460 Overseas Hwy Islamorada (33036) ***(G-6099)***
S & S Precast Inc 239 992-8685
25095 Old 41 Rd Bonita Springs (34135) ***(G-852)***
S & S Propeller Co Inc 718 359-3393
3040 Sw 10th St Pompano Beach (33069) ***(G-14838)***
S & S Welding Inc 863 533-2888
2850 Us Highway 17 S Bartow (33830) ***(G-333)***

S & W Nash Seafood, Apalachicola *Also called Miracle Seafood Manufacturers (G-98)*
S + L Millworks Inc....813 413-6260
18631 Avenue Capri Lutz (33558) **(G-8415)**
S A Feather Co Inc....239 693-6363
5852 Enterprise Pkwy Fort Myers (33905) **(G-4590)**
S A Florikan-E LLC....800 322-8666
2404 Commerce Ct Bowling Green (33834) **(G-868)**
S A Gloria Corp....305 575-2900
6705 S Red Rd Ste 405 South Miami (33143) **(G-16826)**
S A Microtechnologies LLC....954 973-6166
2901 Gateway Dr Pompano Beach (33069) **(G-14839)**
S Aj Cabinets Inc....321 264-2872
4950 Harrison Rd Mims (32754) **(G-10952)**
S and S Morris LLC....404 431-7803
1630 Assisi Dr Sarasota (34231) **(G-16567)**
S B Lighting LLC....850 687-1166
2889 N Highway 81 Ponce De Leon (32455) **(G-14918)**
S C R Precision Tube Bending....813 622-7091
5407 24th Ave S Tampa (33619) **(G-18074)**
S D Modular Displays, Fort Lauderdale *Also called Sdm Acquisition Corporation (G-4226)*
S E Inc....407 859-9317
6448 Pinecastle Blvd # 104 Orlando (32809) **(G-13151)**
S E S, Hialeah *Also called Select Engineered Systems Inc (G-5613)*
S F C, Medley *Also called South Florida Concrete & Rdymx (G-8725)*
S G M, Pompano Beach *Also called Southern Grouts & Mortars Inc (G-14863)*
S Gager Industries Inc....904 268-6727
11436 Philips Hwy Jacksonville (32256) **(G-6743)**
S I P Corporation....813 884-8300
7210 Anderson Rd Ste A Tampa (33634) **(G-18075)**
S J Turbine LLC....954 804-4779
1109 Waterbrook Ln Weston (33326) **(G-19165)**
S King Fulton Div, Hallandale Beach *Also called International Dock Products (G-5191)*
S M D Research Inc....561 451-9895
9151 Pine Springs Dr Boca Raton (33428) **(G-696)**
S M I, Largo *Also called Suncoast Molders Inc (G-8063)*
S M I Cabinetry Inc....407 841-0292
2525 N Orange Blossom Trl Orlando (32804) **(G-13152)**
S N S Auto Sports LLC....727 546-2700
7061 49th St N Pinellas Park (33781) **(G-14386)**
S O S Printing & Office Supply, Destin *Also called Weidenhamer Corporation (G-3211)*
S P Manufacturing LLC....305 362-0456
2208 W 79th St Hialeah (33016) **(G-5607)**
S P Sheet Metal Co Inc....609 698-8800
5500 Military Trl Ste 22 Jupiter (33458) **(G-7107)**
S Printing Inc....305 633-3343
2207 Nw 23rd Ave Miami (33142) **(G-10292)**
S R P, Bradenton *Also called Southern Reinforced Plastics (G-1118)*
S R Q Storm Protection LLC....941 341-0334
1899 Porter Lake Dr # 105 Sarasota (34240) **(G-16568)**
S S Designs Inc....863 965-2576
5558 Commercial Blvd Winter Haven (33880) **(G-19353)**
S T A Sales, Clearwater *Also called Hutchins Co Inc (G-1722)*
S T Wooten Corporation....239 337-9486
16560 Mass Ct Fort Myers (33912) **(G-4591)**
S Tam Cabinets Inc....813 310-2263
5555 W Linebaugh Ave N Tampa (33624) **(G-18076)**
S V Bags America Inc....954 577-9091
1563 Sandpiper Cir Weston (33327) **(G-19166)**
S&B Pallet Corp....305 525-0872
14765 Sw 36th Ter Miami (33185) **(G-10293)**
S&H Arcylic Coatings Inc....352 232-1249
4673 Chamber Ct Spring Hill (34609) **(G-16862)**
S&J 34102 Inc....239 592-9388
609 E Jackson St Ste 100 Tampa (33602) **(G-18077)**
S&J Aluminum Works Inc....850 492-5700
5623 Bauer Rd Pensacola (32507) **(G-14256)**
S&J Logging Inc....904 237-7774
10471 Reid Stafford Rd Glen Saint Mary (32040) **(G-5038)**
S&L Cnstrction Specialists Inc....407 300-5080
13412 Heswall Run Orlando (32832) **(G-13153)**
S&P USA Vntilation Systems LLC....904 731-4711
6393 Powers Ave Jacksonville (32217) **(G-6744)**
S&S Consulting Partners LLC....850 803-8379
139 Bayside Dr Niceville (32578) **(G-11574)**
S&S Craftsmen Inc....813 247-4429
6404 E Columbus Dr Tampa (33619) **(G-18078)**
S&S Global Supply LLC....786 529-4799
730 W 38th Pl Hialeah (33012) **(G-5608)**
S&S Performance Marine, Islamorada *Also called S & S Performance Inc (G-6099)*
S.A. Feather Co., Inc. Florida, Fort Myers *Also called S A Feather Co Inc (G-4590)*
S2 Pass Holdings LLC....706 773-4097
116 Mc Davis Blvd # 230 Santa Rosa Beach (32459) **(G-16166)**
S4j Manufacturing Services Inc....239 574-9400
2685 Ne 9th Ave Cape Coral (33909) **(G-1463)**
Saas Transportation Inc....850 650-7709
3551 Scenic Highway 98 Destin (32541) **(G-3204)**
Saavy Naturals....904 372-0002
241 Atlantic Blvd Neptune Beach (32266) **(G-11477)**
Sab Fuels Inc....786 213-3399
2616 Stickney Point Rd Sarasota (34231) **(G-16569)**
Sabalo Boats....727 243-6767
1005 Gunn Hwy Odessa (33556) **(G-12148)**
Sabcon Underground LLC....863 268-8225
1730 Dundee Rd Winter Haven (33884) **(G-19354)**
Sabic Innovative Plastics....386 409-5540
703 South St New Smyrna Beach (32168) **(G-11541)**
Sabine Inc....386 418-2000
13301 Nw Us Highway 441 Alachua (32615) **(G-17)**
Sabrosol Laboratories LLC....305 290-4038
12585 Ne 7th Ave North Miami (33161) **(G-11653)**
Sachi Tech Inc....813 649-8028
5005 W Laurel St Ste 204 Tampa (33607) **(G-18079)**
Sacyr Environment USA LLC....202 361-4568
3191 Coral Way Ste 510 Miami (33145) **(G-10294)**
SAE, Orlando *Also called Sky Aerospace Engineering Inc (G-13196)*
Saf Aerospace LLC....813 376-0883
8006 N Highland Ave Tampa (33604) **(G-18080)**
Safari Programs Inc....305 621-1000
8010 Westside Indus Dr Jacksonville (32219) **(G-6745)**
Safari Sun LLC....407 339-7291
928 Josiane Ct Ste 1007 Altamonte Springs (32701) **(G-71)**
Safariland LLC....904 741-5400
3041 Faye Rd Jacksonville (32226) **(G-6746)**
Safariland LLC....904 646-0141
3041 Faye Rd Jacksonville (32226) **(G-6747)**
Safariland LLC (HQ)....904 741-5400
13386 International Pkwy Jacksonville (32218) **(G-6748)**
Safariland Group, Jacksonville *Also called Safariland LLC (G-6748)*
Safariland Group, The, Jacksonville *Also called Cadre Holdings Inc (G-6249)*
Safco Software....561 750-7879
7654 Solimar Cir Boca Raton (33433) **(G-697)**
Safe, Saint Augustine *Also called Security and Fire Elec Inc (G-15608)*
Safe Banks and Lock....954 762-3565
2870 Ne 55th Ct Fort Lauderdale (33308) **(G-4221)**
Safe Glass, Riviera Beach *Also called Security Impact GL Hldings LLC (G-15376)*
Safe Industries Inc....321 639-8646
396 Gus Hipp Blvd Ste B Rockledge (32955) **(G-15445)**
Safe Money Report, Jupiter *Also called Weiss Research Inc (G-7146)*
Safe Pro Inc....954 494-5768
1650 W 33rd Pl Hialeah (33012) **(G-5609)**
Safe Strap LLC....239 461-0033
13830 Jtport Cmmerce Pkwy Fort Myers (33913) **(G-4592)**
Safe Stride, Largo *Also called Kmss Products Inc (G-7994)*
Safe Workplace Inc (PA)....813 657-7233
10321 Buncombe Way San Antonio (33576) **(G-15979)**
Safeboot Corp....239 298-7000
2640 Golden Gate Pkwy # 1 Naples (34105) **(G-11388)**
Safecraft Rstraint Systems Inc....813 758-3571
3959 Van Dyke Rd Lutz (33558) **(G-8416)**
Safeguard America Inc (PA)....305 859-9000
3935 Nw 26th St Miami (33142) **(G-10295)**
Safeguard of South Florid....561 499-7600
1395 Nw 17th Ave Ste 104 Delray Beach (33445) **(G-3137)**
Safeprints LLC....305 960-7391
9155 S Dadeland Blvd # 1504 Miami (33156) **(G-10296)**
Safetarp Corp....904 824-7277
1950 State Road 16 Saint Augustine (32084) **(G-15602)**
Safetek International Inc (PA)....702 558-8202
6560 W Rogers Cir Boca Raton (33487) **(G-698)**
Safetogether Ltd Liability Co....954 227-2236
5917 Nw 63rd Way Parkland (33067) **(G-14000)**
Safety Clamps Inc....904 781-2809
233 Santa Barbara Ave Jacksonville (32254) **(G-6749)**
Safety Compliance Publ Inc....844 556-3149
3600 S State Road 7 # 204 Miramar (33023) **(G-11038)**
Safety Intl Bags & Straps....407 830-0888
160 Lyman Rd Casselberry (32707) **(G-1517)**
Safety Systems Barricades....407 674-8440
2513 Industrial Blvd Orlando (32804) **(G-13154)**
Safety Zone Specialists Inc....863 984-1385
2318 Old Combee Rd 107 Lakeland (33805) **(G-7784)**
Safilo Usa Inc....305 262-5727
703 Nw 62nd Ave Ste 100 Miami (33126) **(G-10297)**
Safran Power Uk Ltd....941 739-7207
2250 Whitfield Ave Sarasota (34243) **(G-16288)**
Safran Power Usa LLC....941 758-7726
2250 Whitfield Ave Sarasota (34243) **(G-16289)**
Saftron Manufacturing LLC....305 233-5511
6012 33rd St E Bradenton (34203) **(G-1109)**
Sage Implementations LLC....407 290-6952
7648 San Remo Pl Orlando (32835) **(G-13155)**
Sage Imports Corp....305 962-0631
232 Andalusia Ave Ste 201 Coral Gables (33134) **(G-2192)**
Sagrad Inc....321 726-9400
202 West Dr Melbourne (32904) **(G-8923)**
Sahara Cabinets Inc....239 334-1151
13296 Island Rd Fort Myers (33905) **(G-4593)**

ALPHABETIC

SAI Super Software Solutions......407 445-2520
5230 Cona Reef Ct Orlando (32810) *(G-13156)*
SAI/Rf of Florida......727 394-1012
16012 5th St E Redington Beach (33708) *(G-15259)*
Saikou Optics Incorporated......407 986-4200
3259 Progress Dr Ste 128 Orlando (32826) *(G-13157)*
Sailfish Woodworks LLC......772 708-2791
3061 Ne Heather Ct Jensen Beach (34957) *(G-6973)*
Sailor Made Cstm Woodworks LLC......805 587-1197
190 Wading Bird Cir Sw Palm Bay (32908) *(G-13533)*
Sailor Made Custom Woodworks L......805 587-1197
4260 Dow Rd Ste 401 Melbourne (32934) *(G-8924)*
Saint Augustine Cast Stone......904 794-2626
4960 Cres Technical Ct Saint Augustine (32086) *(G-15603)*
Saint George Industries LLC......786 212-1176
9130 S Dadelnd Blvd 180 Miami (33156) *(G-10298)*
Saint Judas Tadeus Foundry, Hialeah *Also called St Judas Tadeus Foundry Inc (G-5631)*
Saint Petersburg Cabinets Inc......727 327-4800
2547 24th Ave N Saint Petersburg (33713) *(G-15904)*
Saint Petersburg Times, Port Richey *Also called Times Publishing Company (G-15072)*
Saint-Gobain Corporation......863 425-3299
2377 State Road 37 S Mulberry (33860) *(G-11135)*
Saint-Gobain Vetrotex Amer Inc......407 834-8968
110 Atlantic Annex Pt Maitland (32751) *(G-8476)*
Sal Aerospace Engineering LLC......305 791-0593
11990 Sw 128th St Miami (33186) *(G-10299)*
Sal Praschnik Inc......305 866-4323
1090 Kane Cncurse Ste 101 Bay Harbor Islands (33154) *(G-339)*
Salco Industries Inc......941 377-7717
263 Field End St Sarasota (34240) *(G-16570)*
Salerno Pharmaceuticals LP......352 799-9813
16255 Aviation Loop Dr Brooksville (34604) *(G-1266)*
Sales, Tampa *Also called Outreach Corporation (G-17966)*
Salmi and Company Inc......443 243-8537
8328 Randall Dr Navarre (32566) *(G-11474)*
Salon By Destiny & Light, The, Tampa *Also called Destiny & Light Inc (G-17601)*
Salon Technologies Intl......407 301-3726
8810 Com Cir Ste 20-22 Orlando (32819) *(G-13158)*
Salsa Cuba Inc......305 993-9757
1275 W 49th St Hialeah (33012) *(G-5610)*
Salsa Pembroke Pines Inc......954 461-0532
601 Sw 145th Ter Pembroke Pines (33027) *(G-14058)*
Salsa Three Inc......954 990-2223
10167 W Sunrise Blvd Plantation (33322) *(G-14548)*
Salt 1 To 1......407 538-2134
11221 John Wycliffe Blvd Orlando (32832) *(G-13159)*
Salt 1to1 Inc......407 721-8107
214 N Goldenrod Rd Ste 8 Orlando (32807) *(G-13160)*
Salt International Corp......305 698-8889
2798 Sw 32nd Ave Pembroke Park (33023) *(G-14012)*
Salt Life LLC......904 595-5370
240 3rd St S Jacksonville Beach (32250) *(G-6957)*
Saltex Group Corp......305 477-3187
7509 Nw 36th St Miami (33166) *(G-10300)*
Salty Industries LLC......321 626-6331
231 6th Ave Melbourne Beach (32951) *(G-8984)*
Salvia Tile & Stone Inc......239 643-7770
303 Airport Pulling Rd N Naples (34104) *(G-11389)*
Sam S Accrsio Sons Pkg Prod In......305 246-3455
1225 Nw 2nd St Homestead (33030) *(G-5990)*
Sam Weiss Woodworking Inc......954 975-8158
5195 Nw 15th St Margate (33063) *(G-8566)*
Sam-E-Nik Corp......347 992-2123
330 Madeira Ave Coral Gables (33134) *(G-2193)*
Samara Publishing......305 361-3333
104 Crandon Blvd Ste 301 Key Biscayne (33149) *(G-7162)*
Samarian Products LLC......212 781-2121
780 Fifth Ave S Ste 200 Naples (34102) *(G-11390)*
Samark Technology Corporation......941 955-4325
15 Paradise Plz Ste 300 Sarasota (34239) *(G-16571)*
Sameday Printing Inc......800 411-3106
6815 Biscayne Blvd Miami (33138) *(G-10301)*
Saminco Inc (PA)......239 561-1561
10030 Amberwood Rd Ste 5 Fort Myers (33913) *(G-4594)*
Samjay Media Group Orlando LLC......407 865-7526
187 Sabal Palm Dr Ste 200 Longwood (32779) *(G-8333)*
Sampletech......727 239-7055
1953 Whitney Way Clearwater (33760) *(G-1868)*
Sams Gas......386 698-1033
2680 S Us Highway 17 Crescent City (32112) *(G-2341)*
Sams Led Signs & Services......407 492-4934
243 Whispering Pines Way Davenport (33837) *(G-2482)*
Samson Metal and Machine Inc (PA)......863 665-0283
3225 Us Highway 92 E Lakeland (33801) *(G-7785)*
San Bernardo Ice Cream, Miramar *Also called Food Marketing Consultants Inc (G-10992)*
San Marco Place Condo Assn......504 812-0352
1478 Riverplace Blvd Jacksonville (32207) *(G-6750)*
San Sebastian Winery, Saint Augustine *Also called Seavin Inc (G-15607)*
Sanacare, Miami *Also called Ace Sales Corp (G-9063)*
Sanastar Inc......954 323-2485
5079 N Dixie Hwy Ste 303 Oakland Park (33334) *(G-11836)*
Sanborn Resources Ltd......561 551-6161
777 S Flagler Dr West Palm Beach (33401) *(G-19025)*
Sanbornwebdesigns.com, Madeira Beach *Also called A Sanborn Corporation (G-8445)*
Sanbur Inc......941 371-7446
4118 Bee Ridge Rd Sarasota (34233) *(G-16572)*
Sanchelima Dairy Products, Miami *Also called Mambi Cheese Company Inc (G-9940)*
Sanchelima International Inc......305 591-4343
1783 Nw 93rd Ave Doral (33172) *(G-3495)*
Sanchez Brothers Corp......561 992-0062
6500 Us Highway 27 S South Bay (33493) *(G-16797)*
Sanchez Machine Shop LLC......863 494-1212
4 S Parker Ave Arcadia (34266) *(G-204)*
Sanctuary Intl Ministries......954 955-7818
1100 Nw 4th St Fort Lauderdale (33311) *(G-4222)*
Sand Dollar Charters LLC......903 734-5376
147 Middle Way New Smyrna Beach (32169) *(G-11542)*
Sand Hill Rock LLC......772 216-4852
7660 Ne 304th St Okeechobee (34972) *(G-12191)*
Sand Power Volleyball......813 786-8055
1601 Dogwood Ln Brandon (33510) *(G-1177)*
Sandale Utility Products......863 937-5208
2515 Commerce Point Dr Lakeland (33801) *(G-7786)*
Sandar Industries Inc......904 246-4309
1545 Main St Atlantic Beach (32233) *(G-226)*
Sanderson Pipe Corporation (PA)......904 275-3289
1 Enterprise Blvd Sanderson (32087) *(G-15983)*
Sandi Johnson......561 389-1035
10010 Se 125th Ct Dunnellon (34431) *(G-3599)*
Sandlife Volleyball, Brandon *Also called Sand Power Volleyball (G-1177)*
Sandow Media LLC......646 805-0200
3651 Fau Blvd Ste 200 Boca Raton (33431) *(G-699)*
Sandow Media LLC (PA)......561 961-7749
3651 Nw 8th Ave Ste 200 Boca Raton (33431) *(G-700)*
Sandow Media-Airport Linehaul, Boca Raton *Also called Sandow Media LLC (G-700)*
Sandow Specialty Printing Inc......305 255-5697
8260 Sw 151st St Palmetto Bay (33158) *(G-13853)*
Sandpaper Marketing Inc......850 939-8040
7502 Harvest Village Ct Navarre (32566) *(G-11475)*
Sandpaper Publishing Inc......850 939-8040
7502 Harvest Village Ct Gulf Breeze (32566) *(G-5125)*
Sandpiper Turbine LLC......407 377-7220
3955 Merlin Dr Kissimmee (34741) *(G-7294)*
Sands At St Lucie......772 489-9499
2750 S Us Highway 1 Fort Pierce (34982) *(G-4742)*
Sands Molding Inc......813 345-8646
23324 Gracewood Cir Land O Lakes (34639) *(G-7865)*
Sandvik Mining & Cnstr USA LLC (HQ)......386 462-4100
13500 Nw County Road 235 Alachua (32615) *(G-18)*
Sandy Finished Wood Inc......954 615-7271
3163 Sw 13th Ct Fort Lauderdale (33312) *(G-4223)*
Sandy Lender Inc......239 272-8613
2200 Nw 5th St Cape Coral (33993) *(G-1464)*
Sandy-Alexander Inc......727 579-1527
1527 102nd Ave N Saint Petersburg (33716) *(G-15905)*
Sanibel Print & Graphics......239 454-1001
15630 Mcgregor Blvd Ste 1 Fort Myers (33908) *(G-4595)*
Saniflow Corporation......305 424-2433
3325 Nw 70th Ave Miami (33122) *(G-10302)*
Sanit Technologies LLC......941 351-9114
7810 25th Ct E Unit 106 Sarasota (34243) *(G-16290)*
Sanitary Prcess Components Inc......407 650-8988
3711 Vineland Rd Orlando (32811) *(G-13161)*
Sanitation Products of America, Tallahassee *Also called Spa Concepts Inc (G-17328)*
Sanitube LLC (PA)......863 606-5960
180 Contractors Way Lakeland (33801) *(G-7787)*
Sano Associates Inc......239 403-2650
3827 Progress Ave Naples (34104) *(G-11391)*
Sanofi US Services Inc......407 736-0226
2501 Discovery Dr Orlando (32826) *(G-13162)*
Sanomedics Inc (PA)......305 433-7814
7777 Glades Rd Ste 100 Boca Raton (33434) *(G-701)*
Santa Bell Capitav Group, Sanibel *Also called Captiva Current Inc (G-16143)*
Santa Fe Truss Company Inc......386 454-7711
5079 Sw 80th Ave Bell (32619) *(G-343)*
Santa Rosa Auto Parts Inc......850 477-7747
50 Industrial Blvd Pensacola (32503) *(G-14257)*
Santiago......386 527-5822
2477 Guava Dr Port Orange (32128) *(G-15031)*
Santiago Chopper LLC (PA)......813 671-9097
10935 Sonora Dr Gibsonton (33534) *(G-5032)*
Santiago of Key West Inc......305 304-6063
1301 United St Key West (33040) *(G-7202)*
Santillana USA Pubg Co Inc (HQ)......305 591-9522
8333 Nw 53rd St Ste 402 Miami (33166) *(G-10303)*
Santiva Chronicle......239 437-9324
12860 Banyan Creek Dr Fort Myers (33908) *(G-4596)*
Santiva Chronicle LLC......239 472-0559
1420 Albatross Rd Sanibel (33957) *(G-16149)*

Santo Domingo Timber Co LLC......561 627-4000
3910 Rca Blvd Ste 1015 Palm Beach Gardens (33410) ***(G-13623)***
Santonis Jewelry Inc......407 298-4994
3191 Waterbridge Ln Kissimmee (34744) ***(G-7295)***
Santos Frozen Foods Inc......813 875-4901
2746 W Main St Tampa (33607) ***(G-18081)***
Santos Group Inc (PA)......954 605-2954
9736 Nw 1st Mnr Coral Springs (33071) ***(G-2309)***
Sanzay Corporation......305 826-9886
1080 Nw 163rd Dr Miami (33169) ***(G-10304)***
SAP Enterprises Inc......954 871-8688
309 Sw 77th Ave North Lauderdale (33068) ***(G-11621)***
Sapa Extrsons St Augustine LLC......904 794-1500
200 Riviera Blvd Saint Augustine (32086) ***(G-15604)***
Sapa Prcsion Tbing Rckldge LLC, Rockledge *Also called Hydro Precision Tubing USA LLC* ***(G-15420)***
Sapa Prcsion Tubing Adrian Inc......321 636-8147
100 Gus Hipp Blvd Rockledge (32955) ***(G-15446)***
Saphire Disinfection Products, Lake Butler *Also called Saphire Services LLC* ***(G-7341)***
Saphire Services LLC......386 247-1048
250 Sw 9th Ave Lake Butler (32054) ***(G-7341)***
Sapore Di Vino Inc......561 818-8411
6905 Nw 51st St Miami (33166) ***(G-10305)***
Sapphire LLC......561 346-7449
6432 Melaleuca Ln Greenacres (33463) ***(G-5087)***
Saputo Dairy Foods Usa LLC......904 354-0406
2198 W Beaver St Jacksonville (32209) ***(G-6751)***
Sar Wholesale Sign Factory......813 949-8397
1903 Passero Ave Lutz (33559) ***(G-8417)***
Sara Glove Company Inc......866 664-7272
7935 Airprt Pulling N Ste Naples (34109) ***(G-11392)***
Sarah Louise Inc......941 377-9656
8263 Blaikie Ct Sarasota (34240) ***(G-16573)***
Sarasota Architectural Wdwkg......941 684-1614
6110 Clark Center Ave Sarasota (34238) ***(G-16574)***
Sarasota Boat Works Inc......941 366-3357
2245 Whtfeld Indus Way Un Sarasota (34243) ***(G-16291)***
Sarasota Byfront Plg Orgnztion......941 203-5316
655 N Tamiami Trl Sarasota (34236) ***(G-16575)***
Sarasota Cabinetry Inc......941 351-5588
3080 N Washington Blvd # 25 Sarasota (34234) ***(G-16576)***
Sarasota Cattlemen Rm, Sarasota *Also called Cemex Cnstr Mtls Fla LLC* ***(G-16381)***
Sarasota Cottages LLC......941 724-2245
1628 7th St Sarasota (34236) ***(G-16577)***
Sarasota Herald Tribune, Sarasota *Also called Halifax Media Group LLC* ***(G-16457)***
Sarasota Herald-Tribune......941 358-4000
1800 University Pkwy Sarasota (34243) ***(G-16292)***
Sarasota Herald-Tribune......941 745-7808
8713 State Road 70 E Bradenton (34202) ***(G-1110)***
Sarasota Herald-Tribune (HQ)......941 953-7755
801 S Tamiami Trl Sarasota (34236) ***(G-16578)***
Sarasota Herald-Tribune......941 953-7755
1777 Main St Ste 400 Sarasota (34236) ***(G-16579)***
Sarasota Kitchens and Closets......941 722-7505
5822 24th St E Bradenton (34203) ***(G-1111)***
Sarasota Leather Gallery Inc (PA)......800 741-4336
15941 Us Highway 19 Hudson (34667) ***(G-6037)***
Sarasota Precision Engrg Inc (PA)......941 727-3444
2305 72nd Ave E Sarasota (34243) ***(G-16293)***
Sarasota Shower Door Company......941 378-0051
2025e Porter Lake Dr Sarasota (34240) ***(G-16580)***
Sarasota Signs and Visuals......941 355-5746
4070 N Washington Blvd Sarasota (34234) ***(G-16581)***
Sarasota-Manatee Originals Inc......941 365-2800
1215 S Tamiami Trl Sarasota (34239) ***(G-16582)***
Sarasotas Finest MBL Gran Inc......941 365-9697
550 Mango Ave Sarasota (34237) ***(G-16583)***
Sardee Industries Inc......407 295-2114
2211 W Washington St Orlando (32805) ***(G-13163)***
Sargeant Bulk Asphalt Inc......954 763-4796
321 E Hillsboro Blvd Deerfield Beach (33441) ***(G-2906)***
Sargeant Marine Inc......561 999-9916
3020 N Military Trl # 100 Boca Raton (33431) ***(G-702)***
Sargent Aerospace and Defense, Miami *Also called Avborne Accesory Group LLC* ***(G-9194)***
Sargent Auto Upholstery, Jacksonville *Also called Sargent Seat Cover Co Inc* ***(G-6752)***
Sargent Seat Cover Co Inc......904 355-2529
44 E 1st St Jacksonville (32206) ***(G-6752)***
Sarniya Enterprises Inc......352 347-6030
8140 Se 58th Ave Ocala (34480) ***(G-12042)***
Sas Group, Port Saint Lucie *Also called Synergy Ancillary Services LLC* ***(G-15151)***
Sas R & D Services Inc......954 432-2345
2371 Sw 195th Ave Miramar (33029) ***(G-11039)***
Sasco Machining Inc......561 746-8233
904 Penn Trl Jupiter (33458) ***(G-7108)***
Sashay Sourcing LLC......239 454-4940
8904 Tropical Ct Fort Myers (33908) ***(G-4597)***
Sashka Co......941 764-9741
992 Tamiami Trl Unit J Port Charlotte (33953) ***(G-14996)***

Sasquatch Cabinet Company......941 365-4950
6841 Energy Ct Lakewood Ranch (34240) ***(G-7846)***
Satchel Group, Edgewater *Also called Jasmine Purkiss* ***(G-3628)***
Satcom Direct Inc......321 242-6665
1421 General Aviation Dr Melbourne (32935) ***(G-8925)***
Satcom Drect Cmmunications Inc (PA)......321 777-3000
1050 Satcom Ln Melbourne (32940) ***(G-8926)***
Satcom Scientific Inc......407 856-1050
5644 Commerce Dr Ste G Orlando (32839) ***(G-13164)***
Satellite Now Inc......239 945-0520
411 Sw 34th Ter Cape Coral (33914) ***(G-1465)***
Saten Leaf Nursery Inc......305 216-5340
13822 Sw 282nd Ter Homestead (33033) ***(G-5991)***
Satin Sensation Co......786 290-4114
16657 Sw 79th Ter Miami (33193) ***(G-10306)***
Saugus Valley Corp......954 772-4077
8716 Nw 54th St Coral Springs (33067) ***(G-2310)***
Saul Signs Inc......305 266-8484
10631 Nw 123rd Street Rd Medley (33178) ***(G-8722)***
Savage Ventures Inc......772 335-5655
1702 Se Village Green Dr Port Saint Lucie (34952) ***(G-15141)***
Savi Air, Stuart *Also called Gb Airlink Inc* ***(G-16946)***
Saving For College LLC......954 770-5136
444 Brickell Ave Ste 820 Miami (33131) ***(G-10307)***
Savor Sleep LLC......860 577-2867
8805 Tamiami Trl N Naples (34108) ***(G-11393)***
Savory Life LLC......813 981-2022
6766 Waterton Dr Riverview (33578) ***(G-15282)***
Savory Street......941 312-4027
411 N Orange Ave Sarasota (34236) ***(G-16584)***
Savvy Associate Inc......954 941-6986
1480 Sw 3rd St Ste 5 Pompano Beach (33069) ***(G-14840)***
Saw Palmetto Berries Cooperati......239 775-4286
7440 Friendship Ln Naples (34120) ***(G-11394)***
Saw Palmetto Florida LLC......239 775-4286
7440 Friendship Ln Naples (34120) ***(G-11395)***
Sawgrass Nutra Labs LLC......844 688-7244
7018 A C Skinner Pkwy # 230 Jacksonville (32256) ***(G-6753)***
Sawyer Products Inc......727 725-1177
605 7th Ave N Safety Harbor (34695) ***(G-15502)***
Saxton Sign FL Inc......239 458-0845
234 Del Prado Blvd N Cape Coral (33909) ***(G-1466)***
Say What Screen Prtg & EMB Inc......941 745-5822
10912 8th Ave E Bradenton (34212) ***(G-1112)***
Sazon Inc......305 591-9785
2000 Nw 92nd Ave Doral (33172) ***(G-3496)***
Sb Mfg LLC......352 458-0137
15240 Citrus Country Dr Dade City (33523) ***(G-2434)***
Sb Pallets, South Bay *Also called Sanchez Brothers Corp* ***(G-16797)***
Sb Signs Inc......561 688-9100
1300 N Florida Mango Rd # 20 West Palm Beach (33409) ***(G-19026)***
Sb Tactical, Bradenton *Also called Nst Global LLC* ***(G-1088)***
SBC International Group Inc......305 506-5638
8000 W 26th Ave Hialeah (33016) ***(G-5611)***
SBC Laser, Opa Locka *Also called Cm2 Industries Inc* ***(G-12301)***
Sbm Beauty LLC......850 567-7338
831 Sikes St Quincy (32351) ***(G-15253)***
Sbr Custom Cabinets Inc......407 765-8134
4093 Floralwood Ct Orlando (32812) ***(G-13165)***
SBS, Melbourne *Also called SBs Precision Shtmtl Inc* ***(G-8927)***
SBs Precision Shtmtl Inc......321 951-7411
615 Distribution Dr Melbourne (32904) ***(G-8927)***
SBS Promotional Solutions, Jacksonville *Also called Shipping + Business Svcs LLC* ***(G-6765)***
SBT River PIP Project......919 469-5095
4400 N Alafaya Trl Orlando (32826) ***(G-13166)***
SC Cabinet LLC......561 429-5369
7655 Enterprise Dr Riviera Beach (33404) ***(G-15375)***
SC Capital Ventures Inc......954 657-8563
3025 Nw 25th Ave Pompano Beach (33069) ***(G-14841)***
SC Edge, Port Saint Lucie *Also called Catch One Comm* ***(G-15096)***
SC Elearning LLC......561 293-2543
400 Fairway Dr Ste 101 Deerfield Beach (33441) ***(G-2907)***
SC Gastronomic Crew Inc......786 864-1212
127 Miracle Mile Coral Gables (33134) ***(G-2194)***
SC Parent Corporation......703 351-0200
1450 Brickell Ave Fl 31 Miami (33131) ***(G-10308)***
SC Purchaser Corporation......703 351-0200
1450 Brickell Ave Fl 31 Miami (33131) ***(G-10309)***
Scale Models Arts & Tech......305 949-1706
15455 W Dixie Hwy Ste G North Miami Beach (33162) ***(G-11704)***
Scan Technology Inc (PA)......931 723-0304
10305 Nw 4th Pl Gainesville (32607) ***(G-4992)***
Scanid Inc......305 607-3523
444 Brickell Ave Miami (33131) ***(G-10310)***
Scar Heal, Largo *Also called Atlantic Medical Products LLC* ***(G-7901)***
Scarb Industries Inc......772 597-3898
15845 Sw Warfield Blvd Indiantown (34956) ***(G-6074)***
Sccy Firearms, Daytona Beach *Also called Sccy Industries LLC* ***(G-2708)***

ALPHABETIC

Sccy Industries LLC...386 322-6336
1800 Concept Ct Daytona Beach (32114) ***(G-2708)***
Scent Fill, Oldsmar *Also called Aromavalue Inc* ***(G-12205)***
Scents Nature Enterprises Corp...305 547-2334
7850 Nw 98th St Miami Lakes (33016) ***(G-10854)***
Scents of Nature Enterprises...305 547-2334
7850 Nw 98th St Miami Lakes (33016) ***(G-10855)***
Scentsability Candles...954 234-4405
11480 W Sample Rd Coral Springs (33065) ***(G-2311)***
Scentstional Soaps Candles Inc...941 485-1443
730 Commerce Dr Venice (34292) ***(G-18572)***
Scf Processing LLC...352 377-0858
1604 Nw 8th Ave Gainesville (32603) ***(G-4993)***
Schark Skinz, Sebastian *Also called Shark Skinz* ***(G-16672)***
Scheduall Scheduall Scheduall...954 334-5400
2719 Hollywood Blvd Hollywood (33020) ***(G-5904)***
Schering-Plough Corp...407 353-2076
438 E Gore St Orlando (32806) ***(G-13167)***
Schick LLC...718 810-3804
20412 Ne 15th Ct Miami (33179) ***(G-10311)***
Schimmbros Inc...407 796-8361
3726 Grissom Ln Kissimmee (34741) ***(G-7296)***
Schnebly Redlands Winery Inc...786 247-2060
30205 Sw 217th Ave Homestead (33030) ***(G-5992)***
Schneidder Industries LLC...850 207-0929
1690 Dunn Ave Apt 408 Daytona Beach (32114) ***(G-2709)***
Schneider Electric It Corp...305 266-5005
490 Swgrss Corp Pkwy Sunrise (33325) ***(G-17171)***
Schnupp Manufacturing Co Inc...305 325-0520
2113 Nw 17th Ave Miami (33142) ***(G-10312)***
Schoen Industries Inc...305 491-5993
4831 Calasans Ave Saint Cloud (34771) ***(G-15665)***
Schoenhut LLC...904 810-1945
6480b Us Highway 1 N Saint Augustine (32095) ***(G-15605)***
Schoenhut Piano Company, Saint Augustine *Also called Schoenhut LLC* ***(G-15605)***
School New Letter Program, Orlando *Also called Academy Publishing Inc* ***(G-12427)***
School-On-Wheels...239 530-8522
13520 Tamiami Trl E Naples (34114) ***(G-11396)***
Schooner Prints Inc...727 397-8572
8632 115th Ave Largo (33773) ***(G-8045)***
Schrappers Fine Cabinetry, Jupiter *Also called Beverly Acquisitions Inc* ***(G-7007)***
Schrappers Fine Cabinetry Inc...561 746-3827
240 W Indiantown Rd # 101 Jupiter (33458) ***(G-7109)***
Schreiber, Fort Lauderdale *Also called Parkson Corporation* ***(G-4160)***
Schroe Lights LLC...407 748-9300
833 Timber Isle Dr Orlando (32828) ***(G-13168)***
Schur & Company LLC...904 353-8075
9410 Florida Min Blvd E Jacksonville (32257) ***(G-6754)***
Schurco Slurry Pumps, Jacksonville *Also called Schur & Company LLC* ***(G-6754)***
Schurr Sails Inc...850 438-9354
490 S L St Pensacola (32502) ***(G-14258)***
Schwabs Enterprises, Valparaiso *Also called Bayou Outdoor Equipment* ***(G-18506)***
Schwartz Electro-Optics Inc...407 297-8988
8337 Southpark Cir Orlando (32819) ***(G-13169)***
Schwarz Bros Manufacturing Co...309 342-5814
1455 Little Creek Dr Pensacola (32506) ***(G-14259)***
Schwarz Partners Packaging LLC...863 682-0123
2808 New Tampa Hwy Lakeland (33815) ***(G-7788)***
Schwarzmann LLC...561 654-3653
360 N Congress Ave Delray Beach (33445) ***(G-3138)***
Schwing Bioset...239 237-2174
12290 Treeline Ave Fort Myers (33913) ***(G-4598)***
SCI, Deerfield Beach *Also called Sustainable Casework Inds LLC* ***(G-2920)***
SCI, Cocoa *Also called Service Corp International* ***(G-2050)***
SCi Architectural Wdwrk Inc...954 247-9601
2801 Nw 55th Ct Ste 1w Fort Lauderdale (33309) ***(G-4224)***
SCI Materials LLC...352 878-4979
15251 N Highway 329 Reddick (32686) ***(G-15258)***
SCI Undercar Inc (PA)...727 327-2278
2447 5th Ave S Saint Petersburg (33712) ***(G-15906)***
SCI-Chem, Kissimmee *Also called Chemline Inc* ***(G-7230)***
Science Daily LLC...239 596-2624
4034 Roberts Point Rd Sarasota (34242) ***(G-16585)***
Science First LLC...904 225-5558
86475 Gene Lassere Blvd Yulee (32097) ***(G-19500)***
Scientific Instruments Inc...561 881-8500
4400 W Tiffany Dr Mangonia Park (33407) ***(G-8511)***
Scientific Plastics Ltd...305 557-3737
5852 Miami Lakes Dr E Miami Lakes (33014) ***(G-10856)***
Scif Solutions Inc (PA)...904 298-0631
11518 Normandy Blvd Jacksonville (32221) ***(G-6755)***
Scooter Link...813 985-3075
10910 Gillette Ave Temple Terrace (33617) ***(G-18377)***
Scope Worker LLC...917 855-5379
2121 Nw 2nd Ave Ste 203 Miami (33127) ***(G-10313)***
Score Group, The, Doral *Also called Quad Intl Incorporated* ***(G-3474)***
Scorpion Equity LLC...352 512-0800
5817 Nw 44th Ave Ocala (34482) ***(G-12043)***
Scorpion Racing Products, Ocala *Also called Scorpion Equity LLC* ***(G-12043)***
Scosta Corp (PA)...863 385-8242
3670 Commerce Center Dr Sebring (33870) ***(G-16705)***
Scot Pump Company, Fort Lauderdale *Also called Wilo USA LLC* ***(G-4325)***
Scott Brevard Inc...386 698-1121
306 Central Ave Crescent City (32112) ***(G-2342)***
Scott Fischer Enterprises LLC (PA)...844 749-2363
12730 Commwl Dr Ste 2 Fort Myers (33913) ***(G-4599)***
Scott Industrial Systems Inc...904 693-3318
4130 N Canal St Jacksonville (32209) ***(G-6756)***
Scott Paint Company LLC (HQ)...941 371-0015
7839 Fruitville Rd Sarasota (34240) ***(G-16586)***
Scott Safety LLC...239 340-8695
13999 W Sr 78 Moore Haven (33471) ***(G-11089)***
Scott Sign Systems Inc (HQ)...941 355-5171
7525 Pennsylvania Ave C Sarasota (34243) ***(G-16294)***
Scott Slide Fasteners Inc...305 576-3328
545 Nw 26th St Miami (33127) ***(G-10314)***
Scott-Douglas Design Inc...727 535-7900
6275 147th Ave Largo (33770) ***(G-8046)***
Scotties Canvas & Mar Sup LLC...239 995-7479
2211 N Tamiami Trl North Fort Myers (33903) ***(G-11604)***
Scottish Spirits Imports Inc...954 332-1116
3101 N Federal Hwy # 301 Fort Lauderdale (33306) ***(G-4225)***
Scp Commercial Printing...561 998-0870
1100 Holland Dr Boca Raton (33487) ***(G-703)***
SCR, Tampa *Also called Shafers Classic Reproductions* ***(G-18089)***
Scraplife Inc...305 776-0727
12200 Vista Ln Pinecrest (33156) ***(G-14332)***
Scratch Off Store...800 584-9937
876 Geneva Dr Oviedo (32765) ***(G-13456)***
Screaming Banshee LLC...727 744-6808
2003 Freedom Dr Clearwater (33755) ***(G-1869)***
Screen Art Posters Inc...305 681-4641
4333 E 10th Ln Hialeah (33013) ***(G-5612)***
Screen Enclosure Lighting...904 838-9786
64 Evans Dr Jacksonville Beach (32250) ***(G-6958)***
Screen Enclosure Services Inc...239 334-6528
502 South Rd Unit A Fort Myers (33907) ***(G-4600)***
Screen Graphics Florida Inc (PA)...800 346-4420
1801 N Andrews Ave Pompano Beach (33069) ***(G-14842)***
Screen Machines LLC...386 527-1368
2422 Old Samsula Rd Port Orange (32128) ***(G-15032)***
Screen Monkey Corp...352 746-7091
5841 W Kime Ln Homosassa (34448) ***(G-6005)***
Screen Printing Unlimited, Naples *Also called Westview Corp Inc* ***(G-11454)***
Screen Process Printers Inc...904 354-8708
101 S Myrtle Ave Jacksonville (32204) ***(G-6757)***
Screen Savers LLC...321 299-8099
715 Kyle Ct Chuluota (32766) ***(G-1554)***
Screen Tech...321 536-6091
1501 Bermuda Ave Merritt Island (32952) ***(G-9008)***
Screenco North Inc...561 840-3300
11211 81st Ct N Palm Beach Gardens (33412) ***(G-13624)***
Screening Leon & Repair Inc...850 575-2840
1223 Airport Dr Tallahassee (32304) ***(G-17321)***
Screenprint Plus Inc...239 549-7284
1336 Se 47th St Cape Coral (33904) ***(G-1467)***
Screens Fast...239 565-1211
1435 Terra Palma Dr Fort Myers (33901) ***(G-4601)***
Screenworks Usa Inc...407 426-9999
2234 W Taft Vineland Rd Orlando (32837) ***(G-13170)***
Scribe Manufacturing Inc (PA)...727 524-7482
14421 Myerlake Cir Clearwater (33760) ***(G-1870)***
Scribe Manufacturing Inc...727 536-7895
3001 Tech Dr N Saint Petersburg (33716) ***(G-15907)***
Scribe Opco Inc (PA)...727 536-7895
14421 Myerlake Cir Clearwater (33760) ***(G-1871)***
Script Central LLC...954 805-8581
1680 Michigan Ave Ste 800 Miami Beach (33139) ***(G-10708)***
Scrubs 941...941 373-0029
5641 Clark Rd Sarasota (34233) ***(G-16587)***
Scs Software Inc...727 871-8366
2840 West Bay Dr Ste 125 Belleair Bluffs (33770) ***(G-364)***
Scully Industries...941 349-5561
314 Island Cir Sarasota (34242) ***(G-16588)***
Sculpture House Inc...609 466-2986
3804 Crossroads Pkwy Fort Pierce (34945) ***(G-4743)***
Scutti America Inc...954 384-2377
2700 Glades Cir Ste 160 Weston (33327) ***(G-19167)***
Scytl, Tampa *Also called Soe Software Corporation* ***(G-18113)***
Sdi Industries Inc...321 733-1128
1216 Prospect Ave 101 Melbourne (32901) ***(G-8928)***
Sdkc Corp...305 469-7578
9624 Nw 47th Ter Doral (33178) ***(G-3497)***
Sdm Acquisition Corporation...954 462-1919
590 Sw 9th St Ste 9 Fort Lauderdale (33315) ***(G-4226)***
Sdm Industries Inc...904 814-2814
13 Hargrove Grade Palm Coast (32137) ***(G-13708)***

Sdmo Generating Sets Inc 305 863-0012
3801 Commerce Pkwy Miramar (33025) ***(G-11040)***
SDr Specialties Services LLC 386 878-6771
4511n Us Highway 17 De Leon Springs (32130) ***(G-2741)***
SDS Dental Inc 954 730-3636
1280 Sw 27th Ave Pompano Beach (33069) ***(G-14843)***
SE Custom Lift Systems Inc 954 941-8090
1801 Sw 7th Ave Pompano Beach (33060) ***(G-14844)***
SE Smith Llc 772 461-0482
8001 Eden Rd Fort Pierce (34951) ***(G-4744)***
Sea 21-21 LLC 954 366-4677
2211 Nw 30th Pl Pompano Beach (33069) ***(G-14845)***
Sea and Shore Custom Canvas Up 954 983-3060
3629 Washington St Hollywood (33021) ***(G-5905)***
Sea Canvas Inc 954 462-7525
1915 S Federal Hwy Fort Lauderdale (33316) ***(G-4227)***
Sea Cast Curb Adptors Crbs LLC 772 466-2400
2601 Industrial Avenue 3 Fort Pierce (34946) ***(G-4745)***
Sea Creations Inc 407 857-2000
408 Bif Ct Orlando (32809) ***(G-13171)***
Sea Enterprise Adventures, Medley *Also called Ram Investments South Fla Inc* ***(G-8714)***
Sea Force Center Console LLC (PA) 941 417-7017
12277 Us Highway 41 N Palmetto (34221) ***(G-13822)***
Sea Force Ix Inc 941 721-9009
1403 Pinetree Cir Wimauma (33598) ***(G-19223)***
Sea Gear Corporation 321 728-9116
700 S John Rodes Blvd B1 Melbourne (32904) ***(G-8929)***
Sea Hawk Boats, Sebring *Also called Sea Hawk Industries Inc* ***(G-16706)***
Sea Hawk Industries Inc 863 385-1995
523 Pear St Sebring (33870) ***(G-16706)***
Sea King Canvas & Shade, Fort Myers *Also called Sea King Kanvas & Shade Inc* ***(G-4602)***
Sea King Kanvas & Shade Inc 239 481-3535
15581 Pine Ridge Rd Ste A Fort Myers (33908) ***(G-4602)***
Sea Link Holdings LLC 727 523-8660
13151 66th St Largo (33773) ***(G-8047)***
Sea Link International Irb Inc (PA) 727 523-8660
13151 66th St Largo (33773) ***(G-8048)***
Sea Products Inc (PA) 904 781-8200
4925 Bulls Bay Hwy Jacksonville (32219) ***(G-6758)***
Sea Ray Boats Inc 386 439-3401
1958 Unsinkable St Flagler Beach (32136) ***(G-3757)***
Sea Ray Boats Inc 321 459-9463
350 Sea Ray Dr Merritt Island (32953) ***(G-9009)***
Sea Ray Boats Inc 321 459-2930
350 Sea Ray Dr Merritt Island (32953) ***(G-9010)***
Sea Ray Boats Inc 321 452-9876
200 Sea Ray Dr Merritt Island (32953) ***(G-9011)***
Sea Ray PD&e, Merritt Island *Also called Sea Ray Boats Inc* ***(G-9011)***
Sea Side Specialties 561 276-6518
1200 S Swinton Ave Delray Beach (33444) ***(G-3139)***
Sea Site Inc 305 403-3002
1180 Nw 163rd Dr Miami (33169) ***(G-10315)***
Sea Suns, Miami *Also called Sir Winston Garments Inc* ***(G-10355)***
Sea Systems Group Inc 434 374-9553
10631 Whittington Ct Largo (33773) ***(G-8049)***
Seaboard Folding Box Company, Boca Raton *Also called Sfbc LLC* ***(G-707)***
Seaboard Manufacturing LLC 727 497-3572
13214 38th St N Clearwater (33762) ***(G-1872)***
Seabob, Fort Lauderdale *Also called Cayago Americas Inc* ***(G-3885)***
Seabreeze Communications Group 239 278-4222
5630 Halifax Ave Fort Myers (33912) ***(G-4603)***
Seabreeze Publication Centl FL 561 741-7770
1102 W Indiantown Rd # 5 Jupiter (33458) ***(G-7110)***
Seabreeze Publications, Fort Myers *Also called Seabreeze Communications Group* ***(G-4603)***
Seabreeze Publications, Jupiter *Also called Seabreeze Publication Centl FL* ***(G-7110)***
Seacoast Air Conditioning & Sh 772 466-2400
3108 Industrial 31st St Fort Pierce (34946) ***(G-4746)***
Seacor Marine LLC 954 523-2200
2200 Eller Dr Fort Lauderdale (33316) ***(G-4228)***
Seacure Inc 904 353-5353
9485 Regency Square Blvd # 110 Jacksonville (32225) ***(G-6759)***
Seadek, Rockledge *Also called Hyperform Inc* ***(G-15421)***
Seadreams Boat Yacht Works LLC 727 843-0010
5100 Sunset Blvd Port Richey (34668) ***(G-15067)***
Seagate Productions LLC 561 506-7750
1162 Rialto Dr Boynton Beach (33436) ***(G-957)***
Seagear Performance Apparel, Miami *Also called CBI Industries Inc* ***(G-9329)***
Seahill Press Inc 805 845-8636
214 N 3rd St Ste A Leesburg (34748) ***(G-8170)***
Seahunter Inc 305 257-3344
25545 Sw 140th Ave Princeton (33032) ***(G-15186)***
Seaking Inc 954 961-6629
2200 Sw 71st Ter Davie (33317) ***(G-2589)***
Seaking USA, Davie *Also called Seaking Inc* ***(G-2589)***
Seal Outdoors Inc 877 323-7325
5900 Sw 56th Ter South Miami (33143) ***(G-16827)***
Seal Publishing LLC 813 792-5852
14611 Middlefield Ln Odessa (33556) ***(G-12149)***
Seal Shield LLC (PA) 877 325-7443
315 E Robinson St Ste 500 Orlando (32801) ***(G-13172)***
Seal-Tite Plastic Packg Co Inc 305 264-9015
4655 Sw 74th Ave Miami (33155) ***(G-10316)***
Sealift LLC 321 638-0301
3390 N Courtenay Pkwy A Merritt Island (32953) ***(G-9012)***
Sealites, Oakland Park *Also called Arcco Inc* ***(G-11779)***
Seapress Inc 941 366-8494
4281 Clark Rd Sarasota (34233) ***(G-16589)***
Seaquest Marine LLC 781 888-8850
777 Brickell Ave Miami (33131) ***(G-10317)***
Searaven Glauben LLC 727 230-8840
6429 Brevard St Saint Augustine (32080) ***(G-15606)***
Searchlight Inc 407 965-2649
1970 E Osceola Pkwy 327 Kissimmee (34743) ***(G-7297)***
Searobotics Corporation 772 742-3700
7765 Sw Ellipse Way Stuart (34997) ***(G-17006)***
Seaside Aluminum llc 386 252-4940
817 Swift St Ste 130 Daytona Beach (32114) ***(G-2710)***
Seaside Graphics Inc 954 782-7151
100 Sw 5th St Pompano Beach (33060) ***(G-14846)***
Seaside Premium Cabinets 850 533-6801
4010 Commons Dr W Destin (32541) ***(G-3205)***
Seaside Stitching 321 455-6427
1505 Martin Blvd Merritt Island (32952) ***(G-9013)***
Seasucker LLC 941 586-2664
1912 44th Ave E Bradenton (34203) ***(G-1113)***
Seat Savers Plus Inc 305 256-7863
12105 Sw 129th Ct Bay 10 Miami (33186) ***(G-10318)***
Seatbelt Solutions Llc 855 642-3964
15835 Corporate Rd N Jupiter (33478) ***(G-7111)***
Seating Constructors Usa Inc 813 505-7560
2347 Circuit Way Brooksville (34604) ***(G-1267)***
Seating Installation Group LLC 727 289-7652
12100 31st Ct N Saint Petersburg (33716) ***(G-15908)***
Seatorque Control Systems LLC 772 220-3020
2779 Se Monroe St Stuart (34997) ***(G-17007)***
Seattle Engraving Center LLC 206 420-4604
1073 E Brandon Blvd Brandon (33511) ***(G-1178)***
Seavin Inc (PA) 352 394-8627
19239 Us Highway 27 Clermont (34715) ***(G-1973)***
Seavin Inc 904 826-1594
157 King St Saint Augustine (32084) ***(G-15607)***
Seaward Group USA, Tampa *Also called Clare Instruments (us) Inc* ***(G-17538)***
Seaway Plastics Engrg LLC 727 777-6032
6041 Siesta Ln Port Richey (34668) ***(G-15068)***
Seaway Plastics Engrg LLC (HQ) 727 845-3235
6006 Siesta Ln Port Richey (34668) ***(G-15069)***
Sebastian Sea Products In 772 321-3997
1800 Us Highway 1 Vero Beach (32960) ***(G-18662)***
Sebco Industries Inc 954 566-8500
211 E Oakland Park Blvd Oakland Park (33334) ***(G-11837)***
Sebring Custom Tanning Inc 863 655-1600
429 Webster Turn Dr Sebring (33870) ***(G-16707)***
Sebring Septic Tank Precast Co 863 655-2030
8037 Associate Blvd Sebring (33876) ***(G-16708)***
Sebring Software LLC (PA) 941 377-0715
1400 Cattlemen Rd Ste 101 Sarasota (34232) ***(G-16590)***
Sebring's Precast Products, Sebring *Also called Sebring Septic Tank Precast Co* ***(G-16708)***
SEC, Hollywood *Also called Simulated Envmt Concepts Inc* ***(G-5908)***
Seco South II Inc 727 536-1924
2111 34th Way Largo (33771) ***(G-8050)***
Second 2 None Wood Work Inc 786 299-3580
10141 Sw 40th Ter Miami (33165) ***(G-10319)***
Secretbandz, Sunrise *Also called Syi Inc* ***(G-17183)***
Secure Biometric Corporation 813 832-1164
2909 W Bay Court Ave Tampa (33611) ***(G-18082)***
Secure Cnstr Systems LLC 561 687-9512
801b Pike Rd West Palm Beach (33411) ***(G-19027)***
Secure On-Site Shredding, Palm Harbor *Also called Bay Area Security Shred* ***(G-13723)***
Secure Wall, West Palm Beach *Also called Secure Cnstr Systems LLC* ***(G-19027)***
Secure Wrap, Miami *Also called Homyn Enterprises Corp* ***(G-9718)***
Security and Fire Elec Inc (PA) 904 844-0964
2590 Dobbs Rd Saint Augustine (32086) ***(G-15608)***
Security Hmntrian Rlief Envmtl, Tampa *Also called Jade Tactical Disaster Relief* ***(G-17801)***
Security Impact GL Hldings LLC 561 844-3100
6555 Garden Rd Ste 1 Riviera Beach (33404) ***(G-15376)***
Security Oracle Inc 352 988-5985
3614 Solana Cir Clermont (34711) ***(G-1974)***
Security Plastics, Miami Lakes *Also called National Molding LLC* ***(G-10827)***
Security Tech Group Inc 305 631-2228
9425 Sw 72nd St Ste 100 Miami (33173) ***(G-10320)***
Security World Electronics 786 285-5303
19704 Nw 48th Ct Miami Gardens (33055) ***(G-10754)***
Securus Brot LLC 954 532-8065
2400 Sw 132nd Ter Miramar (33027) ***(G-11041)***
See Coastal Media LLC 386 562-2213
404 S Beach St Daytona Beach (32114) ***(G-2711)***
See Magazines, Sarasota *Also called Miles Partnership II LLC* ***(G-16509)***

ALPHABETIC

See-Ray Plumbing Inc 772 489-2474
2020 Old Dixie Hwy Se Vero Beach (32962) ***(G-18663)***
Seelye Acquisitions Inc 407 656-6677
946 Century Ln Apopka (32703) ***(G-184)***
Sef Americas LLC 904 423-0211
14476 Duval Pl W Jacksonville (32218) ***(G-6760)***
Segers Aerospace Corporation 850 689-2198
5582 Fairchild Rd Crestview (32539) ***(G-2357)***
Segutronic International Inc 305 463-8551
11042 Nw 72nd Ter Doral (33178) ***(G-3498)***
Seimens Industries Inc 954 364-6600
3402 Bridge Rd Hollywood (33026) ***(G-5906)***
Seiter Enterprises Inc 813 728-8324
155 E Oakwood St Tarpon Springs (34689) ***(G-18324)***
Sel West Coast Inc 352 373-6354
817 Ne Waldo Rd Gainesville (32641) ***(G-4994)***
Select Engineered Systems Inc 305 823-5410
7991 W 26th Ave Hialeah (33016) ***(G-5613)***
Select Europe Inc 407 931-1820
3000 Sw 15th St Ste E Deerfield Beach (33442) ***(G-2908)***
Select Machinery Inc 941 960-1970
4590 Ashton Rd Sarasota (34233) ***(G-16591)***
Select Publishing LLC 850 464-6477
56 Denny Dr Santa Rosa Beach (32459) ***(G-16167)***
Selectwo Machine Company Inc 407 788-3102
1695 Ee Williamson Rd Longwood (32779) ***(G-8334)***
Self Industries Incorporated 386 882-3644
30 Choctaw Trl Ormond Beach (32174) ***(G-13397)***
Self Made Dynasty LLC 754 303-3134
4811 E Pcf View Ter Fl 33 Flr 333 Fort Lauderdale (33309) ***(G-4229)***
Sellandshipusa, Fleming Island *Also called Earthsoil Inc* ***(G-3761)***
Sellink Aviation Fuel Div LLC 305 336-6627
4019 Nw 28th St Miami (33142) ***(G-10321)***
Sellinkafs, Miami *Also called Sellink Aviation Fuel Div LLC* ***(G-10321)***
Selma's Cookies, Apopka *Also called Lindley Foods LLC* ***(G-156)***
Selmas Cookies Inc (PA) 407 884-9433
2023 Apex Ct Apopka (32703) ***(G-185)***
Sembco Stl Erection Met Bldg 561 863-0606
3450 Dr Mrtn Lther King J Riviera Beach (33404) ***(G-15377)***
Semenario Accion, West Palm Beach *Also called Action Weekly Corp* ***(G-18789)***
Semiconductor Technology Inc 772 341-0800
3131 Se Jay St Stuart (34997) ***(G-17008)***
Semilab Sdi, Temple Terrace *Also called Semilab USA LLC* ***(G-18378)***
Semilab USA LLC (PA) 813 977-2244
12415 Telecom Dr Temple Terrace (33637) ***(G-18378)***
Seminole County Public Schools 407 320-0393
1722 W Airport Blvd Sanford (32771) ***(G-16114)***
Seminole Feed Division, Ocala *Also called Seminole Stores Inc* ***(G-12044)***
Seminole Marico Fertilizer Div, Ocala *Also called Branch Properties Inc* ***(G-11890)***
Seminole Metal Finishing Inc 407 332-8949
967 Explorer Cv Altamonte Springs (32701) ***(G-72)***
Seminole Paper & Printing Co 305 379-8481
60 Nw 3rd St Miami (33128) ***(G-10322)***
Seminole Printing Inc 305 823-7204
2310 W 78th St Hialeah (33016) ***(G-5614)***
Seminole Sign Company LLC 863 623-6600
16900 Reservation Rd Ne Okeechobee (34974) ***(G-12192)***
Seminole State Signs & Ltg 954 316-6030
5071 S State Road 7 # 717 Davie (33314) ***(G-2590)***
Seminole Stores Inc 352 732-4143
335 Ne Watula Ave Ocala (34470) ***(G-12044)***
Semplastics 407 353-6885
269 Aulin Ave Ste 1003 Oviedo (32765) ***(G-13457)***
Semprun & Morales Corporation 305 698-2554
3418 W 84th St Ste 100 Hialeah (33018) ***(G-5615)***
Sen-Dure Products Inc 954 973-1260
6785 Nw 17th Ave Fort Lauderdale (33309) ***(G-4230)***
Sen-Pack Inc 386 763-3312
820 Rasley Rd New Smyrna Beach (32168) ***(G-11543)***
Send It Sweetly LLC 239 850-5500
1309 Se 47th Ter Cape Coral (33904) ***(G-1468)***
Senda De Vida Publishers 305 262-2627
14320 Sw 143rd Ct # 705 Miami (33186) ***(G-10323)***
Seneca Industries 561 626-4999
3825 Pga Blvd Ste 1101 Palm Beach Gardens (33410) ***(G-13625)***
Senelco Iberia Inc (HQ) 561 912-6000
500 Nw 12th Ave Deerfield Beach (33442) ***(G-2909)***
Senior Life of Florida 321 242-1235
7350 Shoppes Dr Ste 102 Melbourne (32940) ***(G-8930)***
Senior Times Magazine, Gainesville *Also called Tower Publications Inc* ***(G-5011)***
Senior Voice America Inc 813 444-1011
3820 Northdale Blvd 205a Tampa (33624) ***(G-18083)***
Seniors Vent Mgmt Inc 305 266-0988
6100 Blue Lagoon Dr # 110 Miami (33126) ***(G-10324)***
Sensatek Propulsion Tech Inc 850 321-5993
1 Aerospace Blvd Daytona Beach (32114) ***(G-2712)***
Sensenich Technologies Inc 813 703-8446
2008 Wood Ct Plant City (33563) ***(G-14464)***
Sensidyne LP 727 530-3602
1000 112th Cir N Ste 100 Saint Petersburg (33716) ***(G-15909)***
Sensor Systems LLC 727 347-2181
2800 Anvil St N Saint Petersburg (33710) ***(G-15910)***
Sensormatic Electronics LLC 561 912-6000
6600 Congress Ave 1b Boca Raton (33487) ***(G-704)***
Sensus Healthcare Inc 561 922-5808
851 Broken Sound Pkwy Nw Boca Raton (33487) ***(G-705)***
Sentech Eas Corporation (PA) 954 426-2965
4900 Lyons Tech Pkwy # 7 Coconut Creek (33073) ***(G-2093)***
Sentinel Cmmnctons News Vntres 407 420-6229
210 Pembrook Pl Longwood (32779) ***(G-8335)***
Sentinel Cmmnctons News Vntres 407 420-5291
75 E Amelia St Orlando (32801) ***(G-13173)***
Sentinel Cmmnctons News Vntres 352 742-5900
2012 Classique Ln Tavares (32778) ***(G-18352)***
Sentinel Communicatns News Ven (HQ) 407 420-5000
633 N Orange Ave Orlando (32801) ***(G-13174)***
Sentinel Direct, Orlando *Also called Sentinel Cmmnctons News Vntres* ***(G-13173)***
Sentinel Inc 239 263-9888
3673 Exchange Ave Ste 1 Naples (34104) ***(G-11397)***
Sentinel Sq Off Bldg MGT & Lsg 727 461-7700
300 S Duncan Ave Ste 291 Clearwater (33755) ***(G-1873)***
Sentinel Storm Protection, Naples *Also called Sentinel Inc* ***(G-11397)***
Sentry Food Solutions LLC 904 482-1900
4339 Roosevelt Blvd # 400 Jacksonville (32210) ***(G-6761)***
Sentry Protection Technology 941 306-4949
6202 Clarity Ct Sarasota (34240) ***(G-16592)***
Sep Communications LLC 561 998-0870
6001 Park Of Commerce Blv Boca Raton (33487) ***(G-706)***
Sepac Corp 305 718-3379
5201 Blue Lagoon Dr Miami (33126) ***(G-10325)***
Separation Systems Inc 850 932-1433
100 Nightingale Ln A Gulf Breeze (32561) ***(G-5126)***
Separation Technologies 352 794-4160
15760 W Power Line St Crystal River (34428) ***(G-2381)***
Sepco, Stuart *Also called Solar Electric Power Company* ***(G-17018)***
Sephora Inside Jcpenney 386 752-2822
2427 W Us Highway 90 Lake City (32055) ***(G-7383)***
Sepronet Inc 305 463-8551
11042 Nw 72nd Ter Doral (33178) ***(G-3499)***
Septic Tank Drain Fld/Nsite Sw, Sarasota *Also called Miller Brothers Contractors* ***(G-16510)***
Septimius LLC 813 484-4168
4910 Savarese Cir Tampa (33634) ***(G-18084)***
Sequa Corporation (HQ) 561 935-3571
3999 Rca Blvd Palm Beach Gardens (33410) ***(G-13626)***
Sequoia Brands Inc 813 969-2000
13100 State Road 54 Odessa (33556) ***(G-12150)***
Ser-Mat International LLC 954 525-1417
3200 Nw 27th Ave Ste 106 Pompano Beach (33069) ***(G-14847)***
Serbin Printing Inc 941 366-0755
1500 N Washington Blvd Sarasota (34236) ***(G-16593)***
Serendipity Publishing 407 905-5076
5432 Tildens Grove Blvd Windermere (34786) ***(G-19243)***
Serenity Hair Extensions LLC 407 917-1788
1235 Providence Blvd R10 Deltona (32725) ***(G-3179)***
Serenity Screen Enclosures LLC 407 692-3031
3700 Timber Trl Orlando (32808) ***(G-13175)***
Serenity Slid Srfaces Amer LLC 352 459-1561
3795 Codding Pl Mount Dora (32757) ***(G-11112)***
Serf Inc 850 476-8203
3065 S Highway 29 Cantonment (32533) ***(G-1347)***
Sergeant Bretts Coffee LLC 561 451-0048
1991 Nw 38th Ter Coconut Creek (33066) ***(G-2094)***
Sergios Printing Inc 305 971-4112
14265 Sw 140th St Miami (33186) ***(G-10326)***
Series Usa LLC 305 932-4626
20900 Ne 30th Ave Ste 901 Miami (33180) ***(G-10327)***
Serigraphia Inc 850 243-9743
223 Troy St Ne Fort Walton Beach (32548) ***(G-4832)***
Serigraphic Arts Inc 813 626-1070
6806 Parke East Blvd Tampa (33610) ***(G-18085)***
Seronix Corporation 352 406-1698
27109 Oak Shadow Ln Mount Dora (32757) ***(G-11113)***
Serv-Pak Corp 954 962-4262
5844 Dawson St Hollywood (33023) ***(G-5907)***
Servdata Inc 305 269-7374
18001 Old Cutler Rd # 631 Palmetto Bay (33157) ***(G-13854)***
Servers 4 Networks, Boynton Beach *Also called M & S Computer Products Inc* ***(G-930)***
Service Bindery Enterprises 727 823-9866
3228 Morris St N Saint Petersburg (33713) ***(G-15911)***
Service Bindery of Pinellas, Saint Petersburg *Also called Service Bindery Enterprises* ***(G-15911)***
Service Corp International 321 636-6041
Us Hwy 1 Frontenac Cocoa (32927) ***(G-2050)***
Service D N D Dumpster 813 989-3867
7909 Professional Pl Tampa (33637) ***(G-18086)***
Service Industry Consultant 561 775-4782
9123 N Military Trl # 216 Palm Beach Gardens (33410) ***(G-13627)***

Services NS 18 LLC...786 546-3295
19900 E Country Club Dr Aventura (33180) *(G-280)*
Services On Demand Print Inc...305 681-5345
917 Sw 10th St Hallandale Beach (33009) *(G-5209)*
Servicing Solutions Group...727 216-4477
28100 Us Highway 19 N # 204 Clearwater (33761) *(G-1874)*
Servision Inc...305 900-4999
2100 E Hallandale Beach B Hallandale Beach (33009) *(G-5210)*
Servo Tech Inc...727 573-7998
4785 110th Ave N Clearwater (33762) *(G-1875)*
Servos and Simulation Inc...407 807-0208
421 Meadowridge Cv Longwood (32750) *(G-8336)*
Servotech, Clearwater *Also called Servo Tech Inc (G-1875)*
Sesolinc Grp Inc (PA)...772 287-9090
50 Se Ocean Blvd Ste 202 Stuart (34994) *(G-17009)*
Sesvalia Usa LLC...305 615-1987
67 Miracle Mile Coral Gables (33134) *(G-2195)*
Set Up Inc...239 542-4142
170 Sw 51st St Cape Coral (33914) *(G-1469)*
Setty Enterprises Inc...561 844-3711
4128 Westroads Dr # 225 West Palm Beach (33407) *(G-19028)*
Seven Defenses Corporation...786 448-5701
10550 Nw 74th St Unit 202 Medley (33178) *(G-8723)*
Seven Group USA Inc...305 392-9193
1681 Nw 79th Ave Doral (33126) *(G-3500)*
Seven Hlls Slution Specialists...850 575-0566
1254 Ocala Rd Tallahassee (32304) *(G-17322)*
Seven Keys Co of Florida...954 946-5010
450 Sw 12th Ave Pompano Beach (33069) *(G-14848)*
Seven-Up Snapple Southeast, Tampa *Also called American Bottling Company (G-17415)*
Seven-Up Snapple Southeast, Jacksonville *Also called American Bottling Company (G-6146)*
Sevilla Cabinets Inc...305 888-2174
1550 W 34th Pl Hialeah (33012) *(G-5616)*
Sew Right, Pompano Beach *Also called Logoxpress Inc (G-14747)*
Sew Whats New Embroidery Inc...954 977-3339
2520 N Powerline Rd # 301 Pompano Beach (33069) *(G-14849)*
Sewell Products Florida LLC...863 967-4463
909 Magnolia Ave Auburndale (33823) *(G-252)*
Sextant Marketing LLC...800 691-9980
1860 N Avnida Rpblica De Tampa (33605) *(G-18087)*
Sexy Winks LLC...407 949-2981
10321 Manderley Way Orlando (32829) *(G-13176)*
Seyer - Tech Industries Inc...305 233-2672
1420 Sw 152nd Pl Miami (33194) *(G-10328)*
Sfa Systems Inc...561 585-5927
1230 Wingfield St Lake Worth (33460) *(G-7586)*
Sfada Tag Agency Inc...305 981-1077
625 Ne 124th St North Miami (33161) *(G-11654)*
Sfbc LLC...978 342-8921
7035 Queenferry Cir Boca Raton (33496) *(G-707)*
Sfi, West Park *Also called Shoreline Foundation Inc (G-19098)*
Sfi Inc...407 834-2258
1730 N Forsyth Rd Orlando (32807) *(G-13177)*
Sfsf Magazine, Fort Lauderdale *Also called South Florida Sport Fishing (G-4248)*
Sg Global LLC (PA)...305 726-3439
12192 Sw 128th St Miami (33186) *(G-10329)*
SGF Inc...813 996-2528
3018 Joan Ct Land O Lakes (34639) *(G-7866)*
Sgm Lighting Inc...407 440-3601
7806 Kingspointe Pkwy Orlando (32819) *(G-13178)*
Sgmc Microwave, Melbourne *Also called Andrew Martin Swift (G-8767)*
SGS Designs Inc...813 258-2691
1515 W Cypress St Tampa (33606) *(G-18088)*
SGS US East Coast LLC...305 571-9700
12062 Nw 27th Ave Miami (33167) *(G-10330)*
Sgt. Bretts Healthy Lifestyles, Coconut Creek *Also called Sergeant Bretts Coffee LLC (G-2094)*
Sh Shower & Tub Enclosures LLC...786 229-2529
4101 Sw 74th Ct Miami (33155) *(G-10331)*
Sh Signs...305 967-8964
215 Sw 17th Ave Ste 203 Miami (33135) *(G-10332)*
Shade Experts USA LLC...561 422-3200
11117 Alameda Bay Ct Wellington (33414) *(G-18730)*
Shade Saver Inc...850 650-0884
3330 Nw 95th Avenue Rd Ocala (34482) *(G-12045)*
Shade Systems Inc...352 237-0135
4150 Sw 19th St Ocala (34474) *(G-12046)*
Shades By Ana Inc...305 238-4858
12240 Sw 128th St Miami (33186) *(G-10333)*
Shades To You LLC...407 889-0049
1676 E Semoran Blvd Apopka (32703) *(G-186)*
Shadow Trailers Inc...352 529-2190
951 Sw 21st Pl Williston (32696) *(G-19215)*
Shadow-Caster Led Lighting LLC...727 474-2877
2060 Calumet St Clearwater (33765) *(G-1876)*
Shafers Classic Reproductions...813 622-7091
5407 24th Ave S Tampa (33619) *(G-18089)*
Shaikh Rizwan...202 740-9796
316 N Canal Ave Lakeland (33801) *(G-7789)*
Shain Inc...813 889-9614
4801 George Rd Ste 180 Tampa (33634) *(G-18090)*
Shamrock Mobile Detl & Pressur...941 286-3572
1029 Eastview Ln Punta Gorda (33982) *(G-15231)*
Shane Laliberte Lift LLC...407 873-0703
6449 Adam St Saint Cloud (34771) *(G-15666)*
Shangri-La Enterprises...305 672-6683
4101 Pine Tree Dr # 1704 Miami Beach (33140) *(G-10709)*
Shanker Industries Realty Inc (PA)...631 940-9889
3900 Fiscal Ct Ste 100 West Palm Beach (33404) *(G-19029)*
Shannon Spray Coatings Inc...850 602-7163
7267 Belgium Rd Pensacola (32526) *(G-14260)*
Shantui America Corp...786 491-9114
5201 Nw 77th Ave Ste 600 Miami (33166) *(G-10334)*
Shapes Group Ltd Co...321 837-0500
1415 Fundation Pk Blvd Se Palm Bay (32909) *(G-13534)*
Shapes Precision Manufacturing, Palm Bay *Also called Shapes Group Ltd Co (G-13534)*
Shapley, Fort Myers *Also called Carfore Ltd (G-4388)*
Shar Family Enterprises Llc...352 365-6988
2207 Aitkin Loop Leesburg (34748) *(G-8171)*
Sharing Three Inc...305 884-8384
575 E 10th Ave Hialeah (33010) *(G-5617)*
Shark Signs of Ne Fl Inc...904 766-6222
5317 Shen Ave Jacksonville (32205) *(G-6762)*
Shark Skinz...772 388-9621
300 Industrial Park Blvd # 5 Sebastian (32958) *(G-16672)*
Shark Tools, Deerfield Beach *Also called T H L Diamond Products Inc (G-2922)*
Shark Tooth Enterprises Inc...904 449-8247
981 Martin Ave Green Cove Springs (32043) *(G-5071)*
Sharp Marketing LLC...954 565-2711
655 W Prospect Rd Oakland Park (33309) *(G-11838)*
Sharper Edge...813 871-3343
4821 N Clark Ave Tampa (33614) *(G-18091)*
Shashi LLC...561 447-8800
6926 Royal Orchid Cir Delray Beach (33446) *(G-3140)*
Shashy Enterprises Inc...352 732-3904
1824 N Magnolia Ave Ocala (34475) *(G-12047)*
Shasta Beverages, Eustis *Also called National Beverage Corp (G-3715)*
Shasta Beverages Intl Inc...954 581-0922
8100 Sw 10th St Ste 4000 Plantation (33324) *(G-14549)*
Shaver Millwork, Vero Beach *Also called Shaver Properties Inc (G-18664)*
Shaver Properties Inc...772 569-3466
6010 Old Dixie Hwy Ste K Vero Beach (32967) *(G-18664)*
Shavers Pavers...407 350-3538
4015 Sunny Day Way Kissimmee (34744) *(G-7298)*
Shaw Development LLC (PA)...239 405-6100
25190 Bernwood Dr Bonita Springs (34135) *(G-853)*
Shaw's Site Preparation, Perry *Also called Shaws Welding Inc (G-14313)*
Shawn William Shumake LLC...813 374-2469
9307 N 14th St Tampa (33612) *(G-18092)*
Shaws Fiberglass Inc...863 425-9176
6925b State Road 60 W Mulberry (33860) *(G-11136)*
Shaws Sthern Blle Frz Fods In...904 768-1591
821 Virginia St Jacksonville (32208) *(G-6763)*
Shaws Welding Inc...850 584-7197
1530 S Dixie Hwy Perry (32348) *(G-14313)*
Sheaffer Boats Inc...813 872-7644
3916 W South Ave Tampa (33614) *(G-18093)*
Sheaffer Marine Inc...813 872-7311
3916 W South Ave Tampa (33614) *(G-18094)*
Shealy Revel B Inc...352 629-1552
606 Ne 35th St Ocala (34479) *(G-12048)*
Shearwater Marine Fl Inc...772 781-5553
4519 Se Commerce Ave Stuart (34997) *(G-17010)*
Sheas Salsa LLC...954 371-7781
11328 Regatta Ln Wellington (33449) *(G-18731)*
Shed4less LLC...863 660-7300
3147 Us Highway 98 S Lakeland (33803) *(G-7790)*
Sheds Galore and More LLC...386 362-1786
1410 Howard St E Live Oak (32064) *(G-8240)*
Sheeituuuu, Miami Beach *Also called Jazanique Wickson (G-10684)*
Sheet Metal Systems Inc...727 548-1711
6482 Park Blvd N Ste A Pinellas Park (33781) *(G-14387)*
Sheet Metal Unlimited, Stuart *Also called Jglc Enterprises LLC (G-16961)*
Sheet Metal Unlimited...772 872-7440
3920 Se Commerce Ave Stuart (34997) *(G-17011)*
Sheffield Steel Corporation...918 245-1335
4221 W Boy Scout Blvd # 600 Tampa (33607) *(G-18095)*
Sheila Shine Inc...305 557-1729
1201 Nw 1st Pl Miami (33136) *(G-10335)*
Shelbie Press Inc...407 896-4600
1203 N Mills Ave Orlando (32803) *(G-13179)*
Sheldon Sign Company Inc...941 321-6313
1236 Webster St North Port (34288) *(G-11749)*
Shelfgenie...877 814-3643
16422 Carrara Way # 102 Naples (34110) *(G-11398)*
Shelia Shine Inc...305 557-1729
7725 W 2nd Ct Hialeah (33014) *(G-5618)*

Shell Aerospace LLC..........786 400-2660
7500 Nw 25th St Unit 1a Miami (33122) ***(G-10336)***
Shelleys Cshions Umbrellas Mfg, Miami *Also called Shelleys Cushions Mfg Inc* ***(G-10337)***
Shelleys Cushions Mfg Inc..........305 633-1790
3640 Nw 52nd St Miami (33142) ***(G-10337)***
Shellie Blum LLC..........863 439-3060
201 C F Kinney Rd Lake Wales (33859) ***(G-7519)***
Shelmet Corp..........561 688-9700
400 Columbia Dr West Palm Beach (33409) ***(G-19030)***
Sheltair Daytona Beach LLC..........386 255-0471
561 Pearl Harbor Dr Daytona Beach (32114) ***(G-2713)***
Shelton Group LLC..........321 676-8981
1333 Gateway Dr Ste 1013 Melbourne (32901) ***(G-8931)***
Shenk Enterprises LLC..........386 753-1959
985 Harley Strcklnd Blvd Orange City (32763) ***(G-12378)***
Shepherd Micro Racing USA, Pompano Beach *Also called Nuggets Racing LLC* ***(G-14777)***
Shermans Welding & Maintence..........904 731-3460
6299 Powers Ave Ste 3 Jacksonville (32217) ***(G-6764)***
Sherry J Bertucelli Inc..........407 760-7585
3827 E Kaley Ave Orlando (32812) ***(G-13180)***
Sherry Manufacturing Co Inc..........305 693-7000
3287 Nw 65th St Miami (33147) ***(G-10338)***
Shgar Kane Couture Inc..........407 205-8038
4900 Silver Oaks Village Orlando (32808) ***(G-13181)***
Shield Products Inc..........904 880-6060
6010 Nw 99th Ave Unit 110 Doral (33178) ***(G-3501)***
Shifted Industries..........561 302-8915
6930 Swamp Dr Groveland (34736) ***(G-5108)***
Shiloh Import/Export LLC..........404 514-4109
7049 Woodmont Way Tamarac (33321) ***(G-17368)***
Shilpico Inc..........561 306-5625
22360 Sands Point Dr Boca Raton (33433) ***(G-708)***
Shima Group Corp..........305 463-0288
10836 Nw 27th St Doral (33172) ***(G-3502)***
Shineline Buffing & Detail..........941 268-1033
11338 1st Ave Punta Gorda (33955) ***(G-15232)***
Shining Tree Inc..........855 688-7987
2952 Payson Way Wellington (33414) ***(G-18732)***
Shiny Prints..........561 200-2872
143 Juno St Jupiter (33458) ***(G-7112)***
Ship Shape Canvas and Awng LLC..........954 480-8889
6101 Heliconia Rd Delray Beach (33484) ***(G-3141)***
Shipping + Business Svcs LLC..........904 240-1737
12627 San Jose Blvd Ste 5 Jacksonville (32223) ***(G-6765)***
Shipping Depot Inc..........813 347-2494
4835 W Cypress St Tampa (33607) ***(G-18096)***
Shipyard Dog Prints, Crystal River *Also called Fretto Prints Inc* ***(G-2378)***
Shirley L Jordan Company Inc..........352 754-1117
15270 Flight Path Dr Brooksville (34604) ***(G-1268)***
Shirley Simon & Associates LLC..........813 247-2100
4951b E Adamo Dr Ste 216 Tampa (33605) ***(G-18097)***
Shirts & Caps Inc..........813 788-7026
9437 Corporate Lake Dr Tampa (33634) ***(G-18098)***
Shirts n Things Inc..........954 434-7480
6001 Orange Dr Davie (33314) ***(G-2591)***
Shiseido Americas Corporation..........305 416-6021
1221 Brickell Ave Fl 26 Miami (33131) ***(G-10339)***
Shl Pharma LLC..........954 725-2008
588 Jim Moran Blvd Deerfield Beach (33442) ***(G-2910)***
Sho ME Natural Products, Brooksville *Also called Sho ME Nutriceuticals Inc* ***(G-1269)***
Sho ME Nutriceuticals Inc..........352 797-9600
15431 Flight Path Dr Brooksville (34604) ***(G-1269)***
Shocksocks LLC..........352 258-0496
727 Nw Federal Hwy Stuart (34994) ***(G-17012)***
Shoe Jewels, Santa Rosa Beach *Also called Jdk Imports Inc* ***(G-16161)***
Shop Munki, Oviedo *Also called Excess Liquidator LLC* ***(G-13429)***
Shopworks LLC..........561 491-6000
1101 N Olive Ave West Palm Beach (33401) ***(G-19031)***
Shore Trendz LLC..........954 608-7375
560 Nw 118th Ave Plantation (33325) ***(G-14550)***
Shoreline Foundation Inc..........954 985-0981
2781 Sw 56th Ave West Park (33023) ***(G-19098)***
Shoreline Plastics LLC..........904 696-2981
7167 Old Kings Rd Jacksonville (32219) ***(G-6766)***
Shoreline Print Group..........727 481-9358
4809 Sw 25th Pl Cape Coral (33914) ***(G-1470)***
Shoreline Printing Company..........954 491-0311
5100 Ne 12th Ave A Oakland Park (33334) ***(G-11839)***
Shoreline Publishing Inc..........914 500-5456
3629 Wilderness Blvd W Parrish (34219) ***(G-14007)***
Shoreline Shutter Systems Inc..........386 299-2219
494 Nash Ln Port Orange (32127) ***(G-15033)***
Shores Automotive..........561 391-0260
2544 Nw 2nd Ave Boca Raton (33431) ***(G-709)***
Shores Global LLC..........305 716-0848
2440 Nw 116th St Ste 600 Miami (33167) ***(G-10340)***
Shorr Enterprises Inc..........954 733-9840
3033 Nw 28th St Lauderdale Lakes (33311) ***(G-8093)***
Short Stop Print Inc..........941 474-4313
1101 S Mccall Rd Unit A Englewood (34223) ***(G-3683)***
Shot of Freon..........305 917-5893
2911 10th St W Lehigh Acres (33971) ***(G-8207)***
Show Publishing LLC..........239 272-8477
1540 Clermont Dr Unit 102 Naples (34109) ***(G-11399)***
Showcase Marble Inc..........386 253-6646
405 6th St Daytona Beach (32117) ***(G-2714)***
Showcase Publications Inc..........863 687-4377
1211 E Main St Lakeland (33801) ***(G-7791)***
Shower Doors & More Inc..........954 358-2014
1196 Nw 23rd Ave Fort Lauderdale (33311) ***(G-4231)***
Shower Doors Unlimited Inc..........561 547-0702
3551 High Ridge Rd Boynton Beach (33426) ***(G-958)***
Showerfloss Inc..........239 947-2855
20930 Persimmon Pl Estero (33928) ***(G-3696)***
Shredded Tire Inc..........954 970-8565
6742 Nw 17th Ave Fort Lauderdale (33309) ***(G-4232)***
Shri Guru Krupa Smoothies Inc..........904 461-9090
112 Sea Grove Main St Saint Augustine (32080) ***(G-15609)***
Shrieve Chemical Co Chemi, Winter Haven *Also called American Vulkan Corporation* ***(G-19299)***
Shriji Swami LLC..........904 727-3434
1301 Monument Rd Ste 22 Jacksonville (32225) ***(G-6767)***
Shukla Medical Inc..........732 474-1769
8300 Sheen Dr Saint Petersburg (33709) ***(G-15912)***
Shurhold Products Company..........772 287-1313
3119 Sw 42nd Ave Palm City (34990) ***(G-13673)***
Shutter Down All Weather Protc..........561 856-0655
2778 S Evergreen Cir Boynton Beach (33426) ***(G-959)***
Shutter Down Storm Protection..........813 957-8936
3940 E Knights Griffin Rd Plant City (33565) ***(G-14465)***
Shutter Lubrication & Service..........561 745-8956
1821 W 10th St Ste 3 Jupiter (33469) ***(G-7113)***
Shutter Southern Cross..........941 276-7064
1401 Henning St North Port (34288) ***(G-11750)***
Shutter Southern Cross..........941 235-2620
1109 Tamiami Trl Unit 5 Port Charlotte (33953) ***(G-14997)***
Shutter2think Inc..........850 291-8301
1014 Raintree Ln Palm Beach Gardens (33410) ***(G-13628)***
Shutterman Storm & Security..........239 455-9166
4186 Domestic Ave Naples (34104) ***(G-11400)***
Shutters On Sale Inc..........386 756-0009
1307 Crepe Myrtle Ln Port Orange (32128) ***(G-15034)***
Shutters Wholesale..........770 410-9525
9440 Philips Hwy Ste 12 Jacksonville (32256) ***(G-6768)***
Shuttertek Inc..........772 828-6149
566 Se Floresta Dr Port Saint Lucie (34983) ***(G-15142)***
Shwinco Industries Inc..........850 271-8900
400 Aberdeen Loop Lynn Haven (32444) ***(G-8438)***
Shyft Group Inc..........954 946-9955
15335 Pk Of Commerce Blvd Jupiter (33478) ***(G-7114)***
Sibe Automation LLC..........352 690-1741
1521 Sw 12th Ave Ste 700 Ocala (34471) ***(G-12049)***
Sibex Inc (PA)..........727 726-4343
430 N Suncoast Blvd Crystal River (34429) ***(G-2382)***
Sibex Systems Division, Crystal River *Also called Sibex Inc* ***(G-2382)***
Sibling Group Holdings Inc (PA)..........786 618-1472
6340 Sunset Dr Miami (33143) ***(G-10341)***
Sic Products LLC..........904 374-2639
5130 Kristin Ct Naples (34105) ***(G-11401)***
Sicamu Inc..........850 270-6283
1066 Strong Rd Quincy (32351) ***(G-15254)***
Sick Ride LLC..........239 300-5995
6355 Naples Blvd Ste 5 Naples (34109) ***(G-11402)***
Sicoma North America Inc..........800 921-7559
11300 47th St N Clearwater (33762) ***(G-1877)***
Sid Signs, Miami *Also called Signs International Distr Corp* ***(G-10348)***
Siding Industries of Nthrn FL..........904 814-7923
225 Ventura Rd Saint Augustine (32080) ***(G-15610)***
Sidus Space Inc..........321 613-0615
175 Imperial Blvd Cape Canaveral (32920) ***(G-1367)***
Siebers Graphic, Port Richey *Also called Prolific Resource Inc* ***(G-15066)***
Siemens Corporation..........407 736-5629
4041 Forest Island Dr Orlando (32826) ***(G-13182)***
Siemens Energy Inc..........407 736-1400
3850 Quadrangle Blvd Orlando (32817) ***(G-13183)***
Siemens Energy Inc..........407 206-5008
11842 Corporate Orlando (32817) ***(G-13184)***
Siemens Energy Inc..........407 736-7957
11950 Corporate Blvd Orlando (32817) ***(G-13185)***
Siemens Gmesa Rnwble Enrgy Inc (HQ)..........407 736-2000
4400 N Alafaya Trl Q2 Orlando (32826) ***(G-13186)***
Siemens Gmesa Rnwble Enrgy Inc..........407 721-3273
11950 Corporate Blvd Orlando (32817) ***(G-13187)***
Siemens Industry Inc..........407 650-3570
4506 L B Mcleod Rd Ste C Orlando (32811) ***(G-13188)***
Siemens Industry Inc..........954 436-8848
2270 Nw 185th Way Pembroke Pines (33029) ***(G-14059)***
Sientra Inc..........813 751-7576
1302 Guiles Hill Ct Brandon (33511) ***(G-1179)***

Sierra Nevada Corporation.....850 659-3600
1150 N Eglin Pkwy Shalimar (32579) *(G-16777)*
Sif Technology Company LLC.....941 225-8363
7245 16th St E Unit 101 Sarasota (34243) *(G-16295)*
Sig, Saint Petersburg *Also called Seating Installation Group LLC (G-15908)*
Sighthound Inc.....650 564-4364
101 S New York Ave # 211 Winter Park (32789) *(G-19442)*
Sigillu, Weston *Also called Gold-Rep Corporation (G-19134)*
Siglo Holdings LLC.....727 369-5220
8285 Bryan Dairy Rd Largo (33777) *(G-8051)*
Sigma Extruding Corp.....904 786-2031
627 Lane Ave N Jacksonville (32254) *(G-6769)*
Sigma Marketing, Orange Park *Also called Sigma Press Inc (G-12405)*
Sigma Press Inc.....904 264-6006
1543 Kingsley Ave Ste 7 Orange Park (32073) *(G-12405)*
Sign & Vehicle Wraps Inc.....407 859-8631
1011 W Lancaster Rd Ste 7 Orlando (32809) *(G-13189)*
Sign A Rama.....954 796-1644
10200 W Sample Rd Coral Springs (33065) *(G-2312)*
Sign A Rama.....813 264-0022
3118 Belmore Rd Tampa (33618) *(G-18099)*
Sign A Rama Inc (HQ).....561 640-5570
2121 Vista Pkwy West Palm Beach (33411) *(G-19032)*
Sign A Rama Inc.....904 998-8880
3633 Southside Blvd Jacksonville (32216) *(G-6770)*
Sign and Design Depot LLC.....239 995-7446
960 Pondella Rd Ste C North Fort Myers (33903) *(G-11605)*
Sign Art Group, The, Tampa *Also called Hanes-Harris Design Cons (G-17742)*
Sign Consultants, Bradenton *Also called Guthman Signs LLC (G-1054)*
Sign Depot Co.....407 894-0090
1100 W Colonial Dr Unit 1 Orlando (32804) *(G-13190)*
Sign Design and Creations.....954 724-2884
5000 Nw 17th St Ste 3 Margate (33063) *(G-8567)*
Sign Design of Florida Inc.....352 787-3882
3602 Parkway Blvd Ste 2 Leesburg (34748) *(G-8172)*
Sign Development Corporation.....305 227-6250
8240 W Flagler St Miami (33144) *(G-10342)*
Sign Effex, Winter Haven *Also called Laporte Inv Holdings Inc (G-19335)*
Sign King, Longwood *Also called Greyson Corp (G-8286)*
Sign Language Interpreting.....386 681-9784
74 Concord Dr Ormond Beach (32176) *(G-13398)*
Sign Man Inc.....321 259-1703
4580 N Us Highway 1 Melbourne (32935) *(G-8932)*
Sign N Drive.....813 999-4837
1015 E Hillsborough Ave Tampa (33604) *(G-18100)*
Sign On LLC.....239 800-9454
4519 Del Prado Blvd S B Cape Coral (33904) *(G-1471)*
Sign Pro America.....412 908-9832
3811 University Blvd W # 37 Jacksonville (32217) *(G-6771)*
Sign Producers Inc.....407 855-8864
555 W Landstreet Rd Orlando (32824) *(G-13191)*
Sign Rockers LLC.....866 212-9697
12485 Sw 137th Ave # 206 Miami (33186) *(G-10343)*
Sign Solutions, Plantation *Also called J Schor R Inc (G-14527)*
Sign Solutions of Tampa Bay.....813 269-5990
3921 W Dr M Lthr Kng Jr Martin Luther Tampa (33614) *(G-18101)*
Sign Source The, Belleview *Also called Raimonda Investment Group Inc (G-375)*
Sign Space.....786 360-2670
2365 Nw 70th Ave Miami (33122) *(G-10344)*
Sign Stapler.....800 775-3971
1969 S Alafaya Trl Orlando (32828) *(G-13192)*
Sign Star, Tampa *Also called West Central Signs Inc (G-18255)*
Sign Systems Grphic Dsigns Inc.....813 281-2400
5031 W Grace St Tampa (33607) *(G-18102)*
Sign Tech Inc.....941 575-1349
25191 Olympia Ave Ste 1 Punta Gorda (33950) *(G-15233)*
Sign Up Now Sign Company LLC.....754 224-9091
620 Se 10th St Pompano Beach (33060) *(G-14850)*
Sign Works Inc.....941 894-7927
2491 15th St Sarasota (34237) *(G-16594)*
Sign X-Press, Largo *Also called International C & C Corp (G-7981)*
Sign Zoo, Sarasota *Also called Zoo Holdings LLC (G-16647)*
Sign-A-Rama, Pompano Beach *Also called Crf Group Inc (G-14651)*
Sign-A-Rama, Lakeland *Also called C&D Sign and Lighting Svcs LLC (G-7652)*
Sign-A-Rama, North Fort Myers *Also called Signarama (G-11606)*
Sign-A-Rama, Lutz *Also called Signs of Tampa Bay LLC (G-8418)*
Sign-A-Rama, Coral Springs *Also called Sign A Rama (G-2312)*
Sign-A-Rama, Naples *Also called Signarama Naples (G-11403)*
Sign-A-Rama, Stuart *Also called Sp Sign LLC (G-17020)*
Sign-A-Rama, Fort Myers *Also called Jbjb Holdings LLC (G-4501)*
Sign-A-Rama, West Palm Beach *Also called Sign A Rama Inc (G-19032)*
Sign-A-Rama, North Miami Beach *Also called White Sands Dmg Inc (G-11712)*
Sign-A-Rama, Orlando *Also called Everything Communicates Inc (G-12722)*
Sign-A-Rama, Miami *Also called Barrau & Coirin Inc (G-9223)*
Sign-A-Rama, Jacksonville *Also called Sign A Rama Inc (G-6770)*
Sign-A-Rama, West Palm Beach *Also called Graphics Designer Inc (G-18889)*
Sign-A-Rama, Delray Beach *Also called Sneids Inc (G-3144)*
Sign-A-Rama, Tampa *Also called Sign A Rama (G-18099)*
Sign-A-Rama, Miami *Also called Kendall Sign and Design Inc (G-9820)*
Sign-O-Saurus Inc.....407 677-8965
3008 S Us Highway 17/92 Casselberry (32707) *(G-1518)*
Sign-O-Saurus of Daytona Inc.....386 322-5222
2127 S Ridgewood Ave South Daytona (32119) *(G-16809)*
Signage Plus LLC.....407 668-3567
484 Abba St Altamonte Springs (32714) *(G-73)*
Signal Dynamics Corporation.....904 342-4008
6500 Nw 21st Ave Ste 1 Fort Lauderdale (33309) *(G-4233)*
Signal Graphics Printing LLC.....303 837-1331
615 Aqui Esta Dr Punta Gorda (33950) *(G-15234)*
Signalvault LLC.....407 878-6365
156 S Charles Richard Bea Debary (32713) *(G-2755)*
Signarama.....239 997-1644
4621 Bayshore Rd North Fort Myers (33917) *(G-11606)*
Signarama.....850 656-3200
897 N Monroe St Tallahassee (32303) *(G-17323)*
Signarama - Woodstock, West Palm Beach *Also called Georgia Mktg & Sign Co LLC (G-18887)*
Signarama Clearwater.....727 784-4500
7211 Us Highway 19 N Pinellas Park (33781) *(G-14388)*
Signarama Dwntwn Fort Lderdale.....954 990-4749
1422 Se 17th St Fort Lauderdale (33316) *(G-4234)*
Signarama Naples.....239 330-3737
1095 5th Ave N Naples (34102) *(G-11403)*
Signarama-Sarasota.....941 554-8798
4435 S Tamiami Trl Sarasota (34231) *(G-16595)*
Signature Athletics Inc.....561 212-9284
1025 W Indiantown Rd # 10 Jupiter (33458) *(G-7115)*
Signature AVI US Holdings Inc (HQ).....407 648-7230
13485 Veterans Way # 600 Orlando (32827) *(G-13193)*
Signature Brands LLC (PA).....352 622-3134
808 Sw 12th St Ocala (34471) *(G-12050)*
Signature Brands LLC.....352 622-3134
1930 Sw 38th Ave Ste 300 Ocala (34474) *(G-12051)*
Signature Cabinets.....954 563-8584
1034 Ne 44th Ct Oakland Park (33334) *(G-11840)*
Signature Computer Svcs Inc.....954 421-0950
7040 W Palmetto Park Rd Boca Raton (33433) *(G-710)*
Signature Granite Inc.....813 443-5597
3904 S 51st St Tampa (33619) *(G-18103)*
Signature Metal Fab LLC.....954 214-1161
400 Farmington Dr Plantation (33317) *(G-14551)*
Signature Printing Inc.....305 828-9992
5725 Nw 151st St Miami Lakes (33014) *(G-10857)*
Signature Printing Technology.....407 963-6291
682 Youngstown Pkwy # 330 Altamonte Springs (32714) *(G-74)*
Signature Signs Inc.....727 725-1044
1450 10th St S Unit C Safety Harbor (34695) *(G-15503)*
Signcorp Inc.....863 224-1331
512 6th St Nw Winter Haven (33881) *(G-19355)*
Signcraft LLC.....561 543-0034
3694 Old Lighthouse Cir Wellington (33414) *(G-18733)*
Signcraft & More Inc.....386 755-4754
1554 E Duval St Lake City (32055) *(G-7384)*
Signcraft Magazine, Fort Myers *Also called Signcraft Publishing Co Inc (G-4604)*
Signcraft Publishing Co Inc.....239 939-4644
3950 Ellis Rd Fort Myers (33905) *(G-4604)*
Signcrafters of Central Fla.....352 323-1862
1134 E North Blvd Leesburg (34748) *(G-8173)*
SIGNGEEK DBA PENSACOLA SIGN & GRAPHICS, Pensacola *Also called Pensacola Sign & Graphics Inc (G-14226)*
Signgraphix Inc.....954 571-7131
242 S Military Trl Deerfield Beach (33442) *(G-2911)*
Significant Solutions Corp.....561 703-7703
3003 W Yamato Rd Ste C8 Boca Raton (33434) *(G-711)*
Signline Signs & Electrical.....904 388-9474
562 King St Jacksonville (32204) *(G-6772)*
Signmasters Inc.....352 335-7000
2530 Sw 34th St Gainesville (32608) *(G-4995)*
Signpost LLC.....813 334-7678
1236 Trust Ln Maitland (32751) *(G-8477)*
Signposts, Maitland *Also called Signpost LLC (G-8477)*
Signprinters, Tallahassee *Also called Mag-Tags Inc (G-17293)*
Signs & Stripes Llc.....305 775-1174
2371 Dunhill Ave Miramar (33025) *(G-11042)*
Signs 2 U Inc.....305 227-6250
8240 W Flagler St Miami (33144) *(G-10345)*
Signs All Signs.....786 285-7900
14121 Nw 19th Ave Opa Locka (33054) *(G-12358)*
Signs By Design of Miami, Cutler Bay *Also called Honchin Inc (G-2397)*
Signs By Ramon, Tampa *Also called Rigal Ramon & Maritza (G-18057)*
Signs By Tomorrow, Fort Myers *Also called Thomas United Inc (G-4628)*
Signs By Tomorrow, West Palm Beach *Also called Sb Signs Inc (G-19026)*
Signs By Tomorrow, Sarasota *Also called J T E Inc (G-16475)*

ALPHABETIC

Signs Connection Inc....305 978-5777
600 Ne 36th St Apt 807 Miami (33137) (G-10346)
Signs Factory USA Inc....786 717-5474
7465 W 19th Ct Hialeah (33014) (G-5619)
Signs For You Inc....305 635-6662
2401 Nw 34th Ave Miami (33142) (G-10347)
Signs Galore Inc....850 683-8010
111 Hammock St Crestview (32536) (G-2358)
Signs In One Day, Sarasota Also called Sanbur Inc (G-16572)
Signs International Distr Corp....305 715-0017
8461 Nw 61st St Miami (33166) (G-10348)
Signs Just For You Inc....407 927-0226
4009 W State Road 46 Sanford (32771) (G-16115)
Signs N Stuff Inc....904 248-8141
60 Canterbury Ct Orange Park (32065) (G-12406)
Signs Now, Hollywood Also called Business Forward Inc (G-5792)
Signs Now, Bradenton Also called Lambs Signs Inc (G-1068)
Signs Now....386 238-5507
1440 N Nova Rd Ste 308 Daytona Beach (32117) (G-2715)
Signs Now....727 524-8500
12350 Belcher Rd S 14a Largo (33773) (G-8052)
Signs Now (PA)....850 383-6500
1551 Capital Cir Se Ste 6 Tallahassee (32301) (G-17324)
Signs Now Inc....407 628-2410
1003 S Orlando Ave Winter Park (32789) (G-19443)
Signs Now St Augustine Inc....904 810-5838
1711 Lakeside Ave Ste 1 Saint Augustine (32084) (G-15611)
Signs of America Tampa Corp....813 243-9243
4025 W Waters Ave Tampa (33614) (G-18104)
Signs of Reilly....954 263-7829
1121 W Mcnab Rd Pompano Beach (33069) (G-14851)
Signs of Tampa Bay LLC....813 526-0484
1903 Passero Ave Lutz (33559) (G-8418)
Signs of Time Inc....772 240-9590
1700 Sw Belgrave Ter Stuart (34997) (G-17013)
Signs of Times Ventures LLC....772 336-4525
151 Ne Naranja Ave Port Saint Lucie (34983) (G-15143)
Signs Plus New IDS-New Tech In....941 378-4262
4242 Mcintosh Ln Sarasota (34232) (G-16596)
Signs Supreme Inc....561 795-0111
17224 Gulf Pine Cir Wellington (33414) (G-18734)
Signs Unlimited Inc....727 845-0330
331 A1a Beach Blvd Saint Augustine (32080) (G-15612)
Signs Unlimited of Bay County....850 785-1061
507 E 7th St Panama City (32401) (G-13949)
Signs Unlimited Sea Inc....352 732-7341
618 S Magnolia Ave Ocala (34471) (G-12052)
Signs Usa Inc....813 901-9333
4123 W Hillsborough Ave Tampa (33614) (G-18105)
Signsations Inc....561 989-1900
5425 N Dixie Hwy Ste 2 Boca Raton (33487) (G-712)
Signsharks Sign Service....904 766-6222
7030 N Main St Jacksonville (32208) (G-6773)
Signsitecom Inc....386 487-0265
162 Sw Spencer Ct Ste 106 Lake City (32024) (G-7385)
Signway Inc....407 696-7446
2964 Forsyth Rd Winter Park (32792) (G-19444)
Sike Usa Inc....786 331-4020
3004 Nw 82nd Ave Doral (33122) (G-3503)
Sikorsky Aircraft Corp....772 210-0849
2324 Se Liberator Ln Stuart (34996) (G-17014)
Silcar Corp....305 557-8391
1475 W 82nd St Hialeah (33014) (G-5620)
Silco Software Technology Inc....813 475-4591
16223 Ivy Lake Dr Odessa (33556) (G-12151)
Silent Standby Power Sup LLC....954 253-9557
3866 Prospect Ave Ste 5 West Palm Beach (33404) (G-19033)
Silestone of Tampa, Ponte Vedra Also called Counter Active Inc (G-14923)
Siligom USA LLC....786 406-6262
5930 Nw 99th Ave Unit 9 Doral (33178) (G-3504)
Silk Safari Inc....561 689-3882
613 Madeline Dr West Palm Beach (33413) (G-19034)
Silkmasters Inc....904 372-8958
1911 Sw 80th Dr Gainesville (32607) (G-4996)
Silly Dandelions Inc....727 400-6590
525 Oakwood Dr Largo (33771) (G-8053)
Silly Grape Inc....407 790-7999
1720 Fennell St Ste 5 Maitland (32751) (G-8478)
Silver Bay LLC....941 306-5812
1431 Tallevast Rd Sarasota (34243) (G-16296)
Silver Enterprises Assoc Inc....239 542-0068
1417 Sw 52nd Ter Cape Coral (33914) (G-1472)
Silver Horn Jerky Inc....850 208-1433
3715 Mobile Hwy Pensacola (32505) (G-14261)
Silver Sheet Florida Inc....850 230-9711
17742 Ashley Dr Panama City (32413) (G-13950)
Silver Springs Citrus Inc....352 324-2101
25411 N Mare Ave Howey In The Hills (34737) (G-6012)
Silver Springs Citrus LLC....352 324-2101
25411 N Mare Ave Howey In The Hills (34737) (G-6013)
Silver Star On Lime LLC....941 312-4566
2739 Aspinwall St Sarasota (34237) (G-16597)
Silver, Sword, and Stone, Pensacola Also called Gems Jewelry & Uniques (G-14162)
Silverhorse Racing LLC....321 722-2813
700 S John Rodes Blvd Melbourne (32904) (G-8933)
Silverline Furniture Corp....305 663-9560
15940 Sw 60th St Miami (33193) (G-10349)
Silverman Fence Mfg Inc....904 730-0882
4698 Dusk Ct Jacksonville (32207) (G-6774)
Silvershore Partners LLC....904 562-0812
10175 Fortune Pkwy # 60 Jacksonville (32256) (G-6775)
Silversphere Holdings, Daytona Beach Also called Tel-Tron Technologies Corp (G-2724)
Silverstar Holdings Ltd (PA)....561 479-0040
1900 Glades Rd Ste 265 Boca Raton (33431) (G-713)
Sima Group, Coral Gables Also called SMR Management Inc (G-2196)
Simar Industries Inc....352 622-2287
805 Nw 25th Ave Ocala (34475) (G-12053)
Simco, Avon Park Also called Standard Injection Molding Inc (G-297)
Simco Machine and Tool Inc....863 452-1151
2029 State Road 64 W Avon Park (33825) (G-295)
Simetri Inc....321 972-9980
7005 University Blvd Winter Park (32792) (G-19445)
Simkins Industries Inc (PA)....305 899-8184
5080 Biscayne Blvd Ste A Miami (33137) (G-10350)
Simmonds Precision Pdts Inc....904 757-3660
6061 Goodrich Blvd Jacksonville (32226) (G-6776)
Simon and Baker Inc....561 892-0494
2901 Clint Moore Rd Boca Raton (33496) (G-714)
Simons Hallandale Inc....561 468-1174
850 Ives Dairy Rd Ste T9 Miami (33179) (G-10351)
Simonsclub LLC....352 246-3636
8 S Main St Gainesville (32601) (G-4997)
Simplepin LLC....800 727-4136
8954 Se Bridge Rd Hobe Sound (33455) (G-5727)
Simpleshow USA Corp....844 468-5447
7300 Biscayne Blvd # 100 Miami (33138) (G-10352)
Simplex Inc....352 357-2828
4085 N Highway 19a Mount Dora (32757) (G-11114)
Simplex Manufacturing Inc....941 378-8700
6300 Tower Ln Unit 4 Sarasota (34240) (G-16598)
Simplex Time Recorder Co....561 988-7200
1501 Nw 51st St Boca Raton (33431) (G-715)
Simplex Tool and Mold, Sarasota Also called Simplex Manufacturing Inc (G-16598)
Simplexgrinnell Holdings LLC (HQ)....978 731-2500
1501 Nw 51st St Boca Raton (33431) (G-716)
Simplicity Esports LLC....855 345-9467
7000 W Plmtt Prk Rd Ste 5 Boca Raton (33433) (G-717)
Simplified Fabricators Inc....561 335-3488
9040 Belvedere Rd West Palm Beach (33411) (G-19035)
Simplified Systems Inc....305 672-7676
4014 Chase Ave Ph Miami Beach (33140) (G-10710)
Simplify, Naples Also called Brightsky LLC (G-11194)
Simplimatic Automation....941 360-6500
7245 16th St E Unit 114 Sarasota (34243) (G-16297)
Simply Cabinets LLC....850 541-3712
630 Malaga Pl Panama City Beach (32413) (G-13984)
Simply Closets & Cabinets....239 994-4264
10105 Amberwood Rd Ste 6 Alva (33920) (G-91)
Simply Cupcakes....239 262-5184
2490 Outrigger Ln Naples (34104) (G-11404)
Simply Group II LLC....407 960-4690
4366 Ronald Reagan Blvd Sanford (32773) (G-16116)
Simply Reliable Inc....800 209-9332
10460 Roosevelt Blvd N Saint Petersburg (33716) (G-15913)
Simply Shutters, Port Saint Lucie Also called Plantation Shutters Inc (G-15129)
Simply Sweet Company Inc (PA)....386 873-6516
1431 Orange Camp Rd Deland (32724) (G-3013)
Simply The Best Magazine, Delray Beach Also called Goodpress Publishing LLC (G-3085)
Simply45 LLC....954 982-2017
3490 Sw 30th Ave Fort Lauderdale (33312) (G-4235)
Simplynas, Sanford Also called Simply Group II LLC (G-16116)
Simpson....954 804-0829
7137 Pinecreek Ln Coconut Creek (33073) (G-2095)
Simpson Construction and Roofg....863 443-0710
418 E Elm St Avon Park (33825) (G-296)
Simpson Screens Inc....904 757-1498
11458 Harlan Dr Jacksonville (32218) (G-6777)
Sims Machine & Controls Inc....352 799-2405
15538 Aviation Loop Dr Brooksville (34604) (G-1270)
Sims Promotions, Jennings Also called Fka Racing Inc (G-6964)
Simtec Silicone Parts LLC....954 656-4212
9658 Premier Pkwy Miramar (33025) (G-11043)
Simulated Envmt Concepts Inc....754 263-3184
3937 Pembroke Rd Hollywood (33021) (G-5908)
Sin Pin Inc....877 805-5665
600 Nw Dixie Hwy Stuart (34994) (G-17015)
Sincere Fuel Inc....954 433-3577
16100 Sw 51st St Miramar (33027) (G-11044)

Sincere Sentiments Inc......352 287-1232
8001 E Shannon Ct Inverness (34450) ***(G-6096)***
Sincerus Pharmaceuticals Inc......800 604-5032
3265 W Mcnab Rd Pompano Beach (33069) ***(G-14852)***
Sinclair Industries LLC (PA)......305 215-0990
101691 Overseas Hwy Key Largo (33037) ***(G-7173)***
Sinergie Printing Inc......786 493-6167
1717 N Bayshore Dr Miami (33132) ***(G-10353)***
Singer Holdings Inc......321 724-0900
7791 Industrial Rd Melbourne (32904) ***(G-8934)***
Singing Machine Company Inc (PA)......954 596-1000
6301 Nw 5th Way Ste 2900 Fort Lauderdale (33309) ***(G-4236)***
Singular Grape Inc......305 508-4000
7380 W Sand Lake Rd Orlando (32819) ***(G-13194)***
Sinmat Commercial LLC......352 334-7270
1912 Nw 67th Pl Gainesville (32653) ***(G-4998)***
Sino Eagle Usa Inc......727 259-3570
1000 Bass Blvd Dunedin (34698) ***(G-3588)***
Sinobec Resources LLC......561 409-2205
1901 Green Rd Ste E Deerfield Beach (33064) ***(G-2912)***
Sinocare Meditech Inc......800 342-7226
2400 Nw 55th Ct Fort Lauderdale (33309) ***(G-4237)***
Sinofresh Healthcare Inc (PA)......941 270-2627
2357 S Tamiami Trl Unit 3 Venice (34293) ***(G-18573)***
Sintavia LLC (PA)......954 474-7800
2500 Sw 39th St Fort Lauderdale (33312) ***(G-4238)***
Sio Cnc Machining Inc......727 533-8271
14241 60th St N Clearwater (33760) ***(G-1878)***
Sipp Technologies LLC......904 374-5606
5245 Old Kings Rd Jacksonville (32254) ***(G-6778)***
Sippers By Design......305 371-5087
555 Ne 15th St Miami (33132) ***(G-10354)***
Sipradius LLC......954 290-2434
11834 Wiles Rd Coral Springs (33076) ***(G-2313)***
Sir Speedy, Orlando *Also called La Mar Orlando LLC* ***(G-12885)***
Sir Speedy, Sarasota *Also called Leda Printing Inc* ***(G-16487)***
Sir Speedy, West Palm Beach *Also called Palm Print Inc* ***(G-18986)***
Sir Speedy, Miami *Also called B D D International Corp* ***(G-9209)***
Sir Speedy, West Palm Beach *Also called Steven K Bakum Inc* ***(G-19044)***
Sir Speedy, Miami *Also called General & Duplicating Services* ***(G-9623)***
Sir Speedy, Orlando *Also called Paper Palm LLC* ***(G-13049)***
Sir Speedy, Palm Harbor *Also called Goforit Inc* ***(G-13737)***
Sir Speedy, Tallahassee *Also called Dvh Macleod Corp* ***(G-17246)***
Sir Speedy, Coral Springs *Also called Saugus Valley Corp* ***(G-2310)***
Sir Speedy, Seminole *Also called Anderson Printing Services Inc* ***(G-16738)***
Sir Speedy, Longwood *Also called Vmak Corp* ***(G-8348)***
Sir Speedy, Clearwater *Also called G L E M Inc* ***(G-1697)***
Sir Speedy, Jacksonville *Also called Hartco Inc* ***(G-6462)***
Sir Speedy, Largo *Also called G J V Inc* ***(G-7955)***
Sir Speedy, Miami Lakes *Also called Rennak Inc* ***(G-10850)***
Sir Speedy, Hollywood *Also called South Broward Printing Inc* ***(G-5912)***
Sir Speedy, Tampa *Also called Phil & Brenda Johnson Inc* ***(G-17988)***
Sir Speedy, Lakeland *Also called Aether Media USA Inc* ***(G-7629)***
Sir Speedy, Tequesta *Also called Premier Global Enterprises* ***(G-18387)***
Sir Speedy, Hialeah *Also called Guimar Inc* ***(G-5439)***
Sir Speedy, Coral Gables *Also called Global Printing Services Inc* ***(G-2150)***
Sir Speedy, Saint Petersburg *Also called Power Printing of Florida* ***(G-15885)***
Sir Speedy, Tampa *Also called Mxn Inc* ***(G-17921)***
Sir Speedy, Spring Hill *Also called J-Kup Corp* ***(G-16855)***
Sir Speedy Printing Center......352 683-8758
1260 Lori Dr Spring Hill (34606) ***(G-16863)***
Sir Winston Garments Inc......305 499-3144
13428 Sw 131st St Miami (33186) ***(G-10355)***
Sira......352 377-4947
912 Nw 13th St Gainesville (32601) ***(G-4999)***
SIRE Cabinetry Inc......909 225-4121
10320 Sw Stephanie Way Port Saint Lucie (34987) ***(G-15144)***
Sirs Commercial Print, Boca Raton *Also called Sirs Publishing Inc* ***(G-718)***
Sirs Publishing Inc (HQ)......800 521-0600
5201 Congress Ave Ste 250 Boca Raton (33487) ***(G-718)***
Sisco Marine LLC......850 265-1383
1725 Buchanan St Panama City (32409) ***(G-13951)***
Site Essentials......813 865-0208
13209 Byrd Dr Odessa (33556) ***(G-12152)***
Sitecrafters of Florida Inc......813 258-4696
3242 Henderson Blvd # 200 Tampa (33609) ***(G-18106)***
Sivance LLC (HQ)......352 376-8246
5002 Ne 54th Pl Gainesville (32609) ***(G-5000)***
Sivo Brick Pavers Inc......813 917-3859
4279 Tremblay Way Palm Harbor (34685) ***(G-13760)***
Siw Solutions LLC......561 274-9392
975 S Congress Ave Delray Beach (33445) ***(G-3142)***
Sixto Packaging, Opa Locka *Also called H Sixto Distributors Inc* ***(G-12322)***
Siyufy International Inc......352 512-0658
925 Se 17th St Ste D Ocala (34471) ***(G-12054)***
Sizemore Ultimate Food Trucks, Bunnell *Also called Sizemore Welding Inc* ***(G-1306)***
Sizemore Welding Inc......386 437-4073
205 N Bay St Bunnell (32110) ***(G-1306)***
Sjg Machine Inc......352 345-3656
316 Marianne St Brooksville (34601) ***(G-1271)***
Sjostrom Electronics, Boca Raton *Also called Sjostrom Industries Inc* ***(G-719)***
Sjostrom Industries Inc......561 368-2000
1400 Nw 9th Ave Apt 1 Boca Raton (33486) ***(G-719)***
SJS Woodworking LLC......561 704-5990
207 Pleasant Wood Dr Wellington (33414) ***(G-18735)***
Sk Worldwide LLC (PA)......786 360-4842
9553 Harding Ave Ste 310 Surfside (33154) ***(G-17206)***
Skagfield Corporation (PA)......850 878-1144
270 Crossway Rd Tallahassee (32305) ***(G-17325)***
Skampas Performance Group......305 974-0047
19201 Collins Ave Cu-137 Sunny Isles Beach (33160) ***(G-17080)***
Skandia Window Fashions, Tallahassee *Also called Skagfield Corporation* ***(G-17325)***
Skateboard Supercross LLC......786 529-8187
725 92nd St Surfside (33154) ***(G-17207)***
Skater Socks......850 424-6764
516 Mountain Dr Ste 104 Destin (32541) ***(G-3206)***
Skd Smoothie Inc......386 931-4953
1 Watermill Pl Palm Coast (32164) ***(G-13709)***
Ski Rixen - Quiet Waters Inc......954 429-0215
401 S Powerline Rd Deerfield Beach (33442) ***(G-2913)***
Ski Rixen USA, Deerfield Beach *Also called Ski Rixen - Quiet Waters Inc* ***(G-2913)***
Skide Llc......305 537-4275
6303 Blue Lagoon Dr Miami (33126) ***(G-10356)***
Skies Limit Printing......772 340-1090
10504 S Us Highway 1 Port Saint Lucie (34952) ***(G-15145)***
Skill-Metric Machine & Tl Inc......561 454-8900
1424 Gwenzell Ave 3c Delray Beach (33444) ***(G-3143)***
Skin Pro International Inc......305 528-9095
14345 Sunset Ln Southwest Ranches (33330) ***(G-16841)***
Skingen USA Inc......727 586-3751
1258 West Bay Dr Ste F Largo (33770) ***(G-8054)***
Skinmetics Inc......305 663-5750
4850 Sw 72nd Ave Miami (33155) ***(G-10357)***
Skinny Mixes LLC......727 826-0306
2849 Executive Dr Ste 210 Clearwater (33762) ***(G-1879)***
Skinutra Inc......813 992-1742
5136 W Clifton St Tampa (33634) ***(G-18107)***
Skip One Seafood Inc......239 463-8788
17650 San Carlos Blvd Fort Myers Beach (33931) ***(G-4666)***
Skipper Wright Inc......904 354-4381
634 Dyal St Jacksonville (32206) ***(G-6779)***
Sklar Bov Solutions Inc (PA)......352 746-6731
1233 E Norvell Bryant Hwy Hernando (34442) ***(G-5247)***
Skwholesalenet......305 372-3751
62 Ne 1st St Miami (33132) ***(G-10358)***
Sky Aerospace Engineering......407 251-7111
4219 Lindy Cir Orlando (32827) ***(G-13195)***
Sky Aerospace Engineering Inc (PA)......407 251-7111
9419 Tradeport Dr Orlando (32827) ***(G-13196)***
Sky Capital Partners Inc......305 934-8259
2900 Sw 28th Ter Ste 401 Miami (33133) ***(G-10359)***
Sky Device, Miami Beach *Also called Sky Phone LLC* ***(G-10711)***
Sky Medical Inc......954 747-3188
5229 Nw 108th Ave Sunrise (33351) ***(G-17172)***
Sky Phone LLC (PA)......305 531-5218
1348 Washington Ave # 350 Miami Beach (33139) ***(G-10711)***
Sky Technics Aviation Sls Inc......305 885-7499
6732 Nw 72nd Ave Miami (33166) ***(G-10360)***
Sky-High Sign & Lighting Inc......813 994-3954
30 Citrus Dr Palm Harbor (34684) ***(G-13761)***
Skycross, Melbourne *Also called Viatech of Delaware Inc* ***(G-8971)***
Skyhigh Accessories Inc......954 316-3936
4344 Peters Rd Plantation (33317) ***(G-14552)***
Skyline Attractions LLC......407 587-0080
5233 Alleman Dr Orlando (32809) ***(G-13197)***
Skylite Signs & Services Inc......305 362-5015
1640 W 32nd Pl Hialeah (33012) ***(G-5621)***
Skymasters Aviation LLC......954 796-7622
6640 Stratford Dr Parkland (33067) ***(G-14001)***
Skymo LLC......305 676-6739
12260 Sw 53rd St Ste 609 Cooper City (33330) ***(G-2115)***
Skyo Industries Inc......631 586-4702
2 Sunshine Blvd Ormond Beach (32174) ***(G-13399)***
Skyway Signs and Wraps LLC......727 692-2786
2911 Arrowsmith Rd Wimauma (33598) ***(G-19224)***
Skyways Technics Americas LLC......786 615-2443
13447 Ne 17th Ave North Miami (33181) ***(G-11655)***
Slabs Plus, Ruskin *Also called Bicentrics Inc* ***(G-15482)***
Slainte Wines Inc (PA)......954 474-4547
12535 Orange Dr Ste 610 Davie (33330) ***(G-2592)***
Slappey Communications LLC......863 619-5600
624 Midflorida Dr Lakeland (33813) ***(G-7792)***
Slasher Printing Center Inc......305 835-7366
6701 Nw 22nd St Sunrise (33313) ***(G-17173)***

ALPHABETIC

Slasher Printing Services, Sunrise *Also called Slasher Printing Center Inc* ***(G-17173)***
Slate Group LLC 786 484-9408
9357 Sw 77th Ave Miami (33156) ***(G-10361)***
Slate Solutions LLC 754 200-6752
7060 W State Road 84 # 12 Davie (33317) ***(G-2593)***
Slater Lighting Solutions, Boca Raton *Also called Brian Slater & Associates LLC* ***(G-464)***
Slb1989 Inc 772 344-3609
1066 Sw Bayshore Blvd Port Saint Lucie (34983) ***(G-15146)***
Sleep Group Solutions, Hollywood *Also called Dhss LLC* ***(G-5811)***
Sleep Group Solutions, North Miami Beach *Also called Dhss LLC* ***(G-11670)***
Sleep International LLC (PA) 813 247-5337
5223 16th Ave S Tampa (33619) ***(G-18108)***
Sleep Please, Hollywood *Also called Function Please LLC* ***(G-5827)***
Sleepmed Incorporated 941 361-3035
5432 Bee Ridge Rd Ste 170 Sarasota (34233) ***(G-16599)***
Sleeprite Industries Inc 650 344-1980
7087 Mandarin Dr Boca Raton (33433) ***(G-720)***
Sleepy Dragon Studios Inc 561 714-6156
22814 Sw 88th Path Cutler Bay (33190) ***(G-2411)***
Sleuth Inc 941 745-9903
3988 E State Road 64 Bradenton (34208) ***(G-1114)***
Slick Designs & AP Miami Inc 305 836-7950
3710 E 10th Ct Hialeah (33013) ***(G-5622)***
Slim and Soft Bread LLC 305 759-2126
15051 Royal Oaks Ln # 2105 North Miami (33181) ***(G-11656)***
SLM Boats Inc 386 738-4425
1948 Sunset Ct Deland (32720) ***(G-3014)***
Sloan Custom Woodworking LLC 850 766-5620
5559 Hampton Woods Way Tallahassee (32311) ***(G-17326)***
Slr Rifleworks LLC 855 757-7435
1232 Wntr Gdn Vnlnd Rd Winter Garden (34787) ***(G-19285)***
Sltons Envirnmntal Group Assoc 305 665-5594
2950 Sw 27th Ave Ste 2 Miami (33133) ***(G-10362)***
Slueth Bldg Sys Investigations, Bradenton *Also called Sleuth Inc* ***(G-1114)***
Slyce Inc 727 408-5272
311 Gulf Blvd Ste 2 Indian Rocks Beach (33785) ***(G-6069)***
Smart Access Inc 407 331-4724
2950 Lake Emma Rd # 1030 Lake Mary (32746) ***(G-7449)***
Smart Floors LLC 239 500-1234
4365 Tamiami Trl N Naples (34103) ***(G-11405)***
Smart Foods, Miami Lakes *Also called Liv LLC* ***(G-10808)***
Smart For Life, Riviera Beach *Also called Doctors Scentific Organica LLC* ***(G-15321)***
Smart For Life Inc (PA) 786 749-1221
990 Biscayne Blvd # 1203 Miami (33132) ***(G-10363)***
Smart Glass Systems Inc 954 801-5349
8201 Peters Rd Plantation (33324) ***(G-14553)***
Smart Group Traders Inc 850 460-5130
47 Indian Bayou Dr Destin (32541) ***(G-3207)***
Smart Guard Shutters LLC 386 227-6295
79 Pritchard Dr Palm Coast (32164) ***(G-13710)***
Smart Guides 813 534-0940
20013 Outpost Point Dr Tampa (33647) ***(G-18109)***
Smart Material Corp (PA) 941 870-3337
2170 Main St Ste 302 Sarasota (34237) ***(G-16600)***
Smart Miles Logistics LLC 754 244-2656
2420 Nw 31st Ave Fort Lauderdale (33311) ***(G-4239)***
Smart Shutters Inc 786 391-1100
3070 Nw 72nd Ave Miami (33122) ***(G-10364)***
Smart Snacks LLC 954 860-8833
2007 Johnson St Hollywood (33020) ***(G-5909)***
Smart Stream Inc 904 223-1511
13500 Sutton Park Dr S # 7 Jacksonville (32224) ***(G-6780)***
Smart Tracks Inc 239 938-1000
6182 Idlewild St Fort Myers (33966) ***(G-4605)***
Smartadvocate LLC (PA) 239 390-1000
27299 Riverview Center Bl Bonita Springs (34134) ***(G-854)***
Smartbear Software 954 312-0188
4611 Johnson Rd Unit 4 Coconut Creek (33073) ***(G-2096)***
Smartcart Ev LLC 727 906-7001
245 10th Ave N Safety Harbor (34695) ***(G-15504)***
Smartcolor Graphics, Jupiter *Also called Edward Thomas Company* ***(G-7032)***
Smartcop Inc 850 429-0082
9165 Roe St Pensacola (32514) ***(G-14262)***
Smarte Carte Inc 407 857-5841
9251 Jeff Fuqua Blvd # 1596 Orlando (32827) ***(G-13198)***
Smarthome-Products Inc (PA) 727 490-7260
1560 Faulds Rd W Clearwater (33756) ***(G-1880)***
Smartmatic Corporation (HQ) 561 862-0747
1001 Broken Sound Pkwy Nw D Boca Raton (33487) ***(G-721)***
Smartpoll Election Solutions, West Palm Beach *Also called Naztec International Group LLC* ***(G-18960)***
Smartsat Inc 727 535-6880
8222 118th Ave Ste 600 Largo (33773) ***(G-8055)***
Smartscience Laboratories Inc 813 925-8454
13760 Reptron Blvd Tampa (33626) ***(G-18110)***
Smartt, North Miami Beach *Also called Scale Models Arts & Tech* ***(G-11704)***
SMC Diversified Services Inc 863 698-9696
7120 Regent Dr Lakeland (33810) ***(G-7793)***
Smdk Corp 239 444-1736
4802 Kittiwake Ct Naples (34119) ***(G-11406)***
SMI Cabinetry Stone Millwork, Orlando *Also called S M I Cabinetry Inc* ***(G-13152)***
SMI Tool & Die Inc 321 632-6200
305 Clearlake Rd Cocoa (32922) ***(G-2051)***
Smilefy Inc 302 465-6606
221 W Hallandale B106 Hallandale Beach (33009) ***(G-5211)***
Smith Boat Designs Inc 954 782-1000
1200 S Dixie Hwy W Pompano Beach (33060) ***(G-14853)***
Smith Challenger Mfg Svcs Inc 863 248-2624
3434 Waterfield Rd Lakeland (33803) ***(G-7794)***
Smith Equipment & Supply Co 863 665-4904
3825 Maine Ave Lakeland (33801) ***(G-7795)***
Smith Machine Services Inc 904 845-2002
552121 Us Highway 1 Hilliard (32046) ***(G-5718)***
Smith Mountain, Coral Springs *Also called Aldora Aluminum & GL Pdts Inc* ***(G-2219)***
Smith Power Boats, Pompano Beach *Also called Smith Boat Designs Inc* ***(G-14853)***
Smith Products Co Inc (PA) 386 325-4534
1005 Kirby St Palatka (32177) ***(G-13492)***
Smith Products Kitchens, Palatka *Also called Smith Products Co Inc* ***(G-13492)***
Smith Steps Inc 386 963-5655
6944 Us Highway 90 Live Oak (32060) ***(G-8241)***
Smith Surface Prep Systems Inc 954 941-9744
2504 Nw 19th St Pompano Beach (33069) ***(G-14854)***
Smith Surface-Prep Solutions, Pompano Beach *Also called Smith Surface Prep Systems Inc* ***(G-14854)***
Smithbilt Industries Inc (PA) 321 690-0902
1061 Us Highway 92 W Auburndale (33823) ***(G-253)***
Smiths Interconnect Inc (HQ) 813 901-7200
4726 Eisenhower Blvd Tampa (33634) ***(G-18111)***
Smiths Interconnect Inc 813 901-7200
4726 Eisenhower Blvd Tampa (33634) ***(G-18112)***
Smiths Interconnect Group Ltd 805 370-5580
8851 Sw Old Kansas Ave Stuart (34997) ***(G-17016)***
Smiths Intrcnnect Americas Inc 772 286-9300
8851 Sw Old Kansas Ave Stuart (34997) ***(G-17017)***
Smiths Woodworks Inc 863 381-6564
4216 Shad Dr Sebring (33870) ***(G-16709)***
Smittys Boat Tops and Mar Eqp 305 245-0229
23701 Sw 212th Ave Homestead (33031) ***(G-5993)***
Smittys Boat Tops Sndwner Bats, Homestead *Also called Smittys Boat Tops and Mar Eqp* ***(G-5993)***
Smittys Welding Shop 321 723-4533
2526 S Harbor City Blvd Melbourne (32901) ***(G-8935)***
Smokers Video IV (PA) 904 646-1324
10150 Beach Blvd Jacksonville (32246) ***(G-6781)***
Smokersvaporcom Incorporated 727 258-4942
1129 Woodbrook Dr Largo (33770) ***(G-8056)***
Smokey Mountain Cabinets Inc 386 325-1677
103 E Lake St Palatka (32177) ***(G-13493)***
Smoothie Corp 305 588-0867
10211 Sw 137th Ct Miami (33186) ***(G-10365)***
Smoothie Operator By JC Inc 786 367-4245
13727 Sw 152nd St Miami (33177) ***(G-10366)***
Smoothies Recharge 954 999-0332
2101 N University Dr Sunrise (33322) ***(G-17174)***
SMR Aggregates Inc 941 907-0041
14400 Covenant Way Lakewood Ranch (34202) ***(G-7841)***
SMR Management Inc (PA) 305 529-2488
1728 Coral Way Coral Gables (33145) ***(G-2196)***
Smurfit Kappa Packaging LLC (HQ) 954 838-9738
1301 Intl Pkwy Ste 550 Sunrise (33323) ***(G-17175)***
Smurfit Kappa The America's, Sunrise *Also called Smurfit Kappa Packaging LLC* ***(G-17175)***
Smx-US Inc 914 840-5631
80 Sw 8th St Ste 2000 Miami (33130) ***(G-10367)***
Sna Software LLC (PA) 866 389-6750
1730 Santa Maria Pl Orlando (32806) ***(G-13199)***
Snapple Beverages 941 758-7010
2919 62nd Ave E Bradenton (34203) ***(G-1115)***
Snappy Structures Inc 954 926-6611
2324 Hayes St Hollywood (33020) ***(G-5910)***
Snapspeed LLC 321 441-3797
131 Tomahawk Dr Ste 19a Indian Harbour Beach (32937) ***(G-6067)***
Sneakz LLC 201 693-5695
2895 Jupiter Park Dr # 500 Jupiter (33458) ***(G-7116)***
Sneakz Organic, Jupiter *Also called Sneakz LLC* ***(G-7116)***
Sneids Inc 561 278-7446
2905 S Congress Ave Ste E Delray Beach (33445) ***(G-3144)***
Snif-Snax Ltd 786 613-7007
540 Brickell Key Dr C2 Miami (33131) ***(G-10368)***
Snk America Inc 407 831-7766
3551 W State Road 46 Sanford (32771) ***(G-16117)***
Snook Industries 352 447-0735
5217 Riverside Dr Yankeetown (34498) ***(G-19491)***
Snow-Nabstedt Power Transmissi 603 661-5551
3007 29th Ave E Bradenton (34208) ***(G-1116)***
Snows Custom Furniture Inc 772 794-4430
4009 Us Highway 1 Vero Beach (32960) ***(G-18665)***

Snug Harbor Dinghies Inc 727 578-0618
10121 Snug Harbor Rd Ne Saint Petersburg (33702) ***(G-15914)***
So NAPA 407 782-0459
3406 S Atlantic Ave New Smyrna Beach (32169) ***(G-11544)***
Soapy Chef, The, Hollywood *Also called Baby Food Chef LLC* ***(G-5781)***
Sobe Express 305 674-4454
1205 Lincoln Rd Ste 209 Miami Beach (33139) ***(G-10712)***
Sobrino Custom Cabinets Inc 786 564-2699
2220 W 10th Ct Hialeah (33010) ***(G-5623)***
Socialmetrix, Miami *Also called Smx-US Inc* ***(G-10367)***
Sockets & Specials Inc 561 582-7022
7110 Georgia Ave West Palm Beach (33405) ***(G-19036)***
Socratic Solutions Inc 813 324-7018
220 W Brandon Blvd # 207 Brandon (33511) ***(G-1180)***
Sod Depot & Gravel Inc 321 728-2766
1378 Malabar Rd Se Palm Bay (32907) ***(G-13535)***
Soda Service of Florida LLC 727 595-7632
14184 Mark Dr Largo (33774) ***(G-8057)***
Sodikart USA 561 493-0290
1025 Gateway Blvd Boynton Beach (33426) ***(G-960)***
Soe Software Corporation 813 490-7150
1111 N West Shore Blvd # 300 Tampa (33607) ***(G-18113)***
Sofie Co 407 321-9076
136 Commerce Way Sanford (32771) ***(G-16118)***
Soft Plastics Florida Inc 904 338-9680
2148 Ellis Rd N Jacksonville (32254) ***(G-6782)***
Soft Tech America Inc (PA) 954 563-3198
401 E Las Olas Blvd # 1400 Fort Lauderdale (33301) ***(G-4240)***
Soft Water Techs, West Palm Beach *Also called Duncanson Dynasty Inc* ***(G-18856)***
Softech International Inc 305 233-4813
1421 Sw 107th Ave Miami (33174) ***(G-10369)***
Softex Paper Inc (PA) 386 328-8488
1400 Reid St Palatka (32177) ***(G-13494)***
Software, Port Saint Lucie *Also called System Data Resource* ***(G-15152)***
Software Nuggets Inc 904 687-9778
743 Palmera Dr E Ponte Vedra Beach (32082) ***(G-14954)***
Software Product Solutions LLC 561 798-6727
12713 Westport Cir West Palm Beach (33414) ***(G-19037)***
Software Teacher Inc 954 593-3333
300 N Highway A1a H104 Jupiter (33477) ***(G-7117)***
Softwarekey.com, Winter Garden *Also called Concept Software Inc* ***(G-19258)***
Sogofishing LLC 800 308-0259
1542 Nw 15th Ave Fort Lauderdale (33311) ***(G-4241)***
Sohacki Industries Inc 904 826-0130
185 Cumberland Park Dr Saint Augustine (32095) ***(G-15613)***
Sokol Vineyards LLC 352 368-4069
101 E Silver Springs Blvd Ocala (34470) ***(G-12055)***
Sol Davis Printing Inc 813 353-3609
5205 N Lois Ave Tampa (33614) ***(G-18114)***
Sol-A-Trol Aluminum Pdts Inc 305 681-2020
4101 Nw 132nd St Opa Locka (33054) ***(G-12359)***
Sol-A-Trol Aluminum Products, Opa Locka *Also called Arso Enterprises Inc* ***(G-12290)***
Sola Therapy, Melbourne *Also called Uroshape LLC* ***(G-8968)***
Solair Group Llc 786 269-0160
10421 Sw 187th Ter Cutler Bay (33157) ***(G-2412)***
Solar Electric Power Company 772 220-6615
1521 Se Palm Ct Stuart (34994) ***(G-17018)***
Solar Energy Specialist Corp 863 514-9532
1130 1st St S Winter Haven (33880) ***(G-19356)***
Solar Enterprises Inc 904 724-2262
8841 Corporate Square Ct Jacksonville (32216) ***(G-6783)***
Solar Erectors US Inc 305 823-8950
10501 Nw 121st Way Medley (33178) ***(G-8724)***
Solar Manufacturing Inc (PA) 954 973-8488
1888 Nw 22nd Ct Pompano Beach (33069) ***(G-14855)***
Solar Shades Draperies & More 954 600-3419
1081 Nw 101st Way Plantation (33322) ***(G-14554)***
Solar Stik Inc (PA) 800 793-4364
226 W King St Saint Augustine (32084) ***(G-15614)***
Solar Tech Universal, Riviera Beach *Also called Solartech Universal LLC* ***(G-15378)***
Solar Tint Inc 305 663-4663
5887 Sw 70th St South Miami (33143) ***(G-16828)***
Solar Turbines Incorporated 305 476-6855
701 Nw 62nd Ave Ste 600 Miami (33126) ***(G-10370)***
Solar Venetian Blinds Inc 305 634-4553
3639 Nw 47th St Miami (33142) ***(G-10371)***
Solar X 386 673-2111
630 S Yonge St Us1 Ormond Beach (32174) ***(G-13400)***
Solar-X of Daytona, Ormond Beach *Also called Solar X* ***(G-13400)***
Solara Inc 305 592-4748
5105 Nw 159th St Miami Lakes (33014) ***(G-10858)***
Solara Industries Inc 863 688-3330
4190 Waring Rd Lakeland (33811) ***(G-7796)***
Solara Labs, Miami Lakes *Also called Solara Inc* ***(G-10858)***
Solarbeam International Inc 305 248-8400
15600 Sw 288th St Ste 307 Homestead (33033) ***(G-5994)***
Solarenergy.com, Jacksonville *Also called Sunset Power Inc* ***(G-6824)***
Solartech Universal LLC 561 440-8000
1800 President Barack Oba Riviera Beach (33404) ***(G-15378)***
Solartex, Apopka *Also called Enviroworks Inc* ***(G-137)***
Sole Inc 305 513-2603
8378 Nw 56th St Doral (33166) ***(G-3505)***
Soleil Capital LP (PA) 954 715-7001
3001 Griffin Rd Fort Lauderdale (33312) ***(G-4242)***
Solid Print Solutions Inc 561 670-4391
1961 10th Ave N Lake Worth Beach (33461) ***(G-7619)***
Solid Start Inc 863 937-9297
2801 Saluda Rd Lakeland (33801) ***(G-7797)***
Solidar Express Coatings LLC 727 585-2192
12912 91st St N Largo (33773) ***(G-8058)***
Solidexperts Inc 954 772-1903
2005 W Cypress Creek Rd Fort Lauderdale (33309) ***(G-4243)***
Solitron Devices Inc 561 848-4311
3301 Electronics Way C West Palm Beach (33407) ***(G-19038)***
Sollunar Energy Inc 352 293-2347
4142 Mariner Blvd Ste 510 Spring Hill (34609) ***(G-16864)***
Solo Printing LLC 305 594-8699
7860 Nw 66th St Miami (33166) ***(G-10372)***
Solseen LLC 727 322-3131
2801 16th St N Saint Petersburg (33704) ***(G-15915)***
Soltec Electronics LLC 321 288-5689
1001 Pelican Ln Rockledge (32955) ***(G-15447)***
Solucnes Elctrcas Intgrles LLC 305 804-4201
2609 Ne 189th St Miami (33180) ***(G-10373)***
Solunet 321 369-9719
1571 Robert J Conlan Blvd Palm Bay (32905) ***(G-13536)***
Solution Asset Management LLC 786 288-9408
1918 Harrison St Hollywood (33020) ***(G-5911)***
Solutions Manufacturing Inc 321 848-0848
570 Haverty Ct Rockledge (32955) ***(G-15448)***
Somatics LLC 847 234-6761
720 Commerce Dr Unit 101 Venice (34292) ***(G-18574)***
Somay Manufacturing Inc (PA) 305 637-4757
4301 Nw 35th Ave Miami (33142) ***(G-10374)***
Somec, Sanford *Also called Snk America Inc* ***(G-16117)***
Somero Enterprises Inc (PA) 906 482-7252
14530 Global Pkwy Fort Myers (33913) ***(G-4606)***
Something In A Tin Inc 305 785-6891
2401 Ne 199th St Miami (33180) ***(G-10375)***
Somfy Systems Inc 561 292-3483
1200 Sw 35th Ave Boynton Beach (33426) ***(G-961)***
Somni Specialty Sleep, Deerfield Beach *Also called Blu Sleep Products LLC* ***(G-2785)***
Son Life Prsthtics Orthtics In (PA) 352 596-2257
4138 Daisy Dr Hernando Beach (34607) ***(G-5251)***
Sondra Roberts, West Palm Beach *Also called Becarro International Corp* ***(G-18815)***
Sonec, Miami Lakes *Also called Scents of Nature Enterprises* ***(G-10855)***
Song-Chuan USA Inc 954 788-5889
2841 Center Port Cir Pompano Beach (33064) ***(G-14856)***
Sonic Boats, Fort Pierce *Also called Arrow Power Boats LLC* ***(G-4678)***
Sonic Leak Locator 954 340-8924
3871 Jasmine Ln Coral Springs (33065) ***(G-2314)***
Sonic Print, Tarpon Springs *Also called Cheany Inc* ***(G-18289)***
Sonnys Strings Inc 407 862-4905
311 E Morse Blvd Apt 1-3 Winter Park (32789) ***(G-19446)***
Sonobrands LLC (PA) 305 418-9367
1970 Nw 129th Ave Ste 108 Miami (33182) ***(G-10376)***
Sonoco Products Company 386 424-0970
1601 Tionia Rd New Smyrna Beach (32168) ***(G-11545)***
Sonshine Digital Graphics Inc 904 858-1000
2752 Park St Jacksonville (32205) ***(G-6784)***
Sonus-USA, Oldsmar *Also called Bell Hearing Instruments Inc* ***(G-12211)***
Sony Discos 305 420-4540
3390 Mary St Ste 220 Miami (33133) ***(G-10377)***
Sony/Atv Music Publishing LLC 305 532-9064
1111 Lincoln Rd Ste 803 Miami Beach (33139) ***(G-10713)***
Sophio Software Inc (PA) 323 446-2172
6300 Ne 1st Ave Ste 201 Fort Lauderdale (33334) ***(G-4244)***
Sophistcted Pllet Woodworx LLC 561 795-0739
7119 Apache Blvd Loxahatchee (33470) ***(G-8364)***
Sophix Solutions Inc 813 837-9555
1228 E 7th Ave Ste 225 Tampa (33605) ***(G-18115)***
Sophtech Ba Solutions LLC 407 389-4011
705 Crosby Dr Altamonte Springs (32714) ***(G-75)***
Soren Technologies Inc 954 236-9998
817 S University Dr # 106 Plantation (33324) ***(G-14555)***
SOS Food Lab LLC (PA) 305 594-9933
14802 Nw 107th Ave Unit 5 Hialeah Gardens (33018) ***(G-5699)***
SOs Services On Prtg Corp 305 225-6000
2738 W 68th Pl Hialeah (33016) ***(G-5624)***
SOS Sign & Lighting Services, South Daytona *Also called Sign-O-Saurus of Daytona Inc* ***(G-16809)***
SOS Software, Minneola *Also called Synergistic Office Solutions* ***(G-10956)***
SOS Software Corp 786 237-4903
950 Brickell Bay Dr # 53 Miami (33131) ***(G-10378)***
Sosumi Holdings Inc 239 634-3430
4408 Corporate Sq Naples (34104) ***(G-11407)***
Sota Manufacturing Inc (PA) 561 368-8007
1561 Sw 6th Ave Boca Raton (33486) ***(G-722)***

ALPHABETIC

Sota Manufacturing LLC.....561 251-3389
124 Ne 32nd Ct Oakland Park (33334) ***(G-11841)***
Soto Industries LLC.....941 830-6000
3420 Bal Harbor Blvd Punta Gorda (33950) ***(G-15235)***
Soto Metal Fabrication Inc (PA).....786 486-7125
7025 Sw 16th Ter Miami (33155) ***(G-10379)***
Soul Fuel Inc.....407 448-6533
155 S Court Ave Unit 2215 Orlando (32801) ***(G-13200)***
Soul Kass Boutique LLC.....682 429-4323
1218 Bet Raines Rd Molino (32577) ***(G-11074)***
Sound Anchors Inc.....321 724-1237
2835 Kirby Cir Ne Ste 110 Palm Bay (32905) ***(G-13537)***
Sound Connections Intl.....813 948-2707
611 Chancellar Dr Lutz (33548) ***(G-8419)***
Source Contract LLC.....305 630-8950
11451 Nw 36th Ave Miami (33167) ***(G-10380)***
Source of Sup In Polyurethanes.....239 573-3637
2645 Ne 9th Ave Unit 12 Cape Coral (33909) ***(G-1473)***
Source Outdoor, Miami *Also called Conquest Financial Management* ***(G-9393)***
Sourcerers Inc (PA).....954 530-2333
10097 Cleary Blvd Ste 289 Plantation (33324) ***(G-14556)***
Sourglass Brewing.....407 262-0056
480 S Ronald Reagan Blvd Longwood (32750) ***(G-8337)***
South Amercn Lbr & Timber LLC.....786 280-8326
78 Sw 7th St Ste 500 Miami (33130) ***(G-10381)***
South Bay Hospital.....813 634-3301
4016 Sun City Center Blvd Sun City Center (33573) ***(G-17072)***
South Bch Orthtics Prsthtics I.....352 512-0262
7305 Sw Gaines Ave Stuart (34997) ***(G-17019)***
South Beach Cigar Factory LLC.....786 216-7475
1059 Collins Ave Ste 108 Miami Beach (33139) ***(G-10714)***
South Beach Helicopters, Pembroke Pines *Also called Climax Am LLC* ***(G-14028)***
South Beach Skin Care Inc (PA).....954 606-5057
701 N Federal Hwy Ste 400 Hallandale Beach (33009) ***(G-5212)***
South Broward Brace Inc.....954 458-0656
1920 E Hallndale Bch 702 Hallandale Beach (33009) ***(G-5213)***
South Broward Printing Inc.....954 962-1309
5845 Hollywood Blvd Ste C Hollywood (33021) ***(G-5912)***
South Carolina Minerals Inc (PA).....352 365-6522
8500 Us Highway 441 Leesburg (34788) ***(G-8174)***
South Country Sheds LLC.....863 491-8700
1460 Sw Price Child St Arcadia (34266) ***(G-205)***
South Dade News Leader, Homestead *Also called Homestead Newspapers Inc* ***(G-5968)***
South East Fuel LLC.....407 392-4668
5600 Butler National Dr Orlando (32812) ***(G-13201)***
South Fla Forklift Doctor Corp.....561 951-6243
523 Industrial St Lake Worth Beach (33461) ***(G-7620)***
South Fla Pavement Coatings.....954 979-5997
1831 Nw 33rd St Pompano Beach (33064) ***(G-14857)***
South Florida Aluminum, Lake Worth *Also called Sfa Systems Inc* ***(G-7586)***
South Florida Con Block LLC.....305 408-3444
5800 Sw 177th Ave Ste 101 Miami (33193) ***(G-10382)***
South Florida Concrete & Rdymx.....305 888-0420
9500 Nw 109th St Medley (33178) ***(G-8725)***
South Florida Core Distrs.....954 452-9091
2030 Sw 71st Ter Ste C6 Davie (33317) ***(G-2594)***
South Florida Cutting.....305 693-6711
3965 E 10th Ct Hialeah (33013) ***(G-5625)***
South Florida Digest Inc.....954 458-0635
305 Nw 10th Ter Hallandale Beach (33009) ***(G-5214)***
South Florida Fabricators LLC.....954 802-6782
4960 Sw 91st Ter Cooper City (33328) ***(G-2116)***
South Florida Field Techs Inc.....954 325-6548
1598 Newhaven Point Ln West Palm Beach (33411) ***(G-19039)***
South Florida Finger Printing.....305 661-1636
5900 Sw 73rd St Ste 304 South Miami (33143) ***(G-16829)***
South Florida Graphics Corp.....954 917-0606
1770 Nw 64th St Ste 500 Fort Lauderdale (33309) ***(G-4245)***
South Florida Institut.....305 668-2853
7600 Sw 57th Ave Ste 201 South Miami (33143) ***(G-16830)***
South Florida Laboratory Llc.....954 889-0335
3395 Lake Worth Rd Palm Springs (33461) ***(G-13780)***
South Florida Marine.....305 232-8788
19301 Sw 106th Ave Ste 13 Cutler Bay (33157) ***(G-2413)***
South Florida Pallet Inc.....305 330-7663
224 Nw 136th Pl Miami (33182) ***(G-10383)***
South Florida Pallets Dist.....305 330-7663
1951 Nw 89th Pl Ste 100 Doral (33172) ***(G-3506)***
South Florida Parenting.....954 747-3050
6501 Nob Hill Rd Tamarac (33321) ***(G-17369)***
South Florida Pavers Corp.....786 517-9100
18506 Nw 67th Ave Hialeah (33015) ***(G-5626)***
South Florida Petro Svcs LLC.....561 793-2102
2550 Eisenhower Blvd # 11 Fort Lauderdale (33316) ***(G-4246)***
South Florida Print.....561 807-8584
3413 Sw 14th St Deerfield Beach (33442) ***(G-2914)***
South Florida Rodents.....954 410-5635
17200 Sw 65th Ct Southwest Ranches (33331) ***(G-16842)***
South Florida Sheet Metal (PA).....954 647-6457
2038 Nw 141st Ave Pembroke Pines (33028) ***(G-14060)***
South Florida Sign Co.....954 973-6649
2133 Nw 22nd St Pompano Beach (33069) ***(G-14858)***
South Florida Sport Fishing.....954 942-7261
2765 Nw 62nd St Ste C Fort Lauderdale (33309) ***(G-4247)***
South Florida Sport Fishing.....954 942-7261
2765 Nw 62nd St Ste C Fort Lauderdale (33309) ***(G-4248)***
South Florida Stairs Inc.....561 822-3110
2901 Commerce Park Dr # 4 Boynton Beach (33426) ***(G-962)***
South Florida Strip Tees Inc.....954 972-4899
1740 Nw 22nd Ct Ste 10 Pompano Beach (33069) ***(G-14859)***
South Florida Suntimes, Hallandale Beach *Also called South Florida Digest Inc* ***(G-5214)***
South Florida Technology Svcs.....786 286-2882
2333 W 3rd Ct Hialeah (33010) ***(G-5627)***
South Florida Textile Inc.....954 973-5677
1301 W Copans Rd Ste E7 Pompano Beach (33064) ***(G-14860)***
South Florida Time, West Palm Beach *Also called Diamond Advertising & Mktg* ***(G-18854)***
South Florida Tissue Paper Co, Miami Lakes *Also called Express Paper Company Inc* ***(G-10787)***
South Florida Trane, Miramar *Also called Trane US Inc* ***(G-11052)***
South Florida Woodworkers Inc.....954 868-5043
2873 Sw 16th St Fort Lauderdale (33312) ***(G-4249)***
South Jacksonville - R/M, B/M, Jacksonville *Also called Cemex Cnstr Mtls Fla LLC* ***(G-6257)***
South Lake Press, Clermont *Also called Republic Newspapers Inc* ***(G-1972)***
South Marion Meats.....352 245-2096
13770 S Highway 475 Summerfield (34491) ***(G-17062)***
South Pacific Trading Company.....352 567-2200
15340 Citrus Country Dr Dade City (33523) ***(G-2435)***
South West Adventure Team LLC.....903 288-4739
505 W Hickpochee Ave # 2001 Labelle (33935) ***(G-7323)***
Southast Auto Acquisition Corp.....305 885-8689
7575 Nw 74th Ave Medley (33166) ***(G-8726)***
Southast Clking Slant Svcs LLC.....813 731-8778
2426 Branchwood Rd Plant City (33567) ***(G-14466)***
Southast Protein Purveyors LLC.....912 354-2770
604 Lake Elizabeth Dr Winter Haven (33884) ***(G-19357)***
Southcoast Marine Products, Clearwater *Also called General Hydraulic Solutions* ***(G-1702)***
Southcoast Marine Products Inc.....727 573-4821
12550 47th Way N Clearwater (33762) ***(G-1881)***
Southeast Atlantic, Lakeland *Also called American Bottling Company* ***(G-7633)***
Southeast Atlantic Bev Corp.....904 731-3644
6001 Bowdendale Ave Jacksonville (32216) ***(G-6785)***
Southeast Atlantic Bevera.....904 739-1000
5900 Nw 72nd Ave Miami (33166) ***(G-10384)***
Southeast Bottling & Bev Co.....352 567-2200
15340 Citrus Country Dr Dade City (33523) ***(G-2436)***
Southeast Carbon Works Inc.....561 422-1798
1243 Canyon Way Wellington (33414) ***(G-18736)***
Southeast Clinical RES LLC.....904 296-3260
6817 Sthpint Pkwy Ste 902 Jacksonville (32216) ***(G-6786)***
Southeast Compounding Phrm LLC.....813 644-7700
3906 Cragmont Dr Tampa (33619) ***(G-18116)***
Southeast Dairy Processors Inc.....813 620-1516
3811 E Columbus Dr Tampa (33605) ***(G-18117)***
Southeast Diesel, Doral *Also called Perkins Power Corp* ***(G-3457)***
Southeast Elevator Llc.....772 461-0030
811 Edwards Rd Fort Pierce (34982) ***(G-4747)***
Southeast Energy Inc.....561 883-1051
23257 State Road 7 # 107 Boca Raton (33428) ***(G-723)***
Southeast Finishing Group Inc (PA).....407 299-4620
2807 Mercy Dr Orlando (32808) ***(G-13202)***
Southeast Food Service News, Naples *Also called Southeast Publishing Co Inc* ***(G-11408)***
Southeast Gen Contrs Group Inc.....877 407-3535
10380 Sw Vlg Ctr Dr 232 Port St Lucie (34987) ***(G-15179)***
Southeast Id LLC.....954 571-6665
5830 Nw 163rd St Miami Lakes (33014) ***(G-10859)***
Southeast Intl Chem Co Inc.....904 992-4007
221 N Hogan St 230 Jacksonville (32202) ***(G-6787)***
Southeast Marketing Concepts.....561 747-7010
801 Maplewood Dr Ste 11 Jupiter (33458) ***(G-7118)***
Southeast Modular Mfg, Leesburg *Also called M S Amtex-N Inc* ***(G-8164)***
Southeast Offset Inc.....305 623-7788
4880 Nw 157th St Miami Lakes (33014) ***(G-10860)***
Southeast Plastics, Daytona Beach *Also called Halifax Plastic Inc* ***(G-2672)***
Southeast Power Group Inc (PA).....305 592-9745
5820 Nw 84th Ave Doral (33166) ***(G-3507)***
Southeast Print Programs Inc.....813 885-3203
5023 W Rio Vista Ave Tampa (33634) ***(G-18118)***
Southeast Publications USA Inc.....954 368-4686
2150 Sw 10th St Ste A Deerfield Beach (33442) ***(G-2915)***
Southeast Publishing Co Inc (PA).....239 213-1277
2539 Avila Ln Naples (34105) ***(G-11408)***
Southeast Review Inc.....850 644-4230
405 Williams Building Tallahassee (32306) ***(G-17327)***
Southeast Security Products.....954 786-5900
1387 Sw 12th Ave Pompano Beach (33069) ***(G-14861)***
Southeast Window Coverings.....904 372-0326
6900 Philips Hwy Ste 46 Jacksonville (32216) ***(G-6788)***

Southeast Woodcrafters Inc....561 392-2929
1566 Nw 1st Ave Boca Raton (33432) **(G-724)**
Southeast Worldwide, Medley *Also called Southast Auto Acquisition Corp* **(G-8726)**
Southeast-Atlantic, Fort Myers *Also called American Bottling Company* **(G-4357)**
Southeastern Aluminum, Jacksonville *Also called Sea Products Inc* **(G-6758)**
Southeastern Aluminum Pdts LLC....800 243-8200
4925 Bulls Bay Hwy Jacksonville (32219) **(G-6789)**
Southeastern Assemblies Inc....727 376-1411
2112 Larchwood Ct Trinity (34655) **(G-18489)**
Southeastern Door Company LLC....561 746-5493
1505 Commerce Ln Jupiter (33458) **(G-7119)**
Southeastern Engineering Inc....321 984-2521
1340 Clearmont St Ne # 304 Palm Bay (32905) **(G-13538)**
Southeastern Fasteners....407 790-4888
955 Charles St Unit 105 Longwood (32750) **(G-8338)**
Southeastern Ltg Solutions....386 238-1711
821 Fentress Ct Daytona Beach (32117) **(G-2716)**
Southeastern Marine Power LLC....727 545-2700
7398 46th Ave N Saint Petersburg (33709) **(G-15916)**
Southeastern Marketing Associa....954 421-7388
1522 Se 10th St Deerfield Beach (33441) **(G-2916)**
Southeastern Ornamental Iron....904 292-0933
11307 Distribution Ave E Jacksonville (32256) **(G-6790)**
Southeastern Pallets Inc....904 783-8363
2203 W Beaver St Jacksonville (32209) **(G-6791)**
Southeastern Paper Group Inc....864 574-0440
7080 Havertys Way Lakeland (33805) **(G-7798)**
Southeastern Pegboard Printers....904 731-0357
2750 Dawn Rd Jacksonville (32207) **(G-6792)**
Southeastern Pipe Precast Inc....850 587-7473
2900 N Highway 95a Cantonment (32533) **(G-1348)**
Southeastern Prestressed Con....561 793-1177
860 N Benoist Farms Rd West Palm Beach (33411) **(G-19040)**
Southeastern Printing Co Inc (PA)....772 287-2141
950 Se 8th St Hialeah (33010) **(G-5628)**
Southeastern Seating Inc....813 273-9858
903 E 17th Ave Tampa (33605) **(G-18119)**
Southeastern Truck Tops Inc....386 761-0002
402 6th St Daytona Beach (32117) **(G-2717)**
Southern Air Comprsr Svc Inc....863 425-9111
2260 Peerless Rd Mulberry (33860) **(G-11137)**
Southern Aluminum and Stl Inc....850 484-4700
2501 S Highway 29 Cantonment (32533) **(G-1349)**
Southern Aluminum Inc....239 275-3367
674 Stonecrest Ln Ste 4 Cape Coral (33909) **(G-1474)**
Southern Automated Systems....863 815-7444
3730 N Galloway Rd Lakeland (33810) **(G-7799)**
Southern Awning Inc (PA)....561 586-0464
313 S H St Lake Worth (33460) **(G-7587)**
Southern Bakeries Inc (HQ)....863 682-1155
3355 W Memorial Blvd Lakeland (33815) **(G-7800)**
Southern Balloon Works, Jacksonville *Also called Aerial Products Corporation* **(G-6126)**
Southern Balloon Works Inc....727 388-8360
11653 Central Pkwy # 209 Jacksonville (32224) **(G-6793)**
Southern Blade & Supply, Ocala *Also called Shashy Enterprises Inc* **(G-12047)**
Southern Boating & Yachting....954 522-5515
1591 E Atl Blvd Ste 200 Pompano Beach (33060) **(G-14862)**
Southern Boating Magazine, Pompano Beach *Also called Southern Boating & Yachting* **(G-14862)**
Southern Brothers Racing LLC....850 509-2223
443 Charlie Harris Loop Quincy (32352) **(G-15255)**
Southern Closet Systems Inc....813 926-9348
13211 Byrd Dr Odessa (33556) **(G-12153)**
Southern Company Entp Inc....904 879-2101
54024 Cravey Rd Callahan (32011) **(G-1329)**
Southern Contracting N FL Inc....850 674-3570
19073 Ne State Road 69 Blountstown (32424) **(G-387)**
Southern Covert, Fort Pierce *Also called Wheeler Consolidated Inc* **(G-4770)**
Southern Cross Boatworks Inc....954 467-5801
2019 Sw 20th St Ste 111 Fort Lauderdale (33315) **(G-4250)**
Southern Cross Shutter Systems....941 585-2152
21271 Dearborn Ave Port Charlotte (33954) **(G-14998)**
Southern Custom Iron & Art LLC....561 586-8400
3787 Boutwell Rd Lake Worth Beach (33461) **(G-7621)**
Southern Die Casting Corp....305 635-6571
3560 Nw 59th St Miami (33142) **(G-10385)**
Southern Door Technologies....386 496-3844
9124 S County Road 231 Lake Butler (32054) **(G-7342)**
Southern Drydock Inc....904 355-9945
8153 Six Mile Way Saint Augustine (32092) **(G-15615)**
Southern Dumpsters Inc....772 413-1228
380 Sagamore St Melbourne (32904) **(G-8936)**
Southern Environmental Inc....850 944-4475
6690 W Nine Mile Rd Pensacola (32526) **(G-14263)**
Southern Exhibits and Graphics....407 423-2860
4360 36th St Unit 1 Orlando (32811) **(G-13203)**
Southern Fabricating Machinery....813 966-3983
10417 S County Road 39 Lithia (33547) **(G-8223)**
Southern Fiber Inc....786 916-3052
4715 Nw 157th St Ste 104 Miami Lakes (33014) **(G-10861)**
Southern Fiberglass Inc....904 387-2246
41 Spring St Jacksonville (32254) **(G-6794)**
Southern Fuel Inc....904 545-5163
7028 E Mount Vernon St Glen Saint Mary (32040) **(G-5039)**
Southern Fuelwood Inc....352 472-4324
28826 W Newberry Rd Newberry (32669) **(G-11561)**
Southern Gear, Miami *Also called Gear Dynamics Inc* **(G-9619)**
Southern Gear & Machine Inc....305 691-6300
3685 Nw 106th St Miami (33147) **(G-10386)**
Southern Graphic Machine LLC....615 812-0778
3441 Juniper Dr Edgewater (32141) **(G-3636)**
Southern Grdns Ctrus Hldg Corp (HQ)....863 983-8121
111 Ponce De Leon Ave Clewiston (33440) **(G-1986)**
Southern Grouts & Mortars Inc (PA)....954 943-2288
1502 Sw 2nd Pl Pompano Beach (33069) **(G-14863)**
Southern Hvac Corporation (PA)....407 917-1800
485 N Keller Rd Ste 515 Maitland (32751) **(G-8479)**
Southern Imaging....727 954-0133
6563 46th St N Ste 705 Pinellas Park (33781) **(G-14389)**
Southern Innovative Energy Inc....321 747-9205
4373 Fletcher Ln Ste 2 Titusville (32780) **(G-18461)**
Southern Interest Co Inc....727 471-2040
2233 3rd Ave S Saint Petersburg (33712) **(G-15917)**
Southern International Svcs....954 349-7321
18970 Ne 4th Ct Miami (33179) **(G-10387)**
Southern Lbr & Treating Co Inc....904 695-0784
1433 Lane Cir E Jacksonville (32254) **(G-6795)**
Southern Lights....727 849-4442
3822 Grayton Dr New Port Richey (34652) **(G-11510)**
Southern Litho II LLC....724 394-3693
9010 Strada Stell Ct # 103 Naples (34109) **(G-11409)**
Southern Machine Tool & Rbldrs....941 749-0988
2923 62nd Ave E Bradenton (34203) **(G-1117)**
Southern Manufacturing Inc....305 267-1943
7064 Sw 10th St Miami (33144) **(G-10388)**
Southern Mfg & Fabrication LLC....407 894-8851
2000 E Lake Mary Blvd Sanford (32773) **(G-16119)**
Southern Mfg Tech Inc....954 953-9537
5910 Johns Rd Tampa (33634) **(G-18120)**
Southern Mfg Upholstery Inc....727 573-1006
3670 131st Ave N Clearwater (33762) **(G-1882)**
Southern Micro Etch Inc....954 781-5999
610 Ne 29th St Pompano Beach (33064) **(G-14864)**
Southern Ordnance, Longwood *Also called Exit Ten Inc* **(G-8277)**
Southern Packaging McHy Corp....305 245-3045
550 Nw 3rd Ave Florida City (33034) **(G-3769)**
Southern Pavers LLC....239 940-3671
111 5th St Unit A2 Fort Myers (33907) **(G-4607)**
Southern Pines Inc....239 947-1515
26300 Southern Pines Dr Bonita Springs (34135) **(G-855)**
Southern Plastics & Rubber Co....386 672-1167
565 Parque Dr Ormond Beach (32174) **(G-13401)**
Southern Power Washing....561 644-2237
16931 W Burns Dr Loxahatchee (33470) **(G-8365)**
Southern Pre Cast Structures L....352 569-1128
4457 Cr 542h Bushnell (33513) **(G-1321)**
Southern Recreation Inc....904 387-4390
4060 Edison Ave Jacksonville (32254) **(G-6796)**
Southern Reinforced Plastics....941 746-8793
2904 29th Ave E Ste F Bradenton (34208) **(G-1118)**
Southern Rock & Lime Inc (PA)....850 674-5089
19073 Ne State Road 69 Blountstown (32424) **(G-388)**
Southern Softwoods Inc....863 666-1404
2425 Lasso Ln Lakeland (33801) **(G-7801)**
SOUTHERN SPRING & STAMPING INC (PA)....941 488-2276
401 Substation Rd Venice (34285) **(G-18575)**
Southern States Gluing Svcs....850 469-9667
3865 N Palafox St Pensacola (32505) **(G-14264)**
Southern Strl Stl Fla Inc....727 327-7123
1000 31st St S Saint Petersburg (33712) **(G-15918)**
Southern Supply and Mfg Co....727 323-7099
1501 22nd St N Saint Petersburg (33713) **(G-15919)**
Southern Surgical Consultants....904 296-7828
11653 Central Pkwy # 201 Jacksonville (32224) **(G-6797)**
Southern Switch & Contacts....727 789-0951
855 Virginia Ave Palm Harbor (34683) **(G-13762)**
Southern Tape & Label Inc....321 632-5275
1107 Peachtree St Cocoa (32922) **(G-2052)**
Southern Technologies....904 266-2100
270 Us Highway 90 E Jacksonville (32234) **(G-6798)**
Southern Tennis Supplies....850 936-1772
92 W Gadsden St Apt 3 Pensacola (32501) **(G-14265)**
Southern Truss Companies Inc....772 464-4160
2590 N Kings Hwy Fort Pierce (34951) **(G-4748)**
Southern Underground Inds....954 226-3865
5979 Nw 151st St Ste 223 Miami Lakes (33014) **(G-10862)**
Southern Welding & Mechanics....305 772-0961
592 W 28th St Hialeah (33010) **(G-5629)**

Southern Wheel & Rim Inc.....904 786-7542
1044 Lane Ave S Jacksonville (32205) ***(G-6799)***
Southern Winding Service Inc.....813 621-6555
5302 Saint Paul St Tampa (33619) ***(G-18121)***
Southern Wood Services LLC.....352 279-3208
6288 California St Brooksville (34604) ***(G-1272)***
Southern Woodworks Fine Wdwkg.....850 456-0550
1170 Mahogany Mill Rd Pensacola (32507) ***(G-14266)***
Southern-Bartlett Intl LLC.....407 374-1613
4070 S Pipkin Rd Lakeland (33811) ***(G-7802)***
Southernstone Cabinets Inc.....727 538-0123
12520 Automobile Blvd Clearwater (33762) ***(G-1883)***
Southernunderground Industries.....954 650-4699
10621 Sw 139th St Miami (33176) ***(G-10389)***
Southfloridagaynewscom.....954 530-4970
2520 N Dixie Hwy Wilton Manors (33305) ***(G-19220)***
Southland Milling Co.....850 674-8448
21474 Se Coastal St Blountstown (32424) ***(G-389)***
Southland Power & Enrgy Co LLC.....800 217-6040
5215 Nw 35th Ave Fort Lauderdale (33309) ***(G-4251)***
Southpoint Sportswear LLC.....305 885-3045
11525 Nw 124th St Medley (33178) ***(G-8727)***
Southpointe Precision.....239 225-1350
12960 Commerce Lk Dr # 10 Fort Myers (33913) ***(G-4608)***
Southprint Corp.....813 237-8000
6816 N River Blvd Tampa (33604) ***(G-18122)***
Southridge Outdoor Storage.....352 516-5598
595 County Road 448 Tavares (32778) ***(G-18353)***
Southstern Arspc Svcs Ltd Lblt.....305 992-8257
1816 Sw 7th Ave Pompano Beach (33060) ***(G-14865)***
Southstern Indus Fbrcators LLC.....941 776-1211
12650 County Road 39 Duette (34219) ***(G-3563)***
Southstern Rail Svcs Mlbrry FL.....863 425-4986
1200 Prairie Mine Rd Mulberry (33860) ***(G-11138)***
Southstern Stnless Fabricators.....904 354-4381
634 Dyal St Jacksonville (32206) ***(G-6800)***
Southwest Aggregates, Punta Gorda *Also called Charlotte County Min & Mtl Inc* ***(G-15201)***
Southwest Choppers Inc.....239 242-1101
2123 Ne 3rd Ter Cape Coral (33909) ***(G-1475)***
Southwest Custom Coatings Inc.....239 682-9462
4498 22nd Ave Se Naples (34117) ***(G-11410)***
Southwest Eqp For Hrnando Cnty.....352 596-5142
13484 Chambord St Brooksville (34613) ***(G-1273)***
Southwest Fla Newspapers Inc.....239 574-9733
308 Se 25th Ter Cape Coral (33904) ***(G-1476)***
Southwest Precision AG Inc.....863 674-5799
14960 S Sr 29 Felda (33930) ***(G-3724)***
Southwest Signal Inc.....813 621-4949
1984 Georgia Ave Englewood (34224) ***(G-3667)***
Southwest Steel Group Inc.....239 283-8980
3405 Yucatan Pkwy Cape Coral (33993) ***(G-1477)***
Southwest Strl Systems Inc.....239 693-6000
5774 Corporation Cir Fort Myers (33905) ***(G-4609)***
Southwest Turbine Inc.....305 769-1765
4550 E 10th Ct Hialeah (33013) ***(G-5630)***
Southwest Woodwork Inc.....239 213-0126
429 Production Blvd Naples (34104) ***(G-11411)***
Southwind Aviation Supply LLC.....405 491-0500
752 Strihal Loop Oakland (34787) ***(G-11771)***
Southwings Avionics and ACC.....305 825-6755
5429 Nw 161st St Miami Lakes (33014) ***(G-10863)***
Southwire Company LLC.....727 535-0572
11211 69th St Largo (33773) ***(G-8059)***
Southwire Company LLC.....850 423-4680
5680 John Givens Rd Crestview (32539) ***(G-2359)***
Souvay Cabinetry Inc.....239 273-5947
4292 Corporate Sq Ste C Naples (34104) ***(G-11412)***
Sovita Retail Inc.....888 871-2408
1317 Edgewater Dr # 1943 Orlando (32804) ***(G-13204)***
Sox LLC.....561 501-0057
950 Pnnsula Corp Cir Ste Boca Raton (33487) ***(G-725)***
Sox Erosion Solutions, Boca Raton *Also called Sox LLC* ***(G-725)***
Soythane Technologies Inc.....904 225-1047
850709 Us Highway 17 Yulee (32097) ***(G-19501)***
SP Publications LLC.....239 595-9040
495 Grand Blvd Ste 206 Miramar Beach (32550) ***(G-11069)***
Sp Sign LLC.....772 562-0955
2201 Se Indian St Unit E4 Stuart (34997) ***(G-17020)***
SP&e, Fort Lauderdale *Also called Southland Power & Enrgy Co LLC* ***(G-4251)***
Spa Concepts Inc.....850 575-0921
3191 W Tharpe St Tallahassee (32303) ***(G-17328)***
Spa Cover Inc.....954 923-8801
2310 Hayes St Hollywood (33020) ***(G-5913)***
Spa World Corporation (PA).....866 588-8008
5701 Nw 35th Ave Miami (33142) ***(G-10390)***
Space Cast Intllgent Sltons In.....321 622-6858
770 North Dr Ste B Melbourne (32934) ***(G-8937)***
Space Coast Distributors.....386 239-0305
726 N Segrave St Daytona Beach (32114) ***(G-2718)***
Space Coast Hydraulics Inc.....321 504-6006
1265 Us Highway 1 Rockledge (32955) ***(G-15449)***
Space Coast Industries Inc.....321 633-9336
700 Cox Rd Ste 1 Cocoa (32926) ***(G-2053)***
Space Coast Map LLC.....321 242-4538
1359 Richmond Dr Melbourne (32935) ***(G-8938)***
Space Coast Storm Shutters LLC.....410 652-5717
10 West Point Dr Cocoa Beach (32931) ***(G-2067)***
Space Exploration Tech Corp.....310 363-6000
Cape Cnaveral A Force Sta Cape Canaveral (32920) ***(G-1368)***
Space Lighting, Miami *Also called IMC Lighting Inc* ***(G-9734)***
Space Machine & Engrg Corp.....727 323-2221
2327 16th Ave N Saint Petersburg (33713) ***(G-15920)***
Space Manufacturing Inc.....727 532-9466
14271 60th St N Clearwater (33760) ***(G-1884)***
Space X Design LLC.....407 592-5147
13022 Sw 142nd Ter Miami (33186) ***(G-10391)***
Space-Eyes, Miami *Also called Channel Logistics LLC* ***(G-9348)***
Spacecast Pltg Met Rfnshing In.....321 254-2880
975 Aurora Rd Melbourne (32935) ***(G-8939)***
Spacecoast Cable & Harness Inc.....321 269-0377
3400 Lillian Blvd Titusville (32780) ***(G-18462)***
Spacelabs Healthcare Inc.....904 786-5113
14476 Duval Pl W Ste 303 Jacksonville (32218) ***(G-6801)***
Spacemakers Closets SW Fla Inc.....239 598-0222
2044 J And C Blvd Naples (34109) ***(G-11413)***
Spaceport Corporation.....305 690-6885
20209 Ne 15th Ave Miami (33179) ***(G-10392)***
Spacewerks Inc.....727 540-9714
13100 56th Ct Ste 711 Clearwater (33760) ***(G-1885)***
Spacios Design Group Inc.....305 696-1766
7370 Nw 36th Ave Miami (33147) ***(G-10393)***
Spancrete Inc.....305 599-8885
7907 Nw 53rd St 347 Miami (33166) ***(G-10394)***
Spancrete of Florida LLC.....863 655-1515
400 Deer Trl E Sebring (33876) ***(G-16710)***
Spancrete Southeast Inc.....863 655-1515
400 Deer Trl E Sebring (33876) ***(G-16711)***
Spanglish Advertising Cor.....305 244-0918
6857 Ne 3rd Ave Miami (33138) ***(G-10395)***
Spanish House Inc.....305 503-1191
8167 Nw 84th St Medley (33166) ***(G-8728)***
Spanish Peri & Bk Sls Inc.....305 592-3919
2105 Nw 102nd Ave Doral (33172) ***(G-3508)***
Spanish Pubg Ventures Inc.....305 220-8044
9385 Sw 21st St Miami (33165) ***(G-10396)***
Spanish Publishers LLC.....305 233-3365
8871 Sw 129th St Miami (33176) ***(G-10397)***
Spanish Trail Lumber Co LLC.....850 592-8512
6112 Old Spanish Trl Marianna (32448) ***(G-8586)***
Sparklean.....305 599-8479
11401 Nw 12th St Miami (33172) ***(G-10398)***
Sparkles and Suspenders FL.....754 701-4528
5405 Nw 67th Ave Lauderhill (33319) ***(G-8120)***
Sparks Cabinetry.....954 367-2750
1685 S State Road 7 Hollywood (33023) ***(G-5914)***
Sparton Corporation (HQ).....847 762-5800
5612 Johnson Lake Rd De Leon Springs (32130) ***(G-2742)***
Sparton Deleon Springs LLC (HQ).....386 985-4631
5612 Johnson Lake Rd De Leon Springs (32130) ***(G-2743)***
Sparton Electronics, Brooksville *Also called Spartronics Brooksville LLC* ***(G-1275)***
Spartronics Brooksville LLC (HQ).....352 799-6520
30167 Power Line Rd Brooksville (34602) ***(G-1274)***
Spartronics Brooksville LLC.....352 799-6520
30167 Power Line Rd Brooksville (34602) ***(G-1275)***
Spaulding Craft Inc.....727 726-2316
1053 Harbor Lake Dr Safety Harbor (34695) ***(G-15505)***
Spaulding Custom Cabinets.....904 768-4640
11857 Duval Rd Jacksonville (32218) ***(G-6802)***
Spec-TEC Manufacturing Inc.....954 749-4204
10794 Nw 53rd St Sunrise (33351) ***(G-17176)***
Special Americas Bbq Inc.....305 637-7377
11411 Nw 107th St Ste 1 Miami (33178) ***(G-10399)***
Special Coatings Inc.....239 301-2714
6210 Shirley St Ste 105 Naples (34109) ***(G-11414)***
Special Editions Publishing, Altamonte Springs *Also called Special Editionspublishing* ***(G-76)***
Special Editionspublishing.....407 862-7737
999 Douglas Ave Ste 3317 Altamonte Springs (32714) ***(G-76)***
Special Nutrients LLC.....305 857-9830
2766 Sw 37th Ave Coconut Grove (33133) ***(G-2105)***
Special Publications Inc.....352 622-2995
743 Se Fort King Rd Ocala (34471) ***(G-12056)***
Special Tool Solutions Inc.....904 356-5671
11699 Camden Rd Jacksonville (32218) ***(G-6803)***
Specialty Contractor, Lehigh Acres *Also called Marathon Engineering Corp* ***(G-8198)***
Specialty Fabrication LLC.....863 683-0708
4015 Drane Field Rd Lakeland (33811) ***(G-7803)***
Specialty Fabrication Wldg Inc.....352 669-9353
680 Goodbar Ave Umatilla (32784) ***(G-18502)***

Specialty Fin Consulting Corp (PA)..........717 246-1661
5541 Gulf Of Mexico Dr Longboat Key (34228) ***(G-8247)***
Specialty Food Group LLC (HQ)..........305 392-5000
9835 Nw 14th St Doral (33172) ***(G-3509)***
Specialty Forged Wheels Inc..........786 332-5925
12146 Sw 114th Pl Miami (33176) ***(G-10400)***
Specialty Glass, Oldsmar *Also called Justi Group Inc* ***(G-12238)***
Specialty Maintenance & Constr..........863 644-8432
4121 Drane Field Rd Lakeland (33811) ***(G-7804)***
Specialty Packaging & Display, Titusville *Also called Richard C Good* ***(G-18458)***
Specialty Pharmacy Services..........321 953-2004
800 E Melbourne Ave Melbourne (32901) ***(G-8940)***
Specialty Powder Coating LLC..........813 782-2720
7640 Chenkin Rd Zephyrhills (33540) ***(G-19536)***
Specialty Productions Inc..........786 399-1393
2476 Sw 25th Ter Miami (33133) ***(G-10401)***
Specialty Products Inc..........850 438-4264
2325 W Cervantes St Pensacola (32505) ***(G-14267)***
Specialty Screen Printing Inc..........561 758-4944
6065 Wolfe St Jupiter (33458) ***(G-7120)***
Specialty Stamp & Sign, Orlando *Also called Liquid Soul Dgtal Graphics LLC* ***(G-12915)***
Specialty Steel Holdco Inc..........305 375-7560
200 Biscayne Blvd Miami (33132) ***(G-10402)***
Specialty Structures Inc..........386 668-0474
218 Plumosa Rd Debary (32713) ***(G-2756)***
Specialty Tank and Eqp Co..........904 353-8761
857 Robinson Ave Jacksonville (32209) ***(G-6804)***
Specialty Wood Manufacturing, Kissimmee *Also called Welshman Investment Corp* ***(G-7310)***
Specilty Strctres Instllations, Debary *Also called Specialty Structures Inc* ***(G-2756)***
Spector Manufacturing Inc..........860 559-6068
22 Sw Riverway Blvd Palm City (34990) ***(G-13674)***
Spectra Chrome LLC..........727 573-1990
13130 56th Ct Ste 611 Clearwater (33760) ***(G-1886)***
Spectra Composites East Fla..........772 461-7747
7445 Commercial Cir Fort Pierce (34951) ***(G-4749)***
Spectra Metal Sales Inc..........727 530-5435
5100 140th Ave N Clearwater (33760) ***(G-1887)***
Spectraflex Inc..........850 892-3900
83 Lancelot Rd Defuniak Springs (32433) ***(G-2947)***
Spectrecology LLC..........727 230-1697
8719 Orient Way Ne Saint Petersburg (33702) ***(G-15921)***
Spectrum Bridge Inc..........407 792-1570
110 Timberlachen Cir # 1012 Lake Mary (32746) ***(G-7450)***
Spectrum Engineering & Mfg Inc..........727 376-5510
11609 Pyramid Dr Odessa (33556) ***(G-12154)***
Spectrum Engineering Inc..........239 277-1182
1342 Clnl Blvd Ste D31 Fort Myers (33907) ***(G-4610)***
Spectrum Microwave Inc..........321 727-1838
1335 Gateway Dr Ste 2016 Melbourne (32901) ***(G-8941)***
Spectrum Packaging, Orlando *Also called R G Management Inc* ***(G-13109)***
Spectrum Rugs & More LLC..........813 453-4242
1009 W Indiana Ave Tampa (33603) ***(G-18123)***
Spectrum Signworks LLC..........239 908-0505
1474 Rail Head Blvd Naples (34110) ***(G-11415)***
Spectrumit Inc..........850 202-5263
1101 N Palafox St Pensacola (32501) ***(G-14268)***
Speech Bin..........772 770-0006
1965 25th Ave Vero Beach (32960) ***(G-18666)***
Speed Custom Cabinet Corp..........407 953-1479
6923 Narcoossee Rd Orlando (32822) ***(G-13205)***
Speed Machine Shop Corp..........305 233-3299
10755 Sw 190th St Ste 59 Cutler Bay (33157) ***(G-2414)***
Speed Print One Inc..........305 374-5936
1 Biscayne Tower Ste 1 # 1 Miami (33131) ***(G-10403)***
Speed Pro Miami..........954 534-9503
11341 Interchange Cir S Miramar (33025) ***(G-11045)***
Speed-D-Print, Pensacola *Also called R K L Enterprises of Pensacola* ***(G-14248)***
Speedline Athletic Wear Inc..........813 876-1375
1804 N Habana Ave Tampa (33607) ***(G-18124)***
Speedline Team Sports Inc..........813 876-1375
1804 N Habana Ave Tampa (33607) ***(G-18125)***
Speedpro Imaging, Boca Raton *Also called Paris Ink Inc* ***(G-663)***
Speedpro Imaging..........772 320-9385
7765 Sw Ellipse Way Stuart (34997) ***(G-17021)***
Speedpro Imaging St Petersburg, Saint Petersburg *Also called McKenny Printing Enterprise* ***(G-15853)***
Speedpro Imaging St Petersburg..........727 266-0956
5111 Queen Palm Ter Ne Saint Petersburg (33703) ***(G-15922)***
Speedpro of Orlando West..........407 509-8956
9032 Della Scala Cir Orlando (32836) ***(G-13206)***
Speedsource Inc..........954 578-7071
4 South Dr Key Largo (33037) ***(G-7174)***
Speedway Press, Daytona Beach *Also called Quality Printing Inc* ***(G-2701)***
Speedy Sign, Lake City *Also called Speedysignscom Inc* ***(G-7386)***
Speedysignscom Inc..........386 755-2006
162 Sw Spencer Ct Ste 101 Lake City (32024) ***(G-7386)***
Speedysignsusa.com,, Lake City *Also called Signsitecom Inc* ***(G-7385)***

Speer Laboratories LLC..........954 586-8700
5821 N Andrews Way Fort Lauderdale (33309) ***(G-4252)***
Spencer Boat Co LLC..........305 324-5211
881 Nw 13th Ave Miami (33125) ***(G-10404)***
Spencer Fabrications Inc..........352 343-0014
29511 County Road 561 Tavares (32778) ***(G-18354)***
Speranza Therapeutics Corp..........844 477-3726
433 Plaza Real Ste 275 Boca Raton (33432) ***(G-726)***
Sperry Manufacturing, Venice *Also called Sperry Marketing Group Inc* ***(G-18576)***
Sperry Marketing Group Inc..........941 483-4667
107 Corporation Way Venice (34285) ***(G-18576)***
Spett Printing Co Inc..........561 241-9758
4115 Georges Way Boca Raton (33434) ***(G-727)***
Sphere Access Inc (PA)..........336 501-6159
400 N Ashley Dr Ste 1775 Tampa (33602) ***(G-18126)***
SPI, Orlando *Also called Sign Producers Inc* ***(G-13191)***
SPI, Doral *Also called Structral Prestressed Inds Inc* ***(G-3514)***
SPI LLC..........786 907-4022
11200 Nw 107th St Ste 8 Miami (33178) ***(G-10405)***
Spice Island Boat Works Inc..........954 632-9453
505 Se 18th St Fort Lauderdale (33316) ***(G-4253)***
Spice World LLC (PA)..........407 851-9432
8101 Presidents Dr Orlando (32809) ***(G-13207)***
Spice Worlds, Orlando *Also called Jenard Fresh Incorporated* ***(G-12855)***
Spicer Industries Inc..........352 732-5300
840 Nw 24th Ct Ocala (34475) ***(G-12057)***
Spiegel Pavers Inc..........954 687-5797
3400 Blue Lake Dr Apt 102 Pompano Beach (33064) ***(G-14866)***
Spiegel Pavers Inc..........954 687-5797
7761 Nw 42nd Pl 1 Coral Springs (33065) ***(G-2315)***
Spiker USA Corporation..........850 710-3043
38 S Blue Angel Pkwy Pensacola (32506) ***(G-14269)***
Spikes Press & Printhouse LLC..........850 438-2293
1201 Barrancas Ave Pensacola (32502) ***(G-14270)***
Spin Magnetics..........863 676-9333
22501 Us Highway 27 Lake Wales (33859) ***(G-7520)***
Spincontrol Gearing LLC..........863 241-9055
4535 Tiger Creek Trl Lake Wales (33898) ***(G-7521)***
Spinenet LLC..........321 439-1806
1300 Minnesota Ave # 200 Winter Park (32789) ***(G-19447)***
Spinnaker Holding Company..........561 392-8626
1609 Nw 2nd Ave Boca Raton (33432) ***(G-728)***
Spinnaker Vero Inc..........772 567-4645
983 12th St Ste A Vero Beach (32960) ***(G-18667)***
Spires Empire LLC..........305 797-0622
1106 Grinnell St Key West (33040) ***(G-7203)***
Spirit Connection..........321 327-3804
588 Waveside Dr Melbourne (32934) ***(G-8942)***
Spirit llc..........954 592-0227
1400 Nw 159th St Ste 101 Miami Gardens (33169) ***(G-10755)***
Spirit Sales Corporation..........850 878-0366
2818 Industrial Plaza Dr D Tallahassee (32301) ***(G-17329)***
Spiritualist Chapel Melbourne, Melbourne *Also called Spirit Connection* ***(G-8942)***
Spiritwear Today..........239 676-7384
28711 N Diesel Dr Unit 9 Bonita Springs (34135) ***(G-856)***
Splash Beverage Group Inc..........954 745-5815
1314 E Las Olas Blvd Fort Lauderdale (33301) ***(G-4254)***
Splash of Color LLC..........732 735-3090
2885 Starshire Cv Jacksonville (32257) ***(G-6805)***
Spliffpuff LLC..........786 493-4529
6961 Nw 111th Ave Doral (33178) ***(G-3510)***
Splinter Woodworking Inc..........305 731-9334
738 Dotterel Rd Delray Beach (33444) ***(G-3145)***
Spmc, Florida City *Also called Southern Packaging McHy Corp* ***(G-3769)***
Sponge Merchant International..........727 919-3523
1028 Peninsula Ave Tarpon Springs (34689) ***(G-18325)***
Sponsor Locker, Winter Park *Also called Playoff Technologies LLC* ***(G-19431)***
Spoons Chilly..........321 610-8966
4980 N Wickham Rd Ste 106 Melbourne (32940) ***(G-8943)***
Sport America Magazine..........727 391-3099
248 144th Ave Madeira Beach (33708) ***(G-8448)***
Sport Products of Tampa Inc..........813 630-5552
8721 Ashworth Dr Tampa (33647) ***(G-18127)***
Sport Section, Lakeland *Also called Advanced Screen Printing & EMB* ***(G-7628)***
Sportailor Inc..........305 754-3255
6501 Ne 2nd Ct Miami (33138) ***(G-10406)***
Sports N Stuff Screen Printing..........407 859-0437
3975 Forrestal Ave # 600 Orlando (32806) ***(G-13208)***
Sports Radar Ltd..........352 503-6825
7397 S Suncoast Blvd Homosassa (34446) ***(G-6006)***
Sports Structure Intl LLC..........305 777-2225
1680 Michigan Ave Ste 700 Miami Beach (33139) ***(G-10715)***
Sportsanity..........386 873-4688
143 N Woodland Blvd Deland (32720) ***(G-3015)***
Sposen Signature Homes LLC..........239 244-8886
2311 Santa Barbara Blvd # 111 Cape Coral (33991) ***(G-1478)***
Spot-On Wldg Met Fbrcation LLC..........239 825-7452
2365 14th Ave Ne Naples (34120) ***(G-11416)***

Spotlight Graphics Inc 941 929-1500
6054 Clark Center Ave Sarasota (34238) ***(G-16601)***
Spray Box LLC 850 567-2724
768 Lupine Ln Tallahassee (32308) ***(G-17330)***
Spray-Tech Staining Inc 407 443-4239
569 Darby Way Longwood (32779) ***(G-8339)***
Spraying Systems Co 813 259-9400
5107 Lena Rd Unit 110 Bradenton (34211) ***(G-1119)***
Spraymation Development Corp 954 484-9700
4180 Nw 10th Ave Fort Lauderdale (33309) ***(G-4255)***
Spring Hill Bakery LLC 954 825-3419
374 Winthrop Dr Spring Hill (34609) ***(G-16865)***
Spring Hill Newsletter, Hudson *Also called Tom Watson Enterprises Inc* ***(G-6040)***
Spring Loaded Inc 561 747-8785
315 Commerce Way Ste 1 Jupiter (33458) ***(G-7121)***
Spring Oaks LLC 352 592-1150
7251 Grove Rd Brooksville (34613) ***(G-1276)***
Sprint Printing Company LLC 239 947-2221
28380 Old 41 Rd Ste 4 Bonita Springs (34135) ***(G-857)***
Spruce Creek Cabinetry Inc 386 756-0041
601 Lemon St Ste C Port Orange (32127) ***(G-15035)***
Spruce Creek Cntl Cndo Associa 386 212-4035
4184 Dairy Ct Ste D Port Orange (32127) ***(G-15036)***
SPX Flow Technology, Ocala *Also called Pneumatic Products Corporation* ***(G-12029)***
SPX Flow Technology Usa Inc (HQ) 352 237-1220
4647 Se 40th Ave Ocala (34474) ***(G-12058)***
Spyder Graphics Inc 954 561-9725
3601 Ne 5th Ave Oakland Park (33334) ***(G-11842)***
Square One Armoring Svcs Co 305 477-1109
12370 Sw 130th St Miami (33186) ***(G-10407)***
Squared Machine & Tool Inc A 678 988-2477
1851 Cowen Rd Unit F Gulf Breeze (32563) ***(G-5127)***
Squeegee Stitch Graphix LLC 850 256-4926
2940 W Highway 4 Century (32535) ***(G-1528)***
Squeeze It Corp 954 851-2443
3610 Yacht Club Dr # 213 Aventura (33180) ***(G-281)***
Squire Industries Inc 813 523-1505
1118 Sparkman Rd Plant City (33566) ***(G-14467)***
Srb Servicing LLC 850 278-1000
249 Mack Bayou Loop # 302 Santa Rosa Beach (32459) ***(G-16168)***
Srm Blinds Inc 321 269-5332
4381 Derbyshire Dr Titusville (32780) ***(G-18463)***
Srm Waterproofing Sealants Inc 407 963-3619
2899 Burwood Ave Orlando (32837) ***(G-13209)***
Srq Media Group, Sarasota *Also called Trafalger Communications Inc* ***(G-16624)***
Srq Sign Partners LLC 941 357-0319
1621 W University Pkwy Sarasota (34243) ***(G-16298)***
Srq Sign Partners LLC 941 417-4000
8466 Lockwood Ridge Rd Sarasota (34243) ***(G-16299)***
SRS Health Software, Tampa *Also called SRS Software LLC* ***(G-18128)***
SRS Software LLC 201 802-1300
4221 W Boy Scout Blvd # 200 Tampa (33607) ***(G-18128)***
Srt Wireless LLC 954 797-7850
1613 Nw 136th Ave Bldg C Sunrise (33323) ***(G-17177)***
Ss & S Industries Inc 321 327-2500
620 Di Lido St Ne Melbourne (32907) ***(G-8944)***
SS White Technologies Inc (PA) 727 626-2800
8300 Sheen Dr Saint Petersburg (33709) ***(G-15923)***
SSE and Associates Inc 954 973-7144
1500 W Copans Rd Ste A9 Pompano Beach (33064) ***(G-14867)***
SSE Publications LLC 954 835-7616
1 Panther Pkwy Sunrise (33323) ***(G-17178)***
Ssh Holding Inc 678 942-1800
10055 Seminole Blvd Seminole (33772) ***(G-16761)***
SSP, Miami *Also called Steering & Suspension Parts* ***(G-10412)***
Ssvm Partners Inc 239 825-6282
8293 Consumer Ct Sarasota (34240) ***(G-16602)***
St Acquisitions LLC 941 753-1095
1701 Desoto Rd Sarasota (34234) ***(G-16603)***
St Agstine Bches News Jrnl LL 904 501-4556
415 Talbot Bay Dr Saint Augustine (32086) ***(G-15616)***
St Agustine Elc Mtr Works Inc 904 829-8211
14 Center St Saint Augustine (32084) ***(G-15617)***
St Augustine Dist Co LLC 904 825-4962
112 Riberia St Saint Augustine (32084) ***(G-15618)***
St Augustine Marina Inc 904 824-4394
404 Riberia St Saint Augustine (32084) ***(G-15619)***
St Augustine Record 904 829-6562
1 News Pl Saint Augustine (32086) ***(G-15620)***
St Augustine Shipbuilding, Saint Augustine *Also called St Augustine Trawlers Inc* ***(G-15621)***
St Augustine Trawlers Inc 904 824-4394
404 Riberia St Saint Augustine (32084) ***(G-15621)***
St Cloud Door Company, Saint Cloud *Also called Aadi Inc* ***(G-15642)***
St Cloud Prtg Signs & Cstm AP, Saint Cloud *Also called Megamalls Inc* ***(G-15659)***
St Cloud Wldg Fabrication Inc 407 957-2344
3724 Hickory Tree Rd Saint Cloud (34772) ***(G-15667)***
St Ives Burrups 305 685-7381
13449 Nw 42nd Ave Opa Locka (33054) ***(G-12360)***
ST Japan Usa Llc 239 433-5566
8813 E Bay Cir Fort Myers (33908) ***(G-4611)***
St Johns Bky & Gourmet Fd Co (PA) 813 727-3528
6301 Powers Ave Jacksonville (32217) ***(G-6806)***
St Johns Optical Systems LLC 407 280-3787
101 Gordon St Sanford (32771) ***(G-16120)***
St Johns Ship Building Inc 386 328-6054
560 Stokes Landing Rd Palatka (32177) ***(G-13495)***
St Johns Turf Case 352 258-3314
1040 Hstngs Federal Pt Rd East Palatka (32131) ***(G-3607)***
St Judas Tadeus Foundry Inc 305 512-3612
2160 W 10th Ct Hialeah (33010) ***(G-5631)***
St Lucie Bakery, Port Saint Lucie *Also called Slb1989 Inc* ***(G-15146)***
St Lucie Signs LLC 772 971-6363
1147 Hernando St Fort Pierce (34949) ***(G-4750)***
St Marks Powder Inc 850 577-2824
7121 Coastal Hwy Crawfordville (32327) ***(G-2336)***
St Mary Pharmacy LLC 727 585-1333
1290 West Bay Dr Largo (33770) ***(G-8060)***
St Pete Auto Aids, Saint Petersburg *Also called Quality Industrial Chem Inc* ***(G-15896)***
St Pete Paper Company 727 572-9868
2324 20th St E Palmetto (34221) ***(G-13823)***
St Petersburg Dist Co LLC 727 581-1544
800 31st St S Saint Petersburg (33712) ***(G-15924)***
St Petersburg Times, Tallahassee *Also called Times Publishing Company* ***(G-17340)***
St. Cloud Wldg & Fabrication, Saint Cloud *Also called St Cloud Wldg Fabrication Inc* ***(G-15667)***
STA Cabinet Depot 719 502-5454
320 State Road 16 Saint Augustine (32084) ***(G-15622)***
STA-Con Incorporated (PA) 407 298-5940
2525 S Orange Blossom Trl Apopka (32703) ***(G-187)***
Stabil Concrete Pavers LLC 941 739-7823
7080 28th Street Ct E Sarasota (34243) ***(G-16300)***
Stabil Concrete Products LLC 727 321-6000
4451 8th Ave S Saint Petersburg (33711) ***(G-15925)***
Stable Concrete Product, Saint Petersburg *Also called A To Z Concrete Products Inc* ***(G-15688)***
Stacy Lee Montgomery 863 662-3163
6320 Cypress Gardens Blvd Winter Haven (33884) ***(G-19358)***
Stacy's Printing, Winter Haven *Also called Stacy Lee Montgomery* ***(G-19358)***
Stadium 1 Software LLC 561 498-8356
7115 Rue Notre Dame Miami Beach (33141) ***(G-10716)***
Stadson Technology Corporation 561 372-2648
3651 Fau Blvd Ste 400 Boca Raton (33431) ***(G-729)***
Stagexchange 239 200-9226
9156 Estero River Cir Estero (33928) ***(G-3697)***
Stainless Fabricators Inc 813 926-7113
11107 Challenger Ave Odessa (33556) ***(G-12155)***
Stainless Marine Inc 305 681-7893
13800 Nw 19th Ave Opa Locka (33054) ***(G-12361)***
Stainless Steel Guide Rods 813 240-7616
9347 Denton Ave Ste C12 Hudson (34667) ***(G-6038)***
Stainless Steel Guide Rods 727 207-0583
17205 Monteverde Dr Spring Hill (34610) ***(G-16877)***
Stainless Steel Kitchens Corp 305 999-1543
7601 E Treasure Dr # 2120 North Bay Village (33141) ***(G-11596)***
Stainless Stl Fbrction Svcs Fl, Palmetto *Also called Westcoast Metalworks Inc* ***(G-13836)***
Stairways By Angel LLC 407 790-7181
5555 Burlwood Dr Orlando (32810) ***(G-13210)***
Stal Creations, Boca Raton *Also called Dolphine Jewelry Contracting* ***(G-506)***
Stall Master Company (PA) 352 279-0089
4377 Commercial Way Spring Hill (34606) ***(G-16866)***
Stallion King LLC 321 503-7368
7901 4th St N Ste 4691 Saint Petersburg (33702) ***(G-15926)***
Stalo Group, Miami *Also called Stalo Modulars LLC* ***(G-10408)***
Stalo Modulars LLC 786 713-2410
5400 Nw 32nd Ave Bay B Miami (33142) ***(G-10408)***
Stamas Yacht Inc 727 937-4118
300 Pampas Ave Tarpon Springs (34689) ***(G-18326)***
Stamm Manufacturing, Fort Pierce *Also called World Industrial Equipment Inc* ***(G-4772)***
Stamp Concrete & Pavers Inc 561 880-1527
230 Cherry Ave Merritt Island (32953) ***(G-9014)***
Stampco Inc 904 737-6144
2930 Mercury Rd Jacksonville (32207) ***(G-6807)***
Stan Weaver & Co Inc 407 581-6940
3663 All American Blvd Orlando (32810) ***(G-13211)***
Stand Vertical Inc 407 474-0456
983 Bennett Rd Apt 103 Orlando (32814) ***(G-13212)***
Standard 3d Systems, Aventura *Also called Iter3d Inc* ***(G-274)***
Standard Carbon LLC 352 465-5959
551 N Us Highway 41 Dunnellon (34432) ***(G-3600)***
Standard Clay Mines 609 466-2986
3804 Crossroads Pkwy Fort Pierce (34945) ***(G-4751)***
Standard Industries Inc 813 248-7000
5138 Madison Ave Tampa (33619) ***(G-18129)***
Standard Injection Molding Inc 863 452-9090
2027 State Road 64 W Avon Park (33825) ***(G-297)***
Standard Kegs & Equipment, Medley *Also called Standard Kegs LLC* ***(G-8729)***

Standard Kegs LLC 305 454-9721
9106 Nw 106th St Medley (33178) ***(G-8729)***
Standard Motor Products Inc 718 392-0200
170 Sunport Ln Ste 100 Orlando (32809) ***(G-13213)***
Standard Motor Products Elec, Orlando *Also called Standard Motor Products Inc* ***(G-13213)***
Standard Precast Inc 904 268-0466
12300 Presidents Ct Jacksonville (32220) ***(G-6808)***
Standard Printing & Copy Ctr, Saint Augustine *Also called Kj Reynolds Inc* ***(G-15564)***
Standard Purification, Dunnellon *Also called Standard Carbon LLC* ***(G-3600)***
Standard Register Inc 954 492-9986
4710 Nw 15th Ave Fort Lauderdale (33309) ***(G-4256)***
Standard Rivet Company Inc 386 872-6477
1640 S Segrave St South Daytona (32119) ***(G-16810)***
Standard Sand & Silica Company (PA) 863 422-7100
1850 Us Highway 17 92 N Davenport (33837) ***(G-2483)***
Standard Sand & Silica Company 352 625-2385
15450 Ne 14th Street Rd Silver Springs (34488) ***(G-16784)***
Standard Sand & Silica Company 863 419-9673
2 Us Highway 17 92 N Haines City (33844) ***(G-5148)***
Standard Technology Inc 386 671-7406
1230 N Us Highway 1 # 18 Ormond Beach (32174) ***(G-13402)***
Standard Truss & Roof Sup Inc 863 422-8293
608 N 12th St Haines City (33844) ***(G-5149)***
Standout Home Servicing LLC 772 708-1110
1202 Sw Empire St Port Saint Lucie (34983) ***(G-15147)***
Stanfords Jerky 813 817-5953
3401 Magenta Way Brandon (33511) ***(G-1181)***
Stanley Chair Company Inc 813 884-1436
5110 W Hanna Ave Tampa (33634) ***(G-18130)***
Stanley Industries of S Fla (PA) 954 929-8770
3001 S Ocean Dr Apt 1423 Hollywood (33019) ***(G-5915)***
Stanron Corporation 954 974-8050
2770 Nw 63rd Ct Fort Lauderdale (33309) ***(G-4257)***
Stanron Steel Specialties Div, Fort Lauderdale *Also called Stanron Corporation* ***(G-4257)***
Stans Septic Svc & Con Pdts 941 639-3976
5287 Duncan Rd Punta Gorda (33982) ***(G-15236)***
Star Bakery Inc 305 633-4284
3914 Nw 32nd Ave Miami (33142) ***(G-10409)***
Star Bedding Mfg Corp 305 887-5209
1053 E 14th St Hialeah (33010) ***(G-5632)***
Star Brite, Davie *Also called Star-Brite Distributing Inc* ***(G-2595)***
Star Editorial Inc 561 997-7733
1000 American Media Way Boca Raton (33464) ***(G-730)***
Star Envirotech Inc 714 427-1244
1010 E 31st St Hialeah (33013) ***(G-5633)***
Star Fabricators 904 899-6569
989 Imeson Park Blvd Jacksonville (32218) ***(G-6809)***
Star Led, Fort Lauderdale *Also called Green Applications LLC* ***(G-4030)***
Star Pharmaceuticals LLC 800 845-7827
2881 E Oakland Park Blvd # 221 Fort Lauderdale (33306) ***(G-4258)***
Star Quality Inc 813 875-9955
4006 W Crest Ave Tampa (33614) ***(G-18131)***
Star Sight Innovations 307 786-2911
107 Tangelo Ter Crescent City (32112) ***(G-2343)***
Star-Brite Distributing Inc 954 587-6280
4041 Sw 47th Ave Davie (33314) ***(G-2595)***
Star-Seal of Florida Inc 954 484-8402
2740 Nw 55th Ct Fort Lauderdale (33309) ***(G-4259)***
Starboard Consulting LLC 407 622-6414
2170 W State Road 434 # 3 Longwood (32779) ***(G-8340)***
Starbridge Networks, Weston *Also called Networks Assets LLC* ***(G-19153)***
Starewell Publishing LLC 561 694-0365
200 Bent Tree Dr Palm Beach Gardens (33418) ***(G-13629)***
Starke Waste Wtr Trtmnt Plant 904 964-7999
602 Edwards Rd Starke (32091) ***(G-16897)***
Starline Education Inc 808 631-1818
1375 War Eagle Blvd Titusville (32796) ***(G-18464)***
Starlite Inc 727 392-2929
10861 91st Ter Seminole (33772) ***(G-16762)***
Starlock Inc 305 477-2303
8252 Nw 30th Ter Doral (33122) ***(G-3511)***
Starmakers Rising Inc (PA) 561 989-8999
17239 Boca Club Blvd # 6 Boca Raton (33487) ***(G-731)***
Starmark, Safety Harbor *Also called Vanlympia Inc* ***(G-15507)***
Starmark International Inc 954 874-9000
701 S Federal Hwy Fort Lauderdale (33316) ***(G-4260)***
Starr Wheel Group Inc 954 935-5536
3659 Nw 124th Ave Coral Springs (33065) ***(G-2316)***
Start Stop.com, Tarpon Springs *Also called Hth Engineering Inc* ***(G-18308)***
Startech Lake City Inc 386 466-1969
109 Nw Spring Hill Ct Lake City (32055) ***(G-7387)***
Startek Services LLC 631 224-9220
920 Almeria Ln Sw Palm Bay (32908) ***(G-13539)***
Stat Biomedical LLC 210 365-1495
2865 Night Heron Dr Mims (32754) ***(G-10953)***
Stat Industry Inc 561 826-7045
90 E Mcnab Rd Pompano Beach (33060) ***(G-14868)***
Statcorp Inc 904 786-5113
7037 Commonwealth Ave Jacksonville (32220) ***(G-6810)***
Statcorp Medical, Jacksonville *Also called Spacelabs Healthcare Inc* ***(G-6801)***
State Lathinginc 786 357-8404
606 N J St Lake Worth (33460) ***(G-7588)***
State Lighting Co Inc 561 371-9529
405 4th Way West Palm Beach (33407) ***(G-19041)***
State of Florida 850 488-1234
250 Marriott Dr Tallahassee (32301) ***(G-17331)***
Statement Marine LLC 727 525-5235
12011 49th St N Clearwater (33762) ***(G-1888)***
Statements 2000 LLC 561 249-1587
1374 N Killian Dr Ste A West Palm Beach (33403) ***(G-19042)***
Stateside Indus Solutions LLC 305 301-4052
14900 Sw 30th St # 278663 Miramar (33027) ***(G-11046)***
Statewide Blnds Shtters More I 813 480-8638
3030 Starkey Blvd New Port Richey (34655) ***(G-11511)***
Statewide Cstm Cbinets Fla Inc 813 788-3856
38535 Palm Grove Dr Zephyrhills (33542) ***(G-19537)***
Statewide Materials, Titusville *Also called Rock Ridge Materials Inc* ***(G-18460)***
Statgear, Fort Lauderdale *Also called Magenav Inc* ***(G-4109)***
Stature Software LLC 888 782-8881
620 Palencia Club Dr # 104 Saint Augustine (32095) ***(G-15623)***
Stay Smart Care LLC 321 682-7113
941 W Morse Blvd Winter Park (32789) ***(G-19448)***
Stay-Sealed Inc 866 978-2973
3454 Airfield Dr W Thonotosassa (33592) ***(G-18404)***
Stayfilm Inc 786 961-1007
2234 Sw 8th St Miami (33135) ***(G-10410)***
Staysealed Inc 866 978-2973
3454 Airfield Dr W Lakeland (33811) ***(G-7805)***
Ste-Ro Inc 754 234-1789
257 S Cypress Rd Apt 427 Pompano Beach (33060) ***(G-14869)***
Stealth Industries 561 747-1471
10782 N Dogwood Trl Jupiter (33478) ***(G-7122)***
Stedi Press, Doral *Also called Capra Graphics Inc* ***(G-3289)***
Steeda Engineering and Mfg LLC 954 960-0774
1351 Nw Steeda Way Pompano Beach (33069) ***(G-14870)***
Steel City Inc 850 785-9596
749 E 15th St Panama City (32405) ***(G-13952)***
Steel Cnstr Systems Holdg Co 407 438-1664
11250 Astronaut Blvd Orlando (32837) ***(G-13214)***
Steel Components Inc 954 427-6820
4701 Johnson Rd Ste 1 Coconut Creek (33073) ***(G-2097)***
Steel Fabricators LLC (HQ) 954 772-0440
721 Ne 44th St Oakland Park (33334) ***(G-11843)***
Steel Monkey Dream Shop LLC 786 356-1077
1369 Nw 74th St Miami (33147) ***(G-10411)***
Steel Plus Service Center Inc 407 328-7169
2525 Magnolia Ave Sanford (32773) ***(G-16121)***
Steel Products Inc 941 351-8128
1821 Myrtle St Sarasota (34234) ***(G-16604)***
Steel Systems, Pensacola *Also called Bell Steel Company* ***(G-14098)***
Steel Technology & Design 863 665-2525
401 Howard Ave Apt C Lakeland (33815) ***(G-7806)***
Steele Defense LLC 786 610-0857
480 Se 26th Dr Homestead (33033) ***(G-5995)***
Steele Industries Inc 800 674-7302
7910 N Tamiami Trl # 104 Sarasota (34243) ***(G-16301)***
Steelgate Global LLC 610 909-8509
1800 N Andrews Ave Fort Lauderdale (33311) ***(G-4261)***
Steen Aero Lab LLC 321 725-4160
1451 Clearmont St Ne Palm Bay (32905) ***(G-13540)***
Steering & Suspension Parts 786 523-3726
2740 Nw 35th St Miami (33142) ***(G-10412)***
Steiner-Atlantic LLC 305 754-4551
1714 Nw 215th St Miami Gardens (33056) ***(G-10756)***
Stella Sealants Corp 941 357-1566
6915 15th St E Ste 201 Sarasota (34243) ***(G-16302)***
Stellar On-Site LLC 904 945-1908
27167 Betina Dr Hilliard (32046) ***(G-5719)***
Stellar Sign and Design LLC 407 660-3174
7005 Stapoint Ct Winter Park (32792) ***(G-19449)***
Stellar Signs Grap 561 721-6060
5401 N Haverhill Rd West Palm Beach (33407) ***(G-19043)***
Stellarnet Inc 813 855-8687
14390 Carlson Cir Tampa (33626) ***(G-18132)***
Stemler Corporation 727 577-1216
1873 64th Ave N Saint Petersburg (33702) ***(G-15927)***
Stemtech Healthsciences Corp 954 715-6000
10370 Usa Today Way Miramar (33025) ***(G-11047)***
Stenner Pump Company Inc (PA) 904 641-1666
3174 Desalvo Rd Jacksonville (32246) ***(G-6811)***
Step Zone LLC 850 983-3758
6674 Elva St Milton (32570) ***(G-10940)***
Stephen B Fine Cabinetry Inc 561 512-2850
1154 Sw 28th Ave Boynton Beach (33426) ***(G-963)***
Stephen J Austin 941 780-7842
120 Gulf Ave Nokomis (34275) ***(G-11588)***
Stephen ODonnell 631 664-3594
5221 Hammock Cir Saint Cloud (34771) ***(G-15668)***

ALPHABETIC

Stephen Shives...352 454-6522
14628 Se 95th Ct Summerfield (34491) ***(G-17063)***
Stephens Advertising Inc...904 354-7004
7029 Commwl Ave Ste 9 Jacksonville (32220) ***(G-6812)***
Stephens Group...941 623-9689
20101 Peachland Blvd # 2 Port Charlotte (33954) ***(G-14999)***
Stephs Woodworking LLC...772 571-2661
6065 21st St Sw Vero Beach (32968) ***(G-18668)***
Stepincorp Auto Solutions LLC...786 864-3222
12480 Nw 25th St Ste 115 Miami (33182) ***(G-10413)***
Steriline North America I...941 405-2039
872 62nd Street Cir E Bradenton (34208) ***(G-1120)***
Steripack (usa) Limited LLC...863 648-2333
4255 S Pipkin Rd Lakeland (33811) ***(G-7807)***
Steritool Inc...904 388-3672
2376 Lake Shore Blvd Jacksonville (32210) ***(G-6813)***
Sterling Eqp Mfg Centl Fla Inc...352 669-3255
803 Line St Umatilla (32784) ***(G-18503)***
Sterling Facility Services LLC...772 871-2161
523 Nw Peacock Blvd Port Saint Lucie (34986) ***(G-15148)***
Sterling Fibers Inc...850 994-5311
5005 Sterling Way Milton (32571) ***(G-10941)***
Sterling Industry LLC...561 845-2440
834 W 13th Ct Riviera Beach (33404) ***(G-15379)***
Sterling Manufacturing, Sarasota *Also called Ssvm Partners Inc* ***(G-16602)***
Sterling Mdr Inc...954 725-2777
741 Nw 42nd Way Deerfield Beach (33442) ***(G-2917)***
Sterling Steel Fabrications...561 366-8600
1139 53rd Ct N Mangonia Park (33407) ***(G-8512)***
Sterling Stl Cstm Alum Fbrcton...561 386-7166
837 W 13th St Riviera Beach (33404) ***(G-15380)***
Stern Bloom Media Inc...954 454-8522
20454 Ne 34th Ct Miami (33180) ***(G-10414)***
Steve Baie Enterprises Inc...407 822-3997
2456 Clark St Apopka (32703) ***(G-188)***
Steve French Entps Ltd LLC...772 692-0222
2871 Se Monroe St C Stuart (34997) ***(G-17022)***
Steve Printer Inc...941 375-8657
601 Cypress Ave Venice (34285) ***(G-18577)***
Steve Prints...561 571-2903
15345 Lake Wildflower Rd Delray Beach (33484) ***(G-3146)***
Steve Unser Cabinetry Inc...239 631-2951
5550 Shirley St Naples (34109) ***(G-11417)***
Steven Chancas...352 629-5016
1519 S Pine Ave Ocala (34471) ***(G-12059)***
Steven Herranz Custom Coatings...941 915-4686
527 37th Street Ct W Palmetto (34221) ***(G-13824)***
Steven K Bakum Inc...561 804-9110
4634 S Dixie Hwy West Palm Beach (33405) ***(G-19044)***
Steven M Roessler LLC...321 773-2300
1859 South Patrick Dr Indian Harbour Beach (32937) ***(G-6068)***
Steven Press...954 434-3694
5820 Sw 115th Ave Cooper City (33330) ***(G-2117)***
Steven R Durante...954 564-9913
1056 Ne 44th Pl Oakland Park (33334) ***(G-11844)***
Stewart Materials Inc (PA)...561 972-4517
2875 Jupiter Park Dr # 1100 Jupiter (33458) ***(G-7123)***
Stewart Signs, Sarasota *Also called Redmont Sign LLC* ***(G-16556)***
Stewart-Hedrick Inc...941 907-0090
6001 Business Blvd Lakewood Ranch (34240) ***(G-7847)***
Stewarts Elc Mtr Works Inc...407 859-1837
8951 Trussway Blvd Orlando (32824) ***(G-13215)***
Sticker Karmer...813 802-1826
5405 W Crenshaw St Tampa (33634) ***(G-18133)***
Still Water Industries Inc...561 845-6033
8400 Garden Rd Ste A West Palm Beach (33404) ***(G-19045)***
Stilldragon North America LLC...561 845-8009
7788 Centl Indus Dr Ste 6 Riviera Beach (33404) ***(G-15381)***
Stimwave LLC...800 965-5134
1310 Park Central Blvd S Pompano Beach (33064) ***(G-14871)***
Stimwave Technologies Inc (PA)...800 965-5134
1310 Park Central Blvd S Pompano Beach (33064) ***(G-14872)***
Stinger Fiberglass Designs Inc...321 268-1118
1525 Armstrong Dr Titusville (32780) ***(G-18465)***
Stinner Pump Company...904 329-2098
11201 St Johns Indstrl Pa Jacksonville (32246) ***(G-6814)***
Stirling Winery...727 734-4025
461 Main St Dunedin (34698) ***(G-3589)***
Stitch Ink Inc...954 203-0868
2668 Nw 31st Ave Lauderdale Lakes (33311) ***(G-8094)***
Stitch Logo Inc...727 446-0228
2165 Sunnydale Blvd Ste H Clearwater (33765) ***(G-1889)***
Stitchez LLC...904 221-9148
13714 Longs Landing Rd W Jacksonville (32225) ***(G-6815)***
Stitching Around Inc...305 665-1600
4862 Sw 72nd Ave Miami (33155) ***(G-10415)***
Stitching Heart LLC...904 379-7990
8174 Lexington Dr Jacksonville (32208) ***(G-6816)***
Stitchnship...216 409-6700
1151 97th St Bay Harbor Islands (33154) ***(G-340)***
Stitchyourphotocom...321 297-6103
7652 Billingham St Windermere (34786) ***(G-19244)***
Stm Industries LLC...813 854-3544
9524 N Trask St Tampa (33624) ***(G-18134)***
Stntex, Hallandale Beach *Also called Syntex America Corporation* ***(G-5217)***
Stockdale Technologies Inc...407 323-5121
104 Commerce St Lake Mary (32746) ***(G-7451)***
Stocking Factory...305 745-2681
30554 5th Ave Big Pine Key (33043) ***(G-382)***
Stoller Chemical Co of Florida...352 357-3173
1451 Pine Grove Rd Eustis (32726) ***(G-3717)***
Stoltz Industries Inc...954 792-3270
9704 E Tree Tops Ct Davie (33328) ***(G-2596)***
Stone and Equipment Inc...305 665-0002
4681 Sw 72nd Ave Ste 104 Miami (33155) ***(G-10416)***
Stone Brick Pavers Inc...407 844-1455
1699 Cambridge Village Ct Ocoee (34761) ***(G-12090)***
Stone Center Inc...863 669-0292
2205 E Edgewood Dr Lakeland (33803) ***(G-7808)***
Stone Central of Central Fla...352 689-0075
3200 Ne 37th Pl Wildwood (34785) ***(G-19201)***
Stone Craft Masters LLC...786 401-7060
7975 Nw 54th St Doral (33166) ***(G-3512)***
Stone Design By Santos LLC...954 366-1919
1440 Nw 14th Ave Pompano Beach (33069) ***(G-14873)***
Stone Harbor Homes LLC...239 672-7687
5225 Sw 22nd Pl Cape Coral (33914) ***(G-1479)***
Stone Metals LLC...813 605-7363
4021 S Frontage Rd Plant City (33566) ***(G-14468)***
Stone Mosaics...321 773-3635
1735 Biltz Ave Ne Palm Bay (32905) ***(G-13541)***
Stone Palace...407 896-0872
1901 N Orange Ave Orlando (32804) ***(G-13216)***
Stone Set Technologies LLC...954 565-4979
12161 Ken Adams Way # 210 Wellington (33414) ***(G-18737)***
Stone Systems South Fla LLC...954 584-4058
3501 Nw 16th St Lauderhill (33311) ***(G-8121)***
Stone Trend International Inc...941 927-9113
6244 Clark Center Ave # 3 Sarasota (34238) ***(G-16605)***
Stonecrfters Archtctral Prcast (PA)...727 544-1210
10820 75th St Ste A Seminole (33777) ***(G-16763)***
Stonehardscapes Intl Inc...954 989-4050
5755 Powerline Rd Fort Lauderdale (33309) ***(G-4262)***
Stonehenge Gems, Pompano Beach *Also called Our Warehouse Inc* ***(G-14782)***
Stonelight LLC...239 514-3272
4775 Aston Gardens Way # 205 Naples (34109) ***(G-11418)***
Stoneworks Inc...305 666-6676
6840 Sw 81st Ter Miami (33143) ***(G-10417)***
Stoneworks of Art, Miami *Also called Stoneworks Inc* ***(G-10417)***
Stonexchange Inc...305 513-9795
9605 Nw 13th St Doral (33172) ***(G-3513)***
Stony Coral Investments LLC...941 704-5391
23410 78th Ave E Myakka City (34251) ***(G-11143)***
Stony Creek Sand & Gravel LLC (PA)...804 229-0015
2103 N Riverside Dr Pompano Beach (33062) ***(G-14874)***
Stop-N-Go 12...386 344-5494
801 Nw Lake Jeffery Rd Lake City (32055) ***(G-7388)***
Storage Building Company LLC...863 738-1319
429 10th Ave W Ste B Palmetto (34221) ***(G-13825)***
Storage Heaven, Plantation *Also called Multimedia Effects Inc* ***(G-14536)***
Store It Cold LLC...720 456-1178
9731 Nw 114th Way Medley (33178) ***(G-8730)***
Storm Depot of Palm Beach...561 721-9800
1202 S Congress Ave Ste A West Palm Beach (33406) ***(G-19046)***
Stormforce Jacksonville LLC...904 288-6639
3030 Hartley Rd Ste 210 Jacksonville (32257) ***(G-6817)***
Storngerrx, Miami *Also called Asb Sports Group LLC* ***(G-9176)***
Storopack Inc...305 805-9696
11825 Nw 100th Rd Ste 5 Medley (33178) ***(G-8731)***
Storterchilds Printing Co Inc...352 376-2658
1540 Ne Waldo Rd Gainesville (32641) ***(G-5001)***
Story Citrus Inc...863 638-1619
20205 Hwy 27 Lake Wales (33853) ***(G-7522)***
Stout Defense PA...352 665-9266
5215 Sw 91st Ter Gainesville (32608) ***(G-5002)***
Stover Manufacturing LLC...386 238-3775
825 Ballough Rd Daytona Beach (32114) ***(G-2719)***
Stover Manufacturing LLC...386 235-7060
919 Alexander Ave Port Orange (32129) ***(G-15037)***
Str Racing Wheels...407 251-7171
7558 Brokerage Dr Orlando (32809) ***(G-13217)***
Straight Polarity Welding Inc...727 530-7224
12855 Belcher Rd S Ste 19 Largo (33773) ***(G-8061)***
Straightline Metals...407 988-2353
1150 Belle Ave Winter Springs (32708) ***(G-19484)***
Strand Core, Milton *Also called Central Wire Industries LLC* ***(G-10926)***
Strands Inc (PA)...415 398-4333
3390 Mary St Ste 116 Miami (33133) ***(G-10418)***
Strang Communications, Lake Mary *Also called Plus Communications Inc* ***(G-7443)***

Strap Shade, Bonita Springs *Also called Strap Shade Inc* ***(G-858)***
Strap Shade Inc 239 450-5844
24841 Old 41 Rd Bonita Springs (34135) ***(G-858)***
Strasse Forged LLC 786 701-3649
13979 Sw 140th St Miami (33186) ***(G-10419)***
Strasser Enterprises 386 677-5163
1504 State Ave Daytona Beach (32117) ***(G-2720)***
Strata Analytics Holdg US LLC 954 349-4630
1560 Sawgrs Corp Pkwy Sunrise (33323) ***(G-17179)***
Stratco Pharmaceuticals LLC 813 403-5060
2600 Lakepointe Pkwy Odessa (33556) ***(G-12156)***
Strategic Brands Inc 516 745-6100
2810 Center Port Cir Pompano Beach (33064) ***(G-14875)***
Strategic Products Inc 321 752-0441
5100 Laguna Vista Dr Melbourne (32934) ***(G-8945)***
Strategy Marketing Group, Fort Myers *Also called Panther Printing Inc* ***(G-4564)***
Stratford Care Usa Inc (HQ) 877 498-2002
2600 Lakepointe Pkwy Odessa (33556) ***(G-12157)***
Stratford Corporation 727 443-1573
1555 Sunshine Dr Clearwater (33765) ***(G-1890)***
Stratgic Trbine Invntory Group 561 427-2007
1330 W Indiantown Rd Jupiter (33458) ***(G-7124)***
Stratonet Inc (PA) 863 382-8503
935 Mall Ring Rd Sebring (33870) ***(G-16712)***
Stratos Light Wave Inc 321 308-4100
1333 Gateway Dr Ste 1007 Melbourne (32901) ***(G-8946)***
Stratos Optical, Melbourne *Also called Stratos Light Wave Inc* ***(G-8946)***
Stratton Home Decor, Sunrise *Also called Jem Art Inc* ***(G-17136)***
Stratton Inc Dm 904 268-6052
7653 Bayard Blvd Jacksonville (32256) ***(G-6818)***
Stratus Pharmaceuticals Inc 305 254-6793
12379 Sw 130th St Miami (33186) ***(G-10420)***
Straw Giant Company 561 430-0729
10290 W Atlantic Ave Delray Beach (33448) ***(G-3147)***
Straw Life Inc 386 935-2850
25434 87th Dr O Brien (32071) ***(G-11766)***
Stream Line Publishing Inc 561 655-8778
331 Se Mizner Blvd Boca Raton (33432) ***(G-732)***
Stream2sea LLC 866 960-9513
2498 Commerce Ct Bowling Green (33834) ***(G-869)***
Streaming Store, The, Jacksonville *Also called Videolinq Streaming Svcs LLC* ***(G-6898)***
Streamline Aluminum Inc 239 561-7200
12651 Metro Pkwy Ste 1 Fort Myers (33966) ***(G-4612)***
Streamline Extrusion Inc 727 796-4277
3105 Ashwood Ln Safety Harbor (34695) ***(G-15506)***
Streamline Numerics Inc 352 271-8841
3221 Nw 13th St Ste A Gainesville (32609) ***(G-5003)***
Streamline Performance Boats C 305 393-8848
7711 W 22nd Ave Hialeah (33016) ***(G-5634)***
Streamline Publishing Inc 561 655-8778
331 Se Mizner Blvd Boca Raton (33432) ***(G-733)***
Streamline Technologies Inc 407 679-1696
1900 Town Plaza Ct Winter Springs (32708) ***(G-19485)***
Street Elements Magazine Inc 813 935-5894
3902 E Powhatan Ave Tampa (33610) ***(G-18135)***
Street Lighting Equipment Corp 954 961-9140
2099 S Park Rd Hallandale Beach (33009) ***(G-5215)***
Street Signs USA Inc 561 848-1411
1137 Silver Beach Rd Lake Park (33403) ***(G-7480)***
Street Talk America 850 547-6186
1007 N Waukesha St Bonifay (32425) ***(G-808)***
Streetrod Productions Inc 352 751-3953
11962 County Road 101 The Villages (32162) ***(G-18393)***
Streetrod Productions Florida, The Villages *Also called Streetrod Productions Inc* ***(G-18393)***
Streetwise Maps Inc (HQ) 941 358-1956
4376 Independence Ct A Sarasota (34234) ***(G-16606)***
Stress Nuts LLC 787 675-3042
10715 Bonne Chance Dr Orlando (32832) ***(G-13218)***
Strictly Ecommerce 352 672-6566
5210 Ne 49th Ter Gainesville (32609) ***(G-5004)***
Strictly Toolboxes 352 672-6566
4820 Ne 49th Rd Gainesville (32609) ***(G-5005)***
Strides Pharma Inc 561 741-6500
3874 Fiscal Ct Ste 200 Riviera Beach (33404) ***(G-15382)***
Striker Orthopedic, Sarasota *Also called Howmedica Osteonics Corp* ***(G-16461)***
Stripping Alpaca LLC 207 208-9687
900 West Ave Apt 713 Miami Beach (33139) ***(G-10717)***
Strive Development Corporation 850 689-2124
3100 Adora Teal Way Crestview (32539) ***(G-2360)***
Strong Enterprises, Orlando *Also called S E Inc* ***(G-13151)***
Strong Hurricane Shutter 786 587-3990
6406 Nw 82nd Ave Miami (33166) ***(G-10421)***
Strong Publications LLC (PA) 813 852-9933
13046 Race Track Rd Tampa (33626) ***(G-18136)***
Strong Tower Vineyard 352 799-7612
17810 Forge Dr Spring Hill (34610) ***(G-16878)***
Strongbridge International LLC 904 278-7499
154 Industrial Loop S Orange Park (32073) ***(G-12407)***
Stronghaven, Jacksonville *Also called K & G Box Inc* ***(G-6529)***

Structall Building Systems Inc (PA) 813 855-2627
350 Burbank Rd Oldsmar (34677) ***(G-12269)***
Structral Prestressed Inds Inc 305 556-6699
11405 Nw 112th Ct Doral (33178) ***(G-3514)***
Structural Cnstr Orlando Inc 407 383-9719
2200 Winter Springs Blvd Oviedo (32765) ***(G-13458)***
Structural Composites Inc 321 951-9464
360 East Dr Melbourne (32904) ***(G-8947)***
Structural Metal Fabricators 786 253-8012
3182 Nw 75th St Miami (33147) ***(G-10422)***
Structural Steel of Brevard 321 726-0271
6951 Vickie Cir Ste A Melbourne (32904) ***(G-8948)***
Structure Glass Solutions LLC 954 499-9450
13202 Nw 107th Ave Unit 8 Hialeah (33018) ***(G-5635)***
Structure Medical LLC (HQ) 239 262-5551
9935 Business Cir Naples (34112) ***(G-11419)***
Structurz Exhibits & Graphics, Fort Lauderdale *Also called J R Wheeler Corporation* ***(G-4073)***
Strumba Media LLC (PA) 800 948-4205
382 Ne 191st St Ste 6920 Miami (33179) ***(G-10423)***
Stryker Mako, Weston *Also called Mako Surgical Corp* ***(G-19149)***
Stryker Orthopaedics, Tampa *Also called Howmedica Osteonics Corp* ***(G-17763)***
Stryker Orthopedics 904 296-6000
7014 A C Skinner Pkwy Jacksonville (32256) ***(G-6819)***
Stryker Spine, Fort Lauderdale *Also called Howmedica Osteonics Corp* ***(G-4051)***
Stryker Spines, Tampa *Also called Howmedica Osteonics Corp* ***(G-17764)***
STS Air-Pro, Miramar *Also called STS Distribution Solutions LLC* ***(G-11048)***
STS Apparel Corp 305 628-4000
325 W 74th Pl Hialeah (33014) ***(G-5636)***
STS Distribution Solutions LLC 844 359-4673
11650 Miramar Pkwy # 500 Miramar (33025) ***(G-11048)***
Stuart Boat Works Inc 772 600-7121
3515 Se Lionel Ter Stuart (34997) ***(G-17023)***
Stuart Building Products LLC 239 461-3100
3601 Work Dr Fort Myers (33916) ***(G-4613)***
Stuart Composites LLC 772 266-4285
6900 Nw 77th Ct Miami (33166) ***(G-10424)***
Stuart Industries Inc 305 651-3474
526 Ne 190th St Miami (33179) ***(G-10425)***
Stuart Magazine 954 332-3214
1401 E Broward Blvd # 206 Fort Lauderdale (33301) ***(G-4263)***
Stuart Magazine 772 207-7895
1950 Se Port St Lucie Blv Port Saint Lucie (34952) ***(G-15149)***
Stuart News, Stuart *Also called Port St Lucie News* ***(G-16991)***
Stuart News (HQ) 772 287-1550
1939 Se Federal Hwy Stuart (34994) ***(G-17024)***
Stuart News 772 287-1550
1939 Se Federal Hwy Stuart (34994) ***(G-17025)***
Stuart Promotional Products, Brooksville *Also called Ped-Stuart Corporation* ***(G-1259)***
Stuart Propeller & Marine, Stuart *Also called E M P Inc* ***(G-16935)***
Stuart Stair & Furniture Mfg 772 287-4097
3220 Se Dominica Ter Stuart (34997) ***(G-17026)***
Stuart Web Inc 772 287-8022
5675 Se Grouper Ave Stuart (34997) ***(G-17027)***
Stuart Web Inc 772 287-8022
1521 Se Palm Ct Stuart (34994) ***(G-17028)***
Stuart Yacht Builders 561 747-1947
450 Sw Salerno Rd Stuart (34997) ***(G-17029)***
Stuart-Dean Co Inc 305 652-9595
2279 Nw 102nd Pl Doral (33172) ***(G-3515)***
Studio 21 Lighting Inc 941 355-2677
1227 Hardin Ave Sarasota (34243) ***(G-16303)***
Studio Luxe Cstm Cabinetry LLC 941 371-4010
2035 Constitution Blvd Sarasota (34231) ***(G-16607)***
Stump Industries LLC 239 940-5754
1300 Lee St Fort Myers (33901) ***(G-4614)***
Stuntwear LLC 305 842-2115
6538 Collins Ave Unit 414 Miami Beach (33141) ***(G-10718)***
Stush AP USA/Stush Style LLC 404 940-3445
2500 N University Dr Sunrise (33322) ***(G-17180)***
Style Crest Products 863 709-8735
5001 Gateway Blvd Ste 14 Lakeland (33811) ***(G-7809)***
Style-View Products Inc 305 634-9688
1800 N Byshore Dr Apt 400 Miami (33132) ***(G-10426)***
Stylecraft Cabinets Mfg Inc 941 474-4824
2780 Ivy St Unit 1 Englewood (34224) ***(G-3668)***
Stylecraft Fine Cabinetry, Stuart *Also called Omt Inc* ***(G-16983)***
Styleline Doors, Sarasota *Also called Commercial Rfrg Door Co Inc* ***(G-16390)***
Styleview Industries, Fort Myers *Also called Fresco Group Inc* ***(G-4459)***
Stylors Inc 904 765-4453
640 W 41st St Jacksonville (32206) ***(G-6820)***
Sublimation Station Inc 407 605-5300
1656 N Goldenrod Rd Orlando (32807) ***(G-13219)***
Sugar Cane Growers Coop Fla (PA) 561 996-5556
1500 George Wedgworth Way Belle Glade (33430) ***(G-351)***
Sugar Development Corp 561 784-0604
1940 S Club Dr West Palm Beach (33414) ***(G-19047)***

ALPHABETIC

Sugar Fancies LLC...786 558-9087
1091 Sw 134th Ct Miami (33184) ***(G-10427)***
Sugar Works Distillery LLC...386 463-0120
1714 State Road 44 New Smyrna Beach (32168) ***(G-11546)***
Sugart, Lauderhill *Also called Add-V LLC* ***(G-8099)***
Suinpla LLC...786 747-4829
12605 Nw 115th Ave # 106 Medley (33178) ***(G-8732)***
Sukalde Inc (PA)...786 399-0087
5271 Sw 8th St Apt 213 Coral Gables (33134) ***(G-2197)***
Sula Too LLC...813 368-1628
1405 Tampa Park Plaza St Tampa (33605) ***(G-18137)***
Sulzer Ems Inc...407 858-9447
7200 Lake Ellenor Dr Orlando (32809) ***(G-13220)***
Sumiflex LLC...954 578-6998
773 Shotgun Rd Sunrise (33326) ***(G-17181)***
Summation Research Inc...321 254-2580
305 East Dr Ste D Melbourne (32904) ***(G-8949)***
Summit ATL Productions LLC...407 930-5488
3320 Vineland Rd Ste A Orlando (32811) ***(G-13221)***
Summit Dental Systems, Pompano Beach *Also called SDS Dental Inc* ***(G-14843)***
Summit Holsters LLC...386 383-4090
843 Superior St Deltona (32725) ***(G-3180)***
Summit Orthopedic Tech Inc...203 693-2727
2975 Horseshoe Dr S # 100 Naples (34104) ***(G-11420)***
Sumter Planning Department, Bushnell *Also called County of Sumter* ***(G-1316)***
Sun 3d Corporation...954 210-6010
2530 N Powerline Rd # 402 Pompano Beach (33069) ***(G-14876)***
Sun Barrier Products Inc...407 830-9085
159 Baywood Ave Longwood (32750) ***(G-8341)***
Sun Belt Graphics Inc...954 424-3139
15431 Sw 14th St Davie (33326) ***(G-2597)***
Sun Business Systems Inc (PA)...727 547-6540
10900 47th St N Clearwater (33762) ***(G-1891)***
Sun Catalina Holdings LLC...305 558-4777
16200 Nw 59th Ave Ste 101 Miami Lakes (33014) ***(G-10864)***
Sun City Blinds LLC (PA)...727 522-6695
2426 63rd Ter E Ellenton (34222) ***(G-3655)***
Sun Coast Converters Inc...850 864-2361
631 Anchors St Nw Fort Walton Beach (32548) ***(G-4833)***
Sun Coast Industries LLC...941 355-7166
7350 26th Ct E Sarasota (34243) ***(G-16304)***
Sun Coast Media Group Inc (HQ)...941 206-1300
23170 Harborview Rd Port Charlotte (33980) ***(G-15000)***
Sun Coast Media Group Inc...941 207-1000
200 E Venice Ave Fl 1 Venice (34285) ***(G-18578)***
Sun Coast Media Group Inc...863 494-7600
23170 Harborview Rd Punta Gorda (33980) ***(G-15237)***
Sun Coast Media Group Inc...941 681-3000
120 W Dearborn St Englewood (34223) ***(G-3684)***
Sun Coast Media Group Inc...941 206-1900
2726 Tamiami Trl Ste B Port Charlotte (33952) ***(G-15001)***
Sun Coast Newspaper, New Port Richey *Also called Wood Television LLC* ***(G-11521)***
Sun Coast Orthotics Assn, Miami *Also called Mahnkes Orthtics Prsthtics of* ***(G-9935)***
Sun Coast Paper & Envelope Inc...727 545-9566
2050 Tall Pines Dr Ste A Largo (33771) ***(G-8062)***
Sun Coast Pavers, Brooksville *Also called Pavers Inc* ***(G-1258)***
Sun Coast Surgical & Med Sup...813 881-0065
2711 N 58th St Tampa (33619) ***(G-18138)***
Sun Coatings Inc...727 531-4100
4701 E 7th Ave Tampa (33605) ***(G-18139)***
Sun Electronic Systems Inc...321 383-9400
1845 Shepard Dr Titusville (32780) ***(G-18466)***
Sun Graphic Technologies Inc...941 753-7541
2310 Whitfield Park Ave Sarasota (34243) ***(G-16305)***
Sun Gro Horticulture Dist Inc...407 291-1676
6021 Beggs Rd Orlando (32810) ***(G-13222)***
Sun Indalex LLC...561 394-0550
5200 Town Center Cir # 470 Boca Raton (33486) ***(G-734)***
Sun Krafts of Volusia County...386 441-1961
217 Royal Dunes Cir Ormond Beach (32176) ***(G-13403)***
Sun Light Products, Miramar *Also called General Metal Intl Inc* ***(G-10997)***
Sun Mackie LLC...561 394-0550
5200 Town Center Cir # 470 Boca Raton (33486) ***(G-735)***
Sun Metals Systems Inc...813 889-0718
5008 Tampa West Blvd Tampa (33634) ***(G-18140)***
Sun Microstamping Technologies, Clearwater *Also called ES Investments LLC* ***(G-1677)***
Sun Nation Corp...954 822-5460
2861 Nw 22nd Ter Pompano Beach (33069) ***(G-14877)***
Sun Nuclear Corp (HQ)...321 259-6862
3275 Suntree Blvd Melbourne (32940) ***(G-8950)***
Sun Orchard LLC...863 422-5062
1200 S 30th St Haines City (33844) ***(G-5150)***
Sun Orchard LLC (PA)...786 646-9200
1198 W Frmont Dr Ste 2350 Miami (33131) ***(G-10428)***
Sun Paints & Coatings, Tampa *Also called Sun Coatings Inc* ***(G-18139)***
Sun Paper Company...305 887-0040
7925 Nw 12th St Ste 321 Doral (33126) ***(G-3516)***
Sun Pipe and Valves LLC...772 408-5530
710 Nw Enterprise Dr Port Saint Lucie (34986) ***(G-15150)***
Sun Power Diesel Inc...954 522-4775
413 Sw 3rd Ave Fort Lauderdale (33315) ***(G-4264)***
Sun Print Management LLC...727 945-0255
5441 Provost Dr Holiday (34690) ***(G-5749)***
Sun Publication of Florida, Clermont *Also called News Leader Inc* ***(G-1970)***
Sun Publications Florida Inc...321 402-0257
108 Church St Kissimmee (34741) ***(G-7299)***
Sun Publications Florida Inc (HQ)...863 583-1202
7060 Havertys Way Lakeland (33805) ***(G-7810)***
Sun Screen Print Inc...904 674-0520
4849 Dawin Rd Ste 3 Jacksonville (32207) ***(G-6821)***
Sun Screenprinting Lindycal, Sarasota *Also called Sun Graphic Technologies Inc* ***(G-16305)***
Sun State Systems Inc...904 269-2544
140 Industrial Loop W Orange Park (32073) ***(G-12408)***
Sun Valley Tech Solutions Inc...480 463-4101
31437 Heatherstone Dr Wesley Chapel (33543) ***(G-18759)***
Sun Works Plastics Inc...727 573-2343
15373 Roosevelt Blvd # 202 Clearwater (33760) ***(G-1892)***
Sun-Art Designs Inc...954 929-6622
2808 N 29th Ave Hollywood (33020) ***(G-5916)***
Sun-Glo Plating Co, Clearwater *Also called Pozin Enterprises Inc* ***(G-1838)***
Sun-Pac Manufacturing Inc...813 925-8787
14201 Mccormick Dr Tampa (33626) ***(G-18141)***
Sun-Ray Setting, Wellington *Also called Stone Set Technologies LLC* ***(G-18737)***
Sun-Rock Inc...727 938-0013
904 Anclote Rd Tarpon Springs (34689) ***(G-18327)***
Sun-Sentinel Company LLC (HQ)...954 356-4000
500 E Broward Blvd # 800 Fort Lauderdale (33394) ***(G-4265)***
Sun-Sentinel Company LLC...954 356-4000
333 Sw 12th Ave Deerfield Beach (33442) ***(G-2918)***
Sun-Sentinel Company Inc...561 736-2208
4935 Park Ridge Blvd # 1 Boynton Beach (33426) ***(G-964)***
Sun-Sentinel Company Inc...954 735-6414
3585 Nw 54th St Fort Lauderdale (33309) ***(G-4266)***
Sun-Tek Manufacturing Inc...407 859-2117
10303 General Dr Orlando (32824) ***(G-13223)***
Sun-Tek Skylights, Orlando *Also called Sun-Tek Manufacturing Inc* ***(G-13223)***
Sunbeam Americas Holdings LLC...561 912-4100
2381 Nw Executive Ctr Dr Boca Raton (33431) ***(G-736)***
Sunbeam Bread, Jacksonville *Also called Flowers Bkg Jacksonville LLC* ***(G-6407)***
Sunbeam Latin America LLC (HQ)...786 845-2540
2381 Executive Ctr Dr Boca Raton (33431) ***(G-737)***
Sunbeam Outdoor Products, Boca Raton *Also called American Household Inc* ***(G-422)***
Sunbeam Products Inc (HQ)...561 912-4100
2381 Nw Executive Ctr Dr Boca Raton (33431) ***(G-738)***
Sunbelt Dimensional Inc...954 424-3139
15431 Sw 14th St Davie (33326) ***(G-2598)***
Sunbelt Lettering, Pensacola *Also called Mid West Lettering Company* ***(G-14209)***
Sunbelt Metals & Mfg Inc...407 889-8960
920 S Bradshaw Rd Apopka (32703) ***(G-189)***
Sunbelt Transformer Ltd...305 517-3657
2063 Blount Rd Pompano Beach (33069) ***(G-14878)***
Sunbelt Usa Inc...239 353-5519
132 Vista Ln Naples (34119) ***(G-11421)***
Sunciti Industries Inc...407 877-8081
3402 Rex Dr Winter Garden (34787) ***(G-19286)***
Sunco Plastics Inc...305 238-2864
8501 Nw 90th St Miami (33166) ***(G-10429)***
Suncoast Accrdted Gmlgical Lab...941 756-8787
4016 Cortez Rd W Ste 1201 Bradenton (34210) ***(G-1121)***
Suncoast Aluminum Furn Inc...239 267-8300
6291 Thomas Rd Fort Myers (33912) ***(G-4615)***
Suncoast Assemblers LLC...407 947-8835
2114 Belle Isle Ave Belle Isle (32809) ***(G-359)***
Suncoast Automotive Pdts Inc...954 973-4822
3024 Nw 25th Ave Pompano Beach (33069) ***(G-14879)***
Suncoast Cartons & Crating LLC...813 242-8477
5601 Airport Blvd Tampa (33634) ***(G-18142)***
Suncoast Diesel, Fort Walton Beach *Also called Sun Coast Converters Inc* ***(G-4833)***
Suncoast Electric Motor Svc...813 247-4104
2502 E 5th Ave Tampa (33605) ***(G-18143)***
Suncoast Fabrics Inc...239 566-3313
5400 Yahl St Ste A Naples (34109) ***(G-11422)***
Suncoast Heat Treat Inc...386 267-0955
400 Fentress Blvd Daytona Beach (32114) ***(G-2721)***
Suncoast Heat Treat Inc (PA)...561 776-7763
507 Industrial Way Boynton Beach (33426) ***(G-965)***
Suncoast Identification Tech...239 277-9922
13300 S Cleveland Ave # 56 Fort Myers (33907) ***(G-4616)***
Suncoast Idntfction Sltons LLC...239 277-9922
618 Danley Dr Fort Myers (33907) ***(G-4617)***
Suncoast Industries of Florida, Fort Myers *Also called E-Z Metals Inc* ***(G-4438)***
Suncoast Investmens of PA...941 722-5391
1511 20th Ave E Palmetto (34221) ***(G-13826)***
Suncoast Kingfish Classic LLC...970 708-7997
12781 Kingfish Dr Treasure Island (33706) ***(G-18478)***
Suncoast Led Displays LLC...727 683-2777
2366 Knoll Ave S Palm Harbor (34683) ***(G-13763)***
Suncoast Lmntion Idntification, Fort Myers *Also called Suncoast Identification Tech* ***(G-4616)***

Suncoast Molders Inc 727 546-0041
10760 76th Ct Largo (33777) **(G-8063)**
Suncoast News 727 815-1023
11321 Us Highway 19 Port Richey (34668) **(G-15070)**
Suncoast Pallets Inc 813 988-1623
11506 Cerca Del Rio Pl Temple Terrace (33617) **(G-18379)**
Suncoast Pavers Llc 813 323-4014
16544 Ivy Lake Dr Odessa (33556) **(G-12158)**
Suncoast Pavers Inc 352 754-3875
3015 W Mustang Blvd Beverly Hills (34465) **(G-379)**
Suncoast Post-Tension Ltd 305 592-5075
7223 Nw 46th St 29 Miami (33166) **(G-10430)**
Suncoast Rebuild Center Inc 813 238-3433
2717 N 58th St Tampa (33619) **(G-18144)**
Suncoast Research Labs Inc 727 344-7627
2901 Anvil St N Saint Petersburg (33710) **(G-15928)**
Suncoast Sign Shop Inc 941 448-5835
8466 Cookwood Rdg Sarasota (34231) **(G-16608)**
Suncoast Signs Inc 813 664-0699
9601 E Us Highway 92 Tampa (33610) **(G-18145)**
Suncoast Specialty Prtg Inc 813 951-0899
6401 N River Blvd Tampa (33604) **(G-18146)**
Suncoast Stone Inc 561 364-2061
151 Nw 18th Ave Delray Beach (33444) **(G-3148)**
Suncoast Toner Cartridge Inc 727 945-0255
5441 Provost Dr Holiday (34690) **(G-5750)**
Suncoast Tool & Gage Inds Inc 727 572-8000
11625 54th St N Clearwater (33760) **(G-1893)**
Suncoast Trends Inc 727 321-4948
2860 21st Ave N Saint Petersburg (33713) **(G-15929)**
Suncoast Welding & Fabrication 254 537-3611
900 Old Combee Rd Lakeland (33805) **(G-7811)**
Suncoast Window Fashion, Naples *Also called Suncoast Fabrics Inc* **(G-11422)**
Suncrest Sheds Inc (PA) 863 675-8600
1451 Commerce Dr Labelle (33935) **(G-7324)**
Suncrest Sheds of South Fla 305 231-1990
9600 Nw 77th Ave Miami Lakes (33016) **(G-10865)**
Sundar Publishing 305 335-1930
234 Cortez Rd West Palm Beach (33405) **(G-19048)**
Sundog Education, Merritt Island *Also called Sundog Software LLC* **(G-9015)**
Sundog Software LLC 425 635-8683
4022 Tradewinds Trl Merritt Island (32953) **(G-9015)**
Sundown Lighting 561 254-3738
417 Se Atlantic Dr Lantana (33462) **(G-7876)**
Sundown Manufacturing Inc 727 828-0826
4505 131st Ave N Ste 26 Clearwater (33762) **(G-1894)**
Sundrinks, Miami *Also called D D B Corporation* **(G-9426)**
Sunflex 800 606-0756
4120 Enterprise Ave # 120 Naples (34104) **(G-11423)**
Sunflex Wall Systems LP 239 220-1570
1494 Pacaya Cv Naples (34119) **(G-11424)**
Sungard, Jacksonville *Also called Fis Avantgard LLC* **(G-6388)**
Sunglass Heaven 305 302-7285
3161 W Oakland Park Blvd Oakland Park (33311) **(G-11845)**
Sunglo Paint, Clearwater *Also called Leto LLC* **(G-1758)**
Sunglow Industries 304 554-2552
700 Iva Pl The Villages (32162) **(G-18394)**
Sungraf Inc 954 456-8500
325 W Ansin Blvd Hallandale Beach (33009) **(G-5216)**
Suniland Press Inc 305 235-8811
7379 Nw 31st St Miami (33122) **(G-10431)**
Sunluver Smoothies Inc 239 331-5431
160 12th Ave Nw Naples (34120) **(G-11425)**
Sunmaster of Naples Inc 239 261-3581
900 Industrial Blvd Naples (34104) **(G-11426)**
Sunnibunni 941 554-8744
1916 Bay Rd Sarasota (34239) **(G-16609)**
Sunnman Inc 305 505-6615
2215 W 9th Ave Hialeah (33010) **(G-5637)**
Sunny Hill International Inc 386 736-5757
901 W New York Ave Deland (32720) **(G-3016)**
Sunny Skies Enterprises Inc 954 316-6015
570 Ne 185th St North Miami Beach (33179) **(G-11705)**
Sunnyland Usa Inc 772 293-0293
600 Citrus Ave Ste 200 Fort Pierce (34950) **(G-4752)**
Sunnypics LLC 407 992-6210
618 E South St Ste 500 Orlando (32801) **(G-13224)**
Sunoptic Technologies LLC (PA) 877 677-2832
6018 Bowdendale Ave Jacksonville (32216) **(G-6822)**
Sunpack of Pensacola Inc 850 476-9838
8500 Fowler Ave Pensacola (32534) **(G-14271)**
Sunpost, Miami Beach *Also called Caxton Newspapers Inc* **(G-10652)**
Sunpost Newspaper Group, Miami Beach *Also called Prestige Publication Group* **(G-10705)**
Sunray Reflections Inc 305 305-6350
956 Harrison St Hollywood (33019) **(G-5917)**
Sunrise 386 627-5029
26 N Village Dr Palm Coast (32137) **(G-13711)**
Sunrise Fiberglass Inc 305 636-4111
3280 Nw 29th St Miami (33142) **(G-10432)**
Sunrise Financial Assoc Inc 321 439-9797
14004 Chcora Crssing Blvd Orlando (32828) **(G-13225)**
Sunrise Foods LLC 904 613-4756
4520 Swilcan Bridge Ln N Jacksonville (32224) **(G-6823)**
Sunrise Manufacturing Intl Inc 813 780-7369
4035 Correia Dr Zephyrhills (33542) **(G-19538)**
Sunrise Printing & Signs 321 284-3803
1218 Dyer Blvd Kissimmee (34741) **(G-7300)**
Sunrise Trampolines and Nets 727 526-9288
6544 44th St N Ste 1205 Pinellas Park (33781) **(G-14390)**
Sunrise Yacht Products, Pinellas Park *Also called Octal Ventures Inc* **(G-14373)**
Sunrise Yacht Products, Pinellas Park *Also called Sunrise Trampolines and Nets* **(G-14390)**
Sunrui Ttnium Prcsion Pdts Inc 727 953-7101
1058 Cephas Rd Clearwater (33765) **(G-1895)**
Suns Eye Inc 407 519-4904
2098 Tall Pine Trl Geneva (32732) **(G-5023)**
Suns Up of Swf LLC 301 470-2678
191 Lee Rd Venice (34292) **(G-18579)**
Sunset Cadillac of Sarasota 941 922-1571
2200 Bee Ridge Rd Sarasota (34239) **(G-16610)**
Sunset Metal Fabrication Inc 386 215-4520
1211 Porter Rd Unit 7 Sarasota (34240) **(G-16611)**
Sunset Pavers Inc 239 208-7293
8210 Katanga Ct Fort Myers (33916) **(G-4618)**
Sunset Power Inc 866 485-2757
5191 Shawland Rd Jacksonville (32254) **(G-6824)**
Sunshine 305 382-6677
15198 Sw 56th St Miami (33185) **(G-10433)**
Sunshine Alance Cabinets Mllwk 954 621-7444
712 S Military Trl Deerfield Beach (33442) **(G-2919)**
Sunshine Avionics LLC 954 517-1294
963 W 81st Pl Hialeah (33014) **(G-5638)**
Sunshine Bottling Co 305 592-4366
8447 Nw 54th St Doral (33166) **(G-3517)**
Sunshine Canvas Inc 352 787-4436
240 State Road 44 Leesburg (34748) **(G-8175)**
Sunshine Cap Company 863 688-8147
1142 W Main St Lakeland (33815) **(G-7812)**
Sunshine Cordage Corporation 305 592-3750
7190 Nw 12th St Miami (33126) **(G-10434)**
Sunshine Driveways Inc 954 394-7373
7750 Nw 35th St Hollywood (33024) **(G-5918)**
Sunshine Filters of Pinellas 727 530-3884
12415 73rd Ct Largo (33773) **(G-8064)**
Sunshine Health Products Inc 954 493-5469
6245 Powerline Rd Ste 106 Fort Lauderdale (33309) **(G-4267)**
Sunshine Lighters 386 322-1300
730 Glades Ct Port Orange (32127) **(G-15038)**
Sunshine Ltd Tape & Label Spc 561 832-9656
516 24th St West Palm Beach (33407) **(G-19049)**
Sunshine Marine Tanks Inc 305 805-9898
8045 Nw 90th St Medley (33166) **(G-8733)**
Sunshine Metal Products Inc 407 331-1300
195 Magnolia St Altamonte Springs (32701) **(G-77)**
Sunshine Nylon Products Inc 352 754-9932
16101 Flight Path Dr Brooksville (34604) **(G-1277)**
Sunshine Oil and Gas Inc (PA) 305 367-3100
13230 Sw 132nd Ave Ste 22 Miami (33186) **(G-10435)**
Sunshine Oil and Gas Fla Inc, Miami *Also called Sunshine Oil and Gas Inc* **(G-10435)**
Sunshine Organics Compost LLC 904 900-3072
6478 Buffalo Ave Jacksonville (32208) **(G-6825)**
Sunshine Packaging Inc 305 887-8141
880 W 19th St Hialeah (33010) **(G-5639)**
Sunshine Packing & Noodle Co 904 355-7561
57 Cantee St Jacksonville (32204) **(G-6826)**
Sunshine Peanut Company (PA) 813 988-6987
7405 Temple Terrace Hwy A Temple Terrace (33637) **(G-18380)**
Sunshine Piping Inc 850 763-4834
6513 Bayline Dr Panama City (32404) **(G-13953)**
Sunshine Printing Inc (PA) 561 478-2602
2605 Old Okeechobee Rd West Palm Beach (33409) **(G-19050)**
Sunshine Printing and Business 407 846-0126
2583 N Orange Blossom Trl Kissimmee (34744) **(G-7301)**
Sunshine Provisions, Hallandale Beach *Also called E&M Innovative Forager LLC* **(G-5182)**
Sunshine Ready Technologies, Miami Lakes *Also called Lewa Group Corp* **(G-10806)**
Sunshine Software 407 297-6253
8043 Sweetgum Loop Orlando (32835) **(G-13226)**
Sunshine Spray Foam Insulation 239 221-8704
10923 K Nine Dr Bonita Springs (34135) **(G-859)**
Sunshine Supplements Inc (PA) 407 751-4299
120 E Marks St Ste 250 Orlando (32803) **(G-13227)**
Sunshine Tape & Label, West Palm Beach *Also called Sunshine Ltd Tape & Label Spc* **(G-19049)**
Sunshine Tool LLC 941 351-6330
7245 16th St E Unit 114 Sarasota (34243) **(G-16306)**
Sunshine Welding, Cape Canaveral *Also called Batech Inc* **(G-1351)**
Sunshine Windows Mfg Inc 305 364-9952
1785 W 33rd Pl Hialeah (33012) **(G-5640)**

ALPHABETIC

Sunsof Inc (PA).....305 691-1875
5821 E 10th Ave Hialeah (33013) ***(G-5641)***
Sunstate Awng Grphic Dsign Inc.....407 260-6118
50 Keyes Ave Sanford (32773) ***(G-16122)***
Sunstate Uav LLC.....904 580-4828
1093 A1a Beach Blvd # 170 Saint Augustine (32080) ***(G-15624)***
Suntech Doors, Sarasota *Also called Ashton Manufacturing LLC* ***(G-16350)***
Suntek Window Films, Fort Lauderdale *Also called Eastman Performance Films LLC* ***(G-3956)***
Suntree Diagnostic Center.....321 259-8800
7970 N Wickham Rd Ste 102 Melbourne (32940) ***(G-8951)***
Suntree Technologies Inc.....321 637-7552
798 Clearlake Rd Ste 2 Cocoa (32922) ***(G-2054)***
Suntyx LLC.....786 558-2233
11550 Interchange Cir N Miramar (33025) ***(G-11049)***
Sunwyre Inc.....904 631-6961
4251 Monument Rd Apt 203 Jacksonville (32225) ***(G-6827)***
Sunybell LLC.....727 301-2832
4344 Cold Harbor Dr New Port Richey (34653) ***(G-11512)***
Super Brite Screw Corp.....305 822-6560
16 Sw 1st Ave Miami (33130) ***(G-10436)***
Super Color Inc.....954 964-4656
5905 Sw 58th Ct Davie (33314) ***(G-2599)***
Super Color Digital LLC.....407 240-1660
3450 Vineland Rd Ste 200 Orlando (32811) ***(G-13228)***
Super Grafix Inc.....561 585-1519
2889 Nw 24th Ter Boca Raton (33431) ***(G-739)***
Super Lite Aluminum Products.....407 682-2121
1090 Rainer Dr Altamonte Springs (32714) ***(G-78)***
Super Screening Incorporated.....239 931-3224
2971 South St Fort Myers (33916) ***(G-4619)***
Super Sensitive String Sls Co.....941 371-0016
1805 Apex Rd Sarasota (34240) ***(G-16612)***
Super Stone Inc (PA).....305 681-3561
1251 Burlington St Opa Locka (33054) ***(G-12362)***
Super Tool Inc.....941 751-9677
2951 63rd Ave E Bradenton (34203) ***(G-1122)***
Super-Pufft Snacks Usa Inc.....905 564-1180
700 Super Pufft St Perry (32348) ***(G-14314)***
Superchips Inc.....407 585-7000
1790 E Airport Blvd Sanford (32773) ***(G-16123)***
Superheat Fgh Services Inc.....519 396-1324
895 E Lemon St Bartow (33830) ***(G-334)***
Superion LLC.....407 304-3235
1000 Business Center Dr Lake Mary (32746) ***(G-7452)***
Superior Asphalt Inc.....941 755-2850
4703 15th St E Bradenton (34203) ***(G-1123)***
Superior Avionics Inc.....954 917-9194
2700 W Cypress Creek Rd Fort Lauderdale (33309) ***(G-4268)***
Superior Cast Stone LLC.....863 634-4771
6344 Se 30th Pkwy Okeechobee (34974) ***(G-12193)***
Superior Chrome Plating Inc.....832 659-0873
861 101st Ave N Naples (34108) ***(G-11427)***
Superior Design Products, Tampa *Also called Bornt Enterprises Inc* ***(G-17483)***
Superior Door Works & More LLC.....850 880-6579
37 Caswell Branch Rd Freeport (32439) ***(G-4852)***
Superior Electronics.....941 355-9500
7519 Pennsylvania Ave # 102 Sarasota (34243) ***(G-16307)***
Superior Electronics Inc.....727 733-0700
1140 Kapp Dr Clearwater (33765) ***(G-1896)***
Superior Fabrication Inc.....941 639-2966
5524 Independence Ct Punta Gorda (33982) ***(G-15238)***
Superior Fabrics Inc.....954 975-8122
7901 S Woodridge Dr Parkland (33067) ***(G-14002)***
Superior Fire & Lf Safety Inc.....850 572-0265
1709 Sw 15th Ave Cape Coral (33991) ***(G-1480)***
Superior Group Companies Inc (PA).....727 397-9611
10055 Seminole Blvd Seminole (33772) ***(G-16764)***
Superior Group Companies Inc.....727 397-9611
10055 Seminole Blvd Seminole (33772) ***(G-16765)***
Superior Kitchens Inc (PA).....772 286-6801
2680 Se Federal Hwy Stuart (34994) ***(G-17030)***
Superior Leaf Inc.....561 480-2464
523 Ogston St Ste A West Palm Beach (33405) ***(G-19051)***
Superior Metal.....407 522-8100
2409 N John Young Pkwy Orlando (32804) ***(G-13229)***
Superior Metal Fabricators Inc.....407 295-5772
2411 N John Young Pkwy Orlando (32804) ***(G-13230)***
Superior Millwork Company Inc.....904 355-5676
501 E 27th St Jacksonville (32206) ***(G-6828)***
Superior Oil 2016 Inc.....305 851-5140
5477 Nw 72nd Ave Miami (33166) ***(G-10437)***
Superior Pallets Llc.....863 875-4041
4353 Fussell Ln Winter Haven (33880) ***(G-19359)***
Superior Pavers and Stone LLC.....904 887-7831
731 Duval Station Rd # 107 Jacksonville (32218) ***(G-6829)***
Superior Printers, Plantation *Also called Admask Inc* ***(G-14486)***
Superior Redi-Mix.....850 575-1532
61 Commerce Ln Midway (32343) ***(G-10918)***
Superior Roof Tile Mfg.....850 892-2299
50 Hugh Adams Rd Defuniak Springs (32435) ***(G-2948)***
Superior Sealers Coatings Inc.....727 807-7851
7849 Riverdale Dr New Port Richey (34653) ***(G-11513)***
Superior Shade & Blind Co Inc.....954 975-8122
11100 Nw 24th St Coral Springs (33065) ***(G-2317)***
Superior Sheds Inc (PA).....386 774-9861
2323 S Volusia Ave Orange City (32763) ***(G-12379)***
Superior Shutters, Sarasota *Also called Greg Valley* ***(G-16224)***
Superior Signs and Prints.....954 780-6351
1800 Nw 15th Ave Pompano Beach (33069) ***(G-14880)***
Superior Signs Inc.....407 601-7964
3975 Forrestal Ave # 600 Orlando (32806) ***(G-13231)***
Superior Sleep Technology Inc.....305 888-0953
705 E 10th Ave Hialeah (33010) ***(G-5642)***
Superior Solid Surface Inc.....727 842-9947
8609 Squib Dr Port Richey (34668) ***(G-15071)***
Superior Storm Solutions.....305 638-8420
1501 Nw 79th St Miami (33147) ***(G-10438)***
Superior Surgical Mfg Co.....800 727-8643
10055 Seminole Blvd Seminole (33772) ***(G-16766)***
Superior Swim Systems Inc.....239 566-2060
2340 Vanderbilt Beach Rd Naples (34109) ***(G-11428)***
Superior Trim & Door Inc (PA).....407 408-7624
615 Sprior Cmmrce Blvd St Apopka (32703) ***(G-190)***
Superior Truss Systems Inc.....305 591-9918
8500 Nw 58th St Doral (33166) ***(G-3518)***
Superior Unlimited Enterprises.....863 294-1683
160 Spirit Lake Rd Winter Haven (33880) ***(G-19360)***
Superior Waterway Services Inc.....561 799-5852
6701 Garden Rd Ste 1 Riviera Beach (33404) ***(G-15383)***
Superiorlaser, Orlando *Also called Superior Metal Fabricators Inc* ***(G-13230)***
Superleaf, West Palm Beach *Also called Superior Leaf Inc* ***(G-19051)***
Supermarket Services Inc.....954 525-0439
4100 Sw 47th Ave Davie (33314) ***(G-2600)***
Supermix Concrete (PA).....954 858-0780
4300 Sw 74th Ave Miami (33155) ***(G-10439)***
Supermix Concrete.....305 265-4465
4550 Glades Cut Off Rd Fort Pierce (34981) ***(G-4753)***
Supersonic Imagine Inc.....954 660-3528
2625 Weston Rd Weston (33331) ***(G-19168)***
Supersweet Frog LLC.....863 386-4917
2932 Us Highway 27 N Sebring (33870) ***(G-16713)***
Supertrak Inc.....941 505-7800
26855 Airport Rd Punta Gorda (33982) ***(G-15239)***
Supliaereos USA LLC.....727 754-4915
21941 Us Highway 19 N Clearwater (33765) ***(G-1897)***
Supper On Wheels Inc.....305 205-8999
2423 Sw 147th Ave Miami (33185) ***(G-10440)***
Supply Expediters Intl Inc.....305 805-4255
911 Nw 209th Ave Ste 103 Pembroke Pines (33029) ***(G-14061)***
Support Aircraft Parts Inc.....305 975-3767
13034 Sw 133rd Ct Miami (33186) ***(G-10441)***
Support Systems Associates Inc.....321 724-5566
700 S John Rodes Blvd Melbourne (32904) ***(G-8952)***
Supreme International LLC (HQ).....305 592-2830
3000 Nw 107th Ave Doral (33172) ***(G-3519)***
Supreme Printing Corp.....305 591-2916
3155 W 81st St Hialeah (33018) ***(G-5643)***
Supreme Seat Covers, Miami *Also called Seat Savers Plus Inc* ***(G-10318)***
Sure Torque, Sarasota *Also called St Acquisitions LLC* ***(G-16603)***
Surefire Laser LLC.....305 720-7118
9611 Sw 130th St Miami (33176) ***(G-10442)***
Surepods LLC.....407 859-7034
2300 Principal Row # 101 Orlando (32837) ***(G-13232)***
Sureshade, Bradenton *Also called Lippert Components Inc* ***(G-1071)***
Sureweld Welding Inc.....813 918-1857
3050 W Socrum Loop Rd Lakeland (33810) ***(G-7813)***
Surf Lighting Inc.....305 888-7851
210 W 24th St Hialeah (33010) ***(G-5644)***
Surf Outfitter.....813 489-4587
1413 S Howard Ave Ste 104 Tampa (33606) ***(G-18147)***
Surf Style Inc.....954 926-6666
4100 N 28th Ter Hollywood (33020) ***(G-5919)***
Surface Engrg & Alloy Co Inc (PA).....727 528-3734
2895 46th Ave N Saint Petersburg (33714) ***(G-15930)***
Surface Finishing Tech Inc.....727 577-7777
12200 34th St N Ste A Clearwater (33762) ***(G-1898)***
Surfskate Industries LLC.....954 349-1116
614 S Federal Hwy Ste 300 Fort Lauderdale (33301) ***(G-4269)***
Surgentec LLC.....561 990-7882
911 Clint Moore Rd Boca Raton (33487) ***(G-740)***
Surgimed Corporation.....912 674-7660
9900 W Sample Rd Coral Springs (33065) ***(G-2318)***
Suriparts Corp.....954 639-7700
20861 Johnson St Ste 116 Pembroke Pines (33029) ***(G-14062)***
Survitec Survivor Cft Mar Inc.....954 374-4276
9640 Premier Pkwy Miramar (33025) ***(G-11050)***
Survival Armor Inc.....239 210-0891
12621 Corp Lakes Dr Ste 8 Fort Myers (33913) ***(G-4620)***

Survival Products Inc...954 966-7329
1655 Nw 136th Ave M Sunrise (33323) ***(G-17182)***
Survivor Industries Inc...805 385-5560
9399 Nw 13th St Doral (33172) ***(G-3520)***
Sustainable Casework Inds LLC...954 980-6506
720 S Deerfield Ave Ste 1 Deerfield Beach (33441) ***(G-2920)***
Sustainable Projects Group Inc...239 316-4593
2316 Pine Ridge Rd # 383 Naples (34109) ***(G-11429)***
Sutherland Armour Rand...863 696-3129
2426 Lake Front Dr Lake Wales (33898) ***(G-7523)***
Sutton Draperies Inc...305 653-7738
1762 Ne 205th Ter Miami (33179) ***(G-10443)***
Suvillaga Construction MGT LLC...305 323-8380
11411 Nw 7th St Apt 206 Miami (33172) ***(G-10444)***
Suwannee American Cem Co LLC (HQ)...352 569-5393
4750 E C 470 Sumterville (33585) ***(G-17069)***
Suwannee Fund LLC...386 963-1149
5790 98th Ter Live Oak (32060) ***(G-8242)***
Suwannee River Shellfish, Cross City *Also called M & R Seafood Inc* ***(G-2365)***
Suwanneearc...386 362-1796
617 Ontario Ave Sw Live Oak (32064) ***(G-8243)***
Suzanne Chalet Foods Inc...863 676-6011
3800 Chalet Suzanne Dr Lake Wales (33859) ***(G-7524)***
Suzano Pulp & Paper...954 772-7716
550 W Cypress Creek Rd # 420 Fort Lauderdale (33309) ***(G-4270)***
Sv Microwave Inc...561 840-1800
2400 Cntre Pk W Dr Ste 10 West Palm Beach (33409) ***(G-19052)***
SW, Miami *Also called Spa World Corporation* ***(G-10390)***
SW Premier Products LLC...941 275-6677
28100 Challenger Blvd # 1 Punta Gorda (33982) ***(G-15240)***
Swah-Rey 2 LLC...727 767-0527
625 Central Ave Saint Petersburg (33701) ***(G-15931)***
Swami Foods LLC...888 697-9264
1617 Kersley Cir Lake Mary (32746) ***(G-7453)***
Swan Neck Winery...850 495-3897
2115 W Nine Mile Rd Pensacola (32534) ***(G-14272)***
Swans Feed Mill...813 782-6969
8916 Fort King Rd Zephyrhills (33541) ***(G-19539)***
Swapper...850 973-6653
115 Se Madison St Madison (32340) ***(G-8454)***
Swarovski North America Ltd...561 791-7757
10300 W Frest Hl Blvd Ste West Palm Beach (33414) ***(G-19053)***
Swatch Group Caribbean...877 839-5224
5301 Blue Lagoon Dr # 620 Miami (33126) ***(G-10445)***
Sweepy Group Products LLC...305 556-3450
14501 Nw 60th Ave Unit 37 Miami Lakes (33014) ***(G-10866)***
Sweet & Saltsy Scrubs...863 853-8874
1854 Kinsman Way Lakeland (33809) ***(G-7814)***
Sweet Additions LLC (PA)...561 472-0178
4440 Pga Blvd Ste 600 Palm Beach Gardens (33410) ***(G-13630)***
Sweet and Vicious LLC (PA)...305 576-0012
111 Ne 21st St Miami (33137) ***(G-10446)***
Sweet and Vicious LLC...772 907-3030
1512 N Lakeside Dr Lake Worth (33460) ***(G-7589)***
Sweet Creations By L S Young...772 584-7206
953 Old Dixie Hwy Ste B11 Vero Beach (32960) ***(G-18669)***
Sweet Industries LLC...904 228-9655
3561 Se Micanopy Ter Stuart (34997) ***(G-17031)***
Sweet Mix LLC...561 227-8332
2644 Starwood Cir West Palm Beach (33406) ***(G-19054)***
Sweet Spot...727 784-2277
2609 Alt 19 Palm Harbor (34683) ***(G-13764)***
Sweet Tooth Inc...305 682-1400
18435 Ne 19th Ave North Miami Beach (33179) ***(G-11706)***
Sweet Treats...239 598-3311
7935 Airprt Plng Rd N 1 Ste 11 Naples (34109) ***(G-11430)***
Sweetlight Systems...239 245-8159
1506 Alhambra Dr Fort Myers (33901) ***(G-4621)***
Sweetreats of Naples Inc...239 598-3311
7935 Airport Pulling Rd N Naples (34109) ***(G-11431)***
Sweetsies...386 566-6762
26 Ullman Pl Palm Coast (32164) ***(G-13712)***
Sweetwater Today Inc...305 456-4724
35 Sw 114th Ave Miami (33174) ***(G-10447)***
Swf Bonita Beach Inc...239 466-6600
3540 Bonita Beach Rd Bonita Springs (34134) ***(G-860)***
Swfl Hurricane Shutters Inc...239 454-4944
422 Sw 2nd Ter Ste 214 Cape Coral (33991) ***(G-1481)***
Swi Publishing Inc...352 538-1438
116 Sw 40th Ter Gainesville (32607) ***(G-5006)***
Swift Print Service Inc...239 458-2212
1431 Se 10th St Unit B Cape Coral (33990) ***(G-1482)***
Swim Buoy...305 953-4101
2596 Ali Baba Ave Opa Locka (33054) ***(G-12363)***
Swim By Chuck Handy Inc...305 519-4946
15415 Ne 21st Ave North Miami Beach (33162) ***(G-11707)***
Swipe K12 School Solutions, Saint Augustine *Also called Webidcard Inc* ***(G-15634)***
Swire Pacific Holdings Inc...305 371-3877
98 Se 7th St Ste 601 Miami (33131) ***(G-10448)***

Swisher International Inc (HQ)...904 353-4311
459 E 16th St Jacksonville (32206) ***(G-6830)***
Swisher Intl Group Inc...904 353-4311
14425 Duval Rd Jacksonville (32218) ***(G-6831)***
Swiss Caps Usa Inc...786 345-5505
14193 Sw 119th Ave Miami (33186) ***(G-10449)***
Swiss Components Inc...321 723-6729
405 West Dr Ste A Melbourne (32904) ***(G-8953)***
Swisscosmet Corp...727 842-9419
5540 Rowan Rd New Port Richey (34653) ***(G-11514)***
Swisstech Machinery LLC...407 416-2383
8815 Conroy Windermere Rd Orlando (32835) ***(G-13233)***
Switchgear Unlimited, Plant City *Also called Resa Pwr Slutions Plant Cy LLC* ***(G-14461)***
Swoogo LLC (PA)...212 655-9810
4646 Ashton Rd Sarasota (34233) ***(G-16613)***
Sws Contracting, Tampa *Also called Shawn William Shumake LLC* ***(G-18092)***
Sws Services Inc...904 802-2120
1453 S 8th St Fernandina Beach (32034) ***(G-3748)***
Sy-Klone Company LLC...904 448-6563
4390 Imeson Rd Jacksonville (32219) ***(G-6832)***
Sy-Klone International, Jacksonville *Also called Sy-Klone Company LLC* ***(G-6832)***
Sybo Composites LLC...904 599-7093
404 Riberia St Saint Augustine (32084) ***(G-15625)***
Syft, Tampa *Also called Management Hlth Solutions Inc* ***(G-17876)***
Syi Inc...954 323-2483
10152 Nw 50th St Sunrise (33351) ***(G-17183)***
Sykleb Inc...305 303-9391
455 Ne 144th St North Miami (33161) ***(G-11657)***
Symbee/Symbee Connect, Vero Beach *Also called Connect Slutions Worldwide LLC* ***(G-18611)***
Symbol Mattress Florida Inc...407 343-4626
5000 Mercantile Ln Kissimmee (34758) ***(G-7302)***
Symetrics Industries LLC...321 254-1500
1615 W Nasa Blvd Melbourne (32901) ***(G-8954)***
Symetrics Technology Group LLC...321 254-1500
1615 W Nasa Blvd Melbourne (32901) ***(G-8955)***
Symme3d LLC...321 220-1584
1 S Orange Ave Ste 502 Orlando (32801) ***(G-13234)***
Symmetrical Stair Inc...561 228-4800
2115 Sw 2nd St Pompano Beach (33069) ***(G-14881)***
Symmetry Pavers Inc...813 340-0724
2407 Vandervort Rd Lutz (33549) ***(G-8420)***
Symrise Inc...904 768-5800
601 Crestwood St Jacksonville (32208) ***(G-6833)***
Symrna Ready Mix...352 330-1001
8302 Ne 44th Dr Wildwood (34785) ***(G-19202)***
Syn-Tech Systems Inc (PA)...850 878-2558
100 Four Points Way Tallahassee (32305) ***(G-17332)***
Synaptic Sparks Inc...205 774-8324
9738 Old Patina Way Orlando (32832) ***(G-13235)***
Sync Footwear, Miami *Also called Violettas LLC* ***(G-10587)***
Syncron Ems Llc...321 409-0025
2330 Commerce Park Dr Ne # 6 Palm Bay (32905) ***(G-13542)***
Syndaver Labs Inc (PA)...813 600-5530
8506 Benjamin Rd Ste C Tampa (33634) ***(G-18148)***
Syndesis Inc...954 483-9548
392 Sw 159th Dr Pembroke Pines (33027) ***(G-14063)***
Syndicated Programming Inc...850 877-0105
1363 Mahan Dr Tallahassee (32308) ***(G-17333)***
Synergistic Office Solutions...352 242-9100
11350 Tuscarora Ln Minneola (34715) ***(G-10956)***
Synergy Ancillary Services LLC...561 249-7238
11350 Sw Village Pkwy Port Saint Lucie (34987) ***(G-15151)***
Synergy Biologics LLC...850 656-4277
2849 Pablo Ave Tallahassee (32308) ***(G-17334)***
Synergy Communication MGT LLC (PA)...800 749-3160
400 Imperial Blvd Cape Canaveral (32920) ***(G-1369)***
Synergy Custom Fixtures Corp...305 693-0055
215 Se 10th Ave Hialeah (33010) ***(G-5645)***
Synergy Labs Inc...954 525-1133
888 Se 3rd Ave Ste 301 Fort Lauderdale (33316) ***(G-4271)***
Synergy Metal Finishing, Titusville *Also called Jssa Inc* ***(G-18435)***
Synergy Rehab Technologies Inc...407 943-7500
1404 Hamlin Ave Unit B Saint Cloud (34771) ***(G-15669)***
Synergy Sports LLC...239 593-9374
6300 Taylor Rd Naples (34109) ***(G-11432)***
Synergy Thermal Foils Inc...954 420-9553
12175 Nw 39th St Coral Springs (33065) ***(G-2319)***
Synergylabs LLC...954 525-1133
888 Se 3rd Ave Ste 301 Fort Lauderdale (33316) ***(G-4272)***
Syneron...407 489-3366
605 W Yale St Orlando (32804) ***(G-13236)***
Synkt Games Inc...305 779-5611
1820 Micanopy Ave Miami (33133) ***(G-10450)***
Syntech, Tallahassee *Also called Syn-Tech Systems Inc* ***(G-17332)***
Syntex America Corporation...954 457-1468
409 Nw 10th Ter Hallandale Beach (33009) ***(G-5217)***
Syntheon LLC...305 255-1745
13755 Sw 119th Ave Miami (33186) ***(G-10451)***

Synthes3d USA Inc...321 946-1303
1800 Pembrook Dr Orlando (32810) ***(G-13237)***
Sypris Electronics LLC (HQ)...813 972-6000
10421 University Ctr Dr Tampa (33612) ***(G-18149)***
Syrac Ordnance Inc...727 612-6090
6626 Osteen Rd Ste 331 New Port Richey (34653) ***(G-11515)***
System 48 Plus Inc...561 844-5305
3866 Prospect Ave Ste 1 West Palm Beach (33404) ***(G-19055)***
System Data Resource...954 213-8008
11422 Sw Hillcrest Cir Port Saint Lucie (34987) ***(G-15152)***
System Enterprises LLC...888 898-3600
319 Windward Is Clearwater (33767) ***(G-1899)***
Systematix Inc...850 983-2213
5953 Commerce Rd Milton (32583) ***(G-10942)***
Systemone Technolgies, Doral *Also called Mansur Industries Inc* ***(G-3423)***
Systemone Technologies Inc (PA)...305 593-8015
8305 Nw 27th St Ste 107 Doral (33122) ***(G-3521)***
Systems Engrg RES & Facilities, Cantonment *Also called Serf Inc* ***(G-1347)***
Syxa Enterprise, North Bay Village *Also called Omniaelectronics llc* ***(G-11594)***
Szabo Pos Displays Inc...941 778-0192
1501 63rd St W Bradenton (34209) ***(G-1124)***
T & C Creations, Lakeland *Also called PM Craftsman* ***(G-7768)***
T & C Godby Enterprises Inc...407 831-6334
915 State Road 436 Casselberry (32707) ***(G-1519)***
T & D Screen Enclosures, Wildwood *Also called Jennifer Yoder Sung* ***(G-19196)***
T & E Pavers Inc...239 243-6229
1319 Sw 10th Pl Cape Coral (33991) ***(G-1483)***
T & M Atlantic Inc...786 332-4773
436 Sw 8th St Miami (33130) ***(G-10452)***
T & M Industries Inc...954 778-2238
1106 Se 14th Dr Deerfield Beach (33441) ***(G-2921)***
T & R Marine Corp...850 584-4261
3309 E Us 27 Hwy Perry (32347) ***(G-14315)***
T & R Store Fixtures Inc...305 751-0377
2700 N Miami Ave Miami (33127) ***(G-10453)***
T & S Mobile Welding LLC...727 505-9407
6152 Tipton Ln Spring Hill (34606) ***(G-16867)***
T & T Concrete Specialties, Orlando *Also called Precast Designs Inc* ***(G-13079)***
T & W Inc...305 887-0258
400 Swallow Dr Miami Springs (33166) ***(G-10898)***
T A C Armatures & Pumps Corp...305 835-8845
800 Nw 73rd St Miami (33150) ***(G-10454)***
T and C Sales Inc...321 632-0920
1950 Murrell Rd Ste 10 Rockledge (32955) ***(G-15450)***
T and M Woodworking Inc...352 748-6655
3321 Ne 37th Pl Wildwood (34785) ***(G-19203)***
T B A, Tampa *Also called Tampa Brass and Aluminum Corp* ***(G-18162)***
T Beattie Enterprises...407 679-2000
7208 Aloma Ave Ste 300 Winter Park (32792) ***(G-19450)***
T Bower Enterprises Inc...863 984-3050
1824 Pearce Rd Polk City (33868) ***(G-14568)***
T Brand Fertilizer Inc...386 437-2970
801 N Bay St Bunnell (32110) ***(G-1307)***
T C B Products Inc...941 723-9820
1507 17th St E Palmetto (34221) ***(G-13827)***
T C Deliveries...813 881-1830
7002 Parke East Blvd Tampa (33610) ***(G-18150)***
T D C S, Davie *Also called Technical Drive Ctrl Svcs Inc* ***(G-2601)***
T D R Inc...941 505-0800
30436 Holly Rd Punta Gorda (33982) ***(G-15241)***
T Disney Trucking & Grading...813 443-6258
9250 Bay Plaza Blvd # 311 Tampa (33619) ***(G-18151)***
T E S S Electrical Sales & Svc, Fort Lauderdale *Also called TESS LLC* ***(G-4278)***
T H L Diamond Products Inc...954 596-5012
312 S Powerline Rd Deerfield Beach (33442) ***(G-2922)***
T H Stone...561 361-3966
4521 N Dixie Hwy Boca Raton (33431) ***(G-741)***
T J Sales Associates Inc...407 328-0777
4355 Saint Johns Pkwy Sanford (32771) ***(G-16124)***
T L Fahringer, Tampa *Also called TL Fahringer Co Inc* ***(G-18190)***
T L Sheet Metal Inc...813 871-3780
4203 N Lauber Way Ste 8 Tampa (33614) ***(G-18152)***
T M Building Products Ltd...954 781-4430
601 Nw 12th Ave Pompano Beach (33069) ***(G-14882)***
T M Tooling Inc...561 712-0903
7341 Westport Pl Ste B West Palm Beach (33413) ***(G-19056)***
T N R Technical Inc (PA)...407 321-3011
301 Central Park Dr Sanford (32771) ***(G-16125)***
T R C, Clearwater *Also called Technology Research LLC* ***(G-1912)***
T R S...407 298-5490
6330 Silver Star Rd Orlando (32818) ***(G-13238)***
T S E Industries Inc (PA)...727 573-7676
5180 113th Ave N Clearwater (33760) ***(G-1900)***
T S E Industries Inc...727 540-1368
5260 113th Ave N Clearwater (33760) ***(G-1901)***
T S F, Tarpon Springs *Also called Tarpon Stnless Fabricators Inc* ***(G-18328)***
T Sals Shirt Co...850 916-9229
1161 Oriole Beach Rd Gulf Breeze (32563) ***(G-5128)***
T Shirt Center Inc...305 655-1955
19900 Ne 15th Ct Miami (33179) ***(G-10455)***
T T Publications Inc...407 327-4817
203 W State Road 434 A Winter Springs (32708) ***(G-19486)***
T V HI Lites Penny Saver Inc...941 378-5353
6950 Webber Rd Sarasota (34240) ***(G-16614)***
T V Trac Ltd...516 371-1111
7 Island Dr Boynton Beach (33436) ***(G-966)***
T W A Sports Inc...727 541-9831
10522 75th St Largo (33777) ***(G-8065)***
T&S Kitchen and Bbq LLC...863 608-6223
4798 S Florida Ave 235 Lakeland (33813) ***(G-7815)***
T&T Detailing Inc...407 414-6710
1801 E Clnl Dr Ste 107 Orlando (32803) ***(G-13239)***
T&T Sons Inc...859 576-3316
1999 N County Road 426 Oviedo (32765) ***(G-13459)***
T&Y Cabinets Inc...305 512-0802
7380 W 20th Ave Ste 102 Hialeah (33016) ***(G-5646)***
T-Formation Inc Tallahassee...850 574-0122
864 Commerce Blvd Midway (32343) ***(G-10919)***
T-M Fabrications LLC...386 295-5302
11 Seaside Dr Ormond Beach (32176) ***(G-13404)***
T-Shirt Florida, Miami *Also called Jose Polanco* ***(G-9804)***
T-Shirts Plus Color Inc...305 267-7664
4156 Sw 74th Ct Miami (33155) ***(G-10456)***
T-Wiz Prtg & EMB Designs LLC...954 280-8949
464 W Melrose Cir Fort Lauderdale (33312) ***(G-4273)***
Taber Incorporated...401 245-2800
9624 Sw Nuova Way Port St Lucie (34986) ***(G-15180)***
Table Golf Llc...813 435-6111
667 W Lumsden Rd Brandon (33511) ***(G-1182)***
Tables Designs, Odessa *Also called Great American Woodworks Inc* ***(G-12124)***
Taco Marine, Seminole *Also called Taco Metals Inc* ***(G-16767)***
Taco Metals Inc...727 224-4282
6950 Bryan Dairy Rd Ste A Seminole (33777) ***(G-16767)***
Taco Mix Corp...239 498-9448
1740 Wilson Blvd N Naples (34120) ***(G-11433)***
Taco Time, Perry *Also called Perry Newspapers Inc* ***(G-14309)***
Tactical Phaser Corp...321 262-4140
2993 Moore Dr Oviedo (32765) ***(G-13460)***
Tactical Prchute Dlvry Systems...813 782-7482
4035 Correia Dr Zephyrhills (33542) ***(G-19540)***
Tactical Products Group LLC...561 265-4066
1914 Corporate Dr Boynton Beach (33426) ***(G-967)***
TAe Trans Atlantic Elec Inc (PA)...631 595-9206
4504 E Hillsborough Ave Tampa (33610) ***(G-18153)***
Tag & Label of Florida Inc...305 255-1050
13375 Sw 128th St Ste 106 Miami (33186) ***(G-10457)***
Tag Heuer...954 846-2103
1800 Sawgrass Mills Cir Sunrise (33323) ***(G-17184)***
Tag Media Group LLC...239 288-0499
16751 Link Ct Fort Myers (33912) ***(G-4622)***
Tagalong Inc...561 585-7400
5485 Old Spanish Trl Lantana (33462) ***(G-7877)***
Tags & Labels Printing Inc...954 455-2867
520 Ne 1st Ave Hallandale Beach (33009) ***(G-5218)***
Tagua Gun Leather, Miami *Also called Zen Distributors Group II LLC* ***(G-10629)***
Tagua Leather Corporation...305 637-3014
2047 Nw 24th Ave Miami (33142) ***(G-10458)***
Tahoe Interactive Systems Inc...614 891-2323
601 Woodstork Ln Punta Gorda (33982) ***(G-15242)***
Taie Inc (PA)...954 966-0233
4171 N State Road 7 Hollywood (33021) ***(G-5920)***
Tail Activewear, Doral *Also called Great Cir Vntures Holdings LLC* ***(G-3372)***
Tailored Living, Fort Lauderdale *Also called Premier Coatings LLC* ***(G-4175)***
Tailored LLC...239 249-9636
603 Cypress Way E Naples (34110) ***(G-11434)***
Tak Paper Corp...786 287-8900
10773 Nw 58th St Ste 651 Doral (33178) ***(G-3522)***
Take A Bed LLC...407 734-8857
1915 Hollywood Blvd Hollywood (33020) ***(G-5921)***
Takeda Phrmceuticals N Amer In...561 818-0925
336 E 5th Ave Windermere (34786) ***(G-19245)***
Taken For Granite...727 235-1559
4481 Pompano Dr Se Saint Petersburg (33705) ***(G-15932)***
Takeria Mix Inc...904 338-9157
6680 Powers Ave Ste 108 Jacksonville (32217) ***(G-6834)***
Talaria Company LLC...239 261-2870
3450 Westview Dr Unit 11 Naples (34104) ***(G-11435)***
Talaria Company LLC...772 403-5387
4550 Se Boatyard Ave Stuart (34997) ***(G-17032)***
Talent Assessment Inc...904 260-4102
6838 Phillips Pkwy Dr S Jacksonville (32256) ***(G-6835)***
Talent Wear LLC...561 624-3030
14812 64th Way N West Palm Beach (33418) ***(G-19057)***
Tallahassee Democrat...850 599-2100
277 N Magnolia Dr Tallahassee (32301) ***(G-17335)***
Tallahassee Engraving & Award...850 878-7187
1387 E Lafayette St Tallahassee (32301) ***(G-17336)***

Tallahassee Magazine, Tallahassee *Also called Rowland Publishing Inc* ***(G-17319)***
Tallahassee Powder Coating, Tallahassee *Also called Tallahassee Welding & Mch Sp* ***(G-17337)***
Tallahassee Welding & Mch Sp 850 576-9596
1220 Lake Bradford Rd Tallahassee (32304) ***(G-17337)***
Tallahassee Woman Magazine, Tallahassee *Also called Mitcham Media Group LLC* ***(G-17302)***
Talon Industries, Odessa *Also called International Imaging Mtls Inc* ***(G-12128)***
Talon Industries Inc 727 517-0052
111 8th St Belleair Beach (33786) ***(G-362)***
Talon Innovations FL Corp 320 251-0390
1217 Tech Blvd Tampa (33619) ***(G-18154)***
Talon Marine 941 753-7400
1968 Whitfield Park Ave Sarasota (34243) ***(G-16308)***
Tamco, Tampa *Also called LV Thompson Inc* ***(G-17866)***
Tamco Group, Port St Lucie *Also called City Electric Supply Company* ***(G-15171)***
Tamlite 772 878-4944
660 Nw Peacock Blvd Port St Lucie (34986) ***(G-15181)***
Tamlite Lighting - New Whse 772 879-7440
660 Nw Peacock Blvd Port Saint Lucie (34986) ***(G-15153)***
Tampa Amalgamated Steel Corp 813 621-0550
5215 Saint Paul St Tampa (33619) ***(G-18155)***
Tampa Amalgamated Steel Corp 813 621-0550
5215 Saint Paul St Tampa (33619) ***(G-18156)***
Tampa Armature Works Inc 904 757-7790
10520 Busch Dr N Jacksonville (32218) ***(G-6836)***
Tampa Armature Works Inc 813 612-2600
440 S 78th St Tampa (33619) ***(G-18157)***
Tampa Bay Business Journal, Tampa *Also called American City Bus Journals Inc* ***(G-17416)***
Tampa Bay Coatings Inc 727 823-9866
3228 Morris St N Saint Petersburg (33713) ***(G-15933)***
Tampa Bay Copack, Dade City *Also called South Pacific Trading Company* ***(G-2435)***
Tampa Bay Grand Prix (PA) 727 527-8464
12350 Automobile Blvd Clearwater (33762) ***(G-1902)***
Tampa Bay Machining Inc 813 855-8456
13601 Mccormick Dr Tampa (33626) ***(G-18158)***
Tampa Bay Magazine, Clearwater *Also called Tampa Bay Publications Inc* ***(G-1903)***
Tampa Bay Newspapers Inc 727 397-5563
9911 Seminole Blvd Seminole (33772) ***(G-16768)***
Tampa Bay Powder Coating Inc 813 964-5667
9601 Norwood Dr Ste B Tampa (33624) ***(G-18159)***
Tampa Bay Powersports LLC 813 968-7888
13521 N Florida Ave Tampa (33613) ***(G-18160)***
Tampa Bay Press Inc 813 886-1415
4710 Eisenhower Blvd B12 Tampa (33634) ***(G-18161)***
Tampa Bay Print Shop LLC 813 321-8790
2904 S Falkenburg Rd Riverview (33578) ***(G-15283)***
Tampa Bay Publications Inc 727 791-4800
2531 Landmark Dr Ste 101 Clearwater (33761) ***(G-1903)***
Tampa Bay Sports Entrmt LLC (PA) 727 893-8111
490 1st Ave S Saint Petersburg (33701) ***(G-15934)***
Tampa Bay Times 352 754-6100
13045 Cortez Blvd Brooksville (34613) ***(G-1278)***
Tampa Bay Times Storefront, Saint Petersburg *Also called Times Holding Co* ***(G-15938)***
Tampa Bays Coatings Screening 813 230-1610
528 Lantern Cir Temple Terrace (33617) ***(G-18381)***
Tampa Brass and Aluminum Corp 813 885-6064
8511 Florida Mining Blvd Tampa (33634) ***(G-18162)***
Tampa Catamarans LLC 813 966-4640
663 Flamingo Dr Apollo Beach (33572) ***(G-106)***
Tampa Contractors Supply Inc 813 418-7284
5017 N Coolidge Ave Tampa (33614) ***(G-18163)***
Tampa Fiberglass Inc 813 248-6828
4209 Raleigh St Tampa (33619) ***(G-18164)***
Tampa Fork Lift Inc 904 674-6899
7033 Commonwealth Ave Jacksonville (32220) ***(G-6837)***
Tampa Machine Products Inc 813 854-3332
151 Vollmer Ave Oldsmar (34677) ***(G-12270)***
Tampa Marine Fabricators LLC 813 664-1700
8702 E Broadway Ave Tampa (33619) ***(G-18165)***
Tampa Media Group Inc 813 259-7711
202 S Parker St Tampa (33606) ***(G-18166)***
Tampa Media Group Inc (PA) 813 259-7711
202 S Parker St Tampa (33606) ***(G-18167)***
Tampa Media Group LLC 813 259-7100
202 S Parker St Tampa (33606) ***(G-18168)***
Tampa Metal Works Inc 813 628-9223
6601 N 50th St Tampa (33610) ***(G-18169)***
Tampa Microwave, Saint Petersburg *Also called E2g Partners LLC* ***(G-15766)***
Tampa Microwave LLC 813 855-2251
16255 Bay Vista Dr # 100 Clearwater (33760) ***(G-1904)***
Tampa Multi Roll Sheet Metal 813 340-3554
4438 Bass St Tampa (33617) ***(G-18170)***
Tampa Pallet Co, Tampa *Also called Haman Industries Inc* ***(G-17741)***
Tampa Pool Company, Tampa *Also called Jlb Enterprises Tampa Inc* ***(G-17806)***
Tampa Powertrain & Hydraulics, Tampa *Also called Florida Pwrtrain Hydrulics Inc* ***(G-17687)***
Tampa Printing Company 813 612-7746
4907 N Florida Ave Tampa (33603) ***(G-18171)***
Tampa Printing Solutions, Tampa *Also called Printing Services Plus LLC* ***(G-18016)***
Tampa Sheet Metal Company 813 251-1845
1402 W Kennedy Blvd Tampa (33606) ***(G-18172)***
Tampa Ship LLC 813 248-9310
1130 Mcclosky Blvd Tampa (33605) ***(G-18173)***
TAMPA STEEL & SUPPLY, Tampa *Also called Urban Metals LLC* ***(G-18225)***
Tampa Steel Erecting Company 813 677-7184
5127 Bloomingdale Ave Tampa (33619) ***(G-18174)***
Tampa Tank & Welding Inc 813 241-0123
12781 S Us Highway 41 Gibsonton (33534) ***(G-5033)***
Tampa Tribune, Lakeland *Also called Nexstar Broadcasting Inc* ***(G-7757)***
Tampa Tribune, Brooksville *Also called Wood Television LLC* ***(G-1292)***
Tampa Tribune Company, The, Tampa *Also called Tampa Media Group Inc* ***(G-18166)***
Tampa Tribune, The, Tampa *Also called Tampa Media Group Inc* ***(G-18167)***
Tampa Wines LLC 727 799-9463
22041 Us Highway 19 N Clearwater (33765) ***(G-1905)***
Tampa Yacht Manufacturing LLC 813 792-2114
3671 131st Ave N Clearwater (33762) ***(G-1906)***
Tampa Yard, Tampa *Also called Vgcm LLC* ***(G-18241)***
Tampabay Custom Door LLC 813 842-3667
447 Arch Ridge Loop Seffner (33584) ***(G-16732)***
Tampatechnik Corporation 727 823-8889
2530 22nd St N Saint Petersburg (33713) ***(G-15935)***
Tan Group USA LLC 954 600-8697
31 Se 5th St Miami (33131) ***(G-10459)***
Tan Printing Inc 954 986-9869
2211 John P Lyons Ln Hallandale Beach (33009) ***(G-5219)***
Tandjteesandcustomizations 904 901-9227
13475 Atlantic Blvd Ste 8 Jacksonville (32225) ***(G-6838)***
Tanks Incorporated 941 320-4371
5150 Wauchula Rd Myakka City (34251) ***(G-11144)***
Tannehill Intl Inds Inc (PA) 850 265-3611
10 Arthur Dr Lynn Haven (32444) ***(G-8439)***
Tanning Research Labs LLC (HQ) 386 677-9559
1190 N Us Highway 1 Ormond Beach (32174) ***(G-13405)***
Tannous Innovations LLC 754 220-6645
2157 Nw 22nd St Pompano Beach (33069) ***(G-14883)***
Tantasia 239 274-5455
5100 S Cleveland Ave # 312 Fort Myers (33907) ***(G-4623)***
Tap Express Inc 305 468-0038
9625 Nw 33rd St Doral (33172) ***(G-3523)***
Tape Technologies Inc 904 284-0284
1272 Harbor Rd Green Cove Springs (32043) ***(G-5072)***
Tapesouth Inc 904 642-1800
1626 Nw 55th Pl Gainesville (32653) ***(G-5007)***
Tapinfluence Inc 720 726-4071
480 N Orlando Ave Ste 200 Winter Park (32789) ***(G-19451)***
Tapioca Fit 954 842-3924
156 N University Dr Pembroke Pines (33024) ***(G-14064)***
Tar Building LLC 407 896-7252
1155 N Orange Ave Orlando (32804) ***(G-13240)***
Tara Biek Creative 772 486-3684
4745 Se Desoto Ave Stuart (34997) ***(G-17033)***
Target Copy Gainesville Inc 352 372-1171
3422 Sw Archer Rd Gainesville (32608) ***(G-5008)***
Target Graphics Inc 941 365-8809
2053 13th St Sarasota (34237) ***(G-16615)***
Target Manufacturing Inc 305 633-0361
3430 Nw 38th St Miami (33142) ***(G-10460)***
Target Marine Inc 863 293-3592
125 Bomber Rd Winter Haven (33880) ***(G-19361)***
Target Marine Manufacturers, Winter Haven *Also called Target Marine Inc* ***(G-19361)***
Target Print & Mail 850 671-6600
2843 Industrial Plaza Dr A1 Tallahassee (32301) ***(G-17338)***
Tarin Services LLC 803 526-9643
5404 24th Ave S Tampa (33619) ***(G-18175)***
Tarmac America, Orlando *Also called Paver Systems LLC* ***(G-13055)***
Tarmac America Inc 386 427-0438
200 N Flagler Ave Edgewater (32132) ***(G-3637)***
Tarmac Florida Inc 954 481-2800
455 Fairway Dr Deerfield Beach (33441) ***(G-2923)***
Tarmac Standard Concrete, Deerfield Beach *Also called Titan America LLC* ***(G-2928)***
Tarpon Springs Distillery, Tarpon Springs *Also called Papous Craft Distillery LLC* ***(G-18319)***
Tarpon Stnless Fabricators Inc 727 942-1821
911 Rivo Pl Ste B Tarpon Springs (34689) ***(G-18328)***
Tarpon Woodworks LLC 407 446-9450
1518 Newbridge Ln Orlando (32825) ***(G-13241)***
Tarps and Beyond, Ocala *Also called Evora Enterprises Inc* ***(G-11934)***
Tarvin Mobile Home Service 727 734-3400
329 Archimedes St Palm Harbor (34683) ***(G-13765)***
Tarzen International LLC 239 243-0711
10060 Amberwood Rd Ste 3 Fort Myers (33913) ***(G-4624)***
Tasco, Tampa *Also called Tampa Amalgamated Steel Corp* ***(G-18156)***
Tassel Depot, Deerfield Beach *Also called Hofmann & Leavy Inc* ***(G-2842)***
Taste Advantage LLC 863 619-8101
3135 Drane Feld Rd Ste 22 Lakeland (33811) ***(G-7816)***
Taste of Thai LLC 850 581-3340
3475 Gulf Breeze Pkwy Gulf Breeze (32563) ***(G-5129)***

ALPHABETIC

Tasteful Delight LLC...305 879-6487
1919 W 10th St Apt 43 Lakeland (33805) ***(G-7817)***
Tata Tea Extractions Inc...813 754-2602
1001 W Dr Mlk Jr Blvd Martin Luther Plant City (33563) ***(G-14469)***
Tattoo Factory Inc (PA)...941 923-4110
2828 Proctor Rd Ste 2 Sarasota (34231) ***(G-16616)***
Tattoo Promotion Factory, Sarasota *Also called Tattoo Factory Inc* ***(G-16616)***
Tatum Brothers Lumber Co Inc...904 782-3690
22796 Nw County Road 200a Lawtey (32058) ***(G-8126)***
Taunton Truss Co Red Lobs...850 785-5566
910 E 23rd St Panama City (32405) ***(G-13954)***
Taurus Chutes Inc...954 445-0146
3030 Nw 23rd Ave Oakland Park (33311) ***(G-11846)***
Tavarez Sporting Goods Inc...347 441-9690
1840 Coral Way Miami (33145) ***(G-10461)***
Tavtek LLC (PA)...904 907-7749
450 State Road 13 Ste 106 Saint Johns (32259) ***(G-15681)***
Tavtek LLC...904 907-7749
2557 Pheasant Ct W Saint Johns (32259) ***(G-15682)***
Taw Jacksonville Service Ctr, Jacksonville *Also called Tampa Armature Works Inc* ***(G-6836)***
Taw Payroll Inc...813 621-5661
440 S 78th St Tampa (33619) ***(G-18176)***
Taw Tampa Service Center, Tampa *Also called Tampa Armature Works Inc* ***(G-18157)***
Tayco Industries Inc...863 318-9264
245 Ruby Lake Ln Winter Haven (33884) ***(G-19362)***
Taylor & Francis Group LLC...800 516-0186
1990 Main St Ste 750 Sarasota (34236) ***(G-16617)***
Taylor & Francis Group LLC (HQ)...561 994-0555
6000 Broken Sound Pkwy Nw # 300 Boca Raton (33487) ***(G-742)***
Taylor Building Elements LLC...863 287-2228
116 Van Fleet Ct Auburndale (33823) ***(G-254)***
Taylor Communications Inc...813 689-5099
12003 Embarcadero Dr Seffner (33584) ***(G-16733)***
Taylor Communications Inc...813 886-5511
5131 Tampa West Blvd Tampa (33634) ***(G-18177)***
Taylor Communications Inc...954 632-6501
1551 Sawgrs Corp Pkwy 1 Sunrise (33323) ***(G-17185)***
Taylor Concrete Inc...941 737-7225
503 10th St E Palmetto (34221) ***(G-13828)***
Taylor Electronics Inc...941 925-3605
7061b S Tamiami Trl Sarasota (34231) ***(G-16618)***
Taylor Farms Florida Inc...407 859-3373
7492 Chancellor Dr Orlando (32809) ***(G-13242)***
Taylor L Max L C...833 346-9963
12751 S Cleveland Ave Fort Myers (33907) ***(G-4625)***
Taylor Made Plastics Inc...941 926-0200
1561 Global Ct Ste A Sarasota (34240) ***(G-16619)***
Taylor Made Scrub Hats LLC...615 348-7802
10044 Creek Bluff Dr Riverview (33578) ***(G-15284)***
Taylor Made Systems Brdnton In (PA)...941 747-1900
2750 Kansas St Oviedo (32765) ***(G-13461)***
Taylor Media LLC...727 317-5800
490 1st Ave S Ste 800 Saint Petersburg (33701) ***(G-15936)***
Taylor Sign & Design Inc...904 396-4652
4162 Saint Augustine Rd Jacksonville (32207) ***(G-6839)***
Taylor-Cotton-Ridley Inc...904 733-8373
4873 Victor St Jacksonville (32207) ***(G-6840)***
Taylors Indus Coatings Inc...800 932-3049
108 Drive J A Wltshire Av Lake Wales (33853) ***(G-7525)***
Tbc Retail Group Inc...702 395-2100
823 Donald Ross Rd Juno Beach (33408) ***(G-6984)***
Tbo, Tampa *Also called Tampa Media Group LLC* ***(G-18168)***
Tca Pool Inc...954 600-2448
350 Sw 32nd Ave Deerfield Beach (33442) ***(G-2924)***
TCH, Boca Raton *Also called Twinlab Cnsld Holdings Inc* ***(G-759)***
Tcm Imagineering Inc...407 323-6494
1835 Bennett Ave Deland (32724) ***(G-3017)***
Tcr Woodworks Inc...561 827-6676
204 Monterey Sq 31 Boynton Beach (33436) ***(G-968)***
Tct Manufacturing...352 735-5070
21911 Us Highway 441 Mount Dora (32757) ***(G-11115)***
Td Coating Inc...786 325-4211
12420 Nw 5th Ave North Miami (33168) ***(G-11658)***
Td Fuel Inc...561 305-2059
1919 Nw 19th St Fort Lauderdale (33311) ***(G-4274)***
Td Tra -Dix Supply Inc...727 869-8662
14196 Us Highway 19 Hudson (34667) ***(G-6039)***
Tdk Electronics Inc...561 509-7771
6530 N Ocean Blvd Ocean Ridge (33435) ***(G-12080)***
Tdr Food Distribution LLC...561 860-7617
7810 Kingspointe Pkwy Orlando (32819) ***(G-13243)***
Tdse Inc...352 399-6413
3187 Ne 37th Pl Wildwood (34785) ***(G-19204)***
Tdt Manufacturing LLC (PA)...239 573-7498
2137 Se 19th Pl Cape Coral (33990) ***(G-1484)***
Te Olde Foundry Shoppe Inc...239 261-3911
4573 Exchange Ave Ste 7 Naples (34104) ***(G-11436)***
Teak Isle Inc...407 656-8885
401 Capitol Ct Ocoee (34761) ***(G-12091)***
Teak Isle Manufacturing, Ocoee *Also called Teak Isle Inc* ***(G-12091)***
Teakdecking Systems Inc...941 756-0600
7061 15th St E Sarasota (34243) ***(G-16309)***
Team Cymru Inc...847 378-3300
901 Intrntl Pkwy Ste 30 Lake Mary (32746) ***(G-7454)***
Team Edition Apparel Inc...941 744-2041
4208 19th Street Ct E Bradenton (34208) ***(G-1125)***
Team Hammer Screen Printing...863 666-1108
2328 E Main St Lakeland (33801) ***(G-7818)***
Team Inkjet...954 554-3250
1440 Coral Ridge Dr 339 Coral Springs (33071) ***(G-2320)***
Team Ip, Stuart *Also called International Prtg Ad Spc Inc* ***(G-16959)***
Team Ip Sports LLC...772 398-4664
850 Nw Federal Hwy 229 Stuart (34994) ***(G-17034)***
Team One Furniture Resources, Zephyrhills *Also called John Eric Madden* ***(G-19524)***
Team Plastics Inc...386 740-9555
2025 Eidson Dr Deland (32724) ***(G-3018)***
TEam Service Corp New York...410 365-1574
1040 Coronado Ct Marco Island (34145) ***(G-8527)***
Team Solutions Dental LLC...407 542-1552
2675 S Design Ct Sanford (32773) ***(G-16126)***
Teamwork Commerce, Clearwater *Also called Retail Cloud Technologies LLC* ***(G-1859)***
Tearepair Inc...813 948-6898
2223 Knight Rd Land O Lakes (34639) ***(G-7867)***
TEC Air Inc...772 335-8220
2195 N Kings Hwy Fort Pierce (34951) ***(G-4754)***
TEC Composites Inc...904 765-6502
10615 New Kings Rd Jacksonville (32219) ***(G-6841)***
Tech Comm Inc...954 712-7777
511 Se 32nd Ct Fort Lauderdale (33316) ***(G-4275)***
Tech Data Education Inc...727 539-7429
5350 Tech Data Dr Clearwater (33760) ***(G-1907)***
Tech Data Resources LLC...727 539-7429
5350 Tech Data Dr Clearwater (33760) ***(G-1908)***
Tech Data Tennessee Inc...727 539-7429
5350 Tech Data Dr Clearwater (33760) ***(G-1909)***
Techbtc, Doral *Also called Bridge Trading Usa LLC* ***(G-3286)***
Techcodes LLC...321 529-4122
2701 Sherwood Dr Titusville (32796) ***(G-18467)***
Techcrete Architectural Precast, Miami *Also called Berkshire Managment Associates* ***(G-9233)***
Techderm LLC...407 795-1517
220 Legendary Cir Palm Beach Gardens (33418) ***(G-13631)***
Technamold Inc...727 561-0030
5190 110th Ave N Clearwater (33760) ***(G-1910)***
Techncal Pntg Jacksonville Inc...904 652-1129
1401 Wheels Rd Bldg 3 Jacksonville (32218) ***(G-6842)***
Technet Corp...305 582-5369
10595 Nw 43rd Ter Doral (33178) ***(G-3524)***
Technetics Group Daytona Inc (HQ)...386 253-0628
305 Fentress Blvd Daytona Beach (32114) ***(G-2722)***
Technetics Group Deland, De Land *Also called Technetics Group LLC* ***(G-2734)***
Technetics Group LLC...386 736-7373
1700 E Intl Speedway Blvd Deland (32724) ***(G-3019)***
Technetics Group LLC...386 736-7373
1700 E Intl Speedway Blvd De Land (32724) ***(G-2734)***
Technical Components Inc (PA)...863 646-3253
3901 Industry Blvd Ste 6 Lakeland (33811) ***(G-7819)***
Technical Drive Ctrl Svcs Inc...954 471-6521
5081 S State Road 7 Davie (33314) ***(G-2601)***
Technical International Corp...305 374-1054
1000 Brickell Ave Ste 625 Miami (33131) ***(G-10462)***
Technical Ord Solutions LLC (PA)...850 223-2393
9495 Puckett Rd Perry (32348) ***(G-14316)***
Technical Sales & Engineering, Venice *Also called General Rubber Corporation* ***(G-18549)***
Technical Service Labs Inc...850 243-3722
95 Ready Ave Nw Fort Walton Beach (32548) ***(G-4834)***
Technico...561 588-8300
507 S G St Lake Worth (33460) ***(G-7590)***
Technico of Central Florida...321 631-4414
1950 Murrell Rd Rockledge (32955) ***(G-15451)***
Technicraft Plastics Inc...954 927-2575
1253 Stirling Rd Dania (33004) ***(G-2458)***
Technicuff Corp...352 326-2833
2525 Industrial St Leesburg (34748) ***(G-8176)***
Technifinish Inc...727 576-5955
5095 113th Ave N Clearwater (33760) ***(G-1911)***
Techniflex LLC...561 235-0844
4400 N Federal Hwy Ste 51 Boca Raton (33431) ***(G-743)***
Technipower LLC...954 346-2442
210 N University Dr # 700 Coral Springs (33071) ***(G-2321)***
Technisys LLC...305 728-5372
701 Brickell Ave Ste 1550 Miami (33131) ***(G-10463)***
Technlogy Integration Svcs LLC...904 565-4050
4600 Touchton Rd E # 1150 Jacksonville (32246) ***(G-6843)***
Techno Aerospace, North Miami *Also called Techno-Coatings Inc* ***(G-11659)***
Techno Cabinets Inc...305 910-9929
1681 Nw 97th Ave Doral (33172) ***(G-3525)***
Techno Solis USA, Saint Petersburg *Also called Techno-Solis Inc* ***(G-15937)***

Techno-Coatings Inc 305 945-2220
1865 Ne 144th St North Miami (33181) ***(G-11659)***
Techno-Solis Inc 727 823-6766
301 20th St S Saint Petersburg (33712) ***(G-15937)***
Techno-Spa Manufacturing Inc (PA) 386 239-8980
320 Fentress Blvd Daytona Beach (32114) ***(G-2723)***
Technocable Wiring Specialist 813 664-0697
3110 Cherry Palm Dr # 380 Tampa (33619) ***(G-18178)***
Technolgy Training Associates 813 249-0303
326 S Plant Ave Tampa (33606) ***(G-18179)***
Technologies Drs Unmanned Inc 850 302-3909
645 Anchors St Nw Fort Walton Beach (32548) ***(G-4835)***
Technologies For Tomorrow Inc 850 478-5222
1106 N 9th Ave Pensacola (32501) ***(G-14273)***
Technology Products Design Inc 321 432-3537
3806 Hield Rd Nw Palm Bay (32907) ***(G-13543)***
Technology RES A Southwire Co, Largo *Also called Southwire Company LLC* ***(G-8059)***
Technology Research, Clearwater *Also called Creating Tech Solutions LLC* ***(G-1642)***
Technology Research LLC (HQ) 727 535-0572
4525 140th Ave N Ste 900 Clearwater (33762) ***(G-1912)***
Technology Research Cons Inc 863 419-8860
2801 Us Highway 17 92 W Haines City (33844) ***(G-5151)***
Technomarine Usa Inc 305 438-0880
7600 Corp Ctr Dr Ste 4 Miami (33126) ***(G-10464)***
Techpubs Ltd 201 541-1192
65 Strathmore Blvd Sarasota (34233) ***(G-16620)***
Techshop Int 713 589-3559
9372 Nw 101st St Medley (33178) ***(G-8734)***
Techtran Lenses Inc 561 623-5490
601 Heritage Dr Ste 118 Jupiter (33458) ***(G-7125)***
Techtron Corporation 239 513-0800
1400 Rail Head Blvd Naples (34110) ***(G-11437)***
Techtronics LLC 407 738-4680
2450 Smith St Ste A Kissimmee (34744) ***(G-7303)***
Teckno Corp 305 677-3487
8640 Nw 101st Pl Doral (33178) ***(G-3526)***
Tecnam US Inc 863 655-2400
29536 Flying Fortress Ln Sebring (33870) ***(G-16714)***
Tecnico Corporation 904 853-6118
490 Levy Rd Atlantic Beach (32233) ***(G-227)***
Tecnografic Inc 954 928-1714
1010 Nw 51st Pl Fort Lauderdale (33309) ***(G-4276)***
Tecnometales Onis Cnc LLC 786 637-8316
21011 Johnson St Ste 110 Pembroke Pines (33029) ***(G-14065)***
Teco Diversified Inc (HQ) 813 228-4111
702 N Franklin St Tampa (33602) ***(G-18180)***
Tecore Government Services LLC 410 872-6000
295 North Dr Ste G Melbourne (32934) ***(G-8956)***
Tecport Optics Inc 407 855-1212
6457 Hazeltine National D Orlando (32822) ***(G-13244)***
Tectron 904 355-5512
546 Ellis Rd S Jacksonville (32254) ***(G-6844)***
Tectron Engineering Company (PA) 904 394-0683
5820 Commonwealth Ave Jacksonville (32254) ***(G-6845)***
Tectron Metal Detection, Jacksonville *Also called Tectron Engineering Company* ***(G-6845)***
Tecvalco USA Inc 866 427-3444
270 Barnes Blvd Rockledge (32955) ***(G-15452)***
Teds Sheds of Tampa 239 344-2900
10311 Bonita Beach Rd Se Bonita Springs (34135) ***(G-861)***
Tee Line Corp 786 350-9526
11883 62nd Ln N West Palm Beach (33412) ***(G-19058)***
Tee-N-Jay Services LLC 407 760-7925
528 Kittredge Dr Orlando (32805) ***(G-13245)***
Teeko Graphics Inc 386 754-5600
2018 Sw Main Blvd Lake City (32025) ***(G-7389)***
Tees By Bo Inc 305 382-8551
13220 Sw 66th St Miami (33183) ***(G-10465)***
Tees Please Inc 857 472-3391
9278 Se Sharon St Hobe Sound (33455) ***(G-5728)***
Teething Egg, The, Boca Raton *Also called Babbala LLC* ***(G-440)***
Teeze International Inc 727 726-3592
2431 Estancia Blvd Clearwater (33761) ***(G-1913)***
Tef-Gel Inc 561 845-1086
1601 Hill Ave West Palm Beach (33407) ***(G-19059)***
Tejeda Sheet Metal & Aluminum 305 609-5477
651 W 43rd Pl Hialeah (33012) ***(G-5647)***
Tek-Lite Inc 410 775-7123
1279 Tipperary Dr Melbourne (32940) ***(G-8957)***
Tekk Supply Inc 954 444-5782
290 Sw 14th Ave Pompano Beach (33069) ***(G-14884)***
Tekmatic Corp 305 972-1300
7522 Sw 143rd Ave Miami (33183) ***(G-10466)***
Tekna Manufacturing LLC 813 782-6700
39248 South Ave Zephyrhills (33542) ***(G-19541)***
Teknatool Usa Inc 727 954-3433
4499 126th Ave N Clearwater (33762) ***(G-1914)***
Teknifab Industries Inc 321 722-1922
179 Park Hill Blvd Melbourne (32904) ***(G-8958)***
Teknocraft Inc 321 729-9634
425 West Dr Melbourne (32904) ***(G-8959)***
Tekquest Inc 321 768-6069
2510 Kirby Cir Ne Ste 106 Palm Bay (32905) ***(G-13544)***
Tektrol Inc 305 305-0937
11013 Nw 30th St Doral (33172) ***(G-3527)***
Tektronix Inc 407 660-2727
151 Southhall Ln Ste 170 Maitland (32751) ***(G-8480)***
Tel Test, Gainesville *Also called Corporate One Hundred Inc* ***(G-4898)***
Tel-Tron Technologies Corp (PA) 386 523-1070
2570 W Intl Spwy Blvd # 200 Daytona Beach (32114) ***(G-2724)***
Teledyne Instruments Inc 386 236-0780
1026 N Williamson Blvd Daytona Beach (32114) ***(G-2725)***
Teledyne Odi, Daytona Beach *Also called Teledyne Instruments Inc* ***(G-2725)***
Teleios Manufacturing Inc 904 490-0600
8940 Western Way Ste 15 Jacksonville (32256) ***(G-6846)***
Telelect East, Wildwood *Also called Terex Corporation* ***(G-19205)***
Telematic Systems Inc 239 217-0629
2029 Club House Rd North Fort Myers (33917) ***(G-11607)***
Telenetpro Inc 954 333-8633
43 S Powerline Rd Ste 499 Pompano Beach (33069) ***(G-14885)***
Telephony Partners LLC 813 769-4690
5215 W Laurel St Ste 210 Tampa (33607) ***(G-18181)***
Telese Inc 813 752-6015
1207 Wood Ct Plant City (33563) ***(G-14470)***
Telese Properties Inc 813 752-6015
1207 Wood Ct Plant City (33563) ***(G-14471)***
Teleview Racing Patrol, Hialeah *Also called International Sound Corp* ***(G-5456)***
Telexpress La Musica Inc 813 879-1914
6310 N Armenia Ave Ste A Tampa (33604) ***(G-18182)***
Teligentems, Havana *Also called Prime Technological Svcs LLC* ***(G-5239)***
Telit Iot Platforms LLC (HQ) 561 982-9898
5300 Broken Sound Blvd Nw S Boca Raton (33487) ***(G-744)***
Tellabs International Inc 954 492-0120
1000 Corporate Dr Ste 300 Fort Lauderdale (33334) ***(G-4277)***
Tellus Products LLC (HQ) 561 996-5556
1500 George Wedgworth Way Belle Glade (33430) ***(G-352)***
Telsec Corporation 561 998-9983
1155 Broken Sound Pkwy Nw E Boca Raton (33487) ***(G-745)***
Tem Systems Inc 407 251-7114
4520 Pkwy Commerce Blvd Orlando (32808) ***(G-13246)***
Tempered Glass Industries Inc 727 499-0284
11116 47th St N Ste B Clearwater (33762) ***(G-1915)***
Temple Terrace Industries Inc 813 752-7546
4208 Business Ln Plant City (33566) ***(G-14472)***
Tempo Fulfillment Inc 727 914-0659
10344 66th St N Unit 100 Pinellas Park (33782) ***(G-14391)***
Ten In Motion LLC 407 226-0204
8544 Commodity Cir Orlando (32819) ***(G-13247)***
Ten Star Promotions, Tampa *Also called Ten Star Supply Co Inc* ***(G-18183)***
Ten Star Supply Co Inc 813 254-6921
7902 Hopi Pl Tampa (33634) ***(G-18183)***
Ten4 Solutions LLC 302 544-1120
2342 Laurel Rd E # 7308 Nokomis (34275) ***(G-11589)***
Tend Skin International Inc 954 382-0800
2090 Sw 71st Ter Ste G9 Davie (33317) ***(G-2602)***
Tendonease LLC 888 224-0319
1738 Sw Foxpoint Trl Palm City (34990) ***(G-13675)***
Tennessee Tool and Fixture LLC 931 954-5316
1750 Barcelona Way Winter Park (32789) ***(G-19452)***
Tennier Industries Inc (PA) 561 999-9710
950 Pnnsula Corp Cir Ste Boca Raton (33487) ***(G-746)***
Tensik Inc 954 937-9505
3955 W Lake Hamilton Dr Winter Haven (33881) ***(G-19363)***
Tensolite LLC 904 829-5600
100 Tensolite Dr Saint Augustine (32092) ***(G-15626)***
Tent Renters Supply, Tampa *Also called M & N Capital Enterprises LLC* ***(G-17868)***
Tentech Corporation 305 938-0389
7330 Nw 66th St Miami (33166) ***(G-10467)***
Tep Manufacturing Co 321 632-1417
1950 Murrell Rd Ste 5 Rockledge (32955) ***(G-15453)***
Tequesta Community Health Ctr 561 713-0798
470 Tequesta Dr Jupiter (33469) ***(G-7126)***
Ter Prints Usa Inc 305 953-7789
3613 N 29th Ave Hollywood (33020) ***(G-5922)***
Tera Industries Inc 561 848-7272
7634 Central Indus Dr Riviera Beach (33404) ***(G-15384)***
Teralife LLC 407 434-0408
5950 Lakehurst Dr Ste 249 Orlando (32819) ***(G-13248)***
Teranex Systems Inc 407 888-4300
2602 Challenger Tech Ct # 240 Orlando (32826) ***(G-13249)***
Terex Corporation 352 330-4044
3400 Ne 37th Pl Wildwood (34785) ***(G-19205)***
Terfa Litter USA Inc 416 358-4495
17720 N Bay Rd Apt 5a Sunny Isles Beach (33160) ***(G-17081)***
Terlyn Industries Inc 727 592-0772
11256 47th St N Clearwater (33762) ***(G-1916)***
Terminal Service Company 850 739-5702
2778 W Tharpe St Tallahassee (32303) ***(G-17339)***
Termine Ravioli Manufacturing (PA) 954 983-3711
5714 Johnson St Hollywood (33021) ***(G-5923)***

Terra Nova Pvers Hrdscape Slto....904 662-2999
7095 Stonelion Cir Jacksonville (32256) ***(G-6847)***
Terracassa LLC....786 581-7741
950 Nw 72nd St Unit 102 Miami (33150) ***(G-10468)***
Terrades Custom Woodworks Inc....305 316-2908
219 W 27th St Hialeah (33010) ***(G-5648)***
Terraferma USA Corporation....305 994-7892
2201 Nw 93rd Ave Doral (33172) ***(G-3528)***
Terrastone Inc....305 234-8384
8747 Sw 134th St Miami (33176) ***(G-10469)***
Terry Boca Inc....561 893-0333
512 Hillsboro Tech Dr Deerfield Beach (33441) ***(G-2925)***
Terry D Triplett Inc....561 251-3641
1103 53rd Ct S Ste B Mangonia Park (33407) ***(G-8513)***
Terry Laboratories LLC....321 259-1630
7005 Technology Dr Melbourne (32904) ***(G-8960)***
Terry M Griffin Welding....407 209-8317
18290 Hewlett Rd Orlando (32820) ***(G-13250)***
Terumo Aortic, Sunrise *Also called Bolton Medical Inc* ***(G-17100)***
Tervis Tumbler Company (PA)....941 966-2114
201 Triple Diamond Blvd North Venice (34275) ***(G-11763)***
Tes America LLC....786 393-2544
10867 Sw 235th Ln Homestead (33032) ***(G-5996)***
Tesco Equipment....954 791-9470
3400 Burris Rd Davie (33314) ***(G-2603)***
Tesco Equipment LLC....954 752-7994
3661 Nw 126th Ave Coral Springs (33065) ***(G-2322)***
Tesco of Swfl Inc....239 234-6490
3992 Prospect Ave Ste C Naples (34104) ***(G-11438)***
Tesla Inc....305 535-7596
513 Lincoln Rd Miami Beach (33139) ***(G-10719)***
Tesla Inc....754 816-3069
1949 Tigertail Blvd Dania Beach (33004) ***(G-2473)***
Tesla Inc....305 774-5965
3851 Bird Rd Ste 100 Miami (33146) ***(G-10470)***
TESS LLC (HQ)....954 583-6262
2900 Sw 2nd Ave Fort Lauderdale (33315) ***(G-4278)***
Tess Enterprises Inc....727 573-9701
13150 38th St N Clearwater (33762) ***(G-1917)***
Tesseract Sensors LLC....407 385-2498
101 Gordon St Sanford (32771) ***(G-16127)***
Testa & Sons Signs, Hollywood *Also called James Testa* ***(G-5851)***
Testmaxx Services Corporation....954 946-7100
1111 W Mcnab Rd Pompano Beach (33069) ***(G-14886)***
Tetra Process Technology....813 886-9331
5415 W Sligh Ave Ste 102 Tampa (33634) ***(G-18184)***
Teva Pharmaceuticals....954 382-7729
13900 Nw 2nd St Sunrise (33325) ***(G-17186)***
Teva Pharmaceuticals Usa Inc....305 575-6000
74 Nw 176th St Miami (33169) ***(G-10471)***
Tex Medical, Weston *Also called Oxigeno Nitrogeno Inc* ***(G-19158)***
Tex Onsite Inc....386 935-4093
2169 Ne 120th Loop Branford (32008) ***(G-1189)***
Tex Z-E Corp....305 769-0202
12815 Nw 45th Ave Opa Locka (33054) ***(G-12364)***
Tex-Coat LLC (HQ)....800 454-0340
2422 E 15th St Panama City (32405) ***(G-13955)***
Tex-Coat LLC....954 581-0771
4101 Ravenswood Rd # 218 Fort Lauderdale (33312) ***(G-4279)***
Texene LLC....305 200-5001
5860 Miami Lakes Dr E Miami Lakes (33014) ***(G-10867)***
Textron Ground Support Eqp Inc....954 359-5730
1800 Sw 34th St Fort Lauderdale (33315) ***(G-4280)***
Textured Coatings....850 360-1451
169 Griffin Blvd Panama City Beach (32413) ***(G-13985)***
Tf Defense LLC....321 961-7596
147 Toluca Dr Kissimmee (34743) ***(G-7304)***
Tfl of Orlando....407 936-1553
2586 N Orange Blossom Trl Orlando (32804) ***(G-13251)***
Tg Oil Services....407 576-9571
14520 Sw 21st St Davie (33325) ***(G-2604)***
Tg United Inc (PA)....352 799-9813
16275 Aviation Loop Dr Brooksville (34604) ***(G-1279)***
TGI, Miami *Also called Tridor Group Inc* ***(G-10506)***
Th Custom Promo Tions....407 704-7921
102 Drennen Rd Orlando (32806) ***(G-13252)***
Thaler's Printing Cetner, Lauderhill *Also called Thalers Printing Center Inc* ***(G-8122)***
Thalers Printing Center Inc....954 741-6522
4970 N University Dr Lauderhill (33351) ***(G-8122)***
Thales E-Security Inc....954 888-6200
900 S Pine Island Rd # 710 Plantation (33324) ***(G-14557)***
Thales Esecurity Inc....954 888-6200
900 S Pine Island Rd Plantation (33324) ***(G-14558)***
Thales Inflight Entertaiment....786 777-9031
6101 Blue Lagoon Dr Miami (33126) ***(G-10472)***
Thalo Assist LLC....786 340-6892
2893 Executive Park Dr # 203 Weston (33331) ***(G-19169)***
That Software Guy Inc....727 533-8109
12825 Pineforest Way W Largo (33773) ***(G-8066)***
Thatcher Chemical Company, Deland *Also called Thatcher Chemical Florida Inc* ***(G-3020)***
Thatcher Chemical Florida Inc (HQ)....386 734-3966
245 Hazen Rd Deland (32720) ***(G-3020)***
Thatcher Chemical Florida Inc....386 490-1642
2905 Inland Transport St Palmetto (34221) ***(G-13829)***
The Alluring Group Inc....800 731-2280
7451 Riviera Blvd Ste 112 Miramar (33023) ***(G-11051)***
The Boston Tea Party Kettle Co, Boca Raton *Also called Trident Trading Inc* ***(G-756)***
The Caldwell Manufacturing Co....386 418-3525
11600 Nw 173rd St Ste 110 Alachua (32615) ***(G-19)***
The Forklift Company Inc....863 595-8156
290 W Harbord St Lake Alfred (33850) ***(G-7334)***
The Hc Companies Inc....863 314-9417
2006 Fortune Blvd Sebring (33870) ***(G-16715)***
The Nanosteel Company LLC (HQ)....407 838-1427
485 N Keller Rd Ste 100 Maitland (32751) ***(G-8481)***
The Natural Light Inc....850 265-0800
1020 Arthur Dr Lynn Haven (32444) ***(G-8440)***
The Press Gazette, Milton *Also called Milton Newspapers Inc* ***(G-10935)***
The Scranton Times L P....407 377-0400
16 W Pine St Orlando (32801) ***(G-13253)***
Theater Ears Inc....561 305-0519
20423 State Road 7 Ste F1 Boca Raton (33498) ***(G-747)***
Thebestcandlescom....732 608-5081
5453 Nw 24th St Ste 1 Margate (33063) ***(G-8568)***
Theblklbl Publishing Group, Orlando *Also called Black Label Group LLC* ***(G-12521)***
Theclipcom Inc....305 599-3871
91766 Overseas Hwy Tavernier (33070) ***(G-18363)***
Theft Protection Com Corp....772 231-6677
656 Broadway St Vero Beach (32960) ***(G-18670)***
Theissen Training Systems Inc....352 490-8020
3705 Sw 42nd Ave Ste 2 Gainesville (32608) ***(G-5009)***
Themeworks Incorporated....386 454-7500
17594 High Sprng Main St High Springs (32643) ***(G-5702)***
Theory Defense Systems, Bradenton *Also called Militek Industries LLC* ***(G-1078)***
Therapeuticsmd Inc (PA)....561 961-1900
951 W Yamato Rd Ste 220 Boca Raton (33431) ***(G-748)***
Theret Bicom Inc....917 796-1443
725 Tanglewood Cir Weston (33327) ***(G-19170)***
Thermacon, West Palm Beach *Also called Vertarib Inc* ***(G-19078)***
Thermal Braze Inc....561 746-6640
231 Venus St Jupiter (33458) ***(G-7127)***
Thermal Conversion Tech Inc....904 358-3720
101 Copeland St Jacksonville (32204) ***(G-6848)***
Thermal Matrix Intl LLC....813 222-3274
101 E Kennedy Blvd # 322 Tampa (33602) ***(G-18185)***
Thermalroll.com, Wesley Chapel *Also called Force Imaging Group LLC* ***(G-18747)***
Thermo Arl US Inc (PA)....800 532-4752
1400 Northpoint Pkwy # 50 West Palm Beach (33407) ***(G-19060)***
Thermo Compaction Systems Inc....863 370-3799
5001 Gateway Blvd Ste 22 Lakeland (33811) ***(G-7820)***
Thermo Electron North Amer LLC (HQ)....561 688-8700
1400 Nrthpint Pkwy Ste 10 West Palm Beach (33407) ***(G-19061)***
Thermo Fisher Scientific....781 327-3261
13859 Progress Blvd Alachua (32615) ***(G-20)***
Thermo Fisher Scientific Inc....561 688-8700
1400 Nrthpint Pkwy Ste 10 West Palm Beach (33407) ***(G-19062)***
Thermocarbon Inc (PA)....407 834-7800
391 W Melody Ln Casselberry (32707) ***(G-1520)***
Thermodyne Powder Coating, Pensacola *Also called Foot-In-Your-mouth Inc* ***(G-14157)***
Thermotech Systems Corporation....407 290-6000
5201 N Orange Blossom Trl Orlando (32810) ***(G-13254)***
Thermoval Solenoid Valves Usa....954 835-5523
4651 Sw 51st St Ste 808 Davie (33314) ***(G-2605)***
Thetradebaycom LLC....954 607-2405
451 Conservation Dr Weston (33327) ***(G-19171)***
Thi E-Commerce LLC....352 327-4058
4414 Sw College Rd # 14 Ocala (34474) ***(G-12060)***
Thida Thai Jewelry....561 455-4249
47 E Flagler St Miami (33131) ***(G-10473)***
Thierry Brouzet Inc....727 449-0158
57 Aster St Clearwater (33767) ***(G-1918)***
Thinglobal LLC....561 923-8559
7700 Congress Ave # 1122 Boca Raton (33487) ***(G-749)***
Think Outloud Printing....239 800-3219
613 Sw Pine Island Rd Cape Coral (33991) ***(G-1485)***
Think Print, Pompano Beach *Also called Tko Print Solutions Inc* ***(G-14887)***
Thinking Foods Inc....305 433-8287
123 Nw 23rd St Miami (33127) ***(G-10474)***
Thinktech Corporation....954 501-3034
1840 Vista Way Margate (33063) ***(G-8569)***
Thomas A Glassman LLC....239 822-2219
3840 7th Ave Nw Naples (34120) ***(G-11439)***
Thomas C Gibbs Custom Cabinets....239 872-6279
12141 Clover Dr Fort Myers (33905) ***(G-4626)***
Thomas J Cola....954 846-0868
12759 Nw 15th St Sunrise (33323) ***(G-17187)***
Thomas Mix Kitchens & Baths....239 229-4323
18070 S Tamiami Trl # 13 Fort Myers (33908) ***(G-4627)***

Thomas Printworks 305 667-4149
801 N Andrews Ave Fort Lauderdale (33311) *(G-4281)*
Thomas Rley Artisans Guild Inc (PA) 239 591-3203
1510 Rail Head Blvd Naples (34110) *(G-11440)*
Thomas Sign and Awning Co Inc 727 573-7757
4590 118th Ave N Clearwater (33762) *(G-1919)*
Thomas Smith & Company Inc 863 858-2199
3828 Knights Station Rd Lakeland (33810) *(G-7821)*
Thomas United Inc 239 561-7446
12700 Metro Pkwy Ste 3 Fort Myers (33966) *(G-4628)*
Thomas White LLC 813 704-4406
1302 N Orange St Plant City (33563) *(G-14473)*
Thompson Awning & Shutter Co 904 355-1616
2036 Evergreen Ave Jacksonville (32206) *(G-6849)*
Thompson Envrmntal Mntring Ctr 321 591-7300
444 Oleander Ln Melbourne (32935) *(G-8961)*
Thompson Manufacturing Inc 239 332-0446
2700 Evans Ave Unit 1 Fort Myers (33901) *(G-4629)*
Thompson Repairs Inc 904 384-5175
4857 Dignan St Jacksonville (32254) *(G-6850)*
Thompson Sales Group Inc 239 332-0446
2700 Evans Ave Unit 1 Fort Myers (33901) *(G-4630)*
Thor Guard Inc (PA) 954 835-0900
1193 Sawgrs Corp Pkwy Sunrise (33323) *(G-17188)*
Thor Guard Weather, Sunrise *Also called Thor Guard Inc* *(G-17188)*
Thor Manufacturing Inc 866 955-8467
7050 W Palmetto Park Rd Boca Raton (33433) *(G-750)*
Thread and Ink 904 568-9688
4629 Trevor Creek Dr N Jacksonville (32257) *(G-6851)*
Thread Graphics Embroidery 407 688-7026
1731 Timber Hills Dr Deland (32724) *(G-3021)*
Thread Pit Inc 352 505-0065
2708 Ne Waldo Rd Gainesville (32609) *(G-5010)*
Threadbird LLC 407 545-6506
3715 Vineland Rd Orlando (32811) *(G-13255)*
Threattrack Security Inc (HQ) 855 885-5566
311 Park Place Blvd # 300 Clearwater (33759) *(G-1920)*
Three Brothers Boards 386 310-4927
212 S Beach St Ste 100 Daytona Beach (32114) *(G-2726)*
Three Cay G LLC 904 930-4554
5121 Bowden Rd Ste 107 Jacksonville (32216) *(G-6852)*
Three D Products Corp 954 971-6511
6889 Nw 28th Way Fort Lauderdale (33309) *(G-4282)*
Threez Company LLC (PA) 904 422-9224
1225 W Beaver St Ste 123 Jacksonville (32204) *(G-6853)*
Threez Company LLC 904 651-1444
7232 Smyrna St Jacksonville (32208) *(G-6854)*
Thrifty Nickle Want ADS, Panama City *Also called American Classifieds* *(G-13863)*
Thriller Clearwater Inc 727 389-2209
669 Lexington St Dunedin (34698) *(G-3590)*
Thriv Industries LLC 404 436-3230
402 W Atlantic Ave 65 Delray Beach (33444) *(G-3149)*
Thrive Frozen Nutrition Inc (PA) 407 960-4883
4767 New Broad St Ste 325 Orlando (32814) *(G-13256)*
Throw Raft LLC 954 366-8004
1202 Ne 8th Ave Fort Lauderdale (33304) *(G-4283)*
Thule Inc 850 584-3448
606 Industrial Park Dr Perry (32348) *(G-14317)*
Thule North America, Perry *Also called Thule Inc* *(G-14317)*
Thunder Bay Enterprises Inc 352 796-9551
5130 Broad St Brooksville (34601) *(G-1280)*
Thunder Bay Foods Corporation 727 943-0606
640 Douglas Rd E Ste A Oldsmar (34677) *(G-12271)*
Thunder Energies Corporation (HQ) 561 560-4302
111 Moorings Dr Lantana (33462) *(G-7878)*
Thunderbird Press Inc 321 269-7616
205 N Mantor Ave Titusville (32796) *(G-18468)*
Ti-Pagos Usa Inc 786 310-7423
20200 W Dixie Hwy Ste 603 Miami (33180) *(G-10475)*
Tias Milkshakes and More 954 391-8753
6768 Stirling Rd Hollywood (33024) *(G-5924)*
Tiba Enterprises Inc 561 575-3037
1601 Commerce Ln Ste 102 Jupiter (33458) *(G-7128)*
Tibor Inc 561 272-0770
255 N Congress Ave Delray Beach (33445) *(G-3150)*
Tic Light Electrical Corp 305 712-3499
11519 Sw 172nd Ter Miami (33157) *(G-10476)*
Tic Logistics, Miami *Also called Tobruk International Corp* *(G-10484)*
Ticket Drop Traffic Defense 305 332-3186
20137 Ne 16th Pl Miami (33179) *(G-10477)*
Tidal Wave Tanks Fabrications 863 425-7795
3275 Mulford Rd Mulberry (33860) *(G-11139)*
Tides Marine Inc 954 420-0949
3251 Sw 13th Dr Ste A Deerfield Beach (33442) *(G-2926)*
Tidwells Orthotics and Prosthe 954 346-5402
4450 Nw 126th Ave Ste 106 Coral Springs (33065) *(G-2323)*
Tie Collection LLC 305 323-1420
8071 Westfield Cir Vero Beach (32966) *(G-18671)*
Tielve Cabinetsinc 561 267-3740
2122 Tarragon Rd West Palm Beach (33415) *(G-19063)*
Tienda Maya 561 965-0900
6082 S Congress Ave Lake Worth (33462) *(G-7591)*
Tier5 Technical Services 904 435-3484
16167 Kayla Cove Ct Jacksonville (32218) *(G-6855)*
Tifco Industries Freedom Alloy 407 474-6747
651 Fox Hunt Cir Longwood (32750) *(G-8342)*
Tiffany and Associates Inc 386 252-7351
500 Mason Ave Daytona Beach (32117) *(G-2727)*
Tiffany Quilting & Drapery 407 834-6386
206 E Palmetto Ave Longwood (32750) *(G-8343)*
Tig Technologies Inc 561 691-3633
4250 Bandy Blvd Fort Pierce (34981) *(G-4755)*
Tiger Business Forms Inc 305 888-3528
7765 W 20th Ave Hialeah (33014) *(G-5649)*
Tiger Composites Inc 386 334-0941
1531 Airway Cir New Smyrna Beach (32168) *(G-11547)*
Tiger Meat & Provisions, Miami *Also called La Montina Inc* *(G-9844)*
Tiger/Southland, Hialeah *Also called Tiger Business Forms Inc* *(G-5649)*
Tightails, Sebastian *Also called Ionemoto Inc* *(G-16663)*
Tightline Publications Inc 954 570-7174
2795 Sw 11th Pl Deerfield Beach (33442) *(G-2927)*
Tigo Inc 954 935-5990
5967 Nw 31st Ave Fort Lauderdale (33309) *(G-4284)*
Tikal Pavers Inc 850 892-2207
5991 Coy Burgess Loop Defuniak Springs (32435) *(G-2949)*
Tiki Water Sports Inc 305 852-9298
94.5 Ocean Side Key Largo (33037) *(G-7175)*
Tikore Industries LLC 954 616-5902
14397 Sw 143rd Ct Ste 106 Miami (33186) *(G-10478)*
Tim Gardners Vitamart Inc (PA) 813 908-7843
3001 N Rocky Point Dr E Tampa (33607) *(G-18186)*
Tim Hardy Plaster Moldings LLC 239 877-8434
232 Palm Dr Apt 2 Naples (34112) *(G-11441)*
Timber Creek Distilling Llc 408 439-0973
146 Country Club Dr W Destin (32541) *(G-3208)*
Timbercraft of Naples Inc 239 566-2559
802 Tallow Tree Ct Naples (34108) *(G-11442)*
Timberland Door LLC 727 539-8600
12555 Entp Blvd Ste 102 Largo (33773) *(G-8067)*
Timberwolf Cabinetry 561 389-5782
530 Business Park Way # 7 Royal Palm Beach (33411) *(G-15478)*
Timberwolf Organics Ltd Lblty 407 877-8779
13506 Summerport Vlg Pkwy Windermere (34786) *(G-19246)*
Timburr Express LLC 850 535-1488
3765 Highway 79 Vernon (32462) *(G-18587)*
Time 4 Learning, Fort Lauderdale *Also called Vkidz Inc* *(G-4310)*
Time Adjusters Conference Inc 386 274-4210
5807 Spruce Creek Wods Dr Port Orange (32127) *(G-15039)*
Time Finance Adjusters, Port Orange *Also called Time Adjusters Conference Inc* *(G-15039)*
Time Industries Inc 321 676-2080
709 Silver Palm Ave Ste J Melbourne (32901) *(G-8962)*
Time Is Money Campaign LLC 352 255-5273
16750 Abbey Hill Ct Clermont (34711) *(G-1975)*
Time Printing Co Inc 904 396-9967
3504 Saint Augustine Rd Jacksonville (32207) *(G-6856)*
Timeless Reflections, Orlando *Also called Art & Frame Direct Inc* *(G-12491)*
Timeless Treasures Doll Club 813 854-6208
12020 Steppingstone Blvd Tampa (33635) *(G-18187)*
Times Holding Co (HQ) 727 893-8111
490 1st Ave S Saint Petersburg (33701) *(G-15938)*
Times Media Services Inc 727 893-8111
490 1st Ave S Saint Petersburg (33701) *(G-15939)*
Times Microwave Systems Inc 203 949-8400
2400 Cntre Pk W Dr Ste 10 West Palm Beach (33409) *(G-19064)*
Times Printing, Quincy *Also called Gadsden County Times Inc* *(G-15250)*
Times Publishing Company (HQ) 727 893-8111
490 1st Ave S Saint Petersburg (33701) *(G-15940)*
Times Publishing Company 727 849-6397
11321 Us Highway 19 Port Richey (34668) *(G-15072)*
Times Publishing Company 850 224-7263
336 E College Ave Ste 303 Tallahassee (32301) *(G-17340)*
Times Publishing Company 352 567-6660
301 W Main St Inverness (34450) *(G-6097)*
Timilon Corporation 239 330-9650
24301 Walden Center Dr # 101 Bonita Springs (34134) *(G-862)*
Timus Inc 904 614-4342
8131 Baymeadows Cir Jacksonville (32256) *(G-6857)*
Tin Cup Catering, Ocala *Also called Ashtin Inc* *(G-11880)*
Tin Man Co 305 365-1926
2828 Coral Way Ste 207 Coral Gables (33145) *(G-2198)*
Tin Man Mobile Welding LLC 239 465-9058
830 93rd Ave N Naples (34108) *(G-11443)*
Tin-Rez Corp Inc 561 654-3133
6615 Boynton Beach Blvd Boynton Beach (33437) *(G-969)*
Tinfoil Hats LLC 407 844-0578
11858 Sw 100th Ter Miami (33186) *(G-10479)*
Tintometer Inc (HQ) 941 756-6410
6456 Parkland Dr Sarasota (34243) *(G-16310)*

ALPHABETIC

Tip Top Canvas and Uphl Inc......954 524-6214
6501 E Tropical Way Plantation (33317) *(G-14559)*
Tip Top Prtg of Volusia Cnty......386 760-7701
1325 Beville Rd Daytona Beach (32119) *(G-2728)*
Tip Tops of America Inc......352 357-9559
100 S Bay St Eustis (32726) *(G-3718)*
Tiptops Inc......352 357-9559
100 S Bay St Eustis (32726) *(G-3719)*
Tire Experts LLC......305 663-3508
10903 Nw 122nd St Medley (33178) *(G-8735)*
Tiregraficx, Orlando *Also called Eminel Corporation Inc (G-12709)*
Tita Itln Import & Export LLC......305 608-4258
1408 Nw 23rd St Miami (33142) *(G-10480)*
Titan America LLC......386 734-5526
407 N Spring Garden Ave Deland (32720) *(G-3022)*
Titan America LLC......561 842-5309
1453 53rd St Mangonia Park (33407) *(G-8514)*
Titan America LLC......305 761-1944
11955 Nw 102nd Rd Medley (33178) *(G-8736)*
Titan America LLC......954 481-2800
10100 Nw 121st Way Medley (33178) *(G-8737)*
Titan America LLC......954 426-8407
455 Fairway Dr Ste 200 Deerfield Beach (33441) *(G-2928)*
Titan America LLC......305 364-2200
10100 Nw 121st Way Medley (33178) *(G-8738)*
Titan Florida, Medley *Also called Titan America LLC (G-8738)*
Titan Florida LLC......800 588-3939
10100 Nw 121st Way Medley (33178) *(G-8739)*
Titan Industries......904 608-3905
3470 Peoria Rd Orange Park (32065) *(G-12409)*
Titan Metalworks Inc......904 503-2941
8350 Arlington Expy Jacksonville (32211) *(G-6858)*
Titan Metalworks LLC......904 574-9828
8531 Alton Ave Jacksonville (32211) *(G-6859)*
Titan Mfg Inc......239 939-5152
6381 Metro Plantation Rd Fort Myers (33966) *(G-4631)*
Titan Natural Focus Corp......305 778-7005
2701 Vista Pkwy West Palm Beach (33411) *(G-19065)*
Titan Oil Tools LLC......941 356-3010
8466 Lockwood Ridge Rd Sarasota (34243) *(G-16311)*
Titan Petroleum Corporation......813 280-4833
4830 W Kennedy Blvd # 60 Tampa (33609) *(G-18188)*
Titan Service Industry Llc......678 313-4707
2044 Anchor Ave Deland (32720) *(G-3023)*
Titan Specialty Cnstr Inc......850 916-7660
8188 Armstrong Rd Milton (32583) *(G-10943)*
Titan Sunrooms, Milton *Also called Titan Specialty Cnstr Inc (G-10943)*
Titan Tools LLC......818 984-1001
2622 Flournoy Cir S # 23 Clearwater (33764) *(G-1921)*
Titan Trailers LLC......813 298-8597
2406 E State Road 60 Valrico (33595) *(G-18525)*
Titanic Brewing Company Inc......305 668-1742
5813 Ponce De Leon Blvd Coral Gables (33146) *(G-2199)*
Titanic Restaurant & Brewery, Coral Gables *Also called Titanic Brewing Company Inc (G-2199)*
Titanium 22 Productions......310 962-0937
800 W 42nd St Apt 1b Miami Beach (33140) *(G-10720)*
Titanium Dance Challenge LLC......813 340-0903
4045 Shoreside Cir Tampa (33624) *(G-18189)*
Titanium Development LLC......407 844-8664
3209 Prkchster Sq Blvd Ap Orlando (32835) *(G-13257)*
Titanium Endeavors LLC......321 728-9732
2205 Botanica Cir Melbourne (32904) *(G-8963)*
Titanium Fusion Tech LLC......435 881-5742
8501 Amber Oak Dr Orlando (32817) *(G-13258)*
Titanium Gymnastics and Cheerl......813 659-2204
402 W Ball St Plant City (33563) *(G-14474)*
Titanium Gynmastics & Cheer......813 689-2200
7017 Lithia Pinecrest Rd Lithia (33547) *(G-8224)*
Titanium Integration LLC......561 775-1898
11211 Prosperity Farms Rd Palm Beach Gardens (33410) *(G-13632)*
Titanium Laser Tech Inc......956 279-0638
4463 Kingslynn Rd Niceville (32578) *(G-11575)*
Titanium Pavers, Orlando *Also called Titanium Development LLC (G-13257)*
Titanium Performance LLC......407 712-5770
1233 Valley Creek Run Winter Park (32792) *(G-19453)*
Titanium Prof Hyraulics......917 929-5044
1853 Sw 31st Ave Hallandale (33009) *(G-5162)*
Titanium Real Estate LLC......863 808-0445
1543 Lakeland Hills Blvd Lakeland (33805) *(G-7822)*
Titanium Tech Corp......407 912-9126
6373 Conroy Rd Orlando (32835) *(G-13259)*
Titans Protective Coatings LLC......561 370-2085
150 Evernia St Jupiter (33458) *(G-7129)*
Titans USA Ltd......727 290-9897
4371 112th Ter N Clearwater (33762) *(G-1922)*
Tite-Dri Industries, Boynton Beach *Also called Premium Absrbent Dspsables LLC (G-944)*
TJ Cabinetry Inc......407 886-8294
4333 Silver Star Rd # 14 Orlando (32808) *(G-13260)*
Tj Cabinetry Inc......407 801-5124
2312 Clark St Ste 3 Apopka (32703) *(G-191)*
Tk - Autek Inc......727 572-7473
270 Foxcroft Dr E Palm Harbor (34683) *(G-13766)*
Tk Cabinets......386 325-6906
500 N Pine St Palatka (32177) *(G-13496)*
Tk Defense Solutions Inc......727 365-6823
5819 10th St N Saint Petersburg (33703) *(G-15941)*
TK Tires & Wheels Inc......321 473-8945
2400 S Harbor City Blvd Melbourne (32901) *(G-8964)*
Tko Print Solutions Inc......954 315-0990
140 Park Central Blvd S Pompano Beach (33064) *(G-14887)*
Tks Printing & Promo Products......904 469-0968
3107 Spring Glen Rd Ste 2 Jacksonville (32207) *(G-6860)*
TL Fahringer Co Inc......813 681-2373
10103 Cedar Run Tampa (33619) *(G-18190)*
TLC Food Truck LLC......305 879-2488
8602 Nw 22nd Ave Miami (33147) *(G-10481)*
Tld LLC......813 927-7554
14512 N Nebraska Ave Tampa (33613) *(G-18191)*
Tm Marketing Group LLC......954 848-9955
3200 S Andrews Ave # 100 Fort Lauderdale (33316) *(G-4285)*
Tm USA Inc......954 801-4649
1628 Nw 82nd Ave Doral (33126) *(G-3529)*
Tmarketing Products, Tampa *Also called Tropical Enterprises Intl (G-18202)*
TMC, Fort Lauderdale *Also called Manning Company (G-4111)*
Tmf Plastic Solutions LLC......941 748-2946
4690 19th Street Ct E Bradenton (34203) *(G-1126)*
Tmg Manufacturing Corp......813 464-2299
5517 W Sligh Ave Ste 100 Tampa (33634) *(G-18192)*
TMI, Jacksonville *Also called Too Many Ideas Inc (G-6862)*
TMMR Holdings LLC (PA)......407 295-5200
301 Enterprise St Unit A Ocoee (34761) *(G-12092)*
Tms Enterprises LLC......850 539-2500
102 Technology Way Havana (32333) *(G-5240)*
Tmt Printing & Mailing, Gulf Breeze *Also called Town Street Print Shop Inc (G-5130)*
TN Cruz, Miami *Also called Whole Coffee Company LLC (G-10604)*
Tni Manufacturing Inc (PA)......954 742-5988
4635 Nw 103rd Ave Sunrise (33351) *(G-17189)*
TNT, Tampa *Also called Shirley Simon & Associates LLC (G-18097)*
TNT Custom Cabinetry Inc......561 662-0964
11093 49th St N West Palm Beach (33411) *(G-19066)*
TNT Custom Marine Inc (PA)......305 931-3157
3030 Ne 188th St Miami (33180) *(G-10482)*
TNT Packaging Inc......305 769-0616
17375 Ne 7th Ave Miami (33162) *(G-10483)*
TNT Supplements, Leesburg *Also called Total Nutrition Technology LLC (G-8178)*
Tobruk International Corp......305 406-0263
6970 Nw 50th St Miami (33166) *(G-10484)*
Today Magazines Group, Ocala *Also called Special Publications Inc (G-12056)*
Todays Frozen Desserts Inc......305 994-9940
7156 Nw 50th St Miami (33166) *(G-10485)*
Todays Restaurant News Inc......561 620-8888
6165 Old Court Rd Apt 224 Boca Raton (33433) *(G-751)*
Todo En Uno......305 263-6934
6601 W Flagler St Miami (33144) *(G-10486)*
Toledo Doors Inc......305 633-4352
4710 Nw 37th Ave Miami (33142) *(G-10487)*
Toledo Iron Works, Miami *Also called Toledo Doors Inc (G-10487)*
Toledo Sales Inc......305 389-3441
835 Nw 7th Street Rd Miami (33136) *(G-10488)*
Tolliver Aluminum Service Inc......561 582-8939
6810 Georgia Ave West Palm Beach (33405) *(G-19067)*
Tolliver Powder Coating, West Palm Beach *Also called Tolliver Aluminum Service Inc (G-19067)*
Tom & Company LLC......321 917-0760
1101 W Hibiscus Blvd # 10 Melbourne (32901) *(G-8965)*
Tom Burke Services......863 940-4504
6244 Troi Ln Lakeland (33813) *(G-7823)*
Tom George Yacht Group......727 734-8707
17166 Us Highway 19 N Clearwater (33764) *(G-1923)*
Tom James Company......813 204-9699
2005 Pan Am Cir Ste 110 Tampa (33607) *(G-18193)*
Tom Watson Enterprises Inc......352 683-5097
9629 Amilia Dr Ste 4 Hudson (34667) *(G-6040)*
Tom's Instant Printing, Jacksonville *Also called Toms Instant Printing Inc (G-6861)*
Tomasa Healthy Passion, Hialeah *Also called Sunsof Inc (G-5641)*
Tomatoes & Olive Oil LLC......941 822-9709
1055 Us Highway 41 Byp S Venice (34285) *(G-18580)*
TOMI Aircraft Inc......863 446-3001
1310 Flight Line Blvd Deland (32724) *(G-3024)*
Tommy & Giordy Buy/Sell......786 797-6973
15060 Nw 22nd Ave Opa Locka (33054) *(G-12365)*
Toms Instant Printing Inc......904 396-0686
3100 Beach Blvd Jacksonville (32207) *(G-6861)*
Tomsons Inc (PA)......248 646-0677
6520 Manasota Key Rd Englewood (34223) *(G-3685)*

Tonbo Imaging Inc...814 441-0475
1351 Sawgrs Corp Pkwy # 104 Sunrise (33323) ***(G-17190)***
Tone Printing LLC (PA)...855 505-8663
1221 Brickell Ave Fl 9 Miami (33131) ***(G-10489)***
Toner Cartridge Recharge Inc...305 968-1045
7923 Nw 163rd Ter Miami Lakes (33016) ***(G-10868)***
Toner City Corp...954 945-5392
4137 Stirling Rd Apt 103 Davie (33314) ***(G-2606)***
Toner Technologies Inc...561 547-9710
2900 Commerce Park Dr # 11 Boynton Beach (33426) ***(G-970)***
Toners Plus LLC...407 756-5787
1969 S Alafaya Trl 218 Orlando (32828) ***(G-13261)***
Tonertype Inc...813 915-1300
5100 W Cypress St Tampa (33607) ***(G-18194)***
Tony Doukas Racing, Punta Gorda *Also called T D R Inc* ***(G-15241)***
Too Many Ideas Inc...904 396-9245
1712 Hendricks Ave Jacksonville (32207) ***(G-6862)***
Toogle Industries LLC...863 688-8975
127 N Lake Parker Ave Lakeland (33801) ***(G-7824)***
Toolinghouse Inc...239 424-8503
1136 Ne Pine Island Rd Cape Coral (33909) ***(G-1486)***
Tools & More, Brooksville *Also called Woodcrafts By Angel Inc* ***(G-1293)***
Tooter Lingo Liquer, Cocoa *Also called Mango Bottling Inc* ***(G-2034)***
Top 10 Floors, Tampa *Also called Proximity Mills LLC* ***(G-18022)***
Top Cters Ycht Restoration LLC...561 818-9259
11852 61st St N West Palm Beach (33412) ***(G-19068)***
Top Drawer Inc...305 620-1102
5190 Nw 165th St Miami Lakes (33014) ***(G-10869)***
Top Drawer Cabinetry & Carpent...772 370-4624
4101 S Indian River Dr Fort Pierce (34982) ***(G-4756)***
Top Drawer Printers Inc...305 620-1102
5190 Nw 165th St Miami Lakes (33014) ***(G-10870)***
Top Drinks USA Corp...305 407-3514
3550 Biscayne Blvd # 507 Miami (33137) ***(G-10490)***
Top Hat Food Services LLC...630 825-2800
11799 Granite Woods Loop Venice (34292) ***(G-18581)***
Top Kitchen Cabinets...305 392-9938
12650 Nw 107th Ave Medley (33178) ***(G-8740)***
Top Line Installation Inc...352 636-4192
2134 Aitkin Loop Leesburg (34748) ***(G-8177)***
Top Notch Diecutting Foil STA...904 346-3511
4246 Saint Augustine Rd Jacksonville (32207) ***(G-6863)***
Top Notch Wood Works Inc...954 445-7861
526 Nw 43rd Pl Miami (33126) ***(G-10491)***
Top of The Line Coating Inc...407 485-8546
13209 Briar Forest Ct Orlando (32828) ***(G-13262)***
Top Optical Lab...305 662-2893
4444 Sw 71st Ave Ste 111 Miami (33155) ***(G-10492)***
Top Quality Finishers Inc...305 688-8174
2780 Nw 122nd St Miami (33167) ***(G-10493)***
Top Quality Yacht Refinishing...954 522-5232
1513 Sw 18th Ave Fort Lauderdale (33312) ***(G-4286)***
Top Sales Co...561 852-4311
17047 Boca Club Blvd 141b Boca Raton (33487) ***(G-752)***
Top Shelf Custom Cabinetry (PA)...941 726-2393
3365 Spring Mill Cir Sarasota (34239) ***(G-16621)***
Top Spec US Inc...904 345-0814
1650 Margaret St Jacksonville (32204) ***(G-6864)***
Top Torch Wldg & Fabrication...352 835-1174
4326 Hedgewood Ave Spring Hill (34608) ***(G-16868)***
Top Trtment Cstomes Accesories...239 936-4600
50 Mildred Dr Unit A Fort Myers (33901) ***(G-4632)***
Topflite Components, Miami *Also called Topflite Manufacturing Inc* ***(G-10494)***
Topflite Manufacturing Inc...800 219-2601
14262 Sw 140th St Ste 108 Miami (33186) ***(G-10494)***
Tophet-Blyth LLC...239 594-5477
1415 Panther Ln Ste 402 Naples (34109) ***(G-11444)***
Topline Cstm Fabrications LLC...850 295-2481
14781 Radcliff Grade Perry (32348) ***(G-14318)***
Topline Hy-Lift Johnson Inc (PA)...352 799-4668
2251 Topline Way Brooksville (34604) ***(G-1281)***
Topline Machine & Tool LLC...352 799-4668
2251 Topline Way Brooksville (34604) ***(G-1282)***
Topline Prtg & Graphics Inc...561 881-2267
1401 W 13th St Ste 104 Riviera Beach (33404) ***(G-15385)***
Tops Cabinet...954 544-2006
2500 Sw 30th Ave Hallandale (33009) ***(G-5163)***
Tops Kitchen Cabinet LLC...954 933-9988
1900 Nw 18th St Pompano Beach (33069) ***(G-14888)***
Tops Software...813 960-8300
2495 Entp Rd Ste 201 Clearwater (33763) ***(G-1924)***
Torque Technologies Products...630 462-1188
1623 W University Pkwy Sarasota (34243) ***(G-16312)***
Torres & Tavara Coating LLC...904 520-9910
705 Putters Green Way S Jacksonville (32259) ***(G-6936)***
Torrington Brush Works Inc (PA)...941 355-1499
4377 Independence Ct Sarasota (34234) ***(G-16622)***
Torro Foods LLC...305 558-3212
6725 Main St Miami Lakes (33014) ***(G-10871)***
Tortilla Bay...941 778-3663
5318 Marina Dr Holmes Beach (34217) ***(G-5947)***
Tortilleria America Inc...239 462-2175
2853 Work Dr Ste 1-2 Fort Myers (33916) ***(G-4633)***
Tortilleria Dona Chela...941 953-4045
1155 N Washington Blvd Sarasota (34236) ***(G-16623)***
Tortilleria El Triunfo LLC...954 270-7832
3981 Sw 12th Ct Fort Lauderdale (33312) ***(G-4287)***
Tortilleria Gallo De Oro...561 503-3751
1302 Lake Ave Ste 2 Lake Worth (33460) ***(G-7592)***
Tortilleria Gallo De Oro LLC...561 818-7829
3511 Se Dixie Hwy Stuart (34997) ***(G-17035)***
Tortilleria La Rancherita...941 747-7949
3010 14th St W Bradenton (34205) ***(G-1127)***
Tortilleria Lamexicana 7 Inc...407 324-3100
2715 S Orlando Dr Sanford (32773) ***(G-16128)***
TOS Manufacturing Inc...407 330-3880
4280 Saint Johns Pkwy Sanford (32771) ***(G-16129)***
Total Koatings Inc...941 870-0369
8161 Misty Oaks Blvd Sarasota (34243) ***(G-16313)***
Total Ntrtn & Therapeutics PA...352 259-5190
809 Highway 466 Ste 202c Lady Lake (32159) ***(G-7329)***
Total Nutrition Technology LLC...352 435-0050
154 Park Center St Ste A Leesburg (34748) ***(G-8178)***
Total of Florida...239 768-9400
12881 Metro Pkwy Fort Myers (33966) ***(G-4634)***
Total Pavers Corp...561 902-7665
2529 Sw Grotto Cir Port Saint Lucie (34953) ***(G-15154)***
Total Performance Inc...203 265-5667
75 N Lakewalk Dr Palm Coast (32137) ***(G-13713)***
Total Print Inc...772 589-9658
1132 Us Highway 1 Sebastian (32958) ***(G-16673)***
Total Sign Solutions...561 264-2551
7655 Enterprise Dr Ste A8 Riviera Beach (33404) ***(G-15386)***
Total Spcalty Publications LLC (PA)...813 405-2610
1715 N West Shore Blvd # 266 Tampa (33607) ***(G-18195)***
Total Vision Design Group...407 438-6933
7552 10th Chancellor Dr Orlando (32809) ***(G-13263)***
Total Window Inc...954 921-0109
1249 Stirling Rd Ste 15 Dania (33004) ***(G-2459)***
Totally Bananas LLC...954 674-9421
5081 S State Road 7 # 803 Davie (33314) ***(G-2607)***
Totally Glass & Blinds Llc...561 929-6125
1027 Egremont Dr West Palm Beach (33406) ***(G-19069)***
Totally Products LLC...786 942-9218
1101 S Rogers Cir Ste 10 Boca Raton (33487) ***(G-753)***
Totally Storage Inc...407 472-6000
59 Skyline Dr Ste 1550 Lake Mary (32746) ***(G-7455)***
Totalprint USA...855 915-1300
5100 W Cypress St Tampa (33607) ***(G-18196)***
Toteum All Trckg Trnsprting L...888 506-5890
5401 S Kirkman Rd Ste 310 Orlando (32819) ***(G-13264)***
Toti Media Inc...239 472-0205
2422 Palm Ridge Rd # 103 Sanibel (33957) ***(G-16150)***
Toucanvas, Fort Myers *Also called Nite-Bright Sign Company Inc* ***(G-4547)***
Touche Software LLC...786 241-9907
15616 Sw 62nd St Miami (33193) ***(G-10495)***
Touchless Cover LLC...407 679-2217
10150 Central Port Dr Orlando (32824) ***(G-13265)***
Touchpoint Group Holdings Inc...305 420-6640
4300 Biscayne Blvd # 203 Miami (33137) ***(G-10496)***
Touchpoint Medical Inc (PA)...813 854-1905
2200 Touchpoint Dr Odessa (33556) ***(G-12159)***
Tow Times, Winter Springs *Also called T T Publications Inc* ***(G-19486)***
Tower Optical Corporation...561 740-2525
3600 S Congress Ave Ste J Boynton Beach (33426) ***(G-971)***
Tower Publications Inc...352 372-5468
4400 Nw 36th Ave Gainesville (32606) ***(G-5011)***
Town Crier Newspaper, Wellington *Also called Newspaper Publishers Inc* ***(G-18725)***
Town Street Print Shop Inc...850 432-8300
1142 Bayview Ln Gulf Breeze (32563) ***(G-5130)***
Townley Engineering & Mfg Co, Candler *Also called Townley Engrg & Mfg Co Inc* ***(G-1332)***
Townley Engrg & Mfg Co Inc (PA)...352 687-3001
10551 Se 110th St Rd Candler (32111) ***(G-1332)***
Townley Foundry & Mch Co Inc...352 687-3001
10551 Se 110th St Rd Candler (32111) ***(G-1333)***
Townsend Ceramics & Glass Inc...321 269-5671
3535 South St Titusville (32780) ***(G-18469)***
Townsend Signs Inc...386 255-1955
515 Lpga Blvd Holly Hill (32117) ***(G-5761)***
Townsend's, Titusville *Also called Townsend Ceramics & Glass Inc* ***(G-18469)***
Toyops, Pensacola *Also called Triops Inc* ***(G-14276)***
Toys For Boys Miami LLC...786 464-0160
1924 N Miami Ave Miami (33136) ***(G-10497)***
TP Aerospace Technics LLC (HQ)...407 730-9988
6470 Narcoossee Rd Ste A Orlando (32822) ***(G-13266)***
Tpg Black LLC...561 777-8989
2108 Corporate Dr Boynton Beach (33426) ***(G-972)***
Tpi Aluminum...239 332-3900
5612 6th Ave Fort Myers (33907) ***(G-4635)***

ALPHABETIC

Tpi Engineered Systems Inc........727 233-2810
17726 Meridian Blvd Hudson (34667) ***(G-6041)***
TPL Manufacturing Inc........954 783-3400
461 Ne 27th St Pompano Beach (33064) ***(G-14889)***
Tpr Systems Inc........850 983-8600
8100 Armstrong Rd Milton (32583) ***(G-10944)***
Tqmuch, Doral *Also called Bella Vista Bakery Inc* ***(G-3266)***
Tra Publishing LLP........305 424-6468
245 Ne 37th St Miami (33137) ***(G-10498)***
Trac Ecological America Inc........954 583-4922
1103 Old Griffin Rd Dania (33004) ***(G-2460)***
Tracking Solutions Corp........877 477-2922
7791 Nw 46th St Ste 306 Doral (33166) ***(G-3530)***
Trackmaster LLC........727 333-7562
22001 Us Highway 19 N Clearwater (33765) ***(G-1925)***
Tracto Parts Corp........305 972-1357
7401 Nw 68th St Ste 122 Miami (33166) ***(G-10499)***
Tracy Publishing LLC........561 799-4690
4025 Community Dr Jupiter (33458) ***(G-7130)***
Tradeland Americas Inc........786 718-1490
7900 Sw 57th Ave Ste 24 South Miami (33143) ***(G-16831)***
Trademark Components Inc........813 948-2233
21432 Keating Way Lutz (33549) ***(G-8421)***
Tradepak Inc........305 871-2247
4041 Nw 25th St A Miami (33142) ***(G-10500)***
Tradestation Technologies Inc (HQ)........954 652-7000
8050 Sw 10th St Ste 2000 Plantation (33324) ***(G-14560)***
Tradewind Custom Cabinetry LLC........239 257-3295
1213 Cape Coral Pkwy E Cape Coral (33904) ***(G-1487)***
Tradewinds Power Corp........863 382-2166
2717 Alt Us Hwy 27 S Sebring (33870) ***(G-16716)***
Tradewinds Power Corp (HQ)........305 592-9745
5820 Nw 84th Ave Doral (33166) ***(G-3531)***
Trading Company, The, Largo *Also called Ttc-The Trading Company Inc* ***(G-8069)***
Trading Post of Central Fla........954 675-2149
7626 Nw 25th St Margate (33063) ***(G-8570)***
Tradingflex Inc........877 522-3535
1395 Brickell Ave Ste 800 Miami (33131) ***(G-10501)***
Trafalger Communications Inc........941 365-7702
331 S Pineapple Ave Sarasota (34236) ***(G-16624)***
Traffic Control Pdts Fla Inc........813 621-8484
4020 Edison Ave Fort Myers (33916) ***(G-4636)***
Traffic Control Pdts Fla Inc........407 521-6777
249 N Ivey Ln Ste A Orlando (32811) ***(G-13267)***
Traffic Control Pdts Fla Inc........352 372-7088
5639 Witten Rd Jacksonville (32254) ***(G-6865)***
Traffipax LLC........561 881-7400
16490 Innovation Dr Jupiter (33478) ***(G-7131)***
Trailblazerai Inc........727 859-2732
10460 Rsvelt Blvd N 298 Saint Petersburg (33716) ***(G-15942)***
Trailer 1, Port Saint Lucie *Also called Sterling Facility Services LLC* ***(G-15148)***
Trailer Source, The, Ocala *Also called U-Dump Trailers LLC* ***(G-12065)***
Trailmate Inc........941 739-5743
6600 Suemac Pl Jacksonville (32254) ***(G-6866)***
Traincat Model Sales Inc........954 385-8999
3709 Heron Ridge Ln Weston (33331) ***(G-19172)***
Trainor Metal Products Inc........561 395-5520
171 Nw 16th St Boca Raton (33432) ***(G-754)***
Trak Engineering Incorporated........850 878-4585
2901 Crescent Dr Tallahassee (32301) ***(G-17341)***
Trakka USA LLC........505 345-0270
4725 Lena Rd Unit 103 Bradenton (34211) ***(G-1128)***
Trane Central America Inc........305 592-8646
7650 Nw 19th St Ste 270 Miami (33126) ***(G-10502)***
Trane Technologies Company LLC........850 873-8200
200 Aberdeen Loop Panama City (32405) ***(G-13956)***
Trane US Inc........239 277-0344
14241 Jtport Loop W Ste 1 Fort Myers (33913) ***(G-4637)***
Trane US Inc........954 499-6900
2884 Corporate Way Miramar (33025) ***(G-11052)***
Trann Technologies Inc........888 668-6700
12526 Us Hwy 90 Mossy Head (32434) ***(G-11094)***
Trans - Cem Dade City, Dade City *Also called New Line Transport LLC* ***(G-2432)***
Trans-Resources LLC........305 933-8301
17780 Collins Ave Sunny Isles Beach (33160) ***(G-17082)***
Transaction Data Systems Inc........407 295-5050
1555 Boren Dr Ocoee (34761) ***(G-12093)***
Transamerica Intl Brdcstg........305 477-0973
3100 Nw 72nd Ave Ste 112 Miami (33122) ***(G-10503)***
Transand, Crestview *Also called G2c Enterprises Inc* ***(G-2349)***
Transdermal Technologies Inc........561 848-2345
521 Northlake Blvd Ste B North Palm Beach (33408) ***(G-11727)***
Transition of Slc Inc........772 461-4486
7300 Commercial Cir Fort Pierce (34951) ***(G-4757)***
Transitions Lenses, Pinellas Park *Also called Transitions Optical Inc* ***(G-14392)***
Transitions Optical Inc........727 545-0400
9251 Belcher Rd N Ste B Pinellas Park (33782) ***(G-14392)***
Transmotion Medical, Ocala *Also called Winco Mfg LLC* ***(G-12076)***
Transport A/C Inc........954 254-4822
91 S Madison Dr Pensacola (32505) ***(G-14274)***
Transport PC USA Inc........813 264-1700
1423 Baythorn Dr Wesley Chapel (33543) ***(G-18760)***
Transprtation Ctrl Systems Inc........813 630-2800
1030 S 86th St Tampa (33619) ***(G-18197)***
Transtat Equipment Inc........407 857-2040
510 Thorpe Rd Orlando (32824) ***(G-13268)***
Trap World LLC........305 517-5676
2125 Biscayne Blvd # 400 Miami (33137) ***(G-10504)***
Trash Express SW Inc........239 340-5291
3040 Oasis Grand Blvd # 2104 Fort Myers (33916) ***(G-4638)***
Trasport John........321 452-6789
645 S Plumosa St Ste 5 Merritt Island (32952) ***(G-9016)***
Trauma Tattoos, Winter Park *Also called Simetri Inc* ***(G-19445)***
Traveling Canvas Corporation........305 259-2001
15400 Sw 67th Ct Palmetto Bay (33157) ***(G-13855)***
Travis Lh LLC........863 967-0628
1800 42nd St Nw Winter Haven (33881) ***(G-19364)***
Treace Medical Concepts Inc........904 373-5940
203 Fort Wade Rd Unit 150 Ponte Vedra (32081) ***(G-14928)***
Treadstone Performance........305 972-9600
10340 Sw 187th St Cutler Bay (33157) ***(G-2415)***
Treadstone Prfmce Engrg Inc........888 789-4586
9486 Sw 222nd Ln Cutler Bay (33190) ***(G-2416)***
Treadway Industries LLC........352 326-3313
410 Virginia St Minneola (34715) ***(G-10957)***
Treasure Cast Prenting Mag Inc........772 672-8588
2162 Nw Reserve Park Trce Port Saint Lucie (34986) ***(G-15155)***
Treasure Chest of Sweetwater........407 788-0020
2901 W State Road 434 # 121 Longwood (32779) ***(G-8344)***
Treasure Coast Canvas........772 210-2588
6538 Se Federal Hwy Stuart (34997) ***(G-17036)***
Treasure Coast Machines Inc........772 283-2024
3081 Se Slater St Stuart (34997) ***(G-17037)***
Treasure Coast Publishing Inc........772 221-4289
1939 S Federal Hwy Stuart (34994) ***(G-17038)***
Treasure Coast Seadoo Yamaha, Stuart *Also called Power Sports Treasure Coast* ***(G-16992)***
Treasure Coast Sealing Co........772 834-5014
8949 Se Bridge Rd Hobe Sound (33455) ***(G-5729)***
Treasure Coastline, Fort Lauderdale *Also called Gulfstream Media Group Inc* ***(G-4035)***
Treasure Cove II Inc........941 966-2004
8927 S Tamiami Trl Sarasota (34238) ***(G-16625)***
Treasure CST Curb & Therm Plas........772 287-0391
2580 Sw Hidden Pond Way Palm City (34990) ***(G-13676)***
Treasured Photo Gifts LLC........407 324-4816
107 Commerce St Lake Mary (32746) ***(G-7456)***
Trebol Florida LLC........904 751-2828
11400 New Berlin Rd Jacksonville (32226) ***(G-6867)***
Trebor USA Corp........954 922-1620
3901 N 29th Ave Hollywood (33020) ***(G-5925)***
Tree Innovations, Maitland *Also called Botanical Innovations Inc* ***(G-8460)***
Tree Stake Solutions LLC........407 920-0507
6713 New Hope Rd Orlando (32824) ***(G-13269)***
Treetop Industries LLC........904 471-4412
219 Marshside Dr Saint Augustine (32080) ***(G-15627)***
Tremonti Project Pubg LLC........407 217-7140
6137 Cartmel Ln Windermere (34786) ***(G-19247)***
Tremron Inc (HQ)........305 825-9000
11321 Nw 138th St Medley (33178) ***(G-8741)***
Tremron LLC (PA)........904 359-5900
2885 Saint Clair St Jacksonville (32254) ***(G-6868)***
Tremron LLC........863 491-0990
3144 Ne Highway 17 Arcadia (34266) ***(G-206)***
Tremron Group, Jacksonville *Also called Tremron LLC* ***(G-6868)***
Tremron Group, Arcadia *Also called Tremron LLC* ***(G-206)***
Trend At LLC........786 300-2550
2627 S Bayshore Dr Miami (33133) ***(G-10505)***
Trend Magazines Inc (HQ)........727 821-5800
490 1st Ave S Ste 800 Saint Petersburg (33701) ***(G-15943)***
Trend Offset Printing Svcs Inc........562 598-2446
10301 Busch Dr N Jacksonville (32218) ***(G-6869)***
Trendy Entertainment Inc........814 384-7123
4910 Sw 78th Ln Gainesville (32608) ***(G-5012)***
Trenwa Inc........863 666-1680
1920 Longhorn Ave Lakeland (33801) ***(G-7825)***
Trepko Inc........813 443-0794
4893 W Waters Ave Ste C-F Tampa (33634) ***(G-18198)***
Tres Leches Factory & Beyond, Doral *Also called Parinto Global Enterprises LLC* ***(G-3454)***
Trese Inc........321 632-7272
2040 Murrell Rd Rockledge (32955) ***(G-15454)***
Trese Printing, Rockledge *Also called Trese Inc* ***(G-15454)***
Tri Inc........813 267-1201
107 S Willow Ave Tampa (33606) ***(G-18199)***
Tri C Petroleum Inc........941 756-3370
6442 Shoal Creek St Cir Bradenton (34202) ***(G-1129)***
Tri County Aerospace Inc........305 639-3356
2080 Nw 96th Ave Doral (33172) ***(G-3532)***

Tri County Aluminum Spc......727 848-4523
16201 Us Highway 19 Hudson (34667) *(G-6042)*
Tri County Printing Co In......561 477-8487
9070 Kimberly Blvd Boca Raton (33434) *(G-755)*
Tri Gas 05, Clearwater *Also called Matheson Tri-Gas Inc (G-1776)*
Tri Tech Metal Inc......727 946-1229
6925 Daubon Ct New Port Richey (34655) *(G-11516)*
Tri-County Bulletin......352 493-4796
624 W Park Ave Chiefland (32626) *(G-1538)*
Tri-County Woodworking LLC......954 850-2222
3001 Sw 10th St Pompano Beach (33069) *(G-14890)*
Tri-Deck LLC (PA)......386 748-3239
3402 Black Willow Trl Deland (32724) *(G-3025)*
Tri-Edge Industries LLC......561 703-5961
6586 Hypoluxo Rd Lake Worth (33467) *(G-7593)*
Tri-H Metal Products Inc......941 753-7311
5815 21st St E Bradenton (34203) *(G-1130)*
Tri-State Demolition LLC......850 597-8722
5272 Crawfordville Rd Tallahassee (32305) *(G-17342)*
Tri-Tech Electronics Inc......407 277-2131
9480 E Colonial Dr Orlando (32817) *(G-13270)*
Tri-Tech of Florida Inc......727 544-8836
5151 Park St N Saint Petersburg (33709) *(G-15944)*
Tria Beauty, Tampa *Also called Channel Investments LLC (G-17531)*
Triach Industries, Hollywood *Also called Triarch International Inc (G-5926)*
Triad Edm Inc......352 489-5336
14872 Sw 111th St Dunnellon (34432) *(G-3601)*
Triad Electric Vehicles, Boca Raton *Also called Valiant Transport Group LLC (G-774)*
Triad Isotopes Inc (PA)......407 455-6700
4205 Vineland Rd Ste L13 Orlando (32811) *(G-13271)*
Trial Exhibits Inc (PA)......813 258-6153
1177 W Cass St Tampa (33606) *(G-18200)*
Trial Prints, Coral Springs *Also called Trial Spectrum Inc (G-2324)*
Trial Spectrum Inc......954 906-5743
12201 Nw 35th St Coral Springs (33065) *(G-2324)*
Trialworks, Coral Gables *Also called Lawex Corporation (G-2171)*
Triangle Reprogressives, Orlando *Also called Repro Plus Inc (G-13131)*
Triangle Shopping Guide, Mount Dora *Also called Mid-Florida Publications Inc (G-11107)*
Triangle Shopping Guide Inc......352 589-8811
4645 N Highway 19a Mount Dora (32757) *(G-11116)*
Triarch International Inc......305 622-3400
4811 Sarazen Dr Hollywood (33021) *(G-5926)*
Triatomic Environmental Inc......561 748-4864
1838 Park Ln S Jupiter (33458) *(G-7132)*
Tricab (usa) Inc......754 210-5490
3876 Pembroke Rd Hollywood (33021) *(G-5927)*
Tricen Technologies Fla LLC (PA)......866 620-9407
500 Farmers Market Rd # 6 Fort Pierce (34982) *(G-4758)*
Tricounty Chemical Co......407 682-3550
2578 Park St Unit 5 Apopka (32712) *(G-192)*
Trident Building Systems Inc......941 755-7073
2812 Tallevast Rd Sarasota (34243) *(G-16314)*
Trident Pontoons Inc......352 253-1400
28240 Lake Indus Blvd Tavares (32778) *(G-18355)*
Trident Trading Inc (PA)......561 488-0458
6340 Via Tierra Boca Raton (33433) *(G-756)*
Tridor Group Inc......786 707-2241
10118 W Flagler St Miami (33174) *(G-10506)*
Trifecta Phrmceuticals USA LLC (PA)......888 296-9067
4100 N Powerline Rd J4 Pompano Beach (33073) *(G-14891)*
Trigeant Ep Ltd......561 999-9916
3020 N Military Trl # 100 Boca Raton (33431) *(G-757)*
Trikaroo......800 679-3415
5525 Commerce Dr Ste 1 Orlando (32839) *(G-13272)*
Trilectron......941 721-1000
11001 Us Highway 41 N Palmetto (34221) *(G-13830)*
Trim Rite Trimmings and Lace, Hialeah *Also called American S-Shore Plting Sttchi (G-5295)*
Trim Spot, Eustis *Also called Kevco Builders Inc (G-3711)*
Trim-Line of Miami Inc......305 556-6210
2755 W 81st St Hialeah (33016) *(G-5650)*
Trim-Pak Corporation (PA)......407 851-8900
8700 S Orange Ave Orlando (32824) *(G-13273)*
Trimtek Leather Inc......706 577-3950
1060 E Cross St Pensacola (32503) *(G-14275)*
Trinity Creamery Inc......813 926-2023
14167 Wadsworth Dr Odessa (33556) *(G-12160)*
Trinity Exterior Solutions LLC......850 393-9682
4292 Sundance Way Holt (32564) *(G-5950)*
Trinity Fabricators Inc......904 284-9657
825 Corporate Sq Green Cove Springs (32043) *(G-5073)*
Trinity Graphic Usa Inc......941 355-2636
885 Tallevast Rd Ste D Sarasota (34243) *(G-16315)*
Trinity Manufacturing Corp......941 727-9595
6205 31st St E Ste A Bradenton (34203) *(G-1131)*
Trinity Materials, Fanning Springs *Also called A Materials Group Inc (G-3721)*
Trinity Mobility......727 389-1438
8343 Royal Hart Dr New Port Richey (34653) *(G-11517)*
Trinity Signs LLC......850 502-7634
1111 N Eglin Pkwy Shalimar (32579) *(G-16778)*
Trio Envmtl Solutions LLC......850 543-9125
301 Friar Tuck Rd Mary Esther (32569) *(G-8592)*
Triops Inc......850 479-4415
3330 Mclemore Dr Ste B Pensacola (32514) *(G-14276)*
Triple Crown Printing......561 939-6440
5801 Congress Ave Boca Raton (33487) *(G-758)*
Triple H Cstm Wldg Fbrction LL......850 851-5097
7420 Kingman St Panama City (32408) *(G-13957)*
Triple J Marketing LLC......813 247-6999
301 W Platt St Tampa (33606) *(G-18201)*
Triple Play Cmmunications Corp......321 327-8997
250 East Dr Ste F Melbourne (32904) *(G-8966)*
Triple Seven Home LLC......321 652-5151
3385 Grant Rd Grant (32949) *(G-5050)*
Tripp Electric Motors Inc......561 996-3333
1233 Nw Avenue L Belle Glade (33430) *(G-353)*
Tristan S Kool Dreemz......772 398-8875
1401 Se Delene Ct Port Saint Lucie (34952) *(G-15156)*
Tritech Industries LLC......954 383-3545
5204 Ne 12th Ave Oakland Park (33334) *(G-11847)*
Triton II Jv LLC......407 894-5575
12802 Science Dr Ste 300 Orlando (32826) *(G-13274)*
Triton Seafood Co......305 888-8999
7301 Nw 77th St Medley (33166) *(G-8742)*
Triton Stone Holdings LLC (PA)......219 669-4890
800 Nw 65th St Fort Lauderdale (33309) *(G-4288)*
Triton Submarines LLC......772 770-1995
10055 102nd Ter Sebastian (32958) *(G-16674)*
Triumph Aerostructures LLC......772 463-8700
1845 Se Airport Rd Stuart (34996) *(G-17039)*
Triumph Arstrctres - Vght Coml, Stuart *Also called Triumph Aerostructures LLC (G-17039)*
Triumph Hosiery Corp......954 929-6021
4624 Hollywood Blvd # 205 Hollywood (33021) *(G-5928)*
Triumph Transport Inc......863 226-7276
1104 Bartow Rd Apt 173 Lakeland (33801) *(G-7826)*
Triumvirate Environmental......407 859-4441
10100 Rocket Blvd Orlando (32824) *(G-13275)*
Trivantis, Deerfield Beach *Also called SC Elearning LLC (G-2907)*
Trivantis Corporation (HQ)......513 929-0188
400 Fairway Dr Ste 101 Deerfield Beach (33441) *(G-2929)*
Trivecta Pharmaceuticals Inc......561 856-0842
1 E Broward Blvd Ste 700 Fort Lauderdale (33301) *(G-4289)*
Trividia Meditech LLC......954 677-9201
2400 Nw 55th Ct Fort Lauderdale (33309) *(G-4290)*
Troika Group Inc......561 313-1119
12300 South Shore Blvd # 20 Wellington (33414) *(G-18738)*
Trojan Fla Powdr Coating Inc......941 351-0500
1300 Hardin Ave Sarasota (34243) *(G-16316)*
Trolley Boats......727 588-1100
9470 Ulmerton Rd Ste 6b Largo (33771) *(G-8068)*
Tromtech, Pompano Beach *Also called Savvy Associate Inc (G-14840)*
Trophy Animal Health Care, Pensacola *Also called Pegasus Laboratories Inc (G-14224)*
Tropic Guard Industries LLC......813 447-3938
6727 Clair Shore Dr Apollo Beach (33572) *(G-107)*
Tropic Isles Co-Op Inc......941 721-8888
1503 28th Ave W Palmetto (34221) *(G-13831)*
Tropic Seal Industries Inc......239 543-8069
1745 Coral Way Fort Myers (33917) *(G-4639)*
Tropic Shield Inc......954 731-5553
3031 Nw 28th St Lauderdale Lakes (33311) *(G-8095)*
Tropic Spa, North Miami *Also called Majestics Business USA LLC (G-11645)*
Tropical Asphalt LLC......954 983-3434
1904 Sw 31st Ave Hallandale (33009) *(G-5164)*
Tropical Assemblies Inc......954 396-9999
4066 Ne 5th Ave Oakland Park (33334) *(G-11848)*
Tropical Awning of Florida......561 276-1144
335 Se 1st Ave Ste A Delray Beach (33444) *(G-3151)*
Tropical Bottling Corporation (PA)......786 636-6169
8074 Nw 74th Ave Medley (33166) *(G-8743)*
Tropical Ceiling Fan Company......877 921-3267
13110 S Dixie Hwy Miami (33156) *(G-10507)*
Tropical Custom Coatings......941 475-3663
11354 Zola Ave Port Charlotte (33981) *(G-15002)*
Tropical Designs, Melbourne *Also called Allgeo & Yerkes Entps Inc (G-8764)*
Tropical Dvrsons Mrina MGT Inc......954 922-0387
3200 N 29th Ave Hollywood (33020) *(G-5929)*
Tropical Enterprises Intl (PA)......813 837-9800
8625 Florida Mining Blvd Tampa (33634) *(G-18202)*
Tropical MBC LLC......727 498-6511
246 75th Ave St Pete Beach (33706) *(G-16884)*
Tropical Mfg Inc......305 394-6280
783 W 18th St Hialeah (33010) *(G-5651)*
Tropical Pallets Inc (PA)......305 634-0346
1500 Nw 23rd St Miami (33142) *(G-10508)*
Tropical Paper Box......305 592-5520
1401 Nw 78th Ave Doral (33126) *(G-3533)*
Tropical Paver Sealing......727 786-4011
4834 Windingbrook Trl Wesley Chapel (33544) *(G-18761)*
Tropical Pcb Design Services......561 784-9536
7960 Banyan Blvd Loxahatchee (33470) *(G-8366)*

ALPHABETIC

Tropical Prints Inc A Corp......305 261-9926
4401 Sw 75th Ave Ste 2 Miami (33155) ***(G-10509)***
Tropical Showers Inc......954 260-5196
1433 Ne 28th St Pompano Beach (33064) ***(G-14892)***
Tropical Signs & Graphics......321 458-7742
425 Deb Ln Merritt Island (32952) ***(G-9017)***
Tropical Skoops Llc......954 440-8736
11635 Red Rd Miramar (33025) ***(G-11053)***
Tropical Stencil Pcb Inc......561 972-5133
1530 Cypress Dr Ste E Jupiter (33469) ***(G-7133)***
Tropical Taffy Naples Inc......239 571-3761
2655 64th St Sw Naples (34105) ***(G-11445)***
Tropicalcreation......941 580-8465
1310 Atwater Dr North Port (34288) ***(G-11751)***
Tropicana Manufacturing Co Inc......312 821-1000
1001 13th Ave E Bradenton (34208) ***(G-1132)***
Tropicana Products Inc (HQ)......941 747-4461
1001 13th Ave E Bradenton (34208) ***(G-1133)***
Tropicana Products Inc......772 465-2030
6500 Glades Cut Off Rd Fort Pierce (34981) ***(G-4759)***
Tropicana Products Inc......850 610-8849
400 E Nelson Ave Defuniak Springs (32433) ***(G-2950)***
Tropichem Research Labs LLC......561 804-7603
15843 Guild Ct Jupiter (33478) ***(G-7134)***
Tropicolor Display Graphics, Miami Beach *Also called Tropicolor Photo Service Inc* ***(G-10721)***
Tropicolor Photo Service Inc......305 672-3720
1442 Alton Rd Miami Beach (33139) ***(G-10721)***
Tropix Marble Company......239 334-2371
17121 Primavera Cir Cape Coral (33909) ***(G-1488)***
Trost Industries LLC......407 690-8603
6300 Parc Corniche Dr Orlando (32821) ***(G-13276)***
Troy Industries Inc......305 324-1742
2100 Nw 102nd Pl Doral (33172) ***(G-3534)***
Troy Industries LLC......401 241-4231
6733 Greenview Ln Englewood (34224) ***(G-3669)***
Troy Thompson Inc......813 716-1598
20255 Denny Dr Brooksville (34601) ***(G-1283)***
Trs, Orlando *Also called T R S* ***(G-13238)***
Trs Industries Inc......561 880-0031
6845 Finamore Cir Lake Worth (33467) ***(G-7594)***
Trs Wireless Inc......407 447-7333
1711 S Division Ave Orlando (32805) ***(G-13277)***
Tru Cane Sugar Corp......561 833-1731
1 N Clematis St Ste 200 West Palm Beach (33401) ***(G-19070)***
Tru Craft Woodworks LLC......561 441-2742
1865 Sw 4th Ave Ste D9 Delray Beach (33444) ***(G-3152)***
Tru Dimensions Printing Inc......407 339-3410
2100 N R Reagan Blvd 10 Longwood (32750) ***(G-8345)***
Tru Mension Mfg Solutions......321 255-4665
3900 Dow Rd Ste C Melbourne (32934) ***(G-8967)***
Tru Simulation + Training Inc......813 792-9300
1551 Gunn Hwy Odessa (33556) ***(G-12161)***
Tru-Art Signs &GRaphix Inc......561 371-2388
5596 Sw Evans Dr Stuart (34997) ***(G-17040)***
Tru-Flo Corp......561 996-5850
924 Nw 13th St Belle Glade (33430) ***(G-354)***
Trubendz Technology Inc......305 378-9337
18495 S Dixie Hwy Ste 213 Cutler Bay (33157) ***(G-2417)***
Trubendz Technology Inc (PA)......305 378-9337
19101 Sw 108th Ave # 19 Cutler Bay (33157) ***(G-2418)***
Trucraft Specialties Inc......561 441-2742
1503 Hummingbird Dr Delray Beach (33444) ***(G-3153)***
True Back, Belleair *Also called Morcent Import Export Inc* ***(G-360)***
True Bloods Colonial Printing, Lakeland *Also called Hunt Enterprises Inc* ***(G-7707)***
True Blue Metal LLC......352 444-9596
14350 Sw 20th Avenue Rd Ocala (34473) ***(G-12061)***
True East Surfboard Inc......407 679-6896
3155 Rider Pl Orlando (32817) ***(G-13278)***
True Grit Abrasives Inc......813 247-5219
7015 E 14th Ave Tampa (33619) ***(G-18203)***
True House Inc......386 325-9085
150 State Road 207 East Palatka (32131) ***(G-3608)***
True House Inc (PA)......904 757-7500
4745 Sutton Park Ct # 501 Jacksonville (32224) ***(G-6870)***
True Line Industries Inc......561 745-4828
13841 151st Ln N Jupiter (33478) ***(G-7135)***
True Loaf, Miami Beach *Also called Corvatsch Corp* ***(G-10658)***
True Plumbing Svc Inc......941 296-5123
11729 Meadowgate Pl Bradenton (34211) ***(G-1134)***
True Stone Corp......772 334-9797
7324 Commercial Cir Fort Pierce (34951) ***(G-4760)***
True Stone Masonry LLC......772 334-9797
7324 Commercial Cir Fort Pierce (34951) ***(G-4761)***
True Truss, Jacksonville *Also called True House Inc* ***(G-6870)***
Truear Inc......352 314-8805
18997 Us Highway 441 Mount Dora (32757) ***(G-11117)***
Truenorth Iq Inc......678 849-5000
1193 Se Port St Lcie Blvd Port Saint Lucie (34952) ***(G-15157)***
Truesouth Marine Corp......813 286-0716
4810 Culbreath Isles Rd Tampa (33629) ***(G-18204)***
Truffles Coffee House & Bakery, Jacksonville *Also called St Johns Bky & Gourmet Fd Co* ***(G-6806)***
Trugard, Doral *Also called Interntnal Tech Sltons Sup LLC* ***(G-3393)***
Trugreen Products LLC......954 629-5794
1010 S Ocean Blvd Apt 408 Pompano Beach (33062) ***(G-14893)***
Trujillo Oil Plant Inc......305 696-8701
3325 Nw 62nd St Miami (33147) ***(G-10510)***
Trulieve Cannabis Corp (HQ)......844 878-5438
6749 Ben Bostic Rd Quincy (32351) ***(G-15256)***
Trumeter Company Inc (HQ)......954 725-6699
6601 Lyons Rd Ste H7 Coconut Creek (33073) ***(G-2098)***
Truplate, Tampa *Also called Photoengraving Inc* ***(G-17992)***
Trurev LLC......800 397-3388
4407 Sw 62nd Ave Davie (33314) ***(G-2608)***
Trusco Manufacturing Company......352 237-0311
545 Nw 68th Ave Ocala (34482) ***(G-12062)***
Truss Spans Unlimited LLC......352 274-0306
12830 Sw 58th Cir Ocala (34473) ***(G-12063)***
Truss Systems LLC......386 255-3009
3615 U S 1 S Bunnell (32110) ***(G-1308)***
Truss Systems of Vlsia Flgler......386 255-3009
3615 S Us Highway 1 Bunnell (32110) ***(G-1309)***
Truss William......954 438-4710
17800 Nw 14th St Pembroke Pines (33029) ***(G-14066)***
Trusscorp International Inc......305 882-8826
9590 Nw 89th Ave Medley (33178) ***(G-8744)***
Trusses Unlimited Inc (PA)......904 355-6611
320 San Juan Dr Ponte Vedra Beach (32082) ***(G-14955)***
Trussway Manufacturing Inc......407 857-2777
8850 Trussway Blvd Orlando (32824) ***(G-13279)***
Trusswood Inc......321 383-0366
3620 Bobbi Ln Titusville (32780) ***(G-18470)***
Trusted Daily Solutions......954 461-5131
3431 Ne 27th Ave Lighthouse Point (33064) ***(G-8213)***
Truth Nutrition LLC......754 400-0382
4302 Hollywood Blvd # 16 Hollywood (33021) ***(G-5930)***
Truvoice Telecom Inc......888 448-5556
3102 Cherry Palm Dr # 145 Tampa (33619) ***(G-18205)***
Trx Integration Inc......727 797-4707
401 Corbett St Ste 470 Belleair (33756) ***(G-361)***
Trxade Inc......727 230-1915
3840 Land O Lakes Blvd Land O Lakes (34639) ***(G-7868)***
Tryana LLC......813 467-9916
4901 W Rio Vista Ave A Tampa (33634) ***(G-18206)***
TSA Rewinds Florida Inc......305 681-2030
13050 Nw 47th Ave Opa Locka (33054) ***(G-12366)***
Tsb Emulsions LLC......904 249-5115
1306 Big Tree Rd Neptune Beach (32266) ***(G-11478)***
Tsd Group Corp......954 940-2111
306 International Pkwy B Sunrise (33325) ***(G-17191)***
Tsfpr LLC......954 691-9031
1501 W Copans Rd Pompano Beach (33064) ***(G-14894)***
Tsl-Reico, Fort Walton Beach *Also called Technical Service Labs Inc* ***(G-4834)***
Tsm Champ LLC......615 806-7900
2359 Trailmate Dr Sarasota (34243) ***(G-16317)***
Tsn Manufacturing......813 740-1876
4011 E 21st Ave Tampa (33605) ***(G-18207)***
Tsn Manufacturing Inc......727 709-9802
807 Hickory Fork Dr Seffner (33584) ***(G-16734)***
TSO Mobile, Doral *Also called Tracking Solutions Corp* ***(G-3530)***
TST Impreso Inc......305 381-5153
9114 Nw 106th St Medley (33178) ***(G-8745)***
TST Industries LLC......973 865-1998
3625 Royal Fern Cir Deland (32724) ***(G-3026)***
TST Industries LLC......386 868-2011
623 Pleasant St Lake Helen (32744) ***(G-7395)***
Ttc-The Trading Company Inc (PA)......503 982-0880
2062 20th Ave Se Largo (33771) ***(G-8069)***
TTI Holdings Inc (PA)......813 623-2675
2710 E 5th Ave Tampa (33605) ***(G-18208)***
Tts Food LLC......305 622-2726
15990 Nw 49th Ave Hialeah (33014) ***(G-5652)***
Tua Systems Inc......321 453-3200
3645 N Courtenay Pkwy Merritt Island (32953) ***(G-9018)***
Tube Services-Division, Jacksonville *Also called Flotech Inc* ***(G-6406)***
Tubos Inc......727 504-0633
718 4th Ave Ne Largo (33770) ***(G-8070)***
Tubos Inc......727 504-0633
2775 Diane Ter Clearwater (33759) ***(G-1926)***
Tucker Lithographic Co......904 276-0568
661 Blanding Blvd Ste 103 Orange Park (32073) ***(G-12410)***
Tucker Trckg Log Jhnny E Tcker......850 258-1982
2371 County Road 381 Wewahitchka (32465) ***(G-19183)***
Tucker-Davis Technologies Inc......386 462-9622
11930 Research Cir Alachua (32615) ***(G-21)***
Tuckers Machine & Stl Svc Inc......352 787-3157
400 County Road 468 Leesburg (34748) ***(G-8179)***

Tuf Top Coatings......727 527-3382
4590 60th Ave N Saint Petersburg (33714) *(G-15945)*
Tuflex Manufacturing Co......954 781-0605
1406 Sw 8th St Pompano Beach (33069) *(G-14895)*
Tuiskombuis......904 484-4509
3790 Winterhawk Ct Saint Augustine (32086) *(G-15628)*
Tuka Imports LLC......305 640-8336
3729 Nw 71st St Miami (33147) *(G-10511)*
Tulipan Bakery Inc (PA)......561 832-6107
740 Belvedere Rd West Palm Beach (33405) *(G-19071)*
Tuly Corporation......305 633-0710
3820 Nw 32nd Ave Miami (33142) *(G-10512)*
Tumbling Pines Inc......386 437-2668
10987 State Road 11 Bunnell (32110) *(G-1310)*
Tumi Holdings Inc......941 866-6304
140 University Town Cente Sarasota (34243) *(G-16318)*
Tupperware Brands Corporation (PA)......407 826-5050
14901 S Ornge Blossom Trl Orlando (32837) *(G-13280)*
Tupperware Products Inc......407 826-5050
14901 S Ornge Blossom Trl Orlando (32837) *(G-13281)*
Tupperware Turkey Inc......407 826-5050
14901 S Orange Blossom Tr Orlando (32837) *(G-13282)*
Tupperware US Inc (HQ)......407 826-5050
14901 S Ornge Blossom Trl Orlando (32837) *(G-13283)*
Turbine Broach Company......352 795-1163
521 E Overdrive Cir Hernando (34442) *(G-5248)*
Turbine Controls LLC......954 517-1706
3501 Enterprise Way Miramar (33025) *(G-11054)*
Turbine Generator Maint Inc (PA)......239 573-1233
125 Sw 3rd Pl Ste 300 Cape Coral (33991) *(G-1489)*
Turbine Kinetics Inc......954 744-7526
3000 Taft St Hollywood (33021) *(G-5931)*
Turbine Parts Repair Inc......850 983-8600
8100 Armstrong Rd Milton (32583) *(G-10945)*
Turbine Resources Intl LLC......850 377-0449
2595a Dog Track Rd Pensacola (32506) *(G-14277)*
Turbine Solution Group, Deland *Also called Diemech Turbine Solution Inc* *(G-2970)*
Turbine Weld Industries LLC......941 485-5113
402 Substation Rd Venice (34285) *(G-18582)*
Turbo Aerospace Corp......786 218-8990
2920 Nw 17th Ter Oakland Park (33311) *(G-11849)*
Turbo Parts LLC......352 351-4510
810 Nw 25th Ave Ste 102 Ocala (34475) *(G-12064)*
Turbo Rotating Spare US, Miami *Also called Multi-Commercial Services Corp* *(G-10054)*
Turbo Vacuum, Orlando *Also called Walden Consulting LLC* *(G-13317)*
Turbocombustor Technology Inc (HQ)......772 287-7770
3651 Se Commerce Ave Stuart (34997) *(G-17041)*
Turbousa Inc......954 767-8631
1867 Ne 33rd St Oakland Park (33306) *(G-11850)*
Turf Care Supply Corp......863 655-2424
422 Webster Turn Dr Sebring (33870) *(G-16717)*
Turin Em Inc......305 825-2004
8045 W 26th Ct Hialeah (33016) *(G-5653)*
Turn Key Industries......813 671-3446
9901 Alafia River Ln Gibsonton (33534) *(G-5034)*
Turner Envirologic Inc......954 422-9566
1140 Sw 34th Ave Deerfield Beach (33442) *(G-2930)*
Turner Machine & Supply Co......772 464-4550
5000 Orange Ave Fort Pierce (34947) *(G-4762)*
Turning Point Propellers Inc......904 900-7739
11762 Marco Beach Dr # 2 Jacksonville (32224) *(G-6871)*
Turnstile Publishing Company (HQ)......407 563-7000
1500 Park Center Dr Orlando (32835) *(G-13284)*
Turtle Publishing Co......904 568-1484
1034 Hendricks Ave Jacksonville (32207) *(G-6872)*
Turtlehue LLC......561 775-6614
11231 Us Highway 1 170 North Palm Beach (33408) *(G-11728)*
Tuscola Wind II LLC......561 691-7171
700 Universe Blvd Juno Beach (33408) *(G-6985)*
Tutela Monitoring Systems LLC......941 462-1067
485 Mariner Blvd Spring Hill (34609) *(G-16869)*
Tuthill Corporation......727 446-8593
2050 Sunnydale Blvd Clearwater (33765) *(G-1927)*
Tutogen Medical Inc (HQ)......386 418-8888
11621 Research Cir Alachua (32615) *(G-22)*
Tutti Hogar International LLC......305 705-4735
19472 Diplomat Dr Miami (33179) *(G-10513)*
Tuuci, Hialeah *Also called Ultimate Umbrella Company Inc* *(G-5657)*
Tuuci LLC......305 634-5116
1000 Se 8th St Ste A Hialeah (33010) *(G-5654)*
Tuuci Worldwide......305 634-5116
1000 Se 8th St Hialeah (33010) *(G-5655)*
Tuuci Worldwide LLC (PA)......305 634-5116
2900 Nw 35th St Miami (33142) *(G-10514)*
TV Film International Inc......305 671-3265
2600 Sw 3rd Ave Ste 850 Miami (33129) *(G-10515)*
TV Publishing......954 773-6967
417 Lake Dora Dr West Palm Beach (33411) *(G-19072)*
TV Shield, The, Altamonte Springs *Also called Protective Enclosures Co LLC* *(G-68)*
TW Byrds Sons Inc......386 935-1544
11860 E Us 27 Branford (32008) *(G-1190)*
Twin Vee Catamarans Inc......772 429-2525
3101 S Us Highway 1 Fort Pierce (34982) *(G-4763)*
Twinlab Cnsld Holdings Inc (PA)......561 443-4301
4800 T Rex Ave Ste 305 Boca Raton (33431) *(G-759)*
Twinlab Consolidation Corp......800 645-5626
4800 T Rex Ave Ste 350 Boca Raton (33431) *(G-760)*
Twinlab Corporation......800 645-5626
4800 T Rex Ave Ste 305 Boca Raton (33431) *(G-761)*
Twinlab Holdings Inc (PA)......800 645-5626
4800 T Rex Ave Ste 305 Boca Raton (33431) *(G-762)*
Twinlab Holdings Inc......800 645-5626
2255 Glades Rd Ste 342w Boca Raton (33431) *(G-763)*
Twinoxide-Usa Inc......321 207-8524
3700 N Courtenay Pkwy Merritt Island (32953) *(G-9019)*
Twins & Martin Equipment Corp......954 802-0345
80 Sw 8th St Ste 2056 Miami (33130) *(G-10516)*
Twinstar Optics & Coatings Inc......727 847-2300
6741 Commerce Ave Port Richey (34668) *(G-15073)*
Twinstar Optics Ctngs Cyrstals, Port Richey *Also called Twinstar Optics & Coatings Inc* *(G-15073)*
Twisted Coffee Canyon Roasters, Pensacola *Also called De Luna Coffee Intl Inc* *(G-14126)*
Twisted Fusion Nutrition......646 719-3041
1305 Kingsway Rd Brandon (33510) *(G-1183)*
TWN Industries Inc (PA)......305 246-5717
25490 Sw 141st Ave Princeton (33032) *(G-15187)*
Two B Printing Inc......954 566-4886
625 Ne 42nd St Oakland Park (33334) *(G-11851)*
Two Brothers Cultivation LLC......954 478-2402
817 Se 2nd Ave Apt 518 Fort Lauderdale (33316) *(G-4291)*
Two Guys Plumbing Supply LLc......321 263-0021
1030 Sunshine Ln Ste 1020 Altamonte Springs (32714) *(G-79)*
Two Little Fishies Inc......305 623-7695
15801 Nw 15th Ave Miami (33169) *(G-10517)*
Two Mermaids Swim & Resort Wr, The Villages *Also called Two Mermaids Villages LLC* *(G-18395)*
Two Mermaids Villages LLC (PA)......352 259-4722
1039 Canal St The Villages (32162) *(G-18395)*
Two Paper Chasers LLC......813 251-5090
3214 W San Miguel St Tampa (33629) *(G-18209)*
Two Roads Consulting LLC......305 395-8821
469 Limewood Ave Dunedin (34698) *(G-3591)*
Two Tree Inc......352 284-1763
24 Nw 33rd Ct Ste A Gainesville (32607) *(G-5013)*
Two Way Radio Gear Inc......800 984-1534
3245 Okeechobee Rd Fort Pierce (34947) *(G-4764)*
Tws Cabinets LLC......863 614-4693
2947 Vermont Ave Lakeland (33803) *(G-7827)*
Tws Fabricators......954 983-9749
2001 N Us Highway 27 Pembroke Pines (33029) *(G-14067)*
TX Trading Inc......786 303-9950
20355 Ne 34th Ct Apt 427 Miami (33180) *(G-10518)*
Tyco Machine Inc......352 544-0210
1400 Ponce De Leon Blvd Brooksville (34601) *(G-1284)*
Tycoon Tutti Inc......305 624-7811
1361 Nw 155th Dr Miami (33169) *(G-10519)*
Tyler Fabricators, Delray Beach *Also called Sea Side Specialties* *(G-3139)*
Tyrex Ore & Minerals Company......305 333-5288
8950 Sw 74th Ct Fl 22 Miami (33156) *(G-10520)*
Tyrolit Company, Trinity *Also called Meopta USA Inc* *(G-18488)*
Tys Hometown Cafe Bistro LLC......786 208-1163
1847 Nw 1st Ct Miami (33136) *(G-10521)*
Tyson Foods Inc......904 693-0688
5441 W 5th St Jacksonville (32254) *(G-6873)*
Tzh Industries Inc......727 807-3000
1731 Swamp Rose Ln Trinity (34655) *(G-18490)*
U B Corp......813 884-1463
9829 Wilsky Blvd Tampa (33615) *(G-18210)*
U C Cabinet Inc......407 322-0968
222 Hickman Dr Sanford (32771) *(G-16130)*
U C Fab of Florida LLC......407 614-4210
301 Enterprise St Unit C Ocoee (34761) *(G-12094)*
U D T Inc......850 784-0537
2304 Grant Ave Panama City (32405) *(G-13958)*
U Got Recovery Inc......407 343-9919
3406 W Vine St Kissimmee (34741) *(G-7305)*
U M P......305 740-4996
6262 Bird Rd Miami (33155) *(G-10522)*
U S A Coatings Inc......904 477-0916
2361 Edwards Ave Jacksonville (32254) *(G-6874)*
U S Awning, Sarasota *Also called United States Awning Company* *(G-16631)*
U S Composites Inc......561 588-1001
5101 Georgia Ave West Palm Beach (33405) *(G-19073)*
U S Hardware Supply Inc......407 657-1551
4675 Metric Dr Winter Park (32792) *(G-19454)*
U S Holdings Inc (PA)......305 885-0301
3200 W 84th St Hialeah (33018) *(G-5656)*
U S Sign and Mill, Fort Myers *Also called US Sign and Mill Inc* *(G-4641)*

ALPHABETIC

U Tech, Brooksville *Also called Unbridled Technologies LLC (G-1285)*
U-Dump Trailers LLC 352 351-8510
2610 Nw 10th St Ocala (34475) ***(G-12065)***
U-Load Dumpsters LLC 352 318-3045
1450 Mitchell Rd Ponce De Leon (32455) ***(G-14919)***
U2 Cloud LLC 888 370-5433
1300 Cooks Ln Green Cove Springs (32043) ***(G-5074)***
UAS Drone Corp (PA) 561 693-1424
420 Royal Palm Way # 100 Palm Beach (33480) ***(G-13562)***
UCI Paints, Boca Raton *Also called Union Chemical Industries Corp (G-766)*
Uct Coatings Inc (PA) 772 872-7110
3300 Sw 42nd Ave Palm City (34990) ***(G-13677)***
Uct Defense, Palm City *Also called Uct Coatings Inc (G-13677)*
Uct2, Miami *Also called Unique Custom Truck & Trlr LLC (G-10531)*
UDC Usa Inc (PA) 813 281-0200
501 E Kennedy Blvd # 801 Tampa (33602) ***(G-18211)***
Ufg Group Inc (PA) 561 425-6829
2121 Vista Pkwy West Palm Beach (33411) ***(G-19074)***
Uflex Usa Inc 941 351-2628
6442 Parkland Dr Sarasota (34243) ***(G-16319)***
Ufp Orlando LLC 407 982-3312
7205 Rose Ave Orlando (32810) ***(G-13285)***
Ufp Palm Bch LLC DBA Ufp Mami 786 837-0552
11400 Nw 32nd Ave Miami (33167) ***(G-10523)***
Ufp Tampa LLC 813 971-3030
1003 E 131st Ave Tampa (33612) ***(G-18212)***
Ufp Technologies Inc 407 933-4880
2175 Partin Settlement Rd Kissimmee (34744) ***(G-7306)***
Ugp, Longwood *Also called American Mentality Inc (G-8254)*
Uip International Inc (PA) 954 785-3539
1350 S Dixie Hwy E Pompano Beach (33060) ***(G-14896)***
Uk Sailmakers Inc (PA) 941 365-7245
324 Bernard Ave Sarasota (34243) ***(G-16320)***
Uk Sailmakers Sarasota, Sarasota *Also called Uk Sailmakers Inc (G-16320)*
Uk Sails Makers, Miami *Also called Atlantic Sails Makers (G-9183)*
Uk Sales LLC 561 239-2980
5300 W Hillsboro Blvd # 215 Coconut Creek (33073) ***(G-2099)***
Uk US Partners LLC T McCuloch 407 217-2978
10806 Woodchase Cir Orlando (32836) ***(G-13286)***
Ukg Inc 954 331-7000
1485 N Park Dr Weston (33326) ***(G-19173)***
Ullman Sails Florida, Sarasota *Also called Douglas A Fisher Inc (G-16414)*
Ullrich's, Wauchula *Also called Franz A Ullrich Jr (G-18692)*
Ultima Design South Fla Inc 305 477-9300
11305 Nw 128th St Medley (33178) ***(G-8746)***
Ultimate Cargo Services LLC 954 251-1680
10752 Deerwood Park Blvd Jacksonville (32256) ***(G-6875)***
Ultimate Compressor LLC 305 720-3079
400 S Hollybrook Dr Apt 1 Pembroke Pines (33025) ***(G-14068)***
Ultimate Containers Pro LLC 786 241-4306
355 Nw 171st St Miami Gardens (33169) ***(G-10757)***
Ultimate Door of Palm Beach 561 642-2828
2800 2nd Ave N Lake Worth (33461) ***(G-7595)***
Ultimate Machining Corporation 954 749-9810
4741 Nw 103rd Ave Sunrise (33351) ***(G-17192)***
Ultimate Outdoor Cabinetry Inc 941 713-5295
2864 48th Way E Bradenton (34203) ***(G-1135)***
Ultimate Overstock LLC 407 851-1017
4967 Intl Dr Ste 3a27 Orlando (32819) ***(G-13287)***
Ultimate Sign Mfg LLC 954 864-7776
4080 Ne 8th Ave Oakland Park (33334) ***(G-11852)***
Ultimate Sign Service LLC 813 210-3166
8328 Civic Rd Tampa (33615) ***(G-18213)***
Ultimate Software 305 559-3052
11900 Sw 46th St Miami (33175) ***(G-10524)***
Ultimate Stnwrks Centl Fla LLC 407 412-5981
9220 Boggy Creek Rd # 221 Orlando (32824) ***(G-13288)***
Ultimate Swimwear Inc 386 668-8900
247 N Westmonte Dr Altamonte Springs (32714) ***(G-80)***
Ultimate Tool Inc 954 489-9996
5105 Ne 12th Ave Oakland Park (33334) ***(G-11853)***
Ultimate Umbrella Company Inc (PA) 305 634-5116
1000 Se 8th St Ste A Hialeah (33010) ***(G-5657)***
Ultimate Wdwkg & Design Inc 754 223-4004
1881 Nw 29th St Oakland Park (33311) ***(G-11854)***
Ultimaxx Inc 877 300-3424
3651 Fau Blvd Ste 400 Boca Raton (33431) ***(G-764)***
Ultimaxx Health, Boca Raton *Also called Ultimaxx Inc (G-764)*
Ultra Aerospace Inc 305 728-6361
12235 Sw 128th St Miami (33186) ***(G-10525)***
Ultra Base Systems, Saint Petersburg *Also called Innovative Base Tech LLC (G-15816)*
Ultra Clean Systems Inc 813 925-1003
110 Douglas Rd E Oldsmar (34677) ***(G-12272)***
Ultra Defense, Tampa *Also called UDC Usa Inc (G-18211)*
Ultra Graphics Corp 305 593-0202
132 Sw 96th Ave Miami (33174) ***(G-10526)***
Ultra Lite Tenders LLC 214 215-2725
4399 Se Whiticar Way Stuart (34997) ***(G-17042)***
Ultra Pharma LLC 954 532-7539
3131 W Mcnab Rd Pompano Beach (33069) ***(G-14897)***
Ultra Prcsion McHning Grnding 321 725-9655
2870 Kirby Cir Ne Ste 6 Palm Bay (32905) ***(G-13545)***
Ultra Tuff Manufacturing Inc 970 252-9457
8845 Se Robwyn St Hobe Sound (33455) ***(G-5730)***
Ultra-Pure Bottled Water Inc 281 731-0258
1801 Ne 123rd St Ste 314 North Miami (33181) ***(G-11660)***
Ultrabox Inc 941 371-0000
5827 17th St E Bradenton (34203) ***(G-1136)***
Ultraclenz LLC 800 931-8911
1201 Jupiter Park Dr # 1 Jupiter (33458) ***(G-7136)***
Ultrafast Systems LLC 941 360-2161
8330 Consumer Ct Sarasota (34240) ***(G-16626)***
Ultraflex Systems Florida Inc (PA) 973 664-6739
6333 Pelican Creek Cir Riverview (33578) ***(G-15285)***
Ultrapanel Marine Inc 772 285-4258
2665 S Byshr Dr Ste 220 Miami (33133) ***(G-10527)***
Ultrasonic Technologies Inc 813 973-1702
27247 Breakers Dr Wesley Chapel (33544) ***(G-18762)***
Ultrasonics and Magnetics 813 740-1800
5275 Causeway Blvd Ste 2 Tampa (33619) ***(G-18214)***
Ultratech International Inc (PA) 904 292-9019
11542 Davis Creek Ct Jacksonville (32256) ***(G-6876)***
Ultroid Technologies Inc 877 858-0555
3140 W Kennedy Blvd Tampa (33609) ***(G-18215)***
Um Kitchen Cabinets Inc 772 224-5445
965 Sw North Globe Ave Port Saint Lucie (34953) ***(G-15158)***
Uma Holdings Inc 786 587-1349
601 S 21st Ave Hollywood (33020) ***(G-5932)***
Umbrella Buses Inc 754 457-4004
9800 Us 192 Davenport (33897) ***(G-2484)***
Umbusa, Davenport *Also called Umbrella Buses Inc (G-2484)*
Umg Recordings Inc 305 532-4754
404 Wshington Ave Ste 800 Miami Beach (33139) ***(G-10722)***
Unaflex LLC (PA) 954 943-5002
1350 S Dixie Hwy E Pompano Beach (33060) ***(G-14898)***
Unbridled Technologies LLC 888 334-8402
21125 Cortez Blvd Brooksville (34601) ***(G-1285)***
Uncle Carlos Gelatos 810 523-8506
141 Melody Ln Fort Pierce (34950) ***(G-4765)***
Uncle Johns Pride LLC 813 685-7745
10250 Woodberry Rd Tampa (33619) ***(G-18216)***
Unconventional Marine, Orlando *Also called Summit ATL Productions LLC (G-13221)*
Undersea Breathing Systems 561 588-7698
2565 N Dixie Hwy Lake Worth (33460) ***(G-7596)***
Underwater Lights Usa LLC 954 760-4447
3406 Sw 26th Ter Ste 5 Fort Lauderdale (33312) ***(G-4292)***
Underwood Butcher Block Co Inc 904 338-2348
51 Nitram St Ste 500 Jacksonville (32211) ***(G-6877)***
Underwter Fish Light Ltd Lblty 941 391-5846
20400 Veterans Blvd Port Charlotte (33954) ***(G-15003)***
Unfoldingword Corporation 407 900-3005
10524 Moss Park Rd # 204 Orlando (32832) ***(G-13289)***
UNI Glide Trailer, Venice *Also called Dills Enterprises LLC (G-18542)*
UNI-Box Inc 954 733-3550
1700 Nw 27th St Oakland Park (33311) ***(G-11855)***
UNI-Pak Corp 407 830-9300
1015 N Ronald Reagan Blvd Longwood (32750) ***(G-8346)***
Unia International Corp 954 404-6076
18501 Pines Blvd Ste 202 Pembroke Pines (33029) ***(G-14069)***
Unico International Trdg Corp 561 338-3338
5499 N Federal Hwy Ste P Boca Raton (33487) ***(G-765)***
Unicomp Corp of America 954 755-1710
10101 W Sample Rd Stop 1 Coral Springs (33065) ***(G-2325)***
Unicornio Bakery LLC 786 665-1602
8255 Lake Dr Doral (33166) ***(G-3535)***
Unicraft Corp 305 633-4945
3640 Nw 52nd St Miami (33142) ***(G-10528)***
Unifab Co, Oakland Park *Also called UNI-Box Inc (G-11855)*
Uniform Authority Inc (PA) 305 625-8050
2263 Sw 12th St Miami (33135) ***(G-10529)***
Uniform Authority, The, Miami *Also called International Clothiers Inc (G-9756)*
Uniform Nametape Company Inc 813 839-6737
5701 S Dale Mabry Hwy Tampa (33611) ***(G-18217)***
Unihold Inc 941 966-7440
2307 Tamiami Trl N Nokomis (34275) ***(G-11590)***
Unik Design & Print Inc 786 355-6877
10220 Nw 80th Ave Miami Lakes (33016) ***(G-10872)***
Unilens Corp USA 727 544-2531
21 N Park Place Blvd Clearwater (33759) ***(G-1928)***
Unilever 904 378-0298
12200 Presidents Ct Jacksonville (32220) ***(G-6878)***
Unimat Industries LLC 305 716-0358
6980 Nw 43rd St Miami (33166) ***(G-10530)***
Unimd Scrubs LLC 954 245-1509
1850 S Ocean Dr Apt 3407 Hallandale Beach (33009) ***(G-5220)***
Unimed Surgical Products Inc 727 546-1900
10401 Belcher Rd S Seminole (33777) ***(G-16769)***

Uninsred Untd Prchute Tech LLC 386 736-7589
1645 Lexington Ave Deland (32724) ***(G-3027)***
Uninsured Relative Workshop 386 736-7589
1645 Lexington Ave Deland (32724) ***(G-3028)***
Union Chemical Industries Corp....716 866-4978
298 Kingsbridge St Boca Raton (33487) ***(G-766)***
Union County Times, Starke *Also called Bradford County Telegraph Inc* ***(G-16887)***
Union Engineering N Amer LLC....386 225-4952
2361 Mason Ave Ste 100 Daytona Beach (32117) ***(G-2729)***
Union Pvc Industries Inc....305 883-1640
295 W 27th St Hialeah (33010) ***(G-5658)***
Unipower, Coral Springs *Also called Technipower LLC* ***(G-2321)***
Unipress Corporation....813 623-3731
3501 Queen Palm Dr Tampa (33619) ***(G-18218)***
Unique Custom Truck & Trlr LLC....305 403-7042
7248 Sw 42nd Ter Miami (33155) ***(G-10531)***
Unique Designs & Finishes Inc....772 335-4884
1443 Se Huffman Rd Port Saint Lucie (34952) ***(G-15159)***
Unique Designs Prof Svcs Inc....407 296-6204
918 Wooden Blvd Orlando (32805) ***(G-13290)***
Unique Electronics Inc (PA)....407 422-3051
1320 26th St Orlando (32805) ***(G-13291)***
Unique Fbrctions Unlimited LLC....352 229-8511
12 Pine Trace Ter Ocala (34472) ***(G-12066)***
Unique Hits Music Pubg Inc....786 525-9525
7302 Nw 107th Pl Doral (33178) ***(G-3536)***
Unique Ink Printing Corp....954 829-2801
1934 Sw 8th Ave Boca Raton (33486) ***(G-767)***
Unique Led Products LLC....440 520-4959
408 Madonna North Port (34287) ***(G-11752)***
Unique Marble Inc....772 766-4432
780 8th Ct Vero Beach (32962) ***(G-18672)***
Unique Marble Polishing Inc....305 969-1554
18093 Sw 135th Ave Miami (33177) ***(G-10532)***
Unique Originals Inc....305 634-2274
19205 Sw 66th St Fort Lauderdale (33332) ***(G-4293)***
Unique Rabbit Studios Inc....954 691-1390
1631 S Dixie Hwy Ste B1 Pompano Beach (33060) ***(G-14899)***
Unique Recording Software Inc....917 854-5403
21218 Saint Andrews Blvd Boca Raton (33433) ***(G-768)***
Unique Technology Inc....941 358-5410
1523 Edgar Pl Sarasota (34240) ***(G-16627)***
Unique Technology Inds LLC....941 358-5410
1523 Edgar Pl Sarasota (34240) ***(G-16628)***
Unique Tool & Die LLC....772 464-5006
3343 S Us Highway 1 Ste 4 Fort Pierce (34982) ***(G-4766)***
Uniroyal Engineered Pdts LLC (HQ)....941 906-8580
1800 2nd St Ste 970 Sarasota (34236) ***(G-16629)***
Uniroyal Globl Engnred Pdts In (PA)....941 906-8580
1800 2nd St Ste 970 Sarasota (34236) ***(G-16630)***
Uniscan LLC....305 322-7669
10913 Nw 30th St Ste 101 Doral (33172) ***(G-3537)***
Unisigns Usa Inc....305 509-5232
5526 Nw 79th Ave Doral (33166) ***(G-3538)***
Unison Industries LLC (HQ)....904 739-4000
7575 Baymeadows Way Jacksonville (32256) ***(G-6879)***
Unisource Graphics and Signs, Fort Myers *Also called Eidolon Analytics Inc* ***(G-4441)***
Unisource Stone Inc....561 493-0660
2575 Se Federal Hwy # 101 Stuart (34994) ***(G-17043)***
Unite Parent Corp (PA)....800 432-1729
2000 Ultimate Way Weston (33326) ***(G-19174)***
Unitech Industries Corp....305 691-0330
7525 Nw 37th Ave Miami (33147) ***(G-10533)***
United Abrasives Inc....239 300-0033
3551 Westview Dr Naples (34104) ***(G-11446)***
United Adhesive Products Inc....863 698-9484
4202 Hammond Dr Winter Haven (33881) ***(G-19365)***
United Advantage Signs Inc....813 855-3300
206 Tower Dr Oldsmar (34677) ***(G-12273)***
United Advg Publications....954 730-9700
3313 W Coml Blvd Ste 130 Fort Lauderdale (33309) ***(G-4294)***
United Advg Publications Inc....407 297-0832
225 S Westmonte Dr # 3050 Altamonte Springs (32714) ***(G-81)***
United Aerospace Corporation....954 364-0085
9800 Premier Pkwy Miramar (33025) ***(G-11055)***
United AG Svcs Amer Inc....352 793-1682
534 Cr 529a Lake Panasoffkee (33538) ***(G-7464)***
United Armour Products LLC....813 767-9624
1601 N 39th St Tampa (33605) ***(G-18219)***
United Associates Group Inc....561 840-0050
6701 Garden Rd Ste 1 Riviera Beach (33404) ***(G-15387)***
United Beddings Corp....786 333-4795
421 W 28th St Hialeah (33010) ***(G-5659)***
United Biosource LLC (ubc)....877 599-7748
680 Century Pt Lake Mary (32746) ***(G-7457)***
United Cabinets Corp....305 887-5050
867 W 30th St Hialeah (33012) ***(G-5660)***
United Chair Industries LLC....386 333-0800
16442 Ivy Lake Dr Odessa (33556) ***(G-12162)***
United Circuits Inc....954 971-6860
1410 Sw 29th Ave Ste 300 Pompano Beach (33069) ***(G-14900)***
United Concrete Products LLC (HQ)....786 402-3536
8351 Nw 93rd St Medley (33166) ***(G-8747)***
United Drones LLC....305 978-1480
9146 Quartz Ln Naples (34120) ***(G-11447)***
United Electric Motor Inc....813 238-7872
905 E Ida St Tampa (33603) ***(G-18220)***
United Electronics Corporation....954 888-1024
1 Se 3rd Ave Ste 158 Miami (33131) ***(G-10534)***
United Energy Corporation....904 296-1168
855-21 St Johns Bluff Rd Jacksonville (32225) ***(G-6880)***
United Express Intl Corp....305 591-3292
7302 Nw 34th St Miami (33122) ***(G-10535)***
United Fabrication & Maint....863 295-9000
622 Snively Ave Eloise (33880) ***(G-3656)***
United Fabrication Shtmtl Inc....407 826-1933
1815 Tallokas Ave Orlando (32805) ***(G-13292)***
United Franchise Group, West Palm Beach *Also called Ufg Group Inc* ***(G-19074)***
United Fuel....305 992-2923
6900 Sw 8th St Miami (33144) ***(G-10536)***
United Granite Inc....813 391-4323
3906 S 51st St Tampa (33619) ***(G-18221)***
United Jice Companies Amer Inc....772 562-5442
505 66th Ave Sw Vero Beach (32968) ***(G-18673)***
United Machining Service Inc....407 422-7710
2410 Coolidge Ave Orlando (32804) ***(G-13293)***
United Manufacturing Services....941 224-1692
2908 29th Ave E Bradenton (34208) ***(G-1137)***
United Metal Fabrications Inc....305 962-1608
1635 Ne 133rd St North Miami (33181) ***(G-11661)***
United Metro Media, Jacksonville *Also called Job News* ***(G-6524)***
United Ntons Space Crps Mltary (PA)....702 373-2351
10310 County Highway 3280 Ponce De Leon (32455) ***(G-14920)***
United Oil Packers Inc....305 687-6457
3200 Nw 125th St Stop 4 Miami (33167) ***(G-10537)***
United Ophthalmics, Doral *Also called Hansa Ophthalmics LLC* ***(G-3378)***
United Pillow Mfg Inc....305 636-9747
5646 Nw 35th Ct Miami (33142) ***(G-10538)***
United Plastic Fabricating Inc....352 291-2477
5000 Nw 5th St Ocala (34482) ***(G-12067)***
United Printing LLC....954 554-7969
2323 Ne 26th Ave Pompano Beach (33062) ***(G-14901)***
United Printing Sales Inc....954 942-4300
51 N Federal Hwy Pompano Beach (33062) ***(G-14902)***
United Rail Inc....904 503-9757
13500 Sutton Park Dr S # 601 Jacksonville (32224) ***(G-6881)***
United Rentals North Amer Inc....239 690-0600
5491 Division Dr Fort Myers (33905) ***(G-4640)***
United Rentals North Amer Inc....850 478-2833
3310 Mclemore Dr Pensacola (32514) ***(G-14278)***
United Rentals North Amer Inc....941 755-3177
6851 26th Ct E Sarasota (34243) ***(G-16321)***
United Seal & Tag Label Corp....941 625-6799
19237 Pine Bluff Ct Port Charlotte (33948) ***(G-15004)***
United Ship Service Corp (PA)....954 583-4588
1341 Sw 21st Ter Fort Lauderdale (33312) ***(G-4295)***
United Sierra Group Corp....305 297-5835
8200 Commerce Way Miami Lakes (33016) ***(G-10873)***
United Signs Systems, Oldsmar *Also called United Advantage Signs Inc* ***(G-12273)***
United Space Coast Cables Inc....321 952-1040
7703 Tech Dr Ste 100 West Melbourne (32904) ***(G-18778)***
United State Postal Service....904 783-7145
1815 Silver St Jacksonville (32206) ***(G-6882)***
United States Awning Company....941 955-7010
1935 18th St Sarasota (34234) ***(G-16631)***
United States Concrete Pipe, Pompano Beach *Also called Mancini Inc* ***(G-14752)***
United States Crene, Orlando *Also called General Clamp Industries Inc* ***(G-12777)***
United States Fndry & Mfg Corp (HQ)....305 885-0301
8351 Nw 93rd St Medley (33166) ***(G-8748)***
United States Fndry & Mfg Corp....305 556-1661
3200 W 84th St Hialeah (33018) ***(G-5661)***
United States Green Enrgy Corp....540 295-4843
1074 Windchime Way Pensacola (32503) ***(G-14279)***
United States Gypsum Company....904 768-2501
6825 Evergreen Ave Jacksonville (32208) ***(G-6883)***
United States Gypsum Company....305 688-8744
3301 Nw 125th St Miami Shores (33167) ***(G-10886)***
United Strings Intl LLC....561 790-4191
352 Tall Pines Rd Ste G West Palm Beach (33413) ***(G-19075)***
United Technologies Carrier, Palm Beach Gardens *Also called Carrier Corporation* ***(G-13573)***
United Technologies Corp....954 538-8900
3601 S Flamingo Rd Miramar (33027) ***(G-11056)***
United Technologies Corp....860 565-4321
17900 Bee Line Hwy Jupiter (33478) ***(G-7137)***
United Trophy Manufacturing (PA)....407 841-2525
610 N Orange Ave Orlando (32801) ***(G-13294)***

ALPHABETIC

United Vertical Blinds LLC.......786 348-8000
1261 Nw 175th St Miami (33169) ***(G-10539)***
United Visual Branding LLC.......813 855-3300
206 Tower Dr Oldsmar (34677) ***(G-12274)***
United Wireless Tech Inc.......561 302-9350
300 Se 5th Ave Apt 8180 Boca Raton (33432) ***(G-769)***
United World Imports LLC.......904 208-1252
2542 Carriage Lamp Dr Jacksonville (32246) ***(G-6884)***
United World Printing Inc.......407 738-0888
236 Outlook Point Dr # 300 Orlando (32809) ***(G-13295)***
Unitime Systems Inc (PA).......407 233-2050
2600 Lake Lucien Dr # 200 Maitland (32751) ***(G-8482)***
Unitron Prcision Machining Inc.......407 299-4180
2482 Clark St Apopka (32703) ***(G-193)***
Unity Marine Inc.......954 321-1727
2860 W State Road 84 # 118 Fort Lauderdale (33312) ***(G-4296)***
Universal Alum Windows & Doors.......305 825-7900
1675 W 31st Pl Hialeah (33012) ***(G-5662)***
Universal Bakery LLC.......786 566-3303
1050 Ali Baba Ave Opa Locka (33054) ***(G-12367)***
Universal Brass Fabrication.......561 691-5445
109 Palm Point Cir Palm Beach Gardens (33418) ***(G-13633)***
Universal Cntact Lenses of Fla.......904 731-3410
3840 Williamsburg Pk Blvd Jacksonville (32257) ***(G-6885)***
Universal Concrete & Ready Mix.......305 512-3400
10505 W Okeechobee Rd # 10 Hialeah (33018) ***(G-5663)***
Universal Concrete & Ready Mix.......305 888-4101
11790 Nw South River Dr Medley (33178) ***(G-8749)***
Universal Crgo Doors & Svc LLC.......305 594-9175
8490 Nw 68th St Miami (33166) ***(G-10540)***
Universal Die Services Inc.......863 665-6092
2646 Lasso Ln Lakeland (33801) ***(G-7828)***
Universal Erectors Inc.......813 621-8111
5668 Fshhawk Crssing Blvd Lithia (33547) ***(G-8225)***
Universal Forest Products, Tampa *Also called Ufp Tampa LLC* ***(G-18212)***
Universal Gear, Tampa *Also called S I P Corporation* ***(G-18075)***
Universal Generators LLC.......954 383-5394
5231 Pinetree Rd Pompano Beach (33067) ***(G-14903)***
Universal Graphics & Prtg Inc.......561 845-6404
120 Us Highway 1 Ste 1 North Palm Beach (33408) ***(G-11729)***
Universal HM Hlth Indus Sups I.......813 493-7904
7320 E Fletcher Ave Tampa (33637) ***(G-18222)***
Universal Kit Cabinets Closets.......305 406-9096
2905 Welcome Cir Kissimmee (34746) ***(G-7307)***
Universal Kitchen Center Inc.......305 218-5108
7836 Nw 193rd Ter Hialeah (33015) ***(G-5664)***
Universal Labeling Systems Inc (PA).......727 327-2123
3501 8th Ave S Saint Petersburg (33711) ***(G-15946)***
Universal Metal Works Inc.......904 765-2600
14600 Duval Pl W Ste 52 Jacksonville (32218) ***(G-6886)***
Universal Microwave Corp (PA).......352 754-2200
6036 Nature Coast Blvd Brooksville (34602) ***(G-1286)***
Universal Networking Svcs Co.......281 825-9790
200 2nd Ave S Ste 432 Saint Petersburg (33701) ***(G-15947)***
Universal Packaging Co, Medley *Also called Universal Transactions Inc* ***(G-8750)***
Universal Paverscapes LLC.......904 428-2010
3760 University Blvd S # 1033 Jacksonville (32216) ***(G-6887)***
Universal PC Organization Inc.......321 285-9206
8082 Wellsmere Cir Orlando (32835) ***(G-13296)***
Universal Polishing Systems.......407 227-9516
4333 Silver Star Rd # 175 Orlando (32808) ***(G-13297)***
Universal Precision Inds Inc.......727 581-7097
1876 Lake Ave Se Ste A Largo (33771) ***(G-8071)***
Universal Printing Company.......305 592-5387
3100 Nw 74th Ave Miami (33122) ***(G-10541)***
Universal Prof Coatings Inc.......954 294-5236
2125 Candlewood Ct Middleburg (32068) ***(G-10913)***
Universal Recording, Miami Beach *Also called Umg Recordings Inc* ***(G-10722)***
Universal Ribbon Corporation.......305 471-0828
8111 Nw 68th St Miami (33166) ***(G-10542)***
Universal School Products Inc.......904 273-8590
2309 Sawgrass Village Dr Ponte Vedra Beach (32082) ***(G-14956)***
Universal Screen Graphics Inc.......813 623-5335
4897 W Waters Ave Ste H Tampa (33634) ***(G-18223)***
Universal Seat Covers Auto ACC (PA).......305 262-3955
2370 Ludlam Rd Miami (33155) ***(G-10543)***
Universal Signs.......954 366-1535
6045 Nw 31st Ave Fort Lauderdale (33309) ***(G-4297)***
Universal Signs & Accessories, Fort Pierce *Also called McCain Sales of Florida Inc* ***(G-4717)***
Universal Software Solutions.......727 298-8877
912 Drew St Ste 104 Clearwater (33755) ***(G-1929)***
Universal Stncling Mkg Systems.......727 894-3027
205 15th Ave Se Saint Petersburg (33701) ***(G-15948)***
Universal Surgical Appliance.......305 652-0810
400 Ne 191st St Miami (33179) ***(G-10544)***
Universal Tech Inc.......786 220-8032
3042 Nw 72nd Ave Miami (33122) ***(G-10545)***
Universal Training Sftwr Inc.......561 981-6421
301 Ne 51st St Ste 1240 Boca Raton (33431) ***(G-770)***
Universal Transactions Inc.......305 887-4677
12870 Nw South River Dr Medley (33178) ***(G-8750)***
Universal Welding Service Co.......305 898-9130
9921 Nw 80th Ave Unit 1u Miami Lakes (33016) ***(G-10874)***
Universal Wood Design.......772 569-5389
1708 Old Dixie Hwy # 102 Vero Beach (32960) ***(G-18674)***
Universalms Inc.......786 285-7531
711 S 20th Ave Apt 7 Hollywood (33020) ***(G-5933)***
Uniware Houseware Corp.......305 952-4958
5275 Nw 163rd St Miami Lakes (33014) ***(G-10875)***
Uniweld Products Inc (PA).......954 584-2000
2850 Ravenswood Rd Fort Lauderdale (33312) ***(G-4298)***
Unlimited Cabinet Designs Inc.......954 923-3269
1798 Sw 31st Ave Hallandale (33009) ***(G-5165)***
Unlimited Impressions, Doral *Also called Restifo Investments LLC* ***(G-3484)***
Unlimited Inpressions Inc.......305 606-2699
1424 Mw 82nd Ave Miami (33176) ***(G-10546)***
Unlimited Marine Mfg Inc.......305 420-6034
2637 W 76th St Hialeah (33016) ***(G-5665)***
Unlimited Printing & Copying, Oldsmar *Also called Print One Inc* ***(G-12262)***
Unlimited Welding Inc.......407 327-3333
235 Old Sanford Oviedo Rd Winter Springs (32708) ***(G-19487)***
Uo Packers, Miami *Also called United Oil Packers Inc* ***(G-10537)***
Up - N - Atom.......904 716-5431
3443 Maiden Voyage Cir S Jacksonville (32257) ***(G-6888)***
Up2speed Printing Inc.......850 508-2620
8081 W 28th Ave Hialeah (33016) ***(G-5666)***
Upright Aluminum Inc.......239 731-6644
7908 Interstate Ct North Fort Myers (33917) ***(G-11608)***
Uproxx Media Inc.......917 603-2374
1602 Alton Rd Ste 447 Miami Beach (33139) ***(G-10723)***
UPS Store 4332, The, Miramar *Also called Lujotex LLC* ***(G-11011)***
Upstream Installation Inc.......904 829-3507
1835 Us Highway 1 S # 119 Saint Augustine (32084) ***(G-15629)***
Upt Vector, Deland *Also called Uninsred Untd Prchute Tech LLC* ***(G-3027)***
Upton House Cooler Corporation.......305 633-2531
2490 Nw 7th Ave Miami (33127) ***(G-10547)***
Uptown Cstm Cabinets of Naples.......239 825-8432
6260 Shirley St Ste 603 Naples (34109) ***(G-11448)***
Ur Cabinets.......813 434-6454
4042 W Kennedy Blvd Tampa (33609) ***(G-18224)***
Ural Associates Inc.......305 446-9462
3608 Anderson Rd Coral Gables (33134) ***(G-2200)***
Urano Publishing Inc.......305 233-3365
8871 Sw 129th Ter Miami (33176) ***(G-10548)***
Urban Charge LLC.......305 809-6625
1330 West Ave Apt 1411 Miami Beach (33139) ***(G-10724)***
Urban Extreme LLC.......954 248-9007
4303 Hayes St Hollywood (33021) ***(G-5934)***
Urban Metals LLC.......813 241-2801
1301 N 26th St Tampa (33605) ***(G-18225)***
Urban Stone Works.......305 754-7171
7025 Ne 2nd Ave Miami (33138) ***(G-10549)***
Urbaprint LLC.......786 502-3223
649 Conservation Dr Weston (33327) ***(G-19175)***
Urecon Systems Inc.......321 638-2364
4046 N Goldenrod Rd 162 Winter Park (32792) ***(G-19455)***
Urecon Systems Inc.......904 695-3332
7136 Smallow Run Winter Park (32792) ***(G-19456)***
Uren North America LLC.......410 924-3478
2990 Ponce De Leon Blvd Coral Gables (33134) ***(G-2201)***
Uribemonica.......305 856-3857
2127 Sw 16th Ter Miami (33145) ***(G-10550)***
Uroshape LLC.......321 960-2484
1130 S Harbor City Blvd Melbourne (32901) ***(G-8968)***
US 1 Truck Sales LLC.......904 545-1233
10126 New Kings Rd Jacksonville (32219) ***(G-6889)***
US American Plastic Corp.......305 200-3683
2164 Nw 22nd Ct Miami (33142) ***(G-10551)***
US Applied Phys Ics Group.......321 567-7270
1650 Chaffee Dr Titusville (32780) ***(G-18471)***
US Applied Physics Group LLC.......321 607-9023
7065 Challenger Ave Titusville (32780) ***(G-18472)***
US Barcodes Inc.......727 849-1196
6740 Commerce Ave Port Richey (34668) ***(G-15074)***
US Bindery Inc.......305 622-7070
5330 Nw 161st St Miami Lakes (33014) ***(G-10876)***
US Blanks LLC.......321 253-3626
282 N Wickham Rd Melbourne (32935) ***(G-8969)***
US Blinds, South Daytona *Also called Florida Plntn Shutters LLC* ***(G-16801)***
US Body Source, Jacksonville *Also called Rfl & Figlio LLC* ***(G-6723)***
US Building Systems Corp.......954 281-2100
401 Fairway Dr Ste 100 Deerfield Beach (33441) ***(G-2931)***
US Bullnosing.......954 567-0404
216 Ne 33rd St Oakland Park (33334) ***(G-11856)***
US China Mining Group Inc.......813 514-2873
15310 Amberly Dr Ste 250 Tampa (33647) ***(G-18226)***
US Chutes Corp.......860 567-4000
751 Park Of Commerce Dr # 108 Boca Raton (33487) ***(G-771)***

US Communications Industries (PA) 772 468-7477
2733 Peters Rd Fort Pierce (34945) ***(G-4767)***
US Composites 561 588-1001
6670 White Dr Riviera Beach (33407) ***(G-15388)***
US Concrete Products Corp 954 973-0368
1878 Nw 21st St Pompano Beach (33069) ***(G-14904)***
US Conveyor Solutions Inc 352 343-0085
3714 County Road 561 Tavares (32778) ***(G-18356)***
US Cremation Equipment, Orlando *Also called American Incinerators Corp* ***(G-12470)***
US Custom Fabrication Inc 954 917-6161
1858 Nw 21st St Pompano Beach (33069) ***(G-14905)***
US Defib Medical Tech LLC (PA) 305 887-7552
7831 Nw 72nd Ave Medley (33166) ***(G-8751)***
US Diagnostics Inc 866 216-5308
6600 Nw 16th St Ste 1 Plantation (33313) ***(G-14561)***
US Foundry, Medley *Also called United States Fndry & Mfg Corp* ***(G-8748)***
US Foundry, Hialeah *Also called United States Fndry & Mfg Corp* ***(G-5661)***
US Fuels Inc 254 559-1212
928 Rotonda Cir Rotonda West (33947) ***(G-15460)***
US Generator Inc 772 778-0131
725 Commerce Center Dr J Sebastian (32958) ***(G-16675)***
US Global Glass LLC 305 651-6630
220 Ne 187th St Miami (33179) ***(G-10552)***
US Granite and Quartz, Weston *Also called National Stoneworks LLC* ***(G-19152)***
US Hemp and Oil LLC 352 817-2455
1010 Ne 16th St Ocala (34470) ***(G-12068)***
US Implant Solutions LLC 407 971-8054
1778 N Park Ave Ste 200 Maitland (32751) ***(G-8483)***
US Ink A Div Sun Chem Corp 904 786-1474
4725 Javeline Cir Middleburg (32068) ***(G-10914)***
US Ink A Division Sun Chemical, Middleburg *Also called US Ink A Div Sun Chem Corp* ***(G-10914)***
US Iron LLC 765 210-4111
755 Grand Blvd Ste 105b Miramar Beach (32550) ***(G-11070)***
US Ironworks Company 850 588-5995
328 Wahoo Rd Panama City (32408) ***(G-13959)***
US Marine Canvas 904 687-5058
2475 Deer Run Rd Saint Augustine (32084) ***(G-15630)***
US Marine Supply, Dania Beach *Also called US Metal Fabricators Inc* ***(G-2474)***
US Metal Fabricators Inc 954 921-0800
800 Old Griffin Rd Dania Beach (33004) ***(G-2474)***
US Mobile Pro LLC 973 365-1812
6422 Milner Blvd Ste 103 Orlando (32809) ***(G-13298)***
US Mold Inc 561 748-2223
612 N Orange Ave Ste A4 Jupiter (33458) ***(G-7138)***
US Natural Gas Corp 727 482-1505
735 Arlington Ave N # 308 Saint Petersburg (33701) ***(G-15949)***
US Nutraceuticals Inc 352 357-2004
2751 Nutra Ln Eustis (32726) ***(G-3720)***
US Orthotics Inc 813 621-7797
8605 Palm River Rd Tampa (33619) ***(G-18227)***
US Pack Group LLC 954 556-1840
5011 N Hiatus Rd Sunrise (33351) ***(G-17193)***
US Patriot LLC 803 787-9398
3108 N Boundary Blvd Tampa (33621) ***(G-18228)***
US Patriot Industries Inc 954 802-7402
100 Golden Isles Dr Hallandale Beach (33009) ***(G-5221)***
US Paver Co 954 292-4373
22809 Horse Shoe Way Boca Raton (33428) ***(G-772)***
US Paverscape LLC 772 223-7287
1735 Se Federal Hwy Stuart (34994) ***(G-17044)***
US Pet Imaging LLC 941 795-3780
4351 Cortez Rd W Bradenton (34210) ***(G-1138)***
US Pet Imaging LLC (PA) 941 921-0383
3830 Bee Ridge Rd Ste 100 Sarasota (34233) ***(G-16632)***
US Pipe Fabrication LLC 860 769-6097
109 5th St Orlando (32824) ***(G-13299)***
US Precast Corp 305 364-8253
3200 W 84th St Hialeah (33018) ***(G-5667)***
US Precast Corporation 305 885-8471
8351 Nw 93rd St Medley (33166) ***(G-8752)***
US Precious Metals Inc 786 814-5804
1825 Ponce De Leon Blvd Coral Gables (33134) ***(G-2202)***
US Precision Manufacturing Inc 954 332-2921
3220 Sw 15th St Deerfield Beach (33442) ***(G-2932)***
US Recreational Alliance Inc 954 782-7279
820 Sw 14th Ct Pompano Beach (33060) ***(G-14906)***
US Sample Corp 954 495-4525
10386 Stonebridge Blvd Boca Raton (33498) ***(G-773)***
US Security Defense Corp 407 979-1478
1181 E Alfred St Tavares (32778) ***(G-18357)***
US Sheet Metal Inc 305 884-7705
7333 Nw 66th St Miami (33166) ***(G-10553)***
US Sign and Mill Inc 239 936-9154
7981 Mainline Pkwy Fort Myers (33912) ***(G-4641)***
US Signs Inc 727 862-7933
16631 Scheer Blvd Port Richey (34667) ***(G-15075)***
US Spars Inc 386 462-3760
6320 Nw 123rd Pl Gainesville (32653) ***(G-5014)***
US Stem Cell Inc (PA) 954 835-1500
1560 Sawgrs Corp Pkwy # 4 Sunrise (33323) ***(G-17194)***
US Submarines Inc (PA) 208 687-9057
9015 17th Pl Vero Beach (32966) ***(G-18675)***
US Truss Inc 561 686-4000
3400 45th St West Palm Beach (33407) ***(G-19076)***
US Wood Work & Service 954 675-7153
372 W Tropical Trce Saint Johns (32259) ***(G-15683)***
USA Aluminum 305 303-9121
1880 S Ocean Dr Hallandale Beach (33009) ***(G-5222)***
USA Corp Airplane 954 399-8472
4601 Sheridan St Hollywood (33021) ***(G-5935)***
USA Express Pallets Corp 786 251-9543
4655 Nw 36th Ave Miami (33142) ***(G-10554)***
USA Exterior LLC 813 515-5181
301 W Platt St Ste 144 Tampa (33606) ***(G-18229)***
USA Keratin, Boca Raton *Also called Eve Corporation* ***(G-524)***
USA Manufacturing Group LLC 786 253-3152
1130 Alfonso Ave Coral Gables (33146) ***(G-2203)***
USA Marine Engines 954 614-4810
2600 Sw 3rd Ave Fort Lauderdale (33315) ***(G-4299)***
USA Marine Engines LLC 954 383-1870
1540 Sw 106th Ter Davie (33324) ***(G-2609)***
USA Maritime Enterprises Inc 954 764-8360
2600 Esnhwer Blvd Lhigh C Lehigh Cement Fort Lauderdale (33308) ***(G-4300)***
USA Plastic Industry, Miami *Also called Emmanuel Holdings Inc* ***(G-9524)***
USA Recmar Corp 786 554-3505
918 Nw 106th Avenue Cir Miami (33172) ***(G-10555)***
USA Scientific Inc (HQ) 352 237-6288
346 Sw 57th Ave Ocala (34474) ***(G-12069)***
USA Sheet Metal Inc 786 517-3482
650 W 18th St Hialeah (33010) ***(G-5668)***
USA Shutter Company LLC 239 596-8883
2141 Flint Dr Fort Myers (33916) ***(G-4642)***
USA Sign Company 954 497-3293
1503 Island Way Weston (33326) ***(G-19176)***
USA Signs Inc 305 470-2333
7230 Nw 46th St Miami (33166) ***(G-10556)***
USA Today, Fort Myers *Also called Anna Andres* ***(G-4364)***
USA Vigil 386 736-8464
1400 Flight Line Blvd Deland (32724) ***(G-3029)***
Usacompressors.com, Miami *Also called Miami Compressor Rbldrs Inc* ***(G-9995)***
Usaop Inc 386 212-9514
578 Sterthaus Dr Ormond Beach (32174) ***(G-13406)***
Usaxray, Saint Petersburg *Also called Burkhart Roentgen Intl Inc* ***(G-15732)***
USB Plastics 727 375-8840
11805 State Road 54 Odessa (33556) ***(G-12163)***
Usbev Plastics LLC 813 855-0700
3874 Tampa Rd Oldsmar (34677) ***(G-12275)***
Usbev Products Inc 727 375-8840
11805 State Road 54 Odessa (33556) ***(G-12164)***
USF Fabrication Inc (PA) 305 556-1661
3200 W 84th St Hialeah (33018) ***(G-5669)***
USG International Ltd 305 688-8744
3001 Nw 125th St Miami (33167) ***(G-10557)***
Usher Land & Timber Inc 352 493-4221
6551 Nw 100th St Chiefland (32626) ***(G-1539)***
Usmi Pallets Inc 813 765-4309
3301 Sam Allen Oaks Cir Plant City (33565) ***(G-14475)***
Uspharma Ltd 954 817-4418
13900 Nw 57th Ct Miami Lakes (33014) ***(G-10877)***
Ussi LLC 941 244-2408
752 Commerce Dr Ste 15 Venice (34292) ***(G-18583)***
Usvi Pharmaceuticals LLC 305 643-8841
1301 Nw 84th Ave Ste 101 Doral (33126) ***(G-3539)***
UTC Aerospace Systems, Miami Gardens *Also called Goodrich Corporation* ***(G-10744)***
UTC Aerospace Systems, Jacksonville *Also called Simmonds Precision Pdts Inc* ***(G-6776)***
UTC Aerospace Systems 954 538-8971
3601 S Flamingo Rd Miramar (33027) ***(G-11057)***
UTC Fire & Security Lincolnton, Palm Beach Gardens *Also called Carrier Fire SEC Americas Corp* ***(G-13574)***
Utilis Usa LLC 850 226-7043
36 Tupelo Ave Se Fort Walton Beach (32548) ***(G-4836)***
Utilitech Inc 863 767-0600
130 W Main St Wauchula (33873) ***(G-18695)***
Utilities Structures Inc 239 334-7757
2700 Evans Ave Unit 2 Fort Myers (33901) ***(G-4643)***
Utility Vault, Wildwood *Also called Oldcastle Infrastructure Inc* ***(G-19198)***
Utilytech Company 813 778-6952
630 Baldwin Dr Kissimmee (34758) ***(G-7308)***
Utopia Grilling LLC 727 488-1355
3511 Cockatoo Dr New Port Richey (34652) ***(G-11518)***
Uts Systems LLC 850 226-4301
36 Tupelo Ave Se Ste A Fort Walton Beach (32548) ***(G-4837)***
Uvisors 813 716-1113
4919 W Bartlett Dr Tampa (33603) ***(G-18230)***
Uvlrx Therapeutics Inc 813 309-1976
640 Brooker Creek Blvd Oldsmar (34677) ***(G-12276)***

Uzzi Amphibious Gear LLC.....954 777-9595
205 Ansin Blvd Hallandale Beach (33009) *(G-5223)*
V & C Supply Ornamental Corp.....305 634-9040
6400 Nw 72nd Ave Miami (33166) *(G-10558)*
V & F Air Conditioning Sup LLC.....305 477-1040
7320 Nw 12th St Ste 107 Miami (33126) *(G-10559)*
V & G Industries Inc.....786 853-1265
4965 E 10th Ct Hialeah (33013) *(G-5670)*
V A Electrical Motors Center.....305 825-3327
4011 W 18th Ave Hialeah (33012) *(G-5671)*
V and N Advanced Auto Sys LLC.....321 504-6440
415 Gus Hipp Blvd Rockledge (32955) *(G-15455)*
V G Carpentry LLC.....786 531-7824
4855 E 10th Ct Hialeah (33013) *(G-5672)*
V G I, Largo *Also called Vgi Medical LLC (G-8073)*
V I P Printing.....386 258-3326
133 W Intl Speedway Blvd Daytona Beach (32114) *(G-2730)*
V J Pro Fabrics, Mount Dora *Also called C P Enterprises of Apopka Inc (G-11098)*
V M P, Boca Raton *Also called Vehicle Maint Program Inc (G-776)*
V M Visual Mdsg Dctr Group Inc.....305 759-9910
600 Nw 62nd St Miami (33150) *(G-10560)*
V P I, Lake Worth *Also called Vertex Precision Inc (G-7597)*
V P Press Inc.....954 581-7531
3934 Davie Blvd Fort Lauderdale (33312) *(G-4301)*
V P R A R T LLC.....786 205-4526
2630 W 81st St Hialeah (33016) *(G-5673)*
V-Blox Corporation.....904 425-4908
3653 Regent Blvd Ste 408 Jacksonville (32224) *(G-6890)*
V-Bro Products LLC.....352 267-6235
28114 County Road 561 Tavares (32778) *(G-18358)*
V-Raptor Aircraft LLC (PA).....772 388-3334
7756 130th St Sebastian (32958) *(G-16676)*
V12 Data, Wesley Chapel *Also called Datamentors LLC (G-18743)*
V2 Cigs (PA).....305 517-1149
1521 Alton Rd Ste 275 Miami Beach (33139) *(G-10725)*
V2 Cigs.....305 240-6387
3050 Biscayne Blvd # 700 Miami (33137) *(G-10561)*
Vac Cubes Inc.....727 944-3337
536 E Tarpon Ave Ste 5 Tarpon Springs (34689) *(G-18329)*
Vac-Con Inc (HQ).....904 284-4200
969 Hall Park Rd Green Cove Springs (32043) *(G-5075)*
Vac-Tron Equipment, Okahumpka *Also called American Mfg & Mch Inc (G-12168)*
Vacation Vault, Doral *Also called Blue Chip Group LLC (G-3280)*
Vade Mecum Pubg Group LLC.....813 969-1623
4327 Honey Vista Cir Tampa (33624) *(G-18231)*
Val DOr Apparel LLC (PA).....954 363-7340
6820 Lyons Tech Cir # 220 Coconut Creek (33073) *(G-2100)*
Valco Group Inc.....813 870-0482
2203 N Lois Ave Ste 937 Tampa (33607) *(G-18232)*
Valdor Apparel, Coconut Creek *Also called Val DOr Apparel LLC (G-2100)*
Valensa International, Eustis *Also called US Nutraceuticals Inc (G-3720)*
Valentina Signa Inc.....305 264-0673
7343 Nw 56th St Miami (33166) *(G-10562)*
Valentines Glass & Metal, Fort Myers *Also called Greg Valentine LLC (G-4473)*
Valentini Italian Spc Co.....305 638-0822
4290 Nw 37th Ct Miami (33142) *(G-10563)*
Valiant Products Inc.....863 688-7998
939 Quincy St Lakeland (33815) *(G-7829)*
Valiant Transport Group LLC.....855 648-7423
5030 Chmpn Blvd Ste G11 Boca Raton (33496) *(G-774)*
Validsoft.....813 334-9745
19103 Centre Rose Blvd Lutz (33558) *(G-8422)*
Valley Forge Textiles LLC.....954 971-1776
1390 Sw 30th Ave Pompano Beach (33069) *(G-14907)*
Valley Proteins (de) Inc.....704 718-6568
6142 Old Soutel Ct Jacksonville (32219) *(G-6891)*
Valley Proteins (de) Inc.....910 282-7900
465 Caboose Pl Mulberry (33860) *(G-11140)*
Valley Surgical Inc.....954 768-9886
1543 Se 13th St Fort Lauderdale (33316) *(G-4302)*
Valleymedia Inc.....510 565-7559
200 Se 6th St Ste 505 Fort Lauderdale (33301) *(G-4303)*
Valmont Newmark Inc.....863 533-6465
4131 Us Highway 17 S Bartow (33830) *(G-335)*
Valmont Stheastern Galvanizing, Miami *Also called Industrial Glvnzers Stheastern (G-9740)*
Valor Latin Group Inc.....305 791-5255
8320 Nw 14th St Doral (33126) *(G-3540)*
Value Providers LLC.....321 567-0919
2441 Bellevue Ave Daytona Beach (32114) *(G-2731)*
Valuesafes Inc.....877 629-6214
24123 Peachland Blvd Port Charlotte (33954) *(G-15005)*
Valve Research & Mfg Co, Deerfield Beach *Also called Jet Research Development Inc (G-2850)*
Valvetrain Amplification.....407 886-7656
560 Sand Wedge Loop Apopka (32712) *(G-194)*
Vampa Tires Supplies Inc.....305 888-1001
7243 Nw 54th St Miami (33166) *(G-10564)*
Vampire Wire, Lutz *Also called Sound Connections Intl (G-8419)*
Van Aernam Logging & Trucking.....352 498-5809
County Rd 351 A Cross City (32628) *(G-2369)*
Van Aernam Timber Management, Cross City *Also called Van Aernam Logging & Trucking (G-2369)*
Van Charles Inc.....954 394-3242
4794 Ne 11th Ave Oakland Park (33334) *(G-11857)*
Van Gogh Signs & Displays.....813 849-7446
5020 N Florida Ave Tampa (33603) *(G-18233)*
Van Linda Iron Works Inc.....561 586-8400
3787 Boutwell Rd Lake Worth Beach (33461) *(G-7622)*
Van Nevel Aerospace LLC.....337 936-2504
1932 Holley Timber Rd Cottondale (32431) *(G-2333)*
Van Teal Hospitality Inc.....305 751-6767
13480 Sw 131st St Miami (33186) *(G-10565)*
Van Teal Inc.....305 751-6767
7240 Ne 4th Ave Miami (33138) *(G-10566)*
Van Tibolli Beauty Corp.....305 390-0044
4800 Nw 15th Ave Unit E Fort Lauderdale (33309) *(G-4304)*
Van Zant Timber Incorporated.....904 845-4661
373120 Kings Ferry Rd Hilliard (32046) *(G-5720)*
Van-Ess Manufacturing Inc.....352 799-1015
15311 Flight Path Dr Brooksville (34604) *(G-1287)*
Vanavac Inc.....813 752-1391
1309 Joe Mcintosh Rd Plant City (33565) *(G-14476)*
Vanbert Corporation.....561 945-5856
1855 Sw 4th Ave Ste B3 Delray Beach (33444) *(G-3154)*
Vandalay Inds Manatee Cnty LLC.....941 756-6028
6832 14th St W Bradenton (34207) *(G-1139)*
Vandeplas Publishing.....407 562-1947
801 International Pkwy # 500 Lake Mary (32746) *(G-7458)*
Vanguard Products Group Inc.....813 855-9639
720 Brooker Creek Blvd Oldsmar (34677) *(G-12277)*
Vanguard Protex Global, Oldsmar *Also called Vanguard Products Group Inc (G-12277)*
Vanguard Systems Corp.....727 528-0121
10460 Roosevelt Blvd N Saint Petersburg (33716) *(G-15950)*
Vanguardistas LLC.....386 868-2919
564 S Yonge St Ormond Beach (32174) *(G-13407)*
Vanity Fair Brands LP.....904 538-0288
10300 Southside Blvd Jacksonville (32256) *(G-6892)*
Vanity Furs of Avondale LLC.....904 387-9900
4555 Saint Johns Ave # 6 Jacksonville (32210) *(G-6893)*
Vanlex Clothing Inc.....305 431-4669
5850 Miami Lakes Dr E Miami Lakes (33014) *(G-10878)*
Vanlympia Inc.....727 725-5055
605 7th Ave N Safety Harbor (34695) *(G-15507)*
Vapeworld, Boca Raton *Also called Warehouse Goods LLC (G-787)*
Vapex Environmental Tech Inc.....407 277-0900
2971 Oxbow Cir Ste A Cocoa (32926) *(G-2055)*
Vapor Artillery, Hialeah *Also called V P R A R T LLC (G-5673)*
Vapor Engineering Inc.....850 434-3191
147 Mirabelle Cir Pensacola (32514) *(G-14280)*
Vapor Group Inc (PA).....954 792-8450
20725 Ne 16th Ave Ste A4 Miami (33179) *(G-10567)*
Vapor Group Inc (PA).....954 792-8450
20200 W Dixie Hwy Ste 906 Miami (33180) *(G-10568)*
Vaprzone LLC.....941 882-4841
448 Us Highway 41 Byp N Venice (34285) *(G-18584)*
Vargas Enterprises Inc.....561 989-0908
2518 Nw 64th Blvd Boca Raton (33496) *(G-775)*
Variance Reynolds Mtc.....954 765-6320
3810 Nw 7th St Lauderhill (33311) *(G-8123)*
Varibelt Incorporated.....305 775-1568
13216 Sw 45th Ln Miami (33175) *(G-10569)*
Various Inc (PA).....561 900-3691
1615 S Congress Ave # 10 Delray Beach (33445) *(G-3155)*
Varnums Rest Home, Bristol *Also called Ruby Vanrum (G-1203)*
Vasco Winds LLC.....561 691-7171
700 Universe Blvd Juno Beach (33408) *(G-6986)*
Vasquez Custom Metals Inc.....813 248-3348
3723 N 15th St Tampa (33610) *(G-18234)*
Vass Holdings Inc (PA).....863 295-5664
146 Avenue B Nw Winter Haven (33881) *(G-19366)*
Vault Spirits Company.....941 306-3331
8437 Tuttle Ave Ste 202 Sarasota (34243) *(G-16322)*
Vault Structures Inc.....239 332-3270
3640 Work Dr Fort Myers (33916) *(G-4644)*
Vaya Space, Cocoa *Also called Rocket Crafters Launch LLC (G-2049)*
Vb Custom Signs Inc.....772 713-5678
2555 27th Ave Ste G4 Vero Beach (32960) *(G-18676)*
Vc Displays Inc.....352 796-0060
15250 Flight Path Dr Brooksville (34604) *(G-1288)*
Vc Serum LLC.....305 778-2190
425 Ne 22nd St Apt 2505 Miami (33137) *(G-10570)*
Vc Technology, Brooksville *Also called Vc Displays Inc (G-1288)*
Vdc Display Systems, Cocoa *Also called Video Display Corporation (G-2056)*
Vdh Worldwide LLC.....866 304-2388
6452 Quail Hollow Blvd Wesley Chapel (33544) *(G-18763)*
Veatic.....888 474-2999
2450 Smith St Ste P Kissimmee (34744) *(G-7309)*

Vecellio & Grogan Inc....305 822-5322
18300 Nw 122nd Ave Hialeah (33018) ***(G-5674)***
Vecellio Management Svcs Inc....561 793-2102
101 Sansburys Way West Palm Beach (33411) ***(G-19077)***
Vecom Usa LLC....813 901-5300
4803 George Rd Ste 300 Tampa (33634) ***(G-18235)***
Vector Group Ltd (PA)....305 579-8000
4400 Biscayne Blvd Miami (33137) ***(G-10571)***
Vector Solutions, Tampa *Also called Vector-Solutionscom Inc* ***(G-18236)***
Vector-Solutionscom Inc (PA)....813 207-0012
4890 W Kennedy Blvd # 30 Tampa (33609) ***(G-18236)***
Vedic Origins Inc....407 712-5614
478 E Altamonte Dr # 108 Altamonte Springs (32701) ***(G-82)***
Vee Enterprises Inc....954 960-0300
4100 N Powerline Rd I5 Pompano Beach (33073) ***(G-14908)***
Vee Industries Inc....561 732-1083
211 Se 9th Ave Boynton Beach (33435) ***(G-973)***
Veeam Software Corporation....614 339-8200
15137 Sw 36th St Davie (33331) ***(G-2610)***
Veedis Clinical Systems....954 344-0498
1380 N University Dr # 102 Plantation (33322) ***(G-14562)***
Veethree Electronics & Mar LLC....941 538-7775
2050 47th Ter E Bradenton (34203) ***(G-1140)***
Veethree Instruments, Bradenton *Also called Veethree Electronics & Mar LLC* ***(G-1140)***
Vega....239 574-1798
447 Ne 8th Ter Cape Coral (33909) ***(G-1490)***
Vegan Suckers LLc....904 265-5263
11111 San Jose Blvd Ste 5 Jacksonville (32223) ***(G-6894)***
Veggiespetit Pois Inc....305 826-7867
2202 W 78th St Hialeah (33016) ***(G-5675)***
Vehicle Maint Program Inc....561 362-6080
3595 N Dixie Hwy Ste 7 Boca Raton (33431) ***(G-776)***
Vei Technologies Inc....954 653-0210
3223 Nw 10th Ter Ste 605 Fort Lauderdale (33309) ***(G-4305)***
Vela Research LP....727 507-5300
5516 Rio Vista Dr Clearwater (33760) ***(G-1930)***
Velcorp Gems Vels, Green Cove Springs *Also called Virginia Electronic & Ltg Corp* ***(G-5076)***
Velez Custom Cabinetry Corp....772 418-9565
5810 Nw Gillespie Ave Port Saint Lucie (34986) ***(G-15160)***
Velgen Wheels, Miami *Also called Sg Global LLC* ***(G-10329)***
Velmaxxx Enterprises Inc....239 689-4343
10941 Gladiolus Dr Unit 9 Fort Myers (33908) ***(G-4645)***
Velocity Aerospace - Nmb Inc....214 396-9030
570 Ne 185th St North Miami Beach (33179) ***(G-11708)***
Velocity Aircraft Inc....772 589-1860
200 Airport Dr W Sebastian (32958) ***(G-16677)***
Velocity Inc....772 589-1860
200 Airport Dr W Sebastian (32958) ***(G-16678)***
Velocity Machine Works LLC....850 727-5066
364 Marpan Ln Tallahassee (32305) ***(G-17343)***
Veltia Usa LLC....305 298-8262
2525 Ponce De Leon Blvd # 300 Coral Gables (33134) ***(G-2204)***
Venair Inc....305 362-8920
16713 Park Centre Blvd Miami Gardens (33169) ***(G-10758)***
Venancio Usa Inc....321 418-9489
2021 Sw 31st Ave Hallandale (33009) ***(G-5166)***
Venchi US Inc....646 448-8663
1111 Brickell Ave # 2650 Miami (33131) ***(G-10572)***
Venco Marine Inc....954 923-0036
2012 Hayes St Hollywood (33020) ***(G-5936)***
Vendapin LLC (PA)....352 796-2693
16381 Cherokee Rd Brooksville (34601) ***(G-1289)***
Vending Company, Boca Raton *Also called Rocket Vending Inc* ***(G-692)***
Vendor Guide Publications Inc....407 399-0745
3574 Gentle Ter The Villages (32163) ***(G-18396)***
Vendornet....954 767-8228
2301 Barbara Dr Fort Lauderdale (33316) ***(G-4306)***
Veneer Source, Tavares *Also called J F V Designs Inc* ***(G-18343)***
Veneta Cucine Inc....305 949-5223
2020 Ne 163rd St Ste 100 North Miami Beach (33162) ***(G-11709)***
Venfood Disrtibutors, Hialeah *Also called Tts Food LLC* ***(G-5652)***
Venga LLC....561 665-8200
955 Nw 17th Ave Delray Beach (33445) ***(G-3156)***
Venice Custom Cabinets Inc....941 488-5000
510 Colonia Ln E Nokomis (34275) ***(G-11591)***
Venice Granit & Marble Inc....941 483-4363
159 Progress Cir Venice (34285) ***(G-18585)***
Venice Print Center....941 206-1414
200 E Venice Ave Venice (34285) ***(G-18586)***
Venice Quarters Inc....954 318-3483
2435 N Dixie Hwy Wilton Manors (33305) ***(G-19221)***
Venkata SAI Corporation....352 746-7076
3502 N Lecanto Hwy Beverly Hills (34465) ***(G-380)***
Venom Allstars LLC....407 575-3484
1205 Crown Park Cir Winter Garden (34787) ***(G-19287)***
Vensoft Corp....786 991-2080
2530 Ne 208th Ter Miami (33180) ***(G-10573)***
Ventex Technology Inc (PA)....561 354-6300
1201 Jupiter Park Dr Jupiter (33458) ***(G-7139)***
Venti Group LLC....949 264-3185
1521 Alton Rd Ste 697 Miami Beach (33139) ***(G-10726)***
Ventilex Inc....954 433-1321
20871 Jhnson St Units 103 Pembroke Pines (33029) ***(G-14070)***
Ventum LLC....786 838-1113
1100 14th St Miami Beach (33139) ***(G-10727)***
Ventura Cleaners, Kissimmee *Also called Chhaya Corporation* ***(G-7231)***
Ventura Foods LLC....772 878-1400
485 Nw Enterprise Dr Port Saint Lucie (34986) ***(G-15161)***
Venture Circle Enterprises LLC....407 678-7489
140 Maritime Dr Sanford (32771) ***(G-16131)***
Venture Circle Intl LLC....407 677-6004
140 Maritime Dr Sanford (32771) ***(G-16132)***
Venue Advertising Inc....561 844-1778
815 S Us Highway 1 103 Jupiter (33477) ***(G-7140)***
Venue Marketing Group, Jupiter *Also called Venue Advertising Inc* ***(G-7140)***
Venus Manufacturing Co Inc....904 645-3187
11711 Marco Beach Dr Jacksonville (32224) ***(G-6895)***
Ver-Val Enterprises Inc....850 244-7931
646 Anchors St Nw Ste 8 Fort Walton Beach (32548) ***(G-4838)***
Veracity Tech Solutions LLC....402 658-4113
7004 Pine Forest Rd Ste D Pensacola (32526) ***(G-14281)***
Vercipia Biofuels, Tampa *Also called Highlands Ethanol LLC* ***(G-17754)***
Verde GSE Inc....888 837-5221
12291 Us Highway 41 N Palmetto (34221) ***(G-13832)***
Verde Speed Machine Shop Corp....305 233-3299
10780 Sw 190th St Cutler Bay (33157) ***(G-2419)***
Verdu-Us LLC....407 776-3017
741 Caribbean Dr Davenport (33897) ***(G-2485)***
Verhi Inc....850 477-4880
824 Creighton Rd Ste A Pensacola (32504) ***(G-14282)***
Veridien Corporation (PA)....727 576-1600
1100 4th St N Ste 202 Saint Petersburg (33701) ***(G-15951)***
Verified Label & Print Inc....813 290-7721
7905 Hopi Pl Tampa (33634) ***(G-18237)***
Verifone Inc (HQ)....800 837-4366
2744 N University Dr Coral Springs (33065) ***(G-2326)***
Verifone Inc....727 953-4000
300 Park Place Blvd # 100 Clearwater (33759) ***(G-1931)***
Verifone Inc....727 535-9200
12501 B 562nd St N Clearwater (33755) ***(G-1932)***
Verifone Inc....754 229-4571
2900 N University Dr Coral Springs (33065) ***(G-2327)***
Verifone Systems Inc (PA)....408 232-7800
2744 N University Dr Coral Springs (33065) ***(G-2328)***
Veritas Farms Inc (PA)....561 288-6603
1512 E Broward Blvd # 30 Fort Lauderdale (33301) ***(G-4307)***
Veriteq Acquisition Corp....561 805-8007
220 Congress Park Dr # 200 Delray Beach (33445) ***(G-3157)***
Vero Beach 32963 Media....772 226-7924
4855 Highway A1a Vero Beach (32963) ***(G-18677)***
Vero Beach Magazine, Vero Beach *Also called Moulton Publications Inc* ***(G-18645)***
Vero Beach Printing Inc....772 562-4267
3280 Quay Dock Rd Vero Beach (32967) ***(G-18678)***
Vero News....772 234-5727
1240 Olde Doubloon Dr Vero Beach (32963) ***(G-18679)***
Veroch LLC....954 990-7544
10573 Nw 53rd St Sunrise (33351) ***(G-17195)***
Veronica Knits Inc....305 887-7333
490 W 18th St Hialeah (33010) ***(G-5676)***
Veronicas Health Crunch LLC....352 409-1124
88 Fanny Ann Way Freeport (32439) ***(G-4853)***
Versacomp Inc....954 561-8778
4021 Ne 5th Ter Oakland Park (33334) ***(G-11858)***
Versailles Lighting Inc....561 945-5744
1305 Poinsettia Dr Ste 6 Delray Beach (33444) ***(G-3158)***
Versatile Manufacturing Inc (PA)....954 561-8083
4021 Ne 5th Ter Oakland Park (33334) ***(G-11859)***
Versatile Manufacturing Inc....954 561-8083
4020 Ne 5th Ter Oakland Park (33334) ***(G-11860)***
Versatile Packagers LLC....813 664-1171
933 Chad Ln Ste C Tampa (33619) ***(G-18238)***
Versatile Water Jet, Oakland Park *Also called Versatile Manufacturing Inc* ***(G-11859)***
Versatus Hpc Inc....561 544-8862
4700 Nw 2nd Ave Boca Raton (33431) ***(G-777)***
Versea Holdings Inc....800 397-0670
1000 N Florida Ave Tampa (33602) ***(G-18239)***
Vertaeon LLC....404 823-6232
747 Sw 2nd Ave Ste 349 Gainesville (32601) ***(G-5015)***
Vertaloc, Plantation *Also called US Diagnostics Inc* ***(G-14561)***
Vertarib Inc (PA)....877 815-8610
9005 Southern Blvd West Palm Beach (33411) ***(G-19078)***
Vertec Inc....850 478-6480
141 Terry Dr Pensacola (32503) ***(G-14283)***
Vertex Precision Inc....561 582-6171
714 S East Coast St Lake Worth (33460) ***(G-7597)***
Vertical Assesment Assoc LLC....850 210-0401
17752 Ne Charlie Johns St Blountstown (32424) ***(G-390)***
Vertical Aviation Technologies....407 322-9488
1609 Hangar Rd Bldg 332 Sanford (32773) ***(G-16133)***

ALPHABETIC

Vertical Bridge Towers LLC...561 948-6367
750 Park Of Commerce Boca Raton (33487) ***(G-778)***
Vertical Cable, Hallandale *Also called Chiptech Inc* ***(G-5154)***
Vertical Flight Technology Inc...407 687-3126
3385 Shady Run Rd Melbourne (32934) ***(G-8970)***
Vertical Land Inc (PA)...850 819-2535
7950 Front Beach Rd Panama City (32407) ***(G-13960)***
Vertical Land Inc...850 244-5263
621 Mckenzie Ave Panama City (32401) ***(G-13961)***
Vertical Reality Inc...305 238-4522
17511 Sw 99th Rd Palmetto Bay (33157) ***(G-13856)***
Vertical Reality Mfg Inc...305 238-4522
17511 Sw 99th Rd Palmetto Bay (33157) ***(G-13857)***
Vertical Systems Inspctons Inc...954 775-6023
899 E Country Club Cir Plantation (33317) ***(G-14563)***
Vertical Village Inc...772 340-0400
10658 S Us Highway 1 Port Saint Lucie (34952) ***(G-15162)***
Verticals Unlimited, Ocoee *Also called TMMR Holdings LLC* ***(G-12092)***
Vertimax LLC...800 699-5867
8108 Benjamin Rd Ste 201 Tampa (33634) ***(G-18240)***
Vertiv, Sunrise *Also called Alber Corp* ***(G-17086)***
Vertiv Corporation...954 377-7101
7775 W Oakland Park Blvd Sunrise (33351) ***(G-17196)***
Vertpac LLC...407 886-9010
520 W Orange Blossom Trl Apopka (32712) ***(G-195)***
Veru Healthcare, Miami *Also called Veru Inc* ***(G-10574)***
Veru Inc (PA)...305 509-6897
48 Nw 25th St Ste 102 Miami (33127) ***(G-10574)***
Very Tasty LLC...305 636-4140
2177 Nw 24th Ct Miami (33142) ***(G-10575)***
Veserca Group Ltd Inc...561 210-7400
20694 Nw 27th Ave Boca Raton (33434) ***(G-779)***
Vestagen Tchnical Textiles Inc...407 781-2570
1301 W Colonial Dr Orlando (32804) ***(G-13300)***
Vestas...561 588-9933
5411 S Olive Ave West Palm Beach (33405) ***(G-19079)***
Vested Metals Intl LLC...904 495-7278
7000 Us Highway 1 N # 503 Saint Augustine (32095) ***(G-15631)***
Vesten Woodworks LLC...407 780-9295
200 Colorado Springs Way Saint Augustine (32092) ***(G-15632)***
Vestex, Orlando *Also called Vestagen Tchnical Textiles Inc* ***(G-13300)***
Vet Sonic Inc...305 681-4486
1099 E 47th St Hialeah (33013) ***(G-5677)***
Vet-Equip LLC...239 537-3402
999 Vanderbilt Beach Rd # 200 Naples (34108) ***(G-11449)***
Vetbiotek Inc...727 308-2030
11401 Belcher Rd S # 260 Largo (33773) ***(G-8072)***
Vetcon Construction Inc...352 234-6668
1825 Ne 17th St Ocala (34470) ***(G-12070)***
Vetcon Construction - Ocala, Ocala *Also called Vetcon Construction Inc* ***(G-12070)***
Vetio Dev't & Mfg Plant, Jupiter *Also called Tropichem Research Labs LLC* ***(G-7134)***
Vette Brakes & Products Inc...727 345-5292
7490 30th Ave N Saint Petersburg (33710) ***(G-15952)***
Vevyan Hanania Inc...800 297-8485
10415 Beach Blvd Jacksonville (32246) ***(G-6896)***
Vf Imagewear Inc...813 671-2986
8221 Eagle Palm Dr Riverview (33578) ***(G-15286)***
Vfinity Inc...239 244-2555
837 5th Ave S Ste 200 Naples (34102) ***(G-11450)***
Vfm Aerosystems LLC...786 567-2348
10050 Nw 44th Ter Apt 301 Doral (33178) ***(G-3541)***
Vgcm LLC...813 247-7625
3510 Pendola Point Rd Tampa (33619) ***(G-18241)***
Vgcm LLC...813 620-4889
2001 Maritime Blvd Tampa (33605) ***(G-18242)***
Vgi Medical LLC...727 565-1235
11651 87th St Largo (33773) ***(G-8073)***
Vgr Holding LLC (HQ)...305 579-8000
4400 S Biscayne Blvd # 10 Miami (33131) ***(G-10576)***
Via Cabinets Corp...407 633-1915
3113 Willie Mays Pkwy Orlando (32811) ***(G-13301)***
Via Optronics LLC...407 745-5031
6220 Hzltine Nat Dr Ste 1 Orlando (32822) ***(G-13302)***
Viadiem LLC...407 571-6845
555 Winderley Pl Ste 300 Maitland (32751) ***(G-8484)***
Vianny Corporation...239 888-4536
6860 Daniels Pkwy Fort Myers (33912) ***(G-4646)***
Viasat Inc...813 880-5000
4211 W Boy Scout Blvd # 550 Tampa (33607) ***(G-18243)***
Viatech of Delaware Inc...321 308-6600
7341 Office Park Pl # 102 Melbourne (32940) ***(G-8971)***
Vibrant Sign Studio LLC...305 363-2181
8890 Sw 129th Ter Miami (33176) ***(G-10577)***
Vicbag LLC...305 423-7042
80 Sw 8th St Ste 2000 Miami (33130) ***(G-10578)***
Viccarbe Inc...305 670-0979
8950 Sw 74th Ct Ste 1406 Miami (33156) ***(G-10579)***
Vice Alliance Corp...954 792-4240
1611 Sw 55th Ave Plantation (33317) ***(G-14564)***
Vicente Gandia Pla...310 699-8559
7300 N Kendall Dr Ste 470 Miami (33156) ***(G-10580)***
Vicente Gandia USA, Miami *Also called Vicente Gandia Pla* ***(G-10580)***
Vicente Gandia Usa Inc...310 699-8559
7300 N Kendall Dr Ste 470 Miami (33156) ***(G-10581)***
Vick Houston, Fort Lauderdale *Also called Attack Communications Inc* ***(G-3831)***
Vickery and Company...813 987-2100
7911 Professional Pl Tampa (33637) ***(G-18244)***
Victores Machine Shop, Miami *Also called Group Heros Inc* ***(G-9675)***
Victoriano Pantoja, Orlando *Also called Causey Machine Works Inc* ***(G-12555)***
Victors Cstm Qilting Bedspread...305 362-1990
2765 W 78th St Hialeah (33016) ***(G-5678)***
Victors Die Cutting Inc...305 599-0255
1385 Se 9th Ave Hialeah (33010) ***(G-5679)***
Victors Trim Molding Crown Bas...727 403-6057
6142 38th Ave N Saint Petersburg (33710) ***(G-15953)***
Victory Custom Cabinetry...727 937-2284
2623 Grand Blvd Holiday (34690) ***(G-5751)***
Victory Tailgate LLC...407 704-8775
2437 E Landstreet Rd Orlando (32824) ***(G-13303)***
Victory Valet Services LLC...904 521-6517
5549 Fort Caroline Rd # 107 Jacksonville (32277) ***(G-6897)***
Victus LLC (PA)...305 663-2129
4918 Sw 74th Ct Miami (33155) ***(G-10582)***
Victus Capital Enterprises Inc (PA)...727 442-6677
1780 102nd Ave N Ste 500 Saint Petersburg (33716) ***(G-15954)***
Vicx LLC...407 674-2073
1273 Wntr Gdn Vnlnd Rd Winter Garden (34787) ***(G-19288)***
Vida 18com LLC...305 935-6657
7499 Nw 31st St Miami (33122) ***(G-10583)***
Vidacann LLC...772 672-1178
4844 Race Track Rd Saint Johns (32259) ***(G-15684)***
Vidal Shutters and Blinds LLC...813 601-1068
275 Byshore Blvd Unit 401 Tampa (33606) ***(G-18245)***
Vidco Industries Inc...305 888-0077
7500 Nw 69th Ave Frnt Ste Medley (33166) ***(G-8753)***
Video Display Corporation...813 854-2259
13948 Lynmar Blvd Tampa (33626) ***(G-18246)***
Video Display Corporation...321 784-4427
5155 King St Cocoa (32926) ***(G-2056)***
Videolinq Streaming Svcs LLC...904 330-1026
4651 Salisbury Rd Jacksonville (32256) ***(G-6898)***
Vidrepur of America LLC...305 468-9008
2301 Nw 84th Ave Miami (33122) ***(G-10584)***
Vienna Beauty Products Co (PA)...937 228-7109
222 Harbour Dr Apt 100 Naples (34103) ***(G-11451)***
Vienna Beef Ltd...941 723-7234
2650 Corporate Way Palmetto (34221) ***(G-13833)***
Viesel Fuel LLC...772 781-4300
1000 Se Monterey Cmns # 206 Stuart (34996) ***(G-17045)***
Viewpoint Systems LLC...850 450-0681
730 W Garden St Pensacola Pensacola (32502) ***(G-14284)***
Vigo Importing Company...813 884-3491
4701 Tony Alessi Sr Ave Tampa (33614) ***(G-18247)***
Viking Aircraft Engines...386 416-8383
735 Air Park Rd 3c Edgewater (32132) ***(G-3638)***
Viking Cases, Saint Petersburg *Also called Stemler Corporation* ***(G-15927)***
Viking Kabinets Inc...305 238-9025
10445 Sw 186th Ln Cutler Bay (33157) ***(G-2420)***
Viking Welding and Fabrication...904 234-5964
835 Camp Frncis Jhnson Rd Orange Park (32065) ***(G-12411)***
Viking Woodworking...352 237-5050
13401 W Highway 328 Ocala (34482) ***(G-12071)***
Vilano Interiors Inc...904 824-3439
112 Oak Ave Saint Augustine (32084) ***(G-15633)***
Village Bread & Bagells, Jacksonville *Also called New Vbb LLC* ***(G-6629)***
Village Door, The, Destin *Also called BMW Entertainment LLC* ***(G-3213)***
Village Scribe Printing Co...727 585-7388
1548 Shirley Pl Largo (33770) ***(G-8074)***
Villar Stone & Paver Works LLC...860 209-2907
1140 Seaside Dr Sarasota (34242) ***(G-16633)***
Vimar Stucco Inc...813 966-4831
2546 Edgewater Falls Dr Brandon (33511) ***(G-1184)***
Vin-Dotco Inc...727 217-9200
2875 Mci Dr N Unit B Pinellas Park (33782) ***(G-14393)***
Vinavil Americas Corporation...954 246-8888
1144 E Newport Center Dr Deerfield Beach (33442) ***(G-2933)***
Vinbillingcom LLC...904 549-5461
540 Phelps St Jacksonville (32206) ***(G-6899)***
Vince & Sons Pasta Co, Boca Raton *Also called Jo MO Enterprises Inc* ***(G-582)***
Vine & Grind, Treasure Island *Also called Vine and Grind LLC* ***(G-18479)***
Vine and Grind LLC...727 420-3122
111 107th Ave Ste 1 Treasure Island (33706) ***(G-18479)***
Vines Worldwide LLC...786 353-2102
13300 Biscayne Island Ter North Miami (33181) ***(G-11662)***
Vineyard 101 LLC...727 819-5300
12930 Us Highway 19 Hudson (34667) ***(G-6043)***
Vingcard, Fort Lauderdale *Also called Assa Abloy Hospitality Inc* ***(G-3827)***

Vinita USA Co...650 260-5161
3250 Ne 1st Ave Ste 305 Miami (33137) ***(G-10585)***
Vinland Corporation...954 475-9093
11600 Nw 20th St Plantation (33323) ***(G-14565)***
Vinland International Inc...954 316-2007
1700 Nw 65th Ave Ste 12 Plantation (33313) ***(G-14566)***
Vinland Marketing Inc...954 602-2177
1152 N University Dr # 304 Pembroke Pines (33024) ***(G-14071)***
Vino Del Grotto...321 508-1478
4758 Coquina Crossing Dr Elkton (32033) ***(G-3652)***
Vintage Art and Sign LLC...770 815-7887
1419 29th St 3 Niceville (32578) ***(G-11576)***
Vintage Fashion...786 631-4048
2450 W 8th Ln Hialeah (33010) ***(G-5680)***
Vintage Ironworks LLC...407 339-2555
671 Newburyport Ave Altamonte Springs (32701) ***(G-83)***
Vintners Collections...407 654-9019
13918 Caywood Pond Dr Windermere (34786) ***(G-19248)***
Vinyl Bros...850 396-5977
5668 Gulf Breeze Pkwy # 4 Gulf Breeze (32563) ***(G-5131)***
Vinyl Corp (HQ)...305 477-6464
8000 Nw 79th Pl Ste 4 Miami (33166) ***(G-10586)***
Vinyl Etchings Inc...727 845-5300
6641 Industrial Ave Port Richey (34668) ***(G-15076)***
Vinylot of Florida Inc...954 978-8424
2048 Mears Pkwy Margate (33063) ***(G-8571)***
Vinylot Signs & Graphics, Margate *Also called Vinylot of Florida Inc* ***(G-8571)***
Violet Defense LLC...407 433-1104
189 S Orange Ave Ste 1400 Orlando (32801) ***(G-13304)***
Violettas LLC (PA)...305 301-3351
145 Sw 8th St Unit 1901 Miami (33130) ***(G-10587)***
VIP Drinks Bottling LLC...239 214-8190
2624 Sw 4th Ave Cape Coral (33914) ***(G-1491)***
Vlp Prtg Night CLB Sups LLC...561 603-2846
1000 Holland Dr Ste 1 Boca Raton (33487) ***(G-780)***
VIP Scooter Rental, Miami Beach *Also called Adir Scooters Inc* ***(G-10636)***
VIP Software Corporation...813 837-4347
6000 S Florida Ave # 6832 Lakeland (33807) ***(G-7830)***
VIP Sports Idrive, Orlando *Also called Ultimate Overstock LLC* ***(G-13287)***
Viper 4x4...305 468-9818
11924 Perspective Dr Windermere (34786) ***(G-19249)***
Viper Communication Systems (HQ)...352 694-7030
4211 Sw 13th St Ocala (34474) ***(G-12072)***
Viper Drones Inc...321 427-5837
409 5th Ave Indialantic (32903) ***(G-6061)***
Viper Drones LLC...205 677-3700
409 5th Ave Indialantic (32903) ***(G-6062)***
Vipre, Clearwater *Also called Threattrack Security Inc* ***(G-1920)***
Virag Biosciences, West Palm Beach *Also called Virag Distribution LLC* ***(G-19080)***
Virag Distribution LLC...844 448-4724
700 S Rosemary Ave # 204 West Palm Beach (33401) ***(G-19080)***
Virco Mfg Corporation...772 834-8261
6882 Se Raintree Ave Stuart (34997) ***(G-17046)***
Virginia Electronic & Ltg Corp (PA)...904 230-2840
1293 Energy Cove Ct Green Cove Springs (32043) ***(G-5076)***
Virginia Kelly...954 415-8056
1825 Bridgepointe Cir # 14 Vero Beach (32967) ***(G-18680)***
Viscomm Publishing LLC...888 511-0900
919 W Pearson St Hernando (34442) ***(G-5249)***
Vishay Americas Inc...407 804-2567
735 Primera Blvd Lake Mary (32746) ***(G-7459)***
Visible Results USA Inc...913 706-8248
1550 Corolla Ct 1 Reunion (34747) ***(G-15261)***
Vision Analytical Inc (PA)...305 801-7140
4444 Sw 71st Ave Ste 112 Miami (33155) ***(G-10588)***
Vision Benefits 4 All Inc...888 317-0606
652 Hummingbird Ct Saint Johns (32259) ***(G-15685)***
Vision Blocks Inc...321 254-7478
1634 Cypress Ave Melbourne (32935) ***(G-8972)***
Vision Candles Inc...305 836-8650
7363 Nw 36th Ave Miami (33147) ***(G-10589)***
Vision Concepts Ink Inc...305 463-8003
8953 Nw 23rd St Doral (33172) ***(G-3542)***
Vision Conveyor Inc...352 343-3300
32834 Lakeshore Dr Tavares (32778) ***(G-18359)***
Vision Engineering Labs...727 812-2000
8787 Enterprise Blvd Largo (33773) ***(G-8075)***
Vision Engineering Labs...727 812-2035
8787 Enterprise Blvd Largo (33773) ***(G-8076)***
Vision Manufacturing Tech Inc...904 579-5272
137 Industrial Loop W Orange Park (32073) ***(G-12412)***
Vision Mt, Orange Park *Also called Vision Manufacturing Tech Inc* ***(G-12412)***
Vision Solution Technology LL...305 477-4480
10367 Nw 41st St Doral (33178) ***(G-3543)***
Vision Source Inc...407 435-9958
9262 Bent Arrow Cv Apopka (32703) ***(G-196)***
Vision Systems North America...321 265-5110
1801 Penn St Ste 104 Melbourne (32901) ***(G-8973)***
Vision Web Offset LLC...305 433-6188
13930 Nw 60th Ave Miami Lakes (33014) ***(G-10879)***
Vision Woodworking Inc...407 493-9665
193 Hidden View Dr Groveland (34736) ***(G-5109)***
Visionare LLC...305 989-7271
12251 Towne Lake Dr Fort Myers (33913) ***(G-4647)***
Visions Auto Spa, Panama City Beach *Also called Bruce Roland* ***(G-13974)***
Visions Millwork Inc...239 390-0811
15674 Spring Line Ln Fort Myers (33905) ***(G-4648)***
Visions Sky Corp...888 788-8609
18154 Cadence St Orlando (32820) ***(G-13305)***
Visiontech Components LLC...727 547-5466
5120 110th Ave N Clearwater (33760) ***(G-1933)***
Visor Versa...239 249-4745
9510 Coralee Ave Estero (33928) ***(G-3698)***
Vista Color Corporation...305 635-2000
1401 Nw 78th Ave Ste 201 Doral (33126) ***(G-3544)***
Vista Magazine, Miami Beach *Also called Vista Publishing Corporation* ***(G-10728)***
Vista Products Inc (HQ)...904 725-2242
8801 Corporate Square Ct Jacksonville (32216) ***(G-6900)***
Vista Publishing Corporation...305 416-4644
6538 Collins Ave Miami Beach (33141) ***(G-10728)***
Vista Semanal...239 263-4785
1100 Immokalee Rd Naples (34110) ***(G-11452)***
Vista System LLC...941 365-4646
1800 N East Ave Ste 102 Sarasota (34234) ***(G-16634)***
Vista-Pro Automotive LLC...352 867-7272
2410 Nw 8th Pl Ocala (34475) ***(G-12073)***
Vistakon, Jacksonville *Also called Johnson Jhnson Vision Care Inc* ***(G-6526)***
Vistakon Pharmaceuticals LLC...904 443-1000
7500 Centurion Pkwy # 100 Jacksonville (32256) ***(G-6901)***
Vistamatic LLC...866 466-9525
11713 Nw 39th St Coral Springs (33065) ***(G-2329)***
Vistapharm Inc...727 530-1633
7265 Ulmerton Rd Largo (33771) ***(G-8077)***
Vistapharm Inc...727 530-1633
13707 66th St Largo (33771) ***(G-8078)***
Visual Acoustics LLC...786 390-6128
591 Nw 35th St Miami (33127) ***(G-10590)***
Visual Comm Specialists Inc...407 936-7300
707 Platinum Pt Ste 2001 Lake Mary (32746) ***(G-7460)***
Visual Concepts In Plastic Inc...941 749-1141
2908 29th Ave E Ste C Bradenton (34208) ***(G-1141)***
Visual Magic...727 271-2702
8255 Tanglewood Dr New Port Richey (34654) ***(G-11519)***
Visual Signs LLC...407 693-0200
7041 Grand National Dr Orlando (32819) ***(G-13306)***
Vital Graphics and Signs Inc...305 557-8181
2131 W 60th St Hialeah (33016) ***(G-5681)***
Vital Health Corp...407 522-1125
6150 Metrowest Blvd # 204 Orlando (32835) ***(G-13307)***
Vital Health Corporation (HQ)...407 522-1125
6000 Metrowest Blvd # 200 Orlando (32835) ***(G-13308)***
Vital Pharma Research Inc...786 666-0592
2300 W 84th St Ste 303 Hialeah (33016) ***(G-5682)***
Vital Pharmaceuticals Inc (PA)...954 641-0570
20311 Sheridan St Fort Lauderdale (33332) ***(G-4308)***
Vital Printing Corporation...561 659-2367
1983 10th Ave N Lake Worth Beach (33461) ***(G-7623)***
Vital Signs of Orlando Inc...407 297-0680
2111 S Division Ave Ste A Orlando (32805) ***(G-13309)***
Vital Solutions LLC...561 848-1717
3755 Fiscal Ct Ste 2 West Palm Beach (33404) ***(G-19081)***
Vital Usa Inc...561 282-6074
525 S Flagler Dr Ste 301 West Palm Beach (33401) ***(G-19082)***
Vitalleo Health, Neptune Beach *Also called Vitalleo LLC* ***(G-11479)***
Vitalleo LLC...904 474-5330
2300 Marsh Point Rd 302c Neptune Beach (32266) ***(G-11479)***
Vitaminmed LLC...727 443-7008
300 S Duncan Ave Ste 263 Clearwater (33755) ***(G-1934)***
Vitapak LLC...954 661-0390
21070 Sheridan St Fort Lauderdale (33332) ***(G-4309)***
Viterra Affordable Shutters...239 738-6364
1104 Se 46th Ln Ste 2 Cape Coral (33904) ***(G-1492)***
Vitsur Industries Inc...561 744-1290
130 Evernia St Ste 3 Jupiter (33458) ***(G-7141)***
Viva 5 LLC (HQ)...561 239-2239
239 2nd Ave S Ste 200 Saint Petersburg (33701) ***(G-15955)***
Vivalize LLC...305 614-3952
201 Alhambra Cir Ste 1205 Coral Gables (33134) ***(G-2205)***
Vive Creole LLC...954 607-1925
2500 Hollywood Blvd Hollywood (33020) ***(G-5937)***
Vivid Images USA Inc...904 620-0303
1730 E Duval St Jacksonville (32202) ***(G-6902)***
Vivid Sportwear, Miami *Also called T Shirt Center Inc* ***(G-10455)***
Vividus LLC...954 326-1954
3265 W Mcnab Rd Pompano Beach (33069) ***(G-14909)***
Vizco Us Inc...941 753-3333
1401 Manatee Ave W # 110 Bradenton (34205) ***(G-1142)***
Vizergy, Jacksonville *Also called Jjj & H Inc* ***(G-6522)***
Viztek Inc...904 448-9936
6491 Powers Ave Jacksonville (32217) ***(G-6903)***

Vj Publications Inc...407 461-0707
1551 W Marvin St Longwood (32750) *(G-8347)*
Vkidz Inc...954 771-0914
6300 Ne 1st Ave Ste 203 Fort Lauderdale (33334) *(G-4310)*
Vladmir Ltd...386 445-6000
32 Hargrove Grade Palm Coast (32137) *(G-13714)*
Vlex 1450 LLC...954 218-5443
1199 Hidden Valley Way Weston (33327) *(G-19177)*
Vloc Incorporated...727 375-8562
6716 Industrial Ave Port Richey (34668) *(G-15077)*
Vm, Jacksonville *Also called Venus Manufacturing Co Inc (G-6895)*
Vm Jewelry, Port Saint Lucie *Also called Corporacion Internacional De J (G-15101)*
Vmak Corp...407 260-1199
131 Applewood Dr Longwood (32750) *(G-8348)*
Vmax Vision Inc...321 972-1823
2600 Mtland Ctr Pkwy Ste Maitland (32751) *(G-8485)*
Vmoviles Inc...954 609-2510
17111 Biscayne Blvd Aventura (33160) *(G-282)*
Vmoviles Power Solar Energy, Aventura *Also called Vmoviles Inc (G-282)*
VMS Usa Inc...727 434-1577
8060 Cypress Garden Ct Seminole (33777) *(G-16770)*
Voda Technologies LLC...727 645-6030
3909 Mimosa Pl Palm Harbor (34685) *(G-13767)*
Voda USA, Miami *Also called Main USA Corp (G-9937)*
Vogue Aerospace & Defense Inc...321 289-0872
1712 Commercial Dr Naples (34112) *(G-11453)*
Voice of South Marion...352 245-3161
5513 Se 113th St Belleview (34420) *(G-376)*
Voice Publishing Co Inc...305 687-5555
4696 E 10th Ct Hialeah (33013) *(G-5683)*
Voicetech, Sarasota *Also called Omnisys LLC (G-16532)*
Voicethread LLC...919 724-4486
21747 Westmont Ct Boca Raton (33428) *(G-781)*
Volaero Drones, Sunrise *Also called Volaero Uav Drnes Hldings Corp (G-17197)*
Volaero Uav Drnes Hldings Corp...954 261-3105
5375 N Hiatus Rd Sunrise (33351) *(G-17197)*
Volcano Industries Inc...770 300-0041
1125 Commerce Blvd N Sarasota (34243) *(G-16323)*
Volpino Corp...904 264-8808
1551 Pine Hammock Trl Orange Park (32003) *(G-12413)*
Volt Lighting...813 978-3700
16011 N Nebraska Ave # 102 Lutz (33549) *(G-8423)*
Volt Resistance, Saint Augustine *Also called H2c Brands LLC (G-15548)*
Volume Cases, Boca Raton *Also called Hut Global Inc (G-560)*
Volunteer Capital LLC...954 366-6659
1911 Nw 40th Ct Deerfield Beach (33064) *(G-2934)*
Volusia Printing LLC...386 873-7442
1919 W Minnesota Ave Deland (32720) *(G-3030)*
Volusia Waste Inc...386 878-3322
1455 Brayton Cir Deltona (32725) *(G-3181)*
Volvox Inc Hollywood...954 961-4942
537 N Rainbow Dr Hollywood (33021) *(G-5938)*
Vonn Lighting, North Miami Beach *Also called Vonn LLC (G-11710)*
Vonn LLC...888 604-8666
3323 Ne 163rd St Ph 706 North Miami Beach (33160) *(G-11710)*
Vonos LLC...888 698-6667
1317 Edgewater Dr Ste 476 Orlando (32804) *(G-13310)*
Vonwidman Designs LLC...727 862-5303
9246 Hilltop Dr New Port Richey (34654) *(G-11520)*
Voodoo Fab LLC...727 916-0014
4717 Bartelt Rd Holiday (34690) *(G-5752)*
Vos Systems LLC...352 317-2954
304 W University Ave Gainesville (32601) *(G-5016)*
Voss Bindery Inc...904 396-3330
2565 Philips Hwy Jacksonville (32207) *(G-6904)*
Vossen Wheels Inc...305 463-7778
1598 Nw 82nd Ave Doral (33126) *(G-3545)*
Vowells Downtown Inc...850 432-5175
1233 Barrancas Ave Pensacola (32502) *(G-14285)*
Vowells Printing, Pensacola *Also called Vowells Downtown Inc (G-14285)*
Voxx Automotive Corp (HQ)...631 231-7750
2351 J Lawson Blvd Orlando (32824) *(G-13311)*
Voxx Automotive Corporation...407 842-7000
2351 J Lawson Blvd Orlando (32824) *(G-13312)*
Voxx Electronics, Orlando *Also called Voxxhirschmann Corporation (G-13314)*
Voxx International Corporation (PA)...800 645-7750
2351 J Lawson Blvd Orlando (32824) *(G-13313)*
Voxxhirschmann Corporation...866 869-7888
2351 J Lawson Blvd Orlando (32824) *(G-13314)*
Voyager Offroad LLC...941 235-7225
1602 Market Cir Unit 8 Port Charlotte (33953) *(G-15006)*
VP Cast Stone Corp...305 691-9306
879 E 25th St 899 Hialeah (33013) *(G-5684)*
Vp Castone, Hialeah *Also called VP Cast Stone Corp (G-5684)*
Vplenish Nutritionals Inc...954 304-4000
101 Plaza Real S Apt 306 Boca Raton (33432) *(G-782)*
Vpr 4x4...305 468-9818
1870 Saturn Blvd Orlando (32837) *(G-13315)*
VPR BRANDS, Fort Lauderdale *Also called Soleil Capital LP (G-4242)*
Vpx Sports, Fort Lauderdale *Also called Vital Pharmaceuticals Inc (G-4308)*
Vreeland Woodworking LLC...727 365-0241
1407 Tampa Rd Palm Harbor (34683) *(G-13768)*
Vs Carbonics Inc...305 903-6501
3491 Nw 79th St Miami (33147) *(G-10591)*
Vs Coatings LLC...305 677-6224
3491 Nw 79th St Miami (33147) *(G-10592)*
VSF Corp...305 769-2202
2800 Nw 125th St Miami (33167) *(G-10593)*
VSI, Fort Myers *Also called Vault Structures Inc (G-4644)*
VSI & Partners Inc...954 205-8653
14501 Sw 39th St Miramar (33027) *(G-11058)*
Vso, Orlando *Also called Vital Signs of Orlando Inc (G-13309)*
Vtech Io, Fort Myers *Also called Computers At Work Inc (G-4407)*
Vtronix LLC...305 471-7600
7900 Nw 68th St Miami (33166) *(G-10594)*
Vuaant Inc (PA)...407 701-6975
7300 Sandlake Commons Blv Orlando (32819) *(G-13316)*
Vuessence Inc...813 792-7123
17633 Gunn Hwy Ste 107 Odessa (33556) *(G-12165)*
Vuflow Filters Co Inc...352 597-2607
13370 Chambord St Brooksville (34613) *(G-1290)*
Vulcan Materials, Ocala *Also called Florida Rock Industries (G-11947)*
Vulcan Materials, Tavares *Also called Legacy Vulcan Corp (G-18345)*
Vulcan Materials Company...352 473-4258
6547 State Road 21 Keystone Heights (32656) *(G-7212)*
Vulcan Materials Company...205 298-3000
2001 Maritime Blvd Tampa (33605) *(G-18248)*
Vulcan Materials Company...863 675-5866
7425 W State Road 78 Moore Haven (33471) *(G-11090)*
Vulcan Mtls Co Vestavia Al, Jacksonville *Also called Florida Rock Industries (G-6402)*
Vulcan Steel, Jacksonville *Also called Fitzlord Inc (G-6390)*
Vulcan Steel...561 945-1259
326 Jupiter Lakes Blvd # 2 Jupiter (33458) *(G-7142)*
Vuram Inc...813 421-8000
12802 Tampa Oaks Blvd # 241 Temple Terrace (33637) *(G-18382)*
Vurb LLC...561 441-8870
2450 W Sample Rd Ste 14 Pompano Beach (33073) *(G-14910)*
Vutec Corporation...954 545-9000
11711 W Sample Rd Coral Springs (33065) *(G-2330)*
Vuziq, Homestead *Also called Duenas Mobile Applications LLC (G-5964)*
Vve, Fort Walton Beach *Also called Ver-Val Enterprises Inc (G-4838)*
Vy Spine LLC...866 489-7746
2236 Capital Cir Ne # 103 Tallahassee (32308) *(G-17344)*
Vycor Medical Inc (PA)...561 558-2020
951 Broken Sound Pkwy Nw # 320 Boca Raton (33487) *(G-783)*
Vyp Services LLC...305 593-8183
3555 Nw 79th Ave Doral (33122) *(G-3546)*
W & B Scientific Inc...954 607-1500
1301 W Copans Rd Ste H7 Pompano Beach (33064) *(G-14911)*
W & W Manufacturing Co...516 942-0011
4504 E Hillsborough Ave Tampa (33610) *(G-18249)*
W C Edge Jewelry Co Division, Hollywood *Also called Mayers Jwly Co Hollywood Inc (G-5872)*
W C H Enterprises Inc...239 267-7549
17640 Holly Oak Ave Fort Myers (33967) *(G-4649)*
W D H Enterprises Inc...941 758-6500
4230 26th St W Bradenton (34205) *(G-1143)*
W D Wilson Inc (PA)...813 626-6989
3005 S 54th St Tampa (33619) *(G-18250)*
W E Connery Boat Builders...239 549-8014
5787 Sw 9th Ct Cape Coral (33914) *(G-1493)*
W E W Enterprises Inc...941 751-6610
6103 28th St E Ste A Bradenton (34203) *(G-1144)*
W H L Business Communications...561 361-9202
2880 N Federal Hwy Boca Raton (33431) *(G-784)*
W Kost Inc...772 286-3700
4175 Sw Martin Hwy Palm City (34990) *(G-13678)*
W R Bonsal Plant 44, Tampa *Also called Bonsal American Inc (G-17482)*
W R Grace & Co - Conn...561 982-7776
6001 Broken Sound Pkwy # 600 Boca Raton (33487) *(G-785)*
W R Kershaw Inc...386 673-0602
12 Aviator Way Ormond Beach (32174) *(G-13408)*
W R Williams Enterprises Inc...813 677-2000
6202 Powell Rd Gibsonton (33534) *(G-5035)*
W&W Engineering Company, Palm Harbor *Also called Westlund Engineering Inc (G-13769)*
W.L. Installers, Hollywood *Also called William Laroque Installers Inc (G-5940)*
W.S.I., Margate *Also called Willson & Son Industry Inc (G-8572)*
W2e International Corp...561 362-9595
2200 Nw Corp Blvd Ste 210 Boca Raton (33431) *(G-786)*
Wafer World Inc...561 842-4441
1100 Tech Pl Ste 104 West Palm Beach (33407) *(G-19083)*
Wagner Pavers Contractor...321 633-5131
403 Hawk St Ste A Rockledge (32955) *(G-15456)*
Wai Corporate - USA, Miramar *Also called Wetherill Associates Inc (G-11060)*

Wake Up Beautiful...941 792-6500
6646 Cortez Rd W Bradenton (34210) ***(G-1145)***
Wakulla News...850 926-7102
3119a Crawfordville Hwy Crawfordville (32327) ***(G-2337)***
Walden Consulting LLC...407 563-3620
1021 E Robinson St Ste A Orlando (32801) ***(G-13317)***
Walden Timber Harvesting Inc...850 674-4884
13851 Nw Sand Cut Trl Altha (32421) ***(G-86)***
Walin Tools LLC...850 226-8632
642a Anchors St Nw Fort Walton Beach (32548) ***(G-4839)***
Walker Electric Inc...941 729-5015
340 42nd Street Ct W Palmetto (34221) ***(G-13834)***
Walker Graphics Inc...954 964-1688
2039 Coolidge St B Hollywood (33020) ***(G-5939)***
Walker Hospitality Inc...407 927-1871
1038 25th St Orlando (32805) ***(G-13318)***
Walker Products...941 723-9820
1507 17th St E Palmetto (34221) ***(G-13835)***
Walker Stainless Eqp Co LLC...352 343-2606
27620 County Road 561 Tavares (32778) ***(G-18360)***
Walker Wood Products Inc...904 448-5202
6112 Quattlebaum Rd Jacksonville (32217) ***(G-6905)***
Walking Bird Publications LLC...954 474-7261
3984 Sw 137th Ave Davie (33330) ***(G-2611)***
Walkup Enterprises Inc...727 571-1244
5040 110th Ave N Clearwater (33760) ***(G-1935)***
Wall Bed Systems Inc...419 738-5207
5040 140th Ave N Clearwater (33760) ***(G-1936)***
Wall Scuplture By Grutan, Pompano Beach *Also called Gurtan Designs* ***(G-14719)***
Wall Way Corporation...305 484-7600
9001 Nw 97th Ter Ste F Medley (33178) ***(G-8754)***
Wall Way USA of Florida, Medley *Also called Wall Way Corporation* ***(G-8754)***
Wallace Industries Inc...561 833-8554
316 Valencia Rd West Palm Beach (33401) ***(G-19084)***
Wallace Industries Inc...561 301-0811
906 N Dixie Hwy Lake Worth (33460) ***(G-7598)***
Waller Pavers Inc...863 644-8187
4909 Tradition Dr Lakeland (33812) ***(G-7831)***
Walling Crate Company...352 787-5211
507 N 14th St Leesburg (34748) ***(G-8180)***
Wallpaper For Windows, Cocoa *Also called Etchart LLC* ***(G-2021)***
Walruss Enterprises Inc...954 525-0342
1509 Sw 1st Ave Fort Lauderdale (33315) ***(G-4311)***
Walt Dittmer and Sons Inc...407 699-1755
1006 Shepard Rd Winter Springs (32708) ***(G-19488)***
Walter Green Inc...850 227-7946
252 Marina Dr Port Saint Joe (32456) ***(G-15084)***
Walter Haas Graphics Inc...305 883-2257
123 W 23rd St Hialeah (33010) ***(G-5685)***
Walters Tools LLC...321 537-4788
2998 Hester Ave Se Palm Bay (32909) ***(G-13546)***
Walton Son Newspapers, Santa Rosa Beach *Also called Emerald Coast Media & Mktg* ***(G-16159)***
Waltzing Waters Inc...239 574-5181
1410 Se 10th St Cape Coral (33990) ***(G-1494)***
Wannagofast LLC...850 585-5168
403 Juniper St Destin (32541) ***(G-3209)***
Wanted Dead or Alive Inc...239 633-5080
1011 April Ln North Fort Myers (33903) ***(G-11609)***
Wantzloeben RES Solutions LLC...972 273-0190
17277 Allamanda Dr Summerland Key (33042) ***(G-17066)***
War Chest River LLC...954 736-7704
675 Nw 97th St Miami (33150) ***(G-10595)***
Warbird Marine Holdings LLC (PA)...844 341-2504
4700 Nw 132nd St Opa Locka (33054) ***(G-12368)***
Warden Enterprises Inc (PA)...954 463-4404
807 Nw 7th St Fort Lauderdale (33311) ***(G-4312)***
Warehouse Goods LLC...877 865-2260
1095 Broken Sound Pkwy Nw # 300 Boca Raton (33487) ***(G-787)***
Warensford Well Drilling Inc...386 738-3257
329 S Blue Lake Ave Deland (32724) ***(G-3031)***
Warfighter Fcsed Logistics Inc...740 513-4692
936 Nw 1st St Fort Lauderdale (33311) ***(G-4313)***
Warren Equipment Inc...813 752-5126
2299 Us Highway 92 E Plant City (33563) ***(G-14477)***
Warren Heim Corp...772 466-8265
3107 Industrial 25th St Fort Pierce (34946) ***(G-4768)***
Warren Manufacturing, Hialeah *Also called Warren Technology Inc* ***(G-5686)***
Warren Technology Inc...305 556-6933
2050 W 73rd St Hialeah (33016) ***(G-5686)***
Warwick Logging...386 328-9358
119 Putnam County Blvd East Palatka (32131) ***(G-3609)***
Warwick, Blane, East Palatka *Also called Warwick Logging* ***(G-3609)***
Washers-R-Us Inc...850 573-0221
2205 Park Rd Alford (32420) ***(G-23)***
Washington CL Inc...813 739-4800
810 N Howard Ave Tampa (33606) ***(G-18251)***
Washington County News (HQ)...850 638-4242
1364 N Railroad Ave Chipley (32428) ***(G-1546)***
Washington Free Weekly, Tampa *Also called Washington CL Inc* ***(G-18251)***
Washington Penn Plastics Co...724 228-1260
4600 Mirabella Ct St Pete Beach (33706) ***(G-16885)***
Washington Shores Element...407 250-6260
944 W Lake Mann Dr Orlando (32805) ***(G-13319)***
Waste Advantage Corporation...800 358-2873
230 Tresana Blvd Unit 64 Jupiter (33478) ***(G-7143)***
Waste Advantage Magazine, Jupiter *Also called Waste Advantage Corporation* ***(G-7143)***
Waste Management Inc Florida...954 984-2000
5400 Rex Dr Winter Garden (34787) ***(G-19289)***
Wastequip Manufacturing Co LLC...863 665-6507
2624 Mine And Mill Ln Lakeland (33801) ***(G-7832)***
Water Bagel Boca East Lllp...347 661-7171
201 N Us Highway 1 Ste C5 Jupiter (33477) ***(G-7144)***
Water Boy Inc...239 461-0860
1520 Lee St Fort Myers (33901) ***(G-4650)***
Water Purification Systems...954 467-8920
2233 S Andrews Ave Fort Lauderdale (33316) ***(G-4314)***
Water Technology of Pensacola...850 477-4789
3000 W Nine Mile Rd Pensacola (32534) ***(G-14286)***
Waterblasting Technologies Inc (PA)...772 223-7393
3920 Se Commerce Ave Stuart (34997) ***(G-17047)***
Waterbox Aquariums, Longwood *Also called Waterbox Usa LLC* ***(G-8349)***
Waterbox Usa LLC (PA)...800 674-2608
320 W Sabal Palm Pl # 10 Longwood (32779) ***(G-8349)***
Waterboy Sports LLC...407 869-9881
1717 Minnesota Ave Ste A Winter Park (32789) ***(G-19457)***
Waterboyz Wbz Inc...850 433-2929
380 N 9th Ave Pensacola (32502) ***(G-14287)***
Waterbrick International Inc...877 420-9283
13506 Smmrport Vlg Pkwy S Windermere (34786) ***(G-19250)***
Waterfall LLC...941 342-7417
4438 Ardale St Sarasota (34232) ***(G-16635)***
Waterfall Industries Inc...407 330-2003
915 Cornwall Rd Sanford (32773) ***(G-16134)***
Waterfilterusa...386 469-0138
3060 Prfmce Cir Ste 2 Deland (32724) ***(G-3032)***
Waterford Press, Safety Harbor *Also called Waterford Publishing Group LLC* ***(G-15509)***
Waterford Press Inc...727 812-0140
1040 Harbor Lake Dr Safety Harbor (34695) ***(G-15508)***
Waterford Publishing Group LLC...727 812-0140
1040 Harbor Lake Dr Safety Harbor (34695) ***(G-15509)***
Waterheaterdepot.com, Sunrise *Also called Peralta Group Inc* ***(G-17157)***
Waterhouse Press LLC...781 975-6191
4481 Legendary Dr Ste 200 Destin (32541) ***(G-3210)***
Waterhuse Archtctral Wdwrk LLC...786 534-4943
4261 Nw 36th Ave Miami (33142) ***(G-10596)***
Waterjet Robotics USA LLC...772 403-2192
86 Cayman Pl Palm Beach Gardens (33418) ***(G-13634)***
Watermakers Inc...954 467-8920
2233 S Andrews Ave Fort Lauderdale (33316) ***(G-4315)***
Waterproof Charters Inc...941 639-7626
320 Cross St Punta Gorda (33950) ***(G-15243)***
Watershpes By Greg Gnstrom Inc...321 777-5432
2163 Ohio St West Melbourne (32904) ***(G-18779)***
Waterway Systems LLC...941 752-3554
7010 28th Street Ct E Sarasota (34243) ***(G-16324)***
Watson Steel Products...716 853-2233
8067 Nw 66th St Miami (33166) ***(G-10597)***
Watson Therapeutics Inc...954 266-1000
3400 Enterprise Way Miramar (33025) ***(G-11059)***
Wattera LLC...954 400-5135
3131 Sw 42nd St Fort Lauderdale (33312) ***(G-4316)***
Watts Juicery...904 372-0693
1013 Atlantic Blvd Atlantic Beach (32233) ***(G-228)***
Watts Technologies LLC...407 512-5750
2647 N Design Ct Sanford (32773) ***(G-16135)***
Watts Water Technologies Inc...352 465-2000
11611 Sw 147th Ct Dunnellon (34432) ***(G-3602)***
Wau USA Corp...305 361-6110
240 Crandon Blvd Ste 278 Key Biscayne (33149) ***(G-7163)***
Way Beyond Bagels Inc...561 638-1320
16850 S Jog Rd Ste 108 Delray Beach (33446) ***(G-3159)***
Way Bright Sign Systems...615 480-4602
93 Dune Lakes Cir E305 Santa Rosa Beach (32459) ***(G-16169)***
Wayloo Inc...954 914-3192
2700 W Cypress Creek Rd Fort Lauderdale (33309) ***(G-4317)***
Wayloomoto LLC...954 636-1510
7060 W State Road 84 # 8 Davie (33317) ***(G-2612)***
Wayne Dixon LLC...352 279-6886
27340 Popiel Rd Brooksville (34602) ***(G-1291)***
Wayne Metal Products Inc...407 321-7168
5461 Benchmark Ln Sanford (32773) ***(G-16136)***
Wb Medical Transport LLC...561 827-8877
177 Sw Hawthorne Cir Port Saint Lucie (34953) ***(G-15163)***
Wbn LLC...786 870-4172
1630 Nw 82nd Ave Doral (33126) ***(G-3547)***
Wbt Apparel Inc...305 891-1107
1175 Ne 125th St Ste 102 North Miami (33161) ***(G-11663)***
Wbz Boarding House, Pensacola *Also called Waterboyz Wbz Inc* ***(G-14287)***

ALPHABETIC

Wccm-USA Ltd Corporation.....904 346-3816
2024 River Rd Jacksonville (32207) ***(G-6906)***
Wcm Group Inc.....516 238-4261
1516 N Daytona Ave Flagler Beach (32136) ***(G-3758)***
Wco Enterprises, Jacksonville *Also called Flamm Industries Inc* ***(G-6393)***
We Bronze Wholesale LLC.....954 922-8826
2736 N Federal Hwy Fort Lauderdale (33306) ***(G-4318)***
We Love Tec LLC.....305 433-4453
2032 Ne 155th St North Miami Beach (33162) ***(G-11711)***
We Make Vitamins LLC.....863 607-6708
2715 Badger Rd Lakeland (33811) ***(G-7833)***
We Mix You Match Inc.....561 615-0253
6524 Patricia Dr West Palm Beach (33413) ***(G-19085)***
We Print Flyers and Shirts.....407 902-7128
210 N Kirkman Rd Orlando (32811) ***(G-13320)***
We RE Organized.....407 323-5133
1441 Kastner Pl Unit 111 Sanford (32771) ***(G-16137)***
We Sign It Inc.....772 800-7373
889 E Prima Vista Blvd Port Saint Lucie (34952) ***(G-15164)***
We Sign It Inc (PA).....772 577-4400
15838 Orange Ave Fort Pierce (34945) ***(G-4769)***
Weapons Systems, Palm Beach Gardens *Also called Northrop Grumman Systems Corp* ***(G-13613)***
Wear Fund LLC.....239 313-3907
93 Mildred Dr Ste B Fort Myers (33901) ***(G-4651)***
Wearable Nalia LLC.....561 629-5804
5081 Palo Verde Pl Haverhill (33415) ***(G-5241)***
Web Offset Printing Co Inc.....727 572-7488
12198 44th St N Clearwater (33762) ***(G-1937)***
Webb-Mason Inc.....727 531-1112
12397 Belcher Rd S # 240 Largo (33773) ***(G-8079)***
Webcom Group Inc (HQ).....904 680-6600
5335 Gate Pkwy Jacksonville (32256) ***(G-6907)***
Webelectric Products Inc.....440 389-5647
333 Colony Blvd The Villages (32162) ***(G-18397)***
Weber Manufacturing, North Venice *Also called Weber Mfg & Supplies Inc* ***(G-11764)***
Weber Mfg & Supplies Inc.....941 488-5185
3430 Technology Dr North Venice (34275) ***(G-11764)***
Weber South Fl LLC.....239 543-7240
40800 Cook Brown Rd Punta Gorda (33982) ***(G-15244)***
Webidcard Inc.....443 280-1577
89 Mitad Cir Saint Augustine (32095) ***(G-15634)***
Webvoip Inc.....305 793-2061
6400 N Andrews Ave # 490 Fort Lauderdale (33309) ***(G-4319)***
Wecando Print LLC.....754 222-9144
424 Sw 12th Ave Deerfield Beach (33442) ***(G-2935)***
Weddings By Tina.....904 235-3740
4720 Salisbury Rd Jacksonville (32256) ***(G-6908)***
Wedgworth Farms Inc.....561 996-2076
2607 Sammonds Rd Plant City (33563) ***(G-14478)***
Wedgworths Inc (PA).....561 996-2076
651 Nw 9th St Belle Glade (33430) ***(G-355)***
Wedgworths Inc.....561 996-2076
211 Sr 70 W Lake Placid (33852) ***(G-7495)***
Weehoo Inc.....720 477-3700
803 Whitcomb Blvd Tarpon Springs (34689) ***(G-18330)***
Weekly Challenger Newspaper.....727 896-2922
2500 Dr Mrtn Lther King J Saint Petersburg (33705) ***(G-15956)***
Weekly Newspaper.....305 743-0844
9709 Overseas Hwy Marathon (33050) ***(G-8521)***
Weekly Planet, Tampa *Also called Creative Loafing Inc* ***(G-17565)***
Weekly Planet of Sarasota Inc.....813 739-4800
810 N Howard Ave Tampa (33606) ***(G-18252)***
Weekly Schulte Valdes.....813 221-1154
1635 N Tampa St Ste 100 Tampa (33602) ***(G-18253)***
Weeks Gas Hme of The Brbc Sprs, Miami *Also called Barbecue Superstore* ***(G-9217)***
Weibel Equipment Inc.....571 278-1989
3870 Hidden Cypress Way Lake Worth (33467) ***(G-7599)***
Weidenhamer Corporation.....850 837-3190
808 Wild Oak Ave Destin (32541) ***(G-3211)***
Weider Publications LLC.....561 998-7424
1000 American Media Way Boca Raton (33464) ***(G-788)***
Weightech USA LLC.....954 666-0877
10384 W State Road 84 # 6 Davie (33324) ***(G-2613)***
Weimer Mechanical Services Inc.....813 645-2258
1701 E Shell Point Rd Ruskin (33570) ***(G-15487)***
Weimer Services, Ruskin *Also called Weimer Mechanical Services Inc* ***(G-15487)***
Weiss Group LLC (PA).....561 627-3300
15430 Endeavor Dr Ste 101 Jupiter (33478) ***(G-7145)***
Weiss Research Inc.....561 627-3300
15430 Endeavor Dr Ste 101 Jupiter (33478) ***(G-7146)***
Welbilt Inc (PA).....727 375-7010
2227 Welbilt Blvd Trinity (34655) ***(G-18491)***
Weldco Mechanical Services, Panama City *Also called Phillip & Roger Inc* ***(G-13941)***
Weldcorp Industries.....561 339-7713
15188 Pk Of Cmmrce Blvd S Jupiter (33478) ***(G-7147)***
Welding, Altamonte Springs *Also called Mag Cleaning Solutions LLC* ***(G-55)***
Welding and Fabrication Inc.....973 508-7267
3150 W Pembroke Rd Hallandale Beach (33009) ***(G-5224)***
Welding Anything Anywhere LLC.....561 762-1404
6231 Pga Blvd Palm Beach Gardens (33418) ***(G-13635)***
Welding LLC.....386 478-0323
23 Silver Cir Edgewater (32141) ***(G-3639)***
Well Bilt Industries, Ocala *Also called M Bilt Enterprises Inc* ***(G-11989)***
Well Bilt Industries Usa LLC.....352 528-5566
3001 Sw 67th Avenue Rd # 100 Ocala (34474) ***(G-12074)***
Well Made Bus Solutions LLC.....754 227-7268
5671 Nw 40th Ter Coconut Creek (33073) ***(G-2101)***
Well Traveled Imports Inc.....904 261-5400
716 S 8th St Amelia Island (32034) ***(G-93)***
Well Traveled Living, Amelia Island *Also called Well Traveled Imports Inc* ***(G-93)***
Wellington Forum, Deerfield Beach *Also called Forum Publishing Group Inc* ***(G-2828)***
Wellington Leather LLC.....561 790-0034
320 Business Park Way Royal Palm Beach (33411) ***(G-15479)***
Wells & Drew Companies, The, Jacksonville *Also called Wells Legal Supply Inc* ***(G-6909)***
Wells Legal Supply Inc.....904 399-1510
3414 Galilee Rd Jacksonville (32207) ***(G-6909)***
Wellstream Inc.....281 249-0900
6521 Bayline Dr Panama City (32404) ***(G-13962)***
Wellstream International Ltd.....850 636-4800
6521 Bayline Dr Panama City (32404) ***(G-13963)***
Welshman Investment Corp.....407 933-4444
1570 Kelley Ave Ste 2 Kissimmee (34744) ***(G-7310)***
Wemerge Inc.....561 305-2070
3620 W Hillsboro Blvd Coconut Creek (33073) ***(G-2102)***
Wemi Sports.....305 446-5178
156 Giralda Ave Coral Gables (33134) ***(G-2206)***
Wep Sourcing, Miami *Also called World Event Promotions LLC* ***(G-10619)***
Weplenish LLC.....954 909-4183
150 S Pine Island Rd Plantation (33324) ***(G-14567)***
Were In Stitches.....813 264-4804
14807 N Florida Ave Tampa (33613) ***(G-18254)***
Werever Products Inc.....813 241-9701
6120 Pelican Creek Cir Riverview (33578) ***(G-15287)***
Werever Waterproof Cabinetry, Riverview *Also called Werever Products Inc* ***(G-15287)***
Wes Holdings Corp.....941 371-4995
818 Cattlemen Rd Sarasota (34232) ***(G-16636)***
Wes Industries Inc (PA).....941 371-7617
6389 Tower Ln Sarasota (34240) ***(G-16637)***
Weschler Instruments, Coral Springs *Also called Hughes Corporation* ***(G-2256)***
Wesco Partners Inc.....941 484-8224
1125 Commerce Blvd N Sarasota (34243) ***(G-16325)***
Wesley Chapel Fuel Inc.....813 907-9994
27616 Wesley Chapel Blvd Wesley Chapel (33544) ***(G-18764)***
Wesol Distribution LLC.....407 921-9248
1486 Seminola Blvd Unit 1 Casselberry (32707) ***(G-1521)***
West Bay Door, Tampa *Also called Florida Made Door Co* ***(G-17681)***
West Bolusia Beacon.....386 734-4622
110 W New York Ave Deland (32720) ***(G-3033)***
West Cast Cbnets Clsets Flrg I.....239 481-8109
6385 Presidential Ct # 102 Fort Myers (33919) ***(G-4652)***
West Central Signs Inc.....813 980-6763
3502 Queen Palm Dr Ste C Tampa (33619) ***(G-18255)***
West Coast Brace & Limb, Temple Terrace *Also called Westcoast Brace & Limb Inc* ***(G-18383)***
West Coast Castings Inc.....941 753-2969
1211 44th Ave E Bradenton (34203) ***(G-1146)***
West Coast Custom Cabinetry.....239 481-8109
17683 Summerlin Rd 10 Fort Myers (33908) ***(G-4653)***
West Coast Shutters Sunburst.....727 894-0044
128 19th St S Ste B Saint Petersburg (33712) ***(G-15957)***
West Coast Signs.....941 755-5686
2310 Whitfield Indus Way Sarasota (34243) ***(G-16326)***
West Coast Wonderworks LLC.....407 351-8800
9067 International Dr Orlando (32819) ***(G-13321)***
West Development Group LLC.....407 308-5020
4520 Malvern Hill Dr Orlando (32818) ***(G-13322)***
West End.....407 322-7475
202 Sanford Ave Sanford (32771) ***(G-16138)***
West Florida Precision Mch LLC.....727 939-0030
728 Anclote Rd Tarpon Springs (34689) ***(G-18331)***
West Fraser Inc.....904 786-4155
109 Halsema Rd S Jacksonville (32220) ***(G-6910)***
West Fraser Inc.....850 587-1000
401 Champion Mc David (32568) ***(G-8602)***
West Harbour Woodworking LLC.....954 822-7543
2543 Nw 49th Ave Apt 203 Lauderdale Lakes (33313) ***(G-8096)***
West Orange Times, Winter Garden *Also called Winter Garden Times Inc* ***(G-19291)***
West Palm Installers Inc.....305 406-3575
5141 Nw 79th Ave Unit 1 Doral (33166) ***(G-3548)***
West Palm Machining & Welding.....561 841-2725
4650 Dyer Blvd Riviera Beach (33407) ***(G-15389)***
West Phrm Svcs Fla Inc.....727 546-2402
5111 Park St N Saint Petersburg (33709) ***(G-15958)***
West Point Industries Inc.....561 848-8381
1300 Old Dixie Hwy # 101 Lake Park (33403) ***(G-7481)***
West Point Stevens.....850 638-9421
1414 Main St Chipley (32428) ***(G-1547)***

West Side Gazette, Fort Lauderdale *Also called Bi-Ads Inc* ***(G-3849)***
West Texas Protein Inc 806 250-5959
601 Riverside Ave Jacksonville (32204) ***(G-6911)***
West Wood Manufacturing, Bradenton *Also called Cabinet Designs of Sarasota* ***(G-1010)***
Westchester Gold Fabricators 941 625-0666
4200 Tamiami Trl Ste F Port Charlotte (33952) ***(G-15007)***
Westcoast Brace & Limb Inc (PA) 813 985-5000
5311 E Fletcher Ave Temple Terrace (33617) ***(G-18383)***
Westcoast Brace & Limb Inc 407 502-0024
341 N Maitland Ave # 210 Maitland (32751) ***(G-8486)***
Westcoast Metalworks Inc 941 920-3201
3308 39th St E Palmetto (34221) ***(G-13836)***
Westech Development Group Inc 954 505-5090
3010 N Andrews Avenue Ext Pompano Beach (33064) ***(G-14912)***
Westech Industries, Pompano Beach *Also called Westech Development Group Inc* ***(G-14912)***
Western Digital Corporation 561 995-1496
1 Park Pl Ste 240nw Boca Raton (33487) ***(G-789)***
Western Fabricating LLC 239 676-5382
17061 Alico Commerce Ct Fort Myers (33967) ***(G-4654)***
Western Graphite Inc (PA) 850 270-2808
1045 E Washington St Monticello (32344) ***(G-11083)***
Western Ivy 352 622-5767
6998 N Us Highway 27 Ocala (34482) ***(G-12075)***
Western Microsystems Inc (PA) 800 547-7082
4230 Pablo Pro Ct Ste 200 Jacksonville (32224) ***(G-6912)***
Western Reserve Tool Machine, Jupiter *Also called North Erie Electronics Inc* ***(G-7084)***
Westime 310 205-5555
701 S Miami Ave Unit 168c Miami (33130) ***(G-10598)***
Westlund Engineering Inc 727 572-4343
3116 Roxmere Dr Palm Harbor (34685) ***(G-13769)***
Weston Magazine Inc 203 451-1967
6103 Aqua Ave Ph 2 Miami Beach (33141) ***(G-10729)***
Weston Park At Longwood STA 321 422-3546
100 Wax Myrtle Ln Longwood (32779) ***(G-8350)***
Westpoint Home Inc 850 415-4100
1056 Commerce Ave Chipley (32428) ***(G-1548)***
Westpoint Home Inc 850 415-4100
1414 Main St Chipley (32428) ***(G-1549)***
Westran Corporation 727 375-7010
2227 Welbilt Blvd Trinity (34655) ***(G-18492)***
Westrock Cp LLC 904 261-5551
600 N 8th St Fernandina Beach (32034) ***(G-3749)***
Westrock Cp LLC 904 356-5611
2002 E 18th St Jacksonville (32206) ***(G-6913)***
Westrock Cp LLC 850 785-4311
1 S Everitt Ave Panama City (32401) ***(G-13964)***
Westrock Cp LLC 239 658-8221
815 E Main St Immokalee (34142) ***(G-6054)***
Westrock Cp LLC 904 714-7151
9469 Eastport Rd Jacksonville (32218) ***(G-6914)***
Westrock Cp LLC 954 522-3684
3251 Sw 1st Ter Fort Lauderdale (33315) ***(G-4320)***
Westrock Cp LLC 407 843-1300
4364 Sw 34th St Orlando (32811) ***(G-13323)***
Westrock CP LLC 407 859-9701
375 W 7th St Orlando (32824) ***(G-13324)***
Westrock Lake Mary 407 936-1277
2950 Lake Emma Rd Lake Mary (32746) ***(G-7461)***
Westrock Rkt LLC 904 714-1643
1660 Prudential Dr # 202 Jacksonville (32207) ***(G-6915)***
Westrom Software 866 480-1879
903 7th Ave Vero Beach (32960) ***(G-18681)***
Westview Corp Inc 239 643-5699
3419 Westview Dr Naples (34104) ***(G-11454)***
Wetherill Associates Inc (PA) 800 773-0005
3300 Corporate Way Miramar (33025) ***(G-11060)***
Wf Brick Pavers Inc 813 506-1941
213 Lexington St Oldsmar (34677) ***(G-12278)***
Wf Fuel 941 706-4953
300 N Washington Blvd Sarasota (34236) ***(G-16638)***
Wgentv, Doral *Also called Mambo LLC* ***(G-3422)***
Wharton Pepper Co 850 997-4359
2873a St Augustine Rd Monticello (32344) ***(G-11084)***
What To Drink B4 You Drink, Orlando *Also called Sunshine Supplements Inc* ***(G-13227)***
Whatever Lo Que Sea LLC 786 429-3462
2087 Nw 135th Ave Miami (33182) ***(G-10599)***
Whats Wrong Publishing Co 904 388-3494
2641 Park St Jacksonville (32204) ***(G-6916)***
Wheel Systems Intl Inc 920 235-9888
7645 Tralee Way Bradenton (34202) ***(G-1147)***
Wheel Wright 850 626-2662
6899 Deception Rd Milton (32583) ***(G-10946)***
Wheelblast Inc 813 715-7117
3951 Copeland Dr Zephyrhills (33542) ***(G-19542)***
Wheeled Coach Industries, Winter Park *Also called Rev Amblance Group Orlando Inc* ***(G-19441)***
Wheeler Consolidated Inc 772 464-4400
1031 Digiorgio Rd Fort Pierce (34982) ***(G-4770)***
Wheeler EMC, Marianna *Also called Wheeler Emergency Management C* ***(G-8587)***
Wheeler Emergency Management C 850 372-4174
2954 Highway 71 Marianna (32446) ***(G-8587)***
Wheeler Trading Inc 305 430-7100
5851 Nw 159th St Miami Lakes (33014) ***(G-10880)***
Wheelhouse Direct LLC 239 246-8788
17595 S Tamiami Trl # 125 Fort Myers (33908) ***(G-4655)***
Wheels A Million 754 444-2869
1100 Nw 54th St Fort Lauderdale (33309) ***(G-4321)***
Whertec Inc (HQ) 904 278-6503
5409 Highway Ave Jacksonville (32254) ***(G-6917)***
Whertec Technologies Inc 866 207-6503
5409 Highway Ave Jacksonville (32254) ***(G-6918)***
Whetstone Chocolate Factory, Saint Augustine *Also called Whetstone Industries Inc* ***(G-15636)***
Whetstone Indus Holdings Inc (PA) 904 824-0888
100 Whetstone Pl Ste 100 # 100 Saint Augustine (32086) ***(G-15635)***
Whetstone Industries Inc 904 824-0888
100 Whetstone Pl Ste 100 # 100 Saint Augustine (32086) ***(G-15636)***
Whigham Citrus Packing House 772 569-7190
10525 State Road 60 Vero Beach (32966) ***(G-18682)***
Whigham Citrus Pkg Hse McHy, Vero Beach *Also called Whigham Citrus Packing House* ***(G-18682)***
Whip-It Inventions Inc (PA) 850 626-6300
5946 Commerce Rd Milton (32583) ***(G-10947)***
Whispering Oaks Winery 352 748-0449
10934 County Road 475 Oxford (34484) ***(G-13465)***
White Aluminum Fabrication Inc 772 219-3245
3195 Se Lionel Ter Stuart (34997) ***(G-17048)***
White Cardboard Corp 786 260-4692
3671 Nw 81st St Miami (33147) ***(G-10600)***
White Cliff, Miami *Also called Kiskeya Minerals Usa LLC* ***(G-9823)***
White County Stone LLC 415 516-0849
135 Churchill Rd West Palm Beach (33405) ***(G-19086)***
White Cross Supply Co, Naples *Also called Vienna Beauty Products Co* ***(G-11451)***
White Horse Fashion Cuisine 561 847-4549
14440 Pierson Rd Wellington (33414) ***(G-18739)***
White Label Liquid Inc 386 256-1826
210 Sentress Blvd Daytona Beach (32114) ***(G-2732)***
White Ladder Inc 904 343-9314
1566 Plantation Oaks Ter Fernandina Beach (32034) ***(G-3750)***
White Miami LLC 305 579-9115
117 Ne 1st Ave Apt 1301 Miami (33132) ***(G-10601)***
White Mop Wringer Company 813 971-2223
10702 N 46th St Tampa (33617) ***(G-18256)***
White Oak Energy Backleverage (HQ) 561 691-7171
700 Universe Blvd Juno Beach (33408) ***(G-6987)***
White Oak Energy Holdings LLC 561 691-7171
700 Universe Blvd Juno Beach (33408) ***(G-6988)***
White Publishing Co Inc 904 389-3622
1531 Osceola St Jacksonville (32204) ***(G-6919)***
White Rose Installation 772 562-6698
1266 14th Ave Sw Vero Beach (32962) ***(G-18683)***
White Sands Dmg Inc 305 947-7731
1798 Ne 163rd St North Miami Beach (33162) ***(G-11712)***
White Sign Company LLC 386 516-6156
909 S Chrles R Beall Blvd Debary (32713) ***(G-2757)***
White Sign Company LLC 407 342-7887
909 S Charles Richard Bea Debary (32713) ***(G-2758)***
White Springs AG Chem Inc 386 397-8101
15843 Se 78th St White Springs (32096) ***(G-19189)***
White Square Chemical Inc 302 212-4555
91760 Overseas Hwy Tavernier (33070) ***(G-18364)***
White Starr Publishing 305 322-5788
12031 Sw 107th St Miami (33186) ***(G-10602)***
Whitecap Promotions LLC 813 960-4918
2523 Cozumel Dr Tampa (33618) ***(G-18257)***
Whitehouse Custom Scrn PR 727 321-7398
7183 30th Ave N Saint Petersburg (33710) ***(G-15959)***
Whites Holdings Inc Centl Fla 727 863-6072
9301 Denton Ave Port Richey (34667) ***(G-15078)***
Whitewater Boat Corp 305 756-9191
280 Nw 73rd St Miami (33150) ***(G-10603)***
Whitewave Foods, Jacksonville *Also called Wwf Operating Company LLC* ***(G-6930)***
Whitfield Timber Co Inc (PA) 850 639-5556
101 N Highway 71 Wewahitchka (32465) ***(G-19184)***
Whiticar Boat Works Inc (PA) 772 287-2883
3636 Se Old St Lucie Blvd Stuart (34996) ***(G-17049)***
Whitley Welding Company L 904 576-3410
4280 Chokeberry Rd Middleburg (32068) ***(G-10915)***
Whitman Industries LLC 239 216-6171
1825 Dogwood Dr Marco Island (34145) ***(G-8528)***
Whittington Energy Co 321 984-2128
730 E Strawbridge Ave # 205 Melbourne (32901) ***(G-8974)***
Whiz Bang LLC 305 296-0160
926 Truman Ave Key West (33040) ***(G-7204)***
Whk Biosystems LLC 727 209-8402
11345 53rd St N Clearwater (33760) ***(G-1938)***

ALPHABETIC

Whole Coffee Company LLC......786 364-4444
1130 Nw 159th Dr Miami (33169) *(G-10604)*
Whole Enchlada Fresh Mxcan Gri......954 561-4040
4115 N Federal Hwy Fort Lauderdale (33308) *(G-4322)*
Whole Tomato Software Inc......408 323-1590
1990 Main St Ste 750 Sarasota (34236) *(G-16639)*
Whole Trade, Lake Worth *Also called Bikekeeper LLC (G-7536)*
Wholesale Cornhole Bags, Orlando *Also called Custom Cornhole Boards Inc (G-12638)*
Wholesale Screen Prtg of Nples......239 263-7061
3584 Mercantile Ave Ste B Naples (34104) *(G-11455)*
Wholesale Sign Superstore Inc......321 212-8458
580 Gus Hipp Blvd Rockledge (32955) *(G-15457)*
Wholesale Signs Fabricators......407 729-5599
2968 Michigan Ave Ste C Kissimmee (34744) *(G-7311)*
Wholesale Trade, Naples *Also called ABC Recyclers Collier Cnty Inc (G-11145)*
Wholesalers, Hialeah *Also called Love Is In The Air Corp (G-5489)*
Wholly Hemp Inc......813 785-6231
187 Brushcreek Dr Sanford (32771) *(G-16139)*
Whr Holdings LLC......954 342-4342
3402 Sw 26th Ter Ste 10 Fort Lauderdale (33312) *(G-4323)*
Whyte Power Industries Corp......786 200-6033
22524 Sw 110th Ct Miami (33170) *(G-10605)*
Wialan Technologies LLC (PA)......954 749-3481
10271 Nw 46th St Sunrise (33351) *(G-17198)*
Wibe Natural......305 594-0158
10860 Nw 27th St Doral (33172) *(G-3549)*
Wicked Dolphin Distillery......239 565-7947
131 Sw 3rd Pl Cape Coral (33991) *(G-1495)*
Wicks Unlimited Inc......631 472-2010
1515 Sw 13th Ct Pompano Beach (33069) *(G-14913)*
Wide Open Armory LLC......727 202-5980
8200 113th St Ste 104 Seminole (33772) *(G-16771)*
Widell Industries Inc (PA)......800 237-5963
6622 Industrial Ave Port Richey (34668) *(G-15079)*
Wilaen, Miami *Also called Wireless Latin Entrmt Inc (G-10614)*
Wilbert E Beran......813 882-0178
7025 Oakview Cir Tampa (33634) *(G-18258)*
Wilcox and Ray Music Pubg Inc......786 220-1362
1275 Nw 50th St Miami (33142) *(G-10606)*
Wilcox Steel Company LLC......727 443-0461
1101 Kapp Dr Clearwater (33765) *(G-1939)*
Wild Diamond Vineyards LLC......305 892-8699
1680 Ne 135th St North Miami (33181) *(G-11664)*
Wild Prints LLC......561 800-6536
12415 76th Rd N West Palm Beach (33412) *(G-19087)*
Wilkenson Hi-Rise, Fort Lauderdale *Also called Whr Holdings LLC (G-4323)*
Wilkerson Instrument Co Inc......863 647-2000
2915 Parkway St Lakeland (33811) *(G-7834)*
Wilkins Lapidary Arts......386 734-8470
413 E Kentucky Ave Deland (32724) *(G-3034)*
Wilkinson Hi-Rise LLC......954 342-4400
3402 Sw 26th Ter Ste 10 Fort Lauderdale (33312) *(G-4324)*
Wilkinson Steel Supply LLC......904 757-1522
3210 Faye Rd Jacksonville (32226) *(G-6920)*
Will & Mia Corp......617 943-6914
1250 Ne 207th Ter Miami (33179) *(G-10607)*
Will Garrett Towers, Plantation *Also called Tip Top Canvas and Uphl Inc (G-14559)*
Will Shutter U Inc......772 285-3600
2087 Nw Marsh Rabbit Ln Jensen Beach (34957) *(G-6974)*
Will Watson Construction LLC......850 586-5349
464 Kanuha Dr Fort Walton Beach (32547) *(G-4840)*
Will-Rite Industries Inc......305 253-1985
10853 Sw 188th St Cutler Bay (33157) *(G-2421)*
Willett Precision Machining......727 573-9299
11339 43rd St N Clearwater (33762) *(G-1940)*
William B Rudow Inc......941 957-4200
1122 Goodrich Ave Sarasota (34236) *(G-16640)*
William Burns......877 462-5872
1800 Via Lago Dr Lakeland (33810) *(G-7835)*
William Byrd & Sons Inc......786 573-3251
14720 Sw 83rd Pl Palmetto Bay (33158) *(G-13858)*
William Fster Entp Embrdme Jck......904 329-1549
2266 Mission Creek Dr Jacksonville (32218) *(G-6921)*
William Laroque Installers Inc......305 769-1717
5820 Sheridan St Hollywood (33021) *(G-5940)*
William Leupold Sr......727 527-7400
3291 40th Ave N Saint Petersburg (33714) *(G-15960)*
Williams & Bennett, Orlando *Also called Fantasy Chocolates Inc (G-12732)*
Williams and King Publishers......407 914-8134
3900 Millenia Blvd Orlando (32839) *(G-13325)*
Williams Communications Inc......850 689-6651
701 Ashley Dr Crestview (32536) *(G-2361)*
Williams Industrial Svcs LLC......904 696-9994
11380 Island Dr 1 Jacksonville (32226) *(G-6922)*
Williams Jewelry and Mfg Co......727 823-7676
3152 Morris St N Saint Petersburg (33713) *(G-15961)*
Williams Minerals Co Inc......304 897-6003
168 Seville Chase Dr Winter Springs (32708) *(G-19489)*
Williams Orthtc-Prosthetic Inc......850 385-6655
2360 Centerville Rd Tallahassee (32308) *(G-17345)*
Williams Specialities, Hialeah *Also called Bros Williams Printing Inc (G-5332)*
Williams Specialties Inc......305 769-9925
4716 E 10th Ct Hialeah (33013) *(G-5687)*
Williams Tenders USA Inc......954 648-6560
451 S Federal Hwy Pompano Beach (33062) *(G-14914)*
Williams Timber Inc......850 584-2760
215 Sunset Ln Perry (32348) *(G-14319)*
Willie D Wood Works Inc......305 969-6522
14185 Sw 142nd St Miami (33186) *(G-10608)*
Willie Maes Pies LLC......407 655-9360
843 Cypress Pkwy 253 Kissimmee (34759) *(G-7315)*
Willies Wild......850 597-8116
4556 Capital Cir Nw Tallahassee (32303) *(G-17346)*
Willis Aeronautical Svcs Inc......561 272-5402
4700 Lyons Tech Pkwy Coconut Creek (33073) *(G-2103)*
Willis Custom Yachts LLC......772 221-9100
6800 Sw Jack James Dr # 1 Stuart (34997) *(G-17050)*
Willis Industries Inc......954 830-6163
5064 S University Dr Davie (33328) *(G-2614)*
Willis Marine Inc......772 283-7189
4361 Se Commerce Ave Stuart (34997) *(G-17051)*
Williston Timber Co Inc......352 528-2699
4351 Ne 176th Ave Williston (32696) *(G-19216)*
Wills Prestress Inc......239 417-9117
680 31st St Sw Naples (34117) *(G-11456)*
Willson & Son Industry Inc......954 972-5073
2000 Banks Rd Ste H1 Margate (33063) *(G-8572)*
Willsonet Inc......813 336-8175
2502 N Rocky Point Dr # 820 Tampa (33607) *(G-18259)*
Willy Walt Inc......727 209-2872
2390 26th Ave N Saint Petersburg (33713) *(G-15962)*
Wilma Schumann Skin Care Pdts, Miami *Also called Skinmetics Inc (G-10357)*
Wilo USA LLC......954 524-6776
3001 Sw 3rd Ave Ste 7 Fort Lauderdale (33315) *(G-4325)*
Wilson Machine & Welding Works......904 829-3737
5760 Us Highway 1 N Saint Augustine (32095) *(G-15637)*
Wilson Manifolds Inc......954 771-6216
4700 Ne 11th Ave Oakland Park (33334) *(G-11861)*
Wilson Msclineous Fabrications, Tampa *Also called W D Wilson Inc (G-18250)*
Wilson Printing USA LLC......727 536-4173
1085 Cephas Rd Clearwater (33765) *(G-1941)*
Wilsons Machine Products Inc......407 644-2020
1844 Kentucky Ave Winter Park (32789) *(G-19458)*
Wilsons Monument LLC......850 743-8605
1343 S Barack Obama Blvd Quincy (32351) *(G-15257)*
Wiltcher Industries Inc......704 907-9838
1034 Sudbury Ln Ormond Beach (32174) *(G-13409)*
Wilton Wind II LLC......561 691-7171
700 Universe Blvd Juno Beach (33408) *(G-6989)*
Wimbledon Health Partners LLC......800 200-8262
7000 W Plmtt Prk Rd # 205 Boca Raton (33433) *(G-790)*
Winans Electric Motors LLC......863 875-5710
1150 Us Highway 92 W Auburndale (33823) *(G-255)*
Winatic Corporation......727 538-8917
5410 115th Ave N Clearwater (33760) *(G-1942)*
Winchster Interconnect Rf Corp......800 881-9689
3950 Dow Rd Melbourne (32934) *(G-8975)*
Winchster Intrcnnect Hrmtics L (HQ)......321 254-4067
3950 Dow Rd Melbourne (32934) *(G-8976)*
Winco Mfg LLC (PA)......352 854-2929
5516 Sw 1st Ln Ocala (34474) *(G-12076)*
Wincor Technology Inc......407 702-0787
3025 Pinenut Dr Apopka (32712) *(G-197)*
Wind Blue Technology LLC......850 218-9398
7502 Sears Blvd Pensacola (32514) *(G-14288)*
Wind River Systems Inc......321 726-9463
100 Rialto Pl Ste 525 Melbourne (32901) *(G-8977)*
Windbrella Products Corp......561 734-5222
2114 Corporate Dr Boynton Beach (33426) *(G-974)*
Windera Power Systems Inc......407 808-1271
703 Progress Way Sanford (32771) *(G-16140)*
Windermere Cabinetry LLC......321 263-5181
13675 Sunset Lakes Cir Winter Garden (34787) *(G-19290)*
Windermere Nannies LLC......407 782-2057
6526 Old Brick Rd Ste 120 Windermere (34786) *(G-19251)*
Windoor Incorporated......407 481-8400
1070 Technology Dr North Venice (34275) *(G-11765)*
Window Craftsmen Inc......941 922-1844
6031 Clark Center Ave Sarasota (34238) *(G-16641)*
Windows Doors Etc, Saint Petersburg *Also called Bay City Window Company (G-15718)*
Windowware Pro......904 584-9191
2085 A1a S Ste 201 Saint Augustine (32080) *(G-15638)*
Windrusher Inc......904 614-5196
602 Miramar Ct Ponte Vedra Beach (32082) *(G-14957)*
Winds......239 948-0777
4555 Bonita Beach Rd Bonita Springs (34134) *(G-863)*
Windsor & York Inc......561 687-8424
7233 Southern Blvd West Palm Beach (33413) *(G-19088)*

Windsor Imaging, Oakland Park *Also called Open Magnetic Scanning Ltd* ***(G-11826)***
Windsor Imaging Delray 561 900-0300
14590 S Military Trl E1 Delray Beach (33484) ***(G-3160)***
Windsor Metal Finishing, Kissimmee *Also called Best Engineered Surfc Tech LLC* ***(G-7223)***
Windsor Window Company 321 385-3880
1450 Shepard Dr Titusville (32780) ***(G-18473)***
Windstar Express Inc 786 252-1569
19499 Ne 10th Ave Miami (33179) ***(G-10609)***
Windstone Development Intl Lc 954 370-7201
7080 W State Road 84 Davie (33317) ***(G-2615)***
Windward Associates Corp 954 336-8085
265 Bryan Rd Dania (33004) ***(G-2461)***
Windward Communications Inc 727 584-7191
2401 West Bay Dr Ste 414 Largo (33770) ***(G-8080)***
Windy City Apparel, Sarasota *Also called CC Sportswear Inc* ***(G-16188)***
Wine Plum Inc 844 856-7586
11 Sw 12th Ave Ste 104 Dania Beach (33004) ***(G-2475)***
Wine Tasters of Naples Inc 239 961-1522
2021 Painted Palm Dr Naples (34119) ***(G-11457)***
Wine World Inc 786 348-8780
12650 Nw 25th St Ste 112 Miami (33182) ***(G-10610)***
Wingard LLC 904 387-2570
76 S Laura St Ste 1501 Jacksonville (32202) ***(G-6923)***
Wings Aircraft Finance, Fort Lauderdale *Also called Aercap Group Services Inc* ***(G-3786)***
Wings Things Monogramming Inc 850 455-3081
3815 W Navy Blvd Pensacola (32507) ***(G-14289)***
Wink Streaming Llc 312 281-5444
6703 Nw 7th St 87872 Miami (33126) ***(G-10611)***
Winner Group, Sebring *Also called Winntel USA* ***(G-16718)***
Winntel USA 863 451-1789
4014 Vilabella Dr Sebring (33872) ***(G-16718)***
Winrise Enterprises LLC 786 621-6705
15701 Sw 29th St 100 Miramar (33027) ***(G-11061)***
Winslow Life Raft Co, Lake Suzy *Also called Winslow Marine Products Corp* ***(G-7497)***
Winslow Marine Products Corp 941 613-6666
11700 Sw Winslow Dr Lake Suzy (34269) ***(G-7497)***
Winslow Microplastics Corp 305 493-3501
20257 Ne 15th Ct Miami (33179) ***(G-10612)***
Winsted Thermographers Inc 305 944-7862
917 Sw 10th St Hallandale Beach (33009) ***(G-5225)***
Winston & Sons Inc 954 562-1984
9735 Nw 76th St Tamarac (33321) ***(G-17370)***
Winston Furniture Company Ala, Saint Augustine *Also called Jordan Brown Inc* ***(G-15562)***
Winston Manufacturing, Opa Locka *Also called Everglades Creations Inc* ***(G-12314)***
Winston Manufacturing Corp 305 822-3344
1745 W 32nd Pl Ste 55 Hialeah (33012) ***(G-5688)***
Winsulator Corporation 941 365-7901
3350 S Osprey Ave Sarasota (34239) ***(G-16642)***
Wintel 407 834-1188
1051 Bennett Dr Ste 101 Longwood (32750) ***(G-8351)***
Winter Garden Times Inc 407 656-2121
661 Garden Commerce Pkwy Winter Garden (34787) ***(G-19291)***
Winter Park Distilling Co LLC 407 801-2714
1288 Orange Ave Winter Park (32789) ***(G-19459)***
Winter Park Publishing Co LLC 941 320-6627
201 W Canton Ave Ste 125b Winter Park (32789) ***(G-19460)***
Winter Qarters Pasco Rv Resort 800 879-2131
21632 State Road 54 Lutz (33549) ***(G-8424)***
Winwood Print 786 615-3188
591 Nw 29th St Miami (33127) ***(G-10613)***
Wire Experts Group Inc (PA) 239 597-8555
3650 Shaw Blvd Naples (34117) ***(G-11458)***
Wire Mesh Corp 706 922-5179
4034 Faye Rd Jacksonville (32226) ***(G-6924)***
Wire Products Inc of Florida (PA) 954 772-1477
4300 Nw 10th Ave Fort Lauderdale (33309) ***(G-4326)***
Wire Tech International Inc 786 258-5746
10225 Collins Ave Bal Harbour (33154) ***(G-304)***
Wired Rite Systems Inc 707 838-1122
1748 Independence Blvd C5 Sarasota (34234) ***(G-16643)***
Wireless Coverage Group Inc 561 429-5032
11718 Se Federal Hwy # 36 Hobe Sound (33455) ***(G-5731)***
Wireless Latin Entrmt Inc 305 858-7740
5301 Blue Lagoon Dr # 180 Miami (33126) ***(G-10614)***
Wiremaid Products Division, Coral Springs *Also called Vutec Corporation* ***(G-2330)***
Wiremil Division, Sanderson *Also called Insteel Wire Products Company* ***(G-15982)***
Wiretec Ignition Inc 407 578-4569
1901 4th St W Palmetto (34221) ***(G-13837)***
Wireworld By David Salz Inc 954 474-4464
6545 Nova Dr Ste 204 Davie (33317) ***(G-2616)***
Wireworld Cable Technology, Davie *Also called Wireworld By David Salz Inc* ***(G-2616)***
Wise Business Forms Inc 770 442-1060
13015 Nw 38th Ave Opa Locka (33054) ***(G-12369)***
Wise Gas Fuel Card LLC 954 636-4291
1058 Bluewood Ter Weston (33327) ***(G-19178)***
Wise Recycling 1 LLC 850 477-5273
601 W Hope Dr Pensacola (32534) ***(G-14290)***
Wish Inc 305 653-9474
33 Nw 168th St North Miami Beach (33169) ***(G-11713)***
Wishbone Woodworking Inc 239 262-7230
121 Pinehurst Cir Naples (34113) ***(G-11459)***
Witts Woodworking Inc 941 544-8812
1963 Racimo Dr Sarasota (34240) ***(G-16644)***
Wizard Labs 321 422-0803
927 Fern St Ste 1000 Altamonte Springs (32701) ***(G-84)***
Wizard Publications 808 823-8815
775 Blvard Of The Chmpons Shalimar (32579) ***(G-16779)***
Wiztel USA Inc 416 457-5513
18281 Via Caprini Dr Miromar Lakes (33913) ***(G-11072)***
Wj Bergin Cabinetry LLC 407 271-8982
1228 28th St Orlando (32805) ***(G-13326)***
WJS Printing Partners Inc 904 731-0357
2750 Dawn Rd Jacksonville (32207) ***(G-6925)***
Wm G Roe & Sons Inc 863 294-3577
500 Avenue R Sw Winter Haven (33880) ***(G-19367)***
Wmr Cycle Performance Inc 772 426-3000
7749 Sw Ellipse Way Stuart (34997) ***(G-17052)***
Wogans Cstm Cbnets Rfacing LLC 904 343-8917
9344 Lockheed Ln Jacksonville (32221) ***(G-6926)***
Wohlers Publishing Inc 305 289-1644
10701 6th Avenue Gulf Marathon (33050) ***(G-8522)***
Wolf Americas LLC 407 704-2051
3113 Willie Mays Pkwy Orlando (32811) ***(G-13327)***
Wolf Rock Drills, Orlando *Also called Wolf Americas LLC* ***(G-13327)***
Wolff Controls Corporation 863 324-0423
2929 Dundee Rd Winter Haven (33884) ***(G-19368)***
Wolverine Advanced Mtls LLC 352 787-3015
10825 County Road 44 Leesburg (34788) ***(G-8181)***
Wolverine Engines 850 462-4160
108 Patrick Dr Fort Walton Beach (32547) ***(G-4841)***
Wonder Emporium Millwork Fab 407 850-3131
10779 Satellite Blvd Orlando (32837) ***(G-13328)***
Wonder Holdings Acquisition 305 379-2322
1450 Brickell Ave # 3100 Miami (33131) ***(G-10615)***
Wonderland Products Inc 904 786-0144
5772 Lenox Ave Jacksonville (32205) ***(G-6927)***
Wonderworld 100 LLC 407 618-3207
2209 S Fern Creek Ave Orlando (32806) ***(G-13329)***
Wood & Glass Works LLC 727 317-9599
8540 29th Way N Apt 207 Pinellas Park (33782) ***(G-14394)***
Wood Arts of India, Sanford *Also called Deep Ocean Woodworks Inc* ***(G-16034)***
Wood Aspects 321 800-8875
1704 Langley Ave Ste D Deland (32724) ***(G-3035)***
Wood Dimensions, Tallahassee *Also called Debruyne Enterprise Inc* ***(G-17242)***
Wood Drams Inc of Palm Beaches 561 842-9814
1137 Silver Beach Rd Lake Park (33403) ***(G-7482)***
Wood Machine Corp 407 851-8714
491 Thorpe Rd Orlando (32824) ***(G-13330)***
Wood One LLC 727 639-5620
2416 52nd Ave N Saint Petersburg (33714) ***(G-15963)***
Wood Product Services Inc 813 248-2221
2417 N 70th St Tampa (33619) ***(G-18260)***
Wood Scapes Interiors 386 454-1540
26509 W Us Highway 27 High Springs (32643) ***(G-5703)***
Wood Splinter Corp 305 721-7215
15451 Sw 60th St Miami (33193) ***(G-10616)***
Wood Stile Inc 561 329-4671
644 Marbella Ln North Palm Beach (33403) ***(G-11730)***
Wood Television LLC 727 815-1000
6214 Us Highway 19 New Port Richey (34652) ***(G-11521)***
Wood Television LLC 352 544-5200
15299 Cortez Blvd Brooksville (34613) ***(G-1292)***
Wood U Envision 561 601-1973
4252 Westroads Dr West Palm Beach (33407) ***(G-19089)***
Wood U LLC 954 560-2000
4321 Nw 19th Ave Oakland Park (33309) ***(G-11862)***
Wood Zone Inc 305 971-5550
13751 Sw 147th Ave Miami (33196) ***(G-10617)***
Woodcraft LLC 850 217-7757
2218 Avenida De Sol Navarre (32566) ***(G-11476)***
Woodcrafters, The, Bradenton *Also called W E W Enterprises Inc* ***(G-1144)***
Woodcrafts By Angel Inc 352 754-9335
15400 Shady St Brooksville (34604) ***(G-1293)***
Wooden It Be Nice 352 797-0427
1442 Culbreath Rd Brooksville (34602) ***(G-1294)***
Woodham Industries Inc 561 863-6666
1400 Old Dixie Hwy Ste 1 Lake Park (33403) ***(G-7483)***
Woodie L Dupree 850 859-2496
409 Sandspur Rd Westville (32464) ***(G-19182)***
Woodies Inc 305 266-9209
2041 Sw 82nd Pl Miami (33155) ***(G-10618)***
Woodman Cabinets Inc 561 558-2550
6911 95th Ln E Palmetto (34221) ***(G-13838)***
Woods Distinctive Designs 941 698-7535
7450 Sawyer Cir Port Charlotte (33981) ***(G-15008)***
Woods n Water Magazine Inc 850 584-3824
3427 Puckett Rd Perry (32348) ***(G-14320)***
Woods Printing of Ocala Inc 352 629-1665
1740 Ne 23rd Ter Ocala (34470) ***(G-12077)***

ALPHABETIC

Woodshed Woodworks LLC 904 540-0354
55 Florida Ave Saint Augustine (32084) ***(G-15639)***
Woodtech Global Inc 941 371-0392
5822 24th St E Bradenton (34203) ***(G-1148)***
Woodwards Cabinets Inc 850 835-0071
17921 Us Highway 331 S Freeport (32439) ***(G-4854)***
Woodwards Custom Cabinets, Freeport *Also called Woodwards Cabinets Inc* ***(G-4854)***
Woodwork In Nova Architectural 954 448-2962
2242 Mears Pkwy Margate (33063) ***(G-8573)***
Woodwork Unlimited Inc 352 267-4051
4075 County Road 106 Oxford (34484) ***(G-13466)***
Woodworkers Cabinet Inc 239 593-1718
6189 Taylor Rd Ste 2 Naples (34109) ***(G-11460)***
Woodworkers Cabinet Naples Inc 239 593-1718
6189 Taylor Rd Naples (34109) ***(G-11461)***
Woodworking Inc 727 442-6876
1458 S Jefferson Ave Clearwater (33756) ***(G-1943)***
Woodworks By Mike Inc 850 567-2086
1527 Coombs Dr Tallahassee (32308) ***(G-17347)***
Woodworks Cabinetry Inc 904 924-5300
4541 Saint Augustine Rd Jacksonville (32207) ***(G-6928)***
Woodworks For You 386 717-4169
1230 Stevens Ave Deland (32720) ***(G-3036)***
Woodworks Kit & Bath Designs 813 926-0570
8717 Gunn Hwy Odessa (33556) ***(G-12166)***
Woodworks of Tampa Bay LLC 813 330-5836
333 N Falkenburg Rd B209 Tampa (33619) ***(G-18261)***
Woodworkx Unlimited Inc 772 882-4197
103 N 13th St Fort Pierce (34950) ***(G-4771)***
Woody Hatcher 850 526-1501
2866 Madison St Marianna (32448) ***(G-8588)***
Woodys Acres LLC 352 345-8145
4000 Crum Rd Brooksville (34604) ***(G-1295)***
Woodys Enterprises LLC 407 892-1900
1110b Quotation Ct Saint Cloud (34772) ***(G-15670)***
Woodys Hedging LLC 863 557-4525
225 Water Tank Rd Lake Hamilton (33851) ***(G-7393)***
Wool Wholesale Plumbing Supply 954 763-3632
1321 Ne 12th Ave Fort Lauderdale (33304) ***(G-4327)***
Woovfu Inc 719 301-1661
7901 4th St N Ste 300 Saint Petersburg (33702) ***(G-15964)***
Workep Inc 787 634-1115
11930 N Bayshore Dr North Miami (33181) ***(G-11665)***
Workforce Audio Inc 866 360-6416
4821 N Grady Ave Tampa (33614) ***(G-18262)***
Working Cow Homemade Inc 727 572-7251
4711 34th St N Unit F Saint Petersburg (33714) ***(G-15965)***
Working Drones Inc 904 647-4511
2180 Emerson St Jacksonville (32207) ***(G-6929)***
Working Mother Media Inc 212 351-6400
480 N Orlando Ave Ste 236 Winter Park (32789) ***(G-19461)***
World Boat Manufacturing Inc 863 824-0015
8040 Nw 144th Trl Okeechobee (34972) ***(G-12194)***
World City, Coral Gables *Also called Worldcity Inc* ***(G-2207)***
World Class Machining Inc 386 437-7036
6650 S Us Highway 1 Bunnell (32110) ***(G-1311)***
World Container Services LLC 305 400-4850
3341 Nw 82nd Ave Doral (33122) ***(G-3550)***
World Electronics Inc 954 318-1044
10794 Nw 53rd St Sunrise (33351) ***(G-17199)***
World Emblem International Inc (PA) 305 899-9006
4601 Sheridan St Ste 300 Hollywood (33021) ***(G-5941)***
World Event Promotions LLC 800 214-3408
4302 Sw 73rd Ave Miami (33155) ***(G-10619)***
World Frost Inc 786 439-4445
14853 Sw 152nd Ter Miami (33187) ***(G-10620)***
World Fuel Cx LLC 305 428-8000
9800 Nw 41st St Ste 400 Doral (33178) ***(G-3551)***
World Golf Collection, Saint Augustine *Also called Golf America Southwest Fla Inc* ***(G-15546)***
World Hlth Enrgy Holdings Inc (PA) 561 870-0440
1825 Nw Corp Blvd Ste 110 Boca Raton (33431) ***(G-791)***
World Indus Resources Corp (HQ) 727 572-9991
13100 56th Ct Ste 710 Clearwater (33760) ***(G-1944)***
World Industrial Equipment Inc 772 461-6056
4850 Orange Ave Fort Pierce (34947) ***(G-4772)***
World Jet Fuel Report, West Palm Beach *Also called Armbrust Aviation Group Inc* ***(G-18801)***
World Manufacturing LLC 843 751-9375
17103 Se 110th Court Rd Summerfield (34491) ***(G-17064)***
World of Awnings Inc 305 884-6699
151 W 21st St Hialeah (33010) ***(G-5689)***
World of Window Coverings, Palm Beach Gardens *Also called L C Clark Publishing Inc* ***(G-13601)***
World Perfumes Inc 305 822-0004
2360 Nw 150th St Opa Locka (33054) ***(G-12370)***
World Plate 386 597-7832
2323 N State St Unit 55 Bunnell (32110) ***(G-1312)***
World Politics Review LLC 202 903-8398
825 S Orleans Ave Tampa (33606) ***(G-18263)***
World Precision Instrs LLC (PA) 941 371-1003
175 Sarasota Center Blvd Sarasota (34240) ***(G-16645)***
World Product Solutions, Saint Petersburg *Also called Private Label Skin Na LLC* ***(G-15890)***
World Publications Inc 407 628-4802
460 N Orlando Ave Ste 200 Winter Park (32789) ***(G-19462)***
World Stone and Design LLC 850 235-0399
19709 Panama Cy Bch Pkwy Panama City (32413) ***(G-13965)***
World Wide Export Management, Coral Gables *Also called Wemi Sports* ***(G-2206)***
World Wide Frozen Foods LLC 954 266-8500
800 W Cypress Creek Rd Fort Lauderdale (33309) ***(G-4328)***
World Wide Hardware, Tampa *Also called Worldwide Door Components Inc* ***(G-18265)***
Worldbox Corporation 305 253-8800
8333 Nw 66th St Miami (33166) ***(G-10621)***
Worldcity Inc 305 441-2244
251 Valencia Ave Coral Gables (33134) ***(G-2207)***
Worldglass Corporation 813 609-2453
5600 Airport Blvd Ste C Tampa (33634) ***(G-18264)***
Worlds Columbian Exonumis 561 734-4433
802 North Rd Boynton Beach (33435) ***(G-975)***
Worlds Greatest Ice Cream Inc 305 538-0207
1626 Michigan Ave Miami Beach (33139) ***(G-10730)***
Worldwide Auto Systems Corp 954 439-6332
900 Tallwood Ave Apt 307 Hollywood (33021) ***(G-5942)***
Worldwide Building Intl Inc 786 744-7076
1840 Coral Way Miami (33145) ***(G-10622)***
Worldwide Challenge Magazine 407 826-2390
100 Lake Hart Dr Ste 1600 Orlando (32832) ***(G-13331)***
Worldwide Door Components Inc (PA) 813 870-0003
5017 N Coolidge Ave Tampa (33614) ***(G-18265)***
Worldwide Draperies West LLC 305 887-9611
705 W 20th St Hialeah (33010) ***(G-5690)***
Worldwide Embroidery Inc 386 761-2688
4471 Eastport Park Way Port Orange (32127) ***(G-15040)***
Worldwide Intl Trade LLC 305 414-9774
601 S 21st Ave Hollywood (33020) ***(G-5943)***
Worldwide Media Svcs Group Inc 561 989-1342
1000 American Media Way Boca Raton (33464) ***(G-792)***
Worldwide Media Svcs Group Inc (PA) 561 989-1342
1000 American Media Way Boca Raton (33464) ***(G-793)***
Worldwide Sportswear Inc 386 761-2688
4471 Eastport Park Way Port Orange (32127) ***(G-15041)***
Worldwide Superabrasives LLC 954 828-9650
2921 Commerce Park Dr Boynton Beach (33426) ***(G-976)***
Worldwide Technology Inc (PA) 813 855-2443
141 Stevens Ave Ste 10 Oldsmar (34677) ***(G-12279)***
Worldwide Ticketcraft, Boynton Beach *Also called Worldwide Tickets & Labels Inc* ***(G-977)***
Worldwide Tickets & Labels Inc 877 426-5754
3606 Quantum Blvd Boynton Beach (33426) ***(G-977)***
Worrell Water Technologies LLC 434 973-6365
14 S Swinton Ave Delray Beach (33444) ***(G-3161)***
Worth Company LLC 888 652-1555
608 Trestle Pt Sanford (32771) ***(G-16141)***
Worth Intl Media Group (PA) 305 826-4763
5979 Nw 151st St Ste 120 Miami Lakes (33014) ***(G-10881)***
Worth Metals Inc 904 626-1434
4135 Highway 17 S Green Cove Springs (32043) ***(G-5077)***
Worthington Industries LLC 813 979-1000
17501 Preserve Walk Ln Tampa (33647) ***(G-18266)***
Worthington Millwork LLC 800 872-1608
17842 Ashley Dr C Panama City Beach (32413) ***(G-13986)***
Wow Business 813 301-2620
400 N Tampa St Ste 1000 Tampa (33602) ***(G-18267)***
Wow Innovations, Fort Lauderdale *Also called Color-Chrome Technologies Inc* ***(G-3910)***
Wpp Group Usa Inc 305 341-8132
601 Brickell Key Dr # 700 Miami (33131) ***(G-10623)***
Wpr Inc 850 626-7713
4175 Briarglen Rd Milton (32583) ***(G-10948)***
Wrap-Art Inc 954 428-1819
712 S Military Trl Deerfield Beach (33442) ***(G-2936)***
Wrapfink, Hollywood *Also called Metro Signs Inc* ***(G-5875)***
Wrico Stamping Co of Florida, Orlando *Also called Griffiths Corporation* ***(G-12790)***
Wright Printery Inc 386 252-6571
735 N Ridgewood Ave Daytona Beach (32114) ***(G-2733)***
Wristband Specialty, Deerfield Beach *Also called Wristband Supply LLC* ***(G-2937)***
Wristband Supply LLC 954 571-3993
3000 Sw 15th St Ste F Deerfield Beach (33442) ***(G-2937)***
Write Stuff Enterprises LLC 954 462-6657
1001 S Andrews Ave # 120 Fort Lauderdale (33316) ***(G-4329)***
Wrobel Industries Inc 727 560-6850
1004 Us Highway 19 # 202 Holiday (34691) ***(G-5753)***
Wrongs Without Wremedies LLC 850 423-0828
6256 Bullet Dr Crestview (32536) ***(G-2362)***
Wurth Wood Group Inc 800 432-1149
5102 W Hanna Ave Tampa (33634) ***(G-18268)***
WW Timber LLC 352 584-4550
8999 Us Highway 19 S Perry (32348) ***(G-14321)***
Wwf Operating Company LLC 904 354-0406
2198 W Beaver St Jacksonville (32209) ***(G-6930)***

Wwgso, Rockledge *Also called Good 4 Tklc Inc* ***(G-15415)***
Wws Contracting LLC 813 868-3100
142 W Platt St Tampa (33606) ***(G-18269)***
Wwsa, Boynton Beach *Also called Worldwide Superabrasives LLC* ***(G-976)***
Wwsa Solids LLC 561 588-9299
2921 Commerce Park Dr Boynton Beach (33426) ***(G-978)***
Www Tcpalm Company 772 287-1550
1939 S Federal Hwy Stuart (34994) ***(G-17053)***
Www.alephgraphics.com, Doral *Also called Aleph Graphics Inc* ***(G-3237)***
Www.tpgus.com, Delray Beach *Also called Platinum Group Usa Inc* ***(G-3119)***
Wwwsureshotsidscom LLC 850 906-0745
3516 Clifden Dr Tallahassee (32309) ***(G-17348)***
Wyla Inc (PA) 904 886-4338
6920 Phillips Ind Blvd Jacksonville (32256) ***(G-6931)***
Wyla Laces, Jacksonville *Also called Wyla Inc* ***(G-6931)***
X-Treme Wood Cabinets Corp 305 537-8378
10930 Sw 188th St Cutler Bay (33157) ***(G-2422)***
Xcalibur Arcft Solutions LLC 305 744-2830
2859 Longleaf Ranch Cir Middleburg (32068) ***(G-10916)***
Xcape Solutions Inc (PA) 813 369-5261
207 Crystal Grove Blvd # 101 Lutz (33548) ***(G-8425)***
Xcelience LLC 813 286-0404
5415 W Laurel St Tampa (33607) ***(G-18270)***
Xcelience LLC 813 286-0404
4901 W Grace St Tampa (33607) ***(G-18271)***
Xcelience LLC (HQ) 813 286-0404
4910 Savarese Cir Tampa (33634) ***(G-18272)***
Xcelience Holdings LLC (HQ) 813 286-0404
4910 Savarese Cir Tampa (33634) ***(G-18273)***
Xcessive Inc 866 919-9527
8714 Nw 153rd Ter Miami Lakes (33018) ***(G-10882)***
Xcessive Engines, Miami Lakes *Also called Xcessive Inc* ***(G-10882)***
Xeleum Lighting LLC (HQ) 954 617-8170
751 Park Of Commerce Dr # 100 Boca Raton (33487) ***(G-794)***
Xerographic Copy Center, Gainesville *Also called Ejco Inc* ***(G-4913)***
Xerox Business Services LLC 407 926-4228
2290 Premier Row Orlando (32809) ***(G-13332)***
Xhale Inc (PA) 352 371-8488
3630 Sw 47th Ave Ste 100 Gainesville (32608) ***(G-5017)***
Xikar Inc 816 474-7555
3350 Entp Ave Ste 120 Weston (33331) ***(G-19179)***
Xilinx Inc 407 365-8644
3518 Buckingham Ct Oviedo (32765) ***(G-13462)***
Xl Carts Inc 904 277-7111
474415 E State Road 200 Fernandina Beach (32034) ***(G-3751)***
Xmre, Hollywood *Also called Nex-Xos Worldwide LLC* ***(G-5882)***
Xothermic Inc 407 951-8008
311 Riverbend Blvd Longwood (32779) ***(G-8352)***
Xoxo Beauty Studio LLC 407 476-7172
937 W State Road 436 # 115 Altamonte Springs (32714) ***(G-85)***
Xperient LLC 407 265-8000
250 W Church Ave Ste 100 Longwood (32750) ***(G-8353)***
Xpondr Corporation 727 541-4149
10751 75th St Seminole (33777) ***(G-16772)***
Xpress Finance Inc (PA) 407 629-0095
807 S Orlando Ave Ste B Deltona (32738) ***(G-3182)***
Xpress Materials LLC 352 748-2200
8302 Ne 44th Dr Wildwood (34785) ***(G-19206)***
Xpress Precision Products Inc 305 685-2127
4432 E 10th Ct Hialeah (33013) ***(G-5691)***
Xscream Inc 727 449-9353
1780 Calumet St Clearwater (33765) ***(G-1945)***
Xterior Shutter Systems 239 872-2327
2523 Sw 24th Ave Cape Coral (33914) ***(G-1496)***
Xtreme Boats, Bonifay *Also called Bd Xtreme Holdings LLC* ***(G-799)***
Xtreme Dumpster Services Corp 407 272-8899
6142 Buford St Orlando (32835) ***(G-13333)***
Xtreme Electronic Designs Inc 561 557-3667
352 Legare Ct Jupiter (33458) ***(G-7148)***
Xtreme Pallets Inc 954 302-8915
5440 Nw 55th Blvd Apt 108 Coconut Creek (33073) ***(G-2104)***
Xtreme Signs Printing Inc 321 438-3954
4401 Vineland Rd Ste A9 Orlando (32811) ***(G-13334)***
Xtreme Tools International Inc 305 622-7474
15400 Nw 34th Ave Opa Locka (33054) ***(G-12371)***
Xts Corp 305 863-7779
8870 Nw 18th Ter Doral (33172) ***(G-3552)***
Xue Wu Inc 727 532-4571
4445 E Bay Dr Ste 302 Clearwater (33764) ***(G-1946)***
Xylem Dewatering Solutions 904 695-2131
240 Hammond Blvd Jacksonville (32254) ***(G-6932)***
Xylitol USA Inc 303 991-1999
11524 Storywood Dr Riverview (33578) ***(G-15288)***
Xymogen Inc (PA) 407 445-0203
6900 Kingspointe Pkwy Orlando (32819) ***(G-13335)***
Xymoprint LLC 407 504-2170
6900 Kingspointe Pkwy Orlando (32819) ***(G-13336)***
Y C Aluminum Welding Corp 786 255-7186
23701 Sw 132nd Ave Unit 2 Homestead (33032) ***(G-5997)***
Y F Leung Inc (PA) 305 651-6851
1155 Ne 177th Ter North Miami Beach (33162) ***(G-11714)***
Y&D Machine Shop Inc 786 717-6356
748 E 51st St Hialeah (33013) ***(G-5692)***
Y3k LLC 561 835-0404
44 Cocoanut Row Ste T1 Palm Beach (33480) ***(G-13563)***
Yacht 10 Inc 954 759-9929
3001 Sw 3rd Ave Ste 1 Fort Lauderdale (33315) ***(G-4330)***
Yacht Furnishing By Eclip 954 792-7339
7050 W State Road 84 Davie (33317) ***(G-2617)***
Yacht International Magazine, Fort Lauderdale *Also called IMS Publishing Inc* ***(G-4056)***
Yacht-Mate Products Inc 954 527-0112
3200 S Andrews Ave Ste 10 Fort Lauderdale (33316) ***(G-4331)***
Yahl Mulching & Recycling Inc 239 352-7888
2250 Washburn Ave Naples (34117) ***(G-11462)***
Yale Ogron Mfg Co Inc (PA) 305 687-0424
15201 Nw 34th Ave Opa Locka (33054) ***(G-12372)***
Yam Machine Shop and Iron Work 786 246-4174
3710 Nw 50th St Miami (33142) ***(G-10624)***
Yandles Quality Roof Trusses 352 732-3000
834 N Magnolia Ave Ocala (34475) ***(G-12078)***
Yarbrough Tire Svc Inc 863 385-1574
1532 Sebring Pkwy Sebring (33870) ***(G-16719)***
Yard House Hallandale Bch LLC 561 691-6901
11701 Lk Vctr Grdn Ave Palm Beach Gardens (33410) ***(G-13636)***
Yarey Inc 954 520-6015
18840 Mariner Inlet Dr Boca Raton (33498) ***(G-795)***
Yatfl Inc 786 643-8660
19425 Sw 188th St Miami (33187) ***(G-10625)***
Yauchler Properties LLC 863 662-5570
119 Avenue D Se Winter Haven (33880) ***(G-19369)***
Yeager Manufacturing Tech LLC 407 573-7033
6869 Stapoint Ct Ste 101 Winter Park (32792) ***(G-19463)***
Yellow Green Aerospace Inc 954 599-4161
2525 Ponce De Leon Blvd # 300 Coral Gables (33134) ***(G-2208)***
Yellow Pages, Deerfield Beach *Also called Global Directories Inc* ***(G-2832)***
Yellowfin Yachts, Inc., Sarasota *Also called Copalo Inc* ***(G-16198)***
Yes Ink Solutions, Ocala *Also called Yes Solutions Gallery LLC* ***(G-12079)***
Yes Solutions Gallery LLC 352 622-7937
4901 E Slver Sprng Blvd Ocala (34470) ***(G-12079)***
Yesco Orlando South 407 922-5856
929 W Oak St Kissimmee (34741) ***(G-7312)***
Yesco Sign and Lighting 407 321-3577
1940 Dolgner Pl Sanford (32771) ***(G-16142)***
Yesil Inc 516 858-0244
23400 Milano Ct Boca Raton (33433) ***(G-796)***
Yetman Industries Inc 239 561-7808
14701 Bald Eagle Dr Fort Myers (33912) ***(G-4656)***
Yfan LLC 786 453-3724
5340 Nw 163rd St Miami Lakes (33014) ***(G-10883)***
Ygaero, Coral Gables *Also called Yellow Green Aerospace Inc* ***(G-2208)***
Yield - St. Augustine, Saint Augustine *Also called Yield Design* ***(G-15640)***
Yield Design 402 321-2196
25 Palmer St Saint Augustine (32084) ***(G-15640)***
Yihong Software Inc 407 391-8450
169 Adler Pt Oviedo (32765) ***(G-13463)***
Yippy Inc (PA) 877 947-7901
999 Brickell Ave Ste 610 Miami (33131) ***(G-10626)***
YKK AP America Inc 561 736-7808
8846 Andy Ct Apt C Boynton Beach (33436) ***(G-979)***
YKK AP America Inc 407 856-0660
7608 Currency Dr Orlando (32809) ***(G-13337)***
Ym Welding Services Inc 502 905-4651
28715 Sw 132nd Ave Homestead (33033) ***(G-5998)***
Ymg Iron Work & Metal Design 305 343-2537
21650 Nw 3rd Pl Pembroke Pines (33029) ***(G-14072)***
Yo Mama's Foods, Clearwater *Also called Magnificat Holdings LLC* ***(G-1771)***
Yogurico, Hialeah *Also called Pura Vida Dairy Inc* ***(G-5584)***
Yogurt Breeze LLC 407 412-5939
10727 Narcoossee Rd B4 Orlando (32832) ***(G-13338)***
Yogurtology 727 895-1393
3043 4th St N Saint Petersburg (33704) ***(G-15966)***
Yogurtology 813 839-4200
3017 W Gandy Blvd Tampa (33611) ***(G-18274)***
Yogurtology 813 969-2500
12400 N Dale Mabry Hwy B Tampa (33618) ***(G-18275)***
Yogurtology 813 926-9090
7889 Gunn Hwy Tampa (33626) ***(G-18276)***
Yolo Consulting LLC 954 993-4517
2364 Nw 159th Ave Pembroke Pines (33028) ***(G-14073)***
Yolo Las Olas LLC 954 522-3002
200 Sw 2nd St Fort Lauderdale (33301) ***(G-4332)***
Yoly Munoz Corp 305 860-3839
102 Se 1st St Miami (33131) ***(G-10627)***
Yonder Woodworks Inc 561 547-5777
4901 Georgia Ave West Palm Beach (33405) ***(G-19090)***
York Bridge Concepts Inc 813 482-0613
2420 Brunello Trce Lutz (33558) ***(G-8426)***

ALPHABETIC

Yos Bottling LLC 863 258-6820
15240 Citrus Country Dr Dade City (33523) *(G-2437)*
You Lucky Dog Inc 954 428-4648
947 S Federal Hwy Deerfield Beach (33441) *(G-2938)*
Youmop LLC 248 343-2013
714 S Atlantic Dr Lake Worth (33462) *(G-7600)*
Younger You Inc (PA) 954 924-4462
5961 Bayview Dr Fort Lauderdale (33308) *(G-4333)*
Youngquist Brothers Rock Inc 239 267-6000
15401 Alico Rd Fort Myers (33913) *(G-4657)*
Your Cabinet Source Inc 352 728-3806
2606 South St Ste 4 Leesburg (34748) *(G-8182)*
Your Dreams Cabinets Corp 305 305-3729
7635 W 28th Ave Hialeah (33016) *(G-5693)*
Your Hometown Newspaper Inc 305 669-7355
6796 Sw 62nd Ave South Miami (33143) *(G-16832)*
Your ID Guard 904 354-8989
4417 Beach Blvd Ste 204 Jacksonville (32207) *(G-6933)*
Your Name Printing 813 621-2400
6502 N 54th St Tampa (33610) *(G-18277)*
Your Name Prtg Envlope Mfg Inc (PA) 813 643-1443
508 Hobbs St Tampa (33619) *(G-18278)*
Yourmembershipcom Inc (PA) 727 827-0046
9620 Exec Ctr Dr N Ste 20 Saint Petersburg (33702) *(G-15967)*
Youthful Innovations LLC 239 596-2200
3066 Tamiami Trl N # 101 Naples (34103) *(G-11463)*
Yovino Printing, Margate *Also called P & G Printing Group Inc (G-8559)*
Yp Advrtising Pubg LLC Not LLC 321 956-5400
100 Rialto Pl Ste 300 Melbourne (32901) *(G-8978)*
Yp General Work & Cabinets 786 317-0973
600 Nw 111th St Miami (33168) *(G-10628)*
Ysi Inc (HQ) 727 565-2201
9843 18th St N Ste 1200 Saint Petersburg (33716) *(G-15968)*
Ysl Graphics LLC 954 916-7255
4642 N Hiatus Rd Sunrise (33351) *(G-17200)*
Yung Payper Chasers Entrmt LLC 727 239-2880
695 Central Ave Saint Petersburg (33701) *(G-15969)*
Yvel Usa Inc 561 391-5119
6000 Glades Rd Ste 1153 Boca Raton (33431) *(G-797)*
Z & L Partners Inc 813 639-0066
4920 W Cypress St Ste 100 Tampa (33607) *(G-18279)*
Z & N Manufacturing Corp 407 518-1114
1732 Kelley Ave Kissimmee (34744) *(G-7313)*
Z Cans LLC 941 748-6688
1111 Brambling Ct Bradenton (34212) *(G-1149)*
Z Haydu Manufacturing Corp 954 925-1779
1980 Grant St Hollywood (33020) *(G-5944)*
Z Spars, Gainesville *Also called US Spars Inc (G-5014)*
Z-2 Metal Artwork Inc 305 804-4974
117 W 24th St Hialeah (33010) *(G-5694)*
Zachey Design Marble Inc 754 367-6261
1649 Moffett St 4 Hollywood (33020) *(G-5945)*
Zag Medical, Miami *Also called Endo-Gear LLC (G-9526)*
Zahn Builders Inc 718 885-2202
4628 N Federal Hwy Lighthouse Point (33064) *(G-8214)*
Zaniboni Lighting LLC 727 213-0410
101 N Garden Ave Ste 230 Clearwater (33755) *(G-1947)*
Zap Skim'ers, Venice *Also called Glaspro (G-18550)*
Zaragoza Pavers Inc 239 273-6665
19049 Murcott Dr E Fort Myers (33967) *(G-4658)*
Zassi Holdings Inc (PA) 904 432-8315
822 A1a N Ste 104 Ponte Vedra Beach (32082) *(G-14958)*
Zayas Fashions Inc (PA) 305 823-1438
665 W 33rd St Hialeah (33012) *(G-5695)*
Zazz Engineering Inc 561 594-0123
7833 Sw Ellipse Way Stuart (34997) *(G-17054)*
Zbc Cabinetry 239 332-2940
3593 Vrnica S Shmker Blvd Fort Myers (33916) *(G-4659)*
Zd Realty LLC 866 672-1212
2135 13th Ave N Saint Petersburg (33713) *(G-15970)*
Zeeeees Corporation 407 624-3796
2008 Jaffa Dr Ste D Saint Cloud (34771) *(G-15671)*
Zefon International, Ocala *Also called Antylia Scientific (G-11877)*
Zel Custom Manufacturing LLC 303 880-8701
11419 Challenger Ave Odessa (33556) *(G-12167)*
Zel Tech Trining Solutions LLC 757 722-5565
7123 University Blvd Winter Park (32792) *(G-19464)*
Zellermayer Supply Corp (PA) 561 848-0057
1231 52nd St Ste B Mangonia Park (33407) *(G-8515)*
Zellwin Farms Company (PA) 407 886-9241
6052 Jones Ave Zellwood (32798) *(G-19505)*
Zen Distributors Group II LLC 305 637-3014
2047 Nw 24th Ave Miami (33142) *(G-10629)*
Zenit Service LLC 407 878-7840
309 Grand Valley Dr Lake Mary (32746) *(G-7462)*
Zenith Rollers Llc 954 493-6484
764 Nw 57th Ct Fort Lauderdale (33309) *(G-4334)*
Zenithtech Industries Inc 386 454-7630
27124 Nw 203rd Pl High Springs (32643) *(G-5704)*
Zennergy LLC 813 382-3460
3918 N Highland Ave Tampa (33603) *(G-18280)*
Zeno Furniture & Mat Mfg Co 954 764-1212
671 Nw 4th Ave Fort Lauderdale (33311) *(G-4335)*
Zeno Mattress and Furn Mfg Co, Fort Lauderdale *Also called Zeno Furniture & Mat Mfg Co (G-4335)*
Zep-Pro, Hallandale Beach *Also called Zeppelin Products Inc (G-5226)*
Zephyr Feed Company Inc 813 782-1578
40140 Lynbrook Dr Zephyrhills (33540) *(G-19543)*
Zeppelin Products Inc 954 989-8808
3178 W Pembroke Rd Hallandale Beach (33009) *(G-5226)*
Zepsa Industries 754 307-2173
41 Sw 6th St Pompano Beach (33060) *(G-14915)*
Zerion Group LLC 877 872-1726
235 S Maitland Ave # 100 Maitland (32751) *(G-8487)*
Zeroc Inc 561 283-1480
4425 Military Trl Ste 209 Jupiter (33458) *(G-7149)*
Zeroll Co (HQ) 772 461-3811
3355 Entp Ave Ste 160 Weston (33331) *(G-19180)*
Zerons Metal Designers Inc 305 688-2240
115 117 W 24th St Hialeah (33010) *(G-5696)*
Zesty Brands LLC 954 348-2827
2160 Premier Row Orlando (32809) *(G-13339)*
Zesty Paws LLC 407 358-6601
12124 High Tech Ave Ste 2 Orlando (32817) *(G-13340)*
Zeta Kitchen & Bath Inc 786 552-2322
6905 Nw 82nd Ave Miami (33166) *(G-10630)*
Zetma LLC 407 237-0233
901 Indiana St Orlando (32805) *(G-13341)*
Zeus Industries 727 530-4373
12545 Creekside Dr Largo (33773) *(G-8081)*
Zhone Technologies Inc 510 777-7151
7340 Bryan Dairy Rd # 150 Seminole (33777) *(G-16773)*
Zhyno Inc 844 313-1900
20815 Ne 16th Ave Ste B22 Miami (33179) *(G-10631)*
Ziami Distillery, Hollywood *Also called Florida Rum Company LLC (G-5823)*
Ziehm Imaging Inc 407 615-8560
6280 Hzltine Nat Dr 100 Orlando (32822) *(G-13342)*
Zilla Inc 904 610-1436
4265 Eldridge Loop Orange Park (32073) *(G-12414)*
Zimmer Biomet CMF Thoracic LLC 574 267-6639
1520 Tradeport Dr Jacksonville (32218) *(G-6934)*
Zimmer Dental Inc 561 776-6700
4555 Riverside Dr Palm Beach Gardens (33410) *(G-13637)*
Zinc Guy Inc (PA) 954 907-2752
3811 Sw 47th Ave Ste 617 Davie (33314) *(G-2618)*
Ziptek LLC 941 953-5509
1250 S Tamiami Trl # 303 Sarasota (34239) *(G-16646)*
Zipx Package Service Inc 305 597-5305
8401 Nw 17th St Doral (33191) *(G-3553)*
Zitec Inc 850 678-9747
1031 Partin Dr N Niceville (32578) *(G-11577)*
Zk Cabinets Inc 407 421-7307
5509 Commerce Dr Orlando (32839) *(G-13343)*
Zmh Publishers Inc 239 404-9259
340 15th St Nw Naples (34120) *(G-11464)*
Zoag LLC 862 591-2969
102 Alegria Way Palm Beach Gardens (33418) *(G-13638)*
Zoho Stone LLC 727 230-6956
34318 Us Highway 19 N Palm Harbor (34684) *(G-13770)*
Zollan, Miami Lakes *Also called Pioneer Led Lighting Corp (G-10839)*
Zom Monterra LP 407 644-6300
2001 Summit Park Dr # 300 Orlando (32810) *(G-13344)*
Zondervan Corporation LLC 616 698-3437
8333 Nw 53rd St Ste 450 Miami (33166) *(G-10632)*
Zoo Holdings LLC 941 355-5653
4139 N Wa Blvd Sarasota (34234) *(G-16647)*
Zpacks Corp 321 215-5658
7703 Technology Dr West Melbourne (32904) *(G-18780)*
Zps Powdercoating 727 465-8131
6225 118th Ave Largo (33773) *(G-8082)*
Zpx LLC 888 943-8849
2106 Nw 4th Pl Gainesville (32603) *(G-5018)*
Zsno Ft Lauderdale 954 792-2223
3801 Commerce Pkwy Miramar (33025) *(G-11062)*
Zumex Usa Inc 305 591-0061
1573 Nw 82nd Ave Doral (33126) *(G-3554)*
Zumro Manufacturing Inc 954 782-7779
650 Sw 16th Ter Pompano Beach (33069) *(G-14916)*
Zurigo Trading Inc 305 244-4681
5077 Nw 7th St Apt 1118 Miami (33126) *(G-10633)*
Zweifel International, Orlando *Also called Creative Events and Exhibits (G-12625)*

PRODUCT INDEX

• **Product categories are listed in alphabetical order.**

A

B

C

D

E

F

G

H

I

J

K

L

M

N

O

P

Q

R

S

T

U

V

W

X

Y

Z

PRODUCT SECTION

See footnotes for symbols and codes identification.

- Refer to the Industrial Product Index preceding this section to locate product headings.

ABRASIVE SAND MINING

Standard Sand & Silica Company..........G...... 863 419-9673
Haines City *(G-5148)*

ABRASIVES

Abrasive Dynamics Inc..........F...... 860 291-0664
Pompano Beach *(G-14573)*
All Polishing Solutions..........G...... 954 505-4041
Miramar *(G-10965)*
Bobs Barricades Inc..........E...... 813 886-0518
Tampa *(G-17478)*
Harsco Corporation..........F...... 717 506-2071
Tampa *(G-17745)*
Kay Diamond Products LLC..........F...... 561 994-5400
Boca Raton *(G-585)*
Maxi-Blast of Florida Inc..........G...... 727 572-0909
Saint Petersburg *(G-15851)*
Microtool and Instrument Inc..........E...... 786 242-8780
Palmetto Bay *(G-13851)*
Sheila Shine Inc..........E...... 305 557-1729
Miami *(G-10335)*
Trident Trading Inc..........G...... 561 488-0458
Boca Raton *(G-756)*
True Grit Abrasives Inc..........E...... 813 247-5219
Tampa *(G-18203)*
United Abrasives Inc..........F...... 239 300-0033
Naples *(G-11446)*
Worldwide Superabrasives LLC..........E...... 954 828-9650
Boynton Beach *(G-976)*
Wwsa Solids LLC..........F...... 561 588-9299
Boynton Beach *(G-978)*

ABRASIVES: Aluminum Oxide Fused

Abracol North America Corp..........G...... 305 431-5596
Miami *(G-9057)*

ABRASIVES: sandpaper

Sandpaper Marketing Inc..........G...... 850 939-8040
Navarre *(G-11475)*

ACCELERATION INDICATORS & SYSTEM COMPONENTS: Aerospace

Moog-Fts..........G...... 407 264-0611
Orlando *(G-12978)*
Praesto Enterprises LLC..........G...... 407 298-9171
Orlando *(G-13077)*
Rover Aerospace Inc..........G...... 305 594-7799
Doral *(G-3491)*
Russell Associates Inc..........G...... 727 815-3100
New Port Richey *(G-11509)*

ACCELERATORS: Electrostatic Particle

Ground Zero Electrostatics Inc..........G...... 941 751-7581
Bradenton *(G-1053)*

ACCELERATORS: Linear

Interntonal Linear Matrix Corp..........F...... 727 549-1808
Seminole *(G-16748)*

ACCELEROMETERS

Impact Register Inc..........G...... 727 585-8572
Largo *(G-7978)*

ACCOUNTING MACHINES & CASH REGISTERS

Logic Controls Inc..........E...... 800 576-9647
Orlando *(G-12934)*
Shade Saver Inc..........G...... 850 650-0884
Ocala *(G-12045)*

ACCOUNTING MACHINES WHOLESALERS

Southeastern Pegboard Printers..........G...... 904 731-0357
Jacksonville *(G-6792)*

ACCOUNTING SVCS, NEC

Copy Van of Florida Inc..........G...... 407 366-7126
Oviedo *(G-13423)*
Excelor LLC..........F...... 321 300-3315
Orlando *(G-12727)*

ACID RESIST: Etching

ACC Holdco Inc..........C...... 863 578-1206
Mulberry *(G-11118)*

ACOUSTICAL BOARD & TILE

Martin Gallagher LLC..........G...... 407 453-1027
Kissimmee *(G-7273)*
Tubos Inc..........G...... 727 504-0633
Clearwater *(G-1926)*

ACRYLIC RESINS

Acrocrete Inc..........E...... 954 917-4114
Pompano Beach *(G-14576)*
Idea Design Studio Inc..........F...... 305 823-6008
Doral *(G-3387)*

ACTOR

Survival Products Inc..........G...... 954 966-7329
Sunrise *(G-17182)*

ADDITIVE BASED PLASTIC MATERIALS: Plasticizers

Rehrig Pacific Company..........F...... 407 857-3888
Orlando *(G-13128)*

ADHESIVES

10 Roof Cottage LLC..........G...... 888 667-6961
Tampa *(G-17371)*
Adhesive Manufacturers Inc..........G...... 305 495-8018
Pembroke Pines *(G-14014)*
Adhesive Technologies Fla LLC..........G...... 941 228-0295
Sarasota *(G-16333)*
Adhesives Technology Corp..........D...... 754 399-1684
Pompano Beach *(G-14578)*
American Acrylic Adhesives LLC..........F...... 877 422-4583
Largo *(G-7893)*
American Adhesives LLC..........G...... 877 422-4583
Largo *(G-7894)*
Foamseal Hurricane Adhesive..........G...... 850 766-2000
Tallahassee *(G-17257)*
HB Fuller Cnstr Pdts Inc..........G...... 352 372-3931
Gainesville *(G-4935)*
Mapei Corporation..........C...... 954 246-8888
Deerfield Beach *(G-2868)*
Palm Labs Adhesives LLC..........F...... 321 710-4850
Debary *(G-2753)*
PPG Architectural Finishes Inc..........G...... 813 877-5841
Tampa *(G-17999)*
Southern Grouts & Mortars Inc..........D...... 954 943-2288
Pompano Beach *(G-14863)*
T S E Industries Inc..........C...... 727 573-7676
Clearwater *(G-1900)*
United Adhesive Products Inc..........G...... 863 698-9484
Winter Haven *(G-19365)*

ADHESIVES & SEALANTS

Anchor Coatings Leesburg Inc..........E...... 352 728-0777
Leesburg *(G-8142)*
Gardner-Gibson Mfg Inc..........E...... 813 248-2101
Tampa *(G-17705)*
Jamo Inc..........D...... 305 885-3444
Medley *(G-8676)*
Lambert Corporation Florida..........E...... 407 841-2940
Orlando *(G-12889)*
Lapolla Industries LLC..........F...... 954 379-0241
Deerfield Beach *(G-2857)*
Lehigh White Cement Co LLC..........C...... 561 812-7441
Tampa *(G-17842)*
Masking Systems of America..........F...... 813 920-2271
Odessa *(G-12133)*
Ocoow LLC..........G...... 805 266-7616
Sopchoppy *(G-16785)*
P S Research Corp..........G...... 954 558-8727
Lauderhill *(G-8119)*
Quality Industrial Chem Inc..........F...... 727 573-5760
Saint Petersburg *(G-15896)*
Rcd Corporation..........G...... 352 589-0099
Eustis *(G-3716)*

ADHESIVES & SEALANTS WHOLESALERS

Nebula Glass International Inc..........E...... 954 975-3233
Pompano Beach *(G-14771)*

ADHESIVES: Adhesives, plastic

Nfk Corporation..........F...... 305 791-2044
Miami *(G-10069)*

ADHESIVES: Epoxy

Dynamis Epoxy LLC..........G...... 941 488-3999
Venice *(G-18544)*
Fasco Epoxies Inc..........F...... 772 464-0808
Fort Pierce *(G-4696)*
Hernon Manufacturing Inc..........D...... 407 322-4000
Sanford *(G-16061)*
S & R Fastener Co Inc..........G...... 352 588-0768
San Antonio *(G-15978)*

ADRENAL DERIVATIVES

Xymogen Inc..........B...... 407 445-0203
Orlando *(G-13335)*

ADVERTISING AGENCIES

Comcept Solutions LLC..........E...... 727 535-1900
Seminole *(G-16744)*
Conric Holdings LLC..........F...... 239 690-9840
Fort Myers *(G-4408)*
Flexofferscom Inc..........G...... 305 999-9940
Miami *(G-9577)*
Jar Advertising LLC..........G...... 844 344-4586
Orlando *(G-12851)*
Jpl Associates Inc..........F...... 954 929-6024
Hallandale Beach *(G-5194)*
King & Grube Inc..........F...... 727 327-6033
Largo *(G-7991)*
Media Digittal LLC..........G...... 305 506-0470
Doral *(G-3428)*

Passport Pblcations Media Corp..........E....... 561 615-3900
West Palm Beach *(G-18988)*
Premier Parties Entertainment..............E....... 352 375-6122
Gainesville *(G-4983)*
Special Publications Inc........................F....... 352 622-2995
Ocala *(G-12056)*
Spirit Connection..................................G....... 321 327-3804
Melbourne *(G-8942)*
Venue Advertising Inc ....E....... 561 844-1778
Jupiter *(G-7140)*
Wpp Group Usa Inc...............................G....... 305 341-8132
Miami *(G-10623)*

ADVERTISING AGENCIES: Consultants

Carlaron Inc...G....... 386 258-1183
Daytona Beach *(G-2639)*
Charisma Media ....D....... 407 333-0600
Lake Mary *(G-7405)*
Mc Squared Group Inc..........................G....... 850 435-4600
Pensacola *(G-14202)*
Reed Brennan Media Associates ....E....... 407 894-7300
Orlando *(G-13125)*

ADVERTISING COPY WRITING SVCS

Las Amrcas Mltimedia Group LLC ....E....... 305 633-3341
Miami *(G-9861)*
Pensacola Voice Inc...............................G....... 850 434-6963
Pensacola *(G-14227)*

ADVERTISING DISPLAY PRDTS

Brandano Displays Inc ....E....... 954 956-7266
Margate *(G-8537)*
Brevard Achievement Center Inc ....B....... 321 632-8610
Rockledge *(G-15395)*
Creative Events and Exhibits.................G....... 407 851-4754
Orlando *(G-12625)*
Look Worldwide Inc................................G....... 305 662-1287
Miami *(G-9910)*
Mediawrite LLC ....G....... 239 344-9988
Fort Myers *(G-4526)*

ADVERTISING MATERIAL DISTRIBUTION

Kenney Communications Inc..................F....... 407 859-3113
Orlando *(G-12869)*
Wayloo Inc...G....... 954 914-3192
Fort Lauderdale *(G-4317)*

ADVERTISING REPRESENTATIVES: Electronic Media

Media Digittal LLC..................................G....... 305 506-0470
Doral *(G-3428)*

ADVERTISING REPRESENTATIVES: Magazine

Rowland Publishing Inc ....E....... 850 878-0554
Tallahassee *(G-17319)*

ADVERTISING REPRESENTATIVES: Newspaper

Nexstar Broadcasting Inc......................F....... 863 683-6531
Lakeland *(G-7757)*
Orange Peel Gazette Inc........................G....... 407 892-5556
Saint Cloud *(G-15663)*
Sarasota Herald-Tribune ....E....... 941 953-7755
Sarasota *(G-16579)*
West Bolusia Beacon ....F....... 386 734-4622
Deland *(G-3033)*

ADVERTISING REPRESENTATIVES: Printed Media

Collins Media & Advg LLC ....F....... 954 688-9758
Margate *(G-8538)*
Mc Squared Group Inc..........................G....... 850 435-4600
Pensacola *(G-14202)*
MGM Cargo LLC.....................................G....... 407 770-1500
Orlando *(G-12966)*
Shipping + Business Svcs LLC ....G....... 904 240-1737
Jacksonville *(G-6765)*
Showcase Publications Inc....................E....... 863 687-4377
Lakeland *(G-7791)*

ADVERTISING SPECIALTIES, WHOLESALE

Above LLC..F....... 850 469-9028
Pensacola *(G-14077)*
Ampersand Graphics Inc ....E....... 772 283-1359
Stuart *(G-16906)*
Apparel Printers ....G....... 352 463-8850
Alachua *(G-4)*
Artworks Printing Enterprises...............G....... 954 893-7984
Hollywood *(G-5775)*
Bros Williams Printing............................G....... 305 769-9925
Hialeah *(G-5331)*
Eagle Athletic Wear Inc ....F....... 727 937-6147
Tarpon Springs *(G-18297)*
Express Signs & Graphics Inc...............F....... 407 889-4433
Winter Garden *(G-19263)*
Independent Resources Inc...................E....... 813 237-0945
Tampa *(G-17777)*
Jar Advertising LLC ....G....... 844 344-4586
Orlando *(G-12851)*
Koala Tee Inc (usa) ....E....... 941 954-7700
Sarasota *(G-16483)*
Laser Creations Incorporated...............E....... 800 771-7151
Apopka *(G-155)*
M & H Enterprises Inc...........................G....... 305 885-5945
Hialeah *(G-5494)*
Metropolis Graphics Inc.........................G....... 407 740-5455
Winter Park *(G-19424)*
Paints N Cocktails Inc ....F....... 954 514-7383
Miami *(G-10130)*
Put Your Name On It LLC ....G....... 813 972-1460
Tampa *(G-18026)*
Serigraphic Arts Inc...............................F....... 813 626-1070
Tampa *(G-18085)*
Tip Top Prtg of Volusia Cnty ....G....... 386 760-7701
Daytona Beach *(G-2728)*
Trident Trading Inc................................G....... 561 488-0458
Boca Raton *(G-756)*
Tru Dimensions Printing Inc ....G....... 407 339-3410
Longwood *(G-8345)*

ADVERTISING SVCS: Direct Mail

Customer First Inc Naples ....E....... 239 949-8518
Bonita Springs *(G-827)*
Direct Impressions Inc ....E....... 239 549-4484
Cape Coral *(G-1415)*
Dxm Marketing Group LLC ....F....... 904 332-6490
Jacksonville *(G-6342)*
Futch Printing & Mailing Inc ....F....... 904 388-3995
Jacksonville *(G-6418)*
Hill Donnelly Corporation......................D....... 800 525-1242
Tampa *(G-17755)*
Microcomputer Services ....G....... 561 988-7000
Boca Raton *(G-623)*
Ncp Solutions LLC.................................D....... 205 849-5200
Jacksonville *(G-6623)*
Original Impressions LLC ....C....... 305 233-1322
Weston *(G-19156)*
Tip Top Prtg of Volusia Cnty ....G....... 386 760-7701
Daytona Beach *(G-2728)*
W D H Enterprises Inc ....G....... 941 758-6500
Bradenton *(G-1143)*

ADVERTISING SVCS: Display

A W R Cabinets Inc................................F....... 407 323-1415
Sanford *(G-15985)*
Fastsigns ....G....... 850 477-9744
Pensacola *(G-14149)*
La Fabrika Retail Services LLC ....G....... 786 525-4491
Miami *(G-9840)*
Sarasota Herald-Tribune ....E....... 941 953-7755
Sarasota *(G-16579)*
Sarasota Signs and Visuals..................G....... 941 355-5746
Sarasota *(G-16581)*

ADVERTISING SVCS: Outdoor

Fast Signs...G....... 239 498-7200
Bonita Springs *(G-830)*
Jar Advertising LLC...............................G....... 844 344-4586
Orlando *(G-12851)*

ADVERTISING SVCS: Poster, Exc Outdoor

Shipping + Business Svcs LLC ....G....... 904 240-1737
Jacksonville *(G-6765)*

ADVERTISING SVCS: Poster, Outdoor

Cutting Edge Sgns Grphics of P ....G....... 727 546-3700
Clearwater *(G-1645)*

Shipping + Business Svcs LLC ....G....... 904 240-1737
Jacksonville *(G-6765)*

AEROSOLS

AVw Inc ....E....... 954 972-3338
Margate *(G-8536)*

AGENTS, BROKERS & BUREAUS: Personal Service

Eem Technologies Corp ....F....... 786 606-5993
Doral *(G-3340)*

AGRICULTURAL CHEMICALS: Trace Elements

Agra Chem Sales Co Inc ....G....... 863 453-6450
Avon Park *(G-283)*
Flottec LLC ....G....... 973 588-4717
Jupiter *(G-7046)*

AGRICULTURAL DISINFECTANTS

Agranco Corp (usa) ....F....... 877 592-0031
South Miami *(G-16811)*
Biochem Manufacturing Inc..................E....... 561 799-1590
Jupiter *(G-7010)*
Redeagle International LLC ....G....... 863 682-6698
Lakeland *(G-7777)*

AGRICULTURAL EQPT: BARN, SILO, POULTRY, DAIRY/LIVESTOCK MACH

Industrial Cnveyor Systems Inc ....F....... 305 255-0200
Cutler Bay *(G-2398)*
Sanchelima International Inc ....F....... 305 591-4343
Doral *(G-3495)*

AGRICULTURAL EQPT: Barn Stanchions & Standards

5 Star Builders Inc ....G....... 561 795-1282
Wellington *(G-18707)*

AGRICULTURAL EQPT: Fertilizing Machinery

Agrifleet Leasing Corporation ....E....... 239 293-3976
Auburndale *(G-229)*
Conibear Equipment Co Inc..................G....... 863 858-4414
Lakeland *(G-7662)*

AGRICULTURAL EQPT: Fertilizng, Sprayng, Dustng/Irrigatn Mach

Neelco Industries Inc............................F....... 321 632-5303
Cocoa *(G-2038)*

AGRICULTURAL EQPT: Grade, Clean & Sort Machines, Fruit/Veg

Delaney Resources Inc.........................G....... 863 670-5924
Dade City *(G-2427)*

AGRICULTURAL EQPT: Harvesters, Fruit, Vegetable, Tobacco

Bag-A-Nut LLC ....G....... 904 641-3934
Jacksonville *(G-6191)*
Okee-B Inc ....D....... 561 996-3040
Belle Glade *(G-350)*

AGRICULTURAL EQPT: Irrigation Eqpt, Self-Propelled

Eastern Irrigation Supply ....G....... 352 472-3323
Newberry *(G-11553)*
K-Rain Manufacturing Corp ....D....... 561 721-3936
Riviera Beach *(G-15338)*
Maxijet Inc..E....... 863 439-3667
Dundee *(G-3566)*
Rainbow Manufacturing Company........G....... 305 477-5541
Miami Lakes *(G-10848)*

AGRICULTURAL EQPT: Soil Preparation Mach, Exc Turf & Grounds

Amega Sciences Inc ....G....... 863 937-9792
Lakeland *(G-7632)*
Fogmaster Corporation ....G....... 954 481-9975
Deerfield Beach *(G-2825)*

Golf Agronomics Sand & Hlg Inc ....G....... 800 626-1359
Sarasota *(G-16451)*
Manley Farms Inc..........G....... 239 597-6416
Naples *(G-11318)*

AGRICULTURAL EQPT: Spreaders, Fertilizer

50 50 Parmley Envmtl Svcs LLC..........G....... 407 593-1165
Saint Cloud *(G-15641)*
Irms Inc..........F....... 321 631-1161
Rockledge *(G-15423)*
Rugby Road Corp..........G....... 407 328-5474
Sanford *(G-16112)*

AGRICULTURAL EQPT: Trailers & Wagons, Farm

Bulk Resources Inc..........G....... 813 764-8420
Plant City *(G-14413)*
C P Enterprises of Apopka Inc..........G....... 407 886-3321
Mount Dora *(G-11098)*

AGRICULTURAL LIMESTONE: Ground

Marianna Lime Products Inc..........G....... 850 526-3580
Marianna *(G-8581)*
Marianna Limestone LLC..........F....... 954 581-1220
Marianna *(G-8582)*

AGRICULTURAL MACHINERY & EQPT REPAIR

Everglades Machine Inc..........G....... 863 983-0133
Clewiston *(G-1979)*
McEs LLC..........G....... 321 363-4977
Sanford *(G-16086)*

AIR CLEANING SYSTEMS

Atco Rubber Products Inc..........E....... 813 754-6678
Plant City *(G-14403)*
Chilly Willys Heating & A Inc..........G....... 904 772-1164
Jacksonville *(G-6264)*
Florida Air Cleaning Inc..........G....... 727 573-5281
Clearwater *(G-1685)*
Fresh Aire Sanitization..........G....... 407 301-9831
Kissimmee *(G-7247)*
Rainbow Eb Buenavista..........G....... 305 982-8153
Miami *(G-10235)*
Triatomic Environmental Inc..........F....... 561 748-4864
Jupiter *(G-7132)*
Worldwide Technology Inc..........E....... 813 855-2443
Oldsmar *(G-12279)*

AIR CONDITIONERS: Motor Vehicle

Classic Auto A Mnfactoring Inc..........F....... 813 251-2356
Tampa *(G-17540)*
Hoseline Inc..........F....... 407 892-2599
Saint Cloud *(G-15654)*
Re-Bus LLC..........G....... 772 418-7711
Fort Pierce *(G-4738)*
Transport A/C Inc..........G....... 954 254-4822
Pensacola *(G-14274)*

AIR CONDITIONING & VENTILATION EQPT & SPLYS: Wholesales

Parker Davis Hvac Intl Inc..........E....... 305 513-4488
Doral *(G-3455)*
Total of Florida..........G....... 239 768-9400
Fort Myers *(G-4634)*

AIR CONDITIONING EQPT

A C Repairs Inc..........G....... 813 909-0809
Lutz *(G-8370)*
Air Source 1 LLC..........G....... 772 626-7604
Port St Lucie *(G-15167)*
Baez Enterprises Corp..........F....... 813 317-7277
Seffner *(G-16721)*
Carrier Corporation..........C....... 800 379-6484
Palm Beach Gardens *(G-13573)*
Chiller Medic Inc..........G....... 904 814-9446
Jacksonville *(G-6263)*
Energetico Inc..........G....... 213 550-5211
North Miami *(G-11637)*
Everest Air Corp..........F....... 407 319-6204
Kissimmee *(G-7243)*
Flagship Marine Inc..........G....... 772 781-4242
Stuart *(G-16940)*
Fusion AC & Appl Svc LLC..........G....... 888 670-8435
Pompano Beach *(G-14707)*
Gem 360 LLC..........E....... 800 436-1932
Miami *(G-9621)*
Innovative Svc Solutions LLC..........E....... 407 296-5211
Orlando *(G-12831)*
Klimaire Products Inc..........F....... 305 593-8358
Doral *(G-3409)*
Kommercial Refrigeration Inc..........G....... 863 299-3000
Winter Haven *(G-19332)*
Mas Hvac Inc..........F....... 904 531-3140
Elkton *(G-3649)*
Monar Corporation..........G....... 954 650-1930
Coral Springs *(G-2287)*
Northrich Florida LLC..........F....... 954 678-6602
Weston *(G-19154)*
Parker Davis Hvac Intl Inc..........E....... 305 513-4488
Doral *(G-3455)*
Proservices Supply LLC..........F....... 858 254-4415
Jacksonville *(G-6696)*
South Florida Marine..........G....... 305 232-8788
Cutler Bay *(G-2413)*
Total of Florida..........G....... 239 768-9400
Fort Myers *(G-4634)*
Trane Central America Inc..........E....... 305 592-8646
Miami *(G-10502)*
V & F Air Conditioning Sup LLC..........F....... 305 477-1040
Miami *(G-10559)*
Warren Technology Inc..........C....... 305 556-6933
Hialeah *(G-5686)*

AIR CONDITIONING REPAIR SVCS

Air Doctor of Swfl LLC..........G....... 239 285-8774
Lehigh Acres *(G-8184)*
Chiller Medic Inc..........G....... 904 814-9446
Jacksonville *(G-6263)*
Con-Air Industries Inc..........D....... 407 298-5733
Orlando *(G-12611)*
Everest Air Corp..........F....... 407 319-6204
Kissimmee *(G-7243)*
Fusion AC & Appl Svc LLC..........G....... 888 670-8435
Pompano Beach *(G-14707)*
Innovative Svc Solutions LLC..........E....... 407 296-5211
Orlando *(G-12831)*
South Florida Marine..........G....... 305 232-8788
Cutler Bay *(G-2413)*

AIR CONDITIONING UNITS: Complete, Domestic Or Indl

Air Doctor of Swfl LLC..........G....... 239 285-8774
Lehigh Acres *(G-8184)*
American Hermetics Georgia Inc..........G....... 305 592-8958
Miami *(G-9143)*
Aquacal Autopilot Inc..........C....... 727 823-5642
Saint Petersburg *(G-15705)*
Electrolux Professional LLC..........F....... 954 327-6778
Fort Lauderdale *(G-3967)*
First America Products..........F....... 904 683-1253
Orange Park *(G-12393)*
First America Products LLC..........G....... 904 215-8075
Miami *(G-9571)*
Innovative Support Systems..........G....... 407 682-7570
Altamonte Springs *(G-51)*
James D Nall Co Inc..........E....... 305 884-8363
Fort Lauderdale *(G-4074)*
Mermaid Mfg Southwest Fla Inc..........F....... 239 418-0535
Fort Myers *(G-4528)*
Mosco Inc..........G....... 561 588-3880
Lake Worth Beach *(G-7617)*
Southern Hvac Corporation..........G....... 407 917-1800
Maitland *(G-8479)*
Trane Technologies Company LLC..........A....... 850 873-8200
Panama City *(G-13956)*
Zenit Service LLC..........G....... 407 878-7840
Lake Mary *(G-7462)*

AIR MATTRESSES: Plastic

Dotchi LLC..........F....... 305 477-0024
Miami *(G-9483)*
Innovative PDT Solutions LLC..........F....... 407 933-2029
Kissimmee *(G-7254)*

AIR PURIFICATION EQPT

Advanced Tech & Tstg Labs..........G....... 352 871-3802
Tampa *(G-17388)*
Air Purifying Systems Inc..........G....... 954 962-0450
Miami *(G-9093)*
Atitlan Enterprises LLC..........F....... 813 362-1909
Tampa *(G-17442)*
Better Air North America LLC..........G....... 844 447-7624
Hollywood *(G-5787)*
Biozone Scientific Intl Inc..........G....... 407 876-2000
Orlando *(G-12517)*
Iaire LLC..........G....... 407 873-2538
Orlando *(G-12818)*
Timilon Corporation..........F....... 239 330-9650
Bonita Springs *(G-862)*
Turner Envirologic Inc..........E....... 954 422-9566
Deerfield Beach *(G-2930)*
Wes Holdings Corp..........F....... 941 371-4995
Sarasota *(G-16636)*

AIR, WATER & SOLID WASTE PROGRAMS ADMINISTRATION SVCS

Platinium Rosis Inc..........G....... 786 617-9973
Miami Beach *(G-10703)*

AIRCRAFT & AEROSPACE FLIGHT INSTRUMENTS & GUIDANCE SYSTEMS

ABC Components Inc..........F....... 954 249-6286
Cooper City *(G-2106)*
Aerospace Automation LLC..........G....... 954 260-2844
Pembroke Pines *(G-14018)*
Avidyne Corporation..........D....... 321 751-8520
Melbourne *(G-8774)*
Dayton-Granger Inc..........C....... 954 463-3451
Fort Lauderdale *(G-3935)*
Gables Engineering Inc..........B....... 305 774-4400
Coral Gables *(G-2147)*
GKN Aerospace Florida LLC..........D....... 314 412-8311
Panama City *(G-13910)*
Green Energy Enterprises Inc..........E....... 904 309-8993
Jacksonville *(G-6447)*
Honeywell International Inc..........B....... 727 539-5080
Clearwater *(G-1717)*
Jormac Aerospace Inc..........F....... 727 549-9600
Clearwater *(G-1745)*
Mercaereo Inc..........G....... 305 307-0672
Doral *(G-3432)*
Nelver Airparts Inc..........G....... 305 378-0072
Miami *(G-10064)*
New Generation Aerospace Inc..........G....... 305 882-1410
Medley *(G-8696)*
Northrop Grumman Corporation..........G....... 352 759-2946
Altoona *(G-87)*
Pratt & Whitney..........E....... 561 796-6701
Jupiter *(G-7097)*
Revolution Air Craft Services..........F....... 954 747-4773
Pompano Beach *(G-14831)*
Sota Manufacturing Inc..........E....... 561 368-8007
Boca Raton *(G-722)*
Supliaereos USA LLC..........G....... 727 754-4915
Clearwater *(G-1897)*
Tef-Gel Inc..........F....... 561 845-1086
West Palm Beach *(G-19059)*
Teleios Manufacturing Inc..........G....... 904 490-0600
Jacksonville *(G-6846)*
Willis Aeronautical Svcs Inc..........F....... 561 272-5402
Coconut Creek *(G-2103)*

AIRCRAFT & HEAVY EQPT REPAIR SVCS

Heico Corporation..........B....... 954 987-4000
Hollywood *(G-5840)*
Interntnal Synrgy For Tchncal..........G....... 321 305-0863
Orlando *(G-12837)*
Southwest Eqp For Hrnando Cnty..........G....... 352 596-5142
Brooksville *(G-1273)*
Ver-Val Enterprises Inc..........F....... 850 244-7931
Fort Walton Beach *(G-4838)*

AIRCRAFT ASSEMBLY PLANTS

Above Ground Level Aerospace..........F....... 305 713-2629
Miami *(G-9056)*
Aercap Inc..........E....... 954 760-7777
Fort Lauderdale *(G-3785)*
Aercap Group Services Inc..........B....... 954 760-7777
Fort Lauderdale *(G-3786)*
Aerial Products Corporation..........F....... 800 973-9110
Jacksonville *(G-6126)*
Aerosmart Enterprise LLC..........E....... 310 499-8878
Saint Petersburg *(G-15692)*
Air Support Tecks..........G....... 386 986-5301
Palm Coast *(G-13681)*

Airbus Oneweb Satellites LLC..............C....... 321 735-8446
Merritt Island *(G-8988)*
Aircraft Systems Group Inc..................G....... 727 376-9292
Odessa *(G-12100)*
Altum Aerospace..................F....... 954 618-6573
Sunrise *(G-17089)*
Amxs Corp..................E....... 904 568-1416
Jacksonville Beach *(G-6938)*
ASG Aerospace LLC..................G....... 305 253-0802
Miami *(G-9177)*
Aviation Parts & Trade Corp..................G....... 954 944-2828
Plantation *(G-14495)*
Bmg Aerospace..................F....... 786 725-4959
Miami *(G-9263)*
Bob Laferriere Aircraft Inc..................G....... 727 709-2704
Tarpon Springs *(G-18284)*
Boeing..................E....... 850 301-6635
Fort Walton Beach *(G-4782)*
Boeing Arospc Operations Inc..................F....... 850 682-2746
Crestview *(G-2344)*
Boeing Company..................C....... 407 306-8782
Orlando *(G-12530)*
Boeing Company..................G....... 321 867-6005
Cape Canaveral *(G-1353)*
Boeing Company..................G....... 321 867-6005
Kennedy Space Center *(G-7151)*
Boeing Company..................G....... 321 867-7380
Kennedy Space Center *(G-7152)*
Boeing Company..................G....... 904 317-2490
Jacksonville *(G-6221)*
Bombardier Trnsp Hldngs USA In..................G....... 407 450-4855
Sanford *(G-16004)*
Bombardiier..................G....... 954 622-1200
Fort Lauderdale *(G-3865)*
C1 Aerospace LLC..................G....... 786 712-9949
Miami *(G-9295)*
Celtic Airspares LLC..................G....... 727 431-0482
Clearwater *(G-1622)*
Coleman Aerospace..................E....... 407 354-0047
Orlando *(G-12599)*
CSC Aerospace Corporation..................G....... 203 300-9760
Doral *(G-3315)*
Diamond Aircraft Logisctics..................G....... 305 456-8400
Doral *(G-3328)*
Diloren Inc..................G....... 786 618-9671
Doral *(G-3330)*
Discovery Aviation Inc..................E....... 321 752-0332
Melbourne *(G-8806)*
Dowe Gallagher Aerospace..................G....... 941 256-2179
Sarasota *(G-16208)*
Dreamline Aerospace..................G....... 954 544-2365
Pembroke Pines *(G-14030)*
ELite Intl Group LLC..................F....... 305 901-5005
Miami *(G-9516)*
Embraer Executive Aircraft Inc..................D....... 321 751-5050
Melbourne *(G-8824)*
Embraer Services Inc..................A....... 954 359-3700
Fort Lauderdale *(G-3970)*
EMC Aerospace Inc..................E....... 954 316-6015
North Miami Beach *(G-11674)*
Estumkeda Ltd..................F....... 954 966-6300
Hollywood *(G-5817)*
Excalibur Aircraft..................G....... 863 385-9486
Sebring *(G-16690)*
Fl Aerospace Solutions Inc..................G....... 786 395-3289
Miami *(G-9565)*
Florida Aerospace Partnership..................G....... 954 617-7700
Fort Lauderdale *(G-3998)*
Full Circle Integration LLC..................F....... 504 615-5501
Valparaiso *(G-18511)*
Garrison Lickle Aircraft..................G....... 561 833-7111
Palm Beach *(G-13555)*
Gb Airlink Inc..................G....... 561 593-7284
Stuart *(G-16946)*
General Dynamics Corporation..................G....... 850 897-9700
Niceville *(G-11567)*
GKN Aerospace Florida LLC..................D....... 314 412-8311
Panama City *(G-13910)*
Global Aerospace..................G....... 407 721-3732
Indialantic *(G-6059)*
Gonzalez Aerospace Services..................G....... 561 227-1575
Wellington *(G-18719)*
Gulf Coast Airways Inc..................G....... 239 403-3020
Naples *(G-11270)*
Gulfstream Mses Invstmnts Grou..................G....... 305 975-6186
Miami Beach *(G-10675)*
Harris Aerial LLC..................F....... 407 725-7886
Casselberry *(G-1505)*
High Standard Aviation Inc..................E....... 305 599-8855
Doral *(G-3383)*
Jade Tactical Disaster Relief..................C....... 850 270-4077
Tampa *(G-17801)*
Kaman Aerospace Corporation..................E....... 904 751-5369
Jacksonville *(G-6532)*
KB Aerospace Co..................G....... 754 366-9194
Fort Lauderdale *(G-4085)*
Landmark Aviation..................G....... 305 296-5422
Key West *(G-7194)*
Lift Aerospace Corp..................F....... 305 851-5237
Miami *(G-9890)*
Lighter Than Air Systems Corp..................F....... 904 834-4400
Jacksonville *(G-6557)*
Lockheed Martin Corporation..................G....... 904 660-6917
Jacksonville *(G-6561)*
Lockheed Mrtin Mllmter Tech In..................E....... 407 356-4186
Orlando *(G-12932)*
Lockheed Training Facility..................G....... 850 883-2144
Eglin Afb *(G-3646)*
Maris Worden Aerospace Inc..................G....... 514 895-8075
South Daytona *(G-16803)*
Max Torque LLC..................F....... 863 701-8000
Lakeland *(G-7746)*
Meridian South Aviation LLC..................G....... 727 536-5387
Clearwater *(G-1781)*
Mia Aerospace LLC..................G....... 786 973-4118
Miami *(G-9987)*
Micro Systems Inc..................C....... 850 244-2332
Fort Walton Beach *(G-4815)*
Mysky Aircraft Inc..................G....... 386 492-6908
Port Orange *(G-15026)*
Nobel Aerospace LLC..................F....... 786 210-0716
Doral *(G-3445)*
Northrop Grmman Feld Spport Sv..................D....... 904 810-4665
Saint Augustine *(G-15574)*
Northstar Aviation USA LLC..................E....... 321 600-4557
Melbourne *(G-8898)*
Onvoi AVI Supp and Inspect Ser..................G....... 805 312-3274
Defuniak Springs *(G-2945)*
Pegasus Aerospace..................G....... 850 376-0991
Destin *(G-3201)*
Perry North Aerospace Inc..................G....... 954 295-9520
Lighthouse Point *(G-8212)*
Progressive Aerodyne Inc..................G....... 352 253-0108
Tavares *(G-18351)*
Puma Aero Marine Inc..................G....... 904 638-5888
Fort Lauderdale *(G-4184)*
R4 Integration Inc..................E....... 850 226-6913
Fort Walton Beach *(G-4825)*
Ronco Aircraft and Marine Inc..................E....... 321 220-0209
Palm Bay *(G-13532)*
Southstern Arspc Svcs Ltd Lblt..................G....... 305 992-8257
Pompano Beach *(G-14865)*
Southwings Avionics and ACC..................G....... 305 825-6755
Miami Lakes *(G-10863)*
Supliaereos USA LLC..................G....... 727 754-4915
Clearwater *(G-1897)*
Tecnam US Inc..................F....... 863 655-2400
Sebring *(G-16714)*
TP Aerospace Technics LLC..................G....... 407 730-9988
Orlando *(G-13266)*
UAS Drone Corp..................G....... 561 693-1424
Palm Beach *(G-13562)*
Veserca Group Ltd Inc..................F....... 561 210-7400
Boca Raton *(G-779)*
Viper Drones LLC..................G....... 205 677-3700
Indialantic *(G-6062)*
Vogue Aerospace & Defense Inc..................G....... 321 289-0872
Naples *(G-11453)*
VSI & Partners Inc..................F....... 954 205-8653
Miramar *(G-11058)*

AIRCRAFT CONTROL SYSTEMS:

Aviation Instrument Tech Inc..................F....... 813 783-3361
Zephyrhills *(G-19508)*
Suriparts Corp..................G....... 954 639-7700
Pembroke Pines *(G-14062)*

AIRCRAFT CONTROL SYSTEMS: Electronic Totalizing Counters

Avalex Technologies Corp..................D....... 850 470-8464
Gulf Breeze *(G-5113)*
GE Aviation Systems LLC..................F....... 727 532-6370
Clearwater *(G-1698)*
GE Aviation Systems LLC..................F....... 727 539-1631
Clearwater *(G-1700)*
Honeywell International Inc..................A....... 727 531-4611
Clearwater *(G-1719)*
Moog Inc..................G....... 716 652-2000
Pembroke Pines *(G-14049)*
Radiant Power Idc LLC..................E....... 760 945-0230
Sarasota *(G-16282)*

AIRCRAFT DEALERS

Veserca Group Ltd Inc..................F....... 561 210-7400
Boca Raton *(G-779)*

AIRCRAFT ENGINES & ENGINE PARTS: Airfoils

Sequa Corporation..................A....... 561 935-3571
Palm Beach Gardens *(G-13626)*

AIRCRAFT ENGINES & ENGINE PARTS: Mount Parts

Dynamic Precision Group Inc..................E....... 772 287-7770
Stuart *(G-16934)*
Propulsion Tech Intl LLC..................B....... 954 874-0274
Miramar *(G-11034)*
Simmonds Precision Pdts Inc..................E....... 904 757-3660
Jacksonville *(G-6776)*
Turbocombustor Technology Inc..................B....... 772 287-7770
Stuart *(G-17041)*

AIRCRAFT ENGINES & ENGINE PARTS: Research & Development, Mfr

V and N Advanced Auto Sys LLC..................G....... 321 504-6440
Rockledge *(G-15455)*

AIRCRAFT ENGINES & PARTS

Acmt South LLC..................F....... 860 645-0592
Lynn Haven *(G-8427)*
Aero-Link Marine & Power LLC..................G....... 561 404-8181
Boca Raton *(G-404)*
Aerojet Rocketdyne De Inc..................C....... 561 882-5150
Jupiter *(G-6996)*
Aerosync Engrg Consulting Inc..................G....... 316 208-3367
Milton *(G-10920)*
Aersale 23440 LLC..................G....... 305 764-3200
Coral Gables *(G-2119)*
Air Alliance Inc..................G....... 305 735-4864
Marathon *(G-8516)*
Air Lion Incorp..................G....... 386 748-9296
Deland *(G-2955)*
Air Marshall Inc..................F....... 954 843-0991
Hollywood *(G-5766)*
Aircraft Technology Inc..................E....... 954 744-7602
Hollywood *(G-5767)*
Airmark Overhaul Inc..................G....... 954 970-3200
Fort Lauderdale *(G-3792)*
Airstox Inc..................G....... 954 618-6573
Sunrise *(G-17085)*
Avstar Fuel Systems Inc..................G....... 561 575-1560
Jupiter *(G-7002)*
Bonus Aerospace Inc..................G....... 305 887-6778
Medley *(G-8624)*
Bonus Tech Inc..................F....... 786 251-4232
Medley *(G-8625)*
Chromalloy Component Svcs Inc..................D....... 954 378-1999
Fort Lauderdale *(G-3898)*
Chromalloy Gas Turbine LLC..................A....... 561 935-3571
Palm Beach Gardens *(G-13578)*
CIT Aerospace Inc..................F....... 954 359-2561
Plantation *(G-14499)*
Csi Aerospace Inc..................E....... 954 961-9800
Hollywood *(G-5807)*
ELite Intl Group LLC..................F....... 305 901-5005
Miami *(G-9516)*
Falcon Commercial Aviation LLC..................F....... 786 340-9464
Miami *(G-9558)*
Flight Source LLC..................G....... 954 249-8449
Fort Lauderdale *(G-3997)*
Florida Aero Precision Inc..................E....... 561 848-6248
Lake Park *(G-7471)*
Florida Turbine Tech Inc..................G....... 561 427-6400
Jupiter *(G-7045)*
Fossco Inc..................G....... 850 983-1330
Milton *(G-10929)*
Global Turbine Services Inc..................F....... 786 476-2166
Medley *(G-8659)*
Goodrich Corporation..................G....... 305 622-4500
Miami Gardens *(G-10744)*
H H Terry Co Inc..................F....... 239 593-0132
Naples *(G-11274)*
Hamilton Sundstrand Corp..................G....... 860 654-6252
Pompano Beach *(G-14721)*

Heico Aerospace Corporation ......E 954 987-6101
Hollywood *(G-5837)*
Heico Aerospace Holdings Corp ......G 954 987-4000
Hollywood *(G-5838)*
Heico Aerospace Holdings Corp ......G 305 463-0455
Miami *(G-9698)*
Heico Aerospace Parts Corp ......G 440 995-3661
Hollywood *(G-5839)*
Heico Corporation ......G 305 374-1745
Miami *(G-9699)*
Heico Corporation ......G 305 463-0455
Miami *(G-9700)*
Heico Corporation ......B 954 987-4000
Hollywood *(G-5840)*
Heico Electronic Tech Corp ......E 954 987-6101
Hollywood *(G-5841)*
Heico Flight Support Corp ......E 954 987-4000
Hollywood *(G-5842)*
Honeywell International Inc ......G 561 479-0639
Boca Raton *(G-558)*
Honeywell International Inc ......G 281 546-0993
Tallahassee *(G-17279)*
Honeywell International Inc ......G 305 525-1950
Miami *(G-9719)*
Honeywell International Inc ......G 850 243-8812
Fort Walton Beach *(G-4809)*
Honeywell International Inc ......G 727 539-3111
Clearwater *(G-1718)*
Honeywell International Inc ......G 727 539-4451
Largo *(G-7972)*
Honeywell International Inc ......G 877 841-2840
Oviedo *(G-13436)*
Honeywell International Inc ......G 904 696-5222
Jacksonville *(G-6477)*
Honeywell International Inc ......G 813 573-1166
Clearwater *(G-1720)*
Honeywell International Inc ......G 904 260-5900
Jacksonville *(G-6478)*
Honeywell International Inc ......G 352 372-4192
Gainesville *(G-4938)*
Honeywell US Corp ......F 617 955-4031
North Miami Beach *(G-11682)*
Iag Engine Center LLC ......E 305 591-0643
Miami *(G-9726)*
Interavia Spares and Svcs Inc ......G 954 794-0174
Boca Raton *(G-567)*
Interntnal Synrgy For Tchncal ......G 321 305-0863
Orlando *(G-12837)*
Ja Engineering II Corp ......G 954 744-7560
Hollywood *(G-5850)*
Jet Avion Corporation ......D 954 987-6101
Hollywood *(G-5854)*
Magellan Aviation Group Lllp ......G 561 266-0845
Boynton Beach *(G-931)*
Miami Leasing Inc ......G 786 431-1215
Miami *(G-10003)*
Miami Ndt Inc ......F 305 599-9393
Medley *(G-8691)*
Miltechnologies Inc ......G 305 817-4244
Miami Lakes *(G-10821)*
MTI Aviation Inc ......E 305 817-4244
Opa Locka *(G-12342)*
Norris Precision Mfg Inc ......D 727 572-6330
Clearwater *(G-1810)*
Northwings Accessories Corp ......C 305 463-0455
Miami *(G-10078)*
Overall-Honeycomb LLC ......D 941 756-8781
Sarasota *(G-16269)*
Palladium Sales LLC ......G 754 423-0517
Davie *(G-2564)*
Palmer Manufacturing Co LLC ......F 772 287-7770
Stuart *(G-16986)*
Parker-Hannifin Corporation ......G 239 304-1000
Naples *(G-11358)*
Pma LLC ......G 407 310-2548
Orlando *(G-13073)*
Pratt & Whitney Eng Svcs Inc ......G 305 512-9882
Miami Lakes *(G-10841)*
Precision Shapes Inc ......E 321 269-2555
Titusville *(G-18453)*
Precision Turbines Inc ......G 561 447-0751
Boca Raton *(G-672)*
PSI Mnfacturing Operations LLC ......G 561 747-6107
Jupiter *(G-7100)*
Radiant-Seacom Repairs Corp ......G 941 739-3200
Sarasota *(G-16283)*
Raytheon Technologies Corp ......A 858 277-7639
Jupiter *(G-7103)*
Saf Aerospace LLC ......G 813 376-0883
Tampa *(G-18080)*
Sidus Space Inc ......E 321 613-0615
Cape Canaveral *(G-1367)*
Skill-Metric Machine & Tl Inc ......E 561 454-8900
Delray Beach *(G-3143)*
Sohacki Industries Inc ......E 904 826-0130
Saint Augustine *(G-15613)*
Sunshine Avionics LLC ......G 954 517-1294
Hialeah *(G-5638)*
Supliaereos USA LLC ......G 727 754-4915
Clearwater *(G-1897)*
Treasure Coast Machines Inc ......F 772 283-2024
Stuart *(G-17037)*
Turbine Kinetics Inc ......D 954 744-7526
Hollywood *(G-5931)*
Turbine Weld Industries LLC ......E 941 485-5113
Venice *(G-18582)*
United Technologies Corp ......E 860 565-4321
Jupiter *(G-7137)*
Vfm Aerosystems LLC ......G 786 567-2348
Doral *(G-3541)*

AIRCRAFT EQPT & SPLYS WHOLESALERS

Aerotools Connection LLC ......G 305 234-3034
Miami *(G-9083)*
M Bilt Enterprises Inc ......F 352 528-5566
Ocala *(G-11989)*
Mirage Systems Inc ......F 386 740-9222
Deland *(G-2997)*
Tobruk International Corp ......G 305 406-0263
Miami *(G-10484)*

AIRCRAFT FLIGHT INSTRUMENTS

Becker Avionics Inc ......F 954 450-3137
Miramar *(G-10974)*
Richards Aviation ......G 954 527-2623
Fort Lauderdale *(G-4205)*
Trilectron ......G 941 721-1000
Palmetto *(G-13830)*

AIRCRAFT FUELING SVCS

Atlantic Jet Center Inc ......G 321 255-7111
Melbourne *(G-8771)*

AIRCRAFT LIGHTING

B/E Aerospace Inc ......E 410 266-2048
Wellington *(G-18710)*
Cobalt Aerospace Inc ......G 305 450-0457
Hialeah *(G-5349)*
Radiant Power Corp ......C 941 739-3200
Sarasota *(G-16281)*

AIRCRAFT MAINTENANCE & REPAIR SVCS

Aviation Instrument Tech Inc ......F 813 783-3361
Zephyrhills *(G-19508)*
High Standard Aviation Inc ......E 305 599-8855
Doral *(G-3383)*
Safran Power Usa LLC ......C 941 758-7726
Sarasota *(G-16289)*

AIRCRAFT PARTS & AUX EQPT: Panel Assy/Hydro Prop Test Stands

Honeycomb Company America Inc ......C 941 756-8781
Sarasota *(G-16229)*

AIRCRAFT PARTS & AUXILIARY EQPT: Accumulators, Propeller

Mt-Propeller Usa Inc ......F 386 736-7762
Deland *(G-3002)*

AIRCRAFT PARTS & AUXILIARY EQPT: Ailerons

Honeycomb Arcft Repr Ctr LLC ......E 850 610-0334
Sarasota *(G-16228)*

AIRCRAFT PARTS & AUXILIARY EQPT: Aircraft Training Eqpt

Cte Jv LLC ......G 407 894-5575
Orlando *(G-12631)*
ELite Intl Group LLC ......F 305 901-5005
Miami *(G-9516)*
Heico Corporation ......B 954 987-4000
Hollywood *(G-5840)*

AIRCRAFT PARTS & AUXILIARY EQPT: Assys, Subassemblies/Parts

AAR Manufacturing Inc ......D 727 539-8585
Clearwater *(G-1561)*
Airplane Services Inc ......G 850 675-1252
Jay *(G-6961)*
Donica International Inc ......F 954 217-7616
Miami *(G-9478)*
Monroy Aerospace ......G 954 344-4936
Coral Springs *(G-2289)*
Omnia Inc ......G 863 619-8100
Lakeland *(G-7758)*
Parker-Hannifin Corporation ......G 239 304-1000
Naples *(G-11358)*
Pioneer Aerospace Corporation ......F 850 623-3330
Milton *(G-10936)*
Simmonds Precision Pdts Inc ......E 904 757-3660
Jacksonville *(G-6776)*
Steen Aero Lab LLC ......G 321 725-4160
Palm Bay *(G-13540)*

AIRCRAFT PARTS & AUXILIARY EQPT: Bodies

Aersale 26346 LLC ......D 305 764-3200
Coral Gables *(G-2120)*

AIRCRAFT PARTS & AUXILIARY EQPT: Body & Wing Assys & Parts

American Enrgy Innovations LLC ......F 772 221-9100
Stuart *(G-16905)*
AMP Aero Services LLC ......G 833 267-2376
Miami *(G-9151)*
Boeing Company ......G 850 882-4912
Eglin Afb *(G-3641)*
Integritrust Solutions LLC ......G 850 685-9801
Navarre *(G-11466)*
Precision Shapes Inc ......E 321 269-2555
Titusville *(G-18453)*
Tri-Tech Electronics Inc ......D 407 277-2131
Orlando *(G-13270)*

AIRCRAFT PARTS & AUXILIARY EQPT: Body Assemblies & Parts

Aerospace Rotables Inc ......F 954 452-0056
Sunrise *(G-17083)*
Avalon Aviation Inc ......G 954 655-0256
Fort Lauderdale *(G-3834)*
Firefly Aircraft Parts Inc ......G 954 505-1470
Plantation *(G-14516)*
Setty Enterprises Inc ......F 561 844-3711
West Palm Beach *(G-19028)*
Shark Skinz ......G 772 388-9621
Sebastian *(G-16672)*

AIRCRAFT PARTS & AUXILIARY EQPT: Gears, Power Transmission

Coast Wcp ......E 727 572-4249
Odessa *(G-12111)*
Southern Gear & Machine Inc ......D 305 691-6300
Miami *(G-10386)*

AIRCRAFT PARTS & AUXILIARY EQPT: Military Eqpt & Armament

General Dynamics-Ots Inc ......D 727 578-8100
Saint Petersburg *(G-15790)*
Lopez & Company Inc ......E 305 302-3045
Miami *(G-9911)*
Zitec Inc ......G 850 678-9747
Niceville *(G-11577)*

AIRCRAFT PARTS & AUXILIARY EQPT: Oxygen Systems

Aerox AVI Oxgn Systems LLC ......F 207 637-2331
Bonita Springs *(G-811)*

AIRCRAFT PARTS & AUXILIARY EQPT: Refueling Eqpt, In Flight

Smart Material Corp ......F 941 870-3337
Sarasota *(G-16600)*

AIRCRAFT PARTS & AUXILIARY EQPT: Research & Development, Mfr

Aire-Tech Rotorcraft Svcs LLC ... F ... 305 696-8001
Miami (G-9096)
Arrowhead Global LLC ... G ... 727 497-7340
Clearwater (G-1589)
Aveoengineering LLC ... G ... 631 747-6671
Palm Coast (G-13684)
Exodus Management LLC ... G ... 954 995-4407
Fort Lauderdale (G-3983)
Interntnal Synrgy For Tchncal ... G ... 321 305-0863
Orlando (G-12837)
Rolin Industries Inc ... G ... 850 654-1704
Fort Walton Beach (G-4831)

AIRCRAFT PARTS & AUXILIARY EQPT: Rotor Blades, Helicopter

Acmt South LLC ... F ... 860 645-0592
Lynn Haven (G-8427)
Aviation Intl Solutions LLC ... G ... 305 267-7117
Hialeah (G-5313)

AIRCRAFT PARTS & EQPT, NEC

A J Assoc Mfg & Engrg Co ... F ... 727 258-0994
Clearwater (G-1560)
A R Components Corp ... F ... 786 703-8456
Miami (G-9042)
AAR Airlift Group Inc ... E ... 321 837-2345
Palm Bay (G-13498)
AAR Corp ... G ... 786 337-4000
Medley (G-8604)
AAR Government Services Inc ... E ... 904 693-7260
Jacksonville (G-6116)
AAR Government Services Inc ... E ... 321 361-3461
Rockledge (G-15390)
AAR Landing Gear LLC ... E ... 305 883-1511
Medley (G-8605)
ABC Intercargo LLC ... G ... 954 908-5200
Weston (G-19102)
Advanced Thermal Tech Inc ... E ... 561 791-5000
Wellington (G-18708)
Advent Aerospace Inc ... E ... 727 549-9600
Largo (G-7887)
Aero Bridgeworks Inc ... G ... 321 689-1912
Orlando (G-12438)
Aero Hose Corp ... F ... 904 215-9638
Orange Park (G-12380)
Aero Mechanical Industries ... G ... 469 645-1620
Coral Gables (G-2118)
Aero South Florida Inc ... G ... 954 363-2376
Deerfield Beach (G-2767)
Aero-Flex Corp ... E ... 561 745-2534
Jupiter (G-6994)
Aerobase Group Inc ... E ... 321 802-5889
Melbourne (G-8759)
Aerojet Rocketdyne Inc ... G ... 386 626-0001
Daytona Beach (G-2622)
Aeronate Inc ... G ... 954 358-7145
Pembroke Pines (G-14017)
Aerosonic LLC ... C ... 727 461-3000
Clearwater (G-1568)
Aerosource Inc ... E ... 941 751-2620
Sarasota (G-16172)
Aerotools Connection LLC ... G ... 305 234-3034
Miami (G-9083)
Aerotools USA Inc ... G ... 305 432-4258
Miami (G-9084)
Aerowest Mfg Corp ... G ... 786 367-6948
Hialeah (G-5273)
Agd Systems Corporation ... G ... 561 722-5561
West Palm Beach (G-18791)
Air Operations ... F ... 305 871-5449
Miami (G-9092)
Aircraft Engrg Instlltion Svcs ... E ... 407 438-4436
Orlando (G-12445)
Airdyne Aerospace Inc ... E ... 352 593-4163
Brooksville (G-1206)
Airframe International Inc ... F ... 218 461-9305
Fort Pierce (G-4671)
Airind Incorporated ... G ... 954 252-0900
Southwest Ranches (G-16836)
Airline Support Group Inc ... E ... 954 971-4567
Fort Lauderdale (G-3790)
Airmark Components Inc ... E ... 954 522-5370
Fort Lauderdale (G-3791)
Aj Associates ... F ... 727 258-0994
Clearwater (G-1571)
Alaris Aerospace Systems LLC ... F ... 954 596-8736
Pompano Beach (G-14583)
Alco Services Inc ... E ... 954 538-2189
Miramar (G-10963)
Allclear Aerospace & Def Inc ... F ... 954 200-9195
Miramar (G-10966)
Allied Aerospace Inc ... F ... 786 616-8484
Doral (G-3239)
Allied Aerospace International ... G ... 954 429-8600
Deerfield Beach (G-2775)
Alm Technologies Inc ... E ... 904 849-7212
Yulee (G-19495)
American Science and Tech Corp ... G ... 312 898-3333
Miami Beach (G-10641)
American Vly Avnics Clbrtion L ... F ... 904 579-5272
Orange Park (G-12381)
Apex Aviation Group LLC ... G ... 305 789-6695
Miami (G-9156)
Arcadia Aerospace Inds LLC ... E ... 941 205-5700
Punta Gorda (G-15191)
Arma Holdings Inc ... E ... 813 402-0667
Tampa (G-17434)
Atlantic Jet Support Inc ... G ... 954 360-7549
Coconut Creek (G-2070)
Atlantic Precision Inc ... D ... 772 466-1011
Port Saint Lucie (G-15089)
Atlas Helicopter Inc ... G ... 321 696-4342
Sanford (G-15997)
Avborne Accesory Group LLC ... C ... 305 593-6038
Miami (G-9194)
Avborne Accessory Group Inc ... E ... 305 593-6038
Miami (G-9195)
Aviacol Usa Corp ... F ... 786 701-2152
Miami (G-9198)
Aviation Worldwide Svcs LLC ... F ... 321 837-2345
Palm Bay (G-13500)
Avionics Support Group Inc ... E ... 305 378-9786
Miami (G-9199)
B & J Atlantic Inc ... E ... 904 338-0088
Jacksonville (G-6185)
B E Aerospace ... E ... 305 459-7000
Medley (G-8619)
B/E Aerospace Inc ... G ... 305 471-8800
Doral (G-3262)
B/E Aerospace Inc ... E ... 410 266-2048
Wellington (G-18710)
Ballistic Recovery Systems Inc ... D ... 651 457-7491
Pompano Beach (G-14612)
Baron LLC ... G ... 239 691-5783
Fort Myers (G-4372)
Bigorre Aerospace Corp ... F ... 727 525-8115
Pinellas Park (G-14337)
Bischoff Aero Llc ... F ... 305 883-4410
Hialeah (G-5328)
Borgesfs Inc ... G ... 786 210-0327
Miami (G-9268)
Cambridge Aeronautical LLC ... G ... 305 987-3851
Miami (G-9303)
Chase Aerospace Inc ... F ... 407 812-4545
Orlando (G-12577)
Choice Products Inc ... F ... 386 426-6450
Edgewater (G-3619)
Clero Enterprises Inc ... G ... 305 681-4877
Opa Locka (G-12300)
Coastal Machine LLC ... G ... 850 769-6117
Panama City (G-13885)
Composite-Fx Sales LLC ... G ... 352 538-1624
Trenton (G-18481)
Crane Electronics Inc ... D ... 850 244-0043
Fort Walton Beach (G-4789)
CSC Textron ... F ... 954 776-5862
Fort Lauderdale (G-3921)
Cvg Aerospace LLC ... G ... 786 293-9923
Miami (G-9421)
Cygnus Aerospace Incorporated ... E ... 850 612-1618
Crestview (G-2346)
Daher Inc ... G ... 954 893-1400
Pompano Beach (G-14658)
Dalimar Corp ... G ... 727 525-8115
Pinellas Park (G-14343)
Dass Logistics Inc ... F ... 954 837-8339
Coconut Creek (G-2074)
Diagma U S LLC ... G ... 407 683-0852
Orlando (G-12669)
Discovery Aviation Inc ... E ... 321 752-0332
Melbourne (G-8806)
Don Industrial Group LLC ... F ... 305 290-4237
Hialeah (G-5377)
Doorway Projects Inc ... G ... 561 523-2040
Lake Worth (G-7544)
Electronic Components Fas Inc ... G ... 407 328-8111
Sanford (G-16040)
Equs Logistics LLC ... F ... 954 618-6573
Sunrise (G-17120)
Flight Aerotech LLC ... F ... 305 901-6001
Miami (G-9578)
Flight Velocity ... G ... 866 937-9371
Palm Coast (G-13694)
Flying Colors Air Parts ... F ... 352 728-1900
Leesburg (G-8158)
Forward Express One Llc ... F ... 305 234-3034
Miami (G-9595)
Free Wing Flight Technologies ... G ... 813 752-8552
Plant City (G-14432)
General Mro Aerospace Inc ... G ... 305 482-9903
Medley (G-8657)
General Scientific Corporation ... G ... 850 866-9636
Panama City (G-13908)
Gigli Enterprises Inc ... G ... 850 871-4777
Panama City (G-13909)
Global Intl Investments LLC ... G ... 305 825-2288
Hialeah (G-5432)
Gold Coast Aero Accessories ... G ... 561 965-7767
Lake Worth (G-7553)
Goodrich Corporation ... G ... 954 538-8900
Miramar (G-11000)
Goodrich Corporation ... G ... 305 622-4565
Miami Gardens (G-10745)
Goodrich Corporation ... G ... 305 622-4500
Miami Gardens (G-10744)
GSE America LLC ... G ... 863 583-4343
Lakeland (G-7702)
GSE Jetall Inc ... G ... 305 688-2111
Opa Locka (G-12321)
Halcyon Aviation Capital LLC ... G ... 305 615-1575
Doral (G-3376)
Heli-Tech Inc ... F ... 850 763-9000
Panama City (G-13914)
Hensoldt Avionics Usa LLC ... G ... 941 306-1328
Sarasota (G-16459)
Hermes Technical Intl Inc ... G ... 305 477-8993
Doral (G-3380)
High Standard Aviation Inc ... E ... 305 599-8855
Doral (G-3383)
Himmel Losungen Group Hlg LLC ... G ... 786 631-5531
Doral (G-3384)
Honeywell International Inc ... G ... 505 358-0676
Largo (G-7973)
Icon Aircraft Inc ... F ... 813 387-6603
Tampa (G-17769)
Interavia Spares and Svcs Inc ... G ... 954 794-0174
Boca Raton (G-567)
Intgrated Arospc Aliance LLC ... G ... 469 703-7093
Lake Mary (G-7426)
Irvin Technologies Inc ... E ... 866 245-9356
Winter Springs (G-19476)
J F Aerospace Inc ... G ... 786 242-6686
Miami (G-9781)
Jetspares International Inc ... G ... 407 876-3978
Windermere (G-19231)
Jormac Aerospace ... D ... 727 549-9600
Largo (G-7989)
Js2 Aerospace Corp ... G ... 954 840-3620
Pompano Beach (G-14738)
Kachemak Bay Flying Service ... F ... 850 398-8699
Crestview (G-2352)
Kaman Aerospace Corporation ... E ... 904 751-5369
Jacksonville (G-6532)
Karob Instrument Inc ... G ... 352 732-2414
Ocala (G-11973)
Kellstrom Coml Arospc Inc ... E ... 305 818-5400
Miami Lakes (G-10801)
L3harris Technologies Inc ... G ... 321 727-4660
Palm Bay (G-13520)
Laminar Flow Systems Inc ... F ... 386 253-8833
Daytona Beach (G-2679)
Landing Aerospace Inc ... G ... 305 687-0100
Opa Locka (G-12332)
Live Aerospace Inc ... G ... 305 910-0091
Miami (G-9903)
Loos & Co Inc ... D ... 239 643-5667
Naples (G-11316)
Lopresti Speed Merchants Inc ... E ... 772 562-4757
Sebastian (G-16666)
Ltb Aerospace LLC ... G ... 954 251-1141
Doral (G-3420)
Mattis Aerospace ... G ... 305 910-2377
Homestead (G-5982)
Maverick Composites Inc ... G ... 561 601-3393
Jupiter (G-7075)

Miami Technics LLC ....F 754 227-5459
Deerfield Beach *(G-2871)*
Micro Systems Inc ....C 850 244-2332
Fort Walton Beach *(G-4815)*
Micro Tool Engineering Inc ....F 561 842-7381
Riviera Beach *(G-15348)*
Milspec Products Inc ....G 352 735-0065
Sorrento *(G-16790)*
Mk Aviation LLC ....F 305 825-4810
Doral *(G-3440)*
Moog Inc ....G 716 652-2000
Pembroke Pines *(G-14049)*
Mro Aerospace Inc ....F 727 546-4820
Largo *(G-8015)*
MSA Aircraft Products ....F 772 562-2243
Fort Pierce *(G-4721)*
N23d Services LLC ....G 754 217-3362
Fort Lauderdale *(G-4128)*
National Aerospace Group Inc ....G 817 226-0315
Vero Beach *(G-18646)*
Northstar Aviation USA LLC ....E 321 600-4557
Melbourne *(G-8898)*
Novo Aero Services LLC ....G 786 319-8637
West Palm Beach *(G-18968)*
Pacific Scientific Company ....E 305 477-4711
Medley *(G-8700)*
Parts Cage Inc ....F 904 373-7800
Saint Augustine *(G-15584)*
Pem-Air LLC ....F 954 321-8726
Davie *(G-2568)*
Pem-Air Turbine Eng Svcs LLC ....F 954 321-8726
Davie *(G-2569)*
Piper Aircraft Inc ....A 772 567-4361
Vero Beach *(G-18653)*
Power Flow Systems Inc ....F 386 253-8833
Daytona Beach *(G-2696)*
Pratt & Whitney Eng Svcs Inc ....G 305 512-9882
Miami Lakes *(G-10841)*
Precision Tech Aero Inc ....F 305 603-8347
Miami Lakes *(G-10842)*
Precision Tl Engrg of Gnsville ....F 352 376-2533
Gainesville *(G-4982)*
Quiet Technology Aerospace Inc ....E 305 687-9808
Hollywood *(G-5899)*
R4 Integration Inc ....E 850 226-6913
Fort Walton Beach *(G-4825)*
Radiant Power Corp ....C 941 739-3200
Sarasota *(G-16281)*
Raytheon Technologies Corp ....A 858 277-7639
Jupiter *(G-7103)*
Redstone Corporation ....G 321 213-2135
Merritt Island *(G-9007)*
Rockwell Collins Inc ....G 321 768-7492
Melbourne *(G-8920)*
Rockwell Collins Inc ....G 305 459-7000
Medley *(G-8719)*
Saf Aerospace LLC ....G 813 376-0883
Tampa *(G-18080)*
Safran Power Uk Ltd ....G 941 739-7207
Sarasota *(G-16288)*
Safran Power Usa LLC ....C 941 758-7726
Sarasota *(G-16289)*
Saint-Gobain Corporation ....C 863 425-3299
Mulberry *(G-11135)*
Sal Aerospace Engineering LLC ....F 305 791-0593
Miami *(G-10299)*
Savvy Associate Inc ....F 954 941-6986
Pompano Beach *(G-14840)*
Segers Aerospace Corporation ....E 850 689-2198
Crestview *(G-2357)*
Sensenich Technologies Inc ....G 813 703-8446
Plant City *(G-14464)*
Sidus Space Inc ....E 321 613-0615
Cape Canaveral *(G-1367)*
Signature AVI US Holdings Inc ....F 407 648-7230
Orlando *(G-13193)*
Sky Aerospace Engineering ....G 407 251-7111
Orlando *(G-13195)*
Sky Aerospace Engineering Inc ....G 407 251-7111
Orlando *(G-13196)*
Sky Capital Partners Inc ....G 305 934-8259
Miami *(G-10359)*
Sky Technics Aviation Sls Inc ....G 305 885-7499
Miami *(G-10360)*
Skyhigh Accessories Inc ....G 954 316-3936
Plantation *(G-14552)*
Skymasters Aviation LLC ....G 954 796-7622
Parkland *(G-14001)*
Skyways Technics Americas LLC ....G 786 615-2443
North Miami *(G-11655)*

SMI Tool & Die Inc ....G 321 632-6200
Cocoa *(G-2051)*
Sohacki Industries Inc ....E 904 826-0130
Saint Augustine *(G-15613)*
Solair Group Llc ....E 786 269-0160
Cutler Bay *(G-2412)*
Southeastern Engineering Inc ....F 321 984-2521
Palm Bay *(G-13538)*
Southern Fiberglass Inc ....F 904 387-2246
Jacksonville *(G-6794)*
Southwind Aviation Supply LLC ....F 405 491-0500
Oakland *(G-11771)*
Stat Industry Inc ....F 561 826-7045
Pompano Beach *(G-14868)*
Sunny Skies Enterprises Inc ....E 954 316-6015
North Miami Beach *(G-11705)*
Superior Avionics Inc ....G 954 917-9194
Fort Lauderdale *(G-4268)*
Supliaereos USA LLC ....G 727 754-4915
Clearwater *(G-1897)*
Support Aircraft Parts Inc ....F 305 975-3767
Miami *(G-10441)*
Support Systems Associates Inc ....E 321 724-5566
Melbourne *(G-8952)*
Survival Products Inc ....G 954 966-7329
Sunrise *(G-17182)*
Technology Research Cons Inc ....G 863 419-8860
Haines City *(G-5151)*
Tesco Equipment LLC ....E 954 752-7994
Coral Springs *(G-2322)*
Thales Inflight Entertaiment ....G 786 777-9031
Miami *(G-10472)*
TL Fahringer Co Inc ....G 813 681-2373
Tampa *(G-18190)*
Tobruk International Corp ....G 305 406-0263
Miami *(G-10484)*
TOMI Aircraft Inc ....G 863 446-3001
Deland *(G-3024)*
Tri-Tech of Florida Inc ....F 727 544-8836
Saint Petersburg *(G-15944)*
Tritech Industries LLC ....F 954 383-3545
Oakland Park *(G-11847)*
Triumph Aerostructures LLC ....E 772 463-8700
Stuart *(G-17039)*
Turbine Controls LLC ....D 954 517-1706
Miramar *(G-11054)*
Turbo Aerospace Corp ....G 786 218-8990
Oakland Park *(G-11849)*
Turbocombustor Technology Inc ....B 772 287-7770
Stuart *(G-17041)*
UDC Usa Inc ....E 813 281-0200
Tampa *(G-18211)*
Ultra Aerospace Inc ....F 305 728-6361
Miami *(G-10525)*
Unison Industries LLC ....A 904 739-4000
Jacksonville *(G-6879)*
United Aerospace Corporation ....E 954 364-0085
Miramar *(G-11055)*
United Technologies Corp ....D 954 538-8900
Miramar *(G-11056)*
Universal Crgo Doors & Svc LLC ....E 305 594-9175
Miami *(G-10540)*
UTC Aerospace Systems ....G 954 538-8971
Miramar *(G-11057)*
V-Raptor Aircraft LLC ....G 772 388-3334
Sebastian *(G-16676)*
Velocity Aerospace - Nmb Inc ....E 214 396-9030
North Miami Beach *(G-11708)*
Velocity Aircraft Inc ....G 772 589-1860
Sebastian *(G-16677)*
Ver-Val Enterprises Inc ....F 850 244-7931
Fort Walton Beach *(G-4838)*
Viking Aircraft Engines ....G 386 416-8383
Edgewater *(G-3638)*
Viper Drones Inc ....F 321 427-5837
Indialantic *(G-6061)*
Vision Manufacturing Tech Inc ....E 904 579-5272
Orange Park *(G-12412)*
Vision Systems North America ....F 321 265-5110
Melbourne *(G-8973)*
Willis Aeronautical Svcs Inc ....F 561 272-5402
Coconut Creek *(G-2103)*
Xcalibur Arcft Solutions LLC ....G 305 744-2830
Middleburg *(G-10916)*
Yellow Green Aerospace Inc ....G 954 599-4161
Coral Gables *(G-2208)*

AIRCRAFT PARTS WHOLESALERS

Exodus Management LLC ....G 954 995-4407
Fort Lauderdale *(G-3983)*

Shark Skinz ....G 772 388-9621
Sebastian *(G-16672)*

AIRCRAFT SEATS

Aviation Intl Solutions LLC ....G 305 267-7117
Hialeah *(G-5313)*
B/E Aerospace Inc ....E 410 266-2048
Wellington *(G-18710)*

AIRCRAFT SERVICING & REPAIRING

Chromalloy Gas Turbine LLC ....A 561 935-3571
Palm Beach Gardens *(G-13578)*
Florida Aero Precision Inc ....E 561 848-6248
Lake Park *(G-7471)*
Heli-Tech Inc ....F 850 763-9000
Panama City *(G-13914)*
Vertical Aviation Technologies ....F 407 322-9488
Sanford *(G-16133)*

AIRCRAFT: Airplanes, Fixed Or Rotary Wing

Aerion Corp ....E 775 337-6682
Fort Lauderdale *(G-3787)*
Aviall Inc ....G 954 625-3930
Davie *(G-2501)*
Boeing Company ....G 904 772-1273
Jacksonville *(G-6220)*
Boeing Company ....G 786 265-9965
Virginia Gardens *(G-18684)*
Boeing Company ....G 850 301-6613
Fort Walton Beach *(G-4783)*
Boeing Company ....G 850 882-4912
Eglin Afb *(G-3641)*
Boeing Company ....G 312 544-2000
Titusville *(G-18416)*
J Cube Inc ....F 407 699-6866
Casselberry *(G-1507)*
Northrop Grumman Systems Corp ....C 904 825-3300
Saint Augustine *(G-15576)*
Northrop Grumman Systems Corp ....C 904 825-3300
Saint Augustine *(G-15578)*
Piper Aircraft Inc ....A 772 567-4361
Vero Beach *(G-18653)*
Velocity Inc ....F 772 589-1860
Sebastian *(G-16678)*

AIRCRAFT: Autogiros

Aero Tech Service Assoc Inc ....F 850 286-1378
Tyndall Afb *(G-18493)*
Extreme Crafts LLC ....G 561 989-7400
Boca Raton *(G-526)*

AIRCRAFT: Motorized

Birds Eye Drones LLC ....G 321 355-3415
Windermere *(G-19226)*
Drone Clips By Majic ....G 407 619-3704
Orlando *(G-12686)*
Drone Defense Systems LLC ....G 305 607-6708
Daytona Beach *(G-2659)*
Drone Imaging Services LLC ....G 407 620-5258
Orlando *(G-12687)*
Drone Master Shots LLC ....G 407 295-7715
Orlando *(G-12688)*
Drone Pics and Vids Corp ....G 786 558-4027
Miami *(G-9487)*
Fix n Fly Drones LLC ....G 321 474-2291
Tampa *(G-17667)*
Florida SW Drones LLC ....G 239 785-8337
Cape Coral *(G-1425)*
Inteli Drone Inc ....G 954 707-9547
Coconut Creek *(G-2083)*
Lockheed Martin Corporation ....G 407 356-2000
Orlando *(G-12927)*
Lumenier Holdco LLC ....G 941 444-0021
Sarasota *(G-16491)*
Lumenier LLC ....F 941 444-0021
Sarasota *(G-16492)*
Navmar Applied Sciences Corp ....C 904 423-0927
Jacksonville *(G-6620)*
Riverview Drones Inc ....G 813 451-4744
Riverview *(G-15281)*
Tiger Composites Inc ....F 386 334-0941
New Smyrna Beach *(G-11547)*
Volaero Uav Drnes Hldings Corp ....F 954 261-3105
Sunrise *(G-17197)*

AIRCRAFT: Research & Development, Manufacturer

Kiss Polymers LLC..................F....... 813 962-2703
Tampa *(G-17827)*
Uts Systems LLC..................G....... 850 226-4301
Fort Walton Beach *(G-4837)*

AIRFRAME ASSEMBLIES: Guided Missiles

Atsg Logistic Support Service..................F....... 904 579-4596
Jacksonville *(G-6179)*

AIRLINE TRAINING

Gleim Publications Inc..................D....... 352 375-0772
Gainesville *(G-4931)*

AIRLOCKS

Airlock USA LLC..................F....... 305 888-6454
Miami Springs *(G-10887)*

AIRPORT TERMINAL SVCS

G S Servicore Corp..................E....... 305 888-0189
Hialeah *(G-5420)*

AIRPORTS, FLYING FIELDS & SVCS

Homyn Enterprises Corp..................D....... 305 870-9720
Miami *(G-9718)*
Lift Aerospace Corp..................F....... 305 851-5237
Miami *(G-9890)*
Raytheon Company..................G....... 850 664-7993
Fort Walton Beach *(G-4826)*

ALARM SYSTEMS WHOLESALERS

Ddci Inc..................D....... 407 814-0225
Orlando *(G-12659)*
Incity Security Inc..................F....... 561 306-9228
West Palm Beach *(G-18902)*

ALARMS: Burglar

Carrier Fire SEC Americas Corp..................G....... 828 695-4000
Palm Beach Gardens *(G-13574)*
Ddci Inc..................D....... 407 814-0225
Orlando *(G-12659)*
Keytroller LLC..................F....... 813 877-4500
Tampa *(G-17823)*
Minuteman Industries Inc..................G....... 813 248-1776
Tampa *(G-17909)*
Security Tech Group Inc..................G....... 305 631-2228
Miami *(G-10320)*
Vanguard Products Group Inc..................D....... 813 855-9639
Oldsmar *(G-12277)*

ALARMS: Fire

Superior Fire & Lf Safety Inc..................F....... 850 572-0265
Cape Coral *(G-1480)*

ALCOHOL: Ethyl & Ethanol

Highlands Ethanol LLC..................G....... 813 421-1090
Tampa *(G-17754)*
Omega Energy Usa LLC..................G....... 786 245-0642
Miami *(G-10097)*

ALKALIES & CHLORINE

Bio-Lab Inc..................F....... 863 709-1411
Lakeland *(G-7646)*
Buckeye International Inc..................G....... 813 621-6260
Tampa *(G-17488)*
Universal Transactions Inc..................E....... 305 887-4677
Medley *(G-8750)*

ALKALOIDS & OTHER BOTANICAL BASED PRDTS

US Nutraceuticals Inc..................E....... 352 357-2004
Eustis *(G-3720)*

ALLOYS: Additive, Exc Copper Or Made In Blast Furnaces

Beehive3d Inc..................G....... 954 560-9513
Deerfield Beach *(G-2784)*

ALTERNATORS & GENERATORS: Battery Charging

Cleva Technologies LLC..................F....... 561 654-5279
Boca Raton *(G-485)*

ALTERNATORS: Automotive

Central Fla Remanufacturing..................G....... 407 299-9011
Orlando *(G-12563)*
Suncoast Automotive Pdts Inc..................F....... 954 973-4822
Pompano Beach *(G-14879)*
T R S..................E....... 407 298-5490
Orlando *(G-13238)*

ALUMINUM

AJs Aluminum Inc..................G....... 352 688-7631
Spring Hill *(G-16845)*
All Coast Manufacturing Inc..................G....... 813 626-2264
Tampa *(G-17398)*
Alumacart Inc..................F....... 772 675-2158
Hobe Sound *(G-5721)*
Benchmark Aluminum Inc..................G....... 941 585-9977
Port Charlotte *(G-14964)*
Charleston Aluminum LLC..................F....... 305 628-4014
Hialeah *(G-5342)*
Eastern Metal Supply Inc..................F....... 863 682-6660
Lakeland *(G-7679)*
Florida Sales & Marketing..................E....... 239 274-3103
Fort Myers *(G-4451)*
Glassarium LLC..................E....... 786 631-7080
Miami *(G-9639)*
Ideal Deals LLC..................C....... 386 736-1700
Saint Augustine *(G-15553)*
Jmn Aluminum..................G....... 813 325-7807
Tampa *(G-17807)*
Mary Lame Wrought Iron & Alum..................G....... 727 934-2879
Holiday *(G-5747)*
Shelmet Corp..................G....... 561 688-9700
West Palm Beach *(G-19030)*
Streamline Aluminum Inc..................F....... 239 561-7200
Fort Myers *(G-4612)*

ALUMINUM PRDTS

Absolute Aluminum Inc..................D....... 941 497-7777
Venice *(G-18526)*
Aldora Aluminum & GL Pdts Inc..................E....... 954 441-5057
Coral Springs *(G-2219)*
Aludisc LLC..................E....... 910 299-0911
Boca Raton *(G-416)*
Alumacart Inc..................F....... 772 675-2158
Hobe Sound *(G-5721)*
Aluminum Products Whl Inc..................G....... 904 268-4895
Jacksonville *(G-6144)*
Alumitech Inc..................F....... 407 826-5373
Orlando *(G-12463)*
American Products Inc..................G....... 813 925-0144
Tampa *(G-17418)*
American Windows Shutters Inc..................E....... 239 278-3066
Fort Myers *(G-4359)*
Architctral Mtal Flashings LLC..................F....... 239 221-0123
Cape Coral *(G-1383)*
Associated Steel & Alum Co Inc..................F....... 954 974-7890
Pompano Beach *(G-14603)*
Benada Aluminum Products LLC..................C....... 407 323-3300
Sanford *(G-16002)*
Cline Aluminum Doors Inc..................E....... 941 746-4104
Bradenton *(G-1021)*
Cross Key Marine Canvas Inc..................G....... 305 451-1302
Key Largo *(G-7167)*
Eagle Metal Distributors Inc..................G....... 407 367-0688
Orlando *(G-12693)*
Expert Shutter Services Inc..................D....... 772 871-1915
Port Saint Lucie *(G-15108)*
Florida Extruders Intl Inc..................D....... 407 323-3300
Sanford *(G-16049)*
Global Aluminum Solutions LLC..................G....... 954 636-4143
Pembroke Pines *(G-14036)*
Gulf Electronics..................F....... 727 595-3840
Largo *(G-7967)*
Jupiter Industries LLC..................G....... 239 225-9041
Fort Myers *(G-4508)*
Karnak South Inc..................F....... 954 761-7606
Fort Lauderdale *(G-4084)*
Keymark Corporation Florida..................C....... 863 858-5500
Lakeland *(G-7727)*
Largo Aluminum Inc..................F....... 305 852-2390
Islamorada *(G-6098)*
Liberty Aluminum Co..................E....... 239 369-3000
Lehigh Acres *(G-8197)*
Magic Tilt Trailer Mfg Co Inc..................E....... 727 535-5561
Clearwater *(G-1769)*
Mary Lame Wrought Iron & Alum..................G....... 727 934-2879
Holiday *(G-5747)*
Metal Container Corporation..................C....... 904 695-7600
Jacksonville *(G-6596)*
Metals USA Holdings Corp..................A....... 954 202-4000
Fort Lauderdale *(G-4118)*
Naples Iron Works Inc..................E....... 239 649-7265
Naples *(G-11336)*
Nav-X LLC..................E....... 954 978-9988
Fort Lauderdale *(G-4134)*
RDS Manufacturing Inc..................C....... 850 584-6898
Perry *(G-14310)*
Rolling Shield Incorporated..................E....... 305 436-6661
Miami Lakes *(G-10852)*
Sapa Prcsion Tubing Adrian Inc..................E....... 321 636-8147
Rockledge *(G-15446)*
Sinobec Resources LLC..................G....... 561 409-2205
Deerfield Beach *(G-2912)*
Snappy Structures Inc..................F....... 954 926-6611
Hollywood *(G-5910)*
Style-View Products Inc..................F....... 305 634-9688
Miami *(G-10426)*
Super Lite Aluminum Products..................G....... 407 682-2121
Altamonte Springs *(G-78)*
T and C Sales Inc..................G....... 321 632-0920
Rockledge *(G-15450)*
Te Olde Foundry Shoppe Inc..................G....... 239 261-3911
Naples *(G-11436)*
Titan Specialty Cnstr Inc..................E....... 850 916-7660
Milton *(G-10943)*

ALUMINUM: Coil & Sheet

Polytech International LLC..................F....... 904 354-9355
Jacksonville *(G-6678)*

ALUMINUM: Ingots & Slabs

Gyrosolar Corp..................G....... 954 554-9990
Weston *(G-19136)*

ALUMINUM: Pigs

Tru Mension Mfg Solutions..................G....... 321 255-4665
Melbourne *(G-8967)*

ALUMINUM: Rolling & Drawing

Aluminium Design Products LLC..................G....... 561 894-8775
Delray Beach *(G-3045)*
Carmacks Quality Aluminum..................G....... 727 846-0305
Port Richey *(G-15044)*
Spectra Metal Sales Inc..................F....... 727 530-5435
Clearwater *(G-1887)*

AMMONIA & AMMONIUM SALTS

Freeport Ammonia LLC..................G....... 813 222-3813
Tampa *(G-17695)*

AMMUNITION

Arma Holdings Inc..................E....... 813 402-0667
Tampa *(G-17434)*
Dse Inc..................E....... 813 443-4809
Tampa *(G-17617)*
General Dynmics Ord Tctcal Sys..................C....... 727 578-8100
Saint Petersburg *(G-15791)*
Global Ordnance LLC..................E....... 941 549-8388
Sarasota *(G-16221)*
Gti Systems Inc..................E....... 863 965-2002
Auburndale *(G-245)*
Kaman Precision Products Inc..................C....... 407 282-1000
Orlando *(G-12865)*

AMMUNITION: Components

Energy Technical Systems Inc..................F....... 850 223-2393
Perry *(G-14299)*
Syrac Ordnance Inc..................G....... 727 612-6090
New Port Richey *(G-11515)*

AMMUNITION: Mines & Parts, Ordnance

Carbon Mine Supply LLC..................G....... 606 437-9905
Bradenton *(G-1013)*

AMMUNITION: Paper Shells, Empty, Blank/Loaded, 30mm & Below

Boland Production Supply Inc..................G....... 863 324-7784
Winter Haven *(G-19304)*

AMMUNITION: Rockets

Cesaroni Aerospace Inc ....E 941 400-1421
Bowling Green *(G-865)*

AMMUNITION: Shot, Steel

Hyperion Munitions Inc ....F 844 622-8339
Largo *(G-7977)*

AMMUNITION: Small Arms

Arms East LLC ....G 561 293-2915
Bradenton *(G-991)*
Degraaff Inc ....G 305 451-4460
Key Largo *(G-7168)*
Energy Technical Systems Inc ....F 850 223-2393
Perry *(G-14299)*
General Dynmics Ord Tctcal Sys ....C 727 578-8100
Saint Petersburg *(G-15791)*
Global Ordnance LLC ....E 941 549-8388
Sarasota *(G-16221)*
Gti Systems Inc ....E 863 965-2002
Auburndale *(G-245)*
Jsn Blue Thunder LLC ....G 786 398-5222
Miami *(G-9809)*
L C Npee ....E 888 316-3718
Hialeah *(G-5479)*
Paul Wong ....G 863 465-1114
Lake Placid *(G-7492)*
Pcp Tactical LLC ....G 772 473-3472
Vero Beach *(G-18652)*
Precision Ammunition LLC ....G 813 626-0077
Tampa *(G-18003)*
Wide Open Armory LLC ....G 727 202-5980
Seminole *(G-16771)*

AMPLIFIERS

Astra Products Co Inc Tampa ....E 813 855-3021
Oldsmar *(G-12206)*
Dj Live Productions LLC ....G 407 383-1740
Altamonte Springs *(G-41)*
Hki Soundigital USA LLC ....G 786 600-1056
Dania *(G-2446)*
Valvetrain Amplification ....G 407 886-7656
Apopka *(G-194)*

AMPLIFIERS: Pulse Amplifiers

Pulse Displays LLC ....G 314 971-8700
Wesley Chapel *(G-18757)*

AMPLIFIERS: RF & IF Power

Analog Modules Inc ....D 407 339-4355
Longwood *(G-8255)*

AMUSEMENT & REC SVCS: Attractions, Concessions & Rides

3 D F X Inc ....F 407 237-6249
Orlando *(G-12416)*

AMUSEMENT & RECREATION SVCS: Gambling & Lottery Svcs

Ocala Breeders Sales Co Inc ....E 352 237-4667
Ocala *(G-12007)*

AMUSEMENT & RECREATION SVCS: Night Club, Exc Alcoholic Bev

A2f LLC ....G 305 984-9205
Miami *(G-9048)*

AMUSEMENT & RECREATION SVCS: Swimming Pool, Non-Membership

South West Adventure Team LLC ....G 903 288-4739
Labelle *(G-7323)*

AMUSEMENT & RECREATION SVCS: Theme Park

3 D F X Inc ....F 407 237-6249
Orlando *(G-12416)*
Anheuser-Busch Companies LLC ....D 407 251-4049
Orlando *(G-12480)*

AMUSEMENT & RECREATION SVCS: Tourist Attraction, Commercial

Biotoxins Inc ....G 407 892-6905
Saint Cloud *(G-15646)*

AMUSEMENT MACHINES: Coin Operated

Flushing Amusement Inc ....G 813 780-7900
Zephyrhills *(G-19520)*
Fuller Amusements ....G 352 629-2792
Ocala *(G-11951)*

AMUSEMENT PARK DEVICES & RIDES

3 D F X Inc ....F 407 237-6249
Orlando *(G-12416)*
Bobs Space Racers Inc ....C 386 677-0761
Daytona Beach *(G-2631)*
Skyline Attractions LLC ....F 407 587-0080
Orlando *(G-13197)*
Vertical Reality Inc ....G 305 238-4522
Palmetto Bay *(G-13856)*
Vertical Reality Mfg Inc ....G 305 238-4522
Palmetto Bay *(G-13857)*
West Coast Wonderworks LLC ....G 407 351-8800
Orlando *(G-13321)*

AMUSEMENT PARK DEVICES & RIDES: Carnival Mach & Eqpt, NEC

Entech Onsite Services LLC ....G 407 956-8980
Rockledge *(G-15409)*
Transport PC USA Inc ....G 813 264-1700
Wesley Chapel *(G-18760)*

AMUSEMENT PARKS

United Trophy Manufacturing ....E 407 841-2525
Orlando *(G-13294)*

ANALGESICS

Grunenthal Services Inc ....F 786 364-6308
Miami *(G-9678)*

ANALYZERS: Network

Akuwa Solutions Group Inc ....F 941 343-9947
Sarasota *(G-16337)*
C2c Innovated Technology LLC ....G 251 382-2277
Bonifay *(G-800)*
Gray Information Solutions Inc ....G 352 684-6655
Spring Hill *(G-16854)*
High Yield AG Solutions LLC ....G 407 592-8089
Lake Mary *(G-7422)*
Ideasgt Corp ....G 786 370-7767
Miami *(G-9730)*
Jones Mediaamerica Inc ....B 305 289-4524
Marathon *(G-8518)*
Lee Net Services Inc ....G 904 777-4833
Jacksonville *(G-6552)*
Meg Systems Inc ....G 239 263-5833
Naples *(G-11326)*
Wink Streaming Llc ....G 312 281-5444
Miami *(G-10611)*

ANALYZERS: Petroleum Prdts

Roper Technologies Inc ....E 941 556-2601
Sarasota *(G-16563)*

ANALYZERS: Respiratory

Airehealth Inc ....F 407 280-4107
Winter Springs *(G-19467)*
Respitrend Inc ....G 407 529-5888
Gainesville *(G-4990)*

ANESTHESIA EQPT

Biorep Technologies Inc ....F 305 330-4449
Miami Lakes *(G-10770)*
Eagle Eye Anesthesia Inc ....G 817 999-9830
Jacksonville *(G-6345)*

ANIMAL BASED MEDICINAL CHEMICAL PRDTS

Ceva Animal Health LLC ....F 727 548-8345
Oldsmar *(G-12214)*

ANIMAL FEED & SUPPLEMENTS: Livestock & Poultry

AB Vista Inc ....G 954 278-3965
Plantation *(G-14483)*
B&K Country Feeds LLC ....G 561 701-1852
West Palm Beach *(G-18810)*
BRT Oakleaf Pet Inc ....G 904 563-1212
Jacksonville *(G-6239)*
Buddy Custard Inc ....G 561 715-3785
Fort Lauderdale *(G-3874)*
Dalian Platinum Chem Ltd Corp ....G 954 501-0564
Fort Lauderdale *(G-3931)*
Furst-Mcness Company ....G 386 755-5605
Lake City *(G-7355)*
Griffin Industries LLC ....E 904 964-8083
Starke *(G-16894)*
Higgins Group Corp ....E 305 681-4444
Miami *(G-9709)*
Nulab Inc ....D 727 446-1126
Clearwater *(G-1813)*
Plantation Botanicals Inc ....E 863 675-2984
Felda *(G-3722)*
Purina Animal Nutrition LLC ....F 863 262-4332
Lakeland *(G-7772)*
Swans Feed Mill ....G 813 782-6969
Zephyrhills *(G-19539)*

ANIMAL FOOD & SUPPLEMENTS: Chicken Feeds, Prepared

Backyard Feed LLC ....G 813 846-5995
Saint Augustine *(G-15521)*
Zephyr Feed Company Inc ....G 813 782-1578
Zephyrhills *(G-19543)*

ANIMAL FOOD & SUPPLEMENTS: Citrus Seed Meal

Tropicana Products Inc ....A 941 747-4461
Bradenton *(G-1133)*

ANIMAL FOOD & SUPPLEMENTS: Dog

Snif-Snax Ltd ....F 786 613-7007
Miami *(G-10368)*
Synergy Labs Inc ....E 954 525-1133
Fort Lauderdale *(G-4271)*

ANIMAL FOOD & SUPPLEMENTS: Dog & Cat

All American Pet Company Inc ....F 561 337-5340
Palm Beach Gardens *(G-13565)*
Natural Crvings Pet Treats LLC ....G 786 404-8099
Homestead *(G-5985)*
Zesty Paws LLC ....E 407 358-6601
Orlando *(G-13340)*

ANIMAL FOOD & SUPPLEMENTS: Feed Premixes

Agranco Corp (usa) ....F 877 592-0031
South Miami *(G-16811)*
Dairy Feeds Inc ....G 863 763-0258
Okeechobee *(G-12175)*

ANIMAL FOOD & SUPPLEMENTS: Feed Supplements

Animal Business Concepts LLC ....F 727 641-6176
Saint Petersburg *(G-15701)*
Coronet Industries Inc ....E 813 752-1161
Plant City *(G-14420)*
Mr Gummy Vitamins LLC ....G 855 674-8669
Opa Locka *(G-12341)*
Special Nutrients LLC ....F 305 857-9830
Coconut Grove *(G-2105)*

ANIMAL FOOD & SUPPLEMENTS: Hay, Cubed

Hay Tech ....G 850 592-2424
Bascom *(G-336)*

ANIMAL FOOD & SUPPLEMENTS: Livestock

Branch Properties Inc ....D 352 732-4143
Ocala *(G-11890)*
Gator Feed Co Inc ....F 863 763-3337
Okeechobee *(G-12179)*

Monticello Milling Co Inc.......................G....... 850 997-5521
Monticello *(G-11079)*
Ocala Breeders Sales Co Inc.................E....... 352 237-4667
Ocala *(G-12007)*

ANIMAL FOOD & SUPPLEMENTS: Mineral feed supplements

Heal and Shine Inc.................................G....... 561 801-3423
Royal Palm Beach *(G-15469)*
Stratford Care Usa Inc...........................G....... 877 498-2002
Odessa *(G-12157)*

ANIMAL FOOD & SUPPLEMENTS: Pet, Exc Dog & Cat, Dry

Perfectus Pet Food LLC.........................G....... 800 774-3296
Hollywood *(G-5890)*

ANIMAL FOOD & SUPPLEMENTS: Pet, Exc Dog & Cat, Frozen

Seminole Stores Inc...............................F....... 352 732-4143
Ocala *(G-12044)*

ANIMAL FOOD & SUPPLEMENTS: Rolled Oats

Paws Off Prime K9 Cuisine LLC...........G....... 305 546-7475
Miami *(G-10145)*

ANIMAL FOOD & SUPPLEMENTS: Specialty, Mice & Other Pets

Karnak Corporation.................................G....... 352 481-4145
East Palatka *(G-3604)*

ANODIZING EQPT

Al Stein Industries LLC...........................F....... 727 329-8755
Largo *(G-7889)*

ANODIZING SVC

AM Metal Finishing...................................E....... 407 843-0182
Orlando *(G-12464)*
Certified Metal Finishing Inc..................E....... 954 979-0707
Pompano Beach *(G-14633)*
David Russell Anodizing.........................G....... 407 302-4041
Sanford *(G-16032)*
Dhs Enterprises Inc.................................G....... 727 572-9470
Clearwater *(G-1651)*
Gti Systems Inc.......................................E....... 863 965-2002
Auburndale *(G-245)*
Peninsula Metal Finishing Inc................E....... 407 291-1023
Orlando *(G-13059)*
Russell Bros Alum Andzing Ctin...........F....... 407 323-5619
Sanford *(G-16113)*

ANTENNAS: Radar Or Communications

ARC Group Worldwide Inc.......................D....... 303 467-5236
Deland *(G-2959)*
Bluesky Mast Inc.....................................F....... 877 411-6278
Largo *(G-7911)*
Frontier Electronics.................................G....... 954 255-0911
Micanopy *(G-10900)*
Maxxfi LLC...F....... 513 289-6521
Cape Coral *(G-1447)*
Pinnacle Cmmncations Group LLC.......F....... 904 910-0444
Jacksonville *(G-6674)*
Techcodes LLC...G....... 321 529-4122
Titusville *(G-18467)*

ANTENNAS: Receiving

Concept Group LLC..................................F....... 856 767-5506
Palm Beach Gardens *(G-13582)*
Digital Antenna Inc..................................F....... 954 747-7022
Sunrise *(G-17115)*
Hascall Engineering and Mfg Co...........F....... 941 723-2833
Palmetto *(G-13805)*
Niftys Inc...F....... 786 878-4725
Miami *(G-10073)*

ANTENNAS: Satellite, Household Use

All Things Digital Inc................................E....... 305 887-9464
Miami *(G-9113)*
Micro-Ant LLC...D....... 904 683-8394
Jacksonville *(G-6602)*

ANTIFREEZE

Global Diversified Products....................E....... 727 209-0854
Pinellas Park *(G-14351)*

ANTIQUE SHOPS

Finns Brass and Silver Polsg................G....... 904 387-1165
Jacksonville *(G-6381)*

APARTMENT LOCATING SVCS

United Advg Publications Inc.................G....... 407 297-0832
Altamonte Springs *(G-81)*

APPAREL ACCESS STORES

Walter Green Inc.......................................G....... 850 227-7946
Port Saint Joe *(G-15084)*
Zayas Fashions Inc...................................E....... 305 823-1438
Hialeah *(G-5695)*

APPAREL DESIGNERS: Commercial

Shgar Kane Couture Inc..........................G....... 407 205-8038
Orlando *(G-13181)*

APPAREL PRESSING SVCS

Blue Ocean Press Inc...............................E....... 954 973-1819
Fort Lauderdale *(G-3859)*

APPAREL: Hand Woven

Point Blank Intrmdate Hldg LLC.............E....... 954 630-0900
Pompano Beach *(G-14802)*

APPLIANCE PARTS: Porcelain Enameled

Boca Stone Designs.................................F....... 561 362-2085
Boca Raton *(G-458)*

APPLIANCE REPAIR

Tri-Tech Electronics Inc..........................D....... 407 277-2131
Orlando *(G-13270)*

APPLIANCES, HOUSEHOLD: Drycleaning Machines, Incl Coin-Op

Japan Fabricare Inc.................................G....... 407 366-9986
Oviedo *(G-13441)*

APPLIANCES, HOUSEHOLD: Kitchen, Major, Exc Refrigs & Stoves

Appliances To Go Usa Llc.......................G....... 239 278-0811
Cape Coral *(G-1381)*
Clean Cut Intl LLC....................................F....... 866 599-7066
Juno Beach *(G-6978)*
Deers Holdings Inc..................................G....... 805 323-6899
Bay Harbor Islands *(G-338)*
Dka Distributing LLC...............................G....... 800 275-4352
Tampa *(G-17610)*
Kappa Metal USA Inc...............................G....... 954 757-7100
Coconut Creek *(G-2087)*
La Cuisine Intl Distrs Inc........................E....... 305 418-0010
Miami *(G-9839)*
Minea Usa Llc...F....... 800 971-3216
Coral Gables *(G-2177)*
Unique Designs & Finishes Inc..............F....... 772 335-4884
Port Saint Lucie *(G-15159)*

APPLIANCES: Household, NEC

Mia Appliances LLC..................................G....... 866 670-4860
Miami *(G-9988)*

APPLIANCES: Household, Refrigerators & Freezers

Acme Service Corp...................................F....... 305 836-4800
Miami *(G-9065)*
GE Consumer Corporation......................D....... 904 696-9775
Jacksonville *(G-6429)*
Wine Plum Inc...F....... 844 856-7586
Dania Beach *(G-2475)*

APPLIANCES: Major, Cooking

Creative Home and Kitchen LLC............F....... 786 233-8621
Doral *(G-3312)*

APPLIANCES: Small, Electric

American Household Inc..........................D....... 561 912-4100
Boca Raton *(G-422)*
Avstar Systems LLC.................................G....... 239 793-5511
Naples *(G-11177)*
Clean Cut Intl LLC....................................F....... 866 599-7066
Juno Beach *(G-6978)*
Eaton Corporation....................................G....... 813 281-8069
Tampa *(G-17628)*
Flash Sales Inc..G....... 954 914-2689
Miami Gardens *(G-10741)*
Sunbeam Americas Holdings LLC........C....... 561 912-4100
Boca Raton *(G-736)*
Sunbeam Products Inc.............................B....... 561 912-4100
Boca Raton *(G-738)*
Uniware Houseware Corp.......................E....... 305 952-4958
Miami Lakes *(G-10875)*

APPLICATIONS SOFTWARE PROGRAMMING

Channel Logistics LLC.............................E....... 856 614-5441
Miami *(G-9348)*
Hummingbirds Ai Inc................................F....... 305 432-2787
Miami Beach *(G-10680)*
Sachi Tech Inc...F....... 813 649-8028
Tampa *(G-18079)*
Sleepy Dragon Studios Inc......................G....... 561 714-6156
Cutler Bay *(G-2411)*

AQUARIUM ACCESS, METAL

Endless Oceans LLC................................G....... 561 274-1990
Delray Beach *(G-3073)*

AQUARIUM DESIGN & MAINTENANCE SVCS

Endless Oceans LLC................................G....... 561 274-1990
Delray Beach *(G-3073)*

AQUARIUMS & ACCESS: Glass

Carib Sea Inc...E....... 772 461-1113
Fort Pierce *(G-4683)*
Endless Oceans LLC................................G....... 561 274-1990
Delray Beach *(G-3073)*
Living Color Enterprises Inc...................E....... 954 970-9511
Deerfield Beach *(G-2863)*
Shark Tooth Enterprises Inc...................E....... 904 449-8247
Green Cove Springs *(G-5071)*
Waterbox Usa LLC....................................G....... 800 674-2608
Longwood *(G-8349)*

AQUARIUMS & ACCESS: Plastic

Endless Oceans LLC................................G....... 561 274-1990
Delray Beach *(G-3073)*

ARCHITECTURAL SVCS

Foam By Design Inc..................................E....... 727 561-7479
Clearwater *(G-1692)*
J A Custom Fabricators Inc....................F....... 561 615-4680
Lake Worth *(G-7559)*
Lightnet Usa Inc..F....... 305 260-6444
Miami *(G-9891)*
Southwest Woodwork Inc.........................F....... 239 213-0126
Naples *(G-11411)*

ARMATURE REPAIRING & REWINDING SVC

New Generation Aerospace Inc..............G....... 305 882-1410
Medley *(G-8696)*

ARMATURES: Automotive

Unia International Corp............................G....... 954 404-6076
Pembroke Pines *(G-14069)*

ARMOR PLATES

Automotive Armor Mfg Inc......................F....... 941 721-3335
Palmetto *(G-13788)*

AROMATIC CHEMICAL PRDTS

Tsd Group Corp...F....... 954 940-2111
Sunrise *(G-17191)*
Warehouse Goods LLC............................E....... 877 865-2260
Boca Raton *(G-787)*

ART & ORNAMENTAL WARE: Pottery

Ronald M Hart Inc.....................................G....... 772 600-8497
Stuart *(G-17003)*

ART DEALERS & GALLERIES

Brandine Woodcraft Inc ....G....... 561 266-9360
Delray Beach *(G-3051)*

ART DESIGN SVCS

Doral Dgtal Reprographics Corp...........G....... 305 704-3194
Doral *(G-3333)*
Liteworks Lighting Productions...........G....... 407 888-8677
Orlando *(G-12916)*

ART MARBLE: Concrete

Geigel Marble & Design LLC.................G....... 305 301-0399
Key Biscayne *(G-7156)*
Kitchen & Bath Center Inc....................E....... 850 244-3996
Fort Walton Beach *(G-4812)*
Maxrodon Marble Inc.............................G....... 772 562-7543
Vero Beach *(G-18642)*

ART SPLY STORES

Art & Frame Direct Inc..........................C....... 407 857-6000
Orlando *(G-12491)*

ARTIFICIAL FLOWERS & TREES

Botanical Innovations Inc......................G....... 407 332-8733
Maitland *(G-8460)*
International Greenscapes LLC............D....... 760 631-6789
Miami *(G-9758)*

ARTISTS' EQPT

Sculpture House Inc..............................F....... 609 466-2986
Fort Pierce *(G-4743)*

ARTISTS' MATERIALS: Clay, Modeling

Standard Clay Mines..............................G....... 609 466-2986
Fort Pierce *(G-4751)*

ARTISTS' MATERIALS: Frames, Artists' Canvases

Art & Frame Direct Inc..........................C....... 407 857-6000
Orlando *(G-12491)*
Art & Frame Source Inc.........................E....... 727 329-6502
Saint Petersburg *(G-15711)*
M&M Studios Inc...................................G....... 561 744-2754
Jupiter *(G-7070)*

ARTISTS' MATERIALS: Pencils & Leads

Dixon Ticonderoga Company................D....... 407 829-9000
Lake Mary *(G-7409)*

ARTWORK: Framed

Crystal Art of Florida Inc......................G....... 305 885-5358
Coral Springs *(G-2235)*
Lakeridge Falls Art League...................G....... 941 360-1046
Sarasota *(G-16247)*
Ngf Distributors Inc..............................F....... 407 816-7554
Oviedo *(G-13449)*

ASBESTOS PRDTS: Pipe Covering, Heat Insulatng Matl, Exc Felt

Cahill Construction Services.................G....... 239 369-9290
Lehigh Acres *(G-8186)*

ASBESTOS PRODUCTS

American Coatings Corporation............G....... 954 970-7820
Margate *(G-8535)*

ASBESTOS REMOVAL EQPT

Mold Remediation Services Inc.............G....... 904 574-5266
Jacksonville *(G-6612)*

ASPHALT & ASPHALT PRDTS

Blacklidge Emulsions Inc.......................F....... 954 275-7225
Pompano Beach *(G-14619)*
Group III Asphalt Inc..............................F....... 850 983-0611
Milton *(G-10931)*

ASPHALT COATINGS & SEALERS

Acryfin Coatings LLC............................G....... 772 631-3899
Stuart *(G-16902)*
All American Sealcoating LLC...............G....... 305 961-1655
Miami *(G-9108)*
Aristcrete Coating Experts LLC.............G....... 386 882-3660
Ormond Beach *(G-13349)*
C C Lead Inc...F....... 863 465-6458
Lake Placid *(G-7486)*
Campen Companies..............................G....... 904 388-6000
Jacksonville *(G-6250)*
Carpenters Roofg & Shtmtl Inc..............E....... 561 833-0341
Riviera Beach *(G-15310)*
Coatings Smples Sltons Etc LLC...........G....... 863 398-8513
Lakeland *(G-7660)*
Coma Cast Corp.....................................E....... 305 667-6797
Miami *(G-9385)*
Elliott Custom Coatings LLC..................G....... 407 734-5221
Orlando *(G-12706)*
Harsco Corporation...............................F....... 717 506-2071
Tampa *(G-17745)*
Hco Holding I Corporation.....................F....... 863 533-0522
Bartow *(G-318)*
High Sierra Terminaling LLC..................F....... 954 764-8818
Fort Lauderdale *(G-4047)*
Knights Powder Coating LLC.................G....... 727 906-5130
Tarpon Springs *(G-18312)*
Metro Roof Tile Inc................................F....... 863 467-0042
Medley *(G-8690)*
Monier Lifetile Inc..................................G....... 561 338-8200
Boca Raton *(G-631)*
Monier Lifetile LLC.................................G....... 561 338-8200
Boca Raton *(G-632)*
NP Industrial Coating Inc.......................G....... 727 485-6113
Tarpon Springs *(G-18317)*
Randel L Rdriguez Coatings LLC...........G....... 386 308-8120
Daytona Beach *(G-2702)*
Sargeant Bulk Asphalt Inc.....................G....... 954 763-4796
Deerfield Beach *(G-2906)*
Standard Industries Inc..........................D....... 813 248-7000
Tampa *(G-18129)*
Super Stone Inc......................................E....... 305 681-3561
Opa Locka *(G-12362)*
Tropical Asphalt LLC.............................F....... 954 983-3434
Hallandale *(G-5164)*

ASPHALT MINING & BITUMINOUS STONE QUARRYING SVCS

Coraldom Usa LLC.................................G....... 305 716-0200
Miami *(G-9402)*

ASPHALT PLANTS INCLUDING GRAVEL MIX TYPE

D A B Constructors Inc..........................G....... 352 797-3537
Brooksville *(G-1224)*
Gencor Industries Inc............................C....... 407 290-6000
Orlando *(G-12776)*
Hco Holding I Corporation.....................F....... 863 533-0522
Bartow *(G-318)*
S T Wooten Corporation.........................E....... 239 337-9486
Fort Myers *(G-4591)*

ASSEMBLIES: Exciter, Motor Or Generator Parts

Chism Manufacturing Svcs LLC.............F....... 941 896-9671
Sarasota *(G-16190)*

ASSEMBLING SVC: Clocks

LP Watch Group Inc...............................E....... 954 985-3827
Hollywood *(G-5863)*
TWN Industries Inc................................G....... 305 246-5717
Princeton *(G-15187)*

ASSEMBLING SVC: Plumbing Fixture Fittings, Plastic

M & C Assemblies Inc............................A....... 800 462-7779
Tarpon Springs *(G-18314)*

ASSOCIATIONS: Business

Raytheon Technologies Corp.................A....... 858 277-7639
Jupiter *(G-7103)*
S E Inc...E....... 407 859-9317
Orlando *(G-13151)*

ASSOCIATIONS: Manufacturers'

William Byrd & Sons Inc........................G....... 786 573-3251
Palmetto Bay *(G-13858)*

ASSOCIATIONS: Trade

American Welding Society Inc...............D....... 305 443-9353
Doral *(G-3247)*

ATHLETIC CLUB & GYMNASIUMS, MEMBERSHIP

Cheval Country Club..............................G....... 813 279-5122
Dunedin *(G-3573)*

ATLASES

American Atlas Corp..............................G....... 904 273-6090
Ponte Vedra Beach *(G-14932)*

ATOMIZERS

Audio Excellence....................................G....... 407 277-8790
Orlando *(G-12500)*
Debut Development LLC........................G....... 863 448-9081
Wauchula *(G-18690)*
Enduris Extrusions Inc...........................E....... 321 914-0897
Melbourne *(G-8825)*
Gulfstream Goodwill Inds Inc.................E....... 561 362-8662
Boca Raton *(G-554)*
Horizon Industries Inc............................F....... 561 315-5439
Royal Palm Beach *(G-15470)*
Jta Industries LLC..................................F....... 321 663-4395
Orlando *(G-12864)*
Lane Shark Usa LLC..............................G....... 864 382-6892
Mc David *(G-8601)*
Lov Industries Inc..................................G....... 407 406-8221
Kissimmee *(G-7272)*
Manufacturing Martin LLC Kls...............F....... 904 641-0421
Jacksonville *(G-6578)*
Massimo Roma LLC...............................G....... 561 302-5998
Miami *(G-9953)*
Rar Industries LLC.................................G....... 561 213-7876
Boynton Beach *(G-953)*
Real Gold Inc..G....... 386 873-4849
Deland *(G-3010)*
Richter Industries Inc.............................G....... 239 732-9440
Naples *(G-11384)*
Riley & Company Inc.............................F....... 407 265-9963
Sanford *(G-16110)*
SBC International Group Inc..................F....... 305 506-5638
Hialeah *(G-5611)*
Seaboard Manufacturing LLC................G....... 727 497-3572
Clearwater *(G-1872)*
Strictly Ecommerce................................G....... 352 672-6566
Gainesville *(G-5004)*
Techniflex LLC.......................................E....... 561 235-0844
Boca Raton *(G-743)*
Tekna Manufacturing LLC......................G....... 813 782-6700
Zephyrhills *(G-19541)*
Thor Manufacturing Inc.........................F....... 866 955-8467
Boca Raton *(G-750)*

AUCTIONEERS: Fee Basis

Ocala Breeders Sales Co Inc.................E....... 352 237-4667
Ocala *(G-12007)*

AUDIO & VIDEO EQPT, EXC COMMERCIAL

Andrew Mj Inc...G....... 561 575-6032
Jupiter *(G-7000)*
Attack Communications Inc...................G....... 954 300-2716
Fort Lauderdale *(G-3831)*
Audioshark Inc..G....... 954 591-9252
Hollywood *(G-5778)*
AVI-Spl Holdings Inc..............................A....... 866 708-5034
Tampa *(G-17446)*
AVI-Spl LLC..A....... 813 884-7168
Tampa *(G-17447)*
Da Vinci Systems Inc..............................G....... 954 688-5600
Coral Springs *(G-2236)*
Gocase LLC..G....... 415 341-6248
Miami Beach *(G-10673)*
Gulf Coast Beach Cams LLC..................G....... 850 792-4617
Miramar Beach *(G-11066)*
K & A Audio Inc......................................F....... 941 925-7648
Sarasota *(G-16478)*
Mdt Technologies Inc.............................G....... 305 308-2902
Medley *(G-8686)*
Nowvision Technologies Inc...................G....... 813 943-4639
Lutz *(G-8406)*
Padgett Communications Inc................E....... 727 323-5800
Tampa *(G-17969)*
Perpetual Marketing Assoc Inc.............G....... 813 949-9385
Lutz *(G-8408)*

PRODUCT

Philips North America LLC ....D 305 969-7447
Miami *(G-10158)*
Raytheon Company ....G 727 768-8468
Largo *(G-8037)*
Raytheon Company ....C 310 647-9438
Largo *(G-8036)*
S N S Auto Sports LLC ....G 727 546-2700
Pinellas Park *(G-14386)*
Voxx International Corporation ....B 800 645-7750
Orlando *(G-13313)*
Wireworld By David Salz Inc ....E 954 474-4464
Davie *(G-2616)*
Wizard Labs ....G 321 422-0803
Altamonte Springs *(G-84)*

AUDIO COMPONENTS

Singing Machine Company Inc ....F 954 596-1000
Fort Lauderdale *(G-4236)*
Sound Anchors Inc ....G 321 724-1237
Palm Bay *(G-13537)*

AUDIO ELECTRONIC SYSTEMS

Audio Video Imagineering Inc ....G 305 947-6991
Biscayne Park *(G-383)*
Fun Electronics Inc ....F 305 933-4646
Miami *(G-9603)*
Koncept Systems LLC ....E 786 610-0122
Homestead *(G-5977)*
Magnum Audio Group Inc ....G 813 870-2857
Tampa *(G-17874)*
MD Audio Engineering Inc ....G 305 593-8361
Miami *(G-9960)*
Mpr Audio System LLC ....G 305 988-8524
Miami *(G-10047)*
Power Evolution Inc ....G 305 318-8476
Orlando *(G-13075)*
Sonobrands LLC ....F 305 418-9367
Miami *(G-10376)*
Spirit llc ....E 954 592-0227
Miami Gardens *(G-10755)*
Sun Mackie LLC ....A 561 394-0550
Boca Raton *(G-735)*

AUDIO-VISUAL PROGRAM PRODUCTION SVCS

Baptist Communications Mission ....F 954 981-2271
Hollywood *(G-5784)*

AUDIOLOGICAL EQPT: Electronic

Megin Us LLC ....G 954 341-2965
Coral Springs *(G-2279)*
Micro Audiometrics Corporation ....G 828 644-0771
Daytona Beach *(G-2684)*

AUDIOLOGISTS' OFFICES

Ear-Tronics Inc ....G 239 275-7655
Fort Myers *(G-4440)*

AUTO & HOME SUPPLY STORES: Auto & Truck Eqpt & Parts

Emergency Vehicle Sup Co LLC ....E 954 428-5201
Pompano Beach *(G-14678)*
Vehicle Maint Program Inc ....F 561 362-6080
Boca Raton *(G-776)*

AUTO & HOME SUPPLY STORES: Auto Air Cond Eqpt, Sell/Install

Kcw Electric Company Inc ....G 850 878-2051
Tallahassee *(G-17287)*

AUTO & HOME SUPPLY STORES: Automotive Access

Hornblasters Inc ....E 813 783-8058
Tampa *(G-17761)*
Reading Truck Body LLC ....E 727 943-8911
Tarpon Springs *(G-18322)*

AUTO & HOME SUPPLY STORES: Automotive parts

Dhs Power Corp ....G 305 599-1022
Miami *(G-9463)*
Gear Dynamics Inc ....G 305 691-0151
Miami *(G-9619)*

T R S ....E 407 298-5490
Orlando *(G-13238)*
Total Performance Inc ....G 203 265-5667
Palm Coast *(G-13713)*

AUTO & HOME SUPPLY STORES: Batteries, Automotive & Truck

Battery Usa Inc ....E 863 665-6317
Lakeland *(G-7643)*
Palm Beach Btry Ventures LLC ....F 561 881-8900
Lake Park *(G-7477)*
Rayovac Corp ....G 727 393-0966
Largo *(G-8035)*

AUTOCLAVES: Laboratory

Genecell International LLC ....F 305 382-6737
Doral *(G-3360)*

AUTOMATED TELLER MACHINE NETWORK

Atmcentral ....G 727 345-8460
Saint Petersburg *(G-15714)*

AUTOMATIC REGULATING CNTRLS: Flame Safety, Furnaces & Boiler

Whertec Technologies Inc ....G 866 207-6503
Jacksonville *(G-6918)*

AUTOMATIC REGULATING CNTRLS: Liq Lvl, Residential/Comm Heat

Intelligent Heater LLC ....G 305 248-4971
Homestead *(G-5973)*

AUTOMATIC REGULATING CONTROL: Building Svcs Monitoring, Auto

Automated Buildings Inc ....F 407 857-0140
Orlando *(G-12501)*
Maintnnce Reliability Tech Inc ....E 863 533-0300
Bartow *(G-323)*
Top Line Installation Inc ....F 352 636-4192
Leesburg *(G-8177)*

AUTOMATIC REGULATING CONTROLS: AC & Refrigeration

Air Authorities of Tampa Inc ....G 727 525-1575
Clearwater *(G-1570)*
C & C Services of Tampa Inc ....G 813 477-8559
Plant City *(G-14414)*
Dais Corp ....F 727 375-8484
Odessa *(G-12115)*
Dsas Air Inc ....F 954 673-5385
Lauderdale Lakes *(G-8087)*
Gulf States Automation Inc ....E 850 475-0724
Pensacola *(G-14167)*
Jireh AC & Rfrgn Inc ....F 305 216-2774
Miami *(G-9798)*
Nautical Specialists ....G 954 761-7130
Fort Lauderdale *(G-4133)*

AUTOMATIC TELLER MACHINES

Adnan Enterprises ....G 305 430-9752
Miami Gardens *(G-10731)*
Americas Atm LLC ....F 954 414-0341
Plantation *(G-14489)*
Atmcentral ....G 727 345-8460
Saint Petersburg *(G-15714)*
Atmfla Inc ....G 407 425-7708
Orlando *(G-12499)*
Eep ....F 407 380-2828
Belle Isle *(G-357)*
Money Tree Atm Mfg LLC ....G 850 244-5543
Fort Walton Beach *(G-4817)*
Motaz Inc ....G 239 334-7699
Fort Myers *(G-4538)*
Sarniya Enterprises Inc ....F 352 347-6030
Ocala *(G-12042)*

AUTOMOBILES: Off-Highway, Electric

Cruise Car Inc ....F 941 929-1630
Sarasota *(G-16200)*
Moran Transport ....G 305 824-3366
Hialeah *(G-5528)*

AUTOMOTIVE & TRUCK GENERAL REPAIR SVC

Fidelity Manufacturing LLC ....E 352 414-4700
Ocala *(G-11940)*
Harberson Rv Pinellas LLC ....E 727 937-6176
Holiday *(G-5742)*
Palatka Welding Shop Inc ....E 386 328-1507
Palatka *(G-13488)*
Tbc Retail Group Inc ....G 702 395-2100
Juno Beach *(G-6984)*
Transtat Equipment Inc ....F 407 857-2040
Orlando *(G-13268)*

AUTOMOTIVE BATTERIES WHOLESALERS

Battery Usa Inc ....E 863 665-6317
Lakeland *(G-7643)*

AUTOMOTIVE BODY, PAINT & INTERIOR REPAIR & MAINTENANCE SVC

Sargent Seat Cover Co Inc ....E 904 355-2529
Jacksonville *(G-6752)*

AUTOMOTIVE GLASS REPLACEMENT SHOPS

Darren Thomas Glass Co Inc ....G 863 655-9500
Sebring *(G-16686)*

AUTOMOTIVE LETTERING & PAINTING SVCS

Doug Bloodworth Enterprises ....G 407 247-9728
Lady Lake *(G-7325)*

AUTOMOTIVE LETTERING SVCS

Thomas United Inc ....G 239 561-7446
Fort Myers *(G-4628)*

AUTOMOTIVE PARTS, ACCESS & SPLYS

AA Performance ....G 772 672-1164
Vero Beach *(G-18589)*
Ach LLC ....G 727 586-4930
Largo *(G-7885)*
Ach Solution USA Inc ....G 941 355-9488
Sarasota *(G-16171)*
Addco Manufacturing Company ....E 828 733-1560
Riviera Beach *(G-15292)*
Aero Seating Technologies LLC ....G 321 264-5600
Titusville *(G-18412)*
Air Temp of America Inc ....G 850 340-3017
Panama City *(G-13861)*
Ameraparts International LLC ....B 904 725-9700
Jacksonville *(G-6145)*
American Ignition Wire LLC ....G 954 974-6500
Fort Lauderdale *(G-3813)*
ARB Optimal Inc ....G 904 487-6874
Jacksonville *(G-6163)*
Autocraft Manufacturing Co ....E 321 453-1850
Merritt Island *(G-8992)*
Balls Rod & Kustom LLC ....G 888 446-2191
Gainesville *(G-4881)*
Battery Usa Inc ....E 863 665-6317
Lakeland *(G-7643)*
Battery Usa Inc ....G 863 665-5401
Lakeland *(G-7644)*
Beach House Engineering ....G 941 727-4488
Bradenton *(G-995)*
Billet Technology ....G 561 582-6171
Lake Worth *(G-7537)*
Blp Racing Products LLC ....F 407 422-0394
Orlando *(G-12524)*
Boat Steering Solutions LLC ....G 727 400-4746
North Venice *(G-11754)*
Boost Lab Inc ....F 813 443-0531
Wesley Chapel *(G-18741)*
Capristo USA ....G 561 882-9885
West Palm Beach *(G-18834)*
Carvizion Inc ....G 772 807-0307
Port St Lucie *(G-15170)*
CC Machine Inc ....F 888 577-0144
Holly Hill *(G-5757)*
Ccp Fabrication ....G 727 946-6024
Holiday *(G-5738)*
Chromalloy Castings Tampa Corp ....C 561 935-3571
Palm Beach Gardens *(G-13577)*

Competition Specialties Inc ....F 386 776-1476
Mc Alpin *(G-8599)*
Crankshaft Rebuilders Inc ....D 407 323-4870
Sanford *(G-16027)*
Cummins Inc ....G 407 298-2080
Orlando *(G-12636)*
Cummins Inc ....G 352 861-1122
Ocala *(G-11912)*
Custom Quality Mfg Inc ....E 813 290-0805
Tampa *(G-17582)*
Dashcovers Plus Depot Distrs ....G 954 961-7774
Davie *(G-2514)*
Delphi of Florida Inc ....F 727 561-9553
Saint Petersburg *(G-15757)*
Desco Machine Company LLC ....G 954 565-2739
Oakland Park *(G-11798)*
Diaz Go Green Inc ....G 407 501-2724
Orlando *(G-12670)*
Dimple Products Inc ....G 704 320-0700
Palm Coast *(G-13691)*
Dover Cylinder Head Inc ....E 850 785-6569
Panama City *(G-13894)*
Dsx Products Inc ....F 904 744-3400
Jacksonville *(G-6331)*
Dynotune Inc ....G 941 753-8899
Bradenton *(G-1033)*
Enforcement One Inc ....F 727 816-9833
Oldsmar *(G-12226)*
Eng Group LLC ....G 954 323-2024
Fort Lauderdale *(G-3972)*
Ensida Energy Afs LLC ....G 954 364-2296
Hollywood *(G-5816)*
Enstar Holdings (us) LLC ....D 727 217-2900
Saint Petersburg *(G-15770)*
Etco Incorporated ....C 941 756-8426
Bradenton *(G-1039)*
Evamped LLC ....G 614 205-4467
Naples *(G-11241)*
Exhaust Technologies Inc ....G 561 744-9500
Jupiter *(G-7037)*
Extreme Corvette Co LLC ....G 941 524-8942
Bradenton *(G-1040)*
Extreme Manufacturing LLC ....F 888 844-7734
Ocala *(G-11938)*
Faes Srt Inc ....G 941 960-6742
Sarasota *(G-16424)*
FCA US LLC ....G 305 597-2222
Doral *(G-3349)*
Federal-Mogul Motorparts LLC ....G 954 585-2500
Fort Lauderdale *(G-3991)*
Florida Dacco/Detroit Inc ....E 813 879-4131
Tampa *(G-17674)*
Florida Motors Inc ....G 786 524-9001
Miami *(G-9585)*
Florida Pwrtrain Hydrulics Inc ....G 954 463-7711
Fort Lauderdale *(G-4003)*
Florida Pwrtrain Hydrulics Inc ....G 813 623-6713
Tampa *(G-17687)*
Florida Pwrtrain Hydrulics Inc ....G 407 291-1441
Orlando *(G-12754)*
Flowmaster Inc ....G 561 249-1145
Loxahatchee *(G-8359)*
Fluid Routing Solutions LLC ....B 352 732-0222
Ocala *(G-11948)*
Forecast Trading Corporation ....E 954 979-1120
Fort Lauderdale *(G-4009)*
Fuelmatics Corp ....F 305 807-4923
Palmetto Bay *(G-13843)*
Gaterman Products LLC ....G 386 253-1899
Daytona Beach *(G-2667)*
Gear Driven LLC ....G 954 681-8394
Coral Springs *(G-2250)*
Hale Products Inc ....C 352 629-5020
Ocala *(G-11963)*
Harry J Honan ....G 405 273-9315
Riviera Beach *(G-15332)*
Hre LLC ....G 317 340-5991
Fort Myers *(G-4485)*
IESC Diesel Corp ....G 305 470-9306
Medley *(G-8668)*
Intertek International Corp ....D 305 883-8700
Hialeah *(G-5457)*
Ionemoto Inc ....G 617 784-1401
Sebastian *(G-16663)*
Isoflex Technologies Intl LLC ....G 561 210-5170
Deerfield Beach *(G-2848)*
J & J Dynamic Products LLC ....G 863 274-5333
Lakeland *(G-7719)*
JMS Corporate Group LLC ....G 786 219-6114
Aventura *(G-275)*
Jodar Inc ....G 561 375-6277
Boca Raton *(G-583)*
Johnsons Management Group Inc ....G 904 261-4044
Fernandina Beach *(G-3741)*
Key Automotive Florida LLC ....B 863 668-6000
Lakeland *(G-7725)*
Key Safety Systems Inc ....G 863 668-6000
Lakeland *(G-7726)*
Kirby Acquisitions LLC ....G 850 687-8703
Santa Rosa Beach *(G-16162)*
Lambs Signs Inc ....F 941 792-4453
Bradenton *(G-1068)*
Latham Marine Inc ....E 954 462-3055
Fort Lauderdale *(G-4096)*
Lightning Connecting Rods LLC ....G 727 733-2054
Clearwater *(G-1760)*
Luminar Technologies Inc ....C 407 900-5259
Orlando *(G-12938)*
Luminar Technologies Inc ....E 407 900-5259
Orlando *(G-12939)*
Luxury Motor Cars LLC ....F 407 398-6933
Orlando *(G-12940)*
M P N Inc ....E 863 606-5999
Lakeland *(G-7741)*
Man-Trans LLC ....F 850 222-6993
Tallahassee *(G-17294)*
March Inc ....E 239 593-4074
Naples *(G-11320)*
Minder Research Inc ....F 772 463-6522
Stuart *(G-16977)*
Mobilepower LLC ....F 843 706-6108
South Miami *(G-16823)*
Motor Coach Inds Intl Inc ....F 407 246-1414
Winter Garden *(G-19277)*
P4rts LLC ....G 305 396-4879
Miami *(G-10125)*
Partsvu LLC ....C 239 643-2292
Naples *(G-11359)*
Paw Inc ....E 904 724-0310
Jacksonville *(G-6661)*
Phoenix Transmission Parts Inc ....G 727 541-0269
Clearwater *(G-1831)*
Pierce Manufacturing Inc ....D 941 748-3900
Bradenton *(G-1097)*
Precision Shaft Technology ....G 727 442-1711
Clearwater *(G-1841)*
Propglide USA Corp ....G 305 520-0150
Miami *(G-10210)*
R C Specialized International ....G 407 681-5905
Casselberry *(G-1516)*
Rally Manufacturing Inc ....C 305 628-2886
Miami *(G-10236)*
RDS Manufacturing Inc ....C 850 584-6898
Perry *(G-14310)*
Reach International Inc ....E 305 863-6360
Hialeah *(G-5596)*
Redat of North America Inc ....G 407 246-1600
Orlando *(G-13122)*
Rehadapt North America ....G 904 687-0130
Saint Augustine *(G-15595)*
Road Master ....G 561 479-6450
Fort Lauderdale *(G-4210)*
Rod-Speed Inc ....G 786 426-3996
Doral *(G-3488)*
Ruke Inc ....G 239 292-2553
Windermere *(G-19242)*
Santa Rosa Auto Parts Inc ....E 850 477-7747
Pensacola *(G-14257)*
Santiago Chopper LLC ....E 813 671-9097
Gibsonton *(G-5032)*
Screaming Banshee LLC ....G 727 744-6808
Clearwater *(G-1869)*
Sea Systems Group Inc ....G 434 374-9553
Largo *(G-8049)*
Shafers Classic Reproductions ....G 813 622-7091
Tampa *(G-18089)*
Shark Skinz ....G 772 388-9621
Sebastian *(G-16672)*
Shearwater Marine Fl Inc ....E 772 781-5553
Stuart *(G-17010)*
Signal Dynamics Corporation ....F 904 342-4008
Fort Lauderdale *(G-4233)*
Silverhorse Racing LLC ....G 321 722-2813
Melbourne *(G-8933)*
Sizemore Welding Inc ....E 386 437-4073
Bunnell *(G-1306)*
Skyo Industries Inc ....E 631 586-4702
Ormond Beach *(G-13399)*
SMR Management Inc ....G 305 529-2488
Coral Gables *(G-2196)*
Southeast Carbon Works Inc ....G 561 422-1798
Wellington *(G-18736)*
Southeastern Engineering Inc ....F 321 984-2521
Palm Bay *(G-13538)*
Square One Armoring Svcs Co ....D 305 477-1109
Miami *(G-10407)*
Standard Motor Products Inc ....G 718 392-0200
Orlando *(G-13213)*
Steering & Suspension Parts ....G 786 523-3726
Miami *(G-10412)*
Strasse Forged LLC ....F 786 701-3649
Miami *(G-10419)*
Tanks Incorporated ....G 941 320-4371
Myakka City *(G-11144)*
Thi E-Commerce LLC ....D 352 327-4058
Ocala *(G-12060)*
Total Performance Inc ....G 203 265-5667
Palm Coast *(G-13713)*
Treadstone Performance ....F 305 972-9600
Cutler Bay *(G-2415)*
Treadstone Prfmce Engrg Inc ....G 888 789-4586
Cutler Bay *(G-2416)*
U S Hardware Supply Inc ....E 407 657-1551
Winter Park *(G-19454)*
Urban Charge LLC ....G 305 809-6625
Miami Beach *(G-10724)*
USA Corp Airplane ....G 954 399-8472
Hollywood *(G-5935)*
Vista-Pro Automotive LLC ....F 352 867-7272
Ocala *(G-12073)*
Voxxhirschmann Corporation ....C 866 869-7888
Orlando *(G-13314)*
Vpr 4x4 ....G 305 468-9818
Orlando *(G-13315)*
Walker Products ....D 941 723-9820
Palmetto *(G-13835)*
Webelectric Products Inc ....G 440 389-5647
The Villages *(G-18397)*
Wetherill Associates Inc ....C 800 773-0005
Miramar *(G-11060)*
Wheels A Million ....G 754 444-2869
Fort Lauderdale *(G-4321)*
Wolverine Advanced Mtls LLC ....G 352 787-3015
Leesburg *(G-8181)*
Woodys Acres LLC ....G 352 345-8145
Brooksville *(G-1295)*
Yarbrough Tire Svc Inc ....G 863 385-1574
Sebring *(G-16719)*

AUTOMOTIVE PARTS: Plastic

Dixie Restorations LLC ....G 813 785-2159
Zephyrhills *(G-19514)*
Fuel Air Spark Technology ....F 901 260-3278
Naples *(G-11252)*
International Power USA LLC ....G 305 534-7993
Miami *(G-9760)*
Jers Group ....G 786 953-6419
Doral *(G-3402)*
Pcm and S L Plota Co LLC ....F 727 547-6277
Largo *(G-8024)*
Sea Link Holdings LLC ....F 727 523-8660
Largo *(G-8047)*
Southast Auto Acquisition Corp ....E 305 885-8689
Medley *(G-8726)*
Sunset Cadillac of Sarasota ....F 941 922-1571
Sarasota *(G-16610)*

AUTOMOTIVE PRDTS: Rubber

Paragon Globl Sup Slutions LLC ....G 813 745-9902
Tampa *(G-17975)*
Polyhistor International Inc ....G 904 646-5666
Jacksonville *(G-6677)*
Ready Containment LLC ....F 941 739-9486
Palmetto *(G-13821)*

AUTOMOTIVE REPAIR SHOPS: Electrical Svcs

L & L Automotive Electric Inc ....F 631 471-5230
Melbourne *(G-8862)*

AUTOMOTIVE REPAIR SHOPS: Engine Rebuilding

Engine Lab of Tampa Inc ....F 813 630-2422
Tampa *(G-17640)*

AUTOMOTIVE REPAIR SHOPS: Engine Repair, Exc Diesel

Godwin and Singer Inc..........................G....... 727 896-8631
Saint Petersburg *(G-15795)*

AUTOMOTIVE REPAIR SHOPS: Machine Shop

Aero Technology Mfg Inc.......................F....... 305 345-7747
Miami *(G-9082)*

AUTOMOTIVE REPAIR SHOPS: Powertrain Components Repair Svcs

Acme Service Corp................................F....... 305 836-4800
Miami *(G-9065)*

AUTOMOTIVE REPAIR SHOPS: Sound System Svc & Installation

Flints Wrecker Service Inc....................G....... 863 676-1318
Lake Wales *(G-7509)*

AUTOMOTIVE REPAIR SHOPS: Tire Repair Shop

Jacksonville Tire Rescue Inc.................F....... 904 783-1296
Jacksonville *(G-6513)*

AUTOMOTIVE REPAIR SHOPS: Torque Converter Repair

Avalanche Corporation..........................D....... 800 708-0087
Brooksville *(G-1213)*

AUTOMOTIVE REPAIR SHOPS: Trailer Repair

A Plus Trailers......................................G....... 786 395-0799
Southwest Ranches *(G-16835)*
Amera Trail Inc......................................E....... 407 892-1100
Saint Cloud *(G-15643)*
J & J Marine Service Inc.......................G....... 813 741-2190
Saint Petersburg *(G-15820)*
Steel Plus Service Center Inc...............G....... 407 328-7169
Sanford *(G-16121)*
Terminal Service Company...................C....... 850 739-5702
Tallahassee *(G-17339)*

AUTOMOTIVE REPAIR SVC

American Auto Marine Wiring...............G....... 954 782-0193
Pompano Beach *(G-14590)*
Toogle Industries LLC...........................G....... 863 688-8975
Lakeland *(G-7824)*

AUTOMOTIVE SPLYS & PARTS, NEW, WHOLESALE: Alternators

T R S...E....... 407 298-5490
Orlando *(G-13238)*

AUTOMOTIVE SPLYS & PARTS, NEW, WHOLESALE: Engines/Eng Parts

Sen-Dure Products Inc..........................D....... 954 973-1260
Fort Lauderdale *(G-4230)*

AUTOMOTIVE SPLYS & PARTS, NEW, WHOLESALE: Pumps, Oil & Gas

Power Equipments Trading LLC............G....... 305 704-7021
Doral *(G-3464)*

AUTOMOTIVE SPLYS & PARTS, NEW, WHOLESALE: Splys

Pro Chem Products Inc..........................G....... 407 425-5533
Orlando *(G-13091)*

AUTOMOTIVE SPLYS & PARTS, USED, WHOLESALE

B & P Motor Heads Inc..........................G....... 305 769-3183
Opa Locka *(G-12291)*

AUTOMOTIVE SPLYS & PARTS, USED, WHOLESALE: Access, NEC

Hornblasters Inc...................................E....... 813 783-8058
Tampa *(G-17761)*

AUTOMOTIVE SPLYS & PARTS, WHOLESALE, NEC

Bukkehave Inc.......................................G....... 954 525-9788
Fort Lauderdale *(G-3876)*
D & L Auto & Marine Supplies...............G....... 305 593-0560
Doral *(G-3319)*
Motor Service Group LLC......................G....... 305 592-2440
Miami *(G-10044)*
Motor Service Inc...................................G....... 305 592-2440
Miami *(G-10045)*
Naztec International Group LLC............F....... 561 802-4110
West Palm Beach *(G-18960)*
Southast Auto Acquisition Corp.............E....... 305 885-8689
Medley *(G-8726)*
Total Performance Inc............................G....... 203 265-5667
Palm Coast *(G-13713)*
Voxx International Corporation..............B....... 800 645-7750
Orlando *(G-13313)*
Wetherill Associates Inc.........................C....... 800 773-0005
Miramar *(G-11060)*

AUTOMOTIVE SPLYS/PART, NEW, WHOL: Spring, Shock Absorb/Strut

Hornblasters Inc...................................E....... 813 783-8058
Tampa *(G-17761)*

AUTOMOTIVE SVCS

Florida Oil Service Inc...........................F....... 813 655-4753
Lithia *(G-8219)*

AUTOMOTIVE SVCS, EXC REPAIR & CARWASHES: Maintenance

Creative Colors International.................G....... 239 573-8883
Cape Coral *(G-1407)*
Kcw Electric Company Inc.....................G....... 850 878-2051
Tallahassee *(G-17287)*

AUTOMOTIVE SVCS, EXC RPR/CARWASHES: High Perf Auto Rpr/Svc

Revology Cars LLC.................................F....... 800 974-4463
Orlando *(G-13133)*

AUTOMOTIVE TOWING & WRECKING SVC

Palatka Welding Shop Inc......................E....... 386 328-1507
Palatka *(G-13488)*

AUTOMOTIVE TOWING SVCS

Arons Towing & Recovery Inc................G....... 772 220-1151
Hobe Sound *(G-5722)*

AUTOMOTIVE TRANSMISSION REPAIR SVC

Phoenix Transmission Parts Inc..............G....... 727 541-0269
Clearwater *(G-1831)*

AUTOMOTIVE WELDING SVCS

Bjb Marine Welding & Svcs Inc...............G....... 954 909-4967
Fort Lauderdale *(G-3856)*
Immokalee Fabrication and Wldg...........G....... 239 675-8299
Immokalee *(G-6051)*
Kingston Automotive & Wldg LLC.........G....... 727 378-4881
Hudson *(G-6031)*
Mims Welding Incorporated...................G....... 863 612-9819
Labelle *(G-7320)*
Tarin Services LLC.................................G....... 803 526-9643
Tampa *(G-18175)*

AUTOMOTIVE: Bodies

Speedsource Inc....................................G....... 954 578-7071
Key Largo *(G-7174)*

AUTOMOTIVE: Seating

Vehicle Maint Program Inc.....................F....... 561 362-6080
Boca Raton *(G-776)*

AUTOTRANSFORMERS: Electric

Backbone Interconnect LLC...................E....... 954 800-4749
Sunrise *(G-17093)*

AVIATION PROPELLER & BLADE REPAIR SVCS

Willis Aeronautical Svcs Inc...................F....... 561 272-5402
Coconut Creek *(G-2103)*

AVIATION SCHOOL

Cae USA Inc...A....... 813 885-7481
Tampa *(G-17500)*
ELite Intl Group LLC..............................F....... 305 901-5005
Miami *(G-9516)*
Gleim Publications Inc...........................D....... 352 375-0772
Gainesville *(G-4931)*

AWNINGS & CANOPIES

Coastal Awngs Hrrcane Prtction............G....... 407 923-9482
Orlando *(G-12592)*
Emerald Sails...F....... 850 240-4777
Shalimar *(G-16774)*
General Metals & Plastics Inc................G....... 904 354-8224
Jacksonville *(G-6432)*
Kenco 2000 Inc......................................F....... 386 672-1590
Daytona Beach *(G-2676)*
No Equal Design Inc..............................G....... 305 971-5177
Miami *(G-10074)*
Parrish Inc...G....... 386 985-4879
De Leon Springs *(G-2740)*

AWNINGS & CANOPIES: Awnings, Fabric, From Purchased Matls

A & A Central Florida.............................F....... 407 648-5666
Altamonte Springs *(G-24)*
ABc Awning & Canvas Co Inc................F....... 321 253-1960
Delray Beach *(G-3039)*
Advanced Awning & Design LLC...........G....... 904 724-5567
Jacksonville *(G-6121)*
American Awning Company Inc.............E....... 561 832-7123
West Palm Beach *(G-18796)*
Ards Awning & Upholstery Inc...............E....... 863 293-2442
Winter Haven *(G-19300)*
Awnings By Coversol.............................E....... 813 251-4774
Tampa *(G-17448)*
Biscayne Awning & Shade Co................E....... 305 638-7933
Miami *(G-9250)*
Canvas Shop Inc.....................................G....... 407 898-6001
Orlando *(G-12548)*
Coastal Canvas and Awning Co..............F....... 239 433-1114
Fort Myers *(G-4400)*
Cross Key Marine Canvas Inc.................G....... 305 451-1302
Key Largo *(G-7167)*
Delray Awning Inc...................................F....... 561 276-5381
Delray Beach *(G-3069)*
Discount Awnings Inc.............................G....... 941 753-5700
Sarasota *(G-16207)*
Florida Shutters Inc................................E....... 772 569-2200
Vero Beach *(G-18619)*
Hoover Canvas Products Co..................E....... 954 764-1711
Oakland Park *(G-11811)*
Hoover Canvas Products Co..................F....... 954 541-9745
Mangonia Park *(G-8502)*
Hoover Canvas Products Co..................F....... 561 844-4444
Mangonia Park *(G-8503)*
Jones Awnings & Canvas Inc..................E....... 954 784-6966
Pompano Beach *(G-14737)*
Major Canvas Products Inc....................F....... 954 764-1711
Oakland Park *(G-11821)*
Miami Beach Awning Co.........................E....... 305 576-2029
Miami *(G-9993)*
Milliken & Milliken Inc...........................E....... 941 474-0223
Englewood *(G-3680)*
Paradise Awnings Corporation..............E....... 305 597-5714
Miami *(G-10141)*
Sunstate Awng Grphic Dsign Inc...........E....... 407 260-6118
Sanford *(G-16122)*
Thomas Sign and Awning Co Inc...........C....... 727 573-7757
Clearwater *(G-1919)*
Thompson Awning & Shutter Co............E....... 904 355-1616
Jacksonville *(G-6849)*
Treasure Coast Canvas...........................G....... 772 210-2588
Stuart *(G-17036)*
Tropical Awning of Florida.....................F....... 561 276-1144
Delray Beach *(G-3151)*
United States Awning Company.............E....... 941 955-7010
Sarasota *(G-16631)*

AWNINGS & CANOPIES: Canopies, Fabric, From Purchased Matls

Apollo Sunguard Systems Inc .... F 941 925-3000
Sarasota *(G-16343)*
Logsdon and Associates Inc .... G 407 292-0084
Windermere *(G-19236)*
Mason-Florida LLC .... F 352 638-9003
Leesburg *(G-8165)*
Portable-Shade USA LLC .... G 321 704-8100
Cocoa *(G-2041)*

AWNINGS & CANOPIES: Fabric

Air Shelters USA LLC .... E 215 957-6128
Pompano Beach *(G-14581)*
Big Top Manufacturing Inc .... D 850 584-7786
Perry *(G-14294)*
Canopy Specialist LLC .... F 813 703-6844
Plant City *(G-14415)*
Coastal Awngs Hrrcane Prtction .... G 407 923-9482
Orlando *(G-12592)*
Fabis Group Corporation .... G 305 718-3638
Miami *(G-9553)*
Got It Inc .... G 954 899-0001
Boca Raton *(G-550)*
Iis Incorporated .... G 561 547-4297
Boynton Beach *(G-918)*
Southern Awning Inc .... E 561 586-0464
Lake Worth *(G-7587)*

AWNINGS: Fiberglass

Coastal Awngs Hrrcane Prtction .... G 407 923-9482
Orlando *(G-12592)*
Iis Incorporated .... G 561 547-4297
Boynton Beach *(G-918)*
Safe Pro Inc .... G 954 494-5768
Hialeah *(G-5609)*

AWNINGS: Metal

Alumflo Inc .... G 727 527-8494
Saint Petersburg *(G-15698)*
Dolphin Sheet Metal Inc .... F 561 744-0242
Jupiter *(G-7025)*
Florida Shutters Inc .... E 772 569-2200
Vero Beach *(G-18619)*
Fresco Group Inc .... F 239 936-8055
Fort Myers *(G-4459)*
Hurst Awning Company Inc .... E 305 693-0600
Hollywood *(G-5847)*
Rolling Shield Incorporated .... E 305 436-6661
Miami Lakes *(G-10852)*
Rolling Shield Parts Inc .... F 305 436-6661
Miami Lakes *(G-10853)*
Style-View Products Inc .... F 305 634-9688
Miami *(G-10426)*
Thompson Awning & Shutter Co .... E 904 355-1616
Jacksonville *(G-6849)*
United States Awning Company .... E 941 955-7010
Sarasota *(G-16631)*

BACKHOES

Anderson Backhoe Service Inc .... G 904 759-9084
Jacksonville *(G-6155)*
Ingrams Backhoe Dumptruck Svc .... G 850 718-6042
Cottondale *(G-2332)*
James Frncisco Backhoe Svc Inc .... G 727 514-1968
New Port Richey *(G-11494)*
Moncada Backhoe Services LLC .... G 786 269-5427
Miami *(G-10039)*

BADGES: Identification & Insignia

Express Badging Services Inc .... F 321 784-5925
Cocoa Beach *(G-2062)*
Hbys Enterprises LLC .... F 855 290-9900
Winter Springs *(G-19473)*
One Source Industries Inc .... G 813 855-3440
Oldsmar *(G-12253)*
Ped-Stuart Corporation .... E 352 754-6001
Brooksville *(G-1259)*
Suncoast Idntfction Sltons LLC .... F 239 277-9922
Fort Myers *(G-4617)*
Superior Group Companies Inc .... A 727 397-9611
Seminole *(G-16764)*

BAGS & CONTAINERS: Textile, Exc Sleeping

Paper Bag Manufacturers Inc .... F 305 685-1100
Opa Locka *(G-12349)*
Suncoast Trends Inc .... G 727 321-4948
Saint Petersburg *(G-15929)*

BAGS & SACKS: Shipping & Shopping

Atlantic Ship Supply Inc .... G 954 961-8885
Hallandale *(G-5153)*
Bryce Foster Inc .... G 800 371-0395
Altamonte Springs *(G-34)*

BAGS: Canvas

Armor Products Mfg Inc .... F 813 764-8844
Plant City *(G-14402)*
Black Ops LLC .... G 305 450-0127
Hialeah *(G-5329)*
Cameron Textiles Inc .... G 954 454-6482
Palm City *(G-13644)*
Safety Intl Bags & Straps .... F 407 830-0888
Casselberry *(G-1517)*
Warren Heim Corp .... E 772 466-8265
Fort Pierce *(G-4768)*

BAGS: Cellophane

Cavadas Ruben & Trisha Wagner .... G 407 248-2659
Orlando *(G-12556)*
H Sixto Distributors Inc .... F 305 688-5242
Opa Locka *(G-12322)*

BAGS: Cement, Made From Purchased Materials

Ready Building Products Inc .... G 941 639-6222
Punta Gorda *(G-15228)*

BAGS: Duffle, Canvas, Made From Purchased Materials

Abco Industries LLC .... G 813 605-5900
Tampa *(G-17383)*

BAGS: Food Storage & Frozen Food, Plastic

Seal-Tite Plastic Packg Co Inc .... D 305 264-9015
Miami *(G-10316)*

BAGS: Food Storage & Trash, Plastic

Inteplast Engineered Films Inc .... D 407 851-6620
Orlando *(G-12834)*

BAGS: Garment Storage Exc Paper Or Plastic Film

Premier Plastics LLC .... E 305 805-3333
Boynton Beach *(G-943)*

BAGS: Laundry, From Purchased Materials

Cameron Textiles Inc .... G 954 454-6482
Palm City *(G-13644)*

BAGS: Laundry, Garment & Storage

Armor Products Mfg Inc .... F 813 764-8844
Plant City *(G-14402)*

BAGS: Paper

Aspen Products Inc .... E 904 579-4366
Fleming Island *(G-3759)*
Harmsco Inc .... D 561 848-9628
Riviera Beach *(G-15331)*
Paper Bag Manufacturers Inc .... F 305 685-1100
Opa Locka *(G-12349)*
Trend At LLC .... F 786 300-2550
Miami *(G-10505)*

BAGS: Paper, Made From Purchased Materials

J S Trading Inc .... G 954 791-9035
Plantation *(G-14526)*
S V Bags America Inc .... G 954 577-9091
Weston *(G-19166)*
Tak Paper Corp .... G 786 287-8900
Doral *(G-3522)*

BAGS: Plastic

Coastal Films of Florida .... D 904 786-2031
Jacksonville *(G-6276)*
Cosner Manufacturing LLC .... F 863 676-2579
Lake Wales *(G-7506)*
Diversitypro Corp .... E 305 691-2348
South Miami *(G-16815)*
H Goicoechea Inc .... F 305 805-3333
Hialeah *(G-5441)*
Jan and Jean Inc .... G 813 645-0680
Ruskin *(G-15485)*
Koszegi Industries Inc .... E 954 419-9544
Deerfield Beach *(G-2855)*
Premium Absrbent Dspsables LLC .... E 561 737-6377
Boynton Beach *(G-944)*
R & D Sleeves Llc .... E 407 886-9010
Apopka *(G-178)*
Sigma Extruding Corp .... G 904 786-2031
Jacksonville *(G-6769)*
Starlock Inc .... G 305 477-2303
Doral *(G-3511)*
Sterling Mdr Inc .... F 954 725-2777
Deerfield Beach *(G-2917)*
US American Plastic Corp .... F 305 200-3683
Miami *(G-10551)*

BAGS: Plastic & Pliofilm

Construction and Elec Pdts Inc .... F 954 972-9787
Pompano Beach *(G-14645)*
Flexsol Holding Corp .... D 954 941-6333
Pompano Beach *(G-14700)*
Jr Plastics Corporation .... D 352 401-0880
Ocala *(G-11972)*

BAGS: Plastic, Made From Purchased Materials

Bags Express Inc .... G 305 500-9849
Doral *(G-3263)*
Biobag Americas Inc .... F 727 789-1646
Dunedin *(G-3570)*
Crown Products LLC .... G 954 917-1118
Pompano Beach *(G-14652)*
CSR Enterprise Ltd .... G 954 624-2284
North Miami *(G-11635)*
Dairy-Mix Inc .... F 813 621-8098
Tampa *(G-17586)*
Dynasel Incorporated .... G 972 733-4447
Deerfield Beach *(G-2819)*
J S Trading Inc .... G 954 791-9035
Plantation *(G-14526)*
Mhms Corp .... E 813 948-0504
Lutz *(G-8401)*
Plastix Usa LLC .... D 305 891-0091
Hollywood *(G-5892)*
Poly Plastic Packaging Co Inc .... E 561 498-9040
Boca Raton *(G-668)*
Pro Pak Enterprises Inc .... F 888 375-2275
Deerfield Beach *(G-2894)*

BAGS: Rubber Or Rubberized Fabric

Bags Unlimited Inc .... G 985 868-3393
Chiefland *(G-1533)*

BAGS: Textile

Matteo Graphics Inc .... F 239 652-1002
Cape Coral *(G-1446)*
Wayloo Inc .... G 954 914-3192
Fort Lauderdale *(G-4317)*
Youthful Innovations LLC .... G 239 596-2200
Naples *(G-11463)*

BAGS: Trash, Plastic Film, Made From Purchased Materials

Litterbin LLC .... G 772 633-7184
Vero Beach *(G-18640)*

BAGS: Vacuum cleaner, Made From Purchased Materials

ACS of West Palm Beach Inc .... G 561 844-5790
West Palm Beach *(G-18787)*

BAGS: Wardrobe, Closet Access, Made From Purchased Materials

Daisies Closets .... G 863 838-5056
Lakeland *(G-7671)*

BAKERIES, COMMERCIAL: On Premises Baking Only

Bauducco Manufacturing Inc................F 305 477-9270
Miami *(G-9225)*
Bauducco USA Holding Company........G....... 305 477-9270
Miami *(G-9226)*
Cedars Bakery Group Inc......................F 407 476-6593
Orlando *(G-12559)*
Corvatsch Corp.......................................F 305 775-2831
Miami Beach *(G-10658)*
Crustys Bread Bakery...........................G....... 727 937-9041
Tarpon Springs *(G-18291)*
Cupcake Inc..G....... 407 644-7800
Maitland *(G-8464)*
Cupcakes Frsting Sprinkles LLC..........G....... 305 769-3393
Opa Locka *(G-12304)*
Delicio Baking Company Inc.................G....... 305 865-5664
Miami Beach *(G-10662)*
Duval Bakery Products Inc....................G....... 904 354-7878
Jacksonville *(G-6339)*
Five Star Bakery.....................................G....... 954 983-6133
Miramar *(G-10991)*
Flowers Bakeries LLC.............................E....... 850 875-4997
Quincy *(G-15249)*
Flowers Baking Co LLC..........................G....... 850 763-2541
Panama City *(G-13904)*
Flowers Baking Co Lakeland Inc...........E....... 863 682-1155
Lakeland *(G-7694)*
Flowers Bkg Co Bradenton LLC............F 941 627-0752
Port Charlotte *(G-14981)*
Flowers Bkg Co Bradenton LLC............E....... 941 758-5656
Lakeland *(G-7695)*
Flowers Bkg Co Bradenton LLC............F 941 758-5656
Avon Park *(G-287)*
Flowers Bkg Co Bradenton LLC............E....... 941 758-5656
Orlando *(G-12760)*
Flowers Bkg Co Bradenton LLC............E....... 941 758-5656
Hudson *(G-6025)*
Flowers Bkg Co Bradenton LLC............E....... 941 758-5656
Kissimmee *(G-7246)*
Flowers Bkg Co Bradenton LLC............E....... 941 758-5656
Bonita Springs *(G-832)*
Flowers Bkg Co Bradenton LLC............E....... 941 758-5656
Bradenton *(G-1043)*
Franklin Baking Company LLC.............G....... 850 478-8360
Pensacola *(G-14159)*
Fresh On Fifth...G....... 305 234-5678
Miami Beach *(G-10669)*
Heara Inc..G....... 305 651-5200
Miami *(G-9694)*
La Province Inc...F 305 538-2406
Miami *(G-9847)*
Marnis Dolce..G....... 407 915-7607
Apopka *(G-157)*
Merenguitoscom LLC...............................G....... 305 685-2709
Hialeah *(G-5505)*
New Marco Foods Inc................................F 305 836-0571
Hialeah *(G-5538)*
Nostalgic Specialty Foods Inc................G....... 561 391-8600
Boca Raton *(G-650)*
Obem Foods Inc...G....... 305 887-0258
Miami Springs *(G-10896)*
On A Roll Distributors Inc......................G....... 352 726-3420
Inverness *(G-6093)*
OPelle Enterprises Inc............................E....... 954 942-7338
Pompano Beach *(G-14780)*
Patticakes Cupcakery LLC.....................G....... 386 383-1782
South Daytona *(G-16807)*
Simply Cupcakes.......................................G....... 239 262-5184
Naples *(G-11404)*
Slb1989 Inc..G....... 772 344-3609
Port Saint Lucie *(G-15146)*
Spring Hill Bakery LLC.............................E....... 954 825-3419
Spring Hill *(G-16865)*
Star Bakery Inc..F 305 633-4284
Miami *(G-10409)*
T & W Inc..G....... 305 887-0258
Miami Springs *(G-10898)*

BAKERIES: On Premises Baking & Consumption

Claddah Corp..F 407 834-8881
Casselberry *(G-1501)*
Edca Bakery Corporation..........................F 305 448-7843
Coral Gables *(G-2141)*
Flowers Baking Co Miami LLC.................D....... 305 652-3416
Miami *(G-9589)*
Pane Rustica Bakery & Cafe....................F 813 902-8828
Tampa *(G-17970)*

Way Beyond Bagels Inc..............................F 561 638-1320
Delray Beach *(G-3159)*

BAKERY FOR HOME SVC DELIVERY

Bks Bakery Inc..G....... 386 216-0540
Deltona *(G-3164)*

BAKERY MACHINERY

Deluxe Equipment Co..................................F 941 753-4184
Bradenton *(G-1029)*

BAKERY PRDTS, FROZEN: Wholesalers

Bks Bakery Inc..G....... 386 216-0540
Deltona *(G-3164)*

BAKERY PRDTS: Bagels, Fresh Or Frozen

Brothers Wholesale Inc..............................E....... 631 831-8484
Port St Lucie *(G-15168)*
Hometown Foods Usa LLC.........................C....... 305 887-5200
Medley *(G-8665)*

BAKERY PRDTS: Bakery Prdts, Partially Cooked, Exc frozen

Fat and Weird Cookie Co LLC....................F 850 832-9150
Panama City *(G-13900)*
Unicornio Bakery LLC................................F 786 665-1602
Doral *(G-3535)*

BAKERY PRDTS: Biscuits, Baked, Baking Powder & Raised

Savory Street..G....... 941 312-4027
Sarasota *(G-16584)*

BAKERY PRDTS: Bread, All Types, Fresh Or Frozen

Caamacosta Inc..G....... 954 987-5895
Hollywood *(G-5793)*
Casino Bakery Inc..F 813 242-0311
Tampa *(G-17513)*
Claddah Corp...F 407 834-8881
Casselberry *(G-1501)*
Flowers Bkg Co Bradenton LLC................C....... 941 758-5656
Sarasota *(G-16215)*
Flowers Bkg Co Thomasville LLC.............F 229 226-5331
Tallahassee *(G-17256)*
Panamerican Food LLC..............................E....... 305 594-5704
Miramar *(G-11026)*
Southern Bakeries Inc................................C....... 863 682-1155
Lakeland *(G-7800)*

BAKERY PRDTS: Cakes, Bakery, Exc Frozen

Babicakes LLC...G....... 561 507-0331
West Palm Beach *(G-18811)*
Churrico Factory LLC..................................G....... 239 989-7616
Fort Myers *(G-4394)*
Cupcake Girls Dessert Company..............G....... 904 372-4579
Jacksonville Beach *(G-6941)*
Cupcake Heaven...G....... 352 610-4433
Spring Hill *(G-16850)*
El Trigal International.................................G....... 305 594-6610
Medley *(G-8646)*
Gigliola Inc...G....... 954 564-7871
Fort Lauderdale *(G-4021)*
Gregomarc LLC...G....... 305 559-9777
Miami *(G-9670)*
Juan F Montano..G....... 305 274-0512
Miami *(G-9811)*
Sweetsies...G....... 386 566-6762
Palm Coast *(G-13712)*
Todo En Uno..G....... 305 263-6934
Miami *(G-10486)*

BAKERY PRDTS: Cakes, Bakery, Frozen

Dawn Foods Inc..G....... 866 218-3801
Medley *(G-8641)*
Sugar Fancies LLC.......................................G....... 786 558-9087
Miami *(G-10427)*

BAKERY PRDTS: Cones, Ice Cream

Carpe Diem Ice Cream LLC.........................G....... 305 504-4469
Key West *(G-7180)*

BAKERY PRDTS: Cookies

Ambo Foods LLC...G....... 941 485-4400
Venice *(G-18531)*
Aventura Cookies Inc..................................G....... 954 447-4525
Pembroke Pines *(G-14021)*
First Grade Food Corporation....................E....... 813 886-6118
Tampa *(G-17666)*
Lavi Enterprises LLC...................................D....... 561 721-7170
Riviera Beach *(G-15342)*
Lindley Foods LLC..G....... 407 884-9433
Apopka *(G-156)*
Selmas Cookies Inc.......................................E....... 407 884-9433
Apopka *(G-185)*
Smart Snacks LLC..G....... 954 860-8833
Hollywood *(G-5909)*

BAKERY PRDTS: Cookies & crackers

Brownie Lady LLC..G....... 954 989-0630
Hollywood *(G-5791)*
Jada Foods LLC..F 305 319-0263
Hallandale Beach *(G-5193)*
Magnolias Gurmet Bky Itln Deli.................G....... 352 207-2667
Ocala *(G-11990)*
Paleo Simplified LLC....................................G....... 813 446-5969
Safety Harbor *(G-15500)*
Ricos Tostaditos Inc.....................................F 305 885-7392
Hialeah *(G-5601)*

BAKERY PRDTS: Crackers

Gilda Industries Inc......................................D....... 305 887-8286
Hialeah *(G-5431)*
Rika Bakeries Inc..F 305 691-5673
Hialeah *(G-5602)*
Tuly Corporation..F 305 633-0710
Miami *(G-10512)*

BAKERY PRDTS: Doughnuts, Exc Frozen

Dip-A-Dee Donuts...E....... 352 460-4266
Leesburg *(G-8150)*
Orlando Donut Mfg LLC.................................F 407 933-7111
Kissimmee *(G-7281)*

BAKERY PRDTS: Dry

Barjor Baking Group LLC..............................G....... 239 325-8591
Naples *(G-11183)*
Bingo Bakery Inc...F 305 545-9993
Miami *(G-9246)*
Megatron Equity Partners Inc......................F 305 789-6688
Miami *(G-9972)*
Star Bakery Inc..F 305 633-4284
Miami *(G-10409)*

BAKERY PRDTS: Frozen

Blue Coast Bakers LLC...................................E....... 386 944-0800
Ormond Beach *(G-13355)*
Caligiuri Corporation....................................E....... 407 324-4441
Sanford *(G-16006)*
Epic Harvests LLC...E....... 904 503-5143
Jacksonville *(G-6369)*
Hometown Foods Usa LLC............................C....... 305 887-5200
Medley *(G-8665)*
OPelle Enterprises Inc...................................E....... 954 942-7338
Pompano Beach *(G-14780)*
Sunsof Inc..E....... 305 691-1875
Hialeah *(G-5641)*

BAKERY PRDTS: Pastries, Danish, Frozen

La Autentica...G....... 786 409-3779
Hialeah *(G-5480)*

BAKERY PRDTS: Pastries, Exc Frozen

Bkn International Inc.......................................G....... 301 518-7153
Miami *(G-9254)*
Panapastry LLC..G....... 305 883-1557
Medley *(G-8702)*
Tuly Corporation..F 305 633-0710
Miami *(G-10512)*

BAKERY PRDTS: Pies, Exc Frozen

Darland Bakery Inc..F 407 894-1061
Orlando *(G-12648)*
Empanada Lady Co...F 786 271-6460
Miami *(G-9525)*

BAKERY PRDTS: Rolls, Bread Type, Fresh Or Frozen

Egg Roll Skins Inc....F....305 836-0571
Hialeah (G-5391)
Martins Fmous Pstry Shoppe Inc....G....800 548-1200
Tallahassee (G-17297)

BAKERY PRDTS: Wholesalers

Gfoodz LLC....G....561 703-4505
Boynton Beach (G-912)
Southern Bakeries Inc....C....863 682-1155
Lakeland (G-7800)

BAKERY PRDTS: Yeast Goods, Sweet, Exc Frozen

Richardson Family Products LLC....G....239 896-3595
Lehigh Acres (G-8205)

BAKERY: Wholesale Or Wholesale & Retail Combined

904 Sweet Treatz Street LLC....G....800 889-3298
Jacksonville (G-6105)
Achsahs Delight Bakery LLC....G....954 533-1843
Fort Lauderdale (G-3778)
Bakerly LLC....E....305 608-4479
Coral Gables (G-2125)
Bimbo Bakeries USA....G....941 875-5945
North Port (G-11732)
Bimbo Bakeries USA....F....954 968-7684
Fort Lauderdale (G-3853)
Brooklyn Water Enterprises Inc....E....877 224-3580
Delray Beach (G-3053)
Brownsugarbae LLC....G....954 554-0318
Fort Lauderdale (G-3872)
Buttercream Cpcakes Cof Sp Inc....F....305 669-8181
Coral Gables (G-2128)
Clear Distribution Inc....G....904 330-5624
Jacksonville (G-6267)
CMC Bakery LLC....E....978 682-2382
Pompano Beach (G-14637)
Coleo LLC....F....215 436-0902
Daytona Beach (G-2645)
Cusanos Italian Bakery Inc....E....786 506-4281
Orlando (G-12637)
Ebs Quality Service Inc....F....305 595-4048
Miami (G-9497)
Edca Bakery Corporation....F....305 448-7843
Coral Gables (G-2141)
Enchanting Creations....G....305 978-2828
Miami Shores (G-10884)
Farartis LLC....G....305 594-5704
Miami (G-9559)
Flowers Baking Co Miami LLC....F....772 778-3990
Vero Beach (G-18620)
Flowers Baking Co Miami LLC....E....305 599-8457
Doral (G-3353)
Flowers Bkg Jacksonville LLC....D....904 354-3771
Jacksonville (G-6407)
Frosting....G....772 234-2915
Vero Beach (G-18622)
Gfoodz LLC....G....561 703-4505
Boynton Beach (G-912)
Giovannis Bakery Inc....F....727 536-2253
Largo (G-7958)
H&K Home Supplies Distrs LLC....F....786 308-6024
Homestead (G-5966)
Ipq Trade Corp....F....786 522-2310
Miami (G-9768)
Kellys Bakery Corp....F....305 685-4622
Opa Locka (G-12330)
La Mansion Latina LLC....G....305 406-1606
Miami (G-9843)
Lisa Bakery Inc....G....305 888-8431
Hialeah (G-5487)
Magnolias Gurmet Bky Itln Deli....G....352 207-2667
Ocala (G-11990)
Mishas Cupcakes Inc....E....786 200-6153
Miami (G-10028)
Mr GS Foods....F....352 799-1806
Brooksville (G-1255)
Nani Sweets LLC....G....305 793-1077
Hialeah (G-5532)
New Vbb LLC....E....904 631-5978
Jacksonville (G-6629)
New York Intl Bread Co....D....407 843-9744
Orlando (G-13000)
Palanjian Enterprises Inc....F....850 244-2848
Fort Walton Beach (G-4820)
Pane Rustica Bakery & Cafe....F....813 902-8828
Tampa (G-17970)
Parinto Global Enterprises LLC....G....305 606-3107
Doral (G-3454)
Payo LLC....G....786 368-8655
Davie (G-2567)
Phils Cake Box Bakeries Inc....D....813 348-0128
Tampa (G-17991)
Pin Hsiao & Associates LLC....F....425 637-3357
Port Orange (G-15028)
Popcorn Cellar LLC....G....239 272-8494
Naples (G-11372)
Rouzbeh Inc....E....727 587-7077
Largo (G-8042)
St Johns Bky & Gourmet Fd Co....F....813 727-3528
Jacksonville (G-6806)
Swah-Rey 2 LLC....G....727 767-0527
Saint Petersburg (G-15931)
Swami Foods LLC....F....888 697-9264
Lake Mary (G-7453)
Sweet Creations By L S Young....G....772 584-7206
Vero Beach (G-18669)
Tulipan Bakery Inc....F....561 832-6107
West Palm Beach (G-19071)
Universal Bakery LLC....G....786 566-3303
Opa Locka (G-12367)
Way Beyond Bagels Inc....F....561 638-1320
Delray Beach (G-3159)
Willie Maes Pies LLC....G....407 655-9360
Kissimmee (G-7315)

BALCONIES: Metal

Clear Horizon Ventures Company....E....727 372-1100
Hudson (G-6018)
Frattle Stairs & Rails Inc....F....904 384-3495
Jacksonville (G-6415)
Solara Industries Inc....E....863 688-3330
Lakeland (G-7796)

BALLOONS: Toy & Advertising, Rubber

Aerial Products Corporation....F....800 973-9110
Jacksonville (G-6126)
Boulder Blimp Company Inc....F....303 664-1122
Miami (G-9271)
Put Your Name On It LLC....G....813 972-1460
Tampa (G-18026)

BANDAGES

Aso LLC....C....941 379-0300
Sarasota (G-16352)

BANDS: Plastic

Price Chpper Med Wrstbands Inc....G....407 505-5809
Orlando (G-13086)

BANKING SCHOOLS, TRAINING

West Texas Protein Inc....F....806 250-5959
Jacksonville (G-6911)

BANNERS: Fabric

AMI Graphics Inc....E....352 629-4455
Ocala (G-11873)
Boulder Blimp Company Inc....F....303 664-1122
Miami (G-9271)
Delray Awning Inc....F....561 276-5381
Delray Beach (G-3069)
Flyrite Banner Makers Inc....F....352 873-7501
Ocala (G-11949)
Gulf Glo Banners and Signs LLC....G....850 234-0952
Panama City (G-13913)
Imprint Promotions LLC....G....321 622-8946
Melbourne (G-8850)
In The News Inc....D....813 882-8886
Tampa (G-17775)
Kiteman Productions Inc....G....407 943-8480
Orlando (G-12874)
Olympus Group Inc....G....407 851-6229
Orlando (G-13021)
Outdoor America Images Inc....E....813 888-8796
Tampa (G-17964)

BAR JOISTS & CONCRETE REINFORCING BARS: Fabricated

Capstone Cg LLC....F....941 371-3321
Sarasota (G-16187)
R&W Distributors Inc....G....239 948-5735
Bonita Springs (G-851)

BARBECUE EQPT

A&J Manufacturing Inc....E....912 638-4724
Tampa (G-17377)
Advanced Outdoor Concepts Inc....G....954 429-1428
Deerfield Beach (G-2765)
American Household Inc....D....561 912-4100
Boca Raton (G-422)
Dryer Vent Wizard of Pb....F....561 901-3464
Boynton Beach (G-899)
Firetainment Inc....G....888 552-7897
Orlando (G-12740)
L C Ch International Inc....G....305 888-1323
Hialeah (G-5478)
Profire Inc....F....305 665-5313
Pinecrest (G-14331)
Sunbeam Americas Holdings LLC....C....561 912-4100
Boca Raton (G-736)
Sunbeam Latin America LLC....E....786 845-2540
Boca Raton (G-737)
Sunbeam Products Inc....B....561 912-4100
Boca Raton (G-738)

BARGES BUILDING & REPAIR

Hendry Shipyard Joint Ventr 1....E....813 241-9206
Tampa (G-17752)

BARRELS: Shipping, Metal

Extreme Coatings....G....727 528-7998
Saint Petersburg (G-15775)
Migrandy Corp....E....321 459-0044
Merritt Island (G-9004)

BARRICADES: Metal

All American Barricades....G....305 685-6124
Fort Lauderdale (G-3796)
Bobs Barricades Inc....E....813 886-0518
Tampa (G-17478)
Bobs Barricades Inc....E....239 656-1183
Fort Myers (G-4379)
L C Acme Barricades....D....904 781-1950
Jacksonville (G-6548)
Lrvs Barricades LLC....G....305 343-6101
Miami (G-9914)
Rssi Barriers Llc....E....850 871-9300
Panama City (G-13948)
Safety Systems Barricades....G....407 674-8440
Orlando (G-13154)
Safety Zone Specialists Inc....G....863 984-1385
Lakeland (G-7784)
Traffic Control Pdts Fla Inc....F....813 621-8484
Fort Myers (G-4636)
Traffic Control Pdts Fla Inc....F....407 521-6777
Orlando (G-13267)
Traffic Control Pdts Fla Inc....F....352 372-7088
Jacksonville (G-6865)

BARS & BAR SHAPES: Steel, Cold-Finished, Own Hot-Rolled

Florida Stl Frame Truss Mfg LL....G....813 460-0006
Wesley Chapel (G-18746)
Sheffield Steel Corporation....A....918 245-1335
Tampa (G-18095)

BARS & BAR SHAPES: Steel, Hot-Rolled

Urban Metals LLC....F....813 241-2801
Tampa (G-18225)

BARS, COLD FINISHED: Steel, From Purchased Hot-Rolled

Stuart Building Products LLC....G....239 461-3100
Fort Myers (G-4613)

BARS: Cargo, Stabilizing, Metal

Gyro-Gale Inc....G....772 283-1711
Stuart (G-16952)

BARS: Concrete Reinforcing, Fabricated Steel

Atlantic Steel Cnstr LLC....G....419 236-2200
Miami (G-9184)
Brunsteel Corp....G....305 251-7607
Miami (G-9281)
Davanti Doors Llc....G....239 842-8341
Fort Myers (G-4426)
Gerdau Ameristeel US Inc....B....813 286-8383
Tampa (G-17711)
Gerdau USA Inc....B....813 286-8383
Tampa (G-17712)
Gulf Coast Rebar Inc....E....813 247-1200
Tampa (G-17734)
Raw Energy Materials Corp....F....954 270-9000
Pompano Beach (G-14825)
S & S Welding Inc....F....863 533-2888
Bartow (G-333)

BASES, BEVERAGE

Al-Rite Fruits and Syrups Inc....G....305 652-2540
Miami (G-9099)
Bev-Co Enterprises Inc....E....786 362-6368
Miami (G-9238)
Bev-Co Enterprises Inc....E....786 953-7109
Doral (G-3270)
Celsius Inc....F....561 276-2239
Boca Raton (G-476)
Coastal Promotions Inc....G....850 460-2270
Destin (G-3186)
Fresh Start Beverage Company....G....561 757-6541
Boca Raton (G-540)
Nutrition Laboratories Inc....E....727 442-2747
Clearwater (G-1815)
Squeeze It Corp....G....954 851-2443
Aventura (G-281)
Sunny Hill International Inc....G....386 736-5757
Deland (G-3016)
Top Drinks USA Corp....G....305 407-3514
Miami (G-10490)
Yos Bottling LLC....F....863 258-6820
Dade City (G-2437)

BATCHING PLANTS: Cement Silos

Scutti America Inc....F....954 384-2377
Weston (G-19167)

BATHING SUIT STORES

Double J of Broward Inc....E....954 659-8880
Weston (G-19121)
Ultimate Swimwear Inc....G....386 668-8900
Altamonte Springs (G-80)

BATHROOM ACCESS & FITTINGS: Vitreous China & Earthenware

Alabama Marble Co Inc....F....305 718-8000
Doral (G-3232)
National Bidet Corp....G....786 325-6593
Miami Beach (G-10696)
Terracassa LLC....G....786 581-7741
Miami (G-10468)

BATHROOM FIXTURES: Plastic

See-Ray Plumbing Inc....E....772 489-2474
Vero Beach (G-18663)
Spa World Corporation....D....866 588-8008
Miami (G-10390)

BATHTUBS: Concrete

Hamsard Usa Inc....C....386 761-1830
Daytona Beach (G-2673)

BATTERIES, EXC AUTOMOTIVE: Wholesalers

Exide Battery....G....904 783-1224
Jacksonville (G-6373)
Rayovac Corp....G....727 393-0966
Largo (G-8035)
TAe Trans Atlantic Elec Inc....E....631 595-9206
Tampa (G-18153)

BATTERIES: Alkaline, Cell Storage

Cleva Technologies LLC....F....561 654-5279
Boca Raton (G-485)
Inspired Energy LLC....C....352 472-4855
Newberry (G-11557)

BATTERIES: Dry

T N R Technical Inc....F....407 321-3011
Sanford (G-16125)

BATTERIES: Rechargeable

Creating Tech Solutions LLC....E....727 914-3001
Clearwater (G-1641)
Kendoo Technology Inc....G....305 592-9688
Doral (G-3407)
Mathews Associates Inc....C....407 323-3390
Sanford (G-16082)

BATTERIES: Storage

Amper Usa LLC....G....305 717-3101
Doral (G-3248)
Authentic Trading Inc....G....347 866-7241
Davie (G-2500)
Caliber Sales Engineering Inc....E....954 430-6234
Sunrise (G-17103)
Chargex LLC....G....855 242-7439
Tampa (G-17532)
Chicago Electronic Distrs Inc....F....312 985-6175
Port Charlotte (G-14969)
Clarios LLC....G....904 786-9161
Jacksonville (G-6265)
Creating Tech Solutions LLC....E....727 914-3001
Clearwater (G-1643)
Duracell Company....E....561 494-7550
West Palm Beach (G-18857)
Enersys Advanced Systems Inc....D....610 208-1934
Pinellas Park (G-14346)
Es Tudios Corp....G....305 300-9262
Miami (G-9535)
Exide Battery....G....904 783-1224
Jacksonville (G-6373)
Geneforce Incorporated....G....786 823-0700
Miami (G-9622)
Kash Corporation....G....786 368-7747
Miami (G-9816)
Lithionics Battery LLC....F....727 726-4204
Clearwater (G-1762)
Lithium Battery Company LLC....F....813 504-0074
Tampa (G-17850)
Max Global North America LLC....G....954 727-6656
Miramar (G-11015)
Palm Beach Btry Ventures LLC....F....561 881-8900
Lake Park (G-7477)
Rainbow Storage....F....386 362-1171
Live Oak (G-8238)
T N R Technical Inc....F....407 321-3011
Sanford (G-16125)
W & W Manufacturing Co....E....516 942-0011
Tampa (G-18249)

BATTERIES: Wet

Adva-Lite Inc....E....727 369-5319
Seminole (G-16735)
Creating Tech Solutions LLC....E....727 914-3001
Clearwater (G-1641)
Creating Tech Solutions LLC....E....727 914-3001
Clearwater (G-1643)
Empire Scientific....G....630 510-8636
Tampa (G-17637)
Future Plus of Florida....G....612 240-7275
Tampa (G-17698)
JW Marketing and Consulting....F....866 323-0001
Coconut Creek (G-2086)
Oakridge Globl Enrgy Sltons In....E....321 610-7959
Palm Bay (G-13528)
Rayovac Corp....G....727 393-0966
Largo (G-8035)
TAe Trans Atlantic Elec Inc....E....631 595-9206
Tampa (G-18153)

BATTERY CHARGERS

Creating Tech Solutions LLC....E....727 914-3001
Clearwater (G-1641)
Lithium Battery Company LLC....F....813 504-0074
Tampa (G-17850)

BATTERY CHARGERS: Storage, Motor & Engine Generator Type

Capacity Inc....E....855 440-7825
Sarasota (G-16186)

BATTERY REPAIR & SVCS

Battery Usa Inc....E....863 665-6317
Lakeland (G-7643)

BEARINGS & PARTS Ball

Centrifugal Rebabbitting Inc....F....954 522-3003
Fort Lauderdale (G-3891)
Faro Industriale Spa Co....G....941 925-3004
Sarasota (G-16428)

BEARINGS: Ball & Roller

Bearing Specialist Inc....G....305 796-3415
Doral (G-3265)
Debway Corporation....G....305 818-6353
Hialeah (G-5366)
NSK Latin America Inc....E....305 477-0605
Miami (G-10083)

BEAUTY & BARBER SHOP EQPT

American Polylactide Inds....G....352 653-5963
Ocala (G-11872)
Bala Industries LLC....E....954 243-9804
Lakeland (G-7642)
Betty Dain Creations LLC....D....305 769-3451
Medley (G-8623)
Brewer International Inc....F....772 562-0555
Vero Beach (G-18603)
C & M Manufacturing LLC....G....407 673-9601
Winter Park (G-19386)
CLJ Industries Inc....G....562 688-0508
Jacksonville (G-6269)
Cmz Industries LLC....G....727 726-1443
Clearwater (G-1629)
Daje Industries Inc....G....305 592-7711
Doral (G-3322)
Deal To Win Inc....E....718 609-1165
Oakland Park (G-11796)
Desco Industries....G....305 255-7744
Miami (G-9457)
Desind Industries Corp....G....212 729-0192
Orlando (G-12665)
Ecotec Manufacturing Inc....E....863 357-4500
Okeechobee (G-12177)
Egm Manufacturing Corp....F....954 440-0445
Sunrise (G-17118)
Elite Flower Services Inc....E....305 436-7400
Miami (G-9515)
Fam Industries Inc....F....281 779-0650
Jacksonville (G-6377)
Gibbons Industries Inc....G....352 330-0294
Lutz (G-8384)
Goodwill Industries S Fla Inc....C....941 745-8459
Bradenton (G-1051)
Hall Industries Incorporated....F....239 768-0372
Fort Myers (G-4480)
Hayes Ivy Manufacturing....G....954 306-2647
Fort Lauderdale (G-4043)
Ibs Manufacturing LLC....G....352 629-9752
Ocala (G-11968)
Its Technologies Logistics LLC....C....904 751-1300
Jacksonville (G-6505)
Jet Factory LLC....G....305 848-8846
Boynton Beach (G-924)
Jtac Industries LLC....G....813 928-0628
Plant City (G-14441)
Kcon Industries LLC....G....917 250-7402
Hialeah (G-5471)
Keystone Rv Company....C....813 228-0625
Tampa (G-17821)
Kirkland Industries LLC....G....386 496-3491
Lake Butler (G-7339)
Kos Industries Inc....G....863 318-1511
Winter Haven (G-19333)
Nigella Industries Inc....G....813 404-7923
Treasure Island (G-18476)
No 1 Beauty Salon Furniture....G....954 981-0403
Oakland Park (G-11825)
Omz Industries LLC....F....786 210-6763
Doral (G-3449)
Power Foam Manufacturing Inc....G....305 303-2956
Hialeah (G-5562)
Premier Plastics LLC....E....305 805-3333
Boynton Beach (G-943)
Premier Plastics LLC....G....305 805-3333
Hallandale Beach (G-5203)
Prime Manufacturing Canada....G....850 332-7193
Pensacola (G-14238)

Reflection Manufacturing......D...... 407 297-5727
Orlando *(G-13126)*
Rytex Industries Inc......F...... 727 557-7450
Largo *(G-8044)*
S P Manufacturing LLC......G...... 305 362-0456
Hialeah *(G-5607)*
Sb Mfg LLC......G...... 352 458-0137
Dade City *(G-2434)*
Scarb Industries Inc......G...... 772 597-3898
Indiantown *(G-6074)*
Sota Manufacturing LLC......E...... 561 251-3389
Oakland Park *(G-11841)*
Sun-Art Designs Inc......E...... 954 929-6622
Hollywood *(G-5916)*
Surfskate Industries LLC......G...... 954 349-1116
Fort Lauderdale *(G-4269)*
Tactical Prchute Dlvry Systems......F...... 813 782-7482
Zephyrhills *(G-19540)*
The Caldwell Manufacturing Co......E...... 386 418-3525
Alachua *(G-19)*
Wcm Group Inc......G...... 516 238-4261
Flagler Beach *(G-3758)*

BEAUTY & BARBER SHOP EQPT & SPLYS WHOLESALERS

Betty Dain Creations LLC......D...... 305 769-3451
Medley *(G-8623)*

BEAUTY SALONS

New York Nails......G...... 904 448-6040
Jacksonville *(G-6631)*
Xoxo Beauty Studio LLC......G...... 407 476-7172
Altamonte Springs *(G-85)*

BEDDING, BEDSPREADS, BLANKETS & SHEETS

Tuka Imports LLC......G...... 305 640-8336
Miami *(G-10511)*

BEDDING, BEDSPREADS, BLANKETS & SHEETS: Bedspread, Lace

Jayco International LLC......D...... 407 855-8880
Orlando *(G-12852)*

BEDDING, FROM SILK OR MANMADE FIBER

Bedding Acquisition LLC......G...... 561 997-6900
Boca Raton *(G-443)*

BEDS: Hospital

Kci......G...... 352 572-2873
Lecanto *(G-8136)*
Medtek Medical Solutions LLC......F...... 786 458-8080
Miami *(G-9968)*
Mhkap LLC......G...... 239 919-0786
Naples *(G-11327)*

BEDSPREADS & BED SETS, FROM PURCHASED MATERIALS

Associated Interior Desgr Svc......F...... 561 655-4926
West Palm Beach *(G-18805)*
Distinctive Creat Intr Wkshp I......F...... 954 921-1861
Hollywood *(G-5812)*
Kenco Hospitality Inc......D...... 954 921-5434
Fort Lauderdale *(G-4087)*
Kenco Quilting & Textiles Inc......F...... 954 921-5434
Fort Lauderdale *(G-4088)*
Mac D&D Inc......G...... 305 821-9452
Hialeah *(G-5495)*
Tiffany Quilting & Drapery......F...... 407 834-6386
Longwood *(G-8343)*

BEDSPREADS, COTTON

Jose Leal Enterprises Inc......D...... 305 887-9611
Hialeah *(G-5467)*

BEEKEEPERS' SPLYS

Rev-Tech Mfg Solutions LLC......F...... 727 577-4999
Saint Petersburg *(G-15901)*

BEEKEEPERS' SPLYS: Honeycomb Foundations

Honeycommcore LLC......G...... 561 747-2678
West Palm Beach *(G-18897)*

BEER & ALE WHOLESALERS

D G Yuengling and Son Inc......D...... 813 972-8500
Tampa *(G-17584)*

BEER, WINE & LIQUOR STORES

Pair ODice Brewing Co LLC......G...... 727 755-3423
Clearwater *(G-1825)*

BELLOWS

Bellowstech LLC......G...... 386 615-7530
Ormond Beach *(G-13352)*
Bellowstech LLC......E...... 386 615-7530
Ormond Beach *(G-13353)*
Tectron......F...... 904 355-5512
Jacksonville *(G-6844)*

BELLS: Electric

Bell Brothers Electric LLC......E...... 954 496-0632
Coral Springs *(G-2225)*

BELTING: Fabric

Signature AVI US Holdings Inc......F...... 407 648-7230
Orlando *(G-13193)*

BELTING: Rubber

Adventry Corp......F...... 305 582-2977
Miami Lakes *(G-10760)*
Gate Petroleum Company......G...... 904 998-7126
Jacksonville *(G-6420)*
Signature AVI US Holdings Inc......F...... 407 648-7230
Orlando *(G-13193)*

BELTS: Conveyor, Made From Purchased Wire

Belt Maintenance Group Inc......G...... 813 907-9316
Wesley Chapel *(G-18740)*
Industrial Conveyor Belt......G...... 904 345-3046
Jacksonville *(G-6492)*
Roro Inc......F...... 561 909-6220
West Palm Beach *(G-19024)*

BELTS: Seat, Automotive & Aircraft

CSC Racing Corporation......F...... 248 548-5727
Jupiter *(G-7021)*
Key Safety Systems Inc......G...... 863 668-6000
Lakeland *(G-7726)*
Seatbelt Solutions Llc......E...... 855 642-3964
Jupiter *(G-7111)*

BEVERAGE BASES & SYRUPS

Splash Beverage Group Inc......G...... 954 745-5815
Fort Lauderdale *(G-4254)*

BEVERAGE PRDTS: Brewers' Grain

Brew Hub LLC......D...... 863 698-7600
Lakeland *(G-7650)*

BEVERAGE PRDTS: Brewers' Rice

Hyperion Managing LLC......G...... 904 612-3987
Jacksonville *(G-6485)*

BEVERAGE STORES

Babys Coffee LLC......G...... 305 744-9866
Key West *(G-7178)*

BEVERAGE, NONALCOHOLIC: Iced Tea/Fruit Drink, Bottled/Canned

Celsius Holdings Inc......D...... 561 276-2239
Boca Raton *(G-477)*
Fresh Start Beverage Company......G...... 561 757-6541
Boca Raton *(G-540)*
Great America Beverage Co LLC......G...... 786 763-2027
Palmetto Bay *(G-13846)*
Home Bistro Inc......G...... 561 227-2727
Miami Beach *(G-10679)*

Polenghi Usa Inc......F...... 954 637-4900
Deerfield Beach *(G-2887)*

BEVERAGES, ALCOHOLIC: Beer

Anheuser-Busch Incorporated......G...... 863 646-7357
Lakeland *(G-7636)*
Anheuser-Busch Companies LLC......D...... 407 251-4049
Orlando *(G-12480)*
Apple A Day Inc......G...... 941 377-5404
Sarasota *(G-16344)*
Canarchy Craft......E...... 813 348-6363
Tampa *(G-17503)*
Cigar City Brewpub LLC......C...... 813 348-6363
Tampa *(G-17534)*
D G Yuengling and Son Inc......D...... 813 972-8500
Tampa *(G-17584)*
Ellipsis Brewing......G...... 407 556-3241
Orlando *(G-12707)*
Florida Craft Distributors LLC......F...... 813 528-7902
Sanford *(G-16048)*
Great Bay Distributors Inc......C...... 727 584-8626
Holiday *(G-5741)*
Indian River Brewery Corp......E...... 321 728-4114
Cape Canaveral *(G-1361)*
International Keg Rental LLC......F...... 407 900-9992
Orlando *(G-12836)*
JJ Taylor Distrg Fla Inc......G...... 239 267-1006
Fort Myers *(G-4504)*
Krome Brewing Company LLC......G...... 786 601-9337
Miami *(G-9832)*
Le Mundo Vino LLC......F...... 786 369-5232
Miami *(G-9875)*
Molson Coors Brewing Company......G...... 305 792-6620
Miami *(G-10037)*
Rpd Management LLC......G...... 904 710-8911
Jacksonville *(G-6738)*
Titanic Brewing Company Inc......F...... 305 668-1742
Coral Gables *(G-2199)*

BEVERAGES, ALCOHOLIC: Beer & Ale

Blind Mouth Brewing Co LLC......G...... 727 318-7664
Saint Petersburg *(G-15722)*
Bold City Braves LLC......F...... 904 545-3480
Jacksonville *(G-6223)*
Brew Central LLC......F...... 936 714-3402
Jacksonville *(G-6236)*
Bru Fl LLC......G...... 813 431-6815
Tampa *(G-17487)*
Cerberus Craft Distillery LLC......G...... 813 789-1556
Tampa *(G-17527)*
Dukes Brewhouse Inc......F...... 813 758-9309
Plant City *(G-14427)*
Fantasy Brewmasters LLC......G...... 239 206-3247
Naples *(G-11244)*
Florida Brewery Inc......G...... 305 621-0099
Miami *(G-9580)*
Florida Brewery Inc......E...... 863 965-1825
Auburndale *(G-242)*
In The Loop Brewing Inc......G...... 813 857-0111
Land O Lakes *(G-7856)*
Main & Six Brewing Company LLC......G...... 904 673-0144
Jacksonville *(G-6575)*
Orlando Brewing Partners......G...... 407 843-6783
Orlando *(G-13032)*
Rock Brothers Brewing LLC......G...... 917 324-8175
Tampa *(G-18066)*
Sourglass Brewing......G...... 407 262-0056
Longwood *(G-8337)*

BEVERAGES, ALCOHOLIC: Bourbon Whiskey

Key West Smuggler Co......G...... 916 995-1873
Key West *(G-7191)*

BEVERAGES, ALCOHOLIC: Cocktails

Buzz Pop Cocktails Corporation......F...... 727 275-9848
Holiday *(G-5736)*
Miami Cocktail Company Inc......F...... 305 482-1974
Miami *(G-9994)*

BEVERAGES, ALCOHOLIC: Cordials & Premixed Cocktails

Arco Globas Trading LLC......E...... 305 707-7702
De Leon Springs *(G-2737)*

BEVERAGES, ALCOHOLIC: Distilled Liquors

Big Cypress Distillery LLC....................G....... 786 228-9740
Miami *(G-9244)*
Black Coral Rum LLC.............................E....... 561 766-2493
Riviera Beach *(G-15302)*
Caribbean Distillers LLC........................F....... 863 508-1175
Winter Haven *(G-19311)*
Chef Distilled LLC..................................G....... 305 747-8236
Key West *(G-7182)*
Diageo North America Inc.......................D....... 305 476-7761
Coral Gables *(G-2139)*
Dr Spirits Company LLC..........................G....... 561 349-5005
Lake Worth *(G-7546)*
Florida Rum Company LLC......................E....... 305 791-1221
Hollywood *(G-5823)*
Four Seas Distilling Co LLC...................G....... 813 645-0057
Apollo Beach *(G-104)*
Island Joys...G....... 561 201-6005
Fort Lauderdale *(G-4067)*
JB Thome & Co Inc.................................G....... 727 642-0588
St Pete Beach *(G-16882)*
Kozuba & Sons Distillery Inc.................F....... 813 857-8197
Saint Petersburg *(G-15834)*
La Tropical Brewing Co LLC...................G....... 786 362-5429
Coral Gables *(G-2170)*
Leblon LLC..G....... 954 649-0148
Miami *(G-9878)*
List Distillery LLC..................................F....... 239 208-7214
Fort Myers *(G-4519)*
Loggerhead Distillery LLC.....................G....... 321 800-8566
Sanford *(G-16081)*
Manifest Distilling LLC..........................F....... 904 619-1479
Jacksonville *(G-6577)*
Marlin & Barrel Distillery LLC...............G....... 321 230-4755
Fernandina Beach *(G-3743)*
Mezcal Hub LLC......................................G....... 561 373-7972
Lake Worth *(G-7569)*
Papous Craft Distillery LLC...................G....... 813 766-9539
Tarpon Springs *(G-18319)*
St Augustine Dist Co LLC.......................E....... 904 825-4962
Saint Augustine *(G-15618)*
St Petersburg Dist Co LLC.....................F....... 727 581-1544
Saint Petersburg *(G-15924)*
Stilldragon North America LLC..............F....... 561 845-8009
Riviera Beach *(G-15381)*
Sugar Works Distillery LLC....................G....... 386 463-0120
New Smyrna Beach *(G-11546)*
Timber Creek Distilling Llc....................G....... 408 439-0973
Destin *(G-3208)*
Wicked Dolphin Distillery........................G....... 239 565-7947
Cape Coral *(G-1495)*
Winter Park Distilling Co LLC................F....... 407 801-2714
Winter Park *(G-19459)*
World Frost Inc..G....... 786 439-4445
Miami *(G-10620)*

BEVERAGES, ALCOHOLIC: Gin

Incity Security Inc..................................F....... 561 306-9228
West Palm Beach *(G-18902)*

BEVERAGES, ALCOHOLIC: Liquors, Malt

Pair ODice Brewing Co LLC...................G....... 727 755-3423
Clearwater *(G-1825)*

BEVERAGES, ALCOHOLIC: Rum

Bacardi Bottling Corporation.................C....... 904 757-1290
Jacksonville *(G-6187)*
Hemingway Rum Company LLC..............F....... 305 414-8754
Key West *(G-7189)*
Ron Matusalem & Matusa Fla Inc..........F....... 305 448-8255
Miami *(G-10279)*

BEVERAGES, ALCOHOLIC: Scotch Whiskey

Scottish Spirits Imports Inc....................F....... 954 332-1116
Fort Lauderdale *(G-4225)*

BEVERAGES, ALCOHOLIC: Vodka

Florida Distillery LLC..............................G....... 813 347-6565
Tampa *(G-17675)*
Italian Moonshiners Inc..........................G....... 954 687-4500
Doral *(G-3395)*

BEVERAGES, ALCOHOLIC: Wine Coolers

Brumate LLC..G....... 317 474-7352
Fort Lauderdale *(G-3873)*

BEVERAGES, ALCOHOLIC: Wines

1506 N Florida LLC..................................G....... 813 229-0900
Tampa *(G-17372)*
Abide Family Winery Inc..........................G....... 850 258-0743
Panama City Beach *(G-13968)*
Amizetta Vineyards..................................G....... 707 963-1460
Marco Island *(G-8523)*
Barton & Guestier Usa Inc......................G....... 305 895-9757
Miami *(G-9224)*
Bea Sue Vineyards Inc............................G....... 352 446-5204
Summerfield *(G-17057)*
Buena Cepa Wines LLC..........................G....... 310 621-2566
Key Biscayne *(G-7154)*
Catanias Winery LLC..............................G....... 941 321-9650
Englewood *(G-3672)*
Cavallo Estate Winery LLC.....................G....... 352 500-9463
Lecanto *(G-8130)*
Charleston Winery...................................G....... 843 425-1265
Vero Beach *(G-18610)*
Chautuqua Vineyards Winery Inc..........F....... 850 892-5887
Defuniak Springs *(G-2940)*
Coopers Hawk Intrmdate Hldg LL.........G....... 904 996-2466
Jacksonville *(G-6288)*
Corkscrew Winery...................................G....... 352 751-1787
Ocala *(G-11909)*
De Vinco Company..................................G....... 941 722-1100
Seffner *(G-16724)*
Elk Creek Wine...G....... 561 529-2822
Jupiter *(G-7033)*
Faraday Inc...F....... 813 536-6104
Tampa *(G-17659)*
Florida Orange Groves Inc.....................F....... 727 347-4025
South Pasadena *(G-16834)*
Florida Winery Inc....................................G....... 727 362-0008
Madeira Beach *(G-8446)*
Fws Distributors LLC..............................G....... 561 312-3318
Miami *(G-9606)*
Fws Distributors LLC..............................G....... 305 677-9663
Orlando *(G-12768)*
Gravity Produce LLC...............................G....... 269 471-9463
Fort Myers Beach *(G-4663)*
Headwaters Management LLC...............G....... 608 209-3111
Fort Lauderdale *(G-4046)*
Henscratch Farms Inc.............................G....... 863 699-2060
Lake Placid *(G-7489)*
JD Wine Concepts LLC...........................G....... 407 730-3082
Orlando *(G-12854)*
Johns Pass Winery...................................G....... 727 362-0008
Madeira Beach *(G-8447)*
Keel & Curley Winery LLC.....................F....... 813 752-9100
Plant City *(G-14442)*
Land O Lakes Winery LLC......................G....... 813 995-9463
Land O Lakes *(G-7859)*
Maestro Winery...G....... 308 627-6436
Jacksonville *(G-6574)*
Masso Estate Winery LLC......................F....... 305 707-7749
Coral Gables *(G-2174)*
Orvino Imports & Distrg Inc...................F....... 954 785-3100
Coral Springs *(G-2300)*
Royal Manor Vineyard & Winery............G....... 386 684-6270
Interlachen *(G-6079)*
Sapore Di Vino Inc...................................F....... 561 818-8411
Miami *(G-10305)*
Schnebly Redlands Winery Inc..............E....... 786 247-2060
Homestead *(G-5992)*
Seavin Inc..E....... 352 394-8627
Clermont *(G-1973)*
Seavin Inc..E....... 904 826-1594
Saint Augustine *(G-15607)*
Slainte Wines Inc......................................G....... 954 474-4547
Davie *(G-2592)*
So NAPA...G....... 407 782-0459
New Smyrna Beach *(G-11544)*
Sokol Vineyards LLC................................G....... 352 368-4069
Ocala *(G-12055)*
Stirling Winery..G....... 727 734-4025
Dunedin *(G-3589)*
Strong Tower Vineyard.............................G....... 352 799-7612
Spring Hill *(G-16878)*
Swan Neck Winery....................................G....... 850 495-3897
Pensacola *(G-14272)*
Tampa Wines LLC.....................................G....... 727 799-9463
Clearwater *(G-1905)*
Tita Itln Import & Export LLC..................G....... 305 608-4258
Miami *(G-10480)*
Vicente Gandia Pla....................................C....... 310 699-8559
Miami *(G-10580)*
Vicente Gandia Usa Inc............................G....... 310 699-8559
Miami *(G-10581)*
Vines Worldwide LLC................................G....... 786 353-2102
North Miami *(G-11662)*
Vinita USA Co..G....... 650 260-5161
Miami *(G-10585)*
Vino Del Grotto..G....... 321 508-1478
Elkton *(G-3652)*
Whispering Oaks Winery..........................G....... 352 748-0449
Oxford *(G-13465)*
Wine World Inc...G....... 786 348-8780
Miami *(G-10610)*

BEVERAGES, MALT

Center For Vital Living DBA....................F....... 239 213-2222
Naples *(G-11205)*

BEVERAGES, MILK BASED

Attitude Drinks Incorporated...................G....... 561 227-2727
North Palm Beach *(G-11717)*
Sneakz LLC..G....... 201 693-5695
Jupiter *(G-7116)*

BEVERAGES, NONALCOHOLIC: Bottled & canned soft drinks

7up Snapple...G....... 561 732-7395
Boynton Beach *(G-871)*
Al-Rite Fruits and Syrups Inc..................G....... 305 652-2540
Miami *(G-9099)*
Bacardi Bottling Corporation...................C....... 904 757-1290
Jacksonville *(G-6187)*
Canada Dry of Florida...............................G....... 941 758-7010
Bradenton *(G-1012)*
Ccbcc Operations LLC...............................D....... 850 785-6171
Panama City *(G-13876)*
Coca Cola Bottling Co...............................E....... 813 569-3030
Brandon *(G-1153)*
Coca Cola Enterprises Inc........................G....... 305 256-3628
Miami *(G-9369)*
Coca-Cola Beverages Fla LLC..................C....... 813 623-5411
Tampa *(G-17544)*
Coca-Cola Beverages Fla LLC..................B....... 800 438-2653
Tampa *(G-17545)*
Coca-Cola Beverages Fla LLC..................B....... 904 786-2720
Jacksonville *(G-6278)*
Coca-Cola Bottling Co...............................F....... 305 378-1073
Miami *(G-9370)*
Coca-Cola Bottling Co...............................G....... 844 863-2653
Sarasota *(G-16387)*
Coca-Cola Btlg Centl Fla LLC..................F....... 832 260-0462
Brandon *(G-1154)*
Coca-Cola Co..G....... 407 287-4527
Clermont *(G-1954)*
Coca-Cola Company...................................G....... 407 886-1568
Apopka *(G-121)*
Coca-Cola Company...................................G....... 941 351-4695
Sarasota *(G-16388)*
Coca-Cola Company...................................G....... 954 985-5000
Hollywood *(G-5802)*
Coca-Cola Company...................................E....... 404 676-2121
Apopka *(G-122)*
Coca-Cola Company...................................G....... 904 342-5609
Saint Augustine *(G-15531)*
Coca-Cola Company...................................G....... 407 560-0107
Orlando *(G-12596)*
Coca-Cola Company...................................G....... 727 736-7101
Dunedin *(G-3574)*
Coca-Cola Company...................................G....... 954 961-8564
Hollywood *(G-5803)*
Coca-Cola Company Distribution............F....... 407 814-1327
Apopka *(G-125)*
Coca-Cola Enterprises...............................F....... 954 917-1108
Pompano Beach *(G-14640)*
Coca-Cola Refreshments USA Inc...........G....... 863 551-3700
Auburndale *(G-235)*
Cutrale Citrus Juices USA Inc..................B....... 352 728-7800
Leesburg *(G-8149)*
Florida Coca-Cola Bottling Co..................B....... 561 848-0055
Riviera Beach *(G-15329)*
Florida Coca-Cola Bottling Co..................B....... 813 569-2600
Brandon *(G-1159)*
Florida Coca-Cola Bottling Co..................B....... 772 461-3636
Fort Pierce *(G-4698)*
Florida Coca-Cola Bottling Co..................B....... 850 678-9370
Valparaiso *(G-18510)*
Florida Coca-Cola Bottling Co..................B....... 850 478-4800
Pensacola *(G-14154)*
Florida Coca-Cola Bottling Co..................B....... 850 575-6122
Tallahassee *(G-17253)*
ICEE Company...F....... 954 966-7502
Dania *(G-2447)*

Kona Gold LLC ....F 844 714-2224
Melbourne *(G-8861)*
Mega 4s Bottling Company LLC ....G 305 815-3775
Miami *(G-9971)*
Milca Bottling Company ....F 305 365-0044
Key Biscayne *(G-7160)*
Opreme Beverage Corp ....G 954 699-0669
Jupiter *(G-7088)*
Panamco LLC ....F 305 856-7100
Miami *(G-10137)*
Pepsico Inc ....G 800 433-2652
Deerfield Beach *(G-2885)*
Pepsico Inc ....G 407 933-5542
Kissimmee *(G-7286)*
Primo Water Corporation ....A 844 237-7466
Tampa *(G-18011)*
Quaker Oats Company ....C 407 846-5926
Kissimmee *(G-7292)*
Refresco Beverages US Inc ....E 813 313-1711
Tampa *(G-18045)*
Sergeant Bretts Coffee LLC ....G 561 451-0048
Coconut Creek *(G-2094)*
Southeast Atlantic Bevera ....G 904 739-1000
Miami *(G-10384)*
Swire Pacific Holdings Inc ....F 305 371-3877
Miami *(G-10448)*
Titan Natural Focus Corp ....G 305 778-7005
West Palm Beach *(G-19065)*
Tropical Bottling Corporation ....G 786 636-6169
Medley *(G-8743)*
Venga LLC ....G 561 665-8200
Delray Beach *(G-3156)*

BEVERAGES, NONALCOHOLIC: Carbonated

APRU LLC ....G 888 741-3777
Orlando *(G-12483)*
Frito-Lay North America Inc ....G 972 334-7000
Seminole *(G-16747)*
Pepsi Beverages Company ....E 407 241-4110
Orlando *(G-13060)*
Pepsi Bottling Group ....G 863 452-9920
Avon Park *(G-292)*
Pepsi Bottling Group Inc ....G 863 687-7605
Lakeland *(G-7765)*
Pepsi St Pete ....F 727 527-8113
Saint Petersburg *(G-15875)*
Pepsi-Cola Bottling Co Tampa ....C 239 643-4642
Naples *(G-11360)*
Pepsi-Cola Bottling Co Tampa ....C 813 971-2550
Tampa *(G-17982)*
Pepsi-Cola Bottling Co Tampa ....C 941 378-1058
Sarasota *(G-16542)*
Pepsi-Cola Bottling Co Tampa ....F 407 857-3301
Orlando *(G-13061)*
Pepsi-Cola Bottling Co Tampa ....C 239 337-2011
Fort Myers *(G-4567)*
Pepsi-Cola Bottling Co Tampa ....C 727 942-3664
Holiday *(G-5748)*
Pepsi-Cola Bottling Co Tampa ....C 407 826-5929
Orlando *(G-13062)*
Pepsi-Cola Btlg Ft Ldrdl-Palm ....D 561 848-1000
Riviera Beach *(G-15361)*
Pepsi-Cola Metro Btlg Co Inc ....C 904 733-1627
Jacksonville *(G-6668)*
Pepsi-Cola Metro Btlg Co Inc ....G 407 354-5800
Orlando *(G-13063)*
Pepsi-Cola Metro Btlg Co Inc ....G 386 752-8956
Lake City *(G-7375)*
Pepsi-Cola Metro Btlg Co Inc ....G 352 376-8276
Gainesville *(G-4980)*
Pepsi-Cola Metro Btlg Co Inc ....G 352 629-8911
Ocala *(G-12024)*
Pepsi-Cola Metro Btlg Co Inc ....G 321 242-2984
Melbourne *(G-8906)*
Pepsi-Cola Metro Btlg Co Inc ....G 352 797-1160
Brooksville *(G-1260)*
Pepsi-Cola Metro Btlg Co Inc ....C 772 464-6150
Fort Pierce *(G-4731)*
Pepsico Inc ....G 305 593-7500
Medley *(G-8703)*
Pepsico Beverage Distributors ....G 305 537-4477
Miami *(G-10152)*
Pepsico Latin America Beverage ....F 305 537-4477
Miami *(G-10153)*

BEVERAGES, NONALCOHOLIC: Carbonated, Canned & Bottled, Etc

Arkay Distributing Inc ....G 954 536-8413
Fort Lauderdale *(G-3822)*
Asterion Beverages Inc ....G 866 335-2672
Doral *(G-3256)*
D D B Corporation ....G 305 721-9506
Miami *(G-9426)*
Dna Brands Inc ....G 561 654-5722
Lauderdale By The SE *(G-8084)*
Everfresh Juice Co Inc ....E 954 581-0922
Plantation *(G-14513)*
Interbeverage LLC ....G 305 961-1110
Miami *(G-9754)*
Mipe Corp ....G 305 825-1195
Hialeah *(G-5521)*
Prodalim USA Inc ....G 407 656-1000
Winter Garden *(G-19281)*
Refresco Beverages US Inc ....C 813 241-0147
Tampa *(G-18046)*
Refresco Beverages US Inc ....E 314 994-7545
Tampa *(G-18048)*
Refresco US Holding Inc ....E 813 313-1863
Tampa *(G-18049)*
Shasta Beverages Intl Inc ....E 954 581-0922
Plantation *(G-14549)*
Vital Pharmaceuticals Inc ....C 954 641-0570
Fort Lauderdale *(G-4308)*

BEVERAGES, NONALCOHOLIC: Cider

Broski Ciderworks LLC ....G 954 657-8947
Pompano Beach *(G-14623)*

BEVERAGES, NONALCOHOLIC: Flavoring extracts & syrups, nec

Buddy Pauls Inc ....G 561 578-9813
West Palm Beach *(G-18830)*
Florida Flvors Cncentrates Inc ....G 561 775-5714
Palm Beach Gardens *(G-13591)*
Florida Natural Flavors Inc ....E 407 834-5979
Casselberry *(G-1503)*
Givaudan Fragrances Corp ....E 863 667-0821
Lakeland *(G-7698)*
Interamericas Beverages Inc ....G 561 881-1340
Riviera Beach *(G-15334)*
Monin Inc ....C 727 461-3033
Clearwater *(G-1791)*
Pouchfill Packaging LLC ....F 386 274-1600
Daytona Beach *(G-2695)*
Royal Cup Inc ....G 813 664-8902
Tampa *(G-18070)*
Skinny Mixes LLC ....G 727 826-0306
Clearwater *(G-1879)*
Taste Advantage LLC ....G 863 619-8101
Lakeland *(G-7816)*

BEVERAGES, NONALCOHOLIC: Fruit Drnks, Under 100% Juice, Can

H & H Products Company ....E 407 299-5410
Orlando *(G-12793)*
Tropicana Products Inc ....A 941 747-4461
Bradenton *(G-1133)*

BEVERAGES, NONALCOHOLIC: Fruit Juices, Concentrtd, Fountain

Coca-Cola Company ....G 407 886-1568
Apopka *(G-121)*
Coca-Cola Company ....G 407 358-6758
Apopka *(G-124)*

BEVERAGES, NONALCOHOLIC: Lemonade, Bottled & Canned, Etc

Lorina Inc ....F 305 779-3085
Doral *(G-3419)*

BEVERAGES, NONALCOHOLIC: Soft Drinks, Canned & Bottled, Etc

7 Up Snapple Southeast ....G 407 839-1706
Orlando *(G-12421)*
American Bottling Company ....F 813 806-2931
Tampa *(G-17415)*
American Bottling Company ....F 561 732-7395
Boynton Beach *(G-875)*
American Bottling Company ....F 772 461-3383
Fort Pierce *(G-4673)*
American Bottling Company ....F 941 758-7010
Bradenton *(G-987)*
American Bottling Company ....F 863 665-6128
Lakeland *(G-7633)*
American Bottling Company ....F 239 489-0838
Fort Myers *(G-4357)*
American Bottling Company ....F 904 739-1000
Jacksonville *(G-6146)*
Anupack LLC ....G 407 850-1960
Orlando *(G-12481)*
Beverage Canners Inc ....G 305 714-7000
Miami *(G-9239)*
Beverage Canners International ....E 305 714-7000
Miami *(G-9240)*
Beverage Corp Intl Inc ....D 305 714-7000
Miami *(G-9241)*
Bighill Corporation ....G 786 497-1875
Miami Beach *(G-10647)*
Camel Enterprises Corp ....F 954 234-2559
Miami *(G-9304)*
Cawy Bottling Co Inc ....E 305 634-8669
Miami *(G-9328)*
Cloudkiss Beverages Inc ....E 407 324-8500
Sanford *(G-16016)*
Coca-Cola Beverages Fla LLC ....C 407 295-9290
Orlando *(G-12595)*
Coca-Cola Company ....C 407 295-9290
Orlando *(G-12597)*
Coca-Cola Company ....G 407 565-2465
Apopka *(G-123)*
Cola Construction Inc ....G 305 218-3985
Miami Beach *(G-10657)*
Cola Group Riverside LLC ....G 305 940-0277
Sunny Isles Beach *(G-17073)*
Dr Pepper/Seven Up Inc ....F 321 433-3622
Cocoa *(G-2015)*
Dr Pepper/Seven Up Inc ....F 352 732-9777
Ocala *(G-11925)*
Dr Pepper/Seven Up Inc ....F 561 995-6260
Boca Raton *(G-508)*
Ibs Partners Ltd ....E 954 581-0922
Plantation *(G-14523)*
Keurig Dr Pepper Inc ....G 561 227-1424
Tampa *(G-17819)*
National Beverage Corp ....B 954 581-0922
Plantation *(G-14537)*
National Beverage Corp ....G 352 357-7130
Eustis *(G-3715)*
Newbevco Inc ....E 954 581-0922
Plantation *(G-14539)*
Pepsi-Cola Metro Btlg Co Inc ....G 863 551-4500
Winter Haven *(G-19340)*
R-Lines LLC ....G 954 457-7777
Hallandale Beach *(G-5207)*
Refresco Beverages US Inc ....C 813 313-1800
Tampa *(G-18047)*
Refreshment Services Inc ....D 850 574-0281
Tallahassee *(G-17315)*
Royal Crown Developers LLC ....G 561 305-4588
Boca Raton *(G-694)*
Snapple Beverages ....F 941 758-7010
Bradenton *(G-1115)*
Southeast Atlantic Bev Corp ....B 904 731-3644
Jacksonville *(G-6785)*
Southeast Bottling & Bev Co ....D 352 567-2200
Dade City *(G-2436)*
Sunshine Bottling Co ....E 305 592-4366
Doral *(G-3517)*
Thomas J Cola ....G 954 846-0868
Sunrise *(G-17187)*
VIP Drinks Bottling LLC ....G 239 214-8190
Cape Coral *(G-1491)*

BEVERAGES, NONALCOHOLIC: Tea, Iced, Bottled & Canned, Etc

Dr Pepper Bottling Co ....G 407 354-5800
Orlando *(G-12682)*
Florida Refresco Inc ....C 863 665-5515
Lakeland *(G-7693)*

BEVERAGES, WINE & DISTILLED ALCOHOLIC, WHOLESALE: Wine

Vicente Gandia Pla ....C 310 699-8559
Miami *(G-10580)*

BEVERAGES, WINE/DISTILLED ALCOHOLIC, WHOL: Bttlg Wine/Liquor

Florida Rum Company LLC ....E 305 791-1221
Hollywood *(G-5823)*
Mango Bottling Inc ....E 321 631-1005
Cocoa *(G-2034)*

BICYCLE ASSEMBLY SVCS

Apollo Retail Specialists LLC ....B....... 813 712-2525
Tampa *(G-17428)*

BICYCLES, PARTS & ACCESS

Epiccycles ....G....... 561 450-6470
Delray Beach *(G-3074)*
First Coast Trikkes ....G....... 904 343-1833
Atlantic Beach *(G-221)*
Hawk Racing ....G....... 941 209-1790
Bradenton *(G-1055)*
Profile Racing Inc ....E....... 727 392-8307
Saint Petersburg *(G-15891)*
Trailmate Inc ....E....... 941 739-5743
Jacksonville *(G-6866)*
Ventum LLC ....G....... 786 838-1113
Miami Beach *(G-10727)*
Vet-Equip LLC ....G....... 239 537-3402
Naples *(G-11449)*
Worldglass Corporation ....G....... 813 609-2453
Tampa *(G-18264)*

BIDETS: Vitreous China

American Bidet Company ....F....... 954 981-1111
Sunrise *(G-17090)*
M F B International Inc ....G....... 305 436-6601
Miami *(G-9925)*
Rinseworks Inc ....F....... 954 946-0070
Pompano Beach *(G-14832)*

BILLFOLD INSERTS: Plastic

Sumiflex LLC ....G....... 954 578-6998
Sunrise *(G-17181)*

BILLIARD & POOL TABLES & SPLYS

Maitland Furniture Inc ....G....... 386 677-7711
Daytona Beach *(G-2682)*
Robertson Billiard Sups Inc ....G....... 813 229-2778
Tampa *(G-18065)*

BILLIARD EQPT & SPLYS WHOLESALERS

Robertson Billiard Sups Inc ....G....... 813 229-2778
Tampa *(G-18065)*

BILLING & BOOKKEEPING SVCS

Elements Accounting Inc ....G....... 305 662-4448
Miami *(G-9513)*

BINDING SVC: Books & Manuals

Abby Press Inc ....E....... 407 847-5565
Kissimmee *(G-7216)*
All-Star Sales Inc ....E....... 904 396-1653
Jacksonville *(G-6137)*
Allied General Engrv & Plas ....F....... 305 626-6585
Opa Locka *(G-12286)*
American Business Cards Inc ....E....... 314 739-0800
Naples *(G-11161)*
Apple Printing & Advg Spc Inc ....E....... 954 524-0493
Fort Lauderdale *(G-3818)*
Armstrongs Printing & Graphics ....G....... 850 243-6923
Fort Walton Beach *(G-4778)*
Assocated Prtg Productions Inc ....E....... 305 623-7600
Miami Lakes *(G-10763)*
B J and ME Inc ....G....... 561 368-5470
Boca Raton *(G-438)*
B R Q Grossmans Inc ....F....... 954 971-1077
Pompano Beach *(G-14609)*
Bava Inc ....F....... 850 893-4799
Tallahassee *(G-17226)*
Bayou Printing Inc ....F....... 850 678-5444
Valparaiso *(G-18507)*
Best Bindery Corp ....G....... 941 505-1779
Punta Gorda *(G-15197)*
Bill & Renee Enterprises ....G....... 321 452-2800
Merritt Island *(G-8993)*
Bindery LLC ....G....... 407 647-7777
Winter Park *(G-19382)*
Bjm Enterprises Inc ....F....... 941 746-4171
Bradenton *(G-1000)*
Boca Color Graphics Inc ....F....... 561 391-2229
Boca Raton *(G-450)*
Bodree Printing Company Inc ....F....... 850 455-8511
Pensacola *(G-14102)*
Bros Williams Printing Inc ....G....... 305 769-9925
Hialeah *(G-5332)*
C & R Designs Inc ....G....... 321 383-2255
Titusville *(G-18419)*
C & R Designs Printing LLC ....G....... 321 383-2255
Titusville *(G-18420)*
Colonial Press Intl Inc ....C....... 305 633-1581
Miami *(G-9379)*
Color Concepts Prtg Design Co ....E....... 813 623-2921
Tampa *(G-17546)*
Color Express Inc ....G....... 305 558-2061
Hialeah *(G-5350)*
Coloramax Printing Inc ....F....... 305 541-0322
Miami *(G-9381)*
Commercial Printers Inc ....D....... 954 781-3737
Fort Lauderdale *(G-3911)*
Copy-Flow Inc ....E....... 305 592-0930
Davie *(G-2509)*
Creative Prtg Grphic Dsign Inc ....E....... 407 855-0202
Orlando *(G-12627)*
Csmc Inc ....E....... 407 246-1567
Orlando *(G-12630)*
Dahlquist Enterprises Inc ....G....... 407 896-2294
Orlando *(G-12644)*
Dannys Prtg Svc Sups & Eqp Inc ....G....... 305 757-2282
Miami *(G-9435)*
Donna Lynn Enterprises Inc ....G....... 772 286-2812
Palm Beach Gardens *(G-13584)*
Durra Print Inc ....E....... 850 222-4768
Tallahassee *(G-17244)*
Ed Vance Printing Company Inc ....F....... 813 882-8888
Tampa *(G-17630)*
Fidelity Printing Corporation ....D....... 727 522-9557
Saint Petersburg *(G-15778)*
First Imprssons Prtg Cmmnctons ....G....... 407 831-6100
Longwood *(G-8282)*
Florida Graphic Printing Inc ....F....... 386 253-4532
Daytona Beach *(G-2666)*
G J V Inc ....G....... 727 584-7136
Largo *(G-7955)*
G L E M Inc ....G....... 727 461-5300
Clearwater *(G-1697)*
G S Printers Inc ....G....... 305 931-2755
Fort Lauderdale *(G-4016)*
Gandy Printers Inc ....F....... 850 222-5847
Tallahassee *(G-17260)*
Gulf Coast Business World Inc ....F....... 850 864-1511
Fort Walton Beach *(G-4806)*
H & H Printing Inc ....F....... 407 422-2932
Orlando *(G-12792)*
H & M Printing Inc ....F....... 407 831-8030
Sanford *(G-16059)*
Hernandez Printing Service ....F....... 305 642-0483
Miami *(G-9705)*
ICM Printing Co Inc ....F....... 352 377-7468
Gainesville *(G-4940)*
Instant Printing Services Inc ....F....... 727 546-8036
Floral City *(G-3768)*
Interprint Incorporated ....D....... 727 531-8957
Clearwater *(G-1734)*
J J M Services Inc ....G....... 954 437-1880
Miramar *(G-11007)*
Jet Graphics Inc ....F....... 305 264-4333
Miami *(G-9796)*
Jet Set Printing Inc ....G....... 407 339-1900
Casselberry *(G-1508)*
K R O Enterprises Ltd ....G....... 309 797-2213
Naples *(G-11302)*
Keithco Inc ....G....... 352 351-4741
Ocala *(G-11976)*
Kights Printing & Office Pdts ....G....... 904 731-7990
Jacksonville *(G-6537)*
Lake Worth Herald Press ....E....... 561 585-9387
Lake Worth *(G-7564)*
Leda Printing Inc ....E....... 941 922-1563
Sarasota *(G-16487)*
Mailing & Bindery Systems Inc ....G....... 813 416-8965
Lutz *(G-8397)*
Midds Inc ....E....... 561 586-6220
Lake Worth Beach *(G-7615)*
Mikes Print Shop Inc ....G....... 407 718-4964
Winter Park *(G-19426)*
Multicolor Printing Inc ....G....... 772 287-1676
Stuart *(G-16979)*
My Print Shop Inc ....F....... 954 973-9369
Deerfield Beach *(G-2878)*
Ngp Corporate Square Inc ....E....... 239 643-3430
Naples *(G-11345)*
Npc of Tampa Inc ....F....... 813 839-0035
Tampa *(G-17942)*
Ocala Print Quick Inc ....G....... 352 629-0736
Ocala *(G-12014)*
Oompha Inc ....G....... 850 222-7210
Tallahassee *(G-17308)*
Output Printing Corp ....F....... 813 228-8800
Tampa *(G-17965)*
Parkinson Enterprises Inc ....F....... 863 688-7900
Lakeland *(G-7762)*
PIP Printing ....G....... 352 622-3224
Ocala *(G-12027)*
Professional Bindery Inc ....F....... 305 633-3761
Miami *(G-10205)*
Reimink Printing Inc ....G....... 813 289-4663
Tampa *(G-18050)*
Roberts Quality Printing Inc ....E....... 727 442-4011
Clearwater *(G-1862)*
Russells Bindery Inc ....G....... 904 829-3100
Saint Augustine *(G-15601)*
Saugus Valley Corp ....G....... 954 772-4077
Coral Springs *(G-2310)*
Schooner Prints Inc ....D....... 727 397-8572
Largo *(G-8045)*
South Broward Printing Inc ....G....... 954 962-1309
Hollywood *(G-5912)*
Southeast Finishing Group Inc ....E....... 407 299-4620
Orlando *(G-13202)*
Southeastern Printing Co Inc ....C....... 772 287-2141
Hialeah *(G-5628)*
Spinnaker Holding Company ....E....... 561 392-8626
Boca Raton *(G-728)*
Steven K Bakum Inc ....G....... 561 804-9110
West Palm Beach *(G-19044)*
Sunshine Printing Inc ....F....... 561 478-2602
West Palm Beach *(G-19050)*
Taie Inc ....F....... 954 966-0233
Hollywood *(G-5920)*
Target Copy Gainesville Inc ....F....... 352 372-1171
Gainesville *(G-5008)*
Thalers Printing Center Inc ....G....... 954 741-6522
Lauderhill *(G-8122)*
Town Street Print Shop Inc ....G....... 850 432-8300
Gulf Breeze *(G-5130)*
United Seal & Tag Label Corp ....G....... 941 625-6799
Port Charlotte *(G-15004)*
Universal Graphics & Prtg Inc ....G....... 561 845-6404
North Palm Beach *(G-11729)*
V I P Printing ....G....... 386 258-3326
Daytona Beach *(G-2730)*
V P Press Inc ....F....... 954 581-7531
Fort Lauderdale *(G-4301)*
Vmak Corp ....F....... 407 260-1199
Longwood *(G-8348)*
Vowells Downtown Inc ....G....... 850 432-5175
Pensacola *(G-14285)*
W D H Enterprises Inc ....G....... 941 758-6500
Bradenton *(G-1143)*
Zetma LLC ....G....... 407 237-0233
Orlando *(G-13341)*

BINDING SVC: Magazines

Rapid Rater Company ....E....... 850 893-7346
Tallahassee *(G-17314)*

BINDING SVC: Trade

Florida Print Finishers Inc ....G....... 850 877-8503
Tallahassee *(G-17255)*

BINOCULARS

Discipline Marketing Inc ....F....... 305 793-7358
Homestead *(G-5963)*

BINS: Prefabricated, Metal Plate

Myrlen Inc ....G....... 800 662-4762
Coral Springs *(G-2293)*

BIOLOGICAL PRDTS: Antitoxins

Vital Solutions LLC ....G....... 561 848-1717
West Palm Beach *(G-19081)*

BIOLOGICAL PRDTS: Bacteriological Media

Becker Microbial Products Inc ....G....... 954 345-9321
Parkland *(G-13989)*

BIOLOGICAL PRDTS: Blood Derivatives

Clearant Inc ....G....... 407 876-3134
Orlando *(G-12589)*
Immunotek Bio Centers LLC ....E....... 337 500-1175
Bradenton *(G-1059)*

Immunotek Bio Centers LLC..........E....... 561 270-6712
Greenacres *(G-5083)*
Immunotek Bio Centers LLC..........E....... 772 577-7194
Fort Pierce *(G-4707)*
Immunotek Bio Centers LLC..........F....... 404 345-3570
Cocoa *(G-2030)*

BIOLOGICAL PRDTS: Exc Diagnostic

Adma Biomanufacturing LLC..........B....... 201 478-5552
Boca Raton *(G-401)*
Amgen USA Inc..........F....... 805 447-1000
Tampa *(G-17422)*
Apexeon Biomedical LLC..........G....... 850 878-2150
Tallahassee *(G-17221)*
Applied Genetic Tech Corp..........D....... 386 462-2204
Alachua *(G-5)*
Bioresource Technology..........E....... 954 792-5222
Weston *(G-19113)*
Demerx Inc..........G....... 954 607-3670
Miami *(G-9454)*
Dyadic International Inc..........G....... 561 743-8333
Jupiter *(G-7027)*
Ecological Laboratories Inc..........E....... 239 573-6650
Cape Coral *(G-1416)*
Empowered Diagnostics LLC..........G....... 206 228-5990
Pompano Beach *(G-14679)*
HCW Biologics Inc..........E....... 954 842-2024
Miramar *(G-11002)*
Lactalogics Inc..........G....... 772 202-0407
Port Saint Lucie *(G-15118)*
Lillian Bay Medical Inc..........F....... 941 815-7373
Saint Petersburg *(G-15840)*
Longeveron Inc..........F....... 305 909-0840
Miami *(G-9909)*
M-Biolabs Inc..........G....... 239 571-0435
Naples *(G-11317)*
Organabio LLC..........F....... 305 676-2586
South Miami *(G-16824)*
Radiation Shield Tech Inc..........F....... 866 733-6766
Coral Gables *(G-2189)*
Stat Biomedical LLC..........G....... 210 365-1495
Mims *(G-10953)*
Synergy Biologics LLC..........G....... 850 656-4277
Tallahassee *(G-17334)*

BIOLOGICAL PRDTS: Extracts

Citrus Extracts LLC..........F....... 772 464-9800
Fort Pierce *(G-4688)*
Extract Downtown Orlando LLC..........G....... 407 722-7379
Orlando *(G-12728)*
Mad Chiller Extracts LLC..........G....... 813 304-1664
Tampa *(G-17872)*
Real Extract Ventures Inc..........G....... 561 371-3532
Wellington *(G-18728)*

BIOLOGICAL PRDTS: Serums

Vc Serum LLC..........G....... 305 778-2190
Miami *(G-10570)*

BIOLOGICAL PRDTS: Vaccines

Iliad Biotechnologies LLC..........G....... 954 336-0777
Weston *(G-19139)*
Pet Doc FL LLC..........G....... 407 437-6614
Oviedo *(G-13453)*

BIOLOGICAL PRDTS: Vaccines & Immunizing

Healthy Schools LLC..........C....... 904 887-4540
Jacksonville *(G-6465)*

BIOLOGICAL PRDTS: Venoms

Biotoxins Inc..........G....... 407 892-6905
Saint Cloud *(G-15646)*
Nature Cast Ant-Vnom Index LLC..........G....... 352 683-0647
Spring Hill *(G-16857)*
Venom Allstars LLC..........G....... 407 575-3484
Winter Garden *(G-19287)*

BIOLOGICAL PRDTS: Veterinary

Amino Cell Inc..........F....... 352 291-0200
Ocala *(G-11874)*
Bioivt LLC..........G....... 516 876-7902
Plantation *(G-14497)*
Medrx Inc..........E....... 727 584-9600
Largo *(G-8008)*

BIRTH CONTROL DEVICES: Rubber

Grove Medical LLC..........G....... 305 903-6402
Miami *(G-9677)*
Veru Inc..........B....... 305 509-6897
Miami *(G-10574)*

BITUMINOUS & LIGNITE COAL LOADING & PREPARATION

Progress Fuels Corporation..........D....... 727 824-6600
Saint Petersburg *(G-15892)*

BLADES: Saw, Hand Or Power

Elliott Diamond Tool Inc..........F....... 727 585-3839
Clearwater *(G-1669)*
Round Table Tools Inc..........G....... 850 877-7650
Tallahassee *(G-17318)*

BLANKBOOKS & LOOSELEAF BINDERS

Beautiful Deluxe Inc..........G....... 305 498-4995
Cutler Bay *(G-2387)*
Cjks Deluxe Inc..........G....... 786 657-8726
Hialeah *(G-5346)*
Deluxe Stone Inc..........G....... 561 236-2322
Boynton Beach *(G-896)*
Dobbs & Brodeur Bookbinders..........G....... 305 885-5215
Hialeah *(G-5376)*
Fastkit Corp..........E....... 305 599-0839
Doral *(G-3347)*
Fastkit Corp..........G....... 754 227-8234
Doral *(G-3348)*
Garcia Deluxe Services Corp..........G....... 786 291-4329
Hialeah *(G-5424)*
I Wentworth Inc..........G....... 561 231-7544
Vero Beach *(G-18627)*
Russells Bindery Inc..........G....... 904 829-3100
Saint Augustine *(G-15601)*

BLANKBOOKS: Account

All-Pro Accnting Bkkeeping LLC..........G....... 561 212-8418
Lake Worth Beach *(G-7602)*

BLANKBOOKS: Albums, Record

Meishboy Productions Inc..........G....... 407 949-1464
Apopka *(G-159)*
Umg Recordings Inc..........C....... 305 532-4754
Miami Beach *(G-10722)*

BLANKBOOKS: Scrapbooks

Scraplife Inc..........G....... 305 776-0727
Pinecrest *(G-14332)*

BLANKETS: Horse

Quality Shavings South Florida..........E....... 561 433-9955
Lake Worth *(G-7584)*

BLAST SAND MINING

Don Schick LLC..........G....... 954 491-9042
Oakland Park *(G-11800)*
In Diversified Plant Services..........F....... 813 453-7025
Lutz *(G-8390)*

BLASTING SVC: Sand, Metal Parts

First Cast Strpping MBL Sndbls..........G....... 904 733-5915
Jacksonville *(G-6383)*
Industrial Marine Inc..........F....... 904 781-4707
Jacksonville *(G-6493)*
Standard Sand & Silica Company..........G....... 863 419-9673
Haines City *(G-5148)*

BLINDS & SHADES: Vertical

1st Vertical Blind Company..........G....... 352 343-3363
Tavares *(G-18332)*
American Blind Corporation..........F....... 305 262-2009
Miami *(G-9140)*
Bornt Enterprises Inc..........E....... 813 623-1492
Tampa *(G-17483)*
Ceco Inc..........F....... 561 265-1111
Boynton Beach *(G-889)*
G K Window Treatments Inc..........F....... 954 786-2927
Pompano Beach *(G-14709)*
Myriam Interiors Inc..........G....... 305 626-9898
Hialeah *(G-5531)*
Ortega Industries and Mfg..........D....... 305 688-0090
Opa Locka *(G-12348)*
Shades To You LLC..........G....... 407 889-0049
Apopka *(G-186)*
Stand Vertical Inc..........G....... 407 474-0456
Orlando *(G-13212)*
Superior Shade & Blind Co Inc..........E....... 954 975-8122
Coral Springs *(G-2317)*
Thompson Awning & Shutter Co..........E....... 904 355-1616
Jacksonville *(G-6849)*
Tropic Shield Inc..........F....... 954 731-5553
Lauderdale Lakes *(G-8095)*
United Vertical Blinds LLC..........F....... 786 348-8000
Miami *(G-10539)*
Vertical Assesment Assoc LLC..........E....... 850 210-0401
Blountstown *(G-390)*
Vertical Flight Technology Inc..........F....... 407 687-3126
Melbourne *(G-8970)*
Vertical Land Inc..........F....... 850 244-5263
Panama City *(G-13961)*
Vertical Systems Inspctons Inc..........G....... 954 775-6023
Plantation *(G-14563)*
Vista Products Inc..........D....... 904 725-2242
Jacksonville *(G-6900)*

BLINDS : Window

A1cm..........G....... 954 716-3216
Miami *(G-9047)*
Affordable Quality Blinds Inc..........G....... 786 412-4840
Miami *(G-9087)*
Blind and Drapery Gallery Inc..........G....... 239 948-7611
Bonita Springs *(G-816)*
Blind Monkey..........G....... 954 533-3090
Fort Lauderdale *(G-3857)*
Blinds 321 Inc..........G....... 305 336-9221
Miami *(G-9257)*
Blinds By Randy LLC..........G....... 305 300-1147
Miami Gardens *(G-10735)*
Blinds Dr LLC..........G....... 305 394-4808
Miami *(G-9258)*
Blinds Express..........G....... 954 826-6185
Oakland Park *(G-11786)*
Blinds Plus Shutters & Shades..........G....... 352 430-7200
Leesburg *(G-8145)*
Blinds Shades Industries Corp..........G....... 786 445-2144
Miami *(G-9260)*
Blinds Side..........G....... 888 610-8366
Cape Canaveral *(G-1352)*
BMW & Associates Inc..........G....... 352 694-2300
Ocala *(G-11888)*
Cardenas Roberto Blinds of Fla..........G....... 315 807-6878
Miami *(G-9312)*
Casa Blinds Interior Corp..........G....... 786 219-7157
Doral *(G-3293)*
Diy Blinds Inc..........G....... 305 692-8877
North Miami Beach *(G-11671)*
Dizenzo Manufacturing Intl..........G....... 954 978-4624
Deerfield Beach *(G-2815)*
Ed Allen Inc..........F....... 941 743-2646
Port Charlotte *(G-14975)*
Falcons Castl Blinds Globl Fla..........G....... 561 727-4332
West Palm Beach *(G-18869)*
Florida Plntn Shutters LLC..........G....... 386 788-7766
South Daytona *(G-16801)*
Florida Prnts Blind Chldren In..........G....... 407 257-7637
Orlando *(G-12753)*
Floridian Blinds Llc..........G....... 786 250-4697
Miami *(G-9587)*
Gator Blinds & Shutters..........G....... 352 375-1995
Ocala *(G-11954)*
Gator Custom Blinds..........G....... 352 867-0448
Ocala *(G-11955)*
Grannys Cheesecake & More Inc..........G....... 561 847-6599
Okeechobee *(G-12180)*
Gulf Coast Shades & Blinds LLC..........F....... 850 332-2100
Gulf Breeze *(G-5118)*
Kelsies Blinds..........G....... 407 977-0827
Oviedo *(G-13445)*
Kristine Window Treatments LLC..........F....... 305 623-8302
Hialeah *(G-5476)*
Lavish Blinds Corp..........G....... 786 229-8134
Cutler Bay *(G-2400)*
Mastercraft Shtters Blinds LLC..........G....... 904 379-7544
Jacksonville *(G-6581)*
Mpalacios Blinds Inc..........G....... 239 601-4864
Lehigh Acres *(G-8200)*
North W Fla Cncil of Blind Cor..........G....... 850 982-7867
Gulf Breeze *(G-5123)*
Orlando Blinds Factory..........F....... 407 697-0521
Orlando *(G-13031)*

PRODUCT

Poseidon Window Treatments LLC.......G....... 954 920-1112
Dania Beach *(G-2472)*
Royal Blinds LLC.......F....... 786 253-8126
Miami *(G-10283)*
Skagfield Corporation.......D....... 850 878-1144
Tallahassee *(G-17325)*
Srm Blinds Inc.......G....... 321 269-5332
Titusville *(G-18463)*
Statewide Blnds Shtters More I.......G....... 813 480-8638
New Port Richey *(G-11511)*
Sun City Blinds LLC.......F....... 727 522-6695
Ellenton *(G-3655)*
Sunrise.......G....... 386 627-5029
Palm Coast *(G-13711)*
Sutton Draperies Inc.......F....... 305 653-7738
Miami *(G-10443)*
Top Trtment Cstomes Accesories.......G....... 239 936-4600
Fort Myers *(G-4632)*
Total Window Inc.......G....... 954 921-0109
Dania *(G-2459)*
Totally Glass & Blinds Llc.......G....... 561 929-6125
West Palm Beach *(G-19069)*
Vidal Shutters and Blinds LLC.......G....... 813 601-1068
Tampa *(G-18245)*

BLINDS, WOOD

S R Q Storm Protection LLC.......G....... 941 341-0334
Sarasota *(G-16568)*
Shades To You LLC.......G....... 407 889-0049
Apopka *(G-186)*
Timbercraft of Naples Inc.......G....... 239 566-2559
Naples *(G-11442)*

BLOCKS & BRICKS: Concrete

Argos-US LLC.......G....... 407 298-1900
Orlando *(G-12488)*
Artistic Paver Mfg Inc.......E....... 305 653-7283
Miami *(G-9174)*
Bell Concrete Products Inc.......E....... 352 463-6103
Bell *(G-341)*
Bluegrass Materials Co LLC.......E....... 919 781-4550
Jacksonville *(G-6216)*
Cement Products Inc.......E....... 727 868-9226
Port Richey *(G-15045)*
Cemex Materials LLC.......D....... 561 746-4556
Jupiter *(G-7018)*
Cemex Materials LLC.......E....... 407 322-8862
Sanford *(G-16008)*
Cemex Materials LLC.......D....... 941 722-4578
Palmetto *(G-13790)*
Central Florida Cnstr Walls.......F....... 407 448-2350
Orlando *(G-12565)*
Devcon International Corp.......C....... 954 926-5200
Boca Raton *(G-499)*
GLC 3 & Rental Corp.......G....... 954 916-1551
Plantation *(G-14520)*
Gulf Coast Ready Mix LLC.......E....... 352 621-3900
Homosassa *(G-6004)*
Jcs Contracting Inc.......G....... 407 348-4555
Kissimmee *(G-7258)*
Kenton Industries LLC.......G....... 863 675-8233
Labelle *(G-7318)*
Miami Quality Pavers Corp.......G....... 305 408-3444
Miami *(G-10008)*
New Line Transport LLC.......E....... 305 223-9200
Dade City *(G-2432)*
Paver Systems LLC.......E....... 407 859-9117
Orlando *(G-13055)*
Roof Tile Inc.......E....... 863 467-0042
Okeechobee *(G-12190)*
Royal Concrete Concepts Inc.......E....... 561 689-5398
Jupiter *(G-7106)*
Shealy Revel B Inc.......G....... 352 629-1552
Ocala *(G-12048)*
Whites Holdings Inc Centl Fla.......F....... 727 863-6072
Port Richey *(G-15078)*

BLOCKS: Acoustical, Concrete

Banaszak Concrete Corp.......E....... 954 476-1004
Davie *(G-2502)*
Cemex Cement Inc.......C....... 850 942-4582
Tallahassee *(G-17231)*

BLOCKS: Drystack Interlocking, Concrete

Labelle Brick Pavers Tile LLC.......F....... 863 230-3100
Labelle *(G-7319)*
Tremron Inc.......F....... 305 825-9000
Medley *(G-8741)*
Tremron LLC.......F....... 863 491-0990
Arcadia *(G-206)*

BLOCKS: Insulating, Concrete

Secure Cnstr Systems LLC.......G....... 561 687-9512
West Palm Beach *(G-19027)*

BLOCKS: Landscape Or Retaining Wall, Concrete

Blue Native of Fla Keys Inc.......G....... 305 345-5305
Big Pine Key *(G-381)*
Ross Pivnik.......G....... 305 254-1635
Miami *(G-10282)*

BLOCKS: Paving

Masters Block - North LLC.......G....... 407 212-7704
Saint Cloud *(G-15658)*
Paver Technologies LLC.......G....... 772 213-8905
Vero Beach *(G-18651)*

BLOCKS: Paving, Asphalt, Not From Refineries

Atlantic Coast Asphalt Co.......E....... 904 268-0274
Jacksonville *(G-6172)*

BLOCKS: Paving, Concrete

American Pavers Manufacturing.......G....... 954 418-0000
Pompano Beach *(G-14593)*
Masters Block - North LLC.......G....... 407 212-7704
Saint Cloud *(G-15658)*
Sunshine Driveways Inc.......G....... 954 394-7373
Hollywood *(G-5918)*

BLOCKS: Paving, Cut Stone

Paver Systems LLC.......E....... 407 859-9117
Orlando *(G-13055)*

BLOCKS: Standard, Concrete Or Cinder

A and A Concrete Block Inc.......G....... 305 986-5128
Miami *(G-9034)*
A-1 Block Corporation.......E....... 407 422-3768
Orlando *(G-12424)*
Bedrock Industries Inc.......F....... 407 859-1300
Orlando *(G-12509)*
Cemex Materials LLC.......C....... 561 833-5555
West Palm Beach *(G-18841)*
Cemex Materials LLC.......E....... 321 636-5121
Titusville *(G-18422)*
Cemex Materials LLC.......D....... 352 435-0783
Okahumpka *(G-12169)*
Cemex Materials LLC.......D....... 305 558-0315
Miami *(G-9337)*
Cemex Materials LLC.......D....... 561 793-1442
West Palm Beach *(G-18842)*
Cemex Materials LLC.......D....... 561 743-4039
Jupiter *(G-7019)*
Cemex Pacific Holdings LLC.......D....... 239 992-1400
Bonita Springs *(G-824)*
Jahna Concrete Inc.......F....... 863 453-4353
Avon Park *(G-289)*
PM Engraving Corp.......F....... 786 573-5292
Miami *(G-10171)*
Titan America LLC.......C....... 305 364-2200
Medley *(G-8738)*

BLOOD RELATED HEALTH SVCS

Morton Plant Mease Health Care.......A....... 727 462-7052
Clearwater *(G-1793)*

BLOWERS & FANS

3t Corporation.......G....... 786 222-2147
Hialeah *(G-5253)*
Breezemaker Fan Company Inc.......E....... 813 248-5552
Tampa *(G-17486)*
Central Florida Central Fla.......E....... 407 674-2626
Orlando *(G-12564)*
Cool Components Inc.......G....... 813 322-3814
Tampa *(G-17554)*
Custom Masters Inc.......E....... 407 331-4634
Longwood *(G-8270)*
Flaire Corporation.......C....... 352 237-1220
Ocala *(G-11944)*
Flanders Corp.......F....... 727 822-4411
Saint Petersburg *(G-15782)*
Hood Depot International Inc.......E....... 954 570-9860
Deerfield Beach *(G-2844)*
Merritt Mfg LLC.......G....... 407 481-1074
Land O Lakes *(G-7862)*
Moffitt Corporation Inc.......F....... 904 241-9944
Jacksonville Beach *(G-6951)*
Pall Aeropower Corporation.......B....... 727 849-9999
Deland *(G-3006)*
Plastec Ventilation Inc.......G....... 941 751-7596
Bradenton *(G-1098)*
Q-Pac Systems Inc.......E....... 229 834-2908
Elkton *(G-3651)*
R & J Mfg of Gainesville.......G....... 352 375-3130
Gainesville *(G-4987)*
Raytheon Technologies Corp.......A....... 858 277-7639
Jupiter *(G-7103)*
RB Kanalflakt Inc.......E....... 941 359-3267
Sarasota *(G-16554)*
Sunshine Filters of Pinellas.......E....... 727 530-3884
Largo *(G-8064)*
Sy-Klone Company LLC.......E....... 904 448-6563
Jacksonville *(G-6832)*

BLOWERS & FANS

Fanam Inc.......G....... 941 955-9788
Sarasota *(G-16427)*
Moffitt Fan Corporation.......F....... 585 768-7010
Jacksonville Beach *(G-6952)*
Robinson Fans Inc.......E....... 724 452-6121
Lakeland *(G-7780)*

BLUEPRINTING SVCS

Target Copy Gainesville Inc.......F....... 352 372-1171
Gainesville *(G-5008)*

BLUING

Felix Reynoso.......G....... 954 497-2330
Oakland Park *(G-11805)*

BOAT & BARGE COMPONENTS: Metal, Prefabricated

Calloway Barge Lines Inc.......G....... 904 284-0503
Green Cove Springs *(G-5056)*
Custom Marine Components Inc.......F....... 904 221-6412
Jacksonville *(G-6303)*

BOAT BUILDING & REPAIR

Aicon Yachts Americas LLC.......G....... 910 583-5299
Miami Beach *(G-10638)*
All Tank Services LLC.......G....... 954 260-9443
Pompano Beach *(G-14585)*
Ameracat Inc.......G....... 772 882-9186
Fort Pierce *(G-4672)*
Americraft Enterprises Inc.......G....... 386 756-1100
Daytona Beach *(G-2624)*
Angler Pro Boats LLC.......G....... 305 525-4943
South Miami *(G-16812)*
Arthur Cox.......G....... 772 286-5339
Stuart *(G-16910)*
Autocraft Manufacturing Co.......E....... 321 453-1850
Merritt Island *(G-8992)*
Barker Boatworks LLC.......F....... 941 233-8640
Sarasota *(G-16180)*
Bausch American Towers LLC.......F....... 772 283-2771
Stuart *(G-16911)*
Bausch Enterprises Inc.......F....... 772 220-6652
Stuart *(G-16912)*
Beavertail Skiffs Inc.......G....... 941 705-2090
Bradenton *(G-997)*
Beez Worx Boats LLC.......G....... 850 678-6548
Niceville *(G-11563)*
Belzona Inc.......E....... 305 512-3200
Doral *(G-3268)*
Bertram Yachts LLC.......C....... 813 527-9899
Tampa *(G-17465)*
Big O Boats LLC.......G....... 863 697-6319
Sebring *(G-16683)*
Bill Shuda.......G....... 772 220-6620
Stuart *(G-16916)*
Birdsall Marine Design Inc.......E....... 561 832-7879
West Palm Beach *(G-18822)*
Bms International Inc.......E....... 813 247-7040
Tampa *(G-17477)*
Boat Works.......G....... 904 389-0090
Jacksonville *(G-6217)*
Boggy Creek Boat Co LLC.......G....... 904 707-0952
Jacksonville *(G-6222)*

Bohemian Boatworks LLC G 941 321-1499
Sarasota *(G-16366)*
Bonadeo Boat Works LLC G 772 341-9820
Stuart *(G-16918)*
Bonefish Boatworks Llc G 727 243-6767
Odessa *(G-12108)*
Brunswick Boat Group G 321 449-8754
Merritt Island *(G-8996)*
C&A Boatworks Inc G 754 366-5549
Pompano Beach *(G-14628)*
C-Worthy Corp F 954 784-7370
Pompano Beach *(G-14629)*
Canyon Bay Boats Llc G 850 838-1400
Perry *(G-14297)*
Carey-Dunn Inc F 561 840-1694
Riviera Beach *(G-15309)*
Cayo Custom Boats LLC G 727 698-7201
Largo *(G-7920)*
CF Boatworks Inc G 954 325-6007
Fort Lauderdale *(G-3892)*
Chardonnay Boat Works LLC G 703 981-6339
Green Cove Springs *(G-5058)*
Chittum Yachts LLC E 386 589-7224
Stuart *(G-16923)*
CK Dockside Services Inc G 954 254-0263
Parkland *(G-13990)*
Composite Holdings Inc E 321 268-9625
Titusville *(G-18424)*
Concept Boats Inc E 305 635-8712
Opa Locka *(G-12303)*
Contender Boats Inc C 305 230-1600
Homestead *(G-5959)*
Corinthian Catamarans LLC F 813 334-1029
Palm Harbor *(G-13730)*
Craig Catamaran Corporation G 407 290-8778
Orlando *(G-12624)*
Creative Marine G 239 437-1010
Fort Myers *(G-4416)*
Custom Marine Components Inc F 904 221-6412
Jacksonville *(G-6303)*
Custom Marine Concepts Inc F 954 782-1111
Pompano Beach *(G-14654)*
Dennis Boatworks G 954 260-6855
Oakland Park *(G-11797)*
Diamondback Manufacturing LLC F 321 305-5995
Cocoa *(G-2012)*
Diamondback Manufacturing LLC E 321 633-5624
Cocoa *(G-2013)*
Diamondback Towers LLC F 800 424-5624
Cocoa *(G-2014)*
Discount Boat Tops Inc G 727 536-4412
Largo *(G-7933)*
Doller Marine Sales & Services F 954 463-9988
Fort Lauderdale *(G-3947)*
Dorado Custom Boats LLC F 727 786-3800
Tarpon Springs *(G-18295)*
Dorado Marine Inc F 727 786-3800
Ozona *(G-13467)*
Double Down Boat Works Inc G 305 984-3000
Miami *(G-9484)*
Duckworth Steel Boats Inc G 727 934-2550
Tarpon Springs *(G-18296)*
Earl Parker Yacht Refinishing F 954 791-1811
Fort Lauderdale *(G-3955)*
Eastward Boats Inc G 772 828-1358
Port Saint Lucie *(G-15104)*
Edgewater Power Boats LLC D 386 426-5457
Edgewater *(G-3622)*
EZ Boatworks Inc G 772 475-8721
Palm City *(G-13653)*
Flat Island Boatworks LLC G 850 434-8295
Pensacola *(G-14153)*
Flatsmaster Marine LLC F 239 574-7800
Cape Coral *(G-1423)*
Floral City Airboat Co Inc F 352 637-4390
Inverness *(G-6087)*
Florida Mkb Holdings LLC E 407 281-7909
Clermont *(G-1959)*
Frank Murray & Sons Inc F 561 845-1366
Fort Lauderdale *(G-4012)*
Gable Enterprises F 727 455-5576
Seffner *(G-16727)*
Gilbane Boatworks LLC G 561 744-2223
Tequesta *(G-18384)*
Glasser Boat Works Inc G 321 626-0061
Rockledge *(G-15414)*
Good Time Outdoors Inc E 352 401-9070
Ocala *(G-11958)*
Gulfstream Boatworks G 239 223-2628
Fort Myers *(G-4479)*
Gulfstream Unsnkable Boats LLC F 813 820-6100
Tampa *(G-17737)*
Hake Yachts Inc G 772 287-3200
Stuart *(G-16954)*
Hamant Airboats LLc G 321 259-6998
Melbourne *(G-8839)*
Hinckley G 239 919-8142
Naples *(G-11277)*
Hohol Marine Products G 386 734-0630
Deland *(G-2983)*
Hutchins Co Inc F 727 442-6651
Clearwater *(G-1722)*
Invincible Boat Company LLC E 305 685-2704
Opa Locka *(G-12327)*
Islamorada Boatworks LLC G 786 393-4752
Edgewater *(G-3626)*
Jabm Advisors Inc G 727 458-3755
Tarpon Springs *(G-18310)*
Jim Smith Boats Inc F 772 286-9049
Stuart *(G-16962)*
Jlb Enterprises Tampa Inc G 813 545-3830
Tampa *(G-17806)*
Jupiter Mar Intl Holdings Inc D 941 729-5000
Palmetto *(G-13809)*
L & S Design & Construction G 772 220-1745
Palm City *(G-13665)*
Lake & Bay Boats LLC G 813 949-7300
Naples *(G-11307)*
Larsen G 305 989-4043
Stuart *(G-16969)*
Lighthouse Boatworks Inc G 561 667-7382
Jupiter *(G-7067)*
Littoral Marine LLC E 352 400-4222
Wildwood *(G-19197)*
Mack Sales Inc G 772 283-2306
Stuart *(G-16971)*
Marine Fiberglass Specialist G 305 821-6667
Hialeah *(G-5502)*
Marine Transportation Svcs Inc E 850 215-4557
Panama City *(G-13927)*
Markcam Inc G 772 283-7189
Stuart *(G-16975)*
Marpro Marine Ways LLC G 727 447-4930
Clearwater *(G-1774)*
Master Marine G 904 329-1541
Jacksonville *(G-6580)*
Maverick Boat Group Inc C 772 465-0631
Fort Pierce *(G-4715)*
Merrill-Stevens Dry Dock Co D 305 640-5676
Miami *(G-9983)*
Michael Rybvich Sons Boat Wrks E 561 627-9168
Palm Beach Gardens *(G-13609)*
Miller Marine Yacht Svc Inc E 850 265-6768
Panama City *(G-13929)*
Motley Enterprises Inc G 703 966-3997
Saint Augustine *(G-15571)*
National Assemblers Inc F 877 915-5505
Lake Worth *(G-7574)*
Novurania of America Inc D 772 567-9200
Vero Beach *(G-18647)*
Parker Boatworks F 954 585-1059
Fort Lauderdale *(G-4159)*
Pemberton Custom Airboats G 352 422-5597
Inverness *(G-6094)*
Performance Sales & Service G 863 465-2814
Lake Placid *(G-7493)*
Perry Composites LLC G 850 584-8400
Perry *(G-14308)*
Peter Welchs Custom Boats G 941 575-8665
Punta Gorda *(G-15219)*
Pitman Allen Boat Repr & Maint G 727 772-9848
Palm Harbor *(G-13750)*
Premier Prfmce Interiors Inc E 941 752-6271
Sarasota *(G-16279)*
Premium Marine Inc E 786 903-0851
Miami *(G-10186)*
Progressive Industrial Inc F 941 723-0201
Palmetto *(G-13818)*
Promarine Boats USA G 305 450-2014
Fort Lauderdale *(G-4183)*
Rabud Inc G 954 925-4199
Dania *(G-2457)*
Resilient Group Inc F 518 434-4414
Jacksonville *(G-6718)*
Roscioli International Inc E 941 755-7411
Fort Lauderdale *(G-4215)*
Roscioli International Inc E 941 755-7411
Bradenton *(G-1107)*
Rupp Marine Inc F 772 286-5300
Stuart *(G-17004)*
S & S Performance Inc G 305 951-9846
Islamorada *(G-6099)*
Sabalo Boats G 727 243-6767
Odessa *(G-12148)*
Sarasota Boat Works Inc G 941 366-3357
Sarasota *(G-16291)*
Schurr Sails Inc F 850 438-9354
Pensacola *(G-14258)*
Sdkc Corp G 305 469-7578
Doral *(G-3497)*
Sea Force Center Console LLC E 941 417-7017
Palmetto *(G-13822)*
Sea Hawk Industries Inc G 863 385-1995
Sebring *(G-16706)*
Seahunter Inc D 305 257-3344
Princeton *(G-15186)*
Sheaffer Boats Inc G 813 872-7644
Tampa *(G-18093)*
Shearwater Marine Fl Inc E 772 781-5553
Stuart *(G-17010)*
Shurhold Products Company G 772 287-1313
Palm City *(G-13673)*
SLM Boats Inc G 386 738-4425
Deland *(G-3014)*
Smittys Boat Tops and Mar Eqp G 305 245-0229
Homestead *(G-5993)*
Snug Harbor Dinghies Inc F 727 578-0618
Saint Petersburg *(G-15914)*
South Florida Field Techs Inc G 954 325-6548
West Palm Beach *(G-19039)*
Southern Fiberglass Inc F 904 387-2246
Jacksonville *(G-6794)*
Spencer Boat Co LLC G 305 324-5211
Miami *(G-10404)*
Spice Island Boat Works Inc G 954 632-9453
Fort Lauderdale *(G-4253)*
Statement Marine LLC F 727 525-5235
Clearwater *(G-1888)*
Streamline Performance Boats C F 305 393-8848
Hialeah *(G-5634)*
Stuart Boat Works Inc F 772 600-7121
Stuart *(G-17023)*
Stuart Composites LLC E 772 266-4285
Miami *(G-10424)*
Talaria Company LLC D 772 403-5387
Stuart *(G-17032)*
Taylor Made Systems Brdnton In C 941 747-1900
Oviedo *(G-13461)*
Tecnografic Inc E 954 928-1714
Fort Lauderdale *(G-4276)*
Toledo Sales Inc G 305 389-3441
Miami *(G-10488)*
Top Cters Ycht Restoration LLC G 561 818-9259
West Palm Beach *(G-19068)*
Trolley Boats G 727 588-1100
Largo *(G-8068)*
Ultrapanel Marine Inc E 772 285-4258
Miami *(G-10527)*
US Spars Inc G 386 462-3760
Gainesville *(G-5014)*
Vilano Interiors Inc G 904 824-3439
Saint Augustine *(G-15633)*
Warbird Marine Holdings LLC G 844 341-2504
Opa Locka *(G-12368)*
Williams Tenders USA Inc F 954 648-6560
Pompano Beach *(G-14914)*
Willis Marine Inc G 772 283-7189
Stuart *(G-17051)*

BOAT BUILDING & REPAIRING: Fiberglass

Atlas Boat Works Inc G 239 574-2628
Cape Coral *(G-1385)*
Bahama Boat Works LLC F 561 882-4069
Mangonia Park *(G-8499)*
Blazer Boats Inc E 321 307-4761
Orlando *(G-12523)*
Boston Whaler Inc B 386 428-0057
Edgewater *(G-3615)*
Canaveral Custom Boats Inc G 321 783-3536
Cape Canaveral *(G-1354)*
Chris Craft Corporation C 941 351-4900
Sarasota *(G-16191)*
Copalo Inc C 941 753-7828
Sarasota *(G-16198)*
Fabbro Marine Group Inc E 321 701-8141
Orlando *(G-12730)*
Floral City Airboat Co Inc G 352 637-4390
Floral City *(G-3767)*
Harley Boat Corporation G 863 533-2800
Bartow *(G-316)*

Hells Bay Boatworks LLC ....E.... 321 383-8223
Titusville ***(G-18432)***
Hells Bay Marine Inc ....E.... 321 383-8223
Titusville ***(G-18433)***
Hydrofoils Incorporated ....G.... 561 964-6399
Lake Worth ***(G-7556)***
Intrepid Powerboats Inc ....B.... 954 324-4196
Dania ***(G-2448)***
Johannsen Boat Works Inc ....G.... 772 567-4612
Vero Beach ***(G-18634)***
Knowles Plastics Inc ....G.... 954 232-8756
Coral Springs ***(G-2270)***
Kz Manufacturing LLC ....G.... 305 257-2628
Princeton ***(G-15185)***
Land Marine Service Inc ....G.... 561 626-2947
West Palm Beach ***(G-18926)***
Little River Marine ....G.... 352 378-5025
Gainesville ***(G-4955)***
Magnum Marine Corporation ....E.... 305 931-4292
Miami ***(G-9934)***
Mark McManus Inc ....F.... 239 454-1300
Fort Myers ***(G-4522)***
Midnight Express Pwr Boats Inc ....E.... 954 745-8284
Miami ***(G-10018)***
Mirage & Co Inc ....E.... 407 301-5850
Saint Cloud ***(G-15661)***
Mirage Manufacturing Inc ....D.... 352 377-4146
Gainesville ***(G-4964)***
Patrick Industries Inc ....E.... 941 556-6311
Sarasota ***(G-16274)***
Pipe Welders Inc ....D.... 954 587-8400
Fort Lauderdale ***(G-4168)***
R J Dougherty Associates LLC ....C.... 386 409-2202
Edgewater ***(G-3635)***
Regal Marine Industries Inc ....B.... 407 851-4360
Orlando ***(G-13127)***
Sea Ray Boats Inc ....C.... 386 439-3401
Flagler Beach ***(G-3757)***
Sea Ray Boats Inc ....C.... 321 459-9463
Merritt Island ***(G-9009)***
Sea Ray Boats Inc ....C.... 321 459-2930
Merritt Island ***(G-9010)***
Sea Ray Boats Inc ....C.... 321 452-9876
Merritt Island ***(G-9011)***
Southern Cross Boatworks Inc ....F.... 954 467-5801
Fort Lauderdale ***(G-4250)***
Stamas Yacht Inc ....D.... 727 937-4118
Tarpon Springs ***(G-18326)***
Stinger Fiberglass Designs Inc ....F.... 321 268-1118
Titusville ***(G-18465)***
Talon Marine ....G.... 941 753-7400
Sarasota ***(G-16308)***
Target Marine Inc ....G.... 863 293-3592
Winter Haven ***(G-19361)***
Tiger Composites Inc ....F.... 386 334-0941
New Smyrna Beach ***(G-11547)***
W E Connery Boat Builders ....G.... 239 549-8014
Cape Coral ***(G-1493)***
Whitewater Boat Corp ....G.... 305 756-9191
Miami ***(G-10603)***
World Boat Manufacturing Inc ....F.... 863 824-0015
Okeechobee ***(G-12194)***

BOAT BUILDING & REPAIRING: Hydrofoil

Alumitech Inc ....F.... 407 826-5373
Orlando ***(G-12463)***

BOAT BUILDING & REPAIRING: Kits, Not Models

Harley Shipbuilding Corp ....G.... 863 533-2800
Bartow ***(G-317)***
Revere Survival Inc ....F.... 904 503-9733
Jacksonville ***(G-6720)***

BOAT BUILDING & REPAIRING: Lifeboats

Survitec Survivor Cft Mar Inc ....G.... 954 374-4276
Miramar ***(G-11050)***

BOAT BUILDING & REPAIRING: Motorboats, Inboard Or Outboard

Andros Boatworks Inc ....F.... 941 351-9702
Sarasota ***(G-16342)***
P B C H Incorporated ....E.... 239 567-5030
Fort Myers ***(G-4560)***
Porta Products ....G.... 386 428-7656
Edgewater ***(G-3633)***
US Recreational Alliance Inc ....F.... 954 782-7279
Pompano Beach ***(G-14906)***

BOAT BUILDING & REPAIRING: Motorized

Acrylico Inc ....G.... 561 304-2921
Lake Worth ***(G-7529)***
All Craft Marine LLC ....E.... 813 236-8879
Zephyrhills ***(G-19506)***
Bd Xtreme Holdings LLC ....F.... 850 703-1793
Bonifay ***(G-799)***
Brunswick Commercial & ....D.... 386 423-2900
Edgewater ***(G-3616)***
Cigarette Racing Team LLC ....D.... 305 769-4350
Opa Locka ***(G-12299)***
CK Prime Investments Inc ....G.... 239 574-7800
Cape Coral ***(G-1403)***
Performance Boats Inc ....F.... 305 956-9549
North Miami Beach ***(G-11697)***
Ram Investments South Fla Inc ....C.... 305 759-6419
Medley ***(G-8714)***
Smith Boat Designs Inc ....E.... 954 782-1000
Pompano Beach ***(G-14853)***
Twin Vee Catamarans Inc ....F.... 772 429-2525
Fort Pierce ***(G-4763)***
Whiticar Boat Works Inc ....E.... 772 287-2883
Stuart ***(G-17049)***

BOAT BUILDING & REPAIRING: Pontoons, Exc Aircraft & Inflat

Fiesta Marine Products Inc ....F.... 727 856-6900
Hudson ***(G-6023)***
Florida Trident Trading LLC ....F.... 352 253-1400
Tavares ***(G-18337)***

BOAT BUILDING & REPAIRING: Rigid, Plastic

Acryplex Inc ....G.... 305 633-7636
Miami ***(G-9066)***
Pompanette LLC ....E.... 813 885-2182
Tampa ***(G-17997)***

BOAT BUILDING & REPAIRING: Tenders, Small Motor Craft

Marine Exhaust Systems Inc ....D.... 561 848-1238
Riviera Beach ***(G-15346)***

BOAT BUILDING & REPAIRING: Yachts

Adler Anb Inc ....G.... 954 581-2572
Davie ***(G-2488)***
Admiral ....G.... 305 493-4355
Miami ***(G-9069)***
Arkup Llc ....G.... 786 448-8635
Miami Beach ***(G-10644)***
Big Eagle LLC ....G.... 305 586-8766
Fort Lauderdale ***(G-3850)***
Bradford Yacht Limited Inc ....C.... 954 791-3800
Fort Lauderdale ***(G-3867)***
Broward Yard & Marine LLC ....D.... 954 927-4119
Dania ***(G-2441)***
Campeones Marina Corp ....G.... 305 491-5738
Miami ***(G-9307)***
Camper & Nicholsons Usa Inc ....E.... 561 655-2121
Palm Beach ***(G-13550)***
Chittum Yachts LLC ....F.... 386 589-7224
Palm City ***(G-13647)***
Classic Yacht Refinishing Inc ....G.... 954 760-9626
Fort Lauderdale ***(G-3903)***
Dania Cut Holdings Inc ....F.... 954 923-9545
Dania Beach ***(G-2464)***
Diversified Yacht Services Inc ....E.... 239 765-8700
Fort Myers Beach ***(G-4661)***
Endeavour Catamaran Corp ....F.... 727 573-5377
Clearwater ***(G-1671)***
Florida Derecktor Inc ....C.... 954 920-5756
Dania Beach ***(G-2465)***
G & S Boats Inc ....F.... 850 835-7700
Freeport ***(G-4847)***
Garlington Landeweer Marine ....E.... 772 283-7124
Stuart ***(G-16945)***
Glass Tech Corp ....E.... 305 633-6491
Miami ***(G-9638)***
Huckins Yacht Corporation ....E.... 904 389-1125
Jacksonville ***(G-6481)***
Island Pcket Saward Yachts LLC ....G.... 727 535-6431
Largo ***(G-7984)***
Ivm Usa Inc ....E.... 786 693-2755
Miami ***(G-9778)***
K C Marine Services Inc ....G.... 954 766-8100
Fort Lauderdale ***(G-4082)***
Luxury Boat Services Inc ....G.... 360 451-2888
Fort Lauderdale ***(G-4105)***
Mariner International Trvl Inc ....G.... 954 925-4150
Dania ***(G-2451)***
McKinna Corporation ....G.... 386 446-8822
Palm Coast ***(G-13703)***
Moores Mar of Palm Beaches Inc ....G.... 561 841-2235
Riviera Beach ***(G-15349)***
Multihull Technologies Inc ....G.... 305 296-2773
Key West ***(G-7198)***
OP Yacht Services Corp ....F.... 954 451-3677
Fort Lauderdale ***(G-4150)***
Ray Eaton Yacht Service Inc ....G.... 954 583-8762
Fort Lauderdale ***(G-4199)***
Sea Force Ix Inc ....E.... 941 721-9009
Wimauma ***(G-19223)***
Seadreams Boat Yacht Works LLC ....G.... 727 843-0010
Port Richey ***(G-15067)***
Sheaffer Marine Inc ....F.... 813 872-7311
Tampa ***(G-18094)***
Stuart Yacht Builders ....F.... 561 747-1947
Stuart ***(G-17029)***
Talaria Company LLC ....D.... 239 261-2870
Naples ***(G-11435)***
Tampa Yacht Manufacturing LLC ....F.... 813 792-2114
Clearwater ***(G-1906)***
Tom George Yacht Group ....G.... 727 734-8707
Clearwater ***(G-1923)***
Top Quality Yacht Refinishing ....F.... 954 522-5232
Fort Lauderdale ***(G-4286)***
Tropical Dvrsons Mrina MGT Inc ....G.... 954 922-0387
Hollywood ***(G-5929)***
Truesouth Marine Corp ....G.... 813 286-0716
Tampa ***(G-18204)***
Willis Custom Yachts LLC ....C.... 772 221-9100
Stuart ***(G-17050)***
Yacht 10 Inc ....G.... 954 759-9929
Fort Lauderdale ***(G-4330)***

BOAT BUILDING & RPRG: Fishing, Small, Lobster, Crab, Oyster

Game Fisherman Inc ....F.... 772 220-4850
Stuart ***(G-16944)***
L & H Boats Inc ....G.... 772 288-2291
Stuart ***(G-16968)***
Maritec Industries Inc ....D.... 352 429-8888
Groveland ***(G-5101)***
Maverick Boat Group Inc ....C.... 772 465-0631
Fort Pierce ***(G-4716)***
Ocean Master Marine Inc ....G.... 561 840-0448
Riviera Beach ***(G-15357)***
Pb Holdco LLC ....B.... 772 465-6006
Fort Pierce ***(G-4730)***
Ros Holding Corporation ....F.... 954 581-9200
Fort Lauderdale ***(G-4214)***

BOAT DEALERS

Camper & Nicholsons Usa Inc ....E.... 561 655-2121
Palm Beach ***(G-13550)***
Concept Boats Inc ....E.... 305 635-8712
Opa Locka ***(G-12303)***
Custom Marine Components Inc ....F.... 904 221-6412
Jacksonville ***(G-6303)***
Doller Marine Sales & Services ....F.... 954 463-9988
Fort Lauderdale ***(G-3947)***
Florida Mkb Holdings LLC ....E.... 407 281-7909
Clermont ***(G-1959)***
G & S Boats Inc ....F.... 850 835-7700
Freeport ***(G-4847)***
Good Time Outdoors Inc ....E.... 352 401-9070
Ocala ***(G-11958)***
Hohol Marine Products ....G.... 386 734-0630
Deland ***(G-2983)***
Kz Manufacturing LLC ....G.... 305 257-2628
Princeton ***(G-15185)***
Little River Marine ....G.... 352 378-5025
Gainesville ***(G-4955)***
Marine Spc Cstm Fabricator ....G.... 813 855-0554
Oldsmar ***(G-12246)***
Midnight Express Pwr Boats Inc ....E.... 954 745-8284
Miami ***(G-10018)***
Multihull Technologies Inc ....G.... 305 296-2773
Key West ***(G-7198)***
Nautical Acquisitions Corp ....C.... 727 541-6664
Largo ***(G-8017)***
Pipewelders Marine Inc ....D.... 954 587-8400
Fort Lauderdale ***(G-4169)***

Ram Investments South Fla Inc..........C....... 305 759-6419
Medley *(G-8714)*
Ray Electric Outboards Inc..........G....... 239 574-1948
Cape Coral *(G-1459)*
Southeastern Marine Power LLC..........F....... 727 545-2700
Saint Petersburg *(G-15916)*
T A C Armatures & Pumps Corp..........F....... 305 835-8845
Miami *(G-10454)*
Turning Point Propellers Inc..........G....... 904 900-7739
Jacksonville *(G-6871)*

BOAT DEALERS: Canoe & Kayak

Bote LLC..........F....... 888 855-4450
Miramar Beach *(G-11064)*

BOAT DEALERS: Marine Splys & Eqpt

Beachcomber Fibrgls Tech Inc..........G....... 772 283-0200
Stuart *(G-16914)*
Ros Holding Corporation..........F....... 954 581-9200
Fort Lauderdale *(G-4214)*

BOAT DEALERS: Outboard

Performance Sales & Service..........G....... 863 465-2814
Lake Placid *(G-7493)*

BOAT LIFTS

Boat Lift Pros of SW Fla Inc..........F....... 239 339-7080
Fort Myers *(G-4376)*
Boat Lifts By Synergy LLC..........G....... 641 676-4785
Fort Myers *(G-4377)*
Boat Lifts of South Florida..........G....... 305 522-1320
Tavernier *(G-18361)*
Deco Power Lift Inc..........F....... 727 736-4529
Safety Harbor *(G-15491)*
Florida Boat Lift..........G....... 813 873-1614
Tampa *(G-17673)*
Golden Manufacturing Inc..........E....... 239 337-4141
North Fort Myers *(G-11598)*
Imm Survivor Inc..........F....... 239 454-7020
Fort Myers *(G-4490)*
Neptune Boat Lifts Inc..........E....... 954 524-3616
Fort Lauderdale *(G-4135)*
Presto Lifts..........G....... 786 615-7256
Hialeah *(G-5566)*
Qlty Alumn Boat Lifts Inc..........G....... 850 434-6446
Pensacola *(G-14244)*
Quality Alum Boat Lifts Inc..........G....... 850 434-6446
Pensacola *(G-14245)*
Rocky Bayou Enterprises Inc..........G....... 850 244-4567
Fort Walton Beach *(G-4829)*
SE Custom Lift Systems Inc..........G....... 954 941-8090
Pompano Beach *(G-14844)*
Touchless Cover LLC..........E....... 407 679-2217
Orlando *(G-13265)*

BOAT REPAIR SVCS

Florida Marine Joiner Svc Inc..........F....... 813 514-1125
Tampa *(G-17682)*
K C Marine Services Inc..........G....... 954 766-8100
Fort Lauderdale *(G-4082)*

BOAT YARD: Boat yards, storage & incidental repair

Diversified Yacht Services Inc..........E....... 239 765-8700
Fort Myers Beach *(G-4661)*
Ros Holding Corporation..........F....... 954 581-9200
Fort Lauderdale *(G-4214)*

BOATS & OTHER MARINE EQPT: Plastic

Composite Holdings Inc..........E....... 321 268-9625
Titusville *(G-18424)*
Hc Grupo Inc..........G....... 954 227-0150
Coral Springs *(G-2252)*
Maritime Custom Designs Inc..........G....... 941 716-0255
Venice *(G-18562)*
Sargeant Marine Inc..........F....... 561 999-9916
Boca Raton *(G-702)*
Seacure Inc..........F....... 904 353-5353
Jacksonville *(G-6759)*
Structural Composites Inc..........F....... 321 951-9464
Melbourne *(G-8947)*
Taco Metals Inc..........F....... 727 224-4282
Seminole *(G-16767)*
W E Connery Boat Builders..........G....... 239 549-8014
Cape Coral *(G-1493)*

BOATS: Plastic, Nonrigid

Pompanette LLC..........E....... 813 885-2182
Tampa *(G-17997)*

BODIES: Truck & Bus

Amer-Con Corp..........E....... 786 293-8004
Palmetto Bay *(G-13839)*
Mickey Truck Bodies Inc..........F....... 352 620-0015
Ocala *(G-12001)*
Pierce Manufacturing Inc..........A....... 727 573-0400
Clearwater *(G-1832)*
Tesco Equipment LLC..........E....... 954 752-7994
Coral Springs *(G-2322)*
Tuflex Manufacturing Co..........E....... 954 781-0605
Pompano Beach *(G-14895)*

BODY PARTS: Automobile, Stamped Metal

Cooper-Standard Automotive Inc..........E....... 407 330-3323
Sanford *(G-16024)*
Cooper-Standard Automotive Inc..........D....... 407 330-3323
Sanford *(G-16025)*
Direct Sales and Design Inc..........F....... 954 522-5477
Fort Lauderdale *(G-3943)*
Excellent Performance Inc..........G....... 561 296-0776
Riviera Beach *(G-15326)*
Glennmar Supply LLC..........F....... 727 536-1955
Largo *(G-7961)*
Lincoln Tactical LLC..........F....... 813 419-3110
Valrico *(G-18521)*
Marquez Brothers Inc..........F....... 305 888-0090
Medley *(G-8683)*
Priko Corp..........F....... 305 556-3558
Miami Lakes *(G-10843)*
Pro Trim of Central Florida..........G....... 863 294-4646
Winter Haven *(G-19346)*
PSi Customs..........G....... 863 661-4211
Winter Haven *(G-19350)*
Rotab Inc..........E....... 954 447-7746
Fort Lauderdale *(G-4217)*
Spicer Industries Inc..........F....... 352 732-5300
Ocala *(G-12057)*
Wish Inc..........F....... 305 653-9474
North Miami Beach *(G-11713)*

BOILER REPAIR SHOP

St Cloud Wldg Fabrication Inc..........E....... 407 957-2344
Saint Cloud *(G-15667)*

BOILERS: Low-Pressure Heating, Steam Or Hot Water

Shilpico Inc..........G....... 561 306-5625
Boca Raton *(G-708)*

BOLTS: Handle, Wooden, Hewn

Davanti Doors Llc..........G....... 239 842-8341
Fort Myers *(G-4426)*

BOLTS: Metal

Sunpack of Pensacola Inc..........F....... 850 476-9838
Pensacola *(G-14271)*

BONDS, RAIL: Electric, Propulsion & Signal Circuit Uses

Douglas Abbott..........G....... 407 422-3597
Orlando *(G-12680)*

BOOK STORES

Books-A-Million Inc..........G....... 813 571-2062
Brandon *(G-1152)*

BOOKS, WHOLESALE

Pro Publishing Inc..........G....... 954 888-7726
Southwest Ranches *(G-16840)*
Spanish House Inc..........E....... 305 503-1191
Medley *(G-8728)*

BOOTHS: Spray, Sheet Metal, Prefabricated

Gibson Wldg Shetmetal Vent Inc..........G....... 850 837-6141
Destin *(G-3190)*
Tk - Autek Inc..........G....... 727 572-7473
Palm Harbor *(G-13766)*

BOOTS: Men's

Ronmar Industries Inc..........F....... 561 630-8035
West Palm Beach *(G-19023)*

BOOTS: Women's

Devon-Aire Inc..........E....... 813 884-9544
Tampa *(G-17602)*
Ronmar Industries Inc..........F....... 561 630-8035
West Palm Beach *(G-19023)*

BORING MILL

A & L Toolings LLC..........G....... 407 242-7114
Sanford *(G-15984)*

BOTTLE CAPS & RESEALERS: Plastic

Anupack LLC..........G....... 407 850-1960
Orlando *(G-12481)*
Berry Global Inc..........G....... 305 887-2040
Medley *(G-8622)*
Sourcerers Inc..........G....... 954 530-2333
Plantation *(G-14556)*

BOTTLED GAS DEALERS: Propane

Airgas Usa LLC..........G....... 407 293-6630
Orlando *(G-12446)*

BOTTLED WATER DELIVERY

Keystone Water Company LLC..........F....... 863 465-1932
Lake Placid *(G-7490)*
Ultra-Pure Bottled Water Inc..........F....... 281 731-0258
North Miami *(G-11660)*

BOTTLES: Plastic

AC Plastics LLC..........G....... 305 826-6333
Hialeah *(G-5266)*
Advance Plastics Unlimited..........E....... 305 885-6266
Hialeah *(G-5270)*
Altira Inc..........D....... 305 687-8074
Miami *(G-9124)*
Altium Packaging LLC..........F....... 813 248-4300
Tampa *(G-17409)*
Amalie Oil Company..........C....... 813 248-1988
Tampa *(G-17412)*
Anupack LLC..........G....... 407 850-1960
Orlando *(G-12481)*
C & G Packaging LLC..........F....... 305 825-5244
Hialeah *(G-5337)*
Captiva Containers LLC..........D....... 800 861-3868
Miami *(G-9310)*
CKS Packaging Inc..........D....... 407 423-0333
Orlando *(G-12586)*
CKS Packaging Inc..........D....... 954 925-9049
Hollywood *(G-5800)*
Compliance Meds Tech LLC..........G....... 786 319-9826
Miami *(G-9389)*
Florida Electromechanics Inc..........G....... 305 825-5244
Hialeah *(G-5412)*
Global Source Imports LLC..........G....... 917 213-6891
Miami *(G-9641)*
Mango Bottling Inc..........E....... 321 631-1005
Cocoa *(G-2034)*
Mesa Industries Inc..........F....... 386 738-3255
Deland *(G-2995)*
Mfx Corp..........F....... 407 429-4051
Orlando *(G-12965)*
New Sentry Marketing Inc..........G....... 561 982-9599
Boca Raton *(G-640)*
Rock Bottom Bottles LLC..........G....... 901 237-9929
Sarasota *(G-16287)*
US Pack Group LLC..........G....... 954 556-1840
Sunrise *(G-17193)*
W R Kershaw Inc..........G....... 386 673-0602
Ormond Beach *(G-13408)*

BOULDER: Crushed & Broken

White County Stone LLC..........E....... 415 516-0849
West Palm Beach *(G-19086)*

BOUTIQUE STORES

Purpleglassboutique LLC..........G....... 407 601-2641
Orlando *(G-13101)*

PRODUCT

BOXES & CRATES: Rectangular, Wood

Millenium Wood Boxes Inc ....G....... 305 969-5510
Miami *(G-10023)*
Quantum Development LLC ....G....... 954 587-4205
Fort Lauderdale *(G-4192)*

BOXES & SHOOK: Nailed Wood

Air-Flite Containers Inc ....G....... 407 679-1200
Orlando *(G-12444)*
Animal Air Service Inc ....E....... 305 218-1759
Doral *(G-3250)*
Cross City Veneer Company Inc ....D....... 352 498-3226
Cross City *(G-2364)*
Haman Industries Inc ....F....... 813 626-5700
Tampa *(G-17741)*
L & M Pallet Services Inc ....F....... 863 519-3502
Bartow *(G-322)*

BOXES, GARBAGE: Concrete

Florida Container Services ....F....... 407 302-2197
Sanford *(G-16047)*

BOXES: Corrugated

Advanced Design & Packg Inc ....F....... 904 356-6063
Jacksonville *(G-6123)*
Aggressive Box Inc ....F....... 813 901-9600
Tampa *(G-17391)*
Air-Flite Containers Inc ....G....... 407 679-1200
Orlando *(G-12444)*
Avatar Packaging Inc ....E....... 813 888-9141
Tampa *(G-17444)*
Avon Corrugated/Florida Corp ....F....... 305 770-3439
Miami *(G-9200)*
Birdiebox LLC ....E....... 786 762-2975
Miami *(G-9249)*
Central Florida Box Corp ....E....... 407 936-1277
Lake Mary *(G-7404)*
Cypress Folding Cartons Inc ....E....... 813 884-5418
Tampa *(G-17583)*
Dusobox Corporation ....D....... 407 855-5120
Orlando *(G-12692)*
Flamm Industries Inc ....G....... 904 356-2876
Jacksonville *(G-6393)*
Florida Packg & Graphics Inc ....F....... 954 781-1440
Fort Lauderdale *(G-4002)*
Ic Industries Inc ....D....... 305 696-8330
Hialeah *(G-5451)*
K & G Box Inc ....D....... 904 356-6063
Jacksonville *(G-6529)*
Macpac Inc ....F....... 904 315-6457
Ponte Vedra Beach *(G-14945)*
Mas Entrprses of Ft Lauderdale ....E....... 904 356-9606
Fort Lauderdale *(G-4113)*
Max-Pak Inc ....C....... 863 682-0123
Lakeland *(G-7747)*
Micon Packaging Inc ....C....... 813 855-4651
Oldsmar *(G-12249)*
Packaging Corporation America ....G....... 386 792-0810
Jasper *(G-6960)*
Plant Foods Inc ....E....... 772 567-5741
Vero Beach *(G-18654)*
Pratt Industries Inc ....G....... 863 439-4184
Dundee *(G-3568)*
Schwarz Partners Packaging LLC ....C....... 863 682-0123
Lakeland *(G-7788)*
Sfbc LLC ....E....... 978 342-8921
Boca Raton *(G-707)*
Smurfit Kappa Packaging LLC ....F....... 954 838-9738
Sunrise *(G-17175)*
St Pete Paper Company ....G....... 727 572-9868
Palmetto *(G-13823)*
Suncoast Cartons & Crating LLC ....G....... 813 242-8477
Tampa *(G-18142)*
Sunshine Packaging Inc ....F....... 305 887-8141
Hialeah *(G-5639)*
Ultrabox Inc ....F....... 941 371-0000
Bradenton *(G-1136)*
UNI-Box Inc ....E....... 954 733-3550
Oakland Park *(G-11855)*
Westrock Cp LLC ....C....... 904 261-5551
Fernandina Beach *(G-3749)*
Westrock Cp LLC ....D....... 850 785-4311
Panama City *(G-13964)*
Westrock Cp LLC ....G....... 239 658-8221
Immokalee *(G-6054)*
Westrock Rkt LLC ....C....... 904 714-1643
Jacksonville *(G-6915)*

BOXES: Mail Or Post Office, Collection/Storage, Sheet Metal

United Express Intl Corp ....G....... 305 591-3292
Miami *(G-10535)*
Worlds Columbian Exonumis ....G....... 561 734-4433
Boynton Beach *(G-975)*

BOXES: Packing & Shipping, Metal

Desapro Inc ....E....... 321 674-6804
Rockledge *(G-15401)*
Edak Inc ....F....... 321 674-6804
Melbourne *(G-8820)*
Lotus Containers Inc ....G....... 786 590-1056
Miami *(G-9913)*

BOXES: Paperboard, Folding

Caribbean Box Company ....F....... 305 667-4900
Miami *(G-9313)*
Cypress Folding Cartons Inc ....E....... 813 884-5418
Tampa *(G-17583)*
Latham Marine Inc ....E....... 954 462-3055
Fort Lauderdale *(G-4096)*
R G Management Inc ....E....... 407 889-3100
Orlando *(G-13109)*
Richard C Good ....G....... 321 639-6383
Titusville *(G-18458)*
Southeast Finishing Group Inc ....E....... 407 299-4620
Orlando *(G-13202)*
Sunshine Packaging Inc ....F....... 305 887-8141
Hialeah *(G-5639)*

BOXES: Paperboard, Set-Up

Goldys Box Co ....G....... 954 648-1623
The Villages *(G-18391)*
McMill LLC ....G....... 561 279-3232
Boca Raton *(G-615)*
Paper Box ....G....... 407 415-7262
Lake Mary *(G-7441)*
Simkins Industries Inc ....F....... 305 899-8184
Miami *(G-10350)*
Spruce Creek Cntl Cndo Associa ....G....... 386 212-4035
Port Orange *(G-15036)*
Tropical Paper Box ....G....... 305 592-5520
Doral *(G-3533)*

BOXES: Plastic

New Generation Packaging LLC ....G....... 786 259-6670
Miami Gardens *(G-10751)*
Nfk Corporation ....F....... 305 378-2116
Miami *(G-10070)*
Profast Corporation ....E....... 305 827-7801
Miami Lakes *(G-10844)*
R P M Industries Inc ....E....... 315 255-1105
Hobe Sound *(G-5726)*

BOXES: Stamped Metal

Daws Manufacturing Company Inc ....C....... 850 478-3298
Pensacola *(G-14125)*

BRAKES & BRAKE PARTS

Coastal RE-Manufacturing Inc ....G....... 727 869-4808
Port Richey *(G-15046)*
Express Brake International ....F....... 352 304-6263
Ocala *(G-11936)*
Extreme Brake Integration Inc ....G....... 352 342-9596
Ocala *(G-11937)*
Mann+hummel Filtration Technol ....G....... 305 499-5100
Medley *(G-8682)*
SCI Undercar Inc ....F....... 727 327-2278
Saint Petersburg *(G-15906)*
Vette Brakes & Products Inc ....E....... 727 345-5292
Saint Petersburg *(G-15952)*

BRASS GOODS, WHOLESALE

James A De Flippo Co ....G....... 407 851-2765
Orlando *(G-12849)*

BRAZING SVCS

Precision Brazing Inc ....G....... 954 942-8971
Pompano Beach *(G-14807)*
Thermal Braze Inc ....G....... 561 746-6640
Jupiter *(G-7127)*

BRICK, STONE & RELATED PRDTS WHOLESALERS

A-1 Block Corporation ....E....... 407 422-3768
Orlando *(G-12424)*
Cement Industries Inc ....D....... 239 332-1440
Fort Myers *(G-4391)*
HG Trading Cia Inc ....G....... 305 986-5702
Hialeah *(G-5443)*
Quality Vaults Inc ....F....... 407 656-8781
Ocoee *(G-12089)*
Triton Stone Holdings LLC ....G....... 219 669-4890
Fort Lauderdale *(G-4288)*
Tropix Marble Company ....F....... 239 334-2371
Cape Coral *(G-1488)*

BRICKS & BLOCKS: Structural

Masters Block - North LLC ....G....... 407 212-7704
Saint Cloud *(G-15658)*

BRICKS : Ceramic Glazed, Clay

Three D Products Corp ....G....... 954 971-6511
Fort Lauderdale *(G-4282)*

BRICKS : Paving, Clay

Florida Brick and Clay Co Inc ....F....... 813 754-1521
Plant City *(G-14430)*
LLC Best Block ....E....... 239 789-3531
Orlando *(G-12918)*
LLC Best Block ....E....... 239 789-3531
Tampa *(G-17855)*

BRICKS: Concrete

Atlas Concrete Products Inc ....G....... 407 277-0841
Orlando *(G-12497)*

BROADCASTING & COMMS EQPT: Antennas, Transmitting/Comms

Altelix LLC ....F....... 561 660-9434
Boca Raton *(G-415)*
CF Motion Inc ....G....... 727 458-7092
Clearwater *(G-1623)*
Commstructures Inc ....D....... 850 968-9293
Pensacola *(G-14118)*
Denke Laboratories Inc ....E....... 941 721-0568
Palmetto *(G-13795)*
Gateway Wreless Communications ....F....... 561 732-6444
Boynton Beach *(G-909)*
Helical Communication Tech Inc ....G....... 561 762-2823
Rockledge *(G-15416)*
Myers Engineering Intl Inc ....E....... 954 975-2712
Margate *(G-8558)*
Venti Group LLC ....G....... 949 264-3185
Miami Beach *(G-10726)*
Viatech of Delaware Inc ....E....... 321 308-6600
Melbourne *(G-8971)*

BROADCASTING & COMMS EQPT: Rcvr-Transmitter Unt, Transceiver

ACR Electronics Inc ....C....... 954 981-3333
Fort Lauderdale *(G-3779)*
Vela Research LP ....D....... 727 507-5300
Clearwater *(G-1930)*

BROADCASTING & COMMS EQPT: Trnsmttng TV Antennas/Grndng Eqpt

Maxxfi LLC ....F....... 513 289-6521
Cape Coral *(G-1447)*

BROADCASTING & COMMUNICATION EQPT: Transmit-Receiver, Radio

Trs Wireless Inc ....E....... 407 447-7333
Orlando *(G-13277)*

BROADCASTING & COMMUNICATIONS EQPT: Cellular Radio Telephone

Sky Phone LLC ....F....... 305 531-5218
Miami Beach *(G-10711)*

BROADCASTING & COMMUNICATIONS EQPT: Studio Eqpt, Radio & TV

Ejm Broadcast Inc.......G....... 321 251-5662
Orlando *(G-12701)*
Self Made Dynasty LLC.......G....... 754 303-3134
Fort Lauderdale *(G-4229)*

BROADCASTING & COMMUNICATIONS EQPT: Transmitting, Radio/TV

Vertical Bridge Towers LLC.......C....... 561 948-6367
Boca Raton *(G-778)*

BROKERS & DEALERS: Securities

Consulier Engineering Inc.......G....... 561 842-2492
Riviera Beach *(G-15314)*

BROKERS' SVCS

Firefly Aircraft Parts Inc.......G....... 954 505-1470
Plantation *(G-14516)*
Global Ordnance LLC.......E....... 941 549-8388
Sarasota *(G-16221)*

BROKERS: Automotive

Uma Holdings Inc.......E....... 786 587-1349
Hollywood *(G-5932)*

BROKERS: Contract Basis

Imported Yarns LLC.......G....... 239 405-2974
Estero *(G-3691)*

BROKERS: Food

Ait USA Corp.......G....... 786 953-5918
Miami *(G-9098)*
Everglades Foods Inc.......G....... 863 655-2214
Sebring *(G-16689)*
Future Foods LLC.......G....... 786 390-5226
Lake Worth *(G-7551)*
Hispanic Certified Foods Inc.......G....... 305 772-6815
Pompano Beach *(G-14723)*
JRP Screen Printing Inc.......E....... 305 333-4244
Hialeah *(G-5469)*
K and G Food Services LLC.......G....... 954 857-9283
West Palm Beach *(G-18917)*
Smart Group Traders Inc.......G....... 850 460-5130
Destin *(G-3207)*

BROKERS: Mortgage, Arranging For Loans

A M Coplan Associates.......G....... 904 737-6996
Jacksonville *(G-6110)*

BROKERS: Printing

Kwikie Dup Ctr of Pinellas Pk.......G....... 727 544-7788
Pinellas Park *(G-14362)*
Power Point Graphics Inc.......G....... 561 351-5599
Boca Raton *(G-670)*

BROKERS: Yacht

Merrill-Stevens Dry Dock Co.......D....... 305 640-5676
Miami *(G-9983)*
Ros Holding Corporation.......F....... 954 581-9200
Fort Lauderdale *(G-4214)*
Tom George Yacht Group.......G....... 727 734-8707
Clearwater *(G-1923)*

BRONZE FOUNDRY, NEC

American Bronze Foundry Inc.......F....... 407 328-8090
Sanford *(G-15992)*
Arte Bronce Monuments Inc.......G....... 305 477-0813
Medley *(G-8614)*
We Bronze Wholesale LLC.......G....... 954 922-8826
Fort Lauderdale *(G-4318)*

BROOMS & BRUSHES

A J Giammanco & Associates.......F....... 386 328-1254
Palatka *(G-13472)*
Industrial Brush Corporation.......F....... 863 647-5643
Lakeland *(G-7709)*
Kleenbore Inc.......G....... 800 347-1200
Jacksonville *(G-6540)*
Smith Equipment & Supply Co.......E....... 863 665-4904
Lakeland *(G-7795)*
Torrington Brush Works Inc.......F....... 941 355-1499
Sarasota *(G-16622)*

BROOMS & BRUSHES: Household Or Indl

Boden Co Inc.......E....... 727 571-1234
Clearwater *(G-1610)*
Shurhold Products Company.......G....... 772 287-1313
Palm City *(G-13673)*

BROOMS & BRUSHES: Paint & Varnish

Elder & Jenks LLC.......G....... 727 538-5545
Largo *(G-7940)*

BROOMS & BRUSHES: Paint Rollers

Rollercoat Industries Inc.......E....... 813 621-4668
Tampa *(G-18067)*

BROOMS & BRUSHES: Paintbrushes

Brawley Distributing Co Inc.......F....... 727 539-8500
Largo *(G-7913)*
Corona Brushes Inc.......D....... 813 885-2525
Tampa *(G-17558)*

BRUCITE MINING

Jlt Custom Works Inc.......E....... 863 245-3371
Wauchula *(G-18694)*

BRUSHES

Premier Brush Inc.......G....... 850 271-5736
Panama City *(G-13942)*

BRUSHES: Rubber

Atlantech Process Technology.......G....... 352 751-4286
Lady Lake *(G-7330)*

BUFFING FOR THE TRADE

American Buffing Solid Surface.......G....... 407 625-6837
Orlando *(G-12468)*
Shineline Buffing & Detail.......G....... 941 268-1033
Punta Gorda *(G-15232)*

BUILDING & STRUCTURAL WOOD MBRS: Timbers, Struct, Lam Lumber

Kennedy Craft Cabinets Inc.......G....... 239 598-1566
Naples *(G-11304)*

BUILDING & STRUCTURAL WOOD MEMBERS

American Truss.......G....... 352 493-9700
Chiefland *(G-1529)*
Architctral Mlding Mllwrks Inc.......E....... 305 638-8900
Miami *(G-9163)*
Fine Archtctral Mllwk Shutters.......F....... 954 491-2055
Fort Lauderdale *(G-3993)*
Florida Forest Products LLC.......E....... 727 585-2067
Largo *(G-7949)*
Florida Truss Corporation.......G....... 407 438-2553
Orlando *(G-12758)*
Georgia-Pacific LLC.......E....... 404 652-4000
Silver Springs *(G-16782)*
Joseph J Taylor Truss.......G....... 321 482-4039
Melbourne *(G-8854)*
Pacific Arches Corporation.......F....... 352 236-7787
Ocala *(G-12020)*
Park Place Manufacturing Inc.......F....... 863 382-0126
Sebring *(G-16701)*
Truss Spans Unlimited LLC.......G....... 352 274-0306
Ocala *(G-12063)*
Truss William.......G....... 954 438-4710
Pembroke Pines *(G-14066)*

BUILDING BOARD & WALLBOARD, EXC GYPSUM

Continental Palatka LLC.......D....... 703 480-3800
Palatka *(G-13475)*

BUILDING BOARD: Gypsum

Continental Palatka LLC.......D....... 703 480-3800
Palatka *(G-13475)*

BUILDING CLEANING & MAINTENANCE SVCS

Apollo Retail Specialists LLC.......B....... 813 712-2525
Tampa *(G-17428)*
Joe Hearn Innovative Tech LLC.......F....... 850 898-3744
Pensacola *(G-14183)*

BUILDING CLEANING SVCS

Extra Time Solutions.......F....... 407 625-2198
Clermont *(G-1957)*

BUILDING COMPONENTS: Structural Steel

Ameribuilt Stl Structures LLC.......G....... 407 340-9401
Oviedo *(G-13411)*
Apex Metal Fabrication Inc.......F....... 386 328-2564
Palatka *(G-13473)*
Banker Steel South LLC.......F....... 407 293-0120
Orlando *(G-12505)*
Bell Steel Company.......D....... 850 432-1545
Pensacola *(G-14097)*
Bell Steel Company.......F....... 850 479-2980
Pensacola *(G-14098)*
Canam Steel Corporation.......G....... 386 252-3730
Daytona Beach *(G-2638)*
Canam Steel Corporation.......G....... 407 295-3864
Orlando *(G-12545)*
Canam Steel Corporation.......G....... 904 781-0898
Jacksonville *(G-6251)*
Central Fla Stl Bldg & Sup LLC.......G....... 352 266-6795
Ocala *(G-11899)*
Dade Engineering Group LLC.......F....... 305 885-2766
Miami *(G-9429)*
Division 5 Florida Inc.......E....... 904 964-4513
Starke *(G-16893)*
Fabricated Products Tampa Inc.......E....... 813 247-4001
Tampa *(G-17657)*
Gainesville Wldg & Fabrication.......G....... 352 373-0384
Gainesville *(G-4930)*
Gem Industries Inc.......E....... 321 302-8985
Cocoa *(G-2027)*
Hall Metal Corp.......G....... 772 460-0706
Fort Pierce *(G-4705)*
Hammer Haag Steel Inc.......C....... 727 216-6903
Clearwater *(G-1710)*
Hmb Steel Corporation.......F....... 321 636-6511
Rockledge *(G-15418)*
Imperial Industries Inc.......F....... 954 917-4114
Pompano Beach *(G-14729)*
Interstate Wldg & Fabrication.......F....... 727 446-1449
Clearwater *(G-1735)*
Met-Con Inc.......D....... 321 632-4880
Cocoa *(G-2035)*
Metal Systems Inc.......G....... 813 752-7088
Plant City *(G-14448)*
RDS Industrial Inc.......F....... 321 631-0121
Cocoa *(G-2045)*
Sea Cast Curb Adptors Crbs LLC.......F....... 772 466-2400
Fort Pierce *(G-4745)*
Storage Building Company LLC.......F....... 863 738-1319
Palmetto *(G-13825)*
Sunbelt Metals & Mfg Inc.......E....... 407 889-8960
Apopka *(G-189)*
Tampa Amalgamated Steel Corp.......F....... 813 621-0550
Tampa *(G-18155)*
West Point Industries Inc.......G....... 561 848-8381
Lake Park *(G-7481)*

BUILDING ITEM REPAIR SVCS, MISCELLANEOUS

Otis Elevator Company.......B....... 561 618-4831
West Palm Beach *(G-18974)*

BUILDING PRDTS & MATERIALS DEALERS

Aluma TEC Aluminun.......G....... 352 732-7362
Ocala *(G-11870)*
Cast-Crete Usa LLC.......D....... 813 621-4641
Seffner *(G-16723)*
Central Florida Lbr & Sup Co.......D....... 407 298-5600
Orlando *(G-12569)*
Cornerstone Kitchens Inc.......C....... 239 332-3020
Fort Myers *(G-4410)*
Finyl Products Inc.......G....... 352 351-4033
Ocala *(G-11942)*
Island Shutter Co Inc.......E....... 386 738-9455
Deland *(G-2985)*
Largo Aluminum Inc.......F....... 305 852-2390
Islamorada *(G-6098)*

Shower Doors & More Inc ....G.... 954 358-2014
Fort Lauderdale *(G-4231)*
Southern Fuelwood Inc ....E.... 352 472-4324
Newberry *(G-11561)*

BUILDING PRDTS: Concrete

Brown (usa) Inc ....F.... 305 593-9228
Miami *(G-9280)*
Knightsbridge Steel LLC ....G.... 786 532-0290
Hialeah *(G-5474)*
Lane Construction Corporation ....E.... 863 665-0457
Lakeland *(G-7732)*
Mark 1 Contracting Inc ....F.... 727 894-3600
New Port Richey *(G-11500)*
Metals USA Holdings Corp ....A.... 954 202-4000
Fort Lauderdale *(G-4118)*

BUILDING PRDTS: Stone

Asv Stone Llc ....G.... 941 268-5321
Sarasota *(G-16354)*
Borders & Accents Inc ....F.... 305 947-6200
North Miami *(G-11629)*
Florida Amico ....G.... 863 688-9256
Lakeland *(G-7689)*
Quartzo LLC ....F.... 888 813-3442
Tampa *(G-18034)*
Stone Design By Santos LLC ....G.... 954 366-1919
Pompano Beach *(G-14873)*

BUILDING STONE, ARTIFICIAL: Concrete

Stonehardscapes Intl Inc ....G.... 954 989-4050
Fort Lauderdale *(G-4262)*

BUILDINGS & COMPONENTS: Prefabricated Metal

Adf International Inc ....F.... 954 931-5150
Pompano Beach *(G-14577)*
Advanced Alum Polk Cnty Inc ....E.... 863 648-5787
Lakeland *(G-7626)*
All American Building Products ....G.... 786 718-7300
Dania *(G-2438)*
All Amrcan Bldg Strctres Contr ....G.... 407 466-4959
Apopka *(G-110)*
All Steel Bldngs Cmponents Inc ....E.... 813 671-8044
Gibsonton *(G-5025)*
Allied Insulated Panels Inc ....G.... 800 599-3905
Fort Lauderdale *(G-3803)*
Allied Steel Buildings Inc ....E.... 800 508-2718
Fort Lauderdale *(G-3804)*
Allied Steel Buildings Inc ....F.... 954 590-4949
Fort Lauderdale *(G-3805)*
Amazon Sheds and Gazebos Inc ....F.... 239 498-5558
Fort Myers *(G-4355)*
Amtex-Nms Holdings Inc ....D.... 352 728-2930
Leesburg *(G-8141)*
Bestway Portable Building Inc ....F.... 850 747-1984
Panama City *(G-13871)*
Carport Solution LLC ....F.... 352 789-1149
Ocala *(G-11896)*
Carports Anywhere Inc ....F.... 352 468-1116
Starke *(G-16888)*
Curvco Steel Structures Corp ....F.... 800 956-6341
Delray Beach *(G-3067)*
Defenshield Inc ....G.... 904 679-3942
Saint Augustine *(G-15535)*
Grays Portable Buildings Inc ....G.... 386 755-6449
Lake City *(G-7356)*
Gulfstream Alum & Shutter Corp ....E.... 772 287-6476
Stuart *(G-16950)*
Jacobsen Manufacturing Inc ....C.... 727 726-1138
Safety Harbor *(G-15496)*
Jax Enterprises LLC ....G.... 904 786-6909
Jacksonville *(G-6518)*
JCs Building Sales ....G.... 386 277-2851
Deland *(G-2988)*
Kingspan Insulated Panels Inc ....C.... 386 626-6789
Deland *(G-2991)*
Kingspan Insulated Panels Inc ....D.... 386 626-6789
Deland *(G-2992)*
Kingspan-Medusa Inc ....C.... 386 626-6789
Deland *(G-2993)*
Majestic Metals Inc ....F.... 813 380-6885
Valrico *(G-18522)*
Marinetek North America Inc ....F.... 727 498-8741
Saint Petersburg *(G-15849)*
Modular Life Solutions LLC ....G.... 904 900-7965
Jacksonville *(G-6611)*
Morin Corp ....G.... 386 626-6789
Deland *(G-2999)*
Neopod Systems LLC ....F.... 954 603-3100
Sunrise *(G-17151)*
Ocala Metal Products Inc ....G.... 352 861-4500
Ocala *(G-12012)*
Premier Buildings of Navarre ....G.... 850 684-3639
Navarre *(G-11472)*
R & K Buildings Inc ....E.... 850 995-9525
Milton *(G-10939)*
R & K Portable Buildings ....G.... 850 857-7899
Pensacola *(G-14247)*
Screens Fast ....G.... 239 565-1211
Fort Myers *(G-4601)*
Shed4less LLC ....G.... 863 660-7300
Lakeland *(G-7790)*
Sheds Galore and More LLC ....G.... 386 362-1786
Live Oak *(G-8240)*
Shoreline Foundation Inc ....C.... 954 985-0981
West Park *(G-19098)*
US Building Systems Corp ....F.... 954 281-2100
Deerfield Beach *(G-2931)*

BUILDINGS: Farm & Utility

Teds Sheds of Tampa ....E.... 239 344-2900
Bonita Springs *(G-861)*

BUILDINGS: Mobile, For Commercial Use

Step Zone LLC ....G.... 850 983-3758
Milton *(G-10940)*

BUILDINGS: Portable

Blue Water Dynamics LLC ....D.... 386 957-5464
Edgewater *(G-3614)*
Eds Aluminum Buildings Inc ....G.... 850 476-2169
Pensacola *(G-14138)*
Florida Pre-Fab Inc ....F.... 813 247-3934
Tampa *(G-17685)*
Forts Services LLC ....F.... 786 942-4389
Coconut Creek *(G-2077)*
Keens Portable Buildings Inc ....F.... 386 364-7995
Live Oak *(G-8234)*
Langstons Utility Buildings ....G.... 813 659-0141
Mulberry *(G-11128)*
Leslie Industries Inc ....F.... 850 422-0099
Tallahassee *(G-17290)*
M S Amtex-N Inc ....C.... 352 326-9729
Leesburg *(G-8164)*
Smithbilt Industries Inc ....D.... 321 690-0902
Auburndale *(G-253)*
Suncrest Sheds of South Fla ....F.... 305 231-1990
Miami Lakes *(G-10865)*
Superior Sheds Inc ....E.... 386 774-9861
Orange City *(G-12379)*

BUILDINGS: Prefabricated, Metal

Dean Steel Buildings Inc ....D.... 239 334-1051
Fort Myers *(G-4429)*
Elite Outdoor Buildings LLC ....G.... 386 364-1364
Live Oak *(G-8231)*
Metal Building Kings ....G.... 412 522-4797
Tamarac *(G-17363)*
Scif Solutions Inc ....F.... 904 298-0631
Jacksonville *(G-6755)*
Trident Building Systems Inc ....C.... 941 755-7073
Sarasota *(G-16314)*
Worth Metals Inc ....F.... 904 626-1434
Green Cove Springs *(G-5077)*

BUILDINGS: Prefabricated, Plastic

Blue Water Dynamics LLC ....D.... 386 957-5464
Edgewater *(G-3614)*

BUILDINGS: Prefabricated, Wood

Advanced Mdular Structures Inc ....G.... 954 960-1550
Pompano Beach *(G-14580)*
Amazon Sheds and Gazebos Inc ....F.... 239 498-5558
Fort Myers *(G-4355)*
Chariot Eagle Inc ....C.... 623 936-7545
Ocala *(G-11901)*
Jacobsen Manufacturing Inc ....C.... 727 726-1138
Safety Harbor *(G-15496)*
Neopod Systems LLC ....F.... 954 603-3100
Sunrise *(G-17151)*
Quality Cmpnents Tampa Bay LLC ....G.... 727 623-4909
Largo *(G-8034)*
South Country Sheds LLC ....F.... 863 491-8700
Arcadia *(G-205)*
Southeastern Seating Inc ....F.... 813 273-9858
Tampa *(G-18119)*
Truss Systems LLC ....G.... 386 255-3009
Bunnell *(G-1308)*
Truss Systems of Vlsia Flgler ....F.... 386 255-3009
Bunnell *(G-1309)*

BUILDINGS: Prefabricated, Wood

Florida Shed Company Inc ....E.... 727 524-9191
Saint Petersburg *(G-15785)*
Riverhead Housing Inc ....G.... 630 688-6791
Fort Lauderdale *(G-4206)*
Suncrest Sheds Inc ....F.... 863 675-8600
Labelle *(G-7324)*
Surepods LLC ....D.... 407 859-7034
Orlando *(G-13232)*

BULLETPROOF VESTS

Dhb Armor Group Inc ....G.... 800 413-5155
Pompano Beach *(G-14662)*
Noguera Holdings LLC ....G.... 305 846-9144
Hialeah *(G-5543)*
Onyx Protective Group Inc ....F.... 305 282-4455
Miami *(G-10108)*
Point Blank Enterprises Inc ....A.... 954 630-0900
Pompano Beach *(G-14801)*
Point Blank Enterprises Inc ....D.... 305 820-4270
Miami Lakes *(G-10840)*
Ppi International Corp ....D.... 954 838-1008
Sunrise *(G-17159)*
Protective Group Inc ....E.... 305 820-4266
Miami Lakes *(G-10846)*
Protective Products Entps Inc ....E.... 954 630-0900
Pompano Beach *(G-14820)*
Telenetpro Inc ....F.... 954 333-8633
Pompano Beach *(G-14885)*
Tpg Black LLC ....G.... 561 777-8989
Boynton Beach *(G-972)*

BUMPERS: Motor Vehicle

Hope Technical Sales & Svcs ....G.... 941 412-1204
Venice *(G-18554)*

BURGLAR ALARM MAINTENANCE & MONITORING SVCS

Cintas Corporation ....G.... 239 693-8722
Fort Myers *(G-4396)*
Quality Cable Contractors Inc ....E.... 407 246-0606
Orlando *(G-13103)*
Vanguard Products Group Inc ....D.... 813 855-9639
Oldsmar *(G-12277)*

BURIAL VAULTS: Concrete Or Precast Terrazzo

Atlas Concrete Products Inc ....G.... 407 277-0841
Orlando *(G-12497)*
Atm Vault Corp ....G.... 561 441-9294
Boca Raton *(G-434)*
Burleys Mmrals Brial Vults LLC ....G.... 561 284-6983
Boynton Beach *(G-885)*
Darkside Vault LLC ....G.... 407 353-3776
Orlando *(G-12647)*
Florida Wilbert Inc ....G.... 904 765-2641
Jacksonville *(G-6405)*
Florida Wilbert Inc ....G.... 352 728-3531
Okahumpka *(G-12171)*
Gulf Coast Wilbert Inc ....G.... 850 682-8004
Crestview *(G-2350)*
Gun Vault ....G.... 850 391-7651
Tallahassee *(G-17271)*
Hicks Industries Inc ....G.... 954 226-5148
Davie *(G-2535)*
Jewish Burial Society America ....G.... 954 424-1899
Delray Beach *(G-3096)*
Latteri & Sons Inc ....G.... 813 876-1800
Tampa *(G-17836)*
Lewis Vault & Precast Inc ....G.... 352 351-2992
Ocala *(G-11982)*
Mack Industries Inc ....G.... 352 742-2333
Astatula *(G-214)*
Quality Vaults Inc ....F.... 407 656-8781
Ocoee *(G-12089)*
Roberts Vault Co Inc ....E.... 352 567-0110
Dade City *(G-2433)*

(G-0000) Company's Geographic Section entry number

Rons Safe & Vault Company G 305 527-2901
Plantation *(G-14545)*
Wilbert E Beran G 813 882-0178
Tampa *(G-18258)*

BURIAL VAULTS: Stone

Florida Funeral Shipping Cntrs G 954 957-9259
Fort Lauderdale *(G-4000)*

BURNERS: Gas, Indl

Micron Fiber - Tech Inc F 386 668-7895
Debary *(G-2752)*

BURNERS: Gas-Oil, Combination

Intertech Worldwide Corp G 561 395-5441
Boca Raton *(G-571)*

BUSHINGS: Cast Steel, Exc Investment

Contemporary Carbide Tech F 386 734-0080
Deland *(G-2964)*

BUSHINGS: Rubber

Stepincorp Auto Solutions LLC G 786 864-3222
Miami *(G-10413)*

BUSINESS ACTIVITIES: Non-Commercial Site

9t Technology LLC G 904 703-9214
Jacksonville *(G-6106)*
Accenius Inc G 415 205-6444
Boca Raton *(G-396)*
Advanced Electronics Labs Inc G 305 255-6401
Pinecrest *(G-14322)*
Beez Worx Boats LLC G 850 678-6548
Niceville *(G-11563)*
Big Star Systems LLC G 954 243-7209
Lauderhill *(G-8102)*
Blinds By Randy LLC G 305 300-1147
Miami Gardens *(G-10735)*
Boostane LLC F 239 908-1615
Bonita Springs *(G-819)*
Cavallo Estate Winery LLC G 352 500-9463
Lecanto *(G-8130)*
Cellec Games Inc G 407 476-3590
Apopka *(G-120)*
Cima Activewear LLC G 239 273-6055
Estero *(G-3687)*
Closeup Inc G 650 284-8831
Miami *(G-9363)*
Comm Dots LLC Connecting F 305 505-6009
Miami *(G-9388)*
Command Print LLC G 716 583-5175
Bonita Springs *(G-826)*
Common Sense Publishing LLC C 561 510-1713
Delray Beach *(G-3063)*
Construction Software Inc G 888 801-0675
Fort Lauderdale *(G-3916)*
Coqui Rdo Pharmaceuticals Corp G 787 685-5046
Doral *(G-3307)*
CP Logging Inc F 850 379-8698
Hosford *(G-6008)*
Custom Carpentry Plus LLC F 305 972-3735
Cutler Bay *(G-2390)*
Custom Install Solutions Inc F 916 601-1190
Boca Raton *(G-494)*
Data Buoy Instrumentation LLC G 239 849-7063
Cape Coral *(G-1410)*
Demelle Biopharma LLC G 908 240-8939
Tarpon Springs *(G-18294)*
Deming Designs Inc F 850 478-5765
Pensacola *(G-14129)*
Dinner Belle Inc G 747 210-6284
Lauderhill *(G-8108)*
Dirtbag Choppers Inc F 904 725-7600
Atlantic Beach *(G-219)*
Dudley Blake LLC G 904 866-2829
Jacksonville *(G-6332)*
East Coast Metalworks LLC G 321 698-0624
Cocoa *(G-2018)*
Everyday Feminism LLC G 202 643-1001
Tallahassee *(G-17249)*
G Haddock Rowland Inc G 904 845-2725
Hilliard *(G-5706)*
H&K Home Supplies Distrs LLC F 786 308-6024
Homestead *(G-5966)*
Hollywood Clctibles Group LLC G 407 985-4613
Orlando *(G-12806)*
Intelligent Robotics Inc G 850 728-7353
Tallahassee *(G-17281)*
Ivengo Software Inc G 321 480-3155
Melbourne *(G-8852)*
Jax Enterprises LLC G 904 786-6909
Jacksonville *(G-6518)*
Jess By Inches LLC G 305 731-1387
North Miami Beach *(G-11686)*
Jmn Aluminum G 813 325-7807
Tampa *(G-17807)*
John Eric Madden G 813 395-3314
Zephyrhills *(G-19524)*
Jsi Scientific Inc G 732 845-1925
Naples *(G-11300)*
Jupiter Wellness Inc G 561 462-2700
Jupiter *(G-7063)*
Karnak Corporation G 352 481-4145
East Palatka *(G-3604)*
Keepmefresh G 502 407-7902
Clermont *(G-1965)*
Lamb Tec Inc G 305 798-6266
Cutler Bay *(G-2399)*
Lit Forklift LLC G 321 271-4626
Cocoa Beach *(G-2065)*
Mauer Sports Nutrition Inc G 888 609-2489
Fort Myers *(G-4524)*
Maydone Ltd Liability Company G 407 399-3287
Orlando *(G-12955)*
Meridian Cable LLC F 847 847-1128
Saint Augustine *(G-15568)*
Militek Industries LLC G 941 544-5636
Bradenton *(G-1078)*
Mobile Auto Solutions LLC G 561 903-5328
West Palm Beach *(G-18954)*
Morgannas Alchemy LLC G 727 505-8376
New Port Richey *(G-11502)*
New Style Wood Work Corp G 305 989-9665
Hialeah *(G-5539)*
OGrady Tool Company F 239 560-3395
Fort Myers *(G-4556)*
Okee-B Inc D 561 996-3040
Belle Glade *(G-350)*
Pallet Direct Inc G 888 433-1727
Naples *(G-11354)*
Paper Free Technology Inc G 515 270-1505
Lehigh Acres *(G-8202)*
Precision Infinity Systems Inc G 407 490-2320
Orlando *(G-13080)*
Pure Wave Organics Inc G 321 368-7002
Melbourne *(G-8915)*
Rapid Composites LLC G 941 322-6647
Sarasota *(G-16284)*
Rbj Timber Inc G 904 879-1597
Callahan *(G-1328)*
RLC Building Inc G 904 704-5614
Jacksonville *(G-6731)*
S2 Pass Holdings LLC G 706 773-4097
Santa Rosa Beach *(G-16166)*
Sandy Lender Inc F 239 272-8613
Cape Coral *(G-1464)*
Sbm Beauty LLC F 850 567-7338
Quincy *(G-15253)*
Seal Outdoors Inc F 877 323-7325
South Miami *(G-16827)*
Seminole Metal Finishing Inc F 407 332-8949
Altamonte Springs *(G-72)*
Sleepy Dragon Studios Inc G 561 714-6156
Cutler Bay *(G-2411)*
Stress Nuts LLC G 787 675-3042
Orlando *(G-13218)*
Stuart Boat Works Inc F 772 600-7121
Stuart *(G-17023)*
Tim Hardy Plaster Moldings LLC G 239 877-8434
Naples *(G-11441)*
Tropical Paver Sealing G 727 786-4011
Wesley Chapel *(G-18761)*
Trs Industries Inc G 561 880-0031
Lake Worth *(G-7594)*
Trugreen Products LLC G 954 629-5794
Pompano Beach *(G-14893)*
Vuaant Inc F 407 701-6975
Orlando *(G-13316)*
Wiztel USA Inc G 416 457-5513
Miromar Lakes *(G-11072)*
Wonderworld 100 LLC F 407 618-3207
Orlando *(G-13329)*
Yesil Inc F 516 858-0244
Boca Raton *(G-796)*

BUSINESS FORMS WHOLESALERS

Dannys Prtg Svc Sups & Eqp Inc G 305 757-2282
Miami *(G-9435)*
Printed Systems Inc G 904 281-0909
Jacksonville *(G-6687)*

BUSINESS FORMS: Printed, Continuous

John Stewart Enterprises Inc F 904 356-9392
Jacksonville *(G-6525)*

BUSINESS FORMS: Printed, Manifold

America Solutions For Business G 305 971-5400
Miami *(G-9138)*
Blackstone Legal Supplies Inc F 305 945-3450
Lauderhill *(G-8103)*
Business Card Ex Tampa Bay Inc D 727 535-7768
Clearwater *(G-1618)*
Economy Printing Co F 904 786-4070
Jacksonville *(G-6354)*
Herald-Advocate Publishing Co F 863 773-3255
Wauchula *(G-18693)*
Independent Resources Inc E 813 237-0945
Tampa *(G-17777)*
K R O Enterprises Ltd G 309 797-2213
Naples *(G-11302)*
Professional Office Svcs Inc G 305 756-8632
Miami *(G-10206)*
Professional Office Svcs Inc G 863 967-6634
Winter Haven *(G-19348)*
Taylor Communications Inc F 813 689-5099
Seffner *(G-16733)*
Taylor Communications Inc F 813 886-5511
Tampa *(G-18177)*
Taylor Communications Inc F 954 632-6501
Sunrise *(G-17185)*
Tiger Business Forms Inc E 305 888-3528
Hialeah *(G-5649)*

BUSINESS FORMS: Strip, Manifold

Arlington Prtg Stationers Inc C 904 358-2928
Jacksonville *(G-6168)*

BUSINESS FORMS: Unit Sets, Manifold

Southeastern Pegboard Printers G 904 731-0357
Jacksonville *(G-6792)*

BUSINESS SUPPORT SVCS

Bill Evans Aluminum Inc G 352 400-1424
Lecanto *(G-8128)*
Exploration Resources Intn Geo G 601 747-0726
Lake Mary *(G-7412)*
Find A Friend LLC G 813 293-1584
Land O Lakes *(G-7855)*
Great America Beverage Co LLC G 786 763-2027
Palmetto Bay *(G-13846)*
Maria Fuentes LLC G 305 717-3404
Miami *(G-9947)*
Natures Power and Energy LLC F 813 907-6279
Wesley Chapel *(G-18753)*
North America Bio Fuel Corp G 877 877-9279
Bradenton *(G-1087)*
Ottica Dante Americas LLC G 561 322-0186
Boca Raton *(G-658)*
R S S Partners Inc G 904 241-6144
Jacksonville Beach *(G-6955)*
Recycled Vinyl G 727 434-1857
Sarasota *(G-16555)*
Saf Aerospace LLC G 813 376-0883
Tampa *(G-18080)*
Sterling Mdr Inc F 954 725-2777
Deerfield Beach *(G-2917)*
Swoogo LLC G 212 655-9810
Sarasota *(G-16613)*
Techpubs Ltd F 201 541-1192
Sarasota *(G-16620)*
Terfa Litter USA Inc F 416 358-4495
Sunny Isles Beach *(G-17081)*
West Texas Protein Inc F 806 250-5959
Jacksonville *(G-6911)*

BUSINESS TRAINING SVCS

Paradigm Leaders LLC G 850 441-3289
Panama City Beach *(G-13982)*

BUTTONS

531 East Inc.......G....... 561 249-2524
Lake Worth *(G-7526)*
M D R International Inc.......F....... 305 944-5335
North Miami *(G-11644)*
Maxant Button & Supply Inc.......G....... 770 460-2227
Plantation *(G-14532)*

CABINETS & CASES: Show, Display & Storage, Exc Wood

Bob & Lees Cabinets.......F....... 352 748-3553
Wildwood *(G-19191)*
New River Cabinet & Fix Inc.......E....... 954 938-9200
Fort Lauderdale *(G-4137)*

CABINETS: Bathroom Vanities, Wood

Avon Cabinet Corporation.......C....... 941 755-2866
Bradenton *(G-993)*
Bailey Industries Inc.......E....... 352 326-2898
Leesburg *(G-8144)*
Beverly Acquisitions Inc.......F....... 561 746-3827
Jupiter *(G-7007)*
Braden Kitchens Inc.......E....... 321 636-4700
Cocoa *(G-1999)*
Clover Interior Systems Inc.......F....... 941 484-1300
Nokomis *(G-11580)*
Counter Productions Inc.......G....... 386 673-6500
Daytona Beach *(G-2647)*
Custom Klosets & Cabinets Inc.......E....... 813 246-4806
Tampa *(G-17579)*
Dj Cabinet Factory Inc.......G....... 786 483-8868
Hialeah *(G-5375)*
Home Art Corporation.......F....... 352 326-3337
Fruitland Park *(G-4865)*
Jim Baird Cabinets.......G....... 772 569-0936
Vero Beach *(G-18633)*
Princeton Industries Inc.......E....... 954 344-9155
Margate *(G-8563)*
Smith Products Co Inc.......F....... 386 325-4534
Palatka *(G-13492)*
Star Quality Inc.......F....... 813 875-9955
Tampa *(G-18131)*

CABINETS: Entertainment

Amick Cstm Woodcraft & Design.......G....... 407 324-8525
Sanford *(G-15994)*
Bon Vivant Interiors Inc.......E....... 305 576-8066
Opa Locka *(G-12296)*
Dons Cabinets and Woodworking.......F....... 727 863-3404
Hudson *(G-6022)*
Elegant House Intl LLC.......G....... 954 457-8836
Hallandale *(G-5157)*
Florida Designer Cabinets Inc.......F....... 352 793-8555
Sumterville *(G-17068)*
Home Pride Cabinets Inc.......F....... 813 887-3782
Tampa *(G-17760)*
J & J Custom Mica Inc.......F....... 239 433-2828
Fort Myers *(G-4498)*
McCallum Cabinets Inc.......F....... 352 372-2344
Gainesville *(G-4957)*
Spruce Creek Cabinetry Inc.......F....... 386 756-0041
Port Orange *(G-15035)*
Williams Minerals Co Inc.......G....... 304 897-6003
Winter Springs *(G-19489)*
Y F Leung Inc.......G....... 305 651-6851
North Miami Beach *(G-11714)*

CABINETS: Entertainment Units, Household, Wood

Still Water Industries Inc.......G....... 561 845-6033
West Palm Beach *(G-19045)*

CABINETS: Factory

Borgzinner Inc.......E....... 561 848-2538
Riviera Beach *(G-15304)*
Byblos Group Inc.......G....... 305 662-6666
Miami *(G-9291)*
Commercial Casework Inc.......D....... 904 264-4222
Jacksonville *(G-6280)*
Distinct Dsgns Cstm Coml Case.......G....... 727 530-0119
Largo *(G-7934)*
Florida Designer Cabinets Inc.......F....... 352 793-8555
Sumterville *(G-17068)*
Gulf South Distributors Inc.......F....... 850 244-1522
Fort Walton Beach *(G-4807)*
Guyton Industries LLC.......E....... 772 208-3019
Indiantown *(G-6073)*
James Spear Design Inc.......G....... 727 592-9600
Largo *(G-7986)*
Morris Mica Cabinets Inc.......G....... 954 979-6838
Pompano Beach *(G-14769)*
Regency Custom Cabinets Inc.......F....... 239 332-7977
Fort Myers *(G-4580)*
Werever Products Inc.......F....... 813 241-9701
Riverview *(G-15287)*
Wj Bergin Cabinetry LLC.......E....... 407 271-8982
Orlando *(G-13326)*
Wood Stile Inc.......G....... 561 329-4671
North Palm Beach *(G-11730)*

CABINETS: Filing, Wood

Kabinets By Kinsey Inc.......E....... 813 222-0460
Tampa *(G-17813)*

CABINETS: Kitchen, Metal

FL Central Cnstr & Rmdlg.......G....... 863 701-3548
Lakeland *(G-7687)*
Kit Residential Designs Inc.......G....... 305 796-5940
Hialeah *(G-5473)*
Mag Works Inc.......E....... 305 823-4440
Hialeah *(G-5496)*
Saint Petersburg Cabinets Inc.......G....... 727 327-4800
Saint Petersburg *(G-15904)*
Schwarzmann LLC.......G....... 561 654-3653
Delray Beach *(G-3138)*
Studio Luxe Cstm Cabinetry LLC.......G....... 941 371-4010
Sarasota *(G-16607)*

CABINETS: Kitchen, Wood

3 Stars Kitchen Cabinets Corp.......G....... 786 285-7147
Hialeah *(G-5252)*
4k Cabinets.......G....... 727 507-0444
Largo *(G-7880)*
A A A Cabinets.......G....... 850 438-8337
Pensacola *(G-14075)*
A Better Kitchen Cabinets Inc.......G....... 786 234-1897
Homestead *(G-5951)*
A RE Door Cabinets Inc.......G....... 813 419-0007
Tampa *(G-17376)*
A W R Cabinets Inc.......F....... 407 323-1415
Sanford *(G-15985)*
A1 Custom Mica Inc.......G....... 954 893-0063
Hollywood *(G-5763)*
Aadi Inc.......E....... 407 957-4557
Saint Cloud *(G-15642)*
About Face Cabinetry & Refacin.......F....... 813 777-4088
Lutz *(G-8371)*
Absolute Wood Creations LLC.......G....... 954 251-2202
Hallandale Beach *(G-5167)*
Adams Bros Cabinetry Inc.......G....... 863 993-0501
Arcadia *(G-198)*
Advanced Cabinetry Inventions.......G....... 305 866-1160
North Bay Village *(G-11592)*
Advanced Cabinets LLC.......G....... 954 515-2675
Pompano Beach *(G-14579)*
Advanced Kitchen & Cabinet.......G....... 305 251-9344
Cutler Bay *(G-2383)*
Aj Originals Inc.......G....... 954 563-9911
Fort Lauderdale *(G-3793)*
Akiknav Inc.......F....... 561 842-8091
Riviera Beach *(G-15296)*
Al-FA Cabinets Inc.......F....... 813 876-4205
Tampa *(G-17396)*
Albrecht Consulting Inc.......F....... 941 377-7755
Sarasota *(G-16339)*
All American Kit & Bath LLC.......G....... 305 599-9000
Doral *(G-3238)*
All Wood Cabinetry LLC.......E....... 866 367-2516
Bartow *(G-305)*
Allen Custom Cabinetry Inc.......G....... 850 625-4713
Panama City *(G-13862)*
Altamonte Woodworking Co Inc.......G....... 407 331-0020
Altamonte Springs *(G-29)*
AM Cabinets LLC.......G....... 321 663-4319
Altamonte Springs *(G-30)*
Amazing Cabinet Store LLC.......F....... 407 270-7865
Orlando *(G-12466)*
Amercn Cabinets Granite Floors.......F....... 727 303-0678
Palm Harbor *(G-13718)*
American Cabinet Works Inc.......G....... 904 672-6649
Jacksonville *(G-6147)*
Amick Cstm Woodcraft & Design.......G....... 407 324-8525
Sanford *(G-15994)*
Amy Cabinetry.......E....... 561 842-8091
Riviera Beach *(G-15298)*
Andrews Cabinet.......F....... 850 994-0836
Milton *(G-10921)*
Antique & Modern Cabinets Inc.......E....... 904 393-9055
Jacksonville *(G-6158)*
Architctral Wdwrks Cbnetry Inc.......F....... 561 848-8595
Palm Beach Gardens *(G-13568)*
Argenal Cabinets Inc.......G....... 863 670-7973
Lakeland *(G-7638)*
Art Wood Cabinets Corp.......G....... 754 367-0742
Deerfield Beach *(G-2779)*
Assocate Cbinetmakers Palm Bch.......G....... 561 743-9566
Jupiter *(G-7001)*
B & K Discount Cabinets LLC.......F....... 321 254-2322
Melbourne *(G-8775)*
B G Cabinets Llc.......G....... 941 485-0040
Venice *(G-18534)*
Bailey Industries.......G....... 352 326-2898
Tampa *(G-17454)*
Batista Cabinets Inc.......G....... 407 922-3459
Kissimmee *(G-7222)*
Bauformat South-East LLC.......G....... 201 693-6635
Fort Lauderdale *(G-3841)*
Bay Cabinets and Millworks.......G....... 850 215-1485
Panama City Beach *(G-13972)*
Beaches Woodcraft Inc.......F....... 904 249-0785
Atlantic Beach *(G-217)*
Beautiful Cabinets Corp.......G....... 813 486-9034
Tampa *(G-17463)*
Bennetts Custom Cabinets Inc.......E....... 904 751-1455
Jacksonville *(G-6206)*
BK Stainless Inc.......G....... 786 474-0203
Miami *(G-9253)*
Bob & Lees Cabinets.......F....... 352 748-3553
Wildwood *(G-19191)*
Braswell Custom Cabinets.......G....... 850 436-2645
Pensacola *(G-14104)*
Bresee Woodwork Inc.......F....... 941 355-2591
Sarasota *(G-16368)*
Broward Custom Woodwork LLC.......G....... 352 376-4732
Deerfield Beach *(G-2791)*
Bruno Danger Custom Cabinets.......G....... 754 366-1302
Sebastian *(G-16656)*
Built Rght Ktchens of Palm Cas.......G....... 386 437-7077
Bunnell *(G-1299)*
Built Rite Cabinets Inc.......G....... 352 447-2238
Inglis *(G-6075)*
Busy Bee Cabinets Inc.......D....... 941 628-2025
North Port *(G-11734)*
Byerly Custom Design Inc.......G....... 941 371-7498
Sarasota *(G-16374)*
Cabinet Cnnction of Trsure Cas.......E....... 772 621-4882
Port Saint Lucie *(G-15095)*
Cabinet Collection Inc.......G....... 239 478-0359
Bonita Springs *(G-822)*
Cabinet Design and Cnstr LLC.......G....... 850 393-9724
Pensacola *(G-14111)*
Cabinet Designs of Central Fla.......G....... 321 636-1101
Rockledge *(G-15397)*
Cabinet Designs of Sarasota.......F....... 941 739-1607
Bradenton *(G-1010)*
Cabinet Dreams & Things Inc.......G....... 727 514-0847
Hudson *(G-6017)*
Cabinet Factory Outlet.......G....... 386 323-0778
Daytona Beach *(G-2637)*
Cabinet Genies.......G....... 239 458-8563
Cape Coral *(G-1399)*
Cabinet Guy 2012 Inc.......G....... 305 796-5242
Davie *(G-2505)*
Cabinet Guy of Englewood Inc.......G....... 941 475-9454
Englewood *(G-3670)*
Cabinet Kings LLC.......G....... 239 288-6740
Fort Myers *(G-4383)*
Cabinet Market LLC.......G....... 321 203-2598
Winter Park *(G-19389)*
Cabinet Masters Inc.......G....... 727 535-0020
Largo *(G-7918)*
Cabinet Mechanics LLC.......G....... 941 626-0735
Port Charlotte *(G-14967)*
Cabinet Options Inc.......G....... 904 434-1564
Saint Johns *(G-15674)*
Cabinet Specialist Inc.......G....... 239 641-6931
Naples *(G-11198)*
Cabinet Systems of Central Fla.......G....... 407 678-0994
Winter Park *(G-19390)*
Cabinetree Collection Inc.......F....... 772 569-4761
Vero Beach *(G-18608)*
Cabinetry Masters LLC.......G....... 954 549-8646
Jacksonville *(G-6248)*

Cabinets & Counters ....G....... 561 444-3083
West Palm Beach *(G-18832)*
Cabinets -N- More Inc ....G....... 321 355-9548
Cocoa *(G-2003)*
Cabinets By Design ....G....... 954 829-2923
Oakland Park *(G-11788)*
Cabinets By Marylin Inc ....G....... 954 729-3995
Pompano Beach *(G-14630)*
Cabinets By Wfc Inc ....F....... 941 355-2703
Sarasota *(G-16375)*
Cabinets Direct USA ....F....... 862 704-6138
Delray Beach *(G-3055)*
Cabinets Extraordinaire Inc ....F....... 618 925-0515
Bradenton *(G-1011)*
Cabinets Moreunlimited Inc ....G....... 813 789-4203
Tampa *(G-17497)*
Cabinets One LLC ....G....... 407 227-1147
Orlando *(G-12542)*
Cabinets Plus Inc ....F....... 239 574-7020
Cape Coral *(G-1400)*
Cabinets Plus of America Inc ....G....... 813 408-0433
Tampa *(G-17498)*
Cabinetscapes LLC ....G....... 941 539-0013
Sarasota *(G-16376)*
Cabinetsync Inc ....G....... 239 690-6122
Fort Myers *(G-4384)*
Camelot Cabinets Inc ....F....... 813 876-9150
Tampa *(G-17502)*
Candi-Lyn Cabinetry ....G....... 863 860-2505
Bartow *(G-311)*
Capri Kitchens Inc ....F....... 813 623-1424
Tampa *(G-17504)*
Captain Cabinets LLC ....G....... 813 685-7179
Seffner *(G-16722)*
Caravaggio Cabinetry Inc ....F....... 561 609-3355
Lake Worth *(G-7539)*
Caribbean Cbinets Counters Inc ....G....... 239 292-8073
Fort Myers *(G-4389)*
Carlos Velez Cabinets & Instal ....G....... 407 929-3402
Orlando *(G-12551)*
Carloss Cabinets Inc ....G....... 863 853-4255
Lakeland *(G-7653)*
Carters Cabinetry Inc ....E....... 386 677-4192
Ormond Beach *(G-13357)*
Castor Inc ....G....... 813 254-1171
Tampa *(G-17514)*
Cayo Hueso Enterprises Inc ....E....... 305 747-0020
Key West *(G-7181)*
CC Kitchen Cabinets Corp ....G....... 786 457-1494
Miami *(G-9330)*
Century Millworks ....F....... 850 256-2565
Century *(G-1527)*
Cepero Remodeling Inc ....G....... 305 265-1888
Miami *(G-9341)*
Chief Cabinets LLC ....G....... 850 545-5055
Tallahassee *(G-17233)*
Choice Cabinets LLC ....G....... 352 629-1556
Ocala *(G-11902)*
Cianos Tile & Marble Inc ....E....... 239 267-8453
Fort Myers *(G-4395)*
Classic Cabinets and More LLC ....G....... 727 239-8869
Largo *(G-7923)*
Classic Kitchens Brevard Inc ....G....... 321 327-5972
Melbourne *(G-8790)*
Clever Cabinetry LLC ....G....... 813 992-0020
Riverview *(G-15267)*
Cljp Inc ....E....... 850 678-8819
Niceville *(G-11564)*
Closet Pros ....G....... 305 240-7775
Key West *(G-7183)*
Cnc Cabinet Components Inc ....F....... 321 956-3470
Melbourne *(G-8791)*
Coastal Cabinets & Countertops ....G....... 850 424-3940
Miramar Beach *(G-11065)*
Coastal Closet Co of Fla LLC ....G....... 239 826-3807
Fort Myers *(G-4401)*
Coastal Custom Woodwork LLC ....G....... 904 945-2299
Jacksonville *(G-6275)*
Coastline Cbntry Cstm Mllwk LL ....F....... 239 208-2876
Fort Myers *(G-4405)*
Coffin Cabinetry & Trim Michae ....G....... 352 217-3729
Umatilla *(G-18497)*
Concept One Custom Cabine ....G....... 954 829-3505
Hollywood *(G-5804)*
Contemporary Cabinets Gulf CST ....G....... 941 758-3060
Sarasota *(G-16195)*
Contractors Cabinet Company ....G....... 786 492-7118
Margate *(G-8540)*
Coral Cabinet Inc ....G....... 305 484-8702
Miami *(G-9400)*

Corn-E-Lee Woodcrafts ....G....... 239 574-2414
Cape Coral *(G-1406)*
Country Cabinets ....G....... 850 547-5477
Bonifay *(G-802)*
Creations In Cabinetry Inc ....G....... 386 237-3082
Palm Coast *(G-13690)*
Creative Cabinet Concepts Inc ....F....... 239 939-1313
Fort Myers *(G-4413)*
Creative Concepts Orlando Inc ....E....... 407 260-1435
Longwood *(G-8268)*
Creative Teaching Cabinets ....G....... 754 205-0886
Deerfield Beach *(G-2806)*
Csi Home Decor Inc ....G....... 754 301-2147
Sunrise *(G-17112)*
Csw Cabinet Services Inc ....G....... 727 267-1767
Spring Hill *(G-16871)*
Curry Cabinetry Inc ....E....... 813 321-3650
Tampa *(G-17574)*
Curtis K Foulks ....G....... 239 454-9663
Fort Myers *(G-4419)*
Custom Cabinet Doors & More In ....G....... 954 318-1881
Fort Lauderdale *(G-3923)*
Custom Cabinet Factory Inc ....G....... 352 429-7722
Groveland *(G-5094)*
Custom Cabinets ....G....... 727 392-1676
Seminole *(G-16745)*
Custom Cabinets By Jensen LLC ....G....... 813 250-0286
Tampa *(G-17576)*
Custom Cabinets Design Inc ....G....... 561 210-3423
Deerfield Beach *(G-2807)*
Custom Cabinets Inc ....F....... 941 366-0428
Sarasota *(G-16398)*
Custom Cabinets SW Florida LLC ....G....... 239 415-3350
Fort Myers *(G-4420)*
Custom Carpentry Plus LLC ....F....... 305 972-3735
Cutler Bay *(G-2390)*
Custom Craft Laminates Inc ....E....... 813 877-7100
Tampa *(G-17577)*
Custom Crafters ....G....... 954 792-6119
Pompano Beach *(G-14653)*
Custom Drawers of Swfl LLC ....G....... 239 226-1699
Fort Myers *(G-4421)*
Custom WD Designs of Pensacola ....F....... 850 476-9663
Pensacola *(G-14122)*
Custom Wood Products Inc ....G....... 904 737-6906
Jacksonville *(G-6304)*
D & G Custom Cabinetry Inc ....F....... 954 561-8822
Tamarac *(G-17353)*
D & G Millwork & Cabinetry LLC ....G....... 305 830-3000
Miami *(G-9424)*
D & N Cabinetry Inc ....F....... 863 471-1500
Sebring *(G-16685)*
D R Nickelson & Company Inc ....F....... 386 755-6565
Lake City *(G-7353)*
D T Woodcrafters Corp ....E....... 305 556-3771
Hialeah *(G-5360)*
Da Vinci Cabinetry LLC ....F....... 239 633-7957
Bonita Springs *(G-828)*
Dade Doors Inc ....F....... 305 556-8980
Hialeah *(G-5362)*
Dale Mabry Heating & Metal Co ....G....... 813 877-1574
Tampa *(G-17588)*
Dale Smith Cabinetry LLC ....G....... 407 625-2274
Orlando *(G-12645)*
Darmar Cabinets Inc ....G....... 786 556-5784
Miami Lakes *(G-10778)*
Daystar International Inc ....G....... 813 281-0200
Tampa *(G-17593)*
Debruyne Enterprise Inc ....F....... 850 562-0491
Tallahassee *(G-17242)*
Deluxe Clsets Cabinets Stn LLC ....G....... 786 879-3371
Miami *(G-9452)*
Demoss Cabinetry LLC ....F....... 863 738-0080
Lakeland *(G-7673)*
Design Your Kit Clset More Inc ....G....... 786 227-6412
Miami *(G-9458)*
Designers Choice Cabinetry ....F....... 321 632-0772
Rockledge *(G-15402)*
Designers Choice Cabinetry Inc ....G....... 321 632-0772
Rockledge *(G-15403)*
Devine Cabinetry LLC ....G....... 941 716-0339
North Port *(G-11737)*
Distinctive Cabinet Designs ....G....... 239 641-5165
Naples *(G-11228)*
District 95 Wood Working Inc ....G....... 888 400-3136
Pompano Beach *(G-14666)*
Dixie Workshop Inc ....G....... 352 629-4699
Ocala *(G-11922)*
Dl Cabinetry Orlando LLC ....G....... 504 669-7847
Orlando *(G-12679)*

Dma Cabinets Inc ....F....... 352 249-8147
Lecanto *(G-8133)*
Doctor Granite and Cabinets ....G....... 321 368-1779
West Melbourne *(G-18772)*
Doerrs Cstm Cabinets Trim LLC ....F....... 904 540-7024
Saint Augustine *(G-15538)*
Doerrs Custom Cabinets & Trim ....G....... 904 540-7024
Saint Augustine *(G-15539)*
Dons Cabinets and Woodworking ....F....... 727 863-3404
Hudson *(G-6022)*
Doormark Inc ....E....... 954 418-4700
Deerfield Beach *(G-2817)*
Dukemans Custom Woodworking ....G....... 904 355-5188
Jacksonville *(G-6333)*
E & D Kitchen Cabinet Inc ....G....... 786 343-8558
Hialeah *(G-5383)*
East Coast Cabinet Co ....G....... 321 392-4686
Rockledge *(G-15407)*
East Coast Fixtures & Mllwk Co ....G....... 904 733-9711
Jacksonville *(G-6349)*
Eastburn Woodworks Inc ....F....... 850 456-8090
Pensacola *(G-14137)*
EC Cabinets Inc ....G....... 305 887-2091
Hialeah *(G-5387)*
Eco Woodwork and Design Inc ....G....... 954 326-8806
Oakland Park *(G-11802)*
Elite Cabinet Coatings ....G....... 352 795-2655
Crystal River *(G-2377)*
Elite Cabinetry Inc ....G....... 239 262-1144
Naples *(G-11235)*
Emerald Coast Cabinets Inc ....F....... 850 267-2290
Santa Rosa Beach *(G-16158)*
Empire Stone and Cabinets ....E....... 305 885-7092
Hialeah *(G-5397)*
Epi Cabinets ....G....... 850 665-0659
Pensacola *(G-14144)*
Esquadro Inc ....G....... 754 367-3098
Deerfield Beach *(G-2823)*
Eternity Cabinets ....G....... 239 482-7172
Fort Myers *(G-4445)*
Eurocraft Cabinets Inc ....G....... 561 948-3034
Boca Raton *(G-523)*
European Cabinets & Design LLC ....G....... 561 684-1440
West Palm Beach *(G-18865)*
Evans Custom Cabinetry LLC ....G....... 904 829-1973
Saint Augustine *(G-15542)*
Everest Cabinets Inc ....G....... 407 790-7819
Orlando *(G-12721)*
F & S Mill Works ....G....... 407 349-9948
Geneva *(G-5021)*
Faba Cabinets & Such LLC ....G....... 813 871-1529
Tampa *(G-17656)*
Factory Direct Cab Refacing ....G....... 954 445-6635
Hollywood *(G-5819)*
Falfas Cabinet & Stone LLC ....G....... 941 960-2065
Sarasota *(G-16425)*
Fgt Cabinetry LLC ....G....... 321 800-2036
Orlando *(G-12737)*
Final Touch Molding Cabinetry ....F....... 239 948-7856
Bonita Springs *(G-831)*
Fine Archtctral Mllwk Shutters ....F....... 954 491-2055
Fort Lauderdale *(G-3993)*
Fine Wood Design Inc ....G....... 727 531-8000
Largo *(G-7947)*
Finecraft Custom Cabinetry ....G....... 941 378-1901
Sarasota *(G-16430)*
Finecraft Custom Cabinets ....G....... 941 312-6598
Sarasota *(G-16431)*
Fisher Cabinet Company LLC ....E....... 850 944-4171
Pensacola *(G-14151)*
FL Central Cnstr & Rmdlg ....G....... 863 701-3548
Lakeland *(G-7687)*
Florida Custom Cabinets Inc ....G....... 850 769-4781
Panama City *(G-13903)*
Florida Designer Cabinets Inc ....F....... 352 793-8555
Sumterville *(G-17068)*
Florida Kit Cbnets Amercn Corp ....G....... 305 828-2830
Hialeah *(G-5414)*
Florida Plywoods Inc ....D....... 850 948-2211
Greenville *(G-5088)*
Florida West Poggenpohl ....G....... 239 948-9005
Estero *(G-3689)*
From Trees Inc ....G....... 813 431-8285
Port Richey *(G-15050)*
Furniture Concepts 2000 Inc ....G....... 954 946-0310
Pompano Beach *(G-14706)*
Furnival Cabinetry LLC ....G....... 321 638-1223
Cocoa *(G-2025)*
Furnival Construction LLC ....F....... 321 638-1223
Cocoa *(G-2026)*

Future Kitchen Corp ....G.... 786 356-3746
Hialeah *(G-5418)*
G K Woodworks ....G.... 941 232-3910
Sarasota *(G-16444)*
G&G Quality Services Inc ....G.... 386 566-0309
Palm Coast *(G-13696)*
Gannon Charles Berchman III ....G.... 239 514-0243
Naples *(G-11258)*
Garcia Armando Custom Cabinets ....G.... 305 775-5674
Miami *(G-9613)*
Garys Cabinets and More LLC ....G.... 941 585-8001
Fort Myers *(G-4466)*
Gater Custom Cabinet & Doors ....G.... 904 778-2300
Jacksonville *(G-6425)*
Gb Cabinets Incorporated ....G.... 863 446-0676
Sebring *(G-16693)*
Gc Cabinet Express LLC ....G.... 561 662-0369
Lake Park *(G-7473)*
Gemstone Cabinetry LLC ....G.... 941 426-5656
North Port *(G-11740)*
General Cabinets Inc ....E.... 727 863-3404
Port Richey *(G-15051)*
George Gillespie Cabinets ....G.... 561 744-6191
West Palm Beach *(G-18886)*
Gilmans Custom Furn & Cabinets ....F.... 352 746-3532
Lecanto *(G-8134)*
Glenny Stone Works Inc ....G.... 786 502-3918
Doral *(G-3367)*
Global Cabinet Distributors ....G.... 305 625-9814
Miami Lakes *(G-10795)*
Global Custom Cabinets LLC ....G.... 407 738-0146
Kissimmee *(G-7250)*
Gontech Custom Wood Corp ....G.... 305 323-0765
Miami *(G-9647)*
Great American Imports Llc ....G.... 786 524-4120
Miami *(G-9661)*
Gregorys Cabinets Inc ....G.... 239 450-8840
Naples *(G-11268)*
Gs Cabinets Inc ....G.... 305 986-4768
Miami *(G-9681)*
Guerra Universal Cabinet I ....G.... 561 317-4079
Lake Worth *(G-7554)*
Gulf Coast Cabinetry Inc ....G.... 850 769-3799
Panama City Beach *(G-13978)*
Gulf Contours Inc ....G.... 941 639-3933
Punta Gorda *(G-15207)*
Hammond Kitchens & Bath LLC ....F.... 321 768-9549
Melbourne *(G-8840)*
Hand Carved Creations ....G.... 561 893-0292
Boca Raton *(G-555)*
Hector & Hector Inc ....F.... 305 629-8864
Miami *(G-9696)*
Heller Cabinetry Inc ....F.... 321 729-9690
Melbourne *(G-8842)*
Herman Cabinets Inc ....G.... 727 459-6730
Largo *(G-7970)*
High End Cabinets LLC ....G.... 561 469-8237
West Palm Beach *(G-18895)*
Highland Cabinet Inc ....G.... 863 385-4396
Sebring *(G-16694)*
HIS Cabinetry Inc ....D.... 727 527-7262
Pinellas Park *(G-14354)*
Home Design Group Corp ....G.... 305 888-5836
Hialeah *(G-5449)*
Home Pride Cabinets Inc ....F.... 813 887-3782
Tampa *(G-17760)*
Home Works Bay County Inc ....G.... 850 215-7880
Panama City *(G-13915)*
House of Cabinets Ltd Inc ....G.... 352 795-5300
Crystal River *(G-2379)*
Hudson Cabinets & Millwork LLC ....F.... 239 218-0451
Fort Myers *(G-4486)*
Imperial Kitchens Inc ....G.... 239 208-9359
Fort Myers *(G-4492)*
Infinite Ret Design & Mfg Corp ....F.... 305 967-8339
Miami *(G-9741)*
Innovations Cabinets Corp ....G.... 305 458-9395
Miami *(G-9748)*
Innovtive Cabinets Closets Inc ....F.... 904 475-2336
Jacksonville *(G-6498)*
Insight Cabinetry LLC ....G.... 352 818-9708
Eustis *(G-3709)*
Integral WD Cstm Cabinetry LLC ....F.... 561 361-5111
Boca Raton *(G-566)*
Interlachen Cabinets Inc ....G.... 352 481-6078
Hawthorne *(G-5244)*
Italian Cabinetry Inc ....F.... 786 534-2742
Miami *(G-9774)*
J & A Custom Cabinetry Inc ....G.... 786 255-4181
Homestead *(G-5974)*

J & D Oldja LLC ....F.... 727 526-3240
Saint Petersburg *(G-15819)*
J & E Custom Cabinets ....F.... 727 868-2820
Port Richey *(G-15055)*
J & J Custom Mica Inc ....F.... 239 433-2828
Fort Myers *(G-4498)*
J & S Cypress Inc ....F.... 352 383-3864
Sorrento *(G-16787)*
J J Cabinets Appliances ....G.... 786 573-0300
Miami *(G-9782)*
J M Interiors Inc ....G.... 305 891-6121
North Miami *(G-11642)*
J V Installations Corp ....E.... 407 849-0262
Orlando *(G-12848)*
Jaiba Cabinets Inc ....G.... 305 364-3646
Hialeah *(G-5461)*
Jam Cabinets & Investments LLC ....F.... 305 823-9020
Hialeah *(G-5462)*
James Simmons Cabinets Inc ....G.... 407 468-1802
Orlando *(G-12850)*
Jamestown Kitchens Inc ....G.... 941 359-1166
Sarasota *(G-16476)*
Jay Robinson Cabinet Sales Inc ....G.... 954 298-3009
Oakland Park *(G-11816)*
JC Best Finish Cabinet Inc ....G.... 786 216-5571
Miami *(G-9788)*
Jcs Limited Corporation ....G.... 954 822-2887
Tamarac *(G-17360)*
Jean Richard Kitchen Cabinets ....G.... 786 285-5506
Miami *(G-9793)*
Jeffrey Bowden Cabinets LLC ....G.... 727 992-9187
New Port Richey *(G-11495)*
Jesus Cabinets Corp ....G.... 786 285-1088
Hialeah *(G-5465)*
Jesus Cabinets Corp ....G.... 786 237-6299
Miami *(G-9795)*
Jfaure LLC ....G.... 239 631-5324
Naples *(G-11296)*
Jim Rinaldos Cabinetry Inc ....F.... 813 788-2715
Dade City *(G-2430)*
Juan Rodriguez Cabinetry Corp ....G.... 305 467-3878
Hialeah *(G-5470)*
K & M Custom Cabinetry Inc ....G.... 727 791-3993
Safety Harbor *(G-15497)*
K P Kitchens Corp ....G.... 954 322-9087
Miramar *(G-11008)*
K-Kraft Cabinets Inc ....G.... 321 632-8800
Rockledge *(G-15426)*
K-Kraft Industries Inc ....F.... 321 632-8800
Rockledge *(G-15427)*
Kasse Cabinets Inc ....G.... 407 285-2738
Orlando *(G-12866)*
Kbf Design Gallery Inc ....G.... 407 830-7703
Maitland *(G-8469)*
Kc & B Custom Inc ....G.... 561 276-1887
Delray Beach *(G-3099)*
Kings & Queens Cabinets ....G.... 863 646-6972
Lakeland *(G-7728)*
Kitchen and Bath Universe Inc ....F.... 813 887-5658
Tampa *(G-17828)*
Kitchen USA Inc ....G.... 904 714-1970
Jacksonville *(G-6539)*
Kitchens By US ....F.... 407 745-4923
Orlando *(G-12872)*
Kitchens Crafters Inc ....G.... 407 788-0560
Longwood *(G-8300)*
Kitchens Rta LLC ....G.... 407 969-0902
Orlando *(G-12873)*
Knothole Creations Inc ....G.... 727 561-9107
Clearwater *(G-1753)*
KR Ward Inc ....G.... 863 325-9070
Winter Haven *(G-19334)*
Lakeshore Custom Wood Products ....G.... 813 623-2790
Tampa *(G-17834)*
Larsen Cabinetmaker Co ....G.... 305 252-1212
Miami *(G-9860)*
Latino Cabinet Center Plus LLC ....G.... 786 663-0909
North Miami Beach *(G-11689)*
Lee Cabinets Corp ....G.... 786 291-5871
Miami *(G-9879)*
Legacy Building Supply Company ....G.... 850 729-5901
Niceville *(G-11570)*
Leiton Decor & Design ....G.... 786 286-4776
Miami *(G-9882)*
Lfh Southernstone LLC ....G.... 727 538-0123
Clearwater *(G-1759)*
Lily Ann Cabinets - Tampa Bay ....G.... 727 877-8180
Largo *(G-8000)*
Londos Fine Cabinetry LLC ....G.... 727 544-2929
Seminole *(G-16751)*

Luxurable Kitchen & Bath Llc ....G.... 727 286-8927
Largo *(G-8004)*
Lyndan Inc ....E.... 813 977-6683
Tampa *(G-17867)*
M & E Kitchen Cabinets Inc ....G.... 786 346-9987
Hialeah *(G-5493)*
M Cabinets ....G.... 305 968-8188
Miami *(G-9924)*
M Wegener Inc ....G.... 561 848-2408
Palm Springs *(G-13775)*
M X Corporation ....G.... 305 597-9881
Pembroke Pines *(G-14046)*
M&L Cabinets Inc ....G.... 941 761-8100
Bradenton *(G-1074)*
MAc Entps Tampa Bay Inc ....G.... 813 363-2601
New Port Richey *(G-11499)*
Madewell Kitchens Inc ....E.... 727 856-1014
Port Richey *(G-15060)*
Maggac Corporation ....G.... 561 439-2707
Lake Worth *(G-7567)*
Magnolia Custom Cabinetry ....G.... 941 906-8744
Sarasota *(G-16496)*
Mahan Cabinets ....G.... 305 255-3325
Cutler Bay *(G-2403)*
Majestic Woodworks ....G.... 352 429-2520
Groveland *(G-5100)*
Manatee Cabinets Inc ....G.... 941 792-8656
Bradenton *(G-1075)*
Marquez Custom Cabinets Inc ....G.... 813 352-8027
Tampa *(G-17885)*
Marx Brothers Cabinets Inc ....G.... 813 695-1473
Valrico *(G-18523)*
Master Cabinet Maker Inc ....G.... 941 723-0278
Palmetto *(G-13811)*
Master Cabinets LLC ....G.... 239 324-9701
Ave Maria *(G-258)*
Master Kitchen Cabinets ....G.... 239 225-9668
Fort Myers *(G-4523)*
Master-Kraft Cabinetry ....G.... 863 661-2083
Auburndale *(G-249)*
McCallum Cabinets Inc ....F.... 352 372-2344
Gainesville *(G-4957)*
Metro Door Brickell LLC ....G.... 786 326-4748
Miami *(G-9986)*
Mg Cabinet Installers LLC ....G.... 561 530-7961
Palm Springs *(G-13777)*
Miacucina LLC ....G.... 305 792-9494
Miami *(G-9990)*
Miacucina LLC ....F.... 305 444-7383
Coral Gables *(G-2176)*
Mica Craft & Design Inc ....F.... 561 863-5354
West Palm Beach *(G-18950)*
Mica Pdts & WD of Boca Raton ....E.... 561 395-4686
Boca Raton *(G-622)*
Micaworks Cabinetry Inc ....G.... 352 336-1707
Gainesville *(G-4962)*
Michigan Avenue Bridge Inc ....F.... 352 236-4044
Ocala *(G-12000)*
Midnite Son II of Sarasota ....G.... 941 377-6029
Sarasota *(G-16508)*
Mike Pulver LLC ....G.... 386 747-8951
Deland *(G-2996)*
Millcreek Fine Cabinetry Inc ....G.... 954 801-8595
Plantation *(G-14534)*
Mister Cabinet Deluxe Inc ....G.... 305 205-3601
Hialeah *(G-5523)*
MJM Cabinet Inc ....G.... 786 953-5000
Hialeah *(G-5524)*
Mobius Business Group Inc ....F.... 239 274-8900
Fort Myers *(G-4535)*
Modern Cabinetry and AMP Mllwk ....F.... 813 426-6941
Tampa *(G-17914)*
Moose Tracts Inc ....G.... 407 491-1412
Orlando *(G-12979)*
Moralmar Kitchen Cabinets ....E.... 305 819-8402
Hialeah *(G-5527)*
Morgan Cabinet Restylers LLC ....G.... 813 931-4663
Lutz *(G-8403)*
Morning Star of Sarasota Inc ....G.... 941 371-0392
Sarasota *(G-16514)*
Morris Mica Cabinets Inc ....G.... 954 979-6838
Pompano Beach *(G-14769)*
Mr Goodwood Inc ....G.... 941 961-4478
Sarasota *(G-16516)*
Mundy Kitchen Cabinet Inc ....G.... 786 298-0131
Miami Lakes *(G-10825)*
National Stoneworks LLC ....E.... 954 349-1609
Weston *(G-19152)*
Neocabinet Inc ....G.... 310 927-1008
Hollywood *(G-5881)*

Nfjb Inc.....E..... 954 771-1100
Fort Lauderdale *(G-4141)*
Nickols Cbinetry Woodworks Inc.....G..... 941 485-7894
Venice *(G-18564)*
Nosta Inc.....G..... 305 634-1435
Miami *(G-10079)*
Nuform Cabinetry.....G..... 954 532-2746
Pompano Beach *(G-14776)*
Ocean Kitchen Cabinets.....G..... 352 745-7110
Gainesville *(G-4974)*
Oldja Enterprises Inc.....F..... 727 526-3240
Saint Petersburg *(G-15871)*
Oliveira Services Corp.....G..... 772 834-4803
Port Saint Lucie *(G-15127)*
Oly Custom Cabinets Miami Inc.....G..... 305 216-3947
Miami *(G-10096)*
Omax Home Inc.....F..... 239 980-2755
Fort Myers *(G-4558)*
Omt Inc.....G..... 772 287-3762
Stuart *(G-16983)*
Orka Cabinets Inc.....G..... 954 907-2456
Coral Springs *(G-2299)*
Ortega & Velazco Cabinet Inc.....G..... 305 726-9097
Miami *(G-10121)*
Ortega Custom Cabinets Inc.....G..... 813 403-7101
Tampa *(G-17961)*
Packard Company Inc.....G..... 941 451-8201
Venice *(G-18565)*
Palm Beach Cstm Cabinetry Inc.....G..... 561 859-9071
Lake Worth *(G-7577)*
Palm Beach Trim Inc.....E..... 561 588-8746
Davie *(G-2565)*
Peace Millwork Co Inc.....E..... 305 573-6222
Miami *(G-10147)*
Pearsons Refacing and Refacing.....G..... 904 591-3850
Saint Augustine *(G-15586)*
Peartree Cabinets and Design.....G..... 941 377-7655
Sarasota *(G-16539)*
Pedano Custom Furniture Inc.....G..... 904 704-9329
Jacksonville *(G-6664)*
Pinellas Custom Cabinets Inc.....G..... 727 864-4263
Largo *(G-8027)*
Pinnacle Cabinets Closets LLC.....G..... 850 477-5402
Pensacola *(G-14230)*
Pioneer Casework LLC.....F..... 305 404-3490
Saint Petersburg *(G-15878)*
Plastic and Products Mktg LLC.....F..... 352 867-8078
Ocala *(G-12028)*
PLC Cabinets Installed Ltd.....G..... 239 641-7565
Naples *(G-11370)*
Porath Fine Cabinetry Inc.....E..... 561 616-9400
West Palm Beach *(G-19002)*
Posh Cabinets.....G..... 954 444-5441
Boca Raton *(G-669)*
Precision Cabinetry LLC.....G..... 386 218-3340
Deltona *(G-3177)*
Premier Cabinets LLC.....G..... 407 760-9060
Oviedo *(G-13454)*
Princeton Custom Cabinetry.....G..... 954 755-7614
Pompano Beach *(G-14813)*
Pro Kitchen Cabinets Corp.....G..... 786 768-4291
Cutler Bay *(G-2409)*
Procraft Cabinetry Florida LLC.....G..... 754 212-2277
Deerfield Beach *(G-2895)*
Professional Kitchen Cabinets.....G..... 305 888-5660
Hialeah *(G-5578)*
Project Pros Woodworking Inc.....G..... 239 454-6800
Fort Myers *(G-4573)*
Prolific Cabinetry & More Inc.....G..... 904 448-6575
Jacksonville *(G-6695)*
PS Cabinet Works Inc.....G..... 239 850-2162
Lehigh Acres *(G-8204)*
Quality Cabinet Recovering.....G..... 941 378-1715
Sarasota *(G-16550)*
Quality Cabinets & Counters.....F..... 239 948-5364
Fort Myers *(G-4577)*
Quality Cbinets By Stewart LLC.....G..... 954 624-6877
Hallandale Beach *(G-5206)*
Quality Creations Inc.....G..... 727 571-4332
Clearwater *(G-1855)*
Quality Custom Cabinet Design.....G..... 352 728-4292
Leesburg *(G-8169)*
R & J Custom Cabinets Inc.....G..... 813 871-5779
Tampa *(G-18036)*
R & R Designer Cabinets Inc.....G..... 954 735-6435
Oakland Park *(G-11834)*
R & R Doors Corp.....G..... 305 982-8106
Hialeah *(G-5592)*
R and D Kitchen Cabinets Corp.....G..... 305 305-2390
Miami *(G-10230)*
Rainbow Cabinets Inc.....G..... 352 236-4044
Ocala *(G-12035)*
RARe Cabinets Inc.....G..... 407 415-3730
Altamonte Springs *(G-70)*
RB Cabinetry LLC.....F..... 850 685-5316
Destin *(G-3203)*
RCS Wood Crafters LLC.....G..... 305 836-0120
Hialeah *(G-5595)*
Regal Cabinets Inc.....F..... 407 678-1003
Winter Park *(G-19440)*
Regency Custom Cabinets Inc.....F..... 239 332-7977
Fort Myers *(G-4580)*
Regent Cabinetry and More Inc.....G..... 239 693-2207
Fort Myers *(G-4581)*
Reliable Cabinet Designs.....F..... 941 473-3403
Englewood *(G-3666)*
Rich Maid Cabinets Inc.....F..... 727 572-4857
Clearwater *(G-1860)*
Richard Bryan Ingram LLC.....G..... 407 677-7779
Orlando *(G-13137)*
Richardsons Cabinet Works.....G..... 850 832-8298
Panama City *(G-13945)*
Riks Cabinetry Inc.....G..... 561 929-5260
Lauderdale Lakes *(G-8092)*
Ritter Kit Bath & Closet LLC.....G..... 239 272-4551
Naples *(G-11385)*
River City Cstm Cabinetry Inc.....F..... 904 247-0807
Jacksonville *(G-6727)*
Rj Unique Cabinets.....G..... 954 708-0893
Pompano Beach *(G-14833)*
RMM Cabinets LLC.....G..... 954 588-6353
Boca Raton *(G-691)*
Robert Duffy Cabinets Inc.....G..... 239 777-0372
Marco Island *(G-8526)*
Rolu Woodcraft Inc.....F..... 305 685-0914
Hialeah *(G-5605)*
Rt22 Creations Inc.....G..... 954 254-8258
Pompano Beach *(G-14835)*
Rta Cabinets & More LLC.....G..... 321 288-3068
Indian Harbour Beach *(G-6066)*
Rubens Custom Cabinets Inc.....G..... 813 510-8397
Tampa *(G-18072)*
S Aj Cabinets Inc.....G..... 321 264-2872
Mims *(G-10952)*
S M I Cabinetry Inc.....E..... 407 841-0292
Orlando *(G-13152)*
S Tam Cabinets Inc.....G..... 813 310-2263
Tampa *(G-18076)*
Sahara Cabinets Inc.....F..... 239 334-1151
Fort Myers *(G-4593)*
Sarasota Cabinetry Inc.....F..... 941 351-5588
Sarasota *(G-16576)*
Sarasota Kitchens and Closets.....G..... 941 722-7505
Bradenton *(G-1111)*
Sasquatch Cabinet Company.....G..... 941 365-4950
Lakewood Ranch *(G-7846)*
Sbr Custom Cabinets Inc.....G..... 407 765-8134
Orlando *(G-13165)*
SC Cabinet LLC.....G..... 561 429-5369
Riviera Beach *(G-15375)*
Seaside Premium Cabinets.....G..... 850 533-6801
Destin *(G-3205)*
Serenity Slid Srfaces Amer LLC.....G..... 352 459-1561
Mount Dora *(G-11112)*
Sevilla Cabinets Inc.....F..... 305 888-2174
Hialeah *(G-5616)*
Showcase Marble Inc.....F..... 386 253-6646
Daytona Beach *(G-2714)*
Signature Cabinets.....G..... 954 563-8584
Oakland Park *(G-11840)*
Simply Cabinets LLC.....F..... 850 541-3712
Panama City Beach *(G-13984)*
Simply Closets & Cabinets.....G..... 239 994-4264
Alva *(G-91)*
SIRE Cabinetry Inc.....G..... 909 225-4121
Port Saint Lucie *(G-15144)*
Smokey Mountain Cabinets Inc.....F..... 386 325-1677
Palatka *(G-13493)*
Snows Custom Furniture Inc.....G..... 772 794-4430
Vero Beach *(G-18665)*
Sobrino Custom Cabinets Inc.....G..... 786 564-2699
Hialeah *(G-5623)*
Southeast Woodcrafters Inc.....F..... 561 392-2929
Boca Raton *(G-724)*
Southernstone Cabinets Inc.....E..... 727 538-0123
Clearwater *(G-1883)*
Souvay Cabinetry Inc.....G..... 239 273-5947
Naples *(G-11412)*
Spacemakers Closets SW Fla Inc.....G..... 239 598-0222
Naples *(G-11413)*
Sparks Cabinetry.....G..... 954 367-2750
Hollywood *(G-5914)*
Spaulding Custom Cabinets.....G..... 904 768-4640
Jacksonville *(G-6802)*
Speed Custom Cabinet Corp.....G..... 407 953-1479
Orlando *(G-13205)*
Spruce Creek Cabinetry Inc.....F..... 386 756-0041
Port Orange *(G-15035)*
STA Cabinet Depot.....G..... 719 502-5454
Saint Augustine *(G-15622)*
Statewide Cstm Cbinets Fla Inc.....G..... 813 788-3856
Zephyrhills *(G-19537)*
Stephen B Fine Cabinetry Inc.....G..... 561 512-2850
Boynton Beach *(G-963)*
Steve Unser Cabinetry Inc.....F..... 239 631-2951
Naples *(G-11417)*
Studio Luxe Cstm Cabinetry LLC.....G..... 941 371-4010
Sarasota *(G-16607)*
Stylecraft Cabinets Mfg Inc.....G..... 941 474-4824
Englewood *(G-3668)*
Sungraf Inc.....F..... 954 456-8500
Hallandale Beach *(G-5216)*
Sunshine Alance Cabinets Mllwk.....F..... 954 621-7444
Deerfield Beach *(G-2919)*
Superior Kitchens Inc.....F..... 772 286-6801
Stuart *(G-17030)*
T&Y Cabinets Inc.....G..... 305 512-0802
Hialeah *(G-5646)*
Tarzen International LLC.....G..... 239 243-0711
Fort Myers *(G-4624)*
Techno Cabinets Inc.....G..... 305 910-9929
Doral *(G-3525)*
Thomas C Gibbs Custom Cabinets.....G..... 239 872-6279
Fort Myers *(G-4626)*
Thomas Rley Artisans Guild Inc.....E..... 239 591-3203
Naples *(G-11440)*
Tielve Cabinetsinc.....G..... 561 267-3740
West Palm Beach *(G-19063)*
Timberwolf Cabinetry.....G..... 561 389-5782
Royal Palm Beach *(G-15478)*
TJ Cabinetry Inc.....F..... 407 886-8294
Orlando *(G-13260)*
Tj Cabinetry Inc.....G..... 407 801-5124
Apopka *(G-191)*
Tk Cabinets.....G..... 386 325-6906
Palatka *(G-13496)*
TNT Custom Cabinetry Inc.....G..... 561 662-0964
West Palm Beach *(G-19066)*
Top Drawer Cabinetry & Carpent.....G..... 772 370-4624
Fort Pierce *(G-4756)*
Top Kitchen Cabinets.....G..... 305 392-9938
Medley *(G-8740)*
Top Shelf Custom Cabinetry.....G..... 941 726-2393
Sarasota *(G-16621)*
Tops Cabinet.....G..... 954 544-2006
Hallandale *(G-5163)*
Tops Kitchen Cabinet LLC.....F..... 954 933-9988
Pompano Beach *(G-14888)*
Tradewind Custom Cabinetry LLC.....G..... 239 257-3295
Cape Coral *(G-1487)*
Trim-Pak Corporation.....E..... 407 851-8900
Orlando *(G-13273)*
Tws Cabinets LLC.....F..... 863 614-4693
Lakeland *(G-7827)*
U C Cabinet Inc.....G..... 407 322-0968
Sanford *(G-16130)*
Ultimate Outdoor Cabinetry Inc.....G..... 941 713-5295
Bradenton *(G-1135)*
Um Kitchen Cabinets Inc.....G..... 772 224-5445
Port Saint Lucie *(G-15158)*
Underwood Butcher Block Co Inc.....F..... 904 338-2348
Jacksonville *(G-6877)*
United Cabinets Corp.....G..... 305 887-5050
Hialeah *(G-5660)*
Universal Kit Cabinets Closets.....G..... 305 406-9096
Kissimmee *(G-7307)*
Universal Kitchen Center Inc.....G..... 305 218-5108
Hialeah *(G-5664)*
Universal Wood Design.....F..... 772 569-5389
Vero Beach *(G-18674)*
Uptown Cstm Cabinets of Naples.....G..... 239 825-8432
Naples *(G-11448)*
Ur Cabinets.....G..... 813 434-6454
Tampa *(G-18224)*
V G Carpentry LLC.....G..... 786 531-7824
Hialeah *(G-5672)*
Vanbert Corporation.....G..... 561 945-5856
Delray Beach *(G-3154)*
Velez Custom Cabinetry Corp.....G..... 772 418-9565
Port Saint Lucie *(G-15160)*

Veneta Cucine Inc..................G....... 305 949-5223
North Miami Beach *(G-11709)*
Venice Custom Cabinets Inc..................G....... 941 488-5000
Nokomis *(G-11591)*
Victory Custom Cabinetry..................G....... 727 937-2284
Holiday *(G-5751)*
Viking Woodworking..................G....... 352 237-5050
Ocala *(G-12071)*
W E W Enterprises Inc..................F....... 941 751-6610
Bradenton *(G-1144)*
Walker Wood Products Inc..................G....... 904 448-5202
Jacksonville *(G-6905)*
We RE Organized..................G....... 407 323-5133
Sanford *(G-16137)*
Welshman Investment Corp..................G....... 407 933-4444
Kissimmee *(G-7310)*
West Cast Cbnets Clsets Flrg I..................F....... 239 481-8109
Fort Myers *(G-4652)*
West Coast Custom Cabinetry..................F....... 239 481-8109
Fort Myers *(G-4653)*
Windermere Cabinetry LLC..................G....... 321 263-5181
Winter Garden *(G-19290)*
Windward Associates Corp..................F....... 954 336-8085
Dania *(G-2461)*
Wogans Cstm Cbnets Rfacing LLC..................G....... 904 343-8917
Jacksonville *(G-6926)*
Wood Aspects..................G....... 321 800-8875
Deland *(G-3035)*
Wood Scapes Interiors..................G....... 386 454-1540
High Springs *(G-5703)*
Wood U Envision..................G....... 561 601-1973
West Palm Beach *(G-19089)*
Wood Zone Inc..................G....... 305 971-5550
Miami *(G-10617)*
Woodman Cabinets Inc..................G....... 561 558-2550
Palmetto *(G-13838)*
Woods Distinctive Designs..................F....... 941 698-7535
Port Charlotte *(G-15008)*
Woodtech Global Inc..................F....... 941 371-0392
Bradenton *(G-1148)*
Woodwards Cabinets Inc..................G....... 850 835-0071
Freeport *(G-4854)*
Woodworkers Cabinet Naples Inc..................G....... 239 593-1718
Naples *(G-11461)*
Woodworks Cabinetry Inc..................G....... 904 924-5300
Jacksonville *(G-6928)*
Woodworks Kit & Bath Designs..................F....... 813 926-0570
Odessa *(G-12166)*
Woodworkx Unlimited Inc..................G....... 772 882-4197
Fort Pierce *(G-4771)*
X-Treme Wood Cabinets Corp..................G....... 305 537-8378
Cutler Bay *(G-2422)*
Y F Leung Inc..................G....... 305 651-6851
North Miami Beach *(G-11714)*
Your Cabinet Source Inc..................G....... 352 728-3806
Leesburg *(G-8182)*
Your Dreams Cabinets Corp..................G....... 305 305-3729
Hialeah *(G-5693)*
Yp General Work & Cabinets..................G....... 786 317-0973
Miami *(G-10628)*
Zbc Cabinetry..................G....... 239 332-2940
Fort Myers *(G-4659)*
Zk Cabinets Inc..................G....... 407 421-7307
Orlando *(G-13343)*

CABINETS: Office, Wood

Braden Kitchens Inc..................E....... 321 636-4700
Cocoa *(G-1999)*
Creative Woodworking Concepts..................E....... 727 937-4165
Tarpon Springs *(G-18290)*
District 95 Wood Working Inc..................G....... 888 400-3136
Pompano Beach *(G-14666)*
F & S Cabinets Inc..................E....... 386 822-9525
Deland *(G-2976)*
Furniture Design of Centl Fla..................F....... 407 330-4430
Sanford *(G-16052)*
McCabinet Inc..................F....... 727 608-5929
Largo *(G-8007)*
Star Quality Inc..................F....... 813 875-9955
Tampa *(G-18131)*

CABINETS: Show, Display, Etc, Wood, Exc Refrigerated

Corry Cabinet Company Inc..................E....... 850 539-6455
Havana *(G-5237)*
Creative Cabinet Concepts Inc..................F....... 239 939-1313
Fort Myers *(G-4413)*
Fisher Cabinet Company LLC..................E....... 850 944-4171
Pensacola *(G-14151)*
Kitchen Dsgns By Joan E Rbbins..................G....... 321 727-0012
Melbourne *(G-8860)*
Lyndan Inc..................E....... 813 977-6683
Tampa *(G-17867)*
Mobius Business Group Inc..................F....... 239 274-8900
Fort Myers *(G-4535)*
Mr Mica Wood Inc..................F....... 561 278-5821
Delray Beach *(G-3109)*
New River Cabinet & Fix Inc..................E....... 954 938-9200
Fort Lauderdale *(G-4137)*
Pro Tech Custom Cabinet..................F....... 727 863-5143
Port Richey *(G-15065)*
S M I Cabinetry Inc..................E....... 407 841-0292
Orlando *(G-13152)*
Spruce Creek Cabinetry Inc..................F....... 386 756-0041
Port Orange *(G-15035)*
Still Water Industries Inc..................G....... 561 845-6033
West Palm Beach *(G-19045)*
Trasport John..................G....... 321 452-6789
Merritt Island *(G-9016)*

CABLE TELEVISION PRDTS

Componexx Corp..................G....... 954 236-6569
Sunrise *(G-17107)*
NC IV Inc..................F....... 941 378-9133
Sarasota *(G-16522)*
Quality Cable Contractors Inc..................E....... 407 246-0606
Orlando *(G-13103)*
Ravic Technologies LLC..................G....... 954 237-3241
Medley *(G-8715)*

CABLE: Fiber

American Wire Group Inc..................F....... 954 455-3050
Aventura *(G-260)*
Applied Fiber Holdings LLC..................E....... 850 539-7720
Havana *(G-5230)*
Applied Fiber Mfg LLC..................E....... 850 539-7720
Havana *(G-5231)*
Chiptech Inc..................F....... 954 454-3554
Hallandale *(G-5154)*
Conexus Technologies Inc..................F....... 513 779-5448
Sarasota *(G-16391)*
E Quality Cables Inc..................F....... 321 242-4820
Melbourne *(G-8817)*
Gulf Cable LLC..................C....... 201 720-2417
Milton *(G-10932)*
Meridian Cable LLC..................F....... 847 847-1128
Saint Augustine *(G-15568)*
Miami Cordage LLC..................E....... 305 636-3000
Miami *(G-9996)*
Newlink Cabling Systems Inc..................F....... 305 477-8063
Medley *(G-8697)*

CABLE: Fiber Optic

AGS Enterprises Inc..................G....... 305 716-7660
Doral *(G-3231)*
American Data Supply Inc..................F....... 866 650-3282
Clearwater *(G-1579)*
Amphenol Custom Cable Inc..................C....... 813 623-2232
Tampa *(G-17423)*
Amphenol Custom Cable Inc..................E....... 407 393-3886
Orlando *(G-12476)*
Commski LLC..................G....... 813 501-0111
Tampa *(G-17548)*
Gulf Photonics Inc..................G....... 813 855-6618
Oldsmar *(G-12231)*
Managed Data Assoc Inc..................G....... 386 449-8419
Palm Coast *(G-13702)*
Newlink Cabling Systems Inc..................F....... 305 477-8063
Medley *(G-8697)*
Oceaneering International Inc..................C....... 985 329-3282
Panama City *(G-13933)*

CABLE: Ropes & Fiber

Bubba Rope LLC..................G....... 877 499-8494
Altamonte Springs *(G-35)*
Consolidated Cordage Corp..................F....... 561 347-7247
Boca Raton *(G-488)*
Rope Works Inc..................F....... 954 525-6575
Fort Lauderdale *(G-4213)*

CABLE: Steel, Insulated Or Armored

Orbital Corporation of Tampa..................G....... 813 782-7300
Zephyrhills *(G-19529)*
Suncoast Post-Tension Ltd..................E....... 305 592-5075
Miami *(G-10430)*

CABS: Indl Trucks & Tractors

Rack It Truck Racks..................F....... 800 354-1900
San Antonio *(G-15977)*

CAFETERIAS

Tulipan Bakery Inc..................F....... 561 832-6107
West Palm Beach *(G-19071)*

CAGES: Wire

Animal Air Service Inc..................E....... 305 218-1759
Doral *(G-3250)*

CALCULATING & ACCOUNTING EQPT

Blue Eagle Alliance Inc..................G....... 904 322-8067
Jacksonville *(G-6213)*
General Business Services..................G....... 904 260-1099
Jacksonville *(G-6431)*
Professional Office Svcs Inc..................G....... 863 967-6634
Winter Haven *(G-19348)*
R S S Partners Inc..................G....... 904 241-6144
Jacksonville Beach *(G-6955)*
Szabo Pos Displays Inc..................G....... 941 778-0192
Bradenton *(G-1124)*
Verifone Inc..................G....... 754 229-4571
Coral Springs *(G-2327)*

CAMERA & PHOTOGRAPHIC SPLYS STORES

Sunnypics LLC..................G....... 407 992-6210
Orlando *(G-13224)*

CAMERA & PHOTOGRAPHIC SPLYS STORES: Cameras

Lester A Dine Inc..................G....... 561 624-3009
Palm Beach Gardens *(G-13603)*

CAMERAS & RELATED EQPT: Photographic

Ar2 Products LLC..................G....... 800 667-1263
Saint Johns *(G-15673)*
Drs Laurel Technologies..................E....... 727 541-6681
Largo *(G-7936)*
Eyeson Dgtal Srvllnce MGT Syst..................G....... 305 808-3344
Miami *(G-9551)*
Imperx Inc..................E....... 561 989-0006
Boca Raton *(G-563)*
Incity Security Inc..................F....... 561 306-9228
West Palm Beach *(G-18902)*
Westech Development Group Inc..................G....... 954 505-5090
Pompano Beach *(G-14912)*
Zd Realty LLC..................F....... 866 672-1212
Saint Petersburg *(G-15970)*

CANDLE SHOPS

Love Is In The Air Corp..................G....... 305 828-8181
Hialeah *(G-5489)*
Scentstional Soaps Candles Inc..................F....... 941 485-1443
Venice *(G-18572)*

CANDLES

2 Guys Company..................G....... 786 970-9275
Miami *(G-9023)*
Candle For You LLC..................G....... 920 883-7900
Jacksonville *(G-6252)*
Cape Candle LLC..................G....... 239 357-6766
Cape Coral *(G-1402)*
Imagination Enterprises LLC..................F....... 504 289-9691
Orlando *(G-12823)*
Je TAime Fragrances..................G....... 727 581-0970
Largo *(G-7987)*
Kaluz LLC..................E....... 786 991-2260
Miami *(G-9814)*
Lemon Grass Industries Inc..................G....... 954 418-6110
Parkland *(G-13995)*
Scents of Nature Enterprises..................E....... 305 547-2334
Miami Lakes *(G-10855)*
Scentsability Candles..................G....... 954 234-4405
Coral Springs *(G-2311)*
Scentstional Soaps Candles Inc..................F....... 941 485-1443
Venice *(G-18572)*
Thebestcandlescom..................G....... 732 608-5081
Margate *(G-8568)*
Vision Candles Inc..................G....... 305 836-8650
Miami *(G-10589)*

Wicks Unlimited Inc..........G...... 631 472-2010
Pompano Beach *(G-14913)*

CANDLES: Wholesalers

Kaluz LLC..........E...... 786 991-2260
Miami *(G-9814)*
Scentstional Soaps Candles Inc..........F...... 941 485-1443
Venice *(G-18572)*

CANDY & CONFECTIONS: Cake Ornaments

Signature Brands LLC..........B...... 352 622-3134
Ocala *(G-12050)*

CANDY & CONFECTIONS: Candy Bars, Including Chocolate Covered

Cozy Bar..........F...... 305 532-2699
Miami Beach *(G-10659)*
Louis Sherry Company LLC..........G...... 904 482-1900
Jacksonville *(G-6565)*
Retreat..........G...... 813 254-2014
Tampa *(G-18055)*

CANDY & CONFECTIONS: Chocolate Candy, Exc Solid Chocolate

Bbx Sweet Holdings LLC..........F...... 954 940-4000
Fort Lauderdale *(G-3843)*
Sweet Tooth Inc..........G...... 305 682-1400
North Miami Beach *(G-11706)*

CANDY & CONFECTIONS: Fruit & Fruit Peel

Kizable LLC..........G...... 727 600-3469
Fort Lauderdale *(G-4090)*

CANDY & CONFECTIONS: Nuts, Candy Covered

Barnard Nut Company Inc..........D...... 305 836-9999
Miami *(G-9221)*

CANDY & CONFECTIONS: Popcorn Balls/Other Trtd Popcorn Prdts

Brownbag Popcorn Company LLC..........G...... 561 212-5664
Boca Raton *(G-467)*
Poppin Box LLC..........G...... 904 484-7030
Saint Johns *(G-15680)*

CANDY, NUT & CONFECTIONERY STORES: Candy

Bbx Sweet Holdings LLC..........F...... 954 940-4000
Fort Lauderdale *(G-3843)*
Sweet Tooth Inc..........G...... 305 682-1400
North Miami Beach *(G-11706)*

CANDY, NUT & CONFECTIONERY STORES: Produced For Direct Sale

Hoffman Commercial Group Inc..........E...... 561 967-2213
Greenacres *(G-5082)*

CANDY: Chocolate From Cacao Beans

Behrs Chocolates By Design..........G...... 407 648-2020
Orlando *(G-12510)*
Hoffman Commercial Group Inc..........E...... 561 967-2213
Greenacres *(G-5082)*
P B C Central..........G...... 407 648-2020
Orlando *(G-13041)*

CANDY: Hard

Candies and Beyond Inc..........G...... 954 828-2255
Miami Lakes *(G-10774)*
Lollipop Children Center Inc..........G...... 386 755-3953
Lake City *(G-7366)*

CANES & TRIMMINGS, EXC PRECIOUS METAL

Fashionable Canes..........F...... 727 547-8866
Largo *(G-7942)*

CANNED SPECIALTIES

Florida International Firm Inc..........G...... 305 450-5920
Sweetwater *(G-17209)*

Kraft Heinz Foods Company..........G...... 407 786-8157
Longwood *(G-8301)*
Olas Foods Specialty Mkt Inc..........E...... 813 447-5127
Kenneth City *(G-7153)*
RL Schreiber Inc..........D...... 954 972-7102
Fort Lauderdale *(G-4208)*

CANOPIES: Sheet Metal

Consolidated Metal Products..........G...... 850 576-2167
Tallahassee *(G-17236)*
Sfa Systems Inc..........E...... 561 585-5927
Lake Worth *(G-7586)*

CANS: Aluminum

Andersons Can Line Fbrction Eq..........F...... 407 889-4665
Apopka *(G-113)*
Anheuser-Busch Companies LLC..........D...... 407 251-4049
Orlando *(G-12480)*
S&J Aluminum Works Inc..........G...... 850 492-5700
Pensacola *(G-14256)*

CANS: Composite Foil-Fiber, Made From Purchased Materials

Rapid Composites LLC..........G...... 941 322-6647
Sarasota *(G-16284)*
Sybo Composites LLC..........G...... 904 599-7093
Saint Augustine *(G-15625)*

CANS: Metal

Metal Container Corporation..........C...... 904 695-7600
Jacksonville *(G-6596)*
Wastequip Manufacturing Co LLC..........E...... 863 665-6507
Lakeland *(G-7832)*

CANVAS PRDTS

American Marine Coverings Inc..........F...... 305 889-5355
Hialeah *(G-5292)*
Bayside Canvas Yacht Interiors..........G...... 954 792-8535
Fort Lauderdale *(G-3842)*
Busch Canvas..........G...... 561 881-1605
Riviera Beach *(G-15306)*
C&D Canvas Inc..........G...... 954 924-3433
Davie *(G-2504)*
Canvas Designers Inc..........E...... 561 881-7663
Riviera Beach *(G-15308)*
Canvas West Inc..........G...... 941 355-0780
Sarasota *(G-16380)*
Creative Energies Inc..........G...... 352 351-9448
Ocala *(G-11911)*
Fabis Group Corporation..........G...... 305 718-3638
Miami *(G-9554)*
Gar Industries Corp..........F...... 954 456-8088
Hallandale Beach *(G-5188)*
Germain Canvas & Awning Co..........G...... 305 751-4963
Miami *(G-9631)*
Gioia Sails South LLC..........D...... 386 597-2876
Palm Coast *(G-13698)*
Innovative Indus Solutions Inc..........G...... 561 733-1548
Boynton Beach *(G-920)*
Mpc Group LLC..........G...... 773 927-4120
Deland *(G-3001)*
Pipe Welders Inc..........D...... 954 587-8400
Fort Lauderdale *(G-4168)*
Schnupp Manufacturing Co Inc..........G...... 305 325-0520
Miami *(G-10312)*
Scotties Canvas & Mar Sup LLC..........G...... 239 995-7479
North Fort Myers *(G-11604)*
Ship Shape Canvas and Awng LLC..........G...... 954 480-8889
Delray Beach *(G-3141)*
Smittys Boat Tops and Mar Eqp..........G...... 305 245-0229
Homestead *(G-5993)*
Taylor Made Systems Brdnton In..........C...... 941 747-1900
Oviedo *(G-13461)*
Tip Top Canvas and Uphl Inc..........G...... 954 524-6214
Plantation *(G-14559)*
US Marine Canvas..........G...... 904 687-5058
Saint Augustine *(G-15630)*
Utilis Usa LLC..........G...... 850 226-7043
Fort Walton Beach *(G-4836)*
World of Awnings Inc..........F...... 305 884-6699
Hialeah *(G-5689)*
Yacht Furnishing By Eclip..........G...... 954 792-7339
Davie *(G-2617)*

CANVAS PRDTS, WHOLESALE

Iis Incorporated..........G...... 561 547-4297
Boynton Beach *(G-918)*

CANVAS PRDTS: Boat Seats

Artful Canvas Design Inc..........E...... 727 521-0212
Saint Petersburg *(G-15713)*
Marine Customs Unlimited..........F...... 772 223-8005
Stuart *(G-16973)*

CANVAS PRDTS: Convertible Tops, Car/Boat, Fm Purchased Mtrl

Boatswains Locker Inc..........E...... 904 388-0231
Jacksonville *(G-6218)*
Discount Boat Tops Inc..........G...... 727 536-4412
Largo *(G-7933)*
J W L Trading Company Inc..........F...... 813 854-1128
Tampa *(G-17800)*

CANVAS PRDTS: Shades, Made From Purchased Materials

Awnings of Hollywood Inc..........E...... 954 963-7717
Hollywood *(G-5780)*
Sea King Kanvas & Shade Inc..........G...... 239 481-3535
Fort Myers *(G-4602)*

CAPACITORS & CONDENSERS

General Capacitor LLC..........G...... 510 371-2700
Tallahassee *(G-17262)*

CAPACITORS: NEC

ABB Inc..........D...... 407 732-2000
Lake Mary *(G-7396)*
ABB Inc..........D...... 305 471-0844
Miami *(G-9053)*
American Tchncal Crmics Fla In..........D...... 904 724-2000
Jacksonville *(G-6152)*
Dynamic Engrg Innovations Inc..........C...... 386 445-6000
Palm Coast *(G-13692)*
Exxelia Usa Inc..........E...... 407 695-6562
Longwood *(G-8279)*
General Capacitor LLC..........G...... 510 371-2700
Tallahassee *(G-17262)*
Kemet Corporation..........A...... 954 766-2800
Fort Lauderdale *(G-4086)*
Kemet Ventures LLC..........G...... 407 403-2958
Orlando *(G-12868)*
Mat-Vac Technology Inc..........F...... 386 238-7017
Daytona Beach *(G-2683)*
Nordquist Dielectrics Inc..........E...... 727 585-7990
Clearwater *(G-1809)*
Nwl Inc..........C...... 561 848-9009
Riviera Beach *(G-15353)*
Vladmir Ltd..........E...... 386 445-6000
Palm Coast *(G-13714)*

CAPACITORS: Series

S&S Consulting Partners LLC..........G...... 850 803-8379
Niceville *(G-11574)*

CAPS: Plastic

Sun Coast Industries LLC..........D...... 941 355-7166
Sarasota *(G-16304)*

CAR WASH EQPT

Andre T Jean..........G...... 305 647-8744
Opa Locka *(G-12288)*
Annellies Car Wash LLC..........G...... 954 990-8436
Lauderhill *(G-8101)*
Car Wash Solutions Florida Inc..........E...... 941 323-8817
Ocala *(G-11894)*
J-Ko Company..........G...... 561 795-7377
Royal Palm Beach *(G-15472)*
Wws Contracting LLC..........E...... 813 868-3100
Tampa *(G-18269)*

CAR WASH EQPT & SPLYS WHOLESALERS

OHanrahan Consultants Inc..........E...... 727 531-3375
Largo *(G-8019)*

CARBIDES

Caribe Express Associates Inc..........F...... 305 222-9057
Miami *(G-9318)*
Creative Carbide Inc..........F...... 239 567-0041
Fort Myers *(G-4414)*

CARBON REMOVING SOLVENT

Akj Industries Inc....G....239 939-1696
Fort Myers *(G-4348)*

CARBURETORS

Daytona Parts Company....G....386 427-7108
New Smyrna Beach *(G-11532)*
Total Performance Inc....G....203 265-5667
Palm Coast *(G-13713)*

CARDIOVASCULAR SYSTEM DRUGS, EXC DIAGNOSTIC

Ivax Corporation....C....305 329-3795
Miami *(G-9775)*

CARDS, PLASTIC, UNPRINTED, WHOLESALE

Card Usa Inc....F....954 862-1300
Hollywood *(G-5795)*

CARDS: Greeting

5 01 Fridays....G....754 444-3561
Pompano Beach *(G-14570)*
Montevista Greetings LLC....G....305 888-9797
Hialeah *(G-5526)*
Sincere Sentiments Inc....G....352 287-1232
Inverness *(G-6096)*
Specialty Productions Inc....G....786 399-1393
Miami *(G-10401)*
Starmakers Rising Inc....E....561 989-8999
Boca Raton *(G-731)*
Zetma LLC....G....407 237-0233
Orlando *(G-13341)*

CARDS: Identification

Card Quest Inc....G....813 288-0004
Tampa *(G-17506)*
Card Usa Inc....F....954 862-1300
Hollywood *(G-5795)*
Checkpoint Card Group Inc....F....954 426-1331
Deerfield Beach *(G-2800)*
Idproductsource LLC....G....772 336-4269
Port Saint Lucie *(G-15114)*
J & P Deerfield Inc....F....954 571-6665
Deerfield Beach *(G-2849)*
Southeast Id LLC....F....954 571-6665
Miami Lakes *(G-10859)*
Your ID Guard....G....904 354-8989
Jacksonville *(G-6933)*

CARDS: Playing

Marketshare LLC....G....631 273-0598
Boca Raton *(G-609)*

CARNIVAL SPLYS, WHOLESALE

Sharp Marketing LLC....G....954 565-2711
Oakland Park *(G-11838)*

CARPET & UPHOLSTERY CLEANING SVCS

Cannida Co LLC....G....727 642-3709
Saint Petersburg *(G-15737)*

CARPET & UPHOLSTERY CLEANING SVCS: Carpet/Furniture, On Loc

John Eric Madden....G....813 395-3314
Zephyrhills *(G-19524)*

CARPETS & RUGS: Tufted

Mohawk Industries Inc....G....918 272-0184
Hollywood *(G-5878)*

CARPETS, RUGS & FLOOR COVERING

Artificial Turf Supply LLC....G....877 525-8873
Ponte Vedra Beach *(G-14934)*
Bearded Mohawk LLC....G....913 680-9829
Deltona *(G-3163)*
BF Hurley Mat Co Inc....E....813 837-0616
Tampa *(G-17468)*
Carpet Clinic LLC....G....850 232-1170
Pensacola *(G-14112)*
Drab To Fab....G....941 475-7700
Englewood *(G-3675)*
Dyn-O-Mat Inc....G....561 747-2301
Jupiter *(G-7029)*
Dynomat Inc....E....561 747-2301
Jupiter *(G-7030)*
Hanteri Enterprises Corp....F....813 949-8729
Lutz *(G-8388)*
International Mdse Sources Inc....C....239 430-9993
Naples *(G-11289)*
Kitchens Xtreme LLC....G....941 387-5181
Sarasota *(G-16482)*
Murse Properties LLC....G....941 966-3380
Sarasota *(G-16518)*
Niba Designs Inc....F....305 456-6230
Hollywood *(G-5883)*
Picket Fence Childrens....G....813 713-8589
Zephyrhills *(G-19532)*
Proximity Mills LLC....F....813 251-3060
Tampa *(G-18022)*
Rampell Software....F....561 628-5102
Palm Beach *(G-13561)*
Ser-Mat International LLC....E....954 525-1417
Pompano Beach *(G-14847)*

CARPETS: Hand & Machine Made

Design-A-Rug Inc....F....954 943-7487
Deerfield Beach *(G-2812)*

CARRIER EQPT: Telephone Or Telegraph

Allied Telecommunications Ltd....F....954 370-9900
Plantation *(G-14487)*

CARRYING CASES, WHOLESALE

Bee Electronics Inc....D....772 468-7477
Fort Pierce *(G-4680)*
Identity Stronghold LLC....E....941 475-8480
Englewood *(G-3679)*

CARS: Electric

Electra Automotive Corp....G....941 623-5563
Hollywood *(G-5815)*
Ev Pilotcar Inc....G....239 243-8023
Fort Myers *(G-4446)*
Valiant Transport Group LLC....E....855 648-7423
Boca Raton *(G-774)*

CARTS: Grocery

Load King Manufacturing Co....C....904 354-8882
Jacksonville *(G-6560)*

CASES, WOOD

Palm Beach Trim Inc....E....561 588-8746
Davie *(G-2565)*

CASES: Carrying

Agora Sales Inc....F....727 490-0499
Clearwater *(G-1569)*
Agora Sales Inc....B....727 321-0707
Saint Petersburg *(G-15695)*
Bee Electronics Inc....D....772 468-7477
Fort Pierce *(G-4680)*
Gar Industries Corp....F....954 456-8088
Hallandale Beach *(G-5188)*
Hut Global Inc....G....561 571-2523
Boca Raton *(G-560)*
Koszegi Industries Inc....E....954 419-9544
Deerfield Beach *(G-2855)*
Stemler Corporation....E....727 577-1216
Saint Petersburg *(G-15927)*
US Communications Industries....E....772 468-7477
Fort Pierce *(G-4767)*

CASES: Carrying, Clothing & Apparel

Intradeco Apparel Inc....C....305 264-8888
Medley *(G-8671)*
Spires Empire LLC....G....305 797-0622
Key West *(G-7203)*

CASES: Jewelry

Yvel Usa Inc....G....561 391-5119
Boca Raton *(G-797)*

CASES: Packing, Nailed Or Lock Corner, Wood

Custom Crate & Logistics Co....G....954 527-5742
Fort Lauderdale *(G-3924)*

CASES: Plastic

Arts Products LLC....G....201 984-7232
Doral *(G-3255)*
Homyn Enterprises Corp....D....305 870-9720
Miami *(G-9718)*
Rehrig Pacific Company....F....407 857-3888
Orlando *(G-13128)*

CASES: Shipping, Nailed Or Lock Corner, Wood

Allcases Reekstin & Assoc Inc....F....813 891-1313
Oldsmar *(G-12200)*

CASES: Shipping, Wood, Wirebound

Allcases Reekstin & Assoc Inc....F....813 891-1313
Oldsmar *(G-12200)*

CASH REGISTERS WHOLESALERS

Eastern Ribbon & Roll Corp....E....813 676-8600
Odessa *(G-12117)*

CASINGS: Storage, Missile & Missile Components

C4 Advnced Tctical Systems LLC....D....407 206-3886
Orlando *(G-12541)*

CASKETS & ACCESS

Service Corp International....G....321 636-6041
Cocoa *(G-2050)*

CAST STONE: Concrete

AAA Cast Stone Inc....E....941 721-8092
Palmetto *(G-13783)*
Art Crete Products Inc....F....386 252-5118
Daytona Beach *(G-2629)*
Hamner Parking Lot Service....G....954 328-3216
Fort Lauderdale *(G-4040)*
Marbon Inc....F....561 822-9999
West Palm Beach *(G-18941)*
Palm Beach Cast Stone Inc....E....561 835-4085
West Palm Beach *(G-18981)*
Pedronis Cast Stone Inc....E....904 783-1690
Jacksonville *(G-6666)*
Premier Stoneworks LLC....D....561 330-3737
Delray Beach *(G-3123)*
Stone Central of Central Fla....F....352 689-0075
Wildwood *(G-19201)*
True Stone Masonry LLC....F....772 334-9797
Fort Pierce *(G-4761)*
VP Cast Stone Corp....G....305 691-9306
Hialeah *(G-5684)*

CASTERS

Shadow-Caster Led Lighting LLC....E....727 474-2877
Clearwater *(G-1876)*

CASTINGS GRINDING: For The Trade

1842 Daily Grind & Mercantile....G....352 543-5004
Cedar Key *(G-1522)*
Big OS Stump Grinding....G....904 945-5900
Jacksonville *(G-6208)*
Daily Grind Stumpgrinding....G....954 588-4640
Sunrise *(G-17114)*
Grind It LLC....G....813 310-9710
Lutz *(G-8386)*
Gulfport Grind Inc....G....727 343-2785
Gulfport *(G-5135)*
James Caldwell Stump Grinding....G....813 843-1262
Plant City *(G-14439)*
Kens Stump Grinding LLC....G....407 948-5031
Orlando *(G-12870)*
Mr Bones Stump Grinding....G....941 927-0790
Sarasota *(G-16515)*
Vine and Grind LLC....G....727 420-3122
Treasure Island *(G-18479)*

CASTINGS: Aerospace Investment, Ferrous

Alm Technologies Inc..........E....... 904 849-7212
Yulee *(G-19495)*
Cloud Investment Partners Lllp..........G....... 561 266-0845
Boynton Beach *(G-891)*
Extant Cmpnnts Group Hldngs In..........G....... 321 254-1500
Melbourne *(G-8828)*
Extant Cmpnnts Group Intrmdate..........C....... 321 254-1500
Melbourne *(G-8829)*
General Pneumatics Inflation..........G....... 941 216-3500
Sarasota *(G-16219)*
Kellstrom Aerospace Group Inc..........E....... 954 538-2482
Boca Raton *(G-586)*

CASTINGS: Aerospace, Aluminum

Gables Engineering Inc..........B....... 305 774-4400
Coral Gables *(G-2147)*

CASTINGS: Aerospace, Nonferrous, Exc Aluminum

Gables Engineering Inc..........B....... 305 774-4400
Coral Gables *(G-2147)*
Inspectech Aeroservice Inc..........F....... 954 359-6766
Fort Lauderdale *(G-4060)*
Kellstrom Aerospace Group Inc..........E....... 954 538-2482
Boca Raton *(G-586)*
Shell Aerospace LLC..........G....... 786 400-2660
Miami *(G-10336)*

CASTINGS: Aluminum

RC Investment Casting..........G....... 305 801-9088
Hialeah *(G-5594)*

CASTINGS: Bronze, NEC, Exc Die

Bronzart Foundry Inc..........F....... 941 922-9106
Sarasota *(G-16370)*

CASTINGS: Commercial Investment, Ferrous

M Austin Forman..........E....... 954 763-8111
Fort Lauderdale *(G-4107)*

CASTINGS: Die, Aluminum

Big Sun Equine Products Inc..........G....... 352 629-9645
Ocala *(G-11886)*
Southern Die Casting Corp..........E....... 305 635-6571
Miami *(G-10385)*
Southern Mfg Upholstery Inc..........F....... 727 573-1006
Clearwater *(G-1882)*
Strive Development Corporation..........F....... 850 689-2124
Crestview *(G-2360)*

CASTINGS: Die, Magnesium & Magnesium-Base Alloy

Fullerton 799 Inc..........E....... 727 572-7040
Clearwater *(G-1696)*

CASTINGS: Die, Nonferrous

Camp Aircraft Inc..........F....... 727 397-6076
Saint Petersburg *(G-15734)*
Motor City Classics Inc..........G....... 954 473-2201
Sunrise *(G-17149)*
Target Manufacturing Inc..........G....... 305 633-0361
Miami *(G-10460)*

CASTINGS: Die, Zinc

Southern Die Casting Corp..........E....... 305 635-6571
Miami *(G-10385)*

CASTINGS: Gray Iron

U S Holdings Inc..........G....... 305 885-0301
Hialeah *(G-5656)*
United States Fndry & Mfg Corp..........C....... 305 885-0301
Medley *(G-8748)*
United States Fndry & Mfg Corp..........F....... 305 556-1661
Hialeah *(G-5661)*

CASTINGS: Lead

Gypsy Mining Inc..........G....... 772 589-5547
Roseland *(G-15459)*

CASTINGS: Machinery, Aluminum

Florida Machine & Casting Co..........G....... 561 655-3771
Riviera Beach *(G-15330)*
Heroal USA Inc..........A....... 888 437-6257
Orlando *(G-12799)*
Simplimatic Automation..........G....... 941 360-6500
Sarasota *(G-16297)*

CASTINGS: Machinery, Brass

Loren/Wtp..........G....... 954 846-9800
Hollywood *(G-5862)*

CASTINGS: Machinery, Nonferrous, Exc Die or Aluminum Copper

Chromalloy Castings Tampa Corp..........C....... 561 935-3571
Palm Beach Gardens *(G-13577)*

CASTINGS: Precision

Collins Mfg Inc..........D....... 321 322-0280
Apopka *(G-126)*
Xl Carts Inc..........G....... 904 277-7111
Fernandina Beach *(G-3751)*

CASTINGS: Zinc

Camp Company St Petersburg..........E....... 727 397-6076
Saint Petersburg *(G-15735)*

CAT BOX FILLER

Terfa Litter USA Inc..........F....... 416 358-4495
Sunny Isles Beach *(G-17081)*

CATALOG & MAIL-ORDER HOUSES

Blue Ocean Press Inc..........E....... 954 973-1819
Fort Lauderdale *(G-3859)*
Gleim Publications Inc..........D....... 352 375-0772
Gainesville *(G-4931)*
Rainbow Lght Ntrtnal Systems I..........G....... 954 233-3300
Sunrise *(G-17167)*
Warehouse Goods LLC..........E....... 877 865-2260
Boca Raton *(G-787)*

CATALOG SALES

South Florida Sport Fishing..........F....... 954 942-7261
Fort Lauderdale *(G-4248)*

CATALYSTS: Chemical

Nano Liquitec LLC..........F....... 813 447-1742
Lutz *(G-8404)*
Vanavac Inc..........G....... 813 752-1391
Plant City *(G-14476)*
W R Grace & Co - Conn..........F....... 561 982-7776
Boca Raton *(G-785)*

CATAPULTS

Catapult 13 Crtive Studios LLC..........G....... 305 788-6948
Miami *(G-9324)*
Catapult Group Inc..........G....... 904 834-7728
Ponte Vedra Beach *(G-14935)*
Catapult Lakeland Inc..........G....... 863 687-3788
Lakeland *(G-7654)*
Catapult Learning LL..........G....... 561 573-6025
Delray Beach *(G-3057)*
Chasco Machine & Manufacturing..........G....... 727 815-3510
Brooksville *(G-1218)*

CATCH BASIN CLEANING SVC

All Liquid Envmtl Svcs LLC..........E....... 800 767-9594
Fort Lauderdale *(G-3797)*

CATCH BASIN COVERS: Concrete

Oldcastle Coastal Inc..........G....... 813 932-1007
Tampa *(G-17954)*
Oldcastle Coastal Inc..........C....... 813 367-9780
Tampa *(G-17955)*

CATERERS

Big Bend Ice Cream Co..........G....... 850 539-7778
Havana *(G-5233)*
Madan Corporation..........G....... 954 925-0077
Dania Beach *(G-2467)*
Sweet Tooth Inc..........G....... 305 682-1400
North Miami Beach *(G-11706)*

CEILING SYSTEMS: Luminous, Commercial

Eran Financial Services LLC..........E....... 844 411-5483
Boca Raton *(G-520)*
R & R American Corporation..........G....... 786 497-8898
Miami *(G-10228)*

CELLULOID PRDTS

Coffee Cllloid Productions LLC..........F....... 305 424-8900
Miami *(G-9375)*

CELLULOSE DERIVATIVE MATERIALS

Rayonier Advanced Mtls Inc..........A....... 904 357-4600
Jacksonville *(G-6707)*
Rayonier AM Sales and Tech Inc..........G....... 904 357-4600
Jacksonville *(G-6708)*

CEMENT, EXC LINOLEUM & TILE

Greencore LLC..........G....... 727 251-9837
Saint Petersburg *(G-15798)*
Lehigh White Cement Co LLC..........D....... 561 812-7439
West Palm Beach *(G-18928)*

CEMENT: Hydraulic

Argos Cement LLC..........E....... 813 247-4831
Tampa *(G-17431)*
Basecrete Technologies LLC..........F....... 941 312-5142
Sarasota *(G-16362)*
Basic Industries Global LLC..........G....... 850 622-5924
Santa Rosa Beach *(G-16152)*
Bonsal American Inc..........G....... 813 621-2427
Tampa *(G-17482)*
Cement Products Inc..........E....... 727 868-9226
Port Richey *(G-15045)*
Gallop Group Inc..........G....... 813 251-6242
Tampa *(G-17702)*
Gulf Cast Mtls Sthwest Fla Inc..........F....... 239 790-0016
Fort Myers *(G-4474)*
Hco Holding I Corporation..........F....... 863 533-0522
Bartow *(G-318)*
Phg Kendall LLC..........F....... 954 392-8788
Hollywood *(G-5891)*
Titan America LLC..........C....... 305 364-2200
Medley *(G-8738)*

CEMENT: Masonry

Argos USA LLC..........E....... 352 472-4722
Newberry *(G-11552)*
David Sayne Masonry Inc..........F....... 386 873-4696
Deland *(G-2966)*

CEMENT: Natural

Euro Gear (usa) Inc..........E....... 518 578-1775
Miami *(G-9539)*

CEMETERY MEMORIAL DEALERS

Bricklser Engrv Monuments Corp..........F....... 786 806-0672
Doral *(G-3285)*

CERAMIC FIBER

Florida Nonwovens Inc..........F....... 407 241-2701
Orlando *(G-12751)*
Trebol Florida LLC..........F....... 904 751-2828
Jacksonville *(G-6867)*

CERAMIC FLOOR & WALL TILE WHOLESALERS

Mosch International Corp..........G....... 786 616-9108
Miami *(G-10043)*
Salvia Tile & Stone Inc..........F....... 239 643-7770
Naples *(G-11389)*

CHAIN: Tire, Made From Purchased Wire

Las Zirh Americas Inc..........G....... 305 942-7597
Miami *(G-9862)*

CHAINS: Power Transmission

Orion Power Systems Inc..........G....... 877 385-1654
Jacksonville *(G-6648)*

CHAMBERS: Space Simulation, Metal Plate

Tru Simulation + Training Inc..........D....... 813 792-9300
Odessa *(G-12161)*

CHANGE MAKING MACHINES

American Changer Corp........................D....... 954 917-3009
Fort Lauderdale *(G-3811)*

CHARCOAL: Activated

American Carbons Inc............................G....... 850 265-4214
Lynn Haven *(G-8428)*
Carbonxt Inc............................E....... 352 378-4950
Gainesville *(G-4892)*
Donau Carbon US Lcc............................E....... 352 465-5959
Dunnellon *(G-3596)*
Puragen LLC............................E....... 561 907-5400
West Palm Beach *(G-19010)*
Puragen LLC............................E....... 760 630-5724
North Palm Beach *(G-11726)*

CHASING SVC: Metal

Extreme Coatings............................G....... 727 528-7998
Saint Petersburg *(G-15775)*

CHASSIS: Automobile Trailer

A&R Xpress Inc............................G....... 954 744-4343
Miramar *(G-10959)*
Itnorlando Inc............................G....... 407 900-7572
Winter Park *(G-19414)*
Safecraft Rstraint Systems Inc..............F....... 813 758-3571
Lutz *(G-8416)*

CHASSIS: Motor Vehicle

Shyft Group Inc............................E....... 954 946-9955
Jupiter *(G-7114)*

CHEESE WHOLESALERS

Goloso Food Llc............................G....... 321 277-2055
Orlando *(G-12786)*
Latin Amercn Meats & Foods USA........G....... 305 477-2700
Miami *(G-9867)*

CHEMICAL ELEMENTS

5thelement Indian Cuisine LLC............G....... 386 302-0202
Palm Coast *(G-13679)*
Drywall Elements............................F....... 407 454-7293
Orlando *(G-12690)*
Element 26 LLC............................G....... 413 519-1146
Fort Pierce *(G-4693)*
Element Mdterranean Steakhouse........G....... 407 873-6829
Sarasota *(G-16418)*
Element Mtls Tech Jupiter LLC..............F....... 321 327-8985
West Melbourne *(G-18773)*
Enchanting Elements............................G....... 321 663-9521
Naples *(G-11237)*
Washington Shores Element..................G....... 407 250-6260
Orlando *(G-13319)*

CHEMICAL PROCESSING MACHINERY & EQPT

Dilution Solutions Inc............................G....... 800 451-6628
Clearwater *(G-1652)*

CHEMICALS & ALLIED PRDTS WHOLESALERS, NEC

Allied USA Incorporated............................G....... 305 235-3950
Miami *(G-9118)*
Ascend Prfmce Mtls Oprtons LLC.........A....... 850 968-7000
Cantonment *(G-1335)*
Auto Gard Qmi Inc............................F....... 727 847-5441
New Port Richey *(G-11481)*
B & R Products Inc............................F....... 305 238-1592
Cutler Bay *(G-2386)*
Bon Brands Inc............................F....... 800 590-7911
Royal Palm Beach *(G-15462)*
Ecological Laboratories Inc..................E....... 239 573-6650
Cape Coral *(G-1416)*
Goho Enterprises Inc............................F....... 407 884-0770
Zellwood *(G-19503)*
Hi-TEC Laboratories Inc..................E....... 850 835-6822
Freeport *(G-4850)*
Illinois Tool Works Inc............................D....... 863 665-3338
Lakeland *(G-7708)*
Latam Group Corp............................G....... 305 793-8961
Miami *(G-9864)*
Mapei Corporation............................C....... 954 246-8888
Deerfield Beach *(G-2868)*
Thatcher Chemical Florida Inc..............F....... 386 734-3966
Deland *(G-3020)*

CHEMICALS & ALLIED PRDTS, WHOL: Chemical, Organic, Synthetic

Pure Wave Organics Inc............................G....... 321 368-7002
Melbourne *(G-8915)*

CHEMICALS & ALLIED PRDTS, WHOLESALE: Chemicals, Indl

Belzona Inc............................E....... 305 594-4994
Doral *(G-3269)*
Dyadic International USA Inc..............G....... 561 743-8333
Jupiter *(G-7028)*
Kraton Chemical LLC............................D....... 850 785-8521
Panama City *(G-13924)*
Morning Star Industries Inc..................E....... 800 440-6050
Jensen Beach *(G-6971)*

CHEMICALS & ALLIED PRDTS, WHOLESALE: Chemicals, Indl & Heavy

American Coatings Corporation............G....... 954 970-7820
Margate *(G-8535)*
Hac International Inc............................E....... 954 584-4530
Davie *(G-2534)*

CHEMICALS & ALLIED PRDTS, WHOLESALE: Compressed Gas

Axi International Corporation..............E....... 239 690-9589
Fort Myers *(G-4370)*
Dilo Production Inc............................G....... 727 376-5593
Odessa *(G-12116)*

CHEMICALS & ALLIED PRDTS, WHOLESALE: Detergents

Campos Chemicals............................F....... 727 412-2774
Saint Petersburg *(G-15736)*

CHEMICALS & ALLIED PRDTS, WHOLESALE: Dry Ice

Atlantic Dry Ice Corportion..................F....... 305 592-7000
Miami *(G-9182)*

CHEMICALS & ALLIED PRDTS, WHOLESALE: Essential Oils

Love Is In The Air Corp............................G....... 305 828-8181
Hialeah *(G-5489)*
Suns Eye Inc............................G....... 407 519-4904
Geneva *(G-5023)*

CHEMICALS & ALLIED PRDTS, WHOLESALE: Indl Gases

Deland Metal Craft Company................G....... 386 734-0828
Deland *(G-2967)*

CHEMICALS & ALLIED PRDTS, WHOLESALE: Oil Additives

Fuel Solutions Distrs LLC....................G....... 305 528-3758
North Miami Beach *(G-11679)*

CHEMICALS & ALLIED PRDTS, WHOLESALE: Plastics Materials, NEC

Bags Unlimited Inc............................G....... 985 868-3393
Chiefland *(G-1533)*
Melt-Tech Polymers Inc............................G....... 305 887-6148
Medley *(G-8688)*
S V Bags America Inc............................G....... 954 577-9091
Weston *(G-19166)*
Seelye Acquisitions Inc............................G....... 407 656-6677
Apopka *(G-184)*

CHEMICALS & ALLIED PRDTS, WHOLESALE: Plastics Prdts, NEC

Action Plastics Inc............................G....... 352 342-4122
Belleview *(G-365)*
Doran Manufacturing Corp Fla............G....... 904 731-3313
Jacksonville *(G-6326)*

CHEMICALS & ALLIED PRDTS, WHOLESALE: Plastics Sheets & Rods

American Plastic Sup & Mfg Inc............E....... 727 573-0636
Clearwater *(G-1581)*
Plastic and Products Mktg LLC............F....... 352 867-8078
Ocala *(G-12028)*
Plastics America Incorporated..............G....... 813 620-3711
Tampa *(G-17995)*

CHEMICALS & ALLIED PRDTS, WHOLESALE: Resins

Composite Essential Mtls LLC..............G....... 772 344-0034
Port St Lucie *(G-15172)*
Pacific Limited Intl Corp............................G....... 305 358-1900
Miami *(G-10128)*

CHEMICALS & ALLIED PRDTS, WHOLESALE: Resins, Plastics

Ravago Americas LLC............................A....... 407 773-7777
Orlando *(G-13114)*

CHEMICALS & ALLIED PRDTS, WHOLESALE: Spec Clean/Sanitation

Ciega Inc............................G....... 727 526-9048
Saint Petersburg *(G-15746)*

CHEMICALS & OTHER PRDTS DERIVED FROM COKING

Matschel of Flagler Inc............................G....... 386 446-4595
Saint Augustine *(G-15567)*

CHEMICALS, AGRICULTURE: Wholesalers

Chemical Dynamics Inc............................E....... 813 752-4950
Plant City *(G-14418)*

CHEMICALS/ALLIED PRDTS, WHOL: Coal Tar Prdts, Prim/Intermdt

Star-Seal of Florida Inc............................F....... 954 484-8402
Fort Lauderdale *(G-4259)*

CHEMICALS: Agricultural

Ai Thomas LLC............................E....... 904 553-6202
Ponte Vedra Beach *(G-14929)*
Ben Hill Griffin Inc............................D....... 863 635-2281
Frostproof *(G-4856)*
Brewer International Inc............................F....... 772 562-0555
Vero Beach *(G-18603)*
Collins and Dupont Interiors..................G....... 239 694-3400
Fort Myers *(G-4406)*
Custom Agronomics Inc............................F....... 772 223-0775
Palm City *(G-13650)*
Diamond R Fertilizer Co Inc..................F....... 863 763-2158
Okeechobee *(G-12176)*
Dupont Fine Homes Inc............................G....... 850 934-8545
Gulf Breeze *(G-5116)*
Excelag Corp............................G....... 305 670-0145
Miami *(G-9544)*
Morse Enterprises Limited Inc..............G....... 407 682-6500
Miami *(G-10042)*
Numerator Technologies Inc..................G....... 941 807-5333
Sarasota *(G-16526)*
Rx For Fleas Inc............................F....... 954 351-9244
Fort Lauderdale *(G-4220)*
Sawyer Products Inc............................E....... 727 725-1177
Safety Harbor *(G-15502)*

CHEMICALS: Alcohols

American Industrial Group Inc..............F....... 703 757-7683
North Miami Beach *(G-11666)*
Florida Rum Company LLC..................E....... 305 791-1221
Hollywood *(G-5823)*

CHEMICALS: Aluminum Compounds

Ceco & Associates Inc............................G....... 727 528-0075
Riverview *(G-15266)*

CHEMICALS: Brine

H20logy Inc............................G....... 904 829-6098
Saint Augustine *(G-15547)*

CHEMICALS: Fire Retardant

Geltech Solutions Inc .... E 561 427-6144
Jupiter *(G-7048)*

CHEMICALS: Fluorine, Elemental

Vestagen Tchnical Textiles Inc .... G 407 781-2570
Orlando *(G-13300)*

CHEMICALS: Fuel Tank Or Engine Cleaning

Penek Chemical Industries Inc .... G 954 978-6501
Pompano Beach *(G-14787)*

CHEMICALS: High Purity Grade, Organic

Nu Earth Labs LLC .... E 727 648-4787
Dunedin *(G-3585)*

CHEMICALS: High Purity, Refined From Technical Grade

Cheltec Inc .... G 941 355-1045
Sarasota *(G-16382)*

CHEMICALS: Inorganic, NEC

5th Element Inc .... G 321 331-7028
Kissimmee *(G-7214)*
All Elements Mechanical Corp .... E 866 306-0359
Longwood *(G-8251)*
Artistic Elements Inc .... G 561 750-1554
Boca Raton *(G-430)*
Auto Gard Qmi Inc .... F 727 847-5441
New Port Richey *(G-11481)*
Basic Elements LLC .... G 386 673-3100
Ormond Beach *(G-13351)*
Bio-Lab Inc .... F 863 709-1411
Lakeland *(G-7646)*
Caliber Elements LLC .... F 352 697-1415
Homosassa *(G-6000)*
Element Aircraft Sales LLC .... G 954 494-2242
Boca Raton *(G-516)*
Element Inc Co .... G 786 208-5693
Miami *(G-9512)*
Element-M LLC .... G 954 288-8683
Plantation *(G-14511)*
Elemental Energy Inc .... G 352 589-5703
Mount Dora *(G-11102)*
Elemental Mobile Services LLC .... G 904 768-9840
Jacksonville *(G-6358)*
Elements Accounting Inc .... G 305 662-4448
Miami *(G-9513)*
Elements of Stylez .... G 813 575-8416
Wesley Chapel *(G-18744)*
Eternal Elements LLC .... G 407 830-6968
Altamonte Springs *(G-44)*
Gns Technologies LLC .... G 561 367-3774
Boca Raton *(G-547)*
Harcros Chemicals Inc .... E 813 247-4531
Tampa *(G-17743)*
Hi-TEC Laboratories Inc .... E 850 835-6822
Freeport *(G-4850)*
Jci Jones Chemicals Inc .... F 904 355-0779
Jacksonville *(G-6520)*
JVI Minerals Inc .... G 561 894-1022
Delray Beach *(G-3098)*
K C Industries LLC .... G 863 425-1195
Mulberry *(G-11127)*
K-Technologies Inc .... G 863 940-4815
Lakeland *(G-7723)*
Kraton Chemical LLC .... D 850 785-8521
Panama City *(G-13924)*
Lambert Corporation Florida .... E 407 841-2940
Orlando *(G-12889)*
National Chemical Sply .... F 800 515-9938
Davie *(G-2556)*
National Chemical Supply Inc .... G 954 683-1645
Plantation *(G-14538)*
Nu-Element Inc .... G 561 322-8904
Deerfield Beach *(G-2880)*
P S Research Corp .... G 954 558-8727
Lauderhill *(G-8119)*
Periodic Elements LLC .... G 561 972-7791
Jupiter *(G-7092)*
Plasmine Technology Inc .... F 850 438-8550
Pensacola *(G-14231)*
Plating Technologies Inc .... G 772 220-4201
Stuart *(G-16989)*
Prince Minerals Inc .... G 832 241-2169
Mount Dora *(G-11111)*
Quest Environmental Products .... G 321 984-4423
Melbourne *(G-8917)*
Royce International LLC .... G 941 894-1228
Sarasota *(G-16565)*
Sesolinc Grp Inc .... F 772 287-9090
Stuart *(G-17009)*
Sinmat Commercial LLC .... F 352 334-7270
Gainesville *(G-4998)*
Sivance LLC .... C 352 376-8246
Gainesville *(G-5000)*
Standard Carbon LLC .... E 352 465-5959
Dunnellon *(G-3600)*
Syndesis Inc .... G 954 483-9548
Pembroke Pines *(G-14063)*
Taylor Building Elements LLC .... G 863 287-2228
Auburndale *(G-254)*
Thatcher Chemical Florida Inc .... F 386 734-3966
Deland *(G-3020)*
Thatcher Chemical Florida Inc .... G 386 490-1642
Palmetto *(G-13829)*
Trac Ecological America Inc .... G 954 583-4922
Dania *(G-2460)*
Trans-Resources LLC .... A 305 933-8301
Sunny Isles Beach *(G-17082)*

CHEMICALS: Iodine, Elemental

Isoaid LLC .... E 727 815-3262
Port Richey *(G-15054)*

CHEMICALS: Medicinal

Germkleen LLC .... G 954 947-5602
Fort Lauderdale *(G-4020)*
Mydor Industries Inc .... G 954 927-1140
Dania *(G-2453)*

CHEMICALS: Medicinal, Inorganic, Uncompounded, Bulk

Real Ketones LLC .... F 801 244-8610
Saint Petersburg *(G-15899)*

CHEMICALS: Medicinal, Organic, Uncompounded, Bulk

Dragons Miracle LLC .... G 561 670-5546
Boca Raton *(G-509)*
One Bio Corp .... B 305 328-8662
Aventura *(G-277)*

CHEMICALS: Muriate Of Potash, Not From Mines

Mosaic Company .... A 813 775-4200
Tampa *(G-17919)*

CHEMICALS: NEC

21st Century Chemical Inc .... G 954 689-7111
Fort Lauderdale *(G-3772)*
Agarose Unlimited Inc .... G 800 850-0659
Gainesville *(G-4869)*
Amaya Solutions Inc .... E 813 246-5448
Plant City *(G-14398)*
Arrmaz Products Inc .... D 863 578-1206
Mulberry *(G-11119)*
Aurum Chemicals Corp .... G 305 412-4141
Miami *(G-9192)*
B & R Products Inc .... F 305 238-1592
Cutler Bay *(G-2386)*
Bbj Environmental LLC .... G 813 622-8550
Tampa *(G-17461)*
Beesfree Inc .... G 561 939-4860
West Palm Beach *(G-18817)*
Belzona Inc .... E 305 594-4994
Doral *(G-3269)*
Blue Planet Envmtl Systems .... G 321 255-1931
Palm Bay *(G-13505)*
Bonsal American Inc .... G 813 621-2427
Tampa *(G-17482)*
Buckeye International Inc .... G 813 621-6260
Tampa *(G-17488)*
Camco Chemical .... G 239 992-4100
Bonita Springs *(G-823)*
Chem Guard Inc .... F 407 402-2798
Casselberry *(G-1500)*
Cjb Industries Inc .... F 941 552-8397
Sarasota *(G-16384)*
Cleanpak Products LLC .... G 813 740-8611
Tampa *(G-17541)*
Clinical Dagnstc Solutions Inc .... E 954 791-1773
Plantation *(G-14500)*
Color-Chrome Technologies Inc .... G 954 335-0127
Fort Lauderdale *(G-3910)*
Compass Service .... G 954 900-4462
Lauderhill *(G-8105)*
Dyadic International USA Inc .... G 561 743-8333
Jupiter *(G-7028)*
E-Liquids Investment Group LLC .... E 954 507-6060
Sunrise *(G-17117)*
Element Solutions Inc .... B 561 207-9600
Fort Lauderdale *(G-3968)*
Enviroseal Corporation .... G 772 335-8225
Port Saint Lucie *(G-15106)*
Euclid Chemical Company .... F 813 886-8811
Odessa *(G-12119)*
Far Research Inc .... E 321 723-6160
Palm Bay *(G-13511)*
Freezetone Products LLC .... F 305 640-0414
Doral *(G-3355)*
Global Seven Inc .... G 973 664-1900
Sarasota *(G-16450)*
Illinois Tool Works Inc .... D 863 665-3338
Lakeland *(G-7708)*
Increte Systems .... G 813 886-8811
Odessa *(G-12126)*
Jamo Inc .... D 305 885-3444
Medley *(G-8676)*
Klp Investments LLC .... G 401 762-4357
Stuart *(G-16966)*
Kraton Chemical LLC .... D 850 785-8521
Panama City *(G-13924)*
Mk Monomers LLC .... G 732 928-5800
Miami *(G-10029)*
Natural Organic Products Intl .... G 352 383-8252
Mount Dora *(G-11108)*
P S Research Corp .... G 954 558-8727
Lauderhill *(G-8119)*
Pharmco Laboratories Inc .... G 321 268-1313
Titusville *(G-18451)*
Plating Resources Inc .... F 321 632-2435
Cocoa *(G-2040)*
Proline Chemical & Plastics LL .... G 850 835-6822
Freeport *(G-4851)*
Pyrotecnico of Florida LLC .... F 352 588-5086
San Antonio *(G-15976)*
S M D Research Inc .... G 561 451-9895
Boca Raton *(G-696)*
Separation Technologies .... G 352 794-4160
Crystal River *(G-2381)*
Shield Products Inc .... G 904 880-6060
Doral *(G-3501)*
Two Little Fishies Inc .... G 305 623-7695
Miami *(G-10517)*
Universal Transactions Inc .... E 305 887-4677
Medley *(G-8750)*
Vass Holdings Inc .... G 863 295-5664
Winter Haven *(G-19366)*

CHEMICALS: Organic, NEC

4 Fuel LLC .... G 954 929-5803
Hollywood *(G-5762)*
Arrmaz Products Inc .... D 863 578-1206
Mulberry *(G-11119)*
Bartow Ethanol Florida LC .... F 863 533-2498
Bartow *(G-307)*
Bastech LLC .... E 904 737-1722
Jacksonville *(G-6196)*
Bn Biofuels LLC .... G 312 239-2680
Riviera Beach *(G-15303)*
Divitae Inc .... G 786 585-5556
Hialeah *(G-5374)*
Envirnmental Mfg Solutions LLC .... F 321 837-0050
Melbourne *(G-8826)*
Ethnergy International Inc .... E 954 499-1582
Pembroke Pines *(G-14033)*
Givaudan Fragrances Corp .... E 863 667-0821
Lakeland *(G-7698)*
Green Biofuels Miami LLC .... F 305 639-3030
Miami *(G-9665)*
Harcros Chemicals Inc .... E 813 247-4531
Tampa *(G-17743)*
Iff Chemical Holdings Inc .... C 904 783-2180
Jacksonville *(G-6488)*
Kraton Chemical LLC .... D 850 785-8521
Panama City *(G-13924)*
Natural Organic Products Intl .... G 352 383-8252
Mount Dora *(G-11108)*
Parabel Inc .... E 321 409-7415
Melbourne *(G-8905)*

Parabel USA Inc..........F....... 978 905-0958
Vero Beach *(G-18650)*
Phlexapeel LLC..........G....... 407 990-1854
Melbourne *(G-8907)*
Pspc Escrow II Corp..........G....... 561 207-9600
West Palm Beach *(G-19009)*
Rat Trap Bait Company Inc..........F....... 863 967-2148
Auburndale *(G-251)*
Rp International LLC..........E....... 941 894-1228
Sarasota *(G-16566)*
St Marks Powder Inc..........B....... 850 577-2824
Crawfordville *(G-2336)*
Symrise Inc..........C....... 904 768-5800
Jacksonville *(G-6833)*
Terry Laboratories LLC..........F....... 321 259-1630
Melbourne *(G-8960)*

CHEMICALS: Reagent Grade, Refined From Technical Grade

Arj Medical Inc..........G....... 813 855-1557
Oldsmar *(G-12203)*
Hac International Inc..........E....... 954 584-4530
Davie *(G-2534)*

CHEMICALS: Water Treatment

American Water Chemicals Inc..........F....... 813 246-5448
Plant City *(G-14400)*
Bluworld Innovations LLC..........D....... 888 499-5433
Orlando *(G-12528)*
Chemline Inc..........G....... 407 847-4181
Kissimmee *(G-7230)*
Duncanson Dynasty Inc..........G....... 561 288-1349
West Palm Beach *(G-18856)*
Ecological Laboratories Inc..........E....... 239 573-6650
Cape Coral *(G-1416)*
Jacks Magic Products Inc..........F....... 727 536-4500
Largo *(G-7985)*
Mydor Industries Inc..........G....... 954 927-1140
Dania *(G-2453)*
Northeast Water Reclamation..........G....... 727 893-7779
Saint Petersburg *(G-15867)*
Premier Water & Enrgy Tech Inc..........E....... 904 268-1152
Jacksonville *(G-6685)*
Terlyn Industries Inc..........F....... 727 592-0772
Clearwater *(G-1916)*

CHESTS: Bank, Metal

Zerons Metal Designers Inc..........F....... 305 688-2240
Hialeah *(G-5696)*

CHILD DAY CARE SVCS

Lincoln-Marti Cmnty Agcy Inc..........A....... 305 643-4888
Miami *(G-9895)*

CHILDBIRTH PREPARATION CLINIC

Advanced Prof Surgical Svcs..........G....... 786 326-0576
Miami *(G-9076)*

CHILDREN'S & INFANTS' CLOTHING STORES

Bossy Princess LLC..........G....... 786 285-4435
Aventura *(G-265)*

CHINA & GLASS: Decalcomania Work

Leonard-Martin Corporation..........G....... 850 434-2203
Pensacola *(G-14192)*

CHLORINE

Jci Jones Chemicals Inc..........F....... 904 355-0779
Jacksonville *(G-6520)*
Odyssey Manufacturing Co..........F....... 813 635-0339
Tampa *(G-17946)*

CHLOROPRENE RUBBER: Neoprene

Unaflex LLC..........E....... 954 943-5002
Pompano Beach *(G-14898)*

CHOCOLATE, EXC CANDY FROM BEANS: Chips, Powder, Block, Syrup

David Delights LLC..........G....... 407 648-2020
Orlando *(G-12654)*
Mvs International Inc..........G....... 954 727-3383
Weston *(G-19151)*
Pinnacle Foods Inc..........G....... 321 952-7926
Melbourne Beach *(G-8981)*
Sweet Tooth Inc..........G....... 305 682-1400
North Miami Beach *(G-11706)*

CHOCOLATE, EXC CANDY FROM PURCH CHOC: Chips, Powder, Block

Araya Inc..........G....... 305 229-6868
Miami *(G-9161)*
Art Edibles Inc..........G....... 407 603-4043
Oviedo *(G-13413)*
Atlantic Candy Company..........E....... 904 429-7250
Saint Augustine *(G-15518)*
Chocolate Guys LLC..........G....... 561 278-5889
Delray Beach *(G-3060)*
Fantasy Chocolates Inc..........E....... 561 276-9007
Orlando *(G-12732)*
Kay Peak Group Inc..........G....... 754 307-5400
Margate *(G-8554)*
Peterbrooke Choclat Fctry LLC..........G....... 904 273-7878
Ponte Vedra Beach *(G-14950)*
Venchi US Inc..........G....... 646 448-8663
Miami *(G-10572)*
Whole Coffee Company LLC..........D....... 786 364-4444
Miami *(G-10604)*

CHURCHES

Grace Bible Church..........G....... 850 623-4671
Milton *(G-10930)*

CHUTES: Metal Plate

US Chutes Corp..........F....... 860 567-4000
Boca Raton *(G-771)*
Valiant Products Inc..........E....... 863 688-7998
Lakeland *(G-7829)*

CIGAR & CIGARETTE HOLDERS

Innevape LLC..........G....... 631 957-6500
Hudson *(G-6029)*

CIGARETTE & CIGAR PRDTS & ACCESS

Double D S Tobacco..........G....... 772 871-9910
Delray Beach *(G-3070)*
Gilla Inc..........G....... 416 843-2881
Daytona Beach *(G-2668)*
Goodcat LLC..........E....... 239 254-8288
Naples *(G-11264)*
International Vapor Group LLC..........D....... 305 824-4027
Miami Lakes *(G-10799)*
Island Lifestyle Importers LLC..........G....... 941 378-3200
Sarasota *(G-16473)*
Smokers Video IV..........G....... 904 646-1324
Jacksonville *(G-6781)*
Xikar Inc..........E....... 816 474-7555
Weston *(G-19179)*

CIRCUIT BOARD REPAIR SVCS

Denver Elevator Systems Inc..........G....... 800 633-9788
Cape Canaveral *(G-1356)*

CIRCUIT BOARDS, PRINTED: Television & Radio

Aw-Tronics LLC..........E....... 786 228-7835
Miami *(G-9202)*
Bare Board Group Inc..........E....... 727 549-2200
Largo *(G-7904)*
Circuitronix LLC..........B....... 786 364-4458
Fort Lauderdale *(G-3900)*
Elreha Printed Circuits..........G....... 727 244-0130
Bradenton *(G-1036)*
Jabil Circuit LLC..........G....... 727 577-9749
Saint Petersburg *(G-15823)*
Profab Electronics Inc..........E....... 954 917-1998
Pompano Beach *(G-14818)*
Ra Co AMO Inc..........F....... 561 626-7232
Palm Beach Gardens *(G-13620)*

CIRCUIT BOARDS: Wiring

American Auto Marine Wiring..........G....... 954 782-0193
Pompano Beach *(G-14590)*

CIRCUIT BREAKERS

Jimenez Enterprises Group..........E....... 561 542-7709
Doral *(G-3403)*
Southwire Company LLC..........E....... 727 535-0572
Largo *(G-8059)*

CIRCUITS, INTEGRATED: Hybrid

Micro Engineering Inc..........E....... 407 886-4849
Apopka *(G-161)*

CIRCUITS: Electronic

ACR Family Components LLC..........E....... 352 243-0307
Groveland *(G-5092)*
Advanced Manufacturing Inc..........E....... 727 573-3300
Saint Petersburg *(G-15691)*
Allied Circuits LLC..........G....... 239 970-2299
Naples *(G-11155)*
American Data Supply Inc..........F....... 866 650-3282
Clearwater *(G-1579)*
American Fibertek Inc..........E....... 732 302-0660
Saint Petersburg *(G-15699)*
Aspen Electronics Inc..........E....... 305 863-2151
Miami *(G-9179)*
Best Circuits Inc..........E....... 321 425-6725
Melbourne *(G-8778)*
Bocatech Inc..........G....... 954 397-7070
Deerfield Beach *(G-2788)*
Built Story LLC..........G....... 305 671-3890
Miami *(G-9283)*
Capacitor and Components LLC..........E....... 954 798-8943
Sunrise *(G-17104)*
Concurrent Mfg Solutions LLC..........E....... 512 637-2540
Doral *(G-3304)*
Continuity Unlimited Inc..........F....... 561 358-8171
Oviedo *(G-13422)*
Custom Mfg & Engrg Inc..........D....... 727 548-0522
Pinellas Park *(G-14342)*
Dbi Services LLC..........E....... 239 218-5204
Fort Myers *(G-4427)*
Delta Group Electronics Inc..........D....... 321 631-0799
Rockledge *(G-15400)*
Flint LLC..........G....... 813 622-8899
Tampa *(G-17670)*
Freshsurety Corporation..........G....... 321 209-8699
Altamonte Springs *(G-47)*
Hiltronics Corporation..........G....... 954 341-9100
Coral Springs *(G-2254)*
I-Con Systems Inc..........D....... 407 365-6241
Oviedo *(G-13438)*
Intellitec Motor Vehicles LLC..........E....... 386 738-7307
Deland *(G-2984)*
Just-In-Time Mfg Corp..........F....... 321 752-7552
Melbourne *(G-8857)*
Kai Limited..........C....... 954 957-8586
Fort Lauderdale *(G-4083)*
KID Group Inc..........G....... 888 805-8851
Greenacres *(G-5084)*
Kimball Electronics Tampa Inc..........C....... 813 814-5229
Tampa *(G-17825)*
Lgl Group Inc..........G....... 407 298-2000
Orlando *(G-12907)*
LMI Components Inc..........F....... 561 994-5896
Boca Raton *(G-604)*
Mdco Inc..........F....... 813 855-4068
Tampa *(G-17898)*
Micro Hybrids Inc..........G....... 772 225-4206
Stuart *(G-16976)*
Micro Technology of Brevard..........G....... 321 733-1766
Melbourne *(G-8889)*
MN Trades Inc..........G....... 954 455-9320
Hallandale Beach *(G-5200)*
Monroe Cable LLC..........D....... 941 429-8484
North Port *(G-11744)*
New ERA Technology Corp..........F....... 352 746-3569
Beverly Hills *(G-377)*
Phantom Technologies Inc..........E....... 407 265-2567
Longwood *(G-8325)*
Protek Electronics Inc..........E....... 941 351-4399
Sarasota *(G-16548)*
Rami Technology USA LLC..........G....... 305 593-6033
Doral *(G-3481)*
Relcom Industries Inc..........G....... 561 304-7717
Greenacres *(G-5086)*
Sam-E-Nik Corp..........G....... 347 992-2123
Coral Gables *(G-2193)*
Sibex Inc..........C....... 727 726-4343
Crystal River *(G-2382)*
Soltec Electronics LLC..........G....... 321 288-5689
Rockledge *(G-15447)*
Spacecoast Cable & Harness Inc..........E....... 321 269-0377
Titusville *(G-18462)*
Sparton Deleon Springs LLC..........D....... 386 985-4631
De Leon Springs *(G-2743)*

Syncron Ems Llc....D....321 409-0025
Palm Bay *(G-13542)*
Sypris Electronics LLC....B....813 972-6000
Tampa *(G-18149)*
Technical Service Labs Inc....E....850 243-3722
Fort Walton Beach *(G-4834)*
Techtronics LLC....G....407 738-4680
Kissimmee *(G-7303)*
Tekquest Inc....F....321 768-6069
Palm Bay *(G-13544)*
Telematic Systems Inc....G....239 217-0629
North Fort Myers *(G-11607)*
Tri-Tech Electronics Inc....D....407 277-2131
Orlando *(G-13270)*

CLAMPS: Metal

Safety Clamps Inc....F....904 781-2809
Jacksonville *(G-6749)*

CLAY PRDTS: Architectural

Glassarium LLC....E....786 631-7080
Miami *(G-9639)*

CLAYS, EXC KAOLIN & BALL

C C Calhoun Inc....E....863 292-9511
Winter Haven *(G-19310)*

CLEANERS: Boiler Tube

CT Natural....G....813 996-6443
Tampa *(G-17572)*
Water Technology of Pensacola....E....850 477-4789
Pensacola *(G-14286)*

CLEANING EQPT: Blast, Dustless

B E Pressure Supply Inc....F....561 688-9246
West Palm Beach *(G-18807)*

CLEANING EQPT: Commercial

A&M Cleaning Solutions LLC....F....786 559-7093
West Palm Beach *(G-18785)*
Consumer Engineering Inc....F....321 984-8550
Palm Bay *(G-13507)*
Douglas Machines Corp....E....727 461-3477
Clearwater *(G-1655)*
Extra Time Solutions....F....407 625-2198
Clermont *(G-1957)*
White Mop Wringer Company....C....813 971-2223
Tampa *(G-18256)*

CLEANING EQPT: Dirt Sweeping Units, Indl

Smith Equipment & Supply Co....E....863 665-4904
Lakeland *(G-7795)*

CLEANING EQPT: Floor Washing & Polishing, Commercial

Genfloor LLC....G....305 477-1557
Doral *(G-3364)*

CLEANING EQPT: High Pressure

A Clean Finish Inc....G....407 516-1311
Jacksonville *(G-6109)*
A1 Cleaning Concepts Inc....G....772 288-7214
Stuart *(G-16899)*
American Pressure Systems Inc....G....321 914-0827
West Melbourne *(G-18765)*
Angel Fernandez....G....239 580-9714
Fort Myers *(G-4363)*
Bateh Networking Solutions LLC....G....904 725-2282
Jacksonville *(G-6197)*
Blast Off Equipment Inc....F....561 964-6199
West Palm Beach *(G-18824)*
Charles Gable Inc....G....239 300-0220
Naples *(G-11207)*
Getitcleaned....F....239 331-2891
Naples *(G-11261)*
Greenlam America Inc....F....305 640-0388
Doral *(G-3373)*
Nilfisk Pressure-Pro LLC....D....772 672-3697
Fort Pierce *(G-4722)*
Pressure Shine LLC....G....727 216-8543
Palm Harbor *(G-13751)*
Richard Lyn....G....954 326-1017
North Lauderdale *(G-11620)*
Southern Power Washing....G....561 644-2237
Loxahatchee *(G-8365)*
Transition of Slc Inc....E....772 461-4486
Fort Pierce *(G-4757)*

CLEANING OR POLISHING PREPARATIONS, NEC

Chemco Corp....E....305 623-4445
Miami Lakes *(G-10776)*
Crown Products LLC....G....954 917-1118
Pompano Beach *(G-14652)*
Marinize Products Corp....G....954 989-7990
Hollywood *(G-5869)*
Power Kleen Corporation....E....813 854-2648
Oldsmar *(G-12258)*
Quality Industrial Chem Inc....F....727 573-5760
Saint Petersburg *(G-15896)*
Sheila Shine Inc....E....305 557-1729
Miami *(G-10335)*
Shelia Shine Inc....G....305 557-1729
Hialeah *(G-5618)*
Vin-Dotco Inc....F....727 217-9200
Pinellas Park *(G-14393)*

CLEANING PRDTS: Automobile Polish

Asi Chemical Inc....F....863 678-1814
Lake Wales *(G-7499)*
Bruce Roland....G....850 775-1497
Panama City Beach *(G-13974)*
Car Care Haven LLC....G....855 464-2836
Englewood *(G-3671)*
Clean & Shine Auto Marine....G....239 261-6563
Naples *(G-11211)*
Distingshed Gntlman MBL Dtling....G....321 200-4331
Orlando *(G-12676)*

CLEANING PRDTS: Bleaches, Household, Dry Or Liquid

Odyssey Manufacturing Co....E....813 635-0339
Tampa *(G-17945)*
Sewell Products Florida LLC....D....863 967-4463
Auburndale *(G-252)*
United Sierra Group Corp....D....305 297-5835
Miami Lakes *(G-10873)*

CLEANING PRDTS: Degreasing Solvent

Petruj Chemical Corp....F....305 556-1271
Miami Lakes *(G-10836)*
Quantum Envmtl Slutions St Inc....G....800 975-8721
Fort Lauderdale *(G-4193)*
Skymo LLC....F....305 676-6739
Cooper City *(G-2115)*

CLEANING PRDTS: Deodorants, Nonpersonal

Falconpro Industries Inc....G....305 556-4456
Hialeah *(G-5404)*
Hinsilblon Ltd Inc....G....239 418-1133
Fort Myers *(G-4483)*
OHanrahan Consultants Inc....E....727 531-3375
Largo *(G-8019)*

CLEANING PRDTS: Disinfectants, Household Or Indl Plant

Eco Concepts Inc....F....954 920-9700
Hollywood *(G-5814)*
Reliox Corporation....G....904 729-5097
Jacksonville *(G-6715)*
Seal Shield LLC....E....877 325-7443
Orlando *(G-13172)*
Vonos LLC....G....888 698-6667
Orlando *(G-13310)*

CLEANING PRDTS: Drain Pipe Solvents Or Cleaners

See-Ray Plumbing Inc....E....772 489-2474
Vero Beach *(G-18663)*

CLEANING PRDTS: Drycleaning Preparations

Holiday Cleaners Inc....G....727 842-6989
New Port Richey *(G-11492)*

CLEANING PRDTS: Indl Plant Disinfectants Or Deodorants

Lee Chemical Corporation....G....407 843-6950
Orlando *(G-12900)*
Northland Manufacturing Inc....G....850 878-5149
Tallahassee *(G-17306)*

CLEANING PRDTS: Laundry Preparations

Chhaya Corporation....G....407 348-9400
Kissimmee *(G-7231)*
Mollys Suds LLC....G....678 361-5456
Saint Petersburg *(G-15858)*

CLEANING PRDTS: Polishing Preparations & Related Prdts

N A Comandulli LLC....G....941 870-2878
Sarasota *(G-16262)*
Ocean Bio-Chem Inc....E....954 587-6280
Davie *(G-2559)*

CLEANING PRDTS: Sanitation Preparations

Ciega Inc....G....727 526-9048
Saint Petersburg *(G-15746)*

CLEANING PRDTS: Sanitation Preps, Disinfectants/Deodorants

Cogswell Innovations Inc....G....954 245-8877
Fort Lauderdale *(G-3907)*
Futurescape Inc....G....386 679-4120
Port Orange *(G-15018)*
Infinity Manufacturing LLC....G....954 531-6918
Coconut Creek *(G-2079)*
Jde Distributors LLC....F....727 498-7886
Pinellas Park *(G-14357)*
Nvip LLC....G....972 435-4097
Naples *(G-11348)*
Paradise Air Fresh LLC....F....561 972-0375
Palm City *(G-13670)*
Relu Co....E....786 717-5665
Doral *(G-3482)*
Samarian Products LLC....E....212 781-2121
Naples *(G-11390)*
Saphire Services LLC....G....386 247-1048
Lake Butler *(G-7341)*
Veridien Corporation....F....727 576-1600
Saint Petersburg *(G-15951)*
Victory Valet Services LLC....F....904 521-6517
Jacksonville *(G-6897)*
Whr Holdings LLC....D....954 342-4342
Fort Lauderdale *(G-4323)*

CLEANING PRDTS: Specialty

1st Enviro-Safety Inc....G....239 283-1222
Saint James City *(G-15672)*
Amazon Cleaning & More Inc....F....239 594-1733
Naples *(G-11158)*
American Coatings Corporation....G....954 970-7820
Margate *(G-8535)*
Beyondclean LLC....F....561 799-5710
Jupiter *(G-7008)*
Brewer International Inc....F....772 562-0555
Vero Beach *(G-18603)*
Buckeye International Inc....G....813 621-6260
Tampa *(G-17488)*
Dudley Blake LLC....G....904 866-2829
Jacksonville *(G-6332)*
Green Bull Products Inc....G....386 402-0409
New Smyrna *(G-11522)*
Impressions Dry Cleaners Inc....F....561 988-3030
Boca Raton *(G-564)*
Kmss Products Inc....G....800 646-3005
Largo *(G-7994)*
Services NS 18 LLC....G....786 546-3295
Aventura *(G-280)*
Spa Concepts Inc....F....850 575-0921
Tallahassee *(G-17328)*
Sparklean....G....305 599-8479
Miami *(G-10398)*
Suncoast Research Labs Inc....F....727 344-7627
Saint Petersburg *(G-15928)*

CLEANING SVCS: Industrial Or Commercial

Florida Elc Mtr Co Miami Inc....E....305 759-3835
Miami *(G-9581)*

CLOSURES: Plastic

Marconi Line Inc....................F....... 321 639-1130
Rockledge *(G-15434)*

CLOTHING & ACCESS STORES

Sew Whats New Embroidery Inc..........G....... 954 977-3339
Pompano Beach *(G-14849)*

CLOTHING & ACCESS, WOMEN, CHILD & INFANT, WHOLESALE: Under

New Concepts Distrs Intl LLC..............F....... 305 463-8735
Doral *(G-3444)*

CLOTHING & ACCESS, WOMEN, CHILD & INFANT, WHSLE: Sportswear

Sportailor Inc..............................D....... 305 754-3255
Miami *(G-10406)*

CLOTHING & ACCESS, WOMEN, CHILDREN & INFANT, WHOL: Handbags

Excel Handbags Co Inc.....................F....... 305 836-8800
Miami *(G-9543)*

CLOTHING & ACCESS, WOMEN, CHILDREN & INFANT, WHOL: Uniforms

JA Uniforms Inc...............................F....... 305 234-1231
Miami *(G-9784)*

CLOTHING & ACCESS, WOMEN, CHILDREN/INFANT, WHOL: Outerwear

Fashion Pool USA Inc..........................G....... 970 367-4797
Jupiter *(G-7040)*

CLOTHING & ACCESS, WOMEN, CHILDREN/INFANT, WHOL: Swimsuits

Swim By Chuck Handy Inc...................G....... 305 519-4946
North Miami Beach *(G-11707)*

CLOTHING & ACCESS, WOMENS, CHILDREN & INFANTS, WHOL: Hats

Royal Headwear & EMB Inc..................G....... 305 889-8480
Medley *(G-8720)*

CLOTHING & ACCESS: Arm bands, Elastic

Price Chopper Inc..............................E....... 407 679-1600
Orlando *(G-13085)*
Wristband Supply LLC........................F....... 954 571-3993
Deerfield Beach *(G-2937)*

CLOTHING & ACCESS: Costumes, Lodge

Greater Miami Elks Lodge Inc..............F....... 305 754-5899
Miami *(G-9663)*

CLOTHING & ACCESS: Costumes, Theatrical

Algy Trimmings Co Inc........................D....... 954 457-8100
Miami *(G-9104)*

CLOTHING & ACCESS: Footlets

Keepmefresh.....................................G....... 502 407-7902
Clermont *(G-1965)*

CLOTHING & ACCESS: Garters

Garflex Inc...D....... 305 436-8915
Doral *(G-3358)*

CLOTHING & ACCESS: Handicapped

David Dobbs Enterprises Inc...............D....... 904 824-6171
Saint Augustine *(G-15533)*
Geekshive Inc.....................................F....... 888 797-4335
Miami *(G-9620)*
Stuntwear LLC...................................G....... 305 842-2115
Miami Beach *(G-10718)*

CLOTHING & ACCESS: Hospital Gowns

Carter-Health Disposables LLC...........G....... 407 296-6689
Orlando *(G-12553)*

Prescient Logistics LLC......................F....... 407 547-2680
Sanford *(G-16106)*
Universal HM Hlth Indus Sups I...........G....... 813 493-7904
Tampa *(G-18222)*

CLOTHING & ACCESS: Men's Miscellaneous Access

Can Can Concealment LLC..................G....... 727 841-6930
Odessa *(G-12109)*
Davis-Wick Talent MGT LLC................E....... 407 369-1614
Margate *(G-8541)*
Exclusive Apparel LLC........................F....... 800 859-6260
Fort Lauderdale *(G-3981)*
Purpleglassboutique LLC....................G....... 407 601-2641
Orlando *(G-13101)*
Sashay Sourcing LLC..........................G....... 239 454-4940
Fort Myers *(G-4597)*
Slate Solutions LLC............................E....... 754 200-6752
Davie *(G-2593)*
Walter Green Inc................................G....... 850 227-7946
Port Saint Joe *(G-15084)*
Wayloo Inc..G....... 954 914-3192
Fort Lauderdale *(G-4317)*
Wesol Distribution LLC.......................G....... 407 921-9248
Casselberry *(G-1521)*
Zeppelin Products Inc........................F....... 954 989-8808
Hallandale Beach *(G-5226)*

CLOTHING & ACCESS: Suspenders

Sparkles and Suspenders FL...............G....... 754 701-4528
Lauderhill *(G-8120)*

CLOTHING & APPAREL STORES: Custom

Cotton Pickin Shirts Plus.....................G....... 850 435-3133
Pensacola *(G-14120)*
Marlin Graphics Inc............................G....... 561 743-5220
Jupiter *(G-7074)*
Outdoor Products LLC........................G....... 352 473-0886
Steinhatchee *(G-16898)*

CLOTHING & FURNISHINGS, MEN'S & BOYS', WHOLESALE: Hats

Royal Headwear & EMB Inc..................G....... 305 889-8480
Medley *(G-8720)*

CLOTHING & FURNISHINGS, MEN'S & BOYS', WHOLESALE: Outerwear

American Lw & Promo Prods LLC........G....... 954 946-5252
Pompano Beach *(G-14591)*
Fashion Pool USA Inc..........................G....... 970 367-4797
Jupiter *(G-7040)*

CLOTHING & FURNISHINGS, MEN'S & BOYS', WHOLESALE: Shirts

CBI Industries Inc...............................G....... 305 796-9346
Miami *(G-9329)*

CLOTHING & FURNISHINGS, MEN'S & BOYS', WHOLESALE: Uniforms

Interntnal Export Uniforms Inc............E....... 305 869-9900
Miami *(G-9761)*

CLOTHING & FURNISHINGS, MENS & BOYS, WHOL: Sportswear/Work

Bid Excellence Co LLC........................G....... 609 929-9019
Miami *(G-9243)*
Sportailor Inc.......................................D....... 305 754-3255
Miami *(G-10406)*

CLOTHING & FURNISHINGS, MENS & BOYS, WHOLESALE: Apprl Belts

Continental Belt Corp..........................G....... 305 573-8871
Miami *(G-9395)*

CLOTHING STORES: Formal Wear

Designs To Shine..................................E....... 727 525-4297
Saint Petersburg *(G-15759)*

CLOTHING STORES: Jeans

Blue Light USA Corp.............................G....... 954 766-4308
Sunrise *(G-17099)*

CLOTHING STORES: Shirts, Custom Made

CBI Industries Inc................................G....... 305 796-9346
Miami *(G-9329)*

CLOTHING STORES: T-Shirts, Printed, Custom

Above LLC..F....... 850 469-9028
Pensacola *(G-14077)*
Expert TS of Jacksonville.....................F....... 904 387-2500
Jacksonville *(G-6374)*
Maddys Print Shop LLC.......................G....... 954 749-0440
Fort Lauderdale *(G-4108)*
STS Apparel Corp................................F....... 305 628-4000
Hialeah *(G-5636)*

CLOTHING STORES: Uniforms & Work

A2z Uniforms Inc..................................G....... 941 254-3194
Sarasota *(G-16330)*
Official Gear Company Inc...................G....... 407 721-9110
Ormond Beach *(G-13387)*

CLOTHING STORES: Unisex

Drench Khari LLC.................................G....... 561 507-4723
Riviera Beach *(G-15322)*
Shirts & Caps Inc.................................F....... 813 788-7026
Tampa *(G-18098)*

CLOTHING STORES: Work

Bags Unlimited Inc...............................G....... 985 868-3393
Chiefland *(G-1533)*

CLOTHING, WOMEN & CHILD, WHLSE: Dress, Suit, Skirt & Blouse

Stush AP USA/Stush Style LLC............F....... 404 940-3445
Sunrise *(G-17180)*

CLOTHING: Academic Vestments

Herff Jones LLC...................................G....... 727 527-0696
Saint Petersburg *(G-15805)*
Regency Cap & Gown Company...........E....... 904 724-3500
Jacksonville *(G-6713)*

CLOTHING: Access

Antonyo Denard Llc.............................F....... 904 290-1579
Jacksonville *(G-6159)*
C&D Sign and Lighting Svcs LLC.........G....... 863 937-9323
Lakeland *(G-7652)*
Jewels Handmade LLC........................F....... 407 283-9951
Orlando *(G-12856)*
Lululemon..G....... 813 973-3879
Wesley Chapel *(G-18752)*
Michael Kors...G....... 813 413-3310
Brandon *(G-1167)*
My Glam Choice Inc.............................G....... 786 586-7927
Miami *(G-10056)*
RES Textiles Inc...................................G....... 813 476-5524
Tampa *(G-18052)*
The Alluring Group Inc.........................F....... 800 731-2280
Miramar *(G-11051)*

CLOTHING: Access, Women's & Misses'

Can Can Concealment LLC...................G....... 727 841-6930
Odessa *(G-12109)*
Coastal Paddle Co LLC........................F....... 850 916-1600
Gulf Breeze *(G-5114)*
Finesta Inc...G....... 786 439-1647
Miami *(G-9569)*
Jazanique Wickson...............................G....... 815 221-7155
Miami Beach *(G-10684)*
Maria Fuentes LLC...............................G....... 305 717-3404
Miami *(G-9947)*

CLOTHING: Aprons, Harness

Hallmark Emblems Inc..........................D....... 813 223-5427
Tampa *(G-17740)*

CLOTHING: Aprons, Work, Exc Rubberized & Plastic, Men's

Cameron Textiles Inc............................G....... 954 454-6482
Palm City *(G-13644)*

CLOTHING: Athletic & Sportswear, Men's & Boys'

Anmapec Corporation ....F 786 897-5389
Miami *(G-9154)*
Armen Co Inc ....D 305 206-1601
Plantation *(G-14490)*
Arno Belo Inc ....G 800 734-2356
Hallandale Beach *(G-5170)*
Athco Inc ....E 941 351-1600
Sarasota *(G-16179)*
B & B Industries of Orlando ....G 407 366-1800
Oviedo *(G-13417)*
Bdc Florida LLC ....F 561 249-0900
West Palm Beach *(G-18814)*
Exist Inc ....D 954 739-7030
Fort Lauderdale *(G-3982)*
Fabrox LLC ....E 904 342-4048
Ormond Beach *(G-13371)*
Fitletic Sports LLC ....G 305 907-6663
Hallandale Beach *(G-5186)*
Golf America Southwest Fla Inc ....G 904 688-0280
Saint Augustine *(G-15546)*
Good Chance Textile Inc ....F 754 263-2792
Pembroke Pines *(G-14038)*
Icon Embroidery Inc ....G 407 858-0886
Windermere *(G-19228)*
In Gear Fashions Inc ....D 305 830-2900
Miami Gardens *(G-10747)*
JMP Fashion Inc ....F 305 633-9920
Miami *(G-9799)*
John M Caldwell Distrg Co Inc ....G 305 685-9822
Opa Locka *(G-12329)*
Onca Gear LLC ....G 857 253-8207
Hialeah *(G-5549)*
Outdoor Products LLC ....G 352 473-0886
Steinhatchee *(G-16898)*
Recover Gear LLC ....G 904 280-9660
Ponte Vedra Beach *(G-14952)*
Richard Appelbaum & Associates ....G 813 920-0300
Odessa *(G-12145)*
Speedline Team Sports Inc ....F 813 876-1375
Tampa *(G-18125)*
Spirit Sales Corporation ....G 850 878-0366
Tallahassee *(G-17329)*
Sportailor Inc ....D 305 754-3255
Miami *(G-10406)*
Sports Structure Intl LLC ....G 305 777-2225
Miami Beach *(G-10715)*
Suncoast Trends Inc ....G 727 321-4948
Saint Petersburg *(G-15929)*
Surf Outfitter ....G 813 489-4587
Tampa *(G-18147)*
Surf Style Inc ....E 954 926-6666
Hollywood *(G-5919)*
T Shirt Center Inc ....G 305 655-1955
Miami *(G-10455)*
Tactical Products Group LLC ....E 561 265-4066
Boynton Beach *(G-967)*
Ultimate Overstock LLC ....E 407 851-1017
Orlando *(G-13287)*
Val DOr Apparel LLC ....G 954 363-7340
Coconut Creek *(G-2100)*

CLOTHING: Athletic & Sportswear, Women's & Girls'

B & B Industries of Orlando ....G 407 366-1800
Oviedo *(G-13417)*
Cima Activewear LLC ....G 239 273-6055
Estero *(G-3687)*
Excess Liquidator LLC ....G 407 247-9105
Oviedo *(G-13429)*
Kamaj Business Group Inc ....F 813 863-9967
Tampa *(G-17815)*
New Concepts Distrs Intl LLC ....F 305 463-8735
Doral *(G-3444)*
Recover Gear LLC ....G 904 280-9660
Ponte Vedra Beach *(G-14952)*
Shgar Kane Couture Inc ....G 407 205-8038
Orlando *(G-13181)*
Tom James Company ....G 813 204-9699
Tampa *(G-18193)*

CLOTHING: Baker, Barber, Lab/Svc Ind Apparel, Washable, Men

Ivory International Inc ....C 305 687-2244
Medley *(G-8672)*
Uzzi Amphibious Gear LLC ....F 954 777-9595
Hallandale Beach *(G-5223)*

CLOTHING: Bathing Suits & Swimwear, Girls, Children & Infant

Agua Viva LLC ....G 954 802-3255
Miami Beach *(G-10637)*
Rme Studio Inc ....G 305 409-0856
Miami *(G-10268)*
Shore Trendz LLC ....G 954 608-7375
Plantation *(G-14550)*
Surf Outfitter ....G 813 489-4587
Tampa *(G-18147)*
Tca Pool Inc ....G 954 600-2448
Deerfield Beach *(G-2924)*

CLOTHING: Bathing Suits & Swimwear, Knit

Absolutely Suitable ....G 561 653-6380
Palm Beach *(G-13548)*
House of Llull Atlier ....G 305 964-7921
Miami *(G-9720)*
Reflections Beach & Resortwear ....G 954 776-1230
Laud By Sea *(G-8083)*
Swim By Chuck Handy Inc ....G 305 519-4946
North Miami Beach *(G-11707)*

CLOTHING: Bathrobes, Mens & Womens, From Purchased Materials

Terry Boca Inc ....G 561 893-0333
Deerfield Beach *(G-2925)*

CLOTHING: Beachwear, Knit

Nrz Inc ....G 305 345-7303
Pinecrest *(G-14329)*
Swf Bonita Beach Inc ....D 239 466-6600
Bonita Springs *(G-860)*

CLOTHING: Belts

Belts Inc ....G 714 572-3636
Hialeah *(G-5320)*
Tagua Leather Corporation ....G 305 637-3014
Miami *(G-10458)*
Zeppelin Products Inc ....F 954 989-8808
Hallandale Beach *(G-5226)*

CLOTHING: Blouses & Shirts, Girls' & Children's

Bossy Princess LLC ....G 786 285-4435
Aventura *(G-265)*

CLOTHING: Blouses, Women's & Girls'

Apyelen Curves LLC ....F 904 434-8768
Jacksonville *(G-6162)*
Daisy Crazy Inc ....G 305 300-5144
Doral *(G-3321)*
Decoy Inc ....F 305 633-6384
Miami *(G-9443)*
Entire Select Inc ....G 954 674-2368
Sunrise *(G-17119)*
H M J Corporation ....F 954 229-1873
Fort Lauderdale *(G-4037)*
Kamtex USA Incorporated ....G 954 733-1044
Lauderdale Lakes *(G-8089)*
Matteo Graphics Inc ....F 239 652-1002
Cape Coral *(G-1446)*
R&S Intrnational Inv Group LLC ....F 305 576-3000
Miami *(G-10234)*
Stanley Industries of S Fla ....G 954 929-8770
Hollywood *(G-5915)*
Supreme International LLC ....A 305 592-2830
Doral *(G-3519)*
Vargas Enterprises Inc ....G 561 989-0908
Boca Raton *(G-775)*
Wbt Apparel Inc ....G 305 891-1107
North Miami *(G-11663)*

CLOTHING: Blouses, Womens & Juniors, From Purchased Mtrls

Argus International Inc ....E 305 888-4881
Weston *(G-19108)*
Co-Edikit ....G 863 802-1000
Lakeland *(G-7658)*
Goen3 Corporation ....G 407 601-6000
Orlando *(G-12785)*
Johnny Devil Inc ....G 305 634-0700
Miami *(G-9800)*
PJ Designs Inc ....E 727 525-0599
Saint Petersburg *(G-15879)*
Stush AP USA/Stush Style LLC ....F 404 940-3445
Sunrise *(G-17180)*
Suncoast Trends Inc ....G 727 321-4948
Saint Petersburg *(G-15929)*

CLOTHING: Brassieres

Universal Brass Fabrication ....F 561 691-5445
Palm Beach Gardens *(G-13633)*

CLOTHING: Bridal Gowns

Designs To Shine ....E 727 525-4297
Saint Petersburg *(G-15759)*

CLOTHING: Children's, Girls'

Armen Co Inc ....D 305 206-1601
Plantation *(G-14490)*
Athco Inc ....E 941 351-1600
Sarasota *(G-16179)*
Dilan Enterprises Inc ....E 305 887-3051
Hialeah *(G-5373)*
Florida Christn Conference Inc ....G 407 460-8259
Kissimmee *(G-7244)*
Ivory International Inc ....C 305 687-2244
Medley *(G-8672)*
Kona Gold LLC ....F 844 714-2224
Melbourne *(G-8861)*
Manatee Bay Enterprises Inc ....F 407 245-3600
Orlando *(G-12947)*
Puppet Workshop Inc ....C 305 666-2655
Hialeah *(G-5583)*
Sarah Louise Inc ....F 941 377-9656
Sarasota *(G-16573)*
Suncoast Trends Inc ....G 727 321-4948
Saint Petersburg *(G-15929)*

CLOTHING: Coats & Jackets, Leather & Sheep-Lined

Tagua Leather Corporation ....G 305 637-3014
Miami *(G-10458)*

CLOTHING: Coats & Suits, Men's & Boys'

Black Mountain Apparel Inc ....E 727 216-6419
Seminole *(G-16743)*
Mario Kenny ....G 786 274-0527
Miami *(G-9949)*
Tycoon Tutti Inc ....E 305 624-7811
Miami *(G-10519)*

CLOTHING: Costumes

Goruck LLC ....E 904 708-2081
Jacksonville Beach *(G-6944)*
Goruck Holdings LLC ....F 904 708-2081
Jacksonville Beach *(G-6945)*
Miss BS Inc ....G 305 981-9900
North Miami Beach *(G-11692)*
Robot-Costumes Technologies ....G 904 535-0074
Saint Augustine *(G-15598)*

CLOTHING: Disposable

Mhms Corp ....E 813 948-0504
Lutz *(G-8401)*
Shore Trendz LLC ....G 954 608-7375
Plantation *(G-14550)*

CLOTHING: Dresses

Amj DOT LLC ....G 646 249-0273
Boca Raton *(G-426)*
Ancient Language Inc ....G 413 344-4042
Orlando *(G-12477)*
Arde Apparel Inc ....E 305 326-0861
Miami *(G-9166)*
Janine of London Inc ....G 954 772-3593
Fort Lauderdale *(G-4075)*
Laura Knit Collection Inc ....C 305 945-8222
North Miami Beach *(G-11690)*
Meek Chic Queen Inc ....G 407 920-8135
Coral Springs *(G-2278)*
Stanley Industries of S Fla ....G 954 929-8770
Hollywood *(G-5915)*
Stush AP USA/Stush Style LLC ....F 404 940-3445
Sunrise *(G-17180)*

CLOTHING: Formal Jackets, Mens & Youth, From Purchased Matls

Apparel Imports Inc....E.... 800 428-6849
Miami *(G-9157)*

CLOTHING: Girdles & Other Foundation Garments, Knit

Fajas Colombianas USA LLC....G.... 786 326-0002
Hialeah *(G-5403)*

CLOTHING: Gowns & Dresses, Wedding

A Fine Affair Dj....G.... 319 899-2071
Kissimmee *(G-7215)*
AA Oldco Inc....D.... 215 659-5300
Delray Beach *(G-3038)*
CD Greeting LLC....G.... 954 530-1301
Fort Lauderdale *(G-3887)*
Classic Stars Inc....G.... 305 871-6767
Miami *(G-9362)*
Miller Creative Works Inc....G.... 904 504-3212
Jacksonville *(G-6608)*
Mori Lee LLC....E.... 954 418-6165
Deerfield Beach *(G-2876)*
Weddings By Tina....G.... 904 235-3740
Jacksonville *(G-6908)*

CLOTHING: Hats & Caps, NEC

Bernard Cap LLC....C.... 305 822-4800
Hialeah *(G-5322)*
Ronmar Industries Inc....F.... 561 630-8035
West Palm Beach *(G-19023)*

CLOTHING: Hats & Caps, Uniform

American Lw & Promo Prods LLC....G.... 954 946-5252
Pompano Beach *(G-14591)*
Feds Apparel....E.... 954 932-0685
Davie *(G-2524)*

CLOTHING: Hats, Harvest, Straw

John Lacquey Enterprises Inc....F.... 386 935-1705
Branford *(G-1187)*

CLOTHING: Helmets, Jungle Cloth, Wool Lined

Coolhead Helmet LLC....G.... 786 292-4829
Miami *(G-9399)*

CLOTHING: Hosiery, Men's & Boys'

Triumph Hosiery Corp....G.... 954 929-6021
Hollywood *(G-5928)*

CLOTHING: Hosiery, Pantyhose & Knee Length, Sheer

New Concepts Distrs Intl LLC....F.... 305 463-8735
Doral *(G-3444)*
Triumph Hosiery Corp....G.... 954 929-6021
Hollywood *(G-5928)*

CLOTHING: Hospital, Men's

Affordable Med Scrubs LLC....F.... 419 222-1088
Miami *(G-9086)*
Fabrox LLC....E.... 904 342-4048
Ormond Beach *(G-13371)*
Samarian Products LLC....E.... 212 781-2121
Naples *(G-11390)*

CLOTHING: Jackets, Knit

Bnj Noble Inc....F.... 954 987-1040
Davie *(G-2503)*

CLOTHING: Knit Underwear & Nightwear

Jockey International Inc....G.... 561 689-7646
West Palm Beach *(G-18913)*
Sweet and Vicious LLC....F.... 772 907-3030
Lake Worth *(G-7589)*

CLOTHING: Leather

Oceanstyle LLC....G.... 305 672-9400
Miami Beach *(G-10699)*

CLOTHING: Leather & sheep-lined clothing

Shaikh Rizwan....G.... 202 740-9796
Lakeland *(G-7789)*

CLOTHING: Lounge, Bed & Leisurewear

A & S Entertainment LLC....F.... 305 627-3456
Miami *(G-9032)*

CLOTHING: Maternity

Olian Inc....E.... 305 233-9116
Miami *(G-10094)*

CLOTHING: Men's & boy's clothing, nec

Jamerica Inc....G.... 561 488-6247
Boca Raton *(G-575)*
Winntel USA....G.... 863 451-1789
Sebring *(G-16718)*

CLOTHING: Men's & boy's underwear & nightwear

Jockey International Inc....G.... 561 689-7646
West Palm Beach *(G-18913)*
Val DOr Apparel LLC....G.... 954 363-7340
Coconut Creek *(G-2100)*

CLOTHING: Neckwear

Bonito & Company LLC....G.... 561 451-7494
Boca Raton *(G-460)*
Breezy Swimwear....G.... 305 763-9570
Miami *(G-9275)*
Caveat....G.... 305 501-4646
Miami *(G-9326)*
Chervo USA Inc....G.... 561 510-2458
North Palm Beach *(G-11721)*
Element Outdoors LLC....G.... 888 589-9589
Pace *(G-13468)*
Exces International LLC....G.... 561 880-8920
Wellington *(G-18716)*
Infotek Groups Inc....G.... 612 666-0535
Saint Petersburg *(G-15814)*
Jblaze Inc....G.... 954 680-3962
Southwest Ranches *(G-16838)*
Mary Angel....G.... 772 299-1392
Vero Beach *(G-18641)*
Prive Porter LLC....G.... 561 479-9200
Boca Raton *(G-675)*
Pure 32 LLC....G.... 813 792-9219
Odessa *(G-12144)*
Siyufy International Inc....G.... 352 512-0658
Ocala *(G-12054)*
Tailored LLC....G.... 239 249-9636
Naples *(G-11434)*

CLOTHING: Outerwear, Knit

Jonel Knitting Mills Inc....E.... 305 887-7333
Hialeah *(G-5466)*
Two Mermaids Villages LLC....G.... 352 259-4722
The Villages *(G-18395)*

CLOTHING: Outerwear, Lthr, Wool/Down-Filled, Men, Youth/Boy

Fashion Pool USA Inc....G.... 970 367-4797
Jupiter *(G-7040)*

CLOTHING: Outerwear, Women's & Misses' NEC

A Living Testimony LLC....G.... 352 406-0249
Eustis *(G-3699)*
Algy Trimmings Co Inc....D.... 954 457-8100
Miami *(G-9104)*
ANue Ligne Inc....G.... 305 638-7979
Miami *(G-9155)*
Big Fish Co Custom Creations....G.... 727 525-5010
Saint Petersburg *(G-15721)*
Dilan Enterprises Inc....E.... 305 887-3051
Hialeah *(G-5373)*
Fashion Pool USA Inc....G.... 970 367-4797
Jupiter *(G-7040)*
Happy Kids For Kids Inc....F.... 954 730-7922
Lauderhill *(G-8111)*
Ivory International Inc....C.... 305 687-2244
Medley *(G-8672)*
Joro Fashions Florida Inc....F.... 305 888-8110
Pinecrest *(G-14328)*
Lagaci Inc....F.... 954 929-1395
Fort Lauderdale *(G-4093)*
Lisa Todd International LLC....G.... 305 445-2632
Miami *(G-9897)*
Manatee Bay Enterprises Inc....F.... 407 245-3600
Orlando *(G-12947)*
Nordic Group LLC....E.... 561 789-8676
Boca Raton *(G-647)*
Ocean Waves Inc....F.... 904 372-4743
Jacksonville Beach *(G-6953)*
Perry Ellis International Inc....B.... 305 592-2830
Doral *(G-3458)*
Salt Life LLC....G.... 904 595-5370
Jacksonville Beach *(G-6957)*
South Florida Textile Inc....F.... 954 973-5677
Pompano Beach *(G-14860)*
Speedline Team Sports Inc....F.... 813 876-1375
Tampa *(G-18125)*
Sport Products of Tampa Inc....G.... 813 630-5552
Tampa *(G-18127)*
Val DOr Apparel LLC....G.... 954 363-7340
Coconut Creek *(G-2100)*

CLOTHING: Robes & Dressing Gowns

Boca Terry LLC....F.... 954 312-4400
Deerfield Beach *(G-2787)*
Lyric Choir Gown Company....G.... 904 725-7977
Jacksonville *(G-6567)*
PJ Designs Inc....E.... 727 525-0599
Saint Petersburg *(G-15879)*

CLOTHING: Service Apparel, Women's

Momentum Comfort Gear Inc....G.... 305 653-5050
Miami *(G-10038)*
Saint George Industries LLC....E.... 786 212-1176
Miami *(G-10298)*
Uzzi Amphibious Gear LLC....F.... 954 777-9595
Hallandale Beach *(G-5223)*

CLOTHING: Shirts

Entire Select Inc....G.... 954 674-2368
Sunrise *(G-17119)*
Feldenkreis Holdings LLC....E.... 305 592-2830
Doral *(G-3350)*
La Providencia Express Co....G.... 305 409-9894
Miami *(G-9846)*
Leo Fashions Inc....F.... 305 887-1032
Hialeah *(G-5484)*
Ronmar Industries Inc....F.... 561 630-8035
West Palm Beach *(G-19023)*
Sashay Sourcing LLC....G.... 239 454-4940
Fort Myers *(G-4597)*
Stanley Industries of S Fla....G.... 954 929-8770
Hollywood *(G-5915)*
Tycoon Tutti Inc....E.... 305 624-7811
Miami *(G-10519)*

CLOTHING: Shirts & T-Shirts, Knit

Eyedose Inc....G.... 786 853-6194
Miami *(G-9550)*
Monkey Shack....G.... 850 234-0082
Panama City *(G-13930)*

CLOTHING: Shirts, Dress, Men's & Boys'

Perry Ellis International Inc....B.... 305 592-2830
Doral *(G-3458)*
Pvh Corp....F.... 850 269-0482
Miramar Beach *(G-11068)*
Regina Behar Enterprises Inc....E.... 305 557-5212
Miramar *(G-11035)*

CLOTHING: Shirts, Sports & Polo, Men's & Boys'

A G A Electronics Corp....F.... 305 592-1860
Miami *(G-9038)*
Dynasty Apparel Corp....D.... 305 685-3490
Opa Locka *(G-12310)*

CLOTHING: Shirts, Uniform, From Purchased Materials

Feds Apparel....E.... 954 932-0685
Davie *(G-2524)*

CLOTHING: Shirts, Women's & Juniors', From Purchased Mtrls

Leo Fashions Inc....F....305 887-1032
Hialeah *(G-5484)*

CLOTHING: Skirts, Knit

Veronica Knits Inc....F....305 887-7333
Hialeah *(G-5676)*

CLOTHING: Socks

American Stock LLC....G....904 641-2055
Jacksonville *(G-6151)*
King of Socks....F....772 204-3286
Port St Lucie *(G-15174)*
Leopard Brands Inc....G....954 794-0007
Boca Raton *(G-599)*
Pop Em Sock Ems....G....850 287-3778
Gulf Breeze *(G-5124)*
Royalty Enterprises LLC....G....786 380-7774
Miami Beach *(G-10706)*
Shashi LLC....G....561 447-8800
Delray Beach *(G-3140)*
Skater Socks....F....850 424-6764
Destin *(G-3206)*

CLOTHING: Sportswear, Women's

American Athletic Uniforms Inc....F....850 729-1205
Valparaiso *(G-18505)*
Anmapec Corporation....F....786 897-5389
Miami *(G-9154)*
Armen Co Inc....D....305 206-1601
Plantation *(G-14490)*
Diane Dal Lago Limited Company....F....813 374-2473
Tampa *(G-17604)*
Fitletic Sports LLC....G....305 907-6663
Hallandale Beach *(G-5186)*
Great Cir Vntures Holdings LLC....D....305 638-2650
Doral *(G-3372)*
Icon Embroidery Inc....G....407 858-0886
Windermere *(G-19228)*
In Gear Fashions Inc....D....305 830-2900
Miami Gardens *(G-10747)*
JMP Fashion Inc....F....305 633-9920
Miami *(G-9799)*
John M Caldwell Distrg Co Inc....G....305 685-9822
Opa Locka *(G-12329)*
Lear Investors Inc....G....305 681-8582
Opa Locka *(G-12333)*
Matteo Graphics Inc....F....239 652-1002
Cape Coral *(G-1446)*
Sir Winston Garments Inc....F....305 499-3144
Miami *(G-10355)*
Southpoint Sportswear LLC....G....305 885-3045
Medley *(G-8727)*
Suncoast Trends Inc....G....727 321-4948
Saint Petersburg *(G-15929)*
T Shirt Center Inc....G....305 655-1955
Miami *(G-10455)*

CLOTHING: Suits, Men's & Boys', From Purchased Materials

Tom James Company....G....813 204-9699
Tampa *(G-18193)*

CLOTHING: Swimwear, Men's & Boys'

Hexskin LLC....G....305 901-1573
Miami *(G-9706)*
Ultimate Swimwear Inc....G....386 668-8900
Altamonte Springs *(G-80)*

CLOTHING: Swimwear, Women's & Misses'

Double J of Broward Inc....E....954 659-8880
Weston *(G-19121)*
Earth & Sea Wear LLC....E....786 332-2236
Doral *(G-3338)*
Regency Cap & Gown Company....E....904 724-3500
Jacksonville *(G-6713)*
Ultimate Swimwear Inc....G....386 668-8900
Altamonte Springs *(G-80)*
Venus Manufacturing Co Inc....D....904 645-3187
Jacksonville *(G-6895)*

CLOTHING: T-Shirts & Tops, Knit

Balzarano John....F....239 455-1231
Naples *(G-11181)*
Coral Club Tee Shirts Inc....G....305 828-6939
Hialeah *(G-5354)*
Daisy Crazy Inc....G....305 300-5144
Doral *(G-3321)*
Mk Brothers Inc....G....407 847-9547
Kissimmee *(G-7277)*
Talent Wear LLC....G....561 624-3030
West Palm Beach *(G-19057)*

CLOTHING: T-Shirts & Tops, Women's & Girls'

Kleids Enterprises Inc....G....727 796-7900
Clearwater *(G-1751)*
Val DOr Apparel LLC....G....954 363-7340
Coconut Creek *(G-2100)*

CLOTHING: Trousers & Slacks, Men's & Boys'

Goen3 Corporation....G....407 601-6000
Orlando *(G-12785)*
Lagaci Inc....F....954 929-1395
Fort Lauderdale *(G-4093)*
Original Pnguin Drect Oprtions....F....305 592-2830
Doral *(G-3452)*
Perry Ellis International Inc....B....305 592-2830
Doral *(G-3458)*
Stanley Industries of S Fla....G....954 929-8770
Hollywood *(G-5915)*
Stush AP USA/Stush Style LLC....F....404 940-3445
Sunrise *(G-17180)*
Supreme International LLC....A....305 592-2830
Doral *(G-3519)*

CLOTHING: Underwear, Knit

Intradeco Apparel Inc....C....305 264-8888
Medley *(G-8671)*

CLOTHING: Underwear, Women's & Children's

Apparel Machinery Services Inc....G....772 335-5350
Port Saint Lucie *(G-15087)*
Decoy Inc....F....305 633-6384
Miami *(G-9443)*
Fenix Wester Corp....G....305 324-9105
Miami *(G-9562)*
Jockey International Inc....G....561 689-7646
West Palm Beach *(G-18913)*
Kamtex USA Incorporated....G....954 733-1044
Lauderdale Lakes *(G-8089)*
Sweet and Vicious LLC....G....305 576-0012
Miami *(G-10446)*

CLOTHING: Uniforms & Vestments

Bold Look Inc....E....305 687-8725
Miami *(G-9265)*
Fashion Connection Miami Inc....G....305 882-0782
Hialeah *(G-5405)*
Point Blank Enterprises Inc....A....954 846-8222
Pompano Beach *(G-14800)*
Superior Group Companies Inc....A....727 397-9611
Seminole *(G-16764)*

CLOTHING: Uniforms, Ex Athletic, Women's, Misses' & Juniors'

Cintas Corporation....G....239 693-8722
Fort Myers *(G-4396)*
International Clothiers Inc....F....914 715-5600
Miami *(G-9756)*
Interntnal Export Uniforms Inc....E....305 869-9900
Miami *(G-9761)*
Uniform Authority Inc....D....305 625-8050
Miami *(G-10529)*

CLOTHING: Uniforms, Men's & Boys'

A G A Electronics Corp....F....305 592-1860
Miami *(G-9038)*
Bid Excellence Co LLC....G....609 929-9019
Miami *(G-9243)*
Burn Proof Gear LLC....G....786 634-7406
Miami *(G-9286)*
Global Trading Inc....F....305 471-4455
Miami *(G-9642)*
Uniform Authority Inc....D....305 625-8050
Miami *(G-10529)*

CLOTHING: Uniforms, Military, Men/Youth, Purchased Materials

Cadre Holdings Inc....C....904 741-5400
Jacksonville *(G-6249)*
Eglin Air Force Base....D....850 882-5422
Eglin Afb *(G-3642)*
Eglin Air Force Base....C....850 882-3315
Eglin Afb *(G-3643)*
L C Industries Inc....E....850 581-0117
Hurlburt Field *(G-6044)*
Point Blank Protective Apprl....A....954 630-0900
Pompano Beach *(G-14803)*
Tennier Industries Inc....G....561 999-9710
Boca Raton *(G-746)*
US Patriot LLC....F....803 787-9398
Tampa *(G-18228)*

CLOTHING: Uniforms, Policemen's, From Purchased Materials

Maui Holdings LLC....A....904 741-5400
Palm Beach *(G-13558)*
Onyx Protective Group Inc....F....305 282-4455
Miami *(G-10108)*

CLOTHING: Uniforms, Team Athletic

Bakers Sports Inc....E....904 388-8126
Jacksonville *(G-6192)*
Speedline Athletic Wear Inc....E....813 876-1375
Tampa *(G-18124)*

CLOTHING: Uniforms, Work

At Work Uniforms....G....850 435-3133
Pensacola *(G-14093)*
Cintas Corporation....F....813 874-1401
Tampa *(G-17536)*
Cintas Corporation....G....239 693-8722
Fort Myers *(G-4396)*
CTI Group Worldwide Svcs Inc....G....954 568-5900
Fort Lauderdale *(G-3922)*
Global Trading Inc....F....305 471-4455
Miami *(G-9642)*
International Clothiers Inc....F....914 715-5600
Miami *(G-9756)*
JA Uniforms Inc....F....305 234-1231
Miami *(G-9784)*
M R M S Inc....G....305 576-3000
Miami *(G-9927)*
R&S Intrnational Inv Group LLC....F....305 576-3000
Miami *(G-10234)*
Wayloo Inc....G....954 914-3192
Fort Lauderdale *(G-4317)*

CLOTHING: Vests

Cameron Textiles Inc....G....954 454-6482
Palm City *(G-13644)*

CLOTHING: Warm Weather Knit Outerwear, Including Beachwear

H2c Brands LLC....E....904 342-7485
Saint Augustine *(G-15548)*

CLOTHING: Waterproof Outerwear

Loksak Inc....G....239 331-5550
Naples *(G-11315)*
Monarch Safety Products Inc....G....407 442-0269
Orlando *(G-12977)*
Sara Glove Company Inc....G....866 664-7272
Naples *(G-11392)*
Seal Outdoors Inc....F....877 323-7325
South Miami *(G-16827)*

CLOTHING: Work Apparel, Exc Uniforms

Bid Excellence Co LLC....G....609 929-9019
Miami *(G-9243)*
Boxseat Inc....F....850 656-1223
Jacksonville *(G-6228)*
Dmr Creative Marketing LLC....G....954 725-3750
Deerfield Beach *(G-2816)*
Gallant Inc....G....800 330-1343
Winter Garden *(G-19265)*
Saint George Industries LLC....E....786 212-1176
Miami *(G-10298)*

CLOTHING: Work, Men's

Anmapec Corporation ....F 786 897-5389
Miami *(G-9154)*
CSC Racing Corporation ....F 248 548-5727
Jupiter *(G-7021)*
Gulfshore Clothier LLC ....G 239 450-8437
Naples *(G-11273)*
Jackie Z Style Co St Pete LLC ....G 727 258-4849
Saint Petersburg *(G-15831)*
Mario Kenny ....G 786 274-0527
Miami *(G-9949)*
Scrubs 941 ....G 941 373-0029
Sarasota *(G-16587)*
Skwholesalenet ....F 305 372-3751
Miami *(G-10358)*
Tees By Bo Inc ....G 305 382-8551
Miami *(G-10465)*
Uniform Authority Inc ....D 305 625-8050
Miami *(G-10529)*
Zayas Fashions Inc ....E 305 823-1438
Hialeah *(G-5695)*

CLOTHS: Polishing, Plain

Coastal Wipers Inc ....E 813 628-4464
Tampa *(G-17543)*
Troy Industries Inc ....E 305 324-1742
Doral *(G-3534)*

COAL MINING EXPLORATION & TEST BORING SVC

Keystone Industries LLC ....F 239 337-7474
Jacksonville *(G-6535)*
US China Mining Group Inc ....D 813 514-2873
Tampa *(G-18226)*

COAL MINING SERVICES

Carbon Resources Inc ....G 941 746-8089
Bradenton *(G-1014)*
Carbon Resources of Florida ....G 941 746-8089
Bradenton *(G-1015)*
Cline Resource and Dev Co ....D 561 626-4999
Palm Beach Gardens *(G-13580)*
Diversified Mining Inc ....G 407 923-3194
Winter Park *(G-19403)*
Mosaic ....E 863 860-1328
Lakeland *(G-7754)*
North American Mining ....G 305 824-3181
Medley *(G-8698)*
Oxbow Carbon LLC ....C 561 907-5400
West Palm Beach *(G-18977)*
Oxbow Enterprises Intl LLC ....G 561 907-5400
West Palm Beach *(G-18978)*
Weber South Fl LLC ....G 239 543-7240
Punta Gorda *(G-15244)*

COAL MINING: Bituminous Coal & Lignite-Surface Mining

North American Coal Corp ....G 305 824-9018
Miami *(G-10077)*
Teco Diversified Inc ....G 813 228-4111
Tampa *(G-18180)*

COAL PREPARATION PLANT: Bituminous or Lignite

Evolving Coal Corp ....G 813 944-3100
Saint Petersburg *(G-15773)*

COAL, MINERALS & ORES, WHOLESALE: Coal

Keystone Industries LLC ....F 239 337-7474
Jacksonville *(G-6535)*
Oxbow Carbon LLC ....C 561 907-5400
West Palm Beach *(G-18977)*
Oxbow Enterprises Intl LLC ....G 561 907-5400
West Palm Beach *(G-18978)*
Puragen LLC ....E 561 907-5400
West Palm Beach *(G-19010)*

COAL, MINERALS & ORES, WHOLESALE: Gold Ore

International Weatherization ....G 954 818-3288
Fort Lauderdale *(G-4065)*

COATING COMPOUNDS: Tar

Marbelite International Corp ....G 941 378-0860
Sarasota *(G-16502)*

COATING SVC

5 Star Coatings LLc ....G 850 628-3743
Panama City Beach *(G-13967)*
88 South Atlantic LLC ....G 386 253-0105
Daytona Beach *(G-2619)*
A J W Coatings Corp ....G 786 357-7580
Hialeah Gardens *(G-5697)*
A Tek Steel Industries Inc ....G 561 745-2858
Jupiter *(G-6992)*
A-Brevard Coatings Inc ....G 321 726-0322
Palm Bay *(G-13497)*
Aerospc/Dfense Coatings GA Inc ....G 407 843-1140
Altamonte Springs *(G-25)*
All American Coatings LLC ....G 941 730-9397
Valrico *(G-18514)*
Alternative Coatings of SW Fla ....G 239 537-6153
Naples *(G-11156)*
Americas Blasting Coatings LLC ....G 754 281-6738
Fort Lauderdale *(G-3815)*
Artistic Custom Coatings Inc ....G 941 822-5608
Sarasota *(G-16349)*
Bacc Coatings LLC ....G 239 424-8843
Cape Coral *(G-1387)*
Bobs Custom Coatings LLC ....G 941 745-9659
Bradenton *(G-1001)*
Boca Coatings Inc ....G 561 400-8183
Boca Raton *(G-449)*
Bold City Spray Coatings LLC ....G 904 655-0825
Jacksonville *(G-6224)*
Caliber Coating Inc ....G 813 928-1461
Zephyrhills *(G-19509)*
Captivated Coatings LLC ....G 321 446-6619
Merritt Island *(G-8997)*
Continental Property LLC ....G 817 613-1890
Orlando *(G-12616)*
Copernicco Coatings LLC ....G 407 948-3434
Orlando *(G-12620)*
Creative Coating LLC ....G 407 346-5725
Kissimmee *(G-7234)*
Critical Coatings Inc ....G 813 515-7119
Tampa *(G-17568)*
Custom Powder Coating LLC ....G 386 758-3973
Lake City *(G-7352)*
D and I Trucking Express Inc ....G 786 443-3320
Miami *(G-9425)*
D and S Superior Coatings Inc ....G 360 388-6099
Fort Myers *(G-4424)*
Dew It Right Coatings ....G 504 272-4981
Edgewater *(G-3621)*
Dna Surface Concepts Inc ....F 561 328-7302
Riviera Beach *(G-15320)*
Ds Coatings Inc ....F 321 848-4719
Avon Park *(G-286)*
E G Coatings LLC ....F 407 624-2615
Kissimmee *(G-7240)*
Ecosmart Surface & Coating TEC ....G 402 319-1607
West Palm Beach *(G-18860)*
Emerald Coast Coatings LLC ....F 850 424-5244
Fort Walton Beach *(G-4798)*
Endless Coatings Inc ....G 813 714-5395
Zephyrhills *(G-19516)*
Exotic Custom Coatings ....G 850 358-1492
Lynn Haven *(G-8432)*
Florida Spcialty Coatings Corp ....G 727 224-6883
Melbourne *(G-8834)*
Genteel Coatings LLC ....G 772 708-1781
Inglis *(G-6076)*
Grindhard Coatings Inc ....G 772 221-9986
Stuart *(G-16949)*
Gwb Coatings LLC ....G 407 271-7732
Orlando *(G-12791)*
Industrial Coating Solutions ....G 813 333-8988
Tampa *(G-17780)*
JM Coatings Inc ....G 407 312-1115
Longwood *(G-8297)*
Jmc Coatings LLC ....G 239 260-5451
Naples *(G-11297)*
Kingdom Coatings Inc ....G 904 600-1424
Middleburg *(G-10908)*
Leisure Furniture Powder CT ....F 239 597-4343
Naples *(G-11310)*
M and T Pro Coating Inc ....G 727 272-4620
Clearwater *(G-1766)*
Magnum Coatings Inc ....G 407 704-0786
Brandon *(G-1166)*
Marlin Coatings LLC ....F 850 224-1370
Tallahassee *(G-17295)*
Modern Coating System LLC ....G 786 326-3652
Miami *(G-10033)*
Monteocha Coatings Inc ....G 352 367-3136
Gainesville *(G-4965)*
Nano Activated Coatings Inc ....G 727 437-1099
Clearwater *(G-1800)*
Nano Safe Coatings Inc ....G 561 747-5758
Jupiter *(G-7079)*
North FL Custom Coatings Inc ....G 904 251-4462
Jacksonville *(G-6639)*
Orellana Coatings Inc ....G 305 389-4610
Miami *(G-10114)*
Petes Seal Coating ....G 857 251-1912
Pompano Beach *(G-14789)*
POm Performance Coatings LLC ....G 561 441-7611
West Palm Beach *(G-19000)*
Power Tek LLC ....G 904 814-7007
Saint Augustine *(G-15590)*
Premium Powder Coating ....G 386 789-0216
Deltona *(G-3178)*
Pro Color Coating LLC ....G 941 661-4769
Port Charlotte *(G-14994)*
Protect All Coating Inc ....G 727 278-7454
Saint Petersburg *(G-15894)*
Protective Coatings LLC ....G 407 535-8535
Apopka *(G-174)*
Protek Custom Coatings LLC ....G 850 656-7923
Tallahassee *(G-17312)*
R & H Air Coatings Inc ....G 863 559-6021
Fort Meade *(G-4339)*
Rigid Coatings & Castings Inc ....G 352 396-8738
Apopka *(G-180)*
Rigid Coatings & Castings Screening ....G 352 396-8738
Apopka *(G-181)*
S&H Arcylic Coatings Inc ....G 352 232-1249
Spring Hill *(G-16862)*
Shannon Spray Coatings Inc ....G 850 602-7163
Pensacola *(G-14260)*
Southwest Custom Coatings Inc ....G 239 682-9462
Naples *(G-11410)*
Steven Herranz Custom Coatings ....G 941 915-4686
Palmetto *(G-13824)*
Superior Sealers Coatings Inc ....G 727 807-7851
New Port Richey *(G-11513)*
Tampa Bays Coatings Screening ....G 813 230-1610
Temple Terrace *(G-18381)*
Titans Protective Coatings LLC ....F 561 370-2085
Jupiter *(G-7129)*
Top of The Line Coating Inc ....G 407 485-8546
Orlando *(G-13262)*
Torres & Tavara Coating LLC ....G 904 520-9910
Jacksonville *(G-6936)*
Tropic Seal Industries Inc ....F 239 543-8069
Fort Myers *(G-4639)*
Tropical Custom Coatings ....G 941 475-3663
Port Charlotte *(G-15002)*
U S A Coatings Inc ....F 904 477-0916
Jacksonville *(G-6874)*
Universal Prof Coatings Inc ....G 954 294-5236
Middleburg *(G-10913)*

COATING SVC: Aluminum, Metal Prdts

Coverall Aluminum Inc ....F 321 377-7874
Sanford *(G-16026)*
Every Thing Aluminum ....G 561 202-9900
Lantana *(G-7873)*
Ideal Deals LLC ....C 386 736-1700
Saint Augustine *(G-15553)*
Jnr International Metals Inc ....G 305 671-3509
North Miami Beach *(G-11687)*
Precision Coat of Florida ....G 813 986-1611
Tampa *(G-18004)*

COATING SVC: Metals & Formed Prdts

904 Powderworx LLC ....G 904 290-6383
Jacksonville *(G-6104)*
AAA Custom Powder Coating Inc ....G 305 531-5983
Miami Beach *(G-10634)*
Abakan Inc ....G 786 206-5368
Miami *(G-9052)*
Absolute Powder Coating Inc ....F 954 917-2715
Pompano Beach *(G-14574)*
Accurate Powder Coating Inc ....G 321 269-6972
Titusville *(G-18410)*
Alpha Coatings Inc ....G 850 324-9454
Cantonment *(G-1334)*
Aluminum Powder Coating ....G 305 628-4155
Hialeah *(G-5285)*

Aluminum Powder Coating Lc..............F 305 628-4155
Hialeah *(G-5286)*
American Prtective Coating Inc............E....... 954 561-0999
Fort Lauderdale *(G-3814)*
Americoat Corporation..........................G....... 863 667-1035
Lakeland *(G-7635)*
Ameritech Powder Coating Inc.............F 239 274-8000
Fort Myers *(G-4361)*
Aml Extreme Powdercoating................G....... 904 794-4313
Saint Augustine *(G-15516)*
Arcoat Coatings Corporation................E....... 561 422-9900
West Palm Beach *(G-18799)*
Automated Services Inc........................F 772 461-3388
Fort Pierce *(G-4679)*
Azz Powder Coating - Tampa LLC.........G....... 813 390-2802
Tampa *(G-17451)*
Bad Fish Powder Coat...........................G....... 904 465-8888
Jacksonville *(G-6188)*
Balpro Powder Coating Inc....................F 954 797-0520
Fort Lauderdale *(G-3838)*
Best Engineered Surfc Tech LLC..........D....... 407 932-0008
Kissimmee *(G-7223)*
Best Finisher...F 305 688-8174
Miami *(G-9234)*
Best Powder Coatings Inc.....................E....... 305 836-9460
Hialeah *(G-5323)*
Brothers Powder Coating Inc................G....... 727 846-0717
New Port Richey *(G-11484)*
Brycoat Inc...E....... 727 490-1000
Oldsmar *(G-12212)*
C2 Powder Coating LLC.......................G....... 941 404-2671
Bradenton *(G-1009)*
Centrex Powdercoating Inc...................G....... 813 390-2802
Tampa *(G-17524)*
Coastal Powder Coatings Inc...............G....... 772 283-5311
Palm City *(G-13648)*
Coating Heaven.....................................G....... 321 300-5464
Orlando *(G-12593)*
Corrocoat USA Inc................................F 904 268-4559
Jacksonville *(G-6294)*
Custom Colors Powder Coating............G....... 941 953-7997
Sarasota *(G-16399)*
Cya Powder Coating LLC......................G....... 727 299-9832
Clearwater *(G-1646)*
Dads Powder Coating............................G....... 813 715-6561
Zephyrhills *(G-19513)*
Decortive Electro Coatings Inc.............F 386 255-7878
Daytona Beach *(G-2658)*
Dps Powder Coating..............................G....... 727 573-2797
Clearwater *(G-1658)*
Ds Powder Coating................................G....... 561 660-7835
Lake Worth Beach *(G-7610)*
Elite Powder Coating.............................G....... 786 616-8084
Miami *(G-9517)*
Excell Coatings Inc...............................E....... 321 868-7968
Cape Canaveral *(G-1358)*
Finns Brass and Silver Polsg...............G....... 904 387-1165
Jacksonville *(G-6381)*
Florida Pwdr Cting Shtters Inc.............F 561 588-2410
Lantana *(G-7874)*
Foot-In-Your-mouth Inc........................F 850 438-0876
Pensacola *(G-14157)*
Glassflake International Inc.................G....... 904 268-4000
Jacksonville *(G-6436)*
Glory Sandblasting Inc..........................F 407 422-0078
Orlando *(G-12784)*
Gml Coatings LLC.................................F 941 755-2176
Bradenton *(G-1050)*
High Performance Systems Inc.............E....... 863 294-5566
Winter Haven *(G-19329)*
Innovative Powder Coating Inc..............G....... 954 537-2558
Oakland Park *(G-11813)*
JAS Powder Coating LLC......................G....... 386 410-6675
Edgewater *(G-3627)*
Majestic Coatings Inc............................G....... 561 722-9593
Lake Worth *(G-7568)*
Matrix Coatings Corp.............................F 561 848-1288
West Palm Beach *(G-18945)*
Matrix Coatings Inc................................G....... 561 848-1288
West Palm Beach *(G-18946)*
Mineral Life Intl Inc...............................G....... 305 661-9854
Miami *(G-10026)*
Mpp Coatings Inc...................................G....... 386 334-4484
Port Orange *(G-15025)*
Naples Powder Coating LLC..................G....... 239 352-3500
Naples *(G-11337)*
National Powdr Coating Fla Inc.............G....... 941 756-1322
Bradenton *(G-1084)*
Palm Bay Coml Coatings Inc.................G....... 321 266-2467
Melbourne *(G-8903)*
Performance Powder Coating...............F 407 339-4000
Longwood *(G-8323)*
Powder Coating Factory LLC................G....... 407 286-4550
Orlando *(G-13074)*
Powdertech Plus Inc..............................G....... 904 269-1719
Orange Park *(G-12404)*
Preferred Coatings LLC........................G....... 231 499-3864
Bradenton *(G-1102)*
Prime Tech Coatings Inc.......................G....... 561 844-2312
Mangonia Park *(G-8510)*
Pro Powder Coating Inc.........................F 941 505-8010
Punta Gorda *(G-15221)*
Quality Aerospace Coatings LLC..........G....... 863 619-2628
Lakeland *(G-7774)*
RSR Industrial Coatings Inc..................F 863 537-1110
Bartow *(G-332)*
Special Coatings Inc..............................G....... 239 301-2714
Naples *(G-11414)*
Specialty Powder Coating LLC.............G....... 813 782-2720
Zephyrhills *(G-19536)*
Tampa Bay Powder Coating Inc............G....... 813 964-5667
Tampa *(G-18159)*
Taylors Indus Coatings Inc...................F 800 932-3049
Lake Wales *(G-7525)*
Td Coating Inc.......................................G....... 786 325-4211
North Miami *(G-11658)*
Tolliver Aluminum Service Inc...............F 561 582-8939
West Palm Beach *(G-19067)*
Top Quality Finishers Inc......................G....... 305 688-8174
Miami *(G-10493)*
Trojan Fla Powdr Coating Inc...............E....... 941 351-0500
Sarasota *(G-16316)*
Tua Systems Inc....................................G....... 321 453-3200
Merritt Island *(G-9018)*
Uct Coatings Inc....................................F 772 872-7110
Palm City *(G-13677)*
V and N Advanced Auto Sys LLC..........G....... 321 504-6440
Rockledge *(G-15455)*
Wheelblast Inc.......................................E....... 813 715-7117
Zephyrhills *(G-19542)*
Zps Powdercoating................................G....... 727 465-8131
Largo *(G-8082)*

COATING SVC: Rust Preventative

L A Rust Inc...F 954 749-5009
Sunrise *(G-17140)*

COATING SVC: Silicon

Industrial Nanotech Inc.........................G....... 800 767-3998
Naples *(G-11286)*

COATINGS: Epoxy

Aquatic Technologies Inc......................F 772 225-4389
Jensen Beach *(G-6966)*
Epoxy Floor Coatings LLC....................G....... 920 471-6913
Holiday *(G-5740)*
Epoxy2u of Florida Inc..........................G....... 239 772-0899
Cape Coral *(G-1418)*
Jodan Technology Inc............................G....... 561 515-5556
Lake Worth *(G-7561)*
Pro-Tech Coatings Inc...........................G....... 813 248-1477
Tampa *(G-18018)*

COATINGS: Polyurethane

Soythane Technologies Inc...................F 904 225-1047
Yulee *(G-19501)*

COFFEE MAKERS: Electric

Grimes Aerospace Company................D....... 407 276-6083
Delray Beach *(G-3088)*
Melitta North America Inc.....................D....... 727 535-2111
Clearwater *(G-1779)*
Melitta Usa Inc.......................................D....... 727 535-2111
Clearwater *(G-1780)*

COFFEE SVCS

Potters Coffee Company........................G....... 850 525-1793
Pensacola *(G-14235)*
Royal Cup Inc...G....... 850 436-4435
Pensacola *(G-14254)*

COILS & TRANSFORMERS

Certified Manufacturing Inc..................E....... 850 537-3777
Holt *(G-5948)*
Exxelia Usa Inc......................................E....... 407 695-6562
Longwood *(G-8279)*
OHM Americas LLC...............................F 800 467-7275
Fort Lauderdale *(G-4148)*
Paal Technologies Inc...........................G....... 954 368-5000
Sunrise *(G-17156)*
Spin Magnetics.......................................E....... 863 676-9333
Lake Wales *(G-7520)*
Standard Technology Inc......................F 386 671-7406
Ormond Beach *(G-13402)*

COILS: Pipe

Custom Fab Inc......................................D....... 407 859-3954
Orlando *(G-12639)*

COIN COUNTERS

Klopp International Inc..........................F 813 855-6789
Oldsmar *(G-12240)*
Klopp of Florida Inc...............................G....... 813 855-6789
Oldsmar *(G-12241)*

COINS & TOKENS: Non-Currency

Promo Daddy LLC..................................F 877 557-2336
Melbourne *(G-8913)*

COKE: Calcined Petroleum, Made From Purchased Materials

Oxbow Carbon LLC................................C....... 561 907-5400
West Palm Beach *(G-18977)*
Oxbow Enterprises Intl LLC..................G....... 561 907-5400
West Palm Beach *(G-18978)*

COKE: Petroleum & Coal Derivative

Agrotek Services Incorporated..............G....... 305 599-3818
Miami *(G-9089)*
Bradley Indus Textiles Inc.....................F 850 678-6111
Valparaiso *(G-18508)*

COKE: Petroleum, Not From Refineries

Oxbow Calcining Usa Inc.......................D....... 580 874-2201
West Palm Beach *(G-18976)*

COLOR PIGMENTS

Dry Color USA LLC................................G....... 407 856-7788
Orlando *(G-12689)*

COLOR SEPARATION: Photographic & Movie Film

Columbia Films Inc................................G....... 800 531-3238
Pompano Beach *(G-14641)*

COLORING & FINISHING SVC: Aluminum Or Formed Prdts

Burn Brite Metals Co Inc.......................G....... 727 360-4408
Treasure Island *(G-18474)*
Titan Specialty Cnstr Inc.......................E....... 850 916-7660
Milton *(G-10943)*

COLORS: Pigments, Inorganic

Keystone Color Works Inc.....................G....... 813 250-1313
Tampa *(G-17820)*
Paver Systems LLC...............................E....... 407 859-9117
Orlando *(G-13055)*

COLORS: Pigments, Organic

Keystone Color Works Inc.....................G....... 813 250-1313
Tampa *(G-17820)*

COLUMNS: Concrete

Artistic Columns Inc..............................G....... 954 530-5537
Oakland Park *(G-11780)*
Ornamental Columns and Statues........F 239 482-3911
Fort Myers *(G-4559)*
Renaissance Entp Group LLC...............G....... 941 284-7854
Englewood *(G-3681)*

COLUMNS: Paper-Mache Or Plaster Of Paris

Spaulding Craft Inc................................F 727 726-2316
Safety Harbor *(G-15505)*

COMMERCIAL & OFFICE BUILDINGS RENOVATION & REPAIR

Moody Construction Svcs Inc .... E 941 776-1542
Duette *(G-3562)*

COMMERCIAL ART & GRAPHIC DESIGN SVCS

C & R Designs Inc .... G 321 383-2255
Titusville *(G-18419)*
C & R Designs Printing LLC .... G 321 383-2255
Titusville *(G-18420)*
Continental Printing Svcs Inc .... G 904 743-6718
Jacksonville *(G-6286)*
Customer First Inc Naples .... E 239 949-8518
Bonita Springs *(G-827)*
E3 Graphics Inc .... G 954 510-1302
Coral Springs *(G-2243)*
Fassidigitalcom Inc .... F 954 385-6555
Weston *(G-19124)*
First Edition Design Inc .... G 941 921-2607
Sarasota *(G-16433)*
Graphic Masters Inc .... D 800 230-3873
Miami *(G-9656)*
Graphics Type Color Entps Inc .... E 305 591-7600
Miami *(G-9658)*
Linographics Inc .... F 407 422-8700
Orlando *(G-12913)*
MGM Cargo LLC .... G 407 770-1500
Orlando *(G-12966)*
Military One Click LLC .... G 904 390-7100
Jacksonville *(G-6605)*
Oakhurst Marketing Inc .... G 727 532-8255
Saint Petersburg *(G-15869)*
Proprint of Naples Inc .... F 239 775-3553
Fort Myers *(G-4574)*
Reliance Media Inc .... G 505 243-1821
Apopka *(G-179)*
Sign Producers Inc .... E 407 855-8864
Orlando *(G-13191)*
Sleepy Dragon Studios Inc .... G 561 714-6156
Cutler Bay *(G-2411)*
Sonshine Digital Graphics Inc .... F 904 858-1000
Jacksonville *(G-6784)*
Trial Exhibits Inc .... F 813 258-6153
Tampa *(G-18200)*
Trim-Line of Miami Inc .... F 305 556-6210
Hialeah *(G-5650)*
Two B Printing Inc .... G 954 566-4886
Oakland Park *(G-11851)*

COMMERCIAL CONTAINERS WHOLESALERS

CKS Packaging Inc .... D 407 423-0333
Orlando *(G-12586)*

COMMERCIAL EQPT WHOLESALERS, NEC

C & D Industrial Maint LLC .... F 833 776-5833
Bradenton *(G-1005)*
Decowall .... G 813 886-5226
Tampa *(G-17597)*
Fast Signs .... G 239 498-7200
Bonita Springs *(G-830)*
Lift Aerospace Corp .... F 305 851-5237
Miami *(G-9890)*
Profire Inc .... F 305 665-5313
Pinecrest *(G-14331)*

COMMERCIAL EQPT, WHOLESALE: Mannequins

R P M Industries Inc .... E 315 255-1105
Hobe Sound *(G-5726)*

COMMERCIAL EQPT, WHOLESALE: Neon Signs

Accent Neon & Sign Company .... G 727 784-8414
Palm Harbor *(G-13716)*
Outdoor Images Central Fla Inc .... G 407 825-9944
Orlando *(G-13040)*

COMMERCIAL EQPT, WHOLESALE: Restaurant, NEC

American Metal Products Inc .... G 407 293-0090
Orlando *(G-12471)*

COMMERCIAL LAUNDRY EQPT

Kemco Systems Co LLC .... D 727 573-2323
Clearwater *(G-1748)*
Psp Industrial Laundry Eqp LLC .... F 305 517-1421
Pompano Beach *(G-14821)*

COMMERCIAL PRINTING & NEWSPAPER PUBLISHING COMBINED

Advanced Cmmncations Holdg Inc .... D 954 753-0100
Coral Springs *(G-2213)*
Coinweek LLC .... F 407 786-5555
Longwood *(G-8266)*
Cooke Communications Fla LLC .... D 305 292-7777
Key West *(G-7184)*
Cottonimagescom Inc .... E 305 251-2560
Doral *(G-3311)*
D-R Media and Investments LLC .... D 941 207-1602
Venice *(G-18540)*
Daily News Inc .... G 386 312-5200
Palatka *(G-13476)*
Gadsden County Times Inc .... F 850 627-7649
Quincy *(G-15250)*
Gainesville Sun Publishing Co .... B 352 378-1411
Gainesville *(G-4929)*
Greentree Marketing Svcs Inc .... F 800 557-9567
Fort Lauderdale *(G-4031)*
Herald-Advocate Publishing Co .... F 863 773-3255
Wauchula *(G-18693)*
Horse & Pony .... G 813 986-1003
Thonotosassa *(G-18401)*
Image Experts Inc .... G 727 488-7556
Saint Petersburg *(G-15813)*
Jewish Press Group of Tmpa Bay .... G 727 535-4400
Largo *(G-7988)*
Newspaper Printing Company .... G 727 572-7488
Clearwater *(G-1808)*
Npc of Tampa Inc .... F 813 839-0035
Tampa *(G-17942)*
Observer Media Group Inc .... D 941 366-3468
Sarasota *(G-16529)*
One World Media LLC .... G 786 762-3030
Miami *(G-10104)*
Osceola Woman Newspaper LLC .... G 407 891-9771
Kissimmee *(G-7283)*
Perry Newspapers Inc .... F 850 584-5513
Perry *(G-14309)*
Polk County Democrat .... F 863 533-4183
Winter Haven *(G-19342)*
Printing Services Plus LLC .... F 813 279-1903
Tampa *(G-18016)*
Ronecker Holdings LLC .... G 813 855-5559
Oldsmar *(G-12268)*
Santiago of Key West Inc .... G 305 304-6063
Key West *(G-7202)*
Sarasota Herald-Tribune .... C 941 745-7808
Bradenton *(G-1110)*
Sentinel Cmmnctons News Vntres .... G 352 742-5900
Tavares *(G-18352)*
Sentinel Communicatns News Ven .... A 407 420-5000
Orlando *(G-13174)*
Sep Communications LLC .... F 561 998-0870
Boca Raton *(G-706)*
Southeast Offset Inc .... E 305 623-7788
Miami Lakes *(G-10860)*
The Scranton Times L P .... E 407 377-0400
Orlando *(G-13253)*
Times Publishing Company .... A 727 893-8111
Saint Petersburg *(G-15940)*
Washington County News .... F 850 638-4242
Chipley *(G-1546)*
Whatever Lo Que Sea LLC .... G 786 429-3462
Miami *(G-10599)*
Your Hometown Newspaper Inc .... E 305 669-7355
South Miami *(G-16832)*

COMMODITY CONTRACT TRADING COMPANIES

Heralpin Usa Inc .... G 305 218-0174
Doral *(G-3379)*

COMMON SAND MINING

Bergeron Sand & Rock Min Inc .... E 954 680-6100
Fort Lauderdale *(G-3847)*
ER Jahna Industries Inc .... F 863 675-3942
La Belle *(G-7316)*

COMMUNICATION HEADGEAR: Telephone

C & C Multiservices Corp .... F 305 200-5851
Miami *(G-9292)*
Ingeant Florida LLC .... G 954 868-2879
Coconut Creek *(G-2080)*
Synergy Communication MGT LLC .... F 800 749-3160
Cape Canaveral *(G-1369)*

COMMUNICATIONS EQPT & SYSTEMS, NEC

Nitv Federal Services LLC .... G 561 798-6280
West Palm Beach *(G-18966)*

COMMUNICATIONS EQPT: Microwave

E2g Partners LLC .... E 813 855-2251
Saint Petersburg *(G-15766)*
Millimeter Wave Products Inc .... E 727 563-0034
Saint Petersburg *(G-15854)*
U B Corp .... G 813 884-1463
Tampa *(G-18210)*

COMMUNICATIONS SVCS: Cellular

Comptech Global Solutions Inc .... G 941 766-8100
Port Charlotte *(G-14972)*

COMMUNICATIONS SVCS: Data

American Data Supply Inc .... F 866 650-3282
Clearwater *(G-1579)*
Satcom Scientific Inc .... F 407 856-1050
Orlando *(G-13164)*

COMMUNICATIONS SVCS: Internet Connectivity Svcs

Connected Life Solutions LLC .... F 407 745-1952
Altamonte Springs *(G-38)*
Sipradius LLC .... G 954 290-2434
Coral Springs *(G-2313)*
Wialan Technologies LLC .... E 954 749-3481
Sunrise *(G-17198)*

COMMUNICATIONS SVCS: Internet Host Svcs

Cloud Veneer LLC .... G 305 230-7379
Miami *(G-9364)*

COMMUNICATIONS SVCS: Online Svc Providers

Digi-Net Technologies Inc .... E 352 505-7450
Gainesville *(G-4905)*
Hardware Online Store .... F 954 565-5678
Fort Lauderdale *(G-4042)*
Kenexa Learning Inc .... G 407 548-0434
Lake Mary *(G-7428)*
Netexpressusa Inc .... G 888 575-1245
Fort Myers *(G-4545)*

COMMUNICATIONS SVCS: Proprietary Online Svcs Networks

Working Mother Media Inc .... D 212 351-6400
Winter Park *(G-19461)*

COMMUNICATIONS SVCS: Satellite Earth Stations

Nic4 Inc .... F 877 455-2131
Tampa *(G-17939)*

COMMUNICATIONS SVCS: Telephone, Data

Techcodes LLC .... G 321 529-4122
Titusville *(G-18467)*

COMMUNITY SVCS EMPLOYMENT TRAINING PROGRAM

PHI CHI Foundation Inc .... G 561 526-3401
Margate *(G-8560)*

COMPACT LASER DISCS: Prerecorded

Akman Inc .... G 407 948-0562
Cocoa Beach *(G-2057)*
Captain Zoom Products Inc .... G 561 989-9119
Boca Raton *(G-470)*

Dubhouse Inc ....G.... 954 524-3658
Fort Lauderdale *(G-3951)*

COMPACTORS: Trash & Garbage, Residential

Lean Green Enterprises LLC ....G.... 954 525-2971
Fort Lauderdale *(G-4099)*

COMPOSITION STONE: Plastic

Commercial Stone Cab Fbrctors ....F.... 727 209-1141
Saint Petersburg *(G-15749)*
Commercial Stone Fbrcators Inc ....F.... 727 209-1141
Saint Petersburg *(G-15750)*

COMPOST

Atlas Orgnics Indian River LLC ....F.... 772 563-9336
Vero Beach *(G-18595)*
Consoldted Rsurce Recovery Inc ....E.... 813 262-8404
Tampa *(G-17552)*
Genesis II Systems Inc ....G.... 954 489-1124
Fort Lauderdale *(G-4019)*
Jfe Compost ....F.... 863 532-9629
Okeechobee *(G-12183)*

COMPRESSORS: Air & Gas

Aircel LLC ....E.... 865 681-7066
Naples *(G-11152)*
American Mfg & Mch Inc ....D.... 352 728-2222
Okahumpka *(G-12168)*
Brownies Marine Group Inc ....G.... 954 462-5570
Pompano Beach *(G-14624)*
Danfoss LLC ....C.... 850 504-4800
Tallahassee *(G-17240)*
Greengood Energy Corp ....G.... 954 417-6117
Hollywood *(G-5831)*
Gssc Inc ....G.... 727 461-6044
Clearwater *(G-1706)*
Hankison ....G.... 352 273-1220
Ocala *(G-11965)*
L M Compressor LLC ....G.... 352 484-0850
Ocala *(G-11979)*
Makai Marine Industries Inc ....G.... 954 425-0203
Deerfield Beach *(G-2867)*
Mat Industries LLC ....E.... 847 821-9630
Dania Beach *(G-2470)*
Q Industries Inc ....G.... 954 689-2263
Fort Lauderdale *(G-4187)*
Roper Technologies Inc ....E.... 941 556-2601
Sarasota *(G-16563)*
Southern Air Comprsr Svc Inc ....G.... 863 425-9111
Mulberry *(G-11137)*
Ultimate Compressor LLC ....G.... 305 720-3079
Pembroke Pines *(G-14068)*

COMPRESSORS: Air & Gas, Including Vacuum Pumps

America Energy Inc ....G.... 954 762-7763
Pembroke Pines *(G-14020)*
Interbay Air Compressors Inc ....G.... 813 831-8213
Tampa *(G-17789)*
Vac Cubes Inc ....G.... 727 944-3337
Tarpon Springs *(G-18329)*

COMPRESSORS: Refrigeration & Air Conditioning Eqpt

Advanced Hermetics Inc ....G.... 407 464-0539
Apopka *(G-109)*
Frascold USA Corporation ....G.... 855 547-5600
Jacksonville *(G-6412)*
R & Y Automotive AC Cmpsr ....E.... 305 919-9232
North Miami Beach *(G-11700)*
R & Y Automotive AC Cmpsr ....F.... 305 947-1173
North Miami Beach *(G-11701)*

COMPRESSORS: Repairing

Aap Industrial Inc ....E.... 941 377-4373
Sarasota *(G-16331)*

COMPUTER & COMPUTER SOFTWARE STORES

Bdt Concepts Inc ....G.... 904 730-2590
Jacksonville *(G-6199)*
Brainchild Corp ....E.... 239 263-0100
Naples *(G-11193)*
Brickmed LLC ....G.... 305 774-0081
Miami *(G-9276)*
Computers At Work Inc ....E.... 239 571-1050
Fort Myers *(G-4407)*
Cybertek Computer Systems Inc ....G.... 352 373-9923
Gainesville *(G-4901)*
Information Mgt Svcs Inc ....F.... 386 677-5073
Ormond Beach *(G-13380)*
Intellgent Haring Systems Corp ....F.... 305 668-6102
Miami *(G-9752)*
Vensoft Corp ....F.... 786 991-2080
Miami *(G-10573)*

COMPUTER & COMPUTER SOFTWARE STORES: Peripheral Eqpt

P S T Computers Inc ....G.... 954 566-1600
Fort Lauderdale *(G-4153)*
Thinglobal LLC ....G.... 561 923-8559
Boca Raton *(G-749)*

COMPUTER & COMPUTER SOFTWARE STORES: Personal Computers

Cloudfactors LLC ....G.... 866 779-9974
Plantation *(G-14501)*

COMPUTER & COMPUTER SOFTWARE STORES: Printers & Plotters

Light Source Business Systems ....F.... 772 562-5046
Port Saint Lucie *(G-15120)*

COMPUTER & COMPUTER SOFTWARE STORES: Software & Access

Advanced Software Inc ....F.... 215 369-7800
Jacksonville Beach *(G-6937)*
Express Badging Services Inc ....F.... 321 784-5925
Cocoa Beach *(G-2062)*

COMPUTER & COMPUTER SOFTWARE STORES: Software, Bus/Non-Game

Telit Iot Platforms LLC ....C.... 561 982-9898
Boca Raton *(G-744)*

COMPUTER & COMPUTER SOFTWARE STORES: Software, Computer Game

Origin Pc LLC ....E.... 305 971-1000
Miami *(G-10119)*

COMPUTER & COMPUTER SOFTWARE STORES: Word Process Eqpt/Splys

Toner Technologies Inc ....G.... 561 547-9710
Boynton Beach *(G-970)*

COMPUTER & DATA PROCESSING EQPT REPAIR & MAINTENANCE

Computer Technician Inc ....G.... 941 479-0242
Palmetto *(G-13793)*

COMPUTER & OFFICE MACHINE MAINTENANCE & REPAIR

Buscar Inc ....G.... 813 877-7272
Tampa *(G-17491)*
Cybertek Computer Systems Inc ....G.... 352 373-9923
Gainesville *(G-4901)*
Fis Avantgard LLC ....E.... 484 582-2000
Jacksonville *(G-6388)*
Kyocera Dcment Sltons Sthast L ....F.... 772 562-0511
Fort Pierce *(G-4710)*
Lightning Phase II Inc ....G.... 727 539-1800
Seminole *(G-16749)*

COMPUTER & SFTWR STORE: Modem, Monitor, Terminal/Disk Drive

Incity Security Inc ....F.... 561 306-9228
West Palm Beach *(G-18902)*
Kos Industries Inc ....G.... 863 318-1511
Winter Haven *(G-19333)*

COMPUTER DISKETTES WHOLESALERS

Tdk Electronics Inc ....F.... 561 509-7771
Ocean Ridge *(G-12080)*

COMPUTER FACILITIES MANAGEMENT SVCS

Arma Holdings Inc ....E.... 813 402-0667
Tampa *(G-17434)*

COMPUTER FORMS

Zilla Inc ....F.... 904 610-1436
Orange Park *(G-12414)*

COMPUTER GRAPHICS SVCS

A Sanborn Corporation ....E.... 727 397-3073
Madeira Beach *(G-8445)*
Maddys Print Shop LLC ....G.... 954 749-0440
Fort Lauderdale *(G-4108)*
Naylor LLC ....C.... 800 369-6220
Gainesville *(G-4969)*
Networked Solutions Inc ....G.... 321 259-3242
Rockledge *(G-15438)*
Sep Communications LLC ....F.... 561 998-0870
Boca Raton *(G-706)*
Signsations Inc ....G.... 561 989-1900
Boca Raton *(G-712)*
Soren Technologies Inc ....F.... 954 236-9998
Plantation *(G-14555)*
Webcom Group Inc ....A.... 904 680-6600
Jacksonville *(G-6907)*

COMPUTER INTERFACE EQPT: Indl Process

Contrologix LLC ....E.... 407 878-2774
Sanford *(G-16023)*
Intellgent Instrumentation Inc ....F.... 520 573-0887
Naples *(G-11288)*
Mmats Inc ....E.... 561 842-0600
Jupiter *(G-7076)*
Noxtak Corp ....G.... 786 586-7927
Pembroke Pines *(G-14052)*

COMPUTER PAPER WHOLESALERS

Computer Forms & Supplies ....G.... 727 535-0422
Largo *(G-7926)*

COMPUTER PERIPHERAL EQPT, NEC

2n USA LLC ....G.... 954 606-6602
Doral *(G-3214)*
Amag Technology Inc ....G.... 407 549-3882
Lake Mary *(G-7399)*
Arco Computer Products LLC ....G.... 954 925-2688
Hollywood *(G-5774)*
Best Iproductscom LLC ....G.... 386 402-7800
Edgewater *(G-3613)*
Boca Systems Inc ....C.... 561 998-9600
Boca Raton *(G-459)*
Braden & Son Construction Inc ....G.... 239 694-8600
Fort Myers *(G-4380)*
Carlos Abascal ....G.... 973 696-1971
Miami *(G-9320)*
Centurion Holdings I LLC ....E.... 636 349-5425
Tampa *(G-17526)*
Component General Inc ....E.... 727 376-6655
Odessa *(G-12112)*
Compro Solution ....G.... 407 733-4130
Sanford *(G-16021)*
Conduent Image Solutions Inc ....C.... 407 849-0279
Orlando *(G-12613)*
Donovan Home Services LLC ....F.... 813 644-9488
Saint Petersburg *(G-15762)*
Electro-Comp Services Inc ....E.... 727 532-4262
Clearwater *(G-1667)*
Electronics For Imaging Inc ....G.... 800 624-5999
Jacksonville Beach *(G-6943)*
Graphic Data Inc ....G.... 954 493-8003
Margate *(G-8547)*
Integrated Dealer Systems Inc ....F.... 800 962-7872
Oldsmar *(G-12236)*
Iter3d Inc ....G.... 718 473-0114
Aventura *(G-274)*
L3 Technologies Inc ....G.... 321 409-6122
Melbourne *(G-8864)*
Lift Spectrum Technologies LLC ....G.... 407 228-8343
Orlando *(G-12910)*
Micro Crane Inc ....G.... 954 755-2225
Coral Springs *(G-2285)*

Nemal Electronics Intl Inc.....E.......305 899-0900
North Miami *(G-11648)*
OConnell Team LLC.....G.......772 201-3848
Port Saint Lucie *(G-15126)*
Select Engineered Systems Inc.....E.......305 823-5410
Hialeah *(G-5613)*
Signature Computer Svcs Inc.....G.......954 421-0950
Boca Raton *(G-710)*
Smdk Corp.....E.......239 444-1736
Naples *(G-11406)*
Suncoast Identification Tech.....G.......239 277-9922
Fort Myers *(G-4616)*
Synthes3d USA Inc.....F.......321 946-1303
Orlando *(G-13237)*
Technetics Group Daytona Inc.....C.......386 253-0628
Daytona Beach *(G-2722)*
Technologies For Tomorrow Inc.....F.......850 478-5222
Pensacola *(G-14273)*
Thinglobal LLC.....G.......561 923-8559
Boca Raton *(G-749)*
Thinktech Corporation.....F.......954 501-3034
Margate *(G-8569)*
Tropical Pcb Design Services.....F.......561 784-9536
Loxahatchee *(G-8366)*
Verifone Inc.....C.......727 535-9200
Clearwater *(G-1932)*
Verifone Inc.....C.......800 837-4366
Coral Springs *(G-2326)*
Western Microsystems Inc.....E.......800 547-7082
Jacksonville *(G-6912)*

COMPUTER PERIPHERAL EQPT, WHOLESALE

Two Way Radio Gear Inc.....F.......800 984-1534
Fort Pierce *(G-4764)*

COMPUTER PERIPHERAL EQPT: Decoders

McEs LLC.....G.......321 363-4977
Sanford *(G-16086)*

COMPUTER PERIPHERAL EQPT: Encoders

AMC Development Group LLC.....G.......305 597-8641
Doral *(G-3245)*

COMPUTER PERIPHERAL EQPT: Graphic Displays, Exc Terminals

Eizo Rugged Solutions Inc.....E.......407 262-7100
Altamonte Springs *(G-43)*
In Touch Electronics LLC.....G.......813 818-9990
Tampa *(G-17776)*
McKenny Printing Enterprise.....G.......727 420-4944
Saint Petersburg *(G-15853)*
Speedpro Imaging St Petersburg.....G.......727 266-0956
Saint Petersburg *(G-15922)*
Suncoast Led Displays LLC.....F.......727 683-2777
Palm Harbor *(G-13763)*

COMPUTER PERIPHERAL EQPT: Input Or Output

American Fibertek Inc.....E.......732 302-0660
Saint Petersburg *(G-15699)*
Datamax International Corp.....B.......407 578-8007
Orlando *(G-12651)*
Datamax-Oneil Corporation.....C.......800 816-9649
Orlando *(G-12652)*
Icloak Inc.....G.......407 422-0876
Orlando *(G-12820)*

COMPUTER PROGRAMMING SVCS

Actigraph LLC.....F.......850 332-7900
Pensacola *(G-14080)*
Ademero Inc.....F.......863 937-0272
Lakeland *(G-7625)*
Asrc Aerospace Corp.....C.......321 867-1462
Kennedy Space Center *(G-7150)*
Atris Technology LLC.....F.......352 331-3100
Gainesville *(G-4880)*
Automation Consulting Inc.....F.......850 477-6477
Pensacola *(G-14095)*
Cellec Games Inc.....G.......407 476-3590
Apopka *(G-120)*
Eizo Rugged Solutions Inc.....E.......407 262-7100
Altamonte Springs *(G-43)*
Engineerica Systems Inc.....F.......407 542-4982
Oviedo *(G-13428)*
Fathym Inc.....F.......303 905-4402
Palmetto *(G-13797)*
Hispacom Inc.....F.......954 255-2622
Coral Springs *(G-2255)*
Information Builders Inc.....E.......407 804-8000
Lake Mary *(G-7424)*
Irvin Technologies Inc.....E.......866 245-9356
Winter Springs *(G-19476)*
Kamel Software Inc.....G.......407 672-0202
Oviedo *(G-13444)*
Landtech Data Corporation.....F.......561 790-1265
Royal Palm Beach *(G-15474)*
Lockheed Martin Corporation.....B.......813 855-5711
Oldsmar *(G-12245)*
Maxit Corporation.....G.......904 998-9520
Ponte Vedra Beach *(G-14946)*
Maydone Ltd Liability Company.....G.......407 399-3287
Orlando *(G-12955)*
Mercury Systems Inc.....E.......352 371-2567
Gainesville *(G-4961)*
Montague Enterprises Inc.....G.......239 631-5292
Naples *(G-11330)*
Ncg Medical Systems Inc.....E.......407 788-1906
Orlando *(G-12996)*
Praxis Software Inc.....F.......407 226-5691
Orlando *(G-13078)*
Tahoe Interactive Systems Inc.....G.......614 891-2323
Punta Gorda *(G-15242)*
Tier5 Technical Services.....G.......904 435-3484
Jacksonville *(G-6855)*
Trivantis Corporation.....D.......513 929-0188
Deerfield Beach *(G-2929)*
Unicomp Corp of America.....G.......954 755-1710
Coral Springs *(G-2325)*
Universal Software Solutions.....G.......727 298-8877
Clearwater *(G-1929)*
Western Microsystems Inc.....E.......800 547-7082
Jacksonville *(G-6912)*
Willsonet Inc.....E.......813 336-8175
Tampa *(G-18259)*

COMPUTER RELATED MAINTENANCE SVCS

Hatalom Corporation.....E.......407 567-2556
Orlando *(G-12796)*

COMPUTER SOFTWARE DEVELOPMENT

Axiom Services Inc.....E.......727 442-7774
Clearwater *(G-1595)*
Hatalom Corporation.....E.......407 567-2556
Orlando *(G-12796)*
It Labs LLC.....D.......310 490-6142
Palm Beach Gardens *(G-13598)*
Pantograms Mfg Co Inc.....E.......813 839-5697
Tampa *(G-17973)*
Retail Cloud Technologies LLC.....D.......727 210-1700
Clearwater *(G-1859)*
Servos and Simulation Inc.....G.......407 807-0208
Longwood *(G-8336)*
Summation Research Inc.....E.......321 254-2580
Melbourne *(G-8949)*
Telit Iot Platforms LLC.....C.......561 982-9898
Boca Raton *(G-744)*

COMPUTER SOFTWARE DEVELOPMENT & APPLICATIONS

Aqualogix Inc.....F.......858 442-4550
Palm Beach Gardens *(G-13567)*
Bca Technologies Inc.....F.......407 659-0653
Maitland *(G-8459)*
Caduceus International Pubg.....F.......866 280-2900
Gainesville *(G-4891)*
Carlees Creations Inc.....G.......786 232-0050
Miami *(G-9319)*
Cloudfactors LLC.....G.......866 779-9974
Plantation *(G-14501)*
Common Sense Publishing LLC.....C.......561 510-1713
Delray Beach *(G-3063)*
Hensoldt Avionics Usa LLC.....G.......941 306-1328
Sarasota *(G-16459)*
Igovsolutions LLC.....E.......407 574-3056
Lake Mary *(G-7423)*
Konnected Inc.....F.......407 286-3138
Orlando *(G-12876)*
Lott Qa Group Inc.....G.......201 693-2224
Bonita Springs *(G-844)*
One Milo Inc.....F.......305 804-0266
Miami *(G-10102)*
Original Impressions LLC.....C.......305 233-1322
Weston *(G-19156)*
Qsrr Corporation.....G.......305 322-9867
Hallandale Beach *(G-5205)*
RTC Software LLC.....G.......407 765-7462
Winter Garden *(G-19284)*
SC Parent Corporation.....D.......703 351-0200
Miami *(G-10308)*
SC Purchaser Corporation.....D.......703 351-0200
Miami *(G-10309)*
Starboard Consulting LLC.....E.......407 622-6414
Longwood *(G-8340)*
Streamline Technologies Inc.....G.......407 679-1696
Winter Springs *(G-19485)*
Techderm LLC.....G.......407 795-1517
Palm Beach Gardens *(G-13631)*
VIP Software Corporation.....F.......813 837-4347
Lakeland *(G-7830)*

COMPUTER SOFTWARE SYSTEMS ANALYSIS & DESIGN: Custom

Informulate LLC.....G.......866 222-2307
Oviedo *(G-13439)*
Roper Technologies Inc.....E.......941 556-2601
Sarasota *(G-16563)*
Utilitech Inc.....F.......863 767-0600
Wauchula *(G-18695)*

COMPUTER STORAGE DEVICES, NEC

Computer Technician Inc.....G.......941 479-0242
Palmetto *(G-13793)*
Computers At Work Inc.....E.......239 571-1050
Fort Myers *(G-4407)*
EMC Quality Group Corp.....G.......786 501-5891
Miami Lakes *(G-10785)*
EMC Representations Corp.....G.......305 305-1776
Hialeah *(G-5394)*
EMC Roofing LLC.....G.......786 597-6604
Tampa *(G-17635)*
EMC South Florida LLC.....G.......786 352-9327
South Miami *(G-16816)*
EMC Ticketing LLC.....G.......813 792-1234
Land O Lakes *(G-7853)*
Gtechusa Inc.....G.......786 281-1803
Hollywood *(G-5834)*
Hatalom Corporation.....E.......407 567-2556
Orlando *(G-12796)*
Hill Donnelly Corporation.....D.......800 525-1242
Tampa *(G-17755)*
Lucid Technology Inc.....G.......727 487-2430
Clearwater *(G-1764)*
Quantem Fbo Group Kssimmee LLC.....G.......407 846-8001
Kissimmee *(G-7293)*
Quantum Assets LLC.....G.......786 484-1187
Miami *(G-10220)*
Quantum Creations LLC.....F.......786 233-6769
Miami Gardens *(G-10752)*
Quantum Limit Partners LLC.....E.......954 849-3720
Fort Lauderdale *(G-4194)*
Quantum Reflex Integration Inc.....E.......352 228-0766
Crystal River *(G-2380)*
Quantum Safety Services Inc.....G.......786 420-0735
Miami *(G-10221)*
Quantum Servicing Corporation.....G.......305 229-6675
Miami *(G-10222)*
Quantum-L/S Dna Labs Intl.....G.......407 246-0484
Orlando *(G-13104)*
Quiantum Creative Group Inc.....G.......954 557-6777
North Bay Village *(G-11595)*
Refly of Miami Inc.....F.......786 762-2748
Miami *(G-10246)*
Rela USA LLC.....G.......786 656-5069
Miami *(G-10249)*
Seagate Productions LLC.....G.......561 506-7750
Boynton Beach *(G-957)*
Simply Group II LLC.....G.......407 960-4690
Sanford *(G-16116)*
Totally Storage Inc.....F.......407 472-6000
Lake Mary *(G-7455)*
Wheeler Emergency Management C.....G.......850 372-4174
Marianna *(G-8587)*

COMPUTER STORAGE UNITS: Auxiliary

IMC Storage.....G.......305 418-0069
Doral *(G-3389)*

COMPUTER SYSTEMS ANALYSIS & DESIGN

Applied Systems Integrator Inc.....G.......321 259-6106
Melbourne *(G-8770)*

COMPUTER TERMINALS

Biosculptor Corporation ....G....... 305 823-8300
Hialeah *(G-5326)*
Verifone Inc ....C....... 800 837-4366
Coral Springs *(G-2326)*

COMPUTER-AIDED MANUFACTURING SYSTEMS SVCS

Edumatics Inc ....F....... 407 656-0661
Orlando *(G-12699)*

COMPUTERS, NEC

9t Technology LLC ....G....... 904 703-9214
Jacksonville *(G-6106)*
Advanced Electronics Labs Inc ....G....... 305 255-6401
Pinecrest *(G-14322)*
Alienware Corp ....G....... 786 260-9625
Miami *(G-9105)*
Ayon Cybersecurity Inc ....E....... 321 953-3033
Cocoa *(G-1998)*
Bio-Logic Systems Corp ....D....... 847 949-0456
Orlando *(G-12515)*
Black Diamond Systems Corp ....D....... 917 539-7309
Vero Beach *(G-18601)*
Buscar Inc ....G....... 813 877-7272
Tampa *(G-17491)*
C & R Designs Inc ....G....... 321 383-2255
Titusville *(G-18419)*
C & R Designs Printing LLC ....G....... 321 383-2255
Titusville *(G-18420)*
Computer Technician Inc ....G....... 941 479-0242
Palmetto *(G-13793)*
Contec Americas Inc ....D....... 321 728-0172
Melbourne *(G-8796)*
Enterprise Tech Partners LLC ....F....... 918 851-3285
Orlando *(G-12713)*
EPC Inc ....F....... 636 443-1999
Tampa *(G-17646)*
Essentials ....G....... 386 677-7444
Ormond Beach *(G-13368)*
Faratech LLC ....G....... 954 651-7287
Sunrise *(G-17122)*
Geekshive Inc ....F....... 888 797-4335
Miami *(G-9620)*
General Dynmics Mssion Systems ....E....... 407 823-7000
Orlando *(G-12779)*
Ibi Systems Inc ....G....... 954 978-9225
Fort Lauderdale *(G-4054)*
Industrial Technology LLC ....F....... 877 224-5534
Fort Myers *(G-4494)*
Konnected Inc ....F....... 407 286-3138
Orlando *(G-12876)*
Kos Industries Inc ....G....... 863 318-1511
Winter Haven *(G-19333)*
Lockheed Martin Corporation ....B....... 813 855-5711
Oldsmar *(G-12245)*
M & S Computer Products Inc ....G....... 561 244-5400
Boynton Beach *(G-930)*
McEs LLC ....G....... 321 363-4977
Sanford *(G-16086)*
Morgan Technical Services ....G....... 772 466-5757
Fort Pierce *(G-4719)*
Oriental Red Apple LLC ....G....... 646 853-1468
Miami *(G-10118)*
Orion Technologies LLC ....E....... 407 476-2120
Orlando *(G-13030)*
P S T Computers Inc ....G....... 954 566-1600
Fort Lauderdale *(G-4153)*
Palm Tree Computer Systems Inc ....F....... 407 359-3356
Oviedo *(G-13452)*
PC Masters Corp ....G....... 305 582-5595
Miami Lakes *(G-10835)*
Phintec LLC ....G....... 321 214-2500
Orlando *(G-13066)*
Phone Wave Inc ....G....... 352 683-8101
Spring Hill *(G-16858)*
Ra Co AMO Inc ....F....... 561 626-7232
Palm Beach Gardens *(G-13620)*
Refly of Miami Inc ....F....... 786 762-2748
Miami *(G-10246)*
Smartmatic Corporation ....F....... 561 862-0747
Boca Raton *(G-721)*
Superchips Inc ....E....... 407 585-7000
Sanford *(G-16123)*
Syn-Tech Systems Inc ....C....... 850 878-2558
Tallahassee *(G-17332)*
Tactical Phaser Corp ....G....... 321 262-4140
Oviedo *(G-13460)*
United Wireless Tech Inc ....F....... 561 302-9350
Boca Raton *(G-769)*
Versatus Hpc Inc ....F....... 561 544-8862
Boca Raton *(G-777)*
Vinland International Inc ....E....... 954 316-2007
Plantation *(G-14566)*

COMPUTERS, NEC, WHOLESALE

Advanced Software Inc ....F....... 215 369-7800
Jacksonville Beach *(G-6937)*
Genel/Landec Inc ....G....... 305 591-9990
Doral *(G-3361)*

COMPUTERS, PERIPHERALS & SOFTWARE, WHOLESALE: Printers

Bluestar Latin America Inc ....E....... 800 354-9776
Miramar *(G-10975)*
Hut Global Inc ....G....... 561 571-2523
Boca Raton *(G-560)*
Toners Plus LLC ....G....... 407 756-5787
Orlando *(G-13261)*

COMPUTERS, PERIPHERALS & SOFTWARE, WHOLESALE: Software

Above Property LLC ....E....... 239 263-7406
Naples *(G-11146)*
Aci Worldwide Inc ....A....... 239 403-4600
Naples *(G-11147)*
Beachchip Technologies LLC ....G....... 727 643-8106
Clearwater *(G-1605)*
Brickmed LLC ....G....... 305 774-0081
Miami *(G-9276)*
Davison Publishing Company LLC ....G....... 407 380-8900
Orlando *(G-12656)*
Incity Security Inc ....F....... 561 306-9228
West Palm Beach *(G-18902)*
Intellgent Haring Systems Corp ....F....... 305 668-6102
Miami *(G-9752)*
Wialan Technologies LLC ....E....... 954 749-3481
Sunrise *(G-17198)*

COMPUTERS: Mini

Acer Latin America Inc ....G....... 305 392-7000
Doral *(G-3223)*
Artex Computer Llc ....G....... 407 844-2253
Miami *(G-9173)*
Energybionics LLC ....G....... 561 229-4985
Stuart *(G-16938)*

COMPUTERS: Personal

Appel 26 Corp ....G....... 305 672-8645
Miami Beach *(G-10643)*
Apple Spice - Jax ....G....... 904 328-6542
Jacksonville *(G-6160)*
Atlantic Multi Family I LLC ....F....... 301 233-1261
Parkland *(G-13988)*
Dell USA LP ....F....... 512 728-8391
Miami *(G-9450)*
Fun Electronics Inc ....F....... 305 933-4646
Miami *(G-9603)*
Gold Network of Miami Inc ....G....... 305 343-7355
Hialeah *(G-5433)*
Industry Standard Technology ....G....... 941 355-2100
Sarasota *(G-16235)*
Integrated Dealer Systems Inc ....F....... 800 962-7872
Oldsmar *(G-12236)*
Motorola Solutions Inc ....G....... 407 562-4000
Lake Mary *(G-7437)*
Nortech Engineering Inc ....G....... 508 823-8520
Port Charlotte *(G-14991)*
Qtronics Inc ....G....... 850 267-0102
Santa Rosa Beach *(G-16165)*

CONCENTRATES, DRINK

Atlantic Bev Group USA Inc ....G....... 239 334-3016
Fort Myers *(G-4368)*
Banana Bag Solutions LLC ....G....... 321 917-4334
Satellite Beach *(G-16648)*
Coca-Cola Company ....G....... 407 565-2465
Apopka *(G-123)*
Coca-Cola Company ....G....... 954 961-8564
Hollywood *(G-5803)*
Prima Foods International Inc ....G....... 352 732-9148
Ocala *(G-12031)*
Rehydrade LLC ....G....... 561 419-5656
Boca Raton *(G-687)*

CONCRETE BUGGIES: Powered

Sicoma North America Inc ....G....... 800 921-7559
Clearwater *(G-1877)*

CONCRETE MIXERS

Ficap ....F....... 407 302-3316
Lake Mary *(G-7415)*
Tarmac America Inc ....G....... 386 427-0438
Edgewater *(G-3637)*

CONCRETE PLANTS

Tensik Inc ....G....... 954 937-9505
Winter Haven *(G-19363)*

CONCRETE PRDTS

A & C Concrete Products Inc ....G....... 305 232-1631
Miami *(G-9030)*
Allstone Casting ....F....... 305 528-1677
Medley *(G-8607)*
Americast Precast Generator ....F....... 772 971-1958
Fort Pierce *(G-4675)*
Architectural Masters LLC ....G....... 239 290-2250
Leesburg *(G-8143)*
Argos USA LLC ....E....... 678 368-4300
Newberry *(G-11551)*
Barreiro Concrete Mtls Inc ....E....... 305 805-0095
Princeton *(G-15182)*
Bayshore Con Prdcts/Chspake In ....D....... 757 331-2300
Maitland *(G-8457)*
Bayshore Concrete Products Inc ....G....... 239 543-3001
Fort Myers *(G-4373)*
Bayshore Precast Concrete Inc ....G....... 239 543-3001
Fort Myers *(G-4374)*
Bonsal American Inc ....G....... 904 783-0605
Jacksonville *(G-6225)*
Bonsal American Inc ....G....... 863 967-9100
Auburndale *(G-230)*
Cement Products Inc ....E....... 727 868-9226
Port Richey *(G-15045)*
Cemex Cnstr Mtls ATL LLC ....D....... 561 833-5555
West Palm Beach *(G-18837)*
Cemex Cnstr Mtls PCF LLC ....D....... 561 833-5555
West Palm Beach *(G-18840)*
Cemex Materials LLC ....D....... 561 746-4556
Jupiter *(G-7018)*
Cemex Materials LLC ....D....... 561 793-1442
West Palm Beach *(G-18842)*
Consolidated Minerals Inc ....F....... 352 365-6522
Leesburg *(G-8148)*
Coreslab Strctures Orlando Inc ....E....... 407 855-3191
Okahumpka *(G-12170)*
Cornerstone Interlocking Inc ....G....... 863 944-1609
Lakeland *(G-7663)*
Crom Corporation ....B....... 352 372-3436
Gainesville *(G-4900)*
Durlach Holdings Inc ....F....... 941 751-1672
Bradenton *(G-1032)*
Elite Cast Stone Inc ....G....... 305 904-3032
Ruskin *(G-15483)*
Ersion Interntnal Ctrl Systems ....G....... 800 821-7462
Tampa *(G-17648)*
Finfrock Design Inc ....E....... 407 293-4000
Apopka *(G-140)*
First Coast Concrete Pumping ....G....... 904 262-6488
Jacksonville *(G-6385)*
Florida Engineered Constru ....G....... 727 863-7451
Hudson *(G-6024)*
Florida Lift Stations Corp ....G....... 305 887-8485
Medley *(G-8652)*
Florida Vault Service Inc ....G....... 727 527-4992
Saint Petersburg *(G-15787)*
Forterra Pipe & Precast LLC ....F....... 386 734-6228
Deland *(G-2979)*
Forterra Pressure Pipe Inc ....C....... 386 328-8841
Palatka *(G-13480)*
Fsp-Ges Inc ....E....... 352 799-7933
Brooksville *(G-1230)*
Gate Petroleum Company ....G....... 904 396-0517
Jacksonville *(G-6421)*
Gulf Coast Precast Inc ....E....... 239 337-0021
Fort Myers *(G-4476)*
Hall Fountains Inc ....F....... 954 484-8530
Fort Lauderdale *(G-4039)*
I A I ....G....... 561 488-6369
Boca Raton *(G-561)*
Imperial Industries Inc ....F....... 954 917-4114
Pompano Beach *(G-14729)*

PRODUCT

Insteel Wire Products Company............E....... 904 275-2100
Sanderson *(G-15982)*
J R C Concrete Products Inc...............G....... 850 456-9665
Pensacola *(G-14181)*
Jahna Concrete Inc..............................F....... 863 453-4353
Avon Park *(G-289)*
Janusz Art Stone Inc..........................G....... 305 754-7171
Miami *(G-9787)*
Lambert Corporation Florida..............E....... 407 841-2940
Orlando *(G-12889)*
Landmark Precast LLC.........................F....... 305 242-8888
Homestead *(G-5979)*
Leesburg Concrete Company Inc..........E....... 352 787-4177
Leesburg *(G-8163)*
Lindsay Precast Inc..............................E....... 800 669-2278
Alachua *(G-11)*
Lotts Concrete Products Inc................E....... 407 656-2112
Winter Garden *(G-19275)*
Lrg Solutions Inc..................................F....... 321 978-1050
Rockledge *(G-15429)*
Metro Roof Tile Inc..............................F....... 863 467-0042
Medley *(G-8690)*
Monroe Concrete Products...................D....... 305 296-5606
Key West *(G-7197)*
Native Nursery.......................................G....... 941 625-2022
Punta Gorda *(G-15216)*
North Florida Vault LLC........................F....... 386 303-2267
Lake City *(G-7372)*
Oldcastle Apg South Inc......................A....... 813 367-9780
Palm Beach Gardens *(G-13614)*
Oldcastle Apg South Inc.......................F....... 863 421-7422
Haines City *(G-5144)*
Oldcastle Architectural Inc..................E....... 813 886-7761
Tampa *(G-17950)*
Oldcastle Building Produc...................G....... 352 377-1699
Gainesville *(G-4975)*
Oldcastle Coastal Inc...........................G....... 813 886-7761
Tampa *(G-17953)*
Oldcastle Coastal Inc...........................G....... 813 783-1970
Zephyrhills *(G-19528)*
Oldcastle Infrastructure Inc...............F....... 800 642-1540
Wildwood *(G-19198)*
Olde World Craftsmen Inc...................G....... 239 229-3806
Fort Myers *(G-4557)*
Paver Systems LLC..............................E....... 561 844-5202
Riviera Beach *(G-15359)*
Paver Systems LLC..............................E....... 407 859-9117
Orlando *(G-13055)*
Pfci LLC...E....... 239 435-3575
Naples *(G-11361)*
Pollak Industries...................................G....... 850 438-4651
Pensacola *(G-14234)*
Ponce De Leon Construction...............G....... 786 554-3685
Miami *(G-10178)*
Quikrete Companies LLC.....................G....... 305 681-8664
Miami *(G-10226)*
Quikrete Companies LLC.....................D....... 863 665-5127
Lakeland *(G-7775)*
Ras Concrete Construction Inc............E....... 239 775-3709
Naples *(G-11381)*
Rinker Materials....................................F....... 305 345-4127
Medley *(G-8717)*
Rj Staab Stone Company Fla LLC.........G....... 352 222-5989
Williston *(G-19214)*
Roof Tile Inc..E....... 863 467-0042
Okeechobee *(G-12190)*
Rudders River Rock...............................G....... 239 574-5656
Cape Coral *(G-1462)*
Silk Safari Inc..G....... 561 689-3882
West Palm Beach *(G-19034)*
Stabil Concrete Products LLC..............D....... 727 321-6000
Saint Petersburg *(G-15925)*
Structural Cnstr Orlando Inc................E....... 407 383-9719
Oviedo *(G-13458)*
Superior Cast Stone LLC.......................F....... 863 634-4771
Okeechobee *(G-12193)*
Suwannee American Cem Co LLC........D....... 352 569-5393
Sumterville *(G-17069)*
Tremron LLC...F....... 863 491-0990
Arcadia *(G-206)*
US Paverscape LLC...............................D....... 772 223-7287
Stuart *(G-17044)*
US Precast Corporation.........................G....... 305 885-8471
Medley *(G-8752)*
Wall Way Corporation............................F....... 305 484-7600
Medley *(G-8754)*
Wesco Partners Inc................................E....... 941 484-8224
Sarasota *(G-16325)*
Zoho Stone LLC......................................G....... 727 230-6956
Palm Harbor *(G-13770)*

CONCRETE PRDTS, PRECAST, NEC

A-1 City Wide Sewer Service.................F....... 352 236-4456
Silver Springs *(G-16780)*
Aercon Florida LLC................................D....... 863 422-6360
Haines City *(G-5137)*
Allied Precast Products Co....................E....... 407 745-5605
Orlando *(G-12460)*
American Concrete Industries...............E....... 772 464-1187
Fort Pierce *(G-4674)*
Anderson Columbia Co Inc....................F....... 352 463-6342
Chiefland *(G-1531)*
Artistic Fence Corporation....................G....... 305 805-1976
Hialeah *(G-5307)*
Atlantic Cast Prcast S Fla LLC...............E....... 954 564-6245
Oakland Park *(G-11783)*
Atlantic Concrete Products Inc.............D....... 941 355-2988
Sarasota *(G-16356)*
Atlantic Tng LLC.....................................E....... 941 355-2988
Sarasota *(G-16357)*
Bailey Sigler Inc......................................G....... 386 428-5566
New Smyrna Beach *(G-11526)*
Building Blocks Gfrc LLC........................D....... 312 243-9960
Kissimmee *(G-7226)*
Cast Systems LLC....................................E....... 941 625-3474
Port Charlotte *(G-14968)*
Castone Creations Inc............................F....... 305 599-3367
Doral *(G-3294)*
Cement Industries Inc.............................D....... 239 332-1440
Fort Myers *(G-4391)*
Cement Precast Products Inc..................E....... 352 372-0953
Gainesville *(G-4894)*
Cemex Cnstr Mtls Fla LLC.......................F....... 800 992-3639
Sarasota *(G-16381)*
Coastal Concrete Products LLC..............E....... 239 208-4079
Fort Myers *(G-4402)*
Coastal Precast of Florida.......................E....... 239 432-0667
Fort Myers *(G-4404)*
Commercial Concrete Pdts Inc................E....... 813 659-3707
Plant City *(G-14419)*
Concraft Inc..G....... 561 689-0149
Greenacres *(G-5078)*
Concrete Pdts of Palm Bches In..............E....... 561 842-2743
Riviera Beach *(G-15313)*
Coreslab Structures Miami Inc................B....... 305 823-8950
Medley *(G-8635)*
Coreslab Structures Tampa Inc...............C....... 602 237-3875
Tampa *(G-17556)*
D Maxwell Company Inc............................G....... 727 868-9151
Port Richey *(G-15048)*
DC Kerckhoff Company..............................F....... 239 597-7218
Naples *(G-11223)*
Delzotto Products Florida Inc..................D....... 352 351-3834
Ocala *(G-11919)*
F T F Construction Company....................F....... 772 571-1850
Fellsmere *(G-3725)*
Florida Engineered Constru.....................C....... 813 621-4641
Seffner *(G-16726)*
Florida Silica Sand Company....................E....... 954 923-8323
Fort Lauderdale *(G-4005)*
Florida Silica Sand Company....................F....... 954 923-8323
Fort Lauderdale *(G-4006)*
Forterra Pipe & Precast LLC....................E....... 863 401-6800
Winter Haven *(G-19323)*
Gate Precast Company..............................C....... 407 847-5285
Kissimmee *(G-7249)*
International Casting Corp.......................E....... 305 558-3515
Miami Lakes *(G-10798)*
J & N Stone Inc..E....... 941 924-6200
Sarasota *(G-16474)*
Johnson Bros Prcsion Prcast Pd..............E....... 239 947-6734
Bonita Springs *(G-842)*
Keystone Precast & Columns Cor...........G....... 305 216-5375
Homestead *(G-5975)*
Mack Concrete Industries Inc.................C....... 352 742-2333
Astatula *(G-213)*
Mother Earth Stone LLC...........................F....... 407 878-2854
Sanford *(G-16091)*
Oldcastle Retail Inc....................................B....... 954 971-1200
Pompano Beach *(G-14778)*
Phoscrete Corporation................................E....... 561 420-0595
Pompano Beach *(G-14793)*
Polly Concrete Products Co.......................F....... 850 897-3314
Niceville *(G-11571)*
Pre-Cast Specialties Inc.............................C....... 954 781-4040
Sanford *(G-16104)*
Pre-Cast Specialties LLC.............................F....... 954 781-4040
Sanford *(G-16105)*
Precast Designs Inc......................................F....... 407 856-5444
Orlando *(G-13079)*
Precast Solution System Inc.......................F....... 813 949-7929
Odessa *(G-12142)*
Pro-Crete Material Corporation..................E....... 352 748-1505
Orlando *(G-13094)*
Quality Precast & Company........................F....... 407 877-1000
Winter Garden *(G-19282)*
Rj Staab Stone Co...G....... 352 377-3313
Williston *(G-19213)*
Royal Concrete Concepts Inc......................E....... 561 689-5398
Jupiter *(G-7106)*
S & S Precast Inc..F....... 239 992-8685
Bonita Springs *(G-852)*
Solar Manufacturing Inc...............................E....... 954 973-8488
Pompano Beach *(G-14855)*
Southeastern Pipe Precast Inc.....................E....... 850 587-7473
Cantonment *(G-1348)*
Spancrete of Florida LLC..............................E....... 863 655-1515
Sebring *(G-16710)*
Spancrete Southeast Inc...............................G....... 863 655-1515
Sebring *(G-16711)*
Treasure CST Curb & Therm Plas..................G....... 772 287-0391
Palm City *(G-13676)*
Trenwa Inc..F....... 863 666-1680
Lakeland *(G-7825)*
Urban Stone Works...F....... 305 754-7171
Miami *(G-10549)*
US Concrete Products Corp...........................D....... 954 973-0368
Pompano Beach *(G-14904)*

CONCRETE REINFORCING MATERIAL

Wire Products Inc of Florida.........................E....... 954 772-1477
Fort Lauderdale *(G-4326)*

CONCRETE: Asphaltic, Not From Refineries

Advanta Asphalt Inc..G....... 386 362-5580
Live Oak *(G-8226)*

CONCRETE: Dry Mixture

Bonsal American Inc.......................................G....... 813 621-2427
Tampa *(G-17482)*
Bonsal American Inc.......................................G....... 850 476-4223
Pensacola *(G-14103)*

CONCRETE: Ready-Mixed

A & J Ready Mix Inc...G....... 863 228-7154
Clewiston *(G-1976)*
A L Materials..G....... 863 551-0980
Winter Haven *(G-19293)*
A Materials Group Inc......................................G....... 352 463-1254
Fanning Springs *(G-3721)*
A Materials Group Inc......................................D....... 386 758-3164
Lake City *(G-7344)*
A-Mari-Mix LLC..F....... 305 603-9134
Miami *(G-9045)*
Adonel Con Pmpg Fnshg S Fla In....................D....... 305 392-5416
Miami *(G-9071)*
All Star Materials LLC......................................F....... 352 598-7590
Ocala *(G-11869)*
Anderson Columbia Co Inc...............................F....... 352 463-6342
Chiefland *(G-1531)*
Argos..E....... 678 368-4300
Jacksonville *(G-6167)*
Argos..F....... 352 376-6491
Gainesville *(G-4875)*
Argos Ready Mix...G....... 941 629-7713
Port Charlotte *(G-14962)*
Argos Ready Mix LLC..G....... 727 321-4667
Saint Petersburg *(G-15709)*
Argos USA..G....... 863 687-1898
Lakeland *(G-7639)*
Argos USA LLC..E....... 850 872-1209
Panama City *(G-13864)*
Argos USA LLC..E....... 850 235-9600
Panama City Beach *(G-13970)*
Argos USA LLC..G....... 850 576-4141
Tallahassee *(G-17223)*
Argos USA LLC..E....... 407 299-9924
Orlando *(G-12487)*
Argos USA LLC..G....... 866 322-4547
Sarasota *(G-16348)*
Argos USA LLC..E....... 813 962-3213
Tampa *(G-17432)*
B M H Concrete Inc...F....... 561 615-0011
West Palm Beach *(G-18809)*
Banaszak Concrete Corp.....................................E....... 954 476-1004
Davie *(G-2502)*
Bell Concrete Products Inc..................................E....... 352 463-6103
Bell *(G-341)*

Berkshire Managment Associates ....G 305 883-3277
Miami *(G-9233)*
Bet Er Mix Inc ....G 352 799-5538
Brooksville *(G-1214)*
BET-Er Mix Holding Inc ....G 727 868-9226
Port Richey *(G-15043)*
Better Mix ....F 800 232-6833
Hudson *(G-6016)*
Brooks Welding & Concrete Shop ....F 850 984-5279
Panacea *(G-13859)*
C Mix Corp ....F 954 670-0208
Fort Lauderdale *(G-3878)*
Cement Miami Terminal ....G 305 221-2502
Miami *(G-9334)*
Cement Products Inc ....E 727 868-9226
Port Richey *(G-15045)*
Cement-It Inc ....G 954 565-7875
Fort Lauderdale *(G-3889)*
Cemex Inc ....E 813 663-9712
Tampa *(G-17521)*
Cemex Cement Inc ....C 904 296-2400
Orange Park *(G-12384)*
Cemex Cement Inc ....C 352 867-5794
Ocala *(G-11897)*
Cemex Cement Inc ....C 727 327-5730
Saint Petersburg *(G-15742)*
Cemex Cement Inc ....C 407 877-9623
Winter Garden *(G-19255)*
Cemex Cement Inc ....C 850 942-4582
Tallahassee *(G-17231)*
Cemex Cnstr Mtls Fla LLC ....F 305 247-3011
Homestead *(G-5957)*
Cemex Cnstr Mtls Fla LLC ....G 321 636-5121
Cape Canaveral *(G-1355)*
Cemex Cnstr Mtls Fla LLC ....F 904 880-4958
Jacksonville *(G-6257)*
Cemex Cnstr Mtls Fla LLC ....G 321 632-0500
Cocoa *(G-2004)*
Cemex Cnstr Mtls Fla LLC ....E 800 992-3639
Fort Pierce *(G-4685)*
Cemex Cnstr Mtls Fla LLC ....G 954 977-9222
Pompano Beach *(G-14632)*
Cemex Cnstr Mtls Fla LLC ....G 561 996-5249
Belle Glade *(G-346)*
Cemex Cnstr Mtls Fla LLC ....F 352 330-1115
Wildwood *(G-19192)*
Cemex Cnstr Mtls Fla LLC ....G 352 746-0136
Lecanto *(G-8131)*
Cemex Cnstr Mtls Fla LLC ....F 813 621-5575
Tampa *(G-17522)*
Cemex Cnstr Mtls Fla LLC ....F 561 745-5240
Jupiter *(G-7017)*
Cemex Cnstr Mtls Fla LLC ....G 352 793-3048
Bushnell *(G-1315)*
Cemex Cnstr Mtls Fla LLC ....F 904 213-8860
Orange Park *(G-12385)*
Cemex Cnstr Mtls Fla LLC ....G 904 827-0369
Saint Augustine *(G-15528)*
Cemex Cnstr Mtls Fla LLC ....F 561 833-5555
West Palm Beach *(G-18839)*
Cemex Cnstr Mtls Fla LLC ....G 772 461-7102
Fort Pierce *(G-4686)*
Cemex Cnstr Mtls Fla LLC ....G 863 419-2875
Davenport *(G-2476)*
Cemex Cnstr Mtls Fla LLC ....G 800 992-3639
Oldsmar *(G-12213)*
Cemex Cnstr Mtls Fla LLC ....F 561 832-6646
West Palm Beach *(G-18838)*
Cemex Concrete Company ....F 305 558-0255
Medley *(G-8628)*
Cemex Corp ....D 561 820-8613
Miami *(G-9335)*
Cemex Materials LLC ....D 386 775-0790
Deland *(G-2963)*
Cemex Materials LLC ....D 305 223-6934
Miami *(G-9336)*
Cemex Materials LLC ....D 321 636-5121
Cocoa *(G-2005)*
Cemex Materials LLC ....D 305 821-5661
Medley *(G-8629)*
Cemex Materials LLC ....D 772 287-0502
Stuart *(G-16921)*
Cemex Materials LLC ....D 305 818-4941
Medley *(G-8630)*
Cemex Materials LLC ....D 904 296-2400
Jacksonville *(G-6258)*
Cemex Materials LLC ....D 941 722-4578
Palmetto *(G-13790)*
Cemex Materials LLC ....D 954 523-9978
Fort Lauderdale *(G-3890)*
Cemex Materials LLC ....E 407 322-8862
Sanford *(G-16008)*
Cemex Materials LLC ....D 850 769-2243
Panama City *(G-13878)*
Cemex Materials LLC ....F 863 688-2306
Lakeland *(G-7655)*
Cemex Materials LLC ....D 954 431-7655
Pembroke Pines *(G-14026)*
Cemex Materials LLC ....D 813 620-3760
Tampa *(G-17523)*
Cemex Materials LLC ....D 239 332-0135
Fort Myers *(G-4392)*
Cemex Materials LLC ....D 561 881-4472
Riviera Beach *(G-15311)*
Cemex Materials LLC ....E 863 678-3945
Lake Wales *(G-7501)*
Cemex Materials LLC ....C 561 833-5555
West Palm Beach *(G-18841)*
Cemex Materials LLC ....D 561 746-4556
Jupiter *(G-7018)*
Cemex Materials LLC ....D 352 435-0783
Okahumpka *(G-12169)*
Cemex Materials LLC ....D 305 558-0315
Miami *(G-9337)*
Cemex Materials LLC ....D 561 793-1442
West Palm Beach *(G-18842)*
Cemex Materials LLC ....D 561 743-4039
Jupiter *(G-7019)*
Central Concrete Supermix Inc ....F 954 480-9333
Deerfield Beach *(G-2799)*
Colonial Ready Mix LLC ....G 941 698-4022
Placida *(G-14395)*
Columbia Ready Mix Concrete ....F 386 755-2458
Lake City *(G-7350)*
Coreyco LLC ....G 813 469-1203
Wesley Chapel *(G-18742)*
Couch Ready Mix Usa Inc ....E 850 236-9042
Cantonment *(G-1337)*
Crestview Ready Mix Inc ....F 850 682-6117
Crestview *(G-2345)*
Crh Americas Inc ....D 843 672-5553
Lakeland *(G-7665)*
Cylinders On Cemex Gas ....G 305 818-4952
Doral *(G-3318)*
Davis Concrete Inc ....E 727 733-3141
Clearwater *(G-1649)*
Devcon International Corp ....C 954 926-5200
Boca Raton *(G-499)*
Drake Inc ....F 239 590-9199
Fort Myers *(G-4436)*
Drake Ready Mix Inc ....D 239 590-9199
Fort Myers *(G-4437)*
Dunco Rock & Gravel Inc ....G 813 752-5622
Plant City *(G-14428)*
Eagle Ready Mix ....G 239 732-9333
Naples *(G-11233)*
Eagle Ready Mix LLC ....E 239 693-1500
Fort Myers *(G-4439)*
Florida Block & Ready Mix LLC ....E 727 585-2852
Clearwater *(G-1686)*
Florida Block & Ready Mix LLC ....E 813 623-3700
Tampa *(G-17672)*
Florida Concrete Recycling ....F 352 495-2044
Archer *(G-208)*
Florida Mining Enterprises LLC ....G 904 270-2646
Atlantic Beach *(G-222)*
Florida Rock ....F 352 472-4722
Newberry *(G-11556)*
Florida Rock Concrete ....G 407 877-6180
Clermont *(G-1960)*
Florida Rock Concrete Inc ....G 904 355-1781
Jacksonville *(G-6401)*
Florida Rock Industries ....G 352 854-6468
Ocala *(G-11947)*
Fort Walton Concrete Co ....F 850 243-8114
Fort Walton Beach *(G-4800)*
Frako Concrete Services Inc ....G 305 551-8196
Miami *(G-9597)*
Frontier Ready Mix Inc ....F 727 544-1000
Pinellas Park *(G-14350)*
Griswold Ready Mix Con Inc ....F 904 751-3796
Jacksonville *(G-6453)*
Gulf Coast Ready Mix LLC ....E 352 621-3900
Homosassa *(G-6004)*
Hanson Lehigh Cement ....F 800 665-6006
Cape Canaveral *(G-1359)*
Hare Lumber & Ready Mix Inc ....F 863 983-8725
Clewiston *(G-1982)*
Hicks Industries Inc ....E 863 425-4155
Mulberry *(G-11125)*
Instacrete Mobile Concrete ....F 813 956-3741
Zephyrhills *(G-19523)*
Jahna Concrete Inc ....E 863 453-4353
Avon Park *(G-290)*
Jahna Concrete Inc ....F 863 453-4353
Avon Park *(G-289)*
Jamo Inc ....D 305 885-3444
Medley *(G-8676)*
Kmr Concrete Inc ....E 863 519-9077
Bartow *(G-321)*
Kuhlman Corporation ....G 239 334-3111
Fort Myers *(G-4514)*
Larrys Mobilcrete Inc ....G 352 336-2525
Gainesville *(G-4950)*
Legacy Vulcan LLC ....G 407 855-9902
Orlando *(G-12903)*
Legacy Vulcan LLC ....G 850 914-9661
Panama City *(G-13925)*
Legacy Vulcan LLC ....G 407 321-5323
Sanford *(G-16080)*
Legacy Vulcan LLC ....G 727 321-4667
Saint Petersburg *(G-15837)*
Legacy Vulcan LLC ....G 352 376-2182
Gainesville *(G-4953)*
Legacy Vulcan LLC ....G 352 473-4258
Keystone Heights *(G-7209)*
Legacy Vulcan LLC ....G 850 951-0562
Defuniak Springs *(G-2944)*
Legacy Vulcan LLC ....G 863 687-7625
Lakeland *(G-7734)*
Legacy Vulcan LLC ....F 386 659-2477
Grandin *(G-5047)*
Legacy Vulcan LLC ....G 850 997-1490
Lloyd *(G-8244)*
Lehigh Cement Company LLC ....E 813 248-4000
Tampa *(G-17841)*
Lehigh Cement Company LLC ....E 954 581-2812
Davie *(G-2545)*
Lehigh Cement Company LLC ....E 321 323-5039
Cape Canaveral *(G-1363)*
Litecrete Inc ....E 305 500-9373
Miami *(G-9901)*
Maschmeyer Concrete Co Fla ....F 386 668-7801
Debary *(G-2751)*
Maschmeyer Concrete Co Fla ....F 407 339-5311
Longwood *(G-8310)*
Maschmeyer Concrete Co Fla ....E 561 848-9112
Lake Park *(G-7476)*
Maschmeyer Concrete Co Fla ....F 863 420-6800
Davenport *(G-2481)*
Metropolitan Mix ....G 904 242-0743
Ponte Vedra Beach *(G-14947)*
Miami Mix Corp ....G 954 704-9682
Miramar *(G-11016)*
Mix It Loop Inc ....G 407 902-9334
Orlando *(G-12973)*
Mix It Up ....G 251 767-1771
Fort Walton Beach *(G-4816)*
Mix Masters Inc ....G 386 846-9239
Port Orange *(G-15024)*
Ocala Concrete Services LLC ....G 352 694-4300
Ocala *(G-12009)*
Okeechobee Asphalt & Ready Mix ....G 863 763-7373
Okeechobee *(G-12187)*
Oldcastle Coastal ....F 813 621-2427
Tampa *(G-17952)*
Organizacion Marketing Mix LLC ....F 407 924-2709
Kissimmee *(G-7279)*
Ozinga South Florida Inc ....G 786 422-4694
Davie *(G-2563)*
Panama City Concrete Inc ....G 850 851-3637
Panama City *(G-13934)*
Pensacola Ready Mix LLC ....F 850 477-0343
Cantonment *(G-1345)*
Phoscrete Corporation ....E 561 420-0595
Pompano Beach *(G-14793)*
Polimix Usa LLC ....F 305 888-4752
Medley *(G-8708)*
Preferred Materials Inc ....E 904 288-0244
Lutz *(G-8412)*
Preferred Materials Inc ....G 407 578-1200
Orlando *(G-13081)*
Prestige/Ab Ready Mix LLC ....E 561 478-9980
West Palm Beach *(G-19006)*
Prestige/Ab Ready Mix LLC ....E 407 654-3330
Clermont *(G-1971)*
Prestige/Ab Ready Mix LLC ....E 321 751-2566
Melbourne *(G-8911)*
Prestige/Ab Ready Mix LLC ....F 407 847-7229
Orlando *(G-13084)*

Prestige/Ab Ready Mix LLC ....E.... 772 468-4666
Fort Pierce *(G-4736)*
Pro-Mix Inc ....G.... 305 556-6699
Medley *(G-8711)*
Quality Block & Supply Inc ....G.... 863 425-3070
Mulberry *(G-11133)*
Quality Ready Mix Inc ....B.... 561 833-5555
West Palm Beach *(G-19014)*
Ready Mix Usa LLC ....F.... 850 227-7677
Port Saint Joe *(G-15083)*
Rinker Materials Corp ....G.... 352 799-7881
Brooksville *(G-1264)*
Rinker Materials Corp ....G.... 305 386-0078
Miami *(G-10265)*
Rinker Materials Corp ....G.... 386 775-0790
Deland *(G-3012)*
Rios Con Pmpg & Rentl Inc ....E.... 305 888-7909
Medley *(G-8718)*
RMC Ewell Inc ....E.... 850 879-0959
Niceville *(G-11573)*
RMC Ewell Inc ....G.... 850 863-5040
Fort Walton Beach *(G-4828)*
RMC Ewell Inc ....F.... 407 282-0984
Orlando *(G-13143)*
Rudys Ready Mix ....G.... 305 382-9283
Miami *(G-10287)*
South Florida Con Block LLC ....G.... 305 408-3444
Miami *(G-10382)*
South Florida Concrete & Rdymx ....E.... 305 888-0420
Medley *(G-8725)*
Superior Redi-Mix ....F.... 850 575-1532
Midway *(G-10918)*
Supermix Concrete ....E.... 954 858-0780
Miami *(G-10439)*
Supermix Concrete ....D.... 305 265-4465
Fort Pierce *(G-4753)*
Sweet Mix LLC ....G.... 561 227-8332
West Palm Beach *(G-19054)*
Symrna Ready Mix ....F.... 352 330-1001
Wildwood *(G-19202)*
T Bower Enterprises Inc ....G.... 863 984-3050
Polk City *(G-14568)*
Taco Mix Corp ....G.... 239 498-9448
Naples *(G-11433)*
Takeria Mix Inc ....F.... 904 338-9157
Jacksonville *(G-6834)*
Tarmac Florida Inc ....F.... 954 481-2800
Deerfield Beach *(G-2923)*
Titan America LLC ....G.... 386 734-5526
Deland *(G-3022)*
Titan America LLC ....F.... 561 842-5309
Mangonia Park *(G-8514)*
Titan America LLC ....E.... 305 761-1944
Medley *(G-8736)*
Titan America LLC ....F.... 954 481-2800
Medley *(G-8737)*
Titan America LLC ....E.... 954 426-8407
Deerfield Beach *(G-2928)*
Titan America LLC ....C.... 305 364-2200
Medley *(G-8738)*
Titan Florida LLC ....A.... 800 588-3939
Medley *(G-8739)*
Tradeland Americas Inc ....G.... 786 718-1490
South Miami *(G-16831)*
Universal Concrete & Ready Mix ....E.... 305 512-3400
Hialeah *(G-5663)*
Universal Concrete & Ready Mix ....F.... 305 888-4101
Medley *(G-8749)*
Vulcan Materials Company ....G.... 352 473-4258
Keystone Heights *(G-7212)*
Vulcan Materials Company ....F.... 205 298-3000
Tampa *(G-18248)*
Vulcan Materials Company ....G.... 863 675-5866
Moore Haven *(G-11090)*
We Mix You Match Inc ....G.... 561 615-0253
West Palm Beach *(G-19085)*
Whites Holdings Inc Centl Fla ....F.... 727 863-6072
Port Richey *(G-15078)*
Wpr Inc ....E.... 850 626-7713
Milton *(G-10948)*
Xpress Materials LLC ....F.... 352 748-2200
Wildwood *(G-19206)*

CONDENSERS & CONDENSING UNITS: Air Conditioner

Heat-Pipe Technology Inc ....E.... 813 470-4250
Tampa *(G-17749)*
Icecold2 LLC ....G.... 855 326-2665
Tampa *(G-17767)*
Preble Enterprises Inc ....G.... 954 480-6919
Deerfield Beach *(G-2889)*

CONDENSERS: Heat Transfer Eqpt, Evaporative

Cook Manufacturing Group Inc ....F.... 863 546-6183
Frostproof *(G-4857)*

CONDENSERS: Motors Or Generators

Air Temp of America Inc ....G.... 850 340-3017
Panama City *(G-13861)*

CONDUITS & FITTINGS: Electric

Camp Aircraft Inc ....F.... 727 397-6076
Saint Petersburg *(G-15734)*
Cantex Inc ....C.... 863 967-4161
Auburndale *(G-231)*
Reditek Corporation ....F.... 954 781-1069
Pompano Beach *(G-14826)*

CONFECTIONS & CANDY

Amazon Origins Inc ....G.... 239 404-1818
Naples *(G-11159)*
B & B Bons LLC ....G.... 954 940-4900
Fort Lauderdale *(G-3836)*
Behrs Chocolates By Design ....G.... 407 648-2020
Orlando *(G-12510)*
Florida Candy Factory Inc ....F.... 727 446-0024
Clearwater *(G-1687)*
Hoffman Commercial Group Inc ....E.... 561 967-2213
Greenacres *(G-5082)*
Jne Candy Co LLC ....F.... 407 622-6292
Orlando *(G-12857)*
Nestle Usa Inc ....D.... 813 301-4638
Thonotosassa *(G-18403)*
P B C Central ....G.... 407 648-2020
Orlando *(G-13041)*
Ricos Tostaditos Inc ....F.... 305 885-7392
Hialeah *(G-5601)*
Send It Sweetly LLC ....G.... 239 850-5500
Cape Coral *(G-1468)*
Signature Brands LLC ....D.... 352 622-3134
Ocala *(G-12051)*
Tropical Taffy Naples Inc ....G.... 239 571-3761
Naples *(G-11445)*

CONFETTI: Made From Purchased Materials

Parti Line International Inc ....F.... 504 522-0300
Largo *(G-8023)*

CONNECTORS & TERMINALS: Electrical Device Uses

ABB Installation Products Inc ....D.... 386 677-9110
Ormond Beach *(G-13347)*
Molex LLC ....F.... 727 521-2700
Pinellas Park *(G-14370)*
National Std Parts Assoc Inc ....D.... 850 456-5771
Pensacola *(G-14211)*
Polaris Sales Co Inc ....C.... 727 372-1703
Odessa *(G-12140)*
Topflite Manufacturing Inc ....F.... 800 219-2601
Miami *(G-10494)*

CONNECTORS: Electrical

Gulf Connectors Inc ....G.... 239 657-2986
Immokalee *(G-6050)*
Multi Contact USA ....G.... 561 738-5637
Boynton Beach *(G-935)*
Tensolite LLC ....A.... 904 829-5600
Saint Augustine *(G-15626)*

CONNECTORS: Electronic

Altelix LLC ....F.... 561 660-9434
Boca Raton *(G-415)*
Arrowhead Global LLC ....G.... 727 497-7340
Clearwater *(G-1589)*
Backbone Interconnect LLC ....E.... 954 800-4749
Sunrise *(G-17093)*
Benchmark Connector Corp ....E.... 954 746-9929
Sunrise *(G-17096)*
Bocatech Inc ....G.... 954 397-7070
Deerfield Beach *(G-2788)*
Carlisle Interconnect Tech Inc ....A.... 904 829-5600
Saint Augustine *(G-15526)*
Diversfied Mtl Specialists Inc ....G.... 941 244-0935
North Venice *(G-11757)*
Eagle I Tech Inc ....E.... 772 221-8188
Palm City *(G-13651)*
Interconnect Cable Tech Corp ....D.... 352 796-1716
Brooksville *(G-1237)*
Lextm3 Systems LLC ....F.... 954 888-1024
Davie *(G-2546)*
Logus Manufacturing Corp ....E.... 561 842-3550
West Palm Beach *(G-18934)*
Molex LLC ....F.... 727 521-2700
Pinellas Park *(G-14370)*
Rde Connectors & Cables Inc ....F.... 954 746-6400
Sunrise *(G-17168)*
Rpp Devices ....G.... 772 807-7098
Port Saint Lucie *(G-15140)*
Stratos Light Wave Inc ....G.... 321 308-4100
Melbourne *(G-8946)*
Sv Microwave Inc ....C.... 561 840-1800
West Palm Beach *(G-19052)*
Teledyne Instruments Inc ....C.... 386 236-0780
Daytona Beach *(G-2725)*
Winchster Interconnect Rf Corp ....E.... 800 881-9689
Melbourne *(G-8975)*

CONNECTORS: Power, Electric

National Std Parts Assoc Inc ....D.... 850 456-5771
Pensacola *(G-14211)*

CONSTRUCTION & MINING MACHINERY WHOLESALERS

American Silica Holdings LLC ....G.... 352 796-8855
Brooksville *(G-1211)*
Emergency Standby Power LLC ....F.... 850 259-2304
Fort Walton Beach *(G-4799)*
Liebherr Cranes Inc ....G.... 305 817-7500
Hialeah *(G-5486)*
Mwi Corporation ....F.... 239 337-4747
Fort Myers *(G-4542)*
Pantropic Power Inc ....D.... 954 797-7972
Fort Lauderdale *(G-4156)*
Tradewinds Power Corp ....F.... 863 382-2166
Sebring *(G-16716)*

CONSTRUCTION EQPT: Airport

Apogee Services Inc ....F.... 561 441-5354
Boynton Beach *(G-878)*

CONSTRUCTION EQPT: Attachments

Advanced Infrstrcture Tech Inc ....G.... 239 992-1700
Bonita Springs *(G-810)*
Masaka LLC ....F.... 786 800-8337
Doral *(G-3426)*
Patriot Foundation Systems LLC ....G.... 352 668-4842
San Antonio *(G-15975)*
Pemberton Inc ....E.... 407 831-6688
Longwood *(G-8322)*

CONSTRUCTION EQPT: Attachments, Backhoe Mounted, Hyd Pwrd

Zennergy LLC ....F.... 813 382-3460
Tampa *(G-18280)*

CONSTRUCTION EQPT: Backhoes, Tractors, Cranes & Similar Eqpt

Bravo Inc ....G.... 239 471-8127
Cape Coral *(G-1394)*
Supertrak Inc ....F.... 941 505-7800
Punta Gorda *(G-15239)*

CONSTRUCTION EQPT: Cranes

Coastal Crane and Rigging Inc ....G.... 850 460-1766
Santa Rosa Beach *(G-16155)*

CONSTRUCTION EQPT: Graders, Road

Duncan and Sons Cnstr Eqp Inc ....F.... 305 216-3115
Miami Gardens *(G-10738)*

CONSTRUCTION EQPT: Ladder Ditchers, Vertical Boom Or Wheel

General Clamp Industries Inc ....F.... 407 859-6000
Orlando *(G-12777)*

CONSTRUCTION EQPT: Roofing Eqpt

Gardner Asphalt Corporation ....C....... 813 248-2101
Tampa *(G-17704)*

CONSTRUCTION EQPT: Trucks, Off-Highway

Iler Group Inc...F 813 600-1738
Wesley Chapel *(G-18749)*

CONSTRUCTION EQPT: Wellpoint Systems

Environmental Mfg & Supply Inc...........F 850 547-5287
Bonifay *(G-803)*

CONSTRUCTION EQPT: Wrecker Hoists, Automobile

Country Man S...G....... 352 472-8699
Trenton *(G-18482)*
Javidco Scratch N Dent...........................G....... 727 494-7611
Port Richey *(G-15057)*
U Got Recovery Inc..................................F 407 343-9919
Kissimmee *(G-7305)*
Wanted Dead or Alive Inc.........................G....... 239 633-5080
North Fort Myers *(G-11609)*

CONSTRUCTION MATERIALS, WHOL: Concrete/Cinder Bldg Prdts

Florida Amico...G....... 863 688-9256
Lakeland *(G-7689)*

CONSTRUCTION MATERIALS, WHOLESALE: Aggregate

LV Thompson Inc.....................................C....... 813 248-3456
Tampa *(G-17866)*

CONSTRUCTION MATERIALS, WHOLESALE: Air Ducts, Sheet Metal

Engineered Air Systems Inc ....F 813 881-9555
Tampa *(G-17641)*

CONSTRUCTION MATERIALS, WHOLESALE: Awnings

Business World Trading Inc...................F 305 238-0724
Miami *(G-9288)*
Iis Incorporated..G....... 561 547-4297
Boynton Beach *(G-918)*

CONSTRUCTION MATERIALS, WHOLESALE: Block, Concrete & Cinder

Bluegrass Materials Co LLC ....E 919 781-4550
Jacksonville *(G-6216)*
Supermix Concrete...................................E 954 858-0780
Miami *(G-10439)*

CONSTRUCTION MATERIALS, WHOLESALE: Blocks, Building, NEC

Masters Block - North LLC.......................G....... 407 212-7704
Saint Cloud *(G-15658)*

CONSTRUCTION MATERIALS, WHOLESALE: Brick, Exc Refractory

Lhoist North America Tenn Inc.................F 352 629-7990
Ocala *(G-11983)*

CONSTRUCTION MATERIALS, WHOLESALE: Building Stone, Granite

Creta Granite & Marble Inc......................G....... 954 956-9993
Pompano Beach *(G-14650)*
LAS & JB Inc ....G....... 772 672-5315
Fort Pierce *(G-4711)*

CONSTRUCTION MATERIALS, WHOLESALE: Building Stone, Marble

Architctural MBL Importers Inc ....E 941 365-3552
Sarasota *(G-16347)*
Azul Stone LLC ....F 561 655-9385
West Palm Beach *(G-18806)*
C L Industries Inc.......................................E 800 333-2660
Orlando *(G-12540)*
Exotic Countertop Inc................................G....... 954 979-8188
Pompano Beach *(G-14685)*
Fantasy Marble & Granite Inc ....G....... 954 788-0433
Pompano Beach *(G-14687)*
Quality Custom Cabinet Design ....G....... 352 728-4292
Leesburg *(G-8169)*
Stone and Equipment Inc..........................E 305 665-0002
Miami *(G-10416)*
Stone Trend International Inc ....E 941 927-9113
Sarasota *(G-16605)*

CONSTRUCTION MATERIALS, WHOLESALE: Building, Exterior

Arso Enterprises Inc..................................E 305 681-2020
Opa Locka *(G-12290)*
Best Manufacturing Company..................F 954 922-1443
Hollywood *(G-5786)*
Florida Engineered Constru......................C 813 621-4641
Seffner *(G-16726)*

CONSTRUCTION MATERIALS, WHOLESALE: Building, Interior

E-Stone USA Corp ....D 863 655-1273
Sebring *(G-16687)*

CONSTRUCTION MATERIALS, WHOLESALE: Cement

Argos USA LLC..E 352 472-4722
Newberry *(G-11552)*
Devcon International Corp.......................C 954 926-5200
Boca Raton *(G-499)*

CONSTRUCTION MATERIALS, WHOLESALE: Ceramic, Exc Refractory

Cug LLC...F 786 858-0499
Plantation *(G-14505)*

CONSTRUCTION MATERIALS, WHOLESALE: Concrete Mixtures

Cemex Cnstr Mtls Fla LLC ....G....... 321 632-0500
Cocoa *(G-2004)*
Cemex Cnstr Mtls Fla LLC ....F 561 832-6646
West Palm Beach *(G-18838)*
Cemex Materials LLC................................D 386 775-0790
Deland *(G-2963)*
Cemex Materials LLC................................D 772 287-0502
Stuart *(G-16921)*
Cemex Materials LLC................................D 941 722-4578
Palmetto *(G-13790)*
Cemex Materials LLC................................D 954 523-9978
Fort Lauderdale *(G-3890)*
Cemex Materials LLC................................D 954 431-7655
Pembroke Pines *(G-14026)*
Jahna Concrete Inc....................................F 863 453-4353
Avon Park *(G-289)*

CONSTRUCTION MATERIALS, WHOLESALE: Door Frames

Davanti Doors Llc ....G....... 239 842-8341
Fort Myers *(G-4426)*

CONSTRUCTION MATERIALS, WHOLESALE: Drywall Materials

Doral Building Supply Corp......................F 305 471-9797
Doral *(G-3332)*
Grabber Construction Pdts Inc.................G....... 813 249-2281
Tampa *(G-17723)*

CONSTRUCTION MATERIALS, WHOLESALE: Glass

Faours Mirror Corp ....E 813 884-3297
Tampa *(G-17658)*
Florida A&G Co Inc...................................A 800 432-8132
Tamarac *(G-17356)*

CONSTRUCTION MATERIALS, WHOLESALE: Gravel

Legacy Vulcan LLC...................................F 352 394-6196
Clermont *(G-1967)*

CONSTRUCTION MATERIALS, WHOLESALE: Joists

Accu-Span Truss Co..................................E 407 321-1440
Longwood *(G-8250)*

CONSTRUCTION MATERIALS, WHOLESALE: Limestone

Helms Hauling & Materials Llc.................F 850 218-6895
Niceville *(G-11569)*
Legacy Vulcan LLC...................................F 352 796-5690
Brooksville *(G-1245)*

CONSTRUCTION MATERIALS, WHOLESALE: Millwork

Builders Door and Supply Inc..................F 941 955-2311
Sarasota *(G-16372)*
Synergy Thermal Foils Inc ....F 954 420-9553
Coral Springs *(G-2319)*
Trusses Unlimited Inc...............................D 904 355-6611
Ponte Vedra Beach *(G-14955)*

CONSTRUCTION MATERIALS, WHOLESALE: Mobile Offices/Comm Units

GOTG LLC ....G....... 800 381-4684
Brooksville *(G-1232)*

CONSTRUCTION MATERIALS, WHOLESALE: Molding, All Materials

Excel Millwork & Moulding Inc ....E 850 576-7228
Midway *(G-10917)*

CONSTRUCTION MATERIALS, WHOLESALE: Pallets, Wood

Pallet Ex Jacksonville Inc ....E 904 781-2500
Jacksonville *(G-6654)*

CONSTRUCTION MATERIALS, WHOLESALE: Paving Materials

Group III Asphalt Inc..................................F....... 850 983-0611
Milton *(G-10931)*
Paver Systems LLC ....E 407 859-9117
Orlando *(G-13055)*
Paver Technologies LLC ....G....... 772 213-8905
Vero Beach *(G-18651)*

CONSTRUCTION MATERIALS, WHOLESALE: Prefabricated Structures

ABC Screen Masters Inc ....G....... 239 772-7336
Cape Coral *(G-1371)*
Consolidated Metal Products ....G....... 850 576-2167
Tallahassee *(G-17236)*
Langstons Utility Buildings ....G....... 813 659-0141
Mulberry *(G-11128)*

CONSTRUCTION MATERIALS, WHOLESALE: Roof, Asphalt/Sheet Metal

Hco Holding I Corporation ....F 863 533-0522
Bartow *(G-318)*
Southeast Gen Contrs Group Inc..........F 877 407-3535
Port St Lucie *(G-15179)*

CONSTRUCTION MATERIALS, WHOLESALE: Roofing & Siding Material

Dj Roof and Solar Supply LLC..................G....... 954 557-1992
Fort Lauderdale *(G-3944)*
Drexel Metals Inc.......................................E 727 572-7900
Tampa *(G-17616)*
Dyplast Products LLC ....D 305 921-0100
Opa Locka *(G-12311)*

CONSTRUCTION MATERIALS, WHOLESALE: Sand

Conrad Yelvington Distrs Inc....................G....... 352 336-5049
Gainesville *(G-4895)*

CONSTRUCTION MATERIALS, WHOLESALE: Septic Tanks

All Liquid Envmtl Svcs LLC..................E....... 800 767-9594
Fort Lauderdale *(G-3797)*
Gunter Septic Tank Mfg.........................G....... 813 654-1214
Seffner *(G-16730)*

CONSTRUCTION MATERIALS, WHOLESALE: Skylights, All Materials

Logsdon and Associates Inc...............G....... 407 292-0084
Windermere *(G-19236)*

CONSTRUCTION MATERIALS, WHOLESALE: Stone, Crushed Or Broken

Dyadic International USA Inc................G....... 561 743-8333
Jupiter *(G-7028)*
Rock Ridge Materials Inc.....................F....... 321 268-8455
Titusville *(G-18460)*

CONSTRUCTION MATERIALS, WHOLESALE: Stucco

Andrew Pratt Stucco & Plst Inc.............F....... 407 501-2609
Orlando *(G-12478)*

CONSTRUCTION MATERIALS, WHOLESALE: Tile & Clay Prdts

Coma Cast Corp.......................................E....... 305 667-6797
Miami *(G-9385)*

CONSTRUCTION MATERIALS, WHOLESALE: Tile, Clay/Other Ceramic

Design Works By Tech Pdts Inc............E....... 941 355-2703
Sarasota *(G-16410)*

CONSTRUCTION MATERIALS, WHOLESALE: Windows

Design Works By Tech Pdts Inc............E....... 941 355-2703
Sarasota *(G-16410)*

CONSTRUCTION MATLS, WHOL: Doors, Combination, Screen-Storm

Sunmaster of Naples Inc......................E....... 239 261-3581
Naples *(G-11426)*

CONSTRUCTION MATLS, WHOLESALE: Struct Assy, Prefab, NonWood

Aldora Aluminum & GL Pdts Inc............E....... 954 441-5057
Coral Springs *(G-2219)*
Atlantic Steel Inc...................................E....... 407 599-3822
Longwood *(G-8258)*
Clock Spring Company Inc...................F....... 561 683-6992
Riviera Beach *(G-15312)*
Quality Custom Cabinet Design............G....... 352 728-4292
Leesburg *(G-8169)*

CONSTRUCTION MTRLS, WHOL: Exterior Flat Glass, Plate/Window

Gopi Glass Sales & Svcs Corp.............E....... 305 592-2089
Miami *(G-9650)*

CONSTRUCTION SAND MINING

Central Sand Inc....................................G....... 321 632-0308
Titusville *(G-18423)*
Charlotte County Min & Mtl Inc.............E....... 239 567-1800
Punta Gorda *(G-15201)*
McDirt Industries Inc...........................F....... 850 944-0112
Pensacola *(G-14203)*
SMR Aggregates Inc.............................E....... 941 907-0041
Lakewood Ranch *(G-7841)*

CONSTRUCTION SITE PREPARATION SVCS

Arons Towing & Recovery Inc..............G....... 772 220-1151
Hobe Sound *(G-5722)*
Consoldted Rsurce Recovery Inc..........E....... 813 262-8404
Tampa *(G-17552)*

CONSTRUCTION: Airport Runway

Neubert Aero Corp..................................G....... 352 345-4828
Brooksville *(G-1256)*

CONSTRUCTION: Bridge

Atlantic Coast Asphalt Co......................E....... 904 268-0274
Jacksonville *(G-6172)*

CONSTRUCTION: Commercial & Institutional Building

A Plus Construction Svcs Inc................E....... 904 612-0597
Jacksonville *(G-6111)*
Elements Restoration LLC....................E....... 813 330-2035
Tampa *(G-17632)*
Waterfall Industries Inc........................F....... 407 330-2003
Sanford *(G-16134)*

CONSTRUCTION: Commercial & Office Building, New

Dean Steel Buildings Inc.......................D....... 239 334-1051
Fort Myers *(G-4429)*
Premier Luxury Group LLC...................E....... 954 358-9885
Fort Lauderdale *(G-4176)*

CONSTRUCTION: Dams, Waterways, Docks & Other Marine

Dolphin Boat Lifts Inc.............................G....... 239 936-1782
Fort Myers *(G-4435)*
Hydroplus Inc..F....... 941 479-7473
Palmetto *(G-13807)*
Rz Service Group LLC............................G....... 904 402-2313
Jacksonville *(G-6741)*

CONSTRUCTION: Dock

Gator Dock & Marine LLC.......................F....... 407 323-0190
Sanford *(G-16054)*

CONSTRUCTION: Drainage System

Purifoy Construction LLC.......................G....... 850 206-2900
Cantonment *(G-1346)*

CONSTRUCTION: Foundation & Retaining Wall

Artistic Fence Corporation.....................G....... 305 805-1976
Hialeah *(G-5307)*

CONSTRUCTION: Heavy Highway & Street

Coastal Concrete Products LLC.............E....... 239 208-4079
Fort Myers *(G-4402)*
Eagle Engrg & Land Dev Inc..................F....... 913 948-4320
Boynton Beach *(G-900)*
Hamner Parking Lot Service..................G....... 954 328-3216
Fort Lauderdale *(G-4040)*

CONSTRUCTION: Indl Building & Warehouse

Environmental Contractors Inc...............F....... 305 556-6942
Hialeah *(G-5399)*
Waterfall Industries Inc..........................F....... 407 330-2003
Sanford *(G-16134)*

CONSTRUCTION: Indl Buildings, New, NEC

A Plus Construction Svcs Inc.................E....... 904 612-0597
Jacksonville *(G-6111)*
Cannida Co LLC......................................G....... 727 642-3709
Saint Petersburg *(G-15737)*
Masters Block - North LLC.....................G....... 407 212-7704
Saint Cloud *(G-15658)*
Met-Con Inc..D....... 321 632-4880
Cocoa *(G-2035)*

CONSTRUCTION: Marine

Digital Antenna Inc..................................F....... 954 747-7022
Sunrise *(G-17115)*
Florida Floats Inc....................................E....... 904 358-3362
Jacksonville *(G-6398)*
Hendry Corporation.................................D....... 813 241-9206
Tampa *(G-17750)*
Hyper-Sub Platform Tech Inc.................F....... 386 365-6021
Lake Butler *(G-7337)*

CONSTRUCTION: Nonresidential Buildings, Custom

A To Z Concrete Products Inc................F....... 727 321-6000
Saint Petersburg *(G-15688)*

CONSTRUCTION: Oil & Gas Pipeline Construction

Aei International Corp............................G....... 904 724-9771
Jacksonville *(G-6125)*

CONSTRUCTION: Parking Lot

Platinium Rosis Inc................................G....... 786 617-9973
Miami Beach *(G-10703)*

CONSTRUCTION: Power & Communication Transmission Tower

American Data Supply Inc......................F....... 866 650-3282
Clearwater *(G-1579)*

CONSTRUCTION: Pumping Station

Central Electric Motor Service...............F....... 863 422-4721
Haines City *(G-5138)*

CONSTRUCTION: Residential, Nec

Cannida Co LLC......................................G....... 727 642-3709
Saint Petersburg *(G-15737)*
Elements Restoration LLC.....................E....... 813 330-2035
Tampa *(G-17632)*
Premier Luxury Group LLC....................E....... 954 358-9885
Fort Lauderdale *(G-4176)*

CONSTRUCTION: Single-Family Housing

A Plus Construction Svcs Inc.................E....... 904 612-0597
Jacksonville *(G-6111)*
Chuculu LLC...F....... 305 595-4577
Miami *(G-9353)*
D & D Building Contractors....................G....... 954 791-2075
Davie *(G-2513)*
F T F Construction Company.................F....... 772 571-1850
Fellsmere *(G-3725)*

CONSTRUCTION: Steel Buildings

Advanced Mdular Structures Inc............G....... 954 960-1550
Pompano Beach *(G-14580)*
Carport Solution LLC..............................F....... 352 789-1149
Ocala *(G-11896)*
Gulf Coast Rebar Inc..............................E....... 813 247-1200
Tampa *(G-17734)*

CONSTRUCTION: Swimming Pools

Jacks Magic Products Inc......................F....... 727 536-4500
Largo *(G-7985)*
South West Adventure Team LLC..........G....... 903 288-4739
Labelle *(G-7323)*

CONSTRUCTION: Tennis Court

Hamner Parking Lot Service...................G....... 954 328-3216
Fort Lauderdale *(G-4040)*

CONSTRUCTION: Utility Line

Clearwater Engineering Inc....................G....... 727 573-2210
Clearwater *(G-1627)*

CONSTRUCTION: Waste Water & Sewage Treatment Plant

American Engineering Svcs Inc..............G....... 813 621-3932
Plant City *(G-14399)*

CONSTRUCTION: Water Main

Hoover Pumping Systems Corp............E....... 954 971-7350
Pompano Beach *(G-14727)*

CONSULTING SVC: Business, NEC

Analytical Research Systems.................F....... 352 466-0051
Micanopy *(G-10899)*
Archer Ellison Inc...................................G....... 800 449-4095
Lake Mary *(G-7400)*
Armbrust Aviation Group Inc.................E....... 561 355-8488
West Palm Beach *(G-18801)*

Calev Systems Inc ....E.... 786 837-2343
Miami Springs (G-10888)
Castle Software Inc....G.... 800 345-7606
Sebastian (G-16657)
Fournies Associates....G.... 561 445-5102
Delray Beach (G-3079)
Game Fisherman Inc....F.... 772 220-4850
Stuart (G-16944)
Global Diversified Products....E.... 727 209-0854
Pinellas Park (G-14351)
Hayes Less Lethal LLC....G.... 561 201-2186
Tequesta (G-18385)
Logical Data Solutions Inc....F.... 561 694-9229
Palm Beach Gardens (G-13606)
Mayn Focus LLC....G.... 603 801-8406
Winter Garden (G-19276)
Ravenswood Import Export Ltd L....G.... 863 800-0210
Lake Placid (G-7494)
Sdi Industries Inc....E.... 321 733-1128
Melbourne (G-8928)
Solara Industries Inc....E.... 863 688-3330
Lakeland (G-7796)

CONSULTING SVC: Chemical

Color-Chrome Technologies Inc....G.... 954 335-0127
Fort Lauderdale (G-3910)

CONSULTING SVC: Computer

Betrock Information Systems....E.... 954 981-2821
Cooper City (G-2110)
Cloud Veneer LLC....G.... 305 230-7379
Miami (G-9364)
Cyipcom Inc....G.... 954 727-2500
Oakland Park (G-11794)
Fis Avantgard LLC....E.... 484 582-2000
Jacksonville (G-6388)
Ivengo Software Inc....G.... 321 480-3155
Melbourne (G-8852)
Kenexa Learning Inc....G.... 407 562-1905
Maitland (G-8470)
Kenexa Learning Inc....G.... 407 548-0434
Lake Mary (G-7428)
Levitech Services LLC....G.... 904 576-0562
Jacksonville Beach (G-6949)
Lott Qa Group Inc....G.... 201 693-2224
Bonita Springs (G-844)
Mercury Systems Inc....E.... 352 371-2567
Gainesville (G-4961)
Microvision Technology Corp....F.... 407 333-2943
Lake Mary (G-7435)
Naztec International Group LLC....F.... 561 802-4110
West Palm Beach (G-18960)
Rperf Technologies Corp....F.... 954 629-2359
Coral Springs (G-2307)
Willsonet Inc....E.... 813 336-8175
Tampa (G-18259)

CONSULTING SVC: Data Processing

Microcomputer Services....G.... 561 988-7000
Boca Raton (G-623)

CONSULTING SVC: Engineering

Calvert Manufacturing Inc....F.... 407 331-5522
Casselberry (G-1499)
Florida Turbine Tech Inc....G.... 561 427-6400
Jupiter (G-7045)
Survival Products Inc....G.... 954 966-7329
Sunrise (G-17182)
Yatfl Inc....G.... 786 643-8660
Miami (G-10625)

CONSULTING SVC: Financial Management

Dion Money Management LLC....F.... 413 458-4700
Naples (G-11227)

CONSULTING SVC: Management

Advantagecare Inc....G.... 407 345-8877
Orlando (G-12435)
Alterna Power Inc....F.... 407 287-9148
Orlando (G-12462)
Applied Technologies Group Inc....G.... 813 413-7025
Tampa (G-17429)
Coastal Communications Corp....F.... 561 989-0600
Boca Raton (G-486)
Custom Masters Inc....E.... 407 331-4634
Longwood (G-8270)
Darmiven Inc....G.... 305 871-1157
Virginia Gardens (G-18686)
Didna Inc....G.... 239 851-0966
Orlando (G-12671)
Diversfied Mtl Specialists Inc....G.... 941 244-0935
North Venice (G-11757)
East Coast Cooling Tower Inc....F.... 904 551-5527
Jacksonville (G-6348)
First Marketing Company....C.... 954 979-0700
Pompano Beach (G-14691)
Integritrust Solutions LLC....G.... 850 685-9801
Navarre (G-11466)
JKS Industries Inc....F.... 727 573-1305
Tampa (G-17805)
Pallet Consultants Corp....E.... 954 946-2212
Pompano Beach (G-14783)
Redstone Corporation....G.... 321 213-2135
Merritt Island (G-9007)
Riley Risk Inc....G.... 202 601-0500
Saint Augustine (G-15597)
Shaws Sthern Blle Frz Fods In....D.... 904 768-1591
Jacksonville (G-6763)
Smart Guides....G.... 813 534-0940
Tampa (G-18109)
Taylor Made Systems Brdnton In....C.... 941 747-1900
Oviedo (G-13461)
Trx Integration Inc....F.... 727 797-4707
Belleair (G-361)

CONSULTING SVC: Marketing Management

Comm Dots LLC Connecting....F.... 305 505-6009
Miami (G-9388)
Connected Life Solutions LLC....F.... 407 745-1952
Altamonte Springs (G-38)
Grand Cypress Group Inc....G.... 407 622-1993
Maitland (G-8467)
Graphic Masters Inc....D.... 800 230-3873
Miami (G-9656)
Greentree Marketing Svcs Inc....F.... 800 557-9567
Fort Lauderdale (G-4031)
Mc Squared Group Inc....G.... 850 435-4600
Pensacola (G-14202)
Mediware Info Systems Inc....F.... 904 281-0467
Jacksonville (G-6589)
Metalhouse LLC....G.... 407 270-3000
Orlando (G-12962)
Mfx Corp....F.... 407 429-4051
Orlando (G-12965)
Military One Click LLC....G.... 904 390-7100
Jacksonville (G-6605)
Monumental Enterprises Inc....G.... 305 803-8493
Pembroke Pines (G-14048)
Pk Group Inc....F.... 239 643-2442
Naples (G-11368)
Smilefy Inc....F.... 302 465-6606
Hallandale Beach (G-5211)
Tm Marketing Group LLC....G.... 954 848-9955
Fort Lauderdale (G-4285)
Venice Quarters Inc....E.... 954 318-3483
Wilton Manors (G-19221)
Wingard LLC....F.... 904 387-2570
Jacksonville (G-6923)
World Event Promotions LLC....E.... 800 214-3408
Miami (G-10619)

CONSULTING SVC: Online Technology

Beachchip Technologies LLC....G.... 727 643-8106
Clearwater (G-1605)
Connected Life Solutions LLC....F.... 407 745-1952
Altamonte Springs (G-38)
Ebs Quality Service Inc....F.... 305 595-4048
Miami (G-9497)

CONSULTING SVC: Sales Management

Flyteone Inc....G.... 813 421-1410
Clearwater (G-1691)
James Reese Enterprises Inc....F.... 727 386-5311
Clearwater (G-1741)
Terfa Litter USA Inc....F.... 416 358-4495
Sunny Isles Beach (G-17081)

CONSULTING SVC: Telecommunications

Itelecom USA Inc....G.... 305 557-4660
Weston (G-19143)
Lugloc LLC....F.... 305 961-1765
Miami (G-9916)
Maxxfi LLC....F.... 513 289-6521
Cape Coral (G-1447)
Prepaid Solutions LLC....F.... 786 257-2714
Miami (G-10188)
Techcodes LLC....G.... 321 529-4122
Titusville (G-18467)

CONSULTING SVCS, BUSINESS: Communications

Connected Life Solutions LLC....F.... 407 745-1952
Altamonte Springs (G-38)
Primal Innovation Tech LLC....F.... 407 558-9366
Tampa (G-18010)

CONSULTING SVCS, BUSINESS: Environmental

Cv Technology Inc....E.... 561 694-9588
Jupiter (G-7022)

CONSULTING SVCS, BUSINESS: Lighting

Lightnet Usa Inc....F.... 305 260-6444
Miami (G-9891)

CONSULTING SVCS, BUSINESS: Sys Engnrg, Exc Computer/Prof

Hatalom Corporation....E.... 407 567-2556
Orlando (G-12796)

CONSULTING SVCS, BUSINESS: Systems Analysis & Engineering

Alterna Power Inc....F.... 407 287-9148
Orlando (G-12462)
Concept Software Inc....G.... 321 250-6670
Winter Garden (G-19258)
Jarden Plastic Solutions....G.... 864 879-8100
Boca Raton (G-577)

CONSULTING SVCS, BUSINESS: Systems Analysis Or Design

Servos and Simulation Inc....G.... 407 807-0208
Longwood (G-8336)
Vinland Corporation....E.... 954 475-9093
Plantation (G-14565)

CONSULTING SVCS, BUSINESS: Test Development & Evaluation

Moore Solutions Inc....G.... 772 337-4005
Port St Lucie (G-15175)

CONSULTING SVCS: Oil

Advance Green Energy Inc....G.... 352 765-3850
Inverness (G-6081)
Foster & Foster Worldwide LLC....F.... 352 362-9102
Apopka (G-145)
Gapv....G.... 786 257-1681
South Miami (G-16817)

CONSULTING SVCS: Scientific

West Texas Protein Inc....F.... 806 250-5959
Jacksonville (G-6911)

CONTACT LENSES

Danker Laboratories Inc....F.... 941 758-7711
Sarasota (G-16203)
Express Vision Care Inc....F.... 786 587-7404
Hialeah (G-5401)
Johnson Jhnson Vision Care Inc....A.... 904 443-1000
Jacksonville (G-6526)
Unilens Corp USA....E.... 727 544-2531
Clearwater (G-1928)
Universal Cntact Lenses of Fla....G.... 904 731-3410
Jacksonville (G-6885)

CONTACTS: Electrical

Micro Contacts Inc....F.... 954 973-6166
Pompano Beach (G-14761)
Southern Switch & Contacts....F.... 727 789-0951
Palm Harbor (G-13762)

CONTAINERS, GLASS: Milk Bottles

Kiinde LLC....G.... 404 368-5382
Melbourne (G-8858)

CONTAINERS, GLASS: Water Bottles

Best Quality Water Sys of Fla ....C....... 407 971-2537
Oviedo *(G-13418)*
Brand You Waters LLC ....G....... 786 312-0840
Pompano Beach *(G-14621)*

CONTAINERS: Air Cargo, Metal

Alpine Systems Associates Inc ....G....... 305 262-3263
Medley *(G-8608)*
John Bean Technologies Corp ....E....... 407 851-3377
Orlando *(G-12858)*

CONTAINERS: Cargo, Wood

Florida Funeral Shipping Cntrs ....G....... 954 957-9259
Fort Lauderdale *(G-4000)*
Williams Jewelry and Mfg Co ....G....... 727 823-7676
Saint Petersburg *(G-15961)*

CONTAINERS: Cargo, Wood & Metal Combination

Compact Container Systems LLC ....F....... 561 392-6910
Boca Raton *(G-487)*
Global Galan Logistics Inc ....G....... 754 263-2708
Miramar *(G-10999)*
Rima Cargo LLC ....G....... 305 477-8002
Miami *(G-10264)*

CONTAINERS: Cargo, Wood & Wood With Metal

Cal Air Forwarding ....G....... 305 871-4552
Miami *(G-9302)*
Container Mfg Solutions ....E....... 888 805-8785
Cutler Bay *(G-2389)*

CONTAINERS: Corrugated

Barco Sales & Mfg Inc ....F....... 954 563-3922
Oakland Park *(G-11784)*
Biodegradable Packaging Corp ....E....... 305 824-1164
Miami Lakes *(G-10769)*
Corrugated Help LLC ....G....... 904 874-7285
Starke *(G-16891)*
Gar Business Group LLC ....G....... 321 632-5133
Rockledge *(G-15413)*
Packaging Alternatives Corp ....F....... 352 867-5050
Ocala *(G-12021)*
Republic Packaging Florida Inc ....E....... 305 685-5175
Opa Locka *(G-12355)*
Two Paper Chasers LLC ....G....... 813 251-5090
Tampa *(G-18209)*
Westrock Cp LLC ....C....... 904 356-5611
Jacksonville *(G-6913)*
Westrock CP LLC ....E....... 407 859-9701
Orlando *(G-13324)*

CONTAINERS: Foil, Bakery Goods & Frozen Foods

R and R Brokerage Co ....G....... 305 592-4329
Doral *(G-3477)*

CONTAINERS: Food & Beverage

Egd Euro Gourmet Deli Inc ....G....... 305 937-1515
Aventura *(G-267)*
La Perrada Del Gordo Boca LLC ....F....... 561 968-6978
West Palm Beach *(G-18923)*
Nardis Enterprises LLC ....G....... 954 529-0691
Fort Lauderdale *(G-4130)*
Outstanding Events Inc ....F....... 772 463-5406
Palm City *(G-13668)*
Weplenish LLC ....G....... 954 909-4183
Plantation *(G-14567)*

CONTAINERS: Food, Folding, Made From Purchased Materials

Beverage Blocks Inc ....F....... 813 309-8711
Tampa *(G-17467)*

CONTAINERS: Frozen Food, Made From Purchased Materials

Hg Brokerage Services Inc ....G....... 407 294-3507
Orlando *(G-12800)*

CONTAINERS: Glass

Anchor Glass Container Corp ....C....... 813 884-0000
Tampa *(G-17425)*
Anchor Glass Container Corp ....C....... 904 786-1010
Jacksonville *(G-6153)*
Rock Bottom Bottles LLC ....G....... 901 237-9929
Sarasota *(G-16287)*
Spiker USA Corporation ....G....... 850 710-3043
Pensacola *(G-14269)*
Van Teal Inc ....E....... 305 751-6767
Miami *(G-10566)*

CONTAINERS: Ice Cream, Made From Purchased Materials

Gesco Ice Cream Vending Corp ....F....... 718 782-3232
Sunny Isles Beach *(G-17078)*

CONTAINERS: Liquid Tight Fiber, From Purchased Materials

Custom Manufacturing Inc ....G....... 607 569-2738
Inverness *(G-6084)*

CONTAINERS: Metal

Standard Kegs LLC ....F....... 305 454-9721
Medley *(G-8729)*
Stemler Corporation ....E....... 727 577-1216
Saint Petersburg *(G-15927)*

CONTAINERS: Plastic

Action Plastics Inc ....G....... 352 342-4122
Belleview *(G-365)*
Altium Packaging LLC ....F....... 813 782-2695
Zephyrhills *(G-19507)*
Altium Packaging LLC ....F....... 813 248-4300
Tampa *(G-17409)*
Altium Packaging LLC ....F....... 386 246-4000
Palm Coast *(G-13683)*
American Composites Engrg ....F....... 352 528-5007
Williston *(G-19209)*
Amerikan LLC ....E....... 863 314-9417
Sebring *(G-16681)*
Associated Materials LLC ....G....... 813 621-7058
Tampa *(G-17439)*
CKS Packaging Inc ....D....... 407 423-0333
Orlando *(G-12586)*
CKS Packaging Inc ....D....... 407 420-9529
Orlando *(G-12587)*
CKS Packaging Inc ....D....... 954 925-9049
Hollywood *(G-5800)*
Cw21 Inc ....E....... 813 754-1760
Plant City *(G-14422)*
Dart Container Company Fla LLC ....C....... 813 752-1990
Plant City *(G-14423)*
Dart Industries Inc ....B....... 407 826-5050
Orlando *(G-12650)*
Delconte Packaging Inc ....F....... 305 885-2800
Hialeah *(G-5368)*
Industrial Plastic Systems Inc ....E....... 863 646-8551
Lakeland *(G-7711)*
Jan and Jean Inc ....G....... 813 645-0680
Ruskin *(G-15485)*
Jarden LLC ....D....... 561 447-2520
Boca Raton *(G-576)*
K & I Plastics Inc ....G....... 904 387-0438
Jacksonville *(G-6531)*
Mesa Industries Inc ....F....... 386 738-3255
Deland *(G-2995)*
MTS Sales & Marketing Inc ....D....... 727 812-2830
Clearwater *(G-1797)*
Myton Industries Inc ....F....... 954 989-0113
Hallandale *(G-5159)*
OPif- Our Plstic Is Fntstic ....G....... 954 636-4228
Lauderhill *(G-8118)*
Perry Fiberglas Products Inc ....E....... 321 609-9036
Rockledge *(G-15439)*
Prototype Plastics LLC ....G....... 941 371-3380
Sarasota *(G-16549)*
Sunbeam Products Inc ....B....... 561 912-4100
Boca Raton *(G-738)*
Ultratech International Inc ....E....... 904 292-9019
Jacksonville *(G-6876)*
Vizco Us Inc ....E....... 941 753-3333
Bradenton *(G-1142)*

CONTAINERS: Sanitary, Food

Estal Usa Inc ....G....... 305 728-3272
Miami *(G-9537)*
Mike and Val Tupper Ind ....G....... 904 757-7566
Jacksonville *(G-6604)*
Tellus Products LLC ....E....... 561 996-5556
Belle Glade *(G-352)*

CONTAINERS: Shipping & Mailing, Fiber

May & Well Inc ....G....... 813 333-5806
Tampa *(G-17895)*

CONTAINERS: Shipping, Wood

Qps Companies Inc ....E....... 813 246-5525
Tampa *(G-18029)*
Stemler Corporation ....E....... 727 577-1216
Saint Petersburg *(G-15927)*

CONTAINERS: Wood

Southern Closet Systems Inc ....G....... 813 926-9348
Odessa *(G-12153)*

CONTRACT FOOD SVCS

GA Fd Svcs Pinellas Cnty LLC ....B....... 727 388-0075
Saint Petersburg *(G-15789)*
GA Fd Svcs Pinellas Cnty LLC ....E....... 954 972-8884
Fort Lauderdale *(G-4017)*
GA Fd Svcs Pinellas Cnty LLC ....E....... 239 693-5090
Fort Myers *(G-4465)*
Lincoln-Marti Cmnty Agcy Inc ....A....... 305 643-4888
Miami *(G-9895)*

CONTRACTOR: Rigging & Scaffolding

Whitewater Boat Corp ....G....... 305 756-9191
Miami *(G-10603)*

CONTRACTORS: Access Control System Eqpt

L A Ornamental & Rack Corp ....G....... 305 696-0419
Miami *(G-9835)*

CONTRACTORS: Access Flooring System Installation

A Clean Finish Inc ....G....... 407 516-1311
Jacksonville *(G-6109)*

CONTRACTORS: Acoustical & Insulation Work

Florida Marine Joiner Svc Inc ....F....... 813 514-1125
Tampa *(G-17682)*

CONTRACTORS: Appliance Installation

Fusion AC & Appl Svc LLC ....G....... 888 670-8435
Pompano Beach *(G-14707)*

CONTRACTORS: Artificial Turf Installation

Easyturf Inc ....F....... 941 753-3312
Ellenton *(G-3653)*

CONTRACTORS: Asphalt

Superior Asphalt Inc ....D....... 941 755-2850
Bradenton *(G-1123)*

CONTRACTORS: Awning Installation

A & A Central Florida ....F....... 407 648-5666
Altamonte Springs *(G-24)*
Eddy Storm Protection ....G....... 386 248-1631
Daytona Beach *(G-2661)*
Florida Shutters Inc ....E....... 772 569-2200
Vero Beach *(G-18619)*
Germain Canvas & Awning Co ....G....... 305 751-4963
Miami *(G-9631)*
Miami Beach Awning Co ....E....... 305 576-2029
Miami *(G-9993)*
Paradise Awnings Corporation ....E....... 305 597-5714
Miami *(G-10141)*

CONTRACTORS: Banking Machine Installation & Svc

Crandon Enterprises Inc........G...... 352 873-8400
Ocala *(G-11910)*

CONTRACTORS: Building Eqpt & Machinery Installation

Accurate Metal Door Inc........G...... 321 305-5951
Titusville *(G-18409)*
Built Right Installers Intl........F...... 305 362-6010
Hialeah *(G-5334)*
Millwork and Design Inc........G...... 352 544-0444
Brooksville *(G-1253)*
Otis Elevator Company........B...... 561 618-4831
West Palm Beach *(G-18974)*

CONTRACTORS: Building Sign Installation & Mntnce

Accent Neon & Sign Company........G...... 727 784-8414
Palm Harbor *(G-13716)*
Adtech Electric Advertising........D...... 786 533-3210
Miami *(G-9073)*
All American Signs Inc........G...... 863 665-7161
Lakeland *(G-7631)*
American Led Technology Inc........F...... 850 863-8777
Naples *(G-11162)*
Art-Kraft Sign Co Inc........E...... 321 727-7324
Palm Bay *(G-13499)*
Budget Signs Inc........F...... 954 941-5710
Pompano Beach *(G-14625)*
Dakim Inc........F...... 561 790-0884
Royal Palm Beach *(G-15465)*
Dynamic Aspects Inc........G...... 407 322-1923
Debary *(G-2748)*
General Signs and Service Inc........G...... 904 372-4238
Atlantic Beach *(G-223)*
Gould Signs Inc........G...... 772 221-1218
Stuart *(G-16947)*
Interstate Signcrafters LLC........D...... 561 547-3760
Boynton Beach *(G-922)*
Jayco Signs Inc........F...... 407 339-5252
Maitland *(G-8468)*
Kenco 2000 Inc........F...... 386 672-1590
Daytona Beach *(G-2676)*
Oakhurst Marketing Inc........G...... 727 532-8255
Saint Petersburg *(G-15869)*
Rogers Sign Corp........E...... 352 799-1923
Brooksville *(G-1265)*
Signs Unlimited of Bay County........G...... 850 785-1061
Panama City *(G-13949)*
Superior Signs Inc........F...... 407 601-7964
Orlando *(G-13231)*

CONTRACTORS: Cable Laying

Quality Cable Contractors Inc........E...... 407 246-0606
Orlando *(G-13103)*

CONTRACTORS: Cable Splicing Svcs

Quality Cable Contractors Inc........E...... 407 246-0606
Orlando *(G-13103)*

CONTRACTORS: Carpentry Work

BMC Services Inc........F...... 954 587-6337
Fort Lauderdale *(G-3862)*
Braden Kitchens Inc........E...... 321 636-4700
Cocoa *(G-1999)*
Bresee Woodwork Inc........F...... 941 355-2591
Sarasota *(G-16368)*
Florida Marine Joiner Svc Inc........F...... 813 514-1125
Tampa *(G-17682)*
Hughes Trim Llc........D...... 863 206-6048
Orlando *(G-12814)*
Kevco Builders Inc........F...... 352 308-8025
Eustis *(G-3711)*
Legend Design and Production........G...... 305 270-1156
Miami *(G-9881)*
Melbourne Architectural Mllwk........F...... 321 308-3297
Melbourne *(G-8887)*
Mirandas Woodcraft LLC........G...... 954 306-3568
Lauderhill *(G-8115)*

CONTRACTORS: Carpentry, Cabinet & Finish Work

Acryplex Inc........G...... 305 633-7636
Miami *(G-9066)*
Amick Cstm Woodcraft & Design........G...... 407 324-8525
Sanford *(G-15994)*
Belets Millwork Inc........F...... 904 353-8600
Jacksonville *(G-6202)*
Custom Cabinets SW Florida LLC........G...... 239 415-3350
Fort Myers *(G-4420)*
Infinite Ret Design & Mfg Corp........F...... 305 967-8339
Miami *(G-9741)*
Juan Pampanas Designs Inc........G...... 305 573-7550
Miami *(G-9812)*
Madison Millwork & Cabinet Co........E...... 954 966-7551
Hollywood *(G-5868)*
Millcreek Fine Cabinetry Inc........G...... 954 801-8595
Plantation *(G-14534)*
Princeton Industries Inc........E...... 954 344-9155
Margate *(G-8563)*
Rik Enterprises Inc........G...... 239 772-9485
Cape Coral *(G-1460)*
River City Cstm Cabinetry Inc........F...... 904 247-0807
Jacksonville *(G-6727)*
S M I Cabinetry Inc........E...... 407 841-0292
Orlando *(G-13152)*
Southern Woodworks Fine Wdwkg........F...... 850 456-0550
Pensacola *(G-14266)*
Spruce Creek Cabinetry Inc........F...... 386 756-0041
Port Orange *(G-15035)*
Welshman Investment Corp........G...... 407 933-4444
Kissimmee *(G-7310)*

CONTRACTORS: Carpentry, Cabinet Building & Installation

Commercial Stone Cab Fbrctors........F...... 727 209-1141
Saint Petersburg *(G-15749)*
Commercial Stone Fbrcators Inc........F...... 727 209-1141
Saint Petersburg *(G-15750)*
Guyton Industries LLC........E...... 772 208-3019
Indiantown *(G-6073)*
Institutional Products Inc........E...... 305 248-4955
Homestead *(G-5972)*
Kc & B Custom Inc........G...... 561 276-1887
Delray Beach *(G-3099)*
Southwest Woodwork Inc........F...... 239 213-0126
Naples *(G-11411)*

CONTRACTORS: Carpentry, Finish & Trim Work

Daystar International Inc........G...... 813 281-0200
Tampa *(G-17593)*
Kmi International Inc........E...... 561 588-5514
Lake Worth *(G-7562)*

CONTRACTORS: Ceramic Floor Tile Installation

Designer Lifestyles LLC........F...... 904 631-8954
Jacksonville *(G-6317)*

CONTRACTORS: Commercial & Office Building

Cannida Co LLC........G...... 727 642-3709
Saint Petersburg *(G-15737)*
Suncrest Sheds of South Fla........F...... 305 231-1990
Miami Lakes *(G-10865)*

CONTRACTORS: Computer Installation

Incity Security Inc........F...... 561 306-9228
West Palm Beach *(G-18902)*
P S T Computers Inc........G...... 954 566-1600
Fort Lauderdale *(G-4153)*

CONTRACTORS: Computer Power Conditioning Svcs

Air & Power Solutions Inc........G...... 954 427-0019
Coconut Creek *(G-2068)*

CONTRACTORS: Computerized Controls Installation

Bridge Trading Usa LLC........F...... 877 848-0979
Doral *(G-3286)*

CONTRACTORS: Concrete

Coastal Concrete Products LLC........E...... 239 208-4079
Fort Myers *(G-4402)*
Foam By Design Inc........E...... 727 561-7479
Clearwater *(G-1692)*
Mack Industries Inc........G...... 352 742-2333
Astatula *(G-214)*
Mother Earth Stone LLC........F...... 407 878-2854
Sanford *(G-16091)*
RG Groundworks LLC........G...... 352 474-7949
Newberry *(G-11560)*
Woodwork Unlimited Inc........F...... 352 267-4051
Oxford *(G-13466)*

CONTRACTORS: Concrete Pumping

Adonel Con Pmpg Fnshg S Fla In........D...... 305 392-5416
Miami *(G-9071)*

CONTRACTORS: Concrete Reinforcement Placing

Florida Wilbert Inc........G...... 904 765-2641
Jacksonville *(G-6405)*

CONTRACTORS: Concrete Repair

Dynamis Epoxy LLC........G...... 941 488-3999
Venice *(G-18544)*

CONTRACTORS: Construction Site Cleanup

Rz Service Group LLC........G...... 904 402-2313
Jacksonville *(G-6741)*

CONTRACTORS: Countertop Installation

Fellowship Enterprises Inc........G...... 727 726-5997
Safety Harbor *(G-15493)*
Florida Design Mfg Assoc Inc........F...... 561 533-0733
West Palm Beach *(G-18879)*
Heller Cabinetry Inc........F...... 321 729-9690
Melbourne *(G-8842)*
International Gran & Stone LLC........E...... 813 920-6500
Odessa *(G-12127)*
Natural Stone Sltons Fnest SRS........E...... 941 954-1100
Sarasota *(G-16519)*

CONTRACTORS: Directional Oil & Gas Well Drilling Svc

Accountble Drctional Drillillc........G...... 239 226-1606
Fort Myers *(G-4343)*
Betwell Oil & Gas Company........G...... 305 821-8300
Hialeah *(G-5325)*
Bore Tech Inc........G...... 904 262-0752
Jacksonville *(G-6226)*
Centerline Drctnal Drlg Svc In........E...... 863 674-0913
Labelle *(G-7317)*
Full Bore Directional Inc........G...... 727 327-7784
Gulfport *(G-5133)*
Full Circle Directional Inc........G...... 352 568-0639
Bushnell *(G-1317)*
Jaffer Wll Drllng A Div of AC........F...... 954 523-6669
Hialeah *(G-5460)*
Precision Directional Drlg LLC........F...... 941 320-8308
Bradenton *(G-1101)*
Pretec Directional Drlg LLC........F...... 786 220-7667
Coral Gables *(G-2186)*
Sabcon Underground LLC........E...... 863 268-8225
Winter Haven *(G-19354)*

CONTRACTORS: Dock Eqpt Installation, Indl

Specialty Products Inc........G...... 850 438-4264
Pensacola *(G-14267)*

CONTRACTORS: Electric Power Systems

Cavok Capital LLC........F...... 727 789-0951
Palm Harbor *(G-13726)*
Megawattage LLC........F...... 954 328-0232
Fort Lauderdale *(G-4117)*

CONTRACTORS: Electrical

AL Covell Electric Inc........G...... 352 544-0680
Brooksville *(G-1207)*
American Data Supply Inc........F...... 866 650-3282
Clearwater *(G-1579)*
ARC Electric Inc........E...... 954 583-9800
Davie *(G-2498)*

Capacity Inc....E....855 440-7825
Sarasota *(G-16186)*
Central Electric Motor Service....F....863 422-4721
Haines City *(G-5138)*
Coastal Electric....G....239 245-7396
Fort Myers *(G-4403)*
Del Air Electric Co....G....407 531-1173
Sanford *(G-16035)*
Enterprise Electric LLC....G....407 884-0668
Apopka *(G-136)*
Gc Electric LLC....G....386 842-7066
Jacksonville *(G-6427)*
Ingram Signalization Inc....E....850 433-8267
Pensacola *(G-14178)*
Keltour US Inc....F....239 424-8901
Cape Coral *(G-1443)*
Walker Electric Inc....G....941 729-5015
Palmetto *(G-13834)*

CONTRACTORS: Electronic Controls Installation

Commercial Gates and Elc LLC....F....386 454-2329
High Springs *(G-5700)*
Electrical Controls Inc....F....954 801-6846
Tamarac *(G-17355)*

CONTRACTORS: Energy Management Control

Integrated Surroundings Inc....F....850 932-0848
Gulf Breeze *(G-5120)*

CONTRACTORS: Excavating

H2r Corp....F....727 541-3444
Pinellas Park *(G-14353)*
Purifoy Construction LLC....G....850 206-2900
Cantonment *(G-1346)*

CONTRACTORS: Exterior Concrete Stucco

Trinity Exterior Solutions LLC....G....850 393-9682
Holt *(G-5950)*

CONTRACTORS: Exterior Insulation & Finish Application

Trinity Exterior Solutions LLC....G....850 393-9682
Holt *(G-5950)*

CONTRACTORS: Fence Construction

Arts Work Unlimited Inc....G....305 247-9257
Miami *(G-9175)*
Coastal Craftsmen Aluminum Inc....E....727 868-8802
Hudson *(G-6019)*
Danielle Fence Mfg Co Inc....D....863 425-3182
Mulberry *(G-11121)*
Df Multi Services LLC....G....407 683-2223
Orlando *(G-12668)*
Nationwide Industries Inc....E....813 988-2628
Tampa *(G-17933)*
RB Custom Welding LLC....G....813 280-9860
Tampa *(G-18040)*
Silverman Fence Mfg Inc....G....904 730-0882
Jacksonville *(G-6774)*

CONTRACTORS: Fiber Optic Cable Installation

C2c Innovated Technology LLC....G....251 382-2277
Bonifay *(G-800)*
Quality Cable Contractors Inc....E....407 246-0606
Orlando *(G-13103)*

CONTRACTORS: Fiberglass Work

Hydes Screening Inc....G....954 345-6743
Coral Springs *(G-2258)*
Precision Auto Tint Dsign Corp....G....727 385-8788
Tarpon Springs *(G-18321)*
Tampa Fiberglass Inc....F....813 248-6828
Tampa *(G-18164)*

CONTRACTORS: Fire Detection & Burglar Alarm Systems

Cv Technology Inc....E....561 694-9588
Jupiter *(G-7022)*
Security and Fire Elec Inc....E....904 844-0964
Saint Augustine *(G-15608)*

CONTRACTORS: Floor Laying & Other Floor Work

Cianos Tile & Marble Inc....E....239 267-8453
Fort Myers *(G-4395)*
Marlyn Steel Products Inc....E....813 621-1375
Tampa *(G-17884)*
Prestige Flrg Instllations Inc....F....407 291-0609
Orlando *(G-13083)*
Triton Stone Holdings LLC....G....219 669-4890
Fort Lauderdale *(G-4288)*

CONTRACTORS: Flooring

Dekscape....G....239 278-3325
Fort Myers *(G-4430)*
Floors Inc....E....813 879-5720
Tampa *(G-17671)*
Jdl Surface Innovations Inc....E....239 772-0077
Cape Coral *(G-1441)*

CONTRACTORS: Foundation & Footing

Continental Concrete Products....G....904 388-1390
Jacksonville *(G-6285)*

CONTRACTORS: Garage Doors

A-1 Door Systems Inc....F....904 327-7206
Jacksonville *(G-6112)*

CONTRACTORS: Gas Detection & Analysis Svcs

Delacom Detection Systems LLC....G....941 544-6636
Sarasota *(G-16408)*

CONTRACTORS: Gas Field Svcs, NEC

Dilo Production Inc....G....727 376-5593
Odessa *(G-12116)*
Hess Express....G....772 335-9975
Port Saint Lucie *(G-15112)*
I C T S America Inc....G....786 307-2993
Doral *(G-3385)*
MCR Compression Services LLC....F....432 552-8720
North Port *(G-11743)*

CONTRACTORS: General Electric

BJ Burns Incorporated....E....305 572-9500
Sunrise *(G-17097)*
Freeman Electric Co Inc....F....850 785-7448
Panama City *(G-13905)*
General Sign Service Inc....F....904 355-5630
Jacksonville *(G-6433)*

CONTRACTORS: Glass Tinting, Architectural & Automotive

Solar Tint Inc....G....305 663-4663
South Miami *(G-16828)*
Solar X....G....386 673-2111
Ormond Beach *(G-13400)*

CONTRACTORS: Glass, Glazing & Tinting

Ad Valorem Corporation....G....561 488-9966
Boca Raton *(G-397)*
Arso Enterprises Inc....E....305 681-2020
Opa Locka *(G-12290)*
BT Glass & Mirror Inc....G....561 841-7676
West Palm Beach *(G-18829)*
Flat Glass Distributors LLC....E....904 354-5413
Jacksonville *(G-6394)*
Greg Valentine LLC....E....239 332-0855
Fort Myers *(G-4473)*
MA Glass & Mirror LLC....F....305 593-8555
Miami *(G-9930)*
Michael Valentines Inc....F....239 332-0855
Fort Myers *(G-4531)*
Neo Metal Glass LLC....G....954 532-0340
Pompano Beach *(G-14772)*
Plazadoor Corp....E....561 578-5450
Riviera Beach *(G-15364)*
Southeast Energy Inc....G....561 883-1051
Boca Raton *(G-723)*

CONTRACTORS: Gutters & Downspouts

Titan Specialty Cnstr Inc....E....850 916-7660
Milton *(G-10943)*

CONTRACTORS: Heating & Air Conditioning

Chiller Medic Inc....G....904 814-9446
Jacksonville *(G-6263)*
Crown Seamless Gutters Inc....F....561 748-9919
West Palm Beach *(G-18852)*
Everest Air Corp....F....407 319-6204
Kissimmee *(G-7243)*
Fusion AC & Appl Svc LLC....G....888 670-8435
Pompano Beach *(G-14707)*
Miles of Smiles Rides Inc....F....727 528-1227
Seminole *(G-16753)*

CONTRACTORS: Highway & Street Construction, General

Woodwork Unlimited Inc....F....352 267-4051
Oxford *(G-13466)*

CONTRACTORS: Highway Sign & Guardrail Construction & Install

Scott Safety LLC....E....239 340-8695
Moore Haven *(G-11089)*

CONTRACTORS: Home & Office Intrs Finish, Furnish/Remodel

Premier Coatings LLC....E....954 797-9275
Fort Lauderdale *(G-4175)*
Y F Leung Inc....G....305 651-6851
North Miami Beach *(G-11714)*

CONTRACTORS: Hydraulic Eqpt Installation & Svcs

Alpha Hydraulics LLC....G....561 355-0318
Riviera Beach *(G-15297)*

CONTRACTORS: Hydraulic Well Fracturing Svcs

American Silica Holdings LLC....G....352 796-8855
Brooksville *(G-1211)*

CONTRACTORS: Indl Building Renovation, Remodeling & Repair

Moody Construction Svcs Inc....E....941 776-1542
Duette *(G-3562)*

CONTRACTORS: Kitchen & Bathroom Remodeling

FL Central Cnstr & Rmdlg....G....863 701-3548
Lakeland *(G-7687)*
Jcs Limited Corporation....G....954 822-2887
Tamarac *(G-17360)*

CONTRACTORS: Kitchen Cabinet Installation

Commercial Stone Cab Fbrctors....F....727 209-1141
Saint Petersburg *(G-15749)*
Commercial Stone Fbrcators Inc....F....727 209-1141
Saint Petersburg *(G-15750)*
Professnal Kit Instller Group....F....954 436-1513
Miramar *(G-11033)*

CONTRACTORS: Machinery Installation

Sdi Industries Inc....E....321 733-1128
Melbourne *(G-8928)*

CONTRACTORS: Marble Installation, Interior

Architctural MBL Importers Inc....E....941 365-3552
Sarasota *(G-16347)*
Marble Doctors LLC....D....203 794-1000
Wellington *(G-18724)*
New England Granite & Marble....G....772 283-8667
Stuart *(G-16980)*
Puma Marble Co Inc....F....305 758-6461
Miami *(G-10214)*

CONTRACTORS: Masonry & Stonework

All Granite & Marble Corp....G....508 248-9393
Sarasota *(G-16340)*
LAS & JB Inc....G....772 672-5315
Fort Pierce *(G-4711)*
Premier Stoneworks LLC....D....561 330-3737
Delray Beach *(G-3123)*

True Stone Masonry LLC ..... F 772 334-9797
Fort Pierce *(G-4761)*

CONTRACTORS: Mechanical

Mechanical Svcs Centl Fla Inc ..... C 407 857-3510
Orlando *(G-12957)*
Southern Welding & Mechanics ..... F 305 772-0961
Hialeah *(G-5629)*

CONTRACTORS: Millwrights

Diverse Co ..... F 863 425-4251
Mulberry *(G-11123)*

CONTRACTORS: Multi-Family Home Remodeling

Jab-B-Inc ..... G 813 803-3995
Lutz *(G-8393)*
Los Primos Express Service ..... G 786 701-3297
Miami *(G-9912)*

CONTRACTORS: Nonresidential Building Design & Construction

Division 5 Florida Inc ..... E 904 964-4513
Starke *(G-16893)*

CONTRACTORS: Office Furniture Installation

Joe Hearn Innovative Tech LLC ..... F 850 898-3744
Pensacola *(G-14183)*
John Eric Madden ..... G 813 395-3314
Zephyrhills *(G-19524)*

CONTRACTORS: Oil & Gas Aerial Geophysical Exploration Svcs

Atlantic Gas Services LLC ..... G 386 957-3668
New Smyrna Beach *(G-11525)*

CONTRACTORS: Oil & Gas Building, Repairing & Dismantling Svc

Sunshine Oil and Gas Inc ..... G 305 367-3100
Miami *(G-10435)*
Warensford Well Drilling Inc ..... G 386 738-3257
Deland *(G-3031)*

CONTRACTORS: Oil & Gas Field Salt Water Impound/Storing Svc

Worrell Water Technologies LLC ..... G 434 973-6365
Delray Beach *(G-3161)*

CONTRACTORS: Oil & Gas Well Casing Cement Svcs

Bukkehave Inc ..... G 954 525-9788
Fort Lauderdale *(G-3876)*

CONTRACTORS: Oil & Gas Well Drilling Svc

AES Services Inc ..... G 941 237-1446
Venice *(G-18529)*
Old City Building ..... G 850 432-7723
Pensacola *(G-14215)*
Perfect Oil Inc ..... G 954 984-8944
Pompano Beach *(G-14788)*
Raven Forest Operating LLC ..... F 727 497-2727
Tampa *(G-18039)*
US Natural Gas Corp ..... G 727 482-1505
Saint Petersburg *(G-15949)*
Warensford Well Drilling Inc ..... G 386 738-3257
Deland *(G-3031)*

CONTRACTORS: Oil & Gas Well Flow Rate Measurement Svcs

Five Star Field Services ..... G 347 446-6816
Boynton Beach *(G-905)*

CONTRACTORS: Oil & Gas Well Redrilling

Titan Petroleum Corporation ..... G 813 280-4833
Tampa *(G-18188)*

CONTRACTORS: Oil & Gas Wells Svcs

Puraglobe Florida LLC ..... E 813 247-1754
Tampa *(G-18023)*
Titan Petroleum Corporation ..... G 813 280-4833
Tampa *(G-18188)*

CONTRACTORS: Oil Field Haulage Svcs

D & S Pallets Inc ..... D 727 540-0061
Clearwater *(G-1647)*

CONTRACTORS: Oil Field Lease Tanks: Erectg, Clng/Rprg Svcs

Ed-Gar Leasing Company Inc ..... F 904 284-1900
Green Cove Springs *(G-5060)*

CONTRACTORS: Oil Field Pipe Testing Svcs

Mechanical Design Corp ..... G 772 388-8782
Sebastian *(G-16670)*
Tricen Technologies Fla LLC ..... F 866 620-9407
Fort Pierce *(G-4758)*

CONTRACTORS: Oil/Gas Field Casing,Tube/Rod Running,Cut/Pull

Mecol Oil Tools Corp ..... F 305 638-7686
Miami *(G-9962)*

CONTRACTORS: Oil/Gas Well Construction, Rpr/Dismantling Svcs

A Plus Construction Svcs Inc ..... E 904 612-0597
Jacksonville *(G-6111)*
Affordble Prsrvtion Rstoration ..... G 941 527-1416
Sarasota *(G-16335)*
All-Jer Construction Usa Inc ..... G 305 257-0225
Miami *(G-9114)*
Blue Tarpon Construction LLC ..... G 251 223-3630
Pensacola *(G-14101)*
Brace Integrated Services Inc ..... E 813 248-6248
Tampa *(G-17484)*
Broit Builders Inc ..... E 239 300-6900
Naples *(G-11195)*
Buena Vista Construction Co ..... E 407 828-2104
Lake Buena Vista *(G-7335)*
Canna Construction LLC ..... G 239 450-2141
Fort Myers *(G-4386)*
Cannida Co LLC ..... G 727 642-3709
Saint Petersburg *(G-15737)*
CB Designing Inc ..... G 407 927-1808
Orlando *(G-12557)*
Certified Mold Free Corp ..... G 954 614-7100
Davie *(G-2508)*
CMR FL Solutions LLC ..... G 586 206-2517
Venice *(G-18537)*
Cohen Capital LLC ..... G 954 661-8270
Fort Lauderdale *(G-3908)*
Compact Contract Inc ..... G 352 817-8058
Ocala *(G-11906)*
D M C Industries Inc ..... G 352 620-9322
Sparr *(G-16843)*
Dbn Investment LLC ..... F 407 917-2525
Orlando *(G-12658)*
DDy Martinez LLC ..... F 786 263-2672
Doral *(G-3325)*
Downes Trading Co ..... G 813 855-7122
Palm Harbor *(G-13734)*
Ducksteins Services ..... G 352 449-5678
Leesburg *(G-8151)*
E 3 Maintenance ..... E 904 708-7208
Jacksonville *(G-6343)*
Elements Restoration LLC ..... E 813 330-2035
Tampa *(G-17632)*
Elyse Installations LLC ..... E 904 322-4754
Jacksonville *(G-6360)*
Genos Construction Inc ..... D 234 303-3427
Dade City *(G-2428)*
House Doctair Inc ..... F 239 349-7497
Ave Maria *(G-257)*
Jab-B-Inc ..... G 813 803-3995
Lutz *(G-8393)*
John A Pulling Jr ..... G 239 593-5247
Naples *(G-11298)*
Kabrit Repair Services LLC ..... F 407 714-1470
Windermere *(G-19232)*
Kr Solutions Group US LLC ..... G 305 307-8353
Doral *(G-3412)*
Legacy Cnstr Rmdlg Clg Svcs LL ..... E 800 638-9646
Hallandale Beach *(G-5197)*
Los Primos Express Service ..... G 786 701-3297
Miami *(G-9912)*
Lucas Construction Inc ..... G 386 623-0088
Ormond Beach *(G-13383)*
MEI Companies Inc ..... G 352 361-6895
Citra *(G-1557)*
Michael L Larviere Inc ..... F 239 267-2738
Fort Myers *(G-4530)*
Muelby Construction Services ..... E 561 376-7614
North Palm Beach *(G-11723)*
Nivcoe International Dev ..... F 321 282-3666
Winter Park *(G-19428)*
Pulling Inc ..... G 305 224-2469
Sunrise *(G-17166)*
Rachel Ally ..... F 727 804-9596
Hudson *(G-6036)*
Randolph Cnstr Group Inc ..... G 954 276-2889
Delray Beach *(G-3133)*
Rapid Response ..... G 407 774-9877
Altamonte Springs *(G-69)*
Rippee Construction Inc ..... G 850 668-6805
Tallahassee *(G-17316)*
Ryan Tire & Petroleum Inc ..... G 239 334-1351
Fort Myers *(G-4588)*
Sherry J Bertucelli Inc ..... G 407 760-7585
Orlando *(G-13180)*
Solution Asset Management LLC ..... G 786 288-9408
Hollywood *(G-5911)*
Sunshine Spray Foam Insulation ..... G 239 221-8704
Bonita Springs *(G-859)*
Suvillaga Construction MGT LLC ..... F 305 323-8380
Miami *(G-10444)*
Ten4 Solutions LLC ..... G 302 544-1120
Nokomis *(G-11589)*
Weldcorp Industries ..... E 561 339-7713
Jupiter *(G-7147)*
Will Watson Construction LLC ..... G 850 586-5349
Fort Walton Beach *(G-4840)*
Williams Industrial Svcs LLC ..... E 904 696-9994
Jacksonville *(G-6922)*
Yatfl Inc ..... G 786 643-8660
Miami *(G-10625)*

CONTRACTORS: On-Site Welding

C & H Baseball Inc ..... G 941 727-1533
Bradenton *(G-1006)*
Custom Wldg & Fabrication Inc ..... E 863 967-1000
Auburndale *(G-237)*
D C Inc Prtble Wldg Fbrication ..... G 863 533-4483
Frostproof *(G-4859)*
Deans Cstm Shtmtl Fabrication ..... G 813 757-6270
Dover *(G-3558)*
Gunns Welding & Fabricating ..... G 727 393-5238
Saint Petersburg *(G-15801)*
L M Industrial Inc ..... G 407 240-8911
Orlando *(G-12879)*
P & A Welding and Machine Inc ..... G 863 425-3198
Mulberry *(G-11132)*
Pk Welding Inc ..... G 407 694-9403
Kissimmee *(G-7287)*
St Cloud Wldg Fabrication Inc ..... E 407 957-2344
Saint Cloud *(G-15667)*
Titan Service Industry Llc ..... G 678 313-4707
Deland *(G-3023)*

CONTRACTORS: Ornamental Metal Work

Barrett Custom Designs LLC ..... G 321 242-2002
Melbourne *(G-8776)*
Custom Fbrications of Freeport ..... F 850 729-0500
Valparaiso *(G-18509)*
Florida Aluminum and Steel Inc ..... F 863 967-4191
Auburndale *(G-241)*
Metal Creations Sarasota Llc ..... F 941 922-7096
Sarasota *(G-16256)*

CONTRACTORS: Painting & Wall Covering

A Clean Finish Inc ..... G 407 516-1311
Jacksonville *(G-6109)*
Ken R Avery Painting Inc ..... E 813 855-5037
Oldsmar *(G-12239)*

CONTRACTORS: Painting, Commercial, Exterior

Glory Sandblasting Inc ..... F 407 422-0078
Orlando *(G-12784)*

CONTRACTORS: Painting, Commercial, Interior

John Eric Madden..........G....... 813 395-3314
Zephyrhills *(G-19524)*

CONTRACTORS: Painting, Indl

Industrial Marine Inc..........F....... 904 781-4707
Jacksonville *(G-6493)*

CONTRACTORS: Painting, Residential

Clear View Coatings LLC..........F....... 850 210-0155
Tallahassee *(G-17234)*
Thomas Smith & Company Inc..........F....... 863 858-2199
Lakeland *(G-7821)*

CONTRACTORS: Parking Lot Maintenance

Traffic Control Pdts Fla Inc..........F....... 352 372-7088
Jacksonville *(G-6865)*

CONTRACTORS: Patio & Deck Construction & Repair

Danielle Fence Mfg Co Inc..........D....... 863 425-3182
Mulberry *(G-11121)*
Fresco Group Inc..........F....... 239 936-8055
Fort Myers *(G-4459)*
Hydes Screening Inc..........G....... 954 345-6743
Coral Springs *(G-2258)*
K C Screen..........G....... 407 977-9636
Oviedo *(G-13442)*
R & K Portable Buildings..........G....... 850 857-7899
Pensacola *(G-14247)*

CONTRACTORS: Pile Driving

Shoreline Foundation Inc..........C....... 954 985-0981
West Park *(G-19098)*

CONTRACTORS: Playground Construction & Eqpt Installation

Southern Recreation Inc..........F....... 904 387-4390
Jacksonville *(G-6796)*

CONTRACTORS: Pole Cutting

Florida Pole Setters & Crane..........G....... 772 283-6820
Palm City *(G-13657)*

CONTRACTORS: Post Disaster Renovations

Elements Restoration LLC..........E....... 813 330-2035
Tampa *(G-17632)*
Kustom Us Inc..........F....... 407 965-1940
Longwood *(G-8303)*

CONTRACTORS: Precast Concrete Struct Framing & Panel Placing

Orange State Steel Cnstr Inc..........E....... 727 544-3398
Pinellas Park *(G-14374)*

CONTRACTORS: Prefabricated Window & Door Installation

Absolute Window and Door Inc..........G....... 941 485-7774
Venice *(G-18527)*
Arso Enterprises Inc..........E....... 305 681-2020
Opa Locka *(G-12290)*
Clear Vue Inc..........E....... 727 726-5386
Safety Harbor *(G-15490)*
Global Performance Windows Inc..........F....... 954 942-3322
Pompano Beach *(G-14715)*
Master Alum & SEC Shutter Co..........G....... 727 725-1744
Safety Harbor *(G-15498)*

CONTRACTORS: Pulpwood, Engaged In Cutting

Barnes & Sons Wood Producers..........G....... 386 935-2229
Branford *(G-1185)*
Breeden Pulpwood Inc..........F....... 352 528-5243
Williston *(G-19210)*
Creamer Corp..........G....... 850 265-2700
Panama City *(G-13888)*
Huntley Stemwood Inc..........G....... 904 237-4005
Middleburg *(G-10906)*
J Q Bell & Sons..........G....... 904 879-1597
Callahan *(G-1325)*
Joiner Land Clearing LLC..........G....... 850 997-5729
Monticello *(G-11078)*
Padgetts Pulpwood Inc..........G....... 904 282-5112
Middleburg *(G-10911)*
Stratton Inc Dm..........G....... 904 268-6052
Jacksonville *(G-6818)*
Whitfield Timber Co Inc..........E....... 850 639-5556
Wewahitchka *(G-19184)*

CONTRACTORS: Refrigeration

Kommercial Refrigeration Inc..........G....... 863 299-3000
Winter Haven *(G-19332)*

CONTRACTORS: Roofing

Chuculu LLC..........F....... 305 595-4577
Miami *(G-9353)*
Coastal Acquisitions Fla LLC..........F....... 850 769-9423
Panama City *(G-13883)*
Largo Aluminum Inc..........F....... 305 852-2390
Islamorada *(G-6098)*
Southeast Gen Contrs Group Inc..........F....... 877 407-3535
Port St Lucie *(G-15179)*

CONTRACTORS: Roofing & Gutter Work

Thomas Smith & Company Inc..........F....... 863 858-2199
Lakeland *(G-7821)*

CONTRACTORS: Roustabout Svcs

Grms Servicing LLC..........G....... 850 278-1000
Santa Rosa Beach *(G-16160)*
Jdt Servicing LLC..........G....... 813 909-8640
Lutz *(G-8394)*
Servicing Solutions Group..........G....... 727 216-4477
Clearwater *(G-1874)*
Srb Servicing LLC..........G....... 850 278-1000
Santa Rosa Beach *(G-16168)*
Standout Home Servicing LLC..........G....... 772 708-1110
Port Saint Lucie *(G-15147)*

CONTRACTORS: Safety & Security Eqpt

Amtel Security Systems Inc..........E....... 305 591-8200
Doral *(G-3249)*
Security Oracle Inc..........F....... 352 988-5985
Clermont *(G-1974)*
Titan Service Industry Llc..........G....... 678 313-4707
Deland *(G-3023)*

CONTRACTORS: Sandblasting Svc, Building Exteriors

RSR Industrial Coatings Inc..........F....... 863 537-1110
Bartow *(G-332)*

CONTRACTORS: Screening, Window & Door

ABC Screen Masters Inc..........G....... 239 772-7336
Cape Coral *(G-1371)*
British Boys & Associates..........G....... 305 278-1790
Miami *(G-9277)*
Liberty Aluminum Co..........E....... 239 369-3000
Lehigh Acres *(G-8197)*
Screen Monkey Corp..........G....... 352 746-7091
Homosassa *(G-6005)*

CONTRACTORS: Septic System

Averett Septic Tank Co Inc..........E....... 863 665-1748
Lakeland *(G-7640)*
Bingham On-Site Sewers Inc..........D....... 813 659-0003
Dover *(G-3556)*
Dixie Sptic Tank Orange Cy LLC..........F....... 386 775-3051
Orange City *(G-12375)*
Miller Brothers Contractors..........F....... 941 371-4162
Sarasota *(G-16510)*
Pilot Corp of Palm Beaches..........F....... 561 848-2928
Riviera Beach *(G-15363)*
Stans Septic Svc & Con Pdts..........G....... 941 639-3976
Punta Gorda *(G-15236)*
Taylor Concrete Inc..........G....... 941 737-7225
Palmetto *(G-13828)*

CONTRACTORS: Sheet Metal Work, NEC

Freeman Electric Co Inc..........F....... 850 785-7448
Panama City *(G-13905)*
Kohtler Elevator Inds Inc..........E....... 305 687-7037
Opa Locka *(G-12331)*
Mechanical Svcs Centl Fla Inc..........C....... 407 857-3510
Orlando *(G-12957)*
Ra Co AMO Inc..........F....... 561 626-7232
Palm Beach Gardens *(G-13620)*

CONTRACTORS: Single-family Home General Remodeling

British Boys & Associates..........G....... 305 278-1790
Miami *(G-9277)*
Kevco Builders Inc..........F....... 352 308-8025
Eustis *(G-3711)*

CONTRACTORS: Solar Energy Eqpt

Alterna Power Inc..........F....... 407 287-9148
Orlando *(G-12462)*
Wes Industries Inc..........F....... 941 371-7617
Sarasota *(G-16637)*

CONTRACTORS: Special Trades, NEC

East Coast Door Inc..........F....... 954 868-4700
Pompano Beach *(G-14672)*

CONTRACTORS: Store Front Construction

Florida Glass of Tampa Bay..........D....... 813 925-1330
Tampa *(G-17677)*

CONTRACTORS: Structural Steel Erection

Aog Detailing Services Inc..........G....... 727 742-7321
Saint Petersburg *(G-15703)*
Central Maintenance & Wldg Inc..........B....... 813 229-0012
Lithia *(G-8216)*
Custom Fbrications of Freeport..........F....... 850 729-0500
Valparaiso *(G-18509)*
Fitzlord Inc..........D....... 904 731-2041
Jacksonville *(G-6390)*
Met-Con Inc..........D....... 321 632-4880
Cocoa *(G-2035)*
Quality Industries America Inc..........G....... 386 755-0220
Lake City *(G-7380)*
Steel City Inc..........F....... 850 785-9596
Panama City *(G-13952)*
Storage Building Company LLC..........F....... 863 738-1319
Palmetto *(G-13825)*
United Fabrication & Maint..........G....... 863 295-9000
Eloise *(G-3656)*
Viper Communication Systems..........E....... 352 694-7030
Ocala *(G-12072)*

CONTRACTORS: Stucco, Interior

Central Florida Cnstr Walls..........F....... 407 448-2350
Orlando *(G-12565)*

CONTRACTORS: Svc Well Drilling Svcs

Danny Brawley..........G....... 239 597-0084
Naples *(G-11220)*

CONTRACTORS: Textile Warping

Dillon Yarn Corporation..........C....... 973 684-1600
Fort Lauderdale *(G-3941)*

CONTRACTORS: Tile Installation, Ceramic

Designer Lifestyles LLC..........F....... 904 631-8954
Jacksonville *(G-6317)*

CONTRACTORS: Underground Utilities

Coastal Concrete Products LLC..........E....... 239 208-4079
Fort Myers *(G-4402)*

CONTRACTORS: Unit Paver Installation

Df Multi Services LLC..........G....... 407 683-2223
Orlando *(G-12668)*

CONTRACTORS: Warm Air Heating & Air Conditioning

Airite Air Conditioning Inc..........E....... 813 886-0235
Tampa *(G-17395)*
Precision Resources Inc..........F....... 321 635-2000
Cocoa *(G-2043)*

CONTRACTORS: Water Well Drilling

Eagle Engrg & Land Dev Inc..........F....... 913 948-4320
Boynton Beach *(G-900)*

H2r Corp F 727 541-3444
Pinellas Park *(G-14353)*

CONTRACTORS: Water Well Servicing

Dependable Water Inc E 772 563-7473
Vero Beach *(G-18615)*

CONTRACTORS: Window Treatment Installation

Bornt Enterprises Inc E 813 623-1492
Tampa *(G-17483)*
Florida Wood Creations Inc G 239 561-5411
Punta Gorda *(G-15205)*
Timbercraft of Naples Inc G 239 566-2559
Naples *(G-11442)*
TMMR Holdings LLC E 407 295-5200
Ocoee *(G-12092)*
Top Trtment Cstomes Accesories G 239 936-4600
Fort Myers *(G-4632)*

CONTRACTORS: Windows & Doors

Gulfstream Alum & Shutter Corp E 772 287-6476
Stuart *(G-16950)*
Pinos Window Corporation F 305 888-9903
Medley *(G-8706)*
Rollshield LLC F 727 441-2243
Clearwater *(G-1864)*
Specialty Products Inc G 850 438-4264
Pensacola *(G-14267)*
Techno Cabinets Inc G 305 910-9929
Doral *(G-3525)*

CONTRACTORS: Wood Floor Installation & Refinishing

Eagle Prof Flrg Removal G 813 520-3027
Riverview *(G-15270)*
Global Prime Wood LLC G 770 292-9200
Aventura *(G-271)*

CONTRACTORS: Wrecking & Demolition

Platinium Rosis Inc G 786 617-9973
Miami Beach *(G-10703)*

CONTROL CIRCUIT DEVICES

Technical Drive Ctrl Svcs Inc G 954 471-6521
Davie *(G-2601)*

CONTROL EQPT: Electric

Barcode Automation Inc F 407 327-2177
Winter Springs *(G-19468)*
ICI Custom Parts Inc E 813 888-7979
Tampa *(G-17768)*
Metal-Tech Controls Corp G 941 575-7677
Punta Gorda *(G-15215)*
Phasetronics Inc C 727 573-1819
Clearwater *(G-1830)*
Pro Co Inc G 321 422-0900
Winter Springs *(G-19481)*
STA-Con Incorporated E 407 298-5940
Apopka *(G-187)*
Sun State Systems Inc F 904 269-2544
Orange Park *(G-12408)*
Technico of Central Florida G 321 631-4414
Rockledge *(G-15451)*
Tel-Tron Technologies Corp E 386 523-1070
Daytona Beach *(G-2724)*
Tentech Corporation F 305 938-0389
Miami *(G-10467)*

CONTROL EQPT: Electric Buses & Locomotives

American Traction Systems Inc E 239 768-0757
Fort Myers *(G-4358)*

CONTROL PANELS: Electrical

America Energy Inc G 954 762-7763
Pembroke Pines *(G-14020)*
Champion Controls Inc E 954 318-3090
Fort Lauderdale *(G-3895)*
Consumer Engineering Inc F 321 984-8550
Palm Bay *(G-13507)*
Custom Control Solutions Inc G 850 937-8902
Cantonment *(G-1338)*
Ff Systems Inc G 239 288-4255
Fort Myers *(G-4449)*
Paneltronics Incorporated D 305 823-9777
Hialeah *(G-5554)*
Quality Building Controls Inc E 813 885-5005
Tampa *(G-18030)*
Technology Research LLC D 727 535-0572
Clearwater *(G-1912)*

CONTROLS & ACCESS: Indl, Electric

CC Control Corp E 561 293-3975
West Palm Beach *(G-18836)*
Hale Products Inc C 352 629-5020
Ocala *(G-11963)*
Hf Scientific Inc E 888 203-7248
Fort Myers *(G-4481)*
Southern Automated Systems G 863 815-7444
Lakeland *(G-7799)*
Sun Electronic Systems Inc F 321 383-9400
Titusville *(G-18466)*
Wolff Controls Corporation F 863 324-0423
Winter Haven *(G-19368)*

CONTROLS & ACCESS: Motor

Eaton & Wolk G 305 249-1640
Miami *(G-9496)*
Eaton Law G 813 264-4800
Tampa *(G-17629)*
Motor Protection Electronics F 407 299-3825
Apopka *(G-163)*
Nidec Motor Corporation C 954 346-4900
Coral Springs *(G-2297)*
Saminco Inc E 239 561-1561
Fort Myers *(G-4594)*
Taylor Electronics Inc F 941 925-3605
Sarasota *(G-16618)*

CONTROLS: Air Flow, Refrigeration

Airflowbalance LLC F 386 871-8136
Lake Mary *(G-7397)*
Molekule Inc G 352 871-3803
Tampa *(G-17916)*
R & J Mfg of Gainesville G 352 375-3130
Gainesville *(G-4987)*

CONTROLS: Automatic Temperature

Moisttech Corp F 941 351-7870
Sarasota *(G-16259)*

CONTROLS: Electric Motor

Faac International Inc G 904 448-8952
Rockledge *(G-15411)*
Industrial Service Solutions C 239 288-5230
Fort Myers *(G-4493)*
Universal Precision Inds Inc G 727 581-7097
Largo *(G-8071)*

CONTROLS: Environmental

AVw Inc E 954 972-3338
Margate *(G-8536)*
F & J Specialty Products Inc F 352 680-1177
Ocala *(G-11939)*
Florida Enviromental Cons G 407 402-2828
Clermont *(G-1958)*
Galtronics Telemetry Inc F 386 202-2055
Palm Coast *(G-13697)*
Leslie Controls Inc C 813 978-1000
Temple Terrace *(G-18371)*
Melbourne-Tillman Wtr Ctrl Dst E 321 723-7233
Palm Bay *(G-13524)*
Micro Control Systems Inc E 239 694-0089
Fort Myers *(G-4532)*
Niagara Industries Inc F 305 876-9010
Miami *(G-10071)*
Noxtak Corp G 786 586-7927
Pembroke Pines *(G-14052)*
Portalp Usa Inc F 800 474-3667
Naples *(G-11373)*
Sacyr Environment USA LLC F 202 361-4568
Miami *(G-10294)*
Sampletech G 727 239-7055
Clearwater *(G-1868)*
Suntree Technologies Inc F 321 637-7552
Cocoa *(G-2054)*
Technico F 561 588-8300
Lake Worth *(G-7590)*
Thompson Envrnmntal Mntring Ctr G 321 591-7300
Melbourne *(G-8961)*
Triumvirate Environmental E 407 859-4441
Orlando *(G-13275)*
Two Tree Inc G 352 284-1763
Gainesville *(G-5013)*

CONTROLS: Marine & Navy, Auxiliary

Artful Arnautic Assemblies LLC G 727 522-0055
Saint Petersburg *(G-15712)*
General Scientific Corporation G 850 866-9636
Panama City *(G-13908)*
L-3 Cmmnctons Ntronix Holdings D 212 697-1111
Melbourne *(G-8863)*
Marine Engine Controls Inc F 727 518-8080
Hudson *(G-6034)*
Panish Controls G 203 333-7371
Largo *(G-8022)*
Seatorque Control Systems LLC E 772 220-3020
Stuart *(G-17007)*
Southeastern Marine Power LLC F 727 545-2700
Saint Petersburg *(G-15916)*

CONTROLS: Relay & Ind

ABB Enterprise Software Inc C 954 752-6700
Coral Springs *(G-2211)*
ABB Inc D 407 732-2000
Lake Mary *(G-7396)*
ABB Inc D 305 471-0844
Miami *(G-9053)*
Action Controls Inc G 253 243-7703
Aventura *(G-259)*
Advance Ctrl Mfg Jean Annette G 941 697-0846
Englewood *(G-3657)*
Alttec Corporation G 727 547-1622
Clearwater *(G-1578)*
Beckwith Electric Co Inc G 727 544-2326
Largo *(G-7905)*
Coast Controls Inc F 941 355-7555
Sarasota *(G-16192)*
Custom Controls Technology Inc E 305 805-3700
Hialeah *(G-5358)*
D & L Auto & Marine Supplies G 305 593-0560
Doral *(G-3319)*
Dynalco Controls Corporation E 323 589-6181
Fort Lauderdale *(G-3952)*
E G Pump Controls Inc E 904 292-0110
Jacksonville *(G-6344)*
Eaton Corporation G 561 998-4111
Boca Raton *(G-512)*
Electrical Controls Inc F 954 801-6846
Tamarac *(G-17355)*
Entech Controls Corp G 954 613-2971
Miami *(G-9528)*
Facts Engineering LLC E 727 375-8888
Trinity *(G-18485)*
Intelligent Heater LLC G 305 248-4971
Homestead *(G-5973)*
Jenzano Incorporated F 386 761-4474
Port Orange *(G-15020)*
Kemco Industries LLC D 407 322-1230
Sanford *(G-16077)*
Kinematics and Controls Corp G 352 796-0300
Brooksville *(G-1243)*
Lextm3 Systems LLC F 954 888-1024
Davie *(G-2546)*
Micro Control Systems Inc E 239 694-0089
Fort Myers *(G-4532)*
Moog Inc G 716 652-2000
Pembroke Pines *(G-14049)*
Quest Controls Inc F 941 729-4799
Palmetto *(G-13820)*
RTC Solutions Inc G 919 439-8680
Davie *(G-2587)*
Scientific Instruments Inc E 561 881-8500
Mangonia Park *(G-8511)*
Select Engineered Systems Inc E 305 823-5410
Hialeah *(G-5613)*
Sepac Corp F 305 718-3379
Miami *(G-10325)*
Song-Chuan USA Inc F 954 788-5889
Pompano Beach *(G-14856)*
Ultrapanel Marine Inc E 772 285-4258
Miami *(G-10527)*

CONTROLS: Remote, Boat

Alamo USA Inc G 954 774-3747
Hallandale Beach *(G-5168)*

Dukane Seacom Inc ....C....941 739-3200
Sarasota *(G-16209)*
Gem Remotes Inc ....F....239 642-0873
Naples *(G-11259)*

CONTROLS: Thermostats

JRS Ventures LLP ....G....715 441-1051
Deltona *(G-3172)*
Simplexgrinnell Holdings LLC ....G....978 731-2500
Boca Raton *(G-716)*
Southern Environmental Inc ....E....850 944-4475
Pensacola *(G-14263)*

CONTROLS: Thermostats, Exc Built-in

Mold Control Systems Inc ....G....561 316-5412
Palm Beach Gardens *(G-13610)*
Vtronix LLC ....G....305 471-7600
Miami *(G-10594)*

CONTROLS: Truck, Indl Battery

Lithium Battery Company LLC ....F....813 504-0074
Tampa *(G-17850)*
Mia Consulting & Trading Inc ....G....305 640-9677
Miami *(G-9989)*

CONTROLS: Water Heater

Qci ....D....407 886-6300
Apopka *(G-175)*

CONVERTERS: Data

Crucial Collision Prod LLC ....F....321 501-1722
Melbourne *(G-8798)*
Cyipcom Inc ....G....954 727-2500
Oakland Park *(G-11794)*
Global Mind USA LLC ....D....305 402-2190
Miami *(G-9640)*
Multimedia Effects Inc ....F....800 367-3054
Plantation *(G-14536)*
Ten In Motion LLC ....F....407 226-0204
Orlando *(G-13247)*
Wau USA Corp ....F....305 361-6110
Key Biscayne *(G-7163)*

CONVERTERS: Frequency

Geneforce Incorporated ....G....786 823-0700
Miami *(G-9622)*

CONVERTERS: Power, AC to DC

Creating Tech Solutions LLC ....E....727 914-3001
Clearwater *(G-1642)*
OHM Americas LLC ....F....800 467-7275
Fort Lauderdale *(G-4148)*
Schneider Electric It Corp ....G....305 266-5005
Sunrise *(G-17171)*

CONVEYOR SYSTEMS

Built Right Installers Intl ....F....305 362-6010
Hialeah *(G-5334)*
UNI-Pak Corp ....E....407 830-9300
Longwood *(G-8346)*

CONVEYOR SYSTEMS: Pneumatic Tube

Eagle Pneumatic Inc ....E....863 644-4870
Lakeland *(G-7678)*
J D B Dense Flow Inc ....F....727 785-8500
Palm Harbor *(G-13741)*

CONVEYOR SYSTEMS: Robotic

American Automtn Systems Inc ....G....305 620-0077
Miami Lakes *(G-10762)*
Emmeti USA LLC ....F....813 490-6252
Safety Harbor *(G-15492)*
Sunshine Tool LLC ....G....941 351-6330
Sarasota *(G-16306)*

CONVEYORS & CONVEYING EQPT

Agri Machinery & Parts Inc ....F....407 299-1592
Orlando *(G-12442)*
Anchor Machine & Fabricating ....F....813 247-3099
Tampa *(G-17426)*
Andersons Can Line Fbrction Eq ....F....407 889-4665
Apopka *(G-113)*
Atlas Metal Industries Inc ....C....305 625-2451
Miami *(G-9186)*
Automated Parking Corporation ....G....754 200-8441
Fort Lauderdale *(G-3833)*
Capitol Conveyors Inc ....G....727 314-7474
Trinity *(G-18483)*
Chris Industries Corp ....G....941 729-7600
Palmetto *(G-13791)*
Container Handling Solutions ....G....941 359-2095
Sarasota *(G-16194)*
Conveyor Concepts Corporation ....G....941 751-1200
Sarasota *(G-16196)*
Conveyor Consulting & Rbr Corp ....G....813 385-1254
Odessa *(G-12113)*
Custom Metal Designs Inc ....D....407 656-7771
Oakland *(G-11769)*
Epperson & Company ....D....813 626-6125
Tampa *(G-17647)*
Erie Manufacturing Inc ....F....863 534-3743
Bartow *(G-315)*
Flite Technology Inc ....F....321 631-2050
Cocoa *(G-2022)*
Franbiz Inc ....G....813 282-1115
Clearwater *(G-1694)*
Gaemmerler (us) Corporation ....G....941 465-4400
Palmetto *(G-13800)*
ISA Group Corp ....F....305 748-1578
Miami *(G-9773)*
Jepsen Tool Company Inc ....F....904 262-2793
Jacksonville *(G-6521)*
Keller-Nglillis Design Mfg Inc ....F....727 733-4111
Dunedin *(G-3582)*
Lynx Products Corp Inc ....G....941 727-9676
Bradenton *(G-1073)*
M A K Manufacturing Inc ....G....352 343-5881
Tavares *(G-18346)*
Material Conveying Maint Inc ....E....813 740-1111
Tampa *(G-17894)*
Multi-Flex LLC ....G....941 360-6500
Sarasota *(G-16260)*
Novak Machining Inc ....G....727 527-5473
Pinellas Park *(G-14372)*
Padgett Manufacturing Inc ....D....941 756-8566
Bradenton *(G-1093)*
Quality Fbrction Mch Works Inc ....F....386 755-0220
Lake City *(G-7379)*
Sardee Industries Inc ....E....407 295-2114
Orlando *(G-13163)*
Sdi Industries Inc ....E....321 733-1128
Melbourne *(G-8928)*
Titan Service Industry Llc ....G....678 313-4707
Deland *(G-3023)*
Tpi Engineered Systems Inc ....G....727 233-2810
Hudson *(G-6041)*
US Conveyor Solutions Inc ....F....352 343-0085
Tavares *(G-18356)*
Ver-Val Enterprises Inc ....F....850 244-7931
Fort Walton Beach *(G-4838)*
William Laroque Installers Inc ....E....305 769-1717
Hollywood *(G-5940)*

COOKING & FOOD WARMING EQPT: Commercial

Atlas Metal Industries Inc ....C....305 625-2451
Miami *(G-9186)*
Bcr Environmental Corporation ....E....904 819-9170
Jacksonville *(G-6198)*
Brake-Funderburk Entps Inc ....E....904 730-6788
Jacksonville *(G-6230)*
Crystal Pool Service Inc ....F....954 444-8282
Sunrise *(G-17111)*
Enodis Holdings Inc ....C....727 375-7010
Trinity *(G-18484)*
Louis Di Rmndo Wrldwide Invstm ....F....786 536-7578
Miami Beach *(G-10689)*
Welbilt Inc ....A....727 375-7010
Trinity *(G-18491)*

COOKING & FOODWARMING EQPT: Coffee Brewing

Jiva Cubes Inc ....G....305 788-1200
Surfside *(G-17203)*

COOKING & FOODWARMING EQPT: Commercial

Euroasia Products Inc ....G....321 221-9398
Orlando *(G-12719)*

COOKING & FOODWARMING EQPT: Microwave Ovens, Commercial

Accommodating Services Inc ....G....863 528-3231
Lake Wales *(G-7498)*
Apollo Worldwide Inc ....G....561 585-3865
Hypoluxo *(G-6048)*

COOKING EQPT, HOUSEHOLD: Convection Ovens, Incldg Portable

Strategic Products Inc ....G....321 752-0441
Melbourne *(G-8945)*

COOKING EQPT, HOUSEHOLD: Ranges, Electric

Tannous Innovations LLC ....G....754 220-6645
Pompano Beach *(G-14883)*

COOKWARE: Fine Earthenware

Comerint Inc ....G....813 443-2466
Tampa *(G-17547)*

COOLERS & ICE CHESTS: Polystyrene Foam

Icemule Company Inc ....F....904 325-9012
Saint Augustine *(G-15552)*

COOLING TOWERS: Wood

East Coast Cooling Tower Inc ....F....904 551-5527
Jacksonville *(G-6348)*

COPPER ORE MINING

Pd Wire & Cable Sales Corp ....F....305 648-7790
Doral *(G-3456)*

COPPER ORES

Chemours Company Fc LLC ....C....904 964-1200
Starke *(G-16890)*
Goldfield Cnsld Mines Co ....D....321 724-1700
Melbourne *(G-8837)*
US Precious Metals Inc ....G....786 814-5804
Coral Gables *(G-2202)*

COPPER: Rolling & Drawing

Technetics Group LLC ....C....386 736-7373
Deland *(G-3019)*
Technetics Group LLC ....E....386 736-7373
De Land *(G-2734)*

CORD & TWINE

Rat Trap Bait Company Inc ....F....863 967-2148
Auburndale *(G-251)*
Shurhold Products Company ....G....772 287-1313
Palm City *(G-13673)*

CORK & CORK PRDTS

Art & Frame Drct/Timeless Inds ....G....407 857-6000
Orlando *(G-12492)*

CORK & CORK PRDTS: Tiles

Delta Mg ....G....561 840-0577
West Palm Beach *(G-18853)*
Designer Lifestyles LLC ....F....904 631-8954
Jacksonville *(G-6317)*

CORRUGATED PRDTS: Boxes, Partition, Display Items, Sheet/Pad

Omni Displays LLC ....E....352 799-9997
Brooksville *(G-1257)*

COSMETIC PREPARATIONS

Agustin Reyes Inc ....F....305 558-8870
Hialeah *(G-5275)*
Airrenu LLC ....G....386 246-8694
Palm Coast *(G-13682)*
Alfa Manufacturing Group LLC ....G....305 979-7344
Miami Gardens *(G-10733)*
American Hygenic Laboratories ....F....305 891-9518
Miami *(G-9144)*
Avon Company ....G....386 405-7208
Jacksonville *(G-6182)*

Beauty Awaits Cosmetics LLC ....G....... 754 226-5800
Miramar *(G-10973)*
Biddiscombe International LLC ....F....... 727 299-9287
Saint Petersburg *(G-15720)*
Bobbie Weiner Enterprises LLC ....G....... 817 615-8610
North Miami *(G-11628)*
Bpj International LLC ....G....... 305 507-8971
Doral *(G-3283)*
Brand Labs USA ....E....... 954 532-5390
Pompano Beach *(G-14620)*
Carfore Ltd ....G....... 239 415-2275
Fort Myers *(G-4388)*
Caribbean Breeze Inc ....G....... 904 261-7831
Fernandina Beach *(G-3732)*
Cemi International Inc ....C....... 407 859-7701
Orlando *(G-12561)*
Coco Cosmetics Inc ....F....... 305 622-3488
Miami *(G-9371)*
Cofran International Corp ....E....... 305 592-2644
Doral *(G-3302)*
Contours Rx LLC ....G....... 727 827-7321
Saint Petersburg *(G-15753)*
Cosmetic Corp of America Inc ....E....... 305 883-8434
Medley *(G-8636)*
Cosmetic Solutions LLC ....E....... 561 226-8600
Boca Raton *(G-490)*
Cosmetics & Cleaners Intl LLC ....E....... 305 592-5504
Doral *(G-3310)*
Custom Manufacturing Corp ....F....... 305 863-1001
Medley *(G-8639)*
Daby Products Carisen ....G....... 305 559-3018
West Miami *(G-18781)*
Dermazone Solutions Inc ....E....... 727 446-6882
Saint Petersburg *(G-15758)*
Diora Professionnel LLC ....F....... 954 628-5163
Hallandale Beach *(G-5181)*
Eagle Labs Incorporated ....D....... 727 548-1816
Saint Petersburg *(G-15767)*
Elizabeth Arden Inc ....A....... 954 364-6900
Pembroke Pines *(G-14031)*
F&J USA LLC ....E....... 800 406-6190
Miami Beach *(G-10666)*
Formulated Solutions LLC ....D....... 727 373-3970
Largo *(G-7953)*
Formulated Solutions LLC ....F....... 727 456-0302
Saint Petersburg *(G-15788)*
Glamer Medspa LLC ....F....... 305 744-6908
Pembroke Pines *(G-14035)*
Image International Inc ....G....... 561 793-9560
West Palm Beach *(G-18901)*
Instanatural LLC ....E....... 800 290-6932
Orlando *(G-12832)*
Kira Labs Inc ....F....... 954 978-4549
Pompano Beach *(G-14739)*
Kookie Kllection Kosmetics LLC ....F....... 954 218-4302
Lauderdale Lakes *(G-8090)*
Lf of America Corp ....G....... 561 988-0303
Boca Raton *(G-601)*
Matherson Organics LLC ....G....... 850 792-4007
Tallahassee *(G-17298)*
Mcllpack Inc ....F....... 561 988-8545
Boca Raton *(G-614)*
Menscience-Mk ....G....... 305 361-0994
Miami *(G-9975)*
Nohbo Labs LLC ....G....... 321 345-5319
Palm Bay *(G-13526)*
Nutra-Luxe MD LLC ....F....... 239 561-9699
Fort Myers *(G-4552)*
Nutraceutical Corporation ....G....... 813 877-4186
Tampa *(G-17943)*
Ollie Pippa International Inc ....G....... 888 851-6533
Boca Raton *(G-653)*
Prime Enterprises LLC ....D....... 305 625-4929
Hialeah *(G-5568)*
Prime Packaging Inc ....E....... 305 625-6737
Hialeah *(G-5569)*
Prive International Inc ....E....... 888 750-5850
North Miami Beach *(G-11698)*
Products By O2 Inc ....E....... 561 392-1892
Boynton Beach *(G-946)*
Promoitalia LLC ....G....... 305 347-5178
Miami *(G-10209)*
Pulsaderm LLC ....F....... 877 474-4038
Fort Myers *(G-4576)*
Pure Source LLC ....E....... 305 477-8111
Doral *(G-3473)*
Rev Personal Care LLC ....G....... 832 217-8585
Wellington *(G-18729)*
Revlon Inc ....G....... 904 693-1254
Jacksonville *(G-6721)*
Revlon Consumer Products Corp ....G....... 904 378-4167
Jacksonville *(G-6722)*
Romano Group LLC ....F....... 305 255-4242
Miami *(G-10278)*
Roux Laboratories Inc ....B....... 904 366-2602
Jacksonville *(G-6736)*
Rxgenesys LLC ....G....... 786 220-8366
Miami *(G-10290)*
Shiseido Americas Corporation ....F....... 305 416-6021
Miami *(G-10339)*
Sincerus Pharmaceuticals Inc ....C....... 800 604-5032
Pompano Beach *(G-14852)*
Skinmetics Inc ....F....... 305 663-5750
Miami *(G-10357)*
South Beach Skin Care Inc ....F....... 954 606-5057
Hallandale Beach *(G-5212)*
Swisscosmet Corp ....G....... 727 842-9419
New Port Richey *(G-11514)*
Tanning Research Labs LLC ....B....... 386 677-9559
Ormond Beach *(G-13405)*
Tend Skin International Inc ....F....... 954 382-0800
Davie *(G-2602)*

COSMETICS & TOILETRIES

4elementum LLC ....G....... 305 989-1106
Miami *(G-9028)*
Aleavia Brands LLC ....G....... 407 289-2632
Orlando *(G-12451)*
Aleavia LLC ....G....... 407 898-5800
Orlando *(G-12452)*
Aquarian Bath Inc ....G....... 310 919-0220
Holly Hill *(G-5756)*
Aromavalue Inc ....G....... 866 223-7561
Oldsmar *(G-12205)*
Ayurdevas Natural Products LLC ....G....... 786 322-0909
Miami *(G-9205)*
Beard Booze LLC ....G....... 352 424-0687
Lakeland *(G-7645)*
Beauty With Kelley Inc ....F....... 786 757-6485
Palmetto Bay *(G-13840)*
Berkant Corp ....F....... 305 771-5578
Miami *(G-9232)*
Brand Builders Rx LLC ....G....... 727 576-4013
Saint Petersburg *(G-15728)*
Cbd Brands Inc ....G....... 561 325-0482
Jupiter *(G-7016)*
Chelly Cosmetics Manufacturing ....G....... 305 471-9608
Miami *(G-9350)*
Christian L International Inc ....G....... 305 947-1722
Miami *(G-9351)*
Cosmo International Corp ....E....... 954 798-4500
Deerfield Beach *(G-2804)*
Coughlan Products Corp ....F....... 973 904-1500
Punta Gorda *(G-15202)*
Crunchi LLC ....G....... 772 600-8082
Stuart *(G-16929)*
Edens Garden Natural H ....G....... 585 353-8547
Deltona *(G-3168)*
Esteemed Brands Inc ....F....... 954 442-3923
Miramar *(G-10990)*
Ewhite LLC ....G....... 954 530-3382
Fort Lauderdale *(G-3979)*
Extreme Care Inc ....G....... 239 898-3709
Cape Coral *(G-1421)*
Facelove Cosmetics Inc ....G....... 786 346-7357
Miami *(G-9556)*
Femmescience LLC ....G....... 305 361-0994
Key Biscayne *(G-7155)*
Fhs Enterprises LLC ....G....... 754 214-9379
Delray Beach *(G-3078)*
Filorga Americas Inc ....F....... 786 266-7429
Miami Beach *(G-10667)*
Fragrance Expresscom LLC ....G....... 800 372-4726
Miami *(G-9596)*
Fresh Brandz LLC ....G....... 813 880-7110
Tampa *(G-17696)*
Fruitful LLC ....G....... 954 534-9828
Miami Lakes *(G-10792)*
Gaias Formula ....G....... 954 655-8095
Delray Beach *(G-3082)*
Get Salted LLC ....G....... 954 826-3947
Boca Raton *(G-544)*
Hydron Technologies Inc ....G....... 727 342-5050
Saint Petersburg *(G-15809)*
Inspec Solutions LLC ....E....... 866 467-7320
Holly Hill *(G-5758)*
Isle of Luxe Inc ....G....... 352 745-0515
Saint Augustine *(G-15558)*
James R Kontorchik LLC ....G....... 904 962-0597
Jacksonville *(G-6516)*
Jessups Specialty Products ....G....... 407 332-7574
Longwood *(G-8296)*
Joya Essentials LLC ....G....... 407 865-0880
Orlando *(G-12862)*
Kayva Distribution LLC ....G....... 305 428-2816
Doral *(G-3406)*
Keralis Inter Inc ....F....... 305 345-0849
Miami *(G-9821)*
Keratronix Inc ....F....... 954 753-5741
Coral Springs *(G-2268)*
Kreyol Essence LLC ....F....... 786 453-8287
Miami *(G-9831)*
Lawton LLC ....G....... 833 493-7226
Sunrise *(G-17141)*
Lush Fresh Handmade Cosmetics ....G....... 850 650-2434
Destin *(G-3198)*
Luxe Brands Inc ....E....... 954 791-6050
Plantation *(G-14529)*
Luxury World LLC ....G....... 954 746-8776
Sunrise *(G-17145)*
Natural4naturalz LLC ....G....... 561 621-1546
Clewiston *(G-1985)*
Odara Kanvas Cosmetics ....F....... 239 785-8013
Lehigh Acres *(G-8201)*
OL Products Inc ....D....... 813 854-3575
Oldsmar *(G-12252)*
Old 97 Company ....F....... 813 246-4180
Tampa *(G-17947)*
Oxygen Development LLC ....C....... 954 480-2675
Palm Springs *(G-13778)*
Oz Naturals LLC ....G....... 561 602-2932
West Palm Beach *(G-18979)*
Palladio Beauty Group LLC ....F....... 954 922-4311
Hollywood *(G-5886)*
Pb Group LLC ....E....... 954 922-4311
Hollywood *(G-5887)*
Personal Brands LLC ....E....... 855 426-7765
Deerfield Beach *(G-2886)*
Pretty Vulgar LLC ....G....... 561 465-8831
Boca Raton *(G-674)*
Prevail Solutions LLC ....G....... 727 210-6600
Clearwater *(G-1846)*
Prime Topco LLC ....G....... 305 625-4929
Hialeah *(G-5570)*
Private Label Skin Na LLC ....C....... 877 516-2200
Saint Petersburg *(G-15890)*
Promex LLC ....G....... 305 884-2400
Hialeah *(G-5581)*
Pure Essential ....G....... 407 732-7225
Sanford *(G-16107)*
Pure Labs LLC ....G....... 561 659-2229
West Palm Beach *(G-19012)*
Saavy Naturals ....G....... 904 372-0002
Neptune Beach *(G-11477)*
Sephora Inside Jcpenney ....G....... 386 752-2822
Lake City *(G-7383)*
Sesvalia Usa LLC ....G....... 305 615-1987
Coral Gables *(G-2195)*
Skin Pro International Inc ....F....... 305 528-9095
Southwest Ranches *(G-16841)*
Stream2sea LLC ....G....... 866 960-9513
Bowling Green *(G-869)*
Sweet & Saltsy Scrubs ....G....... 863 853-8874
Lakeland *(G-7814)*
Terry Laboratories LLC ....F....... 321 259-1630
Melbourne *(G-8960)*
Three Cay G LLC ....G....... 904 930-4554
Jacksonville *(G-6852)*
Tupperware Brands Corporation ....A....... 407 826-5050
Orlando *(G-13280)*
Unilever ....F....... 904 378-0298
Jacksonville *(G-6878)*
United World Imports LLC ....F....... 904 208-1252
Jacksonville *(G-6884)*
V P R A R T LLC ....E....... 786 205-4526
Hialeah *(G-5673)*
Vianny Corporation ....F....... 239 888-4536
Fort Myers *(G-4646)*

COSMETICS WHOLESALERS

Bobbie Weiner Enterprises LLC ....G....... 817 615-8610
North Miami *(G-11628)*
Brand Builders Rx LLC ....G....... 727 576-4013
Saint Petersburg *(G-15728)*
Chelly Cosmetics Manufacturing ....G....... 305 471-9608
Miami *(G-9350)*
Dermazone Solutions Inc ....E....... 727 446-6882
Saint Petersburg *(G-15758)*
Instanatural LLC ....E....... 800 290-6932
Orlando *(G-12832)*

Newbeauty Media Group LLC ....E 561 961-7600
Boca Raton *(G-643)*
Shiseido Americas Corporation ....F 305 416-6021
Miami *(G-10339)*
Sincerus Pharmaceuticals Inc ....C 800 604-5032
Pompano Beach *(G-14852)*
Swisscosmet Corp ....G 727 842-9419
New Port Richey *(G-11514)*

COSMETOLOGY & PERSONAL HYGIENE SALONS

Ecstatic Nails Inc ....G 305 328-9554
North Miami *(G-11636)*

COSTUME JEWELRY & NOVELTIES: Apparel, Exc Precious Metals

Pret-EE LLC ....G 561 839-4338
Palm Beach Gardens *(G-13617)*

COSTUME JEWELRY & NOVELTIES: Bracelets, Exc Precious Metals

Emoji Bracelet LLC ....G 954 987-0515
Fort Lauderdale *(G-3971)*
Inspire ME Bracelets ....F 404 644-7771
Fort Lauderdale *(G-4061)*
Sashka Co ....G 941 764-9741
Port Charlotte *(G-14996)*

COSTUME JEWELRY & NOVELTIES: Exc Semi & Precious

Accent Jewelry Inc ....F 941 391-6687
Punta Gorda *(G-15189)*
James A De Flippo Co ....G 407 851-2765
Orlando *(G-12849)*
Sonnys Strings Inc ....G 407 862-4905
Winter Park *(G-19446)*

COSTUME JEWELRY & NOVELTIES: Pins, Exc Precious Metals

Delray Pin Factory Intl ....G 561 994-1680
Coral Springs *(G-2240)*

COUGH MEDICINES

Ingenus Pharmaceuticals LLC ....F 407 354-5365
Orlando *(G-12830)*

COUNTER & SINK TOPS

AGR Fabricators Inc ....F 904 733-9393
Jacksonville *(G-6129)*
AGR of Florida Inc ....E 904 733-9393
Jacksonville *(G-6130)*
Amercn Cabinets Granite Floors ....F 727 303-0678
Palm Harbor *(G-13718)*
Blues Design Group LLC ....F 305 586-3630
Miami *(G-9262)*
Brazil America Srones Inc ....G 305 915-0123
Hallandale Beach *(G-5174)*
Byblos Group Inc ....G 305 662-6666
Miami *(G-9291)*
Cianos Tile & Marble Inc ....E 239 267-8453
Fort Myers *(G-4395)*
Commercial Stone Cab Fbrctors ....F 727 209-1141
Saint Petersburg *(G-15749)*
Commercial Stone Fbrcators Inc ....F 727 209-1141
Saint Petersburg *(G-15750)*
Counter Active Inc ....F 813 626-0022
Ponte Vedra *(G-14923)*
Countertop Solutions Inc ....G 239 961-0663
Naples *(G-11217)*
Designers Tops Inc ....F 305 599-9973
Miami *(G-9461)*
Furniture Concepts Inc ....G 727 535-0093
Largo *(G-7954)*
Just Counters Other Stuff Inc ....F 941 235-1300
Port Charlotte *(G-14986)*
Lg Hausys America Inc ....E 813 249-7658
Tampa *(G-17844)*
Salvia Tile & Stone Inc ....F 239 643-7770
Naples *(G-11389)*
Ssvm Partners Inc ....D 239 825-6282
Sarasota *(G-16602)*
Superior Solid Surface Inc ....F 727 842-9947
Port Richey *(G-15071)*
Total Koatings Inc ....G 941 870-0369
Sarasota *(G-16313)*
Venice Granit & Marble Inc ....G 941 483-4363
Venice *(G-18585)*

COUNTERS & COUNTING DEVICES

Hedrick-Walker & Associates ....G 352 735-2600
Mount Dora *(G-11104)*
Integ Construction Inc ....G 305 440-9101
Doral *(G-3391)*
Maxogen Group LLC ....E 305 814-0734
Hollywood *(G-5871)*
Power Plus Inc ....G 386 672-7579
Ormond Beach *(G-13392)*
Trumeter Company Inc ....G 954 725-6699
Coconut Creek *(G-2098)*

COUNTERS OR COUNTER DISPLAY CASES, EXC WOOD

East Coast Fixtures & Mllwk Co ....G 904 733-9711
Jacksonville *(G-6349)*
Emjac Industries Inc ....D 305 883-2194
Hialeah *(G-5395)*
Florida Design Mfg Assoc Inc ....F 561 533-0733
West Palm Beach *(G-18879)*
Kitchen Counter Connections ....E 386 677-9471
Ormond Beach *(G-13382)*
Load King Manufacturing Co ....C 904 354-8882
Jacksonville *(G-6560)*

COUNTERS OR COUNTER DISPLAY CASES, WOOD

Akiknav Inc ....F 561 842-8091
Riviera Beach *(G-15296)*

COUNTING DEVICES: Gauges, Press Temp Corrections Computing

Suncoast Tool & Gage Inds Inc ....F 727 572-8000
Clearwater *(G-1893)*

COUNTING DEVICES: Production

Del Monte Fresh Production Inc ....G 863 844-5836
Mulberry *(G-11122)*

COUNTING DEVICES: Tally

Countwise Llc ....F 954 846-7011
Sunrise *(G-17109)*
R S S Partners Inc ....G 904 241-6144
Jacksonville Beach *(G-6955)*

COUPLINGS: Hose & Tube, Hydraulic Or Pneumatic

Florida Hose & Hydraulics Inc ....G 305 887-9577
Miami *(G-9584)*
STS Distribution Solutions LLC ....F 844 359-4673
Miramar *(G-11048)*

COURIER SVCS, AIR: Package Delivery, Private

Leeward Tech ....G 305 215-4526
Homestead *(G-5980)*

COVERS: Automobile Seat

Sargent Seat Cover Co Inc ....E 904 355-2529
Jacksonville *(G-6752)*
Seat Savers Plus Inc ....G 305 256-7863
Miami *(G-10318)*
Universal Seat Covers Auto ACC ....G 305 262-3955
Miami *(G-10543)*

COVERS: Automotive, Exc Seat & Tire

Rolin Industries Inc ....G 850 654-1704
Fort Walton Beach *(G-4831)*

COVERS: Canvas

C-Worthy Corp ....F 954 784-7370
Pompano Beach *(G-14629)*
Evora Enterprises Inc ....F 305 261-4522
Ocala *(G-11934)*
Industrial Shadeports Inc ....G 954 755-0661
Fort Lauderdale *(G-4058)*

COVERS: Hot Tub & Spa

Bdjl Enterprises LLC ....F 407 678-9960
Apopka *(G-116)*
Prestige Spas Inc ....D 727 576-8600
Pinellas Park *(G-14379)*
Spa Cover Inc ....F 954 923-8801
Hollywood *(G-5913)*

CRADLES: Boat

Gyro-Gale Inc ....G 772 283-1711
Stuart *(G-16952)*

CRANE & AERIAL LIFT SVCS

Jayco Signs Inc ....F 407 339-5252
Maitland *(G-8468)*
Perl Inc ....F 352 726-2483
Inverness *(G-6095)*

CRANES & MONORAIL SYSTEMS

J Herbert Corporation ....F 407 846-0588
Kissimmee *(G-7256)*
PM Enterprises Holdings LLC ....E 407 846-0588
Kissimmee *(G-7288)*

CRANES: Indl Plant

Coastal Crane and Rigging Inc ....G 850 460-1766
Santa Rosa Beach *(G-16155)*

CRANES: Overhead

Deshazo LLC ....G 863 272-3107
Lakeland *(G-7674)*
Equipment Fabricators Inc ....E 321 632-0990
Cocoa *(G-2020)*
Nautical Acquisitions Corp ....C 727 541-6664
Largo *(G-8017)*

CRANKSHAFTS & CAMSHAFTS: Machining

Crankshaft Rebuilders Inc ....D 407 323-4870
Sanford *(G-16027)*
Delta Machine LLC ....G 386 738-2204
Deland *(G-2968)*
Diamondback Cnc LLC ....E 321 305-5995
Cocoa *(G-2010)*
Kinship Precision LLC ....F 321 765-3531
Melbourne *(G-8859)*

CRANKSHAFTS: Motor Vehicle

La Experiencia Crankshaft ....G 305 823-6161
Miami Lakes *(G-10802)*

CRATES: Fruit, Wood Wirebound

Walling Crate Company ....F 352 787-5211
Leesburg *(G-8180)*

CRUDE PETROLEUM & NATURAL GAS PRODUCTION

Breitburn Operating LP ....D 713 452-2266
Jay *(G-6963)*
C&C Diversified Services LLC ....G 772 597-1022
Stuart *(G-16919)*
Titan Petroleum Corporation ....G 813 280-4833
Tampa *(G-18188)*

CRUDE PETROLEUM & NATURAL GAS PRODUCTION

E-Direct Oil Inc ....G 518 366-2208
Naples *(G-11232)*
Fromkin Energy LLC ....G 954 683-2509
Coral Springs *(G-2249)*
Jones Field Services Pamela ....G 904 368-9777
Starke *(G-16895)*
K20 Oil LLC ....G 954 421-1735
Deerfield Beach *(G-2852)*
Neptune Petroleum LLC ....G 561 684-2844
West Palm Beach *(G-18962)*
Noumenon Corporation ....G 302 296-5460
Cape Coral *(G-1451)*
South Florida Petro Svcs LLC ....G 561 793-2102
Fort Lauderdale *(G-4246)*
Sustainable Projects Group Inc ....G 239 316-4593
Naples *(G-11429)*
US Natural Gas Corp ....G 727 482-1505
Saint Petersburg *(G-15949)*

CRUDE PETROLEUM PRODUCTION

Delta Oil G 813 323-3113
Brandon *(G-1156)*
Dorward Energy Corporation G 727 490-1778
Saint Petersburg *(G-15765)*
Maverick Natural Resources LLC E 239 657-2171
Immokalee *(G-6053)*
Tg Oil Services G 407 576-9571
Davie *(G-2604)*
Venkata SAI Corporation G 352 746-7076
Beverly Hills *(G-380)*

CRYSTALS

Tdk Electronics Inc F 561 509-7771
Ocean Ridge *(G-12080)*
V-Blox Corporation G 904 425-4908
Jacksonville *(G-6890)*

CRYSTALS & CRYSTAL ASSEMBLIES: Radio

Crystek Crystals Corporation E 239 561-3311
Fort Myers *(G-4418)*

CUBICLES: Electric Switchboard Eqpt

B & J Atlantic Inc E 904 338-0088
Jacksonville *(G-6185)*

CULTURE MEDIA

Acuderm Inc D 954 733-6935
Fort Lauderdale *(G-3781)*
Assoction Hspnic Hritg Fstival G 305 885-5613
Hialeah *(G-5310)*
Caregivercom Inc G 954 893-0550
Oakland Park *(G-11790)*
Creative Clture Mdia Group LLC G 786 237-0206
Coral Gables *(G-2134)*
Culture Cartel Media Inc G 407 680-8923
Sanford *(G-16030)*
Larrick Group Inc E 941 351-2700
Sarasota *(G-16248)*
One Biotechnology Company G 941 355-8451
Sarasota *(G-16268)*
P B C Cultural Counsel F 561 471-2903
West Palm Beach *(G-18980)*
Players Media Group Inc F 509 254-4949
Brooksville *(G-1261)*

CULVERTS: Sheet Metal

Metal Culverts Inc E 727 531-1431
Clearwater *(G-1782)*

CUPS & PLATES: Foamed Plastics

Dart Container Company Fla LLC C 813 752-1990
Plant City *(G-14423)*
Key Packaging Company Inc E 941 355-2728
Sarasota *(G-16245)*

CUPS: Plastic Exc Polystyrene Foam

Compak Companies LLC F 321 249-9590
Sanford *(G-16019)*
Grupo Phoenix Corp Svcs LLC E 954 241-0023
Miami *(G-9680)*
Tervis Tumbler Company C 941 966-2114
North Venice *(G-11763)*

CURBING: Granite Or Stone

Airam Stone Designs Inc G 305 477-8009
Miami *(G-9094)*
Fusion Industries Intl LLC G 239 415-7554
Fort Myers *(G-4462)*
Kadassa Inc F 954 684-8361
Riviera Beach *(G-15339)*
New England Granite & Marble G 772 283-8667
Stuart *(G-16980)*
Terrastone Inc G 305 234-8384
Miami *(G-10469)*

CURLING FEATHERS

Fi-Foil Company Inc E 863 965-1846
Auburndale *(G-240)*

CURTAIN & DRAPERY FIXTURES: Poles, Rods & Rollers

A Albrtini Cstm Win Treatments G 941 925-2556
Sarasota *(G-16328)*
A&I Aluminum Shutters G 561 223-5877
Lake Worth *(G-7527)*
B & D Precision Tools Inc E 305 885-1583
Hialeah *(G-5314)*
Biscayne Awning & Shade Co E 305 638-7933
Miami *(G-9250)*
Coverall Interiors G 813 961-8261
Tampa *(G-17560)*
Deco Abrusci International LLC F 305 406-3401
Doral *(G-3326)*
Deco Shades Solutions Inc G 305 558-9800
Hialeah *(G-5367)*
Designers Wholesale Workroom F 239 434-7633
Naples *(G-11226)*
Etchart LLC G 321 504-4060
Cocoa *(G-2021)*
Island Shutter Co Inc E 386 738-9455
Deland *(G-2985)*
Lucky Blinds Shutters LLC G 352 239-8475
Summerfield *(G-17060)*
Orlando Shutters LLC E 407 495-5250
Lake Mary *(G-7440)*
Reah Group LLC G 727 423-0668
Tampa *(G-18042)*
Resort Window Treatments Inc G 813 355-4877
Zephyrhills *(G-19535)*
Southeast Window Coverings G 904 372-0326
Jacksonville *(G-6788)*
TMMR Holdings LLC E 407 295-5200
Ocoee *(G-12092)*
USA Recmar Corp G 786 554-3505
Miami *(G-10555)*
Vertical Village Inc G 772 340-0400
Port Saint Lucie *(G-15162)*

CURTAIN WALLS: Building, Steel

Fenwall LLC D 813 343-5979
Tampa *(G-17664)*
Freedom Steel Building Corp E 561 330-0447
Fort Lauderdale *(G-4013)*

CUSHIONS & PILLOWS

Bedding Acquisition LLC G 561 997-6900
Boca Raton *(G-443)*
Cushion Solutions Incorporated G 813 253-2131
Tampa *(G-17575)*
Elaine Smith Inc F 561 863-3333
Riviera Beach *(G-15325)*
Florida Pillow Company G 407 648-9121
Orlando *(G-12752)*
General Pillows & Fiber Inc G 305 884-8300
Hialeah *(G-5427)*
Hollander HM Fshons Hldngs LLC F 212 302-6571
Boca Raton *(G-557)*
Pacific Coast Feather LLC C 206 624-1057
Boca Raton *(G-659)*
Superior Sleep Technology Inc F 305 888-0953
Hialeah *(G-5642)*
V M Visual Mdsg Dctr Group Inc F 305 759-9910
Miami *(G-10560)*

CUSHIONS & PILLOWS: Bed, From Purchased Materials

Design Works By Tech Pdts Inc E 941 355-2703
Sarasota *(G-16410)*
Hygenator Pillow Service Inc G 305 325-0250
Miami *(G-9723)*
United Pillow Mfg Inc F 305 636-9747
Miami *(G-10538)*

CUSHIONS & PILLOWS: Boat

Affordable Boat Cushions Inc G 877 350-2628
Riverview *(G-15263)*
Miami Prestige Interiors Inc E 305 685-3343
Miami *(G-10005)*

CUSHIONS: Carpet & Rug, Foamed Plastics

Pmh Homes Inc G 941 234-5121
Bradenton *(G-1099)*

CUSHIONS: Textile, Exc Spring & Carpet

Advanced Sewing G 954 484-2100
Fort Lauderdale *(G-3784)*
Shelleys Cushions Mfg Inc E 305 633-1790
Miami *(G-10337)*

CUT STONE & STONE PRODUCTS

Affordable Granite Concepts F 407 332-0057
Altamonte Springs *(G-26)*
American MBL Restoration Inc G 561 502-0764
Palm Springs *(G-13773)*
Andean Stone Company LLC G 305 460-3320
Hialeah *(G-5300)*
Artistic Columns Inc G 954 530-5537
Oakland Park *(G-11780)*
Bathroom World Manufacturing G 954 566-0451
Oakland Park *(G-11785)*
Cemex Materials LLC D 561 746-4556
Jupiter *(G-7018)*
Custom Cultered Marble Inc G 239 823-8241
Spring Hill *(G-16851)*
Designers Tops Inc F 305 599-9973
Miami *(G-9461)*
Dyadic International USA Inc G 561 743-8333
Jupiter *(G-7028)*
Englert Arts Inc G 561 241-9924
Boca Raton *(G-518)*
F T F Construction Company F 772 571-1850
Fellsmere *(G-3725)*
First Coast Granite & MBL Inc E 904 388-1217
Jacksonville *(G-6386)*
Five Star Marble and Stone G 904 887-4736
Ponte Vedra *(G-14925)*
Global Stone Corp G 786 601-2459
Cutler Bay *(G-2395)*
Granite World Inc E 813 243-6556
Tampa *(G-17725)*
Highlander Stone Corp G 786 333-1151
Opa Locka *(G-12323)*
House of Marble & Granite Inc G 239 261-0099
Naples *(G-11281)*
International Gran & Stone LLC E 813 920-6500
Odessa *(G-12127)*
J & N Stone Inc G 863 422-7369
Davenport *(G-2480)*
Moderno Porcelain Works LLC F 954 607-3535
Sunrise *(G-17147)*
Mother Earth Stone LLC F 407 878-2854
Sanford *(G-16091)*
PSC Building Group Inc F 561 756-6811
Delray Beach *(G-3130)*
Stone Craft Masters LLC F 786 401-7060
Doral *(G-3512)*
Stone Palace F 407 896-0872
Orlando *(G-13216)*
Stone Trend International Inc E 941 927-9113
Sarasota *(G-16605)*
Stonecrfters Archtctral Prcast F 727 544-1210
Seminole *(G-16763)*
Suncoast Stone Inc E 561 364-2061
Delray Beach *(G-3148)*
T H Stone G 561 361-3966
Boca Raton *(G-741)*
Unique Marble Inc F 772 766-4432
Vero Beach *(G-18672)*

CUTLERY

Andritz Iggesund Tools Inc E 813 855-6902
Oldsmar *(G-12202)*
Novelty Crystal Corp D 352 429-9036
Groveland *(G-5103)*

CUTLERY, STAINLESS STEEL

Bastinelli Creations LLC F 407 572-8073
Kissimmee *(G-7221)*

CYLINDER & ACTUATORS: Fluid Power

Dynalco Controls Corporation E 323 589-6181
Fort Lauderdale *(G-3952)*
Leslie Controls Inc C 813 978-1000
Temple Terrace *(G-18371)*

DAIRY PRDTS STORE: Ice Cream, Packaged

Big Bend Ice Cream Co G 850 539-7778
Havana *(G-5233)*
Jeremiahs Original Water Ice G 407 679-2665
Winter Park *(G-19416)*

Lefab Commercial LLC.......F....... 305 456-1306
Coral Gables *(G-2172)*
McConnell Corp.......G....... 305 296-6124
Key West *(G-7196)*
Worlds Greatest Ice Cream Inc.......F....... 305 538-0207
Miami Beach *(G-10730)*

DAIRY PRDTS WHOLESALERS: Fresh

Borden Dairy Company Fla LLC.......D....... 863 298-9742
Winter Haven *(G-19305)*
Darifair Foods Inc.......E....... 904 268-8999
Jacksonville *(G-6311)*
Dean Dairy Holdings LLC.......D....... 239 334-1114
Fort Myers *(G-4428)*

DAIRY PRDTS: Butter

Canal Creamery.......G....... 386 410-4703
New Smyrna Beach *(G-11529)*
Carrollwood Creamery.......G....... 813 926-2023
Tampa *(G-17510)*
Magical Creamery LLC.......G....... 407 719-6866
Lake Mary *(G-7430)*
Trinity Creamery Inc.......G....... 813 926-2023
Odessa *(G-12160)*

DAIRY PRDTS: Cheese

Goloso Food Llc.......G....... 321 277-2055
Orlando *(G-12786)*

DAIRY PRDTS: Cream Substitutes

Saputo Dairy Foods Usa LLC.......G....... 904 354-0406
Jacksonville *(G-6751)*

DAIRY PRDTS: Custard, Frozen

Lilas Desserts Inc.......F....... 305 252-1441
Miami *(G-9893)*

DAIRY PRDTS: Dairy Based Desserts, Frozen

Latin Dairy Foods LLC.......F....... 305 888-1788
Miami *(G-9869)*
Todays Frozen Desserts Inc.......F....... 305 994-9940
Miami *(G-10485)*
Verdu-Us LLC.......F....... 407 776-3017
Davenport *(G-2485)*

DAIRY PRDTS: Dietary Supplements, Dairy & Non-Dairy Based

Allegro Nutrition Inc.......E....... 732 364-3777
Palmetto *(G-13784)*
Amino Cell Inc.......F....... 352 291-0200
Ocala *(G-11874)*
Beauty & Health Corporation.......G....... 305 259-8181
Cutler Bay *(G-2388)*
Betancourt Sports Ntrtn LLC.......G....... 305 593-9296
Miami Lakes *(G-10768)*
Bkn International Inc.......G....... 301 518-7153
Miami *(G-9254)*
Bl Bio Lab LLC.......F....... 727 900-2707
Clearwater *(G-1609)*
Blue Sky Labs LLC.......G....... 901 268-6988
Jacksonville *(G-6214)*
Byoscience.......G....... 754 240-4052
Sunrise *(G-17102)*
Cerno Pharmaceuticals LLC.......G....... 786 763-2766
Miami *(G-9343)*
Cyber Group USA LLC.......F....... 888 574-9555
Pompano Beach *(G-14655)*
Essona Organics Inc.......G....... 716 481-0183
Delray Beach *(G-3076)*
Fleda Pharmaceuticals Corp.......G....... 813 920-9882
Odessa *(G-12120)*
Fresh Start Beverage Company.......G....... 561 757-6541
Boca Raton *(G-540)*
Full Lf Natural Hlth Pdts LLC.......G....... 954 889-4019
Hollywood *(G-5825)*
Function Please LLC.......G....... 305 792-7900
Hollywood *(G-5827)*
Green Essentials LLC.......E....... 786 584-4377
Miami *(G-9666)*
Health & Muscles.......G....... 305 225-2929
Miami *(G-9691)*
Ianorod JB LLC.......G....... 954 217-3014
Weston *(G-19138)*
Iq Formulations Llc.......D....... 954 533-9256
Tamarac *(G-17359)*
Maxam Group LLC.......F....... 305 952-3227
Miami *(G-9958)*
Naturecity LLC.......G....... 800 593-2563
Boca Raton *(G-636)*
Nutrition Laboratories Inc.......E....... 915 496-7531
Clearwater *(G-1814)*
Ohana Liquids LLC.......G....... 888 642-6244
New Smyrna Beach *(G-11540)*
Omnimark Enterprises LLC.......G....... 516 351-9075
Orlando *(G-13022)*
Pangenex Corporation.......G....... 352 346-4045
Tampa *(G-17971)*
Peak Nutritional Products LLC.......E....... 813 884-4989
Tampa *(G-17980)*
Prime Life Ntrtn Companyllc.......G....... 754 307-7137
Deerfield Beach *(G-2890)*
Sawgrass Nutra Labs LLC.......E....... 844 688-7244
Jacksonville *(G-6753)*
Sea 21-21 LLC.......G....... 954 366-4677
Pompano Beach *(G-14845)*
Sun-Pac Manufacturing Inc.......E....... 813 925-8787
Tampa *(G-18141)*
Sunshine Supplements Inc.......F....... 407 751-4299
Orlando *(G-13227)*
Twinlab Cnsld Holdings Inc.......E....... 561 443-4301
Boca Raton *(G-759)*
Vital Health Corporation.......G....... 407 522-1125
Orlando *(G-13308)*
Vitapak LLC.......G....... 954 661-0390
Fort Lauderdale *(G-4309)*

DAIRY PRDTS: Dried & Powdered Milk & Milk Prdts

S A Gloria Corp.......E....... 305 575-2900
South Miami *(G-16826)*

DAIRY PRDTS: Fermented & Cultured Milk Prdts

Borden Dairy Company Fla LLC.......D....... 863 298-9742
Winter Haven *(G-19305)*
Darifair Foods Inc.......E....... 904 268-8999
Jacksonville *(G-6311)*

DAIRY PRDTS: Frozen Desserts & Novelties

Big Bend Ice Cream Co.......G....... 850 539-7778
Havana *(G-5233)*
Brain Freeze Nitrogen.......G....... 786 235-8505
Doral *(G-3284)*
C&A Lozaro Inc.......F....... 407 671-8809
Winter Park *(G-19388)*
Carpe Diem Ice Cream LLC.......G....... 305 504-4469
Key West *(G-7180)*
Cold Stone Creamery-Parkland.......G....... 954 341-8033
Coral Springs *(G-2232)*
Cross Atlantic Commodities Inc.......G....... 954 678-0698
Weston *(G-19118)*
Cupcakes On Main.......G....... 321 693-7236
Titusville *(G-18426)*
Darifair Foods Inc.......E....... 904 268-8999
Jacksonville *(G-6311)*
Dean Dairy Holdings LLC.......D....... 239 334-1114
Fort Myers *(G-4428)*
Deliciosa Food Group Inc.......F....... 954 492-6131
Miami *(G-9448)*
Desserts2go Inc.......G....... 941 379-0488
Sarasota *(G-16411)*
Dolci Peccati LLC.......G....... 954 632-8551
Miami *(G-9475)*
Eden Fast Frozen Dessert LLC.......F....... 787 375-0826
Kissimmee *(G-7242)*
Eds Delight LLC.......G....... 305 632-3051
North Miami Beach *(G-11672)*
Gourmet Parisien Inc.......G....... 305 778-0756
Hollywood *(G-5828)*
GS Gelato and Desserts Inc.......E....... 850 243-5455
Fort Walton Beach *(G-4805)*
HM Factory LLC.......G....... 305 897-0004
Miami *(G-9714)*
Ice Cream & Gifts LLC.......G....... 352 237-2660
Ocala *(G-11969)*
Ice Cream Club Inc.......E....... 561 731-3331
Boynton Beach *(G-917)*
Icecapade Frozen Treats Inc.......G....... 904 314-4190
Jacksonville *(G-6487)*
Island Dream Itln Ice Dssrts L.......F....... 904 778-6839
Jacksonville *(G-6503)*
Ispy Equities.......G....... 813 731-0676
Spring Hill *(G-16873)*
Jeremiahs Original Water Ice.......G....... 407 679-2665
Winter Park *(G-19416)*
Jimmy & Toons Icecream Sp LLC.......G....... 850 752-2291
Quincy *(G-15252)*
Just Now Jennings LLC.......G....... 239 331-0315
Naples *(G-11301)*
Kissimmee Smoke Shop.......G....... 407 952-6181
Kissimmee *(G-7265)*
Lefab Commercial LLC.......F....... 305 456-1306
Coral Gables *(G-2172)*
Los Coquitos.......G....... 407 289-9315
Kissimmee *(G-7271)*
Maria E Acosta.......G....... 305 231-5543
Hialeah *(G-5501)*
Old Meeting House Home Made Ic.......F....... 813 254-0977
Tampa *(G-17949)*
Piccionis Frozen Desserts.......G....... 561 633-5759
Wellington *(G-18727)*
Renacer Bros LLC.......G....... 305 935-6777
Miami *(G-10251)*
Rhonda Clanton.......G....... 305 502-7050
Hialeah *(G-5599)*
Romeo Ohana LLC.......F....... 808 500-3420
Spring Hill *(G-16861)*
Ronnie & Moes Italian Ice LLC.......G....... 786 970-1805
Miami *(G-10280)*
Simply Sweet Company Inc.......G....... 386 873-6516
Deland *(G-3013)*
Smart Stream Inc.......F....... 904 223-1511
Jacksonville *(G-6780)*
Sunnibunni.......F....... 941 554-8744
Sarasota *(G-16609)*
Sweet Treats.......G....... 239 598-3311
Naples *(G-11430)*
Sweetreats of Naples Inc.......G....... 239 598-3311
Naples *(G-11431)*
Tristan S Kool Dreemz.......G....... 772 398-8875
Port Saint Lucie *(G-15156)*
Tropical Skoops Llc.......G....... 954 440-8736
Miramar *(G-11053)*
Vegan Suckers LLc.......F....... 904 265-5263
Jacksonville *(G-6894)*
Working Cow Homemade Inc.......F....... 727 572-7251
Saint Petersburg *(G-15965)*
Y3k LLC.......G....... 561 835-0404
Palm Beach *(G-13563)*
Yogurt Breeze LLC.......G....... 407 412-5939
Orlando *(G-13338)*

DAIRY PRDTS: Ice Cream & Ice Milk

Coco Gelato Corp.......E....... 786 621-2444
Miami *(G-9372)*
Happy Mix LLC.......G....... 954 880-0160
Cooper City *(G-2112)*
Peekaboo Organics LLC.......G....... 305 527-7162
Surfside *(G-17205)*

DAIRY PRDTS: Ice Cream, Bulk

A Means To A Vend Inc.......F....... 954 533-8330
Oakland Park *(G-11772)*
Bobs Twist N Shake.......G....... 941 485-5152
Venice *(G-18535)*
Cesibon.......G....... 239 682-5028
Naples *(G-11206)*
Cholados Y Mas.......G....... 813 935-9262
Tampa *(G-17533)*
Coneheads Frozen Custards.......G....... 772 600-7730
Stuart *(G-16925)*
Cool Cow.......G....... 229 272-5495
Tallahassee *(G-17237)*
Cool Treat.......G....... 407 248-0743
Orlando *(G-12619)*
Daisy V Castillo Vendor.......G....... 305 254-1427
Cutler Bay *(G-2391)*
Eighteen Degrees Eighteen.......G....... 904 686-1892
Ponte Vedra Beach *(G-14940)*
Food Marketing Consultants Inc.......G....... 954 322-2668
Miramar *(G-10992)*
Gelateria Milani LLC.......F....... 305 532-8562
Miami Beach *(G-10672)*
Gelato Petrini LLC.......F....... 561 600-4088
Delray Beach *(G-3084)*
Hulas Market Place LLC.......G....... 941 704-3305
Sarasota *(G-16462)*
Lukes Ice Cream.......F....... 561 588-5853
Riviera Beach *(G-15344)*
Mattheessons.......G....... 305 296-1616
Key West *(G-7195)*
McConnell Corp.......G....... 305 296-6124
Key West *(G-7196)*

Mix It At Loop ....G....... 407 201-8948
Kissimmee *(G-7276)*
Muse Gelato Inc ....F....... 407 363-1443
Orlando *(G-12988)*
Rich Ice Cream Co ....C....... 561 833-7585
West Palm Beach *(G-19020)*
Sweet Spot ....G....... 727 784-2277
Palm Harbor *(G-13764)*
Uncle Carlos Gelatos ....G....... 810 523-8506
Fort Pierce *(G-4765)*
Valentini Italian Spc Co ....G....... 305 638-0822
Miami *(G-10563)*
Worlds Greatest Ice Cream Inc ....F....... 305 538-0207
Miami Beach *(G-10730)*
Yogurtology ....G....... 727 895-1393
Saint Petersburg *(G-15966)*

DAIRY PRDTS: Ice Cream, Packaged, Molded, On Sticks, Etc.

Alcas USA Corp ....G....... 305 591-3325
Fort Lauderdale *(G-3795)*
Clondalkin LLC ....E....... 866 545-8703
Largo *(G-7925)*
Conopco Inc ....E....... 727 573-1591
Clearwater *(G-1635)*

DAIRY PRDTS: Milk, Chocolate

Chocolate Compass LLC ....G....... 407 600-0145
Sanford *(G-16014)*
Louis Sherry Company LLC ....G....... 904 482-1900
Jacksonville *(G-6565)*
Whetstone Industries Inc ....F....... 904 824-0888
Saint Augustine *(G-15636)*

DAIRY PRDTS: Milk, Condensed & Evaporated

Climb Your Mountain Inc ....E....... 571 571-8623
Medley *(G-8632)*
Flayco Products Inc ....E....... 813 879-1356
Tampa *(G-17668)*
Nestle Usa Inc ....C....... 813 273-5355
Thonotosassa *(G-18402)*
New Dairy Opco LLC ....B....... 305 652-3720
North Miami Beach *(G-11694)*
Vital Health Corp ....G....... 407 522-1125
Orlando *(G-13307)*

DAIRY PRDTS: Milk, Fluid

Dfa Dairy Brands Fluid LLC ....F....... 386 775-6700
Jacksonville *(G-6318)*
Dfa Dairy Brands Fluid LLC ....G....... 386 775-6700
Melbourne *(G-8803)*
Dfa Dairy Brands Fluid LLC ....E....... 813 621-7805
Tampa *(G-17603)*
Fluid Handling Support Corp ....F....... 786 623-2105
Doral *(G-3354)*

DAIRY PRDTS: Milk, Processed, Pasteurized, Homogenized/Btld

Dfa Dairy Brands Fluid LLC ....G....... 352 754-1750
Brooksville *(G-1226)*
Southeast Dairy Processors Inc ....E....... 813 620-1516
Tampa *(G-18117)*
Wwf Operating Company LLC ....E....... 904 354-0406
Jacksonville *(G-6930)*

DAIRY PRDTS: Natural Cheese

Bufalinda USA LLC ....G....... 305 979-9258
Miami Beach *(G-10650)*
Kelleys Krafts and Kreations ....G....... 813 508-1051
Spring Hill *(G-16874)*
Lanzas Distributor Inc ....G....... 305 885-5966
Miami *(G-9858)*
Mambi Cheese Company Inc ....F....... 305 324-5282
Miami *(G-9940)*

DAIRY PRDTS: Processed Cheese

Mondelez Global LLC ....E....... 305 774-6273
Coral Gables *(G-2179)*

DAIRY PRDTS: Spreads, Cheese

Massachusetts Bay Clam Co Inc ....F....... 813 855-4599
Tampa *(G-17891)*

DAIRY PRDTS: Whey, Powdered

Naked Whey Inc ....G....... 352 246-7294
Miami *(G-10061)*

DAIRY PRDTS: Yogurt, Exc Frozen

Brain Freeze Nitrogen ....G....... 786 235-8505
Doral *(G-3284)*
Colormet Foods LLC ....F....... 888 775-3966
Miami *(G-9382)*
Dairy Fairy LLC ....G....... 305 865-1506
Surfside *(G-17202)*
Froyolicious Inc ....G....... 561 753-4890
Royal Palm Beach *(G-15467)*
Powerful Foods LLC ....G....... 305 779-2449
Pinecrest *(G-14330)*
Pura Vida Dairy Inc ....F....... 305 817-1762
Hialeah *(G-5584)*
Spoons Chilly ....G....... 321 610-8966
Melbourne *(G-8943)*
Tias Milkshakes and More ....G....... 954 391-8753
Hollywood *(G-5924)*
Yogurt Breeze LLC ....G....... 407 412-5939
Orlando *(G-13338)*
Yogurtology ....G....... 813 839-4200
Tampa *(G-18274)*
Yogurtology ....G....... 813 969-2500
Tampa *(G-18275)*
Yogurtology ....G....... 813 926-9090
Tampa *(G-18276)*

DAIRY PRDTS: Yogurt, Frozen

D I Y Yogert ....G....... 239 471-2177
Cape Coral *(G-1409)*
Faithful Heart Froyo LLC ....G....... 407 325-3052
Winter Park *(G-19407)*
Florida Froyo Inc ....G....... 407 977-4911
Lake Mary *(G-7417)*
HM Froyos LLC ....G....... 561 339-0603
Orlando *(G-12804)*
Miami Foods Distrs USA Inc ....F....... 305 512-3246
Hialeah *(G-5510)*
Millenia Froyo LLC ....G....... 407 694-9938
Windermere *(G-19239)*
Mimzy Froyo Delights LLC ....G....... 917 862-9520
West Palm Beach *(G-18953)*
Supersweet Frog LLC ....G....... 863 386-4917
Sebring *(G-16713)*
Top Hat Food Services LLC ....G....... 630 825-2800
Venice *(G-18581)*

DATA PROCESSING & PREPARATION SVCS

Irvin Technologies Inc ....E....... 866 245-9356
Winter Springs *(G-19476)*
Man Enterprises 3 LLC ....G....... 561 655-4944
West Palm Beach *(G-18940)*
Metavante Holdings LLC ....G....... 904 438-6000
Jacksonville *(G-6600)*
Neptune Tech Services Inc ....E....... 904 646-2700
Jacksonville *(G-6624)*

DATA PROCESSING SVCS

Advanced Xrgrphics Imging Syst ....E....... 407 351-0232
Orlando *(G-12434)*
Locus Solutions LLC ....D....... 561 575-7600
Palm Beach Gardens *(G-13605)*

DAVITS

Davit Master Corp ....F....... 727 573-4414
Clearwater *(G-1650)*
Quick Lift Inc ....G....... 305 471-0147
Doral *(G-3475)*
V-Bro Products LLC ....F....... 352 267-6235
Tavares *(G-18358)*

DECORATIVE WOOD & WOODWORK

Ackue International LLC ....G....... 407 323-8688
Sanford *(G-15986)*
Amick Cstm Woodcraft & Design ....G....... 407 324-8525
Sanford *(G-15994)*
Coral Gables Custom Design Inc ....F....... 305 591-7575
Miami *(G-9401)*
Cubos LLC ....G....... 786 299-2671
Miami *(G-9418)*
Dixie Workshop Inc ....G....... 352 629-4699
Ocala *(G-11922)*
Excel Millwork & Moulding Inc ....E....... 850 576-7228
Midway *(G-10917)*
G and W Craftsman LLC ....G....... 440 453-2770
Naples *(G-11256)*
Generations Metier Inc ....E....... 239 283-9209
Cape Coral *(G-1428)*
Home Works Bay County Inc ....G....... 850 215-7880
Panama City *(G-13915)*
J T S Woodworking Inc ....G....... 561 272-7996
Delray Beach *(G-3094)*
K K Woodworking ....G....... 321 724-1298
Malabar *(G-8491)*
Madden Millworks ....G....... 310 514-2640
Jacksonville *(G-6573)*
Noveltex Miami Inc ....E....... 305 887-8191
Hialeah *(G-5544)*
Pleasure Interiors LLC ....E....... 941 756-9969
Sarasota *(G-16545)*
Round Table Tools Inc ....G....... 850 877-7650
Tallahassee *(G-17318)*
Sira ....G....... 352 377-4947
Gainesville *(G-4999)*
Strasser Enterprises ....G....... 386 677-5163
Daytona Beach *(G-2720)*
Summit ATL Productions LLC ....F....... 407 930-5488
Orlando *(G-13221)*
Welshman Investment Corp ....G....... 407 933-4444
Kissimmee *(G-7310)*
Woodcrafts By Angel Inc ....G....... 352 754-9335
Brooksville *(G-1293)*

DEFENSE SYSTEMS & EQPT

Aerojet Rcktdyne Clman Arspc I ....D....... 407 354-0047
Orlando *(G-12441)*
Alonso Defense Group LLC ....G....... 305 989-0927
Miami *(G-9121)*
American Payment Systems ....G....... 954 968-6920
North Lauderdale *(G-11611)*
Ares Defense Group LLC ....F....... 941 255-0559
Port Charlotte *(G-14961)*
Boca Self Defense ....G....... 954 903-0913
Boca Raton *(G-455)*
Cubic Advnced Lrng Sltions Inc ....F....... 407 859-7410
Orlando *(G-12632)*
Cubic Corporation ....G....... 407 859-7410
Orlando *(G-12633)*
Defense Arts & Sciences LLC ....G....... 321 768-0671
West Melbourne *(G-18771)*
Defense Leadership Forum ....G....... 202 375-9587
Santa Rosa Beach *(G-16157)*
Defenstech International Inc ....F....... 202 688-1988
Boca Raton *(G-497)*
Enki Group Inc ....G....... 305 773-3502
Coral Gables *(G-2143)*
Fab Defense Inc ....G....... 386 263-3054
Ormond Beach *(G-13370)*
Fire Defense Centers Inc ....G....... 904 731-1833
Jacksonville *(G-6382)*
Full Circle Integration LLC ....F....... 504 615-5501
Valparaiso *(G-18511)*
Hyper-Sub Platform Tech Inc ....F....... 386 365-6021
Lake Butler *(G-7337)*
Linx Defense LLC ....G....... 805 233-2472
Destin *(G-3197)*
Lockheed Martin Corporation ....B....... 813 855-5711
Oldsmar *(G-12245)*
Lockheed Martin Corporation ....G....... 850 581-1427
Hurlburt Field *(G-6045)*
Metro Defense Services Inc ....G....... 407 285-2304
Winter Park *(G-19423)*
Microbial Defense Systems LLC ....G....... 989 964-9863
Saint Augustine *(G-15570)*
Microgerm Defense LLC ....E....... 561 309-0842
West Palm Beach *(G-18951)*
Nxgen Brands Inc ....E....... 954 329-2205
Cape Coral *(G-1452)*
O2 Defense LLC ....G....... 704 408-7357
Odessa *(G-12137)*
Offensive Defense Inc ....G....... 786 306-8162
Miramar *(G-11022)*
Orbital Sciences LLC ....B....... 703 406-5474
Merritt Island *(G-9005)*
Patriot Person Defense ....G....... 813 470-8025
Brandon *(G-1172)*
Polyhistor International Inc ....G....... 904 646-5666
Jacksonville *(G-6677)*
Raytheon Company ....G....... 850 286-6343
Tyndall Afb *(G-18494)*
Raytheon Company ....G....... 321 235-6682
Orlando *(G-13116)*

Raytheon Company ....G....... 321 235-1700
Orlando *(G-13118)*
Sas R & D Services Inc.................F....... 954 432-2345
Miramar *(G-11039)*
Seven Defenses Corporation.................F....... 786 448-5701
Medley *(G-8723)*
Space Cast Intllgent Sltons In ....F....... 321 622-6858
Melbourne *(G-8937)*
Steele Defense LLC ....G....... 786 610-0857
Homestead *(G-5995)*
Steele Industries Inc.................G....... 800 674-7302
Sarasota *(G-16301)*
Stout Defense PA.................G....... 352 665-9266
Gainesville *(G-5002)*
Tf Defense LLC.................G....... 321 961-7596
Kissimmee *(G-7304)*
Ticket Drop Traffic Defense ....G....... 305 332-3186
Miami *(G-10477)*
Tk Defense Solutions Inc.................G....... 727 365-6823
Saint Petersburg *(G-15941)*
Truenorth Iq Inc.................G....... 678 849-5000
Port Saint Lucie *(G-15157)*

DEGREASING MACHINES

Akj Industries Inc.................G....... 239 939-1696
Fort Myers *(G-4348)*
Global Manufacturing Tech Inc.................G....... 239 657-3720
Immokalee *(G-6049)*
Instazorb International Inc.................G....... 561 416-7302
Boca Raton *(G-565)*
Systemone Technologies Inc.................G....... 305 593-8015
Doral *(G-3521)*

DEHYDRATION EQPT

Cummins-Wagner-Florida LLC.................E....... 813 630-2220
Tampa *(G-17573)*

DENTAL EQPT

Blitz Micro Turning Inc.................G....... 727 725-5005
Safety Harbor *(G-15489)*
DDS Lab USA Holding.................D....... 813 249-8888
Tampa *(G-17596)*
Dynamic Dental Corp.................G....... 954 344-5155
Coral Springs *(G-2242)*
Med Dental Equipment (import).................G....... 786 417-8486
Miami *(G-9963)*
SDS Dental Inc.................E....... 954 730-3636
Pompano Beach *(G-14843)*
Vet Sonic Inc.................G....... 305 681-4486
Hialeah *(G-5677)*

DENTAL EQPT & SPLYS

Boca Dental Supply LLC.................G....... 800 768-5691
Boca Raton *(G-451)*
Dentsply Sirona Inc.................D....... 941 527-4450
Sarasota *(G-16205)*
Dotamed LLC.................G....... 786 594-0144
Doral *(G-3335)*
Economy Dntres Jcksonville LLC.................F....... 904 696-6767
Jacksonville *(G-6353)*
Glenroe Technologies Inc.................F....... 941 554-5262
Sarasota *(G-16220)*
Hec America Inc.................G....... 786 543-9238
Miami *(G-9695)*
Intralock International Inc.................G....... 561 447-8282
Boca Raton *(G-572)*
Omnia Incorporated.................E....... 863 619-8100
Lakeland *(G-7759)*
Regent Labs Inc.................G....... 954 426-4889
Deerfield Beach *(G-2902)*
Regent Labs Inc.................G....... 954 426-4889
Deerfield Beach *(G-2903)*
Showerfloss Inc.................G....... 239 947-2855
Estero *(G-3696)*
Sunoptic Technologies LLC.................D....... 877 677-2832
Jacksonville *(G-6822)*
Valley Surgical Inc.................G....... 954 768-9886
Fort Lauderdale *(G-4302)*
White Square Chemical Inc.................F....... 302 212-4555
Tavernier *(G-18364)*

DENTAL EQPT & SPLYS WHOLESALERS

Florida Probe Corporation.................G....... 352 372-1142
Gainesville *(G-4922)*

DENTAL EQPT & SPLYS: Autoclaves

Orion Dntl Sls Trning Repr LLC.................G....... 888 674-6657
Kissimmee *(G-7280)*

DENTAL EQPT & SPLYS: Dental Materials

Biomet 3i LLC.................A....... 561 775-9928
Palm Beach Gardens *(G-13570)*
Denterprise International Inc.................F....... 386 672-0450
Ormond Beach *(G-13362)*
Sunshine Health Products Inc.................F....... 954 493-5469
Fort Lauderdale *(G-4267)*

DENTAL EQPT & SPLYS: Enamels

Dental Partners Alliance LLC.................G....... 321 574-8003
Melbourne *(G-8802)*
Dentate Porcelain Inc.................G....... 917 359-7696
Pompano Beach *(G-14660)*
Dr Worthington Orthodonti.................G....... 813 968-4040
Tampa *(G-17615)*

DENTAL EQPT & SPLYS: Impression Materials

Kottler Research Corp.................G....... 850 776-7021
Milton *(G-10934)*

DENTAL EQPT & SPLYS: Laboratory

Dsg Clearwater Laboratory.................F....... 727 530-9444
Clearwater *(G-1659)*

DENTAL EQPT & SPLYS: Metal

L A R Manufacturing LLC.................G....... 727 846-7860
Port Richey *(G-15059)*

DENTAL EQPT & SPLYS: Orthodontic Appliances

Inman Orthodontic Labs Inc.................F....... 954 340-8477
Coral Springs *(G-2260)*

DENTAL EQPT & SPLYS: Sterilizers

3b Global LLC.................G....... 813 350-7872
Tampa *(G-17373)*
Wayne Metal Products Inc.................G....... 407 321-7168
Sanford *(G-16136)*

DENTAL EQPT & SPLYS: Tools, NEC

Florida Probe Corporation.................G....... 352 372-1142
Gainesville *(G-4922)*

DENTAL INSTRUMENT REPAIR SVCS

Dynamic Dental Corp.................G....... 954 344-5155
Coral Springs *(G-2242)*

DEPARTMENT STORES: Army-Navy Goods

Heralpin Usa Inc.................G....... 305 218-0174
Doral *(G-3379)*

DERMATOLOGICALS

Clearly Derm LLC.................E....... 561 353-3376
Boca Raton *(G-484)*
Diva Stuff.................G....... 386 256-2521
Ormond Beach *(G-13363)*
ERA Organics Inc.................G....... 800 579-9817
Clearwater *(G-1676)*
Genesis Health Institute Inc.................G....... 954 561-3175
Wilton Manors *(G-19218)*
Heritage Skin Care Inc.................F....... 305 757-9264
Miami Shores *(G-10885)*
North Fort Myers Prescr Sp.................G....... 239 599-4120
North Fort Myers *(G-11600)*
Pure Wave Organics Inc.................G....... 321 368-7002
Melbourne *(G-8915)*
Sincerus Pharmaceuticals Inc.................C....... 800 604-5032
Pompano Beach *(G-14852)*

DERRICKS

Altec Inc.................G....... 813 372-0058
Tampa *(G-17407)*

DESIGN SVCS, NEC

L and C Science and Tech Inc.................G....... 305 200-3531
Hialeah *(G-5477)*
Metal Creations Sarasota Llc.................F....... 941 922-7096
Sarasota *(G-16256)*
Ollo Usa LLC.................G....... 941 366-0600
Sarasota *(G-16531)*
Virginia Electronic & Ltg Corp.................G....... 904 230-2840
Green Cove Springs *(G-5076)*

DESIGN SVCS: Commercial & Indl

Idea Design Studio Inc.................F....... 305 823-6008
Doral *(G-3387)*
Integrated Design & Develop.................G....... 407 268-4300
Sanford *(G-16068)*
Robotic Parking Systems Inc.................F....... 727 539-7275
Clearwater *(G-1863)*

DESIGN SVCS: Computer Integrated Systems

Aeb Technologies Inc.................G....... 352 417-0009
Homosassa *(G-5999)*
Applied Technologies Group Inc.................G....... 813 413-7025
Tampa *(G-17429)*
Arma Holdings Inc.................E....... 813 402-0667
Tampa *(G-17434)*
Arrowhead Global LLC.................G....... 727 497-7340
Clearwater *(G-1589)*
Asrc Aerospace Corp.................C....... 321 867-1462
Kennedy Space Center *(G-7150)*
Black Knight Inc.................B....... 904 854-5100
Jacksonville *(G-6210)*
C2c Innovated Technology LLC.................G....... 251 382-2277
Bonifay *(G-800)*
Cae USA Inc.................A....... 813 885-7481
Tampa *(G-17500)*
Consulier Engineering Inc.................G....... 561 842-2492
Riviera Beach *(G-15314)*
Contec Americas Inc.................D....... 321 728-0172
Melbourne *(G-8796)*
Donnelley Financial LLC.................F....... 305 371-3900
Miami *(G-9479)*
Eci Telecom Inc.................E....... 954 772-3070
Fort Lauderdale *(G-3960)*
Inceptra LLC.................E....... 954 442-5400
Weston *(G-19141)*
Irvin Technologies Inc.................E....... 866 245-9356
Winter Springs *(G-19476)*
Kreateck International Corp.................F....... 772 925-1216
Vero Beach *(G-18637)*
Lightning Phase II Inc.................G....... 727 539-1800
Seminole *(G-16749)*
Myers Engineering Intl Inc.................E....... 954 975-2712
Margate *(G-8558)*
Simpleshow USA Corp.................E....... 844 468-5447
Miami *(G-10352)*
Uts Systems LLC.................G....... 850 226-4301
Fort Walton Beach *(G-4837)*
Willsonet Inc.................E....... 813 336-8175
Tampa *(G-18259)*

DETECTION APPARATUS: Electronic/Magnetic Field, Light/Heat

Senelco Iberia Inc.................D....... 561 912-6000
Deerfield Beach *(G-2909)*
Sentech Eas Corporation.................F....... 954 426-2965
Coconut Creek *(G-2093)*

DETECTION EQPT: Aeronautical Electronic Field

We Love Tec LLC.................G....... 305 433-4453
North Miami Beach *(G-11711)*

DETECTIVE & ARMORED CAR SERVICES

Jade Tactical Disaster Relief.................C....... 850 270-4077
Tampa *(G-17801)*
Metal 2 Metal Inc.................G....... 954 253-9450
Palmetto Bay *(G-13850)*

DETECTORS: Water Leak

Sleuth Inc.................E....... 941 745-9903
Bradenton *(G-1114)*

DIAGNOSTIC SUBSTANCES

Cojali Usa Inc.................F....... 305 960-7651
Doral *(G-3303)*
Continental Services Group.................E....... 305 633-7700
Miami *(G-9396)*

Continental Services Group..................G....... 954 327-0809
Fort Lauderdale *(G-3917)*
Doctorxs Allergy Formula......................G....... 904 758-2088
Jacksonville *(G-6324)*
Nilsson Nils...G....... 561 790-2400
Royal Palm Beach *(G-15476)*
Opko Health Inc..A....... 305 575-4100
Miami *(G-10111)*
Physicians Imaging LLC...........................G....... 352 383-3716
Mount Dora *(G-11110)*
Sanzay Corporation...................................E....... 305 826-9886
Miami *(G-10304)*
Suntree Diagnostic Center.......................G....... 321 259-8800
Melbourne *(G-8951)*
US Diagnostics Inc....................................E....... 866 216-5308
Plantation *(G-14561)*
US Pet Imaging LLC...................................G....... 941 795-3780
Bradenton *(G-1138)*
US Pet Imaging LLC...................................G....... 941 921-0383
Sarasota *(G-16632)*

DIAGNOSTIC SUBSTANCES OR AGENTS: Enzyme & Isoenzyme

Genzyme Corporation...............................D....... 800 245-4363
Miami *(G-9628)*
Inter Cell Technologies Inc......................G....... 561 575-6868
Jupiter *(G-7058)*

DIAGNOSTIC SUBSTANCES OR AGENTS: Hematology

Clinical Dagnstc Solutions Inc...............E....... 954 791-1773
Plantation *(G-14500)*

DIAGNOSTIC SUBSTANCES OR AGENTS: In Vitro

AP Lifesciences LLC.................................F....... 954 300-7469
Alachua *(G-3)*
Banyan Biomarkers Inc............................G....... 760 710-0460
Gainesville *(G-4882)*
Cambridge Diagnostic Pdts Inc...............F....... 954 971-4040
Fort Lauderdale *(G-3880)*
Lumos Diagnostics Inc..............................E....... 941 556-1850
Lakewood Ranch *(G-7845)*

DIAGNOSTIC SUBSTANCES OR AGENTS: In Vivo

Positiveid Corporation...............................F....... 561 805-8000
Delray Beach *(G-3121)*

DIAGNOSTIC SUBSTANCES OR AGENTS: Microbiology & Virology

Advanced Bioprocess LLC.........................G....... 305 927-3661
Miami *(G-9075)*
Infinty Genome Sciences Inc....................G....... 321 327-7365
Melbourne Beach *(G-8979)*
La Genomics LLC......................................G....... 407 909-1120
Windermere *(G-19234)*
Meridian Life Science Inc.........................F....... 561 241-0223
Boca Raton *(G-620)*
Rapid Genomics LLC.................................G....... 352 213-4741
Jacksonville *(G-6705)*

DIAGNOSTIC SUBSTANCES OR AGENTS: Radioactive

Cardinal Health 414 LLC...........................G....... 954 202-1883
Fort Lauderdale *(G-3883)*
Cardinal Health 414 LLC...........................G....... 813 972-1351
Tampa *(G-17507)*
Evolvegene LLC...G....... 727 623-4052
Saint Petersburg *(G-15772)*
Petnet Solutions Inc..................................G....... 813 627-0022
Tampa *(G-17985)*

DIAMONDS: Cutting & Polishing

Bach Diamonds...G....... 954 921-4069
Hollywood *(G-5782)*
Bashert Diamonds Inc...............................G....... 305 466-1881
Aventura *(G-263)*
Giraldo & Donalisio Corp..........................G....... 239 567-2206
Cape Coral *(G-1429)*
Suncoast Accrdted Gmlgical Lab..........G....... 941 756-8787
Bradenton *(G-1121)*

DIAPERS: Disposable

Impex of Doral Inc.....................................E....... 305 470-0041
Medley *(G-8669)*

DIATOMACEOUS EARTH: Ground Or Treated

Atlas Peat & Soil Inc................................E....... 561 734-7300
Boynton Beach *(G-881)*

DICE & DICE CUPS

Master Mold Corp......................................G....... 941 486-0000
North Venice *(G-11760)*

DIE CUTTING SVC: Paper

Top Notch Diecutting Foil STA................G....... 904 346-3511
Jacksonville *(G-6863)*

DIE SETS: Presses, Metal Stamping

Ebway LLC..E....... 954 971-4911
Fort Lauderdale *(G-3957)*
Ebway LLC..D....... 954 971-4911
Fort Lauderdale *(G-3958)*
Miami Quality Graphics Inc......................E....... 305 634-9506
Miami *(G-10007)*
Sohacki Industries Inc..............................E....... 904 826-0130
Saint Augustine *(G-15613)*
Versatile Manufacturing Inc.....................E....... 954 561-8083
Oakland Park *(G-11859)*
Versatile Manufacturing Inc.....................F....... 954 561-8083
Oakland Park *(G-11860)*

DIES & TOOLS: Special

Accu Metal...G....... 850 912-4855
Pensacola *(G-14078)*
Cob Industries Inc......................................G....... 321 723-3200
West Melbourne *(G-18770)*
Crenshaw Die & Manufacturing...............F....... 949 475-5505
Daytona Beach *(G-2648)*
FDM of Clearwater Inc..............................F....... 727 544-8801
Largo *(G-7944)*
Gregg Tool & Die Co Inc...........................G....... 305 685-6309
Hialeah *(G-5436)*
Gulf Tool Corporation...............................F....... 850 456-0840
Pensacola *(G-14168)*
Kirtech Enterprises Inc.............................F....... 352 742-7222
Tavares *(G-18344)*
Moloney Die Company..............................G....... 904 388-3654
Jacksonville *(G-6613)*
Pace Machine & Tool Inc..........................F....... 561 747-5444
Stuart *(G-16985)*
Pacific Die Cast Inc....................................F....... 813 316-2221
Tampa *(G-17968)*
Rafferty Holdings LLC..............................F....... 352 248-0906
Gainesville *(G-4989)*
Redkeys Dies..G....... 772 463-5824
Stuart *(G-17000)*
Roller Die + Forming.................................E....... 502 804-5571
Green Cove Springs *(G-5068)*
Savage Ventures Inc..................................E....... 772 335-5655
Port Saint Lucie *(G-15141)*
Schwarz Bros Manufacturing Co............G....... 309 342-5814
Pensacola *(G-14259)*
Southpointe Precision..............................G....... 239 225-1350
Fort Myers *(G-4608)*
Tennessee Tool and Fixture LLC.............F....... 931 954-5316
Winter Park *(G-19452)*
Tibor Inc...E....... 561 272-0770
Delray Beach *(G-3150)*
Triad Edm Inc...G....... 352 489-5336
Dunnellon *(G-3601)*
Unique Tool & Die LLC..............................F....... 772 464-5006
Fort Pierce *(G-4766)*
Universal Die Services Inc.......................G....... 863 665-6092
Lakeland *(G-7828)*
Versacomp Inc..F....... 954 561-8778
Oakland Park *(G-11858)*

DIES: Cutting, Exc Metal

Nessmith Dye Cutting & Finshg..............G....... 904 353-6317
Jacksonville *(G-6625)*

DIES: Steel Rule

Victors Die Cutting Inc..............................G....... 305 599-0255
Hialeah *(G-5679)*

DIETICIANS' OFFICES

Kulfi LLC..E....... 855 488-4273
Boca Raton *(G-593)*

DIMENSION STONE: Buildings

Breton USA Customers Svc Corp............F....... 941 360-2700
Sarasota *(G-16369)*

DIODES: Light Emitting

Absen Inc...D....... 407 203-8870
Orlando *(G-12426)*
Adj Inc..F....... 727 289-6173
Tierra Verde *(G-18405)*
American Led Display Solutions.............G....... 561 227-8048
Miami *(G-9145)*
Apollo Metro Solutions Inc......................G....... 239 444-6934
Naples *(G-11165)*
Apure Distribution LLC............................F....... 305 351-1025
Miami *(G-9159)*
Aqualuma LLC..G....... 954 234-2512
Deerfield Beach *(G-2778)*
Itelecom USA Inc.......................................G....... 305 557-4660
Weston *(G-19143)*
Keytroller LLC..F....... 813 877-4500
Tampa *(G-17823)*
Luminoso LLC...G....... 305 364-8099
Miami Lakes *(G-10810)*
Lumiron Inc...G....... 305 652-2599
Miami *(G-9919)*
Nebula Led Lighting Systems of.............G....... 813 907-0001
Wesley Chapel *(G-18754)*
Suncoast Led Displays LLC.....................F....... 727 683-2777
Palm Harbor *(G-13763)*
Tesco of Swfl Inc.......................................G....... 239 234-6490
Naples *(G-11438)*
Tm USA Inc..G....... 954 801-4649
Doral *(G-3529)*
Wbn LLC..G....... 786 870-4172
Doral *(G-3547)*

DIODES: Solid State, Germanium, Silicon, Etc

US Applied Physics Group LLC...............G....... 321 607-9023
Titusville *(G-18472)*

DIRECT SELLING ESTABLISHMENTS, NEC

Shaws Sthern Blle Frz Fods In................D....... 904 768-1591
Jacksonville *(G-6763)*

DIRECT SELLING ESTABLISHMENTS: Bakery Goods, House-To-House

904 Sweet Treatz Street LLC....................G....... 800 889-3298
Jacksonville *(G-6105)*

DIRECT SELLING ESTABLISHMENTS: Encyclopedias & Publications

Great Hse Mdia Group of Pbls I...............F....... 407 779-3846
Orlando *(G-12788)*

DIRECT SELLING ESTABLISHMENTS: Food Svcs

All Naturals Direct.....................................G....... 813 792-3777
Tampa *(G-17399)*

DIRECT SELLING ESTABLISHMENTS: Snacks

Mvs International Inc.................................G....... 954 727-3383
Weston *(G-19151)*

DISCS & TAPE: Optical, Blank

Twinstar Optics & Coatings Inc...............F....... 727 847-2300
Port Richey *(G-15073)*

DISHWASHING EQPT: Commercial

Bar Maid Corporation...............................F....... 954 960-1468
Pompano Beach *(G-14614)*
ICI Custom Parts Inc..................................E....... 813 888-7979
Tampa *(G-17768)*
Seaking Inc..E....... 954 961-6629
Davie *(G-2589)*

DISK DRIVES: Computer

Western Digital Corporation ....G....... 561 995-1496
Boca Raton *(G-789)*

DISPENSERS, TISSUE: Plastic

Hernon Manufacturing Inc ....D....... 407 322-4000
Sanford *(G-16061)*

DISPENSERS: Soap

Ecolab Inc ....F....... 800 931-8911
Jupiter *(G-7031)*
Ultraclenz LLC ....F....... 800 931-8911
Jupiter *(G-7136)*

DISPENSING EQPT & PARTS, BEVERAGE: Coolers, Milk/Water, Elec

International H20 Inc ....G....... 954 854-1638
North Miami Beach *(G-11683)*

DISPENSING EQPT & PARTS, BEVERAGE: Fountain/Other Beverage

Dcg Enterprises LLC ....G....... 813 931-4303
Tampa *(G-17594)*
Gate Cfv Solutions Inc ....G....... 772 388-3387
Sebastian *(G-16661)*
Micro Matic Usa Inc ....G....... 352 544-1081
Brooksville *(G-1251)*
Micro Matic Usa Inc ....E....... 352 544-1081
Brooksville *(G-1252)*

DISPLAY FIXTURES: Wood

Ajb Enterprises of Florida ....G....... 352 331-9569
Gainesville *(G-4870)*
Capital Contracting & Design ....E....... 908 561-8411
Fort Lauderdale *(G-3881)*
Nauset Enterprises Inc ....G....... 727 443-3469
Clearwater *(G-1804)*

DISPLAY ITEMS: Corrugated, Made From Purchased Materials

Hitex Marketing Group Inc ....G....... 305 406-1150
Miami *(G-9713)*

DISPLAY LETTERING SVCS

Firedrake Inc ....G....... 813 713-8902
Zephyrhills *(G-19518)*

DISPLAY STANDS: Merchandise, Exc Wood

La Fabrika Retail Services LLC ....G....... 786 525-4491
Miami *(G-9840)*

DISTANCE MEASURING EQPT OR DME: Aeronautical

Trumeter Company Inc ....G....... 954 725-6699
Coconut Creek *(G-2098)*

DISTILLATION PRDTS: Wood

Kraton Chemical LLC ....C....... 904 928-8700
Jacksonville *(G-6546)*

DISTILLERS DRIED GRAIN & SOLUBLES

Drum Circle Distilling LLC ....F....... 941 358-1900
Sarasota *(G-16415)*
Florida Distillers Co ....F....... 863 967-4481
Auburndale *(G-243)*

DISTRIBUTORS: Motor Vehicle Engine

Carbel LLC ....C....... 305 599-0832
Doral *(G-3290)*
Central Turbos Corp ....F....... 305 406-3933
Doral *(G-3296)*
Goodman Manufacturing Co LP ....G....... 904 355-4520
Jacksonville *(G-6440)*
South Florida Core Distrs ....G....... 954 452-9091
Davie *(G-2594)*

DIVING EQPT STORES

Gigli Enterprises Inc ....G....... 850 871-4777
Panama City *(G-13909)*

DOCK EQPT & SPLYS, INDL

Gator Dock & Marine LLC ....F....... 407 323-0190
Sanford *(G-16054)*
International Dock Products ....F....... 954 964-5315
Hallandale Beach *(G-5191)*
Keys Deck & Dock Supplies Inc ....G....... 305 451-8001
Key Largo *(G-7172)*

DOCKS: Floating, Wood

Crowell Marine Inc ....G....... 813 236-3625
Tampa *(G-17570)*
Hohol Marine Products ....G....... 386 734-0630
Deland *(G-2983)*
W R Williams Enterprises Inc ....G....... 813 677-2000
Gibsonton *(G-5035)*

DOCKS: Prefabricated Metal

Bluewater Marine Systems Inc ....G....... 619 499-7507
Saint Petersburg *(G-15724)*
Florida Floats Inc ....E....... 904 358-3362
Jacksonville *(G-6398)*

DOCUMENT DESTRUCTION SVC

Bay Area Security Shred ....F....... 877 974-7337
Palm Harbor *(G-13723)*

DOCUMENT EMBOSSING SVCS

Chiptech Imaging LLC ....G....... 954 827-1401
Coral Springs *(G-2230)*

DOLOMITE: Crushed & Broken

Crystal River Quarries Inc ....E....... 352 795-2828
Crystal River *(G-2375)*
Dolomite Inc ....E....... 850 482-4962
Marianna *(G-8576)*

DOLOMITE: Dimension

Hatch Enterprises Inc ....G....... 386 935-1419
Branford *(G-1186)*

DOOR & WINDOW REPAIR SVCS

Shutterman Storm & Security ....F....... 239 455-9166
Naples *(G-11400)*

DOOR FRAMES: Wood

Al & Sons Millwork Inc ....E....... 352 245-9191
Belleview *(G-366)*
Dayoris Doors ....G....... 954 374-8538
Miramar *(G-10982)*
Designer Door Products Inc ....G....... 786 800-3855
Miami *(G-9459)*
Door Styles Inc ....E....... 305 653-4447
Miami *(G-9480)*
Doors 4 U Inc ....G....... 786 400-2298
Medley *(G-8643)*
East Coast Door Inc ....F....... 954 868-4700
Pompano Beach *(G-14672)*
Mills & Nebraska Door & Trim ....F....... 407 472-2742
Orlando *(G-12971)*
Southern Door Technologies ....G....... 386 496-3844
Lake Butler *(G-7342)*
Taylor-Cotton-Ridley Inc ....D....... 904 733-8373
Jacksonville *(G-6840)*

DOOR MATS: Rubber

Gallant Inc ....G....... 800 330-1343
Winter Garden *(G-19265)*

DOOR OPERATING SYSTEMS: Electric

First Mate Inc ....G....... 954 475-2750
Plantation *(G-14517)*
Quality Door Service LLC ....G....... 904 588-4817
Jacksonville *(G-6698)*
Somfy Systems Inc ....F....... 561 292-3483
Boynton Beach *(G-961)*

DOOR PARTS: Sashes, Wood

Hill Enterprises LLC ....G....... 850 478-4455
Pensacola *(G-14172)*

DOORS & WINDOWS WHOLESALERS: All Materials

Custom Cft Windows & Doors Inc ....F....... 407 834-5400
Winter Springs *(G-19470)*
Gulfport Industries Inc ....F....... 813 885-1000
Tampa *(G-17736)*
Hartman Windows and Doors LLC ....D....... 561 296-9600
Riviera Beach *(G-15333)*
Quality Engineered Products Co ....E....... 813 885-1693
Tampa *(G-18031)*
R & R Door and Trim Inc ....G....... 561 844-5496
West Palm Beach *(G-19015)*

DOORS & WINDOWS: Screen & Storm

Ashton Manufacturing LLC ....F....... 941 351-5529
Sarasota *(G-16350)*
Dependable Shutter Service Inc ....E....... 954 583-1411
Davie *(G-2516)*
Fortress Impact Wndows Dors LL ....G....... 954 621-2395
Fort Lauderdale *(G-4010)*
G F E Inc ....F....... 954 583-7005
Davie *(G-2530)*
John Screen Service LLC ....G....... 561 798-3132
Wellington *(G-18721)*
Levinson Built LLC ....F....... 561 712-9882
West Palm Beach *(G-18929)*
On Screen Ink ....G....... 724 516-4999
Pompano Beach *(G-14779)*
Pioneer Screen Inc ....G....... 772 260-3068
Palm City *(G-13671)*
Russell Home Imprvmnt Ctr Inc ....G....... 954 436-9186
Davie *(G-2588)*
Window Craftsmen Inc ....E....... 941 922-1844
Sarasota *(G-16641)*

DOORS & WINDOWS: Storm, Metal

American Marine Mfg Inc ....G....... 305 497-7723
Hialeah *(G-5293)*
Coastal Awngs Hrrcane Prtction ....G....... 407 923-9482
Orlando *(G-12592)*
Poma Corporation ....D....... 561 790-5799
West Palm Beach *(G-19001)*
Rolladen Inc ....F....... 954 454-4114
Longwood *(G-8332)*
Rolsafe LLC ....F....... 239 225-2487
Fort Myers *(G-4587)*
Style-View Products Inc ....F....... 305 634-9688
Miami *(G-10426)*

DOORS: Fiberglass

Plazadoor Corp ....E....... 561 578-5450
Riviera Beach *(G-15364)*
Quality Molds USA Inc ....F....... 321 632-6066
Cocoa *(G-2044)*
Sunflex Wall Systems LP ....G....... 239 220-1570
Naples *(G-11424)*

DOORS: Fire, Metal

Omega Garage Doors Inc ....F....... 352 620-8830
Melbourne *(G-8901)*

DOORS: Garage, Overhead, Metal

A Superior Garage Door Company ....E....... 305 556-6624
Hialeah *(G-5258)*
Best Rolling Manufacturer Inc ....D....... 305 821-4276
Miami Lakes *(G-10767)*
C & D Industrial Maint LLC ....F....... 833 776-5833
Bradenton *(G-1005)*
Specialty Products Inc ....G....... 850 438-4264
Pensacola *(G-14267)*

DOORS: Garage, Overhead, Wood

A-1 Door Systems Inc ....F....... 904 327-7206
Jacksonville *(G-6112)*
All Pro Chelo Corp ....G....... 786 317-3914
Hialeah *(G-5280)*
Hire Authority ....F....... 561 477-6663
Miami *(G-9712)*
Marko Garage Doors & Gates Inc ....G....... 561 547-4001
Palm Springs *(G-13776)*
Specialty Products Inc ....G....... 850 438-4264
Pensacola *(G-14267)*

DOORS: Glass

Acryplex Inc..........G....... 305 633-7636
Miami *(G-9066)*
Coastal Industries Inc..........C....... 904 642-3970
Jacksonville *(G-6277)*
Crawford Glass Door Co..........F....... 954 480-6820
Deerfield Beach *(G-2805)*
Eviralum Industries Inc..........F....... 305 752-4411
Miami *(G-9529)*
Florida Glass of Tampa Bay..........D....... 813 925-1330
Tampa *(G-17677)*
Lawson Industries Inc..........B....... 305 696-8660
Medley *(G-8678)*
Martell Glass..........G....... 786 336-0142
Miami *(G-9951)*
Neo Metal Glass LLC..........G....... 954 532-0340
Pompano Beach *(G-14772)*
Sarasota Shower Door Company..........G....... 941 378-0051
Sarasota *(G-16580)*
Sea Products Inc..........D....... 904 781-8200
Jacksonville *(G-6758)*
Southeastern Aluminum Pdts LLC..........G....... 800 243-8200
Jacksonville *(G-6789)*
Sunshine Windows Mfg Inc..........D....... 305 364-9952
Hialeah *(G-5640)*
Windoor Incorporated..........C....... 407 481-8400
North Venice *(G-11765)*

DOORS: Hangar, Metal

M Bilt Enterprises Inc..........F....... 352 528-5566
Ocala *(G-11989)*
Rearden Steel Mfg LLC..........G....... 772 882-8517
Fort Pierce *(G-4739)*
Well Bilt Industries Usa LLC..........F....... 352 528-5566
Ocala *(G-12074)*

DOORS: Rolling, Indl Building Or Warehouse, Metal

Rolling Door Parts Inc..........G....... 305 888-5020
Miami *(G-10276)*

DOORS: Screen, Metal

Simplex Inc..........E....... 352 357-2828
Mount Dora *(G-11114)*
Simpson Screens Inc..........F....... 904 757-1498
Jacksonville *(G-6777)*
Southeastern Door Company LLC..........F....... 561 746-5493
Jupiter *(G-7119)*
Yale Ogron Mfg Co Inc..........D....... 305 687-0424
Opa Locka *(G-12372)*

DOORS: Wooden

Absolute Window and Door Inc..........G....... 941 485-7774
Venice *(G-18527)*
Algoma Hardwoods Inc..........E....... 865 471-6300
Orlando *(G-12453)*
Belets Millwork Inc..........F....... 904 353-8600
Jacksonville *(G-6202)*
Builders Door and Supply Inc..........F....... 941 955-2311
Sarasota *(G-16372)*
Century Millworks..........F....... 850 256-2565
Century *(G-1527)*
D R Nickelson & Company Inc..........F....... 386 755-6565
Lake City *(G-7353)*
Florida Made Door Co..........C....... 352 742-1000
Tampa *(G-17681)*
Gulfport Industries Inc..........F....... 813 885-1000
Tampa *(G-17736)*
Hartman Windows and Doors LLC..........D....... 561 296-9600
Riviera Beach *(G-15333)*
Islandoor Company..........G....... 954 524-3667
Fort Lauderdale *(G-4069)*
Jambco Millwork Inc..........F....... 954 977-4998
Margate *(G-8551)*
Kmi International Inc..........E....... 561 588-5514
Lake Worth *(G-7562)*
Lake Door and Trim Inc..........F....... 352 589-5566
Eustis *(G-3712)*
Masonite Corporation..........D....... 813 877-2726
Tampa *(G-17887)*
Masonite Holdings Inc..........F....... 813 877-2726
Tampa *(G-17888)*
Masonite International Corp..........D....... 800 895-2723
Tampa *(G-17889)*
Masonite US Corporation..........D....... 813 877-2726
Tampa *(G-17890)*
Mill-Rite Woodworking Co Inc..........D....... 727 527-7808
Pinellas Park *(G-14368)*
Premdor Finance LLC..........G....... 813 877-2726
Tampa *(G-18007)*
Quality Engineered Products Co..........E....... 813 885-1693
Tampa *(G-18031)*
R & R Door and Trim Inc..........G....... 561 844-5496
West Palm Beach *(G-19015)*
Shaver Properties Inc..........E....... 772 569-3466
Vero Beach *(G-18664)*
Siw Solutions LLC..........D....... 561 274-9392
Delray Beach *(G-3142)*
Superior Trim & Door Inc..........E....... 407 408-7624
Apopka *(G-190)*
Ultimate Door of Palm Beach..........F....... 561 642-2828
Lake Worth *(G-7595)*
Wow Business..........F....... 813 301-2620
Tampa *(G-18267)*

DRAINAGE PRDTS: Concrete

Cemex Materials LLC..........D....... 561 743-4039
Jupiter *(G-7019)*

DRAPERIES & CURTAINS

Associated Interior Desgr Svc..........F....... 561 655-4926
West Palm Beach *(G-18805)*
Bkbl Holdings Ltd..........G....... 954 920-6772
Sunrise *(G-17098)*
D W A Inc..........F....... 941 444-1134
Sarasota *(G-16401)*
Drapery Masters LLC..........G....... 407 448-6898
Kissimmee *(G-7239)*
Fabric Innovations Inc..........E....... 305 860-5757
Miami *(G-9555)*
G K Window Treatments Inc..........F....... 954 786-2927
Pompano Beach *(G-14709)*
Kenco Hospitality Inc..........D....... 954 921-5434
Fort Lauderdale *(G-4087)*
Mws Drapery Inc..........E....... 305 794-3811
Hialeah *(G-5530)*
Quest Drape..........G....... 407 888-8164
Orlando *(G-13105)*
Remas Draperies Etc Inc..........G....... 904 845-9300
Hilliard *(G-5716)*
Residential Acoustics LLC..........F....... 813 922-2390
Tampa *(G-18053)*
Solar Shades Draperies & More..........G....... 954 600-3419
Plantation *(G-14554)*
Top Trtment Cstomes Accesories..........G....... 239 936-4600
Fort Myers *(G-4632)*
Vertical Land Inc..........F....... 850 244-5263
Panama City *(G-13961)*
Westpoint Home Inc..........B....... 850 415-4100
Chipley *(G-1549)*

DRAPERIES & DRAPERY FABRICS, COTTON

Ards Awning & Upholstery Inc..........E....... 863 293-2442
Winter Haven *(G-19300)*
Associated Interior Desgr Svc..........F....... 561 655-4926
West Palm Beach *(G-18805)*
D W A Inc..........F....... 941 444-1134
Sarasota *(G-16401)*
Designers Wholesale Workroom..........F....... 239 434-7633
Naples *(G-11226)*
Dhf Marketing Inc..........F....... 305 884-8077
Hialeah *(G-5371)*
Distinctive Creat Intr Wkshp I..........F....... 954 921-1861
Hollywood *(G-5812)*

DRAPERIES: Plastic & Textile, From Purchased Materials

Paul Himber Inc..........F....... 561 586-3741
West Palm Beach *(G-18990)*
Powless Drapery Service Inc..........E....... 954 566-7863
Oakland Park *(G-11831)*
Shades By Ana Inc..........G....... 305 238-4858
Miami *(G-10333)*
Suncoast Fabrics Inc..........G....... 239 566-3313
Naples *(G-11422)*
Sutton Draperies Inc..........F....... 305 653-7738
Miami *(G-10443)*
Tiffany Quilting & Drapery..........F....... 407 834-6386
Longwood *(G-8343)*

DRAPERY & UPHOLSTERY STORES: Draperies

D W A Inc..........F....... 941 444-1134
Sarasota *(G-16401)*
Myriam Interiors Inc..........G....... 305 626-9898
Hialeah *(G-5531)*
Remas Draperies Etc Inc..........G....... 904 845-9300
Hilliard *(G-5716)*
Vertical Land Inc..........F....... 850 819-2535
Panama City *(G-13960)*
Vertical Village Inc..........G....... 772 340-0400
Port Saint Lucie *(G-15162)*

DRAPES & DRAPERY FABRICS, FROM MANMADE FIBER

Dti Design Trend Inc..........F....... 954 680-8370
Hialeah *(G-5379)*
Remas Draperies Etc Inc..........G....... 904 845-9300
Hilliard *(G-5716)*
Vertical Village Inc..........G....... 772 340-0400
Port Saint Lucie *(G-15162)*

DRILL BITS

Advantage Drills Inc..........G....... 407 478-2487
Winter Park *(G-19373)*
Approved Performance Tooling..........E....... 305 592-7775
Miami *(G-9158)*
B & A Manufacturing Co..........E....... 561 848-8648
Riviera Beach *(G-15300)*

DRILLING MACHINERY & EQPT: Oil & Gas

Logistic Systems Inc..........G....... 305 477-4999
Miami *(G-9906)*

DRILLING MACHINERY & EQPT: Water Well

Jayco Screens Inc..........G....... 850 456-0673
Pensacola *(G-14182)*
Krausz Usa Inc..........F....... 352 509-3600
Ocala *(G-11977)*
Phoenix Dewatering Inc..........F....... 407 330-7015
Sanford *(G-16101)*

DRILLS & DRILLING EQPT: Mining

Ronnies Welding & Machine..........G....... 305 238-0972
Cutler Bay *(G-2410)*
Wolf Americas LLC..........G....... 407 704-2051
Orlando *(G-13327)*

DRILLS: Core

Sandvik Mining & Cnstr USA LLC..........C....... 386 462-4100
Alachua *(G-18)*

DRINK MIXES, NONALCOHOLIC: Cocktail

Lemon-X Corporation..........G....... 863 635-8400
Frostproof *(G-4861)*

DRINKING PLACES: Bars & Lounges

Burn By Rocky Patel..........G....... 239 653-9013
Naples *(G-11197)*

DRINKING PLACES: Wine Bar

Garvinos LLC..........G....... 352 430-1435
The Villages *(G-18390)*

DRIVE SHAFTS

Broward Power Train Co Inc..........E....... 954 772-0881
Fort Lauderdale *(G-3870)*
Central Florida Driveshaft..........G....... 407 299-1100
Orlando *(G-12567)*

DRIVES: High Speed Indl, Exc Hydrostatic

ABB Enterprise Software Inc..........C....... 954 752-6700
Coral Springs *(G-2211)*

DRUG STORES

Kashiben Say LLC..........G....... 352 489-4960
Dunnellon *(G-3598)*
St Mary Pharmacy LLC..........F....... 727 585-1333
Largo *(G-8060)*

Employee Codes: A=Over 500 employees, B=251-500
C=101-250, D=51-100, E=20-50, F=10-19, G=4-9

DRUG TESTING KITS: Blood & Urine

Advantagecare Inc....G....407 345-8877
Orlando *(G-12435)*
Arcpoint of Tallahassee Inc....D....850 201-2500
Tallahassee *(G-17222)*
Intrinsic Interventions Inc....G....614 205-8465
Bonita Springs *(G-841)*

DRUGS & DRUG PROPRIETARIES, WHOLESALE: Bandages

Aso LLC....C....941 379-0300
Sarasota *(G-16352)*

DRUGS & DRUG PROPRIETARIES, WHOLESALE: Medicinals/Botanicals

Potnetwork Holdings Inc....G....800 433-0127
Fort Lauderdale *(G-4171)*

DRUGS & DRUG PROPRIETARIES, WHOLESALE: Pharmaceuticals

Andrx Corporation....C....954 585-1400
Davie *(G-2497)*
Ceautamed Worldwide LLC....G....866 409-6262
Boca Raton *(G-474)*
Lupin Research Inc....E....800 466-1450
Coral Springs *(G-2275)*
Max Avw Professional LLC....F....954 972-3338
Margate *(G-8557)*
Rowell Laboratories Inc....F....407 929-9445
Apopka *(G-183)*
Shriji Swami LLC....F....904 727-3434
Jacksonville *(G-6767)*
Specialty Pharmacy Services....G....321 953-2004
Melbourne *(G-8940)*
Uspharma Ltd....D....954 817-4418
Miami Lakes *(G-10877)*

DRUGS & DRUG PROPRIETARIES, WHOLESALE: Vitamins & Minerals

Be Whole Nutrition LLC....G....813 420-3057
Plant City *(G-14408)*
Boston Ntrceutical Science LLC....F....617 848-4560
Miami *(G-9270)*
Liv LLC....E....321 276-5302
Miami Lakes *(G-10808)*
Mr Gummy Vitamins LLC....G....855 674-8669
Opa Locka *(G-12341)*
Taylor L Max L C....G....833 346-9963
Fort Myers *(G-4625)*

DRUGS: Parasitic & Infective Disease Affecting

Sinofresh Healthcare Inc....G....941 270-2627
Venice *(G-18573)*

DRUMS: Brake

Multi Parts Supply Usa Inc....E....561 748-1515
Jupiter *(G-7078)*

DRUMS: Fiber

Design Containers Inc....D....904 764-6541
Jacksonville *(G-6316)*

DRYCLEANING & LAUNDRY SVCS: Commercial & Family

One Price Drycleaners Tampa....F....727 734-3353
Dunedin *(G-3586)*

DRYCLEANING EQPT & SPLYS WHOLESALERS

Power Kleen Corporation....E....813 854-2648
Oldsmar *(G-12258)*

DRYCLEANING EQPT & SPLYS: Commercial

Steiner-Atlantic LLC....E....305 754-4551
Miami Gardens *(G-10756)*

DRYERS & REDRYERS: Indl

Bcr Environmental Corporation....E....904 819-9170
Jacksonville *(G-6198)*

DUCTS: Sheet Metal

Advanced Metals LLC....G....352 494-2476
Hawthorne *(G-5242)*
Badger Corporation....G....954 942-5277
Pompano Beach *(G-14611)*
Duct Design Corporation....E....305 827-0110
Hialeah *(G-5380)*
Impulse Air Inc....E....904 475-1822
Jacksonville *(G-6491)*
Jer-Air Manufacturing Inc....E....352 591-2674
Micanopy *(G-10902)*
Lapin Sheet Metal Company....D....407 423-9897
Orlando *(G-12892)*
Metal Mart Systems Inc....E....863 533-4040
Bartow *(G-324)*
South Florida Sheet Metal....F....954 647-6457
Pembroke Pines *(G-14060)*
US Sheet Metal Inc....F....305 884-7705
Miami *(G-10553)*

DUMPSTERS: Garbage

College Hunks Hlg Junk & Mvg....G....407 378-2500
Orlando *(G-12601)*
Dumpstermaxx....G....805 552-6299
University Park *(G-18504)*
Dumpsterme LLC....G....904 647-1945
Jacksonville *(G-6334)*
Elevated Dumpsters LLC....G....813 732-6338
Zephyrhills *(G-19515)*
Empire Dumpsters LLC....G....407 223-8985
Apopka *(G-134)*
Gz Dumpsters LLC....G....407 600-0756
Altamonte Springs *(G-49)*
Interstate Recycling Waste....F....407 812-5555
Orlando *(G-12838)*
L & D Dumpsters LLC....G....352 589-5043
Astatula *(G-212)*
Lr Dumpsters LLC....G....321 279-0169
Winter Park *(G-19419)*
Need A Dumpster LLC....G....888 407-3867
Apopka *(G-164)*
Platinium Rosis Inc....G....786 617-9973
Miami Beach *(G-10703)*
Pro Dumpsters Inc....F....407 910-6341
Kissimmee *(G-7291)*
Service D N D Dumpster....G....813 989-3867
Tampa *(G-18086)*
Southern Dumpsters Inc....G....772 413-1228
Melbourne *(G-8936)*
Trash Express SW Inc....G....239 340-5291
Fort Myers *(G-4638)*
U-Load Dumpsters LLC....G....352 318-3045
Ponce De Leon *(G-14919)*
Wastequip Manufacturing Co LLC....E....863 665-6507
Lakeland *(G-7832)*
Xtreme Dumpster Services Corp....G....407 272-8899
Orlando *(G-13333)*

DYES & PIGMENTS: Organic

Ashwell Label Dies Inc....F....727 527-0098
Pinellas Park *(G-14335)*

DYES & TINTS: Household

Southeast Energy Inc....G....561 883-1051
Boca Raton *(G-723)*

DYES OR COLORS: Food, Synthetic

Allied USA Incorporated....G....305 235-3950
Miami *(G-9118)*

EATING PLACES

Choctaw Trading Co Inc....G....407 905-9917
Winter Garden *(G-19257)*
Culinary Concepts Inc....E....407 228-0069
Orlando *(G-12635)*
Grand Buffet....G....941 752-3388
Bradenton *(G-1052)*
J Squared Management II LLC....F....813 373-5359
Tampa *(G-17799)*
Magnolias Gurmet Bky Itln Deli....G....352 207-2667
Ocala *(G-11990)*
Ronnie & Moes Italian Ice LLC....G....786 970-1805
Miami *(G-10280)*
Suzanne Chalet Foods Inc....G....863 676-6011
Lake Wales *(G-7524)*
White Publishing Co Inc....F....904 389-3622
Jacksonville *(G-6919)*

EDUCATIONAL SVCS

Sibling Group Holdings Inc....D....786 618-1472
Miami *(G-10341)*

ELASTOMERS

Linvatec Corporation....A....727 392-6464
Largo *(G-8001)*

ELECTRIC MOTOR REPAIR SVCS

A & A Electric Mtrs & Pump Svc....G....407 843-5005
Orlando *(G-12422)*
Aap Industrial Inc....E....941 377-4373
Sarasota *(G-16331)*
AC Industrial Service Inc....F....305 887-5541
Hialeah *(G-5265)*
AL Covell Electric Inc....G....352 544-0680
Brooksville *(G-1207)*
Allapattah Electric Motor Repr....G....305 325-0330
Miami *(G-9115)*
American International Mtr Svc....G....727 573-9501
Clearwater *(G-1580)*
Belle Glade Electric Motor Svc....G....561 996-3333
Belle Glade *(G-345)*
Biscayne Electric Motor & Pump....G....305 681-8171
Miami *(G-9251)*
Blueocean Marine Services LLC....F....954 583-9888
Fort Lauderdale *(G-3861)*
Central Electric Motor Service....F....863 422-4721
Haines City *(G-5138)*
Condo Electric Motor Repr Corp....E....305 691-5400
Hialeah *(G-5351)*
Dade Pump & Supply Co....G....305 235-5000
Miami *(G-9430)*
Done Rite Pumps....G....305 953-3380
Opa Locka *(G-12308)*
Electrcal Systems Cmmnications....G....813 248-4275
Tampa *(G-17631)*
Electro Mechanical South Inc....E....941 342-9111
Sarasota *(G-16417)*
Florida Elc Mtr Co Miami Inc....E....305 759-3835
Miami *(G-9581)*
Genesis Electric Motors Inc....G....727 572-1414
Largo *(G-7957)*
Indian River Armature Inc....G....772 461-2067
Fort Pierce *(G-4708)*
Industrial Service Solutions....C....239 288-5230
Fort Myers *(G-4493)*
John Mader Enterprises Inc....E....239 731-5455
Fort Myers *(G-4506)*
Kcw Electric Company Inc....G....850 878-2051
Tallahassee *(G-17287)*
Kolich Electric Motor Co Inc....G....954 969-8605
Pompano Beach *(G-14740)*
M & W Electric Motors Inc....G....850 433-0400
Pensacola *(G-14198)*
Miami Industrial Motors Inc....G....305 593-2370
Doral *(G-3434)*
Michigan Pmps Elc Mtrs Repr Co....G....407 841-6800
Orlando *(G-12967)*
Morgans Elc Mtr & Pump Svc....G....321 960-2209
Cocoa Beach *(G-2066)*
Pinellas Electric Motor Repair....G....727 572-0777
Clearwater *(G-1834)*
Robert E Weissenborn Sr....G....239 262-1771
Naples *(G-11387)*
Rusch Electric Motor Repair Co....G....727 319-3388
Seminole *(G-16760)*
Southern Winding Service Inc....E....813 621-6555
Tampa *(G-18121)*
St Agustine Elc Mtr Works Inc....F....904 829-8211
Saint Augustine *(G-15617)*
Stewarts Elc Mtr Works Inc....E....407 859-1837
Orlando *(G-13215)*
Suncoast Electric Motor Svc....F....813 247-4104
Tampa *(G-18143)*
T A C Armatures & Pumps Corp....F....305 835-8845
Miami *(G-10454)*
Tampa Armature Works Inc....D....904 757-7790
Jacksonville *(G-6836)*
Tampa Armature Works Inc....C....813 612-2600
Tampa *(G-18157)*
Taw Payroll Inc....F....813 621-5661
Tampa *(G-18176)*
TEam Service Corp New York....E....410 365-1574
Marco Island *(G-8527)*
Tripp Electric Motors Inc....G....561 996-3333
Belle Glade *(G-353)*
United Electric Motor Inc....G....813 238-7872
Tampa *(G-18220)*

V A Electrical Motors Center.................G....... 305 825-3327
Hialeah *(G-5671)*

ELECTRIC POWER DISTRIBUTION TO CONSUMERS

FPL Energy Oklahoma Wind LLC.........G....... 561 691-7171
Juno Beach *(G-6980)*
Tuscola Wind II LLC.................................G....... 561 691-7171
Juno Beach *(G-6985)*

ELECTRIC SERVICES

Florida Crystals Corporation.................D....... 561 655-6303
West Palm Beach *(G-18875)*
Florida Crystals Corporation.................C....... 561 515-8080
West Palm Beach *(G-18877)*
Vasco Winds LLC..................................G....... 561 691-7171
Juno Beach *(G-6986)*
White Oak Energy Backleverage............E....... 561 691-7171
Juno Beach *(G-6987)*
Wilton Wind II LLC.................................G....... 561 691-7171
Juno Beach *(G-6989)*

ELECTRIC WATER HEATERS WHOLESALERS

Niagara Industries Inc............................F....... 305 876-9010
Miami *(G-10071)*

ELECTRICAL APPARATUS & EQPT WHOLESALERS

Anuva Manufacturing Svcs Inc...............E....... 321 821-4900
Melbourne *(G-8768)*
Apollo Sunguard Systems Inc................F....... 941 925-3000
Sarasota *(G-16343)*
Arco Marine Inc......................................E....... 850 455-5476
Pensacola *(G-14090)*
Carlisle Interconnect Tech Inc...............A....... 904 829-5600
Saint Augustine *(G-15526)*
Edashop Inc..G....... 786 565-9197
Winter Garden *(G-19262)*
Englander Enterprises Inc......................E....... 727 461-4755
Clearwater *(G-1673)*
Gfx Inc..E....... 305 499-9789
Miami *(G-9634)*
Morning Star Industries Inc....................E....... 800 440-6050
Jensen Beach *(G-6971)*
Robertson Transformer Co.....................E....... 708 388-2315
Sarasota *(G-16560)*
Spaceport Corporation............................G....... 305 690-6885
Miami *(G-10392)*
US Generator Inc.....................................G....... 772 778-0131
Sebastian *(G-16675)*

ELECTRICAL APPLIANCES, TELEVISIONS & RADIOS WHOLESALERS

AVI-Spl Holdings Inc..............................A....... 866 708-5034
Tampa *(G-17446)*
AVI-Spl LLC..A....... 813 884-7168
Tampa *(G-17447)*
Flash Sales Inc...G....... 954 914-2689
Miami Gardens *(G-10741)*
La Cuisine Intl Distrs Inc........................E....... 305 418-0010
Miami *(G-9839)*

ELECTRICAL CURRENT CARRYING WIRING DEVICES

B G Service Company Inc........................E....... 561 659-1471
West Palm Beach *(G-18808)*
Carlisle Interconnect Tech Inc...............A....... 904 829-5600
Saint Augustine *(G-15526)*
Certified Manufacturing Inc....................E....... 850 537-3777
Holt *(G-5948)*
Compulink Corporation...........................B....... 727 579-1500
Saint Petersburg *(G-15752)*
Data Phone Wire & Cable Corp..............F....... 954 761-7171
Fort Lauderdale *(G-3933)*
Dayton-Granger Inc.................................C....... 954 463-3451
Fort Lauderdale *(G-3935)*
Evolution Intrcnnect Systems I..............F....... 954 217-6223
Davie *(G-2521)*
Five Oceans Florida Inc..........................E....... 772 221-8188
Palm City *(G-13655)*
Hytronics Corp..D....... 727 535-0413
Clearwater *(G-1725)*
I C Probotics Inc......................................D....... 407 339-8298
Longwood *(G-8288)*
Interconnect Cable Tech Corp................D....... 352 796-1716
Brooksville *(G-1237)*
J B Nottingham & Co Inc........................E....... 386 873-2990
Deland *(G-2986)*
Kleen Wheels Corporation......................G....... 954 791-9112
Davie *(G-2541)*
Lextm3 Systems LLC...............................F....... 954 888-1024
Davie *(G-2546)*
Lightning Specialists Inc.........................G....... 727 938-3560
Odessa *(G-12131)*
LMI Components Inc...............................F....... 561 994-5896
Boca Raton *(G-604)*
Logus Manufacturing Corp.....................E....... 561 842-3550
West Palm Beach *(G-18934)*
Panamtech Inc...F....... 954 587-3769
Plantation *(G-14541)*
Paramount Industries Inc........................E....... 954 781-3755
Pompano Beach *(G-14784)*
Scan Technology Inc................................G....... 931 723-0304
Gainesville *(G-4992)*
Select Engineered Systems Inc...............E....... 305 823-5410
Hialeah *(G-5613)*
Superior Electronics Inc..........................E....... 727 733-0700
Clearwater *(G-1896)*
Technipower LLC.....................................F....... 954 346-2442
Coral Springs *(G-2321)*
United Electronics Corporation...............D....... 954 888-1024
Miami *(G-10534)*
Vee Industries Inc....................................G....... 561 732-1083
Boynton Beach *(G-973)*
Verifone Inc...C....... 800 837-4366
Coral Springs *(G-2326)*

ELECTRICAL DISCHARGE MACHINING, EDM

Savvy Associate Inc.................................F....... 954 941-6986
Pompano Beach *(G-14840)*
Triad Edm Inc..G....... 352 489-5336
Dunnellon *(G-3601)*

ELECTRICAL EQPT & SPLYS

Advance Solder Technology Inc..............F....... 321 633-4777
Rockledge *(G-15393)*
Aero-Tel Wire Harness Corp...................E....... 407 445-1722
Orlando *(G-12439)*
Aeronautical Systems Engrg Inc.............G....... 727 375-2520
Odessa *(G-12099)*
Airo Industries Inc...................................G....... 239 229-5273
Fort Myers *(G-4347)*
Alectron Inc..G....... 786 397-6827
Doral *(G-3236)*
ARC Electric Inc.......................................E....... 954 583-9800
Davie *(G-2498)*
Asco Power Technologies LP..................G....... 727 450-2730
Clearwater *(G-1593)*
Astronics Test Systems Inc......................C....... 407 381-6062
Orlando *(G-12496)*
BJ Burns Incorporated.............................E....... 305 572-9500
Sunrise *(G-17097)*
Canam Electric...G....... 305 534-7903
Miami Beach *(G-10651)*
Carling Technologies Inc.........................G....... 561 745-0405
Jupiter *(G-7015)*
Clare Instruments (us) Inc.......................G....... 813 886-2775
Tampa *(G-17538)*
Coastal Electric..G....... 239 245-7396
Fort Myers *(G-4403)*
Commercial Gates and Elc LLC...............F....... 386 454-2329
High Springs *(G-5700)*
Custom Mfg & Engrg Inc.........................D....... 727 548-0522
Pinellas Park *(G-14342)*
Del Air Electric Co....................................G....... 407 531-1173
Sanford *(G-16035)*
DMC Components Intl LLC.....................G....... 407 478-4064
Winter Park *(G-19404)*
Eaton Corporation...................................G....... 813 281-8069
Tampa *(G-17628)*
Enterprise Electric LLC............................G....... 407 884-0668
Apopka *(G-136)*
Exploration Resources Intn Geo.............G....... 601 747-0726
Lake Mary *(G-7412)*
Famatel USA LLC.....................................G....... 754 217-4841
Dania *(G-2445)*
Gc Electric LLC..G....... 386 842-7066
Jacksonville *(G-6427)*
Geddis Inc...F....... 800 844-6792
Dunedin *(G-3579)*
General Scientific Corporation................G....... 850 866-9636
Panama City *(G-13908)*
Guerilla Technologies Inc........................F....... 772 283-0500
Palm City *(G-13661)*
Hale Products Inc.....................................C....... 352 629-5020
Ocala *(G-11963)*
Holly Sargent..G....... 954 560-6973
Fort Lauderdale *(G-4049)*
Hooper Corp..F....... 954 382-5711
Davie *(G-2536)*
Hose-Mccann Telephone Co Inc..............E....... 954 429-1110
Deerfield Beach *(G-2845)*
Interrail Power Inc....................................F....... 904 268-6411
Jacksonville *(G-6502)*
Inviro Tek Inc..G....... 215 499-1209
Orlando *(G-12840)*
Invision Industries Inc..............................G....... 407 451-8353
Orlando *(G-12843)*
J B Nottingham & Co Inc..........................E....... 386 873-2990
Deland *(G-2986)*
L3harris Technologies Inc.........................G....... 321 729-2186
Melbourne *(G-8867)*
L3harris Technologies Inc.........................G....... 321 309-7848
Melbourne *(G-8866)*
Laser Interceptor Usa LLC.......................G....... 352 688-0708
Spring Hill *(G-16856)*
Laserstar Technologies Corp....................G....... 407 248-1142
Orlando *(G-12896)*
Lightworks Inc...G....... 305 456-3520
Miami *(G-9892)*
Load Banks Direct LLC..............................F....... 859 554-2522
Venice *(G-18560)*
Lockheed Martin Corporation...................A....... 407 306-1000
Orlando *(G-12920)*
Lui Technical Services Inc........................G....... 954 803-7610
Sunrise *(G-17144)*
M Micro Technologies Inc.........................B....... 954 973-6166
Pompano Beach *(G-14749)*
Marine Digital Integrators LLC.................E....... 772 210-2403
Stuart *(G-16974)*
Microsemi Corp...F....... 407 965-5687
Lake Mary *(G-7434)*
New IEM Power Systems LLC...................C....... 904 365-4444
Jacksonville *(G-6626)*
Nuenergy Technologies Corp....................G....... 866 895-6838
Clearwater *(G-1812)*
Pfi Inc..G....... 407 822-4499
Longwood *(G-8324)*
Probotix...G....... 844 472-9262
Fort Walton Beach *(G-4824)*
Semilab USA LLC......................................E....... 813 977-2244
Temple Terrace *(G-18378)*
Sibex Inc..C....... 727 726-4343
Crystal River *(G-2382)*
Superior Metal Fabricators Inc.................E....... 407 295-5772
Orlando *(G-13230)*
Surf Lighting Inc..F....... 305 888-7851
Hialeah *(G-5644)*
Symetrics Industries LLC..........................C....... 321 254-1500
Melbourne *(G-8954)*
T V Trac Ltd...G....... 516 371-1111
Boynton Beach *(G-966)*
Technipower LLC.......................................F....... 954 346-2442
Coral Springs *(G-2321)*
Top Sales Co..G....... 561 852-4311
Boca Raton *(G-752)*
United Space Coast Cables Inc.................E....... 321 952-1040
West Melbourne *(G-18778)*
Vapor Engineering Inc...............................F....... 850 434-3191
Pensacola *(G-14280)*
Vinland Corporation..................................E....... 954 475-9093
Plantation *(G-14565)*
Vos Systems LLC.......................................F....... 352 317-2954
Gainesville *(G-5016)*
Walker Electric Inc....................................G....... 941 729-5015
Palmetto *(G-13834)*

ELECTRICAL EQPT FOR ENGINES

American Auto Marine Wiring...................G....... 954 782-0193
Pompano Beach *(G-14590)*
Arco Marine Inc...E....... 850 455-5476
Pensacola *(G-14090)*
B G Service Company Inc..........................E....... 561 659-1471
West Palm Beach *(G-18808)*
Battery Power Solutions Inc......................G....... 727 446-8400
Clearwater *(G-1601)*
Bobcat of Wiregrass Inc............................F....... 334 792-5121
Panama City Beach *(G-13973)*
Competition Specialties Inc......................F....... 386 776-1476
Mc Alpin *(G-8599)*
Dynalco Controls Corporation..................E....... 323 589-6181
Fort Lauderdale *(G-3952)*
Gml Industries LLC...................................E....... 352 671-7619
Ocala *(G-11957)*

Ibtm Engineering Inc ....G.... 239 246-1876
Sanibel *(G-16146)*
Inglotech Usa LLC ....G.... 305 479-2770
Coral Gables *(G-2157)*
L & L Automotive Electric Inc ....F.... 631 471-5230
Melbourne *(G-8862)*
Reynoso & Associates Inc ....G.... 954 360-0601
Deerfield Beach *(G-2905)*
Tradewinds Power Corp ....F.... 863 382-2166
Sebring *(G-16716)*

ELECTRICAL EQPT REPAIR & MAINTENANCE

Delta Regis Tools Inc ....E.... 772 465-4302
Fort Pierce *(G-4692)*
Electro Mechanical South Inc ....E.... 941 342-9111
Sarasota *(G-16417)*
Megin Us LLC ....G.... 954 341-2965
Coral Springs *(G-2279)*
Money Tree Atm Mfg LLC ....G.... 850 244-5543
Fort Walton Beach *(G-4817)*
Virginia Electronic & Ltg Corp ....G.... 904 230-2840
Green Cove Springs *(G-5076)*

ELECTRICAL EQPT REPAIR SVCS

Megawattage LLC ....F.... 954 328-0232
Fort Lauderdale *(G-4117)*
Sanbur Inc ....F.... 941 371-7446
Sarasota *(G-16572)*

ELECTRICAL EQPT: Automotive, NEC

Advanced Automotive Designs ....G.... 561 499-8812
Delray Beach *(G-3040)*
D & L Auto & Marine Supplies ....G.... 305 593-0560
Doral *(G-3319)*
Euromotion Inc ....G.... 954 612-0354
Delray Beach *(G-3077)*

ELECTRICAL EQPT: Household

David Chittum ....G.... 386 754-6127
Saint Petersburg *(G-15756)*
Portalp Usa Inc ....F.... 800 474-3667
Naples *(G-11373)*

ELECTRICAL GOODS, WHOLESALE: Answering Machines, Telephone

Tier5 Technical Services ....G.... 904 435-3484
Jacksonville *(G-6855)*

ELECTRICAL GOODS, WHOLESALE: Boxes & Fittings

BJ Burns Incorporated ....E.... 305 572-9500
Sunrise *(G-17097)*
Tic Light Electrical Corp ....G.... 305 712-3499
Miami *(G-10476)*

ELECTRICAL GOODS, WHOLESALE: Cable Conduit

Electriduct Inc ....E.... 954 867-9100
Pompano Beach *(G-14676)*
Quality Cable Contractors Inc ....E.... 407 246-0606
Orlando *(G-13103)*

ELECTRICAL GOODS, WHOLESALE: Capacitors

Aerouno Llc ....F.... 561 767-5597
Margate *(G-8532)*

ELECTRICAL GOODS, WHOLESALE: Connectors

Kai Limited ....C.... 954 957-8586
Fort Lauderdale *(G-4083)*

ELECTRICAL GOODS, WHOLESALE: Electrical Appliances, Major

Quality Custom Cabinet Design ....G.... 352 728-4292
Leesburg *(G-8169)*
US Generator Inc ....G.... 772 778-0131
Sebastian *(G-16675)*

ELECTRICAL GOODS, WHOLESALE: Electronic Parts

Compulink Corporation ....B.... 727 579-1500
Saint Petersburg *(G-15752)*
Next Generation Home Pdts Inc ....G.... 727 834-9400
Tampa *(G-17938)*

ELECTRICAL GOODS, WHOLESALE: Fire Alarm Systems

AB Fire Sprinklers LLC ....G.... 954 973-8054
Pompano Beach *(G-14572)*

ELECTRICAL GOODS, WHOLESALE: Fittings & Construction Mat

Citel America Inc ....F.... 954 430-6310
Miramar *(G-10979)*

ELECTRICAL GOODS, WHOLESALE: Flashlights

Emergency Vehicle Sup Co LLC ....E.... 954 428-5201
Pompano Beach *(G-14678)*

ELECTRICAL GOODS, WHOLESALE: Garbage Disposals

Wastequip Manufacturing Co LLC ....E.... 863 665-6507
Lakeland *(G-7832)*

ELECTRICAL GOODS, WHOLESALE: Generators

Armstrong Power Systems LLC ....F.... 305 470-0058
Miami *(G-9170)*

ELECTRICAL GOODS, WHOLESALE: Household Appliances, NEC

Ce North America LLC ....E.... 305 392-2200
Coral Gables *(G-2130)*

ELECTRICAL GOODS, WHOLESALE: Light Bulbs & Related Splys

Jq Green America Inc ....G.... 786 397-0999
Saint Lucie West *(G-15686)*
Roth Southeast Lighting LLC ....G.... 954 423-6640
Fort Lauderdale *(G-4218)*

ELECTRICAL GOODS, WHOLESALE: Lighting Fixtures, Comm & Indl

Lumilum LLC ....F.... 305 233-2844
Miami *(G-9918)*
Solar Electric Power Company ....F.... 772 220-6615
Stuart *(G-17018)*

ELECTRICAL GOODS, WHOLESALE: Lugs & Connectors

Arrowhead Global LLC ....G.... 727 497-7340
Clearwater *(G-1589)*

ELECTRICAL GOODS, WHOLESALE: Mobile telephone Eqpt

Sky Phone LLC ....F.... 305 531-5218
Miami Beach *(G-10711)*

ELECTRICAL GOODS, WHOLESALE: Motor Ctrls, Starters & Relays

T R S ....E.... 407 298-5490
Orlando *(G-13238)*

ELECTRICAL GOODS, WHOLESALE: Motors

Biscayne Electric Motor & Pump ....G.... 305 681-8171
Miami *(G-9251)*
Dade Pump & Supply Co ....G.... 305 235-5000
Miami *(G-9430)*
Electrcal Systems Cmmnications ....G.... 813 248-4275
Tampa *(G-17631)*
Florida Elc Mtr Co Miami Inc ....E.... 305 759-3835
Miami *(G-9581)*
Indian River Armature Inc ....G.... 772 461-2067
Fort Pierce *(G-4708)*
Industrial Service Solutions ....C.... 239 288-5230
Fort Myers *(G-4493)*
M & W Electric Motors Inc ....G.... 850 433-0400
Pensacola *(G-14198)*
Robert E Weissenborn Sr ....G.... 239 262-1771
Naples *(G-11387)*
Rusch Electric Motor Repair Co ....G.... 727 319-3388
Seminole *(G-16760)*
Tampa Armature Works Inc ....D.... 904 757-7790
Jacksonville *(G-6836)*
Tampa Armature Works Inc ....C.... 813 612-2600
Tampa *(G-18157)*
TEam Service Corp New York ....E.... 410 365-1574
Marco Island *(G-8527)*
United Electric Motor Inc ....G.... 813 238-7872
Tampa *(G-18220)*

ELECTRICAL GOODS, WHOLESALE: Panelboards

Champion Controls Inc ....E.... 954 318-3090
Fort Lauderdale *(G-3895)*

ELECTRICAL GOODS, WHOLESALE: Radio & TV Or TV Eqpt & Parts

Da Vinci Systems Inc ....G.... 954 688-5600
Coral Springs *(G-2236)*
Dayton Industrial Corporation ....G.... 941 351-4454
Sarasota *(G-16405)*

ELECTRICAL GOODS, WHOLESALE: Security Control Eqpt & Systems

Edgewater Technologies Inc ....F.... 954 565-9898
Fort Lauderdale *(G-3962)*
Salco Industries Inc ....F.... 941 377-7717
Sarasota *(G-16570)*
Senelco Iberia Inc ....D.... 561 912-6000
Deerfield Beach *(G-2909)*

ELECTRICAL GOODS, WHOLESALE: Semiconductor Devices

Boca Semiconductor Corporation ....E.... 561 226-8500
Boca Raton *(G-456)*
V and N Advanced Auto Sys LLC ....G.... 321 504-6440
Rockledge *(G-15455)*

ELECTRICAL GOODS, WHOLESALE: Switchboards

Axon Circuit Inc ....F.... 407 265-7980
Longwood *(G-8260)*

ELECTRICAL GOODS, WHOLESALE: Switchgear

Resa Pwr Slutions Plant Cy LLC ....F.... 813 752-6550
Plant City *(G-14461)*

ELECTRICAL GOODS, WHOLESALE: Telephone & Telegraphic Eqpt

Prime Meridian Trading Corp ....G.... 954 727-2152
Sunrise *(G-17161)*

ELECTRICAL GOODS, WHOLESALE: Telephone Eqpt

Allied Telecommunications Ltd ....F.... 954 370-9900
Plantation *(G-14487)*
Cyipcom Inc ....G.... 954 727-2500
Oakland Park *(G-11794)*

ELECTRICAL GOODS, WHOLESALE: Transformer & Transmission Eqpt

Man-Trans LLC ....F.... 850 222-6993
Tallahassee *(G-17294)*

ELECTRICAL GOODS, WHOLESALE: Transformers

Exxelia Usa Inc ....E.... 407 695-6562
Longwood *(G-8279)*

ELECTRICAL GOODS, WHOLESALE: Tubes, Rcvg & Txmtg Or Indl

Renco Usa Inc........F...... 321 637-1000
Miami *(G-10252)*

ELECTRICAL GOODS, WHOLESALE: Video Eqpt

Interntnal Srvillance Tech Inc........E...... 954 574-1100
Deerfield Beach *(G-2847)*

ELECTRICAL GOODS, WHOLESALE: Wire & Cable

American Wire Group Inc........F...... 954 455-3050
Aventura *(G-260)*
Commski LLC........G...... 813 501-0111
Tampa *(G-17548)*
Stampco Inc........F...... 904 737-6144
Jacksonville *(G-6807)*

ELECTRICAL GOODS, WHOLESALE: Wire/Cable, Telephone/Telegraph

Managed Data Assoc Inc........G...... 386 449-8419
Palm Coast *(G-13702)*

ELECTRICAL INDL APPARATUS, NEC

Burlakoff Manufacturing Co........G...... 972 889-2502
Ocala *(G-11891)*
First Look Inc........G...... 954 240-0530
Fort Lauderdale *(G-3995)*

ELECTRICAL MEASURING INSTRUMENT REPAIR & CALIBRATION SVCS

International Ozone Svcs LLC........G...... 352 978-9785
Mount Dora *(G-11105)*

ELECTRICAL SPLYS

Advance Controls Inc........F...... 941 746-3221
Bradenton *(G-983)*
Eaton Corporation........G...... 813 281-8069
Tampa *(G-17628)*
Pressure Systems Innvtions LLC........F...... 561 249-2708
West Palm Beach *(G-19005)*
Ryan Scientific LLC........F...... 904 284-6025
Green Cove Springs *(G-5069)*

ELECTRICAL SUPPLIES: Porcelain

Rock Intl Distributors Inc........E...... 305 513-3314
Miami *(G-10272)*

ELECTROMEDICAL EQPT

Actigraph LLC........G...... 850 332-7900
Pensacola *(G-14079)*
Bio-Logic Systems Corp........D...... 847 949-0456
Orlando *(G-12515)*
Biofuse Medical Tech Inc........G...... 877 466-2434
Melbourne *(G-8780)*
Critical Disposables Inc........E...... 407 330-1154
Sanford *(G-16028)*
Evren Technologies Inc........G...... 352 494-0950
Newberry *(G-11555)*
Geddis Inc........F...... 800 844-6792
Dunedin *(G-3579)*
Innovatia Medical Systems LLC........G...... 908 385-2802
Tampa *(G-17784)*
Invivo Corporation........E...... 352 336-0010
Gainesville *(G-4946)*
Iris International Inc........D...... 818 709-1244
Miami *(G-9770)*
Lasersight Incorporated........F...... 407 678-9900
Orlando *(G-12893)*
Lasersight Technologies Inc........G...... 407 678-9900
Orlando *(G-12894)*
Natus Medical Incorporated........E...... 321 235-8213
Orlando *(G-12994)*
Natus Medical Incorporated........F...... 847 949-5200
Orlando *(G-12995)*
Somatics LLC........G...... 847 234-6761
Venice *(G-18574)*
Stimwave LLC........F...... 800 965-5134
Pompano Beach *(G-14871)*
Syneron........G...... 407 489-3366
Orlando *(G-13236)*
Twinstar Optics & Coatings Inc........F...... 727 847-2300
Port Richey *(G-15073)*
Vevyan Hanania Inc........G...... 800 297-8485
Jacksonville *(G-6896)*

ELECTROMETALLURGICAL PRDTS

Bayside Small Cap Senior Loan........F...... 305 381-4100
Miami *(G-9227)*
Chance Aluminum Corp........F...... 407 789-1606
Orlando *(G-12574)*

ELECTRON BEAM: Cutting, Forming, Welding

Advanced Metal Works Inc........F...... 727 449-9353
Clearwater *(G-1566)*

ELECTRON TUBES

Advanced Manufacturing Inc........E...... 727 573-3300
Saint Petersburg *(G-15691)*
Cathodic Prtection Tech of Fla........G...... 321 799-0046
Cocoa Beach *(G-2060)*
Citel America Inc........F...... 954 430-6310
Miramar *(G-10979)*
L3harris Technologies Inc........G...... 321 727-9100
Melbourne *(G-8870)*
Lextm3 Systems LLC........F...... 954 888-1024
Davie *(G-2546)*
Video Display Corporation........D...... 321 784-4427
Cocoa *(G-2056)*

ELECTRON TUBES: Cathode Ray

Passur Aerospace Inc........G...... 631 589-6800
Orlando *(G-13051)*

ELECTRONIC COMPONENTS

2204 Avenue X LLC........G...... 407 619-1410
Vero Beach *(G-18588)*
Arcco Inc........G...... 954 564-0827
Oakland Park *(G-11779)*
Dry Bonez Inc........G...... 321 926-6399
Boca Raton *(G-510)*
J and A Maintenance........F...... 754 234-0708
Sunrise *(G-17133)*
Leeward Tech........G...... 305 215-4526
Homestead *(G-5980)*
Phil Lau........F...... 813 631-8643
Tampa *(G-17989)*
Pro Fuse........G...... 305 982-8457
Miami *(G-10203)*
Trademark Components Inc........G...... 813 948-2233
Lutz *(G-8421)*
Workforce Audio Inc........E...... 866 360-6416
Tampa *(G-18262)*

ELECTRONIC DETECTION SYSTEMS: Aeronautical

Moog Inc........F...... 321 435-8722
West Melbourne *(G-18777)*

ELECTRONIC DEVICES: Solid State, NEC

Aerouno Llc........F...... 561 767-5597
Margate *(G-8532)*
Gen-Prodics Inc........G...... 772 221-8464
Palm City *(G-13658)*
JAs Business Solutions Inc........E...... 954 975-0025
Pompano Beach *(G-14735)*

ELECTRONIC EQPT REPAIR SVCS

Industry Standard Technology........G...... 941 355-2100
Sarasota *(G-16235)*
Ra Co AMO Inc........F...... 561 626-7232
Palm Beach Gardens *(G-13620)*

ELECTRONIC LOADS & POWER SPLYS

Atlas Marine Systems Inc........F...... 954 735-6767
Fort Lauderdale *(G-3830)*
Edge Power Solutions Inc........F...... 321 499-1919
Melbourne *(G-8821)*
OHM Americas LLC........F...... 800 467-7275
Fort Lauderdale *(G-4148)*
Powerficient LLC........E...... 800 320-2535
Fort Lauderdale *(G-4172)*

ELECTRONIC PARTS & EQPT WHOLESALERS

AVw Inc........E...... 954 972-3338
Margate *(G-8536)*
Carrier Fire SEC Americas Corp........G...... 828 695-4000
Palm Beach Gardens *(G-13574)*
Component General Inc........E...... 727 376-6655
Odessa *(G-12112)*
Englander Enterprises Inc........E...... 727 461-4755
Clearwater *(G-1673)*
Entech Controls Corp........G...... 954 613-2971
Miami *(G-9528)*
Global Telemetry Systems Inc........G...... 850 651-3388
Shalimar *(G-16775)*
Ground Zero Electrostatics Inc........G...... 941 751-7581
Bradenton *(G-1053)*
Hensoldt Avionics Usa LLC........G...... 941 306-1328
Sarasota *(G-16459)*
Hera Cases LLC........G...... 305 714-2274
Miami *(G-9703)*
Interconnect Cable Tech Corp........D...... 352 796-1716
Brooksville *(G-1237)*
Lexmark International Inc........F...... 305 467-2200
Miami *(G-9887)*
Lift Aerospace Corp........F...... 305 851-5237
Miami *(G-9890)*
Logus Manufacturing Corp........E...... 561 842-3550
West Palm Beach *(G-18934)*
Marware Inc........E...... 954 927-6031
Dania Beach *(G-2468)*
Mat-Vac Technology Inc........F...... 386 238-7017
Daytona Beach *(G-2683)*
Minuteman Industries Inc........G...... 813 248-1776
Tampa *(G-17909)*
Nemal Electronics Intl Inc........E...... 305 899-0900
North Miami *(G-11648)*
Phototelesis LP........E...... 321 254-1500
Melbourne *(G-8908)*
Sagrad Inc........F...... 321 726-9400
Melbourne *(G-8923)*
Superior Electronics........G...... 941 355-9500
Sarasota *(G-16307)*
Sv Microwave Inc........C...... 561 840-1800
West Palm Beach *(G-19052)*
Vc Displays Inc........E...... 352 796-0060
Brooksville *(G-1288)*
Voxx International Corporation........B...... 800 645-7750
Orlando *(G-13313)*

ELECTRONIC SECRETARIES

Omnisys LLC........E...... 800 325-2017
Sarasota *(G-16532)*

ELECTRONIC SHOPPING

Bucket Company LLC........G...... 786 473-6484
Miami *(G-9282)*
Drench Khari LLC........G...... 561 507-4723
Riviera Beach *(G-15322)*
Youmop LLC........G...... 248 343-2013
Lake Worth *(G-7600)*

ELECTRONIC TRAINING DEVICES

Cae USA Inc........A...... 813 885-7481
Tampa *(G-17500)*
Cubic Simulation Systems Inc........C...... 407 641-2037
Orlando *(G-12634)*
Environmental Tectonics Corp........F...... 407 282-3378
Orlando *(G-12714)*
Nida Corporation........E...... 321 727-2265
Melbourne *(G-8894)*
Triton II Jv LLC........G...... 407 894-5575
Orlando *(G-13274)*

ELECTROPLATING & PLATING SVC

Biomedtech Laboratories Inc........F...... 813 558-2000
Tampa *(G-17470)*
Freedom Metal Finishing Inc........E...... 727 573-2464
Clearwater *(G-1695)*

ELEMENTARY & SECONDARY MILITARY ACADEMIES

United Ntons Space Crps Mltary........F...... 702 373-2351
Ponce De Leon *(G-14920)*

ELEMENTARY & SECONDARY SCHOOLS, PUBLIC

Brevard Achievement Center Inc ....B....... 321 632-8610
Rockledge *(G-15395)*

ELEMENTARY & SECONDARY SCHOOLS, SPECIAL EDUCATION

Lincoln-Marti Cmnty Agcy Inc ....A....... 305 643-4888
Miami *(G-9895)*

ELEVATORS & EQPT

Concept Elevator Group LLC...............D....... 786 845-8955
Miami *(G-9390)*
E M A C Inc ....E....... 850 526-4111
Marianna *(G-8577)*
Gunderlin Ltd Inc ....D....... 305 696-6071
Hialeah *(G-5440)*
International Machine Works ....F....... 305 635-3585
Miami *(G-9759)*
Kohtler Elevator Inds Inc..........E....... 305 687-7037
Opa Locka *(G-12331)*
Otis Elevator Company ....B....... 561 618-4831
West Palm Beach *(G-18974)*
Precision Lift Industries LLC..........G....... 877 770-5862
Pensacola *(G-14237)*
Qcab LLC..........G....... 305 510-2566
Vero Beach *(G-18655)*

ELEVATORS: Automobile

Armstrong Elevator Company..........G....... 727 323-3800
Largo *(G-7900)*

ELEVATORS: Stair, Motor Powered

A1 Elevators LLC ....G....... 954 773-4443
North Lauderdale *(G-11610)*
Beautiful Homes Inc ....G....... 800 403-1480
Spring Hill *(G-16848)*

EMBALMING FLUID

Hepburn Industries Inc..........G....... 305 757-6688
Miami *(G-9702)*

EMBLEMS: Embroidered

Atticus Screen Printing T..........G....... 407 365-9911
Oviedo *(G-13415)*
Bakers Sports Inc ....E....... 904 388-8126
Jacksonville *(G-6192)*
Blackwell Family Corporation..........G....... 941 639-0200
Punta Gorda *(G-15199)*
Clothesline Inc ....F....... 850 877-9171
Tallahassee *(G-17235)*
Florida Embroidered Patch &..........F....... 561 748-9356
Jupiter *(G-7044)*
Ssh Holding Inc..........D....... 678 942-1800
Seminole *(G-16761)*
STS Apparel Corp ....F....... 305 628-4000
Hialeah *(G-5636)*
Wings Things Monogramming Inc ....F....... 850 455-3081
Pensacola *(G-14289)*
World Emblem International Inc..........C....... 305 899-9006
Hollywood *(G-5941)*

EMBOSSING SVC: Paper

Elton Foil Embossing Inc..........G....... 904 399-1510
Jacksonville *(G-6359)*
Miami Quality Graphics Inc..........E....... 305 634-9506
Miami *(G-10007)*
Tektrol Inc..........G....... 305 305-0937
Doral *(G-3527)*

EMBROIDERING & ART NEEDLEWORK FOR THE TRADE

A2z Uniforms Inc..........G....... 941 254-3194
Sarasota *(G-16330)*
Active Line Corp..........F....... 786 766-1944
Hialeah *(G-5268)*
Aero Stitch Inc..........G....... 305 978-3446
Miami *(G-9081)*
All Stitched Up LLC ....G....... 352 316-4859
Newberry *(G-11550)*
American S-Shore Plting Sttchi..........G....... 305 978-9934
Hialeah *(G-5295)*
Berry Best Stitching and EMB..........G....... 813 763-7716
Plant City *(G-14409)*
Brooklyn Stitch Inc..........G....... 786 280-1730
Miami *(G-9279)*
Capsmith Inc ....E....... 407 328-7660
Sanford *(G-16007)*
CC Sportswear Inc..........G....... 941 351-4205
Sarasota *(G-16188)*
Creative Images Embrodiery ....G....... 904 730-5660
Jacksonville *(G-6298)*
Creative Shirts Intl Inc..........F....... 954 351-0909
Oakland Park *(G-11792)*
Designers Top Shop Inc..........G....... 863 453-3855
Avon Park *(G-285)*
DP EMB & Screen Prints Inc..........G....... 954 245-5902
Sunrise *(G-17116)*
Embroid ME..........G....... 941 312-5494
Sarasota *(G-16419)*
Embroidered Stitches..........G....... 702 751-2770
Port St Lucie *(G-15173)*
Embroidery Chimp LLC..........G....... 561 775-9195
Palm Beach Gardens *(G-13586)*
Embroidery USA Inc ....G....... 305 477-9973
Miami *(G-9521)*
Embroidme - North Miami Beach ....G....... 954 434-2191
Cooper City *(G-2111)*
Embroidme Clearwater Co..........G....... 813 803-0763
Clearwater *(G-1670)*
Embroservice LLC ....F....... 305 267-2323
Miami *(G-9522)*
Florida Embroidme Jacksonville..........G....... 904 309-9535
Jacksonville *(G-6397)*
Fully Promoted..........G....... 239 593-2193
Naples *(G-11253)*
Fully Promoted..........G....... 561 615-8655
West Palm Beach *(G-18885)*
Gravity Ink & Stitch Inc..........G....... 954 558-0119
Sunrise *(G-17127)*
Hitmaster Graphics LLC..........F....... 813 250-0555
Tampa *(G-17757)*
JC Santos Embroidery ....G....... 407 201-8617
Kissimmee *(G-7257)*
Jr Embroidery Inc ....G....... 305 253-6968
Miami *(G-9807)*
Legacy Sports Inc..........E....... 352 732-6759
Ocala *(G-11981)*
Lifes A Stitch..........G....... 386 385-3079
Palatka *(G-13484)*
Mid-Florida Sportswear LLC..........E....... 386 258-5632
Daytona Beach *(G-2686)*
New Tampa Embroidme of..........G....... 813 994-0118
Lutz *(G-8405)*
Paradise Cstm Screening & EMB ....E....... 954 566-9096
Davie *(G-2566)*
Pei Shores Inc..........G....... 407 523-2899
Orlando *(G-13057)*
Pixie Dusted Stitches ....G....... 207 776-3277
Gotha *(G-5041)*
Preferred Stitching Inc ....G....... 813 737-3996
Lithia *(G-8222)*
Print Art Screen Printing Inc..........F....... 386 258-5186
Daytona Beach *(G-2698)*
Prodigy Customs..........G....... 407 832-1752
Altamonte Springs *(G-67)*
Reliable Custom Imprints Corp ....G....... 407 834-0571
Longwood *(G-8331)*
Rhinestntransfersdirectcom Inc..........G....... 484 254-6410
Orlando *(G-13134)*
Say What Screen Prtg & EMB Inc..........G....... 941 745-5822
Bradenton *(G-1112)*
Seaside Stitching..........G....... 321 455-6427
Merritt Island *(G-9013)*
Sew Whats New Embroidery Inc ....G....... 954 977-3339
Pompano Beach *(G-14849)*
Squeegee Stitch Graphix LLC ....G....... 850 256-4926
Century *(G-1528)*
Stitch Ink Inc..........G....... 954 203-0868
Lauderdale Lakes *(G-8094)*
Stitchez LLC ....G....... 904 221-9148
Jacksonville *(G-6815)*
Stitching Heart LLC ....G....... 904 379-7990
Jacksonville *(G-6816)*
Stitchnship..........G....... 216 409-6700
Bay Harbor Islands *(G-340)*
Stitchyourphotocom..........G....... 321 297-6103
Windermere *(G-19244)*
T-Wiz Prtg & EMB Designs LLC..........E....... 954 280-8949
Fort Lauderdale *(G-4273)*
Turin Em Inc ....F....... 305 825-2004
Hialeah *(G-5653)*
Vf Imagewear Inc..........G....... 813 671-2986
Riverview *(G-15286)*
Wearable Nalia LLC ....G....... 561 629-5804
Haverhill *(G-5241)*
Western Ivy..........G....... 352 622-5767
Ocala *(G-12075)*
William Fster Entp Embrdme Jck..........G....... 904 329-1549
Jacksonville *(G-6921)*

EMBROIDERING SVC

Above LLC..........F....... 850 469-9028
Pensacola *(G-14077)*
Acme Cap & Clothing Inc..........G....... 407 321-5100
Sanford *(G-15987)*
Apparel Expressions LLC ....G....... 850 314-0100
Fort Walton Beach *(G-4777)*
Apparel Printers..........G....... 352 463-8850
Alachua *(G-4)*
Atlas Embroidery LLC ....D....... 954 625-2411
Fort Lauderdale *(G-3829)*
Bartman Enterprises Inc ....G....... 321 259-4898
Melbourne *(G-8777)*
Bc Sales..........G....... 941 708-2727
Bradenton *(G-994)*
Ben Kaufman Sales Co Inc ....E....... 305 688-2144
Medley *(G-8621)*
Blue Ocean Press Inc ....E....... 954 973-1819
Fort Lauderdale *(G-3859)*
Caribbean Emblems ....G....... 305 593-8183
Doral *(G-3291)*
Cotton Pickin Shirts Plus..........G....... 850 435-3133
Pensacola *(G-14120)*
Dapp Embroidery Inc..........G....... 407 260-1600
Longwood *(G-8272)*
Eagle Athletic Wear Inc ....F....... 727 937-6147
Tarpon Springs *(G-18297)*
Embroidertoo LLC..........G....... 813 909-0239
Lutz *(G-8382)*
Embroidery Plus ....G....... 561 439-8943
Lantana *(G-7872)*
G J Embroidery Inc..........G....... 407 284-8036
Orlando *(G-12769)*
G6 Embroidery LLC ....G....... 904 729-1191
Jacksonville *(G-6419)*
Gns Embroidery..........G....... 850 775-1147
Panama City Beach *(G-13977)*
Goal Line Embroidery..........G....... 305 295-7585
Key West *(G-7188)*
Good Catch Inc ....G....... 305 757-7700
Miami *(G-9648)*
Hamburg House Inc..........E....... 305 557-9913
Hialeah *(G-5442)*
Island Designs Outlet Inc..........E....... 813 855-0020
Tampa *(G-17794)*
Jax Embroidery..........G....... 904 367-4335
Jacksonville *(G-6517)*
Lidias Embroidery..........G....... 386 447-2293
Palm Coast *(G-13701)*
Logoxpress Inc ....G....... 954 973-4994
Pompano Beach *(G-14747)*
Palm Beach Embroidery USA Inc..........G....... 561 506-6307
West Palm Beach *(G-18982)*
Paradise EMB & Silkscreen Inc..........G....... 305 595-6441
Miami *(G-10142)*
Prologo Branding LLC..........G....... 407 730-9831
Orlando *(G-13097)*
Promowear ....G....... 561 372-0505
Parkland *(G-13999)*
R Y D Enterprises Inc ....E....... 305 655-1045
Miami *(G-10233)*
Ray Graphics Inc..........E....... 863 325-0911
Winter Haven *(G-19352)*
Royal Headwear & EMB Inc..........G....... 305 889-8480
Medley *(G-8720)*
S S Designs Inc..........D....... 863 965-2576
Winter Haven *(G-19353)*
Sharp Marketing LLC..........G....... 954 565-2711
Oakland Park *(G-11838)*
Southern International Svcs ....F....... 954 349-7321
Miami *(G-10387)*
Stitch Logo Inc..........G....... 727 446-0228
Clearwater *(G-1889)*
Thread Graphics Embroidery ....G....... 407 688-7026
Deland *(G-3021)*
Uniform Nametape Company Inc ....F....... 813 839-6737
Tampa *(G-18217)*
VSF Corp..........E....... 305 769-2202
Miami *(G-10593)*
Vyp Services LLC..........G....... 305 593-8183
Doral *(G-3546)*
Were In Stitches..........G....... 813 264-4804
Tampa *(G-18254)*

Worldwide Embroidery Inc..................F....... 386 761-2688
Port Orange *(G-15040)*

EMBROIDERING SVC: Schiffli Machine

Bcb International Inc..........................G....... 727 754-4911
Sunrise *(G-17095)*
Bnj Noble Inc..F....... 954 987-1040
Davie *(G-2503)*
Gattas Corp...G....... 727 733-5886
Dunedin *(G-3578)*
Liquid Edge LLC......................................G....... 904 637-1494
Orange Park *(G-12398)*
Pantograms Mfg Co Inc.........................E....... 813 839-5697
Tampa *(G-17973)*
Royal Headwear & EMB Inc....................G....... 305 889-8480
Medley *(G-8720)*
Screenprint Plus Inc...............................E....... 239 549-7284
Cape Coral *(G-1467)*

EMBROIDERY ADVERTISING SVCS

Acm Screen Printing Inc..........................G....... 305 547-1552
Miami *(G-9064)*
Dowling Graphics Inc..............................E....... 727 573-5997
Clearwater *(G-1657)*
Hes Products Inc.......................................G....... 407 834-0741
Ormond Beach *(G-13376)*
Kikinaz Screen Printing Inc....................G....... 561 512-3134
Royal Palm Beach *(G-15473)*
Koala Tee Inc (usa)..................................E....... 941 954-7700
Sarasota *(G-16483)*
Lucky Dog Screen Printing Mg...............G....... 407 629-8838
Winter Park *(G-19420)*
Shipping + Business Svcs LLC...............G....... 904 240-1737
Jacksonville *(G-6765)*
Signs Unlimited Sea Inc..........................F....... 352 732-7341
Ocala *(G-12052)*

EMBROIDERY KITS

Stitching Around Inc................................G....... 305 665-1600
Miami *(G-10415)*

EMERGENCY ALARMS

Advantor Systems Corporation...............C....... 407 859-3350
Orlando *(G-12436)*
Asp Alarm & Elec Sups Inc.....................G....... 305 556-9047
Hialeah *(G-5309)*
Heritage Medcall LLC..............................F....... 813 221-1000
Tampa *(G-17753)*
Med Alert Response Inc...........................G....... 407 730-3571
Orlando *(G-12958)*
Medattend LLC..F....... 561 465-2735
Boca Raton *(G-616)*
Morganelli & Associates Inc...................G....... 386 738-3669
Deland *(G-2998)*
Old Heritage Medcall Inc.........................F....... 813 221-1000
Tampa *(G-17948)*
Potter Roemer LLC....................................G....... 786 845-0842
Doral *(G-3463)*
Prime Meridian Trading Corp.................G....... 954 727-2152
Sunrise *(G-17161)*
Rossam Industries Inc..............................E....... 305 493-5111
Fort Lauderdale *(G-4216)*
Simplex Time Recorder Co.......................G....... 561 988-7200
Boca Raton *(G-715)*
Spec-TEC Manufacturing Inc..................G....... 954 749-4204
Sunrise *(G-17176)*
Zom Monterra LP......................................G....... 407 644-6300
Orlando *(G-13344)*
Zumro Manufacturing Inc........................E....... 954 782-7779
Pompano Beach *(G-14916)*

EMERGENCY SHELTERS

Air Shelters USA LLC...............................E....... 215 957-6128
Pompano Beach *(G-14581)*

EMPLOYMENT AGENCY SVCS

Windermere Nannies LLC.........................F....... 407 782-2057
Windermere *(G-19251)*

EMPLOYMENT SVCS: Labor Contractors

CTI Group Worldwide Svcs Inc...............G....... 954 568-5900
Fort Lauderdale *(G-3922)*

ENAMELS

Caribbean Paint Company Inc.................G....... 305 594-4500
Doral *(G-3292)*

ENCLOSURES: Electronic

Edwin B Stimpson Company Inc..............B....... 954 946-3500
Pompano Beach *(G-14675)*

ENCLOSURES: Screen

ABC Screen Masters Inc...........................G....... 239 772-7336
Cape Coral *(G-1371)*
Affordble Qlty Drywall Screen................G....... 561 723-0635
Lake Worth *(G-7531)*
Affordble Screen Enclosure LLC.............G....... 561 900-8868
Delray Beach *(G-3042)*
All About Screens......................................G....... 239 398-1798
Bonita Springs *(G-812)*
Allstar Screen Enclosures & St...............G....... 954 266-9757
Davie *(G-2493)*
Aluma TEC Aluminun..............................G....... 352 732-7362
Ocala *(G-11870)*
Alumicenter Inc..G....... 954 674-2631
Miramar *(G-10967)*
Aluminum Creations..................................F....... 386 451-0113
De Leon Springs *(G-2736)*
British Boys & Associates.........................G....... 305 278-1790
Miami *(G-9277)*
Charles Screening & Alum LLC...............G....... 239 369-0551
Lehigh Acres *(G-8188)*
Clupper LLC...G....... 386 956-6396
Deltona *(G-3166)*
Coastal Craftsmen Aluminum Inc...........E....... 727 868-8802
Hudson *(G-6019)*
Coastal Screen & Rail LLC.......................G....... 321 917-4605
Delray Beach *(G-3062)*
Custom Built Screen Enclosures..............F....... 239 242-0224
Cape Coral *(G-1408)*
Design Pro Screens Inc..............................G....... 407 831-6541
Longwood *(G-8273)*
Df Multi Services LLC...............................G....... 407 683-2223
Orlando *(G-12668)*
Florida Screen Enclosures LLC...............G....... 352 398-5679
Spring Hill *(G-16852)*
Gardners Screen Enclosures.....................F....... 813 843-8527
Seffner *(G-16728)*
General Metals & Plastics Inc..................G....... 904 354-8224
Jacksonville *(G-6432)*
Harper Screen Enclosures LLC................G....... 813 417-5937
Riverview *(G-15272)*
Housmans Alum & Screening Inc............F....... 321 255-2778
Melbourne *(G-8847)*
Hydes Screening Inc..................................G....... 954 345-6743
Coral Springs *(G-2258)*
J D Aluminum...G....... 239 543-3558
Fort Myers *(G-4500)*
Jbr Exteriors Inc...G....... 772 873-0600
Port Saint Lucie *(G-15115)*
Jennifer Yoder Sung....................................G....... 352 748-6655
Wildwood *(G-19196)*
K C Screen...G....... 407 977-9636
Oviedo *(G-13442)*
Knox Aluminum Inc...................................F....... 813 645-3529
Ruskin *(G-15486)*
Mark Housman Screen RPS Inc...............E....... 321 255-2778
Melbourne *(G-8883)*
Martin L Matthews.....................................G....... 904 881-3550
Jacksonville *(G-6579)*
New World Enclosures Inc........................F....... 904 334-4752
Green Cove Springs *(G-5067)*
Pace Enclosures Inc....................................F....... 239 275-3818
Fort Myers *(G-4561)*
Pioneer Development Entps Inc...............F....... 239 592-0001
Naples *(G-11367)*
Precision Screen Enclosures......................G....... 239 221-8465
Bonita Springs *(G-848)*
Quality Rescreening...................................G....... 941 625-9765
Fort Myers *(G-4578)*
Quality Screen Enclosure LLC..................G....... 954 226-1980
Hollywood *(G-5898)*
R Townsend Rescreens Inc.........................G....... 239 244-4759
Punta Gorda *(G-15226)*
Screen Enclosure Lighting..........................G....... 904 838-9786
Jacksonville Beach *(G-6958)*
Screen Enclosure Services Inc...................G....... 239 334-6528
Fort Myers *(G-4600)*
Screen Savers LLC.....................................G....... 321 299-8099
Chuluota *(G-1554)*
Screenco North Inc.....................................E....... 561 840-3300
Palm Beach Gardens *(G-13624)*
Serenity Screen Enclosures LLC...............G....... 407 692-3031
Orlando *(G-13175)*
Tdse Inc..E....... 352 399-6413
Wildwood *(G-19204)*

Tri County Aluminum Spc.........................G....... 727 848-4523
Hudson *(G-6042)*

ENGINE PARTS & ACCESS: Internal Combustion

Advanced Engine Tech LLC.......................G....... 727 744-2935
Clearwater *(G-1565)*
Bms-Tek LLC...G....... 321 727-7800
Melbourne *(G-8783)*
Diesel Pro Power Inc..................................F....... 305 545-5588
Miami *(G-9467)*

ENGINE REBUILDING: Diesel

Diesel Machinery Intl USA.......................G....... 305 551-4424
Miami *(G-9466)*
Gfs Corp...E....... 954 693-9657
Weston *(G-19132)*
National Diesel Engine Inc........................F....... 810 516-6855
Tampa *(G-17931)*

ENGINE REBUILDING: Gas

360 Energy Solutions LLC.........................E....... 786 348-2156
Miami *(G-9025)*
Engine Lab of Tampa Inc...........................F....... 813 630-2422
Tampa *(G-17640)*

ENGINEERING SVCS

Agteck Inc...E....... 321 305-5930
Cocoa *(G-1993)*
Analytical Research Systems.....................F....... 352 466-0051
Micanopy *(G-10899)*
Aog Detailing Services Inc........................G....... 727 742-7321
Saint Petersburg *(G-15703)*
Atsg Logistic Support Service...................F....... 904 579-4596
Jacksonville *(G-6179)*
Bca Technologies Inc..................................F....... 407 659-0653
Maitland *(G-8459)*
Big Bend Truss Components Inc...............F....... 850 539-5351
Havana *(G-5234)*
Cae USA Inc...A....... 813 885-7481
Tampa *(G-17500)*
Circuitronics LLC.......................................F....... 407 322-8300
Sanford *(G-16015)*
Corporate One Hundred Inc......................E....... 352 335-0901
Gainesville *(G-4898)*
Custom Mfg & Engrg Inc..........................D....... 727 548-0522
Pinellas Park *(G-14342)*
Defenshield Inc..G....... 904 679-3942
Saint Augustine *(G-15535)*
Diversfied Mtl Specialists Inc..................G....... 941 244-0935
North Venice *(G-11757)*
Dutchy Enterprises LLC............................G....... 321 877-0700
Cocoa *(G-2016)*
Entech Onsite Services LLC......................G....... 407 956-8980
Rockledge *(G-15409)*
Exploration Resources Intn Geo................G....... 601 747-0726
Lake Mary *(G-7412)*
Fathym Inc...F....... 303 905-4402
Palmetto *(G-13797)*
Full Circle Integration LLC......................F....... 504 615-5501
Valparaiso *(G-18511)*
Goodrich Corporation...............................C....... 904 757-3660
Jacksonville *(G-6441)*
Granite Services Intl Inc...........................F....... 813 242-7400
Tampa *(G-17724)*
H2r Corp..F....... 727 541-3444
Pinellas Park *(G-14353)*
Holtec International....................................D....... 561 745-7772
Jupiter *(G-7053)*
Interface Technology Group Inc...............G....... 321 433-1165
Rockledge *(G-15422)*
Irvin Technologies Inc................................E....... 866 245-9356
Winter Springs *(G-19476)*
J A Custom Fabricators Inc.......................F....... 561 615-4680
Lake Worth *(G-7559)*
Lrm Industries Intl Inc..............................E....... 321 635-9797
Rockledge *(G-15430)*
Mgl Engineering Inc..................................E....... 863 648-0320
Lakeland *(G-7750)*
Micro Audiometrics Corporation..............G....... 828 644-0771
Daytona Beach *(G-2684)*
Neptune Tech Services Inc........................E....... 904 646-2700
Jacksonville *(G-6624)*
Osgood Industries LLC..............................C....... 813 448-9041
Oldsmar *(G-12254)*
Patrick Industries Inc................................E....... 941 556-6311
Sarasota *(G-16274)*

PRODUCT

Polyhistor International Inc ....G....... 904 646-5666
Jacksonville (G-6677)
Power Systems Mfg LLC ....B 561 354-1100
Jupiter (G-7095)
Pyramid Imaging Inc..............................G....... 813 984-0125
Tampa (G-18028)
Redstone Corporation ....G....... 321 213-2135
Merritt Island (G-9007)
Sdi Industries Inc ....E 321 733-1128
Melbourne (G-8928)
Serf Inc...E 850 476-8203
Cantonment (G-1347)
Spectrum Engineering & Mfg Inc ....G....... 727 376-5510
Odessa (G-12154)
Tropical Pcb Design Services...............F 561 784-9536
Loxahatchee (G-8366)
UDC Usa Inc ....E 813 281-0200
Tampa (G-18211)
United Rail Inc ....F 904 503-9757
Jacksonville (G-6881)
Verifone Inc...C....... 800 837-4366
Coral Springs (G-2326)

ENGINEERING SVCS: Acoustical

Acoustic Communications LLC...........G....... 305 463-9485
Doral (G-3226)
Belquette Inc ....G....... 727 329-9483
Clearwater (G-1606)
Spectrum Engineering Inc ....G....... 239 277-1182
Fort Myers (G-4610)

ENGINEERING SVCS: Aviation Or Aeronautical

Aercap Inc..E 954 760-7777
Fort Lauderdale (G-3785)
Avalon Aviation Inc...................................G....... 954 655-0256
Fort Lauderdale (G-3834)
R4 Integration Inc.....................................E 850 226-6913
Fort Walton Beach (G-4825)

ENGINEERING SVCS: Chemical

E3 Fluid Recovery Eng...........................G....... 727 754-9792
Largo (G-7939)

ENGINEERING SVCS: Electrical Or Electronic

Beckwith Electric Co Inc ....G....... 727 544-2326
Largo (G-7905)
Digital Lighting Systems Inc..................G....... 305 264-8391
Miami (G-9468)
Gadgetcat LLC ....G....... 802 238-3671
Cocoa Beach (G-2063)
OHM Americas LLC ....F 800 467-7275
Fort Lauderdale (G-4148)
Prime Technological Svcs LLC..............D....... 850 539-2500
Havana (G-5239)
Smartsat Inc ....F 727 535-6880
Largo (G-8055)

ENGINEERING SVCS: Energy conservation

DOT Green Energy Inc............................G....... 717 505-8686
Clearwater (G-1654)

ENGINEERING SVCS: Industrial

Phantom Sales Group Inc ....G....... 888 614-1232
Bartow (G-330)

ENGINEERING SVCS: Marine

L-3 Cmmnctons Ntronix Holdings.........D....... 212 697-1111
Melbourne (G-8863)
Structural Composites Inc ....F 321 951-9464
Melbourne (G-8947)

ENGINEERING SVCS: Mechanical

Electro Mech Solutions Inc....................E 813 792-0400
Odessa (G-12118)
Lumitec LLC ....E 561 272-9840
Delray Beach (G-3102)
Praesto Enterprises LLC ....G....... 407 298-9171
Orlando (G-13077)
Rapid Composites LLC ....G....... 941 322-6647
Sarasota (G-16284)

ENGINEERING SVCS: Petroleum

Gas Turbine Efficiency LLC ....E 407 304-5200
Orlando (G-12772)

ENGINEERING SVCS: Professional

Consumer Engineering Inc ....F 321 984-8550
Palm Bay (G-13507)
I-Con Systems Inc...................................D....... 407 365-6241
Oviedo (G-13438)

ENGINEERING SVCS: Sanitary

Tri-Tech Electronics Inc.........................D....... 407 277-2131
Orlando (G-13270)

ENGINES & ENGINE PARTS: Guided Missile

Topline Hy-Lift Johnson Inc...................E 352 799-4668
Brooksville (G-1281)

ENGINES: Diesel & Semi-Diesel Or Duel Fuel

American Diesel and Gas Inc.................F 561 447-8500
Deerfield Beach (G-2776)

ENGINES: Gasoline, NEC

Fka Racing Inc...G....... 386 938-4211
Jennings (G-6964)
Granite Services Intl Inc..........................F 813 242-7400
Tampa (G-17724)

ENGINES: Internal Combustion, NEC

2g Cenrgy Pwr Systems Tech Inc..........E 904 342-5988
Saint Augustine (G-15511)
Cummins-Wagner-Florida LLC ....E 813 630-2220
Tampa (G-17573)
Cyclone Power Technologies Inc..........F 954 943-8721
Pompano Beach (G-14656)
Environmental Recovery Systems ....G....... 727 344-3301
Saint Petersburg (G-15771)
Fast Forward Race Engines Inc.............G....... 813 788-1794
Zephyrhills (G-19517)
Innovation Marine Corporation...............E 941 355-7852
Sarasota (G-16238)
Just Engines...G....... 561 575-2681
Jupiter (G-7064)
Mars Precision Products Inc...................G....... 727 846-0505
Port Richey (G-15061)
Price Rite Engines LLC ....G....... 727 600-8206
Largo (G-8031)
Progress Rail Services Corp..................D....... 239 643-3013
Naples (G-11376)
Spectrumit Inc ....F 850 202-5263
Pensacola (G-14268)
Topline Hy-Lift Johnson Inc...................E 352 799-4668
Brooksville (G-1281)

ENGINES: Jet Propulsion

Gem Aerospace..G....... 786 464-5900
Doral (G-3359)

ENGINES: Marine

ABB Inc..E 954 450-9544
Miramar (G-10960)
Boat Energy LLC..G....... 954 501-2628
Fort Lauderdale (G-3863)
Cobra Power Corporation ....G....... 305 893-5018
North Miami (G-11633)
Emerald Coast Mfg LLC ....G....... 850 469-1133
Pensacola (G-14143)
Gull Tool & Machine Inc ....G....... 727 527-0808
Saint Petersburg (G-15800)
Keith Eickert Power Pdts LLC ....F 386 446-0660
Palm Coast (G-13700)
Marine Electronics Engine.......................G....... 727 459-5593
Saint Petersburg (G-15847)
Offshore Performance Spc ....F 239 481-2768
Fort Myers (G-4555)
PMC North America Inc ....F 727 530-0714
Largo (G-8029)
Sen-Dure Products Inc ....D....... 954 973-1260
Fort Lauderdale (G-4230)
USA Marine Engines.................................F 954 614-4810
Fort Lauderdale (G-4299)
USA Marine Engines LLC........................G....... 954 383-1870
Davie (G-2609)
Xcessive Inc ....G....... 866 919-9527
Miami Lakes (G-10882)

ENGRAVING SVC, NEC

Allied General Engrv & Plas...................F 305 626-6585
Opa Locka (G-12286)
Friends Professional Sty.........................G....... 561 734-4660
Boynton Beach (G-908)
Worth Company LLC ....G....... 888 652-1555
Sanford (G-16141)

ENGRAVING SVC: Jewelry & Personal Goods

Finlayson Enterprises Inc ....G....... 850 785-7953
Panama City (G-13902)

ENGRAVING SVCS

Carlaron Inc...G....... 386 258-1183
Daytona Beach (G-2639)
Kemco Industries LLC..............................D....... 407 322-1230
Sanford (G-16077)
PM Engraving Corp....................................F 786 573-5292
Miami (G-10171)
Shirts & Caps Inc ....F 813 788-7026
Tampa (G-18098)

ENGRAVING: Currency

Seattle Engraving Center LLC ....G....... 206 420-4604
Brandon (G-1178)

ENGRAVINGS: Plastic

Holmes Stamp Company..........................E 904 396-2291
Jacksonville (G-6476)
Lean Design & Mfg Inc ....F 727 415-3504
Lutz (G-8395)

ENTERTAINERS & ENTERTAINMENT GROUPS

Premier Parties Entertainment ....E 352 375-6122
Gainesville (G-4983)

ENTERTAINMENT GROUP

Davis-Wick Talent MGT LLC ....E 407 369-1614
Margate (G-8541)
Great Hse Mdia Group of Pbls I..............F 407 779-3846
Orlando (G-12788)

ENTERTAINMENT PROMOTION SVCS

A2f LLC ....G....... 305 984-9205
Miami (G-9048)
D-R Media and Investments LLC...........D....... 941 207-1602
Venice (G-18540)
Davis-Wick Talent MGT LLC ....E 407 369-1614
Margate (G-8541)

ENVELOPES

Cenveo Worldwide Limited ....B 321 207-0403
Longwood (G-8265)
Double Envelope Corporation ....B 352 375-0738
Gainesville (G-4907)
Everglades Envelope Co Inc...................G....... 954 783-7920
Fort Lauderdale (G-3976)
Mac Paper Converters LLC ....C....... 800 334-7026
Jacksonville (G-6570)
Services On Demand Print Inc................E 305 681-5345
Hallandale Beach (G-5209)
Starlock Inc...G....... 305 477-2303
Doral (G-3511)
Winsted Thermographers Inc ....F 305 944-7862
Hallandale Beach (G-5225)

ENZYMES

AB Enzymes Inc ....G....... 954 278-3975
Plantation (G-14482)
AB Vista Inc..G....... 954 278-3965
Plantation (G-14484)

EPOXY RESINS

American Epoxy Coatings LLC ....F 954 850-1169
Dania Beach (G-2462)

EQUIPMENT: Pedestrian Traffic Control

Dynasystems LLC.......................................G....... 410 343-7759
Melbourne (G-8816)
N & H Construction Inc.............................F 904 282-2224
Middleburg (G-10910)

EQUIPMENT: Rental & Leasing, NEC

Agrifleet Leasing Corporation .... E 239 293-3976
Auburndale *(G-229)*
Ashberry Acquisition Company .... F 813 248-0055
Tampa *(G-17438)*
Holiday Ice Inc .... E 407 831-2077
Longwood *(G-8287)*
Holland Pump Company .... G 813 626-0599
Tampa *(G-17759)*
Holland Pump Company .... G 561 697-3333
West Palm Beach *(G-18896)*
Holland Pump Company .... G 904 880-0010
Jacksonville *(G-6475)*
Mwi Corporation .... E 954 426-1500
Deerfield Beach *(G-2877)*
Mwi Corporation .... F 239 337-4747
Fort Myers *(G-4542)*
Southeastern Seating Inc .... F 813 273-9858
Tampa *(G-18119)*
United Rentals North Amer Inc .... G 850 478-2833
Pensacola *(G-14278)*

ETCHING & ENGRAVING SVC

Blast Ctings Powdercoating LLC .... F 561 635-7605
Lake Worth Beach *(G-7608)*
Bricklser Engrv Monuments Corp .... F 786 806-0672
Doral *(G-3285)*
Clear View Coatings LLC .... F 850 210-0155
Tallahassee *(G-17234)*
Gws Tool LLC .... F 352 343-8778
Tavares *(G-18340)*
Hialeah Powder Coating Corp .... F 786 275-4107
Hialeah *(G-5446)*
JAS Powder Coating LLC .... G 954 916-7711
Fort Lauderdale *(G-4076)*
Sea Site Inc .... G 305 403-3002
Miami *(G-10315)*

ETCHING SVC: Metal

Cm2 Industries Inc .... G 305 685-4812
Opa Locka *(G-12301)*

ETCHING SVC: Photochemical

Pcm Products Inc .... E 321 267-7500
Titusville *(G-18450)*
Southern Micro Etch Inc .... F 954 781-5999
Pompano Beach *(G-14864)*

ETHERS

Natural Ethercom .... G 954 274-6801
Coral Springs *(G-2295)*

ETHYLENE-PROPYLENE RUBBERS: EPDM Polymers

Fatovich Technologies LLC .... G 772 597-1326
Palm City *(G-13654)*
International Polymer Svcs LLC .... G 401 529-6855
Pensacola *(G-14180)*
Rayonier AM Sales and Tech Inc .... G 904 357-4600
Jacksonville *(G-6708)*
Vinavil Americas Corporation .... D 954 246-8888
Deerfield Beach *(G-2933)*

EXCAVATING EQPT

Florida Dragline Operation .... G 305 824-9755
Hialeah *(G-5411)*

EXHAUST SYSTEMS: Eqpt & Parts

Shaw Development LLC .... C 239 405-6100
Bonita Springs *(G-853)*

EXPLOSIVES

Austin Powder Company .... G 352 690-7060
Anthony *(G-94)*
Austin Powder Company .... G 863 674-0504
Fort Denaud *(G-3770)*
Dyno Nobel Inc .... G 352 796-9018
Brooksville *(G-1227)*
General Dynmics Ord Tctcal Sys .... C 727 578-8100
Saint Petersburg *(G-15791)*
Ireco Inc .... F 239 593-3749
Naples *(G-11292)*
J & G Explosives LLC .... F 407 883-0734
Fort Lauderdale *(G-4072)*

EXPLOSIVES: Secondary High

Boland Production Supply Inc .... G 863 324-7784
Winter Haven *(G-19304)*

EXTENSION CORDS

Evolution Intrcnnect Systems I .... F 954 217-6223
Davie *(G-2521)*

EXTRACTS, FLAVORING

Aromatech Flavorings Inc .... G 407 277-5727
Orlando *(G-12489)*
Cvista LLC .... E 813 405-3000
Riverview *(G-15269)*
Flayco Products Inc .... E 813 879-1356
Tampa *(G-17668)*

EYEGLASSES

Bajio Inc .... G 630 461-0915
New Smyrna Beach *(G-11527)*
Eyedeal Vision Care Inc .... G 321 631-2811
Melbourne *(G-8830)*
For Eyes Optcal Ccnut Grove In .... C 305 557-9004
Miramar *(G-10993)*
Invicta Corporation .... G 561 995-9980
Boca Raton *(G-573)*
Miraflex Corporation .... G 786 380-4494
Doral *(G-3439)*
Pasco Vision Center .... G 813 788-7656
Zephyrhills *(G-19530)*
Tan Group USA LLC .... G 954 600-8697
Miami *(G-10459)*

EYEGLASSES: Sunglasses

Costa Inc .... A 386 274-4000
Daytona Beach *(G-2646)*
Ocean Waves Inc .... F 904 372-4743
Jacksonville Beach *(G-6953)*
Sunglass Heaven .... G 305 302-7285
Oakland Park *(G-11845)*

EYELASHES, ARTIFICIAL

Bare Arii LLC .... G 352 701-6625
Tampa *(G-17455)*
Sexy Winks LLC .... G 407 949-2981
Orlando *(G-13176)*
Xoxo Beauty Studio LLC .... G 407 476-7172
Altamonte Springs *(G-85)*

FABRIC SOFTENERS

Dyadic International USA Inc .... G 561 743-8333
Jupiter *(G-7028)*

FABRICATED METAL PRODUCTS, NEC

All Metal Fabrication .... G 305 666-3312
Pinecrest *(G-14323)*
All Metals Custom Inc .... G 727 709-4297
Pinellas Park *(G-14334)*
American Metal Fabrication LLC .... F 954 736-9819
Tamarac *(G-17350)*
Artcraft Stone Inc .... G 239 253-6696
Naples *(G-11168)*
Atlantic Coast Roofing & Metal .... G 321 449-9494
Merritt Island *(G-8991)*
BHd Precision Products Inc .... G 941 753-0003
Sarasota *(G-16183)*
C & J Cstm Wldg Fbrication LLC .... G 407 414-1739
Kissimmee *(G-7228)*
Constrction Mtal Fbrcators LLC .... G 305 781-9004
Hialeah *(G-5352)*
David Gill Enterprises .... G 863 422-5711
Davenport *(G-2477)*
Doll Marine Metal Fabrica .... G 954 941-5093
Fort Lauderdale *(G-3946)*
East Coast Metalworks LLC .... G 321 698-0624
Cocoa *(G-2018)*
Emerald Coast Met Fabrication .... G 850 465-3517
Pensacola *(G-14142)*
Ernies Metal Fabricating .... G 813 679-0816
Brandon *(G-1157)*
G and G Industries Inc .... G 754 701-4178
Davie *(G-2528)*
International Vault Inc .... E 941 390-4505
Lakewood Ranch *(G-7839)*
J&J Sheet Mtal Fabercation LLC .... G 941 752-0569
Sarasota *(G-16241)*
Jetstream Fabrication LLC .... G 772 287-3338
Stuart *(G-16960)*
JHK LLC .... G 786 871-0150
Miami *(G-9797)*
Jose Rodriguez Met Fabrication .... G 305 305-6110
Miami *(G-9805)*
Lakes Metal Fabrication Inc .... G 954 731-2010
Oakland Park *(G-11818)*
Marble Bridge Inc .... F 239 213-1411
Naples *(G-11319)*
Merritt Hollow Metal Inc .... G 727 656-4380
Largo *(G-8010)*
MSC Metal Fabrication .... G 954 344-8343
Coral Springs *(G-2292)*
Pinellas Precision Laser LLC .... G 727 420-0388
Saint Petersburg *(G-15876)*
Pitts Fabrication LLC .... G 850 259-4548
Fort Walton Beach *(G-4822)*
Robert James Custom Metal Fabr .... F 772 214-0996
Jacksonville *(G-6733)*
Seiter Enterprises Inc .... F 813 728-8324
Tarpon Springs *(G-18324)*
Soto Metal Fabrication Inc .... E 786 486-7125
Miami *(G-10379)*
Spot-On Wldg Met Fbrcation LLC .... G 239 825-7452
Naples *(G-11416)*
Structural Metal Fabricators .... G 786 253-8012
Miami *(G-10422)*
Sunset Metal Fabrication Inc .... G 386 215-4520
Sarasota *(G-16611)*
Tpi Aluminum .... G 239 332-3900
Fort Myers *(G-4635)*
United Metal Fabrications Inc .... G 305 962-1608
North Miami *(G-11661)*
Worth Metals Inc .... F 904 626-1434
Green Cove Springs *(G-5077)*
Yeager Manufacturing Tech LLC .... F 407 573-7033
Winter Park *(G-19463)*

FABRICS: Apparel & Outerwear, Broadwoven

Sourcerers Inc .... G 954 530-2333
Plantation *(G-14556)*

FABRICS: Apparel & Outerwear, Cotton

Ata Group of Companies Inc .... G 352 735-1588
Mount Dora *(G-11097)*
Chrome Connection Corp .... G 305 947-9191
North Miami Beach *(G-11669)*
Diction Wear LLC .... G 954 696-5490
Fort Lauderdale *(G-3940)*
Drench Khari LLC .... G 561 507-4723
Riviera Beach *(G-15322)*
Fury Surf Shack .... G 305 747-0799
Key West *(G-7187)*
Indigo Mountain Inc .... G 239 947-0023
Naples *(G-11285)*
Jode Corporation .... G 321 684-1769
Sebastian *(G-16655)*
New Breed Clothing llc .... G 941 773-7406
Sarasota *(G-16266)*
Official Gear Company Inc .... G 407 721-9110
Ormond Beach *(G-13387)*
Phoenix Custom Gear LLC .... G 561 808-7181
Delray Beach *(G-3116)*
RAD Wear Inc .... G 352 727-4498
Gainesville *(G-4988)*

FABRICS: Apparel & Outerwear, From Manmade Fiber Or Silk

R S Apparel Inc .... F 305 599-4939
Doral *(G-3478)*

FABRICS: Awning Stripes, Cotton

Business World Trading Inc .... F 305 238-0724
Miami *(G-9288)*

FABRICS: Bags & Bagging, Cotton

Zellermayer Supply Corp .... F 561 848-0057
Mangonia Park *(G-8515)*

FABRICS: Balloon Cloth, Cotton

Southern Balloon Works Inc .... G 727 388-8360
Jacksonville *(G-6793)*

FABRICS: Broadwoven, Cotton

Digital Output ....G.... 904 285-9944
Ponte Vedra Beach *(G-14939)*
Energy Services Providers Inc ....F.... 305 947-7880
Miramar *(G-10989)*
International Draperies Inc ....G.... 954 590-3897
Margate *(G-8550)*
Superior Fabrics Inc ....E.... 954 975-8122
Parkland *(G-14002)*
Tex Z-E Corp ....G.... 305 769-0202
Opa Locka *(G-12364)*
Unique Originals Inc ....F.... 305 634-2274
Fort Lauderdale *(G-4293)*
West Point Stevens ....G.... 850 638-9421
Chipley *(G-1547)*
Westpoint Home Inc ....B.... 850 415-4100
Chipley *(G-1549)*

FABRICS: Broadwoven, Synthetic Manmade Fiber & Silk

Anglo Silver Liner Co ....F.... 508 943-1440
Parrish *(G-14003)*
Bradley Indus Textiles Inc ....F.... 850 678-6111
Valparaiso *(G-18508)*
Jaynor Furnishings Inc ....G.... 954 973-8446
Coconut Creek *(G-2085)*
Legend Moto LLC ....G.... 863 946-2002
Moore Haven *(G-11087)*
Point Blank Enterprises Inc ....A.... 954 846-8222
Pompano Beach *(G-14800)*
Reliatex Inc ....E.... 813 621-6021
Tampa *(G-18051)*
Rfl & Figlio LLC ....F.... 904 765-2222
Jacksonville *(G-6723)*
Stylors Inc ....F.... 904 765-4453
Jacksonville *(G-6820)*
Sunshine Nylon Products Inc ....G.... 352 754-9932
Brooksville *(G-1277)*
Superior Fabrics Inc ....E.... 954 975-8122
Parkland *(G-14002)*
Valley Forge Textiles LLC ....G.... 954 971-1776
Pompano Beach *(G-14907)*

FABRICS: Broadwoven, Wool

Valley Forge Textiles LLC ....G.... 954 971-1776
Pompano Beach *(G-14907)*

FABRICS: Canvas

Bahamas Uphl & Mar Canvas Inc ....F.... 305 992-4346
Miami *(G-9214)*
Bay Networks Inc ....F.... 813 249-8103
Tampa *(G-17458)*
Bestcanvas Inc ....F.... 305 759-7800
Miami *(G-9236)*
Busch Canvas & Interiors ....G.... 561 881-1605
Riviera Beach *(G-15307)*
Camera2canvas LLC ....F.... 850 276-6990
Lynn Haven *(G-8431)*
Canvas ....G.... 727 317-5572
Saint Petersburg *(G-15738)*
Canvas Clinical Research ....F.... 561 229-0002
Lake Worth *(G-7538)*
Canvas Foods Corp ....G.... 786 529-8041
Weston *(G-19115)*
Canvas Freaks LLC ....G.... 407 978-6224
Orlando *(G-12547)*
Canvas Land Surveying LLC ....G.... 321 689-5330
Longwood *(G-8263)*
Canvas Studio Inc ....G.... 305 987-5895
Surfside *(G-17201)*
Canvas Tattoo LLC ....G.... 561 870-7929
Boynton Beach *(G-886)*
Captain Canvas & More ....G.... 561 881-2278
Lake Park *(G-7467)*
Caribbean Canvas and Mari ....G.... 786 972-6377
Miami *(G-9314)*
Classic Canvas & Upholstery ....G.... 954 850-4994
Hollywood *(G-5801)*
Creative Canvas Centl Fla Inc ....F.... 407 661-1211
Altamonte Springs *(G-39)*
Custom Canvas and Cushions ....G.... 561 800-8541
Riviera Beach *(G-15315)*
Discovery Canvas East Coast Co ....G.... 786 487-8897
Miami *(G-9471)*
Dreamboat Canvas LLC ....G.... 954 536-2415
Hollywood *(G-5813)*
Fit Canvas Inc ....F.... 954 258-9352
Margate *(G-8544)*
Fortune Canvas Company Inc ....G.... 941 740-4296
Placida *(G-14396)*
JM Ocean Mar Canvas & Uphl Inc ....G.... 786 473-7143
Hallandale *(G-5158)*
Jones Awnings & Canvas Inc ....G.... 407 845-9400
Orlando *(G-12860)*
Latitude 27 Canvas ....G.... 772 321-6361
Vero Beach *(G-18638)*
Lilian Oils On Canvas Inc ....G.... 941 320-6263
Riverview *(G-15276)*
Marine Canvas Inc ....G.... 305 325-1830
Miami *(G-9948)*
Mollys Marine Service LLC ....G.... 239 262-2628
Naples *(G-11329)*
My Blank Canvas ....G.... 386 747-5254
Deland *(G-3003)*
Nautiloft LLC ....G.... 801 712-6692
Punta Gorda *(G-15217)*
Pure Canvas Inc ....G.... 561 818-2655
Greenacres *(G-5085)*
Sea and Shore Custom Canvas Up ....G.... 954 983-3060
Hollywood *(G-5905)*
Sea Canvas Inc ....G.... 954 462-7525
Fort Lauderdale *(G-4227)*
Sunshine Canvas Inc ....G.... 352 787-4436
Leesburg *(G-8175)*
Traveling Canvas Corporation ....G.... 305 259-2001
Palmetto Bay *(G-13855)*

FABRICS: Chemically Coated & Treated

Clock Spring Company Inc ....F.... 561 683-6992
Riviera Beach *(G-15312)*
Enviroworks Inc ....F.... 407 889-5533
Apopka *(G-137)*
Fiskars Brands Inc ....G.... 407 889-5533
Apopka *(G-142)*

FABRICS: Coated Or Treated

Mundi Intl Trading Corp ....G.... 305 205-0062
Weston *(G-19150)*
Patrick Industries Inc ....G.... 352 732-8841
Ocala *(G-12023)*

FABRICS: Cotton, Narrow

Mansfield International Inc ....G.... 954 632-3280
Fort Lauderdale *(G-4112)*

FABRICS: Decorative Trim & Specialty, Including Twist Weave

Lead 2 Design ....G.... 954 757-6116
Coral Springs *(G-2272)*

FABRICS: Denims

Denim Lily LLC ....G.... 754 264-9331
Pompano Beach *(G-14659)*
Genuine Denim ....G.... 305 491-1326
North Miami Beach *(G-11680)*
Intertex Miami LLC ....G.... 305 627-3536
Miami *(G-9763)*
L7 Apparel & Denim Company LLC ....G.... 954 867-8124
Hollywood *(G-5857)*

FABRICS: Felts, Blanketing & Upholstery, Wool

Vertical Land Inc ....F.... 850 819-2535
Panama City *(G-13960)*

FABRICS: Fiberglass, Broadwoven

AA Fiberglass Inc ....G.... 904 355-5511
Jacksonville *(G-6114)*
Accurate Reproductions Inc ....F.... 407 814-1622
Apopka *(G-108)*
Alta Technologies Inc ....G.... 609 538-9500
Ponte Vedra Beach *(G-14931)*
Car Care Haven LLC ....G.... 855 464-2836
Englewood *(G-3671)*
Fastglas ....G.... 904 765-2222
Jacksonville *(G-6380)*
Glasrite Inc ....F.... 863 967-8151
Auburndale *(G-244)*
Merritt Precision Tech Inc ....G.... 321 453-2334
Merritt Island *(G-9003)*
Nida-Core Corporation ....E.... 772 343-7300
Port Saint Lucie *(G-15124)*

FABRICS: Furniture Denim

Guyton Industries LLC ....E.... 772 208-3019
Indiantown *(G-6073)*

FABRICS: Gauze

Ijkb LLC ....G.... 941 953-9046
Sarasota *(G-16464)*

FABRICS: Ginghams

Gingham Gator LLC ....G.... 352 475-1985
Melrose *(G-8985)*

FABRICS: Glass & Fiberglass, Broadwoven

Smittys Boat Tops and Mar Eqp ....G.... 305 245-0229
Homestead *(G-5993)*
Stm Industries LLC ....F.... 813 854-3544
Tampa *(G-18134)*

FABRICS: Hand Woven

South Florida Cutting ....F.... 305 693-6711
Hialeah *(G-5625)*

FABRICS: Jean

Blue Light USA Corp ....G.... 954 766-4308
Sunrise *(G-17099)*

FABRICS: Lace & Lace Prdts

Wyla Inc ....E.... 904 886-4338
Jacksonville *(G-6931)*

FABRICS: Lace, Knit, NEC

Metritek Corporation ....C.... 561 995-2414
Coral Springs *(G-2283)*

FABRICS: Laminated

Madico Inc ....D.... 727 327-2544
Pinellas Park *(G-14366)*
Trann Technologies Inc ....G.... 888 668-6700
Mossy Head *(G-11094)*

FABRICS: Lawns, Cotton

N3xt L3vel 2 Point 0 LLC ....F.... 863 777-3778
Tampa *(G-17927)*

FABRICS: Metallized

Metalex LLC ....D.... 941 918-4431
Nokomis *(G-11585)*

FABRICS: Nonwoven

Cerex Advanced Fabrics Inc ....D.... 850 968-0100
Cantonment *(G-1336)*
Mutual Industries North Inc ....D.... 239 332-2400
Fort Myers *(G-4541)*
Superior Fabrics Inc ....E.... 954 975-8122
Parkland *(G-14002)*

FABRICS: Nylon, Broadwoven

Sport Products of Tampa Inc ....G.... 813 630-5552
Tampa *(G-18127)*

FABRICS: Polyethylene, Broadwoven

K Pro Supply Co Inc ....G.... 941 758-1226
Sarasota *(G-16244)*

FABRICS: Print, Cotton

Genesis 50 20 LLC ....G.... 954 860-8175
Weston *(G-19131)*
John E Anderson ....G.... 305 741-8400
West Palm Beach *(G-18914)*
Team Hammer Screen Printing ....G.... 863 666-1108
Lakeland *(G-7818)*
Team Ip Sports LLC ....F.... 772 398-4664
Stuart *(G-17034)*

FABRICS: Resin Or Plastic Coated

C M I Enterprises Inc ....E.... 305 622-6410
Opa Locka *(G-12297)*
Sabic Innovative Plastics ....G.... 386 409-5540
New Smyrna Beach *(G-11541)*

FABRICS: Sail Cloth

Palafox Marine Inc ......F 850 438-9354
Pensacola *(G-14219)*

FABRICS: Satin

Saten Leaf Nursery Inc ......F 305 216-5340
Homestead *(G-5991)*
Satin Sensation Co ......G 786 290-4114
Miami *(G-10306)*

FABRICS: Scrub Cloths

Firebird Scrubs and More LLC ......G 904 258-7514
Orange Park *(G-12392)*
Taylor Made Scrub Hats LLC ......G 615 348-7802
Riverview *(G-15284)*
Unimd Scrubs LLC ......G 954 245-1509
Hallandale Beach *(G-5220)*

FABRICS: Shirting, From Manmade Fiber Or Silk

CBI Industries Inc ......G 305 796-9346
Miami *(G-9329)*

FABRICS: Specialty Including Twisted Weaves, Broadwoven

Mutual Industries North Inc ......D 239 332-2400
Fort Myers *(G-4541)*

FABRICS: Tapestry, Cotton

Holyland Tapestries Inc ......G 305 255-7955
Palmetto Bay *(G-13847)*

FABRICS: Trimmings

Adva-Lite Inc ......E 727 369-5319
Seminole *(G-16735)*
Ampersand Graphics Inc ......E 772 283-1359
Stuart *(G-16906)*
Automated Services Inc ......F 772 461-3388
Fort Pierce *(G-4679)*
Buchanan Signs Screen Process ......E 904 725-5500
Jacksonville *(G-6243)*
Classic Trim Wtp Inc ......G 305 258-3090
Princeton *(G-15183)*
Creative Car Coats ......G 813 886-2589
Tampa *(G-17564)*
Custom Grafix Industries Inc ......G 727 530-7300
Largo *(G-7929)*
Eastern Shores Printing ......E 305 685-8976
Opa Locka *(G-12312)*
Florida Screen Services Inc ......F 407 316-0466
Orlando *(G-12755)*
Florida Tape & Labels Inc ......F 941 921-5788
Sarasota *(G-16438)*
Full Press Apparel Inc ......F 850 222-1003
Tallahassee *(G-17259)*
H Sixto Distributors Inc ......F 305 688-5242
Opa Locka *(G-12322)*
Hes Products Inc ......G 407 834-0741
Ormond Beach *(G-13376)*
Icon Embroidery Inc ......G 407 858-0886
Windermere *(G-19228)*
Image Depot ......G 813 685-7116
Tampa *(G-17772)*
Island Designs Outlet Inc ......E 813 855-0020
Tampa *(G-17794)*
Joni Industries Inc ......F 352 799-5456
Brooksville *(G-1240)*
Moser Automotive ......E 561 881-5665
Riviera Beach *(G-15350)*
National Traffic Signs Inc ......G 727 446-7983
Clearwater *(G-1802)*
Premier Manufacturing Pdts LLC ......F 239 542-0260
Cape Coral *(G-1456)*
Print Shack ......G 352 799-2972
Brooksville *(G-1262)*
Ray Graphics Inc ......E 863 325-0911
Winter Haven *(G-19352)*
Royal Tees Inc ......F 941 366-0056
Sarasota *(G-16564)*
Screen Art Posters Inc ......E 305 681-4641
Hialeah *(G-5612)*
Southern International Svcs ......F 954 349-7321
Miami *(G-10387)*
Steven Chancas ......F 352 629-5016
Ocala *(G-12059)*
T&T Detailing Inc ......G 407 414-6710
Orlando *(G-13239)*
Universal Screen Graphics Inc ......E 813 623-5335
Tampa *(G-18223)*
Vivid Images USA Inc ......F 904 620-0303
Jacksonville *(G-6902)*

FABRICS: Trimmings, Textile

M & H Enterprises Inc ......G 305 885-5945
Hialeah *(G-5494)*

FABRICS: Umbrella Cloth, Cotton

Fiberbuilt Umbrellas Inc ......E 954 484-9139
Pompano Beach *(G-14690)*
Windbrella Products Corp ......E 561 734-5222
Boynton Beach *(G-974)*

FABRICS: Upholstery, Cotton

Anderson Mfg & Upholstery Inc ......G 321 267-7028
Titusville *(G-18413)*

FABRICS: Varnished Glass & Coated Fiberglass

Blutec Glass Fabrication LLC ......G 941 232-1600
Sarasota *(G-16365)*

FABRICS: Woven, Narrow Cotton, Wool, Silk

American Elastic & Tape Inc ......G 305 888-0303
Hialeah *(G-5289)*
Eastern Shores Printing ......E 305 685-8976
Opa Locka *(G-12312)*
Valley Forge Textiles LLC ......G 954 971-1776
Pompano Beach *(G-14907)*

FACIAL SALONS

Florida Keys Keylime Products ......G 305 853-0378
Key Largo *(G-7169)*
Tend Skin International Inc ......F 954 382-0800
Davie *(G-2602)*

FACILITIES SUPPORT SVCS

Atsg Logistic Support Service ......F 904 579-4596
Jacksonville *(G-6179)*
Kratos Def & SEC Solutions Inc ......G 866 606-5867
Orlando *(G-12877)*

FAMILY CLOTHING STORES

Clothesline Inc ......F 850 877-9171
Tallahassee *(G-17235)*
Simons Hallandale Inc ......E 561 468-1174
Miami *(G-10351)*

FANS, BLOWING: Indl Or Commercial

Certainteed Corporation ......F 863 294-3206
Winter Haven *(G-19313)*
Fan America Inc ......G 941 955-9788
Sarasota *(G-16426)*
Kanalflakt Inc ......F 941 359-3267
Sarasota *(G-16480)*
S&P USA Vntilation Systems LLC ......D 904 731-4711
Jacksonville *(G-6744)*

FANS, VENTILATING: Indl Or Commercial

Air Flow Specialists ......G 954 727-9507
Davie *(G-2490)*
Upton House Cooler Corporation ......G 305 633-2531
Miami *(G-10547)*
Ventilex Inc ......G 954 433-1321
Pembroke Pines *(G-14070)*
Warren Technology Inc ......C 305 556-6933
Hialeah *(G-5686)*
Zazz Engineering Inc ......G 561 594-0123
Stuart *(G-17054)*

FANS: Ceiling

Suns Up of Swf LLC ......G 301 470-2678
Venice *(G-18579)*
Tropical Ceiling Fan Company ......G 877 921-3267
Miami *(G-10507)*

FARM MACHINERY REPAIR SVCS

Channel Industries Inc ......F 561 214-0637
West Palm Beach *(G-18845)*

FARM SPLY STORES

Branch Properties Inc ......D 352 732-4143
Ocala *(G-11890)*
Seminole Stores Inc ......F 352 732-4143
Ocala *(G-12044)*

FARM SPLYS WHOLESALERS

Branch Properties Inc ......D 352 732-4143
Ocala *(G-11890)*
Brinsea Products Inc ......G 321 267-7009
Titusville *(G-18418)*
Farmers Cooperative Inc ......E 386 362-1459
Live Oak *(G-8232)*
Morse Enterprises Limited Inc ......G 407 682-6500
Miami *(G-10042)*

FARM SPLYS, WHOLESALE: Feed

Barber Fertilizer Company ......E 850 263-6324
Campbellton *(G-1330)*

FARM SPLYS, WHOLESALE: Fertilizers & Agricultural Chemicals

Calcium Silicate Corp Inc ......F 863 902-0217
Lake Harbor *(G-7394)*
Harrells LLC ......C 863 687-2774
Lakeland *(G-7703)*
Pioneer Ag-Chem Inc ......E 772 464-9300
Fort Pierce *(G-4734)*

FARM SPLYS, WHOLESALE: Garden Splys

Pottre Gardening Products LLC ......G 941 224-8856
Bradenton *(G-1100)*

FASTENERS WHOLESALERS

Scott Slide Fasteners Inc ......F 305 576-3328
Miami *(G-10314)*

FASTENERS: Metal

Carlisle Interconnect Tech Inc ......A 904 829-5600
Saint Augustine *(G-15526)*
Fk Irons Inc ......E 855 354-7667
Doral *(G-3352)*
Shashy Enterprises Inc ......G 352 732-3904
Ocala *(G-12047)*

FASTENERS: Notions, NEC

Allfast Fastener T ......G 352 727-8464
Gainesville *(G-4872)*
Arrowhead Global LLC ......G 727 497-7340
Clearwater *(G-1589)*
Bisi Fasteners LLC ......G 850 913-0101
Panama City *(G-13873)*
C S Fasteners ......G 813 242-8000
Tampa *(G-17495)*
Captains Fasteners Corp ......G 954 533-9259
Fort Lauderdale *(G-3882)*
Ceco & Associates Inc ......G 727 528-0075
Riverview *(G-15266)*
Coll Builders Supply Inc ......F 407 745-4641
Orlando *(G-12600)*
E-Z Fastening Solutions Inc ......G 813 854-3937
Oldsmar *(G-12223)*
Fastener Solutions LLC ......G 813 324-8372
Tampa *(G-17661)*
Fastener Solutions LLC ......G 813 867-4714
Tampa *(G-17662)*
Fastener Specialty Corp ......G 631 903-4453
Port Charlotte *(G-14980)*
Fator Fasteners Usa LLC ......G 941 479-8518
Palmetto *(G-13798)*
Innovative Fasteners LLC ......F 561 542-2152
Coconut Creek *(G-2082)*
Southeastern Fasteners ......G 407 790-4888
Longwood *(G-8338)*
Tekk Supply Inc ......G 954 444-5782
Pompano Beach *(G-14884)*

FASTENERS: Notions, Zippers

Ideal Fastener Corporation ......D 201 207-6722
Miami *(G-9729)*

FASTENERS: Wire, Made From Purchased Wire

Southwire Company LLC ....C 850 423-4680
Crestview *(G-2359)*

FATTY ACID ESTERS & AMINOS

Originates Inc ....F 954 233-2500
Aventura *(G-279)*

FAUCETS & SPIGOTS: Metal & Plastic

Ecolab Inc ....F 800 931-8911
Jupiter *(G-7031)*
OMalley Manufacturing Inc ....G 727 327-6817
Saint Petersburg *(G-15872)*
Ultraclenz LLC ....F 800 931-8911
Jupiter *(G-7136)*

FEATHERS & FEATHER PRODUCTS

S A Feather Co Inc ....F 239 693-6363
Fort Myers *(G-4590)*

FELT: Acoustic

Valley Forge Textiles LLC ....G 954 971-1776
Pompano Beach *(G-14907)*

FENCE POSTS: Iron & Steel

Friedman & Greenberg PA ....G 954 370-4774
Plantation *(G-14519)*
Just Steel Inc ....F 941 755-7811
Sarasota *(G-16242)*

FENCES & FENCING MATERIALS

Merchants Metals LLC ....F 813 980-0938
Tampa *(G-17902)*
Merchants Metals LLC ....G 561 478-0059
West Palm Beach *(G-18949)*

FENCES OR POSTS: Ornamental Iron Or Steel

Iron-Art & Fence Inc ....F 407 699-1734
Longwood *(G-8293)*
L A Ornamental & Rack Corp ....G 305 696-0419
Miami *(G-9835)*

FENCING DEALERS

Baby Guard Inc ....F 954 741-6351
Coral Springs *(G-2222)*
Florida Fence Post Co Inc ....G 863 735-1361
Ona *(G-12280)*
Luv Enterprises Inc ....F 352 867-8440
Ocala *(G-11988)*

FENCING MADE IN WIREDRAWING PLANTS

Baby Guard Inc ....F 954 741-6351
Coral Springs *(G-2222)*

FENCING MATERIALS: Docks & Other Outdoor Prdts, Wood

Core Outdoors Inc ....G 904 215-6866
Saint Augustine *(G-15532)*
John Hurst Outdoor Svcs LLC ....G 850 556-7459
Tallahassee *(G-17284)*

FENCING MATERIALS: Plastic

Brill Hygienic Products Inc ....F 561 278-5600
Delray Beach *(G-3052)*
V & C Supply Ornamental Corp ....G 305 634-9040
Miami *(G-10558)*

FENCING MATERIALS: Wood

ABC Fence Systems Inc ....F 850 638-8876
Chipley *(G-1540)*
Consolidated Forest Pdts Inc ....G 407 830-7723
Perry *(G-14298)*
Consolidated Forest Pdts Inc ....F 407 830-7723
Longwood *(G-8267)*
Danielle Fence Mfg Co Inc ....D 863 425-3182
Mulberry *(G-11121)*
Florida Cypress & Fence Co ....G 561 392-3011
Palm City *(G-13656)*
Mc Connie Enterprises Inc ....G 813 247-3827
Tampa *(G-17897)*
Silverman Fence Mfg Inc ....G 904 730-0882
Jacksonville *(G-6774)*
Spray-Tech Staining Inc ....F 407 443-4239
Longwood *(G-8339)*

FERROSILICON, EXC MADE IN BLAST FURNACES

Globe Specialty Metals Inc ....F 786 509-6900
Miami *(G-9644)*

FERTILIZER MINERAL MINING

Ostara Usa LLC ....G 813 666-8123
Riverview *(G-15278)*

FERTILIZERS: NEC

Ausoil International Corp ....D 954 249-8060
Sunrise *(G-17092)*
Barber Fertilizer Company ....E 850 263-6324
Campbellton *(G-1330)*
Ben Hill Griffin Inc ....E 863 635-2281
Frostproof *(G-4855)*
Ben Hill Griffin Inc ....D 863 635-2281
Frostproof *(G-4856)*
Chemical Dynamics Inc ....E 813 752-4950
Plant City *(G-14418)*
Diamond R Fertilizer Co Inc ....F 863 763-2158
Okeechobee *(G-12176)*
Farmers Cooperative Inc ....E 386 362-1459
Live Oak *(G-8232)*
Harrells LLC ....C 863 687-2774
Lakeland *(G-7703)*
Lesco Inc ....F 863 655-2424
Sebring *(G-16697)*
Plant Foods Inc ....E 772 567-5741
Vero Beach *(G-18654)*
S A Florikan-E LLC ....D 800 322-8666
Bowling Green *(G-868)*
Sun Gro Horticulture Dist Inc ....G 407 291-1676
Orlando *(G-13222)*
Sunshine Organics Compost LLC ....G 904 900-3072
Jacksonville *(G-6825)*
Wedgworth Farms Inc ....G 561 996-2076
Plant City *(G-14478)*
Wedgworths Inc ....G 561 996-2076
Belle Glade *(G-355)*

FERTILIZERS: Nitrogen Solutions

Pioneer Ag-Chem Inc ....E 772 464-9300
Fort Pierce *(G-4734)*
Trans-Resources LLC ....A 305 933-8301
Sunny Isles Beach *(G-17082)*

FERTILIZERS: Nitrogenous

Agrium Advanced Tech US Inc ....F 407 302-2024
Sanford *(G-15989)*
Ben Hill Griffin Inc ....D 863 635-2281
Frostproof *(G-4856)*
Bionitrogen Holdings Corp ....G 561 600-9550
West Palm Beach *(G-18820)*
Florida Phosphorus ....G 561 983-3208
Key Largo *(G-7170)*
Growers Fertilizer Corporation ....E 863 956-1101
Lake Alfred *(G-7332)*
Natural Organic Products Intl ....G 352 383-8252
Mount Dora *(G-11108)*
Nurserymens Sure-Gro Corp ....G 772 770-0462
Vero Beach *(G-18648)*
Stoller Chemical Co of Florida ....F 352 357-3173
Eustis *(G-3717)*
T Brand Fertilizer Inc ....G 386 437-2970
Bunnell *(G-1307)*
Turf Care Supply Corp ....E 863 655-2424
Sebring *(G-16717)*

FERTILIZERS: Phosphatic

Growers Fertilizer Corporation ....E 863 956-1101
Lake Alfred *(G-7332)*
Mos Holdings Inc ....E 763 577-2700
Mulberry *(G-11131)*
Mosaic Company ....A 813 775-4200
Tampa *(G-17919)*
Mosaic Crop Nutrition LLC ....D 813 500-6800
Lithia *(G-8220)*
Mosaic Fertilizer LLC ....A 813 500-6300
Lithia *(G-8221)*
Nurserymens Sure-Gro Corp ....G 772 770-0462
Vero Beach *(G-18648)*

FIBER & FIBER PRDTS: Acrylic

Mirart Inc ....E 954 974-5230
Pompano Beach *(G-14764)*
Sterling Fibers Inc ....D 850 994-5311
Milton *(G-10941)*

FIBER & FIBER PRDTS: Organic, Noncellulose

Ascend Prfmce Mtls Oprtons LLC ....A 850 968-7000
Cantonment *(G-1335)*
Two Brothers Cultivation LLC ....E 954 478-2402
Fort Lauderdale *(G-4291)*

FIBER & FIBER PRDTS: Protein

Northeast Pro-Tech Inc ....G 772 489-8762
Port Saint Lucie *(G-15125)*

FIBER & FIBER PRDTS: Synthetic Cellulosic

Artificial Turf Supply LLC ....G 877 525-8873
Ponte Vedra Beach *(G-14934)*
Composite Holdings Inc ....E 321 268-9625
Titusville *(G-18424)*
Rayonier Advanced Mtls Inc ....A 904 357-4600
Jacksonville *(G-6707)*
Rayonier Inc ....E 904 277-1343
Yulee *(G-19499)*

FIBER & FIBER PRDTS: Vinyl

American Traffic Safety Mtls ....E 904 284-0284
Green Cove Springs *(G-5051)*
Bay City Window Company ....F 727 323-5443
Saint Petersburg *(G-15718)*
Uniroyal Engineered Pdts LLC ....F 941 906-8580
Sarasota *(G-16629)*
Uniroyal Globl Engnred Pdts In ....F 941 906-8580
Sarasota *(G-16630)*

FIBER OPTICS

Gulf Fiberoptics Inc ....E 813 891-1993
Oldsmar *(G-12229)*
Southern Lights ....G 727 849-4442
New Port Richey *(G-11510)*

FIBER PRDTS: Pressed, Wood Pulp, From Purchased Materials

A M Rayonier Products Inc ....B 904 261-3611
Yulee *(G-19493)*

FIBERS: Carbon & Graphite

Rapid Composites LLC ....G 941 322-6647
Sarasota *(G-16284)*
Steve French Entps Ltd LLC ....G 772 692-0222
Stuart *(G-17022)*

FILLERS & SEALERS: Putty

Rezolin LLC ....G 386 677-8238
Ormond Beach *(G-13396)*

FILM & SHEET: Unsuppported Plastic

Dairy-Mix Inc ....F 813 621-8098
Tampa *(G-17586)*
Guardian AG Plas Corp ....G 813 286-8680
Tampa *(G-17732)*
Madico Inc ....D 727 327-2544
Pinellas Park *(G-14366)*
Miami Cellophane Inc ....E 786 293-2212
Hialeah *(G-5508)*
Nina Plastic Bags Inc ....D 407 802-6828
Orlando *(G-13003)*
Ped-Stuart Corporation ....E 352 754-6001
Brooksville *(G-1259)*
Protex Inc ....F 727 573-4665
Clearwater *(G-1850)*
Seal-Tite Plastic Packg Co Inc ....D 305 264-9015
Miami *(G-10316)*
Solar X ....G 386 673-2111
Ormond Beach *(G-13400)*
Tape Technologies Inc ....E 904 284-0284
Green Cove Springs *(G-5072)*

FILM: Motion Picture

Columbia Films Inc ....G.... 800 531-3238
Pompano Beach (G-14641)
Planet Inhouse Inc ....F.... 321 216-2189
Melbourne (G-8909)
Trap World LLC ....D.... 305 517-5676
Miami (G-10504)

FILTERS

Dha Filter LLC ....G.... 904 269-8701
Orange Park (G-12388)
Eddys Filter Change Inc ....G.... 407 448-4498
Altamonte Springs (G-42)
Federal Eastern Intl Inc ....F.... 954 533-4506
Fort Lauderdale (G-3989)
Ingelub Corp ....F.... 407 656-8800
Winter Garden (G-19270)
JRS Ventures LLP ....G.... 715 441-1051
Deltona (G-3172)
No Flood Inc ....G.... 239 776-1671
Fort Myers (G-4548)
Pall Aeropower Corporation ....B.... 727 849-9999
Deland (G-3006)
Porous Metal Filters Inc ....G.... 407 682-1494
Longwood (G-8327)
Safetek International Inc ....G.... 702 558-8202
Boca Raton (G-698)
Siemens Industry Inc ....G.... 407 650-3570
Orlando (G-13188)
Suinpla LLC ....F.... 786 747-4829
Medley (G-8732)

FILTERS & SOFTENERS: Water, Household

Ashberry Acquisition Company ....F.... 813 248-0055
Tampa (G-17438)
Atlantic Drinking Water Systms ....G.... 252 255-1110
Fort Myers (G-4369)
Dependable Water Inc ....E.... 772 563-7473
Vero Beach (G-18615)
Enviro Water Solutions LLC ....D.... 877 842-1635
Deland (G-2975)
Johnson Well Equipment Inc ....G.... 850 453-3131
Pensacola (G-14185)
Michael P Wahlquist ....G.... 850 643-5139
Bristol (G-1200)
Paragon Water Systems Inc ....E.... 727 538-4704
Tampa (G-17976)
Sawyer Products Inc ....E.... 727 725-1177
Safety Harbor (G-15502)
Voda Technologies LLC ....G.... 727 645-6030
Palm Harbor (G-13767)
Waterfilterusa ....G.... 386 469-0138
Deland (G-3032)

FILTERS & STRAINERS: Pipeline

Wellstream Inc ....E.... 281 249-0900
Panama City (G-13962)

FILTERS: Air

Air Sponge Filter Company Inc ....G.... 954 752-1836
Coral Springs (G-2217)
Andrews Filter and Supply Corp ....E.... 407 423-3310
Orlando (G-12479)
Boair Inc ....G.... 954 426-9226
Deerfield Beach (G-2786)
DOT Blue Trading Inc ....G.... 954 646-0448
Miami (G-9482)
Duststop Filters Inc ....G.... 904 725-1001
Jacksonville (G-6338)
Energenics Corporation ....E.... 239 643-1711
Naples (G-11238)
Filters Plus Inc ....G.... 813 232-2000
Tampa (G-17665)
Glasfloss Industries Inc ....F.... 904 741-9922
Jacksonville (G-6435)
Pall Filtration and Sep ....C.... 386 822-8000
Deland (G-3007)
Polk Air Filter Sales Inc ....G.... 863 688-4436
Lakeland (G-7769)
Rv Air Inc ....G.... 309 657-4300
Clearwater (G-1866)

FILTERS: Air Intake, Internal Combustion Engine, Exc Auto

Lawrence Factor Inc ....E.... 305 430-9152
Miami Lakes (G-10805)

Sunshine Filters of Pinellas ....E.... 727 530-3884
Largo (G-8064)
Topline Machine & Tool LLC ....G.... 352 799-4668
Brooksville (G-1282)

FILTERS: Gasoline, Internal Combustion Engine, Exc Auto

Suinpla LLC ....F.... 786 747-4829
Medley (G-8732)

FILTERS: General Line, Indl

Custom Masters Inc ....E.... 407 331-4634
Longwood (G-8270)
Darly Filtration Inc ....G.... 727 318-7064
Largo (G-7931)
Industrial Filter Pump Mfg Co ....G.... 708 656-7800
Mims (G-10951)
Miami Filter LLC ....E.... 772 466-1440
Fort Pierce (G-4718)
Pall Aeropower Corporation ....B.... 727 849-9999
New Port Richey (G-11507)
Vuflow Filters Co Inc ....G.... 352 597-2607
Brooksville (G-1290)

FILTERS: Motor Vehicle

Puradyn Filter Tech Inc ....E.... 561 547-9499
Boynton Beach (G-947)

FILTRATION DEVICES: Electronic

E3 Fluid Recovery Eng ....G.... 727 754-9792
Largo (G-7939)
Filta Group Inc ....F.... 407 996-5550
Orlando (G-12738)
Nordquist Dielectrics Inc ....E.... 727 585-7990
Clearwater (G-1809)
Pall Filtration and Sep ....C.... 386 822-8000
Deland (G-3007)
Piezo Technology Inc ....C.... 407 298-2000
Orlando (G-13067)
Two Little Fishies Inc ....G.... 305 623-7695
Miami (G-10517)

FINANCIAL INVESTMENT ADVICE

Weiss Research Inc ....C.... 561 627-3300
Jupiter (G-7146)

FINDINGS & TRIMMINGS: Apparel

Hofmann & Leavy Inc ....D.... 954 698-0000
Deerfield Beach (G-2842)

FINDINGS & TRIMMINGS: Fabric

Uniroyal Globl Engnred Pdts In ....F.... 941 906-8580
Sarasota (G-16630)

FINGERNAILS, ARTIFICIAL

Chelly Cosmetics Manufacturing ....G.... 305 471-9608
Miami (G-9350)
Nailboutique of WPB LLC ....G.... 954 756-2699
West Palm Beach (G-18956)
Vicx LLC ....F.... 407 674-2073
Winter Garden (G-19288)

FINGERPRINT EQPT

Armor Holdings Forensics LLC ....E.... 904 485-1836
Jacksonville (G-6169)
Cross Match Technologies Inc ....C.... 561 622-1650
Palm Beach Gardens (G-13583)

FINISHING AGENTS

International Finishes Inc ....F.... 561 948-1066
Boca Raton (G-570)

FINISHING AGENTS: Textile

Vestagen Tchnical Textiles Inc ....G.... 407 781-2570
Orlando (G-13300)

FIRE ARMS, SMALL: Guns Or Gun Parts, 30 mm & Below

Adams Arms Holdings LLC ....E.... 727 853-0550
Brooksville (G-1205)
Artisan Arms Inc ....G.... 321 299-4053
Apopka (G-114)
C Products Defense Inc ....E.... 941 727-0009
Bradenton (G-1008)
Diamondback Firearms LLC ....F.... 321 305-5995
Cocoa (G-2011)
Hitman Industries LLC ....F.... 321 735-8562
Rockledge (G-15417)
Kel-TEC Cnc Industries Inc ....F.... 321 631-0068
Cocoa (G-2033)
Khaled W Akkawi ....G.... 321 396-3108
Apopka (G-154)
Knights Manufacturing Company ....D.... 321 607-9900
Titusville (G-18441)
Mwg Company Inc ....G.... 305 232-7344
Cutler Bay (G-2405)
Naroh Manufacturing LLC ....F.... 321 806-4875
Rockledge (G-15437)
O I Inc ....E.... 321 499-3800
Melbourne (G-8899)
Precision Machine Tech LLC ....F.... 305 594-1789
Doral (G-3467)
R M Equipment Inc ....E.... 305 477-9312
Miami (G-10232)
Rwc Group LLC ....E.... 754 222-1407
Pompano Beach (G-14837)
Sccy Industries LLC ....C.... 386 322-6336
Daytona Beach (G-2708)
US Security Defense Corp ....E.... 407 979-1478
Tavares (G-18357)

FIRE ARMS, SMALL: Machine Guns & Grenade Launchers

Arsenal Democracy LLC ....F.... 850 296-2122
Freeport (G-4844)

FIRE CONTROL EQPT REPAIR SVCS, MILITARY

Done Right Fire Gear Repr Inc ....G.... 727 848-9019
Hudson (G-6021)

FIRE CONTROL OR BOMBING EQPT: Electronic

Lehigh Acrs Fre Cnrl & Rscue ....E.... 239 303-5300
Lehigh Acres (G-8196)

FIRE DETECTION SYSTEMS

Simplexgrinnell Holdings LLC ....G.... 978 731-2500
Boca Raton (G-716)

FIRE OR BURGLARY RESISTIVE PRDTS

Argonide Corporation ....F.... 407 322-2500
Sanford (G-15995)
Centerline Steel LLC ....E.... 904 217-4186
Saint Augustine (G-15529)
Champion Shtmtl Fabrication ....G.... 407 509-7439
Winter Park (G-19392)
Custom Mfg & Engrg Inc ....D.... 727 548-0522
Pinellas Park (G-14342)
East Coast Machine Inc ....F.... 321 632-4817
Cocoa (G-2017)
J A Custom Fabricators Inc ....F.... 561 615-4680
Lake Worth (G-7559)
Metal Creations Sarasota Llc ....F.... 941 922-7096
Sarasota (G-16256)
Preston Works Inc ....G.... 850 932-0888
Holt (G-5949)
Telese Properties Inc ....D.... 813 752-6015
Plant City (G-14471)
Theissen Training Systems Inc ....D.... 352 490-8020
Gainesville (G-5009)

FIRE PROTECTION EQPT

911 Equipment Inc ....F.... 954 217-1745
Weston (G-19100)
Done Right Fire Gear Repr Inc ....G.... 727 848-9019
Hudson (G-6021)
Magenav Inc ....G.... 718 551-1815
Fort Lauderdale (G-4109)
Target Manufacturing Inc ....G.... 305 633-0361
Miami (G-10460)

FIREARMS & AMMUNITION, EXC SPORTING, WHOLESALE

Boland Production Supply Inc ....G.... 863 324-7784
Winter Haven (G-19304)

FIREARMS: Large, Greater Than 30mm

Ballista Tactical Systems ....G.... 954 260-0765
Fort Lauderdale *(G-3837)*
Nst Global LLC ....E.... 941 748-2270
Bradenton *(G-1088)*
Syrac Ordnance Inc ....G.... 727 612-6090
New Port Richey *(G-11515)*

FIREARMS: Small, 30mm or Less

Ao Precision Manufacturing LLC ....G.... 386 274-5882
Daytona Beach *(G-2626)*
Arma Holdings Inc ....E.... 813 402-0667
Tampa *(G-17434)*
Ballista Tactical Systems ....G.... 954 260-0765
Fort Lauderdale *(G-3837)*
Blackbird Armament LLC ....F.... 833 255-2473
Melbourne *(G-8781)*
Crosstac Corporation ....G.... 406 522-9300
Medley *(G-8638)*
Dark Storm Manufacturing LLC ....G.... 516 983-3473
Merritt Island *(G-8999)*
Eric Lemoine ....G.... 407 919-9783
Longwood *(G-8276)*
Global Ordnance LLC ....E.... 941 549-8388
Sarasota *(G-16221)*
Gtgjfe LLC ....G.... 904 800-6333
Jacksonville *(G-6455)*
Mossberg Group Inc ....F.... 386 274-5882
Daytona Beach *(G-2689)*
Wide Open Armory LLC ....G.... 727 202-5980
Seminole *(G-16771)*

FIREPLACE & CHIMNEY MATERIAL: Concrete

Earthcore Industries LLC ....E.... 904 363-3417
Jacksonville *(G-6347)*
Jay Walker Enterprises Inc ....G.... 850 539-7668
Tallahassee *(G-17282)*

FIREPLACE EQPT & ACCESS

Grate Ideas of America LLC ....G.... 844 292-6044
Fort Lauderdale *(G-4027)*
Super Screening Incorporated ....G.... 239 931-3224
Fort Myers *(G-4619)*

FIREPLACES: Concrete

Grate Fireplace & Stone Shoppe ....E.... 239 939-7187
Fort Myers *(G-4471)*

FIREWORKS

Ralph Santore & Sons Inc ....E.... 386 437-2242
Bunnell *(G-1305)*

FIREWORKS DISPLAY SVCS

Ralph Santore & Sons Inc ....E.... 386 437-2242
Bunnell *(G-1305)*

FISH & SEAFOOD MARKETS

Captain Rustys ....G.... 813 244-2799
Lorida *(G-8354)*

FISH & SEAFOOD PROCESSORS: Canned Or Cured

M & R Seafood Inc ....F.... 352 498-5150
Cross City *(G-2365)*

FISH & SEAFOOD PROCESSORS: Fresh Or Frozen

681 Seafood & Southern Bites ....G.... 954 573-7320
Deerfield Beach *(G-2759)*
Del Rosario Enterprises Inc ....F.... 786 547-6812
Medley *(G-8642)*
M & R Seafood Inc ....F.... 352 498-5150
Cross City *(G-2365)*
Miracle Seafood Manufacturers ....G.... 850 653-2114
Apalachicola *(G-98)*

FISH & SEAFOOD WHOLESALERS

Ceh Llc ....G.... 941 518-6747
Bradenton *(G-1017)*
M & R Seafood Inc ....F.... 352 498-5150
Cross City *(G-2365)*

Select Europe Inc ....G.... 407 931-1820
Deerfield Beach *(G-2908)*

FISHING EQPT: Lures

Boone Bait Co Inc ....F.... 407 975-8775
Winter Park *(G-19384)*
Cind-Al Inc ....G.... 863 401-8700
Clermont *(G-1952)*
Classic Fishing Products Inc ....E.... 407 656-6133
Clermont *(G-1953)*
Highroller Fishing Lure Co LLC ....G.... 352 215-2925
Gainesville *(G-4936)*
L & S Bait Co Inc ....E.... 727 584-7691
Largo *(G-7997)*
Mayo Plastics Mfg Inc ....F.... 386 294-1049
Mayo *(G-8595)*
Ryman Hospitality Prpts Inc ....A.... 904 284-2770
Green Cove Springs *(G-5070)*
Stuart Industries Inc ....F.... 305 651-3474
Miami *(G-10425)*

FISHING EQPT: Nets & Seines

Frank Murray & Sons Inc ....F.... 561 845-1366
Fort Lauderdale *(G-4012)*
Lee Fisher International Inc ....E.... 813 875-6296
Tampa *(G-17839)*
Mc Connie Enterprises Inc ....G.... 813 247-3827
Tampa *(G-17897)*

FITTINGS & ASSEMBLIES: Hose & Tube, Hydraulic Or Pneumatic

Awab LLC ....G.... 954 763-3003
Fort Lauderdale *(G-3835)*
Commercial Truck & Trailer Sls ....E.... 863 968-9393
Auburndale *(G-236)*
Ibd Industrial LLC ....G.... 786 655-7577
Coral Gables *(G-2156)*
Mako Hose & Rubber Co ....G.... 561 795-6200
West Palm Beach *(G-18939)*
Space Coast Hydraulics Inc ....F.... 321 504-6006
Rockledge *(G-15449)*

FITTINGS: Pipe

Azex Flow Technologies Inc ....G.... 305 393-8037
Miami *(G-9206)*
Nuflo Inc ....E.... 904 265-4001
Jacksonville *(G-6642)*
Southeast Power Group Inc ....D.... 305 592-9745
Doral *(G-3507)*
Teckno Corp ....G.... 305 677-3487
Doral *(G-3526)*
Tradewinds Power Corp ....D.... 305 592-9745
Doral *(G-3531)*

FIXTURES & EQPT: Kitchen, Metal, Exc Cast Aluminum

Accurate Metal Fabricators ....F.... 407 933-2666
Kissimmee *(G-7217)*
LAtelier Pris Hute Design LLC ....F.... 800 792-3550
Miami *(G-9866)*
Officine Gullo USA LLC ....F.... 800 781-7125
Miami *(G-10091)*
Professnal Kit Instller Group ....F.... 954 436-1513
Miramar *(G-11033)*
R and R Brokerage Co ....G.... 305 592-4329
Doral *(G-3477)*

FIXTURES: Cut Stone

Tropix Marble Company ....F.... 239 334-2371
Cape Coral *(G-1488)*

FLAGS: Fabric

Buchanan Signs Screen Process ....E.... 904 725-5500
Jacksonville *(G-6243)*

FLAGSTONES

Flagstone Pavers South ....G.... 239 225-5646
Pompano Beach *(G-14698)*

FLARES

Edible Flair Inc ....G.... 954 321-3608
Fort Lauderdale *(G-3963)*
Flare Clothing Inc ....G.... 863 859-1800
Lakeland *(G-7688)*

Fort Myers Bch Soccer Leag Inc ....G.... 239 353-7567
Fort Myers Beach *(G-4662)*
Innovative Flare LLC ....G.... 561 247-2776
West Palm Beach *(G-18905)*

FLAT GLASS: Construction

Dynamic Visions Inc ....E.... 941 497-1984
Venice *(G-18543)*
King Construction & Glass LLC ....G.... 407 508-6286
Kissimmee *(G-7261)*

FLAT GLASS: Laminated

Advanced Impact Tech Inc ....E.... 727 287-4620
Largo *(G-7886)*
Cardinal Lg Company ....D.... 352 237-4410
Ocala *(G-11895)*
PGT Innovations Inc ....A.... 941 480-1600
North Venice *(G-11762)*

FLAT GLASS: Picture

Giz Studio Inc ....F.... 305 416-5001
Miami *(G-9637)*

FLAT GLASS: Skylight

Kenny Skylights LLC ....G.... 407 330-5150
Sanford *(G-16078)*
Sun-Tek Manufacturing Inc ....E.... 407 859-2117
Orlando *(G-13223)*

FLAT GLASS: Strengthened Or Reinforced

Ad Valorem Corporation ....G.... 561 488-9966
Boca Raton *(G-397)*

FLAT GLASS: Window, Clear & Colored

American Shield LLC ....G.... 850 697-3066
Lanark Village *(G-7848)*
Assura Windows and Doors LLC ....G.... 954 781-4430
Pompano Beach *(G-14605)*
Central Florida Tinting ....G.... 863 221-0185
Lake Wales *(G-7502)*
Coastal Hurricane Film LLC ....G.... 941 268-9693
Port Charlotte *(G-14970)*
Cws Holding Company LLC ....D.... 352 368-6922
Ocala *(G-11915)*
Erickson International LLC ....G.... 702 853-4800
Boynton Beach *(G-904)*
Global Performance Windows Inc ....F.... 954 942-3322
Pompano Beach *(G-14715)*
Panama City Tint Center ....G.... 850 640-0167
Panama City *(G-13938)*
Sick Ride LLC ....G.... 239 300-5995
Naples *(G-11402)*
US Global Glass LLC ....F.... 305 651-6630
Miami *(G-10552)*
Vistamatic LLC ....E.... 866 466-9525
Coral Springs *(G-2329)*
Windoor Incorporated ....C.... 407 481-8400
North Venice *(G-11765)*

FLEA MARKET

United Trophy Manufacturing ....E.... 407 841-2525
Orlando *(G-13294)*

FLIGHT TRAINING SCHOOLS

Cae USA Inc ....A.... 813 885-7481
Tampa *(G-17500)*

FLOATING DRY DOCKS

Jmh Marine Inc ....F.... 954 785-7557
Pompano Beach *(G-14736)*

FLOOR CLEANING & MAINTENANCE EQPT: Household

Flexshopper LLC ....E.... 561 922-6609
Boca Raton *(G-530)*

FLOOR COVERING STORES: Carpets

Design-A-Rug Inc ....F.... 954 943-7487
Deerfield Beach *(G-2812)*
Quality Carpet ....G.... 727 527-1359
Saint Petersburg *(G-15895)*
Tropic Shield Inc ....F.... 954 731-5553
Lauderdale Lakes *(G-8095)*

FLOOR COVERING STORES: Rugs

Murse Properties LLC.......G....... 941 966-3380
Sarasota *(G-16518)*

FLOOR COVERING: Plastic

BF Hurley Mat Co Inc.......E....... 813 837-0616
Tampa *(G-17468)*

FLOOR COVERINGS WHOLESALERS

Eagle Prof Flrg Removal.......G....... 813 520-3027
Riverview *(G-15270)*

FLOOR COVERINGS: Rubber

Abco Products Inc.......E....... 888 694-2226
Miami *(G-9055)*
Impact Molding Clearwater LLC.......E....... 847 718-9300
Clearwater *(G-1730)*

FLOOR COVERINGS: Textile Fiber

Englert Arts Inc.......G....... 561 241-9924
Boca Raton *(G-518)*
Floors Inc.......E....... 813 879-5720
Tampa *(G-17671)*
Glassflake International Inc.......G....... 904 268-4000
Jacksonville *(G-6436)*
Milliken & Company.......G....... 352 244-2267
Gainesville *(G-4963)*

FLOORING & GRATINGS: Open, Construction Applications

Alabama Metal Industries Corp.......D....... 863 688-9256
Lakeland *(G-7630)*

FLOORING: Baseboards, Wood

Eagle Prof Flrg Removal.......G....... 813 520-3027
Riverview *(G-15270)*

FLOORING: Hard Surface

Amercn Cabinets Granite Floors.......F....... 727 303-0678
Palm Harbor *(G-13718)*

FLOORING: Hardwood

Bona Enterprises Inc.......G....... 954 927-4889
Dania *(G-2439)*
Designer Lifestyles LLC.......F....... 904 631-8954
Jacksonville *(G-6317)*
Goodwin Lumber Company Inc.......F....... 352 466-0339
Micanopy *(G-10901)*
It Is Finished Inc.......G....... 813 598-9585
Land O Lakes *(G-7857)*
New T Management Inc.......G....... 954 927-4889
Dania *(G-2454)*
Smart Floors LLC.......G....... 239 500-1234
Naples *(G-11405)*
Upstream Installation Inc.......G....... 904 829-3507
Saint Augustine *(G-15629)*

FLOORING: Parquet, Hardwood

Cryntel Enterprises Ltd Inc.......G....... 954 577-7844
Davie *(G-2511)*

FLOORING: Rubber

A Clean Finish Inc.......G....... 407 516-1311
Jacksonville *(G-6109)*
Bolidt Cruise Control Corp.......G....... 305 607-4172
Opa Locka *(G-12295)*
Ffo Leesburg LLC.......G....... 352 315-0783
Leesburg *(G-8155)*

FLOORING: Tile

Arcana Tileworks.......G....... 407 492-0668
Winter Garden *(G-19252)*

FLORISTS

Always Flowers Inc.......F....... 305 572-1122
Miami *(G-9128)*
Ebs Quality Service Inc.......F....... 305 595-4048
Miami *(G-9497)*

FLOWER ARRANGEMENTS: Artificial

1800flowerscom.......G....... 954 683-1246
Fort Lauderdale *(G-3771)*
Dianthus Miami Inc.......G....... 786 800-8365
Miami *(G-9464)*
Nearly Natural LLC.......F....... 800 711-0544
Hialeah *(G-5535)*

FLOWER POTS Plastic

Enviroworks Inc.......F....... 407 889-5533
Apopka *(G-137)*
Fiskars Brands Inc.......G....... 407 889-5533
Apopka *(G-142)*
Nursery Supplies Inc.......B....... 407 846-9750
Kissimmee *(G-7278)*

FLOWERS & FLORISTS' SPLYS WHOLESALERS

Ebs Quality Service Inc.......F....... 305 595-4048
Miami *(G-9497)*

FLOWERS, ARTIFICIAL, WHOLESALE

Nearly Natural LLC.......F....... 800 711-0544
Hialeah *(G-5535)*

FLOWERS: Artificial & Preserved

Always Flowers Inc.......F....... 305 572-1122
Miami *(G-9128)*

FLUES & PIPES: Stove Or Furnace

Crown Products Company Inc.......C....... 904 737-7144
Jacksonville *(G-6300)*

FLUID METERS & COUNTING DEVICES

Sandale Utility Products.......G....... 863 937-5208
Lakeland *(G-7786)*
Trak Engineering Incorporated.......E....... 850 878-4585
Tallahassee *(G-17341)*

FLUID POWER PUMPS & MOTORS

Flaire Corporation.......C....... 352 237-1220
Ocala *(G-11944)*
Motors Pumps and Accessories.......G....... 305 883-3181
Medley *(G-8692)*
Scott Industrial Systems Inc.......F....... 904 693-3318
Jacksonville *(G-6756)*

FLUID POWER VALVES & HOSE FITTINGS

Engineered Mtls & Mfg Intl LLC.......G....... 727 546-5580
Largo *(G-7941)*
Hose Power USA.......G....... 863 669-9333
Lakeland *(G-7706)*
Kinetics Usa Inc.......E....... 561 988-8826
Boca Raton *(G-588)*
Leslie Controls Inc.......C....... 813 978-1000
Temple Terrace *(G-18371)*
Teknocraft Inc.......E....... 321 729-9634
Melbourne *(G-8959)*

FLUXES

C & J Cstm Wldg Fbrication LLC.......G....... 407 414-1739
Kissimmee *(G-7228)*
John P Cooksey LLC.......G....... 850 997-8426
Monticello *(G-11077)*

FLY TRAPS: Electrical

Pestwest Usa LLC.......G....... 941 358-1983
Sarasota *(G-16276)*

FOAM CHARGE MIXTURES

Blue Earth Solutions Inc.......E....... 352 729-0150
Clermont *(G-1949)*

FOAM RUBBER

Inspiration Foam Inc.......G....... 407 498-0040
Kissimmee *(G-7255)*
Lapolla Industries LLC.......F....... 954 379-0241
Deerfield Beach *(G-2857)*
Reliatex Inc.......E....... 813 621-6021
Tampa *(G-18051)*
Treadway Industries LLC.......E....... 352 326-3313
Minneola *(G-10957)*

FOIL & LEAF: Metal

Vega.......G....... 239 574-1798
Cape Coral *(G-1490)*

FOOD CONTAMINATION TESTING OR SCREENING KITS

Elisa Technologies Inc.......F....... 352 337-3929
Gainesville *(G-4914)*
Greenscape Laboratories Inc.......G....... 850 723-7496
Pensacola *(G-14163)*

FOOD PRDTS & SEAFOOD: Shellfish, Fresh, Shucked

Juniors Bait and Seafood Inc.......E....... 321 480-5492
Melbourne *(G-8856)*

FOOD PRDTS, BREAKFAST: Cereal, Wheat Flakes

Productos Las Delicias Inc.......G....... 305 760-4223
Hialeah *(G-5577)*

FOOD PRDTS, CANNED OR FRESH PACK: Fruit Juices

Coco Lopez Inc.......G....... 954 450-3100
Miramar *(G-10980)*
Cutrale Citrus Juices USA Inc.......B....... 352 728-7800
Leesburg *(G-8149)*
Florida Refresco Inc.......C....... 863 665-5515
Lakeland *(G-7693)*
Gem Freshco LLC.......D....... 772 595-0070
Fort Pierce *(G-4699)*
M & B Products Inc.......C....... 813 988-2211
Temple Terrace *(G-18372)*
Ouhlala Gourmet Corp.......F....... 305 774-7332
Coral Gables *(G-2182)*
Pepsico Inc.......G....... 407 933-5542
Kissimmee *(G-7286)*
Raw Foods International Llc.......F....... 305 856-1991
Coral Gables *(G-2190)*
Tropicana Products Inc.......G....... 772 465-2030
Fort Pierce *(G-4759)*
United Jice Companies Amer Inc.......D....... 772 562-5442
Vero Beach *(G-18673)*

FOOD PRDTS, CANNED OR FRESH PACK: Vegetable Juices

Florida Food Products LLC.......D....... 352 357-4141
Eustis *(G-3707)*

FOOD PRDTS, CANNED: Barbecue Sauce

Barbecue Superstore.......G....... 305 635-4427
Miami *(G-9217)*
Choctaw Trading Co Inc.......G....... 407 905-9917
Winter Garden *(G-19257)*
Cordoba Foods LLC.......E....... 305 733-4768
Hialeah *(G-5355)*
Flayco Products Inc.......E....... 813 879-1356
Tampa *(G-17668)*
Hot Sauce Harrys Inc.......G....... 941 423-7092
North Port *(G-11741)*

FOOD PRDTS, CANNED: Beans, With Meat

Conchita Foods Inc.......D....... 305 888-9703
Medley *(G-8633)*

FOOD PRDTS, CANNED: Chili Sauce, Tomato

Wharton Pepper Co.......G....... 850 997-4359
Monticello *(G-11084)*

FOOD PRDTS, CANNED: Ethnic

All Naturals Direct.......G....... 813 792-3777
Tampa *(G-17399)*
Alpha Omega Commercial Limited.......G....... 407 925-7913
Windermere *(G-19225)*
Comep Usa Inc.......E....... 786 554-2211
Miami *(G-9386)*
MA Fine Foods LLC.......G....... 305 878-6277
Miami *(G-9929)*

FOOD PRDTS, CANNED: Fruit Juices, Concentrated

Tropicana Manufacturing Co Inc .... G 312 821-1000
Bradenton *(G-1132)*

FOOD PRDTS, CANNED: Fruit Juices, Fresh

Brown International Corp LLC .... G 863 299-2111
Winter Haven *(G-19306)*
Coca-Cola Company .... G 407 565-2465
Apopka *(G-123)*
Cutrale Farms Inc .... D 863 965-5000
Auburndale *(G-238)*
Lakewood Organics LLC .... D 305 324-5900
Miami *(G-9852)*
Sun Orchard LLC .... E 786 646-9200
Miami *(G-10428)*
Tropicana Products Inc .... A 941 747-4461
Bradenton *(G-1133)*
Watts Juicery .... F 904 372-0693
Atlantic Beach *(G-228)*
Wm G Roe & Sons Inc .... B 863 294-3577
Winter Haven *(G-19367)*

FOOD PRDTS, CANNED: Fruits

Ben Hill Griffin Inc .... E 863 635-2281
Frostproof *(G-4855)*
Conchita Foods Inc .... D 305 888-9703
Medley *(G-8633)*
Fruselva Usa LLC .... F 949 798-0061
Miami *(G-9602)*

FOOD PRDTS, CANNED: Fruits

Allapattah Industries Inc .... E 305 324-5900
Miami *(G-9116)*
Ardmore Farms LLC .... D 386 734-4634
Deland *(G-2960)*
Coca-Cola Company .... G 727 736-7101
Dunedin *(G-3574)*
Gma-Food LLC .... G 646 469-8599
Lutz *(G-8385)*
Juice Tyme Inc .... G 631 424-2850
Frostproof *(G-4860)*
Kraft Heinz Foods Company .... G 813 810-5298
Valrico *(G-18520)*
Kraft Heinz Foods Company .... G 305 428-7152
Coral Gables *(G-2167)*
Kraft Heinz Foods Company .... G 305 476-7000
Coral Gables *(G-2168)*
Kraft Heinz Foods Company .... G 239 694-3663
Fort Myers *(G-4513)*
Mancini Packing Company .... D 863 735-2000
Zolfo Springs *(G-19546)*
Sun Orchard LLC .... D 863 422-5062
Haines City *(G-5150)*
Tropicana Products Inc .... G 850 610-8849
Defuniak Springs *(G-2950)*

FOOD PRDTS, CANNED: Fruits & Fruit Prdts

Del Monte Fresh Produce NA Inc .... E 305 520-8400
Coral Gables *(G-2138)*
Freshco Ltd .... E 772 287-2111
Stuart *(G-16942)*
R & Z Ventures Inc .... D 954 532-7938
Pompano Beach *(G-14824)*

FOOD PRDTS, CANNED: Italian

Ait USA Corp .... G 786 953-5918
Miami *(G-9098)*
Delarosa Real Foods LLC .... D 718 333-0333
Lauderdale Lakes *(G-8085)*
Magnificat Holdings LLC .... G 727 798-0512
Clearwater *(G-1771)*
Nanas Original Stromboli Inc .... G 954 771-6262
Fort Lauderdale *(G-4129)*
Richard Meer Investments Inc .... G 941 484-6551
Venice *(G-18570)*

FOOD PRDTS, CANNED: Jams, Jellies & Preserves

Good Jams LLC .... G 702 379-5551
Boca Raton *(G-548)*
Jammin Jams USA LLC .... G 305 494-5617
Miami *(G-9786)*
Kraft Heinz Foods Company .... G 904 695-1300
Jacksonville *(G-6545)*

FOOD PRDTS, CANNED: Jellies, Edible, Including Imitation

Palmetto Canning Company .... F 941 722-1100
Palmetto *(G-13814)*
Seven Keys Co of Florida .... G 954 946-5010
Pompano Beach *(G-14848)*

FOOD PRDTS, CANNED: Mexican, NEC

Rancheritos .... G 561 479-0046
Boca Raton *(G-680)*
Whole Enchlada Fresh Mxcan Gri .... F 954 561-4040
Fort Lauderdale *(G-4322)*

FOOD PRDTS, CANNED: Mushrooms

Idsolution Inc .... G 305 603-9835
Medley *(G-8667)*

FOOD PRDTS, CANNED: Pizza Sauce

Chiantis .... G 407 484-6510
Sanford *(G-16013)*

FOOD PRDTS, CANNED: Soups, Exc Seafood

Suzanne Chalet Foods Inc .... G 863 676-6011
Lake Wales *(G-7524)*

FOOD PRDTS, CANNED: Tamales

Catalina Finer Food Corp .... E 813 872-6359
Tampa *(G-17515)*

FOOD PRDTS, CANNED: Tomato Purees

Gulf Coast Growers Florida LLC .... D 941 737-2532
Palmetto *(G-13802)*

FOOD PRDTS, CANNED: Vegetables

Sam S Accrsio Sons Pkg Prod In .... F 305 246-3455
Homestead *(G-5990)*

FOOD PRDTS, CANNED: Vegetables

Fruit Dynamics LLC .... C 239 643-7373
Naples *(G-11251)*

FOOD PRDTS, CONFECTIONERY, WHOLESALE: Candy

Hoffman Commercial Group Inc .... E 561 967-2213
Greenacres *(G-5082)*
Peterbrooke Choclat Fctry LLC .... G 904 273-7878
Ponte Vedra Beach *(G-14950)*

FOOD PRDTS, DAIRY, WHOLESALE: Frozen Dairy Desserts

Latin Dairy Foods LLC .... F 305 888-1788
Miami *(G-9869)*
Miami Foods Distrs USA Inc .... F 305 512-3246
Hialeah *(G-5510)*

FOOD PRDTS, FISH & SEAFOOD, WHOLESALE: Seafood

Florida Fresh Seafood Corp .... F 305 694-1733
Miami *(G-9583)*

FOOD PRDTS, FISH & SEAFOOD: Canned & Jarred, Etc

Select Europe Inc .... G 407 931-1820
Deerfield Beach *(G-2908)*

FOOD PRDTS, FISH & SEAFOOD: Crab cakes, Frozen

Santos Frozen Foods Inc .... F 813 875-4901
Tampa *(G-18081)*

FOOD PRDTS, FISH & SEAFOOD: Crabmeat, Fresh, Pkgd Nonsealed

Chiefland Crab Company Inc .... E 352 493-4887
Chiefland *(G-1535)*

FOOD PRDTS, FISH & SEAFOOD: Fish, Frozen, Prepared

Masa Trading LLC .... F 561 729-3293
Pompano Beach *(G-14754)*

FOOD PRDTS, FISH & SEAFOOD: Fish, Smoked

Captain Rustys .... G 813 244-2799
Lorida *(G-8354)*

FOOD PRDTS, FISH & SEAFOOD: Fresh, Prepared

Buddy Ward & Sons Seafood .... G 850 653-8522
Apalachicola *(G-97)*
Florida Fresh Seafood Corp .... F 305 694-1733
Miami *(G-9583)*
Massachusetts Bay Clam Co Inc .... F 813 855-4599
Tampa *(G-17891)*
Shaws Sthern Blle Frz Fods In .... D 904 768-1591
Jacksonville *(G-6763)*

FOOD PRDTS, FISH & SEAFOOD: Fresh/Frozen Chowder, Soup/Stew

Skip One Seafood Inc .... G 239 463-8788
Fort Myers Beach *(G-4666)*

FOOD PRDTS, FISH & SEAFOOD: Oysters, Canned, Jarred, Etc

Miracle Seafood Manufacturers .... G 850 653-2114
Apalachicola *(G-98)*

FOOD PRDTS, FISH & SEAFOOD: Oysters, Preserved & Cured

Outlaw Oyster Company LLC .... G 850 841-9344
Panacea *(G-13860)*

FOOD PRDTS, FISH & SEAFOOD: Seafood, Frozen, Prepared

Ceh Llc .... G 941 518-6747
Bradenton *(G-1017)*
Global Aliment Inc .... G 786 536-5261
Doral *(G-3368)*

FOOD PRDTS, FISH & SEAFOOD: Shrimp, Frozen, Prepared

Thetradebaycom LLC .... G 954 607-2405
Weston *(G-19171)*

FOOD PRDTS, FISH & SEAFOOD: Soup, Stew/Chowdr, Canned/Pkgd

Ceh Llc .... G 941 518-6747
Bradenton *(G-1017)*

FOOD PRDTS, FROZEN, WHOLESALE: Dinners

Jo MO Enterprises Inc .... G 708 599-8098
Boca Raton *(G-582)*

FOOD PRDTS, FROZEN: Breakfasts, Packaged

Uren North America LLC .... G 410 924-3478
Coral Gables *(G-2201)*

FOOD PRDTS, FROZEN: Ethnic Foods, NEC

Asian Food Solutions Inc .... E 888 499-6888
Oviedo *(G-13414)*
Comida Vida Inc .... G 855 720-7663
Oviedo *(G-13421)*
International Fd Solutions Inc .... E 888 499-6888
Oviedo *(G-13440)*
Patty King Inc .... E 305 817-1888
Hialeah *(G-5555)*
Tuiskombuis .... G 904 484-4509
Saint Augustine *(G-15628)*
Very Tasty LLC .... F 305 636-4140
Miami *(G-10575)*

FOOD PRDTS, FROZEN: Fruit Juice, Concentrates

Citrus World Inc ....A 863 676-1411
Lake Wales *(G-7503)*
Coca-Cola Company ....G....... 407 565-2465
Apopka *(G-123)*
Country Pure Foods Inc ....B 904 734-4634
Deland *(G-2965)*
Tropicana Products Inc ....A....... 941 747-4461
Bradenton *(G-1133)*
Tropicana Products Inc ....G....... 772 465-2030
Fort Pierce *(G-4759)*

FOOD PRDTS, FROZEN: Fruit Juices

Ardmore Farms LLC ....D....... 386 734-4634
Deland *(G-2960)*
Florida Food Products LLC ....D....... 352 357-4141
Eustis *(G-3707)*
Food Partners Inc ....F....... 863 298-8771
Winter Haven *(G-19322)*
Silver Springs Citrus Inc ....C....... 352 324-2101
Howey In The Hills *(G-6012)*
Sun Orchard LLC ....E....... 786 646-9200
Miami *(G-10428)*

FOOD PRDTS, FROZEN: Fruits

Totally Bananas LLC ....F....... 954 674-9421
Davie *(G-2607)*

FOOD PRDTS, FROZEN: Fruits & Vegetables

World Wide Frozen Foods LLC ....G....... 954 266-8500
Fort Lauderdale *(G-4328)*

FOOD PRDTS, FROZEN: Fruits, Juices & Vegetables

Ata Group of Companies Inc ....G....... 352 735-1588
Mount Dora *(G-11097)*
Boca Smoothies LLC ....G....... 772 323-2117
Jupiter *(G-7013)*
Borden Dairy Company Fla LLC ....D....... 863 298-9742
Winter Haven *(G-19305)*
Brazilian Smoothie Inc ....G....... 305 233-5543
Pinecrest *(G-14325)*
Chunky Plates LLC ....G....... 321 746-3346
Orlando *(G-12583)*
Citrus World ADM Svcs Inc ....G....... 863 676-1411
Lake Wales *(G-7504)*
Clonts Groves Inc ....F....... 407 359-4103
Oviedo *(G-13420)*
Crop LLC ....F....... 941 923-8640
Sarasota *(G-16396)*
Daves Super Smoothies LLC ....G....... 407 293-7334
Orlando *(G-12653)*
Floridas Natural Food Svc Inc ....E....... 888 657-6600
Lake Wales *(G-7510)*
Fresh Blends North America Inc ....F....... 531 665-8200
Delray Beach *(G-3081)*
Green Plant LLC ....E....... 305 397-9394
Miami *(G-9669)*
Juice Tyme Inc ....G....... 631 424-2850
Frostproof *(G-4860)*
Kerry Inc ....G....... 813 359-5181
Plant City *(G-14444)*
Key Biscayne Smoothie Company ....G....... 305 441-7882
Coral Gables *(G-2163)*
Manatee Smoothies LLC ....G....... 985 640-3088
Lakewood Ranch *(G-7840)*
Natural Fruit Corp ....E....... 305 887-7525
Hialeah *(G-5533)*
Oakland Park Smoothie Inc ....G....... 954 567-0871
Fort Lauderdale *(G-4146)*
Palm Beach Smoothies Com Inc ....G....... 561 379-8647
Tequesta *(G-18386)*
Pl Smoothie LLC ....G....... 954 554-0450
Davie *(G-2574)*
Refreshing Smoothie ....G....... 904 549-5366
Jacksonville *(G-6712)*
Shri Guru Krupa Smoothies Inc ....G....... 904 461-9090
Saint Augustine *(G-15609)*
Skd Smoothie Inc ....G....... 386 931-4953
Palm Coast *(G-13709)*
Smoothie Corp ....E....... 305 588-0867
Miami *(G-10365)*
Smoothie Operator By JC Inc ....G....... 786 367-4245
Miami *(G-10366)*
Smoothies Recharge ....G....... 954 999-0332
Sunrise *(G-17174)*
Sunluver Smoothies Inc ....G....... 239 331-5431
Naples *(G-11425)*
Sunnyland Usa Inc ....G....... 772 293-0293
Fort Pierce *(G-4752)*

FOOD PRDTS, FROZEN: NEC

Charles Bryant Enterprises ....G....... 850 785-3604
Panama City *(G-13879)*
Chefs Commissary LLC ....D....... 321 303-2947
Orlando *(G-12578)*
Discos Y Empanadas Argentina ....F....... 305 326-9300
Miami *(G-9469)*
GA Fd Svcs Pinellas Cnty LLC ....B....... 727 388-0075
Saint Petersburg *(G-15789)*
GA Fd Svcs Pinellas Cnty LLC ....E....... 954 972-8884
Fort Lauderdale *(G-4017)*
GA Fd Svcs Pinellas Cnty LLC ....E....... 239 693-5090
Fort Myers *(G-4465)*
Greenie Tots Inc ....G....... 888 316-6126
Plantation *(G-14522)*
Hom Ade Foods Inc ....D....... 850 444-4740
Pensacola *(G-14174)*
Kibby Foods LLC ....F....... 305 456-3635
Hialeah *(G-5472)*
Lillys Gstrnmia Itlana Fla Inc ....G....... 305 655-2111
Hallandale Beach *(G-5198)*
Madan Corporation ....G....... 954 925-0077
Dania Beach *(G-2467)*
Sukalde Inc ....E....... 786 399-0087
Coral Gables *(G-2197)*
Thrive Frozen Nutrition Inc ....F....... 407 960-4883
Orlando *(G-13256)*

FOOD PRDTS, FROZEN: Pizza

Classic Pizza Crusts Inc ....G....... 954 570-8383
Pompano Beach *(G-14636)*
Pizza Spice Packet LLC ....G....... 718 831-7036
Boca Raton *(G-666)*

FOOD PRDTS, FROZEN: Potato Prdts

Interfries Inc ....G....... 786 427-1427
Miami *(G-9755)*

FOOD PRDTS, FROZEN: Snack Items

Krunchy Krisps LLC ....G....... 561 309-7049
Palm City *(G-13664)*
Zesty Brands LLC ....F....... 954 348-2827
Orlando *(G-13339)*

FOOD PRDTS, FROZEN: Spaghetti & Meatballs

Jo MO Enterprises Inc ....G....... 708 599-8098
Boca Raton *(G-582)*

FOOD PRDTS, FRUITS & VEGETABLES, FRESH, WHOLESALE

Del Monte Fresh Produce NA Inc ....E....... 305 520-8400
Coral Gables *(G-2138)*

FOOD PRDTS, MEAT & MEAT PRDTS, WHOLESALE: Cured Or Smoked

La Villarena Meat & Pork Inc ....F....... 305 759-0555
Miami *(G-9849)*

FOOD PRDTS, MEAT & MEAT PRDTS, WHOLESALE: Fresh

Bush Brothers Provision Co ....E....... 561 832-6666
West Palm Beach *(G-18831)*
Latin Amercn Meats & Foods USA ....G....... 305 477-2700
Miami *(G-9867)*
Pinellas Provision Corporation ....E....... 727 822-2701
Saint Petersburg *(G-15877)*

FOOD PRDTS, WHOLESALE: Beverage Concentrates

Egd Euro Gourmet Deli Inc ....G....... 305 937-1515
Aventura *(G-267)*
Nutrition Laboratories Inc ....E....... 727 442-2747
Clearwater *(G-1815)*
Splash Beverage Group Inc ....G....... 954 745-5815
Fort Lauderdale *(G-4254)*

FOOD PRDTS, WHOLESALE: Beverages, Exc Coffee & Tea

Candies and Beyond Inc ....G....... 954 828-2255
Miami Lakes *(G-10774)*
Shasta Beverages Intl Inc ....E....... 954 581-0922
Plantation *(G-14549)*

FOOD PRDTS, WHOLESALE: Chocolate

Chocolate Guys LLC ....G....... 561 278-5889
Delray Beach *(G-3060)*

FOOD PRDTS, WHOLESALE: Coffee & Tea

Babys Coffee LLC ....G....... 305 744-9866
Key West *(G-7178)*
De Luna Coffee Intl Inc ....G....... 850 478-6371
Pensacola *(G-14126)*
Grand Havana Inc ....G....... 305 297-2207
Miami Beach *(G-10674)*
Latitude 235 Coffee and Tea ....F....... 941 556-2600
Sarasota *(G-16250)*
Royal Cup Inc ....G....... 813 664-8902
Tampa *(G-18070)*

FOOD PRDTS, WHOLESALE: Coffee, Green Or Roasted

Aroma Coffee Service Inc ....G....... 239 481-7262
Fort Myers *(G-4367)*
Potters Coffee Company ....G....... 850 525-1793
Pensacola *(G-14235)*
Rae Launo Corporation ....G....... 813 242-4281
Valrico *(G-18524)*

FOOD PRDTS, WHOLESALE: Grains

Southland Milling Co ....G....... 850 674-8448
Blountstown *(G-389)*

FOOD PRDTS, WHOLESALE: Macaroni

Termine Ravioli Manufacturing ....F....... 954 983-3711
Hollywood *(G-5923)*

FOOD PRDTS, WHOLESALE: Natural & Organic

Shining Tree Inc ....F....... 855 688-7987
Wellington *(G-18732)*

FOOD PRDTS, WHOLESALE: Sandwiches

Los Atntcos Sndwich Cuban Cafe ....G....... 407 282-2322
Orlando *(G-12936)*

FOOD PRDTS, WHOLESALE: Sauces

Joys International Foods Inc ....G....... 321 242-6520
Melbourne *(G-8855)*

FOOD PRDTS, WHOLESALE: Spaghetti

Cheney Ofs Inc ....A....... 407 292-3223
Orlando *(G-12579)*

FOOD PRDTS, WHOLESALE: Specialty

All Naturals Direct ....G....... 813 792-3777
Tampa *(G-17399)*
Vigo Importing Company ....C....... 813 884-3491
Tampa *(G-18247)*

FOOD PRDTS, WHOLESALE: Spices & Seasonings

El Sabor Spices Inc ....F....... 305 691-2300
Miami *(G-9507)*

FOOD PRDTS, WHOLESALE: Sugar, Refined

Evergreen Sweeteners Inc ....F....... 954 381-7776
Hollywood *(G-5818)*

FOOD PRDTS, WHOLESALE: Water, Distilled

Ultra-Pure Bottled Water Inc ....F....... 281 731-0258
North Miami *(G-11660)*

FOOD PRDTS, WHOLESALE: Water, Mineral Or Spring, Bottled

Aqua Pure LLC ....G.... 407 521-3055
Orlando *(G-12484)*

FOOD PRDTS: Animal & marine fats & oils

Conchita Foods Inc ....D.... 305 888-9703
Medley *(G-8633)*
Darling Ingredients Inc ....G.... 904 964-8083
Starke *(G-16892)*
Darling Ingredients Inc ....G.... 407 856-7667
Orlando *(G-12649)*
Darling Ingredients Inc ....G.... 863 425-0065
Tampa *(G-17589)*
Darling Ingredients Inc ....G.... 239 693-2300
Fort Myers *(G-4425)*
Griffin Industries LLC ....E.... 407 857-5474
Orlando *(G-12789)*
Valley Proteins (de) Inc ....D.... 704 718-6568
Jacksonville *(G-6891)*
Valley Proteins (de) Inc ....D.... 910 282-7900
Mulberry *(G-11140)*

FOOD PRDTS: Box Lunches, For Sale Off Premises

J Squared Management II LLC ....F.... 813 373-5359
Tampa *(G-17799)*

FOOD PRDTS: Bread Crumbs, Exc Made In Bakeries

Quality Bakery Products LLC ....G.... 954 779-3663
Fort Lauderdale *(G-4189)*

FOOD PRDTS: Butter, Renovated & Processed

Belgium Co Inc ....F.... 407 957-1886
Saint Cloud *(G-15644)*

FOOD PRDTS: Cheese Curls & Puffs

Super-Pufft Snacks Usa Inc ....E.... 905 564-1180
Perry *(G-14314)*

FOOD PRDTS: Chili Pepper Or Powder

Shiloh Import/Export LLC ....G.... 404 514-4109
Tamarac *(G-17368)*

FOOD PRDTS: Citrus Pulp, Dried

Citrus World Services Inc ....F.... 863 676-1411
Lake Wales *(G-7505)*
Cvista LLC ....E.... 813 405-3000
Riverview *(G-15269)*

FOOD PRDTS: Coffee

Allcoffee LLC ....G.... 305 685-6856
Opa Locka *(G-12285)*
Aroma Coffee Service Inc ....G.... 239 481-7262
Fort Myers *(G-4367)*
Babys Coffee LLC ....G.... 305 744-9866
Key West *(G-7178)*
C&D Purveyors Inc ....G.... 305 562-8541
Miami *(G-9294)*
Clr Roasters LLC ....E.... 305 591-0040
Miami *(G-9365)*
De Luna Coffee Intl Inc ....G.... 850 478-6371
Pensacola *(G-14126)*
Distribuidora Giorgio Usa LLC ....F.... 305 685-6366
Opa Locka *(G-12307)*
Grand Havana Inc ....G.... 305 297-2207
Miami Beach *(G-10674)*
Javalution Coffee Company ....F.... 954 568-1747
Fort Lauderdale *(G-4077)*
List + Beisler Corp ....E.... 646 866-6960
Miami *(G-9898)*
Melitta North America Inc ....D.... 727 535-2111
Clearwater *(G-1779)*
Mercers Fresh Roasted Coffees ....G.... 941 286-7054
Punta Gorda *(G-15214)*
Potters Coffee Company ....G.... 850 525-1793
Pensacola *(G-14235)*
Rae Launo Corporation ....G.... 813 242-4281
Valrico *(G-18524)*
Royal Cup Inc ....G.... 813 664-8902
Tampa *(G-18070)*
Royal Cup Inc ....G.... 850 436-4435
Pensacola *(G-14254)*
Sergeant Bretts Coffee LLC ....G.... 561 451-0048
Coconut Creek *(G-2094)*
Ste-Ro Inc ....G.... 754 234-1789
Pompano Beach *(G-14869)*
Whole Coffee Company LLC ....D.... 786 364-4444
Miami *(G-10604)*

FOOD PRDTS: Coffee Extracts

Dupuy Silo Facility LLC ....C.... 904 899-7200
Jacksonville *(G-6337)*

FOOD PRDTS: Coffee Roasting, Exc Wholesale Grocers

Burke Brands LLC ....F.... 305 249-5628
Miami *(G-9285)*
Coffee Unlimited LLC ....F.... 305 685-6366
Opa Locka *(G-12302)*
Conali Express Corp ....G.... 954 531-9573
Fort Lauderdale *(G-3914)*
Espresso Disposition Corp 1 ....D.... 305 594-9062
Miami *(G-9536)*
Gold Coffee Roasters Inc ....F.... 561 746-8110
Jupiter *(G-7050)*
Haven Coffee Roasters LLC ....G.... 863 251-9619
Winter Haven *(G-19327)*
J M Smucker Company ....G.... 305 594-2886
Medley *(G-8674)*
Kraft Heinz Foods Company ....G.... 904 632-3400
Jacksonville *(G-6544)*
Latitude 235 Coffee and Tea ....F.... 941 556-2600
Sarasota *(G-16250)*
Melitta Usa Inc ....D.... 727 535-2111
Clearwater *(G-1780)*
Naviera Coffee Mills Inc ....E.... 813 248-2521
Tampa *(G-17934)*
New Dawn Coffee Company ....G.... 727 321-5155
Saint Petersburg *(G-15865)*
Rcr Coffee Company Inc ....E.... 813 248-6264
Tampa *(G-18041)*

FOOD PRDTS: Coffee Substitutes

Ilex Organics LLC ....F.... 386 566-3826
Edgewater *(G-3625)*

FOOD PRDTS: Cooking Oils, Refined Vegetable, Exc Corn

Grease TEC Holding LLC ....G.... 352 742-2440
Tavares *(G-18339)*

FOOD PRDTS: Corn Chips & Other Corn-Based Snacks

Pepsico Inc ....G.... 800 433-2652
Deerfield Beach *(G-2885)*
Specialty Food Group LLC ....G.... 305 392-5000
Doral *(G-3509)*

FOOD PRDTS: Dessert Mixes & Fillings

Body LLC ....F.... 850 888-2639
Saint Petersburg *(G-15725)*

FOOD PRDTS: Dips, Exc Cheese & Sour Cream Based

Red Diamond Salsa LLC ....G.... 813 672-7707
Wimauma *(G-19222)*
Salsa Cuba Inc ....G.... 305 993-9757
Hialeah *(G-5610)*
Salsa Pembroke Pines Inc ....E.... 954 461-0532
Pembroke Pines *(G-14058)*
Salsa Three Inc ....G.... 954 990-2223
Plantation *(G-14548)*
Sheas Salsa LLC ....G.... 954 371-7781
Wellington *(G-18731)*

FOOD PRDTS: Dough, Pizza, Prepared

Classic Pizza Crusts Inc ....G.... 954 570-8383
Pompano Beach *(G-14636)*

FOOD PRDTS: Doughs, Frozen Or Refrig From Purchased Flour

Burris Investment Group Inc ....E.... 850 623-3845
Pensacola *(G-14110)*
Hom/Ade Food Sales Inc ....G.... 850 623-3845
Bagdad *(G-298)*

FOOD PRDTS: Dressings, Salad, Raw & Cooked Exc Dry Mixes

Mizkan America Inc ....F.... 863 956-0391
Lake Alfred *(G-7333)*

FOOD PRDTS: Dried & Dehydrated Fruits, Vegetables & Soup Mix

Conchita Foods Inc ....D.... 305 888-9703
Medley *(G-8633)*
Culinary Concepts Inc ....E.... 407 228-0069
Orlando *(G-12635)*
Ferris Groves ....G.... 352 860-0366
Floral City *(G-3766)*
Green Leaf Foods LLC ....G.... 305 308-9167
Miramar *(G-11001)*
Kerry Inc ....G.... 813 359-5181
Plant City *(G-14444)*
Mastertaste Inc ....G.... 813 754-7392
Plant City *(G-14446)*
Presage Analytics Inc ....G.... 800 309-1704
Bonita Springs *(G-849)*
Story Citrus Inc ....E.... 863 638-1619
Lake Wales *(G-7522)*

FOOD PRDTS: Edible fats & oils

Ventura Foods LLC ....G.... 772 878-1400
Port Saint Lucie *(G-15161)*

FOOD PRDTS: Flavored Ices, Frozen

Phillys Famous Water Ice Inc ....C.... 813 248-8644
Tampa *(G-17990)*

FOOD PRDTS: Flour & Other Grain Mill Products

Change This World ....G.... 407 900-8840
Orlando *(G-12575)*
Dennis Hernandez & Assoc PA ....G.... 813 470-4545
Tampa *(G-17599)*
Shining Tree Inc ....F.... 855 688-7987
Wellington *(G-18732)*

FOOD PRDTS: Flour Mixes & Doughs

Big L Brands Inc ....F.... 888 552-9768
Boca Raton *(G-447)*

FOOD PRDTS: Freeze-Dried Coffee

Coca-Cola Company ....G.... 407 358-6758
Apopka *(G-124)*

FOOD PRDTS: Fresh Vegetables, Peeled Or Processed

Stripping Alpaca LLC ....F.... 207 208-9687
Miami Beach *(G-10717)*

FOOD PRDTS: Fruit Juices

Allapattah Industries Inc ....E.... 305 324-5900
Miami *(G-9116)*
Bru Bottling Inc ....G.... 561 324-5053
Juno Beach *(G-6977)*
Cebev LLC ....G.... 918 830-4417
Boca Raton *(G-475)*
Corines Frsh Fruits/Vegetbles ....G.... 352 708-6247
Clermont *(G-1955)*
Country Frits Juices Nurs Corp ....G.... 786 302-8487
Miami *(G-9408)*
Cutrale Citrus Juices USA Inc ....B.... 352 728-7800
Leesburg *(G-8149)*
Grand Products International ....G.... 386 736-3528
Deland *(G-2981)*
Healtheintentions Inc ....G.... 954 394-8867
Miami *(G-9693)*
King Brands LLC ....E.... 239 313-2057
Fort Myers *(G-4511)*
Orchid Island Juice Co Inc ....D.... 772 465-1122
Fort Pierce *(G-4727)*
Raw Foods International Llc ....F.... 305 856-1991
Coral Gables *(G-2190)*
Southern Grdns Ctrus Hldg Corp ....G.... 863 983-8121
Clewiston *(G-1986)*

FOOD PRDTS: Fruits & Vegetables, Pickled

Pickled Art Inc ....G....... 954 635-7370
Fort Lauderdale *(G-4167)*
Pickles Plus ....G....... 941 661-6139
North Port *(G-11747)*

FOOD PRDTS: Granola & Energy Bars, Nonchocolate

Mauer Sports Nutrition Inc ....G....... 888 609-2489
Fort Myers *(G-4524)*

FOOD PRDTS: Honey

Bees Brothers LLC ....G....... 305 529-5789
Coral Gables *(G-2126)*

FOOD PRDTS: Ice, Blocks

Nucycle Energy of Tampa LLC ....E....... 813 848-0509
Plant City *(G-14450)*
Reddy Ice Corporation ....F....... 850 433-2191
Pensacola *(G-14251)*

FOOD PRDTS: Ice, Cubes

Fanning Springs Ice Company ....G....... 352 463-1999
Old Town *(G-12196)*

FOOD PRDTS: Instant Coffee

Dna Brands Inc ....G....... 561 654-5722
Lauderdale By The SE *(G-8084)*
Kraken Koffee LLC ....G....... 833 546-3725
Coral Gables *(G-2169)*
Productos Las Delicias Inc ....G....... 305 760-4223
Hialeah *(G-5577)*

FOOD PRDTS: Juice Pops, Frozen

Frio Distributors Inc ....F....... 813 567-1493
Plant City *(G-14433)*
Guanabana & Co LLC ....F....... 904 891-5256
Jacksonville *(G-6456)*

FOOD PRDTS: Macaroni Prdts, Dry, Alphabet, Rings Or Shells

Termine Ravioli Manufacturing ....F....... 954 983-3711
Hollywood *(G-5923)*

FOOD PRDTS: Macaroni, Noodles, Spaghetti, Pasta, Etc

First Grade Food Corporation ....E....... 813 886-6118
Tampa *(G-17666)*
Jo MO Enterprises Inc ....G....... 708 599-8098
Boca Raton *(G-582)*
Lillys Gstrnmia Itlana Fla Inc ....G....... 305 655-2111
Hallandale Beach *(G-5198)*

FOOD PRDTS: Malt

Florida Brewery Inc ....E....... 863 965-1825
Auburndale *(G-242)*
Great Western Malting Co ....D....... 360 991-0888
Plant City *(G-14437)*

FOOD PRDTS: Mixes, Bread & Bread-Type Roll

Majesty Foods LLC ....E....... 305 817-1888
Hialeah *(G-5497)*

FOOD PRDTS: Mixes, Salad Dressings, Dry

Cranco Industries Inc ....G....... 321 690-2695
Rockledge *(G-15399)*

FOOD PRDTS: Mixes, Sauces, Dry

Sunshine Packing & Noodle Co ....G....... 904 355-7561
Jacksonville *(G-6826)*

FOOD PRDTS: Mixes, Seasonings, Dry

Everglades Foods Inc ....G....... 863 655-2214
Sebring *(G-16689)*
My Familys Seasonings LLC ....F....... 863 698-7968
Clearwater *(G-1798)*

FOOD PRDTS: Noodles, Uncooked, Packaged W/Other Ingredients

Massimo & Umberto Inc ....G....... 954 993-0842
Dania Beach *(G-2469)*
Strumba Media LLC ....G....... 800 948-4205
Miami *(G-10423)*

FOOD PRDTS: Nuts & Seeds

Papa Johns Peanuts Inc ....E....... 904 389-2511
Jacksonville *(G-6656)*
Veronicas Health Crunch LLC ....G....... 352 409-1124
Freeport *(G-4853)*

FOOD PRDTS: Oils & Fats, Marine

Openwater Seafood LLC ....G....... 407 440-0656
Orlando *(G-13026)*

FOOD PRDTS: Olive Oil

Bella Blsmic Pressed Olive Inc ....G....... 941 505-1707
Punta Gorda *(G-15194)*
Bella Blsmic Pressed Olive Inc ....E....... 941 249-3571
Punta Gorda *(G-15195)*
Estero FL ....G....... 239 289-9511
Estero *(G-3688)*
Miami Oliveoil & Beyond Llc ....G....... 954 632-2762
Doral *(G-3436)*
Olive 30a Oil Inc ....G....... 850 909-0099
Inlet Beach *(G-6077)*
Olive Amelia LLC ....G....... 904 310-3603
Fernandina Beach *(G-3746)*
Olive Naples Oil Company ....E....... 239 596-3000
Naples *(G-11351)*
Olive Oil Co of Fort Myers ....G....... 239 821-4630
Naples *(G-11352)*
Olive Tree II ....G....... 813 991-8781
Wesley Chapel *(G-18755)*
Ormond Beach Olive Oil ....G....... 386 333-9236
Ormond Beach *(G-13390)*
Tomatoes & Olive Oil LLC ....G....... 941 822-9709
Venice *(G-18580)*
United Oil Packers Inc ....E....... 305 687-6457
Miami *(G-10537)*
Vigo Importing Company ....C....... 813 884-3491
Tampa *(G-18247)*

FOOD PRDTS: Olives, Brine, Bulk

Filthy Food LLC ....D....... 786 916-5556
Miami *(G-9567)*

FOOD PRDTS: Pasta, Rice/Potatoes, Uncooked, Pkgd

Jo MO Enterprises Inc ....G....... 708 599-8098
Boca Raton *(G-582)*
Lillys Gstrnmia Itlana Fla Inc ....G....... 305 655-2111
Hallandale Beach *(G-5198)*
Nex-Xos Worldwide LLC ....F....... 305 433-8376
Hollywood *(G-5882)*

FOOD PRDTS: Pasta, Uncooked, Packaged With Other Ingredients

Brefaros Nobile Food LLC ....E....... 305 621-0074
Miami Lakes *(G-10771)*

FOOD PRDTS: Peanut Oil, Cake & Meal

Hawks Nuts Inc ....F....... 813 872-0900
Tampa *(G-17747)*

FOOD PRDTS: Popcorn, Unpopped

Barnard Nut Company Inc ....D....... 305 836-9999
Miami *(G-9221)*

FOOD PRDTS: Potato & Corn Chips & Similar Prdts

Frito-Lay North America Inc ....G....... 407 295-1810
Orlando *(G-12766)*
Kerry Consulting Corp ....F....... 561 364-9969
Boynton Beach *(G-926)*
Mio Gourment Products LLC ....F....... 305 219-0253
Hialeah *(G-5520)*
Pretz Snacks Corp ....G....... 718 869-2762
Doral *(G-3470)*
R & S Snacks LLC ....G....... 954 839-5482
Port Saint Lucie *(G-15133)*
Rap Snacks Inc ....G....... 305 926-9594
Miami *(G-10239)*

FOOD PRDTS: Potatoes, Fresh Cut & Peeled

Santos Frozen Foods Inc ....F....... 813 875-4901
Tampa *(G-18081)*

FOOD PRDTS: Poultry Sausage, Lunch Meats/Other Poultry Prdts

E&M Innovative Forager LLC ....E....... 954 923-0056
Hallandale Beach *(G-5182)*
Premium Quality Meats Inc ....G....... 239 309-4418
Miramar *(G-11029)*

FOOD PRDTS: Poultry, Processed, Frozen

Asian Food Solutions Inc ....E....... 888 499-6888
Oviedo *(G-13414)*
International Fd Solutions Inc ....E....... 888 499-6888
Oviedo *(G-13440)*

FOOD PRDTS: Preparations

4714 Foods Inc ....G....... 813 787-8911
Tampa *(G-17374)*
Abraaham Rosa Seasonings Inc ....G....... 386 453-4827
Deland *(G-2952)*
Adelheidis Commercial Inc ....G....... 239 384-8642
Naples *(G-11149)*
Al-Rite Fruits and Syrups Inc ....G....... 305 652-2540
Miami *(G-9099)*
Alnoor Import Inc ....G....... 954 683-9897
Plantation *(G-14488)*
Amaranth Lf Sciences Phrm Inc ....F....... 561 756-8291
Boca Raton *(G-419)*
ARA Food Corporation ....D....... 305 592-5558
Miami *(G-9160)*
Argen Foods ....G....... 305 884-0037
Medley *(G-8612)*
Aztlan Foods Corp ....E....... 786 202-8301
Medley *(G-8618)*
Baby Food Chef LLC ....G....... 305 335-5990
Hollywood *(G-5781)*
Best Brand Bottlers Inc ....F....... 941 755-1941
Sarasota *(G-16182)*
Bio-Revival LLC ....F....... 561 667-3990
Jupiter *(G-7009)*
Blue Stone Usa LLC ....F....... 305 494-1141
Coral Gables *(G-2127)*
C & E Innovative MGT LLC ....G....... 727 408-5146
Clearwater *(G-1619)*
Cacao Fruit Company ....G....... 954 449-8704
Weston *(G-19114)*
Captain Foods Inc ....G....... 386 428-5833
New Smyrna Beach *(G-11530)*
Carvalho Naturals LLC ....G....... 813 833-8229
Tampa *(G-17511)*
Catalina Finer Food Corp ....E....... 813 872-6359
Tampa *(G-17515)*
CFM&d LLC ....G....... 772 220-8938
Stuart *(G-16922)*
Champion Nutrition Inc ....G....... 954 233-3300
Sunrise *(G-17105)*
Charles Bryant Enterprises ....G....... 850 785-3604
Panama City *(G-13879)*
Coco Lopez Inc ....G....... 954 450-3100
Miramar *(G-10980)*
Conagra Brands Inc ....G....... 904 417-0964
Elkton *(G-3648)*
Culinary Concepts Inc ....E....... 407 228-0069
Orlando *(G-12635)*
Delicae Gourmet LLC ....G....... 727 942-2502
Tarpon Springs *(G-18293)*
Dinner Belle Inc ....G....... 747 210-6284
Lauderhill *(G-8108)*
Dole ....G....... 305 925-7900
Doral *(G-3331)*
Dolmar Foods Inc ....F....... 262 303-6026
Belleview *(G-368)*
Early Foods LLC ....G....... 850 791-3319
Pensacola *(G-14136)*
Easy Foods Inc ....C....... 321 300-1104
Kissimmee *(G-7241)*
Egg Roll Skins Inc ....F....... 305 836-0571
Hialeah *(G-5391)*
Encompass Mktg & Dev Group Inc ....G....... 407 420-7777
Orlando *(G-12711)*

PRODUCT

Evergreen Sweeteners Inc ....F 305 835-6907
Miami *(G-9541)*
Fathers Table LLC ....C 407 324-1200
Sanford *(G-16045)*
Flavorworks Inc ....E 561 588-8246
West Palm Beach *(G-18873)*
Floribbean Inc ....G 844 282-8459
Miami *(G-9579)*
Florida Algae LLC ....G 954 213-2693
Fort Lauderdale *(G-3999)*
Frito-Lay North America Inc ....G 407 295-1810
Orlando *(G-12766)*
G & G Latin Business Inc ....G 954 385-8085
Weston *(G-19129)*
GA Fd Svcs Pinellas Cnty LLC ....E 239 693-5090
Fort Myers *(G-4465)*
Galloway Foods Inc ....G 305 670-7600
Coral Gables *(G-2148)*
Greenes Reserve Inc ....F 954 304-0791
Ocala *(G-11962)*
Handal Foods LLC ....G 954 753-0649
Coral Springs *(G-2251)*
Hispanic Certified Foods Inc ....G 305 772-6815
Pompano Beach *(G-14723)*
Jenard Fresh Incorporated ....E 407 851-9432
Orlando *(G-12855)*
K and G Food Services LLC ....G 954 857-9283
West Palm Beach *(G-18917)*
Kerry Inc ....G 813 359-5182
Plant City *(G-14443)*
Kulfi LLC ....E 855 488-4273
Boca Raton *(G-593)*
L & A Quality Products Inc ....G 305 326-9300
Miami *(G-9834)*
Lifeco Foods North America ....G 321 348-5896
Winter Garden *(G-19274)*
McM Food Corp ....G 305 885-9254
Medley *(G-8685)*
Mestizo Foods LLC ....C 352 414-4900
Ocala *(G-11998)*
Mobile Meals ....G 813 907-6325
Tampa *(G-17913)*
Mr Bills Fine Foods ....G 727 581-9850
Clearwater *(G-1794)*
Nana Foods Inc ....G 407 363-7183
Orlando *(G-12989)*
Natures Heathy Gourmet ....E 772 873-0180
Port St Lucie *(G-15176)*
New Hope Sugar Company ....G 561 366-5120
West Palm Beach *(G-18963)*
Nutrifusion LLC ....F 404 240-0030
Naples *(G-11347)*
Nutritious You LLC ....G 941 203-5203
Sarasota *(G-16527)*
Oakbrook Sales Inc ....F 800 773-0979
Boca Raton *(G-652)*
OH Catering Inc ....G 305 903-9271
Miami *(G-10092)*
Organic Amazon Corp ....G 305 365-7811
Key Biscayne *(G-7161)*
Paca Foods LLC ....E 813 628-8228
Tampa *(G-17967)*
Plantain Products Company ....E 800 477-2447
Miami *(G-10168)*
Prana Organic Plant Oils Inc ....G 216 288-2054
Tavernier *(G-18362)*
Prege ....G 954 908-1535
Fort Lauderdale *(G-4174)*
Prima Food Corp ....E 954 788-0411
Pompano Beach *(G-14812)*
Qsrr Corporation ....G 305 322-9867
Hallandale Beach *(G-5205)*
Radchen USA Inc ....G 786 270-7628
Doral *(G-3479)*
Respect Foods ....G 561 557-2832
Palm Beach Gardens *(G-13622)*
Rj Foods ....G 863 425-3282
Mulberry *(G-11134)*
Royal Cup Inc ....G 813 664-8902
Tampa *(G-18070)*
Sage Imports Corp ....G 305 962-0631
Coral Gables *(G-2192)*
Savory Life LLC ....G 813 981-2022
Riverview *(G-15282)*
Sentry Food Solutions LLC ....G 904 482-1900
Jacksonville *(G-6761)*
SOS Food Lab LLC ....E 305 594-9933
Hialeah Gardens *(G-5699)*
Spice World LLC ....C 407 851-9432
Orlando *(G-13207)*
Sunrise Foods LLC ....G 904 613-4756
Jacksonville *(G-6823)*
Sunshine Peanut Company ....F 813 988-6987
Temple Terrace *(G-18380)*
Survivor Industries Inc ....E 805 385-5560
Doral *(G-3520)*
Sweet Additions LLC ....F 561 472-0178
Palm Beach Gardens *(G-13630)*
T&S Kitchen and Bbq LLC ....G 863 608-6223
Lakeland *(G-7815)*
Tasteful Delight LLC ....F 305 879-6487
Lakeland *(G-7817)*
Tdr Food Distribution LLC ....G 561 860-7617
Orlando *(G-13243)*
Thunder Bay Foods Corporation ....F 727 943-0606
Oldsmar *(G-12271)*
Torro Foods LLC ....G 305 558-3212
Miami Lakes *(G-10871)*
Total Nutrition Technology LLC ....E 352 435-0050
Leesburg *(G-8178)*
Triton Seafood Co ....F 305 888-8999
Medley *(G-8742)*
Tys Hometown Cafe Bistro LLC ....G 786 208-1163
Miami *(G-10521)*
West Development Group LLC ....G 407 308-5020
Orlando *(G-13322)*
Wwwsureshotsidscom LLC ....G 850 906-0745
Tallahassee *(G-17348)*
Yfan LLC ....G 786 453-3724
Miami Lakes *(G-10883)*

FOOD PRDTS: Prepared Meat Sauces Exc Tomato & Dry

Hoerndler Inc ....G 239 643-2008
Naples *(G-11279)*
La Lechonera Products Inc ....F 305 635-2303
Miami *(G-9841)*

FOOD PRDTS: Prepared Seafood Sauces Exc Tomato & Dry

Destination Bvi II Inc ....G 850 699-9551
Destin *(G-3188)*

FOOD PRDTS: Raw cane sugar

Florida Crystals Food Corp ....A 561 366-5100
West Palm Beach *(G-18878)*
Okeelanta Corporation ....C 561 996-9072
South Bay *(G-16796)*
Organic Cane Company Inc ....G 561 385-4081
Stuart *(G-16984)*
Tru Cane Sugar Corp ....G 561 833-1731
West Palm Beach *(G-19070)*

FOOD PRDTS: Rice, Milled

Conchita Foods Inc ....D 305 888-9703
Medley *(G-8633)*
Deeja Foods Inc ....G 321 402-8300
Kissimmee *(G-7237)*
Florida Crystals Corporation ....D 561 655-6303
West Palm Beach *(G-18875)*
Florida Crystals Corporation ....C 561 515-8080
West Palm Beach *(G-18877)*
Florida Gold Foods LLC ....F 347 595-1983
Kissimmee *(G-7245)*

FOOD PRDTS: Rice, Packaged & Seasoned

Vigo Importing Company ....C 813 884-3491
Tampa *(G-18247)*

FOOD PRDTS: Salads

Brianas Salad LLC ....G 954 608-0953
Boca Raton *(G-465)*

FOOD PRDTS: Sandwiches

Axrdham Corp ....G 813 653-9588
Valrico *(G-18515)*
Deli Fresh Foods Inc ....F 305 652-2848
Miami *(G-9446)*
ME Thompson Inc ....G 904 356-6258
Jacksonville *(G-6587)*
ME Thompson Inc ....D 863 667-3732
Lakeland *(G-7749)*

FOOD PRDTS: Seasonings & Spices

Bavaria Corporation ....F 407 880-0322
Apopka *(G-115)*
Burma Spice Inc ....G 863 254-0960
Moore Haven *(G-11085)*
El Jaliciense Inc ....F 850 481-1232
Panama City *(G-13898)*
Flayco Products Inc ....E 813 879-1356
Tampa *(G-17668)*
Greek Island Spice Inc ....G 954 761-7161
Fort Lauderdale *(G-4029)*
Italian Rose Garlic Pdts LLC ....C 561 863-5556
Riviera Beach *(G-15336)*
Jayshree Holdings Inc ....E 352 429-1000
Groveland *(G-5098)*
Kenart Holdings Llc ....C 561 863-5556
Riviera Beach *(G-15340)*

FOOD PRDTS: Sorbets, Non-dairy Based

Buzz Pop Cocktails Corporation ....F 727 275-9848
Holiday *(G-5736)*

FOOD PRDTS: Soup Mixes

Major Products Company ....E 386 673-8381
Ormond Beach *(G-13384)*
RL Schreiber Inc ....D 954 972-7102
Fort Lauderdale *(G-4208)*

FOOD PRDTS: Soup Mixes, Dried

Flayco Products Inc ....E 813 879-1356
Tampa *(G-17668)*
Geneva Foods LLC ....F 407 302-4751
Sanford *(G-16055)*

FOOD PRDTS: Spices, Including Ground

Bijol and Spices Inc ....G 305 634-9030
Miami *(G-9245)*
Chili Produkt Kft ....E 954 655-4111
Wellington *(G-18713)*
El Sabor Spices Inc ....F 305 691-2300
Miami *(G-9507)*
Life Spice and Ingredients LLC ....E 708 301-0447
Palm Beach *(G-13557)*
McCormick & Company Inc ....G 904 247-7773
Jacksonville Beach *(G-6950)*
McCormick Restaurant Services ....F 561 706-5554
Boca Raton *(G-613)*
Oriental Packing Company Inc ....F 305 235-1829
Miami *(G-10117)*
RL Schreiber Inc ....D 954 972-7102
Fort Lauderdale *(G-4208)*
Sazon Inc ....E 305 591-9785
Doral *(G-3496)*

FOOD PRDTS: Spreads, Garlic

Joys International Foods Inc ....G 321 242-6520
Melbourne *(G-8855)*

FOOD PRDTS: Spreads, Sandwich, Salad Dressing Base

Los Atntcos Sndwich Cuban Cafe ....G 407 282-2322
Orlando *(G-12936)*

FOOD PRDTS: Starch, Liquid

Element Eliquid LLC ....F 754 260-5500
Miramar *(G-10988)*

FOOD PRDTS: Sugar

Evergreen Sweeteners Inc ....F 954 381-7776
Hollywood *(G-5818)*
Evergreen Sweeteners Inc ....F 407 323-4250
Sanford *(G-16042)*
Pantaleon Commodities Corp ....F 786 542-6333
Miami *(G-10139)*
Xylitol USA Inc ....G 303 991-1999
Riverview *(G-15288)*

FOOD PRDTS: Sugar, Cane

American Sugar Refining Inc ....G 561 962-8106
Boca Raton *(G-423)*
Atlantic Sugar Association ....F 561 996-6541
Belle Glade *(G-344)*
B and M Sugar Products LLC ....G 305 897-8427
Miami *(G-9208)*

Florida Crystal Refinery Inc..................G....... 561 366-5200
West Palm Beach *(G-18874)*
Florida Crystals Corporation................D....... 561 655-6303
West Palm Beach *(G-18875)*
Florida Crystals Corporation................C....... 561 366-5000
West Palm Beach *(G-18876)*
Florida Crystals Corporation................C....... 561 992-5635
South Bay *(G-16795)*
Florida Crystals Corporation................C....... 561 515-8080
West Palm Beach *(G-18877)*
Florida Sugar Distributors....................E....... 561 655-6303
West Palm Beach *(G-18880)*
Florida Sugar Farmers...........................F....... 863 983-7276
Clewiston *(G-1980)*
Merkavah International Inc.....................G....... 305 909-6798
Miami *(G-9981)*
Okeelanta Corporation..........................E....... 561 366-5100
West Palm Beach *(G-18971)*
Osceola Farms Co..................................A....... 561 924-7156
Pahokee *(G-13470)*

FOOD PRDTS: Sugar, Dry Cane Prdts, Exc Refined

Add-V LLC..G....... 305 496-2445
Lauderhill *(G-8099)*

FOOD PRDTS: Sugar, Ground

Flo Sun Land Corporation......................E....... 561 655-6303
Palm Beach *(G-13554)*
Osceola Farms Co..................................E....... 561 655-6303
Palm Beach *(G-13560)*
Osceola Farms Co..................................A....... 561 924-7156
Pahokee *(G-13470)*

FOOD PRDTS: Sugar, Raw Cane

Alvean Americas Inc...............................F....... 305 606-0770
Coral Gables *(G-2121)*
Atlantic Sugar Association.....................F....... 561 996-6541
Belle Glade *(G-344)*
Florida Crystals Corporation................D....... 561 655-6303
West Palm Beach *(G-18875)*
Florida Crystals Corporation................C....... 561 366-5000
West Palm Beach *(G-18876)*
Florida Crystals Corporation................C....... 561 992-5635
South Bay *(G-16795)*
Florida Crystals Corporation................C....... 561 515-8080
West Palm Beach *(G-18877)*
Okeelanta Corporation..........................E....... 561 366-5100
West Palm Beach *(G-18971)*
Sugar Cane Growers Coop Fla..............B....... 561 996-5556
Belle Glade *(G-351)*

FOOD PRDTS: Tapioca

Tapioca Fit...G....... 954 842-3924
Pembroke Pines *(G-14064)*

FOOD PRDTS: Tea

Grand Havana Inc...................................G....... 305 297-2207
Miami Beach *(G-10674)*
Mad At SAD LLC.....................................F....... 941 203-8854
Sarasota *(G-16495)*
Mother Kombucha LLC...........................F....... 727 767-0408
Saint Petersburg *(G-15860)*
New Dawn Coffee Company...................G....... 727 321-5155
Saint Petersburg *(G-15865)*
Royal Cup Inc...G....... 850 436-4435
Pensacola *(G-14254)*
Tata Tea Extractions Inc........................E....... 813 754-2602
Plant City *(G-14469)*
Twinlab Corporation...............................B....... 800 645-5626
Boca Raton *(G-761)*

FOOD PRDTS: Tortilla Chips

El Mira Sol Inc.......................................D....... 813 754-5857
Plant City *(G-14429)*

FOOD PRDTS: Tortillas

Carne Asada Tortilleria Nicas................G....... 305 221-7001
Miami *(G-9321)*
De Todos Tortillas Inc............................G....... 305 248-4402
Homestead *(G-5961)*
Easy Foods Inc..E....... 305 599-0357
Doral *(G-3339)*
Fritanga Y Tortilla Modra.......................G....... 305 649-9377
Miami *(G-9598)*
Ipac Inc...G....... 407 699-7507
Winter Springs *(G-19474)*
La Autentica Foods Inc...........................E....... 305 888-6727
Hialeah *(G-5481)*
La Chiquita Tortilla Mfr..........................E....... 407 251-8290
Orlando *(G-12884)*
La Real Foods Inc...................................E....... 305 232-6449
Miami *(G-9848)*
Tortilla Bay..G....... 941 778-3663
Holmes Beach *(G-5947)*
Tortilleria America Inc...........................G....... 239 462-2175
Fort Myers *(G-4633)*
Tortilleria Dona Chela............................G....... 941 953-4045
Sarasota *(G-16623)*
Tortilleria El Triunfo LLC.......................G....... 954 270-7832
Fort Lauderdale *(G-4287)*
Tortilleria Gallo De Oro..........................G....... 561 503-3751
Lake Worth *(G-7592)*
Tortilleria Gallo De Oro LLC..................G....... 561 818-7829
Stuart *(G-17035)*
Tortilleria La Rancherita........................G....... 941 747-7949
Bradenton *(G-1127)*
Tortilleria Lamexicana 7 Inc..................F....... 407 324-3100
Sanford *(G-16128)*

FOOD PRDTS: Vegetable Oil Mills, NEC

C P Vegetable Oil Inc.............................F....... 954 584-0420
Fort Lauderdale *(G-3879)*
Trujillo Oil Plant Inc...............................F....... 305 696-8701
Miami *(G-10510)*

FOOD PRDTS: Vegetables, Dehydrated Or Dried

Wedgworths Inc......................................F....... 561 996-2076
Lake Placid *(G-7495)*

FOOD PRDTS: Vegetables, Pickled

Florida International Firm Inc................G....... 305 450-5920
Sweetwater *(G-17209)*

FOOD PRDTS: Vinegar

Delarosa Real Foods LLC.......................D....... 718 333-0333
Lauderdale Lakes *(G-8085)*
Miami Oliveoil & Beyond Llc.................G....... 954 632-2762
Doral *(G-3436)*
Mizkan America Inc................................F....... 863 956-0391
Lake Alfred *(G-7333)*

FOOD PRDTS: Wheat gluten

Plant Theory LLC....................................G....... 305 672-5785
Miami Beach *(G-10702)*

FOOD PRODUCTS MACHINERY

Alexander Industries Inc.........................G....... 305 888-9840
Hialeah *(G-5277)*
Emerge Interactive Inc............................E....... 772 563-0570
Vero Beach *(G-18616)*
Gruenewald Mfg Co Inc..........................F....... 978 777-0200
Ocklawaha *(G-12081)*
Hoppin Pop Kettle Stop LLC...................G....... 502 220-2372
Jacksonville *(G-6479)*
Jbt Foodtech Citrus Systems.................D....... 863 683-5411
Lakeland *(G-7720)*
Jbt LLC..E....... 407 463-2045
Orlando *(G-12853)*
Jbt LLC..F....... 513 238-4218
Naples *(G-11295)*
John Bean Technologies Corp...............C....... 863 683-5411
Lakeland *(G-7722)*
John Bean Technologies Corp...............E....... 407 851-3377
Orlando *(G-12858)*
Mvp Group LLC.......................................F....... 786 600-4687
North Miami *(G-11647)*
Remco Industries International..............F....... 954 462-0000
Fort Lauderdale *(G-4201)*
Rice Machinery Supply Co Inc................F....... 305 620-2274
Miami *(G-10263)*
Sen-Pack Inc...E....... 386 763-3312
New Smyrna Beach *(G-11543)*
Stephen J Austin......................................G....... 941 780-7842
Nokomis *(G-11588)*
Thinking Foods Inc..................................G....... 305 433-8287
Miami *(G-10474)*

FOOD STORES: Cooperative

Poppin Box LLC.......................................G....... 904 484-7030
Saint Johns *(G-15680)*

FOOD STORES: Frozen Food &Freezer Plans, Exc Meat

Pizza Spice Packet LLC..........................G....... 718 831-7036
Boca Raton *(G-666)*

FOOD STORES: Grocery, Independent

El Mira Sol Inc.......................................D....... 813 754-5857
Plant City *(G-14429)*

FOOD WARMING EQPT: Commercial

International Food Eqp Inc.....................G....... 305 785-5100
Miami Springs *(G-10891)*

FOOTWEAR, WHOLESALE: Boots

Interntnal Tech Sltons Sup LLC..............G....... 305 364-5229
Doral *(G-3393)*

FOOTWEAR: Cut Stock

Aurum Enterprises LLC...........................G....... 561 921-5119
Miami Beach *(G-10646)*
Pitbull Tactical LLC.................................G....... 866 452-4708
Orlando *(G-13069)*

FORGINGS

American Professional Ir Work..............G....... 305 556-9522
Hialeah *(G-5294)*
Enstar Holdings (us) LLC.......................D....... 727 217-2900
Saint Petersburg *(G-15770)*
Grizzly Manufacturing Inc.......................E....... 386 755-0220
Lake City *(G-7360)*
Lubov Manufacturing Inc........................G....... 813 873-2640
Tampa *(G-17862)*
Nav-X LLC..E....... 954 978-9988
Fort Lauderdale *(G-4134)*
Profile Racing Inc.....................................E....... 727 392-8307
Saint Petersburg *(G-15891)*

FORGINGS: Aluminum

Bill Evans Aluminum Inc..........................G....... 352 400-1424
Lecanto *(G-8128)*
Lawrence Commercial Systems.............F....... 850 574-8723
Tallahassee *(G-17289)*
Nav-X LLC..E....... 954 978-9988
Fort Lauderdale *(G-4134)*
Sapa Prcsion Tubing Adrian Inc.............E....... 321 636-8147
Rockledge *(G-15446)*

FORGINGS: Anchors

Anchor & Docking Inc..............................G....... 239 770-2030
Cape Coral *(G-1379)*
Profast Usa Inc...F....... 305 827-7801
Miami Lakes *(G-10845)*

FORGINGS: Armor Plate, Iron Or Steel

Point Blank Enterprises Inc....................A....... 954 630-0900
Pompano Beach *(G-14801)*
Survival Armor Inc...................................E....... 239 210-0891
Fort Myers *(G-4620)*

FORGINGS: Automotive & Internal Combustion Engine

Scorpion Equity LLC................................E....... 352 512-0800
Ocala *(G-12043)*
Xcessive Inc...G....... 866 919-9527
Miami Lakes *(G-10882)*

FORGINGS: Construction Or Mining Eqpt, Ferrous

Masaka LLC..F....... 786 800-8337
Doral *(G-3426)*

FORGINGS: Engine Or Turbine, Nonferrous

Advanced Engine Tech LLC.....................G....... 727 744-2935
Clearwater *(G-1565)*

FORGINGS: Gear & Chain

Rosuca International LLC ......G....... 305 332-5572
Doral *(G-3490)*

FORGINGS: Iron & Steel

Project and Cnstr Wldg Inc ......F....... 239 772-9299
Cape Coral *(G-1458)*

FORGINGS: Mechanical Power Transmission, Ferrous

North Amrcn Prtection Ctrl LLC ......G....... 407 788-3717
Altamonte Springs *(G-58)*

FORMS HANDLING EQPT

New Market Enterprises Ltd ......F....... 484 341-8004
Palm Harbor *(G-13748)*

FORMS: Concrete, Sheet Metal

Dayton Superior Corporation ......G....... 407 859-4541
Orlando *(G-12657)*

FOUNDRIES: Aluminum

Broward Casting Foundry Inc ......E....... 954 584-6400
Fort Lauderdale *(G-3869)*
Cost Cast Aluminum Corp ......E....... 863 422-5617
Haines City *(G-5140)*
G & K Aluminum Inc ......F....... 772 283-1297
Stuart *(G-16943)*
Harberson Rv Pinellas LLC ......E....... 727 937-6176
Holiday *(G-5742)*
HP Preferred Ltd Partners ......F....... 407 298-4470
Orlando *(G-12813)*
Luv Enterprises Inc ......F....... 352 867-8440
Ocala *(G-11988)*
MSC Metal Fabrication ......G....... 954 344-8343
Coral Springs *(G-2292)*
Rebah Fabrication Inc ......F....... 407 857-3232
Orlando *(G-13120)*
Sapa Extrsons St Augustine LLC ......A....... 904 794-1500
Saint Augustine *(G-15604)*
Southern Die Casting Corp ......E....... 305 635-6571
Miami *(G-10385)*
Tarvin Mobile Home Service ......G....... 727 734-3400
Palm Harbor *(G-13765)*
West Coast Castings Inc ......F....... 941 753-2969
Bradenton *(G-1146)*

FOUNDRIES: Brass, Bronze & Copper

Florida Airboat Propeller ......G....... 863 324-1653
Winter Haven *(G-19320)*
Florida Machine & Casting Co ......G....... 561 655-3771
Riviera Beach *(G-15330)*
Hawver Aluminum Foundry Inc ......G....... 813 961-1497
Tampa *(G-17748)*
Henefelt Precision Products ......F....... 727 531-0406
Largo *(G-7969)*
PM Craftsman ......E....... 863 665-0815
Lakeland *(G-7768)*
Robert St Croix Sculpture Stu ......G....... 561 835-1753
West Palm Beach *(G-19021)*

FOUNDRIES: Gray & Ductile Iron

Maddox Foundry & Mch Works LLC ......E....... 352 495-2121
Archer *(G-210)*
Tld LLC ......G....... 813 927-7554
Tampa *(G-18191)*

FOUNDRIES: Iron

United States Fndry & Mfg Corp ......C....... 305 885-0301
Medley *(G-8748)*

FOUNDRIES: Nonferrous

Altis Aju Kingwood LLC ......G....... 305 338-5232
Miami *(G-9125)*
Cost Cast Aluminum Corp ......E....... 863 422-5617
Haines City *(G-5140)*
Flotech Inc ......D....... 904 358-1849
Jacksonville *(G-6406)*
J&N Keystone of Florida ......G....... 305 528-1677
Medley *(G-8675)*
Nav-X LLC ......E....... 954 978-9988
Fort Lauderdale *(G-4134)*
Southern Die Casting Corp ......E....... 305 635-6571
Miami *(G-10385)*
Tampa Brass and Aluminum Corp ......C....... 813 885-6064
Tampa *(G-18162)*

FOUNDRIES: Steel

Hardware Parts Corporation ......G....... 561 994-2121
Boca Raton *(G-556)*
Maddox Foundry & Mch Works LLC ......E....... 352 495-2121
Archer *(G-210)*

FOUNDRIES: Steel Investment

R B Casting Inc ......G....... 407 648-2005
Orlando *(G-13108)*

FOUNDRY MACHINERY & EQPT

Safetarp Corp ......D....... 904 824-7277
Saint Augustine *(G-15602)*

FOUNTAINS, METAL, EXC DRINKING

Aquatectonica LLC ......F....... 941 592-3071
Bradenton *(G-990)*
Architectural Fountains Inc ......G....... 727 323-6068
Saint Petersburg *(G-15708)*
Johnston Archtctral Systems In ......E....... 904 886-9030
Jacksonville *(G-6527)*
Waltzing Waters Inc ......G....... 239 574-5181
Cape Coral *(G-1494)*
Wesco Partners Inc ......E....... 941 484-8224
Sarasota *(G-16325)*

FOUNTAINS: Concrete

Aquatectonica LLC ......F....... 941 592-3071
Bradenton *(G-990)*
Architectural Fountains Inc ......G....... 727 323-6068
Saint Petersburg *(G-15708)*
Artistic Statuary Inc ......F....... 954 975-9533
Pompano Beach *(G-14602)*
Com Pac Filtration Inc ......E....... 904 356-4003
Jacksonville *(G-6279)*
Freeport Fountains LLC ......E....... 407 330-1150
Sanford *(G-16050)*

FOUNTAINS: Plaster Of Paris

Architectural Fountains Inc ......G....... 727 323-6068
Saint Petersburg *(G-15708)*

FRACTIONATION PRDTS OF CRUDE PETROLEUM, HYDROCARBONS, NEC

Kraton Chemical LLC ......C....... 904 928-8700
Jacksonville *(G-6546)*

FRAMES & FRAMING WHOLESALE

Artworks International ......G....... 561 833-9165
West Palm Beach *(G-18804)*
Chez Industries LLC ......F....... 386 698-4414
Crescent City *(G-2339)*

FRANCHISES, SELLING OR LICENSING

BCT International Inc ......E....... 305 563-1224
Fort Lauderdale *(G-3844)*
Ciao Group Inc ......E....... 347 560-5040
Boca Raton *(G-479)*
Matrix Packaging of Florida ......G....... 305 358-9696
Miami *(G-9956)*

FREIGHT FORWARDING ARRANGEMENTS

Custom Crate & Logistics Co ......G....... 954 527-5742
Fort Lauderdale *(G-3924)*
Wetherill Associates Inc ......C....... 800 773-0005
Miramar *(G-11060)*

FREIGHT FORWARDING ARRANGEMENTS: Foreign

Rosuca International LLC ......G....... 305 332-5572
Doral *(G-3490)*

FREIGHT TRANSPORTATION ARRANGEMENTS

Lift Aerospace Corp ......F....... 305 851-5237
Miami *(G-9890)*

FREON

Freon & Fabric ......G....... 386 801-5096
Deltona *(G-3171)*
Shot of Freon ......G....... 305 917-5893
Lehigh Acres *(G-8207)*

FRICTION MATERIAL, MADE FROM POWDERED METAL

ARC Group Worldwide Inc ......D....... 303 467-5236
Deland *(G-2959)*
Atlantic Central Entps Inc ......F....... 386 255-6227
Daytona Beach *(G-2630)*

FRITS

Fritz Duane L Sr Tre Frit ......G....... 727 576-1584
Pinellas Park *(G-14349)*

FRUITS & VEGETABLES WHOLESALERS: Fresh

Florida Flvors Cncentrates Inc ......G....... 561 775-5714
Palm Beach Gardens *(G-13591)*

FUEL ADDITIVES

Boostane LLC ......F....... 239 908-1615
Bonita Springs *(G-819)*
Fuel Solutions Distrs LLC ......G....... 305 528-3758
North Miami Beach *(G-11679)*
Mega Power ......F....... 813 855-6664
Largo *(G-8009)*
Purify Fuels Inc ......G....... 949 842-6159
Davie *(G-2577)*

FUEL TREATING

Bell Performance Inc ......F....... 407 831-5021
Longwood *(G-8262)*
Fuel Reformation Inc ......G....... 954 800-4289
Fort Lauderdale *(G-4015)*

FUEL: Rocket Engine, Organic

Aerojet Rocketdyne De Inc ......C....... 561 882-5150
Jupiter *(G-6996)*

FUELS: Diesel

Clean Energy ESb Inc ......E....... 202 905-6726
Coral Gables *(G-2131)*
Export Diesel LLC ......F....... 305 396-1943
Miami *(G-9547)*
Indian River Biodiesel LLC ......G....... 321 586-7670
West Palm Beach *(G-18903)*
New Energy Fuels LLC ......G....... 281 205-0153
Labelle *(G-7321)*
Renewable Energy Systems Inc ......G....... 727 522-0286
Pinellas Park *(G-14384)*

FUELS: Ethanol

Advanced Fuel Injection ......G....... 561 248-6793
Jupiter *(G-6993)*
Aero Fuel LLC ......G....... 352 728-2018
Leesburg *(G-8139)*
Agri-Source Fuels LLC ......E....... 352 521-3460
Pensacola *(G-14085)*
Ameri Food & Fuel Inc ......G....... 727 584-0120
Largo *(G-7892)*
America Marine & Fuel Inc ......G....... 239 261-3715
Naples *(G-11160)*
American Carbons Inc ......G....... 850 265-4214
Lynn Haven *(G-8428)*
Baa LLC ......F....... 954 292-9449
Miramar *(G-10972)*
Big Bend Fuel Inc ......E....... 727 946-8727
Gibsonton *(G-5027)*
Bio Fuel Professionals ......G....... 239 591-3835
Naples *(G-11188)*
Blue Biofuels Inc ......G....... 561 693-1943
Palm Beach Gardens *(G-13571)*
Body Fuel LLC ......G....... 386 566-1855
Port Orange *(G-15013)*
Caribbean Fuels Inc ......G....... 305 233-3016
Miami *(G-9316)*
Cfuel Energy Corp ......G....... 561 336-4084
Miami *(G-9346)*
Chadwick S Fuel Co Inc ......G....... 754 224-8773
Fort Lauderdale *(G-3894)*

(G-0000) Company's Geographic Section entry number

Coastal Fuels Mktg Inc..........G....... 941 722-7753
Palmetto *(G-13792)*
Collier Parkway Fuel LLC..........G....... 732 492-4791
Land O Lakes *(G-7851)*
Consolidated Forest Pdts Inc..........F....... 407 830-7723
Longwood *(G-8267)*
Consolidated Forest Pdts Inc..........G....... 407 830-7723
Perry *(G-14298)*
Costal Fuels Marketing..........G....... 904 358-6725
Jacksonville *(G-6295)*
Daleo Fuels Inc..........G....... 954 931-3331
Oakland Park *(G-11795)*
Douglas Fuel II Inc..........G....... 305 620-0707
Miami Gardens *(G-10737)*
Excel Fuel Inc..........G....... 727 547-5511
Saint Petersburg *(G-15774)*
Express Fuel Systems Inc..........G....... 904 525-4052
Jacksonville *(G-6375)*
Fast Fuel Corp..........G....... 786 251-0373
Hialeah *(G-5406)*
Fire Fly Fuels Inc..........G....... 941 404-6820
Sarasota *(G-16432)*
Fuel Connection..........G....... 305 354-8115
North Miami *(G-11639)*
Fuel Life 1 LLC..........G....... 954 652-1735
Weston *(G-19128)*
Fuel N Go LLC..........G....... 239 656-1072
Estero *(G-3690)*
Fuel Productions LLC..........G....... 904 342-7826
Saint Augustine *(G-15544)*
Fuel Solutions LLC..........G....... 813 969-2506
Tampa *(G-17697)*
Fuel U Fast Inc..........G....... 561 654-0212
Boca Raton *(G-541)*
Fuelmyschool..........G....... 407 952-1030
Windermere *(G-19227)*
Gaseous Fuel Systems Corp..........G....... 954 693-9475
Weston *(G-19130)*
Green Biofuels LLC..........F....... 305 639-3030
Miami *(G-9664)*
Green Fuel Systems LLC..........G....... 352 483-5005
Eustis *(G-3708)*
Green Marine Fuels Inc..........F....... 305 775-3546
Miami *(G-9668)*
Greenwave Biodiesel LLC..........G....... 239 682-7700
Fort Lauderdale *(G-4032)*
Kendall Fuel Inc..........G....... 305 270-7735
Miami *(G-9819)*
Largent Fuels USA LLC..........G....... 786 431-5981
Miami *(G-9859)*
Lee County Fuels Inc..........G....... 239 349-5322
Fort Myers *(G-4517)*
Liles Oil Company..........F....... 407 739-2083
Casselberry *(G-1509)*
Living Fuel Inc..........G....... 813 254-0777
Tampa *(G-17852)*
Mendez Fuel..........G....... 305 227-0470
Miami *(G-9973)*
Mobil Boat Fuel Inc..........G....... 941 718-3781
Bradenton *(G-1079)*
Montedana Fuels..........G....... 305 887-6754
Hialeah *(G-5525)*
Natures Fuel Inc..........G....... 407 808-4272
Orlando *(G-12993)*
On The Go Food & Fuel Inc..........F....... 727 815-0823
New Port Richey *(G-11506)*
Originclear Inc..........G....... 323 939-6645
Clearwater *(G-1822)*
Pentacles Energy GP LLC..........G....... 786 552-9931
Coral Gables *(G-2184)*
Phillips Energy Inc..........G....... 850 682-5127
Crestview *(G-2355)*
R & A Performance Fuel Inc..........G....... 954 237-9824
Pembroke Pines *(G-14055)*
Renewable Fuels Group LLC..........G....... 305 388-3028
Miami *(G-10253)*
Rhodes Brothers Miami Inc..........G....... 305 456-9682
Miami Springs *(G-10897)*
Romco Fuels Inc..........F....... 954 474-5392
Davie *(G-2586)*
Sab Fuels Inc..........G....... 786 213-3399
Sarasota *(G-16569)*
Safe Industries Inc..........F....... 321 639-8646
Rockledge *(G-15445)*
Sincere Fuel Inc..........G....... 954 433-3577
Miramar *(G-11044)*
Soul Fuel Inc..........G....... 407 448-6533
Orlando *(G-13200)*
South East Fuel LLC..........G....... 407 392-4668
Orlando *(G-13201)*
Southern Fuel Inc..........G....... 904 545-5163
Glen Saint Mary *(G-5039)*
Td Fuel Inc..........G....... 561 305-2059
Fort Lauderdale *(G-4274)*
United Fuel..........G....... 305 992-2923
Miami *(G-10536)*
US Fuels Inc..........F....... 254 559-1212
Rotonda West *(G-15460)*
Viesel Fuel LLC..........E....... 772 781-4300
Stuart *(G-17045)*
Wesley Chapel Fuel Inc..........G....... 813 907-9994
Wesley Chapel *(G-18764)*
Wf Fuel..........G....... 941 706-4953
Sarasota *(G-16638)*
Wise Gas Fuel Card LLC..........G....... 954 636-4291
Weston *(G-19178)*
World Fuel Cx LLC..........F....... 305 428-8000
Doral *(G-3551)*

FUELS: Gas, Liquefied

Nap Impex LLC..........G....... 954 589-2861
Miramar *(G-11020)*

FUELS: Jet

Atlantic Jet Center Inc..........G....... 321 255-7111
Melbourne *(G-8771)*
Jet Fuel Catering LLC..........G....... 954 804-1146
Pembroke Pines *(G-14043)*
Sellink Aviation Fuel Div LLC..........G....... 305 336-6627
Miami *(G-10321)*
Sheltair Daytona Beach LLC..........E....... 386 255-0471
Daytona Beach *(G-2713)*

FUELS: Oil

Otus Corp Intl LLC..........G....... 305 833-6078
Miami *(G-10122)*

FUNGICIDES OR HERBICIDES

Trans-Resources LLC..........A....... 305 933-8301
Sunny Isles Beach *(G-17082)*

FUR: Apparel

Wannagofast LLC..........G....... 850 585-5168
Destin *(G-3209)*

FURNACES & OVENS: Indl

Air Burners Inc..........F....... 772 220-7303
Palm City *(G-13639)*
Clarios LLC..........B....... 727 541-3531
Largo *(G-7922)*
Matthews International Corp..........C....... 407 886-5533
Apopka *(G-158)*
Pillar Inc..........G....... 904 545-4993
Jacksonville *(G-6672)*
Sardee Industries Inc..........E....... 407 295-2114
Orlando *(G-13163)*
Thermotech Systems Corporation..........G....... 407 290-6000
Orlando *(G-13254)*

FURNITURE & CABINET STORES: Cabinets, Custom Work

A A A Cabinets..........G....... 850 438-8337
Pensacola *(G-14075)*
Castor Inc..........G....... 813 254-1171
Tampa *(G-17514)*
Custom Cabinets SW Florida LLC..........G....... 239 415-3350
Fort Myers *(G-4420)*
Guyton Industries LLC..........E....... 772 208-3019
Indiantown *(G-6073)*
Italkraft LLC..........E....... 305 406-1301
Doral *(G-3396)*
McCabinet Inc..........F....... 727 608-5929
Largo *(G-8007)*
Schrappers Fine Cabinetry Inc..........F....... 561 746-3827
Jupiter *(G-7109)*

FURNITURE & CABINET STORES: Custom

Carsons Cabinetry and Design..........G....... 352 373-8292
Archer *(G-207)*
Kennedy Craft Cabinets Inc..........G....... 239 598-1566
Naples *(G-11304)*
Lioher Enterprise Corp..........G....... 305 685-0005
Miami Lakes *(G-10807)*

FURNITURE & FIXTURES Factory

American Technical Furn LLC..........G....... 866 239-4204
Holly Hill *(G-5755)*
England Trading Company LLC..........E....... 888 969-4190
Jacksonville *(G-6365)*
Ultima Design South Fla Inc..........F....... 305 477-9300
Medley *(G-8746)*

FURNITURE COMPONENTS: Porcelain Enameled

Famatel USA LLC..........G....... 754 217-4841
Dania *(G-2445)*

FURNITURE PARTS: Metal

Abraham George Inc..........F....... 850 523-0757
Tallahassee *(G-17211)*
MA Metal Fabricators Inc..........G....... 786 343-0268
Miami *(G-9931)*
Pac Seating Systems Inc..........D....... 772 286-6670
Palm City *(G-13669)*
S & S Metal and Plastics Inc..........E....... 904 731-4655
Jacksonville *(G-6742)*
Spicer Industries Inc..........F....... 352 732-5300
Ocala *(G-12057)*

FURNITURE STOCK & PARTS: Carvings, Wood

Cut Services LLC..........G....... 305 560-0905
Doral *(G-3317)*
Giovanni Art In Custom Furn..........G....... 954 698-1008
Deerfield Beach *(G-2831)*
Juan Pampanas Designs Inc..........G....... 305 573-7550
Miami *(G-9812)*

FURNITURE STOCK & PARTS: Chair Seats, Hardwood

Smittys Boat Tops and Mar Eqp..........G....... 305 245-0229
Homestead *(G-5993)*

FURNITURE STOCK & PARTS: Dimension Stock, Hardwood

Maggac Corporation..........G....... 561 439-2707
Lake Worth *(G-7567)*

FURNITURE STOCK & PARTS: Frames, Upholstered Furniture, Wood

Iverica Industrial Inc..........F....... 305 691-1659
Hialeah *(G-5458)*
Roorda Buiders Inc..........G....... 727 410-7776
Odessa *(G-12147)*

FURNITURE STOCK & PARTS: Hardwood

David R Nassivera Inc..........E....... 352 351-1176
Ocala *(G-11917)*
Stuart Stair & Furniture Mfg..........G....... 772 287-4097
Stuart *(G-17026)*

FURNITURE STORES

Alumatech Manufacturing Inc..........E....... 941 748-8880
Bradenton *(G-986)*
Closetmaid LLC..........B....... 352 401-6000
Orlando *(G-12591)*
Contemporary Interiors Inc..........E....... 352 620-8686
Ocala *(G-11907)*
Cordaroys Wholesale Inc..........G....... 352 332-1837
Gainesville *(G-4897)*
Custom Cabinets Inc..........F....... 941 366-0428
Sarasota *(G-16398)*
Florida Finisher Inc..........G....... 941 722-5643
Palmetto *(G-13799)*
Garcia Iron Works..........G....... 305 888-0080
Hialeah *(G-5425)*
Lakewood Manufacturing Co Inc..........C....... 443 398-5015
West Palm Beach *(G-18925)*
Rex Fox Enterprises Inc..........F....... 386 677-3752
Daytona Beach *(G-2704)*
The Natural Light Inc..........E....... 850 265-0800
Lynn Haven *(G-8440)*
Wall Bed Systems Inc..........G....... 419 738-5207
Clearwater *(G-1936)*
Werever Products Inc..........F....... 813 241-9701
Riverview *(G-15287)*

FURNITURE STORES: Cabinets, Kitchen, Exc Custom Made

R & R Designer Cabinets Inc ....G....... 954 735-6435
Oakland Park *(G-11834)*

FURNITURE STORES: Custom Made, Exc Cabinets

Southwest Woodwork Inc ....F....... 239 213-0126
Naples *(G-11411)*

FURNITURE STORES: Office

Altamonte Office Supply Inc................G....... 407 339-6911
Longwood *(G-8253)*
New Vision Furniture Inc......................G....... 305 562-9428
Opa Locka *(G-12346)*

FURNITURE STORES: Outdoor & Garden

TWN Industries Inc ....G....... 305 246-5717
Princeton *(G-15187)*

FURNITURE UPHOLSTERY REPAIR SVCS

Ards Awning & Upholstery Inc ....E....... 863 293-2442
Winter Haven *(G-19300)*
Jose Leal Enterprises Inc.....................D....... 305 887-9611
Hialeah *(G-5467)*

FURNITURE WHOLESALERS

Contemporary Interiors Inc...................E....... 352 620-8686
Ocala *(G-11907)*
Nordic Line Inc......................................E....... 561 338-5545
Boca Raton *(G-648)*
S&S Global Supply LLC ....G....... 786 529-4799
Hialeah *(G-5608)*
Shores Global LLC................................G....... 305 716-0848
Miami *(G-10340)*

FURNITURE, BARBER & BEAUTY SHOP

Classic Hardwood Design.....................G....... 850 232-6473
Molino *(G-11073)*

FURNITURE, CHURCH: Concrete

Helping Adlscnts Live Optmstcl............G....... 407 257-8221
Orlando *(G-12798)*

FURNITURE, HOUSEHOLD: Wholesalers

Glodea Store Corp ....G....... 888 400-4937
Jacksonville *(G-6439)*

FURNITURE, OUTDOOR & LAWN: Wholesalers

Advanced Sewing..................................G....... 954 484-2100
Fort Lauderdale *(G-3784)*
Well Traveled Imports Inc.....................F....... 904 261-5400
Amelia Island *(G-93)*

FURNITURE, WHOLESALE: Chairs

United Chair Industries LLC ....G....... 386 333-0800
Odessa *(G-12162)*

FURNITURE, WHOLESALE: Lockers

Broward Custom Woodwork LLC..........G....... 352 376-4732
Deerfield Beach *(G-2791)*
List Industries Inc.................................B....... 954 429-9155
Deerfield Beach *(G-2859)*
List Plymouth LLC ....E....... 954 429-9155
Deerfield Beach *(G-2861)*

FURNITURE, WHOLESALE: Restaurant, NEC

Raytash Inc..G....... 561 347-8863
Boca Raton *(G-681)*

FURNITURE, WHOLESALE: Waterbeds

Waterfall Industries Inc ....F....... 407 330-2003
Sanford *(G-16134)*

FURNITURE: Assembly Hall

Apollo Retail Specialists LLC ....B....... 813 712-2525
Tampa *(G-17428)*
I-Pop Inc..E....... 561 567-9000
West Palm Beach *(G-18900)*

FURNITURE: Backs & Seats, Metal Household

Tuuci LLC..C....... 305 634-5116
Hialeah *(G-5654)*

FURNITURE: Bar furniture

Design Furnishings Inc ....E....... 407 294-0507
Orlando *(G-12663)*

FURNITURE: Bean Bag Chairs

Cordaroys Wholesale Inc......................G....... 352 332-1837
Gainesville *(G-4897)*
E-Sea Rider LLC...................................G....... 727 863-3333
Holiday *(G-5739)*

FURNITURE: Bed Frames & Headboards, Wood

Saint Petersburg Cabinets Inc..............G....... 727 327-4800
Saint Petersburg *(G-15904)*

FURNITURE: Bedroom, Wood

Capitol Furniture Mfg LLC.....................G....... 954 485-5000
Boca Raton *(G-469)*

FURNITURE: Beds, Household, Incl Folding & Cabinet, Metal

Cadence Keen Innovations Inc.............G....... 561 249-2219
West Palm Beach *(G-18833)*
Mobilite Corporation..............................D....... 407 321-5630
Sanford *(G-16089)*
Murphy Bed USA Inc ....E....... 954 493-9001
Fort Lauderdale *(G-4127)*
Wall Bed Systems Inc...........................G....... 419 738-5207
Clearwater *(G-1936)*

FURNITURE: Box Springs, Assembled

Star Bedding Mfg Corp.........................E....... 305 887-5209
Hialeah *(G-5632)*

FURNITURE: Buffets

Grand Buffet..G....... 941 752-3388
Bradenton *(G-1052)*

FURNITURE: Cabinets & Filing Drawers, Office, Exc Wood

Cayman Nat Mfg & Installation ....D....... 954 421-1170
Deerfield Beach *(G-2798)*

FURNITURE: Cabinets & Vanities, Medicine, Metal

Gk Inc..E....... 215 223-7207
Fort Lauderdale *(G-4022)*

FURNITURE: Chairs & Couches, Wood, Upholstered

Andrews Warehouse Partnership ....G....... 954 524-3330
Fort Lauderdale *(G-3817)*
Capris Furniture Inds Inc ....C....... 352 629-8889
Ocala *(G-11893)*
Devon Chase & Company ....G....... 407 438-6466
Orlando *(G-12667)*

FURNITURE: Chairs, Dental

Boyd Industries Inc...............................D....... 727 561-9292
Clearwater *(G-1611)*

FURNITURE: Chairs, Household Upholstered

Design Furnishings Inc ....E....... 407 294-0507
Orlando *(G-12663)*
Design Systems South Inc....................G....... 850 293-1905
Pensacola *(G-14130)*
Jordan Brown Inc..................................G....... 904 495-0717
Saint Augustine *(G-15562)*
Pendulum One Inc ....G....... 561 844-8169
Riviera Beach *(G-15360)*

FURNITURE: Chairs, Household Wood

Blue Water Chairs Inc ....E....... 954 318-0840
Fort Lauderdale *(G-3860)*

FURNITURE: Chairs, Office Exc Wood

Systematix Inc.......................................E....... 850 983-2213
Milton *(G-10942)*

FURNITURE: Chairs, Office Wood

Camilo Office Furniture Inc...................D....... 305 261-5366
Miami *(G-9305)*
Pradere Manufacturing Corp ....F....... 305 823-0190
Hialeah *(G-5563)*

FURNITURE: Chests, Cedar

Cedar Fresh Home Products LLC ....G....... 305 975-8524
Miami *(G-9332)*

FURNITURE: Desks, Wood

S M I Cabinetry Inc................................E....... 407 841-0292
Orlando *(G-13152)*

FURNITURE: Fiberglass & Plastic

Arcadia Thrift LLC.................................G....... 863 993-2004
Arcadia *(G-199)*

FURNITURE: Frames, Box Springs Or Bedsprings, Metal

Mantua Manufacturing Co.....................G....... 813 621-3714
Tampa *(G-17878)*

FURNITURE: Garden, Exc Wood, Metal, Stone Or Concrete

Sole Inc ....G....... 305 513-2603
Doral *(G-3505)*

FURNITURE: Hospital

Custom Comfort Medtek LLC ....E....... 407 332-0062
Winter Park *(G-19398)*
Winco Mfg LLC.....................................D....... 352 854-2929
Ocala *(G-12076)*

FURNITURE: Hotel

Blue Leaf Hospitality Inc ....F....... 305 668-3000
Miami *(G-9261)*
Bryan Ashley Inc...................................E....... 954 351-1199
Deerfield Beach *(G-2793)*
Deepstream Designs Inc ....G....... 305 857-0466
Miami *(G-9444)*
Italian Cabinetry Inc..............................F....... 786 534-2742
Miami *(G-9774)*
Kron Designs LLC.................................G....... 954 941-0800
Fort Lauderdale *(G-4091)*
One World Resource LLC ....E....... 305 445-9199
Miami *(G-10105)*

FURNITURE: Household, Metal

Cramco Inc ....G....... 305 634-7500
Miami *(G-9409)*
J M Interiors Inc ....G....... 305 891-6121
North Miami *(G-11642)*
Jordan Brown Inc..................................G....... 904 495-0717
Saint Augustine *(G-15562)*
Suncoast Aluminum Furn Inc................E....... 239 267-8300
Fort Myers *(G-4615)*
Sungraf Inc ....F....... 954 456-8500
Hallandale Beach *(G-5216)*
Tuuci Worldwide ....G....... 305 634-5116
Hialeah *(G-5655)*
Tuuci Worldwide LLC ....C....... 305 634-5116
Miami *(G-10514)*

FURNITURE: Household, Upholstered On Metal Frames

Built LLC..G....... 813 512-6250
Tampa *(G-17489)*

FURNITURE: Household, Upholstered, Exc Wood Or Metal

Flexshopper LLC...................................E....... 561 922-6609
Boca Raton *(G-530)*
GLS Assoc Inc.......................................G....... 561 451-1999
Boca Raton *(G-546)*
Outpost 30a LLC ....F....... 850 909-0138
Inlet Beach *(G-6078)*

FURNITURE: Household, Wood

A A A Cabinets..G...... 850 438-8337
Pensacola *(G-14075)*
Ahus Inc..E....... 305 572-9052
Miami Gardens *(G-10732)*
Aj Originals Inc..G...... 954 563-9911
Fort Lauderdale *(G-3793)*
American Frame Furniture Inc..............G...... 305 548-3018
Miami *(G-9142)*
Annette M Wellington Hall Inc ....G...... 954 437-9880
Hollywood *(G-5772)*
Avrora Inc ....G...... 386 246-9112
Palm Coast *(G-13685)*
B C Cabinetry ....G...... 561 393-8937
Boca Raton *(G-436)*
Beaches Woodcraft Inc ....F....... 904 249-0785
Atlantic Beach *(G-217)*
Belle Isle Furniture LLC........................G...... 407 408-1266
Belle Isle *(G-356)*
Bon Vivant Interiors Inc........................E....... 305 576-8066
Opa Locka *(G-12296)*
Bpc LLC ....F....... 305 987-9517
Miami *(G-9272)*
Carsons Cabinetry and Design..............G...... 352 373-8292
Archer *(G-207)*
Contemporary Interiors Inc..................E....... 352 620-8686
Ocala *(G-11907)*
Cramco Inc ....G...... 305 634-7500
Miami *(G-9409)*
Creative Woodwork Miami Inc..............F....... 305 634-3100
Miami *(G-9411)*
Custom Beach Huts LLC........................G...... 305 439-3991
Coral Gables *(G-2135)*
Custom Cabinets Inc........................F....... 941 366-0428
Sarasota *(G-16398)*
Custom Mica Furniture Inc....................G...... 305 888-8480
Hialeah *(G-5359)*
Davila Woodworking Inc ....G...... 954 458-0460
Hallandale Beach *(G-5180)*
Design Systems South Inc....................G...... 850 293-1905
Pensacola *(G-14130)*
Dixie Workshop Inc........................G...... 352 629-4699
Ocala *(G-11922)*
Ecco Doors LLC..G...... 561 392-3533
Boynton Beach *(G-901)*
Elegant House Intl LLC........................G...... 954 457-8836
Hallandale *(G-5157)*
Fine Archtctral Mllwk Shutters ....F....... 954 491-2055
Fort Lauderdale *(G-3993)*
Furniture Concepts 2000 Inc..................G...... 954 946-0310
Pompano Beach *(G-14706)*
Furniture Design of Centl Fla................F....... 407 330-4430
Sanford *(G-16052)*
Genie Shelf ....G...... 305 213-4382
Miami *(G-9627)*
Gilmans Custom Furn & Cabinets.........F....... 352 746-3532
Lecanto *(G-8134)*
Glodea Store Corp ....G...... 888 400-4937
Jacksonville *(G-6439)*
Gulf South Distributors Inc..................F....... 850 244-1522
Fort Walton Beach *(G-4807)*
IB Furniture Inc..G...... 941 371-5764
Sarasota *(G-16463)*
Infinite Ret Design & Mfg Corp.............F....... 305 967-8339
Miami *(G-9741)*
J & S Cypress Inc..F....... 352 383-3864
Sorrento *(G-16787)*
J M Interiors Inc ....G...... 305 891-6121
North Miami *(G-11642)*
J T S Woodworking Inc ....G...... 561 272-7996
Delray Beach *(G-3094)*
Ken Clearys Two LLC ....F....... 727 573-0700
Clearwater *(G-1749)*
Lakewood Manufacturing Co Inc...........C....... 443 398-5015
West Palm Beach *(G-18925)*
Madison Millwork & Cabinet Co ....E....... 954 966-7551
Hollywood *(G-5868)*
Maggac Corporation........................G...... 561 439-2707
Lake Worth *(G-7567)*
Mantua Manufacturing Co.......................G...... 813 621-3714
Tampa *(G-17878)*
Manufacturing By Skema Inc.................G...... 954 797-7325
Davie *(G-2548)*
McCallum Cabinets Inc........................F....... 352 372-2344
Gainesville *(G-4957)*
Mica Visions Inc..G...... 727 712-3213
Clearwater *(G-1784)*
Mobius Business Group Inc ....F....... 239 274-8900
Fort Myers *(G-4535)*
Mr Mica Wood Inc ....F....... 561 278-5821
Delray Beach *(G-3109)*
N & N Investment Corporation..............E....... 954 590-3800
Pompano Beach *(G-14770)*
Nfjb Inc..E....... 954 771-1100
Fort Lauderdale *(G-4141)*
Noell Design Group Inc ....G...... 561 391-9942
Boca Raton *(G-646)*
Nosta Inc..G...... 305 634-1435
Miami *(G-10079)*
Perri Brothers and Associates ....G...... 305 887-8686
Medley *(G-8704)*
Pinellas Custom Cabinets Inc...............G...... 727 864-4263
Largo *(G-8027)*
PKolino LLC ....G...... 888 403-8992
Miami *(G-10167)*
Princeton Industries Inc........................E....... 954 344-9155
Margate *(G-8563)*
Raytash Inc..G...... 561 347-8863
Boca Raton *(G-681)*
Riverstone Snctary - Cbd - Inc..............G...... 954 473-1254
Fort Lauderdale *(G-4207)*
Rm Custom Woodcraft Inc....................G...... 786 355-7387
Miami *(G-10267)*
Rolu Woodcraft Inc..F....... 305 685-0914
Hialeah *(G-5605)*
Shelfgenie..G...... 877 814-3643
Naples *(G-11398)*
Silverline Furniture Corp.......................G...... 305 663-9560
Miami *(G-10349)*
Smith Products Co Inc ....F....... 386 325-4534
Palatka *(G-13492)*
Spacios Design Group Inc ....F....... 305 696-1766
Miami *(G-10393)*
Thomas Rley Artisans Guild Inc............E....... 239 591-3203
Naples *(G-11440)*
TPL Manufacturing Inc ....G...... 954 783-3400
Pompano Beach *(G-14889)*
Unlimited Cabinet Designs Inc ....F....... 954 923-3269
Hallandale *(G-5165)*
Via Cabinets Corp..G...... 407 633-1915
Orlando *(G-13301)*
Viking Kabinets Inc..E....... 305 238-9025
Cutler Bay *(G-2420)*
Waterfall Industries Inc ....F....... 407 330-2003
Sanford *(G-16134)*
Willson & Son Industry Inc ....G...... 954 972-5073
Margate *(G-8572)*
Winston & Sons Inc..G...... 954 562-1984
Tamarac *(G-17370)*
Woodcraft LLC..G...... 850 217-7757
Navarre *(G-11476)*
Woodcrafts By Angel Inc........................G...... 352 754-9335
Brooksville *(G-1293)*
Y F Leung Inc ....G...... 305 651-6851
North Miami Beach *(G-11714)*
Yonder Woodworks Inc ....G...... 561 547-5777
West Palm Beach *(G-19090)*

FURNITURE: Hydraulic Barber & Beauty Shop Chairs

Advanced Vacuum Systems LLC ....G...... 941 378-4565
Sarasota *(G-16334)*
Sustainable Casework Inds LLC ....G...... 954 980-6506
Deerfield Beach *(G-2920)*

FURNITURE: Institutional, Exc Wood

A & J Commercial Seating Inc..............F....... 352 288-2022
Summerfield *(G-17055)*
Allied Plastics Co Inc........................E....... 904 359-0386
Jacksonville *(G-6138)*
Antique & Modern Cabinets Inc.............E....... 904 393-9055
Jacksonville *(G-6158)*
Ashley Bryan International Inc ....E....... 954 351-1199
Deerfield Beach *(G-2780)*
Benchmark Design Group Inc ....F....... 904 246-5060
Jacksonville Beach *(G-6939)*
Contemporary Interiors Inc....................E....... 352 620-8686
Ocala *(G-11907)*
Divatti & Co LLC..G...... 786 354-1888
Miramar *(G-10985)*
Gt Grandstands Inc..E....... 813 305-1415
Plant City *(G-14438)*
Kron Designs LLC..G...... 954 941-0800
Fort Lauderdale *(G-4091)*

FURNITURE: Kitchen & Dining Room

Pastrana Prime LLC..F....... 407 470-9339
Orlando *(G-13052)*
Utopia Grilling LLC ....G...... 727 488-1355
New Port Richey *(G-11518)*

FURNITURE: Kitchen & Dining Room, Metal

Florida Custom Fabricators ....F....... 407 892-8538
Saint Cloud *(G-15650)*

FURNITURE: Lawn & Garden, Except Wood & Metal

Alumatech Manufacturing Inc................E....... 941 748-8880
Bradenton *(G-986)*
Armored Frog Inc..G...... 850 418-2048
Pensacola *(G-14091)*
Morning Star of Sarasota Inc ....G...... 941 371-0392
Sarasota *(G-16514)*

FURNITURE: Lawn & Garden, Metal

American Household Inc........................D....... 561 912-4100
Boca Raton *(G-422)*
Casual Tone Inc..F....... 941 722-5643
Palmetto *(G-13789)*
Dgp Enterprises Inc..F....... 941 729-2373
Sarasota *(G-16206)*
Florida Finisher Inc..G...... 941 722-5643
Palmetto *(G-13799)*
Got It Inc ....G...... 954 899-0001
Boca Raton *(G-550)*
Sunbeam Americas Holdings LLC ....C....... 561 912-4100
Boca Raton *(G-736)*
Trainor Metal Products Inc....................G...... 561 395-5520
Boca Raton *(G-754)*

FURNITURE: Lawn, Metal

Medallion Leisure Furniture..................E....... 305 626-0000
Miami *(G-9964)*
Metal Craft of Pensacola Inc.................E....... 850 478-8333
Pensacola *(G-14207)*

FURNITURE: Lawn, Wood

Lifetime Environmental Designs ....G...... 352 237-7177
Ocala *(G-11984)*

FURNITURE: Living Room, Upholstered On Wood Frames

Associated Interior Desgr Svc...............F....... 561 655-4926
West Palm Beach *(G-18805)*
Carlton Mfg Inc..G...... 352 465-2153
Dunnellon *(G-3594)*
Koki Interiors Furn Mfg Inc ....F....... 305 558-6573
Hialeah *(G-5475)*
Ruby Vanrum..G...... 850 643-5155
Bristol *(G-1203)*
Spring Oaks LLC..F....... 352 592-1150
Brooksville *(G-1276)*

FURNITURE: Mattresses & Foundations

Devon Chase & Company ....G...... 407 438-6466
Orlando *(G-12667)*
Rex Fox Enterprises Inc........................F....... 386 677-3752
Daytona Beach *(G-2704)*

FURNITURE: Mattresses, Box & Bedsprings

Blu Sleep Products LLC........................G...... 866 973-7614
Deerfield Beach *(G-2785)*
Diaz Brothers Corp ....G...... 305 364-4911
Hialeah *(G-5372)*
Leggett & Platt Incorporated.................D....... 954 846-0300
Sunrise *(G-17142)*
Murphy Bed USA Inc ....E....... 954 493-9001
Fort Lauderdale *(G-4127)*
Plushbeds Inc..G...... 888 449-5738
Boca Raton *(G-667)*
Savor Sleep LLC ....G...... 860 577-2867
Naples *(G-11393)*
Sleep International LLC........................E....... 813 247-5337
Tampa *(G-18108)*

FURNITURE: Mattresses, Innerspring Or Box Spring

Biscayne Bedding Intl LLC ....E....... 305 633-4634
Hialeah *(G-5327)*
Corsicana Bedding LLC ....E....... 863 519-5905
Bartow *(G-313)*

Zeno Furniture & Mat Mfg Co.................G....... 954 764-1212
Fort Lauderdale *(G-4335)*

FURNITURE: NEC

Asemblu Inc...F....... 800 827-4419
Hialeah *(G-5308)*
Nanni Usa LLC...G....... 305 450-4853
Coral Gables *(G-2180)*
Octametro LLC...G....... 305 715-9713
Doral *(G-3448)*
Safeguard of South Florid.......................G....... 561 499-7600
Delray Beach *(G-3137)*
SC Gastronomic Crew Inc.........................E....... 786 864-1212
Coral Gables *(G-2194)*
Smarte Carte Inc.......................................G....... 407 857-5841
Orlando *(G-13198)*

FURNITURE: Novelty, Wood

Yield Design..G....... 402 321-2196
Saint Augustine *(G-15640)*

FURNITURE: Office Panel Systems, Exc Wood

Avl Systems Inc...E....... 352 854-1170
Ocala *(G-11882)*

FURNITURE: Office Panel Systems, Wood

Engineered Equipment Corp.....................F....... 561 839-4008
West Palm Beach *(G-18862)*

FURNITURE: Office, Exc Wood

Advanced Furniture Svcs Inc...................F....... 850 390-3442
Pensacola *(G-14084)*
Allied Plastics Co Inc................................E....... 904 359-0386
Jacksonville *(G-6138)*
Bnb Business Systems Inc........................G....... 954 538-0669
Pembroke Pines *(G-14024)*
Buckeye Used Office Furn Inc..................G....... 727 457-5287
Largo *(G-7916)*
Cayman Manufacturing Inc........................E....... 954 421-1170
Deerfield Beach *(G-2797)*
Dons Cabinets and Woodworking..........F....... 727 863-3404
Hudson *(G-6022)*
Euroker LLC..G....... 305 477-0096
Doral *(G-3345)*
Gk Inc..E....... 215 223-7207
Fort Lauderdale *(G-4022)*
John Eric Madden......................................G....... 813 395-3314
Zephyrhills *(G-19524)*
Manning Company.......................................G....... 954 523-9355
Fort Lauderdale *(G-4111)*
New Vision Furniture Inc...........................G....... 305 562-9428
Opa Locka *(G-12346)*
Office Express Corp...................................F....... 786 503-6800
Miami *(G-10090)*
Sungraf Inc..F....... 954 456-8500
Hallandale Beach *(G-5216)*
Winston & Sons Inc....................................G....... 954 562-1984
Tamarac *(G-17370)*

FURNITURE: Office, Wood

Allied Plastics Co Inc................................E....... 904 359-0386
Jacksonville *(G-6138)*
Antique & Modern Cabinets Inc...............E....... 904 393-9055
Jacksonville *(G-6158)*
Cabinet Masters Inc...................................G....... 727 535-0020
Largo *(G-7918)*
Camilo Office Furniture Inc......................G....... 305 261-5366
Miami *(G-9306)*
Contemporary Interiors Inc......................E....... 352 620-8686
Ocala *(G-11907)*
Corpdesign..F....... 866 323-6055
Miami *(G-9404)*
Creative Concepts Orlando Inc...............E....... 407 260-1435
Longwood *(G-8268)*
Custom Craft Laminates Inc.....................E....... 813 877-7100
Tampa *(G-17577)*
Dons Cabinets and Woodworking..........F....... 727 863-3404
Hudson *(G-6022)*
Edgeline Industries LLC...........................F....... 954 727-5272
Deerfield Beach *(G-2821)*
Gilmans Custom Furn & Cabinets..........F....... 352 746-3532
Lecanto *(G-8134)*
Home Pride Cabinets Inc...........................F....... 813 887-3782
Tampa *(G-17760)*
I Found It..G....... 561 557-2881
West Palm Beach *(G-18899)*
J F V Designs Inc.......................................F....... 321 228-7469
Tavares *(G-18343)*
J T S Woodworking Inc.............................G....... 561 272-7996
Delray Beach *(G-3094)*
Ken Clearys Two LLC................................F....... 727 573-0700
Clearwater *(G-1749)*
Kings & Queens Cabinets..........................G....... 863 646-6972
Lakeland *(G-7728)*
McCallum Cabinets Inc.............................F....... 352 372-2344
Gainesville *(G-4957)*
N & N Investment Corporation................E....... 954 590-3800
Pompano Beach *(G-14770)*
Office Furniture By Tempo Inc................F....... 305 685-3077
Hialeah *(G-5548)*
Pinellas Custom Cabinets Inc..................G....... 727 864-4263
Largo *(G-8027)*
Rolu Woodcraft Inc...................................F....... 305 685-0914
Hialeah *(G-5605)*
Roque Brothers Corp.................................F....... 305 885-6995
Miami *(G-10281)*
TOS Manufacturing Inc.............................F....... 407 330-3880
Sanford *(G-16129)*
Viccarbe Inc...E....... 305 670-0979
Miami *(G-10579)*
Wonder Emporium Millwork Fab...........G....... 407 850-3131
Orlando *(G-13328)*

FURNITURE: Rattan

Capris Furniture Inds Inc..........................C....... 352 629-8889
Ocala *(G-11893)*

FURNITURE: Restaurant

A & J Commercial Seating Inc.................F....... 352 288-2022
Summerfield *(G-17055)*
Four Seas Trading Corp...........................G....... 813 221-0895
Tampa *(G-17692)*
Miranda Eldorado Mfg Co.........................G....... 727 586-0707
Largo *(G-8012)*

FURNITURE: School

Cayman Manufacturing Inc......................E....... 954 421-1170
Deerfield Beach *(G-2797)*
Griffin & Holman Inc..................................G....... 904 781-4531
Jacksonville *(G-6452)*
Series Usa LLC..G....... 305 932-4626
Miami *(G-10327)*

FURNITURE: Ship

Aj Originals Inc...G....... 954 563-9911
Fort Lauderdale *(G-3793)*
BMC Services Inc.......................................F....... 954 587-6337
Fort Lauderdale *(G-3862)*
Seaking Inc...E....... 954 961-6629
Davie *(G-2589)*

FURNITURE: Sleep

Symbol Mattress Florida Inc.....................G....... 407 343-4626
Kissimmee *(G-7302)*

FURNITURE: Stadium

Southeastern Seating Inc..........................F....... 813 273-9858
Tampa *(G-18119)*

FURNITURE: Stools, Household, Wood

Simply45 LLC..G....... 954 982-2017
Fort Lauderdale *(G-4235)*

FURNITURE: Storage Chests, Household, Wood

Closetmaid LLC...B....... 352 401-6000
Orlando *(G-12591)*
Omni Dsgns Ldscp Mngements LLC....G....... 561 339-4800
Jupiter *(G-7087)*

FURNITURE: Table Tops, Marble

Ametrine LLC..F....... 786 300-7946
Brandon *(G-1151)*
Ancient Mosaic Studios LLC....................F....... 772 460-3145
Fort Pierce *(G-4676)*
Galaxy Custom Granite Inc.......................G....... 352 220-2822
Inverness *(G-6088)*
Italy Tile and Marble Inc...........................G....... 941 488-5646
Saint Augustine *(G-15559)*
J & J Stone Tops Inc..................................G....... 305 305-8993
Opa Locka *(G-12328)*
Luxury Stone...G....... 813 985-0850
Tampa *(G-17865)*
National Stoneworks LLC..........................E....... 954 349-1609
Weston *(G-19152)*
Stone and Equipment Inc..........................E....... 305 665-0002
Miami *(G-10416)*
Venice Granit & Marble Inc.......................G....... 941 483-4363
Venice *(G-18585)*

FURNITURE: Tables & Table Tops, Wood

Allied Plastics Co Inc................................E....... 904 359-0386
Jacksonville *(G-6138)*
R & R Mica Works Inc...............................G....... 305 231-1887
Miami Lakes *(G-10847)*

FURNITURE: Theater

Cinema Crafters Inc...................................G....... 305 891-6121
North Miami *(G-11632)*

FURNITURE: Unfinished, Wood

Lawko Inc..G....... 904 389-2850
Jacksonville *(G-6550)*

FURNITURE: Upholstered

American Marine Coverings Inc..............F....... 305 889-5355
Hialeah *(G-5292)*
Architctral Wdwkg Concepts Inc............G....... 239 434-0549
Naples *(G-11166)*
Bon Vivant Interiors Inc............................E....... 305 576-8066
Opa Locka *(G-12296)*
Capitol Furniture Mfg LLC........................G....... 954 485-5000
Boca Raton *(G-469)*
Contemporary Interiors Inc......................E....... 352 620-8686
Ocala *(G-11907)*
Elegant House Intl LLC..............................G....... 954 457-8836
Hallandale *(G-5157)*
Expressions In Wood.................................G....... 954 956-0005
Pompano Beach *(G-14686)*
Grafton Furniture Company.....................E....... 305 696-3811
Miami *(G-9653)*
H317 Logistics LLC...................................G....... 404 307-1621
Vero Beach *(G-18624)*
Home Art Corporation..............................F....... 352 326-3337
Fruitland Park *(G-4865)*
Martinson Mica Wood Pdts Inc...............G....... 305 688-4445
Opa Locka *(G-12335)*
Modern Happy Home Llc..........................G....... 954 436-0055
Fort Lauderdale *(G-4123)*
Nordic Line Inc...E....... 561 338-5545
Boca Raton *(G-648)*
S&S Global Supply LLC............................G....... 786 529-4799
Hialeah *(G-5608)*
Shores Global LLC.....................................G....... 305 716-0848
Miami *(G-10340)*
Stanley Chair Company Inc.....................E....... 813 884-1436
Tampa *(G-18130)*
Unimat Industries LLC..............................G....... 305 716-0358
Miami *(G-10530)*
Unique Originals Inc.................................F....... 305 634-2274
Fort Lauderdale *(G-4293)*

FURNITURE: Vanity Dressers, Wood

Italkraft LLC...E....... 305 406-1301
Doral *(G-3396)*

FURNITURE: Wicker & Rattan

Ashley Bryan International Inc...............E....... 954 351-1199
Deerfield Beach *(G-2780)*
Conquest Financial Management..........D....... 305 630-8950
Miami *(G-9393)*
Source Contract LLC.................................F....... 305 630-8950
Miami *(G-10380)*

FUSES: Electric

Power Grid Pros Inc..................................G....... 716 378-1419
Weston *(G-19160)*

Furs

Made Fur You Inc.......................................G....... 813 444-7707
Hudson *(G-6032)*
Made Fur You Inc.......................................G....... 813 444-7707
Hudson *(G-6033)*
Vanity Furs of Avondale LLC...................G....... 904 387-9900
Jacksonville *(G-6893)*

GAMES & TOYS: Automobiles, Children's, Pedal Driven

Prime Pedal Karts LLC ....F 850 475-0450
Pensacola *(G-14239)*

GAMES & TOYS: Banks

Check Assist ....G 850 857-7752
Pensacola *(G-14113)*

GAMES & TOYS: Board Games, Children's & Adults'

Hasbro Latin America Inc ....E 305 931-3180
Miami *(G-9688)*
Victory Tailgate LLC ....C 407 704-8775
Orlando *(G-13303)*

GAMES & TOYS: Craft & Hobby Kits & Sets

Bob Violett Models Inc ....E 407 327-6333
Winter Springs *(G-19469)*
Brandine Woodcraft Inc ....G 561 266-9360
Delray Beach *(G-3051)*
Safari Programs Inc ....D 305 621-1000
Jacksonville *(G-6745)*

GAMES & TOYS: Dolls & Doll Clothing

American Girl Brands LLC ....F 407 852-9771
Orlando *(G-12469)*

GAMES & TOYS: Dolls, Exc Stuffed Toy Animals

Doll Maker LLC ....G 800 851-5183
Naples *(G-11230)*

GAMES & TOYS: Electronic

Benchmark Entertainment LC ....E 561 588-5200
Lake Worth Beach *(G-7606)*
Benchmark Games Intl LLC ....D 561 588-5200
Lake Worth Beach *(G-7607)*
Iq Dominoes Corp ....G 305 967-8583
Miami *(G-9769)*

GAMES & TOYS: Game Machines, Exc Coin-Operated

Misfit Gaming ....D 954 347-0906
Boca Raton *(G-626)*

GAMES & TOYS: Go-Carts, Children's

Rdd International Inc ....G 954 422-9909
Boca Raton *(G-682)*

GAMES & TOYS: Hobby Horses

Galaxy America Inc ....F 941 697-0324
Port Charlotte *(G-14983)*

GAMES & TOYS: Kits, Science, Incl Microscopes/Chemistry Sets

Triops Inc ....G 850 479-4415
Pensacola *(G-14276)*

GAMES & TOYS: Miniature Dolls, Collectors'

Timeless Treasures Doll Club ....E 813 854-6208
Tampa *(G-18187)*

GAMES & TOYS: Models, Airplane, Toy & Hobby

Atlantic Models Inc ....F 305 883-2012
Medley *(G-8617)*

GAMES & TOYS: Models, Boat & Ship, Toy & Hobby

Maritime Replicas Usa LLC ....E 305 921-9690
Boca Raton *(G-607)*

GAMES & TOYS: Musical Instruments

Schoenhut LLC ....G 904 810-1945
Saint Augustine *(G-15605)*

GAMES & TOYS: Puzzles

Autism Puzzle ME Inc ....G 386 314-4310
Edgewater *(G-3611)*
Puzzle Pieces Support Servic ....G 813 985-3232
Tampa *(G-18027)*
Puzzleme Now Inc ....G 386 957-4987
Edgewater *(G-3634)*

GAMES & TOYS: Scooters, Children's

Ev Rider LLC ....G 239 278-5054
Fort Myers *(G-4447)*

GAMES & TOYS: Strollers, Baby, Vehicle

Nikiani Inc ....G 305 606-1104
West Palm Beach *(G-18965)*

GARAGES: Portable, Prefabricated Metal

Wheel Systems Intl Inc ....F 920 235-9888
Bradenton *(G-1147)*

GARBAGE CONTAINERS: Plastic

Hippo Tampa LLC ....G 813 391-9152
Tampa *(G-17756)*
Quick Cans Inc ....G 407 415-1361
Winter Park *(G-19435)*
Ultimate Containers Pro LLC ....F 786 241-4306
Miami Gardens *(G-10757)*
Volusia Waste Inc ....G 386 878-3322
Deltona *(G-3181)*
Z Cans LLC ....G 941 748-6688
Bradenton *(G-1149)*

GARBAGE DISPOSERS & COMPACTORS: Commercial

C & D Industrial Maint LLC ....F 833 776-5833
Bradenton *(G-1005)*
Ebco Envmtl Bins & Cntrs Inc ....F 954 967-9999
West Park *(G-19092)*
Wastequip Manufacturing Co LLC ....E 863 665-6507
Lakeland *(G-7832)*

GAS & OIL FIELD EXPLORATION SVCS

Albasol LLC ....G 830 334-3280
Miami *(G-9100)*
CP Royalties LLC ....G 888 694-9265
Tampa *(G-17561)*
Dauntless Usa Inc ....F 904 996-8800
Jacksonville *(G-6312)*
Exploration Services LLC ....G 352 505-3578
Gainesville *(G-4917)*
Fuels Unlimited Inc ....G 407 302-3193
Sanford *(G-16051)*
Green Gas America Inc ....D 772 220-0717
Palm City *(G-13660)*
Gulfstream Natural Gas Sys LLC ....G 941 723-7000
Palmetto *(G-13803)*
Hess Station 09307 ....F 407 891-7156
Saint Cloud *(G-15653)*
HRF Exploration & Prod LLC ....F 561 847-4743
Palm Beach *(G-13556)*
Hunt Ventures Inc ....F 941 375-3699
Venice *(G-18555)*
Interntnal Tech Sltons Sup LLC ....G 305 364-5229
Doral *(G-3393)*
Kelton Company LLC ....G 850 434-6830
Pensacola *(G-14188)*
Kens Gas Piping Inc ....G 850 897-4149
Valparaiso *(G-18513)*
Nakasawa Mining and Energy LLC ....G 305 302-4980
Miami *(G-10060)*
O Neill Industries Intl Inc ....G 850 754-0312
Cantonment *(G-1344)*
Pegasus Resources Corp ....G 561 575-2393
Jupiter *(G-7091)*
Platinum Group Usa Inc ....F 561 274-7553
Delray Beach *(G-3119)*
Reliance Petro Holdings LLC ....F 352 390-8039
Ocala *(G-12036)*
Seacor Marine LLC ....D 954 523-2200
Fort Lauderdale *(G-4228)*
Superior Oil 2016 Inc ....G 305 851-5140
Miami *(G-10437)*
Tri C Petroleum Inc ....G 941 756-3370
Bradenton *(G-1129)*
Whittington Energy Co ....G 321 984-2128
Melbourne *(G-8974)*

GAS & OIL FIELD SVCS, NEC

Alfresco Air ....F 786 275-5111
Miami *(G-9103)*
Bodman Oil & Gas LLC ....G 239 430-8545
Naples *(G-11190)*
Charuvil Oil Inc DBA Valero ....G 772 871-9050
Port Saint Lucie *(G-15097)*
Euramerica Gas and Oil Corp ....G 954 858-5714
Plantation *(G-14512)*
Expressway Oil Corp ....G 786 302-9534
Medley *(G-8650)*
Gas One Inc ....G 561 483-0504
Boca Raton *(G-542)*
Norjac Oil & Gas Inc or J ....G 954 779-3192
Fort Lauderdale *(G-4142)*
W2e International Corp ....G 561 362-9595
Boca Raton *(G-786)*

GAS FIELD MACHINERY & EQPT

Carib Energy (usa) LLC ....A 904 727-2559
Jacksonville *(G-6254)*

GAS STATIONS

Reliance Petro Holdings LLC ....F 352 390-8039
Ocala *(G-12036)*

GAS STATIONS WITH CONVENIENCE STORES

Kendall Fuel Inc ....G 305 270-7735
Miami *(G-9819)*

GAS: Refinery

DOT Green Energy Inc ....G 717 505-8686
Clearwater *(G-1654)*

GASES & LIQUIFIED PETROLEUM GASES

Donald Ross Gas Inc ....G 561 776-1324
Jupiter *(G-7026)*
NPC&ug Inc ....G 239 694-7255
Alva *(G-89)*
Omega Gas Inc ....G 786 277-2176
Miami *(G-10098)*

GASES: Flourinated Hydrocarbon

North America Bio Fuel Corp ....G 877 877-9279
Bradenton *(G-1087)*

GASES: Helium

Add Helium ....G 239 300-0913
Fort Lauderdale *(G-3782)*

GASES: Hydrogen

Hydrogen Inc ....G 239 436-6668
Naples *(G-11282)*
Hydrogen One Inc ....G 352 361-6974
Belleview *(G-371)*

GASES: Indl

Air Liquide Large Inds US LP ....G 321 452-2214
Merritt Island *(G-8987)*
Equipment Sales & Service Inc ....G 727 572-9197
Clearwater *(G-1675)*
Liquid Technolgy Corp ....F 832 804-8650
Oldsmar *(G-12244)*
Matheson Treigas ....G 850 679-3024
Cantonment *(G-1342)*
Matheson Tri-Gas Inc ....G 561 615-3000
Riviera Beach *(G-15347)*
Matheson Tri-Gas Inc ....G 727 572-8737
Clearwater *(G-1776)*
Prodair Corporation ....G 850 994-5511
Milton *(G-10937)*
Vs Carbonics Inc ....F 305 903-6501
Miami *(G-10591)*

GASES: Neon

EZ Neon Inc ....G 561 262-7813
Jupiter *(G-7038)*
Neon Cowboys LLC ....G 949 514-5557
Apopka *(G-165)*
Neon Sleevz LLC ....G 239 348-0520
Naples *(G-11344)*

Neon Workforce Technologies.............G....... 305 458-8244
Hialeah *(G-5537)*

GASES: Nitrogen

Frostbite Nitrogen Ice Cream.................G....... 305 933-5482
Miami *(G-9600)*
Messer LLC...F....... 407 851-3311
Orlando *(G-12961)*
Nitrogen Jupiter LLC..............................G....... 561 662-2150
Jupiter *(G-7083)*
Rz Service Group LLC.............................G....... 904 402-2313
Jacksonville *(G-6741)*

GASES: Oxygen

Airgas Usa LLC.......................................G....... 407 293-6630
Orlando *(G-12446)*
Bauer Compressors Inc...........................G....... 757 855-6006
Sunrise *(G-17094)*
Messer LLC...F....... 925 606-2000
Delray Beach *(G-3106)*

GASKETS & SEALING DEVICES

Construction and Elec Pdts Inc..............F....... 954 972-9787
Pompano Beach *(G-14645)*
Fabrico Inc..C....... 386 736-7373
Deland *(G-2977)*
Guy Gasket Inc..F....... 561 703-1774
Lake Worth *(G-7555)*
Technetics Group LLC.............................C....... 386 736-7373
Deland *(G-3019)*
Technetics Group LLC.............................E....... 386 736-7373
De Land *(G-2734)*

GASOLINE BLENDING PLANT

Ares Distributors Inc..............................G....... 305 858-0163
Miami *(G-9167)*
Dion Fuels LLC..F....... 305 296-2000
Key West *(G-7186)*

GATES: Dam, Metal Plate

Ppa Miami Corp.......................................G....... 305 436-0460
Miami *(G-10181)*

GATES: Ornamental Metal

Greg Valentine LLC.................................E....... 239 332-0855
Fort Myers *(G-4473)*

GAUGES

Sohacki Industries Inc.............................E....... 904 826-0130
Saint Augustine *(G-15613)*

GAUGES: Pressure

Uniweld Products Inc..............................C....... 954 584-2000
Fort Lauderdale *(G-4298)*

GEARS

Riley Gear Corporation............................D....... 904 829-5652
Saint Augustine *(G-15596)*

GEARS & GEAR UNITS: Reduction, Exc Auto

Hydraulicnet LLC.....................................F....... 630 543-7630
Saint Augustine *(G-15549)*

GEARS: Power Transmission, Exc Auto

Lubov Manufacturing Inc.........................G....... 813 873-2640
Tampa *(G-17862)*
S I P Corporation.....................................F....... 813 884-8300
Tampa *(G-18075)*
Snow-Nabstedt Power Transmissi........G....... 603 661-5551
Bradenton *(G-1116)*

GELATIN CAPSULES

Enzymedica Inc..E....... 941 505-5565
Venice *(G-18547)*

GEM STONES MINING, NEC: Natural

4 Power International Stones.................G....... 407 286-4677
Orlando *(G-12418)*
Ultimate Stnwrks Centl Fla LLC.............G....... 407 412-5981
Orlando *(G-13288)*

GEMSTONE & INDL DIAMOND MINING SVCS

ER Jahna Industries Inc..........................E....... 863 424-0730
Davenport *(G-2478)*
Waste Management Inc Florida.............E....... 954 984-2000
Winter Garden *(G-19289)*

GENERAL MERCHANDISE, NONDURABLE, WHOLESALE

Lakay Vita LLC...G....... 786 985-7552
Hallandale Beach *(G-5196)*
Pb Group LLC...E....... 954 922-4311
Hollywood *(G-5887)*
Premier Luxury Group LLC......................E....... 954 358-9885
Fort Lauderdale *(G-4176)*
Rokey Corporation...................................G....... 561 470-0164
Boca Raton *(G-693)*
Sourcerers Inc..G....... 954 530-2333
Plantation *(G-14556)*

GENERATING APPARATUS & PARTS: Electrical

Adtec Productions Incorporated............G....... 904 720-2003
Jacksonville *(G-6120)*

GENERATION EQPT: Electronic

American Payment Systems....................F....... 407 856-8524
Orlando *(G-12472)*
Apollo Energy Systems Inc......................G....... 954 969-7755
Pompano Beach *(G-14595)*
Axis Group..F....... 954 580-6000
Pompano Beach *(G-14608)*
Chenega Manufacturing Svcs LLC.........E....... 850 763-6013
Panama City *(G-13880)*
Coastland Specialties LLC......................G....... 239 910-5401
Bonita Springs *(G-825)*
Electrnic Systems Sutheast LLC............G....... 561 955-9006
Fort Myers *(G-4442)*
Industry Standard Technology................G....... 941 355-2100
Sarasota *(G-16235)*
Keytroller LLC..F....... 813 877-4500
Tampa *(G-17823)*
Keytroller LLC..G....... 813 877-4500
Tampa *(G-17824)*
Lightning Master Corporation................E....... 800 749-6800
Clearwater *(G-1761)*
M Micro Technologies Inc.......................B....... 954 973-6166
Pompano Beach *(G-14749)*
Mathews Associates Inc..........................C....... 407 323-3390
Sanford *(G-16082)*
Omniaelectronics llc...............................G....... 631 742-5719
North Bay Village *(G-11594)*
Sagrad Inc...F....... 321 726-9400
Melbourne *(G-8923)*
Sepac Corp..F....... 305 718-3379
Miami *(G-10325)*
Ultrasonic Technologies Inc...................G....... 813 973-1702
Wesley Chapel *(G-18762)*
Universal Networking Svcs Co...............G....... 281 825-9790
Saint Petersburg *(G-15947)*
Veethree Electronics & Mar LLC.............D....... 941 538-7775
Bradenton *(G-1140)*
Watts Technologies LLC..........................F....... 407 512-5750
Sanford *(G-16135)*

GENERATOR REPAIR SVCS

Pinnacle Central Company Inc...............F....... 904 354-5746
Jacksonville *(G-6673)*

GENERATORS SETS: Steam

Southern Innovative Energy Inc.............G....... 321 747-9205
Titusville *(G-18461)*

GENERATORS: Automotive & Aircraft

Create and Company Inc.........................F....... 813 393-8778
Tampa *(G-17562)*
Pcm and S L Plota Co LLC......................F....... 727 547-6277
Largo *(G-8024)*

GENERATORS: Electric

Armstrong Power Systems LLC..............F....... 305 470-0058
Miami *(G-9170)*
Bgt Holdings LLC......................................G....... 239 643-9949
Naples *(G-11187)*
Emergency Standby Power LLC..............F....... 850 259-2304
Fort Walton Beach *(G-4799)*
Jat Power LLC...F....... 305 592-0103
Doral *(G-3400)*
Mtservicer LLC..G....... 305 200-1254
Miami Lakes *(G-10824)*
Southeast Power Group Inc.....................D....... 305 592-9745
Doral *(G-3507)*
Tradewinds Power Corp..........................D....... 305 592-9745
Doral *(G-3531)*

GENERATORS: Electrochemical, Fuel Cell

Dioxide Materials Inc...............................F....... 217 239-1400
Boca Raton *(G-502)*
Kollsman Inc..G....... 407 312-1384
Orlando *(G-12875)*

GENERATORS: Gas

Sams Gas...G....... 386 698-1033
Crescent City *(G-2341)*

GENERATORS: Storage Battery Chargers

Amper Usa LLC..G....... 305 717-3101
Doral *(G-3248)*
Lithium Battery Company LLC.................F....... 813 504-0074
Tampa *(G-17850)*
Solar Stik Inc...E....... 800 793-4364
Saint Augustine *(G-15614)*

GENERATORS: Thermo-Electric

Mitsubishi Power Americas Inc...............D....... 407 688-6100
Lake Mary *(G-7436)*

GIFT SHOP

Baker County Press Inc............................G....... 904 259-2400
Macclenny *(G-8442)*
Treasure Cove II Inc..................................F....... 941 966-2004
Sarasota *(G-16625)*

GIFT WRAP: Paper, Made From Purchased Materials

Wrap-Art Inc...G....... 954 428-1819
Deerfield Beach *(G-2936)*

GIFT, NOVELTY & SOUVENIR STORES: Gifts & Novelties

Big Bend Ice Cream Co.............................G....... 850 539-7778
Havana *(G-5233)*

GIFTS & NOVELTIES: Wholesalers

Birdiebox LLC..E....... 786 762-2975
Miami *(G-9249)*
EMB Wholesale...G....... 904 452-4362
Jacksonville *(G-6361)*
Fanatics Mounted Memories Inc............E....... 866 578-9115
Jacksonville *(G-6378)*
Mounted Memories Inc............................F....... 866 236-2541
Miramar *(G-11018)*
Note It..G....... 954 593-8616
Hollywood *(G-5884)*
PM Craftsman..E....... 863 665-0815
Lakeland *(G-7768)*
Suncoast Identification Tech..................G....... 239 277-9922
Fort Myers *(G-4616)*

GLASS & GLASS CERAMIC PRDTS, PRESSED OR BLOWN: Tableware

Anchor Glass Container Corp.................C....... 904 786-1010
Jacksonville *(G-6153)*
Ecosoulife USA Dist LLC..........................F....... 754 212-5456
Boca Raton *(G-513)*

GLASS FABRICATORS

Ameriglass Engineering Inc....................F....... 305 558-6227
Hialeah *(G-5298)*
Arso Enterprises Inc.................................E....... 305 681-2020
Opa Locka *(G-12290)*
B & K Installations Inc.............................E....... 305 245-6968
Homestead *(G-5956)*
Buchelli Glass Inc.....................................G....... 954 695-8067
Coconut Creek *(G-2072)*
Commercial Insulating Glass Co............D....... 941 378-9100
Sarasota *(G-16389)*
Commercial Rfrg Door Co Inc.................G....... 941 371-8110
Sarasota *(G-16390)*

Custom Cft Windows & Doors Inc........F....... 407 834-5400
Winter Springs *(G-19470)*
Darren Thomas Glass Co Inc................G....... 863 655-9500
Sebring *(G-16686)*
Defenshield Inc...................................G....... 904 679-3942
Saint Augustine *(G-15535)*
Downey Group LLC...............................E....... 954 972-0026
Pompano Beach *(G-14668)*
G F E Inc...F....... 954 583-7005
Davie *(G-2530)*
GE Glass Inc..G....... 305 599-7725
Miami *(G-9618)*
Geltech Inc..D....... 407 382-4003
Orlando *(G-12774)*
Grade A Glass......................................D....... 321 419-6935
Deland *(G-2980)*
Jambco Millwork Inc.............................F....... 954 977-4998
Margate *(G-8551)*
Jensen Scientific Products Inc.............E....... 954 344-2006
Coral Springs *(G-2263)*
Jsl Enterprises of Orlando....................F....... 386 767-9653
Chuluota *(G-1553)*
Justi Group Inc.....................................E....... 813 855-5779
Oldsmar *(G-12238)*
Living Color Aquarium Corp.................E....... 844 522-8265
Deerfield Beach *(G-2862)*
Luv Enterprises Inc..............................F....... 352 867-8440
Ocala *(G-11988)*
MA Glass & Mirror LLC........................F....... 305 593-8555
Miami *(G-9930)*
Ocean Dynamics USA Inc.....................G....... 305 770-1800
Miami *(G-10088)*
PGT Industries Inc...............................A....... 941 480-1600
North Venice *(G-11761)*
Pompanette LLC...................................E....... 813 885-2182
Tampa *(G-17997)*
Security Impact GL Hldings LLC...........G....... 561 844-3100
Riviera Beach *(G-15376)*
Shower Doors Unlimited Inc..................F....... 561 547-0702
Boynton Beach *(G-958)*
Smart Glass Systems Inc......................G....... 954 801-5349
Plantation *(G-14553)*
Square One Armoring Svcs Co.............D....... 305 477-1109
Miami *(G-10407)*
Stony Coral Investments LLC...............F....... 941 704-5391
Myakka City *(G-11143)*
Sunoptic Technologies LLC...................D....... 877 677-2832
Jacksonville *(G-6822)*
Tallahassee Engraving & Award............G....... 850 878-7187
Tallahassee *(G-17336)*
Universal Alum Windows & Doors.........F....... 305 825-7900
Hialeah *(G-5662)*
Waterway Systems LLC.........................G....... 941 752-3554
Sarasota *(G-16324)*
Worldglass Corporation.........................G....... 813 609-2453
Tampa *(G-18264)*

GLASS PRDTS, FROM PURCHASED GLASS: Enameled

LP Auto & Home Glass..........................F....... 772 335-3697
Fort Pierce *(G-4713)*

GLASS PRDTS, FROM PURCHASED GLASS: Glass Beads, Reflecting

Flexstake Inc..E....... 239 481-3539
Fort Myers *(G-4450)*

GLASS PRDTS, FROM PURCHASED GLASS: Glassware

Elegant Reflections...............................G....... 941 627-9275
Port Charlotte *(G-14977)*
Terraferma USA Corporation.................F....... 305 994-7892
Doral *(G-3528)*

GLASS PRDTS, FROM PURCHASED GLASS: Insulating

Omega Garage Doors Inc.......................F....... 352 620-8830
Melbourne *(G-8901)*

GLASS PRDTS, FROM PURCHASED GLASS: Mirrored

AGM Industries Inc................................F....... 954 486-1112
Fort Lauderdale *(G-3789)*
Art & Frame Direct Inc..........................C....... 407 857-6000
Orlando *(G-12491)*
BT Glass & Mirror Inc...........................G....... 561 841-7676
West Palm Beach *(G-18829)*
Friedman Bros Dcrtive Arts Inc.............D....... 800 327-1065
Medley *(G-8653)*
Mirrors & More Inc................................G....... 954 782-7272
Pompano Beach *(G-14765)*

GLASS PRDTS, FROM PURCHASED GLASS: Mirrors, Framed

Venture Circle Intl LLC..........................F....... 407 677-6004
Sanford *(G-16132)*

GLASS PRDTS, PRESSED OR BLOWN: Barware

Foh Inc...C....... 305 757-7940
Miami *(G-9592)*

GLASS PRDTS, PRESSED OR BLOWN: Bowls

Eco Cups International Corp.................F....... 407 308-1764
Orlando *(G-12696)*

GLASS PRDTS, PRESSED OR BLOWN: Bulbs, Electric Lights

Jga Lighting LLC...................................G....... 772 408-8224
Grant *(G-5049)*
Ledradiant LLC.....................................G....... 305 901-1313
Hollywood *(G-5858)*

GLASS PRDTS, PRESSED OR BLOWN: Glass Fibers, Textile

Owens Corning Sales LLC.....................E....... 863 291-3046
Winter Haven *(G-19338)*

GLASS PRDTS, PRESSED OR BLOWN: Glassware, Art Or Decorative

Miracles For Fun Usa Inc......................F....... 561 702-8217
Hallandale Beach *(G-5199)*

GLASS PRDTS, PRESSED OR BLOWN: Ophthalmic, Exc Flat

Transitions Optical Inc..........................B....... 727 545-0400
Pinellas Park *(G-14392)*

GLASS PRDTS, PRESSED OR BLOWN: Optical

Safilo Usa Inc..E....... 305 262-5727
Miami *(G-10297)*

GLASS PRDTS, PRESSED OR BLOWN: Ornaments, Christmas Tree

Edmund C Miga.....................................G....... 941 628-5951
Port Charlotte *(G-14976)*

GLASS PRDTS, PRESSED OR BLOWN: Tubing

Charles Composites LLC.......................F....... 863 357-2500
Okeechobee *(G-12173)*

GLASS PRDTS, PRESSED/BLOWN: Glassware, Art, Decor/Novelty

A Sanborn Corporation..........................E....... 727 397-3073
Madeira Beach *(G-8445)*
Calendar Arts LLC.................................F....... 407 285-8139
Vero Beach *(G-18609)*
Madart..G....... 321 961-9264
Titusville *(G-18444)*
Milano Worldwide Corp..........................G....... 561 266-0201
Boca Raton *(G-625)*
Nebula Glass International Inc..............E....... 954 975-3233
Pompano Beach *(G-14771)*

GLASS PRDTS, PURCHASED GLASS: Glassware, Scientific/Tech

Florida Style Aluminum Inc....................G....... 239 689-8662
Fort Myers *(G-4453)*

GLASS PRDTS, PURCHASED GLASS: Insulating, Multiple-Glazed

Global Performance Windows Inc.........F....... 954 942-3322
Pompano Beach *(G-14715)*

GLASS PRDTS, PURCHD GLASS: Furniture Top, Cut, Beveld/Polshd

Circle Redmont Inc................................E....... 321 259-7374
Melbourne *(G-8789)*
Kron Designs LLC..................................G....... 954 941-0800
Fort Lauderdale *(G-4091)*

GLASS PRDTS, PURCHSD GLASS: Ornamental, Cut, Engraved/Décor

Ace Mirror & Glass Works Inc...............G....... 561 792-7478
Loxahatchee *(G-8355)*

GLASS STORE: Leaded Or Stained

Jsl Enterprises of Orlando.....................F....... 386 767-9653
Chuluota *(G-1553)*

GLASS STORES

Blutec Glass Fabrication LLC................G....... 941 232-1600
Sarasota *(G-16365)*
Creative Glassworks.............................G....... 904 860-0865
Jacksonville *(G-6297)*
Faours Mirror Corp...............................E....... 813 884-3297
Tampa *(G-17658)*
Oldcastle Buildingenvelope Inc............D....... 813 247-3184
Tampa *(G-17951)*
Simplex Inc...E....... 352 357-2828
Mount Dora *(G-11114)*

GLASS: Broadwoven Fabrics

Security Impact GL Hldings LLC...........G....... 561 844-3100
Riviera Beach *(G-15376)*

GLASS: Fiber

Allied Molded Products LLC..................E....... 941 723-3072
Palmetto *(G-13785)*
Merritt Precision Tech Inc.....................G....... 321 453-2334
Merritt Island *(G-9003)*
Perry Composites LLC..........................G....... 850 584-8400
Perry *(G-14308)*
Spectra Composites East Fla................G....... 772 461-7747
Fort Pierce *(G-4749)*

GLASS: Flat

Faours Mirror Corp...............................E....... 813 884-3297
Tampa *(G-17658)*
FMC/Rhyno LLC....................................E....... 813 838-2264
Tampa *(G-17689)*
Guardian Industries Cor........................E....... 954 525-3481
Fort Lauderdale *(G-4034)*
Jsl Enterprises of Orlando.....................F....... 386 767-9653
Chuluota *(G-1553)*
Pilkington North America Inc................F....... 407 295-8560
Orlando *(G-13068)*
Precision Auto Tint Dsign Corp.............G....... 727 385-8788
Tarpon Springs *(G-18321)*

GLASS: Indl Prdts

Flat Glass Distributors LLC...................E....... 904 354-5413
Jacksonville *(G-6394)*

GLASS: Insulating

Commercial Insulating Glass Co...........D....... 941 378-9100
Sarasota *(G-16389)*
Impact Safe Glass Corporation.............G....... 813 247-5528
Tampa *(G-17774)*

GLASS: Pressed & Blown, NEC

Chrome Aerospace Inc...........................G....... 305 506-8182
Miami Beach *(G-10655)*
Hoya Largo...F....... 727 531-8964
Largo *(G-7976)*
Mjr Enterprises Inc................................G....... 352 483-0735
Eustis *(G-3714)*
Perfect Reflections Inc..........................G....... 813 991-4361
Zephyrhills *(G-19531)*

GLASS: Safety

Dependable Shutter Service Inc............E....... 954 583-1411
Davie *(G-2516)*
Vision Blocks Inc..................................F....... 321 254-7478
Melbourne *(G-8972)*

GLASS: Stained

Advent Glass Works Inc........................G....... 386 497-2050
Fort White *(G-4842)*
Conrad Pickel Studio Inc.......................G....... 772 567-1710
Vero Beach *(G-18612)*
Creative Glassworks.............................G....... 904 860-0865
Jacksonville *(G-6297)*

GLASS: Structural

Aldora Aluminum & GL Pdts Inc............E....... 954 441-5057
Coral Springs *(G-2219)*
Structure Glass Solutions LLC..............F....... 954 499-9450
Hialeah *(G-5635)*

GLASS: Tempered

Oldcastle Buildingenvelope Inc.............D....... 813 247-3184
Tampa *(G-17951)*
Tempered Glass Industries Inc..............E....... 727 499-0284
Clearwater *(G-1915)*

GLASSWARE WHOLESALERS

Mjr Enterprises Inc..............................G....... 352 483-0735
Eustis *(G-3714)*
Premier Lab Supply Inc.........................G....... 772 873-1700
Port Saint Lucie *(G-15130)*

GLASSWARE: Cut & Engraved

Hartmans Canine Center LLC................G....... 352 978-6592
Clermont *(G-1963)*

GLOBAL POSITIONING SYSTEMS & EQPT

Anywhere Gps LLC...............................G....... 949 468-6842
Saint Augustine *(G-15517)*
Fleetboss Globl Pstning Sltons............E....... 407 265-9559
Fern Park *(G-3728)*
Gps Industries LLC..............................G....... 941 894-8030
Sarasota *(G-16452)*
Joe Hearn Innovative Tech LLC............F....... 850 898-3744
Pensacola *(G-14183)*
Locus Solutions LLC............................D....... 561 575-7600
Palm Beach Gardens *(G-13605)*
Nxgen Brands LLC...............................E....... 888 315-6339
Plantation *(G-14540)*

GLOVES: Fabric

I ABC Corp..G....... 904 645-6000
Jacksonville *(G-6486)*
Parker Protective Products LLC............F....... 800 879-0329
North Miami *(G-11650)*
Warren Heim Corp...............................E....... 772 466-8265
Fort Pierce *(G-4768)*

GLOVES: Leather, Work

Sara Glove Company Inc......................G....... 866 664-7272
Naples *(G-11392)*

GLOVES: Safety

Grobarty Inc..F....... 786 398-5530
Miami *(G-9674)*

GLOVES: Welders'

Orbi Supply Inc....................................G....... 305 810-8822
Doral *(G-3451)*

GLOVES: Work

Niefeld Group LLC...............................G....... 786 587-7423
Hialeah *(G-5541)*

GLUE

Craig Armstrong...................................F....... 786 319-6514
Miami Beach *(G-10660)*

GLYCERIN

World Hlth Enrgy Holdings Inc.............F....... 561 870-0440
Boca Raton *(G-791)*

GLYCOL ETHERS

Mmt Technologies Inc...........................G....... 863 619-2926
Lakeland *(G-7753)*

GOLD BULLION PRODUCTION

International Weatherization................G....... 954 818-3288
Fort Lauderdale *(G-4065)*

GOLD ORE MINING

Bromide Mining LLC.............................F....... 786 477-6229
Doral *(G-3287)*
Iamgold Purchasing Svcs Inc...............G....... 713 671-5973
Doral *(G-3386)*
Smart Group Traders Inc......................G....... 850 460-5130
Destin *(G-3207)*

GOLD ORES

Chemours Company Fc LLC.................C....... 904 964-1200
Starke *(G-16890)*
Goldfield Cnsld Mines Co.....................D....... 321 724-1700
Melbourne *(G-8837)*
Thierry Brouzet Inc..............................G....... 727 449-0158
Clearwater *(G-1918)*
US Precious Metals Inc.......................G....... 786 814-5804
Coral Gables *(G-2202)*

GOLD ORES PROCESSING

New World Gold Corporation................D....... 561 962-4139
Boca Raton *(G-641)*

GOLF CARTS: Powered

Columbia Parcar Corp...........................F....... 352 753-0244
Leesburg *(G-8147)*
Cricket Mini Golf Carts Inc....................F....... 386 220-3536
Daytona Beach *(G-2649)*
Elite Enclosures....................................F....... 352 323-6005
Leesburg *(G-8154)*
Ljs Tops & Bottoms..............................E....... 561 736-7868
Boynton Beach *(G-929)*
My Custom Cart LLC............................G....... 904 214-3723
Middleburg *(G-10909)*
Nivel Holdings LLC...............................G....... 904 741-6161
Jacksonville *(G-6636)*
Nivel Parts & Mfg Co LLC.....................E....... 904 741-6161
Jacksonville *(G-6637)*
Streetrod Productions Inc.....................G....... 352 751-3953
The Villages *(G-18393)*

GOLF CARTS: Wholesalers

My Custom Cart LLC............................G....... 904 214-3723
Middleburg *(G-10909)*
Nivel Holdings LLC...............................G....... 904 741-6161
Jacksonville *(G-6636)*
Nivel Parts & Mfg Co LLC.....................E....... 904 741-6161
Jacksonville *(G-6637)*

GOLF EQPT

Biomech Golf Equipment LLC...............F....... 401 932-0479
Naples *(G-11189)*
Kent Manufacturing Venice Inc..............F....... 941 485-8871
Nokomis *(G-11584)*
Laird International Corp........................F....... 954 532-3794
Pompano Beach *(G-14742)*
Liquid Ed Inc..G....... 727 943-8616
Tarpon Springs *(G-18313)*
Qwikpik Golf LLC.................................G....... 407 505-5546
Orlando *(G-13106)*

GOURMET FOOD STORES

Classica & Telecard Corp......................G....... 239 354-3727
Naples *(G-11210)*
Plant Theory LLC..................................G....... 305 672-5785
Miami Beach *(G-10702)*
Termine Ravioli Manufacturing..............F....... 954 983-3711
Hollywood *(G-5923)*

GOVERNMENT, EXECUTIVE OFFICES: Mayors'

City of Ocala..E....... 352 622-6803
Ocala *(G-11903)*

GRANITE: Crushed & Broken

Granite World Inc..................................E....... 813 243-6556
Tampa *(G-17725)*
Rock Ridge Materials Inc......................F....... 321 268-8455
Titusville *(G-18460)*

GRANITE: Cut & Shaped

All Granite & Marble Corp.....................G....... 508 248-9393
Sarasota *(G-16340)*
Cantor Design On Granite.....................G....... 407 230-1568
Orlando *(G-12546)*
Creta Granite & Marble Inc...................G....... 954 956-9993
Pompano Beach *(G-14650)*
Cug LLC..F....... 786 858-0499
Plantation *(G-14505)*
D G Morrison Inc..................................F....... 813 865-0208
Odessa *(G-12114)*
Exotic Countertop Inc...........................G....... 954 979-8188
Pompano Beach *(G-14685)*
Fantasy Marble & Granite Inc................G....... 954 788-0433
Pompano Beach *(G-14687)*
Fasulo Granite & Marble Inc..................G....... 561 371-5410
Jupiter *(G-7041)*
Fine Surfaces and More Inc..................G....... 305 691-5752
Miami *(G-9568)*
Grevan Artistic Ventures Inc.................F....... 850 243-8111
Fort Walton Beach *(G-4804)*
HI Tech Granite and Marble..................G....... 407 230-4363
Orlando *(G-12802)*
J V Installations Corp..........................E....... 407 849-0262
Orlando *(G-12848)*
Kusser Graniteworks Usa Inc................G....... 813 248-3428
Tampa *(G-17830)*
LAS & JB Inc.......................................G....... 772 672-5315
Fort Pierce *(G-4711)*
MGM Granite & Marble Company..........G....... 954 894-6802
Fort Lauderdale *(G-4120)*
Naples Stone Consulting LLC................F....... 239 325-8653
Naples *(G-11339)*
Natural Stone Sltons Fnest SRS............E....... 941 954-1100
Sarasota *(G-16519)*
Prestige Flrg Instllations Inc..................F....... 407 291-0609
Orlando *(G-13083)*
Reyes Granite & Marble Corp................F....... 305 599-7330
Miami *(G-10259)*
Ribeiro Stones LLC..............................G....... 407 723-8802
Orlando *(G-13136)*
Rik Enterprises Inc...............................G....... 239 772-9485
Cape Coral *(G-1460)*
Sarasotas Finest MBL Gran Inc.............G....... 941 365-9697
Sarasota *(G-16583)*
Signature Granite Inc............................F....... 813 443-5597
Tampa *(G-18103)*
Taken For Granite.................................G....... 727 235-1559
Saint Petersburg *(G-15932)*
Triton Stone Holdings LLC....................G....... 219 669-4890
Fort Lauderdale *(G-4288)*

GRANITE: Dimension

Commercial Stone Cab Fbrctors............F....... 727 209-1141
Saint Petersburg *(G-15749)*
Commercial Stone Fbrcators Inc............F....... 727 209-1141
Saint Petersburg *(G-15750)*
Granite Imports Inc...............................G....... 732 500-2549
Boynton Beach *(G-915)*
OCC My Stone LLC..............................G....... 786 352-1567
Miami Lakes *(G-10832)*
Paramount Depot LLC..........................F....... 786 275-0107
Doral *(G-3453)*
Quality Stones R US LLC.....................G....... 904 551-5619
Jacksonville *(G-6700)*

GRAPHIC ARTS & RELATED DESIGN SVCS

A-Plus Prtg & Graphic Ctr Inc...............E....... 954 327-7315
Plantation *(G-14481)*
Amelia Island Graphics.........................G....... 904 261-0740
Fernandina Beach *(G-3731)*
Baru Agency Incorporated....................G....... 305 259-8800
Doral *(G-3264)*
Bg Expo Group LLC............................G....... 305 428-3576
Doral *(G-3271)*
Blue Ocean Press Inc...........................E....... 954 973-1819
Fort Lauderdale *(G-3859)*
Design & Print.....................................G....... 561 361-8299
Boca Raton *(G-498)*
Fresh Ink Print LLC..............................G....... 407 412-5905
Orlando *(G-12764)*

Graphic Center Group Corp.................G....... 305 961-1649
Coral Gables *(G-2152)*
Kikinaz Screen Printing Inc....................G....... 561 512-3134
Royal Palm Beach *(G-15473)*
Mc Squared Group Inc..........................G....... 850 435-4600
Pensacola *(G-14202)*
McKenny Printing Enterprise................G....... 727 420-4944
Saint Petersburg *(G-15853)*
Outdoor America Images Inc...............E....... 813 888-8796
Tampa *(G-17964)*
Speedpro Imaging St Petersburg..........G....... 727 266-0956
Saint Petersburg *(G-15922)*
Zeeeees Corporation ....G....... 407 624-3796
Saint Cloud *(G-15671)*

GRAPHITE MINING SVCS

Western Graphite Inc..............................F....... 850 270-2808
Monticello *(G-11083)*

GRASSES: Artificial & Preserved

Easyturf Inc ....F....... 941 753-3312
Ellenton *(G-3653)*
Sike Usa Inc...G....... 786 331-4020
Doral *(G-3503)*

GRAVEL & PEBBLE MINING

Atlantic Earth Materials ....F....... 321 631-0600
Cocoa *(G-1996)*

GRAVEL MINING

Bdc Shell & Aggregate LLC ....F....... 941 875-6615
Punta Gorda *(G-15193)*

GRAVEL: Painted

Ipg Network Corp...................................F....... 305 681-4001
Miami *(G-9766)*

GREASES & INEDIBLE FATS, RENDERED

Griffin Industries LLC ....E....... 904 964-8083
Starke *(G-16894)*

GREASES: Lubricating

Aoclsc Inc..D....... 813 248-1988
Tampa *(G-17427)*

GREENHOUSES: Prefabricated Metal

B & K Installations Inc...........................E....... 305 245-6968
Homestead *(G-5956)*
C P Enterprises of Apopka Inc...............G....... 407 886-3321
Mount Dora *(G-11098)*

GREETING CARDS WHOLESALERS

Montevista Greetings LLC ....G....... 305 888-9797
Hialeah *(G-5526)*

GRILLS & GRILLWORK: Woven Wire, Made From Purchased Wire

Grille Tech Inc ....E....... 305 537-0053
Miami *(G-9672)*

GRITS: Crushed & Broken

South Carolina Minerals Inc...................D....... 352 365-6522
Leesburg *(G-8174)*

GROCERIES WHOLESALERS, NEC

Big L Brands Inc ....F....... 888 552-9768
Boca Raton *(G-447)*
Conchita Foods Inc.................................D....... 305 888-9703
Medley *(G-8633)*
Florida Coca-Cola Bottling Co................B....... 850 478-4800
Pensacola *(G-14154)*
Fresh Start Beverage Company ....G....... 561 757-6541
Boca Raton *(G-540)*
Hot Sauce Harrys Inc.............................G....... 941 423-7092
North Port *(G-11741)*
La Province Inc ....F....... 305 538-2406
Miami *(G-9847)*
ME Thompson Inc ....D....... 863 667-3732
Lakeland *(G-7749)*
Pepsi-Cola Metro Btlg Co Inc.................C....... 904 733-1627
Jacksonville *(G-6668)*
Pepsi-Cola Metro Btlg Co Inc.................G....... 352 376-8276
Gainesville *(G-4980)*
Pepsi-Cola Metro Btlg Co Inc.................G....... 352 797-1160
Brooksville *(G-1260)*
Rcr Coffee Company Inc ....E....... 813 248-6264
Tampa *(G-18041)*
Refresco Beverages US Inc ....C....... 813 241-0147
Tampa *(G-18046)*
Royal Cup Inc...G....... 850 436-4435
Pensacola *(G-14254)*
Twinlab Holdings Inc ....E....... 800 645-5626
Boca Raton *(G-762)*

GROCERIES, GENERAL LINE WHOLESALERS

El Mira Sol Inc ....D....... 813 754-5857
Plant City *(G-14429)*
Johnson Brothers Whl Meats Inc..........E....... 850 763-2828
Panama City *(G-13922)*
La Autentica Foods Inc ....E....... 305 888-6727
Hialeah *(G-5481)*
My Familys Seasonings LLC ....F....... 863 698-7968
Clearwater *(G-1798)*
Vigo Importing Company ....C....... 813 884-3491
Tampa *(G-18247)*

GUARD PROTECTIVE SVCS

Tactical Products Group LLC ....E....... 561 265-4066
Boynton Beach *(G-967)*

GUARDRAILS

Scott Safety LLC ....E....... 239 340-8695
Moore Haven *(G-11089)*

GUIDANCE SYSTEMS & EQPT: Space Vehicle

Lockheed Martin Corporation.................G....... 321 853-5194
Cape Canaveral *(G-1364)*

GUIDED MISSILES & SPACE VEHICLES

Blue Origin Florida LLC.........................D....... 253 437-9300
Merritt Island *(G-8994)*
Chad ....F....... 727 433-0404
Tampa *(G-17530)*
Kratos Def & SEC Solutions Inc ....G....... 866 606-5867
Orlando *(G-12877)*
Lockheed Martin Corporation.................G....... 321 853-5194
Cape Canaveral *(G-1364)*
Micro Systems Inc ....C....... 850 244-2332
Fort Walton Beach *(G-4815)*
Mishaal Aerospace Corporation............G....... 786 353-2685
Miami *(G-10027)*
Moon Express Inc ....E....... 650 241-8577
Cape Canaveral *(G-1365)*
New Source Corp...................................G....... 407 830-7771
Altamonte Springs *(G-57)*
Northrop Grmman Feld Spport Sv ....D....... 904 810-4665
Saint Augustine *(G-15574)*
Redwire Corporation ....G....... 650 701-7722
Jacksonville *(G-6711)*
Space Machine & Engrg Corp................E....... 727 323-2221
Saint Petersburg *(G-15920)*
Space X Design LLC..............................G....... 407 592-5147
Miami *(G-10391)*
Wantzloeben RES Solutions LLC ....G....... 972 273-0190
Summerland Key *(G-17066)*

GUIDED MISSILES & SPACE VEHICLES: Research & Development

Raytheon Company................................G....... 321 235-6682
Orlando *(G-13116)*
Trailblazerai Inc......................................G....... 727 859-2732
Saint Petersburg *(G-15942)*

GUIDED MISSILES/SPACE VEHICLE PARTS/AUX EQPT: Research/Devel

H H Terry Co Inc.....................................F....... 239 593-0132
Naples *(G-11274)*
L3 Aviation Products Inc ....C....... 941 371-0811
Saint Petersburg *(G-15835)*
Moog Inc...F....... 321 435-8722
West Melbourne *(G-18777)*

GUM & WOOD CHEMICALS

AZ Chem Holdings LP ....C....... 800 526-5294
Jacksonville *(G-6183)*
Lignotech Florida LLC............................E....... 904 577-9077
Fernandina Beach *(G-3742)*
Taber Incorporated ....G....... 401 245-2800
Port St Lucie *(G-15180)*

GUN PARTS MADE TO INDIVIDUAL ORDER

Militek Industries LLC.............................G....... 941 544-5636
Bradenton *(G-1078)*

GUN SIGHTS: Optical

Knight Vision Lllp ....F....... 321 607-9900
Titusville *(G-18440)*

GUTTERS

Estradas Fiberglass Mfg Corp...............G....... 954 924-8778
Sunny Isles Beach *(G-17076)*

GUTTERS: Sheet Metal

Benchmark Quality Gutters Inc ....G....... 904 759-9800
Jacksonville *(G-6204)*
Crown Seamless Gutters Inc ....F....... 561 748-9919
West Palm Beach *(G-18852)*
Mr Gutter Cutter Inc ....F....... 772 286-7780
Stuart *(G-16978)*
S&L Cnstrction Specialists Inc..............G....... 407 300-5080
Orlando *(G-13153)*

GYPSUM & CALCITE MINING SVCS

Copaco Inc..F....... 407 333-3041
Orange City *(G-12374)*

GYPSUM BOARD

Gypsum Bd Specialists USA Corp ....G....... 954 348-8869
Pembroke Pines *(G-14039)*
United States Gypsum Company ....D....... 305 688-8744
Miami Shores *(G-10886)*

GYPSUM MINING

Harrison Gypsum LLC...........................E....... 850 762-4315
Marianna *(G-8578)*

GYPSUM PRDTS

Certanteed Gyps Ciling Mfg Inc.............E....... 813 286-3900
Tampa *(G-17528)*
E2 Walls Inc ....E....... 813 374-2010
Tampa *(G-17624)*
H & H Gypsum LLC................................G....... 321 972-5571
Casselberry *(G-1504)*
Lambert Corporation Florida ....E....... 407 841-2940
Orlando *(G-12889)*
Premix-Marbletite Mfg Co......................F....... 407 327-0830
Winter Springs *(G-19480)*
United States Gypsum Company ....D....... 904 768-2501
Jacksonville *(G-6883)*

HAIR & HAIR BASED PRDTS

Beauty Cosmetica...................................F....... 305 406-1022
Opa Locka *(G-12293)*
CCI Hair Boutique LLC ....F....... 407 408-8649
Orlando *(G-12558)*
Condition Culture LLC............................F....... 786 433-8279
Boynton Beach *(G-892)*
Flex Beauty Labs LLC ....F....... 646 302-8542
Orlando *(G-12743)*
Fusion Industries LLC ....F....... 239 415-7554
Fort Myers *(G-4461)*
Italian Hair Extension Inc.......................G....... 954 839-5366
Sunrise *(G-17131)*
Its A 10 Inc ....G....... 954 227-7813
Coral Springs *(G-2262)*
Jess By Inches LLC...............................G....... 305 731-1387
North Miami Beach *(G-11686)*
Lion Locs LLC ....F....... 704 802-2752
Orlando *(G-12914)*
Sbm Beauty LLC ....F....... 850 567-7338
Quincy *(G-15253)*
Serenity Hair Extensions LLC................F....... 407 917-1788
Deltona *(G-3179)*

HAIR CARE PRDTS

365 Sun LLC...G....... 208 357-8062
Palmetto *(G-13781)*
Abdiversified LLC ....E....... 954 791-6050
Plantation *(G-14485)*

PRODUCT

AIG Technologies Inc ....F.... 954 433-0618
Deerfield Beach (G-2769)
B & R Products Inc ....F.... 305 238-1592
Cutler Bay (G-2386)
Beauty Lab Inc ....E.... 305 687-0071
Opa Locka (G-12294)
Celeb Luxury LLC ....F.... 954 763-0333
Davie (G-2507)
CXR Strategies LLC ....G.... 516 998-0400
Royal Palm Beach (G-15464)
Ds Healthcare Group Inc ....C.... 888 404-7770
Doral (G-3336)
Eve Corporation ....E.... 305 599-3832
Boca Raton (G-524)
Fekkai Retail LLC ....D.... 866 514-8048
Plantation (G-14515)
Ladove Industries Inc ....G.... 305 624-2456
Miami Lakes (G-10804)
Luxebrands LLC ....F.... 866 514-8048
Plantation (G-14530)
Pure Life Products LLC ....G.... 321 578-2060
Miami (G-10216)
Roux Laboratories Inc ....G.... 904 378-4167
Jacksonville (G-6737)
Sabrosol Laboratories LLC ....G.... 305 290-4038
North Miami (G-11653)

HAIR CARE PRDTS: Hair Coloring Preparations

Beautyge Brands Usa Inc ....C.... 904 693-1200
Jacksonville (G-6201)
Epitomi Inc ....E.... 305 971-5370
Miami (G-9532)
Pure-Chlor Systems Florida Inc ....F.... 305 437-9937
Tampa (G-18025)
Xtreme Tools International Inc ....E.... 305 622-7474
Opa Locka (G-12371)

HAIR CARE PRDTS: Home Permanent Kits

Stylors Inc ....F.... 904 765-4453
Jacksonville (G-6820)

HAIR CARE PRDTS: Tonics

M & S Computer Products Inc ....G.... 561 244-5400
Boynton Beach (G-930)
Van Tibolli Beauty Corp ....E.... 305 390-0044
Fort Lauderdale (G-4304)

HAIR CURLERS: Beauty Shop

Stylors Inc ....F.... 904 765-4453
Jacksonville (G-6820)

HAIR DRESSING, FOR THE TRADE

Destiny & Light Inc ....F.... 813 476-8386
Tampa (G-17601)
Queen B Hair Collection LLC ....F.... 954 393-2791
Miami (G-10224)

HAND TOOLS, NEC: Wholesalers

Db Tucker LLC ....G.... 561 301-4974
Jupiter (G-7023)
Marbelite International Corp ....G.... 941 378-0860
Sarasota (G-16502)

HANDBAG STORES

Mrkt Deux ....G.... 305 603-9682
Miami (G-10049)

HANDBAGS

Mrkt Deux ....G.... 305 603-9682
Miami (G-10049)

HANDBAGS: Men's

Gar Industries Corp ....F.... 954 456-8088
Hallandale Beach (G-5188)

HANDBAGS: Women's

Becarro International Corp ....G.... 561 737-5585
West Palm Beach (G-18815)
Excel Handbags Co Inc ....F.... 305 836-8800
Miami (G-9543)
Gar Industries Corp ....F.... 954 456-8088
Hallandale Beach (G-5188)

HANDLES: Wood

Davanti Doors Llc ....G.... 239 842-8341
Fort Myers (G-4426)

HANDYMAN SVCS

Los Primos Express Service ....G.... 786 701-3297
Miami (G-9912)

HANG GLIDERS

Miami Hang Gliding Corp ....G.... 863 805-0440
Clewiston (G-1984)

HARDWARE

Advance Panel Corp ....G.... 347 399-6732
Miami Lakes (G-10759)
Alpine Engineered Products ....E.... 954 781-3333
Pompano Beach (G-14589)
American Marine Coverings Inc ....F.... 305 889-5355
Hialeah (G-5292)
Automation Consulting Inc ....F.... 850 477-6477
Pensacola (G-14095)
Beachcomber Fibrgls Tech Inc ....G.... 772 283-0200
Stuart (G-16914)
Biosculptor Corporation ....G.... 305 823-8300
Hialeah (G-5326)
Bms International Inc ....E.... 813 247-7040
Tampa (G-17477)
Brown (usa) Inc ....F.... 305 593-9228
Miami (G-9280)
Consolidated Ace Hdwr Sup Inc ....G.... 850 939-9800
Navarre (G-11465)
CT Hydraulics Inc ....F.... 724 342-3089
Sanibel (G-16145)
Custom Marble Works Inc ....E.... 813 620-0475
Tampa (G-17580)
E-Z Fastening Solutions Inc ....G.... 813 854-3937
Oldsmar (G-12223)
Florida Pool Products Inc ....E.... 727 531-8913
Clearwater (G-1690)
General Clamp Industries Inc ....F.... 407 859-6000
Orlando (G-12777)
Goodrich Corporation ....C.... 904 757-3660
Jacksonville (G-6441)
Halliday Products Inc ....D.... 407 298-4470
Orlando (G-12794)
Hardware Concepts Inc ....G.... 305 685-1337
Miami (G-9687)
Hardware Online Store ....F.... 954 565-5678
Fort Lauderdale (G-4042)
Inland Specialties Inc ....G.... 941 756-1234
Sarasota (G-16237)
Inter Gard R&D LLC ....F.... 954 476-5574
Sunrise (G-17129)
International Dock Products ....F.... 954 964-5315
Hallandale Beach (G-5191)
Ipline LLC ....F.... 305 675-4235
Miami (G-9767)
James D Nall Co Inc ....E.... 305 884-8363
Fort Lauderdale (G-4074)
Jefco Manufacturing Inc ....E.... 954 527-4220
Fort Lauderdale (G-4078)
Loos & Co Inc ....D.... 239 643-5667
Naples (G-11316)
Mermaid Mfg Southwest Fla Inc ....F.... 239 418-0535
Fort Myers (G-4528)
Mobile Rugged Tech Corp ....G.... 781 771-6743
Winter Park (G-19427)
Pompanette LLC ....E.... 813 885-2182
Tampa (G-17997)
Practical Design Products Co ....E.... 561 995-4023
Boca Raton (G-671)
Precise Technologies Inc ....F.... 727 535-5594
Largo (G-8030)
Press-Rite Inc ....G.... 954 963-7373
Miramar (G-11030)
Rampmaster Inc ....F.... 305 691-9090
Miami (G-10238)
Savvy Associate Inc ....F.... 954 941-6986
Pompano Beach (G-14840)
SBs Precision Shtmtl Inc ....E.... 321 951-7411
Melbourne (G-8927)
Southern Die Casting Corp ....E.... 305 635-6571
Miami (G-10385)
Stainless Fabricators Inc ....E.... 813 926-7113
Odessa (G-12155)
Taylor Made Systems Brdnton In ....C.... 941 747-1900
Oviedo (G-13461)
Window Craftsmen Inc ....E.... 941 922-1844
Sarasota (G-16641)

HARDWARE & BUILDING PRDTS: Plastic

Advanced Drainage & Hydro Inc ....G.... 813 957-3162
Lutz (G-8374)
Bruce R Ely Enterprise Inc ....F.... 727 573-1643
Clearwater (G-1614)
Dillco Inc ....F.... 386 734-7510
Deland (G-2971)
Florida Amico ....G.... 863 688-9256
Lakeland (G-7689)
Mercer Products Company Inc ....E.... 352 357-0057
Umatilla (G-18499)
Paragon Plastics Inc ....E.... 321 631-6212
Titusville (G-18448)
Plastic Components Inc ....E.... 305 885-0561
Medley (G-8707)
Protective Enclosures Co LLC ....G.... 321 441-9689
Altamonte Springs (G-68)
Shwinco Industries Inc ....E.... 850 271-8900
Lynn Haven (G-8438)
Vinyl Corp ....F.... 305 477-6464
Miami (G-10586)
Walt Dittmer and Sons Inc ....E.... 407 699-1755
Winter Springs (G-19488)

HARDWARE STORES

Panhandle Paint & Dctg LLC ....G.... 850 596-9248
Panama City Beach (G-13981)

HARDWARE STORES: Builders'

Hare Lumber & Ready Mix Inc ....F.... 863 983-8725
Clewiston (G-1982)
Trim-Pak Corporation ....E.... 407 851-8900
Orlando (G-13273)
W R Williams Enterprises Inc ....G.... 813 677-2000
Gibsonton (G-5035)

HARDWARE STORES: Door Locks & Lock Sets

Architctral Mllwk Slutions Inc ....G.... 727 441-1409
Largo (G-7899)
Visions Millwork Inc ....F.... 239 390-0811
Fort Myers (G-4648)

HARDWARE STORES: Pumps & Pumping Eqpt

Oase North America Inc ....G.... 800 365-3880
Riviera Beach (G-15354)

HARDWARE STORES: Tools

Tekk Supply Inc ....G.... 954 444-5782
Pompano Beach (G-14884)

HARDWARE WHOLESALERS

Deco Truss Company Inc ....E.... 305 257-1910
Homestead (G-5962)
E-Z Fastening Solutions Inc ....G.... 813 854-3937
Oldsmar (G-12223)
Lockheed Martin Corporation ....G.... 407 517-6627
Orlando (G-12921)
Round Table Tools Inc ....G.... 850 877-7650
Tallahassee (G-17318)
Shashy Enterprises Inc ....G.... 352 732-3904
Ocala (G-12047)
Wink Streaming Llc ....G.... 312 281-5444
Miami (G-10611)

HARDWARE, WHOLESALE: Builders', NEC

A-Fabco Inc ....E.... 813 677-8790
Gibsonton (G-5024)
Certified Whl Exterior Pdts ....G.... 407 654-7170
Winter Garden (G-19256)
Hare Lumber & Ready Mix Inc ....F.... 863 983-8725
Clewiston (G-1982)
Suncoast Post-Tension Ltd ....E.... 305 592-5075
Miami (G-10430)
Trim-Pak Corporation ....E.... 407 851-8900
Orlando (G-13273)
W R Williams Enterprises Inc ....G.... 813 677-2000
Gibsonton (G-5035)

HARDWARE: Aircraft

Aerospace Retail Inc..............F...... 888 918-8116
Boca Raton *(G-405)*
Altum Aerospace..............F...... 954 618-6573
Sunrise *(G-17089)*
Aviation Intl Solutions LLC..............G...... 305 267-7117
Hialeah *(G-5313)*
Aviation Parts & Trade Corp..............G...... 954 944-2828
Plantation *(G-14495)*
D I R Inc..............G...... 863 661-5360
Lakeland *(G-7669)*
Pcs Aerospace & Marketing LLC..............E...... 973 352-9159
Cutler Bay *(G-2407)*
Precision Shapes Inc..............E...... 321 269-2555
Titusville *(G-18453)*
Ver-Val Enterprises Inc..............F...... 850 244-7931
Fort Walton Beach *(G-4838)*

HARDWARE: Aircraft & Marine, Incl Pulleys & Similar Items

Longbow Marine Inc..............G...... 954 616-5737
Fort Lauderdale *(G-4102)*
Warfighter Fcsed Logistics Inc..............F...... 740 513-4692
Fort Lauderdale *(G-4313)*

HARDWARE: Builders'

Dayton Superior Corporation..............G...... 407 859-4541
Orlando *(G-12657)*
Doorknob Discount Center LLC..............G...... 813 963-3104
Lutz *(G-8380)*
M&C Hardware LLC..............G...... 305 971-9444
Miami *(G-9928)*
Phg Kendall LLC..............F...... 954 392-8788
Hollywood *(G-5891)*
Td Tra -Dix Supply Inc..............G...... 727 869-8662
Hudson *(G-6039)*
Venture Circle Enterprises LLC..............F...... 407 678-7489
Sanford *(G-16131)*

HARDWARE: Cabinet

Barr Systems LLC..............E...... 352 491-3100
Gainesville *(G-4883)*
Divine Dovetail..............G...... 561 245-7601
Boca Raton *(G-504)*
Strategic Brands Inc..............F...... 516 745-6100
Pompano Beach *(G-14875)*
Woodies Inc..............G...... 305 266-9209
Miami *(G-10618)*

HARDWARE: Door Opening & Closing Devices, Exc Electrical

Marko Garage Doors & Gates Inc..............G...... 561 547-4001
Palm Springs *(G-13776)*

HARDWARE: Furniture

C & S Plastics..............E...... 863 294-5628
Winter Haven *(G-19309)*

HARDWARE: Furniture, Builders' & Other Household

Mica Craft & Design Inc..............F...... 561 863-5354
West Palm Beach *(G-18950)*
Ocean Dynamics USA Inc..............G...... 305 770-1800
Miami *(G-10088)*
Shorr Enterprises Inc..............F...... 954 733-9840
Lauderdale Lakes *(G-8093)*

HARDWARE: Parachute

Jco Metals Inc..............F...... 386 734-5867
Deland *(G-2987)*
Mirage Systems Inc..............F...... 386 740-9222
Deland *(G-2997)*
Uninsred Untd Prchute Tech LLC..............D...... 386 736-7589
Deland *(G-3027)*

HARDWARE: Rubber

Shaw Development LLC..............C...... 239 405-6100
Bonita Springs *(G-853)*
Warfighter Fcsed Logistics Inc..............F...... 740 513-4692
Fort Lauderdale *(G-4313)*

HARNESS ASSEMBLIES: Cable & Wire

Aero Electronics Systems Inc..............G...... 321 269-0478
Titusville *(G-18411)*
Automatic Coax and Cable Inc..............E...... 407 322-7622
Sanford *(G-15999)*
Backbone Interconnect LLC..............E...... 954 800-4749
Sunrise *(G-17093)*
Carlisle Interconnect Tech Inc..............A...... 904 829-5600
Saint Augustine *(G-15526)*
Electro Technik Industries Inc..............D...... 727 530-9555
Clearwater *(G-1666)*
Interconnect Cable Tech Corp..............D...... 352 796-1716
Brooksville *(G-1237)*
Ksm Electronics Inc..............D...... 954 642-7050
Tamarac *(G-17361)*
Paal Technologies Inc..............G...... 954 368-5000
Sunrise *(G-17156)*
Pacer Electronics Florida Inc..............E...... 941 378-5774
Sarasota *(G-16534)*
Paradise Cable Industries..............F...... 941 488-6092
Venice *(G-18566)*
Paramount Electronic Mfg Co..............E...... 954 781-3755
Boca Raton *(G-662)*
Paramount Industries Inc..............E...... 954 781-3755
Pompano Beach *(G-14784)*
Sound Connections Intl..............G...... 813 948-2707
Lutz *(G-8419)*
Spectraflex Inc..............G...... 850 892-3900
Defuniak Springs *(G-2947)*
Superior Electronics..............G...... 941 355-9500
Sarasota *(G-16307)*
Tensolite LLC..............A...... 904 829-5600
Saint Augustine *(G-15626)*
Trinity Manufacturing Corp..............E...... 941 727-9595
Bradenton *(G-1131)*
Unique Electronics Inc..............C...... 407 422-3051
Orlando *(G-13291)*

HARNESSES, HALTERS, SADDLERY & STRAPS

Longchamp Usa Inc..............E...... 305 372-1628
Miami *(G-9908)*

HEADPHONES: Radio

Joyce Telectronics Corp..............F...... 727 461-3525
Zephyrhills *(G-19525)*

HEALTH AIDS: Exercise Eqpt

American Quality Mfg Inc..............F...... 321 636-3434
Cocoa *(G-1995)*
Lifetime Wellness Centers Inc..............F...... 321 693-8698
Melbourne *(G-8873)*
Medx Corporation..............F...... 352 351-2005
Ocala *(G-11997)*
Vertimax LLC..............G...... 800 699-5867
Tampa *(G-18240)*

HEALTH AIDS: Vaporizers

Warehouse Goods LLC..............E...... 877 865-2260
Boca Raton *(G-787)*

HEALTH FOOD & SUPPLEMENT STORES

Natural-Immunogenics Corp..............D...... 888 328-8840
Sarasota *(G-16265)*
Organic Amazon Corp..............G...... 305 365-7811
Key Biscayne *(G-7161)*

HEARING AIDS

Affordable At Home Has Inc..............G...... 786 200-0484
Miami *(G-9085)*
Audina Hearing Instruments..............D...... 407 331-0077
Longwood *(G-8259)*
Bell Hearing Instruments Inc..............E...... 813 814-2355
Oldsmar *(G-12211)*
Captel Inc..............D...... 407 730-3397
Orlando *(G-12549)*
Ear-Tronics Inc..............G...... 239 275-7655
Fort Myers *(G-4440)*
Eartech Inc..............G...... 941 747-8193
Bradenton *(G-1034)*
Florida Best Hearing..............E...... 863 402-0094
Boynton Beach *(G-907)*
Florida North Hearing Solution..............F...... 386 466-0902
Gainesville *(G-4921)*
Hear For You Hearing Aid Ctr..............G...... 850 316-4414
Pensacola *(G-14170)*
Miami..............F...... 954 874-7707
Miami *(G-9991)*
Morton Plant Mease Health Care..............A...... 727 462-7052
Clearwater *(G-1793)*
N-Ear Pro Inc..............E...... 877 290-4599
Tampa *(G-17926)*
Physician Hearing Care..............F...... 239 261-7722
Naples *(G-11364)*
Precision Laboratories Inc..............E...... 407 774-4261
Longwood *(G-8328)*
Truear Inc..............F...... 352 314-8805
Mount Dora *(G-11117)*

HEARING TESTING SVCS

Florida Best Hearing..............E...... 863 402-0094
Boynton Beach *(G-907)*

HEAT EXCHANGERS

Monitor Products Inc..............D...... 352 544-2620
Brooksville *(G-1254)*

HEAT TREATING: Metal

Braddck Mtllgl Arsp Ser Inc..............F...... 561 622-2200
Boynton Beach *(G-884)*
Braddock Metallurgical Inc..............F...... 386 267-0955
Jacksonville *(G-6229)*
Braddock Metallurgical GA Inc..............F...... 386 267-0955
Daytona Beach *(G-2632)*
Braddock Metallurgical MGT LLC..............E...... 386 267-0955
Daytona Beach *(G-2633)*
Braddock Mtllrgcal - Dytona In..............G...... 386 267-0955
Daytona Beach *(G-2634)*
Braddock Mtllurgical Holdg Inc..............G...... 386 323-1500
Daytona Beach *(G-2635)*
Dynamic Alloy..............F...... 352 728-7600
Leesburg *(G-8153)*
Heat Treating Incorporated..............D...... 352 245-8811
Belleview *(G-370)*
Nelco Products Inc..............G...... 727 533-8282
Clearwater *(G-1806)*
Suncoast Heat Treat Inc..............F...... 386 267-0955
Daytona Beach *(G-2721)*
Suncoast Heat Treat Inc..............F...... 561 776-7763
Boynton Beach *(G-965)*
Superheat Fgh Services Inc..............G...... 519 396-1324
Bartow *(G-334)*
Thermal Braze Inc..............G...... 561 746-6640
Jupiter *(G-7127)*
Whertec Inc..............D...... 904 278-6503
Jacksonville *(G-6917)*

HEATERS: Swimming Pool, Electric

Aquacal Autopilot Inc..............C...... 727 823-5642
Saint Petersburg *(G-15705)*

HEATERS: Swimming Pool, Oil Or Gas

Gulf Associates Control Inc..............E...... 954 426-0536
Deerfield Beach *(G-2833)*

HEATING & AIR CONDITIONING UNITS, COMBINATION

Addison Hvac LLC..............C...... 407 292-4400
Orlando *(G-12430)*
Air & Power Solutions Inc..............G...... 954 427-0019
Coconut Creek *(G-2068)*
Data Cooling Tech Canada LLC..............E...... 813 865-4701
Tampa *(G-17590)*
Lorenze & Associates Inc..............G...... 407 682-7570
Altamonte Springs *(G-53)*
Miles of Smiles Rides Inc..............F...... 727 528-1227
Seminole *(G-16753)*
Ross Slade Inc..............G...... 813 250-0488
Tampa *(G-18069)*

HEATING APPARATUS: Steam

Leslie Controls Inc..............C...... 813 978-1000
Temple Terrace *(G-18371)*

HEATING EQPT & SPLYS

Alfa Laval Inc..............G...... 941 727-1900
Sarasota *(G-16173)*
Duststop Filters Inc..............G...... 904 725-1001
Jacksonville *(G-6338)*
Innovative Heat Concepts LLC..............G...... 305 248-4971
Homestead *(G-5971)*

PRODUCT

Employee Codes: A=Over 500 employees, B=251-500
C=101-250, D=51-100, E=20-50, F=10-19, G=4-9

Jer-Air Manufacturing Inc ....E....... 352 591-2674
Micanopy *(G-10902)*
R & J Mfg of Gainesville....................G....... 352 375-3130
Gainesville *(G-4987)*
Southland Power & Enrgy Co LLC........G....... 800 217-6040
Fort Lauderdale *(G-4251)*

HEATING EQPT: Complete

Stan Weaver & Co Inc............................E....... 407 581-6940
Orlando *(G-13211)*

HEATING UNITS & DEVICES: Indl, Electric

Aruki Services LLC................................G....... 850 364-5206
Havana *(G-5232)*

HELICOPTERS

Astrum Travel Intl Ltd..............................F....... 917 779-9462
Miami *(G-9181)*
Aviation Intl Solutions LLC....................G....... 305 267-7117
Hialeah *(G-5313)*
Blue Hole Helicopters Inc........................F....... 561 723-0378
Jupiter *(G-7012)*
Climax Am LLC......................................G....... 786 502-5757
Pembroke Pines *(G-14028)*
Florida Sncast Helicopters LLC..............F....... 941 355-1525
Sarasota *(G-16214)*
Heli Aviation Florida LLC......................G....... 941 355-1525
Sarasota *(G-16226)*
Heli-Tech Inc...F....... 850 763-9000
Panama City *(G-13914)*
Mc Dermott Enterprises Inc....................G....... 262 593-8612
Fort Myers *(G-4525)*
Rockymountain Lifenet..........................G....... 863 533-5168
Bartow *(G-331)*
Van Nevel Aerospace LLC......................G....... 337 936-2504
Cottondale *(G-2333)*
Vertical Aviation Technologies..............F....... 407 322-9488
Sanford *(G-16133)*

HELMETS: Athletic

Jay Squared LLC....................................F....... 386 677-7700
Daytona Beach *(G-2675)*
Tavarez Sporting Goods Inc..................G....... 347 441-9690
Miami *(G-10461)*

HELMETS: Steel

Helicopter Helmet LLC..........................G....... 843 556-0405
Melbourne *(G-8841)*

HELP SUPPLY SERVICES

Granite Services Intl Inc..........................F....... 813 242-7400
Tampa *(G-17724)*

HIDES & SKINS

Adirondack Meat Company Inc............F....... 518 585-2333
Cape Coral *(G-1374)*

HIGH ENERGY PARTICLE PHYSICS EQPT

Natures Power and Energy LLC............F....... 813 907-6279
Wesley Chapel *(G-18753)*
Novena TEC LLC....................................E....... 407 392-1868
Orlando *(G-13011)*

HITCHES: Trailer

Rvcc of Florida..G....... 352 569-5870
Bushnell *(G-1320)*

HOBBY, TOY & GAME STORES: Hobbies, NEC

Daytona Magic Inc..................................G....... 386 252-6767
Daytona Beach *(G-2655)*

HOISTS

Beta Max Inc..E....... 321 727-3737
Palm Bay *(G-13502)*
High Tech Hoist Corp..............................G....... 321 733-3387
Melbourne *(G-8843)*
Hook International Inc............................G....... 727 209-0855
Largo *(G-7974)*

HOLDING COMPANIES, NEC

New World Holdings Inc........................E....... 561 888-4939
Boca Raton *(G-642)*

HOLDING COMPANIES: Investment, Exc Banks

Blue Summit Wind LLC..........................G....... 561 691-7171
Juno Beach *(G-6975)*
Industrial Service Solutions....................C....... 239 288-5230
Fort Myers *(G-4493)*
Laporte Inv Holdings Inc........................G....... 863 294-4498
Winter Haven *(G-19335)*
Ronecker Holdings LLC..........................G....... 813 855-5559
Oldsmar *(G-12268)*

HOME ENTERTAINMENT EQPT: Electronic, NEC

A-N-L Home Solutions LLC....................F....... 954 648-2623
Miami *(G-9046)*
Freshetech LLC..G....... 516 519-3453
Orlando *(G-12765)*
Visual Acoustics LLC..............................G....... 786 390-6128
Miami *(G-10590)*

HOME ENTERTAINMENT REPAIR SVCS

Visual Acoustics LLC..............................G....... 786 390-6128
Miami *(G-10590)*

HOME FURNISHINGS WHOLESALERS

Art & Frame Source Inc..........................E....... 727 329-6502
Saint Petersburg *(G-15711)*
Ben Kaufman Sales Co Inc....................E....... 305 688-2144
Medley *(G-8621)*
Euroasia Products Inc..............................G....... 321 221-9398
Orlando *(G-12719)*
Gfx Inc...E....... 305 499-9789
Miami *(G-9634)*
Kasulik II LLC..F....... 786 629-8978
Hallandale Beach *(G-5195)*
Venture Circle Enterprises LLC..............F....... 407 678-7489
Sanford *(G-16131)*

HOME IMPROVEMENT & RENOVATION CONTRACTOR AGENCY

Tropic Shield Inc......................................F....... 954 731-5553
Lauderdale Lakes *(G-8095)*

HOME MOVIES DEVELOPING & PROCESSING

Columbia Films Inc..................................G....... 800 531-3238
Pompano Beach *(G-14641)*

HOMEFURNISHING STORES: Barbeque Grills

Werever Products Inc..............................F....... 813 241-9701
Riverview *(G-15287)*

HOMEFURNISHING STORES: Beddings & Linens

Fabric Innovations Inc............................E....... 305 860-5757
Miami *(G-9555)*

HOMEFURNISHING STORES: Brushes

Torrington Brush Works Inc....................F....... 941 355-1499
Sarasota *(G-16622)*

HOMEFURNISHING STORES: Lighting Fixtures

Lumilum LLC..F....... 305 233-2844
Miami *(G-9918)*

HOMEFURNISHING STORES: Vertical Blinds

Tropic Shield Inc......................................F....... 954 731-5553
Lauderdale Lakes *(G-8095)*
Vertical Village Inc..................................G....... 772 340-0400
Port Saint Lucie *(G-15162)*

HOMEFURNISHING STORES: Window Shades, NEC

Kelsies Blinds..G....... 407 977-0827
Oviedo *(G-13445)*
Vertical Land Inc......................................F....... 850 819-2535
Panama City *(G-13960)*

HOMEFURNISHINGS & SPLYS, WHOLESALE: Decorative

Crystal Art of Florida Inc........................G....... 305 885-5358
Coral Springs *(G-2235)*
Pastrana Prime LLC................................F....... 407 470-9339
Orlando *(G-13052)*

HOMEFURNISHINGS, WHOLESALE: Blinds, Venetian

Total Window Inc......................................G....... 954 921-0109
Dania *(G-2459)*

HOMEFURNISHINGS, WHOLESALE: Blinds, Vertical

Bornt Enterprises Inc..............................E....... 813 623-1492
Tampa *(G-17483)*
Florida Pwdr Cting Shtters Inc..............F....... 561 588-2410
Lantana *(G-7874)*
Sutton Draperies Inc................................F....... 305 653-7738
Miami *(G-10443)*

HOMEFURNISHINGS, WHOLESALE: Decorating Splys

Fleurissima Inc..F....... 305 572-0203
Miami *(G-9575)*

HOMEFURNISHINGS, WHOLESALE: Draperies

Paul Himber Inc..F....... 561 586-3741
West Palm Beach *(G-18990)*

HOMEFURNISHINGS, WHOLESALE: Kitchenware

La Cuisine Intl Distrs Inc........................E....... 305 418-0010
Miami *(G-9839)*

HOMEFURNISHINGS, WHOLESALE: Mirrors/Pictures, Framed/Unframd

Art Connection Usa LLC..........................E....... 954 781-0125
Pompano Beach *(G-14600)*

HOMEFURNISHINGS, WHOLESALE: Pillowcases

Elaine Smith Inc..F....... 561 863-3333
Riviera Beach *(G-15325)*
Fabric Innovations Inc..............................E....... 305 860-5757
Miami *(G-9555)*

HOMEFURNISHINGS, WHOLESALE: Pottery

Well Traveled Imports Inc........................F....... 904 261-5400
Amelia Island *(G-93)*

HOMEFURNISHINGS, WHOLESALE: Sheets, Textile

Vestagen Tchnical Textiles Inc................G....... 407 781-2570
Orlando *(G-13300)*

HOMEFURNISHINGS, WHOLESALE: Window Covering Parts & Access

Ortega Industries and Mfg......................D....... 305 688-0090
Opa Locka *(G-12348)*
West Coast Shutters Sunburst................F....... 727 894-0044
Saint Petersburg *(G-15957)*

HOMEFURNISHINGS, WHOLESALE: Wood Flooring

Designer Lifestyles LLC..........................F....... 904 631-8954
Jacksonville *(G-6317)*

HOMES, MODULAR: Wooden

All Modular Service Inc............................F....... 352 429-0868
Mascotte *(G-8593)*
HI Tech Construction Svc Inc..................E....... 863 968-0731
Winter Haven *(G-19328)*
Island Style Homes Inc............................G....... 772 464-6259
Fort Pierce *(G-4709)*

Jennings Mobile HM Set Up LLC ....F 863 965-0883
Auburndale *(G-247)*
Stalo Modulars LLC ....F 786 713-2410
Miami *(G-10408)*

HONES

Hone Renovation Specialists........G....... 407 202-3536
Orlando *(G-12808)*

HONEYCOMB CORE & BOARD: Made From Purchased Materials

Nida-Core Corporation ....E....... 772 343-7300
Port Saint Lucie *(G-15124)*

HORMONES OR DERIVATIVES

Natures Botanicals Inc ....G....... 727 443-4524
Clearwater *(G-1803)*

HORSE & PET ACCESSORIES: Textile

Ronmar Industries Inc........F 561 630-8035
West Palm Beach *(G-19023)*

HORSE ACCESS: Harnesses & Riding Crops, Etc, Exc Leather

Sandi Johnson ....G....... 561 389-1035
Dunnellon *(G-3599)*

HORSESHOES

Blue Horseshoe Pools West Inc........G....... 321 287-8758
Clermont *(G-1950)*
Dockside At Horseshoe Beach L........G....... 352 377-4616
Gainesville *(G-4906)*
Horseshoe Knoll Lc........G....... 850 894-0824
Tallahassee *(G-17280)*
Horseshoe Picking Inc ....F 305 345-5778
Homestead *(G-5969)*
Horseshoe Shrimp Boat LLC........G....... 352 356-1982
Horseshoe Beach *(G-6007)*
Jmg Strategies LLC ....G....... 305 606-2117
Miami Beach *(G-10686)*

HOSE: Automobile, Rubber

Hitachi Cable America Inc........C....... 850 476-0907
Pensacola *(G-14173)*

HOSE: Flexible Metal

Microflex Inc........E....... 386 672-1945
Ormond Beach *(G-13386)*
Space Coast Hydraulics Inc........F 321 504-6006
Rockledge *(G-15449)*
Unaflex LLC ....E....... 954 943-5002
Pompano Beach *(G-14898)*

HOSE: Plastic

Uip International Inc ....G....... 954 785-3539
Pompano Beach *(G-14896)*

HOSE: Pneumatic, Rubber Or Rubberized Fabric, NEC

Space Coast Hydraulics Inc........F 321 504-6006
Rockledge *(G-15449)*
Unaflex LLC ....E....... 954 943-5002
Pompano Beach *(G-14898)*

HOSE: Rubber

Fluid Routing Solutions LLC ....B....... 352 732-0222
Ocala *(G-11948)*
Space Coast Distributors........G....... 386 239-0305
Daytona Beach *(G-2718)*

HOSES & BELTING: Rubber & Plastic

Hecht Rubber Corporation........E....... 904 731-3401
Jacksonville *(G-6466)*
Varibelt Incorporated........G....... 305 775-1568
Miami *(G-10569)*

HOSPITAL EQPT REPAIR SVCS

Mobility Freedom Inc........G....... 407 495-1333
Orlando *(G-12974)*

HOT TUBS

Aquacal........E....... 727 898-2412
Saint Petersburg *(G-15704)*
Techno-Spa Manufacturing Inc........G....... 386 239-8980
Daytona Beach *(G-2723)*

HOT TUBS: Plastic & Fiberglass

Hot Tub Parts LLC........G....... 727 573-9611
Saint Petersburg *(G-15808)*

HOUSEHOLD APPLIANCE STORES

AAA Able Appliance Service........G....... 954 791-5222
Fort Lauderdale *(G-3774)*

HOUSEHOLD APPLIANCE STORES: Appliance Parts

Fusion AC & Appl Svc LLC ....G....... 888 670-8435
Pompano Beach *(G-14707)*

HOUSEHOLD ARTICLES, EXC FURNITURE: Cut Stone

Architctural MBL Importers Inc ....E....... 941 365-3552
Sarasota *(G-16347)*
Italian Cast Stones Inc........E....... 813 902-8900
Tampa *(G-17796)*

HOUSEHOLD ARTICLES: Metal

6 Ports LLC........F 561 743-8696
Jupiter *(G-6990)*

HOUSEHOLD FURNISHINGS, NEC

Brenda Naused........G....... 352 344-4729
Daytona Beach *(G-2636)*
C-Worthy Corp ....F 954 784-7370
Pompano Beach *(G-14629)*
D W A Inc........F....... 941 444-1134
Sarasota *(G-16401)*
Elegant House Intl LLC........G....... 954 457-8836
Hallandale *(G-5157)*
Home Source Manufacturing Inc........E....... 404 663-0647
Marianna *(G-8579)*
Mecox Gardens & Pottery Inc ....G....... 561 805-8611
Palm Beach *(G-13559)*
Remas Draperies Etc Inc........G....... 904 845-9300
Hilliard *(G-5716)*
Sands At St Lucie ....G....... 772 489-9499
Fort Pierce *(G-4742)*
Shower Doors & More Inc ....G....... 954 358-2014
Fort Lauderdale *(G-4231)*
Top Trtment Cstomes Accesories ....G....... 239 936-4600
Fort Myers *(G-4632)*
Victors Cstm Qilting Bedspread........G....... 305 362-1990
Hialeah *(G-5678)*
Westpoint Home Inc ....B....... 850 415-4100
Chipley *(G-1549)*

HOUSEWARES, ELECTRIC, EXC COOKING APPLIANCES & UTENSILS

Db Tucker LLC........G....... 561 301-4974
Jupiter *(G-7023)*

HOUSEWARES, ELECTRIC: Air Purifiers, Portable

Airfree USA LLC........F 305 772-6577
Miami *(G-9097)*
Healthquest Technologies LLC ....G....... 850 997-6300
Monticello *(G-11076)*
Pyure Company Inc ....E 561 735-3701
Boynton Beach *(G-948)*

HOUSEWARES, ELECTRIC: Appliances, Personal

Alton Manufacturing Inc........G....... 305 821-0701
Miami *(G-9126)*

HOUSEWARES, ELECTRIC: Broilers

Charcoal Chef Usa LLC ....G 786 273-6511
Miami *(G-9349)*

HOUSEWARES, ELECTRIC: Cooking Appliances

Russell Hobbs Inc........D....... 954 883-1000
Miramar *(G-11037)*

HOUSEWARES, ELECTRIC: Curlers, Hair

Charles & Co LLC ....F....... 404 592-1190
Fort Lauderdale *(G-3896)*
Van Tibolli Beauty Corp........E 305 390-0044
Fort Lauderdale *(G-4304)*

HOUSEWARES, ELECTRIC: Dryers, Hand & Face

Balla De Rodriguez Migdalia M........G....... 305 228-6566
Miami *(G-9216)*
Saniflow Corporation........G....... 305 424-2433
Miami *(G-10302)*
Veltia Usa LLC ....G....... 305 298-8262
Coral Gables *(G-2204)*

HOUSEWARES, ELECTRIC: Fans, Exhaust & Ventilating

Air-Tech of Pensacola Inc ....F 850 433-6443
Pensacola *(G-14087)*
Fan America Inc ....G....... 941 955-9788
Sarasota *(G-16426)*

HOUSEWARES, ELECTRIC: Heaters, Immersion

Intelligent Heater LLC........G....... 305 248-4971
Homestead *(G-5973)*

HOUSEWARES, ELECTRIC: Heating, Bsbrd/Wall, Radiant Heat

and-Dell Corporation ....E....... 954 523-6478
Fort Lauderdale *(G-3816)*

HOUSEWARES, ELECTRIC: Lighters, Cigarette

Vapor Group Inc ....F 954 792-8450
Miami *(G-10568)*

HOUSEWARES, ELECTRIC: Massage Machines, Exc Beauty/Barber

Simulated Envmt Concepts Inc ....F 754 263-3184
Hollywood *(G-5908)*

HOUSEWARES: Dishes, Earthenware

Kitchenista Corp ....G....... 305 400-4992
Coral Gables *(G-2165)*

HOUSEWARES: Dishes, Plastic

Corkcicle LLC........E....... 866 780-0007
Orlando *(G-12621)*
Corrigan & Company ....G....... 904 353-5936
Jacksonville *(G-6293)*
D&W Fine Pack LLC........D....... 305 592-4329
Doral *(G-3320)*
Hans-Mill Corp........D....... 904 395-2288
Jacksonville *(G-6460)*
Kasulik II LLC........F 786 629-8978
Hallandale Beach *(G-5195)*
Novelty Crystal Corp ....D....... 352 429-9036
Groveland *(G-5103)*
Tupperware Turkey Inc ....D....... 407 826-5050
Orlando *(G-13282)*

HOUSEWARES: Toothpicks, Wood

Pixotine Products Inc ....G....... 305 479-1335
Jupiter *(G-7093)*

HUB CAPS: Automobile, Stamped Metal

Clever Covers Inc........G....... 407 423-5959
Orlando *(G-12590)*

HYDRAULIC EQPT REPAIR SVC

Alpha Hydraulics LLC........G....... 561 355-0318
Riviera Beach *(G-15297)*

HYDRAULIC FLUIDS: Synthetic Based

Element Solutions Inc ....B.... 561 207-9600
Fort Lauderdale *(G-3968)*
HB Sealing Products Inc ....C.... 727 796-1300
Clearwater *(G-1712)*

HYDROELECTRIC POWER GENERATION

Sepac Corp ....F.... 305 718-3379
Miami *(G-10325)*

Hard Rubber & Molded Rubber Prdts

General Fine Machine Co Inc ....G.... 727 726-5956
Safety Harbor *(G-15494)*
Hernol Usa Inc ....E.... 786 263-3341
Coral Gables *(G-2155)*
Lakeland Lures Inc ....G.... 863 644-3127
Lakeland *(G-7731)*
Revere Manufactured Pdts Inc ....G.... 904 503-9733
Jacksonville *(G-6719)*
Tomsons Inc ....G.... 248 646-0677
Englewood *(G-3685)*

ICE

Atlantic Dry Ice Corportion ....F.... 305 592-7000
Miami *(G-9182)*
Btu Reps LLC ....F.... 727 235-3591
Saint Petersburg *(G-15730)*
Central Florida Ice Services ....G.... 407 779-0161
Orlando *(G-12568)*
Florida Ice Corporation ....F.... 305 685-9377
Opa Locka *(G-12316)*
Gainesville Ice Company ....F.... 352 378-2604
Gainesville *(G-4926)*
Hialeah Distribution Corp ....E.... 786 200-2498
Hialeah *(G-5444)*
Ice Magic-Orlando Inc ....D.... 407 816-1905
Orlando *(G-12819)*
Orlando Ice Servive Corp ....G.... 407 999-4940
Orlando *(G-13033)*
Reddy Ice Corporation ....G.... 772 461-5046
Fort Pierce *(G-4740)*
Reddy Ice Corporation ....F.... 904 388-2653
Jacksonville *(G-6710)*
Reddy Ice Corporation ....F.... 850 233-0128
Panama City *(G-13944)*
Reddy Ice Corporation ....F.... 561 881-9501
West Palm Beach *(G-19017)*
Reddy Ice Inc ....G.... 407 296-8300
Orlando *(G-13123)*

ICE CREAM & ICES WHOLESALERS

Cross Atlantic Commodities Inc ....G.... 954 678-0698
Weston *(G-19118)*
Lefab Commercial LLC ....F.... 305 456-1306
Coral Gables *(G-2172)*
Muse Gelato Inc ....F.... 407 363-1443
Orlando *(G-12988)*

ICE: Dry

Atlantic Dry Ice Corportion ....F.... 305 592-7000
Miami *(G-9182)*

IDENTIFICATION PLATES

Commercial Metal Photography ....G.... 407 295-8182
Orlando *(G-12605)*

IGNITION APPARATUS & DISTRIBUTORS

Alcolock FL Inc ....G.... 407 207-3337
Orlando *(G-12450)*
Smartcart Ev LLC ....F.... 727 906-7001
Safety Harbor *(G-15504)*

IGNITION COILS: Automotive

T C B Products Inc ....E.... 941 723-9820
Palmetto *(G-13827)*

IGNITION SYSTEMS: Internal Combustion Engine

Motorola Solutions Inc ....G.... 407 562-4000
Lake Mary *(G-7437)*

INCENSE

Kenneth S Jarrell Inc ....F.... 334 215-7774
Pensacola *(G-14189)*
Love Is In The Air Corp ....G.... 305 828-8181
Hialeah *(G-5489)*
Scents Nature Enterprises Corp ....F.... 305 547-2334
Miami Lakes *(G-10854)*

INCINERATORS

Air Burners LLC ....E.... 772 220-7303
Palm City *(G-13640)*
Palmetto Group LLC ....G.... 863 294-8070
Winter Haven *(G-19339)*

INCINERATORS: Concrete

Granite Environmental LLC ....F.... 772 646-0597
Vero Beach *(G-18623)*

INCUBATORS & BROODERS: Farm

Brinsea Products Inc ....G.... 321 267-7009
Titusville *(G-18418)*
Hawkhead International Inc ....G.... 904 264-4295
Orange Park *(G-12396)*
Natureform Hatchery Tech LLC ....F.... 904 358-0355
Jacksonville *(G-6619)*
Pas Reform North America LLC ....E.... 904 358-0355
Jacksonville *(G-6659)*

INDICATORS: Cabin Environment

Drs Advanced Isr LLC ....F.... 321 622-1202
Melbourne *(G-8807)*

INDL & PERSONAL SVC PAPER WHOLESALERS

Atlas Paper Mills LLC ....C.... 305 835-8046
Hialeah *(G-5311)*
Latam Group Corp ....G.... 305 793-8961
Miami *(G-9864)*
World Indus Resources Corp ....E.... 727 572-9991
Clearwater *(G-1944)*

INDL & PERSONAL SVC PAPER, WHOL: Bags, Paper/Disp Plastic

Dairy-Mix Inc ....F.... 813 621-8098
Tampa *(G-17586)*

INDL & PERSONAL SVC PAPER, WHOL: Boxes, Corrugtd/Solid Fiber

Avatar Packaging Inc ....E.... 813 888-9141
Tampa *(G-17444)*

INDL & PERSONAL SVC PAPER, WHOL: Container, Paper/Plastic

Bucket Company LLC ....G.... 786 473-6484
Miami *(G-9282)*

INDL EQPT SVCS

Chemko Technical Services Inc ....E.... 954 783-7673
Pompano Beach *(G-14634)*
Done Rite Pumps ....G.... 305 953-3380
Opa Locka *(G-12308)*
G S Servicore Corp ....E.... 305 888-0189
Hialeah *(G-5420)*
James O Corbett Inc ....G.... 352 483-1222
Eustis *(G-3710)*
Mat-Vac Technology Inc ....F.... 386 238-7017
Daytona Beach *(G-2683)*
Star-Seal of Florida Inc ....F.... 954 484-8402
Fort Lauderdale *(G-4259)*

INDL GASES WHOLESALERS

Airgas Usa LLC ....G.... 407 293-6630
Orlando *(G-12446)*

INDL HELP SVCS

Azex Flow Technologies Inc ....G.... 305 393-8037
Miami *(G-9206)*

INDL MACHINERY & EQPT WHOLESALERS

Breezemaker Fan Company Inc ....E.... 813 248-5552
Tampa *(G-17486)*
Contemprary McHnrey Engrg Svcs ....E.... 386 439-0937
Flagler Beach *(G-3755)*
Costex Corporation ....C.... 305 592-9769
Miami *(G-9407)*
Duramaster Cylinders ....F.... 813 882-0040
Tampa *(G-17620)*
Eidschun Engineering Inc ....E.... 727 647-2300
Clearwater *(G-1664)*
Gas Turbine Efficiency LLC ....E.... 407 304-5200
Orlando *(G-12772)*
Gem Remotes Inc ....F.... 239 642-0873
Naples *(G-11259)*
International Baler Corp ....E.... 904 358-3812
Jacksonville *(G-6500)*
J D B Dense Flow Inc ....F.... 727 785-8500
Palm Harbor *(G-13741)*
Keytroller LLC ....F.... 813 877-4500
Tampa *(G-17823)*
Knight Industrial Eqp Inc ....G.... 863 646-2997
Lakeland *(G-7729)*
Lee Chemical Corporation ....G.... 407 843-6950
Orlando *(G-12900)*
Lexington Cutter Inc ....E.... 941 739-2726
Bradenton *(G-1070)*
Lynx Products Corp Inc ....G.... 941 727-9676
Bradenton *(G-1073)*
Madan Corporation ....G.... 954 925-0077
Dania Beach *(G-2467)*
Marden Industries Inc ....F.... 863 682-7882
Punta Gorda *(G-15213)*
Marine Exhaust Systems Inc ....D.... 561 848-1238
Riviera Beach *(G-15346)*
Maydone Ltd Liability Company ....G.... 407 399-3287
Orlando *(G-12955)*
Performance Pumps Inc ....E.... 407 339-6700
Casselberry *(G-1512)*
Pinellas Electric Motor Repair ....G.... 727 572-0777
Clearwater *(G-1834)*
Pixe International Corp ....G.... 850 574-6469
Tallahassee *(G-17309)*
Rios Con Pmpg & Rentl Inc ....E.... 305 888-7909
Medley *(G-8718)*
Sensidyne LP ....D.... 727 530-3602
Saint Petersburg *(G-15909)*
Southeast Power Group Inc ....D.... 305 592-9745
Doral *(G-3507)*
Southern Packaging McHy Corp ....E.... 305 245-3045
Florida City *(G-3769)*
Teknocraft Inc ....E.... 321 729-9634
Melbourne *(G-8959)*
Tradewinds Power Corp ....D.... 305 592-9745
Doral *(G-3531)*
William Laroque Installers Inc ....E.... 305 769-1717
Hollywood *(G-5940)*

INDL MACHINERY REPAIR & MAINTENANCE

Agranco Corp (usa) ....F.... 877 592-0031
South Miami *(G-16811)*
Diverse Co ....F.... 863 425-4251
Mulberry *(G-11123)*
Matthews International Corp ....C.... 407 886-5533
Apopka *(G-158)*
Megawattage LLC ....F.... 954 328-0232
Fort Lauderdale *(G-4117)*
Power Kleen Corporation ....E.... 813 854-2648
Oldsmar *(G-12258)*

INDL PATTERNS: Foundry Patternmaking

U S Holdings Inc ....G.... 305 885-0301
Hialeah *(G-5656)*

INDL PROCESS INSTR: Transmit, Process Variables

For-A Latin America Inc ....G.... 305 261-2345
Miami *(G-9593)*

INDL PROCESS INSTRUMENTS: Chromatographs

Jsi Scientific Inc ....G.... 732 845-1925
Naples *(G-11300)*

INDL PROCESS INSTRUMENTS: Control

Blue Siren Inc ....E.... 321 242-0300
Melbourne *(G-8782)*
Facts Engineering LLC ....E.... 727 375-8888
Trinity *(G-18485)*

James O Corbett Inc ....G.... 352 483-1222
Eustis (G-3710)
Sepac Corp ....F.... 305 718-3379
Miami (G-10325)

INDL PROCESS INSTRUMENTS: Controllers, Process Variables

ABB Enterprise Software Inc ....C.... 954 752-6700
Coral Springs (G-2211)
Riegl Usa Inc ....E.... 407 248-9927
Winter Garden (G-19283)

INDL PROCESS INSTRUMENTS: Digital Display, Process Variables

Digital Living ....G.... 407 332-9998
Altamonte Springs (G-40)
Electric Pcture Dsplay Systems ....G.... 321 757-8484
Melbourne (G-8822)
Infiniti Digital Equipment Inc ....G.... 305 477-6333
Doral (G-3390)
Outform Inc ....G.... 800 204-0524
Miami (G-10123)

INDL PROCESS INSTRUMENTS: Elements, Primary

AP Buck Inc ....F.... 407 851-8602
Orlando (G-12482)

INDL PROCESS INSTRUMENTS: Fluidic Devices, Circuit & Systems

Bar Beverage Ctrl Systems Fla ....G.... 239 213-3301
Naples (G-11182)
Chicago Electronic Distrs Inc ....F.... 312 985-6175
Port Charlotte (G-14969)
Kinetics Usa Inc ....E.... 561 988-8826
Boca Raton (G-588)
Real-Time Laboratories LLC ....D.... 561 988-8826
Boca Raton (G-683)

INDL PROCESS INSTRUMENTS: Temperature

Atkins Technical Inc ....E.... 860 349-3473
Gainesville (G-4879)
Roper Technologies Inc ....E.... 941 556-2601
Sarasota (G-16563)

INDL PROCESS INSTRUMENTS: Water Quality Monitoring/Cntrl Sys

Aero American Detailing Llc ....G.... 850 459-7425
Tallahassee (G-17213)
Aqualogix Inc ....F.... 858 442-4550
Palm Beach Gardens (G-13567)
Coffman Systems Inc ....F.... 813 891-1300
Oldsmar (G-12218)
Danaher Motion ....G.... 727 789-0446
Palm Harbor (G-13732)
Engineer Service Corporation ....G.... 904 268-0482
Jacksonville (G-6364)
Wes Holdings Corp ....F.... 941 371-4995
Sarasota (G-16636)

INDL SPLYS WHOLESALERS

American Coatings Corporation ....G.... 954 970-7820
Margate (G-8535)
Bryan Nelco Inc ....G.... 727 533-8282
Clearwater (G-1615)
Henefelt Precision Products ....F.... 727 531-0406
Largo (G-7969)
J C S Engineering & Dev ....F.... 305 888-7911
Hialeah (G-5459)
Lap of America Lc ....G.... 561 416-9250
Boynton Beach (G-927)
Lodex Enterprises Corp ....G.... 954 442-3843
Miramar (G-11010)
Matthews International Corp ....C.... 407 886-5533
Apopka (G-158)
Maydone Ltd Liability Company ....G.... 407 399-3287
Orlando (G-12955)
Nasco Industries Inc ....E.... 954 733-8665
Fort Lauderdale (G-4131)
NSK Latin America Inc ....E.... 305 477-0605
Miami (G-10083)
Plastics America Incorporated ....G.... 813 620-3711
Tampa (G-17995)

Rock River Tool Inc ....F.... 941 753-6343
Bradenton (G-1106)
Tekk Supply Inc ....G.... 954 444-5782
Pompano Beach (G-14884)

INDL SPLYS, WHOL: Fasteners, Incl Nuts, Bolts, Screws, Etc

Grabber Construction Pdts Inc ....G.... 813 249-2281
Tampa (G-17723)
Merit Fastener Corporation ....E.... 407 331-4815
Longwood (G-8311)

INDL SPLYS, WHOLESALE: Abrasives

True Grit Abrasives Inc ....E.... 813 247-5219
Tampa (G-18203)

INDL SPLYS, WHOLESALE: Bearings

Shark Skinz ....G.... 772 388-9621
Sebastian (G-16672)

INDL SPLYS, WHOLESALE: Brushes, Indl

Torrington Brush Works Inc ....F.... 941 355-1499
Sarasota (G-16622)

INDL SPLYS, WHOLESALE: Cans, Fruits & Vegetables

Atlantic Intl Distrs Inc ....C.... 904 725-5202
Jacksonville (G-6175)

INDL SPLYS, WHOLESALE: Fasteners & Fastening Eqpt

National Std Parts Assoc Inc ....D.... 850 456-5771
Pensacola (G-14211)

INDL SPLYS, WHOLESALE: Gaskets

Construction and Elec Pdts Inc ....F.... 954 972-9787
Pompano Beach (G-14645)
Hisco Pump South LLC ....F.... 904 786-4488
Jacksonville (G-6472)
Siligom USA LLC ....F.... 786 406-6262
Doral (G-3504)
Sunpack of Pensacola Inc ....F.... 850 476-9838
Pensacola (G-14271)

INDL SPLYS, WHOLESALE: Hydraulic & Pneumatic Pistons/Valves

Alpha Hydraulics LLC ....G.... 561 355-0318
Riviera Beach (G-15297)
Bridgestone Hosepower LLC ....D.... 904 264-1267
Orange Park (G-12383)
Space Coast Hydraulics Inc ....F.... 321 504-6006
Rockledge (G-15449)

INDL SPLYS, WHOLESALE: Mill Splys

Quality Industries America Inc ....G.... 386 755-0220
Lake City (G-7380)

INDL SPLYS, WHOLESALE: Power Transmission, Eqpt & Apparatus

Man-Trans LLC ....F.... 850 222-6993
Tallahassee (G-17294)
Robert E Weissenborn Sr ....G.... 239 262-1771
Naples (G-11387)

INDL SPLYS, WHOLESALE: Seals

HB Sealing Products Inc ....C.... 727 796-1300
Clearwater (G-1712)

INDL SPLYS, WHOLESALE: Signmaker Eqpt & Splys

Mac Papers Inc ....G.... 800 582-0049
Clearwater (G-1768)
National Traffic Signs Inc ....G.... 727 446-7983
Clearwater (G-1802)
Poli Group International Inc ....F.... 305 468-8986
Miami (G-10174)
Rogers Sign Corp ....E.... 352 799-1923
Brooksville (G-1265)

INDL SPLYS, WHOLESALE: Tools

Delta Regis Tools Inc ....E.... 772 465-4302
Fort Pierce (G-4692)

INDL SPLYS, WHOLESALE: Valves & Fittings

Azex Flow Technologies Inc ....G.... 305 393-8037
Miami (G-9206)

INDL TRUCK REPAIR SVCS

Nichols Truck Bodies LLC ....E.... 904 781-5080
Jacksonville (G-6634)

INDUCTORS

Manutech Assembly Inc ....G.... 305 888-2800
Miami (G-9942)

INDUSTRIAL & COMMERCIAL EQPT INSPECTION SVCS

C & D Industrial Maint LLC ....F.... 833 776-5833
Bradenton (G-1005)
Megawattage LLC ....F.... 954 328-0232
Fort Lauderdale (G-4117)
Pdma Corporation ....E.... 813 621-6463
Tampa (G-17979)

INFORMATION RETRIEVAL SERVICES

Tahoe Interactive Systems Inc ....G.... 614 891-2323
Punta Gorda (G-15242)

INFRARED OBJECT DETECTION EQPT

Eltec Instruments Inc ....E.... 386 252-0411
Daytona Beach (G-2662)

INK OR WRITING FLUIDS

International Imaging Mtls Inc ....F.... 727 834-8200
Odessa (G-12128)

INK: Letterpress Or Offset

Allied Graphics Inc ....G.... 954 327-8559
Fort Lauderdale (G-3802)
Folders Tabs Et Cetera ....F.... 813 884-3651
Tampa (G-17691)

INK: Lithographic

Amrob Incorporated ....G.... 813 237-5891
Odessa (G-12101)

INK: Printing

Amrob Inc ....G.... 813 238-6041
Tampa (G-17424)
Florida Ink Mfg Co Inc ....G.... 813 247-2911
Tampa (G-17679)
Hailey Cian LLC ....G.... 954 895-7143
Fort Lauderdale (G-4038)
Indian Toners USA Company ....G.... 954 600-5483
Parkland (G-13991)
J&S Inks LLC ....G.... 305 999-0304
North Miami Beach (G-11685)
One Step Papers LLC ....G.... 305 238-2296
Miami (G-10103)
Peace River Deli Provs Inc ....E.... 941 426-4846
Port Charlotte (G-14993)
Rainbow Ink Products Inc ....G.... 954 252-6030
Davie (G-2579)
T C Deliveries ....G.... 813 881-1830
Tampa (G-18150)
US Ink A Div Sun Chem Corp ....G.... 904 786-1474
Middleburg (G-10914)
Yes Solutions Gallery LLC ....G.... 352 622-7937
Ocala (G-12079)

INK: Screen process

Instorescreen LLC ....G.... 646 301-4690
Naples (G-11287)

INNER TUBES: Airplane

Jimenez Enterprises Group ....E.... 561 542-7709
Doral (G-3403)

INSECTICIDES

Agrosource Inc....F....908 251-3500
Jupiter *(G-6998)*
Fresh Mark Corporation....F....352 394-7746
Clermont *(G-1961)*
Growers Fertilizer Corporation....E....863 956-1101
Lake Alfred *(G-7332)*

INSECTICIDES & PESTICIDES

Consulier Engineering Inc....G....561 842-2492
Riviera Beach *(G-15314)*
Lenoc Chemical Solutions Inc....G....229 499-0665
Bowling Green *(G-866)*
Matrix24 Laboratories LLC....F....941 879-3048
Sarasota *(G-16253)*
Natures Own Pest Control Inc....G....941 378-3334
Sarasota *(G-16521)*
Velmaxxx Enterprises Inc....G....239 689-4343
Fort Myers *(G-4645)*

INSPECTION & TESTING SVCS

Tricen Technologies Fla LLC....F....866 620-9407
Fort Pierce *(G-4758)*

INSTALLATION OF CITIZENS BAND ANTENNAS

C2c Innovated Technology LLC....G....251 382-2277
Bonifay *(G-800)*

INSTRUMENTS & ACCESSORIES: Surveying

Datagrid Inc....G....352 371-7608
Gainesville *(G-4904)*
Leadair Inc....E....407 343-7571
Kissimmee *(G-7267)*

INSTRUMENTS & METERS: Measuring, Electric

Hughes Corporation....F....954 755-7111
Coral Springs *(G-2256)*

INSTRUMENTS, LAB: Spectroscopic/Optical Properties Measuring

Chemplex Industries Inc....F....772 283-2700
Palm City *(G-13646)*

INSTRUMENTS, LABORATORY: Gas Chromatographic

Separation Systems Inc....F....850 932-1433
Gulf Breeze *(G-5126)*

INSTRUMENTS, LABORATORY: Photometers

Mip-Technology Corp....G....239 221-3604
Bonita Springs *(G-845)*

INSTRUMENTS, LABORATORY: Photomicrographic

Polygrama Inc....G....305 577-9716
Miami *(G-10177)*

INSTRUMENTS, LABORATORY: Spectrometers

Stellarnet Inc....F....813 855-8687
Tampa *(G-18132)*
Thermo Arl US Inc....E....800 532-4752
West Palm Beach *(G-19060)*

INSTRUMENTS, MEASURING & CNTRL: Geophysical/Meteorological

Drew Scientific Inc....F....305 418-2320
Miami Lakes *(G-10783)*

INSTRUMENTS, MEASURING & CNTRL: Radiation & Testing, Nuclear

Sun Nuclear Corp....C....321 259-6862
Melbourne *(G-8950)*

INSTRUMENTS, MEASURING & CNTRL: Testing, Abrasion, Etc

AVK Industries Inc....F....904 998-8400
Jacksonville *(G-6181)*
Veroch LLC....G....954 990-7544
Sunrise *(G-17195)*

INSTRUMENTS, MEASURING & CNTRLG: Aircraft & Motor Vehicle

Suncoast Tool & Gage Inds Inc....F....727 572-8000
Clearwater *(G-1893)*

INSTRUMENTS, MEASURING & CNTRLG: Fatigue Test, Indl, Mech

Qualitest USA Lc....F....877 884-8378
Fort Lauderdale *(G-4188)*

INSTRUMENTS, MEASURING & CNTRLG: Thermometers/Temp Sensors

American Household Inc....D....561 912-4100
Boca Raton *(G-422)*
Co2meter Inc....F....386 310-4933
Ormond Beach *(G-13358)*
Electro-Optix Inc....F....954 973-2800
Pompano Beach *(G-14677)*
Marathon Technology Corp....G....305 592-1340
Doral *(G-3425)*
Sunbeam Americas Holdings LLC....C....561 912-4100
Boca Raton *(G-736)*

INSTRUMENTS, MEASURING & CNTRLNG: Press & Vac Ind, Acft Eng

Hydroplus....G....386 341-2768
Edgewater *(G-3624)*

INSTRUMENTS, MEASURING & CONTROLLING: Breathalyzers

Alcohol Countermeasure Systems....F....407 207-3337
Orlando *(G-12449)*

INSTRUMENTS, MEASURING & CONTROLLING: Fuel System, Aircraft

AMD Aero Inc....F....239 561-8622
Fort Myers *(G-4356)*
Stay-Sealed Inc....G....866 978-2973
Thonotosassa *(G-18404)*

INSTRUMENTS, MEASURING & CONTROLLING: Gas Detectors

Core Enterprises Incorporated....G....954 227-0781
Coral Springs *(G-2234)*
LDS Vacuum Products Inc....E....407 862-4643
Longwood *(G-8305)*

INSTRUMENTS, MEASURING & CONTROLLING: Gauges, Rain

K-Rain Manufacturing Corp....D....561 721-3936
Riviera Beach *(G-15338)*

INSTRUMENTS, MEASURING & CONTROLLING: Leak Detection, Liquid

Oriflow....F....727 400-4881
Clearwater *(G-1821)*
Precision Leak Detection Inc....G....904 996-9290
Jacksonville *(G-6681)*

INSTRUMENTS, MEASURING & CONTROLLING: Photogrammetrical

Geodetic Services Inc....F....321 724-6831
Melbourne *(G-8835)*

INSTRUMENTS, MEASURING & CONTROLLING: Polygraph

Asset Guardian Inc....G....727 942-2246
Palm Harbor *(G-13720)*

INSTRUMENTS, MEASURING & CONTROLLING: Ultrasonic Testing

Applus Laboratories USA Inc....G....941 205-5700
Punta Gorda *(G-15190)*
Mri Depot Inc....G....407 696-9822
Longwood *(G-8314)*

INSTRUMENTS, MEASURING/CNTRLG: Fare Registers, St Cars/Buses

Umbrella Buses Inc....G....754 457-4004
Davenport *(G-2484)*

INSTRUMENTS, MEASURING/CNTRLNG: Med Diagnostic Sys, Nuclear

Brrh Corporation....E....954 427-9665
Deerfield Beach *(G-2792)*
Faro Technologies Inc....A....407 333-9911
Lake Mary *(G-7414)*
Homestead Diagnostic Ctr Inc....F....305 246-5600
Homestead *(G-5967)*
New World Holdings Inc....E....561 888-4939
Boca Raton *(G-642)*
Pet Services of Florida LLC....G....352 746-6888
Beverly Hills *(G-378)*
Whk Biosystems LLC....G....727 209-8402
Clearwater *(G-1938)*

INSTRUMENTS, OPTICAL: Aiming Circles, Fire Control

Konus USA Corporation....G....305 884-7618
Medley *(G-8677)*
Oasis Alignment Services Inc....F....850 484-2994
Pensacola *(G-14213)*

INSTRUMENTS, OPTICAL: Elements & Assemblies, Exc Ophthalmic

Ii-Vi Aerospace & Defense Inc....C....727 375-8562
Port Richey *(G-15053)*
Optigrate Corporation....E....407 542-7704
Oviedo *(G-13450)*
Vloc Incorporated....C....727 375-8562
Port Richey *(G-15077)*

INSTRUMENTS, OPTICAL: Lenses, All Types Exc Ophthalmic

Benz Research and Dev LLC....E....941 758-8256
Sarasota *(G-16181)*
Graflex Inc....G....561 691-5959
Jupiter *(G-7051)*
Meopta USA Inc....C....631 436-5900
Trinity *(G-18488)*
Twinstar Optics & Coatings Inc....F....727 847-2300
Port Richey *(G-15073)*

INSTRUMENTS, OPTICAL: Magnifying, NEC

Electro-Optix Inc....F....954 973-2800
Pompano Beach *(G-14677)*

INSTRUMENTS, OPTICAL: Test & Inspection

Direct Optical Research Co....G....727 319-9000
Largo *(G-7932)*
Fiberoptic Engineering Corp....F....850 763-2289
Panama City *(G-13901)*

INSTRUMENTS, SURGICAL & MED: Cleaning Eqpt, Ultrasonic Med

Vapor Engineering Inc....F....850 434-3191
Pensacola *(G-14280)*

INSTRUMENTS, SURGICAL & MED: Fixation Appliances, Internal

Treace Medical Concepts Inc....C....904 373-5940
Ponte Vedra *(G-14928)*

INSTRUMENTS, SURGICAL & MED: Gastroscopes, Exc Electromedcal

Endo-Gear LLC....F....305 710-6662
Miami *(G-9526)*

INSTRUMENTS, SURGICAL & MEDICAL: Biopsy

Mobilehelp LLC .... D 561 347-6285
Boca Raton *(G-628)*

INSTRUMENTS, SURGICAL & MEDICAL: Blood & Bone Work

Alpha Industries Inc .... G 727 443-2673
Clearwater *(G-1577)*
Anew Inc .... G 386 668-7785
Debary *(G-2744)*
Betawave LLC .... F 954 223-8298
Fort Lauderdale *(G-3848)*
Biosafe Supplies LLC .... F 407 281-6658
Orlando *(G-12516)*
Byomed LLC .... F 305 634-6763
North Miami *(G-11630)*
Drew Scientific Inc .... F 305 418-2320
Miami Lakes *(G-10783)*
Endo-Therapeutics Inc .... D 727 538-9570
Clearwater *(G-1672)*
Gulf Coast Hyperberic Inc .... G 850 271-1441
Panama City *(G-13911)*
Hdl Therapeutics Inc .... G 772 453-2770
Vero Beach *(G-18625)*
Medtronic .... E 305 458-7260
Miami Lakes *(G-10816)*
New World Holdings Inc .... E 561 888-4939
Boca Raton *(G-642)*
Steripack (usa) Limited LLC .... E 863 648-2333
Lakeland *(G-7807)*
Surgentec LLC .... F 561 990-7882
Boca Raton *(G-740)*

INSTRUMENTS, SURGICAL & MEDICAL: Blood Pressure

American Household Inc .... D 561 912-4100
Boca Raton *(G-422)*
Sunbeam Americas Holdings LLC .... C 561 912-4100
Boca Raton *(G-736)*
Technicuff Corp .... F 352 326-2833
Leesburg *(G-8176)*

INSTRUMENTS, SURGICAL & MEDICAL: Catheters

Inneuroco Inc .... F 954 742-5988
Sunrise *(G-17128)*
Tni Manufacturing Inc .... G 954 742-5988
Sunrise *(G-17189)*

INSTRUMENTS, SURGICAL & MEDICAL: Clamps

Bravo Inc .... G 239 471-8127
Cape Coral *(G-1394)*

INSTRUMENTS, SURGICAL & MEDICAL: Inhalation Therapy

Mobilite Corporation .... D 407 321-5630
Sanford *(G-16089)*

INSTRUMENTS, SURGICAL & MEDICAL: Inhalators

Lor-Ed Enterprises LLC .... F 352 750-1999
Lady Lake *(G-7328)*

INSTRUMENTS, SURGICAL & MEDICAL: Lasers, Surgical

Aesthetic MBL Laser Svcs Inc .... G 954 480-2600
Deerfield Beach *(G-2768)*
Family of Smith Inc .... E 941 726-0873
Sarasota *(G-16212)*
Ideal Image Brandon .... G 813 982-3420
Brandon *(G-1162)*
Lensar Inc .... E 888 536-7271
Orlando *(G-12904)*
Marysol Technologies Inc .... G 727 712-1523
Clearwater *(G-1775)*

INSTRUMENTS, SURGICAL & MEDICAL: Needles, Suture

Rochester Electro-Medical Inc .... E 813 994-7519
Coral Springs *(G-2306)*

INSTRUMENTS, SURGICAL & MEDICAL: Ophthalmic

Adamas Instrument Corporation .... F 727 540-0033
Clearwater *(G-1564)*
Brain Power Incorporated .... E 305 264-4465
Miami *(G-9273)*
Clinicon Corporation .... F 239 939-1345
Fort Myers *(G-4399)*
Hansa Ophthalmics LLC .... E 305 594-1789
Doral *(G-3378)*
Innovative Designs of Sarasota .... G 941 752-7779
Bradenton *(G-1060)*
Morcent Import Export Inc .... G 727 442-9735
Belleair *(G-360)*

INSTRUMENTS, SURGICAL & MEDICAL: Plates & Screws, Bone

Orthopedic Designs N Amer Inc .... G 813 443-4905
Tampa *(G-17962)*

INSTRUMENTS, SURGICAL & MEDICAL: Skin Grafting

Sensus Healthcare Inc .... E 561 922-5808
Boca Raton *(G-705)*

INSTRUMENTS, SURGICAL/MED: Microsurgical, Exc Electromedical

Medtronic Xomed Inc .... A 904 296-9600
Jacksonville *(G-6592)*
Medtronic Xomed Inc .... B 904 296-9600
Jacksonville *(G-6593)*

INSTRUMENTS: Analytical

1982 Hayworth Avenue LLC .... G 772 873-1700
Port St Lucie *(G-15166)*
Analytical Research Systems .... F 352 466-0051
Micanopy *(G-10899)*
Anton Paar Quantatec Inc .... G 561 731-4999
Boynton Beach *(G-877)*
Antylia Scientific .... D 352 854-8080
Ocala *(G-11877)*
Awareness Technology Inc .... C 772 283-6540
Palm City *(G-13642)*
Beckman Coulter Inc .... F 305 380-2175
Miami *(G-9231)*
Beckman Coulter Inc .... G 954 432-4336
Pembroke Pines *(G-14022)*
Bowman Analytics Inc .... G 847 781-3523
Sarasota *(G-16367)*
Cellmic LLC .... G 310 443-2070
Palm Harbor *(G-13727)*
DOE & Ingalls Florida Oper LLC .... G 813 347-4741
Tampa *(G-17613)*
Edgeone LLC .... F 561 995-7767
Boca Raton *(G-514)*
Field Forensics Inc .... F 727 490-3609
Saint Petersburg *(G-15779)*
Gilson Inc .... G 904 725-7612
Jacksonville *(G-6434)*
Hf Scientific Inc .... E 888 203-7248
Fort Myers *(G-4481)*
L and C Science and Tech Inc .... G 305 200-3531
Hialeah *(G-5477)*
Lablogic Systems Inc .... F 813 626-6848
Tampa *(G-17833)*
Mayn Focus LLC .... G 603 801-8406
Winter Garden *(G-19276)*
Multicore Photonics Inc .... G 407 325-7800
Orlando *(G-12984)*
National Scientific Inc .... G 239 262-4047
Naples *(G-11342)*
Npact America Inc .... G 904 755-6259
Jacksonville *(G-6641)*
Ocean Optics Inc .... E 407 673-0041
Orlando *(G-13016)*
Ocean Optics Inc .... D 727 545-0741
Orlando *(G-13017)*
Pipette Solutions LLC .... G 877 974-7388
Casselberry *(G-1513)*
Rave LLC .... E 561 330-0411
Delray Beach *(G-3134)*
Spectrecology LLC .... G 727 230-1697
Saint Petersburg *(G-15921)*
ST Japan Usa Llc .... G 239 433-5566
Fort Myers *(G-4611)*
Thermo Electron North Amer LLC .... B 561 688-8700
West Palm Beach *(G-19061)*
Thermo Fisher Scientific .... F 781 327-3261
Alachua *(G-20)*
Thermo Fisher Scientific Inc .... B 561 688-8700
West Palm Beach *(G-19062)*
Ultrafast Systems LLC .... F 941 360-2161
Sarasota *(G-16626)*
USA Scientific Inc .... E 352 237-6288
Ocala *(G-12069)*
Vision Analytical Inc .... G 305 801-7140
Miami *(G-10588)*
Windsor Imaging Delray .... G 561 900-0300
Delray Beach *(G-3160)*
World Precision Instrs LLC .... D 941 371-1003
Sarasota *(G-16645)*
Ysi Inc .... F 727 565-2201
Saint Petersburg *(G-15968)*

INSTRUMENTS: Analyzers, Internal Combustion Eng, Electronic

Baytronics Manufacturing Inc .... G 813 434-0401
Tampa *(G-17460)*
Ce North America LLC .... E 305 392-2200
Coral Gables *(G-2130)*
Performance Technology 2000 .... G 772 463-1056
Stuart *(G-16987)*
Rjh Technical Services Inc .... G 813 655-7947
Brandon *(G-1174)*

INSTRUMENTS: Analyzers, Spectrum

Spectrum Bridge Inc .... F 407 792-1570
Lake Mary *(G-7450)*

INSTRUMENTS: Combustion Control, Indl

Axi International Corporation .... E 239 690-9589
Fort Myers *(G-4370)*
Ecombustible Products LLC .... G 305 792-1952
Sunny Isles Beach *(G-17075)*
Gencor Industries Inc .... C 407 290-6000
Orlando *(G-12776)*

INSTRUMENTS: Digital Panel Meters, Electricity Measuring

ID Solutions Inc .... F 407 823-7710
Orlando *(G-12821)*

INSTRUMENTS: Endoscopic Eqpt, Electromedical

Endo-Gear LLC .... F 305 710-6662
Miami *(G-9526)*

INSTRUMENTS: Eye Examination

Sinocare Meditech Inc .... F 800 342-7226
Fort Lauderdale *(G-4237)*
Vmax Vision Inc .... G 321 972-1823
Maitland *(G-8485)*

INSTRUMENTS: Frequency Meters, Electrical, Mech & Electronic

King Han Inc .... G 860 933-8574
Englewood *(G-3662)*
Next Generation Home Pdts Inc .... G 727 834-9400
Tampa *(G-17938)*

INSTRUMENTS: Indl Process Control

Advanced Manufacturing Inc .... E 727 573-3300
Saint Petersburg *(G-15691)*
Amci Technologies Inc .... F 561 596-6288
Boynton Beach *(G-874)*
Ametek Inc .... D 727 536-7831
Largo *(G-7896)*
Applied Technologies Group Inc .... G 813 413-7025
Tampa *(G-17429)*
Atlas South .... G 305 824-3900
Hialeah *(G-5312)*
Automated Sonix Corporation .... G 941 964-1361
Boca Grande *(G-391)*

C E C Controls Company Inc ....F 941 746-5700
Bradenton *(G-1007)*
Centroid Products Inc ....G 386 423-3574
Edgewater *(G-3618)*
Chem-TEC Equipment Co ....F 954 428-8259
Deerfield Beach *(G-2801)*
Clearwater Engineering Inc ....G 727 573-2210
Clearwater *(G-1627)*
Coast Controls Inc ....F 941 355-7555
Sarasota *(G-16192)*
Complete Instrmnttion Cntrls I ....G 813 340-8545
Lithia *(G-8217)*
Computational Systems Inc ....C 954 846-5030
Sunrise *(G-17108)*
Computational Systems Inc ....C 863 648-9044
Lakeland *(G-7661)*
Control Solutions Inc ....F 813 247-2136
Tampa *(G-17553)*
CPS Products Inc ....G 305 687-4121
Miramar *(G-10981)*
Crystal Photonics Inc ....E 407 328-9111
Sanford *(G-16029)*
Dynalco Controls Corporation ....E 323 589-6181
Fort Lauderdale *(G-3952)*
Emcee Electronics Inc ....E 941 485-1515
Venice *(G-18546)*
Emerson Electric Co ....E 904 741-6800
Jacksonville *(G-6362)*
Energy Control Technologies ....G 954 739-8400
Davie *(G-2518)*
Fct-Combustion Inc ....G 610 725-8840
Fort Lauderdale *(G-3988)*
Gkwf Inc ....G 863 644-6925
Lakeland *(G-7699)*
H Q Inc ....F 941 721-7588
Palmetto *(G-13804)*
Hf Scientific Inc ....E 888 203-7248
Fort Myers *(G-4481)*
Hughes Corporation ....F 954 755-7111
Coral Springs *(G-2256)*
I C Probotics Inc ....D 407 339-8298
Longwood *(G-8288)*
Ian-Conrad Bergan LLC ....E 850 434-1286
Pensacola *(G-14175)*
Instrument & Valve Services Co ....G 904 741-6800
Jacksonville *(G-6499)*
Jhn North LLC ....G 561 294-5613
Boynton Beach *(G-925)*
L3harris Technologies Inc ....C 260 451-6814
Tampa *(G-17831)*
Malema Engineering Corporation ....F 561 995-0595
Boca Raton *(G-606)*
Onicon Incorporated ....E 727 447-6140
Largo *(G-8021)*
Optoelectronics Inc ....F 954 642-8997
Boca Raton *(G-655)*
Precision Fabg & Clg Co Inc ....D 321 635-2000
Cocoa *(G-2042)*
Precision Resources Inc ....F 321 635-2000
Cocoa *(G-2043)*
Presys Instruments Inc ....G 305 495-3335
Miami *(G-10191)*
Pyramid Imaging Inc ....G 813 984-0125
Tampa *(G-18028)*
Red Meters LLC ....F 407 337-0110
Orlando *(G-13121)*
Roper Industrial Pdts Inv Co ....F 941 556-2601
Sarasota *(G-16562)*
Saikou Optics Incorporated ....G 407 986-4200
Orlando *(G-13157)*
Scientific Instruments Inc ....E 561 881-8500
Mangonia Park *(G-8511)*
Sensidyne LP ....D 727 530-3602
Saint Petersburg *(G-15909)*
Sunoptic Technologies LLC ....D 877 677-2832
Jacksonville *(G-6822)*
Tutela Monitoring Systems LLC ....G 941 462-1067
Spring Hill *(G-16869)*
Utilytech Company ....F 813 778-6952
Kissimmee *(G-7308)*
Wilkerson Instrument Co Inc ....F 863 647-2000
Lakeland *(G-7834)*
Xothermic Inc ....G 407 951-8008
Longwood *(G-8352)*

INSTRUMENTS: Infrared, Indl Process

Cv Technology Inc ....E 561 694-9588
Jupiter *(G-7022)*
Eltec Instruments Inc ....E 386 252-0411
Daytona Beach *(G-2662)*
Infrared Associates Inc ....F 772 223-6670
Stuart *(G-16958)*

INSTRUMENTS: Instrument Relays, All Types

Creating Tech Solutions LLC ....E 727 914-3001
Clearwater *(G-1642)*
Creating Tech Solutions LLC ....E 727 914-3001
Clearwater *(G-1641)*

INSTRUMENTS: Laser, Scientific & Engineering

Belquette Inc ....G 727 329-9483
Clearwater *(G-1606)*
Data Buoy Instrumentation LLC ....G 239 849-7063
Cape Coral *(G-1410)*
Gam Laser Inc ....F 407 851-8999
Orlando *(G-12770)*
Glo Aesthetic & Laser Institut ....G 561 704-4565
Lake Worth *(G-7552)*
Infrared Systems Dev Corp ....F 407 679-5101
Winter Park *(G-19413)*
Marysol Technologies Inc ....G 727 712-1523
Clearwater *(G-1775)*
South Florida Institut ....G 305 668-2853
South Miami *(G-16830)*
St Johns Optical Systems LLC ....G 407 280-3787
Sanford *(G-16120)*
Twinstar Optics & Coatings Inc ....F 727 847-2300
Port Richey *(G-15073)*

INSTRUMENTS: Liquid Level, Indl Process

Kus Usa Inc ....E 954 463-1075
Davie *(G-2542)*

INSTRUMENTS: Measurement, Indl Process

Core Enterprises Incorporated ....G 954 227-0781
Coral Springs *(G-2234)*
Gas Turbine Efficiency LLC ....E 407 304-5200
Orlando *(G-12772)*
Pulsar Process Measurement Inc ....G 850 279-4882
Largo *(G-8032)*
Vertec Inc ....F 850 478-6480
Pensacola *(G-14283)*

INSTRUMENTS: Measuring & Controlling

Advanced Manufacturing Inc ....E 727 573-3300
Saint Petersburg *(G-15691)*
Airpro Diagnostics LLC ....F 904 717-1711
Jacksonville *(G-6131)*
Alertgy Inc ....G 321 914-3199
Melbourne *(G-8762)*
Ametek Power Instrument Inc ....D 954 344-9822
Coral Springs *(G-2220)*
Anton Paar Quantatec Inc ....G 561 731-4999
Boynton Beach *(G-877)*
Awe Diagnostics LLC ....E 786 285-0755
Miami *(G-9203)*
B & G Instruments Inc ....F 305 871-4445
Miami *(G-9207)*
BEI ....G 561 488-0759
Boca Raton *(G-445)*
Collins Research Inc ....F 321 401-6060
Orlando *(G-12603)*
Colloidal Dynamics LLC ....G 904 686-1536
Ponte Vedra Beach *(G-14937)*
Comten Industries Inc ....G 727 520-1200
Pinellas Park *(G-14340)*
Crumbliss Manufacturing Co ....F 239 693-8588
Fort Myers *(G-4417)*
Dynalco Controls Corporation ....E 323 589-6181
Fort Lauderdale *(G-3952)*
Emcee Electronics Inc ....E 941 485-1515
Venice *(G-18546)*
Exploration Resources Intn Geo ....G 601 747-0726
Lake Mary *(G-7412)*
F & J Specialty Products Inc ....F 352 680-1177
Ocala *(G-11939)*
Florida Level & Transit Co Inc ....G 813 623-3307
Tampa *(G-17680)*
Forceleader Inc ....G 727 521-1808
Pinellas Park *(G-14348)*
Gaslab ....G 386 872-7668
Ormond Beach *(G-13373)*
General Oceanics Inc ....F 305 621-2882
Miami *(G-9625)*
Global Telemetry Systems Inc ....G 850 651-3388
Shalimar *(G-16775)*
Guardian Ign Interlock Mfg Inc ....D 321 205-1730
Cocoa *(G-2028)*
Hytronics Corp ....D 727 535-0413
Clearwater *(G-1725)*
Innovative Instruments Inc ....G 813 727-0676
Temple Terrace *(G-18370)*
Innovative Tech By Design Inc ....F 321 676-3194
Palm Bay *(G-13516)*
Invivo Corporation ....B 301 525-9683
Gainesville *(G-4945)*
IPC Global ....G 727 470-2134
Clearwater *(G-1736)*
James O Corbett Inc ....G 352 483-1222
Eustis *(G-3710)*
Life Proteomics Inc ....F 813 864-7646
Tampa *(G-17845)*
Magnetic Automation Corp ....E 321 635-8585
Rockledge *(G-15431)*
MC Miller Co Inc ....E 772 794-9448
Sebastian *(G-16668)*
Micro Typing Systems Inc ....E 954 970-9500
Pompano Beach *(G-14763)*
Molekule Inc ....G 352 871-3803
Tampa *(G-17916)*
Neubert Aero Corp ....G 352 345-4828
Brooksville *(G-1256)*
Parker Research Corporation ....F 727 796-4066
Clearwater *(G-1826)*
Pixe International Corp ....G 850 574-6469
Tallahassee *(G-17309)*
Quest Controls Inc ....F 941 729-4799
Palmetto *(G-13820)*
Rae Services Inc ....G 727 480-9940
Palm Harbor *(G-13756)*
Redington Counters Inc ....G 954 725-6699
Deerfield Beach *(G-2901)*
Riegl Usa Inc ....E 407 248-9927
Winter Garden *(G-19283)*
Rieker LLC ....G 407 496-1555
Orlando *(G-13138)*
Scientific Instruments Inc ....E 561 881-8500
Mangonia Park *(G-8511)*
Select Engineered Systems Inc ....E 305 823-5410
Hialeah *(G-5613)*
Sensor Systems LLC ....C 727 347-2181
Saint Petersburg *(G-15910)*
Sepac Corp ....F 305 718-3379
Miami *(G-10325)*
Shain Inc ....G 813 889-9614
Tampa *(G-18090)*
Smart Material Corp ....F 941 870-3337
Sarasota *(G-16600)*
Stellarnet Inc ....F 813 855-8687
Tampa *(G-18132)*
Tectron Engineering Company ....F 904 394-0683
Jacksonville *(G-6845)*
Thermo Arl US Inc ....E 800 532-4752
West Palm Beach *(G-19060)*
Tucker-Davis Technologies Inc ....E 386 462-9622
Alachua *(G-21)*
Uk US Partners LLC T McCuloch ....G 407 217-2978
Orlando *(G-13286)*
Veracity Tech Solutions LLC ....F 402 658-4113
Pensacola *(G-14281)*
World Precision Instrs LLC ....D 941 371-1003
Sarasota *(G-16645)*

INSTRUMENTS: Measuring Electricity

Akeyma Broden ....G 309 428-5938
Ocala *(G-11868)*
Amascott LLC ....G 352 683-4895
Spring Hill *(G-16846)*
CPS Products Inc ....G 305 687-4121
Miramar *(G-10981)*
Crumbliss Manufacturing Co ....F 239 693-8588
Fort Myers *(G-4417)*
Crystek Crystals Corporation ....E 239 561-3311
Fort Myers *(G-4418)*
Dash Air Parts LLC ....G 786 659-5013
Miami Lakes *(G-10779)*
Dynalco Controls Corporation ....E 323 589-6181
Fort Lauderdale *(G-3952)*
KLA Aventura LLC ....G 305 931-2322
Miami *(G-9825)*
Logus Manufacturing Corp ....E 561 842-3550
West Palm Beach *(G-18934)*
MC Miller Co Inc ....E 772 794-9448
Sebastian *(G-16668)*
Measurements International Inc ....E 315 393-1323
Lake Mary *(G-7433)*

Nci..........G....... 813 749-1799
Tampa *(G-17935)*
Optronic Laboratories LLC..........F....... 407 422-3171
Orlando *(G-13028)*
Piezo Technology Inc..........C....... 407 298-2000
Orlando *(G-13067)*
Quest International Inc..........F....... 305 592-6991
Miami *(G-10225)*
Salco Industries Inc..........F....... 941 377-7717
Sarasota *(G-16570)*
Semilab USA LLC..........E....... 813 977-2244
Temple Terrace *(G-18378)*
Smartsat Inc..........F....... 727 535-6880
Largo *(G-8055)*
T & M Atlantic Inc..........G....... 786 332-4773
Miami *(G-10452)*
Techtron Corporation..........F....... 239 513-0800
Naples *(G-11437)*
Tektronix Inc..........F....... 407 660-2727
Maitland *(G-8480)*
Universal Microwave Corp..........D....... 352 754-2200
Brooksville *(G-1286)*
W & W Manufacturing Co..........E....... 516 942-0011
Tampa *(G-18249)*

INSTRUMENTS: Measuring, Electrical Energy

Data Flow Systems Inc..........D....... 321 259-5009
Melbourne *(G-8800)*
Energy Control Technologies..........G....... 954 739-8400
Davie *(G-2518)*
Omega Power Systems Inc..........G....... 772 219-0045
Stuart *(G-16982)*
Sota Manufacturing Inc..........E....... 561 368-8007
Boca Raton *(G-722)*
Technical International Corp..........G....... 305 374-1054
Miami *(G-10462)*
Vertiv Corporation..........D....... 954 377-7101
Sunrise *(G-17196)*

INSTRUMENTS: Measuring, Electrical Power

AB Ampere Industrial Panels..........G....... 904 379-4168
Yulee *(G-19494)*
Belle Glade Electric Motor Svc..........G....... 561 996-3333
Belle Glade *(G-345)*

INSTRUMENTS: Medical & Surgical

3d Medical Manufacturing Inc..........C....... 561 842-7175
Riviera Beach *(G-15289)*
Aaron Medical Industries Inc..........G....... 727 384-2323
Saint Petersburg *(G-15689)*
Abbott Labs US Sbsdries Alere..........D....... 877 441-7440
Orlando *(G-12425)*
ABC Enterprises..........G....... 407 656-6503
Oakland *(G-11767)*
Adatif Medical Incorporated..........G....... 561 840-0395
Riviera Beach *(G-15291)*
Advantage Medical Elec LLC..........F....... 954 345-9800
Coral Springs *(G-2214)*
Ahc Ventures Corp..........F....... 954 978-9290
Margate *(G-8533)*
Aiolos Group Inc..........G....... 305 496-7674
Miami *(G-9090)*
Airon Corporation..........G....... 321 821-9433
Melbourne *(G-8761)*
Alicia Diagnostic Inc..........F....... 407 365-8498
Chuluota *(G-1551)*
Amend Surgical Inc..........F....... 844 281-3169
Alachua *(G-2)*
Anew International Corporation..........G....... 386 668-7785
Debary *(G-2745)*
Apollo Renal Therapeutics LLC..........E....... 202 413-0963
Ocala *(G-11878)*
Apyx Medical Corporation..........C....... 727 384-2323
Clearwater *(G-1586)*
Arthrex Inc..........C....... 239 643-5553
Naples *(G-11169)*
Arthrex Trauma Inc..........F....... 239 643-5553
Naples *(G-11171)*
B & M Precision Inc..........B....... 813 645-1188
Ruskin *(G-15481)*
B F Industries Inc..........F....... 561 368-6662
Boca Raton *(G-437)*
Back Lory Lee..........G....... 850 638-5430
Chipley *(G-1541)*
Bio Ceps Inc..........E....... 727 669-7544
Clearwater *(G-1608)*
Bio-Logic Systems Corp..........D....... 847 949-0456
Orlando *(G-12515)*
Bioderm Inc..........D....... 727 507-7655
Largo *(G-7909)*
Bioflex Medical Magnetics..........F....... 954 565-8500
Fort Lauderdale *(G-3855)*
Biosculpture Technology Inc..........E....... 561 651-7816
West Palm Beach *(G-18821)*
Bolton Medical Inc..........B....... 954 838-9699
Sunrise *(G-17100)*
Breathing Systems Inc..........G....... 850 477-2324
Pensacola *(G-14105)*
Central Fla Attrnsfsonists Inc..........G....... 321 299-6019
Orlando *(G-12562)*
CMF Medicon Surgical Inc..........G....... 904 642-7500
Jacksonville *(G-6273)*
Codman & Shurtleff Inc..........F....... 908 704-4024
Miami *(G-9374)*
Command Medical Products Inc..........C....... 386 677-7775
Ormond Beach *(G-13359)*
Contract Mfg Solutions Inc..........F....... 954 424-9813
Weston *(G-19117)*
Cordis Corporation..........B....... 786 313-2000
Miami Lakes *(G-10777)*
Corin USA Limited Inc..........F....... 813 977-4469
Tampa *(G-17557)*
Critical Disposables Inc..........E....... 407 330-1154
Sanford *(G-16028)*
Custom Medical Products Inc..........G....... 407 865-7211
Apopka *(G-129)*
Depuy Synthes Products Inc..........C....... 305 265-6842
Miami *(G-9456)*
Derm-Buro Inc..........E....... 305 953-4025
Hialeah *(G-5369)*
Dhss LLC..........F....... 305 405-4001
North Miami Beach *(G-11670)*
Diabetex Care..........G....... 954 427-9510
Deerfield Beach *(G-2813)*
Digicare Biomedical Tech Inc..........G....... 561 689-0408
Boynton Beach *(G-897)*
Doctor Easy Medical Pdts LLC..........G....... 904 276-7200
Orange Park *(G-12389)*
Dwyer Precision Products Inc..........F....... 904 249-3545
Jacksonville *(G-6341)*
Eclipsys Corp..........G....... 404 847-5000
Riviera Beach *(G-15324)*
EM Adams Inc..........D....... 772 468-6550
Fort Pierce *(G-4694)*
Emcyte Corp..........E....... 239 481-7725
Fort Myers *(G-4443)*
Eusa Global LLC..........G....... 786 483-7490
Medley *(G-8649)*
Evren Technologies Inc..........G....... 352 494-0950
Newberry *(G-11555)*
Flospine LLC..........G....... 561 705-3080
Boca Raton *(G-535)*
Gardco..........G....... 954 946-9454
Pompano Beach *(G-14710)*
Gaumard Scientific Company Inc..........E....... 305 971-3790
Miami *(G-9615)*
Geddis Inc..........F....... 800 844-6792
Dunedin *(G-3579)*
Genicon Inc..........E....... 407 657-4851
Orlando *(G-12782)*
Globalink Mfg Solutions..........F....... 239 455-5166
Naples *(G-11263)*
Gremed Group Corp..........E....... 305 392-5331
Doral *(G-3374)*
Gyrx LLC..........F....... 904 641-2599
Jacksonville *(G-6457)*
H-Cyte Inc..........E....... 844 633-6839
Tampa *(G-17739)*
He Instruments LLC..........G....... 561 832-1249
Lake Worth Beach *(G-7612)*
Health Star Inc..........G....... 321 914-6012
Merritt Island *(G-9002)*
Hnm Stainless LLC..........E....... 866 291-8498
Miami *(G-9715)*
Howmedica Osteonics Corp..........E....... 954 714-7933
Fort Lauderdale *(G-4050)*
Howmedica Osteonics Corp..........E....... 813 288-0760
Tampa *(G-17764)*
Hti..........G....... 941 723-4570
Palmetto *(G-13806)*
Hurricane Medical Inc..........E....... 941 753-1517
Bradenton *(G-1058)*
Hydrogel Vision Corporation..........D....... 941 739-1382
Sarasota *(G-16231)*
Hygreen Inc..........F....... 352 327-9747
Gainesville *(G-4939)*
Imaging Diagnostic Systems Inc..........F....... 954 581-9800
Orlando *(G-12824)*
Innfocus Inc..........F....... 305 378-2651
Miami *(G-9744)*
Innomed Technologies Inc..........C....... 800 200-9842
Coconut Creek *(G-2081)*
Innovative Mfg Solutions LLC..........G....... 904 647-5300
Jacksonville *(G-6497)*
Inspired Therapeutics LLC..........G....... 339 222-0847
Melbourne Beach *(G-8980)*
Integrity Implants Inc..........E....... 800 201-9300
Palm Beach Gardens *(G-13597)*
Intermed Group Inc..........E....... 561 586-3667
Alachua *(G-10)*
International Medical Inds Inc..........E....... 954 917-9570
Pompano Beach *(G-14732)*
Invo Bioscience Inc..........G....... 978 878-9505
Lakewood Ranch *(G-7844)*
Iris International Inc..........D....... 818 709-1244
Miami *(G-9770)*
Ispg Inc..........F....... 941 896-3999
Bradenton *(G-1062)*
Ivan & Ivan LLC..........G....... 305 507-8793
Doral *(G-3397)*
Jepsen Tool Company Inc..........F....... 904 262-2793
Jacksonville *(G-6521)*
Jimenez Enterprises Group..........F....... 561 391-6800
Parkland *(G-13994)*
Jimenez Enterprises Group..........E....... 561 542-7709
Doral *(G-3403)*
JTL Enterprises (delaware)..........E....... 727 536-5566
Clearwater *(G-1746)*
Kalitec Direct LLC..........G....... 407 545-2063
Oviedo *(G-13443)*
Kawasumi Laboratories Amer Inc..........F....... 813 630-5554
Tampa *(G-17816)*
Kerma Medical Products Inc..........G....... 954 744-3480
Miramar *(G-11009)*
Klyo Medical Systems Inc..........F....... 305 330-5025
Doral *(G-3410)*
Kms Medical LLC..........F....... 305 266-3388
Miami *(G-9827)*
Kollsut International Inc..........G....... 305 438-6877
North Miami Beach *(G-11688)*
Lane Care LLC..........F....... 727 316-3708
Palm Harbor *(G-13744)*
Laser Surgical Florida Inc..........G....... 954 609-7639
Miami *(G-9863)*
Led Technologies Incorporated..........F....... 800 337-9565
Largo *(G-7998)*
Lenkbar LLC..........D....... 239 732-5915
Naples *(G-11311)*
Lumenis Ltd..........F....... 305 508-5052
Miami *(G-9917)*
Marina Medical Instruments Inc..........E....... 954 924-4418
Davie *(G-2549)*
Martin-Weston Co..........F....... 727 545-8877
Largo *(G-8005)*
Maven Medical Mfg Inc..........E....... 727 518-0555
Largo *(G-8006)*
MC Johnson Co..........F....... 239 293-0901
Naples *(G-11324)*
McKesson Pharmaceutical..........F....... 863 616-2973
Lakeland *(G-7748)*
Medic Healthcare LLC..........G....... 954 336-1776
Fort Lauderdale *(G-4116)*
Medical Energy Inc..........G....... 850 313-6277
Pensacola *(G-14205)*
Medone Surgical Inc..........F....... 941 359-3129
Sarasota *(G-16255)*
Medrx Inc..........E....... 727 584-9600
Largo *(G-8008)*
Medtrnic Sofamor Danek USA Inc..........G....... 904 645-6925
Jacksonville *(G-6590)*
Medtronic..........F....... 305 206-8487
Miami *(G-9969)*
Medtronic..........D....... 305 818-4100
Miami Lakes *(G-10817)*
Medtronic Usa Inc..........A....... 702 308-1302
Jacksonville *(G-6591)*
Medtronic Usa Inc..........A....... 786 709-4200
Doral *(G-3430)*
Mergenet Medical Inc..........F....... 561 208-3770
Deerfield Beach *(G-2870)*
Merlola Industries LLC..........G....... 888 418-0408
Miami *(G-9982)*
Micro Tool Engineering Inc..........F....... 561 842-7381
Riviera Beach *(G-15348)*
Microtek Medical Inc..........C....... 904 741-2964
Jacksonville *(G-6603)*
Moog Inc..........G....... 716 652-2000
Pembroke Pines *(G-14049)*

Motus Gi LLC....G.... 954 541-8000
Fort Lauderdale *(G-4125)*
Motus GI Holdings Inc....E.... 954 541-8000
Fort Lauderdale *(G-4126)*
N E D LLC....G.... 610 442-1017
Boca Raton *(G-634)*
Nb Products Inc....E.... 904 807-0140
Jacksonville *(G-6621)*
Neocis Inc....D.... 855 963-6247
Miami *(G-10065)*
Neurotronics Inc....G.... 352 372-9955
Gainesville *(G-4971)*
New Wave Surgical Corp....F.... 866 346-8883
Coral Springs *(G-2296)*
Nkem Inc....F.... 800 582-0707
Sarasota *(G-16525)*
Nouveau Cosmetique Usa Inc....G.... 321 332-6976
Orlando *(G-13009)*
Novavision Inc....F.... 561 558-2020
Boca Raton *(G-651)*
Oculus Surgical Inc....E.... 772 236-2622
Port St Lucie *(G-15177)*
One Milo Inc....F.... 305 804-0266
Miami *(G-10102)*
Opko Curna LLC....G.... 305 575-4100
Miami *(G-10110)*
Optima Neuroscience Inc....G.... 352 371-8281
Alachua *(G-12)*
Orbusneich Medical Inc....E.... 954 730-0711
Fort Lauderdale *(G-4151)*
Oscor Inc....C.... 727 937-2511
Palm Harbor *(G-13749)*
Parcus Medical LLC....F.... 941 755-7965
Sarasota *(G-16271)*
Ped-Stuart Corporation....E.... 352 754-6001
Brooksville *(G-1259)*
Pedicraft Inc....F.... 904 348-3170
Jacksonville *(G-6665)*
Perry Baromedical Corporation....E.... 561 840-0395
Riviera Beach *(G-15362)*
Pioneer Surgical Technology....G.... 906 225-5629
Alachua *(G-14)*
Polyhistor International Inc....G.... 904 646-5666
Jacksonville *(G-6677)*
Precheck Health Services Inc....E.... 305 203-4711
Miami *(G-10182)*
Precision Machine Tech LLC....F.... 305 594-1789
Doral *(G-3467)*
Professional Pet Products Inc....E.... 305 592-1992
Doral *(G-3471)*
Promedica Inc....D.... 813 854-1905
Oldsmar *(G-12265)*
Quantum Storage Systems....G.... 305 687-0405
Opa Locka *(G-12352)*
Quick-Med Technologies Inc....G.... 352 379-0611
Gainesville *(G-4986)*
Reddress Usa Inc....G.... 800 674-9615
Ponte Vedra Beach *(G-14953)*
Regeneration Technologies Inc....F.... 386 418-8888
Alachua *(G-15)*
Reliant Medical Systems LLC....G.... 954 977-4224
Pompano Beach *(G-14830)*
Rolls Axle Lc....F.... 813 764-0242
Plant City *(G-14463)*
Rotech Oxygen & Medical Equip....G.... 352 291-1070
Ocala *(G-12041)*
Rti Donor Services Inc....E.... 321 431-2464
Melbourne *(G-8922)*
Rti Surgical Inc....C.... 386 418-8888
Alachua *(G-16)*
Rxenergy LLC....F.... 727 726-4204
Clearwater *(G-1867)*
S4j Manufacturing Services Inc....F.... 239 574-9400
Cape Coral *(G-1463)*
Samark Technology Corporation....G.... 941 955-4325
Sarasota *(G-16571)*
Savvy Associate Inc....F.... 954 941-6986
Pompano Beach *(G-14840)*
Shl Pharma LLC....E.... 954 725-2008
Deerfield Beach *(G-2910)*
Simplified Systems Inc....F.... 305 672-7676
Miami Beach *(G-10710)*
Sky Medical Inc....F.... 954 747-3188
Sunrise *(G-17172)*
Sleepmed Incorporated....F.... 941 361-3035
Sarasota *(G-16599)*
Spacelabs Healthcare Inc....E.... 904 786-5113
Jacksonville *(G-6801)*
Speranza Therapeutics Corp....G.... 844 477-3726
Boca Raton *(G-726)*
Statcorp Inc....G.... 904 786-5113
Jacksonville *(G-6810)*
Stryker Orthopedics....G.... 904 296-6000
Jacksonville *(G-6819)*
Summit Orthopedic Tech Inc....E.... 203 693-2727
Naples *(G-11420)*
Sun Coast Surgical & Med Sup....G.... 813 881-0065
Tampa *(G-18138)*
Sunoptic Technologies LLC....D.... 877 677-2832
Jacksonville *(G-6822)*
Surgimed Corporation....F.... 912 674-7660
Coral Springs *(G-2318)*
Syntheon LLC....G.... 305 255-1745
Miami *(G-10451)*
Techderm LLC....G.... 407 795-1517
Palm Beach Gardens *(G-13631)*
Tequesta Community Health Ctr....G.... 561 713-0798
Jupiter *(G-7126)*
Tutogen Medical Inc....E.... 386 418-8888
Alachua *(G-22)*
Ultra Clean Systems Inc....F.... 813 925-1003
Oldsmar *(G-12272)*
Ultroid Technologies Inc....G.... 877 858-0555
Tampa *(G-18215)*
Universal HM Hlth Indus Sups I....G.... 813 493-7904
Tampa *(G-18222)*
Universal Surgical Appliance....F.... 305 652-0810
Miami *(G-10544)*
Uroshape LLC....F.... 321 960-2484
Melbourne *(G-8968)*
Usaop Inc....G.... 386 212-9514
Ormond Beach *(G-13406)*
Vgi Medical LLC....F.... 727 565-1235
Largo *(G-8073)*
Vital Usa Inc....F.... 561 282-6074
West Palm Beach *(G-19082)*
Viztek Inc....F.... 904 448-9936
Jacksonville *(G-6903)*
Vuessence Inc....G.... 813 792-7123
Odessa *(G-12165)*
Vycor Medical Inc....G.... 561 558-2020
Boca Raton *(G-783)*
Wayne Metal Products Inc....G.... 407 321-7168
Sanford *(G-16136)*
Xhale Inc....G.... 352 371-8488
Gainesville *(G-5017)*
Z Haydu Manufacturing Corp....G.... 954 925-1779
Hollywood *(G-5944)*
Ziptek LLC....F.... 941 953-5509
Sarasota *(G-16646)*

INSTRUMENTS: Nautical

Kus Usa Inc....E.... 954 463-1075
Davie *(G-2542)*
Ocean Test Equipment Inc....G.... 954 474-6603
Davie *(G-2560)*
Waterproof Charters Inc....G.... 941 639-7626
Punta Gorda *(G-15243)*

INSTRUMENTS: Power Measuring, Electrical

Relm Communications Inc....C.... 321 953-7800
Melbourne *(G-8919)*

INSTRUMENTS: Radio Frequency Measuring

Locus Diagnostics LLC....F.... 321 727-3077
Melbourne *(G-8877)*
Parkervision Inc....F.... 904 732-6100
Jacksonville *(G-6658)*
Pinnacle Cmmncations Group LLC....F.... 904 910-0444
Jacksonville *(G-6674)*
SAI/Rf of Florida....G.... 727 394-1012
Redington Beach *(G-15259)*

INSTRUMENTS: Standards & Calibration, Electrical Measuring

Rail Scale Inc....E.... 904 302-5154
Saint Augustine *(G-15593)*

INSTRUMENTS: Temperature Measurement, Indl

Chilly Willys Heating & A Inc....G.... 904 772-1164
Jacksonville *(G-6264)*
Cobex Recorders Inc....F.... 954 425-0003
Coconut Creek *(G-2073)*
Ipeg Corporation....F.... 239 963-1470
Naples *(G-11291)*
Phoenix Calibration Ltd Srl....G.... 786 866-5906
Doral *(G-3460)*

INSTRUMENTS: Test, Digital, Electronic & Electrical Circuits

Florida Veex Inc....F.... 727 442-6677
Largo *(G-7952)*
Sjostrom Industries Inc....F.... 561 368-2000
Boca Raton *(G-719)*
Tucker-Davis Technologies Inc....E.... 386 462-9622
Alachua *(G-21)*
Victus Capital Enterprises Inc....E.... 727 442-6677
Saint Petersburg *(G-15954)*

INSTRUMENTS: Test, Electrical, Engine

Corporate One Hundred Inc....E.... 352 335-0901
Gainesville *(G-4898)*
Tex Onsite Inc....G.... 386 935-4093
Branford *(G-1189)*

INSTRUMENTS: Test, Electronic & Electric Measurement

Core Enterprises Incorporated....G.... 954 227-0781
Coral Springs *(G-2234)*
Finetest Inc....G.... 386 569-6189
Palm Coast *(G-13693)*
Indra Systems Inc....E.... 407 567-1977
Orlando *(G-12827)*
Interstate Electronics Corp....D.... 321 730-0119
Cape Canaveral *(G-1362)*
Pdma Corporation....E.... 813 621-6463
Tampa *(G-17979)*
Peak Electronics Inc....G.... 305 888-1588
Miami *(G-10148)*
Testmaxx Services Corporation....F.... 954 946-7100
Pompano Beach *(G-14886)*

INSTRUMENTS: Test, Electronic & Electrical Circuits

I C Probotics Inc....D.... 407 339-8298
Longwood *(G-8288)*
Kobetron LLC....F.... 850 939-5222
Navarre *(G-11468)*
Mc Assembly International LLC....F.... 321 253-0541
Melbourne *(G-8885)*
Optoelectronics Inc....F.... 954 642-8997
Boca Raton *(G-655)*
Ra Co AMO Inc....F.... 561 626-7232
Palm Beach Gardens *(G-13620)*
Servos and Simulation Inc....G.... 407 807-0208
Longwood *(G-8336)*

INSTRUMENTS: Vibration

Roper Technologies Inc....E.... 941 556-2601
Sarasota *(G-16563)*

INSULATING BOARD, CELLULAR FIBER

Chicago Electronic Distrs Inc....F.... 312 985-6175
Port Charlotte *(G-14969)*

INSULATING COMPOUNDS

Southeast Intl Chem Co Inc....G.... 904 992-4007
Jacksonville *(G-6787)*

INSULATION & CUSHIONING FOAM: Polystyrene

Atlantic Insulation Inc....D.... 904 354-2217
Jacksonville *(G-6174)*
Coastal Foam Systems LLC....G.... 850 470-9827
Pensacola *(G-14115)*
Compsys Inc....D.... 321 255-0399
Melbourne *(G-8795)*
Dyplast Products LLC....D.... 305 921-0100
Opa Locka *(G-12311)*
Foam Masters Inc....E.... 239 403-0755
Naples *(G-11248)*
Imperial Foam & Insul Mfg Co....D.... 386 673-4177
Ormond Beach *(G-13379)*

INSULATION & ROOFING MATERIALS: Wood, Reconstituted

Polyglass USA Inc....D.... 954 246-8888
Deerfield Beach *(G-2888)*

Standard Industries Inc ....D....... 813 248-7000
Tampa (G-18129)

INSULATION: Fiberglass

Owens Corning Sales LLC ....E....... 863 291-3046
Winter Haven (G-19338)
Rossiter Manufacturing ....G....... 386 409-7223
Daytona Beach (G-2706)
Ryan Scientific LLC ....F....... 904 284-6025
Green Cove Springs (G-5069)

INSULATORS & INSULATION MATERIALS: Electrical

Gamma Insulators Corp ....E....... 585 302-0878
Coral Gables (G-2149)
Insulator Seal Incorporated ....E....... 941 751-2880
Sarasota (G-16240)

INSULATORS, PORCELAIN: Electrical

Famatel USA LLC ....G....... 754 217-4841
Dania (G-2445)
Insulator Seal Incorporated ....E....... 941 751-2880
Sarasota (G-16240)

INTEGRATED CIRCUITS, SEMICONDUCTOR NETWORKS, ETC

Akuwa Solutions Group Inc ....F....... 941 343-9947
Sarasota (G-16337)
Hybrid Sources Inc ....F....... 772 563-9100
Vero Beach (G-18626)
L3harris Technologies Inc ....B....... 321 727-9100
Melbourne (G-8865)
Solitron Devices Inc ....D....... 561 848-4311
West Palm Beach (G-19038)
Visiontech Components LLC ....F....... 727 547-5466
Clearwater (G-1933)
Wafer World Inc ....F....... 561 842-4441
West Palm Beach (G-19083)

INTERCOMMUNICATIONS SYSTEMS: Electric

Access Wrless Data Sltions LLC ....G....... 813 751-2039
Lutz (G-8372)
Acoustic Communications LLC ....G....... 305 463-9485
Doral (G-3226)
Attenti Us Inc ....C....... 813 749-5454
Odessa (G-12104)
Automation Consulting Inc ....F....... 850 477-6477
Pensacola (G-14095)
AVI-Spl Emplyee Emrgncy Rlief ....A....... 813 884-7168
Tampa (G-17445)
AVI-Spl Holdings Inc ....A....... 866 708-5034
Tampa (G-17446)
AVI-Spl LLC ....A....... 813 884-7168
Tampa (G-17447)
Gresso LLC ....G....... 305 515-8677
Miami (G-9671)
Lugloc LLC ....F....... 305 961-1765
Miami (G-9916)
Padgett Communications Inc ....E....... 727 323-5800
Tampa (G-17969)
Smiths Interconnect Inc ....C....... 813 901-7200
Tampa (G-18111)
Two Way Radio Gear Inc ....F....... 800 984-1534
Fort Pierce (G-4764)
Vecom Usa LLC ....G....... 813 901-5300
Tampa (G-18235)
Walkup Enterprises Inc ....F....... 727 571-1244
Clearwater (G-1935)

INTERIOR DECORATING SVCS

Fleurissima Inc ....F....... 305 572-0203
Miami (G-9575)

INTERIOR DESIGN SVCS, NEC

Hygenator Pillow Service Inc ....G....... 305 325-0250
Miami (G-9723)
Lastrada Furniture Inc ....F....... 954 485-6000
Fort Lauderdale (G-4095)

INVERTERS: Nonrotating Electrical

GOTG LLC ....G....... 800 381-4684
Brooksville (G-1232)

INVERTERS: Rotating Electrical

Multi-Commercial Services Corp ....G....... 305 235-1373
Miami (G-10054)

INVESTMENT ADVISORY SVCS

Italian Rose Garlic Pdts LLC ....C....... 561 863-5556
Riviera Beach (G-15336)

IRON & STEEL PRDTS: Hot-Rolled

Garcia Iron Works ....G....... 305 888-0080
Hialeah (G-5425)
Gerdau Ameristeel US Inc ....B....... 813 286-8383
Tampa (G-17711)
Gerdau USA Inc ....B....... 813 286-8383
Tampa (G-17712)

IRON ORE MINING

Tyrex Ore & Minerals Company ....G....... 305 333-5288
Miami (G-10520)
US Iron LLC ....F....... 765 210-4111
Miramar Beach (G-11070)

IRON ORE PELLETIZING

Meelko Co ....G....... 845 600-3379
Opa Locka (G-12337)

IRON ORES

Chemours Company Fc LLC ....C....... 904 964-1200
Starke (G-16890)

IRRIGATION EQPT WHOLESALERS

Robert E Weissenborn Sr ....G....... 239 262-1771
Naples (G-11387)

IRRIGATION SYSTEMS, NEC Water Distribution Or Sply Systems

Eagle Engrg & Land Dev Inc ....F....... 913 948-4320
Boynton Beach (G-900)
Sergeant Bretts Coffee LLC ....G....... 561 451-0048
Coconut Creek (G-2094)

JACKS: Hydraulic

Sealift LLC ....F....... 321 638-0301
Merritt Island (G-9012)

JANITORIAL EQPT & SPLYS WHOLESALERS

Skymo LLC ....F....... 305 676-6739
Cooper City (G-2115)

JARS: Plastic

Tupperware US Inc ....B....... 407 826-5050
Orlando (G-13283)

JEWELERS' FINDINGS & MATERIALS

Modern Settings LLC ....G....... 800 645-5585
Sarasota (G-16512)
Our Warehouse Inc ....G....... 954 786-1234
Pompano Beach (G-14782)

JEWELERS' FINDINGS & MATERIALS: Castings

Roma Casting Inc ....G....... 305 577-0289
Miami (G-10277)

JEWELERS' FINDINGS & MTLS: Jewel Prep, Instr, Tools, Watches

Adamas Instrument Corporation ....F....... 727 540-0033
Clearwater (G-1564)

JEWELRY & PRECIOUS STONES WHOLESALERS

Accar Ltd Inc ....G....... 305 375-0620
Miami (G-9059)
Buvin Jewelry of Florida Inc ....F....... 305 358-0170
Miami (G-9290)

JEWELRY APPAREL

Arty-Sun LLC ....G....... 561 705-2222
Boca Raton (G-431)

Corporacion Internacional De J ....G....... 772 343-1721
Port Saint Lucie (G-15101)
Finger Mate Inc ....E....... 954 458-2700
Hallandale Beach (G-5184)
Gnj Manufacturing Inc ....E....... 305 651-8644
West Park (G-19093)
Too Many Ideas Inc ....G....... 904 396-9245
Jacksonville (G-6862)

JEWELRY FINDINGS & LAPIDARY WORK

Finger Mate Inc ....E....... 954 458-2700
Hallandale Beach (G-5184)
Jewelnet Corp ....G....... 561 989-8383
Delray Beach (G-3095)
Jewelswebscom ....G....... 954 993-7744
Fort Lauderdale (G-4079)
Marios Casting Jewelry Inc ....G....... 305 374-2894
Miami (G-9950)
National Custom Insignia Inc ....F....... 813 313-2561
Tampa (G-17929)

JEWELRY REPAIR SVCS

Amber Jewelers Corp ....G....... 305 373-8089
Miami (G-9135)

JEWELRY STORES

Finger Mate Inc ....E....... 954 458-2700
Hallandale Beach (G-5184)
Patrice Inc ....F....... 941 359-2577
Sarasota (G-16537)

JEWELRY STORES: Clocks

TWN Industries Inc ....G....... 305 246-5717
Princeton (G-15187)

JEWELRY STORES: Precious Stones & Precious Metals

Cabus USA Inc ....G....... 305 681-0872
North Miami (G-11631)
Jon Paul Inc ....G....... 954 564-4221
Fort Lauderdale (G-4080)
Marios Casting Jewelry Inc ....G....... 305 374-2894
Miami (G-9950)
Neptune Designs Inc ....G....... 305 294-8131
Key West (G-7199)

JEWELRY STORES: Watches

Original Pnguin Drect Oprtions ....F....... 305 592-2830
Doral (G-3452)

JEWELRY, PRECIOUS METAL: Bracelets

Montesino International Corp ....G....... 954 767-6185
Fort Lauderdale (G-4124)

JEWELRY, PRECIOUS METAL: Cigar & Cigarette Access

Burn By Rocky Patel ....G....... 239 653-9013
Naples (G-11197)
Garvinos LLC ....G....... 352 430-1435
The Villages (G-18390)
Orlando Novelty LLC ....G....... 407 858-9499
Orlando (G-13035)
Royal Splits Inc ....G....... 310 935-6699
Orlando (G-13148)
Smokersvaporcom Incorporated ....G....... 727 258-4942
Largo (G-8056)

JEWELRY, PRECIOUS METAL: Cigarette Lighters

Sunshine Lighters ....G....... 386 322-1300
Port Orange (G-15038)

JEWELRY, PRECIOUS METAL: Medals, Precious Or Semiprecious

Larter & Sons ....D....... 732 290-1515
Jupiter (G-7066)
Williams Jewelry and Mfg Co ....G....... 727 823-7676
Saint Petersburg (G-15961)

JEWELRY, PRECIOUS METAL: Necklaces

Richline Group Inc ....B....... 954 718-3200
Tamarac (G-17366)

JEWELRY, PRECIOUS METAL: Settings & Mountings

Amber Jewelers Corp ....G.... 305 373-8089
Miami *(G-9135)*

JEWELRY, WHOLESALE

Hidalgo Corp ....G.... 305 379-0110
Miami *(G-9708)*
International Jewelry Designs ....G.... 954 577-9099
Oakland Park *(G-11814)*
James A De Filippo Co ....G.... 407 851-2765
Orlando *(G-12849)*
OCon Enterprise Inc ....D.... 954 920-6700
Hollywood *(G-5885)*
Our Warehouse Inc ....G.... 954 786-1234
Pompano Beach *(G-14782)*
Phoenix Jewelry Mfg Inc ....F.... 305 477-2515
Doral *(G-3461)*
Red Bay Berry LLC ....G.... 954 552-9935
Davie *(G-2582)*

JEWELRY: Decorative, Fashion & Costume

Aventura Jewelry & Coin ....G.... 305 933-2646
Miami *(G-9196)*
Curly Girlz Creations ....G.... 386 960-3536
Ocala *(G-11913)*
D Turin & Company Inc ....E.... 305 825-2004
Hialeah *(G-5361)*
Eddys Jewelry ....G.... 321 236-7887
Orlando *(G-12698)*
Galaxy Medals Inc ....G.... 321 269-0840
Titusville *(G-18430)*
International Jewelry Designs ....G.... 954 577-9099
Oakland Park *(G-11814)*
Magnetic Jewellry Inc ....G.... 954 975-5868
Pompano Beach *(G-14750)*
Mz Jazzy Accezzoriez ....G.... 239 275-6975
Fort Myers *(G-4543)*
Patrice Inc ....F.... 941 359-2577
Sarasota *(G-16537)*
Red Bay Berry LLC ....G.... 954 552-9935
Davie *(G-2582)*
Swarovski North America Ltd ....G.... 561 791-7757
West Palm Beach *(G-19053)*
Swatch Group Caribbean ....F.... 877 839-5224
Miami *(G-10445)*

JEWELRY: Precious Metal

Accar Ltd Inc ....G.... 305 375-0620
Miami *(G-9059)*
American Diamond Distributors ....G.... 954 485-7808
Fort Lauderdale *(G-3812)*
Arriaga Originals ....F.... 850 231-0084
Panama City *(G-13966)*
Bashert Diamonds Inc ....G.... 305 466-1881
Aventura *(G-263)*
Bullion International Inc ....C.... 321 773-2727
Indian Harbour Beach *(G-6063)*
Buvin Jewelry of Florida Inc ....F.... 305 358-0170
Miami *(G-9290)*
Classique Style Inc ....F.... 561 995-7557
Boca Raton *(G-483)*
D Turin & Company Inc ....E.... 305 825-2004
Hialeah *(G-5361)*
Dolphine Jewelry Contracting ....G.... 561 488-0355
Boca Raton *(G-506)*
Evan Lloyd Designs ....G.... 772 286-7723
Stuart *(G-16939)*
Gems Jewelry & Uniques ....G.... 850 456-8105
Pensacola *(G-14162)*
Gold Karats Jewelry LLC ....G.... 561 401-5935
Pompano Beach *(G-14716)*
Golden Century Inc ....G.... 954 933-2911
Margate *(G-8546)*
Green Bullion Fincl Svcs LLC ....G.... 954 960-7000
Hollywood *(G-5830)*
Hidalgo Corp ....G.... 305 379-0110
Miami *(G-9708)*
Jld Manufacturing Corp ....G.... 877 358-5462
Sunrise *(G-17137)*
Jon Paul Inc ....G.... 954 564-4221
Fort Lauderdale *(G-4080)*
Lau International Inc ....G.... 305 381-9855
Miami *(G-9871)*
Marios Casting Jewelry Inc ....G.... 305 374-2894
Miami *(G-9950)*
Mayers Jwly Co Hollywood Inc ....D.... 954 921-1422
Hollywood *(G-5872)*
Merit Diamond Corporation ....E.... 954 883-3660
Hollywood *(G-5874)*
Metal Rock Inc ....F.... 407 886-6440
Apopka *(G-160)*
Moba Corp ....F.... 305 868-3700
Bal Harbour *(G-303)*
National Custom Insignia ....G.... 813 781-8806
Palm Harbor *(G-13747)*
Neptune Designs Inc ....G.... 305 294-8131
Key West *(G-7199)*
OCon Enterprise Inc ....D.... 954 920-6700
Hollywood *(G-5885)*
Phoenix Jewelry Mfg Inc ....F.... 305 477-2515
Doral *(G-3461)*
Pin Makers ....G.... 877 825-6120
Winter Park *(G-19430)*
Reyes Jewelers Corp ....G.... 305 431-8303
Miami *(G-10260)*
Rock My World Inc ....G.... 727 623-4646
Redington Shores *(G-15260)*
Roma Casting Inc ....G.... 305 577-0289
Miami *(G-10277)*
Sal Praschnik Inc ....F.... 305 866-4323
Bay Harbor Islands *(G-339)*
Santonis Jewelry Inc ....G.... 407 298-4994
Kissimmee *(G-7295)*
Stone Set Technologies LLC ....G.... 954 565-4979
Wellington *(G-18737)*
Suncoast Accrdted Gmlgical Lab ....G.... 941 756-8787
Bradenton *(G-1121)*
Westchester Gold Fabricators ....G.... 941 625-0666
Port Charlotte *(G-15007)*

JOB PRINTING & NEWSPAPER PUBLISHING COMBINED

American Classifieds ....F.... 850 747-1155
Panama City *(G-13863)*
Breeze Corporation ....C.... 239 574-1110
Cape Coral *(G-1395)*
Breeze Corporation ....G.... 239 425-8860
Fort Myers *(G-4381)*
Defuniak Springs Herald Breeze ....G.... 850 892-3232
Defuniak Springs *(G-2941)*
Lake Worth Herald Press ....E.... 561 585-9387
Lake Worth *(G-7564)*
Observer Group and Gulf Coast ....G.... 239 263-0122
Naples *(G-11349)*

JOB TRAINING & VOCATIONAL REHABILITATION SVCS

Miami Hang Gliding Corp ....G.... 863 805-0440
Clewiston *(G-1984)*
Paradigm Leaders LLC ....G.... 850 441-3289
Panama City Beach *(G-13982)*

JOB TRAINING SVCS

Bluedrop USA Inc ....G.... 407 470-0865
Orlando *(G-12527)*
Veracity Tech Solutions LLC ....F.... 402 658-4113
Pensacola *(G-14281)*

JOINTS: Expansion

Fox Equipment LLC ....E.... 904 531-3150
Green Cove Springs *(G-5061)*

JOINTS: Expansion, Pipe

Microflex Inc ....E.... 386 672-1945
Ormond Beach *(G-13386)*

JOISTS: Concrete

Structral Prestressed Inds Inc ....D.... 305 556-6699
Doral *(G-3514)*

JOISTS: Long-Span Series, Open Web Steel

New Mllennium Bldg Systems LLC ....C.... 386 466-1300
Lake City *(G-7369)*

JUICE, FROZEN: Wholesalers

Gem Freshco LLC ....D.... 772 595-0070
Fort Pierce *(G-4699)*
Raw Foods International Llc ....F.... 305 856-1991
Coral Gables *(G-2190)*

KEYBOARDS: Computer Or Office Machine

Seal Shield LLC ....E.... 877 325-7443
Orlando *(G-13172)*

KEYS, KEY BLANKS

Rokey Corporation ....G.... 561 470-0164
Boca Raton *(G-693)*

KITCHEN CABINET STORES, EXC CUSTOM

Contractors Cabinet Company ....G.... 786 492-7118
Margate *(G-8540)*
Grevan Artistic Ventures Inc ....F.... 850 243-8111
Fort Walton Beach *(G-4804)*
Guyton Industries LLC ....E.... 772 208-3019
Indiantown *(G-6073)*
Kc & B Custom Inc ....G.... 561 276-1887
Delray Beach *(G-3099)*
Oliveri Woodworking Inc ....F.... 561 478-7233
West Palm Beach *(G-18972)*
Princeton Industries Inc ....E.... 954 344-9155
Margate *(G-8563)*
Rta Cabinets & More LLC ....G.... 321 288-3068
Indian Harbour Beach *(G-6066)*

KITCHEN CABINETS WHOLESALERS

Design Your Kit Clset More Inc ....G.... 786 227-6412
Miami *(G-9458)*
Kit Residential Designs Inc ....G.... 305 796-5940
Hialeah *(G-5473)*
Regency Custom Cabinets Inc ....F.... 239 332-7977
Fort Myers *(G-4580)*
Richard Bryan Ingram LLC ....G.... 407 677-7779
Orlando *(G-13137)*
Spruce Creek Cabinetry Inc ....F.... 386 756-0041
Port Orange *(G-15035)*

KITCHEN TOOLS & UTENSILS WHOLESALERS

Classica & Telecard Corp ....G.... 239 354-3727
Naples *(G-11210)*

KITCHEN UTENSILS: Food Handling & Processing Prdts, Wood

JRP Screen Printing Inc ....E.... 305 333-4244
Hialeah *(G-5469)*
West Development Group LLC ....G.... 407 308-5020
Orlando *(G-13322)*

KITCHEN UTENSILS: Wooden

Delet Doors Inc ....F.... 786 250-4506
Miami *(G-9445)*

KITCHENWARE: Plastic

Classica & Telecard Corp ....G.... 239 354-3727
Naples *(G-11210)*
Pacific Link Imports Inc ....G.... 954 605-6071
Parkland *(G-13997)*
Tupperware Brands Corporation ....A.... 407 826-5050
Orlando *(G-13280)*

KITS: Plastic

Tearepair Inc ....E.... 813 948-6898
Land O Lakes *(G-7867)*

KNIT OUTERWEAR DYEING & FINISHING, EXC HOSIERY & GLOVE

Color Touch Inc ....F.... 954 444-1999
Lauderhill *(G-8104)*

KNIVES: Agricultural Or indl

Andritz Iggesund Tools Inc ....E.... 813 855-6902
Oldsmar *(G-12202)*

LABELS: Cotton, Printed

Finotex USA Corp ....E.... 305 593-1102
Miami *(G-9570)*
Florida Marking Products LLC ....E.... 407 834-3000
Longwood *(G-8283)*

LABELS: Paper, Made From Purchased Materials

Consolidated Label Co .... C 407 339-2626
Sanford *(G-16022)*
Express Label Co Inc .... E 407 332-4774
Longwood *(G-8278)*
Palmas Printing Inc .... E 321 984-4451
Melbourne *(G-8904)*
Paradise Label Inc .... F 863 860-8779
Plant City *(G-14455)*

LABELS: Woven

Express Label Co Inc .... E 407 332-4774
Longwood *(G-8278)*

LABORATORIES, TESTING: Food

Elisa Technologies Inc .... F 352 337-3929
Gainesville *(G-4914)*

LABORATORIES: Biological Research

Applied Genetic Tech Corp .... D 386 462-2204
Alachua *(G-5)*
Bpc Plasma Inc .... G 561 989-5800
Boca Raton *(G-461)*
Bpc Plasma Inc .... E 561 569-3100
Boca Raton *(G-462)*
Parallax Health Sciences Inc .... G 888 263-9799
West Palm Beach *(G-18987)*
Sea Gear Corporation .... G 321 728-9116
Melbourne *(G-8929)*

LABORATORIES: Biotechnology

Banyan Biomarkers Inc .... G 760 710-0460
Gainesville *(G-4882)*
Opko Health Inc .... A 305 575-4100
Miami *(G-10111)*

LABORATORIES: Commercial Nonphysical Research

Cole Enterprises Inc .... G 727 441-4101
Clearwater *(G-1632)*

LABORATORIES: Dental

Inman Orthodontic Labs Inc .... F 954 340-8477
Coral Springs *(G-2260)*

LABORATORIES: Dental, Artificial Teeth Production

Dsg Clearwater Laboratory .... F 727 530-9444
Clearwater *(G-1659)*

LABORATORIES: Environmental Research

Greentechnologies LLC .... G 352 379-7780
Gainesville *(G-4932)*

LABORATORIES: Medical

Adams Bros Cabinetry Inc .... D 941 639-7188
North Port *(G-11731)*
Clinicon Corporation .... F 239 939-1345
Fort Myers *(G-4399)*
Logan Laboratories LLC .... G 813 316-4824
Tampa *(G-17858)*
Mri Specialists .... G 561 369-2144
Boynton Beach *(G-934)*
RM Imaging Incorporated .... E 561 361-8090
Boca Raton *(G-690)*
Sanzay Corporation .... E 305 826-9886
Miami *(G-10304)*

LABORATORIES: Noncommercial Research

Uts Systems LLC .... G 850 226-4301
Fort Walton Beach *(G-4837)*

LABORATORIES: Physical Research, Commercial

Beacon Phrm Jupiter LLC .... E 212 991-8988
Jupiter *(G-7005)*
Environmental Recovery Systems .... G 727 344-3301
Saint Petersburg *(G-15771)*
Intellgent Haring Systems Corp .... F 305 668-6102
Miami *(G-9752)*
Knights Manufacturing Company .... D 321 607-9900
Titusville *(G-18441)*
Larrick Group Inc .... E 941 351-2700
Sarasota *(G-16248)*
Mercury Systems Inc .... E 352 371-2567
Gainesville *(G-4961)*
Sensatek Propulsion Tech Inc .... F 850 321-5993
Daytona Beach *(G-2712)*
US Stem Cell Inc .... F 954 835-1500
Sunrise *(G-17194)*
Uts Systems LLC .... G 850 226-4301
Fort Walton Beach *(G-4837)*
Vestagen Tchnical Textiles Inc .... G 407 781-2570
Orlando *(G-13300)*

LABORATORIES: Testing

Homestead Diagnostic Ctr Inc .... F 305 246-5600
Homestead *(G-5967)*

LABORATORIES: Testing

Genesis Reference Laboratories .... D 407 232-7130
Orlando *(G-12781)*
H2r Corp .... F 727 541-3444
Pinellas Park *(G-14353)*
Knights Manufacturing Company .... D 321 607-9900
Titusville *(G-18441)*
Lockheed Martin Corporation .... G 321 853-5194
Cape Canaveral *(G-1364)*
Mc Assembly Holdings Inc .... G 321 253-0541
Melbourne *(G-8884)*
Pharmatech LLC .... G 954 581-7881
Davie *(G-2572)*
Sun Nuclear Corp .... C 321 259-6862
Melbourne *(G-8950)*
Veracity Tech Solutions LLC .... F 402 658-4113
Pensacola *(G-14281)*

LABORATORY APPARATUS & FURNITURE

Ga-MA & Associates Inc .... G 352 687-8840
Ocala *(G-11953)*
Hf Scientific Inc .... E 888 203-7248
Fort Myers *(G-4481)*
Jensen Scientific Products Inc .... E 954 344-2006
Coral Springs *(G-2263)*
Phy-Med .... G 305 925-0141
Miami *(G-10162)*

LABORATORY APPARATUS & FURNITURE: Worktables

AGR of Florida Inc .... E 904 733-9393
Jacksonville *(G-6130)*

LABORATORY APPARATUS, EXC HEATING & MEASURING

Arj Medical Inc .... G 813 855-1557
Oldsmar *(G-12203)*
Cbg Biotech Ltd Co .... G 239 514-1148
Naples *(G-11202)*
Precision Coating Rods Inc .... F 813 855-5054
Oldsmar *(G-12259)*
Tintometer Inc .... F 941 756-6410
Sarasota *(G-16310)*

LABORATORY APPARATUS: Laser Beam Alignment Device

Rj Capital Inc .... F 561 208-7444
Boca Raton *(G-689)*

LABORATORY APPARATUS: Particle Size Reduction

Colloidal Dynamics LLC .... G 904 686-1536
Ponte Vedra Beach *(G-14937)*

LABORATORY APPARATUS: Sample Preparation Apparatus

Premier Lab Supply Inc .... G 772 873-1700
Port Saint Lucie *(G-15130)*

LABORATORY CHEMICALS: Organic

Awareness Technology Inc .... C 772 283-6540
Palm City *(G-13642)*
Bridgeport Chemical .... G 941 753-2520
Bradenton *(G-1002)*
Firstpath Laboratory Svcs LLC .... G 954 977-6977
Pompano Beach *(G-14693)*
Synergy Ancillary Services LLC .... F 561 249-7238
Port Saint Lucie *(G-15151)*
W & B Scientific Inc .... F 954 607-1500
Pompano Beach *(G-14911)*

LABORATORY EQPT: Chemical

South Bay Hospital .... B 813 634-3301
Sun City Center *(G-17072)*
W & B Scientific Inc .... F 954 607-1500
Pompano Beach *(G-14911)*

LABORATORY EQPT: Clinical Instruments Exc Medical

Axiom Diagnostics Inc .... G 813 902-9888
Tampa *(G-17449)*
Etectrx Inc .... E 321 363-3020
Gainesville *(G-4915)*
Genesis Reference Laboratories .... D 407 232-7130
Orlando *(G-12781)*
Lifelink Corporation .... G 813 653-3197
Brandon *(G-1165)*
Logan Laboratories LLC .... G 813 316-4824
Tampa *(G-17858)*
Mrn Biologics LLC .... F 508 989-6090
Coral Springs *(G-2291)*
Ormond Beach Clinical RES LLC .... G 386 310-7462
Ormond Beach *(G-13388)*
South Florida Laboratory Llc .... G 954 889-0335
Palm Springs *(G-13780)*
Southeast Clinical RES LLC .... F 904 296-3260
Jacksonville *(G-6786)*

LABORATORY EQPT: Incubators

Nfi Masks LLC .... E 239 990-6546
Fort Myers *(G-4546)*
Oculus Surgical Inc .... E 772 236-2622
Port St Lucie *(G-15177)*

LADDERS: Metal

Garelick Mfg Co .... D 727 545-4571
Largo *(G-7956)*
Leesburg Concrete Company Inc .... E 352 787-4177
Leesburg *(G-8163)*

LADDERS: Permanent Installation, Metal

Rampmaster Inc .... F 305 691-9090
Miami *(G-10238)*
White Ladder Inc .... G 904 343-9314
Fernandina Beach *(G-3750)*

LADDERS: Wood

Abbott Citrus Ladders Inc .... G 863 773-6322
Bowling Green *(G-864)*

LAMINATED PLASTICS: Plate, Sheet, Rod & Tubes

AA Fiberglass Inc .... G 904 355-5511
Jacksonville *(G-6113)*
American Thrmplastic Extrusion .... C 305 769-9566
Opa Locka *(G-12287)*
Chemclad LLC .... F 863 967-1156
Auburndale *(G-234)*
Echo Plastic Systems .... F 305 655-1300
Deerfield Beach *(G-2820)*
Fun Marine Inc .... G 321 576-1100
Cocoa *(G-2024)*
Innovatier Inc .... G 863 688-4548
Lakeland *(G-7712)*
J Schor R Inc .... F 954 621-5279
Plantation *(G-14527)*
Seal-Tite Plastic Packg Co Inc .... D 305 264-9015
Miami *(G-10316)*
Southern Fiberglass Inc .... F 904 387-2246
Jacksonville *(G-6794)*
Sungraf Inc .... F 954 456-8500
Hallandale Beach *(G-5216)*

LAMINATING SVCS

Plastic Sealing Company Inc .... G 954 956-9797
Pompano Beach *(G-14797)*
Serigraphic Arts Inc .... F 813 626-1070
Tampa *(G-18085)*

Suncoast Identification Tech ....G....... 239 277-9922
Fort Myers *(G-4616)*
Target Copy Gainesville Inc ....F....... 352 372-1171
Gainesville *(G-5008)*

LAMP & LIGHT BULBS & TUBES

Bella Luna Inc ....E....... 305 696-0310
Hialeah *(G-5319)*
Digecon Plastics International ....F....... 850 477-5483
Pensacola *(G-14131)*
Energy Management Products LLC ......G....... 410 320-0200
Bradenton *(G-1038)*
Johnston Archtctral Systems In ....E....... 904 886-9030
Jacksonville *(G-6527)*
Kyp Go Inc ....F....... 386 736-3770
Deland *(G-2994)*
Pearl Academy LLC ....G....... 904 619-6419
Jacksonville *(G-6663)*
Sun Catalina Holdings LLC ....E....... 305 558-4777
Miami Lakes *(G-10864)*
Surf Lighting Inc ....F....... 305 888-7851
Hialeah *(G-5644)*
Vision Engineering Labs ....E....... 727 812-2000
Largo *(G-8075)*

LAMP BULBS & TUBES, ELECTRIC: For Specialized Applications

Eag-Led LLC ....C....... 813 463-2420
Tampa *(G-17625)*
Oceanic Electrical Mfg Co Inc ....F....... 908 355-1900
Clearwater *(G-1816)*

LAMP BULBS & TUBES, ELECTRIC: Health, Infrared/Ultraviolet

Hyperbaric Treatment Assn ....G....... 804 296-4094
Saint Augustine *(G-15551)*

LAMP BULBS & TUBES, ELECTRIC: Light, Complete

AMS Global Suppliers Group LLC ....G....... 305 714-9441
Miami *(G-9152)*
Jq Green America Inc ....G....... 786 397-0999
Saint Lucie West *(G-15686)*

LAMP SHADES: Plastic

Advanced Components Solutions ....G....... 813 884-1600
Lutz *(G-8373)*

LAMPS: Arc Units, Electrotherapeutic

Nuline Sensors LLC ....G....... 407 473-0765
Sanford *(G-16092)*

LAMPS: Desk, Commercial

Evolution Lighting LLC ....E....... 305 558-4777
Pembroke Pines *(G-14034)*
Systematix Inc ....E....... 850 983-2213
Milton *(G-10942)*

LAMPS: Floor, Residential

Studio 21 Lighting Inc ....E....... 941 355-2677
Sarasota *(G-16303)*

LAMPS: Table, Residential

Marios Metalcraft ....G....... 239 649-0085
Naples *(G-11321)*
Papila Design Inc ....G....... 407 240-2992
Orlando *(G-13050)*
The Natural Light Inc ....E....... 850 265-0800
Lynn Haven *(G-8440)*

LAMPS: Ultraviolet

Robertson Transformer Co ....E....... 708 388-2315
Sarasota *(G-16560)*
Seal Shield LLC ....E....... 877 325-7443
Orlando *(G-13172)*

LAMPS: Wall, Residential

Gq Investments LLC ....C....... 305 821-3850
Hialeah *(G-5435)*

LAND SUBDIVISION & DEVELOPMENT

Diatomite Corp of America ....G....... 305 466-0075
Miami *(G-9465)*
Flo Sun Land Corporation ....E....... 561 655-6303
Palm Beach *(G-13554)*
Richland Towers Inc ....E....... 813 286-4140
Tampa *(G-18056)*
Vector Group Ltd ....C....... 305 579-8000
Miami *(G-10571)*
Vgr Holding LLC ....D....... 305 579-8000
Miami *(G-10576)*

LAPIDARY WORK: Contract Or Other

Vee Enterprises Inc ....G....... 954 960-0300
Pompano Beach *(G-14908)*
Wilkins Lapidary Arts ....E....... 386 734-8470
Deland *(G-3034)*

LAPIDARY WORK: Jewel Cut, Drill, Polish, Recut/Setting

L and I Diamonds ....G....... 305 603-7727
Miami *(G-9836)*

LASER SYSTEMS & EQPT

905 East Hillsboro LLC ....F....... 954 480-2600
Deerfield Beach *(G-2760)*
Armalaser Inc ....G....... 954 937-6054
Pompano Beach *(G-14599)*
Boss Laser LLC ....D....... 888 652-1555
Sanford *(G-16005)*
Control Laser Corporation ....E....... 407 926-3500
Orlando *(G-12617)*
Control Micro Systems Inc ....E....... 407 679-9716
Winter Park *(G-19396)*
Edmund Optics Inc ....E....... 813 855-1900
Oldsmar *(G-12224)*
Faro Technologies Inc ....E....... 800 736-0234
Lake Mary *(G-7413)*
Inrad Optics Inc ....G....... 941 544-8278
Sarasota *(G-16466)*
Integrated Laser Systems Inc ....F....... 954 489-8282
Coral Springs *(G-2261)*
L-3 Cmmnctons Advnced Lser Sys ......D....... 407 295-5878
Orlando *(G-12881)*
L3 Technologies Inc ....D....... 407 295-5878
Orlando *(G-12882)*
Lap of America Lc ....G....... 561 416-9250
Boynton Beach *(G-927)*
Laser Assault ....G....... 801 374-3400
Navarre *(G-11469)*
Laserpath Technologies LLC ....G....... 407 247-3930
Oviedo *(G-13446)*
Lasersight Incorporated ....F....... 407 678-9900
Orlando *(G-12893)*
New Laser Tech Inc ....G....... 305 450-0456
Miami Lakes *(G-10829)*
Schwartz Electro-Optics Inc ....F....... 407 297-8988
Orlando *(G-13169)*
Spaceport Corporation ....G....... 305 690-6885
Miami *(G-10392)*
T J Sales Associates Inc ....G....... 407 328-0777
Sanford *(G-16124)*

LASERS: Welding, Drilling & Cutting Eqpt

A and J Sheet Metal Inc ....G....... 561 746-4048
Jupiter *(G-6991)*
Fonon Technologies Inc ....E....... 407 477-5618
Orlando *(G-12761)*

LATH: Woven Wire, Made From Purchased Wire

Best Manufacturing Company ....F....... 954 922-1443
Hollywood *(G-5786)*

LATHES

Amaya Lathing & Plaspering ....G....... 786 953-6420
Miami *(G-9131)*
Amaya Lathing & Plastering LLC ....G....... 305 216-4247
Miami *(G-9132)*
Chase Metals Inc ....E....... 352 669-1254
Umatilla *(G-18496)*
E T Plastering Inc ....F....... 305 874-7082
Virginia Gardens *(G-18688)*
Lathing By Estaban M Perez Inc ....G....... 352 302-8791
Lady Lake *(G-7327)*
LJ&j Lathing Inc ....G....... 386 325-5040
Palatka *(G-13485)*
LPs Lath Plst & Stucco Inc ....G....... 954 444-3727
Fort Lauderdale *(G-4104)*
Martin Munive Inc ....G....... 772 318-8168
Port Saint Lucie *(G-15121)*
Santiago ....G....... 386 527-5822
Port Orange *(G-15031)*
State Lathinginc ....G....... 786 357-8404
Lake Worth *(G-7588)*

LAUNDRIES, EXC POWER & COIN-OPERATED

Southern International Svcs ....F....... 954 349-7321
Miami *(G-10387)*

LAUNDRY & DRYCLEANER AGENTS

Holiday Cleaners Inc ....G....... 727 842-6989
New Port Richey *(G-11492)*

LAUNDRY EQPT: Commercial

PWS International ....G....... 850 432-4222
Pensacola *(G-14243)*

LAWN & GARDEN EQPT

Ames Companies Inc ....B....... 717 737-1500
Orlando *(G-12475)*
Brandfx LLC ....E....... 321 632-2063
Cocoa *(G-2000)*
Electrolux Professional LLC ....F....... 954 327-6778
Fort Lauderdale *(G-3967)*
Iceblox Inc ....F....... 717 697-1900
New Port Richey *(G-11493)*
Morning Glory Lawn Maintenance ....G....... 407 376-5833
Orlando *(G-12980)*
Mulch & Stone Emporium Inc ....G....... 352 237-7870
Ocala *(G-12003)*
Oase North America Inc ....G....... 800 365-3880
Riviera Beach *(G-15354)*
Pickhardt Professional Sr ....G....... 941 737-7262
Palmetto *(G-13816)*
Pottre Gardening Products LLC ....G....... 941 224-8856
Bradenton *(G-1100)*
Precision Small Engine Company ....F....... 954 974-1960
Pompano Beach *(G-14809)*

LAWN & GARDEN EQPT STORES

Peterson Enterprises LLC ....G....... 386 456-3400
Mc Alpin *(G-8600)*

LAWN & GARDEN EQPT: Blowers & Vacuums

Greg Franklin Enterprises Inc ....F....... 904 675-9129
Hilliard *(G-5708)*

LAWN & GARDEN EQPT: Grass Catchers, Lawn Mower

Robomow USA Inc ....G....... 844 762-6669
Vero Beach *(G-18659)*

LAWN & GARDEN EQPT: Lawnmowers, Residential, Hand Or Power

Trailmate Inc ....E....... 941 739-5743
Jacksonville *(G-6866)*

LAWN & GARDEN EQPT: Tractors & Eqpt

All-Pro Equipment & Rental Inc ....F....... 850 656-0208
Tallahassee *(G-17217)*
Bravo Inc ....G....... 239 471-8127
Cape Coral *(G-1394)*
Peterson Enterprises LLC ....G....... 386 456-3400
Mc Alpin *(G-8600)*

LAWN & GARDEN EQPT: Trimmers

Woodys Hedging LLC ....G....... 863 557-4525
Lake Hamilton *(G-7393)*

LAWN MOWER REPAIR SHOP

Peterson Enterprises LLC ....G....... 386 456-3400
Mc Alpin *(G-8600)*

LEAD & ZINC

Envirofocus Technologies LLC ....D....... 813 620-3260
Tampa *(G-17645)*

LEAD & ZINC ORES

Chemours Company Fc LLC................C....... 904 964-1200
Starke *(G-16890)*

LEAD PENCILS & ART GOODS

Bic Corporation..................................A....... 727 536-7895
Clearwater *(G-1607)*

LEASING & RENTAL SVCS: Cranes & Aerial Lift Eqpt

Big Iron Intl Inc..................................G....... 407 222-2573
Orlando *(G-12514)*
Key West Wldg Fabrication Inc ....G....... 305 296-5555
Key West *(G-7192)*
Steel City Inc ....F....... 850 785-9596
Panama City *(G-13952)*

LEASING & RENTAL: Construction & Mining Eqpt

Bobs Barricades Inc ....E....... 813 886-0518
Tampa *(G-17478)*
Repco Equipment Leasing Inc..............F....... 727 584-3329
Largo *(G-8041)*
United Rentals North Amer Inc..............G....... 239 690-0600
Fort Myers *(G-4640)*
United Rentals North Amer Inc..............G....... 941 755-3177
Sarasota *(G-16321)*

LEASING & RENTAL: Medical Machinery & Eqpt

Advanced Prosthetics Amer Inc............F....... 352 383-0396
Eustis *(G-3700)*
Compliance Meds Tech LLC ....G....... 786 319-9826
Miami *(G-9389)*
Vet-Equip LLC ....G....... 239 537-3402
Naples *(G-11449)*

LEASING & RENTAL: Office Machines & Eqpt

It Manex LLC...G....... 954 442-4465
Miramar *(G-11005)*

LEASING & RENTAL: Utility Trailers & RV's

Agrifleet Leasing Corporation ....E....... 239 293-3976
Auburndale *(G-229)*

LEATHER GOODS, EXC FOOTWEAR, GLOVES, LUGGAGE/BELTING, WHOL

Land Leather Inc ....G....... 305 594-2260
Miami *(G-9857)*

LEATHER GOODS: Aprons, Welders', Blacksmiths', Etc

Southern-Bartlett Intl LLC......................F....... 407 374-1613
Lakeland *(G-7802)*

LEATHER GOODS: Boxes

Allcases Reekstin & Assoc Inc..............F....... 813 891-1313
Oldsmar *(G-12200)*
American Commodity Exch Corp..........G....... 904 687-0588
Jacksonville *(G-6148)*
Sarasota Leather Gallery Inc ....G....... 800 741-4336
Hudson *(G-6037)*
Wellington Leather LLC..........................G....... 561 790-0034
Royal Palm Beach *(G-15479)*

LEATHER GOODS: Card Cases

Identity Stronghold LLC.........................E....... 941 475-8480
Englewood *(G-3679)*

LEATHER GOODS: Desk Sets

Creative Colors International.................G....... 239 573-8883
Cape Coral *(G-1407)*

LEATHER GOODS: Harnesses Or Harness Parts

E Quality Cables Inc ....F....... 321 242-4820
Melbourne *(G-8817)*
Milcom Services Inc................................G....... 561 907-6816
Lake Worth Beach *(G-7616)*

LEATHER GOODS: Holsters

Cadre Holdings Inc ....C....... 904 741-5400
Jacksonville *(G-6249)*
High Noon Unlimited Inc ....G....... 727 939-2701
Holiday *(G-5744)*
Summit Holsters LLC ....G....... 386 383-4090
Deltona *(G-3180)*
Zen Distributors Group II LLC ....F....... 305 637-3014
Miami *(G-10629)*

LEATHER GOODS: NEC

Eileen Kramer Inc...................................G....... 315 395-3831
Aventura *(G-268)*
Lachance Leathers LLC ....G....... 407 790-6712
Orlando *(G-12887)*
Land Leather Inc ....G....... 305 594-2260
Miami *(G-9857)*
Mid Flrida Lthersir/Leatherboy ....G....... 352 615-5851
Dade City *(G-2431)*
Rally Leather & More LLC ....G....... 516 643-8572
Port Orange *(G-15030)*
Roof-A-Cide West LLC ....G....... 877 258-8998
Sarasota *(G-16561)*

LEATHER GOODS: Personal

Abco Industries LLC................................G....... 813 605-5900
Tampa *(G-17383)*
Bespoke Stitchery LLC............................G....... 407 412-9937
Orlando *(G-12511)*
Continental Belt Corp ....G....... 305 573-8871
Miami *(G-9395)*
Everglades Creations Inc ....E....... 305 822-3344
Opa Locka *(G-12314)*
Koszegi Industries Inc.............................E....... 954 419-9544
Deerfield Beach *(G-2855)*
Leon Leather Company Inc....................F....... 386 304-1902
Edgewater *(G-3629)*
Ostrich Market Inc...................................G....... 954 873-1957
Melbourne *(G-8902)*
Soul Kass Boutique LLC ....F....... 682 429-4323
Molino *(G-11074)*
Trimtek Leather Inc..................................G....... 706 577-3950
Pensacola *(G-14275)*
Winston Manufacturing Corp.................G....... 305 822-3344
Hialeah *(G-5688)*
Zpacks Corp ....F....... 321 215-5658
West Melbourne *(G-18780)*

LEATHER GOODS: Sewing Cases

Sea Link International Irb Inc.................F....... 727 523-8660
Largo *(G-8048)*

LEATHER GOODS: Stirrups, Wood Or Metal

Ontyte LLC...G....... 561 880-8920
Wellington *(G-18726)*

LEATHER GOODS: Wallets

J Lea LLC..G....... 954 921-1422
Hollywood *(G-5849)*

LEATHER TANNING & FINISHING

Leather Doctor of Doral LLC ....G....... 786 367-6146
Cutler Bay *(G-2401)*
Ti-Pagos Usa Inc......................................G....... 786 310-7423
Miami *(G-10475)*

LEATHER: Artificial

Uniroyal Engineered Pdts LLC ....F....... 941 906-8580
Sarasota *(G-16629)*
Windsor & York Inc ....G....... 561 687-8424
West Palm Beach *(G-19088)*

LEATHER: Handbag

Buonaventura Bag and Cases LLC ....G....... 212 960-3442
Naples *(G-11196)*

LEATHER: Shoe

Jdk Imports Inc ....F....... 850 865-0297
Santa Rosa Beach *(G-16161)*

LEATHER: Upholstery

Octane Seating LLC.................................E....... 888 627-6743
Fort Lauderdale *(G-4147)*

LEGAL OFFICES & SVCS

Lawex Corporation ....F....... 305 259-9755
Coral Gables *(G-2171)*
Pageantry Tlent Entrmt Svcs In..............G....... 407 260-2262
Longwood *(G-8319)*
Time Adjusters Conference Inc ....G....... 386 274-4210
Port Orange *(G-15039)*
Watermakers Inc ....F....... 954 467-8920
Fort Lauderdale *(G-4315)*

LEGAL PROCESS SERVERS

Builders Notice Corporation ....G....... 954 764-1322
Fort Lauderdale *(G-3875)*

LENSES: Plastic, Exc Optical

Latam Optical LLC ....G....... 786 275-3284
Miami *(G-9865)*
Optical Hong Kong ....F....... 305 200-5522
Hialeah *(G-5551)*

LICENSE TAGS: Automobile, Stamped Metal

Eurosign Metalwerke Inc.........................G....... 954 717-4426
Fort Lauderdale *(G-3975)*

LIFE RAFTS: Rubber

Eastern Aero Marine Inc.........................C....... 305 871-4050
Miami *(G-9495)*
Patten Co Inc...E....... 707 826-2887
Lake Worth Beach *(G-7618)*
Winslow Marine Products Corp..............D....... 941 613-6666
Lake Suzy *(G-7497)*

LIFE SAVING & SURVIVAL EQPT REPAIR SVCS, NON-MEDICAL

Eastern Aero Marine Inc.........................C....... 305 871-4050
Miami *(G-9495)*

LIFESAVING & SURVIVAL EQPT, EXC MEDICAL, WHOLESALE

Throw Raft LLC..G....... 954 366-8004
Fort Lauderdale *(G-4283)*

LIGHT SENSITIVE DEVICES

B & R Profiles LLC ....E....... 305 479-8308
Bartow *(G-306)*

LIGHTING EQPT: Area & Sports Luminaries

Lightnet Usa Inc ....F....... 305 260-6444
Miami *(G-9891)*

LIGHTING EQPT: Flashlights

Adva-Lite Inc ....E....... 727 369-5319
Seminole *(G-16735)*
Siglo Holdings LLC...................................C....... 727 369-5220
Largo *(G-8051)*

LIGHTING EQPT: Floodlights

Capstone Companies Inc........................G....... 954 252-3440
Deerfield Beach *(G-2794)*
Eag-Led LLC...C....... 813 463-2420
Tampa *(G-17625)*

LIGHTING EQPT: Motor Vehicle

Brooking Industries Inc...........................G....... 954 533-0765
Saint Augustine *(G-15524)*
Rontan North America Inc......................E....... 305 599-2974
Doral *(G-3489)*

LIGHTING EQPT: Motor Vehicle, Dome Lights

Emergency Vehicle Sup Co LLC............E....... 954 428-5201
Pompano Beach *(G-14678)*

PRODUCT

LIGHTING EQPT: Motor Vehicle, NEC

Sea Link International Irb Inc.................F 727 523-8660
Largo *(G-8048)*

LIGHTING EQPT: Outdoor

Airstar America Inc.................F 407 851-7830
Orlando *(G-12447)*
Lighting Technologies.................F 850 462-1790
Pensacola *(G-14193)*
Logic Illumination LLC.................F 407 906-0126
Kissimmee *(G-7270)*
Nightscenes Inc.................F 813 855-9416
Tampa *(G-17940)*
RLS Lighting Inc.................G....... 954 458-0345
Fort Lauderdale *(G-4209)*

LIGHTING EQPT: Searchlights

Rand Search Light Advertising.................G....... 954 476-7620
Davie *(G-2580)*
Searchlight Inc.................G....... 407 965-2649
Kissimmee *(G-7297)*

LIGHTING FIXTURES WHOLESALERS

Digecon Plastics International.................F 850 477-5483
Pensacola *(G-14131)*
Green Applications LLC.................E 954 900-2290
Fort Lauderdale *(G-4030)*
Green Global Energy Systems.................F 305 253-3413
Cutler Bay *(G-2396)*
Louis Poulsen USA Inc.................D....... 954 349-2525
Weston *(G-19148)*
Nebula Led Lighting Systems of.................G....... 813 907-0001
Wesley Chapel *(G-18754)*
Versailles Lighting Inc.................F 561 945-5744
Delray Beach *(G-3158)*

LIGHTING FIXTURES, NEC

0energy Lighting Inc.................F 855 955-1055
Orlando *(G-12415)*
ACR Electronics Inc.................C....... 954 981-3333
Fort Lauderdale *(G-3779)*
Apollo Metro Solutions Inc.................G....... 239 444-6934
Naples *(G-11165)*
Aquallsion Design Concepts LLC.................G....... 407 440-2972
Orlando *(G-12485)*
Brite Shot Inc.................F 954 418-7125
Deerfield Beach *(G-2790)*
Candela Controls Inc.................E 407 654-2420
Winter Garden *(G-19254)*
CC Lighting Inc.................G....... 805 302-5321
Boynton Beach *(G-888)*
Christie Lites Entps USA LLC.................C....... 407 856-0016
Orlando *(G-12581)*
Christie Lites Orlando LLC.................F 206 223-7200
Orlando *(G-12582)*
Creative Lighting & Power LLC.................F 407 967-0957
Lakeland *(G-7664)*
Cyalume Tech Holdings Inc.................D....... 954 315-4939
Fort Lauderdale *(G-3925)*
Digital Lighting Systems Inc.................G....... 305 264-8391
Miami *(G-9468)*
Energyware LLC.................G....... 540 809-5902
Davie *(G-2519)*
Evolution Lighting LLC.................E 305 558-4777
Pembroke Pines *(G-14034)*
Fanto Group LLC.................F 407 857-5101
Orlando *(G-12733)*
First Block LLC.................D....... 727 462-2526
Clearwater *(G-1682)*
Fos Led Lighting Solution.................G....... 321 208-8174
Rockledge *(G-15412)*
Fusion Energy Solutions LLC.................G....... 941 366-9936
Punta Gorda *(G-15206)*
Hoosier Lightening Inc.................G....... 407 290-3323
Orlando *(G-12809)*
Illuminated Lightpanels Inc.................G....... 954 484-6633
Oakland Park *(G-11812)*
Illuminations Holiday Ltg LLC.................G....... 813 334-4827
Tampa *(G-17771)*
IMC Lighting Inc.................G....... 305 373-4422
Miami *(G-9734)*
Jay Strong Lighting Inc.................G....... 813 253-0490
Tampa *(G-17804)*
Kenneth J Manning Lighting.................G....... 561 702-0169
Boca Raton *(G-587)*
Lanai Bright LLC.................G....... 239 303-4756
Lehigh Acres *(G-8194)*
Lanai Lights LLC.................G....... 239 415-2561
Fort Myers *(G-4515)*
Led Surf Lighting Inc.................G....... 239 687-4458
Naples *(G-11309)*
Ledger 2 Ledger Inc.................G....... 321 961-4017
Orlando *(G-12899)*
Light and Sound Equipment Inc.................G....... 305 233-3737
Cutler Bay *(G-2402)*
Lit Lighting & Grip LLC.................G....... 305 770-0272
Miami *(G-9899)*
Lps Production LLC.................F 786 208-6217
Miami Lakes *(G-10809)*
Lux Unlimited Inc.................G....... 305 871-8774
Miami *(G-9922)*
Mia Led Lighting Inc.................G....... 786 440-2856
Hollywood *(G-5876)*
Next Step Products LLC.................G....... 407 857-9900
Orlando *(G-13001)*
Professional Holiday Lighting.................G....... 208 709-2968
Ormond Beach *(G-13394)*
Pure Bright Lighting LLC.................G....... 954 780-8700
Fort Lauderdale *(G-4185)*
Renos Led Sleds.................G....... 727 593-0340
Largo *(G-8040)*
Reward Lighting Net LLC.................G....... 561 832-1819
West Palm Beach *(G-19019)*
Roth Southeast Lighting LLC.................G....... 954 423-6640
Fort Lauderdale *(G-4218)*
Russell Hobbs Inc.................D....... 954 883-1000
Miramar *(G-11037)*
S B Lighting LLC.................G....... 850 687-1166
Ponce De Leon *(G-14918)*
Sgm Lighting Inc.................G....... 407 440-3601
Orlando *(G-13178)*
State Lighting Co Inc.................G....... 561 371-9529
West Palm Beach *(G-19041)*
Stonelight LLC.................G....... 239 514-3272
Naples *(G-11418)*
Sun Catalina Holdings LLC.................E 305 558-4777
Miami Lakes *(G-10864)*
Sundown Lighting.................G....... 561 254-3738
Lantana *(G-7876)*
Tamlite Lighting - New Whse.................G....... 772 879-7440
Port Saint Lucie *(G-15153)*
Titans USA Ltd.................F 727 290-9897
Clearwater *(G-1922)*
Triarch International Inc.................F 305 622-3400
Hollywood *(G-5926)*
Van Teal Inc.................E 305 751-6767
Miami *(G-10566)*
Volt Lighting.................F 813 978-3700
Lutz *(G-8423)*
Zaniboni Lighting LLC.................D....... 727 213-0410
Clearwater *(G-1947)*

LIGHTING FIXTURES: Airport

Neubert Aero Corp.................G....... 352 345-4828
Brooksville *(G-1256)*
Virginia Electronic & Ltg Corp.................G....... 904 230-2840
Green Cove Springs *(G-5076)*

LIGHTING FIXTURES: Decorative Area

Bluegate Inc.................F 305 628-8391
Miami Gardens *(G-10736)*
Jsm Creations Inc.................G....... 239 229-8746
Cape Coral *(G-1442)*

LIGHTING FIXTURES: Fluorescent, Commercial

Surf Lighting Inc.................F 305 888-7851
Hialeah *(G-5644)*

LIGHTING FIXTURES: Fluorescent, Residential

Blu Sense.................G....... 786 616-8628
Doral *(G-3279)*

LIGHTING FIXTURES: Fountain

Bluworld of Water LLC.................D....... 407 426-7674
Orlando *(G-12529)*

LIGHTING FIXTURES: Indl & Commercial

Affineon Lighting.................F 407 448-3434
Weston *(G-19103)*
Alumination LLC.................G....... 904 361-8174
Jacksonville *(G-6143)*
Apollo Metro Solutions Inc.................G....... 239 444-6934
Naples *(G-11165)*
Brownlee Lighting Inc.................E 407 297-3677
Orlando *(G-12537)*
Candela Controls Inc.................E 407 654-2420
Winter Garden *(G-19254)*
City Electric Supply Company.................C....... 772 878-4944
Port St Lucie *(G-15171)*
Commercial Energy Services.................F 904 589-1059
Green Cove Springs *(G-5059)*
Coresential Energy & Lighting.................E 919 602-0849
Tampa *(G-17555)*
Dauer Manufacturing Corp.................G....... 800 883-2590
Medley *(G-8640)*
Digecon Plastics International.................F 850 477-5483
Pensacola *(G-14131)*
Edsun Lighting Fixtures Mfg.................F 305 888-8849
Hialeah *(G-5390)*
Elc Sales LLC.................G....... 772 285-5230
Stuart *(G-16937)*
Electraled Inc.................F 727 561-7610
Clearwater *(G-1665)*
Energy Harness Corporation.................G....... 239 790-3300
Cape Coral *(G-1417)*
Energy Management Products LLC.................G....... 410 320-0200
Bradenton *(G-1038)*
Energy Sving Solutions USA LLC.................F 305 735-2878
Miami *(G-9527)*
Eran Group Inc.................F 561 289-5021
Boca Raton *(G-521)*
Global Tech Led LLC.................E 877 748-5533
Fort Lauderdale *(G-4024)*
Green Applications LLC.................E 954 900-2290
Fort Lauderdale *(G-4030)*
Green Creative LLC.................E 866 774-5433
Sanford *(G-16057)*
Green Global Energy Systems.................F 305 253-3413
Cutler Bay *(G-2396)*
H I T Lighting Corp.................G....... 772 221-1155
Palm City *(G-13662)*
Harris Manufacturing Inc.................F 877 204-7540
Jacksonville *(G-6461)*
Icpf Development Group LLC.................F 727 474-9927
Clearwater *(G-1727)*
J B Nottingham & Co Inc.................E 386 873-2990
Deland *(G-2986)*
Janoro Fixture Mfg Corp.................G....... 305 887-2524
Hialeah *(G-5463)*
Just Leds Inc.................G....... 727 468-4496
Bradenton *(G-1066)*
Keylon Lighting Services Inc.................G....... 352 279-3249
Brooksville *(G-1241)*
Koncept Systems LLC.................E 786 610-0122
Homestead *(G-5977)*
Led Lghting Slutions Globl LLC.................G....... 855 309-1702
Bradenton *(G-1069)*
Ledradiant LLC.................G....... 305 901-1313
Hollywood *(G-5858)*
Lighting Science Group Corp.................G....... 321 779-5520
Melbourne *(G-8874)*
Lightn Up Inc.................F 954 797-7778
Sunrise *(G-17143)*
Louis Poulsen USA Inc.................D....... 954 349-2525
Weston *(G-19148)*
Lumastream Inc.................E 727 827-2805
Saint Petersburg *(G-15844)*
Lumilum LLC.................F 305 233-2844
Miami *(G-9918)*
Metrotech Media & Lighting Inc.................G....... 844 463-8761
Pensacola *(G-14208)*
Morning Star Industries Inc.................E 800 440-6050
Jensen Beach *(G-6971)*
Municipal Lighting Systems Inc.................G....... 305 666-4210
Miami *(G-10055)*
Pioneer Led Lighting Corp.................G....... 305 620-5300
Miami Lakes *(G-10839)*
Remcraft Lighting Products Inc.................E 305 687-9031
Opa Locka *(G-12353)*
Restoration Arts.................G....... 305 953-9755
Miami Gardens *(G-10753)*
Safetogether Ltd Liability Co.................G....... 954 227-2236
Parkland *(G-14000)*
Schroe Lights LLC.................G....... 407 748-9300
Orlando *(G-13168)*
Sun Catalina Holdings LLC.................E 305 558-4777
Miami Lakes *(G-10864)*
Tek-Lite Inc.................G....... 410 775-7123
Melbourne *(G-8957)*
Underwater Lights Usa LLC.................F 954 760-4447
Fort Lauderdale *(G-4292)*

Van Teal Hospitality Inc......G...... 305 751-6767
Miami *(G-10565)*
Versailles Lighting Inc......F...... 561 945-5744
Delray Beach *(G-3158)*
Violet Defense LLC......E...... 407 433-1104
Orlando *(G-13304)*
Vision Engineering Labs......D...... 727 812-2035
Largo *(G-8076)*
Vonn LLC......F...... 888 604-8666
North Miami Beach *(G-11710)*
Xeleum Lighting LLC......F...... 954 617-8170
Boca Raton *(G-794)*

LIGHTING FIXTURES: Marine

Lumishore Usa LLC......G...... 941 405-3302
Sarasota *(G-16251)*
Lumitec LLC......E...... 561 272-9840
Delray Beach *(G-3102)*

LIGHTING FIXTURES: Motor Vehicle

Autocraft Manufacturing Co......E...... 321 453-1850
Merritt Island *(G-8992)*
Basewest Inc......E...... 727 573-2700
Clearwater *(G-1599)*
Energy Management Products LLC......G...... 410 320-0200
Bradenton *(G-1038)*
Hg2 Emergency Lighting LLC......F...... 407 426-7700
Orlando *(G-12801)*
Light Integration Inc......G...... 407 681-0072
Longwood *(G-8307)*
Phantom Products Inc......F...... 321 690-6729
Rockledge *(G-15440)*

LIGHTING FIXTURES: Residential

Brian Slater & Associates LLC......F...... 561 886-7705
Boca Raton *(G-464)*
Brownlee Lighting Inc......E...... 407 297-3677
Orlando *(G-12537)*
City Electric Supply Company......C...... 772 878-4944
Port St Lucie *(G-15171)*
Dauer Manufacturing Corp......G...... 800 883-2590
Medley *(G-8640)*
Edsun Lighting Fixtures Mfg......F...... 305 888-8849
Hialeah *(G-5390)*
Evolution Lighting LLC......E...... 305 558-4777
Pembroke Pines *(G-14034)*
Janoro Fixture Mfg Corp......G...... 305 887-2524
Hialeah *(G-5463)*
Logic Illumination LLC......F...... 407 906-0126
Kissimmee *(G-7270)*
Louis Poulsen USA Inc......D...... 954 349-2525
Weston *(G-19148)*
Remcraft Lighting Products Inc......E...... 305 687-9031
Opa Locka *(G-12353)*
Smarthome-Products Inc......F...... 727 490-7260
Clearwater *(G-1880)*
Sun Catalina Holdings LLC......E...... 305 558-4777
Miami Lakes *(G-10864)*
Tamlite......G...... 772 878-4944
Port St Lucie *(G-15181)*
Van Teal Inc......E...... 305 751-6767
Miami *(G-10566)*
Versailles Lighting Inc......F...... 561 945-5744
Delray Beach *(G-3158)*
Vonn LLC......F...... 888 604-8666
North Miami Beach *(G-11710)*

LIGHTING FIXTURES: Residential, Electric

Bella Luna Inc......E...... 305 696-0310
Hialeah *(G-5319)*
Jibe Ltg N Amer Ltd Lblty Co......G...... 954 899-4040
Parkland *(G-13993)*
Triple Seven Home LLC......G...... 321 652-5151
Grant *(G-5050)*

LIGHTING FIXTURES: Street

Lighting Science Group Corp......G...... 321 779-5520
Melbourne *(G-8874)*
Southwest Signal Inc......E...... 813 621-4949
Englewood *(G-3667)*
Street Lighting Equipment Corp......F...... 954 961-9140
Hallandale Beach *(G-5215)*

LIGHTING FIXTURES: Swimming Pool

A J Giammanco & Associates......F...... 386 328-1254
Palatka *(G-13472)*

LIGHTING FIXTURES: Underwater

Lumitec LLC......E...... 561 272-9840
Delray Beach *(G-3102)*
Underwter Fish Light Ltd Lblty......G...... 941 391-5846
Port Charlotte *(G-15003)*

LIGHTING MAINTENANCE SVC

Apure Distribution LLC......F...... 305 351-1025
Miami *(G-9159)*
Itelecom USA Inc......G...... 305 557-4660
Weston *(G-19143)*
Signs Unlimited Inc......G...... 727 845-0330
Saint Augustine *(G-15612)*

LIGHTS: Trouble lights

Safety Zone Specialists Inc......G...... 863 984-1385
Lakeland *(G-7784)*

LIME

Crystal River Quarries Inc......E...... 352 795-2828
Crystal River *(G-2375)*
Key Lime Customs LLC......G...... 407 353-9942
Windermere *(G-19233)*
Lemon Lime Catering LLC......G...... 786 332-3636
Miami *(G-9883)*
Lhoist North America Ala LLC......F...... 352 585-3488
Brooksville *(G-1246)*
Lhoist North America Ala LLC......E...... 817 732-8164
Pompano Beach *(G-14744)*
Lime Street Development LLC......G...... 239 594-7777
Naples *(G-11313)*
Marianna Lime Products Inc......G...... 850 526-3580
Marianna *(G-8581)*
Mineral Life Intl Inc......G...... 305 661-9854
Miami *(G-10026)*
Silver Star On Lime LLC......G...... 941 312-4566
Sarasota *(G-16597)*

LIME ROCK: Ground

Anderson Mining Corporation......G...... 352 542-7942
Old Town *(G-12195)*
Blue Rock Inc......G...... 850 584-4324
Perry *(G-14295)*
Florida Rock Industries......C...... 904 355-1781
Jacksonville *(G-6402)*

LIME: Agricultural

Marianna Limestone LLC......F...... 954 581-1220
Marianna *(G-8582)*

LIMESTONE & MARBLE: Dimension

ARC Stone III LLC......F...... 561 478-8805
Lake Worth Beach *(G-7603)*
Azul Stone LLC......F...... 561 655-9385
West Palm Beach *(G-18806)*
Southern Contracting N FL Inc......G...... 850 674-3570
Blountstown *(G-387)*
Stone Metals LLC......G...... 813 605-7363
Plant City *(G-14468)*

LIMESTONE: Crushed & Broken

A Mining Group LLC......E...... 386 752-7585
Lake City *(G-7345)*
Argos......G...... 305 592-3501
Miami *(G-9168)*
Cemex Cnstr Mtls Fla LLC......F...... 855 292-8453
Naples *(G-11203)*
Cemex Materials LLC......C...... 561 833-5555
West Palm Beach *(G-18841)*
Cemex Materials LLC......D...... 352 435-0783
Okahumpka *(G-12169)*
Cemex Materials LLC......D...... 305 558-0315
Miami *(G-9337)*
Cemex Materials LLC......D...... 561 793-1442
West Palm Beach *(G-18842)*
Cemex Materials LLC......D...... 561 743-4039
Jupiter *(G-7019)*
Dixie Lime Andstone Co......F...... 352 512-0180
Ocala *(G-11920)*
Eagle Engrg & Land Dev Inc......F...... 913 948-4320
Boynton Beach *(G-900)*
Evolving Coal Corp......G...... 813 944-3100
Saint Petersburg *(G-15773)*
Helms Hauling & Materials Llc......F...... 850 218-6895
Niceville *(G-11569)*
Lake Point Restoration LLC......E...... 561 924-9100
Wellington *(G-18722)*
Lakeview Dirt Co Inc......E...... 904 824-2586
Saint Augustine *(G-15565)*
Lhoist North America Tenn Inc......F...... 352 629-7990
Ocala *(G-11983)*
Limestone Products Company......G...... 352 472-2116
Newberry *(G-11558)*
Martin Marietta......G...... 850 432-8112
Pensacola *(G-14200)*
Rinker Materials Corp Con......G...... 305 818-4952
Doral *(G-3486)*
Rock Ridge Materials Inc......F...... 321 268-8455
Titusville *(G-18460)*
Waste Management Inc Florida......E...... 954 984-2000
Winter Garden *(G-19289)*

LIMESTONE: Dimension

Denali Investments Inc......G...... 386 364-2979
Live Oak *(G-8230)*
Five Stones Mine LLC......F...... 813 967-2123
Canal Point *(G-1331)*
Southern Rock & Lime Inc......F...... 850 674-5089
Blountstown *(G-388)*

LIMESTONE: Ground

Bedrock Resources LLC......E...... 352 369-8600
Ocala *(G-11885)*
Colitz Mining Co Inc......F...... 352 795-2409
Crystal River *(G-2374)*
Legacy Vulcan LLC......F...... 352 796-5690
Brooksville *(G-1245)*
SCI Materials LLC......E...... 352 878-4979
Reddick *(G-15258)*
Vecellio & Grogan Inc......D...... 305 822-5322
Hialeah *(G-5674)*

LINENS & TOWELS WHOLESALERS

Harbor Linen LLC......D...... 305 805-8085
Medley *(G-8661)*

LINENS: Tablecloths, From Purchased Materials

Sperry Marketing Group Inc......F...... 941 483-4667
Venice *(G-18576)*

LINER BRICK OR PLATES: Sewer Or Tank Lining, Vitrified Clay

Infrastructure Repair Systems......G...... 727 327-4216
Saint Petersburg *(G-15815)*

LINERS & COVERS: Fabric

A B C Canvas Inc......G...... 239 542-0909
Cape Coral *(G-1370)*

LININGS: Apparel, Made From Purchased Materials

Saint George Industries LLC......E...... 786 212-1176
Miami *(G-10298)*

LININGS: Fabric, Apparel & Other, Exc Millinery

Catalyst Fabric Solutions LLC......E...... 850 396-4325
Marianna *(G-8575)*
World Event Promotions LLC......E...... 800 214-3408
Miami *(G-10619)*

LINTELS

Cast-Crete Usa LLC......D...... 813 621-4641
Seffner *(G-16723)*

LINTELS: Steel, Light Gauge

Nichols Truck Bodies LLC......E...... 904 781-5080
Jacksonville *(G-6634)*

LIP BALMS

Floridas Best Inc......G...... 407 682-9570
Altamonte Springs *(G-46)*

LIQUEFIED PETROLEUM GAS DEALERS

Farmers Cooperative Inc........................E....... 386 362-1459
Live Oak *(G-8232)*

LIQUEFIED PETROLEUM GAS WHOLESALERS

Sams Gas........................G....... 386 698-1033
Crescent City *(G-2341)*

LIQUID CRYSTAL DISPLAYS

Digital Pixel Displays LLC........................G....... 321 948-3751
Orlando *(G-12673)*
DMC Components Intl LLC........................G....... 407 478-4064
Winter Park *(G-19404)*
Meck Tech Corp........................G....... 888 225-9403
Orange Park *(G-12400)*
New Vision Display Inc........................G....... 407 480-5800
Orlando *(G-12999)*
Vc Displays Inc........................E....... 352 796-0060
Brooksville *(G-1288)*
Via Optronics LLC........................E....... 407 745-5031
Orlando *(G-13302)*
Video Display Corporation........................E....... 813 854-2259
Tampa *(G-18246)*

LITHOGRAPHIC PLATES

Elicar Printing........................G....... 305 324-5252
Miami *(G-9514)*

LOADS: Electronic

Concept 2 Market Inc........................F....... 954 974-0022
Pompano Beach *(G-14643)*

LOCK & KEY SVCS

Safe Banks and Lock........................G....... 954 762-3565
Fort Lauderdale *(G-4221)*

LOCKERS

List Industries Inc........................B....... 954 429-9155
Deerfield Beach *(G-2859)*
List Plymouth LLC........................E....... 954 429-9155
Deerfield Beach *(G-2861)*
Valiant Products Inc........................E....... 863 688-7998
Lakeland *(G-7829)*

LOCKERS: Wood, Exc Refrigerated

List Industries Inc........................B....... 954 429-9155
Deerfield Beach *(G-2859)*

LOCKS

Assa Abloy Hospitality Inc........................G....... 954 920-0772
Fort Lauderdale *(G-3827)*
Brandon Lock & Safe Inc........................G....... 813 655-4200
Tampa *(G-17485)*
Gator Door East Inc........................E....... 904 824-2827
Saint Augustine *(G-15545)*

LOCKS & LOCK SETS, WHOLESALE

Visions Millwork Inc........................F....... 239 390-0811
Fort Myers *(G-4648)*

LOCKS: Safe & Vault, Metal

Safe Banks and Lock........................G....... 954 762-3565
Fort Lauderdale *(G-4221)*

LOGGING

Agner Timber Services Inc........................G....... 850 251-6615
Perry *(G-14291)*
Bernice I Finch........................G....... 850 638-0082
Wausau *(G-18696)*
Black Creek Logging........................G....... 904 591-9681
Middleburg *(G-10904)*
Bushnell Saw Mill Inc........................G....... 352 793-2740
Bushnell *(G-1313)*
Charlie S Logging Inc........................G....... 850 643-1145
Bristol *(G-1193)*
Coastal Logging Inc........................F....... 850 832-0133
Panama City *(G-13884)*
Dm Stratton LLC........................G....... 904 342-7063
Saint Johns *(G-15677)*
Donald Smith Logging Inc........................G....... 850 697-3975
Carrabelle *(G-1497)*
Feagle Logging LLC........................G....... 386 365-2689
Lake City *(G-7354)*
Florida Cental Logging Inc........................F....... 863 272-5364
Lakeland *(G-7690)*
G Black Logging LLC........................G....... 850 379-8747
Hosford *(G-6009)*
G Haddock Rowland Inc........................G....... 904 845-2725
Hilliard *(G-5706)*
Gulf Coast Timber Company........................G....... 850 271-8818
Panama City *(G-13912)*
H Jones Timber LLC........................G....... 386 312-0603
Palatka *(G-13482)*
Hardy Logging Company Inc........................G....... 850 994-1955
Pace *(G-13469)*
Hbt Forestry Services Inc........................F....... 850 584-9324
Perry *(G-14304)*
Hobbs Trucking LLC........................G....... 904 463-5681
Hilliard *(G-5710)*
John L Shadd Enterprises........................F....... 386 496-3989
Lake Butler *(G-7338)*
Joiners Enterprises Inc........................F....... 850 623-5593
Milton *(G-10933)*
Joyner Inc........................G....... 850 832-6326
Panama City Beach *(G-13979)*
Marvin J Dericho........................G....... 407 290-0109
Orlando *(G-12951)*
Pearce Logging LLC........................G....... 386 365-1880
Lake Butler *(G-7340)*
Randall Birge........................G....... 850 373-6131
Bonifay *(G-807)*
Ridgeway Timber Inc........................G....... 352 463-6013
Bell *(G-342)*
Tucker Trckg Log Jhnny E Tcker........................G....... 850 258-1982
Wewahitchka *(G-19183)*
Usher Land & Timber Inc........................E....... 352 493-4221
Chiefland *(G-1539)*
Van Zant Timber Incorporated........................G....... 904 845-4661
Hilliard *(G-5720)*
West Fraser Inc........................D....... 904 786-4155
Jacksonville *(G-6910)*

LOGGING CAMPS & CONTRACTORS

4 C Timber Inc........................G....... 386 937-0806
Palatka *(G-13471)*
A and H Logging Inc........................G....... 352 528-3868
Williston *(G-19208)*
A L Baxley & Sons Inc........................E....... 352 629-5137
Citra *(G-1555)*
A&H Logging Inc........................G....... 352 528-3868
Morriston *(G-11091)*
B&M Logging Inc........................G....... 386 397-1145
White Springs *(G-19185)*
Bbts Logging LLC........................G....... 850 997-2436
Monticello *(G-11075)*
Boland Timber Company Inc........................E....... 850 997-5270
Perry *(G-14296)*
BTR Logging Inc........................G....... 386 397-0730
White Springs *(G-19186)*
Butler Logging Inc........................G....... 386 963-2720
Wellborn *(G-18706)*
C & G Timber Harvesters Inc........................G....... 850 643-1340
Bristol *(G-1192)*
C F Webb and Sons Logging LLC........................G....... 850 971-5565
Lee *(G-8137)*
Cedar Creek Logging Inc........................F....... 850 832-0133
Panama City *(G-13877)*
Circle C Timber Inc........................G....... 863 735-0383
Zolfo Springs *(G-19544)*
Cooper Timber Harvesting Inc........................F....... 863 494-0240
Arcadia *(G-202)*
CP Logging Inc........................F....... 850 379-8698
Hosford *(G-6008)*
D & S Logging Inc........................G....... 850 638-5500
Chipley *(G-1543)*
Flatwoods Forest Products Inc........................F....... 352 787-1161
Leesburg *(G-8156)*
Flowers Logging Co Inc........................G....... 850 639-2856
Kinard *(G-7213)*
Geiger Logging Inc........................E....... 904 845-7534
Hilliard *(G-5707)*
Gray Logging LLC........................G....... 850 973-3863
Madison *(G-8449)*
Gray Logging LLC........................G....... 850 973-3863
Madison *(G-8450)*
H B Tutun Jr Logging Inc........................G....... 850 584-9324
Perry *(G-14302)*
Harrison Logging........................F....... 352 591-2779
Williston *(G-19211)*
Harry Pickett........................G....... 904 845-4643
Hilliard *(G-5709)*
HB Tuten Jr Logging Inc........................E....... 850 584-9324
Perry *(G-14303)*
Henry W Long........................G....... 352 542-7068
Old Town *(G-12197)*
Howell Logging & Land Clearing........................G....... 352 528-2698
Williston *(G-19212)*
Hoyles Logging........................G....... 813 782-1164
Zephyrhills *(G-19522)*
John A Cruce Jr Inc........................E....... 850 584-9755
Perry *(G-14305)*
Johnny Sellers Logging Inc........................G....... 850 643-5214
Bristol *(G-1196)*
Johns & Conner Inc........................G....... 904 845-4430
Hilliard *(G-5711)*
Johns & Conner Logging Inc........................G....... 904 845-4430
Hilliard *(G-5712)*
Johns & Connor Inc........................G....... 904 845-4541
Hilliard *(G-5713)*
Kenneth P Green........................G....... 850 643-5851
Bristol *(G-1197)*
Key Logging........................G....... 386 328-6984
Hollister *(G-5754)*
L and D Logging........................G....... 850 859-1013
Westville *(G-19181)*
M & L Timber Inc........................G....... 386 437-0895
Bunnell *(G-1302)*
McClellan Logging Inc........................G....... 352 468-1856
Hampton *(G-5227)*
McMillan Logging Inc........................F....... 850 643-4819
Bristol *(G-1199)*
P & S Logging Inc........................F....... 904 845-4256
Hilliard *(G-5715)*
Pine Top Logging LLC........................G....... 386 365-0857
Branford *(G-1188)*
Randy Morris Logging Inc........................F....... 850 773-9010
Chipley *(G-1545)*
Reagan H Fox III Inc........................G....... 850 584-9229
Perry *(G-14311)*
Richard Brown Logging Inc........................F....... 850 379-8674
Hosford *(G-6011)*
Riverland Logging Inc........................G....... 904 845-4326
Hilliard *(G-5717)*
Rozar Logging Inc........................G....... 352 267-0829
Groveland *(G-5107)*
S&J Logging Inc........................G....... 904 237-7774
Glen Saint Mary *(G-5038)*
Tumbling Pines Inc........................F....... 386 437-2668
Bunnell *(G-1310)*
TW Byrds Sons Inc........................E....... 386 935-1544
Branford *(G-1190)*
Van Aernam Logging & Trucking........................F....... 352 498-5809
Cross City *(G-2369)*
Walden Timber Harvesting Inc........................F....... 850 674-4884
Altha *(G-86)*
Warwick Logging........................G....... 386 328-9358
East Palatka *(G-3609)*
Williams Timber Inc........................E....... 850 584-2760
Perry *(G-14319)*
Woodie L Dupree........................G....... 850 859-2496
Westville *(G-19182)*

LOGGING: Timber, Cut At Logging Camp

Ata Group of Companies Inc........................G....... 352 735-1588
Mount Dora *(G-11097)*
B & B Timber Company........................G....... 904 284-5541
Green Cove Springs *(G-5055)*
Bailey Timber Co Inc........................F....... 850 674-2080
Blountstown *(G-384)*
Griffis Timber Inc........................G....... 904 275-2372
Sanderson *(G-15981)*
L W Timber Co Inc........................G....... 850 592-2597
Greenwood *(G-5089)*
M&E Timber Inc........................G....... 850 584-6650
Perry *(G-14307)*
Paul White Logging Inc........................G....... 850 379-8651
Hosford *(G-6010)*
Rbj Timber Inc........................G....... 904 879-1597
Callahan *(G-1328)*
Santo Domingo Timber Co LLC........................G....... 561 627-4000
Palm Beach Gardens *(G-13623)*
Southern Wood Services LLC........................G....... 352 279-3208
Brooksville *(G-1272)*

LOGGING: Wooden Logs

South Amercn Lbr & Timber LLC........................G....... 786 280-8326
Miami *(G-10381)*
Underwood Butcher Block Co Inc........................F....... 904 338-2348
Jacksonville *(G-6877)*

LOOSELEAF BINDERS

Allied Decals-Fla Inc ....F 800 940-2233
Fort Lauderdale *(G-3801)*

LOOSELEAF BINDERS: Library

County of Hernando ....F 352 754-4042
Brooksville *(G-1222)*

LOTIONS OR CREAMS: Face

Cosmesis Skincare Inc ....G 954 963-5090
Hollywood *(G-5805)*
Doerfler Manufacturing Inc ....G 763 772-3728
Umatilla *(G-18498)*
Florida Keys Keylime Products ....G 305 853-0378
Key Largo *(G-7169)*
JP Cosmetics Inc ....F 305 231-4963
Hialeah *(G-5468)*
Jupiter Wellness Inc ....G 561 462-2700
Jupiter *(G-7063)*
Nac USA Corporation ....G 800 396-0149
Miami *(G-10058)*
Product Max Group Inc ....G 813 949-5061
Land O Lakes *(G-7863)*
Tropical Enterprises Intl ....F 813 837-9800
Tampa *(G-18202)*
Vienna Beauty Products Co ....F 937 228-7109
Naples *(G-11451)*
Younger You Inc ....G 954 924-4462
Fort Lauderdale *(G-4333)*

LOUDSPEAKERS

Advanced Cmmnications Tech Inc ....F 954 444-4119
Boca Raton *(G-403)*
Eminent Technology Inc ....G 850 575-5655
Tallahassee *(G-17247)*

LUBRICATING EQPT: Indl

Airgroup Inc ....F 561 279-0680
Boca Raton *(G-409)*
Phantom Sales Group Inc ....G 888 614-1232
Bartow *(G-330)*
Travis Lh LLC ....F 863 967-0628
Winter Haven *(G-19364)*

LUBRICATING SYSTEMS: Centralized

Cirven Usa LLC ....G 305 815-2545
Doral *(G-3299)*

LUGGAGE & BRIEFCASES

Fussion International Inc ....G 305 662-4848
Coral Gables *(G-2146)*
Lug Usa LLC ....F 855 584-5433
Orlando *(G-12937)*
Maleta Import ....G 305 592-2410
Miami *(G-9938)*
Qps Companies Inc ....E 813 246-5525
Tampa *(G-18029)*

LUGGAGE & LEATHER GOODS STORES: Leather, Exc Luggage & Shoes

Land Leather Inc ....G 305 594-2260
Miami *(G-9857)*

LUGGAGE & LEATHER GOODS STORES: Luggage, Exc Footlckr/Trunk

Back Country Inc ....G 772 532-6174
Vero Beach *(G-18598)*

LUGGAGE: Traveling Bags

My Focus Inc ....G 305 826-4480
Miami Lakes *(G-10826)*
Tumi Holdings Inc ....G 941 866-6304
Sarasota *(G-16318)*

LUGGAGE: Wardrobe Bags

Goyard Miami LLC ....E 305 894-9235
Bal Harbour *(G-302)*
Hontus Ltd ....F 786 322-3022
Medley *(G-8666)*

LUMBER & BLDG MATLS DEALER, RET: Garage Doors, Sell/Install

All Pro Chelo Corp ....G 786 317-3914
Hialeah *(G-5280)*
Specialty Products Inc ....G 850 438-4264
Pensacola *(G-14267)*

LUMBER & BLDG MATLS DEALERS, RET: Energy Conservation Prdts

A & A Central Florida ....F 407 648-5666
Altamonte Springs *(G-24)*

LUMBER & BLDG MATRLS DEALERS, RET: Bath Fixtures, Eqpt/Sply

Kitchen & Bath Center Inc ....E 850 244-3996
Fort Walton Beach *(G-4812)*
Location 3 Holdings LLC ....F 941 342-3443
Sarasota *(G-16489)*
Unique Marble Inc ....F 772 766-4432
Vero Beach *(G-18672)*

LUMBER & BLDG MTRLS DEALERS, RET: Closets, Interiors/Access

Cast Art International Corp ....G 727 807-3395
Dunedin *(G-3571)*
Southern Closet Systems Inc ....G 813 926-9348
Odessa *(G-12153)*

LUMBER & BLDG MTRLS DEALERS, RET: Doors, Storm, Wood/Metal

Trim-Pak Corporation ....E 407 851-8900
Orlando *(G-13273)*

LUMBER & BLDG MTRLS DEALERS, RET: Windows, Storm, Wood/Metal

Absolute Window and Door Inc ....G 941 485-7774
Venice *(G-18527)*
Screening Leon & Repair Inc ....G 850 575-2840
Tallahassee *(G-17321)*
Tropic Shield Inc ....F 954 731-5553
Lauderdale Lakes *(G-8095)*
Winsulator Corporation ....G 941 365-7901
Sarasota *(G-16642)*

LUMBER & BUILDING MATERIAL DEALERS, RETAIL: Roofing Material

Yandles Quality Roof Trusses ....G 352 732-3000
Ocala *(G-12078)*

LUMBER & BUILDING MATERIALS DEALER, RET: Door & Window Prdts

Architctral Mllwk Slutions Inc ....G 727 441-1409
Largo *(G-7899)*
Custom Cft Windows & Doors Inc ....F 407 834-5400
Winter Springs *(G-19470)*
Rolladen Inc ....F 954 454-4114
Longwood *(G-8332)*
Solar X ....G 386 673-2111
Ormond Beach *(G-13400)*
Sun Barrier Products Inc ....F 407 830-9085
Longwood *(G-8341)*
USA Shutter Company LLC ....G 239 596-8883
Fort Myers *(G-4642)*
West Coast Shutters Sunburst ....F 727 894-0044
Saint Petersburg *(G-15957)*

LUMBER & BUILDING MATERIALS DEALER, RET: Masonry Matls/Splys

Art Crete Products Inc ....F 386 252-5118
Daytona Beach *(G-2629)*
Concrete Edge Company ....G 407 658-2788
Orlando *(G-12612)*
Marble Designs of FL Inc ....G 321 269-6920
Titusville *(G-18445)*
Paver Systems LLC ....E 407 859-9117
Orlando *(G-13055)*
Trenwa Inc ....F 863 666-1680
Lakeland *(G-7825)*

LUMBER & BUILDING MATERIALS DEALERS, RETAIL: Cement

Anderson Columbia Co Inc ....F 352 463-6342
Chiefland *(G-1531)*

LUMBER & BUILDING MATERIALS DEALERS, RETAIL: Flooring, Wood

Designer Lifestyles LLC ....F 904 631-8954
Jacksonville *(G-6317)*
Tree Stake Solutions LLC ....G 407 920-0507
Orlando *(G-13269)*

LUMBER & BUILDING MATERIALS DEALERS, RETAIL: Sand & Gravel

Bdc Shell & Aggregate LLC ....F 941 875-6615
Punta Gorda *(G-15193)*
Helms Hauling & Materials Llc ....F 850 218-6895
Niceville *(G-11569)*
Rock Ridge Materials Inc ....F 321 268-8455
Titusville *(G-18460)*

LUMBER & BUILDING MATERIALS DEALERS, RETAIL: Tile, Ceramic

Techno Cabinets Inc ....G 305 910-9929
Doral *(G-3525)*

LUMBER & BUILDING MATERIALS RET DEALERS: Millwork & Lumber

Architctural WD Pdts of Naples ....G 239 260-7156
Naples *(G-11167)*
Bay Meadow Architectural Mllwk ....E 407 332-7992
Longwood *(G-8261)*
Commercial Casework Inc ....D 904 264-4222
Jacksonville *(G-6280)*
Cross City Lumber LLC ....F 352 578-8078
Cross City *(G-2363)*
Magnolia Millwork Intl Inc ....G 407 585-3470
Casselberry *(G-1510)*
Millwork and Design Inc ....G 352 544-0444
Brooksville *(G-1253)*

LUMBER & BUILDING MATLS DEALERS, RET: Concrete/Cinder Block

Cemex Cnstr Mtls Fla LLC ....G 321 632-0500
Cocoa *(G-2004)*
Cemex Cnstr Mtls Fla LLC ....F 561 832-6646
West Palm Beach *(G-18838)*
Cemex Materials LLC ....D 386 775-0790
Deland *(G-2963)*
Cemex Materials LLC ....D 772 287-0502
Stuart *(G-16921)*
Cemex Materials LLC ....D 941 722-4578
Palmetto *(G-13790)*
Cemex Materials LLC ....D 954 523-9978
Fort Lauderdale *(G-3890)*
Cemex Materials LLC ....D 954 431-7655
Pembroke Pines *(G-14026)*
Commercial Concrete Pdts Inc ....E 813 659-3707
Plant City *(G-14419)*

LUMBER & BUILDING MATLS DEALERS, RET: Screens, Door/Window

ABC Screen Masters Inc ....G 239 772-7336
Cape Coral *(G-1371)*
Greg Valley ....F 941 739-6628
Sarasota *(G-16224)*
Tag Media Group LLC ....G 239 288-0499
Fort Myers *(G-4622)*

LUMBER: Dimension, Hardwood

Resolute Cross City LLC ....G 352 498-3363
Cross City *(G-2367)*

LUMBER: Furniture Dimension Stock, Softwood

Inox LLC ....G 305 409-2764
Sunny Isles Beach *(G-17079)*

LUMBER: Hardboard

Custom Cornhole Boards Inc ....E 407 203-6886
Orlando *(G-12638)*

LUMBER: Hardwood Dimension

Boyett Timber Inc....G.... 352 583-2138
Webster *(G-18697)*

LUMBER: Hardwood Dimension & Flooring Mills

A L Baxley & Sons Inc....E.... 352 629-5137
Citra *(G-1555)*
Aj Originals Inc....G.... 954 563-9911
Fort Lauderdale *(G-3793)*
Big River Cypress & Hardwood....F.... 850 674-5991
Blountstown *(G-385)*
Bushnell Saw Mill Inc....G.... 352 793-2740
Bushnell *(G-1313)*
Fraser West Inc....D.... 901 620-4200
Jacksonville *(G-6414)*
Heisler Hardwood Inc....G.... 727 410-0401
Clearwater *(G-1713)*
Resolute Cross Cy RE Hldngs LL....F.... 352 498-3363
Cross City *(G-2368)*
Roberts Lumber Company Inc....F.... 850 584-4573
Perry *(G-14312)*
West Fraser Inc....D.... 850 587-1000
Mc David *(G-8602)*
West Fraser Inc....D.... 904 786-4155
Jacksonville *(G-6910)*

LUMBER: Kiln Dried

Roberts Lumber Company Inc....F.... 850 584-4573
Perry *(G-14312)*

LUMBER: Plywood, Hardwood

Coastal Plywood Company....B.... 800 359-6432
Havana *(G-5236)*
Dackor Inc....F.... 407 654-5013
Winter Garden *(G-19259)*
Goodwin Lumber Company Inc....F.... 352 466-0339
Micanopy *(G-10901)*
Plywood Express Inc....E.... 954 956-7576
Pompano Beach *(G-14799)*
Thomas Rley Artisans Guild Inc....E.... 239 591-3203
Naples *(G-11440)*

LUMBER: Plywood, Hardwood or Hardwood Faced

Esco Industries Inc....F.... 863 666-3696
Lakeland *(G-7681)*

LUMBER: Plywood, Softwood

Coastal Forest Resources Co....B.... 850 539-6432
Havana *(G-5235)*
Cross City Veneer Company Inc....D.... 352 498-3226
Cross City *(G-2364)*

LUMBER: Plywood, Softwood

Corelite Inc....F.... 305 921-4292
Hialeah *(G-5356)*
Thomas Rley Artisans Guild Inc....E.... 239 591-3203
Naples *(G-11440)*

LUMBER: Poles & Pole Crossarms, Treated

Apalachee Pole Company Inc....E.... 850 643-2121
Bristol *(G-1191)*

LUMBER: Poles, Wood, Untreated

Apalachee Pole Company Inc....E.... 850 643-2121
Bristol *(G-1191)*

LUMBER: Rails, Fence, Round Or Split

Equity Group Usa Inc....G.... 407 421-6464
Winter Springs *(G-19472)*
L A Ornamental & Rack Corp....G.... 305 696-0419
Miami *(G-9835)*

LUMBER: Treated

Arnold Lumber Company Inc....F.... 850 547-5733
Bonifay *(G-798)*
Great Southern Wood Prsv Inc....E.... 352 793-9410
Lake Panasoffkee *(G-7463)*
Johnny Under Pressure LLC....G.... 850 530-8763
Pensacola *(G-14184)*
Pensacola Wood Treating Co....G.... 850 433-1300
Pensacola *(G-14228)*
Robbins Manufacturing Company....C.... 813 971-3030
Tampa *(G-18063)*
Southern Lbr & Treating Co Inc....F.... 904 695-0784
Jacksonville *(G-6795)*

MACHINE PARTS: Stamped Or Pressed Metal

Aero Technology Mfg Inc....F.... 305 345-7747
Miami *(G-9082)*
Aircraft Tbular Components Inc....E.... 321 757-9020
Melbourne *(G-8760)*
Benton Machine Works Inc....G.... 904 768-9161
Jacksonville *(G-6207)*
Chasco Machine & Mfg Inc....E.... 352 678-4188
Brooksville *(G-1219)*
Cnc Works Service Inc....F.... 813 777-8642
Clearwater *(G-1630)*
Icosi Manufacturing LLC....F.... 813 854-1333
Odessa *(G-12095)*
Iva Parts Broker LLC....G.... 239 222-2604
Miramar *(G-11006)*
Rek Manufacturing Inc....G.... 321 269-3533
Titusville *(G-18455)*
SBs Precision Shtmtl Inc....E.... 321 951-7411
Melbourne *(G-8927)*
Sohacki Industries Inc....E.... 904 826-0130
Saint Augustine *(G-15613)*

MACHINE SHOPS

Aba Engineering & Mfg Inc....F.... 386 672-9665
Ormond Beach *(G-13346)*
Addtad Partners Inc....G.... 727 863-0847
Hudson *(G-6014)*
Aero Technology Mfg Inc....F.... 305 345-7747
Miami *(G-9082)*
AL Garey & Associates Inc....C.... 954 975-7992
Coral Springs *(G-2218)*
Arnold Industries South Inc....G.... 352 867-0190
Ocala *(G-11879)*
Automated Production Eqp Ape....G.... 305 451-4722
Key Largo *(G-7165)*
C4 Group LLC....F.... 850 230-4541
Panama City Beach *(G-13975)*
Dj/Pj Inc....E.... 813 907-6359
Clearwater *(G-1653)*
Euro Gear (usa) Inc....E.... 518 578-1775
Miami *(G-9539)*
Grinder Wear Parts Inc....E.... 503 982-0881
Largo *(G-7966)*
Hammer Haag Steel Inc....C.... 727 216-6903
Clearwater *(G-1710)*
Integritrust Solutions LLC....G.... 850 685-9801
Navarre *(G-11466)*
Koral Precision LLC....F.... 727 548-5040
Pinellas Park *(G-14361)*
Machine Tool Masters Inc....F.... 850 432-2829
Pensacola *(G-14199)*
Madson Inc....F.... 305 863-7390
Medley *(G-8681)*
Marden Industries Inc....F.... 863 682-7882
Punta Gorda *(G-15213)*
Merit Fastener Corporation....E.... 407 331-4815
Longwood *(G-8311)*
Merit Fastener Corporation....G.... 813 626-3748
Tampa *(G-17903)*
Mid-State Machine & Fabg Corp....B.... 863 665-6233
Lakeland *(G-7751)*
Novak Machining Inc....G.... 727 527-5473
Pinellas Park *(G-14372)*
Production Metal Stampings....F.... 850 981-8240
Milton *(G-10938)*
Responsive Machining Inc....F.... 321 225-4011
Titusville *(G-18457)*
Rfg Consulting Services Inc....G.... 786 498-2177
Miami *(G-10261)*
Rodriguez Welding....G.... 305 856-3749
Miami *(G-10275)*
Santa Rosa Auto Parts Inc....E.... 850 477-7747
Pensacola *(G-14257)*
Sulzer Ems Inc....E.... 407 858-9447
Orlando *(G-13220)*
Sunshine Tool LLC....G.... 941 351-6330
Sarasota *(G-16306)*
Sy-Klone Company LLC....E.... 904 448-6563
Jacksonville *(G-6832)*
Tep Manufacturing Co....G.... 321 632-1417
Rockledge *(G-15453)*
Ttc-The Trading Company Inc....E.... 503 982-0880
Largo *(G-8069)*
Van Linda Iron Works Inc....E.... 561 586-8400
Lake Worth Beach *(G-7622)*
Weber Mfg & Supplies Inc....F.... 941 488-5185
North Venice *(G-11764)*

MACHINE TOOL ACCESS: Broaches

Turbine Broach Company....F.... 352 795-1163
Hernando *(G-5248)*

MACHINE TOOL ACCESS: Cutting

Agi-Vr/Wesson Inc....E.... 239 573-5132
Cape Coral *(G-1377)*
Rock River Tool Inc....F.... 941 753-6343
Bradenton *(G-1106)*

MACHINE TOOL ACCESS: Diamond Cutting, For Turning, Etc

Gws Tool LLC....F.... 352 343-8778
Tavares *(G-18340)*
Microtool and Instrument Inc....E.... 786 242-8780
Palmetto Bay *(G-13851)*
Thermocarbon Inc....E.... 407 834-7800
Casselberry *(G-1520)*

MACHINE TOOL ACCESS: Drills

Elliott Diamond Tool Inc....F.... 727 585-3839
Clearwater *(G-1669)*

MACHINE TOOL ACCESS: Files

Mastercut Tool Corp....E.... 727 726-5336
Safety Harbor *(G-15499)*

MACHINE TOOL ACCESS: Knives, Metalworking

Florida Knife Co....E.... 941 371-2104
Sarasota *(G-16437)*

MACHINE TOOL ACCESS: Machine Attachments & Access, Drilling

Tom Burke Services....G.... 863 940-4504
Lakeland *(G-7823)*

MACHINE TOOL ACCESS: Tool Holders

Aaw Products Inc....G.... 305 330-6863
Miami *(G-9049)*

MACHINE TOOL ATTACHMENTS & ACCESS

Dan Lipman and Associates....G.... 561 245-8672
Delray Beach *(G-3068)*
Nasco Industries Inc....E.... 954 733-8665
Fort Lauderdale *(G-4131)*
Polygon Solutions Inc....G.... 239 628-4800
Fort Myers *(G-4569)*

MACHINE TOOLS & ACCESS

A B & B Manufacturing Inc....F.... 904 378-3350
Jacksonville *(G-6108)*
Andritz Iggesund Tools Inc....E.... 813 855-6902
Oldsmar *(G-12202)*
Axiom Automotive Technologies....G.... 407 299-4400
Orlando *(G-12502)*
B & P Motors Inc....G.... 305 687-7337
Opa Locka *(G-12292)*
Construction and Elec Pdts Inc....F.... 954 972-9787
Pompano Beach *(G-14645)*
Creative Carbide Inc....F.... 239 567-0041
Fort Myers *(G-4414)*
Delta International Inc....F.... 305 665-6573
Miami *(G-9451)*
Dse Inc....E.... 813 443-4809
Tampa *(G-17617)*
Gulf Tool Corporation....F.... 850 456-0840
Pensacola *(G-14168)*
Henefelt Precision Products....F.... 727 531-0406
Largo *(G-7969)*
Jacksnvlle Advnced McHning LLC....G.... 904 292-2999
Jacksonville *(G-6508)*
Lexington Cutter Inc....E.... 941 739-2726
Bradenton *(G-1070)*
Micro Quality Corp....G.... 954 354-5572
Deerfield Beach *(G-2872)*
Mitts and Merrill LP....G.... 352 343-7001
Tavares *(G-18349)*
Rhino Tools Inc....F.... 305 332-7750
Hialeah *(G-5598)*

Shaw Development LLC........................C....... 239 405-6100
Bonita Springs *(G-853)*
Suncoast Tool & Gage Inds Inc.............F....... 727 572-8000
Clearwater *(G-1893)*
Swisstech Machinery LLC......................G....... 407 416-2383
Orlando *(G-13233)*
Toolinghouse Inc.................................G....... 239 424-8503
Cape Coral *(G-1486)*

MACHINE TOOLS, METAL CUTTING: Drilling

Aerowest Mfg Corp................................G....... 786 367-6948
Hialeah *(G-5273)*
Levil Technology Corp..........................G....... 407 542-3971
Oviedo *(G-13447)*
M Vb Industries Inc...............................E....... 954 480-6448
Deerfield Beach *(G-2865)*
Technical Ord Solutions LLC.................G....... 850 223-2393
Perry *(G-14316)*

MACHINE TOOLS, METAL CUTTING: Exotic, Including Explosive

Metal Supply and Machining Inc............F....... 561 276-4941
Delray Beach *(G-3107)*
Mitts and Merrill LP...............................G....... 352 343-7001
Tavares *(G-18349)*

MACHINE TOOLS, METAL CUTTING: Jig, Boring & Grinding

Reinecker Grinders Corp.......................G....... 954 974-6190
Pompano Beach *(G-14827)*

MACHINE TOOLS, METAL CUTTING: Numerically Controlled

Gulf Machining Inc..................................F....... 727 571-1244
Clearwater *(G-1707)*

MACHINE TOOLS, METAL CUTTING: Sawing & Cutoff

Americut of Florida Inc..........................F....... 800 692-2187
Fort Myers *(G-4360)*

MACHINE TOOLS, METAL CUTTING: Tool Replacement & Rpr Parts

Icosi Manufacturing LLC........................F....... 813 854-1333
Odessa *(G-12095)*
International Tool Mchs of Fla...............E....... 386 446-0500
Palm Coast *(G-13699)*
Lundy Enterprises Inc............................F....... 727 549-1292
Largo *(G-8003)*

MACHINE TOOLS, METAL CUTTING: Ultrasonic

Bescutter LLC...G....... 888 525-2897
Lehigh Acres *(G-8185)*

MACHINE TOOLS, METAL FORMING: Bending

Phoenix Enterprises Fla LLC..................F....... 813 986-9000
Temple Terrace *(G-18374)*

MACHINE TOOLS, METAL FORMING: Container, Metal Incl Cans

Sequa Corporation.................................A....... 561 935-3571
Palm Beach Gardens *(G-13626)*
Sunrise Manufacturing Intl Inc..............F....... 813 780-7369
Zephyrhills *(G-19538)*

MACHINE TOOLS, METAL FORMING: Crimping, Metal

Bridgestone Hosepower LLC..................D....... 904 264-1267
Orange Park *(G-12383)*

MACHINE TOOLS, METAL FORMING: Forging Machinery & Hammers

G & R Machine Inc...................................G....... 407 324-1600
Sanford *(G-16053)*

MACHINE TOOLS, METAL FORMING: Gear Rolling

B&M RC Racing..G....... 313 518-3999
Winter Haven *(G-19301)*

MACHINE TOOLS, METAL FORMING: Headers

Double Header LLC.................................G....... 352 377-4458
Gainesville *(G-4908)*

MACHINE TOOLS, METAL FORMING: Mechanical, Pneumatic Or Hyd

Aflg Invstmnts-Industrials LLC..............G....... 813 443-8203
Tampa *(G-17390)*
Aflg Invstmnts-Industrials LLC..............F....... 813 443-8203
Hernando Beach *(G-5250)*
Lenco Holdings LLC................................G....... 305 360-0895
Deerfield Beach *(G-2858)*

MACHINE TOOLS, METAL FORMING: Shearing, Power

Hydrapower International Inc................A....... 239 642-5379
Marco Island *(G-8525)*

MACHINE TOOLS: Metal Cutting

Agi-Vr/Wesson Inc..................................E....... 239 573-5132
Cape Coral *(G-1377)*
Andritz Iggesund Tools Inc.....................E....... 813 855-6902
Oldsmar *(G-12202)*
Armada Systems Inc...............................F....... 850 664-5197
Destin *(G-3183)*
Azt Technology LLC................................C....... 239 352-0600
Naples *(G-11179)*
Coastal Machine LLC..............................G....... 850 769-6117
Panama City *(G-13885)*
Elliott Diamond Tool Inc........................F....... 727 585-3839
Clearwater *(G-1669)*
Ems Technologies NA LLC.....................F....... 321 259-5979
Orlando *(G-12710)*
Florida Hytorc..F....... 813 990-9470
Clearwater *(G-1689)*
Florida Knife Co......................................E....... 941 371-2104
Sarasota *(G-16437)*
Giraldo & Donalisio Corp.......................G....... 239 567-2206
Cape Coral *(G-1429)*
Grizzly Manufacturing Inc.......................E....... 386 755-0220
Lake City *(G-7360)*
Heath Corporation..................................G....... 863 638-1819
Lake Wales *(G-7513)*
High Performance Holdings Ltd............E....... 815 874-9421
Lakeland *(G-7705)*
Highvac Co LLC.......................................F....... 407 969-0399
Orlando *(G-12803)*
Huff Carbide Tool Inc...............................F....... 727 848-4001
Port Richey *(G-15052)*
Lexington Cutter Inc................................E....... 941 739-2726
Bradenton *(G-1070)*
Machine Technology Inc..........................G....... 321 254-3886
Melbourne *(G-8880)*
Maydone Ltd Liability Company............G....... 407 399-3287
Orlando *(G-12955)*
Odyssey Fastening Systems Inc..............G....... 561 436-5570
Jupiter *(G-7086)*
Precision Metal Parts Inc.......................E....... 727 526-9165
Saint Petersburg *(G-15888)*
Prime Horizontal......................................G....... 239 471-2357
Cape Coral *(G-1457)*
Rankine-Hinman Mfg Co.........................F....... 904 808-0404
Saint Augustine *(G-15594)*
Reiley Tool Company LLC.......................G....... 360 929-0350
Middleburg *(G-10912)*
Republic Drill/Apt Corp..........................D....... 305 592-7777
Miami *(G-10256)*
Skill-Metric Machine & Tl Inc................E....... 561 454-8900
Delray Beach *(G-3143)*
Snk America Inc......................................F....... 407 831-7766
Sanford *(G-16117)*
Super Tool Inc..E....... 941 751-9677
Bradenton *(G-1122)*
Unbridled Technologies LLC.................G....... 888 334-8402
Brooksville *(G-1285)*
Walin Tools LLC......................................G....... 850 226-8632
Fort Walton Beach *(G-4839)*
Zel Tech Trining Solutions LLC..............E....... 757 722-5565
Winter Park *(G-19464)*

MACHINE TOOLS: Metal Forming

Coastal Machine LLC..............................G....... 850 769-6117
Panama City *(G-13885)*
Daigle Tool & Die Inc..............................G....... 954 785-9989
Deerfield Beach *(G-2811)*
Delta Machine & Tool Inc.......................E....... 386 738-2204
Deland *(G-2969)*
Fuji International LLC............................F....... 941 961-5472
Sarasota *(G-16442)*
Jenzano Incorporated.............................F....... 386 761-4474
Port Orange *(G-15020)*
Maydone Ltd Liability Company............G....... 407 399-3287
Orlando *(G-12955)*
Production Metal Stampings..................F....... 850 981-8240
Milton *(G-10938)*
U S Hardware Supply Inc.......................E....... 407 657-1551
Winter Park *(G-19454)*

MACHINERY & EQPT, AGRICULTURAL, WHOLESALE: Agricultural, NEC

Florida Sprayers Inc...............................G....... 813 989-0500
Temple Terrace *(G-18369)*

MACHINERY & EQPT, AGRICULTURAL, WHOLESALE: Dairy

Sanchelima International Inc.................F....... 305 591-4343
Doral *(G-3495)*

MACHINERY & EQPT, AGRICULTURAL, WHOLESALE: Landscaping Eqpt

Concrete Edge Company.........................G....... 407 658-2788
Orlando *(G-12612)*

MACHINERY & EQPT, AGRICULTURAL, WHOLESALE: Poultry Eqpt

Hawkhead International Inc....................G....... 904 264-4295
Orange Park *(G-12396)*

MACHINERY & EQPT, INDL, WHOL: Brewery Prdts Mfrg, Commercial

Brewfab LLC...G....... 727 823-8333
Saint Petersburg *(G-15729)*
Canarchy Craft...E....... 813 348-6363
Tampa *(G-17503)*
Cigar City Brewpub LLC.........................C....... 813 348-6363
Tampa *(G-17534)*

MACHINERY & EQPT, INDL, WHOLESALE: Cranes

Coastal Crane and Rigging Inc...............G....... 850 460-1766
Santa Rosa Beach *(G-16155)*

MACHINERY & EQPT, INDL, WHOLESALE: Drilling, Exc Bits

Ronnies Welding & Machine...................G....... 305 238-0972
Cutler Bay *(G-2410)*

MACHINERY & EQPT, INDL, WHOLESALE: Engines & Parts, Diesel

All Power Pro Inc.....................................G....... 904 310-3069
Fernandina Beach *(G-3730)*
Amds Trading Inc....................................G....... 305 594-6680
Doral *(G-3246)*
Diesel Pro Power Inc...............................F....... 305 545-5588
Miami *(G-9467)*

MACHINERY & EQPT, INDL, WHOLESALE: Engs & Parts, Air-Cooled

AC Industrial Service Inc.........................F....... 305 887-5541
Hialeah *(G-5265)*

MACHINERY & EQPT, INDL, WHOLESALE: Fans

Kanalflakt Inc..F....... 941 359-3267
Sarasota *(G-16480)*

MACHINERY & EQPT, INDL, WHOLESALE: Fuel Injection Systems

Progress Rail Services Corp.................D....... 239 643-3013
Naples (G-11376)

MACHINERY & EQPT, INDL, WHOLESALE: Machine Tools & Access

Chasco Machine & Mfg Inc ....E....... 352 678-4188
Brooksville (G-1219)

MACHINERY & EQPT, INDL, WHOLESALE: Paper Manufacturing

Sandar Industries Inc ....E....... 904 246-4309
Atlantic Beach (G-226)

MACHINERY & EQPT, INDL, WHOLESALE: Processing & Packaging

Aircel LLC...E....... 865 681-7066
Naples (G-11152)
Wilkinson Hi-Rise LLC..........................C....... 954 342-4400
Fort Lauderdale (G-4324)

MACHINERY & EQPT, INDL, WHOLESALE: Propane Conversion

Aei International Corp ....G....... 904 724-9771
Jacksonville (G-6125)

MACHINERY & EQPT, INDL, WHOLESALE: Safety Eqpt

Cintas Corporation ....G....... 239 693-8722
Fort Myers (G-4396)
Primetime Industries LLC ....G....... 813 781-0196
Wesley Chapel (G-18756)

MACHINERY & EQPT, INDL, WHOLESALE: Waste Compactors

C & D Industrial Maint LLC....................F 833 776-5833
Bradenton (G-1005)

MACHINERY & EQPT, TEXTILE: Fabric Forming

Hills Inc ....D....... 321 723-5560
Melbourne (G-8844)

MACHINERY & EQPT, WHOLESALE: Construction & Mining, Ladders

Atlantic Insulation Inc...........................D....... 904 354-2217
Jacksonville (G-6174)

MACHINERY & EQPT, WHOLESALE: Construction, Cranes

Coastal Crane and Rigging Inc.............G....... 850 460-1766
Santa Rosa Beach (G-16155)

MACHINERY & EQPT, WHOLESALE: Construction, General

Dhs Unlimited Inc...................................G....... 954 532-2142
Pompano Beach (G-14663)

MACHINERY & EQPT, WHOLESALE: Drilling, Wellpoints

Jayco Screens Inc.................................G....... 850 456-0673
Pensacola (G-14182)

MACHINERY & EQPT, WHOLESALE: Tractor-Mounting Eqpt

Longs Wheel & Rim Inc ....D....... 904 757-3710
Jacksonville (G-6564)

MACHINERY & EQPT: Electroplating

Eidschun Engineering Inc ....E....... 727 647-2300
Clearwater (G-1664)
Interplex Labs Ltd ....D....... 954 718-9953
Tamarac (G-17358)
Surface Finishing Tech Inc ....E....... 727 577-7777
Clearwater (G-1898)

MACHINERY & EQPT: Farm

Agri Machinery & Parts Inc ....F....... 407 299-1592
Orlando (G-12442)
Agro & Cnstr Solutions Inc....................F....... 305 593-7011
Doral (G-3230)
Alpha Technology USA Corp ....F....... 407 571-2060
Sanford (G-15990)
Animal Air Service Inc ....E....... 305 218-1759
Doral (G-3250)
Black Widow Custom Cases...................G....... 321 327-8058
Palm Bay (G-13504)
Brush Cases LLC ....G....... 305 340-7214
Miami Beach (G-10649)
Bushhog N Blade Work ....G....... 904 669-2764
Saint Augustine (G-15525)
Chargers and Cases LLC ....G....... 352 587-2539
Winter Park (G-19393)
Cnh Industrial America LLC...................F....... 954 389-9779
Weston (G-19116)
Cory Aun ....G....... 407 957-1133
Saint Cloud (G-15648)
David B Case..G....... 904 262-6224
Jacksonville (G-6313)
David R Case..G....... 727 808-9330
Spring Hill (G-16872)
Erb Roberts Tillage LLC ....G....... 352 376-4888
Fort Lauderdale (G-3974)
Farmco Manufacturers Inc......................F....... 813 645-0611
Ruskin (G-15484)
First Case Cash LLC...............................G....... 954 200-5374
Hallandale Beach (G-5185)
Foley Air LLC..F....... 904 379-2243
Jacksonville (G-6411)
Franz A Ullrich Jr ....G....... 863 773-4653
Wauchula (G-18692)
Free Life Inc..G....... 954 584-8485
Plantation (G-14518)
Hera Cases LLC ....G....... 305 322-8960
Coral Gables (G-2154)
Hera Cases LLC ....G....... 305 714-2274
Miami (G-9703)
Home & Garden Industries Inc ....F....... 305 634-0681
Miami (G-9716)
I Fix & Cases LLC...................................G....... 939 645-5252
Orlando (G-12816)
International Packaging Mchs ....G....... 239 643-2020
Naples (G-11290)
John W Hock Company...........................G....... 352 378-3209
Gainesville (G-4948)
Kochan Cases ....G....... 850 533-4190
Mary Esther (G-8591)
Marden Industries Inc.............................F....... 863 682-7882
Punta Gorda (G-15213)
Marine Metal Products Co......................G....... 727 461-5575
Clearwater (G-1773)
Niteo Products LLC ....F....... 561 745-1812
Jupiter (G-7082)
OSteen Plastic Inc..................................G....... 954 434-4921
Southwest Ranches (G-16839)
Ovipost Inc ....F....... 707 776-6108
Labelle (G-7322)
Performnce Ntrtn Solutions LLC ....G....... 310 435-2995
Loxahatchee Groves (G-8367)
Petersen Industries Inc ....C....... 863 676-1493
Lake Wales (G-7517)
Powercases Inc.......................................G....... 239 415-3846
Miromar Lakes (G-11071)
R & C Sales & Mfg Inc............................F....... 904 824-2223
Palm Coast (G-13707)
R & S Metalworks & Co LLC ....F....... 772 466-3303
Port Saint Lucie (G-15132)
Roccos Custom Cases Corp....................G....... 305 799-2841
Hialeah (G-5603)
Ryan Manufacturing Inc ....F....... 386 325-3644
East Palatka (G-3606)
Sebring Septic Tank Precast Co.............E....... 863 655-2030
Sebring (G-16708)
Southern Fiberglass Inc..........................F....... 904 387-2246
Jacksonville (G-6794)
St Johns Turf Case ....F....... 352 258-3314
East Palatka (G-3607)
Tracto Parts Corp....................................G....... 305 972-1357
Miami (G-10499)
Tru-Flo Corp ....F....... 561 996-5850
Belle Glade (G-354)
Turner Machine & Supply Co ....G....... 772 464-4550
Fort Pierce (G-4762)

MACHINERY & EQPT: Gas Producers, Generators/Other Rltd Eqpt

Casper Engineering Corp.......................G....... 305 666-4046
Pinecrest (G-14326)

MACHINERY & EQPT: Liquid Automation

Aflg Invstmnts-Industrials LLC..............G....... 813 443-8203
Tampa (G-17390)
Aflg Invstmnts-Industrials LLC..............F....... 813 443-8203
Hernando Beach (G-5250)
Keltour US Inc ....F....... 239 424-8901
Cape Coral (G-1443)
Syn-Tech Systems Inc ....C....... 850 878-2558
Tallahassee (G-17332)
Whetstone Indus Holdings Inc ....G....... 904 824-0888
Saint Augustine (G-15635)

MACHINERY & EQPT: Metal Finishing, Plating Etc

Prestige Service Group ....G....... 954 532-9014
Pompano Beach (G-14811)
Recycling Center.....................................G....... 386 364-5865
Live Oak (G-8239)

MACHINERY & EQPT: Petroleum Refinery

Logistic Systems Inc ....G....... 305 477-4999
Miami (G-9906)

MACHINERY BASES

Brady Built Technologies Inc.................G....... 270 692-6866
Melbourne (G-8784)
Dj/Pj Inc..E....... 813 907-6359
Clearwater (G-1653)
JP Donvan Prcsion McHining LLC ....G....... 321 383-1171
Rockledge (G-15424)
Tru Mension Mfg Solutions ....G....... 321 255-4665
Melbourne (G-8967)
Vested Metals Intl LLC............................G....... 904 495-7278
Saint Augustine (G-15631)

MACHINERY, COMMERCIAL LAUNDRY & Drycleaning: Pressing

Unipress Corporation ....D....... 813 623-3731
Tampa (G-18218)

MACHINERY, COMMERCIAL LAUNDRY: Washing, Incl Coin-Operated

Coin-O-Matic Inc ....E....... 305 635-4141
Miami (G-9376)
R&K Mehall Inc..G....... 727 781-8780
Palm Harbor (G-13754)

MACHINERY, EQPT & SUPPLIES: Parking Facility

Lcn Incorporated......................................E....... 305 461-2770
Miami (G-9873)
Park Plus Florida Inc ....F....... 954 929-7511
Dania (G-2456)
Robotic Parking Systems Inc ....F....... 727 539-7275
Clearwater (G-1863)

MACHINERY, FOOD PRDTS: Beverage

BWC Equipment LLC................................G....... 239 443-9925
Cape Coral (G-1398)

MACHINERY, FOOD PRDTS: Dairy & Milk

Authentic Trading Inc ....G....... 347 866-7241
Davie (G-2500)
Carter Day Holding Inc ....D....... 239 280-0361
Naples (G-11199)
Sanchelima International Inc ....F....... 305 591-4343
Doral (G-3495)

MACHINERY, FOOD PRDTS: Distillery

Aquaback Technologies Inc....................F....... 978 863-1000
Port Saint Lucie (G-15088)
Point Distillery LLC..................................F....... 727 269-5588
New Port Richey (G-11508)

MACHINERY, FOOD PRDTS: Juice Extractors, Fruit & Veg, Comm

Zumex Usa Inc.........G....... 305 591-0061
Doral *(G-3554)*

MACHINERY, FOOD PRDTS: Mixers, Commercial

Cei Liquidation Inc.........G....... 281 541-2444
Fort Pierce *(G-4684)*

MACHINERY, FOOD PRDTS: Ovens, Bakery

Californo Corp.........G....... 855 553-6766
Hallandale Beach *(G-5176)*

MACHINERY, FOOD PRDTS: Packing House

Whigham Citrus Packing House.........G....... 772 569-7190
Vero Beach *(G-18682)*

MACHINERY, FOOD PRDTS: Pasta

Defrancisci Machine Co LLC.........F....... 321 952-6600
Melbourne *(G-8801)*

MACHINERY, FOOD PRDTS: Roasting, Coffee, Peanut, Etc.

Group 32 Dev & Engrg Inc.........F....... 305 361-0463
Key Biscayne *(G-7157)*

MACHINERY, FOOD PRDTS: Sugar Plant

Alvean Americas Inc.........F....... 305 606-0770
Coral Gables *(G-2121)*
Czarnikow Group Ltd.........G....... 786 476-0000
Miami *(G-9423)*
Sugar Development Corp.........G....... 561 784-0604
West Palm Beach *(G-19047)*

MACHINERY, MAILING: Postage Meters

Pitney Bowes Inc.........D....... 813 639-1110
Tampa *(G-17994)*

MACHINERY, METALWORKING: Assembly, Including Robotic

Alh Systems Inc.........G....... 727 787-6306
Palm Harbor *(G-13717)*
Centurion Armoring Intl Inc.........F....... 813 426-3385
Tampa *(G-17525)*
Intelligent Robotics Inc.........G....... 850 728-7353
Tallahassee *(G-17281)*
Robotics Fabrication Inc.........E....... 850 896-4987
Panama City *(G-13947)*
Waterjet Robotics USA LLC.........G....... 772 403-2192
Palm Beach Gardens *(G-13634)*
Westlund Engineering Inc.........G....... 727 572-4343
Palm Harbor *(G-13769)*

MACHINERY, METALWORKING: Coilers, Metalworking

Best Closures Inc.........G....... 305 821-6607
Miami Lakes *(G-10766)*

MACHINERY, METALWORKING: Coiling

Prime Global Group Inc.........E....... 386 676-2200
Ormond Beach *(G-13393)*

MACHINERY, OFFICE: Dictating

Dictaphone Corporation.........D....... 321 255-8668
Melbourne *(G-8805)*
Hth Engineering Inc.........E....... 727 939-8853
Tarpon Springs *(G-18308)*

MACHINERY, OFFICE: Duplicating

R & K Marketing Inc.........G....... 904 745-0022
Jacksonville *(G-6701)*

MACHINERY, OFFICE: Embossing, Store Or Office

Cim USA Inc.........G....... 305 369-1040
Doral *(G-3298)*
Diversified Performance System.........F....... 904 765-7181
Jacksonville *(G-6321)*

MACHINERY, OFFICE: Ticket Counting

M C Mieth Manufacturing Inc.........F....... 386 767-3494
Port Orange *(G-15023)*

MACHINERY, OFFICE: Time Clocks &Time Recording Devices

Simplexgrinnell Holdings LLC.........G....... 978 731-2500
Boca Raton *(G-716)*

MACHINERY, OFFICE: Typing & Word Processing

Barclays Business Center LLC.........G....... 786 260-0080
Miami *(G-9218)*

MACHINERY, PACKAGING: Carton Packing

Endflex LLC.........E....... 305 622-4070
Opa Locka *(G-12313)*
Quality Carton Inc.........G....... 941 921-1770
Sarasota *(G-16551)*

MACHINERY, PACKAGING: Vacuum

MDC Engineering Inc.........F....... 941 358-0610
Sarasota *(G-16505)*

MACHINERY, PACKAGING: Wrapping

International Packaging Mchs.........G....... 239 643-2020
Naples *(G-11290)*
Polypack Inc.........D....... 727 578-5000
Pinellas Park *(G-14377)*

MACHINERY, PAPER INDUSTRY: Paper Mill, Plating, Etc

Industrial Cnstr Svcs Dsign In.........D....... 904 827-9795
Saint Augustine *(G-15555)*

MACHINERY, PRINTING TRADES: Bookbinding Machinery

Instabook Corp.........G....... 352 332-1311
Gainesville *(G-4943)*

MACHINERY, PRINTING TRADES: Copy Holders

Kyocera Dcment Sltons Sthast L.........F....... 772 562-0511
Fort Pierce *(G-4710)*

MACHINERY, PRINTING TRADES: Plates

Trinity Graphic Usa Inc.........F....... 941 355-2636
Sarasota *(G-16315)*

MACHINERY, PRINTING TRADES: Printing Trade Parts & Attchts

Equigraph Trading Corp.........G....... 786 237-5665
Miami *(G-9534)*
William B Rudow Inc.........G....... 941 957-4200
Sarasota *(G-16640)*

MACHINERY, SERVICING: Coin-Operated, Exc Dry Clean & Laundry

Sergeant Bretts Coffee LLC.........G....... 561 451-0048
Coconut Creek *(G-2094)*

MACHINERY, TEXTILE: Card Clothing

Baylee & Company LLC.........G....... 305 333-6464
Hialeah *(G-5317)*

MACHINERY, TEXTILE: Cloth Spreading

Unicraft Corp.........F....... 305 633-4945
Miami *(G-10528)*

MACHINERY, TEXTILE: Embroidery

Lac Inc.........G....... 407 671-6610
Winter Park *(G-19417)*
Pantograms Inc.........G....... 813 839-5697
Tampa *(G-17972)*
Pantograms Mfg Co Inc.........E....... 813 839-5697
Tampa *(G-17973)*

MACHINERY, TEXTILE: Silk Screens

B Line Apparel Inc.........F....... 305 953-8300
Hialeah *(G-5315)*
Imprints International Inc.........G....... 561 202-0105
Royal Palm Beach *(G-15471)*
Joni Industries Inc.........F....... 352 799-5456
Brooksville *(G-1240)*

MACHINERY, TEXTILE: Winders

Prime Global Group Inc.........E....... 386 676-2200
Ormond Beach *(G-13393)*
Progressive Machine Co Inc.........F....... 386 333-6850
Ormond Beach *(G-13395)*

MACHINERY, WOODWORKING: Bandsaws

A H Woodcrafter.........G....... 305 885-2136
Miami *(G-9039)*
Inzirillo.........G....... 954 486-0055
Oakland Park *(G-11815)*

MACHINERY, WOODWORKING: Cabinet Makers'

Commercial Cabinetry LLC.........G....... 407 440-4601
Orlando *(G-12604)*
Thomas Mix Kitchens & Baths.........G....... 239 229-4323
Fort Myers *(G-4627)*
Up - N - Atom.........G....... 904 716-5431
Jacksonville *(G-6888)*

MACHINERY, WOODWORKING: Furniture Makers

Lastrada Furniture Inc.........F....... 954 485-6000
Fort Lauderdale *(G-4095)*
Pleasure Interiors LLC.........E....... 941 756-9969
Sarasota *(G-16545)*

MACHINERY, WOODWORKING: Planing Mill

County of Sumter.........G....... 352 689-4460
Bushnell *(G-1316)*

MACHINERY, WOODWORKING: Veneer Mill

Calvert Manufacturing Inc.........F....... 407 331-5522
Casselberry *(G-1499)*

MACHINERY/EQPT, INDL, WHOL: Cleaning, High Press, Sand/Steam

Cress Chemical & Equipment Co.........G....... 407 425-2846
Orlando *(G-12628)*

MACHINERY: Ammunition & Explosives Loading

Amtec Less Lethal Systems Inc.........D....... 850 223-4066
Perry *(G-14293)*

MACHINERY: Assembly, Exc Metalworking

Automatic Mfg Systems Inc.........E....... 954 791-1500
Plantation *(G-14494)*
Buffalo Machine Manufacturing.........G....... 727 321-1905
Saint Petersburg *(G-15731)*
Carter Day Holding Inc.........D....... 239 280-0361
Naples *(G-11199)*
Innovated Industrial Svcs Inc.........F....... 863 701-2711
Bartow *(G-320)*
Jenzano Incorporated.........F....... 386 761-4474
Port Orange *(G-15020)*
Serf Inc.........E....... 850 476-8203
Cantonment *(G-1347)*

MACHINERY: Automobile Garage, Frame Straighteners

Popstops Marketing Inc.........G....... 800 209-4571
Saint Petersburg *(G-15884)*

MACHINERY: Automotive Maintenance

Florida Oil Service Inc.........F....... 813 655-4753
Lithia *(G-8219)*
Solid Start Inc.........E....... 863 937-9297
Lakeland *(G-7797)*
Star Envirotech Inc.........F....... 714 427-1244
Hialeah *(G-5633)*

Sun Nation Corp......F...... 954 822-5460
Pompano Beach (G-14877)

MACHINERY: Automotive Related

Archimaze Logistics Inc......G...... 954 615-7485
Fort Lauderdale (G-3819)
Pcm and S L Plota Co LLC......F...... 727 547-6277
Largo (G-8024)
Rcc Conveyors Inc......F...... 224 338-8841
Estero (G-3694)
Shirley L Jordan Company Inc......F...... 352 754-1117
Brooksville (G-1268)
Wolverine Advanced Mtls LLC......G...... 352 787-3015
Leesburg (G-8181)

MACHINERY: Banking

Greenwise Bankcard......G...... 954 673-0406
Coconut Creek (G-2078)
Metavante Holdings LLC......G...... 904 438-6000
Jacksonville (G-6600)

MACHINERY: Billing

American Respiratory Solutions......F...... 386 698-4446
Crescent City (G-2338)

MACHINERY: Bottle Washing & Sterilzing

Kiinde LLC......G...... 404 368-5382
Melbourne (G-8858)

MACHINERY: Bottling & Canning

Emhart Glass Manufacturing Inc......E...... 727 535-5502
Saint Petersburg (G-15769)

MACHINERY: Brewery & Malting

Union Engineering N Amer LLC......F...... 386 225-4952
Daytona Beach (G-2729)

MACHINERY: Centrifugal

Gea Mechanical Eqp US Inc......G...... 863 669-1500
Lakeland (G-7696)

MACHINERY: Coin Wrapping

Klopp International Inc......F...... 813 855-6789
Oldsmar (G-12240)

MACHINERY: Concrete Prdts

Concrete Edge Company......G...... 407 658-2788
Orlando (G-12612)
Somero Enterprises Inc......D...... 906 482-7252
Fort Myers (G-4606)

MACHINERY: Construction

AA Casey Company......F...... 813 234-8831
Tampa (G-17378)
Altec Industries Inc......F...... 904 647-5219
Jacksonville (G-6140)
Amer-Con Corp......E...... 786 293-8004
Palmetto Bay (G-13839)
American Mfg & Mch Inc......D...... 352 728-2222
Okahumpka (G-12168)
Blasters Ready Jet Inc......E...... 813 985-4500
Tampa (G-17474)
Brutus Roller LLC......G...... 609 393-0007
Bradenton (G-1003)
Caterpillar 2 Butterfly Corp......F...... 786 540-4191
Miami (G-9325)
Caterpllar 2 Bttrfly Otrach CT......G...... 850 515-1143
Fort Walton Beach (G-4786)
Cme Arma Inc......E...... 305 633-1524
Miami (G-9366)
Costex Corporation......C...... 305 592-9769
Miami (G-9407)
Cross Construction Svcs Inc......D...... 813 907-1013
Lutz (G-8379)
Dave Siler Transport......G...... 239 348-3283
Naples (G-11222)
Dhs Unlimited Inc......G...... 954 532-2142
Pompano Beach (G-14663)
Equipment Fabricators Inc......E...... 321 632-0990
Cocoa (G-2020)
Florida General Trading Inc......D...... 813 391-2149
Ocala (G-11946)
Form-Co Inc......G...... 800 745-3700
Orlando (G-12762)
Fw Shoring Company......G...... 813 248-2495
Tampa (G-17700)
Fw Shoring Company......G...... 517 676-8800
Orlando (G-12767)
Gar International......G...... 954 704-9590
Miramar (G-10996)
Industrial Cnveyor Systems Inc......F...... 305 255-0200
Cutler Bay (G-2398)
Jlg Industries Inc......C...... 786 558-8909
Doral (G-3404)
Jones Communications Inc......G...... 407 448-6615
Sanford (G-16074)
Michigan Group Inc......G...... 954 328-6341
Coconut Creek (G-2090)
Nippon Maciwumei Co......F...... 954 533-7747
Sunrise (G-17152)
P3 Fleet LLC......F...... 904 549-5500
Jacksonville (G-6651)
Pantropic Power Inc......D...... 954 797-7972
Fort Lauderdale (G-4156)
Puzzled Caterpillars Inc......G...... 904 379-9219
Jacksonville (G-6697)
Roadsafe Traffic Systems Inc......E...... 386 755-0140
Lake City (G-7382)
Ronnies Welding & Machine......G...... 305 238-0972
Cutler Bay (G-2410)
Shantui America Corp......F...... 786 491-9114
Miami (G-10334)
Sipp Technologies LLC......E...... 904 374-5606
Jacksonville (G-6778)
Smith Challenger Mfg Svcs Inc......F...... 863 248-2624
Lakeland (G-7794)
Space Coast Hydraulics Inc......F...... 321 504-6006
Rockledge (G-15449)
Townley Engrg & Mfg Co Inc......C...... 352 687-3001
Candler (G-1332)
Tyco Machine Inc......G...... 352 544-0210
Brooksville (G-1284)
Waterblasting Technologies Inc......C...... 772 223-7393
Stuart (G-17047)

MACHINERY: Cryogenic, Industrial

Mec Cryo LLC......E...... 813 644-3764
Tampa (G-17899)

MACHINERY: Custom

Blair Machine & Tool Inc......F...... 904 731-4377
Jacksonville (G-6212)
Builders Automtn McHy Co LLC......E...... 727 538-2180
Largo (G-7917)
Cole Machine LLC......G...... 239 571-4364
Naples (G-11214)
Flc Machines Inc......E...... 352 728-2303
Leesburg (G-8157)
General Fine Machine Co Inc......G...... 727 726-5956
Safety Harbor (G-15494)
Gunns Welding & Fabricating......G...... 727 393-5238
Saint Petersburg (G-15801)
La Zero Inc......G...... 727 545-1175
Pinellas Park (G-14363)
Larson-Burton Incorporated......F...... 815 637-9500
Daytona Beach (G-2680)
P D I S Inc......F...... 561 243-8442
Delray Beach (G-3112)
Precision Qulty Machining Inc......G...... 407 831-7240
Casselberry (G-1515)
Real Fleet Solutions LLC......E...... 321 631-2414
Cocoa (G-2046)
Riegl Usa Inc......E...... 407 248-9927
Winter Garden (G-19283)
Schur & Company LLC......D...... 904 353-8075
Jacksonville (G-6754)
Special Tool Solutions Inc......E...... 904 356-5671
Jacksonville (G-6803)

MACHINERY: Dredging

Cavo Development Inc......G...... 305 255-7465
Miami (G-9327)

MACHINERY: Electronic Component Making

Andrew Martin Swift......G...... 321 409-0509
Melbourne (G-8767)
Automated Production Eqp Ape......F...... 631 654-1197
Key Largo (G-7164)
Beachchip Technologies LLC......G...... 727 643-8106
Clearwater (G-1605)
Connectronics US Inc......G...... 954 534-3335
Palm Beach (G-13552)
Hilton International Inds......E...... 941 371-2600
Sarasota (G-16460)
Interactive Cards Inc......F...... 863 688-4548
Lakeland (G-7714)
Lgl Group Inc......G...... 407 298-2000
Orlando (G-12907)
Rubyquartz Technology LLC......F...... 305 406-0211
Doral (G-3493)

MACHINERY: Electronic Teaching Aids

Gadgetcat LLC......G...... 802 238-3671
Cocoa Beach (G-2063)
Holovis Interna Tional......G...... 407 286-3976
Orlando (G-12807)

MACHINERY: Engraving

Elements of Space LLC......G...... 407 718-9690
Orlando (G-12704)

MACHINERY: Extruding

Bedeschi America Inc......D...... 954 602-2175
Boca Raton (G-444)

MACHINERY: Fiber Optics Strand Coating

Force Enterprises Coatings LLC......F...... 561 480-7298
Wellington (G-18718)

MACHINERY: Folding

Profold Inc......E...... 772 589-0063
Sebastian (G-16671)

MACHINERY: Gas Producers

Union Engineering N Amer LLC......F...... 386 225-4952
Daytona Beach (G-2729)

MACHINERY: General, Industrial, NEC

Pneumatic Products Corporation......G...... 352 873-5793
Ocala (G-12029)
Wolverine Engines......G...... 850 462-4160
Fort Walton Beach (G-4841)

MACHINERY: Ice Cream

Brain Freeze Nitrogen......G...... 786 235-8505
Doral (G-3284)
Kenfar Corporation......G...... 813 443-5222
Tampa (G-17818)

MACHINERY: Ice Making

A & V Refrigeration Corp......G...... 305 883-0733
Hialeah (G-5255)
Asbury Manufacturing Co LLC......E...... 814 453-6761
Fort Lauderdale (G-3826)
Holiday Ice Inc......E...... 407 831-2077
Longwood (G-8287)
Ice Link 2018 LLC......G...... 305 988-4023
Lake Worth Beach (G-7613)
Welbilt Inc......A...... 727 375-7010
Trinity (G-18491)

MACHINERY: Industrial, NEC

Ace Tools......G...... 386 302-5152
Palm Coast (G-13680)
Ames Tools......F...... 239 693-1055
Fort Myers (G-4362)
Bryan Nelco Inc......G...... 727 533-8282
Clearwater (G-1615)
Custom Watersports Eqp Inc......G...... 941 753-9949
Bradenton (G-1026)
Electrodes Inc......G...... 727 698-7498
Seminole (G-16746)
Express Tools Inc......G...... 954 663-4333
Davie (G-2522)
JC Marine Service Fabrica......G...... 954 913-8185
Hollywood (G-5852)
Ramac Inc......G...... 813 962-2793
Tampa (G-18038)
S J Turbine LLC......G...... 954 804-4779
Weston (G-19165)
Select Machinery Inc......G...... 941 960-1970
Sarasota (G-16591)
Shores Automotive......G...... 561 391-0260
Boca Raton (G-709)
Southridge Outdoor Storage......G...... 352 516-5598
Tavares (G-18353)

Sun Power Diesel Inc ......G 954 522-4775
Fort Lauderdale *(G-4264)*
System 48 Plus Inc ......G 561 844-5305
West Palm Beach *(G-19055)*
Trurev LLC ......G 800 397-3388
Davie *(G-2608)*
Turbo Parts LLC ......F 352 351-4510
Ocala *(G-12064)*
Tws Fabricators ......F 954 983-9749
Pembroke Pines *(G-14067)*

MACHINERY: Jewelers

Laserstar Technologies Corp ......G 407 248-1142
Orlando *(G-12896)*

MACHINERY: Labeling

Booth Manufacturing Company ......E 772 465-4441
Fort Pierce *(G-4682)*
Flexo Concepts Manufacturing ......G 305 233-7075
Miami *(G-9576)*
Industrial Marking Eqp Co Inc ......G 561 626-8520
Palm Beach Gardens *(G-13596)*
Universal Labeling Systems Inc ......E 727 327-2123
Saint Petersburg *(G-15946)*
White Label Liquid Inc ......E 386 256-1826
Daytona Beach *(G-2732)*

MACHINERY: Logging Eqpt

Timburr Express LLC ......G 850 535-1488
Vernon *(G-18587)*

MACHINERY: Marking, Metalworking

Tophet-Blyth LLC ......F 239 594-5477
Naples *(G-11444)*

MACHINERY: Metalworking

Automatic Mfg Systems Inc ......E 954 791-1500
Plantation *(G-14494)*
Custom Instruments LLC ......G 561 735-9971
Boynton Beach *(G-894)*
Decoral System USA Corporation ......E 954 755-6021
Coral Springs *(G-2239)*
Ebway LLC ......E 954 971-4911
Fort Lauderdale *(G-3957)*
Hilton International Inds ......E 941 371-2600
Sarasota *(G-16460)*
Inen USA Corp ......G 305 343-6666
Opa Locka *(G-12325)*
Jrmetal Ornamental ......G 954 989-2607
Hollywood *(G-5855)*
KCm Mch Sp Broward Cnty Inc ......F 954 475-8732
Davie *(G-2540)*
Marchant Machine Corporation ......G 301 937-4481
Sarasota *(G-16503)*
Mid-State Machine Company LLC ......E 704 636-7029
Fort Myers *(G-4533)*
Precision Tl Engrg of Gnsville ......F 352 376-2533
Gainesville *(G-4982)*
Servo Tech Inc ......G 727 573-7998
Clearwater *(G-1875)*
Smith Machine Services Inc ......G 904 845-2002
Hilliard *(G-5718)*
Symme3d LLC ......F 321 220-1584
Orlando *(G-13234)*
TL Fahringer Co Inc ......G 813 681-2373
Tampa *(G-18190)*
United Machining Service Inc ......G 407 422-7710
Orlando *(G-13293)*

MACHINERY: Milling

Federated Precision Inc ......E 561 288-6500
Deerfield Beach *(G-2824)*

MACHINERY: Mining

Atacama Resources Intl Inc ......G 613 421-9733
Plantation *(G-14492)*
B & A Manufacturing Co ......E 561 848-8648
Riviera Beach *(G-15300)*
Chemours Company Fc LLC ......D 904 964-1230
Starke *(G-16889)*
Knight Industrial Eqp Inc ......G 863 646-2997
Lakeland *(G-7729)*
Microtool and Instrument Inc ......E 786 242-8780
Palmetto Bay *(G-13851)*
Quality Fbrction Mch Works Inc ......F 386 755-0220
Lake City *(G-7379)*

Technical International Corp ......G 305 374-1054
Miami *(G-10462)*
Townley Engrg & Mfg Co Inc ......C 352 687-3001
Candler *(G-1332)*
Townley Foundry & Mch Co Inc ......D 352 687-3001
Candler *(G-1333)*
Vertex Precision Inc ......E 561 582-6171
Lake Worth *(G-7597)*

MACHINERY: Optical Lens

Automated Vacuum Systems Inc ......G 941 378-4565
Sarasota *(G-16359)*
Intuitos LLC ......F 727 522-2301
Largo *(G-7983)*

MACHINERY: Ozone

International Ozone Svcs LLC ......G 352 978-9785
Mount Dora *(G-11105)*
Worldwide Technology Inc ......E 813 855-2443
Oldsmar *(G-12279)*

MACHINERY: Packaging

A & B of Tarpon Corporation ......E 727 940-5333
Tarpon Springs *(G-18281)*
Acasi Machinery Inc ......F 305 805-8533
Miami *(G-9058)*
B & M Industries Inc ......G 813 754-9960
Plant City *(G-14404)*
B H Bunn Company ......F 863 647-1555
Lakeland *(G-7641)*
Balpack Incorporated ......G 941 371-7323
Sarasota *(G-16361)*
Bbull Usa Inc ......G 813 855-1400
Oldsmar *(G-12208)*
Central Florida Sales & Svc ......F 863 967-6678
Auburndale *(G-233)*
Diamond Moba Americas Inc ......D 954 384-5828
Weston *(G-19120)*
Fill Tech Solutions Inc 200 ......E 727 572-8550
Largo *(G-7946)*
Gevas Pckg Converting Tech Ltd ......G 561 202-0800
Boynton Beach *(G-911)*
Hdh Agri Products LLC ......G 352 343-3484
Tavares *(G-18342)*
Ics Inex Inspection Systems ......F 727 535-5502
Clearwater *(G-1728)*
Intellitech Inc ......E 727 914-7000
Saint Petersburg *(G-15817)*
ISA Group Corp ......F 305 748-1578
Miami *(G-9773)*
K H S Inc ......D 941 359-4000
Sarasota *(G-16243)*
Kinematics and Controls Corp ......G 352 796-0300
Brooksville *(G-1243)*
Lanfranchi North America Inc ......F 813 901-5333
Tampa *(G-17835)*
Micron Pharmaworks LLC ......C 727 232-8200
Odessa *(G-12134)*
MTS Medication Tech Inc ......C 727 576-6311
Saint Petersburg *(G-15862)*
Orkan18 ......G 855 675-2618
Lake Worth *(G-7576)*
Osgood Industries LLC ......C 813 448-9041
Oldsmar *(G-12254)*
Pelliconi Florida LLC ......E 407 855-6984
Orlando *(G-13058)*
Pepsico Inc ......G 305 593-7500
Medley *(G-8703)*
Plan Automation LLC ......G 786 502-1812
Miami Beach *(G-10701)*
Pneumatic Scale Angelus ......D 727 535-4100
Clearwater *(G-1836)*
Polypack Limited Partnership ......E 727 578-5000
Pinellas Park *(G-14378)*
Production System Engineering ......F 863 299-7330
Winter Haven *(G-19347)*
R & L Manufacturing Inc ......F 772 770-9300
Vero Beach *(G-18658)*
Sardee Industries Inc ......E 407 295-2114
Orlando *(G-13163)*
Southern Packaging McHy Corp ......E 305 245-3045
Florida City *(G-3769)*
Sweepy Group Products LLC ......G 305 556-3450
Miami Lakes *(G-10866)*
Trepko Inc ......F 813 443-0794
Tampa *(G-18198)*
VMS Usa Inc ......F 727 434-1577
Seminole *(G-16770)*

Westlund Engineering Inc ......G 727 572-4343
Palm Harbor *(G-13769)*

MACHINERY: Paper Industry Miscellaneous

Kazdin Industries Inc ......G 772 223-5511
Palm City *(G-13663)*
Ronco Machine Inc ......G 904 827-9795
Jacksonville *(G-6735)*
Southeastern Paper Group Inc ......C 864 574-0440
Lakeland *(G-7798)*

MACHINERY: Pharmaciutical

Pharmacy Automtn Systems LLC ......G 727 544-6522
Pinellas Park *(G-14375)*

MACHINERY: Photoengraving

Guided Particle Systems Inc ......G 727 424-8790
Pensacola *(G-14165)*

MACHINERY: Photographic Reproduction

Mac Gregor Smith Blueprinters ......F 407 423-5944
Orlando *(G-12943)*

MACHINERY: Plastic Working

Flite Technology Inc ......F 321 631-2050
Cocoa *(G-2022)*
Midgard Inc ......D 863 696-1224
Lake Wales *(G-7516)*
Mold Control Systems Inc ......G 561 316-5412
Palm Beach Gardens *(G-13610)*
Polyumac Inc ......E 305 691-9093
Hialeah *(G-5561)*
Reduction International LLC ......G 954 905-5999
Weston *(G-19164)*

MACHINERY: Polishing & Buffing

Gaynor Group Inc ......G 954 749-1228
Sunrise *(G-17125)*

MACHINERY: Printing Presses

Altamonte Office Supply Inc ......G 407 339-6911
Longwood *(G-8253)*
Palm Prnting/Printers Ink Corp ......E 239 332-8600
Fort Myers *(G-4562)*
Southwest Eqp For Hrnando Cnty ......G 352 596-5142
Brooksville *(G-1273)*

MACHINERY: Recycling

Alto Recycling LLC ......G 813 962-0140
Tampa *(G-17410)*
Progress Rail Services Corp ......G 352 748-8008
Wildwood *(G-19200)*
Tin Man Co ......G 305 365-1926
Coral Gables *(G-2198)*
Wilkinson Hi-Rise LLC ......C 954 342-4400
Fort Lauderdale *(G-4324)*

MACHINERY: Riveting

Fabco-Air Inc ......D 352 373-3578
Gainesville *(G-4918)*
Standard Rivet Company Inc ......F 386 872-6477
South Daytona *(G-16810)*

MACHINERY: Robots, Molding & Forming Plastics

Sunshine Tool LLC ......G 941 351-6330
Sarasota *(G-16306)*

MACHINERY: Rubber Working

BBH General Partnership ......G 863 425-5626
Mulberry *(G-11120)*
Omega Lift Corporation ......F 561 840-0088
Riviera Beach *(G-15358)*

MACHINERY: Screening Eqpt, Electric

Pe Manufacturing Company Fla ......E 727 823-8172
Clearwater *(G-1828)*

MACHINERY: Semiconductor Manufacturing

Adamas Instrument Corporation ......F 727 540-0033
Clearwater *(G-1564)*

Atlantic Intl Distrs Inc....C....904 725-5202
Jacksonville *(G-6175)*
Baytronics Manufacturing Inc....G....813 434-0401
Tampa *(G-17460)*
Guided Particle Systems Inc....G....727 424-8790
Pensacola *(G-14165)*
Novena TEC LLC....E....407 392-1868
Orlando *(G-13011)*

MACHINERY: Service Industry, NEC

Defense Flight Aerospace LLC....F....321 442-7255
Orlando *(G-12660)*
Jamuna1 LLC....G....407 313-5927
Windermere *(G-19230)*
Unihold Inc....G....941 966-7440
Nokomis *(G-11590)*

MACHINERY: Sheet Metal Working

Electro Mech Solutions Inc....E....813 792-0400
Odessa *(G-12118)*

MACHINERY: Specialty

Cisam LLC....G....813 404-4180
Zephyrhills *(G-19511)*
Demaco LLC....G....321 952-6600
Miami *(G-9453)*
Fueltec Systems LLC....G....828 212-1141
Royal Palm Beach *(G-15468)*
Industrial Shredders LLC....F....941 753-2815
Sarasota *(G-16234)*
Lewa Group Corp....G....305 407-9500
Miami Lakes *(G-10806)*
Southern Fabricating Machinery....G....813 966-3983
Lithia *(G-8223)*
Water Purification Systems....G....954 467-8920
Fort Lauderdale *(G-4314)*

MACHINERY: Stone Working

Poseidon Industries Inc....G....305 812-2582
Punta Gorda *(G-15220)*

MACHINERY: Tapping

Rockford Ettco Procunier Inc....F....863 688-0071
Lakeland *(G-7781)*

MACHINERY: Textile

Alpine Industries Corporation....F....941 749-1900
Bradenton *(G-985)*
ISA Group Corp....F....305 748-1578
Miami *(G-9773)*
ISA Group Corp....G....786 201-8360
Coral Gables *(G-2161)*
Monarch Knitting McHy Corp....G....954 345-2091
Coral Springs *(G-2288)*
Ricoma International Corp....G....305 418-4421
Doral *(G-3485)*
Tekmatic Corp....F....305 972-1300
Miami *(G-10466)*
United Associates Group Inc....F....561 840-0050
Riviera Beach *(G-15387)*

MACHINERY: Tire Retreading

Vampa Tires Supplies Inc....G....305 888-1001
Miami *(G-10564)*

MACHINERY: Tire Shredding

Quik Shred....G....561 841-1822
Jupiter *(G-7101)*

MACHINERY: Voting

Naztec International Group LLC....F....561 802-4110
West Palm Beach *(G-18959)*
Naztec International Group LLC....F....561 802-4110
West Palm Beach *(G-18960)*
Smartmatic Corporation....F....561 862-0747
Boca Raton *(G-721)*

MACHINERY: Woodworking

Braid Sales and Marketing Inc....E....321 752-8180
Melbourne *(G-8785)*
Dimar Usa Inc....G....954 590-8573
Fort Lauderdale *(G-3942)*
Lioher Enterprise Corp....G....305 685-0005
Miami Lakes *(G-10807)*

Quality Fbrction Mch Works Inc....F....386 755-0220
Lake City *(G-7379)*
Teknatool Usa Inc....G....727 954-3433
Clearwater *(G-1914)*

MACHINES: Forming, Sheet Metal

AL Garey & Associates Inc....C....954 975-7992
Coral Springs *(G-2218)*

MACHINISTS' TOOLS: Measuring, Precision

Gws Tool Holdings LLC....E....352 343-8778
Tavares *(G-18341)*
Time Industries Inc....G....321 676-2080
Melbourne *(G-8962)*
Trumeter Company Inc....G....954 725-6699
Coconut Creek *(G-2098)*

MACHINISTS' TOOLS: Precision

Armorit Precision LLC....F....941 751-1292
Sarasota *(G-16176)*
E-Z Fastening Solutions Inc....G....813 854-3937
Oldsmar *(G-12223)*
Elite Aero LLC....G....727 244-3382
Saint Petersburg *(G-15768)*
Goss Inc....E....386 423-0311
New Smyrna Beach *(G-11534)*
OGrady Tool Company....F....239 560-3395
Fort Myers *(G-4556)*
Omega One Research Inc....G....561 995-9611
Boca Raton *(G-654)*
Sandar Industries Inc....E....904 246-4309
Atlantic Beach *(G-226)*

MACHINISTS' TOOLS: Scales, Measuring, Precision

Outline Technologies Inc....G....904 858-9933
Jacksonville *(G-6650)*

MAGAZINES, WHOLESALE

Spanish Peri & Bk Sls Inc....D....305 592-3919
Doral *(G-3508)*

MAGNETIC INK & OPTICAL SCANNING EQPT

Uniscan LLC....F....305 322-7669
Doral *(G-3537)*

MAGNETIC INK RECOGNITION DEVICES

Scan Technology Inc....G....931 723-0304
Gainesville *(G-4992)*

MAGNETIC RESONANCE IMAGING DEVICES: Nonmedical

Invivo Corporation....E....352 336-0010
Gainesville *(G-4946)*
Medical Outfitters Inc....G....305 885-4045
Miami *(G-9966)*
Medical Outfitters Inc....E....305 332-9103
North Bay Village *(G-11593)*
One Resonance Sensors....G....407 323-9933
Sanford *(G-16094)*
Open Magnetic Scanning Ltd....G....954 202-5097
Oakland Park *(G-11826)*
Radiance Radiology Inc....G....727 934-5500
Palm Harbor *(G-13755)*
Tonbo Imaging Inc....G....814 441-0475
Sunrise *(G-17190)*

MAGNETIC SHIELDS, METAL

Manufacturers Inv Group LLC....F....630 285-0800
Keystone Heights *(G-7210)*

MAGNETIC TAPE, AUDIO: Prerecorded

Bible Alliance Inc....E....941 748-3031
Bradenton *(G-999)*
Miami Tape Inc....F....305 558-9211
Hialeah *(G-5513)*

MAGNETOHYDRODYNAMIC DEVICES OR MHD

Sunwyre Inc....F....904 631-6961
Jacksonville *(G-6827)*

MAGNETS: Ceramic

Smart Material Corp....F....941 870-3337
Sarasota *(G-16600)*

MAGNIFIERS

Vision Source Inc....G....407 435-9958
Apopka *(G-196)*

MAIL-ORDER BOOK CLUBS

Pro Publishing Inc....G....954 888-7726
Southwest Ranches *(G-16840)*

MAIL-ORDER HOUSE, NEC

Gulf Glo Banners and Signs LLC....G....850 234-0952
Panama City *(G-13913)*

MAIL-ORDER HOUSES: Collectibles & Antiques

Hollywood Cllctibles Group LLC....G....407 985-4613
Orlando *(G-12806)*

MAIL-ORDER HOUSES: Computer Eqpt & Electronics

Gadgetcat LLC....G....802 238-3671
Cocoa Beach *(G-2063)*

MAIL-ORDER HOUSES: Cosmetics & Perfumes

Xtreme Tools International Inc....E....305 622-7474
Opa Locka *(G-12371)*

MAIL-ORDER HOUSES: Fitness & Sporting Goods

Onetown Boards....G....786 704-5921
Miami *(G-10106)*
Ventum LLC....G....786 838-1113
Miami Beach *(G-10727)*

MAIL-ORDER HOUSES: General Merchandise

Imagination Enterprises LLC....F....504 289-9691
Orlando *(G-12823)*
Rokey Corporation....G....561 470-0164
Boca Raton *(G-693)*

MAIL-ORDER HOUSES: Gift Items

EMB Wholesale....G....904 452-4362
Jacksonville *(G-6361)*

MAIL-ORDER HOUSES: Magazines

Mojowax Media Inc....G....805 550-6013
Bradenton *(G-1080)*

MAIL-ORDER HOUSES: Order Taking Office Only

Birdsall Marine Design Inc....E....561 832-7879
West Palm Beach *(G-18822)*

MAIL-ORDER HOUSES: Tools & Hardware

Brown (usa) Inc....F....305 593-9228
Miami *(G-9280)*
Doorknob Discount Center LLC....G....813 963-3104
Lutz *(G-8380)*
Electriduct Inc....E....954 867-9100
Pompano Beach *(G-14676)*

MAILING SVCS, NEC

Advanced Xrgrphics Imging Syst....E....407 351-0232
Orlando *(G-12434)*
Reimink Printing Inc....G....813 289-4663
Tampa *(G-18050)*
Southeast Print Programs Inc....E....813 885-3203
Tampa *(G-18118)*
Town Street Print Shop Inc....G....850 432-8300
Gulf Breeze *(G-5130)*

MALLETS: Rubber

General Rubber Corporation ....G.... 941 412-0001
Venice *(G-18549)*

MANAGEMENT CONSULTING SVCS: Automation & Robotics

Fuelmatics Corp ....F.... 305 807-4923
Palmetto Bay *(G-13843)*
V and N Advanced Auto Sys LLC ....G.... 321 504-6440
Rockledge *(G-15455)*

MANAGEMENT CONSULTING SVCS: Business

Hogan Assessment Systems Inc ....G.... 904 992-0302
Jacksonville *(G-6473)*

MANAGEMENT CONSULTING SVCS: Business Planning & Organizing

Informa Usa Inc ....A.... 561 361-6017
Sarasota *(G-16465)*

MANAGEMENT CONSULTING SVCS: Corporate Objectives & Policies

Interntnal Synrgy For Tchncal ....G.... 321 305-0863
Orlando *(G-12837)*

MANAGEMENT CONSULTING SVCS: Incentive Or Award Program

Gallant Inc ....G.... 800 330-1343
Winter Garden *(G-19265)*

MANAGEMENT CONSULTING SVCS: Industrial

Phelps Dodge Intl Corp ....E.... 305 648-7888
Doral *(G-3459)*

MANAGEMENT CONSULTING SVCS: Industrial & Labor

National Tchncal Cmmunications ....G.... 407 671-7777
Orlando *(G-12991)*

MANAGEMENT CONSULTING SVCS: Industry Specialist

Skide Llc ....F.... 305 537-4275
Miami *(G-10356)*

MANAGEMENT CONSULTING SVCS: Information Systems

Donovan Home Services LLC ....F.... 813 644-9488
Saint Petersburg *(G-15762)*

MANAGEMENT CONSULTING SVCS: Manufacturing

Smartscience Laboratories Inc ....F.... 813 925-8454
Tampa *(G-18110)*

MANAGEMENT CONSULTING SVCS: Restaurant & Food

West Development Group LLC ....G.... 407 308-5020
Orlando *(G-13322)*

MANAGEMENT CONSULTING SVCS: Retail Trade Consultant

Firefly Aircraft Parts Inc ....G.... 954 505-1470
Plantation *(G-14516)*
Tin Man Co ....G.... 305 365-1926
Coral Gables *(G-2198)*

MANAGEMENT CONSULTING SVCS: Transportation

E&P Solutions and Services Inc ....G.... 305 715-9545
Miami *(G-9491)*

MANAGEMENT SERVICES

All Power Pro Inc ....G.... 904 310-3069
Fernandina Beach *(G-3730)*
Archer Ellison Inc ....G.... 800 449-4095
Lake Mary *(G-7400)*
Brickmed LLC ....G.... 305 774-0081
Miami *(G-9276)*
C & E Innovative MGT LLC ....G.... 727 408-5146
Clearwater *(G-1619)*
Merchspin Inc ....E.... 877 306-3651
Orlando *(G-12960)*
Nexogy Inc ....E.... 305 358-8952
Coral Gables *(G-2181)*

MANAGEMENT SVCS, FACILITIES SUPPORT: Environ Remediation

Bcr Environmental Corporation ....E.... 904 819-9170
Jacksonville *(G-6198)*
Robotics Fabrication Inc ....E.... 850 896-4987
Panama City *(G-13947)*

MANAGEMENT SVCS: Administrative

Precision Resources Inc ....F.... 321 635-2000
Cocoa *(G-2043)*

MANAGEMENT SVCS: Business

Consultant MGT Group LLC ....G.... 352 344-4001
Inverness *(G-6083)*
Davis-Wick Talent MGT LLC ....E.... 407 369-1614
Margate *(G-8541)*

MANAGEMENT SVCS: Personnel

Atsg Logistic Support Service ....F.... 904 579-4596
Jacksonville *(G-6179)*

MANAGEMENT SVCS: Restaurant

West Development Group LLC ....G.... 407 308-5020
Orlando *(G-13322)*

MANGANESE ORES MINING

Georgian American Alloys Inc ....E.... 305 375-7560
Miami *(G-9629)*

MANHOLES & COVERS: Metal

Halliday Products Inc ....D.... 407 298-4470
Orlando *(G-12794)*

MANHOLES COVERS: Concrete

Standard Precast Inc ....D.... 904 268-0466
Jacksonville *(G-6808)*

MANICURE PREPARATIONS

Alt Thuyan ....G.... 407 302-3655
Sanford *(G-15991)*

MANNEQUINS

Simetri Inc ....E.... 321 972-9980
Winter Park *(G-19445)*

MANUFACTURED & MOBILE HOME DEALERS

Jacobsen Factory Outlet ....G.... 386 438-8458
Lake City *(G-7362)*
Nobility Homes Inc ....D.... 352 732-5157
Ocala *(G-12006)*

MANUFACTURING INDUSTRIES, NEC

3fdm Inc ....F.... 727 877-3336
Largo *(G-7879)*
A J M O Industries Inc ....G.... 954 587-0206
Plantation *(G-14480)*
A Morris Industries LLC ....G.... 239 308-2199
Lehigh Acres *(G-8183)*
AB Used Pallets Inc ....F.... 305 594-2776
Miami *(G-9050)*
Acroturn Industries Usa LLC ....F.... 754 205-7178
Tavares *(G-18333)*
Adma ....E.... 561 989-5800
Boca Raton *(G-399)*
Adonel Block Mfg Corp ....F.... 561 615-9500
Miami *(G-9070)*
Aesthetics Complete Inc ....G.... 610 265-3535
Venice *(G-18530)*
Air Technical LLC ....F.... 305 837-3274
Saint Petersburg *(G-15696)*
AK Industries LLC ....F.... 954 662-7038
West Park *(G-19091)*
Albixon USA LLC ....G.... 954 297-2000
Fort Lauderdale *(G-3794)*
Allan Industries ....F.... 407 875-0897
Orlando *(G-12456)*
Almar Industries Inc ....F.... 305 385-8284
Miami *(G-9120)*
Alta Industries LLC ....G.... 305 343-6091
Miami *(G-9122)*
Alvis Industries Inc ....G.... 941 377-7800
Sarasota *(G-16341)*
Anchor Industries LLC ....G.... 850 509-8344
Tallahassee *(G-17219)*
Andro Corp Industries ....G.... 917 287-5294
Ocoee *(G-12083)*
Anu Industries Inc ....E.... 813 927-7254
Weeki Wachee *(G-18700)*
ARI Specialties LLC ....G.... 321 269-2244
Mims *(G-10949)*
Arm Almnum Rling Mnfctures LLC ....G.... 813 626-2264
Tampa *(G-17433)*
Armageddon Manufacturing ....G.... 772 208-5288
Stuart *(G-16909)*
Armor Industries Corp ....G.... 813 240-5903
Seffner *(G-16720)*
Armour Companies LLC ....G.... 386 740-7459
Deland *(G-2961)*
Arsenal Industries LLC ....F.... 407 506-2698
Winter Park *(G-19380)*
Arsenal Venture Partners Fla ....G.... 407 838-1400
Winter Park *(G-19381)*
Artec Manufacturing LLC ....G.... 305 888-4375
Hialeah *(G-5305)*
Arthrex Manufacturing Inc ....G.... 239 304-2236
Ave Maria *(G-256)*
Artistic Paver Mfg ....G.... 305 949-0000
Miramar *(G-10969)*
ASG Corp ....G.... 718 641-4500
Miami Beach *(G-10645)*
Astroted Inc ....G.... 786 220-5898
Doral *(G-3257)*
Atria Industry ....G.... 786 334-6621
Doral *(G-3260)*
Aurel Partners LLC ....E.... 203 300-7470
Lake Mary *(G-7401)*
Axiom Manufacturing Inc ....G.... 321 223-3394
West Melbourne *(G-18766)*
Axtonne Inc ....G.... 510 755-7480
Delray Beach *(G-3048)*
Balistic 2400 LLC ....F.... 407 955-0065
Naples *(G-11180)*
Balkan Industries LLC ....F.... 727 485-3357
New Port Richey *(G-11482)*
Bam Industries Inc ....G.... 561 674-2185
Boca Raton *(G-441)*
Barth Industries ....F.... 727 787-6392
Dunedin *(G-3569)*
Basanite Industries LLC ....F.... 954 532-1726
Pompano Beach *(G-14616)*
Bass Auto Industries LLC ....G.... 727 446-4051
Clearwater *(G-1600)*
Belongea Industries ....G.... 574 209-1045
Arcadia *(G-200)*
Bernat Industries Intl LLC ....G.... 727 350-5904
Gulfport *(G-5132)*
Biggs Industries Inc ....G.... 561 775-6944
Palm Beach Gardens *(G-13569)*
Biochem Manufacturing Inc ....G.... 786 210-1290
Miami *(G-9248)*
Biochemical Manufacturing Inc ....G.... 561 799-1590
Jupiter *(G-7011)*
Black Creek Precision LLC ....F.... 888 426-6624
Jacksonville *(G-6209)*
Black Oak Industries Inc ....G.... 863 307-1566
Winter Haven *(G-19303)*
Blackwter Metal Sls NW Fla LLC ....G.... 850 622-1414
Milton *(G-10924)*
Bld Industries ....G.... 321 207-0050
Altamonte Springs *(G-33)*
Body Chemistry Industries In C ....G.... 561 253-4438
Wellington *(G-18711)*
Body Manufactur E Inc ....G.... 386 264-6040
Palm Coast *(G-13686)*
Brads Industries LLC ....G.... 863 646-0051
Lakeland *(G-7649)*

Bri Tin Industries ....G.... 941 580-6345
Plant City *(G-14411)*
Bruns Mfg Homes ....G.... 863 294-4949
Winter Haven *(G-19307)*
Bubblemac Industries Inc ....G.... 352 396-8043
Mc Alpin *(G-8598)*
Burr Industries LLC ....G.... 619 254-2309
Cocoa *(G-2002)*
C&P Industries Inc ....G.... 813 685-3131
Dover *(G-3557)*
Campbell Manufacturing Inc ....G.... 727 443-4508
Clearwater *(G-1621)*
Cannon Industries Inc ....F.... 727 320-5040
New Port Richey *(G-11486)*
Caribbean Basin Industries Inc ....G.... 941 726-7272
Nokomis *(G-11579)*
Cas Industries LLC ....G.... 813 986-2694
Plant City *(G-14416)*
Castle Distributing Industries ....G.... 305 336-0855
Miramar *(G-10978)*
Category 5 Manufacturing Inc ....F.... 561 777-2491
Lantana *(G-7869)*
Category 5 Manufacturing Inc ....G.... 561 502-4153
Lake Worth *(G-7540)*
Cavok Capital LLC ....F.... 727 789-0951
Palm Harbor *(G-13726)*
CCA Industries Inc ....F.... 813 601-6238
Dade City *(G-2424)*
Celios Corporation ....G.... 833 235-4671
Tampa *(G-17520)*
Centurion Residential Inds ....E.... 561 574-1483
West Palm Beach *(G-18843)*
Cgc Industries Inc ....G.... 954 923-2428
Hollywood *(G-5797)*
Chattam Industries Inc ....G.... 727 748-2419
Palm Harbor *(G-13728)*
Classic Industries Inc ....F.... 561 855-4609
Wellington *(G-18714)*
Cloud Industries ....G.... 816 213-2730
Sarasota *(G-16385)*
Coastal Industries USA LLC ....G.... 954 946-5223
Pompano Beach *(G-14638)*
Codsworth Industries Inc ....G.... 203 622-5151
North Miami *(G-11634)*
Colonial Industries Centl Fla ....G.... 407 484-5239
Lake Mary *(G-7406)*
Comiskey Industries Inc ....G.... 201 925-0998
Palm Coast *(G-13688)*
Conquest Manufacturing Fla LLC ....F.... 954 655-0139
Pompano Beach *(G-14644)*
Costa Industries LLC ....G.... 813 453-3171
Riverview *(G-15268)*
Crossroads Industries LLC ....G.... 305 967-8116
Miami *(G-9412)*
Crowe Manufacturing ....G.... 813 334-1921
Tampa *(G-17569)*
Crown Leao Industries Inc ....G.... 561 866-1218
Boca Raton *(G-493)*
Ctr Industries ....G.... 321 264-1458
Mims *(G-10950)*
Dar Industries Inc ....G.... 904 327-9689
Jacksonville *(G-6310)*
Dkm Machine Manufacturing ....F.... 904 733-0103
Jacksonville *(G-6323)*
Dontech Industries Inc ....G.... 847 682-1776
Saint Petersburg *(G-15763)*
Dp Industries Inc ....G.... 321 356-3352
Saint Cloud *(G-15649)*
Dragon Glassing LLC ....G.... 904 509-1860
Jacksonville Beach *(G-6942)*
Dyer Industries Inc ....G.... 954 434-9065
Southwest Ranches *(G-16837)*
Dynamic Manufacturing Inc ....G.... 727 639-8633
Longwood *(G-8275)*
E & A Industries Inc ....F.... 954 278-2428
Fort Lauderdale *(G-3954)*
E Benton Grimsley Inc ....G.... 850 863-4064
Fort Walton Beach *(G-4797)*
E M Chadbourne Inds LLC ....G.... 850 429-1797
Pensacola *(G-14135)*
Echodog Industries Inc ....G.... 407 909-1636
Orlando *(G-12695)*
El Teide North Industries ....G.... 786 830-7506
Miami *(G-9508)*
EMC Manufacturing ....G.... 305 613-9546
Miami *(G-9523)*
Emerging Mfg Tech Inc ....G.... 407 341-3476
Lake Mary *(G-7410)*
Empire Enterprises ....G.... 786 373-8003
Hialeah *(G-5396)*
Endeavor Manufacturing Inc ....F.... 954 752-6828
Deerfield Beach *(G-2822)*
Engitork Industries Llc ....G.... 239 877-8499
Naples *(G-11239)*
Esther Industries Inc ....G.... 850 456-6163
Pensacola *(G-14146)*
Europe Coating Industries LLC ....G.... 786 535-4143
Medley *(G-8648)*
Evergreen Rush Industries Inc ....F.... 954 825-9291
Davie *(G-2520)*
Eye Wall Industries Inc ....G.... 850 607-2288
Pensacola *(G-14147)*
Fagerberg Industries LLC ....F.... 352 318-2254
Gainesville *(G-4919)*
Falco Industries Inc ....G.... 407 956-0045
Longwood *(G-8281)*
FBI Industries Inc ....G.... 239 462-1176
Fort Myers *(G-4448)*
Fbj Engineering & Dev LLC ....G.... 754 423-1309
Coral Springs *(G-2244)*
Fcs Industries Corp ....G.... 407 947-3127
Ocoee *(G-12085)*
Fcs Industries Corp ....G.... 407 412-5642
Orlando *(G-12735)*
Ferrelli Industries Inc ....G.... 305 792-0100
North Miami Beach *(G-11677)*
Field Specialties ....G.... 440 635-0282
Morriston *(G-11092)*
Fine Industries Corporation ....G.... 321 452-6956
Merritt Island *(G-9001)*
Finger Lakes Custom Mfg LLC ....G.... 315 283-4849
Ocala *(G-11941)*
First Cast Fla Mfg Support LLC ....G.... 904 434-4128
Orange Park *(G-12394)*
Five Star Quality Mfg Corp ....G.... 954 972-4772
Fort Lauderdale *(G-3996)*
FL Industries Inc ....G.... 954 422-3766
Pompano Beach *(G-14697)*
Flex Innovations Inc ....G.... 866 310-3539
Venice *(G-18548)*
Florida Elite Industries LLC ....G.... 727 223-4233
Largo *(G-7948)*
Florida Factory Agents Inc ....G.... 754 264-9432
Hollywood *(G-5822)*
Florida Freshner Corp ....G.... 954 349-0348
Weston *(G-19125)*
Florida Manufactured Home ....G.... 407 509-8262
Christmas *(G-1550)*
Florida Nbty Manufacturing ....F.... 561 922-4800
Boca Raton *(G-532)*
Floridas Finest Industries ....F.... 239 333-1777
Fort Myers *(G-4455)*
Fox Industries of Swfl Inc ....F.... 239 732-6199
Naples *(G-11249)*
Fox Manufacturing LLC ....G.... 904 531-3150
Green Cove Springs *(G-5062)*
Fraziers Fabrication ....G.... 813 928-1449
Dover *(G-3559)*
Full Throttle Cnc Inc ....G.... 248 525-1973
Fort Myers *(G-4460)*
Fusion Industries ....G.... 239 592-7070
Naples *(G-11254)*
Fuzion Digital Signs ....G.... 844 529-0505
Tampa *(G-17699)*
Gator Fabrications LLC ....G.... 352 245-7227
Belleview *(G-369)*
Global Composite USA Inc ....E.... 813 898-7987
Tampa *(G-17714)*
Global Industries and Mfg Inc ....G.... 954 766-4656
Plantation *(G-14521)*
Global Seashell Industries LLC ....G.... 813 677-6674
Tampa *(G-17718)*
Grafico Industries Inc ....G.... 941 473-2800
Englewood *(G-3660)*
Gravity Colors Usa Inc ....G.... 561 419-5272
Delray Beach *(G-3086)*
Green Touch Industries Inc ....G.... 561 659-5525
West Palm Beach *(G-18890)*
Guild Mfg Solutions LLC ....G.... 407 366-5165
Oviedo *(G-13433)*
Gvi Industries Inc ....G.... 954 514-7283
Pompano Beach *(G-14720)*
Gvi Industries Inc ....G.... 954 818-6411
Fort Lauderdale *(G-4036)*
Gyrotonic Mfg Inc ....G.... 305 397-8070
Miami Beach *(G-10676)*
H V Payne Mfg LLC ....G.... 941 773-1112
Sarasota *(G-16456)*
Halliday Industries LLC ....G.... 321 288-3979
Melbourne *(G-8838)*
Hardrives Industries Inc ....E.... 561 278-0456
Delray Beach *(G-3090)*
High Temp Industries ....G.... 215 794-0864
Cape Coral *(G-1434)*
Hjr Industries LLC ....G.... 706 761-1200
Gibsonton *(G-5029)*
Homeshield Industries Corp ....G.... 239 573-0802
Cape Coral *(G-1437)*
Hopkins Manufacturing Co ....G.... 620 591-8229
Tarpon Springs *(G-18307)*
Hughes Fabrication ....G.... 239 481-1376
Fort Myers *(G-4487)*
Hunter Industries ....G.... 561 775-3239
Palm Beach Gardens *(G-13595)*
Hurricane Marine Manufacturing ....F.... 772 260-3950
Stuart *(G-16955)*
Hydro Industries-Usa LLC ....G.... 305 440-0893
Miami *(G-9722)*
I-75 Industries Inc ....G.... 352 840-3155
Ocala *(G-11967)*
Ice Bunker A&M Corp ....F.... 786 368-0924
Hialeah *(G-5452)*
Instatech Industries Inc ....G.... 954 415-4392
Lake Worth *(G-7557)*
Intouch Inc ....F.... 702 572-4786
Orlando *(G-12839)*
Inusa Manufacturing LLC ....G.... 786 451-5227
Pembroke Park *(G-14009)*
Invigicom Inc ....G.... 407 491-6929
Apopka *(G-149)*
Iver Services ....F.... 786 329-3018
North Miami Beach *(G-11684)*
J C Industries Inc ....G.... 863 773-9199
Bradenton *(G-1063)*
Jamali Industries LLC ....G.... 954 908-5075
Sunrise *(G-17134)*
Jane and George Industries ....F.... 727 698-4903
Saint Petersburg *(G-15832)*
Jerry Metallo ....G.... 305 972-2927
Princeton *(G-15184)*
Jfliszo Industries Inc ....G.... 239 215-6965
Fort Myers *(G-4503)*
JMTM Anufacturing Inc ....G.... 727 847-7665
Port Richey *(G-15058)*
Jq Industries Inc ....G.... 407 509-3880
Longwood *(G-8298)*
Jsp Manufacturing Holdings LLC ....G.... 727 488-5353
Pinellas Park *(G-14358)*
Jta Industries LLC ....G.... 407 352-4255
Orlando *(G-12863)*
JW Fabrications Inc ....G.... 772 201-7097
Okeechobee *(G-12184)*
K & N Industries Inc ....G.... 850 939-7722
Navarre *(G-11467)*
K Bausch Mfg Corp ....G.... 772 485-2426
Stuart *(G-16963)*
Kamco Industries LLC ....F.... 772 299-1401
Vero Beach *(G-18635)*
Keller Manufacturing Inc ....G.... 863 937-8928
Lakeland *(G-7724)*
Kent Mfg Fla Keys Inc ....F.... 941 488-0355
Venice *(G-18559)*
KLA Industries ....G.... 727 315-4719
Largo *(G-7992)*
Km Coatings Mfg Jr ....F.... 602 253-1168
Deerfield Beach *(G-2854)*
Knight Industries ....G.... 772 344-2053
Port Saint Lucie *(G-15117)*
Kt Fab Inc ....G.... 863 443-0029
Lake Wales *(G-7514)*
Laal Manufacturing Inc ....G.... 786 859-3613
Miami *(G-9850)*
Lancaster Industries Inc ....G.... 954 916-9293
Davie *(G-2543)*
Larson Industries ....G.... 352 226-8512
Gainesville *(G-4951)*
Larson Industries Incorporated ....F.... 352 262-0566
Gainesville *(G-4952)*
Lawless Industries Ltd ....G.... 352 429-3300
Groveland *(G-5099)*
LDM Industries Inc ....G.... 305 216-1545
Miami *(G-9874)*
Legends Fabrications LLC ....G.... 727 642-0578
Largo *(G-7999)*
Lesko Industries Inc ....G.... 904 273-8293
Ponte Vedra *(G-14926)*
Lifetime Products Group Inc ....G.... 813 781-9182
Gibsonton *(G-5031)*
Load King Manufacturing ....G.... 904 633-7352
Jacksonville *(G-6559)*

Lost Fabrication LLC .....G..... 772 971-3467
Fort Pierce *(G-4712)*
Low Life Industries Inc .....G..... 813 609-5599
Tampa *(G-17861)*
Luther Industries LLC .....G..... 813 833-5652
Tampa *(G-17864)*
Luv & Luv Industries Inc .....G..... 954 826-6237
Hialeah *(G-5491)*
M J Boturla Industries Inc .....G..... 386 574-0811
Deltona *(G-3174)*
Maddox Industries Inc .....G..... 561 529-2165
Jupiter *(G-7071)*
Maher Industries Inc .....G..... 407 928-5288
Orlando *(G-12946)*
MAKM Anufacturing Inc .....G..... 352 343-5881
Tavares *(G-18347)*
Manns Diversified Industries .....G..... 407 310-5938
Altamonte Springs *(G-56)*
Manufacturing Inc Sp .....G..... 305 362-0456
Hialeah *(G-5499)*
Margoth Manufacturing Co .....G..... 954 200-3894
Miami Lakes *(G-10813)*
Marker Industries LLC .....G..... 954 907-2647
Pompano Beach *(G-14753)*
Marvelleth Industries Corp .....G..... 754 263-7197
Miramar *(G-11014)*
Maskco Technologies Inc .....F..... 877 261-6405
Miami Beach *(G-10690)*
Matchless Manufacturing .....G..... 352 390-3010
Ocala *(G-11995)*
Matt Talbot Industries LLC .....G..... 407 718-7636
Sanford *(G-16083)*
Maxeff Industries Inc .....G..... 941 893-5804
Sarasota *(G-16254)*
McM Industries Inc .....G..... 727 259-9894
Clearwater *(G-1778)*
Meath Industries Inc .....G..... 954 818-0593
Coral Springs *(G-2276)*
Medical Waste Industries Inc .....E..... 407 325-4832
New Smyrna Beach *(G-11538)*
Metalco Mfg Inc .....G..... 305 592-0704
Hialeah *(G-5506)*
Metropolis Corp .....E..... 954 951-1011
Fort Lauderdale *(G-4119)*
Mft Stamps .....G..... 352 360-5797
Eustis *(G-3713)*
Michael Moore LLC .....G..... 407 716-7325
Deltona *(G-3175)*
Milbank Manufacturing Co .....F..... 813 623-2681
Tampa *(G-17907)*
Mitten Manufacturing .....G..... 941 722-1818
Palmetto *(G-13813)*
Mjk Industries Inc .....G..... 954 788-7494
Pompano Beach *(G-14766)*
Mjr Manufacturing LLC .....G..... 727 460-0636
Clearwater *(G-1788)*
Mmo Industries Inc .....G..... 727 452-8665
Tampa *(G-17912)*
Mmx Manufacturing LLC .....F..... 786 456-5072
Miami *(G-10030)*
Motion Industries Inc .....G..... 727 536-5521
Largo *(G-8014)*
Mt Distributors LLC .....G..... 954 802-2161
Lauderhill *(G-8116)*
Mumford Micro Mch Works LLC .....G..... 814 720-7291
Sarasota *(G-16517)*
Mytek Industries .....F..... 727 536-7891
Largo *(G-8016)*
Namro Industries Inc .....G..... 561 704-8063
Boynton Beach *(G-936)*
Navarre Industries Inc .....G..... 850 554-6682
Navarre *(G-11471)*
Newvida Products LLC .....G..... 863 781-9232
Zolfo Springs *(G-19547)*
Niagratech Industries Inc .....G..... 305 876-9010
Miami *(G-10072)*
Nivel Parts and Mfg Co LLC .....G..... 904 421-3004
Tampa *(G-17941)*
Norton Manufacturing & Svc Inc .....G..... 352 225-1225
Morriston *(G-11093)*
Nova Solid Surfaces Inc .....G..... 239 888-0975
Fort Myers *(G-4550)*
NRG Industries Inc .....G..... 850 510-7174
Tallahassee *(G-17307)*
Nrnb LLC .....G..... 203 769-5995
Hialeah *(G-5545)*
NTS Industries Inc .....F..... 317 847-6675
Orlando *(G-13013)*
Oberon Industries Inc .....G..... 321 245-7338
Orlando *(G-13015)*

Ocala Manufacturing .....G..... 352 433-6643
Ocala *(G-12011)*
Odyssey Manufacturing Co .....G..... 407 582-9051
Orlando *(G-13020)*
Ontic Engineering & Mfg .....G..... 407 206-8459
Orlando *(G-13023)*
Orattac Industries LLC .....G..... 904 415-2162
Jacksonville *(G-6647)*
Panel Armor Products LLC .....G..... 407 960-5946
Longwood *(G-8320)*
Pap-Cap Industries LLC .....G..... 850 209-7377
Grand Ridge *(G-5046)*
Paradise Building Mtls LLC .....G..... 407 267-3378
Altamonte Springs *(G-61)*
Patio Products Mfg Inc .....G..... 813 681-3806
Brandon *(G-1170)*
Patrick German Industries Inc .....G..... 727 251-3015
Brandon *(G-1171)*
Paveway Systems Inc .....F..... 386 659-1316
Florahome *(G-3765)*
Peeke Industries Inc .....G..... 954 796-1938
Parkland *(G-13998)*
Pembroke Office Industries LLC .....G..... 954 589-1329
Hollywood *(G-5889)*
Pemsum Industries Inc .....G..... 561 623-3151
West Palm Beach *(G-18993)*
Pepper Shark Llc .....F..... 305 849-0104
Key West *(G-7201)*
Petainer Manufacturing US .....F..... 786 999-2019
Miami *(G-10156)*
Peterson Manufacturing LLC .....F..... 941 371-4989
Sarasota *(G-16543)*
Petlift Sb Manufacturing Inc .....F..... 941 346-2211
Lakeland *(G-7766)*
Phlintrock Industries Inc .....G..... 904 579-3334
Orange Park *(G-12402)*
Plane It Safe LLC .....G..... 888 840-0499
Apopka *(G-171)*
Platinum Mfg Intl Inc .....F..... 727 544-4555
Pinellas Park *(G-14376)*
PNC Manufacturing Leather .....G..... 407 201-2069
Kissimmee *(G-7289)*
Pond Industries Inc .....G..... 727 526-5483
Saint Petersburg *(G-15883)*
Poseidon Boat Manufacturing .....F..... 239 362-3736
Fort Myers *(G-4570)*
Powers Industries LLC .....F..... 786 444-3616
Wilton Manors *(G-19219)*
Precision Manufacturing I .....G..... 786 547-2683
Miami *(G-10184)*
Printing Services Plus LLC .....F..... 813 279-1903
Tampa *(G-18016)*
Prowin Industries Inc .....G..... 954 584-5686
Sunrise *(G-17165)*
Quality Aluminum Manufacturing .....G..... 850 434-6446
Pensacola *(G-14246)*
R & A Industries Inc .....F..... 352 307-6655
Oviedo *(G-13455)*
R C R Manufacturing Inc .....G..... 786 499-9245
Miami *(G-10231)*
R&R Assembly Services .....G..... 407 797-8325
Titusville *(G-18454)*
Rapid Industries Inc .....F..... 772 287-0651
Stuart *(G-16997)*
Rapidspoolindustries Inc .....G..... 954 850-5300
Davie *(G-2581)*
RCA Machine & Mfg Inc .....G..... 727 561-0150
Clearwater *(G-1857)*
Rdc Manufacturing Inc .....G..... 772 286-6921
Stuart *(G-16998)*
Red Hawk Industries LLC .....G..... 303 779-6272
Boca Raton *(G-686)*
Rederick Metal Industries .....E..... 305 396-3396
Miami *(G-10245)*
Resharp Industries .....G..... 352 362-1730
Ocala *(G-12037)*
Richard K Pratt LLC .....G..... 321 482-9494
Titusville *(G-18459)*
Rm Industries .....G..... 386 428-4454
New Smyrna *(G-11523)*
Rogue Industries LLC .....G..... 850 797-9228
Fort Walton Beach *(G-4830)*
Ronca Industries LLC .....G..... 407 839-0440
Orlando *(G-13146)*
Rossiter Manufacturing .....G..... 386 409-7223
Daytona Beach *(G-2706)*
Royal Canes .....G..... 727 474-0792
Largo *(G-8043)*
RSD Industries Inc .....G..... 954 240-3660
Hollywood *(G-5903)*

Rugged Industries Inc .....G..... 239 565-2723
Estero *(G-3695)*
Ruiz Industries .....G..... 305 218-6258
Miami *(G-10288)*
S & B Industries Inc .....G..... 305 367-1068
Miami *(G-10291)*
Safe Strap LLC .....F..... 239 461-0033
Fort Myers *(G-4592)*
Salty Industries LLC .....G..... 321 626-6331
Melbourne Beach *(G-8984)*
Schneidder Industries LLC .....G..... 850 207-0929
Daytona Beach *(G-2709)*
Schoen Industries Inc .....G..... 305 491-5993
Saint Cloud *(G-15665)*
Scully Industries .....G..... 941 349-5561
Sarasota *(G-16588)*
Sdm Industries Inc .....G..... 904 814-2814
Palm Coast *(G-13708)*
Sebastian Sea Products In .....G..... 772 321-3997
Vero Beach *(G-18662)*
Seimens Industries Inc .....G..... 954 364-6600
Hollywood *(G-5906)*
Self Industries Incorporated .....G..... 386 882-3644
Ormond Beach *(G-13397)*
Seneca Industries .....G..... 561 626-4999
Palm Beach Gardens *(G-13625)*
Service Industry Consultant .....G..... 561 775-4782
Palm Beach Gardens *(G-13627)*
Seyer - Tech Industries Inc .....G..... 305 233-2672
Miami *(G-10328)*
Shade Experts USA LLC .....F..... 561 422-3200
Wellington *(G-18730)*
Shifted Industries .....G..... 561 302-8915
Groveland *(G-5108)*
Siding Industries of Nthrn FL .....G..... 904 814-7923
Saint Augustine *(G-15610)*
Sinclair Industries LLC .....F..... 305 215-0990
Key Largo *(G-7173)*
Snook Industries .....G..... 352 447-0735
Yankeetown *(G-19491)*
Soto Industries LLC .....G..... 941 830-6000
Punta Gorda *(G-15235)*
South Florida Fabricators LLC .....G..... 954 802-6782
Cooper City *(G-2116)*
Southeastern Assemblies Inc .....G..... 727 376-1411
Trinity *(G-18489)*
Southernunderground Industries .....G..... 954 650-4699
Miami *(G-10389)*
Spector Manufacturing Inc .....G..... 860 559-6068
Palm City *(G-13674)*
Squire Industries Inc .....G..... 813 523-1505
Plant City *(G-14467)*
Ss & S Industries Inc .....F..... 321 327-2500
Melbourne *(G-8944)*
State of Florida .....E..... 850 488-1234
Tallahassee *(G-17331)*
Stealth Industries .....G..... 561 747-1471
Jupiter *(G-7122)*
Steeda Engineering and Mfg LLC .....G..... 954 960-0774
Pompano Beach *(G-14870)*
Stover Manufacturing LLC .....G..... 386 238-3775
Daytona Beach *(G-2719)*
Stover Manufacturing LLC .....F..... 386 235-7060
Port Orange *(G-15037)*
Stump Industries LLC .....D..... 239 940-5754
Fort Myers *(G-4614)*
Sunciti Industries Inc .....G..... 407 877-8081
Winter Garden *(G-19286)*
Suncoast Assemblers LLC .....G..... 407 947-8835
Belle Isle *(G-359)*
Sundown Manufacturing Inc .....F..... 727 828-0826
Clearwater *(G-1894)*
Sunglow Industries .....G..... 304 554-2552
The Villages *(G-18394)*
Sunnman Inc .....G..... 305 505-6615
Hialeah *(G-5637)*
Sweet Industries LLC .....G..... 904 228-9655
Stuart *(G-17031)*
T & M Industries Inc .....F..... 954 778-2238
Deerfield Beach *(G-2921)*
Talon Industries Inc .....G..... 727 517-0052
Belleair Beach *(G-362)*
Tayco Industries Inc .....G..... 863 318-9264
Winter Haven *(G-19362)*
Tdt Manufacturing LLC .....G..... 239 573-7498
Cape Coral *(G-1484)*
Team Solutions Dental LLC .....D..... 407 542-1552
Sanford *(G-16126)*
Tesco Equipment .....G..... 954 791-9470
Davie *(G-2603)*

Thompson Manufacturing Inc...............G....... 239 332-0446
Fort Myers *(G-4629)*
Thriv Industries LLC...............F....... 404 436-3230
Delray Beach *(G-3149)*
Tifco Industries Freedom Alloy...............G....... 407 474-6747
Longwood *(G-8342)*
Tikore Industries LLC...............G....... 954 616-5902
Miami *(G-10478)*
Titan Industries...............G....... 904 608-3905
Orange Park *(G-12409)*
Titan Trailers LLC...............G....... 813 298-8597
Valrico *(G-18525)*
Toogle Industries LLC...............G....... 863 688-8975
Lakeland *(G-7824)*
Traincat Model Sales Inc...............G....... 954 385-8999
Weston *(G-19172)*
Treetop Industries LLC...............G....... 904 471-4412
Saint Augustine *(G-15627)*
Tri-Edge Industries LLC...............G....... 561 703-5961
Lake Worth *(G-7593)*
Trividia Meditech LLC...............F....... 954 677-9201
Fort Lauderdale *(G-4290)*
Tropic Guard Industries LLC...............G....... 813 447-3938
Apollo Beach *(G-107)*
Tropical Mfg Inc...............G....... 305 394-6280
Hialeah *(G-5651)*
Trost Industries LLC...............G....... 407 690-8603
Orlando *(G-13276)*
Troy Industries LLC...............G....... 401 241-4231
Englewood *(G-3669)*
True Blue Metal LLC...............G....... 352 444-9596
Ocala *(G-12061)*
True Line Industries Inc...............G....... 561 745-4828
Jupiter *(G-7135)*
Tsn Manufacturing...............F....... 813 740-1876
Tampa *(G-18207)*
Tsn Manufacturing Inc...............F....... 727 709-9802
Seffner *(G-16734)*
TST Industries LLC...............G....... 973 865-1998
Deland *(G-3026)*
TST Industries LLC...............G....... 386 868-2011
Lake Helen *(G-7395)*
Turn Key Industries...............G....... 813 671-3446
Gibsonton *(G-5034)*
Tzh Industries Inc...............G....... 727 807-3000
Trinity *(G-18490)*
Union Pvc Industries Inc...............G....... 305 883-1640
Hialeah *(G-5658)*
Unique Fbrctions Unlimited LLC...............G....... 352 229-8511
Ocala *(G-12066)*
United Manufacturing Services...............G....... 941 224-1692
Bradenton *(G-1137)*
US Patriot Industries Inc...............G....... 954 802-7402
Hallandale Beach *(G-5221)*
USA Manufacturing Group LLC...............G....... 786 253-3152
Coral Gables *(G-2203)*
V & G Industries Inc...............F....... 786 853-1265
Hialeah *(G-5670)*
Vandalay Inds Manatee Cnty LLC...............G....... 941 756-6028
Bradenton *(G-1139)*
Vdh Worldwide LLC...............G....... 866 304-2388
Wesley Chapel *(G-18763)*
Venancio Usa Inc...............G....... 321 418-9489
Hallandale *(G-5166)*
Virco Mfg Corporation...............G....... 772 834-8261
Stuart *(G-17046)*
Volcano Industries Inc...............F....... 770 300-0041
Sarasota *(G-16323)*
Vplenish Nutritionals Inc...............F....... 954 304-4000
Boca Raton *(G-782)*
Wallace Industries Inc...............G....... 561 833-8554
West Palm Beach *(G-19084)*
Wallace Industries Inc...............F....... 561 301-0811
Lake Worth *(G-7598)*
Westrock Lake Mary...............G....... 407 936-1277
Lake Mary *(G-7461)*
Whitman Industries LLC...............G....... 239 216-6171
Marco Island *(G-8528)*
Whyte Power Industries Corp...............G....... 786 200-6033
Miami *(G-10605)*
Willis Industries Inc...............G....... 954 830-6163
Davie *(G-2614)*
Wiltcher Industries Inc...............G....... 704 907-9838
Ormond Beach *(G-13409)*
Woodham Industries Inc...............G....... 561 863-6666
Lake Park *(G-7483)*
World Manufacturing LLC...............G....... 843 751-9375
Summerfield *(G-17064)*
Worldwide Building Intl Inc...............C....... 786 744-7076
Miami *(G-10622)*
Worthington Industries LLC...............G....... 813 979-1000
Tampa *(G-18266)*
Wrobel Industries Inc...............G....... 727 560-6850
Holiday *(G-5753)*
WW Timber LLC...............G....... 352 584-4550
Perry *(G-14321)*
Yeager Manufacturing Tech LLC...............F....... 407 573-7033
Winter Park *(G-19463)*
Yetman Industries Inc...............G....... 239 561-7808
Fort Myers *(G-4656)*
Z & N Manufacturing Corp...............G....... 407 518-1114
Kissimmee *(G-7313)*
Zel Custom Manufacturing LLC...............G....... 303 880-8701
Odessa *(G-12167)*
Zenithtech Industries Inc...............G....... 386 454-7630
High Springs *(G-5704)*
Zepsa Industries...............G....... 754 307-2173
Pompano Beach *(G-14915)*

MAPS

Quantum Spatial Inc...............D....... 920 457-3631
Saint Petersburg *(G-15897)*

MARBLE BOARD

Jabs Investors Corp...............F....... 561 540-2693
Lake Worth Beach *(G-7614)*
Sarasotas Finest MBL Gran Inc...............G....... 941 365-9697
Sarasota *(G-16583)*

MARBLE, BUILDING: Cut & Shaped

Advanced Marble Products Inc...............G....... 941 485-7775
Venice *(G-18528)*
Atlantic Marble Company Inc...............E....... 904 262-6262
Jacksonville *(G-6176)*
Custom Marble Works Inc...............E....... 813 620-0475
Tampa *(G-17580)*
Debanie Inc...............F....... 239 254-1222
Naples *(G-11224)*
Gold Granite & Marble...............F....... 863 439-9794
Lake Hamilton *(G-7390)*
Marble Designs of FL Inc...............G....... 321 269-6920
Titusville *(G-18445)*
Marble Doctors LLC...............D....... 203 794-1000
Wellington *(G-18724)*
Marble Lite Products Corp...............E....... 305 557-8766
Miami Lakes *(G-10812)*
Mont Krest Stone Inc...............G....... 727 209-0864
Largo *(G-8013)*
Old World Marble and Gran Inc...............G....... 239 596-4777
Naples *(G-11350)*
Puma Marble Co Inc...............F....... 305 758-6461
Miami *(G-10214)*
Showcase Marble Inc...............F....... 386 253-6646
Daytona Beach *(G-2714)*
Stoneworks Inc...............F....... 305 666-6676
Miami *(G-10417)*
Unisource Stone Inc...............G....... 561 493-0660
Stuart *(G-17043)*
Yarey Inc...............F....... 954 520-6015
Boca Raton *(G-795)*
Zachey Design Marble Inc...............G....... 754 367-6261
Hollywood *(G-5945)*

MARINAS

Gulfstream Land Company LLC...............F....... 772 286-3456
Stuart *(G-16951)*
Performance Sales & Service...............G....... 863 465-2814
Lake Placid *(G-7493)*

MARINE APPAREL STORES

Hexskin LLC...............G....... 305 901-1573
Miami *(G-9706)*

MARINE ENGINE REPAIR SVCS

Cobra Power Corporation...............G....... 305 893-5018
North Miami *(G-11633)*
Offshore Performance Spc...............F....... 239 481-2768
Fort Myers *(G-4555)*

MARINE HARDWARE

A Extend Life Inc...............G....... 941 505-7766
Punta Gorda *(G-15188)*
Accon Marine Inc...............F....... 727 572-9202
Clearwater *(G-1562)*
Acryplex Inc...............G....... 305 633-7636
Miami *(G-9066)*
Batech Inc...............E....... 321 784-4838
Cape Canaveral *(G-1351)*
Birdsall Marine Design Inc...............E....... 561 832-7879
West Palm Beach *(G-18822)*
Byrd Technologies Inc...............E....... 954 957-8333
Pompano Beach *(G-14627)*
Dolphin Boat Lifts Inc...............G....... 239 936-1782
Fort Myers *(G-4435)*
G G Schmitt & Sons Inc...............C....... 717 394-3701
Sarasota *(G-16216)*
Galley Maid Marine Pdts Inc...............F....... 863 467-6070
Okeechobee *(G-12178)*
Garelick Mfg Co...............D....... 727 545-4571
Largo *(G-7956)*
General Hydraulic Solutions...............G....... 727 561-0719
Clearwater *(G-1702)*
Hc Grupo Inc...............G....... 954 227-0150
Coral Springs *(G-2252)*
Headhunter Inc...............E....... 954 462-5953
Fort Lauderdale *(G-4044)*
Latham Marine Inc...............E....... 954 462-3055
Fort Lauderdale *(G-4096)*
Lenco Marine Solutions LLC...............E....... 772 288-2662
Stuart *(G-16970)*
Marine Manufacturing Inc...............G....... 305 885-3493
Hialeah *(G-5503)*
Orbe Inc...............G....... 954 534-2264
Oakland Park *(G-11827)*
Patrick Industries Inc...............C....... 941 556-6311
Sarasota *(G-16273)*
Patrick Industries Inc...............D....... 239 283-0800
Cape Coral *(G-1454)*
Pipewelders Marine Inc...............D....... 954 587-8400
Fort Lauderdale *(G-4169)*
R J Marine Group Inc...............G....... 772 232-6590
Stuart *(G-16995)*
Rupp Marine Inc...............F....... 772 286-5300
Stuart *(G-17004)*
Southcoast Marine Products Inc...............C....... 727 573-4821
Clearwater *(G-1881)*
Stainless Marine Inc...............E....... 305 681-7893
Opa Locka *(G-12361)*
Stuart Industries Inc...............F....... 305 651-3474
Miami *(G-10425)*
T & R Marine Corp...............G....... 850 584-4261
Perry *(G-14315)*
Tides Marine Inc...............E....... 954 420-0949
Deerfield Beach *(G-2926)*
Vitsur Industries Inc...............G....... 561 744-1290
Jupiter *(G-7141)*
W D Wilson Inc...............E....... 813 626-6989
Tampa *(G-18250)*

MARINE RELATED EQPT

American Boom and Barrier Inc...............E....... 321 784-2110
Cape Canaveral *(G-1350)*
Bogantec Corp...............G....... 954 217-0023
Dania Beach *(G-2463)*
Csa International Inc...............E....... 561 746-7946
Jupiter *(G-7020)*
Enviro-USA American Mfr LLC...............E....... 321 222-9551
Cape Canaveral *(G-1357)*
Flagship Marine Inc...............G....... 772 781-4242
Stuart *(G-16940)*
Frz Marine...............G....... 941 322-2631
Sarasota *(G-16440)*
Jetboatpilot LLC...............F....... 850 960-3236
Panama City *(G-13921)*
Marine Spc Cstm Fabricator...............G....... 813 855-0554
Oldsmar *(G-12246)*
South Florida Marine...............G....... 305 232-8788
Cutler Bay *(G-2413)*
Tecnografic Inc...............E....... 954 928-1714
Fort Lauderdale *(G-4276)*
Uflex Usa Inc...............E....... 941 351-2628
Sarasota *(G-16319)*
Zinc Guy Inc...............E....... 954 907-2752
Davie *(G-2618)*

MARINE RELATED EQPT: Cranes, Ship

Liebherr Cranes Inc...............G....... 305 817-7500
Hialeah *(G-5486)*

MARINE SPLY DEALERS

A B C Canvas Inc...............G....... 239 542-0909
Cape Coral *(G-1370)*
Davit Master Corp...............F....... 727 573-4414
Clearwater *(G-1650)*

Headhunter Inc........E....... 954 462-5953
Fort Lauderdale *(G-4044)*
Rocky Bayou Enterprises Inc........G....... 850 244-4567
Fort Walton Beach *(G-4829)*
Whiticar Boat Works Inc........E....... 772 287-2883
Stuart *(G-17049)*

MARINE SPLYS WHOLESALERS

Doller Marine Sales & Services........F....... 954 463-9988
Fort Lauderdale *(G-3947)*
Jetboatpilot LLC........F....... 850 960-3236
Panama City *(G-13921)*
Veethree Electronics & Mar LLC........D....... 941 538-7775
Bradenton *(G-1140)*
Zinc Guy Inc........E....... 954 907-2752
Davie *(G-2618)*

MARINE SVC STATIONS

S & S Performance Inc........G....... 305 951-9846
Islamorada *(G-6099)*

MARKERS

Trs Industries Inc........G....... 561 880-0031
Lake Worth *(G-7594)*

MARKING DEVICES

Ace Printing Inc........F....... 305 358-2572
Miami *(G-9061)*
Burr Printing Co Inc........G....... 863 294-3166
Winter Haven *(G-19308)*
Four G Enterprises Inc........E....... 407 834-4143
Longwood *(G-8284)*
GBIG Corporation........G....... 866 998-8466
Miami *(G-9617)*
Identity Holding Company LLC........C....... 941 355-5171
Sarasota *(G-16233)*
Mark Master Inc........D....... 813 988-6000
Tampa *(G-17881)*
One Price Drycleaners Tampa........F....... 727 734-3353
Dunedin *(G-3586)*
Sun Graphic Technologies Inc........E....... 941 753-7541
Sarasota *(G-16305)*

MARKING DEVICES: Canceling Stamps, Hand, Rubber Or Metal

Holmes Stamp Company........E....... 904 396-2291
Jacksonville *(G-6476)*

MARKING DEVICES: Embossing Seals & Hand Stamps

Ace Marking Devices Corp........G....... 561 833-4073
West Palm Beach *(G-18786)*
Finlayson Enterprises Inc........G....... 850 785-7953
Panama City *(G-13902)*

MARKING DEVICES: Irons, Marking Or Branding

Sequoia Brands Inc........E....... 813 969-2000
Odessa *(G-12150)*

MARKING DEVICES: Screens, Textile Printing

Say What Screen Prtg & EMB Inc........G....... 941 745-5822
Bradenton *(G-1112)*
Southeast Marketing Concepts........G....... 561 747-7010
Jupiter *(G-7118)*
Vanlex Clothing Inc........E....... 305 431-4669
Miami Lakes *(G-10878)*
Wholesale Screen Prtg of Nples........G....... 239 263-7061
Naples *(G-11455)*

MARKING DEVICES: Seal Presses, Notary & Hand

Nommo International LLC........G....... 866 366-3688
Orlando *(G-13006)*

MARKING DEVICES: Stencil Machines

Universal Stncling Mkg Systems........E....... 727 894-3027
Saint Petersburg *(G-15948)*

MASSAGE MACHINES, ELECTRIC: Barber & Beauty Shops

Beata Bordas........G....... 772 349-2568
Stuart *(G-16915)*
Elastec Inc........F....... 618 382-2525
Cocoa *(G-2019)*

MASSAGE PARLORS

Tom Watson Enterprises Inc........G....... 352 683-5097
Hudson *(G-6040)*

MASTS: Cast Aluminum

Sinobec Resources LLC........G....... 561 409-2205
Deerfield Beach *(G-2912)*
St Judas Tadeus Foundry Inc........G....... 305 512-3612
Hialeah *(G-5631)*

MATERIAL GRINDING & PULVERIZING SVCS NEC

Apex Grinding Inc........G....... 386 624-7350
Deland *(G-2958)*

MATERIALS HANDLING EQPT WHOLESALERS

Ring Power Corporation........G....... 863 606-0512
Lakeland *(G-7779)*

MATS & MATTING, MADE FROM PURCHASED WIRE

D & D Manufacturing LLC........F....... 321 890-0069
Titusville *(G-18427)*

MATS OR MATTING, NEC: Rubber

BF Hurley Mat Co Inc........E....... 813 837-0616
Tampa *(G-17468)*

MATS, MATTING & PADS: Auto, Floor, Exc Rubber Or Plastic

Mobile Auto Solutions LLC........G....... 561 903-5328
West Palm Beach *(G-18954)*

MATS, MATTING & PADS: Door, Paper, Grass, Reed, Coir, Etc

Woovfu Inc........F....... 719 301-1661
Saint Petersburg *(G-15964)*

MATS: Blasting, Rope

Nets Depot Inc........F....... 305 215-5579
Medley *(G-8694)*

MATTRESS PROTECTORS: Rubber

Levita LLC........G....... 954 227-7468
Coral Springs *(G-2273)*

MATTRESS STORES

Plushbeds Inc........G....... 888 449-5738
Boca Raton *(G-667)*
Zeno Furniture & Mat Mfg Co........G....... 954 764-1212
Fort Lauderdale *(G-4335)*

MEAL DELIVERY PROGRAMS

West Development Group LLC........G....... 407 308-5020
Orlando *(G-13322)*

MEAT & MEAT PRDTS WHOLESALERS

Catalina Finer Meat Corp........F....... 813 876-3910
Tampa *(G-17516)*
Del Rosario Enterprises Inc........F....... 786 547-6812
Medley *(G-8642)*

MEAT CUTTING & PACKING

Apakus Inc........F....... 305 403-2603
Coral Gables *(G-2123)*
Azar Industries Inc........E....... 904 358-2354
Jacksonville *(G-6184)*
Bubba Foods LLC........C....... 904 482-1900
Jacksonville *(G-6242)*
Cargill Meat Solutions Corp........B....... 305 826-3699
Hialeah *(G-5340)*
Dutch Packing Co Inc........G....... 305 871-3640
Miami *(G-9488)*
Egea Food LLC........F....... 833 353-6637
Miami *(G-9504)*
El Toro Meat Packing Corp........D....... 305 836-4461
Miami *(G-9509)*
FM Meat Products Ltd Partnr........E....... 352 546-3000
Fort Mc Coy *(G-4337)*
Johnson Brothers Whl Meats Inc........E....... 850 763-2828
Panama City *(G-13922)*
Justice Government Supply Inc........G....... 954 559-3038
West Palm Beach *(G-18916)*
Kelly Foods........G....... 904 354-7600
Jacksonville *(G-6534)*
La Montina Inc........E....... 305 324-0083
Miami *(G-9844)*
Madson Inc........F....... 305 863-7390
Medley *(G-8681)*
Martinez Distributors Corp........E....... 305 882-8282
Miami *(G-9952)*
Polks Meat Products Inc........G....... 813 961-2881
Lutz *(G-8410)*
Prg Packing Corp........E....... 201 242-5500
Madison *(G-8453)*
South Marion Meats........G....... 352 245-2096
Summerfield *(G-17062)*
Special Americas Bbq Inc........E....... 305 637-7377
Miami *(G-10399)*
Tyson Foods Inc........G....... 904 693-0688
Jacksonville *(G-6873)*

MEAT MARKETS

South Marion Meats........G....... 352 245-2096
Summerfield *(G-17062)*

MEAT PRDTS: Bacon, Slab & Sliced, From Slaughtered Meat

Gourmet 3005 Inc........G....... 786 334-6250
Hialeah *(G-5434)*

MEAT PRDTS: Calf's Foot Jelly, From Purchased Meat

Immokalee Ranch........G....... 239 657-2000
Immokalee *(G-6052)*

MEAT PRDTS: Canned

On Base Foods Group LLC........F....... 248 672-7659
Avon Park *(G-291)*
Pamplona Foods Inc........G....... 305 970-4120
Miami *(G-10135)*

MEAT PRDTS: Dried Beef, From Purchased Meat

Moroccan Khlii Inc........G....... 813 699-0096
Tampa *(G-17918)*

MEAT PRDTS: Frozen

Kuando Trading Corp........F....... 786 603-3772
Miami *(G-9833)*
La Villarena Meat & Pork Inc........F....... 305 759-0555
Miami *(G-9849)*
Southast Protein Purveyors LLC........G....... 912 354-2770
Winter Haven *(G-19357)*

MEAT PRDTS: Ham, Boiled, From Purchased Meat

Amba Ham Company Inc........G....... 305 754-0001
Miami *(G-9134)*
Golden Boar Product Corp........G....... 305 500-9392
Miami *(G-9646)*

MEAT PRDTS: Ham, Boneless, From Purchased Meat

High Top Products Corp........D....... 305 633-3287
Miami *(G-9710)*

MEAT PRDTS: Ham, Canned, From Purchased Meat

La Montina Inc........E....... 305 324-0083
Miami *(G-9844)*

Employee Codes: A=Over 500 employees, B=251-500
C=101-250, D=51-100, E=20-50, F=10-19, G=4-9

MEAT PRDTS: Lamb, From Slaughtered Meat

Cedena Carmenn G 305 681-1222
Opa Locka *(G-12298)*

MEAT PRDTS: Pork, From Slaughtered Meat

Henrys Hickory House Inc D 904 493-4420
Jacksonville *(G-6469)*

MEAT PRDTS: Prepared Beef Prdts From Purchased Beef

Vienna Beef Ltd B 941 723-7234
Palmetto *(G-13833)*

MEAT PRDTS: Prepared Pork Prdts, From Purchased Meat

Ddd Hams Inc G 850 205-1426
Tallahassee *(G-17241)*
Get Hams Inc G 850 386-7123
Tallahassee *(G-17265)*
La Coronella Meat Processing F 305 691-2630
Miami *(G-9838)*
La Esquina Del Le Billto E 305 477-4225
Doral *(G-3415)*

MEAT PRDTS: Sausages, From Purchased Meat

Cabreras Spanish Sausages LLC G 305 882-1040
Hialeah *(G-5339)*
Elore Enterprises LLC E 305 477-1650
Miami *(G-9519)*
Elore Holdings Inc G 305 477-1650
Miami *(G-9520)*
Hot Dog Shoppe LLC G 850 682-3649
Crestview *(G-2351)*
New Best Packers Inc E 386 328-5127
Palatka *(G-13487)*
Red Smith Foods Inc E 954 581-1996
Davie *(G-2583)*

MEAT PRDTS: Smoked

Blue Planet Holdings LLC F 863 559-1236
Lakeland *(G-7647)*
Uncle Johns Pride LLC D 813 685-7745
Tampa *(G-18216)*

MEAT PRDTS: Snack Sticks, Incl Jerky, From Purchased Meat

Ben Jammin Island Jerky Llc G 904 220-2067
Jacksonville *(G-6203)*
Country Prime Meats USA Inc G 250 396-4111
Plantation *(G-14503)*
Florida Jerky Enterprises Inc G 256 682-2959
Orlando *(G-12750)*
Grub Company F 347 464-9770
Ormond Beach *(G-13375)*
Lone Star Beef Jerky LLC G 806 241-4188
Palm Harbor *(G-13745)*
Silver Horn Jerky Inc F 850 208-1433
Pensacola *(G-14261)*

MEAT PRDTS: Variety, Fresh Edible Organs

High Top Products Corp D 305 633-3287
Miami *(G-9710)*

MEAT PROCESSED FROM PURCHASED CARCASSES

Adirondack Meat Company Inc F 518 585-2333
Cape Coral *(G-1374)*
Bush Brothers Provision Co E 561 832-6666
West Palm Beach *(G-18831)*
Catalina Finer Meat Corp F 813 876-3910
Tampa *(G-17516)*
Cheney Ofs Inc A 407 292-3223
Orlando *(G-12579)*
Discos Y Empanadas Argentina F 305 326-9300
Miami *(G-9469)*
Dutch Packing Co Inc G 305 871-3640
Miami *(G-9488)*
E&M Innovative Forager LLC E 954 923-0056
Hallandale Beach *(G-5182)*
Future Foods LLC G 786 390-5226
Lake Worth *(G-7551)*
Henrys Hickory House Inc D 904 493-4420
Jacksonville *(G-6469)*
Hillshire Brands Company G 321 637-9765
Cocoa *(G-2029)*
Johnson Brothers Whl Meats Inc E 850 763-2828
Panama City *(G-13922)*
Latin Amercn Meats & Foods USA G 305 477-2700
Miami *(G-9867)*
Majestics Business USA LLC G 305 713-9773
North Miami *(G-11645)*
Pinellas Provision Corporation E 727 822-2701
Saint Petersburg *(G-15877)*
Port of Palm Cold Storage Inc E 386 328-5127
Palatka *(G-13489)*
Richards Brazilian Sausage LLC G 786 609-3554
Pembroke Pines *(G-14057)*
South Marion Meats G 352 245-2096
Summerfield *(G-17062)*
Special Americas Bbq Inc E 305 637-7377
Miami *(G-10399)*
Stanfords Jerky G 813 817-5953
Brandon *(G-1181)*

MEATS, PACKAGED FROZEN: Wholesalers

Latin Amercn Meats & Foods USA G 305 477-2700
Miami *(G-9867)*

MECHANICAL INSTRUMENT REPAIR SVCS

Weimer Mechanical Services Inc G 813 645-2258
Ruskin *(G-15487)*

MEDICAL & HOSPITAL EQPT WHOLESALERS

Dhss LLC F 305 405-4001
North Miami Beach *(G-11670)*
Great Northern Rehab PC G 352 732-8868
Ocala *(G-11960)*
Great Northern Rehab PC F 352 732-8868
Ocala *(G-11961)*
Hygreen Inc F 352 327-9747
Gainesville *(G-4939)*
Mahnkes Orthtics Prsthtics of G 954 772-1299
Miami *(G-9935)*
Medical Outfitters Inc G 305 885-4045
Miami *(G-9966)*
Merits Health Products Inc E 239 772-0579
Fort Myers *(G-4527)*
Oculus Surgical Inc E 772 236-2622
Port St Lucie *(G-15177)*
Pride Florida G 813 621-9262
Tampa *(G-18009)*
Sunoptic Technologies LLC D 877 677-2832
Jacksonville *(G-6822)*

MEDICAL & HOSPITAL SPLYS: Radiation Shielding Garments

Burkhart Roentgen Intl Inc F 727 327-6950
Saint Petersburg *(G-15732)*

MEDICAL & SURGICAL SPLYS: Abdominal Support, Braces/Trusses

A & A Orthopedics Mfg G 305 256-8119
Miami *(G-9029)*
North Shore Hldngs Lghthuse Pt E 954 785-1055
Lighthouse Point *(G-8211)*

MEDICAL & SURGICAL SPLYS: Belts, Linemen's Safety

Ace Sales Corp F 305 835-0310
Miami *(G-9063)*

MEDICAL & SURGICAL SPLYS: Braces, Elastic

Dynorthotics Ltd Partnership G 954 925-5806
Dania *(G-2443)*

MEDICAL & SURGICAL SPLYS: Braces, Orthopedic

Anjon Inc E 904 730-9373
Jacksonville *(G-6157)*
Bolt Systems Inc G 407 425-0012
Orlando *(G-12532)*
Bremer Group Company Inc F 904 645-0004
Jacksonville *(G-6235)*
Restorative Care America Inc D 727 573-1595
Saint Petersburg *(G-15900)*
Restorative Products Inc F 813 342-4432
Tampa *(G-18054)*
Tendonease LLC G 888 224-0319
Palm City *(G-13675)*

MEDICAL & SURGICAL SPLYS: Canes, Orthopedic

Pure Med Mobility Inc G 352 366-8008
Brooksville *(G-1263)*

MEDICAL & SURGICAL SPLYS: Clothing, Fire Resistant & Protect

Safe Workplace Inc G 813 657-7233
San Antonio *(G-15979)*
Simpson Construction and Roofg F 863 443-0710
Avon Park *(G-296)*
Straw Giant Company G 561 430-0729
Delray Beach *(G-3147)*

MEDICAL & SURGICAL SPLYS: Cosmetic Restorations

Ace Restoration Services LLC F 786 487-1870
Miami *(G-9062)*
Debut Development LLC G 863 448-9081
Wauchula *(G-18690)*
JB Effects G 727 348-1865
Pinellas Park *(G-14356)*

MEDICAL & SURGICAL SPLYS: Cotton & Cotton Applicators

Juvent Medical Inc G 732 748-8866
Fort Myers Beach *(G-4665)*

MEDICAL & SURGICAL SPLYS: Cotton, Incl Cotton Balls

Energy Now LLC G 941 276-0935
Port Charlotte *(G-14978)*

MEDICAL & SURGICAL SPLYS: Dressings, Surgical

Depuy Inc E 305 412-8010
Miami *(G-9455)*

MEDICAL & SURGICAL SPLYS: Foot Appliances, Orthopedic

Dr Jills Foot Pads Inc F 954 573-6557
Deerfield Beach *(G-2818)*
Orcom Labs Inc G 321 773-0741
Indian Harbour Beach *(G-6064)*
Rlcjc Inc G 407 370-3338
Orlando *(G-13142)*
Southern Surgical Consultants G 904 296-7828
Jacksonville *(G-6797)*

MEDICAL & SURGICAL SPLYS: Limbs, Artificial

Advanced Prosthetics Amer Inc F 352 383-0396
Eustis *(G-3700)*
All Out On A Limb LLC G 813 407-6497
Ruskin *(G-15480)*
Around and About Inc F 954 584-1954
Plantation *(G-14491)*
Bay Quality Prosthetic LLC G 850 522-5343
Panama City *(G-13868)*
Grace Prsthtic Fabrication Inc G 727 842-2265
New Port Richey *(G-11491)*
Hanger Prsthetcs & Ortho Inc G 850 216-2392
Tallahassee *(G-17273)*
Institute For Prosthetic Advan G 850 784-0320
Panama City *(G-13918)*
Jrs Limb & Tree LLC G 407 383-4843
Sanford *(G-16075)*
Limb Preservation Inst Inc G 954 755-5726
Parkland *(G-13996)*
Limbitless Solutions Inc E 407 494-3661
Orlando *(G-12912)*
Orthotic Prsthtic Rhbltion As G 352 331-3399
Gainesville *(G-4977)*

Ryder Orthopedics Inc ....G.... 239 939-0009
Fort Myers (G-4589)
Westcoast Brace & Limb Inc ....F.... 813 985-5000
Temple Terrace (G-18383)

MEDICAL & SURGICAL SPLYS: Models, Anatomical

Digital Antomy Smltons For HLT ....G.... 937 623-7377
Orlando (G-12672)

MEDICAL & SURGICAL SPLYS: Orthopedic Appliances

Applied Mobility Devices LLC ....G.... 833 439-6266
Bonita Springs (G-813)
Euroinsoles Incorporated ....G.... 786 206-6117
Coral Gables (G-2144)
Evolution Orthotics Inc ....E.... 407 688-2860
Lake Mary (G-7411)
Freedom Fabrication Inc ....F.... 850 539-4194
Havana (G-5238)
Freedom Orthotics Inc ....G.... 813 833-7871
Dunedin (G-3577)
Great Northern Rehab PC ....G.... 352 732-8868
Ocala (G-11960)
Great Northern Rehab PC ....F.... 352 732-8868
Ocala (G-11961)
Hanger Prsthtics Orthotics Inc ....F.... 239 772-4510
Cape Coral (G-1433)
Integrity Prsthetics Orthotics ....G.... 813 416-5905
Tampa (G-17788)
Ko Orthotics Inc ....G.... 954 570-8096
Coconut Creek (G-2088)
Leeder Group Inc ....E.... 305 436-5030
Miami (G-9880)
Mako Surgical Corp ....B.... 866 647-6256
Weston (G-19149)
McCluneys Orthpd Prsthetis Svc ....G.... 352 373-5754
Gainesville (G-4958)
Ongoing Care Solutions Inc ....E.... 727 526-0707
Clearwater (G-1818)
Orthomerica Products Inc ....C.... 407 290-6592
Orlando (G-13039)
Pensacola Orthtc & Prostetic ....G.... 850 478-7676
Pensacola (G-14225)
Potenza Services Inc ....G.... 305 400-4938
Miami (G-10180)
Professional Products Inc ....C.... 850 892-5731
Defuniak Springs (G-2946)
Quirantes Orthopedics Inc ....G.... 305 261-1382
Miami (G-10227)
South Bch Orthtics Prsthtics I ....F.... 352 512-0262
Stuart (G-17019)
Structure Medical LLC ....D.... 239 262-5551
Naples (G-11419)
Tidwells Orthotics and Prosthe ....G.... 954 346-5402
Coral Springs (G-2323)
US Orthotics Inc ....F.... 813 621-7797
Tampa (G-18227)
Visionare LLC ....G.... 305 989-7271
Fort Myers (G-4647)
Williams Orthtc-Prosthetic Inc ....G.... 850 385-6655
Tallahassee (G-17345)
Zimmer Dental Inc ....D.... 561 776-6700
Palm Beach Gardens (G-13637)

MEDICAL & SURGICAL SPLYS: Personal Safety Eqpt

Cadre Holdings Inc ....C.... 904 741-5400
Jacksonville (G-6249)
Cameron Textiles Inc ....G.... 954 454-6482
Palm City (G-13644)
Decimal LLC ....E.... 407 330-3300
Sanford (G-16033)
Hawk Protection Incorporated ....G.... 954 980-9631
Pembroke Pines (G-14040)
Lifesaving Systems Corporation ....E.... 813 645-2748
Apollo Beach (G-105)
Primetime Industries LLC ....G.... 813 781-0196
Wesley Chapel (G-18756)
Universal HM Hlth Indus Sups I ....G.... 813 493-7904
Tampa (G-18222)

MEDICAL & SURGICAL SPLYS: Prosthetic Appliances

A and A Orthopedics Inc ....G.... 305 256-8119
Miami (G-9035)
All American Amputee ....G.... 352 383-0396
Eustis (G-3702)
Alps South LLC ....D.... 727 528-8566
Saint Petersburg (G-15697)
Bader Prosthetics & Orthotics ....E.... 813 962-6100
Tampa (G-17453)
Empowered Prosthetics Corp ....G.... 561 630-9137
Palm Beach Gardens (G-13588)
Evolution Liners Inc ....G.... 407 839-6213
Orlando (G-12723)
Florida Prsthtics Orthtics Inc ....G.... 305 553-1217
Miami (G-9586)
Innovative Spine Care ....G.... 813 920-3022
Tampa (G-17785)
Integrity Prosthetics ....G.... 863 875-7063
Winter Haven (G-19330)
Kinetic Research Inc ....F.... 813 962-6300
Tampa (G-17826)
Lawall Prsthtics Orthtics Inc ....G.... 407 567-5190
Orlando (G-12897)
Mahnkes Orthtics Prsthtics of ....G.... 954 772-1299
Miami (G-9935)
Maramed Precision Corporation ....E.... 305 823-8300
Hialeah (G-5500)
Prosthetic Laboratories ....G.... 305 250-9900
Coral Gables (G-2187)
Santos Group Inc ....F.... 954 605-2954
Coral Springs (G-2309)
Son Life Prsthtics Orthtics In ....F.... 352 596-2257
Hernando Beach (G-5251)
South Broward Brace Inc ....F.... 954 458-0656
Hallandale Beach (G-5213)

MEDICAL & SURGICAL SPLYS: Sponges

Sponge Merchant International ....G.... 727 919-3523
Tarpon Springs (G-18325)

MEDICAL & SURGICAL SPLYS: Stretchers

Dollar & Penny Stretchers LLC ....G.... 941 830-5341
Port Charlotte (G-14973)

MEDICAL & SURGICAL SPLYS: Sutures, Non & Absorbable

Demetech Corporation ....D.... 305 824-1048
Miami Lakes (G-10781)

MEDICAL & SURGICAL SPLYS: Traction Apparatus

C Dyer Development Group LLC ....G.... 727 423-6169
Tarpon Springs (G-18285)

MEDICAL & SURGICAL SPLYS: Walkers

Donna M Walker PA ....G.... 561 289-0437
Boca Raton (G-507)

MEDICAL & SURGICAL SPLYS: Welders' Hoods

Alloy Cladding ....E.... 561 625-4550
Jupiter (G-6999)
Hogg Wild Fabrication ....G.... 904 214-3453
Jacksonville (G-6474)

MEDICAL EQPT: Cardiographs

Medicomp Inc ....C.... 321 676-0010
Melbourne (G-8886)

MEDICAL EQPT: Defibrillators

US Defib Medical Tech LLC ....G.... 305 887-7552
Medley (G-8751)

MEDICAL EQPT: Diagnostic

Advanced Dagnstc Solutions Inc ....F.... 352 293-2810
Port Richey (G-15042)
Clinical Chmstry Spclists Corp ....F.... 919 554-1424
West Palm Beach (G-18847)
Dhss LLC ....E.... 305 830-0327
Hollywood (G-5811)
Diagnostic Test Group LLC ....F.... 561 347-5760
Boca Raton (G-500)
Doral Imaging Institute LLC ....G.... 305 594-2881
Miami (G-9481)
Erba Diagnostics Inc ....D.... 305 324-2300
Miami Lakes (G-10786)
First Check Diagnostics LLC ....E.... 858 805-2425
Orlando (G-12741)
Galix Bmedical Instrumentation ....F.... 305 534-5905
Doral (G-3357)
Home Aide Diagnostics Inc ....F.... 954 794-0212
Deerfield Beach (G-2843)
Intellgent Haring Systems Corp ....F.... 305 668-6102
Miami (G-9752)
Invivo Corporation ....B.... 301 525-9683
Gainesville (G-4945)
Iradimed Corporation ....C.... 407 677-8022
Winter Springs (G-19475)
MEI Development Corporation ....F.... 954 341-3302
Coral Springs (G-2280)
Nuline Sensors LLC ....G.... 407 473-0765
Sanford (G-16092)
Pace Tech Inc ....F.... 727 442-8118
Clearwater (G-1824)
Parallax Health Sciences Inc ....G.... 888 263-9799
West Palm Beach (G-18987)
RM Imaging Incorporated ....E.... 561 361-8090
Boca Raton (G-690)
Sota Manufacturing Inc ....E.... 561 368-8007
Boca Raton (G-722)
Twins & Martin Equipment Corp ....G.... 954 802-0345
Miami (G-10516)
Wimbledon Health Partners LLC ....F.... 800 200-8262
Boca Raton (G-790)

MEDICAL EQPT: Electromedical Apparatus

Conmed Corporation ....A.... 727 392-6464
Largo (G-7927)
H Q Inc ....F.... 941 721-7588
Palmetto (G-13804)
Motus GI Holdings Inc ....E.... 954 541-8000
Fort Lauderdale (G-4126)
Sequa Corporation ....A.... 561 935-3571
Palm Beach Gardens (G-13626)
Tri-Tech Electronics Inc ....D.... 407 277-2131
Orlando (G-13270)
Vertec Inc ....F.... 850 478-6480
Pensacola (G-14283)
Zassi Holdings Inc ....G.... 904 432-8315
Ponte Vedra Beach (G-14958)

MEDICAL EQPT: Electrotherapeutic Apparatus

Axogen Inc ....C.... 386 462-6800
Alachua (G-6)
Curallux LLC ....E.... 786 888-1875
Doral (G-3316)
Orthosensor Inc ....D.... 954 577-7770
Dania Beach (G-2471)

MEDICAL EQPT: Laser Systems

Anti-Ging Asthtic Lser Ctr Inc ....G.... 786 539-4901
Miami Beach (G-10642)
Channel Investments LLC ....G.... 727 599-1360
Tampa (G-17531)
Erchonia Corporation LLC ....E.... 321 473-1251
Melbourne (G-8827)
Estetika Skin & Laser Spe ....F.... 262 646-9222
Sarasota (G-16422)
Home Healthcare 2000 Inc ....G.... 954 977-4450
Pompano Beach (G-14726)
K-O Concepts Inc ....G.... 407 296-7788
Titusville (G-18437)
Lexington International LLC ....E.... 800 973-4769
Boca Raton (G-600)
Meditek-Icot Inc ....F.... 813 909-7476
Lutz (G-8398)
Nova Laserlight LLC ....F.... 407 226-0609
Orlando (G-13010)
Pristine Laser Center ....G.... 407 389-1200
Altamonte Springs (G-66)
Silver Bay LLC ....F.... 941 306-5812
Sarasota (G-16296)
Stimwave Technologies Inc ....G.... 800 965-5134
Pompano Beach (G-14872)
Touchpoint Medical Inc ....B.... 813 854-1905
Odessa (G-12159)

MEDICAL EQPT: MRI/Magnetic Resonance Imaging Devs, Nuclear

Imaging Initiatives Inc ....G.... 239 936-3646
Fort Myers (G-4488)

L&R Imaging....G.... 678 691-3204
Pompano Beach *(G-14741)*
Mri Specialists....G.... 561 369-2144
Boynton Beach *(G-934)*

MEDICAL EQPT: Patient Monitoring

3M Resident Monitoring Inc....E.... 813 749-5453
Odessa *(G-12096)*
Actigraph LLC....F.... 850 332-7900
Pensacola *(G-14080)*
Compliance Meds Tech LLC....G.... 786 319-9826
Miami *(G-9389)*
Infopia USA LLC....F.... 321 225-3620
Cocoa *(G-2031)*

MEDICAL EQPT: Sterilizers

Internl Sterilization Lab LLC....G.... 352 429-3200
Groveland *(G-5097)*
Primus Sterilizer Company LLC....F.... 402 344-4200
Orlando *(G-13087)*

MEDICAL EQPT: Ultrasonic Scanning Devices

Harbor Imaging....E.... 941 883-8383
Port Charlotte *(G-14985)*
Mri Depot Inc....G.... 407 696-9822
Longwood *(G-8314)*
Renal Advantage Inc A44....G.... 772 807-7229
Port Saint Lucie *(G-15136)*
Shenk Enterprises LLC....F.... 386 753-1959
Orange City *(G-12378)*
Supersonic Imagine Inc....G.... 954 660-3528
Weston *(G-19168)*

MEDICAL EQPT: X-Ray Apparatus & Tubes, Therapeutic

Power Wthin Cnsling Cnsltn LLC....G.... 863 242-3023
Haines City *(G-5145)*

MEDICAL HELP SVCS

Medtek Medical Solutions LLC....F.... 786 458-8080
Miami *(G-9968)*

MEDICAL SUNDRIES: Rubber

Medical Defense Company Inc....F.... 954 614-3266
Doral *(G-3429)*

MEDICAL SVCS ORGANIZATION

Advantagecare Inc....G.... 407 345-8877
Orlando *(G-12435)*
Modernizing Medicine....C.... 561 880-2998
Boca Raton *(G-629)*

MEDICAL, DENTAL & HOSPITAL EQPT, WHOL: Hospital Eqpt & Splys

Steripack (usa) Limited LLC....E.... 863 648-2333
Lakeland *(G-7807)*

MEDICAL, DENTAL & HOSPITAL EQPT, WHOL: Hosptl Eqpt/Furniture

Decimal LLC....E.... 407 330-3300
Sanford *(G-16033)*
Galix Bmedical Instrumentation....F.... 305 534-5905
Doral *(G-3357)*
Omega Medical Imaging LLC....E.... 407 323-9400
Sanford *(G-16093)*

MEDICAL, DENTAL & HOSPITAL EQPT, WHOL: Surgical Eqpt & Splys

Kollsut International Inc....G.... 305 438-6877
North Miami Beach *(G-11688)*
Zimmer Biomet CMF Thoracic LLC....C.... 574 267-6639
Jacksonville *(G-6934)*

MEDICAL, DENTAL & HOSPITAL EQPT, WHOLESALE: Hearing Aids

Audina Hearing Instruments....D.... 407 331-0077
Longwood *(G-8259)*
Miami....F.... 954 874-7707
Miami *(G-9991)*

MEDICAL, DENTAL & HOSPITAL EQPT, WHOLESALE: Med Eqpt & Splys

CMF Medicon Surgical Inc....G.... 904 642-7500
Jacksonville *(G-6273)*
Erchonia Corporation LLC....E.... 321 473-1251
Melbourne *(G-8827)*
Healthline Medical Pdts Inc....E.... 407 656-0704
Winter Garden *(G-19267)*
Intermed Group Inc....E.... 561 586-3667
Alachua *(G-10)*
Lane Care LLC....F.... 727 316-3708
Palm Harbor *(G-13744)*
Medone Surgical Inc....F.... 941 359-3129
Sarasota *(G-16255)*
Mmx Manufacturing LLC....F.... 786 456-5072
Miami *(G-10030)*
New World Holdings Inc....E.... 561 888-4939
Boca Raton *(G-642)*
Oscor Inc....C.... 727 937-2511
Palm Harbor *(G-13749)*
Parallax Health Sciences Inc....G.... 888 263-9799
West Palm Beach *(G-18987)*
Technicuff Corp....F.... 352 326-2833
Leesburg *(G-8176)*
Universal HM Hlth Indus Sups I....G.... 813 493-7904
Tampa *(G-18222)*
Vehicle Maint Program Inc....F.... 561 362-6080
Boca Raton *(G-776)*
Warehouse Goods LLC....E.... 877 865-2260
Boca Raton *(G-787)*

MEDICAL, DENTAL & HOSPITAL EQPT, WHOLESALE: Orthopedic

EM Adams Inc....D.... 772 468-6550
Fort Pierce *(G-4694)*
Imc-Heartway LLC....G.... 239 275-6767
Fort Myers *(G-4489)*

MEDICAL, DENTAL & HOSPITAL EQPT, WHOLESALE: Oxygen Therapy

Lor-Ed Enterprises LLC....F.... 352 750-1999
Lady Lake *(G-7328)*

MEDICAL, DENTAL & HOSPITAL EQPT, WHOLESALE: Safety

Cameron Textiles Inc....G.... 954 454-6482
Palm City *(G-13644)*

MEMBERSHIP ORGANIZATIONS, NEC: Charitable

Jade Tactical Disaster Relief....C.... 850 270-4077
Tampa *(G-17801)*

MEMBERSHIP ORGANIZATIONS, PROFESSIONAL: Accounting Assoc

Automated Accounting Assoc Inc....G.... 512 669-1000
Pensacola *(G-14094)*

MEMBERSHIP ORGANIZATIONS, RELIGIOUS: Pentecostal Church

Great Hse Mdia Group of Pbls I....F.... 407 779-3846
Orlando *(G-12788)*

MEN'S & BOYS' CLOTHING STORES

Back Country Inc....G.... 772 532-6174
Vero Beach *(G-18598)*
My Glam Choice Inc....G.... 786 586-7927
Miami *(G-10056)*
Perry Ellis International Inc....B.... 305 592-2830
Doral *(G-3458)*

MEN'S & BOYS' CLOTHING WHOLESALERS, NEC

Apparel Imports Inc....E.... 800 428-6849
Miami *(G-9157)*
Carpe Diem Sales & Mktg Inc....E.... 407 682-1400
Orlando *(G-12552)*
Fresh Thread Llc....F.... 904 677-9505
Jacksonville *(G-6416)*
Indigo Mountain Inc....G.... 239 947-0023
Naples *(G-11285)*

Official Gear Company Inc....G.... 407 721-9110
Ormond Beach *(G-13387)*
Pattern Grading & Marker Svcs....G.... 305 495-9963
Miramar *(G-11027)*
Sarah Louise Inc....F.... 941 377-9656
Sarasota *(G-16573)*
Stush AP USA/Stush Style LLC....F.... 404 940-3445
Sunrise *(G-17180)*
Vf Imagewear Inc....G.... 813 671-2986
Riverview *(G-15286)*

MEN'S & BOYS' SPORTSWEAR CLOTHING STORES

Resort Poolside Shops Inc....G.... 407 256-5853
Belle Isle *(G-358)*

MEN'S & BOYS' SPORTSWEAR WHOLESALERS

Rock N Roll Custom Screened S....G.... 727 528-2111
Pinellas Park *(G-14385)*
Spirit Sales Corporation....G.... 850 878-0366
Tallahassee *(G-17329)*
T Shirt Center Inc....G.... 305 655-1955
Miami *(G-10455)*

MESSAGE CONCENTRATORS

American Impact Media Corp....E.... 954 457-9003
Hallandale Beach *(G-5169)*

METAL & STEEL PRDTS: Abrasive

Liquid Metal Products Inc....G.... 402 895-4436
Ocala *(G-11986)*
Tyrex Ore & Minerals Company....G.... 305 333-5288
Miami *(G-10520)*

METAL COMPONENTS: Prefabricated

Ferrera Tooling Inc....F.... 863 646-8500
Lakeland *(G-7685)*
Fertec Inc....F.... 850 478-6480
Pensacola *(G-14150)*
Sesolinc Grp Inc....F.... 772 287-9090
Stuart *(G-17009)*
U C Fab of Florida LLC....G.... 407 614-4210
Ocoee *(G-12094)*

METAL DETECTORS

Tectron Engineering Company....F.... 904 394-0683
Jacksonville *(G-6845)*

METAL FABRICATORS: Architechtural

Aerotec Aluminium Inc....G.... 407 324-5400
Sanford *(G-15988)*
Agri Metal Supply Inc....G.... 386 294-1720
Mayo *(G-8594)*
Airguide Manufacturing LLC....C.... 305 888-1631
Hialeah *(G-5276)*
Alenac Metals Corp....E.... 561 877-4109
Palm Springs *(G-13771)*
Alse Industries LLC....F.... 305 688-8778
Miami Gardens *(G-10734)*
Alumacart Inc....F.... 772 675-2158
Hobe Sound *(G-5721)*
Amazon Metal Fabricators Inc....F.... 321 631-7574
Cocoa *(G-1994)*
Ambiance Interiors Mfg Corp....G.... 305 668-4995
Miami *(G-9136)*
Architectural Metal Systems....F.... 407 277-1364
Orlando *(G-12486)*
Bachiller Iron Works Inc....E.... 305 751-7773
Miami *(G-9213)*
Bausch American Towers LLC....F.... 772 283-2771
Stuart *(G-16911)*
Buchanan Signs Screen Process....E.... 904 725-5500
Jacksonville *(G-6243)*
Caballero Metals Corp....G.... 305 266-9085
Miami *(G-9298)*
Caballero Metals Corp....F.... 305 266-9085
Miami *(G-9299)*
Casco Services Inc....F.... 727 942-1888
Tarpon Springs *(G-18288)*
Cement Precast Products Inc....E.... 352 372-0953
Gainesville *(G-4894)*
Chancey Metal Products Inc....E.... 904 260-6880
Jacksonville *(G-6261)*

Citory Solutions LLC ......F 407 766-6533
Orlando *(G-12584)*
Classic Iron Decor Inc ......F 904 241-5022
Jacksonville Beach *(G-6940)*
Creative Metal Studio Inc ......E 321 206-6112
Apopka *(G-127)*
D & D MBL Wldg Fabrication Inc ......D 772 489-7900
Fort Pierce *(G-4690)*
D G Morrison Inc ......F 813 865-0208
Odessa *(G-12114)*
David Viera LLC ......G 305 218-3401
Hialeah *(G-5365)*
Deland Metal Craft Company ......G 386 734-0828
Deland *(G-2967)*
English Ironworks Inc ......G 941 364-9120
Sarasota *(G-16420)*
Express Ornamental LLC ......G 813 486-0344
Tampa *(G-17653)*
Fluid Metalworks Inc -105 ......G 850 332-0103
Pensacola *(G-14155)*
Glassarium LLC ......E 786 631-7080
Miami *(G-9639)*
Halliday Products Inc ......D 407 298-4470
Orlando *(G-12794)*
Icon Welding & Fabrication ......E 941 822-8822
Sarasota *(G-16232)*
Ironworks Inc of Orange Park ......E 904 291-9330
Middleburg *(G-10907)*
Jace Fabrication Inc ......G 727 547-6873
Pinellas Park *(G-14355)*
JC Iron Omamental Works Inc ......G 561 508-5966
Mangonia Park *(G-8504)*
Kawneer Company Inc ......C 407 648-4511
Orlando *(G-12867)*
L & L Ornamental Iron Works ......F 561 547-5605
West Palm Beach *(G-18922)*
Largo Aluminum Inc ......F 305 852-2390
Islamorada *(G-6098)*
Laza Iron Works Inc ......F 305 754-8200
Miami *(G-9872)*
Liberty Aluminum Co ......E 239 369-3000
Lehigh Acres *(G-8197)*
Litecrete Inc ......E 305 500-9373
Miami *(G-9901)*
Mantua Manufacturing Co ......G 813 621-3714
Tampa *(G-17878)*
Mary Lame Wrought Iron & Alum ......G 727 934-2879
Holiday *(G-5747)*
Metal Creations Sarasota Llc ......F 941 922-7096
Sarasota *(G-16256)*
Metal Supply and Machining Inc ......F 561 276-4941
Delray Beach *(G-3107)*
Miami Railing Design Corp ......G 305 926-0062
Miami *(G-10009)*
Monumental Fabrication of Amer ......G 850 227-9500
Port Saint Joe *(G-15081)*
Naples Iron Works Inc ......E 239 649-7265
Naples *(G-11336)*
Ornamental Design Ironworks ......E 813 626-8449
Tampa *(G-17960)*
Ornamntal Metal Specialist Inc ......G 786 360-5727
Hialeah *(G-5552)*
RDS Industrial Inc ......F 321 631-0121
Cocoa *(G-2045)*
Regional Cnstr Resources Inc ......E 713 789-5131
Sarasota *(G-16558)*
Reich Metal Fabricators Inc ......E 561 585-3173
West Palm Beach *(G-19018)*
S & S Welding Inc ......F 863 533-2888
Bartow *(G-333)*
Saftron Manufacturing LLC ......F 305 233-5511
Bradenton *(G-1109)*
Screenco North Inc ......E 561 840-3300
Palm Beach Gardens *(G-13624)*
Sfa Systems Inc ......E 561 585-5927
Lake Worth *(G-7586)*
Southeastern Ornamental Iron ......E 904 292-0933
Jacksonville *(G-6790)*
Statements 2000 LLC ......G 561 249-1587
West Palm Beach *(G-19042)*
Sunbelt Metals & Mfg Inc ......E 407 889-8960
Apopka *(G-189)*
Tampa Tank & Welding Inc ......F 813 241-0123
Gibsonton *(G-5033)*
Toledo Doors Inc ......F 305 633-4352
Miami *(G-10487)*
US Ironworks Company ......F 850 588-5995
Panama City *(G-13959)*
Vasquez Custom Metals Inc ......G 813 248-3348
Tampa *(G-18234)*
Vintage Ironworks LLC ......G 407 339-2555
Altamonte Springs *(G-83)*
W D Wilson Inc ......E 813 626-6989
Tampa *(G-18250)*
Wesco Partners Inc ......E 941 484-8224
Sarasota *(G-16325)*
Wilcox Steel Company LLC ......G 727 443-0461
Clearwater *(G-1939)*
Ymg Iron Work & Metal Design ......G 305 343-2537
Pembroke Pines *(G-14072)*

METAL FABRICATORS: Plate

Aluminum Tank Industries Inc ......G 863 401-9474
Winter Haven *(G-19298)*
American Aluminum ACC Inc ......E 850 277-0869
Perry *(G-14292)*
Broach Process Serving ......G 727 385-9467
New Port Richey *(G-11483)*
Central Metal Fabricators Inc ......E 305 261-6262
Miami *(G-9339)*
CJ Mulanix Co Inc ......G 716 423-8010
Clearwater *(G-1626)*
Coastal Machine LLC ......G 850 769-6117
Panama City *(G-13885)*
Duramaster Cylinders ......F 813 882-0040
Tampa *(G-17620)*
Formweld Fitting Inc ......E 850 626-4888
Milton *(G-10928)*
Greenco Manufacturing Corp ......E 813 882-4400
Tampa *(G-17728)*
Halliday Products Inc ......D 407 298-4470
Orlando *(G-12794)*
Hutchins Co Inc ......F 727 442-6651
Clearwater *(G-1722)*
Jacksonville Steel Pdts Inc ......G 904 268-3364
Jacksonville *(G-6512)*
Jim Appleys Tru-ARC Inc ......F 727 571-3007
Clearwater *(G-1743)*
Lizheng Stinless Stl Tube Coil ......G 888 582-8820
Tampa *(G-17853)*
Mantua Manufacturing Co ......G 813 621-3714
Tampa *(G-17878)*
Mid-State Machine & Fabg Corp ......B 863 665-6233
Lakeland *(G-7751)*
Mpc Containment Systems LLC ......D 773 927-4121
Deland *(G-3000)*
Ofab Inc ......D 352 629-0040
Ocala *(G-12019)*
Quality Fbrction Mch Works Inc ......F 386 755-0220
Lake City *(G-7379)*
Riw of Jacksonville Inc ......F 904 356-5635
Jacksonville *(G-6730)*
Ryan Manufacturing Inc ......F 386 325-3644
East Palatka *(G-3606)*
Serf Inc ......E 850 476-8203
Cantonment *(G-1347)*
Spencer Fabrications Inc ......E 352 343-0014
Tavares *(G-18354)*
SPX Flow Technology Usa Inc ......G 352 237-1220
Ocala *(G-12058)*
Style-View Products Inc ......F 305 634-9688
Miami *(G-10426)*
Sunbelt Metals & Mfg Inc ......E 407 889-8960
Apopka *(G-189)*
Swiss Components Inc ......F 321 723-6729
Melbourne *(G-8953)*
Tampa Tank & Welding Inc ......F 813 241-0123
Gibsonton *(G-5033)*
Universal Metal Works Inc ......G 904 765-2600
Jacksonville *(G-6886)*
W D Wilson Inc ......E 813 626-6989
Tampa *(G-18250)*
Walker Stainless Eqp Co LLC ......G 352 343-2606
Tavares *(G-18360)*
World Stone and Design LLC ......G 850 235-0399
Panama City *(G-13965)*
Zahn Builders Inc ......G 718 885-2202
Lighthouse Point *(G-8214)*

METAL FABRICATORS: Sheet

A & A Sheetmetal Contr Corp ......D 305 592-2217
Doral *(G-3219)*
A&K Sheet Metal LLC ......G 786 351-8313
Miami *(G-9044)*
Aba Engineering & Mfg Inc ......F 386 672-9665
Ormond Beach *(G-13346)*
Abele Sheetmetal Works Inc ......F 561 471-1134
Riviera Beach *(G-15290)*
Accord Industries LLC ......D 407 671-6989
Winter Park *(G-19370)*
Adeptus Industries Inc ......F 941 756-7636
Bradenton *(G-982)*
Advanced Alum Polk Cnty Inc ......E 863 648-5787
Lakeland *(G-7626)*
Advanced Sheet Metal & Welding ......G 239 430-1155
Naples *(G-11150)*
Air Distributors Inc ......E 352 522-0006
Dunnellon *(G-3592)*
Airite Air Conditioning Inc ......E 813 886-0235
Tampa *(G-17395)*
AJF Sheet Metals Inc ......G 305 970-6359
North Miami *(G-11623)*
Alacriant Holdings LLC ......E 330 233-0523
Lake Mary *(G-7398)*
All Metal Fab Inc ......E 904 570-9772
Jacksonville *(G-6133)*
All Phase Construction USA LLC ......F 754 227-5605
Deerfield Beach *(G-2772)*
All Southern Fabricators Inc ......E 727 573-4846
Clearwater *(G-1574)*
American Metal Fabricators Inc ......E 561 790-5799
Mangonia Park *(G-8497)*
AMS Fabrications Inc ......F 813 420-0784
Oakland Park *(G-11776)*
Anvil Iron Works Inc ......E 727 375-2884
Odessa *(G-12102)*
Apache Sheet Metal ......G 954 214-4468
Weston *(G-19106)*
Architctral Shtmtl Fabricators ......G 407 672-9086
Winter Park *(G-19379)*
Architectural Metal Systems ......F 407 277-1364
Orlando *(G-12486)*
Architectural Metals S W FL ......E 239 334-7433
Fort Myers *(G-4366)*
B & K Installations Inc ......E 305 245-6968
Homestead *(G-5956)*
B&B Custom Sheet Metal Inc ......G 727 938-8083
Tarpon Springs *(G-18283)*
B&C Sheet Metal Duct Corp ......G 305 316-9212
Miami *(G-9211)*
Barrett Custom Designs LLC ......G 321 242-2002
Melbourne *(G-8776)*
Bausch American Towers LLC ......F 772 283-2771
Stuart *(G-16911)*
Bausch Enterprises Inc ......F 772 220-6652
Stuart *(G-16912)*
Bay Harbor Sheet Metal Inc ......F 813 740-8662
Tampa *(G-17457)*
Beautiful Mailbox Co ......E 305 403-4820
Hialeah *(G-5318)*
Birdsall Marine Design Inc ......E 561 832-7879
West Palm Beach *(G-18822)*
Blackwater Folk Art Inc ......G 850 623-3470
Milton *(G-10922)*
Breiner Machine Co Inc ......F 352 544-0463
Brooksville *(G-1216)*
C C Lead Inc ......F 863 465-6458
Lake Placid *(G-7486)*
Camcorp Industries Inc ......G 941 488-5000
Venice *(G-18536)*
Captive-Aire Systems Inc ......E 813 448-7884
Tampa *(G-17505)*
Carpenters Roofg & Shtmtl Inc ......E 561 833-0341
Riviera Beach *(G-15310)*
Cato Steel Co ......F 407 671-3333
Winter Park *(G-19391)*
Cemex Cnstr Mtls Fla LLC ......F 561 832-6646
West Palm Beach *(G-18838)*
Cemex Materials LLC ......D 561 746-4556
Jupiter *(G-7018)*
Central Metal Fabricators Inc ......E 305 261-6262
Miami *(G-9339)*
Century Metal Products Inc ......E 407 293-8871
Orlando *(G-12571)*
Cladding Systems Inc ......E 813 250-0786
Tampa *(G-17537)*
Clarkwstern Dtrich Bldg System ......F 800 543-7140
Dade City *(G-2426)*
Clear Vue Inc ......E 727 726-5386
Safety Harbor *(G-15490)*
Conklin Metal Industries Inc ......F 407 688-0900
Orlando *(G-12614)*
Corrugated Industries Fla Inc ......E 813 623-6606
Tampa *(G-17559)*
Custom Cft Windows & Doors Inc ......F 407 834-5400
Winter Springs *(G-19470)*
Custom Metal Specialties Inc ......E 727 522-3986
Pinellas Park *(G-14341)*
D C Inc Prtble Wldg Fbrication ......G 863 533-4483
Frostproof *(G-4859)*

Day Metal Products LLC.........G....... 352 799-9258
Brooksville *(G-1225)*
Daytona Sheet Metal and Air.........G....... 386 547-2422
Port Orange *(G-15015)*
Deans Cstm Shtmtl Fabrication.........G....... 813 757-6270
Dover *(G-3558)*
Decon USA.........G....... 440 610-5009
Tarpon Springs *(G-18292)*
Delta International Inc.........F....... 305 665-6573
Miami *(G-9451)*
Dills Enterprises LLC.........G....... 941 493-1993
Venice *(G-18542)*
Dixie Metalcraft Incorporated.........F....... 239 337-4299
Fort Myers *(G-4432)*
Dynamic Precision Group Inc.........E....... 772 287-7770
Stuart *(G-16934)*
Earnest Products Inc.........D....... 407 831-1588
Sanford *(G-16038)*
Electro Mech Solutions Inc.........E....... 813 792-0400
Odessa *(G-12118)*
Europa Manufacturing Inc.........F....... 954 426-2965
Coconut Creek *(G-2076)*
Flamco of Texas LLC.........E....... 904 783-8400
Jacksonville *(G-6392)*
Flash Roofing and Shtmtl LLC.........G....... 786 237-9440
Miami *(G-9574)*
Flite Technology Inc.........F....... 321 631-2050
Cocoa *(G-2022)*
Float-On Corporation.........E....... 772 569-4440
Vero Beach *(G-18617)*
Florida Aluminum and Steel Inc.........F....... 863 967-4191
Auburndale *(G-241)*
Florida Metal-Craft Inc.........F....... 407 656-1100
Winter Garden *(G-19264)*
Flotech Inc.........D....... 904 358-1849
Jacksonville *(G-6406)*
Fowlers Sheet Metal Inc.........F....... 561 659-3309
West Palm Beach *(G-18883)*
Frc Electrical Industries Inc.........G....... 321 676-3300
Palm Bay *(G-13514)*
G & K Aluminum Inc.........F....... 772 283-1297
Stuart *(G-16943)*
G F E Inc.........F....... 954 583-7005
Davie *(G-2530)*
Gautier Fabrication Inc.........E....... 941 485-2464
North Venice *(G-11758)*
Gizmos Lion Sheet Metal Inc.........F....... 561 684-8480
West Palm Beach *(G-18888)*
Gms Sheet Metal Inc.........F....... 772 221-0585
Palm City *(G-13659)*
H Lamm Industries Inc.........C....... 954 491-8929
Oakland Park *(G-11810)*
Halliday Products Inc.........D....... 407 298-4470
Orlando *(G-12794)*
Hendrix Maintenance & Repr LLC.........G....... 863 647-3511
Lakeland *(G-7704)*
Hollywood Design & Concepts.........F....... 954 458-4634
Yalaha *(G-19490)*
Hood Depot International Inc.........E....... 954 570-9860
Deerfield Beach *(G-2844)*
Hurricane Roofing & Shtmtl Inc.........G....... 954 968-8155
Margate *(G-8549)*
Hydro Extrusion Usa LLC.........B....... 904 794-1500
Saint Augustine *(G-15550)*
Ice Sheet Metal LLC.........G....... 850 872-2129
Panama City *(G-13916)*
Infinity Manufactured Inds.........F....... 727 532-4453
Largo *(G-7980)*
Integrated Metal Products Inc.........D....... 863 687-4110
Lakeland *(G-7713)*
International Dock Products.........F....... 954 964-5315
Hallandale Beach *(G-5191)*
Interstate Wldg & Fabrication.........F....... 727 446-1449
Clearwater *(G-1735)*
J & J Steel Services Corp.........G....... 305 878-8929
Medley *(G-8673)*
Jax Metals LLC.........G....... 904 731-4655
Jacksonville *(G-6519)*
JC Industrial Mfg Corp.........E....... 305 634-5280
Miami *(G-9789)*
Jim Appleys Tru-ARC Inc.........F....... 727 571-3007
Clearwater *(G-1743)*
JP Custom Metals.........F....... 786 318-2855
Miami *(G-9806)*
Keene Metal Fabricators Inc.........E....... 813 621-2455
Tampa *(G-17817)*
Kemco Industries LLC.........D....... 407 322-1230
Sanford *(G-16077)*
Kinship Precision LLC.........F....... 321 765-3531
Melbourne *(G-8859)*

Kling Fabrication Inc.........F....... 727 321-7233
Pinellas Park *(G-14359)*
Kustom Industrial Fabricators.........F....... 407 965-1940
Longwood *(G-8302)*
Kustom Us Inc.........F....... 407 965-1940
Longwood *(G-8303)*
L D F Services.........F....... 386 947-9256
Daytona Beach *(G-2678)*
Largo Aluminum Inc.........F....... 305 852-2390
Islamorada *(G-6098)*
Liberty Aluminum Co.........E....... 239 369-3000
Lehigh Acres *(G-8197)*
Lion Sheet Metal Inc.........F....... 561 840-0540
West Palm Beach *(G-18931)*
Lloyd Industries Inc.........D....... 904 541-1655
Orange Park *(G-12399)*
Manning Company.........G....... 954 523-9355
Fort Lauderdale *(G-4111)*
Marion Metal Works Inc.........E....... 352 351-4221
Ocala *(G-11992)*
Marlyn Steel Decks Inc.........F....... 813 621-1375
Tampa *(G-17883)*
Marlyn Steel Products Inc.........E....... 813 621-1375
Tampa *(G-17884)*
Memphis Metal Manufacturing Co.........F....... 901 276-6363
Tampa *(G-17900)*
Mercury Aircraft.........G....... 607 776-7002
Miami *(G-9979)*
Metal Creations Sarasota Llc.........F....... 941 922-7096
Sarasota *(G-16256)*
Metal Essence Inc.........G....... 407 478-8480
Longwood *(G-8312)*
Metal Products Company LC.........F....... 850 526-5593
Marianna *(G-8584)*
Metal Sales Manufacturing Corp.........F....... 904 783-3660
Jacksonville *(G-6597)*
Metal Supply and Machining Inc.........F....... 561 276-4941
Delray Beach *(G-3107)*
Metal Works By Gal.........G....... 407 486-7198
Sanford *(G-16087)*
Metalcraft Industries Inc.........E....... 352 680-3555
Ocala *(G-11999)*
Metalcrafters LLC.........G....... 904 257-9036
Jacksonville *(G-6598)*
Metalfab Inc.........F....... 352 588-9901
San Antonio *(G-15974)*
Metalworks Engineering Corp.........F....... 305 223-0011
Hialeah *(G-5507)*
Miami Tech Inc.........F....... 786 354-1115
Hialeah *(G-5514)*
Mid-State Machine & Fabg Corp.........B....... 863 665-6233
Lakeland *(G-7751)*
Modern Metal Systems Inc.........G....... 727 573-2255
Clearwater *(G-1790)*
N C A Manufacturing Inc.........D....... 727 441-2651
Clearwater *(G-1799)*
Naples Iron Works Inc.........E....... 239 649-7265
Naples *(G-11336)*
Nautical Structures Inds Inc.........D....... 727 541-6664
Largo *(G-8018)*
Normandin LLC.........F....... 941 739-8046
Sarasota *(G-16267)*
Northside Sheet Metal Inc.........G....... 850 769-1461
Panama City *(G-13932)*
Nova Sidera Metal Forming Corp.........G....... 786 717-7149
Miami *(G-10080)*
Ornamental Design Ironworks.........E....... 813 626-8449
Tampa *(G-17960)*
Osborne Metals.........G....... 727 441-1703
Clearwater *(G-1823)*
Osgood Industries LLC.........C....... 813 448-9041
Oldsmar *(G-12254)*
P & M Sheet Metal Corp.........G....... 954 618-8513
Pembroke Pines *(G-14053)*
Perez Industries Inc.........F....... 239 992-2444
Bonita Springs *(G-846)*
Pioneer Development Entps Inc.........F....... 239 592-0001
Naples *(G-11367)*
Pipewelders Marine Inc.........D....... 954 587-8400
Fort Lauderdale *(G-4169)*
Plotkowski Inc.........G....... 561 740-2226
Boynton Beach *(G-940)*
Preferred Metal Products Inc.........F....... 407 296-4449
Orlando *(G-13082)*
Premier Archtctural Shtmtl Inc.........G....... 727 373-8937
Odessa *(G-12143)*
Premier Fabricating Llc.........E....... 813 855-4633
Oldsmar *(G-12260)*
Production Metal Stampings.........F....... 850 981-8240
Milton *(G-10938)*

Rafab Spcialty Fabrication Inc.........F....... 407 422-3750
Orlando *(G-13112)*
Rankine-Hinman Mfg Co.........F....... 904 808-0404
Saint Augustine *(G-15594)*
Rapid Metal Products Inc.........E....... 863 701-0058
Lakeland *(G-7776)*
Reading Truck Body LLC.........E....... 727 943-8911
Tarpon Springs *(G-18323)*
Responsive Machining Inc.........F....... 321 225-4011
Titusville *(G-18457)*
Road Block Fabrication Inc.........G....... 708 417-6091
Fort Myers *(G-4584)*
S & B Metal Products S Fla Inc.........C....... 941 727-3669
Bradenton *(G-1108)*
S & B Metal Products S Fla Inc.........E....... 941 727-3669
Lakeland *(G-7783)*
S & S Welding Inc.........F....... 863 533-2888
Bartow *(G-333)*
Seacoast Air Conditioning & Sh.........F....... 772 466-2400
Fort Pierce *(G-4746)*
Sfi Inc.........E....... 407 834-2258
Orlando *(G-13177)*
Sheet Metal Unlimited.........G....... 772 872-7440
Stuart *(G-17011)*
Silver Sheet Florida Inc.........E....... 850 230-9711
Panama City *(G-13950)*
Sourcerers Inc.........G....... 954 530-2333
Plantation *(G-14556)*
Spectrum Engineering & Mfg Inc.........G....... 727 376-5510
Odessa *(G-12154)*
Spencer Fabrications Inc.........E....... 352 343-0014
Tavares *(G-18354)*
Stainless Fabricators Inc.........E....... 813 926-7113
Odessa *(G-12155)*
Stampco Inc.........F....... 904 737-6144
Jacksonville *(G-6807)*
Stanron Corporation.........E....... 954 974-8050
Fort Lauderdale *(G-4257)*
Steel City Inc.........F....... 850 785-9596
Panama City *(G-13952)*
Sterling Industry LLC.........E....... 561 845-2440
Riviera Beach *(G-15379)*
Straightline Metals.........G....... 407 988-2353
Winter Springs *(G-19484)*
Sunbelt Metals & Mfg Inc.........E....... 407 889-8960
Apopka *(G-189)*
Sunshine Metal Products Inc.........G....... 407 331-1300
Altamonte Springs *(G-77)*
Superior Metal.........F....... 407 522-8100
Orlando *(G-13229)*
Superior Metal Fabricators Inc.........E....... 407 295-5772
Orlando *(G-13230)*
Tampa Metal Works Inc.........F....... 813 628-9223
Tampa *(G-18169)*
Tampa Multi Roll Sheet Metal.........G....... 813 340-3554
Tampa *(G-18170)*
Tampa Sheet Metal Company.........D....... 813 251-1845
Tampa *(G-18172)*
Taurus Chutes Inc.........G....... 954 445-0146
Oakland Park *(G-11846)*
Tejeda Sheet Metal & Aluminum.........G....... 305 609-5477
Hialeah *(G-5647)*
Tibor Inc.........E....... 561 272-0770
Delray Beach *(G-3150)*
Townsend Signs Inc.........G....... 386 255-1955
Holly Hill *(G-5761)*
Tri-H Metal Products Inc.........G....... 941 753-7311
Bradenton *(G-1130)*
Tri-Tech of Florida Inc.........F....... 727 544-8836
Saint Petersburg *(G-15944)*
Turbocombustor Technology Inc.........B....... 772 287-7770
Stuart *(G-17041)*
United Fabrication Shtmtl Inc.........G....... 407 826-1933
Orlando *(G-13292)*
Upton House Cooler Corporation.........G....... 305 633-2531
Miami *(G-10547)*
USA Sheet Metal Inc.........G....... 786 517-3482
Hialeah *(G-5668)*
Versatile Manufacturing Inc.........E....... 954 561-8083
Oakland Park *(G-11859)*
Versatile Manufacturing Inc.........F....... 954 561-8083
Oakland Park *(G-11860)*
W D Wilson Inc.........E....... 813 626-6989
Tampa *(G-18250)*
Wheeler Consolidated Inc.........F....... 772 464-4400
Fort Pierce *(G-4770)*
White Rose Installation.........F....... 772 562-6698
Vero Beach *(G-18683)*
Window Craftsmen Inc.........E....... 941 922-1844
Sarasota *(G-16641)*

METAL FABRICATORS: Structural, Ship

Artful Canvas Design Inc ....E 727 521-0212
Saint Petersburg *(G-15713)*
Bausch American Towers LLC ....F 772 283-2771
Stuart *(G-16911)*
Blue Marlin Towers Inc ....G 954 530-9140
Fort Lauderdale *(G-3858)*
Eastern Shipbuilding Group Inc ....A 850 522-7400
Panama City *(G-13896)*
Pipe Welders Inc ....D 954 587-8400
Fort Lauderdale *(G-4168)*

METAL FINISHING SVCS

Accurate Metal Finshg Fla Inc ....F 321 636-4900
Rockledge *(G-15392)*
Best Engineered Surfc Tech LLC ....D 407 932-0008
Kissimmee *(G-7223)*
Chem-Tek Metal Finishing Corp ....F 321 722-2227
Melbourne *(G-8788)*
Cya Powder Coating LLC ....G 727 299-9832
Clearwater *(G-1646)*
D R C Industries Inc ....G 954 971-0699
Pompano Beach *(G-14657)*
Eps Metal Finishing ....G 954 782-3073
Pompano Beach *(G-14682)*
Metal Spray Painting Powder ....G 954 227-2744
Coral Springs *(G-2281)*
Orlando Plating Co ....G 407 843-1140
Orlando *(G-13036)*
Poly Coatings of South Inc ....F 941 371-8555
Sarasota *(G-16546)*
Pozin Enterprises Inc ....E 727 546-8974
Clearwater *(G-1838)*
Quality Finishers Inc ....G 954 782-3073
Pompano Beach *(G-14822)*
Quality Powder Coating Inc ....F 941 378-0051
Sarasota *(G-16553)*
Seminole Metal Finishing Inc ....F 407 332-8949
Altamonte Springs *(G-72)*
Sintavia LLC ....G 954 474-7800
Fort Lauderdale *(G-4238)*
Stuart-Dean Co Inc ....F 305 652-9595
Doral *(G-3515)*

METAL MINING SVCS

American Aggregates LLC ....F 813 352-2124
Boca Raton *(G-420)*
Evolution Metals Corp ....E 561 531-2314
West Palm Beach *(G-18866)*
Nyrstar Us Inc ....C 954 400-6464
Fort Lauderdale *(G-4145)*
Osler Incorporated ....E 954 767-6339
Fort Lauderdale *(G-4152)*

METAL SERVICE CENTERS & OFFICES

Lloyd Industries Inc ....D 904 541-1655
Orange Park *(G-12399)*
LV Thompson Inc ....C 813 248-3456
Tampa *(G-17866)*
Metal Supply and Machining Inc ....F 561 276-4941
Delray Beach *(G-3107)*
Spectra Metal Sales Inc ....F 727 530-5435
Clearwater *(G-1887)*
Urban Metals LLC ....F 813 241-2801
Tampa *(G-18225)*
Vested Metals Intl LLC ....G 904 495-7278
Saint Augustine *(G-15631)*

METAL SPINNING FOR THE TRADE

Accurate Metals Spinning Inc ....G 305 885-9988
Medley *(G-8606)*
Metal Spinning Systems Inc ....G 305 252-7778
Miami *(G-9985)*

METAL STAMPING, FOR THE TRADE

Aero Precision Products Inc ....D 305 688-2565
Opa Locka *(G-12283)*
D & A Machine Inc ....G 407 275-5770
Orlando *(G-12642)*
ES Investments LLC ....C 727 536-8822
Clearwater *(G-1677)*
Florida Metal Services Inc ....D 727 541-6441
Largo *(G-7950)*
Gator Stampings Intl Inc ....D 941 753-9598
Sarasota *(G-16218)*
Griffiths Corporation ....D 407 851-8342
Orlando *(G-12790)*
Hudson Tool & Die Company Inc ....C 386 672-2000
Ormond Beach *(G-13378)*
Interlake Industries Inc ....G 863 688-5665
Lakeland *(G-7716)*
Interlake Stamping Florida Inc ....C 863 688-5665
Lakeland *(G-7717)*
Kwikprint Manufacturing Co Inc ....G 904 737-3755
Jacksonville *(G-6547)*
Masonite Corporation ....D 813 877-2726
Tampa *(G-17887)*
Mohawk Manufacturing Company ....F 407 849-0333
Longwood *(G-8313)*
P&A Machine ....F 407 275-5770
Orlando *(G-13042)*
Peterson Manufacturing Co Inc ....E 941 371-4989
Sarasota *(G-16544)*
Stanron Corporation ....E 954 974-8050
Fort Lauderdale *(G-4257)*

METAL STAMPINGS: Ornamental

Blue Water Dynamics LLC ....D 386 957-5464
Edgewater *(G-3614)*

METAL: Heavy, Perforated

Supply Expediters Intl Inc ....F 305 805-4255
Pembroke Pines *(G-14061)*

METALS SVC CENTERS & WHOL: Structural Shapes, Iron Or Steel

J & J Wldg Stl Fbrction Fla In ....E 813 754-0771
Auburndale *(G-246)*

METALS SVC CENTERS & WHOLESALERS: Cable, Wire

Meridian Cable LLC ....F 847 847-1128
Saint Augustine *(G-15568)*

METALS SVC CENTERS & WHOLESALERS: Iron & Steel Prdt, Ferrous

Pioneer Welding & Fabrication ....G 407 880-4997
Apopka *(G-170)*

METALS SVC CENTERS & WHOLESALERS: Rails & Access

United Rail Inc ....F 904 503-9757
Jacksonville *(G-6881)*

METALS SVC CENTERS & WHOLESALERS: Reinforcement Mesh, Wire

Metalhouse LLC ....G 407 270-3000
Orlando *(G-12962)*

METALS SVC CENTERS & WHOLESALERS: Steel

Bell Steel Company ....D 850 432-1545
Pensacola *(G-14097)*
Central Fla Stl Bldg & Sup LLC ....G 352 266-6795
Ocala *(G-11899)*
Metals USA Holdings Corp ....A 954 202-4000
Fort Lauderdale *(G-4118)*
Modern Welding Company Fla Inc ....D 407 843-1270
Orlando *(G-12975)*
Quality Industries America Inc ....G 386 755-0220
Lake City *(G-7380)*
Steel City Inc ....F 850 785-9596
Panama City *(G-13952)*

METALS SVC CTRS & WHOLESALERS: Aluminum Bars, Rods, Etc

Ceco & Associates Inc ....G 727 528-0075
Riverview *(G-15266)*
Eastern Metal Supply Inc ....F 863 682-6660
Lakeland *(G-7679)*

METALS: Honeycombed

Composite Essential Mtls LLC ....G 772 344-0034
Port St Lucie *(G-15172)*

METALS: Precious NEC

Allliance Precious Mtls Group ....G 954 480-8676
Coconut Creek *(G-2069)*
CB Precious Metals LLC ....F 407 790-1585
Longwood *(G-8264)*
I J Precious Metals Inc ....G 305 371-3009
Miami *(G-9724)*
Palm Beach Precious Metals ....G 561 662-6025
Palm Springs *(G-13779)*
Pmr Gestion Inc ....G 561 501-5190
Delray Beach *(G-3120)*
Precious Metal Group LLC ....G 904 219-8358
Jacksonville *(G-6680)*
Precious Metals Buyers LLC ....G 813 880-9544
Tampa *(G-18001)*
Precious Metals Buyers LLC ....F 813 417-7857
Tampa *(G-18002)*
Precious Metals Xchange Group ....G 305 556-1696
Doral *(G-3466)*
Premium Precious Metals LLC ....G 954 367-7513
Fort Lauderdale *(G-4178)*
Republic Metals Corporation ....C 305 685-8505
Opa Locka *(G-12354)*
SPI LLC ....C 786 907-4022
Miami *(G-10405)*

METALS: Primary Nonferrous, NEC

C C Lead Inc ....F 863 465-6458
Lake Placid *(G-7486)*
Flotech Inc ....D 904 358-1849
Jacksonville *(G-6406)*

METALWORK: Miscellaneous

Ace Construction Management ....G 407 704-7803
Orlando *(G-12429)*
Alumacart Inc ....F 772 675-2158
Hobe Sound *(G-5721)*
Anvil Iron Works Inc ....E 727 375-2884
Odessa *(G-12102)*
Gerdau Ameristeel US Inc ....B 813 752-7550
Plant City *(G-14434)*
GMF Industries Inc ....D 863 646-5081
Lakeland *(G-7700)*
Hanaya LLC ....F 904 285-7575
Ponte Vedra Beach *(G-14941)*
Mid Florida Steel Corp ....E 321 632-8228
Cocoa *(G-2036)*
Midwest Mtal Fbrction Cstm Rll ....E 317 769-6489
North Fort Myers *(G-11599)*
Specialty Fabrication LLC ....E 863 683-0708
Lakeland *(G-7803)*
Structall Building Systems Inc ....E 813 855-2627
Oldsmar *(G-12269)*
Tri Tech Metal Inc ....G 727 946-1229
New Port Richey *(G-11516)*

METALWORK: Ornamental

AMD Ornamental Inc ....G 239 458-7437
Cape Coral *(G-1378)*
Artistic Welding Inc ....G 954 563-3098
Oakland Park *(G-11782)*
Arts Work Unlimited Inc ....G 305 247-9257
Miami *(G-9175)*
Custom Metal Creations LLC ....G 772 807-0000
Fort Pierce *(G-4689)*
Edwards Ornamental Iron Inc ....F 904 354-4282
Jacksonville *(G-6355)*
Gurtan Designs ....G 954 972-6100
Pompano Beach *(G-14719)*
Hernandez Ornamental Inc ....G 305 592-7296
Doral *(G-3381)*
J A Custom ....G 561 615-4680
West Palm Beach *(G-18910)*
M&B Steel Fabricators Inc ....F 407 486-1774
Orlando *(G-12942)*
Shanker Industries Realty Inc ....G 631 940-9889
West Palm Beach *(G-19029)*
Southern Aluminum Inc ....F 239 275-3367
Cape Coral *(G-1474)*
Wonderland Products Inc ....G 904 786-0144
Jacksonville *(G-6927)*

METALWORKING MACHINERY WHOLESALERS

Lloyd Industries Inc ....D 904 541-1655
Orange Park *(G-12399)*

METEOROLOGIC TRACKING SYSTEMS

Embrace Telecom Inc ....F 866 933-8986
Fort Lauderdale *(G-3969)*

METERING DEVICES: Gas Meters, Domestic & Large Cap, Indl

Ronaele Mustang Inc.....G....... 954 319-7433
Tamarac *(G-17367)*

METERING DEVICES: Measuring, Mechanical

Edc Corporation.....G....... 386 951-4075
Deland *(G-2973)*
Qualitest USA Lc.....F....... 877 884-8378
Fort Lauderdale *(G-4188)*

METERING DEVICES: Water Quality Monitoring & Control Systems

Elster Amco Water LLC.....F....... 352 369-6500
Ocala *(G-11931)*
Fewtek Inc.....F....... 727 736-0533
Dunedin *(G-3576)*

METERS: Altimeters

Alti-2 Inc.....F....... 386 943-9333
Deland *(G-2957)*

METERS: Liquid

Kus Usa Inc.....E....... 954 463-1075
Davie *(G-2542)*

METERS: Power Factor & Phase Angle

Powerficient LLC.....E....... 800 320-2535
Fort Lauderdale *(G-4172)*

MGMT CONSULTING SVCS: Matls, Incl Purch, Handle & Invntry

Hatalom Corporation.....E....... 407 567-2556
Orlando *(G-12796)*
Management Hlth Solutions Inc.....B....... 888 647-4621
Tampa *(G-17876)*
Rz Service Group LLC.....G....... 904 402-2313
Jacksonville *(G-6741)*

MICA PRDTS

Braden Kitchens Inc.....E....... 321 636-4700
Cocoa *(G-1999)*

MICROCIRCUITS, INTEGRATED: Semiconductor

Chip Supply Inc.....D....... 407 298-7100
Orlando *(G-12580)*
City Labs Inc.....G....... 305 909-7593
Miami *(G-9357)*
Florida Micro Devices Inc.....G....... 954 973-7200
Coral Springs *(G-2245)*
Icamr Inc.....G....... 407 742-4253
Kissimmee *(G-7252)*
Micross Minco LLC.....D....... 512 339-3422
Orlando *(G-12969)*
Xilinx Inc.....F....... 407 365-8644
Oviedo *(G-13462)*

MICROFILM EQPT

Ad Valorem Corporation.....G....... 561 488-9966
Boca Raton *(G-397)*

MICROMETERS

Microtex Electronics Inc.....G....... 386 426-1922
Weeki Wachee *(G-18704)*

MICROPHONES

Red Microphone.....G....... 818 806-8545
Miami *(G-10244)*

MICROPROCESSORS

Intelbase Security Corporation.....G....... 703 371-9181
Saint Augustine *(G-15557)*
Micro Control Systems Inc.....E....... 239 694-0089
Fort Myers *(G-4532)*
Spartronics Brooksville LLC.....D....... 352 799-6520
Brooksville *(G-1274)*

MICROSCOPES

A&C Microscopes LLC.....F....... 786 514-3967
Doral *(G-3221)*

MICROSCOPES: Electron & Proton

Jl Optical Inc.....G....... 386 428-6928
New Smyrna Beach *(G-11536)*

MICROWAVE COMPONENTS

API Tech North America Inc.....G....... 929 255-1231
Winter Park *(G-19377)*
Electrosource Inc.....G....... 954 723-0840
Plantation *(G-14510)*
L3 Technologies Inc.....G....... 305 371-7039
Fort Lauderdale *(G-4092)*
Logus Manufacturing Corp.....E....... 561 842-3550
West Palm Beach *(G-18934)*
Microwave Electronics.....G....... 561 432-8511
Lake Worth *(G-7570)*
RES-Net Microwave Inc.....E....... 727 530-9555
Clearwater *(G-1858)*
Smiths Interconnect Inc.....C....... 813 901-7200
Tampa *(G-18112)*
Smiths Interconnect Group Ltd.....G....... 805 370-5580
Stuart *(G-17016)*
Smiths Intrcnnect Americas Inc.....B....... 772 286-9300
Stuart *(G-17017)*
Spectrum Microwave Inc.....C....... 321 727-1838
Melbourne *(G-8941)*
Sv Microwave Inc.....C....... 561 840-1800
West Palm Beach *(G-19052)*

MICROWAVE OVENS: Household

Apollo Worldwide Inc.....G....... 561 585-3865
Hypoluxo *(G-6048)*

MILITARY GOODS & REGALIA STORES

M/V Marine Inc.....F....... 904 633-7992
Jacksonville *(G-6569)*
Telenetpro Inc.....F....... 954 333-8633
Pompano Beach *(G-14885)*

MILK, FLUID: Wholesalers

Dfa Dairy Brands Fluid LLC.....G....... 352 754-1750
Brooksville *(G-1226)*

MILLING: Cereal Flour, Exc Rice

Bay State Milling Company.....E....... 772 597-2056
Indiantown *(G-6071)*

MILLING: Chemical

Powder Systems Inc.....G....... 352 680-3558
Ocala *(G-12030)*

MILLING: Grains, Exc Rice

Southland Milling Co.....G....... 850 674-8448
Blountstown *(G-389)*

MILLWORK

1565 Woodworks LLC.....G....... 904 347-7664
Saint Augustine *(G-15510)*
A Izquierdo Enterprises LLC.....G....... 786 558-6657
Miami *(G-9040)*
A L Custom Wood Corp.....G....... 305 557-2434
Hialeah *(G-5257)*
AB Wood Work Inc.....G....... 786 701-3611
Miami *(G-9051)*
Accent Woodworking Inc.....G....... 727 522-2700
Largo *(G-7883)*
Actual Woodworking Inc.....G....... 305 606-7849
Naples *(G-11148)*
Adams Bros Cabinetry Inc.....D....... 941 639-7188
North Port *(G-11731)*
Advanced Millwork Inc.....E....... 407 294-1927
Orlando *(G-12433)*
AJ AZ Woodwork Inc.....G....... 561 859-4963
Margate *(G-8534)*
Akira Wood Inc.....E....... 352 375-0691
Gainesville *(G-4871)*
Al-FA Cabinets Inc.....F....... 813 876-4205
Tampa *(G-17396)*
Alda Stevens Woodworking.....G....... 850 897-4967
Niceville *(G-11562)*
All American Woodwork.....G....... 727 210-5214
Clearwater Beach *(G-1948)*
All Phase Custom Mill Shop Inc.....E....... 941 474-0903
Port Charlotte *(G-14959)*
Alliance Cabinets & Millwork.....G....... 407 802-9921
Deerfield Beach *(G-2774)*
Alpha Woodwork Inc.....F....... 954 347-6251
Pompano Beach *(G-14588)*
American Archtctural Mllwk LLC.....F....... 844 307-9571
Venice *(G-18533)*
American Fine Woodwork LLC.....G....... 954 261-9793
Davie *(G-2495)*
Architctral WD Wkg Mlding Div.....F....... 727 527-7400
Saint Petersburg *(G-15707)*
Architctural WD Pdts of Naples.....G....... 239 260-7156
Naples *(G-11167)*
Architectural Detail & Wdwkg.....G....... 561 835-4005
West Palm Beach *(G-18798)*
Architectural Spc Trdg Co.....D....... 850 435-2507
Pensacola *(G-14089)*
Ark Woodwork Inc.....G....... 561 809-7957
Boca Raton *(G-429)*
Art Staircase & Woodwork LLC.....G....... 239 440-6591
Cape Coral *(G-1384)*
Artemisa Luxury Mill Work.....G....... 305 439-3246
Medley *(G-8615)*
Artisan Wood Works Inc.....E....... 239 321-9122
Naples *(G-11172)*
Artisanis Guild.....F....... 239 591-3203
Naples *(G-11173)*
Artistic Doors Inc.....G....... 561 582-0348
Lake Worth Beach *(G-7604)*
Atelier Woodworking.....F....... 561 386-0811
Royal Palm Beach *(G-15461)*
Atlantic Custom Woodcraft Corp.....E....... 727 645-6905
Odessa *(G-12103)*
Atlantic West Molding & Mllwk.....F....... 239 261-2874
Naples *(G-11175)*
Aventura Custom Woodwork.....G....... 305 891-9093
North Miami *(G-11626)*
Bach Woodworking LLC.....G....... 651 329-1220
Boynton Beach *(G-882)*
Baer Family Woodworking.....G....... 954 297-2991
Hollywood *(G-5783)*
Bari Millwork & Supply LLC.....E....... 954 969-9440
Pompano Beach *(G-14615)*
Bay Meadow Architectural Mllwk.....E....... 407 332-7992
Longwood *(G-8261)*
Beyette Woodworking LLC.....G....... 727 254-8705
Seminole *(G-16742)*
Bindels Custom Woodwork Inc.....G....... 727 776-5233
North Port *(G-11733)*
Black Pearl Woodworks LLC.....G....... 954 214-0899
Loxahatchee *(G-8358)*
Blumer & Stanton Enterprises.....F....... 561 585-2525
West Palm Beach *(G-18825)*
Blumer & Stanton Inc.....F....... 561 585-2525
West Palm Beach *(G-18826)*
Bodhi Tree Woodwork Inc.....G....... 904 540-2655
Saint Augustine *(G-15523)*
Bosshardt Realty.....G....... 352 494-1400
Gainesville *(G-4889)*
Bosworth Millwork LLC.....G....... 305 942-9017
Key Largo *(G-7166)*
Brazilian Wood Works Inc.....G....... 786 468-5712
Miami *(G-9274)*
C & M Millwork Inc.....F....... 352 588-5050
San Antonio *(G-15971)*
Cabinet Design and Cnstr LLC.....G....... 850 393-9724
Pensacola *(G-14111)*
Carolina Woodworks Inc.....G....... 954 692-4662
Deerfield Beach *(G-2796)*
Casework of America Inc.....G....... 904 695-0996
Jacksonville *(G-6256)*
Casons Quality Care Svcs LLC.....G....... 386 365-1016
Lulu *(G-8368)*
Catharine E Armstrong.....G....... 321 704-5042
Indialantic *(G-6057)*
CG Quality Woodworks Inc.....G....... 305 231-3480
Hialeah *(G-5341)*
Chidsey Custom Woodworks.....G....... 561 632-9728
West Palm Beach *(G-18846)*
Classic Woodworks LLC.....E....... 772 398-6258
Port Saint Lucie *(G-15098)*
Cns Millworks Inc.....G....... 850 259-9206
Santa Rosa Beach *(G-16154)*
Coastal Awngs Hrrcane Prtction.....G....... 407 923-9482
Orlando *(G-12592)*
Coastal Door & Mllwk Svcs LLC.....F....... 561 266-3716
Delray Beach *(G-3061)*

Coastal Millworks Inc ....E 561 881-7755
West Palm Beach *(G-18848)*
Coastal Millworks & More LLC ....G 850 250-6672
Panama City *(G-13886)*
Coastal Woodwork Inc ....G 561 218-3353
Pompano Beach *(G-14639)*
Commercial Instllation Systems ....G 727 525-2372
Saint Petersburg *(G-15748)*
Commercial Millworks Inc ....F 407 648-2787
Orlando *(G-12606)*
Conrad Markle Bldr & Cbnt ....G 904 744-4569
Jacksonville *(G-6283)*
Conway Bldg Cstm Woodworks LLC ....G 407 738-9266
Kissimmee *(G-7232)*
Crawfords Custom Woodwork ....G 904 782-1375
Lawtey *(G-8124)*
Creative Concepts Orlando Inc ....E 407 260-1435
Longwood *(G-8268)*
Creative Custom Stairs ....G 941 505-0336
Punta Gorda *(G-15203)*
Creative Millwork Inc ....G 305 885-5474
Hialeah *(G-5357)*
Creative Woodworking Concepts ....E 727 937-4165
Tarpon Springs *(G-18290)*
Custom Cft Windows & Doors Inc ....F 407 834-5400
Winter Springs *(G-19470)*
Custom Install Solutions Inc ....F 916 601-1190
Boca Raton *(G-494)*
Custom Marine Joinery Inc ....G 954 822-6057
Oakland Park *(G-11793)*
Custom WD Architectural Mllwk ....G 786 290-5412
Miami *(G-9420)*
Custom WD Designs of Pensacola ....F 850 476-9663
Pensacola *(G-14122)*
Custom Woodworking ....G 850 319-4440
Panama City *(G-13890)*
Cwac Custom Woodworking & Cabi ....G 407 343-7774
Kissimmee *(G-7236)*
D & D Building Contractors ....G 954 791-2075
Davie *(G-2513)*
D&D Wood Working Inc ....G 407 427-0106
Orlando *(G-12643)*
Dade Truss Company Inc ....C 305 592-8245
Miami *(G-9431)*
Dana Andrews Woodworking ....G 561 882-0444
Riviera Beach *(G-15318)*
Decor Custom Woodwork LLC ....G 561 631-3240
Greenacres *(G-5079)*
Decosta Woodworking LLC ....G 508 802-7765
Winter Garden *(G-19260)*
Decowall ....G 813 886-5226
Tampa *(G-17597)*
Deep Ocean Woodworks Inc ....G 407 687-2773
Sanford *(G-16034)*
Defender Screens International ....G 866 802-0400
Sarasota *(G-16407)*
Design Custom Millwork Inc ....E 407 878-1267
Sanford *(G-16036)*
Designers Specialty Cab Co Inc ....E 954 776-4500
Miami *(G-9460)*
Diversified Woodworks LLC ....G 321 591-9935
Indialantic *(G-6058)*
Dmr Woodworks LLC ....G 850 969-9261
Pensacola *(G-14134)*
Doyles Fine Wood Working Inc ....G 813 763-7800
Plant City *(G-14426)*
DTF Woodworks ....G 954 317-6443
Fort Lauderdale *(G-3950)*
E & E Woodcraft Corp ....F 305 556-1443
Hialeah *(G-5384)*
Effearredi Usa Inc ....F 786 725-4948
Miami *(G-9503)*
El Custom Wood Creations Inc ....G 786 337-0014
Dania *(G-2444)*
Errico Custom Woodworks Inc ....G 561 306-0046
Jupiter *(G-7036)*
Evm Woodwork Corp ....G 954 970-4352
North Lauderdale *(G-11614)*
Evm Woodworks Corp ....G 954 655-6414
North Lauderdale *(G-11615)*
Evolution Woodworking ....G 407 221-5031
Geneva *(G-5020)*
Excell Woodwork Corp ....G 954 461-0465
Margate *(G-8542)*
Exquisite Wood Works By Al ....G 321 634-5398
Rockledge *(G-15410)*
Extreme Iron & Wood Work Inc ....G 407 925-2448
Lake Alfred *(G-7331)*
F & J Woodworking Inc ....G 239 455-8823
Naples *(G-11242)*
F W I Inc ....F 407 509-9739
Longwood *(G-8280)*
Fine Archtctral Mllwk Shutters ....F 954 491-2055
Fort Lauderdale *(G-3993)*
Fine Woodworking ....G 941 957-0863
Sarasota *(G-16429)*
Fine Woodworks ....G 954 448-9206
Weirsdale *(G-18705)*
First Imprssion Dors Mllwk Inc ....F 561 798-6684
West Palm Beach *(G-18872)*
Five Star Millwork Inc ....F 954 956-7665
Pompano Beach *(G-14696)*
Fj Cabinets & Woodworking LLC ....G 850 433-3925
Pensacola *(G-14152)*
Florida Frames Inc ....F 727 572-4064
Clearwater *(G-1688)*
Florida Heritage Wdwkg LLC ....G 941 705-9980
Sarasota *(G-16435)*
Florida Marine Joiner Svc Inc ....F 813 514-1125
Tampa *(G-17682)*
Foote Woodworking Inc ....F 941 923-6553
Sarasota *(G-16439)*
Fort Lauderdale Woodworking ....E 954 935-0366
Pompano Beach *(G-14704)*
Fraser Millworks Inc ....G 904 768-7710
Jacksonville *(G-6413)*
Fred M Bush LLC ....G 561 394-7292
Pompano Beach *(G-14705)*
Freddie Glenns Woodwork LLC ....G 850 556-7163
Tallahassee *(G-17258)*
Fry Trim Works Inc ....G 772 260-8486
Jensen Beach *(G-6969)*
Fuentes Custom Woodwork LLC ....G 941 232-0635
Sarasota *(G-16441)*
G & H Reclaim LLC ....G 904 879-2091
Callahan *(G-1324)*
Garcia Woodwork Entps Inc ....G 954 226-3906
Oakland Park *(G-11807)*
Gecko Woodworks ....G 239 738-8283
Fort Myers *(G-4467)*
GF Woodworks ....G 407 716-3712
Altamonte Springs *(G-48)*
Gleman Sons Cstm Woodworks LLC ....F 407 314-9638
Sanford *(G-16056)*
Gloval Displays Inc ....E 800 972-0353
Miami Gardens *(G-10742)*
Golden Wood Works LLC ....G 239 677-8540
Cape Coral *(G-1430)*
Goodwin Lumber Company Inc ....F 352 466-0339
Micanopy *(G-10901)*
Grand Woodworking Llc ....F 239 594-9663
Naples *(G-11266)*
Greatwoodworks ....G 239 200-4848
Fort Myers *(G-4472)*
Green Forest Industries Inc ....E 941 721-0504
Palmetto *(G-13801)*
Gulf Coast Custom Wdwkg Inc ....G 941 343-7883
Port Charlotte *(G-14984)*
Gulfshore Custom Woodworks LLC ....F 239 205-0777
Cape Coral *(G-1432)*
Gulfstream Woodwork LLC ....G 561 231-1810
West Palm Beach *(G-18892)*
Habibco Woodworks LLC ....G 954 659-8501
Weston *(G-19137)*
Handcraft Woodworking Inc ....E 954 418-6356
Deerfield Beach *(G-2835)*
Harbor Woodworks ....G 727 669-0808
Safety Harbor *(G-15495)*
Harlen S Woodworking ....G 850 774-2224
Lynn Haven *(G-8433)*
Harris Woodworks LLC ....G 561 543-3265
Palm Beach Gardens *(G-13594)*
Hollywood Woodwork Inc ....D 954 920-5009
Hollywood *(G-5845)*
Ilan Custom Woodwork LLC ....F 727 272-5364
Dunedin *(G-3580)*
Infinite Ret Design & Mfg Corp ....F 305 967-8339
Miami *(G-9741)*
Island Millwork Inc ....F 352 694-5565
Ocala *(G-11971)*
J & J Door Manufacturing Inc ....E 850 769-2554
Panama City *(G-13919)*
J B Woodworking Inc ....G 850 362-6362
Valparaiso *(G-18512)*
J L Finish Woodwork Inc ....G 954 609-4387
North Lauderdale *(G-11616)*
J-Coast Woodworks LLC ....G 561 262-6144
Jupiter *(G-7059)*
Jayco Woodworks Inc ....G 850 814-3041
Panama City *(G-13920)*
JB Wood Werks LLC ....G 239 314-4462
Cape Coral *(G-1440)*
Jehova Jireh Wood Work Prof ....G 850 862-7131
Fort Walton Beach *(G-4810)*
Jireh Woodwork Inc ....G 954 515-8041
Deerfield Beach *(G-2851)*
Jjc Woodworks Inc ....G 954 461-0088
Lauderhill *(G-8112)*
Jk2 Scenic LLC ....E 407 703-2977
Apopka *(G-150)*
JM Custom Millworks Inc ....F 561 582-5600
Mangonia Park *(G-8505)*
JM Custom Woodworking ....F 561 582-5600
Mangonia Park *(G-8506)*
John S Wilson Inc ....F 410 442-2400
Naples *(G-11299)*
Johnson Woodworking ....G 772 473-1404
Malabar *(G-8490)*
Jorges Finest Woodworks Inc ....G 305 491-4380
Miami *(G-9802)*
Jr Wood Works Inc ....G 305 401-6056
Miami *(G-9808)*
Juan Alemany Woodwork ....G 407 350-4072
Kissimmee *(G-7259)*
Kdavid Woodwork & Design Inc ....F 754 205-2433
North Lauderdale *(G-11617)*
Kevins Custom Woodworking ....G 727 804-8422
Palm Harbor *(G-13742)*
Kurts Custom Woodworks ....G 352 693-5407
Summerfield *(G-17059)*
L and TW Oodwork LLC ....G 305 742-4362
Homestead *(G-5978)*
Liberty Woodworking Inc ....G 727 642-9652
Pinellas Park *(G-14364)*
Lightstone Woodworking LLC ....G 727 424-2660
Seminole *(G-16750)*
Local Wood Inc ....G 561 410-2113
North Palm Beach *(G-11722)*
Local Woodwork LLC ....G 954 551-1515
Margate *(G-8556)*
Lombardis Woodworking ....G 305 439-7208
Miami Springs *(G-10894)*
Losobe LLC ....G 850 748-3162
Pensacola *(G-14196)*
Luxury Woodworking Soluti ....G 786 398-1785
Hialeah *(G-5492)*
Lyndan Inc ....E 813 977-6683
Tampa *(G-17867)*
Magnolia Millwork Intl Inc ....G 407 585-3470
Casselberry *(G-1510)*
Magruders Woodworking Inc ....G 954 649-0861
Tamarac *(G-17362)*
Mayworth Showcase Works Inc ....G 813 251-1558
Tampa *(G-17896)*
McKenzie Cabinetry Fine Wdwkg ....G 727 424-3707
Pinellas Park *(G-14367)*
McKinney Woodworking Inc ....G 904 591-1233
Saint Johns *(G-15679)*
Medeiros Custom Wood Work ....G 305 970-0472
Miami *(G-9965)*
Melbourne Architectural Mllwk ....F 321 308-3297
Melbourne *(G-8887)*
Mg Woodwork Inc ....G 561 459-7552
Pompano Beach *(G-14760)*
Miles of Wood Inc ....G 305 300-6370
Miami *(G-10021)*
Millennium Glass Inc ....G 305 638-1785
Miami *(G-10024)*
Millwork 360 LLC ....E 813 854-3100
Tampa *(G-17908)*
Millwork and Design Inc ....G 352 544-0444
Brooksville *(G-1253)*
Millwork Masters LLC ....F 727 807-6221
New Port Richey *(G-11501)*
Millwork Plus Inc ....G 352 343-2121
Tavares *(G-18348)*
Mirage Woodworking Inc ....G 305 606-7043
Hialeah *(G-5522)*
Mitchell Wood Works Inc ....G 727 321-7586
Saint Petersburg *(G-15856)*
Mjr Woodworks LLC ....F 407 403-5430
Apopka *(G-162)*
Mm Wood Designs Inc ....G 561 602-2775
Delray Beach *(G-3108)*
Mohamed Lamrana Jalloh ....G 347 305-5556
Miami Beach *(G-10695)*
Moran Woodworking LLC ....G 941 600-8842
Sarasota *(G-16513)*
N & N Investment Corporation ....E 954 590-3800
Pompano Beach *(G-14770)*

PRODUCT

Naples Woodworks Inc........G....... 239 287-1632
Naples (G-11340)
National Woodworks Inc........G....... 407 489-3572
Orlando (G-12992)
Natural Wood Works LLC........G....... 954 445-1493
Hialeah (G-5534)
Navarre Beach Woodworks........G....... 850 781-7884
Navarre (G-11470)
New Style Wood Work Corp........G....... 305 989-9665
Hialeah (G-5539)
New Woodworks Inc........G....... 954 520-4812
Oakland Park (G-11824)
Noble Wood Works........G....... 561 702-2889
Pompano Beach (G-14774)
Noble Woodworks Inc........G....... 561 702-2889
Boca Raton (G-645)
Ocean Woodworks Inc........G....... 904 246-7178
Atlantic Beach (G-225)
Old Town Timber LLC........G....... 904 217-7046
Saint Augustine (G-15583)
Orlando Commercial Millwork........G....... 407 549-2679
Sanford (G-16097)
Oscars Woodworks Inc........G....... 786 543-9200
Hialeah (G-5553)
Ouro Custom Woodwork Inc........F....... 954 428-0735
Deerfield Beach (G-2881)
Palm Beach Cstm Woodworks LLC........F....... 561 575-5335
Mangonia Park (G-8508)
Pat Clark Custom Woodworking L........G....... 941 376-1387
Sarasota (G-16536)
Pecky Cypress & More LLC........G....... 772 215-0430
Jupiter (G-7090)
Pestanos Woodworking LLC........G....... 954 448-3932
Miami (G-10155)
Peter Flagg Woodwork........G....... 561 307-4200
West Palm Beach (G-18994)
Phil Buckner Woodworks Inc........G....... 904 339-4475
Jacksonville (G-6671)
Pineapple Grove Woodworks........G....... 561 676-1287
West Palm Beach (G-18998)
Powell Woodworking LLC........G....... 407 883-9181
Sanford (G-16103)
Pradere Manufacturing Corp........F....... 305 823-0190
Hialeah (G-5563)
Prime Woodwork Inc........G....... 786 226-5646
Hialeah (G-5571)
Pro Millwork Installations........G....... 561 302-5869
Boynton Beach (G-945)
Pro Trim Millwork Inc........G....... 239 592-5454
Naples (G-11375)
Q & O Custom Woodwork Inc........G....... 954 391-8281
West Park (G-19097)
Quality 1 Appraisal Inc........G....... 786 859-4085
Hialeah (G-5587)
R Dorian Millworks LLC........F....... 561 863-9125
West Palm Beach (G-19016)
R K Constructors of Centl Fla........G....... 407 222-5376
Orlando (G-13110)
Ramos Woodwork LLC........G....... 954 861-7679
Deerfield Beach (G-2899)
Rbs Woodwork Corp........F....... 754 214-7682
Pembroke Pines (G-14056)
Redwood Custom Woodworking........F....... 407 529-9877
Orlando (G-13124)
Renaissance Custom Woodworking........G....... 561 212-9885
Delray Beach (G-3135)
Rich Woodturning Inc........F....... 305 573-9142
Miami Lakes (G-10851)
Richard Griggs Custom Woodwork........G....... 941 223-9376
Venice (G-18569)
River Craft LLC........F....... 407 867-0584
Orlando (G-13141)
Riverview Millworks Inc........G....... 904 764-9571
Jacksonville (G-6729)
Rolu Woodcraft Inc........F....... 305 685-0914
Hialeah (G-5605)
Rubinelli Woodwork Inc........G....... 954 445-0537
Boca Raton (G-695)
S + L Millworks Inc........G....... 813 413-6260
Lutz (G-8415)
S M I Cabinetry Inc........E....... 407 841-0292
Orlando (G-13152)
Sailfish Woodworks LLC........G....... 772 708-2791
Jensen Beach (G-6973)
Sailor Made Cstm Woodworks LLC........G....... 805 587-1197
Palm Bay (G-13533)
Sailor Made Custom Woodworks L........G....... 805 587-1197
Melbourne (G-8924)
Sarasota Architectural Wdwkg........F....... 941 684-1614
Sarasota (G-16574)

SCi Architectural Wdwrk Inc........F....... 954 247-9601
Fort Lauderdale (G-4224)
Second 2 None Wood Work Inc........G....... 786 299-3580
Miami (G-10319)
Security World Electronics........G....... 786 285-5303
Miami Gardens (G-10754)
Simpson........F....... 954 804-0829
Coconut Creek (G-2095)
SJS Woodworking LLC........G....... 561 704-5990
Wellington (G-18735)
Sloan Custom Woodworking LLC........G....... 850 766-5620
Tallahassee (G-17326)
Smiths Woodworks Inc........G....... 863 381-6564
Sebring (G-16709)
South Florida Woodworkers Inc........G....... 954 868-5043
Fort Lauderdale (G-4249)
Southwest Woodwork Inc........F....... 239 213-0126
Naples (G-11411)
Splinter Woodworking Inc........G....... 305 731-9334
Delray Beach (G-3145)
Stairways By Angel LLC........G....... 407 790-7181
Orlando (G-13210)
Stephs Woodworking LLC........G....... 772 571-2661
Vero Beach (G-18668)
Superior Door Works & More LLC........G....... 850 880-6579
Freeport (G-4852)
T and M Woodworking Inc........G....... 352 748-6655
Wildwood (G-19203)
T-M Fabrications LLC........G....... 386 295-5302
Ormond Beach (G-13404)
Tampa Contractors Supply Inc........E....... 813 418-7284
Tampa (G-18163)
Tarpon Woodworks LLC........G....... 407 446-9450
Orlando (G-13241)
Tcr Woodworks Inc........G....... 561 827-6676
Boynton Beach (G-968)
Teak Isle Inc........C....... 407 656-8885
Ocoee (G-12091)
Terrades Custom Woodworks Inc........G....... 305 316-2908
Hialeah (G-5648)
Thomas Rley Artisans Guild Inc........E....... 239 591-3203
Naples (G-11440)
Top Notch Wood Works Inc........G....... 954 445-7861
Miami (G-10491)
Tri-County Woodworking LLC........F....... 954 850-2222
Pompano Beach (G-14890)
Tru Craft Woodworks LLC........G....... 561 441-2742
Delray Beach (G-3152)
Trucraft Specialties Inc........G....... 561 441-2742
Delray Beach (G-3153)
Ultimate Wdwkg & Design Inc........G....... 754 223-4004
Oakland Park (G-11854)
Universal Wood Design........F....... 772 569-5389
Vero Beach (G-18674)
US Wood Work & Service........G....... 954 675-7153
Saint Johns (G-15683)
Vesten Woodworks LLC........G....... 407 780-9295
Saint Augustine (G-15632)
Viking Kabinets Inc........E....... 305 238-9025
Cutler Bay (G-2420)
Vision Woodworking Inc........G....... 407 493-9665
Groveland (G-5109)
Vreeland Woodworking LLC........G....... 727 365-0241
Palm Harbor (G-13768)
Waterhuse Archtctral Wdwrk LLC........F....... 786 534-4943
Miami (G-10596)
West Harbour Woodworking LLC........G....... 954 822-7543
Lauderdale Lakes (G-8096)
William Leupold Sr........G....... 727 527-7400
Saint Petersburg (G-15960)
Willie D Wood Works Inc........G....... 305 969-6522
Miami (G-10608)
Wishbone Woodworking Inc........G....... 239 262-7230
Naples (G-11459)
Witts Woodworking Inc........G....... 941 544-8812
Sarasota (G-16644)
Wonder Emporium Millwork Fab........G....... 407 850-3131
Orlando (G-13328)
Wood One LLC........G....... 727 639-5620
Saint Petersburg (G-15963)
Woodwork In Nova Architectural........G....... 954 448-2962
Margate (G-8573)
Woodwork Unlimited Inc........F....... 352 267-4051
Oxford (G-13466)
Woodworkers Cabinet Inc........F....... 239 593-1718
Naples (G-11460)
Woodworking Inc........G....... 727 442-6876
Clearwater (G-1943)
Woodworks By Mike Inc........G....... 850 567-2086
Tallahassee (G-17347)

Woodworks For You........G....... 386 717-4169
Deland (G-3036)
Woodworks of Tampa Bay LLC........G....... 813 330-5836
Tampa (G-18261)
Worthington Millwork LLC........G....... 800 872-1608
Panama City Beach (G-13986)
Y F Leung Inc........G....... 305 651-6851
North Miami Beach (G-11714)

MIMEOGRAPHING SVCS

G L E M Inc........G....... 727 461-5300
Clearwater (G-1697)

MINE & QUARRY SVCS: Nonmetallic Minerals

Kiskeya Minerals Usa LLC........G....... 305 328-5082
Miami (G-9823)
Standard Sand & Silica Company........G....... 352 625-2385
Silver Springs (G-16784)

MINE DEVELOPMENT SVCS: Nonmetallic Minerals

Diatomite Corp of America........G....... 305 466-0075
Miami (G-9465)

MINE EXPLORATION SVCS: Nonmetallic Minerals

H2r Corp........F....... 727 541-3444
Pinellas Park (G-14353)

MINERAL ABRASIVES MINING SVCS

Marion Rock Inc........E....... 352 687-2023
Ocala (G-11994)

MINERAL MINING: Nonmetallic

Acg Materials........G....... 405 366-9500
Marianna (G-8574)
Engelhard Corp........G....... 850 627-7688
Quincy (G-15248)

MINERAL WOOL

Magnum Venus Plastech........F....... 727 573-2955
Clearwater (G-1772)
Quiet Flex........F....... 352 429-3286
Groveland (G-5106)
Super Sensitive String Sls Co........E....... 941 371-0016
Sarasota (G-16612)
Tubos Inc........G....... 727 504-0633
Largo (G-8070)

MINERAL WOOL INSULATION PRDTS

Bigham Insulation & Sup Co Inc........E....... 954 522-2887
Fort Lauderdale (G-3852)

MINERALS: Ground or Treated

Active Minerals Intl LLC........G....... 410 825-2920
Quincy (G-15245)
Center American Longevity........G....... 305 777-1667
Miami (G-9338)
Chemours Company Fc LLC........C....... 904 964-1200
Starke (G-16890)
Diatomite Corp of America........G....... 305 466-0075
Miami (G-9465)
Imerys Perlite Usa Inc........G....... 850 875-1282
Quincy (G-15251)
Sanborn Resources Ltd........G....... 561 551-6161
West Palm Beach (G-19025)

MINING EQPT: Locomotives & Parts

Jimenez Enterprises Group........E....... 561 542-7709
Doral (G-3403)

MINING EXPLORATION & DEVELOPMENT SVCS

Benchmark Metals Inc........G....... 239 699-0802
Cape Coral (G-1388)
Tri-State Demolition LLC........G....... 850 597-8722
Tallahassee (G-17342)
US Precious Metals Inc........G....... 786 814-5804
Coral Gables (G-2202)

MINING MACHINES & EQPT: Concentration, Metallurgical/Mining

Tmg Manufacturing Corp....F....813 464-2299
Tampa *(G-18192)*

MINING MACHINES & EQPT: Washers, Aggregate & Sand

Blue Water Industries LLC....G....904 512-7706
Jacksonville *(G-6215)*
Bluegrass Materials Co LLC....E....919 781-4550
Jacksonville *(G-6216)*

MINING SVCS, NEC: Lignite

Vecellio Management Svcs Inc....E....561 793-2102
West Palm Beach *(G-19077)*

MISSILES: Ballistic, Complete

Lockheed Martin Corporation....A....407 306-1000
Orlando *(G-12920)*
Rocket Crafters Launch LLC....G....321 222-0858
Cocoa *(G-2049)*

MISSILES: Guided

Boeing Company....G....850 882-4912
Eglin Afb *(G-3641)*
Northrop Grumman Systems Corp....C....904 825-3300
Saint Augustine *(G-15578)*

MIXING EQPT

Premix-Marbletite Mfg Co....F....954 970-6540
Pompano Beach *(G-14810)*

MIXTURES & BLOCKS: Asphalt Paving

A & F Paving LLC....G....352 359-2282
Ocala *(G-11863)*
A&D Pavers LLC....G....954 449-0716
Pompano Beach *(G-14571)*
Aldanas Pavers Inc....G....305 970-5339
Miami *(G-9101)*
All In One Cmplete Hndyman Svc....F....954 708-3463
Deerfield Beach *(G-2771)*
All Pro Pavers Hardscapes Inc....G....954 300-6281
Pompano Beach *(G-14584)*
Artistic Paver Mfg Inc....E....305 653-7283
Miami *(G-9174)*
ASAP Brick Pavers and More....G....850 522-7123
Panama City *(G-13866)*
Atlantic Fence & Pavers LLC....G....386 334-6472
Edgewater *(G-3610)*
Beauty Pavers LLC....G....941 720-3655
Bradenton *(G-996)*
Best Pavers LLC....G....407 259-9020
Orlando *(G-12512)*
Blacklidge Emulsions Inc....G....850 432-3496
Pensacola *(G-14100)*
Brick Pavers By Mendoza Inc....D....772 925-1666
Vero Beach *(G-18604)*
Brick Pavers By Mendoza Inc....F....772 408-2005
Vero Beach *(G-18605)*
Brick Pvers Drveway Big Pavers....G....407 928-1217
Orlando *(G-12535)*
Brickland Pavers Inc....G....561 305-0325
Pompano Beach *(G-14622)*
Btb Refining LLC....G....561 999-9916
Boca Raton *(G-468)*
Btb Refining LLC....G....561 347-5500
Delray Beach *(G-3054)*
Butler Pavers Inc....G....941 423-3977
North Port *(G-11735)*
Central Florida Stone Pavers....G....407 227-3519
Orlando *(G-12570)*
CJL Bricks & Pavers Inc....G....305 527-4240
Miami *(G-9360)*
Clever Pavers Inc....G....239 633-7048
Fort Myers *(G-4398)*
Colossus Pavers LLC....G....239 601-5230
Cape Coral *(G-1405)*
Crystal River Quarries Inc....E....352 795-2828
Crystal River *(G-2375)*
Devcon International Corp....C....954 926-5200
Boca Raton *(G-499)*
Easy Pavers Corp....G....407 967-0511
Winter Garden *(G-19261)*
Express Pavers LLC....G....813 408-9938
Tampa *(G-17654)*
Flamingo Pavers Inc....E....850 974-0094
Freeport *(G-4845)*
Florida North Emulsions Inc....G....386 328-1733
Palatka *(G-13479)*
Freedom Brick Pavers LLC....G....863 224-6008
Lake Wales *(G-7511)*
Gardner Asphalt Corporation....D....813 248-2101
Tampa *(G-17703)*
Gardner-Gibson Mfg Inc....E....813 248-2101
Tampa *(G-17705)*
Gb Brick Pavers Inc....G....407 453-5505
Orlando *(G-12773)*
Gem Asset Acquisition LLC....F....904 268-6063
Jacksonville *(G-6430)*
Gem Asset Acquisition LLC....F....407 888-2080
Orlando *(G-12775)*
Gem Asset Acquisition LLC....F....813 630-1695
Tampa *(G-17706)*
Gemseal Pavement Products....F....305 328-9159
Tampa *(G-17707)*
General Asphalt Co Inc....C....305 592-6005
Miami *(G-9624)*
H & J Asphalt Inc....G....305 635-8110
Miami *(G-9684)*
Impressive Pavers Inc....G....321 508-9991
West Melbourne *(G-18775)*
J & A Big Pavers LLC....G....321 948-0019
Orlando *(G-12847)*
J & V Paverscorp....G....786 510-4389
Miami *(G-9779)*
JCB Brick Pavers Inc....G....941 739-6089
Bradenton *(G-1065)*
JD Pavers Inc....G....904 245-9183
Jacksonville Beach *(G-6946)*
Jml Pavers LLC....G....239 240-0082
Fort Myers *(G-4505)*
Jr Bricks Pavers Inc....G....813 516-3554
Tampa *(G-17810)*
Karnak South Inc....F....954 761-7606
Fort Lauderdale *(G-4084)*
La Pavers Inc....G....407 209-9163
Orlando *(G-12886)*
Lcf Pavers Inc....G....239 826-8177
Fort Myers *(G-4516)*
Local Pavers Inc....G....954 913-6916
Deerfield Beach *(G-2864)*
Melanie R Bush Pavers....G....772 501-7295
Vero Beach *(G-18643)*
Mendoza Pavers Corp....G....305 494-6794
Miami *(G-9974)*
Mfjr Pavers LLC....G....239 440-2580
Fort Myers *(G-4529)*
Most Valuable Pavers....G....239 590-5217
Cape Coral *(G-1450)*
Msh Brick Pavers Inc....F....941 822-6472
Bradenton *(G-1083)*
OB Inc....G....321 223-0332
Cocoa *(G-2039)*
Omega Prof Brick Pavers Inc....G....727 243-4659
Largo *(G-8020)*
P&G Pavers Inc....G....561 716-5113
Jupiter *(G-7089)*
Palermo Pavers Inc....G....239 263-0593
Naples *(G-11353)*
Pan American Cnstr Plant....G....305 477-5058
Medley *(G-8701)*
Pavemax....G....386 206-3113
Daytona Beach *(G-2693)*
Pavemax....G....407 494-1959
Orlando *(G-13054)*
Paver Action Inc....G....954 868-1468
Pompano Beach *(G-14786)*
Pavers Professional Inc....G....239 878-6989
Jacksonville *(G-6660)*
Pavers Solutions Inc....G....754 551-1924
Deerfield Beach *(G-2883)*
Paverscape Solutions LLC....G....850 497-5557
Miramar Beach *(G-11067)*
Paversealingcom Corp....G....407 951-6437
Longwood *(G-8321)*
Pbc Pavers Borba Co....G....407 296-7727
Orlando *(G-13056)*
Perfect Brick Pavers Inc....G....727 534-2506
Port Richey *(G-15062)*
Preferred Materials....G....727 573-3027
Clearwater *(G-1843)*
Prime Pavers Inc....E....941 320-7878
Sarasota *(G-16547)*
Propavers LLC....G....904 403-9033
Fleming Island *(G-3764)*
Quantena Energy Productgs....F....352 332-6630
Gainesville *(G-4985)*
RG Groundworks LLC....G....352 474-7949
Newberry *(G-11560)*
Riani Pavers Inc....G....239 321-1875
Fort Myers *(G-4583)*
Riley Coatings & Pavers LLC....G....352 598-9520
Ocala *(G-12038)*
Rock Brick Pavers Inc....G....407 692-6816
Orlando *(G-13144)*
Southern Pavers LLC....G....239 940-3671
Fort Myers *(G-4607)*
Spiegel Pavers Inc....G....954 687-5797
Pompano Beach *(G-14866)*
Spiegel Pavers Inc....G....954 687-5797
Coral Springs *(G-2315)*
Standard Industries Inc....D....813 248-7000
Tampa *(G-18129)*
Suncoast Pavers Inc....G....352 754-3875
Beverly Hills *(G-379)*
Sunset Pavers Inc....G....239 208-7293
Fort Myers *(G-4618)*
Superior Asphalt Inc....D....941 755-2850
Bradenton *(G-1123)*
Symmetry Pavers Inc....G....813 340-0724
Lutz *(G-8420)*
Terra Nova Pvers Hrdscape Slto....G....904 662-2999
Jacksonville *(G-6847)*
Tikal Pavers Inc....G....850 892-2207
Defuniak Springs *(G-2949)*
Total Pavers Corp....F....561 902-7665
Port Saint Lucie *(G-15154)*
Tremron LLC....F....863 491-0990
Arcadia *(G-206)*
Tsb Emulsions LLC....G....904 249-5115
Neptune Beach *(G-11478)*
Universal Paverscapes LLC....G....904 428-2010
Jacksonville *(G-6887)*
Yolo Consulting LLC....G....954 993-4517
Pembroke Pines *(G-14073)*
Zaragoza Pavers Inc....G....239 273-6665
Fort Myers *(G-4658)*

MOBILE COMMUNICATIONS EQPT

Artex Computer Llc....G....407 844-2253
Miami *(G-9173)*
Brightsky LLC....F....239 919-8551
Naples *(G-11194)*
C E S Wireless Tech Corp....E....407 681-0869
Winter Park *(G-19387)*
Limitless Mobile Wholesale Inc....D....321 710-6936
Ocoee *(G-12087)*
Relm Communications Inc....C....321 953-7800
Melbourne *(G-8919)*
Tridor Group Inc....F....786 707-2241
Miami *(G-10506)*
TX Trading Inc....G....786 303-9950
Miami *(G-10518)*
US Mobile Pro LLC....G....973 365-1812
Orlando *(G-13298)*
Wpp Group Usa Inc....G....305 341-8132
Miami *(G-10623)*

MOBILE HOMES

America Trading Inc....F....305 256-0101
Miami *(G-9139)*
Brightman....G....386 752-4883
Lake City *(G-7349)*
Center Seal Inc....G....863 965-7124
Auburndale *(G-232)*
Chariot Eagle Inc....C....623 936-7545
Ocala *(G-11901)*
Clayton Homes Inc....G....850 785-3302
Panama City *(G-13881)*
Dills Enterprises LLC....G....941 493-1993
Venice *(G-18542)*
Eiq Mobility Inc....G....561 691-7171
Juno Beach *(G-6979)*
Good Rep Inc....G....407 869-6531
Longwood *(G-8285)*
Jacobsen Factory Outlet....G....386 438-8458
Lake City *(G-7362)*
Marlin Darlin Air LLC....G....727 726-1136
Belleair Bluffs *(G-363)*
Nobility Homes Inc....D....352 732-5157
Ocala *(G-12006)*
Southern Pines Inc....G....239 947-1515
Bonita Springs *(G-855)*
Tropic Isles Co-Op Inc....F....941 721-8888
Palmetto *(G-13831)*

Wayne Dixon LLC ....G.... 352 279-6886
Brooksville *(G-1291)*

MOBILE HOMES, EXC RECREATIONAL

Jacobsen Manufacturing Inc ....C.... 727 726-1138
Safety Harbor *(G-15496)*
Linman Inc ....B.... 904 755-6800
Lake City *(G-7365)*
Nobility Homes Inc ....E.... 352 245-5126
Belleview *(G-373)*
Realty Systems Inc ....F.... 386 439-0460
Flagler Beach *(G-3756)*
Rolling Greens Mobile Home Pk ....G.... 352 624-0022
Ocala *(G-12039)*

MOBILE HOMES: Indl Or Commercial Use

Tridor Group Inc ....F.... 786 707-2241
Miami *(G-10506)*

MOBILE HOMES: Personal Or Private Use

Florida Harbor Homes Inc ....F.... 941 284-8363
Englewood *(G-3677)*
Harbor Homes ....G.... 941 320-2670
Sarasota *(G-16458)*
Stone Harbor Homes LLC ....G.... 239 672-7687
Cape Coral *(G-1479)*

MODELS: Airplane, Exc Toy

Coastal Aircraft Parts LLC ....G.... 954 980-6929
Sunrise *(G-17106)*

MODELS: Boat, Exc Toy

C M I Enterprises Inc ....E.... 305 622-6410
Opa Locka *(G-12297)*
Maritime Replicas America Inc ....G.... 305 386-1958
Hialeah *(G-5504)*

MODELS: General, Exc Toy

Designer Services of ....G.... 772 286-0855
Stuart *(G-16932)*
Hollywood Cllctibles Group LLC ....G.... 407 985-4613
Orlando *(G-12806)*
Scale Models Arts & Tech ....F.... 305 949-1706
North Miami Beach *(G-11704)*

MODULES: Computer Logic

David S Stoyka ....G.... 561 848-2599
Riviera Beach *(G-15319)*

MODULES: Solid State

Analog Modules Inc ....D.... 407 339-4355
Longwood *(G-8255)*
Smiths Interconnect Inc ....C.... 813 901-7200
Tampa *(G-18111)*

MOLDED RUBBER PRDTS

Medfab Corporation ....G.... 813 854-2646
Oldsmar *(G-12247)*

MOLDING COMPOUNDS

American Sperior Compounds Inc ....G.... 716 873-1209
Lithia *(G-8215)*
Made In America Plastic Inc ....G.... 786 310-7816
Medley *(G-8680)*
Southern Plastics & Rubber Co ....E.... 386 672-1167
Ormond Beach *(G-13401)*
Tupperware Products Inc ....E.... 407 826-5050
Orlando *(G-13281)*

MOLDING SAND MINING

Marine Concepts ....F.... 239 283-0800
Cape Coral *(G-1445)*

MOLDINGS & TRIM: Metal, Exc Automobile

Oliveri Woodworking Inc ....F.... 561 478-7233
West Palm Beach *(G-18972)*
Windsor Window Company ....F.... 321 385-3880
Titusville *(G-18473)*

MOLDINGS OR TRIM: Automobile, Stamped Metal

Florida Production Engrg Inc ....C.... 386 677-2566
Ormond Beach *(G-13372)*
Sterling Eqp Mfg Centl Fla Inc ....G.... 352 669-3255
Umatilla *(G-18503)*

MOLDINGS, ARCHITECTURAL: Plaster Of Paris

Cutting Edge Archtctral Mldngs ....G.... 941 727-1111
Bradenton *(G-1027)*
Cutting Edge Moldings LLC ....G.... 734 649-1500
Sarasota *(G-16201)*
Sun-Rock Inc ....F.... 727 938-0013
Tarpon Springs *(G-18327)*
Tim Hardy Plaster Moldings LLC ....G.... 239 877-8434
Naples *(G-11441)*
Tri Inc ....F.... 813 267-1201
Tampa *(G-18199)*

MOLDINGS: Picture Frame

Artworks International ....G.... 561 833-9165
West Palm Beach *(G-18804)*
Cinega Custom Framing & Design ....E.... 904 495-1846
Orange Park *(G-12386)*
Duncanmatthews LLC ....G.... 813 466-8290
Tampa *(G-17619)*
Jem Art Inc ....E.... 954 966-7078
Sunrise *(G-17136)*

MOLDS: Indl

American Mfg & Mch Inc ....D.... 352 728-2222
Okahumpka *(G-12168)*
American Mold Removal Inc ....G.... 561 575-7757
Loxahatchee *(G-8357)*
Ameritech Die & Mold South Inc ....G.... 386 677-1770
Ormond Beach *(G-13348)*
Apex Flood Fire Mold Clnup Inc ....G.... 305 975-1710
Boca Raton *(G-427)*
Armoury Property & Mold Inspec ....G.... 813 503-9765
Port Charlotte *(G-14963)*
C & C Tool & Mold ....G.... 863 699-5337
Lake Placid *(G-7485)*
Cavaform International LLC ....D.... 727 384-3676
Saint Petersburg *(G-15741)*
Certified Mold Treatment LLC ....G.... 305 879-1839
Summerland Key *(G-17065)*
Complete Mold Remediators Inc ....G.... 305 903-8885
Homestead *(G-5958)*
D M T Inc ....F.... 321 267-3931
Cocoa *(G-2008)*
Danly Corporation ....G.... 305 285-0111
Miami *(G-9434)*
Diemold Machine Company Inc ....E.... 239 482-1400
Fort Myers *(G-4431)*
Emergency Mold Specialist LLC ....G.... 239 691-3157
Naples *(G-11236)*
Expert Mold Removal Inc ....G.... 407 925-6443
Tavares *(G-18336)*
Florida Mold Mitigators LLC ....G.... 772 633-3415
Vero Beach *(G-18618)*
Florida Mold Stoppers Inc ....G.... 954 445-5560
Davie *(G-2526)*
Fullerton 799 Inc ....E.... 727 572-7040
Clearwater *(G-1696)*
Gama TEC Corporation ....G.... 305 362-0456
Hialeah *(G-5423)*
M D Mold LLC ....G.... 941 214-0854
Port Charlotte *(G-14989)*
Mold Be Gone Plus ....G.... 239 672-5321
Fort Myers *(G-4536)*
Mold Busters LLC ....G.... 786 360-6464
Miami *(G-10036)*
Mold Expert ....G.... 954 829-3102
Coral Springs *(G-2286)*
Mold Pros Franchising Inc ....F.... 239 262-6653
Naples *(G-11328)*
Mold R US Inc ....G.... 954 850-6653
Hollywood *(G-5879)*
Oxygenix Mold and Odor LLC ....G.... 850 926-5421
Crawfordville *(G-2335)*
Papenfuss Holdings Inc ....G.... 239 775-9090
Naples *(G-11356)*
PMC Enterprises Mgmt Division ....F.... 239 949-6566
Naples *(G-11371)*
Precision Mold Restoration LLC ....G.... 239 699-3688
Cape Coral *(G-1455)*
Project Mold ....G.... 561 213-6167
Boca Raton *(G-676)*
Robert Petrucci Inc ....F.... 954 772-2333
Fort Lauderdale *(G-4211)*
Spaulding Craft Inc ....F.... 727 726-2316
Safety Harbor *(G-15505)*
Technamold Inc ....G.... 727 561-0030
Clearwater *(G-1910)*
US Mold Inc ....G.... 561 748-2223
Jupiter *(G-7138)*

MONUMENTS & GRAVE MARKERS, EXC TERRAZZO

Mc Monumental Group Inc ....G.... 305 651-9113
North Miami Beach *(G-11691)*
Monumental Air Inc ....F.... 954 383-9507
Coral Springs *(G-2290)*
Monumental Enterprises Inc ....G.... 305 803-8493
Pembroke Pines *(G-14048)*
Monumental Resolutions Inc ....G.... 407 973-3577
Saint Cloud *(G-15662)*
Wilsons Monument LLC ....G.... 850 743-8605
Quincy *(G-15257)*

MOPS: Floor & Dust

Youmop LLC ....G.... 248 343-2013
Lake Worth *(G-7600)*

MOTION PICTURE & VIDEO PRODUCTION SVCS

Man Enterprises 3 LLC ....G.... 561 655-4944
West Palm Beach *(G-18940)*
Sleepy Dragon Studios Inc ....G.... 561 714-6156
Cutler Bay *(G-2411)*

MOTION PICTURE & VIDEO PRODUCTION SVCS: Educational, TV

Edumatics Inc ....F.... 407 656-0661
Orlando *(G-12699)*
Protege Media LLC ....G.... 310 738-9567
Port Saint Lucie *(G-15131)*

MOTION PICTURE EQPT

Cinevise Inc ....G.... 305 232-8182
Miami *(G-9354)*

MOTION PICTURE PRODUCTION ALLIED SVCS

On-Board Media Inc ....D.... 305 673-0400
Doral *(G-3450)*

MOTOR & GENERATOR PARTS: Electric

AB Electric Motors & Pumps ....E.... 954 322-6900
Hollywood *(G-5764)*
Advanced Mfg & Pwr Systems Inc ....E.... 386 822-5565
Deland *(G-2953)*
Technet Corp ....G.... 305 582-5369
Doral *(G-3524)*

MOTOR REBUILDING SVCS, EXC AUTOMOTIVE

Electric Motors Lift Stn Svcs ....G.... 727 538-4778
Pinellas Park *(G-14345)*
Miami Compressor Rbldrs Inc ....F.... 305 303-2251
Miami *(G-9995)*

MOTOR REPAIR SVCS

Quality Driven ....G.... 941 923-3322
Sarasota *(G-16552)*

MOTOR SCOOTERS & PARTS

Adir Scooters Inc ....G.... 305 532-0019
Miami Beach *(G-10636)*
Pure Med Mobility Inc ....G.... 352 366-8008
Brooksville *(G-1263)*

MOTOR VEHICLE ASSEMBLY, COMPLETE: Ambulances

Rev Amblance Group Orlando Inc ....B.... 407 677-7777
Winter Park *(G-19441)*

Worldwide Auto Systems Corp.............F 954 439-6332
Hollywood *(G-5942)*

MOTOR VEHICLE ASSEMBLY, COMPLETE: Autos, Incl Specialty

Alevo Automotive Inc............................G....... 954 593-4215
Boca Raton *(G-411)*
Barron Boyz Auto..................................F 229 403-2656
Fleming Island *(G-3760)*
Delaware Chassis Works.......................G....... 302 378-3013
Stuart *(G-16931)*
Emergency Vehicles Inc........................E 561 848-6652
Lake Park *(G-7469)*
Giliberti Inc..F 772 597-1870
Indiantown *(G-6072)*
Liyanarchi Design LLC..........................G....... 954 330-5034
Windermere *(G-19235)*
Mike Cope Race Cars LLC.....................G....... 352 585-2810
Clearwater *(G-1787)*
Phelps Motorsports LLC........................G....... 239 417-2042
Naples *(G-11362)*
Revology Cars LLC.................................F 800 974-4463
Orlando *(G-13133)*
Rp High Performance Inc.......................F 561 863-2800
Riviera Beach *(G-15374)*
Uma Holdings Inc...................................E 786 587-1349
Hollywood *(G-5932)*

MOTOR VEHICLE ASSEMBLY, COMPLETE: Bus/Large Spclty Vehicles

Amer-Con Corp.......................................E 786 293-8004
Palmetto Bay *(G-13839)*

MOTOR VEHICLE ASSEMBLY, COMPLETE: Buses, All Types

Florida Bus Unlimited Inc.......................E 407 656-1175
Orlando *(G-12746)*

MOTOR VEHICLE ASSEMBLY, COMPLETE: Cars, Armored

Armour Group Inc...................................F 954 767-2030
Fort Lauderdale *(G-3823)*
F I B US Corp..G....... 239 262-6070
Naples *(G-11243)*
Metal 2 Metal Inc....................................G....... 954 253-9450
Palmetto Bay *(G-13850)*
Noguera Holdings LLC...........................G....... 305 846-9144
Hialeah *(G-5543)*
Nu Trek Inc..G....... 813 920-4348
Odessa *(G-12136)*
Square One Armoring Svcs Co..............D....... 305 477-1109
Miami *(G-10407)*

MOTOR VEHICLE ASSEMBLY, COMPLETE: Fire Department Vehicles

E-One Inc...B 352 237-1122
Ocala *(G-11928)*
E-One Inc...D....... 352 237-1122
Ocala *(G-11929)*
Pierce Manufacturing Inc.......................D....... 941 748-3900
Bradenton *(G-1097)*

MOTOR VEHICLE ASSEMBLY, COMPLETE: Military Motor Vehicle

Fea Inc...F 407 330-3535
Sanford *(G-16046)*
Oshkosh Corporation..............................G....... 863 603-4080
Lakeland *(G-7760)*

MOTOR VEHICLE ASSEMBLY, COMPLETE: Patrol Wagons

Emergency Vehicle Sup Co LLC............E 954 428-5201
Pompano Beach *(G-14678)*

MOTOR VEHICLE ASSEMBLY, COMPLETE: Personnel Carriers

Elite Enclosures......................................F 352 323-6005
Leesburg *(G-8154)*

MOTOR VEHICLE ASSEMBLY, COMPLETE: Truck & Tractor Trucks

Navistar Inc...G....... 305 513-2255
Doral *(G-3443)*

MOTOR VEHICLE ASSEMBLY, COMPLETE: Truck Tractors, Highway

Shirley Simon & Associates LLC..........G....... 813 247-2100
Tampa *(G-18097)*

MOTOR VEHICLE ASSEMBLY, COMPLETE: Wreckers, Tow Truck

Alert Towing Inc.......................................E 561 586-5504
Lake Worth *(G-7532)*
Arons Towing & Recovery Inc...............G....... 772 220-1151
Hobe Sound *(G-5722)*
Flints Wrecker Service Inc.....................G....... 863 676-1318
Lake Wales *(G-7509)*

MOTOR VEHICLE DEALERS: Cars, Used Only

Potnetwork Holdings Inc........................G....... 800 433-0127
Fort Lauderdale *(G-4171)*

MOTOR VEHICLE DEALERS: Trucks, Tractors/Trailers, New & Used

All Amrcan Trlr Connection Inc.............G....... 561 582-1800
Palm Springs *(G-13772)*
East 46th Auto Sales Inc........................F 407 322-3100
Sanford *(G-16039)*

MOTOR VEHICLE PARTS & ACCESS: Acceleration Eqpt

Creative Auto Boutique Llc....................G....... 407 654-7300
Oakland *(G-11768)*
Onaris...F 305 579-0056
Miami *(G-10101)*

MOTOR VEHICLE PARTS & ACCESS: Air Conditioner Parts

Commercial Duct Systems LLC.............D....... 877 237-3828
Thonotosassa *(G-18399)*

MOTOR VEHICLE PARTS & ACCESS: Body Components & Frames

Thule Inc...C....... 850 584-3448
Perry *(G-14317)*
Voodoo Fab LLC......................................G....... 727 916-0014
Holiday *(G-5752)*

MOTOR VEHICLE PARTS & ACCESS: Booster Cables, Jump-Start

Epower 360 LLC......................................F 305 330-6684
Miami *(G-9533)*

MOTOR VEHICLE PARTS & ACCESS: Cleaners, air

Dubbs Fresh Detailing LLC....................G....... 813 770-5194
South Bay *(G-16794)*

MOTOR VEHICLE PARTS & ACCESS: Clutches

Warden Enterprises Inc..........................G....... 954 463-4404
Fort Lauderdale *(G-4312)*

MOTOR VEHICLE PARTS & ACCESS: Cylinder Heads

Dover Cylinder Head of Jackson...........F .....
Orange Park *(G-12390)*
National Cylinder Services LLC............E 407 299-8454
Orlando *(G-12990)*

MOTOR VEHICLE PARTS & ACCESS: Electrical Eqpt

Advanced Automotive Designs..............G....... 561 499-8812
Delray Beach *(G-3040)*
Apollo Sunguard Systems Inc...............F 941 925-3000
Sarasota *(G-16343)*
Daytona Parts Company........................G....... 386 427-7108
New Smyrna Beach *(G-11532)*

MOTOR VEHICLE PARTS & ACCESS: Engines & Parts

Alper Automotive Inc..............................G....... 561 342-1501
Delray Beach *(G-3044)*
Gt Technologies Inc................................C....... 850 575-8181
Tallahassee *(G-17267)*
Gt Technologies I Inc.............................G....... 850 575-8181
Tallahassee *(G-17268)*
Hoerbger Auto Cmfort Systems L..........E 334 321-2292
Deerfield Beach *(G-2839)*
Kleen Wheels Corporation......................G....... 954 791-9112
Davie *(G-2541)*
Kysor Industrial Corporation..................F 727 376-8600
Trinity *(G-18487)*
Premiere Services Inc.............................F 678 815-6078
Tallahassee *(G-17310)*

MOTOR VEHICLE PARTS & ACCESS: Engs & Trans,Factory, Rebuilt

Avalanche Corporation...........................D....... 800 708-0087
Brooksville *(G-1213)*
Sun Coast Converters Inc.......................G....... 850 864-2361
Fort Walton Beach *(G-4833)*

MOTOR VEHICLE PARTS & ACCESS: Frames

Marden Industries Inc.............................F 863 682-7882
Punta Gorda *(G-15213)*

MOTOR VEHICLE PARTS & ACCESS: Fuel Pumps

Progress Rail Services Corp..................D....... 239 643-3013
Naples *(G-11376)*

MOTOR VEHICLE PARTS & ACCESS: Fuel Systems & Parts

National Carburetors Inc........................E 904 636-9400
Jacksonville *(G-6618)*

MOTOR VEHICLE PARTS & ACCESS: Gears

Coast Wcp...E 727 572-4249
Odessa *(G-12111)*
Gear Dynamics Inc...................................G....... 305 691-0151
Miami *(G-9619)*
Profile Racing Inc....................................E 727 392-8307
Saint Petersburg *(G-15891)*

MOTOR VEHICLE PARTS & ACCESS: Horns

Hornblasters Inc.......................................E 813 783-8058
Tampa *(G-17761)*

MOTOR VEHICLE PARTS & ACCESS: Lubrication Systems & Parts

Improved Racing Products LLC.............G....... 407 705-3054
Orlando *(G-12826)*

MOTOR VEHICLE PARTS & ACCESS: Manifolds

Professional Products.............................G....... 323 754-1287
Tampa *(G-18021)*
Wilson Manifolds Inc...............................E 954 771-6216
Oakland Park *(G-11861)*

MOTOR VEHICLE PARTS & ACCESS: PCV Valves

Shipping Depot Inc..................................F 813 347-2494
Tampa *(G-18096)*

MOTOR VEHICLE PARTS & ACCESS: Pumps, Hydraulic Fluid Power

Alpha Hydraulics LLC..............................G....... 561 355-0318
Riviera Beach *(G-15297)*

MOTOR VEHICLE PARTS & ACCESS: Trailer Hitches

B & B Trailers and Accessories............F....... 904 829-6855
Saint Augustine *(G-15520)*
Bulletproof Hitches LLC........................G....... 941 251-8110
Bradenton *(G-1004)*

MOTOR VEHICLE PARTS & ACCESS: Transmission Housings Or Parts

Alto Products Corp Al............................G....... 305 892-7777
Doral *(G-3242)*
Gfx Inc...E....... 305 499-9789
Miami *(G-9634)*
Style Crest Products.............................G....... 863 709-8735
Lakeland *(G-7809)*

MOTOR VEHICLE PARTS & ACCESS: Transmissions

JW Performance Transm Inc..................E....... 321 632-6205
Rockledge *(G-15425)*
Suncoast Rebuild Center Inc.................F....... 813 238-3433
Tampa *(G-18144)*

MOTOR VEHICLE PARTS & ACCESS: Water Pumps

Lusa Supplier LLC..................................G....... 305 885-7634
Miami *(G-9921)*

MOTOR VEHICLE PARTS & ACCESS: Wipers, Windshield

Pylon Manufacturing Corp......................E....... 800 626-4902
Deerfield Beach *(G-2898)*

MOTOR VEHICLE PARTS & ACCESS: Wiring Harness Sets

Iron Strength Corp.................................F....... 305 226-6866
Miami *(G-9772)*

MOTOR VEHICLE SPLYS & PARTS WHOLESALERS: New

B & B Trailers and Accessories............F....... 904 829-6855
Saint Augustine *(G-15520)*
Florida Dacco/Detroit Inc......................E....... 813 879-4131
Tampa *(G-17674)*
National Carburetors Inc........................E....... 904 636-9400
Jacksonville *(G-6618)*
Southeast Power Group Inc...................D....... 305 592-9745
Doral *(G-3507)*
Tradewinds Power Corp.........................D....... 305 592-9745
Doral *(G-3531)*

MOTOR VEHICLE SPLYS & PARTS WHOLESALERS: Used

Battery Usa Inc......................................E....... 863 665-6317
Lakeland *(G-7643)*

MOTOR VEHICLE: Hardware

AME Triton LLC......................................E....... 352 799-1111
Brooksville *(G-1209)*
Dse Inc...E....... 813 443-4809
Tampa *(G-17617)*

MOTOR VEHICLE: Radiators

AM Worldwide Corp................................F....... 786 313-3625
Doral *(G-3244)*

MOTOR VEHICLE: Steering Mechanisms

Ezy-Glide Inc...G....... 850 638-4403
Chipley *(G-1544)*
G-Car Inc..D....... 305 883-8223
Hialeah *(G-5421)*

MOTOR VEHICLE: Wheels

Jpm Import LLC......................................F....... 800 753-3009
Margate *(G-8553)*
Longs Wheel & Rim Inc..........................D....... 904 757-3710
Jacksonville *(G-6564)*
Rhino Tire Usa Llc...................................F....... 407 777-5598
Orlando *(G-13135)*
Southern Wheel & Rim Inc.....................F....... 904 786-7542
Jacksonville *(G-6799)*

MOTOR VEHICLES & CAR BODIES

Citrus Motorsports..................................F....... 352 564-2453
Crystal River *(G-2372)*
Composite Holdings Inc..........................E....... 321 268-9625
Titusville *(G-18424)*
Gar-P Industries Inc...............................E....... 305 888-7252
Medley *(G-8655)*
Jade Tactical Disaster Relief.................C....... 850 270-4077
Tampa *(G-17801)*
Lions Intl MGT Group Inc.......................F....... 813 367-2517
Tampa *(G-17848)*
Lippert Components Inc.........................G....... 267 825-0665
Bradenton *(G-1071)*
Moser Automotive...................................E....... 561 881-5665
Riviera Beach *(G-15350)*
Naples Hotrods & Prfmce LLC..............G....... 239 653-9076
Naples *(G-11334)*
Nev International Inc..............................F....... 407 671-0045
Casselberry *(G-1511)*
Pegasus Clean Air Mtr Cars Inc............G....... 954 682-2000
Fort Lauderdale *(G-4161)*
Pierce Manufacturing Inc.......................A....... 727 573-0400
Clearwater *(G-1832)*
Tesla Inc...G....... 305 535-7596
Miami Beach *(G-10719)*
Tesla Inc...G....... 754 816-3069
Dania Beach *(G-2473)*
Tesla Inc...G....... 305 774-5965
Miami *(G-10470)*
Total Performance Inc............................G....... 203 265-5667
Palm Coast *(G-13713)*
Trikaroo..G....... 800 679-3415
Orlando *(G-13272)*
Vac-Con Inc..B....... 904 284-4200
Green Cove Springs *(G-5075)*
Voxx Automotive Corporation................F....... 407 842-7000
Orlando *(G-13312)*
Voxx International Corporation.............B....... 800 645-7750
Orlando *(G-13313)*

MOTOR VEHICLES, WHOLESALE: Motor scooters

Best Price Mobility Inc...........................F....... 321 402-5955
Kissimmee *(G-7224)*
Pure Med Mobility Inc............................G....... 352 366-8008
Brooksville *(G-1263)*

MOTOR VEHICLES, WHOLESALE: Truck bodies

A&L Hall Investments Inc......................E....... 904 781-5080
Bryceville *(G-1296)*

MOTOR VEHICLES, WHOLESALE: Truck tractors

Heralpin Usa Inc....................................G....... 305 218-0174
Doral *(G-3379)*

MOTOR VEHICLES, WHOLESALE: Trucks, commercial

Iler Group Inc..F....... 813 600-1738
Wesley Chapel *(G-18749)*

MOTORCYCLE & BICYCLE PARTS: Saddles & Seat Posts

Hartco International................................G....... 386 698-4668
Crescent City *(G-2340)*

MOTORCYCLE ACCESS

A1a Sportbike LLC.................................G....... 321 806-3995
Titusville *(G-18407)*
Dirtbags Chopper...................................G....... 904 725-7600
Jacksonville *(G-6320)*
Phxtreme Corp.......................................G....... 305 594-2284
Miami *(G-10161)*
Ride Like Bessie Inc...............................G....... 904 580-3631
Jacksonville *(G-6724)*
Scott Fischer Enterprises LLC...............C....... 844 749-2363
Fort Myers *(G-4599)*

MOTORCYCLE DEALERS

Tampa Bay Powersports LLC.................E....... 813 968-7888
Tampa *(G-18160)*
Versacomp Inc..F....... 954 561-8778
Oakland Park *(G-11858)*

MOTORCYCLE DEALERS: All-Terrain Vehicle Parts & Access

Partsvu LLC..C....... 239 643-2292
Naples *(G-11359)*

MOTORCYCLE DEALERS: Motor Scooters

Vapor Group Inc.....................................F....... 954 792-8450
Miami *(G-10567)*

MOTORCYCLE PARTS & ACCESS DEALERS

Jay Squared LLC....................................F....... 386 677-7700
Daytona Beach *(G-2675)*
Shark Skinz...G....... 772 388-9621
Sebastian *(G-16672)*

MOTORCYCLES & RELATED PARTS

Dirtbag Choppers Inc.............................F....... 904 725-7600
Atlantic Beach *(G-219)*
Florida Grasschoppers...........................G....... 561 718-9346
Lake Worth *(G-7550)*
Grass Choppers......................................G....... 305 253-1217
Miami *(G-9659)*
Grass Choppers South Fla Corp...........G....... 786 586-2767
Miami *(G-9660)*
Kjs Hot Choppers...................................G....... 850 200-4860
Mary Esther *(G-8590)*
Nasty Choppers Inc................................G....... 941 234-7743
Venice *(G-18563)*
Powersports 911 Inc..............................G....... 813 769-2468
Tampa *(G-17998)*
Pro Street Choppers Inc.........................G....... 407 389-2047
Apopka *(G-173)*
Southwest Choppers Inc........................F....... 239 242-1101
Cape Coral *(G-1475)*
Wmr Cycle Performance Inc..................G....... 772 426-3000
Stuart *(G-17052)*
Worldwide Intl Trade LLC.......................E....... 305 414-9774
Hollywood *(G-5943)*

MOTORCYCLES: Wholesalers

Worldwide Intl Trade LLC.......................E....... 305 414-9774
Hollywood *(G-5943)*

MOTORS: Electric

Discovery Technology Intl Inc...............F....... 941 907-4444
Lakewood Ranch *(G-7843)*
Motor Magnetics Inc..............................E....... 727 873-3180
Saint Petersburg *(G-15861)*
Nidec Motor Corporation.......................C....... 954 346-4900
Coral Springs *(G-2297)*
Ray Electric Outboards Inc....................G....... 239 574-1948
Cape Coral *(G-1459)*

MOTORS: Generators

360 Energy Solutions LLC.....................E....... 786 348-2156
Miami *(G-9025)*
Acme Service Corp.................................F....... 305 836-4800
Miami *(G-9065)*
Advanced Manufacturing Inc.................E....... 727 573-3300
Saint Petersburg *(G-15691)*
All Power Pro Inc....................................G....... 904 310-3069
Fernandina Beach *(G-3730)*
American Generator Svcs LLC..............F....... 954 965-1210
Davie *(G-2496)*
Anko Products Inc..................................E....... 941 748-2307
Bradenton *(G-989)*
B & I Generators LLC.............................G....... 407 474-6216
Sanford *(G-16000)*
Fischer Panda Generators Inc...............F....... 954 462-2800
Pompano Beach *(G-14694)*
Fischer Panda Generators LLC.............E....... 954 462-2800
Pompano Beach *(G-14695)*
Fisher Electric Technology Inc..............F....... 727 345-9122
Saint Petersburg *(G-15780)*
G S Servicore Corp................................E....... 305 888-0189
Hialeah *(G-5420)*
GE Aviation Systems LLC......................B....... 727 531-7781
Clearwater *(G-1699)*

Generator Supercenter Orlando..........G....... 407 984-5000
Orlando *(G-12780)*
Genertor Sprcnter Suthwest Fla..........G....... 608 765-5177
Fort Myers *(G-4468)*
Grove Power Inc..........G....... 305 599-2045
Doral *(G-3375)*
Hts Controls Inc..........F....... 813 287-5512
Tampa *(G-17766)*
Hydrogen Diesel Prfmce Inc..........G....... 407 847-6064
Kissimmee *(G-7251)*
Hytronics Corp..........D....... 727 535-0413
Clearwater *(G-1725)*
Innovative Power Solutions LLC..........E....... 732 544-1075
Sarasota *(G-16239)*
JDM of Miami LLC..........G....... 305 253-4650
Miami *(G-9792)*
K&M Power Systems LLC..........G....... 866 945-9100
Riviera Beach *(G-15337)*
Marine Exhaust Systems Inc..........D....... 561 848-1238
Riviera Beach *(G-15346)*
Maymaan Research LLC..........G....... 954 374-9376
Hollywood *(G-5873)*
One Stop Generator Shop Inc..........G....... 561 840-0009
West Palm Beach *(G-18973)*
Peerless Wind Systems..........G....... 516 249-6900
Boynton Beach *(G-939)*
Perkins Power Corp..........F....... 904 278-9919
Doral *(G-3457)*
Robertson Transformer Co..........E....... 708 388-2315
Sarasota *(G-16560)*
Tampa Armature Works Inc..........C....... 813 612-2600
Tampa *(G-18157)*
Universal Generators LLC..........G....... 954 383-5394
Pompano Beach *(G-14903)*
US Generator Inc..........G....... 772 778-0131
Sebastian *(G-16675)*
Winans Electric Motors LLC..........G....... 863 875-5710
Auburndale *(G-255)*

MOTORS: Pneumatic

Evo Motors LLC..........F....... 813 621-7799
Seffner *(G-16725)*

MOUNTING SVC: Display

Creative Concepts Intl LLC..........F....... 888 530-7904
Fort Myers *(G-4415)*
Gloval Displays Inc..........E....... 800 972-0353
Miami Gardens *(G-10742)*
Ollo Usa LLC..........G....... 941 366-0600
Sarasota *(G-16531)*

MOUTHWASHES

H2ocean LLC..........F....... 866 420-2326
Stuart *(G-16953)*

MOVING SVC: Local

Los Primos Express Service..........G....... 786 701-3297
Miami *(G-9912)*

MUSIC BOXES

World Indus Resources Corp..........E....... 727 572-9991
Clearwater *(G-1944)*

MUSIC DISTRIBUTION APPARATUS

Fgmg International..........F....... 305 988-7436
Deltona *(G-3169)*
Time Is Money Campaign LLC..........F....... 352 255-5273
Clermont *(G-1975)*

MUSIC VIDEO PRODUCTION SVCS

Spanish House Inc..........E....... 305 503-1191
Medley *(G-8728)*

MUSICAL INSTRUMENTS & ACCESS: NEC

Englert Arts Inc..........G....... 561 241-9924
Boca Raton *(G-518)*
Flexshopper LLC..........E....... 561 922-6609
Boca Raton *(G-530)*
Gladium LLC..........G....... 305 989-2720
Cutler Bay *(G-2394)*
Isla Instruments LLC..........F....... 561 603-4685
West Palm Beach *(G-18908)*
Jatiga Inc..........G....... 727 793-0079
Clearwater *(G-1742)*
Lan Music Corp..........G....... 305 722-5842
Miami *(G-9855)*
MINd&melody Inc..........G....... 305 582-1006
Miami *(G-10025)*

MUSICAL INSTRUMENTS & PARTS: String

Sabine Inc..........D....... 386 418-2000
Alachua *(G-17)*

MUSICAL INSTRUMENTS WHOLESALERS

Jatiga Inc..........G....... 727 793-0079
Clearwater *(G-1742)*
Lewis-Riggs Custom Guitars Inc..........G....... 407 538-3710
Orlando *(G-12905)*

MUSICAL INSTRUMENTS: Bells

Belsnickel Enterprises Inc..........F....... 386 256-5367
South Daytona *(G-16798)*

MUSICAL INSTRUMENTS: Electric & Electronic

Dok Solution Inc..........F....... 727 209-1313
Largo *(G-7935)*

MUSICAL INSTRUMENTS: Guitars & Parts, Electric & Acoustic

Lewis-Riggs Custom Guitars Inc..........G....... 407 538-3710
Orlando *(G-12905)*

MUSICAL INSTRUMENTS: Marimbas

Marimba Cocina Mexicana II Inc..........G....... 321 268-6960
Titusville *(G-18446)*
Mode Marimba Inc..........G....... 561 512-5001
Jupiter *(G-7077)*

MUSICAL INSTRUMENTS: Mouthpieces

Variance Reynolds Mtc..........G....... 954 765-6320
Lauderhill *(G-8123)*

MUSICAL INSTRUMENTS: Strings, Instrument

Super Sensitive String Sls Co..........E....... 941 371-0016
Sarasota *(G-16612)*

MUSICAL INSTRUMENTS: Violins & Parts

Gatchell Violins Company Inc..........F....... 321 733-1499
West Melbourne *(G-18774)*

NAME PLATES: Engraved Or Etched

Labelpro Inc..........F....... 727 538-2149
Clearwater *(G-1757)*

NAMEPLATES

Hallmark Nameplate Inc..........D....... 352 383-8142
Mount Dora *(G-11103)*

NATIONAL SECURITY FORCES

Dla Document Services..........F....... 813 828-4646
Tampa *(G-17611)*

NATIONAL SECURITY, GOVERNMENT: Air Force

United Ntons Space Crps Mltary..........F....... 702 373-2351
Ponce De Leon *(G-14920)*

NATURAL ETHANE PRODUCTION

Pyrolyzer LLC..........G....... 561 400-1608
Boca Raton *(G-677)*

NATURAL GAS COMPRESSING SVC, On-Site

Epoc CNG LLC..........G....... 561 706-4140
Fort Lauderdale *(G-3973)*
Hoerbiger America Holding Inc..........B....... 954 422-9850
Deerfield Beach *(G-2840)*
Hoerbiger America Holding Inc..........A....... 954 422-9850
Deerfield Beach *(G-2841)*

NATURAL GAS LIQUIDS PRODUCTION

Mar-Co Gas Services Inc..........G....... 561 745-0085
Jupiter *(G-7072)*
Nopetro LLC..........G....... 305 441-9059
Tallahassee *(G-17305)*

NATURAL GAS PRODUCTION

United Energy Corporation..........G....... 904 296-1168
Jacksonville *(G-6880)*

NATURAL PROPANE PRODUCTION

Ideal Gas LLC..........G....... 904 417-6470
Saint Augustine *(G-15554)*

NAUTICAL REPAIR SVCS

Centrifugal Rebabbitting Inc..........F....... 954 522-3003
Fort Lauderdale *(G-3891)*
SDr Specialties Services LLC..........G....... 386 878-6771
De Leon Springs *(G-2741)*

NAVIGATIONAL SYSTEMS & INSTRUMENTS

Bae Systems Info & Elec Sys..........C....... 813 979-4392
Temple Terrace *(G-18366)*
Bae Systems Tech Sol Srvc Inc..........G....... 904 241-1631
Jacksonville *(G-6190)*
Bae Systems Tech Sol Srvc Inc..........G....... 850 236-2428
Panama City Beach *(G-13971)*
Weibel Equipment Inc..........G....... 571 278-1989
Lake Worth *(G-7599)*

NET & NETTING PRDTS

Burbank Trawl Makers Inc..........E....... 904 321-0976
Jacksonville *(G-6244)*
Intermas Nets USA Inc..........G....... 305 442-1416
Coral Gables *(G-2160)*

NETS: Laundry

Superior Group Companies Inc..........G....... 727 397-9611
Seminole *(G-16765)*

NETTING: Plastic

Intermas Nets USA Inc..........G....... 305 442-1416
Coral Gables *(G-2160)*

NETTING: Rope

Csl of America Inc..........F....... 407 849-7070
Orlando *(G-12629)*

NETTING: Woven Wire, Made From Purchased Wire

Octal Ventures Inc..........F....... 727 526-9288
Pinellas Park *(G-14373)*

NEW & USED CAR DEALERS

Evo Motors LLC..........F....... 813 621-7799
Seffner *(G-16725)*
Revology Cars LLC..........F....... 800 974-4463
Orlando *(G-13133)*
Sfada Tag Agency Inc..........F....... 305 981-1077
North Miami *(G-11654)*

NEWSPAPERS & PERIODICALS NEWS REPORTING SVCS

Overseas Radio LLC..........G....... 305 296-1630
Key West *(G-7200)*

NEWSSTAND

Weekly Newspaper..........F....... 305 743-0844
Marathon *(G-8521)*

NICKEL ALLOY

Nickels and Associates LLC..........G....... 863 699-0180
Lake Placid *(G-7491)*

NONCURRENT CARRYING WIRING DEVICES

Afc Cable Systems Inc..........G....... 813 539-0588
Largo *(G-7888)*
Alta Technologies Inc..........G....... 609 538-9500
Ponte Vedra Beach *(G-14931)*
Backbone Interconnect LLC..........E....... 954 800-4749
Sunrise *(G-17093)*
LMI Components Inc..........F....... 561 994-5896
Boca Raton *(G-604)*

Microlumen Inc....D....813 886-1200
Oldsmar (G-12250)

NONDURABLE GOODS WHOLESALERS, NEC

Downes Trading Co....G....813 855-7122
Palm Harbor (G-13734)

NONFERROUS: Rolling & Drawing, NEC

Heartland Metals Inc....E....863 465-7501
Lake Placid (G-7488)
Leadex....G....305 266-2028
Miami (G-9877)
Shar Family Enterprises Llc....G....352 365-6988
Leesburg (G-8171)

NONMETALLIC MINERALS: Support Activities, Exc Fuels

Fcs Holdings Inc....E....352 793-5151
Center Hill (G-1526)
Qci Britannic Inc....G....305 860-0102
Coral Gables (G-2188)

NOTARIES PUBLIC

Carlees Creations Inc....G....786 232-0050
Miami (G-9319)

NOTIONS: Hooks, Crochet

APC Art-Phyl Creations LLC....G....786 571-4665
Hialeah (G-5301)

NOVELTIES

Collectibles of SW Florida....G....239 332-2344
Cape Coral (G-1404)
Joni Industries Inc....F....352 799-5456
Brooksville (G-1240)
Marcela Creations Inc....G....813 253-0556
Tampa (G-17879)
Significant Solutions Corp....G....561 703-7703
Boca Raton (G-711)

NOVELTIES, DURABLE, WHOLESALE

Williams Minerals Co Inc....G....304 897-6003
Winter Springs (G-19489)

NOVELTIES: Plastic

Ei Global Group Llc....G....561 999-8989
Boca Raton (G-515)
Pompadour Products Inc....E....954 345-2700
Coral Springs (G-2303)

NOZZLES & SPRINKLERS Lawn Hose

AB Fire Sprinklers LLC....G....954 973-8054
Pompano Beach (G-14572)
C Mike Roach Inc....F....864 882-1101
Hobe Sound (G-5723)
K-Rain Manufacturing Corp....D....561 721-3936
Riviera Beach (G-15338)
Star Sight Innovations....G....307 786-2911
Crescent City (G-2343)

NOZZLES: Spray, Aerosol, Paint Or Insecticide

Spraying Systems Co....G....813 259-9400
Bradenton (G-1119)

NUCLEAR FUELS SCRAP REPROCESSING

Holtec International....D....561 745-7772
Jupiter (G-7053)

NUCLEAR REACTORS: Military Or Indl

United Ntons Space Crps Mltary....F....702 373-2351
Ponce De Leon (G-14920)

NUCLEAR SHIELDING: Metal Plate

A-Fabco Inc....E....813 677-8790
Gibsonton (G-5024)

NURSERIES & LAWN & GARDEN SPLY STORES, RETAIL

Ronald M Hart Inc....G....772 600-8497
Stuart (G-17003)

NURSERIES & LAWN & GARDEN SPLY STORES, RETAIL: Fertilizer

Clean Energy ESb Inc....E....202 905-6726
Coral Gables (G-2131)

NURSERIES & LAWN & GARDEN SPLY STORES, RETAIL: Sod

Conrad Yelvington Distrs Inc....G....352 336-5049
Gainesville (G-4895)

NURSERIES/LAWN/GARDEN SPLY STORES, RET: Hydroponic Eqpt/Sply

Morgans Elc Mtr & Pump Svc....G....321 960-2209
Cocoa Beach (G-2066)

NURSERIES/LAWN/GRDN SPLY STORE, RET: Nursery Stck, Seed/Bulb

Vertpac LLC....E....407 886-9010
Apopka (G-195)

NURSERY STOCK, WHOLESALE

J T Walker Industries Inc....E....727 461-0501
Clearwater (G-1739)

NUTRITION SVCS

West Development Group LLC....G....407 308-5020
Orlando (G-13322)

NUTS: Metal

Henefelt Precision Products....F....727 531-0406
Largo (G-7969)

NYLON FIBERS

Redsled DBA Bulldog Equipment....F....954 448-5221
Stuart (G-17001)
Tagalong Inc....G....561 585-7400
Lantana (G-7877)

OFFICE EQPT WHOLESALERS

Kyocera Dcment Sltons Sthast L....F....772 562-0511
Fort Pierce (G-4710)
New Market Enterprises Ltd....F....484 341-8004
Palm Harbor (G-13748)
Totalprint USA....G....855 915-1300
Tampa (G-18196)

OFFICE EQPT, WHOLESALE: Blueprinting

Reprographic Solutions Inc....G....772 340-3430
Port Saint Lucie (G-15137)

OFFICE EQPT, WHOLESALE: Dictating Machines

Hth Engineering Inc....E....727 939-8853
Tarpon Springs (G-18308)

OFFICE EQPT, WHOLESALE: Photocopy Machines

R & K Marketing Inc....G....904 745-0022
Jacksonville (G-6701)

OFFICE FIXTURES: Wood

Antique & Modern Cabinets Inc....E....904 393-9055
Jacksonville (G-6158)
Duval Fixtures Inc....E....904 757-3964
Jacksonville (G-6340)

OFFICE FURNITURE REPAIR & MAINTENANCE SVCS

John Eric Madden....G....813 395-3314
Zephyrhills (G-19524)

OFFICE MACHINES, NEC

Solunet....G....321 369-9719
Palm Bay (G-13536)

OFFICE SPLY & STATIONERY STORES

Light Source Business Systems....F....772 562-5046
Port Saint Lucie (G-15120)
Mark Master Inc....D....813 988-6000
Tampa (G-17881)

OFFICE SPLY & STATIONERY STORES: Office Forms & Splys

Ace Marking Devices Corp....G....561 833-4073
West Palm Beach (G-18786)
Ayers Publishing Inc....G....352 463-7135
Trenton (G-18480)
Baker County Press Inc....G....904 259-2400
Macclenny (G-8442)
Bradford County Telegraph Inc....F....904 964-6305
Starke (G-16887)
Express Printing & Office Sups....G....904 765-9696
Jacksonville (G-6376)
Gulf Coast Business World Inc....F....850 864-1511
Fort Walton Beach (G-4806)
H D Quickprint & Disc Off Sups....G....407 678-1355
Winter Park (G-19409)
Independent Resources Inc....E....813 237-0945
Tampa (G-17777)
Marlin Graphics Inc....G....561 743-5220
Jupiter (G-7074)
Nassau Printing & Off Sup Inc....G....904 879-2305
Callahan (G-1327)
Professional Office Svcs Inc....G....863 967-6634
Winter Haven (G-19348)
Scott Brevard Inc....G....386 698-1121
Crescent City (G-2342)
Steven M Roessler LLC....G....321 773-2300
Indian Harbour Beach (G-6068)
Thalers Printing Center Inc....G....954 741-6522
Lauderhill (G-8122)
Wakulla News....F....850 926-7102
Crawfordville (G-2337)
Weidenhamer Corporation....G....850 837-3190
Destin (G-3211)
Wells Legal Supply Inc....E....904 399-1510
Jacksonville (G-6909)

OFFICE SPLYS, NEC, WHOLESALE

Baker County Press Inc....G....904 259-2400
Macclenny (G-8442)
Davison Publishing Company LLC....G....407 380-8900
Orlando (G-12656)
Replenish Ink Inc....G....818 206-2424
Miami (G-10254)

OFFICES & CLINICS OF DRS OF MED: Em Med Ctr, Freestanding

Worldwide Auto Systems Corp....F....954 439-6332
Hollywood (G-5942)

OFFICES & CLINICS OF HEALTH PRACTITIONERS: Physical Therapy

Advanced Prosthetics Amer Inc....F....352 383-0396
Eustis (G-3700)
Great Northern Rehab PC....G....352 732-8868
Ocala (G-11960)
Great Northern Rehab PC....F....352 732-8868
Ocala (G-11961)

OFFICES & CLINICS OF OPTOMETRISTS: Specialist, Optometrists

Institutional Eye Care LLC....F....866 604-2931
Bonita Springs (G-839)

OIL & GAS FIELD MACHINERY

Chromalloy Gas Turbine LLC....A....561 935-3571
Palm Beach Gardens (G-13578)
Enviro Petroleum Inc....G....713 896-6996
Jensen Beach (G-6968)
Fred International LLC....F....786 539-1600
Miramar (G-10995)
Skide Llc....F....305 537-4275
Miami (G-10356)

Tecvalco USA Inc.......E....... 866 427-3444
Rockledge *(G-15452)*

OIL FIELD MACHINERY & EQPT

Sandvik Mining & Cnstr USA LLC.......C....... 386 462-4100
Alachua *(G-18)*

OIL FIELD SVCS, NEC

CA Pipeline Inc.......G....... 305 969-4655
Miami *(G-9297)*
Empirica.......F....... 727 403-0399
Palm Harbor *(G-13736)*
J&D Oil Field Intl Inc.......G....... 305 436-0024
Doral *(G-3399)*
MII Oil Holding Inc.......C....... 321 200-0039
Tallahassee *(G-17301)*
North America Wireline LLC.......G....... 870 365-5401
Gulf Breeze *(G-5122)*
Offshore Inland Mar Olfld Svcs.......C....... 251 443-5550
Pensacola *(G-14214)*
Oils R US 1 800.......G....... 305 681-0909
Miami *(G-10093)*
Southern Underground Inds.......F....... 954 226-3865
Miami Lakes *(G-10862)*
Titan Oil Tools LLC.......G....... 941 356-3010
Sarasota *(G-16311)*
Walters Tools LLC.......G....... 321 537-4788
Palm Bay *(G-13546)*

OILS & ESSENTIAL OILS

Florida Kolmiami Corporation.......G....... 305 582-0114
Miami Lakes *(G-10791)*
Intercit Inc.......D....... 863 646-0165
Lakeland *(G-7715)*
Suns Eye Inc.......G....... 407 519-4904
Geneva *(G-5023)*
Vaprzone LLC.......G....... 941 882-4841
Venice *(G-18584)*

OILS & GREASES: Blended & Compounded

Bell Performance Inc.......F....... 407 831-5021
Longwood *(G-8262)*

OILS & GREASES: Lubricating

Advanced Engine Tech LLC.......G....... 727 744-2935
Clearwater *(G-1565)*
Am2f Energy Inc.......G....... 407 505-1127
Winter Park *(G-19376)*
Armor Oil Products LLC.......G....... 813 248-1988
Tampa *(G-17435)*
Break-Free Inc.......E....... 800 347-1200
Jacksonville *(G-6234)*
Eng Group LLC.......G....... 954 323-2024
Fort Lauderdale *(G-3972)*
Gb Energy Management LLC.......G....... 305 792-4650
Miami *(G-9616)*
Global Diversified Products.......E....... 727 209-0854
Pinellas Park *(G-14351)*
Illinois Tool Works Inc.......D....... 863 665-3338
Lakeland *(G-7708)*
Lubrication Global LLC.......F....... 954 239-9522
Doral *(G-3421)*
Ocean Bio-Chem Inc.......E....... 954 587-6280
Davie *(G-2559)*
Otus Corp Intl LLC.......G....... 305 833-6078
Miami *(G-10122)*
Pro-Tech Coatings Inc.......G....... 813 248-1477
Tampa *(G-18018)*

OILS, ANIMAL OR VEGETABLE, WHOLESALE

Griffin Industries LLC.......E....... 813 626-1135
Tampa *(G-17729)*

OILS: Lubricating

All American Lube.......G....... 561 432-0476
Lake Worth *(G-7533)*
Citilube Inc.......F....... 305 681-6064
Miami *(G-9355)*
Global Gl Lc.......G....... 863 551-1079
Winter Haven *(G-19326)*
Mobile 1 Inc.......F....... 954 283-8100
Lauderdale Lakes *(G-8091)*

OILS: Lubricating

Amalie Oil Company.......C....... 813 248-1988
Tampa *(G-17412)*
D N L Performance Inc.......G....... 786 295-8831
Opa Locka *(G-12305)*
Lubrexx Specialty Products LLC.......G....... 561 988-7500
Pompano Beach *(G-14748)*
United Armour Products LLC.......G....... 813 767-9624
Tampa *(G-18219)*

OINTMENTS

Amerx Health Care Corp.......F....... 727 443-0530
Oldsmar *(G-12201)*
Transdermal Technologies Inc.......G....... 561 848-2345
North Palm Beach *(G-11727)*

OLEFINS

Texene LLC.......F....... 305 200-5001
Miami Lakes *(G-10867)*

OPEN PIT COPPER ORE MINING

Smart Group Traders Inc.......G....... 850 460-5130
Destin *(G-3207)*

OPERATOR TRAINING, COMPUTER

Inceptra LLC.......E....... 954 442-5400
Weston *(G-19141)*

OPHTHALMIC GOODS

Achievia Direct Inc.......F....... 386 615-8708
Daytona Beach *(G-2620)*
Bausch Lomb Surgical Inc.......F....... 727 724-6600
Clearwater *(G-1602)*
Best Price Digital Lenses Inc.......G....... 850 361-4401
Pensacola *(G-14099)*
Bicentrics Inc.......F....... 813 649-0225
Ruskin *(G-15482)*
CL Boca Raton LLC.......G....... 561 660-9485
Boca Raton *(G-481)*
CL Dadeland LLC.......G....... 305 712-6825
Miami *(G-9361)*
CL Gardens LLC.......G....... 561 567-0504
Palm Beach Gardens *(G-13579)*
CL Waterside Naples LLC.......F....... 239 734-8534
Naples *(G-11209)*
Electro-Optix Inc.......F....... 954 973-2800
Pompano Beach *(G-14677)*
Gerber Coburn Optical Inc.......E....... 305 592-4705
Miami *(G-9630)*
Icare Industries Inc.......C....... 727 512-3000
Saint Petersburg *(G-15811)*
M12 Lenses Inc.......G....... 407 973-4403
Altamonte Springs *(G-54)*
Premium Dynamic Lens.......F....... 813 891-9912
Oldsmar *(G-12261)*
Solidar Express Coatings LLC.......G....... 727 585-2192
Largo *(G-8058)*
Techtran Lenses Inc.......G....... 561 623-5490
Jupiter *(G-7125)*
Top Optical Lab.......F....... 305 662-2893
Miami *(G-10492)*
Veriteq Acquisition Corp.......G....... 561 805-8007
Delray Beach *(G-3157)*
Vision Benefits 4 All Inc.......G....... 888 317-0606
Saint Johns *(G-15685)*

OPHTHALMIC GOODS WHOLESALERS

Lip Trading Co.......G....... 954 987-0306
Hollywood *(G-5861)*

OPHTHALMIC GOODS, NEC, WHOLESALE: Contact Lenses

Danker Laboratories Inc.......F....... 941 758-7711
Sarasota *(G-16203)*

OPHTHALMIC GOODS: Eyewear, Protective

Inspecs USA LC.......F....... 727 771-7710
Palm Harbor *(G-13740)*

OPHTHALMIC GOODS: Frames & Parts, Eyeglass & Spectacle

East Ormond Beach Crossfit.......G....... 386 673-3011
Ormond Beach *(G-13366)*

Ottica Dante Americas LLC.......G....... 561 322-0186
Boca Raton *(G-658)*

OPHTHALMIC GOODS: Frames, Lenses & Parts, Eyeglasses

Institutional Eye Care LLC.......F....... 866 604-2931
Bonita Springs *(G-839)*
Pixeloptics Inc.......G....... 954 376-1542
Fort Lauderdale *(G-4170)*

OPHTHALMIC GOODS: Lenses, Ophthalmic

Hoya Largo.......F....... 727 531-8964
Largo *(G-7976)*
Transitions Optical Inc.......B....... 727 545-0400
Pinellas Park *(G-14392)*

OPTICAL GOODS STORES

Premium Dynamic Lens.......F....... 813 891-9912
Oldsmar *(G-12261)*

OPTICAL GOODS STORES: Contact Lenses, Prescription

Icare Industries Inc.......C....... 727 512-3000
Saint Petersburg *(G-15811)*

OPTICAL GOODS STORES: Eyeglasses, Prescription

Vision Benefits 4 All Inc.......G....... 888 317-0606
Saint Johns *(G-15685)*

OPTICAL GOODS STORES: Opticians

For Eyes Optcal Ccnut Grove In.......C....... 305 557-9004
Miramar *(G-10993)*

OPTICAL INSTRUMENTS & APPARATUS

ER Precision Optical Corp.......F....... 407 292-5395
Apopka *(G-138)*
Isp Optics Corporation.......D....... 914 591-3070
Orlando *(G-12845)*
Lenstec Inc.......E....... 727 571-2272
Saint Petersburg *(G-15839)*
Light-Tech Inc.......G....... 863 385-6000
Sebring *(G-16698)*
Low Vision Aids Inc.......G....... 954 722-1580
Ocala *(G-11987)*
Manasota Optics Inc.......G....... 941 359-1748
Sarasota *(G-16500)*
Multicore Photonics Inc.......G....... 407 325-7800
Orlando *(G-12984)*
Tower Optical Corporation.......F....... 561 740-2525
Boynton Beach *(G-971)*

OPTICAL INSTRUMENTS & LENSES

Aldana Laser Miami Inc.......F....... 786 681-7752
Doral *(G-3235)*
Align Optics Inc.......G....... 954 748-1715
Sunrise *(G-17087)*
Amphenol Custom Cable Inc.......C....... 813 623-2232
Tampa *(G-17423)*
Amphenol Custom Cable Inc.......E....... 407 393-3886
Orlando *(G-12476)*
Asphericon Inc.......F....... 941 564-0890
Sarasota *(G-16353)*
Brain Power Incorporated.......E....... 305 264-4465
Miami *(G-9273)*
D R S Optronics Inc.......F....... 321 309-1500
Melbourne *(G-8799)*
En-Vision America Inc.......F....... 309 452-3088
Palmetto *(G-13796)*
Eye Specialists Mid Florida PA.......F....... 863 937-4515
Lakeland *(G-7684)*
Eyes On Go Optical LLC.......G....... 954 242-3243
Davie *(G-2523)*
Grampus Enterprises Inc.......G....... 305 491-9827
Weston *(G-19135)*
Jenoptik North America Inc.......C....... 561 881-7400
Jupiter *(G-7060)*
Jenoptik Optical Systems LLC.......C....... 561 881-7400
Jupiter *(G-7061)*
Laser Lens Tek Inc.......F....... 941 752-5811
Sarasota *(G-16249)*
Lightpath Technologies Inc.......D....... 407 382-4003
Orlando *(G-12911)*

PRODUCT

Mercoframes Optical Corp...G... 305 882-0120
Miami *(G-9978)*
Ocean Optics Inc...E... 407 673-0041
Orlando *(G-13016)*
Ocean Optics Inc...D... 727 545-0741
Orlando *(G-13017)*
Oculus Surgical Inc...E... 772 236-2622
Port St Lucie *(G-15177)*
Pixelteq Inc...G... 727 545-0741
Orlando *(G-13070)*
Plastics For Mankind Inc...F... 305 687-5917
Opa Locka *(G-12351)*
Pyramid Imaging Inc...G... 813 984-0125
Tampa *(G-18028)*
Saikou Optics Incorporated...G... 407 986-4200
Orlando *(G-13157)*
Sunoptic Technologies LLC...D... 877 677-2832
Jacksonville *(G-6822)*
Tecport Optics Inc...F... 407 855-1212
Orlando *(G-13244)*
Thermal Matrix Intl LLC...G... 813 222-3274
Tampa *(G-18185)*
Thermo Arl US Inc...E... 800 532-4752
West Palm Beach *(G-19060)*
Thunder Energies Corporation...G... 561 560-4302
Lantana *(G-7878)*
Vision Solution Technology LL...G... 305 477-4480
Doral *(G-3543)*

OPTOMETRIC EQPT & SPLYS WHOLESALERS

Vision Solution Technology LL...G... 305 477-4480
Doral *(G-3543)*

ORAL PREPARATIONS

Probiora Health LLC...G... 214 559-2994
Tampa *(G-18019)*

ORDNANCE

Ao Precision Manufacturing LLC...G... 386 274-5882
Daytona Beach *(G-2626)*
Avasar Corp...E... 321 723-3456
Melbourne *(G-8773)*
Break-Free Inc...E... 800 347-1200
Jacksonville *(G-6234)*
C4 Advnced Tctical Systems LLC...D... 407 206-3886
Orlando *(G-12541)*
Energy Technical Systems Inc...F... 850 223-2393
Perry *(G-14299)*
Fairbanks and Fairbanks Inc...G... 850 293-1184
Pensacola *(G-14148)*
General Defense Corporation...G... 954 444-0155
Davie *(G-2532)*
General Dynmics Ord Tctcal Sys...C... 727 578-8100
Saint Petersburg *(G-15791)*
Global Ordnance LLC...E... 941 549-8388
Sarasota *(G-16221)*
Gr Dynamics LLC...F... 850 897-9700
Niceville *(G-11568)*
Integrated Design & Develop...G... 407 268-4300
Sanford *(G-16068)*
Iron Sight Precision LLC...G... 561 735-9971
Boynton Beach *(G-923)*
Kaman Precision Products Inc...C... 407 282-1000
Orlando *(G-12865)*
L2d Outdoors Inc...G... 954 757-6116
Coral Springs *(G-2271)*
Leonidas Customs Inc...G... 561 542-4151
Wellington *(G-18723)*
Pace Launcher Casings Llc...G... 813 245-6570
Odessa *(G-12138)*
Slr Rifleworks LLC...G... 855 757-7435
Winter Garden *(G-19285)*
Tom & Company LLC...G... 321 917-0760
Melbourne *(G-8965)*

ORDNANCE: Smoke Generators

Elite Distributors LLC...F... 407 601-6665
Orlando *(G-12705)*

ORGANIZATIONS: Bacteriological Research

Becker Microbial Products Inc...G... 954 345-9321
Parkland *(G-13989)*

ORGANIZATIONS: Civic & Social

Brevard Softball Magazine Inc...F... 321 453-3711
Merritt Island *(G-8995)*

ORGANIZATIONS: Medical Research

Bio Therapeutics Inc...G... 954 321-5553
Plantation *(G-14496)*
Biorep Technologies Inc...F... 305 330-4449
Miami Lakes *(G-10770)*

ORGANIZATIONS: Professional

Netexpressusa Inc...G... 888 575-1245
Fort Myers *(G-4545)*

ORGANIZATIONS: Religious

Action Weekly Corp...G... 561 586-8699
West Palm Beach *(G-18789)*
Florida Catholic Media Inc...G... 407 373-0075
Orlando *(G-12747)*
Orlando Times Inc...G... 407 841-3052
Orlando *(G-13037)*

ORGANIZERS, CLOSET & DRAWER Plastic

Able Closets Inc...G... 772 781-8250
Stuart *(G-16901)*

ORNAMENTS: Christmas Tree, Exc Electrical & Glass

Stocking Factory...G... 305 745-2681
Big Pine Key *(G-382)*

OSCILLATORS

APA Wireless Technologies Inc...F... 954 563-8833
Oakland Park *(G-11777)*
Piezo Technology Inc...C... 407 298-2000
Orlando *(G-13067)*

OSCILLATORS

All-Tag Corporation...E... 561 998-9983
Boca Raton *(G-412)*

OUTBOARD MOTORS & PARTS

Brunswick Corporation...G... 850 769-1011
Panama City *(G-13874)*
JRL Service Co...G... 727 243-4734
Tarpon Springs *(G-18311)*

OUTLETS: Electric, Convenience

123 Dollar Plus Inc...G... 305 456-4561
Miami *(G-9020)*
Tag Heuer...G... 954 846-2103
Sunrise *(G-17184)*
Tienda Maya...G... 561 965-0900
Lake Worth *(G-7591)*

OUTREACH PROGRAM

Quality Life Publishing Co...G... 239 513-9907
Naples *(G-11379)*

OVENS: Cremating

B & L Cremation Systems Inc...D... 727 541-4666
Largo *(G-7903)*
Matthews International Corp...C... 407 886-5533
Apopka *(G-158)*

OVERBURDEN REMOVAL SVCS: Nonmetallic Minerals

Environmental Contractors Inc...F... 305 556-6942
Hialeah *(G-5399)*
Express Removal Service LLC...G... 305 303-8249
Miami Gardens *(G-10739)*

PACKAGE DESIGN SVCS

Private Label Skin Na LLC...C... 877 516-2200
Saint Petersburg *(G-15890)*

PACKAGED FROZEN FOODS WHOLESALERS, NEC

Allapattah Industries Inc...E... 305 324-5900
Miami *(G-9116)*
Borden Dairy Company Fla LLC...D... 863 298-9742
Winter Haven *(G-19305)*
Coca-Cola Company...G... 727 736-7101
Dunedin *(G-3574)*
GA Fd Svcs Pinellas Cnty LLC...E... 954 972-8884
Fort Lauderdale *(G-4017)*
Pizza Spice Packet LLC...G... 718 831-7036
Boca Raton *(G-666)*

PACKAGING & LABELING SVCS

Birdiebox LLC...E... 786 762-2975
Miami *(G-9249)*
Cofran International Corp...E... 305 592-2644
Doral *(G-3302)*
Compliance Meds Tech LLC...G... 786 319-9826
Miami *(G-9389)*
Florida Candy Factory Inc...F... 727 446-0024
Clearwater *(G-1687)*
Scan Technology Inc...G... 931 723-0304
Gainesville *(G-4992)*
Sunsof Inc...E... 305 691-1875
Hialeah *(G-5641)*

PACKAGING MATERIALS, INDL: Wholesalers

Waterbrick International Inc...G... 877 420-9283
Windermere *(G-19250)*

PACKAGING MATERIALS, WHOLESALE

Corrigan & Company...G... 904 353-5936
Jacksonville *(G-6293)*
Peter T Amann...G... 561 848-2770
West Palm Beach *(G-18995)*
Storopack Inc...G... 305 805-9696
Medley *(G-8731)*

PACKAGING MATERIALS: Paper

Apakus Inc...F... 305 403-2603
Coral Gables *(G-2123)*
Dairy-Mix Inc...F... 813 621-8098
Tampa *(G-17586)*
Estal Usa Inc...G... 305 728-3272
Miami *(G-9537)*
Four G Enterprises Inc...E... 407 834-4143
Longwood *(G-8284)*
Full Cut Tabs LLC...F... 941 316-1510
Sarasota *(G-16443)*
Graphics Designer Inc...F... 561 687-7993
West Palm Beach *(G-18889)*
Great Northern Corporation...E... 920 739-3671
Jacksonville *(G-6446)*
Gulf Packaging Co...F... 727 441-1117
Clearwater *(G-1708)*
Holmes Stamp Company...E... 904 396-2291
Jacksonville *(G-6476)*
J & J International Corp...E... 407 349-7114
Sanford *(G-16070)*
Label Graphics Inc...G... 561 798-8180
Lake Worth *(G-7563)*
Labelpro Inc...F... 727 538-2149
Clearwater *(G-1757)*
Storopack Inc...G... 305 805-9696
Medley *(G-8731)*
Trend At LLC...F... 786 300-2550
Miami *(G-10505)*
Tutti Hogar International LLC...G... 305 705-4735
Miami *(G-10513)*
United Seal & Tag Label Corp...G... 941 625-6799
Port Charlotte *(G-15004)*
Zellwin Farms Company...E... 407 886-9241
Zellwood *(G-19505)*

PACKAGING MATERIALS: Paper, Coated Or Laminated

A Plus Lamination & Finshg Inc...F... 305 636-9888
Miami *(G-9041)*
Legar Inc...F... 561 635-5882
Boynton Beach *(G-928)*
Plastic Coated Papers Inc...D... 850 968-6100
Pensacola *(G-14233)*

PACKAGING MATERIALS: Paperboard Backs For Blister/Skin Pkgs

Gulf Packaging Co...F... 727 441-1117
Clearwater *(G-1708)*
Uvisors...G... 813 716-1113
Tampa *(G-18230)*

PACKAGING MATERIALS: Plastic Film, Coated Or Laminated

Almi Intl Plastic Inds Inc..........G....... 954 920-6836
Hollywood *(G-5771)*
Attesa Holdings Group LLC..........G....... 305 777-3567
Miami *(G-9190)*
Jr Plastics Corporation..........D....... 352 401-0880
Ocala *(G-11972)*
Mr Cool Waters Inc..........F....... 305 234-6311
Miami *(G-10048)*

PACKAGING MATERIALS: Polystyrene Foam

3a Products LLC..........G....... 754 263-2968
Miramar *(G-10958)*
Allied Foam Fabricators LLC..........D....... 813 626-0090
Tampa *(G-17401)*
Architectural Foam Supply Inc..........E....... 954 943-6949
Pompano Beach *(G-14598)*
Autopax Inc..........G....... 772 563-0131
Vero Beach *(G-18596)*
Drb Packaging LLC..........G....... 321 877-2802
Rockledge *(G-15405)*
Drb Packaging LLC..........G....... 321 877-2802
Rockledge *(G-15406)*
Foam By Design Inc..........E....... 727 561-7479
Clearwater *(G-1692)*
Foam Factory Inc..........E....... 954 485-6700
Boca Raton *(G-536)*
Great Magnet LLC..........F....... 407 260-0591
Winter Park *(G-19408)*
J C & A of South Florida Inc..........G....... 305 445-6665
Miami *(G-9780)*
Kitko Corp..........G....... 786 287-8900
Doral *(G-3408)*
Magna Manufacturing Inc..........E....... 850 243-1112
Fort Walton Beach *(G-4814)*
Merry Mailman Inc..........G....... 954 786-1146
Pompano Beach *(G-14758)*
Plastix Usa LLC..........D....... 305 891-0091
Hollywood *(G-5892)*
Republic Packaging Florida Inc..........E....... 305 685-5175
Opa Locka *(G-12355)*
Root International Inc..........F....... 813 265-1808
Clearwater *(G-1865)*
Seven Group USA Inc..........G....... 305 392-9193
Doral *(G-3500)*
Source of Sup In Polyurethanes..........G....... 239 573-3637
Cape Coral *(G-1473)*
Storopack Inc..........G....... 305 805-9696
Medley *(G-8731)*
Ufp Technologies Inc..........E....... 407 933-4880
Kissimmee *(G-7306)*
Unity Marine Inc..........G....... 954 321-1727
Fort Lauderdale *(G-4296)*
W R Grace & Co - Conn..........F....... 561 982-7776
Boca Raton *(G-785)*
Zipx Package Service Inc..........G....... 305 597-5305
Doral *(G-3553)*

PACKAGING: Blister Or Bubble Formed, Plastic

Holpack Corp..........G....... 786 565-3969
Hialeah *(G-5448)*
MTS Medication Tech Inc..........C....... 727 576-6311
Saint Petersburg *(G-15862)*
MTS Packaging Systems Inc..........C....... 727 576-6311
Saint Petersburg *(G-15863)*

PACKING & CRATING SVC

Homyn Enterprises Corp..........D....... 305 870-9720
Miami *(G-9718)*

PACKING MATERIALS: Mechanical

TNT Packaging Inc..........F....... 305 769-0616
Miami *(G-10483)*

PADS: Mattress

Pillow Plus Manufacturing Inc..........G....... 305 652-2218
Miami *(G-10163)*

PAGERS: One-way

R F Laboratories Inc..........F....... 920 564-2700
Sorrento *(G-16792)*

PAINT & PAINTING SPLYS STORE: Brushes, Rollers, Sprayers

Greg Franklin Enterprises Inc..........F....... 904 675-9129
Hilliard *(G-5708)*

PAINT STORE

Acrylux Paint Mfg Co Inc..........F....... 954 772-0300
Fort Lauderdale *(G-3780)*
Anvil Paints & Coatings Inc..........F....... 727 535-1411
Largo *(G-7897)*
Hy-Tech Thermal Solutions LLC..........G....... 321 984-9777
Melbourne *(G-8848)*
Povia Paints Inc..........G....... 239 791-0011
Fort Myers *(G-4571)*
Richards Paint Mfg Co Inc..........D....... 321 636-6200
Rockledge *(G-15443)*
Scott Paint Company LLC..........G....... 941 371-0015
Sarasota *(G-16586)*

PAINTING SVC: Metal Prdts

Allstar Lighting & Sound Inc..........F....... 407 767-0111
Longwood *(G-8252)*
Bumper Doctor..........G....... 850 341-1771
Pensacola *(G-14109)*
Electrostatic Industrial Pntg..........G....... 305 696-4556
Miami *(G-9511)*
Industrial Marine Inc..........F....... 904 781-4707
Jacksonville *(G-6493)*
Leto LLC..........G....... 813 486-8049
Clearwater *(G-1758)*
Pozin Enterprises Inc..........E....... 727 546-8974
Clearwater *(G-1838)*
Precision Metal Services Inc..........F....... 407 843-3682
Sorrento *(G-16791)*
Reliable Finishes..........G....... 321 723-3334
Melbourne *(G-8918)*

PAINTS & ADDITIVES

Anchor Coatings Leesburg Inc..........E....... 352 728-0777
Leesburg *(G-8142)*
Anvil Paints & Coatings Inc..........F....... 727 535-1411
Largo *(G-7897)*
Associated Paint Inc..........F....... 305 885-1964
Medley *(G-8616)*
Hy-Tech Thermal Solutions LLC..........G....... 321 984-9777
Melbourne *(G-8848)*
Lapolla Industries LLC..........F....... 954 379-0241
Deerfield Beach *(G-2857)*
Marine Industrial Paint Co..........F....... 727 527-3382
Saint Petersburg *(G-15848)*
Povia Paints Inc..........G....... 239 791-0011
Fort Myers *(G-4571)*
Richards Paint Mfg Co Inc..........D....... 321 636-6200
Rockledge *(G-15443)*
Scott Paint Company LLC..........G....... 941 371-0015
Sarasota *(G-16586)*
Sun Coatings Inc..........E....... 727 531-4100
Tampa *(G-18139)*
Tex-Coat LLC..........E....... 800 454-0340
Panama City *(G-13955)*
Union Chemical Industries Corp..........F....... 716 866-4978
Boca Raton *(G-766)*

PAINTS & ALLIED PRODUCTS

Adsil Inc..........G....... 386 274-1382
Daytona Beach *(G-2621)*
All Florida Marketing..........G....... 813 281-4641
Rocky Point *(G-15458)*
All-Weather Coatings LLC..........G....... 888 405-8904
Orlando *(G-12455)*
Autek Spray Booths..........G....... 727 709-4373
Largo *(G-7902)*
Black Diamond Coatings Inc..........E....... 800 270-4050
Brooksville *(G-1215)*
Coating Application Tech Inc..........F....... 781 850-5080
Sarasota *(G-16193)*
Complementary Coatings Corp..........C....... 386 428-6461
Orlando *(G-12608)*
Cork Industries Inc..........E....... 904 695-2400
Jacksonville *(G-6292)*
Coronado Paint Co Inc..........C....... 386 428-6461
Orlando *(G-12622)*
Deako Coatings Chemical..........F....... 305 323-9914
Cutler Bay *(G-2393)*
Ecosmart..........F....... 561 328-6488
Lake Park *(G-7468)*
Faux Effects International Inc..........E....... 772 778-9044
Fort Pierce *(G-4697)*
Florida Prtctive Coatings Cons..........G....... 407 322-1243
Lake Mary *(G-7419)*
Gulf Coast Paint & Supplies..........F....... 813 932-3093
Tampa *(G-17733)*
Hco Holding I Corporation..........F....... 863 533-0522
Bartow *(G-318)*
Inseco Inc..........F....... 239 939-1072
Fort Myers *(G-4495)*
International Paint LLC..........G....... 321 636-9722
Cocoa *(G-2032)*
International Paint LLC..........G....... 305 620-9220
Opa Locka *(G-12326)*
J & J Inc..........G....... 954 746-7300
Sunrise *(G-17132)*
Ken R Avery Painting Inc..........E....... 813 855-5037
Oldsmar *(G-12239)*
Lambert Corporation Florida..........E....... 407 841-2940
Orlando *(G-12889)*
Lanco & Harris Corp..........D....... 407 240-4000
Orlando *(G-12890)*
Microguard..........G....... 386 274-1382
Daytona Beach *(G-2685)*
Nationwide Prtctive Cting Mfrs..........E....... 941 753-7500
Sarasota *(G-16264)*
Nemec..........G....... 407 829-2679
Lake Mary *(G-7439)*
P S Research Corp..........G....... 954 558-8727
Lauderhill *(G-8119)*
Panhandle Paint & Dctg LLC..........G....... 850 596-9248
Panama City Beach *(G-13981)*
Parasol Films Inc..........G....... 954 478-8661
Tamarac *(G-17364)*
Poly Coatings of South Inc..........F....... 941 371-8555
Sarasota *(G-16546)*
PPG Industries Inc..........E....... 305 477-0541
Doral *(G-3465)*
Reliance Supply Co USA LLC..........G....... 954 971-9111
Pompano Beach *(G-14828)*
Rexpro Services..........G....... 561 328-6488
Lake Park *(G-7479)*
Roberlo Usa Inc..........F....... 786 334-6191
Doral *(G-3487)*
Somay Manufacturing Inc..........G....... 305 637-4757
Miami *(G-10374)*
Tex-Coat LLC..........G....... 954 581-0771
Fort Lauderdale *(G-4279)*
Textured Coatings..........G....... 850 360-1451
Panama City Beach *(G-13985)*
Tuf Top Coatings..........F....... 727 527-3382
Saint Petersburg *(G-15945)*
Ultra Tuff Manufacturing Inc..........G....... 970 252-9457
Hobe Sound *(G-5730)*
Vinavil Americas Corporation..........D....... 954 246-8888
Deerfield Beach *(G-2933)*
Zurigo Trading Inc..........G....... 305 244-4681
Miami *(G-10633)*

PAINTS, VARNISHES & SPLYS WHOLESALERS

Scott Paint Company LLC..........G....... 941 371-0015
Sarasota *(G-16586)*

PAINTS, VARNISHES & SPLYS, WHOLESALE: Paints

Hy-Tech Thermal Solutions LLC..........G....... 321 984-9777
Melbourne *(G-8848)*
Povia Paints Inc..........G....... 239 791-0011
Fort Myers *(G-4571)*

PAINTS: Asphalt Or Bituminous

Good 4 Tklc Inc..........G....... 321 632-4340
Rockledge *(G-15415)*

PAINTS: Marine

All Tank Services LLC..........G....... 954 260-9443
Pompano Beach *(G-14585)*
Car Care Haven LLC..........G....... 855 464-2836
Englewood *(G-3671)*
Dynamis Epoxy LLC..........G....... 941 488-3999
Venice *(G-18544)*
New Nautical Coatings Inc..........E....... 727 523-8053
Clearwater *(G-1807)*

PAINTS: Oil Or Alkyd Vehicle Or Water Thinned

Deako Coating & Chemical Inc..........G....... 305 634-5162
Miami *(G-9442)*
Kel Glo Corp..........G....... 305 751-5641
Miami *(G-9818)*

PAINTS: Waterproof

Acrylux Paint Mfg Co Inc..........F....... 954 772-0300
Fort Lauderdale *(G-3780)*

PALLET REPAIR SVCS

Pallet Consultants Corp..........E....... 954 946-2212
Pompano Beach *(G-14783)*
Pallet Ex Jacksonville Inc..........E....... 904 781-2500
Jacksonville *(G-6654)*

PALLETS

Aaa-Affordable Pallets & Reels..........G....... 813 740-8009
Tampa *(G-17379)*
Amigo Pallets Inc..........F....... 305 302-9751
Miami *(G-9150)*
B & T Pallets Inc..........G....... 941 360-0562
Sarasota *(G-16360)*
Diversified Pallets Inc..........F....... 904 491-6800
Fernandina Beach *(G-3735)*
Gt Pallets LLC..........G....... 786 541-6532
Miami *(G-9682)*
Mac Pallets..........G....... 813 340-3246
Tampa *(G-17870)*
Pallet Exchange Inc..........F....... 386 734-0133
Orange City *(G-12377)*
Pallets Inc..........G....... 407 492-0857
Apopka *(G-169)*
Pauls Pallets..........G....... 850 474-1920
Pensacola *(G-14222)*
Preferred Pallets Llc..........G....... 863 401-9517
Winter Haven *(G-19344)*
Raymond Newkirk..........G....... 772 359-0237
Fort Pierce *(G-4737)*
S&B Pallet Corp..........G....... 305 525-0872
Miami *(G-10293)*
Xtreme Pallets Inc..........G....... 954 302-8915
Coconut Creek *(G-2104)*

PALLETS & SKIDS: Wood

Buckley Pallets LLC..........F....... 727 415-4497
Clearwater *(G-1617)*
Camara Industries LLC..........F....... 407 879-2549
Orlando *(G-12544)*
Global Bamboo Technologies Inc..........E....... 707 730-0288
Ocala *(G-11956)*
Marianna Truss Inc..........E....... 850 594-5420
Marianna *(G-8583)*
Pallet Holdings LLC..........D....... 561 367-0009
Boca Raton *(G-660)*

PALLETS: Plastic

Craemer US Corporation..........G....... 727 312-8859
Palm Harbor *(G-13731)*
Masonways Indstrctble Plas LLC..........E....... 561 478-8838
West Palm Beach *(G-18944)*
Polymer Logistics Inc..........E....... 877 462-6195
Tampa *(G-17996)*

PALLETS: Wooden

A Pallet Co Inc..........G....... 561 798-1564
West Palm Beach *(G-18784)*
A Quallity Pallet Company..........G....... 239 245-0900
Fort Myers *(G-4341)*
A1 Pallets LLC..........G....... 813 598-9165
Thonotosassa *(G-18398)*
AA Florida Pallets..........G....... 305 805-1522
Medley *(G-8603)*
Aarons Pallets..........G....... 813 627-3225
Tampa *(G-17380)*
AB Used Pallets Inc..........F....... 305 594-2776
Miami *(G-9050)*
Advanced Pallets Inc..........E....... 954 785-1215
Margate *(G-8531)*
All State Pallets Company LLC..........F....... 407 855-8087
Orlando *(G-12454)*
Amigo Pallets Inc..........G....... 305 631-2452
Medley *(G-8609)*
Best Pallets of FL LLC..........G....... 386 624-5575
Deland *(G-2962)*
Brothers Pallets..........G....... 863 944-5278
Lakeland *(G-7651)*
Buckley Pallets..........G....... 727 415-4497
Clearwater *(G-1616)*
Cienfuegos Pallets Corp..........G....... 786 703-3686
Medley *(G-8631)*
D & S Pallet Recycle Center..........G....... 352 351-0070
Ocala *(G-11916)*
D & S Pallets Inc..........D....... 727 540-0061
Clearwater *(G-1647)*
Floor Tech LLC..........F....... 407 855-8087
Orlando *(G-12745)*
Florida AA Pallets Inc..........G....... 305 805-1522
Medley *(G-8651)*
Florida Pallet LLC..........G....... 772 562-4900
Sebastian *(G-16659)*
Freeman Pallets Inc..........G....... 352 328-9326
Gainesville *(G-4924)*
Haman Industries Inc..........F....... 813 626-5700
Tampa *(G-17741)*
Jacksonville Box & Woodwork Co..........F....... 904 354-1441
Jacksonville *(G-6510)*
L & M Pallet Services Inc..........F....... 863 519-3502
Bartow *(G-322)*
Lifdek Corporation..........G....... 321 759-3422
Melbourne *(G-8872)*
Manasota Pallets..........F....... 941 360-0562
Sarasota *(G-16501)*
Monison Pallets Inc..........F....... 904 359-0235
Jacksonville *(G-6614)*
Monison Pallets Inc..........F....... 305 637-1600
Miami *(G-10040)*
Muchochos Saw Mill & Pallets..........G....... 786 899-0535
Miami Springs *(G-10895)*
National Pallets..........E....... 305 324-1021
Miami *(G-10062)*
Opa-Locka Pallets Inc..........F....... 305 681-8212
Opa Locka *(G-12347)*
Pal-King Inc..........E....... 904 334-8797
Jacksonville *(G-6652)*
Pallet Consultants Corp..........E....... 954 946-2212
Pompano Beach *(G-14783)*
Pallet Depot LLC..........E....... 863 686-6245
Lakeland *(G-7761)*
Pallet Direct Inc..........G....... 888 433-1727
Naples *(G-11354)*
Pallet Doctor Inc..........G....... 904 444-2514
Jacksonville *(G-6653)*
Pallet Dude LLC..........F....... 941 720-1667
Sarasota *(G-16535)*
Pallet Enterprises of Florida..........G....... 305 836-3204
Miami *(G-10131)*
Pallet Enterprises Orlando Inc..........G....... 407 888-3200
Orlando *(G-13044)*
Pallet Ex Jacksonville Inc..........E....... 904 781-2500
Jacksonville *(G-6654)*
Pallet Express Inc..........F....... 813 752-1600
Plant City *(G-14452)*
Pallet Express of Jkvl Inc..........F....... 904 781-2500
Jacksonville *(G-6655)*
Pallet Industries Inc..........F....... 954 935-5804
Deerfield Beach *(G-2882)*
Pallet One of Mobile LLC..........F....... 251 960-1107
Bartow *(G-326)*
Pallet Racks Plus LLC..........G....... 321 203-6634
Orlando *(G-13045)*
Pallet Recall Inc..........G....... 941 727-1944
Sarasota *(G-16270)*
Pallet Services Inc..........G....... 813 754-7719
Plant City *(G-14453)*
Pallet Solutions Inc..........G....... 305 801-8314
Miami *(G-10132)*
Palletone Inc..........E....... 800 771-1147
Bartow *(G-327)*
Palletone of Texas LP..........D....... 903 628-5695
Bartow *(G-328)*
Palletone of Texas LP..........D....... 863 533-1147
Bartow *(G-329)*
Pallets Plus Inc..........G....... 813 759-6355
Plant City *(G-14454)*
Pallets To Go Inc..........F....... 305 654-0303
Miami *(G-10133)*
Panama City Pallet Inc..........E....... 850 769-1040
Panama City *(G-13936)*
Panama Pallets Co Inc..........G....... 850 769-1040
Panama City *(G-13939)*
Phoenix Wood Products Inc..........E....... 888 304-1131
Ocala *(G-12026)*
Placetas Pallet Corp..........G....... 305 633-4262
Hialeah *(G-5559)*
Premier Pallet Recycler LLC..........G....... 561 722-0457
West Palm Beach *(G-19004)*
Premier Pallets Inc..........G....... 813 986-4889
Tampa *(G-18008)*
Ralph & Llerena Pallets Inc..........G....... 305 446-2651
Hialeah *(G-5593)*
Rass Fast Pallet Inc..........G....... 786 877-2854
Miami *(G-10241)*
Regional Trailer Repair Inc..........F....... 912 484-7729
Jacksonville *(G-6714)*
Ricks Pallet Co Inc..........G....... 305 884-4896
Hialeah *(G-5600)*
Romeros Pallets of Jax..........G....... 904 329-2962
Jacksonville *(G-6734)*
Sanchez Brothers Corp..........F....... 561 992-0062
South Bay *(G-16797)*
Sophistcted Pllet Woodworx LLC..........G....... 561 795-0739
Loxahatchee *(G-8364)*
South Florida Pallet Inc..........G....... 305 330-7663
Miami *(G-10383)*
South Florida Pallets Dist..........F....... 305 330-7663
Doral *(G-3506)*
Southeastern Pallets Inc..........G....... 904 783-8363
Jacksonville *(G-6791)*
Suncoast Pallets Inc..........G....... 813 988-1623
Temple Terrace *(G-18379)*
Superior Pallets Llc..........G....... 863 875-4041
Winter Haven *(G-19359)*
Tropical Pallets Inc..........G....... 305 634-0346
Miami *(G-10508)*
USA Express Pallets Corp..........G....... 786 251-9543
Miami *(G-10554)*
Usmi Pallets Inc..........G....... 813 765-4309
Plant City *(G-14475)*
Walling Crate Company..........F....... 352 787-5211
Leesburg *(G-8180)*

PANEL & DISTRIBUTION BOARDS & OTHER RELATED APPARATUS

Hallmark Nameplate Inc..........D....... 352 383-8142
Mount Dora *(G-11103)*
Techno-Solis Inc..........F....... 727 823-6766
Saint Petersburg *(G-15937)*

PANEL & DISTRIBUTION BOARDS: Electric

Electrical Controls Inc..........F....... 954 801-6846
Tamarac *(G-17355)*
Ultrapanel Marine Inc..........E....... 772 285-4258
Miami *(G-10527)*

PANELS, FLAT: Plastic

Innovative Base Tech LLC..........G....... 727 391-9009
Saint Petersburg *(G-15816)*
Nida-Core Corporation..........E....... 772 343-7300
Port Saint Lucie *(G-15124)*

PANELS: Building, Metal

Dade Engineering Corp..........F....... 305 885-2766
Coral Gables *(G-2136)*
Metal Building Supplies LLC..........F....... 407 935-9714
Kissimmee *(G-7274)*
Ring Power Corporation..........E....... 904 354-1858
Jacksonville *(G-6725)*

PANELS: Building, Plastic, NEC

Elite Aluminum Corporation..........D....... 954 949-3200
Coconut Creek *(G-2075)*

PANELS: Building, Wood

Innova Eco Bldg Systems LLC..........E....... 305 455-7707
Miami *(G-9746)*

PAPER & BOARD: Die-cut

Advanced Printing Finshg Inc..........F....... 305 836-8581
Hialeah *(G-5272)*
Bros Williams Printing Inc..........G....... 305 769-9925
Hialeah *(G-5332)*
C & R Designs Inc..........G....... 321 383-2255
Titusville *(G-18419)*
Florida Print Finishers Inc..........G....... 850 877-8503
Tallahassee *(G-17255)*
Folders Tabs Et Cetera..........F....... 813 884-3651
Tampa *(G-17691)*
Knopf & Sons Bindery Inc..........F....... 904 355-4411
Jacksonville *(G-6543)*

Maq Investments Group Inc...E... 305 691-1468
Miami Lakes *(G-10811)*
Packaging Alternatives Corp...F... 352 867-5050
Ocala *(G-12021)*
Service Bindery Enterprises...F... 727 823-9866
Saint Petersburg *(G-15911)*
Southeast Finishing Group Inc...E... 407 299-4620
Orlando *(G-13202)*
Specialty Fin Consulting Corp...B... 717 246-1661
Longboat Key *(G-8247)*

PAPER CONVERTING

Amerifax Acquisition Corp...G... 305 828-1701
Hialeah *(G-5297)*
Automated Paper Converters...G... 954 925-0721
Hollywood *(G-5779)*
Dietzgen Corporation...E... 813 286-4767
Tampa *(G-17605)*
Express Paper Company Inc...F... 305 685-4929
Miami Lakes *(G-10787)*
Gainesville Sun...F... 352 374-5000
Gainesville *(G-4928)*
Palmland Paper Co Inc...G... 954 764-6910
Fort Lauderdale *(G-4154)*
Putnam Paper & Packaging Inc...F... 904 328-5101
Palatka *(G-13491)*
R & D Sleeves Llc...E... 407 886-9010
Apopka *(G-178)*
Specialty Fin Consulting Corp...B... 717 246-1661
Longboat Key *(G-8247)*
Vinland Marketing Inc...G... 954 602-2177
Pembroke Pines *(G-14071)*

PAPER MANUFACTURERS: Exc Newsprint

Bristol Venture Service LLC...G... 407 844-8629
Orlando *(G-12536)*
Bristols Elite...G... 954 651-3574
Hollywood *(G-5790)*
Commonwealth Brands Inc...C... 800 481-5814
Fort Lauderdale *(G-3912)*
Domtar Industries Inc...G... 727 421-6919
Palm Harbor *(G-13733)*
Excel Converting Inc...F... 786 318-2222
Miami *(G-9542)*
F3 Analytics LLC...G... 404 551-2600
Boca Grande *(G-392)*
Fraser West Inc...D... 901 620-4200
Jacksonville *(G-6414)*
Georgia-Pacific LLC...E... 386 328-8826
Palatka *(G-13481)*
Global Tissue Group Jax...F... 904 861-3290
Jacksonville *(G-6438)*
Gold Bond Building Pdts LLC...E... 813 672-8269
Gibsonton *(G-5028)*
J Bristol LLC...G... 407 488-6744
Winter Park *(G-19415)*
Monadnock Paper Mills Inc...G... 603 588-8672
Lutz *(G-8402)*
N V Texpack Group...F... 305 358-9696
Miami *(G-10057)*
Paper Chase...G... 561 641-5319
Lake Worth *(G-7579)*
Peninsula Tissue Corporation...G... 305 863-0704
Miami *(G-10151)*
Resolute Tissue LLC...F... 305 636-5741
Miami *(G-10258)*
Scratch Off Store...G... 800 584-9937
Oviedo *(G-13456)*
Suzano Pulp & Paper...G... 954 772-7716
Fort Lauderdale *(G-4270)*
Vinland Marketing Inc...G... 954 602-2177
Pembroke Pines *(G-14071)*
West Fraser Inc...D... 850 587-1000
Mc David *(G-8602)*

PAPER PRDTS

Contact Enterprises Inc...G... 561 900-5134
Pompano Beach *(G-14647)*

PAPER PRDTS: Book Covers

David Dobbs Enterprises Inc...D... 904 824-6171
Saint Augustine *(G-15533)*

PAPER PRDTS: Cleansing Tissues, Made From Purchased Material

Anthem South LLC...E... 973 779-1982
Medley *(G-8610)*

Peter Marcus Paradigm LLC...F... 877 887-8696
Winter Park *(G-19429)*

PAPER PRDTS: Feminine Hygiene Prdts

All About Her...F... 954 559-5175
Davie *(G-2491)*
Bk Naturals LLC...G... 561 870-0592
West Palm Beach *(G-18823)*
Esteemed Brands Inc...F... 954 442-3923
Miramar *(G-10990)*
Johnson & Johnson...D... 954 534-1141
Dania Beach *(G-2466)*

PAPER PRDTS: Infant & Baby Prdts

Wonderworld 100 LLC...F... 407 618-3207
Orlando *(G-13329)*

PAPER PRDTS: Napkin Stock

Sun Paper Company...E... 305 887-0040
Doral *(G-3516)*

PAPER PRDTS: Napkins, Made From Purchased Materials

Pacific Link Imports Inc...G... 954 605-6071
Parkland *(G-13997)*

PAPER PRDTS: Pin Tickets, Made From Purchased Paper

Amtec Sales Inc...F... 800 994-3318
Miami *(G-9153)*

PAPER PRDTS: Sanitary

Diversitypro Corp...E... 305 691-2348
South Miami *(G-16815)*
Playtex Manufacturing Inc...E... 386 677-9559
Ormond Beach *(G-13391)*

PAPER PRDTS: Toilet Tissue, Stock

Atlas Paper Mills LLC...F... 800 562-2860
Miami *(G-9187)*
Atlas Paper Mills LLC...C... 305 835-8046
Hialeah *(G-5311)*
Resolute FP Florida Inc...D... 800 562-2860
Miami *(G-10257)*

PAPER PRDTS: Towels, Napkins/Tissue Paper, From Purchd Mtrls

Green Leaf Foods LLC...G... 305 308-9167
Miramar *(G-11001)*
Lifelink Foundation Inc...E... 407 218-8783
Orlando *(G-12909)*
Papers Unlimited Plus Inc...G... 215 947-1155
Palm Beach Gardens *(G-13616)*
Softex Paper Inc...D... 386 328-8488
Palatka *(G-13494)*
SW Premier Products LLC...G... 941 275-6677
Punta Gorda *(G-15240)*
Threez Company LLC...G... 904 422-9224
Jacksonville *(G-6853)*
Threez Company LLC...G... 904 651-1444
Jacksonville *(G-6854)*

PAPER PRDTS: Wrappers, Blank, Made From Purchased Materials

Versatile Packagers LLC...F... 813 664-1171
Tampa *(G-18238)*

PAPER, WHOLESALE: Printing

PHI CHI Foundation Inc...G... 561 526-3401
Margate *(G-8560)*
Trend At LLC...F... 786 300-2550
Miami *(G-10505)*

PAPER: Adhesive

Automatic Business Products Co...F... 888 742-7639
Port Orange *(G-15009)*
Avery Dennison Corporation...C... 727 787-1651
Palm Harbor *(G-13721)*
Online Labels LLC...E... 407 936-3900
Sanford *(G-16096)*
Southern States Gluing Svcs...G... 850 469-9667
Pensacola *(G-14264)*

Tapesouth Inc...G... 904 642-1800
Gainesville *(G-5007)*

PAPER: Art

Art On Paper LLC...G... 305 615-9096
Pinecrest *(G-14324)*
Pro Edge Cutlery LLC...G... 239 304-8000
Naples *(G-11374)*

PAPER: Bag

Probag Inc...F... 305 883-3266
Medley *(G-8712)*

PAPER: Book

John Franklin Mowery...G... 202 468-8644
Venice *(G-18557)*

PAPER: Business Form

Wise Business Forms Inc...E... 770 442-1060
Opa Locka *(G-12369)*

PAPER: Cardboard

Cardboard Only Inc...G... 352 345-5060
Weeki Wachee *(G-18701)*
Tommy & Giordy Buy/Sell...G... 786 797-6973
Opa Locka *(G-12365)*
White Cardboard Corp...G... 786 260-4692
Miami *(G-10600)*

PAPER: Cloth, Lined, Made From Purchased Materials

Terry Boca Inc...G... 561 893-0333
Deerfield Beach *(G-2925)*

PAPER: Coated & Laminated, NEC

Avery Dennison Corporation...C... 305 228-8740
Miami *(G-9197)*
Florida Tape & Labels Inc...F... 941 921-5788
Sarasota *(G-16438)*
Folders Tabs Et Cetera...F... 813 884-3651
Tampa *(G-17691)*
J & P Deerfield Inc...F... 954 571-6665
Deerfield Beach *(G-2849)*
Keithco Inc...G... 352 351-4741
Ocala *(G-11976)*
Labelpro Inc...F... 727 538-2149
Clearwater *(G-1757)*
Midds Inc...E... 561 586-6220
Lake Worth Beach *(G-7615)*
Mikes Print Shop Inc...G... 407 718-4964
Winter Park *(G-19426)*
Southeast Id LLC...F... 954 571-6665
Miami Lakes *(G-10859)*
Suncoast Identification Tech...G... 239 277-9922
Fort Myers *(G-4616)*
Tampa Bay Coatings Inc...F... 727 823-9866
Saint Petersburg *(G-15933)*
Taylor Communications Inc...F... 813 886-5511
Tampa *(G-18177)*

PAPER: Gift Wrap

Gift Wrap My Face LLC...F... 305 788-1473
Weston *(G-19133)*

PAPER: Kraft

Vertpac LLC...E... 407 886-9010
Apopka *(G-195)*

PAPER: Magazine

Niche Digital Media Corp...G... 561 768-9793
Jupiter *(G-7081)*

PAPER: Packaging

Papers Unlimited Plus Inc...G... 215 947-1155
Palm Beach Gardens *(G-13616)*

PAPER: Specialty

Superior Leaf Inc...G... 561 480-2464
West Palm Beach *(G-19051)*

Employee Codes: A=Over 500 employees, B=251-500
C=101-250, D=51-100, E=20-50, F=10-19, G=4-9

PAPER: Tissue

3tissue LLC....G....904 540-4335
Jacksonville *(G-6101)*
Atlas Southeast Papers Inc....D....407 330-9118
Sanford *(G-15998)*
Gtg-Jax LLC....E....904 861-3290
Jacksonville *(G-6454)*
Resolute Tissue Sales....C....800 562-2860
Hialeah *(G-5597)*

PAPER: Transfer, Gold Or Silver, From Purchased Materials

One Step Papers LLC....G....305 238-2296
Miami *(G-10103)*

PAPER: Waxed, Made From Purchased Materials

World Indus Resources Corp....E....727 572-9991
Clearwater *(G-1944)*

PAPER: Wrapping

Great American Rolling Ppr Co....G....813 928-9166
Tampa *(G-17727)*

PAPER: Wrapping & Packaging

Hammer Head Group Inc....E....305 436-5691
Doral *(G-3377)*
Main Packaging Supply....E....305 863-7176
Miami *(G-9936)*

PAPERBOARD

Biodegradable Packaging Corp....E....305 824-1164
Miami Lakes *(G-10769)*
Design Containers Inc....D....904 764-6541
Jacksonville *(G-6316)*
Matrix Packaging of Florida....G....305 358-9696
Miami *(G-9956)*
Sonoco Products Company....E....386 424-0970
New Smyrna Beach *(G-11545)*
Westrock Cp LLC....G....954 522-3684
Fort Lauderdale *(G-4320)*
Westrock Cp LLC....E....407 843-1300
Orlando *(G-13323)*

PAPERBOARD PRDTS: Container Board

Westrock Cp LLC....C....904 714-7151
Jacksonville *(G-6914)*

PAPERBOARD PRDTS: Tagboard

Sfada Tag Agency Inc....F....305 981-1077
North Miami *(G-11654)*

PAPERBOARD: Corrugated

Porter Pizza Box Florida Inc....E....800 626-0828
Lakeland *(G-7770)*

PARACHUTES

Aerodyne Research LLC....F....813 891-6300
Deland *(G-2954)*
Eiff Aerodynamics Inc....F....386 734-3958
Deland *(G-2974)*
Performance Designs Inc....C....386 738-2224
Deland *(G-3009)*
S E Inc....E....407 859-9317
Orlando *(G-13151)*
Tactical Prchute Dlvry Systems....F....813 782-7482
Zephyrhills *(G-19540)*
USA Vigil....G....386 736-8464
Deland *(G-3029)*

PARKING STRUCTURE

Magnetic Automation Corp....E....321 635-8585
Rockledge *(G-15431)*

PARTICLEBOARD

Florida Plywoods Inc....D....850 948-2211
Greenville *(G-5088)*

PARTICLEBOARD: Laminated, Plastic

Allied Plastics Co Inc....E....904 359-0386
Jacksonville *(G-6138)*

PARTITIONS & FIXTURES: Except Wood

Akiknav Inc....F....561 842-8091
Riviera Beach *(G-15296)*
Bass Industries Inc....E....305 751-2716
Hialeah *(G-5316)*
Bruce R Ely Enterprise Inc....F....727 573-1643
Clearwater *(G-1614)*
Ccp of Miami Inc....G....305 233-6534
Miami *(G-9331)*
Dons Cabinets and Woodworking....F....727 863-3404
Hudson *(G-6022)*
Gulf South Distributors Inc....F....850 244-1522
Fort Walton Beach *(G-4807)*
Iverica Industrial Inc....F....305 691-1659
Hialeah *(G-5458)*
James Spear Design Inc....G....727 592-9600
Largo *(G-7986)*
N & N Investment Corporation....E....954 590-3800
Pompano Beach *(G-14770)*
Sam Weiss Woodworking Inc....G....954 975-8158
Margate *(G-8566)*
T & R Store Fixtures Inc....E....305 751-0377
Miami *(G-10453)*
Tcm Imagineering Inc....F....407 323-6494
Deland *(G-3017)*
Teak Isle Inc....C....407 656-8885
Ocoee *(G-12091)*
Telese Inc....E....813 752-6015
Plant City *(G-14470)*

PARTITIONS: Nonwood, Floor Attached

American Sani Partition Corp....E....407 656-0611
Ocoee *(G-12082)*

PARTITIONS: Wood & Fixtures

Amick Cstm Woodcraft & Design....G....407 324-8525
Sanford *(G-15994)*
Braden Kitchens Inc....E....321 636-4700
Cocoa *(G-1999)*
Caseworks International Inc....F....954 933-9102
Fort Lauderdale *(G-3884)*
Central Fla Kit Bath Srfces In....F....352 307-2333
Ocala *(G-11898)*
Corn-E-Lee Woodcrafts....G....239 574-2414
Cape Coral *(G-1406)*
Creative Countertops Inc....F....904 387-2800
Jacksonville *(G-6296)*
Custom Cabinets Inc....F....941 366-0428
Sarasota *(G-16398)*
Custom Marble Works Inc....E....813 620-0475
Tampa *(G-17580)*
Daystar International Inc....G....813 281-0200
Tampa *(G-17593)*
EMI Industries LLC....C....813 626-3166
Tampa *(G-17636)*
Extreme Wood Works S Fla Inc....F....305 463-8614
Doral *(G-3346)*
Featherlite Exhibits....G....800 229-5533
Tampa *(G-17663)*
Florida Designer Cabinets Inc....F....352 793-8555
Sumterville *(G-17068)*
Gds....G....305 764-0920
North Miami *(G-11640)*
Home Pride Cabinets Inc....F....813 887-3782
Tampa *(G-17760)*
J & J Custom Mica Inc....F....239 433-2828
Fort Myers *(G-4498)*
J M Interiors Inc....G....305 891-6121
North Miami *(G-11642)*
Kitchen Counter Connections....E....386 677-9471
Ormond Beach *(G-13382)*
Larsen Cabinetmaker Co....G....305 252-1212
Miami *(G-9860)*
Mahan Cabinets....G....305 255-3325
Cutler Bay *(G-2403)*
Mayworth Showcase Works Inc....G....813 251-1558
Tampa *(G-17896)*
McCallum Cabinets Inc....F....352 372-2344
Gainesville *(G-4957)*
Morning Star of Sarasota Inc....G....941 371-0392
Sarasota *(G-16514)*
N & N Investment Corporation....E....954 590-3800
Pompano Beach *(G-14770)*
Princeton Industries Inc....E....954 344-9155
Margate *(G-8563)*
Sand Dollar Charters LLC....G....903 734-5376
New Smyrna Beach *(G-11542)*
Southern Woodworks Fine Wdwkg....F....850 456-0550
Pensacola *(G-14266)*
Wonder Emporium Millwork Fab....G....407 850-3131
Orlando *(G-13328)*
Y F Leung Inc....G....305 651-6851
North Miami Beach *(G-11714)*

PARTITIONS: Wood, Floor Attached

East Coast Fixtures & Mllwk Co....G....904 733-9711
Jacksonville *(G-6349)*
Hugh Robinson Inc....G....954 484-0660
Lauderdale Lakes *(G-8088)*

PARTS: Metal

Ameri Produ Produ Compa of Pin....G....813 925-0144
Tampa *(G-17413)*
American Products Inc....G....813 925-0144
Tampa *(G-17418)*
G Metal Industries Inc....F....305 633-0300
Miami *(G-9607)*
Heritage Manufacturing Svcs....G....727 906-5599
Saint Petersburg *(G-15806)*
Militek Industries LLC....G....941 544-5636
Bradenton *(G-1078)*
Nautical Structures Inds Inc....D....727 541-6664
Largo *(G-8018)*

PARTY & SPECIAL EVENT PLANNING SVCS

Premier Parties Entertainment....E....352 375-6122
Gainesville *(G-4983)*

PATENT OWNERS & LESSORS

Lasersight Incorporated....F....407 678-9900
Orlando *(G-12893)*

PATIENT MONITORING EQPT WHOLESALERS

Nuline Sensors LLC....G....407 473-0765
Sanford *(G-16092)*

PATROL SVCS: Electric Transmission Or Gas Lines

Mitsubishi Power Americas Inc....D....407 688-6100
Lake Mary *(G-7436)*

PATTERNS: Indl

Cost Cast Aluminum Corp....E....863 422-5617
Haines City *(G-5140)*
Living Pattern LLC....G....561 596-8205
Delray Beach *(G-3101)*
Pattern Grading & Marker Svcs....G....305 495-9963
Miramar *(G-11027)*

PAVERS

A & J Pavers Inc....G....863 559-1920
Lakeland *(G-7624)*
Adriano Gb Brick Pavers LLC....G....407 497-1517
Orlando *(G-12432)*
AM Pavers Inc....G....954 275-1590
Boca Raton *(G-418)*
Artistic Pavers....G....727 572-1998
Clearwater *(G-1590)*
Artistic Pavers LLC....F....727 573-0918
Clearwater *(G-1591)*
Atm Pavers Inc....G....239 322-7010
Cape Coral *(G-1386)*
Baju Professional Brick Pavers....G....727 234-5300
Pinellas Park *(G-14336)*
Baron Pavers Corp....G....786 389-2894
Miami *(G-9222)*
Brazilian Brickpavers Inc....G....850 699-7833
Fort Walton Beach *(G-4785)*
Brito Brick & Pavers Corp....G....727 214-8760
Clearwater *(G-1613)*
C&C Brick Pavers Inc....G....813 716-8291
Tampa *(G-17496)*
Compact Brick Pavers Inc....G....727 278-1544
Bradenton *(G-1022)*
David Thiessens Pavers Inc....G....813 516-1389
Thonotosassa *(G-18400)*
Destination Pavers LLC....G....850 319-6551
Panama City *(G-13891)*
Fine Line Pavers Inc....G....561 389-9819
West Palm Beach *(G-18871)*
First Coast Pavers Corp....F....904 410-0278
Orange Park *(G-12395)*

Herbert Pavers Inc.....G..... 941 447-4909
Bradenton *(G-1056)*
Hightec Con Pavers & Curbing.....G..... 941 412-6077
Englewood *(G-3678)*
Homewood Holdings LLC.....F..... 941 740-3655
Cape Coral *(G-1438)*
Island Paver Sealing & Prssure.....G..... 727 641-3512
Clearwater *(G-1738)*
Keystone Brick Paver.....G..... 239 340-6492
Fort Myers *(G-4510)*
Labelle Brick Pavers Tile LLC.....F..... 863 230-3100
Labelle *(G-7319)*
Lentus Products LLC.....G..... 203 913-7600
Kissimmee *(G-7268)*
Lg Enterprises Pavers Inc.....G..... 813 412-9235
Tampa *(G-17843)*
Martins Pavers & Pools Corp.....G..... 754 368-4413
Deerfield Beach *(G-2869)*
Matao Brick Pavers Inc.....G..... 321 663-1978
Orlando *(G-12954)*
Naia Brick Pavers Inc.....G..... 727 638-4734
Pinellas Park *(G-14371)*
North Florida Brick Pavers LLC.....G..... 850 255-0336
Santa Rosa Beach *(G-16164)*
North Port Pavers Inc.....G..... 941 391-7557
North Port *(G-11745)*
Number 1 Brick Pavers Inc.....G..... 321 388-7889
Orlando *(G-13014)*
Pacific Pavers Inc.....G..... 941 238-7854
Bradenton *(G-1090)*
Paver King.....G..... 407 221-1718
Lake Mary *(G-7442)*
Paver Paradise LLC.....G..... 561 843-3031
Port St Lucie *(G-15178)*
Paver Way LLC.....F..... 321 303-0968
Altamonte Springs *(G-63)*
Pavers Inc.....G..... 352 754-3875
Brooksville *(G-1258)*
Payless Brick Pavers LLC.....G..... 904 629-7436
Jacksonville *(G-6662)*
Perfect Pavers South Fla LLC.....F..... 954 779-1855
Fort Lauderdale *(G-4162)*
Precise Pavers Inc.....F..... 863 528-8000
Auburndale *(G-250)*
Professonal Paver Restorations.....G..... 352 797-8411
Spring Hill *(G-16859)*
Reef Pavers Inc.....G..... 904 471-0859
Jacksonville Beach *(G-6956)*
Reyes Interlocking Pavers Inc.....G..... 863 698-9179
Plant City *(G-14462)*
Rio Pavers Inc.....G..... 321 388-6757
Orlando *(G-13140)*
Rockstone Brick Pavers.....G..... 813 685-3900
Brandon *(G-1175)*
Shavers Pavers.....G..... 407 350-3538
Kissimmee *(G-7298)*
Sivo Brick Pavers Inc.....G..... 813 917-3859
Palm Harbor *(G-13760)*
South Florida Pavers Corp.....G..... 786 517-9100
Hialeah *(G-5626)*
Stabil Concrete Pavers LLC.....E..... 941 739-7823
Sarasota *(G-16300)*
Stamp Concrete & Pavers Inc.....G..... 561 880-1527
Merritt Island *(G-9014)*
Stone Brick Pavers Inc.....G..... 407 844-1455
Ocoee *(G-12090)*
Suncoast Pavers Llc.....G..... 813 323-4014
Odessa *(G-12158)*
Superior Pavers and Stone LLC.....G..... 904 887-7831
Jacksonville *(G-6829)*
Sws Services Inc.....F..... 904 802-2120
Fernandina Beach *(G-3748)*
T & E Pavers Inc.....G..... 239 243-6229
Cape Coral *(G-1483)*
Tremron LLC.....C..... 904 359-5900
Jacksonville *(G-6868)*
Tropical Paver Sealing.....G..... 727 786-4011
Wesley Chapel *(G-18761)*
US Paver Co.....G..... 954 292-4373
Boca Raton *(G-772)*
Villar Stone & Paver Works LLC.....G..... 860 209-2907
Sarasota *(G-16633)*
Wagner Pavers Contractor.....G..... 321 633-5131
Rockledge *(G-15456)*
Waller Pavers Inc.....G..... 863 644-8187
Lakeland *(G-7831)*
Wf Brick Pavers Inc.....G..... 813 506-1941
Oldsmar *(G-12278)*

PAVING MATERIALS: Coal Tar, Not From Refineries

Star-Seal of Florida Inc.....F..... 954 484-8402
Fort Lauderdale *(G-4259)*

PAWN SHOPS

Westchester Gold Fabricators.....G..... 941 625-0666
Port Charlotte *(G-15007)*

PAY TELEPHONE NETWORK

Clinigence Holdings Inc.....G..... 678 607-6393
Fort Lauderdale *(G-3904)*

PEAT GRINDING SVCS

Sun Gro Horticulture Dist Inc.....G..... 407 291-1676
Orlando *(G-13222)*
Sunshine.....G..... 305 382-6677
Miami *(G-10433)*

PEDESTALS: Marble

C L Industries Inc.....E..... 800 333-2660
Orlando *(G-12540)*

PENCILS & PARTS: Mechanical

Dixon Ticonderoga Company.....D..... 407 829-9000
Lake Mary *(G-7409)*

PENS & PENCILS: Mechanical, NEC

Bic Corporation.....A..... 727 536-7895
Clearwater *(G-1607)*
Ross Industries Inc.....D..... 954 752-2800
Pompano Beach *(G-14834)*
Scribe Manufacturing Inc.....B..... 727 524-7482
Clearwater *(G-1870)*
Scribe Manufacturing Inc.....F..... 727 536-7895
Saint Petersburg *(G-15907)*
Scribe Opco Inc.....D..... 727 536-7895
Clearwater *(G-1871)*
Sharp Marketing LLC.....G..... 954 565-2711
Oakland Park *(G-11838)*

PERFUME: Concentrated

Mar Company Distributors LLC.....E..... 786 477-4174
Miami *(G-9943)*

PERFUME: Perfumes, Natural Or Synthetic

Crusellas & Co Inc.....F..... 305 261-9580
Miami *(G-9414)*
Grafton Products Corp.....E..... 561 738-2886
Boynton Beach *(G-914)*
It Smells Good.....G..... 904 899-2818
Jacksonville *(G-6504)*

PERFUMES

B224 USA Co.....G..... 786 598-8805
Holiday *(G-5735)*
Firmenich Lakeland.....G..... 863 646-0165
Lakeland *(G-7686)*
Omnireliant Corporation.....G..... 813 909-9191
Tampa *(G-17956)*
Perfumeland.....F..... 407 354-3342
Orlando *(G-13065)*
Wake Up Beautiful.....G..... 941 792-6500
Bradenton *(G-1145)*

PERLITE: Processed

Conrad Yelvington Distrs Inc.....G..... 352 336-5049
Gainesville *(G-4895)*

PERMANENT WAVE EQPT & MACHINES

Sox LLC.....G..... 561 501-0057
Boca Raton *(G-725)*

PERSONAL CREDIT INSTITUTIONS: Consumer Finance Companies

Eran Financial Services LLC.....E..... 844 411-5483
Boca Raton *(G-520)*

PEST CONTROL IN STRUCTURES SVCS

50 50 Parmley Envmtl Svcs LLC.....G..... 407 593-1165
Saint Cloud *(G-15641)*

PEST CONTROL SVCS

Natures Own Pest Control Inc.....G..... 941 378-3334
Sarasota *(G-16521)*

PESTICIDES

Brandfx LLC.....E..... 321 632-2063
Cocoa *(G-2000)*
Glades Formulating Corporation.....F..... 561 996-4200
Belle Glade *(G-348)*
Levita LLC.....G..... 954 227-7468
Coral Springs *(G-2273)*
North Florida AG Services Inc.....G..... 352 494-3978
Lake City *(G-7371)*
Organic Laboratories Inc.....G..... 772 286-5581
Fort Pierce *(G-4728)*
Pbi/Gordon Corp.....F..... 850 478-2770
Pensacola *(G-14223)*

PESTICIDES WHOLESALERS

Glades Formulating Corporation.....F..... 561 996-4200
Belle Glade *(G-348)*

PET ACCESS: Collars, Leashes, Etc, Exc Leather

Find A Friend LLC.....G..... 813 293-1584
Land O Lakes *(G-7855)*
Pets2go International Inc.....E..... 404 625-9606
Homestead *(G-5987)*

PET COLLARS, LEASHES, MUZZLES & HARNESSES: Leather

Bully Wurld LLC.....G..... 201 466-8185
Cape Coral *(G-1397)*
Dp Pet Products Inc.....F..... 407 888-4627
Orlando *(G-12681)*
N3xt Up Exotic LLC.....G..... 863 777-3778
Tampa *(G-17928)*

PET SPLYS

Be The Solution Inc.....G..... 850 545-2043
Tallahassee *(G-17227)*
Cafco LLC.....G..... 240 848-5574
Miami *(G-9301)*
Crown Products LLC.....G..... 954 917-1118
Pompano Beach *(G-14652)*
Higgins Group Corp.....E..... 305 681-4444
Miami *(G-9709)*
Just Fur Fun.....G..... 561 809-6596
Boca Raton *(G-584)*
King Kanine LLC.....E..... 833 546-4738
Plantation *(G-14528)*
Le Posh Pup.....G..... 561 625-6391
Okeechobee *(G-12186)*
M Pet Group Corp.....G..... 954 455-5003
Aventura *(G-276)*
Matry Group LLC.....F..... 407 461-9797
Kissimmee *(G-7314)*
Miami Tbr LLC.....G..... 786 275-4773
Doral *(G-3437)*
Munro International Inc.....E..... 352 337-1535
Gainesville *(G-4968)*
Nava Pets Inc.....F..... 407 982-7256
Longwood *(G-8315)*
Panagenics Inc.....G..... 888 773-0700
Miami *(G-10136)*
Pet Declaration Inc.....G..... 772 215-1607
Tampa *(G-17984)*
Pet Supplies Plus.....G..... 248 824-4676
North Port *(G-11746)*
Pets2go International Inc.....E..... 404 625-9606
Homestead *(G-5987)*
Professional Pet Products Inc.....E..... 305 592-1992
Doral *(G-3471)*
RDt Business Enterprises Inc.....F..... 954 525-1133
Fort Lauderdale *(G-4200)*
South Florida Rodents.....G..... 954 410-5635
Southwest Ranches *(G-16842)*
Sunshine Nylon Products Inc.....G..... 352 754-9932
Brooksville *(G-1277)*
Synergylabs LLC.....E..... 954 525-1133
Fort Lauderdale *(G-4272)*
Timberwolf Organics Ltd Lblty.....F..... 407 877-8779
Windermere *(G-19246)*
Tropichem Research Labs LLC.....D..... 561 804-7603
Jupiter *(G-7134)*

West Texas Protein Inc....F....806 250-5959
Jacksonville *(G-6911)*
You Lucky Dog Inc....G....954 428-4648
Deerfield Beach *(G-2938)*

PET SPLYS WHOLESALERS

Miami Tbr LLC....G....786 275-4773
Doral *(G-3437)*
Panagenics Inc....G....888 773-0700
Miami *(G-10136)*

PETROLEUM PRDTS WHOLESALERS

Armor Oil Products LLC....G....813 248-1988
Tampa *(G-17435)*
Enviro Petroleum Inc....G....713 896-6996
Jensen Beach *(G-6968)*

PEWTER WARE

Accent Jewelry Inc....F....941 391-6687
Punta Gorda *(G-15189)*
Metal Rock Inc....F....407 886-6440
Apopka *(G-160)*

PHARMACEUTICAL PREPARATIONS: Adrenal

Caq International LLC....G....305 744-1472
Miami *(G-9311)*
Tg United Inc....G....352 799-9813
Brooksville *(G-1279)*

PHARMACEUTICAL PREPARATIONS: Druggists' Preparations

Ambo Health LLC....G....866 414-0188
Venice *(G-18532)*
Beutlich Pharmaceuticals LLC....F....386 263-8860
Bunnell *(G-1297)*
Exactus Pharmacy Solutions Inc....D....888 314-3874
Tampa *(G-17652)*
Navinta III Inc....G....561 997-6959
Boca Raton *(G-637)*
Pack4u LLC....E....407 857-2871
Orlando *(G-13043)*

PHARMACEUTICAL PREPARATIONS: Medicines, Capsule Or Ampule

Assistrx Inc....C....855 421-4607
Orlando *(G-12495)*
Nutrakey LLC....D....321 234-6282
Longwood *(G-8318)*
Nutricorp LLC....G....305 680-4896
Hialeah *(G-5547)*

PHARMACEUTICAL PREPARATIONS: Pills

American Bhvioral RES Inst LLC....D....888 353-1205
Boca Raton *(G-421)*
Liquidcapsule Mfg LLC....F....813 431-0532
Tampa *(G-17849)*
Neuro Pharmalogics Inc....G....240 476-4491
Boca Raton *(G-639)*
Qol Medical LLC....G....772 584-3640
Vero Beach *(G-18656)*

PHARMACEUTICAL PREPARATIONS: Powders

Biolife LLC....E....941 360-1300
Sarasota *(G-16184)*
Celigenex Inc....G....954 957-1058
Fort Lauderdale *(G-3888)*
Rx For Fleas Inc....F....954 351-9244
Fort Lauderdale *(G-4220)*
Xcelience LLC....E....813 286-0404
Tampa *(G-18270)*
Xcelience LLC....E....813 286-0404
Tampa *(G-18271)*

PHARMACEUTICAL PREPARATIONS: Proprietary Drug PRDTS

Lf of America Corp....G....561 988-0303
Boca Raton *(G-601)*
Peak Nutritional Products LLC....E....813 884-4989
Tampa *(G-17980)*
Quantum Pharmaceuticals LLC....G....321 724-0625
Melbourne Beach *(G-8982)*
Rockledge Phrm Mfg LLC....F....321 636-0717
Rockledge *(G-15444)*
Speer Laboratories LLC....F....954 586-8700
Fort Lauderdale *(G-4252)*
Vistapharm Inc....E....727 530-1633
Largo *(G-8078)*

PHARMACEUTICAL PREPARATIONS: Solutions

Abhai LLC....G....215 579-1842
Saint Augustine *(G-15512)*
Gand Inc....G....240 575-0622
Miami Beach *(G-10670)*
Viadiem LLC....G....407 571-6845
Maitland *(G-8484)*

PHARMACEUTICAL PREPARATIONS: Tablets

Capzerpharma Manufacturing LLC....G....561 493-4000
Lake Worth Beach *(G-7609)*
Corerx Pharmaceuticals Inc....E....727 259-6950
Clearwater *(G-1639)*

PHARMACEUTICAL PREPARATIONS: Tranquilizers Or Mental Drug

Alloy Fabricators Inc....G....813 925-0222
Tampa *(G-17403)*

PHARMACEUTICALS

1source Biotechnology LLC....G....305 668-5888
Miami *(G-9022)*
5d Bio Gold LLC....G....561 756-8291
Boca Raton *(G-394)*
Abbott Diabetes Care....G....863 385-7910
Sebring *(G-16679)*
AC Pharma Corp....G....954 773-9735
Margate *(G-8529)*
Accentia Biopharmaceuticals....F....813 864-2554
Tampa *(G-17385)*
Acic Pharmaceuticals Inc....G....954 341-0795
Coral Springs *(G-2212)*
Actavis Laboratories Fl Inc....C....954 305-4414
Davie *(G-2487)*
Advanced Pharma Research Inc....F....786 234-3709
Cutler Bay *(G-2384)*
Advanced Pharmaceutical Inc....G....866 259-7122
North Miami *(G-11622)*
Aegle Therapeutics Corporation....G....305 608-9705
Miami *(G-9080)*
Aenova Doral Manufacturing Inc....C....305 463-2270
Doral *(G-3228)*
Aenova Doral Manufacturing Inc....F....305 463-2263
Doral *(G-3229)*
Aerobotics Technologies Inc....G....407 658-9864
Orlando *(G-12440)*
Aim Immunotech Inc....F....352 448-7797
Ocala *(G-11867)*
Allay Pharmaceutical LLC....G....954 336-1136
Hialeah *(G-5281)*
Allergan Sales LLC....E....787 406-1203
Sunrise *(G-17088)*
Alta Pharma LLC....G....727 942-7645
Tarpon Springs *(G-18282)*
Alternative Medical Entps LLC....F....941 702-9955
Apollo Beach *(G-100)*
Alvita Pharma Usa Inc....G....305 961-1623
Doral *(G-3243)*
Alzamend Neuro Inc....G....844 722-6333
Tampa *(G-17411)*
American Injectables Inc....F....813 435-6014
Brooksville *(G-1210)*
American Pharmaceutical Svcs....G....407 704-5937
Orlando *(G-12473)*
Amicitia Pharma Llc....G....941 722-0172
Palmetto *(G-13786)*
Andrx Corporation....C....954 217-4500
Weston *(G-19105)*
Andrx Corporation....C....954 585-1770
Sunrise *(G-17091)*
Andrx Corporation....C....954 585-1400
Davie *(G-2497)*
Annona Biosciences Inc....G....888 204-4980
Palm Beach Gardens *(G-13566)*
Apical Pharmaceutical Corp....G....786 331-7200
Doral *(G-3251)*
Apotex Corp....E....954 384-8007
Weston *(G-19107)*
Archer Pharmaceuticals Inc....F....941 752-2949
Sarasota *(G-16175)*
Arnet Pharmaceutical Corp....B....954 236-9053
Davie *(G-2499)*
Aveva Drug Dlvry Systems Inc....D....954 430-3340
Miramar *(G-10970)*
Axis Phrm Partners LLC....G....407 936-2949
Lake Mary *(G-7402)*
Azopharma Inc....G....954 536-4738
Miramar *(G-10971)*
Baker Norton US Inc....D....305 575-6000
Miami *(G-9215)*
Barcelona Dr Phillips LLC....G....407 352-9733
Orlando *(G-12506)*
Beach Products Inc....G....813 839-6565
Tampa *(G-17462)*
Beacon Phrm Jupiter LLC....E....212 991-8988
Jupiter *(G-7005)*
Belcher Holdings Inc....C....727 530-1585
Largo *(G-7906)*
Belcher Holdings Inc....F....727 471-0850
Largo *(G-7907)*
Belcher Pharmaceuticals LLC....E....727 471-0850
Largo *(G-7908)*
Berman Products LLC....F....561 743-5197
Jupiter *(G-7006)*
Bio Therapeutics Inc....G....954 321-5553
Plantation *(G-14496)*
Bio-Nucleonics Pharma Inc....F....305 576-0996
Miami *(G-9247)*
Bio-Pharm LLC....G....973 223-7163
Hallandale Beach *(G-5171)*
Biogaia Biologics Inc....G....786 762-4000
Doral *(G-3275)*
Biostem Technologies Inc....G....954 380-8342
Pompano Beach *(G-14617)*
Bishop Pharma LLC....G....954 292-7325
Pompano Beach *(G-14618)*
Bjmjrx Inc....G....941 505-9036
Punta Gorda *(G-15198)*
Bpc Plasma Inc....G....561 989-5800
Boca Raton *(G-461)*
Bpc Plasma Inc....E....561 569-3100
Boca Raton *(G-462)*
Bpi Labs LLC....C....727 471-0850
Largo *(G-7912)*
Briemad Inc....F....561 626-4377
Palm Beach Gardens *(G-13572)*
Britvic North America LLC....F....786 641-5041
Miami *(G-9278)*
Cardinal Health 414 LLC....G....954 202-1883
Fort Lauderdale *(G-3883)*
Cardinal Health 414 LLC....G....813 972-1351
Tampa *(G-17507)*
Catalent Inc....F....727 803-2832
Saint Petersburg *(G-15739)*
Catalyst Pharmaceuticals Inc....E....305 420-3200
Coral Gables *(G-2129)*
Cbc Biotechnologies Inc....G....813 803-6300
Tampa *(G-17517)*
Centro De Diagnostico....G....407 865-7020
Sanford *(G-16011)*
Cerno Pharmaceuticals LLC....G....786 763-2766
Miami *(G-9343)*
Cleveland Diabetes Care Inc....G....904 394-2620
Jacksonville *(G-6268)*
Clinical Dagnstc Solutions Inc....E....954 791-1773
Plantation *(G-14500)*
Cocrystal Pharma Inc....G....877 262-7123
Miami *(G-9373)*
Community Pharmacy Svcs LLC....G....727 431-8261
Clearwater *(G-1634)*
Concordia Pharmaceuticals Inc....G....786 304-2083
Miami *(G-9391)*
Coqui Rdo Pharmaceuticals Corp....G....787 685-5046
Doral *(G-3307)*
Cor International (not Inc)....G....850 766-2866
Tallahassee *(G-17239)*
Corerx Inc....F....727 259-6950
Clearwater *(G-1637)*
Corerx Inc....C....727 259-6950
Clearwater *(G-1638)*
Cryothrapy Pain Rlief Pdts Inc....G....954 364-8192
Hollywood *(G-5806)*
Cyclo Therapeutics Inc....G....386 418-8060
Gainesville *(G-4902)*
Dain M Bayer....G....407 647-0679
Winter Park *(G-19400)*
Darmerica LLC....F....321 219-9111
Casselberry *(G-1502)*

Dazmed Inc....G....561 571-2020
Boca Raton (G-495)
DCS Pharma USA LLC....G....248 979-8866
Miami (G-9441)
Defender SD Manufacturing LLC....F....813 864-2570
Tampa (G-17598)
Demelle Biopharma LLC....G....908 240-8939
Tarpon Springs (G-18294)
Dermatonus....G....305 229-3923
Miramar (G-10983)
Devatis Inc....G....954 316-4844
Fort Lauderdale (G-3939)
Diabetic Care Rx LLC....E....866 348-0441
Pompano Beach (G-14664)
Doctors Scientific Organica LLC....F....888 455-9031
Riviera Beach (G-15321)
Duy Drugs Inc....F....305 594-3667
Doral (G-3337)
Eci Pharmaceuticals LLC....E....954 486-8181
Fort Lauderdale (G-3959)
Elite Fitforever LLC....G....305 902-2358
Miami Beach (G-10664)
EMJ Pharma Inc....G....973 600-9087
Palm Beach Gardens (G-13587)
Enveric Biosciences Inc....F....239 302-1707
Naples (G-11240)
Envoy Therapeutics Inc....G....561 210-7705
Jupiter (G-7035)
Ephs Holdings Inc....G....212 321-0091
Boynton Beach (G-903)
Epigenetix Inc....F....561 543-7569
Delray Beach (G-3075)
Erba Diagnostics Inc....D....305 324-2300
Miami Lakes (G-10786)
Exelan Pharmaceuticals Inc....G....561 287-6631
Boca Raton (G-525)
Farma International Inc....F....305 670-4416
Miami (G-9560)
First Wave Biopharma Inc....F....561 589-7020
Boca Raton (G-529)
Fitteam Global LLC....G....586 260-1487
Palm Beach Gardens (G-13590)
Forest Research Institute Inc....F....631 436-4600
Weston (G-19126)
Forest Research Institute Inc....E....954 622-5600
Sunrise (G-17124)
Fresenius Kabi Usa LLC....E....847 550-2300
Doral (G-3356)
Gadal Laboratories Inc....G....786 732-2571
Miami (G-9609)
Global Pharma Analytics LLC....F....701 491-7770
Jupiter (G-7049)
Global Phrm Compliance....G....239 949-4958
Bonita Springs (G-834)
Global Reach Rx Pbf LLC....F....786 703-1988
Doral (G-3369)
Green Roads of Florida....G....954 626-0574
Davie (G-2533)
Growhealthy Holdings LLC....F....863 223-8882
West Palm Beach (G-18891)
Hanna Pharmaceuticals LLC....G....813 409-9327
Lutz (G-8387)
High Five Products Inc....G....239 449-9268
Naples (G-11276)
Hill Dermaceuticals Inc....E....407 323-1887
Sanford (G-16062)
Hill Labs Inc....E....407 323-1887
Sanford (G-16063)
Immune Therapeutics Inc....E....888 613-8802
Winter Park (G-19412)
Infupharma LLC....G....305 301-3389
Hollywood (G-5848)
Innova Softgel LLC....C....855 536-8872
Miami (G-9747)
Inspire Inc....G....321 557-3247
Palm Bay (G-13517)
Inter Cell Technologies Inc....G....561 575-6868
Jupiter (G-7058)
Intratab Labs Inc....F....305 887-5850
Miami Springs (G-10892)
Ivax Pharmaceuticals LLC....C....305 575-6000
Miami (G-9776)
Ivax Research Inc....D....305 668-7688
Miami (G-9777)
Ivax Teva....G....954 384-5316
Weston (G-19144)
Kashiben Say LLC....G....352 489-4960
Dunnellon (G-3598)
Kavi Skin Solutions Inc....E....415 839-5156
Titusville (G-18438)
Kd-Pharma Usa Inc....G....786 345-5500
Miami (G-9817)
Kempharm Inc....G....321 939-3416
Celebration (G-1523)
King Pharmaceuticals LLC....G....954 575-7085
Coral Springs (G-2269)
King Pharmaceuticals LLC....E....423 989-8000
Saint Petersburg (G-15833)
KMA Pharma LLC....G....754 220-6936
Lighthouse Point (G-8209)
Kova Laboratories Inc....G....954 978-8730
Margate (G-8555)
Kramer Pharmacal Inc....F....305 226-0641
Miami (G-9830)
Krs Global Biotechnology Inc....E....888 502-2050
Boca Raton (G-592)
Krs MSA LLC....G....727 264-7605
New Port Richey (G-11497)
Labelclick Inc....G....727 548-8345
Oldsmar (G-12243)
Linpharma Inc....G....888 989-3237
Tampa (G-17847)
Llorens Phrm Intl Div Inc....F....305 716-0595
Miami (G-9904)
Longeveron Inc....F....305 909-0840
Miami (G-9909)
Lonza....G....727 608-6802
Tampa (G-17859)
Lupin Research Inc....E....800 466-1450
Coral Springs (G-2275)
M3 Biopharma Inc....G....858 603-8296
Sarasota (G-16494)
Magellan Pharmaceuticals Inc....G....813 623-6800
Tampa (G-17873)
Marizyme Inc....G....561 935-9955
Jupiter (G-7073)
Max Avw Professional LLC....F....954 972-3338
Margate (G-8557)
Maximilian Zenho & Co Inc....G....352 875-1190
Ocala (G-11996)
Mayo Clinic....G....904 953-2000
Jacksonville (G-6583)
Mayo Clinic....G....904 953-2000
Jacksonville (G-6584)
MCR Amrcan Pharmaceuticals Inc....E....352 754-8587
Brooksville (G-1248)
Medipharma Inc....G....305 858-7332
Miami (G-9967)
Merck Sharp & Dohme Corp....D....305 512-6062
Miami Lakes (G-10818)
Methapharm Inc....G....954 341-0795
Coral Springs (G-2282)
Mohnark Pharmaceuticals Inc....G....954 607-4559
Davie (G-2554)
Mpact Sales Solutions....G....630 669-5937
Oakland (G-11770)
Mymd Pharmaceuticals Inc....F....813 864-2566
Tampa (G-17925)
Nabi....F....561 989-5800
Boca Raton (G-635)
Nanobiotech Pharma Inc....G....866 568-0178
Coral Springs (G-2294)
Natural-Immunogenics Corp....D....888 328-8840
Sarasota (G-16265)
Natures Bioscience LLC....G....800 570-7450
Sarasota (G-16520)
Neglex Inc....F....305 551-4177
Miami (G-10063)
Nephron Pharmaceuticals....E....407 913-3142
Orlando (G-12997)
Nephron Pharmaceuticals Corp....E....407 999-2225
Orlando (G-12998)
New World Holdings Inc....E....561 888-4939
Boca Raton (G-642)
Nextsource Biotechnology LLC....G....305 753-6360
Miami (G-10068)
Nexus Alliance Corp....G....321 945-4283
Longwood (G-8317)
Northside Pharmacy LLC....G....256 398-7500
Destin (G-3200)
Noven Pharmaceuticals Inc....C....305 964-3393
Miami (G-10081)
Noven Therapeutics LLC....B....212 682-4420
Miami (G-10082)
Nutra Pharma Corp....G....954 509-0911
Coral Springs (G-2298)
Nxgen Brands LLC....E....888 315-6339
Plantation (G-14540)
Ocala Pharmacy LLC....G....352 509-7890
Ocala (G-12013)
Ocean Pharmaceuticals Inc....F....954 473-4717
Sunrise (G-17153)
One Nursing Care LLC....G....954 441-6644
Miramar (G-11025)
Opko Health Inc....A....305 575-4100
Miami (G-10111)
Oragenics Inc....G....813 286-7900
Tampa (G-17959)
Oryza Pharmaceuticals Inc....E....954 881-5481
Coral Springs (G-2301)
PDC....F....386 322-2808
Port Orange (G-15027)
Pharma Formulations Labs Inc....G....786 985-1254
Medley (G-8705)
Pharma Nature LLC....G....305 395-4723
Davie (G-2571)
Pharma Resources Inc....F....973 780-5241
Altamonte Springs (G-64)
Pharmalink Inc....C....800 257-3527
Largo (G-8025)
Pharmamed USA Inc....G....954 533-4462
Fort Lauderdale (G-4163)
Pharmatech LLC....G....954 581-7881
Davie (G-2572)
Pharmatech LLC....F....954 629-2444
Davie (G-2573)
Pharmatech Pharmatech LLC....G....954 583-8778
Fort Lauderdale (G-4164)
Platinum Group Usa Inc....F....561 274-7553
Delray Beach (G-3119)
PLD Acquisitions LLC....D....305 463-2270
Miami (G-10170)
Prestige Brands International....E....914 524-6800
Bonita Springs (G-850)
Procyon Corporation....G....727 447-2998
Clearwater (G-1849)
Product Dev Partners LLC....F....813 908-6775
Tampa (G-18020)
Profounda Health & Beauty....F....407 270-7792
Orlando (G-13096)
Prosolus Inc....G....305 514-0270
Miami (G-10211)
Protech Nutraceuticals Inc....F....727 466-0770
Seminole (G-16758)
Protexin....G....786 310-7233
Doral (G-3472)
R-Da Trading LLC....G....954 278-6983
Weston (G-19162)
Rainbow Lght Ntrtnal Systems I....G....954 233-3300
Sunrise (G-17167)
Rapha Pharmaceuticals Inc....G....727 946-9444
Orlando (G-13113)
Regenerative Proc Plant LLC....E....727 781-0818
Palm Harbor (G-13759)
Reserveage....F....561 443-5301
Boca Raton (G-688)
Rls (usa) Inc....A....561 596-0556
Tampa (G-18061)
Romark Laboratories LC....E....813 282-8544
Tampa (G-18068)
Rowell Laboratories Inc....F....407 929-9445
Apopka (G-183)
Salerno Pharmaceuticals LP....G....352 799-9813
Brooksville (G-1266)
Sanofi US Services Inc....E....407 736-0226
Orlando (G-13162)
Schering-Plough Corp....G....407 353-2076
Orlando (G-13167)
Script Central LLC....F....954 805-8581
Miami Beach (G-10708)
Septimius LLC....G....813 484-4168
Tampa (G-18084)
Shriji Swami LLC....F....904 727-3434
Jacksonville (G-6767)
Skingen USA Inc....G....727 586-3751
Largo (G-8054)
Smartscience Laboratories Inc....F....813 925-8454
Tampa (G-18110)
Sofie Co....F....407 321-9076
Sanford (G-16118)
Southeast Compounding Phrm LLC....G....813 644-7700
Tampa (G-18116)
Specialty Pharmacy Services....G....321 953-2004
Melbourne (G-8940)
St Mary Pharmacy LLC....F....727 585-1333
Largo (G-8060)
Stagexchange....G....239 200-9226
Estero (G-3697)
Star Pharmaceuticals LLC....G....800 845-7827
Fort Lauderdale (G-4258)

PRODUCT

Stemtech Healthsciences Corp............E....... 954 715-6000
Miramar (G-11047)
Steriline North America I........................G....... 941 405-2039
Bradenton (G-1120)
Stratco Pharmaceuticals LLC..............F....... 813 403-5060
Odessa (G-12156)
Stratus Pharmaceuticals Inc...............E....... 305 254-6793
Miami (G-10420)
Strides Pharma Inc...............................D....... 561 741-6500
Riviera Beach (G-15382)
Swiss Caps Usa Inc..............................E....... 786 345-5505
Miami (G-10449)
Takeda Phrmceuticals N Amer In..........G....... 561 818-0925
Windermere (G-19245)
Teva Pharmaceuticals............................F....... 954 382-7729
Sunrise (G-17186)
Teva Pharmaceuticals Usa Inc.............E....... 305 575-6000
Miami (G-10471)
Theret Bicom Inc...................................G....... 917 796-1443
Weston (G-19170)
Triad Isotopes Inc.................................E....... 407 455-6700
Orlando (G-13271)
Trifecta Phrmceuticals USA LLC..........G....... 888 296-9067
Pompano Beach (G-14891)
Trivecta Pharmaceuticals Inc................F....... 561 856-0842
Fort Lauderdale (G-4289)
Tropichem Research Labs LLC.............D....... 561 804-7603
Jupiter (G-7134)
Trxade Inc...G....... 727 230-1915
Land O Lakes (G-7868)
Twinlab Holdings Inc.............................E....... 800 645-5626
Boca Raton (G-762)
Ultra Pharma LLC..................................G....... 954 532-7539
Pompano Beach (G-14897)
United Biosource LLC (ubc)..................G....... 877 599-7748
Lake Mary (G-7457)
US Stem Cell Inc....................................F....... 954 835-1500
Sunrise (G-17194)
Uspharma Ltd...D....... 954 817-4418
Miami Lakes (G-10877)
Usvi Pharmaceuticals LLC.....................G....... 305 643-8841
Doral (G-3539)
Uvlrx Therapeutics Inc..........................F....... 813 309-1976
Oldsmar (G-12276)
Versea Holdings Inc...............................E....... 800 397-0670
Tampa (G-18239)
Veru Inc...B....... 305 509-6897
Miami (G-10574)
Vistakon Pharmaceuticals LLC..............G....... 904 443-1000
Jacksonville (G-6901)
Vistapharm Inc.......................................E....... 727 530-1633
Largo (G-8077)
Vital Pharma Research Inc....................G....... 786 666-0592
Hialeah (G-5682)
Vivalize LLC...G....... 305 614-3952
Coral Gables (G-2205)
Vividus LLC..G....... 954 326-1954
Pompano Beach (G-14909)
Watson Therapeutics Inc.......................E....... 954 266-1000
Miramar (G-11059)
West Phrm Svcs Fla Inc.........................B....... 727 546-2402
Saint Petersburg (G-15958)

PHARMACEUTICALS: Medicinal & Botanical Prdts

Atlantic Medical Products LLC..............F....... 727 535-0022
Largo (G-7901)
Biobotanical LLC...................................F....... 239 458-4534
Cape Coral (G-1392)
Botanica Odomiwale Corp.....................G....... 305 381-5834
Hialeah (G-5330)
Cansortium Charities Inc.......................G....... 305 902-2720
Miami (G-9308)
Cls Holdings Usa Inc..............................D....... 888 438-9132
Pinecrest (G-14327)
Concentrated Aloe Corp........................G....... 386 673-7566
Ormond Beach (G-13360)
Coterie Care Inc.....................................F....... 850 325-0422
Fort Walton Beach (G-4788)
Generex Laboratories LLC....................G....... 239 592-7255
Naples (G-11260)
Immudyne Nutritional LLC.....................G....... 914 714-8901
Jacksonville (G-6489)
Lotus Stress Relief LLC.........................F....... 941 706-2778
Sarasota (G-16490)
Macrocap Labs Inc.................................E....... 321 234-6282
Longwood (G-8308)
Midway Labs Usa LLC............................F....... 561 571-6252
Boca Raton (G-624)
Morgannas Alchemy LLC.......................G....... 727 505-8376
New Port Richey (G-11502)
Natural-Immunogenics Corp..................D....... 888 328-8840
Sarasota (G-16265)
Natures Clear LLC...................................G....... 561 503-1751
Lake Worth (G-7575)
Pain Away LLC.......................................G....... 800 215-8739
Deland (G-3005)
Palmate LLC...E....... 352 508-7800
Tavares (G-18350)
Pharmco Laboratories Inc......................G....... 321 268-1313
Titusville (G-18451)
Potnetwork Holdings Inc.......................G....... 800 433-0127
Fort Lauderdale (G-4171)
Purovite Inc..G....... 305 364-5727
Miami (G-10217)
Socratic Solutions Inc............................G....... 813 324-7018
Brandon (G-1180)
Terry Laboratories LLC..........................F....... 321 259-1630
Melbourne (G-8960)
Twinlab Corporation..............................B....... 800 645-5626
Boca Raton (G-761)
Twinlab Holdings Inc.............................F....... 800 645-5626
Boca Raton (G-763)
Ultimaxx Inc...F....... 877 300-3424
Boca Raton (G-764)
Veritas Farms Inc...................................F....... 561 288-6603
Fort Lauderdale (G-4307)
Wibe Natural...G....... 305 594-0158
Doral (G-3549)
World Perfumes Inc................................F....... 305 822-0004
Opa Locka (G-12370)

PHONOGRAPH RECORDS: Prerecorded

Man Enterprises 3 LLC...........................G....... 561 655-4944
West Palm Beach (G-18940)

PHOSPHATE ROCK MINING

White Springs AG Chem Inc..................A....... 386 397-8101
White Springs (G-19189)

PHOSPHATES

Bastech Inc...F....... 904 737-1722
Jacksonville (G-6195)
Florida Phosphate Council Inc..............G....... 863 904-0641
Tallahassee (G-17254)
Novaphos Inc..E....... 863 285-8607
Fort Meade (G-4338)
White Springs AG Chem Inc..................A....... 386 397-8101
White Springs (G-19189)

PHOTO RECONNAISSANCE SYSTEMS

Moog Inc...F....... 321 435-8722
West Melbourne (G-18777)

PHOTOCOPY MACHINE REPAIR SVCS

Sun Print Management LLC...................E....... 727 945-0255
Holiday (G-5749)
Toner Technologies Inc..........................G....... 561 547-9710
Boynton Beach (G-970)

PHOTOCOPY MACHINES

Florida Copier Connections...................G....... 407 844-9690
Orlando (G-12748)

PHOTOCOPY SPLYS WHOLESALERS

Discount Distributors Inc.......................G....... 772 336-0092
Port Saint Lucie (G-15102)

PHOTOCOPYING & DUPLICATING SVCS

352ink Corp..G....... 352 373-7547
Gainesville (G-4866)
B J and ME Inc.......................................G....... 561 368-5470
Boca Raton (G-438)
Customer First Inc Naples.....................E....... 239 949-8518
Bonita Springs (G-827)
G J V Inc...G....... 727 584-7136
Largo (G-7955)
G S Printers Inc......................................G....... 305 931-2755
Fort Lauderdale (G-4016)
Garvin Management Company Inc........G....... 850 893-4719
Tallahassee (G-17261)
Goforit Inc...G....... 727 785-7616
Palm Harbor (G-13737)
Hobby Press Inc.....................................E....... 305 887-4333
Medley (G-8664)
Instant Printing Services Inc..................F....... 727 546-8036
Floral City (G-3768)
Man Enterprises 3 LLC..........................G....... 561 655-4944
West Palm Beach (G-18940)
Ocala Print Quick Inc.............................G....... 352 629-0736
Ocala (G-12014)
Palm Prnting/Printers Ink Corp.............E....... 239 332-8600
Fort Myers (G-4562)
Palmetto Printing Inc.............................F....... 305 253-2444
Miami (G-10134)
Print One Inc..G....... 813 273-0240
Oldsmar (G-12262)
Printers of Pensacola LLC....................G....... 850 434-2588
Pensacola (G-14240)
Reimink Printing Inc...............................G....... 813 289-4663
Tampa (G-18050)
Signal Graphics Printing LLC................G....... 303 837-1331
Punta Gorda (G-15234)
Tru Dimensions Printing Inc...................G....... 407 339-3410
Longwood (G-8345)

PHOTOGRAPHIC EQPT & SPLYS

Aigean Networks.....................................G....... 754 223-2240
Oakland Park (G-11774)
AVI-Spl Emplyee Emrgncy Rlief.............A....... 813 884-7168
Tampa (G-17445)
AVI-Spl Holdings Inc..............................A....... 866 708-5034
Tampa (G-17446)
AVI-Spl LLC..A....... 813 884-7168
Tampa (G-17447)
Cinidyne Sales Inc..................................G....... 941 473-3914
Englewood (G-3673)
Dale Photo and Digital Inc.....................G....... 954 925-0103
Hollywood (G-5808)
Desysca Inc..G....... 407 724-4148
Orlando (G-12666)
Discount Distributors Inc.......................G....... 772 336-0092
Port Saint Lucie (G-15102)
Innovate Audio Visual Inc......................G....... 561 249-1117
Wellington (G-18720)
Lester A Dine Inc....................................G....... 561 624-3009
Palm Beach Gardens (G-13603)
Light Source Business Systems.............F....... 772 562-5046
Port Saint Lucie (G-15120)
Lip Trading Co..G....... 954 987-0306
Hollywood (G-5861)
Matsu Imaging LLC.................................F....... 305 503-2906
Miami (G-9957)
Uribemonica..G....... 305 856-3857
Miami (G-10550)
Xerox Business Services LLC...............G....... 407 926-4228
Orlando (G-13332)

PHOTOGRAPHIC EQPT & SPLYS WHOLESALERS

Lip Trading Co..G....... 954 987-0306
Hollywood (G-5861)

PHOTOGRAPHIC EQPT & SPLYS, WHOLESALE: Project, Motion/Slide

AVI-Spl LLC..A....... 813 884-7168
Tampa (G-17447)

PHOTOGRAPHIC EQPT & SPLYS: Cameras, Aerial

Harris Aerial LLC....................................F....... 407 725-7886
Casselberry (G-1505)

PHOTOGRAPHIC EQPT & SPLYS: Develpg Mach/Eqpt, Still/Motion

Larmac Development Corp.....................G....... 904 264-5006
Orange Park (G-12397)

PHOTOGRAPHIC EQPT & SPLYS: Film, Sensitized

Eastman Kodak Company.......................D....... 813 908-7910
Tampa (G-17627)

PHOTOGRAPHIC EQPT & SPLYS: Plates, Sensitized

Photoengraving Inc.................................E....... 813 253-3427
Tampa (G-17992)

PHOTOGRAPHIC EQPT & SPLYS: Printing Eqpt

ID Print Inc ....G.... 954 923-8374
Plantation *(G-14524)*

Tonertype Inc ....E.... 813 915-1300
Tampa *(G-18194)*

PHOTOGRAPHIC EQPT & SPLYS: Printing Frames

Chez Industries LLC ....F.... 386 698-4414
Crescent City *(G-2339)*

PHOTOGRAPHIC EQPT & SPLYS: Reels, Film

Premier Plastics LLC ....E.... 305 805-3333
Boynton Beach *(G-943)*

PHOTOGRAPHIC EQPT & SPLYS: Toners, Prprd, Not Chem Plnts

Bdt Concepts Inc ....G.... 904 730-2590
Jacksonville *(G-6199)*

Globaltek Office Supply Inc ....G.... 305 477-2988
Doral *(G-3370)*

Ink & Toner Plus ....G.... 813 783-1650
Dade City *(G-2429)*

Toner City Corp ....G.... 954 945-5392
Davie *(G-2606)*

Toners Plus LLC ....G.... 407 756-5787
Orlando *(G-13261)*

PHOTOGRAPHY SVCS: Passport

Tem Systems Inc ....G.... 407 251-7114
Orlando *(G-13246)*

PHOTOVOLTAIC Solid State

Solar Electric Power Company ....F.... 772 220-6615
Stuart *(G-17018)*

Sollunar Energy Inc ....G.... 352 293-2347
Spring Hill *(G-16864)*

PHYSICIANS' OFFICES & CLINICS: Medical doctors

Wimbledon Health Partners LLC ....F.... 800 200-8262
Boca Raton *(G-790)*

PICTURE FRAMES: Metal

Dillco Inc ....F.... 386 734-7510
Deland *(G-2971)*

Russell Hobbs Inc ....D.... 954 883-1000
Miramar *(G-11037)*

PICTURE FRAMES: Wood

Art & Frame Direct Inc ....C.... 407 857-6000
Orlando *(G-12491)*

Art Connection Usa LLC ....E.... 954 781-0125
Pompano Beach *(G-14600)*

Florida Frames Inc ....F.... 727 572-4064
Clearwater *(G-1688)*

Frametastic Inc ....F.... 954 567-2800
Fort Lauderdale *(G-4011)*

Miami Decor Inc ....F.... 800 235-2197
Miami *(G-9998)*

Russell Hobbs Inc ....D.... 954 883-1000
Miramar *(G-11037)*

Total Vision Design Group ....G.... 407 438-6933
Orlando *(G-13263)*

PIECE GOODS & NOTIONS WHOLESALERS

Bespoke Stitchery LLC ....G.... 407 412-9937
Orlando *(G-12511)*

Valley Forge Textiles LLC ....G.... 954 971-1776
Pompano Beach *(G-14907)*

PIECE GOODS, NOTIONS & DRY GOODS, WHOL: Textiles, Woven

Stanley Industries of S Fla ....G.... 954 929-8770
Hollywood *(G-5915)*

PIECE GOODS, NOTIONS & DRY GOODS, WHOLESALE: Fabrics

J & H Supply Co Inc ....G.... 561 582-3346
Lake Worth *(G-7558)*

PIECE GOODS, NOTIONS & DRY GOODS, WHOLESALE: Fabrics, Knit

Superior Shade & Blind Co Inc ....E.... 954 975-8122
Coral Springs *(G-2317)*

PIECE GOODS, NOTIONS & OTHER DRY GOODS, WHOLESALE: Buttons

Promo Daddy LLC ....F.... 877 557-2336
Melbourne *(G-8913)*

PIECE GOODS, NOTIONS & OTHER DRY GOODS, WHOLESALE: Notions

Florida Thread & Trimming ....G.... 954 240-2474
Hialeah *(G-5415)*

PIECE GOODS, NOTIONS & OTHER DRY GOODS, WHOLESALE: Ribbons

Design Services Inc ....G.... 813 949-4748
Land O Lakes *(G-7852)*

PIECE GOODS, NOTIONS/DRY GOODS, WHOL: Drapery Mtrl, Woven

Kenco Quilting & Textiles Inc ....F.... 954 921-5434
Fort Lauderdale *(G-4088)*

PIECE GOODS, NOTIONS/DRY GOODS, WHOL: Fabrics, Synthetic

Ascend Prfmce Mtls Oprtons LLC ....A.... 850 968-7000
Cantonment *(G-1335)*

Texene LLC ....F.... 305 200-5001
Miami Lakes *(G-10867)*

PIGMENTS, INORGANIC: Black

Pigments Black Diamond ....G.... 904 241-2533
Saint Augustine *(G-15587)*

PILING: Prefabricated, Concrete

Henderson Prestress Con Inc ....F.... 727 938-2828
Tarpon Springs *(G-18306)*

Wills Prestress Inc ....F.... 239 417-9117
Naples *(G-11456)*

PILOT SVCS: Aviation

ELite Intl Group LLC ....F.... 305 901-5005
Miami *(G-9516)*

Florida Sncast Helicopters LLC ....F.... 941 355-1525
Sarasota *(G-16214)*

Flyteone Inc ....G.... 813 421-1410
Clearwater *(G-1691)*

Heli Aviation Florida LLC ....G.... 941 355-1525
Sarasota *(G-16226)*

Helicopter Helmet LLC ....G.... 843 556-0405
Melbourne *(G-8841)*

PINS

Fire Rescue Pins Com ....G.... 561 312-8423
Palm Beach Gardens *(G-13589)*

Lighthouse of Leesburg Inc ....G.... 352 408-6566
Palm Bay *(G-13521)*

Naples Hma LLC ....F.... 239 390-2174
Estero *(G-3692)*

Pin-N-Win Wrestling Club Inc ....G.... 904 276-8038
Orange Park *(G-12403)*

Pins Fever ....G.... 407 619-5314
Altamonte Springs *(G-65)*

Sin Pin Inc ....G.... 877 805-5665
Stuart *(G-17015)*

Xue Wu Inc ....G.... 727 532-4571
Clearwater *(G-1946)*

PINS: Dowel

Dowels Pins & Shafts Inc ....E.... 727 461-1255
Clearwater *(G-1656)*

PIPE & FITTING: Fabrication

Alumacart Inc ....F.... 772 675-2158
Hobe Sound *(G-5721)*

ARC-Rite Inc ....E.... 386 325-3523
Jacksonville *(G-6165)*

Cantex Inc ....C.... 863 967-4161
Auburndale *(G-231)*

Custom Tube Products Inc ....F.... 386 426-0670
Edgewater *(G-3620)*

Customfab Inc ....G.... 786 339-9158
Homestead *(G-5960)*

Energy Task Force LLC ....F.... 407 523-3770
Apopka *(G-135)*

Etf West LLC ....G.... 407 523-3770
Apopka *(G-139)*

Formweld Fitting Inc ....E.... 850 626-4888
Milton *(G-10928)*

GPM Fab & Supply LLC ....G.... 813 689-7107
Seffner *(G-16729)*

Gulf Atlantic Culvert Company ....F.... 850 562-2384
Tallahassee *(G-17270)*

Hines Bending Systems Inc ....F.... 239 433-2132
Fort Myers *(G-4482)*

Insulation Design & Dist LLC ....G.... 850 332-7312
Cantonment *(G-1341)*

Jensen Scientific Products Inc ....E.... 954 344-2006
Coral Springs *(G-2263)*

Marine Exhaust Systems Inc ....D.... 561 848-1238
Riviera Beach *(G-15346)*

MPH Industries Inc ....F.... 352 372-9533
Gainesville *(G-4966)*

Peterson Manufacturing Co Inc ....E.... 941 371-4989
Sarasota *(G-16544)*

Petrotech Services Inc ....F.... 813 248-0743
Tampa *(G-17986)*

Petrotech Services Inc ....D.... 813 248-0743
Tampa *(G-17987)*

Pipeline Fabricators Inc ....F.... 863 678-0977
Lake Wales *(G-7518)*

Price Brothers Company ....G.... 386 328-8841
Palatka *(G-13490)*

Shafers Classic Reproductions ....G.... 813 622-7091
Tampa *(G-18089)*

Specialty Maintenance & Constr ....G.... 863 644-8432
Lakeland *(G-7804)*

Strongbridge International LLC ....E.... 904 278-7499
Orange Park *(G-12407)*

Sunshine Piping Inc ....E.... 850 763-4834
Panama City *(G-13953)*

Townley Engrg & Mfg Co Inc ....C.... 352 687-3001
Candler *(G-1332)*

US Pipe Fabrication LLC ....E.... 860 769-6097
Orlando *(G-13299)*

PIPE & FITTINGS: Cast Iron

Custom Flange Pipe LLC ....F.... 863 353-6602
Winter Haven *(G-19316)*

Urecon Systems Inc ....E.... 904 695-3332
Winter Park *(G-19456)*

PIPE & FITTINGS: Pressure, Cast Iron

Forterra Pressure Pipe Inc ....C.... 386 328-8841
Palatka *(G-13480)*

PIPE & TUBES: Copper & Copper Alloy

Admiralty Industries Corp ....G.... 305 722-7311
Doral *(G-3227)*

Kme Amrica Mar Tube Ftting LLC ....D.... 904 265-4001
Jacksonville *(G-6541)*

Manchester Copper Tube LLC ....F.... 321 636-1477
Rockledge *(G-15433)*

PIPE JOINT COMPOUNDS

Continental Palatka LLC ....D.... 703 480-3800
Palatka *(G-13475)*

PIPE, CULVERT: Concrete

Wheeler Consolidated Inc ....F.... 772 464-4400
Fort Pierce *(G-4770)*

PIPE, CYLINDER: Concrete, Prestressed Or Pretensioned

Nuflo Inc ....E.... 904 265-4001
Jacksonville *(G-6642)*

PIPE: Concrete

Cemex Cnstr Mtls Fla LLC ....G....... 800 992-3639
Oldsmar *(G-12213)*
Cemex Materials LLC....C....... 561 833-5555
West Palm Beach *(G-18841)*
Cemex Materials LLC....D....... 352 435-0783
Okahumpka *(G-12169)*
Cemex Materials LLC....D....... 305 558-0315
Miami *(G-9337)*
Florida Concrete Pipe Corp ....F....... 352 742-2232
Astatula *(G-211)*
Mancini Inc ....E....... 954 583-7220
Pompano Beach *(G-14752)*
RMC Ewell Inc ....E....... 850 879-0959
Niceville *(G-11573)*
RMC Ewell Inc ....G....... 850 863-5040
Fort Walton Beach *(G-4828)*
RMC Ewell Inc ....F....... 407 282-0984
Orlando *(G-13143)*
Valmont Newmark Inc....E....... 863 533-6465
Bartow *(G-335)*

PIPE: Irrigation, Sheet Metal

Home & Garden Industries Inc ....F....... 305 634-0681
Miami *(G-9716)*

PIPE: Plastic

Accord Industries LLC ....D....... 407 671-6989
Winter Park *(G-19370)*
Advanced Drainage Systems Inc ....G....... 850 234-0004
Panama City Beach *(G-13969)*
Advantage Earth Products Inc....F....... 904 329-1430
Saint Augustine *(G-15513)*
Aei International Corp ....G....... 904 724-9771
Jacksonville *(G-6125)*
Atkore Plastic Pipe Corp....E....... 813 884-2525
Tampa *(G-17443)*
Blue Creek Holdings Inc....G....... 814 796-1900
Plant City *(G-14410)*
C & S Plastics....E....... 863 294-5628
Winter Haven *(G-19309)*
Cantex Inc....C....... 863 967-4161
Auburndale *(G-231)*
Charlotte Pipe and Foundry Co....E....... 352 748-8100
Wildwood *(G-19193)*
Ciro Manufacturing Corporation ....E....... 561 988-2139
Deerfield Beach *(G-2802)*
Dixie Sptic Tank Orange Cy LLC ....F....... 386 775-3051
Orange City *(G-12375)*
Hancor Inc ....E....... 863 655-5499
Winter Garden *(G-19266)*
Maruti Technology Inc....F....... 407 704-4775
Orlando *(G-12950)*
Sanderson Pipe Corporation ....D....... 904 275-3289
Sanderson *(G-15983)*
Taylor Made Plastics Inc ....G....... 941 926-0200
Sarasota *(G-16619)*
Wellstream International Ltd....C....... 850 636-4800
Panama City *(G-13963)*

PIPE: Seamless Steel

Berg Pipe Panama City Corp ....C....... 850 769-2273
Panama City *(G-13870)*

PIPE: Sheet Metal

Gulf Atlantic Culvert Company....F....... 850 562-2384
Tallahassee *(G-17270)*
Mechanical Svcs Centl Fla Inc....C....... 407 857-3510
Orlando *(G-12957)*
Metal 2 Metal Inc ....G....... 954 253-9450
Palmetto Bay *(G-13850)*

PIPES & FITTINGS: Fiber, Made From Purchased Materials

Rotary Manufacturing LLC....F....... 941 564-8038
North Port *(G-11748)*

PIPES & TUBES

American Vinyl Company....F....... 813 663-0157
Tampa *(G-17421)*

PIPES & TUBES: Steel

Accord Industries LLC ....D....... 407 671-6989
Winter Park *(G-19370)*
Allsteel Processing LC....F....... 954 587-1900
Fort Lauderdale *(G-3808)*
Atkore International Inc....G....... 800 882-5543
Boca Raton *(G-433)*
Cmn Steel Fabricators Inc....D....... 305 592-5466
Miami *(G-9367)*
Custom Fab Inc....D....... 407 859-3954
Orlando *(G-12639)*
GPM Fab & Supply LLC....G....... 813 689-7107
Seffner *(G-16729)*
Metal Culverts Inc....E....... 727 531-1431
Clearwater *(G-1782)*
Neptune Research Inc....E....... 561 683-6992
Riviera Beach *(G-15352)*
Ride and Tube Inc....F....... 352 454-8194
Summerfield *(G-17061)*
Sanitube LLC....F....... 863 606-5960
Lakeland *(G-7787)*
Southstern Indus Fbrcators LLC....E....... 941 776-1211
Duette *(G-3563)*
Specialty Steel Holdco Inc....G....... 305 375-7560
Miami *(G-10402)*
Theclipcom Inc....G....... 305 599-3871
Tavernier *(G-18363)*
Value Providers LLC....G....... 321 567-0919
Daytona Beach *(G-2731)*
Wellstream International Ltd....C....... 850 636-4800
Panama City *(G-13963)*

PIPES & TUBES: Welded

Florida Steam Services Inc....G....... 407 247-8250
Geneva *(G-5022)*

PIPES: Steel & Iron

Berg Europipe Holding Corp ....C....... 850 769-2273
Panama City *(G-13869)*
Chemko Technical Services Inc ....E....... 954 783-7673
Pompano Beach *(G-14634)*
H & M Steel....G....... 904 765-3465
Jacksonville *(G-6458)*
US Pipe Fabrication LLC....E....... 860 769-6097
Orlando *(G-13299)*

PIPES: Tobacco

Spliffpuff LLC....F....... 786 493-4529
Doral *(G-3510)*

PLANING MILL, NEC

Idaho Timber LLC ....C....... 386 758-8111
Lake City *(G-7361)*

PLANING MILLS: Millwork

Synergy Thermal Foils Inc....F....... 954 420-9553
Coral Springs *(G-2319)*

PLANTERS: Plastic

Bloem LLC....G....... 407 889-5533
Apopka *(G-118)*

PLAQUES: Picture, Laminated

American Trophy Co....G....... 954 782-2250
Pompano Beach *(G-14594)*
Art & Frame Direct Inc....C....... 407 857-6000
Orlando *(G-12491)*
Clifton Studio Inc....G....... 813 240-0286
Tampa *(G-17542)*
In The News Inc....D....... 813 882-8886
Tampa *(G-17775)*
Parrillo Inc ....G....... 386 767-8011
South Daytona *(G-16806)*
Williams Jewelry and Mfg Co....G....... 727 823-7676
Saint Petersburg *(G-15961)*

PLASMAS

Adma Biologics Inc....F....... 561 989-5800
Boca Raton *(G-400)*
Advanced Bioservices LLC....C....... 850 476-7999
Pensacola *(G-14082)*
Aqua Pulsar LLC ....G....... 772 320-9691
Palm City *(G-13641)*
Biolife Plasma Services....G....... 407 388-1052
Casselberry *(G-1498)*
Hemarus Llc-Jcksnvle Plsma Ctr ....G....... 904 642-1005
Jupiter *(G-7052)*
Inter Cell Technologies Inc ....G....... 561 575-6868
Jupiter *(G-7058)*
Plasma Cutting LLC....G....... 954 558-1371
Hallandale *(G-5160)*
Plasma Energy Group LLC ....G....... 813 760-6385
Odessa *(G-12139)*
Plasma-Therm Inc ....E....... 856 753-8111
Saint Petersburg *(G-15880)*

PLASTER WORK: Ornamental & Architectural

Green Forest Industries Inc ....E....... 941 721-0504
Palmetto *(G-13801)*

PLASTIC PRDTS

Acacia Inc ....F....... 813 253-2789
Tampa *(G-17384)*
Aqua Technologies....G....... 305 246-2125
Homestead *(G-5954)*
Envirosafe Technologies Inc ....G....... 904 646-3456
Jacksonville *(G-6367)*
Genpak LLC....F....... 863 243-1068
Lake Placid *(G-7487)*
Jar-Den Llc ....G....... 860 334-7539
Port Richey *(G-15056)*
Latham Plastics Inc ....G....... 813 783-7212
Zephyrhills *(G-19526)*
MTS Packaging System Inc ....G....... 727 812-2830
Clearwater *(G-1796)*
Onelid LLC....G....... 305 335-9730
North Miami Beach *(G-11695)*
Parras Plastic Inc ....G....... 305 972-9537
Miami *(G-10143)*
Profbox of America Inc....G....... 786 454-8148
North Miami Beach *(G-11699)*
Rosier Manufacturing Company....G....... 386 409-7223
Daytona Beach *(G-2705)*
Semplastics....G....... 407 353-6885
Oviedo *(G-13457)*
Stephen ODonnell....G....... 631 664-3594
Saint Cloud *(G-15668)*
Sunflex....G....... 800 606-0756
Naples *(G-11423)*
Visual Concepts In Plastic Inc....G....... 941 749-1141
Bradenton *(G-1141)*
Wb Medical Transport LLC....G....... 561 827-8877
Port Saint Lucie *(G-15163)*
Zeus Industries ....G....... 727 530-4373
Largo *(G-8081)*

PLASTICS FILM & SHEET

American Plastic Sup & Mfg Inc....E....... 727 573-0636
Clearwater *(G-1581)*
Designer Films Inc....F....... 305 828-0605
Hialeah *(G-5370)*
Flexsol Holding Corp....D....... 954 941-6333
Pompano Beach *(G-14700)*
King Plastic Corporation....C....... 941 423-8666
North Port *(G-11742)*
Sungraf Inc ....F....... 954 456-8500
Hallandale Beach *(G-5216)*

PLASTICS FILM & SHEET: Polyethylene

Essex Plastics Midwest LLC Lc....A....... 954 956-1100
Pompano Beach *(G-14683)*

PLASTICS FILM & SHEET: Vinyl

Dynamic Visions Inc ....E....... 941 497-1984
Venice *(G-18543)*
Real Gold Inc....G....... 386 873-4849
Deland *(G-3010)*
Recycled Vinyl....G....... 727 434-1857
Sarasota *(G-16555)*

PLASTICS FINISHED PRDTS: Laminated

Acryplex Inc....G....... 305 633-7636
Miami *(G-9066)*
Enduris Extrusions Inc....D....... 904 421-3304
Jacksonville *(G-6363)*
Fisher Cabinet Company LLC....E....... 850 944-4171
Pensacola *(G-14151)*
Institutional Products Inc....E....... 305 248-4955
Homestead *(G-5972)*
Neptune Tech Services Inc ....E....... 904 646-2700
Jacksonville *(G-6624)*
Red Bud Enterprises Inc ....E....... 386 752-5696
Lake City *(G-7381)*
Streamline Extrusion Inc....F....... 727 796-4277
Safety Harbor *(G-15506)*

Suncoast Identification Tech ....G....... 239 277-9922
Fort Myers *(G-4616)*

PLASTICS MATERIAL & RESINS

3 Miracles Corporation ....G....... 407 796-9292
Orlando *(G-12417)*
Advanced Composite Systems ....F....... 904 765-6502
Jacksonville *(G-6122)*
Anchor Coatings Leesburg Inc ....E....... 352 728-0777
Leesburg *(G-8142)*
Ascend Prfmce Mtls Oprtons LLC ....B....... 734 819-0656
Gulf Breeze *(G-5112)*
Ascend Prfmce Mtls Oprtons LLC ....A....... 850 968-7000
Cantonment *(G-1335)*
Atlantic Marble Company Inc ....E....... 904 262-6262
Jacksonville *(G-6176)*
Atlas Polymers Corp ....F....... 786 312-2131
Miami *(G-9188)*
Automated Services Inc ....F....... 772 461-3388
Fort Pierce *(G-4679)*
Avon Assoc ....G....... 561 391-7188
Boca Raton *(G-435)*
Blue Water Dynamics LLC ....D....... 386 957-5464
Edgewater *(G-3614)*
Braden Kitchens Inc ....E....... 321 636-4700
Cocoa *(G-1999)*
Cellofoam North America Inc ....E....... 407 888-4667
Orlando *(G-12560)*
Charles K Sewell ....G....... 407 423-1870
Orlando *(G-12576)*
Coosa LLC ....G....... 904 268-1187
Jacksonville *(G-6289)*
Creative Countertops Inc ....F....... 904 387-2800
Jacksonville *(G-6296)*
Cup Plus USA ....G....... 321 972-1968
Winter Park *(G-19397)*
Designers Tops Inc ....F....... 305 599-9973
Miami *(G-9461)*
Dynamic Material Systems LLC ....G....... 407 353-6885
Oviedo *(G-13427)*
F O F Plastics Inc ....G....... 727 937-2144
Tarpon Springs *(G-18300)*
Fairing Xchange LLC ....G....... 904 589-5253
Orange Park *(G-12391)*
Fiberflon Usa Inc ....G....... 786 953-7329
Miami *(G-9566)*
G Phillips and Sons LLC ....F....... 248 705-5873
Sarasota *(G-16445)*
Global Holdings and Dev LLC ....G....... 949 500-4997
Pompano Beach *(G-14714)*
Huntsman Properties LLC ....E....... 954 282-1797
Fort Lauderdale *(G-4053)*
Industrial Plastic Pdts Inc ....E....... 305 822-3223
Miami Lakes *(G-10797)*
Ineos New Planet Bioenergy LLC ....E....... 772 794-7900
Vero Beach *(G-18630)*
International Composite ....G....... 206 349-7468
Sarasota *(G-16468)*
Jrf Technology LLC ....F....... 813 443-5273
Tampa *(G-17811)*
Kraton Chemical LLC ....F....... 850 438-9222
Pensacola *(G-14190)*
Linkpoint LLC ....F....... 305 903-9191
Key Biscayne *(G-7159)*
Matrix Composites Inc ....C....... 321 633-4480
Rockledge *(G-15435)*
Nida-Core Corporation ....E....... 772 343-7300
Port Saint Lucie *(G-15124)*
Olevin Compounds LLC ....G....... 954 993-5148
Miramar *(G-11023)*
Orca Composites LLC ....F....... 206 349-5300
Sarasota *(G-16533)*
Pacific Limited Intl Corp ....G....... 305 358-1900
Miami *(G-10128)*
Pacific Ltd Corp ....G....... 305 358-1900
Miami *(G-10129)*
Paradigm Plastics Inc ....G....... 727 797-3555
Safety Harbor *(G-15501)*
Plastic Masters International ....F....... 386 312-9775
East Palatka *(G-3605)*
Plastic Specialties Inc ....F....... 239 643-0933
Naples *(G-11369)*
Plastic Trading Intl Inc ....E....... 863 688-1983
Lakeland *(G-7767)*
Plastics America Incorporated ....G....... 813 620-3711
Tampa *(G-17995)*
Poly-Chem Corp ....G....... 305 593-1928
Miami *(G-10176)*
Polymersan LLC ....G....... 305 887-3824
Hialeah *(G-5560)*
Pro Poly of America Inc ....E....... 352 629-1414
Ocala *(G-12033)*
Profab Corporation ....E....... 352 369-5515
Ocala *(G-12034)*
Ravago Americas LLC ....A....... 407 773-7777
Orlando *(G-13114)*
Ravago Holdings America Inc ....D....... 407 875-9595
Orlando *(G-13115)*
Rayonier A M Products Inc ....D....... 904 357-9100
Jacksonville *(G-6706)*
Syntex America Corporation ....F....... 954 457-1468
Hallandale Beach *(G-5217)*
Teak Isle Inc ....C....... 407 656-8885
Ocoee *(G-12091)*
TEC Composites Inc ....F....... 904 765-6502
Jacksonville *(G-6841)*
The Hc Companies Inc ....D....... 863 314-9417
Sebring *(G-16715)*
Thermo Compaction Systems Inc ....G....... 863 370-3799
Lakeland *(G-7820)*
Tradepak Inc ....G....... 305 871-2247
Miami *(G-10500)*
U S Composites Inc ....G....... 561 588-1001
West Palm Beach *(G-19073)*
US Blanks LLC ....E....... 321 253-3626
Melbourne *(G-8969)*
US Composites ....G....... 561 588-1001
Riviera Beach *(G-15388)*
Washington Penn Plastics Co ....F....... 724 228-1260
St Pete Beach *(G-16885)*
Wheeler Consolidated Inc ....F....... 772 464-4400
Fort Pierce *(G-4770)*

PLASTICS MATERIALS, BASIC FORMS & SHAPES WHOLESALERS

Finyl Products Inc ....G....... 352 351-4033
Ocala *(G-11942)*
Peter T Amann ....G....... 561 848-2770
West Palm Beach *(G-18995)*
Polymer Logistics Inc ....E....... 877 462-6195
Tampa *(G-17996)*

PLASTICS PROCESSING

Bio Bubble Pets LLC ....F....... 561 998-5350
West Palm Beach *(G-18819)*
C & G Packaging LLC ....F....... 305 825-5244
Hialeah *(G-5337)*
Conrad Plastics LLC ....G....... 954 391-9515
Hallandale Beach *(G-5179)*
J W Austin Industries Inc ....G....... 321 723-2422
Melbourne *(G-8853)*
Laser Creations Incorporated ....E....... 800 771-7151
Apopka *(G-155)*
Marlon Inc ....F....... 813 901-8488
Tampa *(G-17882)*
Maxi-Blast of Florida Inc ....G....... 727 572-0909
Saint Petersburg *(G-15851)*
Midgard Inc ....D....... 863 696-1224
Lake Wales *(G-7516)*
Mpc Group LLC ....G....... 773 927-4120
Deland *(G-3001)*
Noveltex Miami Inc ....E....... 305 887-8191
Hialeah *(G-5544)*
Plastic Composites Inc ....F....... 352 669-5822
Umatilla *(G-18501)*
Rainbow Pool Supply Inc ....G....... 407 324-9616
Sanford *(G-16109)*
Sippers By Design ....G....... 305 371-5087
Miami *(G-10354)*

PLASTICS SHEET: Packing Materials

Barco Sales & Mfg Inc ....F....... 954 563-3922
Oakland Park *(G-11784)*
Ifco Systems Us LLC ....E....... 813 463-4103
Tampa *(G-17770)*
J & D Manufacturing Inc ....F....... 813 854-1700
Oldsmar *(G-12237)*
Processing and Packg Sups Co ....E....... 321 723-2723
Melbourne *(G-8912)*
Serv-Pak Corp ....F....... 954 962-4262
Hollywood *(G-5907)*

PLASTICS: Blow Molded

Chrom Industries LLC ....E....... 954 400-5135
Fort Lauderdale *(G-3897)*
Safariland LLC ....E....... 904 646-0141
Jacksonville *(G-6747)*

PLASTICS: Carbohydrate

Plastirex LLC ....F....... 305 471-1111
Avon Park *(G-293)*

PLASTICS: Cast

Bowen Medical Services Inc ....G....... 386 362-1345
Live Oak *(G-8227)*
Stoltz Industries Inc ....F....... 954 792-3270
Davie *(G-2596)*

PLASTICS: Extruded

American Products Inc ....G....... 813 925-0144
Tampa *(G-17418)*
American Thrmplastic Extrusion ....C....... 305 769-9566
Opa Locka *(G-12287)*
C & S Plastics ....E....... 863 294-5628
Winter Haven *(G-19309)*
Emmanuel Holdings Inc ....F....... 305 558-3088
Miami *(G-9524)*
Jmh Marine Inc ....F....... 954 785-7557
Pompano Beach *(G-14736)*
Melt-Tech Polymers Inc ....G....... 305 887-6148
Medley *(G-8688)*
Shoreline Plastics LLC ....E....... 904 696-2981
Jacksonville *(G-6766)*

PLASTICS: Finished Injection Molded

Apollo Renal Therapeutics LLC ....E....... 202 413-0963
Ocala *(G-11878)*
Delta Machine & Tool Inc ....E....... 386 738-2204
Deland *(G-2969)*
Diamond Precision Machine Inc ....F....... 321 729-8453
Palm Bay *(G-13508)*
Ehud Industries Inc ....G....... 904 803-0873
Jacksonville *(G-6357)*
Eurogan-Usa Inc ....F....... 321 356-5248
Orlando *(G-12720)*
Florida Production Engrg Inc ....C....... 386 677-2566
Ormond Beach *(G-13372)*
Gulf Coast Mold & Tool Corp ....F....... 239 643-1017
Bonita Springs *(G-837)*
Hardware Concepts Inc ....G....... 305 685-1337
Miami *(G-9687)*
Integrated Components Corp ....F....... 305 824-0484
Hialeah *(G-5454)*
M O Precision Molders Inc ....F....... 727 573-4466
Clearwater *(G-1767)*
Mdi Products LLC ....F....... 772 228-7371
Sebastian *(G-16669)*
Mid-Florida Plastics Inc ....E....... 407 856-1805
Orlando *(G-12970)*
Nanotechnovation Corporation ....E....... 352 732-3244
Ocala *(G-12004)*
Plastic Concepts & Designs Inc ....G....... 904 396-7500
Jacksonville *(G-6676)*
Rainbow Precision Mfg Corp ....G....... 561 691-1658
Palm Beach Gardens *(G-13621)*
Scientific Plastics Ltd ....F....... 305 557-3737
Miami Lakes *(G-10856)*
Tuthill Corporation ....D....... 727 446-8593
Clearwater *(G-1927)*
William B Rudow Inc ....G....... 941 957-4200
Sarasota *(G-16640)*

PLASTICS: Injection Molded

7 Plastics Inc ....F....... 407 321-5441
Longwood *(G-8249)*
A 1 Fabrications Inc ....G....... 352 410-0752
Weeki Wachee *(G-18699)*
Absolute Plastic Solutions ....F....... 239 313-7779
Fort Myers *(G-4342)*
Acai Investments Llc ....G....... 305 821-8872
Hialeah *(G-5267)*
Accu Metal ....G....... 850 912-4855
Pensacola *(G-14078)*
Accu Tech LLC ....G....... 407 446-6676
Groveland *(G-5091)*
Acrylic Images Inc ....F....... 954 484-6633
Oakland Park *(G-11773)*
Advanced Air International Inc ....E....... 561 845-8212
Riviera Beach *(G-15293)*
Advantage Plastics NY Inc ....F....... 863 291-4407
Winter Haven *(G-19295)*
AIN Plastics of Florida Inc ....F....... 813 242-6400
Riverview *(G-15264)*
Allied General Engrv & Plas ....F....... 305 626-6585
Opa Locka *(G-12286)*

American Molding and Plas LLC ....E 561 676-1987
Boynton Beach *(G-876)*
American Technical Molding Inc ....D 727 447-7377
Clearwater *(G-1582)*
American Tool & Mold Inc ....C 727 447-7377
Clearwater *(G-1583)*
Artisan Tool & Die LLC ....G 765 288-6653
Sarasota *(G-16178)*
Atlantic Molding Inc ....F 954 781-9340
Pompano Beach *(G-14606)*
Autisan International Inc ....G 941 349-7029
Sarasota *(G-16358)*
Automated Mfg Systems Inc ....G 561 833-9898
Mangonia Park *(G-8498)*
Ayanna Plastics & Engrg Inc ....E 727 561-4329
Clearwater *(G-1596)*
B & D Precision Tools Inc ....E 305 885-1583
Hialeah *(G-5314)*
B & R Sales Corporation ....G 727 571-2231
Clearwater *(G-1597)*
Better Plastics Inc ....G 407 480-2909
Orlando *(G-12513)*
Big Sun Plastics Inc ....F 352 671-1844
Ocala *(G-11887)*
C & J Industries Inc ....F 386 589-4907
Ormond Beach *(G-13356)*
Cavaform Inc ....G 727 384-3676
Saint Petersburg *(G-15740)*
Choice Tool & Mold LLC ....F 941 371-6767
Sarasota *(G-16383)*
Covington Plastics Inc ....F 321 632-6775
Cocoa *(G-2006)*
Covocup LLC ....G 855 204-5106
Sarasota *(G-16199)*
Custom Plastic Card Company ....D 954 426-1331
Deerfield Beach *(G-2809)*
Custom Plastic Developments ....D 407 847-3054
Kissimmee *(G-7235)*
D M T Inc ....F 321 267-3931
Cocoa *(G-2008)*
D-Rep Plastics Inc ....G 407 240-4154
Clearwater *(G-1648)*
Diemold Machine Company Inc ....E 239 482-1400
Fort Myers *(G-4431)*
Donarra Extrusions LLC ....F 352 369-5552
Ocala *(G-11923)*
Doran Manufacturing Corp Fla ....G 904 731-3313
Jacksonville *(G-6326)*
Dura-Cast Products Inc ....D 863 638-3200
Lake Wales *(G-7507)*
Dynotec Plastic Inc ....G 813 248-5335
Tampa *(G-17622)*
Ellis Family Holdings Inc ....F 503 785-7400
Hialeah *(G-5393)*
Epic Extrusion Inc ....G 941 378-0835
Sarasota *(G-16421)*
Euro Trim Inc ....G 239 574-6646
Cape Coral *(G-1419)*
Excalibur Manufacturing Corp ....F 352 544-0055
Brooksville *(G-1228)*
Extreme Coatings ....G 727 528-7998
Saint Petersburg *(G-15775)*
Faulkner Inc of Miami ....F 305 885-4731
Hialeah *(G-5408)*
Fimco Manufacturing Inc ....G 561 624-3308
Jupiter *(G-7042)*
First Shot Mold and Tool ....G 321 269-0031
Titusville *(G-18429)*
Florida Central Extrusion Inc ....G 863 324-2541
Winter Haven *(G-19321)*
Florida Custom Mold Inc ....D 813 343-5080
Odessa *(G-12121)*
Florida Electromechanics Inc ....G 305 825-5244
Hialeah *(G-5412)*
Gator Polymers LLC ....F 866 292-7306
Cape Coral *(G-1427)*
Genca Corp ....E 727 524-3622
Clearwater *(G-1701)*
Gerogari Display Manufacture ....G 305 888-0993
Miami *(G-9632)*
Glasspec Corp ....G 305 255-8444
Opa Locka *(G-12320)*
Graduate Plastics Inc ....C 305 687-0405
Miami *(G-9652)*
Gulf View Plastics Inc ....G 727 379-3072
Hudson *(G-6028)*
Harbortech Plastics LLC ....F 727 944-2425
Holiday *(G-5743)*
House Plastics Unlimited Inc ....E 407 843-3290
Orlando *(G-12812)*

Idproductsource ....G 772 336-4269
Port Saint Lucie *(G-15113)*
Industrial Plastic Pdts Inc ....E 305 822-3223
Miami Lakes *(G-10797)*
Jarden Plastic Solutions ....G 864 879-8100
Boca Raton *(G-577)*
Jtf Ventures LLC ....G 305 556-5156
Miami Lakes *(G-10800)*
K & I Creative Plas & WD LLC ....G 904 923-0409
Jacksonville *(G-6530)*
Kinetic Industries LLC ....G 727 572-7604
Clearwater *(G-1750)*
Kramski North America Inc ....F 727 828-1500
Largo *(G-7995)*
L C Southwind Manufacturing ....F 352 687-1999
Ocala *(G-11978)*
Lera Plastics Inc ....G 904 716-5421
Jacksonville *(G-6554)*
M & M Plastics Inc ....E 305 688-4335
Miami *(G-9923)*
M D R International Inc ....F 305 944-5335
North Miami *(G-11644)*
Master Mold Corp ....G 941 486-0000
North Venice *(G-11760)*
Master Tool Co Inc ....E 305 557-1020
Miami Lakes *(G-10815)*
Meltpoint Plastics Intl Inc ....E 305 887-8020
Medley *(G-8689)*
Mikes Precision Inc ....G 305 558-6421
Hialeah *(G-5517)*
Modern Tchncal Molding Dev LLC ....F 727 343-2942
Saint Petersburg *(G-15857)*
Modular Molding Intl Inc ....E 727 541-1333
Seminole *(G-16754)*
Molds and Plastic Machinery ....G 305 828-3456
Opa Locka *(G-12340)*
National Molding LLC ....C 305 823-5440
Miami Lakes *(G-10827)*
Nelson Plastics Inc ....E 407 339-3570
Longwood *(G-8316)*
Novelty Crystal Corp ....E 352 429-9036
Groveland *(G-5104)*
Nylacarb Corp ....E 772 569-5999
Vero Beach *(G-18649)*
Octex Holdings LLC ....D 941 371-6767
Sarasota *(G-16530)*
Paradigm Leaders LLC ....G 850 441-3289
Panama City Beach *(G-13982)*
Paragon Globl Sup Slutions LLC ....G 813 745-9902
Tampa *(G-17975)*
Paramount Mold LLC ....E 954 772-2333
Fort Lauderdale *(G-4157)*
Paramount Molded Products Inc ....E 954 772-2333
Fort Lauderdale *(G-4158)*
Plastic Concepts Ltd Inc ....F 727 942-6684
Tarpon Springs *(G-18320)*
Plastic Kingdom Inc ....G 561 586-9300
Lake Worth *(G-7580)*
Plastic Parts Inc ....E 954 974-3051
Pompano Beach *(G-14796)*
Plastic Parts Inc ....G 954 974-3051
Margate *(G-8561)*
Plastic Solutions Inc ....G 727 202-6815
Largo *(G-8028)*
Plastic Solutions of Pompano ....G 800 331-7081
Pompano Beach *(G-14798)*
Plastimold Products Inc ....G 561 869-0183
Delray Beach *(G-3118)*
Precision Mold & Tool Inc ....E 407 847-5687
Kissimmee *(G-7290)*
Precision Plastics Group Inc ....E 863 299-6639
Winter Haven *(G-19343)*
Precision Tool & Mold Inc ....F 727 573-4441
Clearwater *(G-1842)*
Premier Lab Supply Inc ....G 772 873-1700
Port Saint Lucie *(G-15130)*
Prime Molding Technologies Inc ....E 561 721-2799
Riviera Beach *(G-15366)*
Prospect Plastics Inc ....G 954 564-7282
Oakland Park *(G-11833)*
Proto Corp ....D 727 573-4665
Clearwater *(G-1851)*
Prototype Plstic Extrusion Inc ....E 727 572-0803
Clearwater *(G-1852)*
R S Design Inc ....F 727 525-8292
Pinellas Park *(G-14383)*
Rek Manufacturing Inc ....G 321 269-3533
Titusville *(G-18455)*
S Gager Industries Inc ....E 904 268-6727
Jacksonville *(G-6743)*

Scf Processing LLC ....G 352 377-0858
Gainesville *(G-4993)*
Scott Sign Systems Inc ....E 941 355-5171
Sarasota *(G-16294)*
Seaway Plastics Engrg LLC ....G 727 777-6032
Port Richey *(G-15068)*
Seaway Plastics Engrg LLC ....D 727 845-3235
Port Richey *(G-15069)*
Silcar Corp ....G 305 557-8391
Hialeah *(G-5620)*
Simco Machine and Tool Inc ....F 863 452-1151
Avon Park *(G-295)*
Simtec Silicone Parts LLC ....E 954 656-4212
Miramar *(G-11043)*
Soft Plastics Florida Inc ....G 904 338-9680
Jacksonville *(G-6782)*
Southern Reinforced Plastics ....G 941 746-8793
Bradenton *(G-1118)*
Standard Injection Molding Inc ....F 863 452-9090
Avon Park *(G-297)*
Steven R Durante ....G 954 564-9913
Oakland Park *(G-11844)*
Sun Works Plastics Inc ....G 727 573-2343
Clearwater *(G-1892)*
Sunco Plastics Inc ....F 305 238-2864
Miami *(G-10429)*
Suncoast Molders Inc ....F 727 546-0041
Largo *(G-8063)*
Sunrise Fiberglass Inc ....G 305 636-4111
Miami *(G-10432)*
Team Plastics Inc ....E 386 740-9555
Deland *(G-3018)*
TEC Air Inc ....G 772 335-8220
Fort Pierce *(G-4754)*
Technicraft Plastics Inc ....F 954 927-2575
Dania *(G-2458)*
Tmf Plastic Solutions LLC ....E 941 748-2946
Bradenton *(G-1126)*
Tomsons Inc ....G 248 646-0677
Englewood *(G-3685)*
United Plastic Fabricating Inc ....D 352 291-2477
Ocala *(G-12067)*
USB Plastics ....G 727 375-8840
Odessa *(G-12163)*
Usbev Products Inc ....F 727 375-8840
Odessa *(G-12164)*
Vanguard Systems Corp ....G 727 528-0121
Saint Petersburg *(G-15950)*
Victors Trim Molding Crown Bas ....G 727 403-6057
Saint Petersburg *(G-15953)*
W R Kershaw Inc ....G 386 673-0602
Ormond Beach *(G-13408)*
Wattera LLC ....E 954 400-5135
Fort Lauderdale *(G-4316)*
Winslow Microplastics Corp ....G 305 493-3501
Miami *(G-10612)*

PLASTICS: Molded

A Crown Molding Specialist ....F 954 665-5640
Pembroke Pines *(G-14013)*
American Moulding Corporation ....F 321 676-8929
Melbourne *(G-8766)*
Bas Plastics Inc ....G 954 202-9080
Fort Lauderdale *(G-3840)*
Beachcomber Fibrgls Tech Inc ....G 772 283-0200
Stuart *(G-16914)*
Boyce Engineering Inc ....F 727 572-6318
Saint Petersburg *(G-15727)*
Concealment Express LLC ....D 888 904-2722
Jacksonville *(G-6282)*
Creative Molding Corp ....F 786 251-4241
Doral *(G-3313)*
Custom Molding & Casework Inc ....G 407 709-7377
Deltona *(G-3167)*
Custom Plastic Fabricators ....G 813 884-5200
Tampa *(G-17581)*
Daigle Tool & Die Inc ....G 954 785-9989
Deerfield Beach *(G-2811)*
Darnel Inc ....F 954 929-0085
Hollywood *(G-5809)*
Doors Molding and More ....F 727 498-8552
Saint Petersburg *(G-15764)*
Firstcut ....G 786 740-3683
Miami *(G-9573)*
Foam Molding LLC ....G 813 434-7044
Tampa *(G-17690)*
Glass Works of Largo Inc ....G 727 535-9808
Largo *(G-7960)*
Kincaid Plastics Inc ....D 352 754-9979
Brooksville *(G-1242)*

Mdl Molding LLC.....G..... 954 792-3104
Fort Lauderdale *(G-4114)*
Molded Moments Art.....G..... 954 913-0793
Royal Palm Beach *(G-15475)*
Molded Poly Innovations Inc.....F..... 407 314-1778
Sanford *(G-16090)*
Molding Depot Inc.....E..... 813 348-4837
Tampa *(G-17915)*
Mtng Usa Corp.....G..... 305 670-0979
Miami *(G-10051)*
Paradise Inc.....C..... 813 752-1155
Tampa *(G-17974)*
Plastics Dynamics Inc.....G..... 954 565-7122
Oakland Park *(G-11828)*
Plastics For Mankind Inc.....F..... 305 687-5917
Opa Locka *(G-12351)*
Sands Molding Inc.....G..... 813 345-8646
Land O Lakes *(G-7865)*
T S E Industries Inc.....C..... 727 573-7676
Clearwater *(G-1900)*
T S E Industries Inc.....E..... 727 540-1368
Clearwater *(G-1901)*
Usbev Plastics LLC.....F..... 813 855-0700
Oldsmar *(G-12275)*

PLASTICS: Polystyrene Foam

AAA Architectural Elements.....F..... 941 722-1910
Palmetto *(G-13782)*
Allied Aerofoam Products LLC.....F..... 731 660-2705
Fort Lauderdale *(G-3798)*
Allied Aerofoam Products LLC.....D..... 813 626-0090
Fort Lauderdale *(G-3799)*
American Archtctral Foam Wrks.....F..... 813 443-0791
Tampa *(G-17414)*
Barco Sales & Mfg Inc.....F..... 954 563-3922
Oakland Park *(G-11784)*
Dart Container Corp Florida.....F..... 813 752-6525
Plant City *(G-14424)*
Dart Container Corp Florida.....F..... 941 358-1202
Sarasota *(G-16204)*
Dart Container Corp Florida.....F..... 941 358-1202
Sarasota *(G-16404)*
Design Works By Tech Pdts Inc.....E..... 941 355-2703
Sarasota *(G-16410)*
East Coast Foam Supply Inc.....G..... 321 433-8231
Rockledge *(G-15408)*
Foam & Psp Inc.....G..... 954 816-5648
Fort Lauderdale *(G-4008)*
Foam Decoration Inc.....G..... 786 293-8813
Miami *(G-9591)*
Icorp-Ifoam Specialty Products.....G..... 407 328-8500
Sanford *(G-16064)*
Innocor Foam Tech - Acp Inc.....D..... 305 685-6341
Miami *(G-9745)*
Italian Cast Stones Inc.....E..... 813 902-8900
Tampa *(G-17796)*
Medfab Corporation.....G..... 813 854-2646
Oldsmar *(G-12247)*
Nida-Core Corporation.....E..... 772 343-7300
Port Saint Lucie *(G-15124)*
Novicon Industries.....G..... 813 854-3235
Oldsmar *(G-12251)*
Reilly Foam Corp.....F..... 561 842-8090
Riviera Beach *(G-15369)*
Scott Sign Systems Inc.....E..... 941 355-5171
Sarasota *(G-16294)*
Wind Blue Technology LLC.....F..... 850 218-9398
Pensacola *(G-14288)*

PLASTICS: Thermoformed

Bk Plastics Industry Inc.....F..... 813 920-3628
Odessa *(G-12107)*
Brown Company.....G..... 850 455-0971
Pensacola *(G-14106)*
Dj Plastics Inc.....G..... 407 656-6677
Apopka *(G-131)*
Sibe Automation LLC.....F..... 352 690-1741
Ocala *(G-12049)*
Stockdale Technologies Inc.....D..... 407 323-5121
Lake Mary *(G-7451)*

PLATEMAKING SVC: Color Separations, For The Printing Trade

Diversified Graphics Inc.....F..... 407 425-9443
Orlando *(G-12677)*
Miami Trucolor Offset Svc Co.....G..... 954 962-5230
West Park *(G-19096)*
Rex Three Inc.....C..... 954 452-8301
Davie *(G-2585)*

Venue Advertising Inc.....E..... 561 844-1778
Jupiter *(G-7140)*

PLATES

Ace Printing Inc.....F..... 305 358-2572
Miami *(G-9061)*
All-Star Sales Inc.....E..... 904 396-1653
Jacksonville *(G-6137)*
American Business Cards Inc.....E..... 314 739-0800
Naples *(G-11161)*
Assocated Prtg Productions Inc.....E..... 305 623-7600
Miami Lakes *(G-10763)*
Bellak Color Corporation.....E..... 305 854-8525
Doral *(G-3267)*
Bjm Enterprises Inc.....F..... 941 746-4171
Bradenton *(G-1000)*
Boca Color Graphics Inc.....F..... 561 391-2229
Boca Raton *(G-450)*
Boca Raton Printing Co.....G..... 561 395-8404
Boca Raton *(G-454)*
Coastal Printing Inc Sarasota.....E..... 941 351-1515
Sarasota *(G-16386)*
Creative Prtg Grphic Dsign Inc.....E..... 407 855-0202
Orlando *(G-12627)*
Dobbs & Brodeur Bookbinders.....G..... 305 885-5215
Hialeah *(G-5376)*
Durra Print Inc.....E..... 850 222-4768
Tallahassee *(G-17244)*
H & M Printing Inc.....F..... 407 831-8030
Sanford *(G-16059)*
Impact Design Group Inc.....F..... 904 636-8989
Jacksonville *(G-6490)*
Interprint Incorporated.....D..... 727 531-8957
Clearwater *(G-1734)*
Keithco Inc.....G..... 352 351-4741
Ocala *(G-11976)*
Linographics Inc.....F..... 407 422-8700
Orlando *(G-12913)*
Pfaffco Inc.....F..... 305 635-0986
Miami Lakes *(G-10837)*
Photoengraving Inc.....E..... 813 253-3427
Tampa *(G-17992)*
Press Printing Enterprises Inc.....E..... 239 598-1500
Fort Myers *(G-4572)*
Roberts Quality Printing Inc.....E..... 727 442-4011
Clearwater *(G-1862)*
Southeast Finishing Group Inc.....E..... 407 299-4620
Orlando *(G-13202)*
Trinity Graphic Usa Inc.....F..... 941 355-2636
Sarasota *(G-16315)*
Vowells Downtown Inc.....G..... 850 432-5175
Pensacola *(G-14285)*
Walker Graphics Inc.....G..... 954 964-1688
Hollywood *(G-5939)*

PLATES: Steel

Renaissance Steel LLC.....F..... 941 773-7290
Temple Terrace *(G-18376)*

PLATES: Truss, Metal

Blackwater Truss Systems LLC.....G..... 850 623-1414
Milton *(G-10923)*
Mitek USA Inc.....G..... 813 906-3122
Tampa *(G-17911)*

PLATING & FINISHING SVC: Decorative, Formed Prdts

Kerno LLC.....F..... 954 261-5854
Fort Lauderdale *(G-4089)*
Mil-Spec Metal Finishing Inc.....G..... 386 426-7188
Edgewater *(G-3631)*

PLATING & POLISHING SVC

Accurate Metal Finshg Fla Inc.....F..... 321 636-4900
Rockledge *(G-15391)*
Bent Chrome LLC.....G..... 813 363-3398
Riverview *(G-15265)*
Coating Hues Inc.....G..... 786 626-9241
Naples *(G-11212)*
Exact Inc.....C..... 904 783-6640
Jacksonville *(G-6372)*
Finishing Group of Florid.....G..... 954 981-2171
Hollywood *(G-5821)*
Finns Brass and Silver Polsg.....G..... 904 387-1165
Jacksonville *(G-6381)*
Marios Metalcraft.....G..... 239 649-0085
Naples *(G-11321)*

World Plate.....G..... 386 597-7832
Bunnell *(G-1312)*
Z-2 Metal Artwork Inc.....G..... 305 804-4974
Hialeah *(G-5694)*

PLATING SVC: Chromium, Metals Or Formed Prdts

Ni-Chro Plating Corp.....G..... 727 327-5118
Saint Petersburg *(G-15866)*

PLATING SVC: Electro

Adtec II Tampa Inc.....E..... 786 588-3688
Pinellas Park *(G-14333)*
Airco Plating Company Inc.....E..... 305 633-2476
Miami *(G-9095)*
Allbright Electropolishing.....G..... 727 449-9353
Clearwater *(G-1575)*
B4c Technologies Inc.....G..... 772 463-1557
Palm City *(G-13643)*
Central Florida Plating Inc.....G..... 321 452-7234
Merritt Island *(G-8998)*
Coating Technology Inc.....E..... 813 854-3674
Oldsmar *(G-12216)*
Crown Plating Inc.....E..... 904 783-6640
Jacksonville *(G-6299)*
Delta Metal Finishing Inc.....E..... 954 953-9898
Fort Lauderdale *(G-3936)*
Electro Lab Inc.....F..... 813 818-7605
Oldsmar *(G-12225)*
Gold Effects Inc.....G..... 727 573-1990
Clearwater *(G-1704)*
Hard Chrome Enterprises Inc.....G..... 561 844-2529
Lake Park *(G-7474)*
Hialeah Plating.....G..... 305 953-4143
Hialeah *(G-5445)*
Jssa Inc.....E..... 321 383-7798
Titusville *(G-18435)*
Melmar Cstm Met Finshg Svc Inc.....G..... 954 327-5788
Davie *(G-2551)*
Millenium Engine Plating Inc.....G..... 305 688-0098
Hialeah *(G-5518)*
Purecoat International LLC.....E..... 561 844-0100
West Palm Beach *(G-19013)*
Quality Anodizing Incorporated.....G..... 954 791-8711
Davie *(G-2578)*
Spectra Chrome LLC.....G..... 727 573-1990
Clearwater *(G-1886)*

PLATING SVC: NEC

Action Plating Corp.....F..... 305 685-6313
Opa Locka *(G-12282)*
Alex Robert Silversmith Inc.....G..... 727 442-7333
Clearwater *(G-1573)*
Cfu Plating.....G..... 386 795-5198
Ocala *(G-11900)*
Chrome Plating Shop.....G..... 786 527-5357
Miami *(G-9352)*
Gold Plating Specialties.....G..... 239 851-9323
Fort Myers *(G-4470)*
Innovative Money Concepts.....G..... 954 748-6197
Parkland *(G-13992)*
Mark Plating Co.....G..... 561 655-4370
West Palm Beach *(G-18942)*
PC of Titusville Inc.....F..... 321 267-1161
Titusville *(G-18449)*
Space Coast Map LLC.....G..... 321 242-4538
Melbourne *(G-8938)*
Spacecast Pltg Met Rfnshing In.....F..... 321 254-2880
Melbourne *(G-8939)*
Superior Chrome Plating Inc.....F..... 832 659-0873
Naples *(G-11427)*
Techno-Coatings Inc.....C..... 305 945-2220
North Miami *(G-11659)*

PLAYGROUND EQPT

Florida Playground & Steel Co.....G..... 813 247-2812
Tampa *(G-17684)*
Play Tampa Bay Inc.....G..... 727 803-6838
Saint Petersburg *(G-15882)*
Playcore Wisconsin Inc.....G..... 800 853-5316
Saint Augustine *(G-15589)*
Southern Recreation Inc.....F..... 904 387-4390
Jacksonville *(G-6796)*
Urban Extreme LLC.....F..... 954 248-9007
Hollywood *(G-5934)*

PRODUCT

PLEATING & STITCHING SVC

Cubco Inc....F....386 254-2706
Daytona Beach (G-2650)
Full Press Apparel Inc....F....850 222-1003
Tallahassee (G-17259)
Hes Products Inc....G....407 834-0741
Ormond Beach (G-13376)
HOB Corporation....G....813 988-2272
Tampa (G-17758)
Icon Embroidery Inc....G....407 858-0886
Windermere (G-19228)
Image Depot....G....813 685-7116
Tampa (G-17772)
Joni Industries Inc....F....352 799-5456
Brooksville (G-1240)
Mid West Lettering Company....E....850 477-6522
Pensacola (G-14209)
Shirts & Caps Inc....F....813 788-7026
Tampa (G-18098)
Tiffany Quilting & Drapery....F....407 834-6386
Longwood (G-8343)
Vivid Images USA Inc....F....904 620-0303
Jacksonville (G-6902)

PLUGS: Electric

Broadband International Inc....G....305 882-0505
Medley (G-8626)

PLUMBING & HEATING EQPT & SPLY, WHOLESALE: Hydronic Htg Eqpt

Aruki Services LLC....G....850 364-5206
Havana (G-5232)
St Cloud Wldg Fabrication Inc....E....407 957-2344
Saint Cloud (G-15667)
Vickery and Company....F....813 987-2100
Tampa (G-18244)

PLUMBING & HEATING EQPT & SPLYS WHOLESALERS

Sunset Power Inc....F....866 485-2757
Jacksonville (G-6824)
Wool Wholesale Plumbing Supply....D....954 763-3632
Fort Lauderdale (G-4327)

PLUMBING & HEATING EQPT & SPLYS, WHOL: Pipe/Fitting, Plastic

Sun Pipe and Valves LLC....G....772 408-5530
Port Saint Lucie (G-15150)

PLUMBING & HEATING EQPT & SPLYS, WHOL: Plumbing Fitting/Sply

Design Works By Tech Pdts Inc....E....941 355-2703
Sarasota (G-16410)

PLUMBING & HEATING EQPT & SPLYS, WHOL: Water Purif Eqpt

Aqua Engineering & Equipment....F....407 599-2123
Winter Park (G-19378)
Fshs Inc....G....941 625-5929
Port Charlotte (G-14982)
H20logy Inc....G....904 829-6098
Saint Augustine (G-15547)
H2o International Inc....F....954 570-3464
Deerfield Beach (G-2834)
Siemens Industry Inc....G....407 650-3570
Orlando (G-13188)

PLUMBING FIXTURES

Apollo Retail Specialists LLC....B....813 712-2525
Tampa (G-17428)
Averett Septic Tank Co Inc....E....863 665-1748
Lakeland (G-7640)
Bobs Backflow & Plumbing Co....G....904 268-8009
Jacksonville (G-6219)
Coolcraft Inc....G....954 946-0070
Pompano Beach (G-14648)
Dakota Plumbing Products LLC....F....954 987-3430
Fort Lauderdale (G-3930)
Ddp Holdings LLC....C....813 712-2515
Tampa (G-17595)
Designers Plumbing Studio Inc....G....954 920-5997
Hollywood (G-5810)
Enolgas Usa Inc....G....754 205-7902
Pompano Beach (G-14681)
Home & Garden Industries Inc....F....305 634-0681
Miami (G-9716)
Johnston Archtctral Systems In....E....904 886-9030
Jacksonville (G-6527)
M F B International Inc....G....305 436-6601
Miami (G-9925)
Plumb Rite of Central Florida....G....407 292-0750
Apopka (G-172)
Target Manufacturing Inc....G....305 633-0361
Miami (G-10460)
True Plumbing Svc Inc....G....941 296-5123
Bradenton (G-1134)
Wool Wholesale Plumbing Supply....D....954 763-3632
Fort Lauderdale (G-4327)

PLUMBING FIXTURES: Plastic

Bathroom World Manufacturing....G....954 566-0451
Oakland Park (G-11785)
Coast Products LLC....F....850 235-2090
Panama City Beach (G-13976)
East Coast Fixtures & Mllwk Co....G....904 733-9711
Jacksonville (G-6349)
Elstons Inc....G....727 527-7929
Apollo Beach (G-102)
Hale Products Inc....C....352 629-5020
Ocala (G-11963)
Home & Garden Industries Inc....F....305 634-0681
Miami (G-9716)
Lions Intl MGT Group Inc....F....813 367-2517
Tampa (G-17848)
Lpi Inc....F....702 403-8555
Saint Petersburg (G-15842)
Sh Shower & Tub Enclosures LLC....G....786 229-2529
Miami (G-10331)
Tuflex Manufacturing Co....E....954 781-0605
Pompano Beach (G-14895)
Two Guys Plumbing Supply LLc....F....321 263-0021
Altamonte Springs (G-79)

PLUMBING FIXTURES: Vitreous

Custom Marble Works Inc....E....813 620-0475
Tampa (G-17580)
Ecotech Water LLC....G....877 341-9500
St Pete Beach (G-16879)

PLUMBING FIXTURES: Vitreous China

Wool Wholesale Plumbing Supply....D....954 763-3632
Fort Lauderdale (G-4327)

POINT OF SALE DEVICES

Bluestar Latin America Inc....E....800 354-9776
Miramar (G-10975)
Verifone Inc....C....800 837-4366
Coral Springs (G-2326)
Verifone Inc....B....727 953-4000
Clearwater (G-1931)
Verifone Inc....C....727 535-9200
Clearwater (G-1932)
Verifone Systems Inc....C....408 232-7800
Coral Springs (G-2328)
Zhyno Inc....G....844 313-1900
Miami (G-10631)

POKER CHIPS

Classic Poker Chips....G....207 332-9999
Saint Augustine (G-15530)

POLES & POSTS: Concrete

D & S Logging Inc....G....850 638-5500
Chipley (G-1543)
Utilities Structures Inc....F....239 334-7757
Fort Myers (G-4643)

POLICE PROTECTION: Bureau Of Criminal Investigation, Govt

United Ntons Space Crps Mltary....F....702 373-2351
Ponce De Leon (G-14920)

POLISHING SVC: Metals Or Formed Prdts

A Sotolongo Polishing Marble C....G....305 271-7957
Miami (G-9043)
Amado Wheel Finishing....G....786 732-6249
Miami (G-9130)
Exotic Marble Polishing Inc....G....786 318-6568
North Miami (G-11638)
Florida Polishing....G....305 688-2988
Opa Locka (G-12317)
Hard Surface Polishing LLC....G....850 360-4140
Graceville (G-5043)
Kissimmee Polishing....G....407 923-9446
Kissimmee (G-7263)
Polishing By Wilson O....G....727 203-0100
Port Richey (G-15063)
Unique Marble Polishing Inc....G....305 969-1554
Miami (G-10532)
Universal Polishing Systems....G....407 227-9516
Orlando (G-13297)

POLYCARBONATE RESINS

Midgard Inc....D....863 696-1224
Lake Wales (G-7516)

POLYESTERS

Lrm Industries Intl Inc....E....321 635-9797
Rockledge (G-15430)

POLYETHYLENE RESINS

Flying W Plastics Fl Inc....F....904 800-2451
Jacksonville (G-6410)

POLYPROPYLENE RESINS

Composite Essential Mtls LLC....G....772 344-0034
Port St Lucie (G-15172)
Purecycle Technologies Inc....E....877 648-3565
Orlando (G-13100)

POLYSTYRENE RESINS

Dioxide Materials Inc....F....217 239-1400
Boca Raton (G-502)

POLYURETHANE RESINS

Car Care Haven LLC....G....855 464-2836
Englewood (G-3671)
Hancor Inc....E....863 655-5499
Winter Garden (G-19266)

POLYVINYL CHLORIDE RESINS

Ultraflex Systems Florida Inc....F....973 664-6739
Riverview (G-15285)

POPCORN & SUPPLIES WHOLESALERS

Barnard Nut Company Inc....D....305 836-9999
Miami (G-9221)
Brownbag Popcorn Company LLC....G....561 212-5664
Boca Raton (G-467)

PORCELAIN ENAMELED PRDTS & UTENSILS

Hycomb Usa Inc....F....954 251-1691
Hallandale Beach (G-5190)

POSTAL EQPT: Locker Boxes, Exc Wood

Davis Mail Services Inc....C....904 477-7970
Jacksonville (G-6314)

POSTERS

Paris Ink Inc....G....561 990-1194
Boca Raton (G-663)
Starmakers Rising Inc....E....561 989-8999
Boca Raton (G-731)
Tropicolor Photo Service Inc....G....305 672-3720
Miami Beach (G-10721)

POTTERY

American CCC Ceramic Inc....G....321 356-9317
Apopka (G-112)
Florida Cool Ring Company....F....863 858-2211
Lakeland (G-7691)
Hart S Ceramic & Stone Inc....G....850 217-6145
Destin (G-3193)
Kreative Ceramics Inc....G....321 278-9889
Ocoee (G-12086)
Miy Ceramic....G....305 823-5758
Miami Lakes (G-10822)

POTTING SOILS

Earthsoil Inc .... G 888 282-1920
Fleming Island *(G-3761)*
Forestry Resources Inc .... E 239 332-3966
Fort Myers *(G-4457)*
Klasmann-Deilmann Americas Inc .... G 305 397-8498
Miami *(G-9826)*
United AG Svcs Amer Inc .... F 352 793-1682
Lake Panasoffkee *(G-7464)*

POULTRY & POULTRY PRDTS WHOLESALERS

La Villarena Meat & Pork Inc .... F 305 759-0555
Miami *(G-9849)*

POULTRY & SMALL GAME SLAUGHTERING & PROCESSING

Cedars Food Inc .... G 321 724-2624
West Melbourne *(G-18769)*
Johnson Brothers Whl Meats Inc .... E 850 763-2828
Panama City *(G-13922)*
Martins Fmous Pstry Shoppe Inc .... G 800 548-1200
Lake City *(G-7367)*
Martins Fmous Pstry Shoppe Inc .... G 800 548-1200
Lynn Haven *(G-8434)*
Martins Fmous Pstry Shoppe Inc .... G 800 548-1200
Pensacola *(G-14201)*
Pilgrims Pride Corporation .... G 386 362-4171
Live Oak *(G-8236)*

POWDER: Metal

Azz Powder Coating - Tampa LLC .... G 813 390-2802
Tampa *(G-17451)*
Ceramlock Coatings Inc .... G 772 781-2141
Palm City *(G-13645)*

POWDER: Silver

B-N-J Powder Coatings LLC .... G 407 999-8448
Orlando *(G-12503)*

POWER GENERATORS

GE Renewables North Amer LLC .... C 850 474-4011
Pensacola *(G-14161)*
General Power Limited Inc .... F 800 763-0359
Doral *(G-3362)*
Green Rhino Enrgy Slutions LLC .... D 407 925-5868
Apopka *(G-147)*
Megawattage LLC .... F 954 328-0232
Fort Lauderdale *(G-4117)*
Silent Standby Power Sup LLC .... G 954 253-9557
West Palm Beach *(G-19033)*
Windera Power Systems Inc .... G 407 808-1271
Sanford *(G-16140)*

POWER OUTLETS & SOCKETS

Terracassa LLC .... G 786 581-7741
Miami *(G-10468)*

POWER SUPPLIES: All Types, Static

Electriduct Inc .... E 954 867-9100
Pompano Beach *(G-14676)*
Jfh Technologies LLC .... E 407 938-9336
Lake Buena Vista *(G-7336)*
North Erie Electronics Inc .... F 561 839-8127
Jupiter *(G-7084)*
Technipower LLC .... F 954 346-2442
Coral Springs *(G-2321)*
Vision Engineering Labs .... D 727 812-2035
Largo *(G-8076)*

POWER TOOLS, HAND: Drills & Drilling Tools

Delta International Inc .... F 305 665-6573
Miami *(G-9451)*

POWER TOOLS, HAND: Grinders, Portable, Electric Or Pneumatic

S I P Corporation .... F 813 884-8300
Tampa *(G-18075)*

POWER TRANSMISSION EQPT: Aircraft

Dukane Seacom Inc .... C 941 739-3200
Sarasota *(G-16209)*

POWER TRANSMISSION EQPT: Mechanical

Alto Products Corp Al .... G 305 892-7777
Doral *(G-3242)*
Consultant MGT Group LLC .... G 352 344-4001
Inverness *(G-6083)*
Creative Carbide Inc .... F 239 567-0041
Fort Myers *(G-4414)*
Dowels Pins & Shafts Inc .... E 727 461-1255
Clearwater *(G-1656)*
Easy Flex Couplings LLC .... G 863 665-9374
Clermont *(G-1956)*
Enstar Holdings (us) LLC .... D 727 217-2900
Saint Petersburg *(G-15770)*
Gfx Inc .... E 305 499-9789
Miami *(G-9634)*
Ggb1 LLC .... G 305 387-5334
Miami *(G-9636)*
Ipts Inc .... F 561 844-8216
Riviera Beach *(G-15335)*
JW Performance Transm Inc .... E 321 632-6205
Rockledge *(G-15425)*
Man-Trans LLC .... F 850 222-6993
Tallahassee *(G-17294)*
North Amrcn Prtection Ctrl LLC .... G 407 788-3717
Altamonte Springs *(G-58)*
NSK Latin America Inc .... E 305 477-0605
Miami *(G-10083)*
Suncoast Rebuild Center Inc .... F 813 238-3433
Tampa *(G-18144)*
Torque Technologies Products .... G 630 462-1188
Sarasota *(G-16312)*

POWER TRANSMISSION EQPT: Vehicle

Progressive Power Products Inc .... G 904 354-1819
Jacksonville *(G-6693)*

POWERED GOLF CART DEALERS

My Custom Cart LLC .... G 904 214-3723
Middleburg *(G-10909)*

PRECAST TERRAZZO OR CONCRETE PRDTS

Brothers Pavers and Precast .... G 561 662-9075
West Palm Beach *(G-18828)*
Cds Manufacturing Inc .... D 850 875-4651
Gretna *(G-5090)*
Central Florida Precast Inc .... G 941 730-2158
Bradenton *(G-1019)*
Concrete Structures Inc .... F 305 597-9393
Miami *(G-9392)*
Decorative Precast LLC .... F 239 566-9503
Naples *(G-11225)*
Florida Engineered Constru .... G 321 953-5161
Palm Bay *(G-13513)*
Gate Precast Company .... C 904 520-5795
Jacksonville *(G-6422)*
Hbp Pipe & Precast LLC .... E 904 529-8228
Green Cove Springs *(G-5064)*
Intrepid Precast Inc .... G 352 347-7475
Ocala *(G-11970)*
Km Precast Inc .... F 239 438-2146
Naples *(G-11306)*
Master Construction Pdts Inc .... E 407 857-1221
Orlando *(G-12953)*
Perry Precast Inc .... G 386 294-2710
Mayo *(G-8597)*
Precast and Foam Works LLC .... G 727 657-9195
Clearwater *(G-1839)*
Precast Technical Assistance .... F 850 432-8446
Pensacola *(G-14236)*
Rmmj Inc .... E 239 597-2486
Naples *(G-11386)*
Southern Pre Cast Structures L .... G 352 569-1128
Bushnell *(G-1321)*
United Concrete Products LLC .... G 786 402-3536
Medley *(G-8747)*
US Precast Corp .... E 305 364-8253
Hialeah *(G-5667)*

PRECIOUS METALS

Gold Buyers of America LLC .... C 877 721-8033
Greenacres *(G-5081)*

PREFABRICATED BUILDING DEALERS

Eds Aluminum Buildings Inc .... G 850 476-2169
Pensacola *(G-14138)*

PRERECORDED TAPE, CD & RECORD STORE: Record, Disc/Tape

Singing Machine Company Inc .... F 954 596-1000
Fort Lauderdale *(G-4236)*

PRERECORDED TAPE, CD/RECORD STORES: Audio Tapes, Prerecorded

Muscle Mixes Inc .... F 407 872-7576
Orlando *(G-12987)*

PRERECORDED TAPE, COMPACT DISC & RECORD STORES: Compact Disc

Horizon Duplication Inc .... G 407 767-5000
Winter Park *(G-19411)*

PRESS CLIPPING SVC

Cole Enterprises Inc .... G 727 441-4101
Clearwater *(G-1632)*

PRESSED & MOLDED PULP PRDTS, NEC: From Purchased Materials

Inovart Inc .... G 941 751-2324
Bradenton *(G-1061)*

PRESTRESSED CONCRETE PRDTS

Accord Industries LLC .... D 407 671-6989
Winter Park *(G-19370)*
Bayshore Concrete Pdts Corp .... C 757 331-2300
Maitland *(G-8458)*
Dura-Stress Inc .... C 352 787-1422
Leesburg *(G-8152)*
Finfrock Industries Inc .... C 407 293-4000
Apopka *(G-141)*
Prestressed Systems Inc .... F 305 556-6699
Doral *(G-3469)*
Southeastern Prestressed Con .... F 561 793-1177
West Palm Beach *(G-19040)*
Spancrete Inc .... E 305 599-8885
Miami *(G-10394)*

PRIMARY METAL PRODUCTS

Accurate Metal Finshg Fla Inc .... F 321 636-4900
Rockledge *(G-15391)*
AP Richter Holding Co LLC .... G 239 732-9440
Naples *(G-11164)*
Klocke of America Inc .... D 239 561-5800
Fort Myers *(G-4512)*
Ogre Custom Fabrications LLC .... G 321 544-2142
Melbourne *(G-8900)*

PRINT CARTRIDGES: Laser & Other Computer Printers

Computer Forms & Supplies .... G 727 535-0422
Largo *(G-7926)*
Micromicr Corporation .... F 954 922-8044
Dania *(G-2452)*
Replenish Ink Inc .... G 818 206-2424
Miami *(G-10254)*
Sun Print Management LLC .... E 727 945-0255
Holiday *(G-5749)*
Suncoast Toner Cartridge Inc .... F 727 945-0255
Holiday *(G-5750)*
Team Inkjet .... G 954 554-3250
Coral Springs *(G-2320)*
Toner Cartridge Recharge Inc .... G 305 968-1045
Miami Lakes *(G-10868)*
Toner Technologies Inc .... G 561 547-9710
Boynton Beach *(G-970)*
Universal Ribbon Corporation .... E 305 471-0828
Miami *(G-10542)*
Well Made Bus Solutions LLC .... G 754 227-7268
Coconut Creek *(G-2101)*

PRINTED CIRCUIT BOARDS

4front Solutions LLC .... D 814 464-2000
Deland *(G-2951)*
ACt USA International LLC .... F 321 725-4200
Melbourne *(G-8757)*

Advanced Manufacturing Inc E 727 573-3300
Saint Petersburg *(G-15691)*
Alegro Industries Inc D 702 943-0978
Tamarac *(G-17349)*
AOC Technologies Inc F 727 577-9749
Saint Petersburg *(G-15702)*
Ateei International Corp E 305 597-6408
Doral *(G-3258)*
Axon Circuit Inc F 407 265-7980
Longwood *(G-8260)*
Axon Circuit Inc E 407 265-7980
Tampa *(G-17450)*
Board Shark Pcb Inc G 352 759-2100
Astor *(G-215)*
C K C Industries Inc G 813 888-9468
Tampa *(G-17494)*
Calumet Electronics G 954 668-7689
Hollywood *(G-5794)*
Certified Manufacturing Inc E 850 537-3777
Holt *(G-5948)*
Circuit Works Co G 727 544-5336
Pinellas Park *(G-14338)*
Circuitronics LLC F 407 322-8300
Sanford *(G-16015)*
Concept 2 Market Inc F 954 974-0022
Pompano Beach *(G-14643)*
Continuity Unlimited Inc F 561 358-8171
Oviedo *(G-13422)*
Creonix LLC F 941 758-3340
Brooksville *(G-1223)*
Delta Group Electronics Inc D 321 631-0799
Rockledge *(G-15400)*
Denver Elevator Systems Inc G 800 633-9788
Cape Canaveral *(G-1356)*
Diamond Mt Inc F 321 339-3377
Melbourne *(G-8804)*
Englander Enterprises Inc E 727 461-4755
Clearwater *(G-1673)*
Florida Elreha Corporation E 727 327-6236
Saint Petersburg *(G-15783)*
Global Intrcnnect Slutions LLC G 239 254-0326
Naples *(G-11262)*
H & T Global Circuit Fctry LLC D 727 327-6236
Saint Petersburg *(G-15802)*
I3 Microsystems Inc E 727 235-6532
Saint Petersburg *(G-15810)*
Icmfg & Associates Inc G 727 258-4995
Clearwater *(G-1726)*
Infinity Pcb Inc G 321 804-8045
West Melbourne *(G-18776)*
Itct USA G 352 799-1466
Brooksville *(G-1239)*
Jabil Advnced Mech Sltions Inc E 727 577-9749
Saint Petersburg *(G-15821)*
Jabil Circuit G 727 577-9749
Saint Petersburg *(G-15822)*
Jabil Circuit LLC D 727 577-9749
Saint Petersburg *(G-15824)*
Jabil Def & Arospc Svcs LLC E 727 577-9749
Saint Petersburg *(G-15825)*
Jabil Def & Arospc Svcs LLC F 727 577-9749
Saint Petersburg *(G-15826)*
Jabil Inc A 727 577-9749
Saint Petersburg *(G-15827)*
Jabil Inc E 727 577-9749
Saint Petersburg *(G-15828)*
Jabil Inc C 727 803-3110
Saint Petersburg *(G-15829)*
Jabil Inc D 727 577-9749
Saint Petersburg *(G-15830)*
Jrt Manufacturing LLC F 321 363-4133
Sanford *(G-16076)*
Kimball Electronics Tampa Inc C 813 814-5229
Tampa *(G-17825)*
Laser Photo Tooling Services F 561 393-4710
Boca Raton *(G-596)*
M C Test Service Inc A 321 253-0541
Melbourne *(G-8879)*
Mack Technologies Florida Inc C 321 725-6993
Melbourne *(G-8881)*
Marlo Electronics Inc E 561 477-0856
Boca Raton *(G-610)*
Mathews Associates Inc C 407 323-3390
Sanford *(G-16082)*
Mc Assembly Holdings Inc G 321 253-0541
Melbourne *(G-8884)*
Memo Labs Inc F 561 842-0586
West Palm Beach *(G-18948)*
Micro Engineering Inc E 407 886-4849
Apopka *(G-161)*
Nano Dimension USA Inc E 650 209-2866
Sunrise *(G-17150)*
Nypro Healthcare LLC E 727 577-9749
Saint Petersburg *(G-15868)*
Oum LLC F 407 886-1511
Apopka *(G-168)*
Paramount Industries Inc E 954 781-3755
Pompano Beach *(G-14784)*
Pica Sales and Engineering G 239 992-9079
Estero *(G-3693)*
Precision Circuits Inc E 321 632-8629
Rockledge *(G-15441)*
Prime Technological Svcs LLC D 850 539-2500
Havana *(G-5239)*
Protek Electronics Inc E 941 351-4399
Sarasota *(G-16548)*
Qualitel Inc E 954 464-3991
Hollywood *(G-5897)*
Quality Manufacturing Svcs Inc D 407 531-6000
Lake Mary *(G-7447)*
Rtp Corp G 954 597-5333
Pompano Beach *(G-14836)*
Sibex Inc C 727 726-4343
Crystal River *(G-2382)*
Smiths Interconnect Inc C 813 901-7200
Tampa *(G-18111)*
Solutions Manufacturing Inc D 321 848-0848
Rockledge *(G-15448)*
Sparton Corporation C 847 762-5800
De Leon Springs *(G-2742)*
Sparton Deleon Springs LLC D 386 985-4631
De Leon Springs *(G-2743)*
Specialty Fin Consulting Corp B 717 246-1661
Longboat Key *(G-8247)*
Superior Electronics Inc E 727 733-0700
Clearwater *(G-1896)*
Sypris Electronics LLC B 813 972-6000
Tampa *(G-18149)*
Tms Enterprises LLC B 850 539-2500
Havana *(G-5240)*
Tropical Assemblies Inc D 954 396-9999
Oakland Park *(G-11848)*
Tropical Stencil Pcb Inc F 561 972-5133
Jupiter *(G-7133)*
United Circuits Inc F 954 971-6860
Pompano Beach *(G-14900)*
Xtreme Electronic Designs Inc G 561 557-3667
Jupiter *(G-7148)*

PRINTERS & PLOTTERS

Barrett & Company G 305 293-4501
Key West *(G-7179)*
It Manex LLC G 954 442-4465
Miramar *(G-11005)*
Knight Bacon Associates G 772 388-5115
Sebastian *(G-16665)*
Roberto Valverde G 305 324-5252
Miami *(G-10271)*
Zsno Ft Lauderdale G 954 792-2223
Miramar *(G-11062)*

PRINTERS' SVCS: Folding, Collating, Etc

Midds Inc E 561 586-6220
Lake Worth Beach *(G-7615)*

PRINTERS: Computer

Evolis Inc F 954 777-9262
Fort Lauderdale *(G-3977)*
Lexmark International Inc C 954 345-2442
Coral Springs *(G-2274)*
Lexmark International Inc F 305 467-2200
Miami *(G-9887)*
Nscrypt Inc E 407 275-4720
Orlando *(G-13012)*
Peripheral Services Inc E 813 854-1181
Oldsmar *(G-12256)*
Totalprint USA G 855 915-1300
Tampa *(G-18196)*

PRINTERS: Magnetic Ink, Bar Code

Logiscenter LLC G 800 729-0236
Miami *(G-9905)*
US Barcodes Inc G 727 849-1196
Port Richey *(G-15074)*

PRINTING & BINDING: Books

Sosumi Holdings Inc E 239 634-3430
Naples *(G-11407)*

PRINTING & BINDING: Pamphlets

Tone Printing LLC G 855 505-8663
Miami *(G-10489)*

PRINTING & EMBOSSING: Plastic Fabric Articles

PHI CHI Foundation Inc G 561 526-3401
Margate *(G-8560)*
Williams Specialties Inc G 305 769-9925
Hialeah *(G-5687)*

PRINTING & ENGRAVING: Card, Exc Greeting

Alpha Card Compact Media LLC G 407 698-3592
Winter Park *(G-19375)*

PRINTING & ENGRAVING: Invitation & Stationery

Hey Day G 305 763-8660
Miami Beach *(G-10677)*
Miami Engrv Co-Oxford Prtg Co G 305 371-9595
Miami *(G-9999)*
Pioneer Announcements Inc F 305 573-7000
Miami *(G-10166)*

PRINTING & STAMPING: Fabric Articles

Countrywide Screen Printing G 239 333-4020
Fort Myers *(G-4411)*
Elite Graphics G 305 331-2678
Hialeah *(G-5392)*
McGee Enterprises Inc G 904 328-3226
Jacksonville *(G-6585)*
Open Market Enterprises LLC G 407 322-5434
Orlando *(G-13024)*
Parthenon Prints Inc E 850 769-8321
Panama City *(G-13940)*
Preferred Custom Printing LLC F 727 443-1900
Seminole *(G-16757)*
Walter Haas Graphics Inc E 305 883-2257
Hialeah *(G-5685)*

PRINTING MACHINERY

Amrav Inc G 407 831-1550
Altamonte Springs *(G-31)*
Apex Machine Company D 954 563-0209
Oakland Park *(G-11778)*
CST USA Inc F 404 695-2249
Miami *(G-9415)*
EL Harley Inc F 561 841-9887
Delray Beach *(G-3072)*
Gammerlertech Corporation E 941 803-0150
Bradenton *(G-1045)*
Howard Imprinting Machine Co G 813 884-2398
Tampa *(G-17762)*
Iter3d Inc G 718 473-0114
Aventura *(G-274)*
Man Enterprises 3 LLC G 561 655-4944
West Palm Beach *(G-18940)*
Mark/Trece Inc E 863 647-4372
Lakeland *(G-7745)*
MGI Usa Inc F 321 751-6755
Melbourne *(G-8888)*
Southern Graphic Machine LLC G 615 812-0778
Edgewater *(G-3636)*
Universal Stncling Mkg Systems E 727 894-3027
Saint Petersburg *(G-15948)*
Zenith Rollers Llc G 954 493-6484
Fort Lauderdale *(G-4334)*

PRINTING MACHINERY, EQPT & SPLYS: Wholesalers

Amrav Inc G 407 831-1550
Altamonte Springs *(G-31)*
Howard Imprinting Machine Co G 813 884-2398
Tampa *(G-17762)*

PRINTING TRADES MACHINERY & EQPT REPAIR SVCS

Light Source Business Systems F 772 562-5046
Port Saint Lucie *(G-15120)*
Peripheral Services Inc E 813 854-1181
Oldsmar *(G-12256)*

PRINTING, COMMERCIAL Newspapers, NEC

Island The Reporter Inc ......G...... 727 631-4730
Saint Petersburg *(G-15818)*

PRINTING, COMMERCIAL: Announcements, NEC

Rapid Rater Company ......E...... 850 893-7346
Tallahassee *(G-17314)*

PRINTING, COMMERCIAL: Bags, Plastic, NEC

Vicbag LLC ......G...... 305 423-7042
Miami *(G-10578)*

PRINTING, COMMERCIAL: Business Forms, NEC

American Reprographics Co LLC ......G...... 813 286-8300
Tampa *(G-17419)*
County of Broward ......G...... 954 357-7120
Fort Lauderdale *(G-3919)*
Easy Rent Inc ......G...... 904 443-7446
Jacksonville *(G-6351)*
Ef Enterprises of North Fla ......G...... 904 739-5995
Jacksonville *(G-6356)*
Express Printing Center Inc ......F...... 813 909-1085
Land O Lakes *(G-7854)*
M&M Studios Inc ......G...... 561 744-2754
Jupiter *(G-7070)*
Standard Register Inc ......F...... 954 492-9986
Fort Lauderdale *(G-4256)*

PRINTING, COMMERCIAL: Cards, Playing, NEC

Buddy Bridge Inc ......E...... 941 488-0799
Nokomis *(G-11578)*
Sun Business Systems Inc ......G...... 727 547-6540
Clearwater *(G-1891)*

PRINTING, COMMERCIAL: Cards, Visiting, Incl Business, NEC

Jrg Systems Inc ......F...... 954 962-1020
Fort Lauderdale *(G-4081)*
Print Shop of Chiefland Inc ......G...... 352 493-0322
Chiefland *(G-1537)*

PRINTING, COMMERCIAL: Certificates, Security, NEC

Pasa Services Inc ......E...... 305 594-8662
Opa Locka *(G-12350)*

PRINTING, COMMERCIAL: Decals, NEC

Leonard-Martin Corporation ......G...... 850 434-2203
Pensacola *(G-14192)*

PRINTING, COMMERCIAL: Directories, Telephone, NEC

Safari Sun LLC ......E...... 407 339-7291
Altamonte Springs *(G-71)*

PRINTING, COMMERCIAL: Envelopes, NEC

Services On Demand Print Inc ......E...... 305 681-5345
Hallandale Beach *(G-5209)*

PRINTING, COMMERCIAL: Fashion Plates, NEC

PHI CHI Foundation Inc ......G...... 561 526-3401
Margate *(G-8560)*

PRINTING, COMMERCIAL: Imprinting

Coastal Imprinting ......G...... 321 543-4169
Melbourne *(G-8793)*
Imprint Promotions LLC ......G...... 321 622-8946
Melbourne *(G-8850)*
Put Your Name On It LLC ......G...... 813 972-1460
Tampa *(G-18026)*
Sunybell LLC ......F...... 727 301-2832
New Port Richey *(G-11512)*

PRINTING, COMMERCIAL: Invitations, NEC

Note It ......G...... 954 593-8616
Hollywood *(G-5884)*

PRINTING, COMMERCIAL: Labels & Seals, NEC

A Bar Code Business Inc ......G...... 352 750-0077
The Villages *(G-18388)*
Creaprint Usa Corp ......G...... 786 369-7398
Miami *(G-9410)*
Dongili Investment Group Inc ......F...... 941 927-3003
Sarasota *(G-16413)*
Executive Label Inc ......F...... 954 978-6983
Margate *(G-8543)*
Fast Labels ......G...... 904 626-0508
Jacksonville *(G-6379)*
Florida Tape & Labels Inc ......F...... 941 921-5788
Sarasota *(G-16438)*
L & N Label Company Inc ......E...... 727 442-5400
Clearwater *(G-1755)*
Label Graphics Inc ......G...... 561 798-8180
Lake Worth *(G-7563)*
Prolabel Inc ......F...... 305 620-2202
Hialeah *(G-5579)*
Southern Tape & Label Inc ......F...... 321 632-5275
Cocoa *(G-2052)*
Tradingflex Inc ......F...... 877 522-3535
Miami *(G-10501)*
United Seal & Tag Label Corp ......G...... 941 625-6799
Port Charlotte *(G-15004)*

PRINTING, COMMERCIAL: Letterpress & Screen

Elite Printing & Marketing Inc ......G...... 850 474-0894
Pensacola *(G-14139)*

PRINTING, COMMERCIAL: Literature, Advertising, NEC

Aacecorp Inc ......G...... 904 353-7878
Jacksonville *(G-6115)*
Corporate Printing & Advg Inc ......F...... 305 273-6000
Miami *(G-9405)*
Dxm Marketing Group LLC ......F...... 904 332-6490
Jacksonville *(G-6342)*
Image Depot ......G...... 813 685-7116
Tampa *(G-17772)*
Mark Wsser Graphic Productions ......G...... 305 888-7445
Boynton Beach *(G-932)*
Tone Printing LLC ......G...... 855 505-8663
Miami *(G-10489)*

PRINTING, COMMERCIAL: Magazines, NEC

Vision Web Offset LLC ......F...... 305 433-6188
Miami Lakes *(G-10879)*

PRINTING, COMMERCIAL: Maps, NEC

Reprographic Solutions Inc ......G...... 772 340-3430
Port Saint Lucie *(G-15137)*

PRINTING, COMMERCIAL: Menus, NEC

David Dobbs Enterprises Inc ......D...... 904 824-6171
Saint Augustine *(G-15533)*

PRINTING, COMMERCIAL: Promotional

Clear Choice Inc ......G...... 407 830-6968
Altamonte Springs *(G-37)*
Creative Promotional Products ......G...... 407 383-7114
Orlando *(G-12626)*
Drip Communication LLC ......F...... 407 730-5519
Orlando *(G-12685)*
Hit Promotional Products Inc ......B...... 727 541-5561
Largo *(G-7971)*
Inflatable Design Works Corp ......F...... 786 242-1049
Miami *(G-9742)*
Legacy Sports Inc ......E...... 352 732-6759
Ocala *(G-11981)*
New Image Printing Promotion ......G...... 904 240-1516
Jacksonville *(G-6627)*
Promotional Mktg Online LLC ......G...... 941 347-8564
Punta Gorda *(G-15222)*
Tattoo Factory Inc ......E...... 941 923-4110
Sarasota *(G-16616)*
Vurb LLC ......F...... 561 441-8870
Pompano Beach *(G-14910)*
Whitecap Promotions LLC ......G...... 813 960-4918
Tampa *(G-18257)*
World Event Promotions LLC ......E...... 800 214-3408
Miami *(G-10619)*

PRINTING, COMMERCIAL: Publications

ABC Imaging of Washington ......F...... 954 759-2037
Fort Lauderdale *(G-3775)*
Academic Publication Svcs Inc ......G...... 941 925-4474
Sarasota *(G-16332)*
Baptist Mid-Missions Inc ......F...... 863 382-6350
Sebring *(G-16682)*
Greentex America LLC ......F...... 305 908-8580
Hallandale Beach *(G-5189)*
Mango Publications ......G...... 863 583-4773
Lakeland *(G-7743)*
Marco Polo Publications Inc ......G...... 866 610-9441
Saint Petersburg *(G-15846)*
Mojowax Media Inc ......G...... 805 550-6013
Bradenton *(G-1080)*
Morris Visitor Publications ......F...... 407 423-0618
Orlando *(G-12981)*
Naylor LLC ......C...... 800 369-6220
Gainesville *(G-4969)*
Newbeauty Media Group LLC ......E...... 561 961-7600
Boca Raton *(G-643)*
Print Idea Center LLC ......G...... 954 682-6369
Riviera Beach *(G-15367)*

PRINTING, COMMERCIAL: Schedules, Transportation, NEC

Aw Publishing ......F...... 305 856-7000
Miami *(G-9201)*

PRINTING, COMMERCIAL: Screen

850 Screen Printing LLC ......G...... 850 549-7861
Pensacola *(G-14074)*
A D Coaches Corner Inc ......G...... 786 242-2229
Miami *(G-9036)*
Above LLC ......F...... 850 469-9028
Pensacola *(G-14077)*
Accuprint My Print Shop ......G...... 954 973-9369
Deerfield Beach *(G-2763)*
Acm Screen Printing Inc ......G...... 305 547-1552
Miami *(G-9064)*
Admiral Printing Inc ......G...... 727 938-9589
Holiday *(G-5732)*
Advanced Screen Printing & EMB ......G...... 863 648-1268
Lakeland *(G-7628)*
Adver-T Screen Printing Inc ......F...... 727 443-5525
Clearwater *(G-1567)*
All Florida Engraving ......G...... 352 213-4572
Hawthorne *(G-5243)*
All Pro Ink ......G...... 305 252-7644
Cutler Bay *(G-2385)*
All Purpose Prtg Graphics Inc ......F...... 904 346-0999
Jacksonville *(G-6135)*
All Star Graphix Inc ......G...... 954 772-1972
Oakland Park *(G-11775)*
Allgeo & Yerkes Entps Inc ......F...... 321 255-9030
Melbourne *(G-8764)*
Allied Decals Fla Inc ......G...... 800 940-2233
Fort Lauderdale *(G-3800)*
Allied Decals-Fla Inc ......F...... 800 940-2233
Fort Lauderdale *(G-3801)*
Aloha Screen Printing Inc ......G...... 850 934-4716
Gulf Breeze *(G-5111)*
American Mentality Inc ......G...... 407 599-7255
Longwood *(G-8254)*
American Screen Print Inc ......G...... 904 443-0071
Jacksonville *(G-6149)*
Ampersand Graphics Inc ......E...... 772 283-1359
Stuart *(G-16906)*
Ampersand Shirt Shack ......F...... 772 600-8743
Stuart *(G-16907)*
Anchor Screen Printing LLC ......G...... 850 243-4200
Fort Walton Beach *(G-4775)*
and Tees LLC ......G...... 904 745-0773
Jacksonville *(G-6154)*
Apparel Printers ......G...... 352 463-8850
Alachua *(G-4)*
APS Promotional Solutions Inc ......F...... 904 721-4977
Jacksonville *(G-6161)*
Arj Art Inc ......G...... 727 535-8633
Saint Petersburg *(G-15710)*
Art Printing Miami ......G...... 786 581-9889
Miami *(G-9171)*
Artworks Printing Enterprises ......G...... 954 893-7984
Hollywood *(G-5775)*

ASAP Screen Printing Inc ......G...... 352 505-7574
Gainesville *(G-4877)*
Atticus Screen Printing T ......G...... 407 365-9911
Oviedo *(G-13415)*
Bam Enterprises Inc ......E...... 850 469-8872
Pensacola *(G-14096)*
Bayshore Brand Group Inc ......G...... 813 384-8275
Tampa *(G-17459)*
Beach Embroidery & Screen Ptg ......G...... 386 478-3931
New Smyrna Beach *(G-11528)*
Benner China and Glwr of Fla ......E...... 904 733-4620
Jacksonville *(G-6205)*
Bl Brandhouse LLC ......G...... 305 600-7181
Doral *(G-3277)*
CAM Broc Sports Inc ......G...... 407 933-6524
Kissimmee *(G-7229)*
Capsmith Inc ......E...... 407 328-7660
Sanford *(G-16007)*
Captains Custom Tees Inc ......G...... 239 424-8206
Lakewood Ranch *(G-7842)*
Caribongo ......G...... 727 944-5200
Tarpon Springs *(G-18286)*
Carpe Diem Sales & Mktg Inc ......E...... 407 682-1400
Orlando *(G-12552)*
CC Sportswear Inc ......G...... 941 351-4205
Sarasota *(G-16188)*
Charitees LLC ......G...... 561 542-4616
Hollywood *(G-5798)*
Classic Screen Prtg Design Inc ......G...... 407 850-0112
Orlando *(G-12588)*
Classic Shirts Inc ......F...... 850 875-2200
Quincy *(G-15247)*
Clothing Warehouse ......G...... 904 354-9002
Jacksonville *(G-6271)*
Copy Systems Business Center ......G...... 850 650-0886
Santa Rosa Beach *(G-16156)*
Coral Club Tee Shirts Inc ......G...... 305 828-6939
Hialeah *(G-5354)*
Cotton Pickin Shirts Plus ......G...... 850 435-3133
Pensacola *(G-14120)*
Country Side T-Shirt ......G...... 352 372-1015
Gainesville *(G-4899)*
Cubco Inc ......F...... 386 254-2706
Daytona Beach *(G-2650)*
Custom Graphics Inc ......G...... 954 563-6756
Deerfield Beach *(G-2808)*
DAccord Shirts & Guayaberas ......G...... 305 576-0926
Miami *(G-9428)*
Davie Embroidme ......F...... 954 452-0600
Davie *(G-2515)*
DC Apparel Inc ......G...... 863 325-9273
Winter Haven *(G-19317)*
Deluna Toole LLC ......G...... 850 435-4063
Pensacola *(G-14128)*
Designated Sports Inc ......F...... 904 797-9469
Saint Augustine *(G-15537)*
Designers Top Shop Inc ......G...... 863 453-3855
Avon Park *(G-285)*
Dillco Inc ......F...... 386 734-7510
Deland *(G-2971)*
DNE Pot Sbob Inc ......F...... 239 936-8880
Fort Myers *(G-4434)*
Dorado Graphix LLC ......G...... 904 751-4500
Jacksonville *(G-6325)*
Double H Enterprises Inc ......G...... 972 562-8588
Ormond Beach *(G-13364)*
Douglass Screen Printers Inc ......E...... 863 687-8545
Lakeland *(G-7677)*
Dragonfly Graphics ......G...... 772 879-9800
Port Saint Lucie *(G-15103)*
Dragonfly Graphics Inc ......G...... 352 375-2144
Gainesville *(G-4910)*
Drewlu Enterprises Inc ......G...... 407 478-7872
Winter Park *(G-19405)*
Embroidery Solutions Inc ......G...... 407 438-8188
Orlando *(G-12708)*
Engead Gb Design & Prtg Inc ......G...... 954 783-5161
Pompano Beach *(G-14680)*
Epic Promos LLC ......F...... 561 479-8055
Boca Raton *(G-519)*
Evolutionary Screen Printing L ......G...... 863 248-2692
Lakeland *(G-7682)*
Fassi Equipment Inc ......G...... 954 385-6555
Weston *(G-19123)*
Fassidigitalcom Inc ......F...... 954 385-6555
Weston *(G-19124)*
First Coast Tee Shirt Co Inc ......G...... 904 737-1985
Jacksonville *(G-6387)*
Fla Property Holdings Inc ......E...... 813 888-8796
Miami Lakes *(G-10790)*
Florida Flexible ......G...... 305 512-2222
Hialeah *(G-5413)*
Florida Screen Services Inc ......F...... 407 316-0466
Orlando *(G-12755)*
Fluid Designs Inc ......G...... 904 737-1557
Jacksonville *(G-6408)*
Full Press Apparel Inc ......F...... 850 222-1003
Tallahassee *(G-17259)*
Garment Gear Inc ......F...... 850 215-2121
Panama City *(G-13907)*
Gift Giving Creations Corp ......G...... 786 239-0229
Hialeah *(G-5430)*
Good Catch Inc ......G...... 305 757-7700
Miami *(G-9648)*
Grafx By Caz (fort Pierce) ......G...... 772 284-9258
Fort Pierce *(G-4702)*
Grand Cypress Group Inc ......G...... 407 622-1993
Maitland *(G-8467)*
Graphix Screen Printing ......G...... 727 937-6147
Tarpon Springs *(G-18303)*
Great Atlantic Outfitters ......G...... 904 722-0196
Jacksonville *(G-6445)*
Gulf Breeze Apparel LLC ......G...... 941 488-8337
Venice *(G-18551)*
Halifax Plastic Inc ......F...... 386 252-2442
Daytona Beach *(G-2672)*
Happy Endings of Miami Inc ......G...... 305 759-4467
Miami *(G-9686)*
Hes Products Inc ......G...... 407 834-0741
Ormond Beach *(G-13376)*
Hitking Sports LLC ......G...... 941 661-2753
Treasure Island *(G-18475)*
Hitmaster Graphics LLC ......F...... 813 250-0555
Tampa *(G-17757)*
Hot Action Sportswear Inc ......E...... 386 677-5680
Ormond Beach *(G-13377)*
Hunted Tees LLC ......G...... 407 260-2138
Altamonte Springs *(G-50)*
I P Team Inc ......E...... 772 398-4664
Stuart *(G-16956)*
Impress Ink LLC ......F...... 407 982-5646
Orlando *(G-12825)*
Industrial Marking Svcs Inc ......G...... 727 541-7622
Largo *(G-7979)*
Ink Trax Inc ......F...... 850 235-4849
Panama City *(G-13917)*
International Prtg Ad Spc Inc ......E...... 772 398-4664
Stuart *(G-16959)*
James Hines Printing ......G...... 904 398-5110
Jacksonville *(G-6515)*
Jet Set Printing Inc ......G...... 407 339-1900
Casselberry *(G-1508)*
Joni Industries Inc ......F...... 352 799-5456
Brooksville *(G-1240)*
Jose Polanco ......G...... 305 631-1784
Miami *(G-9804)*
Kenny-Ts Inc ......F...... 850 575-6644
Tallahassee *(G-17288)*
Kikisteescom LLC ......G...... 954 314-7147
Weston *(G-19146)*
Koala Tee Inc (usa) ......E...... 941 954-7700
Sarasota *(G-16483)*
Lifestyle Printworks Inc ......G...... 321 604-1531
Titusville *(G-18442)*
Logos Promote Inc ......G...... 407 447-5646
Orlando *(G-12935)*
Looper Sports Connection Inc ......G...... 352 796-7974
Brooksville *(G-1247)*
Lowe Gear Printing ......G...... 866 714-9965
Lutz *(G-8396)*
Lucky Dog Screen Printing Mg ......G...... 407 629-8838
Winter Park *(G-19420)*
Meektees LLC ......G...... 786 424-8491
Miami *(G-9970)*
Merchspin Inc ......E...... 877 306-3651
Orlando *(G-12960)*
Metropolis Graphics Inc ......G...... 407 740-5455
Winter Park *(G-19424)*
Miami Epic Tees Corp ......G...... 305 224-3465
Hialeah *(G-5509)*
Miami Screenprint Supply ......G...... 305 622-7532
Miami Lakes *(G-10819)*
Miami Tees Inc ......D...... 305 623-3908
Miami Lakes *(G-10820)*
Mid State Screen Graphics LLC ......E...... 727 573-2299
Clearwater *(G-1786)*
Mightees LLC ......G...... 201 450-7470
Fort Myers *(G-4534)*
Mlxl Productions Inx ......G...... 904 350-0048
Jacksonville *(G-6610)*
Morning Star Personalized AP ......G...... 772 569-8412
Vero Beach *(G-18644)*
Notice That Tee Inc ......G...... 954 971-1018
Pompano Beach *(G-14775)*
Ocean Blue Graphics Inc ......G...... 561 881-2022
Riviera Beach *(G-15355)*
Ocean Blue Graphics Design Inc ......G...... 561 881-2022
Riviera Beach *(G-15356)*
Outdoor America Images Inc ......E...... 813 888-8796
Miami Lakes *(G-10833)*
Palmas Printing Inc ......E...... 321 984-4451
Melbourne *(G-8904)*
Pathfinder Shirts ......G...... 407 865-6530
Altamonte Springs *(G-62)*
Paul Wales Inc ......F...... 352 371-2120
Gainesville *(G-4979)*
Picasso Embroidery Systems ......F...... 305 827-9666
Hialeah *(G-5558)*
Positive Screenprint ......G...... 904 381-0963
Jacksonville *(G-6679)*
Premier Tees ......G...... 941 681-2688
Englewood *(G-3664)*
Print Art Screen Printing Inc ......F...... 386 258-5186
Daytona Beach *(G-2698)*
Print Shack ......G...... 352 799-2972
Brooksville *(G-1262)*
Printec Inc ......G...... 813 854-1075
Oldsmar *(G-12263)*
Printex Worldwide Inc ......G...... 954 518-0722
Hallandale *(G-5161)*
Productive Products Inc ......G...... 904 570-5553
Saint Augustine *(G-15591)*
Prographix Inc ......G...... 863 298-8081
Winter Haven *(G-19349)*
Proud Tshirts Corp ......G...... 305 769-3300
Miami *(G-10212)*
Ragz ......G...... 850 656-1223
Tallahassee *(G-17313)*
Ranger Associates Inc ......G...... 407 869-0024
Longwood *(G-8329)*
Ray Graphics Inc ......E...... 863 325-0911
Winter Haven *(G-19352)*
Real Thread Inc ......E...... 407 679-3895
Orlando *(G-13119)*
Recreational Screen Printing ......G...... 561 757-5479
Boca Raton *(G-685)*
Red 7 Tees LLC ......G...... 305 793-1440
Crestview *(G-2356)*
Red Hot Trends Inc ......G...... 305 888-6951
Medley *(G-8716)*
Rex Three Inc ......C...... 954 452-8301
Davie *(G-2585)*
Rinehart Corp ......G...... 850 271-5600
Lynn Haven *(G-8437)*
RMR Distributors Inc ......E...... 813 908-1141
Tampa *(G-18062)*
Schimmbros Inc ......G...... 407 796-8361
Kissimmee *(G-7296)*
Schooner Prints Inc ......D...... 727 397-8572
Largo *(G-8045)*
Screen Art Posters Inc ......E...... 305 681-4641
Hialeah *(G-5612)*
Screen Graphics Florida Inc ......E...... 800 346-4420
Pompano Beach *(G-14842)*
Screen Process Printers Inc ......G...... 904 354-8708
Jacksonville *(G-6757)*
Screen Tech ......G...... 321 536-6091
Merritt Island *(G-9008)*
Seaside Graphics Inc ......G...... 954 782-7151
Pompano Beach *(G-14846)*
Sef Americas LLC ......G...... 904 423-0211
Jacksonville *(G-6760)*
Serigraphic Arts Inc ......F...... 813 626-1070
Tampa *(G-18085)*
SGS Designs Inc ......G...... 813 258-2691
Tampa *(G-18088)*
Sharper Edge ......F...... 813 871-3343
Tampa *(G-18091)*
Shirts n Things Inc ......G...... 954 434-7480
Davie *(G-2591)*
Shocksocks LLC ......G...... 352 258-0496
Stuart *(G-17012)*
Sign Depot Co ......F...... 407 894-0090
Orlando *(G-13190)*
Silkmasters Inc ......G...... 904 372-8958
Gainesville *(G-4996)*
Slick Designs & AP Miami Inc ......F...... 305 836-7950
Hialeah *(G-5622)*
Solseen LLC ......G...... 727 322-3131
Saint Petersburg *(G-15915)*

Southeast Marketing Concepts ....G....... 561 747-7010
Jupiter *(G-7118)*
Splash of Color LLC ....F....... 732 735-3090
Jacksonville *(G-6805)*
Sports N Stuff Screen Printing ....G....... 407 859-0437
Orlando *(G-13208)*
Sportsanity ....G....... 386 873-4688
Deland *(G-3015)*
Sublimation Station Inc ....G....... 407 605-5300
Orlando *(G-13219)*
Sun Graphic Technologies Inc ....E....... 941 753-7541
Sarasota *(G-16305)*
T Sals Shirt Co ....F....... 850 916-9229
Gulf Breeze *(G-5128)*
T-Shirts Plus Color Inc ....G....... 305 267-7664
Miami *(G-10456)*
Tampa Bay Print Shop LLC ....G....... 813 321-8790
Riverview *(G-15283)*
Tandjteesandcustomizations ....G....... 904 901-9227
Jacksonville *(G-6838)*
Tee Line Corp ....E....... 786 350-9526
West Palm Beach *(G-19058)*
Tee-N-Jay Services LLC ....G....... 407 760-7925
Orlando *(G-13245)*
Teeko Graphics Inc ....G....... 386 754-5600
Lake City *(G-7389)*
Tees Please Inc ....G....... 857 472-3391
Hobe Sound *(G-5728)*
Ten Star Supply Co Inc ....G....... 813 254-6921
Tampa *(G-18183)*
Think Outloud Printing ....G....... 239 800-3219
Cape Coral *(G-1485)*
Thread and Ink ....G....... 904 568-9688
Jacksonville *(G-6851)*
Thread Pit Inc ....G....... 352 505-0065
Gainesville *(G-5010)*
Threadbird LLC ....G....... 407 545-6506
Orlando *(G-13255)*
Tip Tops of America Inc ....F....... 352 357-9559
Eustis *(G-3718)*
Trim-Line of Miami Inc ....F....... 305 556-6210
Hialeah *(G-5650)*
Tsfpr LLC ....F....... 954 691-9031
Pompano Beach *(G-14894)*
Universal Screen Graphics Inc ....E....... 813 623-5335
Tampa *(G-18223)*
Vanlex Clothing Inc ....E....... 305 431-4669
Miami Lakes *(G-10878)*
Vivid Images USA Inc ....F....... 904 620-0303
Jacksonville *(G-6902)*
Walter Haas Graphics Inc ....E....... 305 883-2257
Hialeah *(G-5685)*
Waterboyz Wbz Inc ....F....... 850 433-2929
Pensacola *(G-14287)*
Wear Fund LLC ....F....... 239 313-3907
Fort Myers *(G-4651)*
Westview Corp Inc ....G....... 239 643-5699
Naples *(G-11454)*
Whitehouse Custom Scrn PR ....G....... 727 321-7398
Saint Petersburg *(G-15959)*
Wholesale Screen Prtg of Nples ....G....... 239 263-7061
Naples *(G-11455)*
Worldwide Sportswear Inc ....E....... 386 761-2688
Port Orange *(G-15041)*

PRINTING, COMMERCIAL: Stationery, NEC

Pfaffco Inc ....F....... 305 635-0986
Miami Lakes *(G-10837)*

PRINTING, COMMERCIAL: Tags, NEC

Blue Ribbon Tag & Label of PR ....F....... 787 858-5300
Hollywood *(G-5789)*

PRINTING, LITHOGRAPHIC: Advertising Posters

Firehouse Promotions Inc ....G....... 407 990-1600
Maitland *(G-8465)*
Mc Squared Group Inc ....G....... 850 435-4600
Pensacola *(G-14202)*
Outdoor Media Inc ....G....... 305 529-1400
Coral Gables *(G-2183)*

PRINTING, LITHOGRAPHIC: Calendars & Cards

Write Stuff Enterprises LLC ....E....... 954 462-6657
Fort Lauderdale *(G-4329)*

PRINTING, LITHOGRAPHIC: Color

Colorprint Design ....G....... 305 229-8880
Miami *(G-9383)*
Printing Corp of Americas Inc ....E....... 954 943-6087
Pompano Beach *(G-14815)*
Sun Belt Graphics Inc ....F....... 954 424-3139
Davie *(G-2597)*

PRINTING, LITHOGRAPHIC: Decals

National Traffic Signs Inc ....G....... 727 446-7983
Clearwater *(G-1802)*
SMC Diversified Services Inc ....G....... 863 698-9696
Lakeland *(G-7793)*

PRINTING, LITHOGRAPHIC: Forms & Cards, Business

Amtec Sales Inc ....F....... 800 994-3318
Miami *(G-9153)*
Delicate Designs Event Plg Inc ....G....... 305 833-8725
Miami *(G-9447)*
Graphink Incorporated ....G....... 305 468-9463
Doral *(G-3371)*
Ncp Solutions LLC ....D....... 205 849-5200
Jacksonville *(G-6623)*

PRINTING, LITHOGRAPHIC: Letters, Circular Or Form

Manatee Printers Inc ....E....... 941 746-9100
Bradenton *(G-1076)*
Print Rite Co ....G....... 305 757-0611
Miami *(G-10197)*
Scott Brevard Inc ....G....... 386 698-1121
Crescent City *(G-2342)*

PRINTING, LITHOGRAPHIC: Menus

Plastic Sealing Company Inc ....G....... 954 956-9797
Pompano Beach *(G-14797)*

PRINTING, LITHOGRAPHIC: Newspapers

Heritage Centl Fla Jewish News ....F....... 407 834-8277
Fern Park *(G-3729)*

PRINTING, LITHOGRAPHIC: Offset & photolithographic printing

Playlist Live Inc ....E....... 877 306-3651
Orlando *(G-13072)*
Screen Machines LLC ....G....... 386 527-1368
Port Orange *(G-15032)*
Tone Printing LLC ....G....... 855 505-8663
Miami *(G-10489)*

PRINTING, LITHOGRAPHIC: On Metal

Burr Printing Co Inc ....G....... 863 294-3166
Winter Haven *(G-19308)*
C & S Press Inc ....D....... 407 841-3000
Orlando *(G-12539)*
Coastal Printing Inc Sarasota ....E....... 941 351-1515
Sarasota *(G-16386)*
Eastern Shores Printing ....E....... 305 685-8976
Opa Locka *(G-12312)*
John Stewart Enterprises Inc ....F....... 904 356-9392
Jacksonville *(G-6525)*
Lake Worth Herald Press ....E....... 561 585-9387
Lake Worth *(G-7564)*
Tiffany and Associates Inc ....E....... 386 252-7351
Daytona Beach *(G-2727)*

PRINTING, LITHOGRAPHIC: Post Cards, Picture

Hill Printing Inc ....G....... 407 654-4282
Winter Garden *(G-19268)*

PRINTING, LITHOGRAPHIC: Promotional

Area Litho Inc ....G....... 863 687-4656
Lakeland *(G-7637)*
Blue Ocean Press Inc ....E....... 954 973-1819
Fort Lauderdale *(G-3859)*
Pure Postcards Inc ....F....... 877 446-2434
Clearwater *(G-1854)*

PRINTING, LITHOGRAPHIC: Publications

Green Papers Inc ....G....... 305 956-3535
North Miami Beach *(G-11681)*
Guest Service Publications Inc ....F....... 516 333-3474
Bonita Springs *(G-835)*

PRINTING, LITHOGRAPHIC: Tags

Blue Ribbon Tag & Label Corp ....E....... 954 922-9292
Hollywood *(G-5788)*

PRINTING, LITHOGRAPHIC: Trading Stamps

Miami Quality Graphics Inc ....E....... 305 634-9506
Miami *(G-10007)*

PRINTING, LITHOGRAPHIC: Transfers, Decalcomania Or Dry

Dowling Graphics Inc ....E....... 727 573-5997
Clearwater *(G-1657)*
Global Impressions Inc ....F....... 727 531-1290
Largo *(G-7962)*

PRINTING: Books

Jrg Systems Inc ....F....... 954 962-1020
Fort Lauderdale *(G-4081)*

PRINTING: Books

Bce of Tampa Bay Inc ....G....... 727 535-7768
Clearwater *(G-1604)*
Creative Tech Sarasota Inc ....G....... 941 371-2743
Sarasota *(G-16395)*
Digital Direct Corporation ....G....... 813 448-9071
Oldsmar *(G-12220)*
Eaglelithocom Inc ....G....... 786 521-7211
Miami *(G-9494)*
Florida Graphic Printing Inc ....F....... 386 253-4532
Daytona Beach *(G-2666)*
Lincoln-Marti Cmnty Agcy Inc ....A....... 305 643-4888
Miami *(G-9895)*
Lincoln-Marti Cmnty Agcy Inc ....F....... 646 463-6120
Miami *(G-9896)*
On Demand Spclty Envelope Corp ....F....... 305 681-5345
Hallandale Beach *(G-5202)*
Prisna Latino ....G....... 305 525-9292
Miami *(G-10202)*
Reliance Media Inc ....G....... 505 243-1821
Apopka *(G-179)*
Royal Palm Press Inc ....G....... 941 575-4299
Punta Gorda *(G-15230)*
Seminole County Public Schools ....F....... 407 320-0393
Sanford *(G-16114)*
Southeastern Printing Co Inc ....C....... 772 287-2141
Hialeah *(G-5628)*

PRINTING: Commercial, NEC

4 Over LLC ....F....... 818 246-1170
Miami *(G-9027)*
A New World Production ....E....... 321 636-6886
Cocoa *(G-1989)*
A Z Printing Delray ....F....... 561 330-4154
Delray Beach *(G-3037)*
Abby Press Inc ....E....... 407 847-5565
Kissimmee *(G-7216)*
Abeka Print Shop Inc ....E....... 850 478-8496
Pensacola *(G-14076)*
Absolute Graphics Inc ....F....... 954 792-3488
Davie *(G-2486)*
Academy Publishing Inc ....E....... 407 736-0100
Orlando *(G-12427)*
Advanced Cmmncations Holdg Inc ....D....... 954 753-0100
Coral Springs *(G-2213)*
Advantage Prtg Lmnting Fla Inc ....G....... 904 737-1613
Jacksonville *(G-6124)*
Agility Press Inc ....F....... 904 731-8989
Jacksonville *(G-6128)*
All-Star Sales Inc ....E....... 904 396-1653
Jacksonville *(G-6137)*
Altira Inc ....D....... 305 687-8074
Miami *(G-9124)*
Amelia Island Graphics ....G....... 904 261-0740
Fernandina Beach *(G-3731)*
Apis Cor Inc ....F....... 347 404-1481
Melbourne *(G-8769)*
Art of Printing Inc ....G....... 561 640-7344
West Palm Beach *(G-18803)*
Automated Services Inc ....F....... 772 461-3388
Fort Pierce *(G-4679)*

B R Q Grossmans Inc .... F 954 971-1077
Pompano Beach *(G-14609)*
Barjo Printing and Sign .... G 786 332-2661
Medley *(G-8620)*
Bills Prestige Printing Inc .... G 352 589-5833
Eustis *(G-3703)*
Bros Williams Printing .... G 305 769-9925
Hialeah *(G-5331)*
Bros Williams Printing Inc .... G 305 769-9925
Hialeah *(G-5332)*
Business Card Ex Tampa Bay Inc .... D 727 535-7768
Clearwater *(G-1618)*
Commercial Printers Inc .... D 954 781-3737
Fort Lauderdale *(G-3911)*
Comptech Global Solutions Inc .... G 941 766-8100
Port Charlotte *(G-14972)*
Concept Design and Printing .... G 813 516-9798
Tampa *(G-17551)*
Cor Label LLC .... G 407 402-6633
Debary *(G-2746)*
Core Label LLC .... E 772 287-2141
Palm City *(G-13649)*
Couchman Printing Company .... G 386 756-3052
South Daytona *(G-16800)*
Cover Publishing .... G 239 482-4814
Fort Myers *(G-4412)*
Creative Prtg Grphic Dsign Inc .... E 407 855-0202
Orlando *(G-12627)*
Csmc Inc .... E 407 246-1567
Orlando *(G-12630)*
D G Morrison Inc .... F 813 865-0208
Odessa *(G-12114)*
Dahlquist Enterprises Inc .... G 407 896-2294
Orlando *(G-12644)*
Dandy Media Corporation .... F 954 616-6800
Plantation *(G-14508)*
Dannys Prtg Svc Sups & Eqp Inc .... G 305 757-2282
Miami *(G-9435)*
Davis Franklin Printing Co .... G 813 259-2500
Tampa *(G-17592)*
Designers Press Inc .... D 407 843-3141
Orlando *(G-12664)*
Dobbs & Brodeur Bookbinders .... G 305 885-5215
Hialeah *(G-5376)*
Don and Kathy Kesler .... G 305 793-9216
Miami *(G-9477)*
Doral Dgtal Reprographics Corp .... G 305 704-3194
Doral *(G-3333)*
Durra Print Inc .... E 850 222-4768
Tallahassee *(G-17244)*
Durra Quick Print Inc .... G 850 681-2900
Tallahassee *(G-17245)*
Dynamic Color Inc .... G 954 462-0261
Pompano Beach *(G-14669)*
E&P Solutions and Services Inc .... G 305 715-9545
Miami *(G-9491)*
Envision Graphics Inc .... E 305 470-0083
Miami *(G-9530)*
ESP Printing .... G 386 263-2949
Bunnell *(G-1300)*
Fdc Print LLC .... D 305 885-8707
Hialeah *(G-5409)*
FGA Printing .... G 954 763-1122
Pompano Beach *(G-14689)*
Fidelity Printing Corporation .... D 727 522-9557
Saint Petersburg *(G-15778)*
Five Star Sports Tickets .... F 440 899-2000
Hallandale Beach *(G-5187)*
Florida Graphic Printing Inc .... F 386 253-4532
Daytona Beach *(G-2666)*
Florida Sncast Trism Prmotions .... F 727 544-1212
Largo *(G-7951)*
Four G Enterprises Inc .... E 407 834-4143
Longwood *(G-8284)*
Fritz Commercial Printing Inc .... G 561 585-6869
West Palm Beach *(G-18884)*
G S Printers Inc .... G 305 931-2755
Fort Lauderdale *(G-4016)*
Gabrielas Memoirs Inc .... G 305 666-9991
Miami *(G-9608)*
Gadsden County Times Inc .... F 850 627-7649
Quincy *(G-15250)*
Gandy Printers Inc .... F 850 222-5847
Tallahassee *(G-17260)*
Gatlin Group LLC .... G 850 941-0959
Pensacola *(G-14160)*
Genuine Ad Inc .... G 786 399-6484
Sunny Isles Beach *(G-17077)*
Go 2 Print Now Inc .... E 800 500-4276
Saint Petersburg *(G-15794)*

Grace Bible Church .... G 850 623-4671
Milton *(G-10930)*
Granada Prtg & Graphics Corp .... F 305 593-5266
Miami *(G-9655)*
Graphic and Printing Svcs Corp .... G 954 486-8868
Tamarac *(G-17357)*
Graphics Type Color Entps Inc .... E 305 591-7600
Miami *(G-9658)*
Graphix Solutions of America .... F 727 898-6744
Parrish *(G-14006)*
Greater 7th Digital Press Inc .... G 305 681-2412
Miami *(G-9662)*
Greg Allens Inc .... E 904 262-8912
Jacksonville *(G-6450)*
Gulf Coast Printing .... E 239 482-5555
Fort Myers *(G-4477)*
H & H Printing Inc .... F 407 422-2932
Orlando *(G-12792)*
Harvest Print & Bus Svcs Inc .... F 850 681-2488
Tallahassee *(G-17275)*
Harvey Branker and Assoc PA .... F 954 966-4445
Hollywood *(G-5835)*
Herald-Advocate Publishing Co .... F 863 773-3255
Wauchula *(G-18693)*
Hernandez Printing Service .... F 305 642-0483
Miami *(G-9705)*
Hilcraft Engraving Inc .... G 305 871-6100
Miami *(G-9711)*
Holmes Stamp Company .... E 904 396-2291
Jacksonville *(G-6476)*
Howies Instant Printing Inc .... F 561 686-8699
West Palm Beach *(G-18898)*
Hunter Green Group Inc .... G 954 753-9914
Coral Springs *(G-2257)*
ICM Printing Co Inc .... F 352 377-7468
Gainesville *(G-4940)*
Image Graphics 2000 Inc .... G 954 332-3380
Pompano Beach *(G-14728)*
Impact Design Group Inc .... F 904 636-8989
Jacksonville *(G-6490)*
Impressions of Miami Inc .... G 305 666-0277
Miami *(G-9735)*
Instant Printing Services Inc .... F 727 546-8036
Floral City *(G-3768)*
J J M Services Inc .... G 954 437-1880
Miramar *(G-11007)*
Jdjsis Inc .... G 561 732-2388
West Palm Beach *(G-18911)*
JMS Designs of Florida Inc .... G 954 572-6100
Sunrise *(G-17138)*
Keithco Inc .... G 352 351-4741
Ocala *(G-11976)*
Kights Printing & Office Pdts .... G 904 731-7990
Jacksonville *(G-6537)*
King Printing & Graphics Inc .... G 813 681-5060
Brandon *(G-1164)*
Kj Reynolds Inc .... G 904 829-6488
Saint Augustine *(G-15564)*
Knopf & Sons Bindery Inc .... F 904 355-4411
Jacksonville *(G-6543)*
Kover Corp .... G 305 888-0146
Doral *(G-3411)*
Lauderdale Graphics Corp .... E 954 450-0800
Davie *(G-2544)*
Leda Printing Inc .... E 941 922-1563
Sarasota *(G-16487)*
Ledger .... B 863 802-7000
Lakeland *(G-7733)*
Limited Designs LLC .... G 305 547-9909
Miami *(G-9894)*
Lrp Conferences LLC .... E 215 784-0860
Palm Beach Gardens *(G-13607)*
Lujotex LLC .... G 954 322-1001
Miramar *(G-11011)*
Marlin Graphics Inc .... G 561 743-5220
Jupiter *(G-7074)*
Maxigraphics Inc .... F 954 978-0740
Pompano Beach *(G-14755)*
Media Works Inc .... F 904 398-5518
Jacksonville *(G-6588)*
Mendez Brothers LLC .... F 305 685-3490
Opa Locka *(G-12338)*
Microcomputer Services .... G 561 988-7000
Boca Raton *(G-623)*
Miller Creative Graphics .... G 904 771-5855
Jacksonville *(G-6607)*
Minuteman Press .... F 386 255-2767
Daytona Beach *(G-2688)*
Newspaper Printing Company .... G 727 572-7488
Clearwater *(G-1808)*

Nis Print Inc .... E 407 423-7575
Orlando *(G-13004)*
Onsight Industries .... G 407 830-8861
Tampa *(G-17957)*
Platecrafters Corporation .... F 215 997-1990
Longwood *(G-8326)*
Pod Crane Services and Rentals .... G 805 291-2675
Miami *(G-10172)*
Poms Enterprises Inc .... G 954 358-1359
Margate *(G-8562)*
Power Point Graphics Inc .... G 561 351-5599
Boca Raton *(G-670)*
Premier Parties Entertainment .... E 352 375-6122
Gainesville *(G-4983)*
Print Mart Inc .... G 727 796-0064
Dunedin *(G-3587)*
Printers Printer Inc .... F 954 917-2773
Pompano Beach *(G-14814)*
Printhouseusacom Inc .... G 305 231-0202
Hialeah *(G-5574)*
Printing Mart Inc South Fla .... F 954 753-0323
Pompano Beach *(G-14817)*
Printing Services Plus LLC .... F 813 279-1903
Tampa *(G-18016)*
Printnovations Inc .... G 305 322-4041
Hallandale Beach *(G-5204)*
Pro Art America Inc .... G 863 385-4242
Sebring *(G-16704)*
Procorp LLC .... G 904 477-6762
Jacksonville *(G-6690)*
Reporgraphics Unlimited Inc .... G 386 253-7990
Daytona Beach *(G-2703)*
Roberts Quality Printing Inc .... E 727 442-4011
Clearwater *(G-1862)*
Royal Identity Incorporated .... G 813 405-4940
Brandon *(G-1176)*
Scp Commercial Printing .... G 561 998-0870
Boca Raton *(G-703)*
Screen Monkey Corp .... G 352 746-7091
Homosassa *(G-6005)*
Seabreeze Publication Centl FL .... G 561 741-7770
Jupiter *(G-7110)*
Serv-Pak Corp .... F 954 962-4262
Hollywood *(G-5907)*
Signal Graphics Printing LLC .... G 303 837-1331
Punta Gorda *(G-15234)*
Signarama .... G 239 997-1644
North Fort Myers *(G-11606)*
Skies Limit Printing .... G 772 340-1090
Port Saint Lucie *(G-15145)*
Slasher Printing Center Inc .... G 305 835-7366
Sunrise *(G-17173)*
South Florida Finger Printing .... G 305 661-1636
South Miami *(G-16829)*
Southeast Finishing Group Inc .... E 407 299-4620
Orlando *(G-13202)*
St Ives Burrups .... G 305 685-7381
Opa Locka *(G-12360)*
Sticker Karmer .... G 813 802-1826
Tampa *(G-18133)*
Suncoast Specialty Prtg Inc .... G 813 951-0899
Tampa *(G-18146)*
Sunshine Printing and Business .... G 407 846-0126
Kissimmee *(G-7301)*
Super Color Digital LLC .... F 407 240-1660
Orlando *(G-13228)*
T-Wiz Prtg & EMB Designs LLC .... E 954 280-8949
Fort Lauderdale *(G-4273)*
Taie Inc .... F 954 966-0233
Hollywood *(G-5920)*
Tampa Printing Company .... E 813 612-7746
Tampa *(G-18171)*
Target Copy Gainesville Inc .... F 352 372-1171
Gainesville *(G-5008)*
Tonertype Inc .... E 813 915-1300
Tampa *(G-18194)*
Treasured Photo Gifts LLC .... E 407 324-4816
Lake Mary *(G-7456)*
Trend At LLC .... F 786 300-2550
Miami *(G-10505)*
Triple Crown Printing .... E 561 939-6440
Boca Raton *(G-758)*
Tru Dimensions Printing Inc .... G 407 339-3410
Longwood *(G-8345)*
Venue Advertising Inc .... E 561 844-1778
Jupiter *(G-7140)*
W D H Enterprises Inc .... G 941 758-6500
Bradenton *(G-1143)*
Walruss Enterprises Inc .... G 954 525-0342
Fort Lauderdale *(G-4311)*

Wingard LLC ..... F 904 387-2570
Jacksonville (G-6923)

PRINTING: Engraving & Plate

Hilcraft Engraving Inc ..... G 305 871-6100
Miami (G-9711)

PRINTING: Fabric, Narrow

PHI CHI Foundation Inc ..... G 561 526-3401
Margate (G-8560)

PRINTING: Flexographic

Graphic Printing Corp ..... E 561 994-3586
Boca Raton (G-551)
Passion Labels & Packaging ..... E 941 312-5003
Sarasota (G-16272)
Safeprints LLC ..... G 305 960-7391
Miami (G-10296)
Southeastern Printing Co Inc ..... C 772 287-2141
Hialeah (G-5628)
Worldwide Tickets & Labels Inc ..... D 877 426-5754
Boynton Beach (G-977)

PRINTING: Gravure, Business Form & Card

Amtec Sales Inc ..... F 800 994-3318
Miami (G-9153)
Collier Business Systems ..... G 239 649-5554
Naples (G-11215)

PRINTING: Gravure, Color

Unlimited Inpressions Inc ..... G 305 606-2699
Miami (G-10546)

PRINTING: Gravure, Envelopes

Sun Coast Paper & Envelope Inc ..... E 727 545-9566
Largo (G-8062)

PRINTING: Gravure, Forms, Business

Ef Enterprises of North Fla ..... G 904 739-5995
Jacksonville (G-6356)

PRINTING: Gravure, Job

Brut Printing Co Inc ..... E 904 354-5055
Jacksonville (G-6241)
Reprographic Services Inc ..... F 305 859-8282
Miami (G-10255)

PRINTING: Gravure, Labels

Datamax International Corp ..... B 407 578-8007
Orlando (G-12651)
Datamax-Oneil Corporation ..... C 800 816-9649
Orlando (G-12652)
Dongili Investment Group Inc ..... F 941 927-3003
Sarasota (G-16413)

PRINTING: Gravure, Rotogravure

A-Plus Prtg & Graphic Ctr Inc ..... E 954 327-7315
Plantation (G-14481)
Collins Media & Advg LLC ..... F 954 688-9758
Margate (G-8538)
Eti-Label Inc ..... G 305 716-0094
Miami (G-9538)
Miami Engrv Co-Oxford Prtg Co ..... G 305 371-9595
Miami (G-9999)
Restifo Investments LLC ..... F 305 468-0013
Doral (G-3484)
Screen Graphics Florida Inc ..... E 800 346-4420
Pompano Beach (G-14842)
Tone Printing LLC ..... G 855 505-8663
Miami (G-10489)

PRINTING: Gravure, Seals

Starlock Inc ..... G 305 477-2303
Doral (G-3511)
Wells Legal Supply Inc ..... E 904 399-1510
Jacksonville (G-6909)

PRINTING: Gravure, Stationery & Invitation

DK Events LLC ..... G 305 760-2963
Miami (G-9473)
Kreative Drive Inc ..... G 786 845-8605
Doral (G-3413)

PRINTING: Gravure, Visiting Cards

Business Card Ex Tampa Bay Inc ..... D 727 535-7768
Clearwater (G-1618)

PRINTING: Laser

Advanced Xrgrphics Imging Syst ..... E 407 351-0232
Orlando (G-12434)
Light Source Business Systems ..... F 772 562-5046
Port Saint Lucie (G-15120)
Pad Printing Technology Corp ..... G 941 739-8667
Bradenton (G-1091)
Target Graphics Inc ..... F 941 365-8809
Sarasota (G-16615)

PRINTING: Letterpress

Crain Ventures Inc ..... G 407 933-1820
Kissimmee (G-7233)
Futch Printing & Mailing Inc ..... F 904 388-3995
Jacksonville (G-6418)
Rinaldi Printing Company ..... E 813 569-0033
Tampa (G-18058)
Spett Printing Co Inc ..... G 561 241-9758
Boca Raton (G-727)
Steven Chancas ..... F 352 629-5016
Ocala (G-12059)
Woods Printing of Ocala Inc ..... G 352 629-1665
Ocala (G-12077)

PRINTING: Lithographic

3g Enterprises Inc ..... G 754 366-7643
Boynton Beach (G-870)
525 Prnting Prmtional Pdts Inc ..... G 904 580-5943
Jacksonville (G-6103)
5301 Realty LLC ..... C 305 633-9779
Hialeah (G-5254)
5hp Investments LLC ..... F 561 655-5355
West Palm Beach (G-18782)
8 Girls & A Guy Printing LLC ..... G 386 492-5976
Ponce Inlet (G-14921)
A and D Printing & Mailing LLC ..... G 850 244-2400
Fort Walton Beach (G-4773)
Accuprint My Print Shop ..... G 954 973-9369
Deerfield Beach (G-2763)
Adorgraf Corp ..... G 786 752-1680
Miami (G-9072)
Advanced Cmmncations Holdg Inc ..... D 954 753-0100
Coral Springs (G-2213)
Aether Media USA Inc ..... G 863 647-5500
Lakeland (G-7629)
Agpb LLC ..... F 561 935-4147
Jupiter (G-6997)
Aleph Graphics Inc ..... G 305 994-9933
Doral (G-3237)
Align Kpital Usa LLC ..... G 305 423-7100
Miami (G-9106)
All-Star Sales Inc ..... E 904 396-1653
Jacksonville (G-6137)
AlphaGraphics Us658 ..... F 813 689-7788
Tampa (G-17405)
American Business Cards Inc ..... E 314 739-0800
Naples (G-11161)
Anderson Printing Services Inc ..... E 727 545-9000
Seminole (G-16738)
Ard Printing Solutions LL ..... G 305 785-7200
Miami (G-9165)
Arfona Printing LLC ..... G 312 339-0215
Highland Beach (G-5705)
Arise Prints LLC ..... G 561 371-6959
West Palm Beach (G-18800)
Artistic Label Company Inc ..... G 401 737-0666
Estero (G-3686)
B D D International Corp ..... G 305 573-2416
Miami (G-9209)
Baker County Press Inc ..... G 904 259-2400
Macclenny (G-8442)
Banks Sign Systems Inc ..... G 954 979-0055
Pompano Beach (G-14613)
Barnett & Pugliano Inc ..... G 727 826-6075
Saint Petersburg (G-15717)
Bayfront Printing Company ..... G 727 823-1965
Saint Petersburg (G-15719)
BCT International Inc ..... E 305 563-1224
Fort Lauderdale (G-3844)
Beginmyprinting Com ..... G 772 828-2026
Port Saint Lucie (G-15090)
Bema Inc ..... G 954 761-1919
Fort Lauderdale (G-3846)
Bestprintingonlinecom LLC ..... E 239 263-2106
Naples (G-11186)
Bi-Ads Inc ..... F 954 525-1489
Fort Lauderdale (G-3849)
Big Biz Direct ..... G 813 978-0584
Tampa (G-17469)
Bill & Renee Enterprises ..... G 321 452-2800
Merritt Island (G-8993)
Bills Prestige Printing Inc ..... G 352 589-5833
Eustis (G-3703)
Bkr Printing Inc ..... G 813 951-8609
Tampa (G-17472)
Blix Corporate Image LLC ..... F 305 572-9001
Doral (G-3278)
Boostan Inc ..... G 305 223-5981
Miami (G-9267)
Broward Print ..... G 954 272-2272
Pembroke Pines (G-14025)
Burke Printing ..... G 813 549-9886
Tampa (G-17490)
Business Cards Tomorrow Inc ..... D 954 563-1224
Fort Lauderdale (G-3877)
Business Clinic Inc ..... G 786 473-4573
Hialeah (G-5336)
Busy Bee Printer ..... G 772 621-3683
Port Saint Lucie (G-15094)
C & R Designs Inc ..... G 321 383-2255
Titusville (G-18419)
C&D Sign and Lighting Svcs LLC ..... G 863 937-9323
Lakeland (G-7652)
Caribbean Discount Ptg Inc ..... G 954 961-5015
Miramar (G-10977)
Caxton Newspapers Inc ..... E 305 538-9700
Miami Beach (G-10652)
Cincinnati Printing Service ..... G 239 455-0960
Naples (G-11208)
City Prints LLC ..... G 407 409-0509
Orlando (G-12585)
Classic Printing & Finish LLC ..... G 305 817-4242
Hialeah (G-5347)
Coastal Reign Inc ..... G 863 940-4082
Lakeland (G-7659)
Cobalt Laser ..... G 407 855-2833
Orlando (G-12594)
Command Print LLC ..... G 716 583-5175
Bonita Springs (G-826)
Compass Banners & Printing LLC ..... G 727 522-7414
Saint Petersburg (G-15751)
Compass Printing and Marketing ..... G 954 856-8331
Margate (G-8539)
Convicted Printing LLC ..... G 813 304-5568
Brandon (G-1155)
Corona Printing Company Inc ..... G 754 263-2914
Hallandale (G-5155)
Corporate Print Resources Inc ..... G 305 968-2037
Palmetto Bay (G-13842)
Couchman Printing Company ..... G 386 756-3052
South Daytona (G-16800)
Creative Biz Center Inc ..... G 954 918-7322
Lauderhill (G-8106)
Cronus Litho LLC ..... F 239 325-4846
Naples (G-11219)
D Turin & Company Inc ..... E 305 825-2004
Hialeah (G-5361)
Danifer Printing Inc ..... G 727 849-5883
New Port Richey (G-11488)
Dark Horse Signs and Prtg LLC ..... G 850 684-3833
Gulf Breeze (G-5115)
DC Style Corp ..... G 786 391-3780
Miami (G-9440)
Dentz Design Screen Prtg LLC ..... G 609 303-0827
Saint Augustine (G-15536)
Design & Print ..... G 561 361-8299
Boca Raton (G-498)
Design & Print Solutions Inc ..... G 407 703-7861
Apopka (G-130)
Designers Press Inc ..... D 407 843-3141
Orlando (G-12664)
Dg Design and Print Co LLC ..... G 321 446-6435
Rockledge (G-15404)
Di Jam Holdings Inc ..... F 863 967-6949
Auburndale (G-239)
Disbrow Corporation ..... F 813 621-9444
Tampa (G-17608)
Diversified Graphics Inc ..... F 407 425-9443
Orlando (G-12677)
Dla Document Services ..... F 813 828-4646
Tampa (G-17611)
Docuvision Incorporated ..... E 954 791-0091
Davie (G-2517)

Donald Art Company Inc ....G....... 407 831-2525
Longwood *(G-8274)*
Donna Lynn Enterprises Inc ....G....... 772 286-2812
Palm Beach Gardens *(G-13584)*
Doral Dgtal Reprographics Corp ....G....... 305 704-3194
Doral *(G-3333)*
Dugout Sportswear ....G....... 386 615-0024
Ormond Beach *(G-13365)*
DVC Marketing ....G....... 727 442-7125
Tampa *(G-17621)*
Dvh Macleod Corp ....F....... 850 224-6760
Tallahassee *(G-17246)*
E3 Graphics Inc ....G....... 954 510-1302
Coral Springs *(G-2243)*
East Side Printing & Pubg ....G....... 239 369-1244
Lehigh Acres *(G-8189)*
Economy Printing Co ....F....... 904 786-4070
Jacksonville *(G-6354)*
Elite Power Prtg Solutions Inc ....G....... 786 387-7164
Miami *(G-9518)*
Emerald Prints LLC ....G....... 850 460-5532
Niceville *(G-11566)*
Envision Graphics Inc ....E....... 305 470-0083
Miami *(G-9530)*
Eprint Inc ....G....... 407 930-5870
Orlando *(G-12715)*
Everglades Pro Painters Corp ....G....... 786 444-5024
Miami *(G-9540)*
Evolution Signs and Print Inc ....G....... 904 634-5666
Jacksonville *(G-6371)*
Express Prtg Winter Haven Inc ....G....... 863 294-3286
Winter Haven *(G-19319)*
Express Signs & Graphics Inc ....F....... 407 889-4433
Winter Garden *(G-19263)*
Fast Frontier Printing ....F....... 407 538-5621
Largo *(G-7943)*
Ferrera Embroidery & Prtg Ser ....G....... 786 667-2680
Miami *(G-9564)*
Five Star Sports Tickets ....F....... 440 899-2000
Hallandale Beach *(G-5187)*
Flash Prints LLC ....G....... 786 422-3195
Miami Gardens *(G-10740)*
Flexible Prtg Solutions LLC ....G....... 727 446-3014
Clearwater *(G-1684)*
Florida Hospital Assn MGT Corp ....G....... 407 841-6230
Orlando *(G-12749)*
Florida Sentinel Publishing Co ....E....... 813 248-1921
Tampa *(G-17688)*
Florida State Graphics Inc ....G....... 727 328-0733
Saint Petersburg *(G-15786)*
Florida Tape & Labels Inc ....F....... 941 921-5788
Sarasota *(G-16438)*
Form Script - Form Print LLC ....G....... 954 345-3727
Coral Springs *(G-2247)*
Four G Enterprises Inc ....E....... 407 834-4143
Longwood *(G-8284)*
Fresh Prints ....G....... 813 992-1655
Lutz *(G-8383)*
Fresh Thread Llc ....F....... 904 677-9505
Jacksonville *(G-6416)*
Fretto Prints Inc ....G....... 904 687-1985
Crystal River *(G-2378)*
G J V Inc ....G....... 727 584-7136
Largo *(G-7955)*
G L E M Inc ....G....... 727 461-5300
Clearwater *(G-1697)*
G Print Inc ....G....... 305 316-2266
Hialeah *(G-5419)*
Gabol Screen Printing Co ....G....... 305 681-3882
Opa Locka *(G-12319)*
Gadsden County Times Inc ....F....... 850 627-7649
Quincy *(G-15250)*
General & Duplicating Services ....G....... 305 541-2116
Miami *(G-9623)*
Glider Printing LLC ....G....... 813 601-8907
Tampa *(G-17713)*
Global Printing Services Inc ....G....... 305 446-7628
Coral Gables *(G-2150)*
Goforit Inc ....G....... 727 785-7616
Palm Harbor *(G-13737)*
Gold Coast Printing Inc ....G....... 813 853-2219
Tampa *(G-17720)*
Good Impressions ....G....... 305 336-0318
Miami *(G-9649)*
Graphics Designer Inc ....F....... 561 687-7993
West Palm Beach *(G-18889)*
Graphics Type Color Entps Inc ....E....... 305 591-7600
Miami *(G-9658)*
Gregory Michael Genung ....G....... 850 572-4407
Pensacola *(G-14164)*

Grizzly Printing Parlour LLC ....G....... 786 416-2494
Miami *(G-9673)*
Grupo Erik USA LLC ....G....... 305 447-2611
Hialeah *(G-5438)*
Guerrilla Prtg Solutions LLC ....G....... 352 394-7770
Minneola *(G-10954)*
Guimar Inc ....F....... 305 888-1547
Hialeah *(G-5439)*
Hart Graphics ....G....... 727 938-7018
Tarpon Springs *(G-18305)*
Hartco Inc ....G....... 904 353-5259
Jacksonville *(G-6462)*
Herff Jones Inc ....G....... 407 647-4373
Winter Park *(G-19410)*
Herff Jones LLC ....G....... 904 641-4060
Jacksonville *(G-6470)*
HOB Corporation ....G....... 813 988-2272
Tampa *(G-17758)*
Hoipong Customs Inc ....G....... 954 684-9232
Pembroke Pines *(G-14041)*
Hybrid Impressions Inc ....E....... 305 392-5029
Hialeah *(G-5450)*
Impressing Design Print ....G....... 786 615-3695
Hialeah *(G-5453)*
In Stock Printers Inc ....G....... 727 447-2515
Oldsmar *(G-12234)*
Ink Bros Printing LLC ....G....... 407 494-9585
Longwood *(G-8290)*
Instant Call Center LLC ....G....... 321 356-1587
Longwood *(G-8291)*
Instant Imprints ....G....... 224 764-2198
Orlando *(G-12833)*
Instant Imprints ....G....... 850 474-9184
Pensacola *(G-14179)*
Instant Locate Inc ....G....... 800 431-0812
Casselberry *(G-1506)*
Instant Ps LLC ....G....... 786 278-5007
Miami *(G-9751)*
Insty-Prints ....G....... 352 373-7547
Gainesville *(G-4944)*
International Printing & Copyi ....G....... 954 295-5239
Coconut Creek *(G-2084)*
Iprint 3d USA ....G....... 888 868-7329
Pompano Beach *(G-14733)*
It Busness Solutions Group Inc ....F....... 407 260-0116
Longwood *(G-8294)*
J & J International Corp ....E....... 407 349-7114
Sanford *(G-16070)*
J J M Services Inc ....G....... 954 437-1880
Miramar *(G-11007)*
J-Kup Corp ....F....... 352 683-5629
Spring Hill *(G-16855)*
Jet Set Printing Inc ....G....... 407 339-1900
Casselberry *(G-1508)*
Jj Screenprint LLC ....G....... 941 587-1801
Sarasota *(G-16477)*
Jjaz Enterprises Inc ....G....... 407 330-0245
Lake Mary *(G-7427)*
Jmf Dgital Print Solutions Inc ....G....... 954 362-4929
Pembroke Pines *(G-14044)*
JPS Digital LLC ....F....... 813 501-6040
Inverness *(G-6091)*
Just Say Print Inc ....G....... 954 254-7793
Coral Springs *(G-2267)*
Kee Kreative LLC ....G....... 954 931-2579
Lauderhill *(G-8113)*
Kikinaz Screen Printing Inc ....G....... 561 512-3134
Royal Palm Beach *(G-15473)*
Kinane Corp ....F....... 772 288-6580
Stuart *(G-16965)*
King Tech Print LLC ....G....... 786 362-6249
Miami *(G-9822)*
Kuhn Family Enterprises Inc ....G....... 813 671-5353
Riverview *(G-15275)*
La Mar Orlando LLC ....E....... 407 423-2051
Orlando *(G-12885)*
Label Printing Service ....G....... 727 820-1226
Clearwater *(G-1756)*
Labelpro Inc ....F....... 727 538-2149
Clearwater *(G-1757)*
Lakeland Digital Printing Co ....G....... 863 509-8049
Lakeland *(G-7730)*
Lance Printers Service Inc ....G....... 305 256-7982
Miami *(G-9856)*
Leda Printing Inc ....E....... 941 922-1563
Sarasota *(G-16487)*
Legend Printing Company LLC ....G....... 904 268-7079
Jacksonville *(G-6553)*
Leila K Moavero ....G....... 954 978-0018
Pompano Beach *(G-14743)*

Life In A Tee Shirt Prtg LLC ....G....... 941 927-0116
Sarasota *(G-16488)*
Lincoln Smith Ventures LLC ....G....... 863 337-6670
Lakeland *(G-7735)*
Lindsey Macke Bindery Printing ....G....... 727 514-3570
Odessa *(G-12132)*
Linographics Inc ....F....... 407 422-8700
Orlando *(G-12913)*
Lion Ink Print Inc ....G....... 561 358-8925
West Palm Beach *(G-18930)*
Lionheart Printers LLC ....G....... 561 781-8300
Jupiter *(G-7068)*
Lit Prints Inc ....G....... 305 456-0150
Miami *(G-9900)*
Lit Prints Inc ....G....... 305 951-5122
Coral Gables *(G-2173)*
Ljk & TS Partners Inc ....G....... 941 661-5675
Tampa *(G-17854)*
Luxe Prints LLC ....G....... 941 484-4500
Sarasota *(G-16493)*
Lytron Print ....G....... 954 683-1291
Fort Lauderdale *(G-4106)*
M J Embroidery Screen Prtg LLC ....G....... 407 239-0246
Orlando *(G-12941)*
M L Solutions Inc ....G....... 305 506-5113
Miami *(G-9926)*
Maki Printing LLC ....F....... 941 809-7574
Sarasota *(G-16498)*
Maki Printing LLC ....F....... 941 925-4802
Sarasota *(G-16499)*
Man Enterprises 3 LLC ....G....... 561 655-4944
West Palm Beach *(G-18940)*
Marion Nature Park ....G....... 352 817-3077
Belleview *(G-372)*
Masc Aspen Partners LLC ....G....... 212 545-1076
Boca Raton *(G-611)*
Matrix Marketing Solutions ....G....... 407 654-5736
Windermere *(G-19237)*
Maxigraphics Inc ....F....... 954 978-0740
Pompano Beach *(G-14755)*
McGee Enterprises Inc ....G....... 904 328-3226
Jacksonville *(G-6585)*
Miami Stitch and Print Center ....G....... 305 770-4285
Miami *(G-10012)*
Mid West Lettering Company ....E....... 850 477-6522
Pensacola *(G-14209)*
Milton Newspapers Inc ....A....... 850 623-2120
Milton *(G-10935)*
Mint Prints ....G....... 561 900-5432
Deerfield Beach *(G-2873)*
Minute Man Press ....G....... 727 791-1115
Dunedin *(G-3584)*
Minuteman Press ....F....... 727 535-3800
Largo *(G-8011)*
Minuteman Press ....E....... 813 884-2476
Tampa *(G-17910)*
Minuteman Press ....G....... 904 733-5578
Jacksonville *(G-6609)*
Minuteman Press ....F....... 305 242-6800
Cutler Bay *(G-2404)*
Minuteman Press ....G....... 863 337-6670
Lakeland *(G-7752)*
Minuteman Press ....G....... 503 789-5741
Kissimmee *(G-7275)*
Minuteman Press ....F....... 386 255-2767
Daytona Beach *(G-2688)*
Minuteman Press ....G....... 352 728-6333
Leesburg *(G-8166)*
Minuteman Press ....G....... 772 301-0222
Port Saint Lucie *(G-15122)*
Minuteman Press ....G....... 954 804-8304
Lake Worth *(G-7573)*
Mp 93 Screen Print and EMB LLC ....F....... 407 592-3657
Orlando *(G-12982)*
MRM Creative LLC ....G....... 386 218-5940
Orange City *(G-12376)*
Mxn Inc ....G....... 813 654-3173
Tampa *(G-17921)*
NC Printing & Accounting Co ....G....... 904 327-7701
Jacksonville *(G-6622)*
Neat Print Inc ....F....... 941 545-1517
Sarasota *(G-16523)*
New Gnrtion Abndant Mssion Ch ....E....... 772 497-5871
Port Saint Lucie *(G-15123)*
Newsnotes LLC ....G....... 407 949-8185
Satellite Beach *(G-16653)*
Northern Litho Inc ....G....... 239 653-9645
Naples *(G-11346)*
One Nugget LLc ....G....... 904 527-3218
Jacksonville *(G-6644)*

Onesource of Florida Inc ......G...... 904 620-0003
Jacksonville *(G-6645)*
Open Market Enterprises LLC ......G...... 407 322-5434
Orlando *(G-13024)*
Orchid Printing Inc ......G...... 786 523-3324
Cutler Bay *(G-2406)*
Orellana Investments Inc ......G...... 305 477-2817
Miami *(G-10115)*
Palm Print Inc ......F...... 561 833-9661
West Palm Beach *(G-18986)*
Pamatian Group Inc ......G...... 407 291-8387
Orlando *(G-13046)*
Paper Palm LLC ......G...... 407 647-3328
Orlando *(G-13049)*
Paper Pushers of America Inc ......G...... 386 872-7025
Daytona Beach *(G-2692)*
Pasa Services Inc ......E...... 305 594-8662
Opa Locka *(G-12350)*
Pat Cobb Printing ......G...... 772 465-5484
Fort Pierce *(G-4729)*
Pencil Printing ......G...... 407 346-4952
Kissimmee *(G-7285)*
Pfaffco Inc ......F...... 305 635-0986
Miami Lakes *(G-10837)*
Pg Express Inc ......G...... 954 788-3263
Pompano Beach *(G-14791)*
Phantom USA LLC ......G...... 863 353-5972
Dundee *(G-3567)*
Phil & Brenda Johnson Inc ......F...... 813 623-5478
Tampa *(G-17988)*
Phoenix Group Florida Inc ......G...... 954 563-1224
Fort Lauderdale *(G-4166)*
Photoengraving Inc ......E...... 813 253-3427
Tampa *(G-17992)*
Pioneer Announcements Inc ......F...... 305 573-7000
Miami *(G-10166)*
Power Printing of Florida ......F...... 727 823-1162
Saint Petersburg *(G-15885)*
Precious Prints Inc ......G...... 786 346-7740
Miami *(G-10183)*
Precise Print Florida ......G...... 813 960-4958
Lutz *(G-8411)*
Precision Printing of Columbus ......G...... 561 509-7269
Boynton Beach *(G-942)*
Premier Corporate Printing LLC ......F...... 305 378-8480
Jacksonville *(G-6684)*
Premier Global Enterprises ......G...... 561 747-7303
Tequesta *(G-18387)*
Presto Print II Inc ......G...... 203 627-2528
Delray Beach *(G-3124)*
Print Administrate ......G...... 407 877-5923
Winter Garden *(G-19280)*
Print All Promotions LLC ......G...... 800 971-3209
Wildwood *(G-19199)*
Print Hopper ......G...... 954 770-3007
Sunrise *(G-17162)*
Print It 4 Less ......G...... 800 370-5591
Delray Beach *(G-3125)*
Print My Atm LLC ......G...... 866 292-6179
Orlando *(G-13088)*
Print Pro Shop Inc ......F...... 305 859-8282
Miami *(G-10196)*
Print Store LLC ......G...... 727 656-1376
Palm Harbor *(G-13752)*
Print This and That LLC ......F...... 386 752-5905
Lake City *(G-7376)*
Print This and That LLC ......F...... 386 344-4420
Lake City *(G-7377)*
Printerbazaar Usa Inc ......G...... 954 730-3473
Miami *(G-10199)*
Printing and Labels Inc ......G...... 954 578-4411
Sunrise *(G-17163)*
Printing and Promotion Svcs ......G...... 201 612-0800
Delray Beach *(G-3126)*
Printing Department LLC ......G...... 386 253-7990
Daytona Beach *(G-2699)*
Printing For A Cause LLC ......E...... 786 496-0637
Saint Petersburg *(G-15889)*
Printing Services Plus LLC ......F...... 813 279-1903
Tampa *(G-18016)*
Printmor ......F...... 954 247-9405
Coral Springs *(G-2304)*
Printrust Inc ......G...... 954 572-0790
Sunrise *(G-17164)*
Prints 2 Go Inc ......F...... 727 725-1700
Clearwater *(G-1847)*
Prints Hope International Inc ......G...... 305 528-1593
Miramar *(G-11032)*
Prints The Ppr of Wnter Pk LLC ......G...... 407 740-0989
Winter Park *(G-19433)*
Printshaqcom Inc ......G...... 954 678-7286
Hollywood *(G-5895)*
Printworld ......G...... 754 312-5908
Fort Lauderdale *(G-4182)*
Priority Printing Inc ......G...... 727 446-6605
Clearwater *(G-1848)*
Professional Office Svcs Inc ......G...... 863 967-6634
Winter Haven *(G-19348)*
Professional Prtg For Less Inc ......G...... 954 977-3737
Pompano Beach *(G-14819)*
PS & QS Custom Prints LLC ......F...... 352 231-3961
Gainesville *(G-4984)*
Pyramideye Print Corp ......G...... 786 663-1157
Hialeah *(G-5586)*
Quality Arts Lcp LLC ......G...... 305 735-2310
Hialeah *(G-5588)*
Ra Printing Inc ......G...... 904 733-5578
Jacksonville *(G-6703)*
Ramseys Printing & Office Pdts ......G...... 850 227-7468
Port Saint Joe *(G-15082)*
Ranger Associates Inc ......G...... 407 869-0024
Longwood *(G-8329)*
Real Print & Ship Inc ......G...... 727 787-1949
Palm Harbor *(G-13758)*
Reimink Printing Inc ......G...... 813 289-4663
Tampa *(G-18050)*
Rek Design & Print LLC ......G...... 407 331-5100
Winter Springs *(G-19483)*
Relion Enterprises LLC ......G...... 321 287-4225
Orlando *(G-13130)*
Rennak Inc ......G...... 305 558-0144
Miami Lakes *(G-10850)*
Rmf Printing Technologies Inc ......G...... 716 683-7500
Miami *(G-10269)*
Rrhill Printing Solutions Inc ......G...... 786 897-2432
Miami *(G-10285)*
San Marco Place Condo Assn ......G...... 504 812-0352
Jacksonville *(G-6750)*
Sandy-Alexander Inc ......D...... 727 579-1527
Saint Petersburg *(G-15905)*
Saugus Valley Corp ......G...... 954 772-4077
Coral Springs *(G-2310)*
Securus Brot LLC ......G...... 954 532-8065
Miramar *(G-11041)*
Seminole Printing Inc ......G...... 305 823-7204
Hialeah *(G-5614)*
Semprun & Morales Corporation ......F...... 305 698-2554
Hialeah *(G-5615)*
Sergios Printing Inc ......F...... 305 971-4112
Miami *(G-10326)*
Services On Demand Print Inc ......E...... 305 681-5345
Hallandale Beach *(G-5209)*
Shiny Prints ......F...... 561 200-2872
Jupiter *(G-7112)*
Signature Printing Technology ......G...... 407 963-6291
Altamonte Springs *(G-74)*
Sir Speedy Printing Center ......F...... 352 683-8758
Spring Hill *(G-16863)*
Sirs Publishing Inc ......D...... 800 521-0600
Boca Raton *(G-718)*
Sonshine Digital Graphics Inc ......F...... 904 858-1000
Jacksonville *(G-6784)*
SOs Services On Prtg Corp ......G...... 305 225-6000
Hialeah *(G-5624)*
South Broward Printing Inc ......G...... 954 962-1309
Hollywood *(G-5912)*
South Florida Graphics Corp ......G...... 954 917-0606
Fort Lauderdale *(G-4245)*
Southern Imaging ......G...... 727 954-0133
Pinellas Park *(G-14389)*
Southern Litho II LLC ......E...... 724 394-3693
Naples *(G-11409)*
Spanglish Advertising Cor ......G...... 305 244-0918
Miami *(G-10395)*
Specialty Screen Printing Inc ......G...... 561 758-4944
Jupiter *(G-7120)*
Spectrum Rugs & More LLC ......G...... 813 453-4242
Tampa *(G-18123)*
Spinnaker Holding Company ......E...... 561 392-8626
Boca Raton *(G-728)*
Spinnaker Vero Inc ......F...... 772 567-4645
Vero Beach *(G-18667)*
Steve Prints ......G...... 561 571-2903
Delray Beach *(G-3146)*
Steven Chancas ......F...... 352 629-5016
Ocala *(G-12059)*
Steven K Bakum Inc ......G...... 561 804-9110
West Palm Beach *(G-19044)*
Sun Coast Media Group Inc ......D...... 941 206-1300
Port Charlotte *(G-15000)*
Sun Graphic Technologies Inc ......E...... 941 753-7541
Sarasota *(G-16305)*
Sun Print Management LLC ......E...... 727 945-0255
Holiday *(G-5749)*
Sunrise Printing & Signs ......G...... 321 284-3803
Kissimmee *(G-7300)*
Superior Signs and Prints ......G...... 954 780-6351
Pompano Beach *(G-14880)*
Supreme Printing Corp ......G...... 305 591-2916
Hialeah *(G-5643)*
Taie Inc ......F...... 954 966-0233
Hollywood *(G-5920)*
Tara Biek Creative ......G...... 772 486-3684
Stuart *(G-17033)*
Th Custom Promo Tions ......G...... 407 704-7921
Orlando *(G-13252)*
Thomas Printworks ......G...... 305 667-4149
Fort Lauderdale *(G-4281)*
Tiba Enterprises Inc ......G...... 561 575-3037
Jupiter *(G-7128)*
Tks Printing & Promo Products ......D...... 904 469-0968
Jacksonville *(G-6860)*
Totalprint USA ......G...... 855 915-1300
Tampa *(G-18196)*
Tri County Printing Co In ......G...... 561 477-8487
Boca Raton *(G-755)*
Trial Spectrum Inc ......G...... 954 906-5743
Coral Springs *(G-2324)*
Tropical Prints Inc A Corp ......G...... 305 261-9926
Miami *(G-10509)*
Tucker Lithographic Co ......G...... 904 276-0568
Orange Park *(G-12410)*
Unik Design & Print Inc ......G...... 786 355-6877
Miami Lakes *(G-10872)*
Unique Designs Prof Svcs Inc ......F...... 407 296-6204
Orlando *(G-13290)*
Unique Ink Printing Corp ......G...... 954 829-2801
Boca Raton *(G-767)*
United Printing LLC ......G...... 954 554-7969
Pompano Beach *(G-14901)*
United Printing Sales Inc ......G...... 954 942-4300
Pompano Beach *(G-14902)*
United World Printing Inc ......G...... 407 738-0888
Orlando *(G-13295)*
Urbaprint LLC ......G...... 786 502-3223
Weston *(G-19175)*
Van Charles Inc ......G...... 954 394-3242
Oakland Park *(G-11857)*
Venice Print Center ......G...... 941 206-1414
Venice *(G-18586)*
Vinylot of Florida Inc ......G...... 954 978-8424
Margate *(G-8571)*
Vision Concepts Ink Inc ......F...... 305 463-8003
Doral *(G-3542)*
Vital Graphics and Signs Inc ......G...... 305 557-8181
Hialeah *(G-5681)*
Vmak Corp ......F...... 407 260-1199
Longwood *(G-8348)*
Volusia Printing LLC ......G...... 386 873-7442
Deland *(G-3030)*
W H L Business Communications ......G...... 561 361-9202
Boca Raton *(G-784)*
Walter Haas Graphics Inc ......E...... 305 883-2257
Hialeah *(G-5685)*
Wayloo Inc ......G...... 954 914-3192
Fort Lauderdale *(G-4317)*
We Print Flyers and Shirts ......G...... 407 902-7128
Orlando *(G-13320)*
Wild Prints LLC ......G...... 561 800-6536
West Palm Beach *(G-19087)*
Will-Rite Industries Inc ......G...... 305 253-1985
Cutler Bay *(G-2421)*
Winwood Print ......G...... 786 615-3188
Miami *(G-10613)*
Xymoprint LLC ......F...... 407 504-2170
Orlando *(G-13336)*

PRINTING: Offset

24hour Printing Inc ......G...... 954 247-9575
Lauderhill *(G-8097)*
3-Dimension Graphics Inc ......E...... 305 599-3277
Doral *(G-3215)*
321webprint ......G...... 321 285-6771
Melbourne *(G-8755)*
352ink Corp ......G...... 352 373-7547
Gainesville *(G-4866)*
A & A Printing Services LLC ......G...... 786 597-6022
Doral *(G-3218)*
A Fine Print of Miami LLC ......G...... 305 441-5263
Miami *(G-9037)*

PRODUCT

Employee Codes: A=Over 500 employees, B=251-500
C=101-250, D=51-100, E=20-50, F=10-19, G=4-9

A-Plus Prtg & Graphic Ctr Inc.....E..... 954 327-7315
Plantation *(G-14481)*
Aawareness Mktg Prtg & Pubg.....G..... 352 422-3953
Inverness *(G-6080)*
Abbott Printing Co.....D..... 407 831-2999
Maitland *(G-8456)*
Abby Press Inc.....E..... 407 847-5565
Kissimmee *(G-7216)*
Absolute Graphics Inc.....F..... 954 792-3488
Davie *(G-2486)*
AC Graphics Inc.....E..... 305 691-3778
Hialeah *(G-5264)*
Accuprint Corporation.....F..... 954 973-9369
Deerfield Beach *(G-2762)*
Ace Blueprinting Inc.....F..... 954 771-0104
Fort Lauderdale *(G-3777)*
Ace High Printing LLC.....G..... 727 542-3897
Saint Petersburg *(G-15690)*
Ace Press Inc.....G..... 239 334-1118
Fort Myers *(G-4344)*
Ace Printing Inc.....F..... 305 358-2572
Miami *(G-9061)*
Action Printers Inc.....G..... 772 567-4377
Vero Beach *(G-18590)*
Action Printing Inc.....G..... 305 592-4646
Miami *(G-9067)*
Admask Inc.....G..... 954 962-2040
Plantation *(G-14486)*
Advanced Graphics & Prtg Inc.....G..... 954 966-1209
Cooper City *(G-2107)*
Advanced Printing.....G..... 727 545-9000
Seminole *(G-16736)*
Advermarket Corp.....G..... 239 541-1144
Cape Coral *(G-1375)*
Advermarket Corp.....G..... 239 542-1020
Cape Coral *(G-1376)*
Aesthetic Print & Design Inc.....G..... 352 278-3714
Gainesville *(G-4868)*
Agape Graphics & Printing Inc.....G..... 305 252-9147
Miami *(G-9088)*
Aims Printing LLC.....G..... 813 313-9574
Tampa *(G-17394)*
ALC Group Corp.....G..... 786 409-7167
Doral *(G-3233)*
All Because LLC.....G..... 407 884-6700
Apopka *(G-111)*
All In One Mail Shop Inc.....F..... 305 233-6100
Miami *(G-9110)*
All Service Graphics Inc.....F..... 321 259-8957
Melbourne *(G-8763)*
All Star Printing Intl.....G..... 954 974-0333
Deerfield Beach *(G-2773)*
Allegra Direct - South Inc.....F..... 586 226-1400
Orlando *(G-12457)*
Allegra Marketing.....G..... 813 664-1129
Tampa *(G-17400)*
Allegra Marketing Print Design.....G..... 407 848-1721
Altamonte Springs *(G-28)*
Allegra Print and Imaging.....G..... 407 246-1567
Orlando *(G-12458)*
Allegra Print Signs Mail.....G..... 954 963-3886
Hollywood *(G-5770)*
Allied Printing Inc.....D..... 800 749-7683
Jacksonville *(G-6139)*
Alpha Commercial Printing.....G..... 561 841-1415
North Palm Beach *(G-11716)*
Alpha Press Inc.....F..... 407 299-2121
Orlando *(G-12461)*
Alta Systems Inc.....E..... 352 372-2534
Gainesville *(G-4873)*
Amazon Services Inc.....F..... 305 663-0585
Miami *(G-9133)*
Ambassador Printing Company.....G..... 561 330-3668
Delray Beach *(G-3046)*
Amendar Printing Inc.....F..... 786 287-5189
Miami *(G-9137)*
American Specialty Sales Corp.....G..... 305 947-9700
North Miami *(G-11624)*
Apple Printing & Advg Spc Inc.....E..... 954 524-0493
Fort Lauderdale *(G-3818)*
Aquaflex Printing LLC.....G..... 727 914-4922
Saint Petersburg *(G-15706)*
Aquarius Press Inc.....F..... 305 688-0066
Opa Locka *(G-12289)*
Aquinas Inc.....G..... 727 842-2254
New Port Richey *(G-11480)*
Arjay Printing Company Inc.....G..... 904 764-6070
Oldsmar *(G-12204)*
Armstrongs Printing & Graphics.....G..... 850 243-6923
Fort Walton Beach *(G-4778)*

Art In Print Inc.....F..... 561 877-0995
Delray Beach *(G-3047)*
Artcraft Engraving & Prtg Inc.....E..... 305 557-9449
Hialeah *(G-5304)*
Artworks Printing Enterprises.....G..... 954 893-7984
Hollywood *(G-5775)*
Automated Printing Services.....G..... 904 731-3244
Jacksonville *(G-6180)*
B J and ME Inc.....G..... 561 368-5470
Boca Raton *(G-438)*
B R Q Grossmans Inc.....F..... 954 971-1077
Pompano Beach *(G-14609)*
B2b Printing Corp.....G..... 312 953-7446
Cocoa Beach *(G-2058)*
Ballard Printing Inc.....G..... 904 783-4430
Jacksonville *(G-6193)*
Bama Printing LLC.....E..... 561 855-7641
West Palm Beach *(G-18813)*
Bandart Enterprises Inc.....E..... 954 564-1224
Fort Lauderdale *(G-3839)*
Bava Inc.....F..... 850 893-4799
Tallahassee *(G-17226)*
Bay Area Graphics.....G..... 813 247-2400
Tampa *(G-17456)*
Bayou Printing Inc.....F..... 850 678-5444
Valparaiso *(G-18507)*
Beck Graphics Inc.....E..... 727 443-3803
Palm Harbor *(G-13725)*
Bellak Color Corporation.....E..... 305 854-8525
Doral *(G-3267)*
Big Red Q Printing Services.....G..... 305 477-7848
Doral *(G-3272)*
Bizcard Xpress Sanford LLC.....G..... 407 688-8902
Sanford *(G-16003)*
Bjm Enterprises Inc.....F..... 941 746-4171
Bradenton *(G-1000)*
Blackstone Legal Supplies Inc.....F..... 305 945-3450
Lauderhill *(G-8103)*
Blackwell Family Corporation.....G..... 941 639-0200
Punta Gorda *(G-15199)*
Bladorn Investments Inc.....G..... 941 627-0014
Port Charlotte *(G-14965)*
Bobs Quick Prtg & Copy Ctr.....G..... 561 278-0203
Boynton Beach *(G-883)*
Boca Color Graphics Inc.....F..... 561 391-2229
Boca Raton *(G-450)*
Boca Raton Commercial Printing.....G..... 561 549-0126
Boca Raton *(G-452)*
Boca Raton Printing Co.....G..... 561 395-8404
Boca Raton *(G-454)*
Bodree Printing Company Inc.....F..... 850 455-8511
Pensacola *(G-14102)*
Bonita Printshop Inc.....G..... 239 992-8522
Bonita Springs *(G-818)*
Bradford County Telegraph Inc.....F..... 904 964-6305
Starke *(G-16887)*
Brooksville Printing Inc.....G..... 352 848-0016
Brooksville *(G-1217)*
Bros Williams Printing Inc.....G..... 305 769-9925
Hialeah *(G-5332)*
Brut Printing Co Inc.....E..... 904 354-5055
Jacksonville *(G-6241)*
Budget Printing Center LLC.....G..... 561 848-5700
Riviera Beach *(G-15305)*
Business Center & Printshop.....G..... 786 547-6681
Miami *(G-9287)*
Butler Graphics Inc.....G..... 305 477-1344
Miami *(G-9289)*
C & D Printing Company.....D..... 727 572-9999
Saint Petersburg *(G-15733)*
C & H Printing Inc.....G..... 904 620-8444
Jacksonville *(G-6247)*
C F Print Ltd Inc.....F..... 631 567-2110
The Villages *(G-18389)*
C2 Image & Printing Inc.....G..... 310 892-8316
Hialeah *(G-5338)*
Calev Systems Inc.....E..... 786 837-2343
Miami Springs *(G-10888)*
Capra Graphics Inc.....G..... 305 418-4582
Doral *(G-3289)*
Carol Printing Corporation.....G..... 631 315-5061
Tarpon Springs *(G-18287)*
Catapult Print and Packg LLC.....F..... 407 717-4323
Orlando *(G-12554)*
Central Fla Prtg Graphics LLC.....G..... 321 752-8753
Melbourne *(G-8787)*
Central Florida Publishing Inc.....G..... 407 682-1221
Sanford *(G-16009)*
Central Printers Inc.....G..... 727 527-5879
Saint Petersburg *(G-15743)*

Cgi Printers LLC.....G..... 561 969-9999
West Palm Beach *(G-18844)*
Cheany Inc.....G..... 813 443-5271
Tarpon Springs *(G-18289)*
Chromatech Digital Inc.....E..... 727 528-4711
Saint Petersburg *(G-15745)*
City Clors Dgital Prtg Ctr Inc.....E..... 305 471-0816
Doral *(G-3300)*
City Prints Signs & Flyers.....G..... 407 532-6078
Winter Park *(G-19395)*
Class A Printing LLC.....G..... 386 447-0520
Palm Coast *(G-13687)*
Clear Copy Inc.....E..... 561 369-3900
Boynton Beach *(G-890)*
Colonial Press Intl Inc.....C..... 305 633-1581
Miami *(G-9379)*
Color Concepts Prtg Design Co.....E..... 813 623-2921
Tampa *(G-17546)*
Color Express Inc.....G..... 305 558-2061
Hialeah *(G-5350)*
Color Press Print Inc.....G..... 850 763-9884
Panama City *(G-13887)*
Coloramax Printing Inc.....F..... 305 541-0322
Miami *(G-9381)*
Colorfast Printing & Graphics.....G..... 727 531-9506
Clearwater *(G-1633)*
Colorgraphx Inc.....E..... 727 572-6364
Saint Petersburg *(G-15747)*
Commercial Printers Inc.....D..... 954 781-3737
Fort Lauderdale *(G-3911)*
Consolidated Label Co.....C..... 407 339-2626
Sanford *(G-16022)*
Continental Printing Svcs Inc.....G..... 904 743-6718
Jacksonville *(G-6286)*
Copy Cat Printing LLC.....G..... 850 438-5566
Pensacola *(G-14119)*
Copy Right Bgmd Inc.....F..... 904 680-0343
Jacksonville *(G-6291)*
Copy Van of Florida Inc.....G..... 407 366-7126
Oviedo *(G-13423)*
Copy Well Inc.....F..... 850 222-9777
Tallahassee *(G-17238)*
Copy-Flow Inc.....E..... 305 592-0930
Davie *(G-2509)*
Corporate Printing Svcs Inc.....G..... 305 273-6000
Miami *(G-9406)*
Crain Ventures Inc.....G..... 407 933-1820
Kissimmee *(G-7233)*
Creative Color Printing Inc.....G..... 954 701-6763
Davie *(G-2510)*
Creative Design and Print.....G..... 239 325-9163
Naples *(G-11218)*
Creative Printing Bay Cnty Inc.....F..... 850 784-1645
Panama City *(G-13889)*
Creative Prtg Grphic Dsign Inc.....E..... 407 855-0202
Orlando *(G-12627)*
Creative Services of Centl Fla.....G..... 863 385-8383
Sebring *(G-16684)*
Cromer Printing Inc.....F..... 863 422-8651
Haines City *(G-5141)*
Crompco Inc.....F..... 954 584-8488
Plantation *(G-14504)*
Crown Printing Inc.....F..... 863 682-4881
Lakeland *(G-7667)*
Csba Digital Printing.....F..... 813 482-1608
Tampa *(G-17571)*
Csmc Inc.....E..... 407 246-1567
Orlando *(G-12630)*
Curry & Sons Inc.....G..... 305 296-8781
Key West *(G-7185)*
Custom Graphics and Plates Inc.....E..... 407 696-5448
Longwood *(G-8269)*
Customer First Inc Naples.....E..... 239 949-8518
Bonita Springs *(G-827)*
D E B Printing & Graphics Inc.....G..... 954 968-0060
Fort Lauderdale *(G-3929)*
D& R Printing LLC.....G..... 941 378-3311
Sarasota *(G-16402)*
D&R Printing LLC.....G..... 941 378-3311
Sarasota *(G-16403)*
Dagher & Sons Inc.....F..... 904 998-0911
Jacksonville *(G-6307)*
Dahlquist Enterprises Inc.....G..... 407 896-2294
Orlando *(G-12644)*
Dakim Inc.....F..... 561 790-0884
Royal Palm Beach *(G-15465)*
Daniels Offset Printing Inc.....G..... 305 261-3263
Cutler Bay *(G-2392)*
Dannys Prtg Svc Sups & Eqp Inc.....G..... 305 757-2282
Miami *(G-9435)*

Dax Copying and Printing Inc....G.... 954 236-3000
Plantation (G-14509)
Design Litho Inc....G.... 813 238-7494
Tampa (G-17600)
Detailed Services Inc....F.... 239 542-2452
Cape Coral (G-1412)
Digital Printing Solutions Inc....E.... 407 671-8715
Winter Park (G-19402)
Dimension Photo Engrv Co Inc....E.... 813 251-0244
Tampa (G-17607)
Direct Impressions Inc....E.... 239 549-4484
Cape Coral (G-1415)
Dlux Printing Inc....F.... 850 457-8494
Pensacola (G-14133)
Docuprint Corporation....F.... 305 639-8618
Miami (G-9474)
Dominion Printers Inc....G.... 757 340-1300
Port Charlotte (G-14974)
Donnelley Financial LLC....F.... 305 371-3900
Miami (G-9479)
Donoso Printing Corp....G.... 786 508-9426
Miami Lakes (G-10782)
Dpdm Inc....G.... 561 327-4150
Lake Worth (G-7545)
Dpf Solutions Group LLC....G.... 904 580-5343
Jacksonville (G-6327)
Drummond Press Inc....D.... 904 354-2818
Jacksonville (G-6330)
Durra Print Inc....E.... 850 222-4768
Tallahassee (G-17244)
Durra Quick Print Inc....G.... 850 681-2900
Tallahassee (G-17245)
Dynacolor Graphics Inc....E.... 305 625-5388
Hialeah (G-5382)
Dynamic Printing of Brandon....G.... 813 664-6880
Lithia (G-8218)
E & P Printing Corp....G.... 305 715-9545
Miami (G-9489)
Eagle Artistic Printing Inc....G.... 973 476-6301
Boca Raton (G-511)
Eagle Printing....G.... 727 469-8622
Tampa (G-17626)
Ed Vance Printing Company Inc....F.... 813 882-8888
Tampa (G-17630)
Edigitalprintingcom Inc....G.... 305 378-2325
Miami (G-9502)
Edward Thomas Company....G.... 561 746-1441
Jupiter (G-7032)
Ejco Inc....G.... 352 375-0797
Gainesville (G-4913)
Elite Printing & Marketing Inc....G.... 850 474-0894
Pensacola (G-14139)
Ellison Graphics Corp....F.... 561 746-9256
Jupiter (G-7034)
Empire Corp Kit of....G.... 800 432-3028
Doral (G-3343)
EO Painter Printing Company....F.... 386 985-4877
De Leon Springs (G-2738)
Everything Printing Inc....G.... 239 541-2679
Cape Coral (G-1420)
Excaliber Printing Inc....G.... 877 542-1699
Pompano Beach (G-14684)
Express Press Inc....F.... 813 884-3310
Tampa (G-17655)
Express Printing & Office Sups....G.... 904 765-9696
Jacksonville (G-6376)
Express Printing Center Inc....F.... 813 909-1085
Land O Lakes (G-7854)
Express Printing Corporation....G.... 305 546-6369
Miami (G-9549)
Factorymart Inc....F.... 561 202-9820
West Palm Beach (G-18868)
Fermatex Enterprises Inc....G.... 407 332-8320
Orlando (G-12736)
FGA Printing....G.... 954 763-1122
Pompano Beach (G-14689)
Fidelity Printing Corporation....D.... 727 522-9557
Saint Petersburg (G-15778)
First Impressions Printing....F.... 352 237-6141
Ocala (G-11943)
First Imprseesion South Flo....G.... 954 525-0342
Fort Lauderdale (G-3994)
First Imprssons Prtg Cmmnctons....G.... 407 831-6100
Longwood (G-8282)
Flamingo Printing of Brevard....G.... 321 723-2771
Melbourne (G-8833)
Florida Color Printing Inc....G.... 772 286-7264
Stuart (G-16941)
Florida Graphic Printing Inc....F.... 386 253-4532
Daytona Beach (G-2666)
Florida Print Solutions Inc....G.... 727 327-5500
Saint Petersburg (G-15784)
Florida Printing Group Inc....G.... 954 956-8570
Pompano Beach (G-14701)
Flyer Studios Inc....F.... 786 402-9596
Davie (G-2527)
Ford Press Inc....F.... 352 787-4650
Leesburg (G-8159)
Fort Myers Digital LLC....G.... 239 482-3086
Fort Myers (G-4458)
Free Press Publishing Company....E.... 813 254-5888
Tampa (G-17694)
G S Printers Inc....G.... 305 931-2755
Fort Lauderdale (G-4016)
Gandy Printers Inc....F.... 850 222-5847
Tallahassee (G-17260)
Garvin Management Company Inc....G.... 850 893-4719
Tallahassee (G-17261)
Gator Printing & Design LLC....G.... 352 593-4168
Brooksville (G-1231)
Gb Printing....F.... 954 941-3778
Pompano Beach (G-14711)
Gentry Printing Company LLC....E.... 727 441-1914
Clearwater (G-1703)
Global Printing Solutions Inc....G.... 727 458-3483
Saint Petersburg (G-15793)
Gobczynskis Printery Inc....G.... 941 758-5734
Sarasota (G-16222)
Golden Print Inc....G.... 561 833-9661
Boynton Beach (G-913)
Good Time Printing Inc....G.... 352 629-8838
Ocala (G-11959)
Graphic and Printing Svcs Corp....G.... 954 486-8868
Tamarac (G-17357)
Graphic Dynamics Inc....G.... 954 728-8452
Fort Lauderdale (G-4026)
Graphic Masters Inc....D.... 800 230-3873
Miami (G-9656)
Graphic Press Corporation....G.... 850 562-2262
Tallahassee (G-17266)
Graphic Reproductions Inc....G.... 321 267-1111
Titusville (G-18431)
Graphica Services Inc....G.... 305 232-5333
Miami (G-9657)
Graphix Solutions of America....F.... 727 898-6744
Parrish (G-14006)
Green Light Printing Inc....G.... 305 576-5858
Miami (G-9667)
Gulf Coast Business World Inc....F.... 850 864-1511
Fort Walton Beach (G-4806)
Gunn Prtg & Lithography Inc....F.... 813 870-6010
Tampa (G-17738)
H & H Printing Inc....F.... 407 422-2932
Orlando (G-12792)
H & M Printing Inc....F.... 407 831-8030
Sanford (G-16059)
H D Quickprint & Disc Off Sups....G.... 407 678-1355
Winter Park (G-19409)
H&M Phillips Inc....G.... 727 797-4600
Odessa (G-12125)
Hamilton Printing Inc....G.... 772 334-0151
Jensen Beach (G-6970)
Hartley Press Inc....D.... 904 398-5141
Jacksonville (G-6463)
Hartmans Print Center Inc....G.... 941 475-2220
Englewood (G-3661)
Harvest Print Mktg Sltions LLC....G.... 850 681-2488
Tallahassee (G-17276)
Harvest Prtg & Copy Ctr Inc....F.... 850 681-2488
Tallahassee (G-17277)
Herald-Advocate Publishing Co....F.... 863 773-3255
Wauchula (G-18693)
Hernandez Printing Service....F.... 305 642-0483
Miami (G-9705)
Hernando Lithoprinting Inc....G.... 352 796-4136
Brooksville (G-1233)
HI Tech Printing Systems Inc....E.... 954 933-9155
Pompano Beach (G-14722)
Hilcraft Engraving Inc....G.... 305 871-6100
Miami (G-9711)
Hobby Press Inc....E.... 305 887-4333
Medley (G-8664)
Hoffman Brothers Inc....E.... 407 563-5004
Debary (G-2750)
Howies Instant Printing Inc....F.... 561 686-8699
West Palm Beach (G-18898)
Hughes Consolidated Services....G.... 904 438-5710
Jacksonville (G-6482)
Hunt Enterprises Inc....G.... 863 682-6187
Lakeland (G-7707)
Hurricane Graphics Inc....E.... 305 760-9154
Miami Gardens (G-10746)
ICM Printing Co Inc....F.... 352 377-7468
Gainesville (G-4940)
Ideal Publishing Co Inc....F.... 727 321-0785
Saint Petersburg (G-15812)
Iguana Graphics Inc....G.... 813 657-7800
Brandon (G-1163)
Image Printing & Graphics LLC....G.... 321 783-5555
Cape Canaveral (G-1360)
Image Prtg & Digital Svcs Inc....G.... 850 244-3380
Mary Esther (G-8589)
Imperial Imprinting LLC....G.... 772 633-8256
Vero Beach (G-18628)
Imprint....G.... 941 484-5151
Nokomis (G-11581)
Independent Resources Inc....E.... 813 237-0945
Tampa (G-17777)
Infinite Print LLC....G.... 727 942-2121
Holiday (G-5745)
Inkpressions Inc....G.... 305 261-0872
Palmetto Bay (G-13849)
Inky Fingers Printing Inc....G.... 904 384-1900
Jacksonville (G-6495)
Instant Printing & Copy Center....G.... 727 849-1199
Holiday (G-5746)
Instant Printing Services Inc....F.... 727 546-8036
Floral City (G-3768)
Intec Printing Solutions Corp....G.... 813 949-7799
Lutz (G-8391)
Integrity Business Svcs Inc....G.... 321 267-9294
Titusville (G-18434)
Interprint Incorporated....D.... 727 531-8957
Clearwater (G-1734)
Ironhorse Pressworks Inc....G.... 727 462-9988
Clearwater (G-1737)
Island Print Shop....G.... 239 642-0077
Naples (G-11293)
J & J Litho Enterprises Inc....F.... 239 433-2311
Fort Myers (G-4499)
J K & M Ink Corporation....G.... 813 875-3106
Tampa (G-17798)
J M Econo-Print Inc....G.... 305 591-3620
Coral Gables (G-2162)
Jak Corporate Holdings Inc....F.... 813 289-1660
Tampa (G-17802)
Jet Graphics Inc....F.... 305 264-4333
Miami (G-9796)
Jimbob Printing Inc....F.... 850 973-2633
Madison (G-8452)
Jkg Group....G.... 561 866-2850
Boca Raton (G-581)
Jordan Norris Inc....G.... 407 846-1400
Orlando (G-12861)
Jrg Systems Inc....F.... 954 962-1020
Fort Lauderdale (G-4081)
K Color Corp....F.... 305 579-2290
Miami (G-9813)
K R O Enterprises Ltd....G.... 309 797-2213
Naples (G-11302)
K12 Print Inc....F.... 800 764-7600
West Palm Beach (G-18919)
Keithco Inc....G.... 352 351-4741
Ocala (G-11976)
Key West Printing LLC....G.... 305 517-6711
Key West (G-7190)
Keytag1 LLC....G.... 203 982-8448
Deerfield Beach (G-2853)
Kights Printing & Office Pdts....G.... 904 731-7990
Jacksonville (G-6537)
King & Grube Advg & Prtg LLC....G.... 727 327-6033
Largo (G-7990)
King & Grube Inc....F.... 727 327-6033
Largo (G-7991)
King Printing & Graphics Inc....G.... 813 681-5060
Brandon (G-1164)
Kissimmee Printing....G.... 407 518-2514
Kissimmee (G-7264)
Kmg Marketing LLC....G.... 727 376-7200
Odessa (G-12130)
Kwikie Dup Ctr of Pinellas Pk....G.... 727 544-7788
Pinellas Park (G-14362)
L & N Label Company Inc....E.... 727 442-5400
Clearwater (G-1755)
Label Company....F.... 850 438-7334
Pensacola (G-14191)
Laser Light Litho Corp....F.... 305 899-0713
North Miami (G-11643)
Lauderdale Graphics Corp....E.... 954 450-0800
Davie (G-2544)

Lawton Printers Inc.....E..... 407 260-0400
Orlando (G-12898)
Leaderinprint Inc.....G..... 561 200-9412
Lake Worth (G-7565)
Lee Printing Inc.....F..... 904 396-5715
Jacksonville Beach (G-6948)
Lexprint LLC.....G..... 305 661-2424
Miami (G-9888)
Liberty Crtive - Coml Prtg Prm.....G..... 407 960-4270
Longwood (G-8306)
Lightning Prtg & Graphics Inc.....G..... 321 242-7766
Melbourne (G-8875)
Lion Press Inc.....G..... 954 971-6193
Pompano Beach (G-14745)
Litho Art Inc.....G..... 305 232-7098
Miami (G-9902)
Litho Haus Printers Inc.....G..... 850 671-6600
Tallahassee (G-17291)
Lithocraft Inc.....G..... 386 761-3584
Port Orange (G-15022)
Lithotec Commercial Printing.....F..... 727 541-4614
Clearwater (G-1763)
Lmb Consultants Inc.....G..... 954 537-9590
Pompano Beach (G-14746)
Lmn Printing Co Inc.....F..... 386 428-9928
Edgewater (G-3630)
Lori Roberts Print Shop I.....F..... 813 882-8456
Tampa (G-17860)
Lucky Dog Printing Inc.....F..... 407 346-1663
Saint Cloud (G-15657)
Ludaca Printing Corp.....G..... 305 300-4355
Miami (G-9915)
Lufemor Inc.....G..... 305 557-2162
Hialeah (G-5490)
Lumo Print Inc.....G..... 305 246-0003
Homestead (G-5981)
M D H Graphic Services Inc.....F..... 561 533-9000
West Palm Beach (G-18936)
M Victoria Enterprises Inc.....G..... 727 576-8090
Saint Petersburg (G-15845)
Mad Inc.....G..... 813 251-9334
Tampa (G-17871)
Maddys Print Shop LLC.....G..... 954 749-0440
Fort Lauderdale (G-4108)
Magic Print Copy Center.....G..... 239 332-4456
Fort Myers (G-4520)
Magnaprint Corp.....G..... 954 376-8416
Oakland Park (G-11819)
Manci Graphics Corp.....G..... 813 664-1129
Tampa (G-17877)
Mark V Printing LLC.....G..... 954 563-2505
Oakland Park (G-11822)
Market Ink Usa Inc.....G..... 561 502-3438
West Palm Beach (G-18943)
Marrakech Inc.....G..... 727 942-2218
Tarpon Springs (G-18315)
Martin Lithograph Inc.....E..... 813 254-1553
Tampa (G-17886)
Medfare LLC.....F..... 561 998-9444
Boca Raton (G-617)
Media Systems Inc.....G..... 954 427-4411
Coral Springs (G-2277)
Megacolor Print LLC.....F..... 305 499-9395
Miami Beach (G-10692)
Megamalls Inc.....F..... 407 891-2111
Saint Cloud (G-15659)
Menu Men Inc.....E..... 305 633-7925
Miami (G-9976)
Miami Trucolor Offset Svc Co.....G..... 954 962-5230
West Park (G-19096)
Micro Printing Inc.....F..... 954 676-5757
Fort Lauderdale (G-4121)
Midds Inc.....F..... 561 586-6220
Lake Worth (G-7571)
Midds Inc.....E..... 561 586-6220
Lake Worth Beach (G-7615)
Mikes Print Shop Inc.....G..... 407 718-4964
Winter Park (G-19426)
Mmp-Boca Raton LLC.....F..... 561 392-8626
Boca Raton (G-627)
Modern Digital Imaging Inc.....F..... 850 222-7514
Tallahassee (G-17303)
Modern Mail Print Slutions Inc.....E..... 727 572-6245
Clearwater (G-1789)
MOR Printing Inc.....F..... 954 377-1197
Pompano Beach (G-14768)
Morten Enterprises Inc.....F..... 727 531-8957
Clearwater (G-1792)
Multicolor Printing Inc.....G..... 772 287-1676
Stuart (G-16979)

My Print Shop Inc.....F..... 954 973-9369
Deerfield Beach (G-2878)
Myers Printing Inc.....G..... 813 237-0288
Tampa (G-17924)
Nai Print Solutions LLC.....G..... 850 637-1260
Pensacola (G-14210)
Naples Printing Inc.....F..... 239 643-2442
Naples (G-11338)
Nassau Printing & Off Sup Inc.....G..... 904 879-2305
Callahan (G-1327)
National Multiple Listing Inc.....E..... 954 772-8880
Fort Lauderdale (G-4132)
Nebraska Printing Inc.....E..... 813 870-6871
Tampa (G-17936)
Newspaper Printing Company.....C..... 813 839-0035
Tampa (G-17937)
Nexpub Inc.....F..... 954 392-5889
Miramar (G-11021)
Ngp Corporate Square Inc.....E..... 239 643-3430
Naples (G-11345)
No Limit TS and Prints LLC.....G..... 813 933-3424
Spring Hill (G-16876)
North Florida Printing Inc.....G..... 386 362-1080
Live Oak (G-8235)
North Palm Printing Center.....G..... 561 622-2839
Palm Beach Gardens (G-13612)
Nupress of Miami Inc.....E..... 305 594-2100
Doral (G-3446)
Ocala Print Quick Inc.....G..... 352 629-0736
Ocala (G-12014)
Olmedo Printing Corp.....G..... 305 262-4666
Miami (G-10095)
On The Run Printing.....G..... 305 733-2619
Miramar (G-11024)
One Hour Printing.....G..... 386 763-3111
South Daytona (G-16805)
Oompha Inc.....G..... 850 222-7210
Tallahassee (G-17308)
Original Impressions LLC.....C..... 305 233-1322
Weston (G-19156)
Output Printing Corp.....F..... 813 228-8800
Tampa (G-17965)
P & G Printing Group Inc.....F..... 954 971-2511
Margate (G-8559)
P & J Graphics Inc.....F..... 813 626-3243
Temple Terrace (G-18373)
Pad Printing Technology Corp.....G..... 941 739-8667
Bradenton (G-1091)
Pad Printing Technology Group.....F..... 941 739-8667
Bradenton (G-1092)
Palm Beach Junior Clg Prnt Shp.....F..... 561 969-0122
Lake Worth (G-7578)
Palm Prnting/Printers Ink Corp.....E..... 239 332-8600
Fort Myers (G-4562)
Palm Prtg Strgc Solutions LLC.....G..... 239 332-8600
Fort Myers (G-4563)
Palmetto Printing Inc.....F..... 305 253-2444
Miami (G-10134)
Pan American Graphic Inc.....E..... 305 885-1962
Miami Lakes (G-10834)
Panther Printing Inc.....E..... 239 936-5050
Fort Myers (G-4564)
Paper Fish Printing Inc.....G..... 239 481-3555
Fort Myers (G-4565)
Paragon Products Inc.....E..... 407 302-9147
Sanford (G-16099)
Parkinson Enterprises Inc.....F..... 863 688-7900
Lakeland (G-7762)
Parkway Printing Inc.....G..... 239 936-6970
Fort Myers (G-4566)
Patriot Press Inc.....F..... 407 625-7516
Orlando (G-13053)
Paw Print Co.....G..... 561 753-5588
West Palm Beach (G-18991)
PCI Communications Inc.....G..... 941 729-5202
Ellenton (G-3654)
Penstripe Graphics.....G..... 904 726-0200
Jacksonville (G-6667)
Peter Printer Inc.....G..... 305 558-0147
Hialeah (G-5556)
Phillips Graphics Inc.....G..... 352 622-1776
Ocala (G-12025)
Phillips Printing Services LLC.....G..... 941 526-6570
Bradenton (G-1095)
Photo Graphics.....G..... 772 220-1430
Stuart (G-16988)
Photo Offset Inc.....F..... 305 666-1067
Miami (G-10159)
PIP Marketing Signs Print.....G..... 904 825-2372
Saint Augustine (G-15588)

PIP Printing.....G..... 352 622-3224
Ocala (G-12027)
PIP Printing.....G..... 386 258-3326
Daytona Beach (G-2694)
PIP Printing 622 Inc.....G..... 813 935-8113
Tampa (G-17993)
Pk Graphicz.....G..... 305 534-2184
Pompano Beach (G-14795)
Pk Group Inc.....F..... 239 643-2442
Naples (G-11368)
Plasti-Card Corporation.....F..... 305 944-2726
Delray Beach (G-3117)
Podgo Printing LLC.....G..... 954 874-9100
Hollywood (G-5893)
Port Printing Co.....G..... 561 848-1402
Riviera Beach (G-15365)
PPG Inc.....F..... 813 831-9902
Tampa (G-18000)
Precision Litho Service Inc.....D..... 727 573-1763
Clearwater (G-1840)
Premier Corporate Printing.....G..... 305 378-8480
Jacksonville (G-6683)
Premier Printing Signs.....G..... 727 849-2493
Port Richey (G-15064)
Premier Printing Solutions Inc.....G..... 305 490-0244
Fort Lauderdale (G-4177)
Press Print Graphics LLC.....F..... 850 249-3700
Panama City Beach (G-13983)
Press Printing Enterprises Inc.....E..... 239 598-1500
Fort Myers (G-4572)
Press Room Inc.....G..... 954 792-6729
Pembroke Pines (G-14054)
Pressex Inc.....F..... 727 299-8500
Clearwater (G-1845)
Print Basics Inc.....E..... 954 354-0700
Deerfield Beach (G-2891)
Print Big Inc.....G..... 305 398-8898
Hialeah (G-5572)
Print Bold Corp.....F..... 305 517-1281
Miami (G-10193)
Print Direct Inc.....G..... 772 545-9191
Hobe Sound (G-5725)
Print Dynamics.....F..... 954 524-9294
Fort Lauderdale (G-4180)
Print E-Solution Inc.....G..... 954 588-5454
Deerfield Beach (G-2892)
Print Etc Inc.....F..... 813 972-2800
Tampa (G-18013)
Print Express.....G..... 904 737-6641
Jacksonville (G-6686)
Print Factory LLC.....G..... 954 392-5889
Miramar (G-11031)
Print Farm Inc.....E..... 305 592-2895
Miami (G-10194)
Print Headquarters.....F..... 772 286-2812
Palm Beach Gardens (G-13618)
Print It Usacom Inc.....G..... 954 370-2200
Davie (G-2575)
Print Motion Inc.....F..... 305 851-7206
Miami (G-10195)
Print One Inc.....G..... 813 273-0240
Oldsmar (G-12262)
Print Shack.....G..... 813 885-4152
Tampa (G-18014)
Print Shop of Chiefland Inc.....G..... 352 493-0322
Chiefland (G-1537)
Print Solution Digital LLC.....G..... 305 819-7420
Hialeah (G-5573)
Printed Systems Inc.....G..... 904 281-0909
Jacksonville (G-6687)
Printer S Pride Inc.....G..... 813 932-8683
Tampa (G-18015)
Printers Edge LLC.....F..... 407 294-8542
Orlando (G-13089)
Printers For Less LLC.....G..... 954 647-0051
Fort Lauderdale (G-4181)
Printers of Pensacola LLC.....G..... 850 434-2588
Pensacola (G-14240)
Printing Center LLC.....G..... 305 513-9114
Miami (G-10200)
Printing Connection Too Inc.....G..... 954 584-4197
Davie (G-2576)
Printing Depot Inc.....G..... 813 855-6758
Oldsmar (G-12264)
Printing Edge Inc.....G..... 904 399-3343
Jacksonville (G-6688)
Printing Express.....G..... 305 512-0900
Hialeah (G-5575)
Printing Grphics Cnnection Inc.....G..... 305 222-6144
Miami (G-10201)

Printing Impressions Prom .... G 904 465-2223
Jacksonville (G-6689)
Printing Mart Inc .... G 954 753-0323
Pompano Beach (G-14816)
Printing Usa Inc .... F 407 857-7468
Orlando (G-13090)
Printmaster Inc .... G 954 771-6104
Oakland Park (G-11832)
Printnow Inc .... G 850 435-1149
Pensacola (G-14241)
Printworks .... G 850 681-6909
Tallahassee (G-17311)
Pro-Copy Inc .... F 813 988-5900
Temple Terrace (G-18375)
Professional Printing .... G 561 845-0514
North Palm Beach (G-11725)
Professnal Reproduction of Jax .... G 904 389-4141
Jacksonville (G-6691)
Progressive Printing Co Inc .... F 904 388-0746
Jacksonville (G-6694)
Progressive Printing Solutions .... G 800 370-5591
Delray Beach (G-3128)
Prolific Resource Inc .... G 727 868-9341
Port Richey (G-15066)
Proprint of Naples Inc .... F 239 775-3553
Fort Myers (G-4574)
Public Image Printing Inc .... G 727 363-1800
St Pete Beach (G-16883)
Q P Consulting Inc .... G 321 727-2442
Melbourne (G-8916)
Quality Forms & Printing Co .... G 407 671-8026
Winter Park (G-19434)
Quality Printing Inc .... G 386 255-1565
Daytona Beach (G-2701)
Quick Print .... G 954 974-2820
Pompano Beach (G-14823)
Quick Prints LLC .... G 954 526-9013
Fort Lauderdale (G-4196)
Quick Prints LLC .... G 954 594-9415
Plantation (G-14543)
Quickprint Line .... G 561 740-9930
Boynton Beach (G-950)
Quicksilver Prtg & Copying Inc .... G 813 888-6811
Tampa (G-18035)
R K L Enterprises of Pensacola .... F 850 432-2335
Pensacola (G-14248)
R R H Inc .... F 954 966-1209
Hollywood (G-5900)
R Smith Printing Inc .... G 518 827-7700
Hastings (G-5229)
Rainbow Printing Inc .... G 561 364-9000
Boynton Beach (G-952)
Rapid Graphix Inc .... G 941 639-2043
Punta Gorda (G-15227)
Rapid Print Southwest Fla Inc .... G 239 590-9797
Fort Myers (G-4579)
Rapid Printer Solutions .... G 954 769-9553
Fort Lauderdale (G-4198)
Rapid Rater Company .... E 850 893-7346
Tallahassee (G-17314)
Rapid Reproductions LLC .... G 607 843-2221
Melbourne Beach (G-8983)
Redberd Printing .... G 407 622-2292
Winter Park (G-19438)
Redbird Printing .... G 904 654-8371
Winter Park (G-19439)
Repro Plus Inc .... F 407 843-1492
Orlando (G-13131)
Rgu Color Inc .... G 386 252-9979
South Daytona (G-16808)
Ribbon Printers Unlimited .... G 888 546-3310
Boynton Beach (G-955)
Rinaldi Printing Company .... E 813 569-0033
Tampa (G-18058)
Roberts Quality Printing Inc .... E 727 442-4011
Clearwater (G-1862)
Rodes Printing Corp .... G 305 559-5263
Miami (G-10274)
Rose Printing Co Inc .... G 850 339-8093
Tallahassee (G-17317)
Rush Flyers .... F 954 332-0509
Plantation (G-14546)
Rush To Excellence Prtg Inc .... G 904 367-0100
Jacksonville (G-6740)
Rxprinting and Graphics LLC .... G 407 965-3039
Orlando (G-13150)
S Printing Inc .... G 305 633-3343
Miami (G-10292)
Salt 1 To 1 .... G 407 538-2134
Orlando (G-13159)

Sameday Printing Inc .... G 800 411-3106
Miami (G-10301)
Sandow Specialty Printing Inc .... G 305 255-5697
Palmetto Bay (G-13853)
Sanibel Print & Graphics .... G 239 454-1001
Fort Myers (G-4595)
SBT River PIP Project .... E 919 469-5095
Orlando (G-13166)
Seapress Inc .... G 941 366-8494
Sarasota (G-16589)
Seminole Paper & Printing Co .... G 305 379-8481
Miami (G-10322)
Serbin Printing Inc .... E 941 366-0755
Sarasota (G-16593)
Shelbie Press Inc .... G 407 896-4600
Orlando (G-13179)
Shima Group Corp .... G 305 463-0288
Doral (G-3502)
Shoreline Print Group .... G 727 481-9358
Cape Coral (G-1470)
Shoreline Printing Company .... G 954 491-0311
Oakland Park (G-11839)
Short Stop Print Inc .... G 941 474-4313
Englewood (G-3683)
Signal Graphics Printing LLC .... G 303 837-1331
Punta Gorda (G-15234)
Signature Printing Inc .... F 305 828-9992
Miami Lakes (G-10857)
Sobe Express .... G 305 674-4454
Miami Beach (G-10712)
Sol Davis Printing Inc .... E 813 353-3609
Tampa (G-18114)
Solid Print Solutions Inc .... G 561 670-4391
Lake Worth Beach (G-7619)
Solo Printing LLC .... C 305 594-8699
Miami (G-10372)
Sosumi Holdings Inc .... E 239 634-3430
Naples (G-11407)
South Florida Print .... G 561 807-8584
Deerfield Beach (G-2914)
Southeast Print Programs Inc .... E 813 885-3203
Tampa (G-18118)
Southeastern Printing Co Inc .... C 772 287-2141
Hialeah (G-5628)
Southern Company Entp Inc .... E 904 879-2101
Callahan (G-1329)
Southprint Corp .... G 813 237-8000
Tampa (G-18122)
Speed Print One Inc .... G 305 374-5936
Miami (G-10403)
Spett Printing Co Inc .... G 561 241-9758
Boca Raton (G-727)
Spiritwear Today .... G 239 676-7384
Bonita Springs (G-856)
Spotlight Graphics Inc .... E 941 929-1500
Sarasota (G-16601)
Sprint Printing Company LLC .... G 239 947-2221
Bonita Springs (G-857)
Spyder Graphics Inc .... G 954 561-9725
Oakland Park (G-11842)
Stacy Lee Montgomery .... G 863 662-3163
Winter Haven (G-19358)
Steve Printer Inc .... G 941 375-8657
Venice (G-18577)
Steven M Roessler LLC .... G 321 773-2300
Indian Harbour Beach (G-6068)
Stewart-Hedrick Inc .... E 941 907-0090
Lakewood Ranch (G-7847)
Storterchilds Printing Co Inc .... E 352 376-2658
Gainesville (G-5001)
Stuart Web Inc .... E 772 287-8022
Stuart (G-17027)
Stuart Web Inc .... G 772 287-8022
Stuart (G-17028)
Sun 3d Corporation .... G 954 210-6010
Pompano Beach (G-14876)
Sun Screen Print Inc .... G 904 674-0520
Jacksonville (G-6821)
Sunbelt Dimensional Inc .... G 954 424-3139
Davie (G-2598)
Sunbelt Usa Inc .... G 239 353-5519
Naples (G-11421)
Suniland Press Inc .... E 305 235-8811
Miami (G-10431)
Sunshine Printing Inc .... F 561 478-2602
West Palm Beach (G-19050)
Super Color Inc .... F 954 964-4656
Davie (G-2599)
Swift Print Service Inc .... G 239 458-2212
Cape Coral (G-1482)

T Beattie Enterprises .... F 407 679-2000
Winter Park (G-19450)
Tag & Label of Florida Inc .... G 305 255-1050
Miami (G-10457)
Tags & Labels Printing Inc .... E 954 455-2867
Hallandale Beach (G-5218)
Tampa Bay Press Inc .... F 813 886-1415
Tampa (G-18161)
Tampa Printing Company .... E 813 612-7746
Tampa (G-18171)
Tan Printing Inc .... G 954 986-9869
Hallandale Beach (G-5219)
Target Graphics Inc .... F 941 365-8809
Sarasota (G-16615)
Target Print & Mail .... G 850 671-6600
Tallahassee (G-17338)
Tempo Fulfillment Inc .... G 727 914-0659
Pinellas Park (G-14391)
Thalers Printing Center Inc .... G 954 741-6522
Lauderhill (G-8122)
Thunderbird Press Inc .... F 321 269-7616
Titusville (G-18468)
Tiger Business Forms Inc .... E 305 888-3528
Hialeah (G-5649)
Time Printing Co Inc .... G 904 396-9967
Jacksonville (G-6856)
Tip Top Prtg of Volusia Cnty .... G 386 760-7701
Daytona Beach (G-2728)
Tko Print Solutions Inc .... E 954 315-0990
Pompano Beach (G-14887)
Toms Instant Printing Inc .... G 904 396-0686
Jacksonville (G-6861)
Top Drawer Inc .... F 305 620-1102
Miami Lakes (G-10869)
Top Drawer Printers Inc .... E 305 620-1102
Miami Lakes (G-10870)
Topline Prtg & Graphics Inc .... E 561 881-2267
Riviera Beach (G-15385)
Total Print Inc .... G 772 589-9658
Sebastian (G-16673)
Town Street Print Shop Inc .... G 850 432-8300
Gulf Breeze (G-5130)
Trend Offset Printing Svcs Inc .... D 562 598-2446
Jacksonville (G-6869)
Trese Inc .... F 321 632-7272
Rockledge (G-15454)
TST Impreso Inc .... G 305 381-5153
Medley (G-8745)
Two B Printing Inc .... G 954 566-4886
Oakland Park (G-11851)
Ultra Graphics Corp .... G 305 593-0202
Miami (G-10526)
Universal Graphics & Prtg Inc .... G 561 845-6404
North Palm Beach (G-11729)
Universal Printing Company .... F 305 592-5387
Miami (G-10541)
Up2speed Printing Inc .... F 850 508-2620
Hialeah (G-5666)
V I P Printing .... G 386 258-3326
Daytona Beach (G-2730)
V P Press Inc .... F 954 581-7531
Fort Lauderdale (G-4301)
Verified Label & Print Inc .... F 813 290-7721
Tampa (G-18237)
Vero Beach Printing Inc .... G 772 562-4267
Vero Beach (G-18678)
Village Scribe Printing Co .... F 727 585-7388
Largo (G-8074)
Vlp Prtg Night CLB Sups LLC .... G 561 603-2846
Boca Raton (G-780)
Vista Color Corporation .... D 305 635-2000
Doral (G-3544)
Vital Printing Corporation .... F 561 659-2367
Lake Worth Beach (G-7623)
Vowells Downtown Inc .... G 850 432-5175
Pensacola (G-14285)
W D H Enterprises Inc .... G 941 758-6500
Bradenton (G-1143)
Web Offset Printing Co Inc .... D 727 572-7488
Clearwater (G-1937)
Webb-Mason Inc .... G 727 531-1112
Largo (G-8079)
Wecando Print LLC .... F 754 222-9144
Deerfield Beach (G-2935)
Weidenhamer Corporation .... G 850 837-3190
Destin (G-3211)
Wells Legal Supply Inc .... E 904 399-1510
Jacksonville (G-6909)
William Burns .... G 877 462-5872
Lakeland (G-7835)

PRODUCT

Willy Walt Inc..........G....... 727 209-2872
Saint Petersburg *(G-15962)*
Wilson Printing USA LLC..........G....... 727 536-4173
Clearwater *(G-1941)*
WJS Printing Partners Inc..........G....... 904 731-0357
Jacksonville *(G-6925)*
Woods Printing of Ocala Inc..........G....... 352 629-1665
Ocala *(G-12077)*
Wright Printery Inc..........G....... 386 252-6571
Daytona Beach *(G-2733)*
Xperient LLC..........G....... 407 265-8000
Longwood *(G-8353)*
Your Name Printing..........G....... 813 621-2400
Tampa *(G-18277)*

PRINTING: Pamphlets

Dasops Inc..........G....... 386 258-6230
Daytona Beach *(G-2652)*
McGee Enterprises Inc..........G....... 904 328-3226
Jacksonville *(G-6585)*
Peter T Amann..........G....... 561 848-2770
West Palm Beach *(G-18995)*

PRINTING: Photolithographic

Lutimi Nr Corp..........G....... 954 245-7986
Miramar *(G-11012)*

PRINTING: Roller, Broadwoven Fabrics, Cotton

Ripa & Associates Inc..........C....... 813 623-6777
Tampa *(G-18059)*

PRINTING: Screen, Broadwoven Fabrics, Cotton

American Mentality Inc..........G....... 407 599-7255
Longwood *(G-8254)*
Aquarius Silk Screen Inc..........G....... 941 377-3059
Sarasota *(G-16346)*
Blackwell Family Corporation..........G....... 941 639-0200
Punta Gorda *(G-15199)*
Capsmith Inc..........E....... 407 328-7660
Sanford *(G-16007)*
Cubco Inc..........F....... 386 254-2706
Daytona Beach *(G-2650)*
Daytona Trophy Inc..........F....... 386 253-2806
Daytona Beach *(G-2656)*
Happy Endings of Miami Inc..........G....... 305 759-4467
Miami *(G-9686)*
Michelle Lynn Solutions Inc..........G....... 786 413-0455
Miami *(G-10016)*
Mid-Florida Sportswear LLC..........E....... 386 258-5632
Daytona Beach *(G-2686)*
Rock N Roll Custom Screened S..........G....... 727 528-2111
Pinellas Park *(G-14385)*
Royal Tees Inc..........F....... 941 366-0056
Sarasota *(G-16564)*
Screenprint Plus Inc..........E....... 239 549-7284
Cape Coral *(G-1467)*
Screenworks Usa Inc..........C....... 407 426-9999
Orlando *(G-13170)*
Sherry Manufacturing Co Inc..........C....... 305 693-7000
Miami *(G-10338)*
South Florida Strip Tees Inc..........F....... 954 972-4899
Pompano Beach *(G-14859)*

PRINTING: Screen, Fabric

Aloha Screen Printing Inc..........G....... 850 934-4716
Gulf Breeze *(G-5111)*
Ataly Inc..........E....... 813 880-9142
Tampa *(G-17441)*
Bakers Sports Inc..........E....... 904 388-8126
Jacksonville *(G-6192)*
Baru Agency Incorporated..........G....... 305 259-8800
Doral *(G-3264)*
Clothesline Inc..........F....... 850 877-9171
Tallahassee *(G-17235)*
Dixon Screen Printing LLC..........G....... 850 476-3924
Pensacola *(G-14132)*
Eagle Athletic Wear Inc..........F....... 727 937-6147
Tarpon Springs *(G-18297)*
EMB Wholesale..........G....... 904 452-4362
Jacksonville *(G-6361)*
Expert TS of Jacksonville..........F....... 904 387-2500
Jacksonville *(G-6374)*
HOB Corporation..........G....... 813 988-2272
Tampa *(G-17758)*
Kid-U-Not Inc..........E....... 407 324-2112
Sanford *(G-16079)*
Manatee Bay Enterprises Inc..........F....... 407 245-3600
Orlando *(G-12947)*
Paradise Cstm Screening & EMB..........E....... 954 566-9096
Davie *(G-2566)*
Promo Daddy LLC..........F....... 877 557-2336
Melbourne *(G-8913)*
Reliable Custom Imprints Corp..........G....... 407 834-0571
Longwood *(G-8331)*
S S Designs Inc..........D....... 863 965-2576
Winter Haven *(G-19353)*
Serigraphia Inc..........E....... 850 243-9743
Fort Walton Beach *(G-4832)*
Shirts & Caps Inc..........F....... 813 788-7026
Tampa *(G-18098)*
Synergy Sports LLC..........G....... 239 593-9374
Naples *(G-11432)*
Team Edition Apparel Inc..........C....... 941 744-2041
Bradenton *(G-1125)*
Tiptops Inc..........G....... 352 357-9559
Eustis *(G-3719)*
Vanlex Clothing Inc..........E....... 305 431-4669
Miami Lakes *(G-10878)*

PRINTING: Screen, Manmade Fiber & Silk, Broadwoven Fabric

Apparel Printers..........G....... 352 463-8850
Alachua *(G-4)*
Bagindd Prints..........F....... 954 971-9000
Coral Springs *(G-2223)*
Blue Ocean Press Inc..........E....... 954 973-1819
Fort Lauderdale *(G-3859)*
Cottonimagescom Inc..........E....... 305 251-2560
Doral *(G-3311)*
Creative Shirts Intl Inc..........F....... 954 351-0909
Oakland Park *(G-11792)*
Dowling Graphics Inc..........E....... 727 573-5997
Clearwater *(G-1657)*
Metal Spray Painting Powder..........G....... 954 227-2744
Coral Springs *(G-2281)*
Orange Sunshine Graphics Inc..........G....... 954 797-7425
Davie *(G-2562)*

PRINTING: Thermography

American Business Cards Inc..........E....... 314 739-0800
Naples *(G-11161)*
Boostan Inc..........G....... 305 223-5981
Miami *(G-9267)*
Breast Thermgrphy of BRWrd&plm..........G....... 561 852-5789
Boca Raton *(G-463)*
Winsted Thermographers Inc..........F....... 305 944-7862
Hallandale Beach *(G-5225)*

PRODUCT STERILIZATION SVCS

Clearant Inc..........G....... 407 876-3134
Orlando *(G-12589)*

PRODUCTS: Petroleum & coal, NEC

Panama City Petro LLC..........G....... 850 215-9146
Panama City *(G-13937)*

PROFESSIONAL EQPT & SPLYS, WHOLESALE: Bank

Metavante Holdings LLC..........G....... 904 438-6000
Jacksonville *(G-6600)*

PROFESSIONAL EQPT & SPLYS, WHOLESALE: Engineers', NEC

Naztec International Group LLC..........F....... 561 802-4110
West Palm Beach *(G-18960)*

PROFESSIONAL EQPT & SPLYS, WHOLESALE: Optical Goods

Lasersight Technologies Inc..........G....... 407 678-9900
Orlando *(G-12894)*
Low Vision Aids Inc..........G....... 954 722-1580
Ocala *(G-11987)*
Premium Dynamic Lens..........F....... 813 891-9912
Oldsmar *(G-12261)*

PROFESSIONAL EQPT & SPLYS, WHOLESALE: Scientific & Engineerg

A B Survey Supply Entps Inc..........G....... 772 464-9500
Fort Pierce *(G-4667)*
Jensen Scientific Products Inc..........E....... 954 344-2006
Coral Springs *(G-2263)*

PROFESSIONAL EQPT & SPLYS, WHOLESALE: Theatrical

Cinema Crafters Inc..........G....... 305 891-6121
North Miami *(G-11632)*

PROFESSIONAL INSTRUMENT REPAIR SVCS

Marine Exhaust Systems Inc..........D....... 561 848-1238
Riviera Beach *(G-15346)*
Sun Nuclear Corp..........C....... 321 259-6862
Melbourne *(G-8950)*
Superior Unlimited Enterprises..........G....... 863 294-1683
Winter Haven *(G-19360)*

PROFILE SHAPES: Unsupported Plastics

Daniel Bustamante..........G....... 305 779-7777
Coral Gables *(G-2137)*
Firedrake Inc..........G....... 813 713-8902
Zephyrhills *(G-19518)*

PROMOTION SVCS

Grand Cypress Group Inc..........G....... 407 622-1993
Maitland *(G-8467)*
Toms Instant Printing Inc..........G....... 904 396-0686
Jacksonville *(G-6861)*

PROPELLERS: Boat & Ship, Cast

Blair Propeller MA..........G....... 772 283-1453
Stuart *(G-16917)*
Brown Dog Propeller LLC..........G....... 321 254-7767
Satellite Beach *(G-16649)*
Turning Point Propellers Inc..........G....... 904 900-7739
Jacksonville *(G-6871)*

PROPELLERS: Boat & Ship, Machined

E M P Inc..........G....... 772 286-7343
Stuart *(G-16935)*

PROPELLERS: Ship, Nec

S & S Propeller Co Inc..........G....... 718 359-3393
Pompano Beach *(G-14838)*

PROPULSION UNITS: Guided Missiles & Space Vehicles

American Maglev Tech Fla Inc..........F....... 404 386-4036
Amelia Island *(G-92)*
Atk Sales Corp..........G....... 954 701-0465
Hollywood *(G-5777)*
Boeing Company..........G....... 850 882-4912
Eglin Afb *(G-3641)*

PROTECTION EQPT: Lightning

Alico Lighting Group Inc..........G....... 305 542-2648
Hollywood *(G-5768)*
Allstate Lghtning Prtction LLC..........G....... 813 240-2736
Tampa *(G-17404)*
Bren Tuck Inc..........F....... 727 561-7697
Clearwater *(G-1612)*
Cooper Crouse-Hinds Mtl Inc..........C....... 321 725-8000
Melbourne *(G-8797)*
Lightning Prtction Systems Inc..........F....... 239 643-4323
Naples *(G-11312)*
Omega Power Systems Inc..........G....... 772 219-0045
Stuart *(G-16982)*
Thor Guard Inc..........F....... 954 835-0900
Sunrise *(G-17188)*

PROTECTIVE FOOTWEAR: Rubber Or Plastic

Global Trading Inc..........F....... 305 471-4455
Miami *(G-9642)*

PUBLIC RELATIONS SVCS

Conric Holdings LLC ....F 239 690-9840
Fort Myers *(G-4408)*
Military One Click LLC ....G 904 390-7100
Jacksonville *(G-6605)*
Quality Life Publishing Co ....G 239 513-9907
Naples *(G-11379)*

PUBLISHERS: Art Copy & Poster

Sinergie Printing Inc ....G 786 493-6167
Miami *(G-10353)*

PUBLISHERS: Book

2leaf Press Inc ....G 646 801-4227
Plantation *(G-14479)*
Armbrust Aviation Group Inc ....E 561 355-8488
West Palm Beach *(G-18801)*
Athletic Guide Publishing ....G 386 439-2250
Flagler Beach *(G-3752)*
Belvoir Publications Inc ....E 941 929-1720
Sarasota *(G-16364)*
Bisk Education Inc ....B 813 621-6200
Tampa *(G-17471)*
Booklocker Com Inc ....F 727 483-4540
Saint Petersburg *(G-15726)*
Builders Publishing Group LLC ....G 407 539-2938
Maitland *(G-8461)*
Casebriefs LLC ....F 646 240-4401
Boca Raton *(G-471)*
Coeur De Lion Inc ....E 727 442-4808
Clearwater *(G-1631)*
Darmiven Inc ....G 305 871-1157
Virginia Gardens *(G-18686)*
E-Libro Corporation ....F 305 466-0155
Sunny Isles Beach *(G-17074)*
First Edition Design Inc ....G 941 921-2607
Sarasota *(G-16433)*
Fournies Associates ....G 561 445-5102
Delray Beach *(G-3079)*
Getabstract Inc ....E 305 936-2626
Miami *(G-9633)*
Great Hse Mdia Group of Pbls I ....F 407 779-3846
Orlando *(G-12788)*
Houghton Mifflin Harcourt ....D 407 345-2000
Orlando *(G-12811)*
Jabberwocky LLC ....G 310 717-3343
Miami *(G-9785)*
Legacy Publishing Services ....G 407 647-3787
Winter Park *(G-19418)*
Living Parables ....G 407 488-6201
Orlando *(G-12917)*
Lmn Printing Co Inc ....F 386 428-9928
Edgewater *(G-3630)*
Meadowbrook Inc ....E 800 338-2232
Naples *(G-11325)*
Mega Book Inc ....G 352 378-4567
Gainesville *(G-4960)*
Municipal Code Corporation ....D 850 576-3171
Tallahassee *(G-17304)*
New Underground RR Pubg Co ....F 305 825-1444
Miami Lakes *(G-10830)*
On-Board Media Inc ....D 305 673-0400
Doral *(G-3450)*
Plus Communications Inc ....F 407 333-0600
Lake Mary *(G-7444)*
Printers Printer Inc ....F 954 917-2773
Pompano Beach *(G-14814)*
Samjay Media Group Orlando LLC ....G 407 865-7526
Longwood *(G-8333)*
Signcraft Publishing Co Inc ....F 239 939-4644
Fort Myers *(G-4604)*
Spirit Connection ....G 321 327-3804
Melbourne *(G-8942)*
Starline Education Inc ....G 808 631-1818
Titusville *(G-18464)*
Stephens Group ....G 941 623-9689
Port Charlotte *(G-14999)*
Wccm-USA Ltd Corporation ....G 904 346-3816
Jacksonville *(G-6906)*

PUBLISHERS: Book Clubs, No Printing

Rourke Ray Publishing Co Inc ....G 772 234-6001
Vero Beach *(G-18661)*

PUBLISHERS: Books, No Printing

90-Minute Books LLC ....G 863 318-0464
Winter Haven *(G-19292)*
American Accounting Assn ....E 941 921-7747
Lakewood Ranch *(G-7836)*
Archer Ellison Inc ....G 800 449-4095
Lake Mary *(G-7400)*
Artex Publishing Inc ....G 727 944-4117
Holiday *(G-5734)*
Buck Pile Inc ....G 772 492-1056
Vero Beach *(G-18607)*
Center For Business Ownership ....G 239 455-9393
Naples *(G-11204)*
Comex Systems Inc ....G 908 881-6301
Port Charlotte *(G-14971)*
CRC Press LLC ....E 561 994-0555
Boca Raton *(G-491)*
CRC Press LLC ....E 561 361-6000
Boca Raton *(G-492)*
Direct Response Publication ....F 561 620-3010
Boca Raton *(G-503)*
Esperanto Inc ....F 305 513-8980
Doral *(G-3344)*
Frederic Thomas USA Inc ....F 239 593-8000
Naples *(G-11250)*
Gleim Publications Inc ....D 352 375-0772
Gainesville *(G-4931)*
Great Locations Inc ....G 954 943-1188
Pompano Beach *(G-14718)*
Management International Inc ....E 954 763-8811
Fort Lauderdale *(G-4110)*
Maupin House Publishing Inc ....G 800 524-0634
Gainesville *(G-4956)*
Netexpressusa Inc ....G 888 575-1245
Fort Myers *(G-4545)*
New World Publications Inc ....G 904 737-6558
Jacksonville *(G-6630)*
Printing For A Cause LLC ....E 786 496-0637
Saint Petersburg *(G-15889)*
Pro Publishing Inc ....G 954 888-7726
Southwest Ranches *(G-16840)*
Reliance Media Inc ....G 505 243-1821
Apopka *(G-179)*
Rourke Educational Media LLC ....E 772 234-6001
Vero Beach *(G-18660)*
Santillana USA Pubg Co Inc ....D 305 591-9522
Miami *(G-10303)*
Senda De Vida Publishers ....E 305 262-2627
Miami *(G-10323)*
Shellie Blum LLC ....G 863 439-3060
Lake Wales *(G-7519)*
Spanish House Inc ....E 305 503-1191
Medley *(G-8728)*
Taylor & Francis Group LLC ....C 561 994-0555
Boca Raton *(G-742)*
Twinlab Corporation ....B 800 645-5626
Boca Raton *(G-761)*
Two Little Fishies Inc ....G 305 623-7695
Miami *(G-10517)*
Write Stuff Enterprises LLC ....E 954 462-6657
Fort Lauderdale *(G-4329)*
Zondervan Corporation LLC ....G 616 698-3437
Miami *(G-10632)*

PUBLISHERS: Catalogs

Davison Publishing Company LLC ....G 407 380-8900
Orlando *(G-12656)*

PUBLISHERS: Directories, NEC

ED Publications Inc ....F 727 726-3592
Clearwater *(G-1663)*
Gulf Publishing Company Inc ....F 727 596-2863
Largo *(G-7968)*
Homes Magazine Inc ....F 239 334-7168
Fort Myers *(G-4484)*
Yp Advrtising Pubg LLC Not LLC ....D 321 956-5400
Melbourne *(G-8978)*

PUBLISHERS: Guides

Sun Publications Florida Inc ....D 321 402-0257
Kissimmee *(G-7299)*
Waterford Press Inc ....E 727 812-0140
Safety Harbor *(G-15508)*
Waterford Publishing Group LLC ....F 727 812-0140
Safety Harbor *(G-15509)*

PUBLISHERS: Magazines, No Printing

3522091611 ....F 352 671-1909
Newberry *(G-11548)*
A & A Publishing Corp ....E 561 982-8960
Boca Raton *(G-395)*
Action Weekly Corp ....G 561 586-8699
West Palm Beach *(G-18789)*
American Accounting Assn ....E 941 921-7747
Lakewood Ranch *(G-7836)*
American Welding Society Inc ....D 305 443-9353
Doral *(G-3247)*
Around House Publishing Inc ....F 561 969-7412
West Palm Beach *(G-18802)*
Back To Godhead Inc ....F 386 462-0481
Alachua *(G-8)*
Betrock Information Systems ....E 954 981-2821
Cooper City *(G-2110)*
Blackfist Magazine LLC ....F 904 864-8695
Miami *(G-9255)*
Boat International Media Inc ....G 954 522-2628
Fort Lauderdale *(G-3864)*
Bocadelray Life Magazine ....G 954 421-9797
Coconut Creek *(G-2071)*
Bonnier Corporation ....G 954 830-4460
Fort Lauderdale *(G-3866)*
Bonnier Corporation ....C 407 628-4802
Winter Park *(G-19383)*
Brooklands New Media LLC ....G 305 901-9674
Miami Beach *(G-10648)*
CJ Publishers Inc ....F 727 521-6277
Pinellas Park *(G-14339)*
Coastal Communications Corp ....F 561 989-0600
Boca Raton *(G-486)*
Conric Holdings LLC ....F 239 690-9840
Fort Myers *(G-4408)*
Constructconnect Inc ....C 772 770-6003
Vero Beach *(G-18613)*
Country Club Concierge Mag Inc ....G 904 223-0204
Ponte Vedra Beach *(G-14938)*
Desh-Videsh Media Group Inc ....F 954 784-8100
Tamarac *(G-17354)*
Direct Response Publication ....F 561 620-3010
Boca Raton *(G-503)*
Distribuidora Continental SA ....F 305 374-4474
Virginia Gardens *(G-18687)*
Diversityinc Media LLC ....F 973 494-0539
Palm Beach *(G-13553)*
Dolphin/Curtis Publishing Co ....G 305 594-0508
Miami Springs *(G-10890)*
Dupont Publishing Inc ....D 727 573-9339
Clearwater *(G-1661)*
Ebella Magazine ....G 239 431-7231
Naples *(G-11234)*
Et Publishing International ....D 305 871-6400
Virginia Gardens *(G-18689)*
Florida Bid Reporting Service ....F 850 539-7522
Tallahassee *(G-17252)*
Florida Design Inc ....E 561 997-1660
Boca Raton *(G-531)*
Florida Eqine Publications Inc ....F 352 732-8686
Ocala *(G-11945)*
Florida Family Magazine ....G 941 922-5437
Sarasota *(G-16434)*
Florida Homes Magazine ....G 941 227-7331
Sarasota *(G-16436)*
Florida Media Inc ....F 407 816-9596
Lake Mary *(G-7418)*
Floridas Hotspots Publishing ....F 954 928-1862
Oakland Park *(G-11806)*
Grandstand Publishing LLC ....G 847 491-6440
Orlando *(G-12787)*
Gulfshore Business ....G 239 887-1930
Naples *(G-11272)*
Gulfstream Media Group Inc ....E 954 462-4488
Fort Lauderdale *(G-4035)*
Haute Living Inc ....E 305 798-1373
Miami *(G-9689)*
Home and Design Magazine ....G 239 598-4826
Naples *(G-11280)*
Home Improver Inc ....F 239 549-6901
Cape Coral *(G-1435)*
Homemag Inc ....F 239 549-6960
Cape Coral *(G-1436)*
Howard Publications Inc ....G 904 355-2601
Jacksonville *(G-6480)*
IMS Publishing Inc ....G 954 761-8777
Fort Lauderdale *(G-4056)*
Interior Design ....F 646 805-0200
Boca Raton *(G-568)*
Interior Dsign Media Group LLC ....D 561 750-0151
Boca Raton *(G-569)*
International Guidelines Ctr ....G 407 878-7606
Lake Mary *(G-7425)*
Jazziz Magazine Inc ....E 561 893-6868
Boca Raton *(G-578)*

PRODUCT

Jes Publishing Corp E 561 997-8683
Boca Raton *(G-580)*

Judicial & ADM RES Assoc F 850 222-3171
Tallahassee *(G-17285)*

Kenney Communications Inc F 407 859-3113
Orlando *(G-12869)*

L C Clark Publishing Inc F 561 627-3393
Palm Beach Gardens *(G-13601)*

Lakeside Publishing Co LLC G 847 491-6440
Palm Beach Gardens *(G-13602)*

Latin Amrcn Fncl Pblctions Inc F 305 416-5261
Miami *(G-9868)*

Latin Press Inc F 305 285-3133
Miami *(G-9870)*

Los Latinos Magazine Inc F 305 882-9074
Hialeah *(G-5488)*

Lrp Publications Inc C 215 784-0860
Palm Beach Gardens *(G-13608)*

Magazine Morris G 561 963-0231
Lake Worth *(G-7566)*

Magic Magazine G 407 420-6080
Orlando *(G-12945)*

Mailbox Publishing Inc E 772 334-2121
Stuart *(G-16972)*

Maritime Executive LLC G 954 848-9955
Plantation *(G-14531)*

Mary Lake Life Mag Inc G 407 324-2644
Lake Mary *(G-7431)*

Mary Lake Life Magazine Inc F 407 324-2644
Lake Mary *(G-7432)*

Meister Media Worldwide Inc G 407 539-6552
Winter Park *(G-19422)*

Mercantile Two G 941 388-0059
Sarasota *(G-16506)*

Miles Partnership II LLC C 941 342-2300
Sarasota *(G-16509)*

Mio Publication Inc G 941 351-2411
Sarasota *(G-16257)*

More Woodturning Magazine G 508 838-1933
Bradenton *(G-1081)*

Motorsport Marketing Inc E 386 239-0523
Holly Hill *(G-5760)*

Moulton Publications Inc G 772 234-8871
Vero Beach *(G-18645)*

Netexpressusa Inc G 888 575-1245
Fort Myers *(G-4545)*

Nostalgic America Inc F 561 585-1724
Boca Raton *(G-649)*

Ocala Magazine E 352 622-2995
Ocala *(G-12010)*

Ocala Publication Incorported E 352 732-0073
Ocala *(G-12015)*

On-Board Media Inc D 305 673-0400
Doral *(G-3450)*

Open House Magazine Inc G 305 576-6011
Miami *(G-10109)*

Oxendine Publishing Inc E 352 373-6907
Gainesville *(G-4978)*

Oxpecker Enterprise Inc G 305 253-5301
Miami *(G-10124)*

PA C Publishing Inc G 813 814-1505
Oldsmar *(G-12255)*

Pageantry Tlent Entrmt Svcs In G 407 260-2262
Longwood *(G-8319)*

Palm Beach Liquidation Company E 561 659-0210
West Palm Beach *(G-18984)*

Palm Beach Media Group Inc G 239 434-6966
Naples *(G-11355)*

Passport Pblcations Media Corp E 561 615-3900
West Palm Beach *(G-18988)*

Patterson Publishing F 863 701-2707
Lakeland *(G-7763)*

PCI Communications Inc G 941 729-5202
Ellenton *(G-3654)*

Phoenix Media Network Inc E 561 994-1118
Boca Raton *(G-664)*

Pinstripe Magazine LLC G 201 310-5398
Naples *(G-11366)*

Polo Players Edition G 561 968-5208
Lake Worth *(G-7581)*

Quanturo Publishing Inc E 305 373-3700
Miami *(G-10223)*

R T Publishing Inc G 904 886-4919
Jacksonville *(G-6702)*

Recommend Travel Publications F 305 826-4763
Miami Lakes *(G-10849)*

Rowland Publishing Inc E 850 878-0554
Tallahassee *(G-17319)*

Rwla Enterprises LLC F 772 334-1248
Stuart *(G-17005)*

Sandow Media LLC F 646 805-0200
Boca Raton *(G-699)*

Sandow Media LLC D 561 961-7749
Boca Raton *(G-700)*

Sandy Lender Inc F 239 272-8613
Cape Coral *(G-1464)*

Sarasota Cottages LLC G 941 724-2245
Sarasota *(G-16577)*

Seabreeze Communications Group F 239 278-4222
Fort Myers *(G-4603)*

See Coastal Media LLC G 386 562-2213
Daytona Beach *(G-2711)*

South Florida Parenting D 954 747-3050
Tamarac *(G-17369)*

South Florida Sport Fishing F 954 942-7261
Fort Lauderdale *(G-4247)*

South Florida Sport Fishing F 954 942-7261
Fort Lauderdale *(G-4248)*

Southern Boating & Yachting E 954 522-5515
Pompano Beach *(G-14862)*

Spanish Peri & Bk Sls Inc D 305 592-3919
Doral *(G-3508)*

Special Editionspublishing G 407 862-7737
Altamonte Springs *(G-76)*

Sport America Magazine G 727 391-3099
Madeira Beach *(G-8448)*

Stern Bloom Media Inc E 954 454-8522
Miami *(G-10414)*

Stream Line Publishing Inc F 561 655-8778
Boca Raton *(G-732)*

Street Elements Magazine Inc F 813 935-5894
Tampa *(G-18135)*

Stuart Magazine F 954 332-3214
Fort Lauderdale *(G-4263)*

Stuart Magazine G 772 207-7895
Port Saint Lucie *(G-15149)*

Swapper G 850 973-6653
Madison *(G-8454)*

T T Publications Inc E 407 327-4817
Winter Springs *(G-19486)*

Tampa Bay Publications Inc E 727 791-4800
Clearwater *(G-1903)*

Teeze International Inc G 727 726-3592
Clearwater *(G-1913)*

Time Adjusters Conference Inc G 386 274-4210
Port Orange *(G-15039)*

Tm Marketing Group LLC G 954 848-9955
Fort Lauderdale *(G-4285)*

Toti Media Inc G 239 472-0205
Sanibel *(G-16150)*

Trafalger Communications Inc E 941 365-7702
Sarasota *(G-16624)*

Treasure Cast Prenting Mag Inc F 772 672-8588
Port Saint Lucie *(G-15155)*

Trend Magazines Inc E 727 821-5800
Saint Petersburg *(G-15943)*

Turnstile Publishing Company D 407 563-7000
Orlando *(G-13284)*

Valleymedia Inc E 510 565-7559
Fort Lauderdale *(G-4303)*

Venice Quarters Inc E 954 318-3483
Wilton Manors *(G-19221)*

Weiss Group LLC C 561 627-3300
Jupiter *(G-7145)*

Weiss Research Inc C 561 627-3300
Jupiter *(G-7146)*

White Publishing Co Inc F 904 389-3622
Jacksonville *(G-6919)*

Woods n Water Magazine Inc G 850 584-3824
Perry *(G-14320)*

Working Mother Media Inc D 212 351-6400
Winter Park *(G-19461)*

World Publications Inc G 407 628-4802
Winter Park *(G-19462)*

Worldwide Challenge Magazine E 407 826-2390
Orlando *(G-13331)*

Worth Intl Media Group E 305 826-4763
Miami Lakes *(G-10881)*

Write Stuff Enterprises LLC E 954 462-6657
Fort Lauderdale *(G-4329)*

PUBLISHERS: Maps

Map & Globe LLC F 407 898-0757
Maitland *(G-8473)*

Streetwise Maps Inc F 941 358-1956
Sarasota *(G-16606)*

PUBLISHERS: Miscellaneous

2klife LLC G 954 316-9866
Pompano Beach *(G-14569)*

3lions Publishing Inc G 727 744-8683
Palm Harbor *(G-13715)*

4 Horsemen Publications Inc G 727 698-0476
Clearwater *(G-1559)*

4biddenknowledge Inc G 954 245-0086
Weston *(G-19099)*

A Cappela Publishing Inc F 941 351-2050
Sarasota *(G-16329)*

A2f LLC G 305 984-9205
Miami *(G-9048)*

ABC Book Publishers Inc G 904 230-0737
Jacksonville *(G-6935)*

Academic Publication Svcs Inc G 941 925-4474
Sarasota *(G-16332)*

AGM Publishing Inc G 727 934-9993
Holiday *(G-5733)*

Akashic Spirit Publishing LLC G 850 974-4944
Defuniak Springs *(G-2939)*

Aligned Global G 305 731-2117
Miami *(G-9107)*

Aluminum Express Inc G 954 868-2628
Hialeah *(G-5284)*

Amazin Publishing Inc G 954 445-6303
Orlando *(G-12465)*

American Classifieds F 850 747-1155
Panama City *(G-13863)*

AMI Celebrity Publications LLC C 561 997-7733
Boca Raton *(G-424)*

AMI Digital Inc B 561 997-7733
Boca Raton *(G-425)*

Anaiah Press LLC G 727 692-0025
Saint Petersburg *(G-15700)*

Angery American Enterprises G 352 669-2198
Umatilla *(G-18495)*

Arsenex Inc G 407 256-3490
Oviedo *(G-13412)*

Ascendants Publishing LLC G 813 391-2745
Gainesville *(G-4878)*

Atlantic Publishing Group Inc D 352 622-6220
Ocala *(G-11881)*

Attraction Center Pubg LLC G 814 422-5683
Saint Petersburg *(G-15715)*

B&C Publishing Inc G 305 385-8216
Miami *(G-9210)*

Banyan Hill G 561 455-9045
Delray Beach *(G-3049)*

Barbes Publishing Inc F 904 992-9945
Jacksonville *(G-6194)*

Beano Publishing LLC F 954 689-8339
Weston *(G-19110)*

Belleaire Press LLC G 352 377-1870
Gainesville *(G-4885)*

Belocal Pro Inc G 727 379-9576
Spring Hill *(G-16870)*

Bent Pine Publishing Corp G 772 708-0490
Port Saint Lucie *(G-15091)*

Best Publishing Company F 561 776-6066
North Palm Beach *(G-11719)*

Bevel Express & Tops Lac G 813 887-3174
Tampa *(G-17466)*

Bigg Publishing G 772 563-0425
Vero Beach *(G-18599)*

Bioenergetics Press F 386 462-5155
Alachua *(G-9)*

Birdie Publishing LLC G 561 332-1826
Delray Beach *(G-3050)*

Black Label Group LLC G 407 917-1255
Orlando *(G-12521)*

Black Tie Publishing Inc G 954 472-6003
Plantation *(G-14498)*

Bluetoad Inc E 407 992-8744
Gotha *(G-5040)*

Bonita Daily News E 239 213-6060
Naples *(G-11191)*

Books-A-Million Inc G 813 571-2062
Brandon *(G-1152)*

Boyle Publications Inc G 941 255-0187
Port Charlotte *(G-14966)*

Breeze Corporation C 239 765-0400
Fort Myers Beach *(G-4660)*

Breeze Corporation G 239 425-8860
Fort Myers *(G-4381)*

Brown Dog Publishing Inc G 904 262-2114
Jacksonville *(G-6238)*

Bruno Publishing G 561 333-7682
Wellington *(G-18712)*

Builders Publishing Group LLC G 407 539-2938
Maitland *(G-8461)*

Butterfield Press G 813 634-3940
Sun City Center *(G-17070)*

By Invitation Only Pubg Inc ....G....... 954 922-7100
Dania *(G-2442)*
Bythenet Publishing ....G....... 407 691-2806
Winter Park *(G-19385)*
Caduceus International Pubg ....F 866 280-2900
Gainesville *(G-4891)*
Calkins Harbor Publishing Inc ....G....... 561 906-4642
North Palm Beach *(G-11720)*
Campus Publications Inc ....G....... 941 780-1326
Sarasota *(G-16379)*
Canterbury House Publishing ....G....... 941 312-6912
Sarasota *(G-16185)*
Capital Publishing Inc ....G....... 813 286-8444
Spring Hill *(G-16849)*
Carbon Press LLC ....F 239 689-4406
Fort Myers *(G-4387)*
Care and Love Publishing LLC ....G....... 254 462-9134
Tampa *(G-17508)*
Casey Research LLC ....F 561 455-9043
Delray Beach *(G-3056)*
Casey Weston LLC ....G....... 239 229-8375
Naples *(G-11200)*
Castle Publishing LLC ....G....... 904 794-0112
Saint Augustine *(G-15527)*
Catskill Express LLC ....G....... 954 784-5151
Pompano Beach *(G-14631)*
Cda Ventures Inc ....F 305 428-2857
Miami Beach *(G-10653)*
Central Florida Publishing Inc ....F 407 323-5204
Sanford *(G-16010)*
Chelle Walton Publishing ....G....... 239 699-4754
Sanibel *(G-16144)*
Christian Publishing Inc ....G....... 813 920-5664
Odessa *(G-12110)*
Citrus County Life Magazine ....G....... 352 341-4769
Lecanto *(G-8132)*
City Debate Publishing Company ....G....... 305 868-1161
Miami Beach *(G-10656)*
City News Publishing LLC ....G....... 305 332-9101
Boca Raton *(G-480)*
City Publications South FL ....G....... 305 495-3311
Virginia Gardens *(G-18685)*
CJ Publishers Inc ....F 727 521-6277
Pinellas Park *(G-14339)*
Classic Mail Corp ....G....... 386 290-0309
Daytona Beach *(G-2642)*
Classics Reborn Publishing LLC ....G....... 727 232-6739
New Port Richey *(G-11487)*
Collectors International Pubg ....G....... 561 845-7156
Palm Beach *(G-13551)*
Color Press Corp ....G....... 786 621-8491
Miami *(G-9380)*
Common Sense Publishing LLC ....C....... 561 510-1713
Delray Beach *(G-3063)*
Compass Publishing LLC ....G....... 407 328-0970
Sanford *(G-16020)*
Competitor Group Inc ....G....... 858 450-6510
Tampa *(G-17549)*
Connectpress Ltd ....F 505 629-0695
Sarasota *(G-16392)*
Consumer Source Inc ....G....... 407 888-0745
Orlando *(G-12615)*
Convivium Press Inc ....G....... 305 889-0489
Miami *(G-9397)*
Counter Top Publishing Inc ....G....... 941 321-5811
Bradenton *(G-1024)*
Countryside Publishing Co Inc ....F 813 925-0195
Oldsmar *(G-12219)*
County of Orange ....G....... 407 649-0076
Orlando *(G-12623)*
Creative Routes Press ....G....... 561 213-9800
Delray Beach *(G-3066)*
Croft Publishing Inc ....G....... 352 473-3159
Keystone Heights *(G-7206)*
Cuban Press ....G....... 305 304-9419
Miami *(G-9417)*
Cycling Quarterly LLC ....E 786 367-2497
Fort Lauderdale *(G-3926)*
David Jacobs Pubg Group LLC ....F 813 321-4119
Tampa *(G-17591)*
Davison Publishing Co Inc ....G....... 407 657-3710
Orlando *(G-12655)*
Digital Color Publications LLC ....G....... 813 886-0065
Tampa *(G-17606)*
Digital Press ....G....... 407 421-3131
Orlando *(G-12674)*
Digital Publishing of Florida ....G....... 813 749-8640
Oldsmar *(G-12221)*
Dion Money Management LLC ....F 413 458-4700
Naples *(G-11227)*
Diversified Pubg & Design ....G....... 239 598-4826
Naples *(G-11229)*
Dolph Map Company Inc ....F 954 763-4732
Oakland Park *(G-11799)*
Double R Publishing ....G....... 305 525-3573
Boynton Beach *(G-898)*
Down Shift LLC ....G....... 813 431-2389
Lutz *(G-8381)*
Dreamspinner Press LLC ....F 800 970-3759
Tallahassee *(G-17243)*
Educational Pubg Centl Fla LLC ....G....... 407 234-4401
Mount Dora *(G-11101)*
Empyre Music Publishing LLC ....G....... 813 873-7700
Tampa *(G-17638)*
Epigram Publishing Co ....G....... 941 391-5296
Port Charlotte *(G-14979)*
Essential Publishing Group LLC ....G....... 410 440-5777
Boca Raton *(G-522)*
Essential Publishing Group LLC ....E 561 570-7165
Greenacres *(G-5080)*
Everett Pubg - Tampa Bay LLC ....G....... 727 534-3425
New Port Richey *(G-11490)*
Everyday Feminism LLC ....G....... 202 643-1001
Tallahassee *(G-17249)*
Ew Publishing LLC ....G....... 305 358-1100
Fort Lauderdale *(G-3978)*
Ewh Press ....G....... 386 405-5069
Ormond Beach *(G-13369)*
Expert Subjects LLC ....G....... 786 877-8531
Miami *(G-9546)*
Express Care of Tampa Bay ....G....... 813 641-0068
Apollo Beach *(G-103)*
Express Ironing Inc ....G....... 305 261-1072
Miami *(G-9548)*
F L F Corp ....G....... 561 747-7077
Jupiter *(G-7039)*
Fabio Napoleoni Artworks ....G....... 207 952-1561
Orlando *(G-12731)*
Ferrari Express Inc ....E 305 374-5003
Miami *(G-9563)*
Florida Health Publishing LLC ....G....... 847 506-2925
Cape Coral *(G-1424)*
Florida Living LLC ....G....... 352 556-9691
Brooksville *(G-1229)*
Floyd Publications Inc ....G....... 813 707-8783
Plant City *(G-14431)*
Focal Point Publishing LLC ....G....... 877 469-9530
Gainesville *(G-4923)*
Focus Community Publications ....G....... 407 892-0019
Saint Cloud *(G-15651)*
Foley Publishing LLC ....G....... 908 766-6006
Vero Beach *(G-18621)*
Forever Current Music LLC ....G....... 213 458-2880
Boca Raton *(G-537)*
Forum Publishing Group Inc ....D....... 954 596-5650
Deerfield Beach *(G-2828)*
Four WD Consulting & Pubg LLC ....G....... 216 533-2203
West Palm Beach *(G-18881)*
Fresh Press ....F 305 942-8571
North Miami Beach *(G-11678)*
Frog Publications Inc ....G....... 352 588-2082
San Antonio *(G-15972)*
Front Line Publishing Inc ....G....... 813 480-8033
Brandon *(G-1160)*
G S Printers Inc ....G....... 305 931-2755
Fort Lauderdale *(G-4016)*
Galan Express Inc ....G....... 305 438-8738
Miami *(G-9610)*
Gatehouse Media LLC ....F 863 401-6900
Winter Haven *(G-19325)*
General Catagraphy Inc ....G....... 561 455-4398
Boynton Beach *(G-910)*
Genie Publishing ....G....... 863 937-7769
Lakeland *(G-7697)*
GLM Publishing LLC ....G....... 561 409-7696
Boca Raton *(G-545)*
Global Media Press Corp ....G....... 813 857-5898
Tampa *(G-17716)*
Global Publishing Inc ....E 904 262-0491
Jacksonville *(G-6437)*
Gnd Publishing LLC ....G....... 561 625-1242
Palm Beach Gardens *(G-13593)*
Good Life Publishing Inc ....G....... 352 317-6903
Archer *(G-209)*
Grapevine Usa Inc ....G....... 786 510-9122
Fort Lauderdale *(G-4025)*
Great Escape Publishing ....G....... 561 860-8266
Delray Beach *(G-3087)*
Great Hse Mdia Group of Pbls I ....F 407 779-3846
Orlando *(G-12788)*
Great Virtualworks LLC ....F 800 606-6518
Fort Lauderdale *(G-4028)*
Guerrilla Press ....G....... 352 281-7420
Gainesville *(G-4934)*
Gulf Shore Press LLC ....G....... 727 641-2920
Naples *(G-11271)*
Halldale Media Inc ....E 407 322-5605
Lake Mary *(G-7420)*
Harvest Day Press ....G....... 727 822-4961
Saint Petersburg *(G-15804)*
Health Communications Inc ....D....... 954 360-0909
Deerfield Beach *(G-2836)*
Helou Regino Publisher LLC ....G....... 407 370-7300
Orlando *(G-12797)*
Henjaty Publishing Co ....G....... 305 633-9993
Miami *(G-9701)*
Hmh Publishing Co Inc ....D....... 617 351-5000
Orlando *(G-12805)*
Hogan Assessment Systems Inc ....G....... 904 992-0302
Jacksonville *(G-6473)*
Homes Devoted Inc ....G....... 321 473-8567
Melbourne *(G-8845)*
Hoot/Wisdom Music Pubg LLC ....G....... 561 297-3205
Boca Raton *(G-559)*
Hot Off Press ....G....... 386 238-8700
South Daytona *(G-16802)*
Howard Scripts Inc ....G....... 561 746-5111
Jupiter *(G-7054)*
I M I Publishing Inc ....G....... 615 957-9288
Naples *(G-11283)*
Igs LLC ....G....... 800 419-3014
Homestead *(G-5970)*
IMI Publishing Inc ....G....... 239 529-5081
Naples *(G-11284)*
Impact Promotional Pubg LLC ....F 727 736-6228
Dunedin *(G-3581)*
In Press Marketing ....G....... 954 659-9332
Weston *(G-19140)*
Indigo River Publishing ....G....... 256 404-5884
Pensacola *(G-14177)*
Ink Publishing Corporation ....F 786 206-9867
Coral Gables *(G-2158)*
Ink Publishing Corporation ....E 786 482-2065
Coral Gables *(G-2159)*
Insanejournalcom ....G....... 561 315-9311
West Palm Beach *(G-18906)*
Instrument Publication ....G....... 352 542-7716
Old Town *(G-12198)*
Irving Publications LLC ....F 352 219-4688
Gainesville *(G-4947)*
Island Media Publishing LLC ....G....... 904 556-3002
Fernandina Beach *(G-3739)*
It Had To Be Told Pubg LLC ....G....... 813 810-5961
Tampa *(G-17795)*
J Ross Publishing Inc ....G....... 954 727-9333
Plantation *(G-14525)*
Jazzy Dogs Publishing ....G....... 941 726-0343
Nokomis *(G-11583)*
JC 323 Media Pubg Group Inc ....G....... 772 940-3510
Lake Worth *(G-7560)*
JC Publishers LLC ....G....... 863 875-6071
Winter Haven *(G-19331)*
Jeanius Publishing LLC ....G....... 239 560-5229
Lehigh Acres *(G-8193)*
Jencor Publishing Inc ....G....... 772 589-5578
Sebastian *(G-16664)*
Jita Press Inc ....G....... 850 329-0884
Tallahassee *(G-17283)*
Kameleon Press Inc ....G....... 850 566-2522
Tallahassee *(G-17286)*
Kenney Communications Inc ....F 407 859-3113
Orlando *(G-12869)*
Korangy Publishing Inc ....D....... 786 334-5052
Miami *(G-9829)*
Krieger Publishing Co Inc ....F 321 724-9542
Malabar *(G-8493)*
Ksr Publishing Inc ....E 941 388-7050
Sarasota *(G-16484)*
La Ciudad En Sus Manos LLC ....G....... 813 770-4973
Altamonte Springs *(G-52)*
Landslide Publishing Inc ....G....... 561 392-4717
Boca Raton *(G-595)*
Latin Goddess Press Inc ....G....... 917 703-1356
Winter Springs *(G-19477)*
Lawrenceville Press Inc ....F 609 737-1148
Lantana *(G-7875)*
Le Publications Inc ....F 954 766-8433
Fort Lauderdale *(G-4098)*
Legacy Publishing Group ....G....... 407 290-8414
Orlando *(G-12902)*

PRODUCT

Less Frtnate Mus Pubg Ltd Lblt..........G....... 786 663-0385
Miami *(G-9886)*
Lifes A Bch Publications LLC..........G....... 850 650-2780
Destin *(G-3196)*
Lifestyle Publications LLC..........G....... 954 217-1165
Weston *(G-19147)*
Light Age Press Inc..........G....... 352 242-4530
Clermont *(G-1968)*
Lighthouse Express World Inc..........G....... 754 210-6196
Hollywood *(G-5860)*
Limelight Publishing LLC..........G....... 727 384-5999
Saint Petersburg *(G-15841)*
Lioness Publication House..........G....... 561 670-4645
West Palm Beach *(G-18932)*
Live Ultimate Inc..........G....... 305 532-6882
Miami Beach *(G-10688)*
Living Well Spending Less Inc..........G....... 941 209-1811
Punta Gorda *(G-15212)*
Lost Key Publishing LLC..........G....... 850 380-6680
Pensacola *(G-14197)*
LTSC LLC..........G....... 863 678-0011
Lake Wales *(G-7515)*
M30 Freedom Inc..........G....... 813 433-1776
Land O Lakes *(G-7860)*
Mama Bear Lawn Care Press..........G....... 863 517-5322
Clewiston *(G-1983)*
Management International Inc..........E....... 954 763-8811
Fort Lauderdale *(G-4110)*
Manatee Media Inc..........F....... 813 909-2800
Land O Lakes *(G-7861)*
Mark Walters LLC..........G....... 727 742-3091
Saint Petersburg *(G-15850)*
Mark Wayne Adams Inc..........G....... 407 756-5862
Longwood *(G-8309)*
Maverick Press Inc..........G....... 239 331-8379
Naples *(G-11323)*
Mdz Publishing..........G....... 954 680-9956
Cooper City *(G-2114)*
Media Creations Inc..........G....... 954 726-0902
Fort Lauderdale *(G-4115)*
Media Edge Communications LLC..........G....... 352 313-6700
Gainesville *(G-4959)*
Messner Publications Inc..........E....... 863 318-1595
Winter Haven *(G-19337)*
Miami Publicity LLC..........G....... 561 215-5189
Miami *(G-10006)*
Milenium Publishing LLC..........G....... 786 573-9974
Miami *(G-10020)*
Millionaire Publishing LLC..........G....... 305 763-8184
Miami Beach *(G-10693)*
Milpro Publications LLC..........G....... 321 613-2250
Melbourne *(G-8890)*
Miramar Publishing Inc..........G....... 305 695-0639
Miami Beach *(G-10694)*
Mobile Rving..........G....... 954 870-7095
Deerfield Beach *(G-2875)*
Msquared Publishing..........G....... 786 399-0607
Miami *(G-10050)*
My Wild Life Press LLC..........G....... 515 203-9728
Delray Beach *(G-3111)*
Nenem Inc..........G....... 561 389-2010
West Palm Beach *(G-18961)*
New Pelican LLC..........G....... 954 783-8700
Pompano Beach *(G-14773)*
New York Deli Express..........G....... 954 572-1442
Lauderhill *(G-8117)*
New You Media LLC..........F....... 800 606-6518
Fort Lauderdale *(G-4139)*
Newsmax Media Inc..........F....... 561 686-1165
West Palm Beach *(G-18964)*
Nielsen Publishing..........G....... 941 539-7579
Nokomis *(G-11586)*
Nwh Publishing Llc..........F....... 904 217-3911
Saint Augustine *(G-15579)*
Oceanvista Publishing LLC..........G....... 561 547-5730
West Palm Beach *(G-18969)*
Olmstead Publishing LLC..........G....... 954 559-0192
Apopka *(G-167)*
Omega Publishing..........G....... 727 815-0402
New Port Richey *(G-11504)*
Online German Publisher LLC..........G....... 239 344-8953
Cape Coral *(G-1453)*
Open Palm Press Inc..........G....... 813 870-3839
Tampa *(G-17958)*
Orlando Branding Agency LLC..........F....... 407 692-8868
Oviedo *(G-13451)*
Osborn Publications..........G....... 305 899-0501
North Miami *(G-11649)*
Our Florida Publishing..........G....... 904 859-2805
Sunrise *(G-17155)*

Palm Beach Newspapers Inc..........D....... 561 820-3800
West Palm Beach *(G-18985)*
Palm Pheon Music Publishing..........G....... 305 705-2405
North Miami Beach *(G-11696)*
Pandia Press Inc..........F....... 352 789-8156
Mount Dora *(G-11109)*
Panoff Publishing Inc..........D....... 954 377-7777
Fort Lauderdale *(G-4155)*
Paradise Publishing Group Inc..........G....... 941 306-2166
Bradenton *(G-1094)*
Paramount Digital Pubg LLC..........F....... 813 489-5029
Brandon *(G-1169)*
Paramount Marketing Inc..........F....... 352 608-8801
Ocala *(G-12022)*
Parkside Publishing LLC..........G....... 888 386-1115
Delray Beach *(G-3113)*
Patriot Publishing USA LLC..........G....... 904 217-7632
Saint Augustine *(G-15585)*
Patterson Publishing LLC..........G....... 863 701-2707
Lakeland *(G-7764)*
Paxen Publishing LLC..........F....... 321 425-3030
Indian Harbour Beach *(G-6065)*
Pelican Bay Publishing..........G....... 954 610-7787
Coral Springs *(G-2302)*
Peniel Inc..........G....... 305 594-2739
Miramar *(G-11028)*
Peppertree Press LLC..........G....... 941 922-2662
Sarasota *(G-16541)*
Pfa Publishing..........F....... 727 512-5814
Gulfport *(G-5136)*
Phoenix Publications..........F....... 954 609-7586
Pompano Beach *(G-14792)*
Pike Pole Press..........G....... 407 474-7453
Sanford *(G-16102)*
Piloto Music Publisher Corp..........G....... 321 348-0638
Miami *(G-10164)*
Pink Inc Publishing..........G....... 904 834-3118
Jacksonville Beach *(G-6954)*
Plattsco Inc..........G....... 954 744-4099
Sunrise *(G-17158)*
Positive Note Network..........G....... 712 259-1381
Fort Walton Beach *(G-4823)*
Post Mortem Publications Inc..........G....... 352 429-1133
Groveland *(G-5105)*
Precision Press LLC..........G....... 386 872-1639
Daytona Beach *(G-2697)*
Preferred Pcks Pblications Inc..........F....... 954 377-8000
Sunrise *(G-17160)*
Premier Publishing Inc..........G....... 561 394-9066
Boca Raton *(G-673)*
Premium Latin Music Inc..........F....... 212 873-1472
Miami *(G-10185)*
Press Beauty Facial Bar..........G....... 561 281-0631
Lake Worth *(G-7582)*
Press Gourmet Sandwiches..........G....... 954 440-0422
Fort Lauderdale *(G-4179)*
Prism Music Inc..........G....... 954 718-6850
Tamarac *(G-17365)*
Prs Taco Place..........G....... 407 440-2803
Orlando *(G-13098)*
Psychlgcal Assssment Rsrces In..........D....... 813 968-3003
Lutz *(G-8413)*
Publishers Crcltion Flfllment..........E....... 877 723-6668
Pensacola *(G-14242)*
Publishers Direct Choice LLC..........G....... 305 264-5998
Miami *(G-10213)*
Publishers Prmotional Svcs Inc..........G....... 303 431-4080
Clearwater *(G-1853)*
Publishers Whse Sanibel Island..........G....... 239 267-6151
Fort Myers *(G-4575)*
Publishing Research Inc..........G....... 954 921-4026
North Miami *(G-11651)*
Quad Intl Incorporated..........D....... 305 662-5959
Doral *(G-3474)*
Quality Life Publishing Co..........G....... 239 513-9907
Naples *(G-11379)*
Quick Press..........G....... 305 418-8744
Doral *(G-3476)*
Quickseries Publishing Inc..........D....... 954 584-1606
Fort Lauderdale *(G-4197)*
Rafi Publications LLC..........G....... 954 384-4166
Weston *(G-19163)*
Rally Point Publications LLC..........F....... 863 221-6304
Winter Haven *(G-19351)*
Readers Drect Publications Inc..........G....... 727 643-8616
Seminole *(G-16759)*
Red Brick Publishing LLC..........G....... 718 208-3600
Boynton Beach *(G-954)*
Redquin Publishing LLC..........G....... 813 314-4500
Tampa *(G-18043)*

Reflex Pubg Eric Reflex Co..........G....... 813 314-8810
Tampa *(G-18044)*
Robert Gomes Publishing Inc..........G....... 941 637-6080
Punta Gorda *(G-15229)*
Rosebandits LLC..........G....... 305 778-6370
Coral Gables *(G-2191)*
Roselle Publishing..........G....... 813 907-5250
Wesley Chapel *(G-18758)*
Russanos Express LLC..........G....... 772 220-3329
Palm City *(G-13672)*
Safety Compliance Publ Inc..........G....... 844 556-3149
Miramar *(G-11038)*
Sandpaper Publishing Inc..........G....... 850 939-8040
Gulf Breeze *(G-5125)*
Scheduall Scheduall Scheduall..........F....... 954 334-5400
Hollywood *(G-5904)*
SE Smith Llc..........G....... 772 461-0482
Fort Pierce *(G-4744)*
Seahill Press Inc..........G....... 805 845-8636
Leesburg *(G-8170)*
Seal Publishing LLC..........G....... 813 792-5852
Odessa *(G-12149)*
Select Publishing LLC..........G....... 850 464-6477
Santa Rosa Beach *(G-16167)*
Sentinel Cmmnctons News Vntres..........G....... 407 420-5291
Orlando *(G-13173)*
Sentinel Cmmnctons News Vntres..........G....... 352 742-5900
Tavares *(G-18352)*
Serendipity Publishing..........G....... 407 905-5076
Windermere *(G-19243)*
Shoreline Publishing Inc..........G....... 914 500-5456
Parrish *(G-14007)*
Show Publishing LLC..........G....... 239 272-8477
Naples *(G-11399)*
Sigma Press Inc..........F....... 904 264-6006
Orange Park *(G-12405)*
Silly Dandelions Inc..........G....... 727 400-6590
Largo *(G-8053)*
Simon and Baker Inc..........G....... 561 892-0494
Boca Raton *(G-714)*
Simonsclub LLC..........E....... 352 246-3636
Gainesville *(G-4997)*
Sirs Publishing Inc..........D....... 800 521-0600
Boca Raton *(G-718)*
Sony Discos..........G....... 305 420-4540
Miami *(G-10377)*
Southeast Publications USA Inc..........E....... 954 368-4686
Deerfield Beach *(G-2915)*
SP Publications LLC..........G....... 239 595-9040
Miramar Beach *(G-11069)*
Spanish Pubg Ventures Inc..........G....... 305 220-8044
Miami *(G-10396)*
Spanish Publishers LLC..........G....... 305 233-3365
Miami *(G-10397)*
Spikes Press & Printhouse LLC..........G....... 850 438-2293
Pensacola *(G-14270)*
SSE Publications LLC..........F....... 954 835-7616
Sunrise *(G-17178)*
Starewell Publishing LLC..........G....... 561 694-0365
Palm Beach Gardens *(G-13629)*
Steven Press..........G....... 954 434-3694
Cooper City *(G-2117)*
Street Talk America..........G....... 850 547-6186
Bonifay *(G-808)*
Strong Publications LLC..........E....... 813 852-9933
Tampa *(G-18136)*
Sula Too LLC..........G....... 813 368-1628
Tampa *(G-18137)*
Sun Publications Florida Inc..........E....... 863 583-1202
Lakeland *(G-7810)*
Sun-Sentinel Company LLC..........E....... 954 356-4000
Deerfield Beach *(G-2918)*
Sundar Publishing..........G....... 305 335-1930
West Palm Beach *(G-19048)*
Swi Publishing Inc..........F....... 352 538-1438
Gainesville *(G-5006)*
Taylor & Francis Group LLC..........D....... 800 516-0186
Sarasota *(G-16617)*
Taylor Media LLC..........C....... 727 317-5800
Saint Petersburg *(G-15936)*
Telexpress La Musica Inc..........G....... 813 879-1914
Tampa *(G-18182)*
Tightline Publications Inc..........G....... 954 570-7174
Deerfield Beach *(G-2927)*
Total Spcalty Publications LLC..........D....... 813 405-2610
Tampa *(G-18195)*
Tower Publications Inc..........F....... 352 372-5468
Gainesville *(G-5011)*
Toys For Boys Miami LLC..........G....... 786 464-0160
Miami *(G-10497)*

Tracy Publishing LLC ....G.... 561 799-4690
Jupiter (G-7130)
Treasure Coast Publishing Inc ....F.... 772 221-4289
Stuart (G-17038)
Tremonti Project Pubg LLC....F.... 407 217-7140
Windermere (G-19247)
Turtle Publishing Co....G.... 904 568-1484
Jacksonville (G-6872)
TV Publishing....G.... 954 773-6967
West Palm Beach (G-19072)
Unique Hits Music Pubg Inc....G.... 786 525-9525
Doral (G-3536)
United Advg Publications ....G.... 954 730-9700
Fort Lauderdale (G-4294)
Urano Publishing Inc....G.... 305 233-3365
Miami (G-10548)
Vade Mecum Pubg Group LLC ....G.... 813 969-1623
Tampa (G-18231)
Vandeplas Publishing....G.... 407 562-1947
Lake Mary (G-7458)
Vendor Guide Publications Inc....G.... 407 399-0745
The Villages (G-18396)
Vida 18com LLC....G.... 305 935-6657
Miami (G-10583)
Virginia Kelly....G.... 954 415-8056
Vero Beach (G-18680)
Viscomm Publishing LLC....G.... 888 511-0900
Hernando (G-5249)
Vj Publications Inc....G.... 407 461-0707
Longwood (G-8347)
Vlex 1450 LLC....G.... 954 218-5443
Weston (G-19177)
Walking Bird Publications LLC....G.... 954 474-7261
Davie (G-2611)
War Chest River LLC ....G.... 954 736-7704
Miami (G-10595)
Waterhouse Press LLC....G.... 781 975-6191
Destin (G-3210)
Weider Publications LLC....G.... 561 998-7424
Boca Raton (G-788)
Wemerge Inc....G.... 561 305-2070
Coconut Creek (G-2102)
Whats Wrong Publishing Co....G.... 904 388-3494
Jacksonville (G-6916)
White Starr Publishing ....G.... 305 322-5788
Miami (G-10602)
Whiz Bang LLC....G.... 305 296-0160
Key West (G-7204)
Wilcox and Ray Music Pubg Inc....G.... 786 220-1362
Miami (G-10606)
Williams and King Publishers....G.... 407 914-8134
Orlando (G-13325)
Windrusher Inc....G.... 904 614-5196
Ponte Vedra Beach (G-14957)
Windward Communications Inc ....G.... 727 584-7191
Largo (G-8080)
Winter Park Publishing Co LLC....G.... 941 320-6627
Winter Park (G-19460)
Wizard Publications....G.... 808 823-8815
Shalimar (G-16779)
Wohlers Publishing Inc ....G.... 305 289-1644
Marathon (G-8522)
Worldwide Media Svcs Group Inc ....E.... 561 989-1342
Boca Raton (G-793)
Wrongs Without Wremedies LLC ....G.... 850 423-0828
Crestview (G-2362)
Xpress Finance Inc....F.... 407 629-0095
Deltona (G-3182)
Zmh Publishers Inc....G.... 239 404-9259
Naples (G-11464)

PUBLISHERS: Music Book & Sheet Music

Bigg D Entertainment LLC ....G.... 917 204-0292
Weston (G-19112)
Fjh Music Company Inc....E.... 954 382-6061
Davie (G-2525)
Kobalt Music Pubg Amer Inc ....D.... 305 200-5682
Coral Gables (G-2166)
Luna Negra Productions Inc....G.... 786 247-1215
Miami (G-9920)
Yung Payper Chasers Entrmt LLC ....F.... 727 239-2880
Saint Petersburg (G-15969)

PUBLISHERS: Newsletter

Bayou Printing Inc....F.... 850 678-5444
Valparaiso (G-18507)
Builders Notice Corporation....G.... 954 764-1322
Fort Lauderdale (G-3875)
Eastgate Publishing Inc ....G.... 772 286-0101
Hobe Sound (G-5724)
National Subscription Bureau ....E.... 800 508-1311
Naples (G-11343)
Netexpressusa Inc ....G.... 888 575-1245
Fort Myers (G-4545)

PUBLISHERS: Newspaper

Alm Media LLC....G.... 954 468-2600
Fort Lauderdale (G-3809)
Alternative Daily....G.... 561 628-4711
West Palm Beach (G-18794)
ASAP Magazine & Newspaper ....G.... 813 238-0184
Tampa (G-17437)
Aw Publishing....F.... 305 856-7000
Miami (G-9201)
Better Built Group Inc....G.... 850 803-4044
Destin (G-3212)
Bloomingdale Gazette Inc....G.... 813 681-2051
Valrico (G-18516)
Carillon Publishing LLC ....G.... 407 363-0375
Orlando (G-12550)
Cedar Key Beacon ....G.... 352 493-4796
Chiefland (G-1534)
Charisma Media ....D.... 407 333-0600
Lake Mary (G-7405)
Community News Publications ....F.... 813 909-2800
Lutz (G-8378)
Dailys 1113 Shell....F.... 904 608-0219
Ponte Vedra (G-14924)
Distribuidora Continental SA....F.... 305 374-4474
Virginia Gardens (G-18687)
Eco Informativo....G.... 786 362-6789
Miami (G-9499)
El Global News....G.... 305 212-1361
Doral (G-3341)
Europrint Inc....F.... 407 869-9955
Altamonte Springs (G-45)
Fernandina Observer Inc....G.... 904 261-4372
Fernandina Beach (G-3738)
First Class Media Inc ....G.... 561 719-3433
Jupiter (G-7043)
Five Star Sports Tickets ....F.... 440 899-2000
Hallandale Beach (G-5187)
Galactic News Service....G.... 239 431-7470
Naples (G-11257)
Gatehouse Media LLC ....F.... 863 401-6900
Winter Haven (G-19325)
Grass River Publshing ....G.... 954 974-7383
Margate (G-8548)
Hammond Enterprises....G.... 386 575-2402
Leesburg (G-8160)
Horizon Publications Inc....G.... 386 427-1000
New Smyrna Beach (G-11535)
Libre ....G.... 305 267-2000
Miami (G-9889)
Nexstar Broadcasting Inc....F.... 863 683-6531
Lakeland (G-7757)
North Central Advertiser Inc....G.... 386 755-2917
Lake City (G-7370)
Pearcey Enterprise ....G.... 904 235-3096
Tampa (G-17981)
Purple Dove....G.... 904 261-5227
Fernandina Beach (G-3747)
Republic Newspapers Inc ....F.... 352 394-2183
Clermont (G-1972)
Seabreeze Communications Group ....F.... 239 278-4222
Fort Myers (G-4603)
Southeast Publishing Co Inc ....G.... 239 213-1277
Naples (G-11408)
Sweetwater Today Inc....G.... 305 456-4724
Miami (G-10447)
Ter Prints Usa Inc....E.... 305 953-7789
Hollywood (G-5922)
Todays Restaurant News Inc ....G.... 561 620-8888
Boca Raton (G-751)
Treasure Coast Publishing Inc ....F.... 772 221-4289
Stuart (G-17038)
Various Inc....C.... 561 900-3691
Delray Beach (G-3155)
Vista Semanal....G.... 239 263-4785
Naples (G-11452)
Voice Publishing Co Inc ....G.... 305 687-5555
Hialeah (G-5683)
Weekly Schulte Valdes ....E.... 813 221-1154
Tampa (G-18253)
Worldbox Corporation....G.... 305 253-8800
Miami (G-10621)
Worldcity Inc ....G.... 305 441-2244
Coral Gables (G-2207)
Www Tcpalm Company ....F.... 772 287-1550
Stuart (G-17053)

PUBLISHERS: Newspapers, No Printing

A M Coplan Associates ....G.... 904 737-6996
Jacksonville (G-6110)
Aldema Services Inc....G.... 561 860-0693
West Palm Beach (G-18793)
Ali Kamakhi ....F.... 850 405-8591
Tallahassee (G-17216)
American City Bus Journals Inc....G.... 813 873-8225
Tampa (G-17416)
Ayers Publishing Inc ....G.... 352 463-7135
Trenton (G-18480)
Baker County Press Inc....G.... 904 259-2400
Macclenny (G-8442)
Breeze Corporation....C.... 239 765-0400
Fort Myers Beach (G-4660)
Breeze Newspapers....F.... 239 574-1116
Fort Myers (G-4382)
Breeze Newspapers ....G.... 239 574-1110
Cape Coral (G-1396)
Buck Pile Inc....G.... 772 492-1056
Vero Beach (G-18607)
Business Jrnl Publications Inc....E.... 813 342-2472
Tampa (G-17492)
Captiva Current Inc....F.... 239 574-1110
Sanibel (G-16143)
Caxton Newspapers Inc ....E.... 305 538-9700
Miami Beach (G-10652)
Citrus Publishing LLC ....C.... 352 563-6363
Crystal River (G-2373)
Creative Loafing Inc....E.... 813 739-4800
Tampa (G-17565)
Downtown Projects I LLC....G.... 352 226-8288
Gainesville (G-4909)
Florida Catholic Media Inc ....G.... 407 373-0075
Orlando (G-12747)
Florida Sentinel Publishing Co....E.... 813 248-1921
Tampa (G-17688)
Forum Publishing Group Inc ....D.... 954 596-5650
Deerfield Beach (G-2828)
Greenwood Lake News Inc ....F.... 845 477-2575
Hudson (G-6027)
Griffon Graphics Inc....G.... 954 922-1800
Hollywood (G-5833)
Grupo De Diarios America LLC ....G.... 305 577-0094
Miami (G-9679)
Hopkins & Daughter Inc....G.... 941 964-2995
Boca Grande (G-393)
Howard Scripts Inc ....G.... 561 746-5111
Jupiter (G-7054)
La Gaceta Publishing Inc ....F.... 813 248-3921
Tampa (G-17832)
Las Amrcas Mltimedia Group LLC ....E.... 305 633-3341
Miami (G-9861)
Lf Senior Communications Group ....F.... 561 392-4550
Boca Raton (G-602)
Lorken Publications Inc ....G.... 239 395-1213
Sanibel (G-16147)
Macbonner Inc....F.... 941 778-7978
Holmes Beach (G-5946)
Maxwells Sanibel Lime-Elo Inc....G.... 239 472-8618
Sanibel (G-16148)
Miami News 24 Inc....G.... 786 331-8141
Doral (G-3435)
National Tchncal Cmmunications ....G.... 407 671-7777
Orlando (G-12991)
Newspaper Publishers Inc ....E.... 561 793-7606
Wellington (G-18725)
Ocala Centre 6....G.... 305 322-7365
Ocala (G-12008)
Ocala Swamp LLC....G.... 352 732-4260
Ocala (G-12017)
Orange Peel Gazette Inc....G.... 407 892-5556
Saint Cloud (G-15663)
Orlando Times Inc....G.... 407 841-3052
Orlando (G-13037)
Osceola Star....G.... 407 933-0174
Kissimmee (G-7282)
Pensacola Voice Inc....G.... 850 434-6963
Pensacola (G-14227)
Photo Finishing News Inc ....G.... 239 992-4421
Naples (G-11363)
Reed Brennan Media Associates ....E.... 407 894-7300
Orlando (G-13125)
Review Newspapers ....G.... 941 474-4351
Englewood (G-3682)
Samara Publishing....G.... 305 361-3333
Key Biscayne (G-7162)
Southwest Fla Newspapers Inc ....G.... 239 574-9733
Cape Coral (G-1476)

Star Editorial Inc ....G.... 561 997-7733
Boca Raton *(G-730)*
Swapper ....G.... 850 973-6653
Madison *(G-8454)*
Tom Watson Enterprises Inc ....G.... 352 683-5097
Hudson *(G-6040)*
Voice of South Marion ....G.... 352 245-3161
Belleview *(G-376)*
Wakulla News ....F.... 850 926-7102
Crawfordville *(G-2337)*
Washington CL Inc ....F.... 813 739-4800
Tampa *(G-18251)*
West Bolusia Beacon ....F.... 386 734-4622
Deland *(G-3033)*
Worldwide Media Svcs Group Inc ....E.... 561 989-1342
Boca Raton *(G-793)*

PUBLISHERS: Pamphlets, No Printing

Informa Usa Inc ....A.... 561 361-6017
Sarasota *(G-16465)*

PUBLISHERS: Periodical Statistical Reports, No Printing

Twinlab Corporation ....B.... 800 645-5626
Boca Raton *(G-761)*

PUBLISHERS: Periodical, With Printing

Cole Enterprises Inc ....G.... 727 441-4101
Clearwater *(G-1632)*
N Media Group LLC ....E.... 239 594-1322
Naples *(G-11333)*
Sep Communications LLC ....F.... 561 998-0870
Boca Raton *(G-706)*

PUBLISHERS: Periodicals, Magazines

954 Savings Magazine ....G.... 954 900-4649
Weston *(G-19101)*
Aacecorp Inc ....G.... 904 353-7878
Jacksonville *(G-6115)*
Academy Publishing Inc ....E.... 407 736-0100
Orlando *(G-12427)*
Always Fun Inc ....G.... 954 258-4377
Cooper City *(G-2108)*
Armbrust Aviation Group Inc ....E.... 561 355-8488
West Palm Beach *(G-18801)*
Best Community Magazine ....G.... 407 571-2980
Altamonte Springs *(G-32)*
Bonita Gente Magazine ....G.... 239 331-7952
Naples *(G-11192)*
Boswell JM & Associates Inc ....G.... 239 949-2311
Bonita Springs *(G-820)*
Central Florida Publishing Inc ....F.... 407 323-5204
Sanford *(G-16010)*
Coastal Angler Magazine ....G.... 850 586-3474
Satellite Beach *(G-16651)*
Community News Publications ....F.... 813 909-2800
Lutz *(G-8378)*
Construction Bulletin Inc ....F.... 904 388-0336
Jacksonville *(G-6284)*
Data Publishers Inc ....F.... 954 752-2332
Coral Springs *(G-2237)*
Edge of Humanity LLC ....G.... 954 425-0540
Pompano Beach *(G-14674)*
Fathym Inc ....F.... 303 905-4402
Palmetto *(G-13797)*
Gatehouse Media LLC ....F.... 863 401-6900
Winter Haven *(G-19325)*
Green Bench Monthly ....G.... 813 417-3944
Saint Petersburg *(G-15797)*
Gulf Publishing Company Inc ....F.... 727 596-2863
Largo *(G-7968)*
Homes Media Solutions LLC ....F.... 850 350-7800
Tallahassee *(G-17278)*
In Focus Interactive Magazine ....G.... 954 966-1233
Miramar *(G-11003)*
Lf Senior Communications Group ....F.... 561 392-4550
Boca Raton *(G-602)*
Lifestyle Magazine ....G.... 386 423-2772
New Smyrna Beach *(G-11537)*
Local Value Magazine ....G.... 813 421-6781
Tampa *(G-17857)*
Mercaworld and CIA LLC ....G.... 786 212-5905
Pembroke Pines *(G-14047)*
Municipal Code Corporation ....D.... 850 576-3171
Tallahassee *(G-17304)*
Newsmax Media Inc ....F.... 561 686-1165
West Palm Beach *(G-18964)*
Quad Intl Incorporated ....D.... 305 662-5959
Doral *(G-3474)*
Ronald A Ferguson ....G.... 786 488-4019
Fort Lauderdale *(G-4212)*
Showcase Publications Inc ....E.... 863 687-4377
Lakeland *(G-7791)*
Southeast Review Inc ....G.... 850 644-4230
Tallahassee *(G-17327)*
Spanish House Inc ....E.... 305 503-1191
Medley *(G-8728)*
Streamline Publishing Inc ....G.... 561 655-8778
Boca Raton *(G-733)*
Tampa Media Group LLC ....G.... 813 259-7100
Tampa *(G-18168)*
Twinlab Holdings Inc ....E.... 800 645-5626
Boca Raton *(G-762)*
United Advg Publications Inc ....G.... 407 297-0832
Altamonte Springs *(G-81)*
Weston Magazine Inc ....G.... 203 451-1967
Miami Beach *(G-10729)*
Wheelhouse Direct LLC ....F.... 239 246-8788
Fort Myers *(G-4655)*
World Politics Review LLC ....G.... 202 903-8398
Tampa *(G-18263)*

PUBLISHERS: Periodicals, No Printing

Coral Gables Living ....G.... 786 552-6464
Coral Gables *(G-2133)*
In The Bite ....F.... 561 529-3940
Jupiter *(G-7056)*
Naples Illustrated ....G.... 239 434-6966
Naples *(G-11335)*
Our Seniors Guidecom Inc ....G.... 904 655-2130
Jacksonville *(G-6649)*
Taylor & Francis Group LLC ....C.... 561 994-0555
Boca Raton *(G-742)*
Waste Advantage Corporation ....G.... 800 358-2873
Jupiter *(G-7143)*

PUBLISHERS: Technical Manuals

Tomsons Inc ....G.... 248 646-0677
Englewood *(G-3685)*

PUBLISHERS: Technical Manuals & Papers

Bot International Inc ....G.... 407 366-6547
Oviedo *(G-13419)*
Digital Direct Corporation ....G.... 813 448-9071
Oldsmar *(G-12220)*
Techpubs Ltd ....F.... 201 541-1192
Sarasota *(G-16620)*

PUBLISHERS: Telephone & Other Directory

Coastal Directory Company ....F.... 321 777-7076
Melbourne *(G-8792)*
Global Directories Inc ....F.... 954 571-8283
Deerfield Beach *(G-2832)*
Guest Service Publications Inc ....F.... 516 333-3474
Bonita Springs *(G-835)*
Heritage Publishing Inc ....E.... 904 296-1304
Jacksonville *(G-6471)*
Hill Donnelly Corporation ....D.... 800 525-1242
Tampa *(G-17755)*
Nationwide Publishing Company ....E.... 352 253-0017
Deltona *(G-3176)*
North Metro Media ....F.... 850 650-1014
Destin *(G-3199)*
Page Golfs Yellow Directory ....F.... 305 378-8038
Palmetto Bay *(G-13852)*
Time Adjusters Conference Inc ....G.... 386 274-4210
Port Orange *(G-15039)*

PUBLISHERS: Textbooks, No Printing

Logoi Inc ....G.... 305 232-5880
Miami *(G-9907)*
Phillip Roy Inc ....G.... 727 593-2700
Largo *(G-8026)*

PUBLISHERS: Trade journals, No Printing

Construction Journal Ltd ....D.... 772 781-2144
Stuart *(G-16927)*
First Marketing Company ....C.... 954 979-0700
Pompano Beach *(G-14691)*
Industrial Projects Services ....G.... 813 265-2957
Tampa *(G-17782)*
Uproxx Media Inc ....F.... 917 603-2374
Miami Beach *(G-10723)*

PUBLISHING & BROADCASTING: Internet Only

Akua Rage Entertainment Inc ....G.... 904 627-5312
Jacksonville *(G-6132)*
Altered Media Inc ....F.... 813 397-3892
Tampa *(G-17408)*
Bg Expo Group LLC ....G.... 305 428-3576
Doral *(G-3271)*
Brazilian Clssfied ADS-Chei In ....G.... 954 570-7568
Deerfield Beach *(G-2789)*
Broadcast Tech Inc ....E.... 786 351-4227
Medley *(G-8627)*
City of Winter Haven ....E.... 863 291-5858
Winter Haven *(G-19315)*
Citygrader LLC ....G.... 305 635-2686
Miami *(G-9358)*
Closeup Inc ....G.... 650 284-8831
Miami *(G-9363)*
Collidecom LLC ....F.... 407 903-5626
Orlando *(G-12602)*
Comm Dots LLC Connecting ....F.... 305 505-6009
Miami *(G-9388)*
D1 Locker LLC ....G.... 305 446-9041
Miami *(G-9427)*
Direct Media Solutions Inc ....G.... 904 419-3675
Jacksonville *(G-6319)*
Do You Remember Inc ....G.... 305 987-9111
Miami Beach *(G-10663)*
E1w Games Llc ....F.... 561 255-7370
Delray Beach *(G-3071)*
Fbr 1804 Inc ....F.... 305 340-3114
North Miami Beach *(G-11676)*
Flowhance Inc ....F.... 305 690-0784
Miami *(G-9590)*
Gcn Publishing Inc ....G.... 203 665-6211
Pompano Beach *(G-14713)*
Gmv Holdings LLC ....G.... 561 747-7864
Palm Beach Gardens *(G-13592)*
Icome2fix LLC ....F.... 954 789-4102
Miami *(G-9728)*
Igbo Network LLC ....F.... 352 727-4113
Gainesville *(G-4941)*
Isocialmedia Digital Marketing ....G.... 561 510-1124
Boca Raton *(G-574)*
Jjj & H Inc ....E.... 904 389-1130
Jacksonville *(G-6522)*
Levatas ....D.... 561 622-4511
Palm Beach Gardens *(G-13604)*
Media Digittal LLC ....G.... 305 506-0470
Doral *(G-3428)*
Military One Click LLC ....G.... 904 390-7100
Jacksonville *(G-6605)*
Page One LLC ....F.... 833 467-2431
Dania *(G-2455)*
Printing For A Cause LLC ....E.... 786 496-0637
Saint Petersburg *(G-15889)*
Rnn Productions LLC ....F.... 437 238-9501
Miami *(G-10270)*
Romeo Roseau Ecommerce ....F.... 561 633-1352
Boynton Beach *(G-956)*
Sarasota Byfront Plg Orgnztion ....G.... 941 203-5316
Sarasota *(G-16575)*
Saving For College LLC ....F.... 954 770-5136
Miami *(G-10307)*
Simpleshow USA Corp ....E.... 844 468-5447
Miami *(G-10352)*
Sipradius LLC ....G.... 954 290-2434
Coral Springs *(G-2313)*
Slate Group LLC ....G.... 786 484-9408
Miami *(G-10361)*
Smilefy Inc ....F.... 302 465-6606
Hallandale Beach *(G-5211)*
Videolinq Streaming Svcs LLC ....G.... 904 330-1026
Jacksonville *(G-6898)*
Wincor Technology Inc ....G.... 407 702-0787
Apopka *(G-197)*

PUBLISHING & PRINTING: Art Copy

Dakim Inc ....F.... 561 790-0884
Royal Palm Beach *(G-15465)*
Palm Prnting/Printers Ink Corp ....E.... 239 332-8600
Fort Myers *(G-4562)*
Preferred Custom Printing LLC ....F.... 727 443-1900
Seminole *(G-16757)*

PUBLISHING & PRINTING: Book Music

4ever Music LLC ....E.... 407 490-0977
Orlando *(G-12419)*

PUBLISHING & PRINTING: Books

Beacon Publishing Inc ....G....... 888 618-5253
North Palm Beach *(G-11718)*
Creative Tech Sarasota Inc ....G....... 941 371-2743
Sarasota *(G-16395)*
Global Village Ventures ....G....... 813 453-6199
Tampa *(G-17719)*
Plus Communications Inc ....D....... 407 333-0600
Lake Mary *(G-7443)*
Speech Bin ....F....... 772 770-0006
Vero Beach *(G-18666)*
Starlite Inc ....F....... 727 392-2929
Seminole *(G-16762)*
Tra Publishing LLP ....F....... 305 424-6468
Miami *(G-10498)*

PUBLISHING & PRINTING: Catalogs

Sony/Atv Music Publishing LLC ....G....... 305 532-9064
Miami Beach *(G-10713)*
Zetma LLC ....G....... 407 237-0233
Orlando *(G-13341)*

PUBLISHING & PRINTING: Directories, NEC

American Computer & Tech Corp ....G....... 786 738-3220
Miami Beach *(G-10640)*
Municipal Code Corporation ....D....... 850 576-3171
Tallahassee *(G-17304)*

PUBLISHING & PRINTING: Guides

Enterra Inc ....G....... 813 514-0531
Tampa *(G-17643)*

PUBLISHING & PRINTING: Magazines: publishing & printing

Akers Media Group Inc ....F....... 352 787-4112
Leesburg *(G-8140)*
American Chiropractor ....F....... 305 434-8865
Miami *(G-9141)*
Artnexus Online Inc ....E....... 305 891-7270
North Miami *(G-11625)*
Automundo Productions Inc ....G....... 305 541-4198
Coral Gables *(G-2124)*
Black College Monthly Inc ....G....... 352 335-5771
Gainesville *(G-4887)*
Black College Today Inc ....G....... 954 344-4469
Coral Springs *(G-2226)*
Brevard Softball Magazine Inc ....F....... 321 453-3711
Merritt Island *(G-8995)*
Diamond Advertising & Mktg ....F....... 561 833-5129
West Palm Beach *(G-18854)*
Endeavor Publications Inc ....G....... 352 369-1104
Ocala *(G-11932)*
Five Sports Inc ....G....... 727 209-1750
Saint Petersburg *(G-15781)*
Franja Corp ....G....... 954 659-1950
Weston *(G-19127)*
Goodpress Publishing LLC ....G....... 561 865-8101
Delray Beach *(G-3085)*
Grupo Editorial Expansion ....G....... 305 374-9003
Coral Gables *(G-2153)*
Insurance Plus ....G....... 904 567-1553
Ponte Vedra Beach *(G-14942)*
International Cnstr Pubg ....G....... 305 668-4999
Miami *(G-9757)*
Lifestyle Media Group LLC ....F....... 954 377-9470
Fort Lauderdale *(G-4100)*
Mas Editorial Corp ....G....... 305 748-0124
Hollywood *(G-5870)*
Metro Life Media Inc ....G....... 813 745-3658
Tampa *(G-17906)*
Mitcham Media Group LLC ....G....... 850 893-9624
Tallahassee *(G-17302)*
Npc of Tampa Inc ....F....... 813 839-0035
Tampa *(G-17942)*
Old Port Group LLC ....F....... 904 819-5812
Saint Augustine *(G-15582)*
Our City Media of Florida LLC ....F....... 954 306-1007
Sunrise *(G-17154)*
Palm Beach Newspapers Inc ....D....... 561 820-3800
West Palm Beach *(G-18985)*
Playbill Southern Publishing ....F....... 305 595-1984
Miami *(G-10169)*
Plus Communications Inc ....D....... 407 333-0600
Lake Mary *(G-7443)*
Shelton Group LLC ....G....... 321 676-8981
Melbourne *(G-8931)*
Special Publications Inc ....F....... 352 622-2995
Ocala *(G-12056)*
T V HI Lites Penny Saver Inc ....G....... 941 378-5353
Sarasota *(G-16614)*
Times Holding Co ....G....... 727 893-8111
Saint Petersburg *(G-15938)*
Times Publishing Company ....A....... 727 893-8111
Saint Petersburg *(G-15940)*
Vista Publishing Corporation ....F....... 305 416-4644
Miami Beach *(G-10728)*
Vive Creole LLC ....G....... 954 607-1925
Hollywood *(G-5937)*

PUBLISHING & PRINTING: Music, Book

Globe Boyz International LLC ....F....... 305 308-8160
Miami *(G-9643)*

PUBLISHING & PRINTING: Newsletters, Business Svc

Construction Bulletin Inc ....F....... 904 388-0336
Jacksonville *(G-6284)*
Leila K Moavero ....G....... 954 978-0018
Pompano Beach *(G-14743)*

PUBLISHING & PRINTING: Newspapers

925 Nuevos Cubanos Inc ....G....... 954 806-8375
Fort Lauderdale *(G-3773)*
Alachua Today Inc ....G....... 386 462-3355
Alachua *(G-1)*
Almanac LLC ....F....... 415 310-5143
Miami *(G-9119)*
Anna Andres ....G....... 239 335-0233
Fort Myers *(G-4364)*
B Squared of Chiefland LLC ....F....... 352 507-2195
Chiefland *(G-1532)*
Bay County Bullet ....G....... 850 640-0855
Panama City *(G-13867)*
Bcc-Bgle Cmmnctons Crp-Clrin L ....F....... 305 270-3333
Miami *(G-9228)*
Beach Beacon ....F....... 727 397-5563
Seminole *(G-16741)*
Bi-Ads Inc ....F....... 954 525-1489
Fort Lauderdale *(G-3849)*
Bluewaterpress LLC ....G....... 888 247-0793
Saint Augustine *(G-15522)*
Boca Raton Observer ....G....... 561 702-3086
Boca Raton *(G-453)*
Bonita Daily News ....E....... 239 213-6060
Naples *(G-11191)*
Bradford County Telegraph Inc ....F....... 904 964-6305
Starke *(G-16887)*
Brasileiras & Brasileiros Inc ....G....... 407 855-9541
Orlando *(G-12534)*
Brazilian Clssfied ADS-Chei In ....G....... 954 570-7568
Deerfield Beach *(G-2789)*
Brevard Business News ....F....... 321 951-7777
Melbourne *(G-8786)*
Bulletin Net Inc ....F....... 941 468-2569
Sarasota *(G-16373)*
Bus Bulletin Inc ....G....... 850 271-0017
Panama City *(G-13875)*
Business Jrnl Publications Inc ....E....... 904 396-3502
Jacksonville *(G-6246)*
Business Report of N Cntrl FL ....G....... 352 275-9469
Gainesville *(G-4890)*
Caribbean Today News Magazine ....F....... 305 238-2868
Palmetto Bay *(G-13841)*
Carol City Opa Locka News ....E....... 305 669-7355
South Miami *(G-16813)*
Central Florida Publishing Inc ....F....... 407 323-5204
Sanford *(G-16010)*
Chipley Newspapers Inc ....G....... 850 638-0212
Bonifay *(G-801)*
Coffee News Clearwater ....G....... 727 789-6677
Oldsmar *(G-12217)*
Com Miami Corporation ....G....... 305 376-5040
Miami *(G-9384)*
Community News Papers Inc ....G....... 386 752-1293
Lake City *(G-7351)*
Cooppa News Reporter ....G....... 954 437-8864
Pembroke Pines *(G-14029)*
Creative Loafing Inc ....G....... 941 365-6776
Tampa *(G-17566)*
Current ....G....... 954 262-8455
Davie *(G-2512)*
Cve Reporter Inc ....F....... 954 421-5566
Deerfield Beach *(G-2810)*
Daily Buzz ....G....... 407 673-5400
Winter Park *(G-19399)*
Daily Green ....G....... 352 226-8288
Gainesville *(G-4903)*
Daily Melt ....G....... 305 519-2585
Miami *(G-9432)*
Daily Melt ....G....... 305 573-9700
Miami *(G-9433)*
Daily Multiservices Inc ....G....... 786 286-3817
Hialeah *(G-5364)*
Daily Room ....F....... 754 200-5153
Plantation *(G-14506)*
Daily Therapy Services Inc ....G....... 954 649-3620
Lauderhill *(G-8107)*
Daily Trnsfrmtion Mnstries Inc ....G....... 727 847-5152
Tampa *(G-17585)*
Dailychew LLC ....G....... 954 849-0553
Plantation *(G-14507)*
Dailys ....F....... 904 448-0562
Jacksonville *(G-6308)*
Dailys ....F....... 904 880-4784
Jacksonville *(G-6309)*
Destin Log ....C....... 850 837-2828
Fort Walton Beach *(G-4790)*
Doral Family Journal LLC ....G....... 305 300-4594
Doral *(G-3334)*
Eglin Flyer ....G....... 850 678-4581
Niceville *(G-11565)*
El Colusa News ....G....... 786 845-6868
Miami *(G-9505)*
El Hispano ....G....... 772 878-6488
Port Saint Lucie *(G-15105)*
El Latino Newspaper ....G....... 561 835-4913
West Palm Beach *(G-18861)*
Emerald Coast Media & Mktg ....E....... 850 267-4555
Santa Rosa Beach *(G-16159)*
EW Scripps Company ....C....... 772 408-5300
Port Saint Lucie *(G-15107)*
F S View Fla Flambeau Newsppr ....E....... 850 561-6653
Tallahassee *(G-17250)*
Florida E Coast Supersonics Tc ....G....... 386 689-2367
New Smyrna Beach *(G-11533)*
Florida Health Care News Inc ....E....... 813 989-1330
Temple Terrace *(G-18368)*
Florida Star Inc ....F....... 904 766-8834
Jacksonville *(G-6403)*
Florida Weekly ....G....... 239 333-2135
Fort Myers *(G-4454)*
Foliage Enterprises Inc ....E....... 407 886-2777
Apopka *(G-144)*
Forum Publishing Group Inc ....C....... 954 698-6397
Deerfield Beach *(G-2827)*
Forward Defuniak Incorporated ....G....... 850 830-7663
Defuniak Springs *(G-2943)*
Frank The Kit Exprt Palm Coast ....G....... 386 264-6105
Palm Coast *(G-13695)*
Free Press ....G....... 305 853-7277
Key Largo *(G-7171)*
Free Press Publishing Company ....E....... 813 254-5888
Tampa *(G-17694)*
Gainesville ....G....... 352 339-0294
Gainesville *(G-4925)*
Go Latinos Magazine LLC ....G....... 786 601-7693
Homestead *(G-5965)*
Gospel Journal ....G....... 904 389-9635
Jacksonville *(G-6443)*
Greene Publishing Inc ....F....... 850 973-6397
Madison *(G-8451)*
Gulf Breeze News Inc ....G....... 850 932-8986
Gulf Breeze *(G-5117)*
Gulf Coast Business Review ....G....... 941 906-9386
Sarasota *(G-16453)*
Gulfcoast Gabber Inc ....G....... 727 321-6965
Gulfport *(G-5134)*
Halifax Media Group LLC ....B....... 386 265-6700
Daytona Beach *(G-2670)*
Halifax Media Group LLC ....C....... 941 361-4800
Sarasota *(G-16457)*
Halifax Media Holdings LLC ....E....... 386 681-2404
Daytona Beach *(G-2671)*
Hammill Post ....G....... 352 304-8675
Ocala *(G-11964)*
Harborpoint Media LLC ....C....... 352 365-8200
Leesburg *(G-8161)*
Heritage Centl Fla Jewish News ....F....... 407 834-8277
Fern Park *(G-3729)*
Home Examiner Inc ....G....... 786 897-8349
Miami *(G-9717)*
Home Town Journal ....G....... 904 259-9141
Glen Saint Mary *(G-5036)*
Homestead Newspapers Inc ....A....... 305 245-2311
Homestead *(G-5968)*

Hometown News LC ....E 772 465-5656
Fort Pierce (G-4706)
Hometown News LC ....G 321 242-1013
Melbourne (G-8846)
Impremedia LLC ....G 407 767-0070
Longwood (G-8289)
Independent Florida Sun ....G 850 438-8115
Pensacola (G-14176)
Independent Newsmedia Inc USA ....G 863 983-9148
Okeechobee (G-12182)
Inquirer Newspapers Inc ....G 772 257-6230
Vero Beach (G-18631)
Island Sand Paper ....G 239 290-4038
Fort Myers Beach (G-4664)
J&J Suwannee Enterprises LLC ....G 386 658-1721
Live Oak (G-8233)
Jacksonville Free Press ....F 904 634-1993
Jacksonville (G-6511)
Jls of St Augustine Inc ....G 904 797-6098
Saint Augustine (G-15560)
Job News ....E 904 296-3006
Jacksonville (G-6524)
Key West Printing LLC ....G 305 517-6711
Key West (G-7190)
Keynoter Publishing Co Inc ....F 305 743-5551
Marathon (G-8519)
Knight-Rddr/Miami Herald Cr Un ....F 305 376-2181
Miami (G-9828)
Lake News LLC ....F 407 251-1314
Orlando (G-12888)
Leader Group ....E 904 249-7475
Jacksonville Beach (G-6947)
Ledger ....B 863 802-7000
Lakeland (G-7733)
Liberty Calhoun Journal Inc ....G 850 643-3333
Bristol (G-1198)
Linville Enterprises LLC ....G 813 782-1558
Zephyrhills (G-19527)
Local Community News Inc ....G 904 886-4919
Callahan (G-1326)
Localtoolbox Inc ....G 415 250-3232
Pensacola (G-14195)
Longboat Key News Inc ....F 941 387-2200
Longboat Key (G-8245)
McClatchy Shared Services Ctr ....D 305 740-8800
Doral (G-3427)
Medleycom Incorporated ....E 408 745-5418
Delray Beach (G-3105)
Merle Harris Enterprises Inc ....G 386 677-7060
South Daytona (G-16804)
Miami Herald ....F 305 269-7768
Miami (G-10002)
Miami Herald ....G 800 843-4372
Doral (G-3433)
Miami Slice LLC ....G 786 200-2723
Miami (G-10011)
Miami Times ....E 305 694-6210
Miami (G-10015)
Mid-Florida Publications Inc ....G 352 589-8811
Mount Dora (G-11107)
Miller Publishing Co Inc ....F 305 669-7355
South Miami (G-16822)
Milton Newspapers Inc ....A 850 623-2120
Milton (G-10935)
Monticello News ....F 850 997-3568
Monticello (G-11080)
National Newspaper Placem ....G 866 404-5913
Lake Mary (G-7438)
Ne Media Group Inc ....G 954 733-8393
Oakland Park (G-11823)
Neighborhood News & Lifestyles ....F 727 943-0551
Tarpon Springs (G-18316)
News Features USA Inc ....G 305 298-5313
Miami Beach (G-10698)
News Herald ....F 850 785-6550
Panama City (G-13931)
News Leader Inc ....E 352 242-9818
Clermont (G-1970)
News-Journal Corporation ....A 386 252-1511
Daytona Beach (G-2690)
News-Journal Corporation ....F 386 283-5664
Palm Coast (G-13704)
Northwest Florida Daily News ....G 850 863-1111
Fort Walton Beach (G-4819)
Observer Group ....G 407 654-5500
Winter Garden (G-19278)
Observer Group Inc ....E 941 383-5509
Sarasota (G-16528)
Ocala Star Banner Corporation ....C 352 867-4010
Ocala (G-12016)
Ocalanow Com ....G 352 433-2497
Ocala (G-12018)
Office of Medical Examiner ....G 772 464-7378
Fort Pierce (G-4724)
OPC News ....G 904 686-3938
Ponte Vedra Beach (G-14948)
Orange Peel Gazette ....G 407 312-7335
Altamonte Springs (G-60)
Orange Peel Gazette Treasur ....G 772 489-8005
Fort Pierce (G-4726)
Orange Peel Gztte of Oscola CN ....F 407 892-5556
Saint Cloud (G-15664)
Ord of Ahepa Ch 356 Daily & T ....G 727 791-1040
Clearwater (G-1820)
Ormond Beach Observer ....F 386 492-2784
Ormond Beach (G-13389)
Our Town News ....G 954 979-0991
Pompano Beach (G-14781)
Our Village Okeechobee Inc ....G 863 467-0158
Okeechobee (G-12188)
Outpost North Lake ....G 352 669-2430
Umatilla (G-18500)
Overseas Radio LLC ....G 305 296-1630
Key West (G-7200)
P A Vivid Pathology ....G 850 416-7780
Pensacola (G-14218)
Palm Beach Gardens Fla Wkly ....G 561 904-6443
Palm Beach Gardens (G-13615)
Palm Beach Newspapers Inc ....D 561 820-3800
West Palm Beach (G-18985)
Palm Coast Observer LLC ....E 386 447-9723
Palm Coast (G-13706)
Panama City News Herald ....C 850 747-5000
Panama City (G-13935)
Panama City News Herald ....C 850 863-1111
Fort Walton Beach (G-4821)
Pathfnders Palm Bch-Mrtin Cnty ....D 561 820-4262
West Palm Beach (G-18989)
Pennysaver ....G 718 986-6437
Deland (G-3008)
Pinecrest Tribune ....F 305 662-2277
South Miami (G-16825)
Plant City Observer LLC ....G 813 704-6850
Plant City (G-14458)
Plantation Journal Corporation ....G 954 226-6170
Plantation (G-14542)
Pompano Pelican Inc ....G 954 783-8700
Pompano Beach (G-14804)
Ponte Vedra Wns Civic Aliance ....G 904 834-3543
Ponte Vedra Beach (G-14951)
Port St Lucie News ....E 772 287-1550
Stuart (G-16991)
Pressnet Corp ....G 786 728-1369
Miami (G-10189)
Prestige Publication Group ....E 305 538-9700
Miami Beach (G-10705)
Prison Legal News ....F 561 360-2523
Lake Worth (G-7583)
Progress House ....G 321 298-4652
Palm Bay (G-13529)
Real News Real Fast ....G 727 485-6055
Spring Hill (G-16860)
Republic Newspapers Inc ....G 813 782-1558
Zephyrhills (G-19534)
Resident Cmnty News Group Inc ....F 904 962-6876
Jacksonville (G-6716)
Resident Community News ....G 904 388-8839
Jacksonville (G-6717)
Ring of Fire Radio LLC ....G 866 666-6114
Pensacola (G-14253)
Rolling Greens News ....G 352 236-0007
Ocala (G-12040)
Santiva Chronicle ....G 239 437-9324
Fort Myers (G-4596)
Santiva Chronicle LLC ....G 239 472-0559
Sanibel (G-16149)
Sarasota Herald-Tribune ....C 941 358-4000
Sarasota (G-16292)
Sarasota Herald-Tribune ....B 941 953-7755
Sarasota (G-16578)
Sarasota Herald-Tribune ....E 941 953-7755
Sarasota (G-16579)
Science Daily LLC ....G 239 596-2624
Sarasota (G-16585)
Senior Life of Florida ....F 321 242-1235
Melbourne (G-8930)
Senior Voice America Inc ....F 813 444-1011
Tampa (G-18083)
Sentinel Cmmnctons News Vntres ....G 407 420-6229
Longwood (G-8335)
Sentinel Cmmnctons News Vntres ....G 407 420-5291
Orlando (G-13173)
Sentinel Sq Off Bldg MGT & Lsg ....G 727 461-7700
Clearwater (G-1873)
South Florida Digest Inc ....F 954 458-0635
Hallandale Beach (G-5214)
Southfloridagaynewscom ....F 954 530-4970
Wilton Manors (G-19220)
St Agstine Bches News Jrnl LL ....G 904 501-4556
Saint Augustine (G-15616)
St Augustine Record ....E 904 829-6562
Saint Augustine (G-15620)
Stuart News ....C 772 287-1550
Stuart (G-17024)
Stuart News ....C 772 287-1550
Stuart (G-17025)
Sun Coast Media Group Inc ....D 941 206-1300
Port Charlotte (G-15000)
Sun Coast Media Group Inc ....D 941 207-1000
Venice (G-18578)
Sun Coast Media Group Inc ....G 863 494-7600
Punta Gorda (G-15237)
Sun Coast Media Group Inc ....E 941 681-3000
Englewood (G-3684)
Sun Coast Media Group Inc ....F 941 206-1900
Port Charlotte (G-15001)
Sun-Sentinel Company LLC ....B 954 356-4000
Fort Lauderdale (G-4265)
Sun-Sentinel Company LLC ....E 954 356-4000
Deerfield Beach (G-2918)
Sun-Sentinel Company Inc ....G 561 736-2208
Boynton Beach (G-964)
Sun-Sentinel Company Inc ....F 954 735-6414
Fort Lauderdale (G-4266)
Suncoast News ....G 727 815-1023
Port Richey (G-15070)
Suwannee Fund LLC ....G 386 963-1149
Live Oak (G-8242)
Suwanneearc ....G 386 362-1796
Live Oak (G-8243)
Syndicated Programming Inc ....G 850 877-0105
Tallahassee (G-17333)
Tallahassee Democrat ....E 850 599-2100
Tallahassee (G-17335)
Tampa Bay Newspapers Inc ....A 727 397-5563
Seminole (G-16768)
Tampa Bay Sports Entrmt LLC ....B 727 893-8111
Saint Petersburg (G-15934)
Tampa Bay Times ....G 352 754-6100
Brooksville (G-1278)
Tampa Media Group Inc ....C 813 259-7711
Tampa (G-18166)
Tampa Media Group Inc ....B 813 259-7711
Tampa (G-18167)
Tampa Media Group LLC ....G 813 259-7100
Tampa (G-18168)
Times Holding Co ....G 727 893-8111
Saint Petersburg (G-15938)
Times Media Services Inc ....C 727 893-8111
Saint Petersburg (G-15939)
Times Publishing Company ....C 727 849-6397
Port Richey (G-15072)
Times Publishing Company ....G 850 224-7263
Tallahassee (G-17340)
Times Publishing Company ....C 352 567-6660
Inverness (G-6097)
Treasure Chest of Sweetwater ....G 407 788-0020
Longwood (G-8344)
Tri-County Bulletin ....G 352 493-4796
Chiefland (G-1538)
Triangle Shopping Guide Inc ....G 352 589-8811
Mount Dora (G-11116)
Trusted Daily Solutions ....G 954 461-5131
Lighthouse Point (G-8213)
Turtlehue LLC ....G 561 775-6614
North Palm Beach (G-11728)
Vero Beach 32963 Media ....G 772 226-7924
Vero Beach (G-18677)
Vero News ....F 772 234-5727
Vero Beach (G-18679)
Weekly Challenger Newspaper ....G 727 896-2922
Saint Petersburg (G-15956)
Weekly Newspaper ....F 305 743-0844
Marathon (G-8521)
Weekly Planet of Sarasota Inc ....F 813 739-4800
Tampa (G-18252)
White Miami LLC ....G 305 579-9115
Miami (G-10601)
Will & Mia Corp ....F 617 943-6914
Miami (G-10607)

Winter Garden Times Inc....E.... 407 656-2121
Winter Garden (G-19291)
Wood Television LLC....G.... 727 815-1000
New Port Richey (G-11521)
Wood Television LLC....G.... 352 544-5200
Brooksville (G-1292)
Woody Hatcher....G.... 850 526-1501
Marianna (G-8588)
Worldwide Media Svcs Group Inc....D.... 561 989-1342
Boca Raton (G-792)

PUBLISHING & PRINTING: Pamphlets

Baptist Communications Mission....F.... 954 981-2271
Hollywood (G-5784)
Digital Propaganda Inc....F.... 407 644-8444
Orlando (G-12675)
Florida Sncast Trism Prmotions....F.... 727 544-1212
Largo (G-7951)

PUBLISHING & PRINTING: Posters

Cutting Edge Sgns Grphics of P....G.... 727 546-3700
Clearwater (G-1645)
Reimink Printing Inc....G.... 813 289-4663
Tampa (G-18050)

PUBLISHING & PRINTING: Shopping News

Fpc Printing Inc....D.... 813 626-9430
Tampa (G-17693)
Trading Post of Central Fla....G.... 954 675-2149
Margate (G-8570)

PUBLISHING & PRINTING: Technical Manuals

Rapid Rater Company....E.... 850 893-7346
Tallahassee (G-17314)

PUBLISHING & PRINTING: Textbooks

H & H Publishing Co Inc....G.... 727 442-7760
Clearwater (G-1709)
Sirs Publishing Inc....D.... 800 521-0600
Boca Raton (G-718)

PUBLISHING & PRINTING: Trade Journals

Fundacion Educativa Carlos M....G.... 305 859-9617
Miami (G-9604)
Signcraft Publishing Co Inc....F.... 239 939-4644
Fort Myers (G-4604)
Ural Associates Inc....G.... 305 446-9462
Coral Gables (G-2200)

PULP MILLS

Foley Cellulose LLC....A.... 850 584-1121
Perry (G-14300)
Rayonier Inc....E.... 904 277-1343
Yulee (G-19499)
Suzano Pulp & Paper....G.... 954 772-7716
Fort Lauderdale (G-4270)

PULP MILLS: Mechanical & Recycling Processing

Ies Sales and Service LLC....G.... 305 525-6079
Miami (G-9731)
Platinium Rosis Inc....G.... 786 617-9973
Miami Beach (G-10703)
Southern Wood Services LLC....G.... 352 279-3208
Brooksville (G-1272)
Stellar On-Site LLC....F.... 904 945-1908
Hilliard (G-5719)
Universal PC Organization Inc....G.... 321 285-9206
Orlando (G-13296)

PULSE FORMING NETWORKS

Akuwa Solutions Group Inc....F.... 941 343-9947
Sarasota (G-16337)

PUMP JACKS & OTHER PUMPING EQPT: Indl

Stenner Pump Company Inc....C.... 904 641-1666
Jacksonville (G-6811)

PUMPS

Acme Service Corp....F.... 305 836-4800
Miami (G-9065)
Air Supply of Future Inc....F.... 954 977-0877
Pompano Beach (G-14582)
American Incinerators Corp....E.... 321 282-7357
Orlando (G-12470)
American-Marsh Pumps LLC....G.... 863 646-5689
Lakeland (G-7634)
Anko Products Inc....E.... 941 748-2307
Bradenton (G-989)
Channel Industries Inc....F.... 561 214-0637
West Palm Beach (G-18845)
Custom Masters Inc....E.... 407 331-4634
Longwood (G-8270)
D & D Machine & Hydraulics Inc....E.... 239 275-7177
Fort Myers (G-4423)
Delta P Systems Inc....F.... 386 236-0950
Ormond Beach (G-13361)
Fluidra Usa LLC....E.... 904 378-0999
Jacksonville (G-6409)
Global Pump Daytona....G.... 386 426-2411
Edgewater (G-3623)
Hamworthy Inc....G.... 305 597-7520
Fort Lauderdale (G-4041)
Hisco Pump South LLC....F.... 904 786-4488
Jacksonville (G-6472)
Hizer Machine Mfg Inc....G.... 386 755-3155
White Springs (G-19187)
Holland Pump Company....G.... 813 626-0599
Tampa (G-17759)
Holland Pump Company....G.... 561 697-3333
West Palm Beach (G-18896)
Holland Pump Company....G.... 904 880-0010
Jacksonville (G-6475)
Hydrolec Inc....E.... 904 730-3766
Jacksonville (G-6484)
Innovation Marine Corporation....E.... 941 355-7852
Sarasota (G-16238)
ITT Flygt Corp....G.... 239 633-2553
Fort Myers (G-4497)
John Mader Enterprises Inc....E.... 239 731-5455
Fort Myers (G-4506)
Johnston Archtctral Systems In....E.... 904 886-9030
Jacksonville (G-6527)
Lodex Enterprises Corp....G.... 954 442-3843
Miramar (G-11010)
Marine Metal Products Co....G.... 727 461-5575
Clearwater (G-1773)
Multitrode Inc....E.... 561 737-1210
Boca Raton (G-633)
Mwi Corporation....E.... 954 426-1500
Deerfield Beach (G-2877)
Osgood Industries LLC....C.... 813 448-9041
Oldsmar (G-12254)
Performance Pumps Inc....E.... 407 339-6700
Casselberry (G-1512)
Phoenix Dewatering Inc....F.... 407 330-7015
Sanford (G-16101)
Portable Pumping Systems Inc....G.... 727 518-9191
Clearwater (G-1837)
Pulsafeeder Inc....D.... 941 575-2900
Punta Gorda (G-15223)
Pulsafeeder Spo Inc....F.... 941 575-3800
Punta Gorda (G-15224)
Reverso Pumps Inc....F.... 954 523-9396
Davie (G-2584)
RG Groundworks LLC....G.... 352 474-7949
Newberry (G-11560)
Schwing Bioset....G.... 239 237-2174
Fort Myers (G-4598)
Serf Inc....E.... 850 476-8203
Cantonment (G-1347)
Southern Innovative Energy Inc....G.... 321 747-9205
Titusville (G-18461)
Stinner Pump Company....G.... 904 329-2098
Jacksonville (G-6814)
Townley Engrg & Mfg Co Inc....C.... 352 687-3001
Candler (G-1332)
Tradewinds Power Corp....F.... 863 382-2166
Sebring (G-16716)
Turner Machine & Supply Co....G.... 772 464-4550
Fort Pierce (G-4762)
Wilo USA LLC....D.... 954 524-6776
Fort Lauderdale (G-4325)
Xylem Dewatering Solutions....G.... 904 695-2131
Jacksonville (G-6932)

PUMPS & PARTS: Indl

Air Dimensions Inc....E.... 954 428-7333
Deerfield Beach (G-2770)
Azcue Pumps USA Inc....G.... 954 597-7602
Tamarac (G-17352)
G & F Manufacturing Inc....F.... 239 939-7446
Fort Myers (G-4464)
Greylor Dynesco Co Inc....G.... 239 574-2011
Cape Coral (G-1431)
Hoover Pumping Systems Corp....E.... 954 971-7350
Pompano Beach (G-14727)
Jka Pump Specialists....G.... 561 686-4455
West Palm Beach (G-18912)
Pioneer Dredge Inc....G.... 904 732-2151
Jacksonville (G-6675)
Power Equipments Trading LLC....G.... 305 704-7021
Doral (G-3464)
Quantumflo Inc....E.... 407 807-7050
Sanford (G-16108)
Smith Surface Prep Systems Inc....D.... 954 941-9744
Pompano Beach (G-14854)
Tru-Flo Corp....F.... 561 996-5850
Belle Glade (G-354)

PUMPS & PUMPING EQPT REPAIR SVCS

Central Electric Motor Service....F.... 863 422-4721
Haines City (G-5138)
Dade Pump & Supply Co....G.... 305 235-5000
Miami (G-9430)
Gulf Coast Elc Mtr Svc Inc....E.... 850 433-5134
Pensacola (G-14166)
John Mader Enterprises Inc....E.... 239 731-5455
Fort Myers (G-4506)
Kcw Electric Company Inc....G.... 850 878-2051
Tallahassee (G-17287)
Morgans Elc Mtr & Pump Svc....G.... 321 960-2209
Cocoa Beach (G-2066)
Robert E Weissenborn Sr....G.... 239 262-1771
Naples (G-11387)

PUMPS & PUMPING EQPT WHOLESALERS

Dade Pump & Supply Co....G.... 305 235-5000
Miami (G-9430)
Greylor Dynesco Co Inc....G.... 239 574-2011
Cape Coral (G-1431)

PUMPS, HEAT: Electric

Built Right Pool Heaters LLC....G.... 941 505-1600
Punta Gorda (G-15200)
Calorex USA LLC....F.... 239 482-0606
Fort Myers (G-4385)

PUMPS: Aircraft, Hydraulic

Leading Edge Aerospace Llc....G.... 305 608-6826
Miami Gardens (G-10750)

PUMPS: Domestic, Water Or Sump

Awl Manufacturing Inc....G.... 239 643-5780
Naples (G-11178)
United Rentals North Amer Inc....G.... 239 690-0600
Fort Myers (G-4640)
United Rentals North Amer Inc....G.... 850 478-2833
Pensacola (G-14278)
United Rentals North Amer Inc....G.... 941 755-3177
Sarasota (G-16321)
Vickery and Company....F.... 813 987-2100
Tampa (G-18244)

PUMPS: Fluid Power

Eem Technologies Corp....F.... 786 606-5993
Doral (G-3340)
Oase North America Inc....G.... 800 365-3880
Riviera Beach (G-15354)

PUMPS: Hydraulic Power Transfer

Mwi Corporation....F.... 239 337-4747
Fort Myers (G-4542)

PUMPS: Measuring & Dispensing

Stenner Pump Company Inc....C.... 904 641-1666
Jacksonville (G-6811)

PUMPS: Oil Well & Field

Acme Dynamics Inc....F.... 813 752-3137
Winter Haven (G-19294)

PUMPS: Vacuum, Exc Laboratory

Graham & Company LLC....G.... 904 281-0003
Jacksonville (G-6444)

Hisco Pump South LLC ....F 904 786-4488
Jacksonville (G-6472)
Mat-Vac Technology Inc ....F 386 238-7017
Daytona Beach (G-2683)

PUPPETS & MARIONETTES

Duck In The Truck Puppets Inc ....G 772 334-3022
Jensen Beach (G-6967)
Puppet Workshop Inc ....E 305 666-2655
Miami (G-10215)

PURIFICATION & DUST COLLECTION EQPT

Rgf Environmental Group Inc ....C 800 842-7771
Riviera Beach (G-15372)

PUSHCARTS

Advance Carts Inc ....F 561 320-8674
Boca Raton (G-402)

QUARTZ CRYSTALS: Electronic

Daytona Glass Works LLC ....F 386 274-2550
Daytona Beach (G-2654)
Mtn Government Services Inc ....F 954 538-4000
Miramar (G-11019)
Quartz Unlimited Inc ....E 561 720-7460
Boca Raton (G-678)

QUILTING SVC & SPLYS, FOR THE TRADE

Rainbows End ....F 727 733-8572
Palm Harbor (G-13757)

RACEWAYS

Apw ....G 850 332-7023
Pensacola (G-14088)
Bashers RC Raceway LLC ....G 561 889-9386
Jupiter (G-7004)
Gaukaupa Raceway ....G 904 483-3473
Jacksonville (G-6426)
Golden Glades Raceway LLC ....G 305 321-9627
Miami Gardens (G-10743)
Holeshot Raceway Inc ....G 407 864-1095
Oviedo (G-13435)
K-Raceway LLC ....G 407 889-4314
Apopka (G-153)
Mary Symon ....G 813 986-4676
Dover (G-3561)
Montalvos Raceway LLC ....G 239 289-6931
Naples (G-11331)
Nelson Raceway LLC ....G 904 206-1625
Fernandina Beach (G-3744)
Nine Mile Raceway Inc ....G 850 937-1845
Cantonment (G-1343)
Nuggets Racing LLC ....G 954 943-3561
Pompano Beach (G-14777)
Race Way 6800 ....G 904 329-2961
Macclenny (G-8444)
Raceway ....G 850 453-9437
Pensacola (G-14249)
Raceway Electric LLC ....G 772 260-6530
Port Saint Lucie (G-15135)
Raceway Towing LLC ....G 754 244-9597
Oakland Park (G-11835)

RACKS: Bicycle, Automotive

Bikekeeper LLC ....G 561 209-6863
Lake Worth (G-7536)
Weehoo Inc ....G 720 477-3700
Tarpon Springs (G-18330)

RACKS: Display

Szabo Pos Displays Inc ....G 941 778-0192
Bradenton (G-1124)

RACKS: Pallet, Exc Wood

Km Industrial Racking Inc ....G 813 900-7457
Largo (G-7993)
SC Capital Ventures Inc ....E 954 657-8563
Pompano Beach (G-14841)

RACKS: Railroad Car, Vehicle Transportation, Steel

First Class Liaisons LLC ....G 954 882-8634
Wellington (G-18717)

Inversnes Wlldel Asociados Inc ....E 305 591-0931
Doral (G-3394)
Inversnes Wlldel Asociados Inc ....D 305 591-0118
Miami (G-9764)

RADAR SYSTEMS & EQPT

C Speed LLC ....G 321 336-7939
Titusville (G-18421)
Detect Inc ....F 850 763-7200
Panama City (G-13892)
Drs Training Ctrl Systems LLC ....E 850 302-3000
Fort Walton Beach (G-4796)
Northrop Grumman Systems Corp ....A 321 951-5000
Melbourne (G-8897)
Raytheon Company ....G 727 768-8468
Largo (G-8037)
Raytheon Company ....G 310 647-9438
Saint Petersburg (G-15898)

RADIO & TELEVISION COMMUNICATIONS EQUIPMENT

Aero-Mach TCO Manufacturing ....G 239 936-7570
Fort Myers (G-4346)
Airspan Networks Inc ....E 561 893-8670
Boca Raton (G-410)
Aska Communication Corp ....G 954 708-2387
Miami (G-9178)
AVI-Spl Emplyee Emrgncy Rlief ....A 813 884-7168
Tampa (G-17445)
AVI-Spl Holdings Inc ....A 866 708-5034
Tampa (G-17446)
AVI-Spl LLC ....A 813 884-7168
Tampa (G-17447)
Barco LLC ....G 305 677-9600
Miami (G-9219)
Bluazu LLC ....F 386 697-3743
Gainesville (G-4888)
Commscope Technologies LLC ....F 407 944-9116
Orlando (G-12607)
Component General Inc ....E 727 376-6655
Odessa (G-12112)
Da Vinci Systems Inc ....G 954 688-5600
Coral Springs (G-2236)
Electro Technik Industries Inc ....D 727 530-9555
Clearwater (G-1666)
Ericsson Inc ....G 856 230-6268
Orlando (G-12716)
Fiplex Communications Inc ....E 305 884-8991
Doral (G-3351)
Fortune Media Group Inc ....F 954 379-4321
Coral Springs (G-2248)
Gap Antenna Products Inc ....G 772 571-9922
Fellsmere (G-3726)
Global Wrless Sltions Tech Inc ....G 941 744-2511
Bradenton (G-1048)
Gogps USA Inc ....F 941 751-2363
Sarasota (G-16223)
Gps Education LLC ....G 386 756-7575
Port Orange (G-15019)
Hilomast LLC ....G 386 668-6784
Debary (G-2749)
I-Acritas LLC ....G 407 375-5707
Orlando (G-12817)
Imagik International Corp ....F 786 631-5003
Doral (G-3388)
Interface Technology Group Inc ....G 321 433-1165
Rockledge (G-15422)
Interstate Electronics Corp ....D 321 730-0119
Cape Canaveral (G-1362)
L3harris Technologies Inc ....G 321 309-7848
Melbourne (G-8866)
L3harris Technologies Inc ....B 321 727-9100
Melbourne (G-8865)
L3harris Technologies Inc ....D 321 768-4660
Malabar (G-8494)
M C Test Service Inc ....A 321 253-0541
Melbourne (G-8879)
Mackay Communications Inc ....G 904 724-6101
Jacksonville (G-6572)
Mambo LLC ....F 305 860-2544
Doral (G-3422)
Micro Systems Inc ....C 850 244-2332
Fort Walton Beach (G-4815)
Motorola Solutions ....G 239 939-7717
Fort Myers (G-4539)
Motorola Solutions Inc ....G 850 243-4426
Fort Walton Beach (G-4818)
Motorola Solutions Inc ....G 561 369-7164
Boynton Beach (G-933)

Motorola Solutions Inc ....G 850 651-1725
Shalimar (G-16776)
Motorola Solutions Center ....G 863 665-5105
Lakeland (G-7755)
OSI International LLC ....G 561 394-9508
Boca Raton (G-656)
Phototelesis LP ....E 321 254-1500
Melbourne (G-8908)
Radiotronics Inc ....F 772 600-7574
Stuart (G-16996)
Rangevideo Laap ....G 404 421-2574
North Miami Beach (G-11703)
Raytheon Company ....G 310 647-9438
Largo (G-8038)
Raytheon Company ....G 727 768-8468
Largo (G-8037)
Reico Inc ....F 850 243-4400
Fort Walton Beach (G-4827)
Rockwell Collins Inc ....D 321 768-7303
Melbourne (G-8921)
RVr USA LLC ....G 305 471-9091
Doral (G-3494)
Satcom Scientific Inc ....F 407 856-1050
Orlando (G-13164)
Sierra Nevada Corporation ....E 850 659-3600
Shalimar (G-16777)
Tampa Microwave LLC ....E 813 855-2251
Clearwater (G-1904)
Transamerica Intl Brdcstg ....G 305 477-0973
Miami (G-10503)
TV Film International Inc ....G 305 671-3265
Miami (G-10515)
United Wireless Tech Inc ....F 561 302-9350
Boca Raton (G-769)
Viasat Inc ....G 813 880-5000
Tampa (G-18243)
Video Display Corporation ....D 321 784-4427
Cocoa (G-2056)
Visual Comm Specialists Inc ....G 407 936-7300
Lake Mary (G-7460)
Vmoviles Inc ....G 954 609-2510
Aventura (G-282)
Voxx International Corporation ....B 800 645-7750
Orlando (G-13313)
W & W Manufacturing Co ....E 516 942-0011
Tampa (G-18249)
Williams Communications Inc ....G 850 689-6651
Crestview (G-2361)

RADIO & TELEVISION REPAIR

Gulf Electronics ....F 727 595-3840
Largo (G-7967)

RADIO BROADCASTING & COMMUNICATIONS EQPT

Bk Technologies Inc ....F 321 984-1414
West Melbourne (G-18767)
Bk Technologies Corporation ....F 321 984-1414
West Melbourne (G-18768)
Cooper Notification Inc ....D 941 487-2300
Sarasota (G-16197)
First Communications Inc ....D 850 668-7990
Tallahassee (G-17251)
Motorola Solutions Inc ....A 954 723-5000
Plantation (G-14535)
Motorola Solutions Inc ....G 407 562-4000
Lake Mary (G-7437)
Parkervision Inc ....F 904 732-6100
Jacksonville (G-6658)
Pax Catholic Communications ....E 305 638-9729
Miami (G-10146)
Pinnacle Cmmncations Group LLC ....F 904 910-0444
Jacksonville (G-6674)
Sports Radar Ltd ....G 352 503-6825
Homosassa (G-6006)
Tech Comm Inc ....F 954 712-7777
Fort Lauderdale (G-4275)
Tecore Government Services LLC ....G 410 872-6000
Melbourne (G-8956)

RADIO COMMUNICATIONS: Airborne Eqpt

Becker Avionics Inc ....F 954 450-3137
Miramar (G-10974)
Boeing Company ....G 850 882-4912
Eglin Afb (G-3641)
Dayton-Granger Inc ....C 954 463-3451
Fort Lauderdale (G-3935)
Smiths Interconnect Inc ....C 813 901-7200
Tampa (G-18111)

Techcodes LLC .... G 321 529-4122
Titusville (G-18467)
Wialan Technologies LLC .... E 954 749-3481
Sunrise (G-17198)

RADIO EQPT: Citizens Band

Wiztel USA Inc .... G 416 457-5513
Miromar Lakes (G-11072)

RADIO MAGNETIC INSTRUMENTATION

General Dynmics Land Systems I .... G 850 574-4700
Tallahassee (G-17263)

RADIO PRODUCERS

American Impact Media Corp .... E 954 457-9003
Hallandale Beach (G-5169)

RADIO RECEIVER NETWORKS

Antique Automobile Radio Inc .... G 727 785-8733
Palm Harbor (G-13719)

RADIO, TELEVISION & CONSUMER ELECTRONICS STORES: Eqpt, NEC

Fun Electronics Inc .... F 305 933-4646
Miami (G-9603)

RADIOS WHOLESALERS

Marathon Technology Corp .... G 305 592-1340
Doral (G-3425)

RAIL & STRUCTURAL SHAPES: Aluminum rail & structural shapes

Custom Fbrications of Freeport .... F 850 729-0500
Valparaiso (G-18509)
Fabworx LLC .... F 239 573-9353
Cape Coral (G-1422)
Prestige Aluminum Railing Inc .... G 904 966-2163
Starke (G-16896)
White Aluminum Fabrication Inc .... E 772 219-3245
Stuart (G-17048)

RAILINGS: Prefabricated, Metal

Fab Rite Inc .... G 561 848-8181
Riviera Beach (G-15327)
Gelander Industries Inc .... F 352 343-3100
Tavares (G-18338)
Greco Alum Railings USA Inc .... E 727 372-4545
Hudson (G-6026)
Quality Railings Miami Corp .... G 786 400-0462
Hialeah (G-5590)

RAILROAD CARGO LOADING & UNLOADING SVCS

Bridge Trading Usa LLC .... F 877 848-0979
Doral (G-3286)

RAILROAD EQPT

CAF USA Inc .... G 305 753-5371
Miami (G-9300)
Contemprary McHnrey Engrg Svcs .... E 386 439-0937
Flagler Beach (G-3755)
G G Schmitt & Sons Inc .... C 717 394-3701
Sarasota (G-16216)
Progress Rail Services Corp .... F 904 783-1143
Jacksonville (G-6692)
Railings Plus Inc .... F 386 437-4501
Bunnell (G-1304)
Silver Enterprises Assoc Inc .... G 239 542-0068
Cape Coral (G-1472)

RAILROAD EQPT: Cars & Eqpt, Dining

Coulombe Enterprises .... G 407 366-4387
Oviedo (G-13424)

RAILROAD EQPT: Cars & Eqpt, Train, Freight Or Passenger

Hitachi Rail STS Usa Inc .... D 415 397-7010
Medley (G-8662)
Hitachi Rail Usa Inc .... F 415 397-7010
Medley (G-8663)

RAILROAD EQPT: Cars, Maintenance

Adams Street Station .... G 904 304-7222
Jacksonville (G-6119)

RAILROAD EQPT: Cars, Rebuilt

Rescar Companies Inc .... G 386 397-2656
White Springs (G-19188)
Southstern Rail Svcs Mlbrry FL .... F 863 425-4986
Mulberry (G-11138)

RAILROAD RELATED EQPT: Railway Track

Florida E Coast Holdings Corp .... E 904 279-3152
Jacksonville (G-6396)
Mafeks International LLC .... F 561 997-2080
Boca Raton (G-605)

RAILROAD TIES: Concrete

Rocla Concrete Tie Inc .... D 772 800-1855
Fort Pierce (G-4741)

RAILROADS: Long Haul

New Underground RR Pubg Co .... F 305 825-1444
Miami Lakes (G-10830)

RAILS: Rails, rolled & drawn, aluminum

Barrows Aluminum Inc .... F 386 767-3445
Port Orange (G-15011)
Largo Aluminum Inc .... F 305 852-2390
Islamorada (G-6098)
Poma Corporation .... D 561 790-5799
West Palm Beach (G-19001)

RAILS: Steel Or Iron

Rq Welding Inc .... G 786 609-3384
Miami (G-10284)
Sfa Systems Inc .... E 561 585-5927
Lake Worth (G-7586)

RAMPS: Prefabricated Metal

Amramp North FL .... G 904 424-3331
Tallahassee (G-17218)
Rampmaster Inc .... F 305 691-9090
Miami (G-10238)

REAL ESTATE AGENCIES: Residential

Volvox Inc Hollywood .... G 954 961-4942
Hollywood (G-5938)

REAL ESTATE AGENTS & MANAGERS

Feick Corporation .... D 305 271-8550
Miami (G-9561)
Sal Praschnik Inc .... F 305 866-4323
Bay Harbor Islands (G-339)
Seabreeze Communications Group .... F 239 278-4222
Fort Myers (G-4603)
Sun Publications Florida Inc .... D 321 402-0257
Kissimmee (G-7299)

REAL ESTATE APPRAISERS

Suncoast Accrdted Gmlgical Lab .... G 941 756-8787
Bradenton (G-1121)

REAL ESTATE INVESTMENT TRUSTS

Bricklser Engrv Monuments Corp .... F 786 806-0672
Doral (G-3285)

REAL ESTATE OPERATORS, EXC DEVELOPERS: Commercial/Indl Bldg

A M Coplan Associates .... G 904 737-6996
Jacksonville (G-6110)
Atlantic Jet Center Inc .... G 321 255-7111
Melbourne (G-8771)

REAL ESTATE OPERATORS, EXC DEVELOPERS: Property, Retail

Ddp Holdings LLC .... C 813 712-2515
Tampa (G-17595)

RECEIVERS: Radio Communications

Dayton Industrial Corporation .... G 941 351-4454
Sarasota (G-16405)
Summation Research Inc .... E 321 254-2580
Melbourne (G-8949)

RECORDING TAPE: Video, Blank

Triple J Marketing LLC .... E 813 247-6999
Tampa (G-18201)

RECORDS & TAPES: Prerecorded

Axzes LLC .... G 786 626-1611
Doral (G-3261)
Capital Technology Solutions .... G 850 562-3321
Tallahassee (G-17230)
Covis Inc .... G 954 315-3835
Fort Lauderdale (G-3920)
Enterprise Slling Slutions LLC .... G 904 655-9410
Jacksonville (G-6366)
Ibr LLC .... G 407 694-6748
Saint Cloud (G-15655)
Jazziz Magazine Inc .... E 561 893-6868
Boca Raton (G-578)
Mahigaming LLC .... F 561 504-1534
Deerfield Beach (G-2866)
Muscle Mixes Inc .... F 407 872-7576
Orlando (G-12987)
Obsolete Gamer Inc .... G 305 388-3372
Miami (G-10087)
Ocoa LLC .... E 407 898-1961
Orlando (G-13019)
Panoptex Technologies Inc .... F 407 412-0222
Orlando (G-13048)
Piergate LLC .... G 813 938-9170
Lutz (G-8409)
Runaware Inc .... F 954 907-9052
Coral Springs (G-2308)
Singing Machine Company Inc .... F 954 596-1000
Fort Lauderdale (G-4236)
Synaptic Sparks Inc .... G 205 774-8324
Orlando (G-13235)
Workep Inc .... G 787 634-1115
North Miami (G-11665)

RECOVERY SVC: Iron Ore, From Open Hearth Slag

Quest Manufacturing Corp .... F 305 513-8583
Medley (G-8713)

RECOVERY SVCS: Solvents

Agranco Corp (usa) .... F 877 592-0031
South Miami (G-16811)

RECREATIONAL VEHICLE DEALERS

Florida Bus Unlimited Inc .... E 407 656-1175
Orlando (G-12746)
Harberson Rv Pinellas LLC .... E 727 937-6176
Holiday (G-5742)

RECREATIONAL VEHICLE PARTS & ACCESS STORES

Offshore Performance Spc .... F 239 481-2768
Fort Myers (G-4555)

RECYCLING: Paper

ABC Recyclers Collier Cnty Inc .... G 239 643-2302
Naples (G-11145)
All Green Recycling Inc .... F 754 204-3707
Hollywood (G-5769)
Hogenkamp Research Inc .... F 850 677-1072
Gulf Breeze (G-5119)
Reuse Salvage Inc .... G 772 485-3248
Port Salerno (G-15165)

REELS: Wood

Temple Terrace Industries Inc .... F 813 752-7546
Plant City (G-14472)

REFINERS & SMELTERS: Aluminum

Alliance Metals LLC .... G 305 343-9536
Bay Harbor Islands (G-337)
Wise Recycling 1 LLC .... F 850 477-5273
Pensacola (G-14290)

REFINERS & SMELTERS: Copper

EJM Copper Inc......F 407 447-0074
Orlando *(G-12702)*

REFINERS & SMELTERS: Nonferrous Metal

All Metals Fabrication LLC......G....... 904 862-6885
Jacksonville *(G-6134)*
Enviro Focus Technology......G....... 813 744-5000
Tampa *(G-17644)*
Flotech Inc......D....... 904 358-1849
Jacksonville *(G-6406)*
Troika Group Inc......G....... 561 313-1119
Wellington *(G-18738)*

REFINERS & SMELTERS: Silicon, Primary, Over 99% Pure

Globe Specialty Metals Inc......F....... 786 509-6900
Miami *(G-9644)*

REFINING: Petroleum

AZ Chem Holdings LP......C....... 800 526-5294
Jacksonville *(G-6183)*
Comoderm Corp......G....... 561 756-2929
Pompano Beach *(G-14642)*
Ipro Force LLC......G....... 603 766-8716
Windermere *(G-19229)*
Jupiter Petroleum Inc......G....... 561 622-1276
Jupiter *(G-7062)*
Kimberlyn Investments Co......G....... 305 448-6328
Coral Gables *(G-2164)*
Nap Impex LLC......G....... 954 272-8453
Pembroke Pines *(G-14051)*
Okeechobee Petroleum LLC......G....... 561 478-1083
West Palm Beach *(G-18970)*
Oxbow Calcining LLC......C....... 580 874-2201
West Palm Beach *(G-18975)*
Petroleum Group LLC......F....... 352 304-5500
Belleview *(G-374)*
Petroleum Marine LLC......G....... 561 422-9018
West Palm Beach *(G-18996)*
Petrosol Processing & Refining......F....... 305 442-7400
Miami *(G-10157)*
Quality Petroleum Corp......G....... 863 635-6708
Frostproof *(G-4863)*
Searaven Glauben LLC......F....... 727 230-8840
Saint Augustine *(G-15606)*
Stop-N-Go 12......G....... 386 344-5494
Lake City *(G-7388)*

REFRACTORIES: Brick

Gem Paver Systems Inc......E....... 305 805-0000
Medley *(G-8656)*

REFRACTORIES: Cement, nonclay

Natures Earth Products Inc......E....... 561 688-8101
West Palm Beach *(G-18958)*

REFRACTORIES: Clay

Jamo Inc......D....... 305 885-3444
Medley *(G-8676)*

REFRACTORIES: Nonclay

Matthews International Corp......C....... 407 886-5533
Apopka *(G-158)*
Osmi Inc......F....... 561 330-9300
Boca Raton *(G-657)*

REFRACTORIES: Tile & Brick, Exc Plastic

Oldcastle Retail Inc......B....... 954 971-1200
Pompano Beach *(G-14778)*

REFRIGERATION & HEATING EQUIPMENT

1600 Lenox LLC......G....... 786 360-2553
Miami *(G-9021)*
AAA Able Appliance Service......G....... 954 791-5222
Fort Lauderdale *(G-3774)*
Adrick Marine Group Inc......F....... 321 631-0776
Cocoa *(G-1991)*
All Power Pro Inc......G....... 904 310-3069
Fernandina Beach *(G-3730)*
Allied Manufacturing Inc......G....... 813 502-0300
Tampa *(G-17402)*
American Standards Inc......G....... 904 683-2189
Jacksonville *(G-6150)*
Andrews Filter and Supply Corp......E....... 407 423-3310
Orlando *(G-12479)*
Beam Associates LLC......E....... 813 855-5695
Oldsmar *(G-12209)*
Beverage Equipment Repair Co......F....... 239 573-0683
Cape Coral *(G-1389)*
Bmp Usa Inc......D....... 813 443-0757
Tampa *(G-17476)*
Carrier Global Corporation......A....... 561 365-2000
Palm Beach Gardens *(G-13575)*
Climax Inc......G....... 786 264-6082
Doral *(G-3301)*
Con-Air Industries Inc......D....... 407 298-5733
Orlando *(G-12611)*
CPS Products Inc......G....... 305 687-4121
Miramar *(G-10981)*
Crown Products Company Inc......D....... 904 924-8340
Jacksonville *(G-6301)*
Dade Engineering Group LLC......F....... 305 885-2766
Miami *(G-9429)*
Danfoss LLC......G....... 772 219-0745
Stuart *(G-16930)*
Danfoss LLC......C....... 850 504-4800
Tallahassee *(G-17240)*
Drinkable Air Inc......E....... 954 533-6415
Lauderdale Lakes *(G-8086)*
Duststop Filters Inc......G....... 904 725-1001
Jacksonville *(G-6338)*
Eco Products Limited LLC......G....... 863 337-4918
Lakeland *(G-7680)*
Engineered Air Systems Inc......F....... 813 881-9555
Tampa *(G-17641)*
Fireside Holdings Inc......G....... 941 371-0300
Bradenton *(G-1041)*
Gigvaoi Fifth and Lenox......G....... 305 604-0635
Palmetto Bay *(G-13844)*
Green Air Group LLC......D....... 850 608-3065
Freeport *(G-4848)*
Hoseline Inc......F....... 541 258-8984
Ocala *(G-11966)*
Jer-Air Manufacturing Inc......E....... 352 591-2674
Micanopy *(G-10902)*
John Bean Technologies Corp......E....... 407 851-3377
Orlando *(G-12858)*
Lajoie Investment Corp......F....... 954 463-3271
Fort Lauderdale *(G-4094)*
Lennox Global Ltd......D....... 305 718-2921
Doral *(G-3416)*
Lennox Industries......G....... 305 718-2974
Doral *(G-3417)*
Lennox International Inc......G....... 352 379-9630
Gainesville *(G-4954)*
Lennox Miami Corp......E....... 305 763-8655
Miami Beach *(G-10687)*
Lennox National Account S......G....... 954 745-3482
Miami *(G-9884)*
Ml Metals Inc......C....... 813 855-5695
Oldsmar *(G-12248)*
Micro Matic Usa Inc......G....... 352 799-6331
Brooksville *(G-1250)*
Quality Marine Air Refrig......G....... 954 560-0084
Fort Lauderdale *(G-4191)*
Quorum Marine & Elec Inc......E....... 772 220-0038
Stuart *(G-16994)*
R & J Mfg of Gainesville......G....... 352 375-3130
Gainesville *(G-4987)*
Reftec International Inc......E....... 800 214-4883
Bradenton *(G-1104)*
Reftec Intl Systems LLC......F....... 727 290-9830
Largo *(G-8039)*
Sharing Three Inc......F....... 305 884-8384
Hialeah *(G-5617)*
Soda Service of Florida LLC......G....... 727 595-7632
Largo *(G-8057)*
Store It Cold LLC......G....... 720 456-1178
Medley *(G-8730)*
Trane US Inc......G....... 239 277-0344
Fort Myers *(G-4637)*
Trane US Inc......D....... 954 499-6900
Miramar *(G-11052)*
Tsm Champ LLC......D....... 615 806-7900
Sarasota *(G-16317)*
Verde GSE Inc......E....... 888 837-5221
Palmetto *(G-13832)*
Westran Corporation......G....... 727 375-7010
Trinity *(G-18492)*

REFRIGERATION EQPT: Complete

Acme Service Corp......F....... 305 836-4800
Miami *(G-9065)*
American Panel Corporation......C....... 352 245-7055
Ocala *(G-11871)*
Arctic Industries LLC......D....... 305 883-5581
Medley *(G-8611)*
Banks Airconditioning & Rfrgn......G....... 813 917-8685
Plant City *(G-14406)*
Cold Storage Engineering Co......G....... 305 448-0099
Miami *(G-9377)*
Kysor Industrial Corporation......F....... 727 376-8600
Trinity *(G-18487)*
Mainstream Engineering Corp......E....... 321 631-3550
Rockledge *(G-15432)*
Mr Winter Inc......E....... 800 327-3371
Medley *(G-8693)*
Refrigeration Panels Inc......F....... 305 836-6900
Miami *(G-10247)*
Refrigrtion Engnred Systems In......E....... 305 836-6900
Miami *(G-10248)*

REFRIGERATION REPAIR SVCS

A & V Refrigeration Corp......G....... 305 883-0733
Hialeah *(G-5255)*
Mechanical Svcs Centl Fla Inc......C....... 407 857-3510
Orlando *(G-12957)*

REFRIGERATION SVC & REPAIR

AAA Able Appliance Service......G....... 954 791-5222
Fort Lauderdale *(G-3774)*
AAA Monterey Discount Vacuum......G....... 772 288-5233
Stuart *(G-16900)*

REFRIGERATORS & FREEZERS WHOLESALERS

Apollo Worldwide Inc......G....... 561 585-3865
Hypoluxo *(G-6048)*

REFUSE SYSTEMS

Dixie Sptic Tank Orange Cy LLC......F....... 386 775-3051
Orange City *(G-12375)*
Wise Recycling 1 LLC......F....... 850 477-5273
Pensacola *(G-14290)*

REGULATION & ADMIN, GOVT: Public Svc Commission, Exc Transp

County of Broward......G....... 954 357-7120
Fort Lauderdale *(G-3919)*

REGULATORS: Power

Ring Power Corporation......E....... 904 354-1858
Jacksonville *(G-6725)*

REGULATORS: Transmission & Distribution Voltage

Universal Microwave Corp......D....... 352 754-2200
Brooksville *(G-1286)*

RELAYS & SWITCHES: Indl, Electric

Hts Controls Inc......F....... 813 287-5512
Tampa *(G-17766)*
Southern Switch & Contacts......F....... 727 789-0951
Palm Harbor *(G-13762)*
Tic Light Electrical Corp......G....... 305 712-3499
Miami *(G-10476)*

REMOVERS & CLEANERS

Cress Chemical & Equipment Co......G....... 407 425-2846
Orlando *(G-12628)*

RENTAL CENTERS: General

Lotus Containers Inc......G....... 786 590-1056
Miami *(G-9913)*

RENTAL SVCS: Aircraft

Aercap Inc......E....... 954 760-7777
Fort Lauderdale *(G-3785)*
Aercap Group Services Inc......B....... 954 760-7777
Fort Lauderdale *(G-3786)*

RENTAL SVCS: Business Machine & Electronic Eqpt

International Keg Rental LLC ....F 407 900-9992
Orlando (G-12836)
Sun Print Management LLC ....E 727 945-0255
Holiday (G-5749)

RENTAL SVCS: Eqpt & Prop, Motion Picture Production

Boland Production Supply Inc ....G 863 324-7784
Winter Haven (G-19304)

RENTAL SVCS: Floor Maintenance Eqpt

Jdl Surface Innovations Inc ....E 239 772-0077
Cape Coral (G-1441)

RENTAL SVCS: Sound & Lighting Eqpt

Airstar America Inc ....F 407 851-7830
Orlando (G-12447)

RENTAL SVCS: Work Zone Traffic Eqpt, Flags, Cones, Etc

Traffic Control Pdts Fla Inc ....F 813 621-8484
Fort Myers (G-4636)

RENTAL: Passenger Car

Premier Luxury Group LLC ....E 954 358-9885
Fort Lauderdale (G-4176)

RENTAL: Portable Toilet

AAA Event Services LLC ....F 386 454-0929
Newberry (G-11549)
Monty Sanitation Inc ....G 239 597-2486
Naples (G-11332)
P & L Creech Inc ....G 386 547-4182
Daytona Beach (G-2691)

RESEARCH, DEVELOPMENT & TEST SVCS, COMM: Cmptr Hardware Dev

Diversfied Mtl Specialists Inc ....G 941 244-0935
North Venice (G-11757)
Kreateck International Corp ....F 772 925-1216
Vero Beach (G-18637)

RESEARCH, DEVELOPMENT & TEST SVCS, COMM: Research, Exc Lab

Dermazone Solutions Inc ....E 727 446-6882
Saint Petersburg (G-15758)

RESEARCH, DEVELOPMENT & TESTING SVCS, COMM: Research Lab

Dermazone Solutions Inc ....E 727 446-6882
Saint Petersburg (G-15758)
Dioxide Materials Inc ....F 217 239-1400
Boca Raton (G-502)
General Oceanics Inc ....F 305 621-2882
Miami (G-9625)

RESEARCH, DEVELOPMENT & TESTING SVCS, COMMERCIAL: Business

Analytical Research Systems ....F 352 466-0051
Micanopy (G-10899)
Smx-US Inc ....E 914 840-5631
Miami (G-10367)

RESEARCH, DEVELOPMENT & TESTING SVCS, COMMERCIAL: Energy

Authentic Trading Inc ....G 347 866-7241
Davie (G-2500)

RESEARCH, DEVELOPMENT & TESTING SVCS, COMMERCIAL: Medical

Kms Medical LLC ....F 305 266-3388
Miami (G-9827)
Life Proteomics Inc ....F 813 864-7646
Tampa (G-17845)
Quick-Med Technologies Inc ....G 352 379-0611
Gainesville (G-4986)

Sinocare Meditech Inc ....F 800 342-7226
Fort Lauderdale (G-4237)

RESEARCH, DVLPT & TEST SVCS, COMM: Mkt Analysis or Research

Original Impressions LLC ....C 305 233-1322
Weston (G-19156)

RESIDUES

Got Residuals Inc ....G 775 343-9240
Naples (G-11265)
Referral & Residual Exchange L ....G 813 655-5000
Riverview (G-15280)
Residual Innovations LLC ....G 407 459-5497
Orlando (G-13132)

RESINS: Custom Compound Purchased

Bath Junkie of Gainesville ....G 352 331-3012
Gainesville (G-4884)
City of Lakeland ....F 863 834-6780
Lakeland (G-7657)
Seelye Acquisitions Inc ....G 407 656-6677
Apopka (G-184)

RESISTORS

Casa Del Marinero Corp ....G 305 374-5386
Miami (G-9322)
Component General Inc ....E 727 376-6655
Odessa (G-12112)
Electro Technik Industries Inc ....D 727 530-9555
Clearwater (G-1666)
Precision Resistor Co Inc ....E 727 541-5771
Seminole (G-16756)
Solitron Devices Inc ....D 561 848-4311
West Palm Beach (G-19038)
Vishay Americas Inc ....B 407 804-2567
Lake Mary (G-7459)

RESISTORS & RESISTOR UNITS

Hymeg Corporation ....G 800 322-1953
Clearwater (G-1724)

RESOLVERS

Resolver Group Inc ....G 941 387-7410
Longboat Key (G-8246)
Resolvers LLC ....G 954 254-7948
Deerfield Beach (G-2904)

RESORT HOTELS

Arkup Llc ....G 786 448-8635
Miami Beach (G-10644)

RESPIRATORY SYSTEM DRUGS

Wonder Holdings Acquisition ....F 305 379-2322
Miami (G-10615)

RESTAURANT EQPT: Carts

American Metal Products Inc ....G 407 293-0090
Orlando (G-12471)
Klugman Enterprises LLC ....G 352 318-9623
Sarasota (G-16246)
Load King Manufacturing Co ....C 904 354-8882
Jacksonville (G-6560)

RESTAURANT EQPT: Food Wagons

Captain Max ....G 954 987-8552
Miramar (G-10976)
Carley Nigel Holdings LLC ....F 407 212-9341
Rockledge (G-15398)
Cg Burgers ....F 954 618-6450
Fort Lauderdale (G-3893)
Chin & Chin Enterprises Inc ....F 407 478-8726
Winter Park (G-19394)
Drinks On ME 305 LLC ....F 786 488-2356
Miami (G-9486)
Gcato 1959 Enterprises LLC ....G 954 937-6282
Pompano Beach (G-14712)
Honduras Food Services Inc ....E 310 940-2071
Gainesville (G-4937)
Luong Moc III Inc ....E 407 478-8726
Winter Park (G-19421)
Mr Real Deal barbque LLC ....G 561 271-8749
Delray Beach (G-3110)

My Passion On A Plate LLC ....F 954 857-6382
North Lauderdale (G-11618)
TLC Food Truck LLC ....F 305 879-2488
Miami (G-10481)

RESTAURANT EQPT: Sheet Metal

Captive-Aire Systems Inc ....E 407 682-9396
Altamonte Springs (G-36)
Tarpon Stnless Fabricators Inc ....E 727 942-1821
Tarpon Springs (G-18328)

RESTAURANTS: Fast Food

Jeremiahs Original Water Ice ....G 407 679-2665
Winter Park (G-19416)

RESTAURANTS:Full Svc, Cajun

Titanic Brewing Company Inc ....F 305 668-1742
Coral Gables (G-2199)

RESTAURANTS:Full Svc, Chinese

Egg Roll Skins Inc ....F 305 836-0571
Hialeah (G-5391)

RESTAURANTS:Full Svc, Ethnic Food

Patty King Inc ....E 305 817-1888
Hialeah (G-5555)

RESTAURANTS:Full Svc, Family, Independent

Mishas Cupcakes Inc ....E 786 200-6153
Miami (G-10028)

RESTAURANTS:Full Svc, Italian

Richard Meer Investments Inc ....G 941 484-6551
Venice (G-18570)

RESTAURANTS:Full Svc, Mexican

La Esquina Del Le Billto ....E 305 477-4225
Doral (G-3415)

RESTAURANTS:Limited Svc, Coffee Shop

Buttercream Cpcakes Cof Sp Inc ....F 305 669-8181
Coral Gables (G-2128)
Outpost 30a LLC ....F 850 909-0138
Inlet Beach (G-6078)

RESTAURANTS:Limited Svc, Fast-Food, Chain

Frito-Lay North America Inc ....G 972 334-7000
Seminole (G-16747)

RESTAURANTS:Limited Svc, Frozen Yogurt Stand

Top Hat Food Services LLC ....G 630 825-2800
Venice (G-18581)

RESTAURANTS:Limited Svc, Ice Cream Stands Or Dairy Bars

Coco Gelato Corp ....E 786 621-2444
Miami (G-9372)
Cold Stone Creamery-Parkland ....G 954 341-8033
Coral Springs (G-2232)

RESTAURANTS:Limited Svc, Pizza

Classic Pizza Crusts Inc ....G 954 570-8383
Pompano Beach (G-14636)
Pizza Spice Packet LLC ....G 718 831-7036
Boca Raton (G-666)

RESTRAINTS

Safety Intl Bags & Straps ....F 407 830-0888
Casselberry (G-1517)

RESTROOM CLEANING SVCS

Lions Intl MGT Group Inc ....F 813 367-2517
Tampa (G-17848)

RETAIL BAKERY: Cakes

Carlees Creations Inc ....G....... 786 232-0050
Miami *(G-9319)*

RETAIL BAKERY: Cookies

Selmas Cookies Inc ....E....... 407 884-9433
Apopka *(G-185)*

RETAIL BAKERY: Doughnuts

Dip-A-Dee Donuts ....E....... 352 460-4266
Leesburg *(G-8150)*

RETAIL FIREPLACE STORES

Grate Fireplace & Stone Shoppe ....E....... 239 939-7187
Fort Myers *(G-4471)*

RETAIL LUMBER YARDS

Bushnell Truss Enterprises LLC ....F....... 352 793-6090
Bushnell *(G-1314)*
K P Kitchens Corp ....G....... 954 322-9087
Miramar *(G-11008)*

RETAIL STORES, NEC

Splinter Woodworking Inc.....................G....... 305 731-9334
Delray Beach *(G-3145)*

RETAIL STORES: Alcoholic Beverage Making Eqpt & Splys

Leonard-Martin Corporation ....G....... 850 434-2203
Pensacola *(G-14192)*

RETAIL STORES: Aquarium Splys

Endless Oceans LLC ....G....... 561 274-1990
Delray Beach *(G-3073)*
Waterbox Usa LLC ....G....... 800 674-2608
Longwood *(G-8349)*

RETAIL STORES: Artificial Limbs

Son Life Prsthtics Orthtics In ....F....... 352 596-2257
Hernando Beach *(G-5251)*

RETAIL STORES: Audio-Visual Eqpt & Splys

AVI-Spl Emplyee Emrgncy Rlief ....A....... 813 884-7168
Tampa *(G-17445)*
Dj Live Productions LLC ....G....... 407 383-1740
Altamonte Springs *(G-41)*

RETAIL STORES: Autograph Splys

Eartech Inc...G....... 941 747-8193
Bradenton *(G-1034)*

RETAIL STORES: Awnings

A & A Central Florida ....F....... 407 648-5666
Altamonte Springs *(G-24)*
Business World Trading Inc..................F....... 305 238-0724
Miami *(G-9288)*
John R Caito...G....... 850 612-0179
Fort Walton Beach *(G-4811)*
Milliken & Milliken Inc............................E....... 941 474-0223
Englewood *(G-3680)*
Rolling Shield Parts Inc.........................F....... 305 436-6661
Miami Lakes *(G-10853)*
Southern Awning Inc ....E....... 561 586-0464
Lake Worth *(G-7587)*
Sunmaster of Naples Inc ....E....... 239 261-3581
Naples *(G-11426)*

RETAIL STORES: Baby Carriages & Strollers

Best Price Mobility Inc...........................F....... 321 402-5955
Kissimmee *(G-7224)*

RETAIL STORES: Banners

C&D Sign and Lighting Svcs LLC ....G....... 863 937-9323
Lakeland *(G-7652)*
Carlaron Inc..G....... 386 258-1183
Daytona Beach *(G-2639)*
Fastsigns ....G....... 850 477-9744
Pensacola *(G-14149)*
International Quiksigns Inc...................F....... 954 462-7446
Fort Lauderdale *(G-4063)*

Maddys Print Shop LLC ....G....... 954 749-0440
Fort Lauderdale *(G-4108)*
Thomas United Inc.................................G....... 239 561-7446
Fort Myers *(G-4628)*

RETAIL STORES: Binoculars & Telescopes

Jl Optical Inc...G....... 386 428-6928
New Smyrna Beach *(G-11536)*

RETAIL STORES: Business Machines & Eqpt

M & S Computer Products Inc ....G....... 561 244-5400
Boynton Beach *(G-930)*

RETAIL STORES: Cake Decorating Splys

Carlees Creations Inc ....G....... 786 232-0050
Miami *(G-9319)*

RETAIL STORES: Canvas Prdts

Canvas West Inc ....G....... 941 355-0780
Sarasota *(G-16380)*
Sea King Kanvas & Shade Inc ....G....... 239 481-3535
Fort Myers *(G-4602)*

RETAIL STORES: Cleaning Eqpt & Splys

Campos Chemicals................................F....... 727 412-2774
Saint Petersburg *(G-15736)*

RETAIL STORES: Concrete Prdts, Precast

Concraft Inc..G....... 561 689-0149
Greenacres *(G-5078)*

RETAIL STORES: Cosmetics

Inspec Solutions LLC ....E....... 866 467-7320
Holly Hill *(G-5758)*
Matrix Packaging of Florida..................G....... 305 358-9696
Miami *(G-9956)*

RETAIL STORES: Educational Aids & Electronic Training Mat

Gadgetcat LLC ....G....... 802 238-3671
Cocoa Beach *(G-2063)*
Paradigm Leaders LLC..........................G....... 850 441-3289
Panama City Beach *(G-13982)*

RETAIL STORES: Electronic Parts & Eqpt

Interntnal Synrgy For Tchncal ....G....... 321 305-0863
Orlando *(G-12837)*
Spin Magnetics......................................E....... 863 676-9333
Lake Wales *(G-7520)*

RETAIL STORES: Farm Eqpt & Splys

Marden Industries Inc............................F....... 863 682-7882
Punta Gorda *(G-15213)*

RETAIL STORES: Fiberglass Materials, Exc Insulation

Car Care Haven LLC ....G....... 855 464-2836
Englewood *(G-3671)*
Ryan Scientific LLC...............................F....... 904 284-6025
Green Cove Springs *(G-5069)*
Tiki Water Sports Inc ....G....... 305 852-9298
Key Largo *(G-7175)*

RETAIL STORES: Flags

Keystone 75 Inc......................................G....... 954 430-1880
Hollywood *(G-5856)*

RETAIL STORES: Hair Care Prdts

Brand Labs USA......................................E....... 954 532-5390
Pompano Beach *(G-14620)*

RETAIL STORES: Hearing Aids

Audina Hearing Instruments.................D....... 407 331-0077
Longwood *(G-8259)*
Bell Hearing Instruments Inc ....E....... 813 814-2355
Oldsmar *(G-12211)*
Ear-Tronics Inc.......................................G....... 239 275-7655
Fort Myers *(G-4440)*
Miami ....F....... 954 874-7707
Miami *(G-9991)*

RETAIL STORES: Hospital Eqpt & Splys

Med Alert Response Inc ....G....... 407 730-3571
Orlando *(G-12958)*

RETAIL STORES: Ice

Reddy Ice Corporation ....F....... 850 433-2191
Pensacola *(G-14251)*

RETAIL STORES: Maps & Charts

Map & Globe LLC ....F....... 407 898-0757
Maitland *(G-8473)*

RETAIL STORES: Medical Apparatus & Splys

Advanced Prosthetics Amer Inc............F....... 352 383-0396
Eustis *(G-3700)*
Cables and Sensors LLC......................F....... 866 373-6767
Orlando *(G-12543)*

RETAIL STORES: Mobile Telephones & Eqpt

Gnj Manufacturing Inc...........................E....... 305 651-8644
West Park *(G-19093)*
Sky Phone LLC.......................................F....... 305 531-5218
Miami Beach *(G-10711)*

RETAIL STORES: Monuments, Finished To Custom Order

Latteri & Sons Inc ....G....... 813 876-1800
Tampa *(G-17836)*

RETAIL STORES: Motors, Electric

AL Covell Electric Inc ....G....... 352 544-0680
Brooksville *(G-1207)*
Biscayne Electric Motor & Pump...........G....... 305 681-8171
Miami *(G-9251)*
Electrcal Systems Cmmnications ....G....... 813 248-4275
Tampa *(G-17631)*
M & W Electric Motors Inc......................G....... 850 433-0400
Pensacola *(G-14198)*
Stewarts Elc Mtr Works Inc...................E....... 407 859-1837
Orlando *(G-13215)*
Suncoast Electric Motor Svc ....F....... 813 247-4104
Tampa *(G-18143)*
United Electric Motor Inc.......................G....... 813 238-7872
Tampa *(G-18220)*

RETAIL STORES: Orthopedic & Prosthesis Applications

Bolt Systems Inc ....G....... 407 425-0012
Orlando *(G-12532)*
Institute For Prosthetic Advan...............G....... 850 784-0320
Panama City *(G-13918)*
Orthotic Prsthtic Rhblttion As ....G....... 352 331-3399
Gainesville *(G-4977)*
Prosthetic Laboratories.........................G....... 305 250-9900
Coral Gables *(G-2187)*
Quirantes Orthopedics Inc.....................G....... 305 261-1382
Miami *(G-10227)*

RETAIL STORES: Pet Splys

King Kanine LLC ....E....... 833 546-4738
Plantation *(G-14528)*
Miami Tbr LLC ....G....... 786 275-4773
Doral *(G-3437)*

RETAIL STORES: Photocopy Machines

Toner Technologies Inc ....G....... 561 547-9710
Boynton Beach *(G-970)*

RETAIL STORES: Police Splys

Telenetpro Inc...F....... 954 333-8633
Pompano Beach *(G-14885)*

RETAIL STORES: Rubber Stamps

Print Shop of Chiefland Inc....................G....... 352 493-0322
Chiefland *(G-1537)*

RETAIL STORES: Safety Splys & Eqpt

Lifesaving Systems Corporation...........E....... 813 645-2748
Apollo Beach *(G-105)*

RETAIL STORES: Sunglasses

Waterboyz Wbz Inc ....F 850 433-2929
Pensacola *(G-14287)*

RETAIL STORES: Telephone & Communication Eqpt

Cyipcom Inc ....G....... 954 727-2500
Oakland Park *(G-11794)*
Trs Wireless Inc ....E 407 447-7333
Orlando *(G-13277)*

RETAIL STORES: Water Purification Eqpt

Aquasolve Ventures LLC ....G....... 732 570-0707
Daytona Beach *(G-2627)*
Ashberry Acquisition Company ....F 813 248-0055
Tampa *(G-17438)*
Siemens Industry Inc ....G....... 407 650-3570
Orlando *(G-13188)*

RETREADING MATERIALS: Tire

Fedan Corp ....F 305 885-5415
Hialeah *(G-5410)*

REUPHOLSTERY & FURNITURE REPAIR

Antique & Modern Cabinets Inc ....E 904 393-9055
Jacksonville *(G-6158)*

REUPHOLSTERY SVCS

Grafton Furniture Company ....E 305 696-3811
Miami *(G-9653)*
Shorr Enterprises Inc ....F 954 733-9840
Lauderdale Lakes *(G-8093)*

REWINDING SVCS

Aircraft Electric Motors Inc ....D 305 885-9476
Miami Lakes *(G-10761)*
Beltech Generator & Rewinding ....G....... 954 588-2255
Fort Lauderdale *(G-3845)*
Tri County Aerospace Inc ....F 305 639-3356
Doral *(G-3532)*
TSA Rewinds Florida Inc ....G....... 305 681-2030
Opa Locka *(G-12366)*

RIBBONS: Machine, Inked Or Carbon

Eastern Ribbon & Roll Corp ....E 813 676-8600
Odessa *(G-12117)*
Golden Ribbon Corporation ....F 727 545-4499
Largo *(G-7963)*
Ribbon Wholesale Corp ....F 786 457-0555
Miami *(G-10262)*

RIPRAP QUARRYING

Rock Ridge Materials Inc ....F 321 268-8455
Titusville *(G-18460)*

RIVETS: Metal

Standard Rivet Company Inc ....F 386 872-6477
South Daytona *(G-16810)*

ROAD MATERIALS: Bituminous

Ellison Rbm Inc ....G....... 863 679-5283
Lake Wales *(G-7508)*

ROAD MATERIALS: Bituminous, Not From Refineries

Blacklidge Emulsions Inc ....F 813 247-5699
Tampa *(G-17473)*

ROBOTS: Assembly Line

Bcdirect Corp ....F 305 623-3838
Miami *(G-9229)*
Health Robotics Canada LLC ....F 786 388-5339
Miami *(G-9692)*
Sims Machine & Controls Inc ....F 352 799-2405
Brooksville *(G-1270)*

ROCKETS: Space & Military

Space Exploration Tech Corp ....E 310 363-6000
Cape Canaveral *(G-1368)*
United Drones LLC ....G....... 305 978-1480
Naples *(G-11447)*

ROD & BAR: Aluminum

Winrise Enterprises LLC ....F 786 621-6705
Miramar *(G-11061)*

RODS: Plastic

American Plastic Sup & Mfg Inc ....E 727 573-0636
Clearwater *(G-1581)*
King Plastic Corporation ....C 941 423-8666
North Port *(G-11742)*

RODS: Steel & Iron, Made In Steel Mills

Durbal Inc ....G....... 727 531-3040
Clearwater *(G-1662)*
Kissimmee Iron Works Inc ....G....... 407 870-8872
Kissimmee *(G-7262)*

RODS: Welding

Dons Custom Service Inc ....G....... 954 491-4043
Fort Lauderdale *(G-3948)*

ROLLERS & FITTINGS: Window Shade

Solar Venetian Blinds Inc ....G....... 305 634-4553
Miami *(G-10371)*

ROLLING MILL EQPT: Galvanizing Lines

Industrial Galvanizers Miami ....E 305 681-8844
Miami *(G-9738)*
Metalplate Galvanizing LP ....D 904 768-6330
Jacksonville *(G-6599)*

ROLLING MILL MACHINERY

Continental Metals ....G....... 734 362-1144
Fort Myers *(G-4409)*
Metalhouse LLC ....G....... 407 270-3000
Orlando *(G-12962)*

ROOF DECKS

Dynamic Metals LLC ....F 561 629-7304
West Palm Beach *(G-18858)*
Epic Metals Corporation ....G....... 863 533-7404
Bartow *(G-314)*

ROOFING MATERIALS: Asphalt

American Roofing Services LLC ....G....... 305 250-7115
Coral Gables *(G-2122)*
Chuculu LLC ....F 305 595-4577
Miami *(G-9353)*
Coastal Acquisitions Fla LLC ....F 850 769-9423
Panama City *(G-13883)*
Dj Roof and Solar Supply LLC ....G....... 954 557-1992
Fort Lauderdale *(G-3944)*
Drexel Metals Inc ....E 727 572-7900
Tampa *(G-17616)*
Karnak South Inc ....F 954 761-7606
Fort Lauderdale *(G-4084)*
Miami Metal Roofing LLC ....F 305 749-6356
Hialeah *(G-5512)*
Thomas White LLC ....G....... 813 704-4406
Plant City *(G-14473)*

ROOFING MATERIALS: Sheet Metal

Baker Metal Works & Supply LLC ....E 850 537-2010
Baker *(G-300)*
Dans Custom Sheet Metal Inc ....E 239 594-0530
Naples *(G-11221)*
Florida Metal Products LLC ....D 904 783-8400
Jacksonville *(G-6400)*
LV Thompson Inc ....C 813 248-3456
Tampa *(G-17866)*
Metal Roof Factory Inc ....G....... 321 632-8300
Rockledge *(G-15436)*
Thomas Smith & Company Inc ....F 863 858-2199
Lakeland *(G-7821)*

ROOFING MEMBRANE: Rubber

Shredded Tire Inc ....F 954 970-8565
Fort Lauderdale *(G-4232)*
Southeast Gen Contrs Group Inc ....F 877 407-3535
Port St Lucie *(G-15179)*

ROOM COOLERS: Portable

Amerikooler LLC ....C 305 884-8384
Hialeah *(G-5299)*

ROPE

Sunshine Cordage Corporation ....G....... 305 592-3750
Miami *(G-10434)*

RUBBER

Daytona Rubber Company Inc ....F 305 513-4105
Doral *(G-3324)*
Gaddie Construction Co ....G....... 850 215-8421
Panama City *(G-13906)*
Goodrich Corporation ....C 904 757-3660
Jacksonville *(G-6441)*
Latam Group Corp ....G....... 305 793-8961
Miami *(G-9864)*
Maclan Corporation Inc ....E 863 665-4814
Lakeland *(G-7742)*
Modern Silicone Tech Inc ....C 727 873-1805
Pinellas Park *(G-14369)*
T S E Industries Inc ....C 727 573-7676
Clearwater *(G-1900)*

RUBBER BANDS

Premium Rubber Bands Inc ....G....... 305 321-0333
Miami *(G-10187)*

RUBBER PRDTS

Global Force Enterprises LLC ....G....... 786 317-8197
Miramar *(G-10998)*
Liberty Balloons LLC ....G....... 239 947-3338
Bonita Springs *(G-843)*
Professional Ctr At Gardens ....F 561 394-5200
Delray Beach *(G-3127)*
Proform System Inc ....G....... 305 854-2800
Miami *(G-10208)*
Racing Shell Covers LLC ....G....... 732 236-0435
Naples *(G-11380)*
Thriller Clearwater Inc ....G....... 727 389-2209
Dunedin *(G-3590)*

RUBBER PRDTS: Automotive, Mechanical

Archimaze Logistics Inc ....G....... 954 615-7485
Fort Lauderdale *(G-3819)*

RUBBER PRDTS: Mechanical

Etco Incorporated ....C 941 756-8426
Bradenton *(G-1039)*
J B Nottingham & Co Inc ....E 386 873-2990
Deland *(G-2986)*
Modern Silicone Tech Inc ....C 727 873-1805
Pinellas Park *(G-14369)*
Pompadour Products Inc ....E 954 345-2700
Coral Springs *(G-2303)*
Southern Plastics & Rubber Co ....E 386 672-1167
Ormond Beach *(G-13401)*
T S E Industries Inc ....C 727 573-7676
Clearwater *(G-1900)*

RUBBER PRDTS: Oil & Gas Field Machinery, Mechanical

Cables and Sensors LLC ....F 866 373-6767
Orlando *(G-12543)*

RUBBER PRDTS: Reclaimed

Global Tire Rcycl of Smter CNT ....E 352 330-2213
Wildwood *(G-19194)*
Global Tire Recycling Inc ....F 352 330-2213
Wildwood *(G-19195)*

RUBBER PRDTS: Sheeting

Mako Hose & Rubber Co ....G....... 561 795-6200
West Palm Beach *(G-18939)*

RUBBER PRDTS: Silicone

Rowe Industries Inc ....F 302 855-0585
Pembroke Park *(G-14011)*
Venair Inc ....G....... 305 362-8920
Miami Gardens *(G-10758)*

RUBBER PRDTS: Sponge

Re-Think It Inc ....F 407 671-6000
Winter Park *(G-19437)*

RUBBER PRDTS: Wet Suits

Aquatic Fabricators of S Fla ......G...... 954 458-0400
Hallandale *(G-5152)*
J & I Ventures Inc ......E...... 561 845-0030
West Palm Beach *(G-18909)*
Sport Products of Tampa Inc ......G...... 813 630-5552
Tampa *(G-18127)*

RUG BINDING

Area Rugs Mfg Inc ......G...... 904 398-5481
Jacksonville *(G-6166)*

RUGS : Hand & Machine Made

Area Rugs Mfg Inc ......G...... 904 398-5481
Jacksonville *(G-6166)*

RUST REMOVERS

Florida Rust ......G...... 386 259-9940
Deltona *(G-3170)*

SAFES & VAULTS: Metal

Blue Chip Group LLC ......G...... 305 863-9094
Doral *(G-3280)*
Brandon Lock & Safe Inc ......G...... 813 655-4200
Tampa *(G-17485)*
Hayman Safe Co Inc ......F...... 407 365-5434
Oviedo *(G-13434)*
Valuesafes Inc ......G...... 877 629-6214
Port Charlotte *(G-15005)*
Vault Structures Inc ......E...... 239 332-3270
Fort Myers *(G-4644)*

SAFETY EQPT & SPLYS WHOLESALERS

Lifesaving Systems Corporation ......E...... 813 645-2748
Apollo Beach *(G-105)*
Sara Glove Company Inc ......G...... 866 664-7272
Naples *(G-11392)*
Threez Company LLC ......G...... 904 422-9224
Jacksonville *(G-6853)*
Threez Company LLC ......G...... 904 651-1444
Jacksonville *(G-6854)*
Troy Industries Inc ......E...... 305 324-1742
Doral *(G-3534)*

SAFETY INSPECTION SVCS

Titan Service Industry Llc ......G...... 678 313-4707
Deland *(G-3023)*

SAILBOAT BUILDING & REPAIR

Catalina Yachts Inc ......C...... 727 544-6681
Largo *(G-7919)*
Gause Built Marine Inc ......E...... 727 937-9113
Tarpon Springs *(G-18302)*
Sino Eagle Usa Inc ......F...... 727 259-3570
Dunedin *(G-3588)*
Uk Sailmakers Inc ......G...... 941 365-7245
Sarasota *(G-16320)*

SAILS

Atlantic Sails Makers ......G...... 305 567-1773
Miami *(G-9183)*
Delisser Enterprises Inc ......G...... 305 649-6001
Miami *(G-9449)*
Douglas A Fisher Inc ......G...... 941 951-0189
Sarasota *(G-16414)*
Gulfcoast Sailing Inc ......G...... 727 823-1968
Saint Petersburg *(G-15799)*
Schurr Sails Inc ......F...... 850 438-9354
Pensacola *(G-14258)*
Southern Interest Co Inc ......F...... 727 471-2040
Saint Petersburg *(G-15917)*
US Spars Inc ......G...... 386 462-3760
Gainesville *(G-5014)*

SALES PROMOTION SVCS

Deco Abrusci International LLC ......F...... 305 406-3401
Doral *(G-3326)*

SALT

A 2 Z of Lake City Inc ......F...... 386 755-0235
Lake City *(G-7343)*
DSM Lake City LLC ......G...... 352 861-5843
Ocala *(G-11927)*
Island Salt Company LLC ......G...... 954 610-2590
Fort Lauderdale *(G-4068)*
Lake City Mediplex LLC ......F...... 386 752-2209
Lake City *(G-7363)*
Microsalt Inc ......G...... 877 825-0655
West Palm Beach *(G-18952)*
OMI of Lake City LLC ......G...... 386 288-5632
Lake City *(G-7373)*
Salt 1to1 Inc ......F...... 407 721-8107
Orlando *(G-13160)*
Startech Lake City Inc ......F...... 386 466-1969
Lake City *(G-7387)*

SAMPLE BOOKS

Hofmann & Leavy Inc ......D...... 954 698-0000
Deerfield Beach *(G-2842)*
US Sample Corp ......E...... 954 495-4525
Boca Raton *(G-773)*

SAND & GRAVEL

Aurora Stone & Gravel LLC ......G...... 321 253-4808
Melbourne *(G-8772)*
Bermont Excavating LLC ......F...... 866 367-9557
Punta Gorda *(G-15196)*
Cemex Cnstr Mtls Fla LLC ......F...... 800 992-3639
Moore Haven *(G-11086)*
Corbin Sand and Clay Inc ......G...... 850 638-8462
Chipley *(G-1542)*
Dan Frame & Trim Inc ......G...... 352 726-4567
Inverness *(G-6085)*
ER Jahna Industries Inc ......G...... 863 422-7617
Haines City *(G-5142)*
G2c Enterprises Inc ......F...... 850 398-5368
Crestview *(G-2348)*
G2c Enterprises Inc ......F...... 850 585-4166
Crestview *(G-2349)*
Hector Corporation ......G...... 786 308-5853
Miami *(G-9697)*
Helms Hauling & Materials Llc ......F...... 850 218-6895
Niceville *(G-11569)*
James G Dowling ......G...... 407 509-9484
Sanford *(G-16073)*
Professional Site & Trnspt Inc ......F...... 386 239-6800
Daytona Beach *(G-2700)*
Rockpack Inc ......E...... 407 757-0798
Apopka *(G-182)*
Sand Power Volleyball ......G...... 813 786-8055
Brandon *(G-1177)*
Sod Depot & Gravel Inc ......G...... 321 728-2766
Palm Bay *(G-13535)*
Stewart Materials Inc ......G...... 561 972-4517
Jupiter *(G-7123)*
Stony Creek Sand & Gravel LLC ......F...... 804 229-0015
Pompano Beach *(G-14874)*
Vecellio & Grogan Inc ......D...... 305 822-5322
Hialeah *(G-5674)*
Vetcon Construction Inc ......G...... 352 234-6668
Ocala *(G-12070)*

SAND MINING

Bonita Grande Mining LLC ......F...... 239 947-6402
Bonita Springs *(G-817)*
C C Calhoun Inc ......E...... 863 292-9511
Winter Haven *(G-19310)*
Garcia Mining Company LLC ......F...... 863 902-9777
Clewiston *(G-1981)*
Legacy Vulcan LLC ......F...... 352 394-6196
Clermont *(G-1967)*
Legacy Vulcan Corp ......G...... 352 742-2122
Tavares *(G-18345)*

SAND: Hygrade

Chemours Company Fc LLC ......C...... 904 964-1200
Starke *(G-16890)*
Standard Sand & Silica Company ......E...... 863 422-7100
Davenport *(G-2483)*

SAND: Silica

Sand Hill Rock LLC ......G...... 772 216-4852
Okeechobee *(G-12191)*

SANDBLASTING EQPT

Industrial Marine Inc ......F...... 904 781-4707
Jacksonville *(G-6493)*
N-Viro Inc ......G...... 904 781-4707
Jacksonville *(G-6617)*

SANDBLASTING SVC: Building Exterior

Cya Powder Coating LLC ......G...... 727 299-9832
Clearwater *(G-1646)*

SANITARY SVC, NEC

Bingham On-Site Sewers Inc ......D...... 813 659-0003
Dover *(G-3556)*
Joe Hearn Innovative Tech LLC ......F...... 850 898-3744
Pensacola *(G-14183)*

SANITARY SVCS: Environmental Cleanup

Agranco Corp (usa) ......F...... 877 592-0031
South Miami *(G-16811)*

SANITARY SVCS: Liquid Waste Collection & Disposal

All Liquid Envmtl Svcs LLC ......E...... 800 767-9594
Fort Lauderdale *(G-3797)*

SANITARY SVCS: Sanitary Landfill, Operation Of

Waste Management Inc Florida ......E...... 954 984-2000
Winter Garden *(G-19289)*

SANITARY SVCS: Waste Materials, Recycling

College Hunks Hlg Junk & Mvg ......G...... 407 378-2500
Orlando *(G-12601)*
D & S Pallets Inc ......D...... 727 540-0061
Clearwater *(G-1647)*
Global Holdings and Dev LLC ......G...... 949 500-4997
Pompano Beach *(G-14714)*
Purecycle Technologies Inc ......E...... 877 648-3565
Orlando *(G-13100)*
Yahl Mulching & Recycling Inc ......F...... 239 352-7888
Naples *(G-11462)*

SANITARY WARE: Metal

Arya Group LLC ......G...... 561 792-9992
Wellington *(G-18709)*
Bathroom World Manufacturing ......G...... 954 566-0451
Oakland Park *(G-11785)*
East Coast Fixtures & Mllwk Co ......G...... 904 733-9711
Jacksonville *(G-6349)*
Jambco Millwork Inc ......F...... 954 977-4998
Margate *(G-8551)*
Wool Wholesale Plumbing Supply ......D...... 954 763-3632
Fort Lauderdale *(G-4327)*

SANITATION CHEMICALS & CLEANING AGENTS

Allen Shuffleboard LLC ......G...... 727 399-8877
Seminole *(G-16737)*
and Services ......G...... 850 805-6455
Fort Walton Beach *(G-4776)*
Campos Chemicals ......F...... 727 412-2774
Saint Petersburg *(G-15736)*
Caribbean Global Group Corp ......F...... 786 449-2767
Port St Lucie *(G-15169)*
Clorox Healthcare Holdings LLC ......E...... 904 996-7758
Jacksonville *(G-6270)*
Duct Dynasty ......G...... 407 730-9081
Orlando *(G-12691)*
Enozo Technologies Inc ......G...... 512 944-7772
Lakewood Ranch *(G-7838)*
For Life Products LLC ......D...... 954 747-3300
Miramar *(G-10994)*
Four Star Products Inc ......G...... 941 727-6161
Bradenton *(G-1044)*
Freezetone Products LLC ......F...... 305 640-0414
Doral *(G-3355)*
Goho Enterprises Inc ......F...... 407 884-0770
Zellwood *(G-19503)*
Illinois Tool Works Inc ......D...... 863 665-3338
Lakeland *(G-7708)*
NCH FL Funding LLC ......G...... 321 777-7777
Melbourne *(G-8892)*
NCH Marine LLC ......G...... 754 422-4237
Davie *(G-2557)*
Pro Chem Products Inc ......G...... 407 425-5533
Orlando *(G-13091)*
Puritair LLC ......F...... 954 281-5105
Fort Lauderdale *(G-4186)*
Roebic Laboratories Inc ......F...... 561 799-3380
Jupiter *(G-7105)*

Sicamu Inc ....G....850 270-6283
Quincy *(G-15254)*
Sltons Envirnmntal Group Assoc ....F....305 665-5594
Miami *(G-10362)*
Star-Brite Distributing Inc ....E....954 587-6280
Davie *(G-2595)*
Stratford Corporation ....G....727 443-1573
Clearwater *(G-1890)*
Trident Trading Inc ....G....561 488-0458
Boca Raton *(G-756)*
Troy Industries Inc ....E....305 324-1742
Doral *(G-3534)*
Venco Marine Inc ....G....954 923-0036
Hollywood *(G-5936)*

SASHES: Door Or Window, Metal

A Curv Tech Corp ....F....305 888-9631
Hialeah *(G-5256)*
Building Envelope Systems Inc ....G....305 693-0683
Hialeah *(G-5333)*
Hill Enterprises LLC ....G....850 478-4455
Pensacola *(G-14172)*
Hollow Metal Inc ....F....813 246-4112
Valrico *(G-18519)*
Panelfold Inc ....C....305 688-3501
Miami *(G-10138)*
Sea Products Inc ....D....904 781-8200
Jacksonville *(G-6758)*
T M Building Products Ltd ....G....954 781-4430
Pompano Beach *(G-14882)*
Universal Alum Windows & Doors ....F....305 825-7900
Hialeah *(G-5662)*
YKK AP America Inc ....G....561 736-7808
Boynton Beach *(G-979)*
YKK AP America Inc ....F....407 856-0660
Orlando *(G-13337)*

SATCHELS

Jasmine Purkiss ....F....386 244-7726
Edgewater *(G-3628)*

SATELLITE COMMUNICATIONS EQPT

Airbus Onweb Stllites N Amer LL ....C....321 522-6645
Merritt Island *(G-8989)*
Airbus Onweb Stllites N Amer LL ....D....321 522-6645
Merritt Island *(G-8990)*
Julio Garcia Satellite ....G....407 414-3223
Kissimmee *(G-7260)*
Nic4 Inc ....F....877 455-2131
Tampa *(G-17939)*
Raytheon Company ....G....321 235-6682
Orlando *(G-13116)*
Satellite Now Inc ....G....239 945-0520
Cape Coral *(G-1465)*

SATELLITES: Communications

Alphatec Communications ....G....518 580-0520
Doral *(G-3241)*
Antennas For Cmmnctons Ocala F ....E....352 687-4121
Ocala *(G-11876)*
Applied Systems Integrator Inc ....G....321 259-6106
Melbourne *(G-8770)*
Astrumsat Communications LLC ....G....954 368-9980
Sanford *(G-15996)*
Cobham Satcom ....F....407 650-9054
Sanford *(G-16017)*
Comtech Antenna Systems Inc ....D....407 854-1950
Orlando *(G-12609)*
Comtech Systems Inc ....D....407 854-1950
Orlando *(G-12610)*
Crown Castle Intl Corp ....F....305 552-3675
Miami *(G-9413)*
Crystal Communications Inc ....G....954 474-3072
Sunrise *(G-17110)*
Global Satellite Prpts LLC ....G....954 459-3000
Fort Lauderdale *(G-4023)*
Itelecom USA Inc ....G....305 557-4660
Weston *(G-19143)*
J&B Cmmnication Solutions Corp ....G....786 346-7449
Davie *(G-2539)*
Mil-Sat LLC ....G....954 862-3613
Davie *(G-2553)*
Orbsat Corp ....F....305 560-5355
Aventura *(G-278)*
Qualitysat Corp ....G....305 232-4211
Miami *(G-10219)*
Satcom Direct Inc ....G....321 242-6665
Melbourne *(G-8925)*
Satcom Drect Cmmunications Inc ....F....321 777-3000
Melbourne *(G-8926)*
Sidus Space Inc ....E....321 613-0615
Cape Canaveral *(G-1367)*
Southeastern Engineering Inc ....F....321 984-2521
Palm Bay *(G-13538)*
Srt Wireless LLC ....G....954 797-7850
Sunrise *(G-17177)*

SAUNA ROOMS: Prefabricated

East Coast Floats LLC ....G....407 203-5628
Orlando *(G-12694)*

SAW BLADES

Blades Direct LLC ....F....855 225-2337
Coral Springs *(G-2227)*
Diamond Blades 4us ....G....800 659-5843
Deerfield Beach *(G-2814)*
Global Diversified Products ....E....727 209-0854
Pinellas Park *(G-14351)*
Microtool and Instrument Inc ....E....786 242-8780
Palmetto Bay *(G-13851)*
RSC Industries Inc ....F....813 886-4711
Tampa *(G-18071)*

SAWDUST & SHAVINGS

J W Dawson Co Inc ....E....305 634-8618
Miami *(G-9783)*
Tatum Brothers Lumber Co Inc ....E....904 782-3690
Lawtey *(G-8126)*

SAWING & PLANING MILLS

A L Baxley & Sons Inc ....E....352 629-5137
Citra *(G-1555)*
Apalachee Pole Company Inc ....G....850 263-4457
Graceville *(G-5042)*
Bailey Timber Co Inc ....F....850 674-2080
Blountstown *(G-384)*
Big River Cypress & Hardwood ....F....850 674-5991
Blountstown *(G-385)*
Creamer Corp ....G....850 265-2700
Panama City *(G-13888)*
Cross City Lumber LLC ....F....352 578-8078
Cross City *(G-2363)*
David E Ashe Sawmill ....G....904 377-4800
Saint Augustine *(G-15534)*
Florida North Lumber Inc ....E....850 263-4457
Bristol *(G-1195)*
Fraser West Inc ....D....901 620-4200
Jacksonville *(G-6414)*
Gilman Building Products LLC ....F....904 548-1000
Yulee *(G-19498)*
Great South Timber & Lbr Inc ....F....386 755-3046
Lake City *(G-7358)*
International Closet Center ....G....305 883-6551
Medley *(G-8670)*
J & S Cypress Inc ....F....352 383-3864
Sorrento *(G-16787)*
John A Cruce Jr Inc ....E....850 584-9755
Perry *(G-14305)*
Kempfer Sawmill Inc ....F....407 892-2955
Saint Cloud *(G-15656)*
McCain Mills Inc ....G....813 752-6478
Plant City *(G-14447)*
North Florida Woodlands Inc ....F....850 643-2238
Bristol *(G-1201)*
Rex Lumber Graceville LLC ....C....850 263-2056
Graceville *(G-5044)*
Rex Lumber LLC ....F....850 643-2172
Bristol *(G-1202)*
Rex Lumber LLC ....F....850 263-4457
Graceville *(G-5045)*
Robbins Manufactuing Co ....D....352 793-2443
Webster *(G-18698)*
Rulon Company of Georgia ....C....904 584-1400
Saint Augustine *(G-15600)*
West Fraser Inc ....D....904 786-4155
Jacksonville *(G-6910)*
West Fraser Inc ....D....850 587-1000
Mc David *(G-8602)*
Whitfield Timber Co Inc ....E....850 639-5556
Wewahitchka *(G-19184)*
Williston Timber Co Inc ....E....352 528-2699
Williston *(G-19216)*

SAWING & PLANING MILLS: Custom

Fuqua Sawmill Inc ....G....352 236-3456
Ocala *(G-11952)*

SAWS & SAWING EQPT

Bayou Outdoor Equipment ....F....850 729-2711
Valparaiso *(G-18506)*
Tct Manufacturing ....E....352 735-5070
Mount Dora *(G-11115)*

SCALES & BALANCES, EXC LABORATORY

Intercomp ....G....407 637-9766
Delray Beach *(G-3092)*
Mettler Toledo ....F....607 257-6000
Lutz *(G-8399)*

SCALES: Indl

Atlas Industrial Scales Inc ....G....352 610-9989
Spring Hill *(G-16847)*
Mettler-Toledo Inc ....F....407 423-3856
Orlando *(G-12964)*

SCALES: Truck

Pinto Palma Sound LLC ....E....877 959-1815
Cutler Bay *(G-2408)*
US 1 Truck Sales LLC ....G....904 545-1233
Jacksonville *(G-6889)*

SCANNING DEVICES: Optical

Dtsystems Inc ....G....813 994-0030
Tampa *(G-17618)*
Industrial Scan Inc ....E....407 322-3664
Sanford *(G-16066)*

SCHOOL BUS SVC

Amer-Con Corp ....E....786 293-8004
Palmetto Bay *(G-13839)*

SCHOOLS & EDUCATIONAL SVCS, NEC

Titan Tools LLC ....E....818 984-1001
Clearwater *(G-1921)*

SCIENTIFIC INSTRUMENTS WHOLESALERS

Analytical Research Systems ....F....352 466-0051
Micanopy *(G-10899)*
Ocean Test Equipment Inc ....G....954 474-6603
Davie *(G-2560)*
Thermo Fisher Scientific Inc ....B....561 688-8700
West Palm Beach *(G-19062)*

SCREENS: Door, Metal Covered Wood

Omega Garage Doors Inc ....F....352 620-8830
Melbourne *(G-8901)*
Tag Media Group LLC ....G....239 288-0499
Fort Myers *(G-4622)*

SCREENS: Door, Wood Frame

Unique Technology Inds LLC ....F....941 358-5410
Sarasota *(G-16628)*

SCREENS: Projection

General Screen Service Co ....G....305 226-0741
Miami *(G-9626)*
Vutec Corporation ....C....954 545-9000
Coral Springs *(G-2330)*

SCREENS: Window, Metal

Brevard Aluminum Cnstr Co ....G....321 383-9255
Titusville *(G-18417)*
J T Walker Industries Inc ....E....727 461-0501
Clearwater *(G-1739)*
Plotkowski Inc ....G....561 740-2226
Boynton Beach *(G-940)*
Reliable Pool Enclsres Screns ....G....407 731-3408
Orlando *(G-13129)*
Screening Leon & Repair Inc ....G....850 575-2840
Tallahassee *(G-17321)*
Tag Media Group LLC ....G....239 288-0499
Fort Myers *(G-4622)*

SCREENS: Window, Wood Framed

Eagle View Windows Inc ....F....904 647-8221
Jacksonville *(G-6346)*

SCREENS: Woven Wire

Harpers Manufacturing Spc..................G....... 941 629-3490
Punta Gorda *(G-15209)*

SCREW MACHINE PRDTS

Ashley F Ward Inc..................F....... 904 284-2848
Green Cove Springs *(G-5054)*
Blitz Micro Turning Inc..................G....... 727 725-5005
Safety Harbor *(G-15489)*
Coastal Machine LLC..................G....... 850 769-6117
Panama City *(G-13885)*
Consoldted Mch Tl Holdings LLC..................G....... 888 317-9990
Flagler Beach *(G-3754)*
Construction and Elec Pdts Inc..................F....... 954 972-9787
Pompano Beach *(G-14645)*
D J Camco Corporation..................G....... 904 355-5995
Jacksonville *(G-6305)*
Danco Machine Inc..................G....... 727 501-0460
Largo *(G-7930)*
Federated Precision Inc..................E....... 561 288-6500
Deerfield Beach *(G-2824)*
Forcon Precision Products LLC..................F....... 239 574-4543
Cape Coral *(G-1426)*
Gti Systems Inc..................E....... 863 965-2002
Auburndale *(G-245)*
Hunter Aerospace Supply LLC..................G....... 954 321-8848
Fort Lauderdale *(G-4052)*
Integrated Design & Develop..................G....... 407 268-4300
Sanford *(G-16068)*
Klopfer Holdings Inc..................D....... 727 472-2002
Clearwater *(G-1752)*
Merit Screw..................G....... 352 344-3744
Hernando *(G-5246)*
Mkm Sarasota LLC..................E....... 941 358-0383
Sarasota *(G-16511)*
MSP Industries LLC..................C....... 727 443-5764
Clearwater *(G-1795)*
Mtec Trailer Supply..................F....... 813 659-1647
Plant City *(G-14449)*
OMalley Manufacturing Inc..................G....... 727 327-6817
Saint Petersburg *(G-15872)*
Praesto Enterprises LLC..................G....... 407 298-9171
Orlando *(G-13077)*
Precision Metal Parts Inc..................E....... 727 526-9165
Saint Petersburg *(G-15888)*
Precision Shapes Inc..................E....... 321 269-2555
Titusville *(G-18453)*
Precision Turning Corporation..................F....... 386 364-5788
Live Oak *(G-8237)*
Quality Precision Pdts Co Inc..................F....... 305 885-4596
Hialeah *(G-5589)*
Royal Precision Products Inc..................E....... 305 685-5490
Opa Locka *(G-12356)*
Sanctuary Intl Ministries..................G....... 954 955-7818
Fort Lauderdale *(G-4222)*
Sidus Space Inc..................E....... 321 613-0615
Cape Canaveral *(G-1367)*
Walkup Enterprises Inc..................F....... 727 571-1244
Clearwater *(G-1935)*
Weber Mfg & Supplies Inc..................F....... 941 488-5185
North Venice *(G-11764)*

SCREW MACHINES

Precision Turning Corporation..................F....... 386 364-5788
Live Oak *(G-8237)*

SCREWS: Metal

Grabber Construction Pdts Inc..................G....... 813 249-2281
Tampa *(G-17723)*
Migrandy Corp..................E....... 321 459-0044
Merritt Island *(G-9004)*
Quality Socket Screw Mfg Corp..................F....... 941 475-9585
Englewood *(G-3665)*
Sockets & Specials Inc..................F....... 561 582-7022
West Palm Beach *(G-19036)*

SEALANTS

386 Nanotech Inc..................F....... 727 252-9580
South Pasadena *(G-16833)*
ICP Adhesives Sealants..................G....... 954 905-0531
Coral Springs *(G-2259)*
Master Painting & Sealants LLC..................G....... 305 910-5104
Miami *(G-9955)*
Mg Coating and Sealantsllc..................G....... 305 409-0915
North Miami *(G-11646)*
Premium Auto Sealant Usa LLC..................G....... 786 637-2573
Medley *(G-8709)*
Southast Clking Slant Svcs LLC..................G....... 813 731-8778
Plant City *(G-14466)*
Srm Waterproofing Sealants Inc..................G....... 407 963-3619
Orlando *(G-13209)*
Stella Sealants Corp..................G....... 941 357-1566
Sarasota *(G-16302)*
Ussi LLC..................F....... 941 244-2408
Venice *(G-18583)*

SEALS: Hermetic

Frc Electrical Industries Inc..................G....... 321 676-3300
Palm Bay *(G-13514)*
Winchster Intrcnnect Hrmtics L..................D....... 321 254-4067
Melbourne *(G-8976)*

SEALS: Oil, Rubber

Bxd Enterprises Inc..................G....... 727 937-4100
Holiday *(G-5737)*

SEARCH & DETECTION SYSTEMS, EXC RADAR

Northrop Grumman Corporation..................A....... 321 951-5000
Melbourne *(G-8896)*

SEARCH & NAVIGATION SYSTEMS

321 Cpr LLC..................G....... 321 806-3525
Cocoa *(G-1987)*
Aero-Trim Control Systems Inc..................G....... 954 321-1936
Davie *(G-2489)*
Alakai Defense Systems Inc..................F....... 727 541-1600
Largo *(G-7890)*
Asrc Aerospace Corp..................C....... 321 867-1462
Kennedy Space Center *(G-7150)*
Astronics Dme LLC..................C....... 954 975-2100
Fort Lauderdale *(G-3828)*
Astronics Test Systems Inc..................C....... 407 381-6062
Orlando *(G-12496)*
Bae Systems Tech Sltons Svcs I..................G....... 850 244-6433
Fort Walton Beach *(G-4779)*
Bae Systems Tech Sltons Svcs I..................D....... 850 344-0832
Fort Walton Beach *(G-4780)*
Bae Systems Tech Sol Srvc Inc..................F....... 850 664-6070
Fort Walton Beach *(G-4781)*
Boeing Company..................G....... 850 882-4912
Eglin Afb *(G-3641)*
Carbonara Labs Inc..................F....... 321 952-1303
Grant *(G-5048)*
Cobham Mission System Corp..................G....... 850 226-6717
Fort Walton Beach *(G-4787)*
Coda Octopus Group Inc..................F....... 407 735-2402
Orlando *(G-12598)*
CPS Products Inc..................G....... 305 687-4121
Miramar *(G-10981)*
Drs Advanced Isr LLC..................F....... 850 226-4888
Fort Walton Beach *(G-4791)*
Drs C3 Systems Inc..................E....... 850 302-3909
Fort Walton Beach *(G-4792)*
Drs Cengen Llc..................B....... 321 622-1500
Melbourne *(G-8808)*
Drs Consolidated Controls..................F....... 850 302-3000
Fort Walton Beach *(G-4793)*
Drs Land Electronics..................G....... 321 622-1435
Melbourne *(G-8809)*
Drs Leonardo Inc..................G....... 850 302-3000
Fort Walton Beach *(G-4794)*
Drs Leonardo Inc..................G....... 850 302-3514
Fort Walton Beach *(G-4795)*
Drs Ntwork Imaging Systems LLC..................B....... 321 309-1500
Melbourne *(G-8810)*
Drs S and T Optronics Div..................F....... 321 309-1500
Melbourne *(G-8811)*
Drs Sensors Targeting Systems..................E....... 321 309-1500
Melbourne *(G-8812)*
Drs Soneticom Inc..................E....... 321 733-0400
Melbourne *(G-8813)*
Drs Systems Inc..................G....... 973 451-3525
Melbourne *(G-8814)*
Drs Tactical Systems Inc..................C....... 321 727-3672
Melbourne *(G-8815)*
Edgeone LLC..................F....... 561 995-7767
Boca Raton *(G-514)*
Etech Simulation Corp..................E....... 561 922-9792
West Palm Beach *(G-18864)*
Gannet Technologies LLC..................F....... 941 870-3444
Sarasota *(G-16217)*
GE Aviation Systems LLC..................B....... 727 531-7781
Clearwater *(G-1699)*
General Dynamics-Ots Inc..................D....... 727 578-8100
Saint Petersburg *(G-15790)*
General Scientific Corporation..................G....... 850 866-9636
Panama City *(G-13908)*
Heico Aerospace Corporation..................E....... 954 987-6101
Hollywood *(G-5837)*
Hensoldt Avionics Usa LLC..................G....... 941 306-1328
Sarasota *(G-16459)*
Honeywell Aerospace Inc..................G....... 727 539-5197
Clearwater *(G-1716)*
Honeywell International Inc..................G....... 505 358-0676
Largo *(G-7973)*
Ilsc Holdings Lc..................G....... 480 935-4230
Orlando *(G-12822)*
Interstate Electronics Corp..................D....... 321 730-0119
Cape Canaveral *(G-1362)*
Jade Tactical Disaster Relief..................C....... 850 270-4077
Tampa *(G-17801)*
Joe Hearn Innovative Tech LLC..................F....... 850 898-3744
Pensacola *(G-14183)*
Kollsman Inc..................G....... 407 312-1384
Orlando *(G-12875)*
L3 Crestview Aerospace..................G....... 850 682-2746
Crestview *(G-2353)*
L3 Technologies Inc..................G....... 321 409-6122
Melbourne *(G-8864)*
L3 Technologies Inc..................G....... 941 371-0811
Saint Petersburg *(G-15836)*
L3 Technologies Inc..................G....... 305 371-7039
Fort Lauderdale *(G-4092)*
L3harris Technologies Inc..................B....... 321 727-9100
Melbourne *(G-8865)*
L3harris Technologies Inc..................G....... 407 581-3782
Orlando *(G-12883)*
L3harris Technologies Inc..................G....... 305 542-5441
Miami *(G-9837)*
L3harris Technologies Inc..................G....... 727 415-6592
Palm Harbor *(G-13743)*
L3harris Technologies Inc..................D....... 321 768-4660
Malabar *(G-8494)*
L3harris Technologies Inc..................G....... 321 412-6601
Palm Bay *(G-13518)*
L3harris Technologies Inc..................G....... 321 727-4000
Melbourne *(G-8869)*
L3harris Technologies Inc..................G....... 321 674-4589
Melbourne *(G-8871)*
L3harris Technologies Inc..................C....... 260 451-6814
Tampa *(G-17831)*
Lockheed Martin Corporation..................A....... 407 306-6405
Orlando *(G-12919)*
Lockheed Martin Corporation..................G....... 407 517-6627
Orlando *(G-12921)*
Lockheed Martin Corporation..................G....... 407 306-4758
Orlando *(G-12922)*
Lockheed Martin Corporation..................D....... 863 647-0100
Lakeland *(G-7736)*
Lockheed Martin Corporation..................G....... 561 494-2501
West Palm Beach *(G-18933)*
Lockheed Martin Corporation..................G....... 407 365-4254
Oviedo *(G-13448)*
Lockheed Martin Corporation..................C....... 727 578-6940
Pinellas Park *(G-14365)*
Lockheed Martin Corporation..................G....... 407 356-5715
Lake Mary *(G-7429)*
Lockheed Martin Corporation..................F....... 407 356-2000
Orlando *(G-12923)*
Lockheed Martin Corporation..................G....... 850 301-4155
Fort Walton Beach *(G-4813)*
Lockheed Martin Corporation..................G....... 407 356-7424
Kissimmee *(G-7269)*
Lockheed Martin Corporation..................G....... 904 392-9779
Jacksonville *(G-6562)*
Lockheed Martin Corporation..................G....... 407 306-2745
Orlando *(G-12924)*
Lockheed Martin Corporation..................G....... 866 562-2363
Doral *(G-3418)*
Lockheed Martin Corporation..................G....... 407 356-1034
Orlando *(G-12925)*
Lockheed Martin Corporation..................G....... 863 647-0100
Lakeland *(G-7737)*
Lockheed Martin Corporation..................B....... 863 647-0558
Lakeland *(G-7738)*
Lockheed Martin Corporation..................G....... 863 647-0100
Lakeland *(G-7739)*
Lockheed Martin Corporation..................G....... 863 647-0303
Lakeland *(G-7740)*
Lockheed Martin Corporation..................G....... 301 240-7500
Orlando *(G-12926)*
Lockheed Martin Corporation..................G....... 321 264-7924
Titusville *(G-18443)*

Lockheed Martin Corporation ....G....... 407 356-6423
Orlando *(G-12928)*
Lockheed Martin Corporation ....G....... 301 897-6000
Riviera Beach *(G-15343)*
Lockheed Martin Corporation ....G....... 850 581-5710
Hurlburt Field *(G-6046)*
Lockheed Martin Corporation ....G....... 407 356-1947
Orlando *(G-12929)*
Lockheed Mrtin Gyrcam Systems ....D....... 407 356-6500
Orlando *(G-12930)*
Lockheed Mrtin Intgrted System ....C....... 407 356-2000
Orlando *(G-12931)*
Lockheed Mrtin Trning Sltons I ....C....... 856 722-3317
Orlando *(G-12933)*
Loos & Co Inc ....D....... 239 643-5667
Naples *(G-11316)*
Mathews Associates Inc ....C....... 407 323-3390
Sanford *(G-16082)*
Meads International Inc ....D....... 407 356-8400
Orlando *(G-12956)*
Micro Systems Inc ....C....... 850 244-2332
Fort Walton Beach *(G-4815)*
Motorola Solutions Inc ....G....... 407 562-4000
Lake Mary *(G-7437)*
Northrop Grmman Tchncal Svcs I ....G....... 321 837-7000
Melbourne *(G-8895)*
Northrop Grmman Tchncal Svcs I ....F....... 904 825-3300
Saint Augustine *(G-15575)*
Northrop Grumman Corporation ....G....... 321 951-5529
Malabar *(G-8496)*
Northrop Grumman Corporation ....G....... 321 951-5730
Palm Bay *(G-13527)*
Northrop Grumman Systems Corp ....G....... 904 810-5957
Saint Augustine *(G-15577)*
Northrop Grumman Systems Corp ....E....... 561 515-3651
Palm Beach Gardens *(G-13613)*
Northrop Grumman Systems Corp ....C....... 407 737-4900
Orlando *(G-13008)*
Northrop Grumman Systems Corp ....B....... 407 295-4010
Apopka *(G-166)*
Radiant Power Corp ....C....... 941 739-3200
Sarasota *(G-16281)*
Raytheon Company ....G....... 850 664-7993
Fort Walton Beach *(G-4826)*
Raytheon Company ....G....... 321 494-3323
Patrick Afb *(G-14008)*
Raytheon Company ....D....... 407 207-9223
Orlando *(G-13117)*
Raytheon Technologies Corp ....A....... 858 277-7639
Jupiter *(G-7103)*
Riegl Usa Inc ....E....... 407 248-9927
Winter Garden *(G-19283)*
Rockwell Collins Inc ....G....... 866 786-0290
Orlando *(G-13145)*
Rockwell Collins Inc ....D....... 321 768-7303
Melbourne *(G-8921)*
Saikou Optics Incorporated ....G....... 407 986-4200
Orlando *(G-13157)*
Sensormatic Electronics LLC ....G....... 561 912-6000
Boca Raton *(G-704)*
Sequa Corporation ....A....... 561 935-3571
Palm Beach Gardens *(G-13626)*
Sierra Nevada Corporation ....E....... 850 659-3600
Shalimar *(G-16777)*
Sikorsky Aircraft Corp ....G....... 772 210-0849
Stuart *(G-17014)*
Smiths Interconnect Inc ....C....... 813 901-7200
Tampa *(G-18111)*
Sports Radar Ltd ....G....... 352 503-6825
Homosassa *(G-6006)*
Streamline Numerics Inc ....G....... 352 271-8841
Gainesville *(G-5003)*
Super Sensitive String Sls Co ....E....... 941 371-0016
Sarasota *(G-16612)*
Technologies Drs Unmanned Inc ....D....... 850 302-3909
Fort Walton Beach *(G-4835)*
Trakka USA LLC ....G....... 505 345-0270
Bradenton *(G-1128)*
Viewpoint Systems LLC ....F....... 850 450-0681
Pensacola *(G-14284)*

SEARCH & RESCUE SVCS

Exploration Services LLC ....G....... 352 505-3578
Gainesville *(G-4917)*

SEASHELLS, WHOLESALE

Sun Krafts of Volusia County ....G....... 386 441-1961
Ormond Beach *(G-13403)*

SEAT BELTS: Automobile & Aircraft

CSC Racing Corporation ....F....... 248 548-5727
Jupiter *(G-7021)*
Key Safety Systems Inc ....G....... 863 668-6000
Lakeland *(G-7726)*
Seatbelt Solutions Llc ....E....... 855 642-3964
Jupiter *(G-7111)*

SEATING: Bleacher, Portable

Miami Grandstand Entertainment ....G....... 305 636-9665
Hialeah *(G-5511)*

SEATING: Chairs, Table & Arm

F & R General Interiors Corp ....F....... 305 635-4747
Hialeah *(G-5402)*

SEATING: Stadium

Seating Constructors Usa Inc ....F....... 813 505-7560
Brooksville *(G-1267)*
Seating Installation Group LLC ....F....... 727 289-7652
Saint Petersburg *(G-15908)*

SECRETARIAL & COURT REPORTING

Pensacola Voice Inc ....G....... 850 434-6963
Pensacola *(G-14227)*

SECRETARIAL SVCS

Mdintouch Us Inc ....G....... 786 268-1161
Miami *(G-9961)*
Paper Free Technology Inc ....G....... 515 270-1505
Lehigh Acres *(G-8202)*

SECURITY CONTROL EQPT & SYSTEMS

AAA Security Depot Corp ....E....... 305 652-8567
Opa Locka *(G-12281)*
Absolute Automation & Security ....G....... 321 505-9989
Cocoa *(G-1990)*
Abz Marketing Solutions Corp ....E....... 305 340-1887
Doral *(G-3222)*
Advanced Dsign Tech Systems In ....E....... 850 462-2868
Pensacola *(G-14083)*
Alco Advanced Technologies ....G....... 305 333-0831
Doral *(G-3234)*
Amtel Security Systems Inc ....E....... 305 591-8200
Doral *(G-3249)*
Aressco Technologies Inc ....G....... 305 245-5854
Homestead *(G-5955)*
Audio Intelligence Devices ....E....... 954 418-1400
Deerfield Beach *(G-2782)*
Centrys LLC ....E....... 407 476-4786
Sanford *(G-16012)*
Communcations Surveillance Inc ....F....... 305 377-1211
Coral Gables *(G-2132)*
Control and Automtn Cons Inc ....G....... 305 823-8670
Hialeah *(G-5353)*
Control Investments Inc ....F....... 954 491-6660
Fort Lauderdale *(G-3918)*
Edgewater Technologies Inc ....F....... 954 565-9898
Fort Lauderdale *(G-3962)*
Elipter Corp ....G....... 305 593-8355
Doral *(G-3342)*
Etc Palm Beach LLC ....D....... 561 881-8118
West Palm Beach *(G-18863)*
Extreme Digital Video Inc ....G....... 954 792-2818
Fort Lauderdale *(G-3984)*
ICO USA Corp ....G....... 305 253-0871
Palmetto Bay *(G-13848)*
Industrial Smoke & Mirrors Inc ....E....... 407 299-9400
Orlando *(G-12828)*
Integrated Surroundings Inc ....F....... 850 932-0848
Gulf Breeze *(G-5120)*
L3harris Technologies Inc ....B....... 321 727-9100
Melbourne *(G-8865)*
Salco Industries Inc ....F....... 941 377-7717
Sarasota *(G-16570)*
Saltex Group Corp ....G....... 305 477-3187
Miami *(G-10300)*
Select Engineered Systems Inc ....E....... 305 823-5410
Hialeah *(G-5613)*
Sepronet Inc ....F....... 305 463-8551
Doral *(G-3499)*
Simplexgrinnell Holdings LLC ....G....... 978 731-2500
Boca Raton *(G-716)*
Smart Access Inc ....G....... 407 331-4724
Lake Mary *(G-7449)*
Southeast Security Products ....G....... 954 786-5900
Pompano Beach *(G-14861)*
Sunrise Financial Assoc Inc ....G....... 321 439-9797
Orlando *(G-13225)*
Telsec Corporation ....G....... 561 998-9983
Boca Raton *(G-745)*
Validsoft ....G....... 813 334-9745
Lutz *(G-8422)*
Venco Marine Inc ....G....... 954 923-0036
Hollywood *(G-5936)*
World Electronics Inc ....G....... 954 318-1044
Sunrise *(G-17199)*
Xpondr Corporation ....E....... 727 541-4149
Seminole *(G-16772)*

SECURITY DEVICES

Appointment Team Inc ....F....... 561 314-5471
Boynton Beach *(G-879)*
Asecure America Inc ....G....... 352 347-7951
Belleview *(G-367)*
Bridge Trading Usa LLC ....F....... 877 848-0979
Doral *(G-3286)*
Brijot Imaging Systems Inc ....F....... 407 641-4370
Boca Raton *(G-466)*
C-Note Solutions Inc ....F....... 321 952-2490
Indialantic *(G-6056)*
Came Americas Automation LLC ....F....... 305 433-3307
Miami Lakes *(G-10773)*
Danielle Fence Mfg Co Inc ....D....... 863 425-3182
Mulberry *(G-11121)*
Deggy Corp ....G....... 305 377-2233
Miami Lakes *(G-10780)*
Devcon International Corp ....C....... 954 926-5200
Boca Raton *(G-499)*
Devcon Security Services Corp ....E....... 813 386-3849
Pompano Beach *(G-14661)*
Gatecrafterscom ....F....... 800 537-4283
Odessa *(G-12122)*
Gess Technologies LLC ....F....... 305 231-6322
Hialeah *(G-5429)*
Gto Access Systems LLC ....D....... 850 575-0176
Tallahassee *(G-17269)*
Hayes Less Lethal LLC ....G....... 561 201-2186
Tequesta *(G-18385)*
Hemco Industries Inc ....F....... 305 769-0606
North Miami *(G-11641)*
Hummingbirds Ai Inc ....F....... 305 432-2787
Miami Beach *(G-10680)*
Knight Fire & Security Inc ....F....... 561 471-8221
Riviera Beach *(G-15341)*
Point Blank Enterprises Inc ....D....... 305 820-4270
Miami Lakes *(G-10840)*
Protective Group Inc ....E....... 305 820-4266
Miami Lakes *(G-10846)*
Rm Brands Inc ....G....... 904 356-0092
Jacksonville *(G-6732)*
Safeguard America Inc ....F....... 305 859-9000
Miami *(G-10295)*
Secure Biometric Corporation ....G....... 813 832-1164
Tampa *(G-18082)*
Security and Fire Elec Inc ....E....... 904 844-0964
Saint Augustine *(G-15608)*
Segutronic International Inc ....G....... 305 463-8551
Doral *(G-3498)*
Servision Inc ....G....... 305 900-4999
Hallandale Beach *(G-5210)*
Signalvault LLC ....G....... 407 878-6365
Debary *(G-2755)*
Symetrics Technology Group LLC ....E....... 321 254-1500
Melbourne *(G-8955)*
Tem Systems Inc ....G....... 407 251-7114
Orlando *(G-13246)*
Theft Protection Com Corp ....F....... 772 231-6677
Vero Beach *(G-18670)*
Vanguard Products Group Inc ....D....... 813 855-9639
Oldsmar *(G-12277)*
Xts Corp ....F....... 305 863-7779
Doral *(G-3552)*

SECURITY EQPT STORES

Florida Fence Post Co Inc ....G....... 863 735-1361
Ona *(G-12280)*
Throw Raft LLC ....G....... 954 366-8004
Fort Lauderdale *(G-4283)*

SECURITY PROTECTIVE DEVICES MAINTENANCE & MONITORING SVCS

Express Badging Services Inc ....F....... 321 784-5925
Cocoa Beach *(G-2062)*

PRODUCT

Lions Intl MGT Group Inc ....F 813 367-2517
Tampa *(G-17848)*
Security Oracle Inc ....F 352 988-5985
Clermont *(G-1974)*

SECURITY SYSTEMS SERVICES

Ad America ....G 904 781-5900
Jacksonville *(G-6118)*
Ad Valorem Corporation ....G 561 488-9966
Boca Raton *(G-397)*
Amtel Security Systems Inc ....E 305 591-8200
Doral *(G-3249)*
Defenshield Inc ....G 904 679-3942
Saint Augustine *(G-15535)*
Eyeson Dgtal Srvllnce MGT Syst ....G 305 808-3344
Miami *(G-9551)*
Jade Tactical Disaster Relief ....C 850 270-4077
Tampa *(G-17801)*
Kratos Def & SEC Solutions Inc ....G 866 606-5867
Orlando *(G-12877)*
Safe Banks and Lock ....G 954 762-3565
Fort Lauderdale *(G-4221)*
Top Line Installation Inc ....F 352 636-4192
Leesburg *(G-8177)*

SELF-PROPELLED AIRCRAFT DEALER

Atlantic Jet Center Inc ....G 321 255-7111
Melbourne *(G-8771)*

SEMICONDUCTOR CIRCUIT NETWORKS

Aurora Semiconductor LLC ....E 727 235-6500
Saint Petersburg *(G-15716)*

SEMICONDUCTOR DEVICES: Wafers

Hine Automation LLC ....G 813 749-7519
Saint Petersburg *(G-15807)*

SEMICONDUCTORS & RELATED DEVICES

AGS Electronics Inc ....G 850 471-1551
Pensacola *(G-14086)*
American All ....G 561 401-0885
Loxahatchee *(G-8356)*
American Technology Pdts Inc ....F 407 960-1722
Sanford *(G-15993)*
Baytronics Manufacturing Inc ....G 813 434-0401
Tampa *(G-17460)*
Cobham Slip Rings Naples Inc ....D 239 263-3102
Naples *(G-11213)*
Convergent Actuarial Svcs Inc ....G 561 715-4204
Delray Beach *(G-3064)*
Convergent Engineering Inc ....F 352 378-4899
Gainesville *(G-4896)*
Convergent Marketing LLC ....G 561 270-7081
Delray Beach *(G-3065)*
Convergent Technologies ....F 407 482-4381
Orlando *(G-12618)*
Cybortrack Solutions Inc ....G 805 904-5677
Longwood *(G-8271)*
Drt Services ....G 321 549-1431
Palm Bay *(G-13510)*
Exalos Inc ....E 215 669-4488
Fort Lauderdale *(G-3980)*
Intertech Supply Inc ....G 786 200-0561
Miami *(G-9762)*
Legacy Components LLC ....F 813 964-6805
Tampa *(G-17840)*
Mercury Systems Inc ....E 352 371-2567
Gainesville *(G-4961)*
Micross Components Inc ....E 407 298-7100
Orlando *(G-12968)*
Micross Prmier Smcdtr Svcs LLC ....E 727 532-1777
Clearwater *(G-1785)*
Motorola Solutions Inc ....G 407 562-4000
Lake Mary *(G-7437)*
Multicore Photonics Inc ....G 407 325-7800
Orlando *(G-12984)*
Multicore Technologies LLC ....G 407 325-7800
Orlando *(G-12986)*
Neos Technologies Inc ....G 321 242-7818
Melbourne *(G-8893)*
Nor East Materials Inc ....F 386 478-0087
New Smyrna Beach *(G-11539)*
Notice Four LLC ....G 954 652-1168
Fort Lauderdale *(G-4143)*
Oerlikon USA Inc ....E 727 577-4999
Saint Petersburg *(G-15870)*
One Resonance Sensors LLC ....F 407 637-0771
Sanford *(G-16095)*
Parkervision Inc ....F 904 732-6100
Jacksonville *(G-6658)*
Planar Energy Devices Inc ....F 407 459-1440
Orlando *(G-13071)*
Plasma-Therm LLC ....C 727 577-4999
Saint Petersburg *(G-15881)*
Power Production MGT Inc ....G 352 263-0766
Gainesville *(G-4981)*
Premier Semiconductor Svcs LLC ....G 727 532-1777
Clearwater *(G-1844)*
Qorvo Us Inc ....B 407 886-8860
Apopka *(G-176)*
Qualcomm Atheros Inc ....F 407 284-7314
Orlando *(G-13102)*
Quantum Technology Inc ....G 407 333-9348
Lake Mary *(G-7448)*
Quartz Unlimited LLC ....G 561 306-1243
Boca Raton *(G-679)*
Raytheon Company ....C 310 647-9438
Largo *(G-8036)*
Reflectivity Inc ....F 386 738-1008
Deland *(G-3011)*
Renesas Electronics Amer Inc ....A 321 724-7000
Palm Bay *(G-13531)*
Scientific Instruments Inc ....E 561 881-8500
Mangonia Park *(G-8511)*
Semiconductor Technology Inc ....G 772 341-0800
Stuart *(G-17008)*
Semilab USA LLC ....E 813 977-2244
Temple Terrace *(G-18378)*
Sepac Corp ....F 305 718-3379
Miami *(G-10325)*
Spartronics Brooksville LLC ....B 352 799-6520
Brooksville *(G-1275)*
Supliaereos USA LLC ....G 727 754-4915
Clearwater *(G-1897)*
Technology Products Design Inc ....F 321 432-3537
Palm Bay *(G-13543)*
Triple Play Cmmunications Corp ....G 321 327-8997
Melbourne *(G-8966)*
US Applied Phys Ics Group ....G 321 567-7270
Titusville *(G-18471)*

SENSORS: Infrared, Solid State

Drs Ntwork Imaging Systems LLC ....E 321 309-1500
Palm Bay *(G-13509)*
Northrop Grumman Systems Corp ....B 407 295-4010
Apopka *(G-166)*

SENSORS: Radiation

M P I Medical Products Inc ....G 321 676-1299
Palm Bay *(G-13522)*
Tesseract Sensors LLC ....F 407 385-2498
Sanford *(G-16127)*

SENSORS: Temperature, Exc Indl Process

C K C Industries Inc ....G 813 888-9468
Tampa *(G-17494)*

SEPTIC TANK CLEANING SVCS

A & L Septic Tank Products ....G 407 273-2149
Orlando *(G-12423)*
Averett Septic Tank Co Inc ....E 863 665-1748
Lakeland *(G-7640)*
Bingham On-Site Sewers Inc ....D 813 659-0003
Dover *(G-3556)*
Miller Brothers Contractors ....F 941 371-4162
Sarasota *(G-16510)*
Monty Sanitation Inc ....G 239 597-2486
Naples *(G-11332)*
P & L Creech Inc ....G 386 547-4182
Daytona Beach *(G-2691)*

SEPTIC TANKS: Concrete

A & L Septic Tank Products ....G 407 273-2149
Orlando *(G-12423)*
Averett Septic Tank Co Inc ....E 863 665-1748
Lakeland *(G-7640)*
Bingham On-Site Sewers Inc ....D 813 659-0003
Dover *(G-3556)*
Dixie Sptic Tank Orange Cy LLC ....F 386 775-3051
Orange City *(G-12375)*
Gunter Septic Tank Mfg ....G 813 654-1214
Seffner *(G-16730)*
Kt Properties & Dev Inc ....F 386 253-0610
Daytona Beach *(G-2677)*
Miller Brothers Contractors ....F 941 371-4162
Sarasota *(G-16510)*
Monty Sanitation Inc ....G 239 597-2486
Naples *(G-11332)*
Pilot Corp of Palm Beaches ....F 561 848-2928
Riviera Beach *(G-15363)*
Rogers Septic Tanks Inc ....G 203 259-9947
Port Saint Lucie *(G-15139)*
Sebring Septic Tank Precast Co ....E 863 655-2030
Sebring *(G-16708)*
Stans Septic Svc & Con Pdts ....G 941 639-3976
Punta Gorda *(G-15236)*
Taylor Concrete Inc ....G 941 737-7225
Palmetto *(G-13828)*
Wpr Inc ....E 850 626-7713
Milton *(G-10948)*

SEPTIC TANKS: Plastic

All Liquid Envmtl Svcs LLC ....E 800 767-9594
Fort Lauderdale *(G-3797)*
Alpha General Services Inc ....E 863 382-1544
Sebring *(G-16680)*
P & L Creech Inc ....G 386 547-4182
Daytona Beach *(G-2691)*

SEWAGE & WATER TREATMENT EQPT

American Boom and Barrier Inc ....E 321 784-2110
Cape Canaveral *(G-1350)*
Aquasolve Ventures LLC ....G 732 570-0707
Daytona Beach *(G-2627)*
City of Cocoa Beach ....F 321 868-3342
Cocoa Beach *(G-2061)*
Dais Corp ....F 727 375-8484
Odessa *(G-12115)*
Eco Water Technologies Corp ....G 954 599-3672
Fort Lauderdale *(G-3961)*
Enviro-USA American Mfr LLC ....E 321 222-9551
Cape Canaveral *(G-1357)*
Jtm International Inc ....G 954 680-3517
Cooper City *(G-2113)*
Pulsafeeder Inc ....D 941 575-2900
Punta Gorda *(G-15223)*
Pulsafeeder Spo Inc ....F 941 575-3800
Punta Gorda *(G-15224)*
Tetra Process Technology ....G 813 886-9331
Tampa *(G-18184)*

SEWAGE FACILITIES

Alpha General Services Inc ....E 863 382-1544
Sebring *(G-16680)*

SEWAGE TREATMENT SYSTEMS & EQPT

American Engineering Svcs Inc ....G 813 621-3932
Plant City *(G-14399)*
Environmental Services ....E 727 518-3080
Clearwater *(G-1674)*
Resource Management Associates ....G 239 656-0818
Fort Myers *(G-4582)*

SEWER CLEANING EQPT: Power

Gator Drain Cleaning Equipment ....G 954 584-4441
Davie *(G-2531)*
Vac-Con Inc ....B 904 284-4200
Green Cove Springs *(G-5075)*

SEWING CONTRACTORS

Advanced Sewing ....G 954 484-2100
Fort Lauderdale *(G-3784)*

SEWING KITS: Novelty

Dyno LLC ....E 954 971-2910
Pompano Beach *(G-14670)*

SEWING MACHINES & PARTS: Indl

Mid West Lettering Company ....E 850 477-6522
Pensacola *(G-14209)*

SEWING, NEEDLEWORK & PIECE GOODS STORES: Sewing & Needlework

Looper Sports Connection Inc ....G 352 796-7974
Brooksville *(G-1247)*

SEXTANTS

Sextant Marketing LLC ....F 800 691-9980
Tampa *(G-18087)*

SHADES: Lamp & Light, Residential

Allure Shades Inc .... F 954 543-6259
Lauderhill *(G-8100)*
General Metal Intl Inc .... G 305 628-2052
Miramar *(G-10997)*
Morlee Lampshade Co Inc .... E 305 500-9310
Miami *(G-10041)*
Stateside Indus Solutions LLC .... G 305 301-4052
Miramar *(G-11046)*

SHADES: Lamp Or Candle

Lampshades of Florida Inc .... F 954 491-3377
Deerfield Beach *(G-2856)*

SHADES: Window

Aero Shade Technologies Inc .... G 772 562-2243
Fort Pierce *(G-4670)*
Aerospace Tech Group Inc .... D 561 244-7400
Boca Raton *(G-406)*
Eddy Storm Protection .... G 386 248-1631
Daytona Beach *(G-2661)*

SHAFTS: Flexible

American Vulkan Corporation .... E 863 324-2424
Winter Haven *(G-19299)*
Schur & Company LLC .... D 904 353-8075
Jacksonville *(G-6754)*
SS White Technologies Inc .... C 727 626-2800
Saint Petersburg *(G-15923)*

SHAPES & PILINGS, STRUCTURAL: Steel

ABS Structural Corp .... F 321 768-2067
Melbourne *(G-8756)*
Dixie Structures & Maintenance .... F 205 274-4525
Fort Myers *(G-4433)*
Florida Aluminum and Steel Inc .... F 863 967-4191
Auburndale *(G-241)*
Harbor Entps Ltd Lblty Co .... F 229 403-0756
Tallahassee *(G-17274)*
Hollywood Iron Works Inc .... F 954 962-0556
West Park *(G-19094)*
International Iron Works LLC .... G 305 835-0190
Hialeah *(G-5455)*
Mgl Engineering Inc .... E 863 648-0320
Lakeland *(G-7750)*
Renovaship Inc .... G 954 342-9062
Hallandale Beach *(G-5208)*

SHAPES: Extruded, Aluminum, NEC

Anchor Aluminum Products South .... G 305 293-7965
Key West *(G-7177)*
Golden Aluminum Extrusion LLC .... E 330 372-2300
Plant City *(G-14436)*
Hydro Precision Tubing USA LLC .... C 321 636-8147
Rockledge *(G-15420)*
Plastic and Products Mktg LLC .... F 352 867-8078
Ocala *(G-12028)*
Walt Dittmer and Sons Inc .... E 407 699-1755
Winter Springs *(G-19488)*

SHEARS

Southern Supply and Mfg Co .... E 727 323-7099
Saint Petersburg *(G-15919)*

SHEET METAL SPECIALTIES, EXC STAMPED

Actron Entities Inc .... D 727 531-5871
Clearwater *(G-1563)*
Affordable Metal Inc .... F 305 691-8082
Hialeah *(G-5274)*
All County Sheet Metal Inc .... G 561 588-0099
Lake Worth Beach *(G-7601)*
Arrow Sheet Metal Works Inc .... E 813 247-2179
Tampa *(G-17436)*
B & T Metalworks Inc .... E 352 236-6000
Ocala *(G-11884)*
Bob Kline Quality Metal Inc .... G 561 659-4245
West Palm Beach *(G-18827)*
Bohnert Sheet Metal & Roofg Co .... F 305 696-6851
Miami *(G-9264)*
Cornerstone Fabrication LLC .... E 386 310-1110
Debary *(G-2747)*
Crown Products Company Inc .... D 904 924-8340
Jacksonville *(G-6301)*
Custom Metal Fabricators Inc .... G 407 841-8551
Orlando *(G-12640)*
Cwp Sheet Metal Inc .... E 407 349-0926
Geneva *(G-5019)*
Electrnic Shtmtal Crftsmen Fla .... E 321 727-0633
Melbourne *(G-8823)*
Exact Inc .... C 904 783-6640
Jacksonville *(G-6372)*
Florida Storm Panels Inc .... F 305 685-9000
Opa Locka *(G-12318)*
Lajoie Investment Corp .... F 954 463-3271
Fort Lauderdale *(G-4094)*
Magnus Hitech Industries Inc .... E 321 724-9731
Melbourne *(G-8882)*
Masseys Metals .... E 813 626-8275
Tampa *(G-17892)*
Miami Tech Inc .... E 305 693-7054
Miami *(G-10014)*
MJM Manufacturing Inc .... D 305 620-2020
Miami Lakes *(G-10823)*
Pomper Sheet Metal Inc .... G 954 492-9717
Oakland Park *(G-11829)*
Precision Fabrication Corp .... E 941 488-2474
Nokomis *(G-11587)*
Precision Metal Industries Inc .... D 954 942-6303
Pompano Beach *(G-14808)*
Precision Metal Services Inc .... F 407 843-3682
Sorrento *(G-16791)*
S P Sheet Metal Co Inc .... F 609 698-8800
Jupiter *(G-7107)*
SBs Precision Shtmtl Inc .... E 321 951-7411
Melbourne *(G-8927)*
Simar Industries Inc .... E 352 622-2287
Ocala *(G-12053)*
Singer Holdings Inc .... F 321 724-0900
Melbourne *(G-8934)*
Telese Inc .... E 813 752-6015
Plant City *(G-14470)*
Topline Cstm Fabrications LLC .... G 850 295-2481
Perry *(G-14318)*
Ver-Val Enterprises Inc .... F 850 244-7931
Fort Walton Beach *(G-4838)*
Vertec Inc .... F 850 478-6480
Pensacola *(G-14283)*

SHEETING: Window, Plastic

Clear Vue Inc .... E 727 726-5386
Safety Harbor *(G-15490)*

SHELL MINING

Blackhawk Construction Co Inc .... E 321 258-4957
Vero Beach *(G-18602)*
Charlotte County Min & Mtl Inc .... E 239 567-1800
Punta Gorda *(G-15201)*
SMR Aggregates Inc .... E 941 907-0041
Lakewood Ranch *(G-7841)*

SHELLAC

Cathodic Prtection Tech of Fla .... G 321 799-0046
Cocoa Beach *(G-2060)*
Kiss Polymers LLC .... F 813 962-2703
Tampa *(G-17827)*

SHELVING, MADE FROM PURCHASED WIRE

Closetmaid LLC .... E 352 351-6100
Ocala *(G-11905)*

SHELVING: Office & Store, Exc Wood

Adapto Storage Products .... E 305 887-9563
Hialeah *(G-5269)*

SHIP BUILDING & REPAIRING: Cargo Vessels

Bae Systems Sthast Shpyrds Amh .... D 904 251-3111
Jacksonville *(G-6189)*
World Container Services LLC .... E 305 400-4850
Doral *(G-3550)*

SHIP BUILDING & REPAIRING: Cargo, Commercial

Arrow Power Boats LLC .... G 772 429-8888
Fort Pierce *(G-4678)*
Marine Transportation Svcs Inc .... E 850 215-4557
Panama City *(G-13927)*
Premier Luxury Group LLC .... E 954 358-9885
Fort Lauderdale *(G-4176)*

SHIP BUILDING & REPAIRING: Dredges

Florida Dredge and Dock LLC .... E 727 942-7888
Tarpon Springs *(G-18301)*

SHIP BUILDING & REPAIRING: Ferryboats

Trident Pontoons Inc .... G 352 253-1400
Tavares *(G-18355)*

SHIP BUILDING & REPAIRING: Landing

Merced Industrial Corp .... G 908 309-0170
Miami *(G-9977)*
USA Maritime Enterprises Inc .... G 954 764-8360
Fort Lauderdale *(G-4300)*

SHIP BUILDING & REPAIRING: Lighters, Marine

American Marine Mfg Inc .... G 305 497-7723
Hialeah *(G-5293)*

SHIP BUILDING & REPAIRING: Lighthouse Tenders

Ultra Lite Tenders LLC .... G 214 215-2725
Stuart *(G-17042)*

SHIP BUILDING & REPAIRING: Patrol Boats

Old City Marine LLC .... G 904 252-6887
Saint Augustine *(G-15580)*

SHIP BUILDING & REPAIRING: Rigging, Marine

TNT Custom Marine Inc .... G 305 931-3157
Miami *(G-10482)*
Unlimited Marine Mfg Inc .... G 305 420-6034
Hialeah *(G-5665)*

SHIP BUILDING & REPAIRING: Tugboats

Progressive Industrial Inc .... F 941 723-0201
Palmetto *(G-13818)*

SHIP COMPONENTS: Metal, Prefabricated

D W Allen Marine Svcs Inc .... E 904 358-1933
Jacksonville *(G-6306)*

SHIPBUILDING & REPAIR

Advanced Mechanical Entps Inc .... E 954 764-2678
Fort Lauderdale *(G-3783)*
Almaco Group Inc .... F 561 558-1600
Boca Raton *(G-413)*
Amee Bay LLC .... E 904 553-9873
Atlantic Beach *(G-216)*
Atlantic Dry Dock .... E 904 251-1545
Jacksonville *(G-6173)*
Atlantic Marine Inc .... G 904 251-1580
Jacksonville *(G-6177)*
Capt Latham LLC .... G 904 483-6118
Green Cove Springs *(G-5057)*
Colonna Shipyard .... G 904 246-1183
Atlantic Beach *(G-218)*
D W Allen Marine Svcs Inc .... E 904 358-1933
Jacksonville *(G-6306)*
Earl Industries .... G 904 247-1301
Atlantic Beach *(G-220)*
Eastern Shipbuilding Group Inc .... B 850 763-1900
Panama City *(G-13895)*
Eastern Shipyards Inc .... D 850 763-1900
Panama City *(G-13897)*
Fassmer Service America LLC .... E 305 557-8875
Lauderhill *(G-8109)*
Gable Enterprises .... F 727 455-5576
Seffner *(G-16727)*
Gde LLC .... G 305 458-3025
Miami Beach *(G-10671)*
General Dynamics Corporation .... E 407 380-9384
Orlando *(G-12778)*
Gulf County Ship Building Inc .... G 850 229-9300
Port Saint Joe *(G-15080)*
Gulf Marine Repair Corporation .... C 813 247-3153
Tampa *(G-17735)*
Gulfstream Land Company LLC .... F 772 286-3456
Stuart *(G-16951)*
Gulfstream Shipbuilding LLC .... G 850 835-5125
Freeport *(G-4849)*

Hendry Corporation..............D....... 813 241-9206
Tampa *(G-17750)*
Hendry Marine Industries Inc..............E....... 813 241-9206
Tampa *(G-17751)*
Hydrex LLC..............G....... 727 443-3900
Clearwater *(G-1723)*
International Ship Repair & MA..............F....... 813 247-1118
Tampa *(G-17790)*
International Shipyards Ancona..............F....... 305 371-7722
Fort Lauderdale *(G-4064)*
Karepat Group Inc..............G....... 772 286-5339
Stuart *(G-16964)*
M/V Marine Inc..............F....... 904 633-7992
Jacksonville *(G-6569)*
Maritime SEC Strtegies Fla LLC..............G....... 912 704-0300
Tampa *(G-17880)*
Metro Machine Corp..............D....... 904 249-7772
Jacksonville *(G-6601)*
Miller Marine Yacht Svc Inc..............E....... 850 265-6768
Panama City *(G-13929)*
Naiad Dynamics Us Inc..............F....... 954 797-7566
Davie *(G-2555)*
New Yachts Company..............G....... 754 223-5907
Fort Lauderdale *(G-4138)*
Newcastle Shipyards LLC..............C....... 386 312-0000
Saint Augustine *(G-15573)*
Nordic Made Inc..............F....... 954 651-6208
Davie *(G-2558)*
Norseman Shipbuilding Corp..............E....... 305 545-6815
Miami *(G-10076)*
Ocean Marine LLC..............F....... 305 549-6092
Miami *(G-10089)*
OSG America LLC..............D....... 813 209-0600
Tampa *(G-17963)*
Patti Marine Enterprises Inc..............F....... 850 453-1282
Pensacola *(G-14221)*
Port Manatee Ship Repair..............E....... 941 417-2613
Palmetto *(G-13817)*
Professional Coating Systems..............G....... 904 477-7138
Lawtey *(G-8125)*
Propel Builders Inc..............F....... 407 960-5116
Maitland *(G-8475)*
Puma Aero Marine Inc..............G....... 904 638-5888
Fort Lauderdale *(G-4184)*
Riverhawk Fast Sea Frames LLC..............G....... 912 484-3112
Tampa *(G-18060)*
Salmi and Company Inc..............G....... 443 243-8537
Navarre *(G-11474)*
Seaking Inc..............E....... 954 961-6629
Davie *(G-2589)*
Seaquest Marine LLC..............G....... 781 888-8850
Miami *(G-10317)*
Searobotics Corporation..............E....... 772 742-3700
Stuart *(G-17006)*
SGS US East Coast LLC..............E....... 305 571-9700
Miami *(G-10330)*
Shearwater Marine Fl Inc..............E....... 772 781-5553
Stuart *(G-17010)*
Sisco Marine LLC..............E....... 850 265-1383
Panama City *(G-13951)*
Southern Drydock Inc..............E....... 904 355-9945
Saint Augustine *(G-15615)*
St Augustine Marina Inc..............E....... 904 824-4394
Saint Augustine *(G-15619)*
St Augustine Trawlers Inc..............F....... 904 824-4394
Saint Augustine *(G-15621)*
St Johns Ship Building Inc..............C....... 386 328-6054
Palatka *(G-13495)*
Suncoast Kingfish Classic LLC..............G....... 970 708-7997
Treasure Island *(G-18478)*
Tampa Ship LLC..............B....... 813 248-9310
Tampa *(G-18173)*
Tecnico Corporation..............F....... 904 853-6118
Atlantic Beach *(G-227)*
United Ship Service Corp..............G....... 954 583-4588
Fort Lauderdale *(G-4295)*

SHIPPING AGENTS

USA Maritime Enterprises Inc..............G....... 954 764-8360
Fort Lauderdale *(G-4300)*

SHOCK ABSORBERS: Indl

Mustang Vacuum Systems Inc..............E....... 941 377-1440
Sarasota *(G-16261)*

SHOE & BOOT ACCESS

Violettas LLC..............G....... 305 301-3351
Miami *(G-10587)*

SHOE MATERIALS: Counters

AGM Kitchen & Bath LLC..............G....... 239 300-4739
Naples *(G-11151)*
Bean Counters Pro..............G....... 941 504-1157
Sarasota *(G-16363)*
Counter..............G....... 239 566-0644
Naples *(G-11216)*
Counter Impressions LLC..............F....... 352 589-4966
Eustis *(G-3706)*
Creative Countertops Inc..............F....... 904 387-2800
Jacksonville *(G-6296)*
Hospitlity Bean Cnters Plus In..............G....... 954 531-1710
Deerfield Beach *(G-2846)*
Jmg Counters LLC..............F....... 904 551-7006
Jacksonville *(G-6523)*

SHOE MATERIALS: Heel Parts

Tap Express Inc..............G....... 305 468-0038
Doral *(G-3523)*

SHOE MATERIALS: Plastic

Kino Sandals Inc..............F....... 305 294-5044
Key West *(G-7193)*

SHOE MATERIALS: Quarters

Advanced Living Quarters Inc..............G....... 954 684-9392
Pembroke Pines *(G-14015)*
Winter Qarters Pasco Rv Resort..............G....... 800 879-2131
Lutz *(G-8424)*

SHOE MATERIALS: Rands

Ingersoll Rand..............F....... 954 391-4500
Miramar *(G-11004)*
Rand & London LLC..............G....... 727 363-0800
Treasure Island *(G-18477)*
Rand M Rawls..............G....... 904 382-4844
Jacksonville *(G-6704)*
Rand Title Corporation..............G....... 407 622-7263
Winter Park *(G-19436)*
Sutherland Armour Rand..............F....... 863 696-3129
Lake Wales *(G-7523)*

SHOE STORES: Orthopedic

Son Life Prsthtics Orthtics In..............F....... 352 596-2257
Hernando Beach *(G-5251)*

SHOE STORES: Women's

Lerness Shoe Corp..............G....... 305 643-6525
Miami *(G-9885)*

SHOES: Canvas, Rubber Soled

Gold Banner USA Inc..............F....... 305 576-2215
Miami *(G-9645)*

SHOES: Men's

Kino Sandals Inc..............F....... 305 294-5044
Key West *(G-7193)*
Lerness Shoe Corp..............G....... 305 643-6525
Miami *(G-9885)*

SHOES: Men's, Sandals

Zeppelin Products Inc..............F....... 954 989-8808
Hallandale Beach *(G-5226)*

SHOES: Plastic Or Rubber

Protege Media LLC..............G....... 310 738-9567
Port Saint Lucie *(G-15131)*

SHOES: Sandals, Rubber

Rebuild Globally Inc..............E....... 407 801-9936
Lake Worth *(G-7585)*

SHOES: Women's

Grezzo Usa Llc..............G....... 954 885-0331
Hollywood *(G-5832)*
Kino Sandals Inc..............F....... 305 294-5044
Key West *(G-7193)*
Kloth Inc..............G....... 954 578-5687
Sunrise *(G-17139)*
Lerness Shoe Corp..............G....... 305 643-6525
Miami *(G-9885)*

Neighborhood Property Mgmt..............G....... 305 819-2361
Hialeah *(G-5536)*
Stush AP USA/Stush Style LLC..............F....... 404 940-3445
Sunrise *(G-17180)*

SHOES: Women's, Dress

Cedrick McDonald..............G....... 813 279-1442
Tampa *(G-17519)*

SHOES: Women's, Sandals

Zeppelin Products Inc..............F....... 954 989-8808
Hallandale Beach *(G-5226)*

SHOT PEENING SVC

Metal Improvement Company LLC..............G....... 305 592-5960
Miami *(G-9984)*

SHOWCASES & DISPLAY FIXTURES: Office & Store

Acryplex Inc..............G....... 305 633-7636
Miami *(G-9066)*
Asottu Inc..............F....... 626 627-6021
Orlando *(G-12494)*
Caddie Company Inc..............F....... 267 332-0976
Tampa *(G-17499)*
Gulf Coast Installers LLC..............F....... 239 273-4663
Bonita Springs *(G-836)*
Synergy Custom Fixtures Corp..............C....... 305 693-0055
Hialeah *(G-5645)*

SHOWER STALLS: Metal

Martell Glass..............G....... 786 336-0142
Miami *(G-9951)*
Shower Doors Unlimited Inc..............F....... 561 547-0702
Boynton Beach *(G-958)*

SHOWER STALLS: Plastic & Fiberglass

AGM Orlando Inc..............G....... 407 865-9522
Altamonte Springs *(G-27)*
Brian Belitz..............G....... 407 924-5543
Kissimmee *(G-7225)*
Central Fla Kit Bath Srfces In..............F....... 352 307-2333
Ocala *(G-11898)*
KDD Inc..............E....... 239 689-8402
Fort Myers *(G-4509)*
Martell Glass..............G....... 786 336-0142
Miami *(G-9951)*
Sea Products Inc..............D....... 904 781-8200
Jacksonville *(G-6758)*
Shower Doors & More Inc..............G....... 954 358-2014
Fort Lauderdale *(G-4231)*
Woodys Enterprises LLC..............F....... 407 892-1900
Saint Cloud *(G-15670)*

SHREDDERS: Indl & Commercial

Bay Area Security Shred..............F....... 877 974-7337
Palm Harbor *(G-13723)*
R & R Stone Industries Inc..............G....... 888 999-4921
Miami *(G-10229)*

SHUTTERS, DOOR & WINDOW: Metal

5 Day Plantation Shutters..............G....... 727 474-6130
Largo *(G-7881)*
Aabc Inc..............F....... 727 434-4444
Largo *(G-7882)*
ABC Shutters Protection Corp..............G....... 785 547-9527
Miami *(G-9054)*
Adams Hurricane Protection Inc..............F....... 850 434-2336
Pensacola *(G-14081)*
Addison Metal Additions Inc..............G....... 305 245-9860
Homestead *(G-5953)*
Advanced Hurricane Protection..............G....... 772 220-1200
Stuart *(G-16903)*
ANC Shutters LLC..............F....... 561 966-8336
Lake Worth *(G-7534)*
Anchor Aluminum Products South..............G....... 305 293-7965
Key West *(G-7177)*
Before Wind Blows LLC..............G....... 407 977-4833
Chuluota *(G-1552)*
California Shutters Inc..............G....... 305 827-9333
Miami Lakes *(G-10772)*
Camco Corp..............G....... 561 427-0433
Jupiter *(G-7014)*
Caribbean Shutter LLC..............G....... 305 202-0501
Miami Springs *(G-10889)*

Cat 5 Hurricane Products LLC ..... F 941 752-4692
Bradenton *(G-1016)*

Coastal Shutters Inc ..... G 954 759-1115
Port Saint Lucie *(G-15099)*

Coastal Shutters Online LLC ..... G 786 509-2093
Miami *(G-9368)*

Ds Shutters Group Inc ..... G 772 260-6393
Wellington *(G-18715)*

Eclipse Screen and Shutters ..... G 305 216-4716
Miami *(G-9498)*

Eddy Storm Protection ..... G 386 248-1631
Daytona Beach *(G-2661)*

Florida Shutters Inc ..... E 772 569-2200
Vero Beach *(G-18619)*

Florida Storm Shutters Inc ..... G 954 257-8365
Fort Lauderdale *(G-4007)*

Future Modes Inc ..... G 305 654-9995
Miami *(G-9605)*

General Impact GL Windows Corp ..... F 305 558-8103
Hialeah *(G-5426)*

Gotcha Shuttered ..... G 850 450-9137
Destin *(G-3192)*

Guardian Hurricane Protection ..... F 305 805-7050
Miami Lakes *(G-10796)*

Hurricane Shutter & Plus Inc ..... G 786 287-0007
Miami *(G-9721)*

Jansen Shutters & Spc Ltd ..... G 941 484-4700
North Venice *(G-11759)*

Jose Morales Hurricane Shutter ..... G 786 315-1835
Miami *(G-9803)*

Loxahatchee Shutter & Alum Inc ..... G 561 513-9581
Loxahatchee *(G-8361)*

Master Alum & SEC Shutter Co ..... G 727 725-1744
Safety Harbor *(G-15498)*

Orlando Shutters LLC ..... E 407 495-5250
Lake Mary *(G-7440)*

Pinellas Blind and Shutter Inc ..... G 727 481-4461
Clearwater *(G-1833)*

Plantation Shutters Inc ..... G 772 208-8245
Port Saint Lucie *(G-15129)*

Rollertech Corp ..... F 239 645-6698
Fort Myers *(G-4586)*

Rolling Shield Incorporated ..... E 305 436-6661
Miami Lakes *(G-10852)*

Rolling Shield Parts Inc ..... F 305 436-6661
Miami Lakes *(G-10853)*

Rollshield LLC ..... F 727 441-2243
Clearwater *(G-1864)*

Sano Associates Inc ..... E 239 403-2650
Naples *(G-11391)*

Sentinel Inc ..... F 239 263-9888
Naples *(G-11397)*

Shoreline Shutter Systems Inc ..... G 386 299-2219
Port Orange *(G-15033)*

Shutter Down All Weather Protc ..... G 561 856-0655
Boynton Beach *(G-959)*

Shutter Down Storm Protection ..... G 813 957-8936
Plant City *(G-14465)*

Shutter Lubrication & Service ..... G 561 745-8956
Jupiter *(G-7113)*

Shutter Southern Cross ..... G 941 276-7064
North Port *(G-11750)*

Shutter Southern Cross ..... G 941 235-2620
Port Charlotte *(G-14997)*

Shutter2think Inc ..... G 850 291-8301
Palm Beach Gardens *(G-13628)*

Shutters On Sale Inc ..... G 386 756-0009
Port Orange *(G-15034)*

Shuttertek Inc ..... G 772 828-6149
Port Saint Lucie *(G-15142)*

Smart Guard Shutters LLC ..... G 386 227-6295
Palm Coast *(G-13710)*

Smart Shutters Inc ..... G 786 391-1100
Miami *(G-10364)*

Southern Cross Shutter Systems ..... G 941 585-2152
Port Charlotte *(G-14998)*

Space Coast Storm Shutters LLC ..... G 410 652-5717
Cocoa Beach *(G-2067)*

Strong Hurricane Shutter ..... G 786 587-3990
Miami *(G-10421)*

Sun Barrier Products Inc ..... F 407 830-9085
Longwood *(G-8341)*

Swfl Hurricane Shutters Inc ..... G 239 454-4944
Cape Coral *(G-1481)*

Tropic Shield Inc ..... F 954 731-5553
Lauderdale Lakes *(G-8095)*

USA Aluminum ..... G 305 303-9121
Hallandale Beach *(G-5222)*

Valco Group Inc ..... C 813 870-0482
Tampa *(G-18232)*

Valiant Products Inc ..... E 863 688-7998
Lakeland *(G-7829)*

West Coast Shutters Sunburst ..... F 727 894-0044
Saint Petersburg *(G-15957)*

West Palm Installers Inc ..... F 305 406-3575
Doral *(G-3548)*

Will Shutter U Inc ..... G 772 285-3600
Jensen Beach *(G-6974)*

SHUTTERS, DOOR & WINDOW: Plastic

Future Modes Inc ..... G 305 654-9995
Miami *(G-9605)*

USA Shutter Company LLC ..... G 239 596-8883
Fort Myers *(G-4642)*

Viterra Affordable Shutters ..... G 239 738-6364
Cape Coral *(G-1492)*

SHUTTERS: Door, Wood

1st Chice Hrrcane Prtction LLC ..... F 239 325-3400
Bonita Springs *(G-809)*

American Louvered Products Co ..... E 813 884-1441
Tampa *(G-17417)*

Dependable Shutter Service Inc ..... E 954 583-1411
Davie *(G-2516)*

Future Modes Inc ..... G 305 654-9995
Miami *(G-9605)*

Guardian Hurricane Protection ..... F 305 805-7050
Miami Lakes *(G-10796)*

Hurricane Shtters Cntl Fla Inc ..... G 321 639-2622
Rockledge *(G-15419)*

Roy Smith S Screen ..... F 561 792-3381
Loxahatchee *(G-8363)*

Shutterman Storm & Security ..... F 239 455-9166
Naples *(G-11400)*

Shutters Wholesale ..... G 770 410-9525
Jacksonville *(G-6768)*

SHUTTERS: Window, Wood

Ace Shutter & Shelves LLC ..... G 239 314-9136
Cape Coral *(G-1372)*

Florida Wood Creations Inc ..... G 239 561-5411
Punta Gorda *(G-15205)*

Greg Valley ..... F 941 739-6628
Sarasota *(G-16224)*

Island Shutter Co Inc ..... E 386 738-9455
Deland *(G-2985)*

Ita Inc ..... F 386 301-5172
Ormond Beach *(G-13381)*

Orlando Shutters LLC ..... E 407 495-5250
Lake Mary *(G-7440)*

USA Exterior LLC ..... G 813 515-5181
Tampa *(G-18229)*

W C H Enterprises Inc ..... G 239 267-7549
Fort Myers *(G-4649)*

SIDING & STRUCTURAL MATERIALS: Wood

Aw Gates Inc ..... G 954 341-2180
Coral Springs *(G-2221)*

Innovative Cnstr Group LLC ..... C 904 398-5690
Jacksonville *(G-6496)*

Maxville LLC ..... C 904 289-7261
Jacksonville *(G-6582)*

Meridian Centre ..... G 253 620-4542
Boca Raton *(G-619)*

SIDING MATERIALS

Aluminum Products ..... G 904 829-9995
Saint Augustine *(G-15514)*

S&L Cnstrction Specialists Inc ..... G 407 300-5080
Orlando *(G-13153)*

SIDING: Precast Stone

Stonecrfters Archtctral Prcast ..... F 727 544-1210
Seminole *(G-16763)*

SIDING: Sheet Metal

Millennium Metals Inc ..... E 904 358-8366
Jacksonville *(G-6606)*

SIGN LETTERING & PAINTING SVCS

Productive Products Inc ..... G 904 570-5553
Saint Augustine *(G-15591)*

SIGN PAINTING & LETTERING SHOP

Apparel Printers ..... G 352 463-8850
Alachua *(G-4)*

Kevin Jeffers Inc ..... G 352 377-2322
Gainesville *(G-4949)*

Sign Design of Florida Inc ..... E 352 787-3882
Leesburg *(G-8172)*

SIGNALING APPARATUS: Electric

L3 Technologies Inc ..... G 305 371-7039
Fort Lauderdale *(G-4092)*

SIGNALS: Railroad, Electric

Alstom Signaling Operation LLC ..... C 781 740-8111
Melbourne *(G-8765)*

Interrail Engineering Inc ..... E 904 268-6411
Jacksonville *(G-6501)*

United Rail Inc ..... F 904 503-9757
Jacksonville *(G-6881)*

SIGNALS: Traffic Control, Electric

City of Ocala ..... E 352 622-6803
Ocala *(G-11903)*

North American Signal LLC ..... G 850 462-1790
Pensacola *(G-14212)*

North Amrcn Signal Systems LLC ..... G 352 376-8341
Gainesville *(G-4973)*

Southwest Signal Inc ..... E 813 621-4949
Englewood *(G-3667)*

Traffipax LLC ..... B 561 881-7400
Jupiter *(G-7131)*

Transprtation Ctrl Systems Inc ..... E 813 630-2800
Tampa *(G-18197)*

SIGNALS: Transportation

Ingram Signalization Inc ..... E 850 433-8267
Pensacola *(G-14178)*

International C & C Corp ..... E 727 249-0675
Largo *(G-7981)*

Peek Traffic Corporation ..... C 941 366-8770
Sarasota *(G-16275)*

Traffic Control Pdts Fla Inc ..... F 352 372-7088
Jacksonville *(G-6865)*

SIGNS & ADVERTISING SPECIALTIES

2u Service Corp ..... G 786 219-6564
Miami *(G-9024)*

3 D F X Inc ..... F 407 237-6249
Orlando *(G-12416)*

A J Trophies & Awards Inc ..... E 850 878-7187
Tallahassee *(G-17210)*

A Sign ..... G 321 264-0077
Titusville *(G-18406)*

A Sign Shop LLC ..... G 813 334-7765
Apollo Beach *(G-99)*

A World of Signs ..... G 850 267-1331
Santa Rosa Beach *(G-16151)*

A&C Signs Solutions Corp ..... F 786 953-5600
Hialeah *(G-5259)*

Abalux Inc ..... F 305 698-9192
Hialeah *(G-5263)*

Abby Press Inc ..... E 407 847-5565
Kissimmee *(G-7216)*

Accuform Signs ..... F 800 237-1001
Spring Hill *(G-16844)*

Accurate Signs LLC ..... G 754 779-7519
Fort Lauderdale *(G-3776)*

Ace Custom Signs of Winter Pk ..... G 407 257-6475
Winter Park *(G-19371)*

Action Signs & Graphics Inc ..... G 386 752-0121
Lake City *(G-7346)*

ADM II Exhibits & Displays Inc ..... F 813 887-1960
Tampa *(G-17387)*

Adtech Electric Advertising ..... D 786 533-3210
Miami *(G-9073)*

Adwave Graphics Inc ..... G 305 643-8020
Miami *(G-9078)*

Aerial Banners Inc ..... F 954 893-0099
Pembroke Pines *(G-14016)*

Affordable Signs Clermont LLC ..... G 352 241-7645
Groveland *(G-5093)*

Agi Solutions Inc ..... G 888 987-8425
Sarasota *(G-16336)*

All Miami Signs Inc ..... F 305 406-2420
Miami *(G-9112)*

All Signs ..... G 904 262-3795
Jacksonville *(G-6136)*

All Venue Graphics and Signs ....G....... 954 399-7446
Pompano Beach ***(G-14586)***
All-Brite Signs ....G....... 352 628-4910
Lecanto ***(G-8127)***
Allegra Print Signs Mail ....G....... 954 963-3886
Hollywood ***(G-5770)***
Alli Cats Inc ....G....... 239 274-0744
Fort Myers ***(G-4352)***
Allstate Signs Inc ....G....... 305 885-9751
Hialeah ***(G-5282)***
Alternative Sign Group Inc ....G....... 561 722-9272
West Palm Beach ***(G-18795)***
AM Primaclasse Corp ....G....... 305 767-5918
Fort Lauderdale ***(G-3810)***
American Led Technology Inc ....F....... 850 863-8777
Naples ***(G-11162)***
American Lw & Promo Prods LLC ....G....... 954 946-5252
Pompano Beach ***(G-14591)***
American Sign Letters ....G....... 772 643-4012
Sebastian ***(G-16654)***
Anything Display ....F....... 239 433-9738
Fort Myers ***(G-4365)***
ARC Creative Inc ....G....... 904 996-7773
Jacksonville ***(G-6164)***
Architctral Sgnage Systems Inc ....G....... 813 996-6777
Land O Lakes ***(G-7849)***
Architectural Signcrafters ....G....... 772 600-5032
Stuart ***(G-16908)***
Architectural Signs Inc ....G....... 305 282-4427
Miami ***(G-9164)***
Arrive Alive Traffic Ctrl LLC ....F....... 407 578-5431
Orlando ***(G-12490)***
Ash Signs Inc ....G....... 904 724-7446
Jacksonville ***(G-6170)***
Atlas Sign Industries Fla LLC ....C....... 561 863-6659
Riviera Beach ***(G-15299)***
Automotive Advertising Assoc ....G....... 954 389-6500
Weston ***(G-19109)***
Avalon Sign Solutions Inc ....G....... 727 398-6126
Seminole ***(G-16740)***
B R Signs Inc ....G....... 954 973-7700
Pompano Beach ***(G-14610)***
B2b Sign Resource ....F....... 813 855-7446
Tampa ***(G-17452)***
Bach Sign Group Inc ....G....... 561 848-3440
West Palm Beach ***(G-18812)***
Backyard Canvas & Signs Inc ....G....... 813 672-2660
Gibsonton ***(G-5026)***
Baron International LLC ....F....... 800 531-9558
Jupiter ***(G-7003)***
Barrau & Coirin Inc ....G....... 305 571-5051
Miami ***(G-9223)***
Baxter Adventures Inc ....G....... 561 439-4700
Lake Worth Beach ***(G-7605)***
Bayfront Printing Company ....G....... 727 823-1965
Saint Petersburg ***(G-15719)***
Bdnz Associates Inc ....G....... 305 379-7993
Miami ***(G-9230)***
Beautiful Mailbox Co ....E....... 305 403-4820
Hialeah ***(G-5318)***
Big Color Output Inc ....G....... 941 540-4441
Cape Coral ***(G-1390)***
Big Digital Graphics LLC ....G....... 561 844-4708
Lake Park ***(G-7466)***
Big Sign Message LLC ....G....... 954 235-5717
Fort Lauderdale ***(G-3851)***
Binca LLC ....F....... 305 698-8883
Doral ***(G-3274)***
Binney Family of Florida Inc ....F....... 727 376-5596
Odessa ***(G-12106)***
Bolt Signs & Marketing LLC ....F....... 407 865-7446
Apopka ***(G-119)***
BR Signs International In ....G....... 954 464-7999
Coral Springs ***(G-2229)***
Broward Sign Shop ....G....... 305 431-2455
Hallandale Beach ***(G-5175)***
Bruce R Ely Enterprise Inc ....F....... 727 573-1643
Clearwater ***(G-1614)***
Buchanan Signs Screen Process ....E....... 904 725-5500
Jacksonville ***(G-6243)***
Bucks Corporation Inc ....F....... 850 894-2400
Tallahassee ***(G-17229)***
Bundy Signs LLC ....G....... 954 296-0784
Sunrise ***(G-17101)***
Burton Signs Inc ....G....... 727 841-8927
New Port Richey ***(G-11485)***
Business Forward Inc ....G....... 954 967-6730
Hollywood ***(G-5792)***
C & E Cabinets Design LLC ....G....... 386 410-4281
Edgewater ***(G-3617)***
C & H Sign Enterprises Inc ....G....... 407 826-0155
Orlando ***(G-12538)***
C L F Enterprises ....G....... 305 643-3222
Miami ***(G-9293)***
C&D Sign and Lighting Svcs LLC ....G....... 863 937-9323
Lakeland ***(G-7652)***
Calmac Corporation ....F....... 813 493-8700
Tampa ***(G-17501)***
Cardinal Signs Inc ....G....... 352 376-8494
Gainesville ***(G-4893)***
Carlaron Inc ....G....... 386 258-1183
Daytona Beach ***(G-2639)***
Carter Signs Inc ....G....... 239 543-4004
Fort Myers ***(G-4390)***
Catch One Comm ....G....... 772 221-0225
Port Saint Lucie ***(G-15096)***
Central Signs Volusia Cnty Inc ....G....... 386 341-4842
South Daytona ***(G-16799)***
Cesco Signs Inc ....G....... 407 463-6635
Orlando ***(G-12572)***
Channel Letter USA Corp ....G....... 561 243-9699
Delray Beach ***(G-3058)***
Charles Thaggard Inc ....G....... 239 936-8059
Fort Myers ***(G-4393)***
Cheap Banners & Signs Central ....G....... 727 522-7414
Saint Petersburg ***(G-15744)***
Chiliprint LLC ....G....... 863 547-6930
Dundee ***(G-3564)***
Chilton Signs & Designs LLC ....G....... 863 438-0880
Winter Haven ***(G-19314)***
Clark Craig Enterprises ....F....... 813 287-0110
Tampa ***(G-17539)***
Clarks Electrical Signs & Svcs ....G....... 561 248-5932
Lake Worth ***(G-7542)***
Classic Shirts Inc ....F....... 850 875-2200
Quincy ***(G-15247)***
Cns Signs Inc ....G....... 904 733-4806
Jacksonville ***(G-6274)***
Collins Media & Advg LLC ....F....... 954 688-9758
Margate ***(G-8538)***
Corporate Signs Inc ....G....... 305 500-9313
Doral ***(G-3309)***
Countdown Today Inc ....G....... 415 420-2849
South Miami ***(G-16814)***
Crazy 4 Signs LLC ....G....... 813 239-3085
Zephyrhills ***(G-19512)***
Creative Printing Bay Cnty Inc ....F....... 850 784-1645
Panama City ***(G-13889)***
Creative Sign Designs LLC ....D....... 813 818-7100
Tampa ***(G-17567)***
Creative Signs ....G....... 786 636-6969
Doral ***(G-3314)***
Creative Signs Inc ....E....... 407 293-9393
Apopka ***(G-128)***
Crf Group Inc ....F....... 954 428-7446
Pompano Beach ***(G-14651)***
Cso Systems Inc ....F....... 941 355-5653
Sarasota ***(G-16397)***
Custom Cut Rubber ....G....... 979 422-2511
Saint Johns ***(G-15675)***
Custom Mailboxes and Signs ....G....... 239 738-9321
Fort Myers ***(G-4422)***
Custom Sign & Awning ....F....... 727 210-0941
Clearwater ***(G-1644)***
D & R Signs Inc ....G....... 386 252-2777
Daytona Beach ***(G-2651)***
D E E Custom Fabricators Inc ....E....... 863 667-1850
Lakeland ***(G-7668)***
D G Morrison Inc ....F....... 813 865-0208
Odessa ***(G-12114)***
D O B Signs LLC ....G....... 772 466-4913
Fort Pierce ***(G-4691)***
Dakim Inc ....F....... 561 790-0884
Royal Palm Beach ***(G-15465)***
Daniels Whl Sign & Plas Inc ....G....... 386 736-4918
Sanford ***(G-16031)***
Data Graphics Inc ....D....... 352 589-1312
Mount Dora ***(G-11100)***
David Dobbs Enterprises Inc ....D....... 904 824-6171
Saint Augustine ***(G-15533)***
Davie Fastsigns ....G....... 305 423-2332
Miami ***(G-9438)***
Daytona Trophy Inc ....F....... 386 253-2806
Daytona Beach ***(G-2656)***
Delconte Packaging Inc ....F....... 305 885-2800
Hialeah ***(G-5368)***
Design Communications Ltd ....F....... 407 856-9661
Orlando ***(G-12662)***
Design It Wraps & Graphics LLC ....G....... 904 310-6032
Fernandina Beach ***(G-3734)***
Designer Sign Systems Inc ....G....... 954 972-0707
Fort Lauderdale ***(G-3937)***
Designstogo Inc ....G....... 561 432-1313
Palm Springs ***(G-13774)***
Dgs Retail LLC ....F....... 727 388-4975
Saint Petersburg ***(G-15761)***
Digiprint & Design Corp ....G....... 786 464-1770
Sweetwater ***(G-17208)***
Digital Tech of Lakeland Inc ....F....... 863 668-8770
Lakeland ***(G-7675)***
Divinitas Displays LLC ....F....... 407 660-6625
Orlando ***(G-12678)***
Doug Bloodworth Enterprises ....G....... 407 247-9728
Lady Lake ***(G-7325)***
Dynamic Aspects Inc ....G....... 407 322-1923
Debary ***(G-2748)***
E C V Display Corp ....G....... 786 586-1034
Hialeah ***(G-5385)***
E&M Pckging Llcdba Crtive Sign ....G....... 813 839-6356
Tampa ***(G-17623)***
Eagle Signs ....G....... 321 863-9844
Titusville ***(G-18428)***
Eastern Signs LLC ....G....... 305 542-8274
Hialeah ***(G-5386)***
Easy Rent Inc ....G....... 904 443-7446
Jacksonville ***(G-6351)***
Easy Signs Inc ....G....... 954 673-0118
Oakland Park ***(G-11801)***
Econochannel Inc ....E....... 305 255-2113
Hialeah ***(G-5388)***
Eidolon Analytics Inc ....F....... 239 288-6951
Fort Myers ***(G-4441)***
Electronic Sign Supply Corp ....G....... 305 477-0555
Medley ***(G-8647)***
Elite Printing & Marketing Inc ....G....... 850 474-0894
Pensacola ***(G-14139)***
Emerald Coast Signs ....G....... 850 398-1712
Crestview ***(G-2347)***
Ernies Signs ....G....... 239 992-0800
Bonita Springs ***(G-829)***
Everything Communicates Inc ....G....... 407 578-6616
Orlando ***(G-12722)***
Excellent Guarantd Elctrcl ....G....... 407 221-6234
Orlando ***(G-12726)***
Exotics Car Wraps ....G....... 786 768-6798
Miami ***(G-9545)***
F D Signworks LLC ....G....... 561 248-6323
West Palm Beach ***(G-18867)***
Fast Service Signs Inc ....G....... 954 380-0451
Sunrise ***(G-17123)***
Fast Signs ....G....... 813 999-4981
Tampa ***(G-17660)***
Fast Signs ....G....... 239 498-7200
Bonita Springs ***(G-830)***
Fast Signs of Brandon ....G....... 813 655-9036
Brandon ***(G-1158)***
Fastsigns ....F....... 305 628-3278
Miami Lakes ***(G-10788)***
Fastsigns ....G....... 727 341-0084
Saint Petersburg ***(G-15777)***
Fastsigns ....G....... 305 747-7115
Coral Gables ***(G-2145)***
Fastsigns ....G....... 903 629-7204
Orlando ***(G-12734)***
Fastsigns ....G....... 813 625-1800
Valrico ***(G-18518)***
Fastsigns ....F....... 305 945-4700
North Miami Beach ***(G-11675)***
Fastsigns ....G....... 786 615-2179
Hialeah ***(G-5407)***
Fastsigns ....G....... 954 404-8341
Fort Lauderdale ***(G-3987)***
Fastsigns ....F....... 954 416-3434
Hollywood ***(G-5820)***
Fastsigns ....G....... 407 542-1234
Oviedo ***(G-13430)***
Fastsigns ....G....... 850 477-9744
Pensacola ***(G-14149)***
Fastsigns 176101 ....F....... 321 307-2400
Melbourne ***(G-8831)***
Fastsigns2043 ....F....... 305 988-5264
Boca Raton ***(G-527)***
FDA Signs LLC ....G....... 904 800-1776
Saint Augustine ***(G-15543)***
Federal Heath Sign Company LLC ....F....... 817 685-9075
Daytona Beach ***(G-2665)***
Firedrake Inc ....G....... 813 713-8902
Zephyrhills ***(G-19518)***
Flexofferscom Inc ....G....... 305 999-9940
Miami ***(G-9577)***

Florida Roadway Signs Inc ....G.... 561 722-4067
Lake Park *(G-7472)*
Florida Sign Source ....G.... 407 316-0466
Orlando *(G-12756)*
Forge Unlimited Co ....G.... 727 900-7600
Clearwater *(G-1693)*
Frames & Things ....G.... 727 815-0515
Port Richey *(G-15049)*
Fusion Signs ....G.... 407 715-6439
Kissimmee *(G-7248)*
Future Signs and Services Inc ....G.... 786 255-0868
Aventura *(G-269)*
Galaxy Awning and Signs Inc ....G.... 305 262-4224
Hialeah *(G-5422)*
Galea Corporation ....G.... 305 663-0244
Miami *(G-9611)*
Georgia Mktg & Sign Co LLC ....G.... 800 286-8671
West Palm Beach *(G-18887)*
Gibbons Advg DBA Gai Exhibits ....G.... 954 395-2397
Oakland Park *(G-11808)*
Gillette Sign & Lighting Inc ....G.... 352 256-2225
Zephyrhills *(G-19521)*
Gjcb Signs Graphics Inc ....F.... 352 429-0803
Groveland *(G-5095)*
Glow Bench Systems Intl ....G.... 954 315-4615
Sunrise *(G-17126)*
Graph-Plex Corp ....F.... 772 766-3866
Sebastian *(G-16662)*
Graphic Banner LLP ....G.... 954 491-9441
Oakland Park *(G-11809)*
Graphic Designs Intl Inc ....F.... 772 287-0000
Stuart *(G-16948)*
Graphic Difference Inc A ....F.... 954 748-6990
Lauderhill *(G-8110)*
Graphic Images Inc ....F.... 954 984-0015
Pompano Beach *(G-14717)*
Graphic Installers Inc ....G.... 863 646-5543
Lakeland *(G-7701)*
Graphic Jet Signs LLC ....G.... 786 552-2098
Palmetto Bay *(G-13845)*
Graphic Sign Dsign Cntl Fla LL ....G.... 386 547-4569
Daytona Beach *(G-2669)*
Graphics Designer Inc ....F.... 561 687-7993
West Palm Beach *(G-18889)*
Graphics Pdts Excellence Inc ....F.... 813 884-1578
Wesley Chapel *(G-18748)*
Great Bay Signs Inc ....G.... 727 437-1091
Largo *(G-7964)*
Greathouse Signs LLC ....G.... 407 247-2668
Apopka *(G-146)*
Greyson Corp ....F.... 407 830-7443
Longwood *(G-8286)*
Gulf Coast Business World Inc ....F.... 850 864-1511
Fort Walton Beach *(G-4806)*
Guthman Signs LLC ....G.... 941 218-0023
Bradenton *(G-1054)*
Guthman Signs LLC ....G.... 941 218-0014
Sarasota *(G-16455)*
Hd Signs & Lighting ....G.... 850 484-9829
Pensacola *(G-14169)*
Heritage Signs ....G.... 904 529-7446
Green Cove Springs *(G-5065)*
Hermes 7 Communications LLC ....F.... 954 426-1998
Deerfield Beach *(G-2838)*
Hit Promotional Products Inc ....B.... 727 541-5561
Largo *(G-7971)*
HOB Corporation ....G.... 813 988-2272
Tampa *(G-17758)*
Holmes Stamp Company ....E.... 904 396-2291
Jacksonville *(G-6476)*
Honchin Inc ....G.... 305 235-3800
Cutler Bay *(G-2397)*
Human Sign ....F.... 239 573-4292
Cape Coral *(G-1439)*
Hunt RDS Inc ....G.... 813 249-7551
Oldsmar *(G-12232)*
I2k Digital Solutions LLC ....F.... 305 507-0707
Miami *(G-9725)*
Ifoxx LLC ....G.... 305 785-7130
Kissimmee *(G-7253)*
Image 360 ....G.... 561 395-0745
Boca Raton *(G-562)*
Imprint Promotions LLC ....G.... 321 622-8946
Melbourne *(G-8850)*
Infinity Signs & Graphix LLC ....F.... 407 270-6733
Orlando *(G-12829)*
Inklab Signs Inc ....G.... 786 430-8100
Miami *(G-9743)*
Instasign ....G.... 561 272-2323
Delray Beach *(G-3091)*
Integrted Sign Engrg Dsign LLC ....G.... 941 379-5918
Sarasota *(G-16467)*
International Sign Design Corp ....E.... 727 541-5573
Largo *(G-7982)*
J R Wheeler Corporation ....G.... 954 585-8950
Fort Lauderdale *(G-4073)*
J T E Inc ....G.... 941 925-2605
Sarasota *(G-16475)*
Jar Advertising LLC ....G.... 844 344-4586
Orlando *(G-12851)*
Jay Berry Signs ....F.... 352 805-4050
Leesburg *(G-8162)*
Jbjb Holdings LLC ....G.... 239 267-1975
Fort Myers *(G-4501)*
JCP Signs Inc ....G.... 305 790-5336
Miami *(G-9791)*
Joni Industries Inc ....F.... 352 799-5456
Brooksville *(G-1240)*
Jpl Associates Inc ....F.... 954 929-6024
Hallandale Beach *(G-5194)*
Jwn Family Partners LP Ltd ....G.... 352 628-4910
Lecanto *(G-8135)*
K & I Plastics Inc ....G.... 904 387-0438
Jacksonville *(G-6531)*
K R O Enterprises Ltd ....G.... 309 797-2213
Naples *(G-11302)*
Kauffs Ventures LLC ....G.... 561 775-3278
Palm Beach Gardens *(G-13600)*
Kay Enterprises ....G.... 352 732-5770
Ocala *(G-11975)*
Kendal Signs Inc ....E.... 321 636-5116
Rockledge *(G-15428)*
Kendall Sign and Design Inc ....G.... 305 595-2000
Miami *(G-9820)*
Kids Wood ....G.... 407 332-9663
Longwood *(G-8299)*
L R Gator Corporation ....G.... 407 578-6616
Orlando *(G-12880)*
L4 Design LLC ....F.... 224 612-5045
Maitland *(G-8472)*
Labelpro Inc ....F.... 727 538-2149
Clearwater *(G-1757)*
Lambs Signs Inc ....F.... 941 792-4453
Bradenton *(G-1068)*
Laporte Inv Holdings Inc ....G.... 863 294-4498
Winter Haven *(G-19335)*
Lcr Signs & Services ....G.... 772 882-5276
Port Saint Lucie *(G-15119)*
Leon Sign S LLC ....G.... 786 333-4694
Hialeah *(G-5485)*
Liquid Soul Dgtal Graphics LLC ....G.... 407 948-6973
Orlando *(G-12915)*
Local Biz Spot Inc ....G.... 866 446-1790
Wesley Chapel *(G-18751)*
Lords Place Thrift Store ....G.... 561 660-7942
West Palm Beach *(G-18935)*
Lsj Corp ....G.... 954 920-0905
Hollywood *(G-5864)*
Lucke Enterprises Inc ....G.... 727 797-1177
Clearwater *(G-1765)*
Lucke Group Inc ....G.... 727 525-4949
Saint Petersburg *(G-15843)*
M & M Signs ....E.... 904 381-7353
Jacksonville *(G-6568)*
M&D Signs ....G.... 561 296-3636
West Palm Beach *(G-18937)*
Mac Papers Inc ....G.... 800 582-0049
Clearwater *(G-1768)*
Major League Signs Inc ....G.... 954 600-5505
Hialeah *(G-5498)*
Mc Graphix ....G.... 321 725-7243
Palm Bay *(G-13523)*
McColl Display Solutions ....F.... 813 333-6613
Windermere *(G-19238)*
McGrail Signs & Graphics LLC ....G.... 850 435-1017
Pensacola *(G-14204)*
McKenny Printing Enterprise ....G.... 727 420-4944
Saint Petersburg *(G-15853)*
MGM Cargo LLC ....G.... 407 770-1500
Orlando *(G-12966)*
Miami Banners & Signs Inc ....G.... 305 262-4460
Miami *(G-9992)*
Miami Sign Industry ....G.... 305 418-0673
Opa Locka *(G-12339)*
Miami Signage LLC ....G.... 305 877-3924
Miami *(G-10010)*
Miller Signs LLC ....G.... 786 395-9420
Hollywood *(G-5877)*
Milliken & Milliken Inc ....E.... 941 474-0223
Englewood *(G-3680)*
Mobile Sign Service Inc ....G.... 954 579-8628
Coconut Creek *(G-2091)*
Modular Sign ....G.... 727 391-2423
Seminole *(G-16755)*
Morrow Technologies Corp ....E.... 727 531-4000
Saint Petersburg *(G-15859)*
Mwr Sign Enterprises Inc ....G.... 954 914-2709
Pembroke Pines *(G-14050)*
N & N Investment Corporation ....E.... 954 590-3800
Pompano Beach *(G-14770)*
Nation Signs ....G.... 386 466-0043
Lake City *(G-7368)*
National Direct Signs ....E.... 561 320-2102
West Palm Beach *(G-18957)*
National Sign Inc ....F.... 727 572-1503
Clearwater *(G-1801)*
Nauset Enterprises Inc ....G.... 727 443-3469
Clearwater *(G-1804)*
Neon & Sign Mfg Inc ....G.... 443 664-6419
Boca Raton *(G-638)*
New Vision Signs Corp ....G.... 786 514-6822
Miami *(G-10067)*
Nine Enterprises Inc ....G.... 904 998-8880
Jacksonville *(G-6635)*
Nitesol Inc ....G.... 407 557-4042
Orlando *(G-13005)*
Novalux Signs ....G.... 904 329-9607
Jacksonville *(G-6640)*
Novus Clip Signs & Video Prod ....G.... 239 471-5639
Fort Myers *(G-4551)*
Nu-Art Signs Inc ....G.... 305 531-9850
Miami *(G-10084)*
Oceanside Custom LLC ....G.... 386 341-7507
Fort Myers *(G-4554)*
Off The Chart Inc ....G.... 954 654-6541
Davie *(G-2561)*
Omega Sign Service Corporation ....G.... 727 505-7833
New Port Richey *(G-11505)*
On-Site Lighting & Sign Svcs ....G.... 256 693-1018
Pensacola *(G-14216)*
Onsight Industries ....G.... 407 830-8861
Tampa *(G-17957)*
Outdoor Images Central Fla Inc ....G.... 407 825-9944
Orlando *(G-13040)*
Pacheco Creative Group Inc ....F.... 305 541-1400
Miami *(G-10126)*
Paints N Cocktails Inc ....F.... 954 514-7383
Miami *(G-10130)*
Phil Rowe Signs Inc ....G.... 561 832-8688
West Palm Beach *(G-18997)*
Pivotal Sign & Graphics Inc ....G.... 727 462-2266
Clearwater *(G-1835)*
Pk Group Inc ....F.... 239 643-2442
Naples *(G-11368)*
Plastic Art Sign Company Inc ....F.... 850 455-4114
Pensacola *(G-14232)*
Platinum Signs and Design LLC ....G.... 407 971-3640
Casselberry *(G-1514)*
Platinum Signs Inc ....G.... 561 296-3636
West Palm Beach *(G-18999)*
Poblocki Sign Co Southeast LLC ....G.... 407 660-3174
Winter Park *(G-19432)*
Poli Group International Inc ....F.... 305 468-8986
Miami *(G-10174)*
Precision Auto Tint Dsign Corp ....G.... 727 385-8788
Tarpon Springs *(G-18321)*
Premier Printing Signs ....G.... 727 849-2493
Port Richey *(G-15064)*
Premier Sign & Service Inc ....G.... 239 258-6979
Lehigh Acres *(G-8203)*
Premier Sign Company LLC ....F.... 850 621-4524
Destin *(G-3202)*
Print Signs & Banners ....G.... 305 600-1349
Miami *(G-10198)*
Priority 1 Signs ....F.... 954 971-8689
Deerfield Beach *(G-2893)*
Professional Signs ....G.... 305 662-5957
Miami *(G-10207)*
Quality Signs ....G.... 786 261-6242
Hialeah *(G-5591)*
Quick Advertising Inc ....F.... 407 774-0003
Apopka *(G-177)*
Quick Signs ....G.... 904 310-1010
Saint Augustine *(G-15592)*
R & A Power Graphics Inc ....F.... 407 898-5770
Orlando *(G-13107)*
Raimonda Investment Group Inc ....G.... 352 347-8899
Belleview *(G-375)*
Rapid Signs and T Shirts ....G.... 786 486-2804
Homestead *(G-5989)*

Redmont Sign LLC.......D....... 941 378-4242
Sarasota *(G-16556)*
Richard Varney Signs.......G....... 772 873-0454
Port Saint Lucie *(G-15138)*
Ricks Quality Prtg & Signs.......G....... 321 504-7446
Cocoa *(G-2048)*
River City Advg Objectional.......G....... 904 731-3452
Jacksonville *(G-6726)*
Road Runner Highway Sign Inc.......G....... 941 753-0549
Bradenton *(G-1105)*
Rocket Sign Supplies LLC.......G....... 239 995-4684
Fort Myers *(G-4585)*
Royal Atlantic Ventures LLC.......F....... 561 243-9699
Delray Beach *(G-3136)*
RPM Graphics Inc.......G....... 239 275-3278
Lehigh Acres *(G-8206)*
Rush Signs.......G....... 407 308-6362
Orlando *(G-13149)*
Sam Weiss Woodworking Inc.......G....... 954 975-8158
Margate *(G-8566)*
Sams Led Signs & Services.......G....... 407 492-4934
Davenport *(G-2482)*
Sapphire LLC.......G....... 561 346-7449
Greenacres *(G-5087)*
Sarasota Signs and Visuals.......G....... 941 355-5746
Sarasota *(G-16581)*
Saul Signs Inc.......F....... 305 266-8484
Medley *(G-8722)*
Saxton Sign FL Inc.......G....... 239 458-0845
Cape Coral *(G-1466)*
Sb Signs Inc.......G....... 561 688-9100
West Palm Beach *(G-19026)*
Screen Process Printers Inc.......G....... 904 354-8708
Jacksonville *(G-6757)*
Sebco Industries Inc.......G....... 954 566-8500
Oakland Park *(G-11837)*
Seminole Sign Company LLC.......G....... 863 623-6600
Okeechobee *(G-12192)*
Seminole State Signs & Ltg.......G....... 954 316-6030
Davie *(G-2590)*
Sep Communications LLC.......F....... 561 998-0870
Boca Raton *(G-706)*
Sh Signs.......G....... 305 967-8964
Miami *(G-10332)*
Sheldon Sign Company Inc.......G....... 941 321-6313
North Port *(G-11749)*
Shipping + Business Svcs LLC.......G....... 904 240-1737
Jacksonville *(G-6765)*
Shirts & Caps Inc.......F....... 813 788-7026
Tampa *(G-18098)*
Sign & Vehicle Wraps Inc.......G....... 407 859-8631
Orlando *(G-13189)*
Sign A Rama.......G....... 954 796-1644
Coral Springs *(G-2312)*
Sign A Rama.......G....... 813 264-0022
Tampa *(G-18099)*
Sign A Rama Inc.......E....... 561 640-5570
West Palm Beach *(G-19032)*
Sign A Rama Inc.......G....... 904 998-8880
Jacksonville *(G-6770)*
Sign and Design Depot LLC.......G....... 239 995-7446
North Fort Myers *(G-11605)*
Sign Design and Creations.......G....... 954 724-2884
Margate *(G-8567)*
Sign Design of Florida Inc.......E....... 352 787-3882
Leesburg *(G-8172)*
Sign Development Corporation.......G....... 305 227-6250
Miami *(G-10342)*
Sign Language Interpreting.......G....... 386 681-9784
Ormond Beach *(G-13398)*
Sign Man Inc.......G....... 321 259-1703
Melbourne *(G-8932)*
Sign N Drive.......G....... 813 999-4837
Tampa *(G-18100)*
Sign On LLC.......G....... 239 800-9454
Cape Coral *(G-1471)*
Sign Pro America.......F....... 412 908-9832
Jacksonville *(G-6771)*
Sign Rockers LLC.......E....... 866 212-9697
Miami *(G-10343)*
Sign Space.......G....... 786 360-2670
Miami *(G-10344)*
Sign Stapler.......G....... 800 775-3971
Orlando *(G-13192)*
Sign Tech Inc.......G....... 941 575-1349
Punta Gorda *(G-15233)*
Sign Up Now Sign Company LLC.......G....... 754 224-9091
Pompano Beach *(G-14850)*
Sign Works Inc.......G....... 941 894-7927
Sarasota *(G-16594)*

Signage Plus LLC.......G....... 407 668-3567
Altamonte Springs *(G-73)*
Signarama.......G....... 239 997-1644
North Fort Myers *(G-11606)*
Signarama.......G....... 850 656-3200
Tallahassee *(G-17323)*
Signarama Clearwater.......G....... 727 784-4500
Pinellas Park *(G-14388)*
Signarama Dwntwn Fort Lderdale.......G....... 954 990-4749
Fort Lauderdale *(G-4234)*
Signarama Naples.......G....... 239 330-3737
Naples *(G-11403)*
Signarama-Sarasota.......G....... 941 554-8798
Sarasota *(G-16595)*
Signcorp Inc.......G....... 863 224-1331
Winter Haven *(G-19355)*
Signcraft LLC.......G....... 561 543-0034
Wellington *(G-18733)*
Signcraft & More Inc.......G....... 386 755-4754
Lake City *(G-7384)*
Signcraft Publishing Co Inc.......F....... 239 939-4644
Fort Myers *(G-4604)*
Signgraphix Inc.......G....... 954 571-7131
Deerfield Beach *(G-2911)*
Signpost LLC.......G....... 813 334-7678
Maitland *(G-8477)*
Signs & Stripes Llc.......G....... 305 775-1174
Miramar *(G-11042)*
Signs 2 U Inc.......G....... 305 227-6250
Miami *(G-10345)*
Signs Connection Inc.......G....... 305 978-5777
Miami *(G-10346)*
Signs Factory USA Inc.......G....... 786 717-5474
Hialeah *(G-5619)*
Signs International Distr Corp.......G....... 305 715-0017
Miami *(G-10348)*
Signs Just For You Inc.......G....... 407 927-0226
Sanford *(G-16115)*
Signs N Stuff Inc.......G....... 904 248-8141
Orange Park *(G-12406)*
Signs Now.......G....... 386 238-5507
Daytona Beach *(G-2715)*
Signs Now.......F....... 727 524-8500
Largo *(G-8052)*
Signs Now.......G....... 850 383-6500
Tallahassee *(G-17324)*
Signs Now Inc.......G....... 407 628-2410
Winter Park *(G-19443)*
Signs Now St Augustine Inc.......G....... 904 810-5838
Saint Augustine *(G-15611)*
Signs of America Tampa Corp.......G....... 813 243-9243
Tampa *(G-18104)*
Signs of Reilly.......G....... 954 263-7829
Pompano Beach *(G-14851)*
Signs of Tampa Bay LLC.......E....... 813 526-0484
Lutz *(G-8418)*
Signs of Time Inc.......G....... 772 240-9590
Stuart *(G-17013)*
Signs of Times Ventures LLC.......G....... 772 336-4525
Port Saint Lucie *(G-15143)*
Signs Plus New IDS-New Tech In.......F....... 941 378-4262
Sarasota *(G-16596)*
Signs Supreme Inc.......G....... 561 795-0111
Wellington *(G-18734)*
Signs Unlimited Inc.......G....... 727 845-0330
Saint Augustine *(G-15612)*
Signs Unlimited Sea Inc.......F....... 352 732-7341
Ocala *(G-12052)*
Signs Usa Inc.......F....... 813 901-9333
Tampa *(G-18105)*
Signsations Inc.......G....... 561 989-1900
Boca Raton *(G-712)*
Signsitecom Inc.......G....... 386 487-0265
Lake City *(G-7385)*
Site Essentials.......G....... 813 865-0208
Odessa *(G-12152)*
Sitecrafters of Florida Inc.......E....... 813 258-4696
Tampa *(G-18106)*
Skylite Signs & Services Inc.......F....... 305 362-5015
Hialeah *(G-5621)*
Skyway Signs and Wraps LLC.......G....... 727 692-2786
Wimauma *(G-19224)*
Sneids Inc.......G....... 561 278-7446
Delray Beach *(G-3144)*
Solar Enterprises Inc.......E....... 904 724-2262
Jacksonville *(G-6783)*
South Florida Sign Co.......G....... 954 973-6649
Pompano Beach *(G-14858)*
Southeastern Ltg Solutions.......E....... 386 238-1711
Daytona Beach *(G-2716)*

Southern Exhibits and Graphics.......G....... 407 423-2860
Orlando *(G-13203)*
Sp Sign LLC.......F....... 772 562-0955
Stuart *(G-17020)*
Spectrum Signworks LLC.......G....... 239 908-0505
Naples *(G-11415)*
Speed Pro Miami.......G....... 954 534-9503
Miramar *(G-11045)*
Speedpro Imaging.......G....... 772 320-9385
Stuart *(G-17021)*
Speedpro Imaging St Petersburg.......G....... 727 266-0956
Saint Petersburg *(G-15922)*
Speedpro of Orlando West.......G....... 407 509-8956
Orlando *(G-13206)*
Speedysignscom Inc.......E....... 386 755-2006
Lake City *(G-7386)*
Sposen Signature Homes LLC.......F....... 239 244-8886
Cape Coral *(G-1478)*
Srq Sign Partners LLC.......F....... 941 357-0319
Sarasota *(G-16298)*
Srq Sign Partners LLC.......G....... 941 417-4000
Sarasota *(G-16299)*
St Lucie Signs LLC.......G....... 772 971-6363
Fort Pierce *(G-4750)*
Startek Services LLC.......G....... 631 224-9220
Palm Bay *(G-13539)*
Stellar Signs Grap.......G....... 561 721-6060
West Palm Beach *(G-19043)*
Steven Chancas.......F....... 352 629-5016
Ocala *(G-12059)*
Street Signs USA Inc.......G....... 561 848-1411
Lake Park *(G-7480)*
Sun Graphic Technologies Inc.......E....... 941 753-7541
Sarasota *(G-16305)*
Suncoast Investmens of PA.......G....... 941 722-5391
Palmetto *(G-13826)*
Suncoast Sign Shop Inc.......F....... 941 448-5835
Sarasota *(G-16608)*
Sunray Reflections Inc.......G....... 305 305-6350
Hollywood *(G-5917)*
Superior Signs Inc.......F....... 407 601-7964
Orlando *(G-13231)*
Szabo Pos Displays Inc.......G....... 941 778-0192
Bradenton *(G-1124)*
T & C Godby Enterprises Inc.......E....... 407 831-6334
Casselberry *(G-1519)*
Tattoo Factory Inc.......E....... 941 923-4110
Sarasota *(G-16616)*
Thomas United Inc.......G....... 239 561-7446
Fort Myers *(G-4628)*
Tigo Inc.......E....... 954 935-5990
Fort Lauderdale *(G-4284)*
Tone Printing LLC.......G....... 855 505-8663
Miami *(G-10489)*
Total Sign Solutions.......G....... 561 264-2551
Riviera Beach *(G-15386)*
Traffic Control Pdts Fla Inc.......F....... 352 372-7088
Jacksonville *(G-6865)*
Tropical Signs & Graphics.......G....... 321 458-7742
Merritt Island *(G-9017)*
Tru-Art Signs &GRaphix Inc.......G....... 561 371-2388
Stuart *(G-17040)*
Ufg Group Inc.......G....... 561 425-6829
West Palm Beach *(G-19074)*
Ultimate Sign Mfg LLC.......G....... 954 864-7776
Oakland Park *(G-11852)*
Ultimate Sign Service LLC.......G....... 813 210-3166
Tampa *(G-18213)*
Unique Led Products LLC.......G....... 440 520-4959
North Port *(G-11752)*
Unisigns Usa Inc.......G....... 305 509-5232
Doral *(G-3538)*
United Visual Branding LLC.......D....... 813 855-3300
Oldsmar *(G-12274)*
Universal Signs.......G....... 954 366-1535
Fort Lauderdale *(G-4297)*
US Sign and Mill Inc.......E....... 239 936-9154
Fort Myers *(G-4641)*
USA Sign Company.......G....... 954 497-3293
Weston *(G-19176)*
Van Gogh Signs & Displays.......G....... 813 849-7446
Tampa *(G-18233)*
Vb Custom Signs Inc.......G....... 772 713-5678
Vero Beach *(G-18676)*
Vibrant Sign Studio LLC.......G....... 305 363-2181
Miami *(G-10577)*
Vintage Art and Sign LLC.......G....... 770 815-7887
Niceville *(G-11576)*
Vinyl Bros.......G....... 850 396-5977
Gulf Breeze *(G-5131)*

Vinyl Etchings Inc.......G....... 727 845-5300
Port Richey *(G-15076)*
Vista System LLC.......E....... 941 365-4646
Sarasota *(G-16634)*
Visual Signs LLC.......G....... 407 693-0200
Orlando *(G-13306)*
Vivid Images USA Inc.......F....... 904 620-0303
Jacksonville *(G-6902)*
Volunteer Capital LLC.......G....... 954 366-6659
Deerfield Beach *(G-2934)*
Waterboyz Wbz Inc.......F....... 850 433-2929
Pensacola *(G-14287)*
Watershpes By Greg Gnstrom Inc.......G....... 321 777-5432
West Melbourne *(G-18779)*
Way Bright Sign Systems.......G....... 615 480-4602
Santa Rosa Beach *(G-16169)*
We Sign It Inc.......G....... 772 800-7373
Port Saint Lucie *(G-15164)*
We Sign It Inc.......F....... 772 577-4400
Fort Pierce *(G-4769)*
White Sands Dmg Inc.......G....... 305 947-7731
North Miami Beach *(G-11712)*
White Sign Company LLC.......G....... 386 516-6156
Debary *(G-2757)*
White Sign Company LLC.......G....... 407 342-7887
Debary *(G-2758)*
Wholesale Sign Superstore Inc.......F....... 321 212-8458
Rockledge *(G-15457)*
Wholesale Signs Fabricators.......G....... 407 729-5599
Kissimmee *(G-7311)*
Windstone Development Intl Lc.......F....... 954 370-7201
Davie *(G-2615)*
Xtreme Signs Printing Inc.......F....... 321 438-3954
Orlando *(G-13334)*
Yesco Orlando South.......G....... 407 922-5856
Kissimmee *(G-7312)*
Yesco Sign and Lighting.......G....... 407 321-3577
Sanford *(G-16142)*
Ysl Graphics LLC.......G....... 954 916-7255
Sunrise *(G-17200)*
Z & L Partners Inc.......G....... 813 639-0066
Tampa *(G-18279)*
Zoo Holdings LLC.......G....... 941 355-5653
Sarasota *(G-16647)*

SIGNS & ADVERTISING SPECIALTIES: Novelties

Ataly Inc.......E....... 813 880-9142
Tampa *(G-17441)*
Bullet Line LLC.......B....... 305 623-9223
Hialeah *(G-5335)*
Delray Pin Factory Intl.......G....... 561 994-1680
Coral Springs *(G-2240)*
Ellis Family Holdings Inc.......F....... 503 785-7400
Hialeah *(G-5393)*
Inflatable Design Works Corp.......F....... 786 242-1049
Miami *(G-9742)*
Laser Creations Incorporated.......E....... 800 771-7151
Apopka *(G-155)*
Process Automation Corporation.......G....... 727 541-6280
Pinellas Park *(G-14381)*
Promo Daddy LLC.......F....... 877 557-2336
Melbourne *(G-8913)*
Promo Daddy LLC.......F....... 352 390-3081
Melbourne *(G-8914)*
Put Your Name On It LLC.......G....... 813 972-1460
Tampa *(G-18026)*
Ross Industries Inc.......D....... 954 752-2800
Pompano Beach *(G-14834)*
Trident Trading Inc.......G....... 561 488-0458
Boca Raton *(G-756)*

SIGNS & ADVERTISING SPECIALTIES: Signs

Accuform Manufacturing Inc.......B....... 352 799-5434
Brooksville *(G-1204)*
Ad America.......G....... 904 781-5900
Jacksonville *(G-6118)*
All Island Signs.......G....... 631 676-3498
Hudson *(G-6015)*
Allen Industries Inc.......D....... 727 573-3076
Clearwater *(G-1576)*
Annat Inc.......F....... 239 262-4639
Naples *(G-11163)*
Architectural Graphics Inc.......F....... 757 427-1900
Clearwater *(G-1587)*
Artful Signs.......G....... 239 431-7356
Bonita Springs *(G-814)*
ASAP Signs & Graphics of Fla.......G....... 727 443-4878
Clearwater *(G-1592)*
Banks Sign Systems Inc.......G....... 954 979-0055
Pompano Beach *(G-14613)*
Banners-N-Signs Etc Inc.......G....... 904 272-3395
Orange Park *(G-12382)*
Boardwalk Designs Inc.......G....... 850 265-0988
Lynn Haven *(G-8430)*
Boca Signworks.......G....... 561 393-6010
Boca Raton *(G-457)*
C & S Graphics Inc.......G....... 813 251-4411
Tampa *(G-17493)*
Classic Design and Mfg.......G....... 850 433-4981
Pensacola *(G-14114)*
Custom Illusionz.......G....... 386 330-5245
Live Oak *(G-8229)*
Cutting Edge Sgns Grphics of P.......G....... 727 546-3700
Clearwater *(G-1645)*
Delivery Signs LLC.......G....... 407 362-7896
Orlando *(G-12661)*
Dgs Retail LLC.......C....... 727 388-4975
Saint Petersburg *(G-15760)*
Dragonfire Industries Inc.......G....... 407 999-2215
Orlando *(G-12683)*
Finlayson Enterprises Inc.......G....... 850 785-7953
Panama City *(G-13902)*
First Sign Corp.......F....... 954 972-7222
Pompano Beach *(G-14692)*
G G Markers Inc.......G....... 813 873-8181
Tampa *(G-17701)*
Gc Traffic Signs and Sup Inc.......G....... 352 735-8445
Sorrento *(G-16786)*
Glomaster Signs Inc.......G....... 772 464-0718
Fort Pierce *(G-4701)*
Go Mobile Signs.......G....... 239 245-7803
Fort Myers *(G-4469)*
H & H Signs Inc.......G....... 941 485-0556
Venice *(G-18552)*
Innovative Signs Inc.......G....... 407 830-5155
Sanford *(G-16067)*
International Quiksigns Inc.......F....... 954 462-7446
Fort Lauderdale *(G-4063)*
James Testa.......F....... 954 962-5840
Hollywood *(G-5851)*
Kemp Signs Inc.......F....... 561 840-6382
Mangonia Park *(G-8507)*
L4 Design LLC.......E....... 407 262-8200
Maitland *(G-8471)*
Mag-Tags Inc.......G....... 850 294-1809
Tallahassee *(G-17293)*
McCain Sales of Florida Inc.......E....... 772 461-0665
Fort Pierce *(G-4717)*
National Traffic Signs Inc.......G....... 727 446-7983
Clearwater *(G-1802)*
Nite-Bright Sign Company Inc.......E....... 239 466-2616
Fort Myers *(G-4547)*
Oakhurst Marketing Inc.......G....... 727 532-8255
Saint Petersburg *(G-15869)*
Pensacola Sign & Graphics Inc.......G....... 850 433-7878
Pensacola *(G-14226)*
Pope Enterprises Inc.......F....... 850 729-7446
Niceville *(G-11572)*
Productive Products Inc.......G....... 904 570-5553
Saint Augustine *(G-15591)*
Reddi Sign Corporation.......G....... 904 757-0680
Jacksonville *(G-6709)*
Rigal Ramon & Maritza.......G....... 813 968-2380
Tampa *(G-18057)*
S & S Metal and Plastics Inc.......E....... 904 731-4655
Jacksonville *(G-6742)*
Sanbur Inc.......F....... 941 371-7446
Sarasota *(G-16572)*
Sign Producers Inc.......E....... 407 855-8864
Orlando *(G-13191)*
Sign Solutions of Tampa Bay.......G....... 813 269-5990
Tampa *(G-18101)*
Sign Systems Grphic Dsigns Inc.......G....... 813 281-2400
Tampa *(G-18102)*
Sign-O-Saurus Inc.......G....... 407 677-8965
Casselberry *(G-1518)*
Sign-O-Saurus of Daytona Inc.......G....... 386 322-5222
South Daytona *(G-16809)*
Signature Signs Inc.......F....... 727 725-1044
Safety Harbor *(G-15503)*
Signmasters Inc.......G....... 352 335-7000
Gainesville *(G-4995)*
Signway Inc.......G....... 407 696-7446
Winter Park *(G-19444)*
Suncoast Signs Inc.......G....... 813 664-0699
Tampa *(G-18145)*
Superior Unlimited Enterprises.......G....... 863 294-1683
Winter Haven *(G-19360)*
Vital Signs of Orlando Inc.......G....... 407 297-0680
Orlando *(G-13309)*
Zeeeees Corporation.......G....... 407 624-3796
Saint Cloud *(G-15671)*

SIGNS & ADVERTSG SPECIALTIES: Displays/Cutouts Window/Lobby

Artistic Adventures Inc.......G....... 407 297-0557
Orlando *(G-12493)*
Bass Industries Inc.......E....... 305 751-2716
Hialeah *(G-5316)*
Bay Area Signs Inc.......F....... 813 677-0237
Plant City *(G-14407)*
D I H Corporation.......G....... 561 881-8705
Riviera Beach *(G-15317)*
Fiero Enterprises Inc.......F....... 954 454-5004
Hallandale Beach *(G-5183)*
Graph-Plex Inc.......F....... 954 920-0905
Hollywood *(G-5829)*
Pro-Ad Media Inc.......G....... 863 802-5043
Lakeland *(G-7771)*
Sdm Acquisition Corporation.......G....... 954 462-1919
Fort Lauderdale *(G-4226)*

SIGNS, EXC ELECTRIC, WHOLESALE

Redmont Sign LLC.......D....... 941 378-4242
Sarasota *(G-16556)*
River City Advg Objectional.......G....... 904 731-3452
Jacksonville *(G-6726)*
Sign Depot Co.......F....... 407 894-0090
Orlando *(G-13190)*
Suncoast Signs Inc.......G....... 813 664-0699
Tampa *(G-18145)*
Superior Signs Inc.......F....... 407 601-7964
Orlando *(G-13231)*

SIGNS: Electrical

A 1 A Signs & Service Inc.......F....... 305 757-6950
Miami *(G-9033)*
A A A Signs Inc.......G....... 813 949-8397
Lutz *(G-8369)*
Acolite Claude Untd Sign Inc.......E....... 305 362-3333
Doral *(G-3224)*
Acolite Sign Company Inc.......G....... 305 362-3333
Doral *(G-3225)*
Allen Industries.......G....... 561 243-8072
Delray Beach *(G-3043)*
Apple Sign & Awning LLC.......F....... 813 948-2220
Lutz *(G-8375)*
Art Sign Co Inc.......D....... 954 763-4410
Fort Lauderdale *(G-3825)*
Art-Kraft Sign Co Inc.......E....... 321 727-7324
Palm Bay *(G-13499)*
B&C Signs.......G....... 386 426-2373
Edgewater *(G-3612)*
Bengis Signs Inc.......F....... 305 592-3860
Miami Lakes *(G-10765)*
Berry Signs Inc.......G....... 321 631-6150
Rockledge *(G-15394)*
Brite Lite Service Company.......F....... 904 398-5305
Jacksonville *(G-6237)*
Broward Signs.......G....... 954 320-9903
Fort Lauderdale *(G-3871)*
Bryson of Brevard Inc.......E....... 321 636-5116
Rockledge *(G-15396)*
Budget Signs Inc.......F....... 954 941-5710
Pompano Beach *(G-14625)*
C & S Signs Inc.......G....... 850 983-9540
Milton *(G-10925)*
Cadillac Graphics Inc.......G....... 954 772-2440
Oakland Park *(G-11789)*
Central Signs LLC.......F....... 386 322-7446
Daytona Beach *(G-2641)*
Channel Letter Network Corp.......E....... 305 594-3360
Miami *(G-9347)*
Coastline Whl Sgns Led Disp LL.......F....... 386 238-6200
Daytona Beach *(G-2643)*
Coastline Whl Signs Svcs Ltd.......F....... 386 238-6200
Daytona Beach *(G-2644)*
Corporate Signs Inc.......G....... 305 500-9313
Doral *(G-3308)*
Custom Graphics & Sign Design.......G....... 904 264-7667
Orange Park *(G-12387)*
Digital Outdoor LLC.......E....... 305 944-7945
Doral *(G-3329)*
Dixie Signs Inc.......E....... 863 644-3521
Lakeland *(G-7676)*
Don Bell Signs LLC.......D....... 800 824-0080
Port Orange *(G-15016)*

Dvc Signs LLC.......G....... 727 524-8543
Largo *(G-7937)*
Express Signs & Graphics Inc.......F....... 407 889-4433
Winter Garden *(G-19263)*
Ferrin Signs Inc.......E....... 561 802-4242
West Palm Beach *(G-18870)*
Forever Signs Inc.......F....... 305 885-3411
Hialeah *(G-5416)*
Freeman Electric Co Inc.......F....... 850 785-7448
Panama City *(G-13905)*
Fresh Ink Print LLC.......G....... 407 412-5905
Orlando *(G-12764)*
General Sign Service Inc.......F....... 904 355-5630
Jacksonville *(G-6433)*
General Signs and Service Inc.......G....... 904 372-4238
Atlantic Beach *(G-223)*
Gould Signs Inc.......G....... 772 221-1218
Stuart *(G-16947)*
Gpi Signs.......G....... 863 453-4888
Avon Park *(G-288)*
Greyfield Holdings Inc.......E....... 407 830-8861
Sanford *(G-16058)*
Gulf Coast Signs Sarasota Inc.......E....... 941 355-8841
Sarasota *(G-16454)*
Guy Wingo Signs.......G....... 407 578-1132
Apopka *(G-148)*
Hanes-Harris Design Cons.......G....... 813 237-0202
Tampa *(G-17742)*
Himes Signs Inc.......F....... 850 837-1159
Destin *(G-3194)*
International Signs & Ltg Inc.......F....... 407 332-9663
Longwood *(G-8292)*
Interstate Signcrafters LLC.......D....... 561 547-3760
Boynton Beach *(G-922)*
J D M Corp.......G....... 305 947-5876
Doral *(G-3398)*
Jayco Signs Inc.......F....... 407 339-5252
Maitland *(G-8468)*
Kenco 2000 Inc.......F....... 386 672-1590
Daytona Beach *(G-2676)*
Kenco Signs Awning LLC.......F....... 386 672-1590
Holly Hill *(G-5759)*
Kevin Jeffers Inc.......G....... 352 377-2322
Gainesville *(G-4949)*
Lee Designs Llc.......F....... 239 278-4245
Fort Myers *(G-4518)*
Machin Signs Inc.......G....... 305 694-0464
Miami *(G-9932)*
Metro Signs Inc.......E....... 954 410-4343
Hollywood *(G-5875)*
Micole Electric Sign Company.......G....... 954 796-4293
Coral Springs *(G-2284)*
Modulex America LLC.......F....... 786 424-0857
Miami *(G-10034)*
Modulex Americas Group Corp.......G....... 877 808-8049
Miami *(G-10035)*
Olympian Led Inc.......G....... 321 747-3220
Titusville *(G-18447)*
Pete Peterson Signs Inc.......G....... 352 625-2307
Silver Springs *(G-16783)*
Preferred Signs Inc.......G....... 954 922-0126
Hollywood *(G-5894)*
Publi Signs.......G....... 954 927-4411
Hollywood *(G-5896)*
Quality Neon Sign Company.......D....... 904 268-4681
Jacksonville *(G-6699)*
Road Signs Inc.......G....... 941 321-0695
Sarasota *(G-16285)*
Rogers Sign Corp.......E....... 352 799-1923
Brooksville *(G-1265)*
Sar Wholesale Sign Factory.......F....... 813 949-8397
Lutz *(G-8417)*
Shark Signs of Ne Fl Inc.......G....... 904 766-6222
Jacksonville *(G-6762)*
Signcrafters of Central Fla.......F....... 352 323-1862
Leesburg *(G-8173)*
Signs All Signs.......G....... 786 285-7900
Opa Locka *(G-12358)*
Signs For You Inc.......E....... 305 635-6662
Miami *(G-10347)*
Signs Galore Inc.......G....... 850 683-8010
Crestview *(G-2358)*
Signs Unlimited of Bay County.......G....... 850 785-1061
Panama City *(G-13949)*
Signsharks Sign Service.......G....... 904 766-6222
Jacksonville *(G-6773)*
Sky-High Sign & Lighting Inc.......G....... 813 994-3954
Palm Harbor *(G-13761)*
Stellar Sign and Design LLC.......F....... 407 660-3174
Winter Park *(G-19449)*
Stephens Advertising Inc.......G....... 904 354-7004
Jacksonville *(G-6812)*
Sungraf Inc.......F....... 954 456-8500
Hallandale Beach *(G-5216)*
Taylor Sign & Design Inc.......F....... 904 396-4652
Jacksonville *(G-6839)*
Thomas Sign and Awning Co Inc.......C....... 727 573-7757
Clearwater *(G-1919)*
Townsend Signs Inc.......G....... 386 255-1955
Holly Hill *(G-5761)*
Trinity Signs LLC.......G....... 850 502-7634
Shalimar *(G-16778)*
United Advantage Signs Inc.......D....... 813 855-3300
Oldsmar *(G-12273)*
US Signs Inc.......E....... 727 862-7933
Port Richey *(G-15075)*
USA Signs Inc.......G....... 305 470-2333
Miami *(G-10556)*
West Coast Signs.......E....... 941 755-5686
Sarasota *(G-16326)*

SIGNS: Neon

A1a Electric Signs & Neon Inc.......G....... 305 757-6950
Hialeah *(G-5261)*
Accent Neon & Sign Company.......G....... 727 784-8414
Palm Harbor *(G-13716)*
All American Signs Inc.......G....... 863 665-7161
Lakeland *(G-7631)*
Beach Neon & Sign Co.......G....... 904 479-3599
Jacksonville *(G-6200)*
Bulldog Neon Sign Company Inc.......G....... 786 277-6366
Miami *(G-9284)*
Expert Promotions LLC.......F....... 772 643-4012
Sebastian *(G-16658)*
Florida Sign Company Inc.......F....... 941 747-1000
Bradenton *(G-1042)*
McNeill Signs Inc.......F....... 561 737-6304
Pompano Beach *(G-14756)*
McNeill Signs Inc.......G....... 386 586-7100
Bunnell *(G-1303)*
Parrillo Inc.......G....... 386 767-8011
South Daytona *(G-16806)*
Robson Corporation.......E....... 941 753-6935
Sarasota *(G-16286)*
Signline Signs & Electrical.......G....... 904 388-9474
Jacksonville *(G-6772)*
West Central Signs Inc.......E....... 813 980-6763
Tampa *(G-18255)*

SILICONE RESINS

Syi Inc.......G....... 954 323-2483
Sunrise *(G-17183)*

SILICONES

Aerialife Inc.......G....... 561 990-9299
Lake Worth *(G-7530)*
Clock Spring Company Inc.......F....... 561 683-6992
Riviera Beach *(G-15312)*
E T I Incorporated.......E....... 727 546-6472
Largo *(G-7938)*
Syi Inc.......G....... 954 323-2483
Sunrise *(G-17183)*

SILK SCREEN DESIGN SVCS

Commercial Metal Photography.......G....... 407 295-8182
Orlando *(G-12605)*
Koala Tee Inc (usa).......E....... 941 954-7700
Sarasota *(G-16483)*
Signs Unlimited Sea Inc.......F....... 352 732-7341
Ocala *(G-12052)*
Sun-Art Designs Inc.......E....... 954 929-6622
Hollywood *(G-5916)*

SILLS, WINDOW: Cast Stone

FL Precast LLC.......G....... 321 356-9673
Orlando *(G-12742)*

SILO STAVES: Concrete Or Cast Stone

Cast Art International Corp.......G....... 727 807-3395
Dunedin *(G-3571)*

SILVER ORE MINING

Smart Group Traders Inc.......G....... 850 460-5130
Destin *(G-3207)*

SILVER ORES

Goldfield Cnsld Mines Co.......D....... 321 724-1700
Melbourne *(G-8837)*
US Precious Metals Inc.......G....... 786 814-5804
Coral Gables *(G-2202)*

SIMULATORS: Electronic Countermeasure

Sierra Nevada Corporation.......E....... 850 659-3600
Shalimar *(G-16777)*

SIMULATORS: Flight

5dt Inc.......E....... 407 734-5377
Orlando *(G-12420)*
Aero Simulation Inc.......C....... 813 628-4447
Tampa *(G-17389)*
Aviation Instrument Tech Inc.......F....... 813 783-3361
Zephyrhills *(G-19508)*
Bluedrop USA Inc.......G....... 407 470-0865
Orlando *(G-12527)*
Cae Healthcare USA Inc.......E....... 941 377-5562
Sarasota *(G-16378)*
Cubic Advnced Lrng Sltions Inc.......F....... 407 859-7410
Orlando *(G-12632)*
Indra Systems Inc.......E....... 407 567-1977
Orlando *(G-12827)*
James Taylor.......F....... 850 882-5148
Eglin Afb *(G-3644)*
Microsimulators Inc.......G....... 407 696-8722
Winter Springs *(G-19479)*
Opinicus Textron Inc.......D....... 813 792-9300
Lutz *(G-8407)*
Sequa Corporation.......A....... 561 935-3571
Palm Beach Gardens *(G-13626)*
Servos and Simulation Inc.......G....... 407 807-0208
Longwood *(G-8336)*
Tru Simulation + Training Inc.......D....... 813 792-9300
Odessa *(G-12161)*

SIRENS: Vehicle, Marine, Indl & Warning

Bay Design Marine Group Inc.......G....... 239 825-8094
Naples *(G-11184)*
Danas Safty Supply Inc.......F....... 305 639-6024
Doral *(G-3323)*
JB Custom Marine.......G....... 239 877-2784
Naples *(G-11294)*

SIZES

Byte Size It LLC.......G....... 386 785-9311
Deltona *(G-3165)*

SKILL TRAINING CENTER

Vertimax LLC.......G....... 800 699-5867
Tampa *(G-18240)*

SKIN CARE PRDTS: Suntan Lotions & Oils

Breeze Products Inc.......E....... 727 521-4482
Largo *(G-7914)*
Edgewell Personal Care Company.......B....... 386 673-2024
Ormond Beach *(G-13367)*
Florida Glsd Holdings Inc.......C....... 321 633-4644
Cocoa *(G-2023)*
Panama Jack Inc.......F....... 407 843-8110
Orlando *(G-13047)*
Salon Technologies Intl.......G....... 407 301-3726
Orlando *(G-13158)*

SKYLIGHTS

Circle Redmont Inc.......E....... 321 259-7374
Melbourne *(G-8789)*

SLAB & TILE, ROOFING: Concrete

Coma Cast Corp.......E....... 305 667-6797
Miami *(G-9385)*
La Moti Roof & Tile Inc.......G....... 305 635-2641
Miami *(G-9845)*
Roof Tile Administration Inc.......F....... 863 467-0042
Okeechobee *(G-12189)*
Superior Roof Tile Mfg.......F....... 850 892-2299
Defuniak Springs *(G-2948)*

SLAB & TILE: Precast Concrete, Floor

Atlas Walls LLC.......G....... 800 951-9201
Orlando *(G-12498)*

Cug LLC F 786 858-0499
Plantation *(G-14505)*
E T C R Inc E 305 637-0999
Miami *(G-9490)*
E-Stone USA Corporation D 954 266-6793
Sebring *(G-16688)*
E-Stone USA Corporation D 863 214-8281
Miami *(G-9492)*
Heavy Hwy Infrastructure LLC D 407 323-8853
Sanford *(G-16060)*
Kingman Custom Stairs & Trim L G 561 547-9888
West Palm Beach *(G-18921)*
US Bullnosing F 954 567-0404
Oakland Park *(G-11856)*

SLAG PRDTS

Tradeland Americas Inc G 786 718-1490
South Miami *(G-16831)*

SLAG: Crushed Or Ground

Calcium Silicate Corp Inc F 863 902-0217
Lake Harbor *(G-7394)*
Harsco Corporation F 717 506-2071
Tampa *(G-17745)*

SLAUGHTERING & MEAT PACKING

Bruss Company E 904 693-0688
Jacksonville *(G-6240)*
Central Beef Ind LLC C 352 793-3671
Center Hill *(G-1525)*
Florida Beef Inc E 912 632-1183
Zolfo Springs *(G-19545)*

SLIDES & EXHIBITS: Prepared

Gloval Displays Inc E 800 972-0353
Miami Gardens *(G-10742)*
Trial Exhibits Inc F 813 258-6153
Tampa *(G-18200)*

SLINGS: Rope

Atlantic Wire and Rigging Inc G 321 633-1552
Cocoa *(G-1997)*

SLIPPERS: House

Margarita Internl Trading Inc F 305 688-1300
Miami *(G-9946)*

SLOT MACHINES

Banyan Gaming LLC F 954 951-7094
Deerfield Beach *(G-2783)*

SLUGS: Slugs, aluminum

Aludisc LLC E 910 299-0911
Boca Raton *(G-416)*

SOAPS & DETERGENTS

Bar Maid Corporation F 954 960-1468
Pompano Beach *(G-14614)*
Bon Brands Inc F 800 590-7911
Royal Palm Beach *(G-15462)*
Cambra Soap Company G 321 525-7575
Satellite Beach *(G-16650)*
Cambridge Diagnostic Pdts Inc F 954 971-4040
Fort Lauderdale *(G-3880)*
Care-Metix Products Inc F 813 628-8801
Tampa *(G-17509)*
Consulier Engineering Inc G 561 842-2492
Riviera Beach *(G-15314)*
Eco Concepts Inc F 954 920-9700
Hollywood *(G-5814)*
Ecolab Inc G 561 207-6278
Palm Beach Gardens *(G-13585)*
Florida Rum Company LLC E 305 791-1221
Hollywood *(G-5823)*
Go Green Marine Inc G 850 499-5137
Destin *(G-3191)*
Loris 1 Inc G 727 847-4499
New Port Richey *(G-11498)*
Mollys Suds LLC G 678 361-5456
Saint Petersburg *(G-15858)*
Pro Chem Products Inc G 407 425-5533
Orlando *(G-13091)*
Purox Brands Corp F 305 392-0738
Hialeah *(G-5585)*
Sanit Technologies LLC E 941 351-9114
Sarasota *(G-16290)*
Scentstional Soaps Candles Inc F 941 485-1443
Venice *(G-18572)*
Sicamu Inc G 850 270-6283
Quincy *(G-15254)*
Skampas Performance Group G 305 974-0047
Sunny Isles Beach *(G-17080)*
Skymo LLC F 305 676-6739
Cooper City *(G-2115)*
Trugreen Products LLC G 954 629-5794
Pompano Beach *(G-14893)*
Whip-It Inventions Inc E 850 626-6300
Milton *(G-10947)*

SOFT DRINKS WHOLESALERS

Coca-Cola Beverages Fla LLC C 407 295-9290
Orlando *(G-12595)*
Coca-Cola Beverages Fla LLC B 904 786-2720
Jacksonville *(G-6278)*
Hialeah Distribution Corp E 786 200-2498
Hialeah *(G-5444)*
Pepsico Inc G 305 593-7500
Medley *(G-8703)*

SOFTWARE PUBLISHERS: Application

Abawi Fit LLC G 813 215-1833
Tampa *(G-17381)*
Acucall LLC F 855 799-7905
North Palm Beach *(G-11715)*
Advtravl Inc G 978 549-5013
Ocala *(G-11865)*
Applied Software Inc G 215 297-9441
West Palm Beach *(G-18797)*
Atris Technology LLC F 352 331-3100
Gainesville *(G-4880)*
Bitvisory Inc G 801 336-6626
Vero Beach *(G-18600)*
Blackcloak Inc F 833 882-5625
Lake Mary *(G-7403)*
Bond-Pro Inc C 888 789-4985
Tampa *(G-17480)*
Bond-Pro LLC F 813 413-7576
Tampa *(G-17481)*
Cerp Software Inc G 954 607-1417
Pembroke Pines *(G-14027)*
Certusview Technologies LLC G 844 533-1258
Palm Beach Gardens *(G-13576)*
Cloud Business Florida LLC G 954 306-3597
Fort Lauderdale *(G-3905)*
Cloudfactors LLC G 866 779-9974
Plantation *(G-14501)*
Colorproof Software Inc G 813 963-0241
Lutz *(G-8377)*
Community MGT Systems LLC F 561 214-4780
Palm Beach Gardens *(G-13581)*
Cubic Advnced Lrng Sltions Inc F 407 859-7410
Orlando *(G-12632)*
Dark Lake Software Inc F 407 602-8046
Winter Park *(G-19401)*
Duenas Mobile Applications LLC E 305 851-3397
Homestead *(G-5964)*
Dynamic Glucose Hlth Ctrs LLC G 800 610-6422
Fort Lauderdale *(G-3953)*
Encore Analytics LLC G 866 890-4331
Destin *(G-3189)*
Flexiinternational Sftwr Inc G 239 298-5700
Naples *(G-11247)*
Gbi Intralogistics Solutions E 954 596-5000
Deerfield Beach *(G-2830)*
Genius Central Systems Inc E 800 360-2231
Bradenton *(G-1046)*
Georgesoft Inc G 850 329-5517
Tallahassee *(G-17264)*
Hcr Software Solutions Inc E 904 638-6177
Jacksonville *(G-6464)*
Himgc Limited D 213 443-8729
Daytona Beach *(G-2674)*
Hipaat International Inc F 905 405-6299
Naples *(G-11278)*
Hydrogen Technology Corp E 800 315-9554
Miami Beach *(G-10681)*
Icarecom LLC F 954 616-5604
Fort Lauderdale *(G-4055)*
Imagicle Inc F 206 201-2042
Miami *(G-9733)*
Industry Weapon Inc E 877 344-8450
Oldsmar *(G-12235)*
Informulate LLC G 866 222-2307
Oviedo *(G-13439)*
Interactyx Americas Inc E 888 575-2266
Bonita Springs *(G-840)*
Iq Formulations Llc D 954 533-9256
Tamarac *(G-17359)*
It Labs LLC D 310 490-6142
Palm Beach Gardens *(G-13598)*
Keith Dennis Markham G 239 353-4122
Naples *(G-11303)*
Kirchman Corporation D 877 384-0936
Orlando *(G-12871)*
Ld Telecommunications Inc D 954 628-3029
Fort Lauderdale *(G-4097)*
Lightning Phase II Inc G 727 539-1800
Seminole *(G-16749)*
Merkari Group Inc G 305 748-3260
Coral Gables *(G-2175)*
Microsoft Corporation C 425 882-8080
Fort Lauderdale *(G-4122)*
Modernizing Medicine C 561 880-2998
Boca Raton *(G-629)*
Modernizing Medicine Inc B 561 880-2998
Boca Raton *(G-630)*
Multi Soft II Inc F 305 579-8000
Miami *(G-10053)*
Niftys Inc F 786 878-4725
Miami *(G-10073)*
Note Bin Inc F 727 642-8530
Clearwater *(G-1811)*
On-Q Software Inc G 305 553-6566
Miami *(G-10100)*
Opie Choice LLC G 352 331-3741
Gainesville *(G-4976)*
Opie Choice LLC F 727 726-5157
Clearwater *(G-1819)*
Painassist Inc G 248 875-4222
Saint Petersburg *(G-15874)*
Peeks Mobile App Corp F 407 931-3878
Kissimmee *(G-7284)*
Perch Security Inc E 844 500-1810
Tampa *(G-17983)*
Phase Integration LLC G 877 778-8885
Jacksonville *(G-6670)*
Powerline Group Inc C 631 828-1183
Delray Beach *(G-3122)*
Precision Infinity Systems Inc G 407 490-2320
Orlando *(G-13080)*
Prestashop Inc F 888 947-6543
Miami *(G-10190)*
Provictus Inc E 561 437-0232
Palm Beach Gardens *(G-13619)*
Ranorex Inc E 727 835-5570
Clearwater *(G-1856)*
Reliable Business Technologies G 386 561-9944
Longwood *(G-8330)*
Riley Risk Inc G 202 601-0500
Saint Augustine *(G-15597)*
Saas Transportation Inc F 850 650-7709
Destin *(G-3204)*
Sage Implementations LLC G 407 290-6952
Orlando *(G-13155)*
SAI Super Software Solutions G 407 445-2520
Orlando *(G-13156)*
SC Parent Corporation D 703 351-0200
Miami *(G-10308)*
SC Purchaser Corporation D 703 351-0200
Miami *(G-10309)*
Sebring Software LLC E 941 377-0715
Sarasota *(G-16590)*
Seronix Corporation G 352 406-1698
Mount Dora *(G-11113)*
Sighthound Inc F 650 564-4364
Winter Park *(G-19442)*
Simplepin LLC F 800 727-4136
Hobe Sound *(G-5727)*
Simplicity Esports LLC F 855 345-9467
Boca Raton *(G-717)*
Smx-US Inc E 914 840-5631
Miami *(G-10367)*
Starboard Consulting LLC E 407 622-6414
Longwood *(G-8340)*
Stay Smart Care LLC G 321 682-7113
Winter Park *(G-19448)*
Stayfilm Inc G 786 961-1007
Miami *(G-10410)*
Streamline Technologies Inc G 407 679-1696
Winter Springs *(G-19485)*
Stress Nuts LLC G 787 675-3042
Orlando *(G-13218)*
Sun Valley Tech Solutions Inc G 480 463-4101
Wesley Chapel *(G-18759)*

Synergistic Office Solutions ....F 352 242-9100
Minneola (G-10956)
Take A Bed LLC ....G 407 734-8857
Hollywood (G-5921)
Thalo Assist LLC ....G 786 340-6892
Weston (G-19169)
Theater Ears Inc ....G 561 305-0519
Boca Raton (G-747)
Titan Tools LLC ....E 818 984-1001
Clearwater (G-1921)
Tropical MBC LLC ....G 727 498-6511
St Pete Beach (G-16884)
U2 Cloud LLC ....E 888 370-5433
Green Cove Springs (G-5074)
Unicomp Corp of America ....G 954 755-1710
Coral Springs (G-2325)
Universal Training Sftwr Inc ....F 561 981-6421
Boca Raton (G-770)
Universalms Inc ....G 786 285-7531
Hollywood (G-5933)
Utilitech Inc ....F 863 767-0600
Wauchula (G-18695)
Vuaant Inc ....F 407 701-6975
Orlando (G-13316)
Webvoip Inc ....G 305 793-2061
Fort Lauderdale (G-4319)
Westrom Software ....G 866 480-1879
Vero Beach (G-18681)
Wind River Systems Inc ....G 321 726-9463
Melbourne (G-8977)
Windermere Nannies LLC ....F 407 782-2057
Windermere (G-19251)
Yourmembershipcom Inc ....E 727 827-0046
Saint Petersburg (G-15967)
Zeroc Inc ....G 561 283-1480
Jupiter (G-7149)

SOFTWARE PUBLISHERS: Business & Professional

Aci Worldwide Inc ....A 239 403-4600
Naples (G-11147)
Adaptive Insights Inc ....G 800 303-6346
Winter Springs (G-19466)
Advanced Public Safety LLC ....G 954 354-3000
Deerfield Beach (G-2766)
Advanced Software Inc ....F 215 369-7800
Jacksonville Beach (G-6937)
Advantage Software Inc ....E 772 288-3266
Stuart (G-16904)
Agile Risk Management LLC ....G 800 317-5497
Tampa (G-17392)
Alliance Rsrvations Netwrk LLC ....G 602 889-5505
Orlando (G-12459)
Aptum Technologies (usa) Inc ....D 877 504-0091
Doral (G-3253)
Bca Technologies Inc ....F 407 659-0653
Maitland (G-8459)
Bio-Tech Medical Software Inc ....D 800 797-4711
Fort Lauderdale (G-3854)
Bla Software Inc ....G 407 355-0800
Orlando (G-12518)
Ca Inc ....C 305 559-4640
Miami (G-9296)
Capstorm LLC ....G 314 403-2143
Santa Rosa Beach (G-16153)
Carpediem LLC ....F 229 230-1453
Destin (G-3185)
Central Fla Bus Solutions Inc ....G 863 297-9293
Winter Haven (G-19312)
CFS Inc ....F 850 386-2902
Tallahassee (G-17232)
Channel Logistics LLC ....E 856 614-5441
Miami (G-9348)
Cirrus Software LLC ....G 727 450-7804
Palm Harbor (G-13729)
Clinigence Holdings Inc ....G 678 607-6393
Fort Lauderdale (G-3904)
Cloud Veneer LLC ....G 305 230-7379
Miami (G-9364)
Collegefrog Inc ....G 850 696-1500
Pensacola (G-14116)
Connectyx Technologies Corp ....G 772 221-8240
Stuart (G-16926)
Consumer Information Bureau ....G 954 971-5079
Pompano Beach (G-14646)
Contact Center Solutions Inc ....E 305 499-0163
Miami (G-9394)
Coresystems Software USA Inc ....F 786 497-4477
Miami (G-9403)
Crichlow Data Sciences Inc ....G 863 616-1222
Lakeland (G-7666)
Datamentors LLC ....E 813 960-7800
Wesley Chapel (G-18743)
Dealer It Group LLC ....F 904 518-3379
Jacksonville (G-6315)
Drsingh Technologies Inc ....F 352 334-7270
Gainesville (G-4911)
Duos Technologies Group Inc ....G 904 652-1616
Jacksonville (G-6336)
Eclipse Ehr Solutions LLC ....F 352 488-0081
Weeki Wachee (G-18702)
Ei Interactive LLC ....G 407 579-0993
Orlando (G-12700)
Enterprise System Assoc Inc ....F 407 275-0220
Orlando (G-12712)
Estimator Software LLC ....G 203 682-6436
Weston (G-19122)
Etas Timeadmin Corporation ....G 813 464-4175
Tampa (G-17650)
Evolution Voice Inc ....G 407 204-1614
Orlando (G-12724)
Excelor LLC ....F 321 300-3315
Orlando (G-12727)
Fis Avantgard LLC ....E 484 582-2000
Jacksonville (G-6388)
Fis Kiodex LLC ....F 904 438-6000
Jacksonville (G-6389)
Flagshipmd LLC ....G 904 302-6160
Jacksonville (G-6391)
Genensys LLC ....F 407 701-4158
Oviedo (G-13432)
Geocommand Inc ....G 561 347-9215
Boca Raton (G-543)
Global Recash LLC ....D 818 297-4437
Coral Gables (G-2151)
Gooee LLC ....F 727 510-0663
Clearwater (G-1705)
Gotobilling Inc ....F 800 305-1534
Tampa (G-17722)
Govpay Network LLC ....G 866 893-9678
Miami (G-9651)
Green Shades Software Inc ....F 904 807-0160
Jacksonville (G-6449)
Guardia LLC ....E 954 670-2900
Fort Lauderdale (G-4033)
Hr Ease Inc ....G 813 414-0040
Tampa (G-17765)
Igovsolutions LLC ....E 407 574-3056
Lake Mary (G-7423)
Ils Management LLC ....E 321 252-0100
Melbourne (G-8849)
Imago Products ....G 888 400-4122
Boynton Beach (G-919)
Information Mgt Svcs Inc ....F 386 677-5073
Ormond Beach (G-13380)
Inperium Corp ....E 305 901-5650
Miami Beach (G-10683)
Integra Connect LLC ....F 800 742-3069
West Palm Beach (G-18907)
Intermedix Corporation ....D 954 308-8700
Fort Lauderdale (G-4062)
Iomartcloud Inc ....G 954 880-1680
Vero Beach (G-18632)
Iris Inc ....G 561 921-0847
Delray Beach (G-3093)
Ironwifi LLC ....F 800 963-6221
Orlando (G-12844)
Juritis USA LLC ....G 954 529-2168
Weston (G-19145)
Kenexa Learning Inc ....G 407 562-1905
Maitland (G-8470)
Kenexa Learning Inc ....G 407 548-0434
Lake Mary (G-7428)
Lamb Tec Inc ....G 305 798-6266
Cutler Bay (G-2399)
Lawex Corporation ....F 305 259-9755
Coral Gables (G-2171)
Levitech Services LLC ....G 904 576-0562
Jacksonville Beach (G-6949)
Linqs Inc ....F 321 244-2626
Winter Springs (G-19478)
Lobby Docs LLC ....G 850 294-0013
Tallahassee (G-17292)
Lott Qa Group Inc ....G 201 693-2224
Bonita Springs (G-844)
Lps Group LLC ....G 305 668-8780
South Miami (G-16821)
Management Hlth Solutions Inc ....B 888 647-4621
Tampa (G-17876)
Mdintouch Us Inc ....G 786 268-1161
Miami (G-9961)
Method Merchant Inc ....E 954 745-7998
Plantation (G-14533)
Microvision Technology Corp ....F 407 333-2943
Lake Mary (G-7435)
Momenry Inc ....F 318 668-0888
Tampa (G-17917)
Ncg Medical Systems Inc ....E 407 788-1906
Orlando (G-12996)
New Generation Computing Inc ....D 800 690-0642
Miami Lakes (G-10828)
Nexogy Inc ....E 305 358-8952
Coral Gables (G-2181)
Omnivore Technologies Inc ....D 800 293-4058
Clearwater (G-1817)
Ordercounter Inc ....F 850 332-5540
Pensacola (G-14217)
Orion Travel Technologies Inc ....F 407 574-6649
Celebration (G-1524)
Outreach Corporation ....F 888 938-7356
Tampa (G-17966)
Pacemate LLC ....G 305 322-5074
Bradenton (G-1089)
Phocas Software ....F 863 738-9107
Maitland (G-8474)
Powerchord Inc ....D 727 823-1530
Saint Petersburg (G-15886)
Premieretrade Forex LLC ....G 407 287-4149
Lake Mary (G-7445)
Profitsword LLC ....E 407 909-8822
Orlando (G-13095)
Projstream LLC ....F 407 476-1084
Lake Mary (G-7446)
Qgiv Inc ....E 888 855-9595
Lakeland (G-7773)
Radial Inc ....F 561 737-5151
Boynton Beach (G-951)
Raynetcrm LLC ....F 813 489-9565
Venice (G-18568)
Razient LLC ....G 855 747-5911
Miami (G-10242)
Recordsone LLC ....F 301 440-8119
Naples (G-11382)
Retail Cloud Technologies LLC ....D 727 210-1700
Clearwater (G-1859)
Ruvos LLC ....F 850 254-7270
Tallahassee (G-17320)
Silvershore Partners LLC ....F 904 562-0812
Jacksonville (G-6775)
Simply Reliable Inc ....G 800 209-9332
Saint Petersburg (G-15913)
Singular Grape Inc ....G 305 508-4000
Orlando (G-13194)
Smart Guides ....G 813 534-0940
Tampa (G-18109)
Smartadvocate LLC ....E 239 390-1000
Bonita Springs (G-854)
Soe Software Corporation ....E 813 490-7150
Tampa (G-18113)
Softech International Inc ....F 305 233-4813
Miami (G-10369)
Sophio Software Inc ....F 323 446-2172
Fort Lauderdale (G-4244)
Sophix Solutions Inc ....G 813 837-9555
Tampa (G-18115)
Sphere Access Inc ....F 336 501-6159
Tampa (G-18126)
Starmark International Inc ....G 954 874-9000
Fort Lauderdale (G-4260)
Stature Software LLC ....G 888 782-8881
Saint Augustine (G-15623)
Strands Inc ....G 415 398-4333
Miami (G-10418)
Strata Analytics Holdg US LLC ....D 954 349-4630
Sunrise (G-17179)
Sundog Software LLC ....G 425 635-8683
Merritt Island (G-9015)
Swoogo LLC ....G 212 655-9810
Sarasota (G-16613)
Tapinfluence Inc ....E 720 726-4071
Winter Park (G-19451)
Technolgy Training Associates ....E 813 249-0303
Tampa (G-18179)
Telephony Partners LLC ....E 813 769-4690
Tampa (G-18181)
Threattrack Security Inc ....C 855 885-5566
Clearwater (G-1920)
Timus Inc ....G 904 614-4342
Jacksonville (G-6857)

Transaction Data Systems Inc..............E....... 407 295-5050
Ocoee *(G-12093)*
Trx Integration Inc..............F....... 727 797-4707
Belleair *(G-361)*
Two Roads Consulting LLC..............G....... 305 395-8821
Dunedin *(G-3591)*
Ukg Inc..............D....... 954 331-7000
Weston *(G-19173)*
Unite Parent Corp..............D....... 800 432-1729
Weston *(G-19174)*
Unitime Systems Inc..............G....... 407 233-2050
Maitland *(G-8482)*
Veedis Clinical Systems..............G....... 954 344-0498
Plantation *(G-14562)*
Vendornet..............G....... 954 767-8228
Fort Lauderdale *(G-4306)*
Vinbillingcom LLC..............G....... 904 549-5461
Jacksonville *(G-6899)*
VIP Software Corporation..............F....... 813 837-4347
Lakeland *(G-7830)*
Vuram Inc..............F....... 813 421-8000
Temple Terrace *(G-18382)*
Waterfall LLC..............G....... 941 342-7417
Sarasota *(G-16635)*
World Hlth Enrgy Holdings Inc..............F....... 561 870-0440
Boca Raton *(G-791)*
Yippy Inc..............G....... 877 947-7901
Miami *(G-10626)*
Zerion Group LLC..............G....... 877 872-1726
Maitland *(G-8487)*

SOFTWARE PUBLISHERS: Computer Utilities

Green Power Systems LLC..............G....... 904 545-1311
Jacksonville *(G-6448)*
Lidarit Inc..............E....... 407 632-2622
Orlando *(G-12908)*
N2w Software Inc..............F....... 561 225-2483
West Palm Beach *(G-18955)*

SOFTWARE PUBLISHERS: Education

Ai2 Inc..............G....... 407 645-3234
Winter Park *(G-19374)*
Brainchild Corp..............E....... 239 263-0100
Naples *(G-11193)*
Cellec Games Inc..............G....... 407 476-3590
Apopka *(G-120)*
Cookie App LLC..............G....... 305 330-5099
Miami *(G-9398)*
Devclan Inc..............G....... 407 933-8212
Kissimmee *(G-7238)*
Educational Networks Inc..............F....... 866 526-0200
Coral Gables *(G-2142)*
Elogic Learning LLC..............E....... 813 901-8600
Tampa *(G-17634)*
Fluenz Inc..............G....... 305 209-1695
Miami Beach *(G-10668)*
Genel/Landec Inc..............G....... 305 591-9990
Doral *(G-3361)*
Hopscotch Technology Group Inc..............F....... 305 846-0942
Oviedo *(G-13437)*
I T Pacs Pro Software Inc..............G....... 954 678-1270
West Park *(G-19095)*
Impact Education Inc..............G....... 239 482-0202
Fort Myers *(G-4491)*
Maxit Corporation..............G....... 904 998-9520
Ponte Vedra Beach *(G-14946)*
Moore Solutions Inc..............G....... 772 337-4005
Port St Lucie *(G-15175)*
My Reviewers LLC..............G....... 813 404-9734
Tampa *(G-17923)*
Ngweb Solutions LLC..............G....... 904 332-9001
Jacksonville *(G-6633)*
Pogi Beauty LLC..............G....... 305 600-1305
Miami *(G-10173)*
Prekcom LLC..............G....... 877 773-5669
Miami Beach *(G-10704)*
Rperf Technologies Corp..............F....... 954 629-2359
Coral Springs *(G-2307)*
S2 Pass Holdings LLC..............G....... 706 773-4097
Santa Rosa Beach *(G-16166)*
Sibling Group Holdings Inc..............D....... 786 618-1472
Miami *(G-10341)*
Sophtech Ba Solutions LLC..............G....... 407 389-4011
Altamonte Springs *(G-75)*
Stallion King LLC..............G....... 321 503-7368
Saint Petersburg *(G-15926)*
Unfoldingword Corporation..............F....... 407 900-3005
Orlando *(G-13289)*

Vector-Solutionscom Inc..............E....... 813 207-0012
Tampa *(G-18236)*
Vkidz Inc..............F....... 954 771-0914
Fort Lauderdale *(G-4310)*
Voicethread LLC..............E....... 919 724-4486
Boca Raton *(G-781)*

SOFTWARE PUBLISHERS: Home Entertainment

Electronic Arts Inc..............F....... 407 838-8000
Orlando *(G-12703)*
Nuevo Mundo Company..............F....... 305 207-8155
Miami *(G-10085)*
Silverstar Holdings Ltd..............G....... 561 479-0040
Boca Raton *(G-713)*
Sleepy Dragon Studios Inc..............G....... 561 714-6156
Cutler Bay *(G-2411)*

SOFTWARE PUBLISHERS: NEC

1425 N Washington Street LLC..............G....... 904 680-6600
Jacksonville *(G-6100)*
180bytwo..............G....... 202 403-7097
Clearwater *(G-1558)*
24/7 Software Inc..............F....... 954 514-8988
Coral Springs *(G-2209)*
5nine Software Inc..............E....... 561 898-1100
West Palm Beach *(G-18783)*
Above Property LLC..............E....... 239 263-7406
Naples *(G-11146)*
Accenius Inc..............G....... 415 205-6444
Boca Raton *(G-396)*
Accounting & Computer Systems..............G....... 407 353-1570
Orlando *(G-12428)*
Accuware Inc..............G....... 305 894-6874
Miami Beach *(G-10635)*
Actionable Quality Assurance..............F....... 352 562-0005
Gainesville *(G-4867)*
Ademero Inc..............F....... 863 937-0272
Lakeland *(G-7625)*
Advanced Services Intl Inc..............G....... 954 889-1366
Miramar *(G-10961)*
Advanced Software Engineering..............G....... 305 387-0112
Miami *(G-9077)*
Adventurous Entertainment LLC..............F....... 407 483-4057
Orlando *(G-12437)*
Afina Systems Inc..............G....... 305 261-1433
Miramar *(G-10962)*
Alchiba Inc..............G....... 561 832-9292
West Palm Beach *(G-18792)*
American Optimal Decisions Inc..............G....... 352 278-2034
Gainesville *(G-4874)*
Applied Neuroscience Inc..............G....... 727 324-8922
Seminole *(G-16739)*
Appo Group Inc..............G....... 410 992-5500
Aventura *(G-261)*
Archangel Tablets LLC..............F....... 703 981-7732
North Miami Beach *(G-11667)*
ASG Federal Inc..............G....... 239 435-2200
Naples *(G-11174)*
Asure Software Inc..............G....... 702 733-9007
Tampa *(G-17440)*
Asysco Inc..............G....... 850 383-2522
Tallahassee *(G-17224)*
Authority Software LLC..............G....... 877 603-9653
Tamarac *(G-17351)*
Automated Accounting Assoc Inc..............G....... 512 669-1000
Pensacola *(G-14094)*
Avt Technology Solutions LLC..............G....... 727 539-7429
Clearwater *(G-1594)*
Axiom Services Inc..............E....... 727 442-7774
Clearwater *(G-1595)*
B-Scada Inc..............F....... 352 564-9610
Crystal River *(G-2370)*
B2 Integrations LLC..............G....... 727 871-7025
Parrish *(G-14004)*
Backstage Software Inc..............G....... 407 925-8751
Ocoee *(G-12084)*
Backtocad Technologies LLC..............G....... 727 303-0383
Clearwater *(G-1598)*
Bankingly Inc..............E....... 734 201-0007
North Miami *(G-11627)*
Belatrix Software Inc..............E....... 801 673-8331
Naples *(G-11185)*
Bellini Systems Inc..............G....... 813 264-9252
Tampa *(G-17464)*
Best Choice Software Inc..............F....... 941 747-5858
Bradenton *(G-998)*
Big Star Systems LLC..............G....... 954 243-7209
Lauderhill *(G-8102)*

Bigbyte Software Systems Inc..............F....... 917 370-1733
Pembroke Pines *(G-14023)*
Biosculptor Corporation..............G....... 305 823-8300
Hialeah *(G-5326)*
Black Bean Software LLC..............G....... 727 420-6916
Land O Lakes *(G-7850)*
Black Ice Software LLC..............G....... 561 757-4107
Boca Raton *(G-448)*
Black Knight Inc..............B....... 904 854-5100
Jacksonville *(G-6210)*
Black Knight Fincl Svcs Inc..............A....... 904 854-5100
Jacksonville *(G-6211)*
Blue Shoe Software LLC..............G....... 321 438-5708
Orlando *(G-12526)*
Bohemia Intrctive Smltions Inc..............F....... 407 608-7000
Orlando *(G-12531)*
Bond Medical Group Inc..............E....... 813 264-5951
Tampa *(G-17479)*
C Horse Software Inc..............G....... 321 952-0692
Palm Bay *(G-13506)*
Cadcam Software Co..............G....... 727 450-6440
Clearwater *(G-1620)*
Cafm..............F....... 407 658-6531
Cocoa Beach *(G-2059)*
Castle Software Inc..............G....... 800 345-7606
Sebastian *(G-16657)*
Certek Software Designs Inc..............G....... 727 738-8188
Dunedin *(G-3572)*
Checksum Software LLC..............G....... 786 375-8091
Doral *(G-3297)*
Chicago Soft Ltd..............F....... 863 940-2066
Lakeland *(G-7656)*
Citrix Systems Inc..............A....... 954 267-3000
Fort Lauderdale *(G-3901)*
CMA Interactive Corporation..............F....... 954 336-6403
Fort Lauderdale *(G-3906)*
Collaborative Sftwr Solutions..............G....... 954 753-2025
Coral Springs *(G-2233)*
Comcept Solutions LLC..............E....... 727 535-1900
Seminole *(G-16744)*
Comp U Netcom Inc..............F....... 407 539-1800
Maitland *(G-8462)*
Comply Arm..............G....... 772 249-0345
Port Saint Lucie *(G-15100)*
Concept Software Inc..............G....... 321 250-6670
Winter Garden *(G-19258)*
Connect Slutions Worldwide LLC..............G....... 407 492-9370
Vero Beach *(G-18611)*
Connected Life Solutions LLC..............F....... 407 745-1952
Altamonte Springs *(G-38)*
Construction Software Inc..............G....... 888 801-0675
Fort Lauderdale *(G-3916)*
Cooltech Holding Corp..............G....... 786 675-5236
Doral *(G-3306)*
Corellium LLC..............G....... 561 502-2420
Boynton Beach *(G-893)*
Cornerstone Software Inc..............G....... 727 443-5557
Clearwater *(G-1640)*
Creative Data Solutions Inc..............F....... 407 333-4770
Lake Mary *(G-7407)*
Creative Vtran Productions LLC..............F....... 407 656-2743
Maitland *(G-8463)*
Customer Success LLC..............F....... 386 265-4882
Port Orange *(G-15014)*
Cyber Manufacturing Inc..............G....... 786 457-1973
Miami *(G-9422)*
Cybertek Computer Systems Inc..............G....... 352 373-9923
Gainesville *(G-4901)*
Daniel Lampert Communications..............F....... 407 327-7000
Winter Springs *(G-19471)*
Darcy Stephen..............F....... 813 645-3375
Apollo Beach *(G-101)*
Dashclicks LLC..............F....... 866 600-3369
Fort Lauderdale *(G-3932)*
Data Access International Inc..............D....... 305 238-0012
Miami *(G-9437)*
Data Pro Accounting Sftwr Inc..............F....... 727 803-1500
Saint Petersburg *(G-15755)*
Datacore Software Corporation..............D....... 954 377-6000
Fort Lauderdale *(G-3934)*
Dealerups Inc..............F....... 407 557-5368
Lake Mary *(G-7408)*
Digi-Net Technologies Inc..............E....... 352 505-7450
Gainesville *(G-4905)*
Dnt Software Corp..............G....... 407 323-0987
Sanford *(G-16037)*
Duos Technologies Inc..............D....... 904 652-1601
Jacksonville *(G-6335)*
Edashop Inc..............G....... 786 565-9197
Winter Garden *(G-19262)*

PRODUCT

Ellis & Associates of Sanford.....G..... 407 322-1128
Sanford *(G-16041)*
Emerald Technologies Corp.....G..... 773 244-0092
St Pete Beach *(G-16881)*
Emphasys Cmpt Solutions Inc.....E..... 305 599-2531
Pembroke Pines *(G-14032)*
Engineerica Systems Inc.....F..... 407 542-4982
Oviedo *(G-13428)*
Enter Your Hours LLC.....G..... 561 337-7785
Boynton Beach *(G-902)*
Erwin Inc.....F..... 813 933-3323
Tampa *(G-17649)*
Esterel Technologies Inc.....F..... 724 746-3304
Orlando *(G-12717)*
Evolve Technologies Inc.....G..... 239 963-8037
Marco Island *(G-8524)*
Extralink Corporation.....G..... 305 804-1100
Miami Beach *(G-10665)*
Eze Castle Software Llc.....G..... 407 692-9699
Orlando *(G-12729)*
Ezverify & Validate LLC.....G..... 855 398-3981
Sunrise *(G-17121)*
Factorfox Software LLC.....G..... 305 671-9526
Miami *(G-9557)*
Fanwise LLC.....G..... 954 874-9000
Fort Lauderdale *(G-3986)*
Fcbn LLC.....G..... 408 505-1324
Pompano Beach *(G-14688)*
Feick Corporation.....D..... 305 271-8550
Miami *(G-9561)*
Finastra USA Corporation.....C..... 800 989-9009
Lake Mary *(G-7416)*
Finastra USA Corporation.....D..... 800 394-8778
Orlando *(G-12739)*
Fleetmatics.....F..... 727 483-9016
Tampa *(G-17669)*
Forewarn LLC.....G..... 561 757-4550
Boca Raton *(G-538)*
Fyi Software Inc.....E..... 239 272-6016
Naples *(G-11255)*
Gleim Publications Inc.....D..... 352 375-0772
Gainesville *(G-4931)*
Gold-Rep Corporation.....G..... 954 892-5868
Weston *(G-19134)*
Goodrich Corporation.....G..... 305 622-4500
Miami Gardens *(G-10744)*
Gorilladesk Llc.....G..... 561 245-8614
Boca Raton *(G-549)*
Graphic Center Group Corp.....G..... 305 961-1649
Coral Gables *(G-2152)*
Grom Social Enterprises Inc.....C..... 561 287-5776
Boca Raton *(G-553)*
GSM Software Technologies Inc.....G..... 813 907-2124
Tampa *(G-17731)*
Gulf Coast Program.....G..... 727 945-1402
Palm Harbor *(G-13738)*
Hazmat Software LLC.....F..... 407 416-5434
Lake Mary *(G-7421)*
Hilton Software LLC.....F..... 954 323-2244
Coral Springs *(G-2253)*
Hispacom Inc.....F..... 954 255-2622
Coral Springs *(G-2255)*
Ichosen1 Inc.....F..... 844 403-4055
Miami *(G-9727)*
Image One Corporation.....D..... 813 888-8288
Tampa *(G-17773)*
Inceptra LLC.....E..... 954 442-5400
Weston *(G-19141)*
Infor Public Sector Inc.....E..... 813 207-6911
Tampa *(G-17783)*
Information Builders Inc.....E..... 407 804-8000
Lake Mary *(G-7424)*
Innergy.....G..... 941 815-8655
Punta Gorda *(G-15210)*
Innquest Corporation.....F..... 813 288-4900
Tampa *(G-17786)*
Insight Risk Technologies LLC.....G..... 863 804-6038
Indian Shores *(G-6070)*
Insight Software LLC.....D..... 305 495-0022
Weston *(G-19142)*
Inteliathlete Corp.....G..... 305 987-1355
Doral *(G-3392)*
Intouch Gps LLC.....E..... 877 593-2981
Lakeland *(G-7718)*
Ipvision Software LLC.....F..... 813 728-3175
Tampa *(G-17793)*
Iter3d Inc.....G..... 718 473-0114
Aventura *(G-274)*
Itqlick Inc.....G..... 855 487-5425
Hallandale Beach *(G-5192)*
Ityx Solutions Inc.....F..... 407 474-4383
Orlando *(G-12846)*
Ivengo Software Inc.....G..... 321 480-3155
Melbourne *(G-8852)*
Jade Software Corporation USA.....G..... 904 677-5133
Jacksonville *(G-6514)*
Jonas Software USA Inc.....G..... 800 476-0094
Pensacola *(G-14186)*
Jupiter Compass LLC.....G..... 561 444-6740
Palm Beach Gardens *(G-13599)*
Kamel Software Inc.....G..... 407 672-0202
Oviedo *(G-13444)*
Kodiak Software Inc.....G..... 727 599-8839
Clearwater *(G-1754)*
Koho Software Inc.....G..... 813 390-1309
Tampa *(G-17829)*
Kommander Software LLC.....G..... 407 906-2121
Inverness *(G-6092)*
Kreateck International Corp.....F..... 772 925-1216
Vero Beach *(G-18637)*
Landtech Data Corporation.....F..... 561 790-1265
Royal Palm Beach *(G-15474)*
Launcher Solutions LLC.....F..... 904 479-0762
Jacksonville *(G-6549)*
Linenmaster LLC.....E..... 772 212-2710
Vero Beach *(G-18639)*
Linga Pos LLC.....E..... 800 619-5931
Naples *(G-11314)*
Live Source.....G..... 561 573-2994
Boca Raton *(G-603)*
Logical Data Solutions Inc.....F..... 561 694-9229
Palm Beach Gardens *(G-13606)*
Logs Group LLC.....G..... 904 733-6594
Jacksonville *(G-6563)*
Low Code Ip Holding LLC.....G..... 833 260-2151
Fort Lauderdale *(G-4103)*
Manufcturing Systems Group LLC.....G..... 727 642-4677
Cape Coral *(G-1444)*
Marquis Software Dev Inc.....D..... 850 877-8864
Tallahassee *(G-17296)*
Marware Inc.....E..... 954 927-6031
Dania Beach *(G-2468)*
Matchware Inc.....G..... 800 880-2810
Tampa *(G-17893)*
Mau Mau Corporation.....E..... 305 440-5203
Miami Beach *(G-10691)*
Mc Software LLC.....G..... 801 621-3900
West Palm Beach *(G-18947)*
McAfee LLC.....G..... 561 477-6626
Boca Raton *(G-612)*
Med X Change Inc.....E..... 941 746-0538
Bradenton *(G-1077)*
Medaffinity Corporation.....F..... 850 254-9690
Tallahassee *(G-17299)*
Medelite Solutions.....G..... 850 348-0468
Lynn Haven *(G-8435)*
Mediaops Inc.....E..... 516 857-7409
Boca Raton *(G-618)*
Mediware Info Systems Inc.....F..... 904 281-0467
Jacksonville *(G-6589)*
Melodon Software Inc.....G..... 407 654-1234
Orlando *(G-12959)*
Mendeleyes Corp.....G..... 305 597-7370
Doral *(G-3431)*
Mercury Systems Inc.....E..... 352 371-2567
Gainesville *(G-4961)*
Mills & Murphy Sftwr Systems.....E..... 727 577-1236
Saint Petersburg *(G-15855)*
Mobilebits Holdings Corp.....G..... 941 225-6115
Sarasota *(G-16258)*
Mobvious Corp.....G..... 786 497-6620
Miami *(G-10032)*
Montague Enterprises Inc.....G..... 239 631-5292
Naples *(G-11330)*
Morrissy & Co.....G..... 850 934-4243
Gulf Breeze *(G-5121)*
Motionvibe Innovations LLC.....F..... 202 285-0235
Bradenton *(G-1082)*
Motorsport Games Inc.....D..... 305 507-8799
Miami *(G-10046)*
Ms Software Inc.....G..... 813 258-1735
Tampa *(G-17920)*
My Clone Solution.....F..... 813 442-9925
Tampa *(G-17922)*
Navizon Inc.....G..... 305 501-2409
Miami Beach *(G-10697)*
Networked Solutions Inc.....G..... 321 259-3242
Rockledge *(G-15438)*
Nex Software LLC.....G..... 786 200-3396
Homestead *(G-5986)*
Nicraf Software & Creations.....G..... 813 842-9648
Odessa *(G-12135)*
Northpointe Bank.....G..... 239 308-4532
Fort Myers *(G-4549)*
Oaktree Software Inc.....F..... 407 339-5855
Altamonte Springs *(G-59)*
Obitx Inc.....G..... 904 748-9750
Jacksonville *(G-6643)*
Oceana Software Corp.....G..... 813 335-6966
Tampa *(G-17944)*
Openkm Usa LLC.....G..... 407 257-2640
Orlando *(G-13025)*
Oracle America Inc.....E..... 407 458-1200
Orlando *(G-13029)*
Oracle America Inc.....G..... 305 260-7200
Miami *(G-10112)*
Oracle Balloon Decor Inc.....G..... 386 866-0878
Jacksonville *(G-6646)*
Oracle Corporation.....C..... 772 337-4141
Port Saint Lucie *(G-15128)*
Oracle Corporation.....B..... 772 466-0704
Fort Pierce *(G-4725)*
Oracle Elevator Company.....G..... 954 391-5835
Miami *(G-10113)*
Oracle Essence Inc.....F..... 786 258-8153
Weston *(G-19155)*
Orizon 360.....F..... 888 979-0360
Weston *(G-19157)*
Panther Software Inc.....F..... 800 856-8729
Miami *(G-10140)*
Paper Free Technology Inc.....G..... 515 270-1505
Lehigh Acres *(G-8202)*
Patient Portal Tech Inc.....E..... 877 779-6627
North Palm Beach *(G-11724)*
Perii Inc.....G..... 321 253-2269
Merritt Island *(G-9006)*
Platesmart Technologies.....F..... 813 749-0892
Oldsmar *(G-12257)*
Playoff Technologies LLC.....G..... 407 497-2202
Winter Park *(G-19431)*
Posm Software LLC.....G..... 859 274-0041
Cape Canaveral *(G-1366)*
Powerdms Inc.....D..... 407 992-6000
Orlando *(G-13076)*
Praxis Software Inc.....F..... 407 226-5691
Orlando *(G-13078)*
Primal Innovation Tech LLC.....F..... 407 558-9366
Tampa *(G-18010)*
Prism Venture Partners LLC.....F..... 561 427-6565
Jupiter *(G-7098)*
Privi LLC.....G..... 863 294-0373
Winter Haven *(G-19345)*
Professional Sftwr Consortium.....F..... 407 909-9168
Windermere *(G-19240)*
Professor Software Company.....G..... 561 691-5455
Jupiter *(G-7099)*
Program Works Inc.....F..... 407 489-4140
Winter Springs *(G-19482)*
Prolink Software Corporation.....G..... 860 659-5928
Naples *(G-11377)*
Quality Software LLC.....E..... 561 714-2314
Delray Beach *(G-3131)*
Queuelogix LLC.....F..... 404 721-3928
Fort Lauderdale *(G-4195)*
Radixx Solutions Intl Inc.....E..... 407 856-9009
Orlando *(G-13111)*
Recon Group LLP.....G..... 855 874-8741
Miami *(G-10243)*
Restoration Games LLC.....G..... 954 937-1970
Sunrise *(G-17169)*
RTC Software LLC.....G..... 407 765-7462
Winter Garden *(G-19284)*
Sachi Tech Inc.....F..... 813 649-8028
Tampa *(G-18079)*
Safco Software.....G..... 561 750-7879
Boca Raton *(G-697)*
Safeboot Corp.....E..... 239 298-7000
Naples *(G-11388)*
SC Elearning LLC.....D..... 561 293-2543
Deerfield Beach *(G-2907)*
Scanid Inc.....G..... 305 607-3523
Miami *(G-10310)*
Scope Worker LLC.....E..... 917 855-5379
Miami *(G-10313)*
Scs Software Inc.....F..... 727 871-8366
Belleair Bluffs *(G-364)*
Security Oracle Inc.....F..... 352 988-5985
Clermont *(G-1974)*
Seniors Vent Mgmt Inc.....G..... 305 266-0988
Miami *(G-10324)*

Servdata Inc....................G....... 305 269-7374
Palmetto Bay *(G-13854)*
Shopworks LLC....................G....... 561 491-6000
West Palm Beach *(G-19031)*
Silco Software Technology Inc..............F....... 813 475-4591
Odessa *(G-12151)*
Slappey Communications LLC..............G....... 863 619-5600
Lakeland *(G-7792)*
Smartbear Software....................G....... 954 312-0188
Coconut Creek *(G-2096)*
Smartcop Inc....................E....... 850 429-0082
Pensacola *(G-14262)*
Smartmatic Corporation....................F....... 561 862-0747
Boca Raton *(G-721)*
Smdk Corp....................E....... 239 444-1736
Naples *(G-11406)*
Soft Tech America Inc....................F....... 954 563-3198
Fort Lauderdale *(G-4240)*
Software Nuggets Inc....................G....... 904 687-9778
Ponte Vedra Beach *(G-14954)*
Software Product Solutions LLC..............G....... 561 798-6727
West Palm Beach *(G-19037)*
Software Teacher Inc....................G....... 954 593-3333
Jupiter *(G-7117)*
Solidexperts Inc....................F....... 954 772-1903
Fort Lauderdale *(G-4243)*
Soren Technologies Inc....................F....... 954 236-9998
Plantation *(G-14555)*
SOS Software Corp....................G....... 786 237-4903
Miami *(G-10378)*
Southeastern Marketing Associa..............G....... 954 421-7388
Deerfield Beach *(G-2916)*
SRS Software LLC....................F....... 201 802-1300
Tampa *(G-18128)*
Stadium 1 Software LLC....................E....... 561 498-8356
Miami Beach *(G-10716)*
Stadson Technology Corporation..............E....... 561 372-2648
Boca Raton *(G-729)*
Steelgate Global LLC....................G....... 610 909-8509
Fort Lauderdale *(G-4261)*
Stratonet Inc....................G....... 863 382-8503
Sebring *(G-16712)*
Sunshine Software....................G....... 407 297-6253
Orlando *(G-13226)*
Superion LLC....................A....... 407 304-3235
Lake Mary *(G-7452)*
Synkt Games Inc....................F....... 305 779-5611
Miami *(G-10450)*
System Data Resource....................G....... 954 213-8008
Port Saint Lucie *(G-15152)*
Tahoe Interactive Systems Inc..............G....... 614 891-2323
Punta Gorda *(G-15242)*
Team Cymru Inc....................C....... 847 378-3300
Lake Mary *(G-7454)*
Tech Data Education Inc....................F....... 727 539-7429
Clearwater *(G-1907)*
Tech Data Resources LLC....................E....... 727 539-7429
Clearwater *(G-1908)*
Tech Data Tennessee Inc....................E....... 727 539-7429
Clearwater *(G-1909)*
Technisys LLC....................B....... 305 728-5372
Miami *(G-10463)*
Thales E-Security Inc....................F....... 954 888-6200
Plantation *(G-14557)*
Thales Esecurity Inc....................E....... 954 888-6200
Plantation *(G-14558)*
That Software Guy Inc....................G....... 727 533-8109
Largo *(G-8066)*
Tops Software....................F....... 813 960-8300
Clearwater *(G-1924)*
Touche Software LLC....................G....... 786 241-9907
Miami *(G-10495)*
Tracking Solutions Corp....................E....... 877 477-2922
Doral *(G-3530)*
Tradestation Technologies Inc..............C....... 954 652-7000
Plantation *(G-14560)*
Trendy Entertainment Inc....................E....... 814 384-7123
Gainesville *(G-5012)*
Ultimate Software....................F....... 305 559-3052
Miami *(G-10524)*
Unique Recording Software Inc..............G....... 917 854-5403
Boca Raton *(G-768)*
Universal Software Solutions..............G....... 727 298-8877
Clearwater *(G-1929)*
Vanguardistas LLC....................G....... 386 868-2919
Ormond Beach *(G-13407)*
Veeam Software Corporation..............G....... 614 339-8200
Davie *(G-2610)*
Vensoft Corp....................F....... 786 991-2080
Miami *(G-10573)*
Vertaeon LLC....................G....... 404 823-6232
Gainesville *(G-5015)*
Vfinity Inc....................F....... 239 244-2555
Naples *(G-11450)*
Vice Alliance Corp....................G....... 954 792-4240
Plantation *(G-14564)*
Visible Results USA Inc....................F....... 913 706-8248
Reunion *(G-15261)*
Visions Sky Corp....................G....... 888 788-8609
Orlando *(G-13305)*
Webcom Group Inc....................A....... 904 680-6600
Jacksonville *(G-6907)*
Webidcard Inc....................G....... 443 280-1577
Saint Augustine *(G-15634)*
Western Microsystems Inc....................E....... 800 547-7082
Jacksonville *(G-6912)*
Whole Tomato Software Inc..............G....... 408 323-1590
Sarasota *(G-16639)*
Willsonet Inc....................E....... 813 336-8175
Tampa *(G-18259)*
Windowware Pro....................G....... 904 584-9191
Saint Augustine *(G-15638)*
Xcape Solutions Inc....................E....... 813 369-5261
Lutz *(G-8425)*
Yihong Software Inc....................G....... 407 391-8450
Oviedo *(G-13463)*

SOFTWARE PUBLISHERS: Operating Systems

Audio Storage Technologies..............G....... 954 229-5050
Fort Lauderdale *(G-3832)*
Dpi Information Inc....................F....... 813 258-8004
Tampa *(G-17614)*
Ecoprintq Inc....................F....... 305 681-7445
Miami Lakes *(G-10784)*
Optimus-Fleet LLC....................F....... 407 590-5060
Orlando *(G-13027)*
Sipradius LLC....................G....... 954 290-2434
Coral Springs *(G-2313)*
Verifone Inc....................C....... 800 837-4366
Coral Springs *(G-2326)*
Verifone Systems Inc....................C....... 408 232-7800
Coral Springs *(G-2328)*

SOFTWARE PUBLISHERS: Publisher's

Azure Computing Inc....................G....... 407 359-8787
Oviedo *(G-13416)*
Didna Inc....................G....... 239 851-0966
Orlando *(G-12671)*
Mas Editorial Corp....................G....... 305 748-0124
Hollywood *(G-5870)*
Pepper Tree....................G....... 941 922-2662
Sarasota *(G-16540)*
Seven Hlls Slution Specialists..............G....... 850 575-0566
Tallahassee *(G-17322)*
Sna Software LLC....................F....... 866 389-6750
Orlando *(G-13199)*
Trivantis Corporation....................D....... 513 929-0188
Deerfield Beach *(G-2929)*

SOFTWARE PUBLISHERS: Word Processing

Emerson Prcess MGT Pwr Wtr Slt..........E....... 941 748-8100
Bradenton *(G-1037)*

SOFTWARE TRAINING, COMPUTER

C2c Innovated Technology LLC..............G....... 251 382-2277
Bonifay *(G-800)*
Utilitech Inc....................F....... 863 767-0600
Wauchula *(G-18695)*

SOIL CONDITIONERS

Humic Growth Solutions Inc..............F....... 904 392-7201
Jacksonville *(G-6483)*
Humic Growth Solutions Inc..............G....... 904 329-1012
Green Cove Springs *(G-5066)*
Humic Growth Solutions Inc..............G....... 904 329-1012
Saint Johns *(G-15678)*

SOLAR CELLS

Alterna Power Inc....................F....... 407 287-9148
Orlando *(G-12462)*
Atlas Renewable Energy USA LLC..........F....... 786 358-5614
Miami *(G-9189)*
Brightwatts Inc....................F....... 954 513-3352
Oakland Park *(G-11787)*
Gb Energy Tech....................F....... 561 450-6047
Delray Beach *(G-3083)*
Guardian Solar LLC....................F....... 727 504-2790
Tarpon Springs *(G-18304)*
Solarbeam International Inc..............G....... 305 248-8400
Homestead *(G-5994)*
Solartech Universal LLC....................E....... 561 440-8000
Riviera Beach *(G-15378)*

SOLAR HEATING EQPT

Ameritech Energy Corporation..............F....... 386 589-7501
Daytona Beach *(G-2625)*
Coast To Coast Solar Inc....................F....... 813 406-6501
Lutz *(G-8376)*
Eco Solar Technology....................G....... 904 219-0807
Jacksonville *(G-6352)*
Florida Solar Energy LLC....................G....... 561 206-2324
Boca Raton *(G-533)*
Gain Solar LLC....................G....... 305 933-1060
Aventura *(G-270)*
Solar Energy Specialist Corp..............G....... 863 514-9532
Winter Haven *(G-19356)*
Sunset Power Inc....................F....... 866 485-2757
Jacksonville *(G-6824)*
Thermal Conversion Tech Inc..............E....... 904 358-3720
Jacksonville *(G-6848)*
United States Green Enrgy Corp..........E....... 540 295-4843
Pensacola *(G-14279)*

SOLVENTS

Skymo LLC....................F....... 305 676-6739
Cooper City *(G-2115)*

SOLVENTS: Organic

Skymo LLC....................F....... 305 676-6739
Cooper City *(G-2115)*

SONAR SYSTEMS & EQPT

Erapsco....................G....... 386 740-5335
De Leon Springs *(G-2739)*
Goodrich Corporation....................C....... 904 757-3660
Jacksonville *(G-6441)*
Raytheon Company....................G....... 850 882-8015
Eglin Afb *(G-3647)*
Raytheon Company....................C....... 310 647-9438
Largo *(G-8036)*

SOUND EQPT: Electric

35 Technologies Group Inc..............E....... 407 402-2119
Longwood *(G-8248)*
Bongiovi Aviation LLC....................F....... 772 879-0578
Port Saint Lucie *(G-15093)*
Sabine Inc....................D....... 386 418-2000
Alachua *(G-17)*

SOUND EQPT: Underwater

Argotec Inc....................F....... 954 491-6550
Fort Lauderdale *(G-3821)*
Argotec Inc....................G....... 407 331-9372
Longwood *(G-8257)*
L-3 Cmmnctons Ntronix Holdings..........D....... 212 697-1111
Melbourne *(G-8863)*

SOUVENIRS, WHOLESALE

Image Depot....................G....... 813 685-7116
Tampa *(G-17772)*

SOYBEAN PRDTS

Amerifood Corp....................G....... 305 305-5951
Miami *(G-9149)*

SPACE FLIGHT OPERATIONS, EXC GOVERNMENT

Agd Systems Corporation....................G....... 561 722-5561
West Palm Beach *(G-18791)*

SPACE PROPULSION UNITS & PARTS

Aerojet Rocketdyne Inc....................B....... 561 796-2000
Jupiter *(G-6995)*
Chromalloy Gas Turbine LLC..............A....... 561 935-3571
Palm Beach Gardens *(G-13578)*
Raytheon Technologies Corp..............G....... 561 796-2000
Jupiter *(G-7102)*
Sensatek Propulsion Tech Inc..............F....... 850 321-5993
Daytona Beach *(G-2712)*

Sequa Corporation..........A....... 561 935-3571
Palm Beach Gardens *(G-13626)*

SPACE RESEARCH & TECHNOLOGY PROGRAMS ADMINISTRATION

Intelligent Robotics Inc..........G....... 850 728-7353
Tallahassee *(G-17281)*

SPACE VEHICLE EQPT

Chromalloy Gas Turbine LLC..........A....... 561 935-3571
Palm Beach Gardens *(G-13578)*
Livetv..........F....... 321 722-0783
Melbourne *(G-8876)*
Micro Systems Inc..........C....... 850 244-2332
Fort Walton Beach *(G-4815)*
Micro Tool Engineering Inc..........F....... 561 842-7381
Riviera Beach *(G-15348)*
Moog Inc..........G....... 716 652-2000
Pembroke Pines *(G-14049)*
Precise Technologies Inc..........F....... 727 535-5594
Largo *(G-8030)*
Precision Fabg & Clg Co Inc..........D....... 321 635-2000
Cocoa *(G-2042)*
Savvy Associate Inc..........F....... 954 941-6986
Pompano Beach *(G-14840)*
Sidus Space Inc..........E....... 321 613-0615
Cape Canaveral *(G-1367)*
Stuart Industries Inc..........F....... 305 651-3474
Miami *(G-10425)*

SPACE VEHICLES

Lockheed Martin Corporation..........G....... 850 885-3583
Eglin Afb *(G-3645)*

SPARK PLUGS: Internal Combustion Engines

Wiretec Ignition Inc..........F....... 407 578-4569
Palmetto *(G-13837)*

SPEAKER SYSTEMS

Light and Sound Equipment Inc..........G....... 305 233-3737
Cutler Bay *(G-2402)*
Peter Fogel..........G....... 561 245-5252
Delray Beach *(G-3115)*

SPECIALTY FOOD STORES: Coffee

Aroma Coffee Service Inc..........G....... 239 481-7262
Fort Myers *(G-4367)*
Melitta North America Inc..........D....... 727 535-2111
Clearwater *(G-1779)*

SPECIALTY FOOD STORES: Dietetic Foods

Real Ketones LLC..........F....... 801 244-8610
Saint Petersburg *(G-15899)*

SPECIALTY FOOD STORES: Health & Dietetic Food

Great Amercn Natural Pdts Inc..........E....... 727 521-4372
Saint Petersburg *(G-15796)*
Pure Solutions Inc..........E....... 813 925-1098
Tampa *(G-18024)*

SPECIALTY FOOD STORES: Juices, Fruit Or Vegetable

Healtheintentions Inc..........G....... 954 394-8867
Miami *(G-9693)*
Watts Juicery..........F....... 904 372-0693
Atlantic Beach *(G-228)*

SPECIALTY FOOD STORES: Tea

Socratic Solutions Inc..........G....... 813 324-7018
Brandon *(G-1180)*

SPECIALTY FOOD STORES: Vitamin

Function Please LLC..........G....... 305 792-7900
Hollywood *(G-5827)*
Tim Gardners Vitamart Inc..........E....... 813 908-7843
Tampa *(G-18186)*

SPECIALTY SAWMILL PRDTS

Griffin Sawmill & Woodworking..........G....... 863 241-5180
Lake Wales *(G-7512)*

SPECULATIVE BUILDERS: Single-Family Housing

Lucas Construction Inc..........G....... 386 623-0088
Ormond Beach *(G-13383)*

SPICE & HERB STORES

Bijol and Spices Inc..........G....... 305 634-9030
Miami *(G-9245)*
El Sabor Spices Inc..........F....... 305 691-2300
Miami *(G-9507)*
Everglades Foods Inc..........G....... 863 655-2214
Sebring *(G-16689)*

SPIKES: Steel, Wire Or Cut

Gerdau Ameristeel US Inc..........B....... 813 286-8383
Tampa *(G-17711)*
Gerdau USA Inc..........B....... 813 286-8383
Tampa *(G-17712)*

SPINDLES: Textile

Levil Technology Corp..........G....... 407 542-3971
Oviedo *(G-13447)*

SPORTING & ATHLETIC GOODS: Arrows, Archery

United Strings Intl LLC..........G....... 561 790-4191
West Palm Beach *(G-19075)*

SPORTING & ATHLETIC GOODS: Balls, Baseball, Football, Etc

Nitro Leisure Products Inc..........E....... 414 272-5084
Stuart *(G-16981)*

SPORTING & ATHLETIC GOODS: Boomerangs

Aussie Boomerang Bar On Ave In..........F....... 561 436-9741
Lake Worth *(G-7535)*

SPORTING & ATHLETIC GOODS: Bowling Alleys & Access

50 Hwy 17 S Inc..........G....... 904 225-1077
Yulee *(G-19492)*
Jawil Enterprises Corps..........G....... 954 366-4212
Margate *(G-8552)*

SPORTING & ATHLETIC GOODS: Bows, Archery

SGF Inc..........G....... 813 996-2528
Land O Lakes *(G-7866)*

SPORTING & ATHLETIC GOODS: Bridges, Billiard & Pool

La Bodeguita De Hialeah Inc..........G....... 305 240-7421
Hialeah *(G-5482)*

SPORTING & ATHLETIC GOODS: Buckets, Fish & Bait

Marine Metal Products Co..........G....... 727 461-5575
Clearwater *(G-1773)*

SPORTING & ATHLETIC GOODS: Driving Ranges, Golf, Electronic

Custom Carts of Sarasota LLC..........E....... 941 953-4445
Bradenton *(G-1025)*
Easy Picker Golf Products Inc..........E....... 239 368-6600
Lehigh Acres *(G-8190)*
Evies Golf Center..........G....... 941 377-2399
Sarasota *(G-16423)*

SPORTING & ATHLETIC GOODS: Fishing Eqpt

Back Country Inc..........G....... 772 532-6174
Vero Beach *(G-18598)*
Black Bart International LLC..........G....... 561 842-4045
Riviera Beach *(G-15301)*
Contagious Fishing Charters..........G....... 727 595-6277
Largo *(G-7928)*
Crowder Custom Rods Inc..........G....... 772 220-8108
Stuart *(G-16928)*
Renzetti Inc..........F....... 321 267-7705
Titusville *(G-18456)*
Volvox Inc Hollywood..........G....... 954 961-4942
Hollywood *(G-5938)*

SPORTING & ATHLETIC GOODS: Fishing Tackle, General

Fishermans Center Inc..........G....... 561 844-5150
Riviera Beach *(G-15328)*
Gypsy Mining Inc..........G....... 772 589-5547
Roseland *(G-15459)*
Larrys Rigs..........G....... 561 967-7791
West Palm Beach *(G-18927)*
Lead Enterprises Inc..........F....... 305 635-8644
Miami *(G-9876)*
New World Trade Inc..........F....... 941 205-5873
Punta Gorda *(G-15218)*
Rat Trap Bait Company Inc..........F....... 863 967-2148
Auburndale *(G-251)*
Rigrap LLC..........G....... 561 200-5958
Jupiter *(G-7104)*
T W A Sports Inc..........G....... 727 541-9831
Largo *(G-8065)*

SPORTING & ATHLETIC GOODS: Gymnasium Eqpt

Pure Global Brands Inc..........G....... 866 498-5269
West Palm Beach *(G-19011)*

SPORTING & ATHLETIC GOODS: Hooks, Fishing

Hook Fish & Chkn - Mangonia Pk..........G....... 561 855-6385
Mangonia Park *(G-8501)*
O Mustad & Son USA Inc..........E....... 206 284-7871
Doral *(G-3447)*

SPORTING & ATHLETIC GOODS: Hunting Eqpt

Jrh Sport Industries Inc..........G....... 904 940-3381
Saint Augustine *(G-15563)*

SPORTING & ATHLETIC GOODS: Ping-Pong Tables

Alternative Vision LLC..........G....... 904 642-3566
Jacksonville *(G-6141)*

SPORTING & ATHLETIC GOODS: Pools, Swimming, Exc Plastic

Tricounty Chemical Co..........G....... 407 682-3550
Apopka *(G-192)*

SPORTING & ATHLETIC GOODS: Pools, Swimming, Plastic

All Safe of Big Pine Key..........G....... 305 872-7233
Key West *(G-7176)*
Blue Hawaiian Products Inc..........E....... 727 535-5677
Largo *(G-7910)*
Florida North Inc..........G....... 352 606-2408
Weeki Wachee *(G-18703)*
Sonic Leak Locator..........G....... 954 340-8924
Coral Springs *(G-2314)*

SPORTING & ATHLETIC GOODS: Protective Sporting Eqpt

Macho Products Inc..........E....... 800 327-6812
Sebastian *(G-16667)*

SPORTING & ATHLETIC GOODS: Racket Sports Eqpt

Diadem Sports LLC..........G....... 844 434-2336
Pompano Beach *(G-14665)*

SPORTING & ATHLETIC GOODS: Rackets/Frames, Tennis, Etc

Bard Sports Corp.....G..... 305 233-2200
Miami *(G-9220)*
Pickle Pro LLC.....G..... 844 332-7069
Naples *(G-11365)*

SPORTING & ATHLETIC GOODS: Reels, Fishing

Tibor Inc.....E..... 561 272-0770
Delray Beach *(G-3150)*

SPORTING & ATHLETIC GOODS: Rods & Rod Parts, Fishing

Halo Fishing LLC.....G..... 321 373-2055
Malabar *(G-8489)*
Rod Biscayne Manufacturing.....G..... 305 884-0808
Hialeah *(G-5604)*

SPORTING & ATHLETIC GOODS: Shafts, Golf Club

Cheval Country Club.....G..... 813 279-5122
Dunedin *(G-3573)*
First Tee Miami Daga.....F..... 305 633-4583
Miami *(G-9572)*
First Tee Sarasota/Manatee.....G..... 941 685-5072
Sarasota *(G-16213)*
Golf Shaft Deals Inc.....G..... 321 591-7824
Indialantic *(G-6060)*
Pro Duffers Orlando.....G..... 407 641-7626
Orlando *(G-13092)*
Quail Height Golf Club.....F..... 386 752-3339
Lake City *(G-7378)*

SPORTING & ATHLETIC GOODS: Shooting Eqpt & Splys, General

Atg Specialty Products Corp.....G..... 888 455-5499
Doral *(G-3259)*
Bag-A-Nut LLC.....G..... 904 641-3934
Jacksonville *(G-6191)*

SPORTING & ATHLETIC GOODS: Shuffleboards & Shuffleboard Eqpt

Allen Shuffleboard LLC.....G..... 727 399-8877
Seminole *(G-16737)*

SPORTING & ATHLETIC GOODS: Skateboards

Boris Skateboards Mfg Inc.....G..... 305 519-3544
Miami *(G-9269)*
Fiik Skateboards LLC.....G..... 561 405-9541
Fort Lauderdale *(G-3992)*
Fiik Skateboards LLC.....F..... 561 316-8234
Boca Raton *(G-528)*
Magneto Sports LLC.....G..... 760 593-4589
Miami *(G-9933)*
Onetown Boards.....G..... 786 704-5921
Miami *(G-10106)*
Skateboard Supercross LLC.....G..... 786 529-8187
Surfside *(G-17207)*
Tri-Deck LLC.....G..... 386 748-3239
Deland *(G-3025)*

SPORTING & ATHLETIC GOODS: Skates & Parts, Roller

Cheezeballs LLC.....G..... 904 716-3709
Jacksonville *(G-6262)*

SPORTING & ATHLETIC GOODS: Team Sports Eqpt

Sterling Facility Services LLC.....G..... 772 871-2161
Port Saint Lucie *(G-15148)*
Tendonease LLC.....G..... 888 224-0319
Palm City *(G-13675)*
Waterboy Sports LLC.....G..... 407 869-9881
Winter Park *(G-19457)*

SPORTING & ATHLETIC GOODS: Tennis Eqpt & Splys

All Tennis LLC.....G..... 561 842-0070
Lake Park *(G-7465)*
Biscayne Tennis LLC.....G..... 786 231-8372
Miami *(G-9252)*
M P Tennis Inc.....G..... 813 961-8844
Tampa *(G-17869)*

SPORTING & ATHLETIC GOODS: Trampolines & Eqpt

Indoor Trampoline Arena Inc.....F..... 321 222-1300
Sanford *(G-16065)*
Sunrise Trampolines and Nets.....G..... 727 526-9288
Pinellas Park *(G-14390)*

SPORTING & ATHLETIC GOODS: Water Skis

Ski Rixen - Quiet Waters Inc.....G..... 954 429-0215
Deerfield Beach *(G-2913)*

SPORTING & ATHLETIC GOODS: Water Sports Eqpt

Cayago Americas Inc.....F..... 754 216-4600
Fort Lauderdale *(G-3885)*
Foil Inc.....G..... 442 233-3645
Pensacola *(G-14156)*
Island Fever LLC.....G..... 941 639-6400
Punta Gorda *(G-15211)*
Lake Area Watersports LLC.....G..... 352 475-3434
Melrose *(G-8986)*
Liquid Force.....G..... 904 813-1490
Jacksonville *(G-6558)*
Reef Runner Charters LLC.....G..... 941 921-0560
Sarasota *(G-16557)*

SPORTING & REC GOODS, WHOLESALE: Boats, Canoes, Etc/Eqpt

Lake Area Watersports LLC.....G..... 352 475-3434
Melrose *(G-8986)*
Nautical Acquisitions Corp.....C..... 727 541-6664
Largo *(G-8017)*
Survitec Survivor Cft Mar Inc.....G..... 954 374-4276
Miramar *(G-11050)*
Waterbrick International Inc.....G..... 877 420-9283
Windermere *(G-19250)*

SPORTING & RECREATIONAL GOODS & SPLYS WHOLESALERS

Bote LLC.....F..... 888 855-4450
Miramar Beach *(G-11064)*
Fluidra Usa LLC.....E..... 904 378-0999
Jacksonville *(G-6409)*
Jmh Marine Inc.....F..... 954 785-7557
Pompano Beach *(G-14736)*
Salt Life LLC.....G..... 904 595-5370
Jacksonville Beach *(G-6957)*
Sergeant Bretts Coffee LLC.....G..... 561 451-0048
Coconut Creek *(G-2094)*
Stuart Yacht Builders.....F..... 561 747-1947
Stuart *(G-17029)*

SPORTING & RECREATIONAL GOODS, WHOLESALE: Boat Access & Part

Beach House Engineering.....G..... 941 727-4488
Bradenton *(G-995)*
Uflex Usa Inc.....E..... 941 351-2628
Sarasota *(G-16319)*

SPORTING & RECREATIONAL GOODS, WHOLESALE: Diving

A Plus Marine Supply Inc.....G..... 850 934-3890
Gulf Breeze *(G-5110)*
Bauer Compressors Inc.....G..... 757 855-6006
Sunrise *(G-17094)*
Lamartek Inc.....E..... 386 752-1087
Lake City *(G-7364)*
Undersea Breathing Systems.....G..... 561 588-7698
Lake Worth *(G-7596)*

SPORTING & RECREATIONAL GOODS, WHOLESALE: Golf

Flexstake Inc.....E..... 239 481-3539
Fort Myers *(G-4450)*
Liquid Ed Inc.....G..... 727 943-8616
Tarpon Springs *(G-18313)*

SPORTING & RECREATIONAL GOODS, WHOLESALE: Gymnasium

Pure Global Brands Inc.....G..... 866 498-5269
West Palm Beach *(G-19011)*

SPORTING & RECREATIONAL GOODS, WHOLESALE: Watersports

Crystal Pool Service Inc.....F..... 954 444-8282
Sunrise *(G-17111)*

SPORTING GOODS

3n2 LLC.....G..... 407 862-3622
Maitland *(G-8455)*
All Golf.....G..... 954 441-1333
Pembroke Pines *(G-14019)*
Alpha Sun & Sport - As & S LLC.....G..... 954 782-2300
Boca Raton *(G-414)*
Anzio Ironworks Corp.....G..... 727 895-2019
Clearwater *(G-1585)*
Armalaser Inc.....G..... 800 680-5020
Gainesville *(G-4876)*
Arno Belo Inc.....G..... 800 734-2356
Hallandale Beach *(G-5170)*
Asb Sports Group LLC.....F..... 305 775-4689
Miami *(G-9176)*
B & D Precision Tools Inc.....E..... 305 885-1583
Hialeah *(G-5314)*
Baby Guard Inc.....F..... 954 741-6351
Coral Springs *(G-2222)*
Blue Gardenia LLC.....G..... 727 560-0040
Saint Petersburg *(G-15723)*
BRC Sports Llc.....F..... 904 388-8126
Jacksonville *(G-6233)*
Brownies Marine Group Inc.....G..... 954 462-5570
Pompano Beach *(G-14624)*
Burn Proof Gear LLC.....G..... 786 634-7406
Miami *(G-9286)*
Caseworks International Inc.....F..... 954 933-9102
Fort Lauderdale *(G-3884)*
Chandler Bats.....G..... 484 674-7175
Boca Raton *(G-478)*
Clawson Custom Cues Inc.....E..... 904 448-8748
Jacksonville *(G-6266)*
Covert Armor LLC.....F..... 561 459-8077
West Palm Beach *(G-18851)*
D G Morrison Inc.....F..... 813 865-0208
Odessa *(G-12114)*
Deers Holdings Inc.....G..... 805 323-6899
Bay Harbor Islands *(G-338)*
Dreams Inc.....G..... 954 377-0002
Miramar *(G-10986)*
Durabody Usa LLC.....G..... 954 357-2333
Miramar *(G-10987)*
Eagle Athletica LLC.....G..... 305 209-7002
Miami *(G-9493)*
Ecx Online Inc.....G..... 407 442-6834
Orlando *(G-12697)*
Exclusive Bats LLC.....G..... 305 450-3858
Hialeah *(G-5400)*
Florida Fishing Products.....G..... 239 938-4612
Tampa *(G-17676)*
Florida Pool Products Inc.....E..... 727 531-8913
Clearwater *(G-1690)*
Florida Stucco Corp.....E..... 561 487-1301
Boca Raton *(G-534)*
G & K Aluminum Inc.....F..... 772 283-1297
Stuart *(G-16943)*
Gar Industries Corp.....F..... 954 456-8088
Hallandale Beach *(G-5188)*
Garbo Sport International Inc.....G..... 305 599-8797
Miami *(G-9612)*
Georgia Usssa Baseball.....G..... 678 794-1630
Melbourne *(G-8836)*
Gorilla Bats LLC.....G..... 813 285-9409
Riverview *(G-15271)*
Headhunter Spearfishing Co.....G..... 954 745-0747
Fort Lauderdale *(G-4045)*
Homerun Derby Bats Only LLC.....G..... 813 545-3887
Riverview *(G-15273)*

Just For Nets....F.... 813 871-1133
Tampa *(G-17812)*
Kj Collections....G.... 904 285-7745
Ponte Vedra Beach *(G-14944)*
Ljs Tops & Bottoms....E.... 561 736-7868
Boynton Beach *(G-929)*
Lucas 5135 Inc....E.... 800 835-7665
Jacksonville *(G-6566)*
Lure Course Brevard LLC....G.... 321 412-7143
Malabar *(G-8495)*
Marconi Line Inc....F.... 321 639-1130
Rockledge *(G-15434)*
McSkis....G.... 863 513-0422
Clermont *(G-1969)*
Mirage Systems Inc....F.... 386 740-9222
Deland *(G-2997)*
Mor Sports LLC....G.... 239 671-5759
Cape Coral *(G-1449)*
Nighthawk Running LLC....F.... 407 443-8404
Orlando *(G-13002)*
Pocketec Inc....G.... 772 692-8020
Stuart *(G-16990)*
Pompanette LLC....E.... 813 885-2182
Tampa *(G-17997)*
Precision Paddleboards....G.... 954 616-8046
Fort Lauderdale *(G-4173)*
Primetime Sports Agents Inc....G.... 561 371-4421
West Palm Beach *(G-19007)*
Salt Life LLC....G.... 904 595-5370
Jacksonville Beach *(G-6957)*
Seasucker LLC....E.... 941 586-2664
Bradenton *(G-1113)*
Showcase Marble Inc....F.... 386 253-6646
Daytona Beach *(G-2714)*
Simons Hallandale Inc....E.... 561 468-1174
Miami *(G-10351)*
Sogofishing LLC....G.... 800 308-0259
Fort Lauderdale *(G-4241)*
Southern Tennis Supplies....G.... 850 936-1772
Pensacola *(G-14265)*
Sport Products of Tampa Inc....G.... 813 630-5552
Tampa *(G-18127)*
Sports Radar Ltd....G.... 352 503-6825
Homosassa *(G-6006)*
SSE and Associates Inc....E.... 954 973-7144
Pompano Beach *(G-14867)*
Stuart Yacht Builders....F.... 561 747-1947
Stuart *(G-17029)*
Swim Buoy....G.... 305 953-4101
Opa Locka *(G-12363)*
Tampa Catamarans LLC....G.... 813 966-4640
Apollo Beach *(G-106)*
Tess Enterprises Inc....G.... 727 573-9701
Clearwater *(G-1917)*
Top Spec US Inc....G.... 904 345-0814
Jacksonville *(G-6864)*
Uninsured Relative Workshop....E.... 386 736-7589
Deland *(G-3028)*
Vertical Reality Inc....G.... 305 238-4522
Palmetto Bay *(G-13856)*
Visor Versa....G.... 239 249-4745
Estero *(G-3698)*
Wayloomoto LLC....G.... 954 636-1510
Davie *(G-2612)*
Wemi Sports....G.... 305 446-5178
Coral Gables *(G-2206)*

SPORTING GOODS STORES, NEC

Bakers Sports Inc....E.... 904 388-8126
Jacksonville *(G-6192)*
Boone Bait Co Inc....F.... 407 975-8775
Winter Park *(G-19384)*
Classic Fishing Products Inc....E.... 407 656-6133
Clermont *(G-1953)*
Crowder Custom Rods Inc....G.... 772 220-8108
Stuart *(G-16928)*
L & S Bait Co Inc....E.... 727 584-7691
Largo *(G-7997)*
Looper Sports Connection Inc....G.... 352 796-7974
Brooksville *(G-1247)*
Synergy Sports LLC....G.... 239 593-9374
Naples *(G-11432)*

SPORTING GOODS STORES: Firearms

Nst Global LLC....E.... 941 748-2270
Bradenton *(G-1088)*

SPORTING GOODS STORES: Fishing Eqpt

Back Country Inc....G.... 772 532-6174
Vero Beach *(G-18598)*
Fishermans Center Inc....G.... 561 844-5150
Riviera Beach *(G-15328)*
Toledo Sales Inc....G.... 305 389-3441
Miami *(G-10488)*

SPORTING GOODS STORES: Pool & Billiard Tables

Robertson Billiard Sups Inc....G.... 813 229-2778
Tampa *(G-18065)*

SPORTING GOODS STORES: Surfing Eqpt & Splys

Bote LLC....F.... 888 855-4450
Miramar Beach *(G-11064)*
Waterboyz Wbz Inc....F.... 850 433-2929
Pensacola *(G-14287)*

SPORTING GOODS STORES: Team sports Eqpt

Dixon Screen Printing LLC....G.... 850 476-3924
Pensacola *(G-14132)*

SPORTING GOODS: Fishing Nets

Brunken Manufacturing Co Inc....G.... 850 438-2478
Pensacola *(G-14108)*
Burbank Trawl Makers Inc....E.... 904 321-0976
Jacksonville *(G-6244)*
Lee Fisher International Inc....E.... 813 875-6296
Tampa *(G-17839)*

SPORTING GOODS: Skin Diving Eqpt

A Plus Marine Supply Inc....G.... 850 934-3890
Gulf Breeze *(G-5110)*
Halcyon Manufacturing Inc....E.... 386 454-0811
High Springs *(G-5701)*
Lamartek Inc....E.... 386 752-1087
Lake City *(G-7364)*
Mine Survival Inc....G.... 850 774-0025
Panama City Beach *(G-13980)*
Undersea Breathing Systems....G.... 561 588-7698
Lake Worth *(G-7596)*

SPORTING GOODS: Surfboards

Billabong Destin....G.... 850 424-3553
Miramar Beach *(G-11063)*
Bote LLC....F.... 888 855-4450
Miramar Beach *(G-11064)*
Bote Boards....G.... 850 855-4046
Fort Walton Beach *(G-4784)*
Bote Paddle Boards....G.... 850 460-2250
Destin *(G-3184)*
Glaspro....E.... 941 488-4586
Venice *(G-18550)*
Hyperform Inc....E.... 321 632-6503
Rockledge *(G-15421)*
Inspired Surf Boards....G.... 904 347-8879
Saint Augustine *(G-15556)*
Knightmare Surfboards LLC....G.... 321 720-4157
Malabar *(G-8492)*
McG Surfboards....G.... 904 305-8801
Atlantic Beach *(G-224)*
R & D Surf....F.... 321 636-4456
Rockledge *(G-15442)*
True East Surfboard Inc....G.... 407 679-6896
Orlando *(G-13278)*

SPORTS APPAREL STORES

Concealment Express LLC....D.... 888 904-2722
Jacksonville *(G-6282)*
Rock N Roll Custom Screened S....G.... 727 528-2111
Pinellas Park *(G-14385)*
Spirit Sales Corporation....G.... 850 878-0366
Tallahassee *(G-17329)*

SPOUTING: Plastic & Fiberglass Reinforced

Building Blocks Management Inc....F.... 214 289-9737
Kissimmee *(G-7227)*
Saint-Gobain Vetrotex Amer Inc....C.... 407 834-8968
Maitland *(G-8476)*

SPRAYING & DUSTING EQPT

Desco Manufacturing Inc....F.... 941 925-7029
Sarasota *(G-16409)*
Irms Inc....F.... 321 631-1161
Rockledge *(G-15423)*

SPRAYING EQPT: Agricultural

Castillos Farms Inc....G.... 305 232-0771
Miami *(G-9323)*
Florida Sprayers Inc....G.... 813 989-0500
Temple Terrace *(G-18369)*
Spray Box LLC....G.... 850 567-2724
Tallahassee *(G-17330)*

SPRINGS: Automobile

S N S Auto Sports LLC....G.... 727 546-2700
Pinellas Park *(G-14386)*

SPRINGS: Clock, Precision

Forceleader Inc....G.... 727 521-1808
Pinellas Park *(G-14348)*

SPRINGS: Gun, Precision

Militek Industries LLC....G.... 941 544-5636
Bradenton *(G-1078)*

SPRINGS: Mechanical, Precision

Harper Limbach LLC....G.... 813 207-0057
Tampa *(G-17744)*

SPRINGS: Precision

SOUTHERN SPRING & STAMPING INC E.... 941 488-2276
Venice *(G-18575)*

SPRINGS: Steel

Easylift N Bansbach Amer Inc....E.... 321 253-1999
Melbourne *(G-8819)*
Goodrich Corporation....C.... 904 757-3660
Jacksonville *(G-6441)*
Industrial Spring Corp....F.... 954 524-2558
Davie *(G-2537)*
J C S Engineering & Dev....F.... 305 888-7911
Hialeah *(G-5459)*
SOUTHERN SPRING & STAMPING INC E.... 941 488-2276
Venice *(G-18575)*
Vette Brakes & Products Inc....E.... 727 345-5292
Saint Petersburg *(G-15952)*

SPRINGS: Wire

Barnes Group Inc....G.... 941 255-0978
Lake Suzy *(G-7496)*
Carlo Morelli....G.... 954 241-1426
Hollywood *(G-5796)*
Cook Spring Co....D.... 941 377-5766
Sarasota *(G-16394)*
Gilco Spring of Florida Inc....E.... 813 855-4631
Oldsmar *(G-12228)*
Goodrich Corporation....C.... 904 757-3660
Jacksonville *(G-6441)*
J C S Engineering & Dev....F.... 305 888-7911
Hialeah *(G-5459)*
Optimum Spring Mfg Inc....G.... 904 567-5999
Ponte Vedra *(G-14927)*
Z Haydu Manufacturing Corp....G.... 954 925-1779
Hollywood *(G-5944)*

SPRINKLER SYSTEMS: Field

K-Rain Manufacturing Corp....D.... 561 721-3936
Riviera Beach *(G-15338)*

SPRINKLING SYSTEMS: Fire Control

Grinnell LLC....B.... 561 988-3658
Boca Raton *(G-552)*
Muller Fire Protection Inc....E.... 305 636-9780
Miami *(G-10052)*

SPROCKETS: Power Transmission

Grizzly Manufacturing Inc....E.... 386 755-0220
Lake City *(G-7360)*
Quality Industries America Inc....G.... 386 755-0220
Lake City *(G-7380)*
Southern Gear & Machine Inc....D.... 305 691-6300
Miami *(G-10386)*

STAGE LIGHTING SYSTEMS

Armadillo Sounds Inc..........G....... 305 801-7906
Miami *(G-9169)*
Dj Live Productions LLC..........G....... 407 383-1740
Altamonte Springs *(G-41)*
Koncept Systems LLC..........E....... 786 610-0122
Homestead *(G-5977)*
Liteworks Lighting Productions..........G....... 407 888-8677
Orlando *(G-12916)*
Platinum Ltg Productions LLC..........G....... 941 320-1906
Sarasota *(G-16278)*
Sweetlight Systems..........G....... 239 245-8159
Fort Myers *(G-4621)*

STAINLESS STEEL

American Stainless Mfrs..........D....... 786 275-4458
Miami *(G-9147)*
ATI Accurate Technology..........G....... 239 206-1240
Palmetto *(G-13787)*
ATI Agency Inc..........F....... 954 895-7909
Boca Raton *(G-432)*
ATI By Sea Co..........G....... 954 483-0526
Hollywood *(G-5776)*
ATI Pro AV LLC..........G....... 941 322-1008
Sarasota *(G-16355)*
ATI Sales Inc..........G....... 954 909-4639
Plantation *(G-14493)*
Ati2 Inc..........G....... 904 396-3766
Jacksonville *(G-6171)*
Brewfab LLC..........G....... 727 823-8333
Saint Petersburg *(G-15729)*
Custom Stainless Stl Eqp Inc..........E....... 305 627-6049
Miami *(G-9419)*
Fabmaster Inc..........G....... 727 216-6750
Clearwater *(G-1680)*
Florida Stainless Steel ACC..........G....... 727 207-2575
Spring Hill *(G-16853)*
Neo Metal Glass LLC..........G....... 954 532-0340
Pompano Beach *(G-14772)*
Shaws Fiberglass Inc..........G....... 863 425-9176
Mulberry *(G-11136)*
Stainless Steel Guide Rods..........G....... 813 240-7616
Hudson *(G-6038)*
Stainless Steel Guide Rods..........G....... 727 207-0583
Spring Hill *(G-16877)*
Stainless Steel Kitchens Corp..........F....... 305 999-1543
North Bay Village *(G-11596)*
Uk Sales LLC..........G....... 561 239-2980
Coconut Creek *(G-2099)*
Zerons Metal Designers Inc..........F....... 305 688-2240
Hialeah *(G-5696)*

STAINLESS STEEL WARE

Roden International Inc..........F....... 954 929-1900
Hollywood *(G-5902)*

STAINS: Biological

Inter Cell Technologies Inc..........G....... 561 575-6868
Jupiter *(G-7058)*

STAIRCASES & STAIRS, WOOD

Cedrus Inc..........E....... 772 286-2082
Stuart *(G-16920)*
General Stair Corporation..........E....... 305 769-9900
Hialeah *(G-5428)*
Remior Industries Inc..........E....... 305 883-8722
Miami *(G-10250)*
Scott-Douglas Design Inc..........G....... 727 535-7900
Largo *(G-8046)*
Symmetrical Stair Inc..........F....... 561 228-4800
Pompano Beach *(G-14881)*

STAMPED ART GOODS FOR EMBROIDERING

Ocean Blue Graphics Inc..........G....... 561 881-2022
Riviera Beach *(G-15355)*

STAMPINGS: Metal

Blackwater Folk Art Inc..........G....... 850 623-3470
Milton *(G-10922)*
Chasco Machine & Manufacturing..........G....... 727 815-3510
Brooksville *(G-1218)*
Defense Stamping & Engineering..........E....... 850 438-6105
Pensacola *(G-14127)*
Ebway LLC..........E....... 954 971-4911
Fort Lauderdale *(G-3957)*
Exact Inc..........C....... 904 783-6640
Jacksonville *(G-6372)*
Global Friction Products Inc..........F....... 813 241-2700
Tampa *(G-17715)*
Gregg Tool & Die Co Inc..........G....... 305 685-6309
Hialeah *(G-5436)*
Hoffstetter Tool & Die Inc..........F....... 727 573-7775
Clearwater *(G-1715)*
Industrial Spring Corp..........F....... 954 524-2558
Davie *(G-2537)*
Iron Container LLC..........E....... 305 726-2150
Miami *(G-9771)*
Koszegi Industries Inc..........E....... 954 419-9544
Deerfield Beach *(G-2855)*
Leader Tech Inc..........D....... 813 855-6921
Tampa *(G-17838)*
Metal Products Company LC..........F....... 850 526-5593
Marianna *(G-8584)*
Mikes Aluminum Products LLC..........G....... 407 855-1989
Saint Cloud *(G-15660)*
Plastic and Products Mktg LLC..........F....... 352 867-8078
Ocala *(G-12028)*
Premier Fabricating Llc..........E....... 813 855-4633
Oldsmar *(G-12260)*
Press-Rite Inc..........G....... 954 963-7373
Miramar *(G-11030)*
Production Metal Stampings..........F....... 850 981-8240
Milton *(G-10938)*
RDS Manufacturing Inc..........C....... 850 584-6898
Perry *(G-14310)*
SOUTHERN SPRING & STAMPING INC..........E....... 941 488-2276
Venice *(G-18575)*
Spicer Industries Inc..........F....... 352 732-5300
Ocala *(G-12057)*
Strictly Toolboxes..........G....... 352 672-6566
Gainesville *(G-5005)*
Top Notch Diecutting Foil STA..........G....... 904 346-3511
Jacksonville *(G-6863)*
Trident Trading Inc..........G....... 561 488-0458
Boca Raton *(G-756)*
U S Hardware Supply Inc..........E....... 407 657-1551
Winter Park *(G-19454)*
Wastequip Manufacturing Co LLC..........E....... 863 665-6507
Lakeland *(G-7832)*

STAPLES

CMC Steel Us LLC..........E....... 904 266-4261
Jacksonville *(G-6272)*

STAPLES: Steel, Wire Or Cut

Tecnometales Onis Cnc LLC..........G....... 786 637-8316
Pembroke Pines *(G-14065)*

STARTERS: Electric Motor

T R S..........E....... 407 298-5490
Orlando *(G-13238)*

STARTERS: Motor

Central Fla Remanufacturing..........G....... 407 299-9011
Orlando *(G-12563)*

STATIC ELIMINATORS: Ind

Kinetronics Corporation..........F....... 941 951-2432
Bradenton *(G-1067)*
Ksm Electronics Inc..........D....... 954 642-7050
Tamarac *(G-17361)*
Patlon Industries Inc..........G....... 305 255-7744
Miami *(G-10144)*

STATIONARY & OFFICE SPLYS, WHOLESALE: Laser Printer Splys

It Manex LLC..........G....... 954 442-4465
Miramar *(G-11005)*
Sun Print Management LLC..........E....... 727 945-0255
Holiday *(G-5749)*
Toners Plus LLC..........G....... 407 756-5787
Orlando *(G-13261)*
Totalprint USA..........G....... 855 915-1300
Tampa *(G-18196)*

STATIONERY & OFFICE SPLYS WHOLESALERS

Greg Allens Inc..........E....... 904 262-8912
Jacksonville *(G-6450)*
Ramseys Printing & Office Pdts..........G....... 850 227-7468
Port Saint Joe *(G-15082)*
Toner Technologies Inc..........G....... 561 547-9710
Boynton Beach *(G-970)*
Well Made Bus Solutions LLC..........G....... 754 227-7268
Coconut Creek *(G-2101)*

STATIONERY PRDTS

Universal Tech Inc..........G....... 786 220-8032
Miami *(G-10545)*

STATORS REWINDING SVCS

Gulf Coast Elc Mtr Svc Inc..........E....... 850 433-5134
Pensacola *(G-14166)*

STATUARY & OTHER DECORATIVE PRDTS: Nonmetallic

Fleurissima Inc..........F....... 305 572-0203
Miami *(G-9575)*
Treasure Cove II Inc..........F....... 941 966-2004
Sarasota *(G-16625)*

STATUARY GOODS, EXC RELIGIOUS: Wholesalers

3 D F X Inc..........F....... 407 237-6249
Orlando *(G-12416)*

STEEL & ALLOYS: Tool & Die

Alpine Tool Inc..........G....... 727 587-0407
Largo *(G-7891)*
Sarasota Precision Engrg Inc..........F....... 941 727-3444
Sarasota *(G-16293)*

STEEL FABRICATORS

3 D F X Inc..........F....... 407 237-6249
Orlando *(G-12416)*
3lmetals Inc..........G....... 305 497-4038
Miami *(G-9026)*
A & K Machine & Fab Shop Inc..........F....... 904 388-7772
Jacksonville *(G-6107)*
A&L Hall Investments Inc..........E....... 904 781-5080
Bryceville *(G-1296)*
A/C Cages..........G....... 407 446-9259
Deltona *(G-3162)*
AAA Steel Fabricators Inc..........G....... 954 570-7211
Deerfield Beach *(G-2761)*
Aat Omega LLC..........E....... 352 473-6673
Keystone Heights *(G-7205)*
Ace Fabricators Inc..........F....... 904 355-3724
Jacksonville *(G-6117)*
Adelman Steel Corp..........F....... 305 691-7740
Miami *(G-9068)*
Advanced Manufacturing & Engrg..........G....... 352 629-1494
Ocala *(G-11864)*
AGlsupreme Llc..........E....... 818 232-6699
Hollywood *(G-5765)*
Air Duct Systems Inc..........F....... 407 839-3313
Orlando *(G-12443)*
Ajl Fabrication Llc..........F....... 407 654-1950
Kissimmee *(G-7218)*
Al-Mar Metals Inc..........G....... 386 734-3377
De Leon Springs *(G-2735)*
Alchemist Holdings LLC..........F....... 772 340-7774
Port Saint Lucie *(G-15085)*
Alchemist Holdings LLC..........E....... 772 343-1111
Port Saint Lucie *(G-15086)*
Alico Metal Fabricators LLC..........G....... 239 454-4766
Fort Myers *(G-4349)*
Allensteel Inc..........G....... 239 454-1331
Fort Myers *(G-4351)*
Allied Steel Structures Inc..........F....... 877 997-8335
Fort Lauderdale *(G-3806)*
Allied-360 LLC..........E....... 954 590-4940
Fort Lauderdale *(G-3807)*
Allpro Fbricators Erectors Inc..........G....... 954 797-7300
Davie *(G-2492)*
Alse Industries LLC..........F....... 305 688-8778
Miami Gardens *(G-10734)*
Aluminum Designs LLC..........G....... 239 289-3388
Naples *(G-11157)*
American Archtctral Mtls GL LL..........G....... 305 688-8778
Hialeah *(G-5288)*
American Metal Fab of Ctrl Fl..........G....... 813 653-2788
Brandon *(G-1150)*
American Wtrjet Fbrcation Svcs..........G....... 407 826-0497
Orlando *(G-12474)*

Aminsa Corp....G.... 954 865-1289
Weston *(G-19104)*
Anthony Spagna Svc & Maint Inc....G.... 352 796-2109
Brooksville *(G-1212)*
Aog Detailing Services Inc....G.... 727 742-7321
Saint Petersburg *(G-15703)*
Apex Fabrication Inc....F.... 904 259-4666
Macclenny *(G-8441)*
ARC Transition LLC....G.... 386 626-0001
Daytona Beach *(G-2628)*
ARC-Rite Inc....E.... 386 325-3523
Jacksonville *(G-6165)*
Arcosa Trffic Ltg Strctres LLC....E.... 352 748-4258
Sumterville *(G-17067)*
Artec Metal Fabrication Inc....G.... 305 888-4375
Hialeah *(G-5306)*
Artemis Holdings LLC....C.... 904 284-5611
Green Cove Springs *(G-5053)*
Artistic Gate Railing....G.... 954 348-9752
Oakland Park *(G-11781)*
Atlantic Central Entps Inc....F.... 386 255-6227
Daytona Beach *(G-2630)*
Atlantic Steel Inc....E.... 407 599-3822
Longwood *(G-8258)*
Automated Metal Products Inc....G.... 863 638-4404
Lake Wales *(G-7500)*
B & K Installations Inc....E.... 305 245-6968
Homestead *(G-5956)*
Baker Metalworks and Sup Inc....F.... 850 537-2010
Baker *(G-301)*
Barrett Custom Designs LLC....G.... 321 242-2002
Melbourne *(G-8776)*
Best Fabrications Inc....F.... 863 519-6611
Bartow *(G-310)*
Best Industries....F.... 772 460-8310
Fort Pierce *(G-4681)*
Big Bend Rebar Inc....F.... 850 875-8000
Quincy *(G-15246)*
Big Iron Intl Inc....G.... 407 222-2573
Orlando *(G-12514)*
Bostic Steel Inc....D.... 305 592-7276
Doral *(G-3282)*
Brantley Machine & Fabrication....F.... 904 359-0554
Jacksonville *(G-6232)*
Breton USA Customers Svc Corp....F.... 941 360-2700
Sarasota *(G-16369)*
Burch Welding & Fabrication....G.... 904 353-6513
Jacksonville *(G-6245)*
Capital Steel Inc....F.... 352 628-1700
Homosassa *(G-6001)*
Capitol Rental Bldg Eqp Inc....F.... 305 633-5008
Miami *(G-9309)*
Cato Steel Co....F.... 407 671-3333
Winter Park *(G-19391)*
Cemex Materials LLC....D.... 941 722-4578
Palmetto *(G-13790)*
Central Metal Fabricators Inc....E.... 305 261-6262
Miami *(G-9339)*
Central Steel Fabricators LLC....G.... 904 503-1660
Jacksonville *(G-6259)*
Clarkwestern Dietrich Building....D.... 800 693-3018
Ocala *(G-11904)*
Clarkwstern Dtrich Bldg System....E.... 954 772-6300
Fort Lauderdale *(G-3902)*
Classic Metal Fabrication Inc....G.... 561 305-9532
Boca Raton *(G-482)*
Coastal Acquisitions Fla LLC....F.... 850 769-9423
Panama City *(G-13882)*
Coastal Mfg & Fabrication Inc....G.... 352 799-8706
Brooksville *(G-1221)*
Coastal Sheet Mtalof S Fla LLC....E.... 561 718-6044
Lake Worth *(G-7543)*
Complete Metal Solutions Intl....G.... 954 560-0583
Fort Lauderdale *(G-3913)*
Cornerstone Fabrication LLC....E.... 386 310-1110
Debary *(G-2747)*
Custom Fabrication Inc....E.... 813 754-7571
Plant City *(G-14421)*
Custom Metal Specialties Inc....E.... 727 522-3986
Pinellas Park *(G-14341)*
Custom Wldg & Fabrication Inc....E.... 863 967-1000
Auburndale *(G-237)*
D & D MBL Wldg Fabrication Inc....F.... 954 791-3385
Fort Lauderdale *(G-3927)*
D & D MBL Wldg Fabrication Inc....D.... 772 489-7900
Fort Pierce *(G-4690)*
D & D Wldg & Fabrication LLC....F.... 954 791-3385
Fort Lauderdale *(G-3928)*
D & I Carbide Tool Co Inc....F.... 727 848-3356
Hudson *(G-6020)*
Daytona Welding & Fabrication....F.... 386 562-0093
Daytona Beach *(G-2657)*
DEC Sheet Metal Inc....F.... 863 669-0707
Lakeland *(G-7672)*
Deltana Enterprises Inc....E.... 305 592-8188
Doral *(G-3327)*
Dixie Metal Products Inc....D.... 352 873-2554
Ocala *(G-11921)*
Dixie-Southern Arkansas LLC....G.... 479 751-9183
Bradenton *(G-1031)*
DK International Assoc Inc....E.... 954 828-1256
Fort Lauderdale *(G-3945)*
Domestic Custom Metals Company....G.... 239 643-2422
Naples *(G-11231)*
Dutchy Enterprises LLC....G.... 321 877-0700
Cocoa *(G-2016)*
Dynabilt Technologies Corp....F.... 305 919-9800
Hialeah *(G-5381)*
E-Z Metals Inc....E.... 239 936-7887
Fort Myers *(G-4438)*
Eagle Metal Products Inc....G.... 561 964-4192
Lake Worth *(G-7549)*
East Coast Medal....G.... 561 619-6753
Lantana *(G-7870)*
East Coast Metal Decks Inc....E.... 561 433-8259
Lantana *(G-7871)*
Eastern Metal Supply NC Inc....F.... 800 432-2204
West Palm Beach *(G-18859)*
Ed Steel Fabricator Inc....G.... 305 926-4904
Hialeah *(G-5389)*
Elro Manufacturing LLC....F.... 407 410-6006
Apopka *(G-133)*
Emerald Coast Fabricators....G.... 850 554-6172
Pensacola *(G-14141)*
Emf Inc....C.... 321 453-3670
Merritt Island *(G-9000)*
Emjac Industries Inc....D.... 305 883-2194
Hialeah *(G-5395)*
Entertainment Metals Inc....E.... 800 817-2683
Fort Myers *(G-4444)*
Fab Rite Inc....G.... 561 848-8181
Riviera Beach *(G-15327)*
Fabco Metal Products LLC....D.... 386 252-3730
Daytona Beach *(G-2664)*
Fabricating Technologies LLC....G.... 352 473-6673
Keystone Heights *(G-7207)*
Fabsouth LLC....D.... 954 938-5800
Oakland Park *(G-11804)*
Fis Group Inc....G.... 786 622-3308
Opa Locka *(G-12315)*
Fitzlord Inc....D.... 904 731-2041
Jacksonville *(G-6390)*
FK Instrument Co LLC....D.... 727 472-2003
Clearwater *(G-1683)*
Florida Aluminum and Steel Inc....F.... 863 967-4191
Auburndale *(G-241)*
Florida CMC Rebar....G.... 407 518-5101
Jacksonville *(G-6395)*
Florida Custom Fabricators....F.... 407 892-8538
Saint Cloud *(G-15650)*
Florida Fabrication Inc....F.... 407 212-0105
Apopka *(G-143)*
Florida Glass of Tampa Bay....D.... 813 925-1330
Tampa *(G-17677)*
Fsf Manufacturing Inc....C.... 407 971-8280
Oviedo *(G-13431)*
G & A Manufacturing Inc....F.... 352 473-6882
Keystone Heights *(G-7208)*
G Bauman Fabrications Inc....G.... 954 914-8037
Pompano Beach *(G-14708)*
Gardner-Watson Decking Inc....E.... 813 891-9849
Oldsmar *(G-12227)*
General Saw Company....F.... 813 231-3167
Tampa *(G-17708)*
Georges Welding Services Inc....D.... 305 822-2445
Medley *(G-8658)*
Gerdau Ameristeel US Inc....B.... 813 752-7550
Plant City *(G-14434)*
Gill Manufacturing Inc....F.... 863 422-5711
Davenport *(G-2479)*
Greenes Wldg & Fabrication LLC....G.... 904 773-3101
Middleburg *(G-10905)*
Grizzly Products Corp....F.... 813 545-3828
Tampa *(G-17730)*
Group Steel Inc....G.... 786 319-1222
Hialeah *(G-5437)*
Group Steel Inc....G.... 305 965-0614
Miami *(G-9676)*
Gulf Coast Fabricators Inc....G.... 850 584-5979
Perry *(G-14301)*
Gunns Welding & Fabricating....G.... 727 393-5238
Saint Petersburg *(G-15801)*
Harrison Metals Inc....G.... 352 588-2436
San Antonio *(G-15973)*
Henley Metal LLC....F.... 904 353-4770
Jacksonville *(G-6468)*
Herco Sheet Metal Inc....E.... 850 244-7424
Fort Walton Beach *(G-4808)*
Hernandez Metal Fabricators....G.... 305 970-4145
Miami *(G-9704)*
Highway Systems Incorporated....F.... 813 907-7512
Lutz *(G-8389)*
Holbrook Metal Fabrication LLC....G.... 386 937-5441
Palatka *(G-13483)*
Hollywood Iron Works Inc....F.... 954 962-0556
West Park *(G-19094)*
Imagine That Inc....F.... 813 728-8324
Tarpon Springs *(G-18309)*
Industrial Welding & Maint....G.... 352 799-3432
Brooksville *(G-1236)*
Innovative Fabricators Fla Inc....G.... 941 375-8668
Nokomis *(G-11582)*
Inox Stainless Specialist LLC....F.... 407 764-2456
Pompano Beach *(G-14731)*
Inprodelca Inc....G.... 865 687-7921
Pembroke Pines *(G-14042)*
J & J Steel Services Corp....G.... 305 878-8929
Medley *(G-8673)*
J & J Wldg Stl Fbrction Fla In....E.... 813 754-0771
Auburndale *(G-246)*
J A Custom....G.... 561 615-4680
West Palm Beach *(G-18910)*
J2b Industrial LLC....G.... 904 805-0745
Jacksonville *(G-6506)*
J2b Industrial LLC....F.... 904 574-8919
Jacksonville *(G-6507)*
Jacksonville Steel Pdts Inc....G.... 904 268-3364
Jacksonville *(G-6512)*
Jamar Cnstr Fabrication Inc....G.... 321 400-0333
Sanford *(G-16071)*
Jglc Enterprises LLC....E.... 772 223-7393
Stuart *(G-16961)*
Jnc Welding & Fabricating Inc....E.... 954 227-9424
Coral Springs *(G-2265)*
Jomar Metal Fabrication Inc....G.... 407 857-1259
Orlando *(G-12859)*
Juno Ironcraft....G.... 561 352-0471
Lake Park *(G-7475)*
Just Steel Inc....F.... 941 755-7811
Sarasota *(G-16242)*
Just-In-Time Mfg Corp....F.... 321 752-7552
Melbourne *(G-8857)*
K&T Manufacturing Inc....G.... 407 814-7700
Apopka *(G-152)*
Keene Metal Fabricators Inc....E.... 813 621-2455
Tampa *(G-17817)*
Kemco Industries LLC....D.... 407 322-1230
Sanford *(G-16077)*
L & D Steel USA Inc....F.... 727 538-9917
Largo *(G-7996)*
L M Industrial Inc....G.... 407 240-8911
Orlando *(G-12879)*
Latham Marine Inc....E.... 954 462-3055
Fort Lauderdale *(G-4096)*
Lexington Dsign + Fbrction E L....F.... 407 578-4720
Orlando *(G-12906)*
Manning Company....G.... 954 523-9355
Fort Lauderdale *(G-4111)*
Mares Services Corp....F.... 305 752-0093
Miami *(G-9944)*
Marlyn Steel Products Inc....E.... 813 621-1375
Tampa *(G-17884)*
Martin & Vleminckx Rides LLC....G.... 407 566-0036
Sarasota *(G-16504)*
Master Fabricators Inc....F.... 786 537-7440
Miami *(G-9954)*
McCarthy Fabrication LLC....F.... 407 943-4909
Sanford *(G-16085)*
McDs Pro LLC....G.... 954 302-3054
Davie *(G-2550)*
Meachem Steel Inc....G.... 352 735-7333
Sorrento *(G-16789)*
Mechanical Dynamics Inc....E.... 863 292-0709
Winter Haven *(G-19336)*
Merlin Industries Inc....F.... 954 472-6891
Davie *(G-2552)*
Metal Magix Inc....G.... 754 235-9996
Pompano Beach *(G-14759)*
Metal Supply and Machining Inc....F.... 561 276-4941
Delray Beach *(G-3107)*

Metalcraft Services Tampa Inc..............G....... 813 558-8700
Tampa *(G-17905)*
Metpro Supply Inc..............E....... 863 425-7155
Mulberry *(G-11130)*
Miami Fabricator Inc..............G....... 305 505-1908
Miami *(G-10000)*
Miami Fabricator Inc..............G....... 305 505-1908
Miami *(G-10001)*
Michael Valentines Inc..............F....... 239 332-0855
Fort Myers *(G-4531)*
Mid Florida Steel Corp..............E....... 321 632-8228
Cocoa *(G-2036)*
Miller-Leaman Inc..............E....... 386 248-0500
Daytona Beach *(G-2687)*
Misc Metal Fabrication LLC..............F....... 754 264-1026
Deerfield Beach *(G-2874)*
MO Steel Fbricator Erector Inc..............G....... 305 945-4855
Miami *(G-10031)*
Moody Construction Svcs Inc..............E....... 941 776-1542
Duette *(G-3562)*
MPH Industries Inc..............F....... 352 372-9533
Gainesville *(G-4966)*
Naples Iron Works Inc..............E....... 239 649-7265
Naples *(G-11336)*
Nautical Structures Inds Inc..............D....... 727 541-6664
Largo *(G-8018)*
Orange State Steel Cnstr Inc..............E....... 727 544-3398
Pinellas Park *(G-14374)*
Orlando Metal Fabrication Inc..............F....... 407 850-4313
Orlando *(G-13034)*
Palatka Welding Shop Inc..............E....... 386 328-1507
Palatka *(G-13488)*
Palm Beach Iron Works Inc..............E....... 561 683-1816
West Palm Beach *(G-18983)*
Peters Structural Products..............G....... 863 229-5275
Winter Haven *(G-19341)*
Petrotech Services Inc..............D....... 813 248-0743
Tampa *(G-17987)*
Phoenix Metal Products Inc..............E....... 772 595-6386
Fort Pierce *(G-4732)*
Piecemakers LLC..............F....... 786 517-1829
Doral *(G-3462)*
Piecemakers LLC..............F....... 786 517-1829
Brandon *(G-1173)*
Pilot Steel Inc..............E....... 954 978-3615
Pompano Beach *(G-14794)*
Pipewelders Marine Inc..............D....... 954 587-8400
Fort Lauderdale *(G-4169)*
Plant City Powder Coating..............G....... 813 763-6028
Plant City *(G-14459)*
Precision Metal Fabrications..............G....... 305 691-0616
Hialeah *(G-5564)*
Premier Fabricators LLC..............G....... 772 323-2042
Fort Pierce *(G-4735)*
Pro Fab..............G....... 813 545-2861
Tampa *(G-18017)*
Protek Systems Inc..............G....... 561 395-8155
Delray Beach *(G-3129)*
Quality Fbrction Mch Works Inc..............F....... 386 755-0220
Lake City *(G-7379)*
Quality Industries America Inc..............G....... 386 755-0220
Lake City *(G-7380)*
Quality Metal Fabricators Inc..............E....... 813 831-7320
Tampa *(G-18032)*
Quality Metal Worx..............G....... 863 353-6638
Haines City *(G-5147)*
Quality Steel Fabricators Inc..............F....... 813 247-7110
Tampa *(G-18033)*
Raber Industries Inc..............G....... 239 728-5527
Alva *(G-90)*
Rafab Spcialty Fabrication Inc..............F....... 407 422-3750
Orlando *(G-13112)*
Rebah Fabrication Inc..............F....... 407 857-3232
Orlando *(G-13120)*
Reeds Metal Manufacturing Inc..............E....... 352 498-0100
Cross City *(G-2366)*
Renaissance Man Incorporated..............G....... 850 432-1177
Pensacola *(G-14252)*
Renova Land and Sea LLC..............G....... 786 916-2695
Miramar *(G-11036)*
Republic Industries..............G....... 954 627-6000
Fort Lauderdale *(G-4203)*
Rev-Tech Mfg Solutions LLC..............F....... 727 577-4999
Saint Petersburg *(G-15901)*
Rm Brands Inc..............G....... 904 356-0092
Jacksonville *(G-6732)*
Robert Ojeda Metalsmith Inc..............G....... 561 507-5511
Royal Palm Beach *(G-15477)*
Robotic Security Systems Inc..............E....... 850 871-9300
Panama City *(G-13946)*
Roof Hugger Inc..............G....... 813 909-4424
Lutz *(G-8414)*
Rubin Iron Works LLC..............E....... 904 356-5635
Jacksonville *(G-6739)*
Ryder Welding Service Inc..............F....... 305 685-6630
Opa Locka *(G-12357)*
S & B Metal Products E Fla Inc..............E....... 386 274-0092
Daytona Beach *(G-2707)*
SBs Precision Shtmtl Inc..............E....... 321 951-7411
Melbourne *(G-8927)*
Seaside Aluminum llc..............F....... 386 252-4940
Daytona Beach *(G-2710)*
Sembco Stl Erection Met Bldg..............F....... 561 863-0606
Riviera Beach *(G-15377)*
Shapes Group Ltd Co..............D....... 321 837-0500
Palm Bay *(G-13534)*
Shaws Fiberglass Inc..............G....... 863 425-9176
Mulberry *(G-11136)*
Sheet Metal Systems Inc..............F....... 727 548-1711
Pinellas Park *(G-14387)*
Snappy Structures Inc..............F....... 954 926-6611
Hollywood *(G-5910)*
Southern Aluminum and Stl Inc..............G....... 850 484-4700
Cantonment *(G-1349)*
Southern Custom Iron & Art LLC..............E....... 561 586-8400
Lake Worth Beach *(G-7621)*
Southern Strl Stl Fla Inc..............E....... 727 327-7123
Saint Petersburg *(G-15918)*
Southstern Stnless Fabricators..............F....... 904 354-4381
Jacksonville *(G-6800)*
Southwest Steel Group Inc..............G....... 239 283-8980
Cape Coral *(G-1477)*
Specialty Structures Inc..............F....... 386 668-0474
Debary *(G-2756)*
Spencer Fabrications Inc..............E....... 352 343-0014
Tavares *(G-18354)*
Spring Loaded Inc..............G....... 561 747-8785
Jupiter *(G-7121)*
Star Fabricators..............G....... 904 899-6569
Jacksonville *(G-6809)*
Steel City Inc..............F....... 850 785-9596
Panama City *(G-13952)*
Steel Components Inc..............F....... 954 427-6820
Coconut Creek *(G-2097)*
Steel Fabricators LLC..............C....... 954 772-0440
Oakland Park *(G-11843)*
Steel Monkey Dream Shop LLC..............G....... 786 356-1077
Miami *(G-10411)*
Steel Products Inc..............G....... 941 351-8128
Sarasota *(G-16604)*
Sterling Steel Fabrications..............E....... 561 366-8600
Mangonia Park *(G-8512)*
Sterling Stl Cstm Alum Fbrcton..............F....... 561 386-7166
Riviera Beach *(G-15380)*
Structural Steel of Brevard..............G....... 321 726-0271
Melbourne *(G-8948)*
Stuart Yacht Builders..............F....... 561 747-1947
Stuart *(G-17029)*
Superior Swim Systems Inc..............G....... 239 566-2060
Naples *(G-11428)*
T L Sheet Metal Inc..............G....... 813 871-3780
Tampa *(G-18152)*
Tampa Amalgamated Steel Corp..............G....... 813 621-0550
Tampa *(G-18156)*
Tampa Marine Fabricators LLC..............G....... 813 664-1700
Tampa *(G-18165)*
Tampa Steel Erecting Company..............D....... 813 677-7184
Tampa *(G-18174)*
Tampa Tank & Welding Inc..............F....... 813 241-0123
Gibsonton *(G-5033)*
Teknifab Industries Inc..............G....... 321 722-1922
Melbourne *(G-8958)*
Tidal Wave Tanks Fabrications..............G....... 863 425-7795
Mulberry *(G-11139)*
Trinity Fabricators Inc..............E....... 904 284-9657
Green Cove Springs *(G-5073)*
Tryana LLC..............G....... 813 467-9916
Tampa *(G-18206)*
TTI Holdings Inc..............G....... 813 623-2675
Tampa *(G-18208)*
Tuckers Machine & Stl Svc Inc..............D....... 352 787-3157
Leesburg *(G-8179)*
United Fabrication & Maint..............G....... 863 295-9000
Eloise *(G-3656)*
United Granite Inc..............F....... 813 391-4323
Tampa *(G-18221)*
United States Fndry & Mfg Corp..............C....... 305 885-0301
Medley *(G-8748)*
United States Fndry & Mfg Corp..............F....... 305 556-1661
Hialeah *(G-5661)*
Universal Erectors Inc..............G....... 813 621-8111
Lithia *(G-8225)*
Universal Welding Service Co..............G....... 305 898-9130
Miami Lakes *(G-10874)*
Unlimited Welding Inc..............E....... 407 327-3333
Winter Springs *(G-19487)*
US Custom Fabrication Inc..............G....... 954 917-6161
Pompano Beach *(G-14905)*
US Metal Fabricators Inc..............F....... 954 921-0800
Dania Beach *(G-2474)*
USF Fabrication Inc..............C....... 305 556-1661
Hialeah *(G-5669)*
Van Linda Iron Works Inc..............E....... 561 586-8400
Lake Worth Beach *(G-7622)*
Veatic..............G....... 888 474-2999
Kissimmee *(G-7309)*
Viper Communication Systems..............E....... 352 694-7030
Ocala *(G-12072)*
Vision Conveyor Inc..............F....... 352 343-3300
Tavares *(G-18359)*
Vulcan Steel..............G....... 561 945-1259
Jupiter *(G-7142)*
W D Wilson Inc..............E....... 813 626-6989
Tampa *(G-18250)*
Welding and Fabrication Inc..............G....... 973 508-7267
Hallandale Beach *(G-5224)*
Western Fabricating LLC..............G....... 239 676-5382
Fort Myers *(G-4654)*
Wheeler Consolidated Inc..............F....... 772 464-4400
Fort Pierce *(G-4770)*
Wilcox Steel Company LLC..............G....... 727 443-0461
Clearwater *(G-1939)*
Wilkinson Steel Supply LLC..............G....... 904 757-1522
Jacksonville *(G-6920)*

STEEL MILLS

Associated Steel & Alum Co Inc..............F....... 954 974-7890
Pompano Beach *(G-14603)*
Associated Steel & Alum Ltd..............F....... 954 974-7890
Pompano Beach *(G-14604)*
Belt Corp..............G....... 954 505-7400
Hollywood *(G-5785)*
Berg LLC..............F....... 786 201-2625
Aventura *(G-264)*
Commercial Metals Company..............G....... 904 781-4780
Jacksonville *(G-6281)*
Conc-Steel Inc..............G....... 516 882-5551
Palm Coast *(G-13689)*
Diverse Co..............F....... 863 425-4251
Mulberry *(G-11123)*
Gerdau Ameristeel Corp..............A....... 813 286-8383
Tampa *(G-17710)*
Gerdau Ameristeel US Inc..............E....... 813 752-7550
Plant City *(G-14435)*
Gulf Atlantic Culvert Company..............F....... 850 562-2384
Tallahassee *(G-17270)*
Home & Garden Industries Inc..............F....... 305 634-0681
Miami *(G-9716)*
Inductoweld Tube Corp..............G....... 646 734-7094
Fort Lauderdale *(G-4057)*
Industrial Galvanizers Miami..............E....... 305 681-8844
Miami *(G-9738)*
Innovative Steel Tech Inc..............F....... 813 767-1746
Gibsonton *(G-5030)*
Iron Sharpens Ir Training LLC..............G....... 407 614-4500
Winter Garden *(G-19271)*
Latham Marine Inc..............E....... 954 462-3055
Fort Lauderdale *(G-4096)*
Maclan Corporation Inc..............E....... 863 665-4814
Lakeland *(G-7742)*
Manor Steel Fabricators..............G....... 941 722-8077
Palmetto *(G-13810)*
Marilyn Jeffcoat..............G....... 407 382-1783
Orlando *(G-12949)*
Metal Culverts Inc..............E....... 727 531-1431
Clearwater *(G-1782)*
Metal Processors Inc..............E....... 813 654-0050
Tampa *(G-17904)*
Nucor LLC..............G....... 786 290-9328
Surfside *(G-17204)*
Nucor Steel Florida Inc..............G....... 863 546-5800
Frostproof *(G-4862)*
Phlebotomists On Wheels Inc..............G....... 954 873-7591
Fort Lauderdale *(G-4165)*
Sea Side Specialties..............G....... 561 276-6518
Delray Beach *(G-3139)*
Sel West Coast Inc..............E....... 352 373-6354
Gainesville *(G-4994)*
Spectrum Engineering Inc..............G....... 239 277-1182
Fort Myers *(G-4610)*

Stainless Fabricators Inc ....E 813 926-7113
Odessa *(G-12155)*
T&T Sons Inc ....G 859 576-3316
Oviedo *(G-13459)*
Wheel Wright ....G 850 626-2662
Milton *(G-10946)*

STEEL: Cold-Rolled

Hydro Extrusion Usa LLC ....B 904 794-1500
Saint Augustine *(G-15550)*
Hydro Precision Tubing USA LLC ....C 321 636-8147
Rockledge *(G-15420)*
Suncoast Post-Tension Ltd ....E 305 592-5075
Miami *(G-10430)*

STEEL: Laminated

Poly Coatings of South Inc ....F 941 371-8555
Sarasota *(G-16546)*

STENCILS

Design Services Inc ....G 813 949-4748
Land O Lakes *(G-7852)*
Ipg (us) Holdings Inc ....D 941 727-5788
Sarasota *(G-16471)*
Ipg (us) Inc ....G 941 727-5788
Sarasota *(G-16472)*

STENCILS & LETTERING MATERIALS: Die-Cut

Super Grafix Inc ....F 561 585-1519
Boca Raton *(G-739)*

STERILIZERS, BARBER & BEAUTY SHOP

Ecstatic Nails Inc ....G 305 328-9554
North Miami *(G-11636)*

STOCK CAR RACING

Tom Watson Enterprises Inc ....G 352 683-5097
Hudson *(G-6040)*

STOKERS: Mechanical, Domestic Or Indl

Snapspeed LLC ....G 321 441-3797
Indian Harbour Beach *(G-6067)*

STONE: Cast Concrete

Coral Reef Cast Stone Inc ....F 561 586-1900
West Palm Beach *(G-18850)*
K&T Stoneworks Inc ....F 561 798-8486
West Palm Beach *(G-18918)*
Saint Augustine Cast Stone ....G 904 794-2626
Saint Augustine *(G-15603)*
True Stone Corp ....E 772 334-9797
Fort Pierce *(G-4760)*

STONE: Dimension, NEC

Cavastone LLC ....G 561 994-9100
Boca Raton *(G-472)*
Central State Aggregates LLC ....F 813 788-0454
Zephyrhills *(G-19510)*
Custom Marble Works Inc ....E 813 620-0475
Tampa *(G-17580)*
Keystone Products Inc ....F 305 245-4716
Homestead *(G-5976)*
LW Rozzo Inc ....E 954 435-8501
Pembroke Pines *(G-14045)*
Old World Marble and Gran Inc ....G 239 596-4777
Naples *(G-11350)*
Plaza Materials Corp ....D 813 788-0454
Zephyrhills *(G-19533)*
Reyes Granite & Marble Corp ....F 305 599-7330
Miami *(G-10259)*
Rockers Stone Inc ....G 305 447-1231
Miami *(G-10273)*
Stone Center Inc ....F 863 669-0292
Lakeland *(G-7808)*
Stone Mosaics ....G 321 773-3635
Palm Bay *(G-13541)*
Stone Systems South Fla LLC ....F 954 584-4058
Lauderhill *(G-8121)*
Stone Trend International Inc ....E 941 927-9113
Sarasota *(G-16605)*
Vgcm LLC ....F 813 247-7625
Tampa *(G-18241)*
Vgcm LLC ....D 813 620-4889
Tampa *(G-18242)*

STONE: Quarrying & Processing, Own Stone Prdts

Center Sand Mine ....G 800 366-7263
Clermont *(G-1951)*
Devcon International Corp ....C 954 926-5200
Boca Raton *(G-499)*
Keystone Products Inc ....F 305 245-4716
Homestead *(G-5976)*
Palm Beach Aggregates LLC ....E 561 795-6550
Loxahatchee *(G-8362)*

STONEWARE PRDTS: Pottery

Florida Stoneware Tops Inc ....G 239 340-0492
Fort Myers *(G-4452)*

STOOLS: Factory

E&T Horizons Ltd Liability Co ....F 321 704-1244
Melbourne *(G-8818)*

STORE FIXTURES: Wood

Artco Group Inc ....D 305 638-1785
Miami *(G-9172)*
Ellis Wood Collection Ltd ....F 610 372-2880
St Pete Beach *(G-16880)*
Load King Manufacturing Co ....C 904 354-8882
Jacksonville *(G-6560)*
Synergy Custom Fixtures Corp ....C 305 693-0055
Hialeah *(G-5645)*
T & R Store Fixtures Inc ....E 305 751-0377
Miami *(G-10453)*

STORE FRONTS: Prefabricated, Metal

Architectural Metal Systems ....F 407 277-1364
Orlando *(G-12486)*
Gopi Glass Sales & Svcs Corp ....E 305 592-2089
Miami *(G-9650)*
Metal Fronts Inc ....G 727 547-6700
Seminole *(G-16752)*

STORES: Auto & Home Supply

Shafers Classic Reproductions ....G 813 622-7091
Tampa *(G-18089)*

STORES: Drapery & Upholstery

Southeast Energy Inc ....G 561 883-1051
Boca Raton *(G-723)*

STRAPPING

JKS Industries Inc ....E 863 425-1745
Mulberry *(G-11126)*
JKS Industries Inc ....F 727 573-1305
Tampa *(G-17805)*

STRAW GOODS

Straw Life Inc ....G 386 935-2850
O Brien *(G-11766)*

STRAWS: Drinking, Made From Purchased Materials

CU Holdings LLC ....D 904 483-5700
Jacksonville *(G-6302)*
Pride Straws LLC ....G 407 754-5833
Miami *(G-10192)*

STRUCTURAL SUPPORT & BUILDING MATERIAL: Concrete

A To Z Concrete Products Inc ....F 727 321-6000
Saint Petersburg *(G-15688)*
Gate Precast Company ....G 904 732-7668
Jacksonville *(G-6423)*
Gate Precast Erection Co ....D 904 737-7220
Jacksonville *(G-6424)*
Solar Erectors US Inc ....F 305 823-8950
Medley *(G-8724)*
Thompson Sales Group Inc ....E 239 332-0446
Fort Myers *(G-4630)*

STUCCO

Andrew Pratt Stucco & Plst Inc ....F 407 501-2609
Orlando *(G-12478)*
Best of Orlando Pntg & Stucco ....G 407 947-4174
Apopka *(G-117)*
Best Products Mix Inc ....G 305 512-9920
Hialeah *(G-5324)*
Bill Praus Stucco LLC ....G 386 453-8400
Flagler Beach *(G-3753)*
Bluewater Finishing LLC ....G 772 460-9457
Port Saint Lucie *(G-15092)*
Custom Stucco Inc ....G 941 650-5649
Englewood *(G-3659)*
Custom Wall Systems Inc ....G 772 408-3006
Vero Beach *(G-18614)*
E T Plastering Inc ....F 305 874-7082
Virginia Gardens *(G-18688)*
Fekel Stucco Plastering Inc ....G 239 571-5464
Naples *(G-11245)*
Florida Stucco Corp ....E 561 487-1301
Boca Raton *(G-534)*
Florida Sunshine Stucco LLC ....G 407 947-2088
Orlando *(G-12757)*
G & R Stucco Inc ....G 941 780-1561
North Port *(G-11739)*
Gold Coast Plst & Stucco Inc ....F 954 275-9132
Margate *(G-8545)*
J&Jh Stucco Inc ....G 813 482-5282
Riverview *(G-15274)*
Jag Stucco Inc ....G 813 210-6577
Land O Lakes *(G-7858)*
John S Smith Stucco Inc ....G 813 928-4320
New Port Richey *(G-11496)*
Juan Diaz Stucco Spc Inc ....G 407 402-1912
Minneola *(G-10955)*
MDK Enterpises Inc ....F 904 288-6855
Jacksonville *(G-6586)*
Pitelka Plastering Stucco ....G 630 235-5611
Venice *(G-18567)*
Pre-Mix Marble Tite Inc ....E 954 917-7665
Pompano Beach *(G-14806)*
Premix-Marbletite Mfg Co ....F 954 970-6540
Pompano Beach *(G-14810)*
Premix-Marbletite Mfg Co ....F 407 327-0830
Winter Springs *(G-19480)*
Q Plastering and Stucco Inc ....G 239 530-1712
Naples *(G-11378)*
Reyes Stucco Inc ....G 321 557-1319
Cocoa *(G-2047)*
Right Stucco Inc ....G 407 468-6119
Orlando *(G-13139)*
River City Stucco Inc ....G 904 234-9526
Jacksonville *(G-6728)*
S&L Cnstrction Specialists Inc ....G 407 300-5080
Orlando *(G-13153)*
Trinity Exterior Solutions LLC ....G 850 393-9682
Holt *(G-5950)*
Vimar Stucco Inc ....G 813 966-4831
Brandon *(G-1184)*

STUDIOS: Artist

Seaboard Manufacturing LLC ....G 727 497-3572
Clearwater *(G-1872)*

STUDS & JOISTS: Sheet Metal

Doral Building Supply Corp ....F 305 471-9797
Doral *(G-3332)*
Steel Cnstr Systems Holdg Co ....E 407 438-1664
Orlando *(G-13214)*

SUBMARINE BUILDING & REPAIR

Triton Submarines LLC ....E 772 770-1995
Sebastian *(G-16674)*
US Submarines Inc ....F 208 687-9057
Vero Beach *(G-18675)*

SUNDRIES & RELATED PRDTS: Medical & Laboratory, Rubber

Acuderm Inc ....D 954 733-6935
Fort Lauderdale *(G-3781)*
Ga-MA & Associates Inc ....G 352 687-8840
Ocala *(G-11953)*
Integrity Technologies LLC ....G 561 768-9023
Jupiter *(G-7057)*
Liquiguard Technologies Inc ....E 954 566-0996
Fort Lauderdale *(G-4101)*
Omt LLC ....F 954 327-1447
Fort Lauderdale *(G-4149)*
Rubber 2 Go Llc ....G 305 688-8566
Miami *(G-10286)*
Victus LLC ....E 305 663-2129
Miami *(G-10582)*

(G-0000) Company's Geographic Section entry number

SUNROOMS: Prefabricated Metal

Titan Specialty Cnstr Inc ....E 850 916-7660
Milton *(G-10943)*

SUPERMARKETS & OTHER GROCERY STORES

ABC Fence Systems Inc ....F 850 638-8876
Chipley *(G-1540)*
Delarosa Real Foods LLC ....D 718 333-0333
Lauderdale Lakes *(G-8085)*
Healthier Choices MGT Corp ....C 305 600-5004
Hollywood *(G-5836)*

SURFACE ACTIVE AGENTS

Paraflow Energy Solutions LLC ....E 713 239-0336
Boca Raton *(G-661)*

SURFACE ACTIVE AGENTS: Oils & Greases

Global Gl Lc ....G 863 551-1079
Winter Haven *(G-19326)*

SURFACERS: Concrete Grinding

A Clean Finish Inc ....G 407 516-1311
Jacksonville *(G-6109)*
Jdl Surface Innovations Inc ....E 239 772-0077
Cape Coral *(G-1441)*

SURGICAL & MEDICAL INSTRUMENTS WHOLESALERS

Camel Enterprises Corp ....F 954 234-2559
Miami *(G-9304)*
Gremed Group Corp ....E 305 392-5331
Doral *(G-3374)*
Uroshape LLC ....F 321 960-2484
Melbourne *(G-8968)*

SURGICAL APPLIANCES & SPLYS

Consolidated Polymer Tech ....E 727 531-4191
Clearwater *(G-1636)*
Halkey-Roberts Corporation ....C 727 471-4200
Saint Petersburg *(G-15803)*
Johnson & Johnson ....E 305 261-3500
Miami *(G-9801)*
Universal Surgical Appliance ....F 305 652-0810
Miami *(G-10544)*

SURGICAL APPLIANCES & SPLYS

360 O and P Inc ....G 813 985-5000
Temple Terrace *(G-18365)*
Aso Corporation ....D 941 378-6600
Sarasota *(G-16351)*
Atlantic Tactical Inc ....G 909 923-7300
Jacksonville *(G-6178)*
Baycare Home Care Inc ....F 727 461-5878
Clearwater *(G-1603)*
Biosculptor Corporation ....G 305 823-8300
Hialeah *(G-5326)*
Blue Diamond Orthopedic LLC ....G 407 613-2001
Orlando *(G-12525)*
C C Lead Inc ....F 863 465-6458
Lake Placid *(G-7486)*
Comfort Brace LLC ....G 954 899-1563
Lighthouse Point *(G-8208)*
Elmridge Protection Pdts LLC ....G 561 244-8337
Boca Raton *(G-517)*
Encore Inc ....F 941 359-3599
Sarasota *(G-16211)*
Exactech Inc ....A 352 377-1140
Gainesville *(G-4916)*
Foot Function Lab Inc ....G 954 753-2500
Coral Springs *(G-2246)*
Hans Rudolph Inc ....F 561 877-8775
Boynton Beach *(G-916)*
Healthline Medical Pdts Inc ....E 407 656-0704
Winter Garden *(G-19267)*
Howmedica Osteonics Corp ....G 941 378-4600
Sarasota *(G-16461)*
Howmedica Osteonics Corp ....G 813 886-3450
Tampa *(G-17763)*
Intermed Group Inc ....E 561 586-3667
Alachua *(G-10)*
Invacare Florida Corporation ....B 407 321-5630
Sanford *(G-16069)*
Johnson & Johnson ....G 813 972-0204
Tampa *(G-17809)*
Kericure Inc ....F 855 888-5374
Wesley Chapel *(G-18750)*
Linvatec Corporation ....A 727 392-6464
Largo *(G-8001)*
Main Tape Co Inc ....G 561 248-8867
West Palm Beach *(G-18938)*
Maven Medical Mfg Inc ....E 727 518-0555
Largo *(G-8006)*
Medtronic Usa Inc ....A 702 308-1302
Jacksonville *(G-6591)*
Neutral Guard LLC ....G 954 249-6600
Fort Lauderdale *(G-4136)*
Quick Protective Systems Inc ....G 772 220-3315
Stuart *(G-16993)*
Restoration Medical LLC ....G 863 272-0250
Lakeland *(G-7778)*
RS&m Consultants ....G 727 323-6983
Saint Petersburg *(G-15903)*
Safariland LLC ....F 904 741-5400
Jacksonville *(G-6746)*
Safariland LLC ....B 904 741-5400
Jacksonville *(G-6748)*
Shukla Medical Inc ....E 732 474-1769
Saint Petersburg *(G-15912)*
Sientra Inc ....G 813 751-7576
Brandon *(G-1179)*
Sky Medical Inc ....F 954 747-3188
Sunrise *(G-17172)*
Superior Surgical Mfg Co ....F 800 727-8643
Seminole *(G-16766)*
Surefire Laser LLC ....G 305 720-7118
Miami *(G-10442)*
Syndaver Labs Inc ....D 813 600-5530
Tampa *(G-18148)*
Vy Spine LLC ....G 866 489-7746
Tallahassee *(G-17344)*
Walker Hospitality Inc ....G 407 927-1871
Orlando *(G-13318)*
Westcoast Brace & Limb Inc ....D 407 502-0024
Maitland *(G-8486)*
Zassi Holdings Inc ....G 904 432-8315
Ponte Vedra Beach *(G-14958)*

SURGICAL EQPT: See Also Instruments

American Surgical Mask LLC ....E 813 606-4510
Tampa *(G-17420)*
Arthrex Manufacturing Inc ....C 239 643-5553
Naples *(G-11170)*
Cae Healthcare Inc ....C 941 377-5562
Sarasota *(G-16377)*
Conmed Corporation ....A 727 392-6464
Largo *(G-7927)*
Gulf Medical Fiberoptics Inc ....G 813 855-6618
Oldsmar *(G-12230)*
Howmedica Osteonics Corp ....E 954 791-6078
Fort Lauderdale *(G-4051)*
Linvatec Corporation ....A 727 392-6464
Largo *(G-8001)*
Ndh Medical Inc ....G 727 570-2293
Saint Petersburg *(G-15864)*
Pablo Surgical Solutions LLC ....G 904 237-4864
Ponte Vedra Beach *(G-14949)*
Rotburg Instruments Amer Inc ....F 954 331-8046
Sunrise *(G-17170)*
Unimed Surgical Products Inc ....E 727 546-1900
Seminole *(G-16769)*
Zimmer Biomet CMF Thoracic LLC ....C 574 267-6639
Jacksonville *(G-6934)*

SURGICAL IMPLANTS

Axogen Corporation ....E 386 462-6800
Alachua *(G-7)*
Catalyst Orthoscience Inc ....F 239 325-9976
Naples *(G-11201)*
Ctm Biomedical LLC ....F 561 650-4027
Miami *(G-9416)*
Innovative Mfg Solutions LLC ....G 904 647-5300
Jacksonville *(G-6497)*
Medtronic Xomed Inc ....A 904 296-9600
Jacksonville *(G-6592)*
Medtronic Xomed Inc ....B 904 296-9600
Jacksonville *(G-6593)*
Physiorx LLC ....F 407 718-5549
Ocoee *(G-12088)*
Spinenet LLC ....F 321 439-1806
Winter Park *(G-19447)*
US Implant Solutions LLC ....G 407 971-8054
Maitland *(G-8483)*

SURVEYING & MAPPING: Land Parcels

A B Survey Supply Entps Inc ....G 772 464-9500
Fort Pierce *(G-4667)*
Quantum Spatial Inc ....D 920 457-3631
Saint Petersburg *(G-15897)*

SURVEYING SVCS: Aerial Digital Imaging

Drs Training Ctrl Systems LLC ....E 850 302-3000
Fort Walton Beach *(G-4796)*

SVC ESTABLISH EQPT, WHOLESALE: Carpet/Rug Clean Eqpt & Sply

Quality Carpet ....G 727 527-1359
Saint Petersburg *(G-15895)*

SVC ESTABLISHMENT EQPT & SPLYS WHOLESALERS

Quality Industrial Chem Inc ....F 727 573-5760
Saint Petersburg *(G-15896)*

SVC ESTABLISHMENT EQPT, WHOL: Cleaning & Maint Eqpt & Splys

Florida Rum Company LLC ....E 305 791-1221
Hollywood *(G-5823)*
Threez Company LLC ....G 904 651-1444
Jacksonville *(G-6854)*
Threez Company LLC ....G 904 422-9224
Jacksonville *(G-6853)*

SVC ESTABLISHMENT EQPT, WHOL: Liquor Dispensing Eqpt/Sys

Micro Matic Usa Inc ....E 352 544-1081
Brooksville *(G-1252)*

SVC ESTABLISHMENT EQPT, WHOLESALE: Beauty Parlor Eqpt & Sply

Matrix Packaging of Florida ....G 305 358-9696
Miami *(G-9956)*
No 1 Beauty Salon Furniture ....G 954 981-0403
Oakland Park *(G-11825)*

SVC ESTABLISHMENT EQPT, WHOLESALE: Vending Machines & Splys

Sunnypics LLC ....G 407 992-6210
Orlando *(G-13224)*

SWIMMING POOL & HOT TUB CLEANING & MAINTENANCE SVCS

Fibre Tech Inc ....E 727 539-0844
Largo *(G-7945)*
National Chemical Sply ....F 800 515-9938
Davie *(G-2556)*
South West Adventure Team LLC ....G 903 288-4739
Labelle *(G-7323)*

SWIMMING POOL EQPT: Filters & Water Conditioning Systems

Aladdin Equipment Company ....D 941 371-3732
Sarasota *(G-16338)*
Com Pac Filtration Inc ....E 904 356-4003
Jacksonville *(G-6279)*
Esse Sales Inc ....G 954 368-3900
Oakland Park *(G-11803)*
Fluidra Usa LLC ....E 904 378-0999
Jacksonville *(G-6409)*
Harmsco Inc ....D 561 848-9628
Riviera Beach *(G-15331)*
South West Adventure Team LLC ....G 903 288-4739
Labelle *(G-7323)*
Yauchler Properties LLC ....F 863 662-5570
Winter Haven *(G-19369)*

SWIMMING POOL SPLY STORES

Jacks Magic Products Inc ....F 727 536-4500
Largo *(G-7985)*
South West Adventure Team LLC ....G 903 288-4739
Labelle *(G-7323)*
Tricounty Chemical Co ....G 407 682-3550
Apopka *(G-192)*

SWIMMING POOLS, EQPT & SPLYS: Wholesalers

South West Adventure Team LLC ....G....... 903 288-4739
Labelle *(G-7323)*
Superior Swim Systems Inc ....G....... 239 566-2060
Naples *(G-11428)*

SWITCHBOARD APPARATUS, EXC INSTRUMENTS

Siemens Industry Inc ....D....... 954 436-8848
Pembroke Pines *(G-14059)*

SWITCHES

S A Microtechnologies LLC ....F....... 954 973-6166
Pompano Beach *(G-14839)*

SWITCHES: Electric Power

Resa Pwr Slutions Plant Cy LLC ....F....... 813 752-6550
Plant City *(G-14461)*

SWITCHES: Electric Power, Exc Snap, Push Button, Etc

Entech Controls Corp ....G....... 954 613-2971
Miami *(G-9528)*
Powerficient LLC ....E....... 800 320-2535
Fort Lauderdale *(G-4172)*

SWITCHES: Electronic

Mini Circuits Lab Inc ....D....... 305 558-6381
Hialeah *(G-5519)*
Molex LLC ....F....... 727 521-2700
Pinellas Park *(G-14370)*

SWITCHES: Electronic Applications

International Specialists Inc ....G....... 813 631-8643
Lutz *(G-8392)*

SWITCHES: Flow Actuated, Electrical

Malema Engineering Corporation ....F....... 561 995-0595
Boca Raton *(G-606)*

SWITCHES: Solenoid

Standard Technology Inc ....F....... 386 671-7406
Ormond Beach *(G-13402)*

SWITCHES: Time, Electrical Switchgear Apparatus

Miami Switchgear Company ....G....... 786 336-5783
Miami *(G-10013)*

SWITCHGEAR & SWITCHBOARD APPARATUS

ABB Enterprise Software Inc ....C....... 954 752-6700
Coral Springs *(G-2211)*
ABB Inc ....D....... 407 732-2000
Lake Mary *(G-7396)*
ABB Inc ....D....... 305 471-0844
Miami *(G-9053)*
Control Solutions Inc ....F....... 813 247-2136
Tampa *(G-17553)*
Evolution Intrcnnect Systems I ....F....... 954 217-6223
Davie *(G-2521)*
Gas Turbine Efficiency LLC ....E....... 407 304-5200
Orlando *(G-12772)*
Hughes Corporation ....F....... 954 755-7111
Coral Springs *(G-2256)*
J B Nottingham & Co Inc ....E....... 386 873-2990
Deland *(G-2986)*
Kemco Industries LLC ....D....... 407 322-1230
Sanford *(G-16077)*
Lextm3 Systems LLC ....F....... 954 888-1024
Davie *(G-2546)*
Motor Protection Electronics ....F....... 407 299-3825
Apopka *(G-163)*
Rapid Switch Systems LLC ....G....... 941 720-7380
Bradenton *(G-1103)*
TESS LLC ....F....... 954 583-6262
Fort Lauderdale *(G-4278)*

SYNCHROS

Miramar Mrmids Synchro Team LL ....G....... 954 646-6350
Miramar *(G-11017)*

SYNTHETIC RESIN FINISHED PRDTS, NEC

County Plastics Corp ....G....... 954 971-9205
Pompano Beach *(G-14649)*
Fellowship Enterprises Inc ....G....... 727 726-5997
Safety Harbor *(G-15493)*
Octal Ventures Inc ....F....... 727 526-9288
Pinellas Park *(G-14373)*
Petroleum Containment Inc ....E....... 904 358-1700
Jacksonville *(G-6669)*

SYRUPS, FLAVORING, EXC DRINK

H & H Products Company ....E....... 407 299-5410
Orlando *(G-12793)*
Pinzon Caramel Syrup ....G....... 305 591-2472
Miami *(G-10165)*

SYSTEMS ENGINEERING: Computer Related

R4 Integration Inc ....E....... 850 226-6913
Fort Walton Beach *(G-4825)*
Rapid Composites LLC ....G....... 941 322-6647
Sarasota *(G-16284)*

SYSTEMS INTEGRATION SVCS

Diversfied Mtl Specialists Inc ....G....... 941 244-0935
North Venice *(G-11757)*
Trx Integration Inc ....F....... 727 797-4707
Belleair *(G-361)*
UDC Usa Inc ....E....... 813 281-0200
Tampa *(G-18211)*

SYSTEMS INTEGRATION SVCS: Local Area Network

Akuwa Solutions Group Inc ....F....... 941 343-9947
Sarasota *(G-16337)*
Techcodes LLC ....G....... 321 529-4122
Titusville *(G-18467)*

SYSTEMS SOFTWARE DEVELOPMENT SVCS

5dt Inc ....E....... 407 734-5377
Orlando *(G-12420)*
Bca Technologies Inc ....F....... 407 659-0653
Maitland *(G-8459)*
It Labs LLC ....D....... 310 490-6142
Palm Beach Gardens *(G-13598)*
Itelecom USA Inc ....G....... 305 557-4660
Weston *(G-19143)*

TABLE OR COUNTERTOPS, PLASTIC LAMINATED

Cabinet Cnnction of Trsure Cas ....E....... 772 621-4882
Port Saint Lucie *(G-15095)*
Front of House Inc ....E....... 305 757-7940
Miami *(G-9599)*
Global Stone Collection LLC ....E....... 772 467-1924
Fort Pierce *(G-4700)*

TABLE TOPS: Porcelain Enameled

Roden International Inc ....F....... 954 929-1900
Hollywood *(G-5902)*

TABLECLOTHS & SETTINGS

Bust Out Promotions LLC ....G....... 561 305-8313
Pompano Beach *(G-14626)*

TABLETS & PADS

3nstar Inc ....F....... 786 233-7011
Doral *(G-3216)*

TABLETS & PADS: Book & Writing, Made From Purchased Material

Peter T Amann ....G....... 561 848-2770
West Palm Beach *(G-18995)*

TAGS & LABELS: Paper

American Label Group Inc ....F....... 386 274-5234
Daytona Beach *(G-2623)*
Force Imaging Group LLC ....G....... 888 406-2120
Wesley Chapel *(G-18747)*
Nadco Tapes & Labels Inc ....E....... 941 751-6693
Sarasota *(G-16263)*
Passion Labels & Packaging ....E....... 941 312-5003
Sarasota *(G-16272)*
Prosegur Eas Usa LLC ....F....... 561 900-2744
Deerfield Beach *(G-2897)*

TAGS: Paper, Blank, Made From Purchased Paper

Auto Tag of America Inc ....D....... 941 739-8841
Bradenton *(G-992)*

TALLOW: Animal

Griffin Industries LLC ....E....... 813 626-1135
Tampa *(G-17729)*
Kane-Miller Corp ....G....... 941 346-2003
Sarasota *(G-16481)*

TANK COMPONENTS: Military, Specialized

C4 Advnced Tctical Systems LLC ....D....... 407 206-3886
Orlando *(G-12541)*
Florida Ordnance Corporation ....F....... 954 493-8691
Fort Lauderdale *(G-4001)*

TANK TOWERS: Metal Plate

Vertarib Inc ....E....... 877 815-8610
West Palm Beach *(G-19078)*

TANKS & OTHER TRACKED VEHICLE CMPNTS

Aba-Con Inc ....F....... 321 567-4967
Titusville *(G-18408)*
Clogic LLC ....G....... 860 324-2227
Ponte Vedra Beach *(G-14936)*
Fidelity Manufacturing LLC ....E....... 352 414-4700
Ocala *(G-11940)*
Memco Inc ....E....... 352 241-2302
Bushnell *(G-1319)*

TANKS: Concrete

Heralpin Usa Inc ....G....... 305 218-0174
Doral *(G-3379)*
Precon Corporation ....C....... 352 332-1200
Newberry *(G-11559)*

TANKS: Fuel, Including Oil & Gas, Metal Plate

Dl Myers Corp ....F....... 609 698-8800
Jupiter *(G-7024)*
Envirovault LLC ....F....... 904 354-1858
Jacksonville *(G-6368)*
Fuel Tanks To Go LLC ....G....... 865 604-4726
Ocala *(G-11950)*
Midwest Mtal Fbrction Cstm Rll ....E....... 317 769-6489
North Fort Myers *(G-11599)*
RDS Manufacturing Inc ....C....... 850 584-6898
Perry *(G-14310)*
Staysealed Inc ....G....... 866 978-2973
Lakeland *(G-7805)*

TANKS: Lined, Metal

Keller-Nglillis Design Mfg Inc ....F....... 727 733-4111
Dunedin *(G-3582)*

TANKS: Plastic & Fiberglass

Bucket Company LLC ....G....... 786 473-6484
Miami *(G-9282)*
Dura-Weld Inc ....G....... 561 586-0180
Lake Worth Beach *(G-7611)*
Industrial Cmpsite Systems LLC ....F....... 863 646-8551
Lakeland *(G-7710)*
Tiki Water Sports Inc ....G....... 305 852-9298
Key Largo *(G-7175)*
Tuflex Manufacturing Co ....E....... 954 781-0605
Pompano Beach *(G-14895)*
Waterbrick International Inc ....G....... 877 420-9283
Windermere *(G-19250)*

TANKS: Standard Or Custom Fabricated, Metal Plate

Aly Fabrication Inc...G... 724 898-2990
Saint Augustine *(G-15515)*
American Stainless & Alum Pdts...G... 423 472-4832
Kissimmee *(G-7219)*
ARC-Rite Inc...E... 386 325-3523
Jacksonville *(G-6165)*
Modern Welding Company Fla Inc...D... 407 843-1270
Orlando *(G-12975)*
Ring Power Corporation...E... 904 354-1858
Jacksonville *(G-6725)*
Southern Mfg & Fabrication LLC...F... 407 894-8851
Sanford *(G-16119)*
Specialty Tank and Eqp Co...G... 904 353-8761
Jacksonville *(G-6804)*
Sunshine Marine Tanks Inc...G... 305 805-9898
Medley *(G-8733)*
TTI Holdings Inc...G... 813 623-2675
Tampa *(G-18208)*

TANKS: Storage, Farm, Metal Plate

Nelson and Affiliates Inc...F... 352 316-5641
Gainesville *(G-4970)*

TANKS: Water, Metal Plate

Dixie Tank Company...E... 904 781-9500
Jacksonville *(G-6322)*
Durapoly Industries Inc...G... 352 622-3455
Silver Springs *(G-16781)*
Krausz Usa Inc...F... 352 509-3600
Ocala *(G-11977)*
Wes Industries Inc...F... 941 371-7617
Sarasota *(G-16637)*

TANNERIES: Leather

Sebring Custom Tanning Inc...G... 863 655-1600
Sebring *(G-16707)*

TAPE DRIVES

Quality Contract Mfg Svcs LLC...F... 941 355-7787
Sarasota *(G-16280)*

TAPES, ADHESIVE: MedicaL

Advanced Prof Surgical Svcs...G... 786 326-0576
Miami *(G-9076)*

TAPES: Coated Fiberglass, Pipe Sealing Or Insulating

Access Able Technologies Inc...G... 407 834-2999
Winter Springs *(G-19465)*
RSR Industrial Coatings Inc...F... 863 537-1110
Bartow *(G-332)*
Urecon Systems Inc...C... 321 638-2364
Winter Park *(G-19455)*

TAPES: Fabric

Nadco Tapes & Labels Inc...E... 941 751-6693
Sarasota *(G-16263)*

TAPES: Pressure Sensitive

Intertape Polymer Corp...C... 888 898-7834
Sarasota *(G-16469)*
Intertape Polymer Corp...F... 813 621-8410
Tampa *(G-17791)*
Ipg (us) Holdings Inc...D... 941 727-5788
Sarasota *(G-16471)*
Ipg (us) Inc...G... 941 727-5788
Sarasota *(G-16472)*
Sunshine Ltd Tape & Label Spc...F... 561 832-9656
West Palm Beach *(G-19049)*

TAPES: Pressure Sensitive, Rubber

Florida Tape & Labels Inc...F... 941 921-5788
Sarasota *(G-16438)*

TAPES: Tie, Woven Or Braided

Tie Collection LLC...G... 305 323-1420
Vero Beach *(G-18671)*

TAPES: Zipper

Lg-TEC Corporation...G... 305 770-4005
Hollywood *(G-5859)*

TAPS

Widell Industries Inc...D... 800 237-5963
Port Richey *(G-15079)*

TAR

Ad-Tar...G... 561 732-2055
Boynton Beach *(G-872)*
Tar Building LLC...G... 407 896-7252
Orlando *(G-13240)*

TARGET DRONES

Censys Technologies Corp...F... 850 321-2278
Daytona Beach *(G-2640)*
Drones Shop LLC...G... 772 224-8118
Stuart *(G-16933)*
Sunstate Uav LLC...F... 904 580-4828
Saint Augustine *(G-15624)*
Working Drones Inc...G... 904 647-4511
Jacksonville *(G-6929)*

TARPAULINS

Aer-Flo Canvas Products Inc...D... 941 747-4151
Bradenton *(G-984)*
Cosner Manufacturing LLC...F... 863 676-2579
Lake Wales *(G-7506)*
Texene LLC...F... 305 200-5001
Miami Lakes *(G-10867)*

TEETHING RINGS: Rubber

Babbala LLC...G... 844 869-5747
Boca Raton *(G-440)*

TELECOMMUNICATION EQPT REPAIR SVCS, EXC TELEPHONES

Tridor Group Inc...F... 786 707-2241
Miami *(G-10506)*
Wintel...F... 407 834-1188
Longwood *(G-8351)*

TELECOMMUNICATION SYSTEMS & EQPT

Antennas For Cmmnctons Ocala F...E... 352 687-4121
Ocala *(G-11876)*
Avaya Inc...G... 239 498-2737
Bonita Springs *(G-815)*
Avaya Inc...C... 305 264-7021
Miami *(G-9193)*
Black Box Corporation...G... 407 276-3171
Orlando *(G-12520)*
Cellphone Parts Express LLC...F... 954 635-5525
Hallandale Beach *(G-5177)*
Ciao Group Inc...E... 347 560-5040
Boca Raton *(G-479)*
Communication Eqp & Engrg Co...F... 863 357-0798
Okeechobee *(G-12174)*
Communications Labs Inc...F... 321 701-9000
Melbourne *(G-8794)*
Converlogic Inter LLC...G... 786 623-4747
Doral *(G-3305)*
Coppercom Inc...D... 561 322-4000
Boca Raton *(G-489)*
Coretek Industries Inc...G... 321 385-2860
Titusville *(G-18425)*
Dasan Zhone Solutions Inc...G... 305 789-6680
Miami *(G-9436)*
Eci Telecom Inc...E... 954 772-3070
Fort Lauderdale *(G-3960)*
Hemco Industries Inc...F... 305 769-0606
North Miami *(G-11641)*
J I S Associates...G... 321 777-6829
Satellite Beach *(G-16652)*
L3harris Technologies Inc...E... 321 727-4255
Palm Bay *(G-13519)*
L3harris Technologies Inc...E... 321 984-0782
Melbourne *(G-8868)*
L3harris Technologies Inc...G... 321 727-9100
Melbourne *(G-8870)*
Monroe Cable LLC...D... 941 429-8484
North Port *(G-11744)*
Primal Innovation Tech LLC...F... 407 558-9366
Tampa *(G-18010)*
Raytheon Company...C... 310 647-9438
Largo *(G-8036)*
Recall Technologies Inc...G... 321 952-4422
Palm Bay *(G-13530)*
Select Engineered Systems Inc...E... 305 823-5410
Hialeah *(G-5613)*
Tellabs International Inc...E... 954 492-0120
Fort Lauderdale *(G-4277)*
Touchpoint Group Holdings Inc...G... 305 420-6640
Miami *(G-10496)*
Wintel...F... 407 834-1188
Longwood *(G-8351)*

TELECOMMUNICATIONS CARRIERS & SVCS: Wired

Ciao Group Inc...E... 347 560-5040
Boca Raton *(G-479)*

TELECOMMUNICATIONS CARRIERS & SVCS: Wireless

Eng Group LLC...G... 954 323-2024
Fort Lauderdale *(G-3972)*
First Communications Inc...D... 850 668-7990
Tallahassee *(G-17251)*

TELEGRAPH EQPT WHOLESALERS

Engineered Air Systems Inc...F... 813 881-9555
Tampa *(G-17641)*

TELEMARKETING BUREAUS

Superior Group Companies Inc...A... 727 397-9611
Seminole *(G-16764)*

TELEMETERING EQPT

L3 Technologies Inc...G... 850 678-9444
Eglin A F B *(G-3640)*
L3 Technologies Inc...G... 305 371-7039
Fort Lauderdale *(G-4092)*
L3 Technologies Inc...G... 941 377-5562
Sarasota *(G-16485)*

TELEPHONE ANSWERING SVCS

US Communications Industries...E... 772 468-7477
Fort Pierce *(G-4767)*

TELEPHONE CENTRAL OFFICE EQPT: Dial Or Manual

Cleartel Voice and Data LLC...G... 239 220-5545
Fort Myers *(G-4397)*

TELEPHONE EQPT INSTALLATION

Tier5 Technical Services...G... 904 435-3484
Jacksonville *(G-6855)*

TELEPHONE EQPT: Modems

Motorola Solutions Inc...G... 407 562-4000
Lake Mary *(G-7437)*

TELEPHONE EQPT: NEC

CCM Clllar Cnnection Miami Inc...E... 305 406-1656
Doral *(G-3295)*
Cyipcom Inc...G... 954 727-2500
Oakland Park *(G-11794)*
L3harris Technologies Inc...B... 321 727-9100
Melbourne *(G-8865)*
Medtel Services LLC...E... 941 753-5000
Palmetto *(G-13812)*
Networks Assets LLC...F... 954 334-1390
Weston *(G-19153)*
Precision Comm Svcs Inc...C... 813 238-1000
Tampa *(G-18005)*
Pss Communications Inc...F... 408 496-3330
Sun City Center *(G-17071)*
Siemens Corporation...G... 407 736-5629
Orlando *(G-13182)*
Sk Worldwide LLC...G... 786 360-4842
Surfside *(G-17206)*
Steve Baie Enterprises Inc...G... 407 822-3997
Apopka *(G-188)*
Tier5 Technical Services...G... 904 435-3484
Jacksonville *(G-6855)*

TELEPHONE STATION EQPT & PARTS: Wire

Altanet Corporation .... G 786 228-5758
Miami *(G-9123)*
Smiths Interconnect Inc .... C 813 901-7200
Tampa *(G-18111)*

TELEPHONE SVCS

Cyipcom Inc .... G 954 727-2500
Oakland Park *(G-11794)*
Telephony Partners LLC .... E 813 769-4690
Tampa *(G-18181)*

TELEPHONE: Fiber Optic Systems

Adcon Telemetry Inc .... G 561 989-5309
Boca Raton *(G-398)*
American Data Supply Inc .... F 866 650-3282
Clearwater *(G-1579)*
Arden Photonics LLC .... F 727 478-2651
Clearwater *(G-1588)*
Florida Veex Inc .... F 727 442-6677
Largo *(G-7952)*
Multicore Photonics Inc .... F 407 325-7800
Orlando *(G-12985)*
Nextera Fibernet LLC .... D 866 787-2637
Juno Beach *(G-6981)*
Photon Towers Inc .... G 305 235-7337
Miami *(G-10160)*
Prime Meridian Trading Corp .... G 954 727-2152
Sunrise *(G-17161)*
Victus Capital Enterprises Inc .... E 727 442-6677
Saint Petersburg *(G-15954)*
Wireless Coverage Group Inc .... G 561 429-5032
Hobe Sound *(G-5731)*
Zhone Technologies Inc .... G 510 777-7151
Seminole *(G-16773)*

TELEPHONE: Headsets

Truvoice Telecom Inc .... G 888 448-5556
Tampa *(G-18205)*

TELEPHONE: Sets, Exc Cellular Radio

Anuva Manufacturing Svcs Inc .... E 321 821-4900
Melbourne *(G-8768)*
Milsav LLC .... G 407 556-5055
Orlando *(G-12972)*
Prepaid Solutions LLC .... F 786 257-2714
Miami *(G-10188)*

TELEPHONES: Sound Powered, Without Battery

Hose-Mccann Telephone Co Inc .... E 954 429-1110
Deerfield Beach *(G-2845)*

TELEVISION BROADCASTING & COMMUNICATIONS EQPT

Balsys Technology Group Inc .... G 407 656-3719
Winter Garden *(G-19253)*
Black News Channel LLC .... D 844 262-3968
Tallahassee *(G-17228)*
Cybercellulars Inc .... G 407 608-7888
Orlando *(G-12641)*
Florical Systems Inc .... E 352 372-8326
Gainesville *(G-4920)*
International Sound Corp .... D 305 556-1000
Hialeah *(G-5456)*
Nahuel Trading Corp .... F 305 999-9944
Miami *(G-10059)*
RES-Net Microwave Inc .... E 727 530-9555
Clearwater *(G-1858)*

TELEVISION: Closed Circuit Eqpt

Flagship Marine Inc .... G 772 781-4242
Stuart *(G-16940)*
Keytroller LLC .... F 813 877-4500
Tampa *(G-17823)*

TELEVISION: Monitors

Monroe Cable LLC .... D 941 429-8484
North Port *(G-11744)*

TEMPERING: Metal

American Metal Processors Inc .... F 386 754-9367
Lake City *(G-7347)*

TEMPORARY RELIEF SVCS

Waterbrick International Inc .... G 877 420-9283
Windermere *(G-19250)*

TENTS: All Materials

Ae Tent LLC .... E 305 691-0191
Miami *(G-9079)*
Economy Tent International Inc .... D 305 691-0191
Miami *(G-9500)*
M & N Capital Enterprises LLC .... F 800 865-5064
Tampa *(G-17868)*
Uts Systems LLC .... G 850 226-4301
Fort Walton Beach *(G-4837)*

TERMINAL BOARDS

Etco Incorporated .... C 941 756-8426
Bradenton *(G-1039)*

TEST BORING, METAL MINING

Allied Metals LLC .... F 305 635-3360
Miami *(G-9117)*

TESTERS: Battery

Alber Corp .... D 954 377-7101
Sunrise *(G-17086)*

TESTERS: Environmental

Clearwater Engineering Inc .... G 727 573-2210
Clearwater *(G-1627)*
F & J Specialty Products Inc .... F 352 680-1177
Ocala *(G-11939)*
Lindorm Inc .... F 305 888-0762
Miami Springs *(G-10893)*
Professional Laboratories Inc .... E 954 384-4446
Weston *(G-19161)*
Sun Electronic Systems Inc .... F 321 383-9400
Titusville *(G-18466)*

TESTERS: Physical Property

Giebner Enterprises Inc .... F 727 520-1200
Saint Petersburg *(G-15792)*
St Acquisitions LLC .... G 941 753-1095
Sarasota *(G-16603)*

TESTERS: Spark Plug

Awl Manufacturing Inc .... G 239 643-5780
Naples *(G-11178)*

TESTERS: Water, Exc Indl Process

Mydor Industries Inc .... G 954 927-1140
Dania *(G-2453)*
Sea Gear Corporation .... G 321 728-9116
Melbourne *(G-8929)*

TESTING SVCS

Testmaxx Services Corporation .... F 954 946-7100
Pompano Beach *(G-14886)*

TEXTILE & APPAREL SVCS

Royal Tees Inc .... F 941 366-0056
Sarasota *(G-16564)*

TEXTILE FABRICATORS

Emerald Coast Fabrication .... G 850 235-1174
Panama City *(G-13899)*
Fluid Wings LLC .... F 888 245-5843
Deland *(G-2978)*
Gail P Scherer DBA/Flag Lady O .... G 941 926-9460
Sarasota *(G-16446)*
Paradigm Parachute and Defense .... F 928 580-9013
Pensacola *(G-14220)*
South Florida Cutting .... F 305 693-6711
Hialeah *(G-5625)*

TEXTILE FINISHING: Chemical Coating Or Treating, Narrow

Colortone Inc .... E 954 455-0200
Hallandale Beach *(G-5178)*

TEXTILE FINISHING: Dyeing, Broadwoven, Cotton

Arca Knitting Inc .... D 305 836-0155
Hialeah *(G-5303)*
Bam Enterprises Inc .... E 850 469-8872
Pensacola *(G-14096)*

TEXTILE: Finishing, Cotton Broadwoven

Armen Co Inc .... D 305 206-1601
Plantation *(G-14490)*
Colortone Inc .... E 954 455-0200
Hallandale Beach *(G-5178)*

TEXTILE: Finishing, Raw Stock NEC

Armen Co Inc .... D 305 206-1601
Plantation *(G-14490)*
Lance Lashelle .... G 425 820-8888
Boca Raton *(G-594)*
Technifinish Inc .... F 727 576-5955
Clearwater *(G-1911)*

TEXTILE: Goods, NEC

Good Chance Inc .... G 754 263-2792
Pembroke Pines *(G-14037)*
Lahia America Corp .... F 305 254-6212
Miami *(G-9851)*
Vintage Fashion .... G 786 631-4048
Hialeah *(G-5680)*
White Horse Fashion Cuisine .... G 561 847-4549
Wellington *(G-18739)*

TEXTILES: Jute & Flax Prdts

Apparel Industries .... G 786 362-5958
Doral *(G-3252)*
Divas Fashion .... G 786 717-7039
Miami *(G-9472)*

TEXTILES: Linen Fabrics

Hamburg House Inc .... E 305 557-9913
Hialeah *(G-5442)*
Harbor Linen LLC .... D 305 805-8085
Medley *(G-8661)*
Niba Designs Inc .... F 305 456-6230
Hollywood *(G-5883)*

TEXTILES: Recovering Textile Fibers From Clippings & Rags

Yesil Inc .... F 516 858-0244
Boca Raton *(G-796)*

THEATRICAL SCENERY

Themeworks Incorporated .... C 386 454-7500
High Springs *(G-5702)*

THERMOMETERS: Medical, Digital

7 Holdings Group LLC .... E 754 200-1365
Doral *(G-3217)*
Oculus Surgical Inc .... E 772 236-2622
Port St Lucie *(G-15177)*
Potenza Services Inc .... G 305 400-4938
Miami *(G-10180)*
Sanomedics Inc .... G 305 433-7814
Boca Raton *(G-701)*

THERMOPLASTIC MATERIALS

Dj Plastics Inc .... G 407 656-6677
Apopka *(G-131)*
Plastic and Products Mktg LLC .... F 352 867-8078
Ocala *(G-12028)*
T S E Industries Inc .... E 727 540-1368
Clearwater *(G-1901)*

THERMOSETTING MATERIALS

Preform LLC .... F 888 826-5161
Elkton *(G-3650)*
Pro Poly of America Inc .... G 352 629-1414
Ocala *(G-12032)*

THREAD & YARN, RUBBER: Fabric Covered

Garflex Inc .... D 305 436-8915
Doral *(G-3358)*

THREAD: Embroidery

John & Betsy Hovland............G....... 727 449-2032
Clearwater *(G-1744)*

THREAD: Thread, From Manmade Fiber

Florida Thread & Trimming............G....... 954 240-2474
Hialeah *(G-5415)*

TIE SHOPS

Tie Collection LLC............G....... 305 323-1420
Vero Beach *(G-18671)*

TILE: Brick & Structural, Clay

Acme Brick Company............F....... 850 531-0725
Tallahassee *(G-17212)*
American Pavers Consultants............E....... 954 418-0000
Pompano Beach *(G-14592)*
Artistic Paver Mfg Inc............E....... 305 653-7283
Miami *(G-9174)*
Brick Markers USA Inc............F....... 561 842-1338
Mangonia Park *(G-8500)*
Cemex Materials LLC............D....... 941 722-4578
Palmetto *(G-13790)*
Dyadic International USA Inc............G....... 561 743-8333
Jupiter *(G-7028)*
HG Trading Cia Inc............G....... 305 986-5702
Hialeah *(G-5443)*

TILE: Clay, Drain & Structural

James Hardie Building Pdts Inc............D....... 813 478-1758
Plant City *(G-14440)*

TILE: Clay, Roof

Ceramica Verea USA Corp............F....... 305 665-3923
Miami *(G-9342)*
Metro Roof Tile Inc............F....... 863 467-0042
Medley *(G-8690)*
Southeast Gen Contrs Group Inc............F....... 877 407-3535
Port St Lucie *(G-15179)*

TILE: Concrete, Drain

Purifoy Construction LLC............G....... 850 206-2900
Cantonment *(G-1346)*

TILE: Mosaic, Ceramic

Custom Mosaics Inc............G....... 954 610-9436
Sunrise *(G-17113)*
Manotiles LLC............G....... 954 803-3303
Delray Beach *(G-3104)*
Vidrepur of America LLC............F....... 305 468-9008
Miami *(G-10584)*

TILE: Quarry, Clay

Florida Brick and Clay Co Inc............F....... 813 754-1521
Plant City *(G-14430)*

TILE: Stamped Metal, Floor Or Wall

Floridian Title Group Inc............G....... 305 792-4911
Miami *(G-9588)*
John Trent Construction LLC............G....... 904 753-2942
Fernandina Beach *(G-3740)*

TILE: Terrazzo Or Concrete, Precast

E-Stone USA Corp............D....... 863 655-1273
Sebring *(G-16687)*
Herpel Inc............F....... 561 585-5573
West Palm Beach *(G-18894)*

TILE: Wall & Floor, Ceramic

William Byrd & Sons Inc............G....... 786 573-3251
Palmetto Bay *(G-13858)*

TILE: Wall, Ceramic

Colaianni Italian Flr Tile Mfg............G....... 954 321-8244
Fort Lauderdale *(G-3909)*
Precision Ceramics Usa Inc............F....... 727 388-5060
Saint Petersburg *(G-15887)*

TIN

Ashtin Inc............G....... 352 867-1900
Ocala *(G-11880)*
Custom Tin Works LLC............G....... 352 728-1788
Fruitland Park *(G-4864)*
Garrett Tin & Brother Inc............G....... 727 236-5434
Trinity *(G-18486)*
Larrys Extreme Audio Tint LLC............G....... 941 766-8468
Port Charlotte *(G-14987)*
Something In A Tin Inc............G....... 305 785-6891
Miami *(G-10375)*
Tin-Rez Corp Inc............F....... 561 654-3133
Boynton Beach *(G-969)*

TIRE & INNER TUBE MATERIALS & RELATED PRDTS

Elite Wheel Distributors Inc............F....... 813 673-8393
Tampa *(G-17633)*
Eminel Corporation Inc............F....... 407 900-0190
Orlando *(G-12709)*
Noahs MBL Tire Auto Solutions............G....... 904 250-1502
Jacksonville *(G-6638)*
Tire Experts LLC............G....... 305 663-3508
Medley *(G-8735)*

TIRE DEALERS

Fedan Corp............F....... 305 885-5415
Hialeah *(G-5410)*

TIRE RECAPPING & RETREADING

Fedan Corp............F....... 305 885-5415
Hialeah *(G-5410)*

TIRES & INNER TUBES

BF American Business LLC............G....... 561 856-7094
Boca Raton *(G-446)*
BF One LLC............F....... 239 939-5251
Fort Myers *(G-4375)*
BF Weston LLC............D....... 561 844-5528
Weston *(G-19111)*
Db Motoring Group Inc............G....... 305 685-0707
Miami *(G-9439)*
Jacksonville Tire Rescue Inc............F....... 904 783-1296
Jacksonville *(G-6513)*
Rsss 1 LLC............G....... 941 483-3293
Venice *(G-18571)*
S N S Auto Sports LLC............G....... 727 546-2700
Pinellas Park *(G-14386)*
Tbc Retail Group Inc............G....... 702 395-2100
Juno Beach *(G-6984)*

TIRES & TUBES WHOLESALERS

Fedan Corp............F....... 305 885-5415
Hialeah *(G-5410)*
Rhino Tire Usa Llc............F....... 407 777-5598
Orlando *(G-13135)*

TIRES & TUBES, WHOLESALE: Truck

Longs Wheel & Rim Inc............D....... 904 757-3710
Jacksonville *(G-6564)*

TIRES: Auto

Vossen Wheels Inc............F....... 305 463-7778
Doral *(G-3545)*

TIRES: Motorcycle, Pneumatic

Rhino Tire Usa Llc............F....... 407 777-5598
Orlando *(G-13135)*

TIRES: Plastic

Chacho Customs............G....... 239 369-4664
Lehigh Acres *(G-8187)*
Jerae Inc............F....... 954 989-6665
Hollywood *(G-5853)*

TITANIUM MILL PRDTS

Sunrui Ttnium Prcsion Pdts Inc............F....... 727 953-7101
Clearwater *(G-1895)*
Titanium 22 Productions............G....... 310 962-0937
Miami Beach *(G-10720)*
Titanium Dance Challenge LLC............G....... 813 340-0903
Tampa *(G-18189)*
Titanium Development LLC............G....... 407 844-8664
Orlando *(G-13257)*
Titanium Endeavors LLC............G....... 321 728-9732
Melbourne *(G-8963)*
Titanium Fusion Tech LLC............G....... 435 881-5742
Orlando *(G-13258)*
Titanium Gymnastics and Cheerl............G....... 813 659-2204
Plant City *(G-14474)*
Titanium Gynmastics & Cheer............G....... 813 689-2200
Lithia *(G-8224)*
Titanium Integration LLC............G....... 561 775-1898
Palm Beach Gardens *(G-13632)*
Titanium Laser Tech Inc............G....... 956 279-0638
Niceville *(G-11575)*
Titanium Performance LLC............G....... 407 712-5770
Winter Park *(G-19453)*
Titanium Prof Hyraulics............G....... 917 929-5044
Hallandale *(G-5162)*
Titanium Real Estate LLC............G....... 863 808-0445
Lakeland *(G-7822)*
Titanium Tech Corp............G....... 407 912-9126
Orlando *(G-13259)*

TOBACCO & PRDTS, WHOLESALE: Cigarettes

International Vapor Group LLC............D....... 305 824-4027
Miami Lakes *(G-10799)*

TOBACCO & PRDTS, WHOLESALE: Cigars

J C Newman Cigar Co............D....... 813 248-2124
Tampa *(G-17797)*

TOBACCO & TOBACCO PRDTS WHOLESALERS

Bridge Trading Usa LLC............F....... 877 848-0979
Doral *(G-3286)*

TOBACCO: Chewing & Snuff

Drew Estate LLC............E....... 786 581-1800
Miami *(G-9485)*
Jti Duty-Free USA Inc............G....... 305 377-3922
Miami *(G-9810)*

TOBACCO: Cigarettes

Commonwealth Brands Inc............C....... 800 481-5814
Fort Lauderdale *(G-3912)*
Dosal Tobacco Corporation............E....... 305 685-2949
Opa Locka *(G-12309)*
Flavana LLC............G....... 561 285-7034
Pompano Beach *(G-14699)*
Healthier Choices MGT Corp............C....... 305 600-5004
Hollywood *(G-5836)*
R J Reynolds Tobacco Company............D....... 772 873-6955
Port Saint Lucie *(G-15134)*
Soleil Capital LP............D....... 954 715-7001
Fort Lauderdale *(G-4242)*
V2 Cigs............F....... 305 517-1149
Miami Beach *(G-10725)*
V2 Cigs............E....... 305 240-6387
Miami *(G-10561)*
Vapor Group Inc............F....... 954 792-8450
Miami *(G-10567)*
Vaprzone LLC............G....... 941 882-4841
Venice *(G-18584)*
Vector Group Ltd............C....... 305 579-8000
Miami *(G-10571)*
Vgr Holding LLC............D....... 305 579-8000
Miami *(G-10576)*

TOBACCO: Cigars

Consolidated Cigr Holdings Inc............A....... 954 772-9000
Fort Lauderdale *(G-3915)*
Domrey Cigar Ltd Company............G....... 941 360-8200
Pinellas Park *(G-14344)*
Dosal Tobacco Corporation............E....... 305 685-2949
Opa Locka *(G-12309)*
Havana Dreams LLC............G....... 305 322-7599
Miami *(G-9690)*
Itg Cigars Inc............D....... 954 772-9000
Fort Lauderdale *(G-4071)*
J C Newman Cigar Co............D....... 813 248-2124
Tampa *(G-17797)*
La Luna Ltd............G....... 305 644-0444
Miami *(G-9842)*
Luis Martinez Cigar Co............G....... 800 822-4427
Tampa *(G-17863)*
Moore & Bode Group LLC............G....... 786 615-9389
Homestead *(G-5984)*
New Century............G....... 305 670-3510
Miami *(G-10066)*

South Beach Cigar Factory LLC............G....... 786 216-7475
Miami Beach *(G-10714)*
Swisher International Inc.....................G....... 904 353-4311
Jacksonville *(G-6830)*

TOBACCO: Smoking

Accendo Tobacco LLC...........................G....... 305 407-2222
Miami *(G-9060)*
Commonwealth Brands Inc..................C....... 800 481-5814
Fort Lauderdale *(G-3912)*
Eternal Smoke Inc...............................G....... 407 984-5090
Orlando *(G-12718)*
Lakay Vita LLC......................................G....... 786 985-7552
Hallandale Beach *(G-5196)*
Swisher Intl Group Inc..........................A....... 904 353-4311
Jacksonville *(G-6831)*

TOILET PREPARATIONS

Cosmetic Creations Inc........................G....... 904 261-7831
Fernandina Beach *(G-3733)*
World Perfumes Inc..............................F....... 305 822-0004
Opa Locka *(G-12370)*

TOILETRIES, COSMETICS & PERFUME STORES

Dermazone Solutions Inc......................E....... 727 446-6882
Saint Petersburg *(G-15758)*
Nu Earth Labs LLC................................E....... 727 648-4787
Dunedin *(G-3585)*
Tend Skin International Inc..................F....... 954 382-0800
Davie *(G-2602)*

TOILETRIES, WHOLESALE: Toilet Preparations

Vianny Corporation................................F....... 239 888-4536
Fort Myers *(G-4646)*

TOILETRIES, WHOLESALE: Toiletries

Fresh Brandz LLC..................................G....... 813 880-7110
Tampa *(G-17696)*
T H Stone...G....... 561 361-3966
Boca Raton *(G-741)*
Tend Skin International Inc..................F....... 954 382-0800
Davie *(G-2602)*

TOILETS: Metal

AAA Event Services LLC.......................F....... 386 454-0929
Newberry *(G-11549)*

TOILETS: Portable Chemical, Plastics

Bingham On Site Portables LLC............G....... 813 659-0003
Dover *(G-3555)*

TOMBSTONES: Terrazzo Or Concrete, Precast

Perl Inc...F....... 352 726-2483
Inverness *(G-6095)*

TOOL & DIE STEEL

Defense Stamping & Engineering.........E....... 850 438-6105
Pensacola *(G-14127)*

TOOLS & EQPT: Used With Sporting Arms

Applied Fiber Concepts Inc..................G....... 754 581-2744
Hialeah *(G-5302)*

TOOLS: Carpenters', Including Levels & Chisels, Exc Saws

Conrado Salas Jr LLC...........................G....... 941 587-5919
Sarasota *(G-16393)*
Daves All Around...................................G....... 407 325-6693
Oviedo *(G-13426)*
Just Door Toolz LLC..............................G....... 954 448-6872
Port Saint Lucie *(G-15116)*
Sykleb Inc...G....... 305 303-9391
North Miami *(G-11657)*
Thomas A Glassman LLC.......................G....... 239 822-2219
Naples *(G-11439)*

TOOLS: Hand

ABC Hammers...G....... 708 343-9900
Sarasota *(G-16170)*
Automated Production Eqp Ape............F....... 631 654-1197
Key Largo *(G-7164)*
B & A Manufacturing Co........................E....... 561 848-8648
Riviera Beach *(G-15300)*
Daniels Manufacturing Corp..................C....... 407 855-6161
Orlando *(G-12646)*
Es Manufacturing Inc.............................F....... 727 323-4040
Pinellas Park *(G-14347)*
Florida Knife Co.....................................E....... 941 371-2104
Sarasota *(G-16437)*
Grip Tooling Technologies LLC.............G....... 813 654-6832
Brandon *(G-1161)*
Halex Corporation..................................G....... 239 216-4444
Naples *(G-11275)*
Iron Bridge Tools Inc..............................G....... 954 596-1090
Fort Lauderdale *(G-4066)*
Merit International Entps Inc................E....... 305 635-1011
Miami *(G-9980)*
Micro Jig Inc...G....... 855 747-7233
Winter Park *(G-19425)*
Nasco Industries Inc..............................E....... 954 733-8665
Fort Lauderdale *(G-4131)*
Pettit Tools & Supplies Inc....................F....... 954 781-2640
Pompano Beach *(G-14790)*
Skyo Industries Inc................................E....... 631 586-4702
Ormond Beach *(G-13399)*
Steritool Inc..F....... 904 388-3672
Jacksonville *(G-6813)*
Vs Coatings LLC.....................................F....... 305 677-6224
Miami *(G-10592)*

TOOLS: Hand, Carpet Layers

Quality Carpet...G....... 727 527-1359
Saint Petersburg *(G-15895)*

TOOLS: Hand, Engravers'

Imperial Photoengraving........................G....... 772 924-1731
Stuart *(G-16957)*
Infinite Lasers LLC.................................G....... 850 424-3759
Destin *(G-3195)*

TOOLS: Hand, Jewelers'

Arca LLC..F....... 305 470-1430
Miami *(G-9162)*
Benchmark of Palm Beach.....................G....... 706 258-3553
Palm Beach *(G-13549)*
Frank Bennardello..................................G....... 561 470-4838
Boca Raton *(G-539)*
George Birney Jr.....................................G....... 407 851-5604
Orlando *(G-12783)*
La Perlelle LLC.......................................G....... 941 388-2458
Sarasota *(G-16486)*
Thida Thai Jewelry.................................G....... 561 455-4249
Miami *(G-10473)*
Volpino Corp...F....... 904 264-8808
Orange Park *(G-12413)*

TOOLS: Hand, Masons'

Exit Ten Inc...G....... 407 574-2433
Longwood *(G-8277)*

TOOLS: Hand, Mechanics

Cob Industries Inc..................................G....... 321 723-3200
West Melbourne *(G-18770)*
Mayhew/Bestway LLC............................E....... 631 586-4702
Ormond Beach *(G-13385)*

TOOLS: Hand, Power

Air Turbine Technology Inc....................F....... 561 994-0500
Boca Raton *(G-408)*
Black & Decker (us) Inc.........................G....... 407 657-0474
Orlando *(G-12519)*
Daniels Manufacturing Corp..................C....... 407 855-6161
Orlando *(G-12646)*
Delta Regis Tools Inc.............................E....... 772 465-4302
Fort Pierce *(G-4692)*
Es Manufacturing Inc.............................F....... 727 323-4040
Pinellas Park *(G-14347)*
Fabco-Air Inc..D....... 352 373-3578
Gainesville *(G-4918)*
Laycock Systems Inc.............................F....... 813 248-3555
Tampa *(G-17837)*
Nasco Industries Inc..............................E....... 954 733-8665
Fort Lauderdale *(G-4131)*
Ronnies Welding & Machine..................G....... 305 238-0972
Cutler Bay *(G-2410)*
Tdk Electronics Inc.................................F....... 561 509-7771
Ocean Ridge *(G-12080)*

TOOTHBRUSHES: Exc Electric

Marketshare LLC....................................G....... 631 273-0598
Boca Raton *(G-609)*

TOOTHPASTES, GELS & TOOTHPOWDERS

Lively Company LLC...............................F....... 617 737-1199
Tampa *(G-17851)*

TOPS, DISPENSER OR SHAKER, ETC: Plastic

Proandre Hygiene Systems Inc.............F....... 305 433-3493
Miami *(G-10204)*

TOWELETTES: Premoistened

Med-Nap LLC..F....... 352 796-6020
Brooksville *(G-1249)*
Unico International Trdg Corp...............G....... 561 338-3338
Boca Raton *(G-765)*

TOWELS: Fabric & Nonwoven, Made From Purchased Materials

Beyond White Spa LLC..........................G....... 866 399-8867
Miami *(G-9242)*

TOWELS: Indl

Alcee Industries Inc...............................F....... 407 468-4573
Orlando *(G-12448)*

TOWERS, SECTIONS: Transmission, Radio & Television

Aluma Tower Company Inc....................E....... 772 567-3423
Vero Beach *(G-18592)*
Aluma Tower Company Inc....................F....... 772 567-3423
Vero Beach *(G-18593)*
Chism Manufacturing Svcs LLC............F....... 941 896-9671
Sarasota *(G-16190)*
Heights Tower Systems Inc....................G....... 850 455-1210
Pensacola *(G-14171)*
Locus Location Systems LLC................E....... 321 727-3077
Melbourne *(G-8878)*
Nextower LLC...G....... 407 907-7984
Gainesville *(G-4972)*
Richland Towers Inc..............................E....... 813 286-4140
Tampa *(G-18056)*

TOWERS: Bubble, Cooling, Fractionating, Metal Plate

Eileen Ruth Bendis..................................G....... 954 565-5470
Fort Lauderdale *(G-3966)*

TOWING BARS & SYSTEMS

Pauls Twing Dsptch Cntl Fla I...............G....... 407 323-4446
Sanford *(G-16100)*

TOYS

Basic Fun Inc..D....... 561 997-8901
Boca Raton *(G-442)*
Correll Services Inc................................G....... 561 358-6952
Royal Palm Beach *(G-15463)*
Daytona Magic Inc..................................G....... 386 252-6767
Daytona Beach *(G-2655)*
Dennys Electronics Inc...........................E....... 941 485-5400
North Venice *(G-11756)*
Florida Pool Products Inc.......................E....... 727 531-8913
Clearwater *(G-1690)*
George & Company LLC.........................F....... 239 949-3650
Bonita Springs *(G-833)*
Getfpv LLC..E....... 941 444-0021
Sarasota *(G-16449)*
Groovy Toys LLC.....................................G....... 772 878-0790
Port Saint Lucie *(G-15111)*
GT Scale Models Inc...............................G....... 305 310-8998
Key Biscayne *(G-7158)*
Herbko Inc...G....... 305 932-3572
Aventura *(G-273)*

Jazwares LLC ....D.... 954 845-0800
Sunrise *(G-17135)*
JC Toys Group Inc ....F.... 305 592-3541
Doral *(G-3401)*
KNex Industries Inc ....C.... 215 997-7722
Boca Raton *(G-589)*
KNex Ltd Partnership Group ....D.... 215 997-7722
Boca Raton *(G-590)*
Law Offces Rbecca A Beddow LLC ....G.... 516 671-6566
Naples *(G-11308)*
Leisure Activities Usa LLC ....G.... 727 417-7128
Saint Petersburg *(G-15838)*
Lumberstak Inc ....G.... 386 546-3745
Palatka *(G-13486)*
Lumenier Holdco LLC ....G.... 941 444-0021
Sarasota *(G-16491)*
Majic Wheels Corp ....G.... 239 313-5672
Fort Myers *(G-4521)*
Never Wrong Toys & Games LLC ....G.... 941 371-0909
Sarasota *(G-16524)*
Pcp Group LLC ....G.... 727 388-7171
Clearwater *(G-1827)*
Performance Aircraft Unlimited ....G.... 808 782-7171
Orlando *(G-13064)*
Scale Models Arts & Tech ....F.... 305 949-1706
North Miami Beach *(G-11704)*
Schick LLC ....F.... 718 810-3804
Miami *(G-10311)*
System Enterprises LLC ....G.... 888 898-3600
Clearwater *(G-1899)*

TOYS & HOBBY GOODS & SPLYS, WHOLESALE: Amusement Goods

Daytona Magic Inc ....G.... 386 252-6767
Daytona Beach *(G-2655)*

TOYS & HOBBY GOODS & SPLYS, WHOLESALE: Toys & Games

Jazwares LLC ....D.... 954 845-0800
Sunrise *(G-17135)*
Safari Programs Inc ....D.... 305 621-1000
Jacksonville *(G-6745)*

TOYS, HOBBY GOODS & SPLYS WHOLESALERS

Hasbro Latin America Inc ....E.... 305 931-3180
Miami *(G-9688)*

TOYS: Dolls, Stuffed Animals & Parts

Baby Abuelita Productions LLC ....G.... 305 662-7320
Miami *(G-9212)*
Basic Fun Inc ....D.... 561 997-8901
Boca Raton *(G-442)*
JC Toys Group Inc ....F.... 305 592-3541
Doral *(G-3401)*
Mascot Factory Inc ....G.... 877 250-2244
Orlando *(G-12952)*

TOYS: Kites

Kgb Kiteboarding Inc ....F.... 904 705-9235
Jacksonville *(G-6536)*
Kite Bum Inc ....G.... 321 267-6393
Titusville *(G-18439)*
Kite Runner LLC ....G.... 305 785-5056
Miami *(G-9824)*
Kite Technology Group LLC ....F.... 407 557-0512
Kissimmee *(G-7266)*
Kite Vn Corporation ....G.... 772 234-3484
Vero Beach *(G-18636)*

TOYS: Video Game Machines

Blingka Inc ....G.... 800 485-6793
Tampa *(G-17475)*

TRADE SHOW ARRANGEMENT SVCS

National Tchncal Cmmunications ....G.... 407 671-7777
Orlando *(G-12991)*

TRAFFIC CONTROL FLAGGING SVCS

L C Acme Barricades ....D.... 904 781-1950
Jacksonville *(G-6548)*

TRAILER COACHES: Automobile

Excalibur Coach ....G.... 407 302-9139
Sanford *(G-16043)*

TRAILERS & PARTS: Boat

Amera Trail Inc ....E.... 407 892-1100
Saint Cloud *(G-15643)*
Boat Master Aluminum Trailers ....G.... 239 768-2224
Fort Myers *(G-4378)*
Bonefish Boats and Trlrs LLC ....G.... 239 707-4656
Cape Coral *(G-1393)*
Caribbean Trailers Corp ....G.... 305 256-1505
Miami *(G-9317)*
EZ Loder Adjstble Boat Trlrs S ....G.... 800 323-8190
Port Saint Lucie *(G-15109)*
Float-On Corporation ....E.... 772 569-4440
Vero Beach *(G-18617)*
Harbor View Boat Trailers ....G.... 941 916-3777
Punta Gorda *(G-15208)*
J & J Marine Service Inc ....G.... 813 741-2190
Saint Petersburg *(G-15820)*
Jdci Enterprises Inc ....E.... 239 768-2292
Fort Myers *(G-4502)*
Magic Tilt Trailer Mfg Co Inc ....E.... 727 535-5561
Clearwater *(G-1769)*
Owens & Sons Marine Inc ....F.... 727 323-1088
Saint Petersburg *(G-15873)*
Rocket International Inc ....G.... 239 275-0880
Cape Coral *(G-1461)*
Rolls Axle Lc ....F.... 813 764-0242
Plant City *(G-14463)*
Thule Inc ....C.... 850 584-3448
Perry *(G-14317)*

TRAILERS & PARTS: Horse

East 46th Auto Sales Inc ....F.... 407 322-3100
Sanford *(G-16039)*
Florida Trailer Ranch LLC ....F.... 904 289-7710
Jacksonville *(G-6404)*

TRAILERS & PARTS: Truck & Semi's

All Amrcan Trlr Connection Inc ....G.... 561 582-1800
Palm Springs *(G-13772)*
Alumne Manufacturing Inc ....G.... 352 748-3229
Wildwood *(G-19190)*
Axxium Engineering LLC ....G.... 786 573-9808
Miami *(G-9204)*
Bt-Twiss Transport LLC ....G.... 866 584-1585
Largo *(G-7915)*
Dills Enterprises LLC ....G.... 941 493-1993
Venice *(G-18542)*
Draggin Trailers Inc ....G.... 352 351-8790
Ocala *(G-11926)*
EZ Truck Services Inc ....F.... 239 728-3022
Alva *(G-88)*
Freight Train Trucking Corp ....G.... 407 509-0611
Saint Cloud *(G-15652)*
Interglobal Capital Inc ....G.... 727 585-1500
Clearwater *(G-1733)*
Nelsons Truck and Trlr Sls LLC ....F.... 352 732-8908
Ocala *(G-12005)*
Pedro Truck Parts & Trailers ....G.... 786 439-8652
Miami *(G-10149)*
Pierce Manufacturing Inc ....D.... 941 748-3900
Bradenton *(G-1097)*
Rolls Rite Trailers Inc ....F.... 850 526-2290
Marianna *(G-8585)*
Terminal Service Company ....C.... 850 739-5702
Tallahassee *(G-17339)*
Thunder Bay Enterprises Inc ....E.... 352 796-9551
Brooksville *(G-1280)*
U-Dump Trailers LLC ....D.... 352 351-8510
Ocala *(G-12065)*
Unique Custom Truck & Trlr LLC ....F.... 305 403-7042
Miami *(G-10531)*
Warren Equipment Inc ....E.... 813 752-5126
Plant City *(G-14477)*

TRAILERS & TRAILER EQPT

A Plus Trailers ....G.... 786 395-0799
Southwest Ranches *(G-16835)*
Central Florida Cstm Trlrs Inc ....E.... 407 851-1144
Orlando *(G-12566)*
Chambers Body Works Inc ....G.... 352 588-3072
Dade City *(G-2425)*
Liles Custom Trailers ....G.... 352 368-2652
Ocala *(G-11985)*

Mbf Industries Inc ....E.... 407 323-9414
Sanford *(G-16084)*
Precision Equipment Co Inc ....G.... 561 689-4400
West Palm Beach *(G-19003)*
Space Coast Industries Inc ....G.... 321 633-9336
Cocoa *(G-2053)*
Ver-Val Enterprises Inc ....F.... 850 244-7931
Fort Walton Beach *(G-4838)*

TRAILERS OR VANS: Horse Transportation, Fifth-Wheel Type

RPM Co ....G.... 352 542-3110
Old Town *(G-12199)*
Shadow Trailers Inc ....E.... 352 529-2190
Williston *(G-19215)*

TRAILERS: Bodies

Loadmaster Alum Boat Trlrs Inc ....E.... 813 689-3096
Tampa *(G-17856)*

TRAILERS: Demountable Cargo Containers

Cepods LLC ....G.... 786 520-1412
Miami Beach *(G-10654)*

TRAILERS: House, Exc Permanent Dwellings

Chariot Eagle Inc ....C.... 623 936-7545
Ocala *(G-11901)*

TRAILERS: Semitrailers, Missile Transportation

Ultimate Cargo Services LLC ....F.... 954 251-1680
Jacksonville *(G-6875)*

TRAILERS: Semitrailers, Truck Tractors

Arnold Manufacturing Inc ....G.... 850 470-9200
Pensacola *(G-14092)*
Globe Trailers Florida Inc ....E.... 941 753-6425
Bradenton *(G-1049)*

TRAILERS: Truck, Chassis

Chassis King LLC ....G.... 727 585-1500
Clearwater *(G-1625)*

TRANSFORMERS: Control

Wired Rite Systems Inc ....F.... 707 838-1122
Sarasota *(G-16643)*

TRANSFORMERS: Distribution

ABB Inc ....D.... 407 732-2000
Lake Mary *(G-7396)*
ABB Inc ....D.... 305 471-0844
Miami *(G-9053)*
Digitrax Inc ....E.... 850 872-9890
Panama City *(G-13893)*
Evolution Intrcnnect Systems I ....F.... 954 217-6223
Davie *(G-2521)*
OHM Americas LLC ....F.... 800 467-7275
Fort Lauderdale *(G-4148)*
Power Quality Intl LLC ....G.... 727 478-7284
Odessa *(G-12141)*
Sunbelt Transformer Ltd ....G.... 305 517-3657
Pompano Beach *(G-14878)*

TRANSFORMERS: Electric

Bright Manufacturing LLC ....G.... 954 603-4950
Fort Lauderdale *(G-3868)*
Manutech Assembly Inc ....G.... 305 888-2800
Miami *(G-9942)*
Nwl Inc ....D.... 800 742-5695
Lake Hamilton *(G-7391)*
Nwl Inc ....C.... 561 848-9009
Riviera Beach *(G-15353)*
Payton America Inc ....F.... 954 428-3326
Deerfield Beach *(G-2884)*

TRANSFORMERS: Electronic

Bocatech Inc ....G.... 954 397-7070
Deerfield Beach *(G-2788)*
Filter Research Corporation ....E.... 321 802-3444
Palm Bay *(G-13512)*
Renco Usa Inc ....F.... 321 637-1000
Miami *(G-10252)*

Vision Engineering Labs ....D....... 727 812-2035
Largo *(G-8076)*

TRANSFORMERS: Florescent Lighting

Robertson Transformer Co ....E....... 708 388-2315
Sarasota *(G-16560)*

TRANSFORMERS: Fluorescent Lighting

Hatch Transformers Inc ....E....... 813 288-8006
Tampa *(G-17746)*

TRANSFORMERS: Furnace, Electric

Solucnes Elctrcas Intgrles LLC ....G....... 305 804-4201
Miami *(G-10373)*

TRANSFORMERS: Instrument

Arteche USA Inc ....F....... 954 438-9499
Miramar *(G-10968)*
Instrument Transformers LLC ....B....... 727 461-9413
Clearwater *(G-1732)*

TRANSFORMERS: Lighting, Street & Airport

Neubert Aero Corp ....G....... 352 345-4828
Brooksville *(G-1256)*

TRANSFORMERS: Power Related

ABB Partners LLC ....F....... 917 843-4430
Palm Beach *(G-13547)*
Central Turbos Corp ....F....... 305 406-3933
Doral *(G-3296)*
Control Solutions Inc ....F....... 813 247-2136
Tampa *(G-17553)*
Discrete Electronics Inc ....G....... 941 575-8700
Punta Gorda *(G-15204)*
Edisonecoenergycom Corporation ....G....... 954 417-5326
Fort Lauderdale *(G-3964)*
Exxelia Usa Inc ....E....... 407 695-6562
Longwood *(G-8279)*
Florida Transformer Inc ....C....... 850 892-2711
Defuniak Springs *(G-2942)*
Gfsf Inc ....G....... 727 478-7284
Odessa *(G-12123)*
Hytronics Corp ....D....... 727 535-0413
Clearwater *(G-1725)*
Inductive Technologies Inc ....F....... 727 536-7861
Clearwater *(G-1731)*
Lextm3 Systems LLC ....F....... 954 888-1024
Davie *(G-2546)*
Miami Transformers Corp ....E....... 305 257-1491
Homestead *(G-5983)*
Spin Magnetics ....E....... 863 676-9333
Lake Wales *(G-7520)*
Technipower LLC ....F....... 954 346-2442
Coral Springs *(G-2321)*

TRANSFORMERS: Specialty

Magnatronix Corporation Inc ....F....... 727 536-7861
Clearwater *(G-1770)*
Ventex Technology Inc ....F....... 561 354-6300
Jupiter *(G-7139)*

TRANSFORMERS: Voltage Regulating

Powerficient LLC ....E....... 800 320-2535
Fort Lauderdale *(G-4172)*

TRANSISTORS

Boca Semiconductor Corporation ....E....... 561 226-8500
Boca Raton *(G-456)*

TRANSPORTATION ARRANGEMENT SVCS, PASSENGER: Airline Ticket

CTI Group Worldwide Svcs Inc ....G....... 954 568-5900
Fort Lauderdale *(G-3922)*

TRANSPORTATION ARRANGEMNT SVCS, PASS: Travel Tour Pkgs, Whol

Mario Kenny ....G....... 786 274-0527
Miami *(G-9949)*

TRANSPORTATION EPQT & SPLYS, WHOL: Aeronautical Eqpt & Splys

Aero-Marine Technologies Inc ....G....... 941 205-5420
Englewood *(G-3658)*
Sky Technics Aviation Sls Inc ....G....... 305 885-7499
Miami *(G-10360)*

TRANSPORTATION EPQT & SPLYS, WHOLESALE: Helicopter Parts

Florida Sncast Helicopters LLC ....F....... 941 355-1525
Sarasota *(G-16214)*

TRANSPORTATION EPQT & SPLYS, WHOLESALE: Marine Crafts/Splys

Keith Eickert Power Pdts LLC ....F....... 386 446-0660
Palm Coast *(G-13700)*
Miami Cordage LLC ....E....... 305 636-3000
Miami *(G-9996)*
Turning Point Propellers Inc ....G....... 904 900-7739
Jacksonville *(G-6871)*

TRANSPORTATION EPQT & SPLYS, WHOLESALE: Nav Eqpt & Splys

L3harris Technologies Inc ....G....... 321 727-4000
Melbourne *(G-8869)*

TRANSPORTATION EPQT/SPLYS, WHOL: Marine Propulsn Mach/Eqpt

E M P Inc ....G....... 772 286-7343
Stuart *(G-16935)*

TRANSPORTATION EQPT & SPLYS WHOLESALERS, NEC

Advanced Air West Palm Bch Inc ....E....... 561 845-8289
Riviera Beach *(G-15294)*
Asrc Aerospace Corp ....C....... 321 867-1462
Kennedy Space Center *(G-7150)*
Cme Arma Inc ....E....... 305 633-1524
Miami *(G-9366)*
Lift Aerospace Corp ....F....... 305 851-5237
Miami *(G-9890)*
Marine Exhaust Systems Inc ....D....... 561 848-1238
Riviera Beach *(G-15346)*
Radiant Power Corp ....C....... 941 739-3200
Sarasota *(G-16281)*
Ultimate Cargo Services LLC ....F....... 954 251-1680
Jacksonville *(G-6875)*
Xl Carts Inc ....G....... 904 277-7111
Fernandina Beach *(G-3751)*

TRANSPORTATION EQUIPMENT, NEC

A Cheaper Shot LLC ....F....... 727 221-3237
Saint Petersburg *(G-15687)*
Agile Cargo Transportation LLC ....F....... 407 747-0812
Jacksonville *(G-6127)*
Andrews 1st Choice Trckg LLC ....G....... 205 703-5717
Jacksonville *(G-6156)*
Bollou Transportation LLC ....F....... 800 548-1768
Miami *(G-9266)*
D & R Delivery Services of Pb ....F....... 561 602-6427
Riviera Beach *(G-15316)*
Lnl Logistics LLC ....G....... 386 977-9276
Deltona *(G-3173)*
Lotus Containers Inc ....G....... 786 590-1056
Miami *(G-9913)*
Sodikart USA ....G....... 561 493-0290
Boynton Beach *(G-960)*
Triumph Transport Inc ....G....... 863 226-7276
Lakeland *(G-7826)*

TRANSPORTATION SVCS, AIR, SCHEDULED: Helicopter Carriers

Heli Aviation Florida LLC ....G....... 941 355-1525
Sarasota *(G-16226)*

TRANSPORTATION SVCS, DEEP SEA: Intercoastal, Freight

Ultimate Cargo Services LLC ....F....... 954 251-1680
Jacksonville *(G-6875)*

TRANSPORTATION SVCS, WATER: Boathouses, Commercial

Arkup Llc ....G....... 786 448-8635
Miami Beach *(G-10644)*

TRANSPORTATION SVCS, WATER: Canal & Intracoastal, Freight

Copaco Inc ....F....... 407 333-3041
Orange City *(G-12374)*

TRANSPORTATION: Air, Scheduled Passenger

Agd Systems Corporation ....G....... 561 722-5561
West Palm Beach *(G-18791)*

TRANSPORTATION: Bus Transit Systems

Amer-Con Corp ....E....... 786 293-8004
Palmetto Bay *(G-13839)*

TRAP ROCK: Dimension

Youngquist Brothers Rock Inc ....D....... 239 267-6000
Fort Myers *(G-4657)*

TRAPS: Animal & Fish, Wire

Aquateko International LLC ....G....... 904 273-7200
Ponte Vedra Beach *(G-14933)*
Ellis Trap and Cage Mfg Inc ....G....... 850 969-1302
Pensacola *(G-14140)*

TRAPS: Animal, Iron Or Steel

Ellis Trap and Cage Mfg Inc ....G....... 850 969-1302
Pensacola *(G-14140)*
H B Sherman Traps Inc ....G....... 850 575-8727
Tallahassee *(G-17272)*

TRAVEL AGENCIES

Mariner International Trvl Inc ....G....... 954 925-4150
Dania *(G-2451)*
On-Board Media Inc ....D....... 305 673-0400
Doral *(G-3450)*
Thalo Assist LLC ....G....... 786 340-6892
Weston *(G-19169)*

TRAVEL TRAILERS & CAMPERS

Big Time Tailgate LLC ....G....... 407 509-5163
Titusville *(G-18414)*
East 46th Auto Sales Inc ....F....... 407 322-3100
Sanford *(G-16039)*
Pierce Manufacturing Inc ....D....... 941 748-3900
Bradenton *(G-1097)*
Rolls Axle Lc ....F....... 813 764-0242
Plant City *(G-14463)*
Southeastern Truck Tops Inc ....F....... 386 761-0002
Daytona Beach *(G-2717)*
Stephen Shives ....G....... 352 454-6522
Summerfield *(G-17063)*

TRAVELER ACCOMMODATIONS, NEC

Allen Shuffleboard LLC ....G....... 727 399-8877
Seminole *(G-16737)*

TRAVELERS' AID

Built Story LLC ....G....... 305 671-3890
Miami *(G-9283)*

TROPHIES, NEC

A J Trophies & Awards Inc ....E....... 850 878-7187
Tallahassee *(G-17210)*
American Trophy Co ....G....... 954 782-2250
Pompano Beach *(G-14594)*
M D R International Inc ....F....... 305 944-5335
North Miami *(G-11644)*
Michelsons Trophies Inc ....G....... 305 687-9898
Miami *(G-10017)*
Parrillo Inc ....G....... 386 767-8011
South Daytona *(G-16806)*

TROPHIES, PLATED, ALL METALS

United Trophy Manufacturing ....E....... 407 841-2525
Orlando *(G-13294)*

TROPHIES: Metal, Exc Silver

Cabus USA Inc ....G.... 305 681-0872
North Miami *(G-11631)*

TROPHY & PLAQUE STORES

Daytona Trophy Inc ....F.... 386 253-2806
Daytona Beach *(G-2656)*
In The News Inc ....D.... 813 882-8886
Tampa *(G-17775)*
Looper Sports Connection Inc ....G.... 352 796-7974
Brooksville *(G-1247)*

TRUCK & BUS BODIES: Car Carrier

Express Auto Carriers LLC ....G.... 352 541-0040
Ocala *(G-11935)*

TRUCK & BUS BODIES: Dump Truck

Armor Supply Metals LLC ....G.... 305 640-9901
Medley *(G-8613)*
Nichols Truck Bodies LLC ....E.... 904 781-5080
Jacksonville *(G-6634)*
T Disney Trucking & Grading ....E.... 813 443-6258
Tampa *(G-18151)*
Warren Equipment Inc ....E.... 813 752-5126
Plant City *(G-14477)*

TRUCK & BUS BODIES: Tank Truck

Bulk Manufacturing Florida Inc ....F.... 813 757-2313
Plant City *(G-14412)*
Terminal Service Company ....C.... 850 739-5702
Tallahassee *(G-17339)*

TRUCK & BUS BODIES: Truck Beds

Miami Dade Truck & Eqp Svc ....F.... 305 691-2932
Miami *(G-9997)*
Reading Truck Body LLC ....E.... 727 943-8911
Tarpon Springs *(G-18323)*

TRUCK & BUS BODIES: Truck Tops

Southeastern Truck Tops Inc ....F.... 386 761-0002
Daytona Beach *(G-2717)*

TRUCK & BUS BODIES: Truck, Motor Vehicle

A&L Hall Investments Inc ....E.... 904 781-5080
Bryceville *(G-1296)*
Advanced Truck Equipment Inc ....E.... 561 424-0442
Boynton Beach *(G-873)*
Gar-P Industries Inc ....E.... 305 888-7252
Medley *(G-8655)*
Reading Truck Body LLC ....E.... 727 943-8911
Tarpon Springs *(G-18322)*
Transtat Equipment Inc ....F.... 407 857-2040
Orlando *(G-13268)*

TRUCK BODIES: Body Parts

Florida Truck Parts ....G.... 786 251-8614
Hialeah Gardens *(G-5698)*
Simplified Fabricators Inc ....E.... 561 335-3488
West Palm Beach *(G-19035)*
World Industrial Equipment Inc ....E.... 772 461-6056
Fort Pierce *(G-4772)*

TRUCK BODY SHOP

Gar-P Industries Inc ....E.... 305 888-7252
Medley *(G-8655)*
Reading Truck Body LLC ....E.... 727 943-8911
Tarpon Springs *(G-18322)*
Transtat Equipment Inc ....F.... 407 857-2040
Orlando *(G-13268)*

TRUCK PAINTING & LETTERING SVCS

Suncoast Signs Inc ....G.... 813 664-0699
Tampa *(G-18145)*

TRUCK PARTS & ACCESSORIES: Wholesalers

Gar-P Industries Inc ....E.... 305 888-7252
Medley *(G-8655)*
Warren Equipment Inc ....E.... 813 752-5126
Plant City *(G-14477)*

TRUCKING & HAULING SVCS: Hazardous Waste

Environmental Contractors Inc ....F.... 305 556-6942
Hialeah *(G-5399)*

TRUCKING & HAULING SVCS: Lumber & Timber

Richard Brown Logging Inc ....F.... 850 379-8674
Hosford *(G-6011)*
Southern Wood Services LLC ....G.... 352 279-3208
Brooksville *(G-1272)*

TRUCKING & HAULING SVCS: Timber, Local

Paul White Logging Inc ....G.... 850 379-8651
Hosford *(G-6010)*

TRUCKING, AUTOMOBILE CARRIER

Trio Envmtl Solutions LLC ....F.... 850 543-9125
Mary Esther *(G-8592)*

TRUCKING, DUMP

Rock Ridge Materials Inc ....F.... 321 268-8455
Titusville *(G-18460)*

TRUCKING: Except Local

Harrison Gypsum LLC ....E.... 850 762-4315
Marianna *(G-8578)*
Titan America LLC ....C.... 305 364-2200
Medley *(G-8738)*

TRUCKING: Local, With Storage

Bt-Twiss Transport LLC ....G.... 866 584-1585
Largo *(G-7915)*
Ofab Inc ....D.... 352 629-0040
Ocala *(G-12019)*

TRUCKING: Local, Without Storage

Buddy Ward & Sons Seafood ....G.... 850 653-8522
Apalachicola *(G-97)*
Donald Smith Logging Inc ....G.... 850 697-3975
Carrabelle *(G-1497)*
Tumbling Pines Inc ....F.... 386 437-2668
Bunnell *(G-1310)*
Usher Land & Timber Inc ....E.... 352 493-4221
Chiefland *(G-1539)*
Yahl Mulching & Recycling Inc ....F.... 239 352-7888
Naples *(G-11462)*

TRUCKS & TRACTORS: Industrial

Alliance Commercial Eqp Inc ....G.... 772 232-8149
Pompano Beach *(G-14587)*
Alta Equipment Holdings Inc ....G.... 813 519-4097
Tampa *(G-17406)*
Amer-Con Corp ....E.... 786 293-8004
Palmetto Bay *(G-13839)*
Amera Trail Inc ....E.... 407 892-1100
Saint Cloud *(G-15643)*
Bms International Inc ....E.... 813 247-7040
Tampa *(G-17477)*
Dhs Power Corp ....G.... 305 599-1022
Miami *(G-9463)*
Earthmover Cnstr Eqp LLC ....E.... 407 401-8956
Apopka *(G-132)*
Grass Pro Shops Inc ....F.... 813 381-3890
Tampa *(G-17726)*
Lake County Forklift Solutions ....G.... 352 735-4024
Sorrento *(G-16788)*
Lite Cart Corp ....G.... 727 584-7364
Largo *(G-8002)*
Mettler-Toledo Inc ....C.... 607 257-6000
Lutz *(G-8400)*
Rampmaster Inc ....F.... 305 691-9090
Miami *(G-10238)*
Rolls Rite Trailers Inc ....F.... 850 526-2290
Marianna *(G-8585)*
Sardee Industries Inc ....E.... 407 295-2114
Orlando *(G-13163)*
Sdi Industries Inc ....E.... 321 733-1128
Melbourne *(G-8928)*
Terex Corporation ....G.... 352 330-4044
Wildwood *(G-19205)*
Tesco Equipment LLC ....E.... 954 752-7994
Coral Springs *(G-2322)*
Tfl of Orlando ....G.... 407 936-1553
Orlando *(G-13251)*
The Forklift Company Inc ....F.... 863 595-8156
Lake Alfred *(G-7334)*
Windstar Express Inc ....G.... 786 252-1569
Miami *(G-10609)*
World Industrial Equipment Inc ....E.... 772 461-6056
Fort Pierce *(G-4772)*

TRUCKS: Forklift

A & S Equipment Co ....F.... 305 436-8207
Doral *(G-3220)*
All Lift Solutions Inc ....G.... 786 295-3946
Miami *(G-9111)*
Benitez Forklift Corp ....G.... 786 307-3872
Hialeah *(G-5321)*
Cholift Forklift USA Co ....G.... 786 483-6930
Hialeah *(G-5344)*
Florida Jacksonville Forklift ....G.... 904 674-6898
Jacksonville *(G-6399)*
Forklift ....G.... 305 468-1824
Miami *(G-9594)*
Jamco Industrial Inc ....F.... 866 848-5400
Sanford *(G-16072)*
Lit Forklift LLC ....G.... 321 271-4626
Cocoa Beach *(G-2065)*
Onsite Rlble Forklift Svcs Inc ....F.... 305 305-8638
Hialeah *(G-5550)*
Orlandos Forklift Service LLC ....G.... 407 761-9104
Orlando *(G-13038)*
Ring Power Corporation ....G.... 863 606-0512
Lakeland *(G-7779)*
RJ Forklift Services Inc ....G.... 786 539-6613
Miami *(G-10266)*
Shane Laliberte Lift LLC ....G.... 407 873-0703
Saint Cloud *(G-15666)*
South Fla Forklift Doctor Corp ....G.... 561 951-6243
Lake Worth Beach *(G-7620)*
Tampa Fork Lift Inc ....F.... 904 674-6899
Jacksonville *(G-6837)*

TRUCKS: Indl

B R Express ....G.... 904 881-2556
Jacksonville *(G-6186)*
Big Man Friendly Trnsp LLC ....G.... 941 229-3454
Lakewood Ranch *(G-7837)*
Carriers Direct Inc ....F.... 941 776-2979
Parrish *(G-14005)*
Dmoney365 Logistic LLC ....F.... 954 529-8202
North Lauderdale *(G-11613)*
First Coast Cargo Inc ....F.... 844 774-7711
Jacksonville *(G-6384)*
Iscar GSE Corp ....E.... 305 364-8886
Miami Gardens *(G-10748)*
Iscar GSE Corp ....E.... 305 364-8886
Miami Gardens *(G-10749)*
LUnion Logistics LLC ....F.... 866 586-4660
Hollywood *(G-5866)*
MC Intl Transportation ....F.... 305 805-8228
Miami *(G-9959)*
Modest Logistics LLC ....F.... 321 314-2825
Orlando *(G-12976)*
Runn-It LLC ....G.... 800 932-8052
Miami *(G-10289)*
Toteum All Trckg Trnsprtng L ....E.... 888 506-5890
Orlando *(G-13264)*

TRUSSES & FRAMING: Prefabricated Metal

A-1 Roof Trusses Ltd Company ....F.... 270 316-9409
Coral Springs *(G-2210)*
Cmn Steel Fabricators Inc ....D.... 305 592-5466
Miami *(G-9367)*
Park Place Manufacturing Inc ....F.... 863 382-0126
Sebring *(G-16701)*
Steel Technology & Design ....F.... 863 665-2525
Lakeland *(G-7806)*

TRUSSES: Wood, Floor

True House Inc ....F.... 904 757-7500
Jacksonville *(G-6870)*

TRUSSES: Wood, Roof

A-1 Roof Trusses Ltd Company ....F.... 270 316-9409
Coral Springs *(G-2210)*
A-1 Roof Trusses Ltd Company ....C.... 772 409-1010
Fort Pierce *(G-4668)*
Accu-Span Truss Co ....E.... 407 321-1440
Longwood *(G-8250)*

American Truss Chiefland LL ....G....... 352 493-9700
Chiefland *(G-1530)*
Anderson Truss LLC................................E....... 386 752-3103
Lake City *(G-7348)*
Angle Truss Co Inc ....F....... 352 343-7477
Tavares *(G-18334)*
Arban & Associates Inc..........................E....... 850 836-4362
Ponce De Leon *(G-14917)*
B and B Roof and Floor Trusses ....G....... 850 265-4119
Lynn Haven *(G-8429)*
Best Truss Company ....D....... 305 667-6797
Miami *(G-9235)*
Big Bend Truss Components Inc ....F....... 850 539-5351
Havana *(G-5234)*
Bruce Component Systems Inc............F....... 352 628-0522
Lecanto *(G-8129)*
Bushnell Truss Enterprises LLC ....F....... 352 793-6090
Bushnell *(G-1314)*
Casmin Inc...G....... 352 253-5000
Mount Dora *(G-11099)*
Central Florida Truss Inc........................E....... 863 533-0821
Bartow *(G-312)*
Chambers Truss Inc................................D....... 772 465-2012
Fort Pierce *(G-4687)*
CMF Truss Inc ....E....... 352 796-5805
Brooksville *(G-1220)*
Custom Truss LLC...................................F....... 561 266-3451
Boynton Beach *(G-895)*
D & M Truss Co ....E....... 850 944-4864
Pensacola *(G-14124)*
D J Trusses Unlimited Inc ....F....... 863 687-4796
Lakeland *(G-7670)*
Dade Truss Company Inc.......................C....... 305 592-8245
Miami *(G-9431)*
Dan Boudreau Inc ....G....... 407 491-7611
Oviedo *(G-13425)*
Deco Truss Company Inc.......................E....... 305 257-1910
Homestead *(G-5962)*
Duley Truss Inc ....E....... 352 465-0964
Dunnellon *(G-3593)*
Emerald Coast Truss LLC ....E....... 850 623-1967
Milton *(G-10927)*
Florida Engineered Constru...................C....... 813 621-4641
Seffner *(G-16726)*
Florida Quality Truss Inc ....G....... 954 975-3384
Pompano Beach *(G-14702)*
Florida Quality Truss Inds Inc................F....... 954 971-3167
Pompano Beach *(G-14703)*
Freeport Truss Company Inc ....F....... 850 835-4541
Freeport *(G-4846)*
Gulf Coast Truss Co Inc ....F....... 239 278-1819
Fort Myers *(G-4478)*
Hitech Truss Inc......................................G....... 352 797-0877
Brooksville *(G-1234)*
Hitek Property LLC ....F....... 352 797-0877
Brooksville *(G-1235)*
K & M Truss Inc.......................................G....... 407 880-4551
Zellwood *(G-19504)*
Lemon Bay Truss & Supply Co...............G....... 941 698-0800
Placida *(G-14397)*
Marianna Truss Inc ....E....... 850 594-5420
Marianna *(G-8583)*
Martinez Builders Supply LLC ....D....... 772 466-2480
Fort Pierce *(G-4714)*
Martinez Truss Company Inc ....F....... 305 883-6261
Medley *(G-8684)*
Mayo Truss Co Inc ....F....... 386 294-3988
Mayo *(G-8596)*
Mid-Flrida Lbr Acqisitions Inc ....E....... 863 533-0155
Bartow *(G-325)*
Nexgen Framing System LLC ....F....... 321 508-6763
Palm Bay *(G-13525)*
Old Oak Truss Company ....G....... 813 689-6597
Seffner *(G-16731)*
Park Place Truss Inc...............................F....... 863 382-0126
Sebring *(G-16702)*
Park Place Truss & Design Inc ....E....... 863 382-0126
Sebring *(G-16703)*
Pelliccione Builders Sup Inc...................F....... 941 334-3014
North Fort Myers *(G-11602)*
Ridgway Roof Truss Company ....D....... 352 376-4436
Gainesville *(G-4991)*
Royal Truss Corp.....................................F....... 786 222-1100
Medley *(G-8721)*
Santa Fe Truss Company Inc.................F....... 386 454-7711
Bell *(G-343)*
Scosta Corp...C....... 863 385-8242
Sebring *(G-16705)*
Southern Truss Companies Inc..............D....... 772 464-4160
Fort Pierce *(G-4748)*
Southwest Strl Systems Inc...................E....... 239 693-6000
Fort Myers *(G-4609)*
Standard Truss & Roof Sup Inc ....E....... 863 422-8293
Haines City *(G-5149)*
Superior Truss Systems Inc...................D....... 305 591-9918
Doral *(G-3518)*
Taunton Truss Co Red Lobs ....G....... 850 785-5566
Panama City *(G-13954)*
True House Inc..C....... 386 325-9085
East Palatka *(G-3608)*
Truss Systems LLC.................................G....... 386 255-3009
Bunnell *(G-1308)*
Truss Systems of Vlsia Flgler ....F....... 386 255-3009
Bunnell *(G-1309)*
Trusscorp International Inc....................E....... 305 882-8826
Medley *(G-8744)*
Trusses Unlimited Inc.............................D....... 904 355-6611
Ponte Vedra Beach *(G-14955)*
Trussway Manufacturing Inc.................F....... 407 857-2777
Orlando *(G-13279)*
Trusswood Inc..D....... 321 383-0366
Titusville *(G-18470)*
US Truss Inc..E....... 561 686-4000
West Palm Beach *(G-19076)*
W Kost Inc..E....... 772 286-3700
Palm City *(G-13678)*
Wood Product Services Inc ....E....... 813 248-2221
Tampa *(G-18260)*
Yandles Quality Roof Trusses ....G....... 352 732-3000
Ocala *(G-12078)*

TUBE & TUBING FABRICATORS

Blue Water Dynamics LLC ....D....... 386 957-5464
Edgewater *(G-3614)*
Gunns Welding & Fabricating................G....... 727 393-5238
Saint Petersburg *(G-15801)*
S C R Precision Tube Bending ....F....... 813 622-7091
Tampa *(G-18074)*
Trubendz Technology Inc.......................F....... 305 378-9337
Cutler Bay *(G-2417)*
Trubendz Technology Inc.......................E....... 305 378-9337
Cutler Bay *(G-2418)*

TUBES: Extruded Or Drawn, Aluminum

Hydro Extrusion Usa LLC ....B....... 904 794-1500
Saint Augustine *(G-15550)*
Sapa Extrsons St Augustine LLC..........A....... 904 794-1500
Saint Augustine *(G-15604)*

TUBES: Finned, For Heat Transfer

Admiralty Industries Corp......................G....... 305 722-7311
Doral *(G-3227)*
Applied Cooling Technology LLC ....G....... 239 217-5080
Cape Coral *(G-1382)*

TUBES: Paper Or Fiber, Chemical Or Electrical Uses

Caraustar Indus Cnsmr Pdts Gro..........E....... 386 328-8335
Palatka *(G-13474)*

TUBES: Steel & Iron

Calnat International Inc..........................G....... 239 839-2581
Cape Coral *(G-1401)*

TUBING, COLD-DRAWN: Mech Or Hypodermic Sizes, Stainless

Ace Mechanical Inc..................................G....... 727 304-6277
Largo *(G-7884)*

TUBING: Flexible, Metallic

Custom Tube Products Inc ....F....... 386 426-0670
Edgewater *(G-3620)*

TUBING: Plastic

Consolidated Polymer Tech....................E....... 727 531-4191
Clearwater *(G-1636)*
Flexsol Holding Corp..............................D....... 954 941-6333
Pompano Beach *(G-14700)*
Microlumen Inc...D....... 813 886-1200
Oldsmar *(G-12250)*
Processing and Packg Sups Co............E....... 321 723-2723
Melbourne *(G-8912)*

TUBING: Rubber

Bowsmith Inc..G....... 863 453-6666
Avon Park *(G-284)*
Florida Pool Products Inc ....E....... 727 531-8913
Clearwater *(G-1690)*

TUBING: Seamless

Driveshaft Power Inc ....F....... 561 433-0022
Lake Worth *(G-7547)*

TUCKING FOR THE TRADE

Wheeler Trading Inc................................F....... 305 430-7100
Miami Lakes *(G-10880)*

TURBINE GENERATOR SET UNITS: Hydraulic, Complete

Hoerbger Auto Cmfort Systems L..........E....... 334 321-2292
Deerfield Beach *(G-2839)*
Hydroplus Inc...F....... 941 479-7473
Palmetto *(G-13807)*

TURBINES & TURBINE GENERATOR SET UNITS, COMPLETE

Jupiter Bach North America Inc ....C....... 850 476-6304
Pensacola *(G-14187)*
Marajo Diesel Power Corp......................G....... 786 212-1485
Doral *(G-3424)*

TURBINES & TURBINE GENERATOR SET UNITS: Gas, Complete

2jcp LLC...G....... 904 834-3818
Ponte Vedra *(G-14922)*
Power Equipments Trading LLC............G....... 305 704-7021
Doral *(G-3464)*
Power Systems Inc ....E....... 561 354-1100
Jupiter *(G-7094)*
Powerphase LLC......................................F....... 561 299-3970
Jupiter *(G-7096)*
Solar Turbines Incorporated ....F....... 305 476-6855
Miami *(G-10370)*
Stratgic Trbine Invntory Group..............G....... 561 427-2007
Jupiter *(G-7124)*
Turbine Resources Intl LLC ....G....... 850 377-0449
Pensacola *(G-14277)*

TURBINES & TURBINE GENERATOR SETS

Alterntive Repr McHning Svcs L ....E....... 904 861-3040
Jacksonville *(G-6142)*
Belac LLC ....D....... 813 749-3200
Oldsmar *(G-12210)*
Chromalloy Castings Tampa Corp ....C....... 561 935-3571
Palm Beach Gardens *(G-13577)*
Diemech Turbine Solution Inc ....G....... 386 804-0179
Deland *(G-2970)*
Escue Energy LLC...................................G....... 561 762-1486
Royal Palm Beach *(G-15466)*
Florida Hydro Power & Light Co.............G....... 386 328-2470
Palatka *(G-13478)*
GE..G....... 904 570-3151
Jacksonville *(G-6428)*
GSE Jetall Inc...G....... 305 688-2111
Opa Locka *(G-12321)*
Locust Usa Inc ....F....... 305 889-5410
Medley *(G-8679)*
Peerless Wind Systems...........................G....... 516 249-6900
Boynton Beach *(G-939)*
Siemens Energy Inc.................................D....... 407 736-1400
Orlando *(G-13183)*
Siemens Energy Inc.................................D....... 407 206-5008
Orlando *(G-13184)*
Siemens Gmesa Rnwble Engry Inc.......A....... 407 736-2000
Orlando *(G-13186)*
Siemens Gmesa Rnwble Engry Inc.......D....... 407 721-3273
Orlando *(G-13187)*
Southwest Turbine Inc.............................G....... 305 769-1765
Hialeah *(G-5630)*
Turbine Generator Maint Inc ....E....... 239 573-1233
Cape Coral *(G-1489)*
Vestas...G....... 561 588-9933
West Palm Beach *(G-19079)*
Vonwidman Designs LLC ....G....... 727 862-5303
New Port Richey *(G-11520)*

TURBINES & TURBINE GENERATOR SETS & PARTS

Chromalloy Mtl Solutions LLC...............E...... 954 378-1999
Fort Lauderdale *(G-3899)*
Sandpiper Turbine LLC...............F...... 407 377-7220
Kissimmee *(G-7294)*

TURBINES: Gas, Mechanical Drive

Mitsubishi Power Americas Inc...............D...... 407 688-6100
Lake Mary *(G-7436)*
Power Systems Mfg LLC...............B...... 561 354-1100
Jupiter *(G-7095)*
Raytheon Technologies Corp...............A...... 858 277-7639
Jupiter *(G-7103)*

TURBINES: Hydraulic, Complete

Brady Wind LLC...............G...... 561 304-5136
Juno Beach *(G-6976)*
Southstern Indus Fbrcators LLC...............E...... 941 776-1211
Duette *(G-3563)*

TURBINES: Steam

Gas Turbine Efficiency Inc...............E...... 407 304-5200
Orlando *(G-12771)*
Gas Turbine Efficiency LLC...............E...... 407 304-5200
Orlando *(G-12772)*
Siemens Energy Inc...............D...... 407 736-7957
Orlando *(G-13185)*

TURBO-SUPERCHARGERS: Aircraft

Approved Turbo Components Inc...............F...... 559 627-3600
Vero Beach *(G-18594)*

TYPESETTING SVC

Abby Press Inc...............E...... 407 847-5565
Kissimmee *(G-7216)*
Advanced Typesetting...............G...... 407 834-1741
Fern Park *(G-3727)*
Aether Media USA Inc...............G...... 863 647-5500
Lakeland *(G-7629)*
Alta Systems Inc...............E...... 352 372-2534
Gainesville *(G-4873)*
American Business Cards Inc...............E...... 314 739-0800
Naples *(G-11161)*
Apple Printing & Advg Spc Inc...............E...... 954 524-0493
Fort Lauderdale *(G-3818)*
Armstrongs Printing & Graphics...............G...... 850 243-6923
Fort Walton Beach *(G-4778)*
Assocated Prtg Productions Inc...............E...... 305 623-7600
Miami Lakes *(G-10763)*
B J and ME Inc...............G...... 561 368-5470
Boca Raton *(G-438)*
B R Q Grossmans Inc...............F...... 954 971-1077
Pompano Beach *(G-14609)*
Bava Inc...............F...... 850 893-4799
Tallahassee *(G-17226)*
Bayou Printing Inc...............F...... 850 678-5444
Valparaiso *(G-18507)*
Bjm Enterprises Inc...............F...... 941 746-4171
Bradenton *(G-1000)*
Boca Color Graphics Inc...............F...... 561 391-2229
Boca Raton *(G-450)*
Boca Raton Printing Co...............G...... 561 395-8404
Boca Raton *(G-454)*
Bros Williams Printing Inc...............G...... 305 769-9925
Hialeah *(G-5332)*
Burr Printing Co Inc...............G...... 863 294-3166
Winter Haven *(G-19308)*
Caxton Newspapers Inc...............E...... 305 538-9700
Miami Beach *(G-10652)*
Central Florida Publishing Inc...............F...... 407 323-5204
Sanford *(G-16010)*
Coastal Printing Inc Sarasota...............E...... 941 351-1515
Sarasota *(G-16386)*
Color Concepts Prtg Design Co...............E...... 813 623-2921
Tampa *(G-17546)*
Color Express Inc...............G...... 305 558-2061
Hialeah *(G-5350)*
Coloramax Printing Inc...............F...... 305 541-0322
Miami *(G-9381)*
Commercial Printers Inc...............D...... 954 781-3737
Fort Lauderdale *(G-3911)*
Creative Prtg Grphic Dsign Inc...............E...... 407 855-0202
Orlando *(G-12627)*
Csmc Inc...............E...... 407 246-1567
Orlando *(G-12630)*
Dahlquist Enterprises Inc...............G...... 407 896-2294
Orlando *(G-12644)*
Dannys Prtg Svc Sups & Eqp Inc...............G...... 305 757-2282
Miami *(G-9435)*
Durra Print Inc...............E...... 850 222-4768
Tallahassee *(G-17244)*
Dvh Macleod Corp...............F...... 850 224-6760
Tallahassee *(G-17246)*
Ed Vance Printing Company Inc...............F...... 813 882-8888
Tampa *(G-17630)*
Edward Thomas Company...............G...... 561 746-1441
Jupiter *(G-7032)*
Express Printing & Office Sups...............G...... 904 765-9696
Jacksonville *(G-6376)*
FGA Printing...............G...... 954 763-1122
Pompano Beach *(G-14689)*
Fidelity Printing Corporation...............D...... 727 522-9557
Saint Petersburg *(G-15778)*
First Imprssons Prtg Cmmnctons...............G...... 407 831-6100
Longwood *(G-8282)*
Florida Graphic Printing Inc...............F...... 386 253-4532
Daytona Beach *(G-2666)*
Ford Press Inc...............F...... 352 787-4650
Leesburg *(G-8159)*
Four G Enterprises Inc...............E...... 407 834-4143
Longwood *(G-8284)*
G J V Inc...............G...... 727 584-7136
Largo *(G-7955)*
G S Printers Inc...............G...... 305 931-2755
Fort Lauderdale *(G-4016)*
Graphics Type Color Entps Inc...............E...... 305 591-7600
Miami *(G-9658)*
Gulf Coast Business World Inc...............F...... 850 864-1511
Fort Walton Beach *(G-4806)*
Halifax Media Holdings LLC...............E...... 386 681-2404
Daytona Beach *(G-2671)*
Hartco Inc...............G...... 904 353-5259
Jacksonville *(G-6462)*
Hilcraft Engraving Inc...............G...... 305 871-6100
Miami *(G-9711)*
ICM Printing Co Inc...............F...... 352 377-7468
Gainesville *(G-4940)*
Image Prtg & Digital Svcs Inc...............G...... 850 244-3380
Mary Esther *(G-8589)*
Impact Design Group Inc...............F...... 904 636-8989
Jacksonville *(G-6490)*
Instant Printing Services Inc...............F...... 727 546-8036
Floral City *(G-3768)*
J J M Services Inc...............G...... 954 437-1880
Miramar *(G-11007)*
Jet Graphics Inc...............F...... 305 264-4333
Miami *(G-9796)*
Jet Set Printing Inc...............G...... 407 339-1900
Casselberry *(G-1508)*
K R O Enterprises Ltd...............G...... 309 797-2213
Naples *(G-11302)*
Keithco Inc...............G...... 352 351-4741
Ocala *(G-11976)*
Kights Printing & Office Pdts...............G...... 904 731-7990
Jacksonville *(G-6537)*
Lake Worth Herald Press...............E...... 561 585-9387
Lake Worth *(G-7564)*
Lauderdale Graphics Corp...............E...... 954 450-0800
Davie *(G-2544)*
Leda Printing Inc...............E...... 941 922-1563
Sarasota *(G-16487)*
Leila K Moavero...............G...... 954 978-0018
Pompano Beach *(G-14743)*
Liberty Calhoun Journal Inc...............G...... 850 643-3333
Bristol *(G-1198)*
Linographics Inc...............F...... 407 422-8700
Orlando *(G-12913)*
Menu Men Inc...............E...... 305 633-7925
Miami *(G-9976)*
Mikes Print Shop Inc...............G...... 407 718-4964
Winter Park *(G-19426)*
Multicolor Printing Inc...............G...... 772 287-1676
Stuart *(G-16979)*
My Print Shop Inc...............F...... 954 973-9369
Deerfield Beach *(G-2878)*
Ngp Corporate Square Inc...............E...... 239 643-3430
Naples *(G-11345)*
Ocala Print Quick Inc...............G...... 352 629-0736
Ocala *(G-12014)*
Oompha Inc...............G...... 850 222-7210
Tallahassee *(G-17308)*
Output Printing Corp...............F...... 813 228-8800
Tampa *(G-17965)*
Paper Fish Printing Inc...............G...... 239 481-3555
Fort Myers *(G-4565)*
Parkinson Enterprises Inc...............F...... 863 688-7900
Lakeland *(G-7762)*
PIP Printing...............G...... 352 622-3224
Ocala *(G-12027)*
Precision Printing of Columbus...............G...... 561 509-7269
Boynton Beach *(G-942)*
Premier Global Enterprises...............G...... 561 747-7303
Tequesta *(G-18387)*
Print One Inc...............G...... 813 273-0240
Oldsmar *(G-12262)*
Printers of Pensacola LLC...............G...... 850 434-2588
Pensacola *(G-14240)*
Reimink Printing Inc...............G...... 813 289-4663
Tampa *(G-18050)*
Roberts Quality Printing Inc...............E...... 727 442-4011
Clearwater *(G-1862)*
S Printing Inc...............G...... 305 633-3343
Miami *(G-10292)*
Saugus Valley Corp...............G...... 954 772-4077
Coral Springs *(G-2310)*
Sergios Printing Inc...............F...... 305 971-4112
Miami *(G-10326)*
Set Up Inc...............G...... 239 542-4142
Cape Coral *(G-1469)*
South Broward Printing Inc...............G...... 954 962-1309
Hollywood *(G-5912)*
Spinnaker Holding Company...............E...... 561 392-8626
Boca Raton *(G-728)*
Steven K Bakum Inc...............G...... 561 804-9110
West Palm Beach *(G-19044)*
Sunshine Printing Inc...............F...... 561 478-2602
West Palm Beach *(G-19050)*
Supreme Printing Corp...............G...... 305 591-2916
Hialeah *(G-5643)*
Tampa Printing Company...............E...... 813 612-7746
Tampa *(G-18171)*
Thalers Printing Center Inc...............G...... 954 741-6522
Lauderhill *(G-8122)*
Toms Instant Printing Inc...............G...... 904 396-0686
Jacksonville *(G-6861)*
Town Street Print Shop Inc...............G...... 850 432-8300
Gulf Breeze *(G-5130)*
Universal Graphics & Prtg Inc...............G...... 561 845-6404
North Palm Beach *(G-11729)*
Universal Screen Graphics Inc...............E...... 813 623-5335
Tampa *(G-18223)*
V I P Printing...............G...... 386 258-3326
Daytona Beach *(G-2730)*
V P Press Inc...............F...... 954 581-7531
Fort Lauderdale *(G-4301)*
Vmak Corp...............F...... 407 260-1199
Longwood *(G-8348)*
Vowells Downtown Inc...............G...... 850 432-5175
Pensacola *(G-14285)*
W D H Enterprises Inc...............G...... 941 758-6500
Bradenton *(G-1143)*
Walker Graphics Inc...............G...... 954 964-1688
Hollywood *(G-5939)*

ULTRASONIC EQPT: Cleaning, Exc Med & Dental

Geneva Systems Inc...............G...... 352 235-2990
Green Cove Springs *(G-5063)*
Neat Clean Group Inc...............F...... 727 459-6079
Clearwater *(G-1805)*
Power Vac Corporation...............G...... 954 491-0188
Oakland Park *(G-11830)*
Pressure Systems Innvtions LLC...............F...... 561 249-2708
West Palm Beach *(G-19005)*

ULTRASONIC EQPT: Dental

Simplified Systems Inc...............F...... 305 672-7676
Miami Beach *(G-10710)*

UMBRELLAS & CANES

Strap Shade Inc...............G...... 239 450-5844
Bonita Springs *(G-858)*
Ultimate Umbrella Company Inc...............B...... 305 634-5116
Hialeah *(G-5657)*

UMBRELLAS: Garden Or Wagon

Advanced Sewing...............G...... 954 484-2100
Fort Lauderdale *(G-3784)*
Schnupp Manufacturing Co Inc...............G...... 305 325-0520
Miami *(G-10312)*
Shelleys Cushions Mfg Inc...............E...... 305 633-1790
Miami *(G-10337)*

Suntyx LLC ... F ... 786 558-2233
Miramar *(G-11049)*

UNDERCOATINGS: Paint

Paints & Coatings Inc ... E ... 239 997-6645
North Fort Myers *(G-11601)*
Sfa Systems Inc ... E ... 561 585-5927
Lake Worth *(G-7586)*
Techncal Pntg Jacksonville Inc ... E ... 904 652-1129
Jacksonville *(G-6842)*

UNIFORM SPLY SVCS: Indl

Cintas Corporation ... G ... 239 693-8722
Fort Myers *(G-4396)*

UNIFORM STORES

Bnj Noble Inc ... F ... 954 987-1040
Davie *(G-2503)*
Sharp Marketing LLC ... G ... 954 565-2711
Oakland Park *(G-11838)*
Uniform Authority Inc ... D ... 305 625-8050
Miami *(G-10529)*

UNISEX HAIR SALONS

Fekkai Retail LLC ... D ... 866 514-8048
Plantation *(G-14515)*

UNIVERSITY

Current ... G ... 954 262-8455
Davie *(G-2512)*

UNSUPPORTED PLASTICS: Floor Or Wall Covering

Architexture LLC ... G ... 954 907-8000
Fort Lauderdale *(G-3820)*
Tropicalcreation ... G ... 941 580-8465
North Port *(G-11751)*

UPHOLSTERERS' EQPT & SPLYS WHOLESALERS

Design Works By Tech Pdts Inc ... E ... 941 355-2703
Sarasota *(G-16410)*

UPHOLSTERY MATERIALS, BROADWOVEN

J & H Supply Co Inc ... G ... 561 582-3346
Lake Worth *(G-7558)*
Miami Prestige Interiors Inc ... E ... 305 685-3343
Miami *(G-10005)*

UPHOLSTERY WORK SVCS

Top Trtment Cstomes Accesories ... G ... 239 936-4600
Fort Myers *(G-4632)*

URNS: Cut Stone

Eterna Urn Co Inc ... G ... 386 258-6491
Daytona Beach *(G-2663)*

USED CAR DEALERS

Addco Manufacturing Company ... E ... 828 733-1560
Riviera Beach *(G-15292)*
Evo Motors LLC ... F ... 813 621-7799
Seffner *(G-16725)*

USED MERCHANDISE STORES

Gems Jewelry & Uniques ... G ... 850 456-8105
Pensacola *(G-14162)*
Nfjb Inc ... E ... 954 771-1100
Fort Lauderdale *(G-4141)*

UTENSILS: Cast Aluminum, Household

Kitchen Sink Express LLC ... G ... 800 888-6604
Dunedin *(G-3583)*

UTENSILS: Household, Cooking & Kitchen, Metal

All Southern Fabricators Inc ... E ... 727 573-4846
Clearwater *(G-1574)*
Epare LLC ... F ... 347 682-5121
Miami *(G-9531)*
Global Marketing Corp ... E ... 973 426-1088
Bradenton *(G-1047)*
Royal Prestige ... F ... 813 464-9872
Fort Lauderdale *(G-4219)*

UTENSILS: Household, Metal, Exc Cast

Zeroll Co ... F ... 772 461-3811
Weston *(G-19180)*

UTILITY TRAILER DEALERS

A Plus Trailers ... G ... 786 395-0799
Southwest Ranches *(G-16835)*
All Amrcan Trlr Connection Inc ... G ... 561 582-1800
Palm Springs *(G-13772)*
Amera Trail Inc ... E ... 407 892-1100
Saint Cloud *(G-15643)*
Eds Aluminum Buildings Inc ... G ... 850 476-2169
Pensacola *(G-14138)*
Loadmaster Alum Boat Trlrs Inc ... E ... 813 689-3096
Tampa *(G-17856)*

VACUUM CLEANER REPAIR SVCS

AAA Monterey Discount Vacuum ... G ... 772 288-5233
Stuart *(G-16900)*

VACUUM CLEANERS: Household

AAA Monterey Discount Vacuum ... G ... 772 288-5233
Stuart *(G-16900)*
Intelliclean Solutions LLC ... G ... 615 293-2299
Miami *(G-9753)*

VACUUM CLEANERS: Indl Type

LDS Vacuum Products Inc ... E ... 407 862-4643
Longwood *(G-8305)*

VACUUM CLEANERS: Wholesalers

Pro Chem Products Inc ... G ... 407 425-5533
Orlando *(G-13091)*

VACUUM PUMPS & EQPT: Laboratory

Walden Consulting LLC ... G ... 407 563-3620
Orlando *(G-13317)*

VALUE-ADDED RESELLERS: Computer Systems

Cloudfactors LLC ... G ... 866 779-9974
Plantation *(G-14501)*
Commski LLC ... G ... 813 501-0111
Tampa *(G-17548)*
Phintec LLC ... G ... 321 214-2500
Orlando *(G-13066)*

VALVE REPAIR SVCS, INDL

Flotech Inc ... D ... 904 358-1849
Jacksonville *(G-6406)*
Hoerbiger Compression Tech AME ... B ... 954 974-5700
Pompano Beach *(G-14724)*

VALVES

Control Southern Inc ... D ... 904 353-0004
Jacksonville *(G-6287)*
Florida Marine Products Inc ... F ... 813 248-2283
Tampa *(G-17683)*
Innovative Products LLC ... G ... 888 764-6478
Fort Lauderdale *(G-4059)*

VALVES & PARTS: Gas, Indl

Petroleum Equipment and Mfg Co ... F ... 305 558-9573
Hialeah *(G-5557)*

VALVES & PIPE FITTINGS

A & N Corporation ... D ... 352 528-4100
Williston *(G-19207)*
Andersons Can Line Fbrction Eq ... F ... 407 889-4665
Apopka *(G-113)*
Depend-O-Drain Inc ... E ... 941 756-1710
Bradenton *(G-1030)*
Eagle Pneumatic Inc ... E ... 863 644-4870
Lakeland *(G-7678)*
Enolgas Usa Inc ... G ... 754 205-7902
Pompano Beach *(G-14681)*
Flotech Inc ... D ... 904 358-1849
Jacksonville *(G-6406)*
Formweld Fitting Inc ... E ... 850 626-4888
Milton *(G-10928)*
Gate Cfv Solutions Inc ... G ... 772 388-3387
Sebastian *(G-16661)*
Gil Industries Inc ... G ... 850 479-3400
Cantonment *(G-1340)*
Hoerbiger Compression Tech AME ... B ... 954 974-5700
Pompano Beach *(G-14724)*
Leslie Controls Inc ... C ... 813 978-1000
Temple Terrace *(G-18371)*
Mat-Vac Technology Inc ... F ... 386 238-7017
Daytona Beach *(G-2683)*
Precision Fabg & Clg Co Inc ... D ... 321 635-2000
Cocoa *(G-2042)*
Serf Inc ... E ... 850 476-8203
Cantonment *(G-1347)*
Southern Innovative Energy Inc ... G ... 321 747-9205
Titusville *(G-18461)*
Sun Pipe and Valves LLC ... G ... 772 408-5530
Port Saint Lucie *(G-15150)*
Target Manufacturing Inc ... G ... 305 633-0361
Miami *(G-10460)*
Teknocraft Inc ... E ... 321 729-9634
Melbourne *(G-8959)*

VALVES Solenoid

Jefferson Solenoid Valves USA ... D ... 305 249-8120
Miami *(G-9794)*
Thermoval Solenoid Valves Usa ... G ... 954 835-5523
Davie *(G-2605)*

VALVES: Aerosol, Metal

Ees Design LLC ... F ... 954 541-2660
Fort Lauderdale *(G-3965)*
Medway Hall Dev Group Inc ... F ... 904 786-0622
Jacksonville *(G-6594)*
Sfi Inc ... E ... 407 834-2258
Orlando *(G-13177)*
Sklar Bov Solutions Inc ... G ... 352 746-6731
Hernando *(G-5247)*

VALVES: Aircraft

Flyteone Inc ... G ... 813 421-1410
Clearwater *(G-1691)*

VALVES: Aircraft, Control, Hydraulic & Pneumatic

Micro Pneumatic Logic Inc ... C ... 954 935-6821
Pompano Beach *(G-14762)*

VALVES: Aircraft, Fluid Power

Moog Inc ... G ... 716 652-2000
Pembroke Pines *(G-14049)*

VALVES: Aircraft, Hydraulic

Jet Research Development Inc ... D ... 954 427-0404
Deerfield Beach *(G-2850)*

VALVES: Control, Automatic

Doch LLC ... G ... 571 491-7578
Tampa *(G-17612)*
Roper Technologies Inc ... E ... 941 556-2601
Sarasota *(G-16563)*

VALVES: Fluid Power, Control, Hydraulic & pneumatic

Eem Technologies Corp ... F ... 786 606-5993
Doral *(G-3340)*
Helios Technologies Inc ... A ... 941 362-1200
Sarasota *(G-16227)*
Industrial Mobile Hydraulics ... G ... 904 866-7592
Jacksonville *(G-6494)*
Innovative Products LLC ... G ... 888 764-6478
Fort Lauderdale *(G-4059)*
Zennergy LLC ... F ... 813 382-3460
Tampa *(G-18280)*

VALVES: Gas Cylinder, Compressed

S A Microtechnologies LLC ... F ... 954 973-6166
Pompano Beach *(G-14839)*

VALVES: Indl

Alfa Laval Inc ... G ... 941 727-1900
Sarasota *(G-16173)*

Chem-TEC Equipment Co F 954 428-8259
Deerfield Beach *(G-2801)*
Chemseal Inc G 305 433-8362
Hialeah *(G-5343)*
Circor International Inc G 813 978-1000
Temple Terrace *(G-18367)*
Dresser Inc E 318 640-2250
Jacksonville *(G-6328)*
Dresser LLC B 904 781-7071
Jacksonville *(G-6329)*
Hoerbiger Corp America Inc B 954 974-5700
Pompano Beach *(G-14725)*
Hose Power USA G 863 669-9333
Lakeland *(G-7706)*
Inovinox Usa LLC G 800 780-1017
Miami *(G-9749)*
Iq Valves Co E 321 729-9634
Melbourne *(G-8851)*
Merit Fastener Corporation G 813 626-3748
Tampa *(G-17903)*
Micro Matic Usa Inc E 352 544-1081
Brooksville *(G-1252)*
Morris Valves Inc G 305 477-6525
Doral *(G-3441)*
Target Manufacturing Inc G 305 633-0361
Miami *(G-10460)*
Tsm Champ LLC D 615 806-7900
Sarasota *(G-16317)*

VALVES: Regulating & Control, Automatic

Azex Flow Technologies Inc G 305 393-8037
Miami *(G-9206)*
Chicago Electronic Distrs Inc F 312 985-6175
Port Charlotte *(G-14969)*
Fabco-Air Inc D 352 373-3578
Gainesville *(G-4918)*
Grinnell LLC B 561 988-3658
Boca Raton *(G-552)*
Guard Dog Valves Inc G 239 793-6886
Naples *(G-11269)*
Leslie Controls Inc C 813 978-1000
Temple Terrace *(G-18371)*

VALVES: Regulating, Process Control

Abbey Rogers G 813 645-1400
Tampa *(G-17382)*

VALVES: Water Works

Gate Cfv Solutions Inc G 772 388-3387
Sebastian *(G-16661)*

VAN CONVERSIONS

Interntnal Srvillance Tech Inc E 954 574-1100
Deerfield Beach *(G-2847)*

VAN CONVERSIONS

Interntnal Srvillance Tech Inc E 954 574-1100
Deerfield Beach *(G-2847)*

VASES: Pottery

Americraft Cookware LLC E 352 483-7600
Mount Dora *(G-11095)*

VAULTS & SAFES WHOLESALERS

Safe Banks and Lock G 954 762-3565
Fort Lauderdale *(G-4221)*

VEGETABLE OILS: Medicinal Grade, Refined Or Concentrated

Ravenswood Import Export Ltd L G 863 800-0210
Lake Placid *(G-7494)*

VEHICLES FINANCE LEASING, EXC AUTOMOBILES & TRUCKS

Bulk Resources Inc G 813 764-8420
Plant City *(G-14413)*

VEHICLES: All Terrain

Power Sports Treasure Coast G 772 463-6428
Stuart *(G-16992)*
River City Powersports LLC G 386 259-5724
Debary *(G-2754)*
Southern Brothers Racing LLC G 850 509-2223
Quincy *(G-15255)*

Viper 4x4 F 305 468-9818
Windermere *(G-19249)*
Xscream Inc G 727 449-9353
Clearwater *(G-1945)*

VEHICLES: Recreational

B & E Rv Service & Repair LLC G 352 401-7930
Ocala *(G-11883)*
Lakeside Recreational Inc G 863 467-1530
Okeechobee *(G-12185)*

VENDING MACHINES & PARTS

Hylton & Assoc G 321 303-2862
Orlando *(G-12815)*
Optima Associates Inc F 877 371-1555
Lake City *(G-7374)*
Optimal Vending Systems G 301 633-2353
Alachua *(G-13)*
Rocket Vending Inc F 561 672-1373
Boca Raton *(G-692)*
SAP Enterprises Inc F 954 871-8688
North Lauderdale *(G-11621)*
Sunnypics LLC G 407 992-6210
Orlando *(G-13224)*
Vendapin LLC F 352 796-2693
Brooksville *(G-1289)*

VENETIAN BLINDS & SHADES

Blind Wizard Too Inc G 954 755-3828
Coral Springs *(G-2228)*
Blinds R Us Corp G 305 303-2072
Miami *(G-9259)*
D W A Inc F 941 444-1134
Sarasota *(G-16401)*
Louvers Window Fashions G 941 275-2655
Venice *(G-18561)*
Privacy Window Design Inc G 386 761-7306
Port Orange *(G-15029)*

VENTURE CAPITAL COMPANIES

Sphere Access Inc F 336 501-6159
Tampa *(G-18126)*

VESSELS: Process, Indl, Metal Plate

Brewfab LLC G 727 823-8333
Saint Petersburg *(G-15729)*

VETERINARY PHARMACEUTICAL PREPARATIONS

American Vet Sciences LLC G 727 471-0850
Largo *(G-7895)*
Amino Cell Inc F 352 291-0200
Ocala *(G-11874)*
D V M Pharmaceuticals Inc D 305 575-6950
Weston *(G-19119)*
Pegasus Laboratories Inc D 850 478-2770
Pensacola *(G-14224)*
Synergylabs LLC E 954 525-1133
Fort Lauderdale *(G-4272)*
Vetbiotek Inc F 727 308-2030
Largo *(G-8072)*

VETERINARY PRDTS: Instruments & Apparatus

Earth Vets Inc G 352 332-9991
Fernandina Beach *(G-3736)*

VIALS: Glass

Jensen Scientific Products Inc E 954 344-2006
Coral Springs *(G-2263)*

VIDEO & AUDIO EQPT, WHOLESALE

Armadillo Sounds Inc G 305 801-7906
Miami *(G-9169)*
AVI-Spl Emplyee Emrgncy Rlief A 813 884-7168
Tampa *(G-17445)*
Hitex Marketing Group Inc G 305 406-1150
Miami *(G-9713)*
Interntnal Srvillance Tech Inc E 954 574-1100
Deerfield Beach *(G-2847)*
Perpetual Marketing Assoc Inc G 813 949-9385
Lutz *(G-8408)*

VIDEO PRODUCTION SVCS

Collins Media & Advg LLC F 954 688-9758
Margate *(G-8538)*

VIDEO TRIGGERS EXC REMOTE CONTROL TV DEVICES

Adtec Productions Incorporated G 904 720-2003
Jacksonville *(G-6120)*

VINYL RESINS, NEC

American Vinyl Company E 305 687-1863
Hialeah *(G-5296)*
Certified Whl Exterior Pdts G 407 654-7170
Winter Garden *(G-19256)*

VISUAL COMMUNICATIONS SYSTEMS

First Communications Inc D 850 668-7990
Tallahassee *(G-17251)*
Kaltec Electronics Inc F 813 888-9555
Tampa *(G-17814)*
Salt International Corp G 305 698-8889
Pembroke Park *(G-14012)*
Viper Communication Systems E 352 694-7030
Ocala *(G-12072)*

VITAMINS: Natural Or Synthetic, Uncompounded, Bulk

Alfa Manufacturing LLC F 305 436-8150
Miami *(G-9102)*
Alive By Nature Inc G 800 810-1935
Ponte Vedra Beach *(G-14930)*
American Natural Pdts Lab Inc G 305 261-5152
Miami *(G-9146)*
Boston Ntrceutical Science LLC F 617 848-4560
Miami *(G-9270)*
CJ Labs Inc F 305 234-9644
Miami *(G-9359)*
De Lima Consultants Group Inc F 954 933-7030
Coral Springs *(G-2238)*
Fdc Vitamins LLC B 305 468-1600
Miami Lakes *(G-10789)*
Great Amercn Natural Pdts Inc E 727 521-4372
Saint Petersburg *(G-15796)*
Guardian Essentials LLC G 817 401-0200
Delray Beach *(G-3089)*
Lab Kingz LLC G 561 808-4216
Delray Beach *(G-3100)*
Lan Industries LLC F 305 889-2087
Miami *(G-9854)*
Liv LLC E 321 276-5302
Miami Lakes *(G-10808)*
Live Wise Naturals LLC G 866 866-0075
Bradenton *(G-1072)*
Modular Thermal Tech LLC E 954 785-1055
Pompano Beach *(G-14767)*
National Health Alliance LLC G 727 504-3915
Tampa *(G-17932)*
Nulab Inc D 727 446-1126
Clearwater *(G-1813)*
Nutop International LLC G 954 909-0010
Fort Lauderdale *(G-4144)*
Rainbow Lght Ntrtnal Systems I G 954 233-3300
Sunrise *(G-17167)*
Totally Products LLC G 786 942-9218
Boca Raton *(G-753)*
Twinlab Cnsld Holdings Inc E 561 443-4301
Boca Raton *(G-759)*
Twinlab Consolidation Corp F 800 645-5626
Boca Raton *(G-760)*
Twinlab Holdings Inc E 800 645-5626
Boca Raton *(G-762)*
Vedic Origins Inc G 407 712-5614
Altamonte Springs *(G-82)*
Vitalleo LLC G 904 474-5330
Neptune Beach *(G-11479)*
Vitaminmed LLC G 727 443-7008
Clearwater *(G-1934)*
Viva 5 LLC D 561 239-2239
Saint Petersburg *(G-15955)*
We Make Vitamins LLC G 863 607-6708
Lakeland *(G-7833)*

VITAMINS: Pharmaceutical Preparations

Avanti Nutritional Labs LLC C 305 822-3880
Miami Lakes *(G-10764)*

Employee Codes: A=Over 500 employees, B=251-500
C=101-250, D=51-100, E=20-50, F=10-19, G=4-9

Be Whole Nutrition LLC..........G....... 813 420-3057
Plant City *(G-14408)*
Ceautamed Worldwide LLC..........G....... 866 409-6262
Boca Raton *(G-474)*
Dextrum Laboratories Inc..........G....... 305 594-4020
Miami *(G-9462)*
Florida Nutri Labs LLC..........F....... 863 607-6708
Lakeland *(G-7692)*
Full Life Direct LLC..........F....... 800 305-3043
Hollywood *(G-5826)*
Glucorell Inc..........F....... 407 384-3388
Maitland *(G-8466)*
Interntnal Ntrctcals Group Inc..........G....... 786 518-2903
Sunrise *(G-17130)*
Master Nutrition Labs Inc..........G....... 786 847-2000
Opa Locka *(G-12336)*
Mdr LLC..........C....... 954 845-9500
Sunrise *(G-17146)*
Natural Vitamins Lab Corp..........C....... 305 265-1660
Opa Locka *(G-12343)*
Natural Vitamins Lab Corp..........C....... 305 265-1660
Opa Locka *(G-12344)*
Nutrition Laboratories Inc..........E....... 727 442-2747
Clearwater *(G-1815)*
Pharmalab Enterprises Inc..........E....... 305 821-4002
Miami Lakes *(G-10838)*
Taylor L Max L C..........G....... 833 346-9963
Fort Myers *(G-4625)*
Twinlab Corporation..........B....... 800 645-5626
Boca Raton *(G-761)*

VOCATIONAL REHABILITATION AGENCY

Brevard Achievement Center Inc..........B....... 321 632-8610
Rockledge *(G-15395)*

WALKWAYS: Moving

Mobile Specialties Inc..........G....... 407 878-5469
Sanford *(G-16088)*

WALL & CEILING SQUARES: Concrete

USG International Ltd..........F....... 305 688-8744
Miami *(G-10557)*

WALLBOARD: Decorated, Made From Purchased Materials

Panelfold Inc..........C....... 305 688-3501
Miami *(G-10138)*

WALLPAPER & WALL COVERINGS

Nicolette Mayer Collection Inc..........G....... 561 241-6906
Boca Raton *(G-644)*
Parthenon Prints Inc..........E....... 850 769-8321
Panama City *(G-13940)*
Richard Wagner LLC..........G....... 239 450-1721
Naples *(G-11383)*

WALLS: Curtain, Metal

Johnson & Jackson Glass Pdts..........F....... 813 630-9774
Tampa *(G-17808)*

WAREHOUSING & STORAGE FACILITIES, NEC

Refreshment Services Inc..........D....... 850 574-0281
Tallahassee *(G-17315)*

WAREHOUSING & STORAGE, REFRIGERATED: Cold Storage Or Refrig

West Texas Protein Inc..........F....... 806 250-5959
Jacksonville *(G-6911)*

WAREHOUSING & STORAGE: General

Dip-A-Dee Donuts..........E....... 352 460-4266
Leesburg *(G-8150)*
Regent Labs Inc..........G....... 954 426-4889
Deerfield Beach *(G-2903)*

WAREHOUSING & STORAGE: Liquid

Kus Usa Inc..........E....... 954 463-1075
Davie *(G-2542)*

WAREHOUSING & STORAGE: Lumber Terminal Or Storage For Hire

Mid-Flrida Lbr Acqisitions Inc..........E....... 863 533-0155
Bartow *(G-325)*

WAREHOUSING & STORAGE: Self Storage

GOTG LLC..........G....... 800 381-4684
Brooksville *(G-1232)*

WARFARE COUNTER-MEASURE EQPT

Sparton Deleon Springs LLC..........D....... 386 985-4631
De Leon Springs *(G-2743)*
Spartronics Brooksville LLC..........B....... 352 799-6520
Brooksville *(G-1275)*

WARM AIR HEATING & AC EQPT & SPLYS, WHOLESALE Air Filters

Air Sponge Filter Company Inc..........G....... 954 752-1836
Coral Springs *(G-2217)*
Andrews Filter and Supply Corp..........E....... 407 423-3310
Orlando *(G-12479)*
Con-Air Industries Inc..........D....... 407 298-5733
Orlando *(G-12611)*
Rv Air Inc..........G....... 309 657-4300
Clearwater *(G-1866)*

WARM AIR HEATING/AC EQPT/SPLYS, WHOL Warm Air Htg Eqpt/Splys

Innovative Support Systems..........G....... 407 682-7570
Altamonte Springs *(G-51)*

WASHERS

Angela Zieglers Window Washers..........G....... 239 849-0310
Cape Coral *(G-1380)*
Pressure Washers USA..........G....... 561 848-7970
Lake Park *(G-7478)*
Shamrock Mobile Detl & Pressur..........G....... 941 286-3572
Punta Gorda *(G-15231)*
Siligom USA LLC..........F....... 786 406-6262
Doral *(G-3504)*
Washers-R-Us Inc..........G....... 850 573-0221
Alford *(G-23)*

WASHERS: Metal

Edwin B Stimpson Company Inc..........B....... 954 946-3500
Pompano Beach *(G-14675)*

WASHROOM SANITATION SVCS

AAA Event Services LLC..........F....... 386 454-0929
Newberry *(G-11549)*

WATCH STRAPS, EXC METAL

Rubber B LLC..........G....... 305 771-2369
Miami Beach *(G-10707)*

WATCHES

Lucien Piccard/Arnex Watch Co..........D....... 954 241-2745
Hollywood *(G-5865)*

WATCHES & PARTS, WHOLESALE

LP Watch Group Inc..........E....... 954 985-3827
Hollywood *(G-5863)*

WATER HEATERS

Marey International LLC..........G....... 787 727-0277
Miami *(G-9945)*
Peralta Group Inc..........G....... 954 502-8100
Sunrise *(G-17157)*

WATER HEATERS WHOLESALERS EXCEPT ELECTRIC

Marey International LLC..........G....... 787 727-0277
Miami *(G-9945)*

WATER PURIFICATION EQPT: Household

Action Manufacturing & Sup Inc..........F....... 239 574-3443
Cape Coral *(G-1373)*
Aquathin Corp..........E....... 800 462-7634
Pompano Beach *(G-14596)*
Astro Pure Incorporated..........F....... 954 422-8966
Deerfield Beach *(G-2781)*
Atmospheric Wtr Solutions Inc..........F....... 954 306-6763
Cooper City *(G-2109)*
Biozone Scientific Intl Inc..........G....... 407 876-2000
Orlando *(G-12517)*
Clearwater Enviro Tech Inc..........E....... 727 209-6400
Largo *(G-7924)*
Focus On Water Inc..........G....... 239 275-1880
Fort Myers *(G-4456)*
Great Lakes Wtr Trtmnt Systems..........G....... 269 381-0210
Naples *(G-11267)*
H2o International Inc..........F....... 954 570-3464
Deerfield Beach *(G-2834)*
Hydro-Dyne Engineering Inc..........E....... 727 532-0777
Oldsmar *(G-12233)*
K V Water Equipment & Krane Co..........F....... 941 723-0707
Venice *(G-18558)*
Lifegard Prfcation Systems LLC..........G....... 813 875-7777
Tampa *(G-17846)*
Main USA Corp..........G....... 305 499-4994
Miami *(G-9937)*
Membrane Systems Corp..........G....... 239 283-8590
Cape Coral *(G-1448)*
Pristine Environment LLC..........F....... 727 541-5748
Pinellas Park *(G-14380)*
Rgf Environmental Group Inc..........C....... 800 842-7771
Riviera Beach *(G-15372)*
Watermakers Inc..........F....... 954 467-8920
Fort Lauderdale *(G-4315)*
Watts Water Technologies Inc..........G....... 352 465-2000
Dunnellon *(G-3602)*
Worldwide Technology Inc..........E....... 813 855-2443
Oldsmar *(G-12279)*

WATER PURIFICATION PRDTS: Chlorination Tablets & Kits

Biomar Products LLC..........G....... 800 216-2080
Doral *(G-3276)*
Dependable Water Inc..........G....... 904 599-0560
Saint Johns *(G-15676)*
Dependable Water Inc..........E....... 772 563-7473
Vero Beach *(G-18615)*
Xcelience LLC..........D....... 813 286-0404
Tampa *(G-18272)*
Xcelience Holdings LLC..........D....... 813 286-0404
Tampa *(G-18273)*

WATER SOFTENER SVCS

Aqualogix Inc..........F....... 858 442-4550
Palm Beach Gardens *(G-13567)*

WATER SOFTENING WHOLESALERS

Enviro Water Solutions LLC..........D....... 877 842-1635
Deland *(G-2975)*

WATER SUPPLY

City of Hollywood..........F....... 954 967-4230
Hollywood *(G-5799)*
Sergeant Bretts Coffee LLC..........G....... 561 451-0048
Coconut Creek *(G-2094)*

WATER TREATMENT EQPT: Indl

Action Mfg & Sup WPB LLC..........G....... 239 574-3443
West Palm Beach *(G-18788)*
Advatech Corporation..........G....... 732 803-8000
West Palm Beach *(G-18790)*
Aesinc Advanced Eqp & Svcs..........G....... 954 857-1895
Coral Springs *(G-2216)*
AFL Industries Inc..........G....... 561 848-1826
Riviera Beach *(G-15295)*
Agua Control LLC..........G....... 813 663-0701
Tampa *(G-17393)*
Aqua Engineering & Equipment..........F....... 407 599-2123
Winter Park *(G-19378)*
Aqua Wholesale Inc..........G....... 941 341-0847
Sarasota *(G-16345)*
Aquatec Solutions LLC..........F....... 561 717-6933
Boca Raton *(G-428)*
Aquatech Manufacturing LLC..........F....... 813 664-0300
Tampa *(G-17430)*
Ce Hooton Sales LLC..........F....... 305 255-9722
Sarasota *(G-16189)*
Central Processing Corp..........G....... 352 787-3004
Leesburg *(G-8146)*
Chlorinators Inc..........E....... 772 288-4854
Stuart *(G-16924)*

City of Bradenton....E....941 727-6360
Bradenton (G-1020)
City of Hollywood....F....954 967-4230
Hollywood (G-5799)
Crane Co....G....941 480-9101
Venice (G-18538)
Crane Environmental Inc....D....941 480-9101
Venice (G-18539)
Dyco....G....941 484-9057
Sarasota (G-16416)
Ecosphere Technologies Inc....F....772 287-4846
Stuart (G-16936)
Electrolytic Tech Svcs LLC....G....305 655-2755
North Miami Beach (G-11673)
Electrolytic Technologies Corp....F....305 655-2755
Miami (G-9510)
Esd Waste2water Inc....D....800 277-3279
Ocala (G-11933)
Evoqua Water Technologies LLC....G....813 620-0900
Tampa (G-17651)
Evoqua Water Technologies LLC....G....407 650-1765
Orlando (G-12725)
Fovico Inc....F....561 624-5400
West Palm Beach (G-18882)
Fshs Inc....G....941 625-5929
Port Charlotte (G-14982)
Genesis Systems LLC....G....417 499-3301
Tampa (G-17709)
Harn Ro Systems Inc....E....941 488-9671
Venice (G-18553)
Kemco Systems Co LLC....D....727 573-2323
Clearwater (G-1748)
Latitude Clean Tech Group Inc....F....561 417-0687
Boca Raton (G-597)
Lenntech USA LLC....G....877 453-8095
South Miami (G-16820)
Lodex Enterprises Corp....G....954 442-3843
Miramar (G-11010)
Mar Cor Purification Inc....E....484 991-0220
Lakeland (G-7744)
Originclear Inc....G....323 939-6645
Clearwater (G-1822)
Parkson Corporation....G....954 974-6610
Fort Lauderdale (G-4160)
Poseidon Services Inc....G....786 294-8529
Miami (G-10179)
Premier Water & Enrgy Tech Inc....E....904 268-1152
Jacksonville (G-6685)
Pro Water Treatment Inc....G....954 650-1955
Margate (G-8564)
Pure Water Changes Inc....F....407 699-2837
Windermere (G-19241)
Randazza Enterprises Inc....F....813 677-0041
Riverview (G-15279)
Rgf Marine Envmtl Tech Inc....E....561 848-1826
Riviera Beach (G-15373)
Rz Service Group LLC....G....904 402-2313
Jacksonville (G-6741)
Starke Waste Wtr Trtmnt Plant....G....904 964-7999
Starke (G-16897)
Superior Waterway Services Inc....F....561 799-5852
Riviera Beach (G-15383)
Tampa Fiberglass Inc....F....813 248-6828
Tampa (G-18164)
Technical International Corp....G....305 374-1054
Miami (G-10462)
Twinoxide-Usa Inc....G....321 207-8524
Merritt Island (G-9019)
Vapex Environmental Tech Inc....G....407 277-0900
Cocoa (G-2055)
Water Bagel Boca East Lllp....G....347 661-7171
Jupiter (G-7144)
Yacht-Mate Products Inc....G....954 527-0112
Fort Lauderdale (G-4331)

WATER: Mineral, Carbonated, Canned & Bottled, Etc

Aqua Pure LLC....G....407 521-3055
Orlando (G-12484)
Chem-Free System Inc....G....954 258-5415
Delray Beach (G-3059)
Clewiston Water Btlg Co LLC....G....863 902-1317
Clewiston (G-1977)
South Pacific Trading Company....E....352 567-2200
Dade City (G-2435)

WATER: Pasteurized & Mineral, Bottled & Canned

AMA Waters LLC....G....786 400-1630
Miami (G-9129)
Aqua Pure Water Co Inc....G....954 744-4210
Hollywood (G-5773)
Pure Water Sulotins LLC....G....727 784-7400
Palm Harbor (G-13753)
Silver Springs Citrus Inc....C....352 324-2101
Howey In The Hills (G-6012)
Silver Springs Citrus LLC....E....352 324-2101
Howey In The Hills (G-6013)

WATER: Pasteurized, Canned & Bottled, Etc

Beverage Blocks Inc....F....813 309-8711
Tampa (G-17467)
Car Care Haven LLC....G....855 464-2836
Englewood (G-3671)
Cg Roxane LLC....E....407 241-1640
Orlando (G-12573)
Crystal River Water Pollution....F....352 795-3199
Crystal River (G-2376)
Keystone Water Company LLC....F....863 465-1932
Lake Placid (G-7490)
Lee McCullough Inc....G....352 796-7100
Brooksville (G-1244)
Mvs International Inc....G....954 727-3383
Weston (G-19151)
Niagara Bottling LLC....G....352 429-3611
Groveland (G-5102)
Nubo Bottle Company LLC....G....954 283-9057
Boynton Beach (G-938)
SOS Food Lab LLC....E....305 594-9933
Hialeah Gardens (G-5699)
Ultra-Pure Bottled Water Inc....F....281 731-0258
North Miami (G-11660)
Water Boy Inc....F....239 461-0860
Fort Myers (G-4650)

WATERING POTS Plastic

Peaktop Technologies Inc....G....561 598-6005
West Palm Beach (G-18992)

WATERPROOFING COMPOUNDS

Pressure Point Water Proofing....G....352 337-9905
Hawthorne (G-5245)

WAX REMOVERS

Ft Lauderdale Wax....G....954 256-9291
Fort Lauderdale (G-4014)

WAXES: Petroleum, Not Produced In Petroleum Refineries

Gaynor Group Inc....G....954 749-1228
Sunrise (G-17125)
Trigeant Ep Ltd....F....561 999-9916
Boca Raton (G-757)

WEAVING MILL, BROADWOVEN FABRICS: Wool Or Similar Fabric

Cool Ocean LLC....G....954 848-4060
Plantation (G-14502)

WEDDING CHAPEL: Privately Operated

Carlees Creations Inc....G....786 232-0050
Miami (G-9319)

WEIGHING MACHINERY & APPARATUS

Keytroller LLC....F....813 877-4500
Tampa (G-17823)
Merrick Industries Inc....C....850 265-3611
Lynn Haven (G-8436)
Mettler-Toledo Inc....C....607 257-6000
Lutz (G-8400)
Radwag USA LLC....G....305 651-3522
North Miami Beach (G-11702)
Tannehill Intl Inds Inc....C....850 265-3611
Lynn Haven (G-8439)
Weightech USA LLC....F....954 666-0877
Davie (G-2613)

WELDING & CUTTING APPARATUS & ACCESS, NEC

Applied Design & Fabrication....G....954 524-6619
Lake Placid (G-7484)
Jdci Enterprises Inc....E....239 768-2292
Fort Myers (G-4502)
Seelye Acquisitions Inc....G....407 656-6677
Apopka (G-184)
Smittys Boat Tops and Mar Eqp....G....305 245-0229
Homestead (G-5993)

WELDING EQPT

Alloy Cladding Company LLC....F....561 625-4550
Fort Myers (G-4353)
American Torch Tip Company....C....941 753-7557
Bradenton (G-988)
Automated Production Eqp Ape....F....631 654-1197
Key Largo (G-7164)
Goss Inc....E....386 423-0311
New Smyrna Beach (G-11534)
TL Fahringer Co Inc....G....813 681-2373
Tampa (G-18190)
V & C Supply Ornamental Corp....G....305 634-9040
Miami (G-10558)

WELDING EQPT & SPLYS WHOLESALERS

Matheson Tri-Gas Inc....G....561 615-3000
Riviera Beach (G-15347)
Matheson Tri-Gas Inc....G....727 572-8737
Clearwater (G-1776)
R & S Metalworks & Co LLC....F....772 466-3303
Port Saint Lucie (G-15132)
Seelye Acquisitions Inc....G....407 656-6677
Apopka (G-184)

WELDING EQPT & SPLYS: Arc Welders, Transformer-Rectifier

R & S Metalworks & Co LLC....F....772 466-3303
Port Saint Lucie (G-15132)

WELDING EQPT & SPLYS: Gas

Uniweld Products Inc....C....954 584-2000
Fort Lauderdale (G-4298)

WELDING EQPT & SPLYS: Resistance, Electric

Alphatron Industries Inc....G....954 581-1418
Davie (G-2494)

WELDING EQPT: Electric

J B Nottingham & Co Inc....E....386 873-2990
Deland (G-2986)
Parodi General Group Corp....G....954 306-1098
Coconut Creek (G-2092)

WELDING EQPT: Electrical

Crandon Enterprises Inc....G....352 873-8400
Ocala (G-11910)

WELDING MACHINES & EQPT: Ultrasonic

Complete Access Ctrl Centl Fla....G....407 498-0067
Saint Cloud (G-15647)
Surface Engrg & Alloy Co Inc....D....727 528-3734
Saint Petersburg (G-15930)

WELDING REPAIR SVC

4f Mobile Welding LLC....G....850 537-2290
Baker (G-299)
5571 Halifax Inc....E....239 454-4999
Fort Myers (G-4340)
A & E Machine Inc....F....321 636-3110
Cocoa (G-1988)
A Mobile Mechanic & Wldg Svc....G....813 900-8764
Riverview (G-15262)
A Plus Trailers....G....786 395-0799
Southwest Ranches (G-16835)
Aarons Equipment Repair Inc....G....904 879-3249
Callahan (G-1323)
Able Railing & Welding LLC....G....850 243-5444
Fort Walton Beach (G-4774)
Accurate Wldg Fabrication LLC....G....727 483-3125
Tampa (G-17386)

PRODUCT

Ace-Pipe Welding LLC.......G....... 561 727-6345
Palm Beach Gardens *(G-13564)*
Advanced Machine and Tool Inc.......D....... 772 465-6546
Fort Pierce *(G-4669)*
Advanced Wldg Fbrction Dsign L.......G....... 352 237-9800
Summerfield *(G-17056)*
Ajs Fabrication Llc.......G....... 863 514-9630
Winter Haven *(G-19296)*
Alexis Welding Express Corp.......G....... 786 626-4090
Opa Locka *(G-12284)*
Alfredo Welding Service LLC.......G....... 954 770-8744
Winter Haven *(G-19297)*
All Phase Welding LLC.......G....... 772 834-2980
Vero Beach *(G-18591)*
All Weld Inc.......G....... 239 348-9550
Naples *(G-11154)*
Allied Welding & Maint Inc.......G....... 863 634-7718
Okeechobee *(G-12172)*
Amax Welding & Fabrication.......G....... 352 544-8484
Brooksville *(G-1208)*
American Fence Shop LLC.......F....... 305 681-3511
Hialeah *(G-5290)*
American Wldg & Installation.......G....... 786 391-4800
Miami *(G-9148)*
Anthony Wright Welding.......G....... 850 544-1831
Tallahassee *(G-17220)*
ARC Dimensions Inc.......G....... 727 524-6139
Largo *(G-7898)*
ARC-Rite Inc.......E....... 386 325-3523
Jacksonville *(G-6165)*
Armor Supply Metals LLC.......G....... 305 640-9901
Medley *(G-8613)*
Arnold Industries South Inc.......G....... 352 867-0190
Ocala *(G-11879)*
Art of Iron Inc.......G....... 850 819-1500
Panama City *(G-13865)*
Atlas Innovative Services Inc.......F....... 617 259-4529
Punta Gorda *(G-15192)*
Attila Services Corp.......G....... 305 255-6776
Miami *(G-9191)*
B & B of Saint Augustine Inc.......G....... 904 829-6855
Saint Augustine *(G-15519)*
B & N Wldg & Fabrication Inc.......E....... 813 719-3956
Plant City *(G-14405)*
Badger Welding Orlando LLC.......G....... 407 648-1100
Orlando *(G-12504)*
Barrs Equipment Service Inc.......F....... 407 999-5214
Orlando *(G-12507)*
Bartow Machine Works Inc.......G....... 863 533-6361
Bartow *(G-308)*
Baxley Services Inc.......G....... 850 675-4459
Jay *(G-6962)*
Beasley Welding LLC.......G....... 352 595-4086
Anthony *(G-95)*
Bee Welding Inc.......F....... 561 616-9003
West Palm Beach *(G-18816)*
Beyers Welding Inc.......G....... 407 892-2834
Saint Cloud *(G-15645)*
Billys Welding Inc.......G....... 239 229-8723
Cape Coral *(G-1391)*
Blackies Weldng & Boiler Svc.......G....... 954 961-5777
Hallandale Beach *(G-5172)*
Blaine E Taylor Welding Inc.......G....... 386 931-1242
Bunnell *(G-1298)*
Blane E Taylor Welding Inc.......G....... 386 931-1240
Ormond Beach *(G-13354)*
Bluepoint Fabrication Inc.......F....... 321 269-0073
Titusville *(G-18415)*
Blunts Welding LLC.......G....... 352 274-6014
Citra *(G-1556)*
Bob Kline Quality Metal Inc.......G....... 561 659-4245
West Palm Beach *(G-18827)*
Bobs Wldg Fbrcation Maint Inc.......E....... 863 665-0135
Lakeland *(G-7648)*
Boyd Welding LLC.......G....... 352 447-2405
Ocala *(G-11889)*
Brannen Wldg & Fabrication Inc.......G....... 352 583-4849
Dade City *(G-2423)*
Brownsville Orna Ir Works Inc.......G....... 850 433-0521
Pensacola *(G-14107)*
Burton JC Companies Inc.......G....... 239 992-2377
Bonita Springs *(G-821)*
Cannons of Jack LLC.......G....... 904 733-3524
Jacksonville *(G-6253)*
Central Florida Weld & Fab LLC.......G....... 407 919-8706
Orange City *(G-12373)*
Central Maintenance & Wldg Inc.......F....... 352 795-2817
Crystal River *(G-2371)*
Central Maintenance & Wldg Inc.......B....... 813 229-0012
Lithia *(G-8216)*
Certified Wldg Fbrction Svcs L.......G....... 813 323-4090
Tampa *(G-17529)*
Champagne Welding Inc.......G....... 585 738-8611
Jacksonville *(G-6260)*
Champion Welding Services LLC.......G....... 786 262-5727
Miami Lakes *(G-10775)*
Channel Industries Inc.......F....... 561 214-0637
West Palm Beach *(G-18845)*
Chviek.......G....... 239 567-1511
North Fort Myers *(G-11597)*
Ciron Custom Welding Inc.......G....... 786 259-7589
Hialeah *(G-5345)*
Coastal Wldg Fabrications Inc.......F....... 954 938-7933
Oakland Park *(G-11791)*
Copeland Welding & Muffler Sp.......G....... 904 355-6383
Jacksonville *(G-6290)*
Cornelius Welding Inc.......E....... 863 635-3668
Frostproof *(G-4858)*
Crown Welding & Fabg Inc.......G....... 941 737-6844
Myakka City *(G-11142)*
D & D MBL Wldg Fabrication Inc.......F....... 954 791-3385
Fort Lauderdale *(G-3927)*
D & D Welding Inc.......G....... 850 438-9011
Pensacola *(G-14123)*
D & S Steel.......G....... 352 489-8791
Dunnellon *(G-3595)*
D B Welding Fabrication.......G....... 941 379-2319
Sarasota *(G-16400)*
Dade Made.......G....... 305 846-9482
Hialeah *(G-5363)*
Dcwfab LLC.......G....... 941 320-6095
Sarasota *(G-16406)*
Diligent Services Inc.......G....... 561 368-1478
Boca Raton *(G-501)*
Discount Welds LLC.......G....... 305 637-3939
Miami *(G-9470)*
Diversified Welding Inc.......G....... 561 996-9398
Belle Glade *(G-347)*
Docs Welding LLC.......G....... 813 846-5022
Plant City *(G-14425)*
Doll Marine Metal Fabrication.......G....... 954 941-5093
Pompano Beach *(G-14667)*
Double R Mfg Ocala Inc.......F....... 352 873-1441
Ocala *(G-11924)*
Dumont Welder Services Inc.......G....... 863 969-7498
Winter Haven *(G-19318)*
Dynamic Welding & Fab LLC.......G....... 904 669-4682
Saint Augustine *(G-15540)*
E M P Inc.......G....... 772 286-7343
Stuart *(G-16935)*
East Coast Metalworks LLC.......G....... 321 698-0624
Cocoa *(G-2018)*
East Coast Ornamental Welding.......F....... 386 672-4340
Daytona Beach *(G-2660)*
Electron Beam Development.......F....... 772 219-4600
Palm City *(G-13652)*
Elkins Welding Inc.......G....... 352 362-4577
Dunnellon *(G-3597)*
Emf Inc.......C....... 321 453-3670
Merritt Island *(G-9000)*
ENG Manufacturing Inc.......G....... 727 942-3868
Tarpon Springs *(G-18299)*
Escambia Welding and Fab Inc.......G....... 850 477-3901
Pensacola *(G-14145)*
Exact Inc.......C....... 904 783-6640
Jacksonville *(G-6372)*
F P General Welding.......G....... 786 812-6673
Miami *(G-9552)*
First Coast Fabrication Inc.......G....... 904 849-7426
Yulee *(G-19496)*
Floyd Fabrication LLC.......G....... 330 289-7351
Haines City *(G-5143)*
Franz A Ullrich Jr.......G....... 863 773-4653
Wauchula *(G-18692)*
Friendly Welding Inc.......F....... 786 953-8413
Hialeah *(G-5417)*
Fusion Welding.......F....... 239 288-6530
Fort Myers *(G-4463)*
G B Welding & Fabrication LLC.......F....... 954 967-2573
Davie *(G-2529)*
G Welding Contractor Corp.......G....... 305 896-0311
Miami Lakes *(G-10793)*
Gator Welding Inc.......F....... 561 746-0049
Jupiter *(G-7047)*
General Welding Svc Entps Inc.......G....... 305 592-9483
Doral *(G-3363)*
Grahams Welding Fabrication.......G....... 850 865-0899
Fort Walton Beach *(G-4803)*
Greenes Wldg & Fabrication LLC.......G....... 904 773-3101
Middleburg *(G-10905)*
Greg Clark Welding Inc.......G....... 904 226-2952
Jacksonville *(G-6451)*
Griffiths Corporation.......D....... 407 851-8342
Orlando *(G-12790)*
Gunns Welding & Fabricating.......G....... 727 393-5238
Saint Petersburg *(G-15801)*
Hay Tech.......G....... 850 592-2424
Bascom *(G-336)*
Hernandez Mobile Welding Inc.......G....... 954 347-4071
Okeechobee *(G-12181)*
HI Tech Aviation Welding LLC.......G....... 305 591-3393
Miami *(G-9707)*
Hialeah Welding & Ornamental.......G....... 305 685-3196
Hialeah *(G-5447)*
Holmes Tool & Engineering Inc.......E....... 850 547-4417
Bonifay *(G-804)*
Hot Shot Welding Inc.......F....... 727 585-1900
Largo *(G-7975)*
House of Metal LLC.......G....... 727 540-0637
Clearwater *(G-1721)*
Hudsons Wldg & Fabrication Inc.......G....... 941 355-4858
Bradenton *(G-1057)*
Industrial & Marine Maint.......G....... 813 622-8338
Tampa *(G-17779)*
Industrial Repair Inc.......F....... 239 368-7435
Lehigh Acres *(G-8192)*
Interstate Wldg & Fabrication.......F....... 727 446-1449
Clearwater *(G-1735)*
Ironclad Welding Inc.......G....... 954 925-7987
Dania *(G-2449)*
J L M Machine Co Inc.......F....... 941 748-4288
Bradenton *(G-1064)*
Jackson Equipment Inc.......G....... 904 845-3696
Jacksonville *(G-6509)*
Jam Welding Service Inc.......F....... 305 662-3787
South Miami *(G-16818)*
JC Industrial Mfg Corp.......E....... 305 634-5280
Miami *(G-9789)*
Jim Appleys Tru-ARC Inc.......F....... 727 571-3007
Clearwater *(G-1743)*
JL Welding Inc.......F....... 786 442-4319
South Miami *(G-16819)*
Just Steel Inc.......F....... 941 755-7811
Sarasota *(G-16242)*
K & D Welding LLC.......G....... 941 586-0258
Sarasota *(G-16479)*
Kevin Murray Welding Proj DBA.......G....... 813 323-3543
Spring Hill *(G-16875)*
Key West Wldg Fabrication Inc.......G....... 305 296-5555
Key West *(G-7192)*
Kickin It LLC.......G....... 954 648-1405
Oakland Park *(G-11817)*
Kinetic Fusion Corp.......G....... 561 352-1670
West Palm Beach *(G-18920)*
King Mobile Welding Andrew.......G....... 386 437-1007
Bunnell *(G-1301)*
Knight Welding Supply LLC.......G....... 561 889-5342
Stuart *(G-16967)*
L & C Metals LLC.......G....... 407 859-2600
Orlando *(G-12878)*
L T Weld II LLC.......G....... 352 454-2735
Clermont *(G-1966)*
Leeroys Fabrication & Wldg LLC.......G....... 850 398-1997
Crestview *(G-2354)*
Lynn Industrial Welding Inc.......G....... 850 584-4494
Perry *(G-14306)*
M&S Strong Welding Inc.......G....... 623 299-5336
Dundee *(G-3565)*
Madson Inc.......F....... 305 863-7390
Medley *(G-8681)*
Mag Cleaning Solutions LLC.......G....... 321 317-3298
Altamonte Springs *(G-55)*
Matlocks Welding & Fab.......G....... 305 942-9201
Marathon *(G-8520)*
MB Welding Inc.......G....... 727 548-0923
Saint Petersburg *(G-15852)*
Metal Craft of Pensacola Inc.......E....... 850 478-8333
Pensacola *(G-14207)*
Metal Fabrication and.......G....... 850 205-2300
Tallahassee *(G-17300)*
Mid-State Machine & Fabg Corp.......B....... 863 665-6233
Lakeland *(G-7751)*
Mike Blackburn Welding LLC.......G....... 850 643-8464
Blountstown *(G-386)*
Milans Machine Shop & Wldg Svc.......E....... 305 592-2447
Doral *(G-3438)*
MPH Industries Inc.......F....... 352 372-9533
Gainesville *(G-4966)*
Ms Mobile Wldg & Fabrication.......F....... 904 591-1488
Jacksonville *(G-6616)*

Ms Welding ....G.... 941 629-2597
Port Charlotte *(G-14990)*
National Pipe Welding Inc ....F.... 904 588-2589
Glen Saint Mary *(G-5037)*
Native Welding ....G.... 561 348-0100
Palm City *(G-13667)*
O R Welding Service LLC ....G.... 561 707-4325
Belle Glade *(G-349)*
Omni Marine Enterprises LLC ....G.... 941 474-4614
Englewood *(G-3663)*
On Site Svcs of Mid FL ....G.... 407 444-2951
Deland *(G-3004)*
Ornamental Alasco Iron & Wldg ....G.... 813 254-4883
Brandon *(G-1168)*
P & A Welding and Machine Inc ....G.... 863 425-3198
Mulberry *(G-11132)*
Paire Jr Weld Inc ....G.... 754 281-1803
North Lauderdale *(G-11619)*
Palatka Welding Shop Inc ....E.... 386 328-1507
Palatka *(G-13488)*
Paradise Wldg Cstm Fabrication ....G.... 239 961-8864
Naples *(G-11357)*
Parts Central Inc ....F.... 850 547-1660
Bonifay *(G-806)*
Patriot Welding Inc ....G.... 954 798-8819
Pompano Beach *(G-14785)*
Pena General Welding Inc ....G.... 786 255-2153
Miami *(G-10150)*
Phillip & Roger Inc ....G.... 850 763-6415
Panama City *(G-13941)*
Pk Welding Inc ....G.... 407 694-9403
Kissimmee *(G-7287)*
Precision Svcs Jcksonville Inc ....F.... 904 781-3770
Jacksonville *(G-6682)*
Pro Weld of South Florida Inc ....G.... 954 984-0104
Margate *(G-8565)*
Pro-Weld Inc ....G.... 863 453-9353
Avon Park *(G-294)*
Production Metal Stampings ....F.... 850 981-8240
Milton *(G-10938)*
Promax Welding Inc ....G.... 305 962-5033
Hialeah *(G-5580)*
Quality Metal Worx ....G.... 863 353-6638
Haines City *(G-5147)*
R & K Welding and Fabrication ....G.... 863 422-8728
Lake Hamilton *(G-7392)*
Ramsay Marine Services LLC ....F.... 561 881-1234
Riviera Beach *(G-15368)*
Rankine-Hinman Mfg Co ....F.... 904 808-0404
Saint Augustine *(G-15594)*
RB Custom Welding LLC ....G.... 813 280-9860
Tampa *(G-18040)*
Real Pro Welding Inc ....G.... 850 939-3469
Navarre *(G-11473)*
Responsive Machining Inc ....F.... 321 225-4011
Titusville *(G-18457)*
Richards Mobile Welding ....G.... 954 913-0487
Coral Springs *(G-2305)*
Right Way Wldg Fabrication LLC ....G.... 850 212-9672
Monticello *(G-11082)*
RLC Building Inc ....G.... 904 704-5614
Jacksonville *(G-6731)*
Rodriguez Welding ....G.... 305 856-3749
Miami *(G-10275)*
Rq Inc ....G.... 305 879-1773
Hialeah *(G-5606)*
Rudd & Son Welding Inc ....F.... 850 476-2110
Pensacola *(G-14255)*
Ryder Welding Service Inc ....F.... 305 685-6630
Opa Locka *(G-12357)*
S & S Welding Inc ....F.... 863 533-2888
Bartow *(G-333)*
SDr Specialties Services LLC ....G.... 386 878-6771
De Leon Springs *(G-2741)*
Serf Inc ....E.... 850 476-8203
Cantonment *(G-1347)*
Shawn William Shumake LLC ....G.... 813 374-2469
Tampa *(G-18092)*
Shaws Welding Inc ....F.... 850 584-7197
Perry *(G-14313)*
Shermans Welding & Maintence ....F.... 904 731-3460
Jacksonville *(G-6764)*
Signature Metal Fab LLC ....G.... 954 214-1161
Plantation *(G-14551)*
Smittys Boat Tops and Mar Eqp ....G.... 305 245-0229
Homestead *(G-5993)*
Smittys Welding Shop ....G.... 321 723-4533
Melbourne *(G-8935)*
Southern Awning Inc ....E.... 561 586-0464
Lake Worth *(G-7587)*
Southern Welding & Mechanics ....F.... 305 772-0961
Hialeah *(G-5629)*
Specialty Fabrication Wldg Inc ....G.... 352 669-9353
Umatilla *(G-18502)*
St Cloud Wldg Fabrication Inc ....E.... 407 957-2344
Saint Cloud *(G-15667)*
Steel Plus Service Center Inc ....G.... 407 328-7169
Sanford *(G-16121)*
Steel Products Inc ....G.... 941 351-8128
Sarasota *(G-16604)*
Straight Polarity Welding Inc ....G.... 727 530-7224
Largo *(G-8061)*
Suncoast Welding & Fabrication ....G.... 254 537-3611
Lakeland *(G-7811)*
Superior Fabrication Inc ....G.... 941 639-2966
Punta Gorda *(G-15238)*
Sureweld Welding Inc ....E.... 813 918-1857
Lakeland *(G-7813)*
T & S Mobile Welding LLC ....G.... 727 505-9407
Spring Hill *(G-16867)*
Tallahassee Welding & Mch Sp ....E.... 850 576-9596
Tallahassee *(G-17337)*
Tampa Amalgamated Steel Corp ....F.... 813 621-0550
Tampa *(G-18155)*
Tera Industries Inc ....E.... 561 848-7272
Riviera Beach *(G-15384)*
Terry M Griffin Welding ....G.... 407 209-8317
Orlando *(G-13250)*
Tes America LLC ....G.... 786 393-2544
Homestead *(G-5996)*
Tig Technologies Inc ....G.... 561 691-3633
Fort Pierce *(G-4755)*
Tin Man Mobile Welding LLC ....G.... 239 465-9058
Naples *(G-11443)*
Titan Metalworks LLC ....G.... 904 574-9828
Jacksonville *(G-6859)*
Titan Mfg Inc ....F.... 239 939-5152
Fort Myers *(G-4631)*
Titan Service Industry Llc ....G.... 678 313-4707
Deland *(G-3023)*
Top Torch Wldg & Fabrication ....G.... 352 835-1174
Spring Hill *(G-16868)*
Triple H Cstm Wldg Fbrction LL ....G.... 850 851-5097
Panama City *(G-13957)*
Unlimited Welding Inc ....E.... 407 327-3333
Winter Springs *(G-19487)*
Viking Welding and Fabrication ....G.... 904 234-5964
Orange Park *(G-12411)*
Voyager Offroad LLC ....G.... 941 235-7225
Port Charlotte *(G-15006)*
Weimer Mechanical Services Inc ....G.... 813 645-2258
Ruskin *(G-15487)*
Welding Anything Anywhere LLC ....G.... 561 762-1404
Palm Beach Gardens *(G-13635)*
Welding LLC ....G.... 386 478-0323
Edgewater *(G-3639)*
West Palm Machining & Welding ....G.... 561 841-2725
Riviera Beach *(G-15389)*
West Point Industries Inc ....G.... 561 848-8381
Lake Park *(G-7481)*
Westcoast Metalworks Inc ....G.... 941 920-3201
Palmetto *(G-13836)*
Whitley Welding Company L ....G.... 904 576-3410
Middleburg *(G-10915)*
Wilson Machine & Welding Works ....G.... 904 829-3737
Saint Augustine *(G-15637)*
World Class Machining Inc ....F.... 386 437-7036
Bunnell *(G-1311)*
Xpress Precision Products Inc ....G.... 305 685-2127
Hialeah *(G-5691)*
Y C Aluminum Welding Corp ....G.... 786 255-7186
Homestead *(G-5997)*
Ym Welding Services Inc ....G.... 502 905-4651
Homestead *(G-5998)*

WELDMENTS

Metal 2 Metal Inc ....G.... 954 253-9450
Palmetto Bay *(G-13850)*
SMI Tool & Die Inc ....G.... 321 632-6200
Cocoa *(G-2051)*

WESTERN APPAREL STORES

Farmers Cooperative Inc ....E.... 386 362-1459
Live Oak *(G-8232)*

WHEELBARROWS

Ames Companies Inc ....B.... 717 737-1500
Orlando *(G-12475)*

WHEELCHAIRS

Affordable Wheelchair Transprt ....G.... 727 432-4089
Saint Petersburg *(G-15694)*
Best Price Mobility Inc ....F.... 321 402-5955
Kissimmee *(G-7224)*
Buffalo Wheelchair Inc ....G.... 941 921-6331
Sarasota *(G-16371)*
Custom Medical Systems Inc ....G.... 941 722-3434
Palmetto *(G-13794)*
Deming Designs Inc ....F.... 850 478-5765
Pensacola *(G-14129)*
Gulf Coast Non Emergency Trans ....G.... 239 825-1350
Fort Myers *(G-4475)*
Hoveround Corporation ....B.... 941 739-6200
Sarasota *(G-16230)*
Imc-Heartway LLC ....G.... 239 275-6767
Fort Myers *(G-4489)*
Merits Health Products Inc ....E.... 239 772-0579
Fort Myers *(G-4527)*
Mobility Freedom Inc ....G.... 407 495-1333
Orlando *(G-12974)*
Noa International Inc ....G.... 954 835-5258
West Palm Beach *(G-18967)*
Pride Florida ....G.... 813 621-9262
Tampa *(G-18009)*
Scooter Link ....G.... 813 985-3075
Temple Terrace *(G-18377)*
Synergy Rehab Technologies Inc ....G.... 407 943-7500
Saint Cloud *(G-15669)*
Trackmaster LLC ....G.... 727 333-7562
Clearwater *(G-1925)*
Trinity Mobility ....G.... 727 389-1438
New Port Richey *(G-11517)*
Verhi Inc ....E.... 850 477-4880
Pensacola *(G-14282)*

WHEELS

Advance One Wheels Inc ....F.... 305 238-5833
Miami *(G-9074)*
American Force Wheels Inc ....F.... 786 345-6301
Hialeah *(G-5291)*
Bigg Wills Wheels LLC ....G.... 352 222-6170
Gainesville *(G-4886)*
Drt Express Inc ....G.... 305 827-5005
Hialeah *(G-5378)*
Elite Wheel Distributors Inc ....F.... 813 673-8393
Tampa *(G-17633)*
Frozen Wheels LLC ....F.... 305 799-2258
Miami *(G-9601)*
Leals Tires & Wheels ....G.... 239 491-2214
Lehigh Acres *(G-8195)*
Manna On Wheels Inc ....G.... 813 754-2277
Dover *(G-3560)*
Miami Power Wheels ....G.... 305 553-1888
Miami *(G-10004)*
New Bs Wheel LLC ....G.... 309 657-4899
Saint Augustine *(G-15572)*
School-On-Wheels ....G.... 239 530-8522
Naples *(G-11396)*
Sg Global LLC ....G.... 305 726-3439
Miami *(G-10329)*
Specialty Forged Wheels Inc ....G.... 786 332-5925
Miami *(G-10400)*
Starr Wheel Group Inc ....F.... 954 935-5536
Coral Springs *(G-2316)*
Str Racing Wheels ....G.... 407 251-7171
Orlando *(G-13217)*
TK Tires & Wheels Inc ....G.... 321 473-8945
Melbourne *(G-8964)*

WHEELS, GRINDING: Artificial

Global Diversified Products ....E.... 727 209-0854
Pinellas Park *(G-14351)*

WHEELS: Iron & Steel, Locomotive & Car

Skipper Wright Inc ....F.... 904 354-4381
Jacksonville *(G-6779)*

WHIRLPOOL BATHS: Hydrotherapy

Bathroom World Manufacturing ....G.... 954 566-0451
Oakland Park *(G-11785)*
Royal Baths Manufacturing Co ....E.... 407 854-1740
Orlando *(G-13147)*

WIGS & HAIRPIECES

Advanced Hair Products Inc ....G.... 561 347-2799
Deerfield Beach *(G-2764)*

PRODUCT

WINDINGS: Coil, Electronic

Electro Technik Industries Inc...............D....... 727 530-9555
Clearwater *(G-1666)*
Hytronics Corp...............D....... 727 535-0413
Clearwater *(G-1725)*
Precision Econowind LLC...............F....... 239 997-3860
North Fort Myers *(G-11603)*
Winatic Corporation...............D....... 727 538-8917
Clearwater *(G-1942)*

WINDMILLS: Electric Power Generation

Blue Summit Wind LLC...............G....... 561 691-7171
Juno Beach *(G-6975)*
FPL Energy Oklahoma Wind LLC...............G....... 561 691-7171
Juno Beach *(G-6980)*
Pheasant Run Wind LLC...............G....... 561 691-7171
Juno Beach *(G-6982)*
Pheasant Run Wind Holdings II...............E....... 561 691-7171
Juno Beach *(G-6983)*
Tuscola Wind II LLC...............G....... 561 691-7171
Juno Beach *(G-6985)*
Vasco Winds LLC...............G....... 561 691-7171
Juno Beach *(G-6986)*
White Oak Energy Backleverage...............E....... 561 691-7171
Juno Beach *(G-6987)*
White Oak Energy Holdings LLC...............G....... 561 691-7171
Juno Beach *(G-6988)*
Wilton Wind II LLC...............G....... 561 691-7171
Juno Beach *(G-6989)*

WINDMILLS: Farm Type

Jmp Marine LLC...............E....... 305 599-0009
Doral *(G-3405)*

WINDOW & DOOR FRAMES

Alutech Corporation...............G....... 305 593-2080
Miami *(G-9127)*
Arso Enterprises Inc...............E....... 305 681-2020
Opa Locka *(G-12290)*
Coyote Acquisition Co...............D....... 941 480-1600
North Venice *(G-11755)*
Custom Cft Windows & Doors Inc...............F....... 407 834-5400
Winter Springs *(G-19470)*
Custom Window Systems Inc...............A....... 352 368-6922
Ocala *(G-11914)*
Eastman Performance Films LLC...............G....... 954 920-2001
Fort Lauderdale *(G-3956)*
First Windows Incorporated...............G....... 813 508-9388
Wesley Chapel *(G-18745)*
Garcia Door & Window Inc...............G....... 305 635-0644
Miami *(G-9614)*
Innovtive Win Cncpts Doors Inc...............F....... 561 493-2303
Boynton Beach *(G-921)*
Larry Johnson Inc...............F....... 305 888-2300
Hialeah *(G-5483)*
Majestic Ultimate Design Inc...............F....... 954 533-8677
Oakland Park *(G-11820)*
Miami Wall Systems Inc...............C....... 305 888-2300
Hialeah *(G-5515)*
PGT Industries Inc...............A....... 941 480-1600
North Venice *(G-11761)*
PGT Innovations Inc...............A....... 941 480-1600
North Venice *(G-11762)*
Pinos Window Corporation...............F....... 305 888-9903
Medley *(G-8706)*
Quality Engineered Products Co...............E....... 813 885-1693
Tampa *(G-18031)*
Ram Sales LLC...............D....... 844 726-6382
Miami *(G-10237)*

WINDOW CLEANING SVCS

Island Shutter Co Inc...............E....... 386 738-9455
Deland *(G-2985)*

WINDOW FRAMES & SASHES: Plastic

Bay City Window Company...............F....... 727 323-5443
Saint Petersburg *(G-15718)*
J T Walker Industries Inc...............E....... 727 461-0501
Clearwater *(G-1739)*
Pvc Windoors Inc...............F....... 305 940-3608
North Miami *(G-11652)*
Southern Die Casting Corp...............E....... 305 635-6571
Miami *(G-10385)*

WINDOW FRAMES, MOLDING & TRIM: Vinyl

Sun-Tek Manufacturing Inc...............E....... 407 859-2117
Orlando *(G-13223)*

WINDOW FURNISHINGS WHOLESALERS

BMW & Associates Inc...............G....... 352 694-2300
Ocala *(G-11888)*
Greg Valley...............F....... 941 739-6628
Sarasota *(G-16224)*
Swfl Hurricane Shutters Inc...............G....... 239 454-4944
Cape Coral *(G-1481)*

WINDOWS: Frames, Wood

Cws Holding Company LLC...............D....... 352 368-6922
Ocala *(G-11915)*

WINDOWS: Storm, Wood

Eco Window Systems LLC...............B....... 305 885-5299
Medley *(G-8645)*
Gravitystorm Inc...............F....... 772 519-3009
Fort Pierce *(G-4703)*
Innovtive Win Cncpts Doors Inc...............F....... 561 493-2303
Boynton Beach *(G-921)*

WINDOWS: Wood

Delet Doors Inc...............F....... 786 250-4506
Miami *(G-9445)*

WINDSHIELDS: Plastic

Waterway Systems LLC...............G....... 941 752-3554
Sarasota *(G-16324)*

WINE & DISTILLED ALCOHOLIC BEVERAGES WHOLESALERS

D G Yuengling and Son Inc...............D....... 813 972-8500
Tampa *(G-17584)*

WINE CELLARS, BONDED: Wine, Blended

Luxe Vintages LLC...............G....... 561 558-7399
Delray Beach *(G-3103)*

WIRE

Merchants Metals Inc...............D....... 813 333-5515
Tampa *(G-17901)*
Phosco Electric Supply Co Inc...............G....... 941 708-9633
Bradenton *(G-1096)*
Repwire LLC...............G....... 786 486-1823
Doral *(G-3483)*
Wire Products Inc of Florida...............E....... 954 772-1477
Fort Lauderdale *(G-4326)*
Wire Tech International Inc...............G....... 786 258-5746
Bal Harbour *(G-304)*

WIRE & CABLE: Aluminum

American Wire Group Inc...............F....... 954 455-3050
Aventura *(G-260)*

WIRE & CABLE: Nonferrous, Aircraft

Sunmaster of Naples Inc...............E....... 239 261-3581
Naples *(G-11426)*

WIRE & CABLE: Nonferrous, Automotive, Exc Ignition Sets

Wiretec Ignition Inc...............F....... 407 578-4569
Palmetto *(G-13837)*

WIRE & CABLE: Nonferrous, Building

Conduit Space Rcvery Systems L...............F....... 330 416-0887
Bradenton *(G-1023)*
Ford Wire and Cable Corp...............E....... 772 388-3660
Sebastian *(G-16660)*
Technlogy Integration Svcs LLC...............G....... 904 565-4050
Jacksonville *(G-6843)*

WIRE & WIRE PRDTS

Alp Industries Inc...............F....... 786 845-8617
Doral *(G-3240)*
Artistic Fence Corporation...............G....... 305 805-1976
Hialeah *(G-5307)*
Baby Guard Inc...............F....... 954 741-6351
Coral Springs *(G-2222)*
Blue Water Dynamics LLC...............D....... 386 957-5464
Edgewater *(G-3614)*
Brandano Displays Inc...............E....... 954 956-7266
Margate *(G-8537)*
Central Wire Industries LLC...............E....... 850 983-9926
Milton *(G-10926)*
Clear Vue Inc...............E....... 727 726-5386
Safety Harbor *(G-15490)*
Cross City Veneer Company Inc...............D....... 352 498-3226
Cross City *(G-2364)*
Eastern Wire Products Inc...............E....... 904 781-6775
Jacksonville *(G-6350)*
Fabricated Wire Products Inc...............G....... 813 802-8463
Valrico *(G-18517)*
Florida Wire & Cable...............G....... 904 275-2101
Sanderson *(G-15980)*
Florida Wire & Rigging Sup Inc...............G....... 407 422-6218
Orlando *(G-12759)*
Insteel Wire Products Company...............E....... 904 275-2100
Sanderson *(G-15982)*
Jayco Screens Inc...............G....... 850 456-0673
Pensacola *(G-14182)*
Johnson Well Equipment Inc...............G....... 850 453-3131
Pensacola *(G-14185)*
Ludlow Fibc Corp...............G....... 305 702-5000
Opa Locka *(G-12334)*
Mansur Industries Inc...............F....... 305 593-8015
Doral *(G-3423)*
Marmon Aerospace & Defense LLC...............D....... 239 643-6400
Naples *(G-11322)*
Merchants Metals LLC...............F....... 904 781-3920
Jacksonville *(G-6595)*
Miami Cordage LLC...............E....... 305 636-3000
Miami *(G-9996)*
Mutual Industries North Inc...............D....... 239 332-2400
Fort Myers *(G-4541)*
Rat Trap Bait Company Inc...............F....... 863 967-2148
Auburndale *(G-251)*
Rowe Industries Inc...............F....... 302 855-0585
Pembroke Park *(G-14011)*
SOUTHERN SPRING & STAMPING INC E....... 941 488-2276
Venice *(G-18575)*
St Judas Tadeus Foundry Inc...............G....... 305 512-3612
Hialeah *(G-5631)*
TL Fahringer Co Inc...............G....... 813 681-2373
Tampa *(G-18190)*
Vutec Corporation...............C....... 954 545-9000
Coral Springs *(G-2330)*
Wire Experts Group Inc...............D....... 239 597-8555
Naples *(G-11458)*

WIRE CLOTH & WOVEN WIRE PRDTS, MADE FROM PURCHASED WIRE

John W Hock Company...............G....... 352 378-3209
Gainesville *(G-4948)*

WIRE FENCING & ACCESS WHOLESALERS

American All Scure Gtes Fnce L...............F....... 407 423-4962
Orlando *(G-12467)*

WIRE MATERIALS: Copper

American Wire Group Inc...............F....... 954 455-3050
Aventura *(G-260)*

WIRE MATERIALS: Steel

Green Mountain Specialties...............F....... 386 469-0057
Deland *(G-2982)*
Keystone Steel Products Co...............G....... 813 248-9828
Tampa *(G-17822)*
List Manufacturing Inc...............E....... 954 429-9155
Deerfield Beach *(G-2860)*
Macias Gabions Inc...............G....... 850 910-8000
Lauderhill *(G-8114)*
Metalhouse LLC...............G....... 407 270-3000
Orlando *(G-12962)*
Peninsula Steel Inc...............G....... 956 795-1966
Plant City *(G-14456)*
Peninsula Steel Inc...............E....... 813 473-8133
Plant City *(G-14457)*
Phelps Dodge Intl Corp...............E....... 305 648-7888
Doral *(G-3459)*
Pte Systems International LLC...............E....... 305 863-3409
Hialeah *(G-5582)*

WIRE PRDTS: Steel & Iron

Atlantic Wire and Rigging Inc...............G....... 321 633-1552
Cocoa *(G-1997)*

Industrial Spring Corp ....F 954 524-2558
Davie (G-2537)
Maschmeyer Concrete Co Fla....E 561 848-9112
Lake Park (G-7476)

WIRE ROPE CENTERS

Hofmann & Leavy Inc ....D 954 698-0000
Deerfield Beach (G-2842)

WIRE WHOLESALERS

Southwire Company LLC ....C 850 423-4680
Crestview (G-2359)

WIRE WINDING OF PURCHASED WIRE

Wire Mesh Corp....E 706 922-5179
Jacksonville (G-6924)

WIRE: Communication

Carlisle Interconnect Tech Inc ....A 904 829-5600
Saint Augustine (G-15526)
Diversfied Mtl Specialists Inc ....G 941 244-0935
North Venice (G-11757)
Fibertronics Inc....E 321 473-8933
Melbourne (G-8832)
Molex LLC....F 727 521-2700
Pinellas Park (G-14370)
Wireless Latin Entrmt Inc....G 305 858-7740
Miami (G-10614)

WIRE: Magnet

Advanced Magnet Lab Inc....F 321 728-7543
Melbourne (G-8758)

WIRE: Mesh

Equity Group Usa Inc ....G 407 421-6464
Winter Springs (G-19472)

WIRE: Nonferrous

Dekoron Unitherm LLC....E 800 633-5015
Cape Coral (G-1411)
Electro Technik Industries Inc ....D 727 530-9555
Clearwater (G-1666)
Equity Group Usa Inc ....G 407 421-6464
Winter Springs (G-19472)
Integrated Cable Solutions ....E 813 769-5740
Tampa (G-17787)
Kai Limited....C 954 957-8586
Fort Lauderdale (G-4083)
Logus Manufacturing Corp....E 561 842-3550
West Palm Beach (G-18934)
Marathon Fiber Optics LLC....G 305 902-9010
Riverview (G-15277)
Monroe Cable LLC ....D 941 429-8484
North Port (G-11744)
Phelps Dodge Intl Corp ....E 305 648-7888
Doral (G-3459)
Tensolite LLC ....A 904 829-5600
Saint Augustine (G-15626)
Times Microwave Systems Inc ....F 203 949-8400
West Palm Beach (G-19064)
Tricab (usa) Inc....G 754 210-5490
Hollywood (G-5927)

WIRING DEVICES WHOLESALERS

Pacer Electronics Florida Inc....E 941 378-5774
Sarasota (G-16534)

WOMEN'S & CHILDREN'S CLOTHING WHOLESALERS, NEC

Apparel Imports Inc ....E 800 428-6849
Miami (G-9157)
Carpe Diem Sales & Mktg Inc ....E 407 682-1400
Orlando (G-12552)
Chrome Connection Corp ....G 305 947-9191
North Miami Beach (G-11669)
Decoy Inc....F 305 633-6384
Miami (G-9443)
Kamtex USA Incorporated ....G 954 733-1044
Lauderdale Lakes (G-8089)
La Providencia Express Co....G 305 409-9894
Miami (G-9846)
My Glam Choice Inc....G 786 586-7927
Miami (G-10056)
Pattern Grading & Marker Svcs ....G 305 495-9963
Miramar (G-11027)
Sarah Louise Inc ....F 941 377-9656
Sarasota (G-16573)
Sharp Marketing LLC ....G 954 565-2711
Oakland Park (G-11838)
Vf Imagewear Inc....G 813 671-2986
Riverview (G-15286)

WOMEN'S & GIRLS' SPORTSWEAR WHOLESALERS

Lear Investors Inc ....G 305 681-8582
Opa Locka (G-12333)
T Shirt Center Inc ....G 305 655-1955
Miami (G-10455)

WOMEN'S CLOTHING STORES

Amj DOT LLC....G 646 249-0273
Boca Raton (G-426)
Excess Liquidator LLC....G 407 247-9105
Oviedo (G-13429)
Exist Inc ....D 954 739-7030
Fort Lauderdale (G-3982)
Jackie Z Style Co St Pete LLC ....G 727 258-4849
Saint Petersburg (G-15831)
Original Pnguin Drect Oprtions ....F 305 592-2830
Doral (G-3452)
Perry Ellis International Inc....B 305 592-2830
Doral (G-3458)
Uniform Authority Inc....D 305 625-8050
Miami (G-10529)

WOMEN'S CLOTHING STORES: Ready-To-Wear

Yoly Munoz Corp....G 305 860-3839
Miami (G-10627)

WOMEN'S SPORTSWEAR STORES

JMP Fashion Inc....F 305 633-9920
Miami (G-9799)
Lan Designs Inc ....G 305 661-7878
Miami (G-9853)

WOOD & WOOD BY-PRDTS, WHOLESALE

Tree Stake Solutions LLC....G 407 920-0507
Orlando (G-13269)

WOOD FENCING WHOLESALERS

Florida Cypress & Fence Co....G 561 392-3011
Palm City (G-13656)

WOOD PRDTS

4303 Silverwood LLC....G 904 900-1702
Jacksonville (G-6102)
6425 Hollywood Blvd LLC ....G 941 923-2954
Sarasota (G-16327)
Backwoods Crossing Llc ....F 850 765-3753
Tallahassee (G-17225)
Burnham Woods Untd Civic Group....G 954 532-2675
North Lauderdale (G-11612)
C & S Foliage....G 352 357-4847
Eustis (G-3704)
Del Mar Hollywood LLC....G 786 325-8335
Miami Beach (G-10661)
Hollywood Houndz LLC....G 407 614-2108
Winter Garden (G-19269)
Hollywood Lodging Inc ....G 305 803-7455
Hollywood (G-5843)
Linenwood Home LLC ....G 850 607-7445
Pensacola (G-14194)
Mamalu Wood LLC....G 305 261-6332
Miami (G-9939)
Mm Wildwood LLC....G 917 609-7128
Oxford (G-13464)
Weston Park At Longwood STA ....G 321 422-3546
Longwood (G-8350)
Wood & Glass Works LLC....G 727 317-9599
Pinellas Park (G-14394)
Wood Splinter Corp ....G 305 721-7215
Miami (G-10616)
Wood U LLC....G 954 560-2000
Oakland Park (G-11862)
Wooden It Be Nice ....G 352 797-0427
Brooksville (G-1294)

WOOD PRDTS: Applicators

Carpentree Creation ....G 904 300-4008
Jacksonville (G-6255)
Konadocks LLC....G 407 909-0606
Winter Garden (G-19272)
Teakdecking Systems Inc ....D 941 756-0600
Sarasota (G-16309)

WOOD PRDTS: Barrels & Barrel Parts

Diamondback Barrels LLC ....F 321 305-5995
Cocoa (G-2009)

WOOD PRDTS: Beekeeping Splys

Agp Holding Corp ....G 850 668-0006
Tallahassee (G-17214)
Agri-Products Inc....G 850 668-0006
Tallahassee (G-17215)

WOOD PRDTS: Extension Planks

Wurth Wood Group Inc....F 800 432-1149
Tampa (G-18268)

WOOD PRDTS: Hampers, Laundry

Laundromart....G 561 487-4343
Boca Raton (G-598)

WOOD PRDTS: Laundry

Fine Line Custom Millwork LLC ....E 941 628-9611
Arcadia (G-203)
Petit Custom Wood Works....G 954 200-3111
Davie (G-2570)
Sandy Finished Wood Inc ....E 954 615-7271
Fort Lauderdale (G-4223)

WOOD PRDTS: Mauls

Boyett Timber Inc....G 352 583-2138
Webster (G-18697)

WOOD PRDTS: Moldings, Unfinished & Prefinished

Architctral Mlding Mllwrks Inc ....E 305 638-8900
Miami (G-9163)
Excel Millwork & Moulding Inc ....E 850 576-7228
Midway (G-10917)
Hughes Trim Llc....D 863 206-6048
Orlando (G-12814)
M & M Enterprises Daytona LLC ....G 386 672-1554
Daytona Beach (G-2681)
S&S Craftsmen Inc....F 813 247-4429
Tampa (G-18078)
Spacewerks Inc ....F 727 540-9714
Clearwater (G-1885)
Terry D Triplett Inc ....G 561 251-3641
Mangonia Park (G-8513)
Windsor Window Company ....F 321 385-3880
Titusville (G-18473)

WOOD PRDTS: Mulch Or Sawdust

Agri-Source Inc ....E 352 351-2700
Ocala (G-11866)
E & M Recycling Inc....G 561 718-1092
Lake Worth (G-7548)

WOOD PRDTS: Mulch, Wood & Bark

Forestry Resources Inc....E 239 332-3966
Fort Myers (G-4457)
K & B Landscape Supplies Inc ....G 800 330-8816
Deland (G-2990)
Randy Wheeler....G 850 997-1248
Monticello (G-11081)
Southern Softwoods Inc....E 863 666-1404
Lakeland (G-7801)
Yahl Mulching & Recycling Inc ....F 239 352-7888
Naples (G-11462)

WOOD PRDTS: Novelties, Fiber

Fanatics Mounted Memories Inc ....E 866 578-9115
Jacksonville (G-6378)
Mounted Memories Inc....F 866 236-2541
Miramar (G-11018)

WOOD PRDTS: Oars & Paddles

Coastal Paddle Co LLC ....F 850 916-1600
Gulf Breeze *(G-5114)*
Dolphin Paddlesports Inc ....F 941 924-2785
Sarasota *(G-16412)*
Three Brothers Boards ....G 386 310-4927
Daytona Beach *(G-2726)*

WOOD PRDTS: Outdoor, Structural

Ecosan LLC ....G 954 446-5929
Coral Gables *(G-2140)*
Global Prime Wood LLC ....G 770 292-9200
Aventura *(G-271)*
Shade Systems Inc ....E 352 237-0135
Ocala *(G-12046)*
Ufp Palm Bch LLC DBA Ufp Mami ....D 786 837-0552
Miami *(G-10523)*

WOOD PRDTS: Panel Work

Unique Originals Inc ....F 305 634-2274
Fort Lauderdale *(G-4293)*

WOOD PRDTS: Poles

Banaghan Wood Products Inc ....E 386 788-6114
Port Orange *(G-15010)*

WOOD PRDTS: Shoe Trees

R P M Industries Inc ....E 315 255-1105
Hobe Sound *(G-5726)*

WOOD PRDTS: Survey Stakes

A B Survey Supply Entps Inc ....G 772 464-9500
Fort Pierce *(G-4667)*

WOOD PRDTS: Trophy Bases

Paul Tinsley Engraving ....G 407 656-4344
Winter Garden *(G-19279)*

WOOD PRODUCTS: Reconstituted

Enviva Pellets Cottondale LLC ....E 850 557-7357
Cottondale *(G-2331)*
Fatezzi Inc ....G 407 323-8688
Sanford *(G-16044)*
GL Shavings LLC ....G 352 360-0063
Groveland *(G-5096)*

WOOD SHAVINGS BALES, MULCH TYPE, WHOLESALE

Griffis Lumber LLC ....G 352 372-9965
Gainesville *(G-4933)*

WOOD TREATING: Bridges & Trestles

York Bridge Concepts Inc ....E 813 482-0613
Lutz *(G-8426)*

WOOD TREATING: Millwork

Commercial Casework Inc ....D 904 264-4222
Jacksonville *(G-6280)*
Commercial Wood Designs Inc ....F 407 302-9063
Sanford *(G-16018)*
F & R General Interiors Corp ....F 305 635-4747
Hialeah *(G-5402)*
Infinite Ret Design & Mfg Corp ....F 305 967-8339
Miami *(G-9741)*
Ufp Orlando LLC ....F 407 982-3312
Orlando *(G-13285)*
Ufp Tampa LLC ....E 813 971-3030
Tampa *(G-18212)*

WOOD TREATING: Structural Lumber & Timber

All Moldings Inc ....G 305 556-6171
Hialeah *(G-5279)*
Coastal Forest Resources Co ....B 850 539-6432
Havana *(G-5235)*
International Weatherization ....G 954 818-3288
Fort Lauderdale *(G-4065)*
John Andersen ....G 407 702-4891
Apopka *(G-151)*
Larry C Cribb ....G 904 845-2804
Hilliard *(G-5714)*

WOOD TREATING: Wood Prdts, Creosoted

Mirandas Woodcraft LLC ....G 954 306-3568
Lauderhill *(G-8115)*

WOODWORK & TRIM: Exterior & Ornamental

Mr Foamy Southwest Fl LLC ....F 239 461-3110
Fort Myers *(G-4540)*

WOODWORK & TRIM: Interior & Ornamental

Designers Specialty Cab Co Inc ....E 954 868-3440
Fort Lauderdale *(G-3938)*
Hollywood Woodwork LLC ....F 954 920-5009
Hollywood *(G-5846)*
Peace Millwork Co Inc ....E 305 573-6222
Miami *(G-10147)*
Pleasure Interiors LLC ....E 941 756-9969
Sarasota *(G-16545)*
Visions Millwork Inc ....F 239 390-0811
Fort Myers *(G-4648)*

WOODWORK: Carved & Turned

Rich Woodturning Inc ....F 305 573-9142
Miami Lakes *(G-10851)*

WOODWORK: Interior & Ornamental, NEC

Architctral Wdwrks Cbnetry Inc ....F 561 848-8595
Palm Beach Gardens *(G-13568)*
Cubos LLC ....G 786 299-2671
Miami *(G-9418)*
Johnsons Woodwork Incorporated ....G 904 826-4100
Saint Augustine *(G-15561)*
Newmil Inc ....F 954 444-4471
Fort Lauderdale *(G-4140)*
Oliveri Woodworking Inc ....F 561 478-7233
West Palm Beach *(G-18972)*
Superior Millwork Company Inc ....F 904 355-5676
Jacksonville *(G-6828)*
Woodshed Woodworks LLC ....G 904 540-0354
Saint Augustine *(G-15639)*

WOODWORK: Ornamental, Cornices, Mantels, Etc.

Federal Millwork Corp ....E 954 522-0653
Fort Lauderdale *(G-3990)*
Legend Design and Production ....G 305 270-1156
Miami *(G-9881)*
Palm Beach Woodwork Co Inc ....G 561 844-8818
Mangonia Park *(G-8509)*

WRENCHES

James Reese Enterprises Inc ....F 727 386-5311
Clearwater *(G-1741)*

X-RAY EQPT & TUBES

Atlantic Mobile Imaging Svcs ....G 386 239-8271
Ormond Beach *(G-13350)*
L and C Science and Tech Inc ....G 305 200-3531
Hialeah *(G-5477)*
Lead Enterprises Inc ....F 305 635-8644
Miami *(G-9876)*
Omega Medical Imaging LLC ....E 407 323-9400
Sanford *(G-16093)*
Orlando Flores ....G 305 898-2111
Miami *(G-10120)*
Osko Inc ....F 305 599-7161
Medley *(G-8699)*
Ziehm Imaging Inc ....E 407 615-8560
Orlando *(G-13342)*

YACHT BASIN OPERATIONS

Broward Yard & Marine LLC ....D 954 927-4119
Dania *(G-2441)*

YARN : Crochet, Spun

Four Purls ....G 863 293-6261
Winter Haven *(G-19324)*

YARN MILLS: Texturizing

Dillon Yarn Corporation ....C 973 684-1600
Fort Lauderdale *(G-3941)*

YARN, ELASTIC: Fabric Covered

Nissi Elastic Corp ....G 305 968-3812
Hialeah *(G-5542)*

YARN, ORGANIC SYNTHETIC

Artificial Turf Supply LLC ....G 877 525-8873
Ponte Vedra Beach *(G-14934)*

YARN: Manmade & Synthetic Fiber, Spun

Southern Fiber Inc ....F 786 916-3052
Miami Lakes *(G-10861)*

YOGURT WHOLESALERS

Colormet Foods LLC ....F 888 775-3966
Miami *(G-9382)*

ZINC OINTMENT

Gensco Laboratories LLC ....F 754 263-2898
Doral *(G-3365)*